AUTO ENGINE PERFORMANCE & DRIVEABILITY MANUAL

CHRYSLER CORPORATION & FORD MOTOR COMPANY

2nd Edition, Volume 2

First Printing

John R. Lypen, SAE
Editor

Marian A. Maasshoff, SAE
Managing Editor

Warren Schildknecht, SAE
Senior Editor

Daniel Reynolds
Associate Editor

Brad A. Harris
Assistant Editor

Michele L. Hawley
Assistant Editor

James M. Pirkola
Assistant Editor

Ron Lathrop
Assistant Editor

Richard C. Grunz
Assistant Editor

Glenn D. Loisel
Assistant Editor

Richard G. Glover, SAE
Assistant Editor

Thomas H. Nash
Assistant Editor

Scott E. Mason
Assistant Editor

Donald J. Schall
Assistant Editor

Charles D. Leibrand
Assistant Editor

Richard H. Sparkes
Assistant Editor

Kirk D. Lashbrook
Electronic Data Manager

Lynda Slater
Production Assistant

Richard F. Cahoon
Product Support Specialist

Kristen Parsons
Graphic Development Specialist

Published by

MOTOR

A Division of Hearst Business Publishing, Inc.

5600 Crooks Road, Troy, MI 48098

Printed in the U.S.A.

Copyright © 1995 Hearst Business Publishing, Inc.
All rights reserved
ISBN 0-87851-863-0

Frank A. Bennack, Jr.
President

Gilbert C. Maurer
Executive Vice President

Richard P. Malloch
Vice President/General Manager Hearst Books/Business Publishing Group

Nelson J. Maione
Vice President & Resident Controller

Randolph A. Hearst
Chairman

Victor F. Ganzi
Senior Vice President

William K. Baker
Vice President/General Manager Motor Books

Kevin F. Carr
Vice President/Publisher Motor Books

Richard B. Laimbeer
Publisher Motor Books

LONGWOOD PUBLIC LIBRARY

VEHICLE IDENTIFICATION

TABLE OF CONTENTS

	Page No.		Page No.
CHRYSLER CORP.:		**FORD MOTOR CO:**	
Domestic........................	2	1993-94........................	4
Imports.........................	3	1995-96........................	5

CHRYSLER DOMESTIC
V.I.N. DEFINED

1st POSITION
COUNTRY
1 = United States
2 = Canada
3 = Mexico
4 = United States

2nd POSITION
MAKE
B = Dodge
C = Chrysler
E = Eagle
P = Plymouth

3rd POSITION
VEHICLE TYPE
3 = Passenger Car
4 = Multipurpose Vehicle
7 = Truck

4th POSITION
RESTRAINT/G.V.W.R.
RESTRAINT
A = Dual Air Bags
A = Air Bag
A = Auto Belts & Driver Air Bag
B = Automatic Belts
B = Manual Belts
C = Automatic Belts
C = Manual Belts
E = Active, Passenger Air Bag
E = Manual Belts & Dual Air
    Bags
F = Manual Belts (Mexico)
H = HYBRID Air Bag
X = Air Bag, Passenger Manual
Y = Air Bag, Passenger
    Automatic
G.V.W.R.
D = 1-3000 LB
E = 3001-4000 LB
F = 4001-5000 LB
G = 5001-6000 LB

5th POSITION
CARLINE
A = LeBaron LE/Landau
A = Spirit/Spirit LE
A = Acclaim
C = New Yorker
C = Chrysler "LHS"
C = New Yorker Salon
C = Dynasty/Dynasty LE
D = Eagele Concorde
D = Intrepid
D = Vision
D = New Yorker
D = Chrysler "LHS"
E = Chrysler Vision
F = Laser/Talon (FWD)
G = Laser/Talon (AWD)
H = Minivan (FWD)
J = Stratus / Cirrus LXI / Breeze
K = Minivan (AWD)
K = Talon (FWD)
L = Concorde

5th POSITION (Cont'd)
L = Talon (AWD)
L = Sebring (JX)
M = LeBaron
P = Shadow/Shadow ES
P = Sundance/Duster
P = Minivan (FWD)
R = Viper
S = Laser/Talon (FWD)
S = Neon
T = Laser/Talon (AWD)
T = Minivan (AWD)
U = LeBaron/LeBaron LS
U = LeBaron GTC/Convertible
U = Sebring/Avenger
V = Imperial
V = New Yorker Fifth Ave
W = Daytona/Daytona ES
W = Daytona IROC
W = Daytona IROC R/T

6th POSITION
SERIES
1 = Economy (E)
2 = Low Line (L)
3 = Medium Line (M)
4 = High Line (H)
4 = Talon ESI
4 = Avenger
5 = Premium (P)
5 = Talon TSI (FWD)
5 = Sebring LXI
6 = Special/Sport (S)
6 = Sebring LX
7 = Performance/Image (X)
8 = Talon TSI (AWD)
8 = Avenger ES

7th POSITION
BODY STYLE
PASSENGER CAR
1 = 2 Door Coupe/Sedan
2 = 2 Door Pillared H.T.
4 = 2 Door Hatchback
4 = 3 Door Hatchback
5 = 2 Door Convertible
6 = 4 Door Sedan
7 = 4 Door Pillared H.T.
8 = 4 Door Hatchback
9 = 4 Door Wagon
TRUCK
1 = Van
4 = Extended Wagon/Van
5 = Wagon

8th POSITION
ENGINE CODE
A = 2.2-L4, 16V Turbo III
B = 2.5-L4, TBI
B = 1.8-L4, MFI
B = 2.4-L4, 16V MPI
B = 2.0-L4, DOHC MPI
C = 2.0-L4, SFI
C = 2.2-L4, Turbo
D = 2.2-L4, TBI
E = 8.0-V10, MPI

8th POSTION (Cont'd)
E = 2.0-L4, MEI
E = 2.0-L4, MPI Turbo
F = 3.5-V6, 24V MPI
F = 2.0-L4, MFI Turbo
G = 2.4-V6, MPI
H = 2.5-L4, SPI
H = 2.5-V6, SFI
J = 2.5-L4, Turbo
J = 3.3-V6, CNG
K = 2.5-L4, TBI
L = 3.8-V6, MPI
L = 3.8-V6, SFI
M = 2.5-L4, Eurostar Diesel
N = 2.0-L4, SFI-SOHC
N = 2.5-V6, 24 Valve
P = 2.5-L4, SFI Turbo II
R = 3.3-V6, MPI
R = 2.0-L4, MPI
S = 2.4-L4, DOHC Turbo
T = 1.8-L4, MPI
T = 3.3-V6, MPI
U = 2.0-L4, MPI Turbo
U = 3.3-V6, Flex Fuel MPI
V = 2.5-L4, Flex Fuel TBI
W = 2.5-L4, TBI
X = 2.4-L4, SFI
Y = 2.0-L4, SFI-DOHC
Y = 2.0-L4, MPI
2 = 2.5-L4, SFI Turbo
3 = 3.0-V6, MPI
9 = 54-KW, Electric

9th POSITION
CHECK DIGIT

10th POSITION
MODEL YEAR
N = 1992
P = 1993
R = 1994
S = 1995
T = 1996

11th POSITION
ASSEMBLY PLANT
A = CTC Preproduction Pilot
A = Outer Drive
B = St. Louis
D = Belvidere
E = Bloomington (DSM)
F = Newark
G = St. Louis-1
H = Bramalea, ON
N = Sterling Heights
R = Windsor
T = Toluca, Mexico
U = Eurostar
U = Graz, Austria
V = New Mack
X = St. Louis-2

12th Thru 17th POSITION
PRODUCTION SEQUENCE
NUMBER

CHRYSLER IMPORTS

V.I.N. DEFINED

1st POSITION
COUNTRY
- J = Japan
- M = Thailand
- 4 = USA (Diamond Star Motors)

2nd POSITION
MAKE
- B = Dodge
- C = Chrysler
- E = Eagle
- J = Chrysler
- L = Dodge, Thailand
- N = Eagle, Thailand
- P = Plymouth

3rd POSITION
VEHICLE TYPE
- 3 = Passenger Car
- 4 = MPV
- 7 = Truck

4th POSITION
G.V.W.R. & RESTRAINT SYSTEM
PASSENGER CAR
- A = Air Bag
- A = Dual Air Bags
- B = Manual Belts
- B = Manual Belts (Driver Air Bag)
- C = Passive Belts
- D = Manual Belts
- E = Passive Belts (Driver Air Bag)
- X = Driver Air Bag

TRUCK or MPV
- D = 0001-3000 LB
- E = 3001-4000 LB
- F = 4001-5000 LB
- G = 5001-6000 LB
- J = 0001-3000 LB
- K = 3001-4000 LB
- L = 4001-5000 LB
- M = 5001-6000 LB

5th POSITION
LINE
PASSENGER CAR
- A = Summit DL & ESI
- A = Summit LX
- A = Colt E, Colt DL
- A = Colt Premier/Summit
- A = Colt 100/Vista (Canada)
- B = Colt Vista/Summit, FWD
- B = Summit DL & LX
- C = Conquest TSI
- C = Colt Vista/Summit, AWD
- C = Summit Wagon
- D = Stealth, Stealth ES & R/T
- E = Stealth R/T Turbo, AWD
- G = Colt Vista, 2WD
- H = Colt Vista, 4WD
- H = 2000 GTX
- M = Stealth & Stealth R/T, FWD
- N = Stealth & Stealth R/T, AWD
- R = 2000 GTX
- U = Colt, Colt E

5th POSITION (Cont'd)
- U = Colt 200 (Canada)
- U = Colt GT, Summit
- U = Colt GL
- U = Summit DL & LX
- U = Summit ES
- V = Colt DL Wagon, 2WD
- V = Summit Wagon, 2WD
- V = Colt Vista (2WD), Summit
- W = Colt DL Wagon, AWD
- W = Summit Wagon, AWD
- W = Colt Vista, AWD
- X = 2000 GTX, AWD

TRUCK
- J = Raider
- L = Ram 50, Custom & SE
- L = Ram 50 Sport
- L = Power Ram 50 SE & LE
- M = Power Ram 50
- M = Power Ram 50 SE & LE
- M = Power Ram 50 Custom
- M = Power Ram 50 Sport

6th POSITION
SERIES
- 1 = (E) Economy (S)
- 1 = Colt, Summit (E)
- 2 = Low (Base) (L)
- 2 = Colt GL, Summit ES (L)
- 3 = Medium (M)
- 3 = Colt Vista, 2WD (H)
- 3 = Colt Vista, 4WD (M)
- 3 = Summit DL (H)
- 3 = Summit, AWD (M)
- 4 = High (H)
- 4 = Stealth, Summit LX (H)
- 4 = Colt Vista SE (L)
- 5 = Premium (P)
- 5 = Sports (S)
- 5 = Stealth ES (T)
- 6 = Special/Sport (S)
- 6 = Stealth R/T (R)
- 7 = Performance/Image (X)
- 7 = Ultimate (U)
- 7 = Stealth R/T Turbo (U)
- 8 = Sports Line (T)

7th POSITION
BODY STYLE
PASSENGER CAR
- 0 = 4 Door Wagon
- 1 = 2 Door Sedan
- 1 = 2 Door Coupe
- 4 = 2 Door Hatchback
- 4 = 3 Door Hatchback
- 4 = Colt, Colt GL, Summit
- 4 = 2 Door Pillard H.T.
- 6 = 4 Door Sedan
- 6 = Summit, Summit ES
- 9 = 4 Door Wagon
- 9 = 5 Door Wagon

TRUCK
- 3 = Van
- 4 = Conventional Cab-Short
- 5 = Club Cab
- 5 = Extended Cab-Long
- 9 = Conventional Cab-Long

7th POSITION (Cont'd)
MPV
- 1 = 4 Door Wagon
- 1 = 5 Door Wagon
- 3 = 3 Door Metal Top
- 4 = 4 Door Wagon

8th POSITION
ENGINE CODE
- A = 1.5L, 3 Valve MPI
- B = 1.8L, MPI
- B = 2.0L, DOHC MPI
- B = 3.0L, DOHC MPI
- C = 1.8L, MPI
- C = 3.0L, DOHC Turbo
- D = 2.0L, Gas
- D = 1.8L, MPI
- E = 2.0L, MPI
- E = 2.6L, Gas
- F = 1.6L, Turbo
- F = 2.0L, MPI Turbo
- G = 2.4L, MPI
- H = 2.6L, Turbo
- H = 3.0L
- J = 3.0L, DOHC-MPI
- K = 1.5L, Gas
- K = 3.0L, DOHC-MPI-Turbo
- L = 2.4L, DOHC
- M = 3.5L, DOHC
- N = 2.6L, Turbo-Intercooler
- P = 1.5L, MPI
- R = 2.0L, DOHC MPI
- S = 3.0L, MPI-18 Valve
- T = 1.8L, MPI
- U = 2.0L, DOHC-MPI-Turbo
- V = 2.0L, MPI
- W = 2.4L, MPI
- X = 1.5L, MPI
- Y = 1.6L, DOHC MPI
- Z = 1.6L, DOHC Turbo

9th POSITION
CHECK DIGIT

10th POSITION
MODEL YEAR
- H = 1987
- J = 1988
- K = 1989
- L = 1990
- M = 1991
- N = 1992
- P = 1993
- R = 1994
- S = 1995
- T = 1996

11th POSITION
ASSEMBLY PLANT
- A = Misushima-2
- E = Bloomington (DSM), USA
- G = Thailand
- J = Nagoya-3
- O = Thailand
- P = Nagoya-2
- U = Mizushima-1
- Y = Nagoya-1
- Z = Okazaki

12th Thru 17th POSITION
PRODUCTION SEQUENCE NUMBER

1993-94 FORD MOTOR CO.
V.I.N. DEFINED

1st POSITION
COUNTRY
1 = United States
2 = Canada
3 = South America
4 = United States
5 = Mexico
6 = Australia
9 = Brazil
J = Japan
K = Korea
L = Taiwan
W = Germany

2nd POSITION
MAKE
B = Ford
C = Imported Truck
F = Ford
F = Mazda
L = Lincoln
M = Mercury
N = Continental
Z = Ford

3rd POSITION
TYPE
A = Passenger Car
A = Imported Mercury Tracer
B = Bus
B = Passenger Car
C = Truck, Stripped Chassis
C = Basic, Stripped Chassis
D = Incomplete Vehicle
E = Passenger Car
F = Equiped Without Power Train
F = Imported, Incomplete Truck
H = Incomplete Vehicle
I = Passenger Car
J = Incomplete Vehicle
J = Passenger Car
J = Imported Car, Festiva
M = Multi Purpose Vehicle
N = Passenger Car, Imported
P = Passenger Car, Imported
R = Passenger Car
T = Truck, Complete
V = Passenger Car
0 = Imported - Fiesta
1 = Imported - Merkur/Scorpio
2 = Courier - Complete
2 = Multi Purpose Vehicle
3 = Multi Purpose Vehicle
4 = Courier - Complete
4 = Courier - Incomplete
5 = Truck, Complete
6 = Courier - Festiva

4th POSITION
RESTRAINT SYSTEM
B = Active Belts
C = Air Bags & Active Belts
D = Active Belts
L = Air Bags & Active Belts
P = Passive & Active Belts

5th POSITION
IDENTIFICATION
M = Lincoln/Mercury Make
P = Passenger Car (82-89)
P = Ford Make (90-94)
T = Imported & Non-Ford Built

6th & 7th POSITION
BODY SERIES NUMBER
See The Body Series Pages

8th POSITION
ENGINE CODE
A = 2.3-L4, EFI/OHC
A = 2.0-L4, MFI, Mazda (93-94)
B = 3.3-V6, 1 Barrel
B = 2.5-V6, MFI, Mazda (93-94)
C = 2.2-L4, EFI (89-92)
C = 3.8-V6, 2 Barrel (84-86)
C = 3.8-V6, EFI (87-90)
D = 2.3-L4, EFI/Turbo (83)
D = 2.5-L4, CFI (85-90)
E = 5.0-V8, MFI (93-94)
E = 5.0-V8, EFI/HO
F = 5.0-V8, CFI/EFI
F = 5.8-V8, 2 Barrel
H = 1.3-L4, EFI, Mazda (93-94)
H = 2.0-L4, Diesel
J = 1.9-L4, CVH SEFI (93-94)
J = 1.9-L4, SFI
K = 1.3-L4, 2-V, Mazda
K = 1.9-L4, HO-CVH-SEFI (94)
L = 2.4-V6, Diesel/Turbo (84-85)
L = 2.2-L4, MFI/TC (93)
L = 2.2-L4, MFI/TC (93)
L = 5.0-V8, CFI or EFI/High
    Output
M = 2.3-L4, EFI (91-92)
M = 2.3-L4, MFI (93)
N = 3.2-V6, DOHC (93)
P = 3.2-V6, SHO DOHC (93-94)
R = 2.3-L4, EFI/Turbo (89-90)
R = 3.8-V6, OHV
S = 2.3-L4, HSC/CFI/High
    Output/EFI
T = 2.3-L4, EFI/TurboIC
T = 5.0-V8, EFI (91-92)
T = 5.0-V8, MFI (33-94)
U = 3.0-V6, EFI
U = 2.9-V6, Fuel Injected
V = 4.6-V8, EFI (93-94)
W = 4.6-V8, EFI (91-92)
W = 4.6-V8, MFI (93-94)
X = 3.3-V6, Fuel Injected
X = 3.0-L4, MFI (93-94)
Y = 3.0-V6, SHO-EFI
Z = 3.0-V6, MFI 93-94)
Z = 1.6-L4, MFI (93-94)
1 = 1.3-L4, Fuel Injected
1 = 3.0-V6, MFI Flex Fuel (93-94)
2 = 1.6-L4, Fuel Injected

8th POSITION (CONT'D)
3 = 3.8-V6, CFI
3 = 3.8-V6, 2 Barrel (Canada)
4 = 1.6-L4, FI/High Output (83-85)
4 = 3.8-V6, EFI/SEFI (87-92)
4 = 3.8-V6, MFI (93-94)
5 = 1.6-L4, EFI/Mazda
6 = 1.6-L4, EFI/Turbo
6 = 2.3-L4, EFI/Turbo
6 = 1.6-L4, EFI/TC/Mazda (91-92)
6 = 1.6-L4, MFI/TC/Mazda (93-94)
7 = 1.6-L4, Methanol/High Output
8 = 1.6-L4, EFI/Turbo
8 = 1.8-L4, EFI/Mazda
8 = 1.8-L4, MFI/Mazda (93-94)
9 = 1.9-L4, CFI

9th POSITION
CHECK DIGIT

10th POSITION
MODEL YEAR
C = 1982
D = 1983
E = 1984
F = 1985
G = 1986
H = 1987
J = 1988
K = 1989
L = 1990
M = 1991
N = 1992
P = 1993
R = 1994

11th POSITION
ASSEMBLY PLANT
A = Atlanta, GA
B = Oakville, Ontario, Canada
D = Avon Lake, OH
E = Mahwah
E = Niehl, West Germany
F = Dearborn, MI
G = Chicago, IL
H = Lorain, OH
J = Los Angeles, CA
J = Monterrey
K = Kansas City, MO
M = West Germany
N = Norfolk, VA
P = Twin Cities, MN
R = Hermosillo, Mexico
R = San Jose, CA
S = Allen Park, MI
T = Metuchen, WI
T = Edison
U = Louisville, KY
W = Wayne, MI
X = St. Thomas, Canada
Y = Wixom, MI
Z = St. Louis, MO
2 = Taiwan
5 = Flat Rock, MI
6 = Kia, Korea
8 = Broadmeadows, Australia

12th Thru 17th POSITION
PRODUCTION SEQUENCE
NUMBER

1995-96 FORD MOTOR CO.
V.I.N. DEFINED

1st POSITION
COUNTRY
1 = United States
2 = Canada
3 = Mexico
4 = United States
9 = Brazil
J = Japan
K = Korea
L = Taiwan

2nd POSITION
MAKE
B = Ford
F = Ford
F = Mazda
L = Lincoln
M = Mercury
N = Continental
N = Ford
N = Nissan
Z = Ford

3rd POSITION
TYPE
A = Passenger Car
A = Imported Mercury Tracer
B = Bus
C = Basic, Stripped Chassis
D = Incomplete Vehicle
E = Equipped Without Power Train
F = Imported, Incomplete Truck
H = Incomplete Vehicle
I = Passenger Car
J = Incomplete Vehicle
J = Passenger Car
J = Imported Car, Asp're
M = Multi Purpose Vehicle
P = Passenger Car, Imported
T = Basic, Complete
T = Truck, Complete
V = Passenger Car
2 = Multi Purpose Vehicle
3 = Incomplete Vehicle
4 = Truck, Complete

4th POSITION
RESTRAINT SYSTEM
A = Active Driver, Passive Passenger
A = Active Rear & Driver Air Bag
B = Active Belts
C = Air Bags & Active Belts
D = Active Belts
L = Air Bags & Active Belts
P = Passive & Active Belts
R = Passive, Active & Driver Air Bag
S = Passive, Active & Dual Air Bags

5th POSITION
IDENTIFICATION
M = Lincoln/Mercury Make
P = Ford Make
T = Imported & Non-Ford Built

6th & 7th POSITION
BODY SERIES NUMBER
See The Body Series Pages

8th POSITION
ENGINE CODE
A = 2.0-L4, MFI, Mazda
B = 2.5-V6, MFI, Mazda
C = 5.8-V8, MFI
D = 5.0-V8, MFI
H = 1.3-L4, MFI, Mazda
J = 1.9-L4, CVH SEFI
K = 1.9-L4, HO-CVH-SEFI
L = 2.5-V6, MFI
N = 3.4-V8, MFI, SHO-DOHC
P = 3.2-V6, SHO DOHC
R = 3.8-V6, SUPERCHARGED
S = 3.0-V6, MFI, DOHC
T = 5.0-V8, MFI, OHV
U = 3.0-V6, MFI
V = 4.6-V8, MFI, DOHC
W = 4.6-V8, MFI, SOHC
X = 2.3-L4, MFI, OHV
Z = 1.6-L4, MFI, Mazda
3 = 2.0-L4, MFI-ZETA
4 = 3.8-V6, MFI-SEFI
6 = 1.6-L4, MFI/TC, Mazda
8 = 1.8-L4, MFI, Mazda
9 = 4.6-V8, Natural Gas

9th POSITION
CHECK DIGIT

10th POSITION
MODEL YEAR
S = 1995
T = 1996

11th POSITION
ASSEMBLY PLANT
A = Atlanta, GA
F = Dearborn, MI
G = Chicago, IL
H = Lorain, OH
K = Kansas City, MO
M = Cuautitlan
R = Hermosillo, Mexico
S = Allen Park, MI
W = Wayne, MI
X = St. Thomas, Canada
Y = Wixom, MI
5 = Flat Rock, MI
6 = Kia, Korea
8 = Broadmeadows, Australia

12th Thru 17th POSITION
PRODUCTION SEQUENCE NUMBER

AIR BAG SYSTEM PRECAUTIONS

TABLE OF CONTENTS

Page No.

CHRYSLER CORP. 5

FORD MOTOR CO. 5

Chrysler Corp.

INDEX

Page No.

Air Bag System Arming 5
Air Bag System Disarming 5

AIR BAG SYSTEM DISARMING

1. Place ignition switch in lock position.
2. Disconnect and tape battery ground cable connector. Allow at least two minutes for back-up power supply to deplete. The SRS is designed to retain enough voltage to deploy air bag for a short time even after battery is disconnected.

AIR BAG SYSTEM ARMING

1. Connect battery ground cable.
2. From passenger side of vehicle turn ignition switch to On position.
3. SRS warning light should illuminate for six to eight seconds, then remain off for 45 seconds to indicate SRS is functioning properly. If SRS warning light does not perform as described, refer to **MOTOR'S AIR BAG MANUAL** for diagnosis and testing.

Ford Motor Co.

INDEX

Page No.	Page No.	Page No.
Air Bag System Arming: 8	Town Car 10	Crown Victoria & Grand Marquis. 6
Aspire 8	1993 Capri Early Production 8	Mark VIII 7
Continental. 8	1993 Capri Late Production 8	Probe 7
Contour & Mystique 8	1994-96 Mustang 9	Sable & Taurus. 7
Cougar & Thunderbird. 8	1994 Capri, 1994-96 Escort & Tracer 8	Tempo, Topaz & 1993 Mustang 7
Crown Victoria & Grand Marquis. 9	**Air Bag System Disarming:** 5	Town Car 7
Mark VIII 9	Aspire 5	1993 Capri Early Production 5
Probe 9	Continental. 6	1993 Capri Late Production 6
Sable & Taurus. 10	Contour & Mystique 6	1994-96 Mustang 7
Tempo, Topaz & 1993 Mustang 10	Cougar & Thunderbird. 6	1994 Capri, 1994-96 Escort & Tracer 6

AIR BAG SYSTEM DISARMING

ASPIRE

1. Disconnect battery ground cable.
2. Wait one minute for back-up power supply to deplete stored energy.

3. Remove four bolts retaining air bag module to steering wheel.
4. Disconnect driver side air bag connector.
5. Connect air bag simulator to vehicle harness above glove compartment.
6. Remove Passenger side air bag module.
7. Connect Rotunda Air Bag Simulator 105-00009 to passenger side air bag vehicle harness.
8. Connect battery ground cable.

1993 CAPRI EARLY PRODUCTION

1. Disconnect positive battery cable and back-up power supply.
2. Remove four nut and washer assemblies retaining air bag module to steering wheel.

3. Disconnect air bag connector.
4. Connect Rotunda Air Bag Simulator 105-00008 or equivalent, to clock spring connector in base of steering wheel.
5. Connect positive battery cable and back-up power supply.

1993 CAPRI LATE PRODUCTION

1. Disconnect battery ground cable.
2. Wait one minute for back-up power supply to deplete stored energy.
3. Remove four bolts retaining air bag module to steering wheel.
4. Disconnect air bag connector.
5. Connect Rotunda Air Bag Simulator 105-00008 to vehicle harness at top of steering column.
6. Connect battery ground cable.

1994 CAPRI, 1994–96 ESCORT & TRACER

1. Disconnect battery positive cable.
2. Wait one minute for back-up power supply to deplete stored energy.
3. Remove bolts retaining air bag module to steering wheel.
4. Disconnect air bag connector.
5. Connect Rotunda Air Bag Simulator 105-00010 to vehicle harness at top of steering column.
6. **On 1995-96 models, proceed as follows:**
   a. Remove glove compartment, then the two passenger side air bag module bolts.
   b. Pull passenger side air bag module from instrument panel, then disconnect electrical connector. **To avoid injury by accidental deployment, place module on a bench with trim cover facing up. Do not pull on wires during removal or handling.**
7. **On all models,** connect battery positive cable.

CONTINENTAL

1. Disconnect battery positive cable
2. Wait one minute for backup power supply to deplete.
3. Remove four nut and washer assemblies retaining driver air bag module to the steering wheel.
4. Disconnect driver air bag module connector.
5. Attach Rotunda Air Bag Simulator 105-00010 or equivalent, to air bag terminals on clock spring assembly to simulate air bag.
6. Open glove compartment and rotate completely past stops. Disconnect

passenger side air bag connector.
7. Attach Rotunda Air Bag Simulator 105-00010 or equivalent, to air bag terminals on wiring harness side of passenger air bag module connector.
8. Connect positive battery cable.

CONTOUR & MYSTIQUE

1. Disconnect battery ground cable, then disconnect battery positive cable and allow at least one minute for back-up power supply to deplete.
2. Remove five retaining screws and steering column shrouds from column tube, then rotate steering wheel as necessary to access and remove air bag retaining bolts.
3. Disconnect driver side air bag module connector, then carefully remove module from vehicle. **To prevent injury by accidental deployment, place module on a bench with trim cover facing upward.**
4. Connect Rotunda air bag simulator tool No. 105-00010 or equivalent to air bag sliding contact connector at top of steering column.
5. Open glove compartment, then lower compartment to floor by pressing inward on sides.
6. Remove four screws, then disconnect glove compartment lamp and remove compartment upper cover.
7. Remove A/C evaporator register duct, then remove two retaining nuts from passenger side air bag module.
8. Remove two bolts from passenger side air bag module, then disconnect electrical connector and carefully remove module from vehicle. **To prevent injury by accidental deployment, place module on a bench with trim cover facing upward.**
9. Connect a second Rotunda air bag simulator tool No. 105-00010 or equivalent to passenger air bag module wiring harness.
10. Reconnect positive battery cable, then the ground cable.

COUGAR & THUNDERBIRD

1. Disconnect battery ground cable, then disconnect battery positive cable and allow at least one minute for back-up power supply to deplete.
2. Remove two bolt and washer assemblies retaining driver side air bag assembly to steering wheel.
3. Disconnect driver side air bag connector, then remove air bag from steering wheel. Position air bag module on work bench with trim cover facing upward.
4. Connect Rotunda air bag similar tool No. 105-00010 or equivalent to vehicle air bag wiring harness at top of steering column.
5. Remove passenger side air bag module as follows:

   a. Using a small screwdriver, detach dampening rod from righthand side of glove compartment.
   b. Pull lefthand side of glove compartment inward and allow glove compartment to drop downward.
   c. Remove air duct attaching screws, then the air duct.
   d. Remove two vertically positioned bolts from each side of air bag module.
   e. Remove the two remaining air bag module attaching bolts.
   f. Push air bag module outward from instrument panel. Do not handle air bag module by deployment doors.
   g. Disconnect electrical connector, then remove air bag module. Position air bag module on work bench with trim cover facing upward.
6. Connect Rotunda air bag simulator tool No. 105-00010 or equivalent to vehicle air bag wiring harness in place of the passenger side air bag module.
7. Reconnect battery positive cable, then the ground cable.

CROWN VICTORIA & GRAND MARQUIS

1. **On 1993 models,** disconnect battery positive cable.
2. **On 1994-96 models,** disconnect battery ground cable, then the battery positive cable.
3. **On all models,** wait one minute for backup power supply to discharge.
4. Remove four nut and washer assemblies retaining driver air bag module to the steering wheel.
5. Disconnect driver air bag module connector.
6. Connect Rotunda Air Bag simulator 105-00010 or equivalent, to vehicle harness at top of steering column.
7. **On models with passenger side air bag,** remove passenger air bag as follows:
   a. Remove righthand instrument panel lower molding.
   b. **On Crown Victoria,** remove righthand instrument cluster finish panel retaining screws, then the panel.
   c. **On Grand Marquis,** remove righthand register applique retaining screws, then the applique.
   d. Remove cluster finish panel retaining screws, then the panel.
   e. **On all models,** open glove compartment, press sides inward and lower glove compartment to floor.
   f. Working through glove compartment opening, remove two front air bag module retaining screws.
   g. Remove two rear air bag module retaining screws, then disconnect electrical connector and remove air bag module.

FORD MOTOR CO.

8. Install Rotunda Air Bag simulator 105-00010 or equivalent, on vehicle air bag harness connector.
9. **On 1993 models,** connect battery positive cable.
10. **On 1994-96 models,** connect battery positive cable, then the battery ground cable.

PROBE

1. Disconnect battery ground cable.
2. Wait one minute for back-up power supply to deplete stored energy.
3. Remove four bolts retaining air bag module to steering wheel.
4. Remove air bag part way.
5. Disconnect air bag, horn and speed control electrical connectors.
6. Connect Rotunda Air Bag simulator 105-00009 to vehicle harness at top of steering column.
7. **On models equipped with passenger air bag,** proceed as follows:
   a. Disconnect two passenger air bag diagnostic module connectors under lefthand instrument panel pad.
   b. Open glove compartment door, then press in compartment sides to disengage retainers and lower compartment from instrument panel, then remove screws and glove compartment from vehicle.
   c. Remove screws from glove compartment upper cover, then remove upper cover and disconnect passenger side air bag module electrical connectors.
   d. Remove passenger side air bag module bolts, then remove module from vehicle by pressing outward from inside instrument panel. **Do not pull on wiring during removal or handling of air bag module. Place module on a bench with trim cover facing up to avoid injury by accidental deployment.**
   e. Connect a second Rotunda air bag simulator tool No. 105-00009 or equivalent to passenger side air bag harness.
8. **On all models,** connect battery ground cable.

MARK VIII

1. **On 1993 models,** disconnect battery positive cable.
2. **On 1994-96 models,** disconnect battery ground cable, then the battery positive cable.
3. **On all models,** wait one minute for backup power supply to discharge.
4. Remove two screw and washer assemblies retaining driver air bag module to the steering wheel.
5. Disconnect driver air bag module connector.
6. Connect Rotunda Air Bag Simulator 105-00010 or equivalent, to vehicle harness at top of steering column.
7. Remove passenger air bag as follows:
   a. Remove righthand and lefthand finish panel.

b. Open glove compartment, press sides inward and lower glove compartment to floor.
c. Working through glove compartment opening, remove two lower air bag module retaining bolts.
d. Remove three remaining air bag module retaining screws from side of air bag cover.
e. Disconnect electrical connector attached to lefthand side of air bag while removing air bag module.
8. Install Rotunda Air Bag Simulator 105-00010 or equivalent, on vehicle air bag harness connector in place of air bag.
9. **On 1993 models,** connect battery positive cable.
10. **On 1994-96 models,** connect battery positive cable, then the battery ground cable.

1994-96 MUSTANG

1. Disconnect battery ground cable.
2. **On 1994 models,** disconnect battery positive cable.
3. **On all models,** allow at least one minute for back-up power supply to deplete, then remove two rear cover plugs from steering wheel in order to access driver side air bag module screws.
4. Remove driver side air bag module screws and washers, then disconnect electrical connector and carefully remove module from vehicle.
5. Connect Rotunda air bag simulator tool No. 105-00010 or equivalent to air bag harness at top of steering column.
6. Open glove compartment door and push inward on sides of compartment to release it from instrument panel, then lower compartment assembly to floor.
7. Remove righthand A/C duct, then remove passenger side air bag retaining bolts from instrument panel steel reinforcement.
8. Disconnect electrical connector at lower lefthand corner of passenger side air bag module, then remove connector from instrument panel reinforcement.
9. Pull gently upon each corner of air bag cover to disengage from instrument panel, then push air bag module out from behind instrument panel. To avoid injury by accidental deployment, place module on a bench with trim cover facing up.
10. Install a second air bag Rotunda simulator tool No. 105-00010 or equivalent to passenger side air bag harness, then connect battery ground cable.

SABLE & TAURUS

1. **On 1993 models,** disconnect battery positive cable.
2. **On 1994 models,** disconnect battery ground cable, then the battery positive cable.

3. **On 1995-96 models,** disconnect battery ground cable.
4. **On all models,** wait one minute for backup power supply to discharge.
5. **On 1993-95 models,** remove four nut and washer assemblies retaining driver air bag module to the steering wheel.
6. **On 1996 models,** remove steering wheel spoke cover and two nut and washer assemblies retaining driver air bag module to the steering wheel.
7. Disconnect driver air bag module connector.
8. Connect Rotunda Air Bag Simulator 105-00010 or equivalent, on clock spring to simulate air bag.
9. **On models with passenger side air bag,** remove passenger air bag as follows:
   a. Remove righthand and lefthand finish panel.
   b. Remove instrument panel finish panel retaining spear clips.
   c. open glove compartment, press sides inward and lower glove compartment to floor.
   d. Working through glove compartment opening, remove two lower air bag module retaining bolts.
   e. Remove four remaining air bag module retaining screws from side of air bag cover, then disconnect electrical connector attached to lefthand side of air bag and remove air bag module.
10. Connect Rotunda Air Bag Simulator 105-00010 or equivalent, to wiring harness.
11. **On 1993 models,** connect battery positive cable.
12. **On 1994 models,** connect battery positive cable, then the battery ground cable.
13. **On 1995-96 models,** connect battery ground cable.

TEMPO, TOPAZ & 1993 MUSTANG

1. **On 1993 models,** disconnect battery positive cable.
2. **On 1994 models,** disconnect battery ground cable, then the battery positive cable.
3. **On all models,** wait one minute for back-up power supply to deplete stored energy.
4. Remove four nut and washer assemblies retaining driver air bag module to steering wheel.
5. Disconnect air bag module connector.
6. Attach Rotunda Air Bag simulator 105-00010 or equivalent, to vehicle harness at top of steering wheel.
7. **On 1993 models,** connect battery positive cable.
8. **On 1994 models,** connect battery positive cable, then the battery ground cable.

TOWN CAR

1. **On 1993 models,** disconnect battery positive cable.

2. **On 1994 models,** disconnect battery ground cable, then the battery positive cable.
3. **On 1995-96 models,** disconnect battery ground cable.
4. **On all models,** wait one minute for backup power supply to discharge.
5. Remove four nut and washer assemblies retaining driver air bag module to the steering wheel.
6. Disconnect driver air bag module connector.
7. Attach Rotunda Air Bag Simulator 105-00010 or equivalent, to vehicle harness at top of steering column.
8. Remove instrument panel moldings, instrument panel finish panel retaining screws, then the panel.
9. Open glove compartment, press sides inward and lower glove compartment to floor.
10. Working through glove compartment opening, remove two lower air bag module retaining bolts.
11. Remove four remaining air bag module retaining screws, then disconnect electrical connector and remove air bag module.
12. Install Rotunda Air Bag simulator 105-00010 or equivalent, on vehicle passenger side air bag harness connector.
13. **On 1993 models,** connect battery positive cable.
14. **On 1994 models,** connect battery positive cable, then the battery ground cable.
15. **On 1995-96 models,** connect battery ground cable.

AIR BAG SYSTEM ARMING

ASPIRE

1. Disconnect battery ground cable.
2. Wait one minute for backup power supply to deplete stored energy.
3. Remove air bag simulator from vehicle harness at top of steering column.
4. Connect driver side air bag connector.
5. Position driver side air bag on steering wheel and secure with four bolts. **Torque** to 80-115 inch lbs.
6. Remove air bag simulator from vehicle harness above glove compartment.
7. Install passenger side air bag module.
8. Connect battery ground cable.
9. Place ignition switch from in the Run position and note air bag warning lamp operation. Indicator lamp should illuminate for approximately 6 seconds, and then turn off. If warning lamp does not illuminate or remains illuminated continuously or flashes, refer to "Diagnosis and Testing." Verify system operation.

1993 CAPRI EARLY PRODUCTION

1. Disconnect positive battery cable and backup power supply.

2. Remove air bag Simulator from clock spring connector at base of steering wheel.
3. Connect air bag connector.
4. Position air bag on steering wheel and secure with four nut and washer assemblies. **Torque** to 17-26 ft. lbs.
5. Connect positive battery cable and back-up power supply.
6. Place ignition switch from in the Run position and note air bag warning lamp operation. Indicator lamp should illuminate for approximately 6 seconds, and then turn off. If warning lamp does not illuminate or remains illuminated continuously or flashes, refer to "Diagnosis and Testing."

1993 CAPRI LATE PRODUCTION

1. Disconnect battery ground cable.
2. Wait one minute for backup power supply to deplete stored energy.
3. Remove air bag Simulator from vehicle harness at top of steering column.
4. Connect air bag connector.
5. Position air bag on steering wheel and secure with four bolts. **Torque** to 17-26 ft. lbs.
6. Connect battery ground cable.
7. Place ignition switch from in the Run position and note air bag warning lamp operation. Indicator lamp should illuminate for approximately 6 seconds, and then turn off. If warning lamp does not illuminate or remains illuminated continuously or flashes, refer to "Diagnosis and Testing."

1994 CAPRI, 1994–96 ESCORT & TRACER

1. Disconnect battery positive cable.
2. Wait one minute for backup power supply to deplete stored energy.
3. Remove air bag simulator from vehicle harness at top of steering column.
4. Connect air bag connector.
5. Position air bag on steering wheel and secure with two bolts. **Torque** to 35-53 inch lbs.
6. **On 1995-96 models,** install passenger side air bag module as follows:
   a. Press air bag module mounting tabs in instrument panel down slightly, then connect module electrical connector and position module in instrument panel.
   b. Install two air bag module bolts and torque to 61-79 inch lbs.
   c. Install glove compartment in instrument panel and **torque** glove compartment door hinge to instrument panel screws to 69-104 inch lbs.
7. **On all models,** connect battery positive cable.
8. Place ignition switch from in the Run position and note air bag warning lamp operation. Indicator lamp should illuminate for approximately 6 seconds, and then turn off. If warning lamp does not illuminate or remains illuminated continuously or flashes, refer to "Diagnosis and Testing."

CONTINENTAL

1. Disconnect battery positive cable.
2. Wait one minute for backup power supply to discharge.
3. Remove air bag simulator from vehicle harness connector at top of steering column.
4. Connect driver air bag connector.
5. Position air bag assembly on steering wheel and secure with four nut and washer assemblies. **Torque** to 35-50 inch lbs.
6. Remove air bag simulator from vehicle harness connector at passenger air bag.
7. Connect passenger air bag connector.
8. Connect battery positive cable.
9. Place ignition switch from in the Run position and note air bag warning lamp operation. Indicator lamp should illuminate for approximately 6 seconds, and then turn off. If warning lamp does not illuminate or remains illuminated continuously or flashes, refer to "Diagnosis and Testing."

CONTOUR & MYSTIQUE

1. Disconnect battery ground cable, then disconnect battery positive cable and allow at least one minute for back-up power supply to deplete.
2. Disconnect drivers side air bag simulator tool from air bag sliding contact connector at top of steering column.
3. Connect driver side air bag module connector, then carefully install module into vehicle.
4. Rotate steering wheel as necessary to access and install air bag retaining bolts. **Torque** to 7-10 ft. lbs.
5. Install steering column shrouds onto column tube, then install five retaining screws.
6. Disconnect passenger side air bag simulator from air bag module wiring harness.
7. Connect air bag electrical connector and carefully install module into vehicle, then install and **torque** two attaching bolts to 7-10 ft. lbs.
8. Install A/C evaporator register duct and attaching screws.
9. Install glove compartment upper cover, lamp and four attaching screws.
10. By pressing inward on sides install glove compartment.
11. Reconnect positive battery cable, then the ground cable.

COUGAR & THUNDERBIRD

1. Disconnect battery ground cable, then disconnect battery positive cable and allow at least one minute for back-up power supply to deplete.
2. Disconnect Rotunda air bag similar tool from air bag wiring harness at top of steering column.
3. Install driver side air bag and connect air bag electrical connector.
4. Install two bolt and washer air bag retaining assemblies.

5. Disconnect Rotunda air bag simulator from vehicle air bag wiring harness.
6. Install passenger side air bag module as follows:
   a. Connect air bag module electrical connector.
   b. Install air bag module.
   c. Install four air bag module attaching bolts. **Torque** to 7 to 10 ft. lbs.
   d. Install air duct and attaching screws.
   e. Install lefthand side of glove compartment.
   f. Attach dampening rod from righthand side of glove compartment.
7. Reconnect battery positive cable, then the ground cable.

CROWN VICTORIA & GRAND MARQUIS

1. **On 1993 models,** disconnect battery positive cable.
2. **On 1994 models,** disconnect battery ground cable, then the battery positive cable.
3. **On 1995-96 models,** disconnect battery ground cable.
4. **On all models,** wait one minute for backup power supply to deplete stored energy.
5. Remove air bag simulator from vehicle harness at top of steering column.
6. Connect driver air bag connector.
7. Position driver air bag on steering wheel and secure with four nut and washer assemblies. **Torque** to 24-33 inch lbs.
8. **On models with passenger side air bag,** remove air bag Simulator from vehicle harness connector.
9. Install passenger air bag as follows:
   a. Connect electrical connector to air bag module and position module in instrument panel.
   b. **On 1993-94,** install two rear retaining screws and **torque** to 24-33 inch lbs.
   c. Install two front retaining screws and **torque** to 67-92 inch lbs.
   d. **On 1995-96 models,** install front retaining screws and **torque** to 19-25 ft. lbs., then install lower retaining screws and **torque** to 6-8 ft. lbs.
   e. **On all models,** return glove compartment to correct position, then install instrument cluster finish panel.
   f. **On Grand Marquis,** install righthand register applique and **torque** retaining screws to 17-27 inch lbs.
   g. **On 1993-94 models,** install instrument panel lower molding.
   h. **On 1995-96 models,** snap instrument panel upper molding into place.
10. **On 1993 models,** connect battery positive cable.
11. **On 1994 models,** connect battery positive cable, then the battery ground cable.

12. **On 1995-96 models,** connect battery ground cable.
13. **On all models,** place ignition switch from in the Run position and note air bag warning lamp operation. Indicator lamp should illuminate for approximately six seconds, and then turn off. If warning lamp does not illuminate or remains illuminated continuously or flashes, refer to "Diagnosis and Testing."

PROBE

1. Disconnect battery ground cable.
2. Wait one minute for backup power supply to deplete stored energy.
3. Remove air bag simulator from vehicle harness at top of steering column.
4. Connect air bag connector.
5. Position air bag on steering wheel and secure with four bolts. **Torque** to 61-86 inch lbs.
6. **On 1995-96 models,** disconnect air bag simulator tool from passenger side air bag harness, then install passenger side air bag module as follows:
   a. Insert air bag module into instrument panel, aligning guide pins with guide holes, then engage module tab with instrument panel clip. **Ensure** wiring is not pinched between air bag module and instrument panel pad.
   b. Install air bag module bolts and **torque** to 23-33 inch lbs., then connect air bag module electrical connectors securely.
   c. Insert connector pin into hole on rear of air bag module, then install glove compartment upper cover and glove compartment.
   d. Connect two diagnostic module connectors.
7. **On all models,** connect battery ground cable.
8. Place ignition switch from in the Run position and note air bag warning lamp operation. Indicator lamp should illuminate for approximately 6 seconds, and then turn off. If warning lamp does not illuminate or remains illuminated continuously or flashes, refer to "Diagnosis and Testing."Verify system operation.

MARK VIII

1. **On 1993 models,** disconnect battery positive cable.
2. **On 1994 models,** disconnect battery ground cable, then the battery positive cable.
3. **On 1995-96 models,** disconnect battery ground cable.
4. **On all models,** wait one minute for backup power supply to deplete stored energy.
5. Remove air bag Simulator from clock spring connector at top of steering column.
6. Connect driver air bag connector.
7. Position driver air bag on steering

wheel and secure with two screw and washer assemblies. **Torque** to 8-10 ft. lbs.
8. Remove air bag Simulator from passenger harness connector.
9. Install passenger air bag as follows:
   a. Connect electrical connector to air bag module and position module in instrument panel.
   b. Install three upper retaining screws and **torque** to 9-18 inch lbs.
   c. Install lower module retaining bolts and **torque** to 62-97 inch lbs.
   d. Return glove compartment to correct position, then install instrument panel finish panel.
10. **On 1993 models,** connect battery positive cable.
11. **On 1994 models,** connect battery positive cable, then the battery ground cable.
12. **On 1995-96 models,** connect battery ground cable.
13. **On all models,** place ignition switch in the Run position and note air bag warning lamp operation. Indicator lamp should illuminate for approximately six seconds, and then turn off. If warning lamp does not illuminate or remains illuminated continuously or flashes, refer to "Diagnosis and Testing."

1994–96 MUSTANG

1. Disconnect battery ground cable.
2. **On 1994 models,** disconnect battery positive cable.
3. **On all models,** allow at least one minute for back-up power supply to deplete, then remove air bag simulator tool from harness connector at top of steering column.
4. Connect driver side air bag module, then position module in steering wheel and install screws and washers. **Torque** to 8-10 ft. lbs.
5. Remove air bag simulator tool from passenger side air bag module harness, then position module in instrument panel.
6. Attach connector to instrument panel reinforcement, then connect to wiring harness.
7. Install passenger air bag module retaining bolts and **torque** to 62-97 inch lbs.
8. Press gently upon air bag module corners to engage with instrument panel trim, then install righthand A/C duct.
9. Press sides of glove compartment assembly together and lift into position in instrument panel, then close glove compartment door.
10. **On 1994 models,** connect battery positive cable.
11. **On all models,** connect battery ground cable.
12. Place ignition switch in run position and note air bag warning lamp operation. Indicator lamp should illuminate for approximately six seconds, then turn off. If warning lamp does not illuminate, remains illuminated continuously or flashes, refer to "Diagnosis and Testing."

TEMPO, TOPAZ & 1993 MUSTANG

1. **On 1993 models,** disconnect battery positive cable.
2. **On 1994 models,** disconnect battery ground cable, then the battery positive cable.
3. **On all models,** wait one minute for backup power supply to deplete stored energy.
4. Remove air bag simulator from vehicle harness connector at top of steering column.
5. Connect driver air bag connector.
6. Position driver air bag on steering wheel and secure with four nut and washer assemblies. **Torque** to 35-50 inch lbs.
7. **On 1993 models,** connect battery positive cable.
8. **On 1994 models,** connect battery positive cable, then the battery ground cable.
9. **On all models,** place ignition switch from in the Run position and note air bag warning lamp operation. Indicator lamp should illuminate for approximately 6 seconds, and then turn off. If warning lamp does not illuminate or remains illuminated continuously or flashes, refer to "Diagnosis and Testing."

SABLE & TAURUS

1. **On 1993 models,** disconnect battery positive cable.
2. **On 1994 models,** disconnect battery ground cable, then the battery positive cable.
3. **On 1995-96 models,** disconnect battery ground cable.
4. **On all models,** wait one minute for backup power supply to deplete stored energy.
5. Remove air bag Simulator from clock spring connector.
6. Connect driver air bag connector.
7. **On 1993-95 models,** position driver air bag on steering wheel and secure with four nut and washer assemblies. **Torque** to 35-50 inch lbs.
8. **On 1996 models,** position driver air bag on steering wheel. Install two nut and washer assemblies retaining driver air bag module to the steering wheel, then install wheel spoke cover.
9. **On models with passenger side air bag,** remove air bag Simulator from vehicle harness connector.
10. Install passenger air bag as follows:
    a. Connect electrical connector to air bag module and position module in instrument panel.
    b. Install four upper retaining screws and **torque** to 11-16 inch lbs.
    c. Install lower module retaining bolts and **torque** to 62-97 inch lbs.
    d. Return glove compartment to correct position.
    e. Install instrument panel finish panel locator pin into air bag bushing locator, then align spear clips and press finish panel into place.
11. **On 1992-93 models,** connect battery positive cable.
12. **On 1994 models,** connect battery positive cable, then the battery ground cable.
13. **On 1995-96 models,** connect battery ground cable.
14. **On all models,** place ignition switch from in the Run position and note air bag warning lamp operation. Indicator lamp should illuminate for approximately 6 seconds, and then turn off. If warning lamp does not illuminate or remains illuminated continuously or flashes, refer to "Diagnosis and Testing."

TOWN CAR

1. **On 1993 models,** disconnect battery positive cable.
2. **On 1994 models,** disconnect battery ground cable, then the battery positive cable.
3. **On 1995-96 models,** disconnect battery ground cable.
4. **On all models,** wait one minute for backup power supply to deplete stored energy.
5. Remove air bag Simulator from vehicle harness at top of steering column.
6. Connect driver air bag connector.
7. Position driver air bag on steering wheel and secure with four nut and washer assemblies. **Torque** to 35-50 inch lbs.
8. Remove air bag Simulator from passenger harness connector.
9. Install passenger air bag as follows:
    a. Connect electrical connector to air bag module and position module in instrument panel.
    b. Install four upper retaining screws and **torque** to 24-35 inch lbs.
    c. Install lower module retaining bolts and **torque** to 4-8 ft. lbs.
    d. Return glove compartment to correct position, then install instrument panel finish panel.
    e. Install instrument panel moldings.
10. **On 1993 models,** connect battery positive cable.
11. **On 1994 models,** connect battery positive cable, then the battery ground cable.
12. **On 1995-96 models,** connect battery ground cable.
13. **On all models,** place ignition switch from in the Run position and note air bag warning lamp operation. Indicator lamp should illuminate for approximately six seconds, and then turn off. If warning lamp does not illuminate or remains illuminated continuously or flashes, refer to "Diagnosis and Testing."

Computer Relearn

DESCRIPTION

A computer relearn procedure may be required on any vehicle equipped with body, engine or transmission control computers whenever battery power to the computer is interrupted. These computers gather and store information on vehicle operation. They use this information to provide maximum driveability and vehicle performance.

RELEARN PROCEDURES

CHRYSLER

Engine Performance

The PCM receives input signals from various switches and sensors. Based on these inputs, the PCM adjusts fuel injector pulse width, idle speed, ignition timing and canister purge operation. If the battery is disconnected, the PCM will need to relearn values sent by the sensors and switches. During the PCM relearning period, a change may be noted in vehicle performance. To allow the PCM to relearn its values, ensure engine is at operating temperature. Drive the vehicle at part throttle, with moderate acceleration and idle conditions until normal performance returns.

Shift Quality

This procedure must be performed whenever battery voltage is interrupted to the Transmission Control Module (TCM) or any transmission internal components are replaced. A Chrysler Diagnostic Readout Box (DRB) or equivalent scan tool with the specified transmission cartridge must be used to perform this procedure.

1. To perform the shift quality reset procedure the following conditions must exist:
   a. Transmission oil temperature must be between 60-200°F (16-94° C).
   b. Engine speed greater than 500 RPM.
   c. Throttle angle less than 3 degrees.
2. Connect DRB or equivalent scan tool to Data Link Connector (DLC), the DLC is located under the lefthand side of the instrument panel, near the top of the brake pedal.
3. With correct cartridge installed, select "ADJUSTMENTS" function.
4. Apply brakes and select "QUICK LEARN" function.
5. Place gearshift in NEUTRAL, then "OD" when indicated.
6. Wait until "TEST COMPLETE" is indicated by the DRB.
7. Place gearshift in PARK, release brakes and disconnect DRB.

Theft Alarm

This procedure must be done any time the battery is disconnected or the battery is boosted. If the theft alarm is not reset, the alarm system will power up and the vehicle will not start.

1. Before reconnecting battery or connecting booster cables to battery, insert door key into driver side door lock.
2. Connect battery or booster cables and cycle driver's door lock once.
3. Vehicle can now be started.

FORD

ENGINE PERFORMANCE

Disconnect negative battery cable for a minimum of five minutes. After clearing memory, it is necessary to drive vehicle a minimum of 10 miles to allow processor time to relearn values.

SHIFT QUALITY
AOD-E & AXOD-E Transaxle

1. With gear selector in "OD," drive vehicle at 50 mph for approximately 15 seconds.
2. Holding speed steady, lightly apply and release brake for about five seconds.
3. Stop and park vehicle for at least 20 seconds with gearshift in DRIVE.
4. Repeat steps 1 through 3 five times.

E4OD Transmission

1. Shift gear selector to DRIVE, then press Overdrive Cancel Switch (LED should light).
2. Accelerate vehicle to 40 mph for minimum of 15 seconds (30 seconds above 4000 feet elevation), transmission should be in 3rd gear.
3. Holding speed steady, press Overdrive Cancel Switch (LED should go off) and accelerate to 50 mph
4. Transmission should shift from 3rd to 4th gear.
5. Hold speed at 50 mph for 15 seconds, then while holding speed steady, lightly apply and release brakes enough to turn the brake lights on.
6. Maintain 50 mph for at least five more seconds.
7. Stop and park vehicle for at least 20 seconds with gearshift in DRIVE.
8. Repeat steps 1 through 7 five times.

S VIC MIND & WA NING LAMP RESET PROCEDURES

TABLE OF CONTENTS

	Page No.
CHRYSLER CORP./EAGLE/AMC..	12
FORD MOTOR CO...............	20

Chrysler Corp./Eagle/AMC

Page No.

Air Bag System Warning Lamp....... 12
Anti-Lock Warning Lamp............ 12
Brake Pad Wear Warning Lamp:...... 12
  Eagle Medallion 12
Check Engine Lamp:............... 12
  Chrysler, Dodge & Plymouth 12
  Eagle Medallion 12
  Dodge Monaco & Eagle Premier..... 12
Check Engine Or Malfunction
  Indicator Lamp: 12
  Dodge & Plymouth Colt Vista & Eagle
    Summit......................... 12
EGR Warning Lamp:................ 12
  1985-87 Dodge & Plymouth Colt Vista 12
Electronic Monitor: 13
  1988-89 Chrysler LeBaron 13

Page No.

Electronic Vehicle Information Center:13
  1988-92 Chrysler New Yorker & New
    Yorker Landau & Dodge Dynasty,
    1990-92 Chrysler Fifth Avenue &
    Imperial....................... 13
Emission Maintenance Reminder
  Indicator:......................... 14
  1980-81 AMC Concord, Eagle, Pacer
    & Spirit 14
  1982-83 AMC Concord & Spirit &
    1982-87 Eagle................ 15
  1988 Eagle Except Medallion &
    Premier...................... 15
Low Coolant Warning Lamp:......... 15
  1990-92 Plymouth Laser & Eagle

Page No.

  Talon............................. 15
Maintenance Required Lamp: 15
  1988-91 Dodge & Plymouth Colt Vista15
Oxygen Sensor Maintenance
  Reminder Lamp:.................. 15
  1980 Chrysler, Dodge & Plymouth 15
Power Loss/Limit Lamp:............. 15
  Chrysler, Dodge & Plymouth 15
Overhead Travel Information System
  (OTIS):............................ 14
  Concorde, Intrepid, LHS, New Yorker &
    Vision 14
Vehicle Maintenance Monitor (VMM)
  System............................ 16
  Dodge Monaco & Eagle Premier...... 16

ANTI-LOCK WARNING LAMP

This lamp will be illuminated when the ignition switch is placed in the ON position. The lamp maybe illuminated for as long as 30 seconds as a bulb and system check. If lamp remains illuminated or comes on while operating the vehicle, a problem in the anti-lock brake system is indicated. When lamp is illuminated, place ignition switch in OFF position, then restart engine. If lamp still remains illuminated, the anti-lock brake system should be serviced. The brake system will remain functional, but without the anti-lock function. After servicing the anti-lock brake system the lamp will automatically reset when the ignition switch is cycled to the OFF position.

AIR BAG SYSTEM WARNING LAMP

On models equipped with an air bag system, if the air bag warning lamp illuminates and stays on, diagnosis and repair of the air bag system will be necessary to reset the lamp.

BRAKE PAD WEAR WARNING LAMP
EAGLE MEDALLION

When this message is displayed, the disc brake pads should be inspected and replaced as necessary. After completing service, the message will be reset automatically.

EGR WARNING LAMP
1985–87 DODGE & PLYMOUTH COLT VISTA

This lamp will be illuminated every 50,000 miles to indicate interval for EGR system service. After performing EGR system service, the lamp can be reset by moving the reset switch lever located at the rear of the instrument cluster, **Fig. 1.**

CHECK ENGINE LAMP
CHRYSLER, DODGE & PLYMOUTH

The Check Engine lamp will be illuminated for approximately 3 seconds after the ignition switch has been placed in the ON position as a bulb check. If incorrect or no signals are received by the Single Board Engine Controller (SMEC) from various sensors, the SBEC will illuminate the Check Engine lamp. After diagnosing and servicing the fuel injection system or emission related systems, the SBEC memory will be cleared after approximately 50 to 100 ignition key on-off cycles.

EAGLE MEDALLION

This lamp will be illuminated during engine starting as a bulb check. Once the engine has started, the lamp should go off. If lamp remains illuminated, the fuel injection and emission control system diagnosis should be performed using tester M.S. 1700. During the diagnosis and repair procedure with tester M.S. 1700, the check engine lamp will be reset.

DODGE MONACO & EAGLE PREMIER

This lamp will be illuminated during engine starting as a bulb check. Once the engine has started, the lamp should go off. If lamp remains illuminated, the fuel injection and emission control system diagnosis should be performed using tester DRB II. During the diagnosis and repair procedure with tester DRB II, the check engine lamp will be reset.

CHECK ENGINE OR MALFUNCTION INDICATOR LAMP
DODGE & PLYMOUTH COLT & EAGLE SUMMIT

This lamp is used to monitor fuel injection and emission control system components for malfunctions. When the ignition switch is placed in the ON position, the lamp will illuminate for 2 to 3 seconds as a bulb check. If lamp remains on, a malfunction in the fuel injection or emission control system is indicated. If malfunction is intermittent, the lamp will go off when Electronic Control Unit (ECU) receives a normal signal from the malfunctioning component. If the ECU receives an improper signal from a malfunctioning component for a time longer than that programmed into the ECU, a code will be stored in the ECU memory and the Malfunction Indicator Lamp will be illuminated. After servicing the indicated component, Malfunction Indicator Lamp can be reset

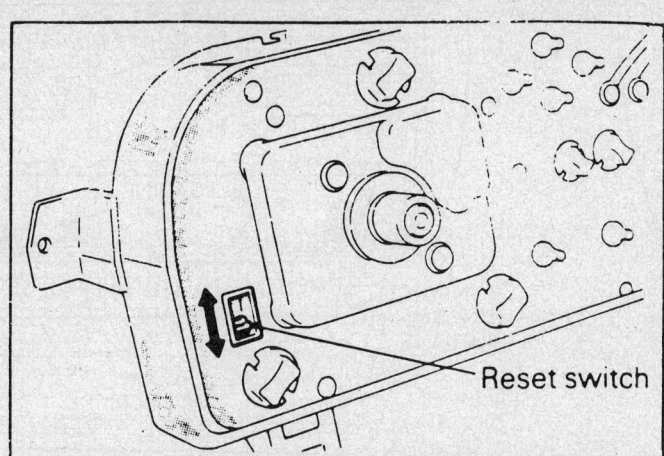

Fig. 1 EGR or Maintenance Required Lamp reset switch location. 1985–91 Dodge & Plymouth Colt Vista

by clearing the ECU memory. The ECU memory is cleared by disconnecting the battery ground cable for approximately 10 seconds.

ELECTRONIC MONITOR

1988–89 CHRYSLER LEBARON

This system is an electronic monitor system with sensors, which displays messages on an instrument panel mounted console. If no messages are stored, the message "Monitored Systems OK" will be displayed approximately 6 seconds after ignition switch has been placed in th ON position. The system is actuated by depressing the check button located on the front of the message display. When this button is depressed, the system will sound a tone and cycle through the messages and then return to normal operation. If the monitor detects a fault, the component will be noted on the display. The fault messages are as follows:

BRAKE FLUID LOW—When this message is displayed, bring brake to proper level. The message will be reset after the ignition switch has been cycled to the OFF position.

COOLANT LEVEL LOW—When this message is displayed, bring coolant to proper level. The message will be reset after the ignition switch has been cycled to the OFF position.

DISC BRAKE PADS WORN—When this message is displayed, the disc brake pads should be inspected and replaced as necessary. After completing service, the message will be reset after the ignition switch has been cycled to the OFF position.

DRIVER, PASSENGER OR HATCH AJAR—Close door or hatch indicated to cancel message.

ENGINE TEMPERATURE HIGH—This message will be indicated when an engine overheating condition is encountered. Af-

ter repairing cause of engine overheating condition or when engine speed is less than 300 RPM, the message will be automatically cancelled.

EXTERIOR LAMPS ON—This message will appear when the ignition switch is in OFF, LOCK or ACC positions, the driver's door is open and the light switch is in the ON position. This message will be cancelled when light switch is placed in the OFF position or the door is closed.

HEADLAMP, BRAKE OR TAIL LAMP OUT—The display will be illuminated when brake is applied or light switch is in the ON position and a burned out lamp bulb is present. To reset message, replace burned out bulb, then actuate lamp circuit.

KEY IN IGNITION—This message will appear when the ignition switch is in the OFF, LOCK or ACC position and the driver's door is open. This message will be cancelled when the keys are removed or the door is closed.

LOW FUEL LEVEL—When this message is displayed, add fuel to vehicle to reset message.

LOW OIL PRESSURE—This message will be displayed when a low engine oil pressure condition exist. If message is encountered with vehicle operating at idle speed, increase engine RPM. If message remains or if message is encountered while operating vehicle, the engine lubricating system should be checked and serviced immediately. After engine lubricating system has been serviced, the message will be automatically cancelled.

LOW TRANS PRESSURE—When this message is displayed, a problem in the automatic transaxle is present. After completing automatic transaxle service, the message will be reset after the ignition switch has been cycled to the OFF position.

VOLTAGE LOW—When this message is displayed, a problem in the charging or electrical system exist. After servicing, the message will be reset after the ignition switch has been cycled to the OFF position.

WASHER FLUID LOW—When this message is displayed, bring washer fluid to proper level to reset message.

ELECTRONIC VEHICLE INFORMATION CENTER

1988–92 CHRYSLER NEW YORKER & NEW YORKER LANDAU & DODGE DYNASTY, 1990–92 CHRYSLER FIFTH AVENUE & IMPERIAL

On 1988-89 models, this system is a computer controlled monitor system, which displays messages on an overhead console, **Fig. 2**. When the vehicle is started and no faults are present, the display will indicate "MONITORED SYSTEMS OK." If the monitor detects a fault, a tone will be sounded and component will be noted on the display.

On 1990-92 models, the Electronic Vehicle Information Center is a computer controlled warning system which monitors various sensors used on the vehicle. The system supplements the warning indicators in the instrument cluster. When a warning message has been activated, a tone will sound to attract the driver's attention. The warning message will then be displayed on the overhead console, **Fig. 3**, until the condition has been corrected or a new display function is called up. A tone will announce each new warning condition. The warning messages are as follows:

CHECK ENGINE OIL LEVEL—When this message is displayed, check engine oil and adjust to proper level. The message will be reset after the ignition switch has been cycled to the OFF position.

CHECK TRANS—When this message is displayed, a problem in the automatic transaxle is present. After completing automatic transaxle service, the message will be reset after the ignition switch has been cycled to the OFF position.

COOLANT LEVEL LOW—When this message is displayed, bring coolant to proper level. The message will be reset after the ignition switch has been cycled to the OFF position.

DISC BRAKE PADS WORN—When this message is displayed, the disc brake pads should be inspected and replaced as necessary. After completing service, the message will be reset after the ignition switch has been cycled to the OFF position.

DRIVER, PASSENGER, LEFT REAR, RIGHT REAR DOOR OR TRUNK AJAR—Close door to cancel message.

ENGINE TEMPERATURE CRITICAL—This message will be indicated when an engine overheating condition is encountered. After repairing cause of engine overheating condition, the message will be automatically cancelled.

EXTERIOR LAMPS ON—This message will appear when the ignition switch is in OFF, LOCK or ACC, the driver's door is open and the light switch is in the ON position. This message will be cancelled when light switch is placed in the OFF position or the door is closed.

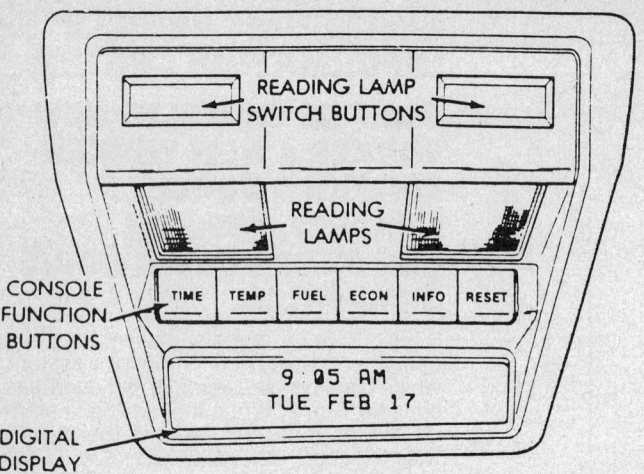

Fig. 2 Electronic Vehicle Information Center display console. 1988–89 Chrysler New Yorker & Dodge Dynasty

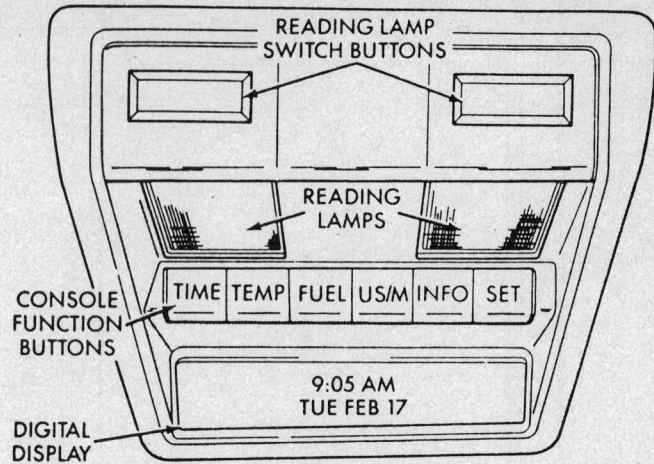

Fig. 3 Electronic Vehicle Information Center display console. 1990–92 Chrysler New Yorker, Fifth Avenue, Imperial & Dodge Dynasty

HEADLAMP, BRAKE OR TAIL LAMP OUT—The display will be illuminated when brake is applied or light switch is in the ON position and a burned out lamp bulb is present. To reset message, replace burned out bulb, then actuate lamp circuit.

KEY IN IGNITION—This message will appear when the ignition switch is in the OFF, LOCK or ACC position and the driver's door is open. This message will be cancelled when the keys are removed or the door is closed.

LOW BRAKE FLUID—When this message is displayed, bring brake to proper level. The message will be reset after the ignition switch has been cycled to the OFF position.

LOW FUEL LEVEL—When this message is displayed, add fuel to vehicle. The message will be reset after the ignition switch has been cycled to the OFF position.

OVERHEAD TRAVEL INFORMATION SYSTEM (OTIS)

CONCORDE, INTREPID, LHS, NEW YORKER & VISION

Overhead Travel Information System (OTIS) is a module with six informational displays and four buttons, **Fig. 4.** When the ignition switch is turned On, OTIS blanks the display for one second, then returns to the display active when the vehicle was last turned Off.

LOW OIL PRESSURE—This message will be displayed when a low engine oil pressure condition exist. If message is encountered with vehicle operating at idle speed, increase engine RPM. If message remains or if message is encountered while operating vehicle, the engine lubricating system should be checked and serviced immediately. After engine lubricating system has been serviced, the message will be automatically cancelled.

SERVICE REMINDER—This message will be indicated at 7,500 mile or 12 month intervals to indicate that required service is to be performed. After performing the required service, with the Service Reminder message displayed, depress the Vehicle Electronic Information Center Reset button.

TURN SIGNAL ON—This message will be indicated when the turn is on and vehicle has traveled a distance over 1/2 mile at a speed above 15 MPH. The message will be reset when the turn signal has been placed in the OFF position.

VOLTAGE IMPROPER—When this message is displayed, a problem in the charging or electrical system exist. After servicing, the message will be reset after the ignition switch has been cycled to the OFF position.

WASHER FLUID LOW—When this message is displayed, bring washer fluid to proper level. The message will be reset after the ignition switch has been cycled to the OFF position.

The six informational displays on the OTIS are as follows:
1. Compass/Temperature.
2. Average fuel economy.
3. Distance to empty.
4. Instantaneous fuel economy.
5. Trip odometer.
6. Elapsed time.

The four buttons on the OTIS are as follows:
1. Step-Depress this button to select display modes except Compass/Temperature.
2. C/T-Depress this button to display compass (vehicle direction) and temperature.
3. U/SM-Switches display information between English and Metric readings.
4. RESET-Depress this button to reset the current display (for displays that can be reset).

Compass Calibration

Do not attempt to set compass calibration near large metal objects, such as other vehicles, buildings or bridges.

1. Remove all magnetic devises from roof panel.
2. Turn key to On position.
3. Press C/T button to select compass/temperature display.
4. Depress and hold RESET button for about 5 seconds. The VAR symbol will light during this time.
5. Continue to hold RESET button for about 10 seconds until CAL symbol illuminates.
6. Drive vehicle through three complete 360° turns in no less than 48 seconds. The compass will be calibrated when the CAL symbol is extinguished.
7. Reset compass variance as follows:
   a. Press and hold reset button for about five seconds until VAR symbol is lit.
   b. The OTIS will display variance zone and VAR.
   c. Press STEP button to display variance zone, **Fig. 5.**
   d. Press RESET button to set new variance zone and resume normal operation.

EMISSION MAINTENANCE REMINDER INDICATOR

1980–81 AMC CONCORD, EAGLE, PACER & SPIRIT

On 1980-81 models, at 30,000 miles intervals, a warning lamp will be illuminated on the instrument panel to indicate oxygen sensor replacement. After performing the required service, the reminder lamp switch must be reset. The switch is located between the upper and lower speedometer cables in the engine compartment on the lefthand side of the dash panel. Rotate the reset screw located on the switch 1/4 turn counterclockwise, **Fig. 6.**

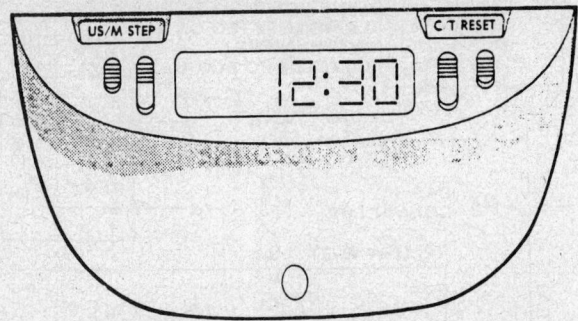

Fig. 4 Overhead Travel Information System (OTIS). Concorde, Intrepid, LHS, New Yorker & Vision

1982–83 AMC CONCORD & SPIRIT & 1982–87 EAGLE

The emission maintenance lamp will, **Fig. 7**, illuminate after 1000 hours of engine operation to indicate that the oxygen sensor must be replaced. After performing the required service, the emission maintenance E-Cell timer must be replaced for the next 1000 hour interval.

This timer is located in the passenger compartment, attached to the wiring harness leading to the MCU. To replace timer, remove printed circuit board, then remove timer from its enclosure and insert replacement timer.

1988 EAGLE EXCEPT MEDALLION & PREMIER

The emission maintenance timer will illuminate an indicator lamp on the instrument cluster when vehicle mileage has reached 82,500 miles. At this time, the oxygen sensor and PCV valve should be replaced, in addition to the other required emission maintenance scheduled for this mileage.

If the timer should fail before vehicle has accumulated 82,500 miles, the timer and oxygen sensor should both be replaced to maintain a proper sensor replacement interval.

After performing the required service, replace the emission maintenance timer as follows:

1. Remove emission maintenance timer to dash bracket attaching screws. The timer is located on the dash panel to the right of the steering column.
2. Remove timer from bracket, then disconnect electrical connector and remove timer from vehicle, **Fig. 8**.
3. Connect electrical connector to replacement timer, then position timer to mounting bracket and install and tighten attaching screws.

LOW COOLANT WARNING LAMP

1990–92 PLYMOUTH LASER & EAGLE TALON

The Low Coolant Warning Lamp will be illuminated whenever coolant level in the coolant reservoir is below a pre-determined level. Add coolant to bring reservoir to proper level to turn lamp off.

MAINTENANCE REQUIRED LAMP

1988–91 DODGE & PLYMOUTH COLT VISTA

This lamp will be illuminated at 50,000, 80,000, 100,000 and 150,000 miles to indicate interval for emission control system inspection. After performing emission control system inspection at the 50,000, 80,000 or 100,00 mile interval, the lamp can be reset by moving the reset switch lever located at the rear of the instrument cluster, **Fig. 1**. At the 150,000 mile interval, after performing inspection, remove bulb from lamp socket, **Fig. 9**.

OXYGEN SENSOR MAINTENANCE REMINDER LAMP

1980 CHRYSLER, DODGE & PLYMOUTH

At 30,000 miles intervals, a warning lamp will be illuminated on the instrument panel to indicate oxygen sensor replacement. The reminder can either be mechanical, **Fig. 10**, or electronic, **Fig. 11**. After performing the required service, the reminder lamp must be reset.

On the mechanical system, rotate the reset screw located on the switch counterclockwise until it stops, **Fig. 6**.

On the electronic system, remove 9 volt battery from module, which is located under the lefthand side of the instrument panel. Insert a suitable rod into hole on module case to reset switch. After resetting switch, install a replacement 9 volt battery.

POWER LOSS/LIMIT LAMP

CHRYSLER, DODGE & PLYMOUTH

The Power Loss/Limit lamp will be illuminated for approximately 3 seconds after the ignition switch has been placed in the ON position as a bulb check. If incorrect or no signals are received by the logic module from various sensors, the logic module will illuminate the Power Loss/Limit lamp. After diagnosing and servicing the fuel injection system or EGR system (California models with EGR sensor), the logic module memory can be cleared by disconnecting and reconnecting the battery quick disconnect.

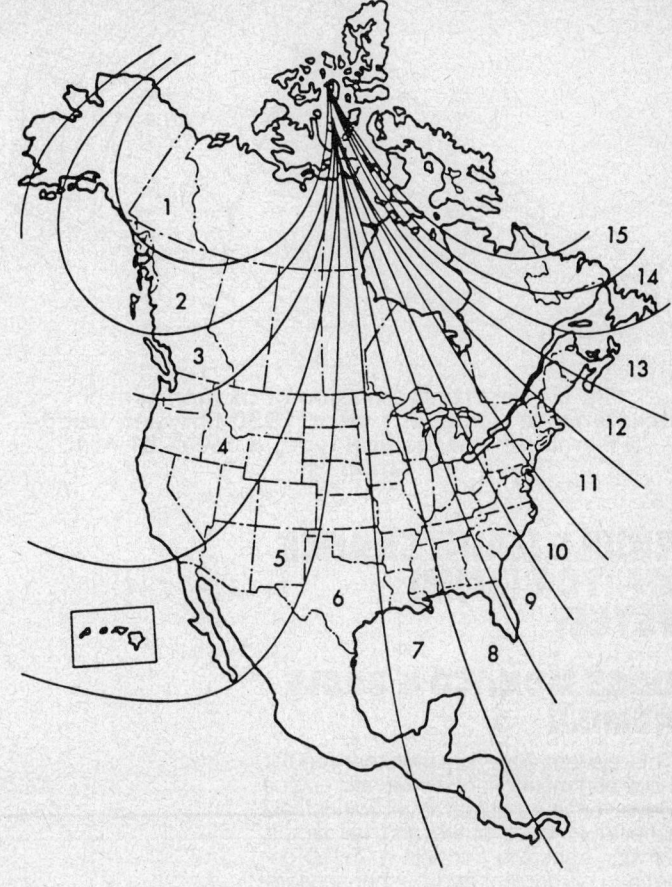

Fig. 5 Variance zone map

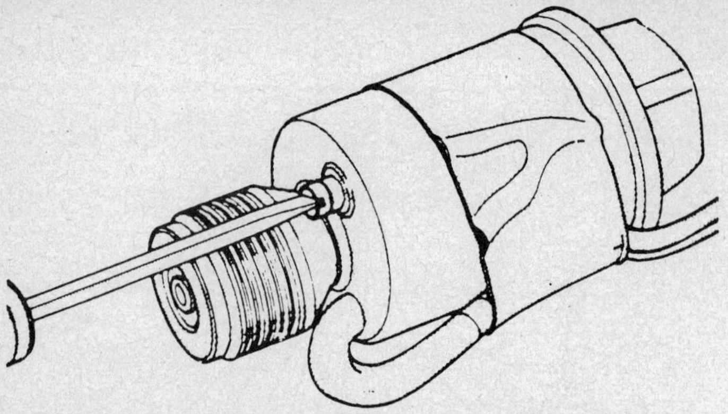

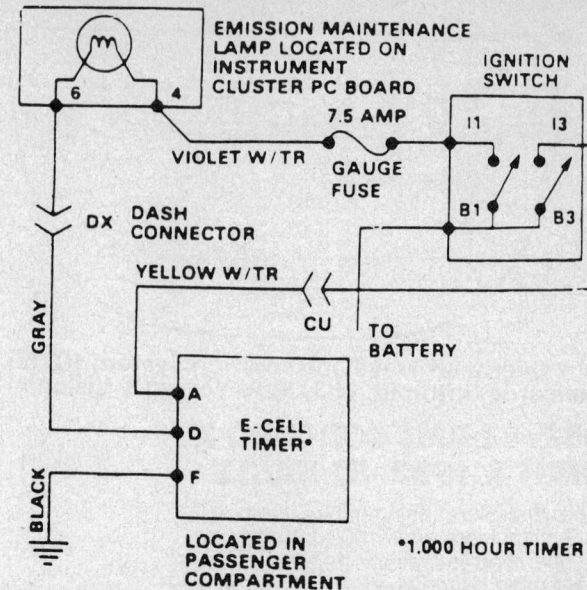

Fig. 6   Resetting emission or oxygen sensor maintenance reminder switch. 1980 Chrysler, Dodge & Plymouth (mechanical type) & 1980–81 AMC models

Fig. 7   Emission maintenance reminder indicator wiring schematic. 1982–83 AMC Concord & Spirit & 1982–87 Eagle

VEHICLE MAINTENANCE MONITOR (VMM) SYSTEM

DODGE MONACO & EAGLE PREMIER

This system, **Fig. 12,** monitors regular service and maintenance intervals, engine oil level, engine coolant level, windshield washer fluid level, brake and tail lamps, door ajar, transaxle (models w/4-150 engine) and oil, coolant and washer sensors.

When the vehicle is started and no faults are present, the display will indicate "MONITOR." If the monitor detects a fault, it will be noted on the display. If more than one fault is noted, the fault of the highest priority will be displayed first. The display will then note all existing faults and return to the fault of highest priority. The VMM fault messages are as follows:

DOOR—Door Ajar—Close door indicated on vehicle outline display to reset monitor.
LAMP—Brake Or Tail Lamp Outage—The display will be illuminated when brake is applied or light switch is in the ON position and a burned out lamp bulb is present. To reset monitor, replace burned out bulb.
COOLANT—Low Engine Coolant Level—Bringing coolant to proper level will reset monitor.
OIL—Low Engine Oil Level—The system will check engine oil level approximately 12 minutes after the ignition switch has been placed in the OFF position. A low oil level condition must be indicated three consecutive times before the monitor will display "Oil." To reset monitor, add oil to bring to proper level, then while display is indicating the "Oil" message, depress Reset select switch until a beep is noted. Even if Reset select switch is not depressed, the system will automatically reset monitor after three proper oil level readings have been obtained.
WASHER—Low Washer Fluid Level—Bringing washer fluid to proper level will reset monitor.
TRANS—Service Transaxle (Models w/4-150 Engine)—Indicates defect in automatic transaxle.

SERVICE—Perform Required Service and Maintenance—This message will be indicated at 7,500 mile intervals to indicate that required service is to be performed. After performing the required service, depress Reset select switch until a beep is noted.
SENSOR—This message will be indicated when a defect in the oil, coolant or washer sensor circuit is noted. Refer to "Self-Diagnosis."
MILES (KMS)—Miles to next scheduled service interval.

Self-Diagnosis

To diagnosis, depress and hold the Check and List select switches, then place ignition switch in ON position. With the instrument cluster switch in the English mode, all diagnosis will be performed automatically in sequence. With the instrument cluster in the Metric mode, the Check select switch will have to be depressed to proceed to the next test. The display will

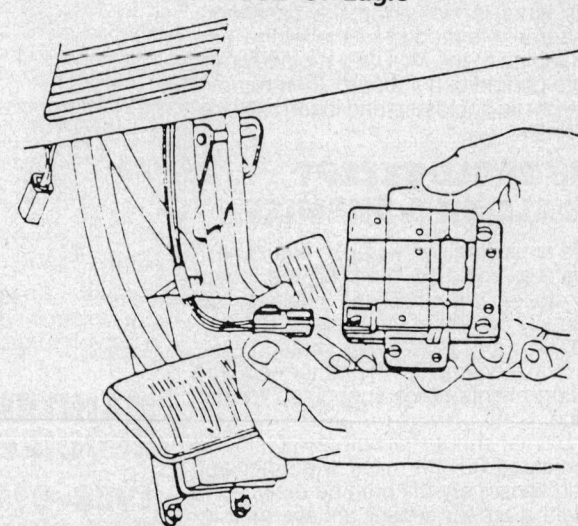

Fig. 8   Emission maintenance timer replacement. 1988 Eagle except Medallion & Premier

indicate which components are defective or satisfactory, refer to **Fig. 13.** After completing diagnosis, depress Check and List select switches to exit diagnosis mode.

Troubleshooting

1. If a condition of no display or incorrect information exist, start engine and check the following:
   a. On models less passive restraint check fuses 8 and 19 in fuse panel. On models with passive restraint, check fuses 2 and 8 in fuse panel. Replace any blown fuses.
   b. Using a suitable voltmeter, check terminal Nos. 1 and 5 of connector A, **Fig. 12.** Voltmeter should indicate battery voltage, if not check for open circuit to fuse panel.
   c. Connect a suitable ohmmeter between terminal Nos. 15 and 18 of connector A, **Fig. 12.** Ohmmeter should indicate zero ohms. If a no display condition is present, re-

Fig. 9 Maintenance Required Lamp bulb location. 1988–91 Dodge & Plymouth Colt Vista

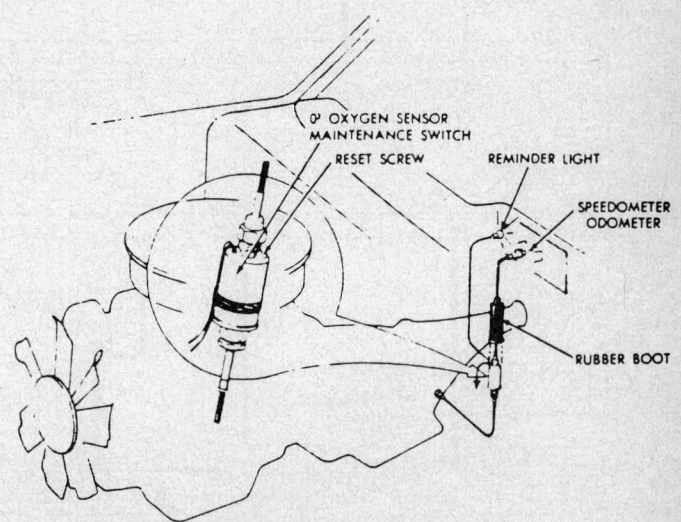

Fig. 10 Oxygen sensor maintenance reminder system. 1980 Chrysler, Dodge & Plymouth mechanical type

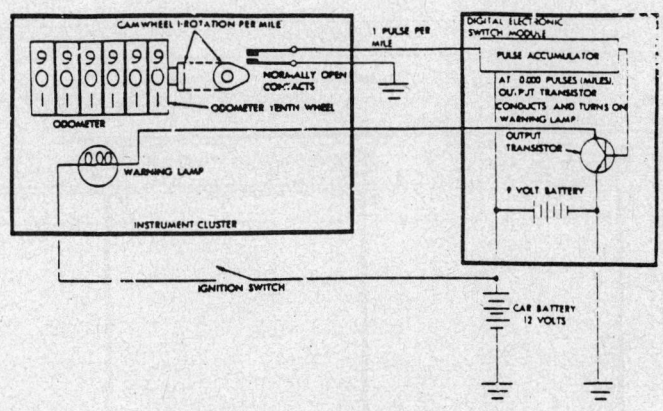

Fig. 11 Oxygen sensor maintenance reminder system. 1980 Chrysler, Dodge & Plymouth electronic type

place monitor. If a incorrect information condition is present, refer to "Self-Diagnosis." If reading is other than zero ohms, check for open circuit to ground.

d. With all doors closed, connect an ohmmeter between terminal Nos. 6, 7, 8 and 9 of connector A, **Fig. 12.** Ohmmeter should indicate an infinite reading. If reading is other than infinite, check for short circuit to ground.

2. If monitor fails to change modes, dis-connect electrical connector B, **Fig. 12,** and proceed as follows:

a. With Check select switch depressed, connect ohmmeter between terminal Nos. 2 and 4 of connector B. If ohmmeter reading is zero ohms, proceed to step b. If ohmmeter reading is other than zero ohms, replace mode select switches.

b. With List select switch depressed, connect ohmmeter between termi-nal Nos. 2 and 3 of connector B. If ohmmeter reading is zero ohms, proceed to step c. If ohmmeter reading is other than zero ohms, replace mode select switches.

c. With Reset select switch depressed, connect ohmmeter between terminal Nos. 2 and 5 of connector B. Ohmmeter reading should be zero ohms. If ohmmeter reading is other than zero ohms, replace mode select switches.

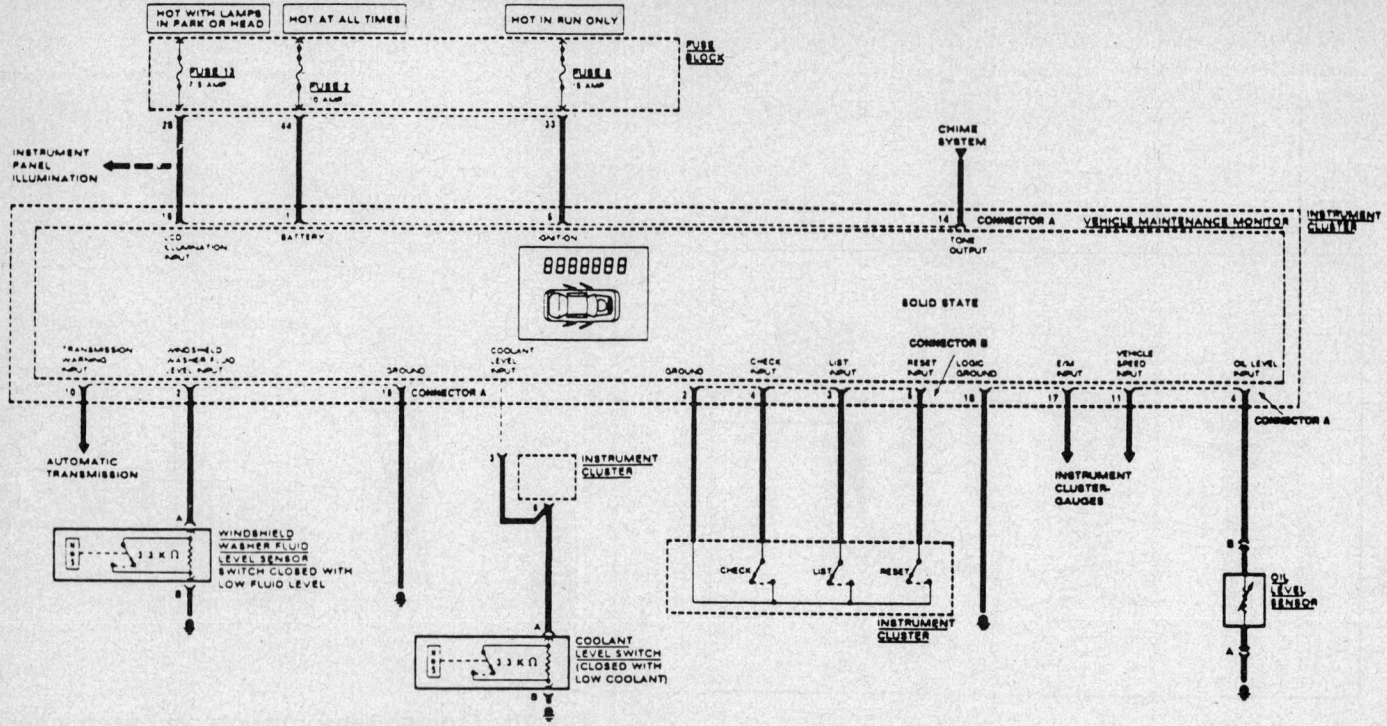

Fig. 12   Vehicle Maintenance Monitor (VMM) System wiring schematic (Part 1 of 2). Dodge Monaco & Eagle Premier

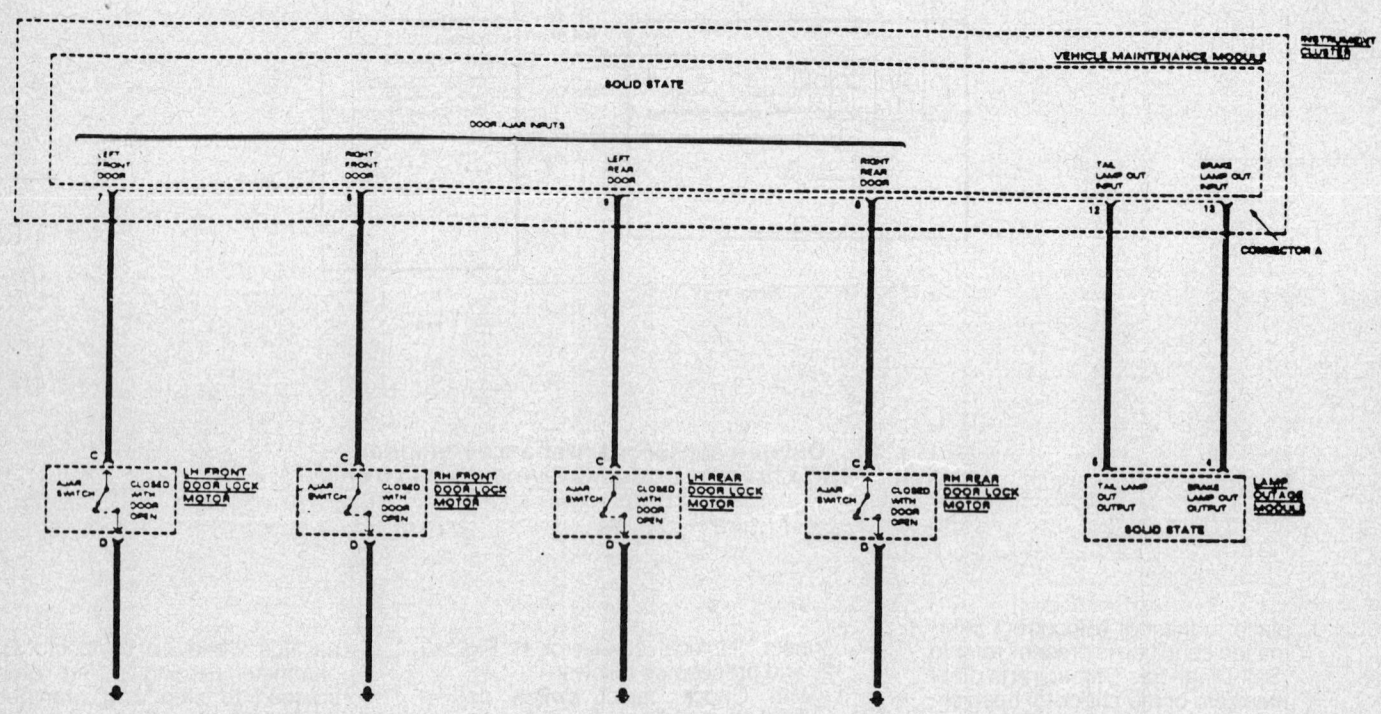

Fig. 12   Vehicle Maintenance Monitor (VMM) System wiring schematic (Part 2 of 2). Dodge Monaco & Eagle Premier

TEST 1 Initially, a number will be displayed on the monitor's screen. This number indicates the version of the maintenance module installed in the vehicle.

TEST 2

In Display	Meaning
"CAL O"	Monitor Bad
"CAL 1-7"	Monitor OK
"CAL F"	Monitor Bad

TEST 3 The module internal memory is tested.

In Display	Meaning
"RAM P"	Monitor OK
"RAM F"	Monitor Bad

TEST 4 The module program is tested.

In Display	Meaning
"ROM P"	Monitor OK
"ROM F"	Monitor Bad

TEST 5 The monitor's clocks are tested.

In Display	Meaning
"TIME P"	Monitor OK
"TIME F"	Monitor Bad

TEST 6 The monitor's storage capability is tested.

In Display	Meaning
"NVM P"	Monitor OK
"NVM F"	Monitor Bad

TEST 7 The monitor's internal synchronization is tested.

In Display	Meaning
"PAR 0"	Monitor OK
"PAR N"	Monitor Bad

TEST 8 The monitor's display screen is tested.

In Display	Meaning
All Segments ON	Monitor OK
All Segments OFF	Monitor OK
"0"	Monitor OK
"1"	Monitor OK
"10"	Monitor OK
"100"	Monitor OK
"1000"	Monitor OK
"10000"	Monitor OK
"100000"	Monitor OK
"111111"	Monitor OK
"122222"	Monitor OK
"133333"	Monitor OK
"144444"	Monitor OK
"155555"	Monitor OK
"166666"	Monitor OK
"177777"	Monitor OK
"188888"	Monitor OK
"199999"	Monitor OK

The graphic segments will light one at a time in the following order: the engine symbol, the car outline, right front door, right rear door, rear tail lamps, left rear door, and left front door. Any deviation from the above patterns signifies a bad monitor. Should any of the segments fail to light, the monitor is bad.

TEST 9 This test can only be performed while the test program is in the manual mode. OIL will flash. Release CHECK button and press and hold LIST button until OIL flashes three times, then release LIST button and OIL will stop flashing. There will be a 30-45 second delay while system is testing. Oil level faults are displayed at this time. The engine oil level is tested.

In Display	Meaning
"OIL H"	Monitor OK, Oil Level Normal
"OIL L"	Monitor OK, but Oil Level Is Low
"OIL O"	Monitor OK, but Oil Level Sensor Is Open
"OIL S"	Monitor OK, but Oil Level Sensor Is Shorted

TEST 10 The oil level probe is tested. The intermittent fault can be cleared in diagnostic program by pressing RESET switch while message is displayed.

In Display	Meaning
"OIL IF"	Intermittent Fault With Oil Sensor
NO MESSAGE	Monitor OK, Sensor OK

TEST 11 The washer fluid level is tested.

In Display	Meaning
"WASH H"	Washer Fluid Level Normal
"WASH L"	Washer Fluid Level Low
"WASH O"	Washer Fluid Level Probe Open

TEST 12 The washer level sensor is tested. The intermittent fault can be cleared in diagnostic program by pressing RESET switch while message is displayed.

In Display	Meaning
"WASHER IF"	Intermittent Fault With Washer Fluid Sensor
NO MESSAGE	Monitor OK, Sensor OK

TEST 13 The coolant fluid level is tested.

In Display	Meaning
"COOL H"	Coolant Fluid Level Is Normal
"COOL L"	Coolant Fluid Level Is Low
"COOL O"	Coolant Fluid Level Probe Is Open

TEST 14 The coolant fluid level sensor is tested. The intermittent fault can be cleared in diagnostic program by pressing RESET switch while message is displayed.

In Display	Meaning
"COOL IF"	Intermittent Fault With the Coolant Level Sensor
NO MESSAGE	Monitor OK, Sensor OK

TEST 15 The tail lamp circuit is tested.

In Display	Meaning
"TLO P"	Tail Lamp Circuit OK
"TLO F"	Tail Lamp Circuit Open

TEST 16 The brake lamp circuit is tested.

In Display	Meaning
"BLO P"	Brake Lamp Circuit OK
"BLO F"	Brake Lamp Circuit Open

TEST 17 The status of the transmission diagnostic module is tested.

In Display	Meaning
"TRANS P"	Transmission Module OK
"TRANS F"	Transmission Module Fault

TEST 18 The frequency of the road speed sensor is displayed. When in manual mode, continuous monitoring is possible.

In Display	Meaning
"SPD XXX"*	Frequency of Vehicle Speed Sensor

*Note: XXX will vary from 0 and increase as vehicle speed increases.

Fig. 13   Vehicle Maintenance Monitor (VMM) System self diagnosis test chart. Dodge Monaco & Eagle Premier

Ford Motor Co.

INDEX

Page No.

Air Bag System Warning Lamp....... 21
Anti-Lock Warning Lamp............. 21
Auxiliary Warning Indicator & Graphic
   Display Module:.................... 21
   Merkur........................... 21
Check Engine Lamp:................ 21
   1987-93 Models w/EEC-IV 21
   1994-95 Models w/EEC-IV.......... 22
   1994-96 Models w/EEC-V.......... 22

Page No.

Low Coolant Warning System........ 23
Low Oil Level Warning Indicator...... 23
Maintenance Reminder Indicator 23
Malfunction Indicator Lamp (MIL):.... 23
   Except 1988-89 Tracer 23
   1988-89 Tracer 23
Message Center:.................... 23
   Mark VIII......................... 23
Multiple Function Warning Indicator: . 23

Page No.

1987-89 Mustang GT................ 23
Service Interval Reminder:........... 24
   Continental....................... 24
   Probe 24
   1985-88 Cougar & Thunderbird...... 24
   1986-89 Sable & Taurus w/Electronic
     Instrument Cluster 24
   1989-93 Cougar & Thunderbird...... 24

ANTI-LOCK WARNING LAMP

This lamp will be illuminated when the ignition switch is placed in the ON position. The lamp maybe illuminated for as long as 30 seconds as a bulb and system check. If lamp remains illuminated or comes on while operating the vehicle, a problem in the anti-lock brake system is indicated. When lamp is illuminated, place ignition switch in OFF position, then restart engine. If lamp still remains illuminated, the anti-lock brake system should be serviced. The brake system will remain functional, but without the anti-lock function. After servicing the anti-lock brake system, the lamp will automatically be reset when vehicle is operated at a speed over 25 MPH.

AIR BAG SYSTEM WARNING LAMP

On models equipped with an air bag system, if the air bag warning lamp illuminates and stays on, diagnosis and repair of the air bag system will be necessary to reset the lamp.

AUXILIARY WARNING INDICATOR & GRAPHIC DISPLAY MODULE
MERKUR

This system monitors engine oil level, engine coolant level, windshield washer fluid level, brake pad wear, fuel level, seat belt usage, headlamp, brake and tail lamps, door ajar, liftgate ajar and ambient temperature.

When ignition switch is placed in the ON position, the graphic display module and all warning indicators will illuminate for 5 seconds. After 5 seconds, all warning lamps should go off and graphic display should indicate outline of vehicle and the two brake lights. The two brake light indications should go out once the brake pedal is depressed. If warning lamps remain illuminated or graphic display indicates a fault, check the following:

The low engine oil warning lamp is used to indicate when engine oil level is 12 mm

or more below the specified level. The lamp will be illuminated during engine starting. If oil level is sufficient, the lamp will go off when engine is operating. If oil level is low the lamp will remain on until engine oil is added and the ignition switch is placed in the OFF position. The module will take approximately 3 minutes to reset. If the engine is started during this period, the last recorded reading will be displayed.

The Low Coolant Warning Lamp will be illuminated whenever coolant level in the coolant recovery bottle is below the specified mark. Raise coolant level in recovery bottle to turn lamp off.

The low fuel warning lamp will be illuminated whenever fuel level drops below 1.4 gals. Add fuel to vehicle to turn lamp off.

The Washer Fluid Warning Lamp will be illuminated whenever fluid drops below the specified reservoir level. Raise washer fluid level in reservoir to turn lamp off.

The brake pad wear warning lamp will be illuminated when disc brake pads wear down to 1.5 mm. At 1.5 mm a wire loop in the brake pad is exposed and severed, which in turn illuminates the brake pad warning lamp. To turn lamp off, replace brake pads.

Air temperature is monitored by a sensor located on the righthand side of the vehicle behind the front bumper. The signal from the sensor is evaluated by the control assembly, which controls the low air temperature (ICE) indication on the graphic display. When air temperature is approximately 39°F, the ICE indication will be illuminated in yellow. When temperature drops to 32°F the triangle located around the ICE indication will be illuminated in red. If a short circuit in wiring between sensor and control assembly is present, the ICE indication on the graphic will flash. If an open circuit between the sensor and control assembly exist, the triangle will flash.

The graphic display will indicate when doors and liftgate are closed (green) and when doors and liftgate are ajar (red). To cancel door or liftgate ajar indication, close door or liftgate indicated.

The graphic will also indicate lamp bulb outage. Replacement of lamp bulb indicated will turn off graphic display indicator. A lamp out indication will also be present if an open or circuit in lamp wiring is present.

CHECK ENGINE LAMP
1987—93 MODELS W/EEC-IV
Except Capri, Festiva, Merkur, Probe w/2.2L Engine & Escort/Tracer w/1.8L Engine

This lamp will be illuminated when the ignition switch is placed in the ON position. After engine is started the lamp should go off, unless a problem has been detected by the EEC-IV system. Following diagnosis and repair, the Check Engine/MIL lamp will automatically reset when stored codes are cleared from the EEC-IV system memory. After diagnosis and repair, EEC-IV memory may be cleared of stored codes as follows:

1. With ignition switch in the OFF position, connect a jumper wire between Self Test and Self Test Input (STI) connectors, **Fig. 1.** On Ford Crown Victoria, Mercury Grand Marquis and Lincoln Town Car models, the Self Test and STI connectors are gray in color and are located on the front of lefthand fender apron, near the Electronic Engine Control (EEC) relay. On Ford Mustang models, the Self Test and STI connectors are gray in color and are located on the lefthand fender apron. On Ford Tempo, Topaz, 1987-90 Escort and Mercury Lynx, the Self Test connector is gray in color and the STI connector is black in color and they are both located on the righthand fender apron near the front of the strut tower. On Ford Taurus and Mercury Sable, the Self Test and STI connectors are gray in color and are located on the righthand fender apron near the front of the engine in the area of the AIR pump and alternator. On 1987-88 Ford Thunderbird and Mercury Cougar, the Self Test and STI connectors are gray in color and are located on the lefthand fender apron near the strut tower. On 1989-93 Ford Thunderbird and Mercury Cougar, the Self Test and STI connectors are gray in color and are located on the righthand fender apron near the

CHECK ENGINE LIGHT (WITH JUMPER WIRE)

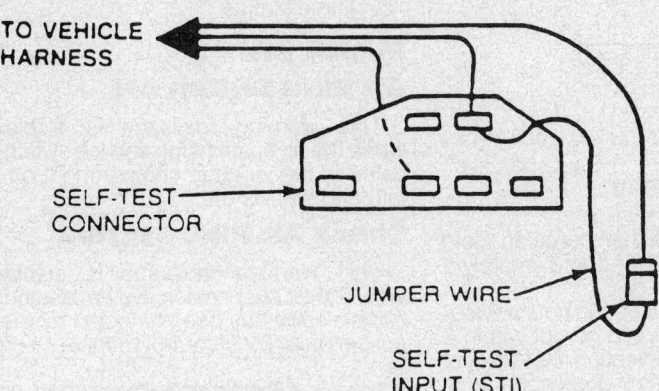

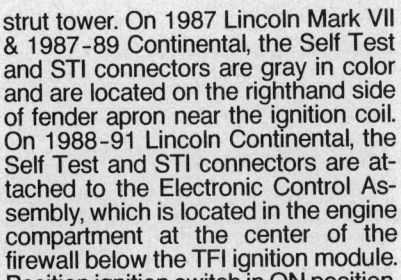

Fig. 1 Jumper wire connections for resetting Check Engine Lamp

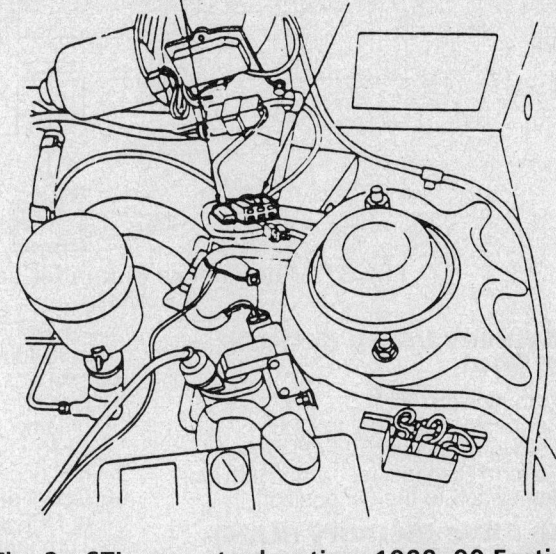

Fig. 2 STI connector location. 1988–90 Festiva

strut tower. On 1987 Lincoln Mark VII & 1987-89 Continental, the Self Test and STI connectors are gray in color and are located on the righthand side of fender apron near the ignition coil. On 1988-91 Lincoln Continental, the Self Test and STI connectors are attached to the Electronic Control Assembly, which is located in the engine compartment at the center of the firewall below the TFI ignition module.

2. Position ignition switch in ON position, then disconnect jumper wire from test connector terminals. Disconnect jumper as soon as check engine lamp starts flashing.

Festiva

The Check Engine Indicator lamp will be illuminated when the ignition switch in in the RUN position with engine not operating. When the engine is started, the Check Engine lamp should go off. If lamp remains on, a service code has been stored in the EEC-IV self test system memory. After diagnosis and repair, the self test memory may be cleared of stored codes as follows:

1. With ignition switch in the OFF position, connect a jumper wire between Self Test Input (STI) connector terminal and ground. The STI connector is located in the engine compartment at the rear lefthand side, **Fig. 2.**
2. Position ignition switch in ON position, then disconnect and reconnect jumper wire connected between STI connector and ground.
3. Disconnect jumper from STI connector as soon as check engine lamp stops flashing.
4. Disconnect battery ground cable and depress brake pedal for approximately 5 to 10 seconds.
5. Reconnect battery ground cable.

Merkur

This lamp will be illuminated when the ignition switch is placed in the ON position. After engine is started the lamp should go off, unless a problem has been detected by

the EEC-IV system. After diagnosis and repair, the Check Engine lamp will automatically reset when stored codes are cleared from the EEC-IV system memory. After diagnosis and repair, EEC-IV memory may be cleared of stored codes as follows:

1. With ignition switch in the OFF position, connect a jumper wire between Self Test and Self Test Input (STI) connectors, **Fig. 1.** The Self Test and STI connectors located on the right-hand fender apron between the strut tower and the battery.
2. Position ignition switch in ON position, then disconnect jumper wire from test connector terminals. Disconnect jumper as soon as check engine lamp starts flashing.

Capri, Probe w/2.2L Engine & Escort/Tracer w/1.8L Engine

This lamp will be illuminated when the ignition switch is placed in the ON position. After engine is started the lamp should go off, unless a problem has been detected by the system. After diagnosis and repair, the Check Engine lamp will automatically reset when stored codes are cleared from the system memory. After diagnosis and repair, memory may be cleared of stored codes as follows:

1. Disconnect battery ground cable, then depress brake pedal for approximately 5 to 10 seconds.
2. Reconnect battery ground cable.

1994-95 MODELS W/EEC-IV

This lamp will be illuminated when the ignition switch is placed in the On position. After engine is started the lamp should go off, unless a problem has been detected by the EEC-IV system a diagnostic trouble code is stored in the PCM. Following diagnosis and repair, the Check Engine/MIL lamp will automatically reset when stored

diagnostic trouble codes are cleared from PCM memory. After diagnosis and repair, PCM memory may be cleared of stored codes as follows:

1. Connect electronic self-tester link connector of NGS and Data Link Connector (DLC) and Self-Test Input (STI) connector on vehicle.
2. Using tester, retrieve DTC's from PCM.
3. When DTC's begin to be displayed, deactivate tester as follows:
   a. With Super/Star II tester, unlatch center button (up position). With other scan tool, press STOP button.
   b. Except Super Star II tester/scan tool, remove jumper wire between Self-Test Input (STI) connector and Signal Return Pin Of DLC. 4.

1994-96 MODELS W/EEC-V

This lamp will be illuminated when the ignition switch is placed in the On position. After engine is started the lamp should go off, unless a problem has been detected by the EEC-V system and diagnostic trouble codes are stored in the PCM. Following diagnosis and repair, the Check Engine/MIL lamp will automatically reset when the codes are cleared from the PCM memory. The PCM reset procedure allows the scan tool to command the PCM to clear all diagnostic trouble codes.

PCM Reset Using STAR Tester

1. Turn ignition Off.
2. Perform necessary vehicle preparation and visual inspection.
3. Connect Star tester, then select vehicle model and year.
4. Follow operating instructions on tester screen. Select Generic OBD II Functions.
5. Press CONT button if all OBD II monitors are not complete.
6. Turn ignition switch to On position.
7. Select Clear Diagnostic codes and press Start Key.

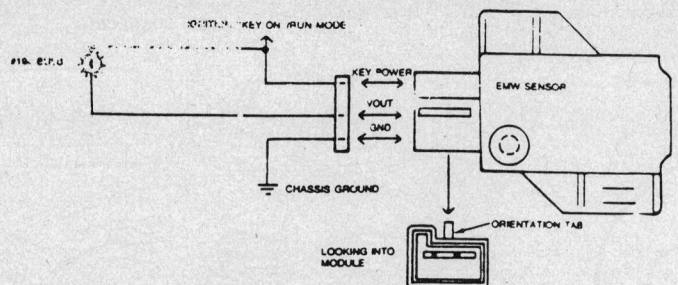

Fig. 3   Maintenance Reminder Lamp wiring schematic

PCM Reset Using Generis Scan Tool

1. Turn ignition Off.
2. Connector scan tool to DLC.
3. Turn ignition switch to On position.
4. Perform scan tool reset, then turn ignition switch to the Off position.

Keep Alive Memory (KAM) Reset & PCM Reset Less Electronic Tester

To clear KAM, disconnect battery ground cable for at least five minutes. This will also result in PCM reset.

LOW COOLANT WARNING SYSTEM

The Low Coolant Warning Lamp will be illuminated whenever coolant level in the coolant recovery bottle is 1/4 to 3/4 inch or more below the cold full mark. Raise coolant level in recovery bottle to the cold full mark to turn lamp off.

LOW OIL LEVEL WARNING INDICATOR

This system is used to indicate when engine oil level is 1½ quarts or more below the specified level. The lamp will be illuminated during engine starting. If oil level is sufficient, the lamp will go off when engine is operating. If oil level is low the lamp will remain on until engine oil is added and the ignition switch is placed in the OFF position. The module will take approximately 5 minutes to reset. If the engine is started during this period, the last recorded reading will be displayed.

MAINTENANCE REMINDER INDICATOR

This lamp, **Fig. 3**, is used on some not equipped with electronic engine controls. The lamp will be illuminated after approximately 2000 engine starts (60,000 miles of vehicle operation). After performing the required emission control service, the lamp maybe reset as follows:

1. Turn ignition switch to OFF position.
2. Install a suitable screwdriver through the .2 inch hole labeled Reset, then lightly press down and hold.
3. While pressing screwdriver down, turn ignition switch to RUN position. The advisory lamp will then come on. Hold screwdriver down for approximately 5 seconds.
4. Remove screwdriver and note advisory lamp. Lamp should go out within 2 to 10 seconds indicating that a reset has occurred. If lamp does not go out, repeat procedure. Turn ignition switch to OFF position.
5. Turn ignition switch to RUN position. The advisory lamp should light for approximately 2 to 10 seconds indicating that a proper reset has been accomplished.

MALFUNCTION INDICATOR LAMP (MIL)

EXCEPT 1988–89 TRACER

Refer to "Check Engine Lamp" for lamp reset procedure.

1988–89 TRACER

The malfunction indicator lamp is used only on EFI models. This lamp indicates a malfunction in the Electronic Engine Control system. If a malfunction occurs, the lamp will illuminate. The malfunction detected may or may not be a noticeable driveability problem. The lamp will be automatically reset during diagnosis and repair of the system.

This indicator system monitors the following:

1. Air Temperature sensor (ACT).
2. Barometric Pressure (BP) sensor.
3. Clutch switch, manual transaxle.
4. Engine coolant temperature (ECT) sensor.
5. Engine coolant temperature (ECT) switch.
6. Exhaust gas oxygen (EGO) sensor.
7. Ignition coil (−) terminal.

MESSAGE CENTER

CROWN VICTORIA, GRAND MARQUIS & TOWN CAR

The message center is located to the right of the instrument cluster. It consists of three buttons: Select, E/M and Reset. The E/M button switches the display between English and Metric. The Reset button set data to zero of instantaneous information. The Select button cycles the message display through the following selections;

1. Average Speed.
2. Fuel remaining.
3. Average fuel economy and instantaneous fuel economy.
4. Distance to empty.
5. Trip distance.

MARK VIII

Air Ride Switch Off

This warning message is displayed when the air suspension service switch, located in the luggage compartment on the lefthand side, is off.

Check Air Ride System

This warning message is displayed when an air suspension system diagnostic trouble code has been detected by the air suspension/EVO control module.

Check Charging System

This warning message is displayed when the electrical system is not maintaining a proper voltage at the message center.

Check Engine Temp

This warning message is displayed when the coolant is overheating.

Low Engine Coolant

This warning message is displayed when the engine coolant level is below the cold line of the coolant recovery reservoir.

Check Exterior Lamps

This warning message is displayed when one of the following lamps is turned on and at least one is burned out: a stop lamp, rear parking lamp, or low beam headlamp.

Change Oil Soon Or Oil Change Required

The oil life functions include oil life, change oil soon and oil change required. The oil life is determined by three functions: Smart Tach pulses, miles driven and time elapsed.

When the oil life drops down to the range of 1-5%, the "Change Oil Soon" message will appear. When oil life is 0%, the "Oil Change Required" message will appear.

Depressing the oil change reset button will reset the oil life to 100%.

MULTIPLE FUNCTION WARNING INDICATOR

1987–89 MUSTANG GT

This system monitors engine oil, cooling system, fuel and washer reservoir levels for low fluid level conditions. During engine starting the lamps will be illuminated for approximately 3 seconds as a bulb check out. After approximately 3 seconds, when the bulb check is completed, low fluid level conditions will be verified, if present.

The low engine oil warning lamp is used to indicate when engine oil level is 1½

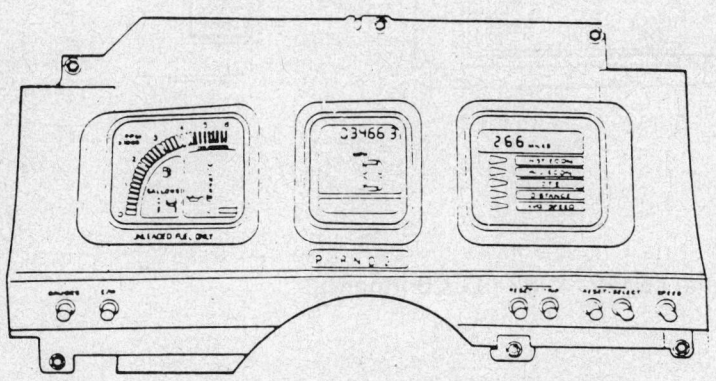

Fig. 4   Trip & reset button locations. 1985–88 Cougar & Thunderbird

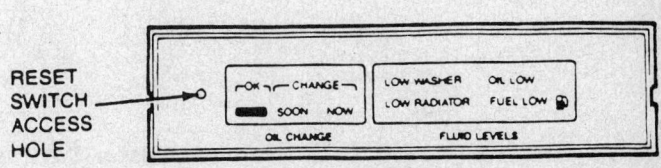

Fig. 5   Oil change interval indicator reset switch access hole location. 1989–93 Cougar & Thunderbird

quarts or more below the specified level. The lamp will be illuminated during engine starting. If oil level is sufficient, the lamp will go off when engine is operating. If oil level is low the lamp will remain on until engine oil is added and the ignition switch is placed in the OFF position. The module will take approximately 90 to 150 seconds to reset. If the engine is started during this period, the last recorded reading will be displayed.

The Low Coolant Warning Lamp will be illuminated whenever coolant level in the coolant recovery bottle is below the cold full mark. Raise coolant level in recovery bottle to the cold full mark to turn lamp off.

The low fuel warning lamp will be illuminated whenever fuel level is 1/8 tank capacity or less. Add fuel to vehicle to turn lamp off.

The Washer Fluid Warning Lamp will be illuminated whenever reservoir level is below 1/3 capacity. Raise washer fluid level in reservoir to turn lamp off.

SERVICE INTERVAL REMINDER

1985–88 COUGAR & THUNDERBIRD

At approximately 5,000 or 7,500 miles, depending on engine installation, the word SERVICE will appear on the display for approximately 1 1/2 miles to indicate time for service interval. After completing the required service, reset service interval reminder by depressing and holding the Trip and Trip Reset buttons until three beeps are heard, **Fig. 4.**

1989–93 COUGAR & THUNDERBIRD

At approximately 7,500 miles, for models less super charged engine, the engine oil change indicator on the Vehicle Maintenance Monitor will indicate an oil change is needed. On models with super charged engine, the need for engine oil change will be indicated at 5,000 miles. After completing the required service, the oil change indicate can be reset by depressing the reset switch, **Fig. 5.** The reset switch is accessed through a switch access hole located to the left of the oil change indicator on the monitor display.

CONTINENTAL

After performing the require interval service, the service interval reminder mileage display on the instrument cluster can be reset as follows:
1. Depress System Check button on instrument panel, service interval reminder mileage should be displayed on fuel computer display, **Fig. 6.**
2. Depress Reset button, the service interval reminder mileage should start flashing.
3. Depress Reset and System Check buttons at the same time to reset mileage.

PROBE
Electronic Instrument Cluster

At 7,500 mile intervals, a Service Check message will be displayed under the System

tem Scanner nomenclature on the instrument cluster for three minutes after engine start, **Fig. 7.** After performing the required interval service, reset the service interval by depressing and holding the Service reset button, located on the speed alarm keyboard, until three tones have sounded, **Fig. 8.**

Vehicle Maintenance Monitor

On models with Vehicle Maintenance Monitor, at 7,500 mile intervals a Service lamp, located on the overhead map lamp console, will be illuminated for 3 minutes after engine start, **Fig. 9.** After performing the required interval service, reset the service interval. On models with speed alarm keypad, depress and hold the Service reset button, until three tones have sounded. On models less speed alarm keypad, locate reset hole in overhead console, then using a suitable tool depress the reset button located behind the hole.

1986–89 SABLE & TAURUS w/ELECTRONIC INSTRUMENT CLUSTER

At 7,200 mile intervals, a Service message will be displayed under the System Scanner nomenclature on the instrument cluster for 30 seconds after engine start, **Fig. 10.** After performing the required interval service, reset the service interval by simultaneously depressing the ODO Sel and Trip Reset buttons located on the instrument panel. The word service will disappear from the display and three tones will sound to indicate the service interval has been reset.

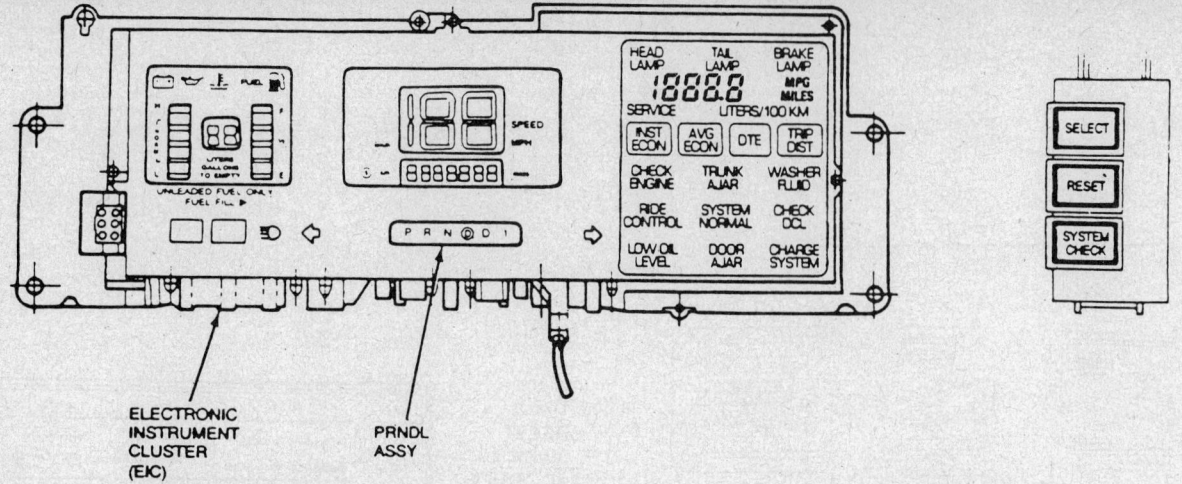

Fig. 6   Instrument cluster & message center. 1988–91 Continental

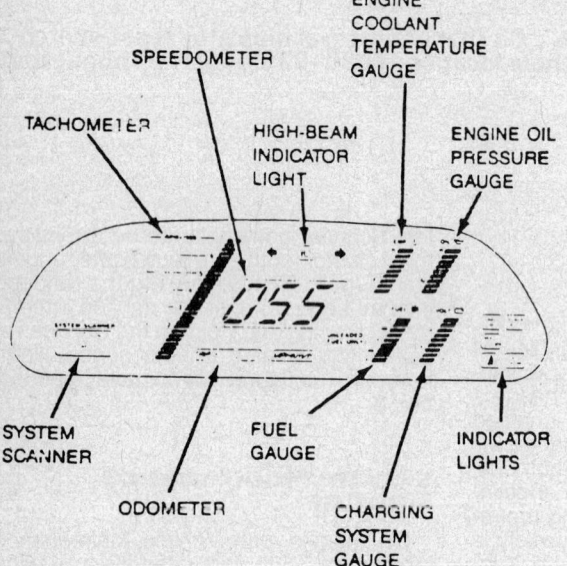

Fig. 7   Electronic instrument cluster. Probe

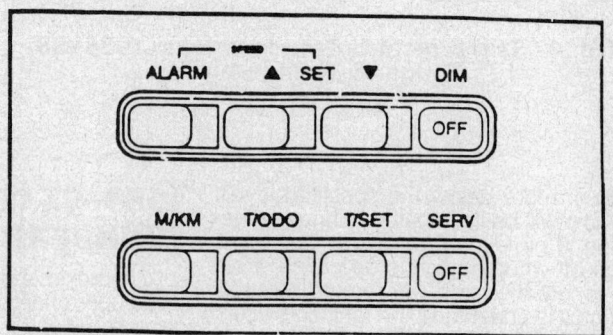

Fig. 8   Speed alarm keyboard. Probe

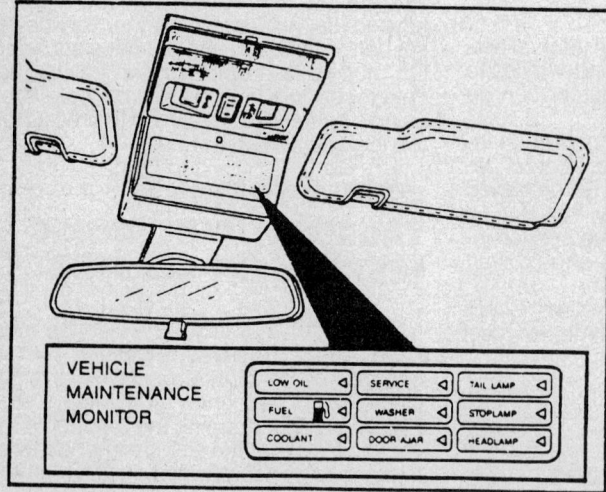

Fig. 9   Vehicle maintenance monitor. Probe

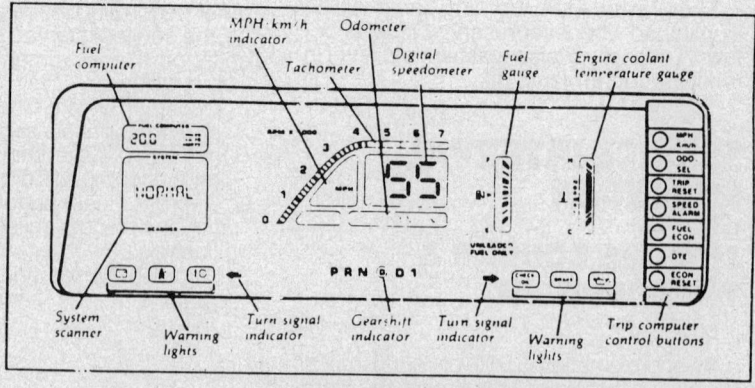

Fig. 10   Instrument cluster & trip control buttons. 1986–89 Sable & Taurus

FORD MOTOR CO.

AIR QUALITY STANDARDS

TABLE OF CONTENTS

Page No.

FEDERAL MANDATED
STANDARDS. 25

Page No.

STATE & DISTRICT OF
COLUMBIA MANDATED
STANDARDS. 26

Federal Mandated Standards

USE THIS CHART ONLY IF THE STATE IN WHICH THE VEHICLE IS OPERATED HAS NOT SET ITS OWN EMISSIONS STANDARDS

Year	Hydrocarbon (HC) gpm		Carbon Monoxide (CO) gpm		Nitrogen Oxide (NOX) gpm	
	Composite	Phase 2	Composite	Phase 2	Composite	Phase 2
LIGHT DUTY VEHICLES						
1968—72	10.0	6.0	150	120	10.0	②
1973—74	10.0	6.0	150	120	9.0	②
1975—76	7.5	5.0	90.0	72.0	9.0	②
1977—79	7.5	5.0	90.0	72.0	6.0	②
1980	2.0	1.25	60.0	48.0	6.0	②
1981—82	2.0	1.25	60.0	48.0	3.0	②
1983—90	2.0	1.25	30.0	24.0	3.0	②
1991—95 ③	1.2	.75	20.0	16.0	2.5	②
1994—95 ④	0.8	.5	15.0	12.0	2.0	②
HIGH ALTITUDE LIGHT DUTY VEHICLES						
1982	2.0	1.25	75.0	60.0	3.0	②
1983—84	2.0	1.25	60.0	48.0	3.0	②
LIGHT DUTY TRUCKS (LESS THAN 6000 LBS. GVWR)						
1973—74	10.0	6.0	150.0	120.0	9.0	②
1975—78	8.0	5.0	120.0	96.0	9.0	②
1979—83	7.5	5.0	100.0	80.0	7.0	②
1984—87	3.2	2.0	80.0	64.0	7.0	②
1988—90	3.2	2.0	80.0	64.0	3.5	②
1991—95 ③	2.4	1.5	60.0	48.0	3.0	②
1994—95 ⑤	0.8	.5	15.0	12.0	2.0	②
1994—95 ⑥	1.0	.63	20.0	16.0	2.5	②
HIGH ALTITUDE LIGHT DUTY TRUCKS (LESS THAN 6000 LBS. GVWR)						
1982—83	8.0	5.0	130.0	104.0	7.0	②
1984—87	4.0	2.5	90.0	72.0	7.0	②
1988—90	4.0	2.5	90.0	72.0	3.5	②
1991—95	3.0	2.0	70.0	56.0	3.0	②
LIGHT DUTY TRUCKS (GREATER THAN 6000 LBS. GVWR)						
1968—72	10.0	6.0	150.0	120.0	10.0	②
1973—74	10.0	6.0	150.0	120.0	9.0	②
1975—78	8.0	5.0	120.0	96.0	9.0	②
1979—83	7.5	5.0	100.0	80.0	7.0	②
1984—87	3.2	2.0	80.0	64.0	7.0	②
1988—90	3.2	2.0	80.0	64.0	5.0	②

Continued

FEDERAL MANDATED STANDARDS–Continued

Year	Hydrocarbon (HC) gpm		Carbon Monoxide (CO) gpm		Nitrogen Oxide (NOX) gpm	
	Composite	Phase 2	Composite	Phase 2	Composite	Phase 2
LIGHT DUTY TRUCKS (GREATER THAN 6000 LBS. GVWR)						
1991—95 ③	2.4	1.5	60.0	48.0	4.5	②
1994—95 ⑦	1.0	.63	20.0	16.0	2.5	②
1994—95 ⑧	2.4	1.5	60.0	48.0	4.0	②
HIGH ALTITUDE LIGHT DUTY TRUCKS (GREATER THAN 6000 LBS. GVWR)						
1982—83	8.0	5.0	130.0	104.0	7.0	②
1984—87	4.0	2.5	90.0	72.0	7.0	②
1988—90	4.0	2.5	90.0	72.0	5.0	②
1991—95	3.0	2.0	70.0	56.0	4.5	②

gpm—grams per mile
LVW—Loaded Vehicle Weight
① —If the corrected, composite emission rate exceed standards for any exhaust component, additional analysis of test results shall look at

the second phase of the driving cycle separately. Phase 2 shall include second 94 through second 239.
② —Reserved.
③ —Exc. Tier 1.

④ —Tier 1.
⑤ —Tier 1 under 3750 lbs. LVW.
⑥ —Tier 1 over 3750 lbs LVW.
⑦ —Tier 1 under 5750 lbs. LVW.
⑧ —Tier 1 over 5750 lbs LVW.

State & District Of Columbia Mandated Standards

The Following Specifications Are The Maximum Allowable Gasoline Engine HC & CO Limits, Unless Otherwise Noted.

INDEX

	Page No.		Page No.		Page No.
Alaska	27	Indiana	34	North Carolina	41
Arizona	27	Kentucky	34	Ohio	41
California	29	Maine	37	Oregon	41
Colorado	29	Maryland	38	Pennsylvania	42
Connecticut	31	Massachusetts	38	Rhode Island	43
Delaware	32	Missouri	38	Tennessee	44
District Of Columbia	32	Nevada	39	Texas	44
Florida	33	New Hampshire	39	Utah	44
Georgia	33	New Jersey	40	Virginia	45
Idaho	33	New Mexico	40	Washington	46
Illinois	34	New York	41	Wisconsin	46

ALASKA

Vehicle Classification (GVW)	Model Year	Hydrocarbons (HC) ppm At Idle		Carbon Monoxide (CO) % At Idle	
		4 Cylinder Engines	5 Or More Cylinder Engines	4 Cylinder Engines	5 Or More Cylinder Engines
Less Than 6000 Lbs.	1968-71 ①	1000	1000	4.0	4.0
	1968—71 ②	1000	1000	5.0	5.0
	1972—74 ①	1000	1000	3.0	3.0
	1972—74 ②	1000	1000	4.0	4.0
	1975—83 ③	1000	1000	2.5	2.5
	1975—83 ① ④	1000	1000	1.5	1.5
	1975—83 ② ④	1000	1000	2.0	2.0
	1975—83 ⑤	1000	1000	1.0	1.0
	1984 & Newer	600	600	1.0	1.0
6000 To 8500 Lbs.	1968-72 ①	1000	1000	4.0	4.0
	1968—72 ②	1000	1000	5.0	5.0
	1973—78 ①	1000	1000	3.0	3.0
	1973—78 ②	1000	1000	4.0	4.0
	1979—83 ③	1000	1000	2.5	2.5
	1979—83 ① ④	1000	1000	1.5	1.5
	1979—83 ② ④	1000	1000	2.0	2.0
	1979—83 ⑤	1000	1000	1.0	1.0
	1984 & Newer	600	600	1.0	1.0
Greater Than 8500 Lbs.	1968-73	—	1000	—	5.0
	1974—83	—	1000	—	4.0
	1984 & Newer	—	600	—	3.0

GVW—Gross Vehicle Weight
ppm—parts per million
①—W/air injection reactor (AIR).
②—Less air injection reactor (AIR).
③—Less catalytic converter.
④—W/oxygen sensor (O2S) & catalytic converter.
⑤—W/three-way catalytic converter (TWC).

ARIZONA
MAXIMUM ALLOWABLE EMISSION STANDARDS ANNUAL TESTS

Engine Type/ Vehicle	Model Year	GVWR	No. of Cylinders	Conditioning Mode		Curb Idle Mode Test		Loaded Cruise Mode Test	
				HC ppm	CO%	HC ppm	CO%	HC ppm	CO%
4 Stroke Motorcycles	All	All	All	500	5.0	1800	5.5	—	—
4 Stroke	1967—71	All	4 Cylinders or Less	450	3.75	500	5.5	500	4.2
4 Stroke	1967—71	All	More Than 4 Cylinders	380	3.0	450	5.0	450	3.75
4 Stroke	1972—74	All	4 Cylinders or Less	380	3.5	400	5.5	400	4.2
4 Stroke	1972—74	All	More Than 4 Cylinders	300	3.0	400	5.0	400	3.75
4 Stroke	1975—78	6000 Lbs. or Less	4 Cylinders or Less	120	1.0	250	2.2	250	1.65
4 Stroke	1975—78	6000 Lbs. or Less	More Than 4 Cylinders	120	1.0	250	2.0	250	1.5
4 Stroke	1975—78	Greater Than 6000 Lbs.	All	300	3.0	350	4.0	350	3.0
4 Stroke	1979	8500 Lbs. or Less	4 Cylinders or Less	120	1.0	220	2.2	220	1.65
4 Stroke	1979	8500 Lbs. or Less	More Than 4 Cylinders	120	1.0	220	2.2	220	1.5
4 Stroke	1979-80	Greater Than 8500 Lbs.	All	300	3.0	300	4.0	300	3.0
4 Stroke	1980	8500 Lbs. or Less	All	100	.5	220	1.2	220	1.2

Continued

ARIZONA–Continued

Engine Type/ Vehicle	Model Year	GVWR	No. of Cylinders	Conditioning Mode		Curb Idle Mode Test		Loaded Cruise Mode Test	
				HC ppm	CO%	HC ppm	CO%	HC ppm	CO%
4 Stroke	1981 & Newer	8500 Lbs. or Less	All	100	.5	220	1.2	220	1.2
4 Stroke	1981 & Newer	Greater Than 8500 Lbs.	All	300	3.0	300	4.0	300	3.0
4 Stroke	Reconstructed 1981 Or Newer	All	All	700	5.25	1200	7.5	700	5.25
4 Stroke	Reconstructed 1980 & Older	All	All	700	5.25	1200	7.5	1200	5.6
4 Stroke Motor Cycle	All	All	All	500	5.0	1800	5.5	—	—
2 Stroke	All	All	All	18,000	5.0	18,000	5.0	18,000	5.0

GVWR—Gross Vehicle Weight Rating
ppm—Parts Per Million.

MAXIMUM ALLOWABLE EMISSION STANDARDS BIENNIAL TESTS

Model Year	Hydrocarbon (HC) gpm [1]		Carbon Monoxide (CO) gpm [1]		Nitrogen Oxide (NOX) gpm [1]	
	Composite	Phase 2	Composite	Phase 2	Composite	Phase 2
LIGHT DUTY VEHICLES						
1981—82	2.0	1.25	60.0	48.0	3.0	[2]
1983—90	2.0	1.25	30.0	24.0	3.0	[2]
1991—96	1.2	.75	20.0	16.0	2.5	[2]
HIGH ALTITUDE LIGHT DUTY VEHICLES						
1982	2.0	1.25	75.0	60.0	3.0	[2]
1983—84	2.0	1.25	60.0	48.0	3.0	[2]
LIGHT DUTY TRUCKS (LESS THAN 6000 LBS. GVWR)						
1981—83	7.5	5.0	100.0	80.0	7.0	[2]
1984—87	3.2	2.0	80.0	64.0	7.0	[2]
1988—90	3.2	2.0	80.0	64.0	3.5	[2]
1991—96	2.4	1.5	60.0	48.0	3.0	[2]
HIGH ALTITUDE LIGHT DUTY TRUCKS (LESS THAN 6000 LBS. GVWR)						
1982—83	8.0	5.0	130.0	104.0	7.0	[2]
1984—87	4.0	2.5	90.0	72.0	7.0	[2]
1988—90	4.0	2.5	90.0	72.0	3.5	[2]
1991—96	3.0	2.0	70.0	56.0	3.0	[2]
LIGHT DUTY TRUCKS (GREATER THAN 6000 LBS. GVWR)						
1981—83	7.5	5.0	100.0	80.0	7.0	[2]
1984—87	3.2	2.0	80.0	64.0	7.0	[2]
1988—90	3.2	2.0	80.0	64.0	5.0	[2]
1991—96	2.4	1.5	60.0	48.0	4.5	[2]
HIGH ALTITUDE LIGHT DUTY TRUCKS (GREATER THAN 6000 LBS. GVWR)						
1982—83	8.0	5.0	130.0	104.0	7.0	[2]
1984—87	4.0	2.5	90.0	72.0	7.0	[2]
1988—90	4.0	2.5	90.0	72.0	5.0	[2]
1991—96	3.0	2.0	70.0	56.0	4.5	[2]

gpm—grams per mile
[1]—If the corrected, composite emission rate exceed standards for any exhaust component, additional analysis of test results shall look at the second phase of the driving cycle separately. Phase 2 shall include second 94 through second 239.
[2]—Reserved.

CALIFORNIA

Due to frequent revisions in the various regional HC & CO limits, it is recommended that the California Air Resources Board (CARB) be consulted for current emission standards.

COLORADO

BASIC PROGRAM AREA & HEAVY DUTY & PRE-1982 ENHANCED PROGRAM AREA VEHICLES SUBJECT TO IDLE SHORT TEST

The maximum allowable emission control limits will be changed from Emission Test Limits B to Emission Test Limits A, as necessary, to provide transition to more stringent emission control limits & to comply with EPA requirements.

Vehicle Classification	Year	Carbon Monoxide (CO) %	Hydrocarbon (HC) ppm
EMISSION CONTROL LIMITS A			
Light Duty Vehicles (Including Light Duty Trucks)	Pre-1970	5.5	1000
	1971—74	4.5	1000
	1975—76	3.5	600
	1977—78	3.0	400
	1979	2.0	400
	1980	1.5	400
	1981—95	1.2	220
Heavy Duty Vehicles [3]	Pre-1967	7.0	1500
	1968—69	6.5	1200
	1970—78	5.5	1000
	1979	4.0	800
	1980	3.5	800
	1981—85	3.0	600
	1986—95	2.0	300
EMISSION CONTROL TEST LIMITS B			
Light Duty Vehicles (Including Light Duty Trucks)	Pre-1970	5.5	1000
	1971—74	4.5	1000
	1975—76	3.5	600
	1977—78	3.0	400
	1979	2.0	400
	1980—88	1.5	400
	1989—95	1.2	220
Heavy Duty Vehicles [1]	Pre-1967	7.0	1500
	1968—69	6.5	1200
	1970—78	6.0	1200
	1979	5.0	1000
	1980	4.0	1000
	1981—85	3.5	800
	1986—95	3.0	600

GVWR—Gross Vehicle Weight Rating
ppm—parts per million
[1]—1966-78 models w/GVWR over 6000 lbs. & 1979-95 models w/GVWR over 8500 lbs.

AIR QUALITY STANDARDS

1982–95 ENHANCED PROGRAM AREA VEHICLES GVWR 8500 LBS. OR LESS

The maximum allowable emission control limits will be changed from Emission Test Limits B to Emission Test Limits A, as necessary, to provide transition to more stringent emission control limits & to comply with EPA requirements.

Vehicle Classification	Year	Carbon Monoxide (CO) GPM ①	Hydrocarbon (HC) GPM ①	NOx GPM ②
EMISSION CONTROL TEST LIMITS A				
Light Duty Vehicles (Excluding Light Duty Trucks)	1982	45	1.25	3
	1983	30	1.25	3
	1984	45	1.25	3
	1985	15	1.25	3
	1986—93	15	.8	2
	1994—95 Exc. Tier 1	15	.7	1.5
	1994—95 Tier 1	10	.7	1.5
Light Duty Vehicles (Light Duty Trucks GVWR 8500 Lbs. & Less)	1982-85	60	1.35	5
	1986—93 ②	15	.8	2.5
	1986—93 ①	15	7	2
	1994—95 Exc. Tier 1	15	.8	2.5
	1994—95 Tier 1	15	7	2
EMISSION CONTROL TEST LIMITS B				
Light Duty Vehicles (Excluding Light Duty Trucks)	1982	75	5	8
	1983—84	60	5	8
	1985	30	5	8
	1986—90	30	4	6
	1991—94 Exc. Tier 1	20	4	6
	1994 Tier 1	15	4	6
	1995	20	4	4
Light Duty Vehicles (Light Duty Trucks GVWR 8500 Lbs. & Less)	1982-83	130	8	12
	1984—85	90	8	12
	1986—90	90	6	9
	1991—95	70	6	9

gpm—grams per mile
① —GVWR 6000 Lbs. or less.
② —GVWR 8500 Lbs. or less.

CONNECTICUT
GASOLINE ENGINE MAXIMUM ALLOWABLE LIMITS FOR IDLE EXHAUST EMISSION TEST

Model Year	Carbon Monoxide (CO) % At Idle	Total Hydrocarbon (THC) ppm At Idle
1968-69	5.0	500
1970	4.75	475
1971	4.4	450
1972	4.25	425
1973	4.0	390
1974	3.8	350
1975	3.0	300
1976	2.8	300
1977	2.7	300
1978	2.4	275
1979	2.1	250
1980	2.0	225
1981-82	1.2	200
1983	1.0	175
1984-87	1.0	150
1988-96	1.0	125

ppm—parts per million

GASOLINE ENGINE MAXIMUM ALLOWABLE LIMITS FOR TRANSIENT EXHAUST EMISSION TEST

Vehicle Weight Classification GVWR	Model Year	Total Hydrocarbon (THC) grams per Mile	Carbon Monoxide (CO) grams per Mile	NOx grams per Mile
Light Duty Vehicle	1981-82	2.00	60.0	3.00
	1983-90	2.00	30.0	3.00
	1991-95	1.20	20.0	2.50
	1996 & Newer	.80	15.0	2.00
Light Duty Truck GVWR 6000 Lbs. Or Less	1981-83	7.50	100.0	7.00
	1984-87	3.20	80.0	7.00
	1988-90	3.20	80.0	3.50
	1991-95	2.40	60.0	3.00
	1996 & Later ①	.80	15.0	2.00
	1996 & Later ②	1.00	20.0	2.50
Light Duty Truck GVWR 6001 To 8500 Lbs.	1981-83	7.50	100.0	7.00
	1984-87	3.20	80.0	7.00
	1988-90	3.20	80.0	5.00
	1991-95	2.40	60.0	4.00
	1996 & Later ③	1.00	20.0	2.50
	1996 & Later ④	2.40	60.0	4.00
Light Duty Truck GVWR 8501 to 10,000 Lbs.	1981-84	6.00	100.0	8.00
	1985-86	5.00	75.0	8.00
	1987-97	3.00	60.0	6.00

GVWR—Gross Vehicle Weight Rating
LVW—Loaded Vehicle Weight

①—Models w/LVW of 3750 lbs. or less.
②—Models w/LVW of above 3750 lbs.
③—Models w/LVW of 5750 lbs. or less.
④—Models w/LVW of above 5750 lbs.

AIR QUALITY STANDARDS

GASOLINE ENGINE EVAPOARATIVE SYSTEM TEST STANDARDS

Evaporatve system test standards for 1981 through 1996 models.

Evaporative system integrity test. An evaporative system pressure of at least 8 inches of water shall be maintained for 2 minutes following system pressuration to 14 + /- .5 inches of water.

Evaporative canister transient purge test. A total purge system flow of at least 1 liter shall be observed over the coarse of thre transient test.

DIESEL ENGINE INSPECTION STANDARDS

Maximum allowable visible emissions for 1988 & later diesel engine light duty vehicles & light duty trucks shall be of 20 percent particulates opacity as determine.

DELAWARE

Model Year	Hydrocarbon (HC) ppm At Idle	Carbon Monoxide (CO) % At Idle
PASSENGER CARS		
1968—70	900	9.0
1971—74	600	6.0
1975—79	400	4.0
1980	220	2.0
1981 & Newer	220	1.2
LIGHT TRUCKS & VANS		
1970—72	900	9.0
1973—78	600	6.0
1979—83	400	4.0
1984 & Newer	220	1.2

ppm—parts per million

DISTRICT OF COLUMBIA

Model Year	Hydrocarbons (HC) ppm At Idle	Carbon Monoxide (CO) % At Idle
Pre-1968	2000	12.5
1968—70	1250	11.0
1971—74	1200	9.0
1975—79	600	6.5
1980 & Newer	300	1.5

ppm—parts per million

FLORIDA

GASOLINE ENGINE INSPECTION STANDARDS

Vehicle Classification	Model Year	Hydrocarbons (HC) ppm At Idle	Carbon Monoxide (CO) % At Idle
Passenger Vehicles (Net Weight 6000 Lbs. Or Less)	1975-77	500	5.0
	1978—79	400	4.0
	1980	300	3.0
	1981 & Newer	220	1.2
Passenger Vehicles (6001 To 10,000 Lbs. GVWR)	1975-77	750	6.5
	1978—79	600	5.5
	1980	400	4.5
	1981—84	300	3.0
	1985 & Newer	220	1.2

ppm—parts per million
GVWR—Gross Vehicle Weight Rating

DIESEL ENGINE INSPECTION STANDARDS

Models with diesel engine shall not emit emissions in excess of 20 percent smoke opacity for 5 consecutive seconds while being operated on a dynamometer. On models with GVWR (Gross Vehicle Weight Rating) 4000 Lbs. or less, test vehicle on a dynamometer with a load of 8 HP and a drive wheel speed of 30 MPH. On models with GVWR (Gross Vehicle Weight Rating) 4001 to 10,000 Lbs., test vehicle on a dynamometer with a load of 30 HP and a drive wheel speed of 50 MPH.

GEORGIA

Vehicle Classification (GVW)	Model Year	Hydrocarbons (HC) ppm At Idle	Carbon Monoxide (CO) % At Idle
8500 Lbs. Or Less	1976-79	400	4.0
	1980	250	2.5
	1981 & Newer	220	1.2

GVW—Gross Vehicle Weight
ppm—parts per million

IDAHO

Vehicle Classification (GVW)	Model Year	Carbon Monoxide (CO) % At Idle
Less Than 8500 Lbs.	1965-74	5.5
	1975—79	3.5
	1980	1.5
	1981 Newer	1.2
Greater Than 8500 Lbs.	1965-74	6.0
	1975—80	5.0
	1981 & Newer	3.0

GVW—Gross Vehicle Weight

AIR QUALITY STANDARDS

ILLINOIS

Vehicle Classification (GVW)	Model Year	Hydrocarbons (HC) ppm At Idle	Carbon Monoxide (CO) % At Idle
8000 Lbs. & Under	1968—71	900	9.0
	1972—74	800	8.0
	1975—77	700	7.0
	1978—79	600	6.0
	1980	300	3.0
	1981 & Newer	220	1.2
8001 Lbs. & Above	1968-71	1550	9.5
	1972—78	900	9.0
	1979—84	700	7.0
	1985 & Newer	300	3.0

GVW—Gross Vehicle Weight.
ppm—parts per million.

INDIANA

Vehicle Classification	Model Year	Idle Test Limits		2500 RPM Test Limits	
		Hydrocarbons (HC) ppm	Carbon Monoxide (CO) %	Hydrocarbons (HC) ppm	Carbon Monoxide (CO) %
Light Duty Vehicles	1976-79	350	3.5	—	—
	1980	250	2.0	—	—
	1981 & Newer	220	1.2	200	1.0
Medium Duty Vehicles	1976-78	500	5.0	—	—
	1979—83	350	3.5	—	—
	1984 & Newer	220	1.2	200	1.0

GVW—Gross Vehicle Weight
ppm—parts per million

KENTUCKY
EXCEPT JEFFERSON COUNTY
1968—80 GASOLINE ENGINE VEHICLES

Model Year	Hydrocarbons (HC) ppm [2] At Idle	Carbon Monoxide (CO) % At Idle
AUTOMOBILES		
1968	950	8.5
1969	900	8.5
1970	850	8.4
1971	850	8.1
1972	800	8.0
1973	800	7.8
1974	800	7.6
1975	700	7.5
1976	700	6.5
1977	650	6.3
1978	600	5.5
1979	600	4.5
1980	250	2.5
VEHICLES GVW 6000 LESS GVW (EXC. AUTOMOBILES)		
1968	1300	8.0
1969	1200	8.0
1970—71	1100	8.0

Model Year	Hydrocarbons (HC) ppm [2] At Idle	Carbon Monoxide (CO) % At Idle
VEHICLES GVW 6000 LESS GVW (EXC. AUTOMOBILES)-CONTINUED		
1972—73	1000	7.8
1974	950	7.8
1975	900	7.0
1976—77	700	7.0
1978	700	6.3
1979	450	5.5
1980	450	4.0
VEHICLES GVW 6001 TO 10,000 LBS.		
1968	1500	9.0
1969—70	1100	8.0
1971	1000	8.0
1972—75	950	7.5
1976	900	7.5
1977	850	7.5
1978	700	6.0
1979	650	5.5
1980	550	5.0

Continued

KENTUCKY
EXCEPT JEFFERSON COUNTY
1968—80 GASOLINE ENGINE VEHICLES

Model Year	Hydrocarbons (HC) ppm② At Idle	Carbon Monoxide (CO) % At Idle	Model Year	Hydrocarbons (HC) ppm② At Idle	Carbon Monoxide (CO) % At Idle
VEHICLES GVW 10,001 TO 18,000 LBS.			**VEHICLES GVW 10,001 TO 18,000 LBS.**		
1968	1500	9.0	1979	650	5.5
1969—70	1300	8.5	1980	550	5.0
1971	1200	8.5			
1972—76	1000	7.0			
1977—80	900	6.5			

①—GVW: Gross Vehicle Weight.
②—ppm: parts per million.

1981 & NEWER GASOLINE ENGINE VEHICLES

Model Year	Hydrocarbon (HC) gpm		Carbon Monoxide (CO) gpm		Nitrogen Oxide (NOX) gpm	
	Composite	Phase 2	Composite	Phase 2	Composite	Phase 2
LIGHT DUTY VEHICLES						
1981—82	2.0	1.25	60.0	48.0	3.0	③
1983—90	2.0	1.25	30.0	24.0	3.0	③
1991 & Newer④	1.2	.75	20.0	16.0	2.5	③
1994 & Newer⑤	0.8	.5	15.0	12.0	2.0	③
HIGH ALTITUDE LIGHT DUTY VEHICLES						
1982	2.0	1.25	75.0	60.0	3.0	③
1983—84	2.0	1.25	60.0	48.0	3.0	③
LIGHT DUTY TRUCKS (LESS THAN 6000 LBS. GVWR)						
1981—83	7.5	5.0	100.0	80.0	7.0	③
1984—87	3.2	2.0	80.0	64.0	7.0	③
1988—90	3.2	2.0	80.0	64.0	3.5	③
1991—95④	2.4	1.5	60.0	48.0	3.0	③
1994 & Newer⑥	0.8	.5	15.0	12.0	2.0	③
1994 & Newer⑦	1.0	.63	20.0	16.0	2.5	③
HIGH ALTITUDE LIGHT DUTY TRUCKS (LESS THAN 6000 LBS. GVWR)						
1982—83	8.0	5.0	130.0	104.0	7.0	③
1984—87	4.0	2.5	90.0	72.0	7.0	③
1988—90	4.0	2.5	90.0	72.0	3.5	③
1991 & Newer	3.0	2.0	70.0	56.0	3.0	③
LIGHT DUTY TRUCKS (GREATER THAN 6000 LBS. GVWR)						
1981—83	7.5	5.0	100.0	80.0	7.0	③
1984—87	3.2	2.0	80.0	64.0	7.0	③
1988—90	3.2	2.0	80.0	64.0	5.0	③
1991 & Newer④	2.4	1.5	60.0	48.0	4.5	③
1994 & Newer⑧	1.0	.63	20.0	16.0	2.5	③
1994 & Newer①	2.4	1.5	60.0	48.0	4.0	③
HIGH ALTITUDE LIGHT DUTY TRUCKS (GREATER THAN 6000 LBS. GVWR)						
1982—83	8.0	5.0	130.0	104.0	7.0	③
1984—87	4.0	2.5	90.0	72.0	7.0	③
1988—90	4.0	2.5	90.0	72.0	5.0	③
1991 & Newer	3.0	2.0	70.0	56.0	4.5	③

gpm—grams per mile.
①—Tier 1 over 5750 lbs LVW.
②—If the corrected, composite emission rate exceed standards for any exhaust component, additional analysis of test results shall look at the second phase of the driving cycle separately. Phase 2 shall include second 94 through second 239.
③—Reserved.
④—Exc. Tier 1.
⑤—Tier 1.
⑥—Tier 1 under 3750 lbs. LVW.
⑦—Tier 1 over 3750 lbs LVW.
⑧—Tier 1 under 5750 lbs. LVW.

KENTUCKY –Continued
JEFFERSON COUNTY
GASOLINE ENGINE INSPECTION
STANDARDS (EXC. MOTORCYCLES)

Model Year	Hydrocarbons (HC) ppm② At Idle	Carbon Monoxide (CO) % At Idle
AUTOMOBILES		
Pre-1968	1200	8.0
1968—69	900	7.5
1970—71	800	7.5
1972—74	700	7.5
1975	600	6.5
1976—77	600	6.0
1978	500	5.5
1979	500	4.5
1980	300	2.5
1981—96	220	1.2
TRUCKS, RECREATIONAL VEHICLES & HOUSECARS 6000 TO 9999 LBS. GVW		
Pre-1968	1200	8.0
1968—69	1100	7.5
1970—71	1000	7.5
1972—73	900	7.5
1974	800	7.5
1975	800	6.5
1976—77	700	6.5
1978	700	6.0
1979	500	5.5
1980	500	4.0
1981	400	2.5
1982—96	220	1.2
VEHICLES 10,000-13,999 LBS. GVW		
Pre-1969	1300	8.0
1969—70	1100	7.5
1971	1000	7.5
1972—75	950	7.5

Model Year	Hydrocarbons (HC) ppm② At Idle	Carbon Monoxide (CO) % At Idle
VEHICLES 10,000-13,999 LBS. GVW-CONTINUED		
1976	900	7.5
1977	850	7.5
1978—79	700	6.0
1980	550	5.0
1981	450	3.5
1982	400	3.0
1983	350	3.0
1984	350	2.0
1985—96	220	1.2
BUSES & VEHICLES 14,000 LBS. TO 21,999 LBS. GVW; ALSO VEHICLES 22,000 LBS. GVW OR MORE INCLUDED BY SECTIONS 1.1.2, 2.16.4 OR 2.16.6 (GOVERNMENTOWNED OR OFFICALLY LICENSED)		
Pre-1969	1300	8.0
1969—70	1100	7.5
1971—72	1000	7.5
1973—75	950	7.5
1976-77	900	7.5
1978—80	900	6.0
1981	500	5.0
1982	500	4.0
1983—84	350	3.0
1985	300	2.0
1986	300	1.5
1987—92	250	1.5
1993—96	220	1.2

①—GVW: Gross Vehicle Weight.
②—ppm: parts per million.

GASOLINE ENGINE INSPECTION
STANDARDS (MOTORCYCLES)

Model Year	Hydrocarbons (HC) ppm① At Idle	Carbon Monoxide (CO) % At Idle
Pre-1980	1600	8.0
1980—96	1000	4.0

①—ppm: parts per million.

DIESEL & 2 STROKE GASOLINE
ENGINE INSPECTION STANDARDS

Vehicle Type	Model Year	Exhaust Opacity Limit %
IDLE MODE OPACITY STANDARD		
Motorcycle 2 Stroke	All	5
Diesel	All	5
LOADED MODE OPACITY STANDARD		
Diesel	All	20

MAINE

Year	Hydrocarbon (HC) gpm		Carbon Monoxide (CO) gpm		Nitrogen Oxide (NOX) Composite & Phase 2 ①
	Composite	Phase 2	Composite	Phase 2	
LIGHT DUTY VEHICLES					
1968—72	10.0	6.0	150.0	120.0	10.0
1973—74	10.0	6.0	150.0	120.0	9.0
1975—76	7.5	5.0	90.0	72.0	9.0
1977—79	7.5	5.0	90.0	72.0	6.0
1980	2.0	1.25	60.0	48.0	6.0
1981—82	2.0	1.25	60.0	48.0	3.0
1983—90	2.0	1.25	30.0	24.0	3.0
1991 & Newer	1.2	.75	20.0	16.0	2.5
LIGHT DUTY TRUCKS UP TO & INCLUDING 6000 LBS. GVWR					
1968—72	10.0	6.0	150.0	120.0	10.0
1973—74	10.0	6.0	150.0	120.0	9.0
1975—78	8.0	5.0	120.0	96.0	9.0
1979—83	7.5	5.0	100.0	80.0	7.0
1984—87	3.2	2.0	80.0	64.0	7.0
1988—90	3.2	2.0	80.0	64.0	3.5
1991 & Newer	2.4	1.5	60.0	48.0	3.0
LIGHT DUTY TRUCKS GREATER THAN 6000 LBS. GVWR					
1968—72	10.0	6.0	150.0	120.0	10.0
1973—74	10.0	6.0	150.0	120.0	9.0
1975—78	8.0	5.0	120.0	96.0	9.0
1979—83	7.5	5.0	100.0	80.0	7.0
1984—87	3.2	2.0	80.0	64.0	7.0
1988—90	3.2	2.0	80.0	64.0	5.0
1991 & Newer	2.4	1.5	60.0	48.0	4.5
HEAVY DUTY					
Pre 1970	20.0	12.5	200.0	160.0	15.0
1970—73	10.0	6.3	175.0	140.0	10.0
1974—78	10.0	6.3	150.0	120.0	10.0
1979—84	6.0	3.8	100.0	80.0	8.0
1985—86	5.0	3.1	75.0	60.0	8.0
1987—90	3.0	1.9	60.0	48.0	8.0
1991 & Newer	3.0	1.9	60.0	48.0	6.0

gpm—grams per mile
① —If the corrected, composite emission rate exceed standards for any exhaust component, additional analysis of test results shall look at the second phase of the driving cycle separately. Phase 2 shall include second 94 through second 239.

AIR QUALITY STANDARDS

MARYLAND

Vehicle Classification (GVW)	Model Year	Hydrocarbons (HC) ppm At Idle	Carbon Monoxide (CO) % At Idle
Less Than 6000 Lbs.	1977	500	6.0
	1978	430	5.5
	1979	400	4.0
	1980	220	1.7
	1981 & Newer	220	1.2
6001 To 10,000 Lbs.	1977	580	7.0
	1978	550	6.7
	1979	470	5.0
	1980	350	5.0
	1981	250	3.0
	1982	220	2.5
	1983	220	1.5
	1984 & Newer	220	1.2
10,001 To 26,000 Lbs.	1977-78	650	7.0
	1979	650	6.5
	1980—82	500	6.0
	1983	500	3.5
	1984—85	440	3.0
	1986	280	2.5
	1987 & Newer	220	1.2

GVW—Gross Vehicle Weight
ppm—parts per million

MASSACHUSETTS

Model Year	Hydrocarbons (HC) ppm At Idle	Carbon Monoxide (CO) % At Idle
1978—79	400	4.0
1980	300	2.7
1981 & Newer	220	1.2

ppm—parts per million

MISSOURI

ST. LOUIS AREA

Model Year	Hydrocarbons (HC) ppm At Idle	Carbon Monoxide (CO) % At Idle
1971—74	700	7.0
1975—79	600	6.0
1980	300	3.0
1981—96	220	1.2
1980-96 Specially Constructed Vehicles	500	1.2

ppm—parts per million

NEVADA
1968–85 MAXIMUM ALLOWABLE EMISSION CONTROL STANDARDS

Model Year	Maximum CO%	Maximum HC ppm
1968—69	4.0	800
1970—74	3.5	700
1975—78	2.5	500
1979—80	2.0	500
1981—85	1.2	220

ppm—Parts Per Million

1986—95 MAXIMUM ALLOWABLE EMISSION CONTROL STANDARDS

Model Year	Carbon Monoxide (CO) GPM ①		Hydrocarbon (HC) GPM ①		Nitrogen Oxide (NOX) Composite gpm ①
	Composite	Phase 2	Composite	Phase 2	
LIGHT DUTY VEHICLES					
1986—90	30.0	24.0	2.0	1.25	3.0
1991 & Newer	20.0	16.0	1.2	.75	2.5
LIGHT DUTY TRUCKS UP TO & INCLUDING 6000 LBS. GVWR					
1986—87	80.0	64.0	3.2	2.0	7.0
1988—90	80.0	64.0	3.2	2.0	3.5
1991 & Newer	60.0	48.0	2.4	1.5	3.0
LIGHT DUTY TRUCKS 6000 LBS.OR MORE GVWR					
1986—87	80.0	64.0	3.2	2.0	7.0
1988—90	80.0	64.0	3.2	2.0	5.0
1991 & Newer	60.0	48.0	2.4	1.5	4.5

gpm—grams per mile
① —If the corrected, composite emission rate exceed standards for any exhaust component, additional analysis of test results shall look at the second phase of the driving cycle separately. Phase 2 shall include second 94 through second 239.

NEW HAMPSHIRE

Model Year	Hydrocarbons (HC) ppm At Idle	Carbon Monoxide (CO) % At Idle
1980	220	1.5
1981 & Newer	220	1.2

ppm—parts per million.

AIR QUALITY STANDARDS

NEW JERSEY

GASOLINE ENGINE INSPECTION STANDARDS

Vehicle Classification (GVW)	Model Year	Hydrocarbons (HC) ppm At Idle	Carbon Monoxide (CO) % At Idle
6,000 Lbs. Or Less	Pre 1968	1400	8.5
	Pre-1968	1400	8.5
	1971—74	500	5.0
	1975—80	300	3.0
	1981 & Newer	220	1.2
6,001 To 10,000 Lbs.	Pre 1968	1400	8.5
	1968—70	1200	8.5
	1971—74	700	6.0
	1975—78	500	4.0
	1979 & Newer	300	3.0

GVW—Gross Vehicle Weight
ppm—parts per million as Hexane

DIESEL ENGINE INSPECTION STANDARDS

Models subject to New Jersey Division Of Motor Vehicles Inspection Regulations, performed by owner or operator, shall not emit smoke emissions in excess of 20 percent smoke opacity standard.

Models subject to New Jersey Department Of Transportation Inspection Regulations, shall not emit smoke emissions in excess of 12 percent smoke opacity standard.

NEW MEXICO

ALBUQUERQUE/BERNALILLO COUNTY

Vehicle Classification (GVWR)	Groupe Code	Model Year	Idle Mode		Unloaded 2500 RPM Test	
			Hydrocarbons (HC) ppm	Carbon Monoxide %	Hydrocarbons (HC) ppm	Carbon Monoxide %
0 to 6000 Lbs.	C/T	1975—76	700	6.5	700	6.0
		1977—78	600	5.0	600	5.0
		1979—80	500	4.0	500	4.0
		1981—96	220	1.2	220	1.2
6001 To 8000 Lbs.	LT	1975-78	900	6.0	900	6.0
		1979—80	750	4.5	750	4.5
		1981—82	650	2.7	400	3.0
		1983—96	400	1.2	300	3.0
8001—10,000 Lbs.	MT	1975—80	950	6.5	950	6.5
		1981-83	800	5.4	450	3.5
		1984—96	630	4.0	400	3.0
10,001—25,999 Lbs.	HT	1975-80	950	6.5	950	6.5
		1981—86	800	5.5	500	3.5
		1987-96	440	2.0	400	3.0

GVW—Gross Vehicle Weight
ppm—parts per million

NEW YORK

Vehicle Classification (GVW)	Model Year	Hydrocarbons (HC) ppm At Idle	Carbon Monoxide (CO) % At Idle
Less Than 8,500 Lbs.	Pre-1974	700	6.0
	1975—78	300	3.0
	1979—80	300	2.5
	1981 & Newer	220	1.2
Greater Than 8,500 Lbs.	Pre-1969	800	7.0
	1970—73	700	6.0
	1974—78	600	4.5
	1979 & Newer	300	3.0

GVW—Gross Vehicle Weight
ppm—parts per million

NORTH CAROLINA

Vehicle Classification (GVW)	Model Year	Carbon Monoxide (CO) % At Idle	Hydrocarbon (HC) ppm At Idle
Light Duty Vehicles	1975-77	4.5	450
	1978—79	3.5	350
	1980	2.0	250
	1981 & Newer	1.2	220
Heavy Duty Vehicles	1975-78	5.0	500
	1979 & Newer	4.0	400

GVW—Gross Vehicle Weight
ppm—parts per million

OHIO

Model Year	Hydrocarbons (HC) ppm	Carbon Monoxide (CO) %
1975—77	450	5.5
1978	350	4.0
1979	275	3.0
1980	230	2.0
1981 & Newer	220	1.2

ppm—parts per million

OREGON

	4 Cylinders Or Less				5 Cylinders Or More			
	At Idle		At 2500 RPM		At Idle		At 2500 RPM	
Model Year	Carbon Monoxide (CO) %	Hydrocarbon (HC) ppm	Carbon Monoxide (CO) %	Hydrocarbon (HC) ppm	Carbon Monoxide (CO) %	Hydrocarbon (HC) ppm	Carbon Monoxide (CO) %	Hydrocarbon (HC) ppm
PASSENGER GASOLINE ENGINE CARS (FOUR STROKE CYCLE)								
Pre-1968	7.0	1600	—	—	6.5	1300	—	—
1968—69	6.0	900	—	—	5.5	700	—	—
1970—71	5.0	600	—	—	5.0	600	—	—
1972—74	4.5	500	—	—	3.5	500	—	—
1975—80 ②	2.5	300	—	—	2.5	300	—	—
1975—80 ③	1.0	220	—	—	1.0	220	—	—
1981 & Newer	1.0	220	1.0	220	1.0	220	1.0	220

Continued

OREGON –Continued

Model Year	4 Cylinders Or Less				5 Cylinders Or More			
	At Idle		At 2500 RPM		At Idle		At 2500 RPM	
	Carbon Monoxide (CO) %	Hydrocarbon (HC) ppm	Carbon Monoxide (CO) %	Hydrocarbon (HC) ppm	Carbon Monoxide (CO) %	Hydrocarbon (HC) ppm	Carbon Monoxide (CO) %	Hydrocarbon (HC) ppm
LIGHT DUTY GASOLINE ENGINE TRUCKS (GVWR 6000 LBS. OR LESS)								
Pre-1968	7.0	1600	—	—	7.0	1300	—	—
1968—69	6.0	900	—	—	5.5	700	—	—
1970—71	5.0	600	—	—	5.0	600	—	—
1972—74	4.5	500	—	—	3.5	500	—	—
1975—80②	2.5	300	—	—	2.5	300	—	—
1975—80③	1.0	220	—	—	1.0	220	—	—
1981 & Newer	1.0	220	1.0	220	1.0	220	1.0	220
LIGHT DUTY GASOLINE ENGINE TRUCKS (GVWR 6001 TO 8500 LBS.)								
Pre-1968	6.5	1600	—	—	6.5	1300	—	—
1968—69	5.5	700	—	—	5.5	700	—	—
1970—71	5.0	600	—	—	5.0	600	—	—
1972—74	3.5	400	—	—	3.5	400	—	—
1975—78	2.5	300	—	—	2.5	300	—	—
1979—80②	2.5	300	—	—	2.5	300	—	—
1979—80③	1.0	220	—	—	1.0	220	—	—
1981 & Newer	1.0	220	—	—	1.0	220	—	—
HEAVY DUTY GASOLINE ENGINE VEHICLES								
Pre-1970	6.5	900	4.0	—	6.5	900	4.0	—
1970—73	5.0	700	①	—	5.0	700	①	—
1974—78	4.0	500	①	—	4.0	500	①	—
1979—95③	3.0	350	①	—	3.0	350	①	—
1985 & Newer ①	1.0	220	1.0	220	1.0	220	1.0	220
LIGHT DUTY GASOLINE (2 STROKE CYCLE) ENGINES								
All	7.0	—	—	—	7.0	—	—	—
LIGHT DUTY DIESEL ENGINES								
All	1.5	—	—	—	1.5	—	—	—

GVWR—Gross Vehicle Weight Rating
ppm—parts per million
①—Models equipped w/carburetor, 3.0%; models equipped w/fuel injection, no check.
②—Non-catalyst.
③—Catalyst.

PENNSYLVANIA

Model Year	Hydrocarbon (HC)①②		Carbon Monoxide (CO)①②		Nitrogen Oxide (NOX) Composite & Phase 2① ②
	Composite	Phase 2	Composite	Phase 2	
LIGHT DUTY VEHICLES					
1977—79	7.5	5.0	90.0	72.0	6.0
1980	2.0	1.25	60.0	48.0	6.0
1981—82	2.0	1.25	60.0	48.0	3.0
1983—90	2.0	1.25	30.0	24.0	3.0
1991 & Newer	1.2	0.75	20.0	16.0	2.5
1994 & Newer Tier 1	0.80	0.50	15.0	12.0	2.0
LIGHT DUTY TRUCKS LESS THAN 6000 LBS GVWR					
1977—78	8.0	5.0	120.0	96.0	9.0
1979—83	7.5	5.0	100.0	80.0	7.0
1984—87	3.2	2.0	80.0	64.0	7.0
1988—90	3.2	2.0	80.0	64.0	3.5

Continued

PENNSYLVANIA –Continued

Model Year	Hydrocarbon (HC)① ②		Carbon Monoxide (CO)① ②		Nitrogen Oxide (NOX) Composite & Phase 2① ②
	Composite	Phase 2	Composite	Phase 2	
LIGHT DUTY TRUCKS LESS THAN 6000 LBS GVWR -CONTINUED					
1991 & Newer	2.4	1.5	60.0	48.0	3.0
1994 & Newer Tier 1 (3750 Lbs. Or Less LVW)	0.8	0.5	15.0	12.0	2.0
1994 & Newer Tier 1 (Over 3750 Lbs. LVW)	1.0	0.63	20.0	16.0	2.5
LIGHT DUTY TRUCKS GREATER THAN 6000 LBS GVWR					
1977—78	8.0	5.0	120.0	96.0	9.0
1979—83	7.5	5.0	100.0	80.0	7.0
1984—87	3.2	2.0	80.0	64.0	7.0
1988—90	3.2	2.0	80.0	64.0	5.0
1991 & Newer	2.4	1.5	60.0	48.0	4.5
1994 & Newer Tier 1 (5750 Lbs. Or Less LVW)	1.0	0.63	20.0	16.0	2.5
1994 & Newer Tier 1 (Over 5750 Lbs. LVW)	2.4	1.5	60.0	48.0	4.0

①—GVWR: Gross Vehicle Weight Rating.
②—ppm: parts per million.

RHODE ISLAND

Model Year	Hydrocarbons (HC) ppm ①	Carbon Monoxide (CO) % ①
Pre-1967	1600	10.0
1968—69	800	8.0
1970—74	600	6.0
1975 & Newer	300	3.0

ppm—parts per million.
①—At idle speed. Pre-condition vehicle prior to testing, by operating engine at a fast idle speed of (approximately 2000 RPM) for approximately 15 seconds.

AIR QUALITY STANDARDS

TENNESSEE

Vehicle Classification (GVWR)	Model Year	Hydrocarbons (HC) ppm At Idle	Carbon Monoxide (CO) % At Idle
MEMPHIS			
All Cars & Trucks Under 9000 Lbs.	1972	900	8.9
	1973—74	700	8.2
	1975—79	600	7.5
	1980	400	4.7
	1981—96	220	1.2
All Trucks Over 9000 Lbs. But Under 26,000 Lbs.	1972	1000	8.9
	1973—74	1000	8.2
	1975—79	1000	8.0
	1980	800	6.0
	1981—96	400	4.0
NASHVILLE & DAVIDSON COUNTY			
Light Weight 0 to 6000 Lbs. GVWR	1975—77	500	5.0
	1978—79	400	4.0
	1980	300	3.0
	1981—96	220	1.2
Heavy Weight 6001 to 8500 Lbs. GVWR	1975—77	750	6.5
	1978—79	600	6.0
	1980	400	4.5
	1981—96	400	4.0

GVWR—Gross Vehicle Weight Rating.
ppm—parts per million.

TEXAS

Model Year	Carbon Monoxide (CO) % At Idle	Hydrocarbons (HC) ppm At Idle
1975—77	7.5	750
1978	6.5	650
1979	6.0	600
1980	4.0	400
1981 & Newer	1.2	220

ppm—parts per million.

UTAH
ADA COUNTY

Vehicle Classification (GVW)	Model Year	Carbon Monoxide (CO) % At Idle
Light Duty Vehicles GVW 8500 Lbs. Or Less	1965—74	5.5
	1975—79	3.5
	1980	1.5
	1981—96	1.2
Heavy Duty Vehicles GVW Over 8500 Lbs.	1965-74	6.0
	1975—80	5.0
	1981—96	3.0

GVW—Gross Vehicle Weight.

UTAH –Continued

DAVIS COUNTY & UTAH COUNTY

Vehicle Classification (GVWR)	Model Year	Carbon Monoxide (CO) % At Idle	Hydrocarbons (HC) ppm At Idle
All Passenger Vehicles: 1978 & Older Light Duty Trucks 6000 Lbs. GVWR Or Less; 1979 & Newer Light Duty Trucks 8500 Lbs. GVWR Or Less	1968—69	6.0	800
	1970—74	5.0	700
	1975—76	4.0	600
	1977—79	3.0	500
	1980	2.0	300
	1981—96	1.2	220
Heavy Duty Trucks & Vans, 1978 & Older 6001 Lbs. GVWR Or Greater: 1979 & Newer Over 8500 Lbs. GVWR	1968-69	7.0	1500
	1970—78	5.0	1200
	1979—80	4.0	1000
	1981—96	3.5	800

GVWR—Gross Vehicle Weight Rating.
ppm—parts per million.

SALT LAKE LAKE COUNTY & WEBER COUNTY

Vehicle Classification (GVW)	Model Year	Carbon Monoxide (CO) % At Idle	Hydrocarbons (HC) ppm At Idle
Below 6000 Lbs.	1968—69	6.0	800
	1970—74	5.0	700
	1975—76	4.0	600
	1977—79	3.0	500
	1980	2.0	300
	1981 & Newer	1.2	220
Greater Than 6000 Lbs.	1968-69	7.0	1500
	1970—78	5.0	1200
	1979—80	4.0	1000
	1981 & Newer	3.5	800

GVW—Gross Vehicle Weight.
ppm—parts per million.

VIRGINIA

Model Year	Hydrocarbons (HC) ppm At Idle	Carbon Monoxide (CO) % At Idle
1968—69	800	8.0
1970—74	600	6.0
1975—79	400	4.0
1980	220	2.0
1981 & Newer	220	1.2

ppm—parts per million.

AIR QUALITY STANDARDS

WASHINGTON

GASOLINE ENGINE INSPECTION STANDARDS

Vehicle Classification (GVWR)	Model Year	Hydrocarbons (HC) ppm At Idle ①	Carbon Monoxide (CO) % At Idle ② ③
All	1968—74	900	6.0
All	1975—80	600	3.0
0 to 8500 Lbs.	1981—96	220	1.2
Greater Than 8500 Lbs.	1981—96	400	3.0

GVWR—Gross Vehicle Weight Rating
ppm—parts per million
① —Optimum emission readings. Properly adjusted to manufacturer's specifications, most vehicle's emission readings for Hydrocarbons should be less than 300 ppm for vehicles without catalytic converter; 100 ppm for vehicles with catalytic converter.
② —For test results to be official, CO reading added to CO2 reading must equal or exceed 6 percent.
③ —Optimum emission readings.

Properly adjusted to manufacturer's specifications, most vehicle's emission readings for Carbon Monoxide should be less than 1.5 percent for vehicles without catalytic converter; .5 percent for vehicles with catalytic converter.

DIESEL ENGINE INSPECTION STANDARDS

Model Year	Diesel Opacity Limits %
1968-73	70
1974—91	60
1992—96	40

① —Spokane 10% more.

WISCONSIN

EMISSION LIMITATIONS FOR TRANSIENT EMISSION TEST FOR MOTOR VEHICLES INSPECTED BETWEEN 12-1-95 & 11-30-96

Model Year	Hydrocarbon (HC) gpm ①		Carbon Monoxide (CO) gpm ①		Nitrogen Oxide (NOX) gpm Composite ①
	Composite	Phase 2	Composite	Phase 2	
LIGHT DUTY VEHICLES					
1968-72	11.5	7.25	175	140	11.5
1973-74	11.5	7.25	175	140	10.5
1975-76	8.5	5.3	100	80	10.5
1977-79	8.5	5.3	100	80	7.0
1980	2.3	1.4	70	55	7.0
1981-82	2.3	1.4	70	55	3.5
1983—90	2.3	1.4	35	28	3.5
1991—95	1.4	.90	23	18.5	3.0
1996 & Newer	.90	.60	17.5	14	2.3
LIGHT DUTY TRUCKS WITH GVWR OF 6000 LBS. OR LESS					
1968-72	11.5	7.25	175	140	11.5
1973-74	11.5	7.25	175	140	10.5
1975-78	9.2	5.8	140	110	10.5
1979-83	8.5	5.3	115	90	8.0
1984—87	3.7	2.3	90	72	8.0
1988—90	3.7	2.3	90	72	4.0
1991—95	2.75	1.75	70	55	3.5
1996 & Newer	1.15	.75	23	18.5	3.0

Continued

WISCONSIN –Continued
EMISSION LIMITATIONS FOR TRANSIENT EMISSION TEST FOR MOTOR VEHICLES INSPECTED BETWEEN 12–1–95 & 11–30–96 –Continued

Model Year	Hydrocarbon (HC) gpm①		Carbon Monoxide (CO) gpm①		Nitrogen Oxide (NOX) gpm Composite①
	Composite	Phase 2	Composite	Phase 2	
LIGHT DUTY TRUCKS WITH GVWR OF 6001 TO 8500 LBS. & HEAVY DUTY VEHICLES WITH GVWR OF 8500 LBS. OR LESS					
1968-72	11.5	7.25	175	140	11.5
1973-74	11.5	7.25	175	140	10.5
1975-78	9.2	5.8	140	110	10.5
1979-83	8.5	5.3	115	90	8.0
1984—87	3.7	2.3	90	72	8.0
1988—90	3.7	2.3	90	72	5.8
1991—96	2.75	1.75	70	55	5.2
1997 & Newer	1.15	.75	23	18.5	3.0
HEAVY DUTY VEHICLES WITH GVWR OF 8501 TO 10,000 LBS.					
1968-69	23.0	14.5	230	185	17.5
1970-73	11.5	7.25	200	160	11.5
1974-78	11.5	7.25	175	140	11.5
1979-84	8.5	5.3	115	90	9.0
1985—86	5.75	3.6	90.	72	9.0
1987—90	3.7	2.3	90	72	9.0
1991—97	3.7	2.3	70	55	7.0
HEAVY DUTY VEHICLES WITH GVWR GREATER THAN 10,000 LBS.					
1968-69	27.0	17.0	290	230	35.0
1970-73	15.0	9.5	260	210	23.0
1974-78	15.0	9.5	230	185	23.0
1979-84	13.0	8.2	205	165	18.5
1985-86	11.5	7.25	185	150	18.5
1987-90	7.4	4.7	185	150	18.5
1991-97	7.4	4.7	140	110	14.0

gpm—grams per mile
①—If the corrected, composite emission rate exceed standards for any exhaust component, additional analysis of test results shall look at the second phase of the driving cycle separately. Phase 2 shall include second 94 through second 239.
②—Reserved.

EMISSION LIMITATIONS FOR TRANSIENT EMISSION TEST FOR MOTOR VEHICLES INSPECTED BETWEEN 12–1–96 & 11–30–97

Model Year	Hydrocarbon (HC) gpm①		Carbon Monoxide (CO) gpm①		Nitrogen Oxide (NOX) gpm Composite①
	Composite	Phase 2	Composite	Phase 2	
LIGHT DUTY VEHICLES					
1968-72	10.0	6.0	150	120	10.0
1973-74	10.0	6.0	150	120	9.0
1975-76	7.5	5.0	90	72	9.0
1977-79	7.5	5.0	90	72	6.0
1980	2.0	1.25	60	48	6.0
1981-82	2.0	1.25	60	48	3.0
1983—90	2.0	1.25	30	24	3.0
1991—95	1.25	.75	20	16	2.5
1996 & Newer	.80	.50	15	12	2.0
LIGHT DUTY TRUCKS WITH GVWR OF 6000 LBS. OR LESS					
1968-72	10.0	6.0	150	120	10.0
1973-74	10.0	6.0	150	120	9.0
1975-78	8.0	5.0	120	96	9.0
1979-83	7.5	5.0	100	80	7.0
1984—87	3.2	2.0	80	64	7.0

Continued

EMISSION LIMITATIONS FOR TRANSIENT EMISSION TEST FOR MOTOR VEHICLES INSPECTED BETWEEN 12–1–96 & 11–30–97 –Continued

Model Year	Hydrocarbon (HC) gpm ①		Carbon Monoxide (CO) gpm ①		Nitrogen Oxide (NOX) gpm Composite ①
	Composite	Phase 2	Composite	Phase 2	
LIGHT DUTY TRUCKS WITH GVWR OF 6000 LBS. OR LESS-CONTINUED					
1988—90	3.2	2.0	80	64	3.5
1991—95	2.4	1.5	60	48	3.0
1996 & Newer	1.0	.63	20	16	2.5
LIGHT DUTY TRUCKS WITH GVWR OF 6001 TO 8500 LBS. & HEAVY DUTY VEHICLES WITH GVWR OF 8500 LBS. OR LESS					
1968-72	10.0	6.0	150	120	10.0
1973-74	10.0	6.0	150	120	9.0
1975-78	8.0	5.0	120	96	9.0
1979-83	7.5	5.0	100	80	7.0
1984—87	3.2	2.0	80	64	7.0
1988—90	3.2	2.0	80	64	5.0
1991—96	2.4	1.5	60	48	4.5
1997 & Newer	1.0	.63	20	16	2.5
HEAVY DUTY VEHICLES WITH GVWR OF 8501 TO 10,000 LBS.					
1968-69	20.0	12.5	200	160	15.0
1970-73	10.0	6.0	175	140	10.0
1974-78	10.0	6.0	150	120	10.0
1979-84	7.5	5.0	100	80	8.0
1985—86	5.0	3.1	80	64	8.0
1987—90	3.2	2.0	80	64	8.0
1991—97	3.2	2.0	60	48	6.0
HEAVY DUTY VEHICLES WITH GVWR GREATER THAN 10,000 LBS.					
1968-69	24.0	15.0	250	200	30.0
1970-73	13.0	8.0	225	180	20.0
1974-78	13.0	8.0	200	160	20.0
1979-84	11.5	7.0	180	145	16.0
1985-86	10.0	6.0	160	128	16.0
1987-90	6.4	4.0	160	128	16.0
1991-97	6.4	4.0	120	96	12.0

gpm—grams per mile
① —If the corrected, composite emission rate exceed standards for any exhaust component, additional analysis of test results shall look at the second phase of the driving cycle separately. Phase 2 shall include second 94 through second 239.
② —Reserved.

EMISSION LIMITATIONS FOR STEADY-STATE TESTS

I. Idle Test
II. Two Speed Idle Test
III. Loaded Test
IV. Preconditioned Idle Test
V. Idle Test With Loaded Preconditioning
VI. Preconditioned Two Speed Idle Test

Vehicle Classification	Model Year	Hydrocarbons (HC) ppm At Idle	Carbon Monoxide (CO) % At Idle
Light Duty Vehicles	1968—71	800	8.0
	1972—74	550	7.0
	1975—77	450	5.5
	1978	350	4.0
	1979	275	3.0
	1980	230	2.0
	1981—96	220	1.2

Continued

EMISSION LIMITATIONS FOR STEADY-STATE TESTS –Continued

Vehicle Classification	Model Year	Hydrocarbons (HC) ppm At Idle	Carbon Monoxide (CO) % At Idle
Light Duty Trucks W/GVWR 6000 Lbs. Or Less	1968—71	800	8.0
	1972—74	700	7.0
	1975—77	500	6.0
	1978	450	5.0
	1979	300	3.0
	1980	275	2.5
	1981—84	250	2.0
	1985—96	220	1.2
Light Duty Trucks W/GVWR 6001 to 8500 Lbs. & Heavy Duty Vehicles W/GVWR 8500 Lbs. Or Less	1968-69	1450	9.0
	1970-71	800	8.0
	1972-74	700	7.0
	1975—77	550	6.5
	1978	450	5.5
	1979	300	3.0
	1980	275	2.5
	1981—84	250	2.0
	1985—96	220	1.2
Heavy Duty Vehicles W/GVWR Greater Than 8500 Lbs.	1968-71	1500	9.5
	1972-78	900	9.0
	1979-84	700	7.0
	1985-96	300	3.0

ppm—parts per million

VEHICLE MAINTENANCE SCHEDULES

TABLE OF CONTENTS

Page No.

CHRYSLER CORP. 49
FORD MOTOR CO. 58

Chrysler Corp.

INDEX

Page No.

Cirrus, Neon & Stratus 56
Colt & Summit Sedan 50
Colt Vista & Summit Wagon 51
Concorde, Intrepid, LHS, Vision & 1994-95 New Yorker 56
Stealth 54

Page No.

1993-94 Laser & Talon 52
Dynasty, New Yorker, Acclaim, Daytona, Laser, LeBaron, Shadow, Spirit & Sundance 55
1995-96 Talon 53

COLT & SUMMIT SEDAN

SCHEDULED MAINTENANCE FOR EMISSION CONTROL & PROPER VEHICLE PERFORMANCE

EMISSION CONTROL SYSTEM MAINTENANCE	SERVICE INTERVALS	MILEAGE IN THOUSANDS	7.5	15	22.5	30	37.5	45
		KILOMETERS IN THOUSANDS	12	24	36	48	60	72
ENGINE OIL (EXCEPT TURBO) CHANGE EVERY 12 MONTHS	OR		X	X	X	X	X	X
ENGINE OIL (TURBO) CHANGE EVERY 6 MONTHS	OR		X	X	X	X	X	X
ENGINE OIL FILTER REPLACE AT EVERY SECOND OIL CHANGE (1)	OR			X		X		X
REPLACE SPARK PLUGS	AT						X	
INSPECT AND ADJUST TENSION ON DRIVE BELTS, REPLACE AS NECESSARY	AT			X		X		X

(1) Note: If mileage is less than 7,500 miles each 12 months, replace oil filter at each oil change.

SEVERE SERVICE MAINTENANCE

Maintenance Item	Service to be Performed	Mileage Intervals Kilometers in Thousands (Miles in Thousands)									Severe Usage Conditions						
		12 (7.5)	24 (15)	36 (22.5)	48 (30)	60 (37.5)	72 (45)	80 (50)	84 (52.5)	96 (60)	A	B	C	D	E	F	G
Air Cleaner Element	Replace	More Frequently									X				X		
Spark Plugs	Replace		X		X		X			X		X		X			
Engine Oil	Change Every 3 Months or	Every 4,800 Km (3,000 Miles)									X	X	X	X			X
Engine Oil Filter	Replace Every 6 Months or	Every 9,600 Km (6,000 Miles)									X	X	X	X			X
Disc Brake Pads	Inspect for Wear	More Frequently									X					X	
Rear Drum Brake Linings and Rear Wheel Cylinders	Inspect for Wear and Leaks	More Frequently									X					X	

Severe usage conditions

A – Driving in dusty conditions
B – Trailer towing or police, taxi, or commercial type operation
C – Extensive idling
D – Short-trip operation at freezing temperatures (engine not thoroughly warmed up)

E – Driving in sandy areas
F – Driving in salty areas
G – More than 50% operation in heavy city traffic during hot weather above 32°C (90°F)

GENERAL MAINTENANCE SERVICE FOR PROPER VEHICLE PERFORMANCE

General Maintenance		Service Intervals		Kilometers in Thousands: 24	48	72	80	96
				Mileage in Thousands: 15	30	45	50	60
Timing Belt		Replace	at					X
Drive Belt (for Water Pump and Alternator)		Replace	at		X			X
Engine Oil	<N/A>	Change Every Year	or	Every 12,000 km (7,500 miles)				
	<T/C>	Change Every 6 Months	or	Every 8,000 km (5,000 miles)				
Engine Oil Filter	<N/A>	Change Every Year	or	X	X	X		X
	<T/C>	Change Every Year	or	Every 16,000 km (10,000 miles)				
Manual Transaxle Oil		Inspect Oil Level	at		X			X
Automatic Transaxle Oil		Inspect Oil Level Every Year	or	X	X	X		X
		Change Oil			X			X
Engine Coolant		Replace Every 2 Years	or		X			X
Disc Brake Pads		Inspect for Wear Every Year	or	X	X	X		X
Drum Brake Linings and Rear Wheel Cylinders		Inspect for Wear and Leaks Every 2 Years	or		X			X
Brake Hoses		Check for Deterioration or Leaks Every Year	or	X	X	X		X
Ball Joint and Steering Linkage Seals		Inspect for Grease Leaks and Damage Every 2 Years	or		X			X
Drive Shaft Boots		Inspect for Grease Leaks and Damage Every Year	or	X	X	X		X
Rear Wheel Bearings		Lubricate Grease Every 2 Years	or		X			X
Exhaust System (Connection Portion of Muffler, Pipings and Converter Heat Shields)		Check and Service as Required Every 2 Years	or		X			X

COLT VISTA & SUMMIT WAGON

2WD

Emission Control System Maintenance	Service Intervals	Kilometers in Thousands: 24	48	72	80	96
		Mileage in Thousands: 15	30	45	50	60
Check Fuel System (Tank, Line and Connections and Fuel filler Cap) for Leaks Every 5 Years	or				X	
Replace Fuel Hoses and Vapor Hoses Every 5 Years	or				X	
Replace Air Cleaner Element	at		X			X
Replace Spark Plugs	at		X			X

4WD

Emission Control System Maintenance	Service Intervals	Kilometers in Thousands: 12	24	36	48	60	72	80	84	96	108	120	128	132	144	156	160	168	180	192
		Mileage in Thousands: 7.5	15	22.5	30	37.5	45	50	52.5	60	67.5	75	80	82.5	90	97.5	100	105	112.5	120
Check Fuel System (Tank, Line and Connections and Fuel Filler Cap) for Leaks Every 5 Years	or							X									X			
Replace Vacuum Hoses, Secondary Air Hoses, Crankcase Ventilation Hoses and Water Hoses Every 5 Years	or								X											X
Replace Fuel Hoses and Vapor Hoses Every 5 Years	or							X									X			
Replace Air Cleaner Element	at				X					X					X					X
Clean Crankcase Emission-control System (PCV Valve)*	at												X							
Check Evaporative Emission-control System (except Canister)* for Leaks and Clogging Every 5 Years	or								X											X
Replace Canister*	at															X				
Replace Spark Plugs	at				X					X					X					X
Replace Ignition Cables* Every 5 Years	or								X											X
Replace EGR Valve*	at						X									X				
Replace Oxygen Sensor*	at												X							

NOTE
* Except for California

GENERAL MAINTENANCE SERVICE FOR PROPER VEHICLE PERFORMANCE

General Maintenance	Service Interval	Kilometers in Thousands	12	24	36	48	60	72	84	96
		Mileage in Thousands	7.5	15	22.5	30	37.5	45	52.5	60
Timing Belt (Including the Balancer Belt)	Replace	at								x
Drive Belt (for Water Pump and Alternator)	Replace	at				x				x
Engine Oil	Change Every Year	or	x	x	x	x	x	x	x	x
Engine Oil Filter	Change Every Year	or	x	x	x	x	x	x	x	x
Manual Transaxle Oil	Check Oil Level	at				x			x	x
Transfer Case*	Check Oil Level	at				x				x
Automatic Transaxle Fluid	Inspect Fluid Level Every Year	or				x			x	x
	Change Fluid	at				x				x
Engine Coolant*	Replace Every 2 Years	or				x				x
Front Disc Brake Pads	Inspect for Wear Every Year	or		x		x		x		x
Drum Brake Linings and Rear Wheel Cylinders	Inspect for Wear and Leaks Every 2 years	or				x				x
Brake Hoses	Check for Deterioration or Leaks Every Year	or		x		x		x		x
Ball Joint and Steering Linkage Seals	Inspect for Grease Leaks and Damage Every 2 Years	or				x				x
Drive Shaft Boots	Inspect for Grease Leaks and Damage Every Years	or		x		x		x		x
Rear Axle*	With LSD Change Oil	at				x				x
	Without LSD Inspect Oil Level	at				x				x
Rear Wheel Bearings	Lubricate Grease Every 2 Years	or				x				x
Propeller Shaft Joint*	Lubricate Grease Every 2 Years	or				x				x
Exhaust System (Connection Portion of Muffler, Pipings and Converter Heat Shields)	Check and Service as Required Every Years	or				x				x

NOTE
LSD Limited-slip Differential
* 4WD

SEVERE SERVICE MAINTENANCE

Maintenance Item	Service to be Performed	Mileage Intervals Kilometers in Thousands (Miles in Thousands)				Severe Usage Conditions							
		24 (15)	48 (30)	72 (45)	96 (60)	A	B	C	D	E	F	G	H
Engine Oil	Change Every 3 Months or	Every 4,800 km (3,000 miles)				x	x	x	x			x	
Engine Oil Filter	Replace Every 6 Months or	Every 9,600 km (6,000 miles)				x	x	x	x			x	
Air Cleaner Element	Replace	More Frequently								x			x
Crankcase Emission-control System*	Check and Clean as Required	More Frequently				x							
Spark Plugs	Replace at	x	x	x	x			x				x	
Front Disc Brake Pads	Inspect for Wear	More Frequently									x		
Rear Drum Brake Linings and Rear Wheel Cylinders	Inspect for Wear and Leaks	More Frequently				x							
Manual Transaxle and Transfer Case*	Change Oil at		x									x	x

NOTE
* 4WD

Severe usage conditions
A – Driving in dusty conditions
B – Trailer towing, or police, taxi, or commercial type operation
C – Extensive idling
D – Short-trip operation at freezing temperatures (engine not thoroughly warmed up)
E – Driving in sandy areas
F – Driving in salty areas
G – More than 50% operation in heavy city traffic during hot weather above 32°C (90°F)
H – Driving on off-road

1993-94 LASER & TALON
SCHEDULED MAINTENANCE FOR EMISSION CONTROL & PROPER VEHICLE PERFORMANCE

No.	Emission Control System Maintenance	Service Intervals	Kilometers in Thousands	24	48	72	80	96
			Mileage in Thousands	15	30	45	50	60
1	Check Fuel System (Tank, Line and Connections and Fuel Filler Cap) for Leaks Every 5 Years		or			x		
2	Replace Fuel Hoses and Vapor Hoses Every 5 Years		or			x		
3	Replace Air Cleaner Element		at	x	x			x
4	Replace Spark Plugs		at	x	x			x

GENERAL MAINTENANCE SERVICE FOR PROPER VEHICLE PERFORMANCE

No.	General Maintenance		Service Intervals	Kilometers in Thousands	24	48	72	80	96
				Mileage in Thousands	15	30	45	50	60
5	Timing Belt (Including the Balancer Belt)		Replace	at					x
6	Drive Belt (for Water Pump and Alternator)		Replace	at	x				x
7	Engine Oil	Non-Turbo	Change Every Year	or	Every 12,000 km (7,500 miles)				
		Turbo	Change Every 6 Months		Every 8,000 km (5,000 miles)				
8	Engine Oil Filter	Non-Turbo	Change Every Year	or	x	x	x		x
		Turbo	Change Every Year		Every 16,000 km (10,000 miles)				
9	Manual Transaxle Oil		Inspect Oil Level						
10	Automatic Transaxle Fluid		Inspect Fluid Level Every Year	or	x	x	x		x
			Change Fluid	at		x			x
11	Engine Coolant		Replace Every 2 Years			x			x
12	Disc Brake Pads		Inspect for Wear Every Year	or	x	x	x		x
13	Brake Hoses		Check for Deterioration or Leaks Every Year	or	x	x	x		x
14	Ball Joint and Steering Linkage Seals		Inspect for Grease Leaks and Damage Every 2 Years			x			x
15	Drive Shaft Boots		Inspect for Grease Leaks and Damage Every Year	or	x	x	x		x
16	Rear Axle <4WD>	With LSD	Change Oil			x			x
		Without LSD	Inspect Oil Level			x			x
17	Exhaust System (Connection Portion of Muffler, Pipings and Converter Heat Shields)		Check and Service as Required Every 2 Years	or	x	x			x

NOTE
LSD Limited-slip differential

SEVERE SERVICE MAINTENANCE

Maintenance Item	Service to be Performed	Mileage Intervals Kilometers in Thousands (Miles in Thousands)									Severe Usage Conditions						
		12 (7.5)	24 (15)	36 (22.5)	48 (30)	60 (37.5)	72 (45)	80 (50)	84 (52.5)	96 (60)	A	B	C	D	E	F	G
Air Cleaner Element	Replace	More Frequently									x			x			
Spark Plugs	Replace		x		x		x			x	x	x					
Engine Oil	Change Every 3 Months or	Every 4,800 km (3,000 miles)									x	x	x	x			x
Engine Oil Filter	Replace Every 6 Months or	Every 9,600 km (6,000 miles)									x	x	x	x			x
Disc Brake Pads	Inspect for Wear	More Frequently														x	

Severe usage conditions
A – Driving in dusty conditions
B – Trailer towing, or police, taxi, or commercial type operation
C – Extensive idling
D – Short trip operation at freezing temperatures (engine not thoroughly warmed up)
E – Driving in sandy areas
F – Driving in salty areas
G – More than 50% operation in heavy city traffic during hot weather above 32°C (90°F)

1995-96 TALON

GENERAL MAINTENANCE SERVICE FOR PROPER VEHICLE PERFORMANCE

No.	General maintenance		Service to be performed		Kilometers in thousands	24	48	72	96	120	144	168
					Mileage in thousands	15	30	45	60	75	90	105
7	Timing belts		Replace	at					x *1		160,000 km *2 (100,000 miles)	
8	Drive belt (for generator, water pump, power steering pump)		Check condition	at			×		×		×	
9	Engine oil	Non-turbo	Change Every 6 months	or		Every 12,000 km (7,500 miles)						
			Change Every year	or								
		Turbo	Change Every 6 months	or		Every 8,000 km (5,000 miles)						
10	Engine oil filter	Non-turbo	Replace Every Year *3	or		×	×	×	×	×	×	×
		Turbo	Replace Every Year	or		Every 16,000 km (10,000 miles)						
11	Manual transaxle oil (including transfer)		Inspect oil level	at			×		×		×	
12	Automatic transaxle fluid		Inspect fluid level Every year	or		×	×	×	×	×	×	×
			Change fluid *4	at			×		×		×	
13	Engine coolant		Change Every 2 years	or			×		×		×	
14	Disc brake pads		Inspect for wear Every year	or		×	×	×	×	×	×	×
15	Brake hoses		Check for deterioration or leaks Every year	or		×	×	×	×	×	×	×
16	Ball joint and steering linkage seals		Inspect for grease leaks and damage Every 2 years	or			×		×		×	
17	Drive shaft boots		Inspect for grease leaks and damage Every year	or		×	×	×	×	×	×	×
18	Rear axle oil		Inspect oil level	at			×		×		×	
19	SRS *5 system		Inspect system			At 10 years						
20	Exhaust system (connection portion of muffler, pipings and converter heat shields)		Check and service as required Every 2 years	or			×		×		×	

NOTES
*1: For California, this maintenance is recommended but not required
*2: Not required if belt was previously changed.
*3: If the mileage is less than 12,000 km (7,500 miles) each year, the oil filter should be replaced at every oil change.
*4: Vehicles with turbocharger
*5: Supplemental Restraint system

SEVERE SERVICE MAINTENANCE

No.	Maintenance item	Service to be performed		Kilometers in thousands	24	48	72	96	120	144	168	Severe usage conditions							
				Mileage in Thousands	15	30	45	60	75	90	105	A	B	C	D	E	F	G	H
3	Air cleaner element	Replace			×	×	×	×	×	×	×	×			×				
5	Spark plugs	Replace			×	×	×	×	×	×	×		×	×					
9	Engine oil	Change Every 3 months	or		Every 4,800 km (3,000 miles)							×	×	×	×			×	
10	Engine oil filter	Replace Every 6 months	or		Every 9,600 km (6,000 miles)							×	×	×	×			×	
12	Automatic transaxle fluid	Change fluid *1			×	×	×	×	×	×	×	×		×				×	×
14	Disc brake pads	Inspect for wear Every 6 months	or				×					×			×			
22	Manual transaxle oil (Include transfer)	Change oil *2				×		×		×		×	×					×	×

*1: Vehicles without turbocharger.
*2: Vehicles with turbocharger.

STEALTH
SCHEDULED MAINTENANCE FOR EMISSION CONTROL
& PROPER VEHICLE PERFORMANCE

Inspection and services should be performed any time a malfunction is observed or suspected. Retain receipts for all vehicle emission services to protect your emission warranty.

No	Emission Control System Maintenance	Service Intervals	Kilometers in Thousands	24	48	72	80	96
			Mileage in Thousands	15	30	45	50	60
1	Check Fuel System (Tank, Line and Connections and Fuel Filler Cap) for Leaks Every 5 Years	or					X	
2	Check Fuel Hoses for Leaks or Damage Every 2 Years	or			X			X
3	Replace Air Cleaner Element	at			X			X
4	Replace Spark Plugs at	SOHC			X			X
		DOHC						X

GENERAL MAINTENANCE SERVICE FOR PROPER VEHICLE PERFORMANCE

No.	General Maintenance	Service Intervals	Kilometers in Thousands	24	48	72	80	96
			Mileage in Thousands	15	30	45	50	60
5	Timing Belt	Replace at						X
6	Drive Belt (for Alternator)	Inspect for Tension at			X			X
7	Engine Oil — Non-Turbo	Change Every Year or	Every 12,000 km (7,500 miles)					
	Engine Oil — Turbo	Change Every 6 Months	Every 8,000 km (5,000 miles)					
8	Engine Oil Filter — Non-Turbo	Change Every Year or		X	X	X		X
	Engine Oil Filter — Turbo	Change Every Year	Every 16,000 km (10,000 miles)					
9	Manual Transaxle Oil	Inspect Oil Level at			X			X
10	Automatic Transaxle Fluid	Inspect Fluid Level Every Year or		X	X	X		X
		Change Fluid at			X			X
11	Engine Coolant	Replace Every 2 Years or			X			X
12	Disc Brake Pads	Inspect for Wear Every Year or		X	X	X		X
13	Brake Hoses	Check for Deterioration or Leaks Every Year or		X	X	X		X
14	Ball Joint and Steering Linkage Seals	Inspect for Grease Leaks and Damage Every 2 Years or			X			X
15	Drive Shaft Boots	Inspect for Grease Leaks and Damage Every Year or		X	X	X		X
16	Rear Axle <AWD> — With LSD	Change Oil			X			X
	Rear Axle <AWD> — Without LSD	Inspect Oil Level			X			X
17	Exhaust System (Connection Portion of Muffler, Pipings and Converter Heat Shields)	Check and Service as Required Every 2 Years or			X			X

NOTE
LSD Limited-slip differential

SEVERE SERVICE MAINTENANCE

The maintenance items should be performed according to the following table:

Maintenance Item	Service to be Performed	Mileage Intervals Kilometers in Thousands (Miles in Thousands)									Severe Usage Conditions						
		12 (7.5)	24 (15)	36 (22.5)	48 (30)	60 (37.5)	72 (45)	80 (50)	84 (52.5)	96 (60)	A	B	C	D	E	F	G
Air Cleaner Element	Replace	More Frequently									X				X		
Spark Plugs	Replace		X		X		X			X		X		X			
Engine Oil	Change Every 3 Months or	Every 4,800 Km (3,000 Miles)									X	X	X	X			X
Engine Oil Filter	Replace Every 6 Months or	Every 9,600 Km (6,000 Miles)									X	X	X	X			X
Disc Brake Pads	Inspect for Wear	More Frequently									X					X	

Severe usage conditions

- A Driving in dusty conditions
- B Police, taxi, or commercial type operation
- C Extensive idling
- D Short trip operation at freezing temperatures (engine not thoroughly warmed up)
- E Driving in sandy areas
- F Driving in salty areas
- G More than 50% operation in heavy city traffic during hot weather above 32°C (90°F)

FORD MOTOR CO.

DYNASTY, NEW YORKER, ACCLAIM, DAYTONA, LEBARON, SHADOW, SPIRIT & SUNDANCE

ALL VEHICLES EXCEPT CALIFORNIA 2.5 L & 3.0 L ENGINE WITH AUTO TRANSAXLE

EMISSION RELATED COMPONENT MAINTENANCE

Where time and mileage are shown, follow interval listed first.	miles X 1000	7.5	15	22.5	30	37.5	45	52.5	60	67.5	75	82.5	90	97.5
	kilometers X 1000	12	24	36	48	60	72	84	96	108	120	132	144	156
Air Cleaner Air Filter—Replace	AT			X					X				X	
Ignition Cables—Replace	AT								X					
PCV Valve—Check and Replace if Necessary	AT								X				0#	
Spark Plugs—Replace	AT			X					X				X	
Timing Belt 2.2-2.5 L Engine—Replace	AT												X	

NON-EMISSION RELATED COMPONENT MAINTENANCE

Where time and mileage are shown, follow interval listed first.	miles X 1000	7.5	15	22.5	30	37.5	45	52.5	60	67.5	75	82.5	90	97.5
	kilometers X 1000	12	24	36	48	60	72	84	96	108	120	132	144	156
Engine Coolant Flush and Replace at 36 Months**	OR							X**						
Engine Coolant Level, Hoses and Clamps—Inspect	AT	X	X	X	X	X	X	X	X	X	X	X	X	X
Engine Oil—Change Every 6 Months (4)	OR	X	X	X	X	X	X	X	X	X	X	X	X	X
Engine Oil Filter—Replace Every Second Oil Change	*		X		X		X		X		X		X	
Crankcase Filter (if equipped)—Replace	AT				X				X				X	
Accessory Drive Belts—Adjust Tension	AT		X		X				X				X	
Replace	AT							X						
Accessory Drive Belts—Auto Tension, Inspect***	AT							X			X#		X#	
Exhaust System—Inspect Every		X	X	X	X	X	X	X	X	X	X	X	X	X
Tire Rotation	AT	X	X	X	X	X	X	X	X	X	X	X	X	X

SEVERE SERVICE MAINTENANCE

Severe service is defined as: Stop-and-go driving in dusty conditions, extensive idling, frequent short trips, operating at sustained high speeds during hot weather above +90°F (+32°C), police, taxi, limousine, commercial type operation, or trailer towing. Including California 2.5 L & 3.0 L Engines with Auto Transaxle.

Where time and mileage are shown, follow interval listed first.	miles X 1000	3	6	9	12	15	18	21	24	27	30	33	36	39	42	45	48
	kilometers X 1000	5	10	15	20	24	29	34	39	43	48	53	58	62	67	72	77
Engine Oil	Refer to engine oil paragraph	X	X	X	X	X	X	X	X	X	X	X	X	X	X	X	X
Engine Oil Filter	Replace every second oil change		X		X		X		X		X		X		X		X
Brake Linings—Front and Rear	Inspect every			X				X				X				X	
CV Joint & Front Suspension Ball Joints	Inspect every oil change	X	X	X	X	X	X	X	X	X	X	X	X	X	X	X	X
Tie Rod Ends & Steering Linkage	Lubricate every 18 months OR					X					X					X	
Air Cleaner Air Filter	Replace if required every					X					X					X	
Automatic Transaxle	Change filter and fluid every					X					X					X	
PCV Valve	Replace if required every										X						

0 = Recommended maintenance for proper performance.
X = Scheduled maintenance.
# = Not required if previously replaced.
* = If accumulated mileage is less than 7,500 miles for 12 months, replace oil filter at each oil change.
** = Flush and replace engine coolant every 24 months or 30,000 miles thereafter.
*** = Replace if required.
(4) = Flexible Fuel Vehicles — Change engine oil every 6 months or 8 000 km (5,000 miles).

CALIFORNIA VEHICLES W/2.5 & 3.0 L ENGINES & AUTO TRANSAXLE

EMISSION RELATED COMPONENT MAINTENANCE

Where time and mileage are shown, follow interval listed first.	miles X 1000	7.5	15	22.5	30	37.5	45	52.5	60	67.5	75	82.5	90	97.5
	kilometers X 1000	12	24	36	48	60	72	84	96	108	120	132	144	156
Air Cleaner Air Filter—Replace	AT			X					X				X	
Ignition Cables—Replace	AT								X					
PCV Valve—Check and Replace if Necessary	AT								0(3)					
Spark Plugs—Replace	AT			X					X				X	
Timing Belt 2.5 L Engine, Replace if Required	AT												0(3)	
Timing Belt 3.0 L Engine, Replace if Required	AT								0(3)				0(3)#	

NON-EMISSION RELATED COMPONENT MAINTENANCE

Where time and mileage are shown, follow interval listed first.	miles X 1000	7.5	15	22.5	30	37.5	45	52.5	60	67.5	75	82.5	90	97.5
	kilometers X 1000	12	24	36	48	60	72	84	96	108	120	132	144	156
Engine Coolant Flush and Replace at 36 Months**	OR							X**						
Engine Coolant Level, Hoses and Clamps—Inspect	AT	X	X	X	X	X	X	X	X	X	X	X	X	X
Engine Oil—Change Every 6 Months	OR	X	X	X	X	X	X	X	X	X	X	X	X	X
Engine Oil Filter—Replace Every Second Oil Change	*		X		X		X		X		X		X	
Crankcase Filter (if equipped)—Replace	AT				X				X				X	
Accessory Drive Belts—Adjust Tension	AT		X		X		X				X		X	
Replace	AT							X						
Accessory Drive Belts—Auto Tension, Inspect***	AT							X			X#		X#	
Exhaust System—Inspect Every		X	X	X	X	X	X	X	X	X	X	X	X	X
Tire Rotation	AT	X	X	X	X	X	X	X	X	X	X	X	X	X

0 = Recommended maintenance for proper performance.
X = Scheduled maintenance.
# = Not required if previously replaced.
* = If accumulated mileage is less than 7,500 miles for 12 months, replace oil filter at each oil change.
** = Flush and replace engine coolant every 24 months or 30,000 miles thereafter.
*** = Replace if required.
(3) = Recommended by Chrysler but not required to maintain warranty on drive belts and PCV valve.

CONCORDE, INTREPID, LHS, VISION & 1994–95 NEW YORKER

EMISSION RELATED COMPONENT MAINTENANCE

Where time and mileage are shown, follow interval listed first.	miles X 1000 / kilometers X 1000	7.5 / 12	15 / 24	22.5 / 36	30 / 48	37.5 / 60	45 / 72	52.5 / 84	60 / 96	67.5 / 108	75 / 120	82.5 / 132	90 / 144	97.5 / 156
Air Cleaner Air Filter-Replace	AT				X				X				X	
Ignition Cables-Replace	AT								X					
PCV Valve-Check and Replace if Necessary	AT								X				0#	
Spark Plugs-Replace	AT			X					X				X	

NON-EMISSION RELATED COMPONENT MAINTENANCE

Where time and mileage are shown, follow interval listed first.	miles X 1000 / kilometers X 1000	7.5 / 12	15 / 24	22.5 / 36	30 / 48	37.5 / 60	45 / 72	52.5 / 84	60 / 96	67.5 / 108	75 / 120	82.5 / 132	90 / 144	97.5 / 156
Engine Coolant Flush and Replace at 36 Months **	OR							X**						
Engine Coolant Level, Hoses and Clamps-Inspect	AT	X	X	X	X	X	X	X	X	X	X	X	X	X
Engine Oil-Change Every 6 Months	OR	X	X	X	X	X	X	X	X	X	X	X	X	X
Engine Oil Filter-Replace Every Second Oil Change	*		X		X		X		X		X		X	
Crankcase Filter (if equipped)-Replace	AT				X				X				X	
Accessory Drive Belts-Adjust Tension	AT		X		X		X				X		X	
Replace	AT								X					
Exhaust System-Inspect Every		X	X	X	X	X	X	X	X	X	X	X	X	X
Tire Rotation	AT	X	X	X	X	X	X	X	X	X	X	X	X	X

SEVERE SERVICE MAINTENANCE

Severe service is defined as: Stop-and-go driving in dusty conditions, extensive idling, frequent short trips, operating at sustained high speeds during hot weather above +90°F (+32°C), police, taxi, limousine, commercial type operation, or trailer towing.

Where time and mileage are shown, follow interval listed first.		miles X 1000: 3 / km 5	6 / 10	9 / 15	12 / 20	15 / 24	18 / 29	21 / 34	24 / 39	27 / 43	30 / 48	33 / 53	36 / 58	39 / 62	42 / 67	45 / 72	48 / 77
Engine Oil	Refer to engine oil paragraph	X	X	X	X	X	X	X	X	X	X	X	X	X	X	X	X
Engine Oil Filter	Replace every second oil change		X		X		X		X		X		X		X		X
Brake Linings-Front and Rear	Inspect every			X		X		X			X			X		X	
CV Joint & Front Suspension Ball Joints	Inspect every oil change	X	X	X	X	X	X	X	X	X	X	X	X	X	X	X	X
Tie Rod Ends & Steering Linkage	Lubricate every 18 months OR					X					X					X	
Air Cleaner Air Filter	Replace if required every					X					X					X	
Automatic Transaxle	Change filter and fluid every					X					X					X	
PCV Valve	Replace if required every										X						

0 = Recommended maintenance for proper performance.
X = Scheduled maintenance for LH vehicles.
# = Not required if previously replaced.
* = If accumulated mileage is less than 7,500 miles for 12 months, replace oil filter at each oil change.
** = Flush and replace engine coolant every 24 months or 30,000 miles thereafter.

CIRRUS, NEON & STRATUS

No.	Emission control system maintenance	Service to be performed	Kilometers in thousands / Mileage in thousands	24 / 15	48 / 30	72 / 45	96 / 60	120 / 75	144 / 90	168 / 105
1	Fuel system (Tank, pipe line and connection, and fuel tank filler tube cap)	Check for leaks Every 5 years or					X			
2	Fuel hoses	Check condition Every 2 years or			X		X		X	
3	Air cleaner element	Replace at			X		X		X	
4	Evaporative emission control system (except evaporative emission canister)	Check for leaks and clogging Every 5 years or					X			
5	Spark plugs	Replace at			X		X		X	
6	Ignition cables	Replace Every 5 years or					X			

CIRRUS, NEON & STRATUS

GENERAL MAINTENANCE SERVICE FOR PROPER VEHICLE PERFORMANCE

Miles	Months	Recomended Maintenance
3,000	—	Change Engine Oil
7,500	6	Change Engine Oil
15,000	12	Change Engine Oil
		Replace Oil Filter
		Adjust Drive Belt Tension
22,500	18	Change Engine Oil
		Inspect Front Brake Pads And Rear Brake Linings
30,000	24	Change Engine Oil
		Replace Air Cleaner Element
		Replace Spark Plugs
37,500	30	Change Engine Oil
45,000	36	Change Engine Oil
		Replace Oil Filter
		Adjust Drive Belt Tension
		Flush And Fill Engine Coolant
52,500	42	Change Engine Oil
60,000	48	Change Engine Oil
		Replace Oil Filter
		Inspect & Replace PCV Valve, If Necessary
		Lubricate Front & Rear Suspension Ball Joints
		Replace Drive Belts
		Replace Air Cleaner Element
		Replace Spark Plugs
		Replace Ignition Cables

Miles	Months	Recomended Maintenance
67,500	54	Change Engine Oil
		Inspect Front Brake Pads & Rear Brake Pad Linings
75,000	60	Change Engine Oil
		Replace Oil Filter
		Adjust Drive Belt Tension
		Flush & Fill Engine Coolant If It Has Been 30,000 Miles Or 24 Months Since Last Changed
82,500	66	Change Engine Oil
		Flush & Fill Engine Coolant If It Has Been 30,000 Miles Or 24 Months Since Last Changed
90,000	72	Change Engine Oil
		Replace Oil Filter
		Inspect & Replace PCV Valve, If Necessary
		Lubricate Front & Rear Suspension Ball Joints
		Adjust Drive Belt Tension
		Replace Air Cleaner Element
97,500	78	Change Engine Oil
105,000	84	Change Engine Oil
		Replace Oil Filter
		Replace Engine Timing Belt

SEVERE SERVICE MAINTENANCE

Miles	Recomended Maintenance
3,000	Change Engine Oil
6,000	Change Engine Oil
	Replace Oil Filter
9,000	Change Engine Oil
12,000	Change Engine Oil
	Replace Oil Filter
	Inspect Front Brake Pads & Rear Brake Linings
15,000	Change Engine Oil
	Adjust Drive Belt Tension
	Inspect & Replace Air Cleaner Element, If Necessary
	Change Automatic Transaxle Fluid & Filter
	Adjust Transaxle Bands, If Equipped
18,000	Change Engine Oil
	Replace Oil Filter
21,000	Change Engine Oil
24,000	Change Engine Oil
	Replace Oil Filter
	Inspect Front Brake Pads And Rear Brake Linings
27,000	Change Engine Oil

Miles	Recomended Maintenance
30,000	Change Engine Oil
	Replace Oil Filter
	Inspect & Replace PCV Valve, If Necessary
	Lubricate Front & Rear Suspension Ball Joints
	Adjust Drive Belt Tension
	Replace Air Cleaner Element
	Replace Spark Plugs
	Change Automatic Transaxle Fluid & Filter
	Adjust Transaxle Bands, If Equipped
33,000	Change Engine Oil
36,000	Change Engine Oil
	Replace Oil Filter
	Flush & Fill Engine Coolant
	Inspect Front Brake Pads & Rear Brake Linings
39,000	Change Engine Oil
42,000	Change Engine Oil
	Replace Oil Filter
45,000	Change Engine Oil
	Inspect & Repalce Air Cleaner Element, If Necessary

Continued

VEHICLE MAINTENANCE SCHEDULES

SEVERE SERVICE MAINTENANCE

Miles	Recomended Maintenance	Miles	Recomended Maintenance
45,000 (cont.)	Adjust Drive Belt Tension	75,000 (cont.)	Inspect & Replace Air Cleaner Element, If Necessary
	Change Automatic Transaxle Fluid & Filter		Change Automatic Transaxle Fluid & Filter
	Adjust Transaxle Bands, If Equipped		Adjust Transaxle Bands, If Equipped
48,000	Change Engine Oil	78,000	Change Engine Oil
	Replace Oil Filter		Replace Oil Filter
	Inspect Front Brake Pads & Rear Brake Linings	81,000	Change Engine Oil
51,000	Change Engine Oil		Flush & Fill Engine Coolant
	Flush & Fill Engine Coolant	84,000	Change Engine Oil
54,000	Change Engine Oil		Replace Oil Filter
	Replace Oil Filter		Inspect Front Brake Pads & Rear Brake Linings
57,000	Change Engine Oil	87,000	Change Engine Oil
60,000	Change Engine Oil	90,000	Change Engine Oil
	Replace Oil Filter		Replace Oil Filter
	Inspect & Replace PCV Valve, If Necessary		Inspect & Replace PCV Valve, If Necessary
	Lubricate Front & Rear Suspension Ball Joints		Lubricate Front & Rear Suspension Ball Joints
	Replace Drive Belts		Adjust Drive Belt Tension
	Replace Air Cleaner Element		Replace Air Cleaner Element
	Replace Spark Plugs		Replace Spark Plugs
	Replace Ignition Cables		Change Automatic Transaxle Fluid & Filter
	Change Automatic Transaxle Fluid & Filter		Adjust Transaxle Bands, If Equipped
	Adjust Transaxle Bands, If Equipped	93,000	Change Engine Oil
	Inspect Front Brake Pads & Rear Brake Linings	96,000	Change Engine Oil
63,000	Change Engine Oil		Replace Oil Filter
66,000	Change Engine Oil		Inspect Front Brake Pads & Rear Brake Linings
	Replace Oil Filter	99,000	Change Engine Oil
69,000	Change Engine Oil	100,000	Replace Spark Plugs
72,000	Change Engine Oil	102,000	Change Engine Oil
	Replace Oil Filter		Replace Oil Filter
	Inspect Front Brake Pads & Rear Brake Linings		Replace Engine Timing Belt
75,000	Change Engine Oil		
	Adjust Drive Belt Tension		

Ford Motor Co.

INDEX

Page No.

Aspire & Festiva 61
Capri 66
Continental 59
Crown Victoria, Grand Marquis & Town Car 60
Escort & Tracer 67
Mustang 62

Page No.

Tempo & Topaz 59
1993-94 Cougar & Thunderbird 59
1993-95 Sable & Taurus 64
Probe 63
1995-96 Cougar & Thunderbird 68
1996 Sable & Taurus 65

TEMPO & TOPAZ — NORMAL SERVICE MAINTENANCE

SERVICE INTERVAL Perform at the months or distances shown, whichever comes first.	3	6	9	12	15	18	21	24	27	30	33	36	39	42	45	48	51	54	57	60
Miles x 1000 / Kilometers x 1000	4.8	9.6	14.4	19.2	24	28.8	33.6	38.4	43.2	48	52.8	57.6	62.4	67.2	72	76.8	81.6	86.4	91.2	96
EMISSION CONTROL SERVICE																				
Change Engine Oil and Oil Filter (every 3 months)	X	X	X	X	X	X	X	X	X	X	X	X	X	X	X	X	X	X	X	X
Spark Plugs. Replace																				X
Inspect Accessory Drive Belt(s)										X										X
Replace Air Cleaner Filter①										X										X
Replace Crankcase Emission Filter①										X										X
Replace Engine Coolant (every 36 months) or																				
GENERAL MAINTENANCE																				
Check Engine Coolant Protection, Hoses and Clamps	ANNUALLY																			
Inspect Exhaust Heat Shields										X						X				X
Change Automatic Transaxle Fluid②										X										X
Inspect Disc Brake Pads and Rotors (Front)②										X						X				X
Inspect Brake Linings and Drums (Rear)②										X										X
Inspect and Repack Rear Wheel Bearings④																				

① If operating in severe dust, more frequent intervals may be required — consult your dealer.
② Change automatic transaxle fluid if your driving habits frequently include one or more of the following conditions:
  • Operation during HOT WEATHER (above 32°C (90°F))
  • Towing a trailer or using a car top carrier.
  • Police, taxi or door-to-door delivery service.
③ If your driving includes continuous stop and go driving or driving in mountainous areas, more frequent intervals may be required.
④ Replace rear wheel bearings at 100,000 miles (160,930 km).

SEVERE SERVICE MAINTENANCE (Tempo & Topaz)

SERVICE INTERVAL Perform at the months or distances shown, whichever comes first.	3	6	9	12	15	18	21	24	27	30	33	36	39	42	45	48	51	54	57	60
Miles x 1000 / Kilometers x 1000	4.8	9.6	14.4	19.2	24	28.8	33.6	38.4	43.2	48	52.8	57.6	62.4	67.2	72	76.8	81.6	86.4	91.2	96
EMISSION CONTROL SERVICE																				
Replace Engine Oil and Oil Filter Every 3 months OR	X	X	X	X	X	X	X	X	X	X	X	X	X	X	X	X	X	X	X	X
Replace Spark Plugs																				X
Inspect Accessory Drive Belt(s)										X										X
Replace Air Cleaner Filter ①										X										X
Replace Crankcase Filter ①										X										X
Replace Engine Coolant Every 36 Months OR																				
GENERAL MAINTENANCE																				
Check Engine Coolant Protection, Hoses and Clamps	ANNUALLY																			
Inspect Exhaust Heat Shields										X										X
Change Automatic Transaxle Fluid ②										②										②
Inspect Disc Brake Pads and Rotors Front and Rear										X③										X③
Inspect and Repack Rear Wheel Bearings										X										X
Rotate Tires		X																		X

1 If operating in severe dust, more frequent intervals may be required — consult your dealer.
2 Change automatic transaxle fluid if your driving habits frequently include one or more of the following conditions:
  • Operation during HOT WEATHER (above 32°C (90°F)).
  • Towing a trailer or using a car top carrier.
  • Police, taxi or door-to-door delivery service.
3 If your driving includes continuous stop and go driving or driving in mountainous areas, more frequent intervals may be required.
x All items designated by an X must be performed in all states.

SEVERE SERVICE MAINTENANCE (Continental)

SERVICE INTERVALS Perform at the months or distances shown, whichever comes first.	7.5	15	22.5	30	37.5	45	52.5	60
Miles x 1000 / Kilometers x 1000	12	24	36	48	60	72	84	96
EMISSIONS CONTROL SERVICE								
Change Engine Oil and Oil Filter (Every 6 Months) or 7500 miles whichever occurs first	X	X	X	X	X	X	X	X
Replace Spark Plugs								X
Change crankcase emission filter				X				X
Inspect Accessory Drive Belt(s)				X				X
Replace Air Cleaner Filter①				X				X①
Change Engine Coolant Every 36 Months or								
Check Engine Coolant Protection, Hoses and Clamps	ANNUALLY							
GENERAL MAINTENANCE								
Check Exhaust Heat Shields				X				X
Inspect Disc Brake Pads and Rotors (Front)②	X②	X②	X②	X②	X②	X②	X②	X②
Inspect Brake Linings and Drums (Rear)②				X②				X②
Inspect and Repack Rear Wheel Bearing③				X③				X③

① If operating in severe dust, more frequent intervals may be required. Consult your dealer.
② If your driving includes continuous stop-and-go driving or driving in mountainous areas, more frequent intervals may be required.
③ Replace rear wheel bearings at 100,000 miles (160,930 km).

CONTINENTAL — NORMAL SERVICE MAINTENANCE

SERVICE INTERVALS Perform at the months or distances shown, whichever comes first.	7.5	15	22.5	30	37.5	45	52.5	60
Miles x 1000 / Kilometers x 1000	12	24	36	48	60	72	84	96
EMISSIONS CONTROL SERVICE								
Replace Engine Oil and Oil Filter Every 6 Months OR	X	X	X	X	X	X	X	X
Replace Spark Plugs								X
Replace Crankcase Filter①				X				X
Inspect Accessory Drive Belt(s)				X				X
Replace Air Cleaner Filter①				X				X
Replace Engine Coolant Every 36 Months OR				X				X
Check Engine Coolant Protection, Hoses and Clamps				X				X
GENERAL MAINTENANCE								
Check Exhaust Heat Shields	ANNUALLY							
Inspect Disc Brake Pads and Rotors (Front and Rear)				X②				X②②
Rotate Tires		X				X		

① If operating in severe dust, more frequent intervals may be required. Consult your dealer.
② If your driving includes continuous stop-and-go driving or driving in mountainous areas, more frequent intervals may be required.
X All items designated by an X must be performed in all states.

1993-94 COUGAR & THUNDERBIRD — NORMAL SERVICE MAINTENANCE

SERVICE INTERVALS Perform at the months or distances shown, whichever comes first.	7.5	15	22.5	30	37.5	45	52.5	60
Miles x 1000 / Kilometers x 1000	12	24	36	48	60	72	84	96
EMISSIONS CONTROL SERVICE								
Supercharged Engines — Change Oil and Filter	As Indicated by the Vehicle Maintenance Monitor, But Not Beyond Every 5,000 Miles (8 000 km) or 6 Months, Whichever Comes First							
Replace Engine Oil and Oil Filter As Indicated by the Vehicle Maintenance Monitor (if equipped), But Not Beyond Every 6 Months or 7,500 Miles Whichever Occurs First — Except Supercharged	X	X	X	X	X	X	X	X
Replace Spark Plugs — Except Supercharged				X				X
Replace Spark Plugs — Platinum Type Supercharged								X
Check Supercharger Lubricant				X				X
Replace Accessory Emission Filter①				X				X
Inspect Accessory Drive Belt(s)				X				X
Replace Air Cleaner Filter①				X				X
Replace Engine Coolant Every 36 Months OR				X				X
Check Engine Coolant Protection, Hoses and Clamps				X				X
GENERAL MAINTENANCE								
Check Exhaust Heat Sheilds	ANNUALLY							
Inspect Disc Brake Pads and Rotors (Front and Rear Super Coupe/XR7)②				X②				X②
Inspect Brake Linings and Drums (Rear)②				X②				X②
Rotate Tires		X				X		

① If operating in severe dust, more frequent intervals may be required. Consult your dealer.
② If your driving includes continuous stop-and-go driving or driving in mountainous areas, more frequent intervals may be required.
x All items designated by an X must be performed in all states.

SEVERE SERVICE MAINTENANCE

SERVICE INTERVAL Perform at the months or distances shown, whichever comes first.	Miles × 1000	3	6	9	12	15	18	21	24	27	30	33	36	39	42	45	48	51	54	57	60
	Kilometers × 1000	4.8	9.6	14.4	19.2	24	28.8	33.6	38.4	43.2	48	52.8	57.6	62.4	67.2	72	76.8	81.6	86.4	91.2	96
EMISSION CONTROL SERVICE																					
Replace Engine Oil and Oil Filter Every 3 Months OR		X	X	X	X	X	X	X	X	X	X	X	X	X	X	X	X	X	X	X	X
Replace Spark Plugs											X										
Replace Spark Plugs (Supercharged use Platinum Type)																					X
Check Supercharger Lubricant											X										X
Inspect Accessory Drive Belt(s)											X										X
Replace Air Cleaner Filter①											X										X
Replace Engine Coolant, EVERY 36 Months OR											X										X
Check Engine Coolant Protection, Hoses and Clamps		ANNUALLY																			
GENERAL MAINTENANCE																					
Inspect Exhaust Heat Shields											X										X
Change Automatic Transmission Fluid②											X										X
Inspect Brake Pads and Rotors (front)③ (Front and Rear — Super Coupe/XR7)③											X										X
Inspect Brake Linings and Drums (Rear)③											X										X
Rotate Tires			X					X					X					X			

① If operating in severe dust, more frequent intervals may be required. Consult your dealer.
② Change automatic transmission fluid if your driving habits frequently include one or more of the following conditions:
  • Operation during hot weather (above 32°C (90°F)) carrying heavy loads and in hilly terrain.
  • Towing a trailer or using a car top carrier.
  • Police, taxi or door-to-door delivery service.
  • Vehicle accumulates 5,000 miles (8 000 km) or more per month or is used in CONTINUOUS stop-and-go service.
③ If your driving includes continuous stop-and-go driving or driving in mountainous areas, more frequent intervals may be required.
X All items designated by an X must be performed in all states.

CROWN VICTORIA, GRAND MARQUIS & TOWN CAR

NORMAL SERVICE MAINTENANCE

SERVICE INTERVALS Perform at the months or distances shown, whichever comes first.	Miles x 1000	7.5	15	22.5	30	37.5	45	52.5	60
	Kilometers x 1000	12	24	36	48	60	72	84	96
EMISSIONS CONTROL SERVICE									
Replace Engine Oil and Filter (Every 6 Months) OR 7,500 Miles Whichever Occurs First		X	X	X	X	X	X	X	X
Replace Spark Plugs					X				X
Replace Crankcase Emission Filter①					X				X
Inspect Accessory Drive Belt(s)					X				X
Replace Air Cleaner Filter①					X				X
Replace PCV Valve and Crankcase Emission Filter — 5.0L Engine			(X)		(X)		(X)		X
Check/Clean Choke Linkage (5.8L only)					X				X
Change Engine Coolant Every 36 Months OR					X				X
Check Engine Coolant Protection, Hoses and Clamps				ANNUALLY					
GENERAL MAINTENANCE									
Check Exhaust Heat Shields					X				X
Lube Suspension (Lincoln)			X③		X		X③		X
Lubricate Steering Linkage (Lincoln)		X			X		X		X
Inspect Disc Brake Pads and Rotors (Front)②					X				X
Inspect Brake Linings and Drums (Rear)②					X				X
Inspect and Repack Front Wheel Bearings					X				X
Rotate Tires		X		X		X			X

① If operating in severe dust, more frequent intervals may be required. Consult your dealer.
② If your driving includes continuous stop-and-go driving or driving in mountainous areas, more frequent intervals may be required.
③ All vehicles except Lincoln Town Car.
X All items designated by an X must be performed in all states.
(X) This item not required to be performed, however, Ford recommends that you also perform maintenance on items designated by an (X) in order to achieve best vehicle operation. Failure to perform this recommended maintenance will not invalidate the vehicle emissions warranty or manufacturer recall liability.

FORD MOTOR CO.

VEHICLE MAINTENANCE SCHEDULES

SEVERE SERVICE MAINTENANCE

SERVICE INTERVAL Perform at the months or distances shown, whichever comes first.	3	6	9	12	15	18	21	24	27	30	33	36	39	42	45	48	51	54	57	60
Miles × 1000	3	6	9	12	15	18	21	24	27	30	33	36	39	42	45	48	51	54	57	60
Kilometers × 1000	4.8	9.6	14.4	19.2	24	28.8	33.6	38.4	43.2	48	52.8	57.6	62.4	67.2	72	76.8	81.6	86.4	91.2	96
EMISSION CONTROL SERVICE																				
Replace Engine Oil and Oil Filter Every 3 Months OR	X	X	X	X	X	X	X	X	X	X	X	X	X	X	X	X	X	X	X	X
Replace Spark Plugs										X										X
Inspect Accessory Drive Belt(s)										X										X
Replace PCV Valve and Crankcase Emission Filter (5.0L Engine)					(X)					(X)					(X)					
Replace Air Cleaner Filter (1)										X										X
Replace Crankcase Emission Filter (1) (5.8L Engine)										X										X
Check/Clean Choke Linkage (5.8L Engine)										X										X
Replace Engine Coolant, EVERY 36 Months OR										X										X
Check Engine Coolant Protection, Hoses and Clamps	ANNUALLY																			
GENERAL MAINTENANCE																				
Inspect Exhaust Heat Shields										X										X
Change Automatic Transmission Fluid (2)										X										X
Lubricate Suspension (Lincoln)										X										X
Lubricate Steering Linkage (Lincoln)					X					X				X						X
Inspect Disc Brake Pads and Rotors (3)										X										X
Inspect Brake Linings and Drums (Rear) (Lincoln) (3)										X										X
Inspect and Repack Front Wheel Bearings										X										X
Rotate Tires		X			X						X				X					

(1) If operating in severe dust, more frequent intervals may be required. Consult your dealer.
(2) Change automatic transmission fluid if your driving habits frequently include one or more of the following conditions:
 ● Operation during hot weather (above 32°C (90°F)) carrying heavy loads and in hilly terrain.
 ● Towing a trailer or using a car top carrrier.
 ● Police, taxi or door to door delivery service.
(3) If your driving includes continuous stop-and-go driving or driving in mountainous areas, more frequent intervals may be required.
X All items designated by an X must be performed in all states.
(X) This item not required to be performed, however, Ford recommends that you also perform maintenance on items designated by an (X) in order to achieve best vehicle operation. Failure to perform this recommended maintenance will not invalidate the vehicle emissions warranty or manufacturer recall liability

ASPIRE & FESTIVA
NORMAL SERVICE MAINTENANCE

	7.5	15.0	22.5	30.0	37.5	45.0	52.5	60.0
MILES × (1000)	7.5	15.0	22.5	30.0	37.5	45.0	52.5	60.0
KILOMETERS × (1000)	12	24	36	48	60	72	84	96
EMISSION CONTROL SERVICE								
Change Engine Oil (whichever occurs first) Every 6 Months or	X	X	X	X	X	X	X	X
Change Engine Oil Filter (whichever occurs first) Every 6 Months or	X	X	X	X	X	X	X	X
Spark Plugs Inspect/Clean		(2)				(2)		
Replace				X				X
Check Idle Speed		X		X		X		X
Inspect Cooling System Every 12 Months or		X		X		X		X
Replace Engine Coolant Every 36 Months or				X				X
Check Accessory Drive Belts				X				X
Replace Air Cleaner Element				(1)				(1)
Replace Fuel Filter				X				X
Replace Engine Timing Belt								X
GENERAL MAINTENANCE								
Inspect Brake Lines and Connections				X		X		X
Inspect Clutch Pedal				X		X		X
Inspect Front Disc Brakes				X		X		X
Inspect Drum Brakes				X				X
Inspect Safety Belts, Buckles, Retractors, & Anchors				X		X		X
Inspect Steering Linkage, Rack Guides & Tie Rod Ends				X		X		X
Tighten Bolts & Nuts on Chassis & Body				X		X		
Inspect Steering Operations & Gear Housing				X		X		X
Inspect Rack Seal Boots				X				X
Inspect Front Suspension Ball Joints				X				X
Inspect Drive Shaft Dust Boots				X				X
Inspect Exhaust System Heat Shield				X				X
Inspect Fuel Lines				(2)				X
Inspect Transaxle, Change Rod Boots							X	
Lubricate Front and Rear Wheel Bearings								X

(1) If operating in severe dusty conditions, ask your dealer for proper replacement interval.
(2) Recommended, but not required.

SEVERE SERVICE MAINTENANCE

	3	6	9	12	15	18	21	24	27	30	33	36	39	42	45	48	51	54	57	60
MILES × (1000)	3	6	9	12	15	18	21	24	27	30	33	36	39	42	45	48	51	54	57	60
KILOMETERS × (1000)	4.8	9.6	14.	19.	24.	28.	33.	38.	43.	48.	52.	57.	62.	67.	72.	76.	81.	86.	91.	96.
EMISSION CONTROL SERVICE																				
Change Engine Oil (whichever occurs first) Every 3 Months or	X	X	X	X	X	X	X	X	X	X	X	X	X	X	X	X	X	X	X	X
Change Engine Oil Filter (whichever occurs first) Every 3 Months or	X	X	X	X	X	X	X	X	X	X	X	X	X	X	X	X	X	X	X	X
Spark Plugs Inspect/Clean		X		X		X		X				X		X		X				
Replace										X										X
Check Idle Speed					X					X					X					X
Inspect Cooling System Every 12 Months or						X				X					X					X
Replace Engine Coolant Every 36 Months or										X										X
Check Accessory Drive Belts										X										X
Replace Air Cleaner Element										(1)										(1)
Replace Fuel Filter										X										
Replace Engine Timing Belt																				X

GENERAL MAINTENANCE	3	6	9	12	15	18	21	24	27	30	33	36	39	42	45	48	51	54	57	60
Inspect Brake Lines, Connections & Hoses						X				X					X					X
Inspect, Adjust Clutch Pedal						X				X					X					X
Inspect Front Disc Brakes						X				X					X					X
Inspect Rear Drum Brakes										X										X
Inspect Safety Belts, Buckles, Retractors & Anchors						X				X					X					X
Inspect Steering Linkage, Rack Guides, & Tie Rod Ends						X				X					X					X
Tighten Bolts & Nuts on Chassis & Body						X									X					
Inspect Steering Operations and Gear Housing										X		X								X
Inspect Rack Seal Boots										X										X
Inspect Front Suspension Ball Joints										X										X
Inspect Drive Shaft Dust Boots										X										X
Inspect Exhaust System Heat Shield										X										X
Inspect Fuel Lines										(2)										X
Inspect Transaxle, Change Rod Boots																X				
Lubricate Front and Rear Wheel Bearings																				X

(1) If operating in severe dusty conditions, ask your dealer for proper replacement interval.
(2) Recommended, but not required.

MUSTANG
NORMAL SERVICE MAINTENANCE

SERVICE INTERVALS Perform at the months or distances shown, whichever comes first.	Miles x 1000	7.5	15	22.5	30	37.5	45	52.5	60
	Kilometers x 1000	12	24	36	48	60	72	84	96
EMISSIONS CONTROL SERVICE									
Replace Engine Oil and Filter Every 6 Months OR 7,500 Miles Whichever Occurs First		X	X	X	X	X	X	X	X
Replace Spark Plugs					X				X
Replace Crankcase Emission Filter ①					X				X
Inspect Accessory Drive Belt(s)					X				X
Replace Air Cleaner Filter ①					X				X
Replace PCV Valve and Crankcase Emission Filter — 5.0L			(X)		(X)		(X)		X
Replace Engine Coolant Every 36 Months OR					X				X
Check Engine Coolant Protection, Hoses and Clamps		ANNUALLY							
GENERAL MAINTENANCE									
Check Exhaust Heat Shields					X				X
Lube Tie Rods			X③		X		X③		X
Inspect Disc Brake Pads and Rotors②					X				X
Inspect Brake Linings and Drums (Rear)②					X②				X②
Inspect and Repack Front Wheel Bearings					X				X
Rotate Tires		X		X		X		X	

① If operating in severe dust, more frequent intervals may be required. Consult your dealer.
② If your driving includes continuous stop-and-go driving or driving in mountainous areas, more frequent intervals may be required.
③ All vehicles.
X All items designated by an X must be performed in all states.
(X) This item not required to be performed, however, Ford recommends that you also perform maintenance on items designated by an (X) in order to achieve best vehicle operation. Failure to perform this recommended maintenance will not invalidate the vehicle emissions warranty or manufacturer recall liability.

SEVERE SERVICE MAINTENANCE

SERVICE INTERVAL Perform at the months or distances shown, whichever comes first.	Miles x 1000	3	6	9	12	15	18	21	24	27	30	33	36	39	42	45	48	51	54	57	60
	Kilometers × 1000	4.8	9.6	14.4	19.2	24	28.8	33.6	38.4	43.2	48	52.8	57.6	62.4	67.2	72	76.8	81.6	86.4	91.2	96
EMISSION CONTROL SERVICE																					
Replace Engine Oil and Oil Filter Every 3 Months OR		X	X	X	X	X	X	X	X	X	X	X	X	X	X	X	X	X	X	X	X
Replace Spark Plugs											X										X
Inspect Accessory Drive Belt(s)											X										X
Replace PCV Valve and Crankcase Emission Filter — 5.0L						(X)					(X)					(X)					X
Replace Air Cleaner Filter ①											X										X
Replace Engine Coolant, EVERY 36 Months OR											X										X
Check Engine Coolant Protection, Hoses and Clamps		ANNUALLY																			
GENERAL MAINTENANCE																					
Inspect Exhaust Heat Shields											X										X
Change Automatic Transmission Fluid②											X										X
Lubricate Tie Rods											X										X
Inspect Disc Brake Pads and Rotors②											X										X
Inspect Brake Linings and Drums (Rear)③											X										X
Inspect and Repack Front Wheel Bearings											X										X
Rotate Tires			X				X					X					X				

1 If operating in severe dust, more frequent intervals may be required. Consult your dealer.
2 Change automatic transmission fluid if your driving habits frequently include one or more of the following conditions:
• Operation during hot weather (above 32°C (90°F)) carrying heavy loads and in hilly terrain.
• Towing a trailer or using a car top carrier.
• Police, taxi or door to door delivery service.
3 If your driving includes continuous stop-and-go driving or driving in mountainous areas, more frequent intervals may be required.
X All items designated by an X must be performed in all states.
(X) This item not required to be performed, however, Ford recommends that you also perform maintenance on items designated by an (X) in order to achieve best vehicle operation. Failure to perform this recommended maintenance will not invalidate the vehicle emissions warranty or manufacturer recall liability.

FORD MOTOR CO.

PROBE
NORMAL SERVICE MAINTENANCE

Perform at the Months or Distances Shown, Whichever Occurs First

	67.5	75	77.5	90	97.5	105	112.5	120
Miles x 1000	67.5	75	77.5	90	97.5	105	112.5	120
Kilometers x 1000	108.5	120.5	125.5	144.5	156.5	168.5	181	193
Emission Control Service								
• Change engine oil and oil filter every 6 months OR 7,500 miles, (12 000 kilometers)	x	x	x	x	x	x	x	x
• Replace spark plugs				x				x
• Replace crankcase ventilation filter (1)				x				x
• Inspect accessory drive belt(s)				x				x
• Replace air cleaner filter (1)				x				x
• Replace engine coolant (every 36 months) OR				x				x
• Check engine coolant system, coolant, hoses and clamps	ANNUALLY							
• Inspect cooling system components every 36 months OR				x				x
• Replace engine timing belt (3)								x
• Inspect idle speed (4)					x			x
• Inspect fuel lines (2)					x			x
• Replace fuel filter								x

	67.5	75	77.5	90	97.5	105	112.5	120
Miles x 1000	67.5	75	77.5	90	97.5	105	112.5	120
Kilometers x 1000	108.5	120.5	125.5	144.5	156.5	168.5	181	193
General Maintenance								
• Inspect exhaust heat shields				x				x
• Inspect front and/or rear disc brakes				x				x
• Inspect drum brakes				x				x
• Rotate tires	x	x	x	x	x		x	
• Inspect halfshaft dust boots				x				x
• Inspect steering operation and linkage				x				x
• Inspect front suspension ball joints				x				x
• Inspect brake lines, hoses and connections				x				x
• Inspect bolts and nuts on chassis and body				x				x
• Inspect clutch pedal operation (if equipped)				x				x

(1) If operating in severe dust, more frequent intervals may be required. Consult your dealer.

(2) This item not required to be performed, however, Ford recommends that you perform maintenance on this item in order to achieve best vehicle operation. Failure to perform this recommended maintenance will not invalidate the emissions warranty or manufacturer recall liability.

(3) Replacement of the timing belt is required at every 60,000 miles (96 000 km). Failure to replace the timing belt may result in damage to the engine.

(4) Recommended, but not required. Adjustment should be made if fault is found.

SEVERE SERVICE MAINTENANCE

Perform at the Months or Distances Shown, Whichever Occurs First

	3	6	9	12	15	18	21	24	27	30	33	36	39	42	45	48	51	54	57	60
Miles x 1000	3	6	9	12	15	18	21	24	27	30	33	36	39	42	45	48	51	54	57	60
Kilometers x 1000	4.8	9.6	14.4	19.2	24	28.8	33.6	38.4	43.2	48	52.8	57.6	62.4	67.2	72	76.8	81.6	86.4	91.2	96
Emission Control Service																				
• Change engine oil and oil filter every 3,000 miles (4 800 kilometers) or 3 months	x	x	x	x	x	x	x	x	x	x	x	x	x	x	x	x	x	x	x	x
• Replace spark plugs										x										x
• Inspect accessory drive belt(s)										x										x
• Inspect/clean air cleaner filter (2)					x										x					
• Replace air cleaner filter (1)										x										x
• Inspect fuel lines (2)										x										x
• Replace engine coolant every 36 months OR										x										x
• Check cooling system, coolant, hoses and clamps	ANNUALLY																			
• Inspect cooling system components every 36 months OR										x										x
• Replace engine timing belt (4)																				x
• Inspect idle speed (5)										x										x
• Replace fuel filter																				x

	3	6	9	12	15	18	21	24	27	30	33	36	39	42	45	48	51	54	57	60
Miles x 1000	3	6	9	12	15	18	21	24	27	30	33	36	39	42	45	48	51	54	57	60
Kilometers x 1000	4.8	9.6	14.4	19.2	24	28.8	33.6	38.4	43.2	48	52.8	57.6	62.4	67.2	72	76.8	81.6	86.4	91.2	96
General Maintenance																				
• Inspect exhaust heat shields										x										x
• Change automatic transaxle fluid (3)										x										x
• Inspect front and/or rear disc brakes					x					x					x					x
• Inspect rear drum brakes (3)										x										x
• Rotate tires		x				x				x					x					
• Inspect clutch pedal operation (if equipped)										x										x
• Inspect halfshaft dust boots										x										x
• Inspect brake line, hoses and connections										x										x
• Inspect front suspension ball joints										x										x
• Inspect bolts and nuts on chassis and body				x						x					x					x
• Inspect steering operation and linkage										x										x

(1) If operating in severe dust, more frequent intervals may be required. Consult your dealer.

(2) This item not required to be performed, however, Ford recommends that you also perform maintenance on these items in order to achieve best vehicle operation. Failure to perform this recommended maintenance will not invalidate the emissions warranty or manufacturer recall liability.

(3) Change automatic transaxle fluid if your driving habits frequently include one or more of the following conditions:
- Operation during hot weather (above 90°F, 32°C), carrying heavy loads and in hilly terrain.
- Police, taxi or door-to-door delivery service.

(4) Replacement of the timing belt is required every 60,000 miles (96 000 km). Failure to replace the timing belt may result in damage to the engine.

(5) Recommended but not required. Adjustment should be made if any fault is found.

VEHICLE MAINTENANCE SCHEDULES

1993-95 SABLE & TAURUS
NORMAL SERVICE MAINTENANCE

SERVICE INTERVALS Perform at the months or distances shown, whichever comes first.	Miles x 1000	7.5	15	22.5	30	37.5	45	52.5	60
	Kilometers x 1000	12	24	36	48	60	72	84	96
EMISSIONS CONTROL SERVICE									
Replace Engine Oil and Oil Filter Every 6 Months OR		X	X	X	X	X	X	X	X
Replace Spark Plugs 2.5L, 3.8L					X				X
3.0L, SHO Platinum Plugs									X
Replace Cam Belt and Adjust Valve Lash — SHO									X
Replace Crankcase Filter — Four Cylinder Engine Only					X				X
Inspect Accessory Drive Belt(s)					X				X
Replace Air Cleaner Filter①					X				X
Replace Engine Coolant Every 36 Months OR					X				X
Check Engine Coolant Protection, Hoses and Clamps		ANNUALLY							
GENERAL MAINTENANCE									
Inspect Battery Fluid Level (SHO only)③					X		X		
Check Exhaust Heat Shields					X				X
Inspect Disc Brake Pads and Rotors (Front) (Front and Rear — SHO)②					X②				X②
Inspect Brake Linings and Drums (Rear)②					X②				X②
Rotate Tires		X		X		X		X	

① If operating in severe dust, more frequent intervals may be required. Consult your dealer.

② If your driving includes continuous stop-and-go driving or driving in mountainous areas, more frequent intervals may be required.

X All items designated with an "X" must be performed in all states.

③ If operating in temperatures above 32°C (90°F) check more often.

SEVERE SERVICE MAINTENANCE

SERVICE INTERVAL Perform at the months or distances shown, whichever comes first.	Miles x 1000	3	6	9	12	15	18	21	24	27	30	33	36	39	42	45	48	51	54	57	60
	Kilometers x 1000	4.8	9.6	14.4	19.2	24	28.8	33.6	38.4	43.2	48	52.8	57.6	62.4	67.2	72	76.8	81.6	86.4	91.2	96
EMISSION CONTROL SERVICE																					
Replace Engine Oil and Oil Filter Every 3 Months OR		X	X	X	X	X	X	X	X	X	X	X	X	X	X	X	X	X	X	X	X
Spark Plugs SHO Platinum Plugs																					X
											X										X
Inspect Accessory Drive Belt(s)											X										X
Replace Air Cleaner Filter①											X										X
Replace Crankcase Filter Four Cylinder Engines Only①											X										X
Replace Cam Belt and Adjust Valve Lash — SHO																					X
Replace Engine Coolant Every 36 Months OR											X										X
Check Engine Coolant Protection, Hoses and Clamps		ANNUALLY																			
GENERAL MAINTENANCE																					
Inspect Exhaust Heat Shields											X										X
Change Automatic Transaxle Fluid②											X										X
Inspect Disc Brake Pads and Rotors (Front)③ (Front and Rear — SHO)											X										X
Inspect Brake Linings and Drums③											X										X
Inspect Battery Fluid Level (SHO only)④						X											X				
Rotate Tires			X			X						X					X				

① If operating in severe dust, more frequent intervals may be required — consult your dealer.

② Change automatic transaxle fluid if your driving habits frequently include one or more of the following conditions:
- Operation during HOT WEATHER (above 32°C (90°F)).
- Towing a trailer or using a car top carrier.
- Police, taxi or door-to-door delivery service.

③ If your driving includes continuous stop and go driving or driving in mountainous areas, more frequent intervals may be required.

X All items designated with an "X" must be performed in all states.

④ If operating in temperatures above 32°C (90°F) check more often.

FORD MOTOR CO.

1996 SABLE & TAURUS

- Replace MicronAir® air filter.

85,000 MILES (136,000 Kilometers)

- Change engine oil and oil filter. (4)
- Rotate tires and adjust air pressure.

90,000 MILES (144,000 Kilometers)

- Change engine oil and oil filter. (4)
- Inspect accessory drive belts. (4)
- Replace air cleaner element. (4)
- Inspect engine cooling system, hoses and clamps; check coolant strength every 15,000 miles (24,000 km) or 12 months.
- Inspect exhaust heat shield(s).
- Inspect front and rear brake shoes and linings and front disc brake rotors and rear disc brake rotors or brake drum (if equipped). (1)
- Change automatic transaxle fluid.
- Replace spark plugs—(3.0L flexible fuel vehicle). (4)

95,000 MILES (152,000 Kilometers)

- Change engine oil and oil filter. (4)
- Rotate tires and adjust air pressure.

100,000 MILES (160,000 Kilometers)

- Change engine oil and oil filter. (4)
- Replace spark plug (except 3.0L flexible fuel vehicle). (4)
- Replace positive crankcase ventilation valve (3.0L (4V) (Duratec) only). (3)
- Replace MicronAir® air filter.

105,000 MILES (169,000 Kilometers)

- Change engine oil and oil filter. (4)
- Inspect engine cooling system, hoses and clamps; check coolant strength every 15,000 miles (24,000 km) or 12 months.
- Rotate tires and adjust air pressure.

110,000 MILES (176,000 Kilometers)

- Change engine oil and oil filter. (4)
- Change engine coolant every 30,000 miles (48,000 km) or 36 months. (4)

115,000 MILES (184,000 Kilometers)

- Change engine oil and oil filter. (4)

120,000 MILES (192,000 Kilometers)

- Change engine oil and oil filter. (4)
- Inspect accessory drive belts. (4)
- Replace air cleaner element. (4)
- Replace positive crankcase ventilation valve (3.0L (2V) (Vulcan) and 3.0L flexible fuel vehicle).
- Inspect engine cooling system, hoses and clamps; check coolant strength every 15,000 miles (25,000 km) or 12 months. (4)
- Replace MicronAir® air filter.
- Change automatic transaxle fluid. (3)
- Inspect exhaust heat shield(s).
- Inspect front and rear brake shoes and linings and front disc brake rotors and rear disc brake rotors or brake drum (if equipped). (1)
- Replace spark plugs (3.0L flexible fuel vehicle). (4)

(1) If your driving includes continuous stop-and-go driving or driving in hilly areas, more frequent intervals may be required.

(2) At 60,000 miles (96,000 km) your dealer will replace the positive crankcase ventilation valve at no cost on 3.0L (2V) (Vulcan) and 3.0L flexible fuel vehicle engines except California and Canada vehicles.

(3) At 100,000 miles (160,000 km) your dealer will replace the positive crankcase ventilation valve at no cost on 3.0L (4V) (Duratec) engine except California and Canada vehicles.

(4) Item for Emission Control Service.

CAUTION: Engine oil, spark plugs and fuel filters for the flexible fuel (FF) vehicle are unique and are not to be substituted with gasoline engine components.

Maintenance Intervals for Normal Duty Schedule

5,000 MILES (8,000 Kilometers)

- Change engine oil and oil filter (6731). (4)
- Rotate tires and adjust air pressure.

10,000 MILES (16,000 Kilometers)

- Change engine oil and oil filter. (4)

15,000 MILES (24,000 Kilometers)

- Change engine oil and oil filter. (4)
- Inspect engine cooling system, hoses and clamps; check coolant strength every 15,000 miles (24,000 km) or 12 months. (4)
- Rotate tires and adjust air pressure.

20,000 MILES (32,000 Kilometers)

- Change engine oil and oil filter. (4)
- Replace MicronAir® air filter.

25,000 MILES (40,000 Kilometers)

- Change engine oil and oil filter. (4)
- Rotate tires and adjust air pressure.

30,000 MILES (48,000 Kilometers)

- Change engine oil and oil filter. (4)
- Replace spark plug (12405) (3.0L flexible fuel vehicle).
- Replace air cleaner element (ACL element)(9601). (4)
- Inspect engine cooling system, hoses and clamps; check coolant strength every 15,000 miles (24,000 km) or 12 months. (4)
- Inspect exhaust heat shield(s).
- Inspect front and rear brake shoes and linings and front disc brake rotors (1125) and rear disc brake rotors (2C026) or brake drum (1126) (if equipped). (1) (4)
- Change automatic transaxle fluid.

35,000 MILES (56,000 Kilometers)

- Change engine oil and oil filter. (4)
- Rotate tires and adjust air pressure.

40,000 MILES (64,000 Kilometers)

- Change engine oil and oil filter. (4)
- Replace MicronAir® air filter.

45,000 MILES (72,000 Kilometers)

- Change engine oil and oil filter. (4)

- Inspect engine cooling system, hoses and clamps; check coolant strength every 15,000 miles (24,000 km) or 12 months.
- Rotate tires and adjust air pressure.

50,000 MILES (80,000 Kilometers)

- Change engine oil and oil filter. (4)
- Change engine coolant initially at 50,000 miles (80,000 km) or 48 months. Thereafter, change engine coolant every 30,000 miles (48,000 km) or 36 months. (4)

55,000 MILES (88,000 Kilometers)

- Change engine oil and oil filter. (4)
- Rotate tires and adjust air pressure.

60,000 MILES (96,000 Kilometers)

- Change engine oil and oil filter. (4)
- Inspect accessory drive belts (8620). (4)
- Replace spark plug (3.0L flexible fuel vehicle only)
- Replace air cleaner element. (4)
- Replace positive crankcase ventilation valve (PCV valve)(6A666) (3.0L (2V) (Vulcan) and 3.0L flexible fuel vehicle). (2) (4)
- Inspect engine cooling system, hoses and clamps; check coolant strength every 15,000 miles (25,000 km) or 12 months. (4)
- Replace MicronAir® air filter.
- Inspect exhaust heat shield(s).
- Inspect front and rear brake shoes and linings and front disc brake rotors and rear disc brake rotors or brake drum (if equipped). (1)
- Change automatic transaxle fluid.

65,000 MILES (104,000 Kilometers)

- Change engine oil and oil filter. (4)
- Rotate tires and adjust air pressure.

70,000 MILES (112,000 Kilometers)

- Change engine oil and oil filter. (4)

75,000 MILES (120,000 Kilometers)

- Change engine oil and oil filter. (4)
- Inspect engine cooling system, hoses and clamps; check coolant strength every 15,000 miles (24,000 km) or 12 months. (4)
- Rotate tires and adjust air pressure.

80,000 MILES (128,000 Kilometers)

- Change engine oil and oil filter. (4)
- Change engine coolant every 30,000 miles (48,000 km) or 36 months. (4)

SEVERE SERVICE MAINTENANCE

CUSTOMER MAINTENANCE SCHEDULE B
Follow maintenance Schedule B if, generally, you drive your vehicle on a daily basis for more than 10 miles (16 km) and NONE OF THE UNIQUE DRIVING CONDITIONS SHOWN IN SCHEDULE A APPLY TO YOUR DRIVING HABITS.

SERVICE INTERVAL — Perform at the months or distances shown, whichever comes first.								
Miles x 1000	7.5	15	22.5	30	37.5	45	52.5	60
Kilometers x 1000	12	24	36	48	60	72	84	96
EMISSION CONTROL SERVICE								
Change Engine Oil & Filter whichever occurs first) Every 6 Months or	X	X	X	X	X	X	X	X
Turbocharged Vehicles Replace Engine Oil & Filter	EVERY 5,000 MILES (8,000 KM) OR 6 MONTHS WHICHEVER OCCURS FIRST							
Replace Spark Plugs: Turbocharged				④		④		④
Non-Turbocharged								X
Check Engine Coolant Protection, Hoses and Clamps			ANNUALLY					
Replace Engine Coolant Every 36 Months or				X				X
Check Accessory Drive Belts				X				X
Replace Air Cleaner Element		X		X		X		X
Replace Fuel Filter				X⑴				X⑴
Replace Engine Timing Belt	REPLACE EVERY 60,000 MILES (96,000 km)							
Check Engine Idle Speed				X⑶				X⑶
GENERAL MAINTENANCE								
Inspect Brake Lines and Connections				X				X
Inspect Clutch Pedal Operation		X		X		X		X
Inspect Front and Rear Disc Brakes		X		X		X		X
Inspect Safety Belts, Buckles, Retractors & Anchors				X		X		X
Inspect Steering Linkage, Rack Guides & Tie Rod Ends				X				X
Tighten Bolts & Nuts on Chassis & Body				X				X
Inspect Steering Operations, Gear Housing and Rack Seal Boots				X				X
Inspect Front Suspension Ball Joints				X				X
Inspect Hall Shaft Dust Boots				X				X
Inspect Exhaust System Heat Shield				X				X
Inspect Fuel Lines				②				X
Lubricate Rear Wheel Bearings				X				X
Rotate Tires	X	X	X	X	X	X	X	X

① If operating in severe dust, more frequent intervals may be required. Consult your dealer.
② Recommended, but not required.
③ This item not required to be performed, however, Ford recommends that you perform maintenance on this item in order to achieve best vehicle operation.
Failure to perform this recommended maintenance will not invalidate the vehicle emissions warranty or manufacturer recall liability.

CAPRI
NORMAL SERVICE MAINTENANCE

CUSTOMER MAINTENANCE SCHEDULE A
Follow this Schedule if your driving habits MAINLY include one or more of the following conditions:
- Short trips of less than 10 miles (16 km) when outside temperatures remain below freezing.
- Operating in severe dust conditions.
- Operating during hot weather, in stop-and-go "rush hour" traffic.
- Extensive idling, such as police, taxi or door-to-door delivery service.

SERVICE INTERVAL — Perform at the months or distances shown, whichever comes first.																				
Miles x 1000	3	6	9	12	15	18	21	24	27	30	33	36	39	42	45	48	51	54	57	60
Kilometers x 1000	4.8	9.6	14	19	24	28	33	38	43	48	52	57	62	67	72	76	81	86	91	96
EMISSION CONTROL SERVICE																				
Change Engine Oil and Oil Filter (whichever occurs first) Every 3 Months or	X	X	X	X	X	X	X	X	X	X	X	X	X	X	X	X	X	X	X	X
Replace Spark Plugs: Turbocharged					④															
Non-Turbocharged										X										X
Check Engine Coolant Protection, Hoses and Clamps						ANNUALLY														
Replace Engine Coolant Every 36 Months or												X								
Check Accessory Drive Belts												X								
Inspect Air Cleaner Filter															X⑴					
Replace Air Cleaner Element										X										X
Replace Fuel Filter										X⑴										
Replace Engine Timing Belt	EVERY 60,000 MILES (96,000 km)																			
Check Engine Idle Speed										X⑷										
GENERAL MAINTENANCE																				
Rotate Tires		X																		
Inspect Brake Lines, Connections & Hoses						X				X								X		
Inspect Clutch Pedal Operation										X										
Inspect Front and Rear Disc Brakes					X					X					X					
Inspect Safety Belts, Buckles, Retractors & Anchors										X										
Inspect Steering Linkage, Rack Guides & Tie Rod Ends										X										
Tighten Bolts & Nuts on Chassis & Body										X										
Inspect Steering Operations, Gear Housing and Rack Seal Boots										X					X					
Inspect Front Suspension Ball Joints										X										
Inspect Hall Shaft Dust Boots										X										
Inspect Exhaust System Heat Shield										X										
Inspect Fuel Lines										②										
Lubricate Rear Wheel Bearings										X										X
Change Automatic Transaxle Fluid										³										

¹ If operating on severe dusty conditions, consult dealer for proper replacement interval.
² Recommended, but not required.
³ This item not required to be performed, however, Ford recommends that you perform maintenance on this item in order to achieve best vehicle operation.
⁴ Change automatic transaxle fluid if your driving habits frequently include one or more of the following conditions:
  • Operation during hot weather (above 90°F, 32°C), carrying heavy loads and in hilly terrain.
  • Police, taxi or door-to-door delivery service.
This item not required to be performed, however, Ford recommends that you perform maintenance on this item in order to achieve best vehicle operation.
Failure to perform this recommended maintenance will not invalidate the vehicle emissions warranty or manufacturer recall liability.

This maintenance is required in all states except California. However, we recommend that it also be performed on California vehicles.

ESCORT & TRACER
NORMAL SERVICE MAINTENANCE

Follow maintenance [Schedule A] if your driving habits **MAINLY** include one or more of the following conditions:
- Short trips of less than 10 miles (16 km) when outside temperatures remain below freezing.
- Towing a trailer, or using a car-top carrier.
- Operating in severe dust conditions.
- Operating during hot weather in stop-and-go "rush hour" traffic.
- Extensive idling, such as police, taxi or door-to-door delivery service.

PERFORM AT THE MONTHS OR DISTANCES SHOWN, WHICHEVER OCCURS FIRST

MILES x 1000	3	6	9	12	15	18	21	24	27	30	33	36	39	42	45	48	51	54	57	60
KILOMETERS x 1000	4.8	9.6	14.4	19.2	24	28.8	33.6	38.4	43.2	48	52.8	57.6	62.4	67.2	72	76.8	81.6	86.4	91.2	96
EMISSION CONTROL SERVICE																				
Change engine oil and oil filter (every 3 months) OR 3,000 miles whichever occurs first	x	x	x	x	x	x	x	x	x	x	x	x	x	x	x	x	x	x	x	x
Replace spark plugs										x										x
Inspect accessory drive belt(s)										x										x
Inspect air cleaner filter (1.8L only)					x(4)										x(4)					
Replace air cleaner filter (all engines) (1)										x(1)										x(1)
Replace crankcase ventilation filter (1) (1.9L only)										x(1)										x(1)
Replace engine coolant EVERY 36 months OR										x										x
Check engine coolant protection, hoses and clamps	ANNUALLY																			
Engine timing belt (1.8L only)	REPLACE EVERY 60,000 MILES (96 000 Km)																			x

MILES x 1000	3	6	9	12	15	18	21	24	27	30	33	36	39	42	45	48	51	54	57	60
KILOMETERS x 1000	4.8	9.6	14.4	19.2	24	28.8	33.6	38.4	43.2	48	52.8	57.6	62.4	67.2	72	76.8	81.6	86.4	91.2	96
GENERAL MAINTENANCE																				
Inspect exhaust heat shields										x										x
Change automatic transaxle fluid										(2)										(2)
Inspect disc brake pads and rotors (3)										x(3)										x(3)
Inspect brake linings and drums (3)										x(3)										x(3)
Inspect and repack rear wheel bearings										x										x
Rotate tires	x					x						x				x				
Inspect clutch pedal operation										x										x
Inspect halfshaft dust boots										x										x
Inspect brake line hoses and connections										x										x
Inspect front suspension ball joints										x										x
Inspect bolts and nuts on chassis and body										x										x
Inspect steering operation and linkage										x										x

(1) If operating in severe dust, more frequent intervals may be required, consult your dealer.

(2) Change automatic transmission fluid if your driving habits frequently include one or more of the following conditions:
- Operation during hot weather (above 90°F, 32°C), carrying heavy loads and in hilly terrain.
- Towing a trailer or using a car-top carrier.
- Police, taxi or door-to-door delivery service.

(3) If your driving includes continuous stop-and-go driving or driving in mountainous areas, more frequent intervals may be required.

(4) This maintenance is required in all states except California. However, we recommend that it also be performed on California vehicles.

SEVERE SERVICE MAINTENANCE

Follow maintenance [Schedule B] if, generally, you drive your vehicle on a daily basis for more than 10 miles (16 km) and **NONE OF THE DRIVING CONDITIONS SHOWN IN SCHEDULE A APPLY TO YOUR DRIVING HABITS.**

PERFORM AT THE MONTHS OR DISTANCES SHOWN, WHICHEVER OCCURS FIRST

MILES x 1000	7.5	15	22.5	30	37.5	45	52.5	60
KILOMETERS x 1000	12	24	36	48	60	72	84	96
EMISSION CONTROL SERVICE								
Change engine oil and oil filter — every 6 months OR 7,500 miles, whichever occurs first	x	x	x	x	x	x	x	x
Replace spark plugs				x				x
Change crankcase ventilation filter (1) (1.9L only)				x(1)				x(1)
Inspect accessory drive belt(s)				x				x
Replace air cleaner filter (1)				x(1)				x(1)
Replace engine coolant (every 36 months) OR				x				x
Check engine coolant protection, hoses and clamps	ANNUALLY							
Engine timing belt (1.8L only)	REPLACE EVERY 60,000 MILES (96 000 Km)							x

MILES x 1000	7.5	15	22.5	30	37.5	45	52.5	60
KILOMETERS x 1000	12	24	36	48	60	72	84	96
GENERAL MAINTENANCE								
Check exhaust heat shields				x				x
Inspect disc brake pads and rotors (2)				x(2)				x(2)
Inspect brake linings and drums (2)				x(2)				x(2)
Inspect and repack rear wheel bearings				x				x
Rotate tires	x		x		x		x	
Inspect halfshaft dust boots				x				x
Inspect steering operation and linkage				x				x
Inspect front suspension ball joints				x				x
Inspect brake line hoses and connections				x				x
Inspect bolts and nuts on chassis and body				x				x
Inspect clutch pedal operation (if equipped)				x				x

(1) If operating in severe dust, more frequent intervals may be required. Consult your dealer.
(2) If your driving includes continuous stop-and-go driving or driving in mountainous areas, more frequent intervals may be required.

VEHICLE MAINTENANCE SCHEDULES

1995-96 COUGAR & THUNDERBIRD
NORMAL SERVICE MAINTENANCE

Miles	Recommended Maintenance
5,000	Change Engine Oil
	Rotate Tires & Adjust Air Pressure
10,000	Change Engine Oil
15,000	Change Engine Oil
	Inspect Engine Cooling System, Hoses & Clamps
	Rotate Tires & Adjust Air Pressure
	Lubricate Steering Linkage
20,000	Change Engine Oil
25,000	Change Engine Oil
	Rotate Tires & Adjust Air Pressure
30,000	Change Engine Oil
	Inspect Engine Cooling System, Hoses & Clamps
	Replace Spark Plugs (Except 3.8L Supercharged Engine)
	Change Automatic Transmission Fluid
	Replace Air Cleaner Element
	Inspect Exhaust Heat Shields
	Lubricate Steering Linkage
	Check Clutch Hydraulic Fluid Level (3.8L Supercharged Engine Only)
	Inspect Front & Rear Brake Shoes And Linings
	Inspect Front & Rear Disc Brake Rotors, If Equipped
	Inspect Rear Brake Shoes, Linings & Brake Drums, If Equipped
35,000	Change Engine Oil
	Rotate Tires & Adjust Air Pressure
40,000	Change Engine Oil
45,000	Change Engine Oil
	Inspect Engine Cooling System, Hoses & Clamps
	Rotate Tires & Adjust Air Pressure
	Lubricate Steering Linkage
50,000	Change Engine Oil
	Change Engine Coolant Every 50,000 Miles Or 48 Months
55,000	Change Engine Oil
60,000	Change Engine Oil
	Change Automatic Transmission Fluid
	Inspect Engine Cooling System, Hoses & Clamps
	Replace Spark Plugs (Except 3.8L Supercharged Engine)
	Replace Air Cleaner Element
	Replace PCV Valve
	Inspect Exhaust Heat Shields
	Inspect Accessory Drive Belts
	Lubricate Steering Linkage
	Check Clutch Hydraulic Fluid Level (3.8L Supercharged Engine Only)
	Inspect Front & Rear Brake Shoes And Linings
	Inspect Front & Rear Disc Brake Rotors, If Equipped
	Inspect Rear Brake Shoes, Linings & Brake Drums, If Equipped
65,000	Change Engine Oil
	Rotate Tires & Adjust Air Pressure
70,000	Change Engine Oil

Miles	Recommended Maintenance
75,000	Change Engine Oil
	Rotate Tires & Adjust Air Pressure
	Inspect Engine Cooling System, Hoses & Clamps
	Lubricate Steering Linkage
80,000	Change Engine Oil
85,000	Change Engine Oil
	Rotate Tires & Adjust Air Pressure
90,000	Change Engine Oil
	Change Automatic Transmission Fluid
	Inspect Engine Cooling System, Hoses & Clamps
	Replace Spark Plugs (Except 3.8L Supercharged Engine)
	Replace Air Cleaner Element
	Inspect Exhaust Heat Shields
	Inspect Accessory Drive Belts
	Lubricate Steering Linkage
	Check Clutch Hydraulic Fluid Level (3.8L Supercharged Engine Only)
	Inspect Front & Rear Brake Shoes And Linings
	Inspect Front & Rear Disc Brake Rotors, If Equipped
	Inspect Rear Brake Shoes, Linings & Brake Drums, If Equipped
95,000	Change Engine Oil
	Rotate Tires & Adjust Air Pressure
100,000	Change Engine Oil
	Replace Rear Axle Lubricant
105,000	Change Engine Oil
	Rotate Tires & Adjust Air Pressure
	Lubricate Steering Linkage
	Inspect Engine Cooling System, Hoses & Clamps
110,000	Change Engine Oil
	Change Engine Coolant Every 30,000 Miles Or 36 Months
115,000	Change Engine Oil
	Rotate Tires & Adjust Air Pressure
120,000	Change Engine Oil
	Change Automatic Transmission Fluid
	Inspect Engine Cooling System, Hoses & Clamps
	Replace Spark Plugs
	Replace Air Cleaner Element
	Inspect Exhaust Heat Shields
	Inspect Accessory Drive Belts
	Change Engine Coolant Every 30,000 Miles Or 36 Months
	Lubricate Steering Linkage
	Check Supercharger Fluid Level (3.8L SC Only)
	Check Clutch Hydraulic Fluid Level (3.8L SC Only)
	Inspect Front & Rear Brake Shoes And Linings
	Inspect Front & Rear Disc Brake Rotors, If Equipped
	Inspect Rear Brake Shoes, Linings & Brake Drums, If Equipped

CHRYSLER CORP.

SEVERE SERVICE MAINTENANCE

Miles	Recommended Maintenance
3,000	Change Engine Oil & Filter
6,000	Change Engine Oil & Filter
	Rotate Tires & Adjust Air Pressure
9,000	Change Engine Oil & Filter
12,000	Change Engine Oil & Filter
15,000	Change Engine Oil & Filter
	Inspect Engine Cooling System, Hoses & Clamps
	Rotate Tires & Adjust Air Pressure
	Lubricate Steering Linkage
18,000	Change Engine Oil & Filter
21,000	Change Engine Oil & Filter
	Change Automatic Transmission Fluid
24,000	Change Engine Oil & Filter
	Rotate Tires And Adjust Air Pressure
27,000	Change Engine Oil & Filter
30,000	Change Engine Oil & Filter
	Replace Engine Coolant
	Replace Spark Plugs (Except 3.8L Supercharged Engine)
	Replace Air Cleaner Element
	Inspect Engine Cooling System, Hoses & Clamps
	Inspect Exhaust Heat Shields
	Lubricate Steering Linkage
	Check Clutch Hydraulic Fluid Level (3.8L Supercharged Engine Only)
	Inspect Front & Rear Brake Shoes And Linings
	Inspect Front & Rear Disc Brake Rotors, If Equipped
	Inspect Rear Brake Shoes, Linings & Brake Drums, If Equipped
33,000	Change Engine Oil & Filter
36,000	Change Engine Oil & Filter
42,000	Change Engine Oil & Filter
	Rotate Tires And Adjust Air Pressure
	Change Automatic Transmission Fluid
45,000	Change Engine Oil & Filter
	Inspect Engine Cooling System, Hoses & Clamps
	Lubricate Steering Linkage
48,000	Change Engine Oil & Filter
	Change Engine Coolant Every 30,000 Miles Or 36 Months
51,000	Change Engine Oil & Filter
	Rotate Tires And Adjust Air Pressure
54,000	Change Engine Oil & Filter
57,000	Change Engine Oil & Filter
60,000	Change Engine Oil & Filter
	Change Engine Coolant Every 30,000 Miles Or 36 Months
	Replace PCV Valve
	Check Supercharger Fluid Level (3.8L SC)
	Check Clutch Hydraulic Fluid Level (3.8L SC)
	Replace Spark Plugs
	Inspect Accessory Drive Belts
	Inspect Engine Cooling System, Hoses & Clamps
	Replace Air Cleaner Element
	Inspect Exhaust Heat Shields

Miles	Recommended Maintenance
	Inspect Front & Rear Disc Brake Rotors, If Equipped
	Inspect Rear Brake Shoes, Linings & Brake Drums, If Equipped
	Lubricate Steering Linkage
	Rotate Tires And Adjust Air Pressure
63,000	Change Engine Oil & Filter
	Change Automatic Transmission Fluid
66,000	Change Engine Oil & Filter
69,000	Change Engine Oil & Filter
	Rotate Tires And Adjust Air Pressure
72,000	Change Engine Oil & Filter
75,000	Change Engine Oil & Filter
	Inspect Engine Cooling System, Hoses & Clamps
	Lubricate Steering Linkage
78,000	Change Engine Oil & Filter
	Change Engine Coolant Every 30,000 Miles Or 36 Months
	Rotate Tires And Adjust Air Pressure
81,000	Change Engine Oil & Filter
84,000	Change Engine Oil & Filter
	Change Automatic Transmission Fluid
87,000	Change Engine Oil
	Rotate Tires And Adjust Air Pressure
90,000	Change Engine Oil
	Inspect Engine Cooling System, Hoses & Clamps
	Inspect Accessory Drive Belts
	Replace Air Cleaner Element
	Inspect Exhaust Heat Shields
	Lubricate Steering Linkage
	Replace Spark Plugs (3.8L SC)
	Check Clutch Hydraulic Fluid Level (3.8L)
	Inspect Front & Rear Disc Brake Rotors, If Equipped
	Inspect Rear Brake Shoes, Linings & Brake Drums, If Equipped
93,000	Change Engine Oil
96,000	Change Engine Oil
	Rotate Tires And Adjust Air Pressure
99,000	Change Engine Oil
100,000	Replace Rear Axle Lubricant
	Change Engine Coolant Every 100,000 Miles Or Every 12 Months
102,000	Change Engine Oil
105,000	Change Engine Oil
	Inspect Engine Cooling System, Hoses & Clamps
	Lubricate Steering Linkage
	Rotate Tires And Adjust Air Pressure
	Change Automatic Transmission Fluid
108,000	Change Engine Oil
	Change Engine Coolant Every 30,000 Miles Or 36 Months

SEVERE SERVICE MAINTENANCE

Miles	Recomended Maintenance
111,000	Change Engine Oil
114,000	Change Engine Oil
	Rotate Tires And Adjust Air Pressure
117,000	Change Engine Oil
120,000	Change Engine Oil
	Change Engine Coolant Every 30,000 Miles Or 36 Months
	Replace PCV Valve
	Check Supercharger Fluid Level (3.8L SC)

Miles	Recomended Maintenance
120,000 (cont.)	Check Clutch Hydraulic Fluid Level (3.8L SC)
	Inspect Engine Cooling System, Hoses & Clamps
	Lubricate Steering Linkage
	Inspect Exhaust Heat Shields
	Replace Air Cleaner Element
	Inspect Accessory Drive Belts
	Replace Spark Plugs
	Inspect Front & Rear Disc Brake Rotors, If Equipped
	Inspect Rear Brake Shoes, Linings & Brake Drums, If Equipped

ELECTRICAL SYMBOL & WIRE COLOR CODE IDENTIFICATION

TABLE OF CONTENTS

Page No.

ELECTRICAL SYMBOL IDENTIFICATION. 70

Page No.

WIRE COLOR CODE IDENTIFICATION. 72

Electrical Symbol Identification

INDEX

Page No.

Chrysler:
  Domestic. 71
  Imports 71

Page No.

Ford:
  1992 71
  1993-95 71

LEGEND OF SYMBOLS USED ON WIRING DIAGRAMS

Symbol	Name	Symbol	Name
+	POSITIVE		CONNECTOR
−	NEGATIVE		MALE CONNECTOR
	GROUND		FEMALE CONNECTOR
	FUSE		DENOTES WIRE CONTINUES ELSEWHERE
	GANG FUSES WITH BUSS BAR		DENOTES WIRE GOES TO ONE OF TWO CIRCUITS
	CIRCUIT BREAKER		SPLICE
	CAPACITOR		SPLICE IDENTIFICATION
	OHMS		THERMAL ELEMENT
	RESISTOR	TIMER	TIMER
	VARIABLE RESISTOR		MULTIPLE CONNECTOR
	SERIES RESISTOR		OPTIONAL WIRING WITH / WIRING WITHOUT
	COIL		"Y" WINDINGS
	STEP UP COIL	88:88	DIGITAL READOUT
	OPEN CONTACT		SINGLE FILAMENT LAMP
	CLOSED CONTACT		DUAL FILAMENT LAMP
	CLOSED SWITCH		L.E.D. — LIGHT EMITTING DIODE
	OPEN SWITCH		THERMISTOR
	CLOSED GANGED SWITCH		GAUGE
	OPEN GANGED SWITCH		SENSOR
	TWO POLE SINGLE THROW SWITCH		FUEL INJECTOR
	PRESSURE SWITCH		DENOTES WIRE GOES THROUGH BULKHEAD DISCONNECT
	SOLENOID SWITCH		DENOTES WIRE GOES THROUGH STEERING COLUMN CONNECTOR
	MERCURY SWITCH		DENOTES WIRE GOES THROUGH INSTRUMENT PANEL CONNECTOR
	DIODE OR RECTIFIER		DENOTES WIRE GOES THROUGH GROMMET TO ENGINE COMPARTMENT
	BY-DIRECTIONAL ZENER DIODE		DENOTES WIRE GOES THROUGH GROMMET
	MOTOR		HEATED GRID ELEMENTS
	ARMATURE AND BRUSHES		

Fig. 1   Chrysler Domestic

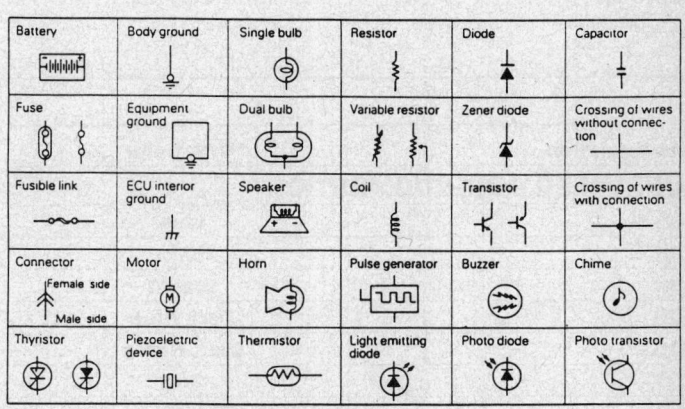

Fig. 2   Chrysler Imports

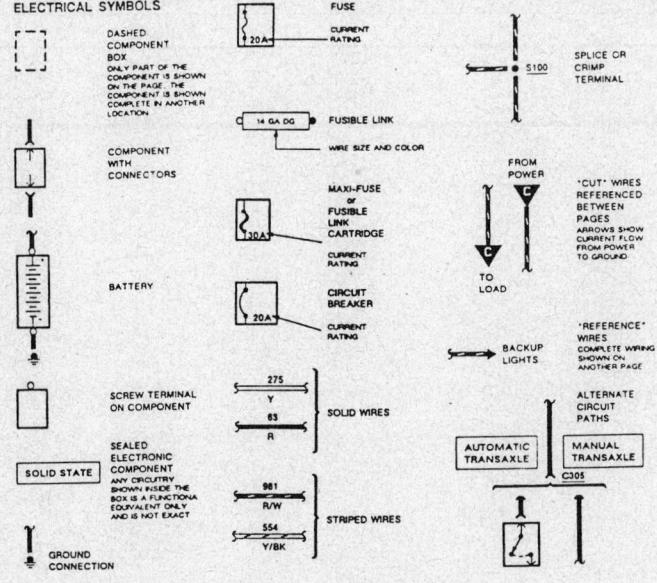

Fig. 3   Ford (Part 1 of 2)

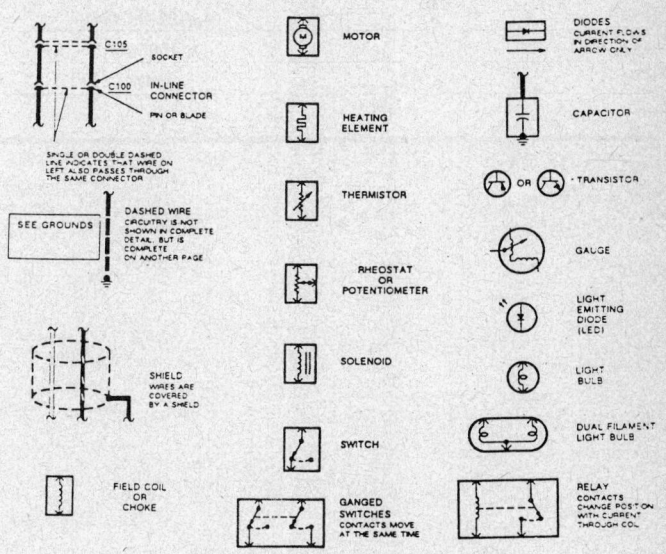

Fig. 3   Ford (Part 2 of 2)

Wire Color Code Identification

INDEX

Page No.

Chysler: 72   Imports 72
  Domestic. 72   **Ford** 72

Abbreviation	Wire Color
CHRYSLER CORP. DOMESTIC	
BL	Blue
BK	Black
BR	Brown
DB	Dark Blue
DG	Dark Green
GY	Gray
LB	Light Blue
LG	Light Green
OR	Orange
PK	Pink
RD	Red
TN	Tan
VT	Violet
WT	White
YL	Yellow
CHRYSLER CORP. IMPORTS	
B	Black
BR	Brown
G	Green
GR	Gray
L	Blue
LG	Light Green
O	Orange
P	Pink

Abbreviation	Wire Color
CHRYSLER CORP. IMPORTS (Cont.)	
R	Red
SB	Sky Blue
V	Violet
W	White
Y	Yellow
FORD MOTOR CO.	
BL	Blue
BK	Black
BR	Brown
DB	Dark Blue
DG	Dark Green
GN	Green
GY	Gray
LB	Light Blue
LG	Light Green
N	Natural
O	Orange
PK	Pink
P	Purple
R	Red
T	Tan
W	White
Y	Yellow

CHRYSLER CORPORATION

Page No.

ABBREVIATIONS & ACRONYMS........................ 23-1
APPLICATION CHARTS 17-1
ELECTRIC FUEL PUMPS............................. 15-1
ELECTRONIC BODY CONTROLS 21-1
ELECTRONIC INSTRUMENTATION..................... 21-1
EMISSION CONTROLS 20-1
EMISSION CONTROL SYSTEM APPLICATION CHARTS.. 17-1
ENGINE COMPARTMENT REFERENCE DIAGRAMS...... 19-1
ENGINE SYSTEMS IDENTIFICATION 1-1
ENGINE TUNE UP & PERFORMANCE
  4 Cylinder Engine:
    Compression Pressure 3-1
    Engine Identification 3-1
    Fuel Injection Cleaning........................... 3-10
    Idle Speed & Mixture Adjustments.................. 3-4
    Ignition Timing................................... 3-1
    Ignition Wire Resistance........................... 3-1
    Sensor Adjustments 3-10
    Spark Plugs..................................... 3-1
    Valves... 3-8
  V6 Engine:
    Compression Pressure 3-12
    Engine Identification 3-12
    Fuel Injection Cleaning.......................... 3-14
    Idle Speed & Mixture Adjustments................. 3-13
    Ignition Timing.................................. 3-12
    Ignition Wire Resistance.......................... 3-12
    Sensor Adjustments 3-14
    Spark Plugs 3-12
    Valves... 3-13
FUEL INJECTION
  Single Point Fuel Injection........................... 5-1
  Multi-Point Fuel Injection
    Models w/1.5L/4-90 Engine........................ 6-1

Page No.

Models w/1.8L/4-107, 1.8L/4-110 & 2.4L/4-143
  Engines, 1993-94 Models w/2.0L/4-122 Engine &
  1995-96 Talon w/2.0L/4-122 Turbocharged Engines 7-1
Models w/2.5L/4-153 Flexible Fuel, 2.2L/4-135
  Turbocharged & 2.5L/4-153 Engines............... 9-1
Models w/3.0L/V6-181, 3.3L/V6-201 & 3.8L/V6-231
  Engines Except Concorde, Intrepid, LHS, Stealth,
  Vision & 1994-96 New Yorker..................... 12-1
Stealth 11-1
1993-95 Concorde, Intrepid, Stealth, Vision &
  1994-95 LHS & New Yorker....................... 13-1
1995 Avenger, Cirrus, Sebring & Stratus
  w/2.5L/V6-152 Engine........................... 10-1
1995 Avenger, Cirrus, Neon, Sebring, Stratus & Talon
  w/2.0L/4-112 Non-Turbocharged Engine 8-1
1996 Models w/2.0L/4-122 Non-Turbocharged,
  2.4L/4-148, 2.5L/V6-152, 3.3L/V6-201 &
  3.5L/V6-215 Engines............................ 14-1
FUEL PUMPS 15-1
HOW TO USE THIS MANUAL 0-1
IGNITION SYSTEMS 4-1
QUICK REFERENCE.................................. 0-1
SERVICE BULLETINS 22-1
SPECIFICATIONS
  Tune Up 2-1
TECHNICAL SERVICE BULLETINS 22-1
TURBOCHARGERS.................................. 16-1
TUNE UP PROCEDURES:
  4 Cylinder Gasoline Engine........................ 3-1
  V6 Gasoline Engine 3-12
TUNE UP SPECIFICATIONS........................... 2-1
VACUUM HOSE ROUTINGS.......................... 18-1

CHRYSLER CORPORATION

Page No.

ABBREVIATIONS & ACRONYMS....................... 23-1
APPLICATION CHARTS 17-1
ELECTRIC FUEL PUMPS............................... 15-1
ELECTRONIC BODY CONTROLS 21-1
ELECTRONIC INSTRUMENTATION.................... 21-1
EMISSION CONTROLS 20-1
EMISSION CONTROL SYSTEM APPLICATION CHARTS.. 17-1
ENGINE COMPARTMENT REFERENCE DIAGRAMS...... 19-1
ENGINE SYSTEMS IDENTIFICATION 1-1
ENGINE TUNE UP & PERFORMANCE
  4 Cylinder Engine:
    Compression Pressure........................... 3-1
    Engine Identification........................... 3-1
    Fuel Injection Cleaning......................... 3-10
    Idle Speed & Mixture Adjustments................. 3-4
    Ignition Timing................................. 3-1
    Ignition Wire Resistance......................... 3-1
    Sensor Adjustments 3-10
    Spark Plugs.................................... 3-1
    Valves... 3-8
  V6 Engine:
    Compression Pressure......................... 3-12
    Engine Identification......................... 3-12
    Fuel Injection Cleaning....................... 3-14
    Idle Speed & Mixture Adjustments.............. 3-13
    Ignition Timing............................... 3-12
    Ignition Wire Resistance...................... 3-12
    Sensor Adjustments 3-14
    Spark Plugs 3-12
    Valves.. 3-13
FUEL INJECTION
  Single Point Fuel Injection........................ 5-1
  Multi-Point Fuel Injection
    Models w/1.5L/4-90 Engine...................... 6-1

Page No.

Models w/1.8L/4-107, 1.8L/4-110 & 2.4L/4-143
  Engines, 1993-94 Models w/2.0L/4-122 Engine &
  1995-96 Talon w/2.0L/4-122 Turbocharged Engines 7-1
Models w/2.5L/4-153 Flexible Fuel, 2.2L/4-135
  Turbocharged & 2.5L/4-153 Engines.............. 9-1
Models w/3.0L/V6-181, 3.3L/V6-201 & 3.8L/V6-231
  Engines Except Concorde, Intrepid, LHS, Stealth,
  Vision & 1994-96 New Yorker..................... 12-1
Stealth 11-1
1993-95 Concorde, Intrepid, Stealth, Vision &
  1994-95 LHS & New Yorker...................... 13-1
1995 Avenger, Cirrus, Sebring & Stratus
  w/2.5L/V6-152 Engine......................... 10-1
1995 Avenger, Cirrus, Neon, Sebring, Stratus & Talon
  w/2.0L/4-112 Non-Turbocharged Engine 8-1
1996 Models w/2.0L/4-122 Non-Turbocharged,
  2.4L/4-148, 2.5L/V6-152, 3.3L/V6-201 &
  3.5L/V6-215 Engines........................... 14-1
FUEL PUMPS 15-1
HOW TO USE THIS MANUAL 0-1
IGNITION SYSTEMS 4-1
QUICK REFERENCE................................. 0-1
SERVICE BULLETINS 22-1
SPECIFICATIONS
  Tune Up 2-1
TECHNICAL SERVICE BULLETINS...................... 22-1
TURBOCHARGERS.................................. 16-1
TUNE UP PROCEDURES:
  4 Cylinder Gasoline Engine....................... 3-1
  V6 Gasoline Engine 3-12
TUNE UP SPECIFICATIONS........................... 2-1
VACUUM HOSE ROUTINGS.......................... 18-1

QUICK REFERENCE

Application	Page No.
ACCESSING DIAGNOSTIC TROUBLE CODES, MULTI-POINT	
1995 Avenger, Cirrus, Neon, Sebring, Stratus & Talon w/Non-Turbocharged 2.0L/4-122 Engine	8-2
1995 Avenger, Cirrus, Sebring & Stratus w/2.5L/V6-152 Engine	10-4
Dodge Stealth	11-2
1993-95 Concorde, Intrepid, LHS, Vision & 1994—95 New Yorker	13-4
Models w/1.5L/4-90 Engine	6-1
Models w/1.8L/4-107, 1.8L/4-110 & 2.4L/4-146 Engines, 1993—94 Models w/2.0L/4-122 Engine & 1995-96 Talon w/2.0L/4-122 Turbocharged Engine	7-2
Models w/2.2L/4-135 & 2.5L/4-153 Turbo & 2.5L/4-153 Flexible Fuel Engines	9-4
1993-95 Models w/3.0L/V6-181, 3.3L/V6-201 & 3.8L/V6-231 Engines Except Concorde, Intrepid, LHS & 1994 = 95 New Yorker	12-3
1996 Models w/2.0L/4-122, 2.5L/V6-152, 3.3L/V6-201 & 3.5L/V6-215	14-3
ACCESSING DIAGNOSTIC TROUBLE CODES, SINGLE-POINT	
All	5-4
CLEARING DIAGNOSTIC TROUBLE CODES, MULTI-POINT	
1995 Avenger, Cirrus, Neon, Sebring, Stratus & Talon w/Non-Turbocharged 2.0L/4-122 Engine	8-4
1995 Avenger, Cirrus, Sebring & Stratus w/2.5L/V6-152 Engine	10-4
Dodge Stealth	11-34
1993-95 Concorde, Intrepid, LHS, Vision & 1994—95 New Yorker	13-4
Models w/1.5L/4-90 Engine	6-4
Models w/1.8L/4-107, 1.8L/4-110 & 2.4L/4-146 Engines, 1993—94 Models w/2.0L/4-122 Engine & 1995-96 Talon w/2.0L/4-122 Turbocharged Engine	7-3

Application	Page No.
CLEARING DIAGNOSTIC TROUBLE CODES, MULTI-POINT-CONTINUED	
Models w/2.2L/4-135 & 2.5L/4-153 Turbo & 2.5L/4-153 Flexible Fuel Engines	9-4
1993-95 Models w/3.0L/V6-181, 3.3L/V6-201 & 3.8L/V6-231 Engines Except Concorde, Intrepid, LHS & 1994 = 95 New Yorker	12-4
1996 Models w/2.0L/4-122, 2.5L/V6-152, 3.3L/V6-201 & 3.5L/V6-215	14-3
CLEARING DIAGNOSTIC TROUBLE CODES, SINGLE-POINT	
All	5-8
COMPRESSION PRESSURE SPECIFICATIONS	
Inline 4 Cylinder Gasoline Engines	3-1
V6 Gasoline Engines	3-12
DIAGNOSTIC CHART INDEX, MULTI-POINT	
1995 Avenger, Cirrus, Neon, Sebring, Stratus & Talon w/Non-Turbocharged 2.0L/4-122 Engine	8-11
1995 Avenger, Cirrus, Sebring & Stratus w/2.5L/V6-152 Engine	10-7
1993-95 Concorde, Intrepid, LHS, Vision & 1994—95 New Yorker	13-24
Models w/1.5L/4-90 Engine	6-10
Models w/1.8L/4-107, 1.8L/4-110 & 2.4L/4-146 Engines, 1993—94 Models w/2.0L/4-122 Engine & 1995-96 Talon w/2.0L/4-122 Turbocharged Engine	7-116
Models w/2.2L/4-135 & 2.5L/4-153 Turbo & 2.5L/4-153 Flexible Fuel Engines	9-17
1993-95 Models w/3.0L/V6-181, 3.3L/V6-201 & 3.8L/V6-231 Engines Except Concorde, Intrepid, LHS & 1994 = 95 New Yorker	12-23
1996 Models w/2.0L/4-122, 2.5L/V6-152, 3.3L/V6-201 & 3.5L/V6-215	14-45
DIAGNOSTIC CHART INDEX, SINGLE-POINT	
All	5-12

Continued

Application	Page No.
FUEL PRESSURE SPECIFICATIONS	
All	15-3
IGNITION COIL SPECIFICATIONS	
Type 1	4-2
Type 2	4-7
Type 3	4-10
Type 4	4-13
Type 5	4-15
Type 6	4-19
SENSOR SPECIFICATIONS, MULTI-POINT	
1995 Avenger, Cirrus, Neon, Sebring, Stratus & 1995-96 Talon w/Non-Turbocharged 2.0L/4-122 Engine	8-1
1995 Avenger, Cirrus, Sebring & Stratus w/2.5L/V6-152 Engine	10-1

Application	Page No.
SENSOR SPECIFICATIONS, MULTI-POINT -CONTINUED	
Dodge Stealth	11-1
Concorde, Intrepid, LHS, Vision & 1994—95 New Yorker	13-1
Models w/1.5L/4-90 Engine	6-1
Models w/1.8L/4-107, 1.8L/4-110 & 2.4L/4-146 Engines, 1993—94 Models w/2.0L/4-122 Engine & 1995-96 Talon w/2.0L/4-122 Turbocharged Engine	7-1
Models w/2.2L/4-135 & 2.5L/4-153 Turbo & 2.5L/4-153 Flexible Fuel Engines	9-1
1995 Models w/3.0L/V6-181, 3.3L/V6-201 & 3.8L/V6-231 Engines Except Concorde, Intrepid, LHS, Monaco, Premier, Stealth, Vision & 1994—95 New Yorker	14-1
SENSOR SPECIFICATIONS, SINGLE-POINT	
All	5-2

HOW TO USE THIS MANUAL

Be aware of the possibility that replacement underhood labels may be incorrect for the application. Replacement labels may also be more current than this publication. Check for existing Technical Service Bulletins (TSBs) and emission recall notices. Some states may fasten an official "Engine Identification" label to the vehicle if it has had an engine change, if it is a kit-car, or gray-market car, or for other reasons. If so, observe the ECS information on the state-installed label.

It is the technician's responsibility to cross-check available information sources. If a discrepancy exists between label information on the vehicle and this publication, the vehicle appears to be as originally equipped, and you are unable to make a positive determination or are unfamiliar with the vehicle to be tested, refer the motorist to a dealership or other inspection facility specializing in that make of vehicle. If a conflict still exists in determining the required ECS, refer the motorist to the state's referee facility for verification.

You may contact MOTOR at 1-800-4A MOTOR to report errors or missing information.

WHAT IS & IS NOT CONTAINED IN THIS MANUAL

This manual contains specifications, diagnostic and service procedures related to fuel, ignition, emissions, engine control and other electronic automotive systems. Information on mechanical systems and components such as engines and brakes can be found in **MOTOR's Auto Repair Manual.** A detailed breakdown of individual systems and procedures can be found inside the back cover of this manual.

GETTING STARTED

All testing should begin with verification of the customer complaint and a basic visual inspection. Successful isolation of a specific problem in a suspected system must follow a thorough and logical approach.

Before performing any detailed system diagnostics, review the various manufacturer's Technical Service Bulletin (TSB) information found in that chapter. The TSBs are listed according to symptom and vehicle application. Many times, you will find that driveability complaints can be readily identified and easily repaired using the information contained in this section.

If a basic vehicle inspection and a check of the TSBs leave the problem unresolved, further testing will be necessary.

The following outline divides this manual into three categories; Engine Control Systems, Related Information and Additional Features. The time you invest in familiarizing yourself with the books contents before attempting to use it will be time well spent.

For immediate access to frequently used information each manufacturer chapter includes a Quick Reference chart. These charts, located on the first page of each chapter allow easy access to information, such as accessing diagnostic trouble codes, diagnostic chart index, fuel pressure and compression pressure, ignition coil and sensor specifications.

ENGINE CONTROL SYSTEMS

ENGINE SYSTEMS IDENTIFICATION

Before beginning any diagnostic work on a vehicle, the vehicle as well as its engine and related systems must be properly identified. This often-overlooked step is **the key to successful diagnosis and repair.**

Presented in chart form, the Engine Systems Identification will identify the Fuel, Ignition and Computer systems used on the vehicle and direct you to the specific page that information on each system can be found.

To verify the engine used in the vehicle, check the Engine Code in the Vehicle Identification Number (VIN). If you are unfamiliar with the VIN system, consult the Vehicle Identification section found in the front of this manual as well as the Engine Identification portion of the Engine Tune Up & Performance Procedure section.

IGNITION SYSTEMS

Information found in this section will include basic testing and servicing of the ignition system and its components. Use the information in this section if the ignition system is suspect and you have been directed here from the Engine Systems Identification Chart. If the problem is more than basic you will be referred to the Electronic Fuel Injection section.

FUEL INJECTION

If an engine fuel problem is suspected (check engine light, etc.), or a reference from another section has been made, the application chart found at the front of this chapter will identify the vehicle's fuel system and where it may be found.

After identifying the system, familiarize yourself with its operation by reviewing the descriptive information found at the beginning of the section. Always begin with a visual inspection. **If trouble (fault) codes are present,** read and record trouble (fault) codes as found in the front of the section.

Using the Diagnostic Chart Index, refer to the appropriate diagnostic chart based on whether a no start or driveability problem exists. Once referred to a specific chart, these charts will take you through the system and component testing and required repairs. When specified repairs have been completed, perform the appropriate verification test.

When using the diagnostic charts, connector pin usage and wiring diagrams are provided near the front of each section. When a test gives a sensor specification, refer to Sensor Specifications listed in the front of each section. At some point in a Diagnostic Chart, you may be instructed to clear the memory of codes. This information will be found in the verification charts.

Also included are basic component testing and replacement procedures.

RELATED INFORMATION

TUNE UP SPECIFICATIONS

These charts provide basic tune up specifications including spark plug gap, ignition timing, idle speeds and fuel pump pressure. Illustrations of firing orders and timing marks are also included.

ENGINE TUNE UP & PERFORMANCE

These sections are grouped by engine configuration and offer procedures for such maintenance routines as measuring compression pressures, spark plug replacement and fuel injector cleaning. Also included in these sections are valve, throttle position sensor, idle speed and mixture adjustments.

ELECTRIC FUEL PUMPS

This section contains basic system service such as fuel pressure testing, fuel pressure relief and component replacement.

TURBOCHARGERS

Descriptions, diagnosis, testing and service procedures for turbochargers can be found in this section.

EMISSION CONTROL SYSTEM APPLICATION CHARTS

Application charts provide a quick reference for identifying the emission control systems and devices used on a vehicle.

VACUUM HOSE ROUTINGS

Vacuum hose routings provide a visual reference to these devices and systems and their installation on the vehicle. This information may be used for inspection, hose rerouting or tracing components that may not be readily visible.

ENGINE COMPARTMENT REFERENCE DIAGRAMS

This section will help to readily identify various fuel, ignition and emission-related components on the vehicle. These illustrations are intended to avoid wasted time when searching for components that require servicing.

EMISSION CONTROLS

After consulting the Emission Control Systems Application Chart, detailed emission system information can be found in this section. Information will include descriptions, basic testing and servicing procedures.

TECHNICAL SERVICE BULLETINS

The Technical Service Bulletins are listed according to symptom and vehicle application. Many common driveability complaints can be readily identified and easily repaired using the information contained in this section.

ADDITIONAL FEATURES
VEHICLE IDENTIFICATION

This section, located in the front of this manual, provides a explanation and breakdown of the Vehicle Identification Number (VIN) system.

VEHICLE MAINTENANCE SCHEDULES

Located in the front of this manual, Vehicle Maintenance Schedules provide a handy reference for identifying factory-recommended maintenance operations and service intervals.

ELECTRICAL SYMBOL & WIRE COLOR CODE IDENTIFICATION

Throughout this manual, many wiring diagrams and schematics will be found. The Electrical Symbol Identification information, located in the front of this manual provides explanations of the various symbols and wire color abbreviations used in the diagrams.

SERVICE REMINDER & WARNING LAMP RESET PROCEDURES

This section, located in the front of the manual, includes illustrated procedures for resetting the various service reminder lights found on Chrysler vehicles.

AIR QUALITY STANDARDS

This section, located in the front of this manual, includes Federal, State and District Of Columbia mandated emissions specifications.

ELECTRONIC INSTRUMENTATION & BODY CONTROLS

Refer to this section when an electronic instrumentation or body control problem is suspected or when referred from a previous section. Determine the applicable section through the Table Of Contents. Once in the proper area, begin with Test 1 Step A and proceed as directed.

ENGINE SYSTE I IDENTIFICATION

The eighth digit of the VIN denotes engine code.

Engine Code	Identification Engine	Fuel/Computer System	Page No.	Ignition System	Page No.
1993					
A	1.5L/4-90 ③	Multi-Point Fuel Injection	6-1	Type 3	4-10
B	1.8L/4-107 ⑨	Multi-Point Fuel Injection	7-1	Type 3	4-10
C	1.8L/4-110 ② ③	Multi-Point Fuel Injection	7-1	Type 3	4-10
E	2.0L/4-122 ⑤ ⑨	Multi-Point Fuel Injection	7-1	Type 6	4-18
F	2.0L/4-122 ④ ⑤ ⑨	Multi-Point Fuel Injection	7-1	Type 6	4-18
A	2.2L/4-135 ④	Multi-Point Fuel Injection	9-1	Type 1	4-1
D	2.2L/4-135	Single Point Fuel Injection	5-1	Type 1	4-1
G	2.4L/4-146	Multi-Point Fuel Injection	7-1	Type 3	4-10
K	2.5L/4-153 ⑩	Single Point Fuel Injection	5-1	Type 1	4-1
B	2.5L/4-153 ⑥	Multi-Point Fuel Injection	9-1	Type 1	4-1
J	3.0L/V6-181 ⑤ ⑧	Multi-Point Fuel Injection	11-1	Type 5	4-15
K	3.0L/V6-181 ⑤ ⑦ ⑧	Multi-Point Fuel Injection	11-1	Type 5	4-15
H	3.0L/V6-181 ⑧	Multi-Point Fuel Injection	11-1	Type 5	4-15
3	3.0L/V6-181 ⑪	Multi-Point Fuel Injection	12-1	Type 1	4-1
R	3.3L/V6-201 ⑫	Multi-Point Fuel Injection	12-1	Type 1	4-1
T	3.3L/V6-201 ①	Multi-Point Fuel Injection	13-1	Type 1	4-1
F	3.5L/V6-215	Multi-Point Fuel Injection	13-1	Type 1	4-1
L	3.8L/V6-231	Multi-Point Fuel Injection	13-1	Type 1	4-1

①—Concorde, Intrepid & Vision.
②—Colt Vista & Summit Wagon.
③—Colt & Summit.
④—Turbocharged engine.
⑤—DOHC engine.
⑥—Models w/Flex Fuel (FF).
⑦—Twin turbocharged engine.
⑧—Stealth.
⑨—Laser & Talon.
⑩—Models less Flex Fuel (FF).
⑪—Except Stealth.
⑫—Except Concorde, Intrepid & Vision.

ENGINE SYSTEM IDENTIFICATION–Continued

Engine Code	Identification		Fuel/Computer System	Page No.	Ignition System	Page No.
	Engine					
1994						
A	1.5L/4-90 ③		Multi-Point Fuel Injection	6-1	Type 3	4-10
B	1.8L/4-107 ⑧		Multi-Point Fuel Injection	7-1	Type 3	4-10
C	1.8L/4-110 ② ③		Multi-Point Fuel Injection	7-1	Type 3	4-10
E	2.0L/4-122 ⑤ ⑧		Multi-Point Fuel Injection	7-1	Type 6	4-18
F	2.0L/4-122 ④ ⑤ ⑧		Multi-Point Fuel Injection	7-1	Type 3	4-10
D	2.2L/4-135		Single Point Fuel Injection	5-1	Type 1	4-1
G	2.4L/4-146		Multi-Point Fuel Injection	7-1	Type 3	4-10
K	2.5L/4-153 ⑨		Single Point Fuel Injection	5-1	Type 1	4-1
V	2.5L/4-153 ⑩		Multi-Point Fuel Injection	9-1	Type 1	4-1
J	3.0L/V6-181 ⑤ ⑦		Multi-Point Fuel Injection	11-1	Type 5	4-15
K	3.0L/V6-181 ⑤ ⑥ ⑦		Multi-Point Fuel Injection	11-1	Type 5	4-15
H	3.0L/V6-181 ⑦		Multi-Point Fuel Injection	11-1	Type 5	4-15
3	3.0L/V6-181 ①		Multi-Point Fuel Injection	12-1	Type 1	4-1
T	3.3L/V6-201		Multi-Point Fuel Injection	12-1	Type 1	4-1
F	3.5L/V6-215		Multi-Point Fuel Injection	13-1	Type 1	4-1

① —Except Stealth.
② —Colt Vista & Summit Wagon.
③ —Colt & Summit.
④ —Turbocharged engine.
⑤ —DOHC engine.
⑥ —Twin turbocharged engine.
⑦ —Stealth.
⑧ —Laser & Talon.
⑨ —Models less Flex Fuel (FF).
⑩ —Models w/Flex Fuel (FF).

ENGINE SYSTEM IDENTIFICATION–Continued

Engine Code	Identification		Fuel/Computer System	Page No.	Ignition System	Page No.
	Engine					
1995						
A	1.5L/4-90		Multi-Point Fuel Injection	6-1	Type 3	4-10
C	1.8L/4-110		Multi-Point Fuel Injection	7-1	Type 3	4-10
Y	2.0L/4-122 ①		Multi-Point Fuel Injection	8-1	Type 6	4-18
F	2.0L/4-122 ②		Multi-Point Fuel Injection	7-1	Type 6	4-18
C	2.0L/4-122 ③		Multi-Point Fuel Injection	8-1	Type 2	4-5
C	2.0L/4-122 ④		Multi-Point Fuel Injection	8-1	Type 4	4-12
C	2.0L/4-122 ⑥		Multi-Point Fuel Injection	8-1	Type 6	4-18
D	2.2L/4-135		Single Point Fuel Injection	5-1	Type 1	4-1
G	2.4L/4-146 ⑤		Multi-Point Fuel Injection	7-1	Type 3	4-10
X	2.4L/4-148 ③		Multi-Point Fuel Injection	7-1	Type 2	4-5
H	2.5L/V6-152		Multi-Point Fuel Injection	9-1	Type 2	4-5
K	2.5L/4-153 ⑦		Single Point Fuel Injection	5-1	Type 1	4-1
V	2.5L/4-153 ⑧		Multi-Point Fuel Injection	10-1	Type 1	4-1
3	3.0L/V6-181 ⑪		Multi-Point Fuel Injection	12-1	Type 1	4-1
H	3.0L/V6-181 ⑨		Multi-Point Fuel Injection	11-1	Type 5	4-15
J	3.0L/V6-181 ⑨ ⑩		Multi-Point Fuel Injection	11-1	Type 5	4-15
K	3.0L/V6-181 ⑨ ⑩ ⑫		Multi-Point Fuel Injection	11-1	Type 5	4-15
T	3.3L/V6-201 ⑦		Multi-Point Fuel Injection	13-1	Type 1	4-1
U	3.3L/V6-201 ⑧		Multi-Point Fuel Injection	13-1	Type 1	4-1
F	3.5L/V6-215		Multi-Point Fuel Injection	13-1	Type 1	4-1

①—Talon w/non-turbocharged engine.
②—Talon w/turbocharged engine.
③—Cirrus & Stratus.
④—Neon.
⑤—Summit Wagon.
⑥—Avenger & Sebring.
⑦—Models less Flex Fuel (FF).
⑧—Models w/Flex Fuel (FF).
⑨—Stealth.
⑩—DOHC engine.
⑪—Except Stealth.
⑫—Twin turbocharged engine.

ENGINE SYSTEM IDENTIFICATION–Continued

Engine Code	Identification		Fuel/Computer System	Page No.	Ignition System	Page No.
		Engine				
1996						
A		1.5L/4-90	Multi-Point Fuel Injection	6-1	Type 3	4-10
C		1.8L/4-110	Multi-Point Fuel Injection	7-1	Type 3	4-10
Y		2.0L/4-122 ① ⑥	Multi-Point Fuel Injection	14-1	Type 6	4-18
F		2.0L/4-122 ②	Multi-Point Fuel Injection	14-1	Type 6	4-18
C		2.0L/4-122 ③	Multi-Point Fuel Injection	14-1	Type 2	4-5
C		2.0L/4-122 ④	Multi-Point Fuel Injection	14-1	Type 4	4-12
G		2.4L/4-146 ⑤	Multi-Point Fuel Injection	7-1	Type 3	4-10
X		2.4L/4-148 ③	Multi-Point Fuel Injection	14-1	Type 1	4-1
H		2.5L/V6-152 ⑪	Multi-Point Fuel Injection	14-1	Type 2	4-5
N		2.5L/V6-152 ⑬	Multi-Point Fuel Injection	14-1	Type 2	4-5
H		3.0L/V6-181 ⑨	Multi-Point Fuel Injection	14-1	Type 5	4-15
J		3.0L/V6-181 ⑨ ⑩	Multi-Point Fuel Injection	11-1	Type 5	4-15
K		3.0L/V6-181 ⑨ ⑩ ⑫	Multi-Point Fuel Injection	14-1	Type 5	4-15
T		3.3L/V6-201 ⑦	Multi-Point Fuel Injection	14-1	Type 1	4-1
U		3.3L/V6-201 ⑧	Multi-Point Fuel Injection	14-1	Type 1	4-1
F		3.5L/V6-215	Multi-Point Fuel Injection	14-1	Type 1	4-1

① —Talon w/non-turbocharged engine.
② —Talon w/turbocharged engine.
③ —Cirrus & Stratus.
④ —Neon.
⑤ —Summit Wagon.
⑥ —Avenger & Sebring.
⑦ —Models less Flex Fuel (FF).
⑧ —Models w/Flex Fuel (FF).
⑨ —Stealth.
⑩ —DOHC engine.
⑪ —Except Sebring convertible.
⑫ —Twin turbocharged engine.
⑬ —Sebring convertible.

TUNE UP SPECIFICATIONS

INDEX

Page No.

Acclaim/Spirit, Daytona,
Dynasty/Imperial, LeBaron,
Shadow/Sundance & 1993 New
Yorker........................... 2-1
Chrysler Cirrus, Dodge Stratus &
Plymouth Breeze 2-3

Page No.

Chrysler Concorde, LHS & 1994-96
New Yorker, Dodge Intrepid &
Eagle Vision 2-9
Chrysler Sebring & Dodge Avenger .. 2-4
Colt, Colt Vista, Summit & Summit
Wagon 2-6

Page No.

Dodge & Plymouth Neon 2-3
Dodge Stealth 2-8
Eagle Talon & Plymouth Laser....... 2-4

ACCLAIM/SPIRIT, DAYTONA, DYNASTY/IMPERIAL, LEBARON, SHADOW/SUNDANCE & 1993 NEW YORKER

| Engine/ VIN Code ① | Spark Plug Gap | Ignition Timing BTDC | | | | Curb Idle Speed ③ | | Fast Idle Speed | | Fuel Pump Pressure psi | Valve Clearance, Inch |
		Firing Order Fig. ②	Man. Trans.	Auto. Trans.	Mark Fig.	Man. Trans.	Auto Trans.	Man. Trans.	Auto. Trans.		
1993											
2.2L/4-135 (D)	.035	C	12⑨	12⑨	D	850	850N	⑧	⑧	39⑦	⑩
2.2L/4-135 Turbo III (A)	.035	B④	⑤	⑤	⑥	750	750N	⑧	⑧	53—57⑦	⑩
2.5L/4-153 (K)	.035	C	12⑨	12⑨	D	850	850N	⑧	⑧	39⑦	⑩
2.5L/4-153 (B)	.035	C	12⑨	12⑨	D	900	900N	⑧	⑧	48⑦	⑩
2.5L/4-153 (V)	.035	C	12⑨	12⑨	D	700-1400	700-1400N	⑧	⑧	—	⑩
3.0L/V6-181 (3)	.041	F	12⑨	12⑨	E	700	700N	⑧	⑧	48⑦	⑩
3.3L/V6-201 (R)	.050	A⑪	⑤	⑤	⑥	—	750N	⑧	⑧	48⑦	⑩
3.8L/V6-231 (L)	.050	A⑪	⑤	⑤	⑥	—	750N	⑧	⑧	48⑦	⑩
1994-95											
2.2L/4-135 (D)	.035	C	12⑨	12⑨	D	850	850N	⑧	⑧	39⑦	⑩
2.5L/4-153 (K, V)	.035	C	12⑨	12⑨	D	850	850N	⑧	⑧	39⑦	⑩
3.0L/V6-181 (3)	.041	F	12⑨	12⑨	E	700	700N	⑧	⑧	48⑦	⑩

BTDC—Before Top Dead Center.
①—The eighth digit of the Vehicle Identification Number (VIN) denotes engine code.
②—Before removing wires from distributor cap or coil, determine location of No. 1 wire, as position may have been altered from that shown at the end of this chart.
③—N: Neutral.
④—Cylinder numbering from front of engine to rear, 1, 2, 3, 4. Firing order, 1—3—4—2.

⑤—Direct Ignition System (DIS), not adjustable.
⑥—Equipped w/crankshaft position sensor.
⑦—Loosen gas cap to release pressure in tank. Ground one terminal of any injector with a jumper wire. connect remaining terminal of injector to the battery positive post using a jumper for no longer that 10 seconds, this will release fuel system pressure. Remove cover from service valve on fuel rail. Connect a suitable fuel

pressure tester to service valve. Check fuel pressure with engine running.
⑧—Controlled by Powertrain Control Module (PCM).
⑨—Check ignition timing with coolant sensor wire disconnected.
⑩—Automatic lash adjusters used; no adjustment necessary.
⑪—Cylinder numbering front to rear of engine, front bank, 2, 4, 6; rear bank, 1, 3, 5. Firing order 1-2-3-4-5-6.

ACCLAIM/SPIRIT, DAYTONA, DYNASTY/IMPERIAL, LEBARON, SHADOW/SUNDANCE & 1993 NEW YORKER—Continued

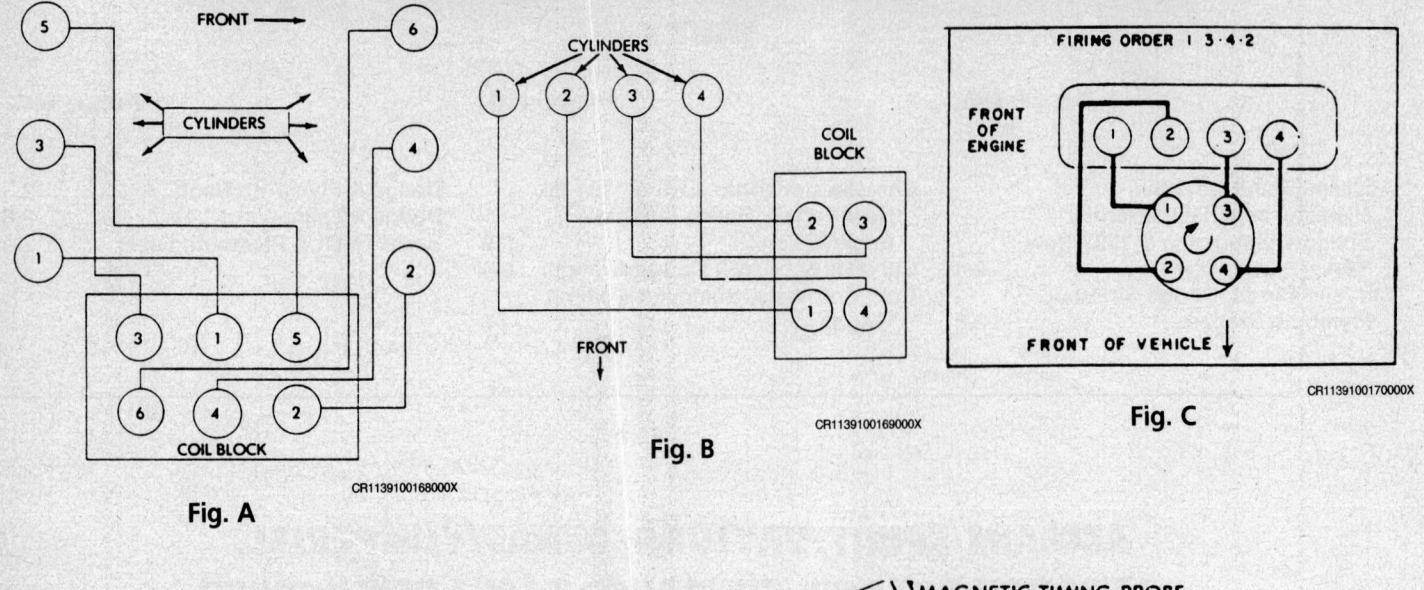

Fig. A

Fig. B

Fig. C

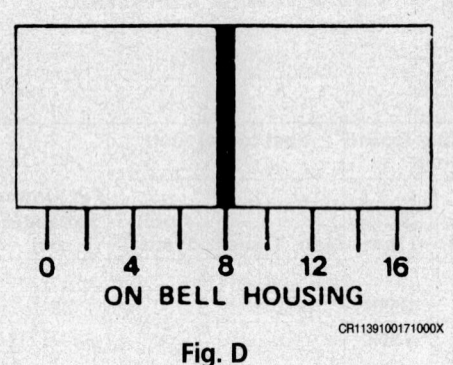

Fig. D

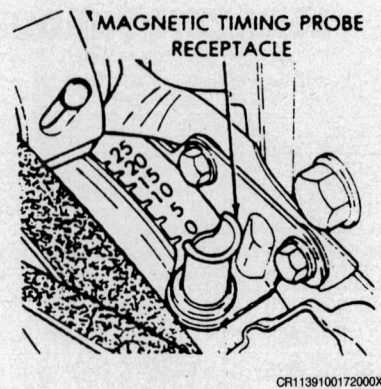

Fig. E

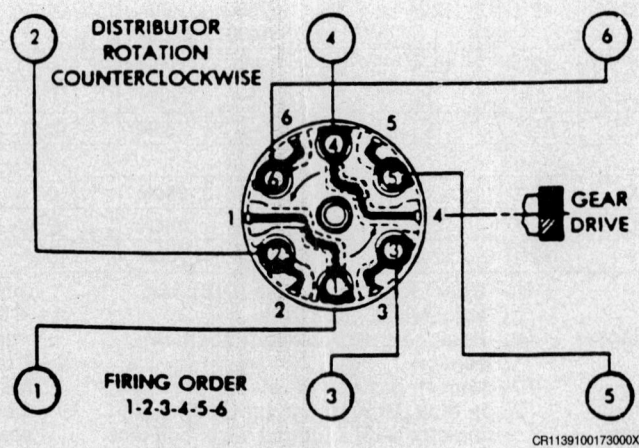

Fig. F

DODGE & PLYMOUTH NEON

Liter/CID	Spark Plug Gap, Inch	Ignition Timing @ BTDC			Curb Idle Speed	Fuel Pump Pressure psi.	Valve Clearance, Inch
		Firing Order ④	Man. Trans.	Auto. Trans.			
1995-96							
2.0L/4—122	.035	1-3-4-2	①	①	③	48②	⑤

①—Direct Ignition System (DIS), not adjustable.
②—Without vacuum applied to pressure regulator.
③—Below 1000 miles, 550—1300 RPM. Above 1000 miles, 600—1300 RPM.
④—Refer to Fig. A.
⑤—Equipped with non-adjustable hydraulic lash adjusters.

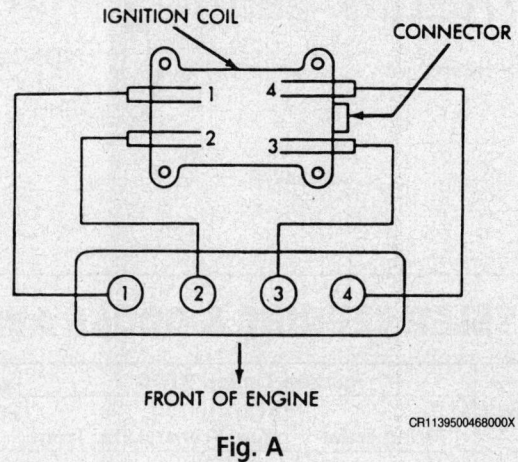

Fig. A

CHRYSLER CIRRUS, DODGE STRATUS & PLYMOUTH BREEZE

Year & Engine/ VIN Code ①	Spark Plug Gap	Ignition Timing BTDC				Minimum Air Flow Idle RPM ②	Fuel Pump Pressure psi	Valve Clearance, Inch ④	
		Firing order	Firing Order Fig.	Man. Trans.	Auto. Trans.			Int.	Exh.
2.0L/4-122/C	.035	1-3-4-2	A	③	③	600-1300	48⑦	⑥	⑥
2.4L/4-148/X	.050	1-3-4-2	A	—	③	600-1300	48⑦	⑥	⑥
2.5L/V6-152/H	.041	1-2-3-4-5-6	B	—	③	500-1100	47-51⑤	⑥	⑥

BTDC-Before Top Dead Center.
①—The eighth digit of the Vehicle Identification Number (VIN) denotes engine code.
②—Engine idle is controlled by the PCM & is not adjustable.
③—Ignition timing is controlled by the PCM & is not adjustable.
④—Equipped with hydraulic valve lash adjusters.
⑤—Disconnect fuel rail wiring harness. Connect a jumper wire between 12 volt power source & A142 circuit terminal of fuel rail wiring harness connector. Connect one end of a jumper wire to ground, then contact other end of jumper wire to each injector terminal in harness. Disconnect fuel line from fuel rail & connect a suitable fuel pressure test gauge between fuel line & fuel rail. Connect DRB scan tool, or equivalent. Place ignition switch in the On position, the using scan tool activate ADSD fuel system test.
⑥—Equipped with hydraulic valve adjusters. No adjustment is necessary.
⑦—Remove cap from fuel pressure test port on fuel rail. Connect a suitable fuel pressure gauge to fuel rail test port. Connect DRB scan tool or equivalent. Place ignition switch in the On position, then using scan tool activate ADSD fuel system test.

CHRYSLER CIRRUS, DODGE STRATUS & PLYMOUTH BREEZE—Continued

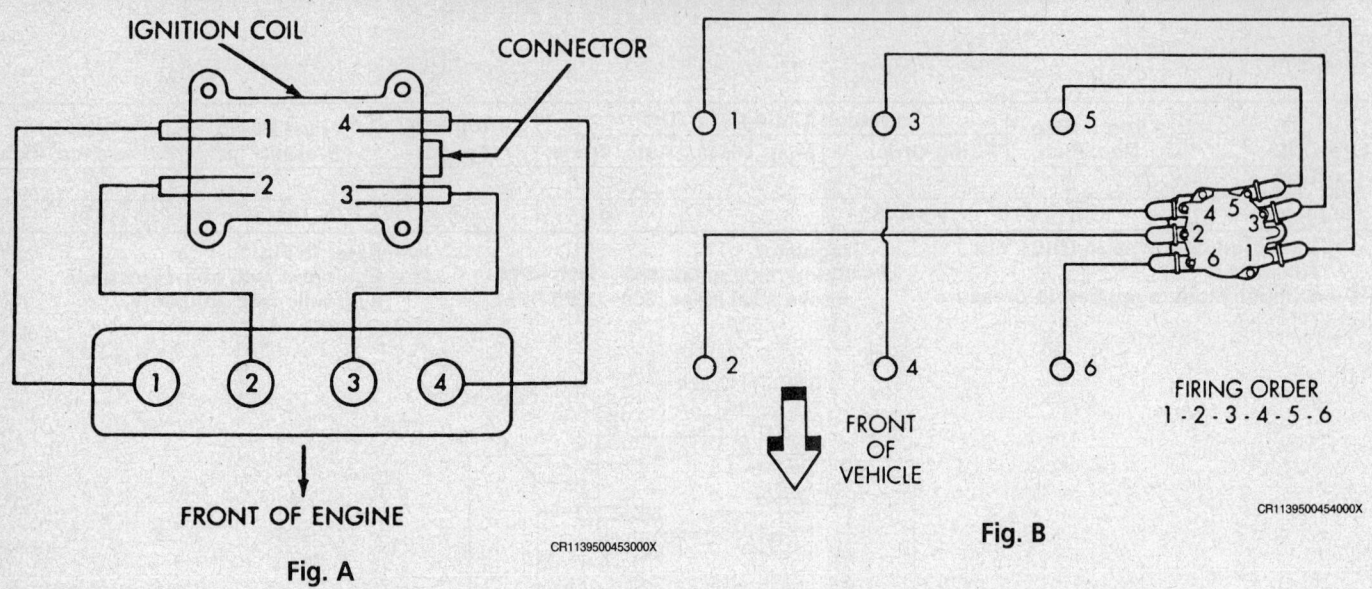

Fig. A

Fig. B

FIRING ORDER
1 - 2 - 3 - 4 - 5 - 6

CHRYSLER SEBRING & DODGE AVENGER

Year & Engine (VIN Code) ①	Spark Plug Gap	Ignition Timing BTDC			Minimum Air Flow Idle RPM ②	Fuel Pump Pressure, psi	Valve Clearance, Inch
		Firing order	Man. Trans.	Auto. Trans.			
1995							
2.0L/4-122 (Y)	.033-.038	1-3-4-2	③	③	700-900	47-50	④
2.5L/V6-152 (N)	.039-.043	1-2-3-4-5-6	③	③	650-850	47-50	④
1996							
2.0L/4-122 (Y)	.033-.038	1-3-4-2	③	③	700-900	47-50	④
2.4L/4-148 (X) ⑤	.051	1-3-4-2	—	③	600-1300	47-51	④
2.5L/V6-152 (N) ⑥	.039-.043	1-2-3-4-5-6	③	③	650-850	47-50	④
2.5L/V6-152 (H) ⑤	.039-.043	1-2-3-4-5-6	—	③	650-850	47-50	④

BTDC–Before top dead center
①—The eighth digit of the Vehicle Identification Number (VIN) denotes engine code.
②—Engine idle is controlled by the PCM & is not adjustable.
③—Ignition timing is electronically controlled. No adjustment is necessary.
④—Equipped with hydraulic valve lash adjusters. No adjustment is necessary.
⑤—Sebring convertible.
⑥—Except convertible.

EAGLE TALON & PLYMOUTH LASER

Year & Engine (VIN Code) ①	Spark Plug Gap	Ignition Timing BTDC				Curb Idle Speed		Fast Idle Speed		Fuel Pump Pressure, Psi.	Valve Clearance, inch
		Firing Order Fig. ④	Man. Trans.	Auto. Trans.	Mark Fig.	Man. Trans.	Auto Trans.	Man. Trans.	Auto. Trans.		
1993—94											
1.8L/4-107 (B)	.041	A	5⑥⑪	5⑥⑪	B	700	700N	②	②	38⑨	⑬
2.0L/4-122 (E) ⑧	.041	C	5⑦⑪	5⑦⑪	B	750	750N	②	②	47—50⑨	⑬
2.0L/4-122 (F) ⑤	.030	C	5⑦⑪	5⑦⑪	B	750	750N	②	②	⑨⑩	⑬
1995											
2.0L/4-122 (Y) ⑧	.050	F	12⑫	12⑫	B	700②	700②	②	②	46-49③	⑬
2.0L/4-122 (F) ⑤	.030	G	5⑫	5⑫	B	750②	750②	②	②	41-44⑨	⑬

Continued

EAGLE TALON & PLYMOUTH LASER—Continued

Year & Engine (VIN Code) ①	Spark Plug Gap	Ignition Timing BTDC				Curb Idle Speed		Fast Idle Speed		Fuel Pump Pressure, Psi.	Valve Clearance, inch
		Firing Order Fig. ④	Man. Trans.	Auto. Trans.	Mark Fig.	Man. Trans.	Auto Trans.	Man. Trans.	Auto. Trans.		
1996											
2.0L/4-122 (Y) ⑧	.050	F	12⑫	12⑫	B	800②	800②	②	②	47-50③	⑬
2.0L/4-122 (F) ⑤	.030	G	5⑫	5⑫	B	750②	750②	②	②	42-45⑨	⑬

BTDC—Before Top Dead Center.
N—Neutral.
①—The eighth digit of the Vehicle Identification Number (VIN) denotes engine code.
②—Controlled by the idle air control motor.
③—Disconnect fuel pump electrical connector, located at fuel tank. Start engine & operate until it stalls. Disconnect battery ground cable, then reconnect fuel pump electrical connector. Install suitable fuel pressure gauge to fuel pressure test port on fuel rail. Connect battery, then place ignition switch in the On position & use scan tool to perform fuel system pressure test. Note fuel pressure reading.

④—Before disconnecting wires from distributor cap, determine location of No. 1 wire in cap, as distributor position may have been altered from that shown at the end of this chart.
⑤—Turbocharged.
⑥—At 700 RPM.
⑦—At 750 RPM.
⑧—Except turbocharged.
⑨—Disconnect fuel pump electrical connector, located at fuel tank. Start engine & operate until it stalls. Disconnect battery ground cable, then reconnect fuel pump electrical connector. Place shop towels around fuel high pressure hose at fuel delivery pipe side, then disconnect hose. Install suitable fuel pressure gauge between fuel

delivery pipe & high pressure hose. Disconnect & plug vacuum hose from fuel pressure regulator. Connect battery ground cable & check fuel pressure w/engine idling.
⑩—Man. trans., 36—38 psi.; auto. trans., 41 = 46 psi.
⑪—With jumper wire connected between ignition timing adjustment connector & ground. Refer to Figs. D for 1.8L engine & Fig. E for 2.0L engine.
⑫—With jumper wire connected between ignition timing adjustment connector & ground. Refer to Fig. H.
⑬—Equipped with hydraulic lash adjusters.

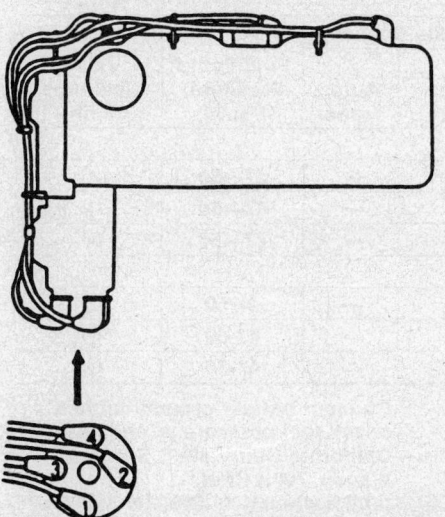

Fig. A

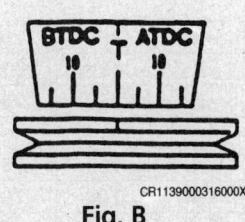

Fig. B

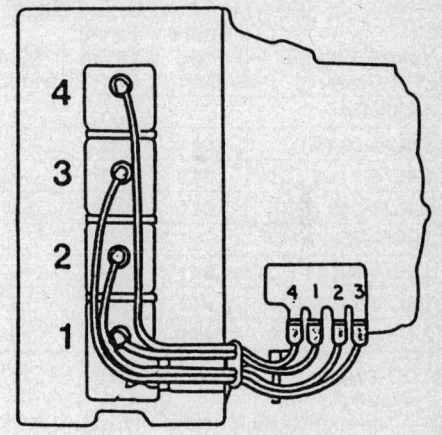

Fig. C

Fig. D

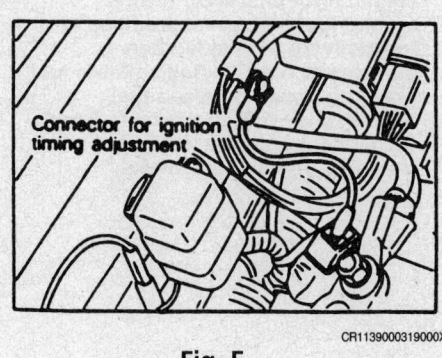

Fig. E

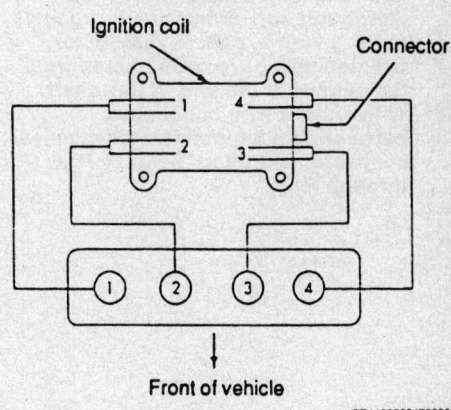

Fig. F

EAGLE TALON & PLYMOUTH LASER–Continued

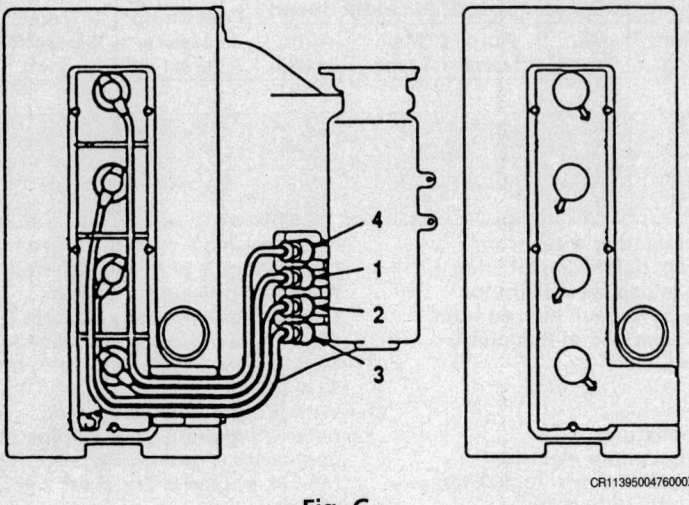

Fig. G

CR1139500476000X

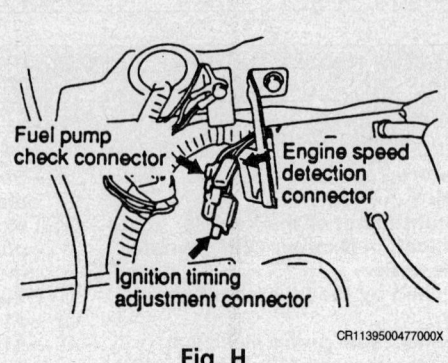

Fuel pump check connector

Engine speed detection connector

Ignition timing adjustment connector

Fig. H

CR1139500477000X

COLT, COLT VISTA, SUMMIT & SUMMIT WAGON

Year & Engine (VIN Code)①	Spark Plug Gap	Ignition Timing BTDC				Curb Idle Speed④		Fast Idle Speed④		Fuel Pump Pressure, Psi.⑤	Valve Clearance, Inch
		Firing Order Fig.②	Man. Trans.③	Auto. Trans.③	Mark Fig.	Man. Trans.	Auto Trans.	Man. Trans.	Auto. Trans.		
1993-94											
1.5L/4-90 (A)	.041	B	5	5	A	750	750N	—	—	47—50	⑦
1.8L/4-111.9 (C)	.041	C	5	5	A	750⑥	750N⑥	—	—	47—50	⑧
2.4L/4-143 (G)	.041	C	5	5	A	750	750N	—	—	47—50	⑨
1995-96											
1.5L/4-90(A)	.041	B	5	5	A	750	750N	—	—	47-50	⑦
1.8L/4-111.9 (C)	.041	C	5	5	A	700	700N	—	—	47-50	⑧
2.4L/4-143 (G)	.041	C	5	5	A	750	750	—	—	47-50	⑨

BTDC—Before Top Dead Center.
N—Neutral.
① —The eighth digit of the Vehicle Identification Number (VIN) denotes engine code.
② —Before disconnecting wires from distributor cap, determine location of No. 1 wire in cap, as distributor position may have been altered from that shown at the end of this chart.
③ —With jumper wire connected between ignition timing adjustment connector & ground. Refer to Figs. D through F.

④ —Controlled by idle speed control.
⑤ —Disconnect fuel pump electrical connector, located at fuel tank. Start engine & operate until it stalls. Disconnect battery ground cable, then reconnect fuel pump electrical connector. Place shop towels around fuel high pressure hose at fuel delivery pipe side, then disconnect hose. Install suitable fuel pressure gauge between fuel delivery pipe & high pressure hose. Disconnect & plug vacuum hose from fuel pressure regulator.

Connect battery ground cable & check fuel pressure w/engine idling.
⑥ —California Colt Vista & Summit Wagon, 700N RPM.
⑦ —Intake when hot, .0080 inch; intake when cold, .0040 inch; exhaust when hot, .0100 inch; exhaust when cold, .0070.
⑧ —Intake when hot, .0080 inch; intake when cold, .0040 inch; exhaust when hot, .0120 inch; exhaust when cold, .0080.
⑨ —Equipped with hydraulic lash adjusters.

COLT, COLT VISTA, SUMMIT & SUMMIT WAGON—Continued

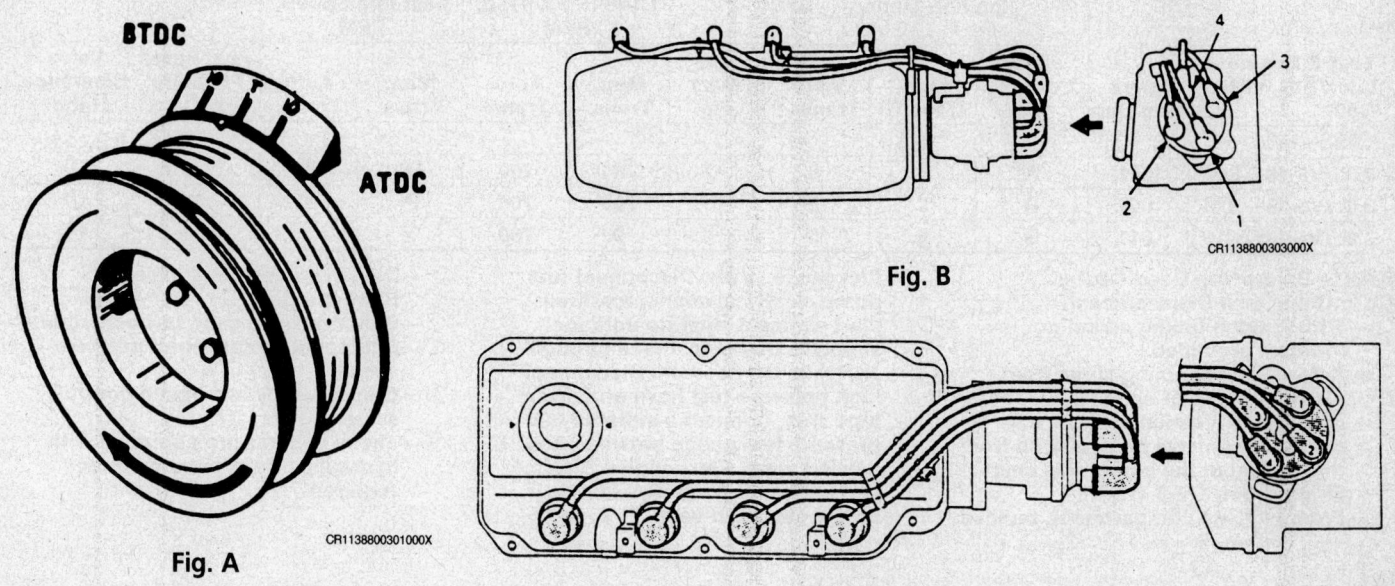

Fig. A

Fig. B

Fig. C

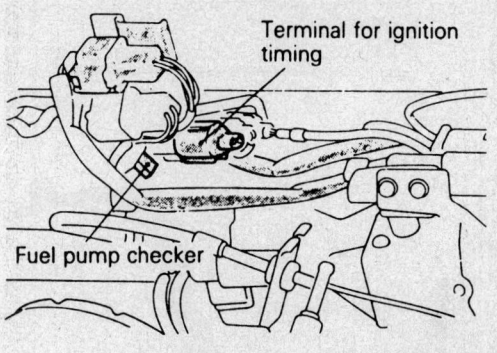

Fig. D   Ignition timing adjustment connector. Colt & Summit w/1.5L/4-90 engine

Fig. E   Ignition timing adjustment connector. Colt & Summit w/1.8L/4-110 engine

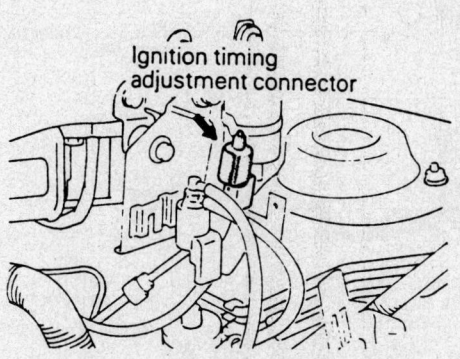

Fig. F   Ignition timing adjustment connector. Colt Vista & Summit Wagon w/1.8L/4-110 & 2.4L/4-143 engines

DODGE STEALTH

Year & Engine Liter/CID, VIN Code	Spark Plug Gap	Ignition Timing @ BTDC				Curb Idle Speed, RPM		Fast Idle Speed, RPM		Fuel Pump Pressure, psi ③	Valve Clearance, Inch
		Firing Order Fig. ②	Man. Trans. ①	Auto. Trans. ①	Mark Fig.	Man. Trans.	Auto. Trans.	Man. Trans.	Auto Trans.		
1993—96											
3.0L/V6-181, S ④	.041	A	5	5	C	700	700	⑧	⑧	38	⑨
3.0L/V6-181, B ⑤	.041	B	5	5	⑦	700	700	⑧	⑧	38	⑨
3.0L/V6-181, C ⑥	.041	B	5	5	⑦	700	700	⑧	⑧	34	⑨

BTDC—Before Top Dead Center.
CID—Cubic Inch Displacement.
①—With ignition timing adjusting terminal grounded.
②—Before disconnecting wires from distributor cap or coil unit, determine location of No. 1 wire, as position may have been altered from that shown at the end of this chart. Firing order, 1-2-3-4-5-6.
③—From luggage compartment, remove fuel gauge cover. Disconnect fuel pump electrical connector, then start engine & operate until fuel supply is depleted. Place ignition switch in Off position. Disconnect high pressure fuel hose at delivery pipe side. Connect a suitable fuel pressure test gauge between hose & delivery pipe. Start engine & check fuel pressure at idle speed.
④—Single overhead cam.
⑤—Dual overhead cam, except turbocharged.
⑥—Dual overhead cam, turbocharged.
⑦—Equipped w/crankshaft position sensor.
⑧—Controlled by idle speed control system.
⑨—These engines are equipped with hydraulic lifters, no adjustment required.

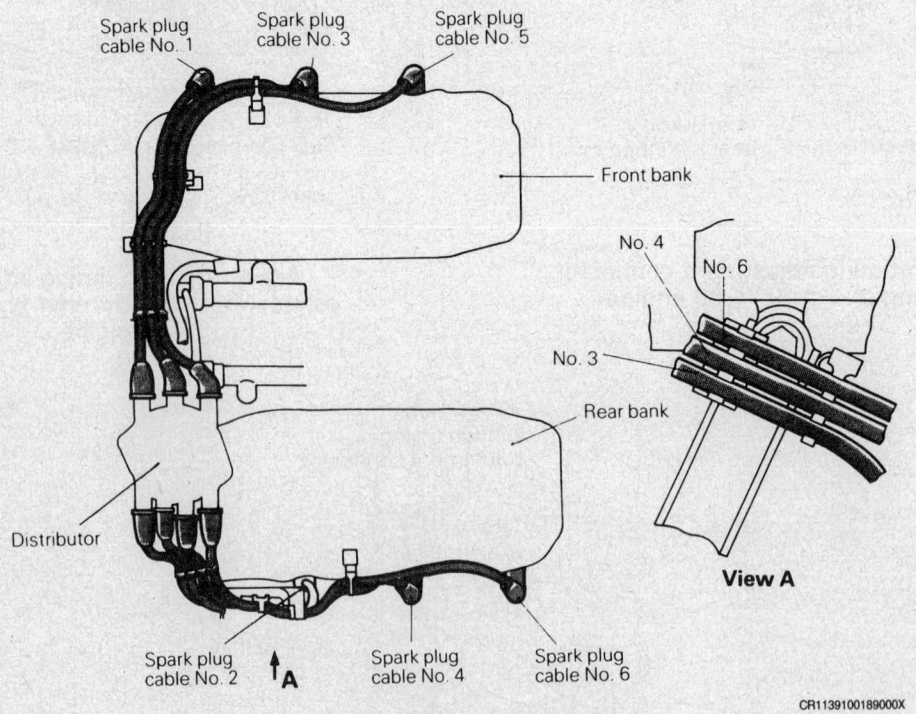

Fig. A

CR1139100189000X

DODGE STEALTH—Continued

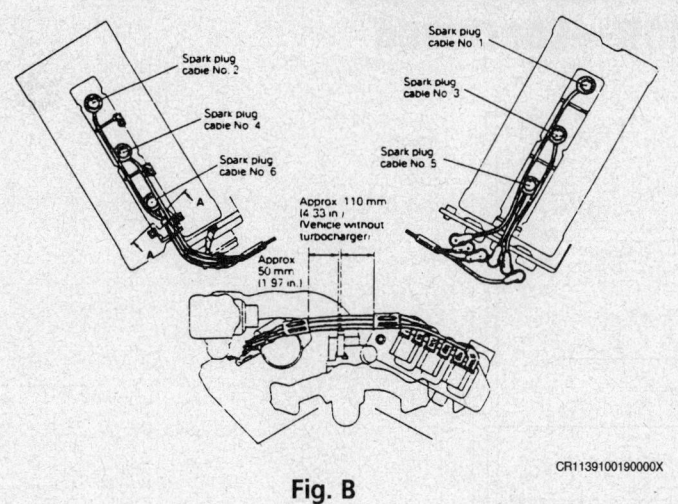

Fig. B

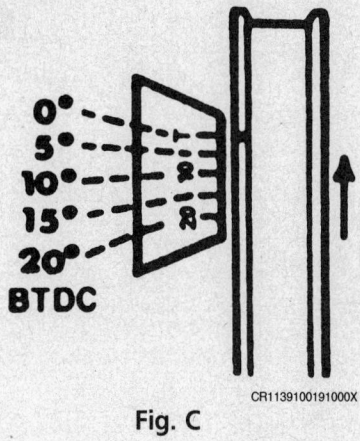

Fig. C

CHRYSLER CONCORDE,
LHS & 1994–96 NEW YORKER, DODGE INTREPID & EAGLE VISION

| Engine Liter/ CID ① (VIN Code ②) | Spark Plug Gap | Ignition Timing BTDC | | | | Curb Idle Speed | | Fast Idle Speed | | Fuel Pump Pressure, psi | Valve Clearance, inch |
		Firing Order Fig. ④	Man. Trans.	Auto. Trans.	Mark Fig.	Man. Trans.	Auto. Trans.	Man. Trans.	Auto. Trans.		
1993											
3.3L/V6-201 (T)	.050	A	—	⑧	⑤	—	③	—	⑧	55⑨	⑩
3.5L/V6-215 (F)	.050	A	—	⑧	⑤	—	③	—	⑥	48⑨	⑩
1994											
3.3L/V6-201 (T)	.050	A	—	⑧	⑤	—	⑦	—	⑦	55⑨	⑩
3.5L/V6-215 (F)	.050	A	—	⑧	⑤	—	⑦	—	⑦	48⑨	⑩
1995											
3.3L/V6-201 (T)	.050	A	—	⑧	⑤	—	⑦	—	⑦	55⑨	⑩
3.3L/V6-201 (U)	.045	A	—	⑧	⑤	—	⑦	—	⑦	55⑨	⑩
3.5L/V6-215 (F)	.050	A	—	⑧	⑤	—	⑦	—	⑦	48⑨	⑩
1996											
3.3L/V6-201 (T)	.050	A	—	⑧	⑤	—	⑦	—	⑦	55⑨	⑩
3.3L/V6-201 (U)	.050	A	—	⑧	⑤	—	⑦	—	⑦	55⑨	⑩
3.5L/V6-215 (F)	.036	A	—	⑧	⑤	—	⑦	—	⑦	48⑨	⑩

① —CID: Cubic Inch Displacement.
② —The eighth digit of the Vehicle Identification Number (VIN) denotes engine code.
③ —Models w/less than 1000 miles, 700 = 1000 RPM; models w/more than 1000 miles, 750—1100 RPM.
④ —Before disconnecting wires from coil unit, determine location of No. 1 wire, as position may have been altered from that shown at the end of this chart. Firing order, 1-2-3-4-5-6.
⑤ —Equipped w/crankshaft position sensor.
⑥ —Idle speeds are controlled by the Automatic Idle Speed (AIS) motor.
⑦ —Controlled by PCM.
⑧ —Direct (Distributorless) Ignition System (DIS), not adjustable.
⑨ —Remove cover from service valve on fuel rail. Connect a suitable fuel pressure test gauge to service valve. With ignition switch in Run position, use Diagnostic Readout Box (DRB) to activate fuel pump & pressurize system.
⑩ —Equipped with hydraulic lash adjusters, no adjustment is necessary.

CHRYSLER CONCORDE, LHS, 1994-96 NEW YORKER, DODGE INTREPID & EAGLE VISION—Continued

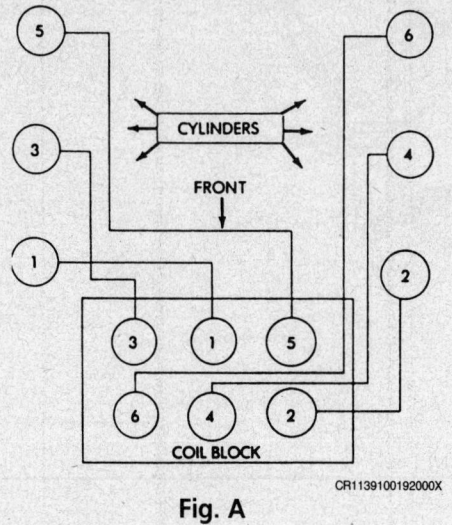

Fig. A

NGINE TUNE U & PERFORMANCE

TABLE OF CONTENTS

Page No.   Page No.

V6 GASOLINE ENGINE........... 3-12   **4 CYLINDER GASOLINE ENGINES**   3-1

4 Cylinder Gasoline Engines

If Uncertain About The Proper Use Of Information Contained In This Section, Please Refer To "How To Use This Manual" Located In The Front Of This Tabbed Section.

Prior To Performing Any Service Operations Listed In This Section, Consult The Technical Service Bulletin Section For Related Information.

INDEX

Page No.

Compression Pressure.............. 3-1
Engine Identification................ 3-1
Fuel Injection Cleaning............ 3-10
Idle Speed & Mixture Adjustments:.. 3-4
  Base Idle Speed:.................. 3-5
    Avenger, Laser, Sebring & Talon... 3-5
    Colt & Summit.................... 3-8
    Colt Vista & Summit Wagon....... 3-7
    Except Avenger, Colt, Colt Vista,
      Laser, Sebring, Summit, Summit
      Wagon & Talon w/2.0/4-122
      Engine......................... 3-5
  Curb Idle Speed:.................. 3-5
    Avenger, Colt, Colt Vista, Laser,
      Sebring, Summit, Summit Wagon
      & Talon w/2.0/4-122 Engine.... 3-5
    Except Avenger, Colt, Colt Vista,
      Laser, Sebring, Summit, Summit
      Wagon & Talon w/2.0/4-122
      Engine......................... 3-5

Page No.

Ignition Timing:...................... 3-1
  Breeze, Cirrus, Neon, Sebring
    Convertible & Stratus............. 3-2
  Colt & Summit.................... 3-2
  Colt Vista & Summit Wagon....... 3-2
  Except Avenger, Breeze, Cirrus, Colt,
    Colt Vista, Neon, Sebring, Sebring
    Convertible, Stratus, Summit,
    Summit Wagon, Laser & Talon:.... 3-1
    Except 2.2L/4-135 Turbo III Engine 3-1
    2.2L/4-135 Turbo III Engine....... 3-2
  Laser, 1993-94 Talon & 1995-96
    Talon w/2.0L/4-122 Turbocharged
    Engine......................... 3-3
  1995-96 Avenger, Sebring & Talon
    w/2.0L/4-122 Non-Turbocharged
    Engine......................... 3-4

Page No.

Ignition Wire Resistance............. 3-1
Sensor Adjustments:............... 3-10
  Closed Throttle Position Switch (Idle
    Position Switch) & Throttle
    Position Sensor (TPS):.......... 3-10
    Colt & Summit................... 3-11
    Colt Vista & Summit Wagon...... 3-10
  Throttle Position Sensor (TPS):..... 3-10
    Avenger, Laser, Sebring & Talon.. 3-10
Spark Plugs......................... 3-1
Valves:............................... 3-8
  Valve Adjustment:................ 3-8
    Intake & Exhaust Valves.......... 3-8
    Jet Valve....................... 3-9
  Valve Arrangement:............... 3-8
    Flywheel To Crankshaft Pulley 3-8

ENGINE IDENTIFICATION

The eighth digit of the vehicle identification number (VIN) denotes the engine code. The VIN plate is attached to the top left corner of the instrument panel and is visible through the outside of the vehicle. Refer to Tune Up Specifications chart for VIN identification.

SPARK PLUGS

Spark plugs should be replaced every 30,000 miles. **Torque** spark plugs to 20 ft. lbs. on all models except Avenger, Colt, Colt Vista, Laser, Sebring, Summit, Summit Wagon and Talon. **Torque** spark plugs to 15-21 ft. lbs. on Avenger, Colt, Colt Vista, Laser, Sebring, Summit, Summit Wagon and Talon. Refer to Tune Up Specifications chart for spark plug gap.

IGNITION WIRE RESISTANCE

Refer to appropriate ignition section for ignition wire resistance specifications.

COMPRESSION PRESSURE

Refer to **Fig. 1** for engine compression pressure specifications.

IGNITION TIMING

Refer to "Tune Up Specifications Chart" for ignition timing and firing order.

Except Avenger, Breeze, Cirrus, Colt, Colt Vista, Neon, Sebring, Sebring Convertible, Stratus, Summit, Summit Wagon, Laser & Talon

EXCEPT 2.2L/4-135 TURBO III ENGINE

1. Connect suitable timing light to No. 1 cylinder spark plug wire following tool manufacturer's instructions.
2. With engine running at normal operating temperature, disconnect coolant temperature sensor electrical connector on thermostat housing. This will il-

luminate Power Loss or Check Engine lamp on instrument panel.

3. Aim timing light at timing scale. If flash occurs when timing mark is before specified degree mark, timing is advanced. To adjust, loosen distributor hold-down and turn distributor housing in direction of rotor rotation. If flash occurs when timing mark is after specified degree mark, timing is retarded. To adjust, loosen distributor hold-down and turn distributor housing against direction of rotor rotation. Adjust as necessary.

4. Stop engine, tighten distributor hold-down, remove timing light and reconnect coolant temperature sensor electrical connector.

5. Cancel "Check Engine" lamp by cycling ignition switch 50 to 100 times.

2.2L/4-135 TURBO III ENGINE

Ignition timing cannot be set or changed on this engine.

Breeze, Cirrus, Neon, Sebring Convertible & Stratus

Ignition timing is electronically controlled and is not adjustable.

Colt & Summit

1. Ensure all lights, accessories and cooling fan are off, manual transaxle is in neutral or automatic transaxle is in park, wheels are in straight ahead position and engine is at operating temperature.

2. Insert a paper clip into 1 pin blue connector, **Fig. 2**, then connect a suitable tachometer to paper clip.

3. Connect timing light according to tool manufacturer's instructions.

4. Start engine and run at idle. Check curb idle speed and adjust if necessary. Refer to "Tune Up Specifications for curb idle setting.

5. Stop engine, then disconnect and ground female connector from ignition timing connector, **Fig. 3**.

6. Start and run engine at curb idle speed, then check basic ignition timing. Results should be as follows:
   a. **On 1993-94 models and 1995-96 Federal models,** basic timing should be 2-8° BTDC.
   b. **On 1995-96 California models,** basic timing should be 2-8° BTDC.

7. If basic timing is not as specified, loosen distributor mounting nut and rotate distributor housing as necessary.

8. Tighten mounting nut, then remove ground from adjusting connector. Start engine and check actual ignition timing. Timing should now be within specifications as listed in "Tune Up Specifications Chart."

Colt Vista & Summit Wagon

1. Start and run engine until coolant

Year	VIN	Engine	Minimum psi	Maximum Variation Between Cylinders, psi
1993	A,D	2.2L/4-135	100	①
	B,K	2.5L/4-153	100	①
	C⑤	1.8L/4-110	142	14
	C②	1.8L/4-110	151	14
	B	1.8L/4-107	131	14
	E	2.0L/4-122 ③	145	14
	F	2.0L/4-122 ④	121	14
	G	2.4L/4-146	139	14
	A②	1.5L/4-90	137	14
1994	D	2.2L/4-135	100	①
	K	2.5L/4-153	100	①
	V⑥	2.5L/4-153	100	①
	C⑤	1.8L/4-110	142	14
	C②	1.8L/4-110	151	14
	B	1.8L/4-107	131	14
	E	2.0L/4-122 ③	145	14
	F	2.0L/4-122 ④	121	14
	G	2.4L/4-146	139	14
	A	1.5L/4-90	137	14
1995	A	1.5L/4-90	137	14
	C⑦	1.8L/4-110	151	14
	C⑧	1.8L/4-110	142	14
	Y⑨	2.0L/4-122 ③	133	14
	F⑨	2.0L/4-122 ④	100	①
	C⑩	2.0L/4-122	170	①
	D	2.2L/4-135	100	①
	G	2.4L/4-146	139	14
	X⑪	2.4L/4-148	170	①
	K	2.5L/4-153	100	①
	V⑥	2.5L/4-153	100	①
1996	A	1.5L/4-90	137	14
	C⑦	1.8L/4-110	151	14
	C⑧	1.8L/4-110	142	14
	Y⑨	2.0L/4-122 ③	133	14
	F⑨	2.0L/4-122 ④	133	①
	C⑩	2.0L/4-122	170	①
	G	2.4L/4-146	139	14
	X⑪	2.4L/4-148	170	①
	N⑥	2.5L/4-153	139	①

①—Psi readings should not vary more than 25 percent from cylinder to cylinder.
②—Colt & Summit.
③—Non-Turbocharged.
④—Turbocharged.
⑤—Colt Vista & Summit Wagon.
⑥—Avenger & Sebring.
⑦—Summit.
⑧—Summit Wagon.
⑨—Avenger, Sebring & Talon.
⑩—Breeze, Cirrus, Neon & Stratus.
⑪—Breeze, Cirrus & Stratus.

Fig. 1 Compression pressure specifications

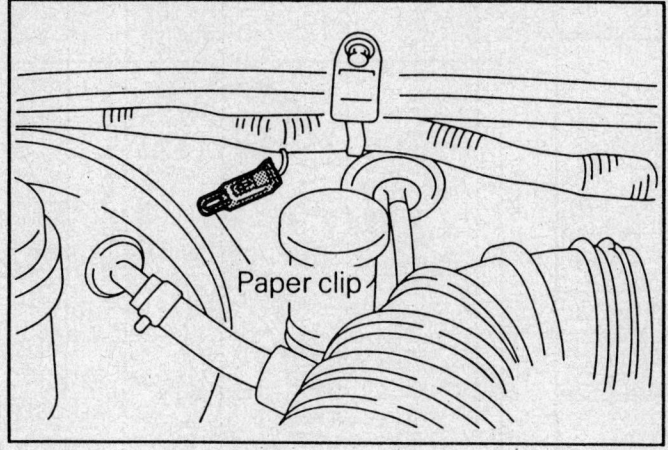

Fig. 2 Tachometer connection point. 1993–94 Colt & 1993–96 Summit

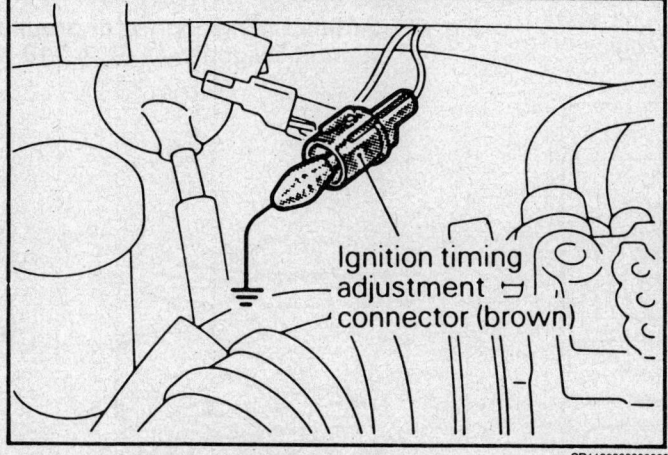

Fig. 3 Ignition timing connector ground. 1993–94 Colt & 1993–96 Summit

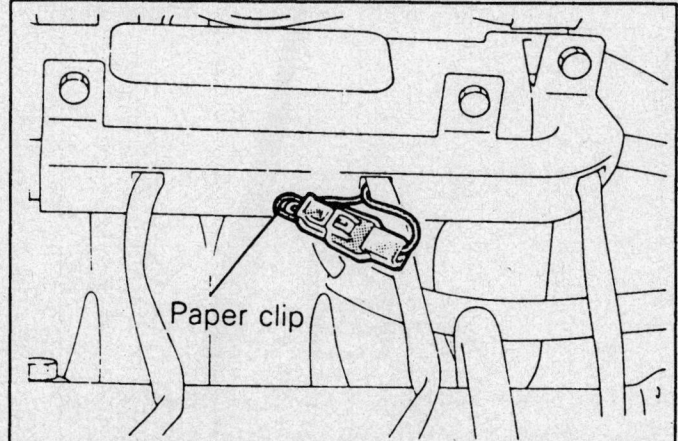

Fig. 4 Tachometer connection point. 1993 Colt Vista & Summit Wagon w/1.8L/4-110 engine

reaches normal operating temperature.
2. Ensure all vehicle lamps and accessories are off, then place manual transaxle in Neutral or automatic transaxle in Park.
3. Place wheels in straight ahead position, then set parking brake.
4. Connect suitable timing light to engine in accordance with tool manufacturer's instructions.
5. Insert a paper clip into engine speed detection terminal, then connect tachometer to paper clip, **Figs. 4 and 5.**
6. Start and run engine. Check curb idle speed; adjust if necessary. Refer to

"Tune Up Specifications" for curb idle setting.
7. Stop engine, then disconnect female connector from ignition timing adjustment connector and connect to ground, **Figs. 6 and 7.**
8. Start and run engine at curb idle speed, then check basic ignition timing. If basic timing is not 3-7° BTDC, loosen distributor mounting nut, then rotate distributor housing as necessary.
9. Tighten mounting nut, then remove ground from adjusting connector. Start engine and check actual ignition timing. Timing should now be within specifications as listed in "Tune Up Specifications."

Laser, 1993–94 Talon & 1995–96 Talon w/2.0L/4-122 Turbocharged Engine

1. Ensure all lights, accessories, and cooling fan are off, manual transaxle is in Neutral or automatic transaxle is in Park, wheels are in straight ahead position and engine is at operating temperature.
2. Connect timing light to engine according to tool manufacturer's instructions.
3. **On 1.8L/4-107 engine,** connect tachometer by inserting a paper clip into 3 pin CRC filter connector, **Fig. 8.** Connect tachometer to paper clip.
4. Start engine and check curb idle speed. Refer to "Tune Up Specifications" for curb idle setting.
5. **On 2.0L/4-122 engine,** connect tachometer by inserting a paper clip into engine revolution speed detection terminal, **Figs. 9 and 10.** Connect tachometer to paper clip. **One half of actual engine RPM is indicated by tachometer, so actual engine RPM is twice tachometer reading.**
6. Start engine and check curb idle speed. Refer to "Tune Up Specifications" for curb idle setting.
7. **On all models,** stop engine, then disconnect connector from ignition timing adjustment connector and connect to ground, **Figs. 11 and 12.**
8. Start and run engine at curb idle speed, then check basic ignition timing. Results should be as follows:
   a. **On 1993-94 models,** basic timing should be 3-7° BTDC.
   b. **On 1995-96 Talon,** basic timing should be 2-8° BTDC.
9. If results are not as specified, proceed as follows:
   a. **On models with 1.8L/4-107 engine,** loosen distributor mounting nut, then rotate distributor housing as necessary.
   b. **On 1993-94 models with 2.0L/4-122 engine,** loosen crank angle sensor mounting nut, then rotate crank angle sensor as necessary.
   c. **On 1995-96 Talon with 2.0L/4-122 turbocharged engine,** inspect MFI components as necessary.

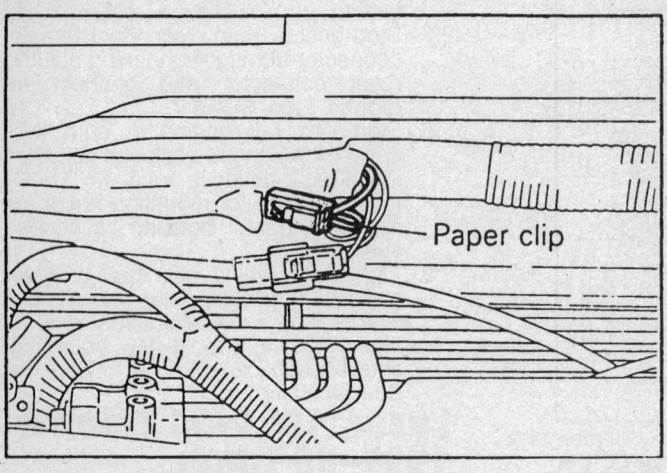

Fig. 5   Tachometer connection point. Colt Vista & Summit Wagon w/2.4L/4-146 engine & 1994 Colt Vista & 1994–96 Summit Wagon w/1.8L/4-110 engine

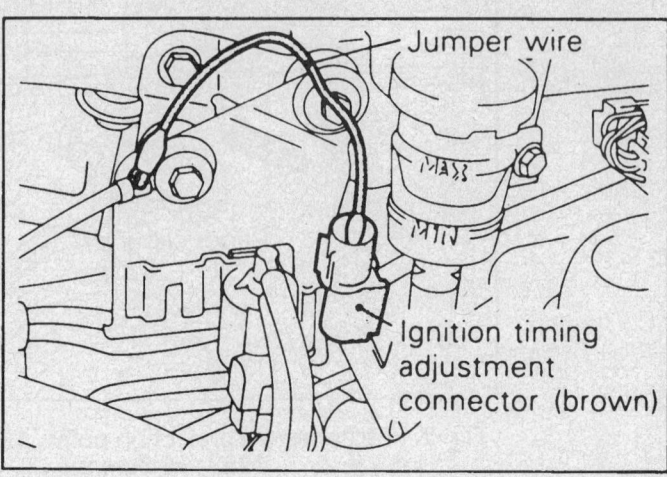

Fig. 6   Ignition timing connector ground. Colt Vista & Summit Wagon w/1.8L/4-110 engine

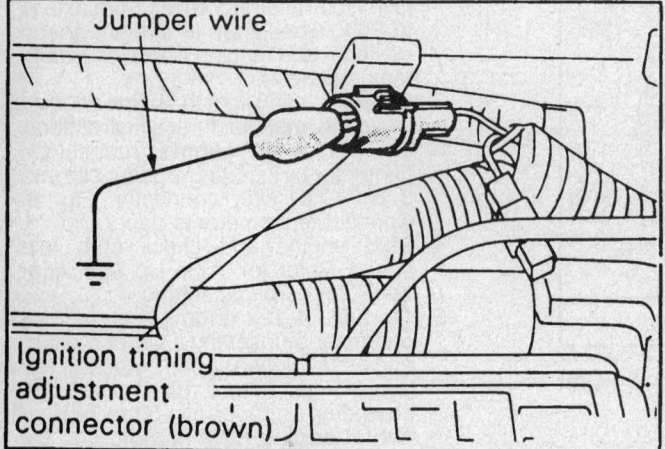

Fig. 7   Ignition timing connector ground. Colt Vista & Summit Wagon w/2.4L/4-146 engine

10. **On 1993-94 models,** tighten mounting nut, then remove ground from adjusting connector. Start engine and check actual ignition timing. Timing should now be within specifications as listed in "Tune Up Specifications Chart."

1995–96 Avenger, Sebring & Talon w/2.0L/4-122 Non-Turbocharged Engine

Because crankshaft position is detected directly and ignition timing is controlled electronically, timing inspection and adjustment is not necessary.

IDLE SPEED & MIXTURE ADJUSTMENTS

Refer to "Tune Up Specifications" chart for idle speed settings.

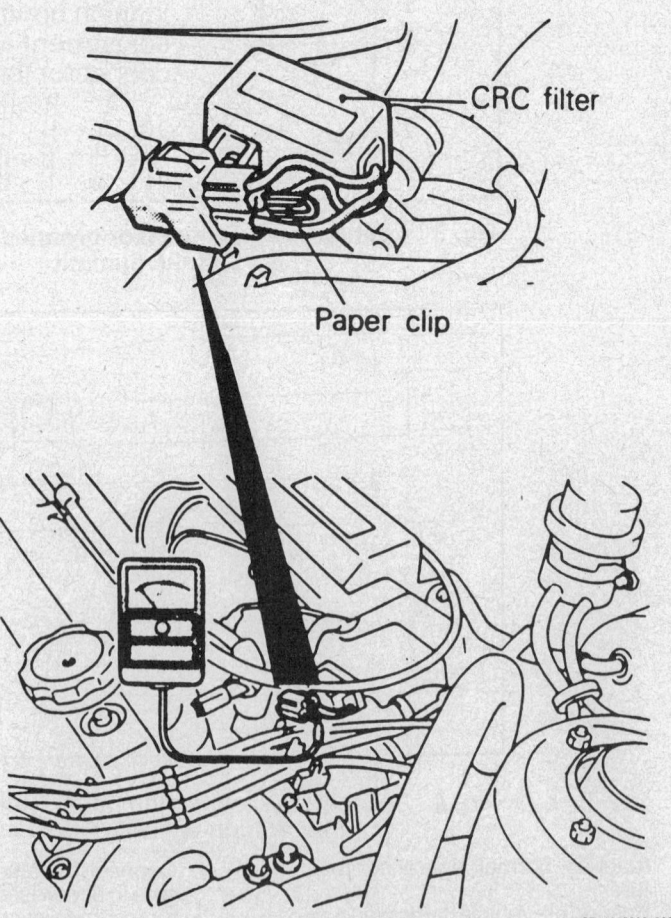

Fig. 8   Tachometer connection. Laser & Talon w/1.8L/4-107 engine

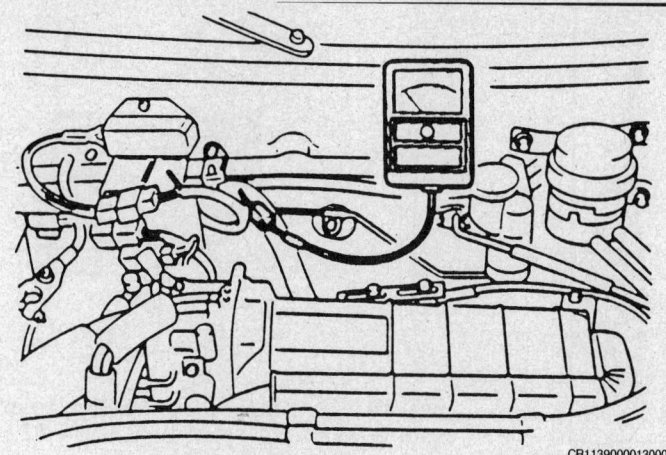

Fig. 9 Tachometer connection. Laser & 1993–94 Talon w/2.0L/4-122 engine

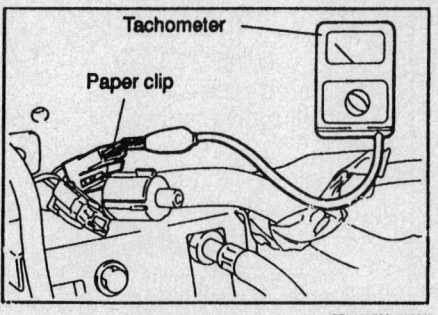

Fig. 10 Tachometer connection. 1995–96 Talon w/2.0L/4-122 turbocharged engine

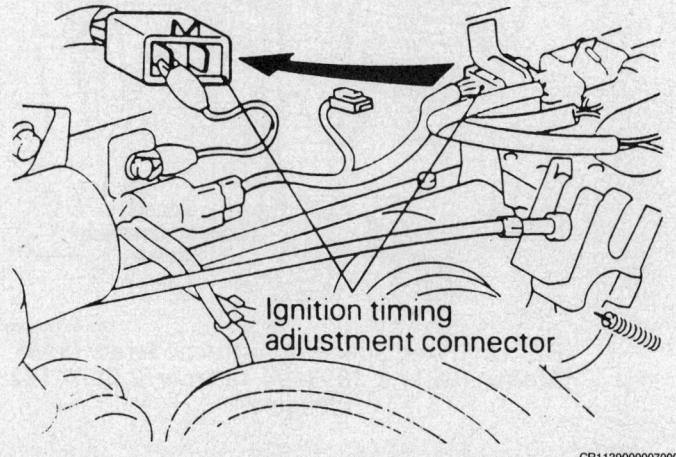

Fig. 11 Ignition timing connector ground. Laser & 1993–94 Talon

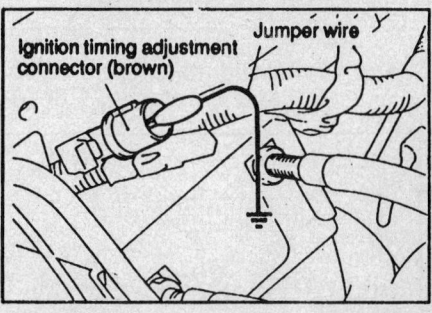

Fig. 12 Ignition timing connector ground. 1995–96 Talon w/2.0L/4-122 turbocharged engine

Curb Idle Speed

EXCEPT AVENGER, COLT, COLT VISTA, LASER, SEBRING, SUMMIT, SUMMIT WAGON & TALON w/2.0L/4-122 ENGINE

The idle speed on these models is electronically controlled by the SBEC II, SBEC III, ECU or PCM.

AVENGER, COLT, COLT VISTA, LASER, SEBRING, SUMMIT, SUMMIT WAGON & TALON w/2.0L/4-122 ENGINE

Curb idle speed on fuel injected models is controlled by the idle speed control servo and the throttle position sensor. Under normal circumstances, there should never be a need to adjust idle speed. Use the following procedure to check idle speed.
1. Ensure all lights, accessories and cooling fan are off, manual transaxle is in Neutral or automatic transaxle is in Park, wheels are in straight ahead position and engine is at operating temperature.
2. Check and adjust ignition timing as outlined under "Ignition Timing."
3. Connect tachometer to engine as outlined under "Ignition Timing."
4. Increase engine speed to 2000–3000 RPM for five seconds or more, then decrease engine speed to idle for approximately two minutes.
5. Check curb idle speed. Refer to "Tune Up Specifications" for curb idle specifications.
6. If curb idle speed is not within specifications, further inspection of idle speed control system is required. Refer to "Fuel Injection" section for further diagnosis.

Base Idle Speed

EXCEPT AVENGER, COLT, COLT VISTA, LASER, SEBRING, SUMMIT, SUMMIT WAGON & TALON w/2.0L/4-122 ENGINE

The idle speed on these models is electronically controlled by the SBEC II, SBEC III, ECU or PCM.

AVENGER, LASER, SEBRING & TALON

The base idle speed has been preset by the manufacturer. Under normal circumstances, there should never be a need to adjust the base idle speed. Use the following procedures to adjust base idle speed when the idling speed drops due to an incorrect adjustment, high idling speed or when a load such as air conditioning has been added to the system.

1993–94 1.8L/4-107 Engine

1. Ensure all lights, accessories and cooling fan are off, engine is at normal operating temperature, and manual transaxle is in Neutral or automatic transaxle is in Park.
2. Loosen accelerator cable.
3. Connect tachometer to engine as outlined under "Ignition Timing."
4. Turn ignition switch to On position (engine off). Leave ignition switch in this position for 15 seconds or longer.
5. Turn ignition switch to Off position, then disconnect idle speed control motor electrical connector. Secure idle speed control motor at initial position.
6. Loosen fixed Speed Adjusting Screw (SAS), Fig. 13, then start and run engine at idle.
7. Check base idle speed. Base idle speed should be 650–750 RPM, noting the following:
   a. The engine speed may be 20–100 RPM lower than specified for a vehicle that has been driven 300 miles or less; no adjustment is necessary.

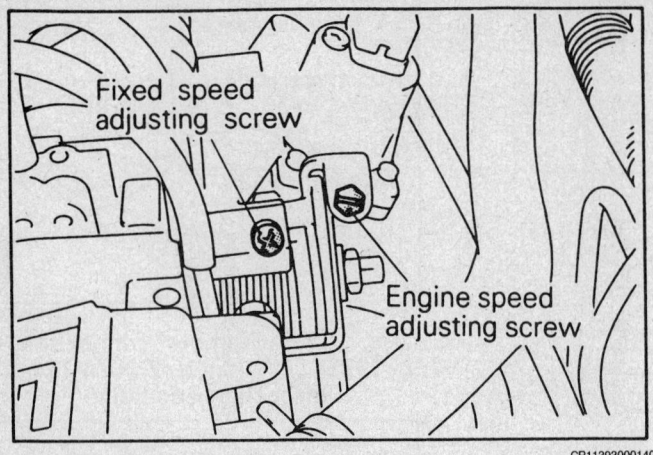

Fig. 13   Speed adjustment screw locations. 1993–94 Laser & Talon w/1.8L/4-107 engine

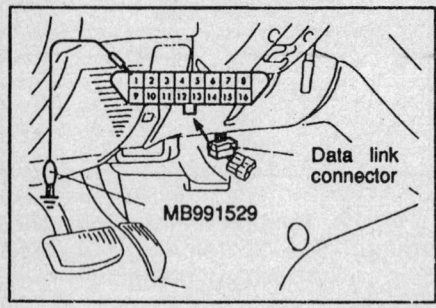

Fig. 15   Terminal 1 connection to ground. 1995–96 Avenger, Sebring & Talon w/2.0L/4-122 engine

Fig. 14   Terminal 10 connection to ground. Laser & 1993–94 Talon w/2.0L/4-122 engine

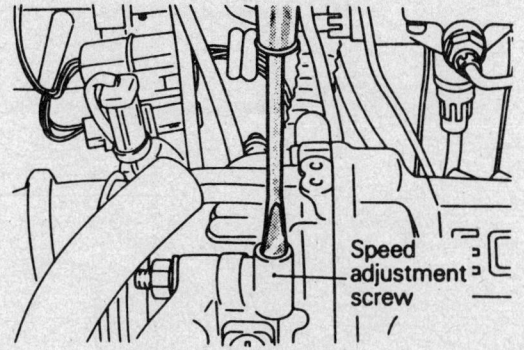

Fig. 16   Fixed Speed Adjustment Screw (SAS) location. Laser & 1993–94 Talon w/2.0L/4-122 engine

b. If engine stalls or RPM is low even though vehicle has been driven more than 300 miles, it is probable that deposits have adhered to throttle valve.

8. If there is a deviation from specifications, turn engine speed adjusting screw, **Fig. 13,** to adjust speed. When engine speed adjusting screw is turned to make adjustment, use a hexagonal wrench if possible, and in order to prevent backlash of screw, make final adjustment at tightening side.

9. Tighten fixed speed adjusting screw, **Fig. 13,** until engine speed increases, then return screw to find point at which engine speed does not decrease. From this point, return fixed speed adjusting screw and additional 1/2 turn.

10. Turn ignition switch to Off position, then adjust accelerator cable.

11. Connect idle speed control motor electrical connector, then adjust throttle position sensor.

12. Start and idle engine for 10 minutes. Ensure idle speed is within specifications.

2.0L/4-122 Engine

1. Ensure all lights, accessories and cooling fan are off, engine is at normal operating temperature, and manual transaxle is in Neutral or automatic transaxle is in Park.

2. Connect tachometer to engine as outlined under "Ignition Timing." **One half of actual engine RPM is indicated by tachometer, so actual engine RPM is twice tachometer reading.**

3. **On 1993-94 models,** use jumper wire to connect terminal No. 10 of data link connector (self diagnosis connector) to ground, **Fig. 14.**

4. **On 1995-96 models,** use diagnostic trouble code check harness tool No. MB991529 or equivalent to ground terminal 1 of data link connector, **Fig. 15.**

5. **On all models,** use jumper wire to ground ignition timing adjustment connector as outlined under "Ignition Timing."

6. Start engine and run at idle.

7. Check base idle speed and note the following:
   a. Base idle speed should be 700-800 RPM.
   b. The engine speed may be 20-100 RPM lower than specified for a vehicle that has been driven 300 miles or less; no adjustment is necessary.
   c. If engine stalls or RPM is low even though vehicle has been driven more than 300 miles, it is probable that deposits have adhered to throttle valve.

8. If base idle speed is not within specifications, turn engine speed adjusting screw, **Figs. 16 and 17,** to make necessary adjustments, noting the following:
   a. If idling speed is higher than specified valve even when speed adjusting screw is fully closed, check for any indication that Closed Throttle Position (CTP) switch (fixed Speed Adjusting Screw (SAS) or idle position switch) position has changed. If there is such and indication, adjust CTP switch (fixed SAS or idle position switch).
   b. If there is no evidence of CTP switch position change, it is probable that there is leakage resulting from deterioration of fast idle air valve. If this condition exists, replace throttle body.

9. Adjust CTP switch (fixed SAS or idle position switch) only if position has changed, as follows:
   a. Loosen accelerator cable, then disconnect switch electrical connector.
   b. Loosen switch locknut, **Fig. 18,** then turn switch counterclockwise until loosened.
   c. Fully close throttle valve. **Throttle valve must be completely closed.**
   d. Connect an ohmmeter between

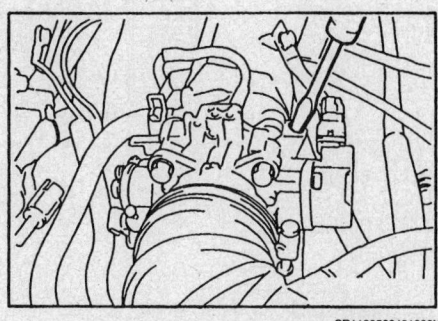

Fig. 17   Fixed Speed Adjustment Screw (SAS) location. 1995–96 Avenger, Sebring & Talon w/2.0L/4-122 engine

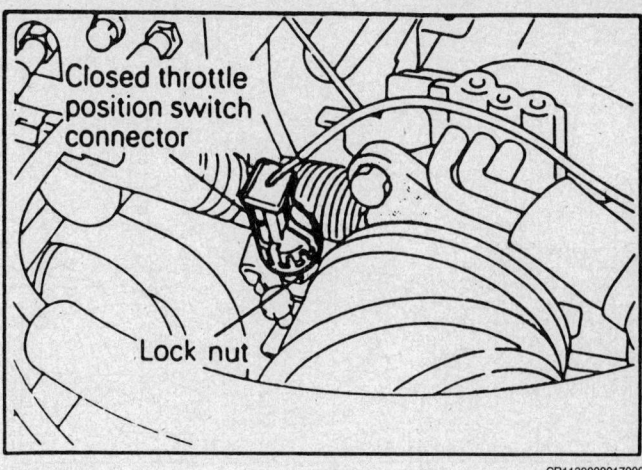

Fig. 18   CTP switch (fixed SAS or idle position switch) location. Laser & Talon w/2.0L/4-122 engine

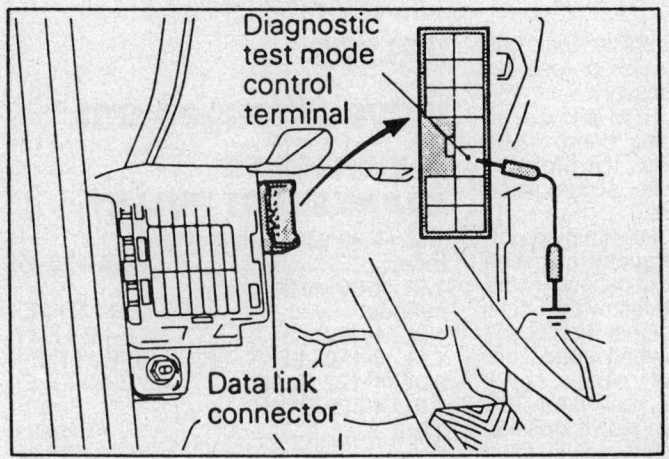

Fig. 19   Diagnostic terminal ground. 1993 Colt Vista & Summit Wagon

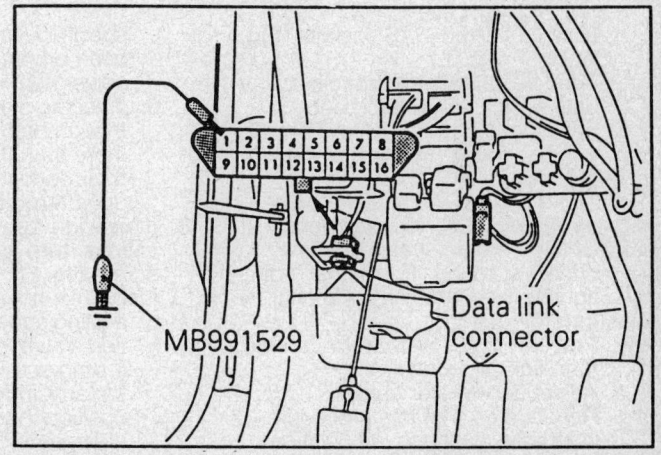

Fig. 20   Data link connector terminal 1 ground. 1994 Colt & Colt Vista & 1994–96 Summit & Summit Wagon

switch terminal and body.
  e. Slowly tighten switch to locate point at which switch is conductive with body (point at which throttle valve begins to open). From that point, tighten switch an additional 15/16 turn.
  f. Prevent switch from turning, then tighten locknut.
  g. Adjust accelerator cable.
  h. Repeat step 8 of this procedure.
10. Turn ignition switch to Off position.
11. Disconnect jumper wire from data link connector (self diagnosis connector).
12. Disconnect jumper wire from ignition timing adjustment connector.
13. Start and idle engine for 10 minutes. Ensure idle speed is within specifications.

COLT VISTA & SUMMIT WAGON

The base idle speed has been preset by the manufacturer. Under normal circumstances, there should never be a need to adjust the base idle speed. Use the following procedures to adjust base idle speed when the idling speed drops due to an incorrect adjustment, high idling speed or when a load such as air conditioning has been added to the system.

1. Ensure all lights, accessories and cooling fan are off, manual transaxle is in Neutral or automatic transaxle is in Park and engine is at operating temperature.
2. Connect tachometer to engine as outlined under "Ignition Timing."
3. **On 1993 models,** use a jumper wire to connect diagnostic terminal of data link connector (self diagnosis connector) to ground as shown in **Fig. 19.**
4. **On 1994-96 models,** use check harness No. MB991529 or equivalent to ground terminal 1 of data link connector as shown in **Fig. 20.**
5. **On all models,** use a jumper wire to ground ignition timing adjustment cinsertonnector as outlined under "Ignition Timing."
6. Start engine and run at idle.
7. Check base idle speed, noting the following:
  a. **On 1993 Federal models,** base idle speed should be 700-800 RPM.
  b. **On 1993 California models and all 1994-95 models,** base idle speed should be 650-750 RPM.
  c. **On all 1996 models,** base idle speed should be 700-800 RPM.

  d. Engine speed may be 20-100 RPM lower than specified for a vehicle that has been driven 300 miles or less; no adjustment is necessary.
  e. If engine stalls or RPM is low even though vehicle has been driven more than 300 miles, it is probable that deposits have accumulated upon throttle valve.
8. If base idle speed is not within specifications, turn engine speed adjusting screw, **Fig. 21,** to make necessary adjustments, noting the following:
  a. If idling speed is higher than specified value even when speed adjusting screw is fully closed, check for any indication that fixed SAS position has changed. If there is such an indication, adjust fixed SAS.
  b. If there is no evidence of fixed SAS position change, it is probable that there is leakage resulting from deterioration of fast idle air valve. If this condition exists, replace throttle body.
9. Adjust fixed SAS only if position has changed, as follows:
  a. Loosen accelerator cable, then

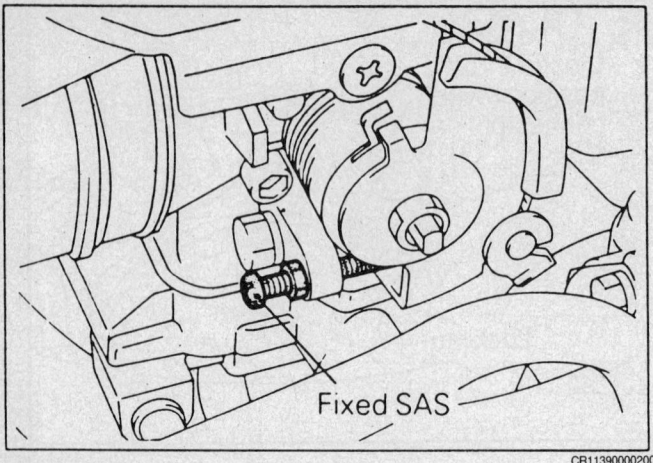

Fig. 21 Fixed Speed Adjustment Screw (SAS) location. Colt Vista & Summit Wagon

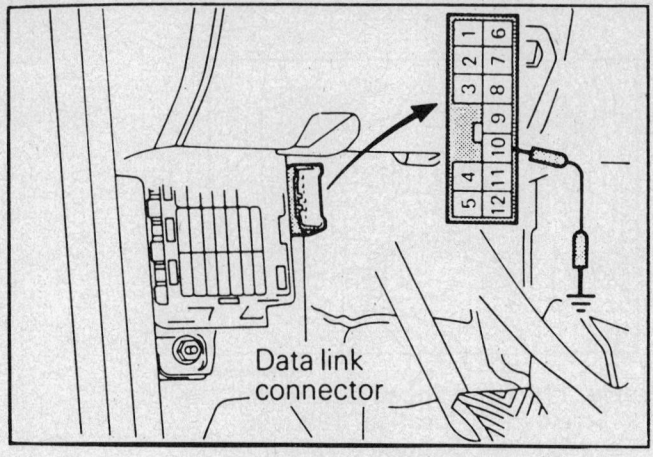

Fig. 22 Data link connector terminal 10 ground. 1993 Colt & Summit

back out fixed SAS locknut, **Fig. 21.**

b. Turn fixed SAS counterclockwise until sufficiently backed out.

c. Fully close throttle valve. **Throttle valve must be completely closed.**

d. Tighten fixed SAS until point where throttle lever is touched (point at which throttle valve begins to open) is found. From that point, tighten fixed SAS an additional 1/4 turn to 1 full turn.

e. Prevent fixed SAS from turning, then tighten locknut.

f. Adjust accelerator cable.

g. Repeat step 7 of this procedure.

10. Turn ignition switch to Off position.

11. Disconnect jumper wire from data link connector (self diagnosis connector).

12. Disconnect jumper wire from ignition timing adjustment connector.

13. Start and idle engine for 10 minutes. Ensure idle speed is normal and meets specified RPM.

COLT & SUMMIT

1. Ensure all lights, accessories and cooling fan are off, manual transaxle is in Neutral or automatic transaxle is in Park and engine is at operating temperature.

2. Connect tachometer to engine as outlined under "Ignition Timing."

3. **On 1993 models,** use jumper wire to ground terminal 10 of data link connector, **Fig. 22.**

4. **On 1994-96 models,** use check harness set No. MB991529 or equivalent to ground terminal 1 of data link connector, **Fig. 20.**

5. **On all models,** ground ignition timing adjustment connector as outlined under "Ignition Timing."

6. Start engine and run at idle.

7. Check base idle speed, noting the following:

a. **On 1993 models,** base idle speed should be 750-850 RPM.

b. **On 1994-96 models,** base idle speed should be 700-800 RPM.

c. **On all models,** the engine speed may be 20-100 RPM lower than

specified for a vehicle that has been driven 300 miles or less. No adjustment is necessary.

d. If engine stalls or RPM is low even though vehicle has been driven more than 300 miles, it is probable that deposits have accumulated upon throttle valve.

8. If base idle speed is not within specifications, turn engine speed adjusting screw, **Fig. 23,** to make necessary adjustments, noting the following:

a. If idling speed is higher than specified valve even when speed adjusting screw is fully closed, check for any indication that fixed SAS position has changed; if position change is indicated, adjust fixed SAS.

b. If there is no evidence of fixed SAS position change, it is probable that there is leakage resulting from deterioration of fast idle air valve. If this condition exists, replace throttle body.

9. Adjust fixed SAS only if position has changed, as follows:

a. Loosen accelerator cable, then back out fixed SAS locknut, **Fig. 24.**

b. Turn fixed SAS counterclockwise until sufficiently backed out.

c. Close throttle valve fully. **Throttle valve must be completely closed.**

d. Tighten fixed SAS until point where throttle lever is touched (point at which throttle valve begins to open) is found. From that point, tighten fixed SAS an additional 1/4 turn to 1 full turn.

e. Prevent fixed SAS from turning, then tighten locknut.

f. Adjust accelerator cable.

g. Repeat step 7 of this procedure.

10. Turn ignition switch to Off position.

11. Disconnect harness or jumper wire or from data link connector.

12. Disconnect jumper wire from ignition timing adjustment connector.

13. Start and idle engine for 10 minutes. Ensure idle speed is normal and meets RPM specification.

VALVES

Valve Arrangement

FLYWHEEL TO CRANKSHAFT PULLEY

1.5L/4-90 w/2 valve cylinder .... I-E-E-I-I-E-E-I

1.5L/4-90 w/3 valve cylinder .... I-E-I-I-E-I-I-E-I-I-E-I

1.8L/4-107 .... I-E-I-E-I-E-I-E

1.8L/4-110 . I-E-E-I-I-E-E-I-I-E-E-I-I-E-E-I

2.0L/4-122 SOHC .... I-E-E-I-I-E-E-I

2.0L/4-122 DOHC:

Front .... Exhaust

Rear .... Intake

2.2L/4-135, 2.5L/4-153 .. I-E-I-E-I-E-I-E

2.4L/4-146:

Front .... Exhaust

Rear .... Intake

2.4L/4-146:2.4L/4-148:

Front .... Exhaust

Rear .... Intake

Valve Adjustment

INTAKE & EXHAUST VALVES

Colt & Summit w/1.5L/4-90 Engine

Adjust intake valve clearance to .008 inch and exhaust valve clearance to .010 inch.

1. With engine at operating temperature, remove spark plugs and rocker arm cover.

2. Turn crankshaft clockwise until notch on pulley is lined up with "T" mark on timing belt lower cover. Move rocker arms on No. 1 and No. 4 cylinders. If intake and exhaust valve rocker arms are both movable, that piston in that cylinder is at top dead center on compression stroke.

3. Measure valve clearance at points shown in **Figs. 25 and 26.** If valve clearance is not as specified, loosen rocker arm locknut and adjust clearance using a feeler gauge while turning adjusting screw.

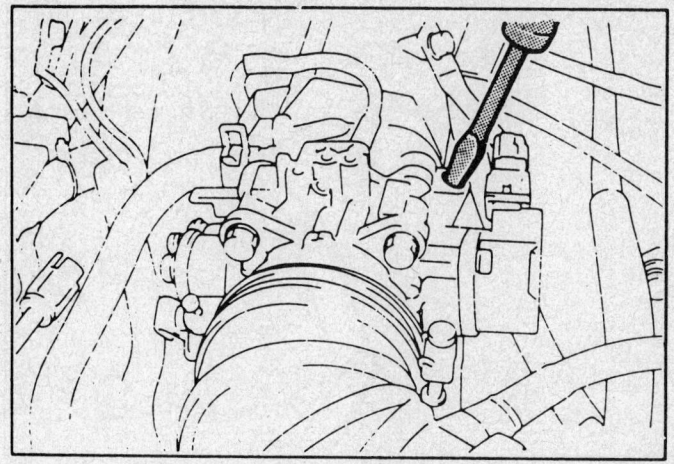

Fig. 23   Speed adjustment screw location. 1993–94 Colt & 1993–96 Summit

CR1139300022000X

Fig. 24   Fixed Speed Adjustment Screw (SAS) location. 1993–94 Colt & 1993–96 Summit

CR1139300023000X

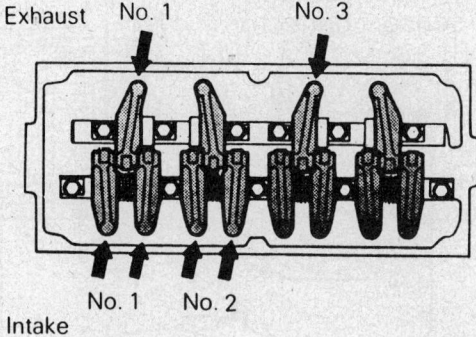

Exhaust   No. 1   No. 3

No. 1   No. 2

Intake

CR1139100024000X

Fig. 25   Valve clearance adjustment w/No. 1 cylinder at TDC. 1.5L/4-90 engine

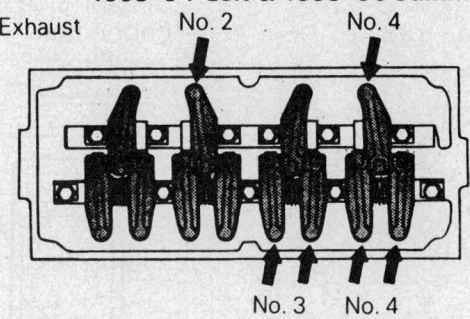

Exhaust   No. 2   No. 4

No. 3   No. 4

Intake

CR1139100025000X

Fig. 26   Valve clearance adjustment w/No. 4 cylinder at TDC. 1.5L/4-90 engine

4. Hold valve adjusting screw and tighten locknut.
5. Turn crankshaft one complete turn (360°) and adjust remaining valves.
6. After completing adjustment, install spark plugs and rocker arm cover.

Colt, Colt Vista, Summit & Summit Wagon w/1.8L/4-110 Engine

Adjust intake valve clearance to .008 inch and exhaust valve clearance to .012 inch.

1. With engine at operating temperature, remove spark plugs and rocker arm cover.
2. Turn crankshaft clockwise until notch on pulley is lined up with "T" mark on timing belt lower cover. Move rocker arms on No. 1 and No. 4 cylinders. If intake and exhaust valve rocker arms are both movable, piston is at top dead center on compression stroke.
3. With No. 1 cylinder at TDC on compression stroke (both rocker arms are movable), check and adjust valves with white arrows, **Fig. 27**. With No. 4 cylinder at TDC on compression stroke (both rocker arms are movable) check and adjust valves with black arrows, **Fig. 27**.
4. If valve clearance is not as specified, loosen rocker arm locknut and adjust clearance using a feeler gauge while turning adjusting screw.

5. Hold valve adjusting screw and tighten locknut.
6. Turn crankshaft one complete turn (360°) and adjust remaining valves.
7. After completing adjustment, install spark plugs and rocker arm cover.

1.8L/4-107, 2.0L/4-122, 2.2L/4-135, 2.4L/4-146, 2.4L/4-148 & 2.5L/4-153 Engines

These engines are equipped with hydraulic valve lash adjusters. No valve adjustment is required.

JET VALVE

Models w/Mechanical Lifters

The jet valve must be adjusted prior to adjusting the intake valve. Adjust jet valve clearance to .010 inch as follows:

1. Following procedure for intake and exhaust valve adjustment, position No. 1 cylinder at top dead center of compression stroke.
2. Loosen intake valve adjusting screw at least 2 turns, then loosen jet valve adjusting screw locknut.
3. Rotate jet valve adjusting screw counterclockwise, then insert a .010 inch feeler gauge blade between jet valve stem and adjusting screw, **Fig. 28**.

4. Tighten jet valve adjusting screw until it contacts feeler gauge blade, then while holding adjusting screw in position, tighten locknut.
5. After jet valve adjustment has been completed, adjust intake valve clearance. Continue to follow intake and exhaust valve adjustment procedure and adjust jet valves as necessary.

Models w/Hydraulic Lifters

Although these engines are equipped with hydraulic valve lash adjusters, periodic adjustment of jet valve lash is recommended.

1. Position No. 1 cylinder at top dead center of compression stroke.
2. Loosen jet valve adjusting screw locknut.
3. Back off jet valve adjusting screw, then insert a .010 inch feeler gauge between jet valve stem and adjusting screw, **Fig. 28**.
4. Tighten jet valve adjusting screw until it contacts feeler gauge blade, then while holding screw in position, tighten locknut.
5. Position remaining cylinders at top dead center and repeat jet valve adjustment procedure.

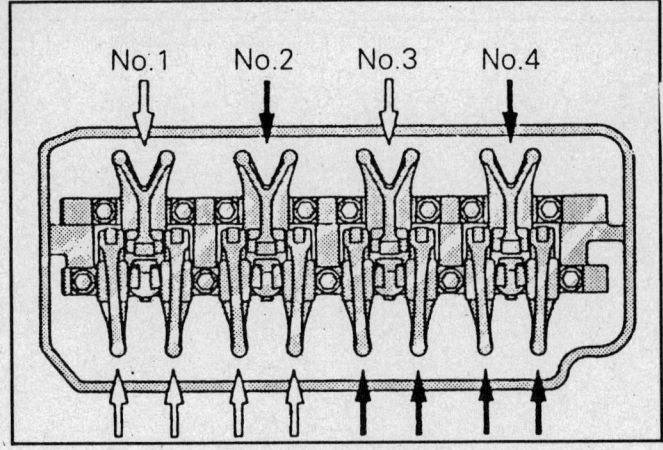

**Fig. 27   Valve clearance adjustment.
1.8L/4-110 engine**

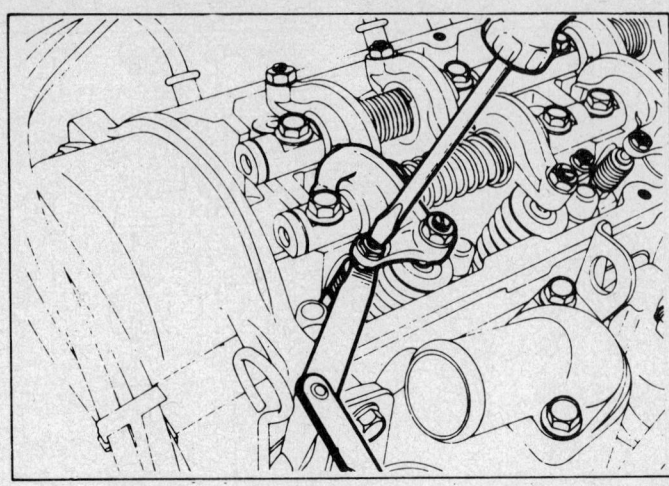

Fig. 28   Jet valve clearance inspection

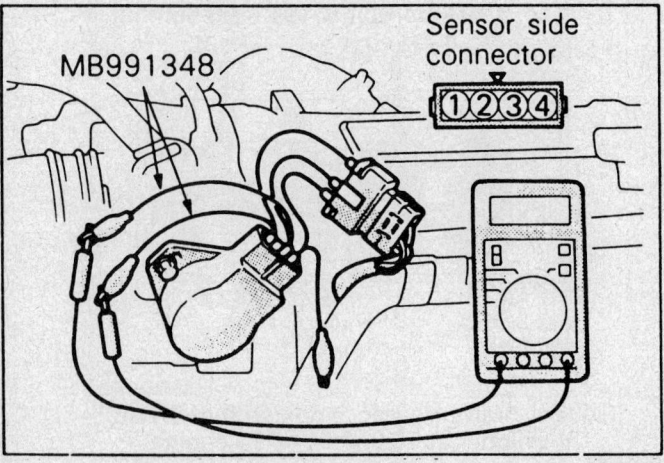

**Fig. 29   Test tool & digital voltmeter installation. 1993–94
Laser & Talon**

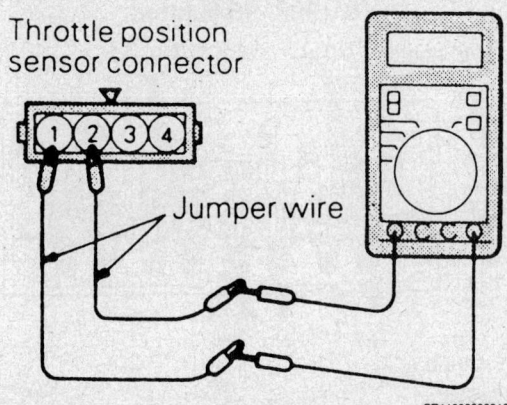

**Fig. 30   Throttle position sensor jumper wire
installation. Colt Vista & Summit Wagon**

SENSOR ADJUSTMENTS

Throttle Position Sensor (TPS)

AVENGER, LASER, SEBRING & TALON

2.0L/4-122 ENGINE

1993–94

1. Disconnect TPS electrical connector, then connect test harness tool No. MB991348, or equivalent, between TPS and electrical connector, Fig. 29.
2. Connect digital voltmeter between sensor output terminal 2 and sensor ground terminal 4, Fig. 29.
3. Turn ignition switch to On position (do not start engine) and check output voltage from TPS. TPS output voltage should be .48-.52 volt.
4. If output voltage is not as specified, adjust by loosening TPS mounting screws and rotating TPS assembly.

Tighten screw after adjustment.
5. Turn ignition switch to Off position.
6. Disconnect battery ground cable for ten seconds, then reconnect battery cable. This erases data stored in diagnosis memory during TPS adjustment.

1995–96

There is no provision for Throttle Position Sensor (TPS) adjustment. If the TPS is not functioning properly, it must be replaced.

1.8L/4-107 ENGINE

1993–94

Base idle speed must be adjusted before adjusting the throttle position sensor.
1. Disconnect TPS electrical connector, then connect test harness tool No. MB991348, or equivalent, between TPS and electrical connector, Fig. 29.
2. Connect digital voltmeter between sensor output terminal 2 and sensor ground terminal 4, Fig. 29.
3. Turn ignition switch On (do not start engine). Hold switch in this position for 15 seconds or more.
4. Check output voltage from TPS. TPS output voltage should be .48-.52 volt.

5. If output voltage is not as specified, adjust by loosening TPS mounting screws and rotating TPS sensor. Tighten screw after adjustment.
6. Turn ignition switch to Off position.
7. Disconnect battery ground cable for ten seconds, then reconnect battery cable. This erases data stored in diagnosis memory during TPS adjustment.

Closed Throttle Position Switch (Idle Position Switch) & Throttle Position Sensor (TPS)

COLT VISTA & SUMMIT WAGON

1. Disconnect electrical connector from throttle position sensor.
2. Using jumper wires, connect an ohmmeter between terminal 2 and terminal 1, Fig. 30.
3. Insert a feeler gauge with a thickness of 0.0256 inch. between fixed SAS and throttle lever, Fig. 31.
4. Loosen throttle position sensor mounting bolt, then turn throttle position sensor body clockwise. In this condition, check for continuity between terminals 1 and 2.

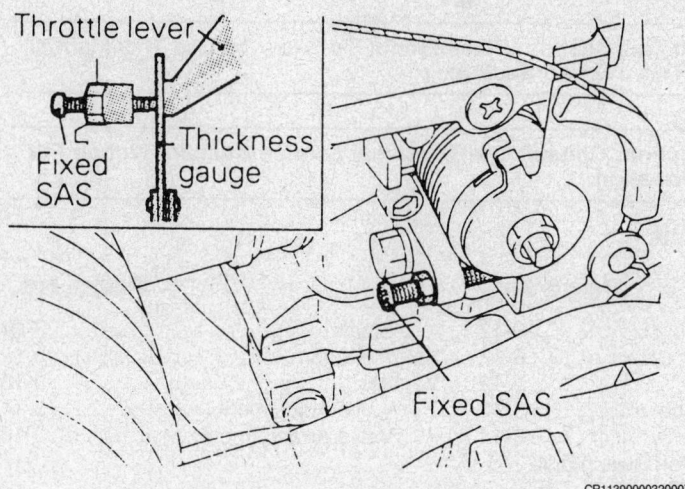

Fig. 31 Thickness gauge installation

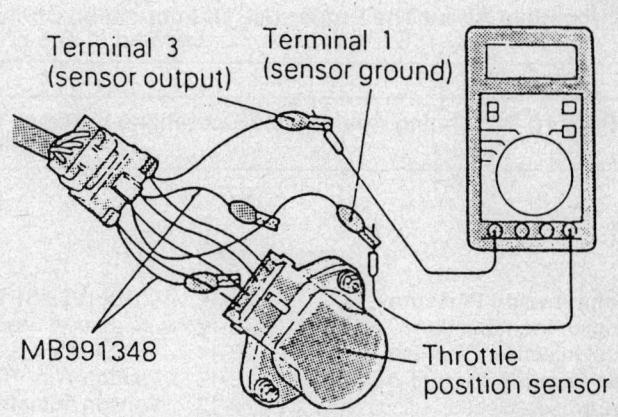

Fig. 32 Test tool & digital voltmeter installation. Colt Vista & Summit Wagon

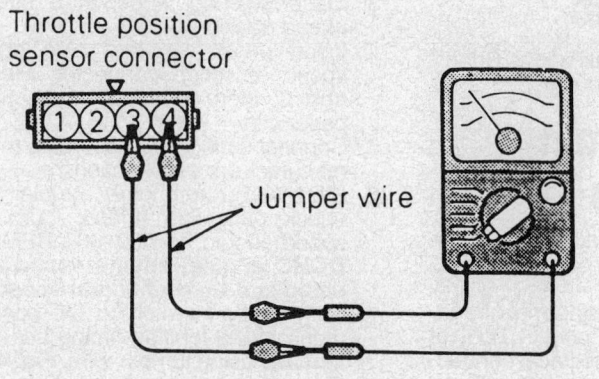

Fig. 33 Throttle position sensor jumper wire installation. Colt & Summit

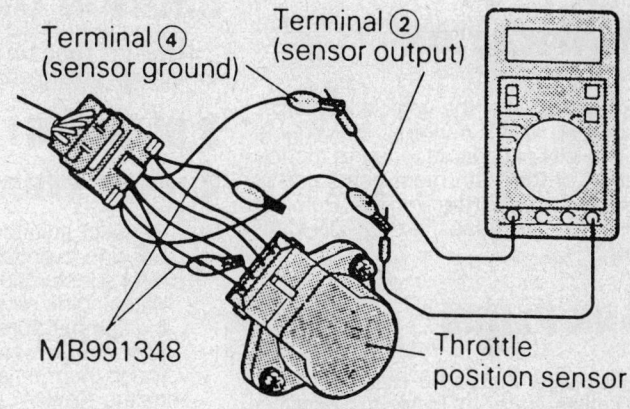

Fig. 34 Test tool & digital voltmeter installation. Colt & Summit

5. Slowly turn throttle position sensor counterclockwise until continuity between terminals 1 and 2 no longer exists. Tighten throttle position sensor retaining bolt at that position.
6. Connect test harness set tool No. MB991348 or equivalent between electrical connector and throttle position sensor as shown in **Fig. 32.**
7. Connect a digital voltmeter between throttle position sensor terminal 3 and terminal 1.
8. Turn ignition switch to On position.
9. Check throttle position sensor output voltage. Reading obtained should be 400–1000mV.
10. If reading is not as specified, check throttle position sensor and related wiring. Repair or replace as necessary.

11. Turn ignition switch to Off position, then remove feeler gauge.

COLT & SUMMIT

1. Disconnect electrical connector from throttle position sensor.
2. Using jumper wires, connect an ohmmeter between terminals 3 and 4, **Fig. 33.**
3. Insert a feeler gauge with a thickness of 0.0256 inch between fixed SAS and throttle lever, **Fig. 31.**
4. Loosen throttle position sensor mounting bolt, then turn throttle position sensor body fully counterclockwise and Check for continuity between terminals 3 and 4.
5. Slowly turn throttle position sensor clockwise until continuity between terminals 3 and 4 does not exist.

Tighten throttle position sensor retaining bolt at that position.
6. Connect test harness set tool No. MB991348 or equivalent between electrical connector and throttle position sensor as shown in **Fig. 34.**
7. Connect a digital voltmeter between throttle position sensor terminal 2 and terminal 4.
8. Turn ignition switch to On position (engine not running).
9. Check throttle position sensor output voltage. Reading obtained should be 400–1000mV.
10. If reading is not as specified, check throttle position sensor and related wiring. Repair or replace as necessary.
11. Turn ignition switch to Off position, then remove feeler gauge.

V6 Gasoline Engine

If Uncertain About The Proper Use Of Information Contained In This Section, Please Refer To "How To Use This Manual" Located In The Front Of This Tabbed Section.

Prior To Performing Any Service Operations Listed In This Section, Consult The Technical Service Bulletin Section For Related Information.

INDEX

	Page No.
Compression Pressure	3-12
Engine Identification	3-12
Fuel Injection Cleaning	3-14
Idle Speed & Mixture Adjustments:	3-13
Curb Idle Speed:	3-13
Except Stealth	3-13
Stealth	3-13
Ignition Timing:	3-12
2.5L/V6-152, 3.3L/V6-201, 3.5L/V6-215 & 3.8L/V6-231 Engines	3-13

	Page No.
3.0L/V6-181 Engine:	3-12
Except Stealth	3-12
Stealth	3-12
Ignition Wire Resistance	3-12
Sensor Adjustments:	3-14
Closed Throttle Position Switch (Idle Position Switch) & Throttle Position Sensor:	3-14

	Page No.
Stealth	3-14
Spark Plugs	3-12
Valves:	3-13
Valve Adjustment	3-14
Valve Arrangement	3-13

ENGINE IDENTIFICATION

The eighth digit of the vehicle identification number (VIN) denotes the engine code. The VIN plate is attached to the top left corner of the instrument panel and is visible from outside the vehicle. Refer to Tune Up Specifications chart for VIN identification.

SPARK PLUGS

Spark plugs should be replaced every 30,000 miles. Refer to Tune Up Specifications chart for spark plug gap.

On all models with 2.5L/V6-152, 3.3L/V6-201, 3.5L/V6-215 and 3.8L/V6-231 engines and all models with 3.0L/V6-181 engine except Stealth, torque spark plugs to 20 ft. lbs.

On Stealth, torque spark plugs to 15-18 ft. lbs.

On Avenger and Sebring, torque spark plugs to 18 ft. lbs.

IGNITION WIRE RESISTANCE

Refer to appropriate ignition section for ignition wire resistance specifications.

COMPRESSION PRESSURE

Perform compression test with engine at normal operating temperature, spark plugs removed and throttle wide open. Results should be as indicated in the compression pressure specifications chart, Fig. 1.

IGNITION TIMING

Refer to "Tune Up Specifications Chart" for ignition timing and firing order.

3.0L/V6-181 Engine

EXCEPT STEALTH

1. Connect suitable timing light to number one cylinder, following manufacturer's instructions.
2. With engine running at normal operating temperature, disconnect coolant temperature sensor electrical connector on thermostat housing, thus illuminating Power Loss or Check Engine lamp on instrument panel.
3. Aim timing light at front crankshaft pulley. If flash occurs when timing mark is before specified degree mark, timing is advanced. To adjust, loosen distributor hold-down and turn distributor housing in direction of rotor rotation. If flash occurs when timing mark is after specified degree mark, timing is retarded. To adjust, loosen distributor hold-down and turn distributor housing against direction of rotor rotation. Adjust as necessary.
4. Stop engine, tighten distributor hold-down, remove timing light and reconnect coolant temperature sensor electrical connector.

STEALTH

1. Start and run engine until normal operating temperature (176°F to 205°F) is reached, then turn ignition switch to Off position.
2. Ensure all lights, accessories and electric cooling fan are off, then place manual transaxle in Neutral position or automatic transaxle in Park.

3. Place steering wheel in a straight ahead position.
4. Insert paper clip into blue engine speed detection connector, Figs. 2 and 3, then connect tachometer to paper clip.
5. Connect timing light according to tool manufacturer's instructions.
6. Start and run engine at idle, then check curb idle speed. Curb idle speed should be 600-800 RPM. On DOHC engine, engine speed indicated is a third of actual speed.
7. Turn ignition switch to Off position, then ground ignition timing adjusting terminal using jumper wire, Fig. 4.
8. Start engine and run at idle. Check basic ignition timing, noting the following:
   a. On 1993 models, basic ignition timing should be 3° BTDC to 7° BTDC.
   b. On 1994-95 SOHC models, basic ignition timing should be 3° BTDC to 7° BTDC.
   c. On 1994-95 DOHC models, basic ignition timing should be 2° BTDC to 8° BTDC.
   d. On all 1996 models, basic ignition timing should be 2° BTDC to 8° BTDC.
9. If basic timing is not within standard value range, loosen distributor (SOHC) or crank angle sensor (DOHC) mounting nut and adjust by turning distributor (SOHC) or crank angle sensor (DOHC).
10. After adjustment, tighten mounting nut on distributor (SOHC) or crank angle sensor (DOHC).
11. Turn ignition switch to Off position, then disconnect jumper wire from timing adjusting terminal.
12. Start and run engine at idle speed, then ensure actual ignition timing is approximately 15° BTDC.

3-12

Year	Engine	Minimum psi	Maximum Variation Between Cylinders, psi
1993	3.0L/V6-181 ①	178 ③	14
	3.0L/V6-181 ②	127	14
	3.0L/V6-181 ④	139	14
	3.0L/V6-181 ⑤	115	14
	3.3L/V6-201	100	⑥
	3.5L/V6-215	155	⑥
	3.8L/V6-231	100	⑥
1994	3.0L/V6-181 ①	178 ③	14
	3.0L/V6-181 ②	127	14
	3.0L/V6-181 ④	139	14
	3.0L/V6-181 ⑤	115	14
	3.3L/V6-201	100	⑥
	3.5L/V6-215	155	⑥
1995	2.5L/V6-152	178 ③	14
	3.0L/V6-181 ①	178 ③	14
	3.0L/V6-181 ②	127	14
	3.0L/V6-181 ④	139	14
	3.0L/V6-181 ⑤	115	14
	3.3L/V6-201	100	⑥
	3.5L/V6-215	155	⑥
1996	2.5L/V6-152	178 ③	14
	3.0L/V6-181 ②	127	14
	3.0L/V6-181 ④	139	14
	3.0L/V6-181 ⑤	115	14
	3.3L/V6-201	100	⑥
	3.5L/V6-215	155	⑥

①—Except Stealth.
②—Stealth w/SOHC engine.
③—Standard pressure @ 250 RPM.
④—Stealth w/DOHC non-turbocharged engine.
⑤—Stealth w/DOHC turbocharged engine.
⑥—Readings should not vary more than 25% from cylinder to cylinder.

Fig. 1 Compression pressure specifications

2.5L/V6-152, 3.3L/V6-201, 3.5L/V6-215 & 3.8L/V6-231 Engines

Ignition timing cannot be set or changed on these engines.

IDLE SPEED & MIXTURE ADJUSTMENTS

Curb Idle Speed

EXCEPT STEALTH

The idle speed on these models is electronically controlled by the SBEC, SBEC II, ECU or PCM.

STEALTH
1993

1. Start and run engine until normal operating temperature (176 to 205°F) is reached, then turn ignition switch to Off position.
2. Ensure all lights, accessories and electric cooling fan are off, then place manual transaxle in Neutral position or automatic transaxle in Park.
3. Place steering wheel in a straight ahead position.
4. Insert paper clip into blue engine speed detection connector, **Figs. 2 and 3**, then connect tachometer to paper clip.
5. Use jumper wire to ground terminal 10 of white diagnosis connector, **Fig. 5**.
6. Ground ignition timing adjusting terminal using jumper wire, **Fig. 4**.
7. Start engine and run at idle, then check idle speed. Basic idle speed should be 650-750 RPM.
8. If basic idle speed is not as specified,

adjust by turning speed adjusting screw (SAS), **Fig. 6**. If idle speed is higher than standard value even with SAS fully tightened, check if closed throttle position switch (idle position switch or fixed SAS) has been moved. If closed throttle position switch (idle position switch or fixed SAS) has not been moved a leak may be caused by deteriorated fast idle air valve. In such a case, replace throttle body.
9. Turn ignition switch to Off position, then remove all jumper wires and tachometer.

1994—96

1. Start and run engine until normal operating temperature (176°F to 205°F) is reached, then turn ignition switch to Off position.
2. Ensure all lights, accessories, and electric cooling fan are off, then place manual transaxle in Neutral position or automatic transaxle in Park.
3. Position steering wheel straight ahead, then insert paper clip into blue engine speed detection connector, **Figs. 2 and 3**. Connect tachometer to clip.
4. Connect timing light according to tool manufacturer's instructions, then use a jumper wire to ground ignition timing adjusting terminal.
5. Start engine and run at idle, then ensure basic ignition timing is within standard value range. Refer to "Ignition Timing, Adjust" for specifications and adjust basic timing as necessary.
6. Remove jumper wire from ignition timing adjusting terminal, and allow engine to idle for 2 minutes.
7. Check idle speed, noting the following:
   a. Curb idle speed should be 600-800 RPM.
   b. Idle RPM is regulated automatically by idle speed control system.
   c. **On DOHC models**, engine speed indicated is 1/3 actual speed.

VALVES
Valve Arrangement

2.5L/V6-152:
Left .... E-I-E-I-E-I
Right .... I-E-I-E-I-E
3.0L/V6-181 Except Stealth:
Left .... E-I-E-I-E-I
Right .... I-E-I-E-I-E
3.0L/V6-181 Stealth w/SOHC:
Left .... E-I-E-I-E-I
Right .... E-I-E-I-E-I
3.0L/V6-181 Stealth w/DOHC
Left:
Bottom camshaft .... Exhaust
Top camshaft .... Intake
Right:
Bottom camshaft .... Exhaust
Top camshaft .... Intake
3.3L/V6-201:
Left .... I-E-I-E-I-E
Right .... E-I-E-I-E-I
3.5L/V6-215:
Left .... I-E-E-I-I-E-E-I-I-E-E-I
Right .... I-E-E-I-I-E-E-I-I-E-E-I
3.8L/V6-231:
Left .... I-E-I-E-I-E
Right .... E-I-E-I-E-I

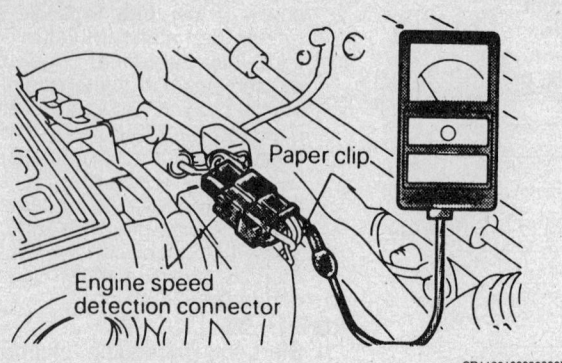

Fig. 2   Tachometer connection. Stealth w/SOHC engine

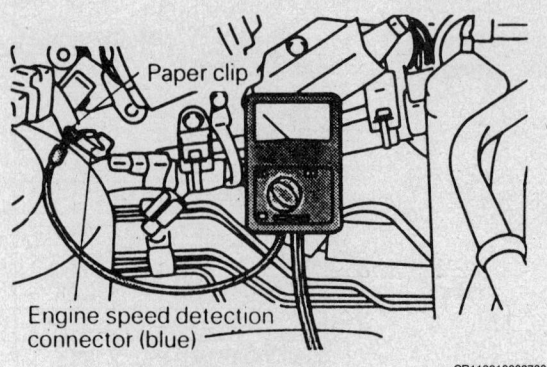

Fig. 3   Tachometer connection. Stealth w/DOHC engine

Valve Adjustment

These engines are equipped with hydraulic lifters. There are no provisions for adjustment.

FUEL INJECTION CLEANING

Fuel injector cleaning parameters are not available from the manufacturer.

SENSOR ADJUSTMENTS

Closed Throttle Position Switch (Idle Position Switch) & Throttle Position Sensor

STEALTH

1. Disconnect TPS electrical connector; then, using jumper wires, connect an ohmmeter across terminals 3 and 4 of TPS, **Fig. 7.**
2. Insert a .65 mm feeler gauge between fixed SAS and throttle lever.
3. Loosen TPS mounting bolts and turn TPS body fully counterclockwise. In this condition, check that there is continuity across terminals 3 and 4.
4. Slowly turn TPS clockwise until point at which there is no continuity across terminals 3 and 4. Tighten TPS mounting bolts securely.
5. Connect test harness No. MB991348 between electrical connector and throttle position sensor as shown in **Fig. 8.**
6. Connect a digital voltmeter between throttle position sensor terminals 2 and 4.
7. Turn ignition switch to On position (engine Off).
8. Check throttle position sensor output voltage. Reading obtained should be 400-1000mV.
9. If reading is not as specified, check throttle position sensor and related wiring. Repair or replace as necessary.
10. Turn ignition switch to Off position, then remove feeler gauge.

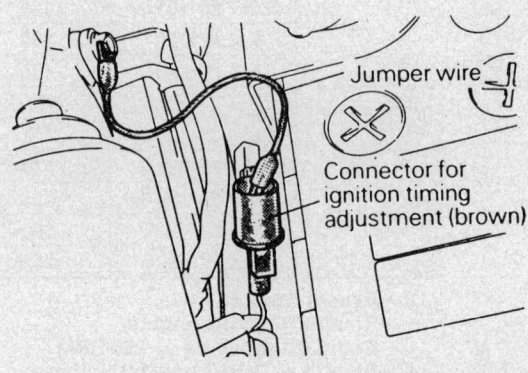

Fig. 4   Ignition timing adjustment connector ground. Stealth

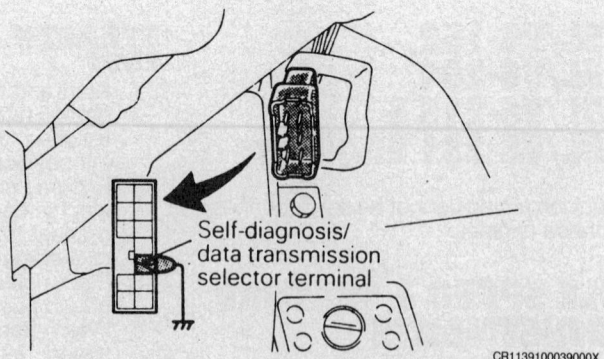

Fig. 5   ECU terminal 10 location. Stealth

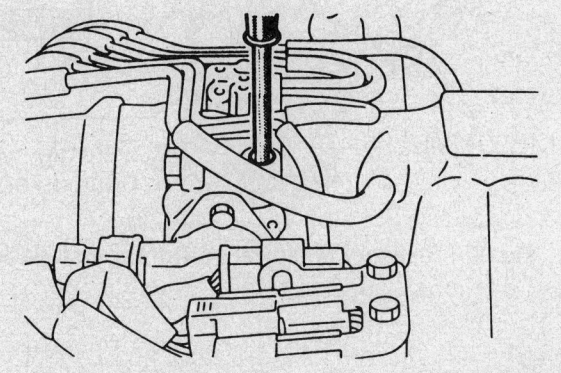

CR1139100040000X

Fig. 6 Speed adjusting screw location. Stealth

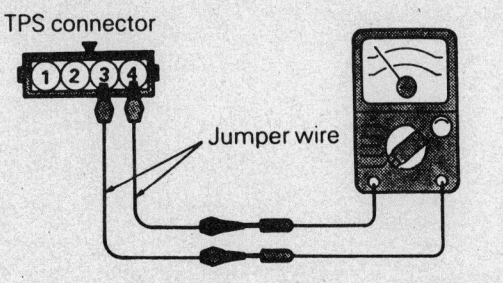

TPS connector

Jumper wire

CR1139100041000X

**Fig. 7 Voltmeter connection to TPS
connector. Stealth**

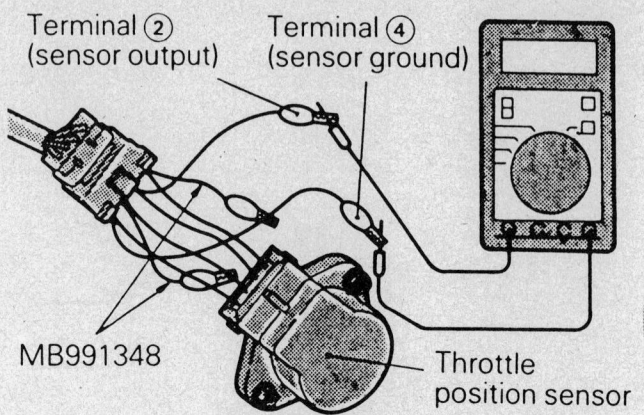

Fig. 8 **Test tool & digital voltmeter installation. Stealth**

IGNITION SYSTEMS

TABLE OF CONTENTS

	Page No.		Page No.
TYPE 1	4-1	TYPE 4	4-12
TYPE 2	4-5	TYPE 5	4-15
TYPE 3	4-10	TYPE 6	4-18

Type 1

NOTE: Prior To Performing Any Service Operations Listed In This Section, Consult The Technical Service Bulletins Section For Related Information.

NOTE: If Unsure Of The System Used On The Vehicle Being Serviced, Refer To The "Engine Systems Identification Chart." Further Assistance For The Proper Use Of Information Contained In This Section Can Also Be Found In The Front Of This Tabbed Section Under "How To Use This Manual."

INDEX

	Page No.		Page No.		Page No.
Description:	4-1	Optical Distributor System	4-2	Ignition Wire Resistance	4-2
Auto Shutdown (ASD) Relay	4-2	Diagnosis & Testing:	4-2	Specifications.	4-5
Coolant Temperature Sensor	4-1	Check Coil Test.	4-2	System Service:	4-4
Electronic Ignition (EI) (Direct		Coolant Temperature Sensor Test	4-3	Component Replacement	4-4
Ignition System)	4-2	Failure To Start Test	4-2	Component Service	4-4
Hall Effect Pickup	4-1	Ignition System Starting Test	4-2		
Manifold Absolute Pressure (MAP)					
Sensor	4-2				

DESCRIPTION

The ignition system is controlled by the Single Board Engine Controller II (SBEC II), Single Board Engine Controller III (SBEC III) or the Powertrain Control Module (PCM), used on Chrysler Domestic models except Avenger, Breeze, Cirrus, Laser, Neon, Sebring, Sebring Convertible, Stealth & Stratus. These engine controllers use the signals from various sensors to provide optimum driveability under all operating conditions by advancing or retarding the ignition timing.

Under cranking and starting conditions, the engine controller provides a set amount of advanced timing to ensure a quick and efficient start. The amount of electronic spark advance provided by the engine controller is determined by coolant temperature, engine RPM and available manifold vacuum.

The oxygen sensor also sends signals to the engine controller which electronically adjusts the air/fuel mixture to provide the most efficient fuel burn possible.

HALL EFFECT PICKUP

The Hall Effect pickup, used on 2.2L/4-135 and 2.5L/4-153 engines, is located in the distributor assembly. The pickup supplies engine RPM data, ignition timing data and, on turbocharged engines, fuel injection synchronization to the engine controller to advance or retard ignition spark as needed.

COOLANT TEMPERATURE SENSOR

The coolant temperature sensor, mounted near the thermostat housing, monitors coolant temperature and provides engine operating temperature data to the engine controller. The sensor, which is a variable resistor, is also used to activate the radiator fan.

MANIFOLD ABSOLUTE PRESSURE (MAP) SENSOR

The MAP sensor monitors manifold vacuum and transmits information to the engine controller to determine the correct air/fuel mixture.

AUTO SHUTDOWN (ASD) RELAY

The ASD relay interrupts power to the electrical fuel pump, fuel injectors and ignition coil when there is no ignition signal present with the ignition key in the Run position.

OPTICAL DISTRIBUTOR SYSTEM

The optical distributor, used on 3.0L/V6-181 engines, sends engine speed and crankshaft position signals to the engine controller to control fuel injection, ignition timing and idle speed. The distributor also delivers the firing pulses from the coil to each cylinder through a cap and rotor. Protection against high voltage damage to the electronic circuitry and optical system contamination is provided by a cover between the rotor and case.

ELECTRONIC IGNITION (EI) (DIRECT IGNITION SYSTEM)

Electronic Ignition (EI) (Direct Ignition System), used on 2.2L/4-135 turbo III, 3.3L/V6-201, 3.5L/V6-215 and 3.8L/V6-231 engines, is controlled by the engine controller. This controller receives engine speed and crankshaft position signals from a crank sensor located in the transaxle housing and a cam sensor located on the timing chain case cover. These sensors control ignition timing and fuel injection synchronization.

High tension ignition leads connect each spark plug to the molded coil, mounted on the intake manifold. The coil fires two spark plugs every power stroke; one to the cylinder under compression, the other to the cylinder on the power stroke. The coil is also controlled by the engine controller.

DIAGNOSIS & TESTING

For service procedures not covered in this section, refer to appropriate fuel injection section.

IGNITION WIRE RESISTANCE

Minimum wire resistance is 250 ohms per inch; maximum resistance is 1000 ohms per inch (measured at 70° F).

IGNITION SYSTEM STARTING TEST

EXCEPT ELECTRONIC IGNITION (EI) (DIRECT IGNITION SYSTEM)

1. Remove coil secondary lead from dis-

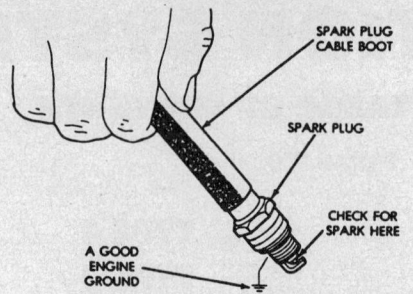

Fig. 1   Testing for spark

tributor cap, then crank engine while holding coil secondary lead ¼ inch from a good ground.
2. If a spark occurs, it must be constant and bright blue in color. If spark is as described, continue to crank engine while slowly moving coil wire away from ground. If arcing occurs at coil tower, replace coil. If the spark is weak or inconsistent, or there is no spark at all, proceed to "Failure To Start Test." If spark is satisfactory, the ignition system is producing the proper secondary voltage. Inspect the cap, wires and plugs. If satisfactory, it will be necessary to check the fuel system and engine mechanical components.

ELECTRONIC IGNITION (EI) (DIRECT IGNITION SYSTEM)

2.2L/4-135 Turbo III Engine

The coil pack consists of two independent coils, cylinders 1-4 and 2-3. Each coil must be checked individually as follows:
1. Remove ignition wire from No. 1 spark plug. Insert a clean spark plug into ignition wire, then ground spark plug to engine, **Fig. 1.**
2. Crank engine and look for spark across electrodes of spark plug.
3. Repeat steps 1 and 2 for remaining cylinders.
4. If there is no spark during cylinder tests, proceed to "Failure To Start Test." If one or more tests indicate irregular or weak spark, proceed to "Check Coil Test."

3.3L/V6-201 & 3.8L/V6-231 ENGINES

The coil consists of three independent coils, cylinders 1-4, 2-5 and 3-6. Each coil must be checked individually as follows:
1. Remove cable from No. 2 spark plug. Insert a clean spark plug into ignition wire, then ground spark plug to engine, **Fig. 1.**
2. Crank engine and look for spark across electrodes of spark plug.
3. Repeat steps 1 and 2 for remaining cylinders.
4. If there is no spark during cylinder tests, proceed to "Failure To Start Test." If one or more tests indicate irregular or weak spark, proceed to "Check Coil Test."

CHECK COIL TEST

ELECTRONIC IGNITION (EI) (DIRECT IGNITION SYSTEM)

2.2L/4-135 Turbo III Engine

The coil pack consists of two independent coils, cylinders 1-4 and 2-3. Each coil must be checked individually as follows:
1. Remove ignition cables, then measure resistance in each cable. Resistance should be 3,000-12,000 ohms per foot. Replace defective cables.
2. Disconnect electrical connector from coil pack.
3. Measure primary resistance of each coil. At the coil, connect an ohmmeter between the B + pin and the pin corresponding to the cylinder to be tested, **Fig. 2.** Resistance should be 0.5-0.7 ohm. Replace coil if not within specifications.
4. Remove ignition cables from secondary coil tower, then measure secondary resistance between towers of each individual coil. Resistance should be 11,600-15,800 ohms. Replace coil if not within specifications.

3.3L/V6-201, 3.5L/V6-215 & 3.8L/V6-231 ENGINES

The molded coil consists of three independent coils, cylinders 1-4, 2-5 and 3-6. Each coil must be checked individually as follows:
1. Remove ignition cables, then measure resistance in each cable. Resistance should be 3000-12000 ohms per foot. Replace defective cables.
2. Disconnect electrical connector from coil pack.
3. Measure primary resistance of each coil. At the coil, connect an ohmmeter between the B + pin and the pin corresponding to the cylinder to be tested, **Fig. 3,** noting the following:
   a. **On 1993 models,** primary resistance should be 0.5-0.7 ohm.
   b. **On 1994-96 models,** primary resistance should be 0.45-0.65 ohm.
4. **On all models,** replace coil if not within specifications.
5. Remove ignition cables from secondary coil tower, then measure secondary resistance between towers of each individual coil, noting the following:
   a. **On 1993 models with Diamond coils,** secondary resistance should be 11,600-15,800 ohms.
   b. **On 1993 models with Toyodenso coils,** secondary resistance should be 11,500-13,500 ohms.
   c. **On 1994-96 models with Diamond or Toyodenso coils,** secondary resistance should be 7,000-15,800 ohms.
6. **On all models,** replace coil if not within specifications.

FAILURE TO START TEST

EXCEPT ELECTRONIC IGNITION (EI) (DIRECT IGNITION SYSTEM)

Before proceeding with this test, perform

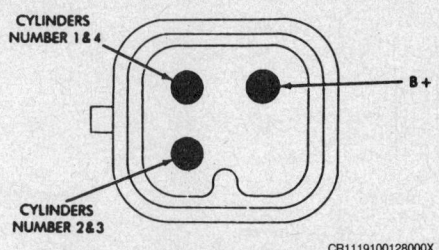

Fig. 2 Ignition coil electrical connector (coil side). 2.2L/4-135 Turbo III engine

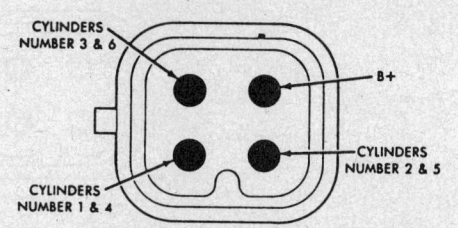

Fig. 3 Ignition coil electrical connector (coil side). 3.3L/V6-201 & 3.8L/V6-231 engines

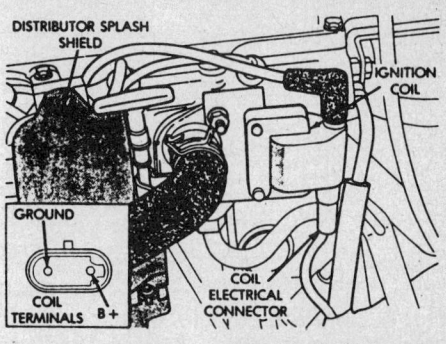

Fig. 4 Ignition coil terminal identification. 1993 2.2L/4-135 & 2.5L/4-153 engines

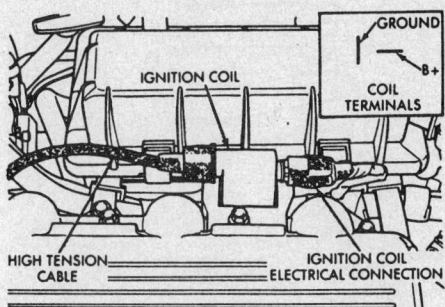

Fig. 5 Ignition coil terminal identification. 3.0L/V6-181 engine

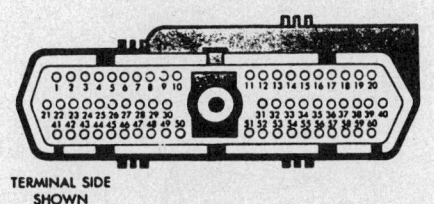

Fig. 6 SBEC 60-way electrical connector

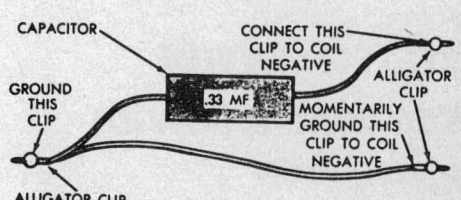

Fig. 7 Coil negative terminal jumper wire

"Ignition System Starting Test." Failure to do so may lead to unnecessary diagnostic time and incorrect test results. **Be sure to block drive wheels or apply parking brake before proceeding with this test.**

1. Measure battery voltage using a suitable voltmeter. Battery voltage must be at least 12.4 volts to deliver the necessary voltage to operate the cranking and ignition systems properly.
2. Crank engine for five seconds while noting voltage at coil (+) terminal, **Figs. 4 and 5.**
3. If voltage does not remain near battery voltage during cranking, problem is contained within engine electronic system.
4. If voltage remains near battery voltage during cranking, turn ignition Off and disconnect 60-way electrical connector, **Fig. 6,** from the engine controller and inspect connector for any loose terminals.
5. Remove coil (+) lead, then connect suitable jumper wire between battery (+) and coil (+) terminals.
6. Momentarily ground terminal 19 of 60-way connector using a suitable jumper wire, **Fig. 7.** A spark should be present when ground is removed.
7. If a spark is present, replace engine controller. If spark is not present, use special jumper to directly ground coil (-) terminal.
8. If spark is present, locate and repair open circuit in wiring harness. If spark is not present, replace ignition coil.

ELECTRONIC IGNITION (EI) (DIRECT IGNITION SYSTEM)

2.2L/4-135 Turbo III Engine

1. Measure battery voltage using a suitable voltmeter. Battery voltage must

be at least 12.4 volts to deliver the necessary voltage to operate the cranking and ignition systems properly.

2. Disconnect harness connector from coil pack, then connect voltmeter to B+ terminal of wiring harness coil connector, **Fig. 8.**
3. Crank engine for five seconds while noting voltage at B+ terminal.
4. If voltage is zero during entire cranking period, problem exists in engine controller or in auto shutdown relay of engine electronic system.
5. If voltage is near battery voltage, then drops to zero after 1-2 seconds of cranking, problem exists in cam or crank sensor circuits of engine electronic system.
6. If voltage remains near battery voltage during cranking, turn ignition off and disconnect engine controller 60-way electrical connector, **Fig. 6.** Inspect connector for any loose terminals.

1993 3.3L/V6-201 & 3.8L/V6-231 ENGINES

1. Measure battery voltage using a suitable voltmeter. Battery voltage must be at least 12.66 volts to deliver the necessary voltage to operate the cranking and ignition systems properly.
2. Disconnect harness connector from coil pack, then connect test light to B+ terminal of wiring harness coil connector and ground, **Fig. 9.**
3. Turn ignition key to On position. Test light should flash On, then turn Off. **Do not turn key to Off position; leave it in On position.** Note the following:
   a. If test light flashes momentarily, engine controller grounded auto

shutdown (ASD) relay. Proceed to step 4.
   b. If test light does not flash, ASD relay did not energize. Problem exists within relay or in a relay circuit.
4. Crank engine. If key was placed in Off position after step 3, place key in On position before cranking. Wait for test light to flash once, then crank engine, noting the following:
   a. If test light flashes momentarily during cranking, engine controller is not receiving a camshaft position sensor signal.
   b. If test light does not flash during cranking, unplug camshaft position sensor connector. Turn ignition key to Off position. Turn key to On position, wait for test light to flash once, then crank engine. If test light flashes, camshaft position sensor is shorted and must be replaced, If test light again does not flash, problem exists in crankshaft position sensor/camshaft position sensor 8.0 volt supply circuit, crankshaft position sensor 5 volt output or ground circuits.

COOLANT TEMPERATURE SENSOR TEST

1. Place ignition switch in Off position, then disconnect coolant temperature sensor electrical connector.
2. Connect suitable ohmmeter across coolant temperature sensor terminals and measure sensor resistance.
3. Resistance should measure 700-1000 ohms with sensor at normal operating temperature (200° F) and 7000-13000 ohms with sensor at room temperature (70° F). If ohmmeter reading is not as specified, replace coolant temperature sensor.

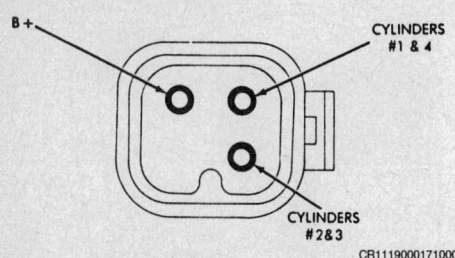

Fig. 8 Ignition coil electrical connector (wiring harness side). 2.2L/4-135 Turbo III engine

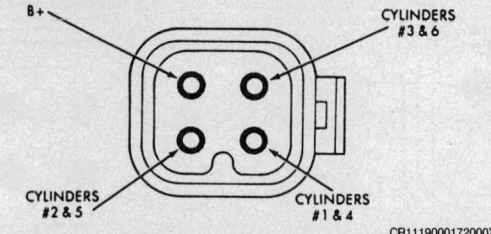

Fig. 9 Ignition coil electrical connector (wiring harness side). 3.3L/V6-201 & 3.8L/V6-231 engines

SYSTEM SERVICE
Component Service
DISTRIBUTOR

2.2L/4-135 & 2.5L/4-153 Engines

1. Remove rotor from shaft, then disconnect pickup electrical connector.
2. Remove Hall Effect pickup retaining screws or clips, then the pickup.
3. Remove distributor drive gear roll pin then the drive gear.
4. Remove drive gear thrust washer and distributor shaft.
5. Remove distributor-to-block seat.
6. Reverse procedure to assemble, noting the following:
   a. Lubricate distributor housing bushings with clean engine oil prior to installing engine seal onto distributor housing.
   b. Ensure pickup lead wire is properly engaged in retaining slot.
   c. Ensure rotor is fully seated when pressing rotor onto shaft.

3.0L/V6-181 Engine

1. Remove distributor cap screws, then the distributor cap, **Fig. 10.** Inspect cap for cracks in shell or in carbon button, burned terminals, or flashover.
2. Remove rotor attaching screw, then the rotor. Inspect rotor for cracks or burned electrode.
3. Remove distributor housing cover, then the lead wire clamp screw and lead wire.
4. Remove disk assembly attaching screw, disk spacers, then the disk. Inspect disk for warpage or damage and replace as necessary.
5. Remove bushing, photo optic sensing unit fasteners, then the sensing unit.
6. Remove two bearing retainer screws.
7. Mark distributor gear and shaft for assembly reference.
8. Drive roll pin out of distributor drive gear, then remove gear.
9. Remove distributor shaft and bearing assembly.
10. Reverse procedure to assemble.

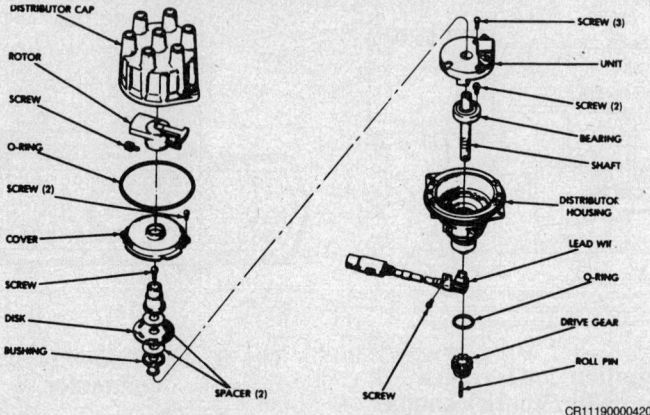

Fig. 10 Exploded view of optical distributor assembly. 3.0L/V6-181 engine

Component Replacement
DISTRIBUTOR

2.2L/4-135 & 2.5L/4-153 Engines

1. Disconnect pickup lead wires from electrical connector.
2. Remove splash shield screws, then the shield.
3. Loosen distributor cap screws, then remove cap.
4. Rotate crankshaft until rotor is pointing in direction of engine block, then scribe a line on block for assembly reference.
5. Remove distributor hold-down bolt, then carefully lift distributor from engine.
6. Position distributor into engine. **Ensure gasket is installed on distributor base.**
7. Engage distributor drive gear with auxiliary drive gear so rotor aligns with scribe mark on engine block.
8. If engine was cranked while distributor was removed, proceed as follows:
   a. Rotate crankshaft until No. 1 piston is at top dead center of compression stroke. Damper clutch housing pointer should align with "O" mark on flywheel.
   b. Rotate rotor to a position ahead of No. 1 distributor cap terminal.
   c. Install distributor into engine, engaging distributor drive with auxiliary shaft. Rotor must be positioned under No. 1 terminal in distributor cap.

9. Install distributor cap, then the distributor hold-down screw.
10. Install splash shield, then connect primary wiring connector to distributor.
11. Adjust ignition timing to specifications.

3.0L/V6-181 Engine

1. Disconnect distributor lead wire from electrical connector.
2. Loosen distributor cap screws, then remove cap.
3. Rotate crankshaft until rotor is pointing in direction of intake plenum, then scribe a line on plenum for assembly reference.
4. Remove distributor hold-down nut, then carefully lift distributor from engine.
5. Position distributor into engine. **Ensure gasket is installed on distributor base.**
6. Engage distributor drive gear with camshaft drive gear so distributor rotor aligns with scribe marks made during removal.
7. If engine was cranked while distributor was removed, proceed as follows:
   a. Rotate crankshaft until No. 1 piston is at top dead center of compression stroke.
   b. Rotate rotor to No. 1 terminal in distributor cap.
   c. Install distributor into engine, engaging distributor drive with camshaft. Rotor must be positioned under No. 1 terminal in distributor cap.
8. Install distributor cap, then the distributor hold-down nut.
9. Connect distributor lead wire to electrical connector.
10. Adjust ignition timing to specifications.

SPECIFICATIONS

Engine	Basic Timing	Spark Advance Test @ 2000 RPM ①	
		Man. Trans,	Auto. Trans.
2.2L/4-135 & 2.5L/4-153 TBI	12°	21°±4°	16°±4°
2.5L/4-153 MPFI	12°	18°±4°	18°±4°
3.0L/V6-181	12°	34°±4°	38°±4°

①—Basic timing included.

Type 2

NOTE: If Unsure Of The System Used On The Vehicle Being Serviced, Refer To The "Engine Systems Identification Chart." Further Assistance For The Proper Use Of Information Contained In This Section Can Also Be Found In The Front Of This Tabbed Section Under "How To Use This Manual."

INDEX

Page No.		Page No.		Page No.
Description: 4-5		2.4L/4-148 Engine 4-7		2.4L/4-148 Engine 4-8
2.4L/4-148 Engine 4-5		2.5L/V6-152 Engine 4-7		2.5L/V6-152 Engine 4-8
2.5L/V6-152 Engine 4-6		**System Service:** 4-8		
Diagnosis & Testing: 4-7		Component Replacement 4-8		

DESCRIPTION

2.4L/4-148 ENGINE

The 2.4L/4-148 DOHC engine uses a fixed ignition timing system. The distributorless electronic ignition system is referred to as the Direct Ignition System (DIS). Basic ignition timing is not adjustable.

The Powertrain Control Module (PCM) determines spark advance. The system's three main components are the coil pack, crankshaft position sensor and camshaft position sensor.

The crankshaft position sensor and camshaft position sensor are Hall Effect devices that generate pulses which are input to the PCM. The PCM then calculates injector sequence and ignition timing. The PCM also supplies battery voltage to the ignition coil through the Automatic Shutdown (ASD) Relay. The PCM also controls the ground circuit for the ignition coil. By switching the path for the coil on and off, the PCM adjusts ignition timing to meet changing engine operating conditions.

During the crank-start period, the PCM maintains spark advance at 9° BTDC. During engine operation, the PCM adjusts spark advance based on inputs from the intake air temperature, coolant, engine RPM, intake manifold vacuum and knock sensors. The PCM also regulates the fuel injection system.

Automatic Shutdown (ASD) Relay

The ASD relay supplies battery voltage to the fuel injectors, electronic ignition coil, and heating element in the oxygen sensors.

A buss bar in the Power Distribution Center (PDC) supplies voltage to the solenoid side and contact side of the relay. The ASD relay power circuit contains a 20 amp fuse between the buss bar in the PDC and the relay. The fuse also protects the power circuit for the fuel pump relay and pump.

The PCM controls the ASD relay by switching the ground path for the solenoid side of the relay on and off. The PCM turns the ground path off when the ignition switch is in the Off position. When the ignition switch is in On or Start positions, the PCM monitors the crankshaft and camshaft position sensors to determine engine speed and ignition timing. If the PCM does not receive crankshaft and camshaft position sensor signals when the ignition switch is in the Run position, it will de-energize the ASD relay.

Camshaft Position Sensor

The PCM determines fuel injector synchronization and cylinder identification from inputs provided by the camshaft position sensor and the crankshaft position sensor. From the two inputs, the PCM determines crankshaft position.

Crankshaft Position Sensor

The PCM determines which cylinder to fire from inputs provided by the camshaft position sensor and the crankshaft position sensor. From the input, the PCM determines engine speed and crankshaft angle (position).

Electronic Ignition Coils

The coil pack consists of two coils molded together. High tension leads route to each cylinder. The coil fires two spark plugs on every power stroke; one plug is the cylinder under compression, the other is the cylinder on exhaust stroke. Coil number one fires cylinders 1 and 4, while coil number two fires cylinders 2 and 3.

CHRYSLER—Ignition Systems

The ASD relay provides voltage to the ignition coil. The PCM provides a ground circuit for energizing the coil. When the PCM breaks the contact, the energy in the coil primary transfers to the secondary, creating the spark. The PCM will not energize the ASD relay if it does not receive the crankshaft position sensor and camshaft position sensor inputs.

Engine Coolant Temperature Sensor

The engine coolant temperature sensor provides an input voltage to the PCM and a separate input voltage to the temperature gauge on the instrument panel. As coolant temperature varies, the sensor resistance changes, resulting in a different input voltage to the PCM.

When the engine is cold, the PCM will demand slightly richer air-fuel mixtures and higher idle speeds until normal operating temperatures are reached.

Intake Air Temperature Sensor

The intake air temperature sensor measures the temperature of the air as it enters the engine. The sensor supplies one of the inputs to the PCM to determine injector pulse-width.

Knock Sensor

When the knock sensor detects a knock in one of the cylinders, it sends an input signal to the PCM. In response, the PCM retards ignition timing for all cylinders by a scheduled amount.

The knock sensor contains a piezoelectric crystal assembly which constantly vibrates and sends an input signal to the PCM. When a knock causes the crystal's vibration to increase, the sensor output voltage also increases.

Manifold Absolute Pressure (MAP) Sensor

The PCM supplies 5 volts to the MAP sensor. The MAP sensor converts intake manifold pressure into voltage. The PCM monitors the MAP sensor output voltage. As vacuum increases, the MAP sensor voltage decreases proportionately. As vacuum decreases, the MAP sensor voltage increases proportionately.

During cranking, before the engine starts running, the PCM determines atmospheric air pressure from MAP sensor voltage. During engine operation, the PCM determines intake manifold pressure from the MAP sensor voltage. Based on MAP sensor voltage and inputs from other sensors, the PCM adjusts spark advance and the air/fuel mixture.

2.5L/V6-152 ENGINE

The 2.5L/V6-152 SOHC engine uses a fixed ignition timing system. Basic ignition timing is not adjustable.

The Powertrain Control Module (PCM) determines spark advance. The system's main components are the ignition coil, distributor, crankshaft position sensor and camshaft position sensor.

The crankshaft position sensor and camshaft position sensor are Hall Effect devices that generate pulses which are input to the PCM. The PCM then calculates injector sequence and ignition timing. The PCM also supplies battery voltage to the ignition coil through the Automatic Shutdown (ASD) Relay. The PCM also controls the ground circuit for the ignition coil. By switching the path for the coil on and off, the PCM adjusts ignition timing to meet changing engine operating conditions.

Automatic Shutdown (ASD) Relay

The ASD relay supplies battery voltage to the fuel injectors, alternator field, electronic ignition coil, and heating element in the oxygen sensors.

The PCM controls the ASD relay by switching the ground path for the solenoid side of the relay on and off. The PCM turns the ground path off when the ignition switch is in the Off position unless the O2 Heater Monitor is being run. When the ignition switch is in On or Start positions, the PCM momentarily turns on the ASD relay. While the relay is on, the PCM monitors the crankshaft and camshaft position sensors signals to determine engine speed and ignition timing (coil dwell). If the PCM does not receive crankshaft and camshaft position sensor signals when the ignition switch is in the Run position, it will de-energize the ASD relay.

The ASD relay is located in the Power Distribution Center.

Camshaft Position Sensor

The PCM determines fuel injector synchronization and cylinder identification from inputs provided by the camshaft position sensor and the crankshaft position sensor. The PCM determines crankshaft position from these two inputs.

The 2.5L/V6-152 engine is equipped with a camshaft driven mechanical distributor, containing a shaft driven rotor. The distributor is also equipped with an internal camshaft position sensor. This sensor provides fuel injection synchronization and cylinder identification to the PCM.

The camshaft position sensor contains a Hall effect device called a sync signal generator which detects a rotating pulse ring (shutter) on the distributor shaft. The signal generated by the sync signal generator is used in conjunction with the crankshaft position sensor to differentiate between fuel injection and spark events.

Crankshaft Position Sensor

The PCM determines which cylinder to fire from inputs provided by the camshaft position sensor and the crankshaft position sensor. From the input, the PCM determines engine speed and crankshaft angle (position).

The crankshaft position sensor detects slots cut into the transmission driveplate extension. There are three sets of slots, each set containing four slots representing 69°, 49°, 29°, and 9° BTDC. The PCM senses the last slot in the series and calculates the crankshaft position.

Distributor

The distributor directs the ignition spark to the individual cylinders to ignite the air/fuel mixture. The distributor is driven by the camshaft and the spark command is given by the PCM, based on inputs from the various sensors.

Engine Coolant Temperature Sensor

The engine coolant temperature sensor provides an input voltage to the PCM and a separate input voltage for radiator fan control. As coolant temperature varies, the sensor resistance changes, resulting in a different input voltage to the PCM.

When the engine is cold, the PCM will demand slightly richer air-fuel mixtures and higher idle speeds until normal operating temperatures are reached.

Ignition Coil

The PCM operates the ignition coil through the ASD relay. When the relay is energized by the PCM, battery voltage is directed to the ignition coil positive terminal. The PCM will not energize the ASD relay if it does not receive an input signal from the distributor pick-up.

The ignition coil used on this engine has its windings embedded in heat and vibration resistant epoxy. The ignition transistor is located in the distributor. The PCM controls ignition timing by turning the ignition transistor on and off. By switching the ground path for the coil on and off, the PCM adjusts ignition timing to meet changing engine operating conditions.

Intake Air Temperature Sensor

The intake air temperature sensor measures the temperature of the air as it enters the engine. The sensor supplies one of the inputs to the PCM to determine injector pulse-width.

Manifold Absolute Pressure (MAP) Sensor

The PCM supplies 5 volts to the MAP sensor. The MAP sensor converts intake manifold pressure into voltage. The PCM monitors the MAP sensor output voltage. As vacuum increases, the MAP sensor voltage decreases proportionately. As vacuum decreases, the MAP sensor voltage increases proportionately.

During cranking, before the engine starts running, the PCM determines atmospheric air pressure from MAP sensor voltage. During engine operation, the PCM determines intake manifold pressure from the MAP sensor voltage. Based on MAP sensor voltage and inputs from other sensors, the PCM adjusts spark advance and the air/fuel mixture.

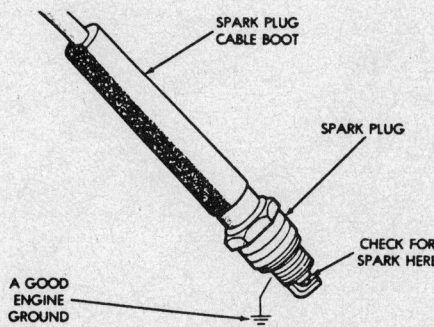

Fig. 1 Spark plug test. 2.4L/4-148 & 2.5L/V6-152 engines

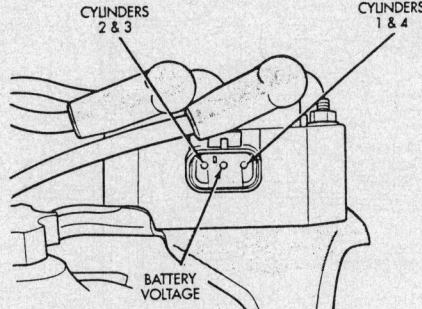

Fig. 2 Primary resistance test. 2.4L/4-148 engine

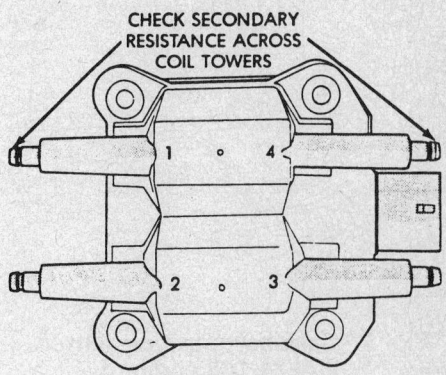

Fig. 3 Secondary resistance test. 2.4L/4-148 engine

DIAGNOSIS & TESTING

2.4L/4-148 ENGINE

Ignition Wire Resistance

Minimum wire resistance is 250 ohms per inch; maximum resistance is 1000 ohms per inch (measured at 70° F).

Spark Test

1. Remove ignition wire from No. 1 spark plug. Insert a clean spark plug into ignition wire, then ground spark plug to engine, **Fig. 1.**
2. Crank engine and look for spark across electrodes of spark plug.
3. Repeat steps 1 and 2 for remaining cylinders.
4. If there is no spark during cylinder tests, proceed to "Failure To Start Test." If one or more tests indicate irregular or weak spark, proceed to "Check Coil Test."

Check Coil Test

The coil pack consists of two independent coils, cylinders 1-4 and 2-3. **Each coil must be checked individually as follows:**
1. Remove ignition cables, then measure resistance in each cable. Resistance should be 3,000-12,000 ohms per foot. Replace defective cables.
2. Disconnect electrical connector from coil pack.
3. Measure primary resistance of each coil. At coil, connect an ohmmeter between the B + pin and the pin corresponding to cylinder to be tested, **Fig. 2.** Resistance should be 0.51-0.61 ohm. Replace coil if not within specifications.
4. Remove ignition cables from secondary coil tower, then measure secondary resistance between towers of each individual coil, **Fig. 3. Resistance should be 11,500-13,500 ohms. Replace coil if not within specifications.**

Failure To Start

1. Measure battery voltage using a suitable voltmeter. Battery voltage must be at least 12.7 volts to deliver necessary voltage to operate cranking and ignition systems properly.

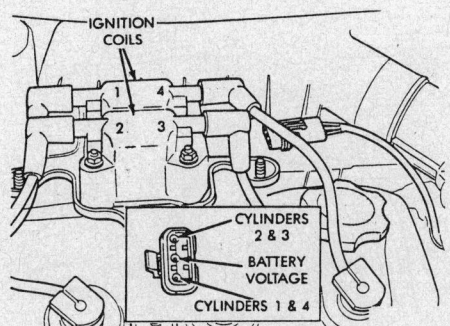

Fig. 4 Harness connector test. 2.4L/4-148 engine

2. Disconnect harness connector from coil pack, then connect voltmeter to B + terminal of wiring harness coil connector, **Fig. 4.**
3. Turn ignition switch to On position. Test light should flash momentarily on then off. **Do not turn ignition switch to Off position.**
   a. If test light flashes momentarily, the PCM grounded the ASD relay. Proceed to step 4.
   b. If test light did not flash, ASD relay did not energize. The cause is either the relay or one of the relay circuits. A suitable DRB scan tool and proper diagnostic procedures will be needed to locate and correct problem.
4. Crank engine.
   a. If test light flashes momentarily during cranking, the PCM is not receiving a camshaft position sensor signal. A suitable DRB scan tool and proper diagnostic procedures will be needed to locate and correct problem.
   b. If test light did not flash during cranking, unplug camshaft position sensor connector. Turn ignition switch Off, then On. Wait for test light to flash momentarily, then crank engine. If test light flashes momentarily, camshaft position sensor is shorted and must be replaced. If test light did not flash, cause of no-start is either crankshaft or camshaft position sensor 8 volt supply circuit, or the crank-

shaft position sensor 5 volt output or ground circuits. A suitable DRB scan tool and proper diagnostic procedures will be needed to locate and correct problem.

2.5L/V6-152 ENGINE

Ignition Wire Resistance

Minimum wire resistance is 250 ohms per inch; maximum resistance is 1000 ohms per inch (measured at 70° F).

Spark Test

1. Remove ignition wire from No. 1 spark plug. Insert a clean spark plug into ignition wire, then ground spark plug to engine, **Fig. 1.**
2. Crank engine and look for spark across electrodes of spark plug.
3. Repeat steps 1 and 2 for remaining cylinders.
4. If there is no spark during cylinder tests, proceed to "Failure To Start Test." If one or more tests indicate irregular or weak spark, proceed to "Check Coil Test."

Check Coil Test

Measure primary resistance at the 2 pin distributor connector. Resistance should be 0.6-0.8 ohms. Measure secondary resistance between coil tower and each terminal of the 2 pin distributor connector. Resistance should be 12,000-18,000 ohms. Replace coil if not within specifications.

Distributor Cap Resistance Test

There is a resistor built into the distributor cap. Connect an ohmmeter between the center button and the ignition coil terminal. Resistance should be 5,000 ohms. Replace cap if not within specifications.

Failure To Start Test

1. Measure battery voltage using a suitable voltmeter. Battery voltage must be at least 12.7 volts to deliver the necessary voltage to operate the cranking and ignition systems properly.
2. Use of a suitable DRB scan tool and proper diagnostic procedures will be needed to locate and correct the problem.

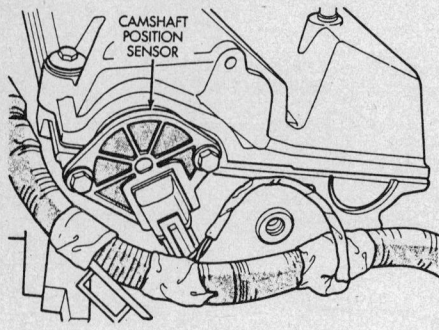

Fig. 5 Camshaft position sensor. 2.4L/4-148 engine

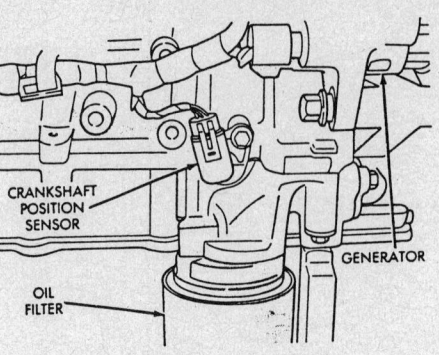

Fig. 6 Crankshaft position sensor. 2.4L/4-148 engine

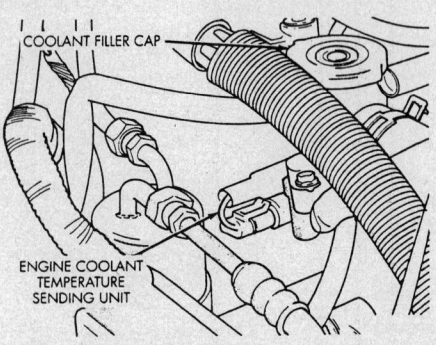

Fig. 7 Engine coolant temperature sensor. 2.4L/4-148 engine

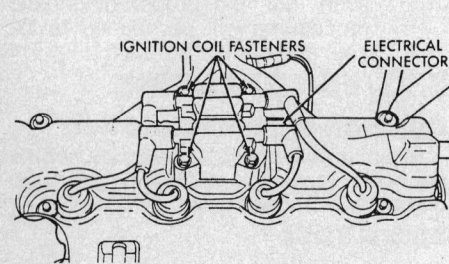

Fig. 8 Electronic Ignition coil pack. 2.4L/4-148 engine

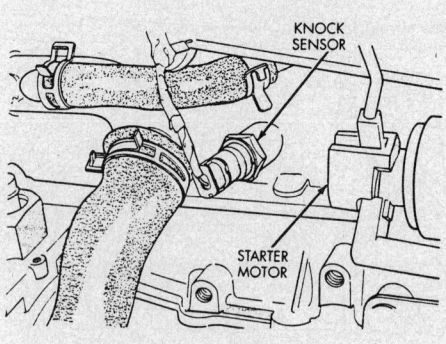

Fig. 9 Knock sensor. 2.4L/4-148 engine

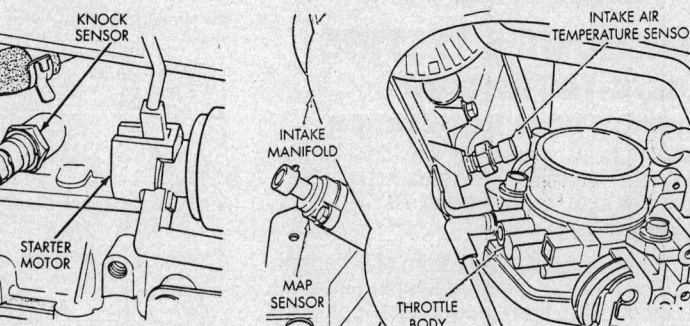

Fig. 10 MAP sensor. 2.4L/4-148 engine

SYSTEM SERVICE

Component Replacement

2.4L/4-148 ENGINE

Camshaft Position Sensor

The camshaft position sensor is mounted to the rear of the cylinder head, **Fig. 5**.
1. Disconnect filtered air tube from throttle body and air cleaner housing.
2. Remove air cleaner inlet tube.
3. Disconnect electrical connectors from engine coolant temperature sensor and camshaft position sensor.
4. Remove brake booster hose and electrical connector from holders on end of cylinder head cover.
5. Remove camshaft position sensor mounting screws, then the sensor.
6. Reverse procedure to install. **Torque** sensor screws to 80 inch lbs.

Crankshaft Position Sensor

The crankshaft position sensor mounts to engine block behind alternator, just above the oil filter, **Fig. 6**.
1. Disconnect electrical connector from sensor.
2. Remove crankshaft position sensor mounting screws, then the sensor.
3. Reverse procedure to install. **Torque** screws to 80 inch lbs.

Engine Coolant Temperature Sensor

The engine coolant temperature sensor is located at the rear of the cylinder head, next to the camshaft position sensor, **Fig. 7.**
1. While engine is cold, properly drain cooling system until coolant level drops below sensor.
2. Disconnect electrical connector from sensor.
3. Remove engine coolant temperature sensor mounting screws, then the sensor.
4. Reverse procedure to install. **Torque** screws to 60 inch lbs.

Electronic Ignition Coil Pack

The electronic ignition coil pack attaches to a bracket mounted on top of the cylinder cover, **Fig. 8**.
1. Disconnect battery ground cable.
2. Disconnect electrical connector from coil pack.
3. Remove mounting screws, then the coil pack.
4. Reverse procedure to install. **Torque** bracket to head cover nuts to 200 inch lbs., and coil pack to bracket screws to 105 inch lbs.

Knock Sensor

The knock sensor threads into the side of cylinder block in front of starter, **Fig. 9**.
1. Disconnect electrical connector from knock sensor.
2. Using a suitable crow foot socket, remove sensor.
3. Reverse procedure to install. **Torque** screws to 90 inch lbs. **Undertightening or overtightening sensor may cause improper spark control.**

Manifold Absolute Pressure (MAP) Sensor

The MAP sensor attaches to the intake manifold plenum, **Fig. 10**.
1. Disconnect electrical connector from MAP sensor.
2. Remove MAP sensor mounting screws, then the sensor.
3. Reverse procedure to install. **Torque** screws to 20 inch lbs.

Powertrain Control Module (PCM)

The PCM attaches to the inner fender panel, next to the washer fluid reservoir, on the passenger side of the vehicle.
1. Disconnect battery ground cable.
2. Remove PCM mounting screws.
3. Lift PCM and disconnect 60-way connector.
4. Reverse procedure to install. **Torque** screws to 35 inch lbs.

2.5L/V6-152 ENGINE

Crankshaft Position Sensor

The crankshaft position sensor is located on the lefthand rear of the transmission housing, above the differential housing, **Fig. 11**.
1. Remove speed control servo from lefthand side strut tower.

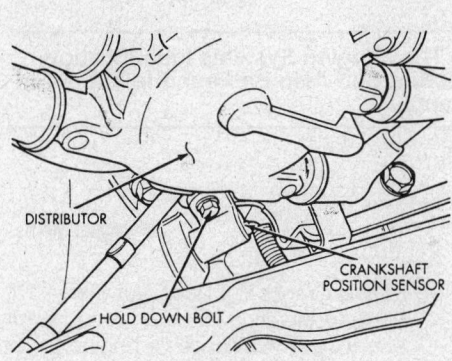

Fig. 11 Crankshaft position sensor. 2.5L/V6-152 engine

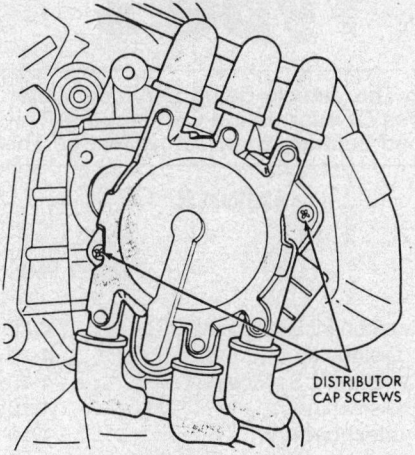

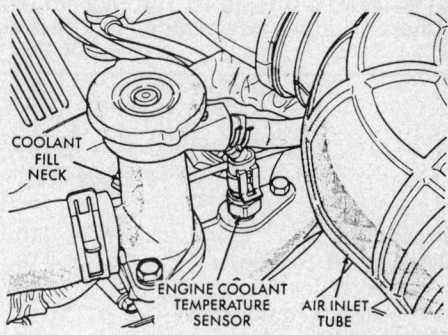

Fig. 13 Engine coolant temperature sensor. 2.5L/V6-152 engine

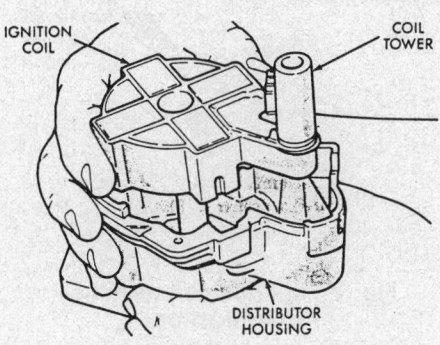

Fig. 14 Ignition coil. 2.5L/V6-152 engine

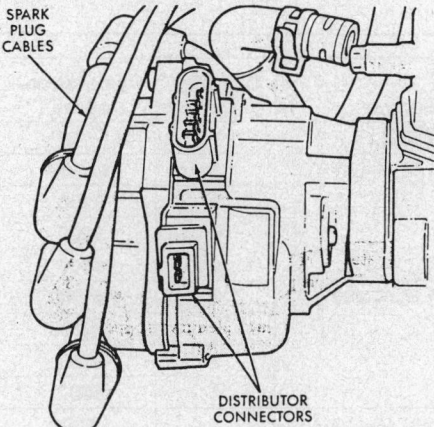

Fig. 12 Distributor. 2.5L/V6-152 engine

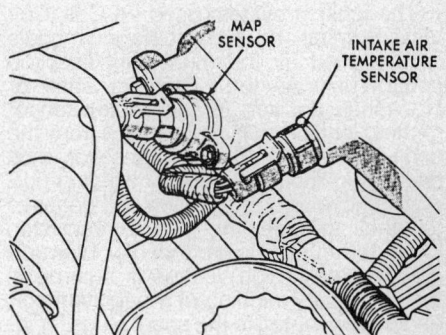

Fig. 15 Intake air temperature and MAP sensors. 2.5L/V6-152 engine

2. Remove crankshaft position sensor retaining bolt.
3. Pull sensor straight up and out of transmission housing.
4. Disconnect electrical connector from sensor.
5. Reverse procedure to install. **Torque** screws to 80 inch lbs.

Distributor

1. Position No. 1 cylinder at TDC of compression stroke.
2. Remove bolt holding air inlet resonator to intake manifold.
3. Loosen clamps holding air cleaner cover to air cleaner housing.
4. Remove PCV make-up air hose from air inlet hose.
5. Loosen hose clamp at throttle body.
6. Remove air inlet tube, resonator and air cleaner cover.
7. Remove EGR tube.
8. Remove spark plug wires from distributor cap.
9. Remove distributor cap, **Fig. 12**.
10. Mark rotor position, then remove rotor.
11. Remove harness connectors from distributor.
12. Remove distributor hold-down nuts.
13. Remove spark plug cable bracket from top of distributor housing.

14. Remove transmission dipstick tube.
15. Carefully remove distributor.
16. Reverse procedure to install. **Torque** distributor hold-down to 9 ft. lbs., and EGR tube to 95 inch lbs.

Engine Coolant Temperature Sensor

The engine coolant temperature sensor is located next to the thermostat housing, **Fig. 13**.
1. While engine is cold, properly drain cooling system until coolant level drops below sensor.
2. Disconnect electrical connector from sensor.
3. Remove engine coolant temperature sensor mounting screws, then the sensor.
4. Reverse procedure to install. **Torque** screws to 60 inch lbs.

Ignition Coil

The ignition coil is located in the distributor housing, **Fig. 14**. If ignition coil is defective, replace distributor assembly.

Intake Air Temperature Sensor

The intake air temperature sensor threads into the intake air manifold, **Fig. 15**.

1. Disconnect electrical connector from sensor.
2. Remove sensor mounting screws, then the sensor.
3. Reverse procedure to install. **Torque** screws to 20 inch lbs.

Manifold Absolute Pressure (MAP) Sensor

The MAP sensor is located near the intake air temperature sensor, **Fig. 15**.
1. Disconnect electrical connector from sensor.
2. Remove sensor mounting screws, then the sensor.
3. Reverse procedure to install. **Torque** screws to 30 inch lbs.

Powertrain Control Module (PCM)

The PCM attaches to the inner fender panel, next to the washer fluid reservoir, on the passenger side of the vehicle.
1. Disconnect battery ground cable.
2. Remove PCM mounting screws.
3. Lift PCM and disconnect 60-way connector.
4. Reverse procedure to install. **Torque** screws to 35 inch lbs.

NOTE: If Unsure Of The System Used On The Vehicle Being Serviced, Refer To The "Engine Systems Identification Chart." Further Assistance For The Proper Use Of Information Contained In This Section Can Also Be Found In The Front Of This Tabbed Section Under "How To Use This Manual."

INDEX

	Page No.			Page No.			Page No.

Description 4-10
Diagnosis & Testing: 4-10
   Ignition Coil Test. 4-10
   Ignition Wire Resistance 4-10
Specifications 4-12
System Service: 4-10

Component Replacement 4-10
   Distributor. 4-10
Component Service 4-10
   Distributor. 4-10
Troubleshooting: 4-10

Engine Cranks But Does Not Start 4-10
Poor Acceleration. 4-10
Poor Gasoline Mileage Or Engine
   Overheats 4-10
Rough Idle Or Stalling. 4-10

DESCRIPTION

The ignition system used on Colt, Colt Vista, Summit and Summit Wagon models is controlled by the multi-point injection control unit. As the distributor shaft or crankshaft position (crank angle) sensor rotates, ignition signals are sent from the control unit to the power transistor, thus causing ignition coil primary winding current to flow from the ignition coil negative terminal through the power transistor. When this current is grounded or interrupted repeatedly, high voltage is built up in the secondary winding of the ignition coil, and is then routed to the spark plugs for ignition.

TROUBLESHOOTING

ENGINE CRANKS BUT DOES NOT START

1. Incorrect ignition timing.
2. Faulty ignition coil.
3. Faulty distributor (if equipped).
4. Faulty crankshaft position (crank angle) sensor, if equipped.
5. Faulty power transistor.
6. Faulty spark plugs.
7. Faulty ignition wires.

ROUGH IDLE OR STALLING

1. Faulty spark plugs.
2. Incorrect ignition timing.
3. Faulty ignition coil.
4. Faulty ignition wires.

POOR ACCELERATION

1. Incorrect ignition timing.
2. Faulty ignition coil.
3. Faulty ignition wires.

POOR GASOLINE MILEAGE OR ENGINE OVERHEATS

1. Incorrect ignition timing.

DIAGNOSIS & TESTING

IGNITION WIRE RESISTANCE

Refer to **Fig. 1** for ignition wire resistance specifications.

Engine	Cylinder wire	Resistance, ohms
1993		
1.5L/4-90	1	11,500
	2	9100
	3	9000
	4	6600
1.8L/4-110 ①	1	12,500
	2	11,700
	3	9300
	4	8500
1.8L/4-110 ②	1	12,600
	2	11,700
	3	9400
	4	8500
2.4L/4-146	1	12,500
	2	11,700
	3	9300
	4	8500
1994—96		
All	—	③

①—Colt Vista & Summit Wagon.
②—Colt & Summit.
③—22,000 ohms maximum.

Fig. 1   Ignition wire resistance specifications

IGNITION COIL TEST

Measure resistance of ignition primary coil between terminal 11 and terminal 12, **Fig. 2**, and secondary coil between terminal 11 and high voltage terminal. Refer to **Fig. 3** for ignition coil specifications.

SYSTEM SERVICE

Component Service

DISTRIBUTOR

1.5L/4—90, 1993 1.8L/4—110 & 2.4L/4—146 Engines

Refer to **Fig. 4** for disassembly and assembly procedure.

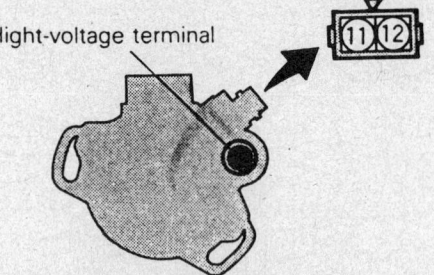

Hight-voltage terminal

CR1119200047000X

Fig. 2   Ignition coil terminal identification

1994—96 1.8L/4—110 & 2.4L/4—146 engines

Refer to **Fig. 5** for disassembly and assembly procedure.

Component Replacement

DISTRIBUTOR

Removal

1. Disconnect battery ground cable.
2. Disconnect distributor wiring harness, then lift off distributor cap with ignition cables attached and position aside.
3. Remove distributor mounting bolt, then the distributor assembly.

Installation

1. Rotate crankshaft until piston of No. 1 cylinder is at top dead center on compression stroke.
2. Align mating marks on distributor housing and distributor gear, **Fig. 6**.
3. **On all models except Colt and Summit**, Install distributor onto cylinder head or cylinder block.
4. **On Colt and Summit**, install distributor with coupling key fitted in keyway in camshaft end, **Fig. 7**.
5. **On all models**, align mating mark on distributor attaching flange with center of distributor flange stud, **Fig. 8**.
6. Install mounting nut, then install wiring harness and distributor cap.
7. Check and reset ignition timing as necessary.

Year	Engine	Primary Coil Resistance, Ohms	Secondary Coil Resistance, Ohms
1993—96	1.5L/4-90	.9—1.2	20,000—29,000
	1.8L/4-110	.9—1.2	20,000—29,000
	2.4L/4-146	.9—1.2	20,000—29,000

Fig. 3   Ignition coil specifications

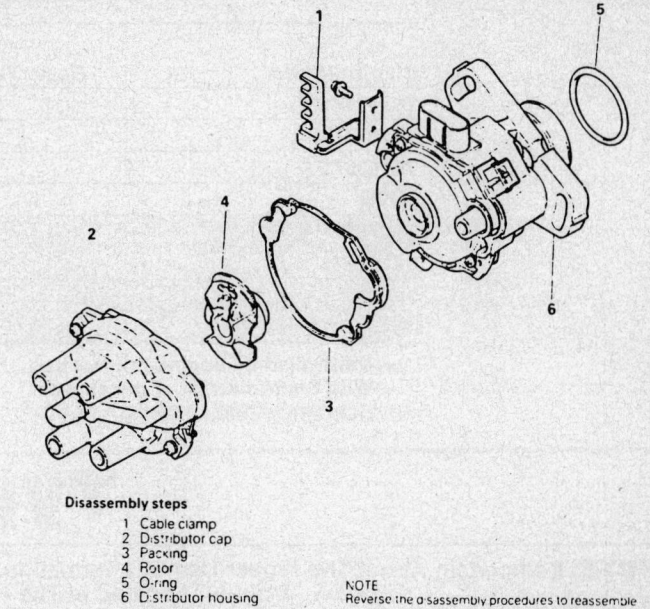

Disassembly steps

1 Cable clamp
2 Distributor cap
3 Packing
4 Rotor
5 O-ring
6 Distributor housing

NOTE
Reverse the disassembly procedures to reassemble

CR1119100053000X

Fig. 4   Distributor disassembly procedure. 1.5L/4–110 & 1993 1.8L/4–110 & 2.4L/4–146 engines

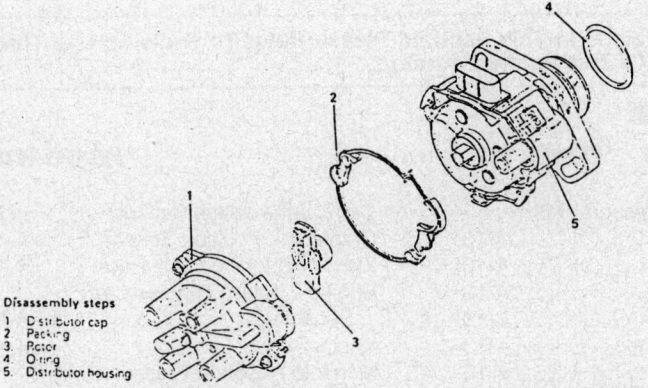

Disassembly steps

1 Distributor cap
2 Packing
3 Rotor
4 O-ring
5 Distributor housing

CR1119400131000X

Fig. 5   Distributor disassembly procedure. 1995–96 1.8L/4–110 & 2.4L/4–146 engines

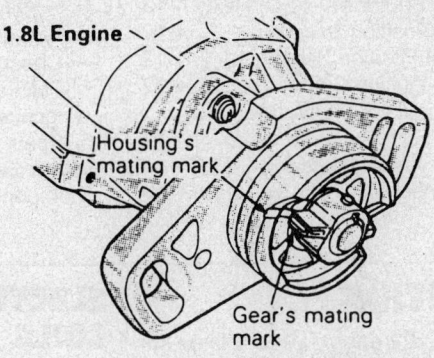

1.8L Engine

Housing's mating mark

Gear's mating mark

CR1119100132000X

Fig. 6   Distributor housing to driven gear alignment.

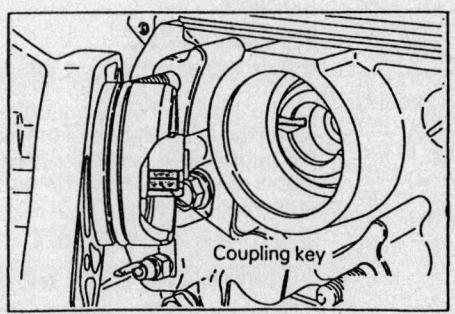

Coupling key

CR1119300133000X

Fig. 7   Coupling key alignment. Colt & Summit

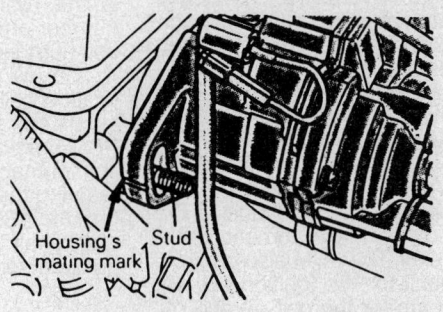

Housing's mating mark   Stud

CR1119100134000X

Fig. 8   Distributor installation

SPECIFICATIONS

Distributor No.	Basic Timing @ Idle	Spark Advance Test @ 2000 RPM
T6T57171②	5°	①
T6T57671②	5°	①
T6T58071②	5°	①
1996		
T6T58771② ③	5°	①
T6T58571② ④	5°	①
T2T60171② ⑤	5°	①
T2T59771② ⑥	5°	①

①—Controlled by engine control unit.
②—With built-in crank angle sensor.
③—Summit w/ 1.5L/4-90 engine.
④—Summit w/ 1.8L/4-110 engine.
⑤—Summit Wagon w/1.8L/4-110 engine.
⑥—Summit Wagon w/2.4L/4-146 engine.

Type 4

NOTE: If Uncertain About The Proper Use Of Information Contained In This Section, Please Refer To "How To Use This Manual" Located In The Front Of This Tabbed Section.

INDEX

Page No.

Description: 4-12
   Automatic Shutdown (ASD) Relay 4-13
   Camshaft Position Sensor 4-12
   Crankshaft Position Sensor 4-12
   Electronic Ignition Coils.......... 4-12
   Engine Coolant Temperature
      Sensor 4-12
   Intake Air Temperature Sensor ... 4-12
   Knock Sensor 4-13

Page No.

Manifold Absolute Pressure (MAP)
   Sensor 4-13
Diagnosis & Testing: 4-13
   Check Coil Test 4-13
   Failure To Start Test 4-13
   Ignition Wire Resistance 4-13
   Spark Test 4-13
System Service: 4-14
   Component Replacement 4-14

Page No.

Camshaft Position Sensor 4-14
Crankshaft Position Sensor 4-14
Electronic Ignition Coil Pack...... 4-14
Engine Coolant Temperature
   Sensor 4-14
Knock Sensor 4-14
Manifold Absolute Pressure (MAP)
   Sensor 4-14
Powertrain Control Module (PCM) 4-14

DESCRIPTION

The 2.0L/4-122 engine uses a fixed ignition timing system. The distributorless electronic ignition system is referred to as the Direct Ignition System (DIS). Basic ignition timing is not adjustable.

The Powertrain Control Module (PCM) determines spark advance. The system's three main components are the coil pack, crankshaft position sensor and camshaft position sensor.

The crankshaft position sensor and camshaft position sensor are Hall Effect devices that generate pulses which are input to the PCM. The PCM then calculates injector sequence and ignition timing. The PCM also supplies battery voltage to the ignition coil through the Automatic Shutdown (ASD) Relay. The PCM also controls the ground circuit for the ignition coil. By switching the path for the coil on and off, the PCM adjusts ignition timing to meet changing engine operating conditions.

During the crank-start period, the PCM maintains spark advance at 9° BTDC. During engine operation, the PCM adjusts spark advance based on inputs from the intake air temperature, coolant, engine RPM, intake manifold vacuum and knock sensors. The PCM also regulates the fuel injection system.

ELECTRONIC IGNITION COILS

The coil pack consists of two coils molded together. High tension leads route to each cylinder. The coil fires two spark plugs on every power stroke; one plug is the cylinder under compression, the other is the cylinder on exhaust stroke. Coil number one fires cylinders 1 and 4, while coil number two fires cylinders 2 and 3.

The ASD relay provides voltage to the ignition coil. The PCM provides a ground circuit for energizing the coil. When the PCM breaks the contact, the energy in the coil primary transfers to the secondary, creating the spark. The PCM will not energize the ASD relay if it does not receive the crankshaft position sensor and camshaft position sensor inputs.

CAMSHAFT POSITION SENSOR

The PCM determines fuel injector synchronization and cylinder identification from inputs provided by the camshaft position sensor and the crankshaft position sensor. From the two inputs, the PCM determines crankshaft position.

CRANKSHAFT POSITION SENSOR

The PCM determines which cylinder to fire from inputs provided by the camshaft position sensor and the crankshaft position sensor. From the input, the PCM determines engine speed and crankshaft angle (position).

INTAKE AIR TEMPERATURE SENSOR

The intake air temperature sensor measures the temperature of the air as it enters the engine. The sensor supplies one of the inputs to the PCM to determine injector pulse-width.

ENGINE COOLANT TEMPERATURE SENSOR

The engine coolant temperature sensor provides an input voltage to the PCM and a separate input voltage to the temperature gauge on the instrument panel. As coolant temperature varies, the sensor resistance changes, resulting in a different input voltage to the PCM.

When the engine is cold, the PCM will demand slightly richer air-fuel mixtures and higher idle speeds until normal operating temperatures are reached.

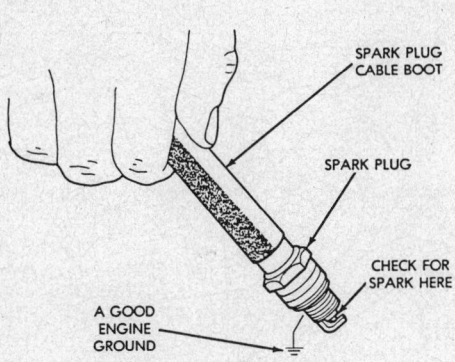

Fig. 1   Spark test

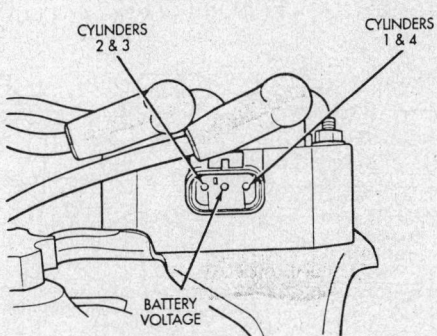

Fig. 2   Coil primary resistance test

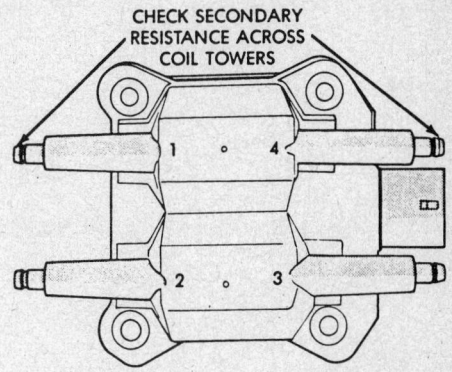

Fig. 3   Coil secondary resistance test

KNOCK SENSOR

When the knock sensor detects a knock in one of the cylinders, it sends an input signal to the PCM. In response, the PCM retards ignition timing for all cylinders by a scheduled amount.

The knock sensor contains a piezoelectric crystal assembly which constantly vibrates and sends an input signal to the PCM. When a knock causes the crystal's vibration to increase, the sensor output voltage also increases.

MANIFOLD ABSOLUTE PRESSURE (MAP) SENSOR

The PCM supplies 5 volts to the MAP sensor. The MAP sensor converts intake manifold pressure into voltage. The PCM monitors the MAP sensor output voltage. As vacuum increases, the MAP sensor voltage decreases proportionately. As vacuum decreases, the MAP sensor voltage increases proportionately.

During cranking, before the engine starts running, the PCM determines atmospheric air pressure from MAP sensor voltage. During engine operation, the PCM determines intake manifold pressure from the MAP sensor voltage. Based on MAP sensor voltage and inputs from other sensors, the PCM adjusts spark advance and the air/fuel mixture.

AUTOMATIC SHUTDOWN (ASD) RELAY

The ASD relay supplies battery voltage to the fuel injectors, electronic ignition coil, and heating element in the oxygen sensors.

A buss bar in the Power Distribution Center (PDC) supplies voltage to the solenoid side and contact side of the relay. The ASD relay power circuit contains a 20 amp fuse between the buss bar in the PDC and the relay. The fuse also protects the power circuit for the fuel pump relay and pump.

The PCM controls the ASD relay by switching the ground path for the solenoid side of the relay on and off. The PCM turns the ground path off when the ignition switch is in the Off position. When the ignition switch is in On or Start positions, the PCM monitors the crankshaft and camshaft position sensors to determine engine speed and ignition timing. If the PCM does

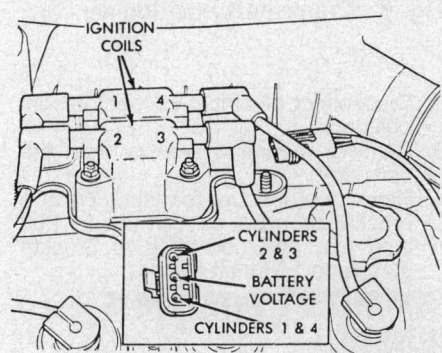

Fig. 4   Coil harness connector

not receive crankshaft and camshaft position sensor signals when the ignition switch is in the Run position, it will de-energize the ASD relay.

DIAGNOSIS & TESTING
IGNITION WIRE RESISTANCE

Minimum wire resistance is 250 ohms per inch; maximum resistance is 1000 ohms per inch (measured at 70° F).

SPARK TEST

1. Remove ignition wire from No. 1 spark plug. Insert a clean spark plug into ignition wire, then ground spark plug to engine, **Fig. 1.**
2. Crank engine and look for spark across electrodes of spark plug.
3. Repeat steps 1 and 2 for remaining cylinders.
4. If there is no spark during cylinder tests, proceed to "Failure To Start Test." If one or more tests indicate irregular or weak spark, proceed to "Check Coil Test."

CHECK COIL TEST

The coil pack consists of two independent coils, cylinders 1-4 and 2-3. **Each coil must be checked individually as follows:**

1. Remove ignition cables, then measure resistance in each cable. Resistance should be 3,000-12,000 ohms per foot. Replace defective cables.
2. Disconnect electrical connector from coil pack.

3. Measure primary resistance of each coil. At the coil, connect an ohmmeter between the B+ pin and the pin corresponding to the cylinder to be tested, **Fig. 2.** Resistance should be 0.51-0.61 ohm. Replace coil if not within specifications.
4. Remove ignition cables from secondary coil tower, then measure secondary resistance between towers of each individual coil, **Fig. 3. Resistance should be 11,500-13,500 ohms. Replace coil if not within specifications.**

FAILURE TO START TEST

1. Measure battery voltage using a suitable voltmeter. Battery voltage must be at least 12.7 volts to deliver necessary voltage to operate cranking and ignition systems properly.
2. Disconnect harness connector from coil pack, then connect voltmeter to B+ terminal of wiring harness coil connector, **Fig. 4.**
3. Turn ignition switch to On position. Test light should flash momentarily on, then off. **Do not turn ignition switch to Off position.**
   a. If test light flashes momentarily, the PCM grounded the ASD relay. Proceed to step 4.
   b. If test light did not flash, ASD relay did not energize. The cause is either the relay or one of the relay circuits. A suitable DRB scan tool and proper diagnostic procedures will be needed to locate and correct the problem.
4. Crank the engine.
   a. If test light flashes momentarily during cranking, PCM is not receiving a camshaft position sensor signal. A suitable DRB scan tool and proper diagnostic procedures will be needed to locate and correct problem.
   b. If test light did not flash during cranking, unplug camshaft position sensor connector. Turn ignition switch Off, then back On. Wait for test light to flash momentarily, then crank engine. If test light flashes momentarily, camshaft position sensor is shorted and must be replaced. If test light did not flash,

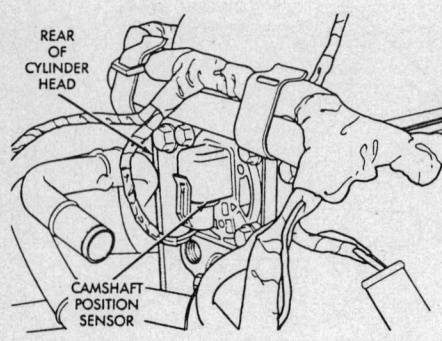

Fig. 5   Camshaft position sensor

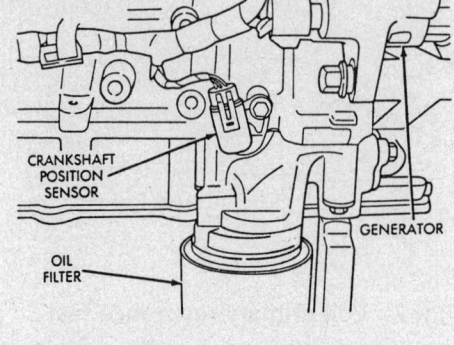

Fig. 6   Crankshaft position sensor

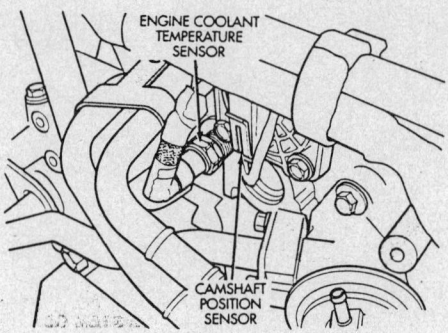

Fig. 7   Engine coolant temperature sensor

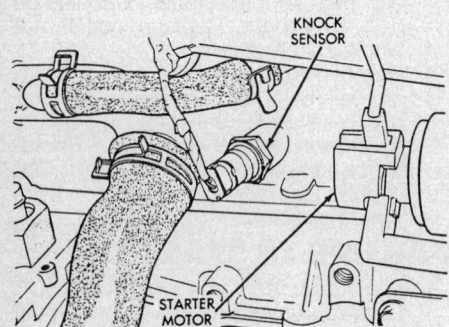

Fig. 8   MAP sensor

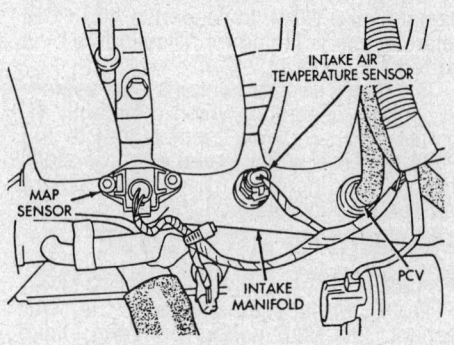

Fig. 9   Knock sensor

cause of no-start is either crankshaft or camshaft position sensor 8 volt supply circuit, or crankshaft position sensor 5 volt output or ground circuits. A suitable DRB scan tool and proper diagnostic procedures will be needed to locate and correct problem.

SYSTEM SERVICE Component Replacement

POWERTRAIN CONTROL MODULE (PCM)

The PCM attaches to the inner fender panel, next to the washer fluid reservoir, on the passenger side of the vehicle.
1. Disconnect battery ground cable.
2. Remove PCM mounting screws.
3. Lift PCM and disconnect 60-way connector.
4. Reverse procedure to install. **Torque** screws to 35 inch lbs.

ELECTRONIC IGNITION COIL PACK

The electronic ignition coil pack attaches to a bracket mounted on top of the cylinder cover.
1. Disconnect battery ground cable.

2. Disconnect electrical connector from coil pack.
3. Remove mounting screws, then the coil pack.
4. Reverse procedure to install. **Torque** bracket to head cover nuts to 200 inch lbs., and coil pack to bracket screws to 105 inch lbs.

CAMSHAFT POSITION SENSOR

The camshaft position sensor is mounted to the rear of the cylinder head, **Fig. 5.**
1. Disconnect filtered air tube from throttle body and air cleaner housing. Disconnect air tube from oil separator hose. Remove filtered air tube.
2. Remove air cleaner inlet tube.
3. Disconnect electrical connectors from engine coolant temperature sensor and camshaft position sensor.
4. Remove brake booster hose and electrical connector from holders on end of cylinder head cover.
5. Remove camshaft position sensor mounting screws, then the sensor.
6. Reverse procedure to install. **Torque** screws to 80 inch lbs.

CRANKSHAFT POSITION SENSOR

The crankshaft position sensor mounts to the engine block behind the alternator, just above the oil filter, **Fig. 6.**
1. Disconnect electrical connector from sensor.
2. Remove crankshaft position sensor mounting screws, then the sensor.
3. Reverse procedure to install. **Torque** screws to 80 inch lbs.

ENGINE COOLANT TEMPERATURE SENSOR

The engine coolant temperature sensor is located at the rear of the cylinder head, next to the camshaft position sensor, **Fig. 7.**
1. While engine is cold, properly drain cooling system until coolant level drops below sensor.

2. Disconnect electrical connector from sensor.
3. Remove engine coolant temperature sensor mounting screws, then the sensor.
4. Reverse procedure to install. **Torque** screws to 60 inch lbs.

MANIFOLD ABSOLUTE PRESSURE (MAP) SENSOR

The MAP sensor attaches to the intake manifold plenum, **Fig. 8.**
1. Disconnect electrical connector from MAP sensor.
2. Remove MAP sensor mounting screws, then the sensor.
3. Reverse procedure to install. **Torque** screws to 20 inch lbs.

KNOCK SENSOR

The knock sensor threads into the side of the cylinder block in front of the starter, **Fig. 9.**
1. Disconnect electrical connector from knock sensor.
2. Using a suitable crow foot socket, remove sensor.
3. Reverse procedure to install. **Torque** screws to 7 ft lbs. **Undertightening or overtightening sensor may cause improper spark control.**

NOTE: If Uncertain About The Proper Use Of Information Contained In This Section, Please Refer To "How To Use This Manual" Located In The Front Of This Tabbed Section.

INDEX

Page No.		Page No.		Page No.
Description 4-15		Power Transistor 4-15		Crank Angle Sensor 4-16
Diagnosis & Testing: 4-15		Specifications 4-17		Distributor 4-16
Ignition Coil 4-15		System Service: 4-16		Component Service 4-16
Ignition Wire Resistance 4-15		Component Replacement 4-16		Distributor 4-16

Engine	Cylinder wire	Resistance, ohms
1993		
All	1	7800
	2	6400
	3	9600
	4	7500
	5	10,400
	6	8600
1994—96		
All	—	①

① —22,000 ohms maximum.

Fig. 1 Ignition wire resistance specifications

DESCRIPTION

The ignition system used on these models is controlled by the engine control unit. As the distributor shaft on Single Over Head Cam models (SOHC) or crank angle sensor on Dual Over Head Cam models (DOHC) rotates, ignition signals are sent from the control unit to the power transistor, thus causing ignition coil primary winding current to flow from the ignition coil negative terminal through the power transistor. When this current is grounded or interrupted repeatedly, high voltage is built up in the secondary winding of the ignition coil, and is then routed to the spark plugs for ignition.

DIAGNOSIS & TESTING

IGNITION WIRE RESISTANCE

Refer to **Fig. 1** for ignition wire resistance specifications.

IGNITION COIL

SOHC Engine

1. Measure resistance of ignition coil between the positive and negative terminals, **Fig. 2.**
2. If resistance is not within the .72-.88 ohm specification, replace ignition coil.
3. Measure resistance of ignition coil between the positive terminal and the high voltage terminal, **Fig. 2.**

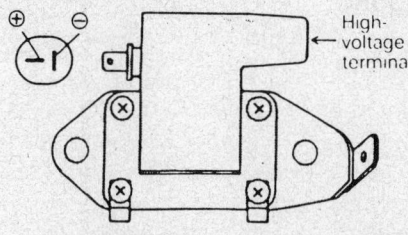

Fig. 2 Ignition coil resistance measurement. SOHC engine

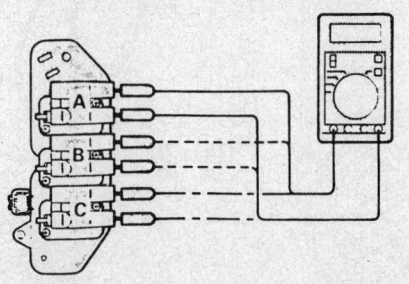

Fig. 4 Secondary coil resistance measurement. DOHC engine

4. If resistance is not within the 10,300-13,900 ohms specification, replace ignition coil.

DOHC Engine

The molded coil consists of three independent coils, cylinders 1-4, 2-5 and 3-6. **Each coil must be checked individually as follows:**

1. Measure primary coil resistance between terminals, **Fig. 3**, for each coil as follows:
   a. For coil A, measure between terminals two and three.
   b. For coil B, measure between terminals one and three.
   c. For coil C, measure between terminals four and three.
2. If resistance is not within .67-.81 ohms, replace ignition coil pack.
3. Measure secondary coil resistance between each coil high voltage terminals, **Fig. 4.**
4. If resistance is not within 11,300-15,300 ohms, replace ignition coil pack.

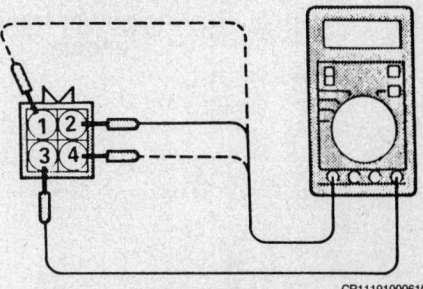

Fig. 3 Primary coil resistance measurement. DOHC engine

POWER TRANSISTOR

SOHC Engine

1. Connect negative lead of 1.5 volt power supply to terminal 2 of power transistor and positive lead to terminal 1, **Fig. 5.**
2. Connect negative probe of an analog type circuit tester to terminal 3 and positive probe to terminal 2.
3. Ensure continuity exists when power supply positive lead is connected to terminal 1 and there is no continuity when positive lead is disconnected.
4. If results are not as specified in step 3, replace power transistor.

DOHC Engine

1. Test power transistor for number one and number four cylinder as follows:
   a. Connect negative lead of 1.5 volt power supply to terminal 7 of power transistor and positive lead to terminal 6, **Fig. 6.**
   b. Connect negative probe of an analog type circuit tester to terminal 3 and positive probe to terminal 7.
   c. Ensure continuity exists when power supply positive lead is connected to Terminal 6 and there is no continuity when positive lead is disconnected.
   d. If result are not as specified in step c, replace power transistor.
2. Repeat step 1 for cylinder numbers 2 and 5 by connecting power supply to terminals 7 (-) and 5 (+), then checking continuity between terminals 2 (-) and 7 (+).
3. Repeat step 1 for cylinder numbers 3 and 6 by connecting power supply to terminals 7 (-) and 4, then checking continuity between terminals 1 (-) and 7 (+).

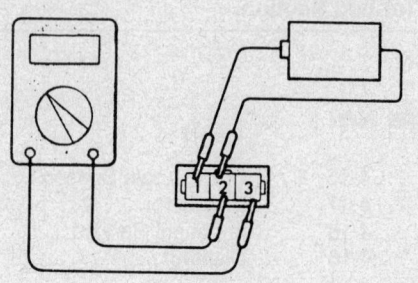

Fig. 5 Testing power transistor. SOHC
engine

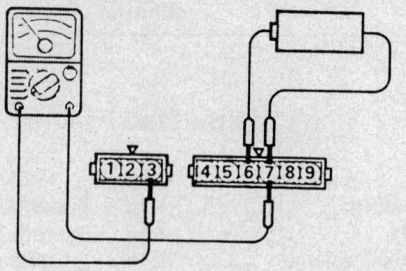

Fig. 6 Testing power transistor.
DOHC engine

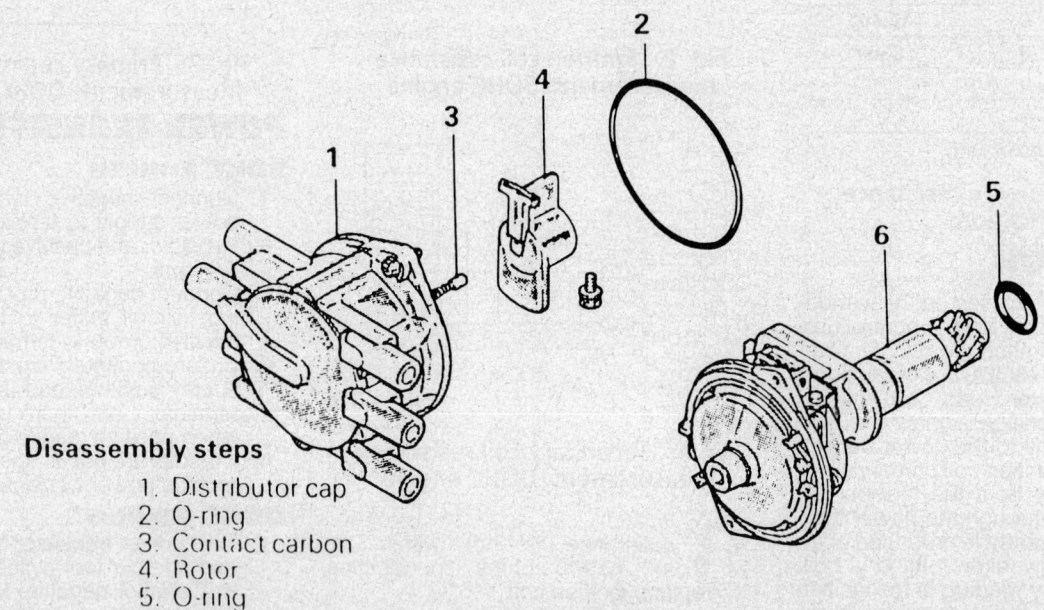

Disassembly steps

1. Distributor cap
2. O-ring
3. Contact carbon
4. Rotor
5. O-ring
6. Housing & crank angle sensor assembly

Fig. 7 Distributor disassembly. SOHC engine

SYSTEM SERVICE
Component Service
DISTRIBUTOR

Refer to **Fig. 7** for distributor overhaul procedure.

Component Replacement
DISTRIBUTOR

Refer to **Fig. 8** for replacement proce-

dures, noting the following:
1. Turn crankshaft until No. 1 cylinder is at compression top dead center.
2. Align distributor housing and gear mating marks, **Fig. 9.**
3. Install distributor into engine while aligning distributor installation flange with mounting stud.

CRANK ANGLE SENSOR
Removal

1. Disconnect crank angle sensor electrical connections.

2. Remove retaining nut and washer.
3. Remove crank angle sensor.

Installation

1. Turn crankshaft until No. 1 cylinder is at compression top dead center.
2. Align sensor housing and gear mating marks, **Fig. 10.**
3. Install crank angle sensor into engine while aligning installation flange with mounting stud.

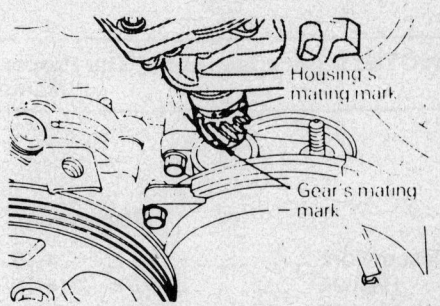

Housing's mating mark.

Gear's mating mark

CR1119100067000X

Fig. 9   Distributor mark alignment. SOHC engine

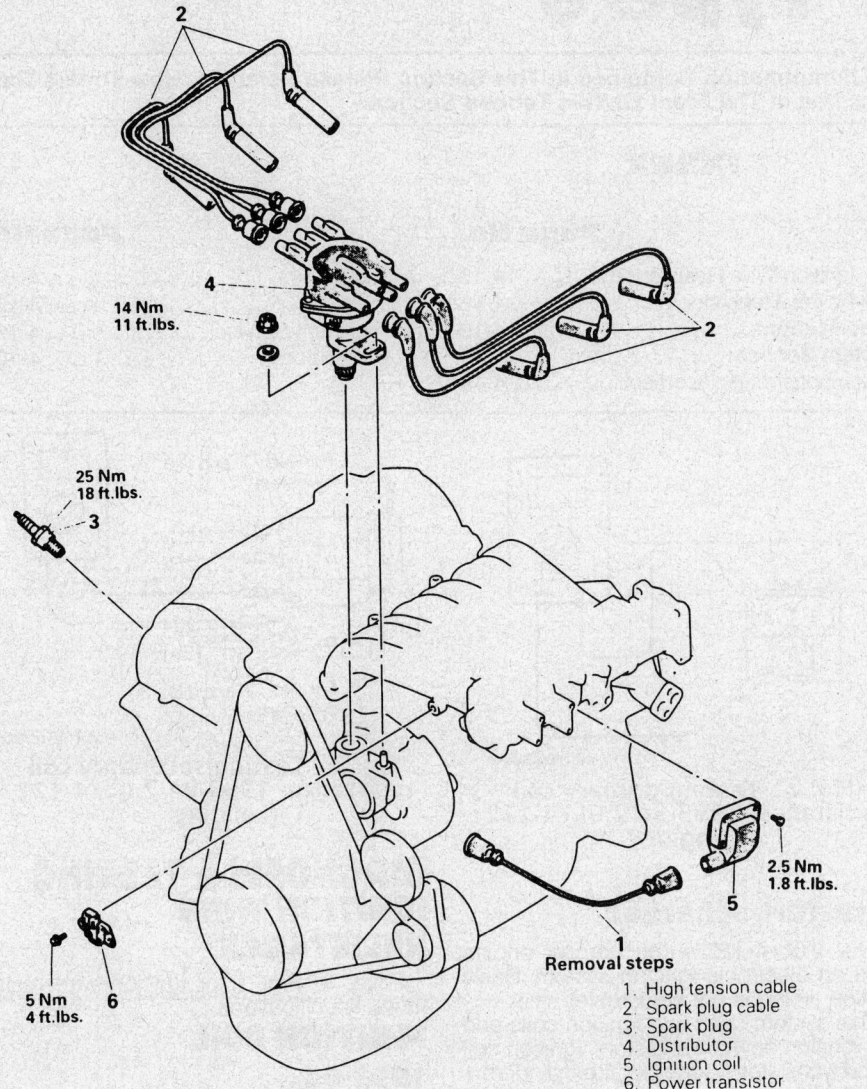

14 Nm
11 ft.lbs.

25 Nm
18 ft.lbs.

2.5 Nm
1.8 ft.lbs.

5 Nm
4 ft.lbs.

Removal steps

1. High tension cable
2. Spark plug cable
3. Spark plug
4. Distributor
5. Ignition coil
6. Power transistor

CR1119100066000X

Fig. 8   Distributor replacement. SOHC engine

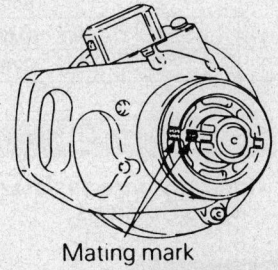

Mating mark

CR1119100135000X

Fig. 10   Crank angle sensor mark alignment. DOHC engine

SPECIFICATIONS

Distributor No.	Basic Timing	Spark Advance Test @ 2000 RPM
1993—95		
T5T42671	5°	①
1996		
T5T43071	5°	①

①—Controlled by engine control unit.

NOTE: If Uncertain About The Proper Use Of Information Contained In This Section, Please Refer To "How To Use This Manual" Located In The Front Of This Tabbed Section.

INDEX

	Page No.
Description:	4-18
1993-94	4-18
1995-96	4-18
Diagnosis & Testing:	4-18
Ignition Coil	4-18

	Page No.
Ignition Wire Resistance	4-18
Power Transistor	4-18
Specifications	4-19
System Service:	4-19
Component Replacement	4-19

	Page No.
1993-94	4-19
1995-96	4-19
Component Service	4-19
Distributor	4-19

Engine	Cylinder wire	Resistance, Ohms
1993–94		
1.8L	1	10,100
	2	11,500
	3	12,000
	4	13,000
2.0L	1	5800
	2	8400
	3	10,600
	4	9700
1995–96		
All	—	22,000

Fig. 1 Ignition wire resistance specifications

DESCRIPTION

1993-94

The ignition system used on these models is controlled by the multi-point injection control unit. As the distributor shaft (1.8L/4-107 models) or crank angle sensor (2.0L/4-122 models) rotates, ignition signals are sent from the control unit to the power transistor, thus causing ignition coil primary winding current to flow from the ignition coil negative terminal through the power transistor. When this current is grounded or interrupted repeatedly, high voltage is built up in the secondary winding of the ignition coil, and is then routed to the spark plugs for ignition.

1995-96

Less Turbocharger

The 2.0L/4-122 non-turbo engine uses an electronic ignition system. Basic ignition timing is not adjustable.

The Powertrain Control Module (PCM) determines spark advance. The system's three main components are the coil pack, crankshaft position sensor and camshaft position sensor.

The crankshaft position sensor and camshaft position sensor are Hall Effect devices that generate pulses which are input to the PCM. The PCM then calculates injector sequence and ignition timing.

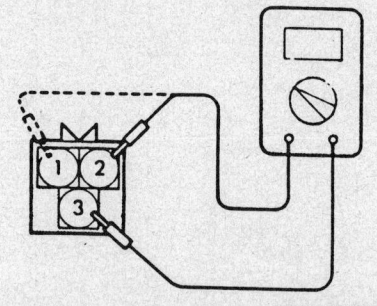

Fig. 2 Testing primary coil resistance. 1993-94 2.0L/4-122 engine

With Turbocharger

The 2.0L/4-122 turbocharged engine uses an electronic ignition system. Basic ignition timing is not adjustable.

This system uses two ignition coils and two ignition power transistors. Ignition coil A and transistor A together fire cylinders 1 and 4, while ignition coil B and transistor B fire together fire cylinder 2 and 3.

Interruption of the primary current flowing in the primary side of ignition coil A generates a high voltage in the secondary side of coil A. The high voltage generated is applied to the spark plugs of cylinder 1 and 4. At the same time the sparks are generated at both spark plugs, if one cylinder is on the compression stroke, the other cylinder is on the exhaust stroke. Ignition of the compressed air/fuel mixture occurs only in the cylinder which is on the compression stroke. The same system uses coil B to ignite cylinder 2 and 3.

The Engine Control Module (ECM) controls the two ignition power transistors (A and B) to turn them alternately on and off. This causes the primary currents in the ignition coils (A and B) to be alternately interrupted and allowed to fire the cylinders.

The ECM determines which ignition coil should be controlled by input signals from camshaft position sensor and crankshaft position sensor.

When the engine is cold or operated at high altitude, the ignition timing is advanced to provide optimum performance. If knocking occurs, the ignition timing is gradually retarded until knocking ceases.

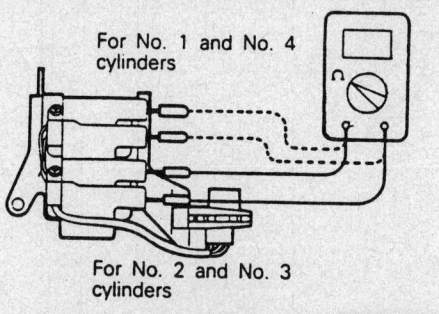

Fig. 3 Testing secondary coil resistance. 1993-94 2.0L/4-122 engine

DIAGNOSIS & TESTING
IGNITION WIRE RESISTANCE

Refer to **Fig. 1** for ignition wire resistance specifications.

IGNITION COIL

1993-94
1.8L/4-107 Engine

1. Measure resistance between primary coil terminals 1 and 2.
2. Replace ignition coil if resistance is not within .9-1.2 ohms.
3. Measure resistance between secondary terminal and terminal 1 or 2.
4. Replace ignition coil if resistance is not within 19,000-27,000 ohms.

2.0L/4-122 Engine

1. Measure resistance between ignition coil connector terminals 2 and 3, then between terminals 1 and 3, **Fig. 2**.
2. If resistance is not within .70-.86 ohm on 1993 models, replace ignition coil.
3. Disconnect ignition coil and measure resistance between high-voltage terminals for cylinder numbers 1 and 4, then between terminals for cylinder numbers 2 and 3, **Fig. 3**.
4. If resistance is not within 11,300-15,300 on 1993 models, replace ignition coil.

1995-96

1. Measure primary coil resistance between connector terminal 3 (power) and each coil terminal, **Fig. 4**.

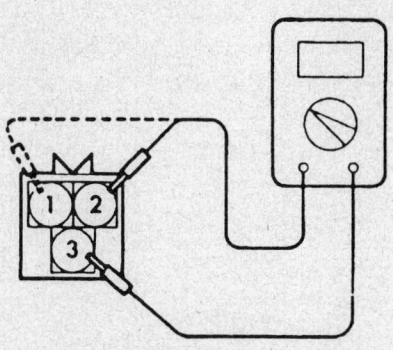

Fig. 4 Testing primary coil resistance. 1995–96

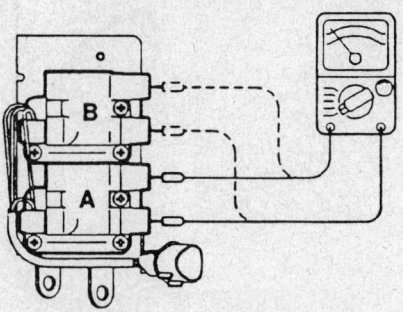

Fig. 5 Testing secondary coil resistance. 1995–96

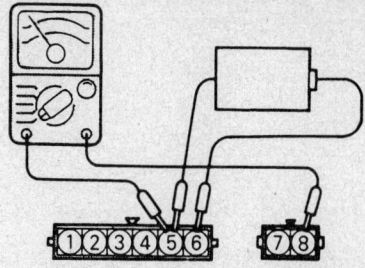

CR1119000072000X

Fig. 6 Testing power transistor. 1993–94 1.8L/4-107 engine

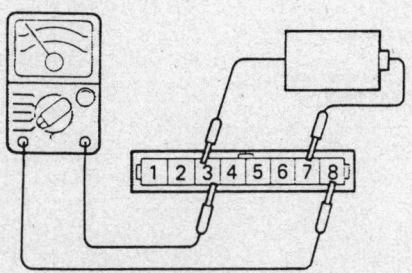

Fig. 7 Testing power transistor for cylinder Nos. 1 & 4. 1993–94 w/2.0L/4-122 engine

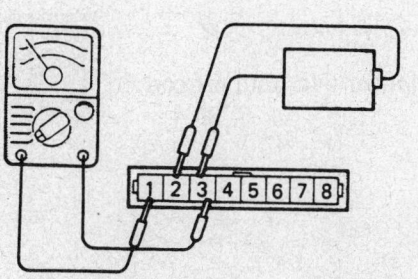

CR1119200174000X

Fig. 8 Testing power transistor for cylinder Nos. 2 & 3. 1993–94 2.0L/4-122 engine

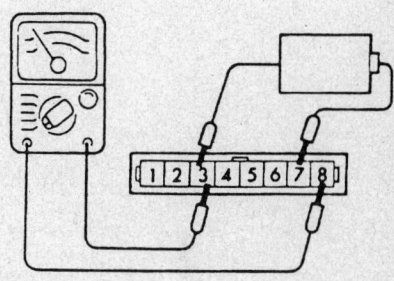

Fig. 9 Testing power transistor for cylinder Nos. 1 & 4. 1995–96

Terminal 7 and (+) terminal	Terminal 8 and terminal 3
Connected	Continuity
Unconnected	No continuity

Fig. 10 Continuity testing chart for cylinder Nos. 1 & 4. 1995–96

Terminal 2 and (+) terminal	Terminal 1 and terminal 3
Connected	Continuity
Unconnected	No continuity

Fig. 12 Continuity testing chart for cylinder Nos. 2 & 3. 1995–96

2. Resistance should be within .70-.86 ohms.
3. Measure secondary coil resistance between coil high voltage terminals, **Fig. 5.**
4. Resistance should be within 11,3000-15,000 ohms.

POWER TRANSISTOR

1993–94

1.8L/4-107 Engine

1. Connect negative lead of 1.5 volt power supply to terminal 5 of power transistor and positive lead to terminal 6, **Fig. 6.**
2. Connect negative probe of an analog type circuit tester to terminal 8 and positive probe to terminal 5.
3. Ensure continuity exists when power supply positive lead is connected to terminal 6 and there is no continuity

Fig. 11 Testing power transistor for cylinder Nos. 2 & 3. 1995–96

when positive lead is disconnected.
4. If results are not as specified in step 3, replace power transistor.

2.0L/4-122 Engine

1. Test power transistor for cylinder numbers 1 and 4 as follows:
   a. Connect negative lead of 1.5 volt power supply to terminal 3 of power transistor and positive lead to terminal 7, **Fig. 7.**
   b. Connect negative probe of an analog type circuit tester to terminal 8 and positive probe to terminal 3, **Fig. 7.**
   c. Ensure continuity exists when power supply positive lead is connected to terminal 7 and that there

is no continuity when positive lead is disconnected.
   d. Replace power transistor if results are not as specified in steps e and

2. Repeat step 1 for cylinder numbers 2 and 3 by connecting power supply to terminals 3 (-) and 2 (+), then checking continuity between terminals 1 (-) and 3 (+), **Fig. 8.**

1995–96

1. Using a suitable analog type ohmmeter, test Nos. 1 and 4 on coil side as follows:
   a. Connect negative terminal of 1.5V power supply to terminal 3 of ignition power transistor.
   b. Test for continuity between terminal 8 and terminal 3, while terminal 7 and the positive terminal are connected and disconnected, **Figs. 9 and 10.**

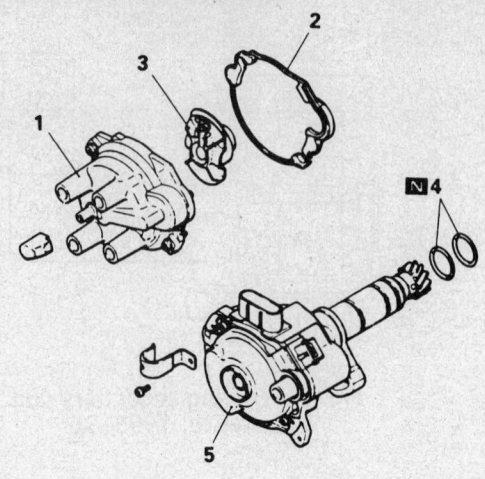

Disassembly steps
1. Distributor cap
2. Packing
3. Rotor
4. O-ring
5. Housing & shaft assembly

NOTE
(1) Reverse the disassembly procedures to reassemble
(2) **N** : Non-reusable parts

CR1119000074000X

Fig. 13 Distributor overhaul procedure. 1993–94 1.8L/4-107 engine

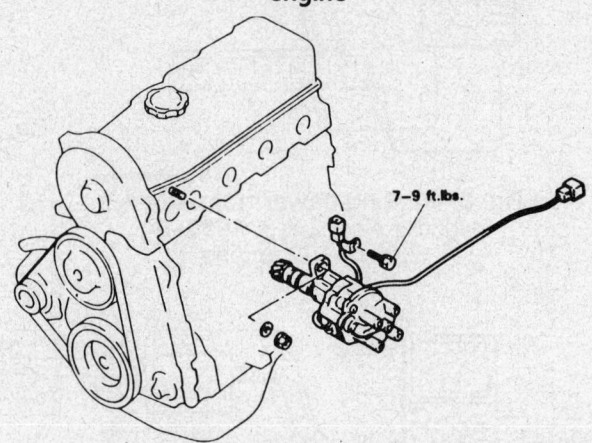

7–9 ft.lbs.

CR1119000075000X

Fig. 14 Distributor replacement. 1993–94 1.8L/4-107 engine

c. Replace ignition power transistor if not to specifications.
2. Using a suitable analog type ohmmeter, test Nos. 2 and 3 on coil side as follows:
   a. Connect negative terminal of 1.5V power supply to terminal 3 of ignition power transistor.
   b. Test for continuity between terminal 1 and terminal 3 while terminal 2 and the positive terminal are connected and disconnected, **Figs. 11 and 12.**
   c. Replace ignition power transistor if not to specifications.

SYSTEM SERVICE
Component Service
DISTRIBUTOR
1993–94

Refer to **Fig. 13** for distributor overhaul procedures.

Component Replacement
1993–94
DISTRIBUTOR
1.8L/4-107 Engine

Refer to **Fig. 14** during replacement of distributor, noting the following during installation:
1. Ensure No. 1 cylinder is at TDC.
2. Before sliding distributor into cylinder block, align mating mark on distributor housing with corresponding mark on distributor gear.
3. When installing distributor gear, align mating mark on distributor flange with center of installation stud.

CRANK ANGLE SENSOR
2.0L/4-122 Engine

Refer to **Fig. 15** during replacement of crank angle sensor, noting the following during installation:
1. Ensure No. 1 cylinder is at TDC.
2. Align mating mark on crank angle sensor housing with notch in plate.

1995–96
CAMSHAFT POSITION SENSOR

Refer to **Fig. 16** during camshaft position sensor replacement.

CRANKSHAFT POSITION SENSOR

Refer to **Fig. 16** during crankshaft position sensor replacement.

KNOCK SENSOR

Refer to **Fig. 17** during knock sensor replacement.

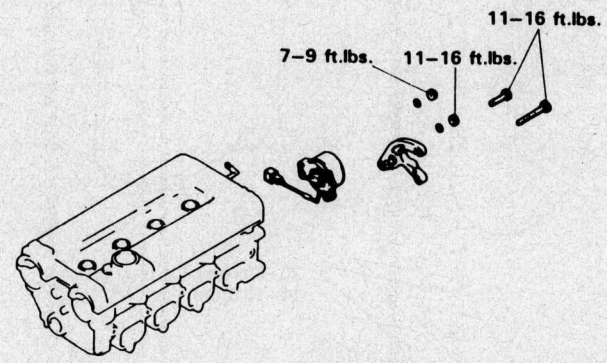

CR1119000076000X

Fig. 15 Crank angle sensor replacement. 1993–94 2.0L/4-122 engine

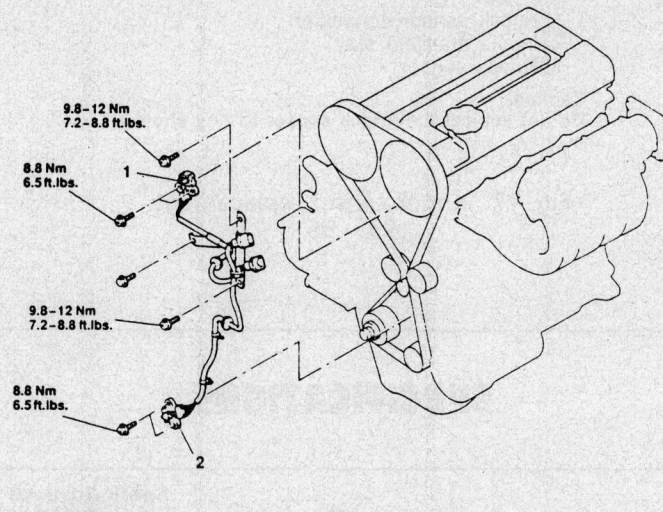

Removal steps
1. Camshaft position sensor
2. Crankshaft position sensor

Fig. 16 Camshaft and crankshaft position sensor replacement. 1995–96

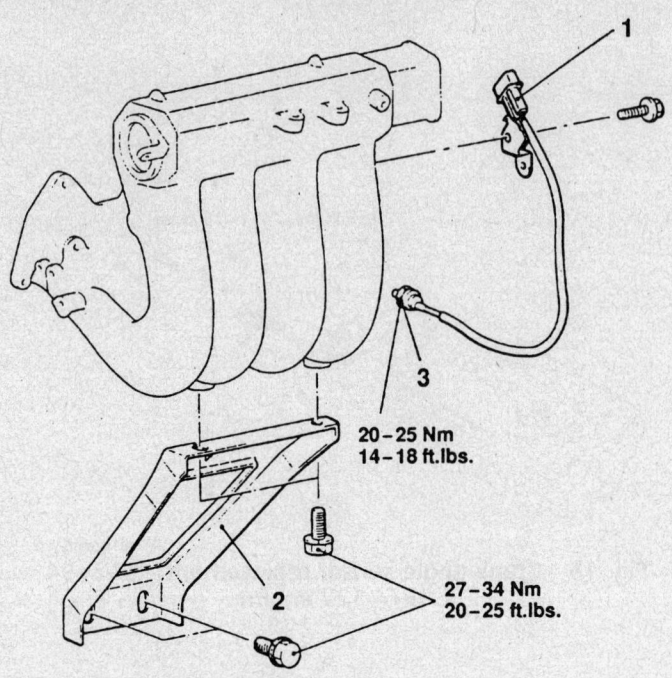

**20–25 Nm
14–18 ft.lbs.**

**27–34 Nm
20–25 ft.lbs.**

Removal steps
1. Knock sensor connector
2. Intake manifold stay
3. Knock sensor

Caution
Do not subject the knock sensor to any shocks.

Fig. 17   Knock sensor replacement.
1995–96

SPECIFICATIONS

Distributor No.	Basic Timing	Spark Advance Test @ 2000 RPM
1993—94		
T6T57371	5°	①

①—Controlled by engine control unit.

FUEL INJECTIⱭN

TABLE OF CONTENTS

	Page No.
MULTI-POINT FUEL INJECTION	6-1
SINGLE POINT FUEL INJECTION	5-1

Single Point Fuel Injection

NOTE: If Uncertain About The Proper Use Of Information Contained In This Section, Please Refer To "How To Use This Manual" Located In The Front Of This Manual.

NOTE: On Air Bag Equipped Models, Refer To "Air Bag System Precautions" Located In The Front Of This Manual For System Disarming & Arming Procedures.

NOTE: Electrical Symbol & Wire Color Code Identification Located In The Front Of This Manual May Be Used As An Aid When Using Wiring Circuits Found In This Section.

INDEX

	Page No.
Body Code Identification	5-1
Description:	5-2
Components	5-2
Diagnosis & Testing:	5-4
Accessing Diagnostic Trouble Codes	5-4
Using Diagnostic Readout Box (DRB)	5-4
Using Malfunction Indicator (Power Loss/Check Engine) Lamp	5-4
Clearing Diagnostic Trouble Codes	5-8
Component Testing	5-8
Throttle Body Minimum Air Flow Test	5-8
Diagnostic Trouble Code Interpretation	5-4
Diagnostic Trouble Code (TC) Tests	5-7
No Diagnostic Trouble Code (NTC)	

	Page No.
Tests	5-7
No Start (NS) Tests	5-7
Verification (VER) Tests	5-7
Visual Inspection	5-4
Diagnostic Chart Index	5-12
Precautions:	5-2
Air Bag Systems	5-2
Fuel System Pressure Relief	5-2
Sensor Specifications	5-2
System Service:	5-53
Adjustments	5-54
Ignition Timing	5-54
Component Replacement	5-53
Automatic Idle Speed (AIS) Motor Assembly & Idle Air Control (IAC) Motors	5-54
Canister Purge Solenoid	5-54
Electric Exhaust Gas Recirculation	

	Page No.
Transducer (EET)	5-54
Fuel Injector	5-53
Manifold Absolute Pressure Sensor	5-54
Oxygen Sensor	5-54
Pressure Regulator	5-53
Single Board Engine Controller (SBEC), Single Board Engine Controller II (SBEC II) Or Powertrain Control Module (PCM)	5-54
Throttle Body	5-53
Throttle Body Temperature Sensor	5-54
Throttle Position Sensor	5-54
Fuel System Pressure Relief	5-53

BODY CODE IDENTIFICATION

Body Code	Model	Body Code	Model
1993		**1994**	
AA	Acclaim	AA	Acclaim
	LeBaron Landau		Spirit
	Spirit	AJ	LeBaron Convertible
AC	Dynasty	AP	Shadow
	New Yorker Salon		Sundance
AG	Daytona	**1995**	
AJ	LeBaron Coupe/Convertible	AA	Acclaim
AP	Shadow		Spirit
	Sundance	AJ	LeBaron Convertible
AY	Imperial		
	New Yorker Fifth Ave.		

SENSOR SPECIFICATIONS

Sensor	Resistance, Ohms	
	At 70°F	At 200°F
Charge Temp.	7000—13,000	700—1000
Coolant Temp.	7000—13,000	700—1000
Throttle Body Temp.	5600—14,600	400—1500

PRECAUTIONS

AIR BAG SYSTEMS

Refer to "Air Bag System Precautions" in the front of this manual for system disarming and arming procedures.

FUEL SYSTEM PRESSURE RELIEF

The electronic fuel injection system is under a constant pressure of approximately 39 psi. Before servicing the fuel pump, fuel lines, fuel filter, throttle body or fuel injector, the fuel system pressure must be released as described under "System Service."

DESCRIPTION

The electronic, single point fuel injection system, **Figs. 1 and 2**, uses a pre-programmed Single Board Engine Controller II (SBEC II) or a Powertrain Control Module (PCM) that regulates ignition timing, air/fuel ratio, emission control devices, cooling fan, charging system and idle speed. The engine controller has the capability to update and revise its programming to meet changing operating conditions.

The engine controller receives inputs from various sensors, switches and relays. All inputs to the engine controller are converted into signals. These signals cause change to either fuel flow at injector or ignition timing or both.

If a problem is found in a major system, this information is stored in the engine controller memory. Information on this problem can be displayed by a instrument panel malfunction indicator (check engine) lamp or by connecting a suitable diagnostic read out tool and reading a numbered display code (trouble code) which directly relates to a general problem.

COMPONENTS

Single Board Engine Controller II (SBEC II) & Powertrain Control Module (PCM)

The SMEC and SBEC contains circuits necessary to energize the ignition coil, fuel injectors and alternator field in order to minimize electrical noise in the passenger compartment. The engine controller is a digital computer containing a microprocessor. This module receives input signals

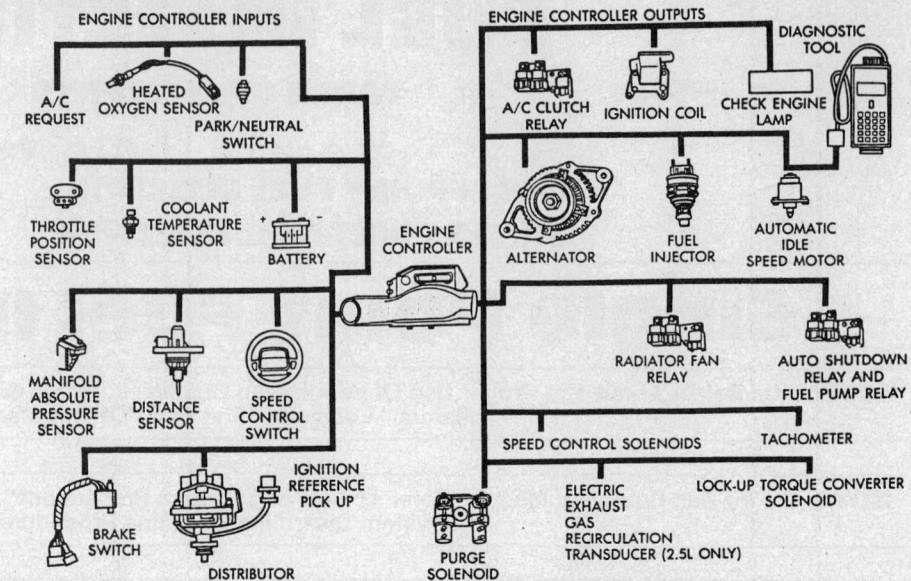

Fig. 1 Fuel injection system schematic

Fig. 2 Engine controller

from various switches and sensors. It then computes fuel injector pulse width, spark advance, ignition coil dwell, idle speed, purge, and cooling fan turn on and alternator charge rate.

The Automatic Shutdown (ASD) relay, mounted externally, is turned On and Off by the engine controller in response to distributor pickup signal. If no distributor signal is present, the ADS relay is not activated and power is shutoff from fuel injector and ignition coil. The engine controller contains a voltage converter which converts battery voltage to a regulated 8 volts output which powers distributor pickup.

Manifold Absolute Pressure (MAP) Sensor

The MAP sensor is mounted under hood on the strut tower. The MAP sensor monitors intake manifold vacuum through a line connected to the throttle body. The sensor converts manifold vacuum (negative pressure) and barometric pressure into electrical signals and transmits these signals to the engine controller. The module uses these signals to monitor engine load and is used with data from other sensors to determine correct air fuel mixture for vehicle operating conditions.

Oxygen Sensor (O2S)

The oxygen sensor produces voltage signals when exposed to oxygen in the exhaust gasses. The oxygen content in the exhaust gasses is directly proportional to the air fuel mixture entering the engine, and the voltage signal produced by the sensor is inversely proportional to the amount of oxygen remaining in the exhaust gasses. The engine controller uses these signals to determine air fuel mixtures entering the engine.

The oxygen sensor is mounted in the exhaust manifold, and the sensing element must be heated by exhaust gasses before the sensor begins to produce voltage signals. When exhaust gas oxygen content is high (lean mixtures), the sensor produces a low voltage. When oxygen content is low (rich mixtures), the sensor produces a higher voltage.

Coolant Temperature Sensor

The coolant temperature sensor is mounted in the thermostat housing and allows the engine controller to monitor engine operating temperature in order to provide proper air/fuel mixtures. The sensor provides a variable resistance which is proportional to coolant temperature. When the engine is cold and sensor resistance is low, the engine controller provides richer air/fuel mixtures and increases engine idle speed to provide acceptable cold engine performance and allow quick warm up. The coolant temperature sensor is also used for cooling fan control.

Throttle Body Temperature Sensor

The throttle body mounted temperature sensor allows the engine controller to monitor fuel temperature. The engine controller uses this information to provide the proper air/fuel mixtures for a hot restart condition.

Throttle Position Sensor (TPS)

The TPS is mounted on the throttle body and is senses the angle of the throttle plate opening. The sensor produces a voltage signal which increases and decreases according to throttle position. The engine controller uses these voltage signals to

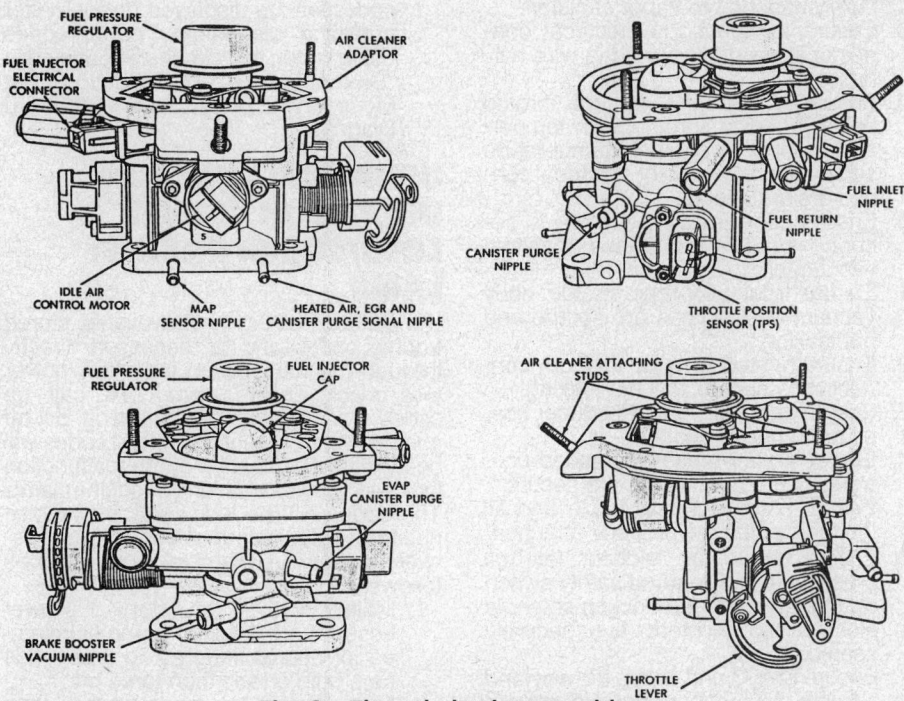

Fig. 3 Throttle body assembly component identification

tailor air/fuel mixtures for varying conditions such as idle, wide open throttle, acceleration and deceleration.

Switch Inputs

Various switches provide information to the engine controller. These switches include the idle, neutral safety, A/C compressor clutch, speed control and brake lamp switches. If one or more of these switches is sensed as being On, the engine controller signals the idle speed motor to change idle speed to a pre-set RPM. In addition, when the A/C is on and the throttle plate is above a specified angle, the wide open throttle cutout relay prevents the A/C clutch from being energized until throttle angle is reduced.

Automatic Idle Speed (AIS) Motor & Idle Air Control (IAC) Motors

The AIS and IAC motors is operated by the engine controller and controls engine idle speed by controlling air flow through the throttle body bypass channel. The engine controller computes proper idle speed based in signals from vehicle and engine sensors and the switch inputs, and transmits voltage signals to the AIS and IAC motors to open or close the bypass channel in order to maintain the proper engine speed.

Basic, no-load idle speed is determined by the amount of air flowing through the throttle body past the closed throttle plate. The AIS and IAC motors alters idle speed by allowing increased air flow through the bypass channel; increasing idle speed when the channel is opened and decreasing idle speed when the channel is closed. In addition, the AIS and IAC motors is signaled to open the bypass channel during deceleration to prevent stalling and mixture enrichment caused by sudden closing of the throttle plate.

Auto Shutdown (ASD) & Fuel Pump Relays

The engine controller operates the ASD relay and fuel pump relay through one ground path. The engine controller operates the relays by switching the ground path on and off. The ASD relay connects battery voltage to the fuel injector and ignition coil. The fuel pump relay connects battery voltage to the fuel pump and oxygen sensor heating element.

On except Acclaim, LeBaron Landau, and Spirit, the ASD and fuel pump relay are located in the power distribution center. On Acclaim, LeBaron Landau, and Spirit, the ASD and fuel pump relay are mounted on the LH fenderwell, next to the strut tower.

Malfunction Indicator (Check Engine) Lamp

The malfunction indicator (check engine) lamp illuminates for three seconds each time the ignition key is turned to the On position as a bulb check. The malfunction indicator (check engine) lamp warns the operator that the engine controller has entered a limp-in mode. During limp-in mode, the engine controller attempts to keep the system operational. The malfunction indicator (check engine) lamp signals the need for immediate service.

Signals that can trigger the malfunction indicator lamp (check engine) are as follows:
1. Coolant temperature sensor.
2. Manifold absolute pressure sensor.
3. Throttle position sensor.
4. Battery voltage input.
5. An emissions related system.
6. Charging system.

Electronic EGR Transducer (EET)

The EET is a backpressure transducer/electric vacuum solenoid assembly.

The EET assembly mounts above the EGR valve.

The solenoid turns the vacuum supply to the transducer On and Off. When the solenoid energizes, vacuum is prevented from flowing to the transducer. The solenoid energizes during engine warm-up, closed throttle, wide open throttle and rapid acceleration/deceleration.

Throttle Body & Fuel Injector

The throttle body assembly is mounted on the intake manifold and houses the throttle plate, fuel injector, fuel pressure regulator, temperature and position sensors, and the AIS and IAC motors, **Fig. 3.** Intake air flow is controlled by the cable operated throttle plate and by a separate bypass channel which is controlled by the AIS and IAC motors. The throttle body provides the chamber for fuel metering, atomization, and mixing atomized fuel with incoming air.

The fuel injector is a solenoid operated valve which is driven by the engine controller. Fuel is supplied to the injector at a constant pressure of 39 psi, and excess fuel is returned to the tank. When voltage is applied to the injector solenoid, a spring loaded ball is lifted off its seat and fuel is sprayed into the throttle body through 6 spray orifices. The spray orifices and injector tip design cause the fuel to be sprayed in an even conical pattern prior to entering the intake air stream.

Fuel Pressure Regulator

The mechanical fuel pressure regulator is used to maintain fuel pressure at the injector tip at a constant 39 psi. The pressure regulator uses a spring loaded diaphragm to control the fuel return port in order to maintain constant pressure. Pressurized fuel is delivered first to the fuel injector and then flows to the pressure regulator. When fuel pressure acting on the regulator diaphragm exceeds 39 psi, the regulator spring is compressed and the fuel return port is opened. When fuel pressure drops below 39 psi, spring tension causes the diaphragm to block the fuel return port. The diaphragm and spring move constantly between the open and closed positions in order to maintain constant fuel pressure at the injector tip.

Fuel Pump & Reservoir

An electric fuel pump is located in a specially designed reservoir within the fuel tank. The reservoir ensures that fuel is available at the pump inlet during all operating conditions, particularly when little fuel remains in the tank. The fuel pump is energized by the ASD relay and operates whenever the relay is activated. Fuel is drawn into the pump through a "sock type filter screen, and the pump contains an integral fuel inlet check valve to prevent drain back.

Emission Controls

The charcoal canister purge control solenoid is operated by the engine controller. When engine temperature is below a predetermined value, the engine controller completes the purge solenoid ground circuit, the solenoid is energized and purge vacuum is prevented from being applied to the canister. When engine temperature is above a predetermined value, the solenoid is de-energized and purge vacuum is applied from the port on the throttle body.

DIAGNOSIS & TESTING

The engine controller has been programmed to monitor several different circuits of the fuel injection system in order to provide a self-diagnosis function. In conjunction with the self-diagnosis function, a malfunction indicator (power loss/check engine) lamp is wired into the system to indicate a failure in the monitored circuits. The malfunction indicator (power loss/check engine) lamp is illuminated for 3 seconds whenever the engine is started as a "bulb test." However, if the engine controller detects a malfunction in one of the monitored circuits the malfunction indicator (power loss/check engine) lamp will be illuminated and will remain on as long as the ignition key remains in the on position. Illumination of the malfunction indicator (power loss/check engine) lamp indicates that the system has entered the "limp-in" mode and signals an immediate need for system service.

If vehicle performance or the malfunction indicator (power loss/check engine) lamp indicate fuel injection system malfunctions, certain procedures should be followed. Prior to suspecting the fuel injection service as the cause for complaints, ensure engine and all related systems are in proper operating condition. After checking related systems, inspect fuel injection components and connecting harnesses as outlined in "Visual Inspection," repair system as indicated, the road test vehicle to check system operation. If service performed during visual inspection does not correct observed malfunctions, or if malfunction indicator (power loss) lamp remains illuminated, refer to "Accessing Diagnostic Trouble Codes" to call up diagnostic trouble codes stored in the engine controller memory and correct as needed.

Refer to **Figs. 4 through 7** for wiring diagrams and connector terminal identification.

Visual Inspection

A visual inspection for loose, disconnected or improperly routed wiring and hoses should be made prior to attempting to diagnose fuel injection system malfunctions. The visual inspection should include the following checks:

1. Check ignition coil electrical connectors.
2. Ensure canister purge solenoid and MAP sensor electrical connector is secure.
3. Ensure EGR diagnostic solenoid electrical connector is secure, if equipped.
4. Ensure vacuum connection at canister purge solenoid and EGR diagnostic solenoid is secure and not leaking.
5. Ensure MAP sensor vacuum hose is attached at MAP sensor.
6. Ensure alternator wiring and belt are correctly installed and tightened.
7. Ensure vapor canister hoses are securely attached to vapor canister.
8. Ensure throttle body electrical connector is securely seated in wire harness.
9. Ensure AIS and IAC motors, throttle position sensor, throttle body temperature sensor, coolant temperature sensor and fuel injector electrical connectors are secure.
10. Ensure hose from PCV valve is securely attached to intake manifold vacuum port.
11. Ensure front and rear throttle body vacuum connections are secure and not leaking.
12. Ensure heated air door vacuum connection is secure and not leaking.
13. Ensure backpressure transducer hoses are properly attached.
14. Ensure power brake and speed control vacuum connectors are secure.
15. Ensure battery ground cable and all ignition cables are properly attached.
16. Ensure distributor, radiator fan, oil pressure switch, neutral safety switch and torque converter lockup solenoid electrical connectors are securely seated.
17. Ensure SMEC and SBEC 60-way and 14-way electrical connectors are securely seated in socket.
18. Ensure oxygen sensor, distance sensor and starter relay ground electrical connectors are securely seated.
19. Ensure engine ground strap is attached at engine and dash panel.
20. Ensure fuel pump hose and electrical connectors are properly attached.

Accessing Diagnostic Trouble Codes

If a problem is sensed by the engine controller, often enough to be considered a malfunction, a diagnostic trouble code is stored in the module memory. If the problem is repaired, or ceases to occur, the module will cancel the diagnostic trouble code after 50-100 vehicle key On/Off cycles. Diagnostic trouble codes that remain in the module memory can be called up and displayed either by using diagnostic tool or by observing flashes of the malfunction indicator (power loss) lamp. Diagnostic trouble codes can be obtained using the following procedures:

USING DIAGNOSTIC READOUT BOX (DRB)

1. Connect tester to diagnostic connector located in engine compartment near the engine controller, **Figs. 8 through 10.**
2. Start engine, if possible, move transmission selector through range and cycle A/C compressor on and off, then stop engine.
3. Place tester read/hold switch in the read position.
4. Turn ignition switch on, off, on, off and on within 5 seconds.
5. Malfunction indicator (power loss/check engine) lamp should light for approximately 2 to 3 seconds, then go out and stored diagnostic trouble codes will be displayed on tool. After obtaining diagnostic trouble codes using tester, test circuits as outlined in "Switch Tests" and "Actuation Test Mode (ATM) Tests" under "On-Board Diagnosis."

USING MALFUNCTION INDICATOR (POWER LOSS/CHECK ENGINE) LAMP

If suitable tester is not available, stored trouble codes and be accessed directly through the malfunction indicator (power loss/check engine) lamp. To call up codes, cycle ignition switch on, off, on, off and on within 5 seconds. Stored codes will be indicated by flashes of the malfunction indicator (power loss/check engine) lamp. The codes will be indicated as two digit numbers, with a four second pause between codes. An example of a code is as follows:

1. Malfunction Indicator (Power Loss/Check Engine) Lamp illuminated for approximately 2 to 3 seconds as a bulb check, then turns off.
2. Lamp flashes two times, pauses, then flashes six times.
3. Lamp pauses for approximately four seconds.
4. Lamp flashes three times, pauses, then flashes one time.
5. This would indicate that code 26 and 31 are stored. The lamp will continue to flash until all stored codes have been displayed.

Once the lamp starts flashing the stored diagnostic trouble codes, it cannot be stopped. If a code is missed, the entire procedure must be repeated. The lamp will not indicate if oxygen feedback system is switching lean-rich or if idle motor system is operational. The lamp also cannot be used to perform actuation test mode, sensor test mode or engine running test mode.

Diagnostic Trouble Code Interpretation

The following diagnostic trouble codes indicate the result of a failure, but do not identify the failed component. The diagnostic charts use diagnostic trouble codes as accessed by a diagnostic scan tool rather than by the vehicle Malfunction Indicator Lamp (MIL) because the scan tool can pinpoint a wider range of problems with greater accuracy. The MIL diagnostic trouble codes, however, can be used in some cases as a starting point for diagnosis. The following are examples of available MIL diagnostic trouble codes:

Code 11—No distributor reference during engine cranking.

Code 12 (1994-95 models)—Battery input to PCM disconnect indicator.

Code 13—Little or no change in MAP sensor signal.① ②

Code 14—MAP sensor electrical circuit. ①

Code 15—Vehicle speed/distance sensor.②

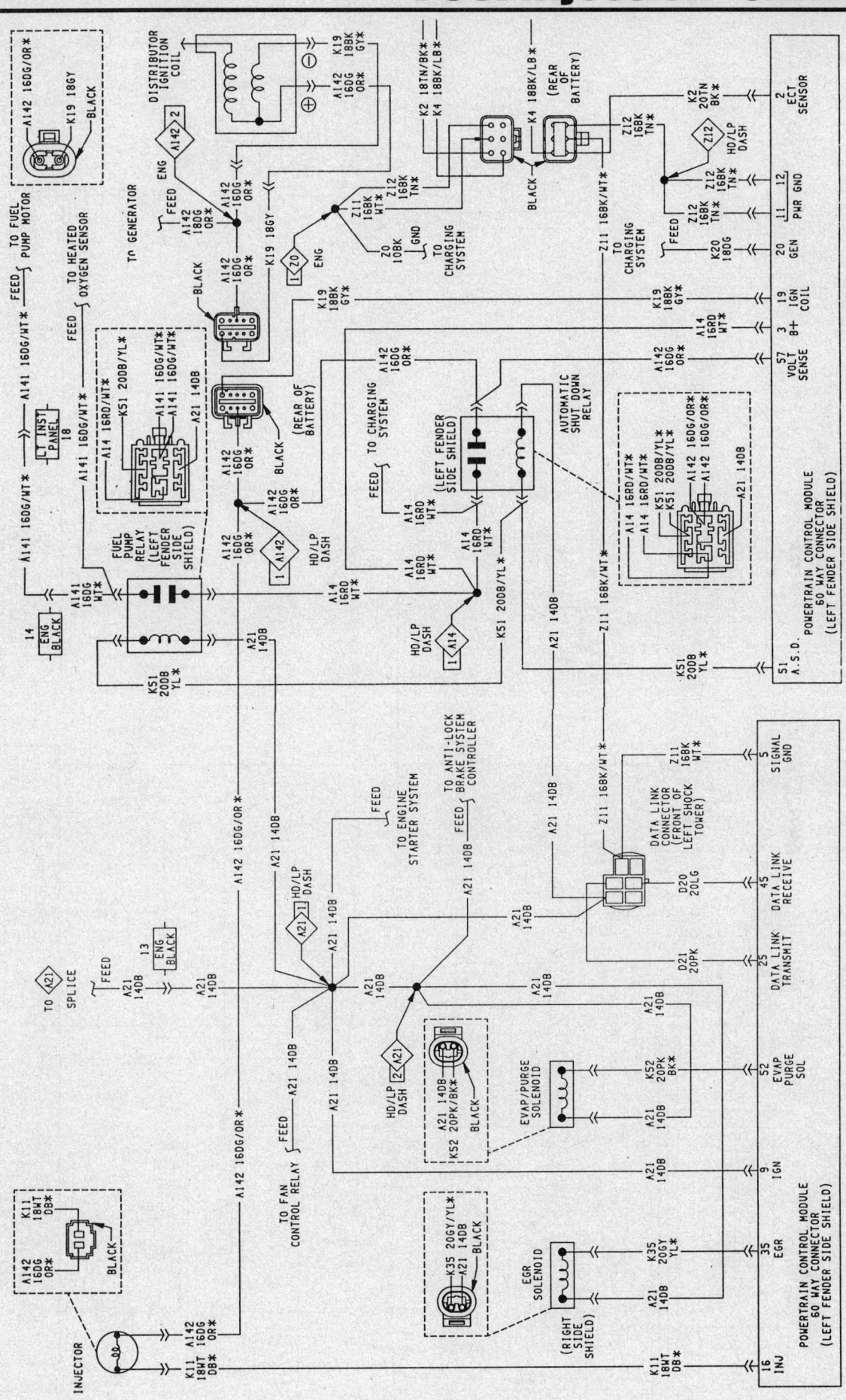

Fig. 4 Single point fuel injection system wiring circuit (Part 2 of 5). 1993

Fig. 4 Single point fuel injection system wiring circuit (Part 1 of 5). 1993

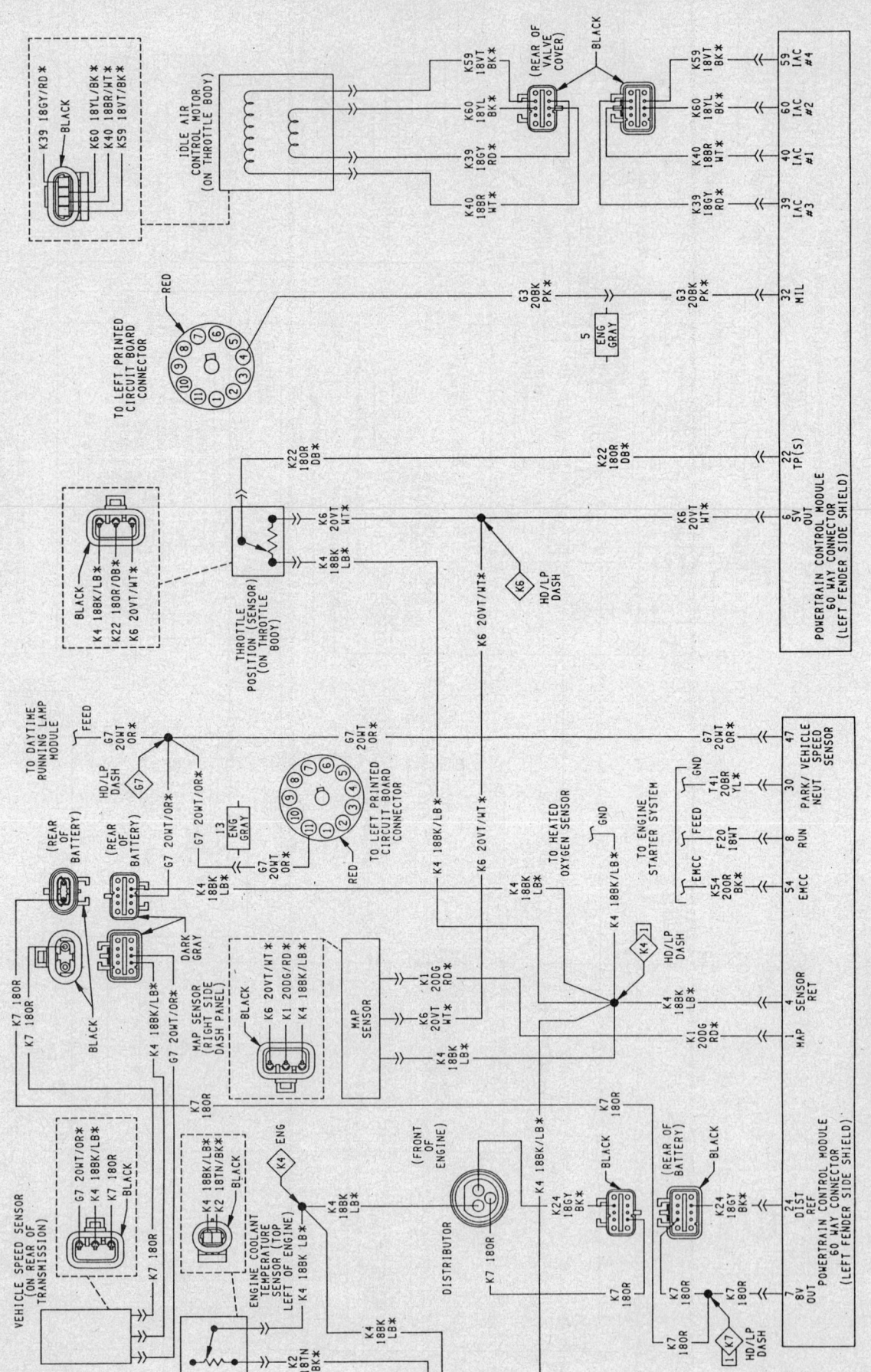

Fig. 4 Single point fuel injection system wiring circuit (Part 4 of 5). 1993

Fig. 4 Single point fuel injection system wiring circuit (Part 3 of 5). 1993

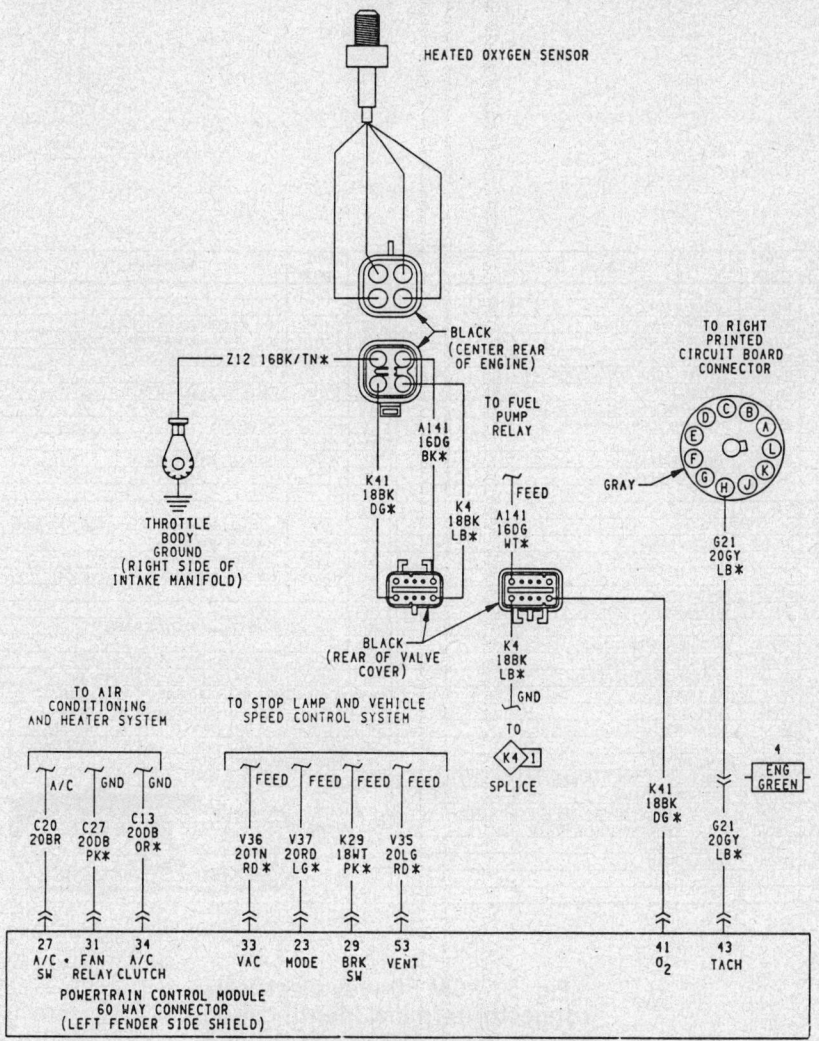

Fig. 4 Single point fuel injection system wiring circuit (Part 5 of 5). 1993

Code 17—Engine running too cool.
Code 21—Oxygen sensor circuit.②
Code 22—Coolant temperature sensor circuit.
Code 24—Throttle position sensor.① ②
Code 25—AIS motor driven circuit.②
Code 27—Fuel injector control problem.
Code 31—Purge solenoid circuit.②
Code 32—EGR diagnosis.②
Code 33—A/C cutout relay circuit.
Code 34—Speed control solenoid driver circuit.
Code 35—Fan control relay circuit.
Code 37 (1993 models)—Part throttle unlock solenoid circuit.
Code 37 (1994-95 models)—Torque converter clutch solenoid circuit.
Code 41—Charging system excess or no field circuit.① ②
Code 42—ASD relay driver.
Code 46—Battery voltage too high.① ②
Code 47—Battery voltage too low.① ②
Code 51—Oxygen feedback system stuck at lean position.②
Code 52—Oxygen feedback system stuck at rich position.②
Code 53—Internal engine controller problem.
Code 55—End of message.

Code 62—EMR mileage accumulation.
Code 63—Controller failure, EEPROM write denied.
①—**Indicates check engine lamp on.**
②—**Indicates check engine lamp on, California only.**
The following tests are used to further diagnose systems monitored by the On-Board Diagnosis (OBD) system and to also test systems or parts of a system which are not monitored by the OBD system. Prior to performing any of the following tests, check electrical and vacuum component connections as described under "Visual Inspection." **Always start at the first No Start, Driveability, No Trouble or Verification test. Starting at any other test may give inaccurate results.** After completing the test, perform appropriate verification test. Also check electrical connector terminal blades or pins for alignment and damage prior to replacing any component. Refer to **Figs. 4 through 7** as necessary for wiring diagrams and connector terminal identification.

NO START (NS) TESTS

Refer to the first No Start diagnosis chart **Fig. 11**, and the remaining charts, **Figs. 12 through 32**, for No Start diagnosis and testing.

NO DIAGNOSTIC TROUBLE CODE (NTC) TESTS

Refer to the No Diagnostic Trouble Code charts, **Figs. 33 through 49**, for diagnosis and testing.

DIAGNOSTIC TROUBLE CODE (TC) TESTS

Refer to the first Diagnostic Trouble Code chart, **Fig. 50**, and the remaining Diagnostic Trouble Code charts, **Figs. 51 through 98**, for diagnosis and testing. Refer to **Fig. 99** for Inactive Diagnostic Trouble Code Condition.

VERIFICATION (VER) TESTS

After completing diagnosis operations, perform verification tests, **Figs. 100 and 101.**

CAV	WIRE COLOR	DESCRIPTION	CAV	WIRE COLOR	DESCRIPTION
1	DG/RD*	MAP SENSOR SIGNAL	37		
2	TN/BK*	COOLANT SENSOR	38		
3	RD/WT*	DIRECT BATTERY VOLTAGE	39	GY/RD*	IDLE AIR CONTROL MOTOR #3 DRIVER
4	BK/LB*	SENSOR RETURN	40	BR/WT*	IDLE AIR CONTROL MOTOR #1 DRIVER
5	BK/WT*	SIGNAL GROUND	41	BK/DG*	OXYGEN SENSOR SIGNAL
6	VT/WT*	5.0 VOLT OUTPUT (MAP AND TPS)	42		
7	OR	8.0 VOLT OUTPUT	43	GY/LB*	TACHOMETER SIGNAL OUTPUT
8	WT	B1 VOLTAGE SENSE (START SIGNAL)	44		
9	DB	A21 SUPPLY (IGNITION START/RUN)	45	LG	SCI RECEIVE
10			46	WT/BK*	CCD (-) BUS
11	BK/TN*	POWER GROUND	47	WT/OR*	DISTANCE SENSOR SIGNAL
12	BK/TN*	POWER GROUND	48		
13			49		
14			50		
15			51	DB/YL*	AUTO SHUTDOWN RELAY AND FUEL PUMP RELAY
16	WT/DB*	INJECTOR DRIVER	52	PK/BK*	PURGE SOLENOID
17			53	LG/RD*	SPEED CONTROL VENT SOLENOID
18			54	LG/WT*	TORQUE CONVERTER CLUTCH SOLENOID
19	BK/GY*	IGNITION COIL	55		
20	DG	GENERATOR FIELD CONTROL	56		
21			57	DG/OR*	A142 CIRCUIT VOLTAGE SENSE
22	OR/DB*	THROTTLE POSITION SENSOR	58		
23	RD/LG*	SPEED CONTROL SENSE	59	VT/BK*	IDLE AIR CONTROL MOTOR #4 DRIVER
24	GY/BK*	IGNITION REFERENCE PICK-UP	60	YL/BK*	IDLE AIR CONTROL MOTOR #2 DRIVER
25	PK	SCI TRANSMIT			
26	VT/BR*	CCD (+) BUS			
27	BR	A/C SWITCH SENSE			
28					
29	WT/PK*	BRAKE SWITCH			
30	BR/LB*	PARK/NEUTRAL SWITCH (AUTO TRANS.)			
31	DB/PK*	RADIATOR FAN RELAY			
32	BK/PK*	MALFUNCTION INDICATOR LAMP (CHECK ENGINE)			
33	TN/RD*	SPEED CONTROL VACUUM SOLENOID			
34	DB/OR*	A/C CLUTCH RELAY			
35	GY/YL*	EGR SOLENOID			
36					

WIRE COLOR CODES				
		LB	LIGHT BLUE	VT	VIOLET
BK	BLACK	LG	LIGHT GREEN	WT	WHITE
BR	BROWN	OR	ORANGE	YL	YELLOW
DB	DARK BLUE	PK	PINK	*	WITH TRACER
DG	DARK GREEN	RD	RED		
GY	GRAY	TN	TAN		

CONNECTOR TERMINAL SIDE SHOWN

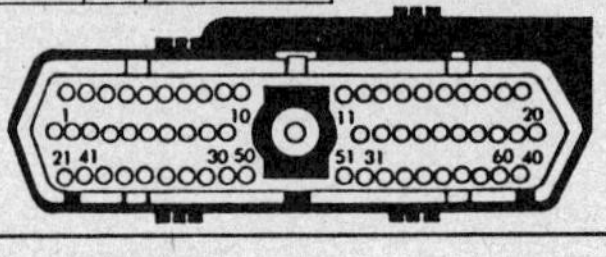

Fig. 5 PCM 60-way electrical connector terminal identification. 1993

Clearing Diagnostic Trouble Codes

Clearing diagnostic trouble codes can be accomplished in one of two ways. They may be erased by selecting "Erase Troubles" under the "Read Troubles" display on the DRB or by disconnecting the battery ground cable for at least two minutes.

Component Testing

THROTTLE BODY MINIMUM AIR FLOW TEST

1. Connect the DRB II scan tool.
2. Remove air cleaner assembly, then plug heated air door vacuum hose.
3. Start engine and allow cooling fan to cycle on and off at least once.
4. Connect suitable timing light, then disconnect coolant thermistor and set basic timing to 12° BTDC.
5. Stop engine and reconnect coolant thermistor wire.
6. Disconnect PCV valve hose from intake manifold nipple.
7. Attach tool No. C-6457, or equivalent (.125 inch orifice in attached hose), to intake manifold PCV nipple.
8. Start engine and allow to idle for at least 1 minute.
9. Using read-out tool, access Min Airflow Idle Spd in the sensor read test mode, then the following should occur:
   a. AIS and IAC motors will fully close.
   b. Idle spark advance will become fixed.
   c. Idle fuel will become enriched.
   d. Engine RPM will be displayed on diagnostic read-out tool in units of RPM x 10. For example, display 95 equals 95 x 10 which indicates 950 RPM.
10. Check idle RPM. Idle RPM should be 600-1200 RPM on models with odometer reading less than 1000 miles, or 800-1200 RPM for models with odometer reading above 1000 miles. If idle speed is not as specified, replace throttle body.
11. Shutoff engine, then remove tool No. C-6457, or equivalent, from intake manifold PCV nipple. Install PVC valve hose.
12. Remove read-out tool, then install air cleaner assembly and heated air door vacuum hose.

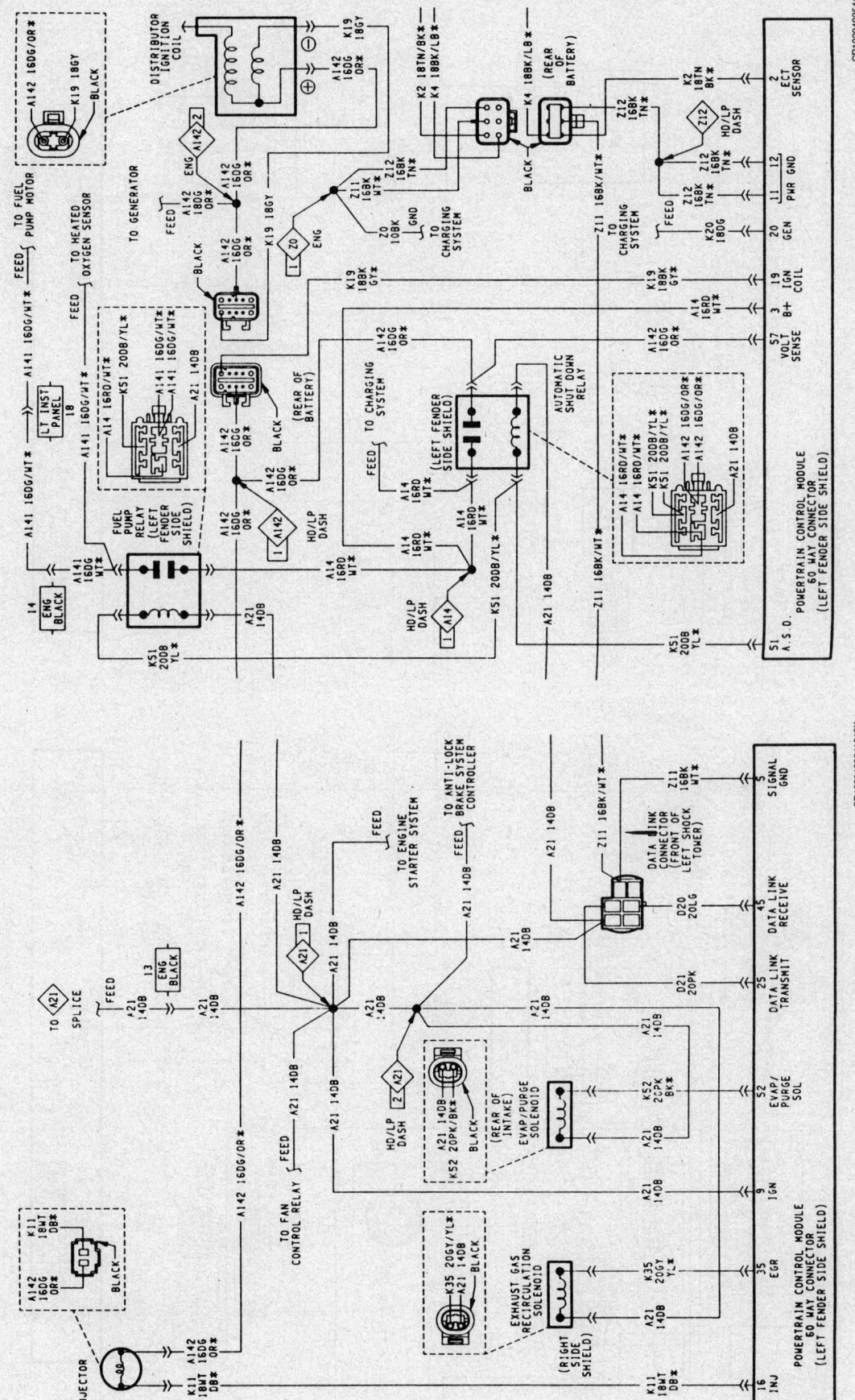

Fig. 6 Single point fuel injection system wiring circuit (Part 2 of 5). 1994-95

Fig. 6 Single point fuel injection system wiring circuit (Part 1 of 5). 1994-95

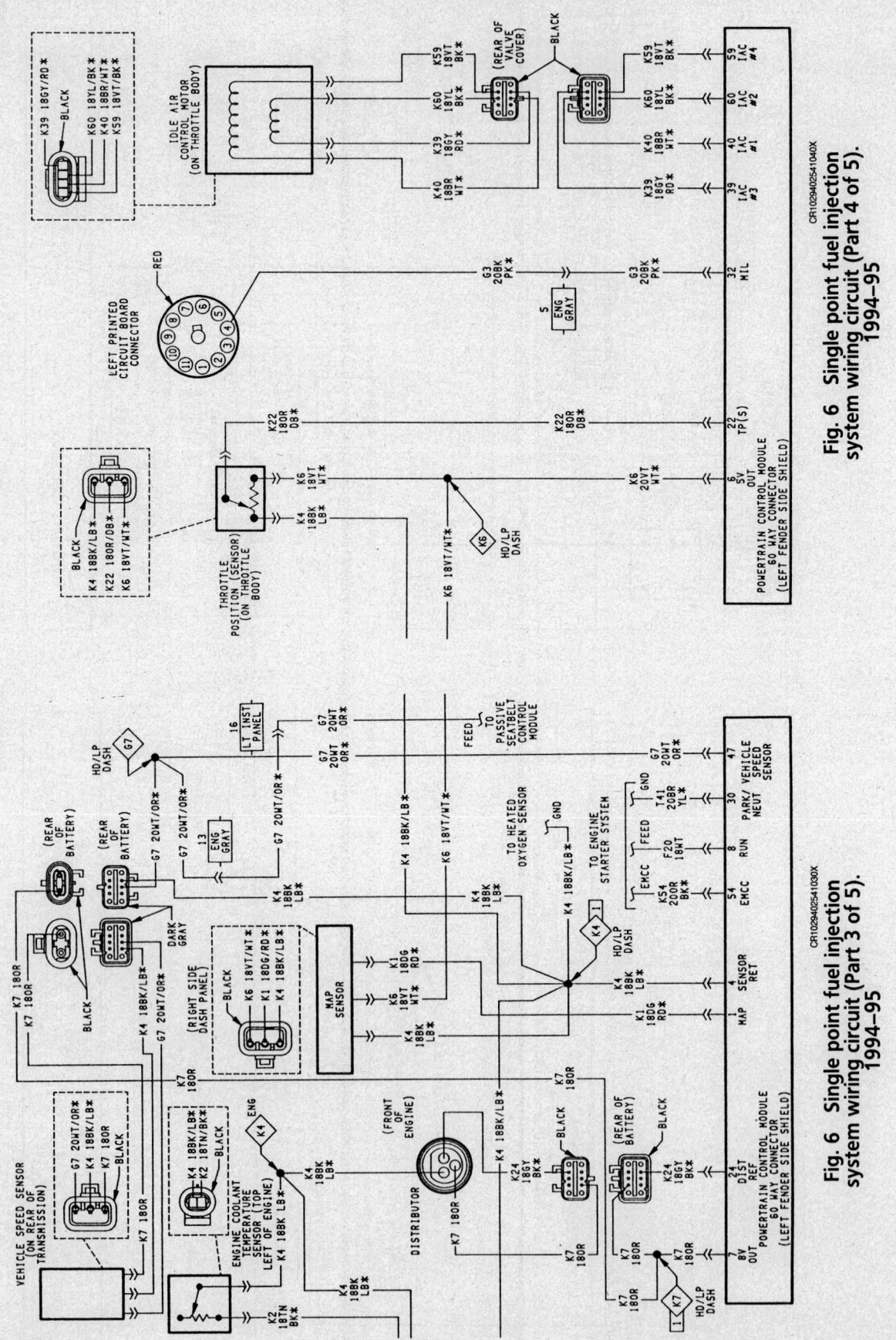

Fig. 6 Single point fuel injection system wiring circuit (Part 4 of 5). 1994–95

Fig. 6 Single point fuel injection system wiring circuit (Part 3 of 5). 1994–95

CR102940254200X

Fig. 7 PCM 60-way electrical connector terminal identification. 1994–95

CAV	WIRE COLOR	DESCRIPTION
1	DG/RD*	MAP SENSOR SIGNAL
2	TN/BK*	ENGINE COOLANT TEMPERATURE SENSOR
3	RD/WT*	DIRECT BATTERY VOLTAGE
4	BK/LB*	SENSOR RETURN
5	BK/WT*	SIGNAL GROUND
6	VT/WT*	5.0 VOLT OUTPUT (MAP and TPS)
7	OR	8.0 VOLT OUTPUT
8	WT	B1 VOLTAGE SENSE (START SIGNAL)
9	DB	A21 SUPPLY (IGNITION START/RUN)
10		
11	BK/TN*	POWER GROUND
12	BK/TN*	POWER GROUND
13		
14		
15		
16	WT/DB*	INJECTOR DRIVER
17		
18		
19	BK/GY*	IGNITION COIL
20	DG	GENERATOR FIELD CONTROL
21		
22	OR/DB*	THROTTLE POSITION SENSOR
23	RD/LG*	SPEED CONTROL SENSE
24	GY/BK*	IGNITION REFERENCE PICK-UP (DISTRIBUTOR PICK-UP)
25	PK	SCI TRANSMIT
26	VT/BR*	CCD BUS (+)
27	BR	A/C SWITCH SENSE
28		
29	WT/PK*	BRAKE SWITCH
30	BR/LB*	PARK/NEUTRAL SWITCH (AUTO TRANS)
31	DB/PK*	RADIATOR FAN RELAY
32	BK/PK*	MALFUNCTION INDICATOR LAMP (CHECK ENGINE)
33	TN/RD*	SPEED CONTROL VACUUM SOLENOID
34	DB/OR*	A/C CLUTCH RELAY
35	GY/YL*	EGR SOLENOID
36		
37		
38		
39	GY/RD*	IDLE AIR CONTROL MOTOR #3 DRIVER
40	BR/WT*	IDLE AIR CONTROL MOTOR #1 DRIVER
41	BK/DG*	HEATED OXYGEN SENSOR
42		
43	GY/LB*	TACHOMETER SIGNAL OUTPUT
44		SCI RECEIVE
45	LG	CCD BUS (-)
46	WT/BK*	
47	WT/OR*	VEHICLE SPEED SENSOR
48		
49		
50		
51	DB/YL*	AUTOMATIC SHUTDOWN RELAY AND FUEL PUMP RELAY
52	PK/BK*	EVAP PURGE SOLENOID
53	LG/RD*	SPEED CONTROL VENT SOLENOID
54	OR/BK*	TORQUE CONVERTER CLUTCH SOLENOID
55		
56		
57	DG/OR*	A1/#2 CIRCUIT VOLTAGE SENSE
58		
59	VT/BK*	IDLE AIR CONTROL MOTOR #4 DRIVER
60	YL/BK*	IDLE AIR CONTROL MOTOR #2 DRIVER

WIRE COLOR CODES:
BK BLACK   LB LIGHT BLUE   VT VIOLET
BR BROWN   LG LIGHT GREEN WT WHITE
DB DARK BLUE   OR ORANGE   YL YELLOW
DG DARK GREEN PK PINK   * WITH TRACER
GY GRAY   RD RED

CONNECTOR TERMINAL SIDE SHOWN

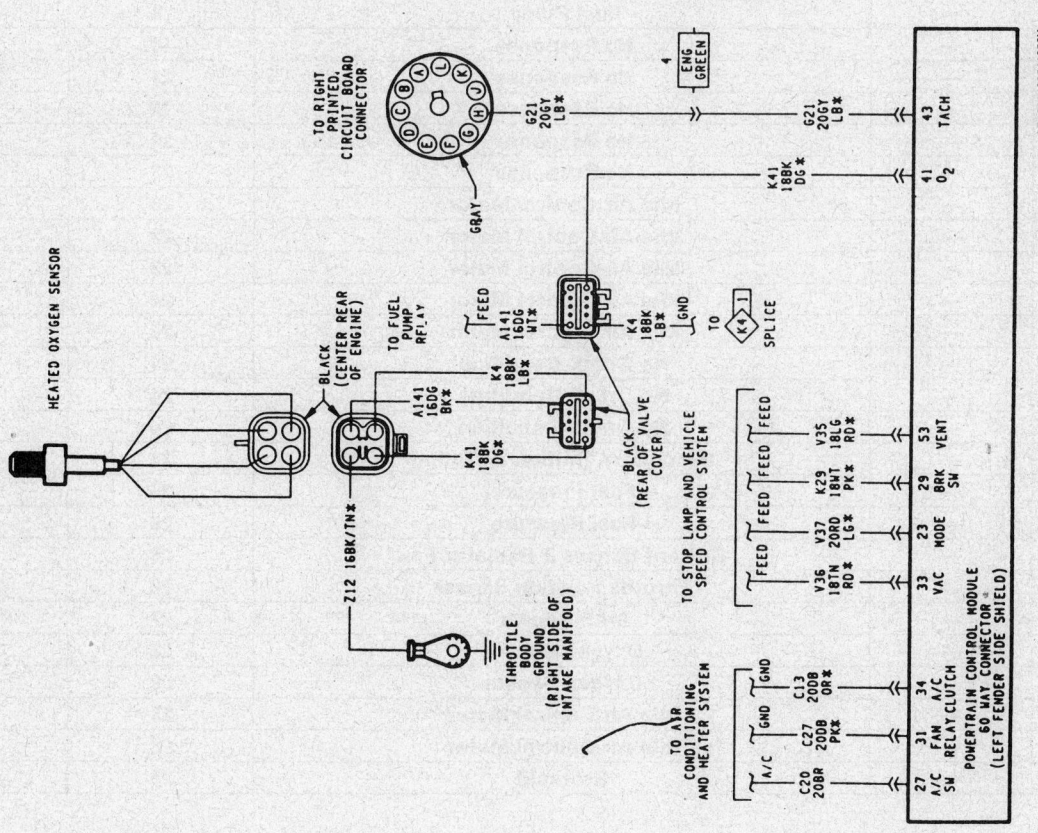

CR102940254105OX

Fig. 6 Single point fuel injection system wiring circuit (Part 5 of 5). 1994–95

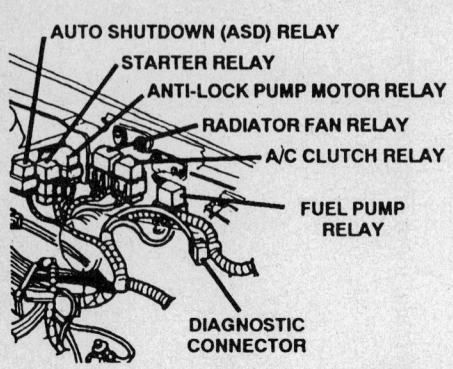

Fig. 8 Diagnostic link connector. 1993

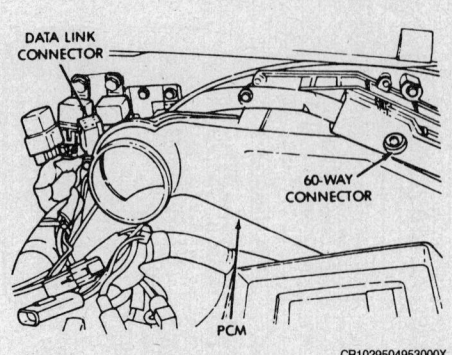

Fig. 9 Diagnostic link connector at PCM. 1994–95

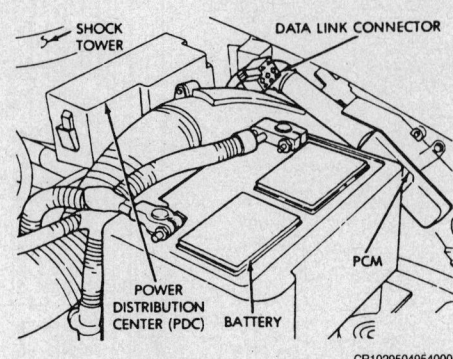

Fig. 10 Diagnostic link connector at PDC. 1994–95

DIAGNOSTIC CHART INDEX

Test	MIL Code	Description	Page No. 5-	Fig. No.
Test NS-1A	—	Qualifying No Start Condition	14	11
Test NS-2A	—	Fuel System	15	12
Test NS-3A	—	Mechanical System	15	13
Test NS-4A	—	Fuel Delivery	16	14
Test NS-4B	—	Fuel Delivery	17	15
Test NS-4C	—	Fuel Delivery	17	16
Test NS-5A	—	Fuel Pump	17	17
Test NS-5B	—	Fuel Pump	18	18
Test NS-5C	—	Fuel Pump	18	19
Test NS-6A	—	No Response	18	20
Test NS-6B	—	No Response	21	21
Test NS-6C	—	No Response	22	22
Test NS-6D	—	No Response	22	23
Test NS-6E	—	No Response	23	24
Test NS-7A	—	Idle Air Control Motor	23	25
Test NS-7B	—	Idle Air Control Motor	23	26
Test NS-7C	—	Idle Air Control Motor	23	27
Test NS-7D	—	Idle Air Control Motor	24	28
Test NS-7E	—	Idle Air Control Motor	24	29
Test NS-9A	—	No Crank Condition	24	30
Test NS-9B	—	No Crank Condition	24	31
Test NS-9C	—	No Crank Condition	24	32
Test NTC-2A	—	Secondary Ignition & Timing	25	33
Test NTC-3A	—	Fuel Pressure	25	34
Test NTC-3B	—	Fuel Pressure	26	35
Test NTC-4A	—	Coolant Sensor & Radiator Fan	26	36
Test NTC-5A	—	Throttle Position Sensor	26	37
Test NTC-6A	—	MAP Sensor	27	38
Test NTC-7A	—	Oxygen Sensor	27	39
Test NTC-7B	—	Oxygen Sensor	28	40
Test NTC-8A	—	Idle Air Control Motor	28	41
Test NTC-8B	—	Idle Air Control Motor	28	42
Test NTC-9A	—	Solenoid	28	43

Continued

DIAGNOSTIC CHART INDEX-Continued

Test	MIL Code	Description	Page No. 5-	Fig. No.
Test NTC-10A	—	PNP Switch	29	44
Test NTC-11A	—	PCM Circuits	29	45
Test NTC-12A	—	EGR System	29	46
Test NTC-13A	—	Engine Vacuum	30	47
Test NTC-14A	—	Idle Air Flow	30	48
Test NTC-15A	—	Mechanical Test	31	49
Test TC-2A	11	No Crank Reference Signal At PCM	31	50
Test TC-2B	11	No Crank Reference Signal At PCM	31	51
Test TC-2C	11	No Crank Reference Signal At PCM	32	52
Test TC-2D	11	No Crank Reference Signal At PCM	32	53
Test TC-3A	—	No Cam Sync Signal At PCM	33	54
Test TC-4A	14	MAP Sensor Voltage Too Low	33	55
Test TC-5A	14	MAP Sensor Voltage Too High	34	56
Test TC-6A	—	Improper Change In MAP Sensor Signal	34	57
Test TC-7A	21	O2 Signal Stays At Center	35	58
Test TC-8A	52	O2 Signal Above Center (Rich)	35	59
Test TC-9A	51	O2 Signal Below Center (Lean)	36	60
Test TC-10A	21	O2 Signal Shorted To Voltage	36	61
Test TC-11A	—	No Vehicle Speed Sensor Signal	36	62
Test TC-11B	—	No Vehicle Speed Sensor Signal	37	63
Test TC-11C	—	No Vehicle Speed Sensor Signal	37	64
Test TC-11D	—	No Vehicle Speed Sensor Signal	37	65
Test TC-11E	—	No Vehicle Speed Sensor Signal	38	66
Test TC-12A	25	Idle Air Control Motor Circuits	38	67
Test TC-12B	25	Idle Air Control Motor Circuits	39	68
Test TC-12C	25	Idle Air Control Motor Circuits	39	69
Test TC-12D	25	Idle Air Control Motor Circuits	39	70
Test TC-13A	27	Injector Control Circuits	39	71
Test TC-13B	27	Injector Control Circuits	40	72
Test TC-17A	32	EGR System Failure	40	73
Test TC-18A	32	EGR Solenoid Circuit	41	74
Test TC-19A	31	EVAP Solenoid Circuit	41	75
Test TC-20A	37	Torque Converter Clutch Solenoid Circuit	42	76
Test TC-21A	—	Throttle Position Sensor Voltage Low	43	77
Test TC-22A	—	Throttle Position Sensor Voltage High	43	78
Test TC-23A	—	Throttle Body Temp Sensor Voltage Low	44	79
Test TC-24A	—	Throttle Body Temp Sensor Voltage High	45	80
Test TC-25A	—	EGR Sensor Voltage Low	45	81
Test TC-26A	—	EGR Sensor Voltage High	46	82
Test TC-27A	42	No ASD Relay Output Voltage At PCM	46	83
Test TC-28A	42	Auto Shutdown Relay Control Circuit	47	84
Test TC-29A	35	Radiator Fan Control Relay Circuit	47	85
Test TC-30A	—	Low Speed Fan Control Relay Circuit	48	86
Test TC-31A	—	High Speed Fan Control Relay Circuit	48	87
Test TC-32A	—	A/C Clutch Relay Circuit	49	88
Test TC-36A	62	PCM Failure SRI Mileage Not Stored	50	89
Test TC-37A	—	Battery Temp Sensor Voltage	50	90
Test TC-38A	47	Charging System Voltage Too Low	50	91
Test TC-39A	46	Charging System Voltage Too High	50	92
Test TC-39B	—	PCM Regulating Circuit	51	93
Test TC-40A	41	Generator Field Not Switching	51	94
Test TC-40B	41	Generator Field Not Switching	52	95

Continued

DIAGNOSTIC CHART INDEX–Continued

Test	MIL Code	Description	Page No. 5-	Fig. No.
Test TC-41A	34	Speed Control Solenoid Circuits	52	96
Test TC-41B	34	Speed Control Solenoid Circuits	52	97
Test TC-41C	34	Speed Control Solenoid Circuits	53	98
Test TC-42A	—	Inactive Trouble Code Condition	53	99
Test VER-1	—	No Start Verification Test	53	100
Test VER-2	—	Road Test Verification	53	101

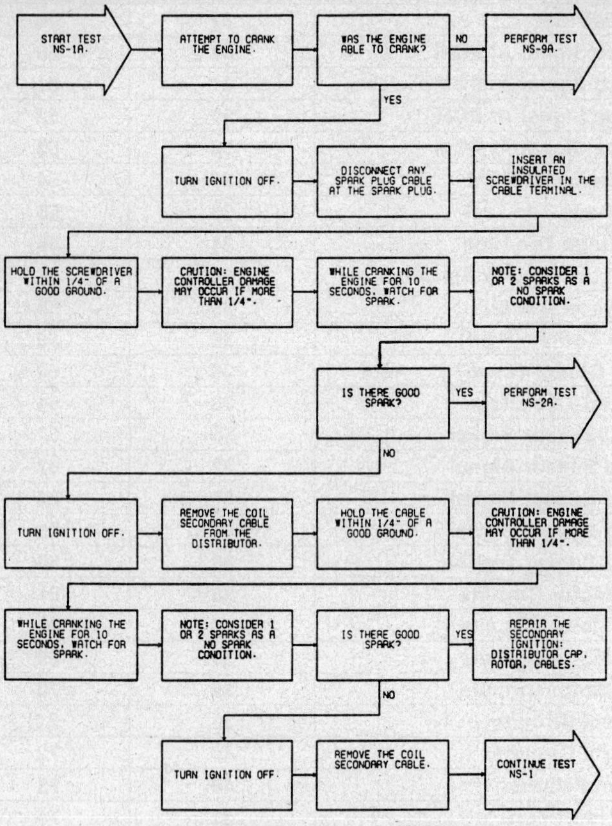

Fig. 11 Test NS-1A: Qualifying No Start Condition (Part 1 of 4)

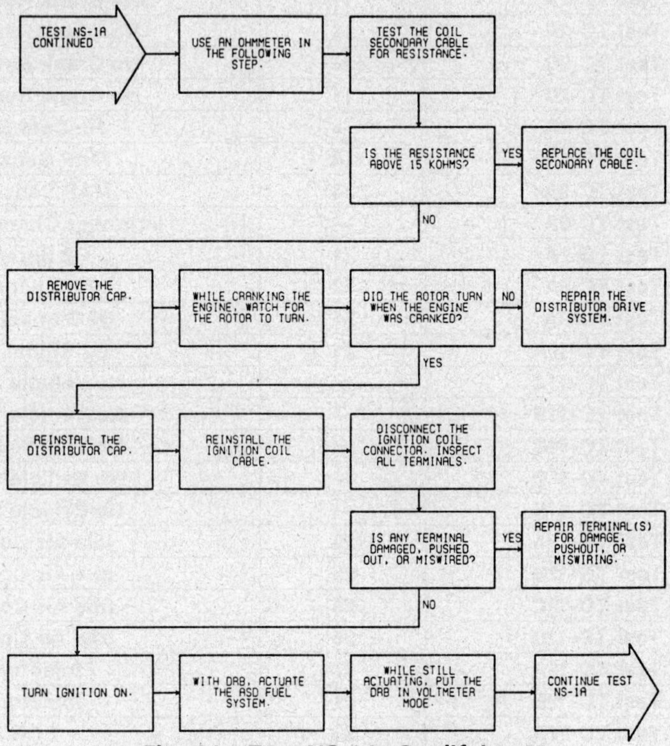

Fig. 11 Test NS-1A: Qualifying No Start Condition (Part 2 of 4)

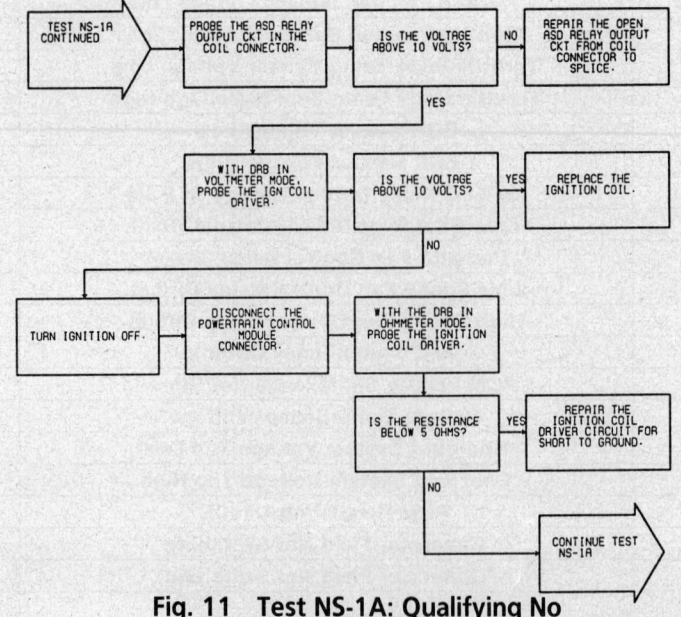

Fig. 11 Test NS-1A: Qualifying No Start Condition (Part 3 of 4)

SINGLE POINT FUEL INJECTION

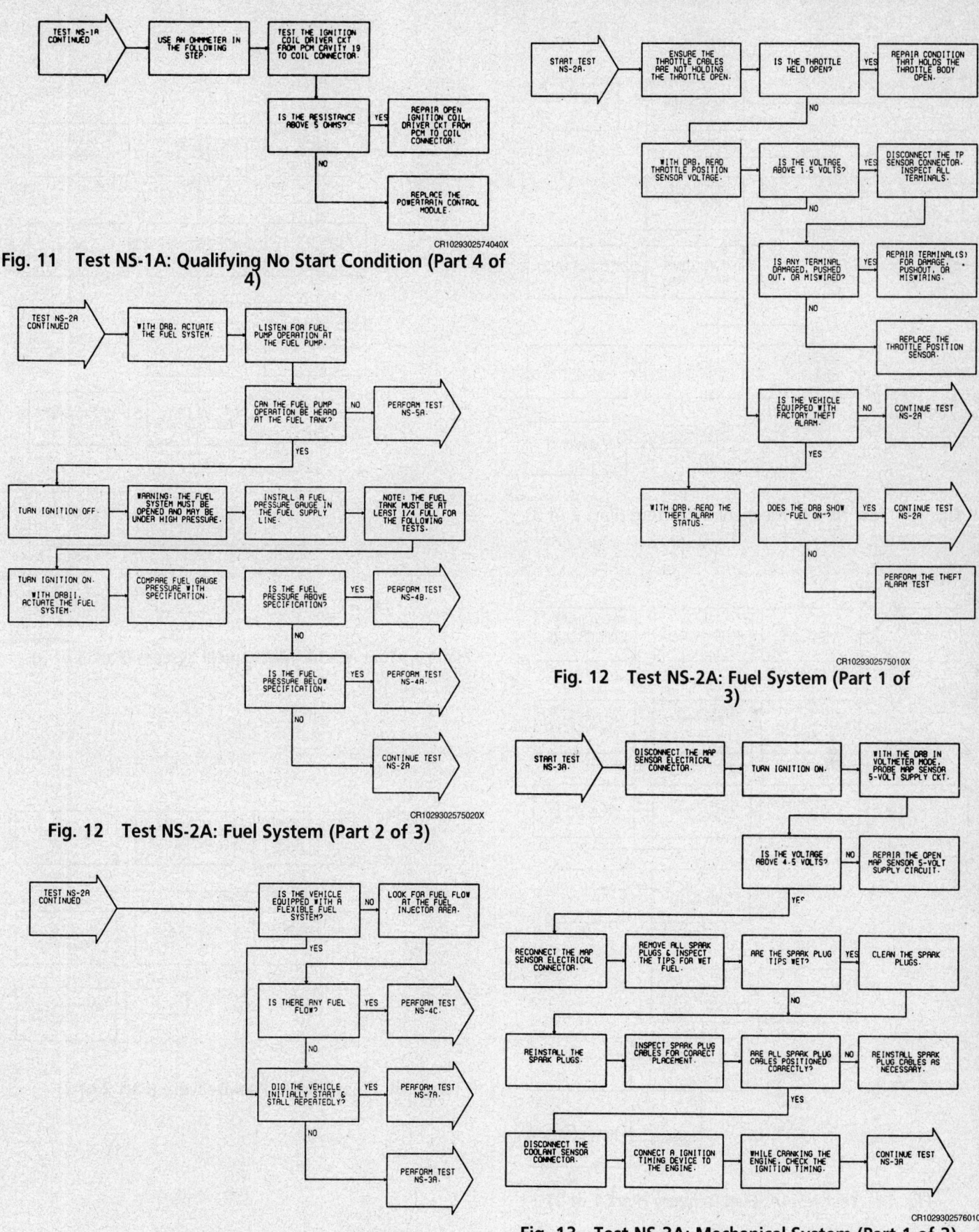

Fig. 11 Test NS-1A: Qualifying No Start Condition (Part 4 of 4)

CR1029302574040X

Fig. 12 Test NS-2A: Fuel System (Part 2 of 3)

CR1029302575020X

Fig. 12 Test NS-2A: Fuel System (Part 3 of 3)

CR1029302575030X

Fig. 12 Test NS-2A: Fuel System (Part 1 of 3)

CR1029302575010X

Fig. 13 Test NS-3A: Mechanical System (Part 1 of 3)

CR1029302576010X

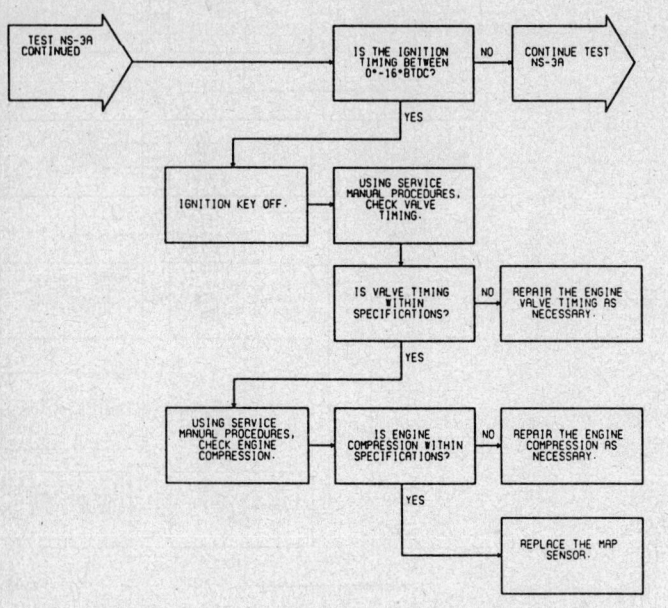

Fig. 13   Test NS-3A: Mechanical System (Part 2 of 3)

CR1029302576020X

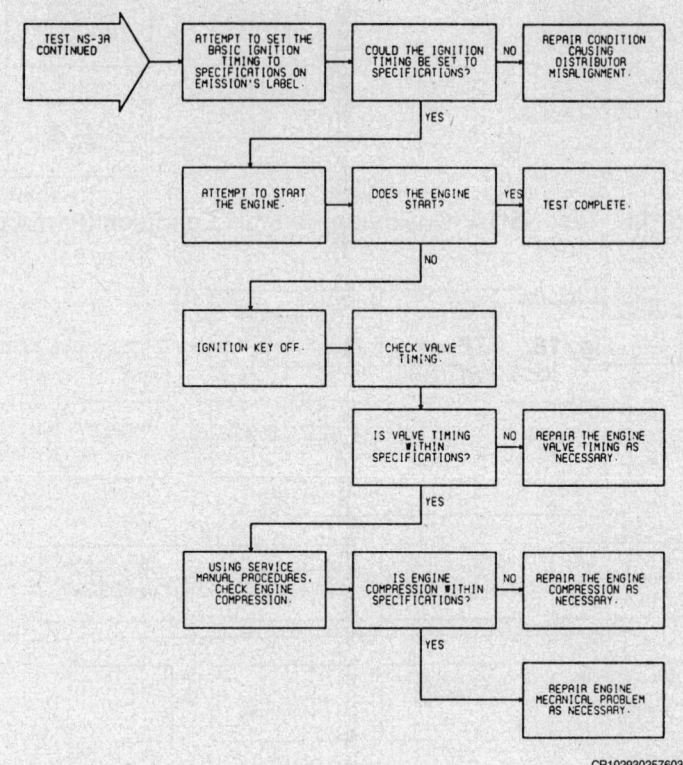

CR1029302576030X

Fig. 13   Test NS-3A: Mechanical System (Part 3 of 3)

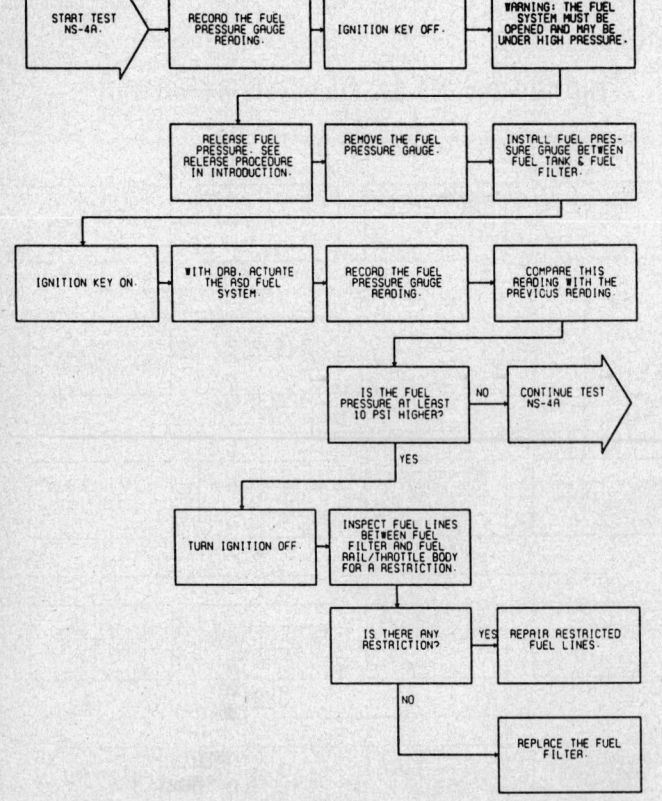

CR1029302577010X

Fig. 14   Test NS-4A: Fuel Delivery (Part 1 of 2)

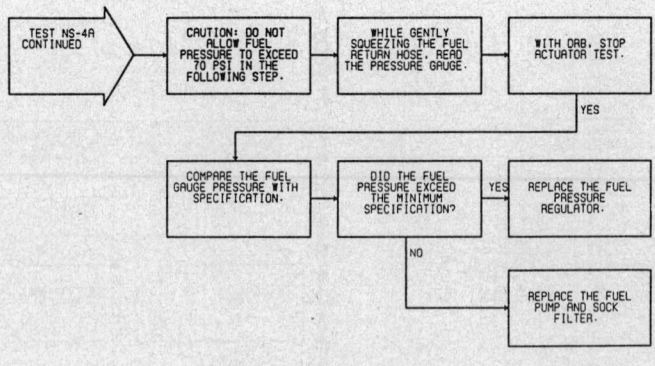

CR1029302577020X

Fig. 14   Test NS-4A: Fuel Delivery (Part 2 of 2)

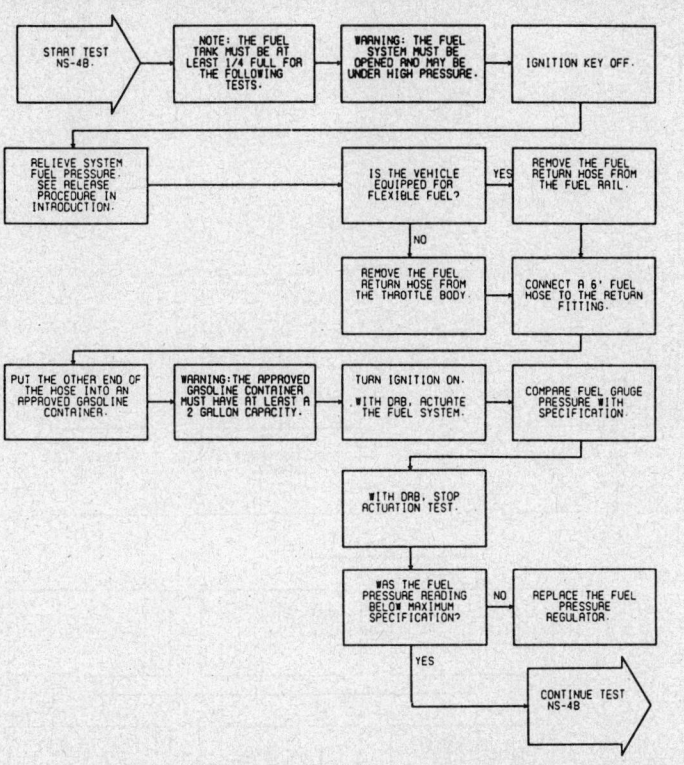

Fig. 15   Test NS-4B: Fuel Delivery (Part 1 of 2)

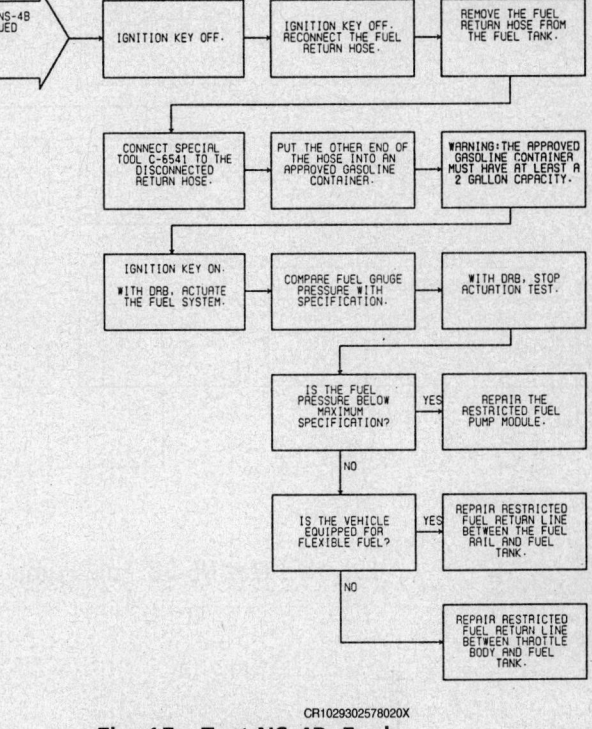

Fig. 15   Test NS-4B: Fuel Delivery (Part 2 of 2)

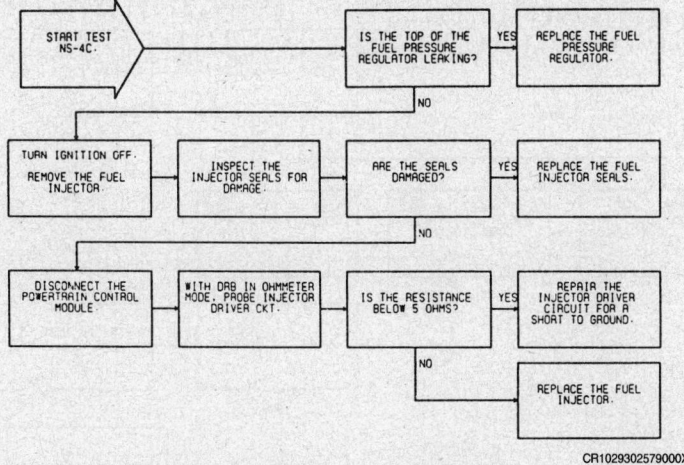

Fig. 16   Test NS-4C: Fuel Delivery

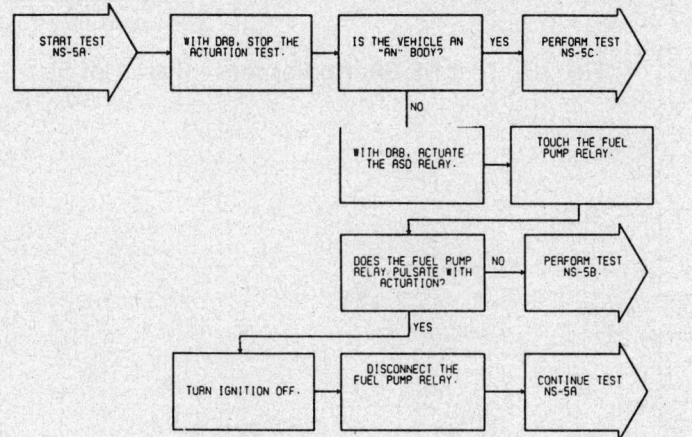

Fig. 17   Test NS-5A: Fuel Pump (Part 1 of 2)

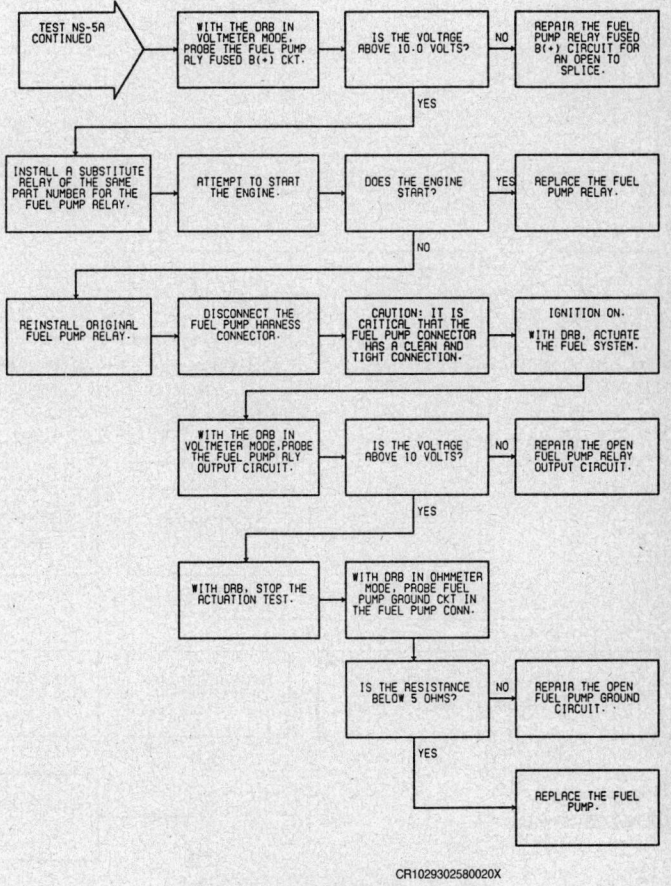

Fig. 17   Test NS-5A: Fuel Pump (Part 2 of 2)

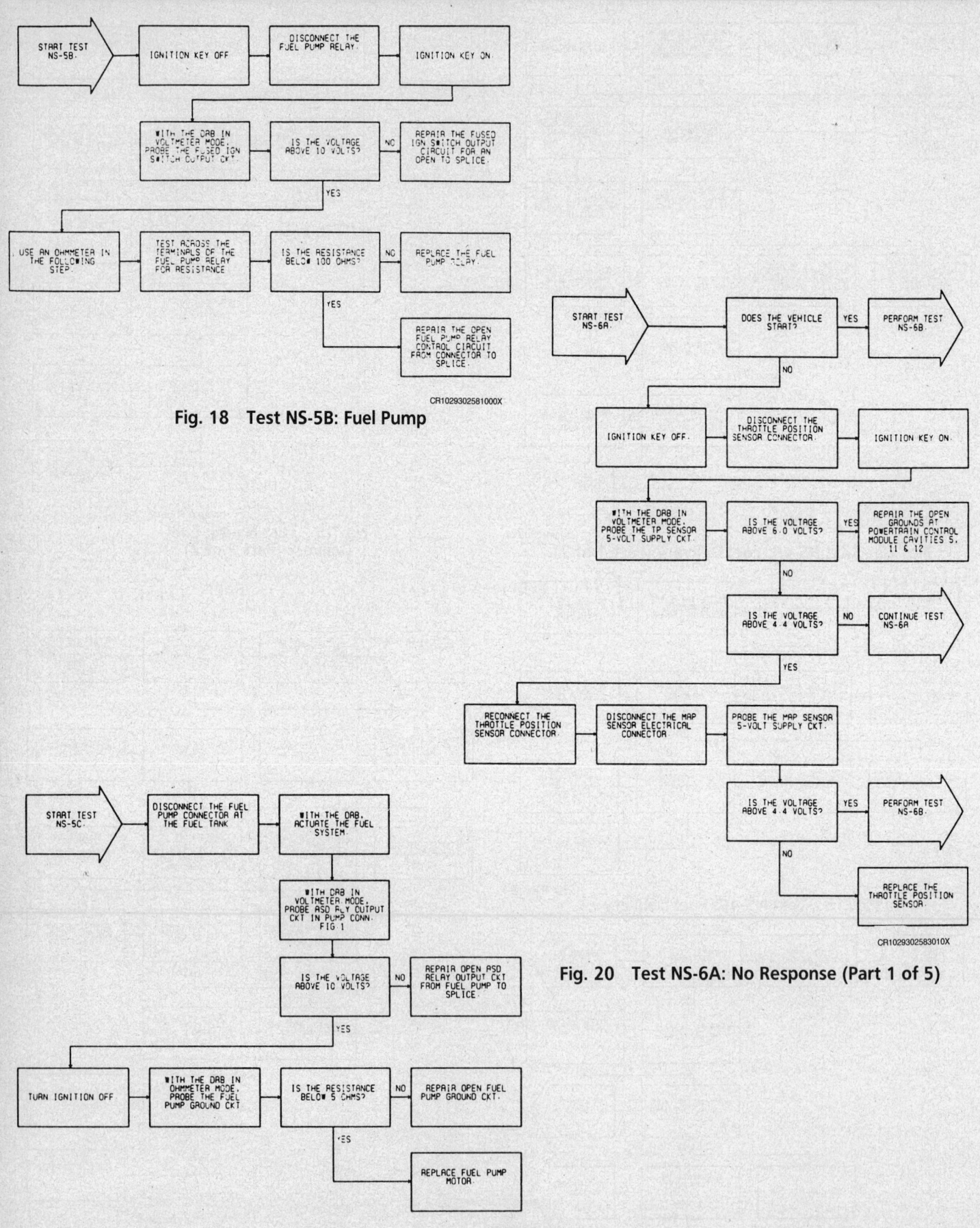

Fig. 18   Test NS-5B: Fuel Pump

CR1029302581000X

Fig. 19   Test NS-5C: Fuel Pump

CR1029302582000X

Fig. 20   Test NS-6A: No Response (Part 1 of 5)

CR1029302583010X

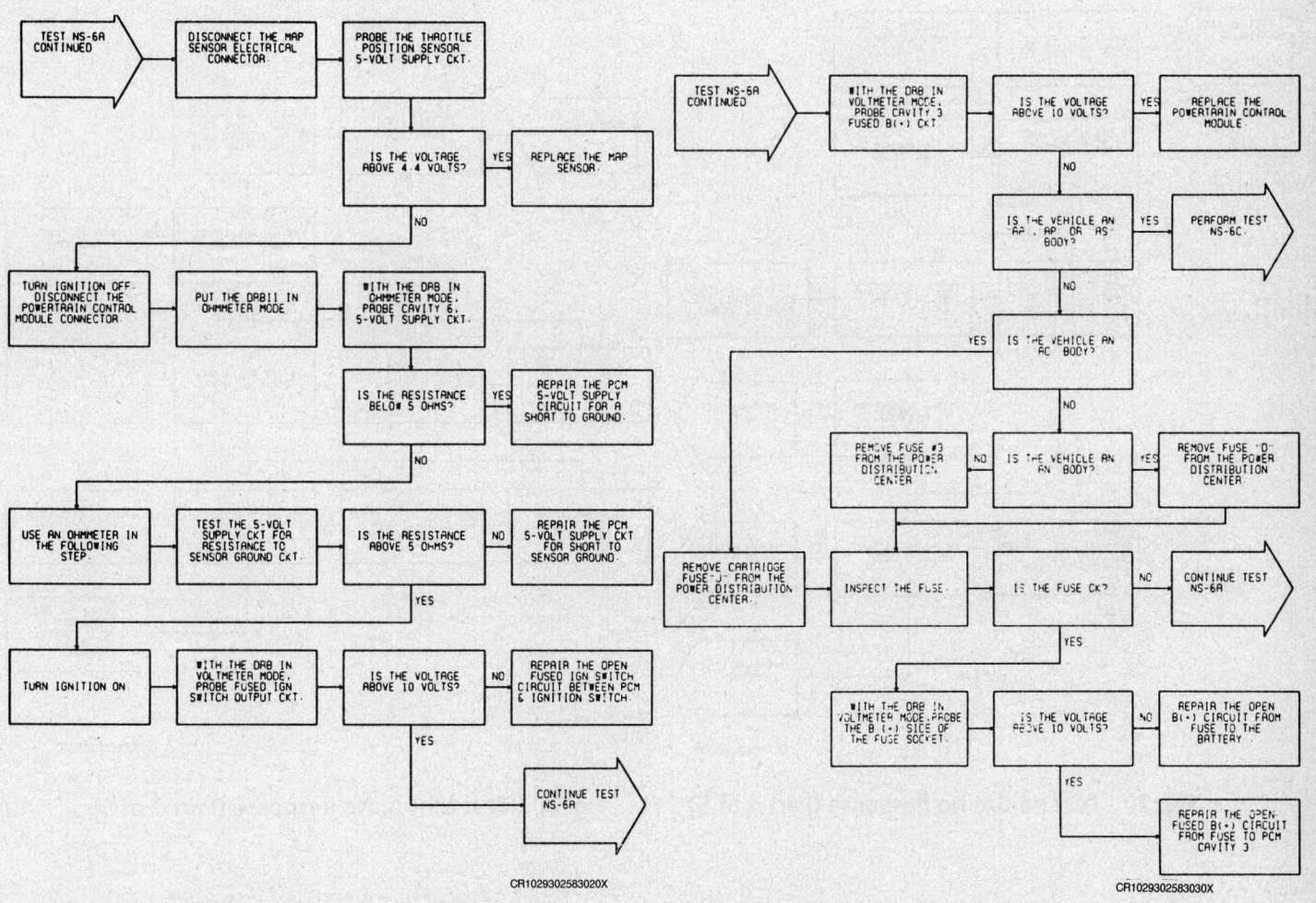

CR1029302583020X

CR1029302583030X

Fig. 20   Test NS-6A: No Response (Part 2 of 5)   **Fig. 20   Test NS-6A: No Response (Part 3 of 5)**

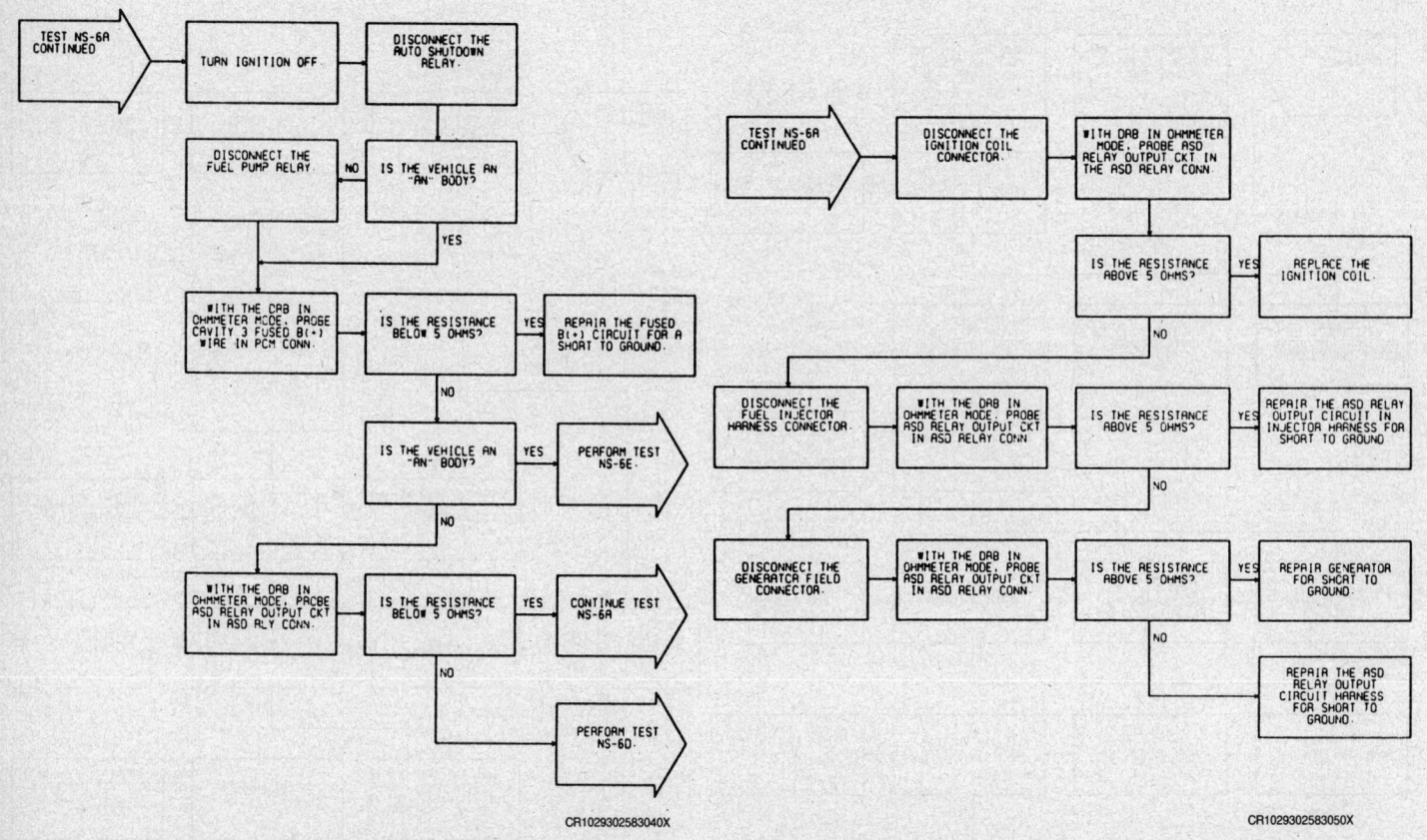

Fig. 20   Test NS-6A: No Response (Part 4 of 5)   **Fig. 20   Test NS-6A: No Response (Part 5 of 5)**

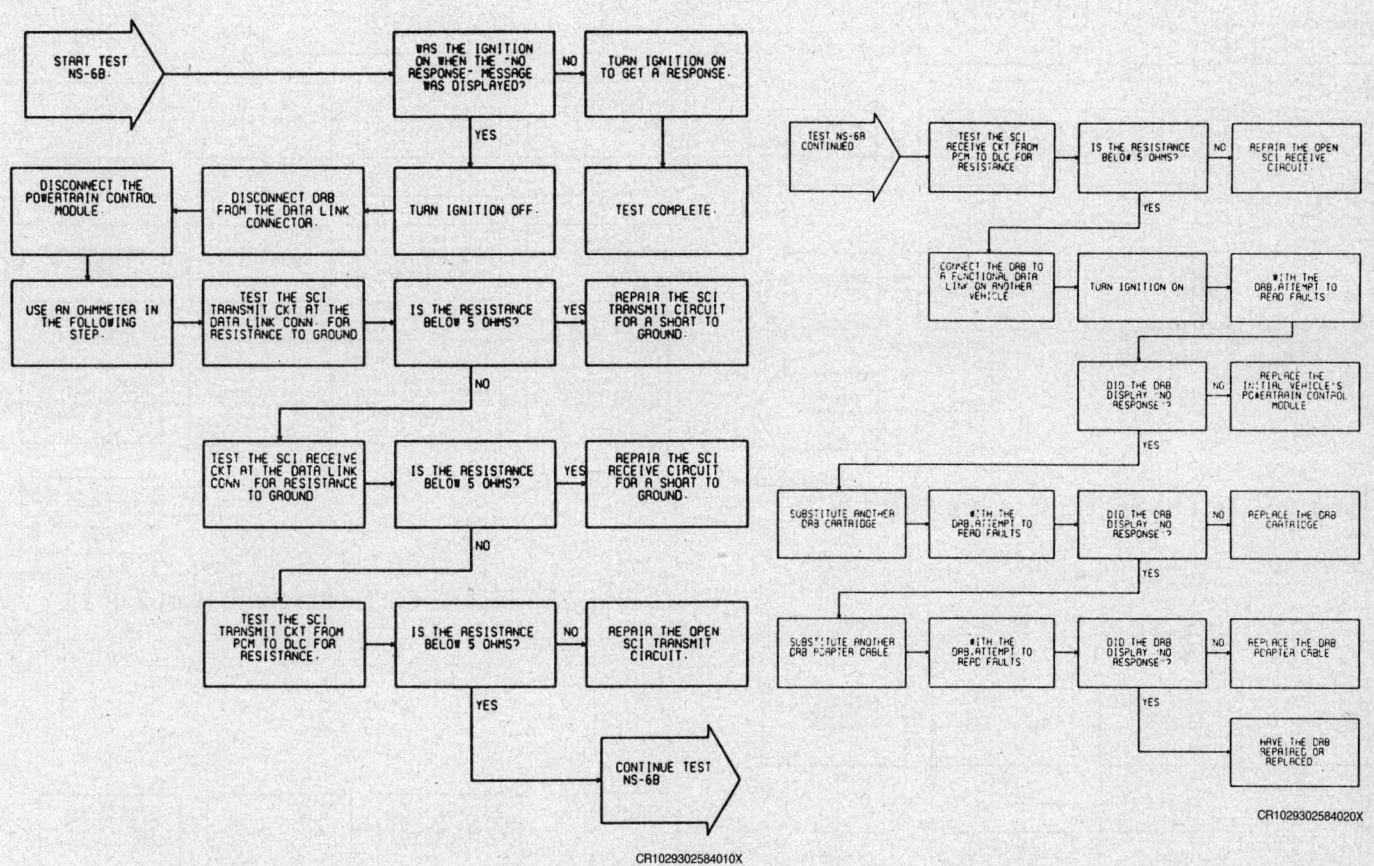

Fig. 21 Test NS-6B: No Response (Part 1 of 2)

Fig. 21 Test NS-6B: No Response (Part 2 of 2)

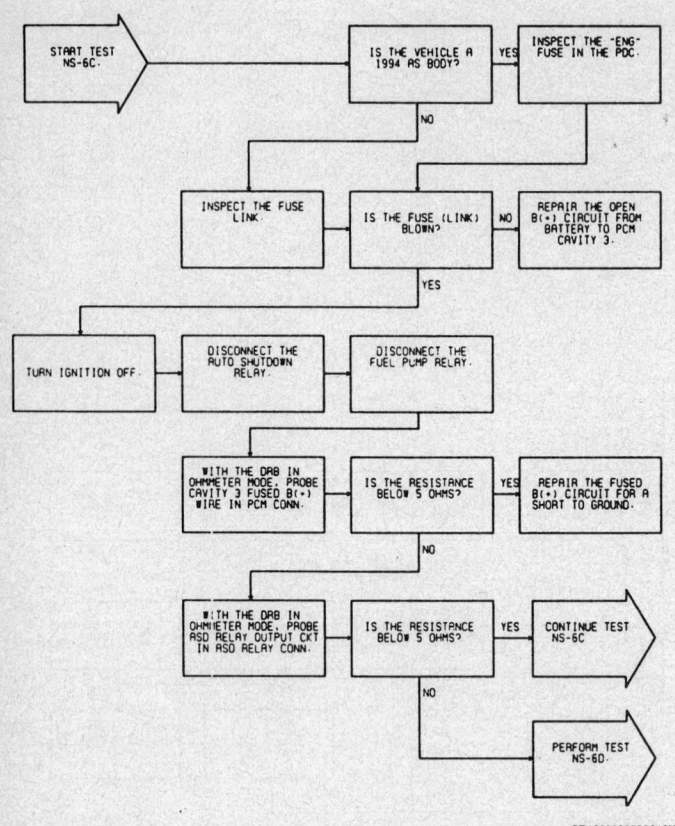

Fig. 22   Test NS-6C: No Response (Part 1 of 2)

CR1029302585010X

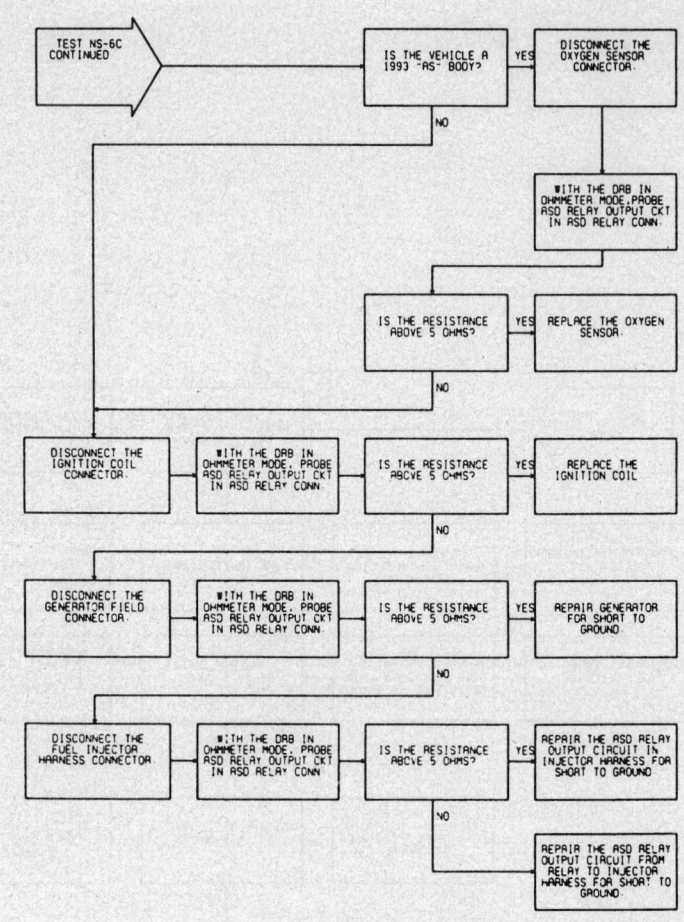

CR1029302585020X

Fig. 22   Test NS-6C: No Response (Part 2 of 2)

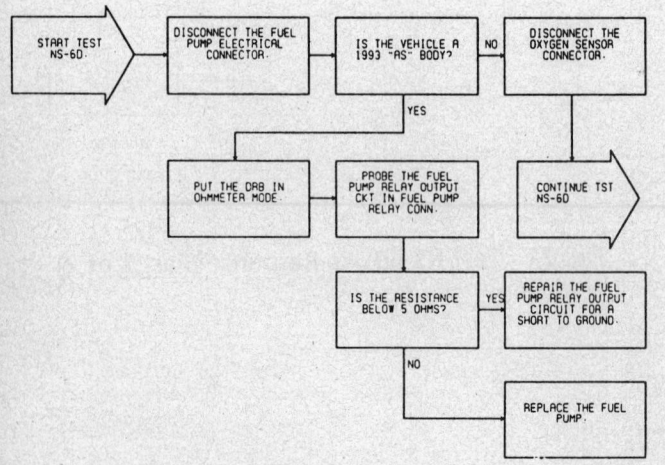

CR1029302586010X

Fig. 23   Test NS-6D: No Response (Part 1 of 2)

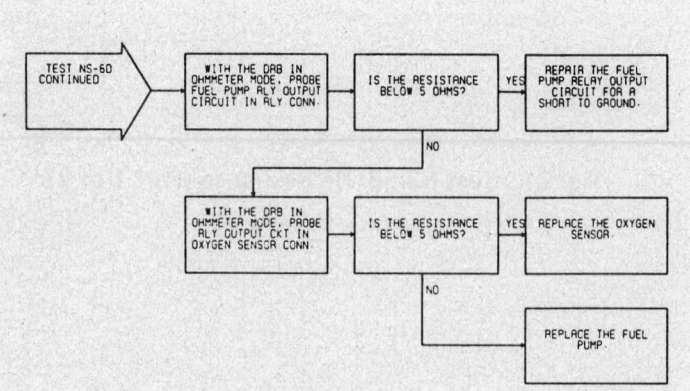

CR1029302586020X

Fig. 23   Test NS-6D: No Response (Part 2 of 2)

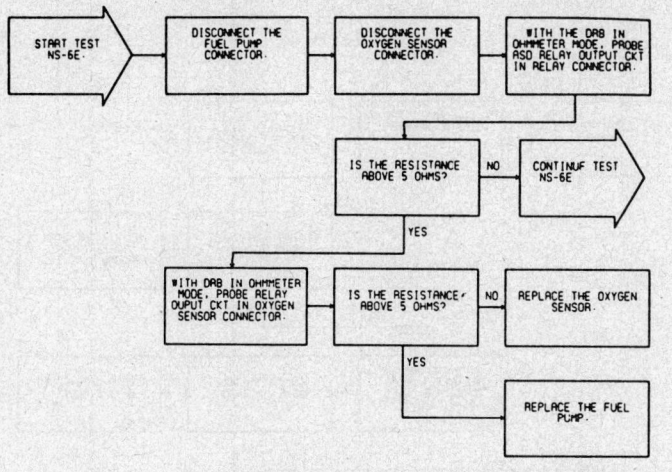

Fig. 24   Test NS-6E: No Response (Part 1 of 2)

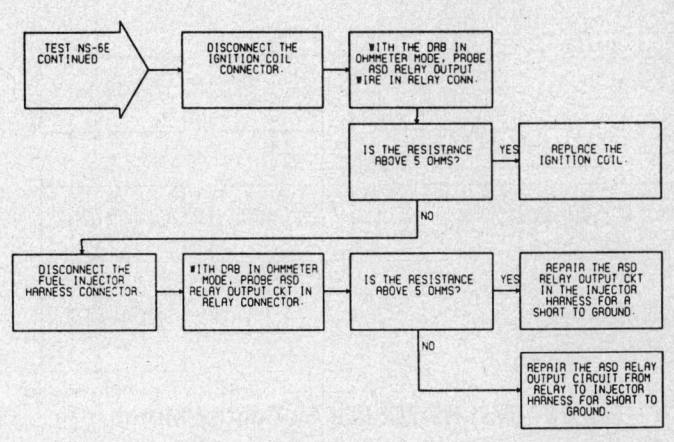

Fig. 24   Test NS-6E: No Response (Part 2 of 2)

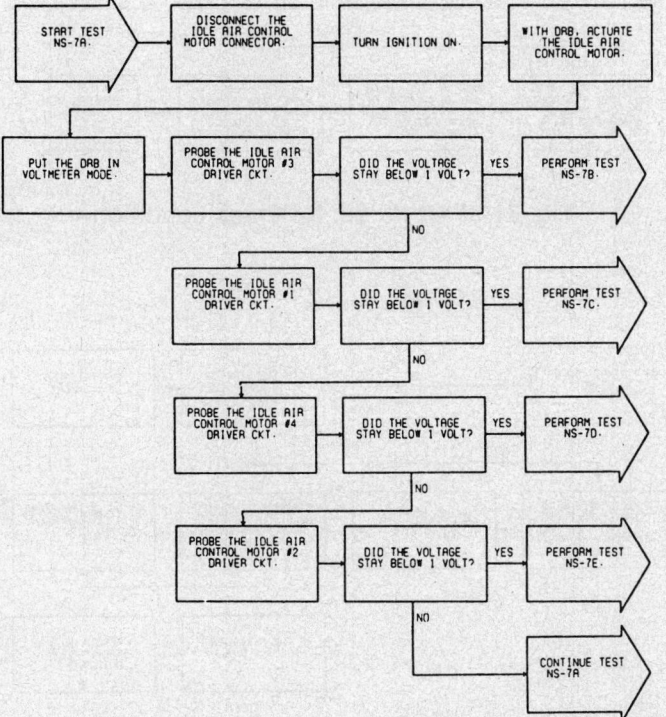

Fig. 25   Test NS-7A: Idle Air Control Motor (Part 1 of 2)

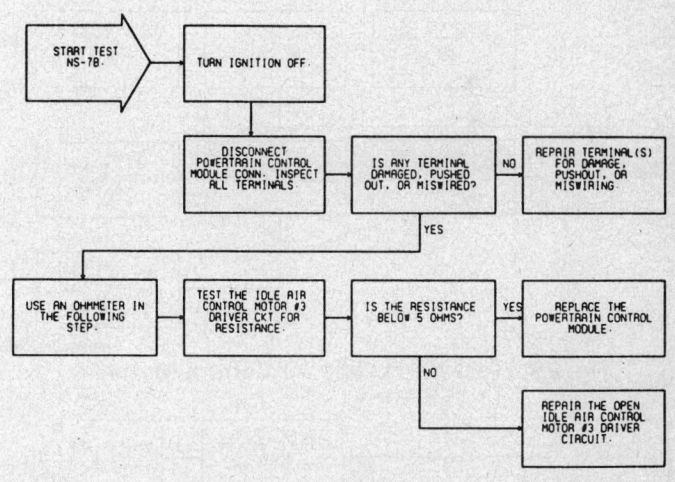

Fig. 26   Test NS-7B: Idle Air Control Motor

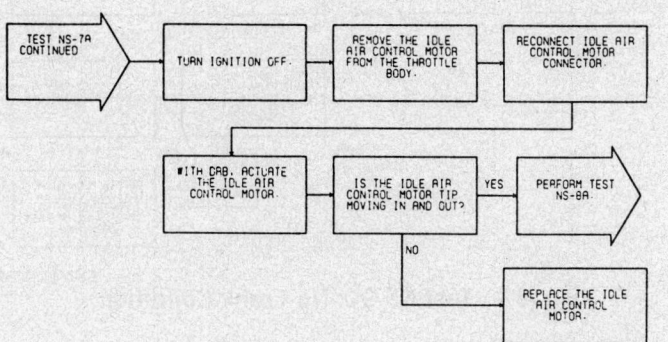

Fig. 25   Test NS-7A: Idle Air Control Motor (Part 2 of 2)

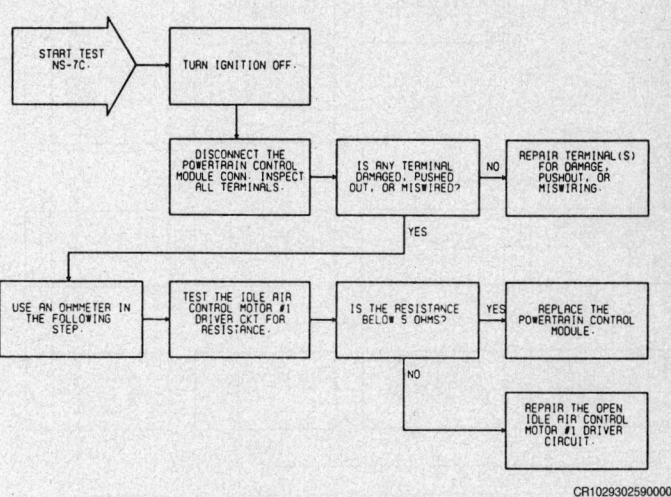

Fig. 27   Test NS-7C: Idle Air Control Motor

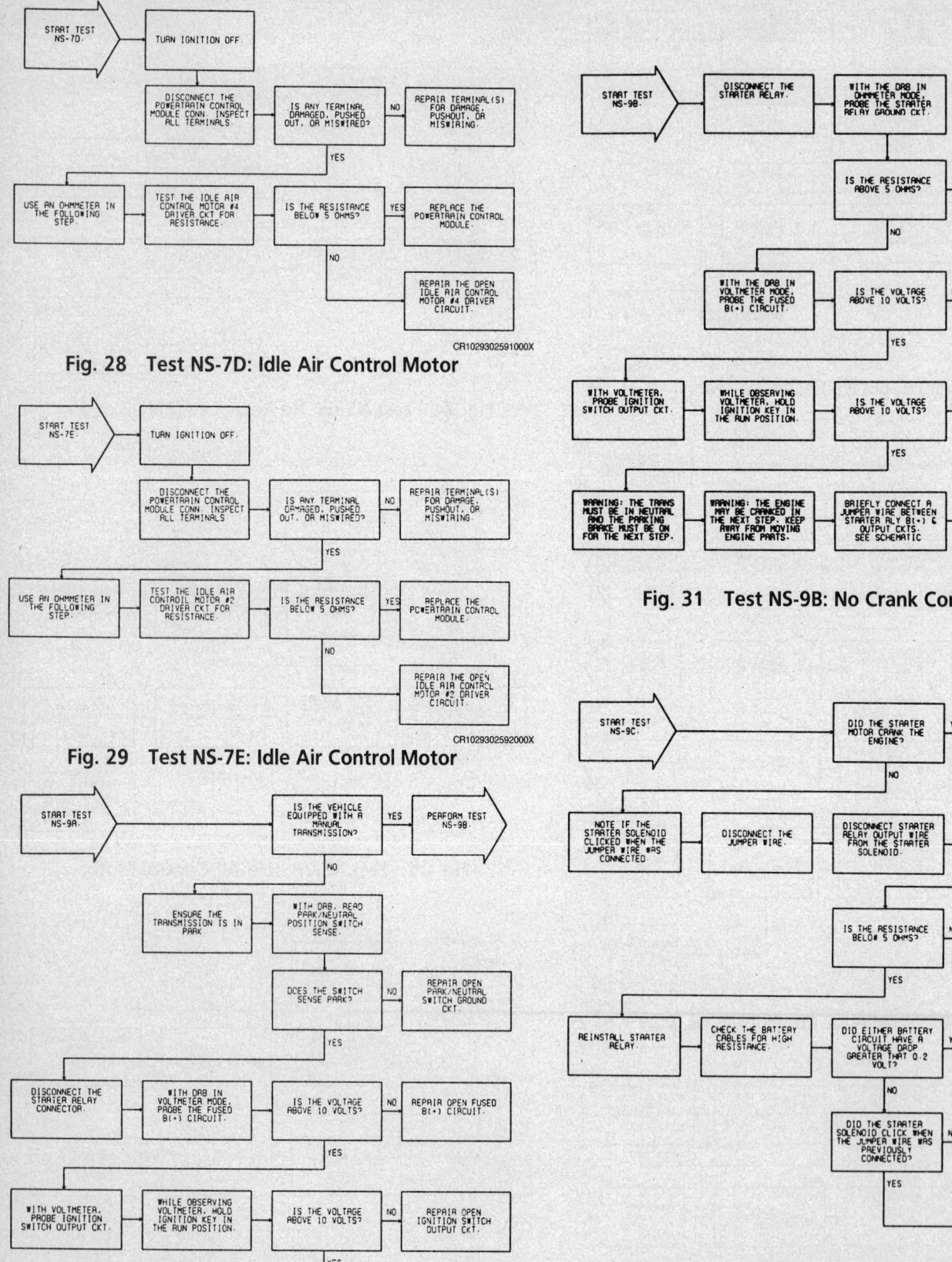

Fig. 28   Test NS-7D: Idle Air Control Motor

Fig. 29   Test NS-7E: Idle Air Control Motor

Fig. 30   Test NS-9A: No Crank Condition

Fig. 31   Test NS-9B: No Crank Condition

Fig. 32   Test NS-9C: No Crank Condition

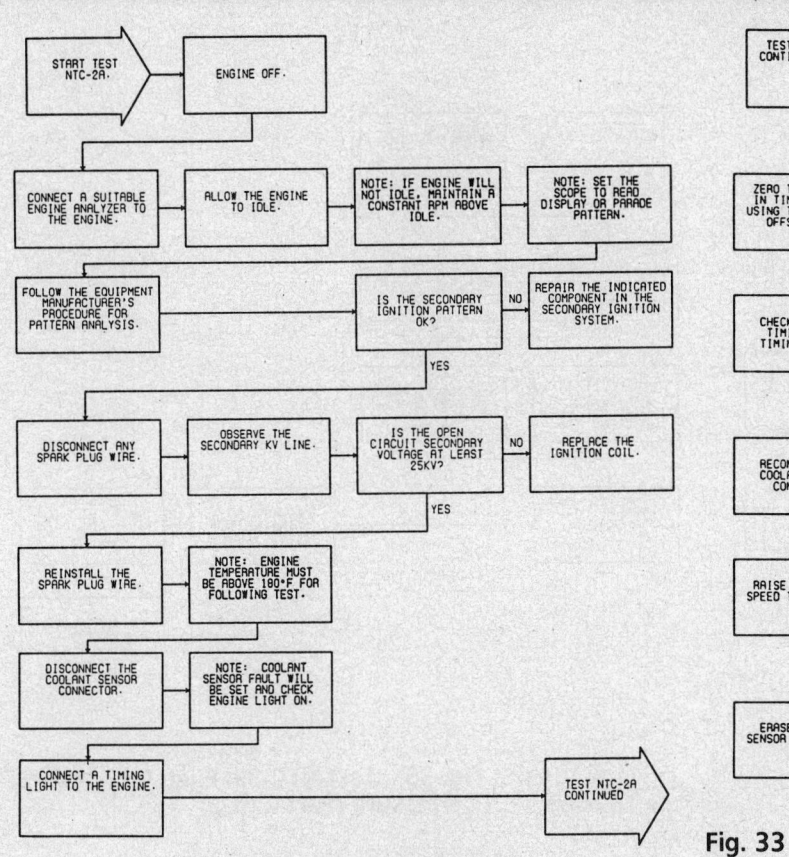

Fig. 33   Test NTC-2A: Secondary Ignition & Timing (Part 1 of 2)

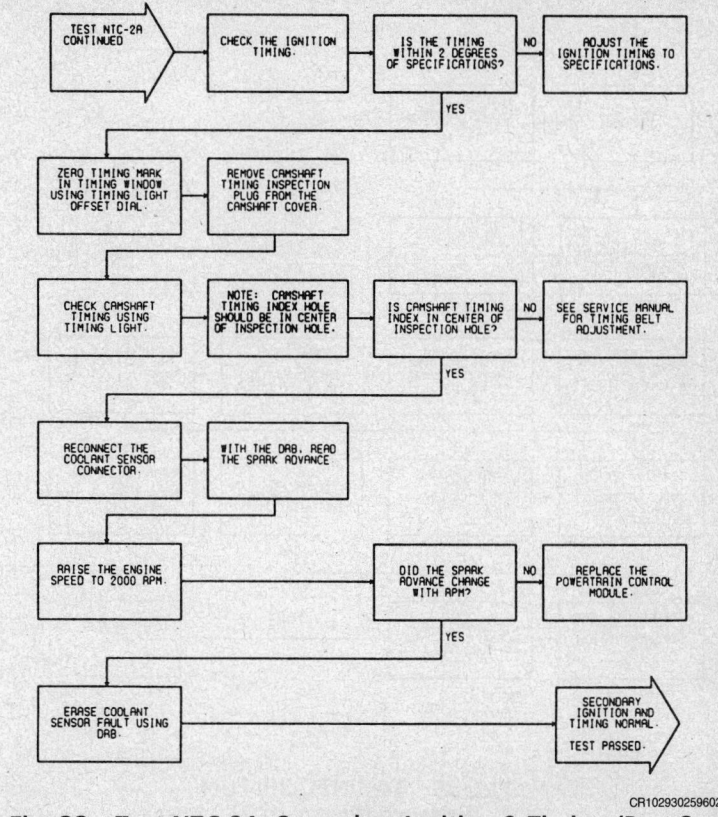

Fig. 33   Test NTC-2A: Secondary Ignition & Timing (Part 2 of 2)

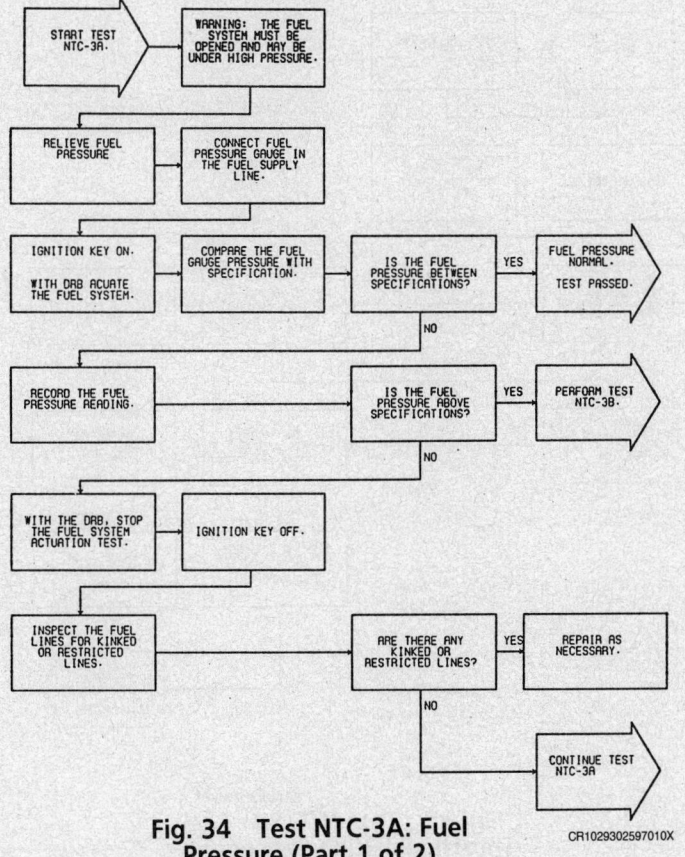

Fig. 34   Test NTC-3A: Fuel Pressure (Part 1 of 2)

Fig. 34   Test NTC-3A: Fuel Pressure (Part 2 of 2)

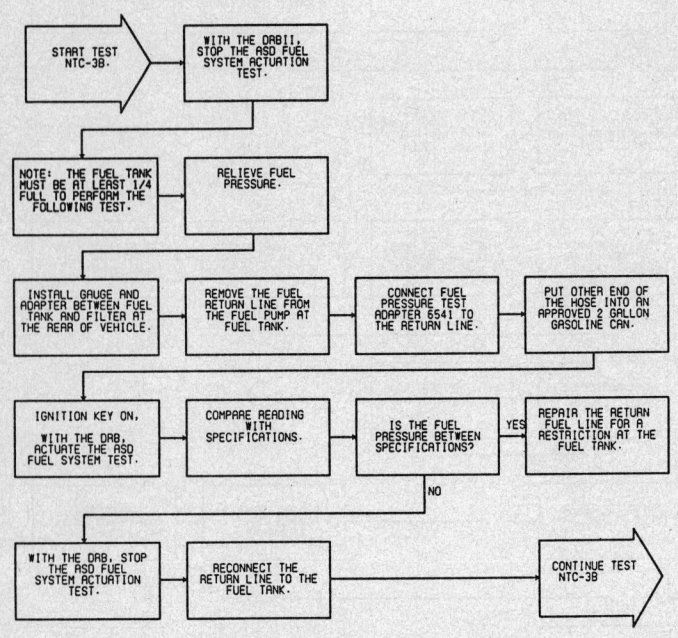

Fig. 35 Test NTC-3B: Fuel Pressure (Part 1 of 2)

CR1029302598010X

Fig. 35 Test NTC-3B: Fuel Pressure (Part 2 of 2)

CR1029302598020X

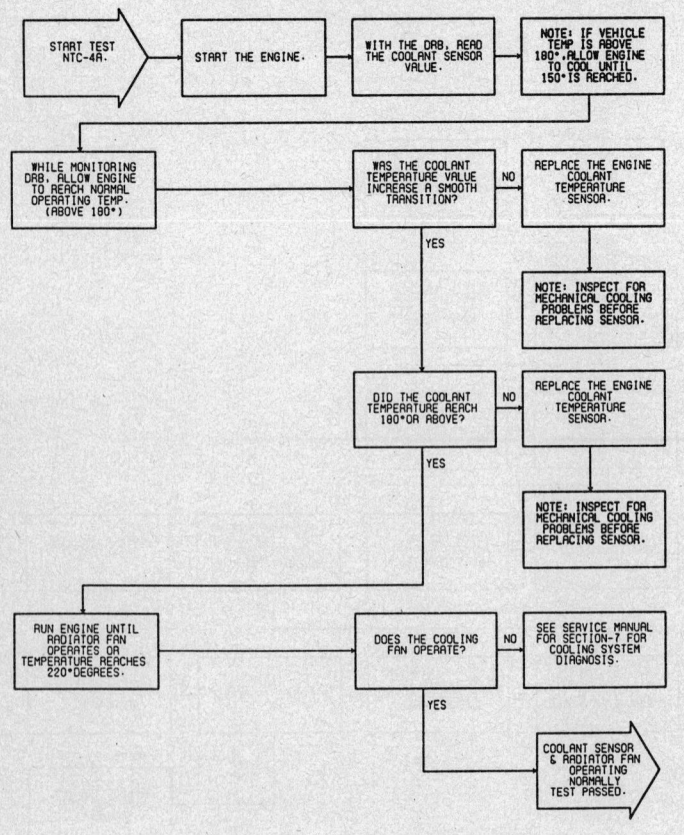

Fig. 36 Test NTC-4A: Coolant Sensor & Radiator Fan

CR1029302599000X

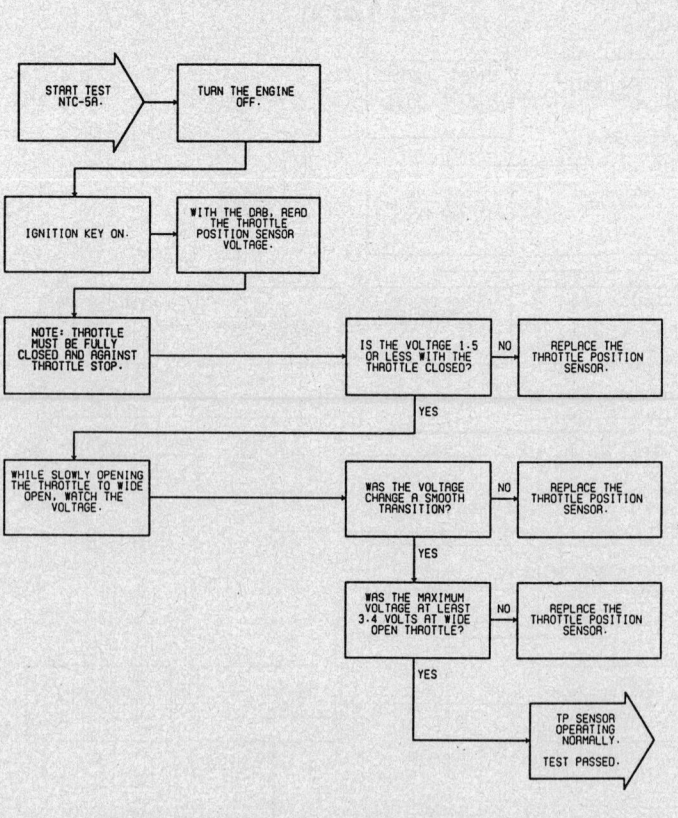

Fig. 37 Test NTC-5A: Throttle Position Sensor

CR1029302600000X

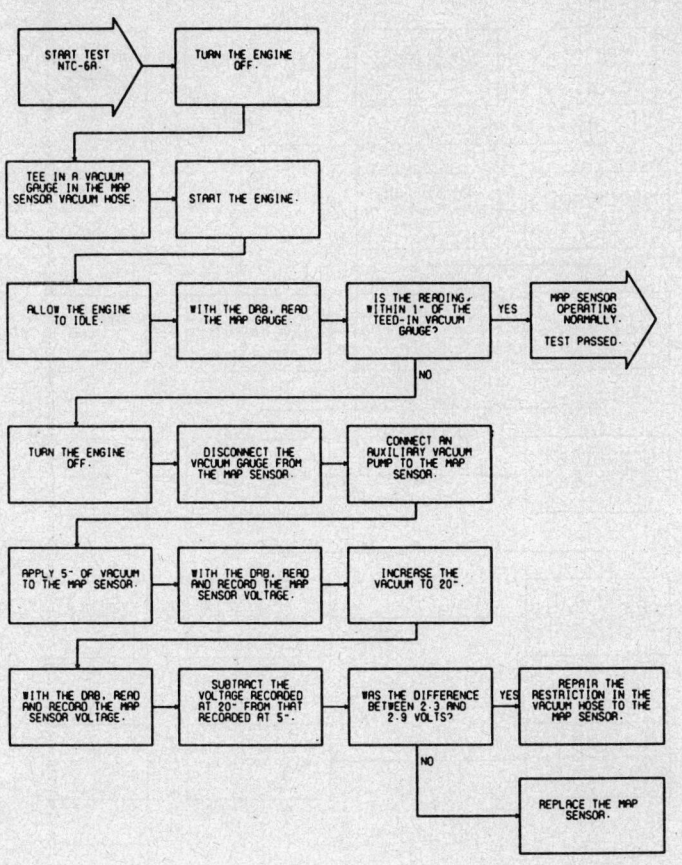

Fig. 38 Test NTC-6A: MAP Sensor

CR1029302601000X

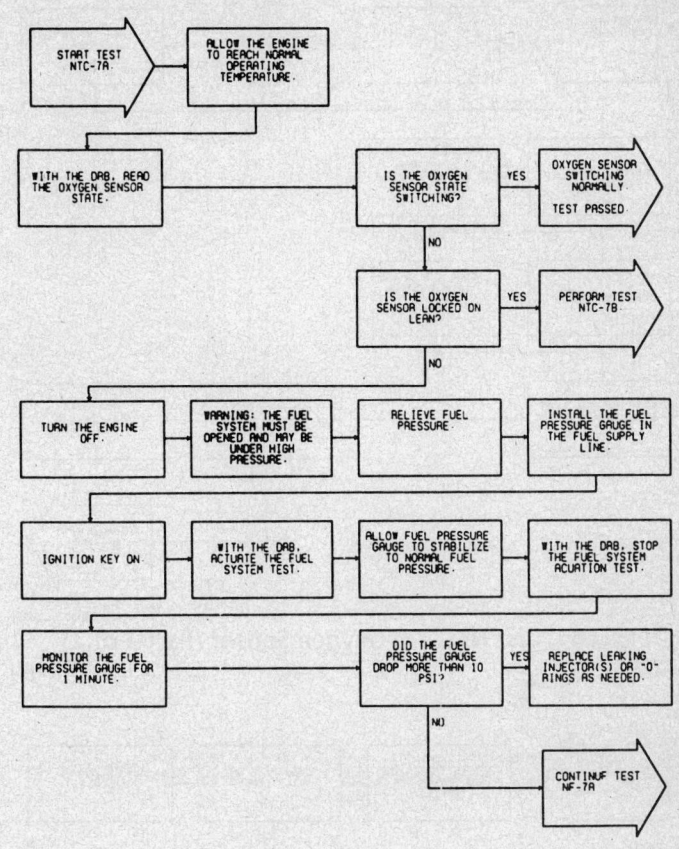

Fig. 39 Test NTC-7A: Oxygen Sensor (Part 1 of 2)

CR1029302602010X

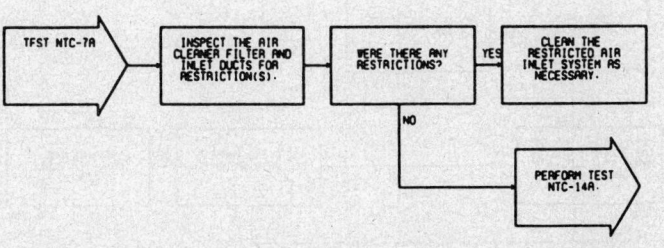

CR1029302602020X

Fig. 39 Test NTC-7A: Oxygen Sensor (Part 2 of 2)

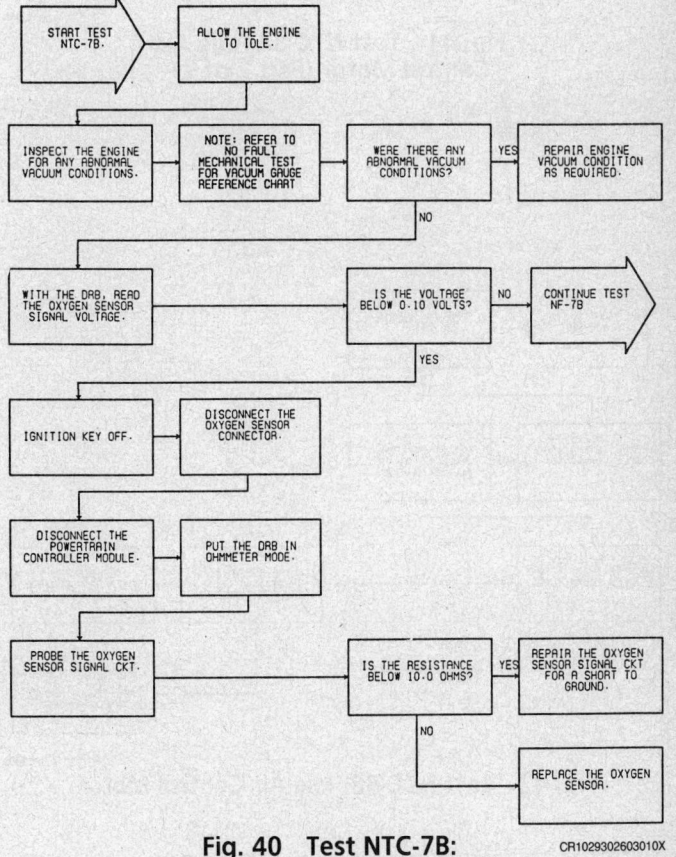

Fig. 40 Test NTC-7B: Oxygen Sensor (Part 1 of 2)

CR1029302603010X

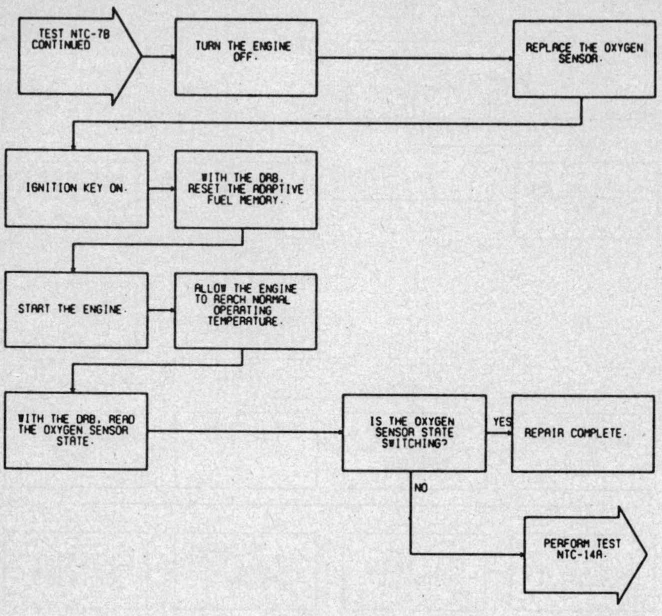

Fig. 40 — Test NTC-7B: Oxygen Sensor (Part 2 of 2)

TEST NTC-7B CONTINUED → TURN THE ENGINE OFF. → REPLACE THE OXYGEN SENSOR.

IGNITION KEY ON. → WITH THE DRB, RESET THE ADAPTIVE FUEL MEMORY.

START THE ENGINE. → ALLOW THE ENGINE TO REACH NORMAL OPERATING TEMPERATURE.

WITH THE DRB, READ THE OXYGEN SENSOR STATE. → IS THE OXYGEN SENSOR STATE SWITCHING? — YES → REPAIR COMPLETE.

NO → PERFORM TEST NTC-14A.

Fig. 40   Test NTC-7B: Oxygen Sensor (Part 2 of 2)

CR1029302603020X

Fig. 41 — Test NTC-8A: Idle Air Control Motor (Part 1 of 2)

START TEST NTC-8A → WITH THE DRBII, SET ENGINE SPEED TO 1100 RPM. → DID THE ENGINE SPEED SET AT 1100 RPM ±50 RPM? — YES → IDLE AIR CONTROL MOTOR OPERATING NORMALLY. TEST PASSED.

NO → RETURN THE ENGINE TO NORMAL IDLE SPEED. → DISCONNECT THE IDLE AIR CONTROL MOTOR CONNECTOR. **

PUT THE DRBII IN VOLTMETER MODE. → WHILE PROBING THE IAC #1 DRIVER CKT, MOMENTARILY OPEN AND CLOSE THE THROTTLE. → DID THE VOLTAGE STAY BELOW 1.0 VOLT? — YES → PERFORM TEST NTC-8B.

NO → WHILE PROBING THE IAC #2 DRIVER CKT, MOMENTARILY OPEN AND CLOSE THE THROTTLE. → DID THE VOLTAGE STAY BELOW 1.0 VOLT? — YES → PERFORM TEST NTC-8B.

NO → WHILE PROBING THE IAC #3 DRIVER CKT, MOMENTARILY OPEN AND CLOSE THE THROTTLE. → DID THE VOLTAGE STAY BELOW 1.0 VOLT? — YES → PERFORM TEST NTC-8B.

NO → WHILE PROBING THE IAC #4 DRIVER CKT, MOMENTARILY OPEN AND CLOSE THE THROTTLE. → DID THE VOLTAGE STAY BELOW 1.0 VOLT? — YES → PERFORM TEST NTC-8B.

NO → CONTINUE TEST NTC-8A

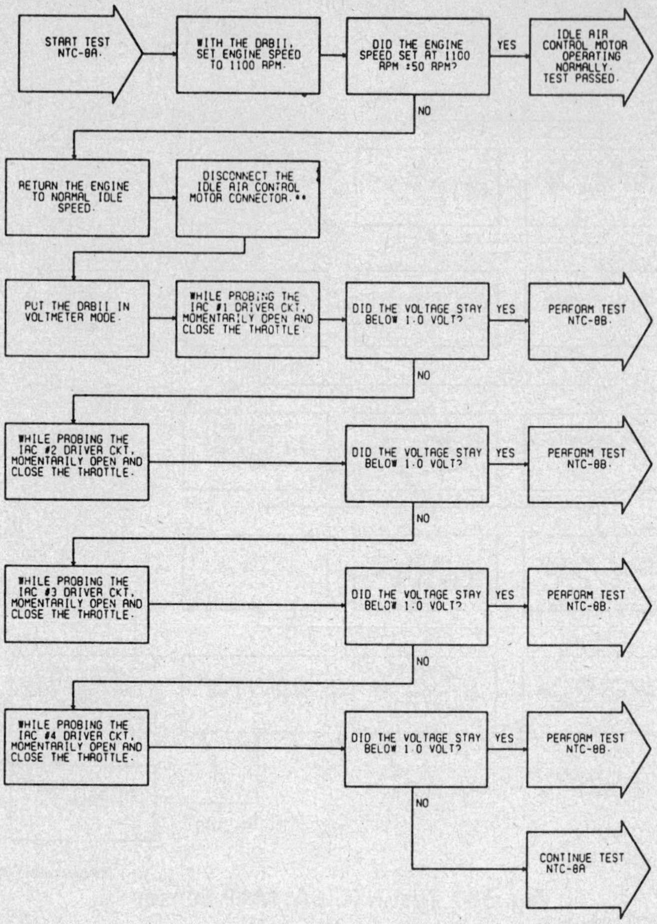

CR1029302604010X

Fig. 41   Test NTC-8A: Idle Air Control Motor (Part 1 of 2)

Fig. 41 — Test NTC-8A: Idle Air Control Motor (Part 2 of 2)

TEST NTC-8A CONTINUED → INSPECT THE ENGINE FOR ANY VACUUM LEAK(S). → WERE THERE ANY VACUUM LEAKS? — YES → REPAIR VACUUM LEAK(S).

NO → REPLACE THE IDLE AIR CONTROL MOTOR.

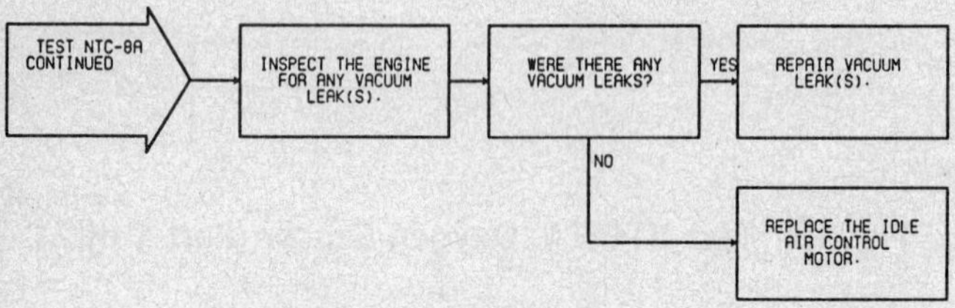

CR1029302604020X

Fig. 41   Test NTC-8A: Idle Air Control Motor (Part 2 of 2)

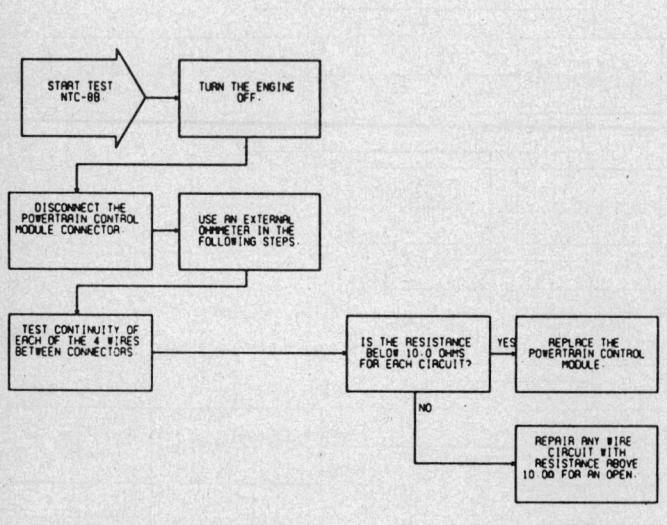

Fig. 42 — Test NTC-8B: Idle Air Control Motor

START TEST NTC-8B → TURN THE ENGINE OFF.

DISCONNECT THE POWERTRAIN CONTROL MODULE CONNECTOR → USE AN EXTERNAL OHMMETER IN THE FOLLOWING STEPS.

TEST CONTINUITY OF EACH OF THE 4 WIRES BETWEEN CONNECTORS → IS THE RESISTANCE BELOW 10.0 OHMS FOR EACH CIRCUIT? — YES → REPLACE THE POWERTRAIN CONTROL MODULE.

NO → REPAIR ANY WIRE CIRCUIT WITH RESISTANCE ABOVE 10 OHMS FOR AN OPEN.

CR1029302605000X

Fig. 42   Test NTC-8B: Idle Air Control Motor

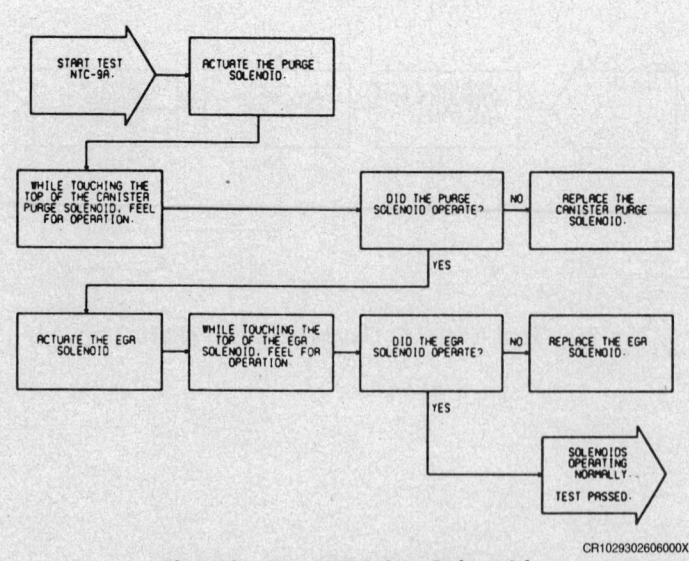

Fig. 43 — Test NTC-9A: Solenoid

START TEST NTC-9A → ACTUATE THE PURGE SOLENOID.

WHILE TOUCHING THE TOP OF THE CANISTER PURGE SOLENOID, FEEL FOR OPERATION. → DID THE PURGE SOLENOID OPERATE? — NO → REPLACE THE CANISTER PURGE SOLENOID.

YES → ACTUATE THE EGR SOLENOID → WHILE TOUCHING THE TOP OF THE EGR SOLENOID, FEEL FOR OPERATION. → DID THE EGR SOLENOID OPERATE? — NO → REPLACE THE EGR SOLENOID.

YES → SOLENOIDS OPERATING NORMALLY. TEST PASSED.

CR1029302606000X

Fig. 43   Test NTC-9A: Solenoid

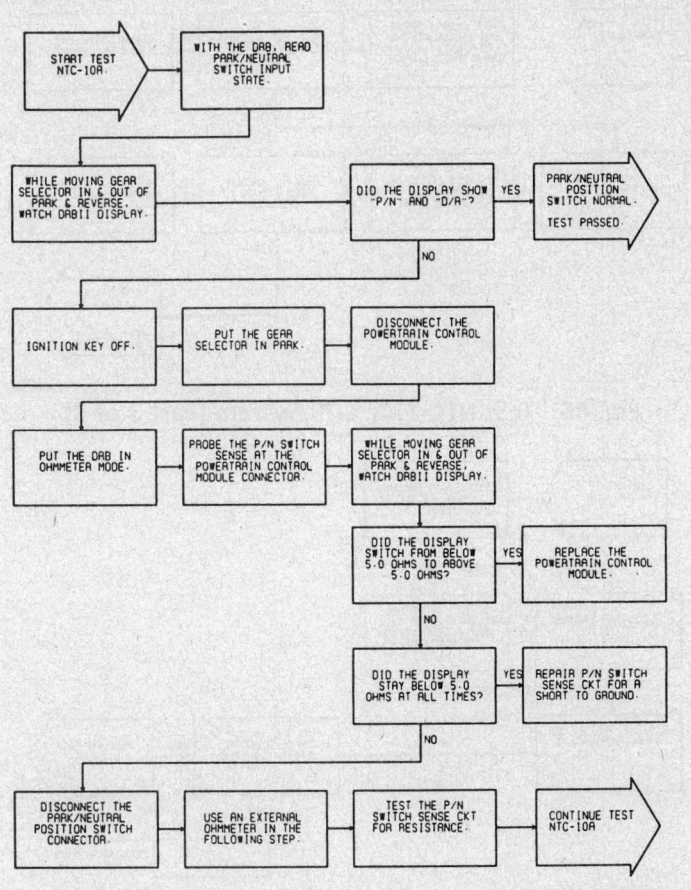

Fig. 44   Test NTC-10A: PNP Switch (Part 1 of 2)

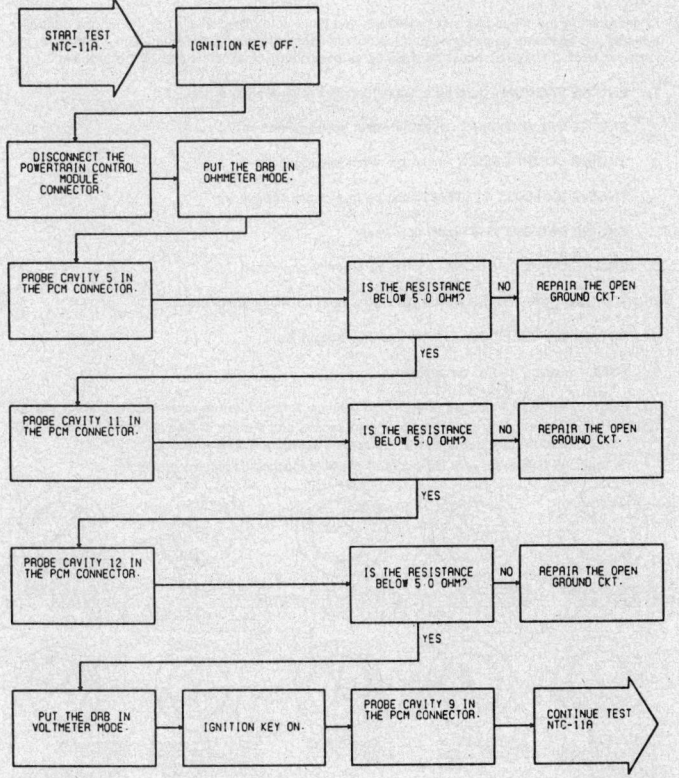

Fig. 45   Test NTC-11A: PCM Circuits (Part 1 of 2)

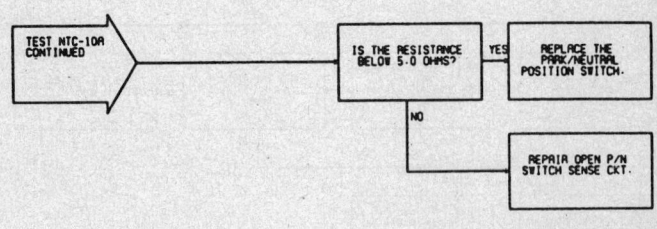

Fig. 44   Test NTC-10A: PNP Switch (Part 2 of 2)

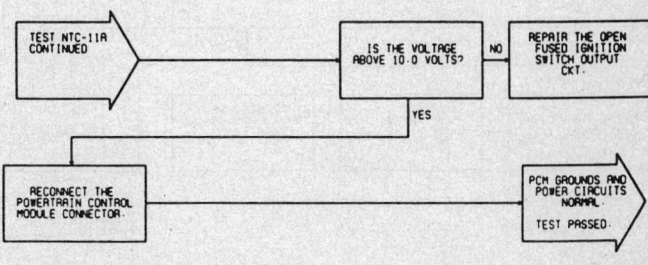

Fig. 45   Test NTC-11A: PCM Circuits (Part 2 of 2)

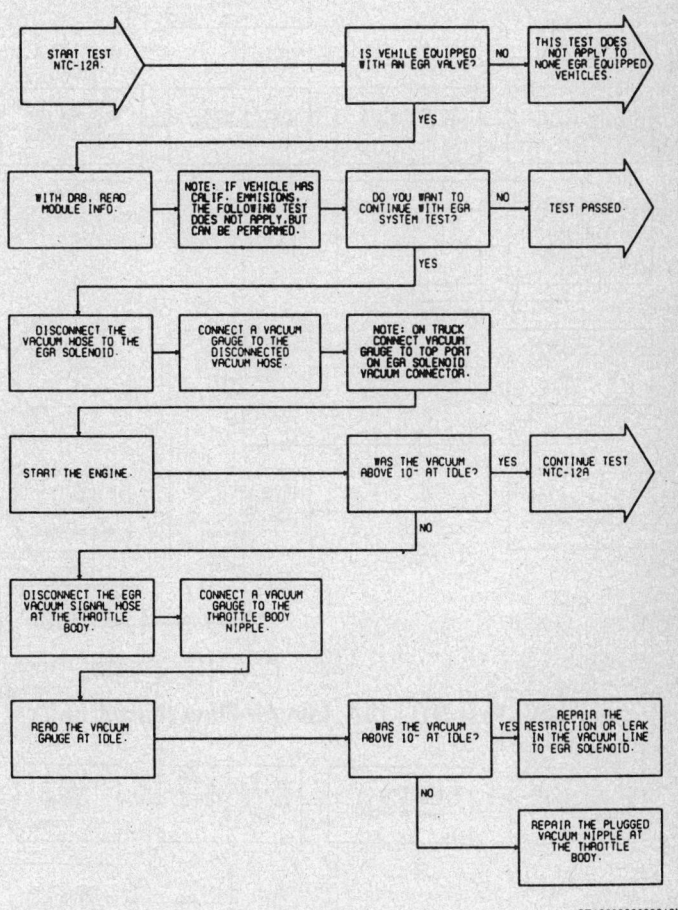

Fig. 46   Test NTC-12A: EGR System (Part 1 of 3)

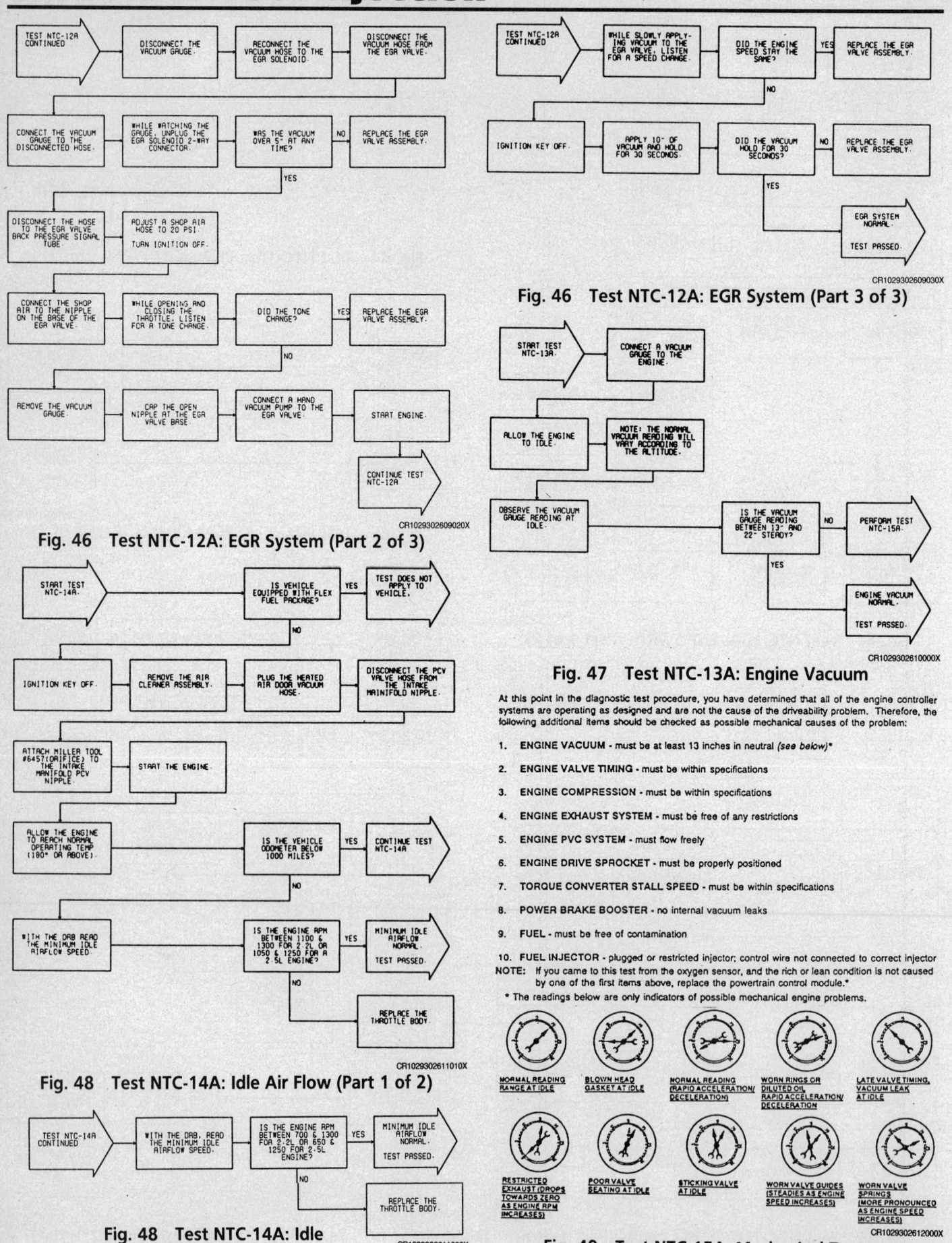

Fig. 46 Test NTC-12A: EGR System (Part 2 of 3)

Flowchart (top left):

TEST NTC-12A CONTINUED → DISCONNECT THE VACUUM GAUGE. → RECONNECT THE VACUUM HOSE TO THE EGR SOLENOID. → DISCONNECT THE VACUUM HOSE FROM THE EGR VALVE.

CONNECT THE VACUUM GAUGE TO THE DISCONNECTED HOSE. → WHILE WATCHING THE GAUGE, UNPLUG THE EGR SOLENOID 2-WAY CONNECTOR. → WAS THE VACUUM OVER 5" AT ANY TIME? — NO → REPLACE THE EGR VALVE ASSEMBLY.

YES ↓

DISCONNECT THE HOSE TO THE EGR VALVE BACK PRESSURE SIGNAL TUBE. → ADJUST A SHOP AIR HOSE TO 20 PSI. TURN IGNITION OFF.

CONNECT THE SHOP AIR TO THE NIPPLE ON THE BASE OF THE EGR VALVE. → WHILE OPENING AND CLOSING THE THROTTLE, LISTEN FOR A TONE CHANGE. → DID THE TONE CHANGE? — YES → REPLACE THE EGR VALVE ASSEMBLY.

NO ↓

REMOVE THE VACUUM GAUGE. → CAP THE OPEN NIPPLE AT THE EGR VALVE BASE. → CONNECT A HAND VACUUM PUMP TO THE EGR VALVE. → START ENGINE. → CONTINUE TEST NTC-12A

CR1029302609020X

Fig. 46 Test NTC-12A: EGR System (Part 3 of 3)

Flowchart (top right):

TEST NTC-12A CONTINUED → WHILE SLOWLY APPLYING VACUUM TO THE EGR VALVE, LISTEN FOR A SPEED CHANGE. → DID THE ENGINE SPEED STAY THE SAME? — YES → REPLACE THE EGR VALVE ASSEMBLY.

NO ↓

IGNITION KEY OFF. → APPLY 10" OF VACUUM AND HOLD FOR 30 SECONDS. → DID THE VACUUM HOLD FOR 30 SECONDS? — NO → REPLACE THE EGR VALVE ASSEMBLY.

YES ↓

EGR SYSTEM NORMAL. TEST PASSED.

CR1029302609030X

Fig. 47 Test NTC-13A: Engine Vacuum

Flowchart (middle right):

START TEST NTC-13A. → CONNECT A VACUUM GAUGE TO THE ENGINE.

ALLOW THE ENGINE TO IDLE. → NOTE: THE NORMAL VACUUM READING WILL VARY ACCORDING TO THE ALTITUDE.

OBSERVE THE VACUUM GAUGE READING AT IDLE. → IS THE VACUUM GAUGE READING BETWEEN 13" AND 22" STEADY? — NO → PERFORM TEST NTC-15A.

YES ↓

ENGINE VACUUM NORMAL. TEST PASSED.

CR1029302610000X

At this point in the diagnostic test procedure, you have determined that all of the engine controller systems are operating as designed and are not the cause of the driveability problem. Therefore, the following additional items should be checked as possible mechanical causes of the problem:

1. ENGINE VACUUM - must be at least 13 inches in neutral *(see below)**

2. ENGINE VALVE TIMING - must be within specifications

3. ENGINE COMPRESSION - must be within specifications

4. ENGINE EXHAUST SYSTEM - must be free of any restrictions

5. ENGINE PVC SYSTEM - must flow freely

6. ENGINE DRIVE SPROCKET - must be properly positioned

7. TORQUE CONVERTER STALL SPEED - must be within specifications

8. POWER BRAKE BOOSTER - no internal vacuum leaks

9. FUEL - must be free of contamination

10. FUEL INJECTOR - plugged or restricted injector; control wire not connected to correct injector

NOTE: If you came to this test from the oxygen sensor, and the rich or lean condition is not caused by one of the first items above, replace the powertrain control module.*

* The readings below are only indicators of possible mechanical engine problems.

Fig. 48 Test NTC-14A: Idle Air Flow (Part 1 of 2)

Flowchart (lower left):

START TEST NTC-14A. → IS VEHICLE EQUIPPED WITH FLEX FUEL PACKAGE? — YES → TEST DOES NOT APPLY TO VEHICLE.

NO ↓

IGNITION KEY OFF. → REMOVE THE AIR CLEANER ASSEMBLY. → PLUG THE HEATED AIR DOOR VACUUM HOSE. → DISCONNECT THE PCV VALVE HOSE FROM THE INTAKE MANIFOLD NIPPLE.

ATTACH MILLER TOOL #6457(ORIFICE) TO THE INTAKE MANIFOLD PCV NIPPLE. → START THE ENGINE.

ALLOW THE ENGINE TO REACH NORMAL OPERATING TEMP (180° AND ABOVE). → IS THE VEHICLE ODOMETER BELOW 1000 MILES? — YES → CONTINUE TEST NTC-14A

NO ↓

WITH THE DRB READ THE MINIMUM IDLE AIRFLOW SPEED. → IS THE ENGINE RPM BETWEEN 1100 & 1300 FOR 2.2L OR 1050 & 1250 FOR A 2.5L ENGINE? — YES → MINIMUM IDLE AIRFLOW NORMAL. TEST PASSED.

NO ↓

REPLACE THE THROTTLE BODY.

CR1029302611010X

Fig. 48 Test NTC-14A: Idle Air Flow (Part 2 of 2)

Flowchart (bottom left):

TEST NTC-14A CONTINUED → WITH THE DRB, READ THE MINIMUM IDLE AIRFLOW SPEED. → IS THE ENGINE RPM BETWEEN 700 & 1300 FOR 2.2L OR 650 & 1250 FOR 2.5L ENGINE? — YES → MINIMUM IDLE AIRFLOW NORMAL. TEST PASSED.

NO ↓

REPLACE THE THROTTLE BODY.

CR1029302611020X

Fig. 49 Test NTC-15A: Mechanical Test

Vacuum gauge readings (top row):
- NORMAL READING RANGE AT IDLE
- BLOWN HEAD GASKET AT IDLE
- NORMAL READING (RAPID ACCELERATION/ DECELERATION)
- WORN RINGS OR DILUTED OIL (RAPID ACCELERATION/ DECELERATION)
- LATE VALVE TIMING, VACUUM LEAK AT IDLE

Vacuum gauge readings (bottom row):
- RESTRICTED EXHAUST (DROPS TOWARDS ZERO AS ENGINE RPM INCREASES)
- POOR VALVE SEATING AT IDLE
- STICKING VALVE AT IDLE
- WORN VALVE GUIDES (STEADIES AS ENGINE SPEED INCREASES)
- WORN VALVE SPRINGS (MORE PRONOUNCED AS ENGINE SPEED INCREASES)

CR1029302612000X

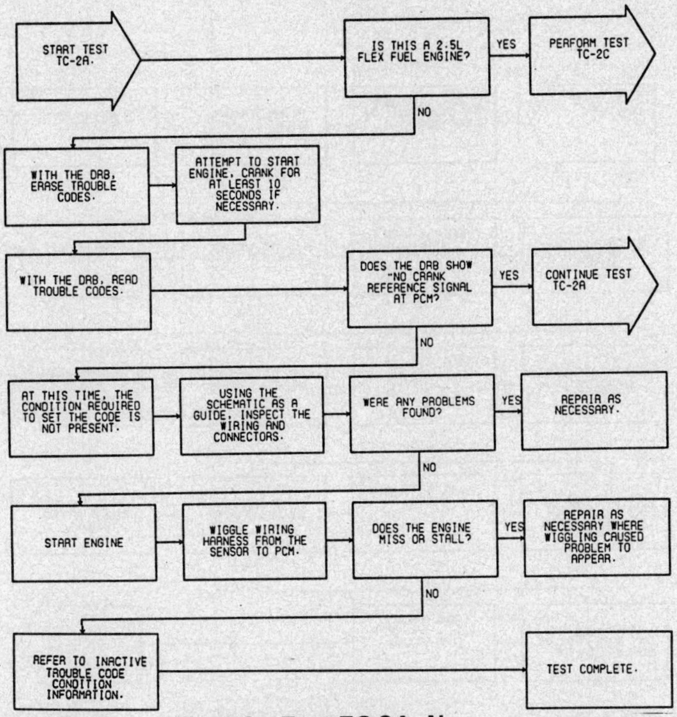

Part 1 (Fig. 50)

START TEST TC-2A. → IS THIS A 2.5L FLEX FUEL ENGINE? → YES → PERFORM TEST TC-2C.

NO ↓

WITH THE DRB, ERASE TROUBLE CODES. → ATTEMPT TO START ENGINE. CRANK FOR AT LEAST 10 SECONDS IF NECESSARY.

WITH THE DRB, READ TROUBLE CODES. → DOES THE DRB SHOW "NO CRANK REFERENCE SIGNAL AT PCM"? → YES → CONTINUE TEST TC-2A.

NO ↓

AT THIS TIME, THE CONDITION REQUIRED TO SET THE CODE IS NOT PRESENT. → USING THE SCHEMATIC AS A GUIDE, INSPECT THE WIRING AND CONNECTORS. → WERE ANY PROBLEMS FOUND? → YES → REPAIR AS NECESSARY.

NO ↓

START ENGINE. → WIGGLE WIRING HARNESS FROM THE SENSOR TO PCM. → DOES THE ENGINE MISS OR STALL? → YES → REPAIR AS NECESSARY WHERE WIGGLING CAUSED PROBLEM TO APPEAR.

NO ↓

REFER TO INACTIVE TROUBLE CODE CONDITION INFORMATION. → TEST COMPLETE.

CR1029302613010X

Fig. 50   Test TC-2A: No Crank Reference Signal At PCM (Part 1 of 3)

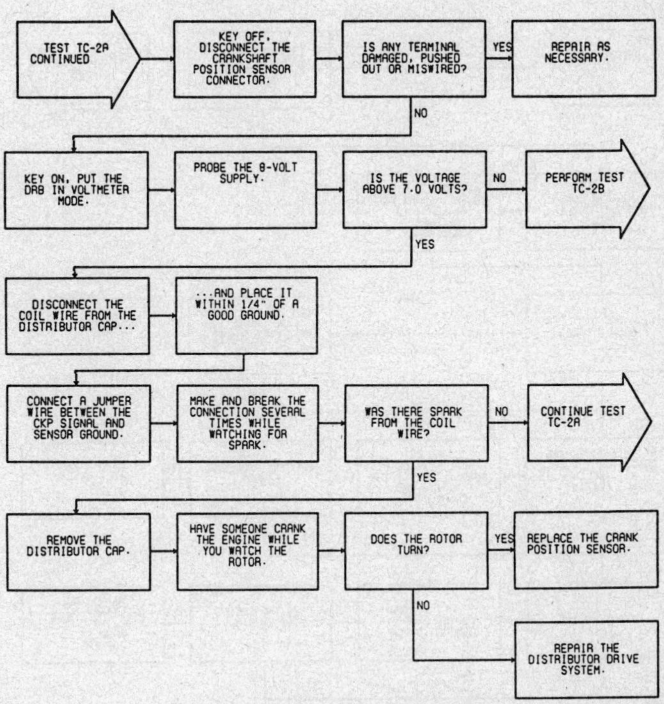

Part 2 (Fig. 50)

TEST TC-2A CONTINUED → KEY OFF. DISCONNECT THE CRANKSHAFT POSITION SENSOR CONNECTOR. → IS ANY TERMINAL DAMAGED, PUSHED OUT OR MISWIRED? → YES → REPAIR AS NECESSARY.

NO ↓

KEY ON. PUT THE DRB IN VOLTMETER MODE. → PROBE THE 8-VOLT SUPPLY. → IS THE VOLTAGE ABOVE 7.0 VOLTS? → NO → PERFORM TEST TC-2B.

YES ↓

DISCONNECT THE COIL WIRE FROM THE DISTRIBUTOR CAP... → ...AND PLACE IT WITHIN 1/4" OF A GOOD GROUND.

CONNECT A JUMPER WIRE BETWEEN THE CKP SIGNAL AND SENSOR GROUND. → MAKE AND BREAK THE CONNECTION SEVERAL TIMES WHILE WATCHING FOR SPARK. → WAS THERE SPARK FROM THE COIL WIRE? → NO → CONTINUE TEST TC-2A.

YES ↓

REMOVE THE DISTRIBUTOR CAP. → HAVE SOMEONE CRANK THE ENGINE WHILE YOU WATCH THE ROTOR. → DOES THE ROTOR TURN? → YES → REPLACE THE CRANK POSITION SENSOR.

NO ↓

REPAIR THE DISTRIBUTOR DRIVE SYSTEM.

CR1029302613020X

Fig. 50   Test TC-2A: No Crank Reference Signal At PCM (Part 2 of 3)

Part 3 (Fig. 50)

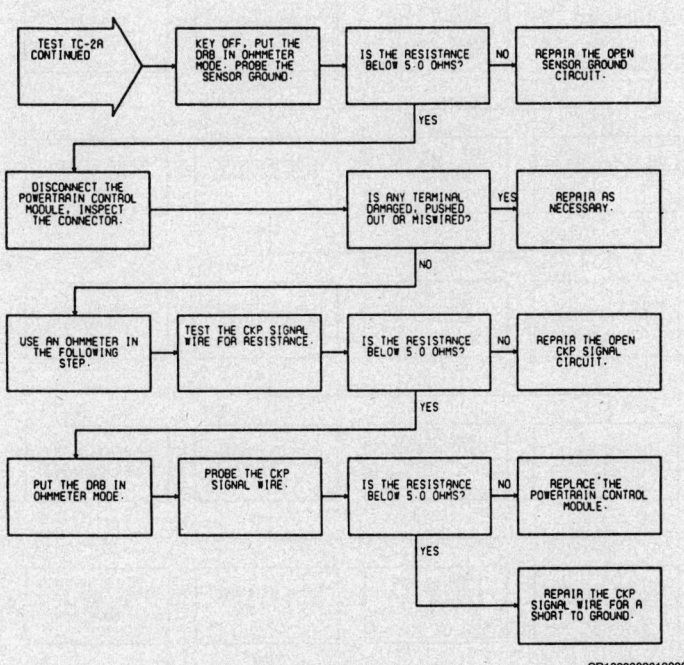

TEST TC-2A CONTINUED → KEY OFF, PUT THE DRB IN OHMMETER MODE. PROBE THE SENSOR GROUND. → IS THE RESISTANCE BELOW 5.0 OHMS? → NO → REPAIR THE OPEN SENSOR GROUND CIRCUIT.

YES ↓

DISCONNECT THE POWERTRAIN CONTROL MODULE. INSPECT THE CONNECTOR. → IS ANY TERMINAL DAMAGED, PUSHED OUT OR MISWIRED? → YES → REPAIR AS NECESSARY.

NO ↓

USE AN OHMMETER IN THE FOLLOWING STEP. → TEST THE CKP SIGNAL WIRE FOR RESISTANCE. → IS THE RESISTANCE BELOW 5.0 OHMS? → NO → REPAIR THE OPEN CKP SIGNAL CIRCUIT.

YES ↓

PUT THE DRB IN OHMMETER MODE. → PROBE THE CKP SIGNAL WIRE. → IS THE RESISTANCE BELOW 5.0 OHMS? → NO → REPLACE THE POWERTRAIN CONTROL MODULE.

YES ↓

REPAIR THE CKP SIGNAL WIRE FOR A SHORT TO GROUND.

CR1029302613030X

Fig. 50   Test TC-2A: No Crank Reference Signal At PCM (Part 3 of 3)

Fig. 51

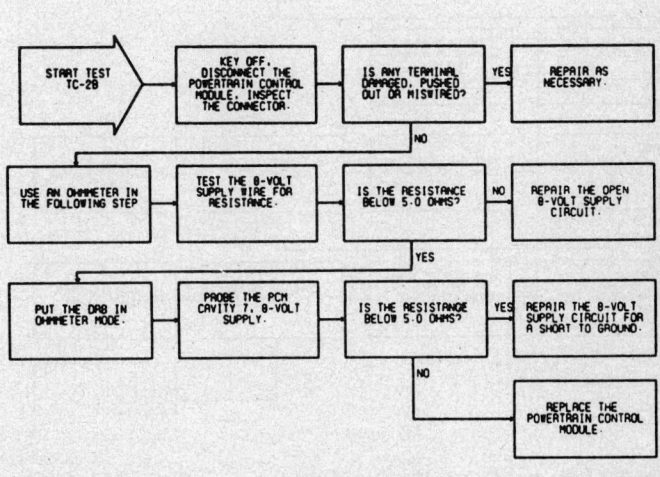

START TEST TC-2B. → KEY OFF. DISCONNECT THE POWERTRAIN CONTROL MODULE. INSPECT THE CONNECTOR. → IS ANY TERMINAL DAMAGED, PUSHED OUT OR MISWIRED? → YES → REPAIR AS NECESSARY.

NO ↓

USE AN OHMMETER IN THE FOLLOWING STEP. → TEST THE 8-VOLT SUPPLY WIRE FOR RESISTANCE. → IS THE RESISTANCE BELOW 5.0 OHMS? → NO → REPAIR THE OPEN 8-VOLT SUPPLY CIRCUIT.

YES ↓

PUT THE DRB IN OHMMETER MODE. → PROBE THE PCM CAVITY 7, 8-VOLT SUPPLY. → IS THE RESISTANCE BELOW 5.0 OHMS? → YES → REPAIR THE 8-VOLT SUPPLY CIRCUIT FOR A SHORT TO GROUND.

NO ↓

REPLACE THE POWERTRAIN CONTROL MODULE.

CR1029302614000X

Fig. 51   Test TC-2B: No Crank Reference Signal At PCM

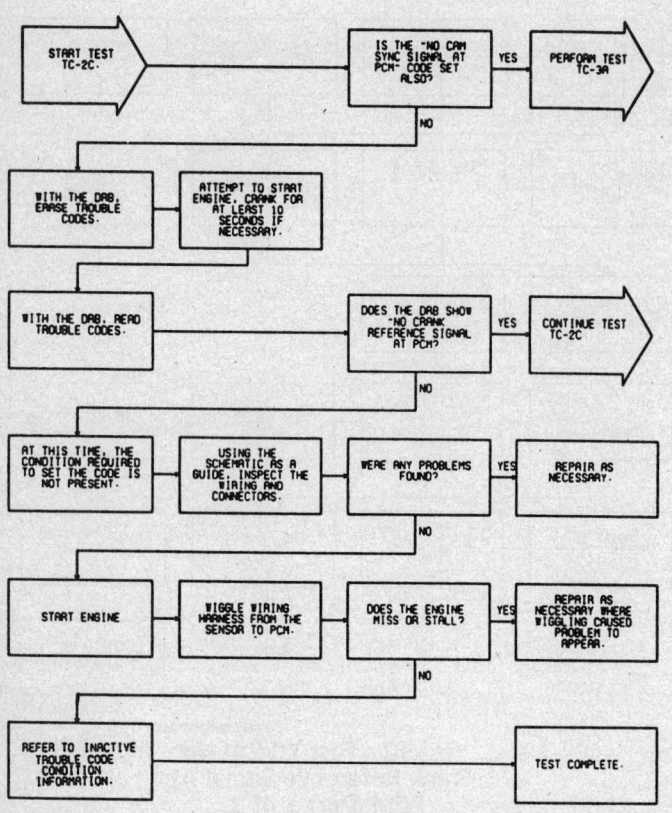

Fig. 52   Test TC-2C: No Crank Reference Signal At PCM (Part 1 of 3)

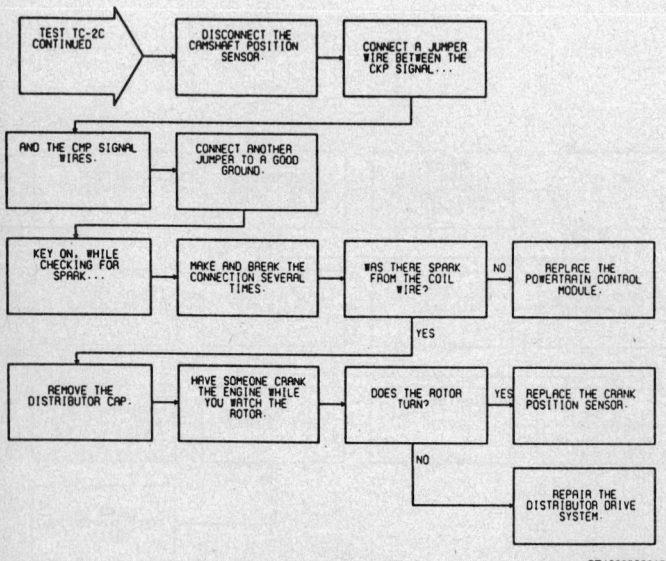

Fig. 52   Test TC-2C: No Crank Reference Signal At PCM (Part 3 of 3)

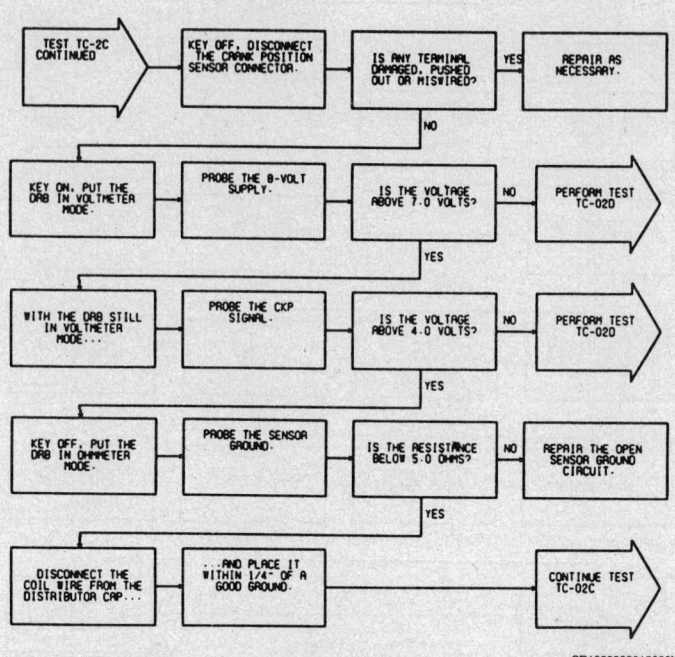

Fig. 52   Test TC-2C: No Crank Reference Signal At PCM (Part 2 of 3)

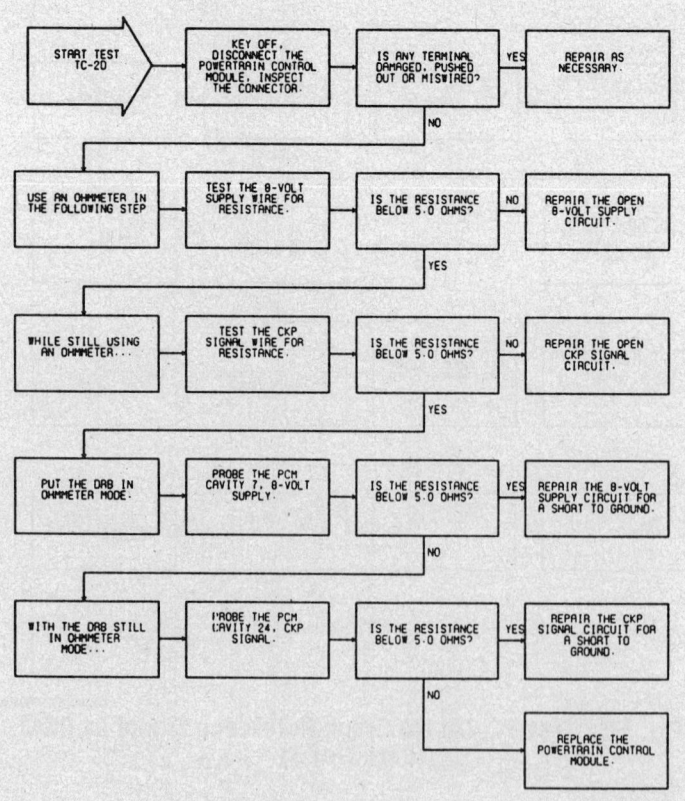

Fig. 53   Test TC-2D: No Crank Reference Signal At PCM

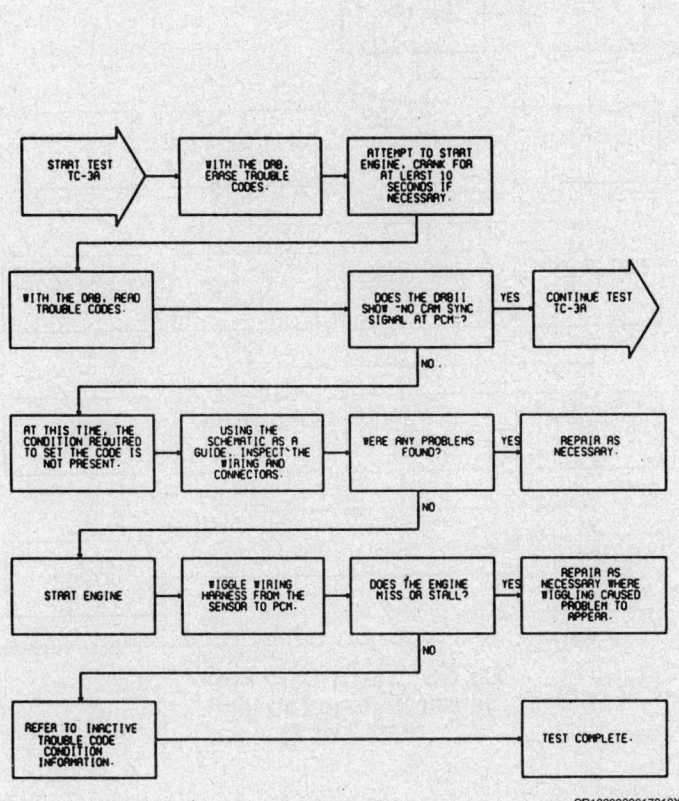

Fig. 54 Test TC-3A: No Cam Sync Signal At PCM (Part 1 of 3)

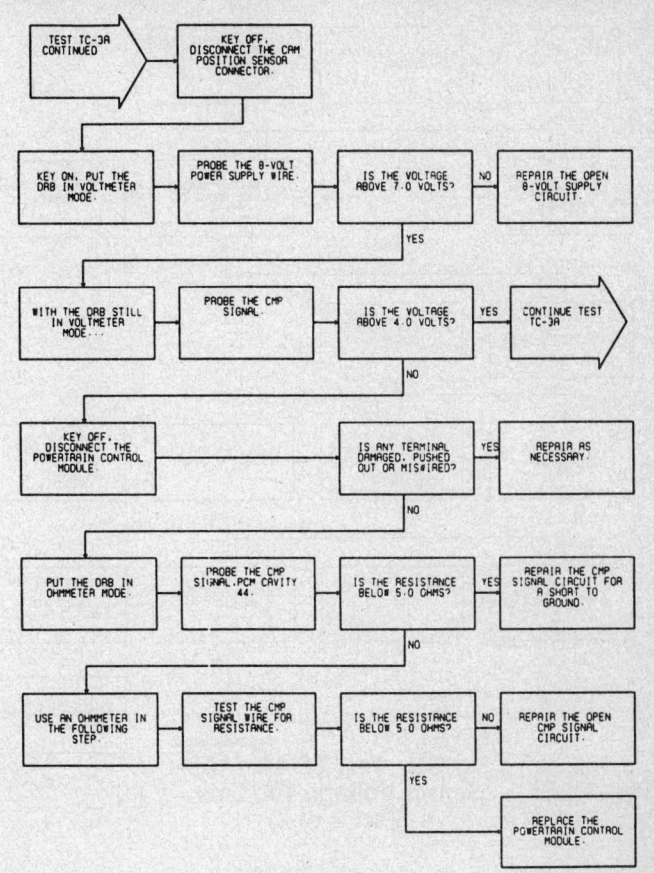

Fig. 54 Test TC-3A: No Cam Sync Signal At PCM (Part 2 of 3)

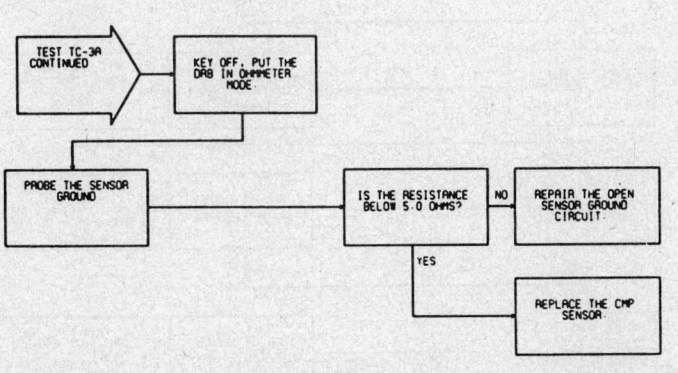

Fig. 54 Test TC-3A: No Cam Sync Signal At PCM (Part 3 of 3)

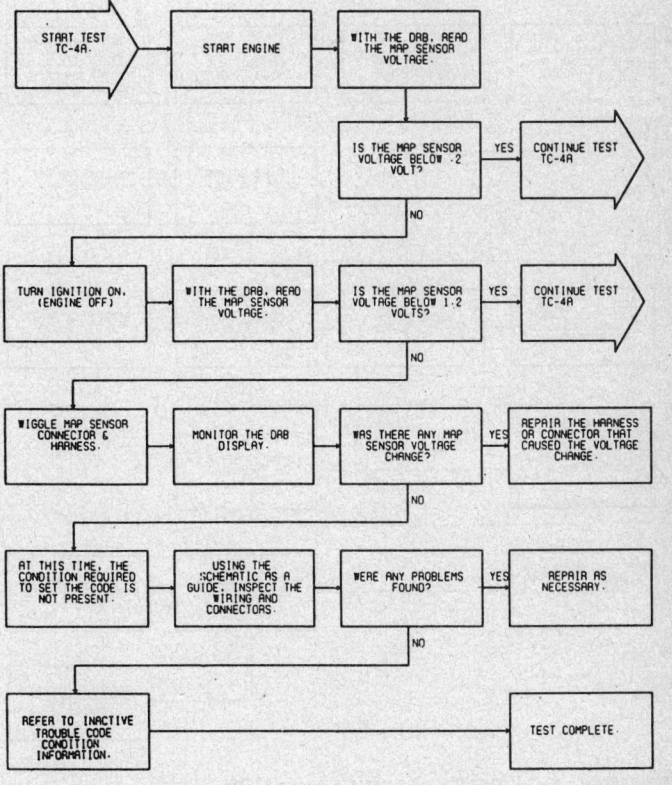

Fig. 55 Test TC-4A: MAP Sensor Voltage Too Low (Part 1 of 2)

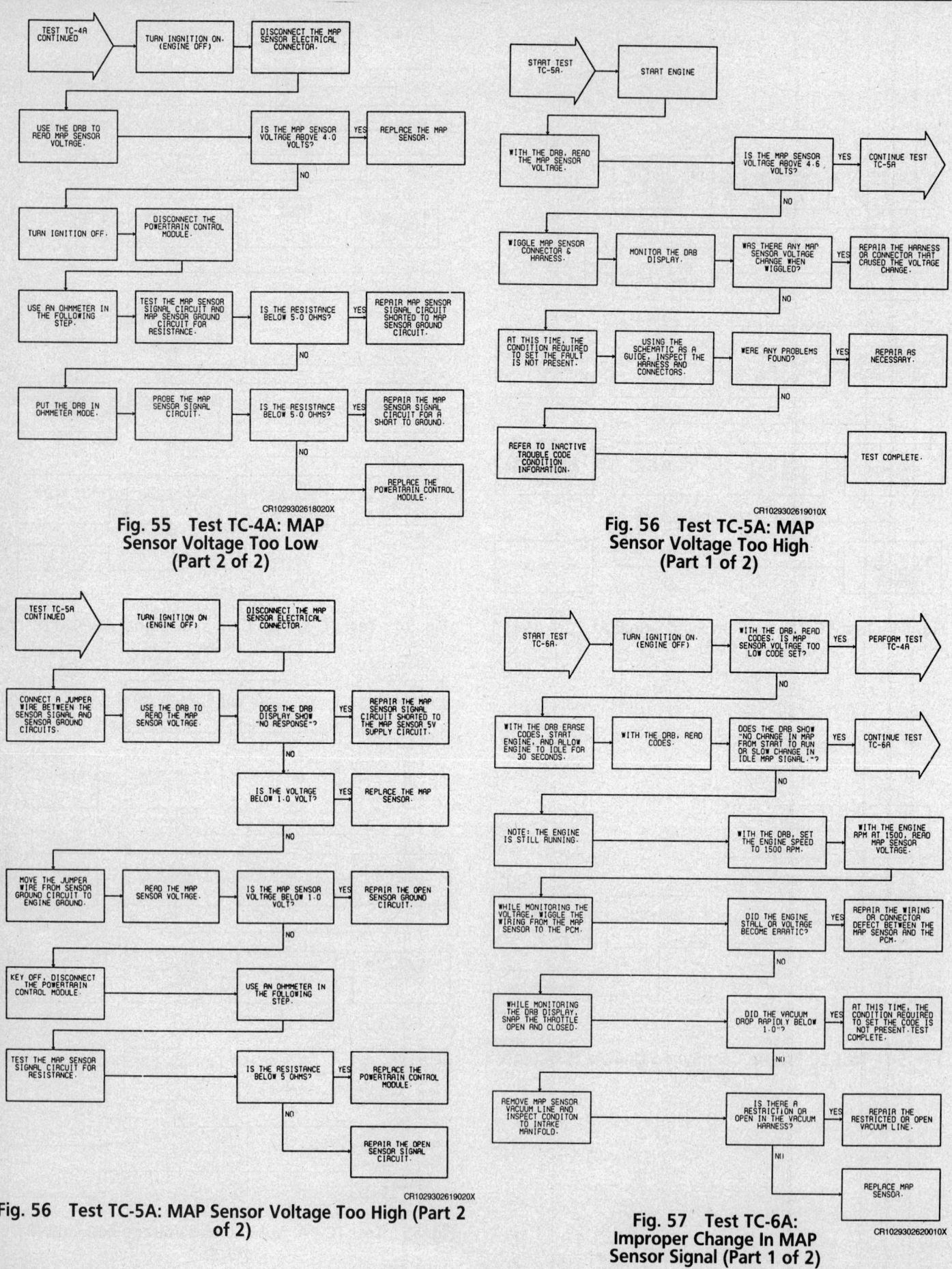

Fig. 55   Test TC-4A: MAP Sensor Voltage Too Low (Part 2 of 2)

Fig. 56   Test TC-5A: MAP Sensor Voltage Too High (Part 1 of 2)

Fig. 56   Test TC-5A: MAP Sensor Voltage Too High (Part 2 of 2)

Fig. 57   Test TC-6A: Improper Change In MAP Sensor Signal (Part 1 of 2)

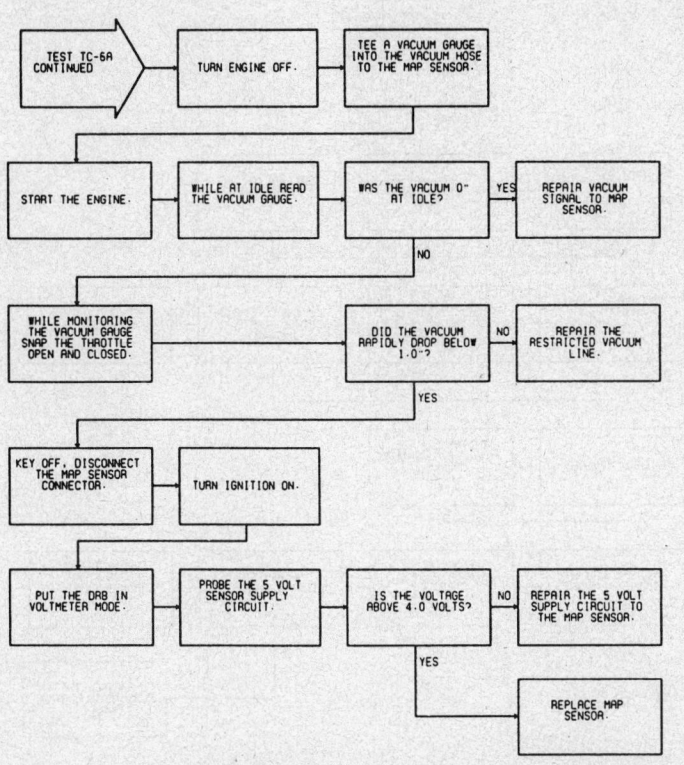

CR1029302620020X

Fig. 57 Test TC-6A: Improper Change In MAP Sensor Signal (Part 2 of 2)

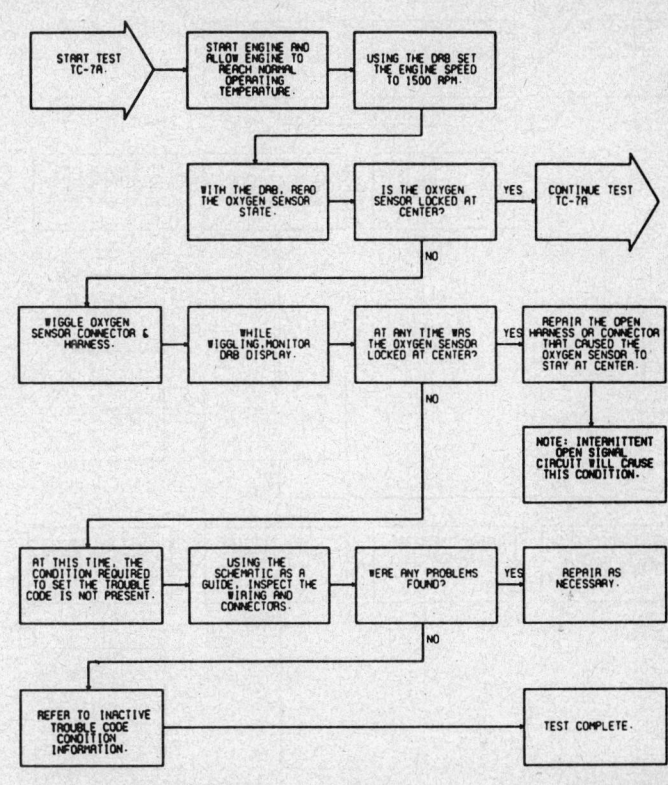

CR1029302621010X

Fig. 58 Test TC-7A: O2 Signal Stays At Center (Part 1 of 2)

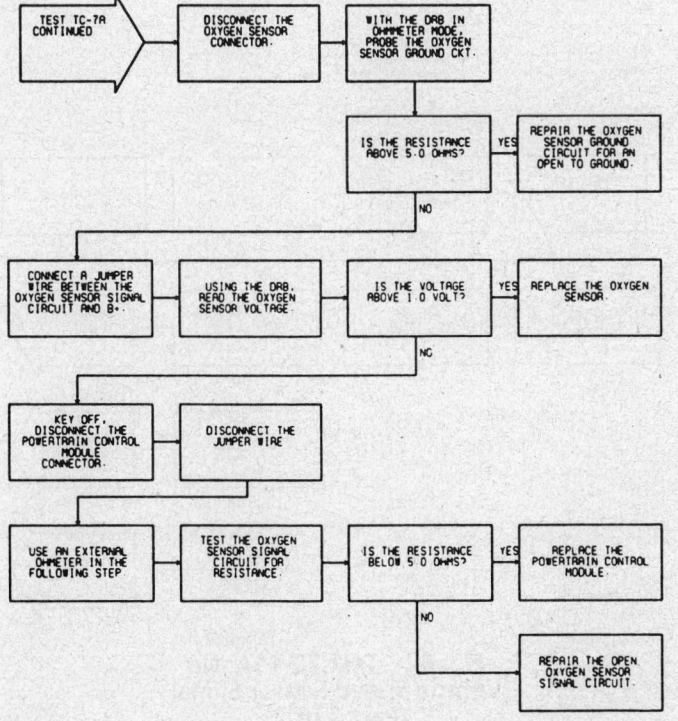

CR1029302621020X

Fig. 58 Test TC-7A: O2 Signal Stays At Center (Part 2 of 2)

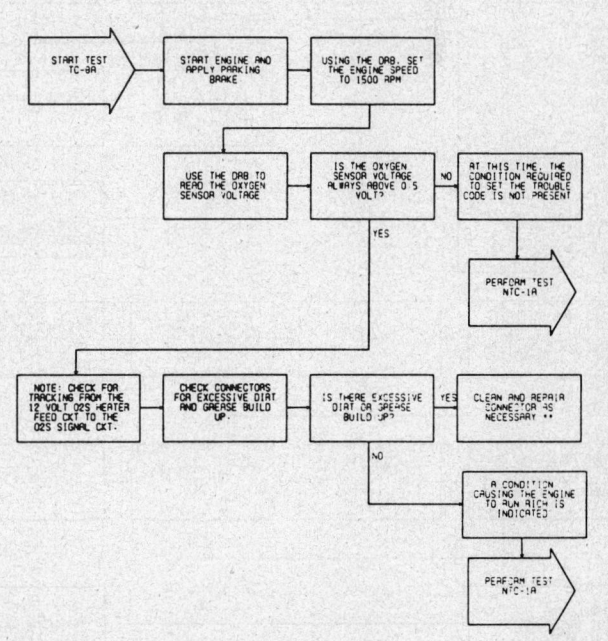

CR1029302622000X

Fig. 59 Test TC-8A: O2 Signal Above Center (Rich)

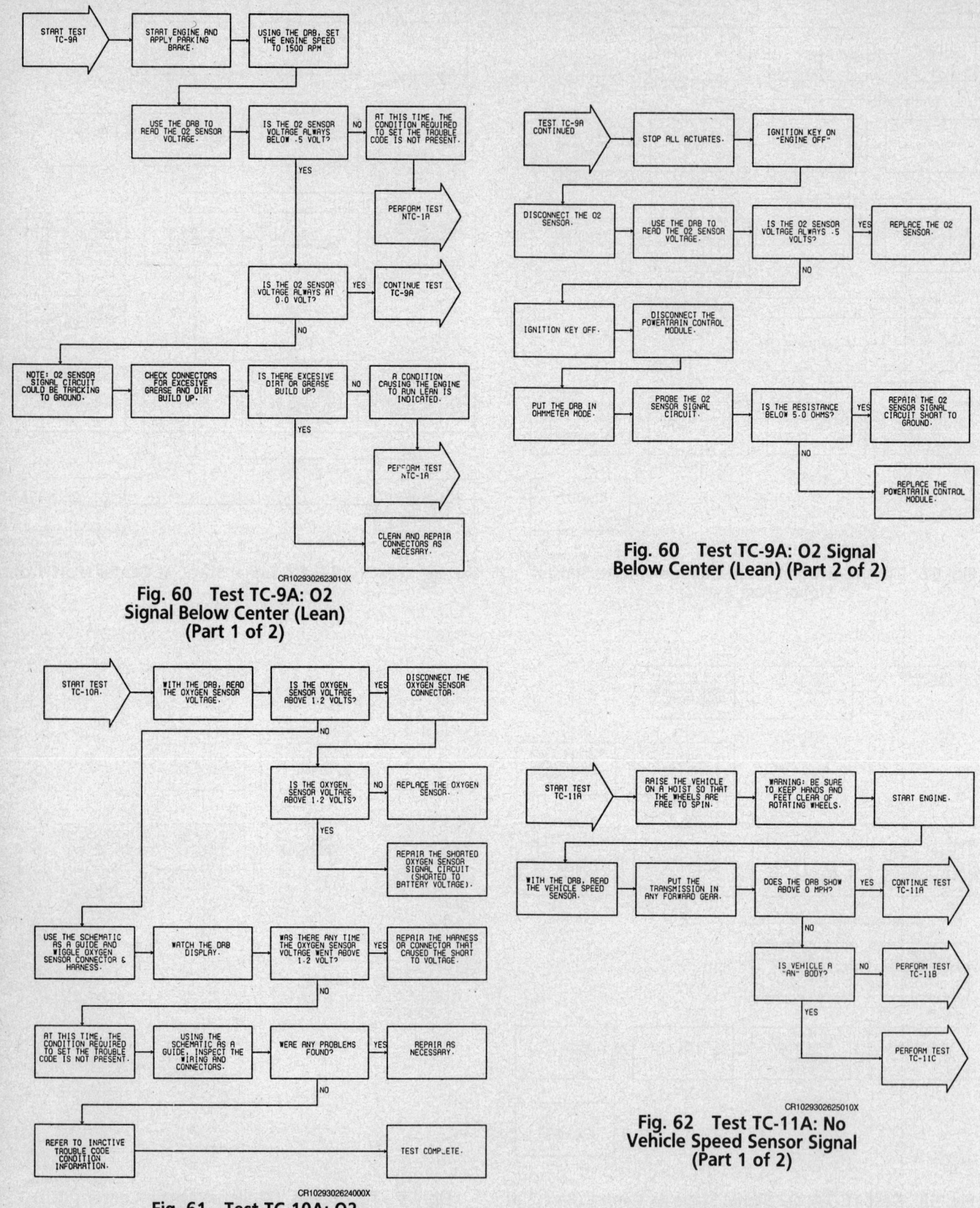

Fig. 60   Test TC-9A: O2 Signal Below Center (Lean) (Part 1 of 2)

Fig. 60   Test TC-9A: O2 Signal Below Center (Lean) (Part 2 of 2)

Fig. 61   Test TC-10A: O2 Signal Shorted To Voltage

Fig. 62   Test TC-11A: No Vehicle Speed Sensor Signal (Part 1 of 2)

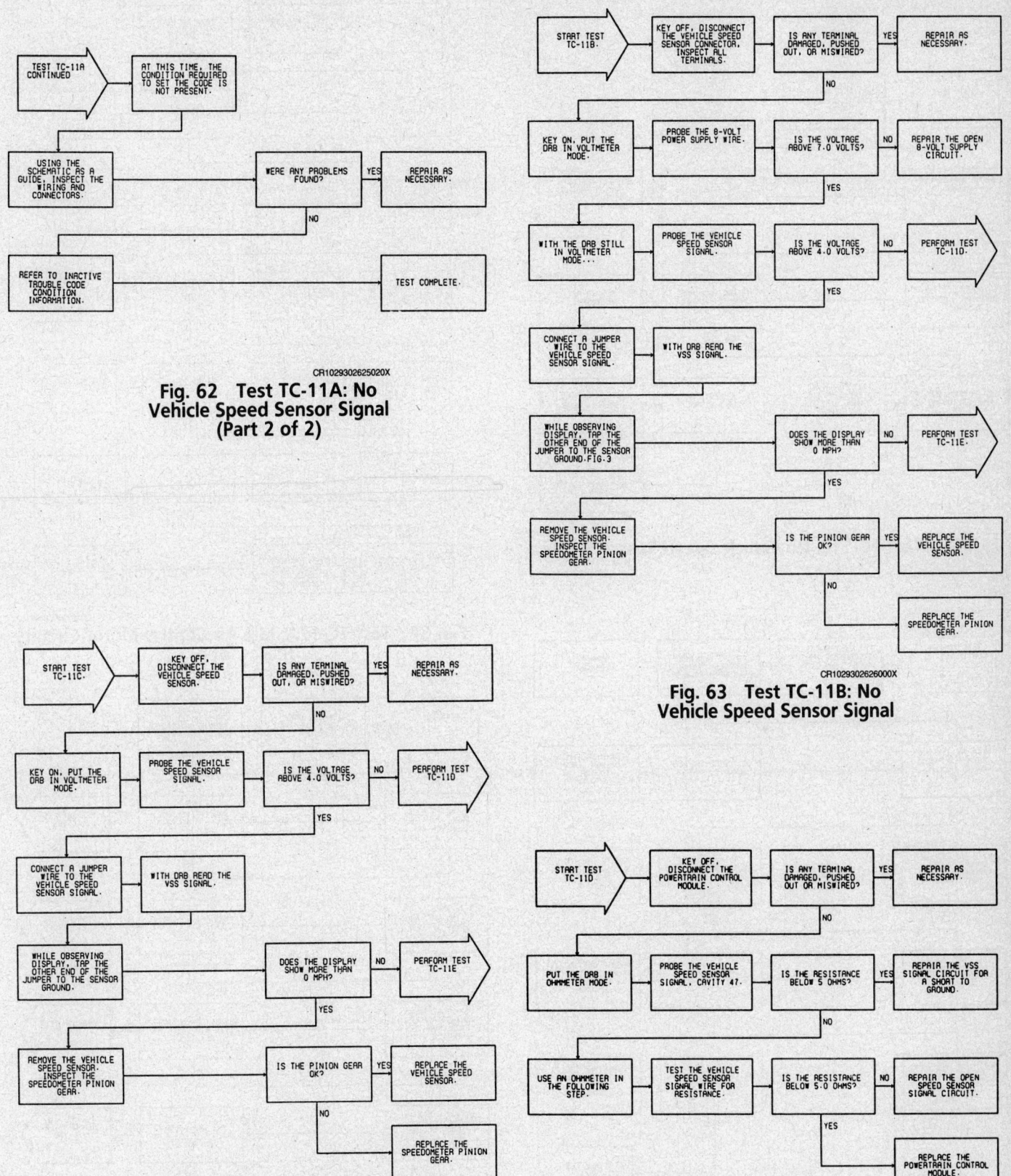

Fig. 62 Test TC-11A: No
Vehicle Speed Sensor Signal
(Part 2 of 2)

Fig. 63 Test TC-11B: No
Vehicle Speed Sensor Signal

Fig. 64 Test TC-11C: No
Vehicle Speed Sensor Signal

Fig. 65 Test TC-11D: No Vehicle Speed Sensor Signal

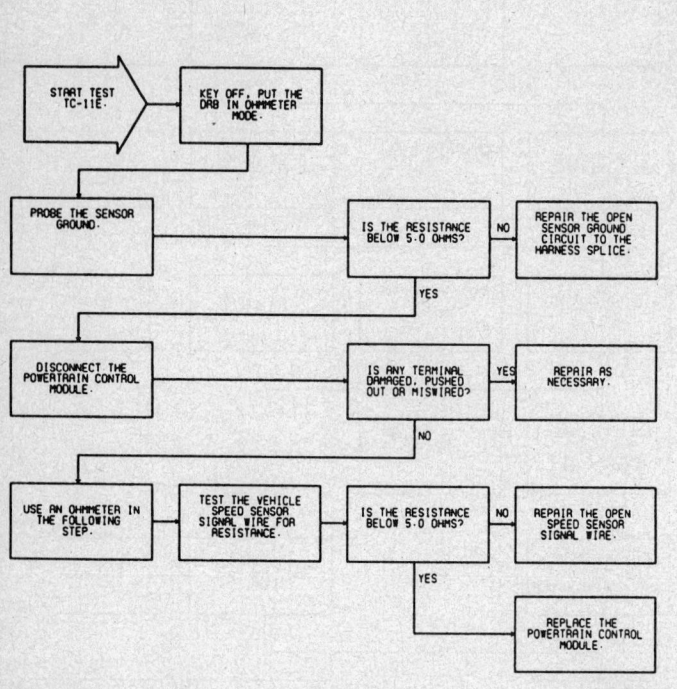

Fig. 66 Test TC-11E: No Vehicle Speed Sensor Signal

CR1029302629000X

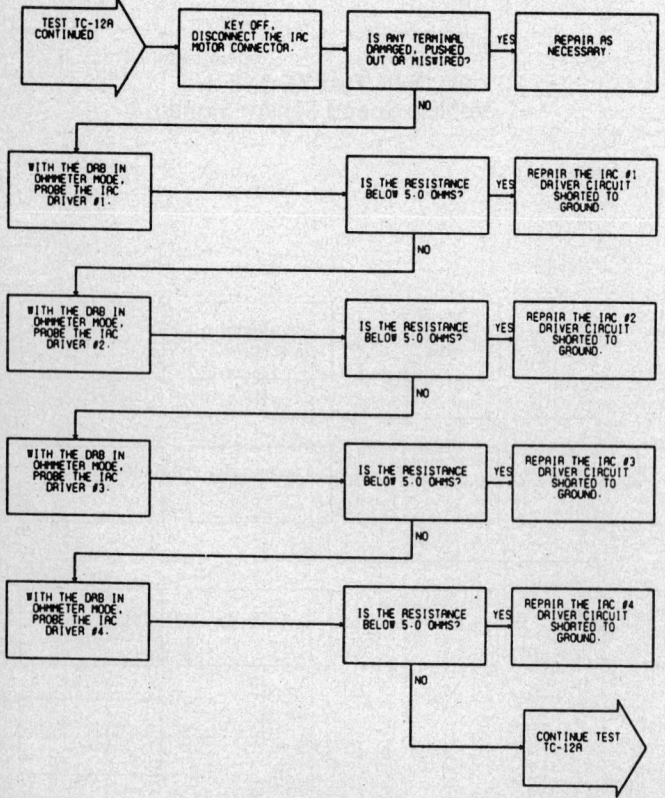

Fig. 67 Test TC-12A: Idle Air Control Motor Circuits
(Part 2 of 4)

CR1029302630020X

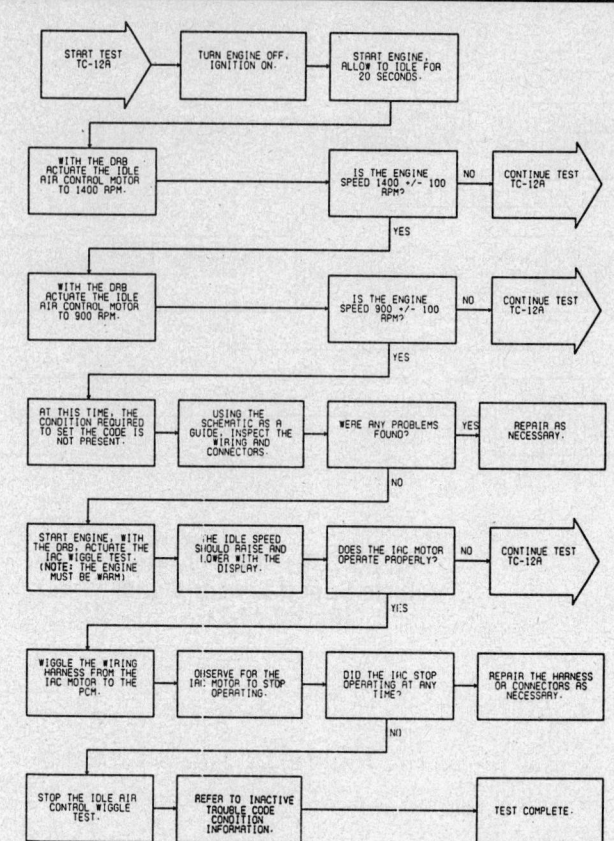

Fig. 67 Test TC-12A: Idle Air Control Motor Circuits
(Part 1 of 4)

CR1029302630010X

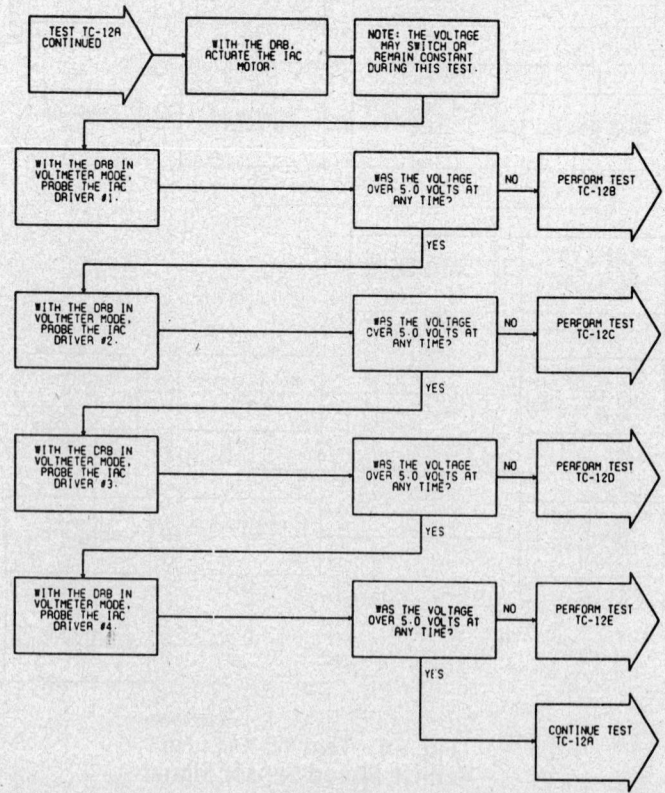

Fig. 67 Test TC-12A: Idle Air Control Motor Circuits (Part
3 of 4)

CR1029302630030X

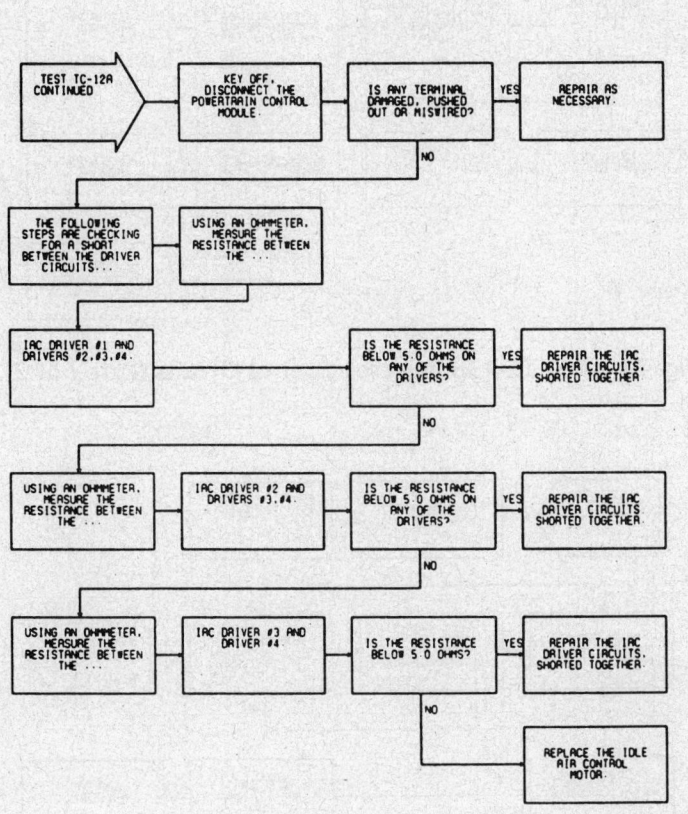

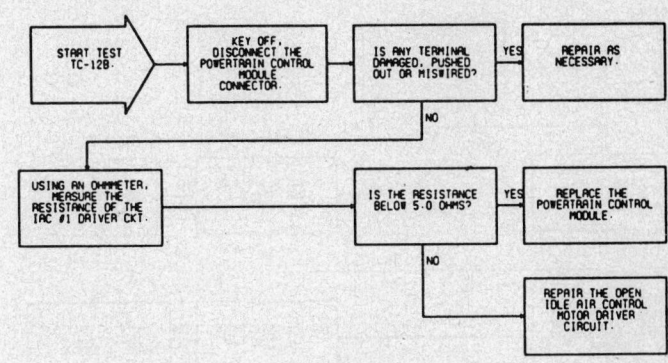

Fig. 68   Test TC-12B: Idle Air Control Motor Circuits

Fig. 67   Test TC-12A: Idle Air Control Motor Circuits (Part 4 of 4)

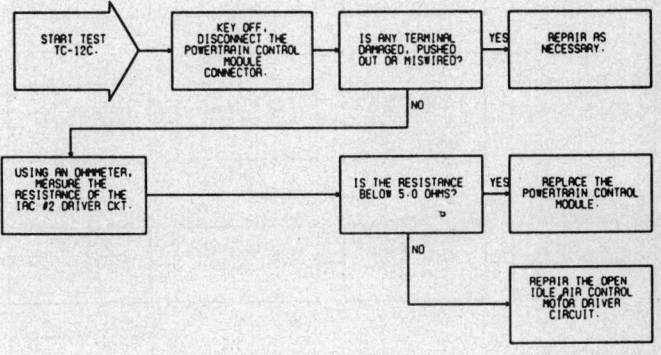

Fig. 69   Test TC-12C: Idle Air Control Motor Circuits

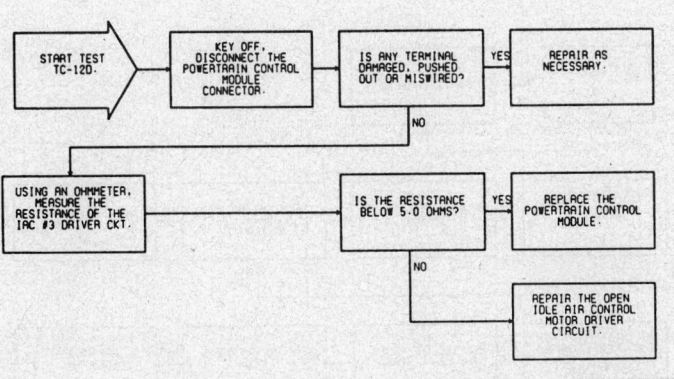

Fig. 70   Test TC-12D: Idle Air Control Motor Circuits

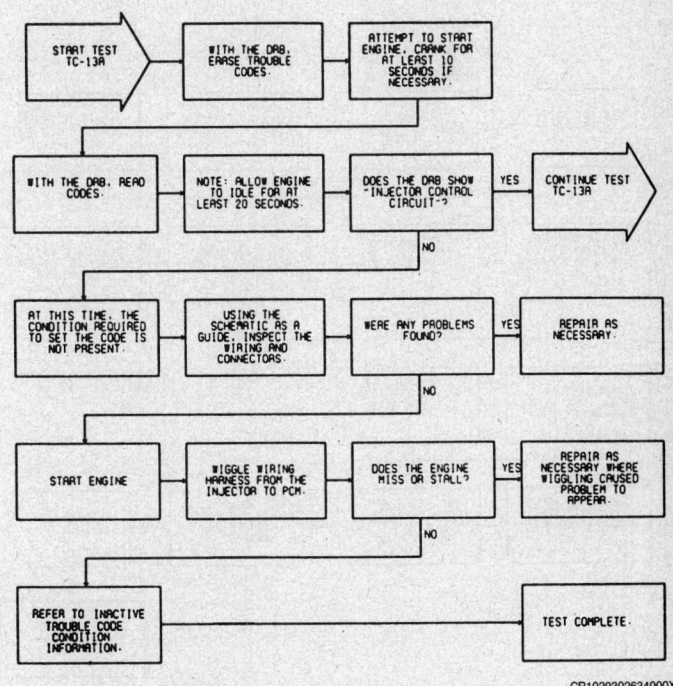

Fig. 71   Test TC-13A: Injector Control Circuits

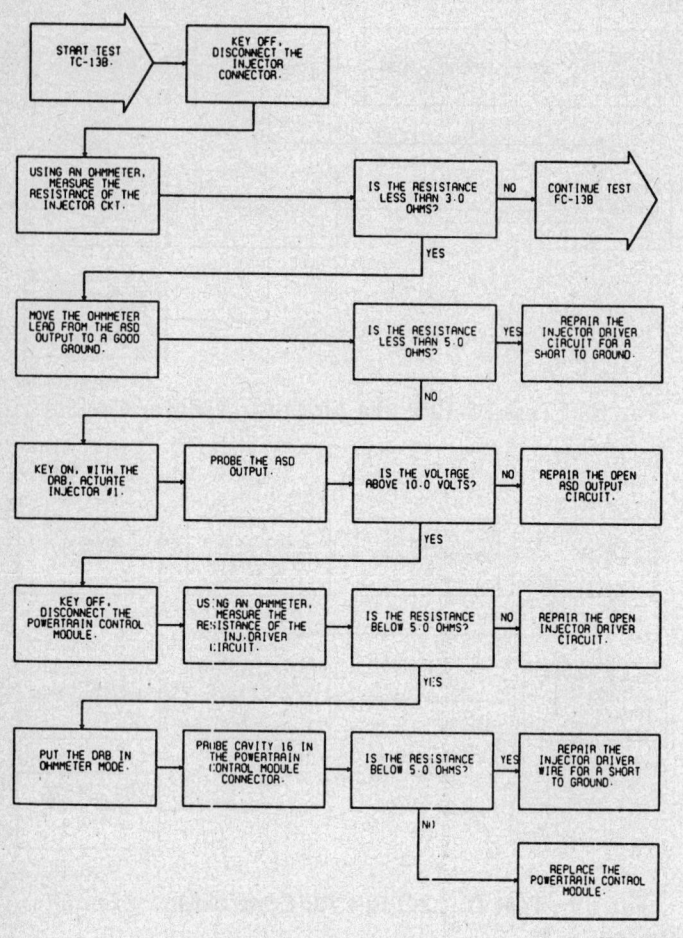

Fig. 72   Test TC-13B: Injector Control Circuits (Part 1 of 2)

CR1029302635010X

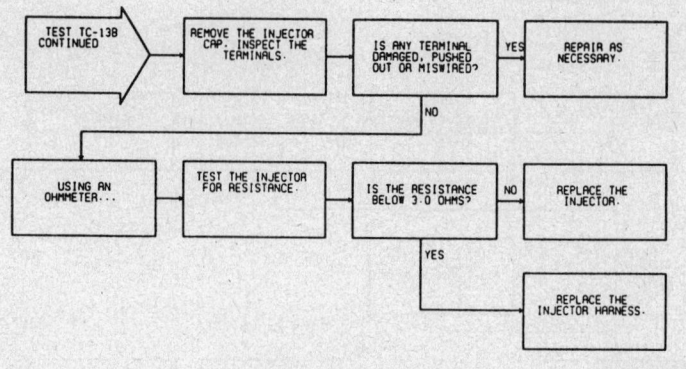

Fig. 72   Test TC-13B: Injector Control Circuits (Part 2 of 2)

CR1029302635020X

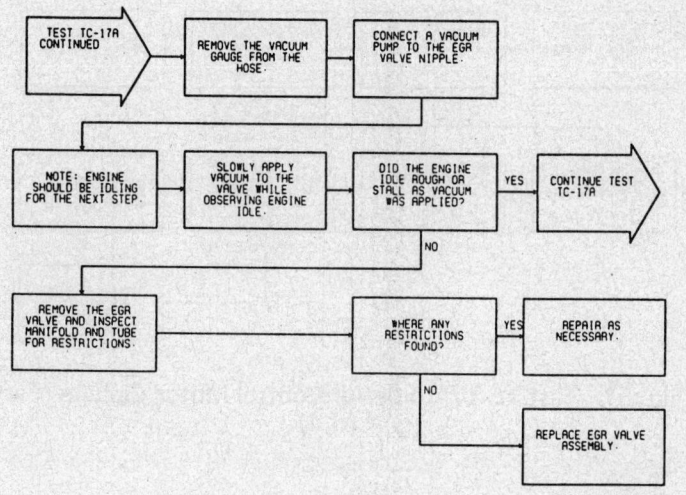

Fig. 73   Test TC-17A: EGR System Failure (Part 2 of 3)

CR1029302636020X

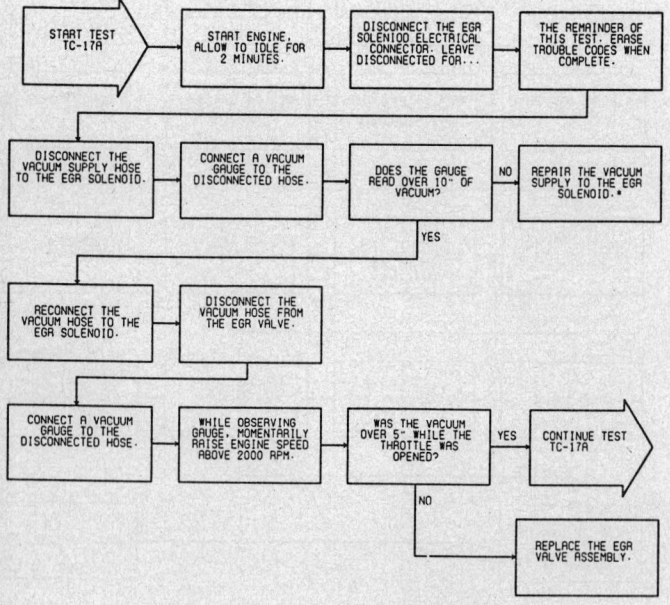

Fig. 73   Test TC-17A: EGR System Failure (Part 1 of 3)

CR1029302636010X

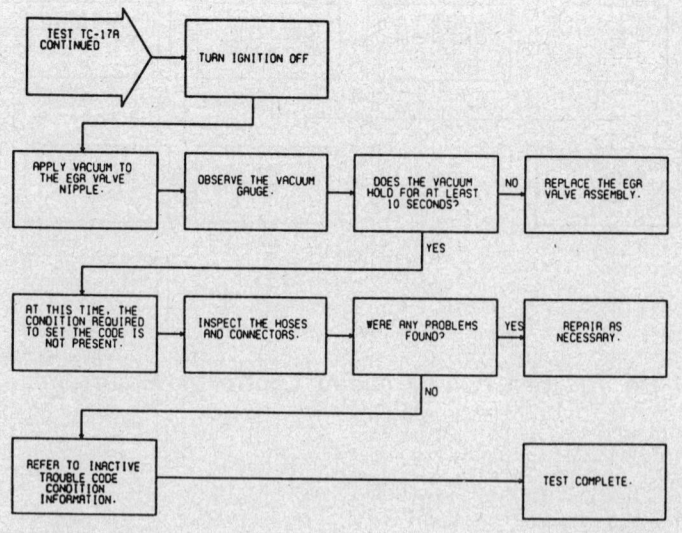

Fig. 73   Test TC-17A: EGR System Failure (Part 3 of 3)

CR1029302636030X

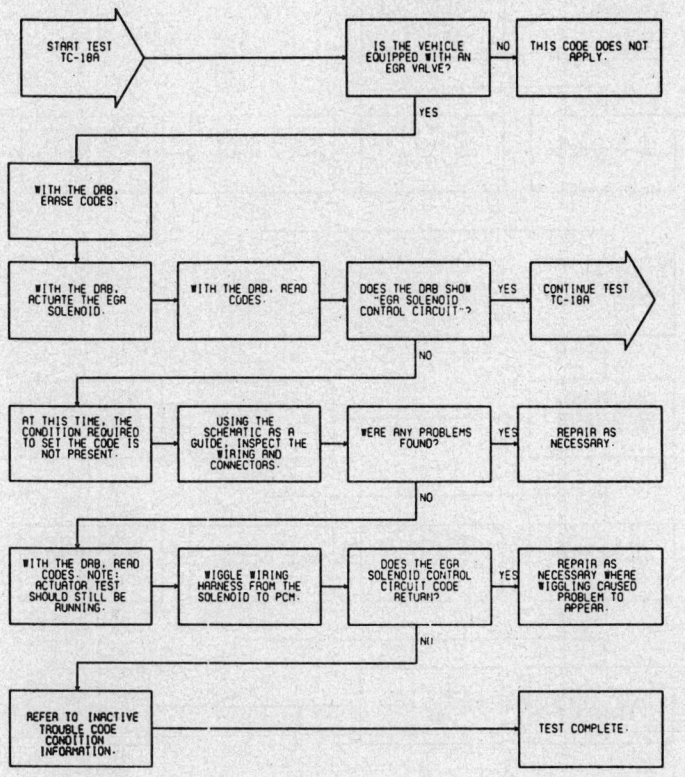

Fig. 74   Test TC-18A: EGR Solenoid Circuit (Part 1 of 3)

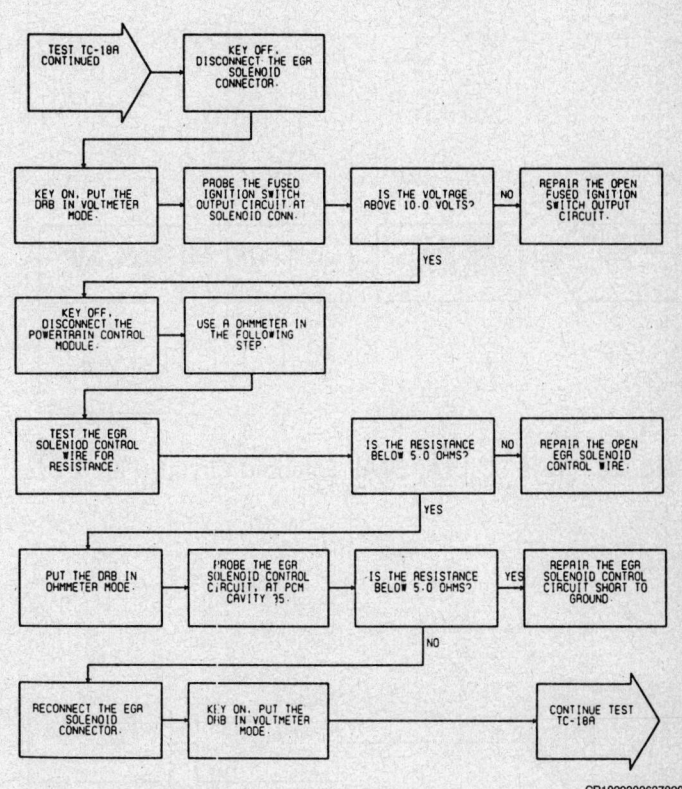

Fig. 74   Test TC-18A: EGR Solenoid Circuit (Part 2 of 3)

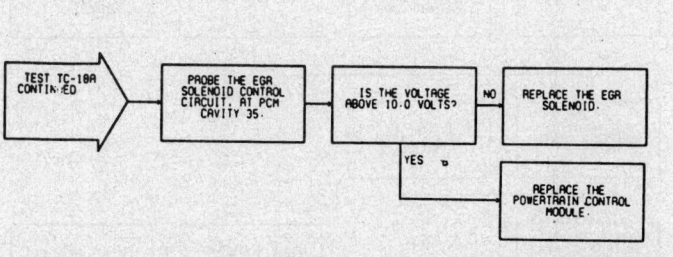

Fig. 74   Test TC-18A: EGR Solenoid Circuit (Part 3 of 3)

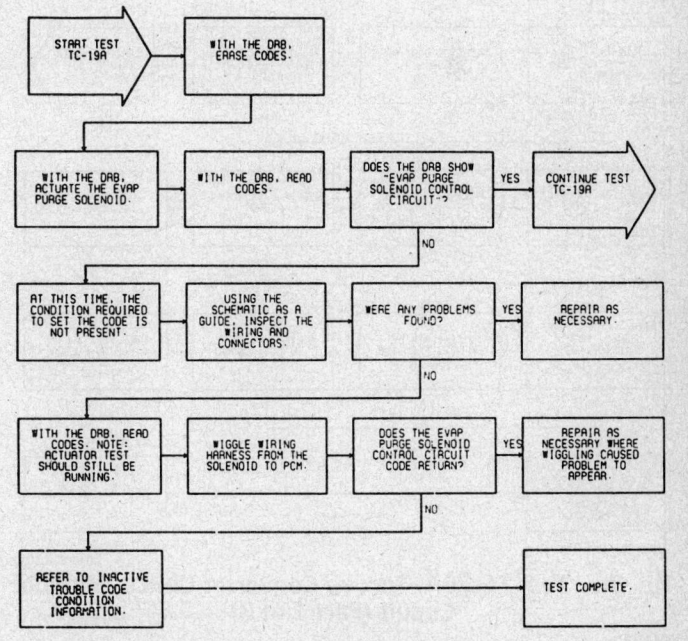

Fig. 75   Test TC-19A: EVAP Solenoid Circuit (Part 1 of 3)

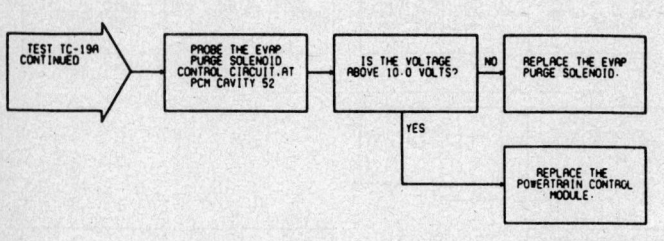

Fig. 75   Test TC-19A: EVAP Solenoid Circuit (Part 2 of 3)

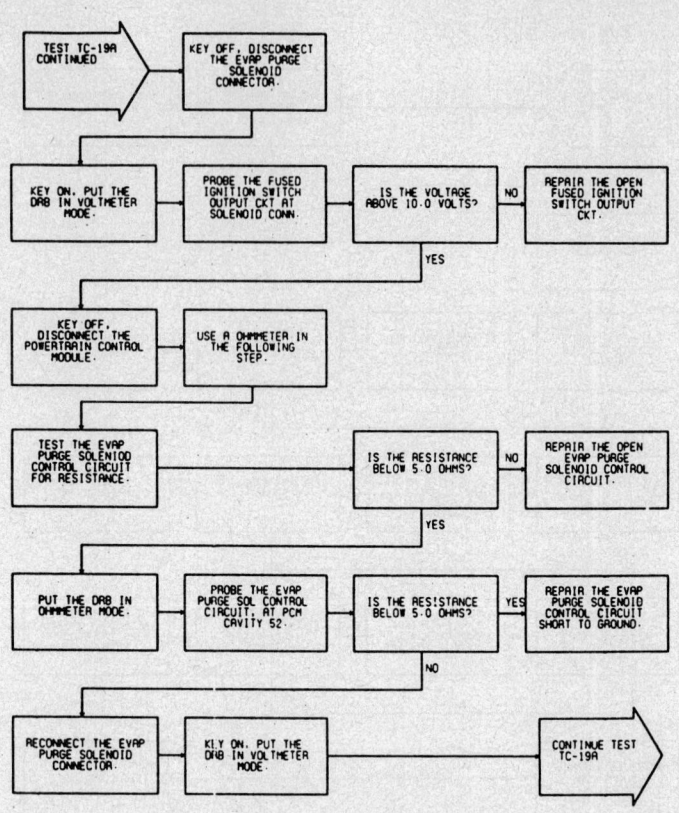

Fig. 75   Test TC-19A: EVAP Solenoid Circuit (Part 3 of 3)

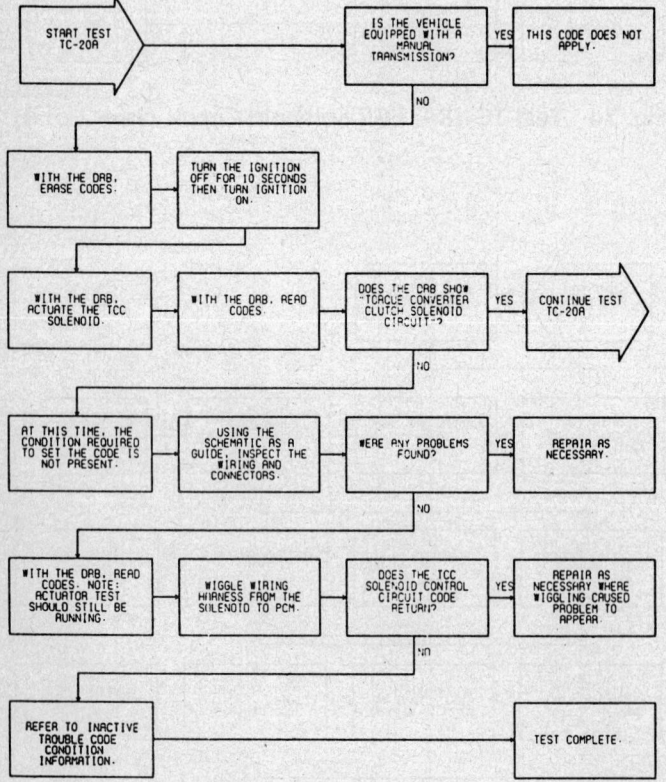

Fig. 76   Test TC-20A: Torque Converter Clutch Solenoid Circuit (Part 1 of 3)

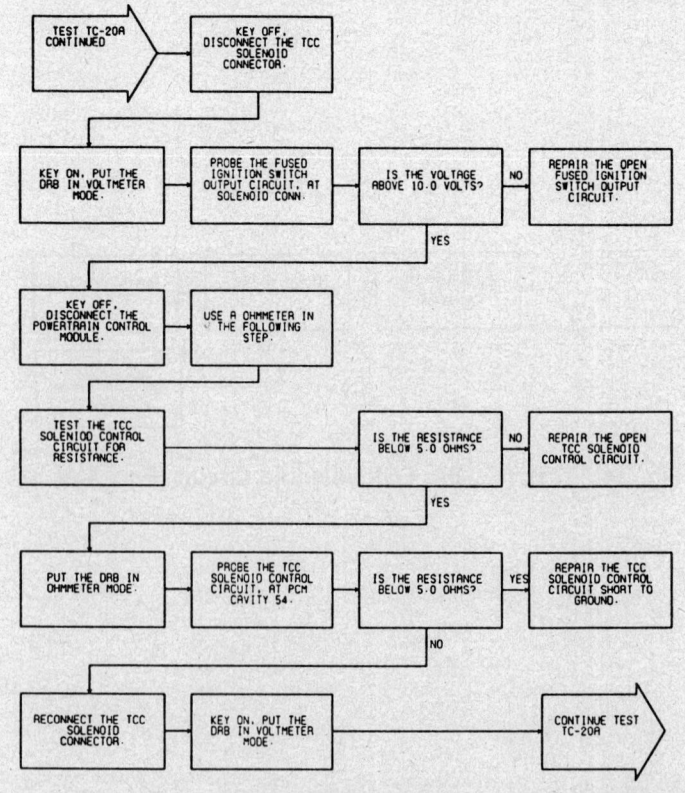

Fig. 76   Test TC-20A: Torque Converter Clutch Solenoid Circuit (Part 2 of 3)

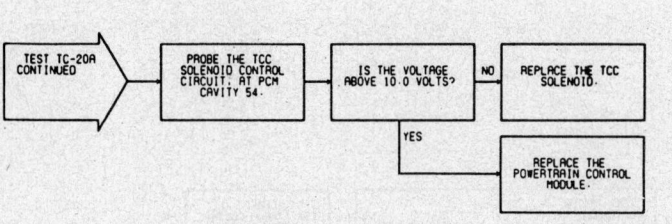

Fig. 76 Test TC-20A: Torque Converter Clutch Solenoid Circuit (Part 3 of 3)

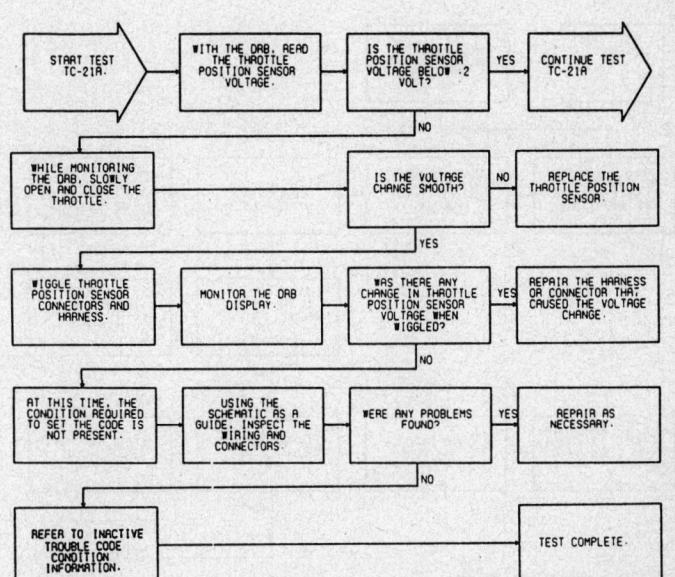

CR1029302640010X

Fig. 77 Test TC-21A: Throttle Position Sensor Voltage Low (Part 1 of 2)

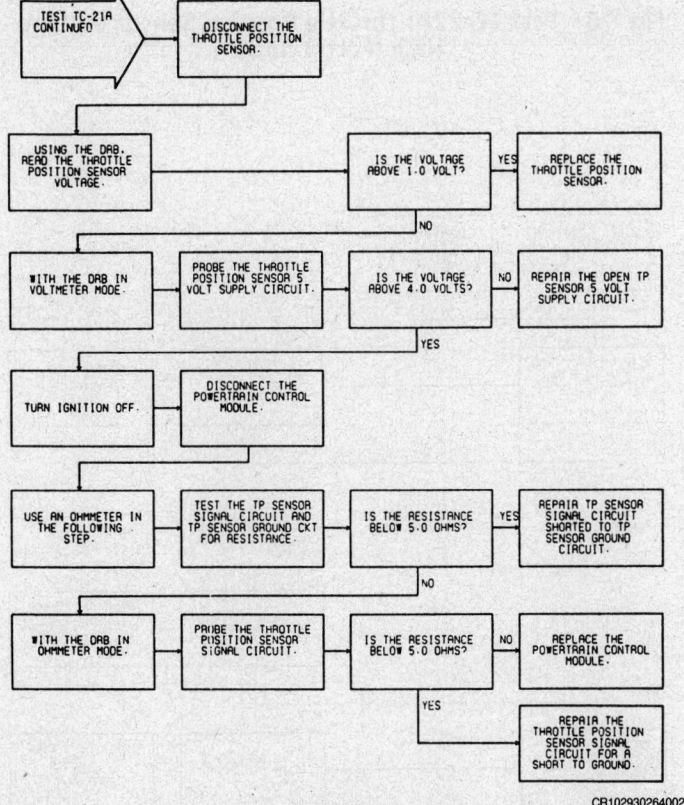

CR1029302640020X

Fig. 77 Test TC-21A: Throttle Position Sensor Voltage Low (Part 2 of 2)

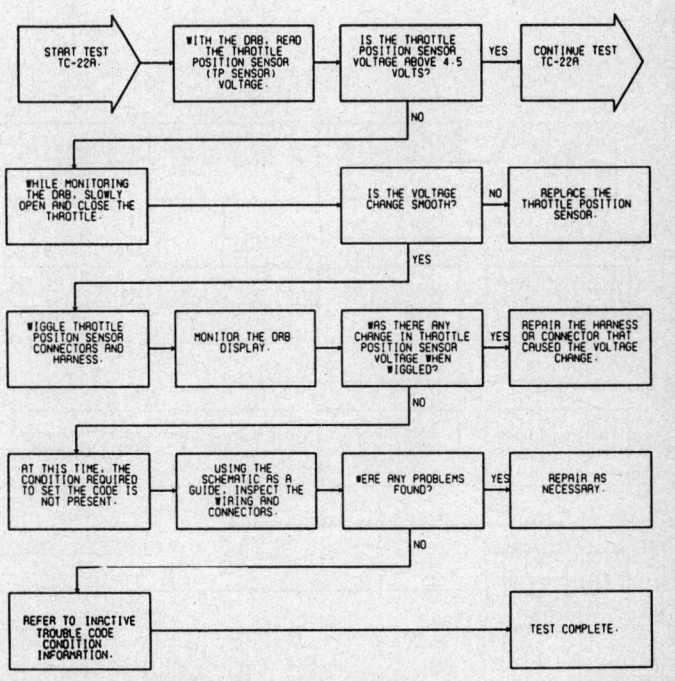

CR1029302641010X

Fig. 78 Test TC-22A: Throttle Position Sensor Voltage High (Part 1 of 3)

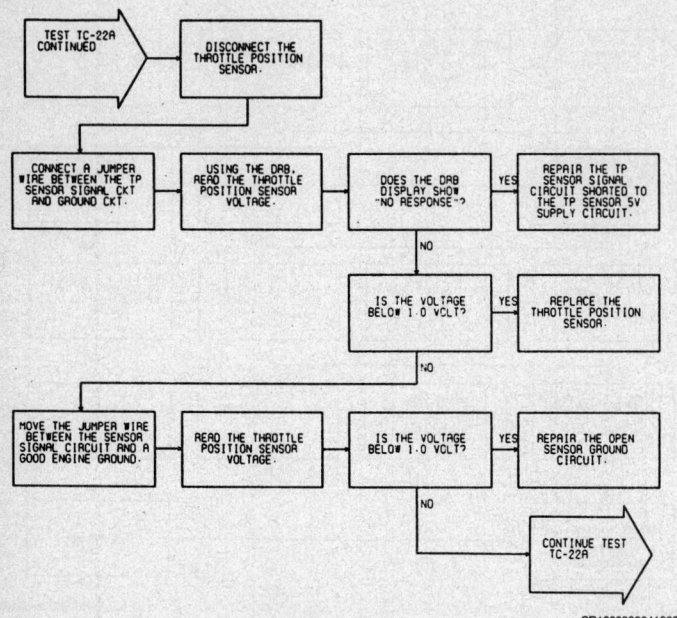

Fig. 78 Test TC-22A: Throttle Position Sensor Voltage High (Part 2 of 3)

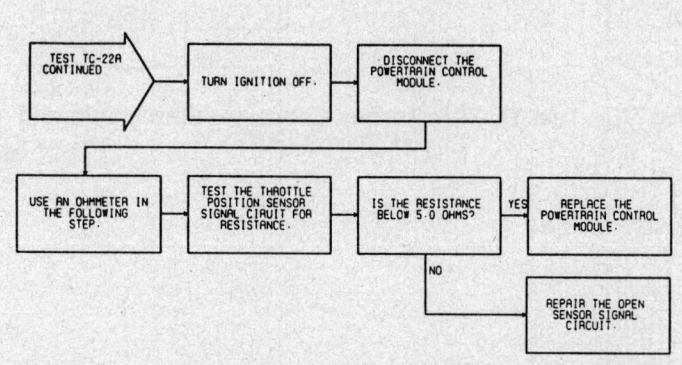

Fig. 78 Test TC-22A: Throttle Position Sensor Voltage High (Part 3 of 3)

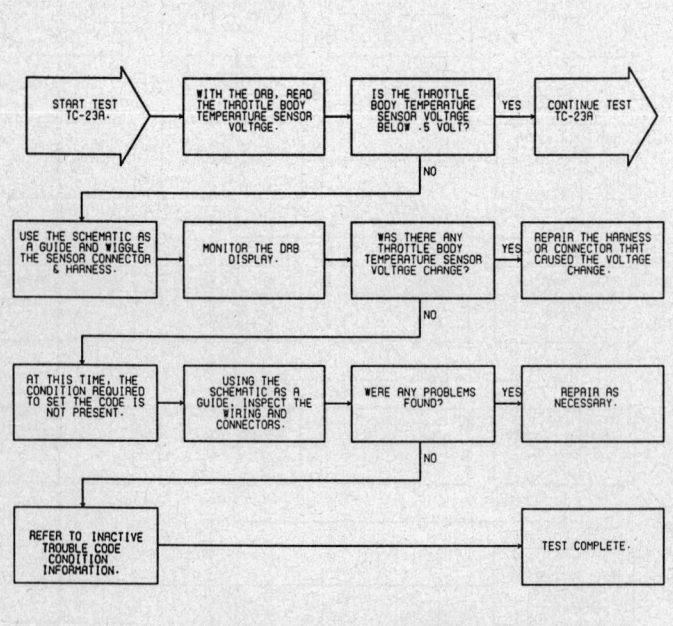

Fig. 79 Test TC-23A: Throttle Body Temp Sensor Voltage Low (Part 1 of 2)

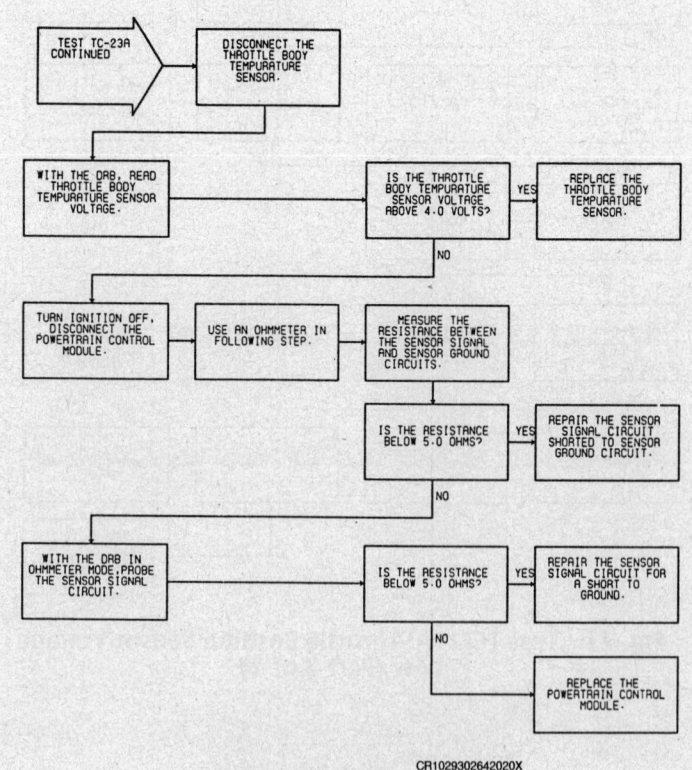

Fig. 79 Test TC-23A: Throttle Body Temp Sensor Voltage Low (Part 2 of 2)

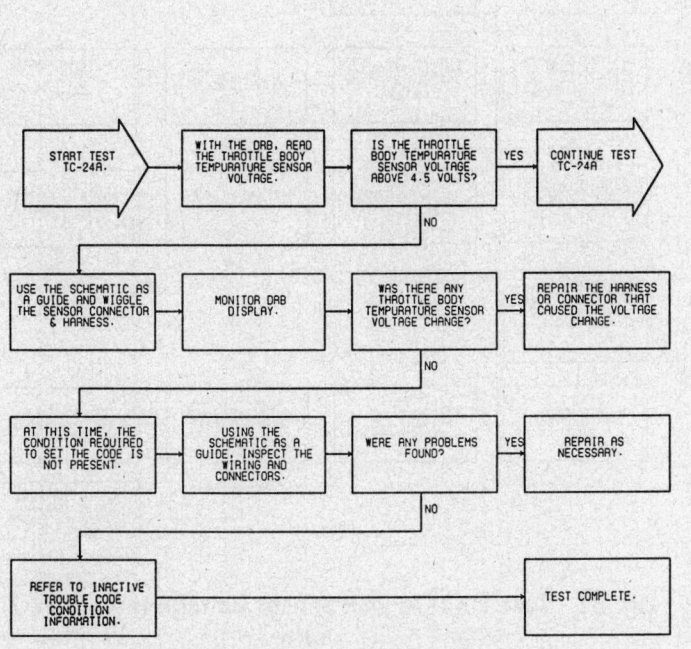

Fig. 80   Test TC-24A:
Throttle Body Temp Sensor
Voltage High (Part 1 of 2)

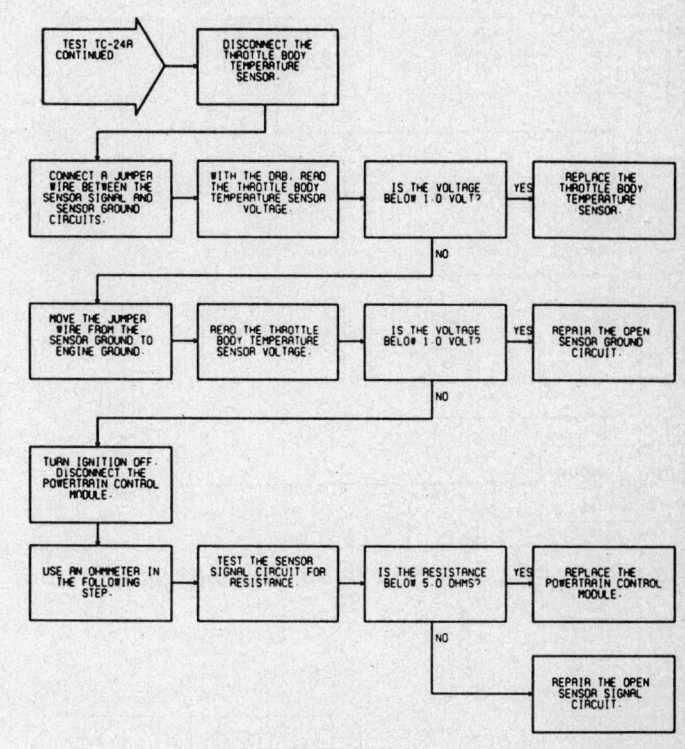

Fig. 80   Test TC-24A: Throttle Body Temp Sensor
Voltage High (Part 2 of 2)

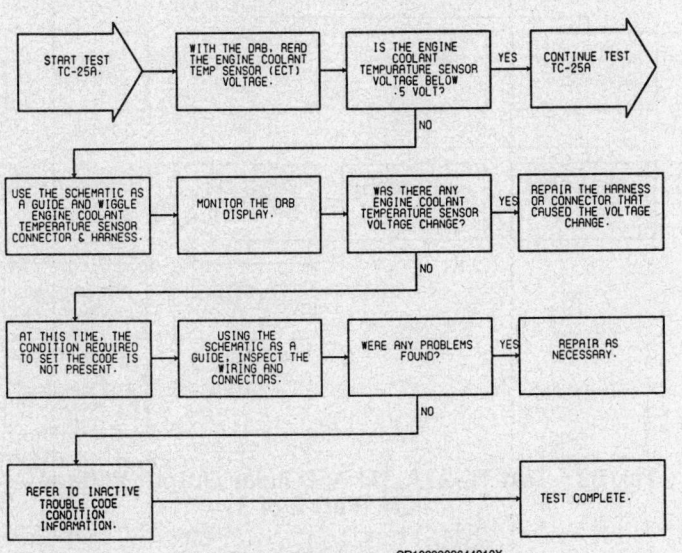

Fig. 81   Test TC-25A: EGR
Sensor Voltage Low (Part 1
of 2)

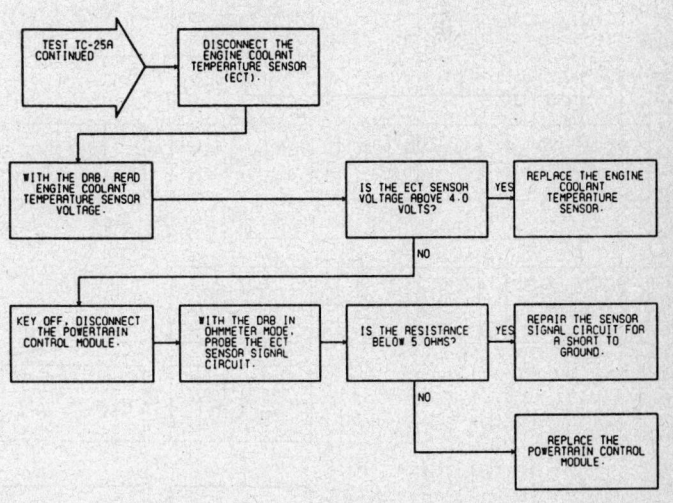

Fig. 81   Test TC-25A: EGR Sensor Voltage Low (Part 2 of
2)

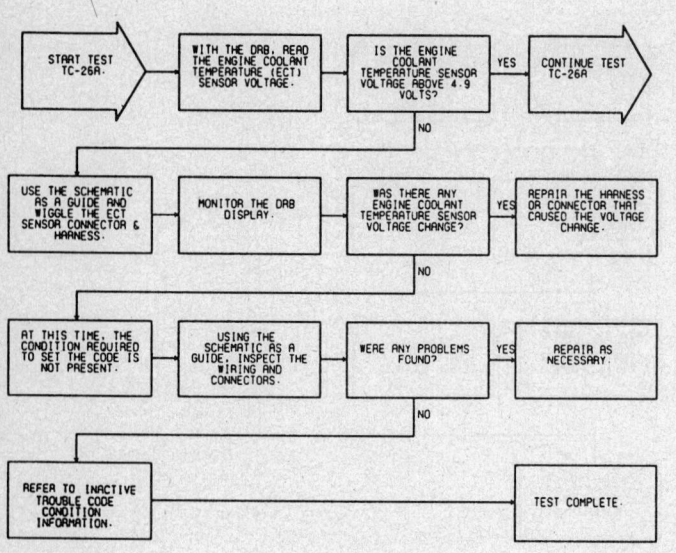

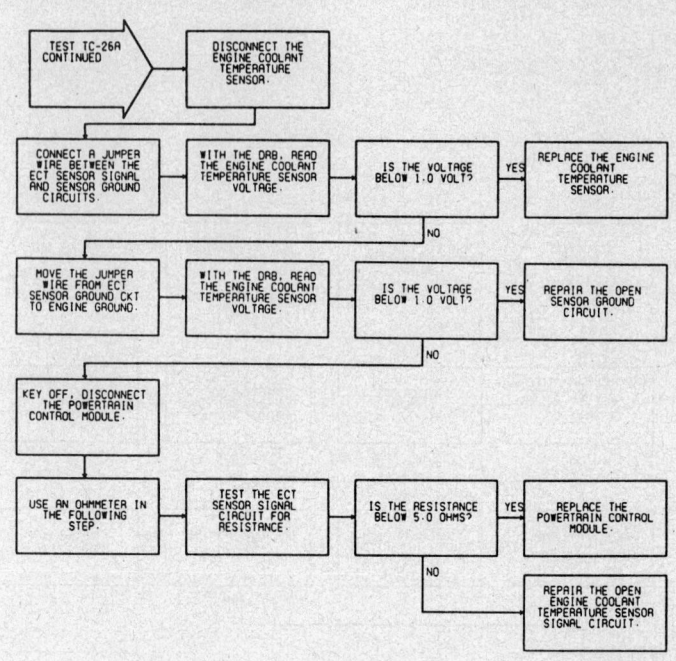

Fig. 82   Test TC-26A: EGR Sensor Voltage High (Part 1 of 2)

Fig. 82   Test TC-26A: EGR Sensor Voltage High (Part 2 of 2)

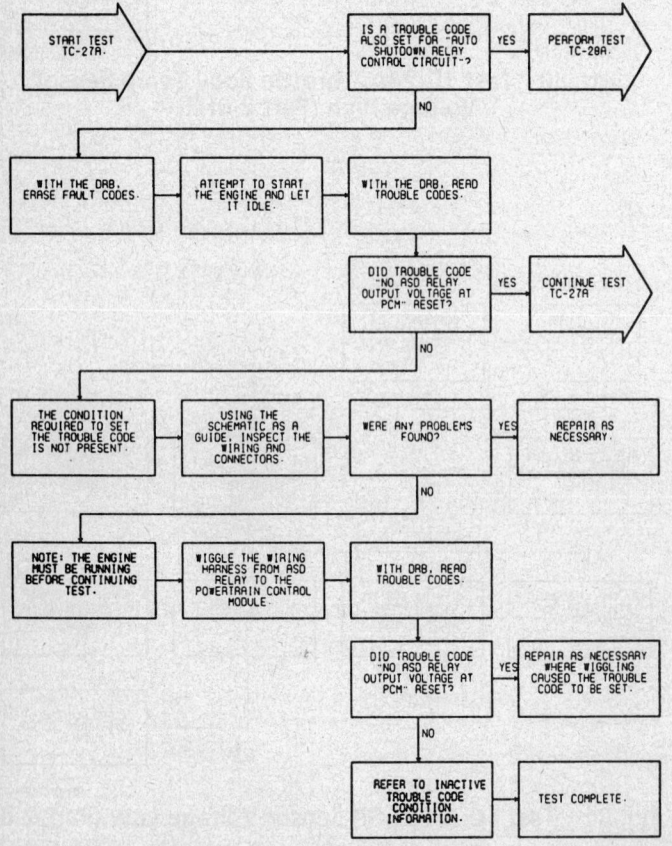

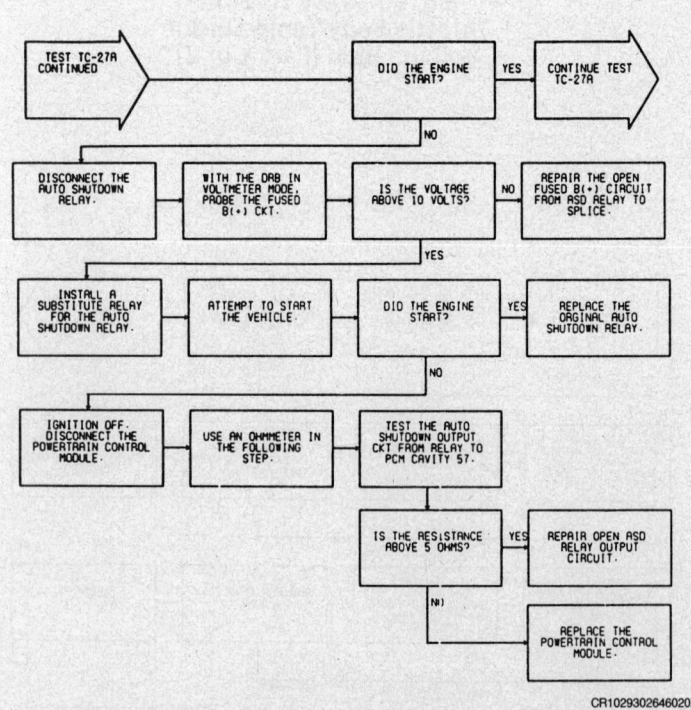

Fig. 83   Test TC-27A: No ASD Relay Output Voltage At PCM (Part 1 of 3)

Fig. 83   Test TC-27A: No ASD Relay Output Voltage At PCM (Part 2 of 3)

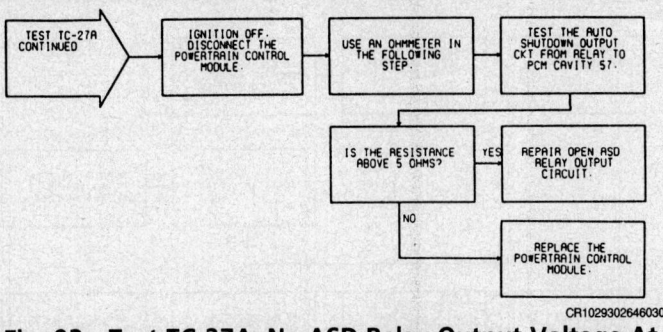

Fig. 83   Test TC-27A: No ASD Relay Output Voltage At PCM (Part 3 of 3)

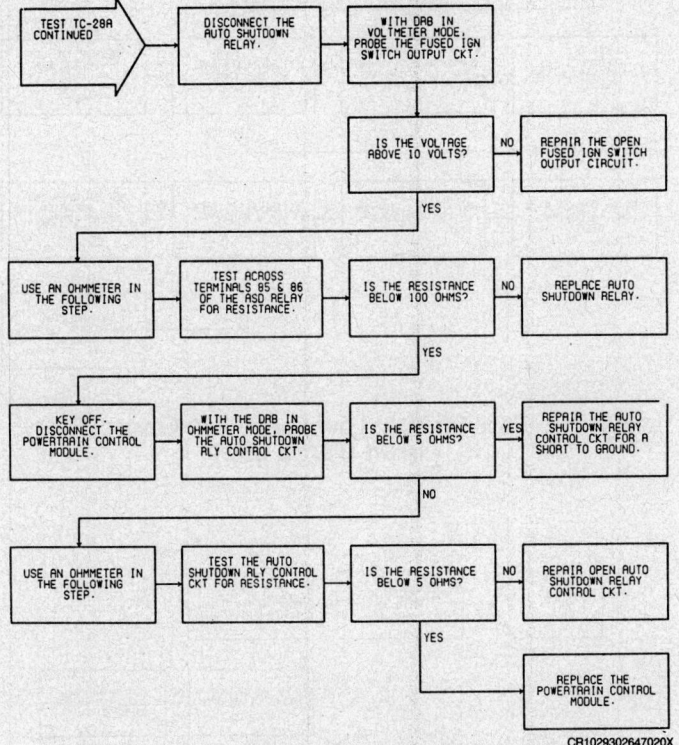

Fig. 84   Test TC-28A: Auto Shutdown Relay Control Circuit (Part 2 of 2)

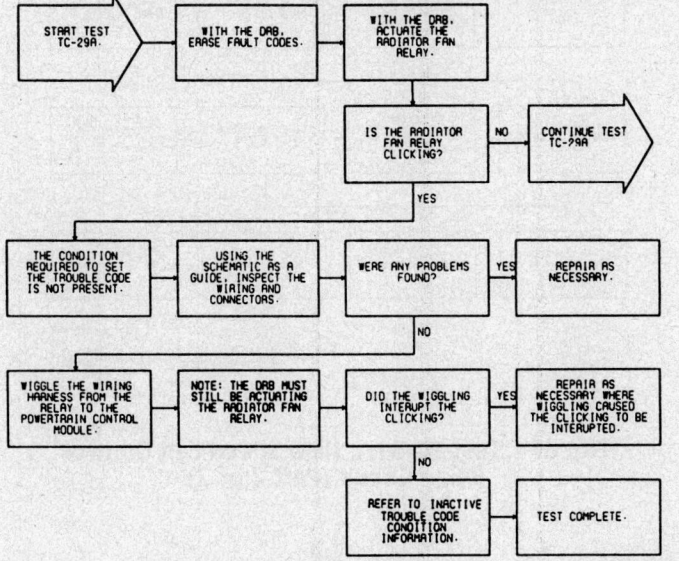

Fig. 85   Test TC-29A: Radiator Fan Control Relay Circuit (Part 1 of 2)

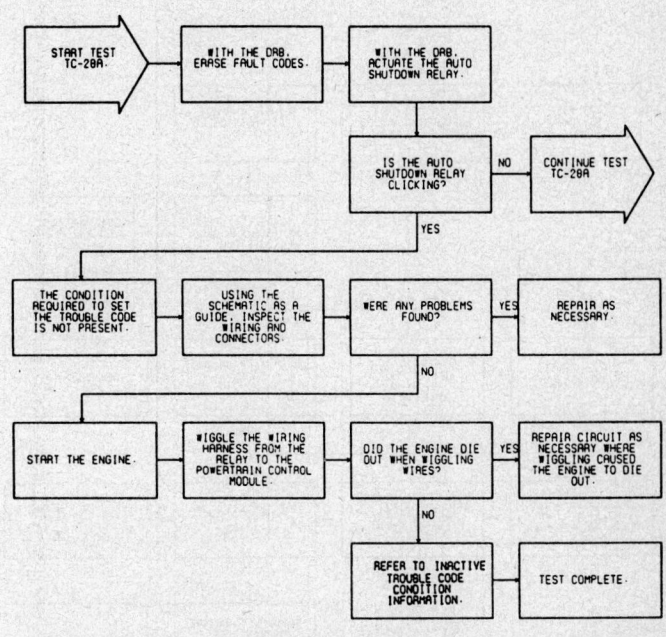

Fig. 84   Test TC-28A: Auto Shutdown Relay Control Circuit (Part 1 of 2)

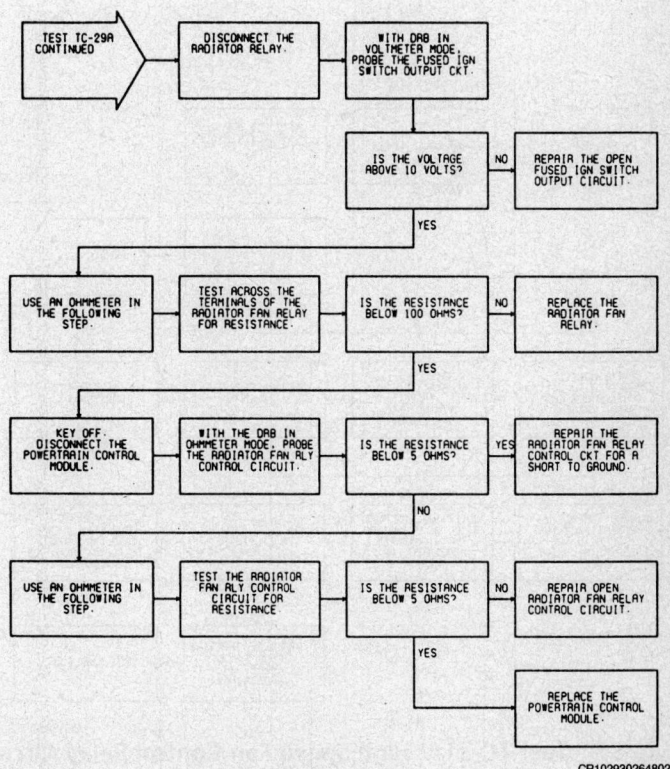

Fig. 85   Test TC-29A: Radiator Fan Control Relay Circuit (Part 2 of 2)

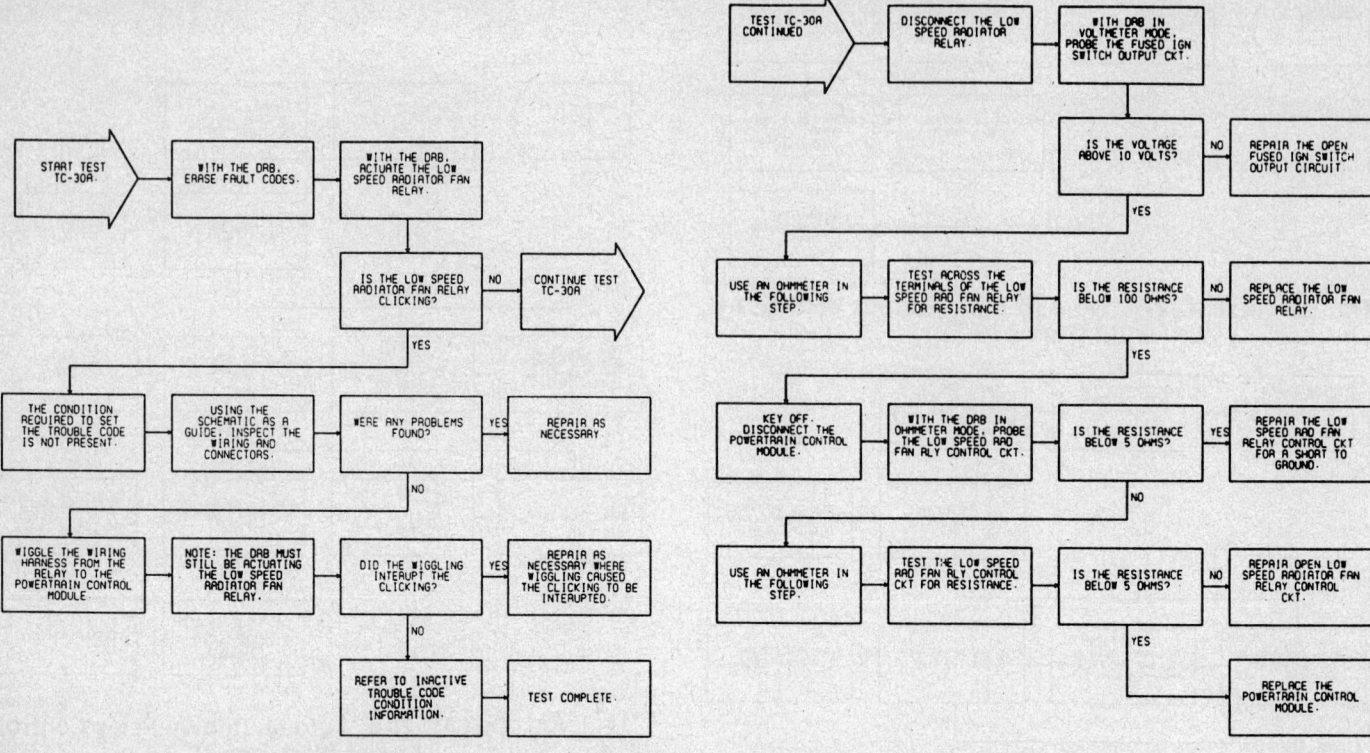

CR1029302649010X

Fig. 86 Test TC-30A: Low Speed Fan Control Relay Circuit (Part 1 of 2)

CR1029302649020X

Fig. 86 Test TC-30A: Low Speed Fan Control Relay Circuit (Part 2 of 2)

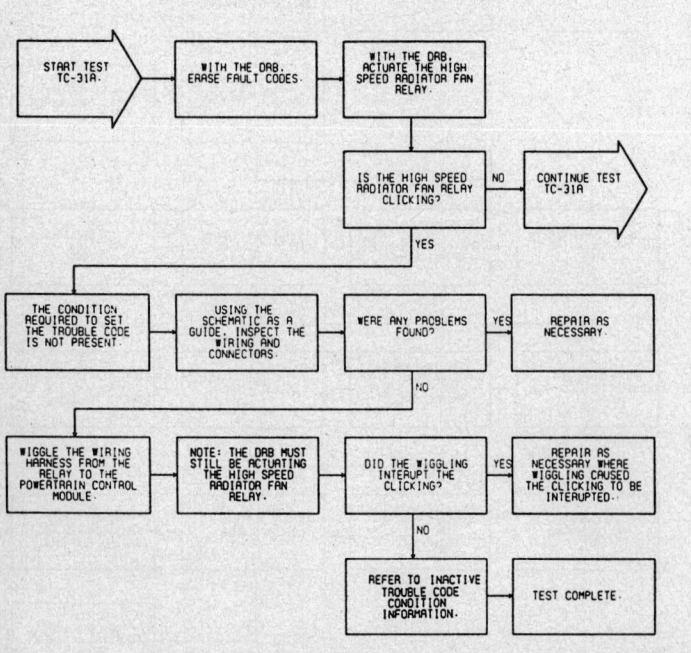

CR1029302650010X

Fig. 87 Test TC-31A: High Speed Fan Control Relay Circuit (Part 1 of 2)

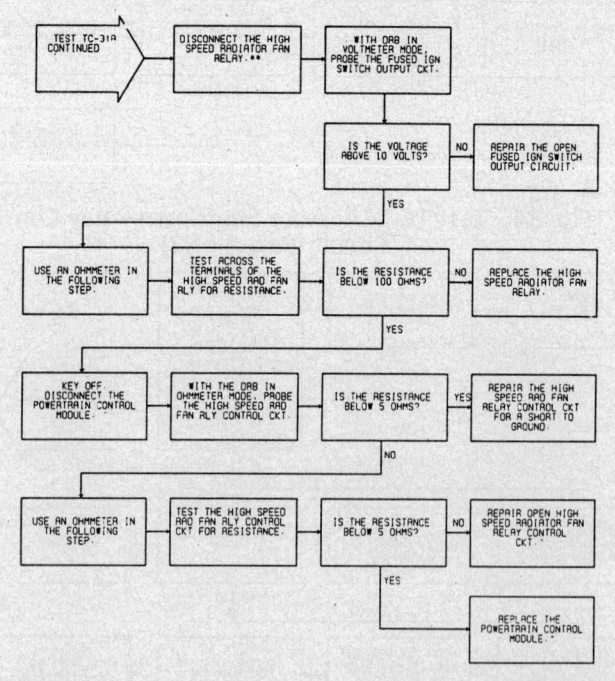

CR1029302650020A

Fig. 87 Test TC-31A: High Speed Fan Control Relay Circuit (Part 2 of 2)

Fuel Injection—CHRYSLER

5-49

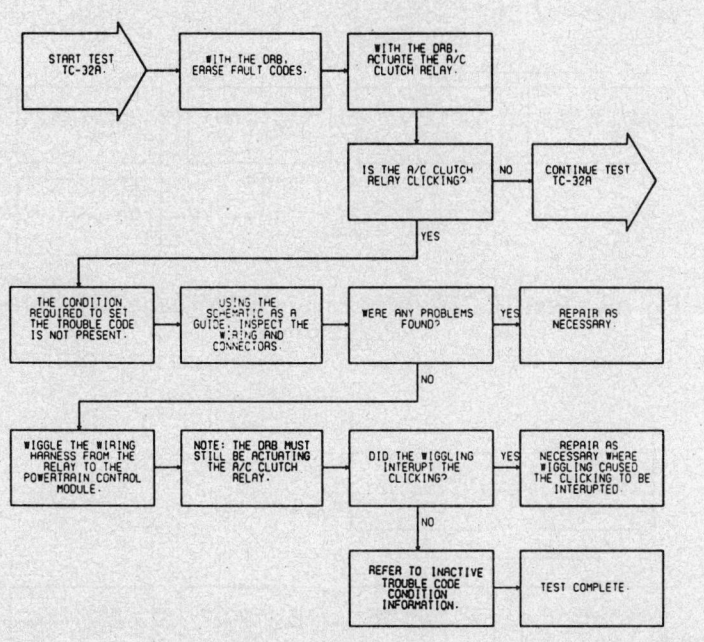

Fig. 88 Test TC-32A: A/C Clutch Relay Circuit (Part 1 of 4)

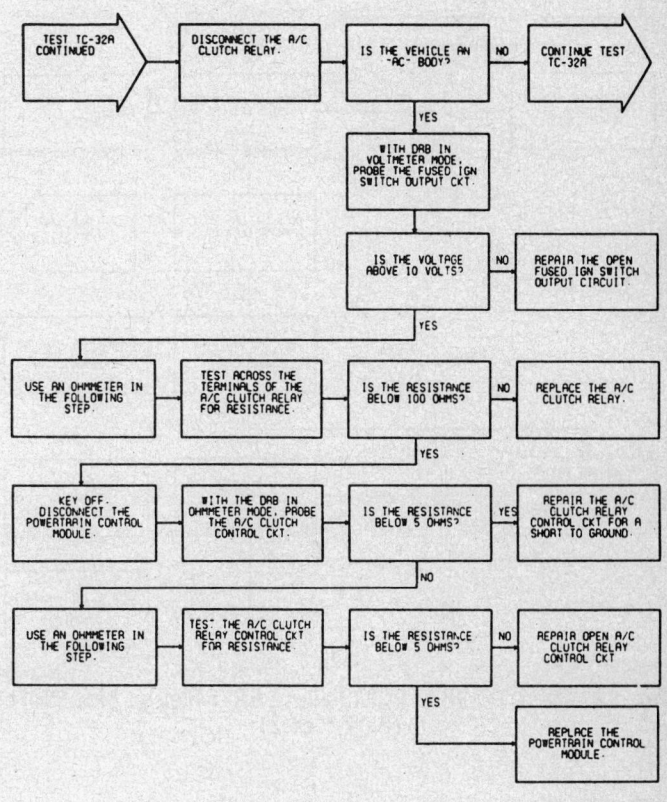

Fig. 88 Test TC-32A: A/C Clutch Relay Circuit (Part 2 of 4)

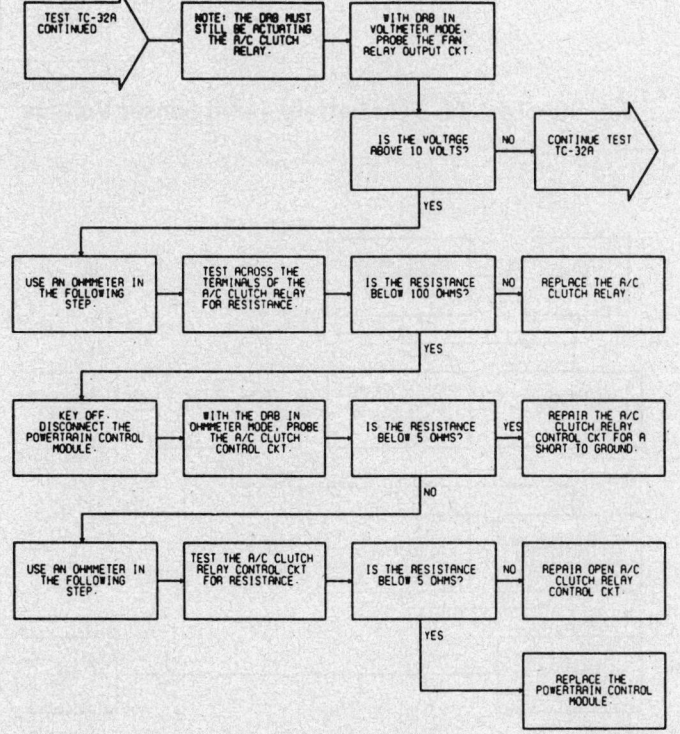

Fig. 88 Test TC-32A: A/C Clutch Relay Circuit (Part 3 of 4)

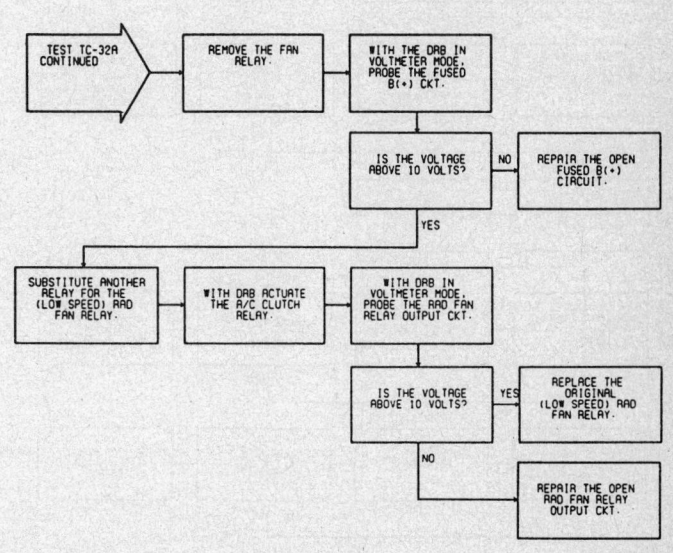

Fig. 88 Test TC-32A: A/C Clutch Relay Circuit (Part 4 of 4)

SINGLE POINT FUEL INJECTION

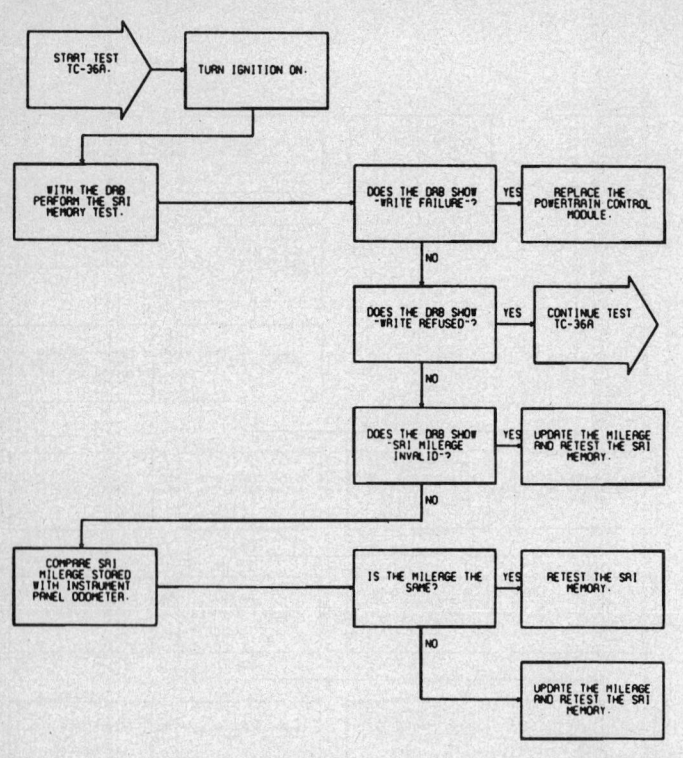

Fig. 89   Test TC-36A: PCM Failure SRI Mileage Not Stored (Part 1 of 2)

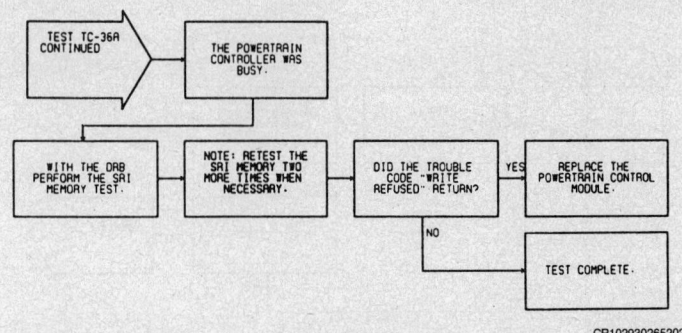

Fig. 89   Test TC-36A: PCM Failure SRI Mileage Not Stored (Part 2 of 2)

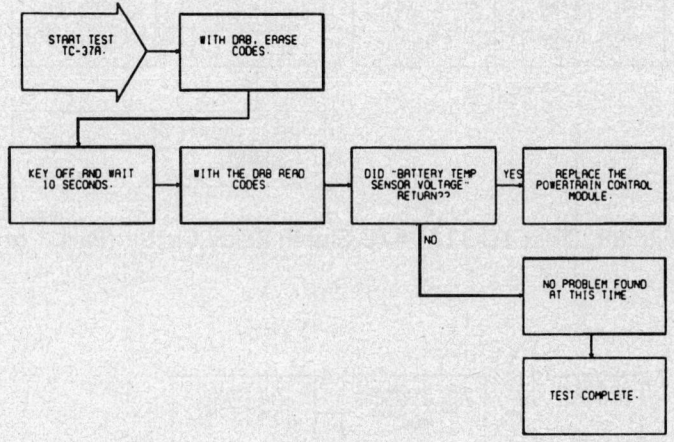

Fig. 90   Test TC-37A: Battery Temp Sensor Voltage

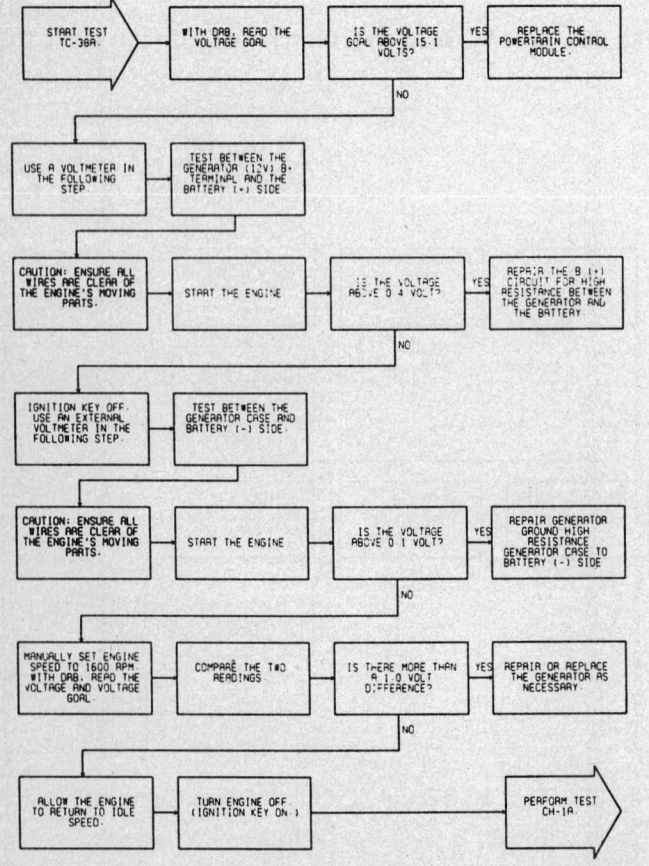

Fig. 91   Test TC-38A: Charging System Voltage Too Low

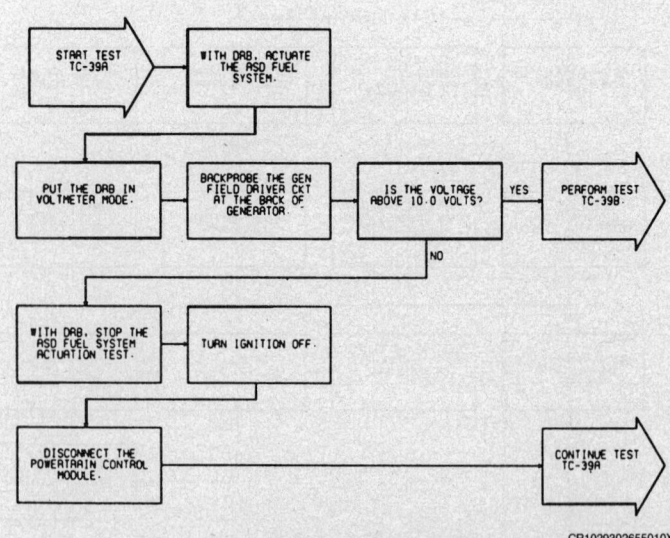

Fig. 92   Test TC-39A: Charging System Voltage Too High (Part 1 of 2)

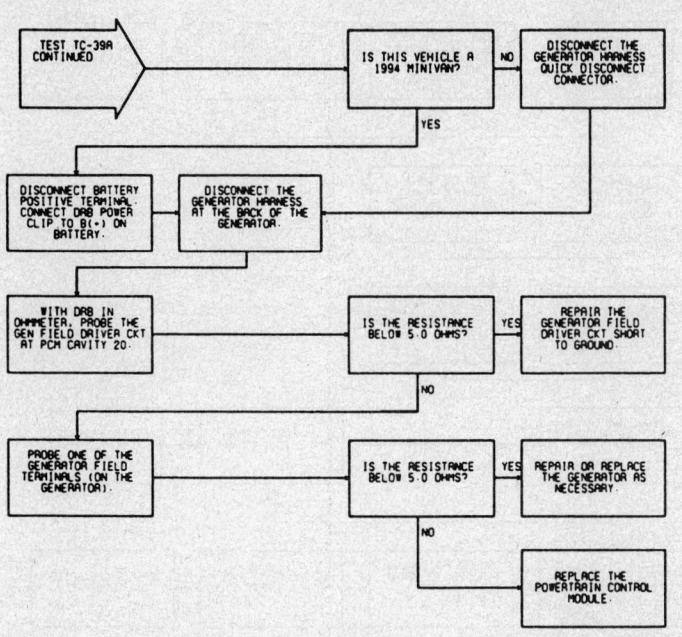

Fig. 92   Test TC-39A: Charging System Voltage Too High (Part 2 of 2)

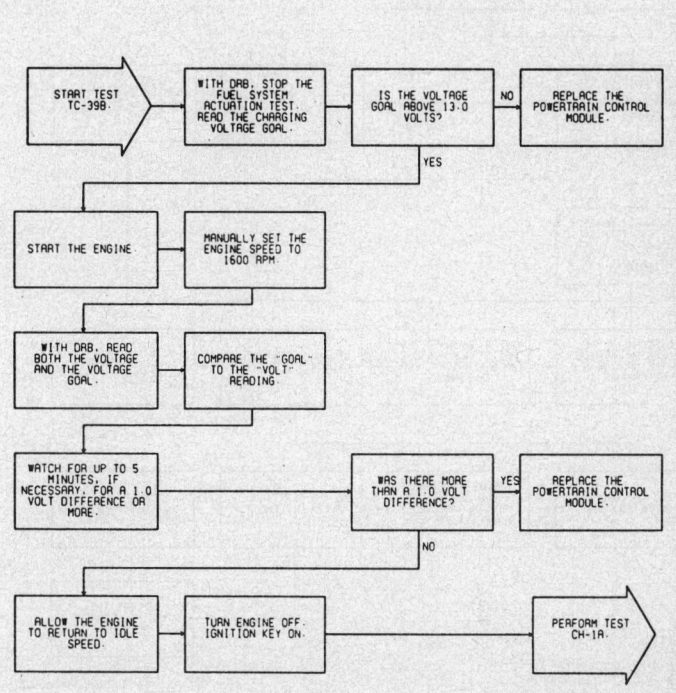

Fig. 93   Test TC-39B: PCM Regulating Circuit

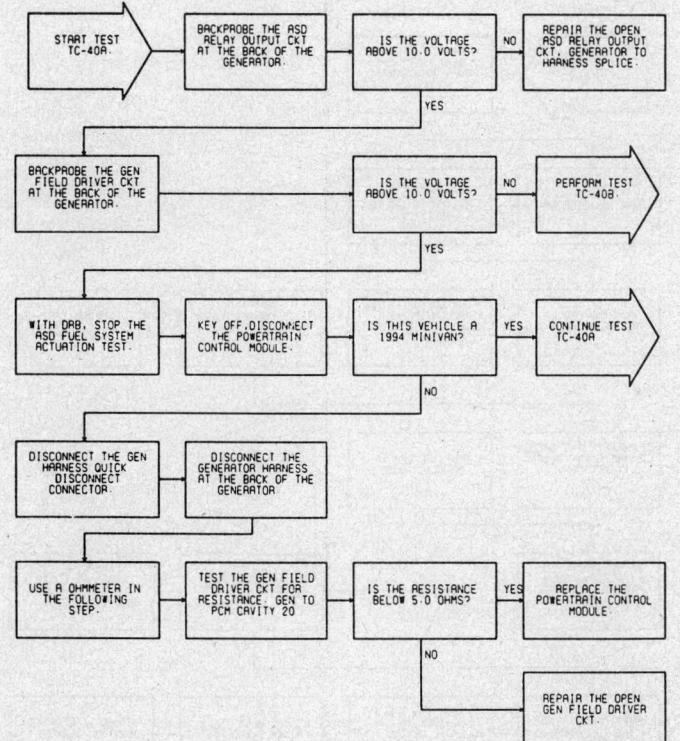

Fig. 94   Test TC-40A: Generator Field Not Switching (Part 1 of 2)

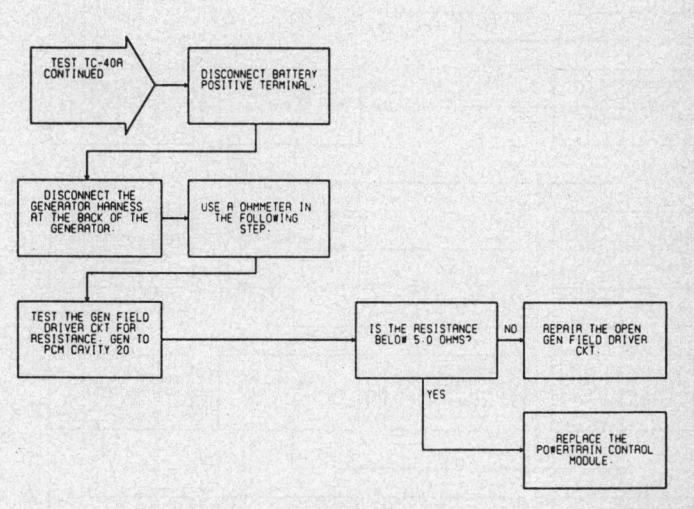

Fig. 94   Test TC-40A: Generator Field Not Switching (Part 2 of 2)

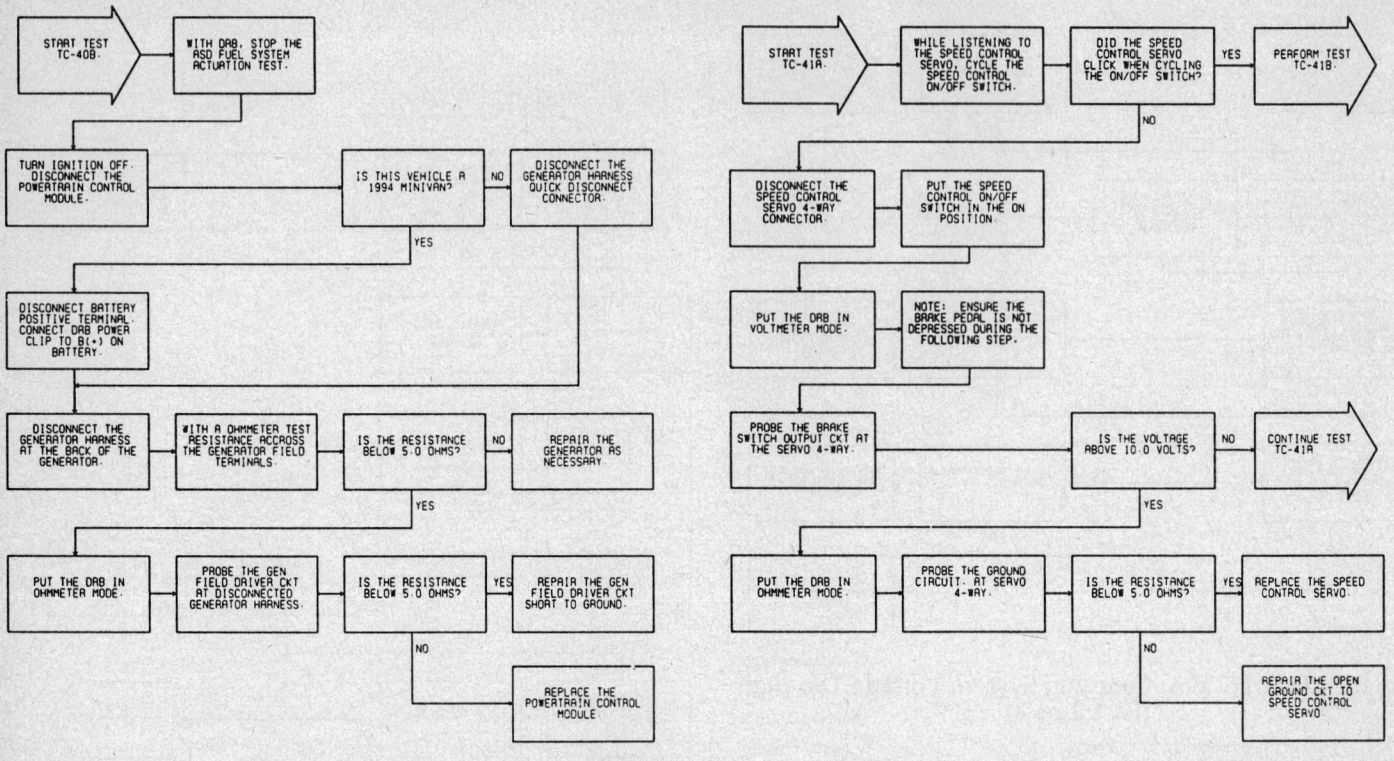

Fig. 95   Test TC-40B: Generator Field Not Switching

Fig. 96   Test TC-41A: Speed Control Solenoid Circuits (Part 1 of 2)

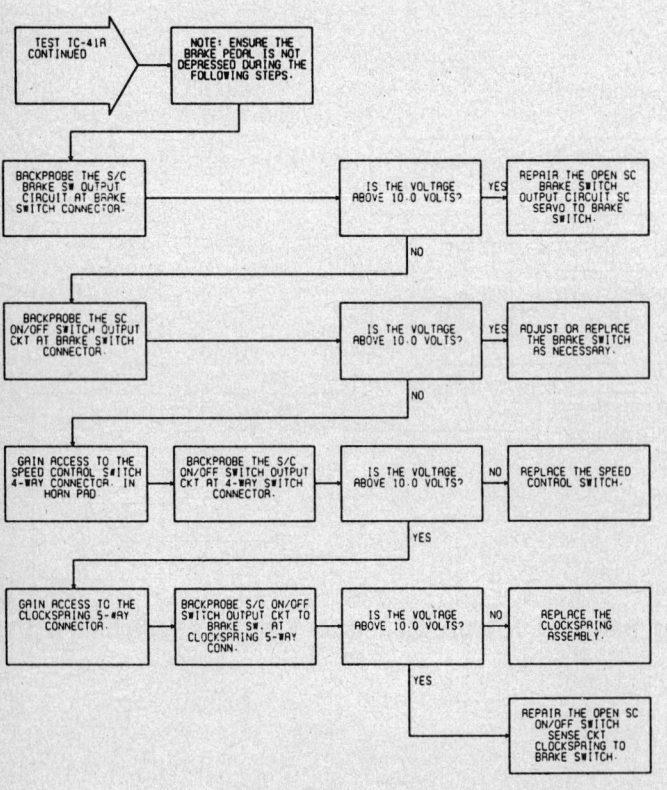

Fig. 96   Test TC-41A: Speed Control Solenoid Circuits (Part 2 of 2)

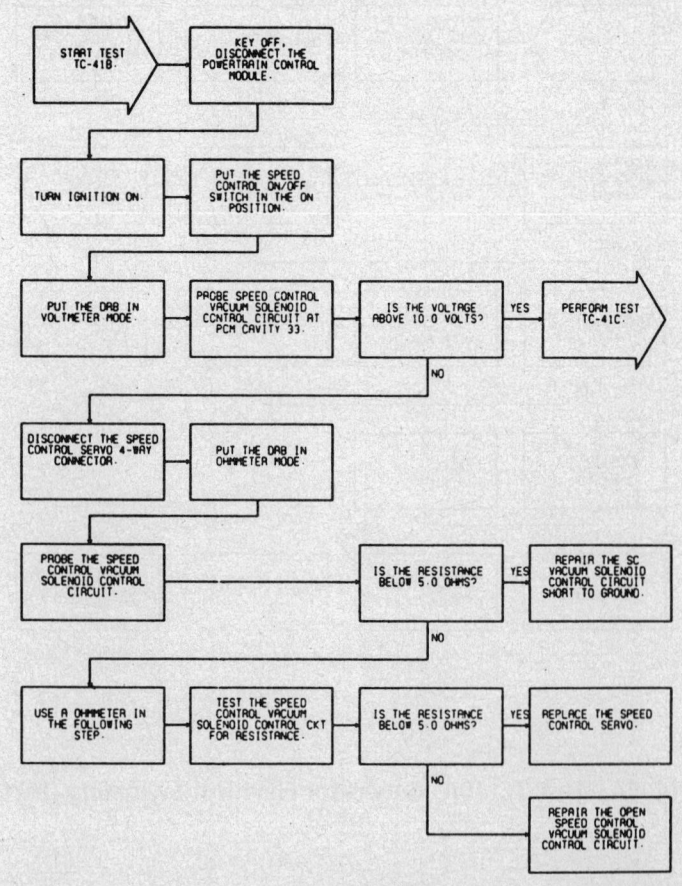

Fig. 97   Test TC-41B: Speed Control Solenoid Circuits

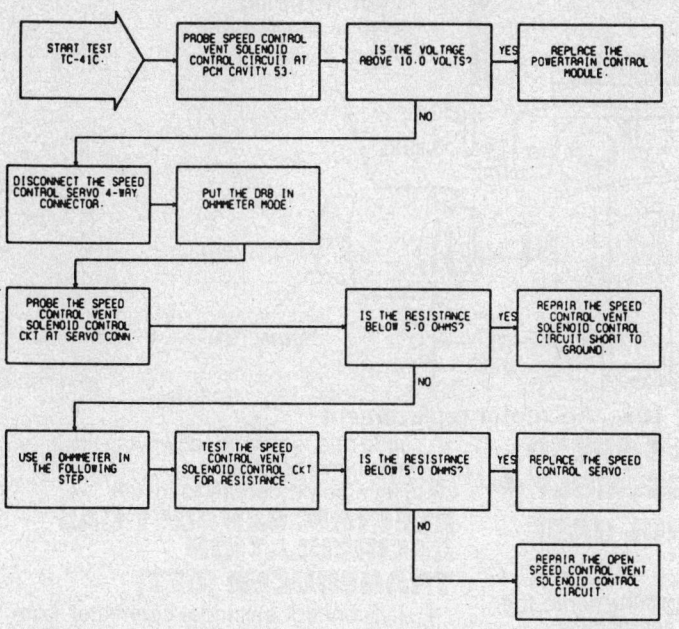

Fig. 98   Test TC-41C: Speed Control Solenoid Circuits

Inspect the vehicle to ensure that all engine components are connected. Reassemble and reconnect components as necessary.

Inspect the engine for contamination. If it is contaminated, change the oil and filter.

Attempt to start the engine.

If the engine is **unable** to start, check all pertinent Technical Service Bulletins, and return to TEST TC-1A if necessary.

If the engine is **able** to start, and the powertrain control module **has been changed,** connect the DRB to the PCM data link connector and erase trouble codes. The repair is now complete.

CR1029302663000X

Fig. 100   Test VER-1: No Start Verification Test

SYSTEM SERVICE
Fuel System Pressure Relief

The electronic fuel injection system is under a constant pressure of approximately 39 psi. Before servicing the fuel pump, fuel lines, fuel filter, throttle body or fuel injector, the fuel system pressure must be released as follows:

1. Loosen filler cap to release any tank pressure.
2. Disconnect injector wiring harness at throttle body.
3. Connect a jumper wire between terminal No. 1 of the fuel injector connector and engine ground, **Fig. 102.**
4. Connect a jumper wire between terminal No. 2 of the fuel injector connector and the positive battery post. **Do not energize injector for more than 10 seconds.**
5. Remove jumper wires.
6. Before opening any fuel supply lines, cover connection with a suitable rag to prevent residual fuel pressure from spraying.

Component Replacement

THROTTLE BODY

1. Remove air cleaner.

2. Perform fuel system pressure release procedures as previously described.
3. Disconnect battery ground cable.
4. Disconnect vacuum hoses, then the electrical connector.
5. Remove throttle cable, then if equipped, the speed control and transaxle kickdown cables.
6. Remove return spring, then the fuel system intake and return hoses.
7. Remove throttle body attaching bolts, then lift throttle body from vehicle.
8. Reverse procedure to install. **Torque** attaching bolts to 175 inch lbs.

PRESSURE REGULATOR

1. Remove air cleaner assembly.
2. Perform fuel system pressure release procedures as previously described.
3. Disconnect battery ground cable.
4. Place a suitable shop towel around

You have just attempted to simulate the condition that initially set the trouble code message. The following additional checks may assist you in identifying a possible intermittent problem:

— Visually inspect related wire harness connectors. Look for broken, bent, pushed out, or corroded terminals.

— Visually inspect the related harnesses. Look for chafed, pierced, or partially broken wire.

CR1029302662000X

Fig. 99   Test TC-42A: Inactive Trouble Code Condition

Inspect the vehicle to ensure that all engine components are connected. Reassemble and reconnect components as necessary.

If this verification procedure is being performed subsequent to a NO TROUBLE CODE test, do the following:

1. Check to see if the initial symptom still exists.
2. If the initial or another symptom exists, the repair is not complete. Check all pertinent Technical Service Bulletins and return to TEST NTC-1A if necessary.

If this verification procedure is being performed subsequent to a TROUBLE CODE test, do the following:

For previously read trouble codes that have not been dealt with, return to TEST TC-1A and follow the path specified by the other code. Otherwise, continue.

If the powertrain control module has not been changed:

> Connect the DRB to the PCM data link connector and erase trouble codes.
> With the DRB, reset all values in the adaptive memory.
> Disconnect the DRB.

Ensure no other trouble code remains by doing the following:

1. If the vehicle is equipped with air conditioning, turn on the air conditioning and blower.
2. Drive the vehicle for at least five minutes and at some point attain a speed of 40 mph. Ensure the transmission shifts through all gears. Upon completion of the road test, turn the engine off.
3. Start the engine. Allow the engine to idle for at least two minutes.
4. Turn the engine off.
5. Connect the DRB to the PCM data link connector, and with the DRB, read all trouble codes.

If the repaired code has reset, the repair is not complete. Check all pertinent Technical Service Bulletins and return to TEST TC-1A if necessary.

If another trouble code has set, return to TEST TC-1A and follow the path specified by the other trouble code.

If there are no trouble codes, the repair is now complete.

CR1029302664000X

Fig. 101   Test VER-2: Road Test Verification

fuel inlet chamber as to contain any remaining fuel in system, then remove three pressure regulator to throttle body attaching screws.
5. Pull pressure regulator from throttle body.
6. Remove O-ring from pressure regulator, then the gasket.
7. Reverse procedure to install, noting the following:
   a. Install new pressure regulator gasket and new O-ring.
   b. **Torque** pressure regulator to throttle body attaching screws to 40 inch lbs.
   c. Pressurize system and check for leaks after assembly.

FUEL INJECTOR

1. Remove air cleaner.
2. Perform fuel system pressure release procedures as previously described.

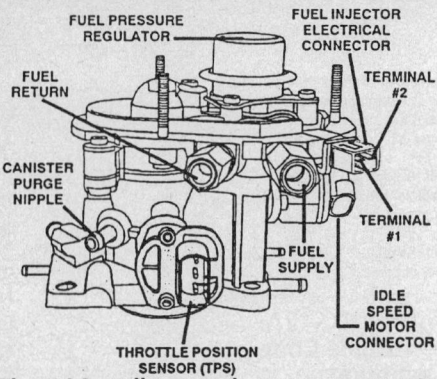

Fig. 102   Idle speed motor terminals

3. Disconnect battery ground cable.
4. Remove Torx screw retaining injector cap, then lift cap from injector using two suitable screwdrivers.
5. Pry injector from pod by placing a suitable screwdriver into hole at side of electrical connector.
6. Remove lower O-ring from pod.
7. Place new lower O-ring on injector and new O-ring on injector cap.
8. Place injector in pod, positioning injector as to allow cap to be installed without interference.
9. Rotate cap and injector to align attachment hold, then press down on cap to ensure proper seal.
10. Install Torx screw, then **torque** to 35-45 inch lbs.
11. Connect battery ground cable, then pressurize system and check for leaks.
12. Reinstall air cleaner.

THROTTLE POSITION SENSOR

1. Disconnect battery ground cable, then remove air cleaner.
2. Disconnect 3-way connector at throttle position sensor (TPS), then remove TPS to throttle body mounting screws.
3. Lift TPS from throttle shaft, then remove O-ring.
4. Reverse procedure to install. Install new O-ring and **torque** TPS to throttle body mounting screw to 20 inch lbs.

THROTTLE BODY TEMPERATURE SENSOR

1. Remove air cleaner, then disconnect throttle cables from throttle body linkage.
2. Remove two throttle cable bracket attaching screws, then position bracket aside.
3. Disconnect electrical connector, then unscrew sensor.
4. Apply heat transfer compound to tip of new sensor.
5. Install new sensor, then **torque** to 80-120 inch lbs.
6. Reconnect electrical connector, then install throttle cable bracket with attaching screws.
7. Connect throttle cables to throttle body linkage, then install retaining clips.
8. Install air cleaner.

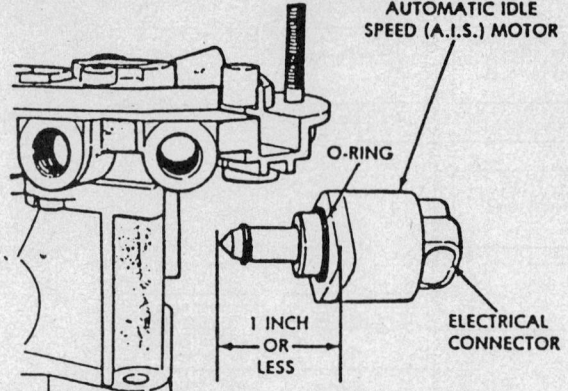

Fig. 103   AIS motor replacement

AUTOMATIC IDLE SPEED (AIS) MOTOR ASSEMBLY & IDLE AIR CONTROL (IAC) MOTORS

1. Disconnect battery ground cable, then remove air cleaner assembly.
2. Disconnect four pin connector from AIS or IAC Motors, then remove temperature sending unit from throttle body housing.
3. Remove two AIS or IAC Motors to throttle body Torx head retaining screws, **Fig. 103.**
4. Remove AIS or IAC Motors from throttle body housing with O-ring.
5. Reverse procedure to install, noting the following:
   a. Ensure pintle is in the retracted position using DRB II Actuation Test Mode or Idle Air Control Motor Open/Close displays.
   b. Install new O-ring and **torque** retaining screws to 20 inch lbs.

MANIFOLD ABSOLUTE PRESSURE SENSOR

1. Remove vacuum hose from sensor.
2. Remove sensor attaching screws, then the sensor.
3. Reverse procedure to install. Ensure proper installation of vacuum hose to sensor.

SINGLE BOARD ENGINE CONTROLLER (SBEC), SINGLE BOARD ENGINE CONTROLLER II (SBEC II) OR POWERTRAIN CONTROL MODULE (PCM)

1. Remove air cleaner duct from engine controller.
2. Remove battery.
3. Remove two module attaching screws.
4. Remove module electrical connectors, then the engine controller.
5. Reverse procedure to install.

CANISTER PURGE SOLENOID

1. Remove vacuum hose and electrical connections from solenoid.
2. Depress tab on top of solenoid and slide the solenoid downward out of mounting bracket.
3. Reverse procedure to install.

ELECTRIC EXHAUST GAS RECIRCULATION TRANSDUCER (EET)

1. Disconnect electrical connector from the EGR transducer.
2. Disconnect vacuum hoses.
3. Remove EET from vehicle.
4. Reverse procedure to install.

OXYGEN SENSOR

The oxygen sensor is to be removed using tool No. C-4589, or equivalent. After removal, clean threads in exhaust manifold using an 18 mm X 1.5 X 6E tap. If reinstalling the same sensor, apply a suitable sealant to threads of sensor. New sensors are packaged with an anti-seize compound already applied to the threads and no further application is required. When installing sensor, **torque** to 20 ft. lbs.

Adjustments
IGNITION TIMING

1. Connect a suitable timing light to No. 1 cylinder, or a magnetic timing unit to engine.
2. Connect tachometer to engine, then start engine and run until operating temperature is reached.
3. Disconnect, then reconnect the water temperature sensor connector on thermostat housing. The malfunction indicator (loss of power) lamp must illuminate and engine RPM should be within specifications given on vehicle emission label.
4. Direct timing light at timing hole in bellhousing, or read magnetic timing unit, and adjust timing as necessary by loosening distributor and turning until specifications are met.
5. Shut engine off, then disconnect and reconnect positive battery quick disconnect.
6. Start engine and observe malfunction indicator (loss of power) lamp, which should be off.
7. Shut engine off, then cycle ignition switch on and off twice.
8. Turn ignition on and observe trouble code display. trouble codes should be clear with Diagnostic Trouble Codes 88, 51, and 55 displayed.

lulti- oint u l Inj tiun

INDEX

	Page No.
MODELS w/1.5L/4-90 ENGINE	6-1
MODELS w/1.8L/4-107, 1.8L/4-110 & 2.4L/4-143 ENGINES, 1993-94 MODELS w/2.0L/4-122 ENGINE & 1995-96 TALON w/2.0L/4-122 TURBOCHARGED ENGINES	7-1
MODELS w/2.5L/4-153 FLEXIBLE FUEL, 2.2L/4-135 TURBOCHARGED & 2.5L/4-153 ENGINES	9-1
MODELS w/3.0L/V6-181, 3.3L/V6-201 & 3.8L/V6-231 ENGINES EXCEPT CONCORDE, INTREPID, LHS, STEALTH, VISION & 1994-96 NEW YORKER	12-1
1995 AVENGER, CIRRUS, SEBRING & STRATUS w/2.5L/V6-152 ENGINE	10-1

	Page No.
1995 AVENGER, CIRRUS, NEON, SEBRING, STRATUS & TALON w/2.0L/4-112 NON-TURBOCHARGED ENGINE	8-1
1996 MODELS w2.0L/4-122 NON-TURBOCHARGED, 2.4L/4-148, 2.5L/V6-152, 3.3L/V6-201 & 3.5L/V6-215 ENGINES	14-1
STEALTH	11-1
1993-95 CONCORDE, INTREPID, STEALTH, VISION & 1994-95 LHS & NEW YORKER	12-1
MODELS w/3.0L/V6-181, 3.3L/V6-201 & 3.8L/V6-231 ENGINES EXCEPT CONCORDE, INTREPID, LHS, STEALTH, VISION & 1994-96 NEW YORKER	12-1

MODELS w/1.5L/4-90 ENGINE

If Unsure Of The System Used On The Vehicle Being Serviced, Refer To The "Engine Systems Identification Chart." Further Assistance For The Proper Use Of Information Contained In This Section Can Also Be Found In The Front Of This Tabbed Section Under "How To Use This Manual."

On Air Bag Equipped Models, Refer To "Air Bag System Precautions" Located In The Front Of This Manual For System Disarming & Arming Procedures.

Prior To Performing Any Service Operations Listed In This Section, Consult The "Technical Service Bulletins" Section For Related Information.

Electrical Symbol & Wire Color Code Identification Located In The Front Of This Manual May Be Used As An Aid When Using Wiring Circuits Found In This Section.

INDEX

	Page No.
Description	6-2
Diagnosis & Testing:	6-2
Accessing Diagnostic Trouble Codes:	6-2
Voltmeter	6-2
Clearing Diagnostic Trouble Codes	6-2
Diagnostic Trouble Code Interpretation	6-2
Precautions:	6-2
Fuel System Pressure Relief	6-2
Sensor Specifications	6-2
System Service:	6-2
Adjustments:	6-13
Closed Throttle Position Switch & Throttle Position Sensor	6-13
Fixed SAS	6-14
Component Replacement:	6-13
Injector	6-13
Throttle Body	6-13

	Page No.
Component Service:	6-2
Air Conditioning Switch & Compressor Clutch	6-8
Camshaft Position Sensor	6-5
Closed Throttle Position Sensor	6-5
Crankshaft Position Sensor	6-5
Ecm Power Ground	6-3
EGR Solenoid	6-11
EGR Temperature Sensor	6-12
Engine Coolant Temperature Sensor	6-4
Evaporative Emission Purge Solenoid	6-11
Fuel Pressure Test	6-13
Fuel Pump	6-3
Generator	6-8
Heated Oxygen Sensor	6-8
Idle Air Control Motor	6-11

	Page No.
Idle Air Control Valve Position Sensor	6-5
Ignition Coil & Ignition Power Transistor	6-11
Ignition Switch (M/T)	6-8
Ignition Switch & Park/Neutral Position Switch (A/T)	6-8
Injectors	6-10
Intake Air Temperature Sensor	6-3
Manifold Air Pressure Sensor	6-3
Oxygen Sensor	6-8
Power Steering Pressure Switch	6-8
Power Supply (MFI Relay)	6-2
Throttle Position Sensor	6-5
Vehicle Speed Sensor	6-5
Fuel System Pressure Relief	6-2
Troubleshooting	6-2

SENSOR SPECIFICATIONS

Sensor	Voltage	Resistance, ohms	Sensor	Voltage	Resistance, ohms
Crankshaft Position	0-5	—	Manifold Absolute Pressure	④	—
Camshaft Position	0-5	—	Oxygen ⑤	0.6-1.0	—
Engine Coolant Temperature	—	①	Throttle Position	0.4-1.0	3500-6500
Heated Oxygen ②	0.6—1.0	—	Vehicle Speed	0-5	—
Intake Air Temperature	—	③			

①—2400 ohms @ 68°F, 300 ohms @ 176°F.
②—Except 1993 Federal emissions.
③—2600 ohms @ 68°F, 300 ohms @ 176°F.
④—Voltage increases as intake manifold pressure increases.
⑤—1993 Federal emissions.

PRECAUTIONS

Wear eye protection when servicing the fuel system. Do not smoke or allow open flame near fuel system components during fuel system service. Wrap shop towels around fuel line quick disconnect fittings before disconnecting them from components being serviced in order to prevent fuel spillage.

FUEL SYSTEM PRESSURE RELIEF

Refer to "Fuel System Pressure Relief" under "System Service" for fuel pressure release procedure.

DESCRIPTION

The multi-point fuel injection system, **Figs. 1 and 2,** is a computer controlled system which provides precise engine regulatory functions under all driving conditions. The system utilizes a preprogrammed electronic control unit (ECU) to regulate ignition timing, idle speed, emission devices and the air/fuel ratio. Various sensors and switches located throughout the engine compartment provide information to the ECU. The system also incorporates a self diagnosis function which monitors various parameters for proper operation.

TROUBLESHOOTING

Refer to **Fig. 3** for troubleshooting information and refer to "Component Service" for component test procedures.

DIAGNOSIS & TESTING
Accessing Diagnostic Trouble Codes

Diagnostic trouble code indications are made by reading analog voltmeter deflections on 1993-95 models or by using a DRB scan tool on all models.

VOLTMETER

1. Ensure ignition switch is in Off position, then locate diagnostic connector, **Figs. 4 through 6.**
2. Connect a suitable analog voltmeter between MFI-diagnosis terminal and ground, **Figs. 7 and 8.**
3. **On 1994-95 models,** use check harness tool No. MB991529 or equivalent when connecting voltmeter to ground terminal.
4. **On all models,** turn ignition switch

On and note that an immediate indication of ECU memory contents will begin and voltmeter will deflect accordingly.
5. After recording abnormal readings, check and repair each part as directed, **Fig. 9.**
6. Turn ignition switch to Off position, then clear diagnostic trouble codes as described under "Clearing Diagnostic Trouble Codes."

DRB SCAN TOOL

1. Ensure ignition switch is in Off position. **Scan tool should only be connected or disconnected when ignition switch is off.**
2. Connect scan tool to data link connector, **Figs. 4 through 6,** then turn ignition switch to On position.
3. Read scan tool diagnostic output, then refer to "Diagnostic Trouble Code Interpretation" to interpret reading.
4. Turn ignition switch to Off position, then return to On position and erase diagnostic trouble code as described under "Clearing Diagnostic Trouble Codes."

Diagnostic Trouble Code Interpretation

Input signals for sensors, injector and fuel pump are monitored by the computer (ECU or ECM). The computer stores improper operating conditions of these components in its memory, which can be accessed using a voltmeter or DRB scan tool. The malfunction is stored in the computer's memory by power supplied directly from the battery so it cannot be erased by turning the ignition key off. **However, if the battery or ECU electrical connector is disconnected for 10 seconds or more, memory will be erased.**

There are many numbered diagnostic trouble codes. For example, Diagnostic Trouble Code 36 (ignition timing adjust signal) is logged when the terminal line for ignition timing adjustment is shorted to ground. Therefore, this diagnostic trouble code is also logged when the terminal for ignition timing adjust is grounded during timing adjustment, but does not indicate any problems.

Voltmeter deflections, shown in **Fig. 9,** correspond with DRB scan tool readings. **Fig. 10** illustrates how diagnostic trouble code wave forms are interpreted and gives an example of a waveform under normal operating conditions.

Diagnostic trouble codes **Figs. 9 and 11** indicate the result of a failure, but do not identify the failed component. Diagnosis is performed in a symptom driven format.

Prior to performing any step in the harness inspection procedures, visually inspect electrical and vacuum components to determine whether further diagnosis is necessary.

Clearing Diagnostic Trouble Codes

If the DRB scan tool is not available for diagnostic trouble code erasure, proceed as follows:
1. Turn ignition switch to Off position.
2. After repairs have been completed, disconnect battery ground cable for at least 10 to 15 seconds to erase diagnostic trouble codes from ECU memory.
3. Recheck readings to ensure normal system operation.

SYSTEM SERVICE
Fuel System Pressure Relief

Prior to disconnecting fuel hoses, fuel system pressure must be relieved.
1. Remove rear seat, if necessary, then disconnect fuel pump electrical connector.
2. Start and run engine until remaining fuel in system is consumed and engine stalls, then turn ignition switch to Off position.
3. Reconnect fuel pump electrical connector, then install any interior trim parts removed to gain access to fuel pump wiring.

Component Service
POWER SUPPLY (MFI RELAY)

HARNESS INSPECTION

1. Inspect for ECM power voltage. Voltage should be indicated with ignition switch in on position.
2. If results are not as specified, then refer to **Fig. 12** for harness inspection.

SENSOR INSPECTION

Refer to **Fig. 13** when testing MFI relay.
1. Remove MFI relay, then check for continuity between relay terminals, noting the following:

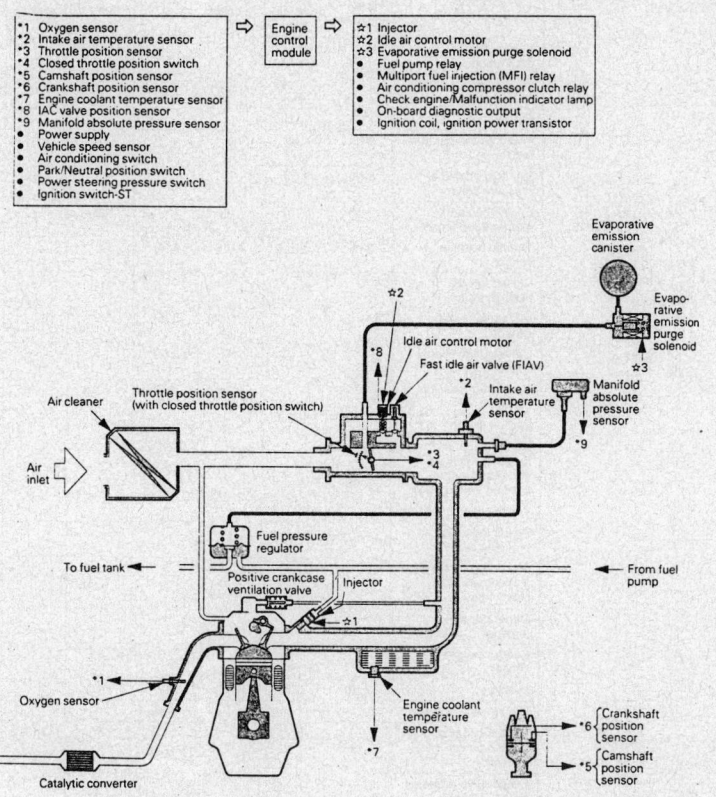

Fig. 1   MFI system. 1993 Federal

CR1029303361000X

*1 Oxygen sensor
*2 Intake air temperature sensor
*3 Throttle position sensor
*4 Closed throttle position switch
*5 Camshaft position sensor
*6 Crankshaft position sensor
*7 Engine coolant temperature sensor
*8 IAC valve position sensor
*9 Manifold absolute pressure sensor
• Power supply
• Vehicle speed sensor
• Air conditioning switch
• Park/Neutral position switch
• Power steering pressure switch
• Ignition switch-ST

Engine control module

☆1 Injector
☆2 Idle air control motor
☆3 Evaporative emission purge solenoid
• Fuel pump relay
• Multiport fuel injection (MFI) relay
• Air conditioning compressor clutch relay
• Check engine/Malfunction indicator lamp
• On-board diagnostic output
• Ignition coil, ignition power transistor

---

*1 Heated oxygen sensor (front)
*2 Intake air temperature sensor
*3 Throttle position sensor
*4 Closed throttle position switch
*5 Camshaft position sensor
*6 Crankshaft position sensor
*7 Engine coolant temperature sensor
*8 IAC valve position sensor
*9 Manifold absolute pressure sensor
*10 EGR temperature sensor
*11 Heated oxygen sensor (Rear)
• Power supply
• Vehicle speed sensor
• Air conditioning switch
• Park/Neutral position switch
• Power steering pressure switch
• Ignition switch-ST

Engine control module

☆1 Injector
☆2 Idle air control motor
☆3 Evaporative emission purge solenoid
☆4 EGR solenoid
• Fuel pump relay
• Multiport fuel injection (MFI) relay
• Air conditioning compressor clutch relay
• Check engine/Malfunction indicator lamp
• On-board diagnostic output
• Ignition coil, ignition power transistor

Fig. 2   MFI system. 1993 California & 1994–96

CR1029303362000X

---

a. Between terminals 5 and 7, value should be approximately 90 ohms.

b. Between terminals 6 and 8, continuity should exist in one direction only.

2. Using jumper wires, connect terminal 7 of MFI relay to B + and terminal 5 to battery ground.

3. Check voltage at MFI relay terminal 1 while connecting and disconnecting jumper wire at battery ground. When wire is connected, voltage should exist; when wire is disconnected, there should be no voltage.

4. Using jumper wires, connect terminal 8 of MFI relay to B + and terminal 6 to battery ground.

5. Check continuity between terminals 2 and 4 of MFI relay, then between terminals 3 and 4 while connecting and disconnecting jumper wire at battery ground. When wire is connected, continuity should exist (0 ohms resistance); when wire is disconnected, there should be no continuity (infinite resistance).

6. If results are not as specified, replace MFI relay.

ECM POWER GROUND

Refer to **Fig. 14** for harness inspection.

FUEL PUMP

1. While cranking engine, grip fuel return hose between fingers; pulsation should be indicated.

2. Listen for fuel pump operation noise near fuel tank; pump noise should be indicated during cranking.

3. If results are not as indicated, refer to **Fig. 15** for harness inspection.

INTAKE AIR TEMPERATURE SENSOR

HARNESS INSPECTION

1. With engine running or ignition switch in On position, measure intake air temperature and sensor temperature. Sensor temperature should correspond with intake air temperature.

2. If results are not as indicated, refer to **Fig. 16** for harness inspection.

SENSOR INSPECTION

1. Disconnect intake air temperature sensor, then measure resistance between terminals No. 1 and 2.

2. Resistance should be 6000 ohms at 32°F, 2600 ohms at 68°F or 300 ohms at 176°F.

3. Remove intake air temperature sensor from intake manifold, then measure resistance of sensor while heating with a hair drier.

4. Resistance should decrease as temperature increases.

MANIFOLD AIR PRESSURE SENSOR

On vehicles with less than 300 miles, intake manifold plenum pressure may be approximately 10 percent higher than standard pressure.

1. Bring engine to normal operating temperature (176-203°F) and ensure all lights, accessories and cooling fan are off.

Items	Starting			Idling stability	
	Will not start	Fires up and dies, Hard starting	Idling instability (rough idling)	Incorrect idle speed	Engine stall
Power supply (MFI relay)	1 (1)				
Engine control module power ground	2 (2)				
Fuel pump	3 (3)	1 (1)			1 (1)
Intake air temperature sensor			6		
Manifold absolute pressure sensor			8		
Engine coolant temperature sensor		(3)	7 (6)	1 (1)	6 (6)
Throttle position sensor					
Closed throttle position switch			4 (4)	2 (2)	5 (5)
IAC valve position sensor			3 (3)	7 (3)	4 (4)
Camshaft position sensor	5 (5)	6 (7)			9 (8)
Crankshaft position sensor	6 (6)	7 (8)			10 (9)
Ignition switch – ST (M/T)	4 (4)	3 (4)			
Ignition switch – ST and Park/Neutral position switch (A/T)	4 (4)	3 (4)		6	
Vehicle speed sensor					7
Power steering pressure switch				3	
Air conditioning switch and compressor clutch relay				4	
Generator (FR terminal, G terminal)				5	
Heated oxygen sensor			10		
Injectors	8 (8)	2 (2)	2 (2)		3 (3)
Idle air control motor		4 (5)	1 (1)	8 (4)	2 (2)
Ignition coil and ignition power transistor	7 (7)				11 (10)
Evaporative emission purge solenoid			9		
EGR solenoid					
Fuel pressure		5 (6)	5 (5)		8 (7)

NOTE
The numbers in the table indicate the check order. [with ( ): cold engine, without ( ): warm engine]

CR1029606552010X

Fig. 3 Troubleshooting (Part 1 of 2)

Items	Driving						Stopping
	Hesita-tion, Sag	Poor accelera-tion	Stumble	Shock	Surge	Knocking	Run-on (diesel-ing)
Power supply (MFI relay)							
Engine control module power ground							
Fuel pump	1 (1)	1 (1)					
Intake air temperature sensor	5 (5)	4 (4)				1 (1)	
Manifold absolute pressure sensor	8 (8)	6 (6)				2 (2)	
Engine coolant temperature sensor	7 (7)	5 (5)	4 (4)		3 (3)		
Throttle position sensor	6 (6)		3 (3)	4 (4)			
Closed throttle position switch							
IAC valve position sensor				5 (5)			
Camshaft position sensor				2 (2)			
Crankshaft position sensor				3 (3)			
Ignition switch – ST (M/T)							
Ignition switch – ST and Park/Neutral position switch (A/T)							
Vehicle speed sensor			6				
Power steering pressure switch							
Air conditioning switch and compressor clutch relay							
Generator (FR terminal, G terminal)							
Heated oxygen sensor							
Injectors	2 (2)	2 (2)	1 (1)		1 (1)		1
Idle air control motor				7 (6)			
Ignition coil and ignition power transistor		7 (7)	1 (1)			3 (3)	
Evaporative emission purge solenoid							
EGR solenoid	4 (4)		5 (5)		4 (4)		
Fuel pressure	3 (3)	3 (3)	2 (2)		2 (2)		

NOTE
The numbers in the table indicate the check order. [with ( ): cold engine, without ( ): warm engine]

CR1029606552020X

Fig. 3 Troubleshooting (Part 2 of 2)

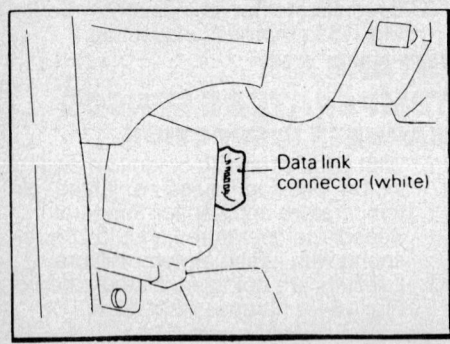

CR1029303365000X

Fig. 4 Diagnostic connector location. 1993

2. Place transaxle in Neutral position and turn ignition switch to On position.
3. With engine stopped, measure intake manifold plenum pressure. Results should be as follows:
   a. At sea level, pressure should be 760 mm Hg.
   b. At 1969 ft. altitude, pressure should be 710 mm Hg.
   c. At 3937 ft. altitude, pressure should be 660 mm Hg.
   d. At 5906 ft. altitude, pressure should be 610 mm Hg.
4. With engine idling, measure intake manifold plenum pressure. Pressure should be 170-270 mm Hg.
5. Race engine abruptly. Pressure should increase as engine speed increases from idle.
6. If results are not as indicated, refer to

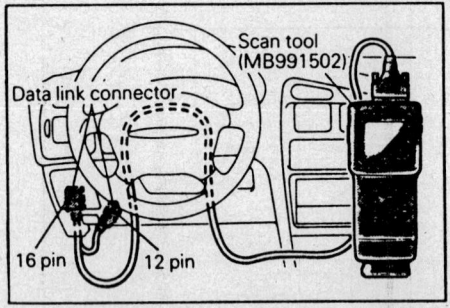

CR1029403366000X

Fig. 5 Diagnostic tool connection. 1994–95

Figs. 17 and 18 for harness inspection.

ENGINE COOLANT TEMPERATURE SENSOR
HARNESS INSPECTION

1. With engine running or ignition switch in On position, measure coolant temperature and sensor temperature. Sensor temperature should correspond with coolant temperature.
2. If results are not as indicated, refer to **Fig. 19** for harness inspection.

SENSOR INSPECTION

1. Remove sensor from intake manifold, then immerse sensing portion of sensor in a suitable heating container filled with water. **Do not allow tem-**

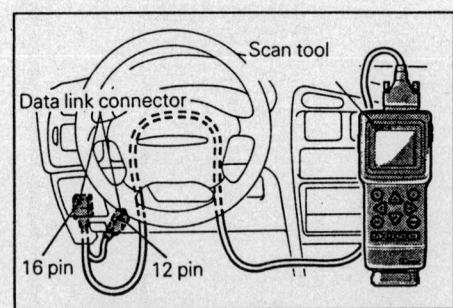

Fig. 6 Diagnostic connector locations. 1994–95

perature sensing portion of sensor to touch heated portion of container. Ensure hot water is continually stirred and connector terminal is held approximately .12 inch above water.

2. Insert a suitable thermometer into container, then connect an ohmmeter to sensor and raise water temperature slowly.
3. Ohmmeter should indicate the following values:
   a. At 32°F, ohmmeter should indicate 5800 ohms.

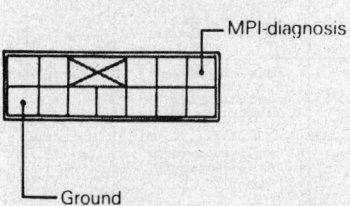

Fig. 7 Diagnostic connector terminal identification. 1993

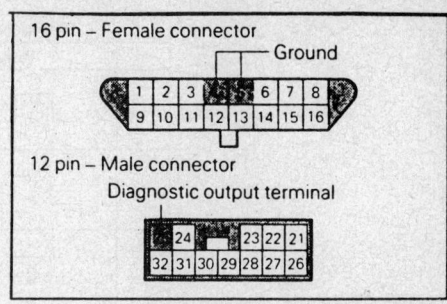

Fig. 8 Diagnostic connector terminal identification. 1994–95

Diagnostic trouble code		On-board diagnostic items	Check items (Remedy)	Memory
No.	Output signal pattern			
–	H ⎍ L	Engine control module	• Fuse • Harness and connector • Ground (Replace ECM if power + ground available)	–
11	H ⎍⎍ L	Heated oxygen sensor (front)	• Harness and connector • Fuel pressure • Injectors (Replace if defective) • Intake air leaks • Heated oxygen sensor	Retained
13	H ⎍⎍⎍ L	Intake air temperature sensor	• Harness and connector • Intake air temperature sensor	Retained
14	H ⎍⎍⎍ L	Throttle position sensor	• Harness and connector • Throttle position sensor • Closed throttle position switch	Retained
21	H ⎍⎍⎍ L	Engine coolant temperature sensor	• Harness and connector • Engine coolant temperature sensor	Retained

Fig. 9 Self diagnosis test chart. 1993–95 (Part 1 of 2)

b. At 68°F, ohmmeter should indicate 2400 ohms.
c. At 104°F, ohmmeter should indicate 1100 ohms.
d. At 176°F, ohmmeter should indicate 300 ohms.
4. If resistance values are as specified, coolant temperature sensor is satisfactory. If resistance values are not as specified, replace sensor.

THROTTLE POSITION SENSOR

HARNESS INSPECTION

1. With ignition switch in On position, allow throttle valve to rest at idle position and measure sensor voltage. Voltage should be 300-1000 mV.
2. Open throttle valve slowly while measuring sensor voltage. Voltage should increase as valve opens.
3. Open throttle valve widely, then measure sensor voltage. Voltage should be 4500-5500 mV.
4. If results are not as indicated, refer to **Fig. 20** for harness inspection.

SENSOR INSPECTION

1. Disconnect TPS electrical connector.
2. Measure resistance between terminals 1 (power supply) and 4 (ground). Ohmmeter should indicate 3500-6500 ohms.

3. Connect ohmmeter between terminals 2 (sensor output) and 4 (ground).
4. Operate throttle valve slowly between idle and wide open throttle. Ensure resistance values change in proportion to throttle valve operation.
5. If resistance values are not as specified, replace TPS.

CLOSED THROTTLE POSITION SENSOR

HARNESS INSPECTION

1. With ignition switch in on position, operate accelerator pedal repeatedly. When throttle valve is at idle position, closed throttle switch should be in On position. When pedal is depressed and valve opens slightly, switch should be in Off position.
2. Refer to **Fig. 21** for harness inspection.

SENSOR INSPECTION

Refer to **Fig. 22** when servicing closed throttle position switch.
1. Disconnect throttle position sensor connector.
2. Check for continuity between connector side terminals 3 and 4, **Fig. 23**. Continuity should exist when throttle valve is in idle position, but should not

exist when throttle valve is opened.
3. If continuity is not as described, replace throttle position sensor.

IDLE AIR CONTROL VALVE POSITION SENSOR

On vehicles with less than 300 miles, IAC valve position may exceed specification by approximately 20 steps.
1. Start engine and allow coolant temperature to reach 176-203°F, then ensure lights, accessories, and cooling fan are off.
2. Place transaxle in Neutral position. Closed throttle position switch should be activated, and engine should be at idle.
3. Note IAC valve position step. With A/C switch in Off position, valve position should be 2-20 steps. When A/C switch is turned to On position, valve position should increase from 8-50 steps.
4. Place A/C switch in Off position, then place transaxle in Drive position. IAC valve position should increase from 3-40 steps.
5. If results are not as indicated, refer to **Fig. 24** for harness inspection.

CAMSHAFT POSITION SENSOR

Refer to **Figs. 25 and 26** for harness inspection.

CRANKSHAFT POSITION SENSOR

CRANKING SPEED TEST

1. With engine cranking and tachometer connected, compare cranking speed with scan tool reading. Scan tool indication should correspond with tachometer indication.
2. If results are not as indicated, refer to **Figs. 27 and 28** for harness inspection.

IDLE SPEED TEST

1. With engine idling, tachometer connected and closed throttle position switch in On position, check RPM at various engine temperatures. Results should be as follows:
a. At -4°F, engine speed should be 1460-1660 RPM.
b. At 32°F, engine speed should be 1350-1550 RPM.
c. At 68°F, engine speed should be 1180-1380 RPM.

No.	Output signal pattern	On-board diagnostic items	Check items (Remedy)	Memory
22	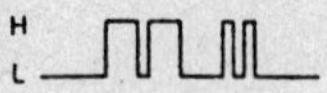	Crankshaft position sensor	• Harness and connector (If harness and connector are normal, replace distributor assembly.)	Retained
23	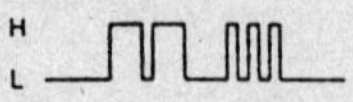	Camshaft position sensor	• Harness and connector (If harness and connector are normal, replace distributor assembly.)	Retained
24	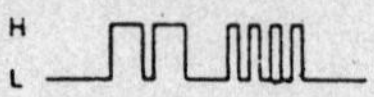	Vehicle speed sensor (reed switch)	• Harness and connector • Vehicle speed sensor (reed switch)	Retained
32	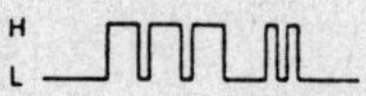	Manifold absolute pressure sensor	• Harness and connector (If harness and connector are normal, replace manifold absolute pressure sensor.)	Retained
36	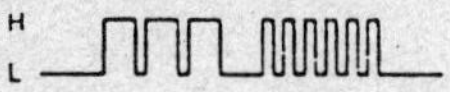	Ignition timing adjustment signal	• Harness and connector	–
41	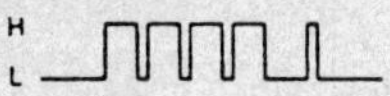	Injector	• Harness and connector • Injector coil resistance	Retained
43	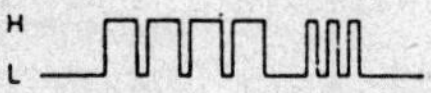	EGR <Federal California>	• Harness and connector • EGR valve • EGR solenoid • EGR valve control vacuum • EGR temperature sensor	Retained
55	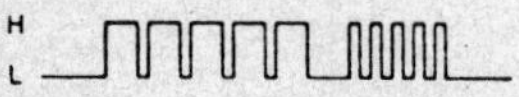	IAC valve position sensor	• Harness and connector • IAC valve movement (If harness, connector and IAC valve movement are normal, replace Idle air control motor assembly.)	Retained
59	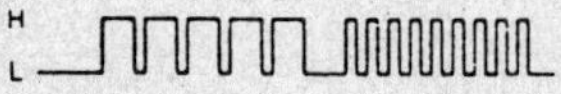	Heated oxygen sensor (rear)	• Harness and connector • Heated oxygen sensor	Retained
–		Normal state	–	–

Diagnostic trouble code

CR1029303370020X

Fig. 9 Self diagnosis test chart. 1993–95 (Part 2 of 2)

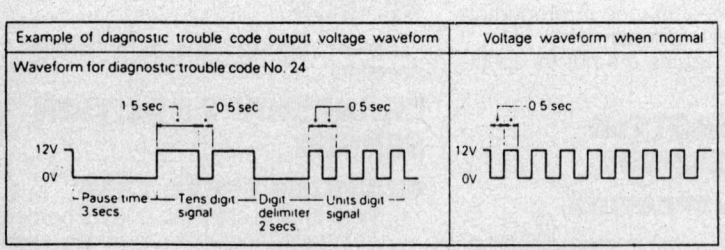

CR1029103371000X

Fig. 10 Diagnostic result indication by voltmeter

DTC No. <General scan tool mode>	DTC No. <Scan tool (MUT-II) mode>	Diagnostic items	Check items (Remedy)	Memory
P0105	P0105	Manifold Absolute Pressure Circuit Malfunction	• Harness and connector (If harness and connector are normal, replace manifold absolute pressure sensor assembly.)	Retained
P0110	P0110	Intake Air Temperature Circuit Malfunction	• Harness and connector • Intake air temperature sensor	Retained
P0115	P0115	Engine Coolant Temperature Circuit Malfunction	• Harness and connector • Engine coolant temperature sensor	Retained
P0120	P0120	Throttle Position Circuit Malfunction	• Harness and connector • Throttle position sensor • Closed throttle position switch	Retained
P0125	–	Excessive Time to Enter Closed Loop Fuel Control*	• Heated oxygen sensor • Heated oxygen sensor and connector • Injector	Retained
P0130	–	Heated Oxygen Sensor Circuit Malfunction (Bank 1 Sensor 1)	• Harness and connector (If harness and connector are normal, replace heated oxygen sensor front.)	Retained
P0135	–	Heated Oxygen Sensor Heater Circuit Malfunction (Bank 1 Sensor 1)	• Harness and connector • Heated oxygen sensor (front) heater	Retained
P0136	–	Heated Oxygen Sensor Circuit Malfunction (Bank 1 Sensor 2)	• Harness and connector • Heated oxygen sensor (rear)	Retained
P0141	–	Heated Oxygen Sensor Heater Circuit Malfunction (Bank 1 Sensor 2)	• Harness and connector • Heated oxygen sensor (rear) heater	Retained
P0170	–	Fuel Trim Malfunction (Bank 1)	• Volume air flow sensor output frequency • Injector • Fuel pressure • Intake air leaks • Engine coolant temperature sensor • Intake air temperature sensor • Barometric pressure sensor • Heated oxygen sensor • Exhaust manifold cracked	Retained

CR1029606564010X

Fig. 11 Self diagnosis test chart (Part 1 of 3). 1996

MODELS w/1.5L/4-90 ENGINE

DTC No. <General scan tool mode>	DTC No. <Scan tool (MUT-II) mode>	Diagnostic items	Check items (Remedy)	Memory
P0201	–	Injector Circuit Malfunction – Cylinder 1	• Harness and connector • Injector	Retained
P0202	–	Injector Circuit Malfunction – Cylinder 2		
P0203	–	Injector Circuit Malfunction – Cylinder 3		
P0204	–	Injector Circuit Malfunction – Cylinder 4		
P0300	–	Random Misfire Detected*	• Ignition coil • Ignition power transistor • Spark plug • Ignition circuit • Injector • Heated oxygen sensor • Compression pressure • Timing belt • Crankshaft position sensor • Air intake • Fuel pressure • Crankshaft position sensor circuit and connector	Retained
P0301	–	Cylinder 1 Misfire Detected*		
P0302	–	Cylinder 2 Misfire Detected*		
P0303	–	Cylinder 3 Misfire Detected*		
P0304	–	Cylinder 4 Misfire Detected*		
P0335	P0335	Crankshaft Position Sensor Circuit Malfunction	• Harness and connector (If harness and connector are normal, replace crankshaft position sensor.)	Retained
P0340	P0340	Camshaft Position Sensor Circuit Malfunction	• Harness and connector (If harness and connector are normal, replace camshaft position sensor.)	Retained
P0400	–	Exhaust Gas Recirculation Flow Malfunction	• Harness and connector • EGR valve • EGR solenoid • EGR valve control vacuum • Manifold differential pressure sensor	Retained
P0403	–	Exhaust Gas Recirculation Solenoid Malfunction	• Harness and connector • EGR valve	Retained
P0420	–	Catalyst System Efficiency Below Threshold (Bank 1) <Federal and Canada>	• Exhaust manifold (Replace the catalytic converter if there is no crack, etc.)	Retained
P0421	–	Warm Up Catalyst Efficiency Below Threshold (Bank 1) <California>	• Exhaust manifold (Replace the catalytic converter if there is no cracks, etc.)	Retained
P0440	–	Evaporative Emission Control System Malfunction	• Harness and connector • Evaporative emission purge solenoid • Purge control valve • Vacuum hoses routing	Retained

CR1029606564020X

Fig. 11   Self diagnosis test chart (Part 2 of 3). 1996

DTC No. <General scan tool mode>	DTC No. <Scan tool (MUT-II) mode>	Diagnostic items	Check items (Remedy)	Memory
P0443	–	Evaporative Emission Control System Purge Control Valve Circuit Malfunction	• Harness and connector • Evaporative emission purge solenoid	Retained
P0500	P0500	Vehicle Speed Sensor Malfunction	• Harness and connector • Vehicle speed sensor	Retained
P0505	P0505	Idle Control System Malfunction	• Harness and connector • Idle air control motor	Retained
P0510	–	Closed Throttle Position Switch Malfunction	• Harness and connector • Closed throttle position switch	Retained
P1300	P1300	Ignition Timing Adjustment Circuit Malfunction	• Harness and connector	–
P1500	P1500	Generator FR Terminal Circuit Malfunction	• Harness and connector	Retained

CR1029606564030X

Fig. 11   Self diagnosis test chart (Part 3 of 3). 1996

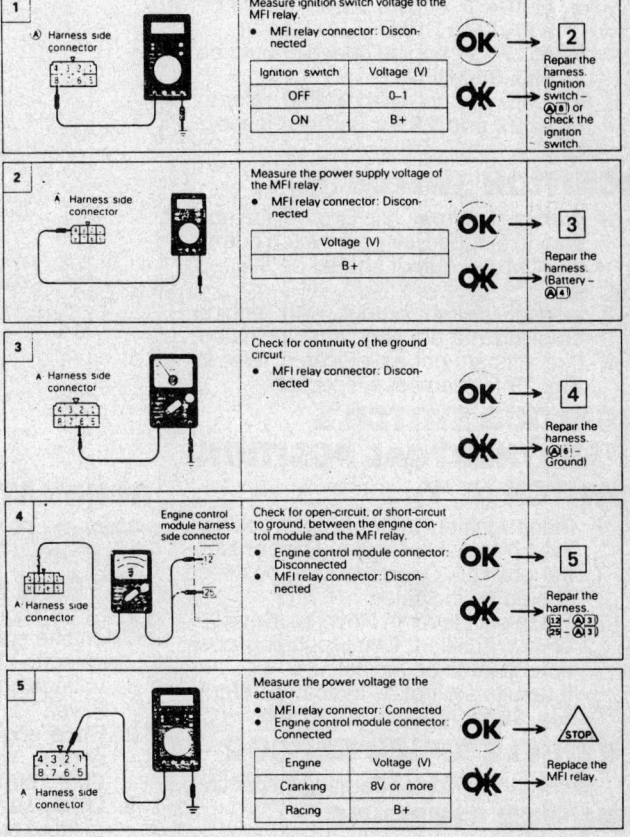

CR1029303405000X

Fig. 12   MFI (control) relay harness inspection

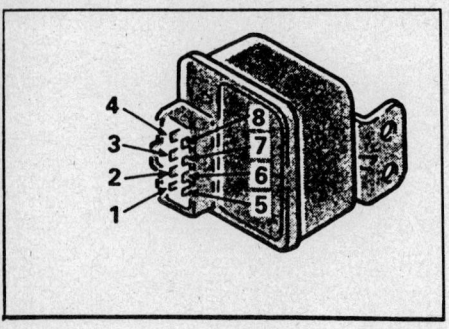

CR1029103426000X

Fig. 13 MFI (control) relay terminal identification

d. At 104°F, engine speed should be 940-1140 RPM.
e. At 176°F, engine speed should be 650-850 RPM.
2. If results are not as indicated, refer to **Figs. 27 and 28** for harness inspection.

IGNITION SWITCH (M/T)

1. With ignition switch in On position and engine stopped, inspect switch output to ECM. No output should be indicated.
2. Inspect switch output with engine cranking. out put should be indicated.
3. If results are not as indicated, refer to **Fig. 29** for harness inspection.

IGNITION SWITCH & PARK/NEUTRAL POSITION SWITCH (A/T)

1. Place ignition switch in On position, then place shift lever in Park or Neutral position. Corresponding positions should be indicated.
2. Place shift lever in Reverse, Drive "2" or low position. Corresponding positions should be indicated.
3. If results are not as indicated, refer to **Fig. 30** for harness inspection.

VEHICLE SPEED SENSOR

Refer to **Fig. 31** for harness inspection.

POWER STEERING PRESSURE SWITCH

1. With engine idling inspect switch state. Switch should be in Off position.
2. Inspect switch state while turning steering wheel. Switch should be in On position.
3. If results are not as indicated, refer to **Fig. 32** for harness inspection.

AIR CONDITIONING SWITCH & COMPRESSOR CLUTCH

1. With engine idling, inspect switch output when switch is in Off position. No output should be indicated.
2. Turn switch to On position and inspect output. Output should be indicated.
3. If results are not as indicated, refer to **Fig. 33** for harness inspection.

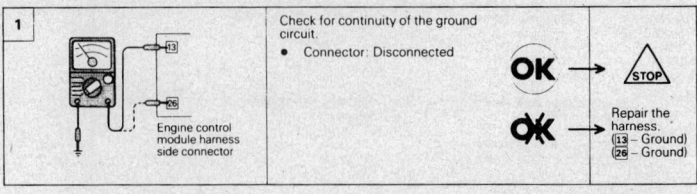

CR1029303418000X

Fig. 14 ECM power ground harness inspection

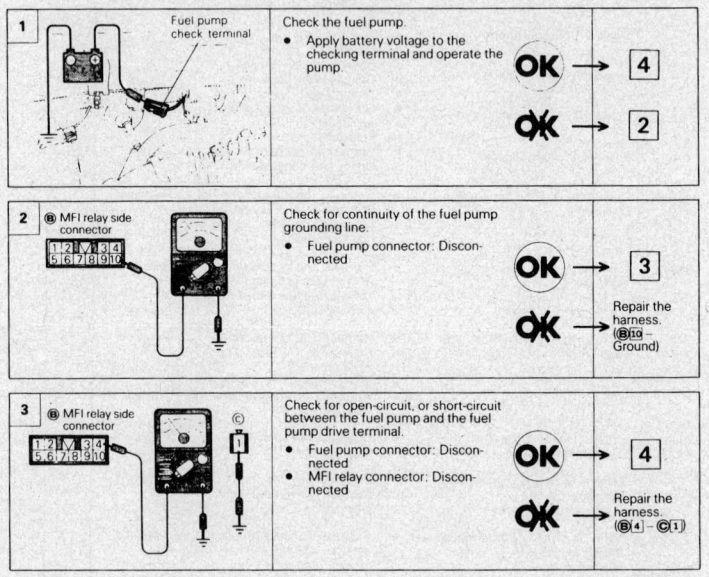

CR1029303398010X

Fig. 15 Fuel pump harness inspection (Part 1 of 2)

GENERATOR

Refer to **Fig. 34** for harness inspection procedure.

OXYGEN SENSOR

1. Start engine. During warm-up raise engine speed to 4000 RPM, then decelerate abruptly and measure sensor voltage. Voltage should be 200 mV or lower.
2. Race engine abruptly, then measure sensor voltage. Voltage should be 600-1000 mV.
3. Using sensor signal, inspect fuel/air mixture ratio and inspect control condition of engine control module. At 750 RPM (idle speed), voltage should be 400 mV or lower. At 2000 RPM, voltage should be 600-1000 mV.
4. If results are not as indicated, refer to **Fig. 35** for harness inspection.

HEATED OXYGEN SENSOR
VOLTAGE INSPECTION
Front

1. Start engine. During warm-up raise engine speed to 4000 RPM, then decelerate abruptly and measure sensor voltage. Voltage should be 200 mV or lower.
2. Race engine abruptly, then measure sensor voltage. Voltage should be 600-1000 mV.
3. Using sensor signal, inspect fuel/air mixture ratio and inspect control condition of engine control module. At 750 RPM (idle speed), voltage should be 400 mV or lower. At 2000 RPM, voltage should be 600-1000 mV.
4. If results are not as indicated, then refer to harness inspection.

Rear

1. **On models equipped with manual transaxle,** drive vehicle in second gear with throttle wide open until engine speed reaches 3500 RPM.
2. **On models equipped with automatic transaxle,** drive vehicle in low gear ("L") range with throttle wide open until engine speed reaches 3500 RPM.
3. **On all models,** measure sensor voltage. Voltage Should be 600-1000 mV with engine at 3500 RPM.
4. If results are not as indicated, then refer to harness inspection.

CONDITION INSPECTION

1. Start engine and allow to warm up, then inspect heater. At 750 RPM, heater should be activated; at 5000 RPM heater should not be activated.
2. If results are not as indicated, then refer to harness inspection.

HARNESS INSPECTION

Refer to **Figs. 36 through 40** for harness inspection.

SENSOR INSPECTION
Front (Federal)

1. Disconnect heated oxygen sensor connector, then connect test harness

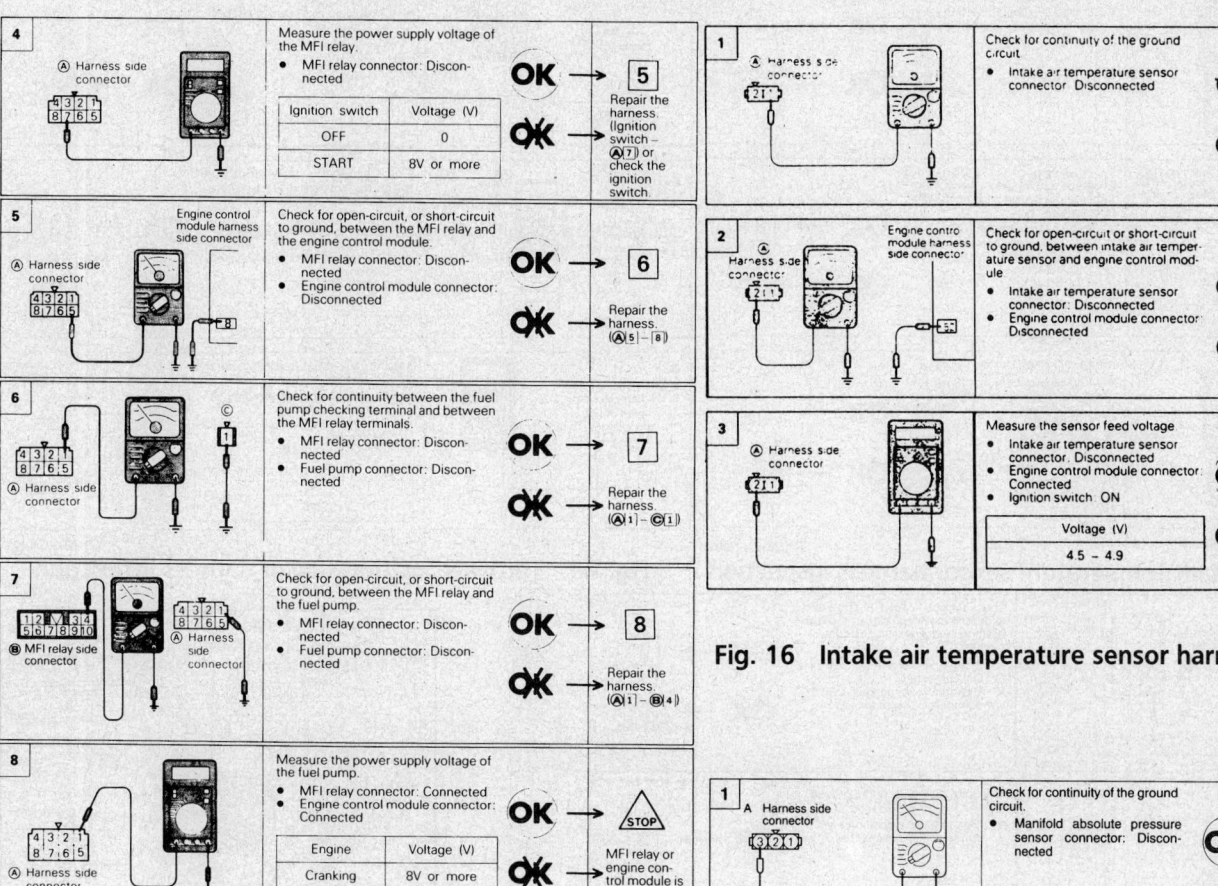

4 Harness side connector

Measure the power supply voltage of the MFI relay.
- MFI relay connector: Disconnected

Ignition switch	Voltage (V)
OFF	0
START	8V or more

OK → **5**

OX → Repair the harness. (Ignition switch – Ⓐ7) or check the ignition switch.

5 Ⓐ Harness side connector / Engine control module harness side connector

Check for open-circuit, or short-circuit to ground, between the MFI relay and the engine control module.
- MFI relay connector: Disconnected
- Engine control module connector: Disconnected

OK → **6**

OX → Repair the harness. (Ⓐ5 – 8)

6 Ⓐ Harness side connector / ©1

Check for continuity between the fuel pump checking terminal and between the MFI relay terminals.
- MFI relay connector: Disconnected
- Fuel pump connector: Disconnected

OK → **7**

OX → Repair the harness. (Ⓐ1 – ©1)

7 Ⓑ MFI relay side connector / Ⓐ Harness side connector

Check for open-circuit, or short-circuit to ground, between the MFI relay and the fuel pump.
- MFI relay connector: Disconnected
- Fuel pump connector: Disconnected

OK → **8**

OX → Repair the harness. (Ⓐ1 – Ⓑ4)

8 Ⓐ Harness side connector

Measure the power supply voltage of the fuel pump.
- MFI relay connector: Connected
- Engine control module connector: Connected

Engine	Voltage (V)
Cranking	8V or more
Racing	B+

OK → STOP

OX → MFI relay or engine control module is defective.

CR1029303398020X

Fig. 15   Fuel pump harness inspection (Part 2 of 2)

1 Ⓐ Harness side connector

Check for continuity of the ground circuit.
- Intake air temperature sensor connector: Disconnected

OK → **2**

OX → Repair the harness (Ⓐ1 – 72)

2 Ⓐ Harness side connector / Engine control module harness side connector

Check for open-circuit or short-circuit to ground, between intake air temperature sensor and engine control module.
- Intake air temperature sensor connector: Disconnected
- Engine control module connector: Disconnected

OK → **3**

OX → Repair the harness. (Ⓐ2 – 52)

3 Ⓐ Harness side connector

Measure the sensor feed voltage.
- Intake air temperature sensor connector: Disconnected
- Engine control module connector: Connected
- Ignition switch: ON

Voltage (V)
4.5 – 4.9

OK → STOP

OX → Repair the engine control module.

CR1029303403000X

Fig. 16   Intake air temperature sensor harness inspection

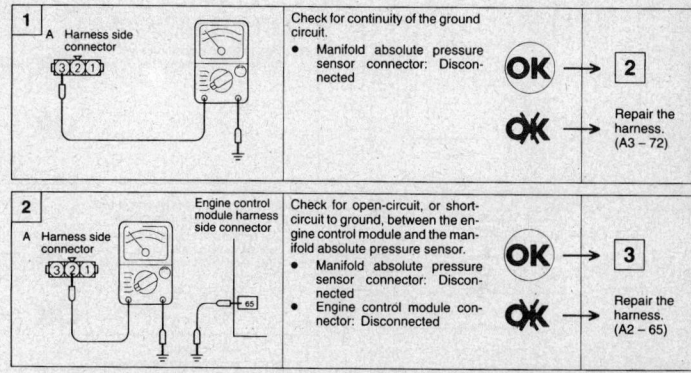

1 A Harness side connector

Check for continuity of the ground circuit.
- Manifold absolute pressure sensor connector: Disconnected

OK → **2**

OX → Repair the harness. (A3 – 72)

2 A Harness side connector / Engine control module harness side connector

Check for open-circuit, or short-circuit to ground, between the engine control module and the manifold absolute pressure sensor.
- Manifold absolute pressure sensor connector: Disconnected
- Engine control module connector: Disconnected

OK → **3**

OX → Repair the harness. (A2 – 65)

CR1029606553010X

Fig. 18   Manifold absolute pressure sensor harness inspection (Part 1 of 2). 1995 California & 1996

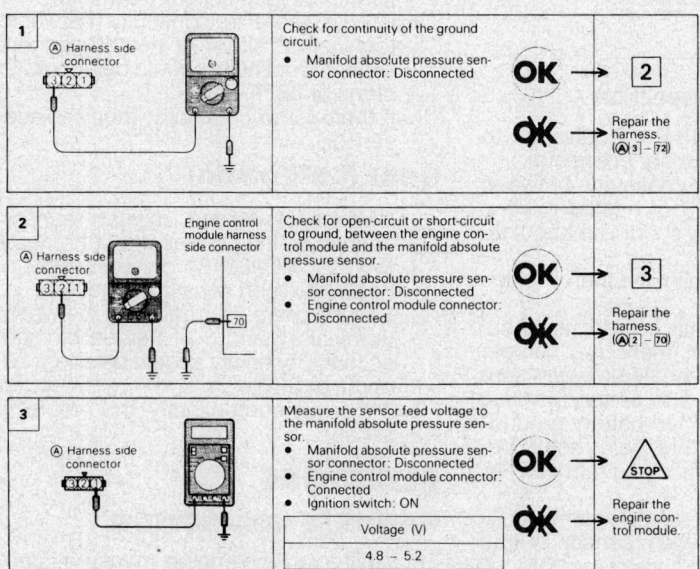

1 Ⓐ Harness side connector

Check for continuity of the ground circuit.
- Manifold absolute pressure sensor connector: Disconnected

OK → **2**

OX → Repair the harness. (A3 – 72)

2 Ⓐ Harness side connector / Engine control module harness side connector

Check for open-circuit or short-circuit to ground, between the engine control module and the manifold absolute pressure sensor.
- Manifold absolute pressure sensor connector: Disconnected
- Engine control module connector: Disconnected

OK → **3**

OX → Repair the harness. (Ⓐ2 – 70)

3 Ⓐ Harness side connector

Measure the sensor feed voltage to the manifold absolute pressure sensor.
- Manifold absolute pressure sensor connector: Disconnected
- Engine control module connector: Connected
- Ignition switch: ON

Voltage (V)
4.8 – 5.2

OK → STOP

OX → Repair the engine control module.

CR1029303413000X

Fig. 17   Manifold absolute pressure sensor harness inspection. 1993–94 & 1995 Federal

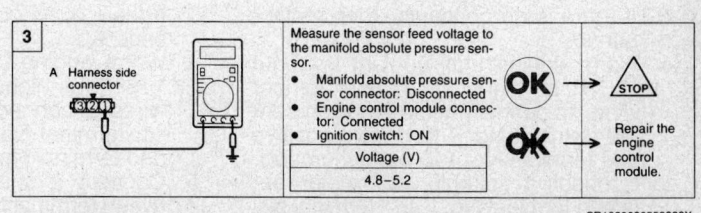

3 A Harness side connector

Measure the sensor feed voltage to the manifold absolute pressure sensor.
- Manifold absolute pressure sensor connector: Disconnected
- Engine control module connector: Connected
- Ignition switch: ON

Voltage (V)
4.8–5.2

OK → STOP

OX → Repair the engine control module.

CR1029606553020X

Fig. 18   Manifold absolute pressure sensor harness inspection (Part 2 of 2). 1995 California & 1996

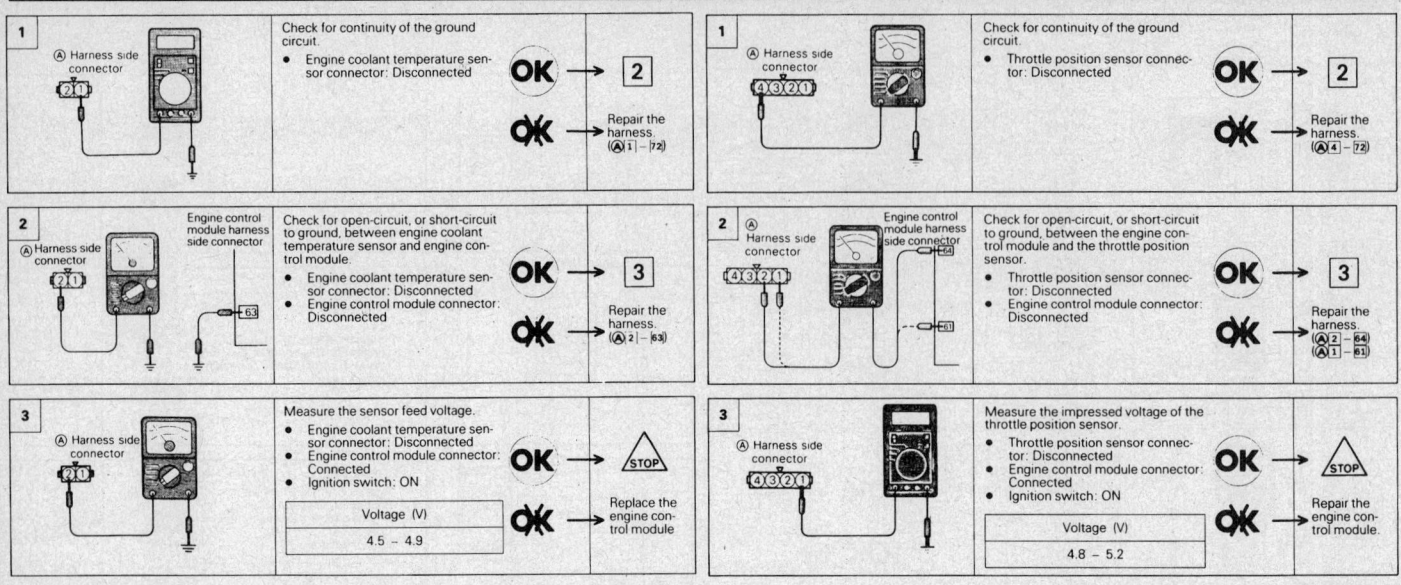

Fig. 19   Coolant temperature sensor harness inspection

Fig. 20   Throttle position sensor harness inspection

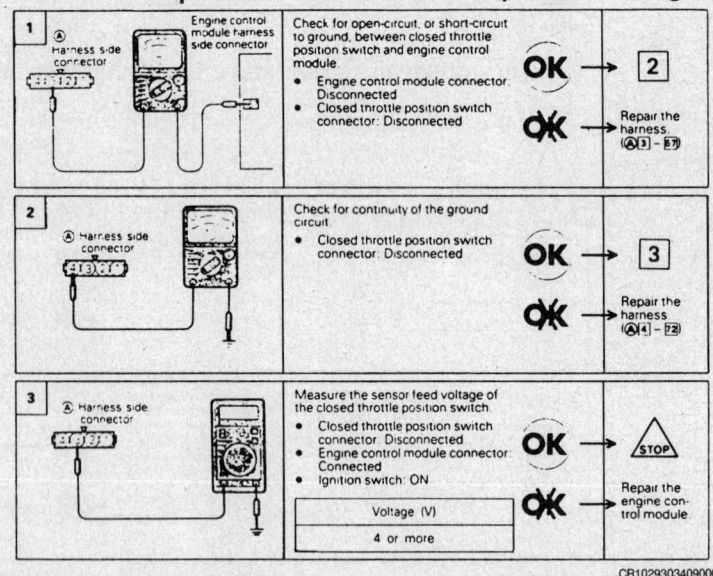

Fig. 21   Closed throttle position switch harness inspection

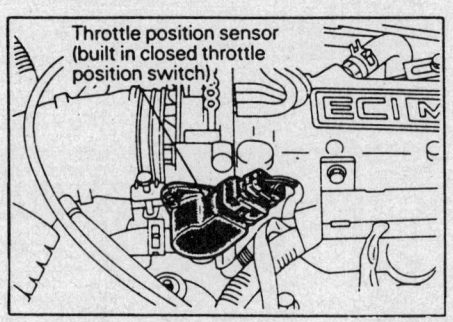

Fig. 22   Closed throttle position switch/throttle position sensor assembly

tool No. MD998464 or equivalent to heated oxygen sensor connector.
2. Ensure there is continuity between terminals 2 and 4 of heated oxygen sensor. Continuity should be about 20 ohms at 68°F.
3. If there is no continuity, then replace sensor.
4. Warm engine until coolant is about 176°F or higher, then user jumper wires, to connect heated oxygen sensor terminal No. 2 to battery positive and terminal No. 4 to battery ground.
5. Connect a suitable volt meter between terminal No. 1 and terminal No. 3.
6. While repeatedly racing engine, measure heated oxygen sensor output voltage. voltage should be 0.6-1.0 volts when racing engine. If voltage is not as specified, then replace sensor.

Front (California)

1. Disconnect heated oxygen sensor connector, then connect test harness

tool No. MD998464 or equivalent to heated oxygen sensor connector.
2. Ensure there is continuity between terminals 1 and 3 of heated oxygen sensor. Continuity should be about 20 ohms at 68°F.
3. If there is no continuity, then replace sensor.
4. Warm engine until coolant is about 176°F or higher, then user jumper wires, to connect heated oxygen sensor terminal No. 1 to battery positive and terminal No. 3 to battery ground.
5. Connect a suitable volt meter between terminal No. 2 and terminal No. 4.
6. While repeatedly racing engine, measure heated oxygen sensor output voltage. voltage should be 0.6-1.0 volts when racing engine. If voltage is not as specified, then replace sensor.

Rear (Federal)

1. Disconnect heated oxygen sensor connector, then connect test harness

tool No. MD998464 or equivalent to heated oxygen sensor connector.
2. Ensure there is continuity between terminals 2 and 4 of heated oxygen sensor. Continuity should be about 20 ohms at 68°F.
3. If there is no continuity, then replace sensor.

Rear (California)

1. Disconnect heated oxygen sensor connector, then connect test harness tool No. MD998464 or equivalent to heated oxygen sensor connector.
2. Ensure there is continuity between terminals 1 and 3 of heated oxygen sensor. Continuity should be about 20 ohms at 68°F.
3. If there is no continuity, then replace sensor.

INJECTORS

HARNESS INSPECTION

1. While cranking engine, measure coolant temperature and injector drive time. Results should be as follows:
   a. At 32°F, drive time should be 16.2-19.8 ms.
   b. At 68°F, drive time should be 32-39 ms.

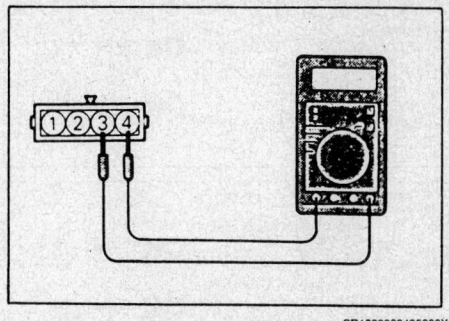

Fig. 23 TPS connector side terminals continuity inspection

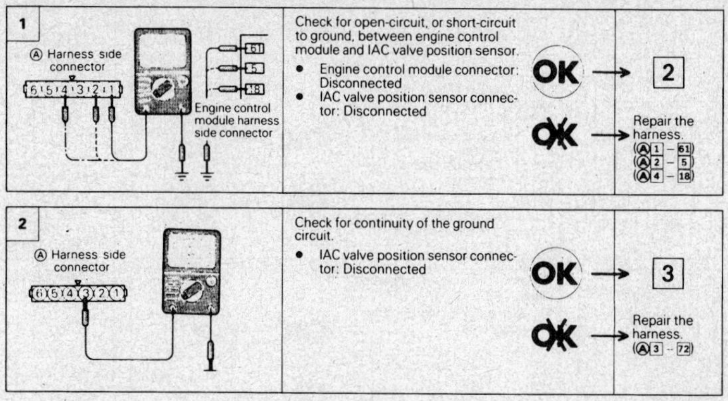

Fig. 24 Idle air control (IAC) valve position sensor harness inspection (Part 1 of 2)

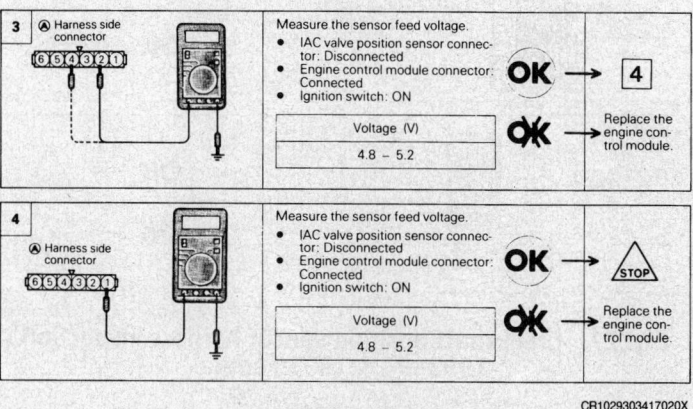

Fig. 24 Idle air control (IAC) valve position sensor harness inspection (Part 2 of 2)

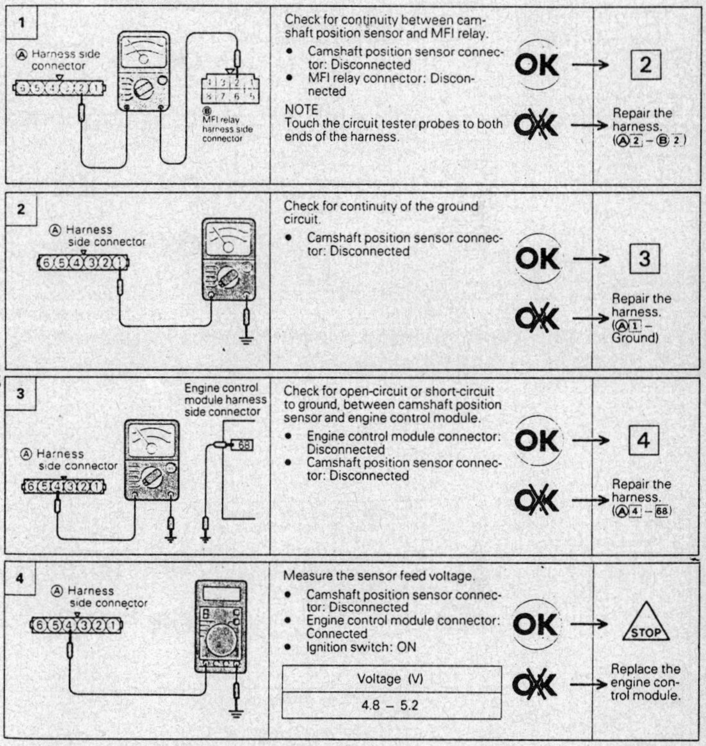

Fig. 25 Camshaft position sensor harness inspection. 1993–94 & 1995 Federal

c. At 176°F, drive time should be 8.1-9.9 ms.
2. If results are not as indicated, refer to **Fig. 41** for harness inspection.

ACTUATOR INSPECTION

1. With ignition switch in Off position, disconnect electrical connectors from injectors.
2. Measure resistance across injector terminals. Ohmmeter should indicate 13-16 ohms at 68°F. If resistance is not within this range, replace injector.

IDLE AIR CONTROL MOTOR

Refer to **Fig. 42** for harness inspection.

IGNITION COIL & IGNITION POWER TRANSISTOR

1. With engine warming up, set timing lights to check actual ignition timing. At idle, timing should be 2-18°BTDC; at 2500 RPM, timing should be 25-45°BTDC.
2. If results are not as indicated, refer to **Figs. 43 and 44** for harness inspection.

EVAPORATIVE EMISSION PURGE SOLENOID

HARNESS INSPECTION

1. Turn ignition switch to On position to activate solenoid valve. Valve operating noise should be indicated during activation.
2. If results are not as indicated, refer to **Fig. 45** for harness inspection.

ACTUATOR INSPECTION

1. Disconnect black, red striped vacuum hose from solenoid valve. **Mark vacuum hose for installation reference.**
2. Disconnect harness connector, then connect hand vacuum pump to vacuum hose nipple.
3. Apply vacuum pressure, then check air tightness while connecting and removing voltage supply at purge solenoid. When voltage is present, vacuum pressure should leak down; when voltage is removed, vacuum pressure should remain constant.
4. Measure resistance between purge solenoid valve terminals.
5. **On 1993-95 models,** resistance should be 36-44 ohms at 68°F.
6. **On 1996 models,** resistance should

be 62-74 ohms at 68°F.
7. **On all models,** if results are not as specified, replace evaporative emission purge solenoid.

EGR SOLENOID

HARNESS INSPECTION

1. Turn ignition switch to On position to activate solenoid valve. Valve operating noise should be indicated during activation.
2. If results are not as indicated, refer to **Fig. 46** for harness inspection.

ACTUATOR INSPECTION

1. Disconnect yellow/green striped vacuum hose from solenoid valve. **Mark vacuum hose for installation reference.**

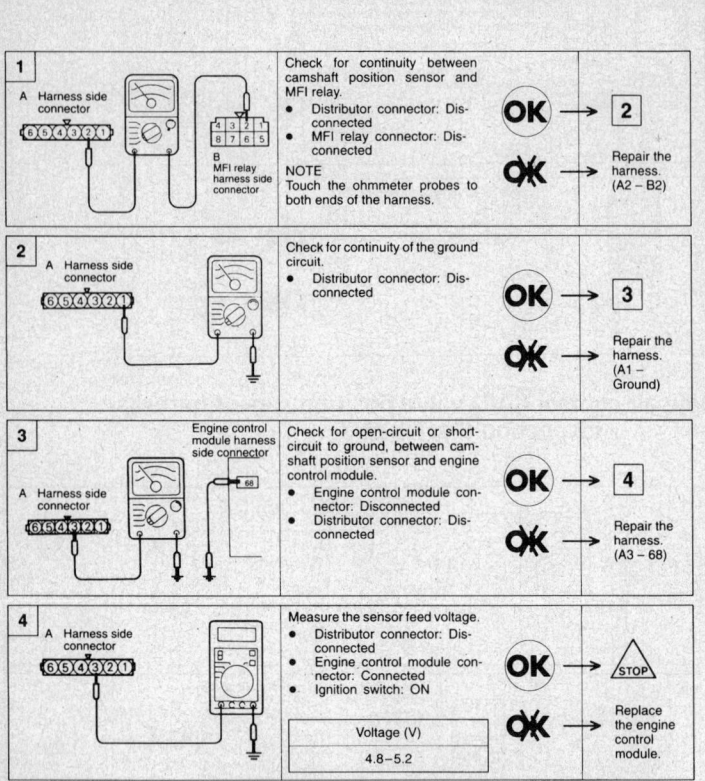

**Fig. 26 Camshaft position sensor harness inspection.
1995 California & 1996**

CR1029606554000X

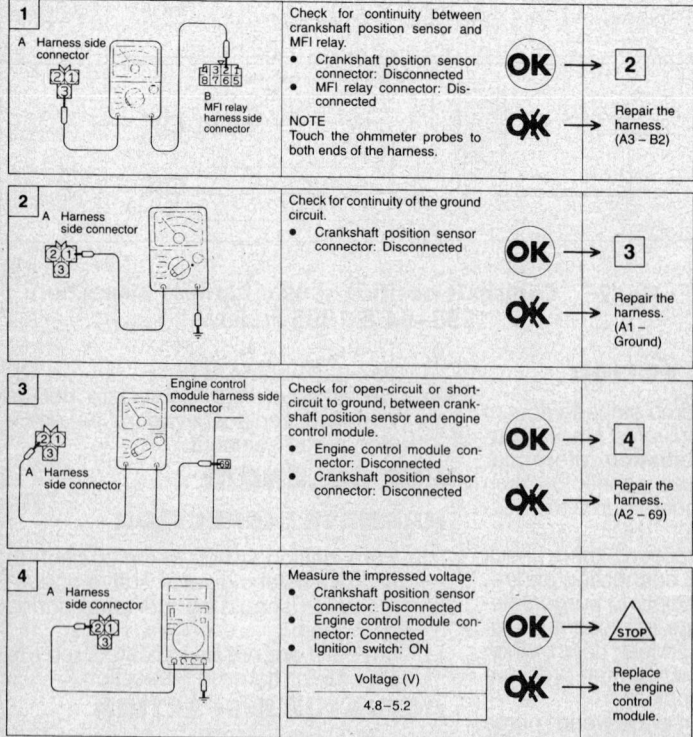

**Fig. 28 Crankshaft position sensor harness inspection.
1995 California & 1996**

CR1029606555000X

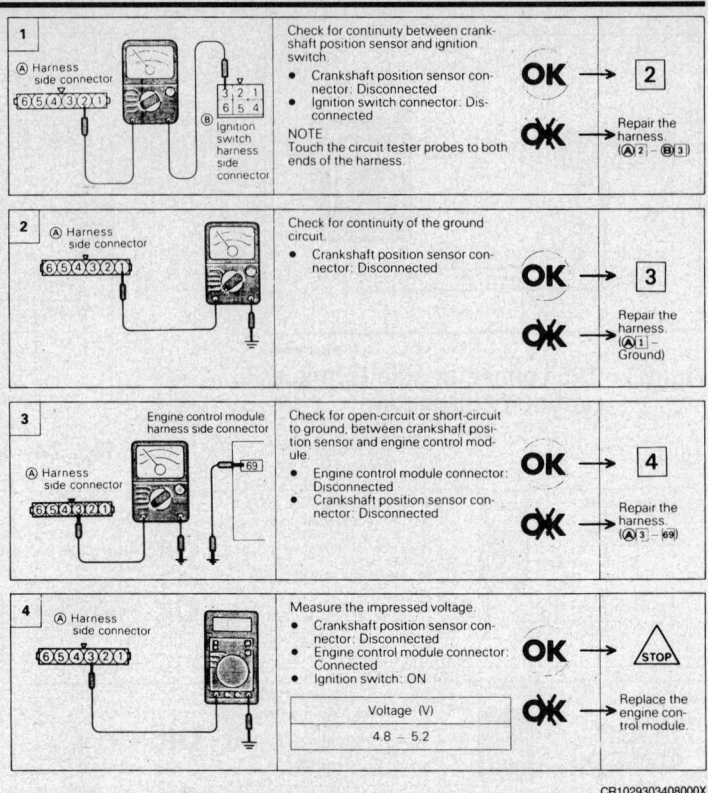

**Fig. 27 Crankshaft position sensor harness inspection.
1993–94 & 1995 Federal**

CR1029303408000X

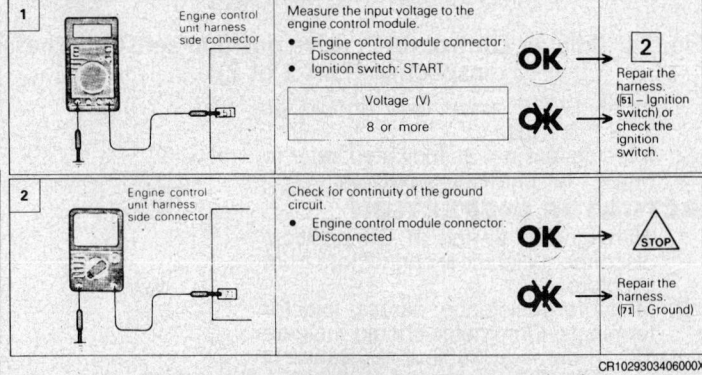

Fig. 29 Ignition switch harness inspection

CR1029303406000X

2. Disconnect harness connector, then connect hand vacuum pump to vacuum hose nipple.
3. Apply vacuum pressure, then check for air tightness while connecting and removing voltage supply at EGR solenoid. When voltage is present, vacuum pressure should remain constant; when voltage is removed, vacuum pressure should leak down.
4. Measure resistance between EGR solenoid valve terminals.
5. **On 1993-95 models**, resistance should be 36-44 ohms at 68°F.
6. **On 1996 models**, resistance should be 62-74 ohms at 68°F.
7. **On all models**, if results are not as specified, replace EGR solenoid.

EGR TEMPERATURE SENSOR
HARNESS INSPECTION
1. Start engine and allow to warm up, then maintain constant engine condi-

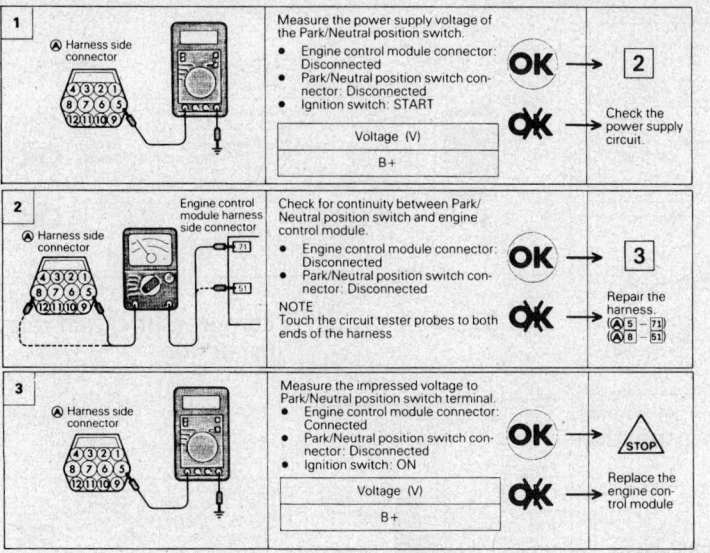

Fig. 30   Ignition switch & park/neutral position switch harness inspection

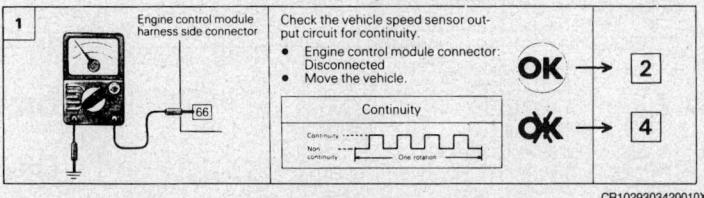

Fig. 31   Vehicle speed sensor harness inspection (Part 1 of 2)

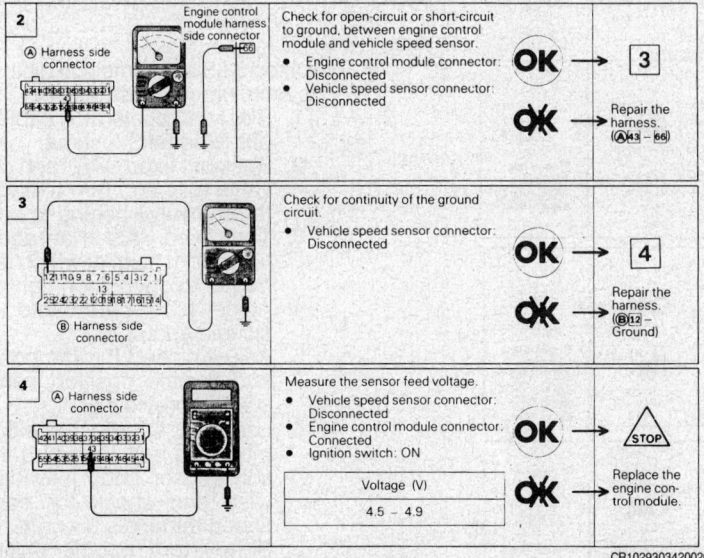

Fig. 31   Vehicle speed sensor harness inspection. (Part 2 of 2)

tions for 2 or more minutes.
2. Measure sensor temperature. At 750 RPM, temperature should be 158°F or less; at 3500 RPM, temperature should be 158°F or more.
3. Pinch green striped vacuum hose between EGR valve and EGR solenoid, then measure temperature. At idle there should be no change in temperature; at 3500 RPM, there should be a significant temperature change.
4. If results are not as indicated, refer to for harness inspection.

SENSOR INSPECTION

1. Remove EGR temperature sensor, then place in suitable container of water.
2. Measure resistance between terminals 1 and 2 while increasing water temperature. At 122°F, resistance should be 60,000-83,000 ohms; at 212°F, resistance should be 11,000-14,000 ohms.
3. If results deviate significantly from specifications, replace EGR tempera-

ture sensor. **Torque** sensor to 7.3-8.6 ft. lbs.

FUEL PRESSURE TEST

1. Relive fuel system pressure as outlined under "System Service" in this chapter.
2. Disconnect high pressure fuel hose at fuel rail side. **Cover hose with shop towel to prevent splash of excess fuel.**
3. Install fuel pressure gauge adapter hose tool Nos. MD998709 and MD998742 or equivalents, between fuel rail and high pressure hose.
4. With a jumper wire connect fuel pump drive terminal with battery positive terminal to drive fuel pump, then inspect fuel pressure gauge and adapter hose for leaks.
5. Disconnect jumper wire, then start and idle engine.
6. Measure fuel pressure at idle, pressure should be 38 psi.
7. Disconnect vacuum hose from fuel pressure regulator and measure fuel pressure with hose end closed by a finger. Fuel pressure should be 47-50 psi at idle.
8. Ensure pressure does not drop when engine is raced.
9. If fuel pressure is not as specified then troubleshoot and repair according to **Fig. 48.**
10. Stop engine and inspect change of fuel pressure reading. Fuel pressure reading should not drop for about two minutes. If reading is not as specified, then trouble shoot according to **Fig. 49.**

Component Replacement
INJECTOR

Prior to disconnecting fuel hoses, relieve fuel system pressure as described under "Fuel System Pressure Relief."

Refer to **Fig. 50** for injector replacement procedure.

THROTTLE BODY

Prior to disconnecting fuel hoses, fuel system pressure must be relieved as described under "Fuel System Pressure Relief."

Refer to **Fig. 51** for throttle body replacement procedure.

Adjustments
CLOSED THROTTLE POSITION SWITCH & THROTTLE POSITION SENSOR

1. Disconnect electrical connector from throttle position sensor.
2. Using jumper wires, connect an ohmmeter between terminals 3 and 4, **Fig. 52.**
3. Insert a feeler gauge with a thickness of 0.0256 inch between fixed SAS and throttle lever, **Fig. 53.**

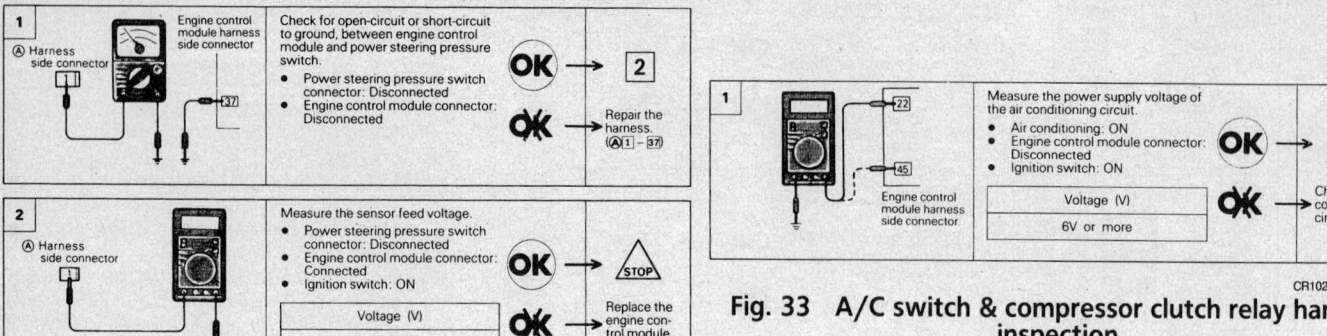

Fig. 32 Power steering pressure switch harness inspection

Fig. 33 A/C switch & compressor clutch relay harness inspection

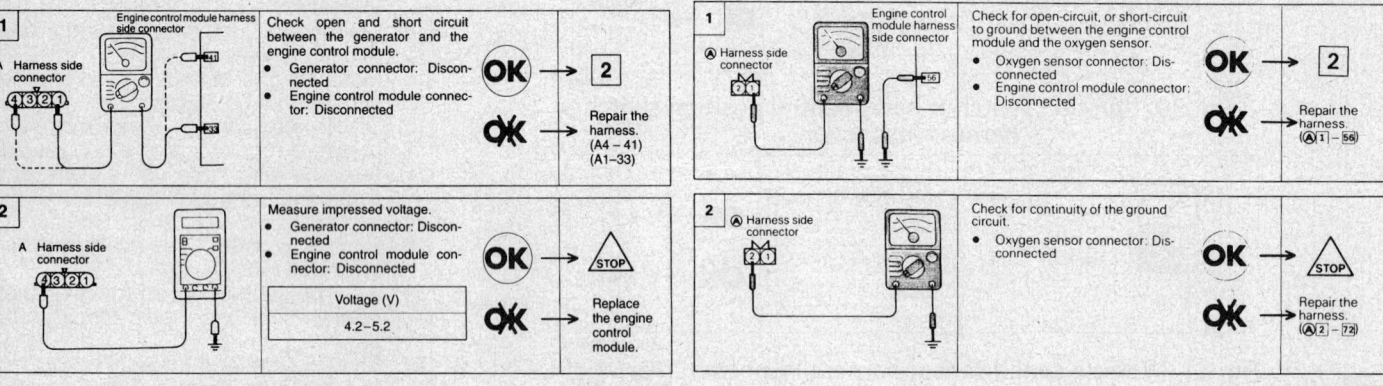

Fig. 34 Generator harness inspection

Fig. 35 Oxygen sensor harness inspection. 1993 Federal

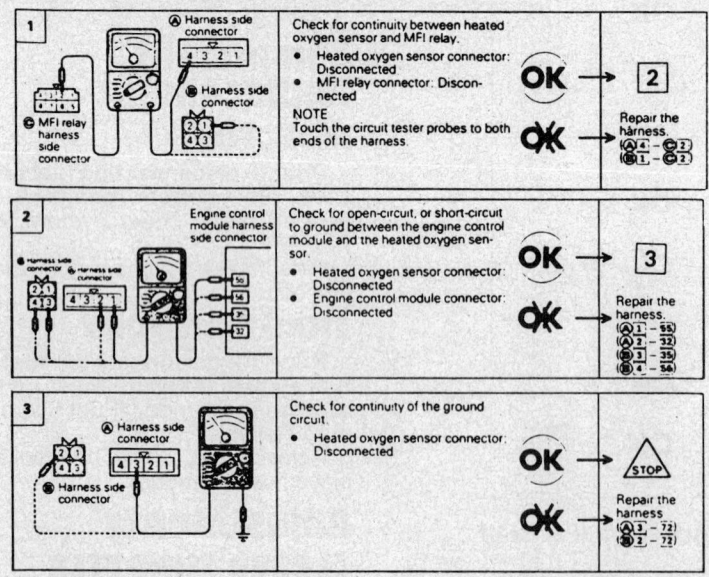

Fig. 36 Heated oxygen sensor harness inspection. 1993 California

10. If reading is not as specified, check throttle position sensor and related wiring. Repair or replace as necessary.
11. Turn ignition switch to Off position, then remove feeler gauge.

FIXED SAS

The fixed SAS should never be adjusted unnecessarily; its adjustment has been set by the manufacturer and, under ordinary circumstances, will not change. However,

if fixed SAS adjustment is disturbed for any reason, proceed as follows:

1. Slacken accelerator cable, then back out fixed SAS locknut.
2. Back out fixed SAS, then close throttle valve fully and turn fixed SAS in until throttle valve begins to open.
3. Turn fixed SAS in an additional 1 1/4 turns from point at which throttle valve began to open, then tighten locknut.
4. Adjust the basic idle speed.
5. Adjust closed throttle position switch and throttle position sensor as described previously.
4. Loosen throttle position sensor mounting bolt, then turn throttle position sensor body fully counterclockwise and check for continuity between terminals 3 and 4.
5. Slowly turn throttle position sensor clockwise until continuity does not exist between terminals 3 and 4. Tighten throttle position sensor retaining bolt at that position.
6. Connect Test Harness Set tool No. MB991348 or equivalent between electrical connector and throttle position sensor as shown in **Fig. 54**.
7. Connect a digital voltmeter between throttle position sensor terminal 2 and terminal 4.
8. Turn ignition switch to On position (do not start engine).
9. Check throttle position sensor output voltage. Reading obtained should be 400-1000 mV.

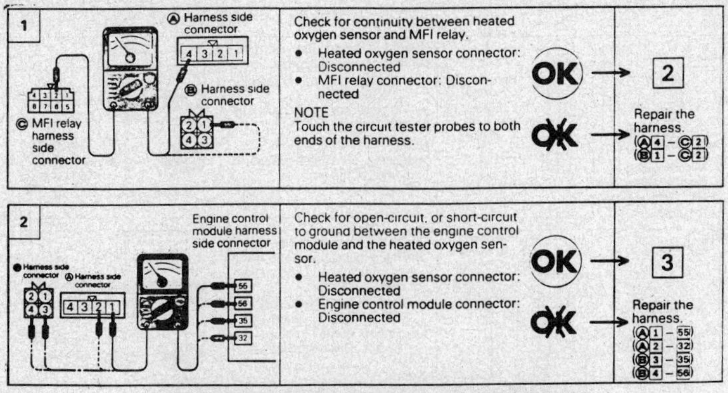

Fig. 37 Heated oxygen sensor harness inspection (Part 1 of 2). 1994

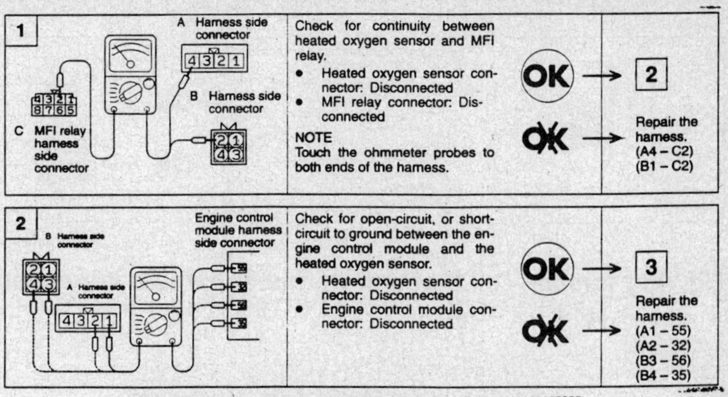

1. Check for continuity between heated oxygen sensor and MFI relay.
   - Heated oxygen sensor connector: Disconnected
   - MFI relay connector: Disconnected
   NOTE
   Touch the circuit tester probes to both ends of the harness.
   OK → 2
   OK̶ → Repair the harness. (A4 – C2) (B1 – C2)

2. Check for open-circuit, or short-circuit to ground between the engine control module and the heated oxygen sensor.
   - Heated oxygen sensor connector: Disconnected
   - Engine control module connector: Disconnected
   OK → 3
   OK̶ → Repair the harness. (A1 – 55) (A2 – 32) (B3 – 35) (B4 – 90)

Fig. 37 Heated oxygen sensor harness inspection (Part 2 of 2). 1994

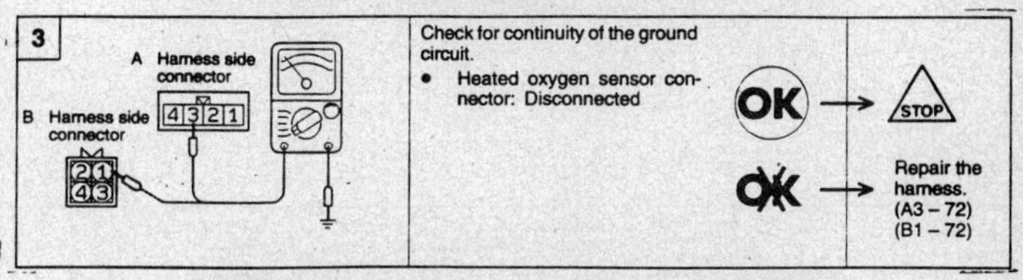

3. Check for continuity of the ground circuit.
   - Heated oxygen sensor connector: Disconnected
   OK → STOP
   OK̶ → Repair the harness. (A3 – 72) (B2 – 72)

Fig. 38 Heated oxygen sensor harness inspection (Part 1 of 2). 1995 Federal

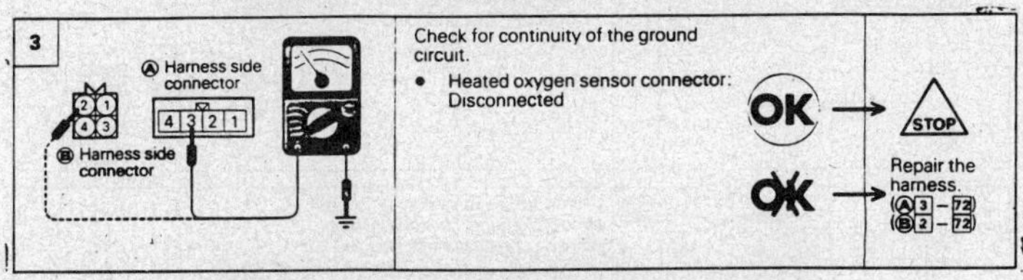

1. Check for continuity between heated oxygen sensor and MFI relay.
   - Heated oxygen sensor connector: Disconnected
   - MFI relay connector: Disconnected
   NOTE
   Touch the ohmmeter probes to both ends of the harness.
   OK → 2
   OK̶ → Repair the harness. (A4 – C2) (B1 – C2)

2. Check for open-circuit, or short-circuit to ground between the engine control module and the heated oxygen sensor.
   - Heated oxygen sensor connector: Disconnected
   - Engine control module connector: Disconnected
   OK → 3
   OK̶ → Repair the harness. (A1 – 55) (A2 – 32) (B3 – 56) (B4 – 35)

Fig. 38 Heated oxygen sensor harness inspection (Part 2 of 2). 1995 Federal

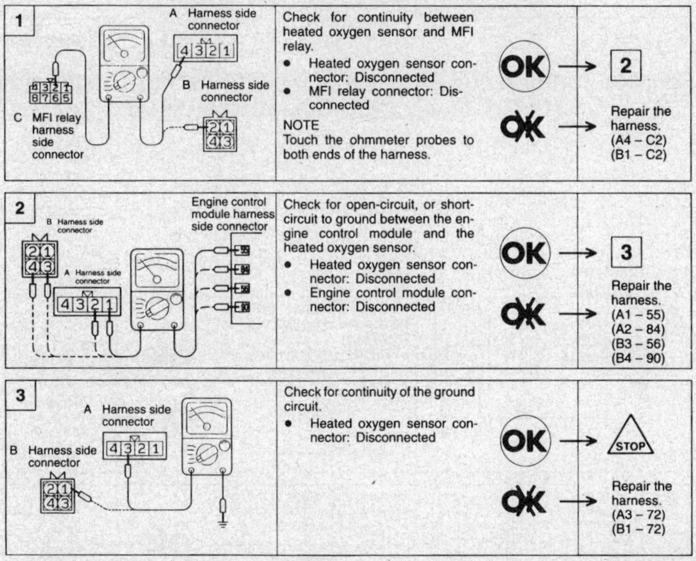

3. Check for continuity of the ground circuit.
   - Heated oxygen sensor connector: Disconnected
   OK → STOP
   OK̶ → Repair the harness. (A3 – 72) (B1 – 72)

Fig. 39 Heated oxygen sensor harness inspection. 1996 Federal

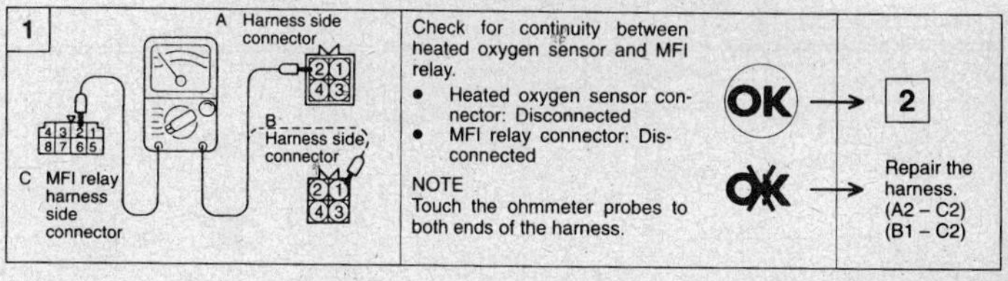

1. Check for continuity between heated oxygen sensor and MFI relay.
   - Heated oxygen sensor connector: Disconnected
   - MFI relay connector: Disconnected
   NOTE
   Touch the ohmmeter probes to both ends of the harness.
   OK → 2
   OK̶ → Repair the harness. (A4 – C2) (B1 – C2)

2. Check for open-circuit, or short-circuit to ground between the engine control module and the heated oxygen sensor.
   - Heated oxygen sensor connector: Disconnected
   - Engine control module connector: Disconnected
   OK → 3
   OK̶ → Repair the harness. (A1 – 55) (A2 – 84) (B3 – 56) (B4 – 90)

3. Check for continuity of the ground circuit.
   - Heated oxygen sensor connector: Disconnected
   OK → STOP
   OK̶ → Repair the harness. (A3 – 72) (B1 – 72)

CR1029606557000X

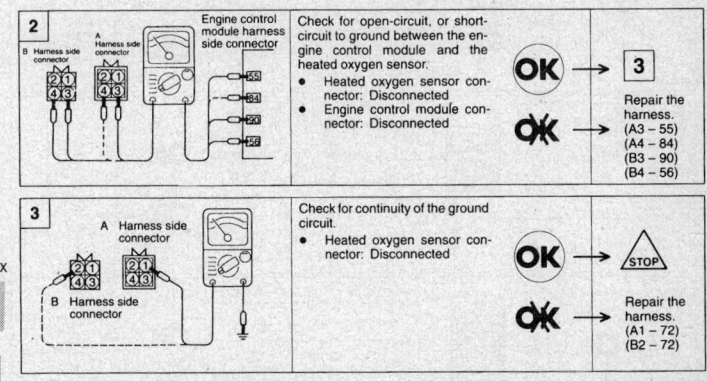

Fig. 40 Heated oxygen sensor harness inspection (Part 1 of 2). 1995–96 California

1. Check for continuity between heated oxygen sensor and MFI relay.
   - Heated oxygen sensor connector: Disconnected
   - MFI relay connector: Disconnected
   NOTE
   Touch the ohmmeter probes to both ends of the harness.
   OK → 2
   OK̶ → Repair the harness. (A2 – C2) (B1 – C2)

CR1029606559010X

2. Check for open-circuit, or short-circuit to ground between the engine control module and the heated oxygen sensor.
   - Heated oxygen sensor connector: Disconnected
   - Engine control module connector: Disconnected
   OK → 3
   OK̶ → Repair the harness. (A3 – 55) (A4 – 84) (B3 – 90) (B4 – 56)

3. Check for continuity of the ground circuit.
   - Heated oxygen sensor connector: Disconnected
   OK → STOP
   OK̶ → Repair the harness. (A1 – 72) (B2 – 72)

CR1029606559020X

Fig. 40 Heated oxygen sensor harness inspection (Part 2 of 2). 1995–96 California

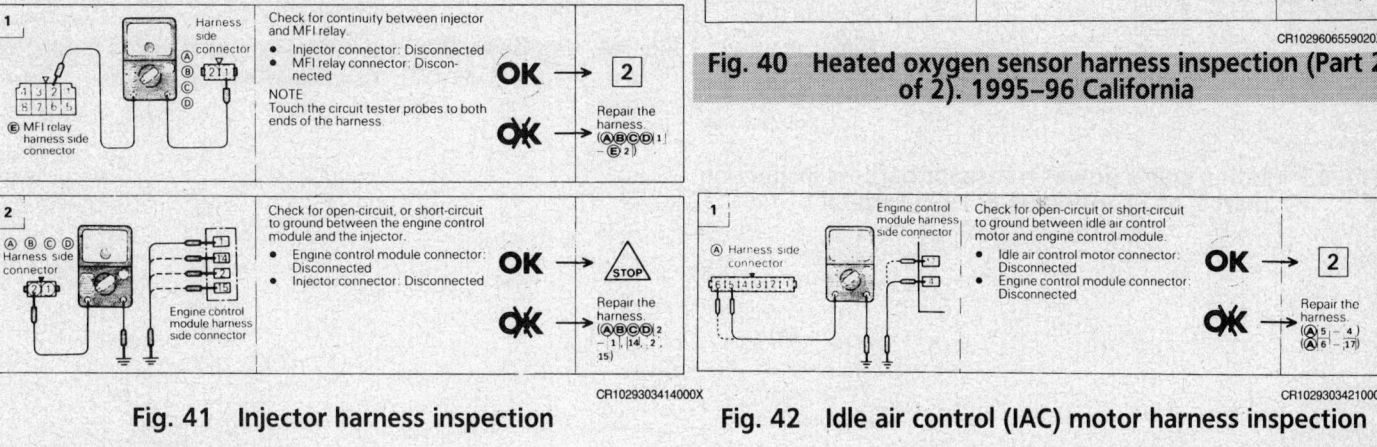

Fig. 41 Injector harness inspection

1. Check for continuity between injector and MFI relay.
   - Injector connector: Disconnected
   - MFI relay connector: Disconnected
   NOTE
   Touch the circuit tester probes to both ends of the harness.
   OK → 2
   OK̶ → Repair the harness. (A B C D) 1 (E 2)

2. Check for open-circuit, or short-circuit to ground between the engine control module and the injector.
   - Engine control module connector: Disconnected
   - Injector connector: Disconnected
   OK → STOP
   OK̶ → Repair the harness. (A B C D) 2 – 1, 14, 2, 15

CR1029303414000X

Fig. 42 Idle air control (IAC) motor harness inspection

1. Check for open-circuit or short-circuit to ground between idle air control motor and engine control module.
   - Idle air control motor connector: Disconnected
   - Engine control module connector: Disconnected
   OK → 2
   OK̶ → Repair the harness. (A 5 – 4) (A 6 – 17)

CR1029303421000X

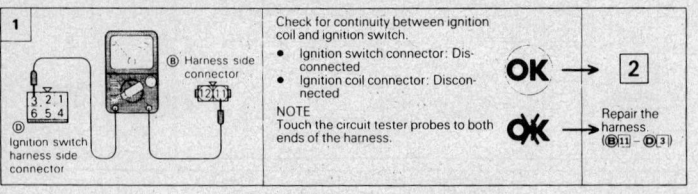

1 — Check for continuity between ignition coil and ignition switch.
- Ignition switch connector: Disconnected
- Ignition coil connector: Disconnected

NOTE
Touch the circuit tester probes to both ends of the harness.

OK → **2**

OK✗ → Repair the harness. (B11 – D3)

Ignition switch harness side connector
(B) Harness side connector

CR1029303416010X

Fig. 43 Ignition coil & power transistor harness inspection (Part 1 of 2). 1993–94 & 1995 Federal

2 — Engine control module harness side connector
(A) Harness side connector

Check for open-circuit or short-circuit to ground, between ignition power transistor and engine control module.
- Ignition power transistor connector: Disconnected
- Engine control module connector: Disconnected

OK → **3**

OK✗ → Repair the harness. (A 6 – 10)

3 — (A) Harness side connector

Check for continuity of the ground circuit of a ignition power transistor.
- Ignition power transistor connector: Disconnected

OK → **4**

OK✗ → Repair the harness. (A 5 – Ground)

4 — (B) Harness side connector

Check to be sure that there is no continuity between the ignition coil and the ground.
- Ignition coil connector: Disconnected

OK → **5**

OK✗ → Check for short in the ignition coil primary circuit.

5 — (A) Harness side connector

Measure the voltage of the control signal circuit of the ignition power transistor.
- Ignition power transistor connector: Disconnected
- Ignition switch: START

Voltage (V)
2–6

OK → **6**

OK✗ → Repair the harness. (A 6 – 10)

6 — C Ignition timing adjustment connector

Measure the voltage of the ignition timing adjustment terminal.
- Ignition switch: ON

Voltage (V)
4.0–5.2

OK → STOP

OK✗ → Repair the harness. (C 1 – 34)

CR1029303416020X

Fig. 43 Ignition coil & power transistor harness inspection (Part 2 of 2). 1993–94 & 1995 Federal

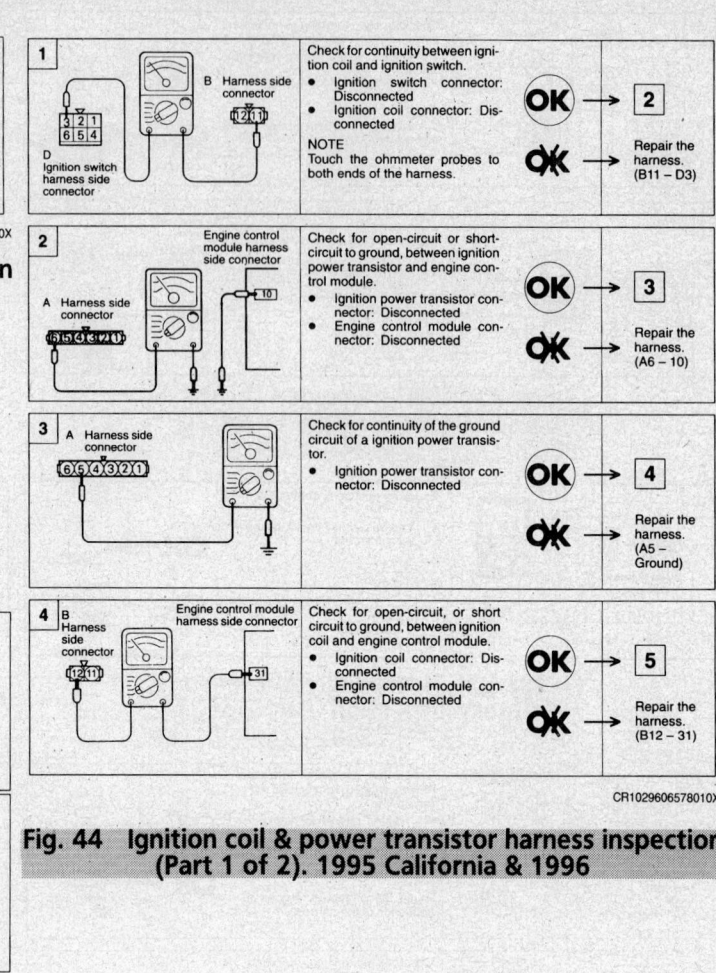

1 — Check for continuity between ignition coil and ignition switch.
- Ignition switch connector: Disconnected
- Ignition coil connector: Disconnected

NOTE
Touch the ohmmeter probes to both ends of the harness.

B Harness side connector
D Ignition switch harness side connector

OK → **2**

OK✗ → Repair the harness. (B11 – D3)

2 — Engine control module harness side connector
A Harness side connector

Check for open-circuit or short-circuit to ground, between ignition power transistor and engine control module.
- Ignition power transistor connector: Disconnected
- Engine control module connector: Disconnected

OK → **3**

OK✗ → Repair the harness. (A6 – 10)

3 — A Harness side connector

Check for continuity of the ground circuit of a ignition power transistor.
- Ignition power transistor connector: Disconnected

OK → **4**

OK✗ → Repair the harness. (A5 – Ground)

4 — B Harness side connector
Engine control module harness side connector

Check for open-circuit, or short circuit to ground, between ignition coil and engine control module.
- Ignition coil connector: Disconnected
- Engine control module connector: Disconnected

OK → **5**

OK✗ → Repair the harness. (B12 – 31)

CR1029606578010X

Fig. 44 Ignition coil & power transistor harness inspection (Part 1 of 2). 1995 California & 1996

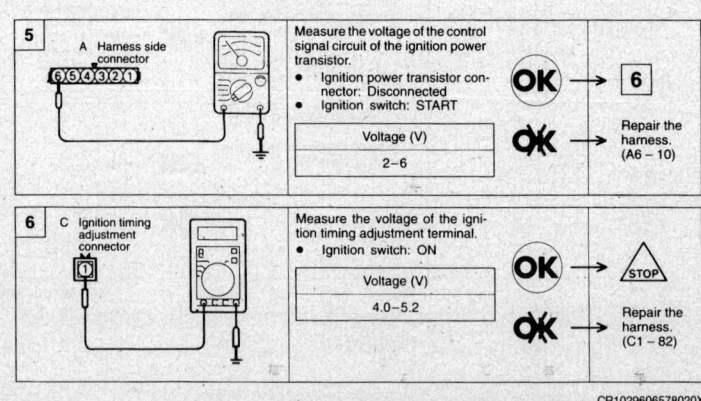

5 — A Harness side connector

Measure the voltage of the control signal circuit of the ignition power transistor.
- Ignition power transistor connector: Disconnected
- Ignition switch: START

Voltage (V)
2–6

OK → **6**

OK✗ → Repair the harness. (A6 – 10)

6 — C Ignition timing adjustment connector

Measure the voltage of the ignition timing adjustment terminal.
- Ignition switch: ON

Voltage (V)
4.0–5.2

OK → STOP

OK✗ → Repair the harness. (C1 – 82)

CR1029606578020X

Fig. 44 Ignition coil & power transistor harness inspection (Part 2 of 2). 1995 California & 1996

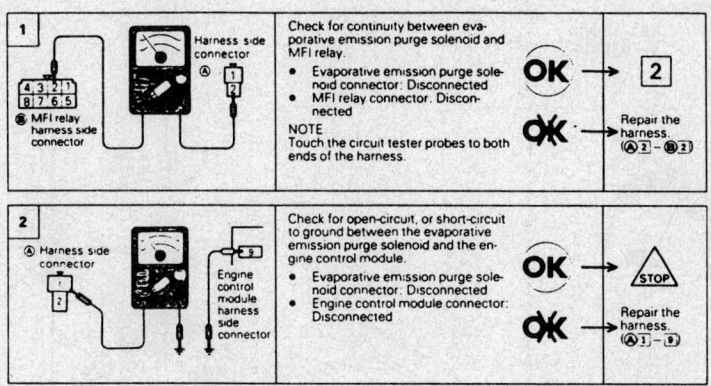

Fig. 45 Evaporative emission purge solenoid harness inspection

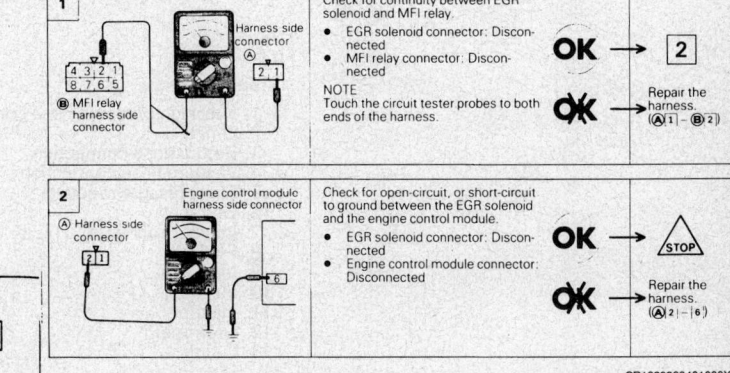

Fig. 46 EGR solenoid harness inspection

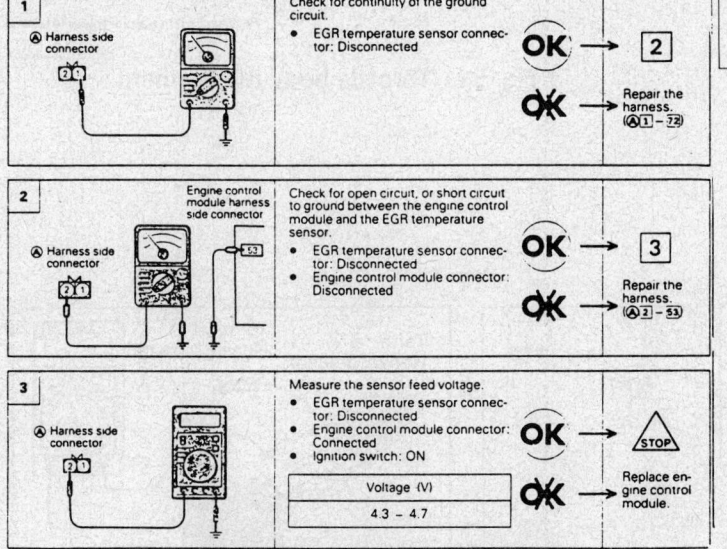

Fig. 47 EGR temperature sensor harness inspection. 1993-94 California & 1994-95 Federal

Symptom	Probable cause	Remedy
• Fuel pressure too low • Fuel pressure drops after racing • No fuel pressure in fuel return hose	Clogged fuel filter	Replace fuel filter
	Fuel leaking to return side due to poor fuel regulator valve seating or settled spring	Replace fuel pressure regulator
	Low fuel pump delivery pressure	Replace fuel pump
Fuel pressure too high	Binding valve in fuel pressure regulator	Replace fuel pressure regulator
	Clogged fuel return hose or pipe	Clean or replace hose or pipe
Same fuel pressure when vacuum hose is connected and when disconnected	Damaged vacuum hose or clogged nipple	Replace vacuum hose or clean nipple

CR1029606562000X

Fig. 48 Incorrect fuel pressure

Symptom	Probable cause	Remedy
Fuel pressure drops gradually after engine is stopped	Leaky injector	Replace injector
	Leaky fuel regulator valve seat	Replace fuel pressure regulator
Fuel pressure drops sharply immediately after engine is stopped	Check valve in fuel pump is held open	Replace fuel pump

CR1029606563000X

Fig. 49 Incorrect fuel pressure drop off

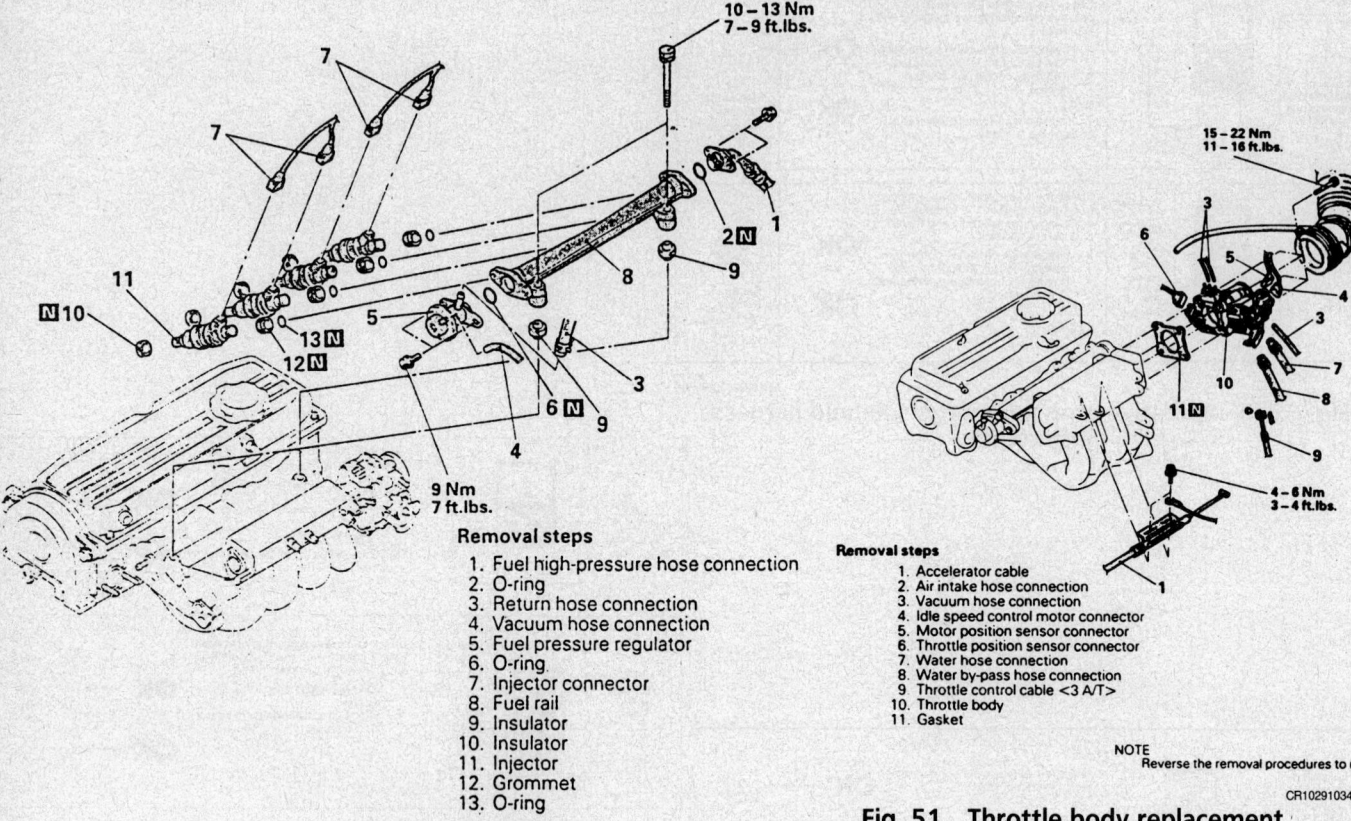

10 – 13 Nm
7 – 9 ft.lbs.

9 Nm
7 ft.lbs.

Removal steps

1. Fuel high-pressure hose connection
2. O-ring
3. Return hose connection
4. Vacuum hose connection
5. Fuel pressure regulator
6. O-ring
7. Injector connector
8. Fuel rail
9. Insulator
10. Insulator
11. Injector
12. Grommet
13. O-ring

Fig. 50   Injector replacement

15 – 22 Nm
11 – 16 ft.lbs.

4 – 6 Nm
3 – 4 ft.lbs.

Removal steps

1. Accelerator cable
2. Air intake hose connection
3. Vacuum hose connection
4. Idle speed control motor connector
5. Motor position sensor connector
6. Throttle position sensor connector
7. Water hose connection
8. Water by-pass hose connection
9. Throttle control cable <3 A/T>
10. Throttle body
11. Gasket

NOTE
Reverse the removal procedures to reinstall.

CR1029103441000X

Fig. 51   Throttle body replacement

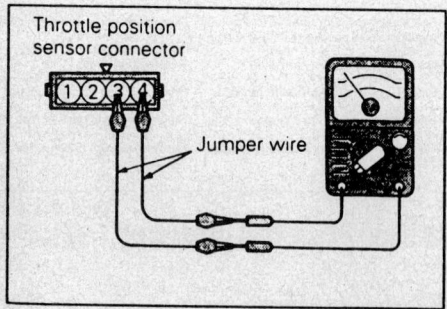

CR1029303442000X

Fig. 52   Ohmmeter connection to TPS connector terminals. 1993–95

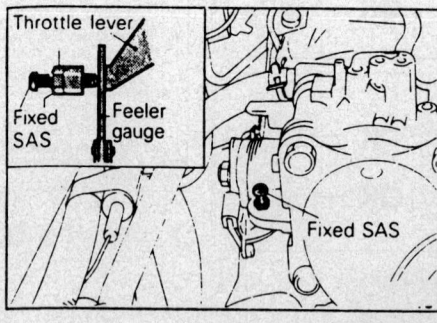

CR1029303443000X

Fig. 53   Feeler gauge, throttle lever & fixed SAS location. 1993–95

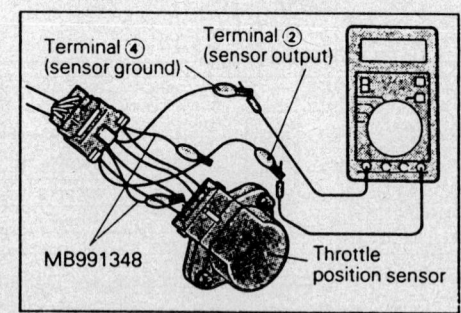

CR1029303444000X

Fig. 54   TPS test harness and voltmeter connection. 1993–95

MODELS w/1.8L/4-107, 1.8L/4-110 & 2.4L/4-143 ENGINES, 1993-94 MODELS w/2.0L/4-122 ENGINE & 1995 TALON w/2.0L/4-122 TURBOCHARGED ENGINE

NOTE: If Uncertain About The Proper Use Of Information Contained In This Section, Please Refer To "How To Use This Manual" Located In The Front Of This Manual.

NOTE: On Air Bag Equipped Models, Refer To "Air Bag System Precautions" Located In The Front Of This Manual For System Disarming & Arming Procedures.

NOTE: Electrical Symbol & Wire Color Code Identification Located In The Front Of This Manual May Be Used As An Aid When Using Wiring Circuits Found In This Section.

INDEX

Page No.	Page No.	Page No.

Description 7-2
Diagnosis & Testing: 7-2
  Accessing Diagnostic Trouble Codes: 7-2
    Using Diagnostic Readout Box
     (DRB II/III) 7-3
    Using General Scan Tool Or
     Multi-Use Tester (MUT). 7-3
    Using Malfunction Indicator Lamp
     (MIL) 7-3
    Using Voltmeter. 7-2
  Clearing Diagnostic Trouble Codes . . 7-3

Component Testing 7-24
Diagnostic Trouble Code
  Interpretation 7-3
System & Component Diagnosis: 7-3
  Colt, Colt Vista, Summit & Summit
    Wagon 7-3
  1993-94 Laser & Talon 7-7
  1995-96 Talon 7-24
  Visual Inspection. 7-2
Diagnostic Chart Index. 7-116
Precautions: 7-2

Air Bag Systems 7-2
Fuel System Pressure Relief 7-2
System Service Precautions. 7-2
Sensor & Fuel Injector Specifications 7-1
System Service: 7-124
  Component Replacement. 7-124
  Fuel System Pressure Relief 7-124
Troubleshooting: 7-2
  Colt, Colt Vista, Laser, Summit,
    Summit Wagon & 1993-94 Talon 7-2
  1995-96 Talon. 7-2

SENSOR & FUEL INJECTOR SPECIFICATIONS

Component	Year	Resistance, Ohms		
		@ 32°F	@ 68°F	@ 176°F
COLT, COLT VISTA, SUMMIT & SUMMIT WAGON				
Barometric Pressure Sensor	1993	5800	2400	1100
EGR Control Solenoid Valve	1993—95	—	36—44	—
EGR Solenoid Coil	1996	—	62—74	—
EGR Temperature Sensor	1993—95	①	①	①
Engine Coolant Temperature Sensor	1993—96	5800	2400	300
Evaporative Emission Purge Solenoid Coil	1996	—	62—74	—
Injector	1993—96	—	13—16	—
Intake Air Temperature Sensor	1993—96	6000	2700	400
Motor Position Sensor	1993	4—6	4—6	4—6
Purge Control Solenoid	1993—95	—	36—44	—
Throttle Position Sensor	1993—96	3500—6500	3500—6500	3500—6500
LASER & TALON				
EGR Control Solenoid	1993—96	—	36—44	—

Continued

_E._SO ^ FUEL I._JECTO SPECIFICATIO._S-Continued

Component	Year	Resistance, Ohms		
		@ 32°F	@ 68°F	@ 176°F
LASER & TALON-CONTINUED				
EGR Temperature Sensor	1993—94	①	①	①
Engine Coolant Temperature Sensor	1993—94	—	2221—2269	264—328
	1995—96	5100—6500	2100—2700	260—360
Fuel Pressure Control Valve	1993	—	36—44	—
Fuel Pressure Solenoid	1995—96	—	36—44	—
Idle Air Control Motor Coil	1995—96	—	28—33	—
Idle Speed Control Motor Position Sensor	1993—94	4000—6000	4000—6000	4000—6000
Idle Speed Control Servo	1993—94	—	5—35	—
Injector	1993—94	—	13—16	—
	1995—96	—	2—3	—
Intake Air Temperature Sensor	1993—94	6000	2700	400
	1995—96	—	2300—3000	300—420
Purge Control Solenoid	1993—96	—	36—44	—
Resistor	1995—96	—	5.5—6.5	—
Throttle Position Sensor	1993—96	3500—6500	3500—6500	3500—6500
Turbocharger Wastegate Solenoid	1995—96	—	36—44	—

① —60,000—83,000 ohms resistance at 122°F; 11,000—14,000 ohms resistance at 212°F.

PRECAUTIONS
AIR BAG SYSTEMS

Refer to "Air Bag System Precautions" in the front of this manual for system disarming and arming procedures.

SYSTEM SERVICE PRECAUTIONS

Wear eye protection when servicing the fuel system. Do not smoke or allow open flame near fuel system components during fuel system service. Wrap shop towels around fuel line quick disconnect fittings before disconnecting them from the component being serviced. The shop towels will prevent fuel spillage.

FUEL SYSTEM PRESSURE RELIEF

To avoid personal injury and vehicle damage, it is necessary to relieve fuel system pressure prior to servicing any fuel-related component. Proceed as follows:
1. Disconnect fuel pump harness connector at fuel tank.
2. Start engine and run until it stops, then turn ignition switch to Off position.
3. Reconnect fuel pump harness connector.

DESCRIPTION

The electronic fuel injection system on these models is equipped with an on-board diagnostic system. This system utilizes test procedures which enable the technician to diagnose specific problems quickly using special tools and, in some cases, the vehicle's Malfunction Indicator Lamp (MIL).

TROUBLESHOOTING

Refer to wiring diagrams, **Figs. 1 through 19**, for fuel injection system circuits and connector and terminal identification.

COLT, COLT VISTA, LASER, SUMMIT, SUMMIT WAGON & 1993–94 TALON

Refer to **Figs. 20 through 29** for troubleshooting procedures.

1995–96 TALON

Refer to troubleshooting reference chart, **Fig. 30**, then proceed as directed to troubleshooting inspection procedures, **Figs. 31 through 62.**

DIAGNOSIS & TESTING
Visual Inspection

All diagnostic procedures must start with a visual inspection of the vehicle as follows:
1. Inspect all electrical connections and harnesses for damage, loose terminals or terminals that are pushed out of connectors.
2. Look for any added accessories that may affect normal operation of MPI system.
3. Ensure all vacuum lines are connected and are in good condition.
4. Ensure intake hoses and air cleaner housing are in place and secure for normal operation.
5. Battery must be fully charged. **Do not disconnect battery until all diagnostic trouble codes are retrieved from MPI system.**
6. The following items cannot be overlooked as possible driveability problems:
   a. Dirt buildup at throttle valve area.
   b. Proper engine timing.
   c. Proper engine vacuum.
   d. Proper engine valve timing.
   e. Proper engine compression.
   f. Proper idle speed.
   g. Restricted PCV system.
   h. Restricted exhaust system.
   i. Internal vacuum leaks at power brake booster.
   j. Incorrect fuel pressure.
7. Inspect fuel system components including fuel lines, fuel filter and fuel pump.
8. Inspect ignition system components including spark plugs, high tension cable, distributor or crank angle sensor and ignition coil.
9. Inspect emission control devices, including crankcase ventilation system and exhaust gas recirculation systems.

Accessing Diagnostic Trouble Codes

On **1993 models and 1994 Laser and Talon models,** diagnostic trouble codes may be accessed using a voltmeter or a DRB scan tool, or equivalent.

On **1994 Colt, Colt Vista, Summit and Summit Wagon models,** diagnostic trouble codes may be accessed using the vehicle's Malfunction Indicator Lamp (MIL) or a DRB scan tool, or equivalent.

On **1995 Summit and Summit Wagon models,** diagnostic trouble codes may be accessed using the vehicle's MIL or a DRB III scan tool, or equivalent.

On **1996 Summit and Summit Wagon models,** diagnostic trouble codes may be accessed using a Multi-Use Tester (MUT) or a general scan tool.

On **1995-96 Talon models,** diagnostic trouble codes may be accessed using a DRB III scan tool or a general scan tool.

USING VOLTMETER
1993 COLT, COLT VISTA, SUMMIT, SUMMIT WAGON & 1993–94 LASER & TALON

1. Place ignition switch in Off position.
2. Connect an analog voltmeter between on-board diagnostic output and ground terminals of white data link connector located under lefthand side of instrument panel, **Fig. 63.**

3. Turn ignition switch to On position.
4. Read and record diagnostic output pattern as indicated by voltmeter deflections. For example, two long pulses, followed by a pause and four brief pulses, indicates Diagnostic Trouble Code 24 is present.
5. Repair condition indicated. Refer to "Diagnostic Trouble Code Interpretation" for diagnostic trouble code meanings.
6. Erase diagnostic trouble codes as described under "Clearing Diagnostic Trouble Codes."
7. Recheck to ensure vehicle condition is corrected.

USING GENERAL SCAN TOOL OR MULTI-USE TESTER (MUT)

1995–96 TALON & 1996 SUMMIT & SUMMIT WAGON

1. Place ignition switch in Off position.
2. Connect diagnostic scan tool to data link connector, **Fig. 64**, located under lefthand side of instrument panel.
3. Plug power cord of scan tool into cigarette lighter receptacle.
4. Place ignition switch in On position.
5. Read and record diagnostic output.
6. Repair condition indicated. Refer to "Diagnostic Trouble Code Interpretation" for diagnostic trouble code meanings.
7. After repairs have been performed, turn ignition switch to Off position, then back to On position.
8. Erase diagnostic trouble codes as described under "Clearing Diagnostic Trouble Codes."
9. Recheck to ensure vehicle condition is corrected.

USING DIAGNOSTIC READOUT BOX (DRB II/III)

COLT, COLT VISTA, LASER, TALON & 1993–95 SUMMIT & SUMMIT WAGON

1. Connect DRB and MMC adapter to diagnostic connector, **Fig. 65**.
2. Once connected, DRB will perform a self-test. **Do not touch keypad during self-test.** If message "Ram Test Failure" is displayed, DRB is defective and must be repaired.
3. After self-test, identification logos will be displayed, then display will read "Select Model Year" with appropriate year displayed. Press Yes key.
4. The display will now read "Select System, Engine." Press Yes key. **From this point on, pressing No key will return display to previous screen.**
5. After a few seconds display will read "Select Engine." Press F1 or F2 key until engine to be tested is displayed, then press Yes key.
6. The display will now read "Select Certification, California." Press F1 or F2 key to select California or Federal standards, then press Yes key.
7. Read and record diagnostic trouble codes.

8. Repair condition indicated. Refer to "Diagnostic Trouble Code Interpretation" for diagnostic trouble code meanings.
9. Erase diagnostic trouble codes as described under "Clearing Diagnostic Trouble Codes."

USING MALFUNCTION INDICATOR LAMP (MIL)

1994 COLT & COLT VISTA & 1994–95 SUMMIT & SUMMIT WAGON

1. Using diagnostic trouble code check harness tool, ground terminal 1 of data link connector as shown, **Fig. 66**, then turn ignition switch to On position.
2. Read and record diagnostic output as indicated by MIL flashes, **Fig. 67**.
3. Repair condition indicated. Refer to "Diagnostic Trouble Code Interpretation" for diagnostic trouble code meanings.
4. Erase diagnostic trouble codes as described under "Clearing Diagnostic Trouble Codes."

Diagnostic Trouble Code Interpretation

Refer to **Figs. 68 through 75** for diagnostic trouble code interpretation.

Clearing Diagnostic Trouble Codes

Clearing diagnostic trouble codes can be accomplished by either selecting Erase Faults on the DRB or scan tool, or by disconnecting the battery ground cable for at least two minutes.

System & Component Diagnosis

When diagnosing system, always start with a thorough visual inspection. Refer to "Visual Inspection" procedures in this section. If a visual inspection does not reveal the cause of the vehicle's condition, proceed to "Accessing Diagnostic Trouble Codes." If any diagnostic trouble codes are present, proceed then to diagnostic trouble code interpretation charts, **Figs. 68 through 75**.

COLT, COLT VISTA, SUMMIT & SUMMIT WAGON

Each of the following diagnostic procedures corresponds to a specific harness inspection procedure. Refer to "Diagnostic Trouble Code Interpretation" to determine which procedures must be followed in response to specific diagnostic trouble codes; then, if necessary, refer to **Figs. 76 through 118** for harness inspections.

Fuel Pump Actuator Test

1. While cranking engine, grip fuel return hose between fingers; pulsation should be indicated.
2. Listen for fuel pump operation noise

near fuel tank; pump noise should be indicated during cranking.
3. If results are not as indicated, refer to **Figs. 76 and 77** for harness inspection.

Evaporative Emission Purge Solenoid Actuator Test

1. Turn ignition switch to On position to activate solenoid valve. Valve operating noise should be indicated during activation.
2. If results are not as indicated, refer to **Fig. 78** for harness inspection.

EGR Solenoid Actuator Test (Except 1993 w/Federal Emissions)

1. Turn ignition switch to On position to activate solenoid valve. Valve operating noise should be indicated during activation.
2. If results are not as indicated, refer to **Fig. 79** for harness inspection.

Oxygen Sensor & Front Heated Oxygen Sensor Voltage Test

1. Start engine. During warm-up, raise engine speed to 4,000 RPM, then decelerate abruptly and measure sensor voltage. Voltage should be 200 mV or lower.
2. Race engine abruptly, then measure sensor voltage. Voltage should be 600–1,000 mV.
3. Using sensor signal, check fuel/air mixture ratio and check control condition of engine control module. At 750 RPM (idle speed), voltage should be 400 mV or lower. At 2,000 RPM, voltage should be 600–1,000 mV.
4. If results are not as indicated, refer to **Figs. 80 through 84** for harness inspections.

Volume Air Flow Sensor Air Volume (Frequency) Test

1. Start engine and allow coolant to reach 176-203°F, then ensure all lights, accessories, and cooling fan are off.
2. Place manual transaxle in Neutral position or automatic in Park.
3. Measure frequency at sensor. Results should be as follows:
   a. **On models with 1.8L/4-110 engine,** frequency should be 23-49 Hz at idle.
   b. At 2,000 RPM, frequency should be 51-91 Hz.
   c. **On models with 2.4L/4-143 engine,** frequency should be 18-44 Hz at idle.
   d. At 2,000 RPM, frequency should be 43-83 Hz.
   e. **On all models,** frequency should increase proportionally when engine is raced abruptly.
4. If results are not as indicated, refer to **Fig. 85** for harness inspection.

Intake Air Temperature Sensor Temperature Test

1. With engine running or ignition switch in On position, measure intake air

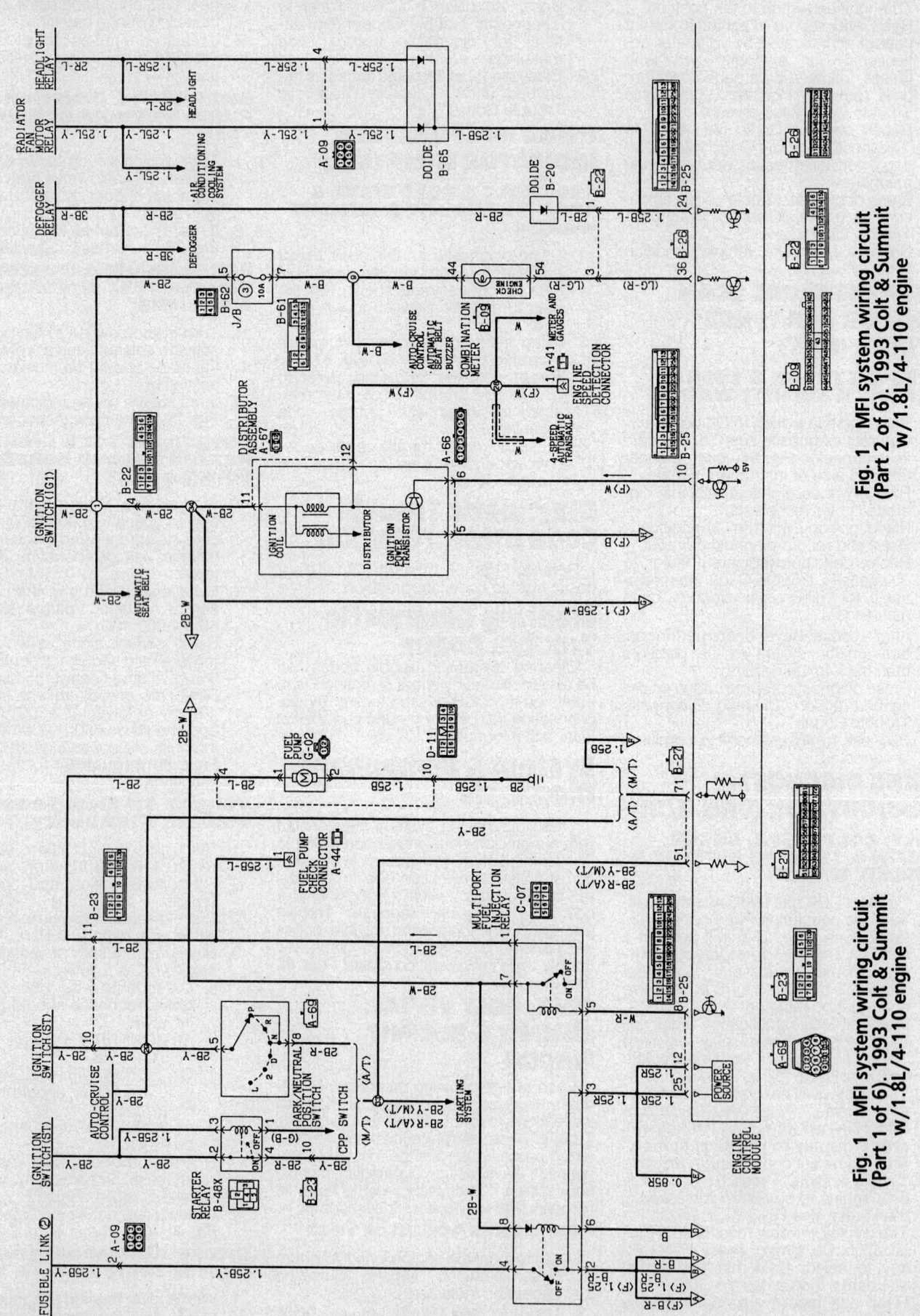

Fig. 1 MFI system wiring circuit (Part 2 of 6). 1993 Colt & Summit w/1.8L/4-110 engine

Fig. 1 MFI system wiring circuit (Part 1 of 6). 1993 Colt & Summit w/1.8L/4-110 engine

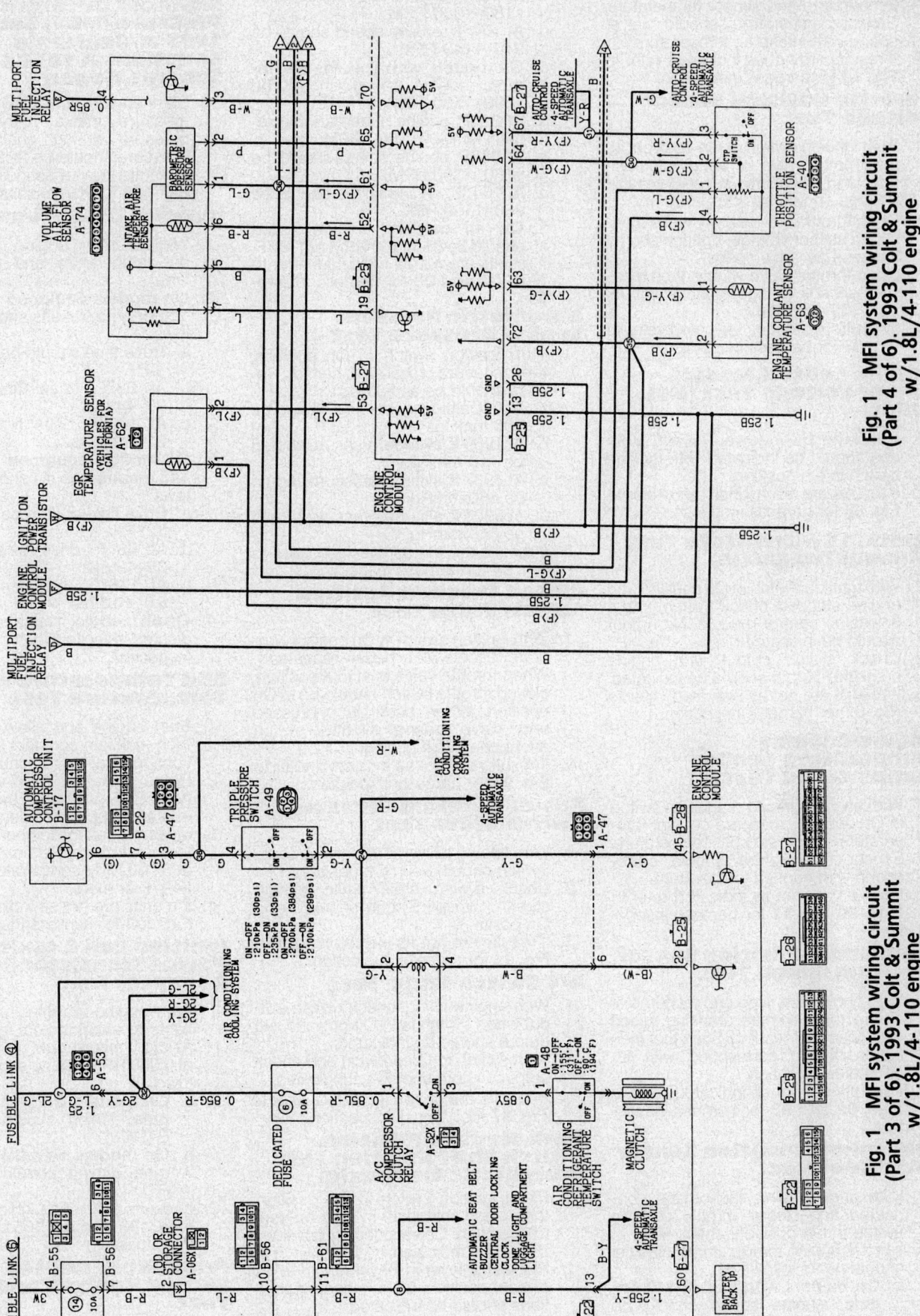

Fig. 1 MFI system wiring circuit (Part 4 of 6). 1993 Colt & Summit w/1.8L/4-110 engine

Fig. 1 MFI system wiring circuit (Part 3 of 6). 1993 Colt & Summit w/1.8L/4-110 engine

MULTI-POINT FUEL INJECTION (MODELS w/1.8L/4-107, 1.8L/4-110 & 2.4L/4-143 ENGINES, 1993-94 MODELS w/2.0L/4-122 ENGINE & 1995 TALON w/2.0L/4-122 TURBOCHARGED ENGINE)

7-5

temperature and sensor temperature. Sensor temperature should correspond with intake air temperature.

2. If results are not as indicated, refer to **Fig. 86** for harness inspection.

Throttle Position Sensor Voltage Test

1. With ignition switch in On position, allow throttle valve to rest at idle position and measure sensor voltage. Voltage should be 300-1,000 mV.
2. Open throttle valve slowly while measuring sensor voltage. Voltage should increase as valve opens.
3. Open throttle valve widely, then measure sensor voltage. Voltage should be 4,500-5,500 mV.
4. If results are not as indicated, refer to **Fig. 87** for harness inspection.

Engine Control Module Power Voltage Test (MFI Relay)

1. Check for ECM power voltage. Voltage should be indicated with ignition switch in On position.
2. If results are not as indicated, refer to **Fig. 88** for harness inspection.

Ignition Switch State Test (Manual Transaxle)

1. With ignition switch in On position and engine stopped, check switch output to engine control module. No output should be indicated.
2. Check switch output with engine cranking. Output should be indicated.
3. If results are not as indicated, refer to **Fig. 89** for harness inspection.

Engine Coolant Temperature Sensor Temperature Test

1. With engine running or ignition switch in On position, measure coolant temperature and sensor temperature. Sensor temperature should correspond with coolant temperature.
2. If results are not as indicated, refer to **Figs. 90 and 91** for harness inspection.

Crankshaft Position Sensor Cranking Speed Test

1. With engine cranking and tachometer connected, compare cranking speed with scan tool reading. Scan tool indication should correspond with tachometer indication.
2. If results are not as indicated, refer to **Figs. 92 and 93** for harness inspection.

Crankshaft Position Sensor Idle Speed Test

1. With engine idling, tachometer connected and closed throttle position switch in On position, check RPM at various engine temperatures. Results should be as follows:
   a. **On models with 1.8L/4-110 engine,** engine speed should be 1,460-1,660 RPM at -4°F.
   b. At 32°F, engine speed should be 1350-1550 RPM.

c. At 68°F, engine speed should be 1180-1380 RPM.
   d. At 104°F, engine speed should be 940-1140 RPM.
   e. **On models with 2.4L/4-143 engine,** engine speed should be 1300-1500 RPM at -4°F.
   f. At 32°F, engine speed should remain at 1300-1500 RPM.
   g. At 68°F, engine speed should be 1150-1350 RPM.
   h. At 104°F, engine speed should be 950-1150 RPM.
   i. **On all models,** engine speed should be 650-850 RPM at 176°F.
2. If results are not as indicated, refer to **Figs. 92 and 93** for harness inspection.

Barometric Pressure Sensor Pressure Test

1. Turn ignition switch to On position, then measure pressure at sensor. Results should be as follows:
   a. At 0 ft. altitude, pressure should be 760 mmHg.
   b. At 1969 ft. altitude, pressure should be 710 mmHg.
   c. At 3937 ft. altitude, pressure should be 660 mmHg.
   d. At 5906 ft. altitude, pressure should be 610 mmHg.
2. If results are not as specified, refer to **Fig. 94** for harness inspection.

Closed Throttle Position Switch State Test

1. With ignition switch in On position, operate accelerator pedal repeatedly. When throttle valve is at idle position, closed throttle switch should be in On position. When pedal is depressed and valve opens slightly, switch should be in Off position.
2. If results are not as indicated, refer to **Fig. 95** for harness inspection.

Power Steering Pressure Switch State Test

1. With engine idling, check switch state. Switch should be in Off position.
2. Check switch state while turning steering wheel. Switch should be in On position.
3. If results are not as indicated, refer to **Fig. 96** for harness inspection.

A/C Switch State Test

1. With engine idling, check switch output when switch is in Off position. No output should be indicated.
2. Turn switch to On position and check output. Output should be indicated.
3. If results are not as indicated, refer to **Fig. 97** for harness inspection.

Park/Neutral Position Switch Shift Position Test (Automatic Transaxle)

1. Place ignition switch in On position, then place shift lever in Park or Neutral position. Corresponding positions should be indicated.
2. Place shift lever in Reverse, Drive, "2" or Low position. Corresponding positions should be indicated.
3. If results are not as indicated, refer to **Figs. 98 and 99** for harness inspection.

Manifold Differential Pressure (MDP) Sensor Test 1995 w/California Emissions & 1996 Summit & Summit Wagon

1. Start engine and allow to idle, then measure intake manifold plenum pressure during engine warm-up. Pressure should be 22.3-35.7 kPa.
2. If results are not as indicated, refer to **Fig. 100** for harness inspection.

Injector Drive Time Test

1. While cranking engine, measure coolant temperature and injector drive time.
2. **On models equipped with 1.8L/4-110 engine,** results should be as follows:
   a. Drive time should be 16-20 ms at 32°F.
   b. At 68°F, drive time should be 36-44 ms.
   c. At 176°F, drive time should be 8.7-10.7 ms.
3. **On models equipped with 2.4L/4-143 engine,** results should be as follows:
   a. Drive time should be 17-21 ms at 32°F.
   b. At 68°F, drive time should be 35-43 ms.
   c. At 176°F, drive time should be 8.6-10.6 ms.
4. **On all models,** if results are not as indicated, refer to **Fig. 101** for harness inspection.

EGR Temperature Sensor Temperature Test

1. Start engine and allow to warm up, then maintain constant engine conditions for 2 or more minutes.
2. Remove green striped vacuum hose from EGR solenoid, then cap hose end and nipple on solenoid.
3. Measure sensor temperature. At idle, temperature should be 212°F or less; at 3,500 RPM, temperature should be 248°F or more.
4. If results are not as indicated, refer to **Fig. 102** for harness inspection.

Ignition Coil & Ignition Power Transistor (Ignition Advance) Test

1. With engine warming up, set timing lights to check actual ignition timing. At idle, timing should be 2-18° BTDC; at 2,000 RPM, timing should be as follows:
   a. **On models with 1.8L/4-110 engine,** timing should be 20-40° BTDC.
   b. **On models with 2.4L/4-143 engine,** timing should be 24-44° BTDC.
2. If results are not as indicated, refer to **Figs. 103 through 105** for harness inspections.

Front/Rear Heated Oxygen Sensor Heater Condition Test

1. Start engine and allow to warm up, then check heater. At 750 RPM, heater should be activated; at 5,000 RPM,

heater should not be activated.
2. If results are not as indicated, refer to Fig. 81 for harness inspection.

A/C Compressor Clutch Relay State Test

1. Start engine and allow to warm up, then check compressor clutch operation with engine at idle. With A/C switch in Off position, clutch should not be activated; with switch in On position, clutch should be activated.
2. If results are not as indicated, refer to Fig. 97 for harness inspection.

IAC Valve Position Step Test

On vehicles with less than 300 miles, IAC valve position may exceed specification by approximately 20 steps.
1. Start engine and allow coolant temperature to reach 176-203°F, then ensure lights, accessories, and cooling fan are off.
2. Place transaxle in Neutral position. Closed throttle position switch should be activated, and engine should be at idle.
3. Note IAC valve position step. With A/C switch in Off position, valve position should be 2-20 steps. When A/C switch is turned to On position, valve position should increase from 8-50 steps.
4. Place A/C switch in Off position, then place transaxle in Drive position. IAC valve position should increase from 3-40 steps.
5. If results are not as indicated, refer to Fig. 106 for harness inspection.

Rear Heated Oxygen Sensor Voltage Test

1. **On models with manual transaxle,** drive vehicle in second gear with throttle wide open until engine speed reaches 3,500 RPM. **Do so in a safe, open area in which all traffic laws can be observed.**
2. **On models with automatic transaxle,** drive vehicle in low gear ("L" range) with throttle wide open until engine speed reaches 3,500 RPM. **Do so in a safe, open area in which all traffic laws can be observed.**
3. **On all models,** measure sensor voltage. Voltage should be 600-1,000 mV with engine at 3,500 RPM.
4. If results are not as indicated, refer to Fig. 81 for harness inspection.

Engine Control Module Power Ground Test

Refer to **Fig. 107** for engine control module power ground harness inspection.

Camshaft Position Sensor Test

Refer to **Figs. 108 and 109** for camshaft position sensor harness inspection.

Vehicle Speed Sensor Test

Refer to **Fig. 110** for vehicle speed sensor harness inspection.

Fan Motor Relay & Air Conditioning Refrigerant Medium Pressure Switch Test

Refer to **Figs. 111 through 113** for fan motor relay and air conditioning refrigerant medium pressure switch harness inspection.

Transaxle Failure Signal Test

Refer to **Figs. 114 and 115** for transaxle failure signal harness inspections.

Idle Air Control Motor Test

Refer to **Fig. 116** for idle air control motor harness inspection.

Engine & Transaxle Total Control Signal Test

Refer to **Figs. 117 and 118** for engine/transaxle total control signal harness inspections.

1993–94 LASER & TALON

Each of the following diagnostic procedures corresponds to a specific harness inspection procedure. Refer to "Diagnostic Trouble Code Interpretation" to determine which procedures must be followed in response to specific diagnostic trouble codes; then, if necessary, refer to **Figs. 119 through 159** for harness inspections.

Fuel Pump Actuator Test

1. While cranking engine, grip fuel return hose between fingers; pulsation should be indicated.
2. Listen for fuel pump operation noise near fuel tank; pump noise should be indicated during cranking.
3. If results are not as indicated, refer to **Figs. 119 and 120** for harness inspection.

Evaporative Emission Purge Solenoid Actuator Test

1. Turn ignition switch to On position to activate solenoid valve. Valve operating noise should be indicated during activation.
2. If results are not as indicated, refer to **Fig. 121** for harness inspection.

Fuel Pressure Solenoid Off/On Test

1. Turn ignition switch to On position. Solenoid operating sound should be heard.
2. If results are not as indicated, refer to **Fig. 122** for harness inspection.

EGR Solenoid Actuator Test (California)

1. Turn ignition switch to On position to activate solenoid valve. Valve operating noise should be indicated during activation.
2. If results are not as indicated, refer to **Fig. 123** for harness inspection.

Oxygen Sensor & Heated Oxygen Sensor Voltage Test

1. Start engine. During warm-up, raise engine speed to 4,000 RPM, then de-

celerate abruptly and measure sensor voltage. Voltage should be 200 mV or lower.
2. Race engine abruptly, then measure sensor voltage. Voltage should be 600-1,000 mV.
3. Using sensor signal, check fuel/air mixture ratio and check control condition of engine control module. At idle, voltage should be 400 mV or lower. At 2,000 RPM, voltage should be 600-1,000 mV.
4. If results are not as indicated, refer to **Figs. 124 and 125** for harness inspection.

Volume Air Flow Sensor Air Volume (Frequency) Test

1. Start engine and allow coolant to reach 176-203°F, then ensure all lights, accessories, and cooling fan are off.
2. Place manual transaxle in Neutral position or automatic in Park.
3. Measure frequency at sensor. Results should be as follows:
   a. **On models with 1.8L/4-107 engine,** frequency should be 25-40 Hz at idle.
   b. At 2,000 RPM, frequency should be 67-88 Hz.
   c. **On models with 2.0L/4-122 engine,** frequency should be 25-50 Hz at idle.
   d. **On models with 2.0L/4-122 turbocharged engine,** frequency should be 60-85 Hz at 2,000 RPM.
   e. **On models with 2.0L/4-122 non-turbocharged engine,** frequency should be 70-90 Hz at 2,000 RPM.
   f. **On all models,** frequency should increase proportionally when engine is raced abruptly.
4. If results are not as indicated, refer to **Figs. 126 and 127** for harness inspection.

Intake Air Temperature Sensor Temperature Test

1. With engine running or ignition switch in On position, measure intake air temperature and sensor temperature. Sensor temperature should correspond with intake air temperature.
2. If results are not as indicated, refer to **Figs. 128 and 129** for harness inspection.

Throttle Position Sensor Voltage Test

1. Turn ignition switch to On position.
2. **On models with 1.8L/4-107 engine,** leave switch in On position for 15 seconds or more.
3. **On all models,** allow throttle valve to rest at idle position and measure sensor voltage. Voltage should be 480-520 mV.
4. Open throttle valve slowly while measuring sensor voltage. Voltage should increase as valve opens.
5. Open throttle valve widely, then measure sensor voltage. Voltage should be 4,500-5,500 mV.
6. If results are not as indicated, refer to **Figs. 130 and 131** for harness inspection.

Continued on page 7-23

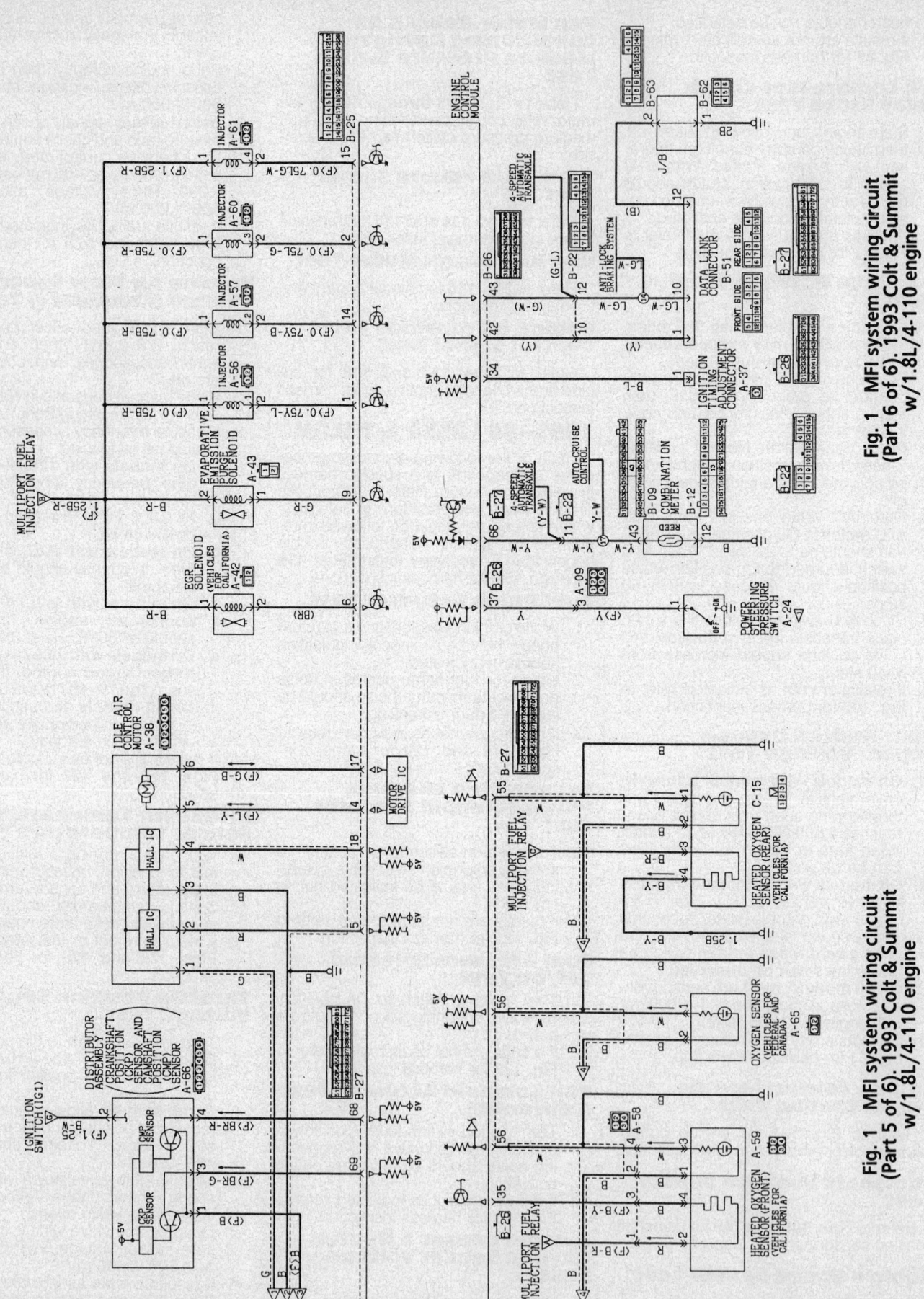

Fig. 1 MFI system wiring circuit (Part 6 of 6). 1993 Colt & Summit w/1.8L/4-110 engine

Fig. 1 MFI system wiring circuit (Part 5 of 6). 1993 Colt & Summit w/1.8L/4-110 engine

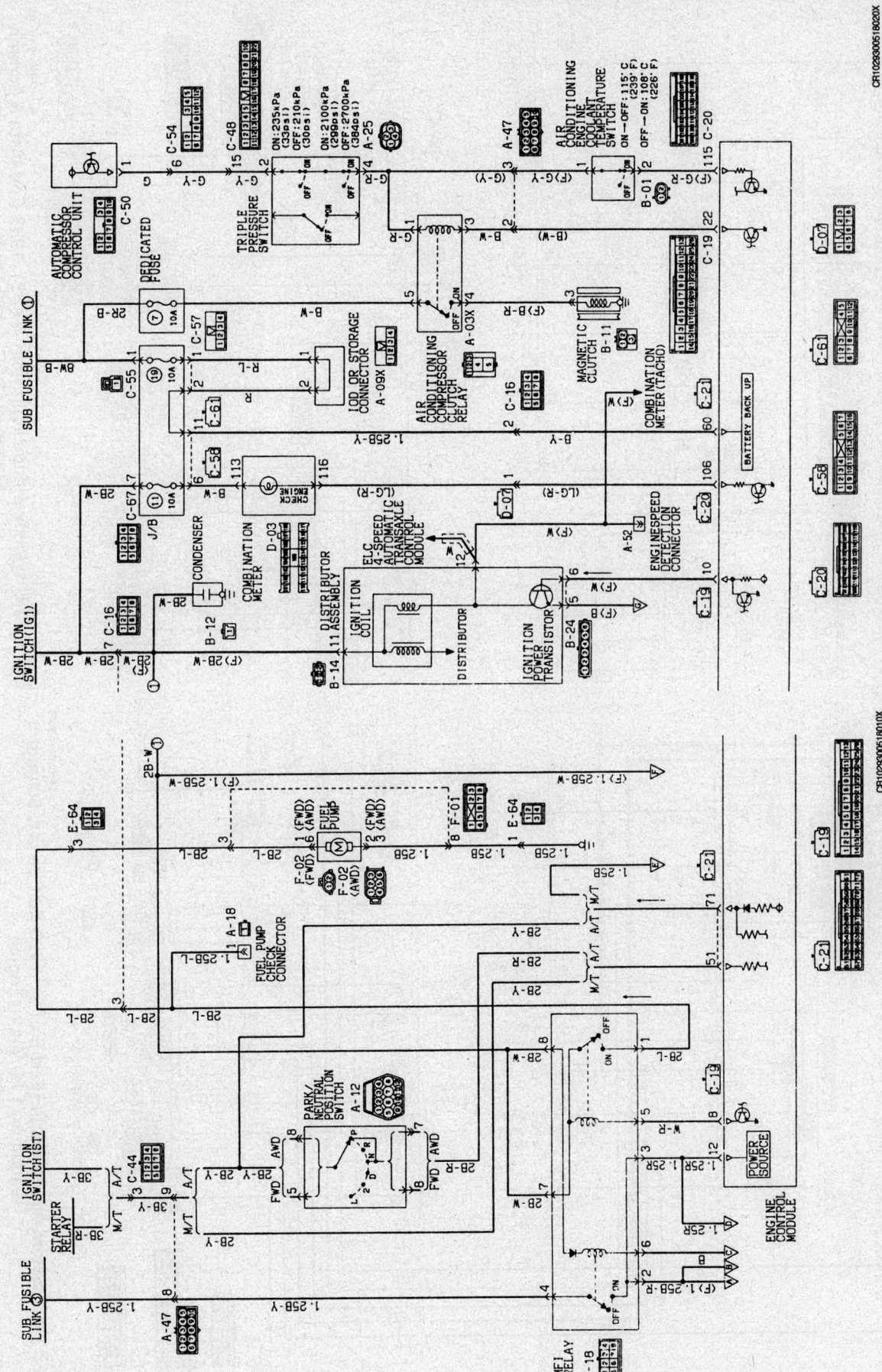

Fig. 2 MFI system wiring circuit (Part 2 of 5). 1993 Colt Vista & Summit Wagon w/1.8L/4-110 Engine

Fig. 2 MFI system wiring circuit (Part 1 of 5). 1993 Colt Vista & Summit Wagon w/1.8L/4-110 Engine

MULTI-POINT FUEL INJECTION (MODELS w/1.8L/4-107, 1.8L/4-110 & 2.4L/4-143 ENGINES, 1993-94 MODELS w/2.0L/4-122 ENGINE & 1995 TALON w/2.0L/4-122 TURBOCHARGED ENGINE)

7-9

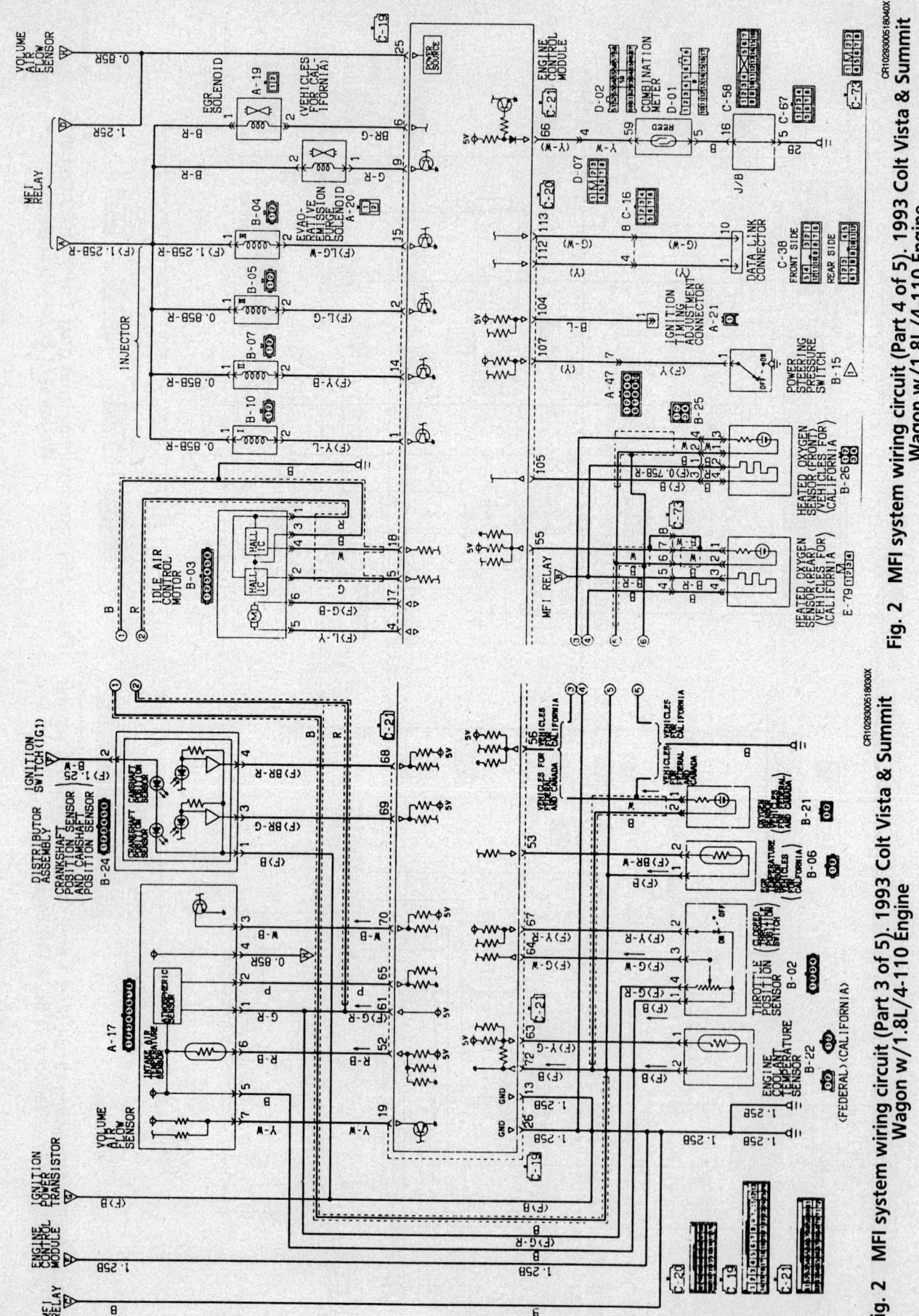

Fig. 2 MFI system wiring circuit (Part 4 of 5). 1993 Colt Vista & Summit Wagon w/1.8L/4-110 Engine

Fig. 2 MFI system wiring circuit (Part 3 of 5). 1993 Colt Vista & Summit Wagon w/1.8L/4-110 Engine

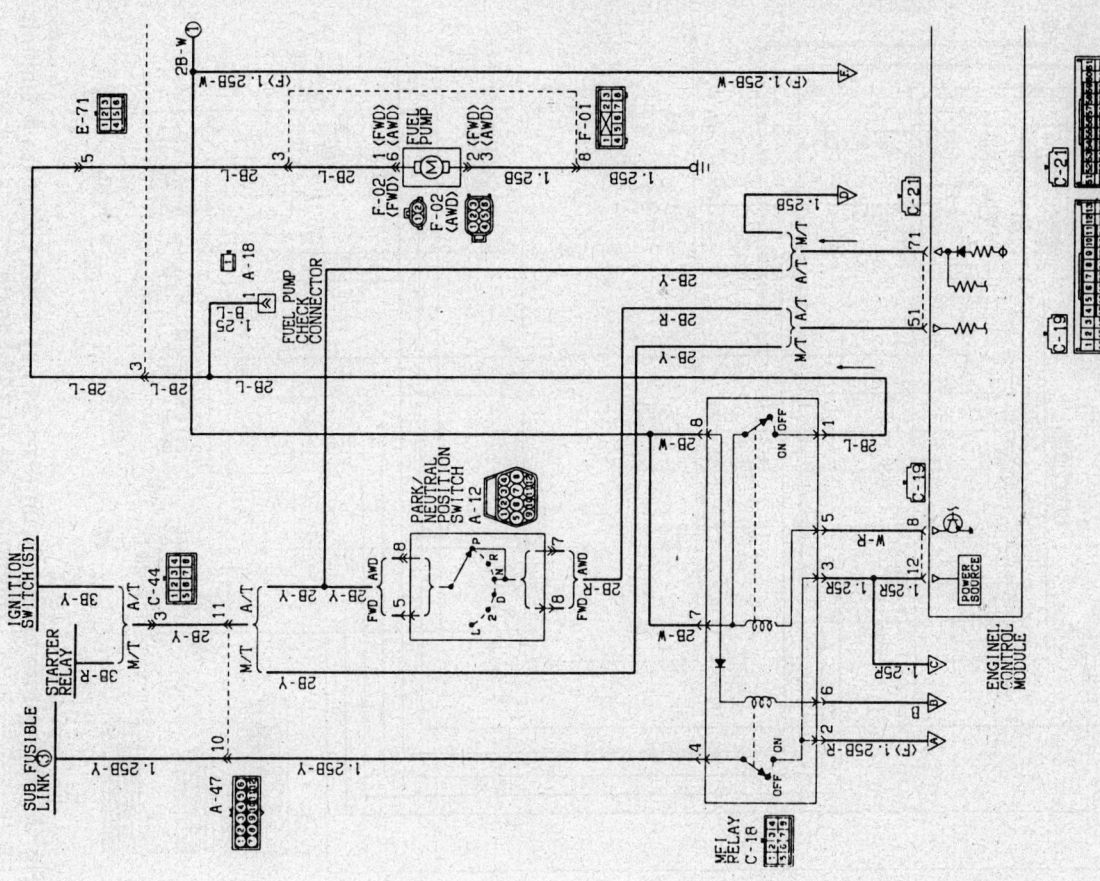

Fig. 3 MFI system wiring circuit (Part 1 of 5). 1993 Colt Vista & Summit Wagon w/2.4L/4-143 Engine

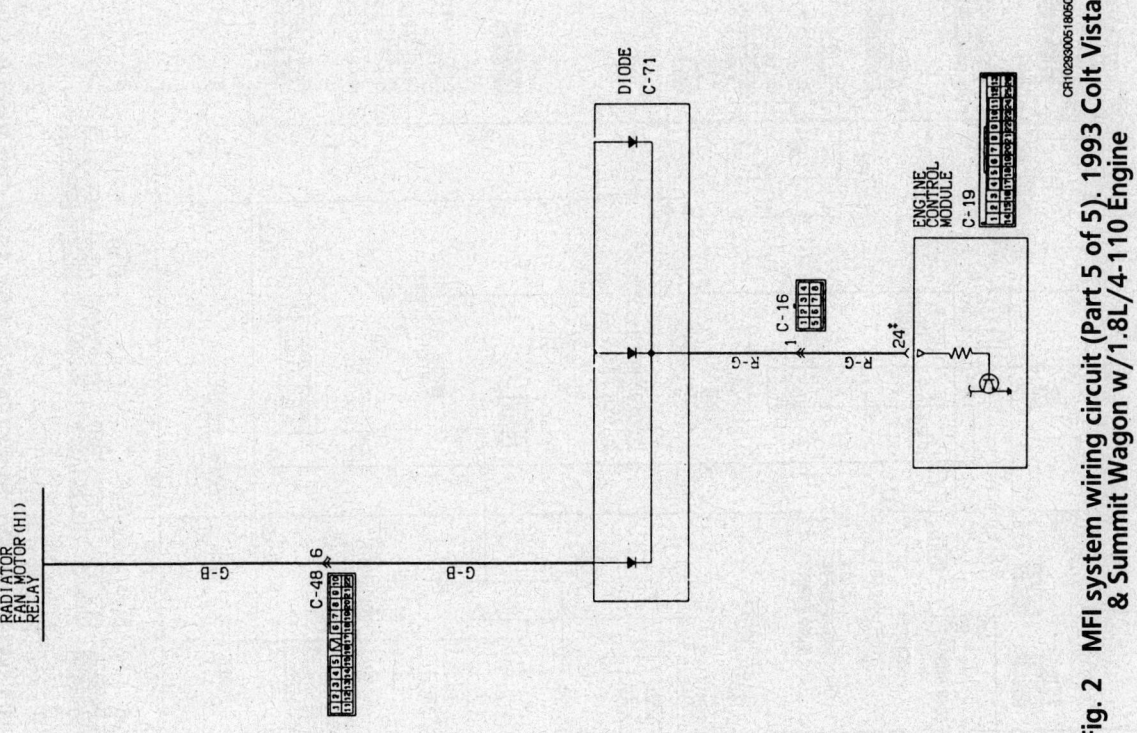

Fig. 2 MFI system wiring circuit (Part 5 of 5). 1993 Colt Vista & Summit Wagon w/1.8L/4-110 Engine

MULTI-POINT FUEL INJECTION (MODELS w/1.8L/4-107, 1.8L/4-110 & 2.4L/4-143 ENGINES, 1993-94 MODELS w/2.0L/4-122 ENGINE & 1995 TALON w/2.0L/4-122 TURBOCHARGED ENGINE)

7-11

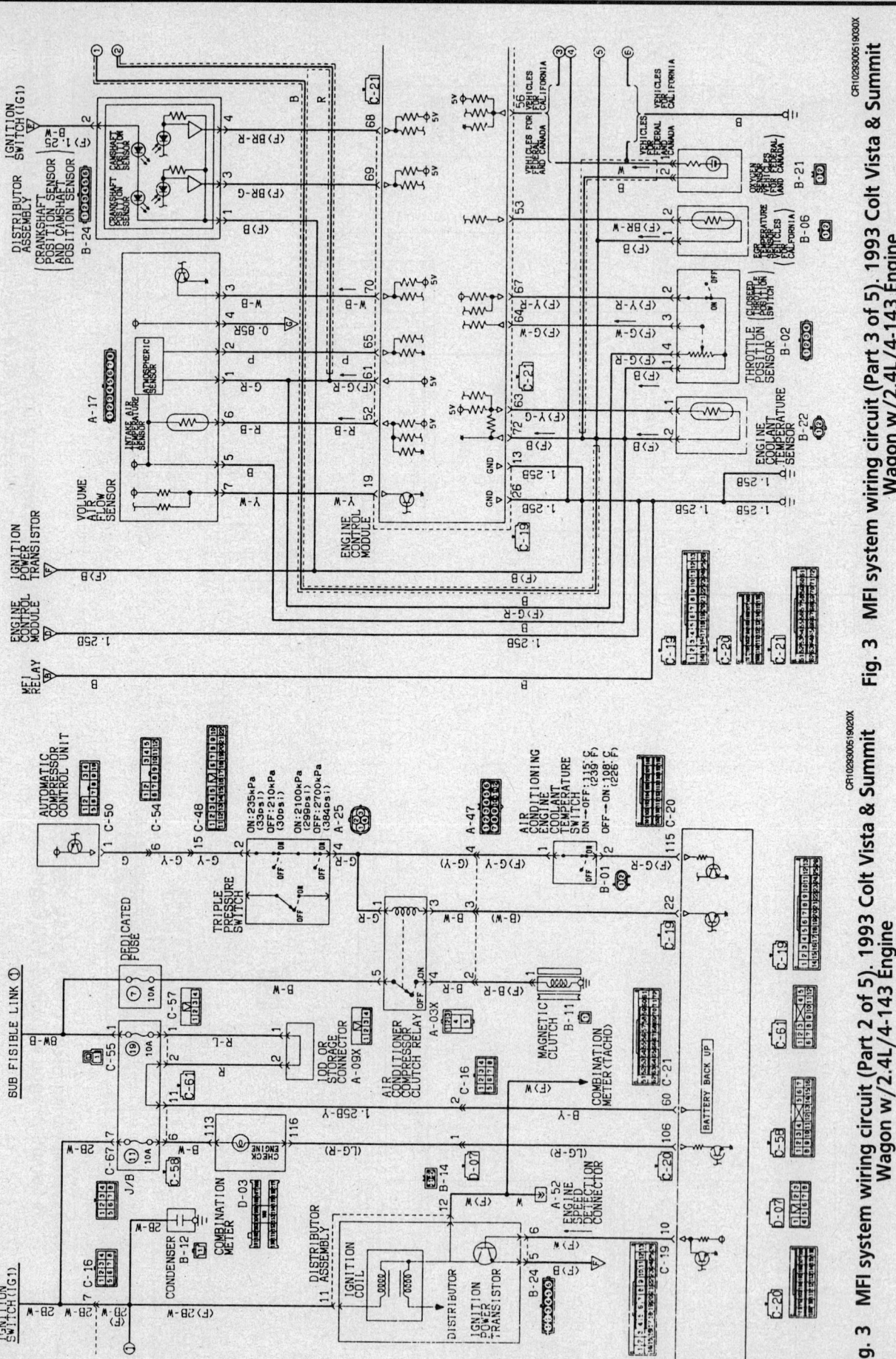

Fig. 3   MFI system wiring circuit (Part 3 of 5). 1993 Colt Vista & Summit Wagon w/2.4L/4-143 Engine

Fig. 3   MFI system wiring circuit (Part 2 of 5). 1993 Colt Vista & Summit Wagon w/2.4L/4-143 Engine

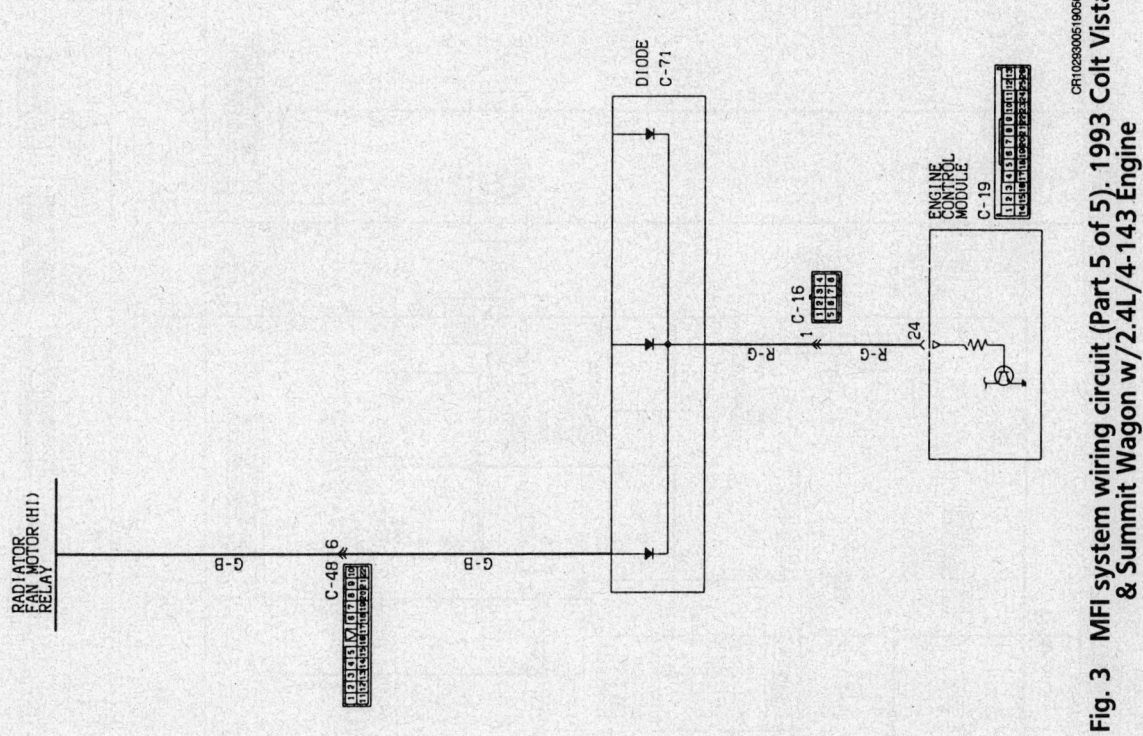

Fig. 3 MFI system wiring circuit (Part 5 of 5). 1993 Colt Vista & Summit Wagon w/2.4L/4-143 Engine

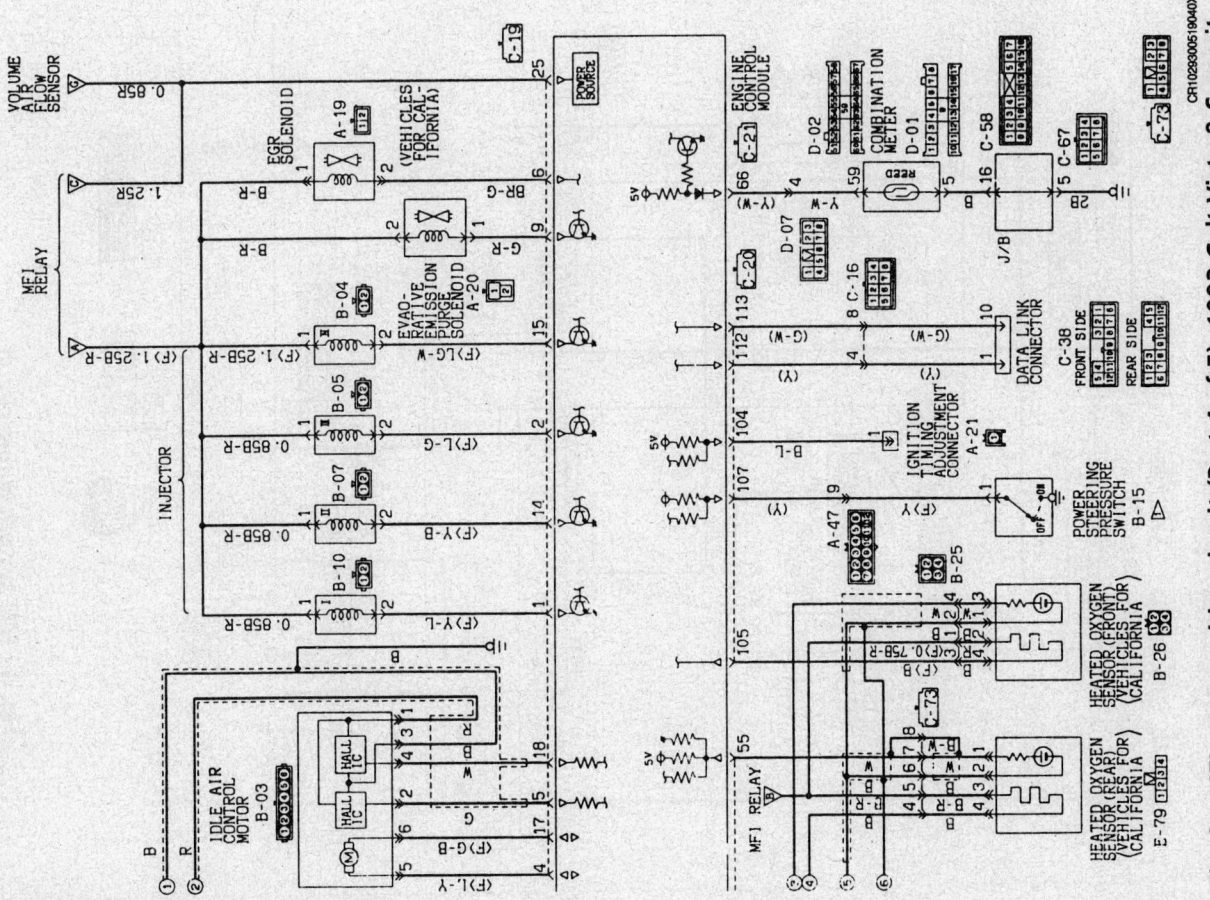

Fig. 3 MFI system wiring circuit (Part 4 of 5). 1993 Colt Vista & Summit Wagon w/2.4L/4-143 Engine

MULTI-POINT FUEL INJECTION (MODELS w/1.8L/4-107, 1.8L/4-110 & 2.4L/4-143 ENGINES, 1993-94 MODELS w/2.0L/4-122 ENGINE & 1995 TALON w/2.0L/4-122 TURBOCHARGED ENGINE)

7-13

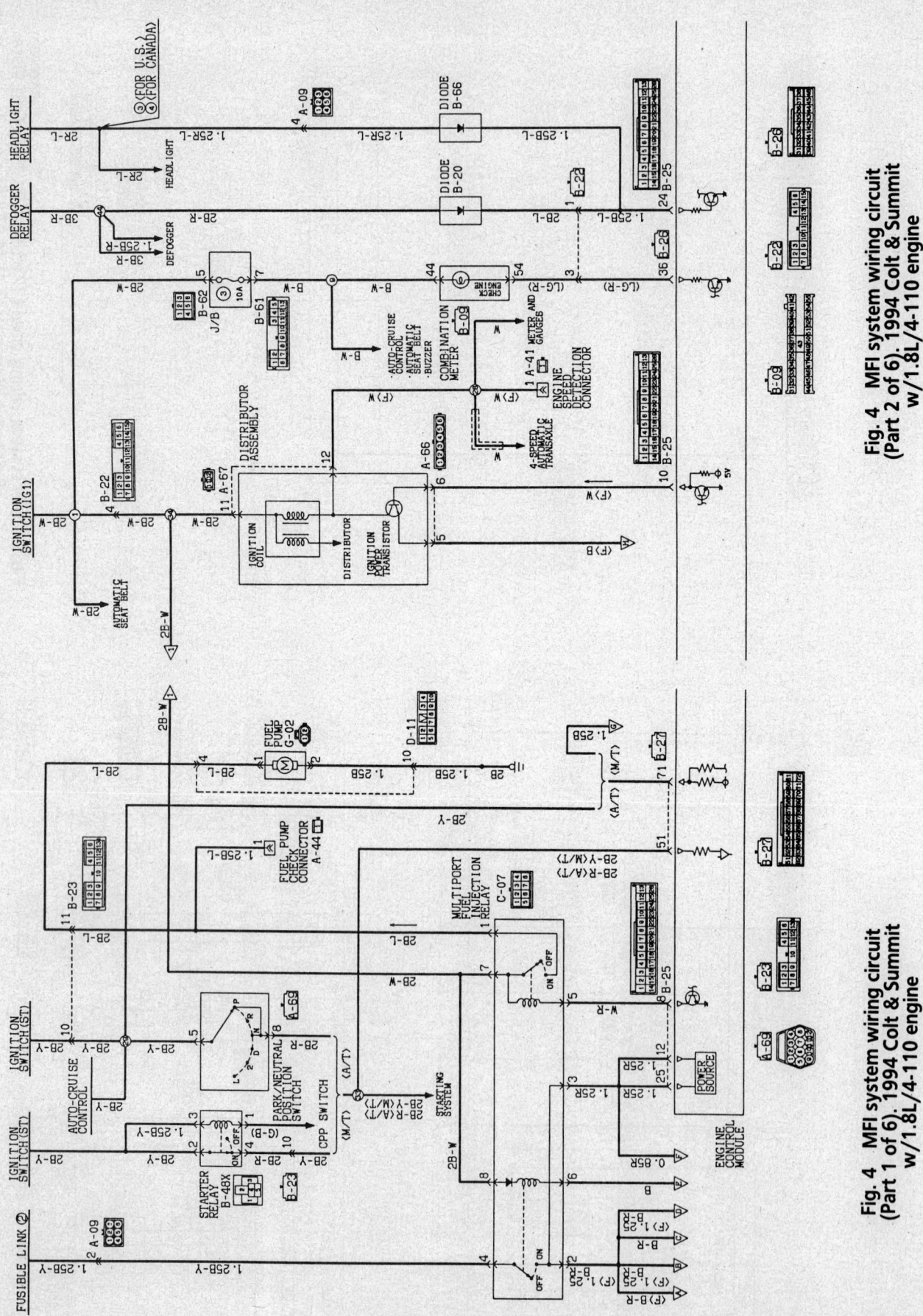

Fig. 4 MFI system wiring circuit (Part 2 of 6). 1994 Colt & Summit w/1.8L/4-110 engine

Fig. 4 MFI system wiring circuit (Part 1 of 6). 1994 Colt & Summit w/1.8L/4-110 engine

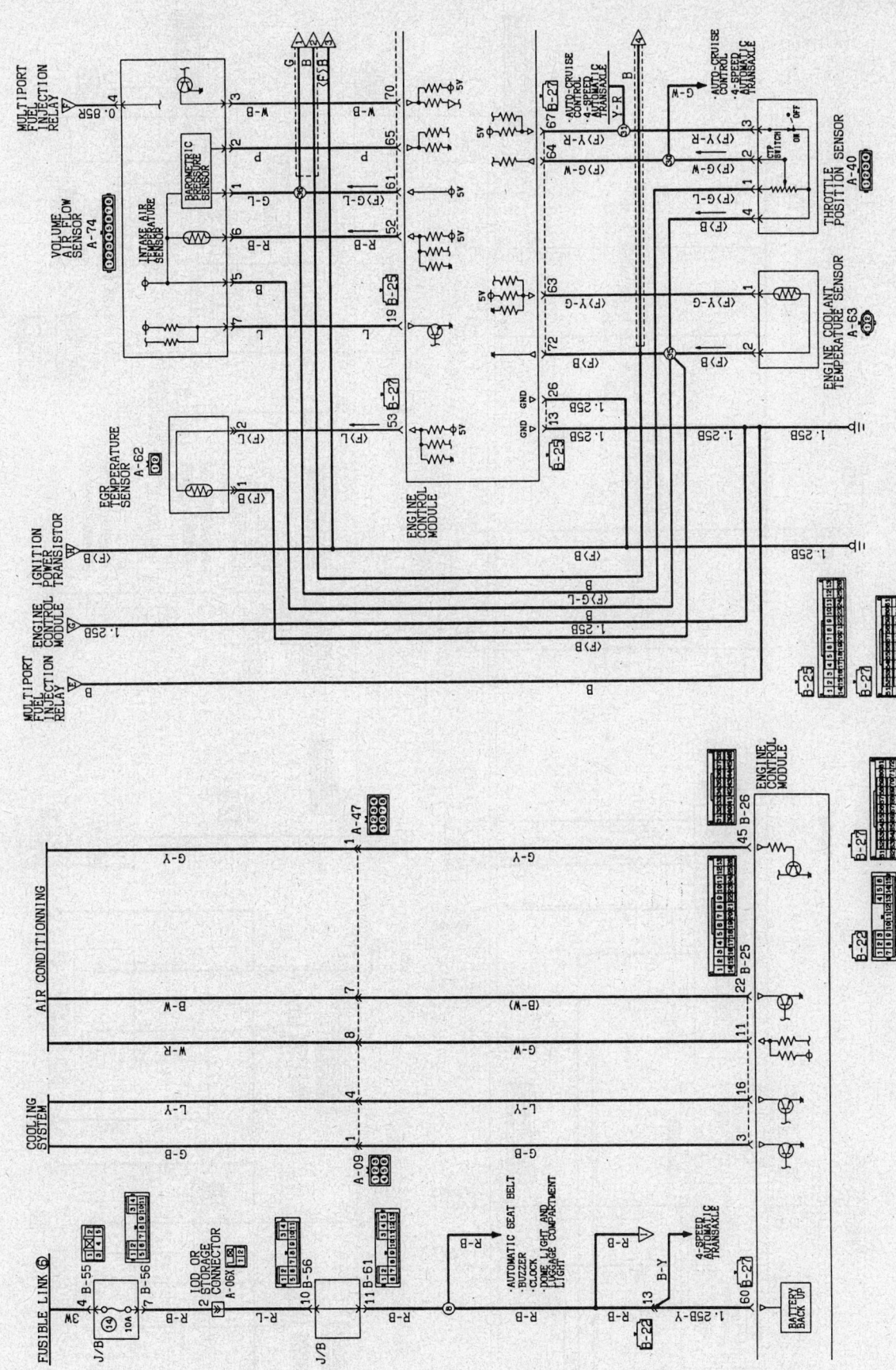

Fig. 4 MFI system wiring circuit (Part 4 of 6). 1994 Colt & Summit w/1.8L/4-110 engine

Fig. 4 MFI system wiring circuit (Part 3 of 6). 1994 Colt & Summit w/1.8L/4-110 engine

MULTI-POINT FUEL INJECTION (MODELS w/1.8L/4-107, 1.8L/4-110 & 2.4L/4-143 ENGINES, 1993-94 MODELS w/2.0L/4-122 ENGINE & 1995 TALON w/2.0L/4-122 TURBOCHARGED ENGINE)

7-15

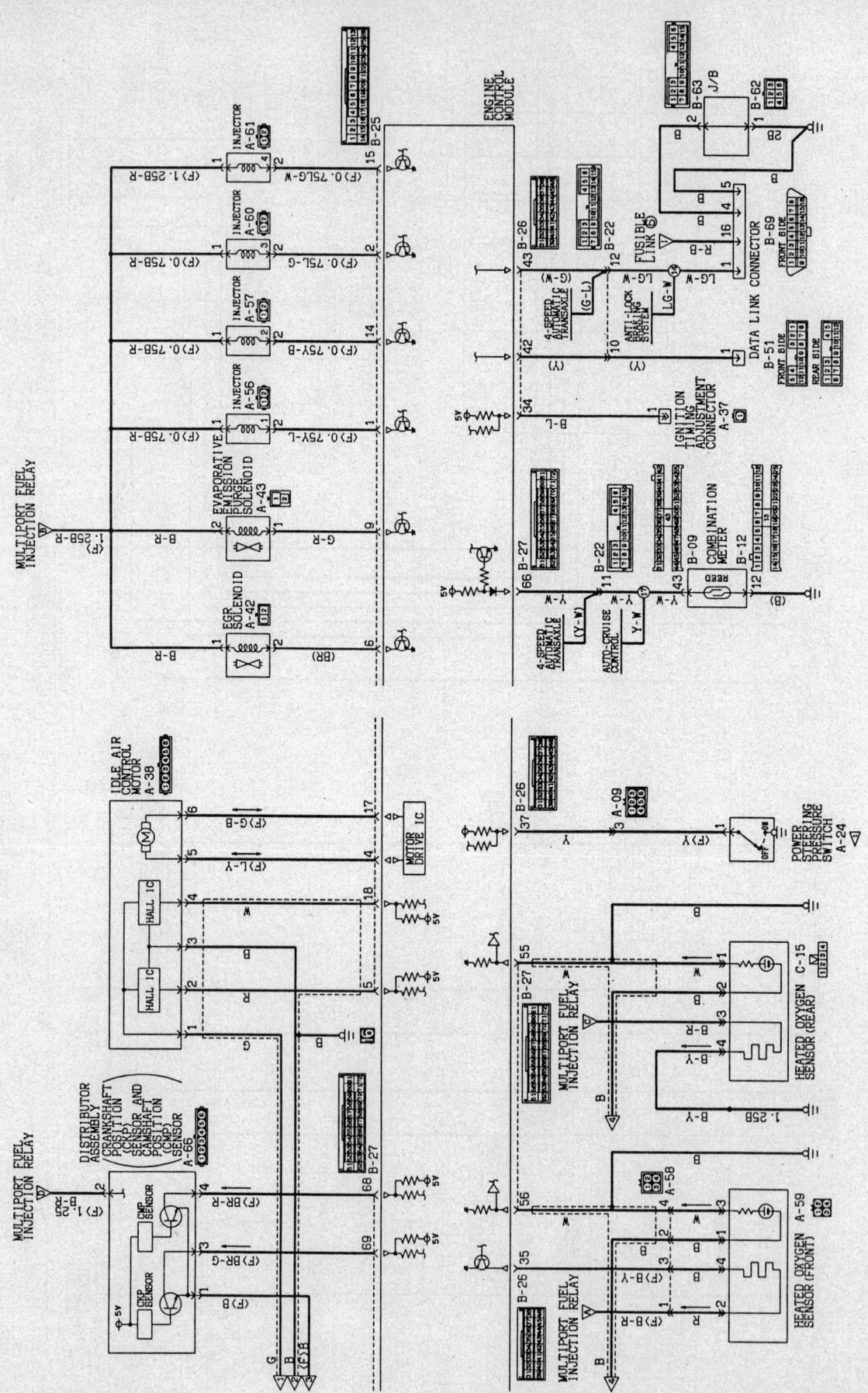

Fig. 4 MFI system wiring circuit (Part 6 of 6). 1994 Colt & Summit w/1.8L/4-110 engine

Fig. 4 MFI system wiring circuit (Part 5 of 6). 1994 Colt & Summit w/1.8L/4-110 engine

MULTI-POINT FUEL INJECTION (MODELS w/1.8L/4-107, 1.8L/4-110 & 2.4L/4-143 ENGINES, 1993-94 MODELS w/2.0L/4-122 ENGINE & 1995 TALON w/2.0L/4-122 TURBOCHARGED ENGINE)

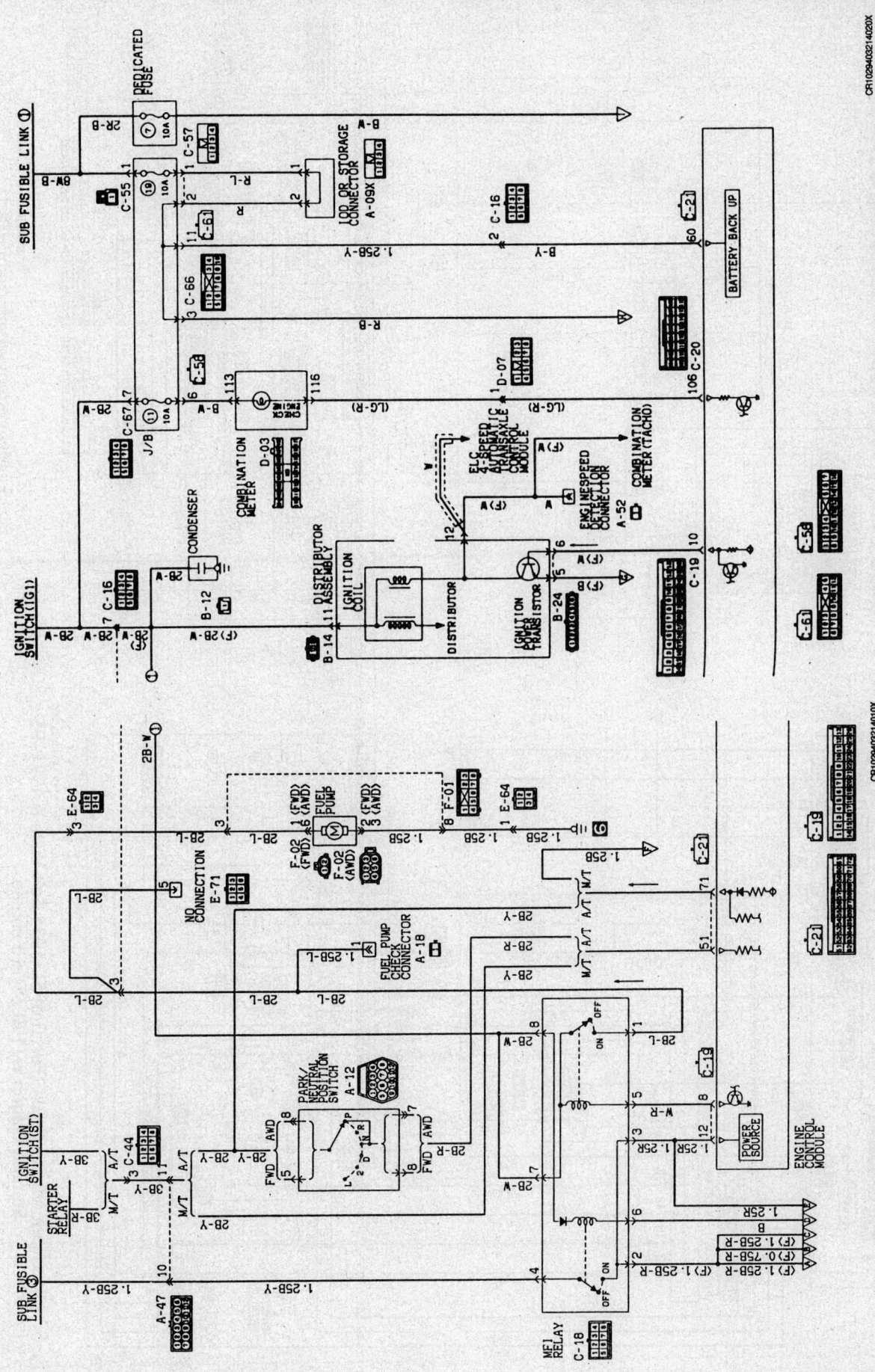

Fig. 5   MFI system wiring circuit (Part 2 of 5). 1994 Colt Vista & 1994–95 Summit Wagon w/1.8L/4-110 engine

Fig. 5   MFI system wiring circuit (Part 1 of 5). 1994 Colt Vista & 1994–95 Summit Wagon w/1.8L/4-110 engine

MULTI-POINT FUEL INJECTION (MODELS w/1.8L/4-107, 1.8L/4-110 & 2.4L/4-143 ENGINES, 1993-94 MODELS w/2.0L/4-122 ENGINE & 1995 TALON w/2.0L/4-122 TURBOCHARGED ENGINE)

7-17

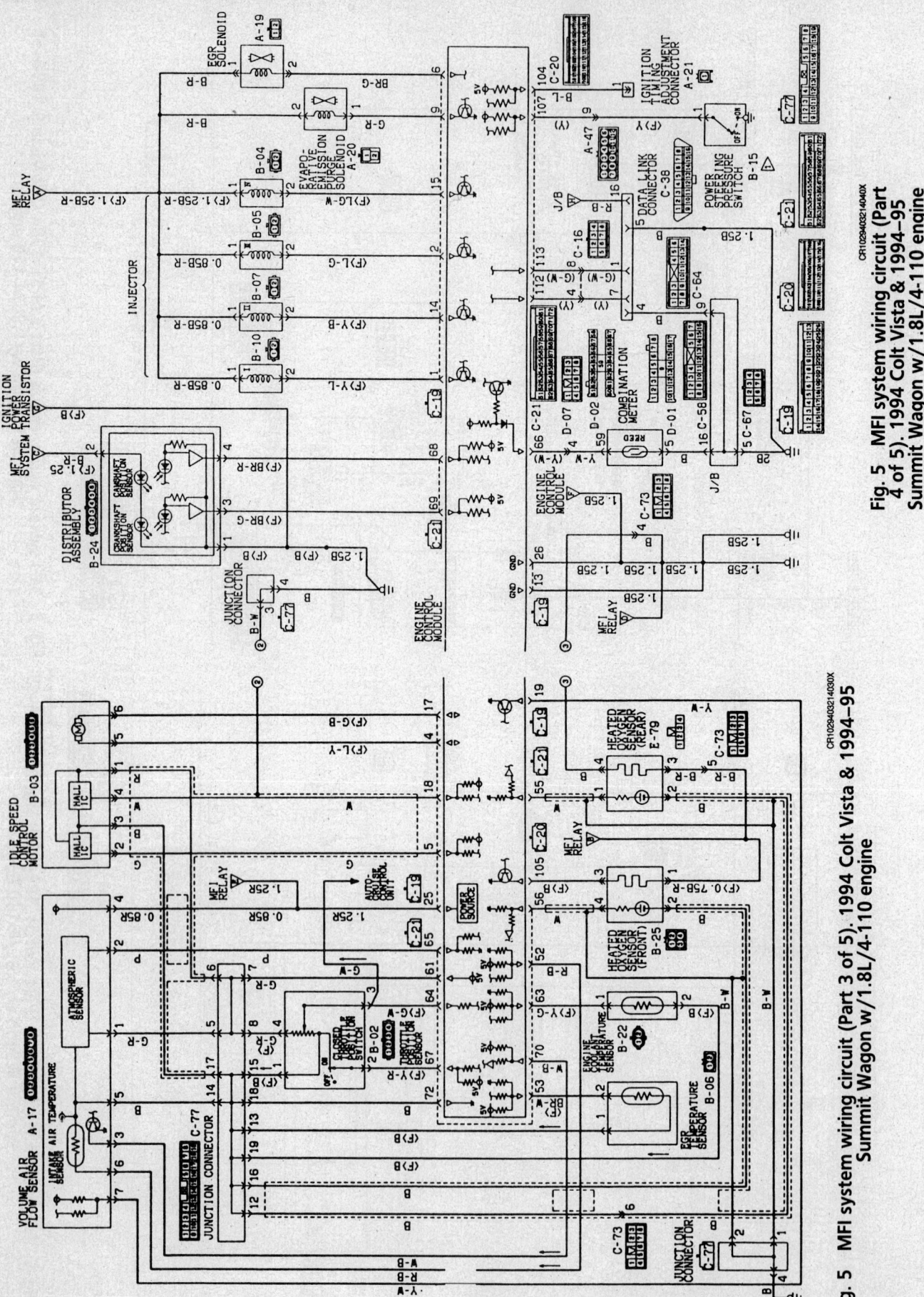

Fig. 5 MFI system wiring circuit (Part 4 of 5). 1994 Colt Vista & 1994–95 Summit Wagon w/1.8L/4-110 engine

Fig. 5 MFI system wiring circuit (Part 3 of 5). 1994 Colt Vista & 1994–95 Summit Wagon w/1.8L/4-110 engine

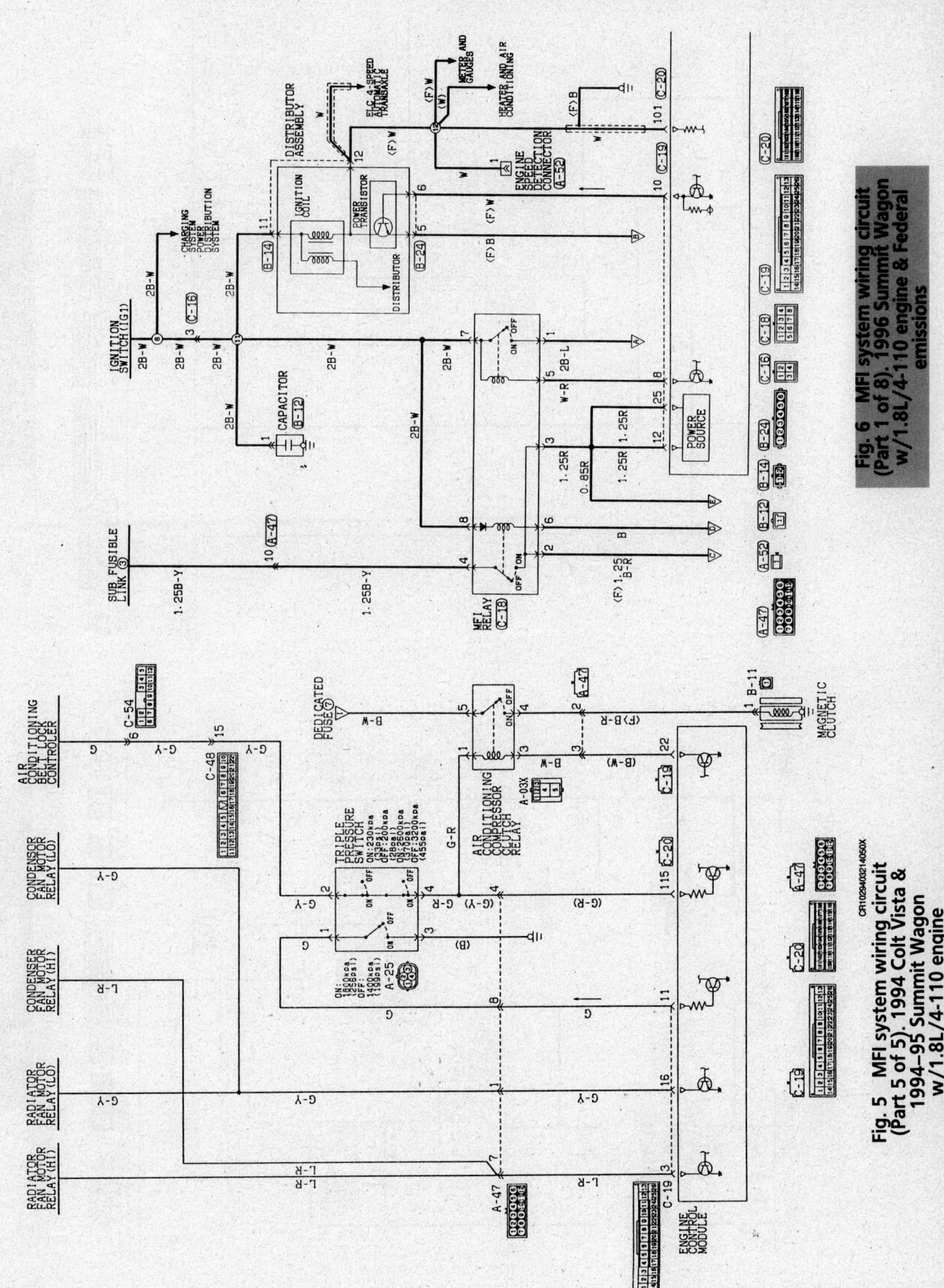

Fig. 6 MFI system wiring circuit (Part 1 of 8). 1996 Summit Wagon w/1.8L/4-110 engine & Federal emissions

Fig. 5 MFI system wiring circuit (Part 5 of 5). 1994 Colt Vista & 1994–95 Summit Wagon w/1.8L/4-110 engine

MULTI-POINT FUEL INJECTION (MODELS w/1.8L/4-107, 1.8L/4-110 & 2.4L/4-143 ENGINES, 1993-94 MODELS w/2.0L/4-122 ENGINE & 1995 TALON w/2.0L/4-122 TURBOCHARGED ENGINE)

7-19

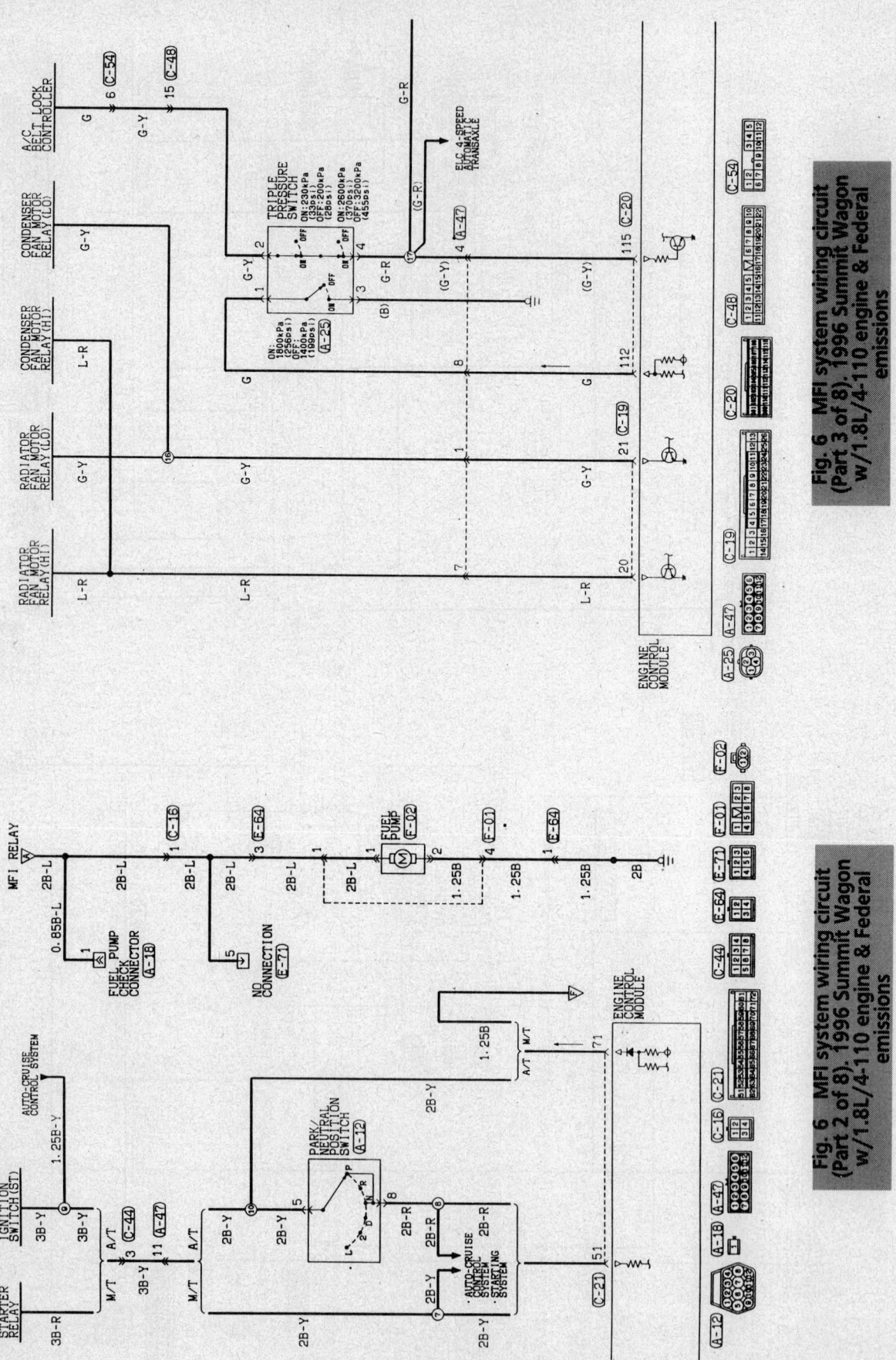

Fig. 6 MFI system wiring circuit (Part 3 of 8). 1996 Summit Wagon w/1.8L/4-110 engine & Federal emissions

Fig. 6 MFI system wiring circuit (Part 2 of 8). 1996 Summit Wagon w/1.8L/4-110 engine & Federal emissions

7-20

MULTI-POINT FUEL INJECTION (MODELS w/1.8L/4-107, 1.8L/4-110 & 2.4L/4-143 ENGINES, 1993-94 MODELS w/2.0L/4-122 ENGINE & 1995 TALON w/2.0L/4-122 TURBOCHARGED ENGINE)

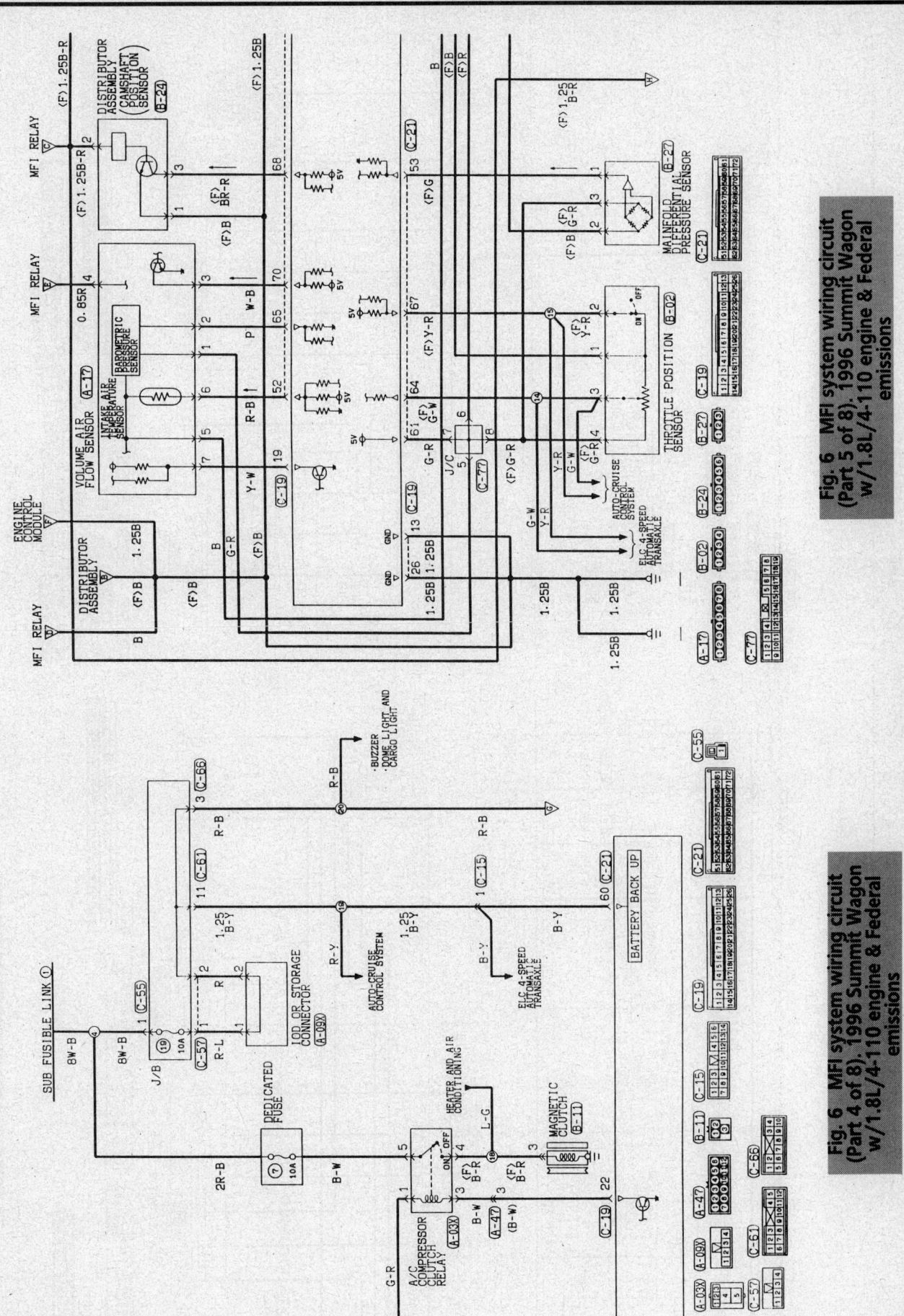

Fig. 6 MFI system wiring circuit (Part 5 of 8), 1996 Summit Wagon w/1.8L/4-110 engine & Federal emissions

Fig. 6 MFI system wiring circuit (Part 4 of 8), 1996 Summit Wagon w/1.8L/4-110 engine & Federal emissions

MULTI-POINT FUEL INJECTION (MODELS w/1.8L/4-107, 1.8L/4-110 & 2.4L/4-143 ENGINES, 1993-94 MODELS w/2.0L/4-122 ENGINE & 1995 TALON w/2.0L/4-122 TURBOCHARGED ENGINE)

7-21

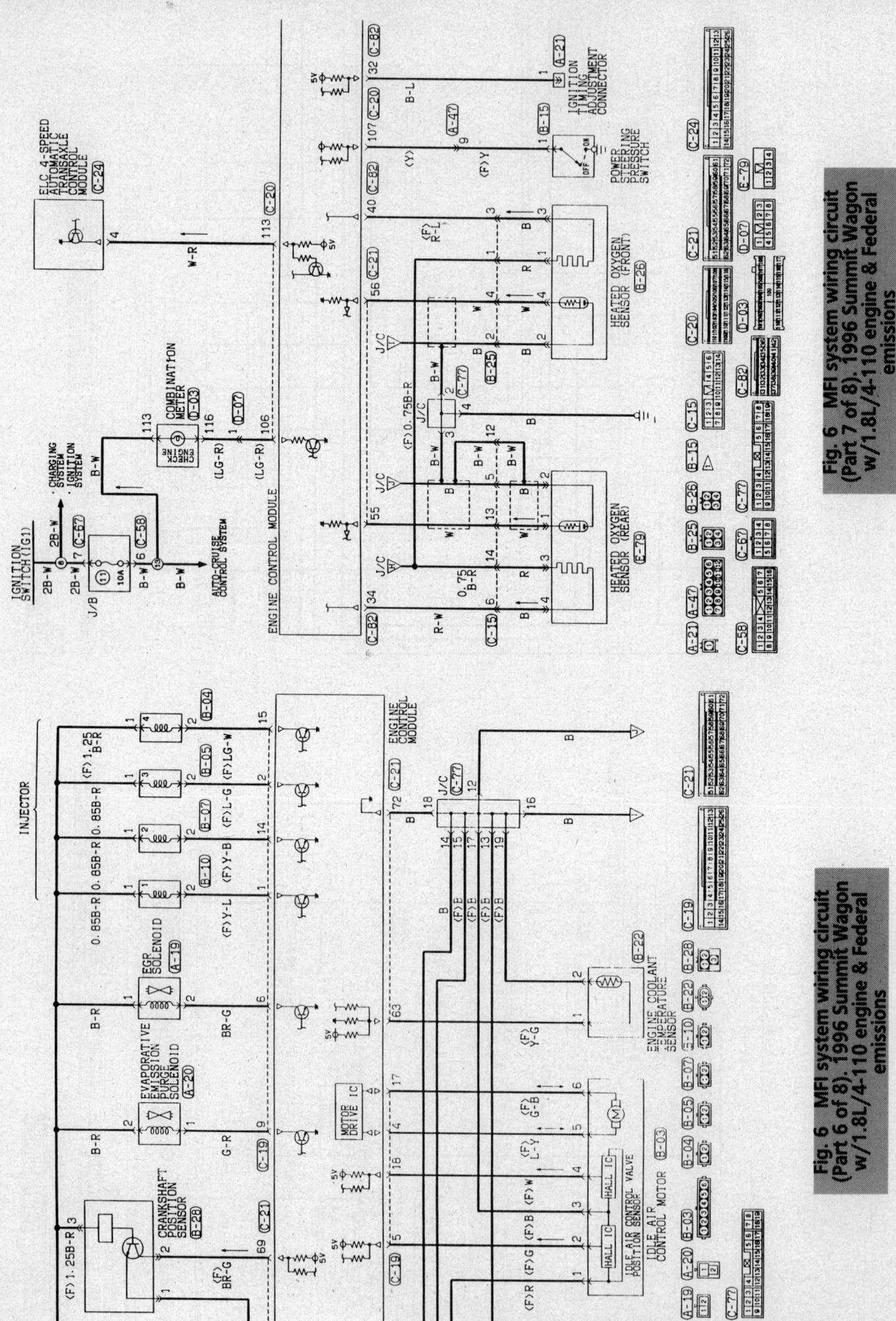

Fig. 6 MFI system wiring circuit (Part 7 of 8). 1996 Summit Wagon w/1.8L/4-110 engine & Federal emissions

Fig. 6 MFI system wiring circuit (Part 6 of 8). 1996 Summit Wagon w/1.8L/4-110 engine & Federal emissions

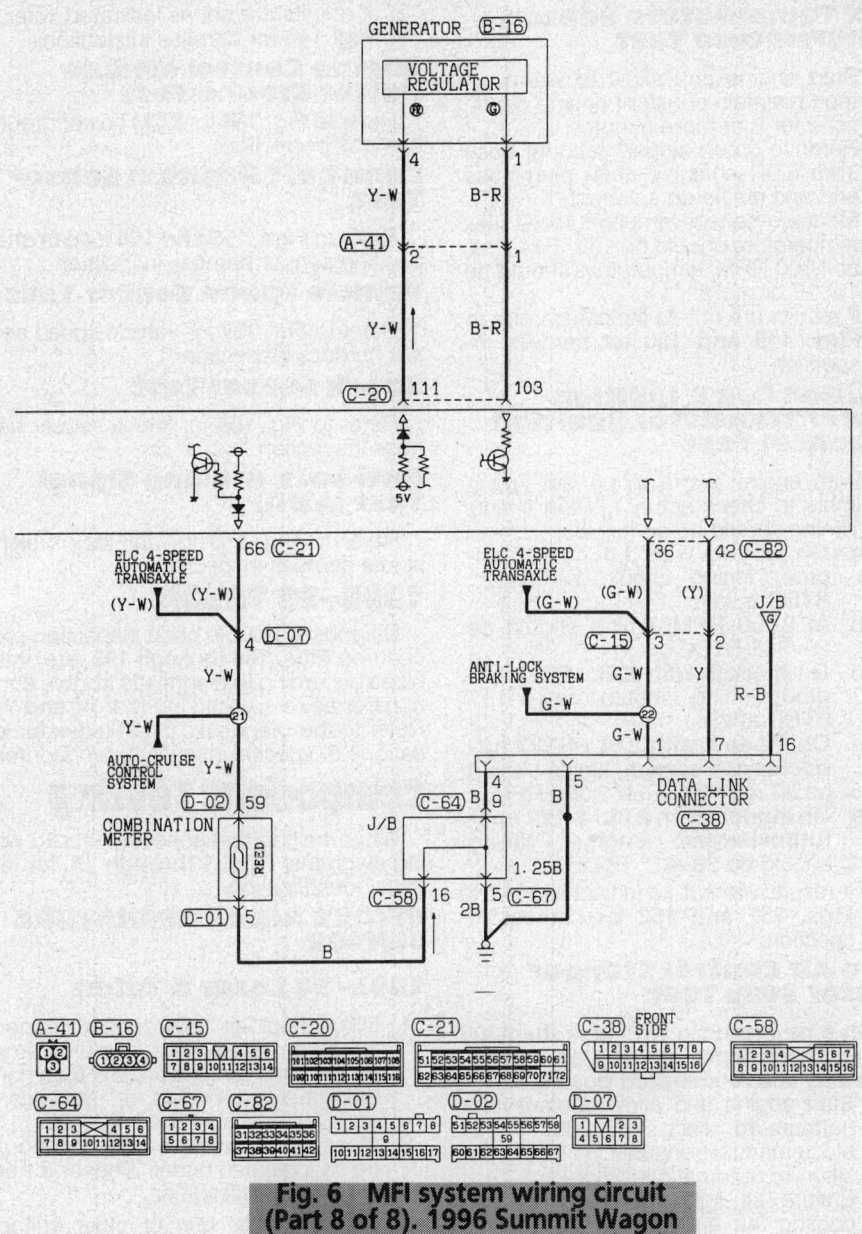

Fig. 6   MFI system wiring circuit (Part 8 of 8). 1996 Summit Wagon w/1.8L/4-110 engine & Federal emissions

Idle Speed Control Motor Position Sensor Voltage Test

1. Start engine and allow coolant temperature to reach 185-205°F, then place manual transaxle in Neutral or automatic in Park.
2. Ensure all lights, accessories and cooling fan are off and engine is at idle.
3. Ensure closed throttle position switch is in On position.
4. With A/C switch in Off position, measure sensor voltage. Voltage should be 500-1,300 mV.
5. With A/C switch in On position, measure sensor voltage. Voltage should be 800-1,800 mV.
6. **On models with automatic transaxle**, place A/C switch in On position and shift lever in "D" range, then measure sensor voltage. Voltage should be 900-1,900 mV.
7. **On all models**, if results are not as indicated, refer to **Fig. 132** for harness inspection.

Power Supply Voltage Test

1. Check for ECM power voltage. Voltage should be indicated with ignition switch in On position.
2. If results are not as indicated, refer to **Figs. 133 and 134** for harness inspection.

Ignition Switch On/Off Test (Manual Transaxle)

1. With ignition switch in On position and engine stopped, check switch output to engine control module. No output should be indicated.
2. Check switch output with engine cranking. Output should be indicated.
3. If results are not as indicated, refer to **Fig. 135** for harness inspection.

Engine Coolant Temperature Sensor Temperature Test

1. With engine running or ignition switch in On position, measure coolant temperature and sensor temperature. Sensor temperature should correspond with coolant temperature.
2. If results are not as indicated, refer to **Figs. 136 and 137** for harness inspection.

Crankshaft Position Sensor Cranking Speed Test

1. With engine cranking and tachometer connected, compare cranking speed with scan tool reading. Scan tool indication should correspond with tachometer indication.
2. If results are not as indicated, refer to **Figs. 138 and 139** for harness inspection.

Crankshaft Position Sensor Idle Speed Test

1. With engine idling, tachometer connected and closed throttle position switch in On position, check RPM at various engine temperatures. Results should be as follows:
   a. At -4°F, engine speed should be 1,500-1,700 RPM.
   b. At 32°F, engine speed should be 1,350-1,550 RPM.
   c. **On models with 1.8L/4-107 engine**, engine speed should be 1,150-1,350 RPM at 68°F.
   d. **On models with 2.0L/4-122 engine**, engine speed should be 1,180-1,380 RPM at 68°F.
   e. **On models with 1.8L/4-107 engine**, engine speed should be 950-1,150 RPM at 104°F.
   f. **On models with 2.0L/4-122 engine**, engine speed should be 1,000-1,200 RPM at 104°F.
   g. **On models with 1.8L/4-107 engine**, engine speed should be 600-800 RPM at 176°F.
   h. **On models with 2.0L/4-122 engine**, engine speed should be 650-850 RPM at 176°F.
2. If results are not as indicated, refer to **Figs. 138 and 139** for harness inspection.

Barometric Pressure Sensor Pressure Test

1. Turn ignition switch to On position, then measure pressure at sensor. Results should be as follows:
   a. At 0 ft. altitude, pressure should be 760 mmHg.
   b. At 1,969 ft. altitude, pressure should be 710 mmHg.
   c. At 3,937 ft. altitude, pressure should be 660 mmHg.
   d. At 5,906 ft. altitude, pressure should be 610 mmHg.
2. If results are not as specified, refer to **Figs. 140 and 141** for harness inspection.

Closed Throttle Position Switch State Test

1. With ignition switch in On position, operate accelerator pedal repeatedly. When throttle valve is at idle position, closed throttle switch should be in On position. When pedal is depressed and valve opens slightly, switch should be in Off position.
2. If results are not as indicated, refer to **Figs. 142 and 143** for harness inspection.

Power Steering Pressure Switch State Test

1. With engine idling, check switch state. Switch should be in Off position.
2. Check switch state while turning steering wheel. Switch should be in On position.
3. If results are not as indicated, refer to **Fig. 144** for harness inspection.

A/C Switch State Test

1. With engine idling, check switch output when switch is in Off position. No output should be indicated.
2. Turn switch to On position and check output. Output should be indicated.
3. If results are not as indicated, refer to **Fig. 145** for harness inspection.

Park/Neutral Position Switch Shift Position Test (Automatic Transaxle)

1. Place ignition switch in On position, then place shift lever in Park or Neutral position. Corresponding positions should be indicated.
2. Place shift lever in Reverse, Drive, "2" or Low position. Corresponding positions should be indicated.
3. If results are not as indicated, refer to **Fig. 146** for harness inspection.

Injector Drive Time Test

1. While cranking engine, measure coolant temperature and injector drive time.
2. **On models with 1.8L/4-107 engine**, results should be as follows:
   a. Drive time should be 17-21 ms at 32°F.
   b. At 68°F, drive time should be 37-45 ms.
   c. At 176°F, drive time should be 8.7-10.7 ms.
3. **On models with 2.0L/4-122 turbocharged engine**, results should be as follows:
   a. Drive time should be 22-26 ms at 32°F.
   b. At 68°F, drive time should be 11-13 ms.
   c. At 176°F, drive time should be 4.1-5 ms.
4. **On models with 2.0L/4-122 nonturbocharged engine**, results should be as follows:
   a. Drive time should be 15-19 ms at 32°F.
   b. At 68°F, drive time should be 34-42 ms.
   c. At 176°F, drive time should be 8.1-9.9 ms.
5. **On all models**, if results are not as indicated, refer to **Figs. 147 and 148** for harness inspection.

EGR Temperature Sensor Temperature Test

1. Start engine and allow to warm up, then maintain constant engine conditions for 2 or more minutes.
2. Remove green striped vacuum hose from EGR solenoid, then plug hose end and nipple on solenoid.
3. Measure sensor temperature. At idle, temperature should be 158°F or less; at 4,000 RPM, temperature should be 158°F or more.
4. If results are not as indicated, refer to **Figs. 149 and 150** for harness inspection.

Ignition Coil & Ignition Power Transistor (Ignition Advance) Test

1. With engine warming up, set timing lights to check actual ignition timing. Timing should be as follows:
   a. **On models with 1.8L/4-107 engine**, timing should be 8-12° BTDC at idle.
   b. At 2,000 RPM, timing should be 26-34° BTDC.
   c. **On models with 2.0L/4-122 engine**, timing should be 5-15° BTDC at idle.
   d. **On models with 2.0L/4-122 turbocharged engine**, timing should be 30-40° BTDC at 2,000 RPM.
   e. **On models with 2.0L/4-122 nonturbocharged engine**, timing should be 33-41° BTDC.
2. If results are not as indicated, refer to **Figs. 151 and 152** for harness inspection.

Idle Air Control Stepper Motor Step Test

On a new vehicle with less than 300 miles, the stepper motor step may be 30 steps above standard position.

1. Start engine and allow coolant temperature to reach 185-205°F, then place manual transaxle in Neutral position or automatic in Park.
2. Ensure all lights, accessories, and cooling fan are off and that closed throttle position switch is in On position.
3. Place A/C switch in Off position, then observe motor step position. Position should be 4-14 steps.
4. Place A/C switch in On position, then observe motor step position. Position should be 20-60 steps.
5. **On models with automatic transaxle**, place A/C switch in On position, then place shift lever in "D" range and observe motor step position. Position should be 38-68 steps.
6. **On all models**, if results are not as indicated, refer to **Fig. 153** for harness inspection.

A/C Compressor Clutch Relay State Test

1. Start engine and allow to warm up, then check compressor clutch operation with engine at idle. With A/C switch in Off position, clutch should not be activated; with switch in On position, clutch should be activated.

2. If results are not as indicated, refer to **Fig. 145** for harness inspection.

Engine Control Module Power Ground Test

Refer to **Fig. 154** for ECM power ground harness inspection.

Camshaft Position Sensor Test

Refer to **Figs. 155 and 156** for camshaft position sensor harness inspection.

Vehicle Speed Sensor Test

Refer to **Fig. 157** for vehicle speed sensor harness inspection.

Knock Sensor Test

Refer to **Fig. 158** for knock sensor harness inspection.

Anti-Lock Braking Signal Test (AWD)

Refer to **Fig. 159** for anti-lock braking signal harness inspection.

1995–96 TALON

Diagnostic trouble code inspection procedures, **Figs. 160 through 195**, are organized according to diagnostic trouble code number as referenced in **Figs. 74 and 75**. Refer to the Diagnostic Chart Index for locations of specific inspection procedures.

Component Testing

When testing components, refer to wiring diagrams, **Figs. 1 through 19**, for terminal identification.

INTAKE AIR TEMPERATURE SENSOR

1993–94 Laser & Talon

1. Disconnect air flow sensor connectors, then connect a suitable ohmmeter between terminals 4 and 6 on nonturbocharged models, or terminals 6 and 8 on turbocharged models.
2. Measure resistance. Results should be as indicated under "Sensor & Fuel Injector Specifications."
3. Using a heat gun or other suitable tool, heat the intake air temperature sensor. Resistance should drop as temperature increases.
4. If resistance is not as specified, replace sensor.

Colt, Colt Vista, Summit, Summit Wagon & 1995–96 Talon

1. Disconnect air flow sensor connectors.
2. **On 1993-94 models and 1995-96 Talon models**, connect a suitable ohmmeter between terminals 5 and 6.
3. **On 1995-96 Summit and Summit Wagon models**, connect a suitable ohmmeter between terminals 1 and 2.
4. **On all models**, measure resistance. Results should be as indicated under "Sensor & Fuel Injector Specifications."
5. Use a heat gun or other suitable tool to heat sensor. Resistance should drop as temperature increases.
6. If resistance is not as indicated, replace sensor. *Continued on page 7-29*

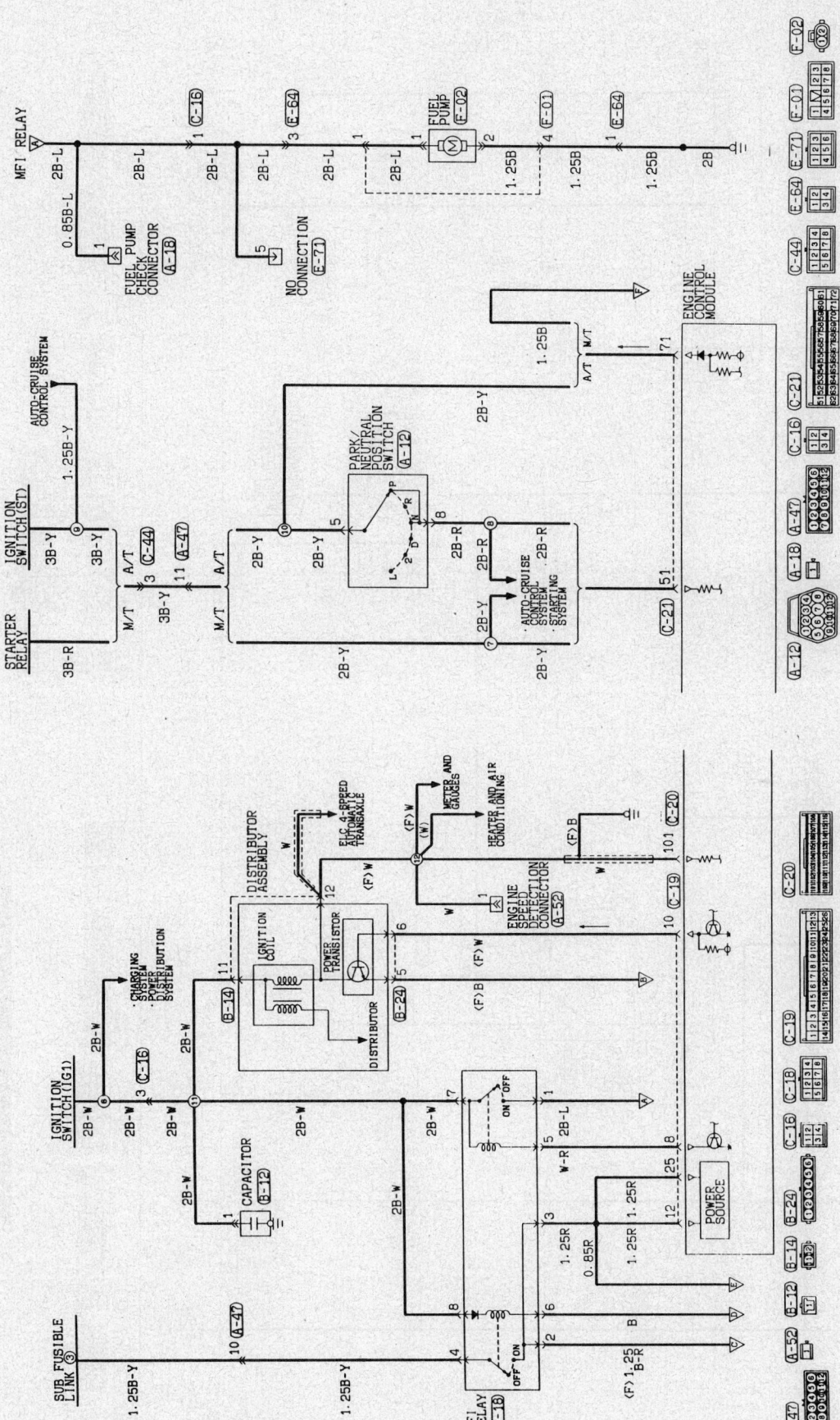

Fig. 7 MFI system wiring circuit (Part 2 of 8). 1996 Summit Wagon w/1.8L/4-110 engine & California emissions

Fig. 7 MFI system wiring circuit (Part 1 of 8). 1996 Summit Wagon w/1.8L/4-110 engine & California emissions

MULTI-POINT FUEL INJECTION (MODELS w/1.8L/4-107, 1.8L/4-110 & 2.4L/4-143 ENGINES, 1993-94 MODELS w/2.0L/4-122 ENGINE & 1995 TALON w/2.0L/4-122 TURBOCHARGED ENGINE)

7-25

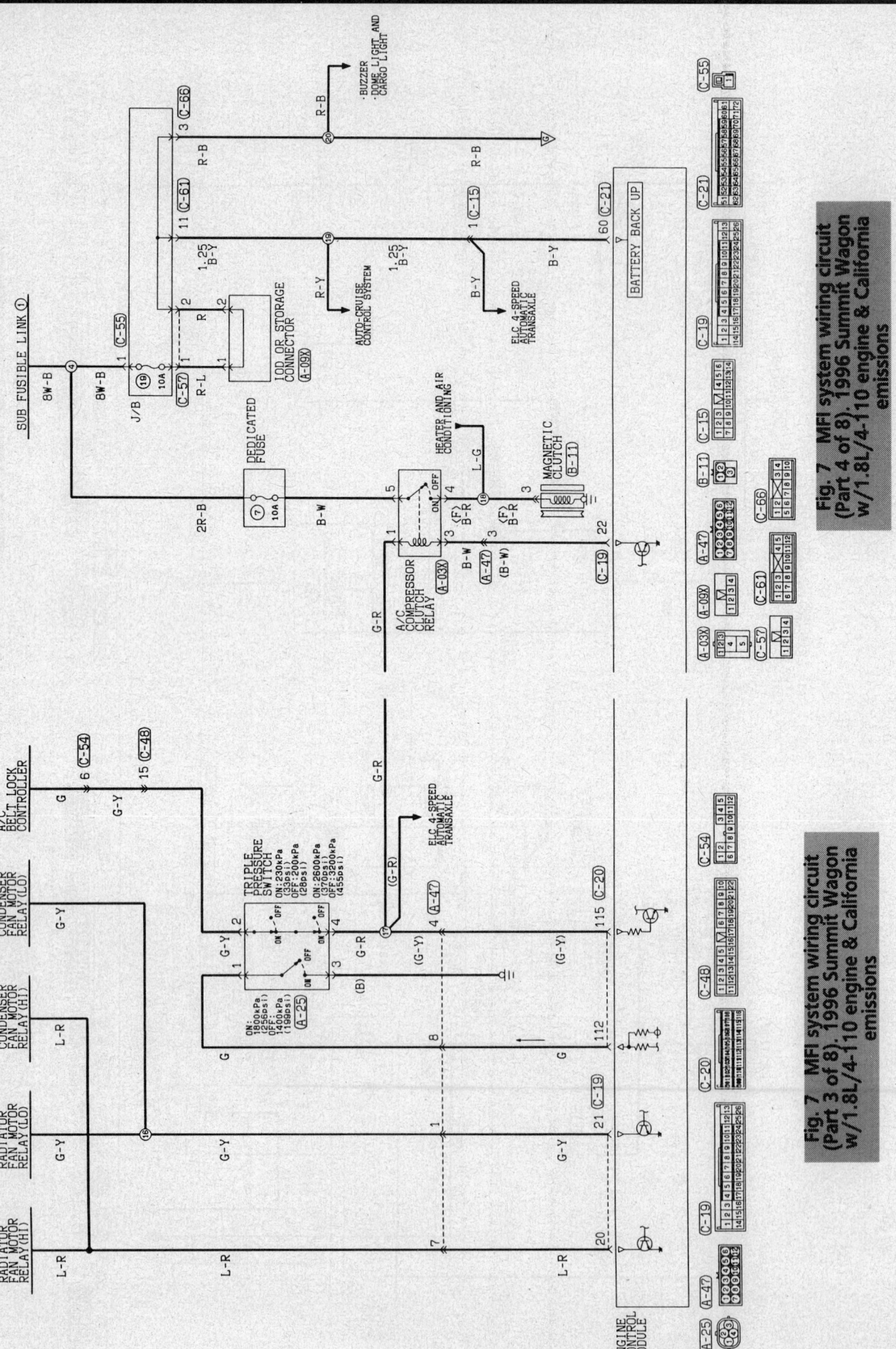

Fig. 7 MFI system wiring circuit (Part 4 of 8). 1996 Summit Wagon w/1.8L/4-110 engine & California emissions

Fig. 7 MFI system wiring circuit (Part 3 of 8). 1996 Summit Wagon w/1.8L/4-110 engine & California emissions

MULTI-POINT FUEL INJECTION (MODELS w/1.8L/4-107, 1.8L/4-110 & 2.4L/4-143 ENGINES, 1993-94 MODELS w/2.0L/4-122 ENGINE & 1995 TALON w/2.0L/4-122 TURBOCHARGED ENGINE)

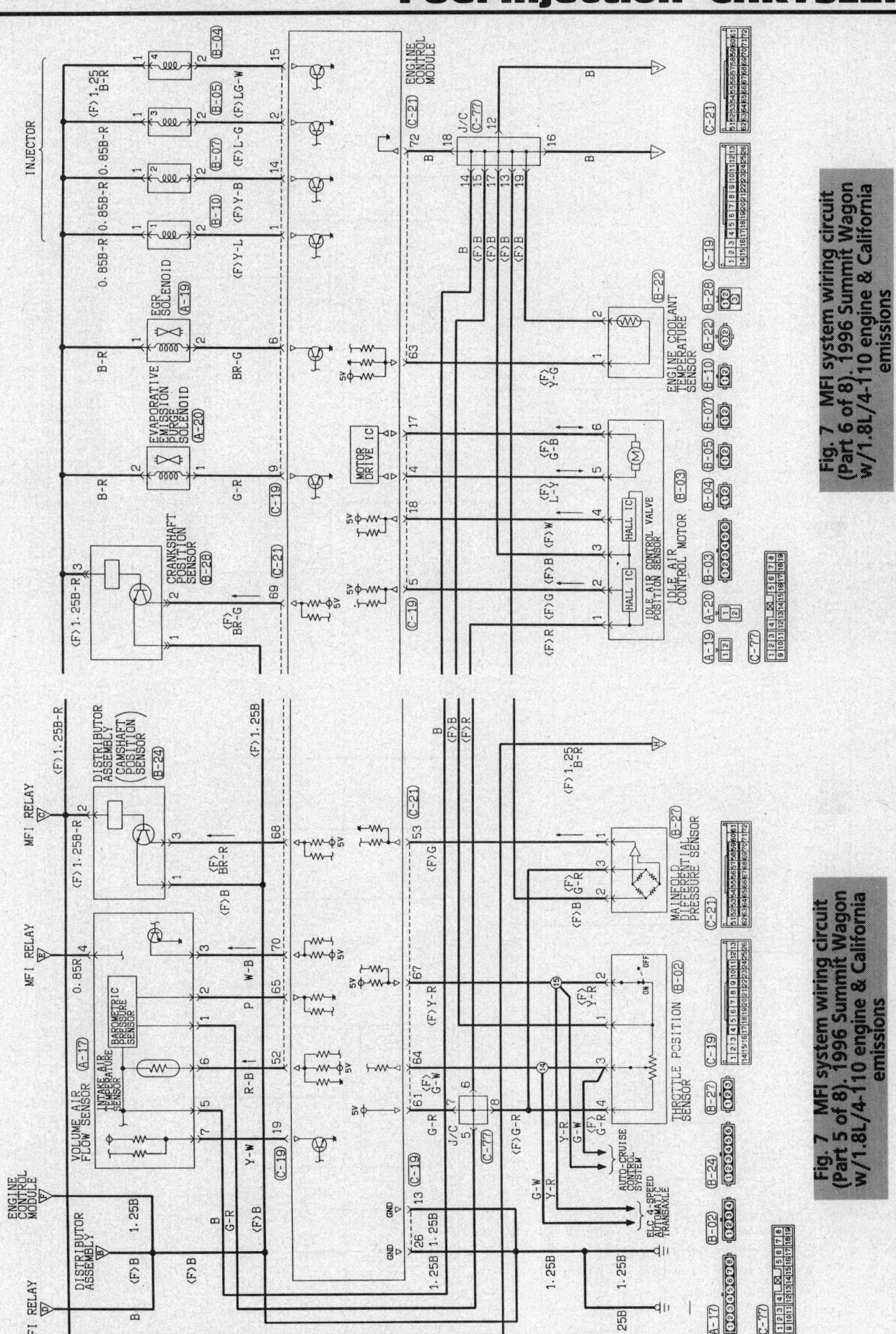

Fig. 7 MFI system wiring circuit (Part 6 of 8), 1996 Summit Wagon w/1.8L/4-110 engine & California emissions

Fig. 7 MFI system wiring circuit (Part 5 of 8), 1996 Summit Wagon w/1.8L/4-110 engine & California emissions

MULTI-POINT FUEL INJECTION (MODELS w/1.8L/4-107, 1.8L/4-110 & 2.4L/4-143 ENGINES, 1993-94 MODELS w/2.0L/4-122 ENGINE & 1995 TALON w/2.0L/4-122 TURBOCHARGED ENGINE)

7-27

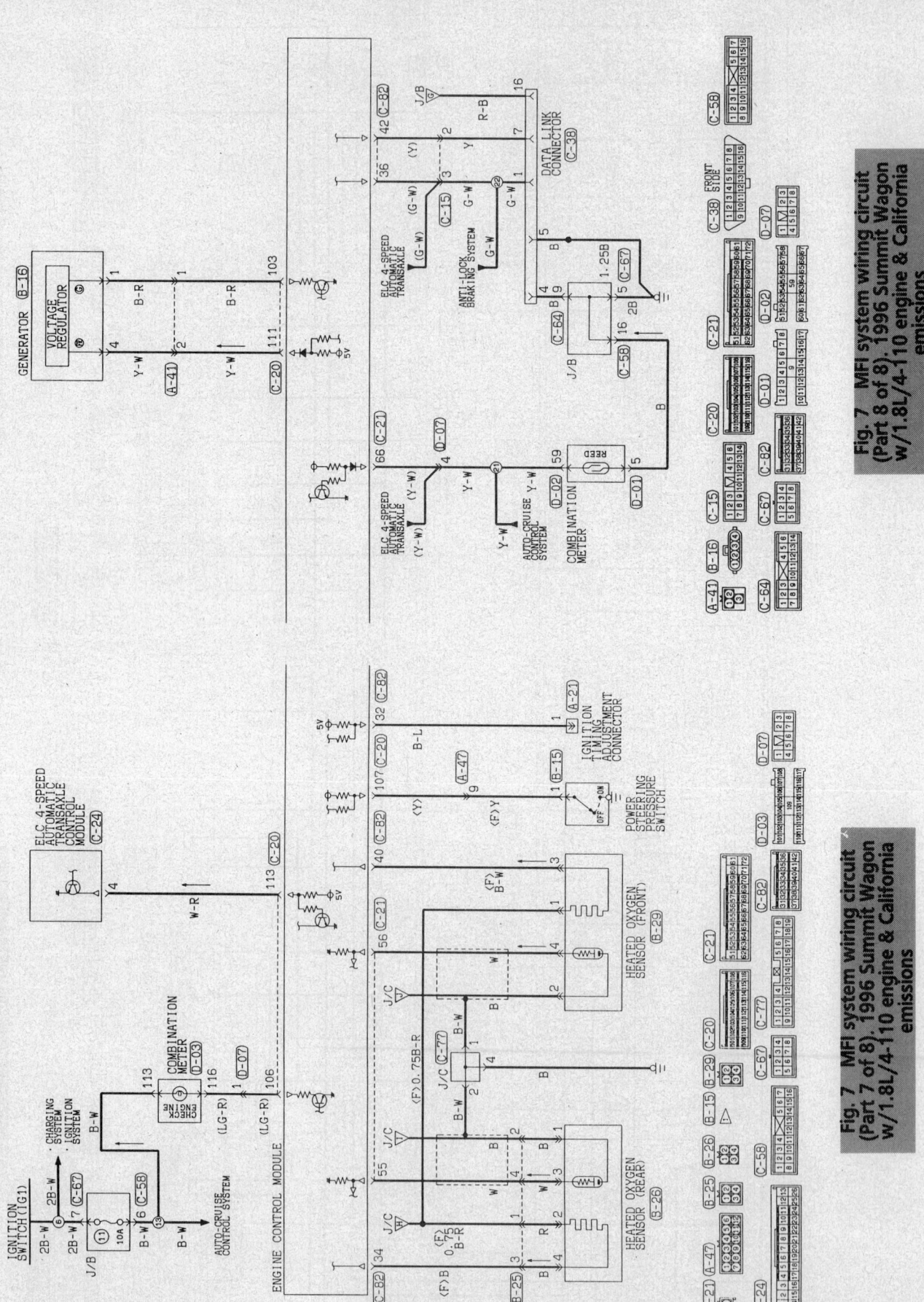

Fig. 7 MFI system wiring circuit (Part 8 of 8). 1996 Summit Wagon w/1.8L/4-110 engine & California emissions

Fig. 7 MFI system wiring circuit (Part 7 of 8). 1996 Summit Wagon w/1.8L/4-110 engine & California emissions

ENGINE COOLANT TEMPERATURE SENSOR

1. Remove sensor from intake manifold.
2. Place sensing portion of coolant sensor in hot water, then check resistance. Results should be as indicated under "Sensor & Fuel Injector Specifications."
3. If results are not as specified, replace.

THROTTLE POSITION SENSOR (TPS)

Laser & Talon

1. Disconnect TPS electrical connector.
2. Connect a suitable ohmmeter and measure resistance between terminal 4 (sensor ground) and terminal 1 (sensor power). Resistance should be as indicated under "Sensor & Fuel Injector Specifications."
3. Connect a pointer type ohmmeter between terminal 2 (sensor output) and terminal 4 (sensor ground), then operate throttle valve slowly from closed position to wide open throttle position. Resistance changes should be smooth.
4. If resistance is not within specifications or change is not smooth when changing throttle opening, replace sensor.

Colt, Colt Vista, Summit & Summit Wagon

1. Disconnect TPS electrical connector.
2. Connect a suitable ohmmeter and measure resistance between side connector terminals 1 and 4. Resistance should be as indicated under "Sensor & Fuel Injector Specifications."
3. Measure resistance between terminals 1 and 3, then operate throttle valve slowly from closed position to wide open throttle position. Resistance changes should be smooth.
4. If resistance is not within specifications or change is not smooth when changing throttle opening, replace sensor.

MOTOR POSITION SENSOR

1993 Laser & Talon W/1.8L/4-107 Engine

1. Disconnect motor position sensor and measure resistance between terminals 2 and 3; resistance should be 4000-6000 ohms.
2. Disconnect idle speed control servo connector.
3. Connect DC 6 volts between terminals 1 and 2 of idle speed control servo, then measure resistance between terminals 3 and 5 of motor position sensor connector when idle speed control is activated. Ensure smooth increase and decrease in extension and retraction of idle speed control servo plunger.
4. If not within specification, or movement is not smooth, replace idle speed control servo assembly.

OXYGEN SENSOR (O₂S)

1993 Laser & Talon W/2.0L/4-122 Engine

1. Start engine and run until operating temperature is reached.
2. Disconnect O₂S connector and connect a suitable ohmmeter between terminals 3 and 4 of oxygen sensor connector.
3. At 68°F, resistance should be approximately 12 ohms, and at 176°F resistance should be 30 ohms or more.
4. Replace oxygen sensor if not within specifications.
5. Apply battery across terminals 3 and 4 of oxygen sensor connector, then connect a digital voltmeter between terminals 1 and 2.
6. Increase engine speed several times and measure output voltage.
7. With engine raced, output voltage should be approximately one volt.
8. If not within specification, replace sensor.

1993–94 Laser & Talon W/1.8L/4-107 Engine & 1993 Colt Vista & Summit Wagon (Except 1993 California)

1. Start engine and run until normal operating temperature is reached.
2. Disconnect O₂S connector and connect a digital voltmeter to O₂S connector.
3. Increase engine speed several times and note oxygen sensor output voltage. When engine is raced voltage should be 0.6-1.0 volts.
4. If not within specifications, replace.

HEATED OXYGEN SENSOR(S)

1994 Laser & Talon W/2.0L/4-122 Engine

1. Disconnect oxygen sensor connector, then check for continuity between sensor connector terminals 3 and 4. Resistance should be approximately 12 ohms at 68°F.
2. If continuity does not exist, replace sensor.
3. Start engine and allow coolant temperature to reach 176°F or above, then use jumper wires to connect sensor terminals 3 and 4 to B+ and battery ground.
4. Connect a digital voltmeter between sensor terminals 1 and 2, then measure output voltage while racing engine. Voltage should be .6-1 volt.
5. If results are not as indicated, replace sensor.

1993 Colt, Colt Vista, Summit & Summit Wagon W/California Emissions, 1994 Colt & Colt Vista, 1994–96 Summit & Summit Wagon & 1995–96 Talon

1. Disconnect front heated oxygen sensor connector, then connect test harness tool No. MD998464, or equivalent, to connector, Fig. 196.
2. Measure resistance between red clip on test harness and blue clip. Resistance should be approximately 12 ohms at 68°F. If there is no continuity, replace front heated oxygen sensor.
3. Start engine and allow coolant temperature to reach 176°F or more, then use jumper wires to connect red clip on test harness to B+ and blue clip to battery ground.
4. Connect a digital voltmeter across black clip on test harness and white clip, Fig. 196, then race engine repeatedly and measure sensor output voltage. Voltage should be .6-1 volt when engine is raced.
5. If results are not as indicated, replace front heated oxygen sensor.
6. Disconnect rear heated oxygen sensor connector, then check for continuity between terminals 3 and 4 of connector. Resistance should be approximately 20 ohms at 68°F.
7. If there is no continuity, replace rear heated oxygen sensor.

EGR TEMPERATURE SENSOR

1. Remove EGR temperature sensor, place sensor in water and measure resistance across terminals while increasing water temperature.
2. At 122°F, resistance should be between 60,000-83,000 ohms, and at 212°F resistance should be between 11,000-14,000 ohms.
3. If resistance is not within specifications, replace sensor.

EGR SOLENOID

1. Disconnect yellow/green striped vacuum hose from solenoid valve. **Mark for installation reference.**
2. Disconnect harness connector, then connect a hand vacuum pump to nipple from which vacuum hose was removed.
3. Apply vacuum pressure to solenoid valve, then connect and disconnect battery voltage while observing hand pump pressure gauge. Results should be as follows:
   a. When voltage is applied to solenoid, vacuum pressure is maintained.
   b. When voltage is removed, vacuum pressure leaks down.
4. If results are not as indicated, replace EGR solenoid.

INJECTORS

1. Using a stethoscope, check operating sound of injector at idle and at various engine speeds. Ticking noise should increase with higher engine RPM.
2. If ticking noise is not heard, check injectors or engine control unit.
3. Disconnect injector connectors, then measure resistance between terminals. Results should be as indicated under "Sensor & Fuel Injector Specifications."
4. If resistance is not within specifications, replace injectors.

IDLE AIR CONTROL (IAC) (IDLE SPEED CONTROL) MOTOR

Colt, Colt Vista, Summit & Summit Wagon

Using a stethoscope, check for motor operation sound immediately after ignition

MULTI-POINT FUEL INJECTION (MODELS w/1.8L/4-107, 1.8L/4-110 & 2.4L/4-143 ENGINES, 1993-94 MODELS w/2.0L/4-122 ENGINE & 1995 TALON w/2.0L/4-122 TURBOCHARGED ENGINE)

7-29

CHRYSLER–Fuel Injection

switch is turned to On position. If no sound can be heard. check motor drive circuit.

Laser & Talon w/2.0L/4-122 Engine

Place ignition switch in On position; operating sound of stepper motor should be heard. If no sound can be heard, check stepper motor circuit or engine control unit.

Laser & Talon w/1.8L/4-107 Engine

1. Disconnect idle speed control motor connector, then connect a suitable ohmmeter to terminals 1 and 2 of idle speed motor coil.
2. Measure continuity of motor coil. Resistance should be as specified under "Sensor & Fuel Injector Specifications.
3. Connect 6 volt DC between terminals 1 and 2 of idle speed control motor connector.
4. Ensure idle speed control motor operates. If not, replace.

CONTROL (MFI) RELAY

Laser & Talon w/1.8L/4-107 Engine

1. Remove control relay from vehicle, check continuity between terminals as shown in **Fig. 197.**
2. Connect terminal 7 to B + and terminal 6 to battery ground.
3. Check continuity between relay terminals 1 and 4. With battery connected, there should be no resistance between terminals 1 and 4. With battery ground jumper disconnected, resistance should be infinite.
4. Connect control relay terminal 2 to battery positive, and terminal 5 to battery negative.
5. Check continuity between relay terminals 1 and 4. With battery connected, there should be no resistance between terminals 1 and 4. With battery ground jumper disconnected, resistance should be infinite.
6. Connect control relay terminal 8 to battery positive, and terminal 6 to battery negative.
7. Check continuity between relay terminals 2 and 4. With battery connected, there should be no resistance between terminals 1 and 4. With battery ground jumper disconnected, resistance should be infinite.
8. If not within specifications, replace control relay.

1993 Laser & Talon w/2.0L/4-122 Engine

Failure of the control relay prevents power to fuel pump, injectors and engine control unit, causing a no start condition.
1. Disconnect control relay connector.
2. Connect battery positive to terminal 10 of control relay, measure voltage at terminals 4 then terminal 5 with battery negative connected to terminal 8, battery voltage should be present. Remove battery negative from terminal 8, voltage should not be present at terminals 4 or 5.

3. Connect battery negative to terminal 6 of control relay, check continuity between terminals 2 and 3 when battery positive is connected to terminal 9, continuity should exist. Remove battery positive from terminal 9, continuity should not be present at terminals 2 and 3.
4. Connect battery positive to terminal 3 of control relay, measure voltage at terminal 2 with battery negative connected to terminal 7, battery voltage should be present. Remove battery negative from terminal 7, voltage should not be present at terminals 2.

1994 Laser & Talon w/2.0L/4-122 Engine

1. Remove MFI relay, then use jumper wires to connect relay terminal 10 to B + and terminal 8 to battery ground.
2. While connecting and disconnecting battery ground jumper, measure voltage at MFI relay terminals 4 and 5. When jumper is connected, battery voltage should be indicated; when jumper is removed, no voltage should be indicated.
3. Using jumper wires, connect MFI relay terminal 9 to B + and terminal 6 to battery ground.
4. While connecting and disconnecting battery ground jumper, measure continuity between MFI relay terminals 2 and 3. When jumper is connected, continuity should be indicated; when jumper is removed, no continuity should be indicated.
5. Using jumper wires, connect MFI relay terminal 3 to B + and terminal 7 to battery ground.
6. While connecting and disconnecting battery ground jumper, measure voltage at relay terminal 2. When jumper is connected, battery voltage should be indicated; when disconnected, no voltage should be indicated.
7. If results are not as indicated, replace MFI relay.

1995–96 Talon

1. Remove MFI relay and check continuity between terminals 5 and 7. Approximately 90 ohms resistance should be indicated.
2. Check continuity between terminals 6 and 8. Continuity should exist in one direction only.
3. Using suitable jumper leads, connect relay terminal 7 to B + and terminal 5 to battery ground, then check voltage at terminal 1 while connecting and disconnecting lead at battery ground source. When connected, battery voltage should be indicated; when disconnected, no voltage should be indicated.
4. Using suitable jumper leads, connect relay terminal 8 to B + and terminal 6 to battery ground, then check continuity between terminals 2 and 4 while connecting and disconnecting lead at battery ground source. When connected, continuity should exist; when disconnected, continuity should not exist.

5. Check continuity between terminals 3 and 4 while connecting and disconnecting lead at battery ground source. When connected, continuity should exist; when disconnected, continuity should not exist.
6. If results are not as indicated, replace relay.

Colt, Colt Vista, Summit & Summit Wagon

1. Remove control relay, then check for continuity between terminals 5 and 7. Continuity should exist.
2. Check for continuity between terminals 6 and 8. Continuity should exist in one direction only.
3. Connect B + to relay terminal 7, and battery ground to terminal 5.
4. Check voltage at control relay terminal 1 with battery voltage connected. Battery voltage should be indicated. Disconnect battery ground from relay; no voltage should be indicated.
5. Connect B + to relay terminal 8, and battery ground to terminal 6.
6. Check continuity at control relay terminals 2 and 4. With battery voltage connected, resistance should be zero ohms. Disconnect battery ground from relay; resistance should be infinite.
7. Check continuity at control relay terminals 3 and 4. With battery voltage connected, resistance should be zero ohms. Disconnect battery ground from relay; resistance should be infinite.
8. If not within specifications, replace control relay.

EVAPORATIVE EMISSION PURGE CONTROL SOLENOID

1. Disconnect purge control solenoid vacuum hoses. **Mark for installation reference.**
2. Disconnect harness electrical connector from solenoid.
3. Connect a hand held vacuum pump to nipple from which red striped vacuum hose was disconnected.
4. Apply vacuum and check for vacuum leakage when voltage is applied to purge control solenoid valve and when voltage is disconnected.
5. Refer to **Fig. 198** for purge control solenoid valve vacuum leakage chart.
6. Measure resistance across terminals of solenoid valve. Resistance should be as indicated under "Sensor & Fuel Injector Specifications."
7. If resistance is not within specifications, replace solenoid.

VEHICLE SPEED SENSOR (REED SWITCH)

1993 Colt Vista & Summit Wagon

Use a suitable ohmmeter and check that circuit repeats Off/On between terminals when speedometer is turned several times, **Fig. 199.**

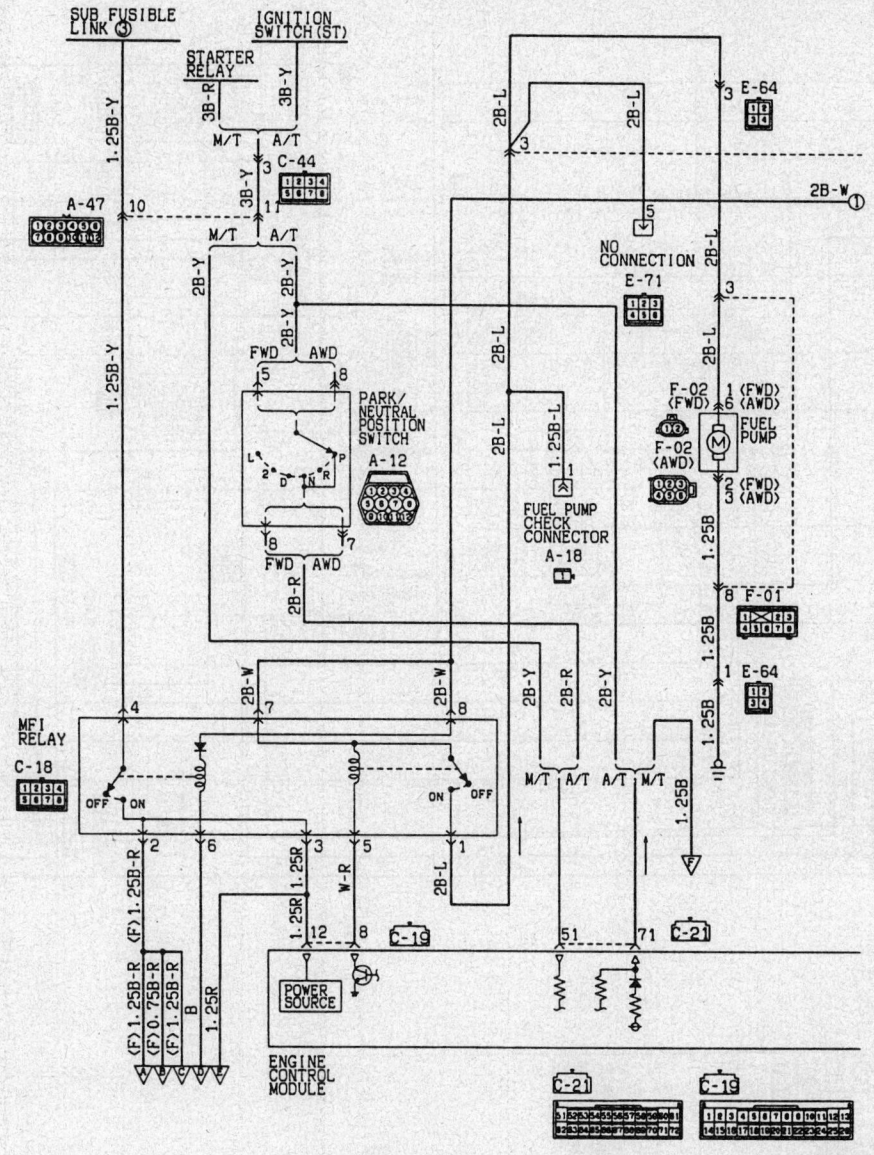

Fig. 8 MFI system wiring circuit (Part 1 of 5). 1994 Colt Vista & 1994–95 Summit Wagon w/2.4L/4-143 engine

Laser & Talon

When performing test, use a tester which uses a measurement current of 4mA or less.

Use a suitable ohmmeter and check that circuit repeats Off/On between terminals when speedometer is turned several times, **Fig. 200.**

POWER STEERING PRESSURE SWITCH

1. Disconnect pressure hose from oil pump, then connect adapter tool Nos. MB991217 and MB990994, or equivalents, and pressure gauge tool No. MB990662, or equivalent, as shown in **Fig. 201.**

2. Bleed air from system, then turn steering wheel several times with vehicle stationary in order to increase fluid temperature to 122-140°F.

3. With engine at idle, disconnect pressure switch connector and connect ohmmeter as shown in **Fig. 201.**

4. Close pressure gauge shutoff valve gradually, then check pressure at which switch would be activated. Correct activation pressure is 213-284 psi.

5. Open pressure gauge shutoff valve gradually, then check pressure at which switch would be deactivated. Correct deactivation pressure is as follows:

   a. **On Colt, Colt Vista, Summit and Summit Wagon models,** deactivation pressure is 100-284 psi.

   b. **On Laser and 1993-94 Talon models,** deactivation pressure is 100-171 psi.

   c. **On 1995-96 Talon models,** deactivation pressure is 114 psi.

6. If results are as specified but switch still does not operate properly, replace switch. Remove tools, reconnect hoses and bleed air from system.

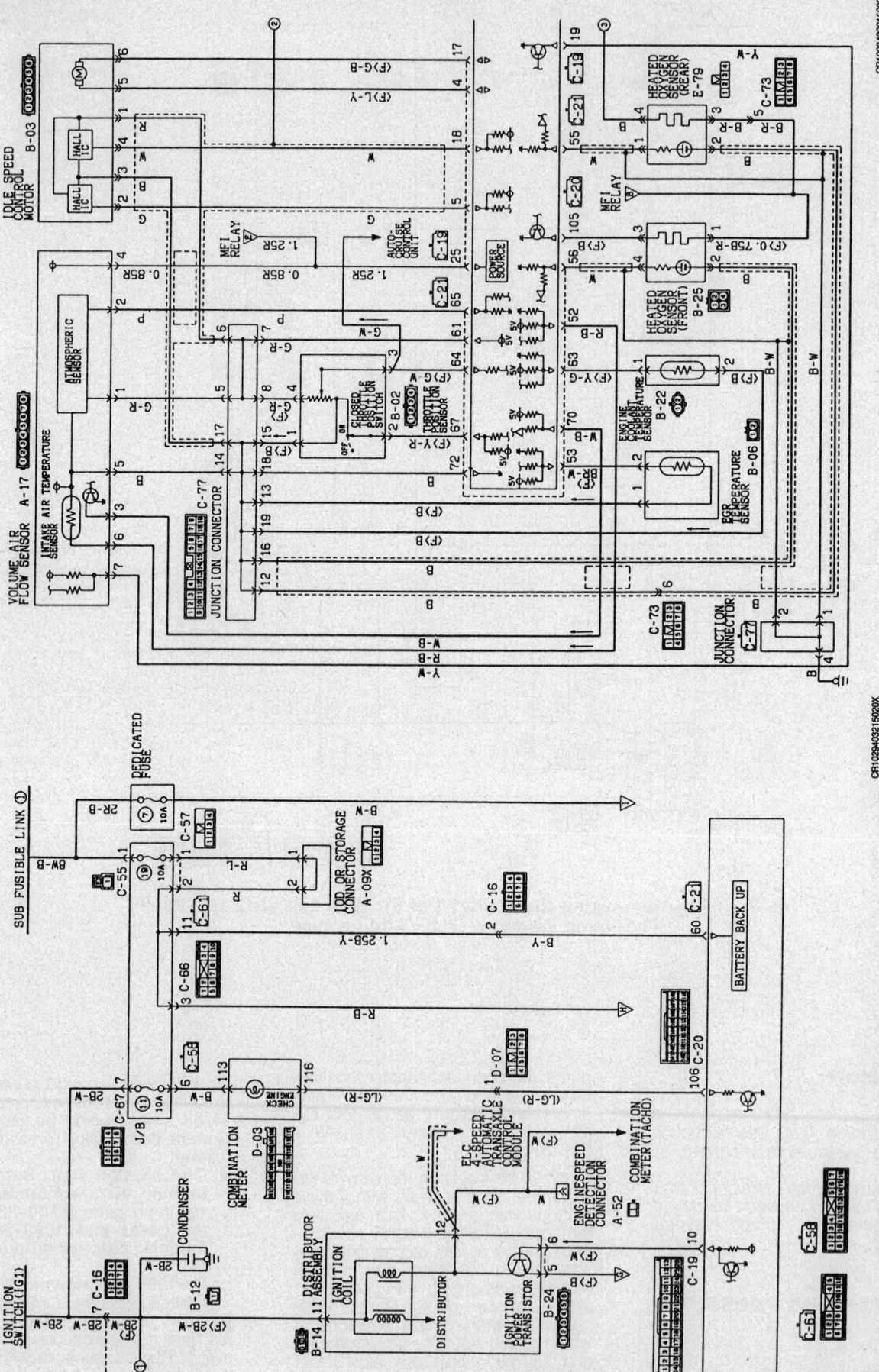

Fig. 8   MFI system wiring circuit (Part 3 of 5). 1994 Colt Vista & 1994–95 Summit Wagon w/2.4L/4-143 engine

Fig. 8   MFI system wiring circuit (Part 2 of 5). 1994 Colt Vista & 1994–95 Summit Wagon w/2.4L/4-143 engine

MULTI-POINT FUEL INJECTION (MODELS w/1.8L/4-107, 1.8L/4-110 & 2.4L/4-143 ENGINES, 1993-94 MODELS w/2.0L/4-122 ENGINE & 1995 TALON w/2.0L/4-122 TURBOCHARGED ENGINE)

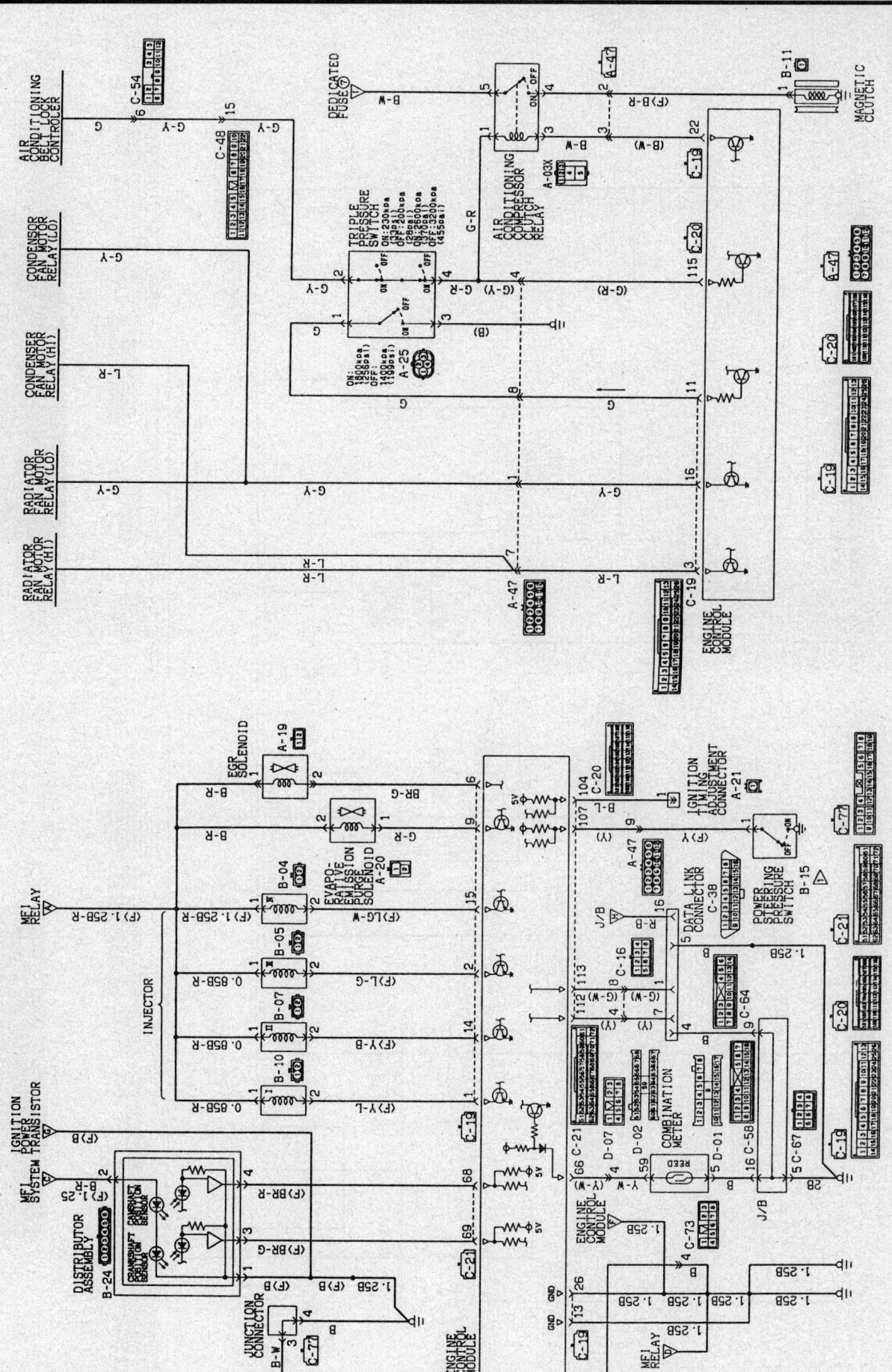

Fig. 8   MFI system wiring circuit (Part 5 of 5), 1994 Colt Vista & 1994–95 Summit Wagon w/2.4L/4-143 engine

Fig. 8   MFI system wiring circuit (Part 4 of 5), 1994 Colt Vista & 1994–95 Summit Wagon w/2.4L/4-143 engine

MULTI-POINT FUEL INJECTION (MODELS w/1.8L/4-107, 1.8L/4-110 & 2.4L/4-143 ENGINES, 1993-94 MODELS w/2.0L/4-122 ENGINE & 1995 TALON w/2.0L/4-122 TURBOCHARGED ENGINE)

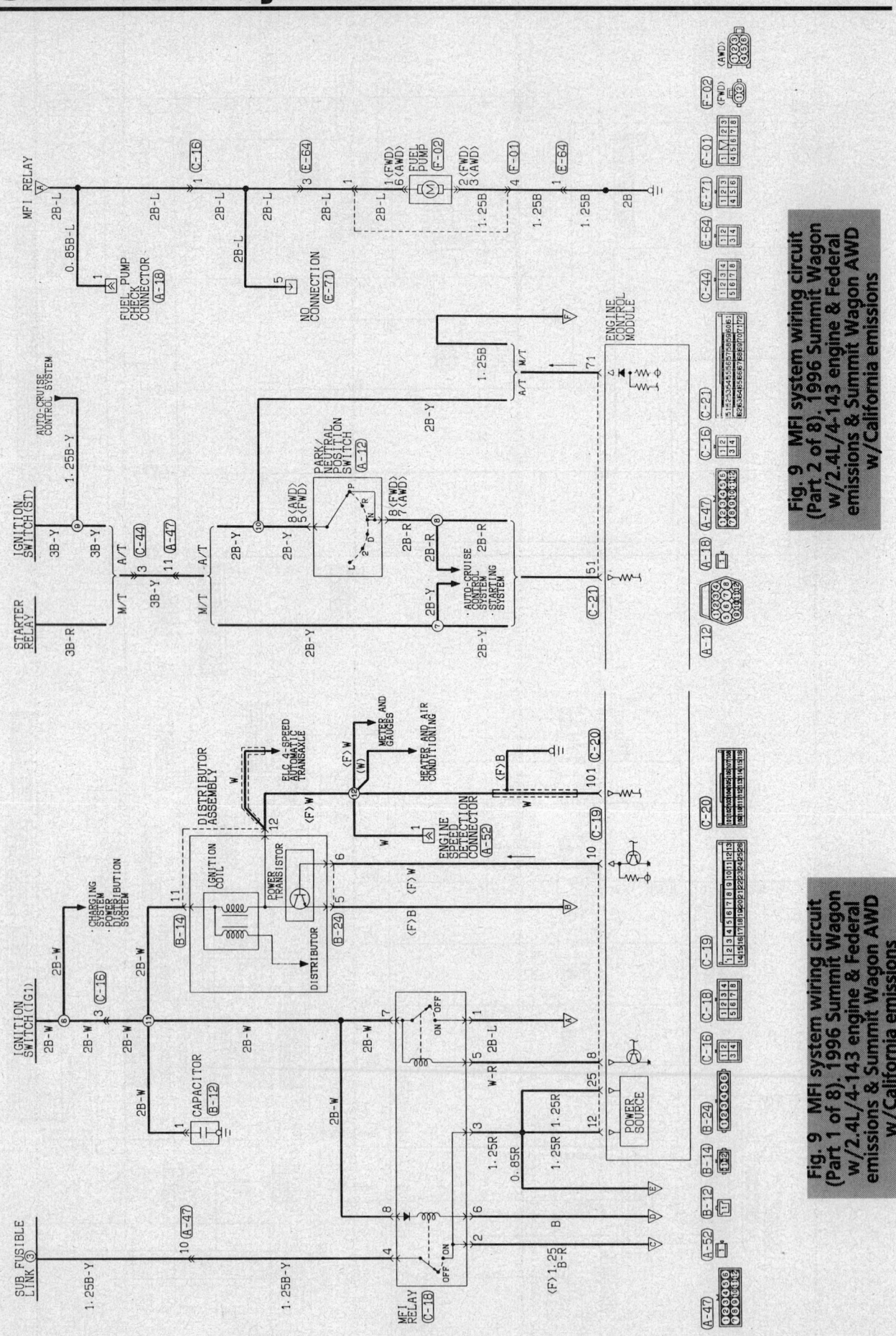

Fig. 9 MFI system wiring circuit (Part 2 of 8). 1996 Summit Wagon w/2.4L/4-143 engine & Federal emissions & Summit Wagon AWD w/California emissions

Fig. 9 MFI system wiring circuit (Part 1 of 8). 1996 Summit Wagon w/2.4L/4-143 engine & Federal emissions & Summit Wagon AWD w/California emissions

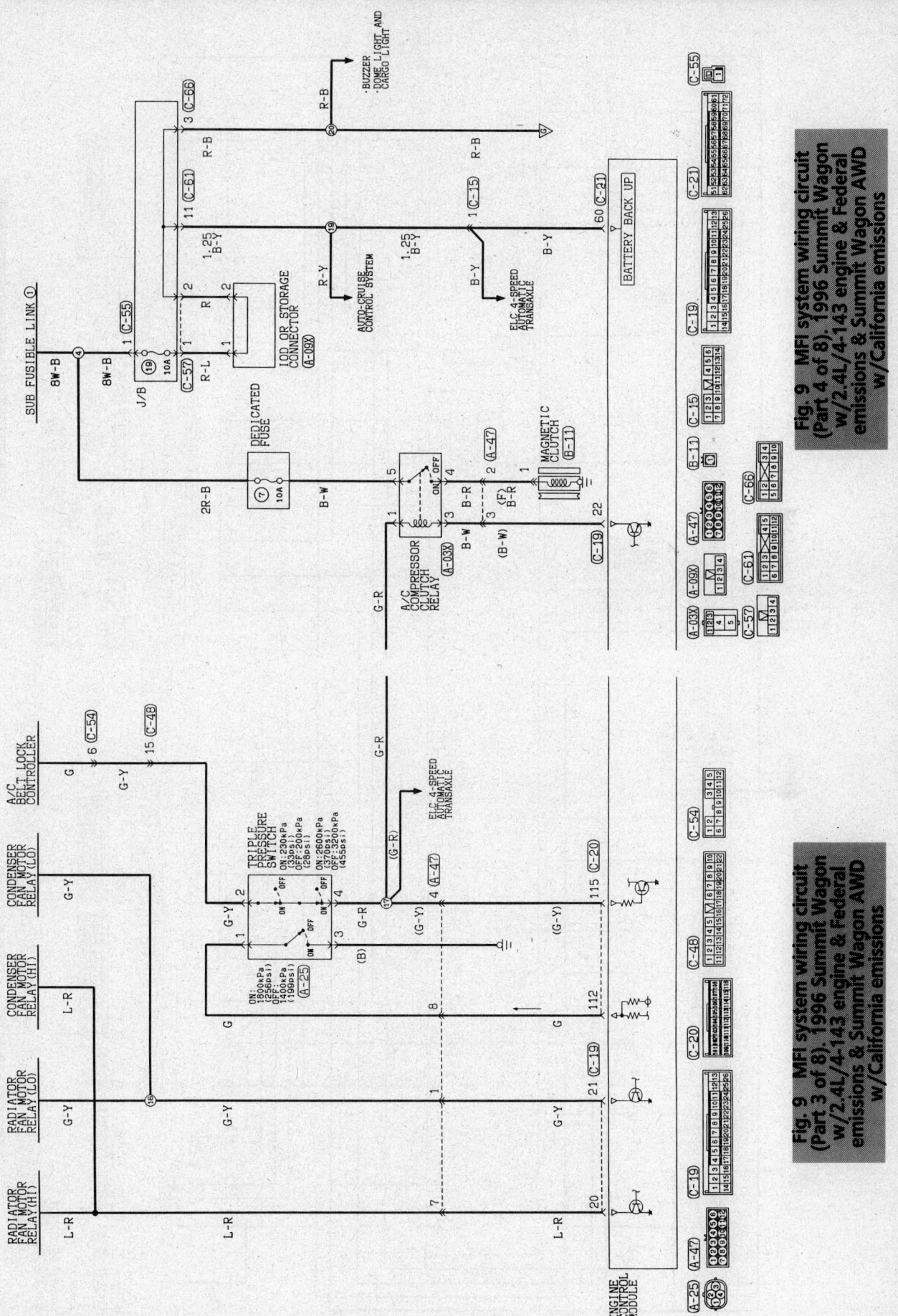

Fig. 9 MFI system wiring circuit (Part 4 of 8), 1996 Summit Wagon w/2.4L/4-143 engine & Federal emissions & Summit Wagon AWD w/California emissions

Fig. 9 MFI system wiring circuit (Part 3 of 8), 1996 Summit Wagon w/2.4L/4-143 engine & Federal emissions & Summit Wagon AWD w/California emissions

MULTI-POINT FUEL INJECTION (MODELS w/1.8L/4-107, 1.8L/4-110 & 2.4L/4-143 ENGINES, 1993-94 MODELS w/2.0L/4-122 ENGINE & 1995 TALON w/2.0L/4-122 TURBOCHARGED ENGINE)

7-35

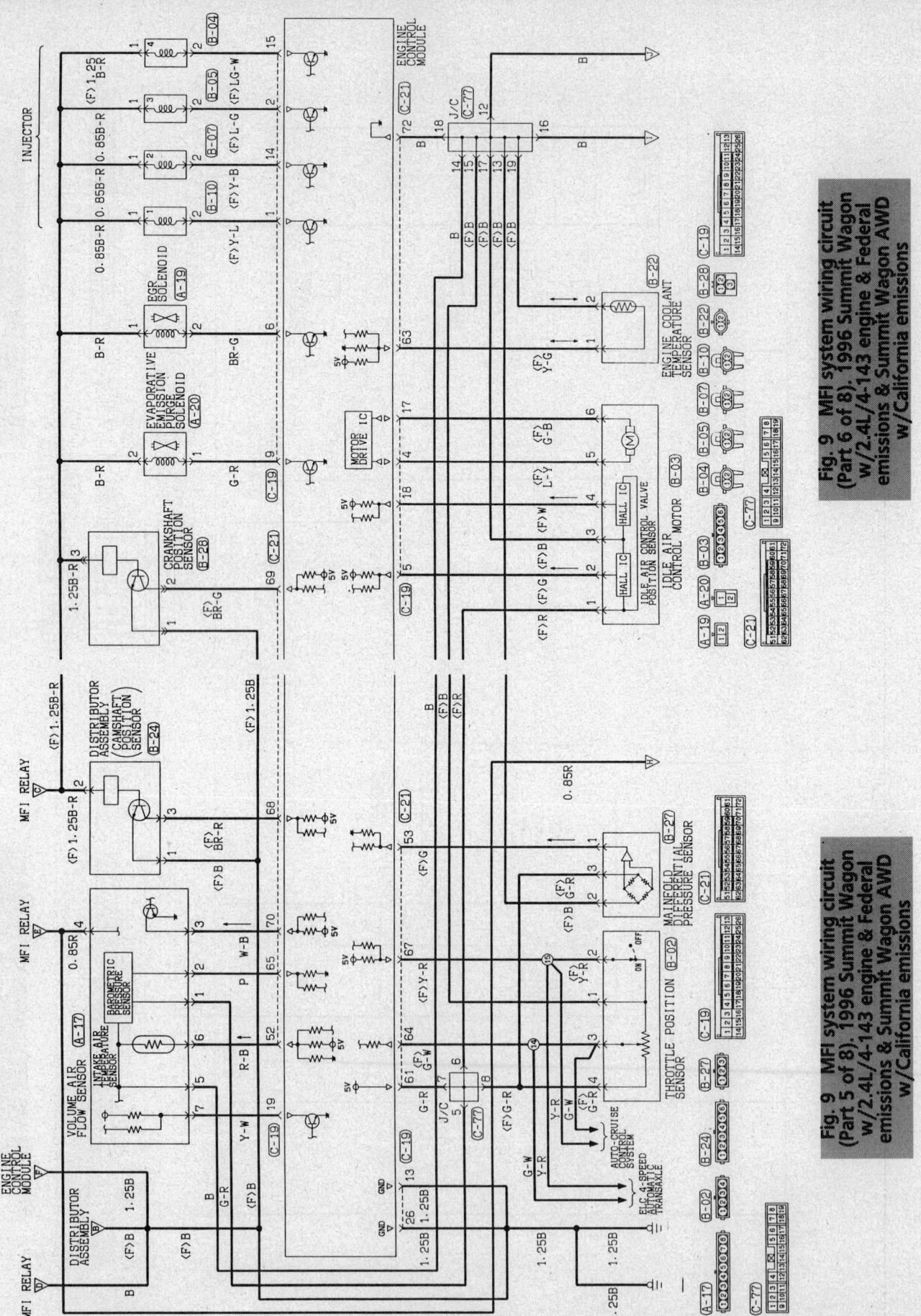

Fig. 9 MFI system wiring circuit (Part 6 of 8). 1996 Summit Wagon w/2.4L/4-143 engine & Federal emissions & Summit Wagon AWD w/California emissions

Fig. 9 MFI system wiring circuit (Part 5 of 8). 1996 Summit Wagon w/2.4L/4-143 engine & Federal emissions & Summit Wagon AWD w/California emissions

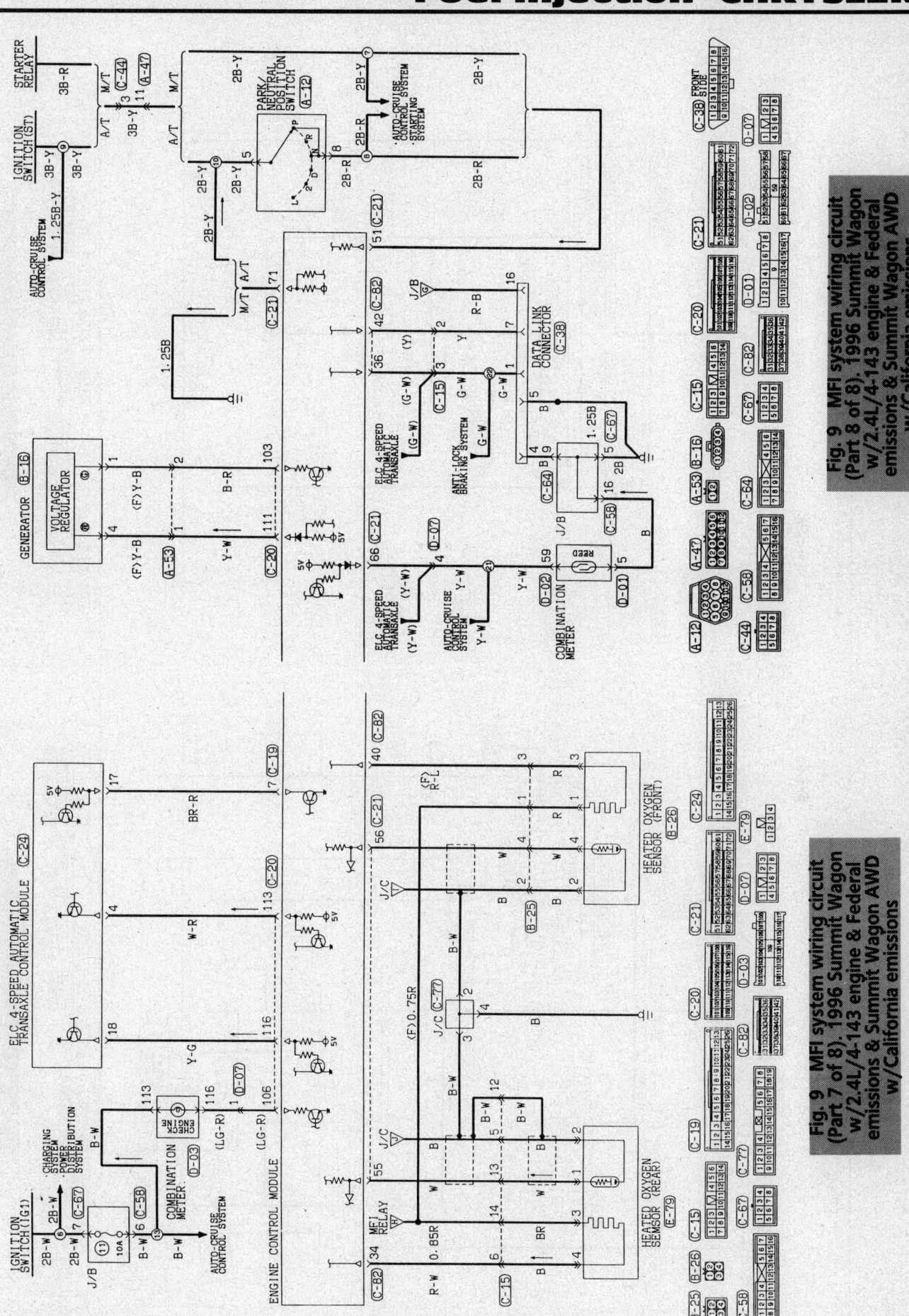

Fig. 9 MFI system wiring circuit (Part 8 of 8). 1996 Summit Wagon w/2.4L/4-143 engine & Federal emissions & Summit Wagon AWD w/California emissions

Fig. 9 MFI system wiring circuit (Part 7 of 8). 1996 Summit Wagon w/2.4L/4-143 engine & Federal emissions & Summit Wagon AWD w/California emissions

MULTI-POINT FUEL INJECTION (MODELS w/1.8L/4-107, 1.8L/4-110 & 2.4L/4-143 ENGINES, 1993-94 MODELS w/2.0L/4-122 ENGINE & 1995 TALON w/2.0L/4-122 TURBOCHARGED ENGINE)

7-37

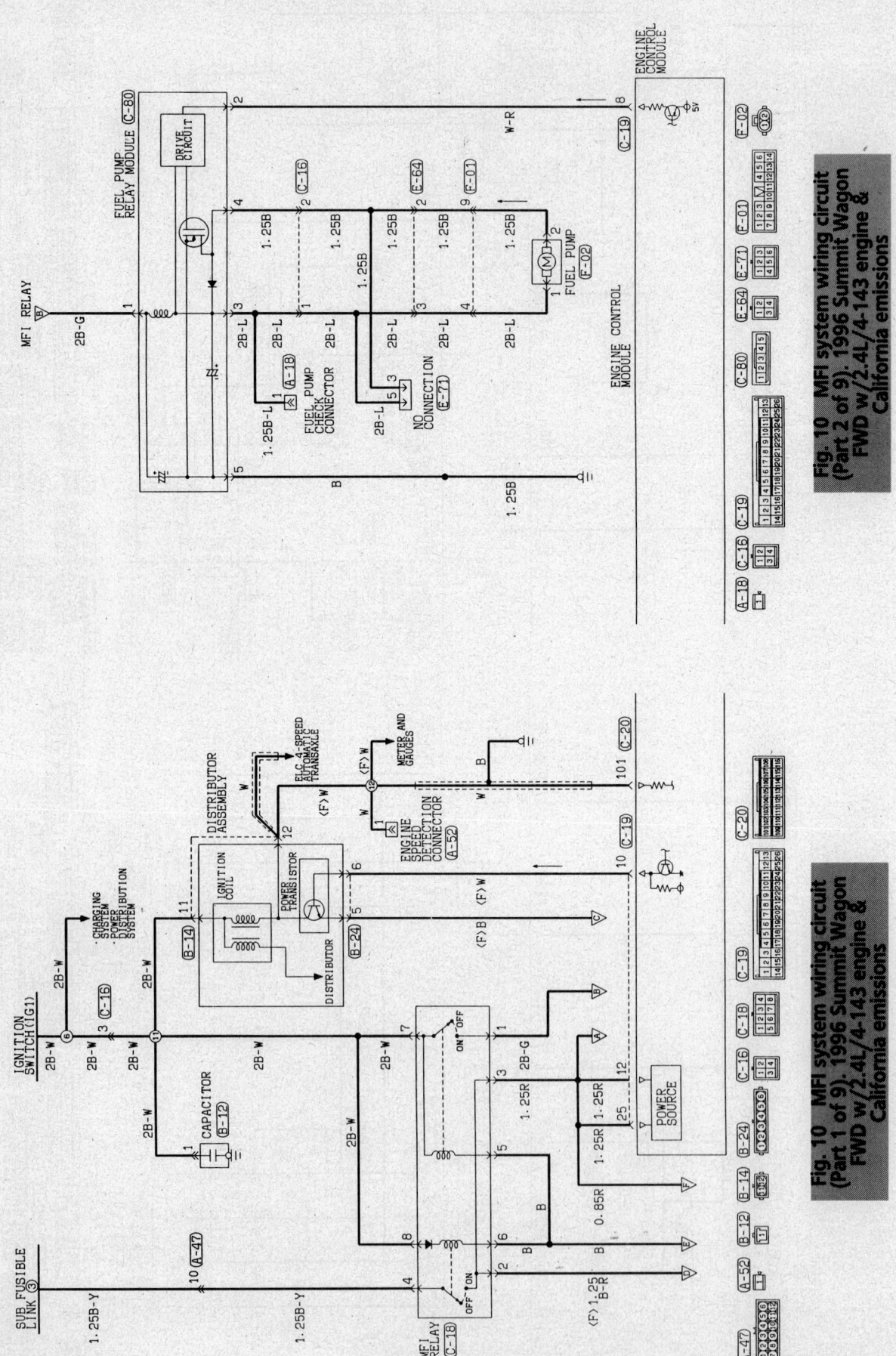

Fig. 10 MFI system wiring circuit
(Part 2 of 9). 1996 Summit Wagon
FWD w/2.4L/4-143 engine &
California emissions

Fig. 10 MFI system wiring circuit
(Part 1 of 9). 1996 Summit Wagon
FWD w/2.4L/4-143 engine &
California emissions

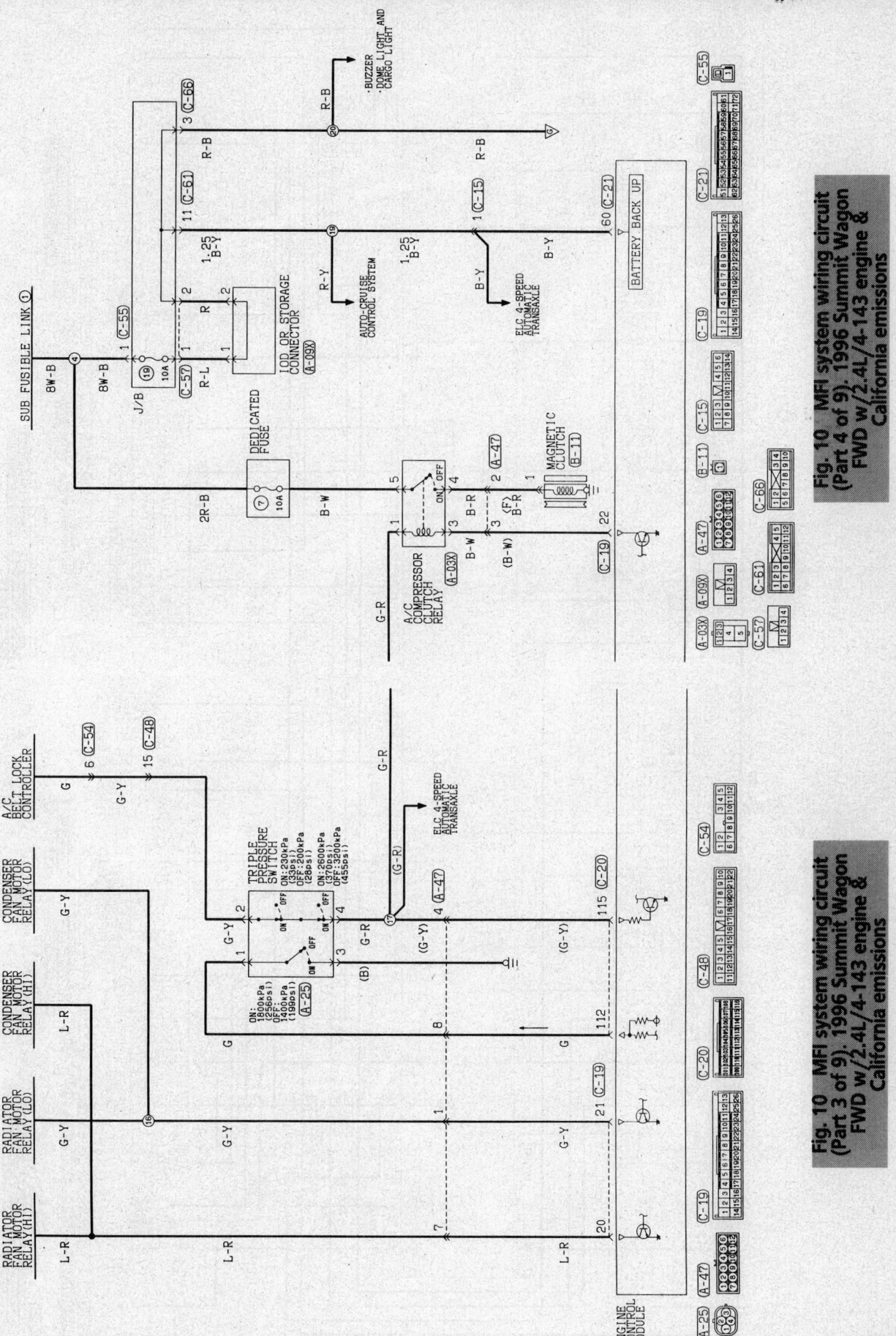

Fig. 10 MFI system wiring circuit
(Part 4 of 9). 1996 Summit Wagon
FWD w/2.4L/4-143 engine &
California emissions

Fig. 10 MFI system wiring circuit
(Part 3 of 9). 1996 Summit Wagon
FWD w/2.4L/4-143 engine &
California emissions

MULTI-POINT FUEL INJECTION (MODELS w/1.8L/4-107, 1.8L/4-110 & 2.4L/4-143 ENGINES, 1993-94 MODELS w/2.0L/4-122
ENGINE & 1995 TALON w/2.0L/4-122 TURBOCHARGED ENGINE)

7-39

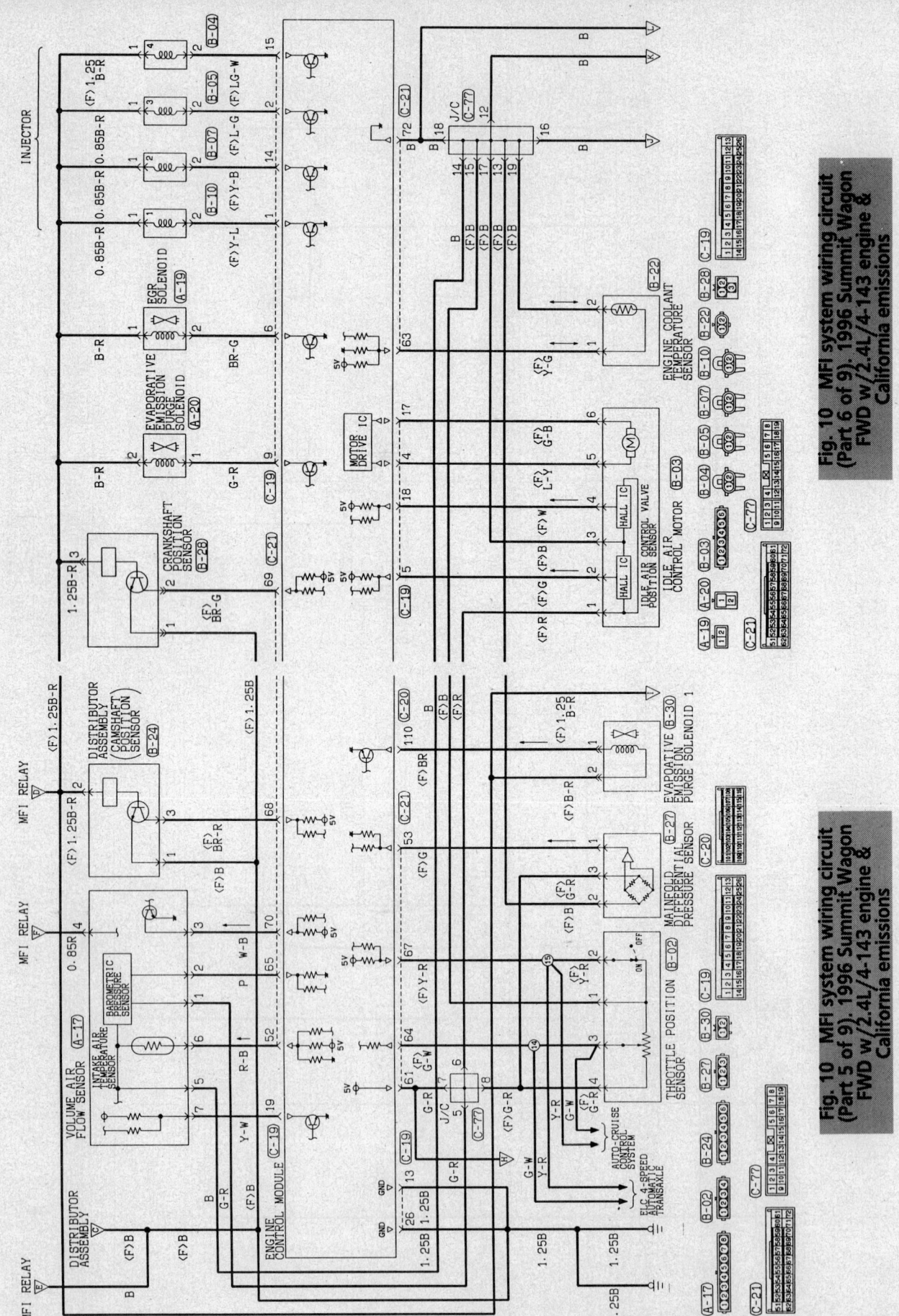

MULTI-POINT FUEL INJECTION (MODELS w/1.8L/4-107, 1.8L/4-110 & 2.4L/4-143 ENGINES, 1993-94 MODELS w/2.0L/4-122 ENGINE & 1995 TALON w/2.0L/4-122 TURBOCHARGED ENGINE)

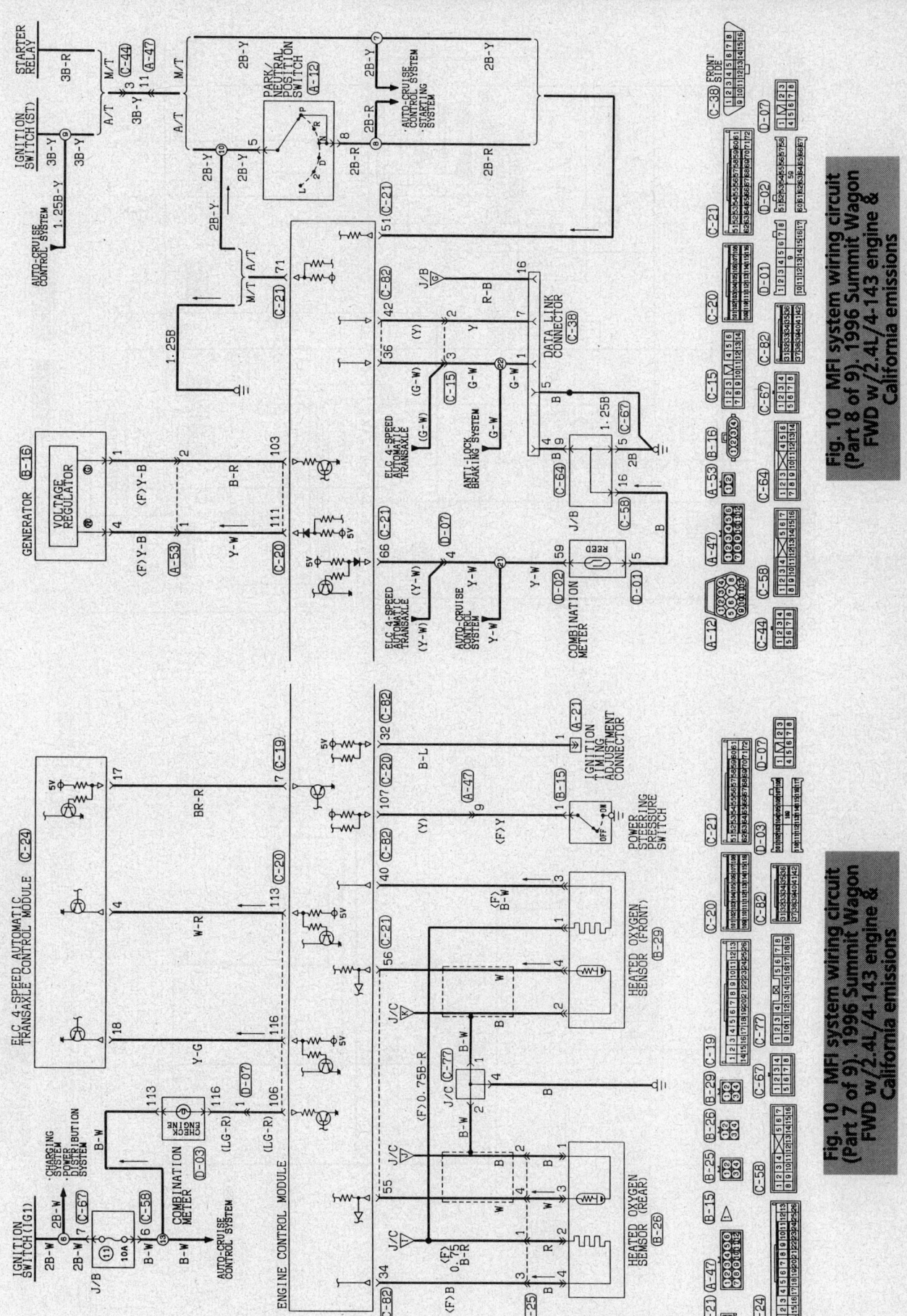

Fig. 10 MFI system wiring circuit (Part 8 of 9). 1996 Summit Wagon FWD w/2.4L/4-143 engine & California emissions

Fig. 10 MFI system wiring circuit (Part 7 of 9). 1996 Summit Wagon FWD w/2.4L/4-143 engine & California emissions

MULTI-POINT FUEL INJECTION (MODELS w/1.8L/4-107, 1.8L/4-110 & 2.4L/4-143 ENGINES, 1993-94 MODELS w/2.0L/4-122 ENGINE & 1995 TALON w/2.0L/4-122 TURBOCHARGED ENGINE)

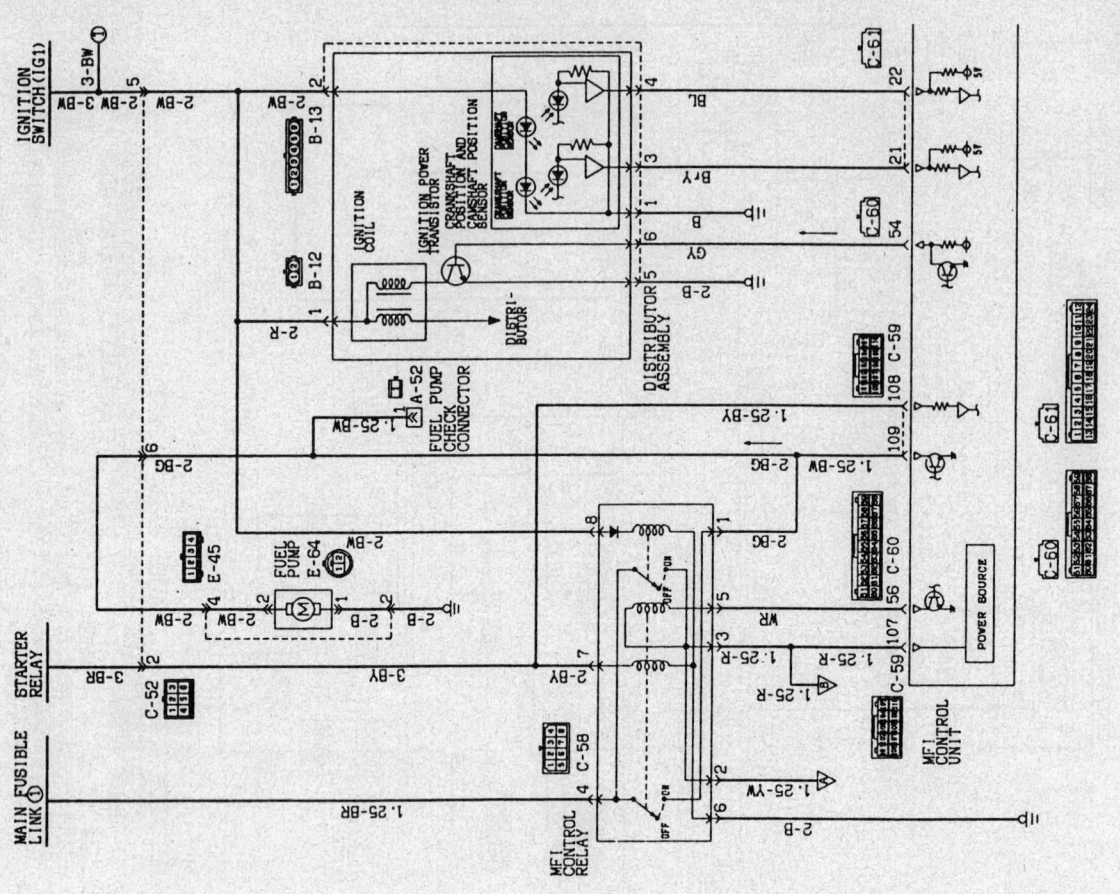

Fig. 11 MFI system wiring circuit (Part 1 of 4). 1993-94 Laser & Talon w/1.8L/4-107 engine & manual transaxle

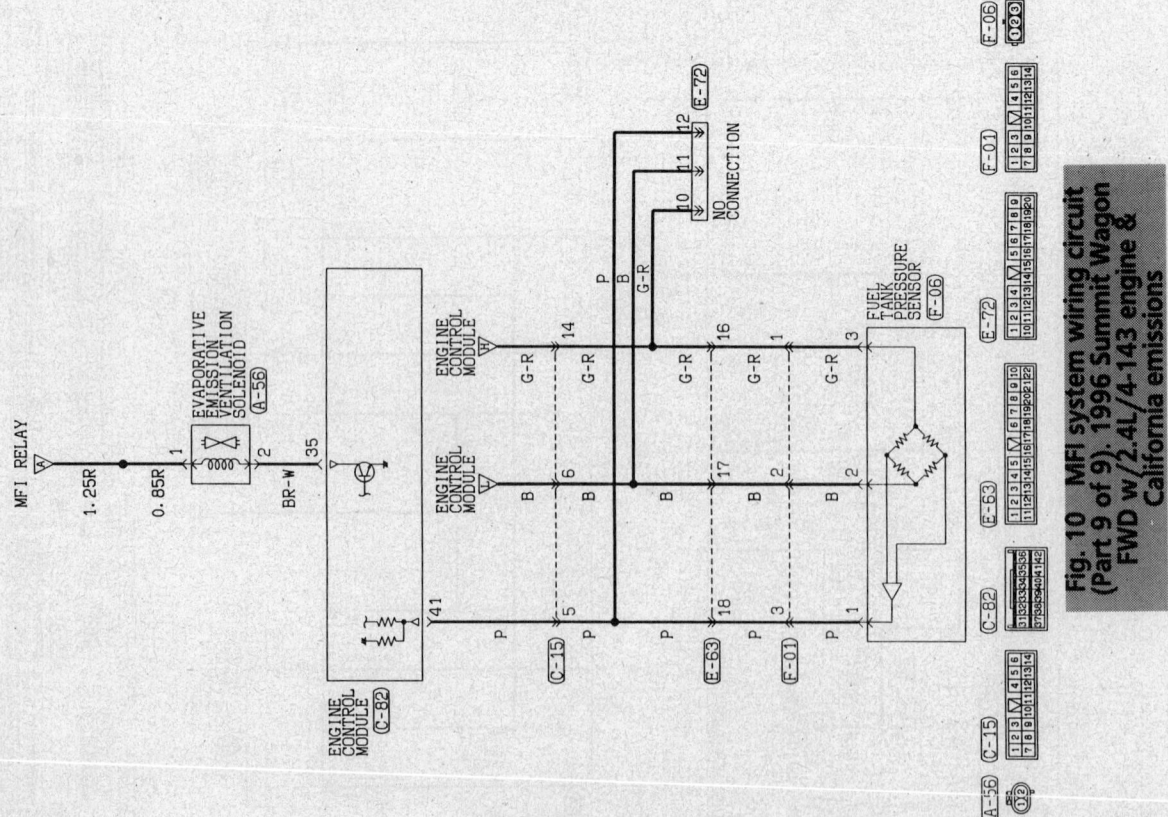

Fig. 10 MFI system wiring circuit (Part 9 of 9). 1996 Summit Wagon FWD w/2.4L/4-143 engine & California emissions

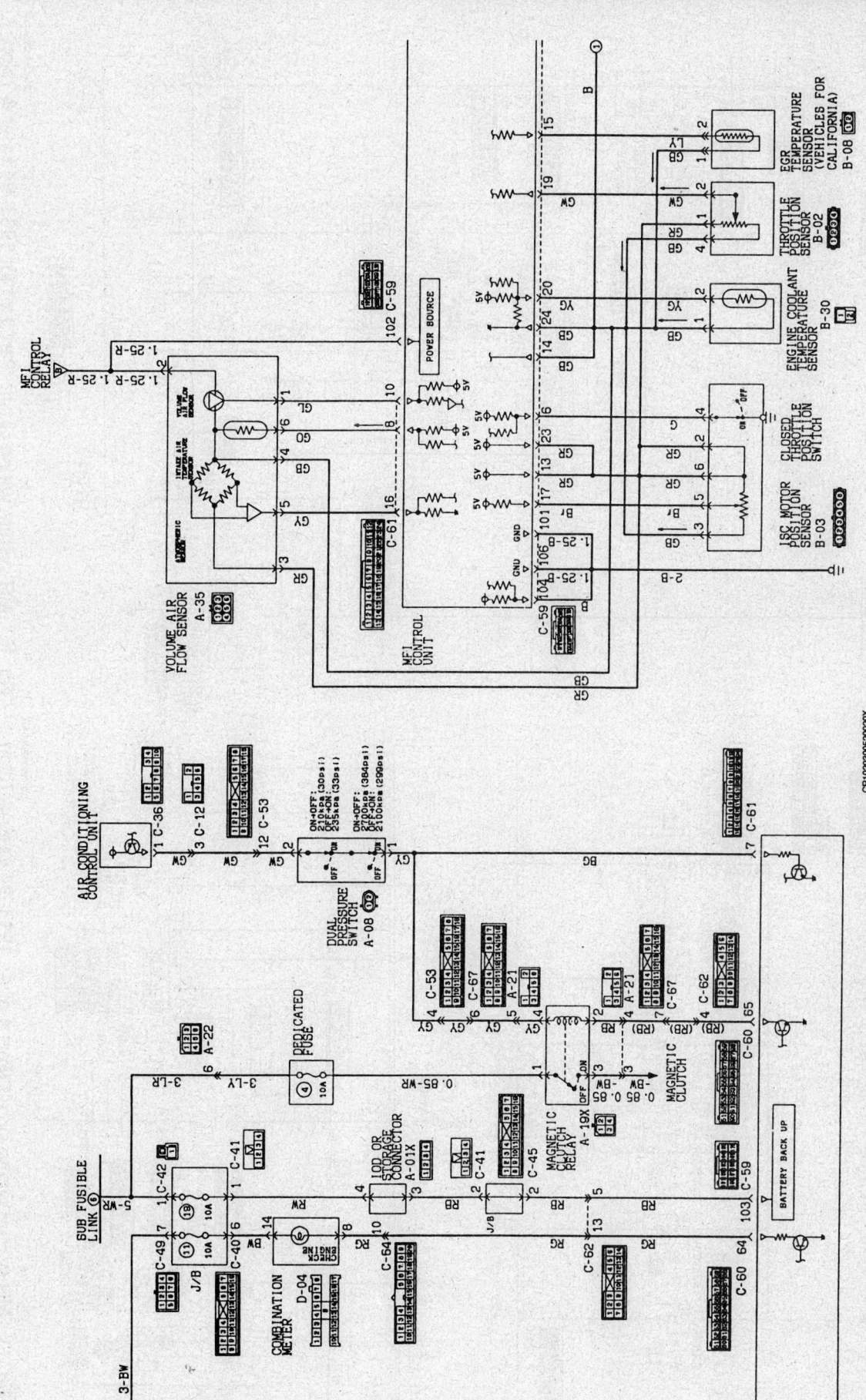

Fig. 11   MFI system wiring circuit (Part 3 of 4). 1993-94 Laser & Talon w/1.8L/4-107 engine & manual transaxle

Fig. 11   MFI system wiring circuit (Part 2 of 4). 1993-94 Laser & Talon w/1.8L/4-107 engine & manual transaxle

MULTI-POINT FUEL INJECTION (MODELS w/1.8L/4-107, 1.8L/4-110 & 2.4L/4-143 ENGINES, 1993-94 MODELS w/2.0L/4-122 ENGINE & 1995 TALON w/2.0L/4-122 TURBOCHARGED ENGINE)

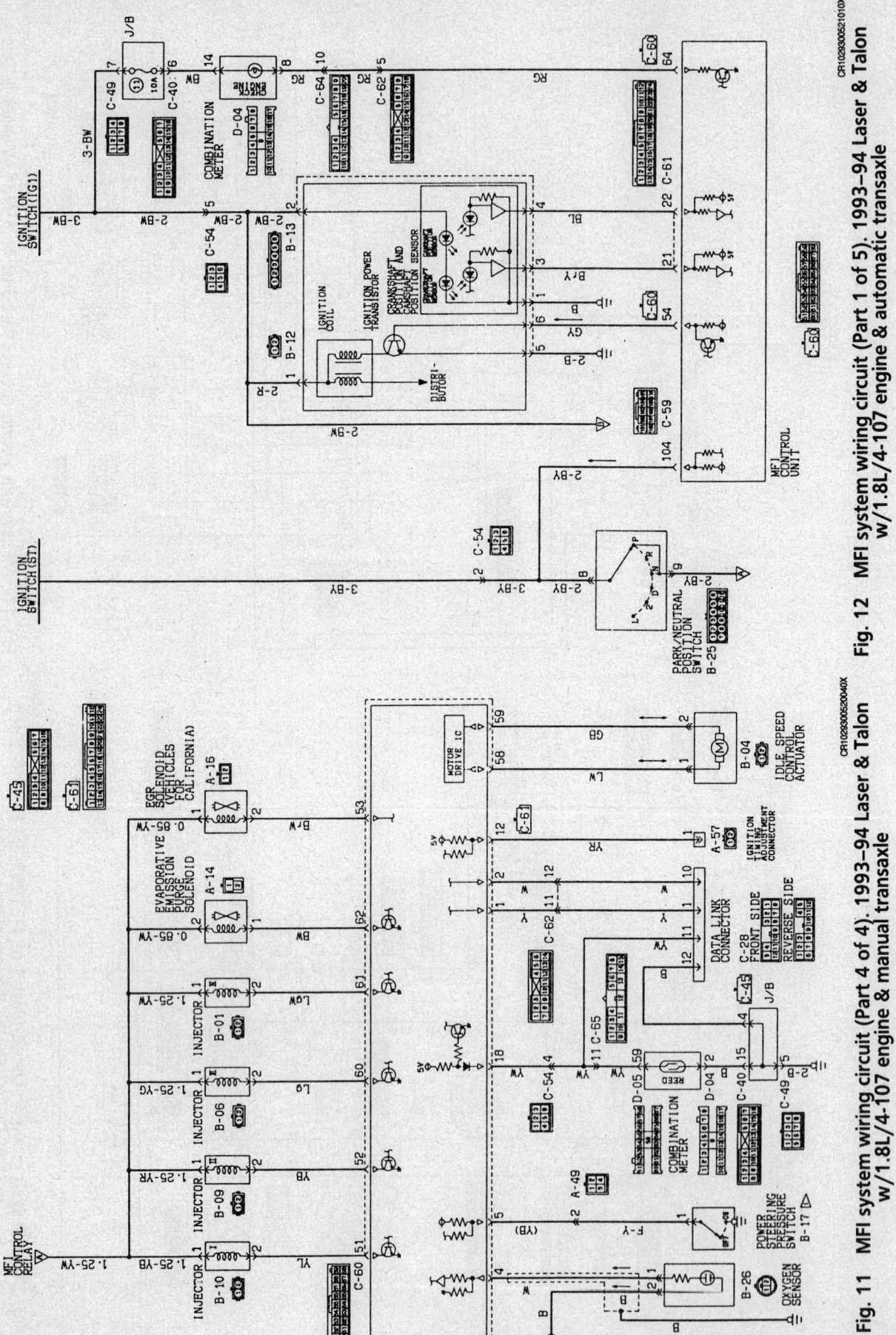

Fig. 12 MFI system wiring circuit (Part 1 of 5). 1993–94 Laser & Talon w/1.8L/4-107 engine & automatic transaxle

Fig. 11 MFI system wiring circuit (Part 4 of 4). 1993–94 Laser & Talon w/1.8L/4-107 engine & manual transaxle

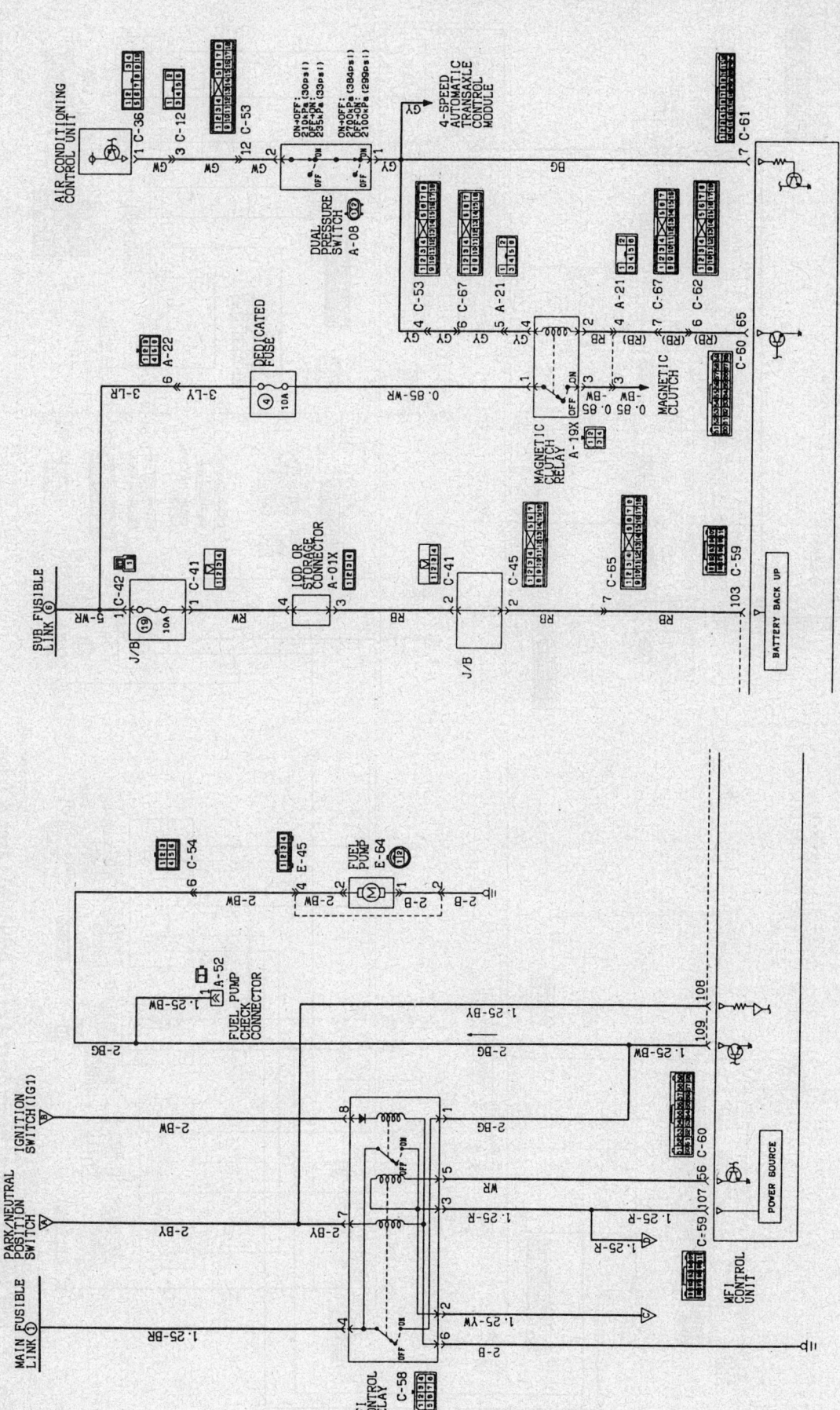

Fig. 12   MFI system wiring circuit (Part 3 of 5). 1993–94 Laser & Talon w/1.8L/4-107 engine & automatic transaxle

Fig. 12   MFI system wiring circuit (Part 2 of 5). 1993–94 Laser & Talon w/1.8L/4-107 engine & automatic transaxle

MULTI-POINT FUEL INJECTION (MODELS w/1.8L/4-107, 1.8L/4-110 & 2.4L/4-143 ENGINES, 1993-94 MODELS w/2.0L/4-122 ENGINE & 1995 TALON w/2.0L/4-122 TURBOCHARGED ENGINE)

7-45

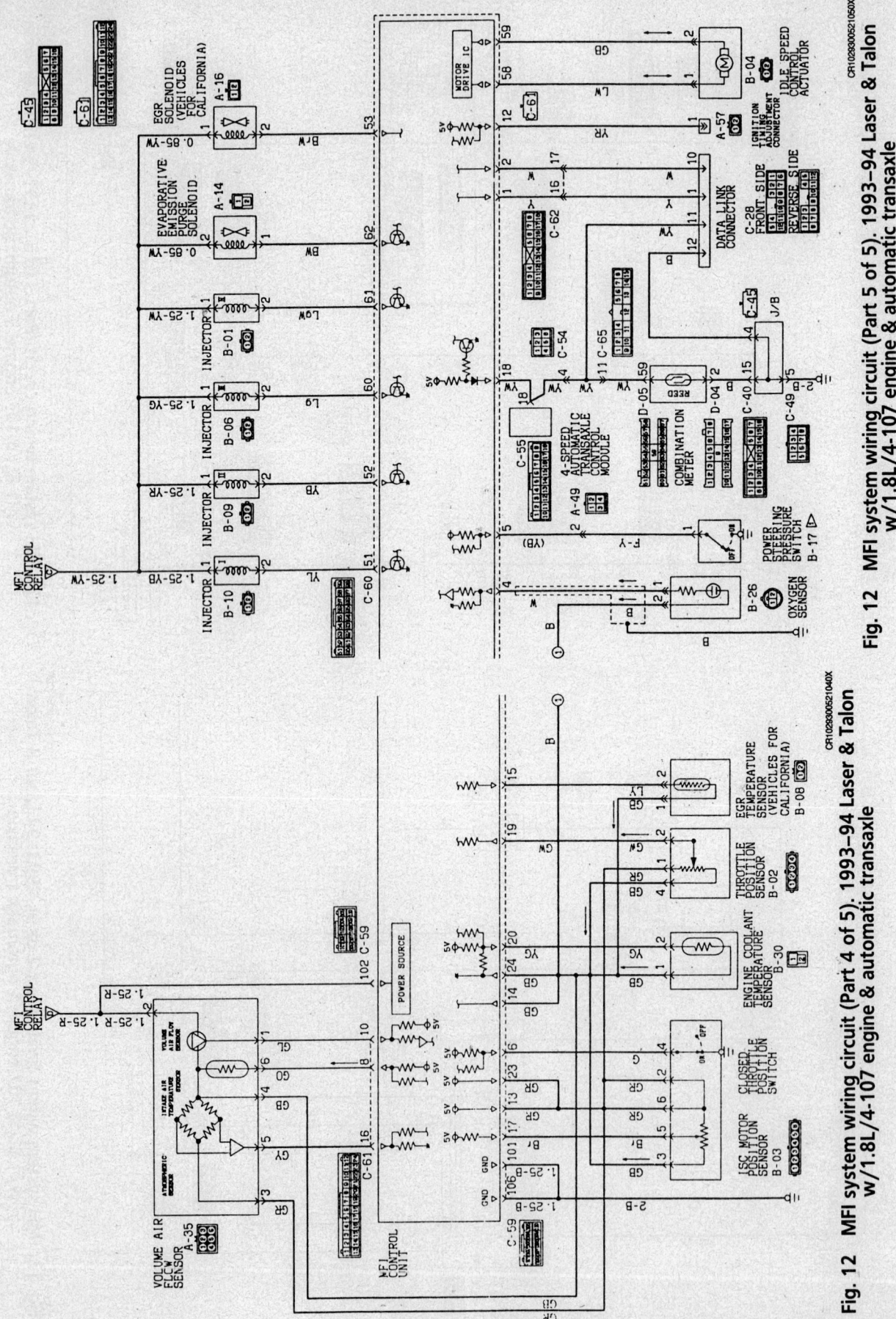

Fig. 12 MFI system wiring circuit (Part 5 of 5). 1993–94 Laser & Talon w/1.8L/4-107 engine & automatic transaxle

Fig. 12 MFI system wiring circuit (Part 4 of 5). 1993–94 Laser & Talon w/1.8L/4-107 engine & automatic transaxle

7-46

MULTI-POINT FUEL INJECTION (MODELS w/1.8L/4-107, 1.8L/4-110 & 2.4L/4-143 ENGINES, 1993-94 MODELS w/2.0L/4-122 ENGINE & 1995 TALON w/2.0L/4-122 TURBOCHARGED ENGINE)

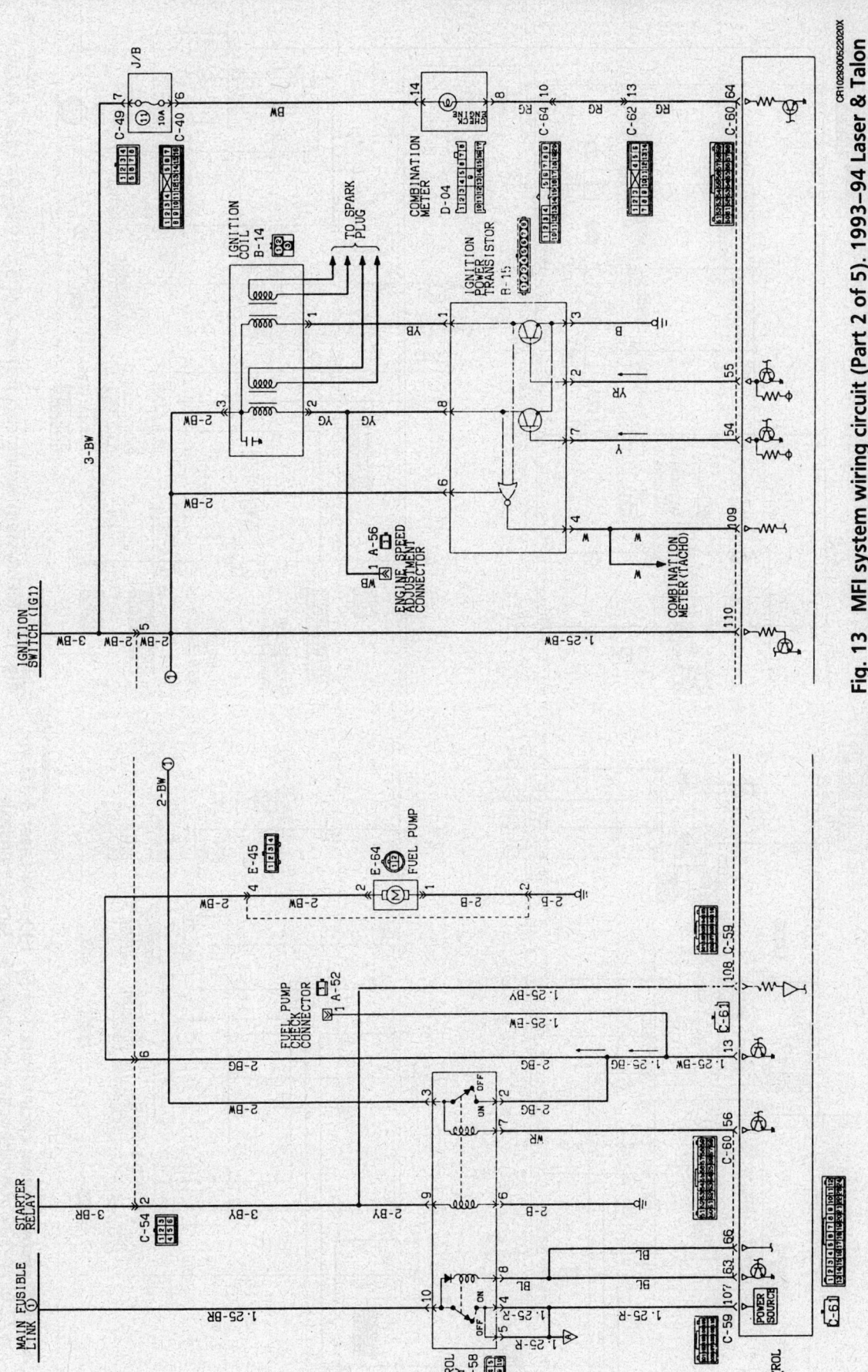

Fig. 13 MFI system wiring circuit (Part 2 of 5). 1993–94 Laser & Talon w/2.0L/4-122 non-turbocharged engine & manual transaxle

Fig. 13 MFI system wiring circuit (Part 1 of 5). 1993–94 Laser & Talon w/2.0L/4-122 non-turbocharged engine & manual transaxle

MULTI-POINT FUEL INJECTION (MODELS w/1.8L/4-107, 1.8L/4-110 & 2.4L/4-143 ENGINES, 1993-94 MODELS w/2.0L/4-122 ENGINE & 1995 TALON w/2.0L/4-122 TURBOCHARGED ENGINE)

7-47

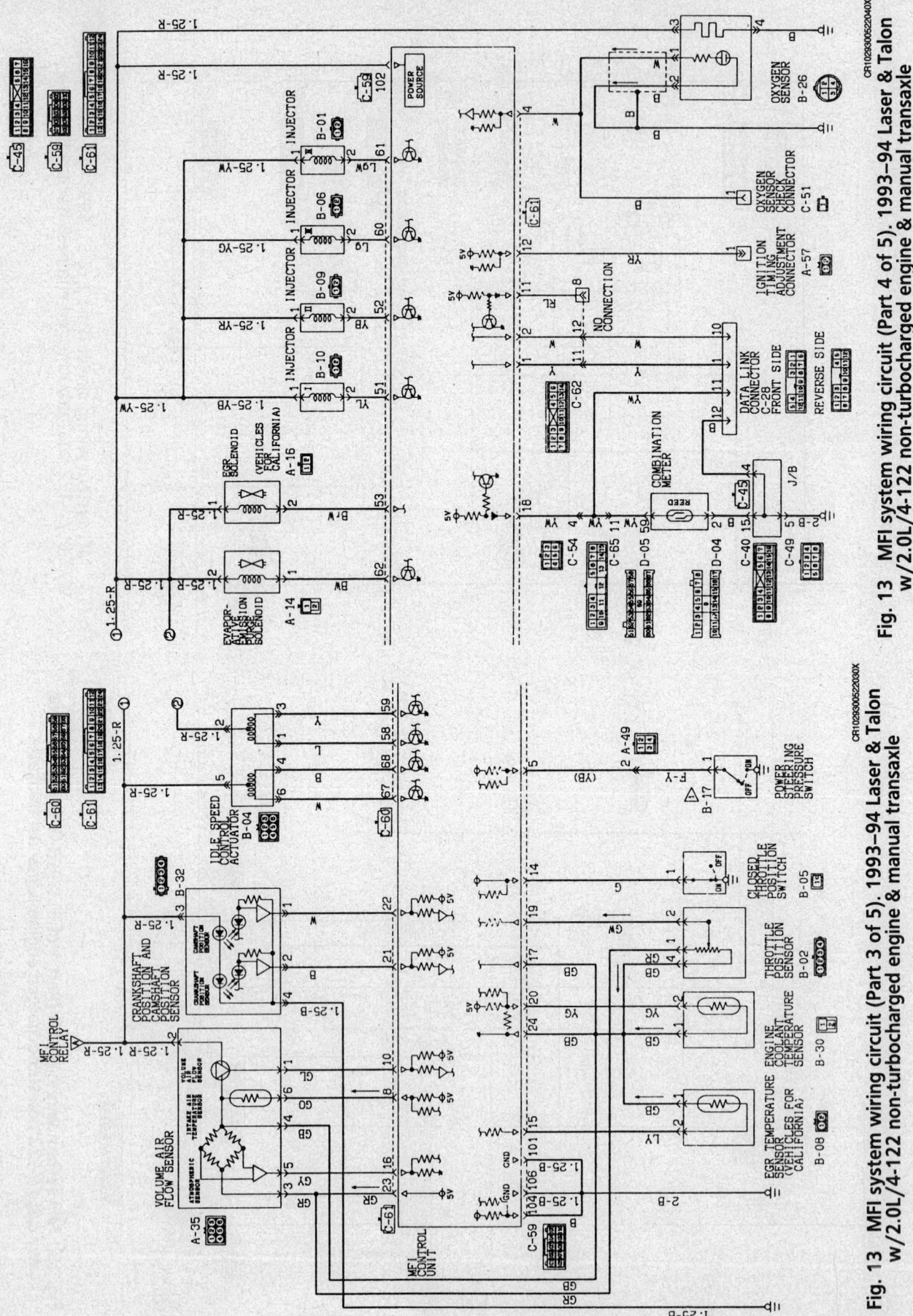

Fig. 13 MFI system wiring circuit (Part 4 of 5). 1993-94 Laser & Talon w/2.0L/4-122 non-turbocharged engine & manual transaxle

Fig. 13 MFI system wiring circuit (Part 3 of 5). 1993-94 Laser & Talon w/2.0L/4-122 non-turbocharged engine & manual transaxle

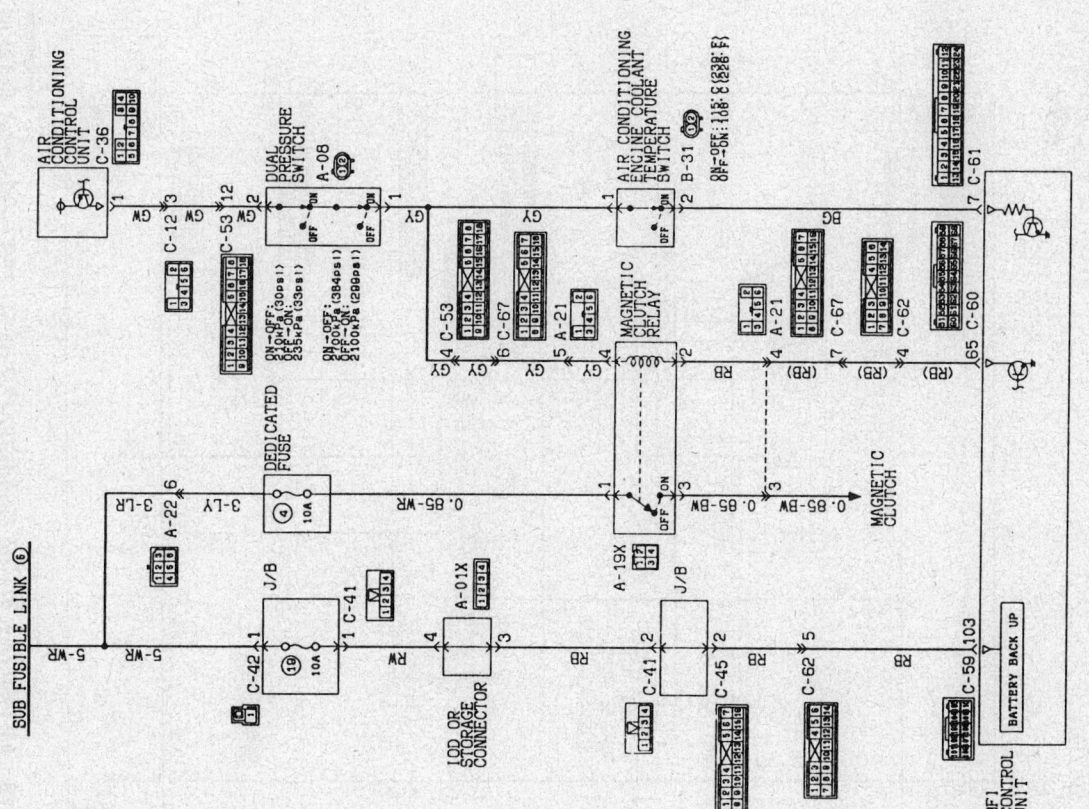

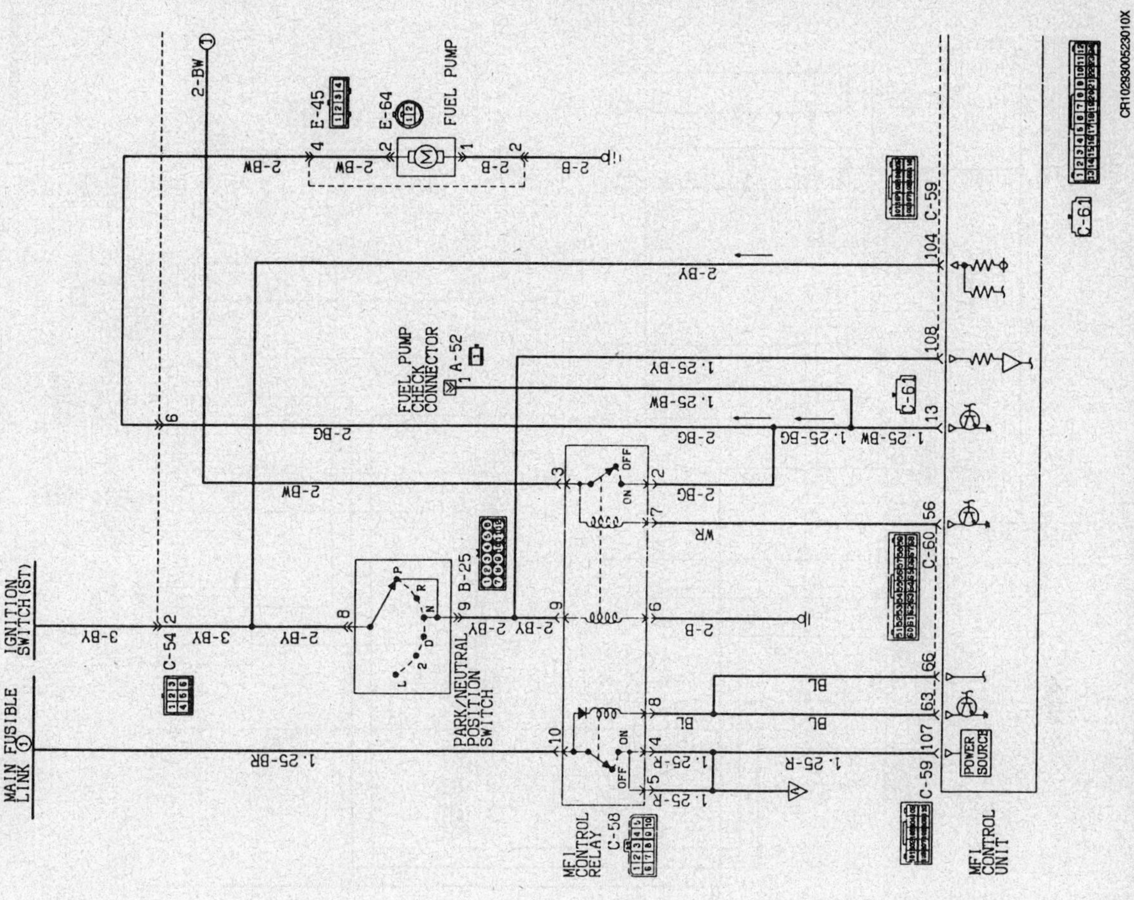

Fig. 14 MFI system wiring circuit (Part 1 of 5). 1993–94 Laser & Talon w/2.0L/4-122 non-turbocharged engine & automatic transaxle

Fig. 13 MFI system wiring circuit (Part 5 of 5). 1993–94 Laser & Talon w/2.0L/4-122 non-turbocharged engine & manual transaxle

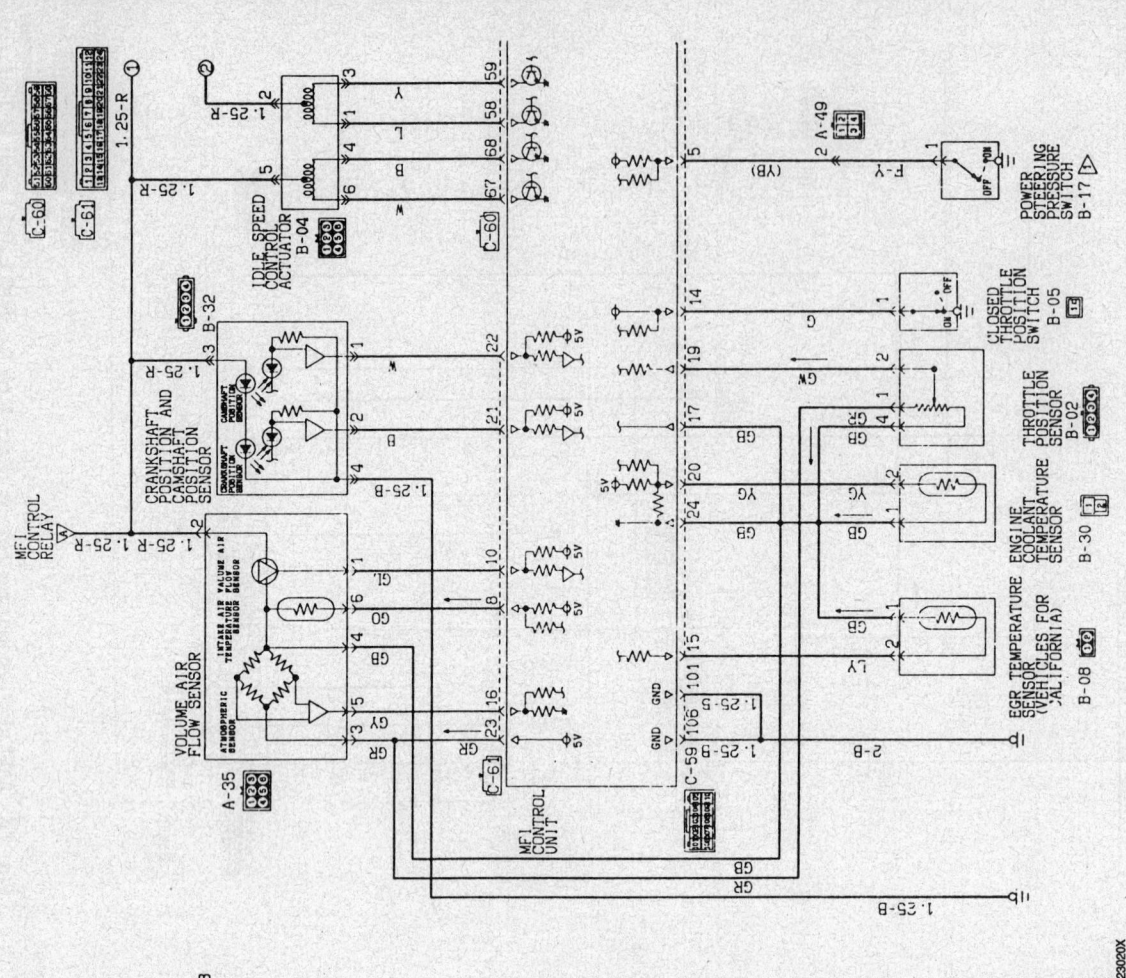

Fig. 14 MFI system wiring circuit (Part 3 of 5). 1993–94 Laser & Talon w/2.0L/4-122 non-turbocharged engine & automatic transaxle

Fig. 14 MFI system wiring circuit (Part 2 of 5). 1993–94 Laser & Talon w/2.0L/4-122 non-turbocharged engine & automatic transaxle

MULTI-POINT FUEL INJECTION (MODELS w/1.8L/4-107, 1.8L/4-110 & 2.4L/4-143 ENGINES, 1993-94 MODELS w/2.0L/4-122 ENGINE & 1995 TALON w/2.0L/4-122 TURBOCHARGED ENGINE)

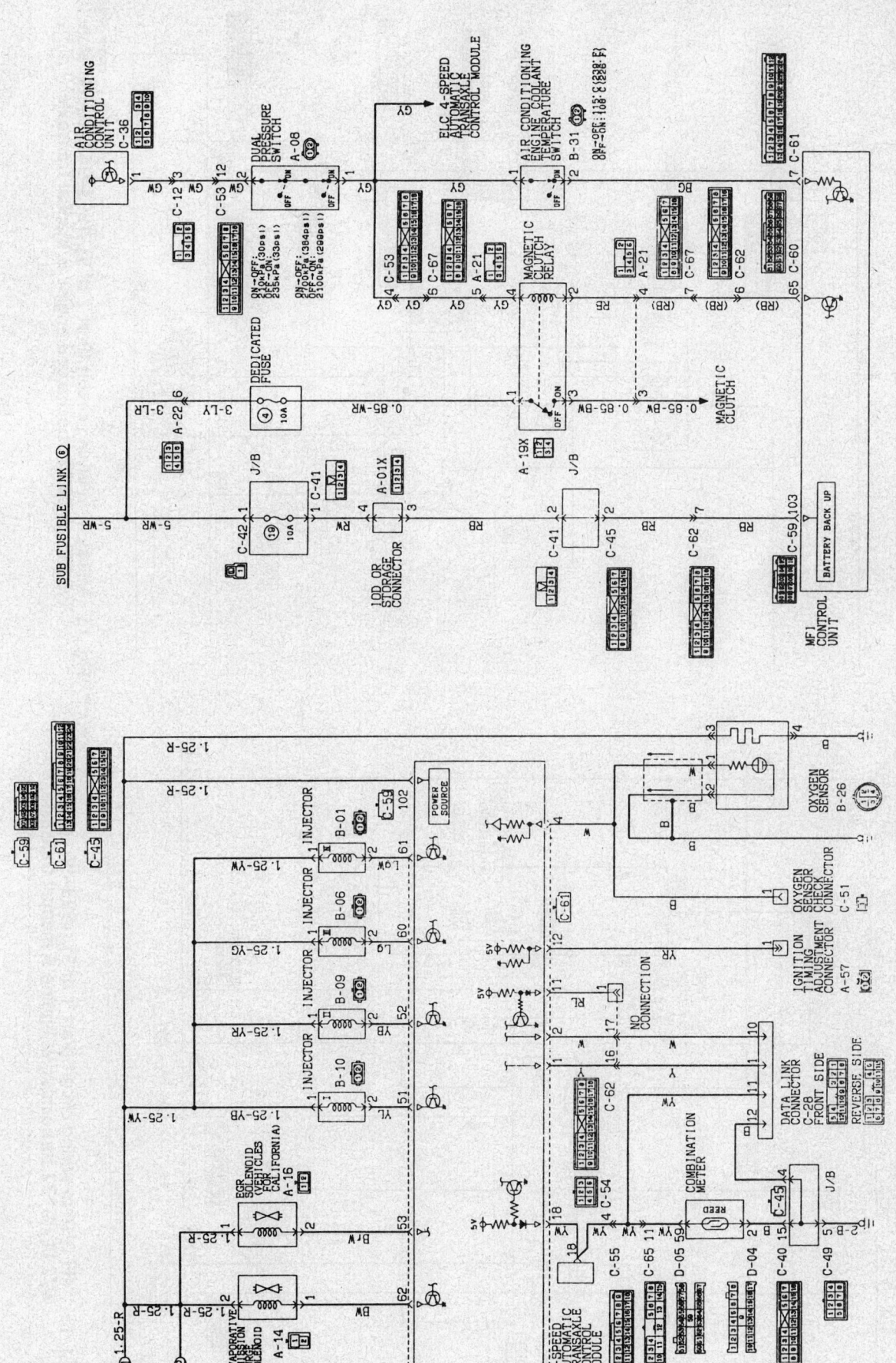

Fig. 14 MFI system wiring circuit (Part 5 of 5). 1993–94 Laser & Talon w/2.0L/4-122 non-turbocharged engine & automatic transaxle

Fig. 14 MFI system wiring circuit (Part 4 of 5). 1993–94 Laser & Talon w/2.0L/4-122 non-turbocharged engine & automatic transaxle

MULTI-POINT FUEL INJECTION (MODELS w/1.8L/4-107, 1.8L/4-110 & 2.4L/4-143 ENGINES, 1993-94 MODELS w/2.0L/4-122 ENGINE & 1995 TALON w/2.0L/4-122 TURBOCHARGED ENGINE)

7-51

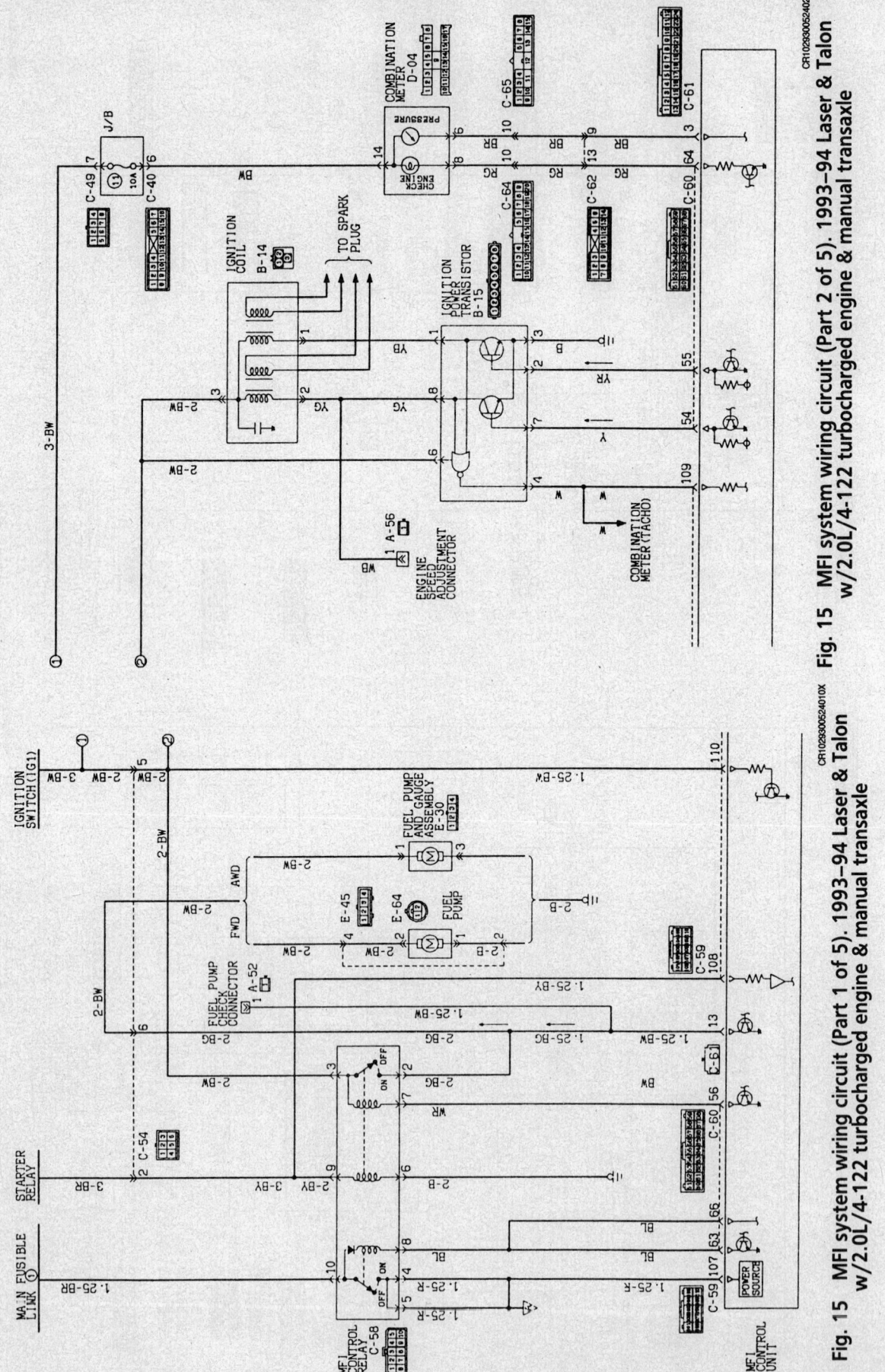

Fig. 15 MFI system wiring circuit (Part 2 of 5). 1993–94 Laser & Talon w/2.0L/4-122 turbocharged engine & manual transaxle

Fig. 15 MFI system wiring circuit (Part 1 of 5). 1993–94 Laser & Talon w/2.0L/4-122 turbocharged engine & manual transaxle

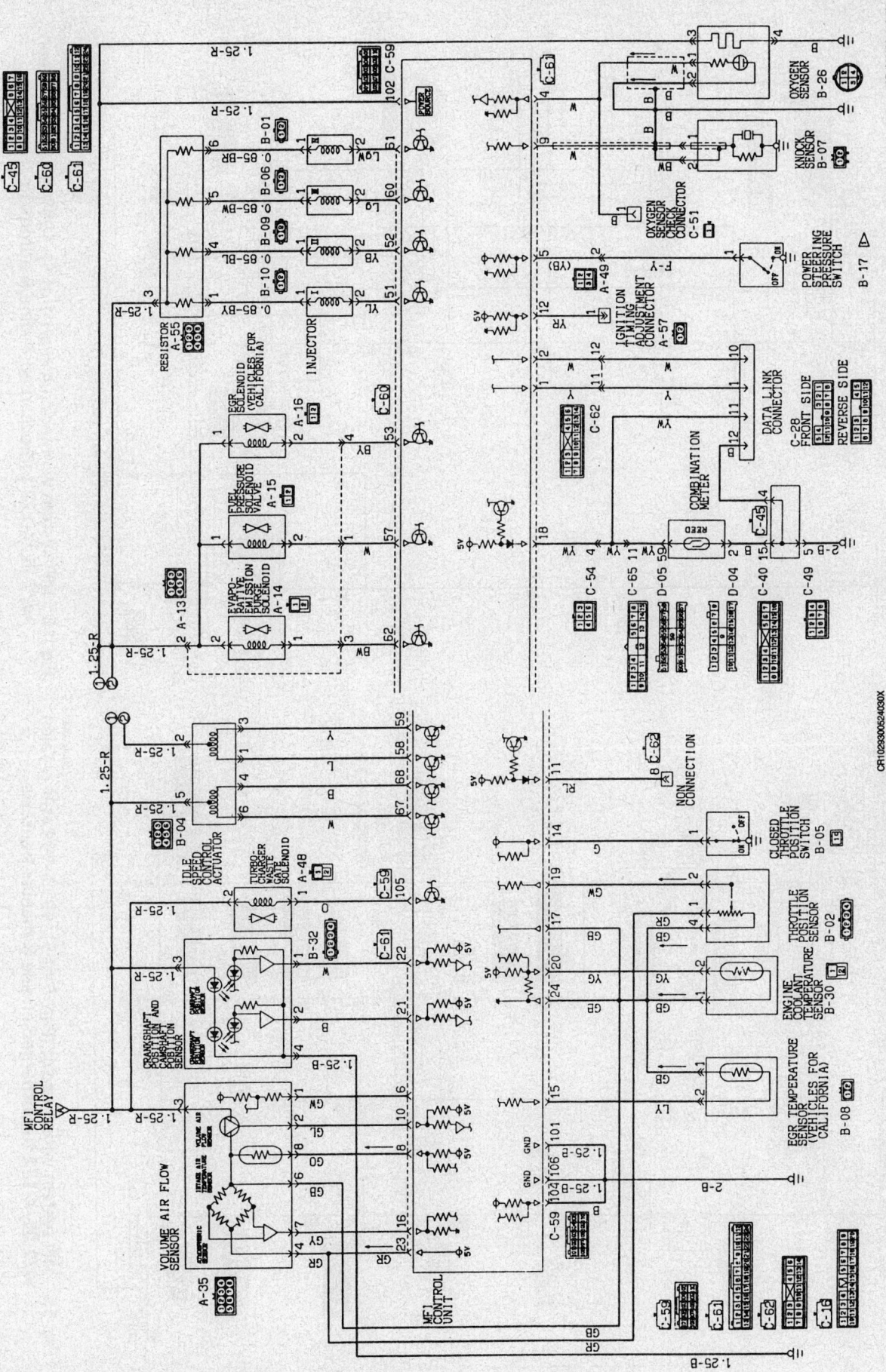

Fig. 15 MFI system wiring circuit (Part 4 of 5). 1993–94 Laser & Talon w/2.0L/4-122 turbocharged engine & manual transaxle

Fig. 15 MFI system wiring circuit (Part 3 of 5). 1993–94 Laser & Talon w/2.0L/4-122 turbocharged engine & manual transaxle

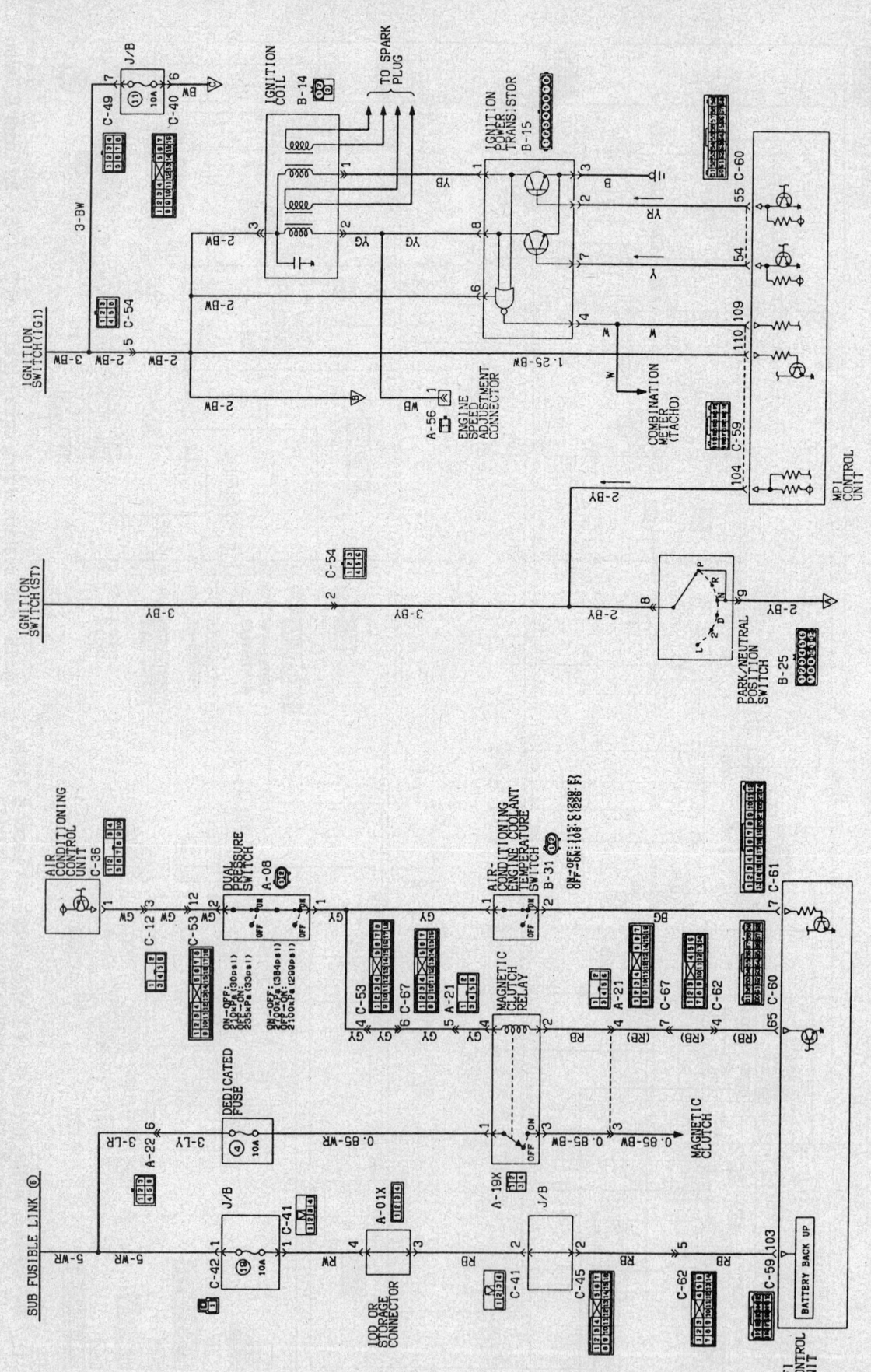

Fig. 16 MFI system wiring circuit (Part 1 of 5). 1993–94 Laser & Talon w/2.0L/4-122 turbocharged engine & automatic transaxle

Fig. 15 MFI system wiring circuit (Part 5 of 5). 1993–94 Laser & Talon w/2.0L/4-122 turbocharged engine & manual transaxle

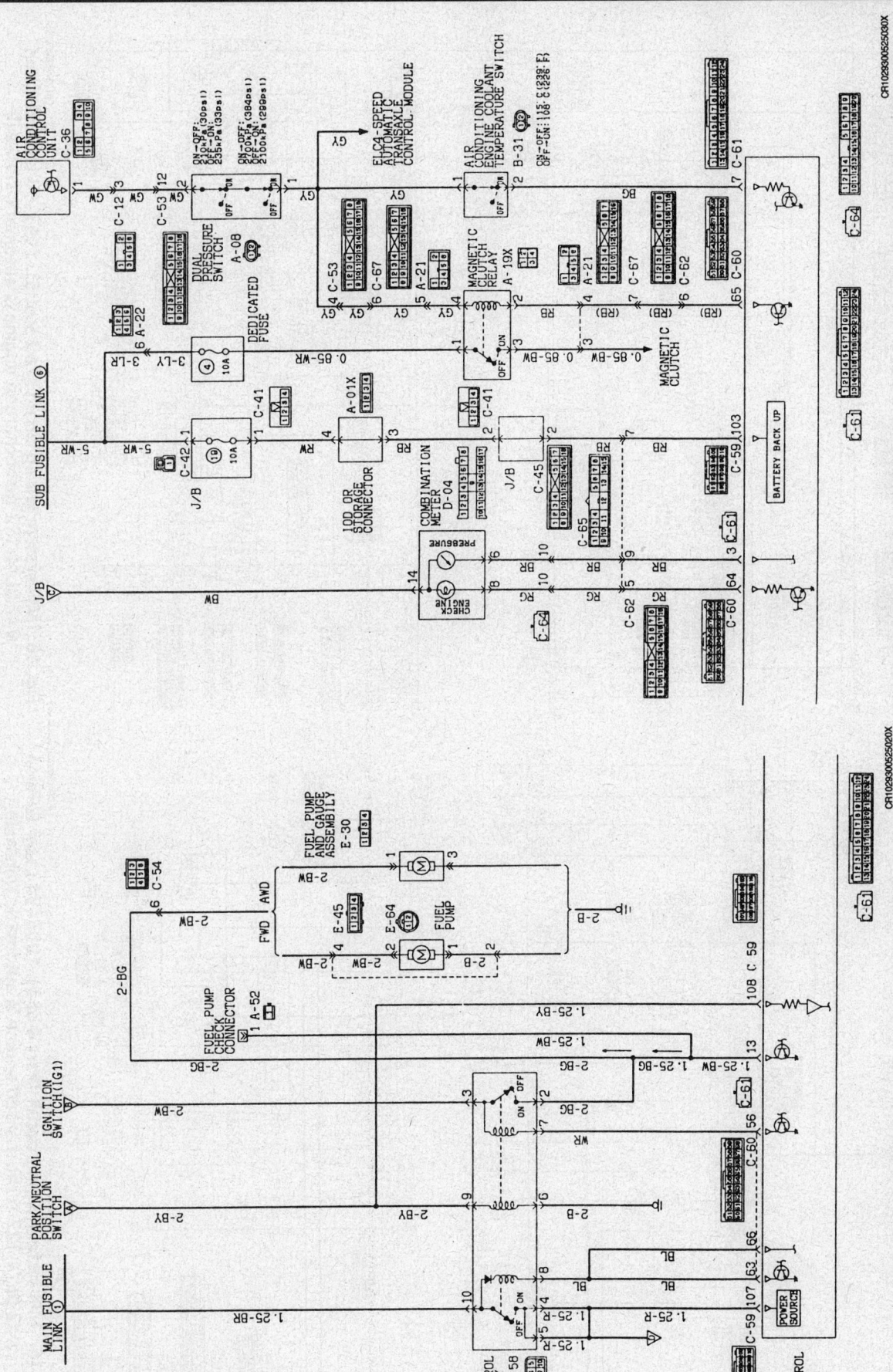

Fig. 16 MFI system wiring circuit (Part 3 of 5). 1993-94 Laser & Talon w/2.0L/4-122 turbocharged engine & automatic transaxle

Fig. 16 MFI system wiring circuit (Part 2 of 5). 1993-94 Laser & Talon w/2.0L/4-122 turbocharged engine & automatic transaxle

MULTI-POINT FUEL INJECTION (MODELS w/1.8L/4-107, 1.8L/4-110 & 2.4L/4-143 ENGINES, 1993-94 MODELS w/2.0L/4-122 ENGINE & 1995 TALON w/2.0L/4-122 TURBOCHARGED ENGINE)

7-55

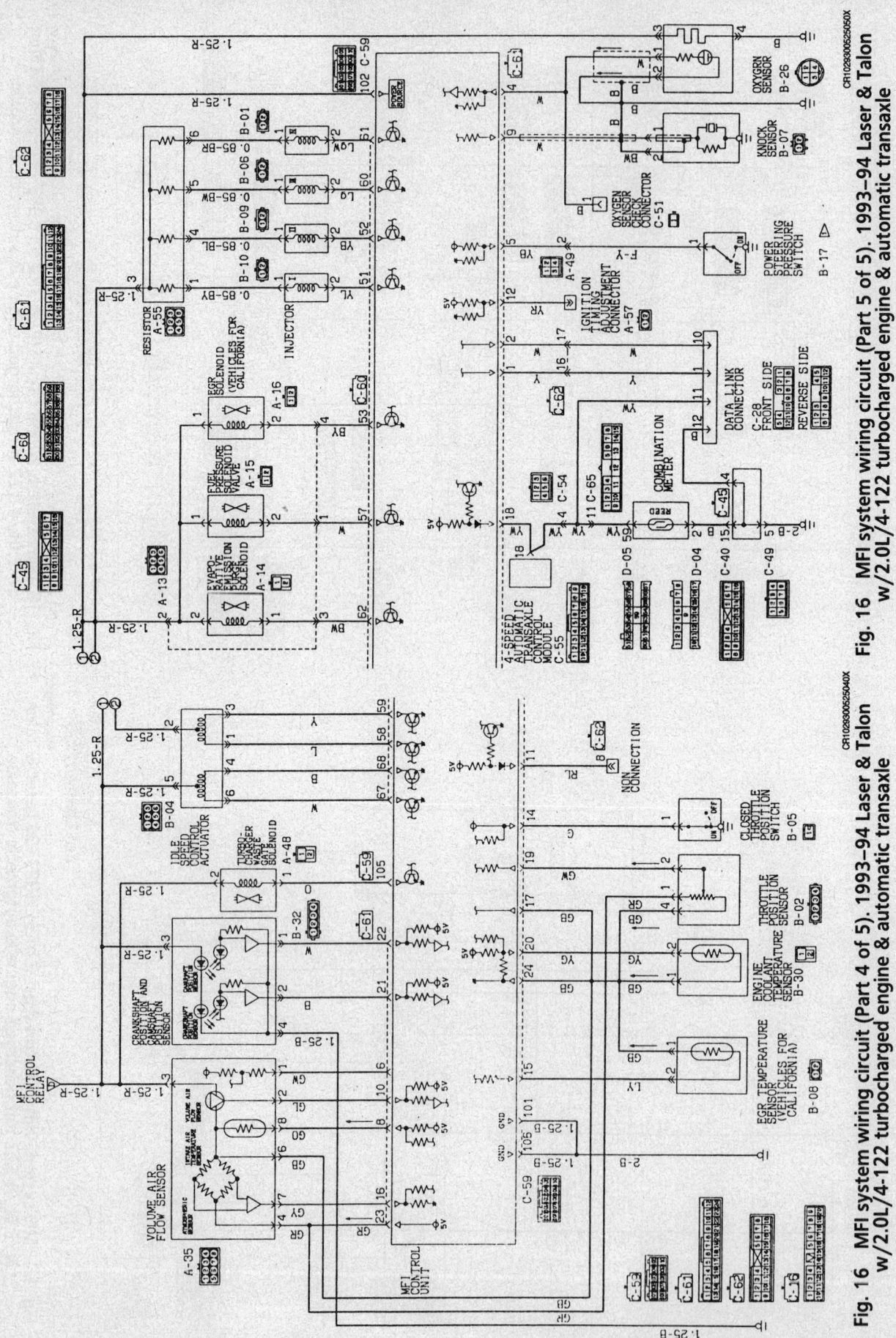

Fig. 16 MFI system wiring circuit (Part 5 of 5). 1993–94 Laser & Talon w/2.0L/4-122 turbocharged engine & automatic transaxle

Fig. 16 MFI system wiring circuit (Part 4 of 5). 1993–94 Laser & Talon w/2.0L/4-122 turbocharged engine & automatic transaxle

Fig. 17 MFI system wiring circuit (Part 2 of 6). 1995–96 Summit w/1.8L/4-110 engine & Federal emissions

Fig. 17 MFI system wiring circuit (Part 1 of 6). 1995–96 Summit w/1.8L/4-110 engine & Federal emissions

MULTI-POINT FUEL INJECTION (MODELS w/1.8L/4-107, 1.8L/4-110 & 2.4L/4-143 ENGINES, 1993-94 MODELS w/2.0L/4-122 ENGINE & 1995 TALON w/2.0L/4-122 TURBOCHARGED ENGINE)

7-57

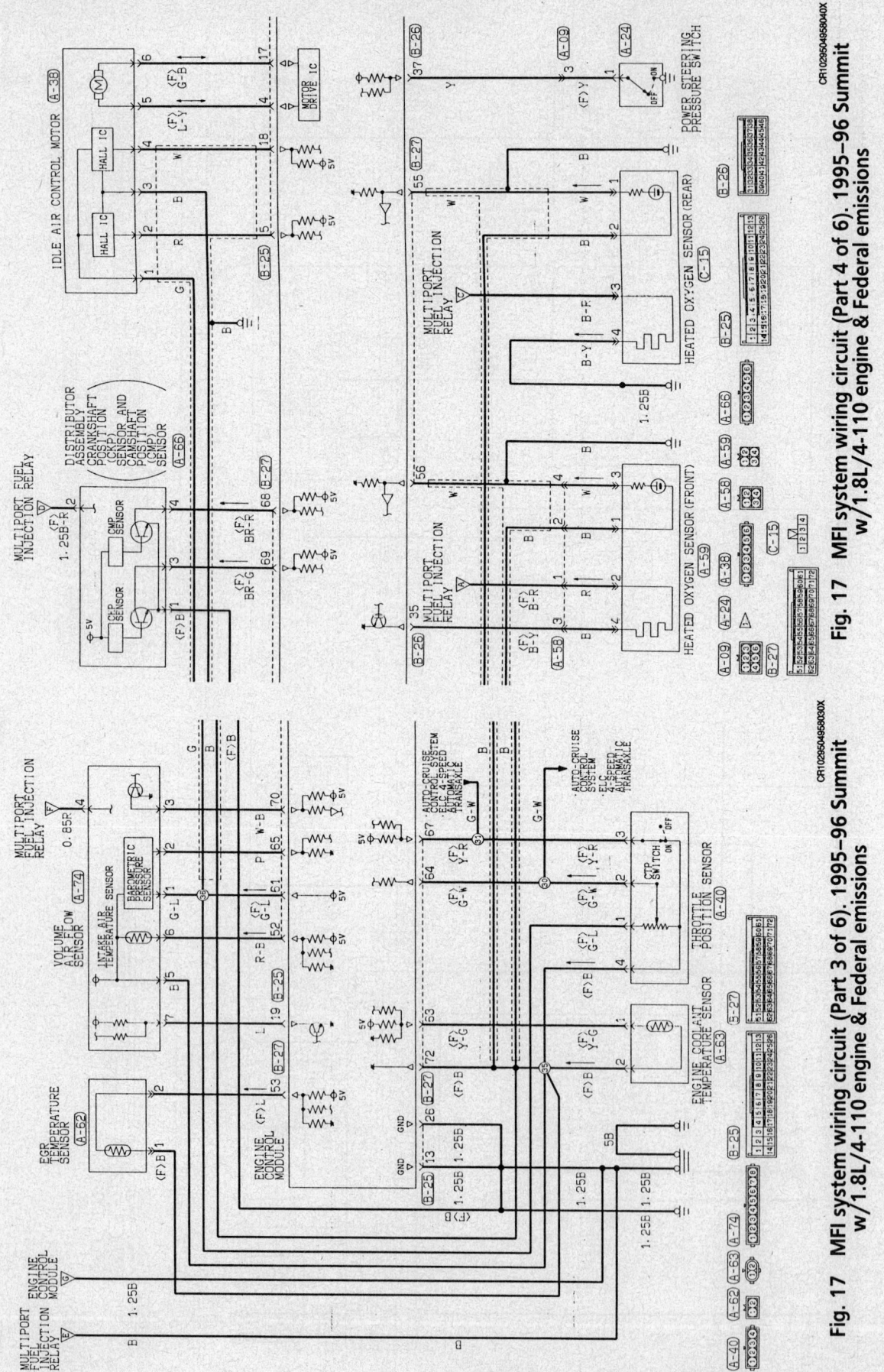

Fig. 17 MFI system wiring circuit (Part 4 of 6). 1995–96 Summit w/1.8L/4-110 engine & Federal emissions

Fig. 17 MFI system wiring circuit (Part 3 of 6). 1995–96 Summit w/1.8L/4-110 engine & Federal emissions

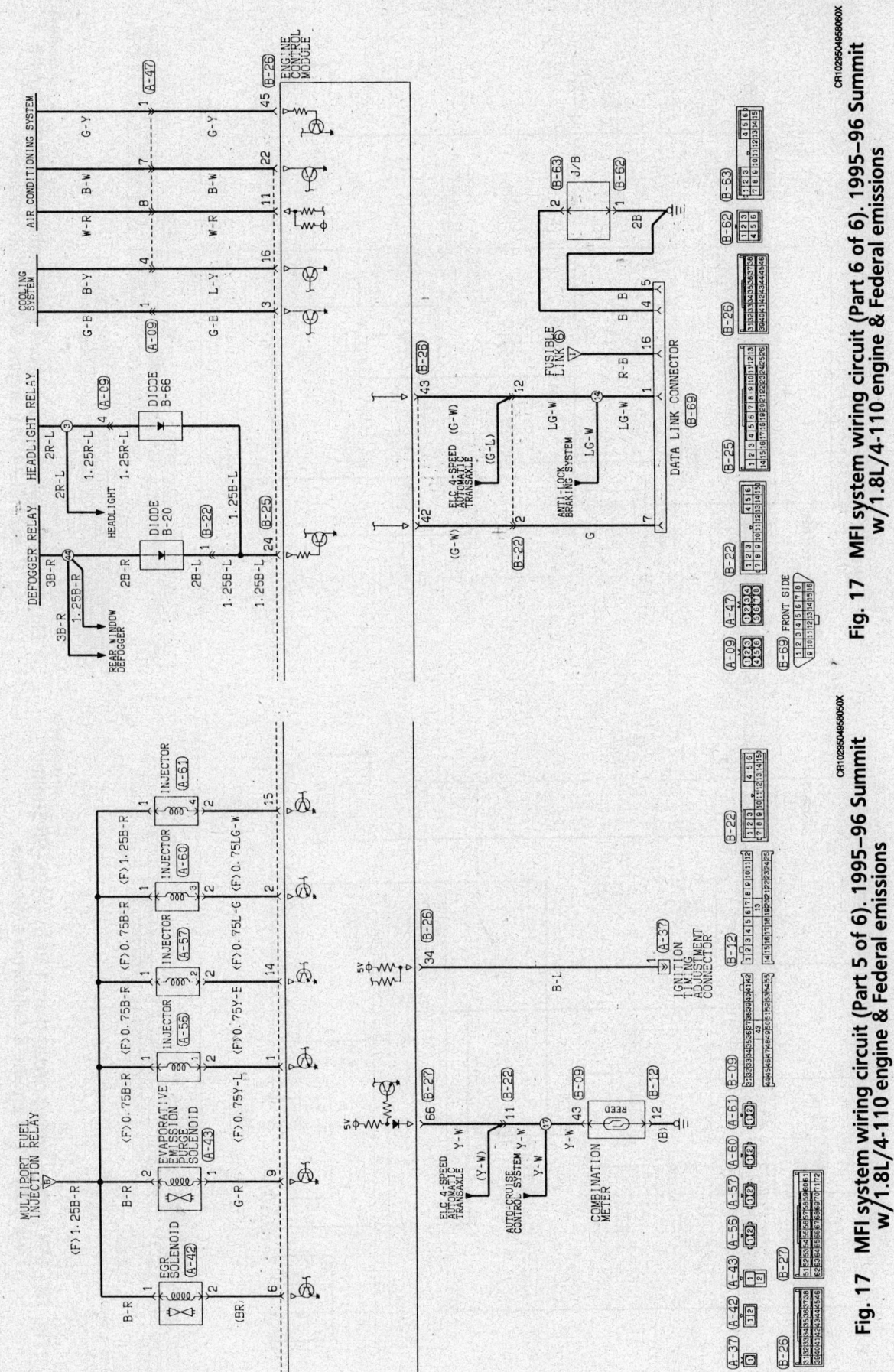

Fig. 17 MFI system wiring circuit (Part 6 of 6). 1995–96 Summit w/1.8L/4-110 engine & Federal emissions

Fig. 17 MFI system wiring circuit (Part 5 of 6). 1995–96 Summit w/1.8L/4-110 engine & Federal emissions

MULTI-POINT FUEL INJECTION (MODELS w/1.8L/4-107, 1.8L/4-110 & 2.4L/4-143 ENGINES, 1993-94 MODELS w/2.0L/4-122 ENGINE & 1995 TALON w/2.0L/4-122 TURBOCHARGED ENGINE)

7-59

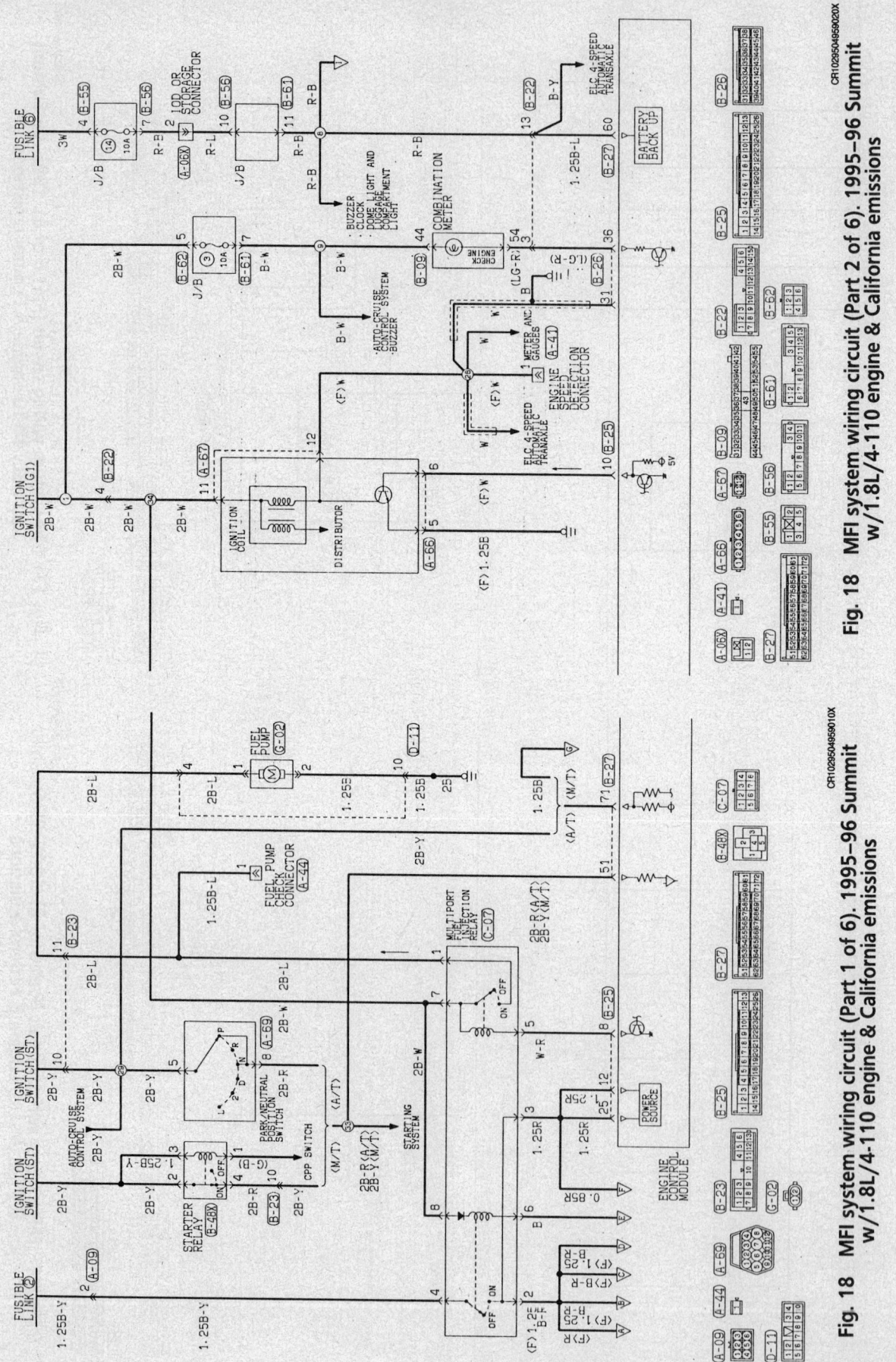

Fig. 18   MFI system wiring circuit (Part 2 of 6). 1995–96 Summit w/1.8L/4-110 engine & California emissions

Fig. 18   MFI system wiring circuit (Part 1 of 6). 1995–96 Summit w/1.8L/4-110 engine & California emissions

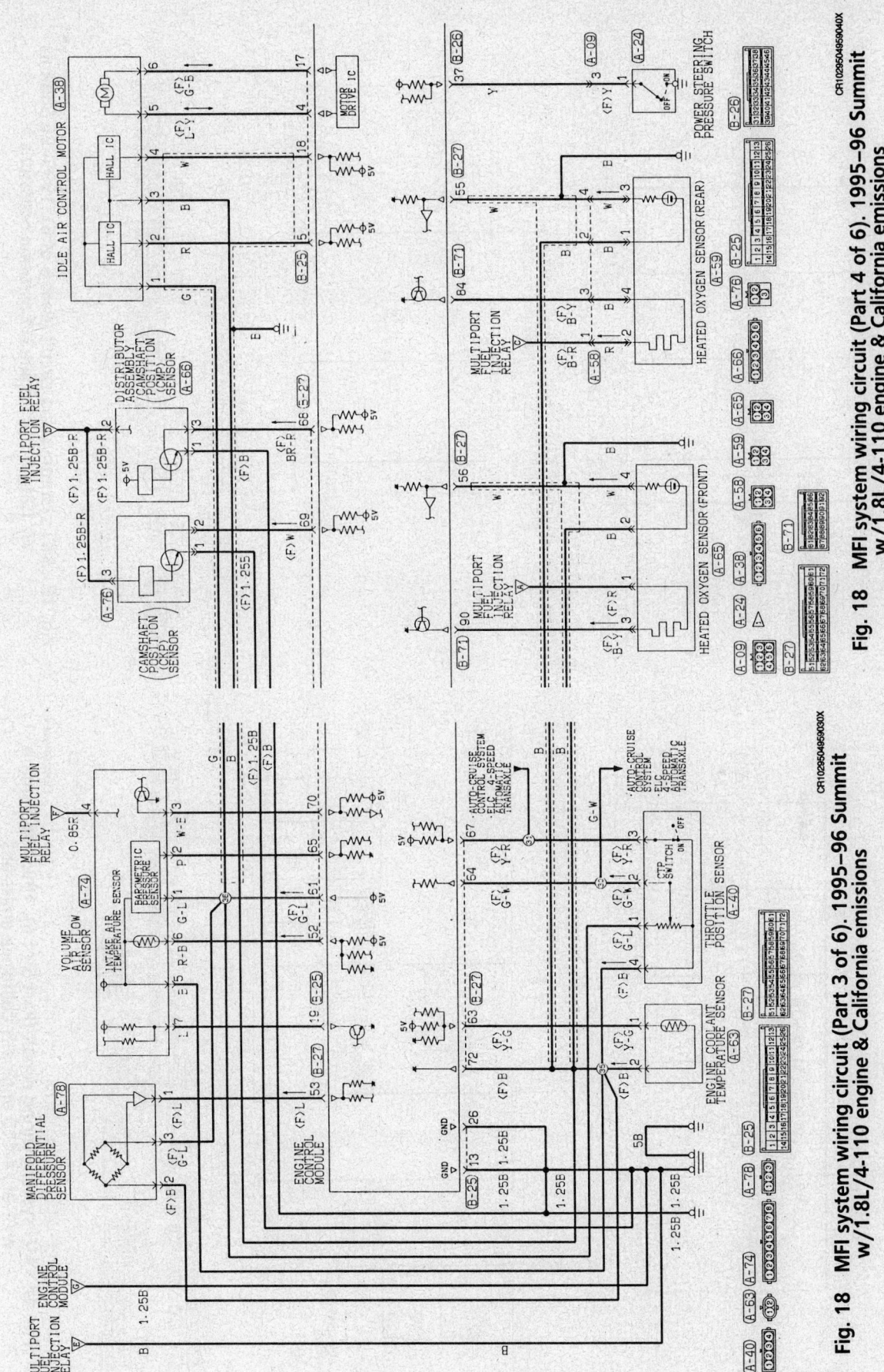

Fig. 18 MFI system wiring circuit (Part 4 of 6). 1995-96 Summit w/1.8L/4-110 engine & California emissions

Fig. 18 MFI system wiring circuit (Part 3 of 6). 1995-96 Summit w/1.8L/4-110 engine & California emissions

MULTI-POINT FUEL INJECTION (MODELS w/1.8L/4-107, 1.8L/4-110 & 2.4L/4-143 ENGINES, 1993-94 MODELS w/2.0L/4-122 ENGINE & 1995 TALON w/2.0L/4-122 TURBOCHARGED ENGINE)

7-61

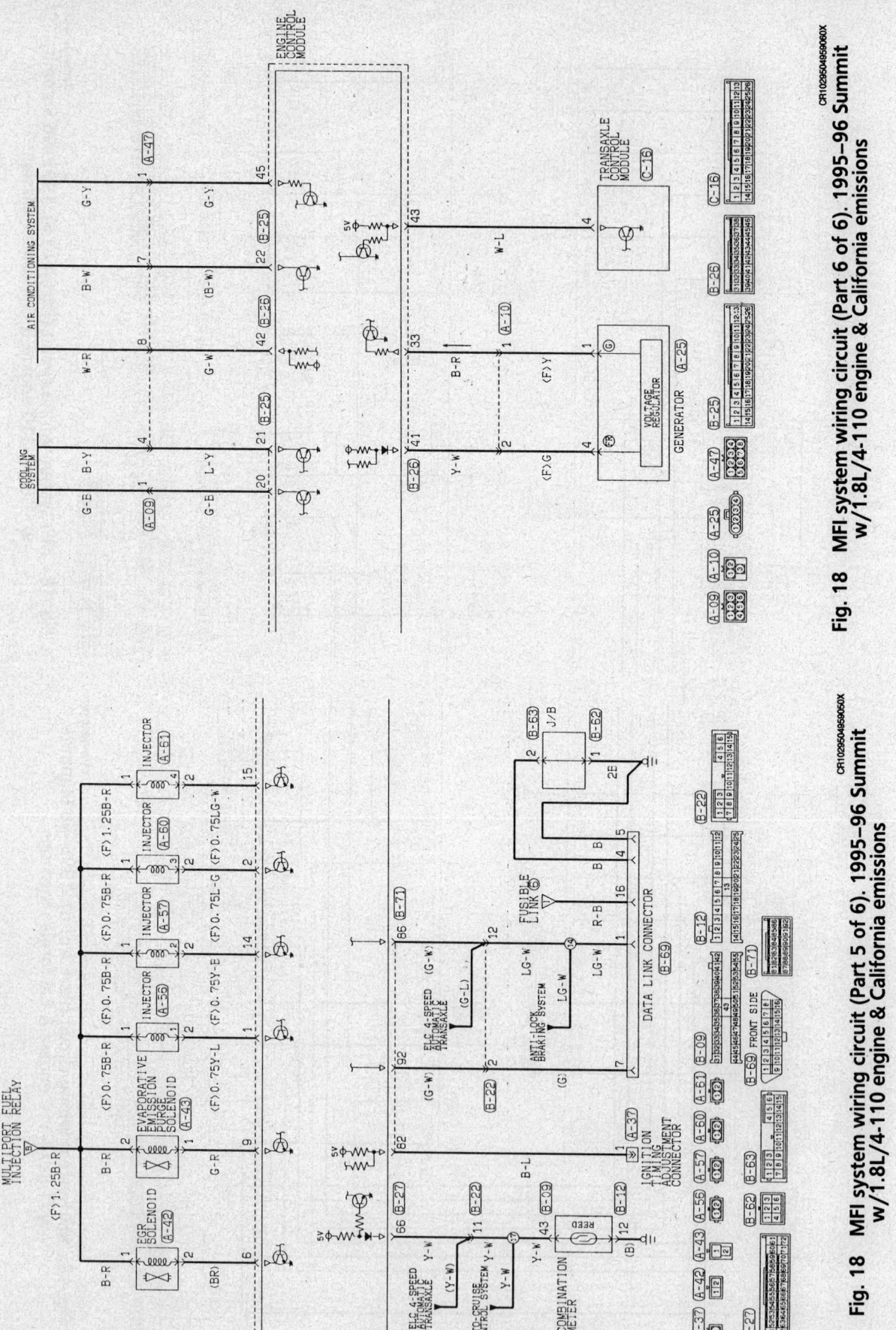

Fig. 18 MFI system wiring circuit (Part 6 of 6). 1995–96 Summit w/1.8L/4-110 engine & California emissions

Fig. 18 MFI system wiring circuit (Part 5 of 6). 1995–96 Summit w/1.8L/4-110 engine & California emissions

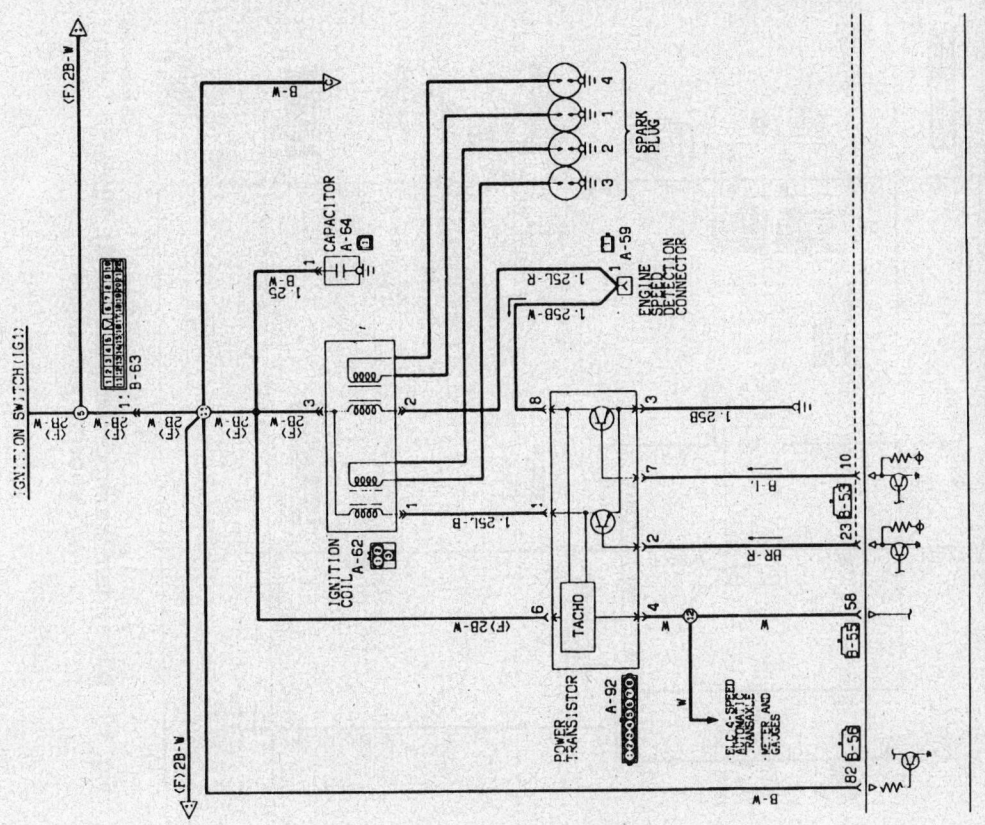

Fig. 19   MFI system wiring circuit (Part 2 of 8). 1995–96 Talon w/turbocharged engine

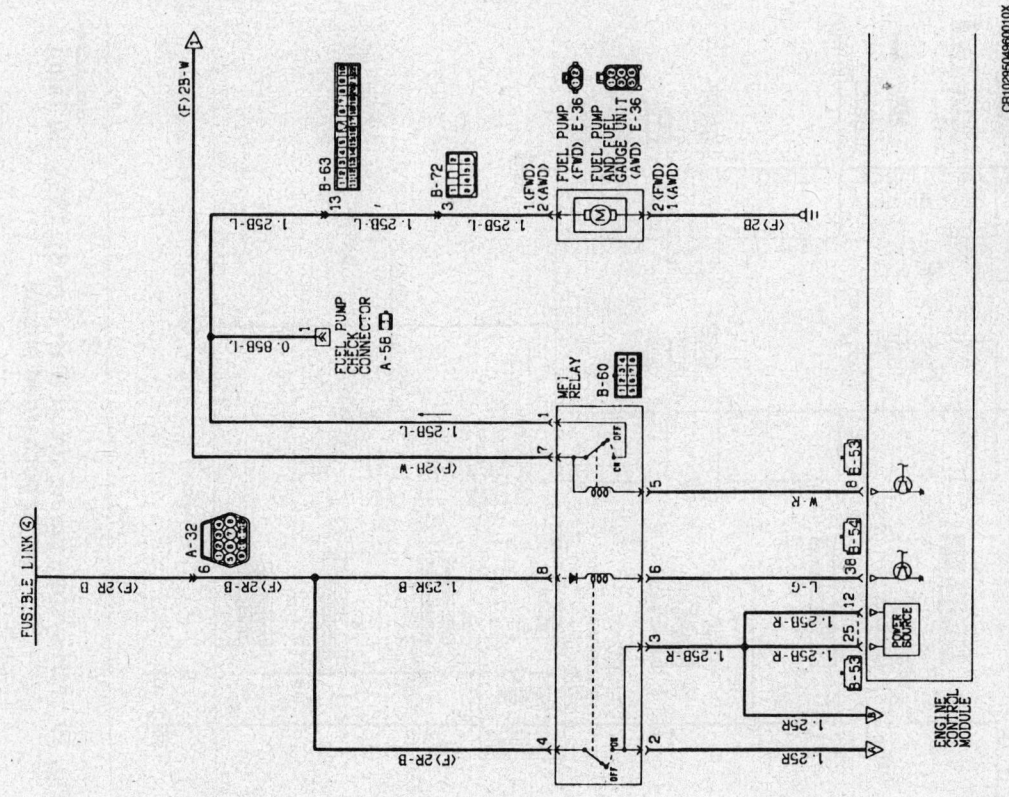

Fig. 19   MFI system wiring circuit (Part 1 of 8). 1995–96 Talon w/turbocharged engine

MULTI-POINT FUEL INJECTION (MODELS w/1.8L/4-107, 1.8L/4-110 & 2.4L/4-143 ENGINES, 1993-94 MODELS w/2.0L/4-122 ENGINE & 1995 TALON w/2.0L/4-122 TURBOCHARGED ENGINE)

7-63

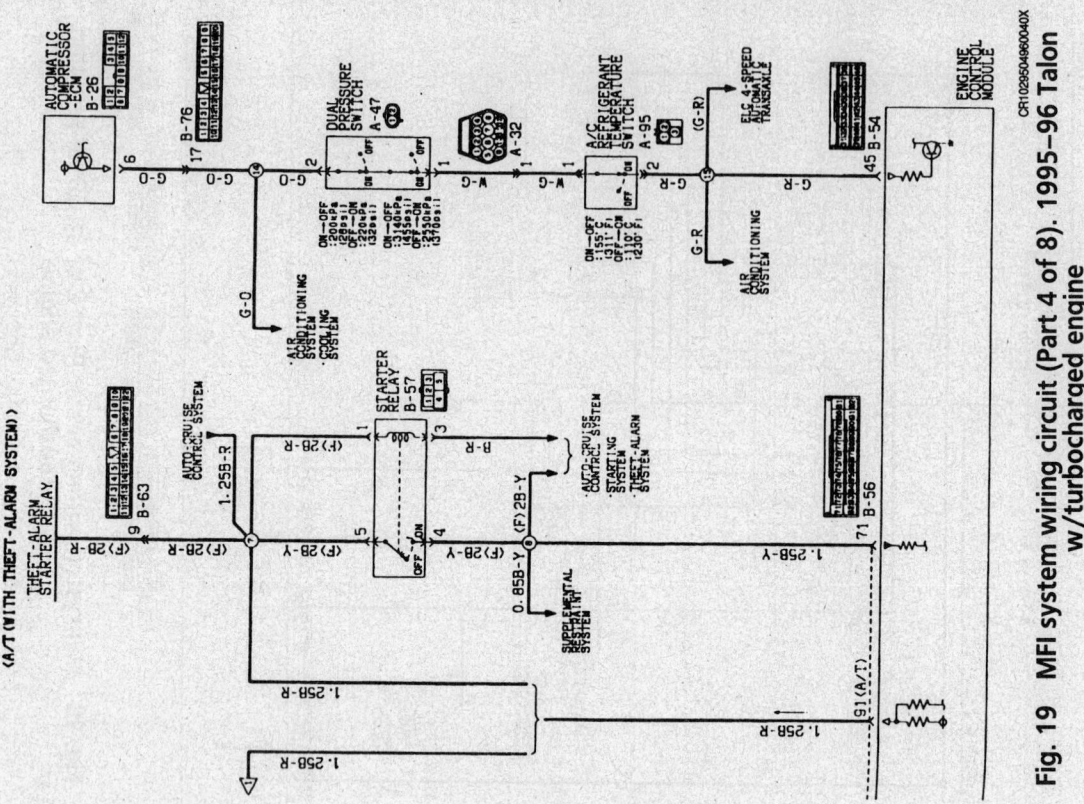

Fig. 19 MFI system wiring circuit (Part 4 of 8). 1995–96 Talon w/turbocharged engine

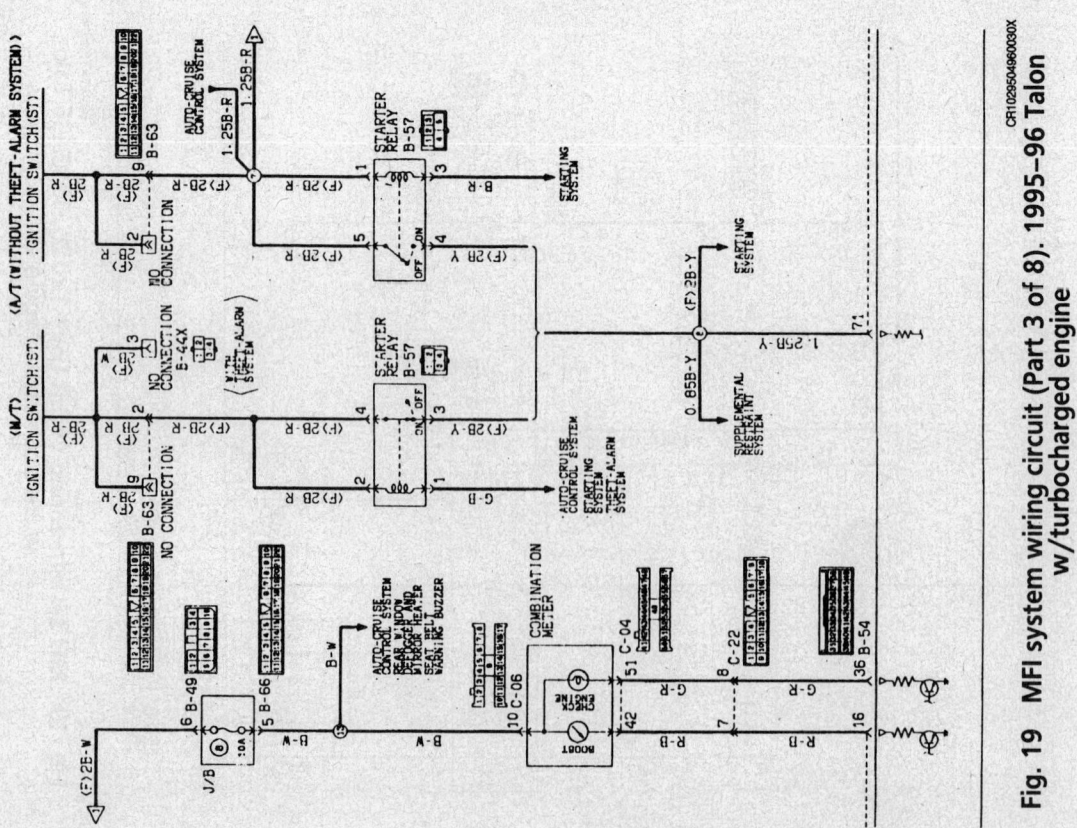

Fig. 19 MFI system wiring circuit (Part 3 of 8). 1995–96 Talon w/turbocharged engine

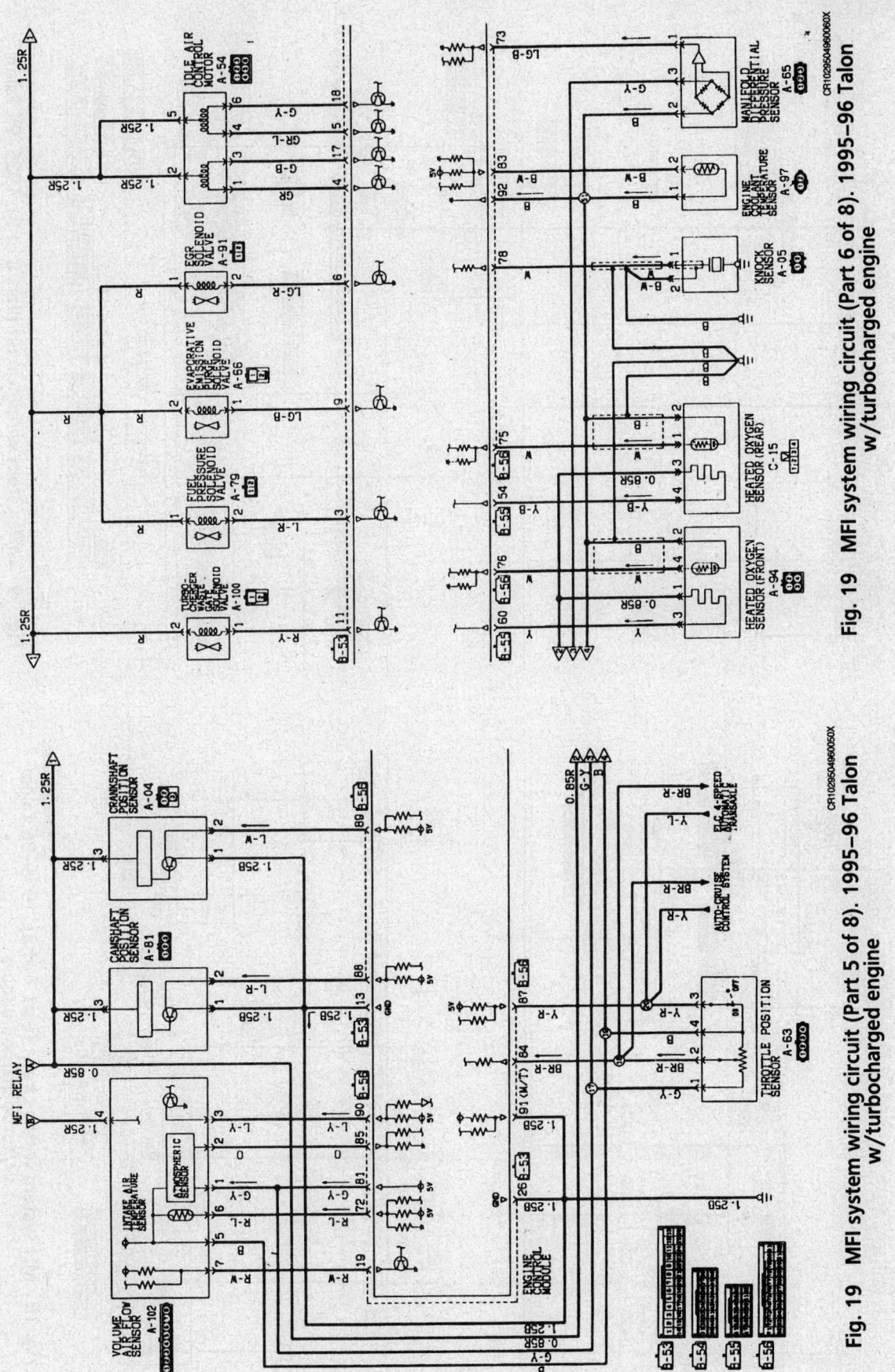

Fig. 19 MFI system wiring circuit (Part 6 of 8). 1995–96 Talon w/turbocharged engine

Fig. 19 MFI system wiring circuit (Part 5 of 8). 1995–96 Talon w/turbocharged engine

MULTI-POINT FUEL INJECTION (MODELS w/1.8L/4-107, 1.8L/4-110 & 2.4L/4-143 ENGINES, 1993-94 MODELS w/2.0L/4-122 ENGINE & 1995 TALON w/2.0L/4-122 TURBOCHARGED ENGINE)

7-65

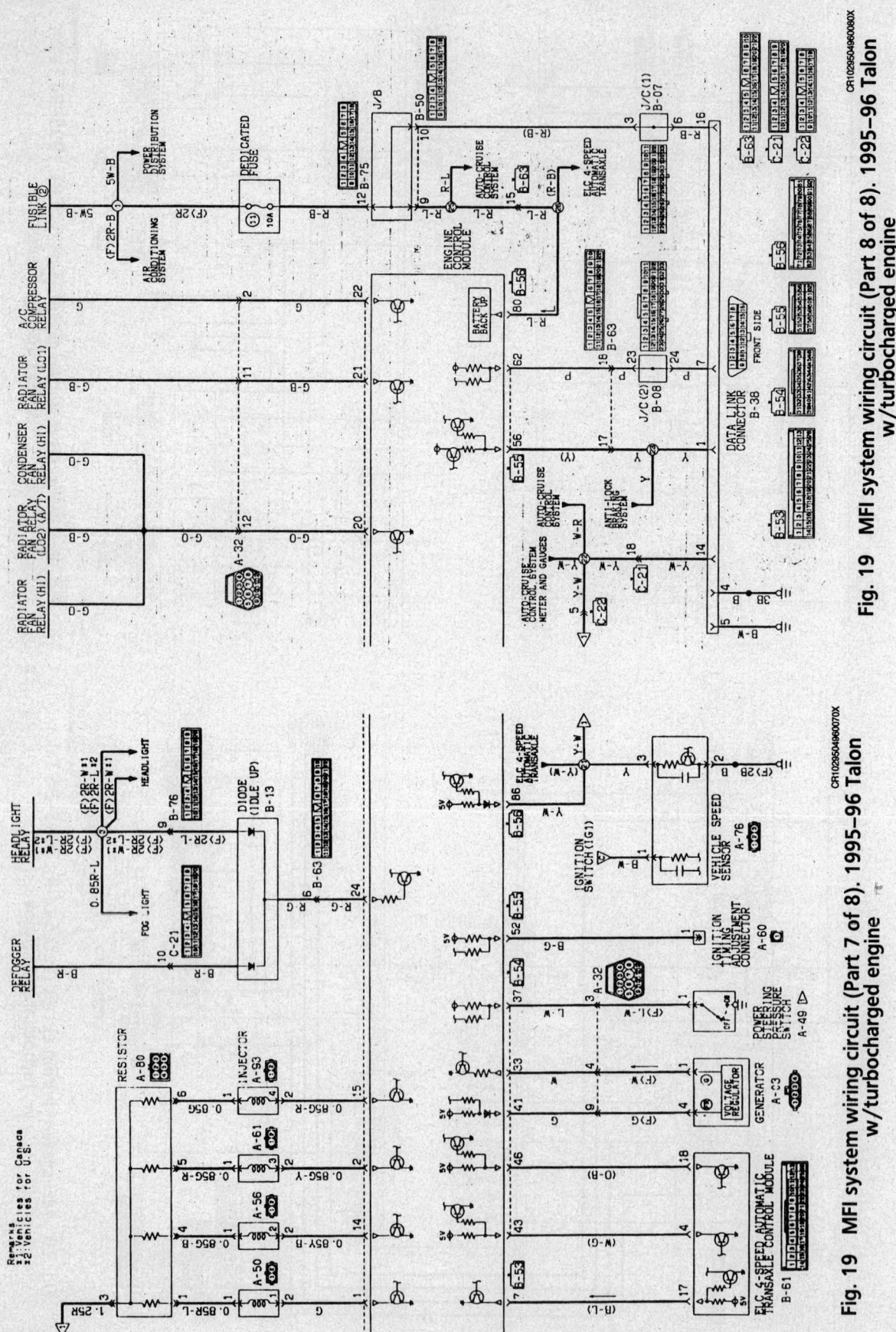

Fig. 19 MFI system wiring circuit (Part 8 of 8). 1995-96 Talon
w/turbocharged engine

Fig. 19 MFI system wiring circuit (Part 7 of 8). 1995-96 Talon
w/turbocharged engine

Check items \ Problem symptoms	Starting: Will not start	Starting: Starting problem	Idling stability: Idling instability (Rough idling)	Idling stability: Incorrect idling speed	Idling stability: Improper idling continuity	Driving: Hesitation, sag	Driving: Poor acceleration	Driving: Stumble	Driving: Shock	Driving: Surge	Driving: Knocking	Stopping: Run-on (Dieseling)
Power supply	①[1]											
Engine control module power ground	②[2]											
Fuel pump	③[3]	①[1]			①[1]	①[1]	①[1]					
Volume air flow sensor					⑫[10]	⑨[9]		⑤[5]	⑥[6]		③[3]	
Intake air temperature sensor			⑥			⑤[5]	③[4]				①[1]	
Barometric pressure sensor			⑧			⑧[8]	⑥[6]				②[2]	
Engine coolant temperature sensor		[3]	⑦[6]	①[1]	⑥[6]	⑦[7]	⑤[5]	④[4]		③[3]		
Throttle position sensor						⑥[6]		③[3]	④[4]			
Closed throttle position switch			④[4]	②[2]	⑤[5]							
IAC valve position sensor			③[3]	⑦[3]	④				⑤[5]			
Camshaft position sensor	⑤[5]	⑥[7]			⑨[8]				②[2]			
Crankshaft position sensor	⑥[6]	⑦[8]			⑪[9]				③[3]			
Ignition switch-ST <M/T>	④[4]	③[4]										
Ignition switch-ST and park/neutral position switch <A/T>	④[4]	③[4]		⑥								
Vehicle speed sensor					⑦				⑦			
Power steering pressure switch				③								
Air conditioning switch and A/C compressor clutch relay				④								
Radiator fan motor switch <California>				⑤								
Oxygen sensor <Federal and Canada>			⑩									
Heated oxygen sensor <California>			⑩									
Injectors	⑧[8]	②[2]	②[2]		③[3]	②[2]	②[2]	①[1]		①[1]		①
Idle air control motor (DC motor)		④[5]	①[1]	⑧[4]	②[2]				⑨[7]			
Ignition coil and ignition power transistor	⑦[7]				⑪[10]		⑦[7]		①[1]		④[4]	
Evaporative emission purge solenoid			⑨									
EGR solenoid <California>						④[4]		⑥[6]		④[4]		
Anti-lock brake signal <AWD-M/T>									⑧			
Fuel pressure		⑤[6]	⑤[5]		⑧[7]	③[3]	③[3]	②[2]		②[2]		

CR1029300495000X

Fig. 20 Troubleshooting chart. 1993 Colt, Colt Vista, Summit & Summit Wagon w/1.8L/4-110 engine

Check items \ Problem symptoms	Starting: Will not start	Starting: Starting problem	Idling stability: Idling instability (Rough idling)	Idling stability: Incorrect idling speed	Idling stability: Improper idling continuity	Driving: Hesitation, sag	Driving: Poor acceleration	Driving: Stumble	Driving: Shock	Driving: Surge	Driving: Knocking	Stopping: Run-on (Dieseling)
Power supply	①[1]											
Engine control module power ground	②[2]											
Fuel pump	③[3]	①[1]			①[1]	①[1]	①[1]					
Volume air flow sensor					⑫[10]	⑨[9]		⑤[5]	⑥[6]		③[3]	
Intake air temperature sensor			⑥			⑤[5]	③[4]				①[1]	
Barometric pressure sensor			⑧			⑧[8]	⑥[6]				②[2]	
Engine coolant temperature sensor		[3]	⑦[6]	①[1]	⑥[6]	⑦[7]	⑤[5]	④[4]		③[3]		
Throttle position sensor						⑥[6]		③[3]	④[4]			
Closed throttle position switch			④[4]	②[2]	⑤[5]							
IAC valve position sensor			③[3]	⑦[3]	④				⑤[5]			
Camshaft position sensor	⑤[5]	⑥[7]			⑨[8]				②[2]			
Crankshaft position sensor	⑥[6]	⑦[8]			⑪[9]				③[3]			
Ignition switch-ST <M/T>	④[4]	③[4]										
Ignition switch-ST and park/neutral position switch <A/T>	④[4]	③[4]		⑥								
Vehicle speed sensor					⑦				⑦			
Power steering pressure switch				③								
Air conditioning switch and A/C compressor clutch relay				④								
Oxygen sensor <Federal and Canada>			⑩									
Heated oxygen sensor <California>			⑩									
Injectors	⑧[8]	②[2]	②[2]		③[3]	②[2]	②[2]	①[1]		①[1]		①
Idle air control motor (DC motor)		④[5]	①[1]	⑧[4]	②[2]				⑨[7]			
Ignition coil and ignition power transistor	⑦[7]				⑪[10]		⑦[7]		①[1]		④[4]	
Evaporative emission purge solenoid			⑨									
EGR solenoid <California>						④[4]		⑥[6]		④[4]		
Anti-lock brake signal <AWD-M/T>									⑧			
Fuel pressure		⑤[6]	⑤[5]		⑧[7]	③[3]	③[3]	②[2]		②[2]		

CR1029300496000X

Fig. 21 Troubleshooting chart. 1993 Colt Vista & Summit Wagon w/2.4L/4-143 engine

Fig. 23 — Troubleshooting chart. 1993–94 Laser & Talon w/2.0L/4-122 engine

	Starting		Idling stability			Operation					
	Impossible start	Defective start	Unstable idling	Unstable idling revolution speed	Defective idling continuation	Hesitation, sag	Defective acceleration	Stumble	Shock	Surge	Knocking
Control system											
Power supply / Fuel pump control	⊗								⊗	⊗	
Volume air flow sensor		⊗	⊗			⊗	⊗	⊗	⊗	⊗	
Intake air temperature sensor		⊗	⊗			⊗	○	⊗			
Barometric pressure sensor						○					
Engine coolant temperature sensor		⊗	⊗	⊗		⊗	⊗	⊗			
TPS											
Closed throttle position switch					⊗						
Camshaft position sensor	⊗										
Crankshaft position sensor	⊗	⊗									
Ignition switch [ST] & Park/Neutral position switch	⊗			⊗							
Vehicle speed sensor					○			○			
PSP switch			○		⊗						
Air conditioning control		⊗	⊗	⊗	⊗						
Injector		⊗	⊗	⊗	⊗	⊗	⊗	⊗			
Idle air control motor		⊗	⊗	⊗	⊗		⊗	⊗			
Ignition power transistor (turbo)							○				
Knock sensor (turbo)		○									○
Fuel pressure solenoid (turbo)											
TC waste gate solenoid (turbo)									○		
Anti-lock braking signal									○		
Ignition system											
Ignition coil	⊗	⊗	⊗		⊗	⊗	⊗	⊗			
Spark plug cable	⊗	⊗	⊗			⊗	⊗	⊗		⊗	
Spark plug										⊗	
Fuel system											
Fuel pressure regulator											
Air intake system											
Throttle body					⊗	⊗	⊗	⊗			
Air hose					○		○				
Turbo-charging system											
Turbocharger							○		○		○
Waste gate											

Fig. 23 Troubleshooting chart. 1993–94 Laser & Talon w/2.0L/4-122 engine

CR102930049800X

Fig. 22 — Troubleshooting chart. 1993–94 Laser & Talon w/1.8L/4-107 engine

	Starting		Idling stability			Operation					
	Impossible start	Defective start	Unstable idling	Unstable idling revolution speed	Defective idling continuation	Hesitation, sag	Defective acceleration	Stumble	Shock	Surge	Knocking
Control system											
Power supply / Fuel pump control	⊗										
Volume air flow sensor		⊗	⊗			⊗	⊗	⊗	⊗	⊗	
Intake air temperature sensor		⊗	⊗			⊗	⊗	⊗			
Barometric pressure sensor						○	○				
Engine coolant temperature sensor		⊗	⊗		⊗	⊗	⊗	⊗			
TPS					⊗	⊗					
Closed throttle position switch											
Idle speed control motor position sensor				○	⊗						
Camshaft position sensor	⊗	⊗	⊗		⊗						
Crankshaft position sensor	⊗	⊗									
Ignition switch [ST] & park/neutral position switch		⊗	⊗	○							
Vehicle speed sensor											
PSP switch			○		○			○			
Air conditioning control			⊗	⊗	⊗					⊗	
Injector		⊗	⊗		⊗	⊗	⊗	⊗			
ISC motor		⊗	⊗		⊗						
Ignition power transistor		⊗	⊗		⊗	⊗	⊗	⊗		⊗	
Ignition system											
Ignition coil	⊗	⊗	⊗		⊗	⊗	⊗	⊗		⊗	
Spark plug cable	⊗	⊗	⊗		○	⊗	⊗	⊗		⊗	
Spark plug		⊗	⊗								
Fuel system											
Fuel pressure regulator	⊗	⊗	⊗		○	⊗	⊗	⊗	⊗	⊗	
Air intake system											
Throttle body											
Air hose		⊗	⊗			⊗	⊗	⊗	⊗	⊗	

Fig. 22 Troubleshooting chart. 1993–94 Laser & Talon w/1.8L/4-107 engine

CR102930049700X

MULTI-POINT FUEL INJECTION (MODELS w/1.8L/4-107, 1.8L/4-110 & 2.4L/4-143 ENGINES, 1993-94 MODELS w/2.0L/4-122 ENGINE & 1995 TALON w/2.0L/4-122 TURBOCHARGED ENGINE)

CR1029403210000X

Fig. 25 Troubleshooting chart. 1994 Colt Vista & 1994–95 Summit Wagon w/2.4L/4-143 Engine

Column groups: Problem Symptoms — Starting (Will not start; Fires up and dies / Hard starting); Idling stability (Hunting Rough idle; Incorrect idle speed; Engine stall); Driving (Hesitation, sag; Poor acceleration; Stumble; Shock; Surge; Knocking); Stopping (Run-on (Dieseling))

Check items:
- Power supply (MFI relay)
- Engine control module power ground
- Fuel pump
- Volume air flow sensor
- Intake air temperature sensor
- Barometric pressure sensor
- Engine coolant temperature sensor
- Throttle position sensor
- Closed throttle position switch
- IAC valve position sensor
- Camshaft position sensor
- Crankshaft position sensor
- Ignition switch -ST <M/T>
- Ignition switch -ST and park/neutral position switch <A/T>
- Vehicle speed sensor
- Power steering pressure switch
- Air conditioning switch and A/C compressor clutch relay
- Fan motor relay and air conditioning refrigerant medium pressure switch
- Heated oxygen sensor
- Injectors
- Idle air control motor (DC motor)
- Ignition coil and ignition power transistor
- Evaporative emission purge solenoid
- EGR solenoid
- Engine and transaxle total control signal
- Fuel pressure

Legend: ○ : Warm engine (number inside indicates check order) □ : Cold engine (number inside indicates check order)

CR1029403209000X

Fig. 24 Troubleshooting chart. 1994 Colt, Colt Vista & Summit & 1994–95 Summit Wagon w/1.8L/4-110 Engine

Column groups: Problem Symptoms — Starting (Will not start; Fires up and dies / Hard starting); Idling stability (Hunting Rough idle; Incorrect idle speed; Engine stall); Driving (Hesitation, sag; Poor acceleration; Stumble; Shock; Surge; Knocking); Stopping (Run-on (Dieseling))

Check items:
- Power supply (MFI relay)
- Engine control module power ground
- Fuel pump
- Volume air flow sensor
- Intake air temperature sensor
- Barometric pressure sensor
- Engine coolant temperature sensor
- Throttle position sensor
- Closed throttle position switch
- IAC valve position sensor
- Camshaft position sensor
- Crankshaft position sensor
- Ignition switch -ST <M/T>
- Ignition switch -ST and park/neutral position switch <A/T>
- Vehicle speed sensor
- Power steering pressure switch
- Air conditioning switch and A/C compressor clutch relay
- Fan motor relay and air conditioning refrigerant medium pressure switch
- Heated oxygen sensor
- Injectors
- Idle air control motor (DC motor)
- Ignition coil and ignition power transistor
- Evaporative emission purge solenoid
- EGR solenoid
- Fuel pressure

Legend: ○ : Warm engine (number inside indicates check order) □ : Cold engine (number inside indicates check order)

MULTI-POINT FUEL INJECTION (MODELS w/1.8L/4-107, 1.8L/4-110 & 2.4L/4-143 ENGINES, 1993-94 MODELS w/2.0L/4-122 ENGINE & 1995 TALON w/2.0L/4-122 TURBOCHARGED ENGINE)

Fig. 26 Troubleshooting chart (Part 2 of 2). 1996 Summit Wagon w/1.8L/4-110 engine

Items	Driving Hesitation, Sag	Driving Poor acceleration	Driving Stumble	Driving Shock	Driving Surge	Driving Knocking	Stopping Run-on (dieseling)
Power supply (MFI relay)							
Engine control module power ground							
Fuel pump	1 (1)	1 (1)					
Volume air flow sensor	9 (9)	4 (4)	5 (5)	6 (6)		3 (3)	
Intake air temperature sensor	5 (5)	6 (6)				1 (1)	
Barometric pressure sensor	8 (8)	6 (6)				2 (2)	
Engine coolant temperature sensor	7 (7)	5 (5)	4 (4)		3 (3)		
Throttle position sensor	6 (6)		3 (3)	4 (4)			
Closed throttle position switch							
IAC valve position sensor				5 (5)			
Camshaft position sensor				2 (2)			
Crankshaft position sensor				3 (3)			
Ignition switch – ST (M/T)							
Ignition switch – ST and Park/Neutral position switch (A/T)							
Vehicle speed sensor				7			
Power steering pressure switch							
Air conditioning switch and compressor clutch relay							
Fan motor relay and air conditioning refrigerant medium pressure switch							
Heated oxygen sensor							
Generator (FR terminal, G terminal)							
Injectors	2 (2)	2 (2)	1 (1)		1 (1)		
Idle air control motor				8 (7)			
Ignition coil and ignition power transistor		7 (7)		1 (1)		4 (4)	1
Evaporative emission purge solenoid							
EGR solenoid	4 (4)	3 (3)	6 (6)		4 (4)		
Fuel pressure	3 (3)		2 (2)		2 (2)		

NOTE
The numbers inside the table indicate the check order.
• With ( ) : for cold engine
•• Without ( ) : for warm engine

Fig. 26 Troubleshooting chart (Part 1 of 2). 1996 Summit Wagon w/1.8L/4-110 engine

Items	Starting Will not start	Starting Fires up and dies, Hard starting	Idling stability Idling instability (rough idling)	Idling stability Incorrect idle speed	Idling stability Engine stall
Power supply (MFI relay)	1 (1)				
Engine control module power ground	2 (2)				
Fuel pump	3 (3)	1 (1)			1 (1)
Volume air flow sensor					12 (11)
Intake air temperature sensor			6		
Barometric pressure sensor			8		
Engine coolant temperature sensor			7 (6)	1 (1)	6 (6)
Throttle position sensor			4 (4)	2 (2)	5 (5)
Closed throttle position switch			3 (3)	8 (3)	4 (4)
IAC valve position sensor	5 (6)	6 (7)			9 (8)
Camshaft position sensor	6 (6)	7 (8)			10 (9)
Crankshaft position sensor	4 (4)	3 (4)			
Ignition switch – ST (M/T)	4 (4)	4 (4)			
Ignition switch – ST and Park/Neutral position switch (A/T)		3 (4)			
Vehicle speed sensor				7	7
Power steering pressure switch				3	
Air conditioning switch and compressor clutch relay				4	
Fan motor relay and air conditioning refrigerant medium pressure switch				5	
Heated oxygen sensor			10	6	
Generator (FR terminal, G terminal)					
Injectors	8 (8)	2 (2)	2 (2)	9 (4)	3 (3)
Idle air control motor		4 (5)	1 (1)	2 (2)	2 (2)
Ignition coil and ignition power transistor	7 (7)			11 (10)	
Evaporative emission purge solenoid			9		
EGR solenoid					
Fuel pressure		5 (6)	5 (5)		8 (7)

NOTE
The numbers inside the table indicate the check order.
• With ( ) : for cold engine
•• Without ( ) : for warm engine

Fig. 27 Troubleshooting chart (Part 2 of 2), 1996 Summit Wagon w/2.4L/4-143 engine

Items	Driving — Hesitation, Sag	Driving — Poor acceleration	Driving — Stumble	Driving — Shock	Driving — Surge	Driving — Knocking	Stopping — Run-on (dieseling)
Power supply (MFI relay)							
Engine control module power ground							
Fuel pump	1 (1)	1 (1)					
Volume air flow sensor	9 (9)	5 (5)	5 (5)	6 (6)		3 (3)	
Intake air temperature sensor	5 (5)	4 (4)				1 (1)	
Barometric pressure sensor	8 (8)	6 (6)				2 (2)	
Engine coolant temperature sensor	7 (7)	5 (5)	4 (4)		3 (3)		
Throttle position sensor	6 (6)		3 (3)	4 (4)			
Closed throttle position switch				5 (5)			
IAC valve position sensor				2 (2)			
Camshaft position sensor				3 (3)			
Crankshaft position sensor							
Ignition switch-ST (M/T)							
Ignition switch-ST and park/neutral position switch (A/T)							
Vehicle speed sensor				7			
Power steering pressure switch							
Air conditioning switch and compressor clutch relay							
Fan motor relay and air conditioning refrigerant medium pressure switch							
Heated oxygen sensor							
Generator (FR terminal, G terminal)							
Injectors	2 (2)	2 (2)	1 (1)		1 (1)		
Idle air control motor				9 (8)			
Ignition coil and ignition power transistor		7 (7)		1 (1)		4 (4)	1
Evaporative emission purge solenoid							
EGR solenoid	4 (4)		6 (6)		4 (4)		
Engine and transaxle total control signal				8 (7)	5 (5)		
Fuel pressure	3 (3)	3 (3)	2 (2)		2 (2)		

NOTE
The numbers inside the table indicate the checking order.
• With ( ) : for cold engine
•• Without ( ) : for warm engine

Fig. 27 Troubleshooting chart (Part 1 of 2), 1996 Summit Wagon w/2.4L/4-143 engine

Items	Starting — Will not start	Starting — Fires up and dies, Hard starting	Idling stability — Idling instability (rough idling)	Idling stability — Incorrect idle speed	Idling stability — Engine stall
Power supply (MFI relay)	1 (1)				
Engine control module power ground	2 (2)				
Fuel pump	3 (3)	1 (1)			1 (1)
Volume air flow sensor					12 (11)
Intake air temperature sensor			6		
Barometric pressure sensor			8		
Engine coolant temperature sensor		(3)	7 (6)	1 (1)	6 (6)
Throttle position sensor					
Closed throttle position switch			4 (4)	2 (2)	5 (5)
IAC valve position sensor			3 (3)	8 (3)	4 (4)
Camshaft position sensor	5 (5)	6 (7)			9 (8)
Crankshaft position sensor	6 (6)	7 (8)			10 (9)
Ignition switch-ST (M/T)		3 (4)			
Ignition switch-ST and Park/Neutral position switch (A/T)	4 (4)	3 (4)			
Vehicle speed sensor				7	7
Power steering pressure switch				3	
Air conditioning switch and compressor clutch relay				4	
Fan motor relay and air conditioning refrigerant medium pressure switch				5	
Heated oxygen sensor			10	6	
Generator (FR terminal, G terminal)					
Injectors	8 (8)	2 (2)	2 (2)		3 (3)
Idle air control motor		4 (5)	1 (1)	9 (4)	2 (2)
Ignition coil and ignition power transistor	7 (7)				11 (10)
Evaporative emission purge solenoid			9		
EGR solenoid					
Engine and transaxle total control signal					
Fuel pressure		5 (6)	5 (5)		8 (7)

NOTE
The numbers inside the table indicate the checking order.
• With ( ) : for cold engine
•• Without ( ) : for warm engine

Fig. 28 Troubleshooting chart (Part 1 of 2). 1995 Summit w/Federal emissions

Items	Starting: Will not start	Fires up and dies, Hard starting	Idling stability: Idling instability (rough idling)	Incorrect idle speed	Engine stall
Power supply (MFI relay)	1 (1)				
Engine control module power ground	2 (2)				
Fuel pump	3 (3)				1 (1)
Volume air flow sensor		1 (1)			12 (11)
Intake air temperature sensor			6		
Barometric pressure sensor			8		
Engine coolant temperature sensor		(3)	7 (6)	1 (1)	6 (6)
Throttle position sensor					
Closed throttle position switch			4 (4)	2 (2)	5 (5)
IAC valve position sensor			3 (3)	6 (3)	4 (4)
Camshaft position sensor		6 (7)			9 (8)
Crankshaft position sensor		7 (8)			10 (9)
Ignition switch – ST (M/T)	4 (4)	3 (4)			
Ignition switch – ST and Park/Neutral position switch (A/T)	4 (4)	3 (4)		7	
Vehicle speed sensor				3	7
Power steering pressure switch					
Air conditioning switch and compressor clutch relay				4	
Fan motor relay				5	
Heated oxygen sensor			10		
Electrical load switch				6	
Injectors	8 (8)		2 (2)	3 (3)	
Idle air control motor		4 (5)	1 (1)	9 (4)	2 (2)
Ignition coil and ignition power transistor	7 (7)				11 (10)
Evaporative emission purge solenoid			9		
EGR solenoid					
Fuel pressure		5 (6)	5 (5)		8 (7)

NOTE
The numbers in the table indicate the check order. [with ( ): cold engine, without ( ): warm engine]

CR1029504961010X

Fig. 28 Troubleshooting chart (Part 2 of 2). 1995 Summit w/Federal emissions

Items	Driving: Hesitation, Sag	Poor acceleration	Stumble	Shock	Surge	Knocking	Stopping: Run-on (dieseling)
Power supply (MFI relay)							
Engine control module power ground							
Fuel pump	1 (1)	1 (1)					
Volume air flow sensor	9 (9)		5 (5)	6 (6)		3 (3)	
Intake air temperature sensor	5 (5)	4 (4)		4 (4)		1 (1)	
Barometric pressure sensor	8 (8)	6 (6)				2 (2)	
Engine coolant temperature sensor	7 (7)	5 (5)	4 (4)		3 (3)		
Throttle position sensor	6 (6)		3 (3)	4 (4)			
Closed throttle position switch							
IAC valve position sensor				5 (5)			
Camshaft position sensor				2 (2)			
Crankshaft position sensor				3 (3)			
Ignition switch – ST (M/T)							
Ignition switch – ST and Park/Neutral position switch (A/T)							
Vehicle speed sensor				7			
Power steering pressure switch							
Air conditioning switch and compressor clutch relay							
Fan motor relay							
Heated oxygen sensor							
Electrical load switch							
Injectors	2 (2)	2 (2)	1 (1)		1 (1)		
Idle air control motor				8 (7)			
Ignition coil and ignition power transistor		7 (7)		1 (1)		4 (4)	1
Evaporative emission purge solenoid							
EGR solenoid	4 (4)		6 (6)		4 (4)		
Fuel pressure	3 (3)	3 (3)	2 (2)		2 (2)		

NOTE
The numbers in the table indicate the check order. [with ( ): cold engine, without ( ): warm engine]

CR1029504961020X

MULTI-POINT FUEL INJECTION (MODELS w/1.8L/4-107, 1.8L/4-110 & 2.4L/4-143 ENGINES, 1993-94 MODELS w/2.0L/4-122 ENGINE & 1995 TALON w/2.0L/4-122 TURBOCHARGED ENGINE)

Troubleshooting chart (Part 2 of 2) — Driving / Stopping

Items	Hesitation, Sag	Poor acceleration	Stumble	Shock	Surge	Knocking	Run-on (dieseling)
Power supply (MFI relay)							
Engine control module power ground							
Fuel pump	1 (1)	1 (1)					
Volume air flow sensor	9 (9)	5 (5)	5 (5)	6 (6)		3 (3)	
Intake air temperature sensor	5 (5)	4 (4)				1 (1)	
Barometric pressure sensor	8 (8)	6 (6)				2 (2)	
Engine coolant temperature sensor	7 (7)	5 (5)	4 (4)				
Throttle position sensor	6 (6)		3 (3)	4 (4)			
Closed throttle position switch					3 (3)		
IAC valve position sensor				5 (5)			
Camshaft position sensor				2 (2)			
Crankshaft position sensor				3 (3)			
Ignition switch – ST (M/T)							
Ignition switch – ST and Park/Neutral position switch (A/T)							
Vehicle speed sensor				7			
Power steering pressure switch							
Air conditioning switch and compressor clutch relay							
Fan motor relay							
Heated oxygen sensor							
Generator (FR terminal, G terminal)							
Injectors	2 (2)	2 (2)	1 (1)		1 (1)		
Idle air control motor				8 (7)			
Ignition coil and ignition power transistor		7 (7)		1 (1)		4 (4)	1
Evaporative emission purge solenoid							
EGR solenoid	4 (4)		6 (6)		4 (4)		
Fuel pressure	3 (3)	3 (3)	2 (2)		2 (2)		

NOTE
The numbers in the table indicate the check order. [with ( ): cold engine, without ( ): warm engine]

CR1029504962020X

Fig. 29 Troubleshooting chart (Part 2 of 2). 1995 Summit w/California emissions & 1996 Summit

Troubleshooting chart (Part 1 of 2) — Starting / Idling stability

Items	Will not start	Fires up and dies, Hard starting	Idling instability (rough idling)	Incorrect idle speed	Engine stall
Power supply (MFI relay)	1 (1)				
Engine control module power ground	2 (2)				
Fuel pump	3 (3)	1 (1)			1 (1)
Volume air flow sensor					12 (11)
Intake air temperature sensor			6		
Barometric pressure sensor			8		
Engine coolant temperature sensor		(3)	7 (6)	1 (1)	6 (6)
Throttle position sensor					
Closed throttle position switch			4 (4)	2 (2)	5 (5)
IAC valve position sensor			3 (3)	8 (3)	4 (4)
Camshaft position sensor	5 (5)	6 (7)			9 (8)
Crankshaft position sensor	6 (6)	7 (8)			10 (9)
Ignition switch – ST (M/T)	4 (4)	3 (4)			
Ignition switch – ST and Park/Neutral position switch (A/T)	4 (4)	3 (4)			
Vehicle speed sensor					7
Power steering pressure switch				3	
Air conditioning switch and compressor clutch relay				4	
Fan motor relay				5	
Heated oxygen sensor			10	6	
Generator (FR terminal, G terminal)					
Injectors	8 (8)	2 (2)	2 (2)	9 (4)	11 (10)
Idle air control motor		4 (5)	1 (1)		
Ignition coil and ignition power transistor	7 (7)		11 (10)		
Evaporative emission purge solenoid			9		
EGR solenoid					
Fuel pressure		5 (6)	5 (5)		8 (7)

NOTE
The numbers in the table indicate the check order. [with ( ): cold engine, without ( ): warm engine]

CR1029504962010X

Fig. 29 Troubleshooting chart (Part 1 of 2). 1995 Summit w/California emissions & 1996 Summit

MULTI-POINT FUEL INJECTION (MODELS w/1.8L/4-107, 1.8L/4-110 & 2.4L/4-143 ENGINES, 1993-94 MODELS w/2.0L/4-122 ENGINE & 1995 TALON w/2.0L/4-122 TURBOCHARGED ENGINE)

INSPECTION PROCEDURE 1

	Probable cause
Communication with scan tool is not possible. (Communication with all systems is not possible.)	• Malfunction of the connector • Malfunction of the harness wire

[Comment] The cause is probably a defect in the power supply system (including ground) for the on-board diagnostic test mode line.

Measure at the data link connector (16-pin.) B-38
• Voltage between 16 and ground
OK: Battery positive voltage

→ NG → Check the following connectors:
B-07, B-50, B-75 → OK → Check trouble symptom → NG → Check the harness wire between the power supply and data link connector (16-pin.), and repair if necessary.

Measure at the data link connector (16-pin.) B-38
• Continuity between 4 and ground
• Continuity between 5 and ground
OK: Continuity

→ NG → Check the harness wire between the data link connector (16-pin.) and ground, and repair if necessary.

→ OK →

Replace the scan tool

INSPECTION PROCEDURE 2

	Probable cause
Scan tool communication with ECM is not possible.	• Malfunction of ECM power supply circuit • Malfunction of the ECM • Open circuit between ECM and data link connector

[Comment] One of the following causes may be suspected.
• No power supply to ECM
• Defective ground circuit of ECM
• Defective ECM
• Improper communication line between ECM and scan tool

Check the following connection: B-38, B-55, B-63 → NG → Repair

→ OK →

Check trouble symptom → NG

Check the harness wire between ECM and data link connector → NG → Repair

→ OK →

Check the power supply and ignition switch-IG system.

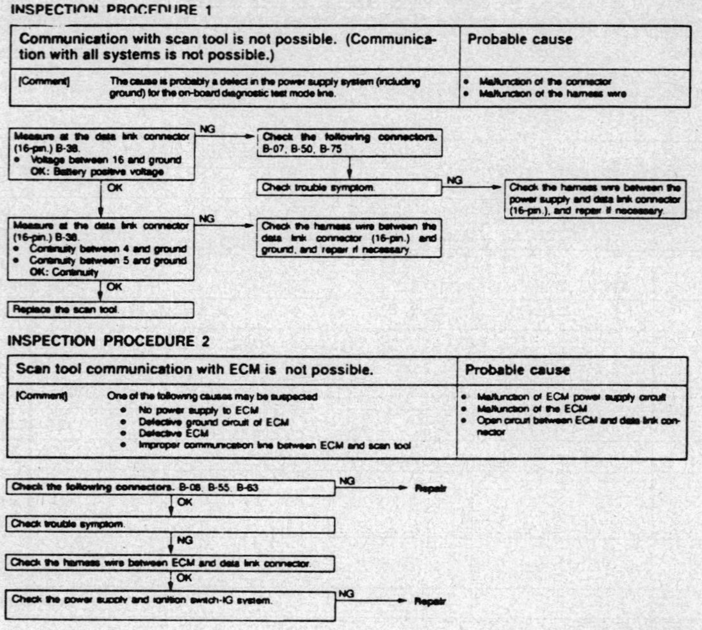

Fig. 31 Troubleshooting inspection procedures 1 & 2. 1995–96 Talon

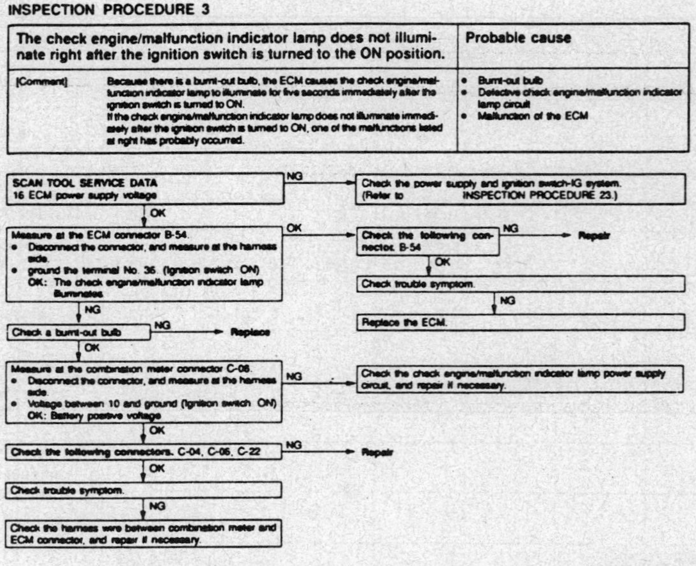

INSPECTION PROCEDURE 3

	Probable cause
The check engine/malfunction indicator lamp does not illuminate right after the ignition switch is turned to the ON position.	• Burnt-out bulb • Defective check engine/malfunction indicator lamp circuit • Malfunction of the ECM

[Comment] Because there is a burnt-out bulb, the ECM causes the check engine/malfunction indicator lamp to illuminate for five seconds immediately after the ignition switch is turned to ON.
If the check engine/malfunction indicator lamp does not illuminate immediately after the ignition switch is turned to ON, one of the malfunctions listed at right has probably occurred.

SCAN TOOL SERVICE DATA
16 ECM power supply voltage

→ NG → Check the power supply and ignition switch-IG system. (Refer to INSPECTION PROCEDURE 23.)

→ OK →

Measure at the ECM connector B-54.
• Disconnect the connector, and measure at the harness side.
• Voltage between No. 35. (Ignition switch ON) and ground No. 35. (Ignition switch ON)
OK: The check engine/malfunction indicator lamp illuminates.

→ OK → Check the following connector B-54. → OK → Check trouble symptom → NG → Replace the ECM

→ NG →

Check a burnt-out bulb → NG → Replace

→ OK →

Measure at the combination meter connector C-06.
• Disconnect the connector, and measure at the harness side.
• Voltage between 10 and ground (Ignition switch ON)
OK: Battery positive voltage

→ NG → Check the following connectors, C-04, C-06, C-22 → OK → Check trouble symptom → NG → Repair

→ OK →

Check the check engine/malfunction indicator lamp power supply circuit, and repair if necessary.

→ NG →

Check the harness wire between combination meter and ECM connector, and repair if necessary.

Fig. 32 Troubleshooting inspection procedure 3. 1995–96 Talon

	Trouble symptom	Inspection procedure No.
Communication with scan tool is impossible.	Communication with all systems is not possible.	1
	Communication with PCM only is not possible.	2
Check engine/ malfunction indicator lamp and related parts	The check engine/malfunction indicator lamp does not illuminate right after the ignition switch is turned to the ON position.	3
	The check engine/malfunction indicator lamp remains illuminated and never goes out.	4
Starting	Cranks, won't start	5
	Fires up and dies	6
	Hard starting	7
Idling stability (Improper idling)	Unstable idle. (Rough idle, hunting)	8
	Idle speed is high. (Improper idle speed)	9
	Idle speed is low. (Improper idle speed)	10
	When the engine is cold, it stalls at idle. (Die out)	11
	When the engine becomes hot, it stalls at idle. (Die out)	12
Idling stability (Engine stalles)	The engine stalls when accelerating. (Pass out)	13
	The engine stalls when decelerating.	14
	Hesitation, sag or stumble	15
	Acceleration shock	16
	Deceleration shock	17
Driving	Poor acceleration	18
	Surge	19
	Knocking	20
Dieseling		21
Too high CO and HC concentration when idling		22

Fig. 30 Troubleshooting reference chart. 1995–96 Talon

MULTI-POINT FUEL INJECTION (MODELS w/1.8L/4-107, 1.8L/4-110 & 2.4L/4-143 ENGINES, 1993-94 MODELS w/2.0L/4-122 ENGINE & 1995 TALON w/2.0L/4-122 TURBOCHARGED ENGINE)

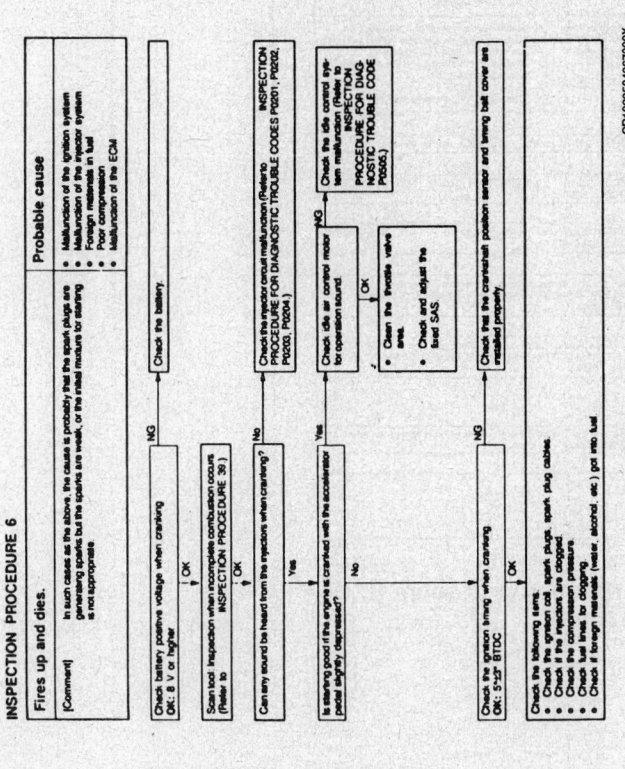

Fig. 33 Troubleshooting inspection procedures 4 & 5. 1995–96 Talon

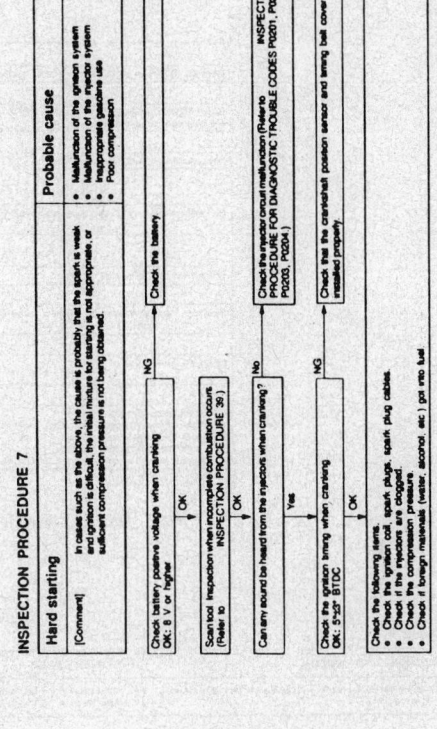

Fig. 34 Troubleshooting inspection procedure 6. 1995–96 Talon

Fig. 35 Troubleshooting inspection procedure 7. 1995–96 Talon

MULTI-POINT FUEL INJECTION (MODELS w/1.8L/4-107, 1.8L/4-110 & 2.4L/4-143 ENGINES, 1993-94 MODELS w/2.0L/4-122 ENGINE & 1995 TALON w/2.0L/4-122 TURBOCHARGED ENGINE)

7-75

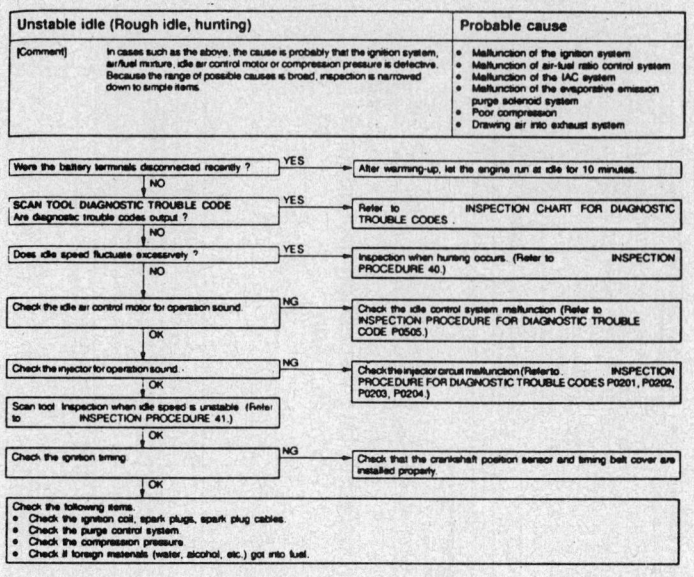

Unstable idle (Rough idle, hunting)		Probable cause
[Comment]	In cases such as the above, the cause is probably that the ignition system, air/fuel mixture, idle air control motor or compression pressure is defective. Because the range of possible causes is broad, inspection is narrowed down to simple items.	• Malfunction of the ignition system • Malfunction of air-fuel ratio control system • Malfunction of the IAC system • Malfunction of the evaporative emission purge solenoid system • Poor compression • Drawing air into exhaust system

Were the battery terminals disconnected recently? — YES → After warming-up, let the engine run at idle for 10 minutes.
NO ↓

SCAN TOOL DIAGNOSTIC TROUBLE CODE — Are diagnostic trouble codes output? — YES → Refer to INSPECTION CHART FOR DIAGNOSTIC TROUBLE CODES.
NO ↓

Does idle speed fluctuate excessively? — YES → Inspection when hunting occurs. (Refer to INSPECTION PROCEDURE 40.)
NO ↓

Check the idle air control motor for operation sound. — NG → Check the idle control system malfunction (Refer to INSPECTION PROCEDURE FOR DIAGNOSTIC TROUBLE CODE P0505.)
OK ↓

Check the injector for operation sound. — NG → Check the injector circuit malfunction (Refer to INSPECTION PROCEDURE FOR DIAGNOSTIC TROUBLE CODES P0201, P0202, P0203, P0204.)
OK ↓

Scan tool inspection when idle speed is unstable (Refer to INSPECTION PROCEDURE 41.)
OK ↓

Check the ignition timing — NG → Check that the crankshaft position sensor and timing belt cover are installed properly.
OK ↓

Check the following items.
• Check the ignition coil, spark plugs, spark plug cables.
• Check the purge control system.
• Check the compression pressure.
• Check if foreign materials (water, alcohol, etc.) got into fuel.

CR1029504969000X

Fig. 36   Troubleshooting inspection procedure 8.
1995–96 Talon

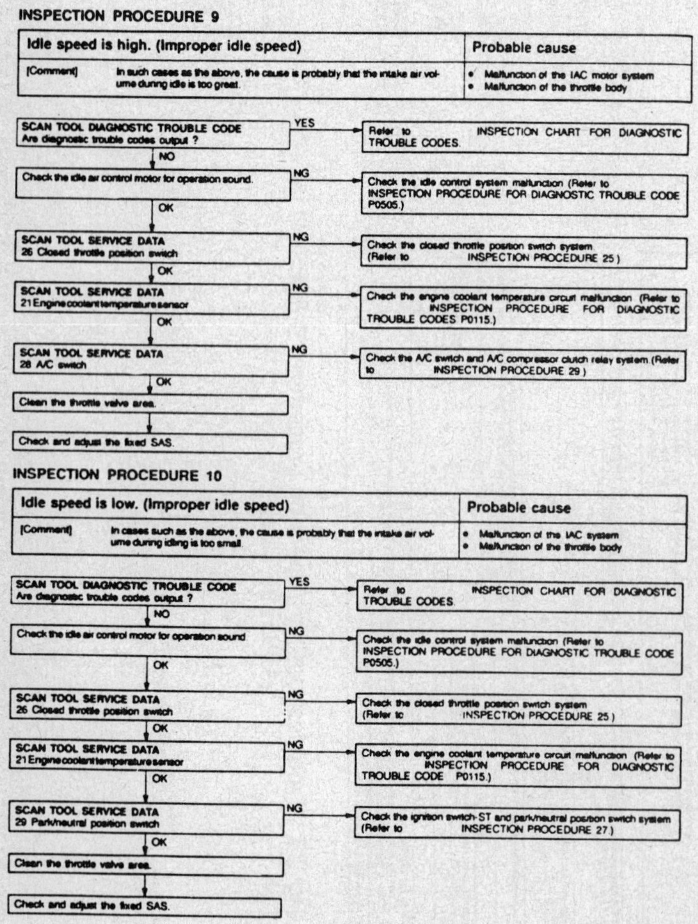

INSPECTION PROCEDURE 9

Idle speed is high. (Improper idle speed)		Probable cause
[Comment]	In such cases as the above, the cause is probably that the intake air volume during idle is too great.	• Malfunction of the IAC motor system • Malfunction of the throttle body

SCAN TOOL DIAGNOSTIC TROUBLE CODE — Are diagnostic trouble codes output? — YES → Refer to INSPECTION CHART FOR DIAGNOSTIC TROUBLE CODES.
NO ↓

Check the idle air control motor for operation sound. — NG → Check the idle control system malfunction (Refer to INSPECTION PROCEDURE FOR DIAGNOSTIC TROUBLE CODE P0505.)
OK ↓

SCAN TOOL SERVICE DATA — 26 Closed throttle position switch — NG → Check the closed throttle position switch system. (Refer to INSPECTION PROCEDURE 25.)
OK ↓

SCAN TOOL SERVICE DATA — 21 Engine coolant temperature sensor — NG → Check the engine coolant temperature circuit malfunction (Refer to INSPECTION PROCEDURE FOR DIAGNOSTIC TROUBLE CODES P0115.)
OK ↓

SCAN TOOL SERVICE DATA — 28 A/C switch — NG → Check the A/C switch and A/C compressor clutch relay system (Refer to INSPECTION PROCEDURE 29.)
OK ↓

Clean the throttle valve area.
↓
Check and adjust the fixed SAS.

INSPECTION PROCEDURE 10

Idle speed is low. (Improper idle speed)		Probable cause
[Comment]	In cases such as the above, the cause is probably that the intake air volume during idling is too small.	• Malfunction of the IAC system • Malfunction of the throttle body

SCAN TOOL DIAGNOSTIC TROUBLE CODE — Are diagnostic trouble codes output? — YES → Refer to INSPECTION CHART FOR DIAGNOSTIC TROUBLE CODES.
NO ↓

Check the idle air control motor for operation sound. — NG → Check the idle control system malfunction (Refer to INSPECTION PROCEDURE FOR DIAGNOSTIC TROUBLE CODE P0505.)
OK ↓

SCAN TOOL SERVICE DATA — 26 Closed throttle position switch — NG → Check the closed throttle position switch system (Refer to INSPECTION PROCEDURE 25.)
OK ↓

SCAN TOOL SERVICE DATA — 21 Engine coolant temperature sensor — NG → Check the engine coolant temperature circuit malfunction (Refer to INSPECTION PROCEDURE FOR DIAGNOSTIC TROUBLE CODE P0115.)
OK ↓

SCAN TOOL SERVICE DATA — 29 Park/neutral position switch — NG → Check the ignition switch-ST and park/neutral position switch system (Refer to INSPECTION PROCEDURE 27.)
OK ↓

Clean the throttle valve area.
↓
Check and adjust the fixed SAS.

CR1029504970000X

Fig. 37   Troubleshooting inspection procedures 9 & 10.
1995–96 Talon

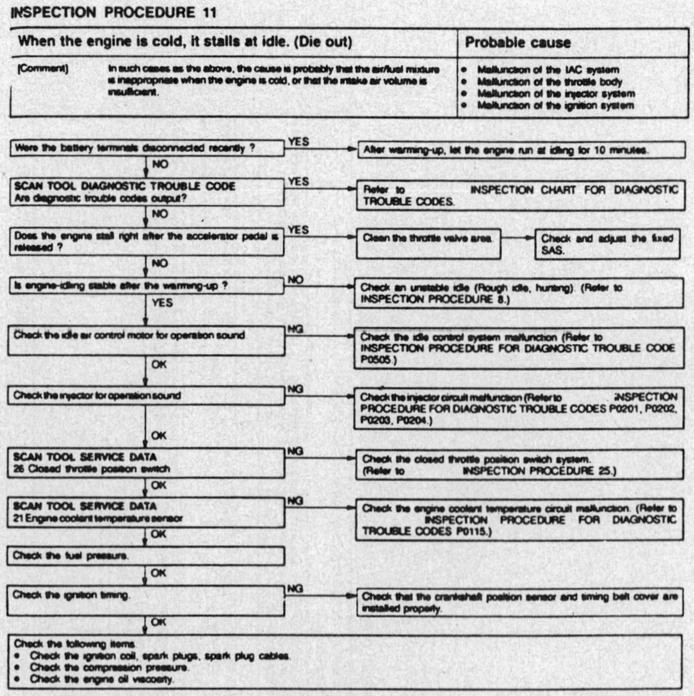

INSPECTION PROCEDURE 11

When the engine is cold, it stalls at idle. (Die out)		Probable cause
[Comment]	In such cases as the above, the cause is probably that the air/fuel mixture is inappropriate when the engine is cold, or that the intake air volume is insufficient.	• Malfunction of the IAC system • Malfunction of the throttle body • Malfunction of the injector system • Malfunction of the ignition system

Were the battery terminals disconnected recently? — YES → After warming-up, let the engine run at idling for 10 minutes.
NO ↓

SCAN TOOL DIAGNOSTIC TROUBLE CODE — Are diagnostic trouble codes output? — YES → Refer to INSPECTION CHART FOR DIAGNOSTIC TROUBLE CODES.
NO ↓

Does the engine stall right after the accelerator pedal is released? — YES → Clean the throttle valve area. → Check and adjust the fixed SAS.
NO ↓

Is engine-idling stable after the warming-up? — NO → Check an unstable idle (Rough idle, hunting). (Refer to INSPECTION PROCEDURE 8.)
YES ↓

Check the idle air control motor for operation sound. — NG → Check the idle control system malfunction (Refer to INSPECTION PROCEDURE FOR DIAGNOSTIC TROUBLE CODE P0505.)
OK ↓

Check the injector for operation sound — NG → Check the injector circuit malfunction (Refer to INSPECTION PROCEDURE FOR DIAGNOSTIC TROUBLE CODES P0201, P0202, P0203, P0204.)
OK ↓

SCAN TOOL SERVICE DATA — 26 Closed throttle position switch — NG → Check the closed throttle position switch system. (Refer to INSPECTION PROCEDURE 25.)
OK ↓

SCAN TOOL SERVICE DATA — 21 Engine coolant temperature sensor — NG → Check the engine coolant temperature circuit malfunction. (Refer to INSPECTION PROCEDURE FOR DIAGNOSTIC TROUBLE CODES P0115.)
OK ↓

Check the fuel pressure.
OK ↓

Check the ignition timing. — NG → Check that the crankshaft position sensor and timing belt cover are installed properly.
OK ↓

Check the following items.
• Check the ignition coil, spark plugs, spark plug cables.
• Check the compression pressure.
• Check the engine oil viscosity.

CR1029504971000X

Fig. 38   Troubleshooting inspection procedure 11.
1995–96 Talon

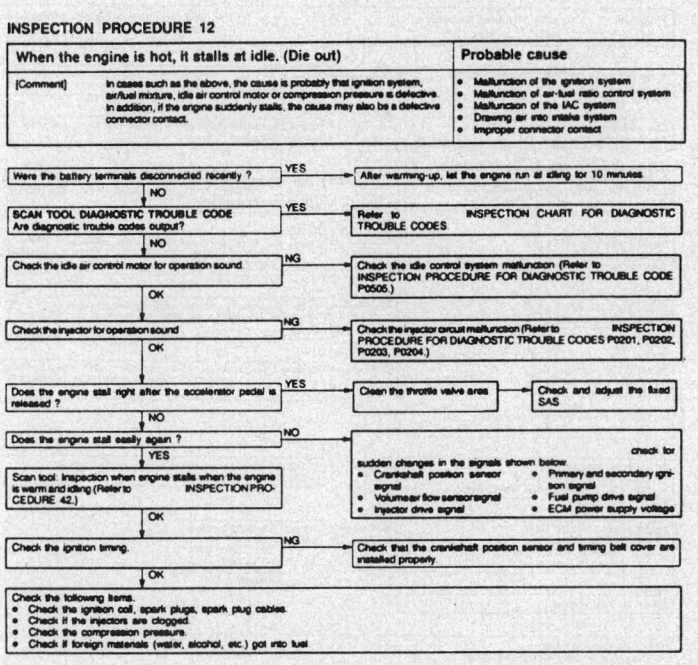

Fig. 39 Troubleshooting inspection procedure 12.
1995–96 Talon

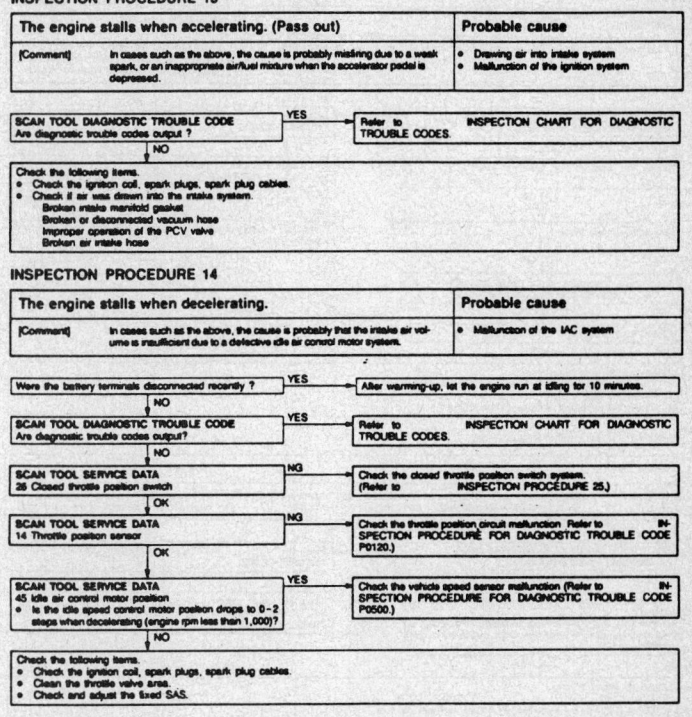

Fig. 40 Troubleshooting inspection procedures 13 & 14.
1995–96 Talon

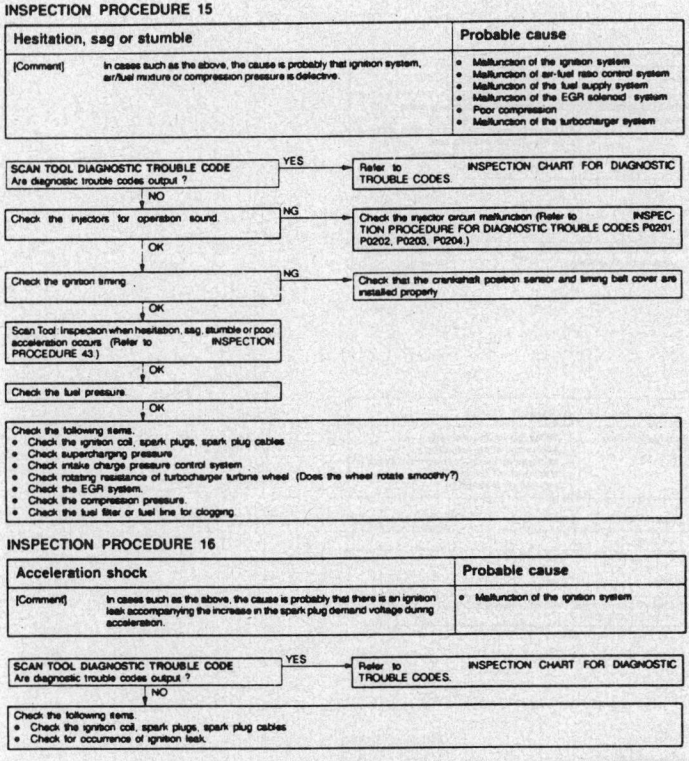

Fig. 41 Troubleshooting inspection procedures 15 & 16.
1995–96 Talon

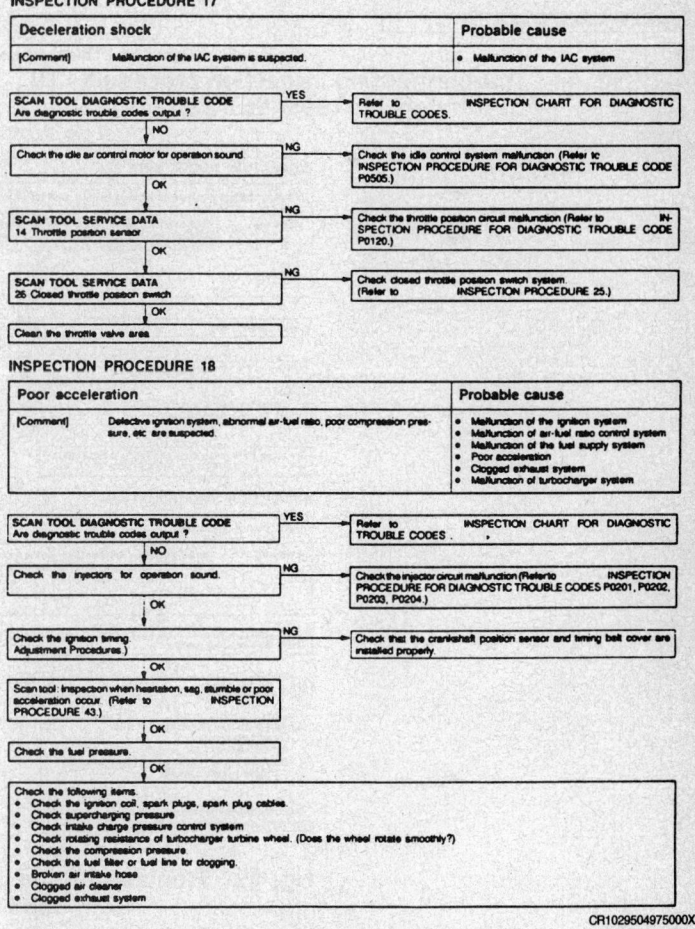

Fig. 42 Troubleshooting inspection procedures 17 & 18.
1995–96 Talon

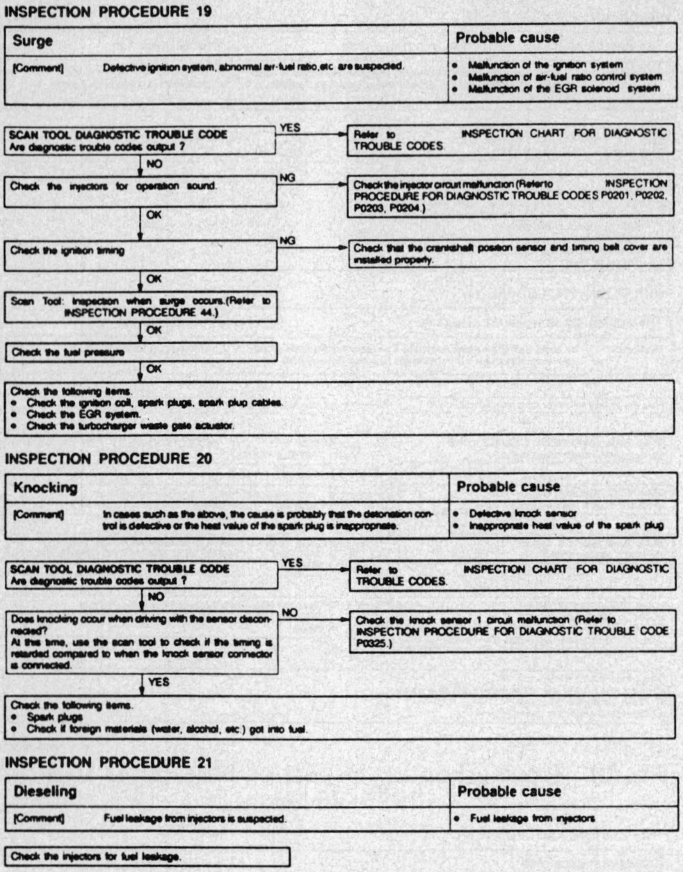

INSPECTION PROCEDURE 19

Surge	Probable cause
[Comment] Defective ignition system, abnormal air-fuel ratio, etc. are suspected.	• Malfunction of the ignition system • Malfunction of air-fuel ratio control system • Malfunction of the EGR solenoid system

SCAN TOOL DIAGNOSTIC TROUBLE CODE
Are diagnostic trouble codes output ? — YES → Refer to INSPECTION CHART FOR DIAGNOSTIC TROUBLE CODES.

NO ↓

Check the injectors for operation sound. — NG → Check the injector circuit malfunction (Refer to INSPECTION PROCEDURE FOR DIAGNOSTIC TROUBLE CODES P0201, P0202, P0203, P0204.)

OK ↓

Check the ignition timing — NG → Check that the crankshaft position sensor and timing belt cover are installed properly.

OK ↓

Scan Tool: Inspection when surge occurs. (Refer to INSPECTION PROCEDURE 44.)

OK ↓

Check the fuel pressure

OK ↓

Check the following items.
• Check the ignition coil, spark plugs, spark plug cables.
• Check the EGR system.
• Check the turbocharger waste gate actuator.

INSPECTION PROCEDURE 20

Knocking	Probable cause
[Comment] In cases such as the above, the cause is probably that the detonation control is defective or the heat value of the spark plug is inappropriate.	• Defective knock sensor • Inappropriate heat value of the spark plug

SCAN TOOL DIAGNOSTIC TROUBLE CODE
Are diagnostic trouble codes output ? — YES → Refer to INSPECTION CHART FOR DIAGNOSTIC TROUBLE CODES.

NO ↓

Does knocking occur when driving with the sensor disconnected?
At this time, use the scan tool to check if the timing is retarded compared to when the knock sensor connector is connected. — NO → Check the knock sensor 1 circuit malfunction (Refer to INSPECTION PROCEDURE FOR DIAGNOSTIC TROUBLE CODE P0325.)

YES ↓

Check the following items.
• Spark plugs
• Check if foreign materials (water, alcohol, etc.) got into fuel.

INSPECTION PROCEDURE 21

Dieseling	Probable cause
[Comment] Fuel leakage from injectors is suspected.	• Fuel leakage from injectors

Check the injectors for fuel leakage.

CR1029504976000X

Fig. 43 Troubleshooting inspection procedures 19 through 21. 1995–96 Talon

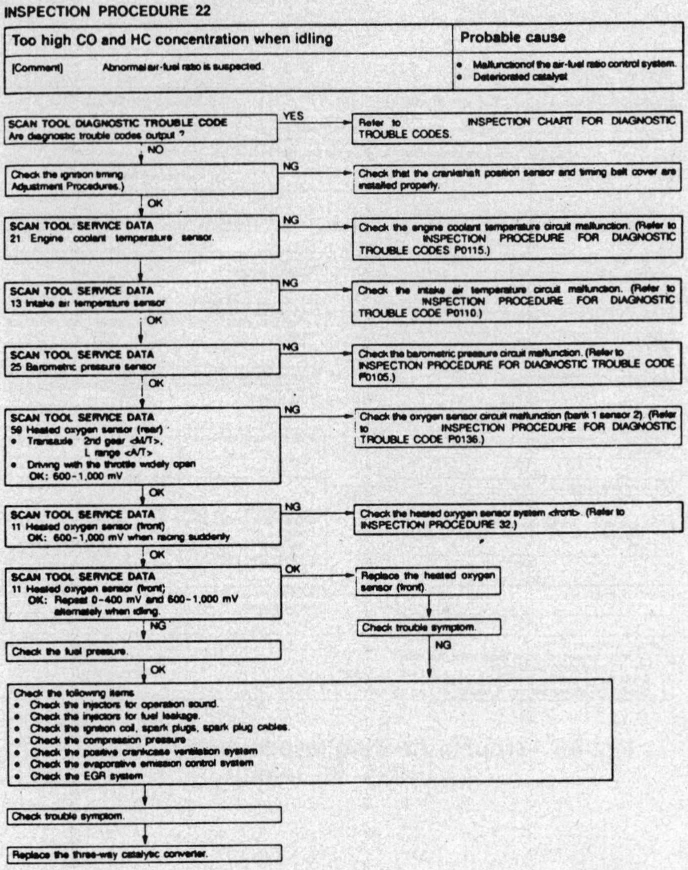

INSPECTION PROCEDURE 22

Too high CO and HC concentration when idling	Probable cause
[Comment] Abnormal air-fuel ratio is suspected.	• Malfunction of the air-fuel ratio control system • Deteriorated catalyst

SCAN TOOL DIAGNOSTIC TROUBLE CODE
Are diagnostic trouble codes output ? — YES → Refer to INSPECTION CHART FOR DIAGNOSTIC TROUBLE CODES.

NO ↓

Check the ignition timing (Refer to Adjustment Procedures.) — NG → Check that the crankshaft position sensor and timing belt cover are installed properly.

OK ↓

SCAN TOOL SERVICE DATA
21 Engine coolant temperature sensor. — NG → Check the engine coolant temperature circuit malfunction. (Refer to INSPECTION PROCEDURE FOR DIAGNOSTIC TROUBLE CODES P0115.)

OK ↓

SCAN TOOL SERVICE DATA
13 Intake air temperature sensor — NG → Check the intake air temperature circuit malfunction. (Refer to INSPECTION PROCEDURE FOR DIAGNOSTIC TROUBLE CODE P0110.)

OK ↓

SCAN TOOL SERVICE DATA
25 Barometric pressure sensor — NG → Check the barometric pressure circuit malfunction. (Refer to INSPECTION PROCEDURE FOR DIAGNOSTIC TROUBLE CODE P0105.)

OK ↓

SCAN TOOL SERVICE DATA
59 Heated oxygen sensor (rear)
• Transaxle 2nd gear <A/T>, L range <A/T>
• Driving with the throttle widely open
OK: 600~1,000 mV — NG → Check the oxygen sensor circuit malfunction (bank 1 sensor 2) (Refer to INSPECTION PROCEDURE FOR DIAGNOSTIC TROUBLE CODE P0136.)

OK ↓

SCAN TOOL SERVICE DATA
11 Heated oxygen sensor (front)
OK: 600~1,000 mV when racing suddenly — NG → Check the heated oxygen sensor system <front> (Refer to INSPECTION PROCEDURE 32.)

OK ↓

SCAN TOOL SERVICE DATA
11 Heated oxygen sensor (front)
OK: Repeat 0~400 mV and 600~1,000 mV alternately when idling — OK → Replace the heated oxygen sensor (front).

NG ↓   → Check trouble symptom.

Check the fuel pressure

NG ↓

OK ↓

Check the following items.
• Check the injectors for operation sound.
• Check the injectors for fuel leakage.
• Check the ignition coil, spark plugs, spark plug cables.
• Check the compression pressure.
• Check the positive crankcase ventilation system.
• Check the evaporative emission control system.
• Check the EGR system.

Check trouble symptom.

Replace the three-way catalytic converter.

CR1029504977000X

Fig. 44 Troubleshooting inspection procedure 22. 1995–96 Talon

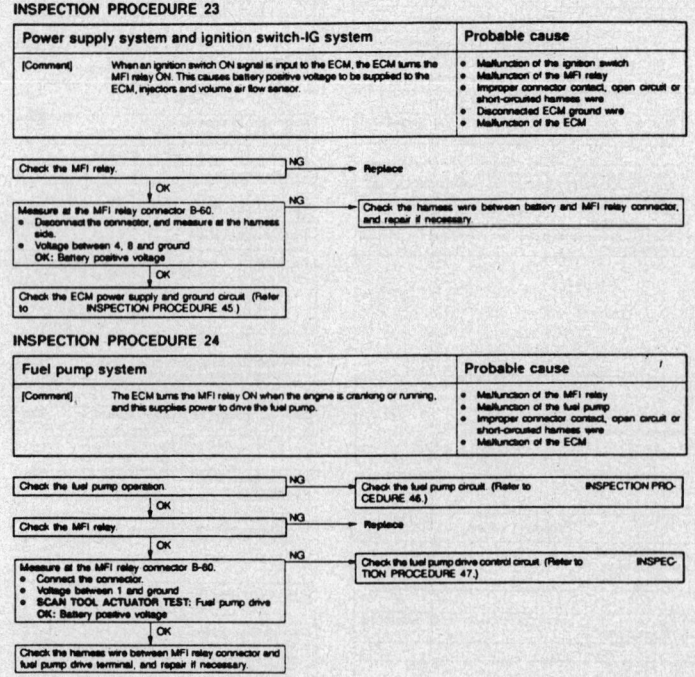

INSPECTION PROCEDURE 23

Power supply system and ignition switch-IG system	Probable cause
[Comment] When an ignition switch ON signal is input to the ECM, the ECM turns the MFI relay ON. This causes battery positive voltage to be supplied to the ECM, injectors and volume air flow sensor.	• Malfunction of the ignition switch • Malfunction of the MFI relay • Improper connector contact, open circuit or short-circuited harness wire • Disconnected ECM ground wire • Malfunction of the ECM

Check the MFI relay. — NG → Replace

OK ↓

Measure at the MFI relay connector B-60.
• Disconnect the connector, and measure at the harness side.
• Voltage between 4, 8 and ground
OK: Battery positive voltage — NG → Check the harness wire between battery and MFI relay connector, and repair if necessary.

OK ↓

Check the ECM power supply and ground circuit (Refer to INSPECTION PROCEDURE 45.)

INSPECTION PROCEDURE 24

Fuel pump system	Probable cause
[Comment] The ECM turns the MFI relay ON when the engine is cranking or running, and this supplies power to drive the fuel pump.	• Malfunction of the MFI relay • Malfunction of the fuel pump • Improper connector contact, open circuit or short-circuited harness wire • Malfunction of the ECM

Check the fuel pump operation. — NG → Check the fuel pump circuit (Refer to INSPECTION PROCEDURE 46.)

OK ↓

Check the MFI relay. — NG → Replace

OK ↓

Measure at the MFI relay connector B-60.
• Connect the connector.
• Voltage between 1 and ground
• SCAN TOOL ACTUATOR TEST: Fuel pump drive
OK: Battery positive voltage — NG → Check the fuel pump drive control circuit (Refer to INSPECTION PROCEDURE 47.)

OK ↓

Check the harness wire between MFI relay connector and fuel pump drive terminal, and repair if necessary.

CR1029504978000X

Fig. 45 Troubleshooting inspection procedures 23 & 24. 1995–96 Talon

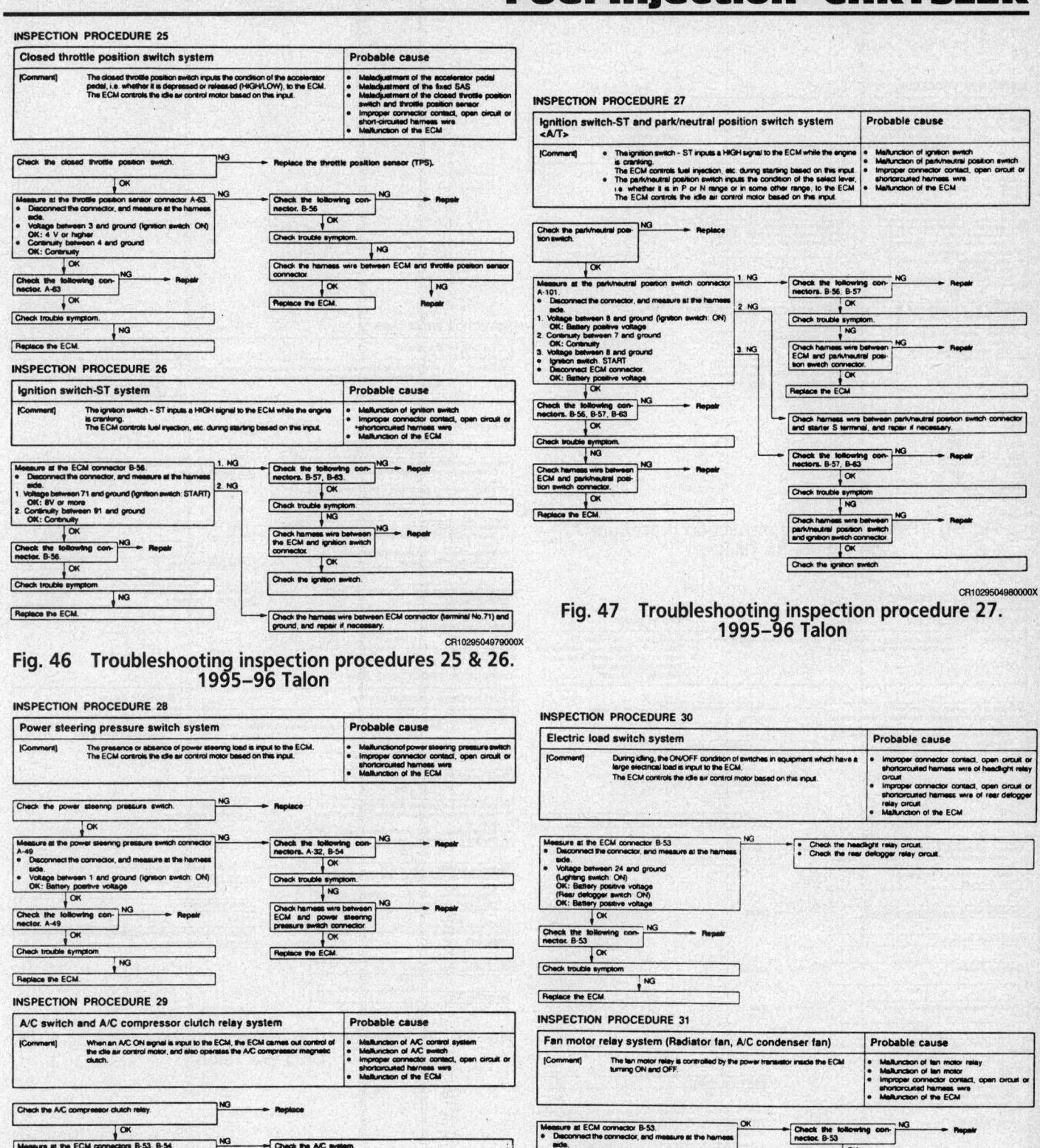

Fig. 46   Troubleshooting inspection procedures 25 & 26.
1995–96 Talon

Fig. 47   Troubleshooting inspection procedure 27.
1995–96 Talon

Fig. 48   Troubleshooting inspection procedures 28 & 29.
1995–96 Talon

Fig. 49   Troubleshooting inspection procedures 30 & 31.
1995–96 Talon

MULTI-POINT FUEL INJECTION (MODELS w/1.8L/4-107, 1.8L/4-110 & 2.4L/4-143 ENGINES, 1993-94 MODELS w/2.0L/4-122
ENGINE & 1995 TALON w/2.0L/4-122 TURBOCHARGED ENGINE)

7-79

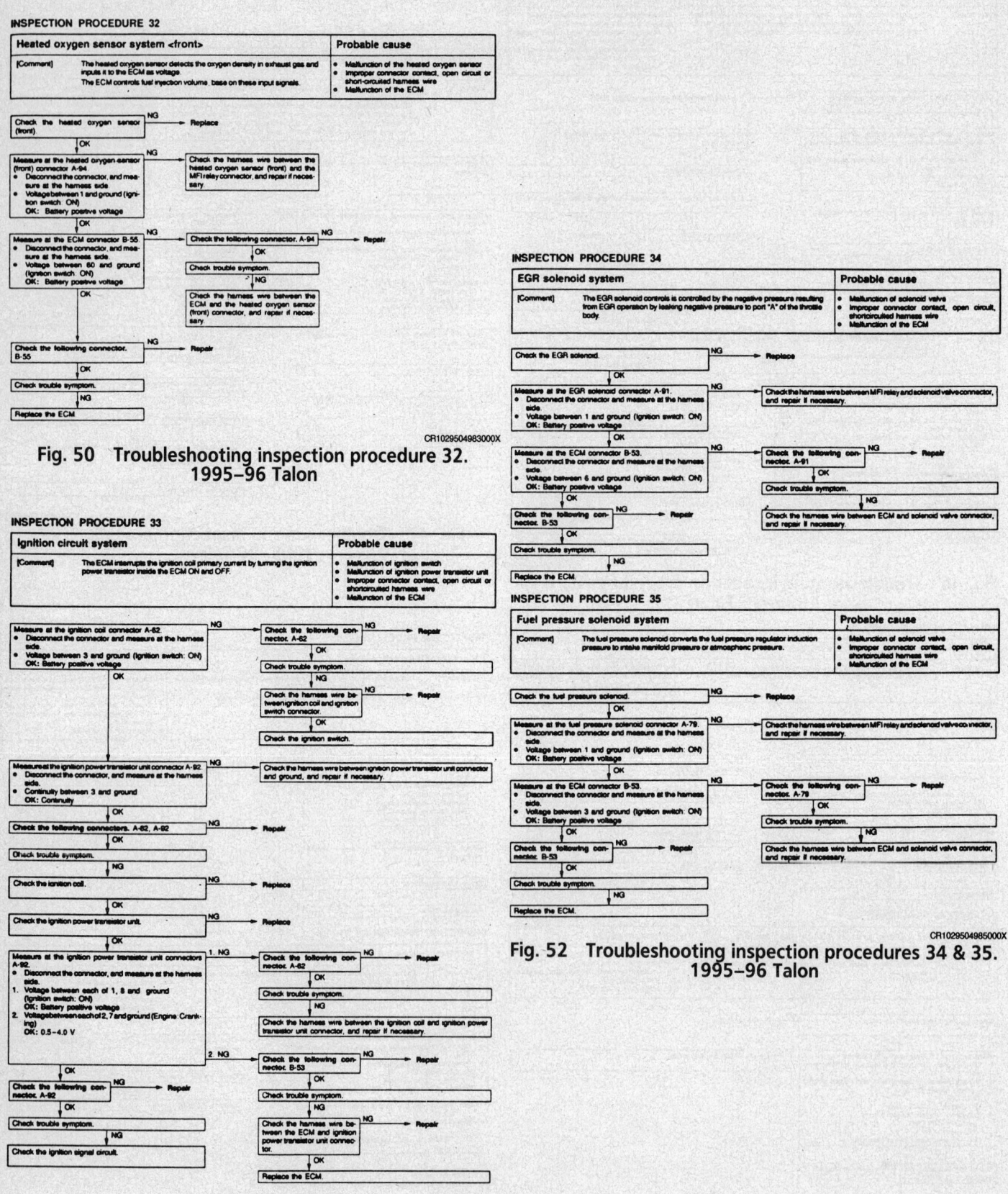

Fig. 50   Troubleshooting inspection procedure 32.
1995–96 Talon

Fig. 51   Troubleshooting inspection procedure 33.
1995–96 Talon

Fig. 52   Troubleshooting inspection procedures 34 & 35.
1995–96 Talon

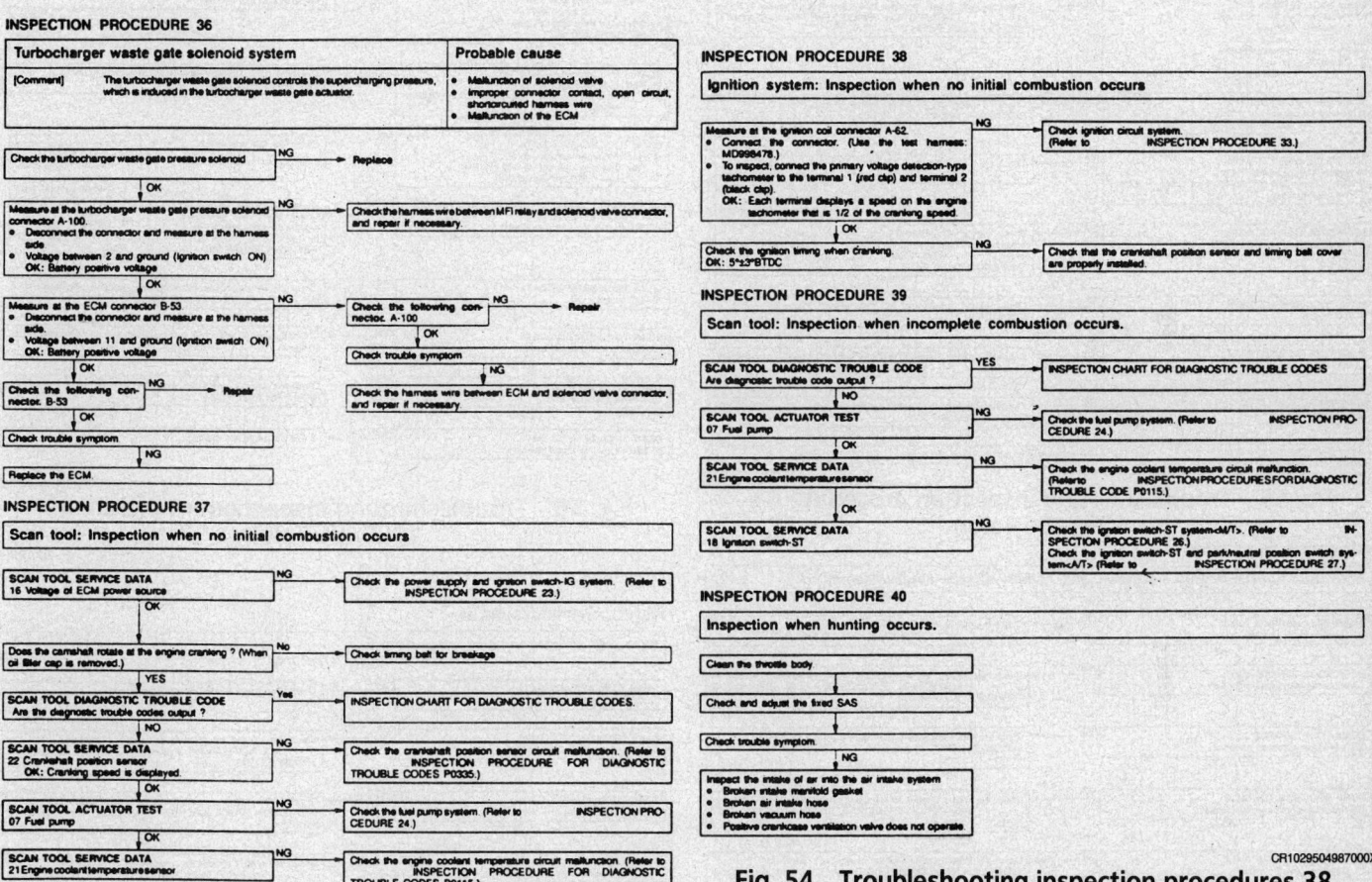

Fig. 53 Troubleshooting inspection procedures 36 & 37. 1995–96 Talon

CR1029504986000X

Fig. 54 Troubleshooting inspection procedures 38 through 40. 1995–96 Talon

CR1029504987000X

MULTI-POINT FUEL INJECTION (MODELS w/1.8L/4-107, 1.8L/4-110 & 2.4L/4-143 ENGINES, 1993-94 MODELS w/2.0L/4-122 ENGINE & 1995 TALON w/2.0L/4-122 TURBOCHARGED ENGINE)

7-81

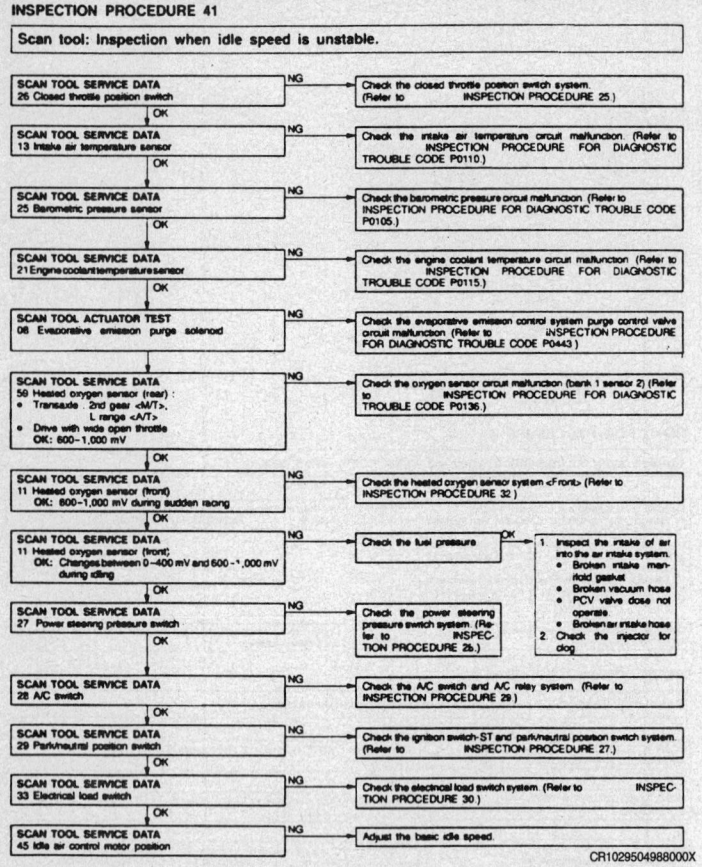

Fig. 55 Troubleshooting inspection procedure 41.
1995–96 Talon

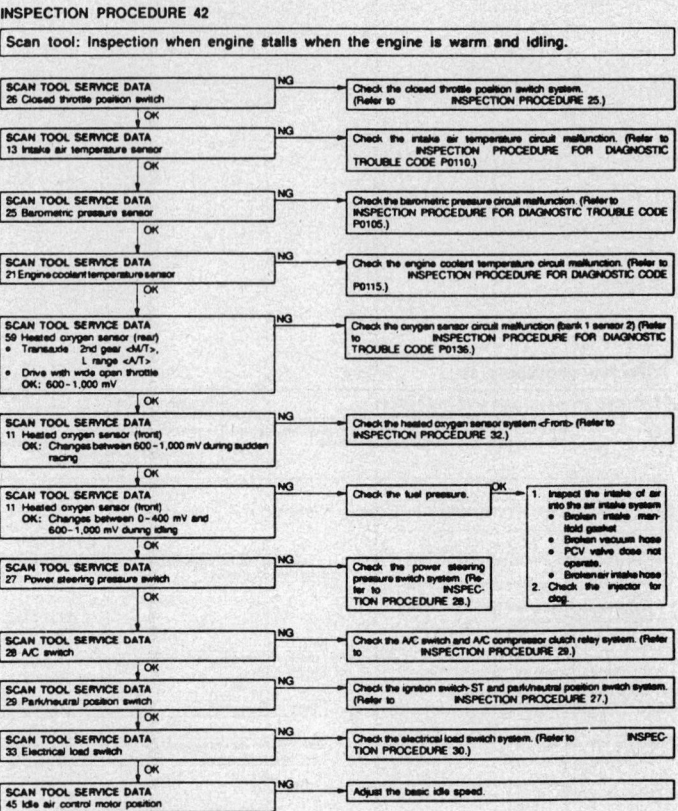

Fig. 56 Troubleshooting inspection procedure 42.
1995–96 Talon

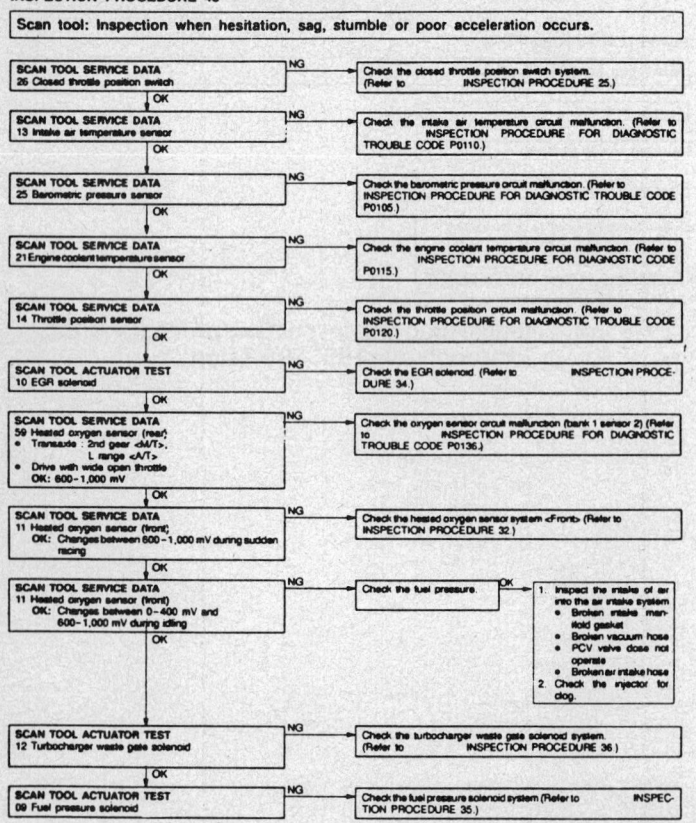

Fig. 57 Troubleshooting inspection procedure 43.
1995–96 Talon

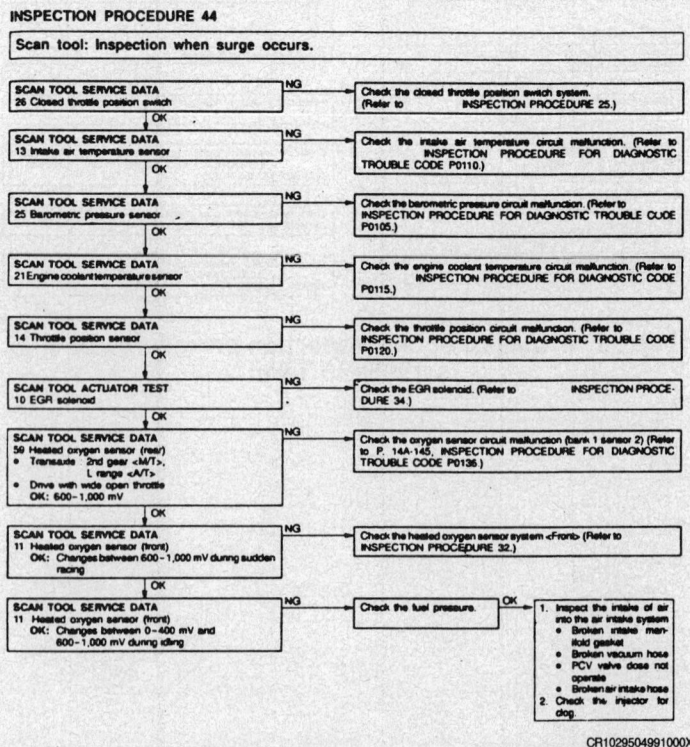

Fig. 58 Troubleshooting inspection procedure 44.
1995–96 Talon

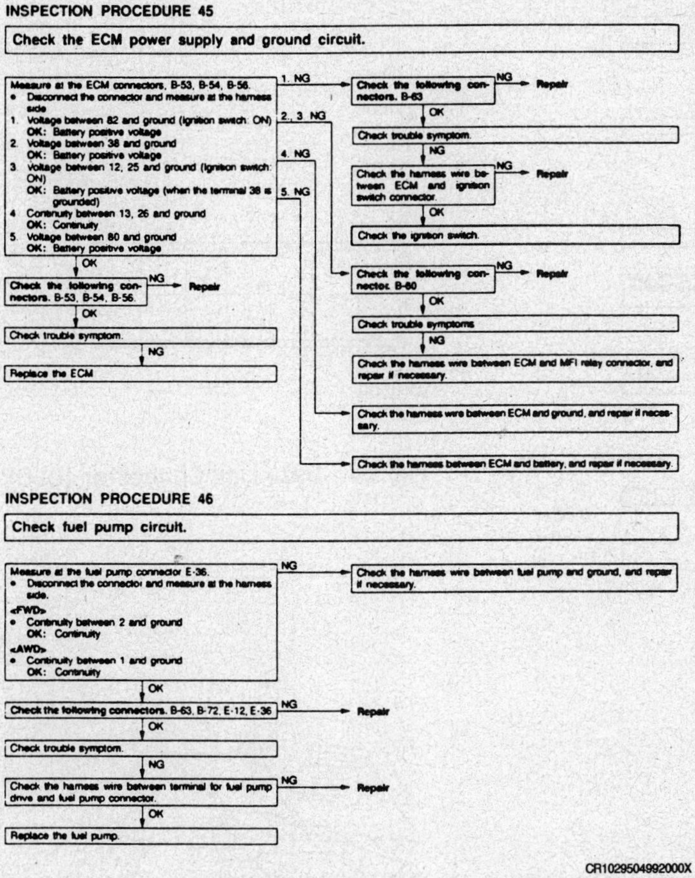

INSPECTION PROCEDURE 45

Check the ECM power supply and ground circuit.

Measure at the ECM connectors, B-53, B-54, B-56.
- Disconnect the connector and measure at the harness side.
1. Voltage between 82 and ground (ignition switch: ON)
   OK: Battery positive voltage
2. Voltage between 38 and ground
   OK: Battery positive voltage
3. Voltage between 12, 25 and ground (ignition switch: ON)
   OK: Battery positive voltage (when the terminal 38 is grounded)
4. Continuity between 13, 26 and ground
   OK: Continuity
5. Voltage between 80 and ground
   OK: Battery positive voltage

1. NG → Check the following connectors. B-63 → NG → Repair
   ↓ OK
   Check trouble symptom.
   ↓
   Check the harness wire between ECM and ignition switch connector. → NG → Repair
   ↓
   Check the ignition switch.

2, 3 NG → Check the following connector. B-60 → NG → Repair
   ↓ OK
   Check trouble symptoms.
   ↓ NG
   Check the harness wire between ECM and MFI relay connector, and repair if necessary.

4. NG → Check the harness wire between ECM and ground, and repair if necessary.

5. NG → Check the harness between ECM and battery, and repair if necessary.

↓ OK
Check the following connectors. B-53, B-54, B-56. → NG → Repair
↓ OK
Check trouble symptom.
↓ NG
Replace the ECM.

INSPECTION PROCEDURE 46

Check fuel pump circuit.

Measure at the fuel pump connector E-36.
- Disconnect the connector and measure at the harness side.
<FWD>
- Continuity between 2 and ground
  OK: Continuity
<AWD>
- Continuity between 1 and ground
  OK: Continuity

NG → Check the harness wire between fuel pump and ground, and repair if necessary.

↓ OK
Check the following connectors. B-63, B-72, E-12, E-36 → NG → Repair
↓ OK
Check trouble symptom.
↓ NG
Check the harness wire between terminal for fuel pump drive and fuel pump connector. → Repair
↓ OK
Replace the fuel pump.

CR1029504992000X

Fig. 59 Troubleshooting inspection procedures 45 & 46. 1995–96 Talon

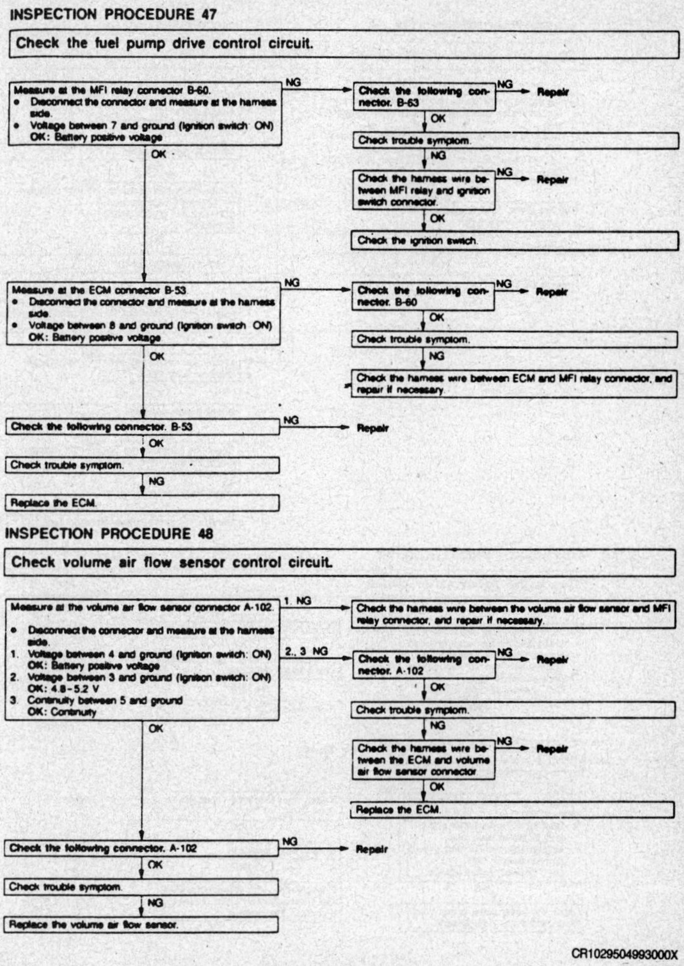

INSPECTION PROCEDURE 47

Check the fuel pump drive control circuit.

Measure at the MFI relay connector B-60.
- Disconnect the connector and measure at the harness side.
- Voltage between 7 and ground (ignition switch: ON)
  OK: Battery positive voltage

NG → Check the following connector. B-63 → NG → Repair
↓ OK
Check trouble symptom.
↓
Check the harness wire between MFI relay and ignition switch connector. → NG → Repair
↓ OK
Check the ignition switch.

↓ OK
Measure at the ECM connector B-53.
- Disconnect the connector and measure at the harness side.
- Voltage between 8 and ground (ignition switch: ON)
  OK: Battery positive voltage

NG → Check the following connector. B-60 → NG → Repair
↓ OK
Check trouble symptom.
↓
Check the harness wire between ECM and MFI relay connector, and repair if necessary.

↓ OK
Check the following connector. B-53 → NG → Repair
↓ OK
Check trouble symptom.
↓ NG
Replace the ECM.

INSPECTION PROCEDURE 48

Check volume air flow sensor control circuit.

Measure at the volume air flow sensor connector A-102.
- Disconnect the connector and measure at the harness side.
1. Voltage between 4 and ground (ignition switch: ON)
   OK: Battery positive voltage
2. Voltage between 3 and ground (ignition switch: ON)
   OK: 4.8–5.2 V
3. Continuity between 5 and ground
   OK: Continuity

1. NG → Check the harness wire between the volume air flow sensor and MFI relay connector, and repair if necessary.

2, 3 NG → Check the following connector. A-102 → NG → Repair
   ↓ OK
   Check trouble symptom.
   ↓ NG
   Check the harness wire between the ECM and volume air flow sensor connector. → NG → Repair
   ↓ OK
   Replace the ECM.

↓ OK
Check the following connector. A-102 → NG → Repair
↓ OK
Check trouble symptom.
↓ NG
Replace the volume air flow sensor.

CR1029504993000X

Fig. 60 Troubleshooting inspection procedures 47 & 48. 1995–96 Talon

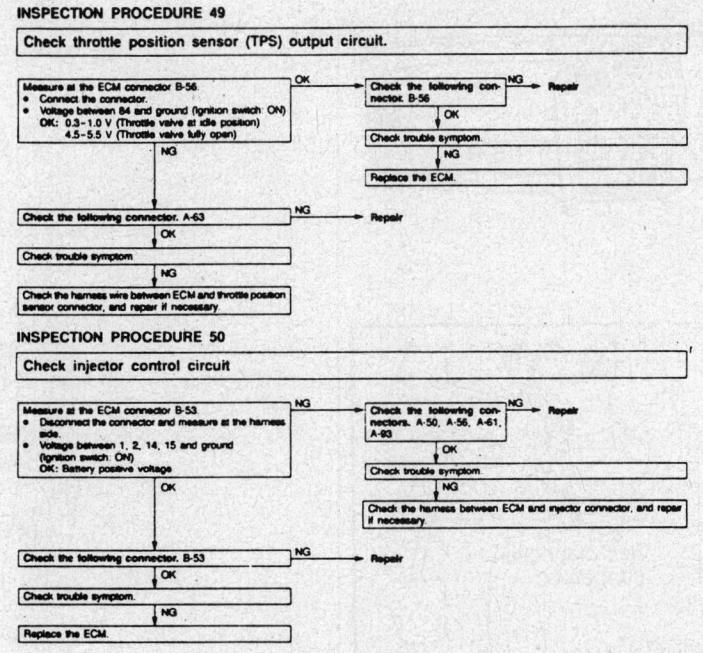

INSPECTION PROCEDURE 49

Check throttle position sensor (TPS) output circuit.

Measure at the ECM connector B-56.
- Connect the connector.
- Voltage between 84 and ground (ignition switch: ON)
  OK: 0.3–1.0 V (Throttle valve at idle position)
     4.5–5.5 V (Throttle valve fully open)

OK → Check the following connector. B-56 → NG → Repair
   ↓ OK
   Check trouble symptom.
   ↓ NG
   Replace the ECM.

↓ NG
Check the following connector. A-63 → NG → Repair
↓ OK
Check trouble symptom.
↓ NG
Check the harness wire between ECM and throttle position sensor connector, and repair if necessary.

INSPECTION PROCEDURE 50

Check injector control circuit.

Measure at the ECM connector B-53.
- Disconnect the connector and measure at the harness side.
- Voltage between 1, 2, 14, 15 and ground (ignition switch: ON)
  OK: Battery positive voltage

→ Check the following connectors. A-50, A-56, A-61, A-93 → NG → Repair
   ↓ OK
   Check trouble symptom.
   ↓ NG
   Check the harness between ECM and injector connector, and repair if necessary.

↓ OK
Check the following connector. B-53 → NG → Repair
↓ OK
Check trouble symptom.
↓ NG
Replace the ECM.

CR1029504994000X

Fig. 61 Troubleshooting inspection procedures 49 & 50. 1995–96 Talon

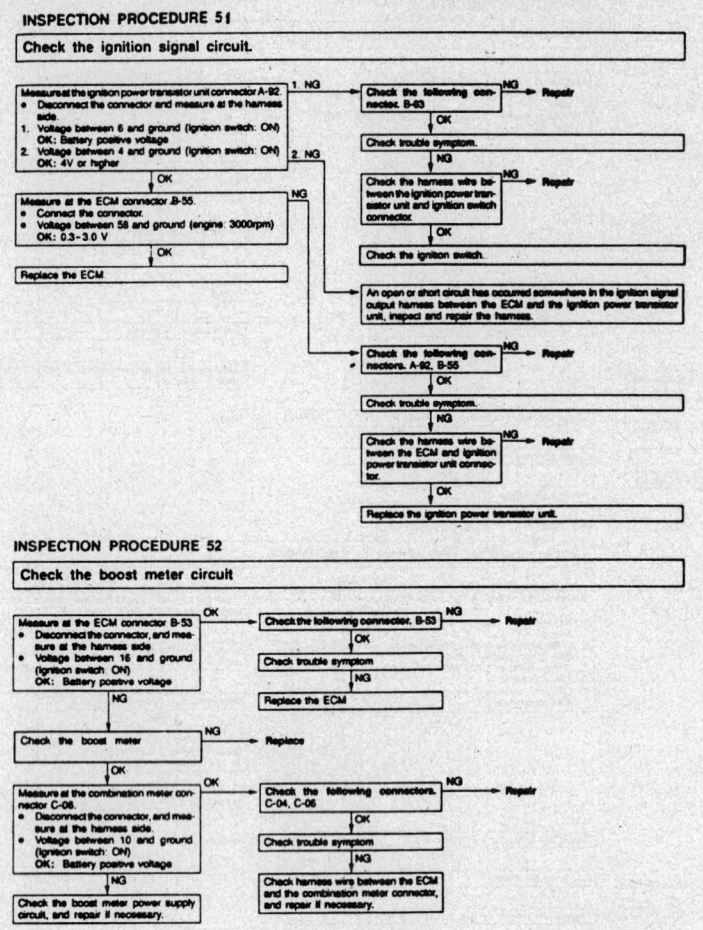

INSPECTION PROCEDURE 51

Check the ignition signal circuit.

Measure at the ignition power transistor unit connector A-92.
- Disconnect the connector and measure at the harness side.
1. Voltage between 6 and ground (ignition switch: ON) OK: Battery positive voltage
2. Voltage between 4 and ground (ignition switch: ON) OK: 4V or higher

Check the following connector. B-63
OK
Check trouble symptom.
NG
Check the harness wire between the ignition power transistor unit and ignition switch connector.
NG → Repair
OK
Check the ignition switch.

Measure at the ECM connector B-55.
- Connect the connector.
- Voltage between 58 and ground (engine: 3000rpm) OK: 0.3–3.0 V
OK
Replace the ECM

An open or short circuit has occurred somewhere in the ignition signal output harness between the ECM and the ignition power transistor unit, inspect and repair the harness.

Check the following connectors. A-92, B-55
OK
Check trouble symptom.
NG
Check the harness wire between the ECM and ignition power transistor unit connector.
OK
Replace the ignition power transistor unit.

INSPECTION PROCEDURE 52

Check the boost meter circuit

Measure at the ECM connector B-53
- Disconnect the connector, and measure at the harness side.
- Voltage between 16 and ground (ignition switch: ON) OK: Battery positive voltage

Check the following connector. B-53
OK
Check trouble symptom
NG
Replace the ECM

Check the boost meter
NG → Replace
OK

Measure at the combination meter connector C-06.
- Disconnect the connector, and measure at the harness side.
- Voltage between 10 and ground (ignition switch: ON) OK: Battery positive voltage
NG
Check the boost meter power supply circuit, and repair if necessary.

Check the following connectors. C-04, C-06
OK
Check trouble symptom
NG
Check harness wire between the ECM and the combination meter connector, and repair if necessary.

Fig. 62 Troubleshooting inspection procedures 51 & 52. 1995–96 Talon

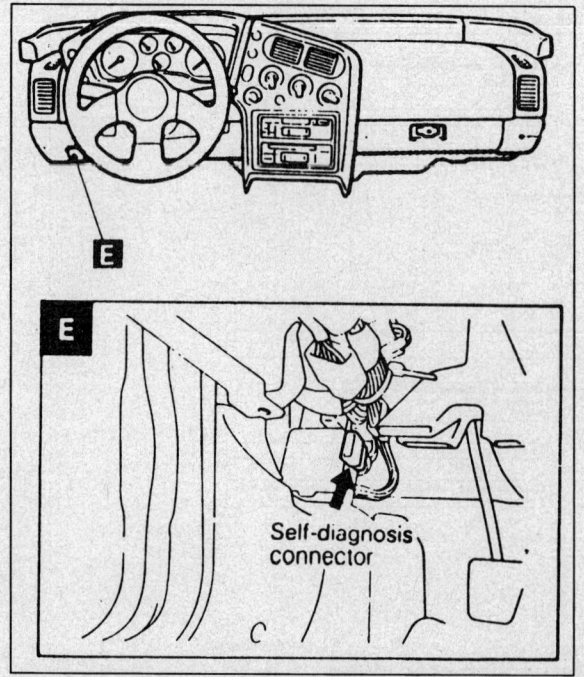

Fig. 65 Diagnostic connector location

Self-diagnosis connector

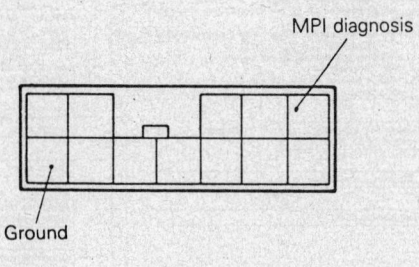

MPI diagnosis

Ground

Fig. 63 Data Link Connector (DLC)

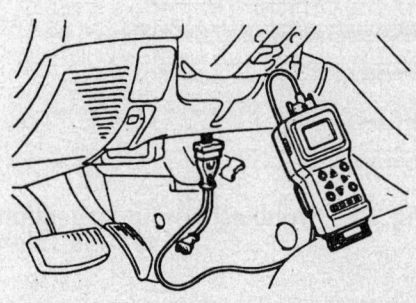

Fig. 64 Scan tool connection to data link connector

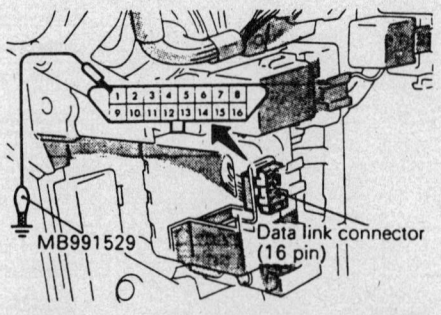

MB991529

Data link connector (16 pin)

Fig. 66 MIL diagnostic trouble code output check harness connection. 1994 Colt & Colt Vista & 1994–95 Summit & Summit Wagon

MULTI-POINT FUEL INJECTION (MODELS w/1.8L/4-107, 1.8L/4-110 & 2.4L/4-143 ENGINES, 1993-94 MODELS w/2.0L/4-122 ENGINE & 1995 TALON w/2.0L/4-122 TURBOCHARGED ENGINE)

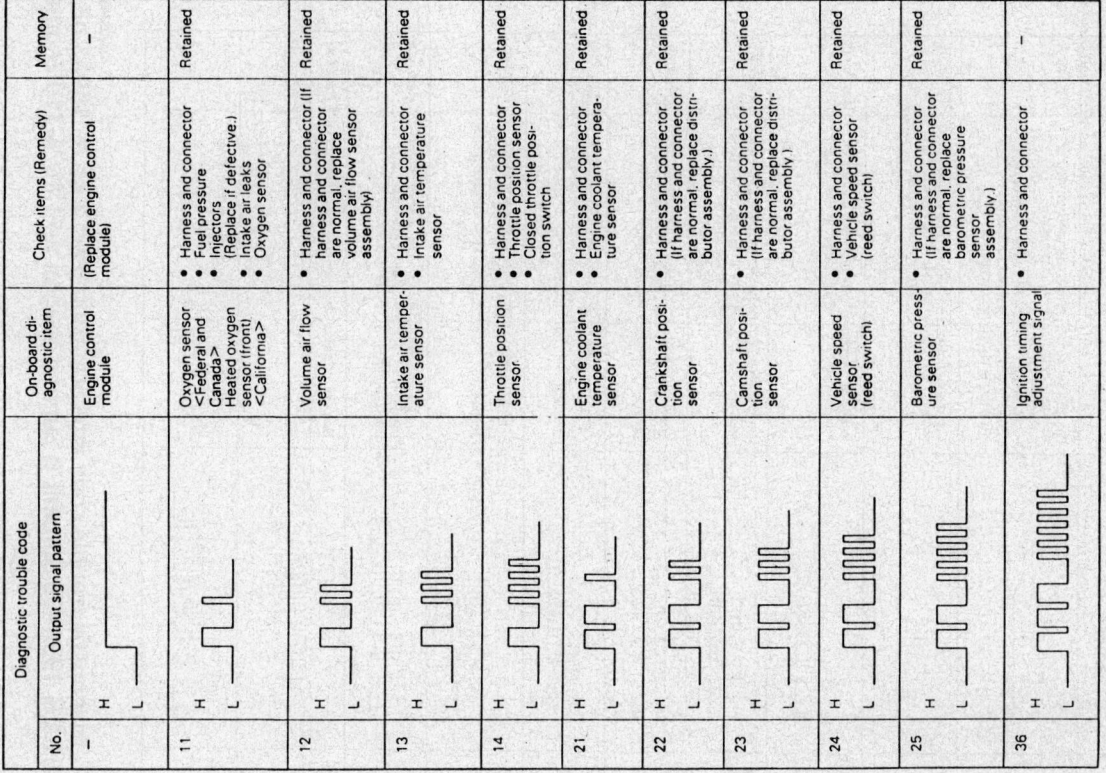

No.	Diagnostic trouble code / Output signal pattern	On-board diagnostic item	Check items (Remedy)	Memory
—		Engine control module	(Replace engine control module)	—
11		Oxygen sensor <Federal and Canada> Heated oxygen sensor (front) <California>	• Harness and connector • Fuel pressure • Injectors (Replace if defective.) • Intake air leaks • Oxygen sensor	Retained
12		Volume air flow sensor	• Harness and connector (If harness and connector are normal, replace volume air flow sensor assembly.)	Retained
13		Intake air temperature sensor	• Harness and connector • Intake air temperature sensor	Retained
14		Throttle position sensor	• Harness and connector • Throttle position sensor • Closed throttle position switch	Retained
21		Engine coolant temperature sensor	• Harness and connector • Engine coolant temperature sensor	Retained
22		Crankshaft position sensor	• Harness and connector (If harness and connector are normal, replace distributor assembly.)	Retained
23		Camshaft position sensor	• Harness and connector (If harness and connector are normal, replace distributor assembly.)	Retained
24		Vehicle speed sensor (reed switch)	• Harness and connector • Vehicle speed sensor (reed switch)	Retained
25		Barometric pressure sensor	• Harness and connector (If harness and connector are normal, replace barometric pressure sensor assembly.)	Retained
36		Ignition timing adjustment signal	• Harness and connector	—

Fig. 68 Diagnostic trouble code interpretation (Part 1 of 2). 1993 Colt, Colt Vista, Summit & Summit Wagon

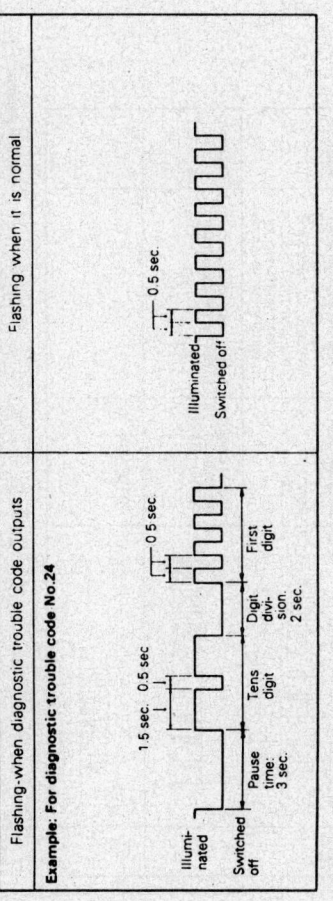

Flashing-when diagnostic trouble code outputs	Flashing when it is normal

Example: For diagnostic trouble code No.24

CR102950499800X

NOTE
Other diagnostic trouble codes also output as the same code numbers as when using the scan tool.

Fig. 67 MIL diagnostic trouble code output interpretation. 1994 Colt & Colt Vista & 1994–95 Summit & Summit Wagon

MULTI-POINT FUEL INJECTION (MODELS w/1.8L/4-107, 1.8L/4-110 & 2.4L/4-143 ENGINES, 1993-94 MODELS w/2.0L/4-122 ENGINE & 1995 TALON w/2.0L/4-122 TURBOCHARGED ENGINE)

7-85

Diagnostic trouble code		On-board diagnostic item	Check items (Remedy)	Memory
No.	Output signal pattern			
41	H L	Injector	• Harness and connector • Injector coil resistance	Retained
43	H L	EGR <California>	• Harness and connector • EGR valve • EGR solenoid • EGR valve control vacuum • EGR temperature sensor	Retained
55	H L	IAC valve position sensor	• Harness and connector • IAC valve movement (If harness, connector and IAC valve movement are normal, replace idle air control motor assembly)	Retained
59	H L	Heated oxygen sensor (rear) <California>	• Harness and connector • Heated oxygen sensor	Retained
–	H L	Normal state	–	–

CR1029300505020X

Fig. 68 Diagnostic trouble code interpretation (Part 2 of 2). 1993 Colt, Colt Vista, Summit & Summit Wagon

Diagnostic trouble code		On-board diagnostic item	Check items (Remedy)	Memory
No.	Output signal pattern			
–	H L	Engine control module	(Replace engine control module)	–
11	H L	Oxygen sensor <Federal and Canada> Heated oxygen sensor (front) <California>	• Harness and connector • Fuel pressure • Injectors (Replace if defective.) • Intake air leaks • Oxygen sensor	Retained
12	H L	Volume air flow sensor	• Harness and connector (If harness and connector are normal, replace volume air flow sensor assembly)	Retained
13	H L	Intake air temperature sensor	• Harness and connector • Intake air temperature sensor	Retained
14	H L	Throttle position sensor	• Harness and connector • Throttle position sensor • Closed throttle position switch	Retained
21	H L	Engine coolant temperature sensor	• Harness and connector • Engine coolant temperature sensor	Retained
22	H L	Crankshaft position sensor	• Harness and connector (If harness and connector are normal, replace distributor assembly.)	Retained
23	H L	Camshaft position sensor	• Harness and connector (If harness and connector are normal, replace distributor assembly.)	Retained
24	H L	Vehicle speed sensor (reed switch)	• Harness and connector • Vehicle speed sensor (reed switch)	Retained
25	H L	Barometric pressure sensor	• Harness and connector (If harness and connector are normal, replace barometric pressure sensor assembly.)	Retained
36	H L	Ignition timing adjustment signal	• Harness and connector	–

CR10294032110010X

Fig. 69 Diagnostic trouble code interpretation (Part 1 of 2). 1994 Colt & Colt Vista & 1994–95 Summit & Summit Wagon w/1.8L/4-110 Engine

No.	Diagnostic trouble code / Output signal pattern	Diagnostic item	Check items (Remedy)	Memory
—		Engine control module	• Fuse • Ground (Replace ECM if power + ground available)	
11		Heated oxygen sensor (front)	• Harness and connector • Fuel pressure • Injectors (Replace if defective.) • Intake air leaks • Oxygen sensor	Retained
12		Volume air flow sensor	• Harness and connector (If harness, and connector are normal, replace volume air flow sensor assembly)	Retained
13		Intake air temperature sensor	• Harness and connector • Intake air temperature sensor	Retained
14		Throttle position sensor	• Harness and connector • Throttle position sensor • Closed throttle position switch	Retained
21		Engine coolant temperature sensor	• Harness and connector • Engine coolant temperature sensor	Retained
22		Crankshaft position sensor	• Harness and connector (If harness and connector are normal, replace distributor assembly.)	Retained
23		Camshaft position sensor	• Harness and connector (If harness and connector are normal, replace distributor assembly.)	Retained
24		Vehicle speed sensor	• Harness and connector • Vehicle speed sensor	Retained
25		Barometric pressure sensor	• Harness and connector (If harness and connector are normal, replace baromatic pressure sensor assembly.)	Retained
36		Ignition timing adjustment signal	• Harness and connector	—

Fig. 70 Diagnostic trouble code interpretation (Part 1 of 2). 1994 Colt Vista & 1994–95 Summit Wagon w/2.4L/4-143 Engine

CR1029403212010X

No.	Diagnostic trouble code / Output signal pattern	Diagnostic item	Check items (Remedy)	Memory
41		Injector	• Harness and connector • Injector coil resistance	Retained
43		EGR	• Harness and connector • EGR valve • EGR solenoid • EGR valve control vacuum • EGR temperature sensor	Retained
55		IAC valve position sensor	• Harness and connector • IAC valve movement (If harness, connector and IAC valve movement are normal, replace idle air control motor assembly)	Retained
59		Heated oxygen sensor (rear)	• Harness and connector • Heated oxygen sensor	Retained
—	(Continuous)	Normal state	—	—

NOTE
1 Do not replace the ECM until a thorough terminal check reveals there are no short/open circuits.
2 The code numbers will be displayed in order, starting from the lowest.

Fig. 69 Diagnostic trouble code interpretation (Part 2 of 2). 1994 Colt & Colt Vista & 1994–95 Summit & Summit Wagon w/1.8L/4-110 Engine

CR1029403211020X

MULTI-POINT FUEL INJECTION (MODELS w/1.8L/4-107, 1.8L/4-110 & 2.4L/4-143 ENGINES, 1993-94 MODELS w/2.0L/4-122 ENGINE & 1995 TALON w/2.0L/4-122 TURBOCHARGED ENGINE)

7-87

DTC No. <General scan tool mode>	DTC No. <Scan tool (MUT-II) mode>	Diagnostic items	Check items (Remedy)	Memory
P0100	P0100	Volume Air Flow Circuit Malfunction	• Harness and connector (If harness and connector are normal, replace volume air flow sensor assembly.)	Retained
P0105	P0105	Barometric Pressure Circuit Malfunction	• Harness and connector (If harness and connector are normal, replace volume air flow sensor assembly.)	Retained
P0110	P0110	Intake Air Temperature circuit Malfunction	• Harness and connector • Intake air temperature sensor	Retained
P0115	P0115	Engine Coolant Temperature Circuit Malfunction	• Harness and connector • Engine coolant temperature sensor	Retained
P0120	P0120	Throttle position Circuit Malfunction	• Harness and connector • Throttle position sensor • Closed throttle position switch	Retained
P0125	–	Excessive Time to Enter Closed Loop Fuel Control	• O₂ sensor (front) • O₂ sensor harness and connector • Injector	Retained
P0130	–	O₂ Sensor Circuit Malfunction (Bank 1 Sensor 1)	• Harness and connector (If harness and connector are normal, replace O₂ sensor front.)	Retained
P0135	–	O₂ Sensor Heater Circuit Malfunction (Bank 1 Sensor 1)	• Harness and connector • O₂ Sensor (front) heater	Retained
P0136	–	O₂ Sensor Circuit Malfunction (Bank 1 Sensor 2)	• Harness and connector • O₂ Sensor (rear)	Retained
P0141	–	O₂ Sensor Heater Circuit Malfunction (Bank 1 Sensor 2)	• Harness and connector • O₂ Sensor (rear) heater	Retained
P0170	–	Fuel Trim Malfunction (Bank 1)	• Volume air flow sensor output frequency • Injector • Fuel pressure • Intake air leaks • Engine coolant temperature sensor • Intake air temperature sensor • Barometric pressure sensor • O₂ Sensor • Exhaust manifold cracked	Retained

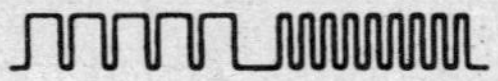

CR1029403212020X

Fig. 71 Diagnostic trouble code interpretation (Part 1 of 3). 1996 Summit Wagon

No.	Diagnostic trouble code (Output signal pattern)	Diagnostic item	Check items (Remedy)	Memory
41	[output signal pattern]	Injector	• Harness and connector • Injector coil resistance	Retained
43	[output signal pattern]	EGR	• Harness and connector • EGR valve • EGR solenoid • EGR valve control vacuum • EGR temperature sensor	Retained
55	[output signal pattern]	IAC valve position sensor	• Harness and connector • IAC valve movement (If harness, connector and IAC valve movement are normal, replace idle air control motor assembly)	Retained
59	[output signal pattern]	Heated oxygen sensor (rear)	• Harness and connector • Heated oxygen sensor	Retained
61	[output signal pattern]	A cable from transaxle control module for transaxle of torque reduction signal	• Harness and connector (If harness and connector are normal, replace only transaxle control module)	Retained
(Continuous)	[output signal pattern]	Normal state		

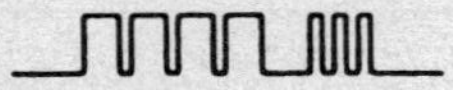

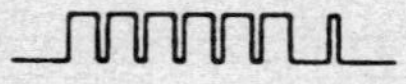

NOTE
1 Do not replace the ECM until a thorough terminal check reveals there are no short/open circuits
2 The code numbers will be displayed in order, starting from the lowest

Fig. 70 Diagnostic trouble code interpretation (Part 2 of 2). 1994 Colt Vista & 1994–95 Summit Wagon w/2.4L/4-143 Engine

MULTI-POINT FUEL INJECTION (MODELS w/1.8L/4-107, 1.8L/4-110 & 2.4L/4-143 ENGINES, 1993-94 MODELS w/2.0L/4-122 ENGINE & 1995 TALON w/2.0L/4-122 TURBOCHARGED ENGINE)

Fig. 71 Diagnostic trouble code interpretation (Part 3 of 3). 1996 Summit Wagon

DTC No. <General scan tool mode>	DTC No. <Scan tool (MUT-II) mode>	Diagnostic items	Check items (Remedy)	Memory
P0442	-	Evaporative Emission Control System Leak Detected <California-FWD>	• Fuel tank • Vapor hose	Retained
P0443	-	Evaporative Emission Control System Purge Control Valve Circuit Malfunction	• Harness and connector • Evaporative emission purge solenoid	Retained
P0446	-	Evaporative Emission Control System Vent Control Malfunction <California-FWD>	• Harness and connector • Evaporative emission purge solenoid	Retained
P0450	-	Evaporative Emission Control System Pressure Sensor Malfunction <California-FWD>	• Harness and connector • Fuel tank differential pressure sensor	Retained
P0500	P0500	Vehicle Speed Sensor Malfunction	• Harness and connector • Vehicle speed sensor	Retained
P0505	P0505	Idle Control System Malfunction	• Harness and connector • Idle air control motor	Retained
P0510	-	Closed Throttle Position Switch Malfunction	• Harness and connector • Closed throttle position switch	Retained
P0705	-	Transmission Range Sensor Circuit Malfunction (RPNDL Input)	• Harness and connector • Park/Neutral position switch	Retained
P0710	-	Transmission Fluid Temperature Sensor Circuit Malfunction	• Harness and connector • Transaxle oil temperature sensor	Retained
P1300	P1300	Ignition Timing Adjustment Circuit Malfunction	• Harness and connector	–
P1400	-	Manifold Differential Pressure (MDP) Sensor Circuit Malfunction	• Harness and connector • MDP sensor	Retained
P1443	-	Evaporative Emission Control System Purge Control Valve 2 Circuit Malfunction <California-FWD>	• Harness and connector • Evaporative emission purge solenoid No.2	Retained
P1500	P1500	Generator FR Terminal Circuit Malfunction	• Harness and connector	Retained
P1715	-	PG Assy Malfunction	• Harness and connector • Pulse generator	Retained
P1750	-	Solenoid Assy Malfunction	• Harness and connector • Converter clutch solenoid • Shift control solenoid • Pressure control solenoid	Retained

Fig. 71 Diagnostic trouble code interpretation (Part 2 of 3). 1996 Summit Wagon

DTC No. <General scan tool mode>	DTC No. <Scan tool (MUT-II) mode>	Diagnostic items	Check items (Remedy)	Memory
P0201	P0201	Injector Circuit Malfunction - Cylinder 1	• Harness and connector • Injector	Retained
P0202	P0202	Injector Circuit Malfunction - Cylinder 2		
P0203	P0203	Injector Circuit Malfunction - Cylinder 3		
P0204	P0204	Injector Circuit Malfunction - Cylinder 4		
P0300	-	Random Misfire Detected	• Ignition coil • Ignition power transistor • Spark plug • Ignition circuit • Injector • O2 Sensor • Compression pressure • Timing belt • Crankshaft position sensor • Air intake • Fuel pressure	Retained
P0301	-	Cylinder 1 Misfire Detected		
P0302	-	Cylinder 2 Misfire Detected		
P0303	-	Cylinder 3 Misfire Detected		
P0304	-	Cylinder 4 Misfire Detected		
P0335	P0335	Crankshaft Position sensor Circuit Malfunction	• Harness and connector (If harness and connector are normal, replace crankshaft position sensor.)	Retained
P0340	P0340	Camshaft Position sensor Circuit Malfunction	• Harness and connector (If harness and connector are normal, replace camshaft position sensor.)	Retained
P0400	-	Exhaust Gas Recirculation Flow Malfunction <Federal, California-AWD, Canada>	• Harness and connector • EGR valve • EGR solenoid • EGR valve control vacuum • Manifold differential pressure sensor	Retained
P0403	-	Exhaust Gas Recirculation solenoid Malfunction	• Harness and connector • EGR solenoid	Retained
P0420	-	Catalyst System Efficiency Below Threshold (Bank 1) <Federal, California-AWD, Canada>	• Exhaust manifold (Replace the catalytic converter if there is no cracks, etc.)	Retained
P0421	-	Warm Up Catalyst Efficiency Below Threshold (Bank 1) <California-FWD>	• Exhaust manifold (Replace the catalytic converter if there is no cracks.)	Retained
P0440	-	Evaporative Emission Control System Malfunction <Federal, California-AWD, Canada>	• Harness and connector • Evaporative emission purge solenoid • Purge control valve • Vacuum hoses routing	Retained

MULTI-POINT FUEL INJECTION (MODELS w/1.8L/4-107, 1.8L/4-110 & 2.4L/4-143 ENGINES, 1993-94 MODELS w/2.0L/4-122 ENGINE & 1995 TALON w/2.0L/4-122 TURBOCHARGED ENGINE)

Fig. 72 Diagnostic trouble code interpretation (Part 1 of 2). 1993–94 Laser & Talon w/1.8L/4-107 engine

No.	Output signal pattern	Diagnostic item	Check item (Remedy)	Memory
–	 (waveform)	Engine control module	• (Replace engine control module)	–
11	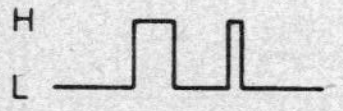 (waveform)	Oxygen sensor	• Harness and connector • Oxygen sensor • Fuel pressure • Injectors (Replace if defective.) • Intake air leaks	Retained
12	 (waveform)	Volume air flow sensor	• Harness and connector (If harness and connector are normal, replace volume air flow sensor assembly.)	Retained
13	 (waveform)	Intake air temperature sensor	• Harness and connector • Intake air temperature sensor	Retained
14	 (waveform)	Throttle position sensor	• Harness and connector • Throttle position sensor • Closed throttle position switch	Retained
15	 (waveform)	Idle speed control motor position sensor	• Harness and connector • Idle speed control motor position sensor • Throttle position sensor	Retained
21	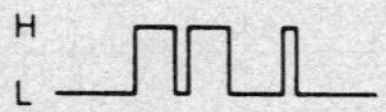 (waveform)	Engine coolant temperature sensor	• Harness and connector • Engine coolant temperature sensor	Retained
22	 (waveform)	Crankshaft position sensor	• Harness and connector (If harness and connector are normal, replace distributor assembly.)	Retained

Fig. 72 Diagnostic trouble code interpretation (Part 2 of 2). 1993–94 Laser & Talon w/1.8L/4-107 engine

No.	Output signal pattern	Diagnostic item	Check item (Remedy)	Memory
23	(waveform)	Camshaft position sensor	• Harness and connector (If harness and connector are normal, replace distributor assembly.)	Retained
24	(waveform)	Vehicle speed sensor (reed switch)	• Harness and connector • Vehicle speed sensor (reed switch)	Retained
25	(waveform)	Barometric pressure sensor	• Harness and connector (If harness and connector are normal, replace barometric pressure sensor assembly.)	Retained
36	(waveform)	Ignition timing adjustment signal	• Harness and connector	–
41	(waveform)	Injector	• Harness and connector • Injector coil resistance	Retained
42	(waveform)	Fuel pump	• Harness and connector • MFI relay	Retained
43	(waveform)	EGR <California>	• Harness and connector • EGR temperature sensor • EGR valve • EGR solenoid • EGR valve control vacuum	Retained
–	(waveform)	Normal state	–	–

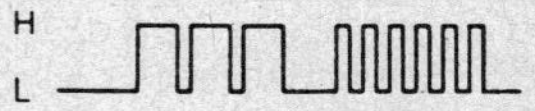

CR1029300506020X

CR1029300506010X

MULTI-POINT FUEL INJECTION (MODELS w/1.8L/4-107, 1.8L/4-110 & 2.4L/4-143 ENGINES, 1993-94 MODELS w/2.0L/4-122 ENGINE & 1995 TALON w/2.0L/4-122 TURBOCHARGED ENGINE)

Diagnostic trouble code interpretation (Part 2 of 2)

No.	Output signal pattern	Diagnostic item	Check item (Remedy)	Memory
24	(waveform)	Vehicle speed sensor (reed switch)	• Harness and connector • Vehicle speed sensor (reed switch)	Retained
25	(waveform)	Barometric pressure sensor	• Harness and connector (If harness and connector are normal, replace barometric pressure sensor assembly.)	Retained
31	(waveform)	Knock sensor <Turbo>	• Harness and connector (If harness and connector are normal, replace knock sensor.)	Retained
41	(waveform)	Injector	• Harness and connector • Injector coil resistance	Retained
42	(waveform)	Fuel pump	• Harness and connector • MFI relay	Retained
43	(waveform)	EGR <California>	• Harness and connector • EGR temperature sensor • EGR valve • EGR solenoid • EGR valve control vacuum	Retained
44	(waveform)	Ignition coil, ignition power transistor unit	• Harness and connector • Ignition coil • Ignition power transistor	Retained
—	(waveform)	Normal state	—	—

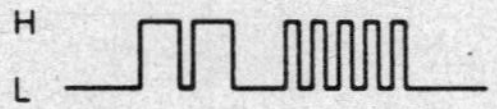

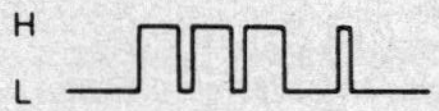

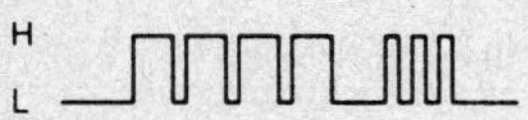

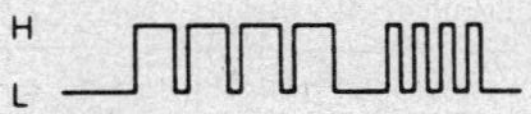

CR102930050702OX

Fig. 73 Diagnostic trouble code interpretation (Part 2 of 2). 1993–94 Laser & Talon w/2.0L/4-122 engine

Diagnostic trouble code interpretation (Part 1 of 2)

No.	Output signal pattern	Diagnostic item	Check item (Remedy)	Memory
—	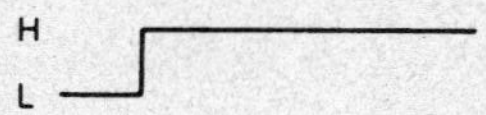 (waveform)	Engine control module	(Replace engine control module)	—
11	 (waveform)	Heated oxygen sensor	• Harness and connector • Heated oxygen sensor • Fuel pressure • Injectors (Replace if defective.) • Intake air leaks	Retained
12	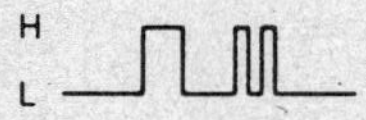 (waveform)	Volume air flow sensor	• Harness and connector (If harness and connector are normal, replace volume air flow sensor assembly.)	Retained
13	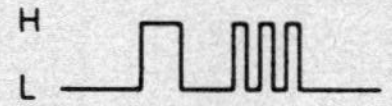 (waveform)	Intake air temperature sensor	• Harness and connector • Intake air temperature sensor	Retained
14	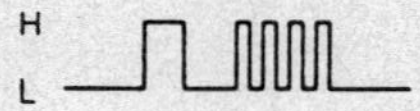 (waveform)	Throttle position sensor	• Harness and connector • Throttle position sensor • Closed throttle position switch	Retained
21	 (waveform)	Engine coolant temperature sensor	• Harness and connector • Engine coolant temperature sensor	Retained
22	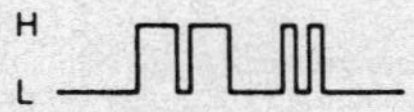 (waveform)	Crankshaft position sensor	• Harness and connector (If harness and connector are normal, replace crankshaft position assembly.)	Retained
23	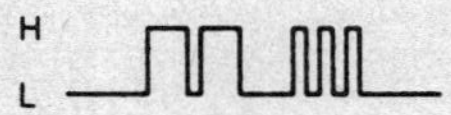 (waveform)	Camshaft position sensor	• Harness and connector (If harness and connector are normal, replace crankshaft position assembly.)	Retained

CR102930050701OX

Fig. 73 Diagnostic trouble code interpretation (Part 1 of 2). 1993–94 Laser & Talon w/2.0L/4-122 engine

MULTI-POINT FUEL INJECTION (MODELS w/1.8L/4-107, 1.8L/4-110 & 2.4L/4-143 ENGINES, 1993-94 MODELS w/2.0L/4-122 ENGINE & 1995 TALON w/2.0L/4-122 TURBOCHARGED ENGINE)

7-91

Diagnostic trouble code No. — General scan tool mode	Scan tool (DRB-III) mode	Diagnostic items	Check items (Remedy)	Memory
P0201	P0201	Injector circuit malfunction – Cylinder 1	• Harness and connector • Injector	Retained
P0202	P0202	Injector circuit malfunction – Cylinder 2		
P0203	P0203	Injector circuit malfunction – Cylinder 3		Retained
P0204	P0204	Injector circuit malfunction – Cylinder 4		
P0300	–	Random misfire detected*	• Ignition coil • Ignition power transistor • Spark plug • Ignition circuit • Injector • O_2 Sensor • Compression pressure • Timing belt • Crankshaft position sensor • Air intake • Fuel pressure • Crankshaft position sensor circuit and connector	Retained
P0301	–	Cylinder 1 misfire detected*		
P0302	–	Cylinder 2 misfire detected*		
P0303	–	Cylinder 3 misfire detected*		
P0304	–	Cylinder 4 misfire detected*		
P0325	P0325	Knock sensor 1 circuit malfunction	• Harness and connector (If harness and connector are not defective, replace knock sensor.)	Retained
P0335	P0335	Crankshaft position sensor circuit malfunction	• Harness and connector (If harness and connector are not defective, replace crankshaft position sensor.)	Retained
P0340	P0340	Camshaft position sensor circuit malfunction	• Harness and connector (If harness and connector are not defective, replace camshaft position sensor.)	Retained
P0400	P0400	Exhaust gas recirculation flow malfunction	• Harness and connector • EGR valve • EGR solenoid • EGR valve control vacuum • Manifold differential pressure sensor	Retained
P0420	–	Catalyst efficiency below threshold (Bank1)	• Exhaust manifold (Replace the catalytic converter if there is no cracks)	Retained
P0440	–	Evaporative emission control system malfunction	• Harness and connector • Evaporative emission purge solenoid • Purge control valve • Vacuum hoses routing	Retained

Fig. 74   Diagnostic trouble code interpretation (Part 2 of 3). 1995 Talon w/turbocharged engine

Diagnostic trouble code No. — General scan tool mode	Scan tool (DRB-III) mode	Diagnostic items	Check items (Remedy)	Memory
P0100	P0100	Volume air flow circuit malfunction	• Harness and connector (If harness and connector are not defective, replace volume air flow sensor assembly.)	Retained
P0105	P0105	Barometric pressure circuit malfunction	• Harness and connector (If harness and connector are not defective, replace volume air flow sensor assembly.)	Retained
P0110	P0110	Intake air temperature circuit malfunction	• Harness and connector • Intake air temperature sensor	Retained
P0115	P0115	Engine coolant temperature circuit malfunction	• Harness and connector • Engine coolant temperature sensor	Retained
P0120	P0120	Throttle position circuit malfunction	• Harness and connector • Throttle position sensor • Closed throttle position switch	Retained
P0125	–	Excessive time to enter closed Loop Fuel Control*	• O_2 sensor (front) • O_2 sensor harness and connector • Injector	Retained
P0130	P0130	O_2 sensor circuit malfunction (Bank 1 Sensor 1)	• Harness and connector (If harness and connector are not defective, replace O_2 sensor (front).)	Retained
P0135	P0135	O_2 sensor heater circuit malfunction (Bank 1 Sensor 1)	• Harness and connector • O_2 sensor (front)	Retained
P0136	P0136	O_2 sensor circuit malfunction (Bank 1 Sensor 2)	• Harness and connector • O_2 sensor (rear)	Retained
P014-1	–	O_2 sensor heater circuit malfunction (Bank 1 Sensor 2)	• Harness and connector • O_2 sensor (rear) heater	Retained
P0170	–	Fuel trim malfunction (Bank 1)	• Volume air flow sensor output frequency • Injector • Fuel pressure • Intake air leaks • Engine coolant temperature sensor • Intake air temperature sensor • Barometric pressure sensor • O_2 Sensor • Exhaust manifold cracks	Retained

Fig. 74   Diagnostic trouble code interpretation (Part 1 of 3). 1995 Talon w/turbocharged engine

DTC No. <General scan tool mode>	DTC No. <Scan tool (DRB-III) mode>	Diagnostic items	Check items (Remedy)	Memory
P0100	P0100	Volume air flow circuit malfunction	• Harness and connector (If harness and connector are not defective, replace volume air flow sensor assembly.)	Retained
P0105	P0105	Barometric pressure circuit malfunction	• Harness and connector (If harness and connector are not defective, replace volume air flow sensor assembly.)	Retained
P0110	P0110	Intake air temperature circuit malfunction	• Harness and connector • Intake air temperature sensor	Retained
P0115	P0115	Engine coolant temperature circuit malfunction	• Harness and connector • Engine coolant temperature sensor	Retained
P0120	P0120	Throttle position circuit malfunction	• Harness and connector • Throttle position sensor • Closed throttle position switch	Retained
P0125	—	Excessive time to enter closed Loop Fuel Control*	• O_2 sensor (front) • O_2 sensor harness and connector • Injector	Retained
P0130	—	O_2 sensor circuit malfunction (Bank 1 Sensor 1)	• Harness and connector (If harness and connector are not defective, replace O_2 sensor (front).)	Retained
P0135	—	O_2 sensor heater circuit malfunction (Bank 1 Sensor 1)	• Harness and connector • O_2 sensor (front)	Retained
P0136	—	O_2 sensor circuit malfunction (Bank 1 Sensor 2)	• Harness and connector • O_2 sensor (rear)	Retained
P0141	—	O_2 sensor heater circuit malfunction (Bank 2)	• Harness and connector • O_2 sensor (rear) heater	Retained
P0170	—	Fuel trim malfunction (Bank 1)	• Volume air flow sensor output frequency • Injector • Fuel pressure • Intake air leaks • Engine coolant temperature sensor • Intake air temperature sensor • Barometric pressure sensor • O_2 Sensor • Exhaust manifold cracks	Retained
P0201	P0201	Injector circuit malfunction – Cylinder 1	• Harness and connector • Injector	Retained
P0202	P0202	Injector circuit malfunction – Cylinder 2		
P0203	P0203	Injector circuit malfunction – Cylinder 3		

Fig. 75 Diagnostic trouble code interpretation (Part 1 of 3). 1996 Talon

Diagnostic trouble code No. — General scan tool mode	Scan tool (DRB-III) mode	Diagnostic items	Check items (Remedy)	Memory
P0443	—	Evaporative emission control system purge control valve circuit malfunction	• Harness and connector • Evaporative emission purge solenoid	Retained
P0500	P0500	Vehicle speed sensor malfunction	• Harness and connector • Vehicle speed sensor	Retained
P0505	—	Idle control system malfunction	• Harness and connector • Idle air control motor	Retained
P0700	—	Transmission*	• Automatic transaxle control system • Harness and connector	Retained
P1300	P1300	Ignition timing adjustment circuit malfunction	• Harness and connector	—
P1400	—	Manifold differential pressure (MDP) sensor circuit malfunction	• Harness and connector • MDP sensor	Retained
P1500	P1500	Generator FR terminal circuit malfunction	• Harness and connector	Retained

NOTE
1. Do not replace the engine control module (ECM) until a thorough terminal check reveals there are no short/open circuits.
2. After the ECM detects a malfunction, a diagnostic trouble code is recorded when the engine is next started and the same malfunction is re-detected. However, for items marked with a "*", the diagnostic trouble code is recorded on the first detection of the malfunction.
3. O_2 : Heated oxygen sensor
4. Sensor 1: indicates sensors which are mounted closest to the engine.
5. Sensor 2: indicates sensors which are mounted next-closest to the engine.

CR10296049990630X

Fig. 74 Diagnostic trouble code interpretation (Part 3 of 3). 1995 Talon w/turbocharged engine

DTC No. \<General scan tool mode\>	DTC No. \<Scan tool (DRB-III) mode\>	Diagnostic items	Check items (Remedy)	Memory
P0204	P0204	Injector circuit malfunction – Cylinder 4	• Harness and connector • Injector	Retained
P0300	-	Random misfire detected*	• Ignition coil • Ignition power transistor • Spark plug • Ignition circuit	Retained
P0301	-	Cylinder 1 misfire detected*	• Injector	Retained
P0302	-	Cylinder 2 misfire detected*	• O₂ Sensor • Compression pressure • Timing belt • Crankshaft position sensor • Air intake	
P0303	-	Cylinder 3 misfire detected*	• Fuel pressure	
P0304	-	Cylinder 4 misfire detected*	• Crankshaft position sensor circuit and connector	
P0325	P0325	Knock sensor 1 circuit malfunction	• Harness and connector (If harness and connector are not defective, replace knock sensor.)	Retained
P0335	P0335	Crankshaft position sensor circuit malfunction	• Harness and connector (If harness and connector are not defective, replace crankshaft position sensor.)	Retained
P0340	P0340	Camshaft position sensor circuit malfunction	• Harness and connector (If harness and connector are not defective, replace camshaft position sensor.)	Retained
P0400	-	Exhaust gas recirculation flow malfunction	• Harness and connector • EGR valve • EGR solenoid • EGR valve control vacuum • Manifold differential pressure sensor	Retained
P0403	-	Exhaust gas recirculation solenoid malfunction	• Harness and connector • EGR solenoid	Retained
P0420	-	Catalyst system efficiency below threshold (Bank1)	• Exhaust manifold (Replace the catalytic converter if there is no cracks)	Retained
P0440	-	Evaporative emission control system malfunction	• Harness and connector • Evaporative emission purge solenoid • Purge control valve • Vacuum hoses routing	Retained
P0443	-	Evaporative emission control system purge control valve circuit malfunction	• Harness and connector • Evaporative emission purge solenoid	Retained
P0500	P0500	Vehicle speed sensor malfunction	• Harness and connector • Vehicle speed sensor	Retained
P0505	-	Idle control system malfunction	• Harness and connector • Idle air control motor	Retained

Fig. 75 Diagnostic trouble code interpretation (Part 2 of 3). 1996 Talon

DTC No. \<General scan tool mode\>	DTC No. \<Scan tool (DRB-III) mode\>	Diagnostic items	Check items (Remedy)	Memory
P0510	-	Closed throttle position switch malfunction	• Harness and connector • Closed throttle position switch	Retained
P0705	-	Transaxle range sensor circuit malfunction (RPNDL Input)	• Harness and connector • Park/neutral position switch	Retained
P0710	-	Transaxle fluid temperature sensor circuit malfunction	• Harness and connector • Transaxle oil temperature sensor	Retained
P1103	-	Turbocharger waste gate actuator malfunction	• Harness and connector • Turbocharger waste gate solenoid • Turbocharger waste gate actuator • Vacuum hose routing	Retained
P1104	-	Turbocharger waste gate solenoid malfunction	• Harness and connector • Turbocharger waste gate solenoid	Retained
P1105	-	Fuel pressure solenoid malfunction	• Harness and connector • Fuel pressure solenoid	Retained
P1300	P1300	Ignition timing adjustment circuit malfunction	• Harness and connector	-
P1400	-	Manifold differential pressure (MDP) sensor circuit malfunction	• Harness and connector • MDP sensor	Retained
P1500	P1500	Generator FR terminal circuit malfunction	• Harness and connector	Retained
P1715	-	PG assy malfunction	• Harness and connector • Pulse generator	Retained
P1750	-	Solenoid assy malfunction	• Harness and connector • Converter clutch solenoid • Shift control solenoid • Pressure control solenoid	Retained

Fig. 75 Diagnostic trouble code interpretation (Part 3 of 3). 1996 Talon

NOTE
1. Do not replace the engine control module (ECM) until a thorough terminal check reveals there are no short/open circuits.
2. After the ECM detects a malfunction, a diagnostic trouble code is recorded when the engine is next started and the same malfunction is re-detected. However, for items marked with a "*", the diagnostic trouble code is recorded on the first detection of the malfunction.
3. O₂ : Heated oxygen sensor
4. Sensor 1: indicates sensors which are mounted closest to the engine.
5. Sensor 2: indicates sensors which are mounted next-closest to the engine.

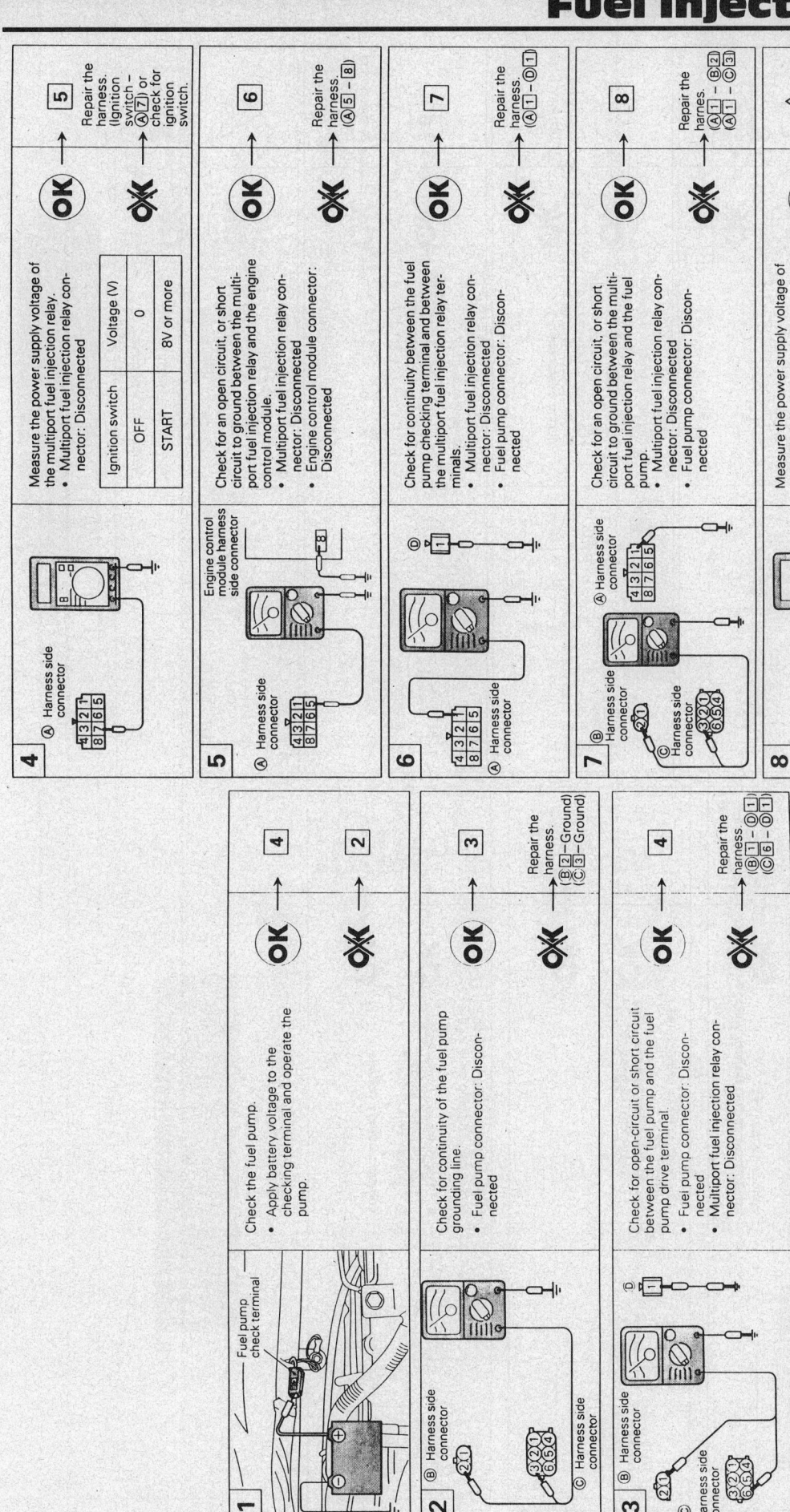

Fig. 76 Fuel pump harness inspection (Part 2 of 2). Colt, Colt Vista, Summit, Summit Wagon AWD, 1993–95 Summit Wagon FWD & 1996 Summit Wagon FWD w/2.4L/4-143 engine & Federal emissions

Fig. 76 Fuel pump harness inspection (Part 1 of 2). Colt, Colt Vista, Summit, Summit Wagon AWD, 1993–95 Summit Wagon FWD & 1996 Summit Wagon FWD w/2.4L/4-143 engine & Federal emissions

MULTI-POINT FUEL INJECTION (MODELS w/1.8L/4-107, 1.8L/4-110 & 2.4L/4-143 ENGINES, 1993-94 MODELS w/2.0L/4-122 ENGINE & 1995 TALON w/2.0L/4-122 TURBOCHARGED ENGINE)

7-95

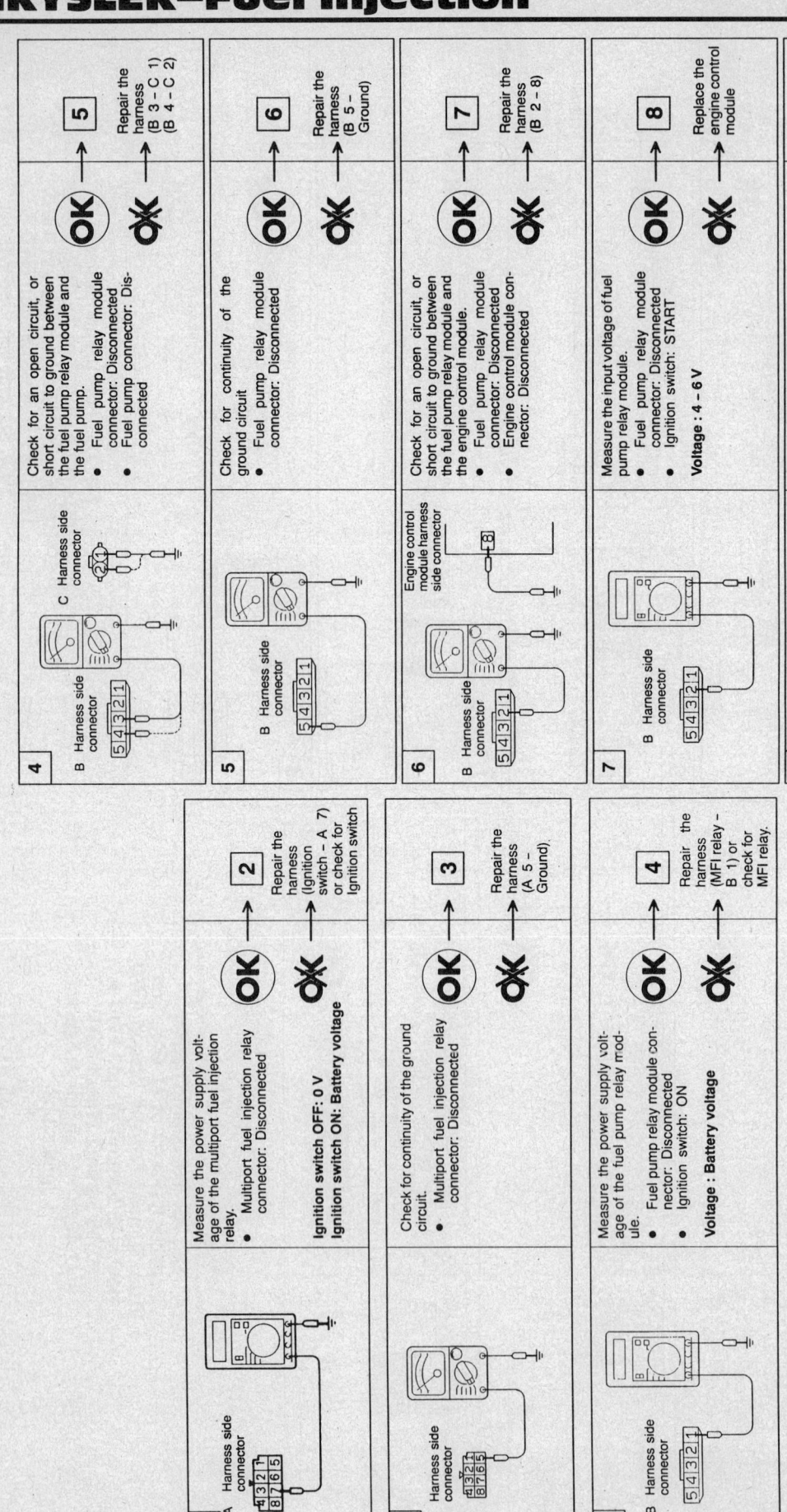

Fig. 77 Fuel pump harness inspection (Part 2 of 2). 1996 Summit Wagon FWD w/2.4L/4-143 engine & California emissions

Fig. 77 Fuel pump harness inspection (Part 1 of 2). 1996 Summit Wagon FWD w/2.4L/4-143 engine & California emissions

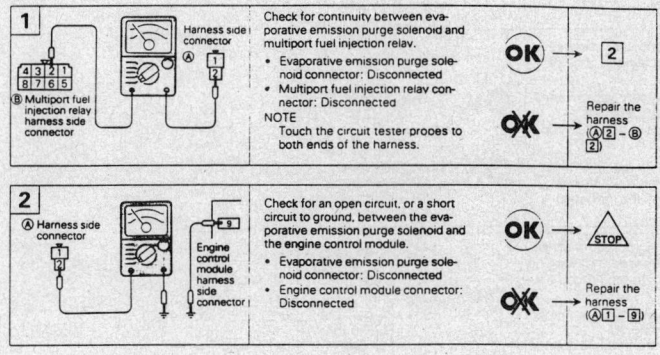

Fig. 78 Evaporative emission purge solenoid harness inspection. Colt, Colt Vista, Summit & Summit Wagon w/1.8L/4-110 engine

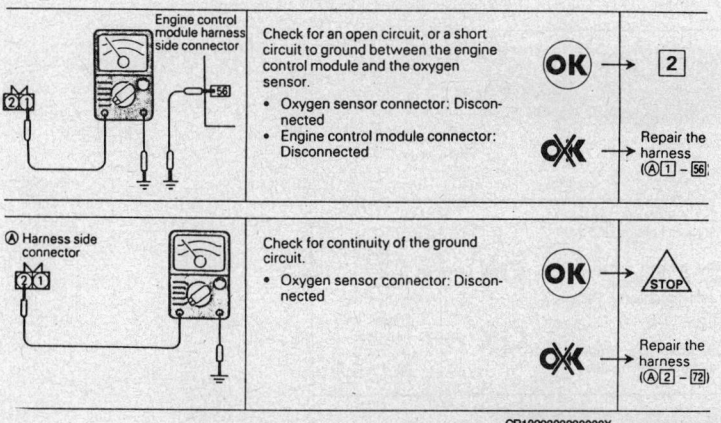

Fig. 80 Oxygen sensor harness inspection. 1993 Colt, Colt Vista, Summit & Summit Wagon w/Federal emissions

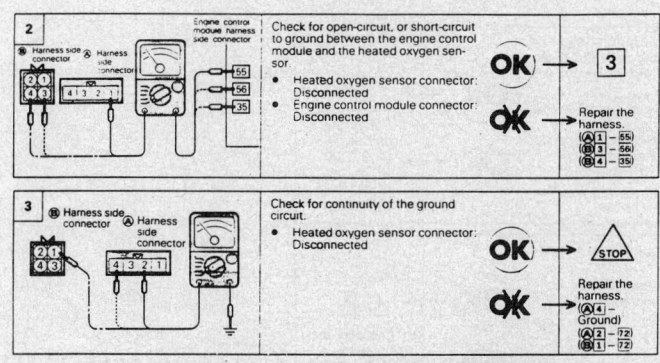

Fig. 81 Heated oxygen sensor harness inspection (Part 2 of 2). 1993 Colt, Colt Vista, Summit & Summit Wagon w/California emissions, 1994 Colt & Colt Vista & 1994–95 Summit & Summit Wagon

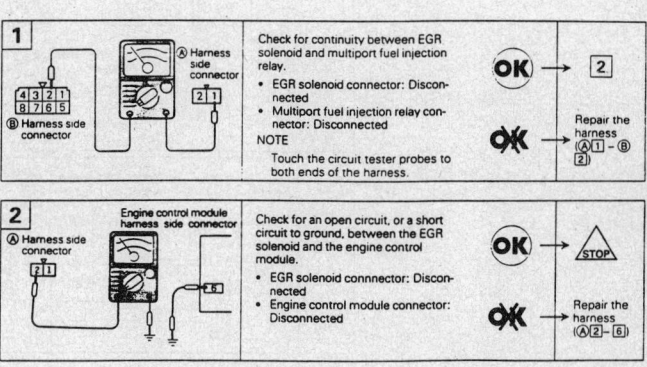

Fig. 79 EGR solenoid harness inspection. Colt, Colt Vista, Summit & Summit Wagon w/1.8L/4-110 engine

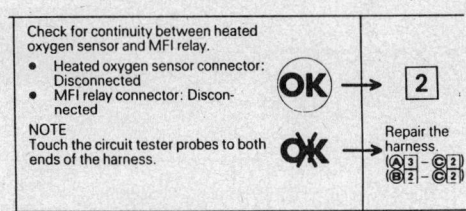

Fig. 81 Heated oxygen sensor harness inspection (Part 1 of 2). 1993 Colt, Colt Vista, Summit & Summit Wagon w/California emissions, 1994 Colt & Colt Vista & 1994–95 Summit & Summit Wagon

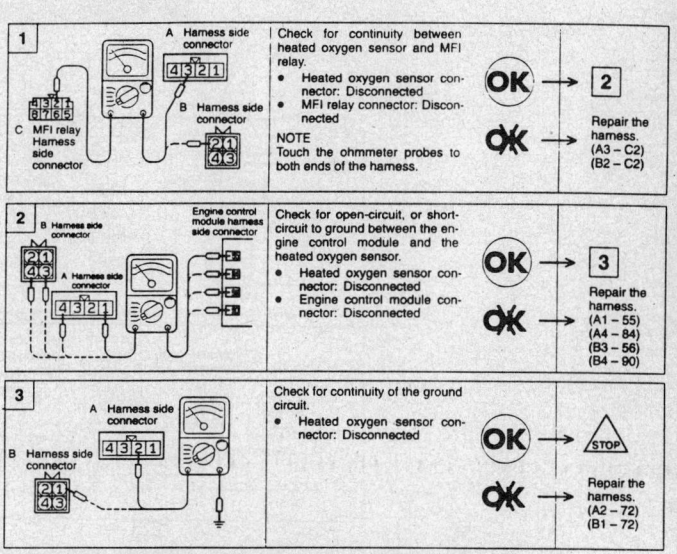

Fig. 82 Heated oxygen sensor harness inspection. 1996 Summit w/Federal emissions

MULTI-POINT FUEL INJECTION (MODELS w/1.8L/4-107, 1.8L/4-110 & 2.4L/4-143 ENGINES, 1993-94 MODELS w/2.0L/4-122 ENGINE & 1995 TALON w/2.0L/4-122 TURBOCHARGED ENGINE)

7-97

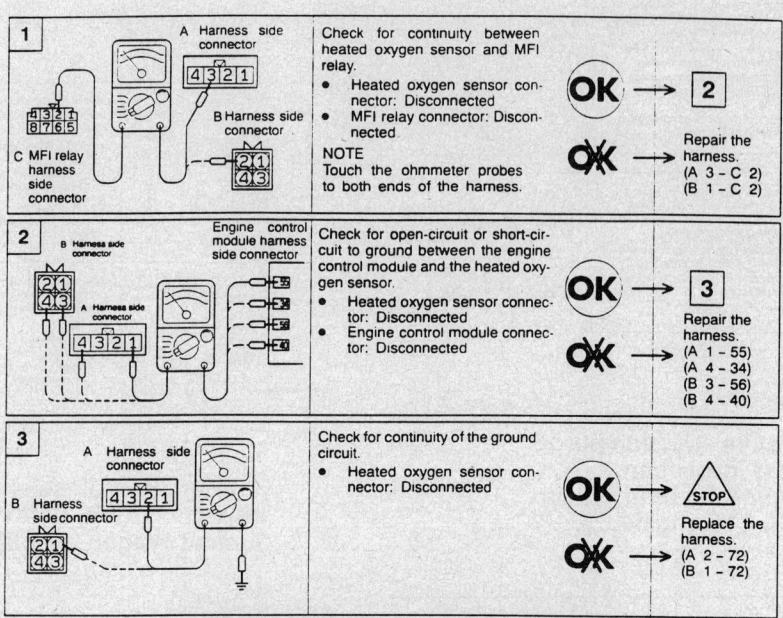

Fig. 83 Heated oxygen sensor harness inspection. 1996 Summit Wagon w/Federal emissions

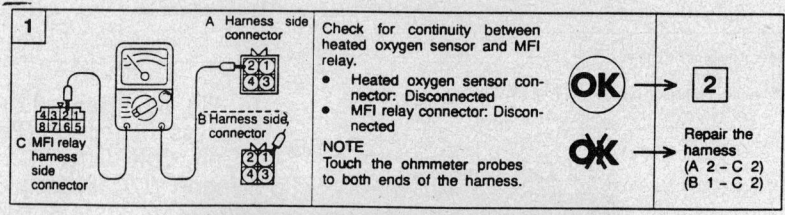

Fig. 84 Heated oxygen sensor harness inspection (Part 1 of 2). 1996 Summit & Summit Wagon w/California emissions

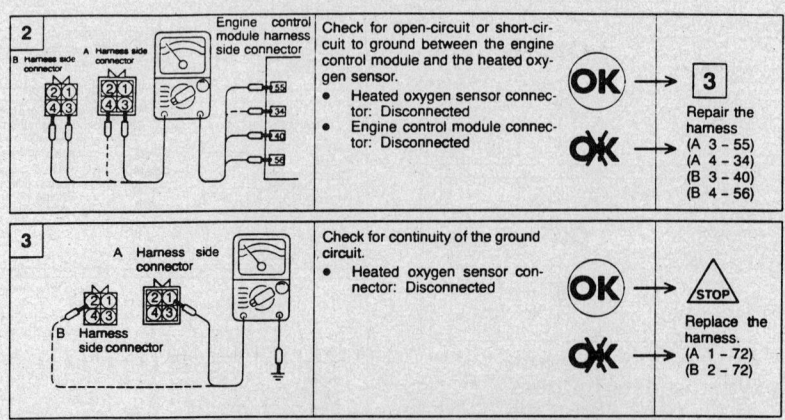

Fig. 84 Heated oxygen sensor harness inspection (Part 2 of 2). 1996 Summit w/California emissions

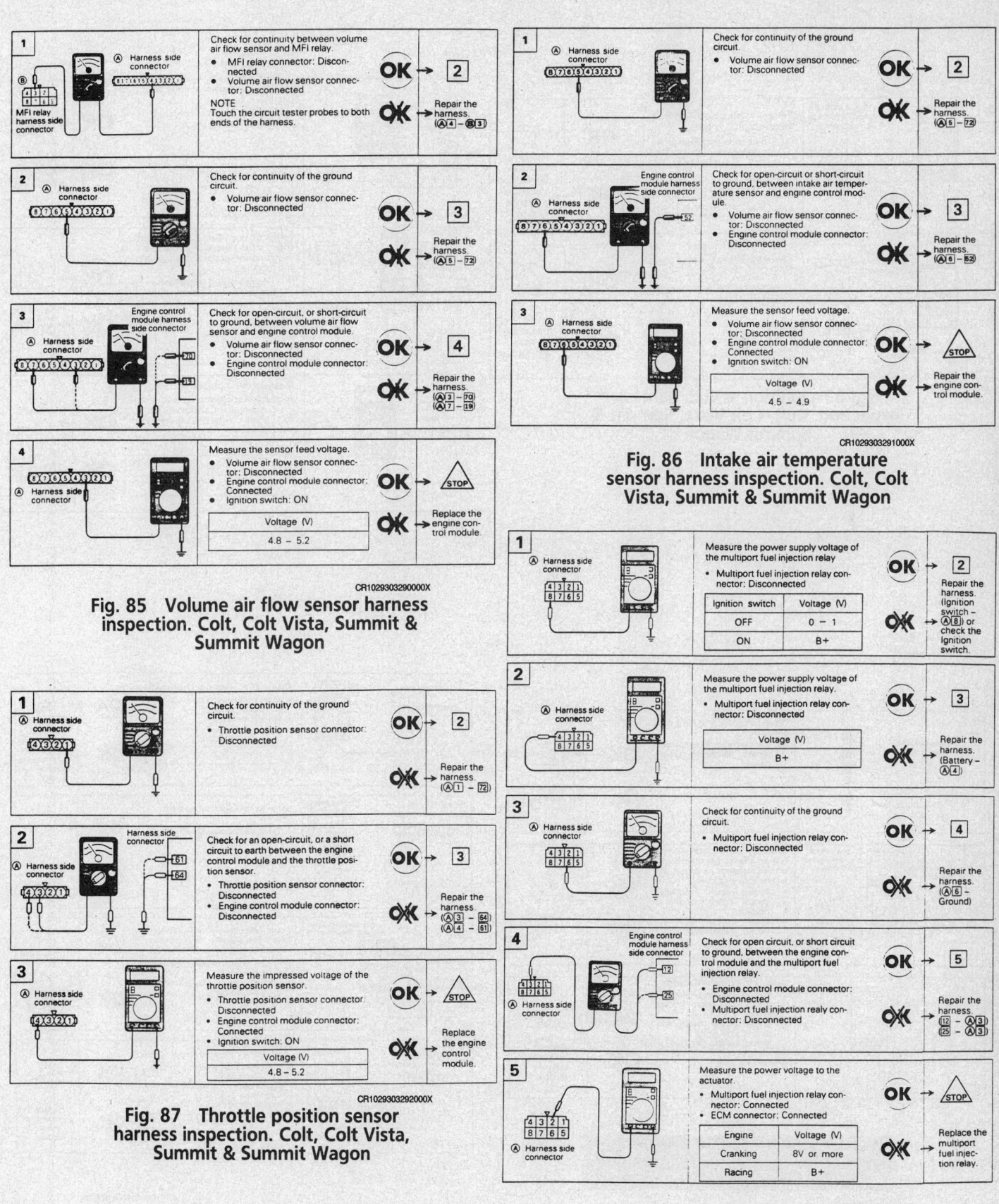

Fig. 85   Volume air flow sensor harness inspection. Colt, Colt Vista, Summit & Summit Wagon

Fig. 86   Intake air temperature sensor harness inspection. Colt, Colt Vista, Summit & Summit Wagon

Fig. 87   Throttle position sensor harness inspection. Colt, Colt Vista, Summit & Summit Wagon

Fig. 88   Power supply (MFI relay) harness inspection. Colt, Colt Vista, Summit & Summit Wagon

MULTI-POINT FUEL INJECTION (MODELS w/1.8L/4-107, 1.8L/4-110 & 2.4L/4-143 ENGINES, 1993-94 MODELS w/2.0L/4-122 ENGINE & 1995 TALON w/2.0L/4-122 TURBOCHARGED ENGINE)

7-99

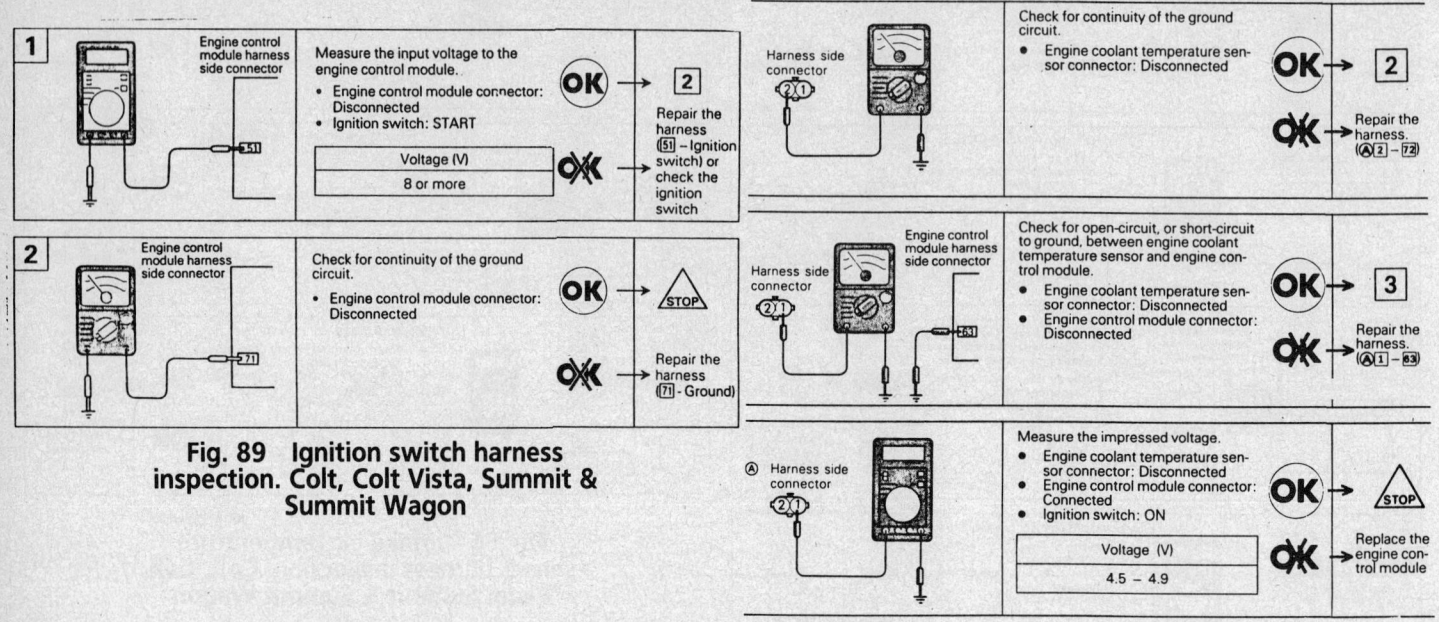

Fig. 89 Ignition switch harness inspection. Colt, Colt Vista, Summit & Summit Wagon

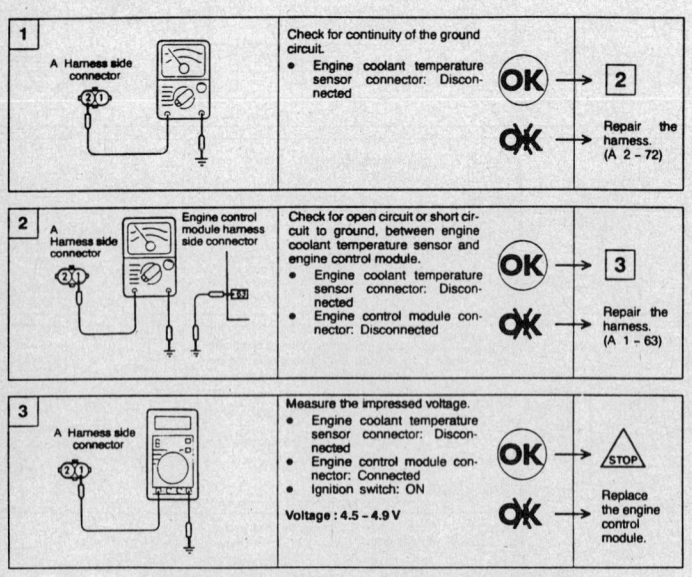

Fig. 91 Coolant temperature sensor harness inspection. 1996 Summit & Summit Wagon

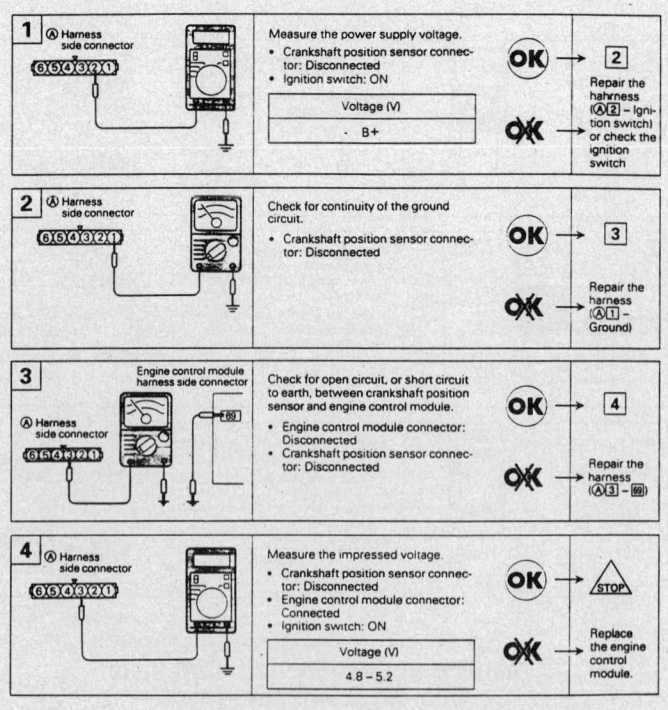

CR1029303296000X

Fig. 92 Crankshaft position sensor harness inspection. Colt, Colt Vista & 1993–95 Summit & Summit Wagon

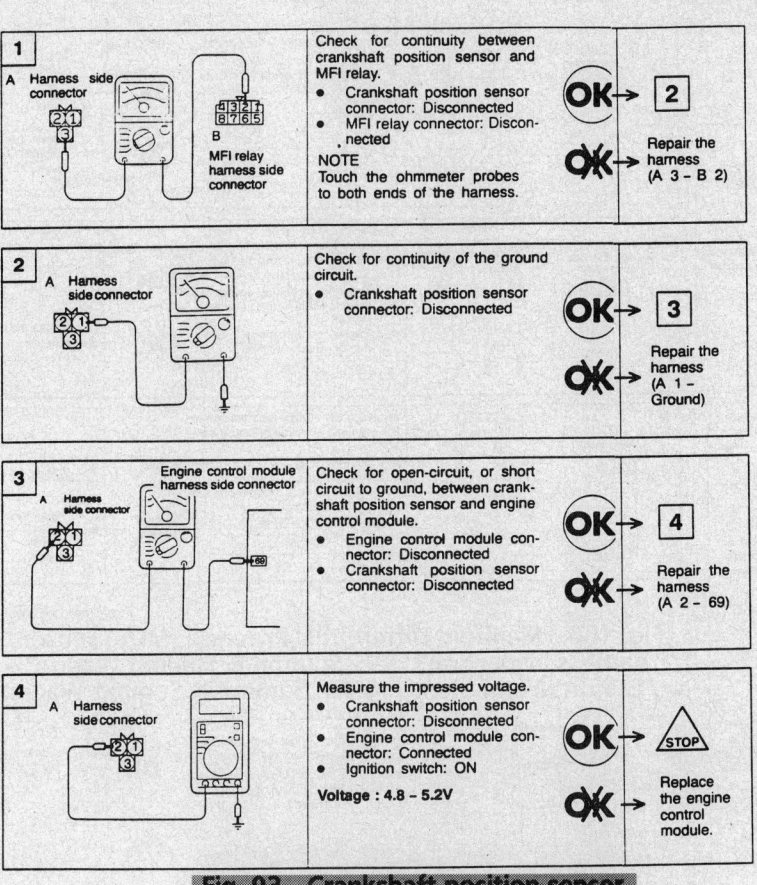

Fig. 93 Crankshaft position sensor harness inspection. 1996 Summit & Summit Wagon

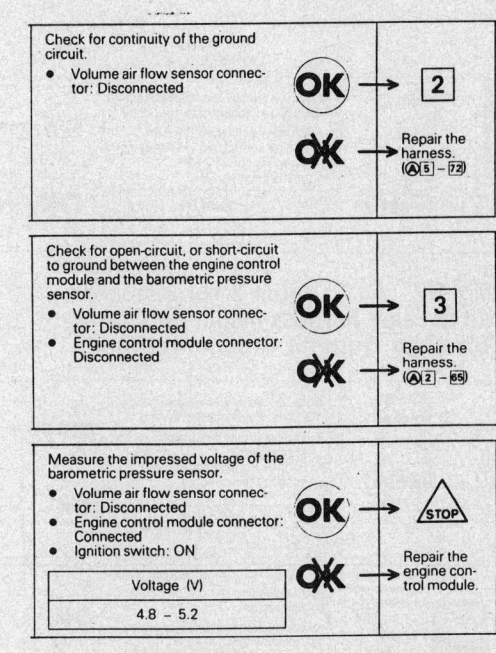

Fig. 94 Barometric pressure sensor harness inspection. Colt, Colt Vista, Summit & Summit Wagon

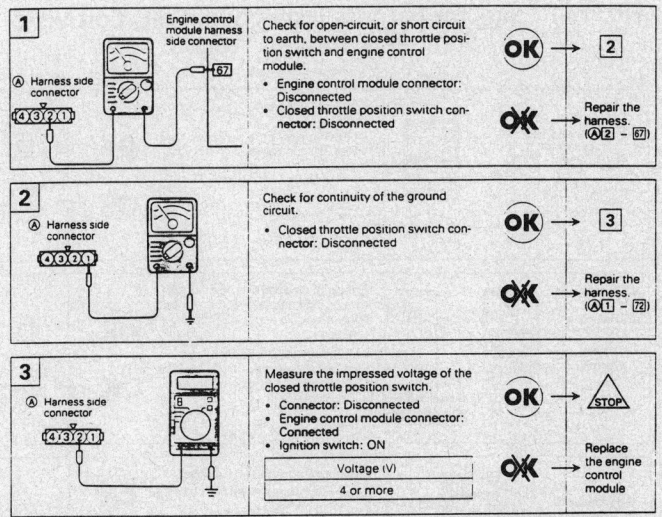

CR1029303298000X

Fig. 95 Closed throttle position switch harness inspection. Colt, Colt Vista, Summit & Summit Wagon

CR1029303299000X

Fig. 96 Power steering pressure switch harness inspection. Colt, Colt Vista, Summit & Summit Wagon

MULTI-POINT FUEL INJECTION (MODELS w/1.8L/4-107, 1.8L/4-110 & 2.4L/4-143 ENGINES, 1993-94 MODELS w/2.0L/4-122 ENGINE & 1995 TALON w/2.0L/4-122 TURBOCHARGED ENGINE)

7-101

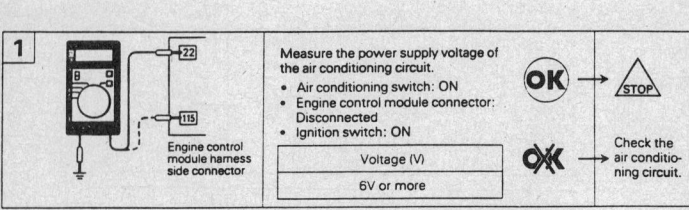

Fig. 97 A/C switch & compressor clutch relay harness inspection. Colt, Colt Vista, Summit & Summit Wagon

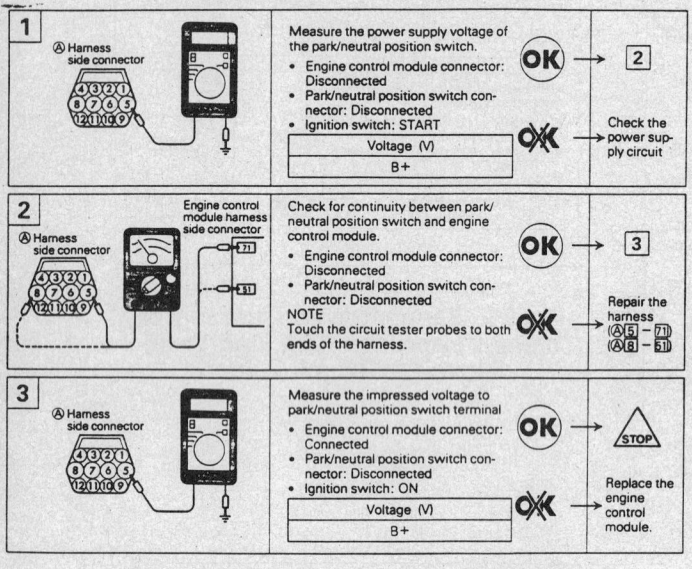

Fig. 98 Park/Neutral position switch harness inspection. Colt & Summit, Colt Vista & Summit Wagon FWD & 1996 Summit Wagon AWD

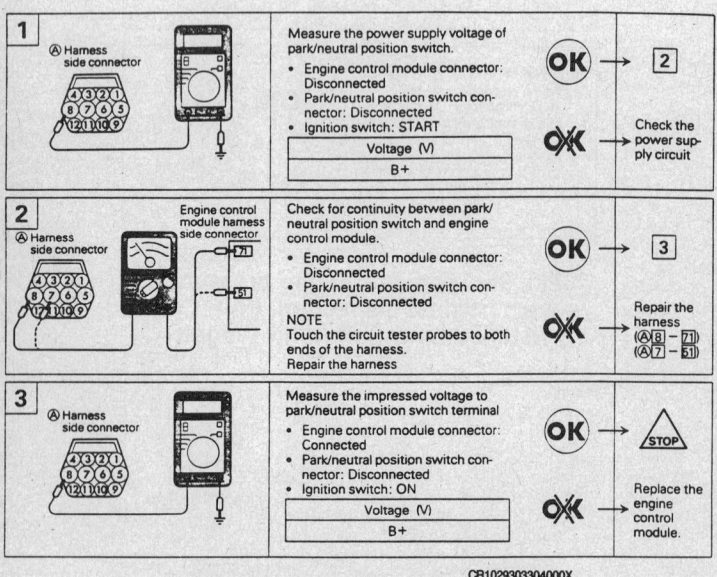

Fig. 99 Park/Neutral position switch harness inspection. Colt Vista & 1993–95 Summit Wagon AWD

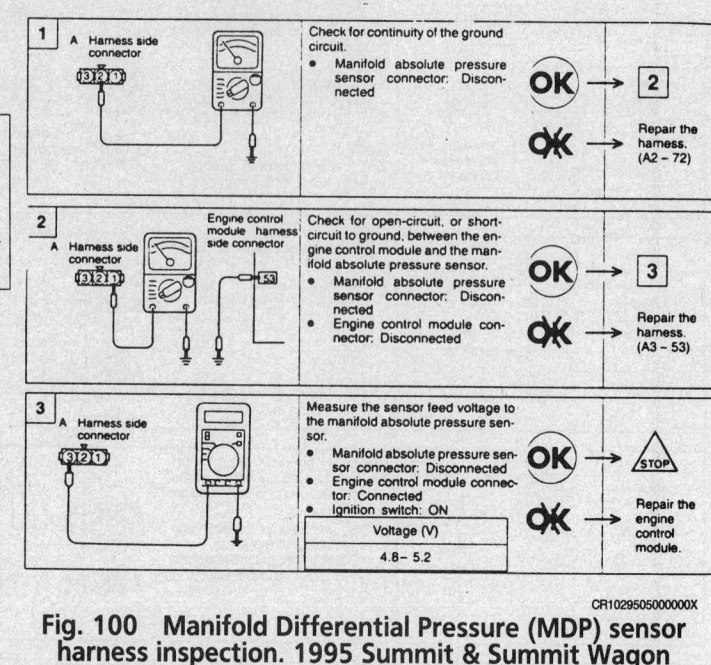

Fig. 100 Manifold Differential Pressure (MDP) sensor harness inspection. 1995 Summit & Summit Wagon w/California emissions & 1996 Summit & Summit Wagon

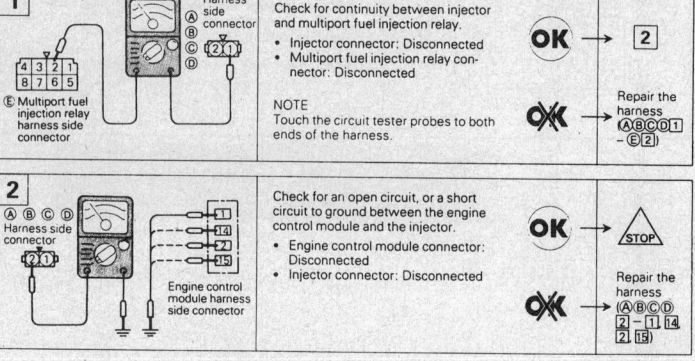

Fig. 101 Injector harness inspection. Colt, Colt Vista, Summit & Summit Wagon

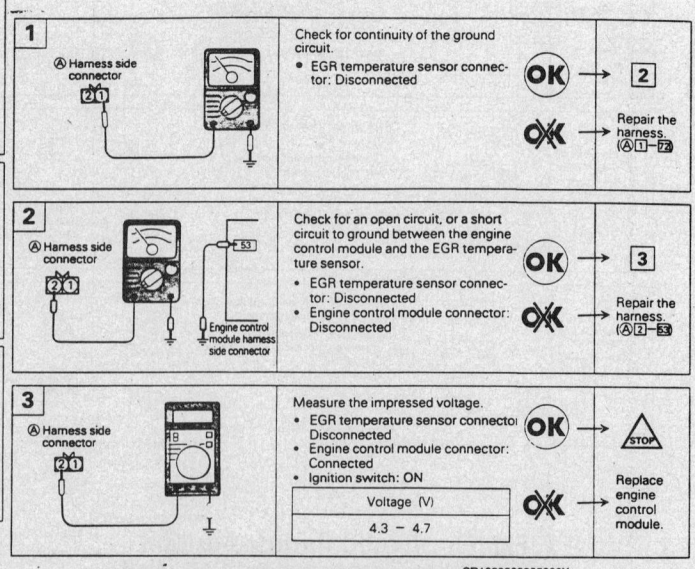

Fig. 102 EGR temperature sensor harness inspection. Colt, Colt Vista & 1993–95 Summit & Summit Wagon

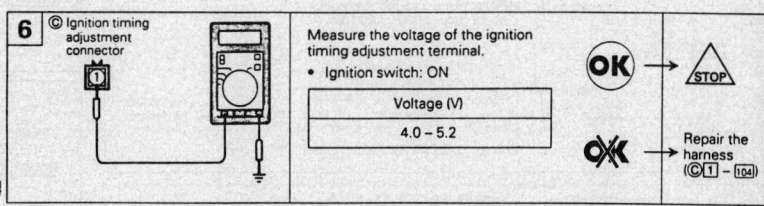

Fig. 103 Ignition coil & ignition power transistor harness inspection (Part 2 of 2). Colt, Colt Vista & 1993–95 Summit & Summit Wagon

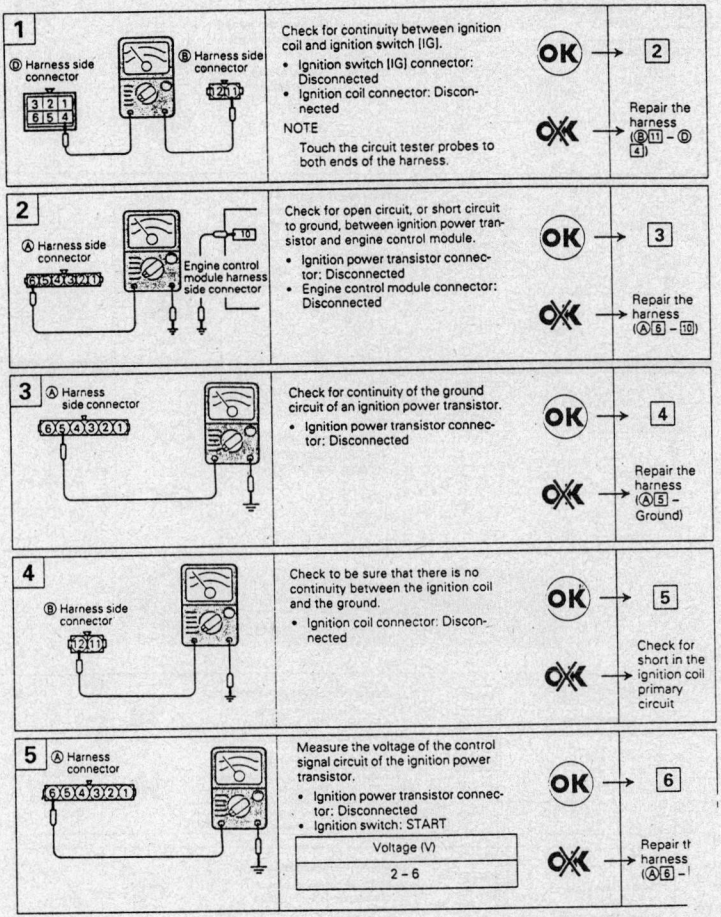

Fig. 103 Ignition coil & ignition power transistor harness inspection (Part 1 of 2). Colt, Colt Vista & 1993–95 Summit & Summit Wagon

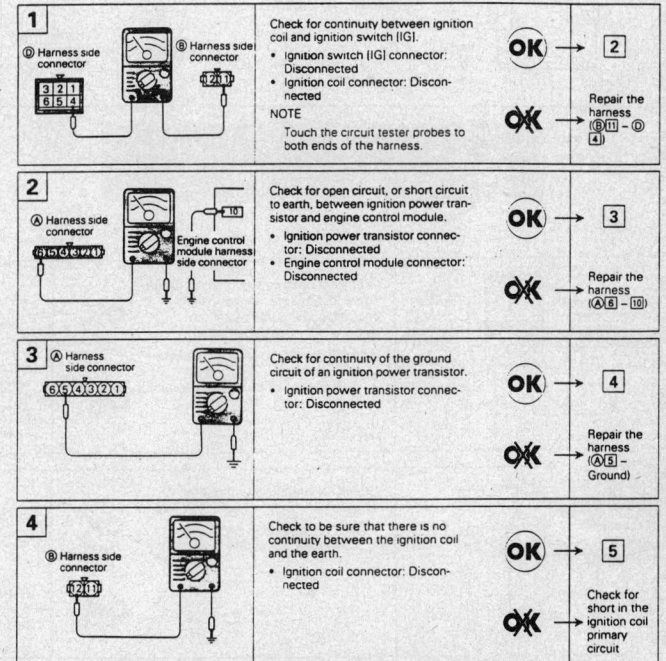

Fig. 104 Power transistor harness inspection (Part 1 of 2). 1996 Summit

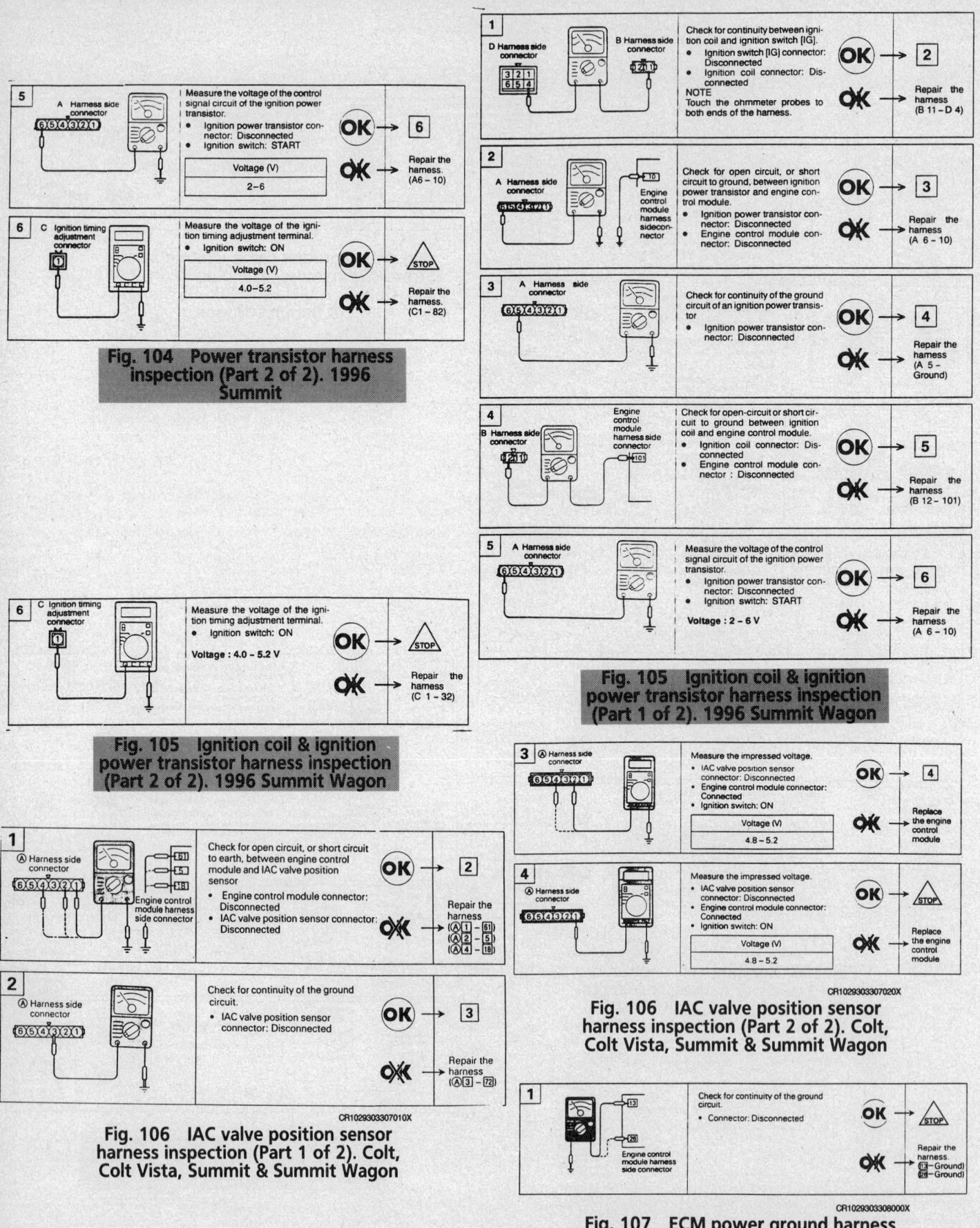

Fig. 104   Power transistor harness inspection (Part 2 of 2). 1996 Summit

Fig. 105   Ignition coil & ignition power transistor harness inspection (Part 2 of 2). 1996 Summit Wagon

Fig. 106   IAC valve position sensor harness inspection (Part 1 of 2). Colt, Colt Vista, Summit & Summit Wagon

Fig. 105   Ignition coil & ignition power transistor harness inspection (Part 1 of 2). 1996 Summit Wagon

Fig. 106   IAC valve position sensor harness inspection (Part 2 of 2). Colt, Colt Vista, Summit & Summit Wagon

Fig. 107   ECM power ground harness inspection. Colt, Colt Vista, Summit & Summit Wagon

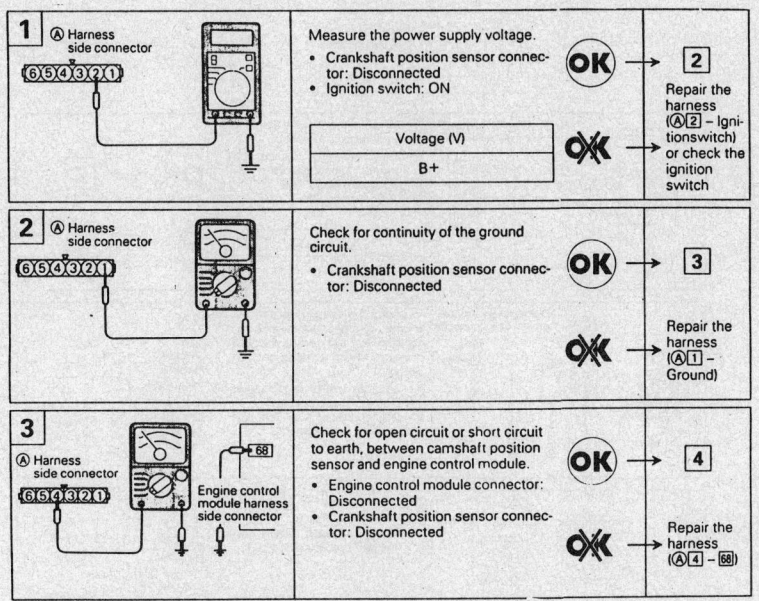

Fig. 108   Camshaft position sensor
harness inspection (Part 1 of 2). Colt,
Colt Vista & 1993–95 Summit &
Summit Wagon

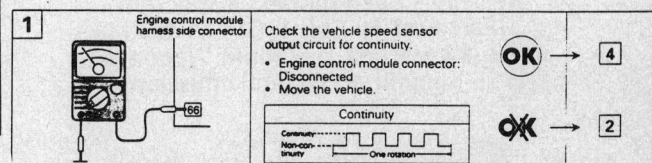

CR1029303309020X

Fig. 108   Camshaft position sensor
harness inspection (Part 2 of 2). Colt,
Colt Vista & 1993–95 Summit &
Summit Wagon

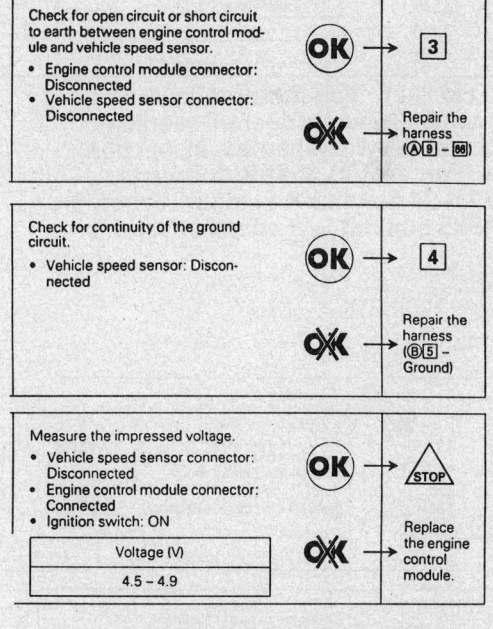

CR1029303310010X

Fig. 110   Vehicle speed sensor harness
inspection (Part 1 of 2). Colt, Colt
Vista, Summit & Summit Wagon

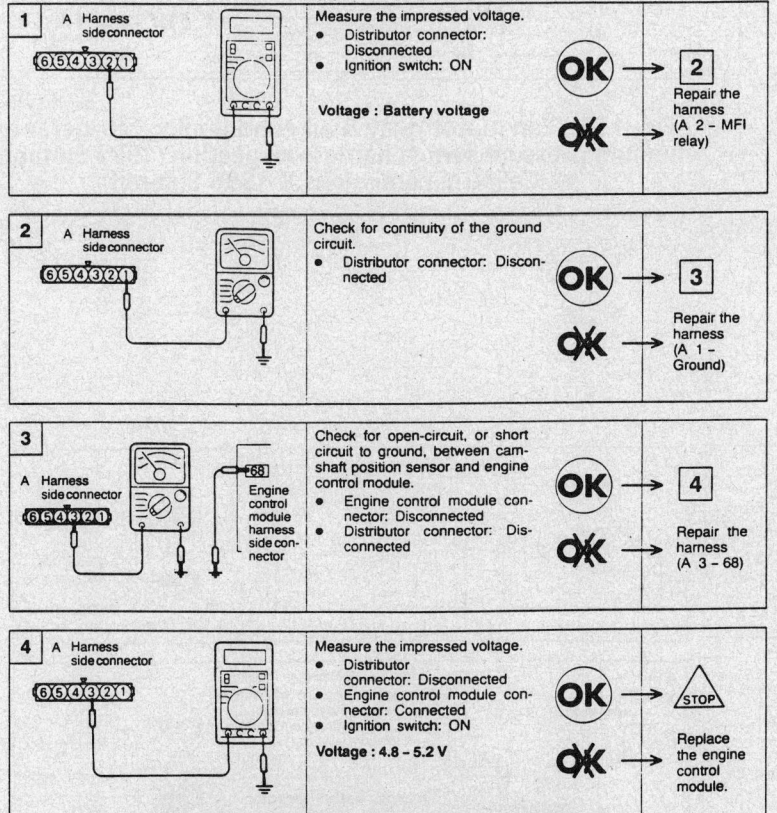

Fig. 109   Camshaft position sensor
harness inspection. 1996 Summit &
Summit Wagon

Fig. 110   Vehicle speed sensor
harness inspection (Part 2 of 2). Colt,
Colt Vista, Summit & Summit Wagon

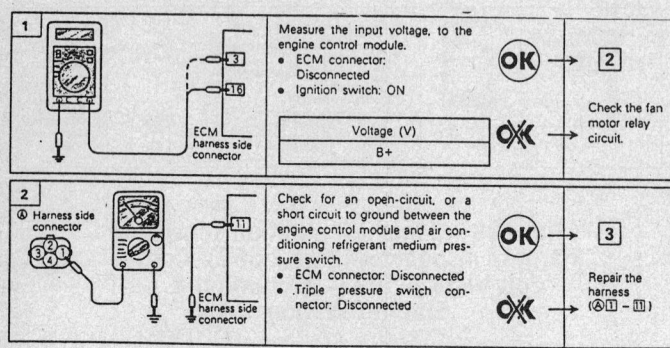

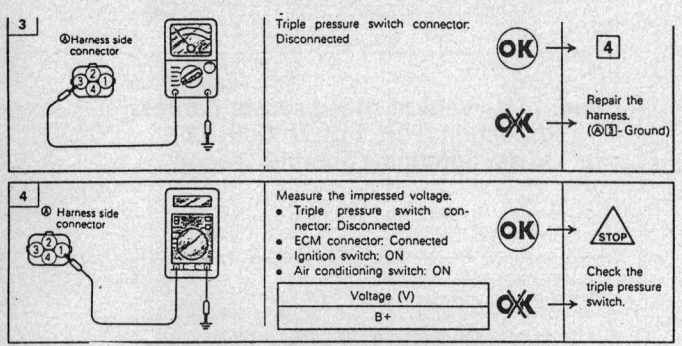

Fig. 111 Fan motor relay & air conditioning refrigerant medium pressure switch harness inspection (Part 1 of 2). Colt & Colt Vista, 1993–94 Summit & Summit Wagon & 1995 Summit w/Federal emissions

Fig. 111 Fan motor relay & air conditioning refrigerant medium pressure switch harness inspection (Part 2 of 2). Colt & Colt Vista, 1993–94 Summit & Summit Wagon & 1995 Summit w/Federal emissions

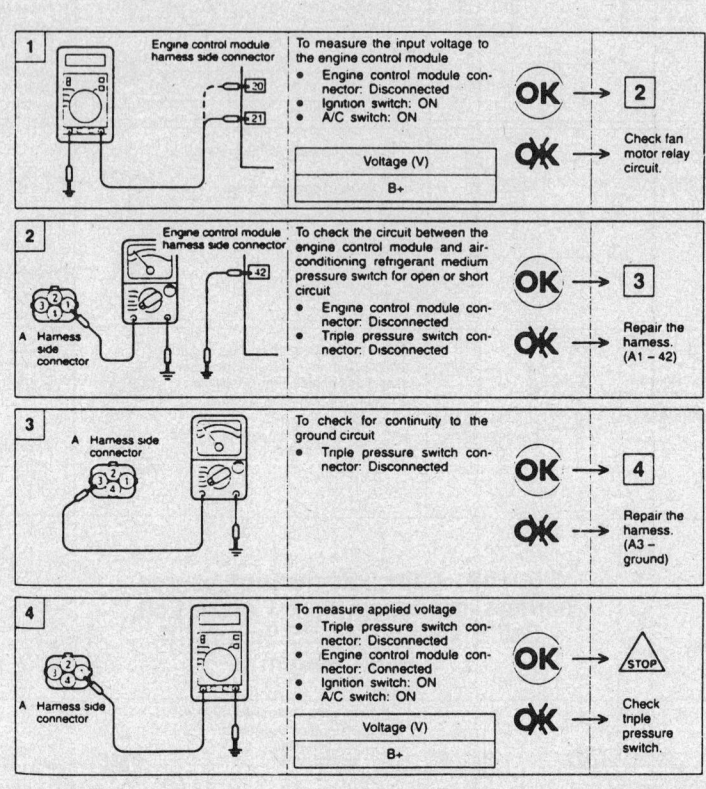

CR1029505001000X

Fig. 112 Fan motor relay & air conditioning refrigerant medium pressure switch harness inspection. 1995 Summit w/California emissions & 1996 Summit

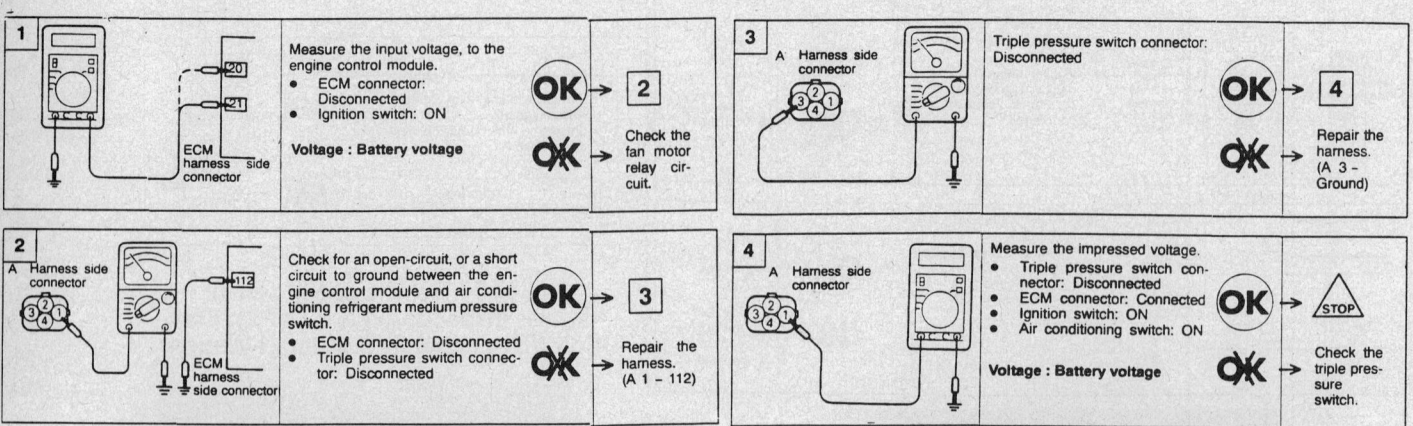

Fig. 113 Fan motor relay & A/C refrigerant medium pressure switch harness inspection (Part 1 of 2). 1996 Summit Wagon

Fig. 113 Fan motor relay & A/C refrigerant medium pressure switch harness inspection (Part 2 of 2). 1996 Summit Wagon

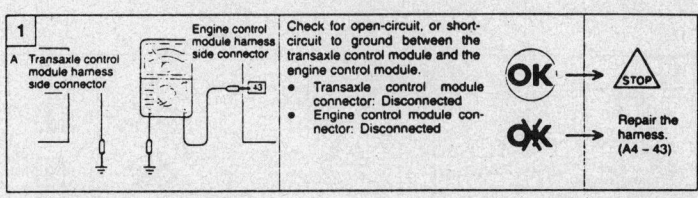

Fig. 114 Transaxle failure signal harness inspection. 1995 Summit & Summit Wagon w/California emissions & 1996 Summit

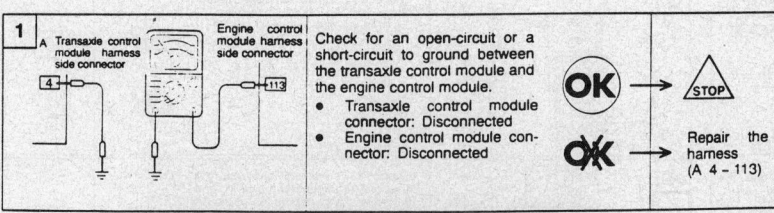

Fig. 115 Transaxle failure signal harness inspection. 1996 Summit Wagon w/1.8L/4-110 engine

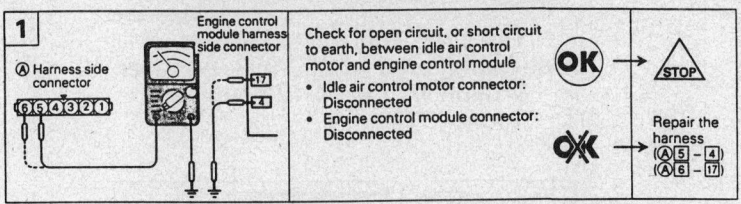

Fig. 116 Idle air control motor harness inspection. Colt, Colt Vista, Summit & Summit Wagon

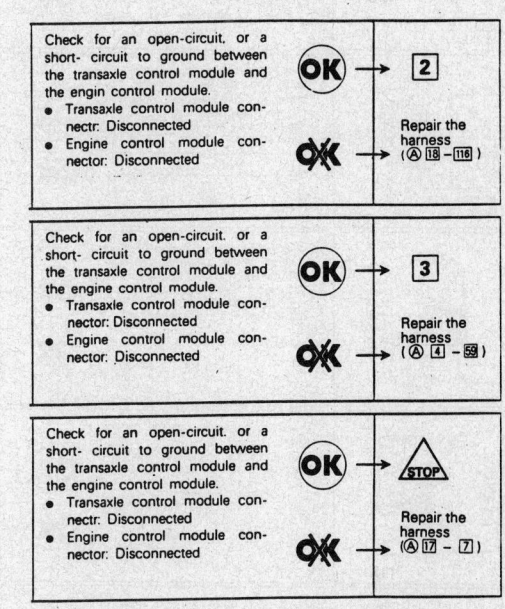

Fig. 117 Engine & transaxle total control signal harness inspection. 1993–94 Colt & Colt Vista & 1993–95 Summit & Summit Wagon

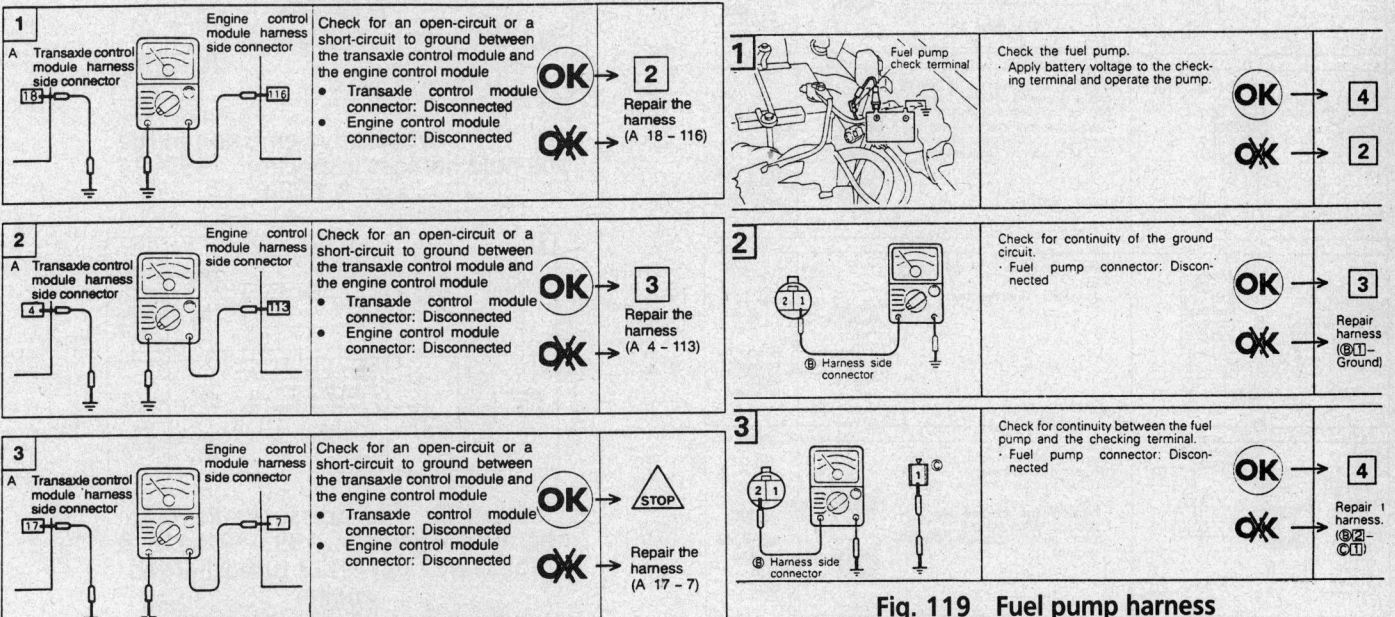

Fig. 118 Engine & transaxle total control signal harness inspection. 1996 Summit Wagon

Fig. 119 Fuel pump harness inspection (Part 1 of 2). 1993–94 Laser & Talon w/1.8L/4-107 engine

MULTI-POINT FUEL INJECTION (MODELS w/1.8L/4-107, 1.8L/4-110 & 2.4L/4-143 ENGINES, 1993-94 MODELS w/2.0L/4-122 ENGINE & 1995 TALON w/2.0L/4-122 TURBOCHARGED ENGINE)

7-107

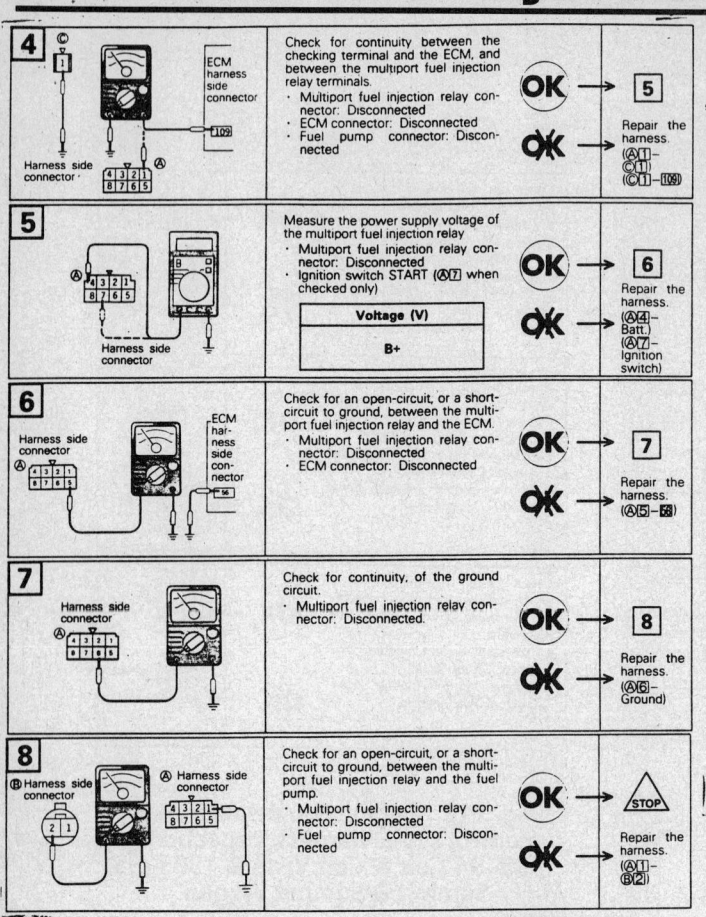

Fig. 119 Fuel pump harness inspection (Part 2 of 2). 1993–94 Laser & Talon w/1.8L/4-107 engine

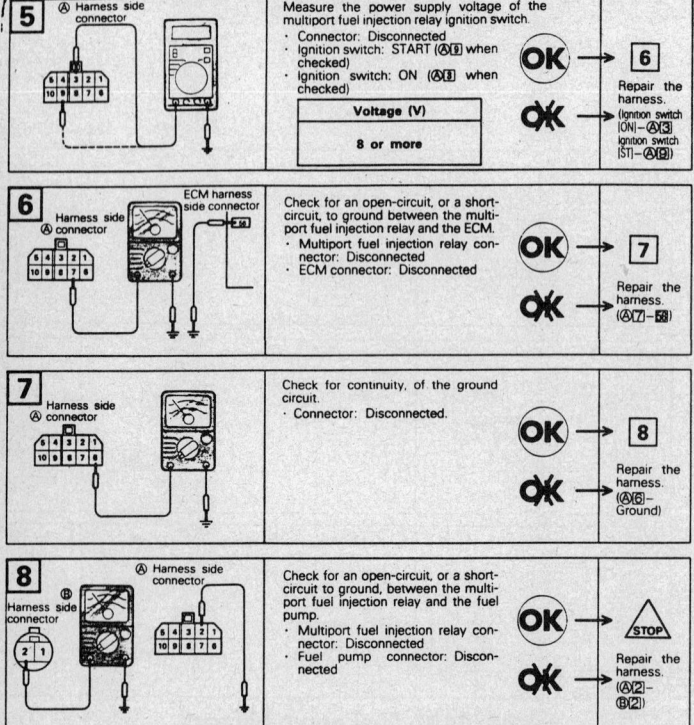

Fig. 120 Fuel pump harness inspection (Part 2 of 2). 1993–94 Laser & Talon w/2.0L/4-122 engine

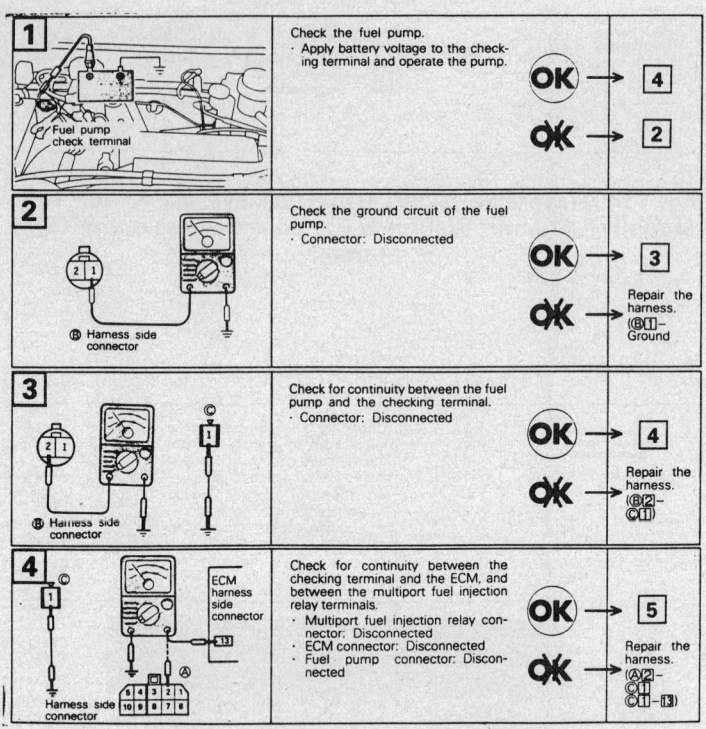

Fig. 120 Fuel pump harness inspection (Part 1 of 2). 1993–94 Laser & Talon w/2.0L/4-122 engine

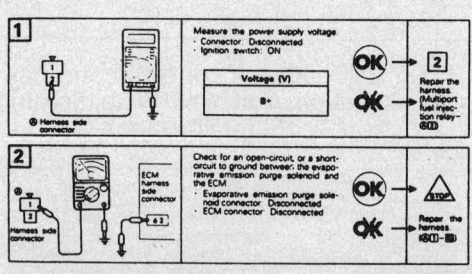

Fig. 121 Evaporative emission purge solenoid harness inspection. 1993–94 Laser & Talon

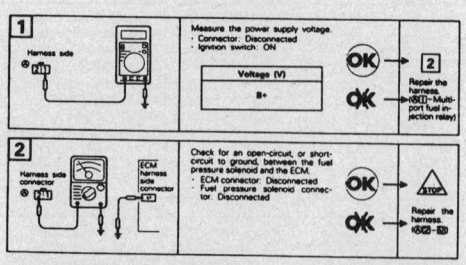

Fig. 122 Fuel pressure solenoid harness inspection. 1993–94 Laser & Talon w/2.0L/4-122 turbocharged engine

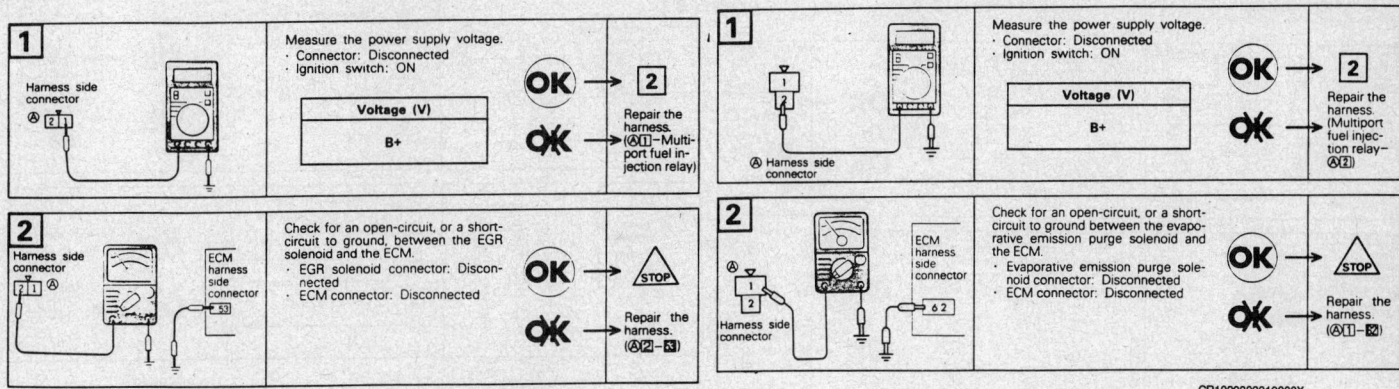

Fig. 123   EGR solenoid harness
inspection. 1993–94 Laser & Talon

Fig. 124   Oxygen sensor harness
inspection. 1993–94 Laser & Talon
w/1.8L/4-107 engine

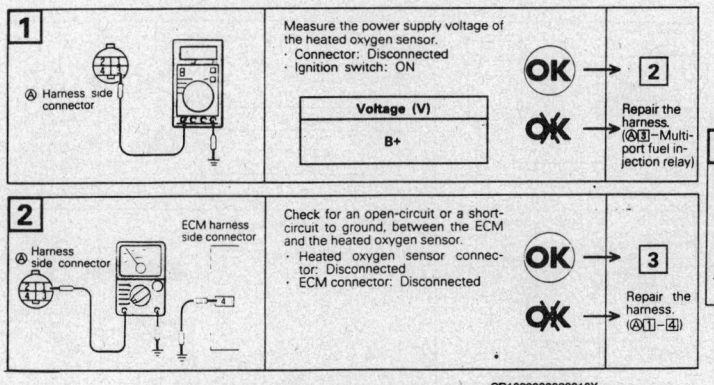

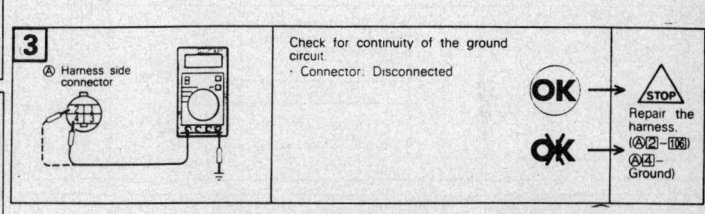

Fig. 125   Heated oxygen sensor
harness inspection (Part 1 of 2).
1993–94 Laser & Talon w/2.0L/4-122
engine

Fig. 125   Heated oxygen sensor
harness inspection (Part 2 of 2).
1993–94 Laser & Talon w/2.0L/4-122
engine

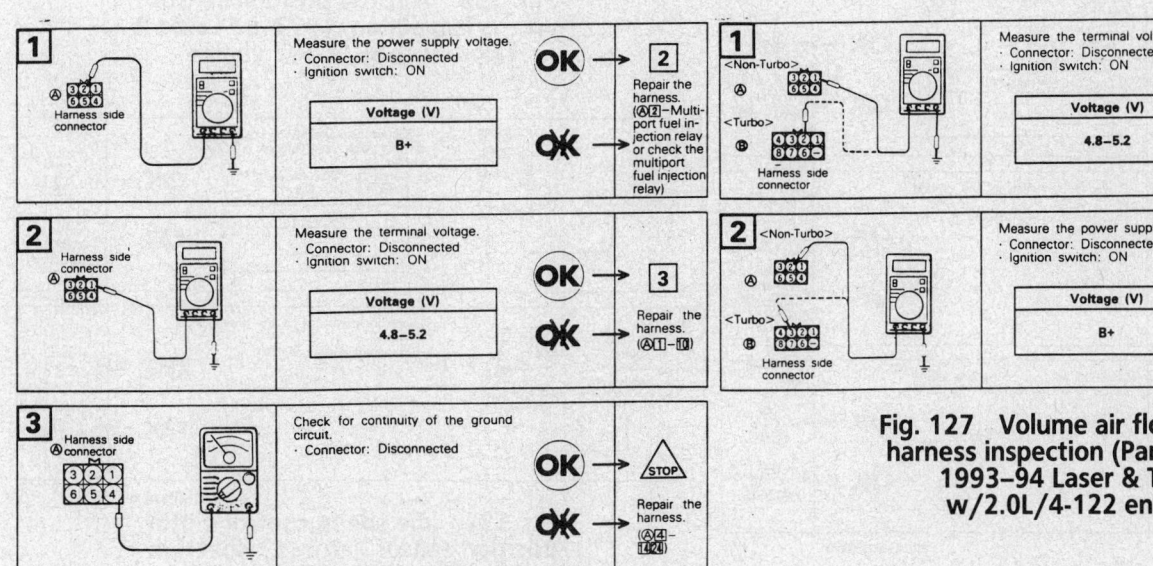

Fig. 127   Volume air flow sensor
harness inspection (Part 1 of 2).
1993–94 Laser & Talon
w/2.0L/4-122 engine

Fig. 126   Volume air flow sensor
harness inspection. 1993–94 Laser &
Talon w/1.8L/4-107 engine

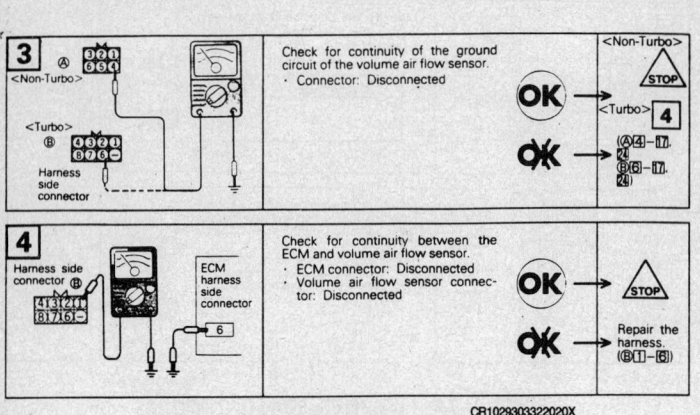

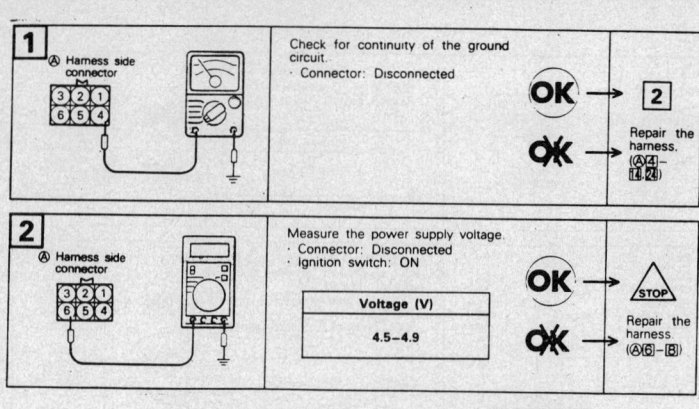

Fig. 127 Volume air flow sensor harness inspection (Part 2 of 2). 1993–94 Laser & Talon w/2.0L/4-122 engine

Fig. 128 Intake air temperature sensor harness inspection. 1993–94 Laser & Talon w/1.8L/4-107 engine

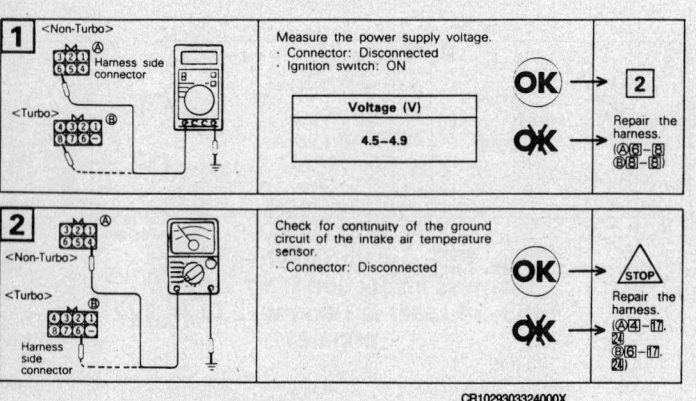

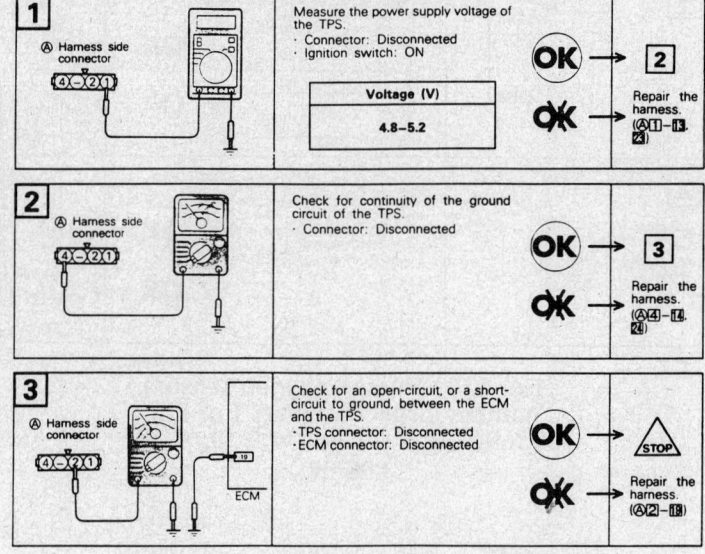

Fig. 129 Intake air temperature sensor harness inspection. 1993–94 Laser & Talon w/2.0L/4-122 engine

Fig. 130 Throttle position sensor harness inspection. 1993–94 Laser & Talon w/1.8L/4-107 engine

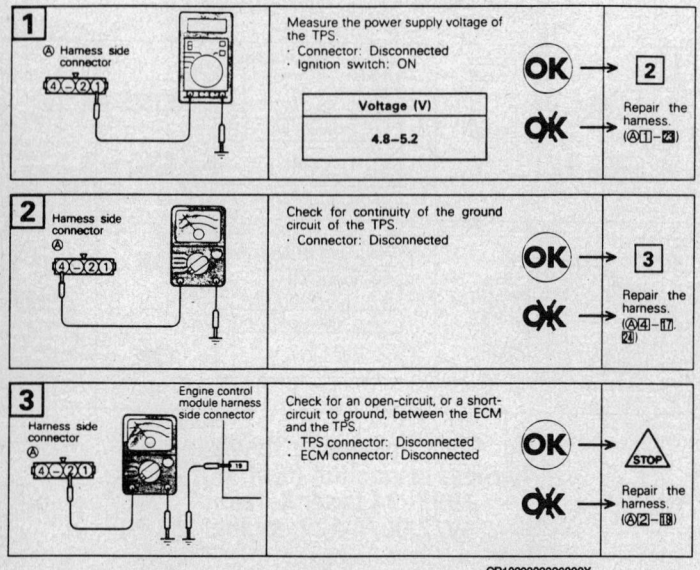

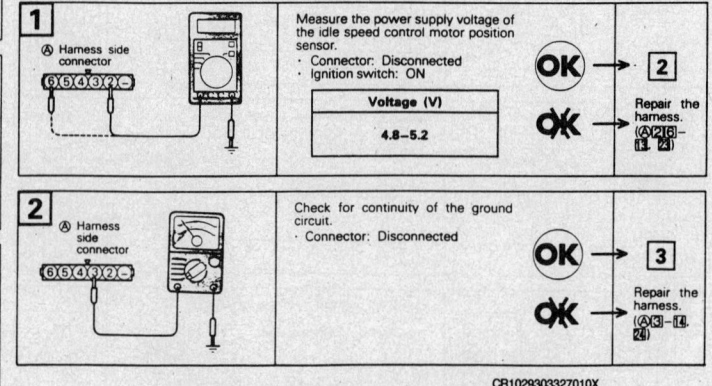

Fig. 131 Throttle position sensor harness inspection. 1993–94 Laser & Talon w/2.0L/4-122 engine

Fig. 132 Idle speed control motor position sensor harness inspection (Part 1 of 2). 1993–94 Laser & Talon w/1.8L/4-107 engine

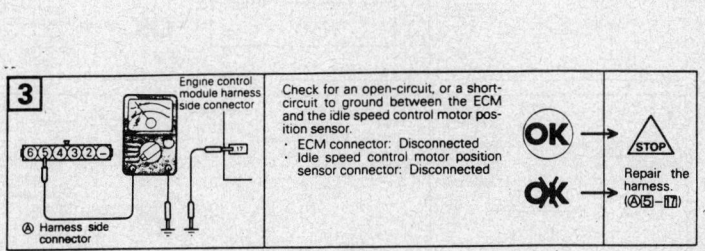

Fig. 132 Idle speed control motor position sensor harness inspection (Part 2 of 2). 1993–94 Laser & Talon w/1.8L/4-107 engine

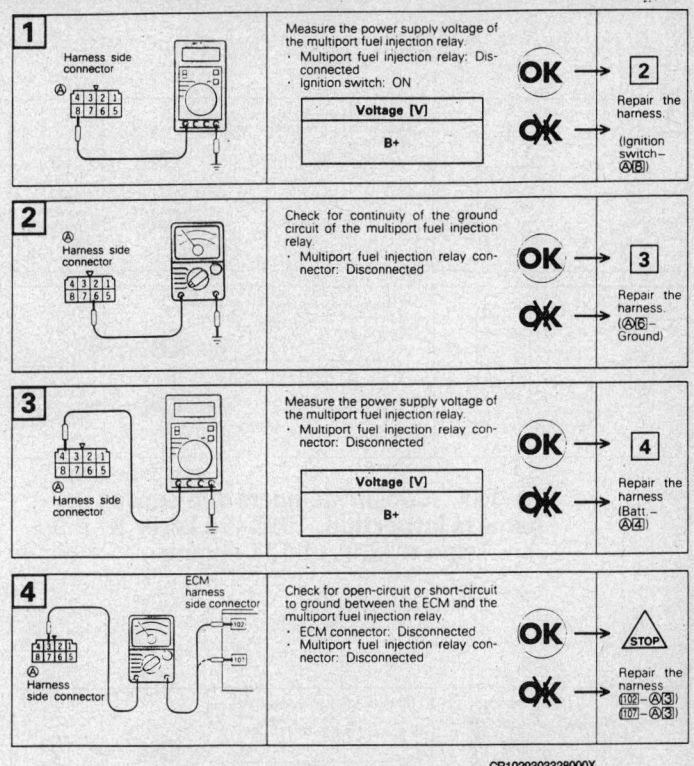

Fig. 133 Power supply harness inspection. 1993–94 Laser & Talon w/1.8L/4-107 engine

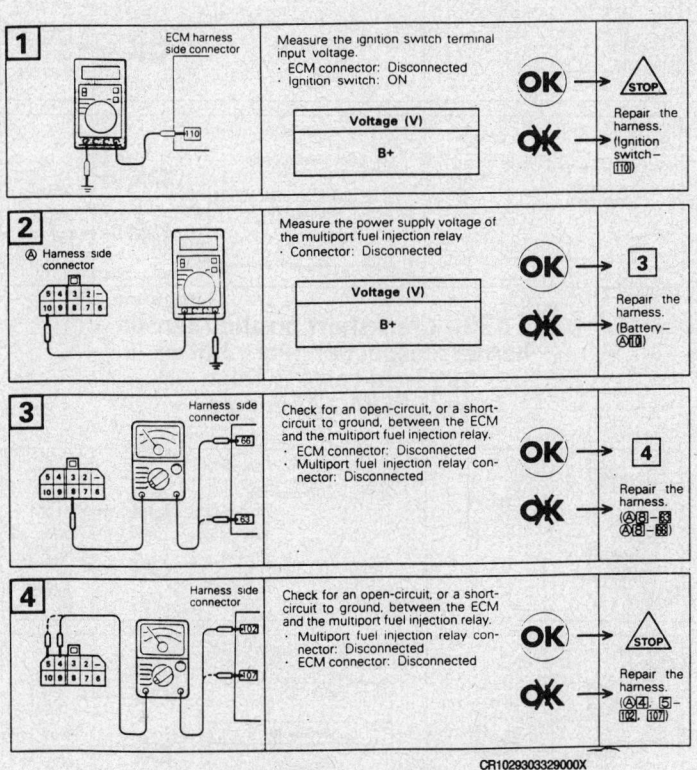

Fig. 134 Power supply harness inspection. 1993–94 Laser & Talon w/2.0L/4-122 engine

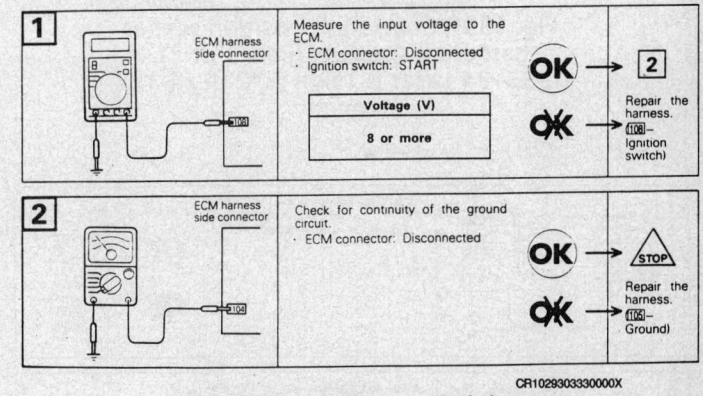

Fig. 135 Ignition switch harness inspection. 1993–94 Laser & Talon w/manual transaxle

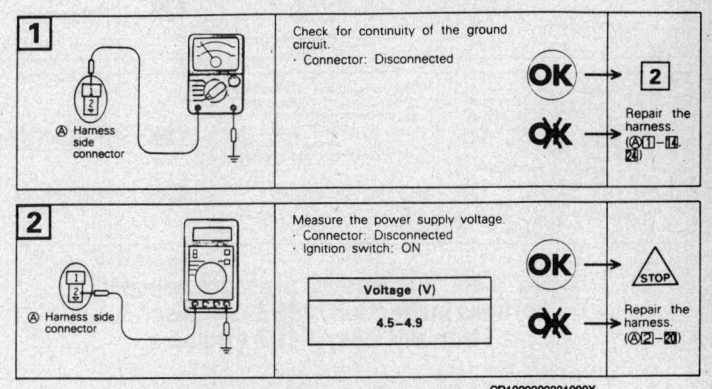

Fig. 136 Coolant temperature sensor harness inspection. 1993–94 Laser & Talon w/1.8L/4-107 engine

MULTI-POINT FUEL INJECTION (MODELS w/1.8L/4-107, 1.8L/4-110 & 2.4L/4-143 ENGINES, 1993-94 MODELS w/2.0L/4-122 ENGINE & 1995 TALON w/2.0L/4-122 TURBOCHARGED ENGINE)

7-111

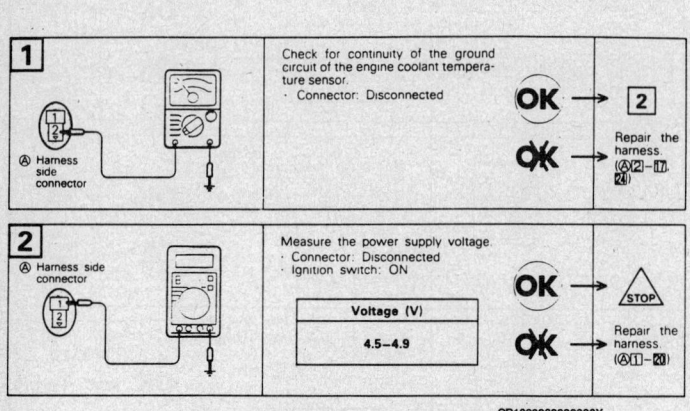

Fig. 137 Coolant temperature sensor harness inspection. 1993–94 Laser & Talon w/2.0L/4-122 engine

CR1029303332000X

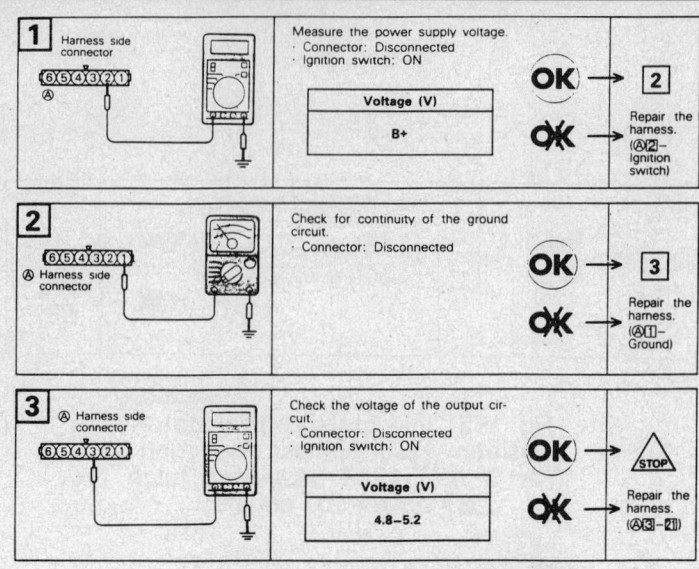

Fig. 138 Crankshaft position sensor harness inspection. 1993–94 Laser & Talon w/1.8L/4-107 engine

CR1029303333000X

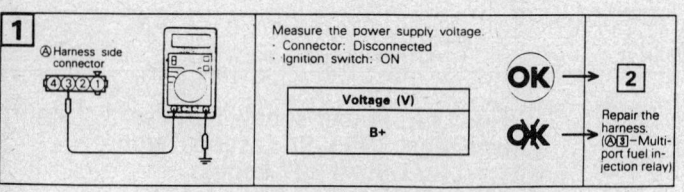

Fig. 139 Crankshaft position sensor harness inspection (Part 1 of 2). 1993–94 Laser & Talon w/2.0L/4-122 engine

CR1029303334010X

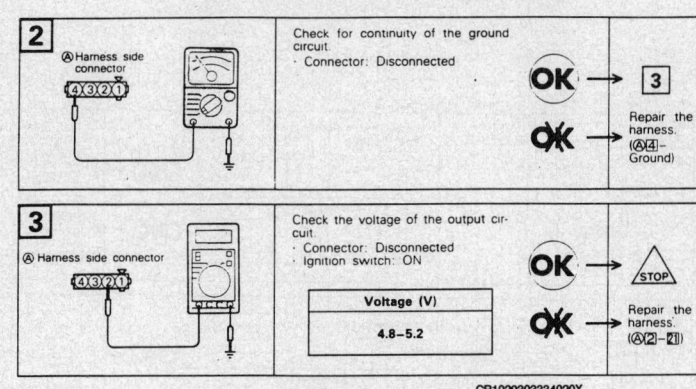

Fig. 139 Crankshaft position sensor harness inspection (Part 2 of 2). 1993–94 Laser & Talon w/2.0L/4-122 engine

CR1029303334020X

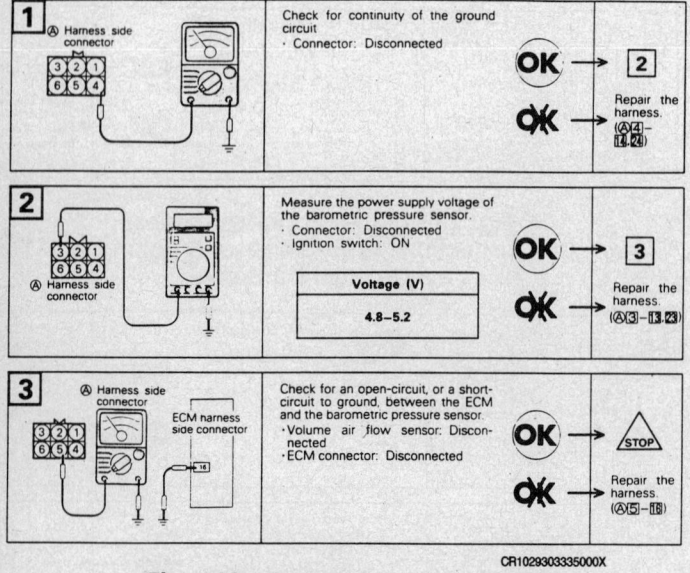

Fig. 140 Barometric pressure sensor harness inspection. 1993–94 Laser & Talon w/1.8L/4-107 engine

CR1029303335000X

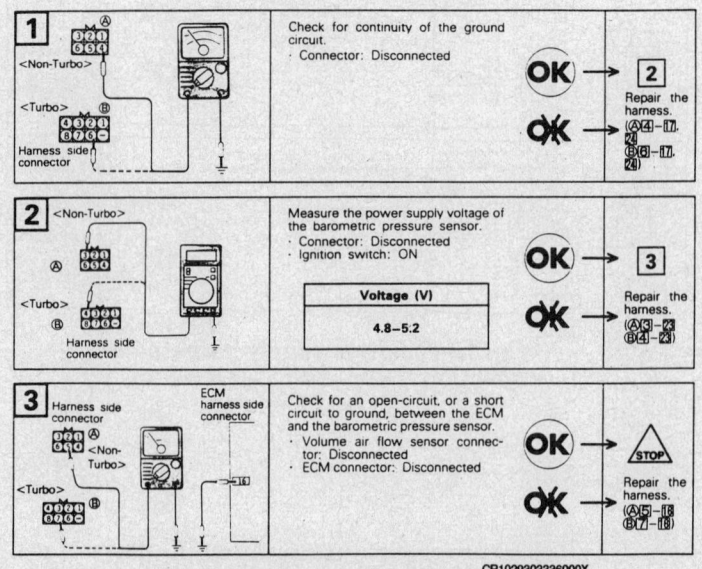

Fig. 141 Barometric pressure sensor harness inspection. 1993–94 Laser & Talon w/2.0L/4-122 engine

CR1029303336000X

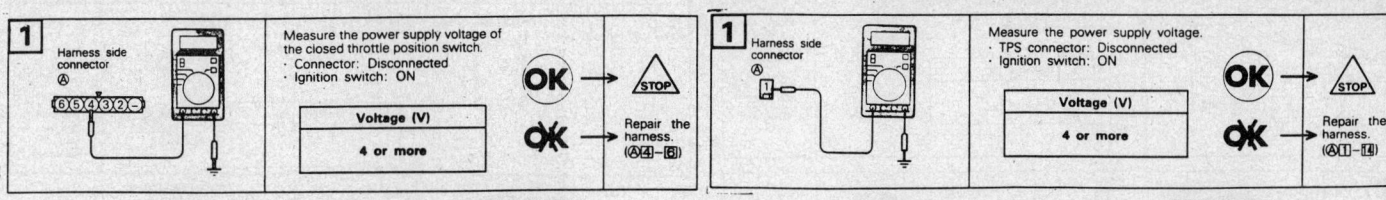

Fig. 142 Closed throttle position switch harness inspection. 1993–94 Laser & Talon w/1.8L/4-107 engine

Fig. 143 Closed throttle position switch harness inspection. 1993–94 Laser & Talon w/2.0L/4-122 engine

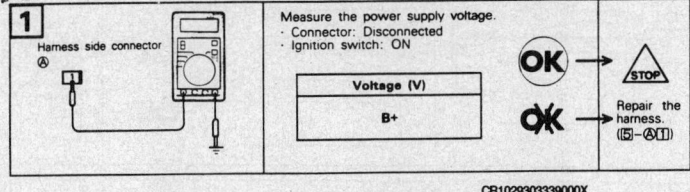

Fig. 144 Power steering pressure switch harness inspection. 1993–94 Laser & Talon

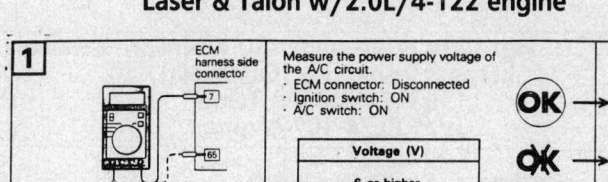

Fig. 145 A/C switch & compressor clutch relay harness inspection. 1993–94 Laser & Talon

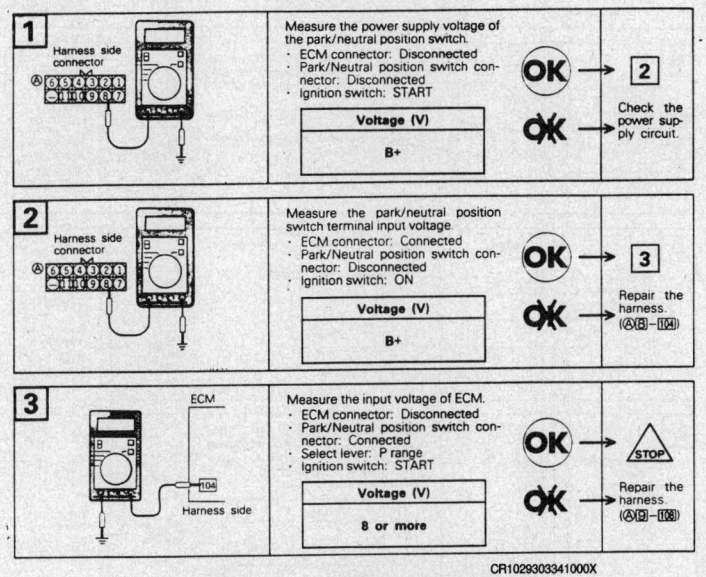

Fig. 146 Ignition switch & Park/Neutral position switch harness inspection. 1993–94 Laser & Talon w/automatic transaxle

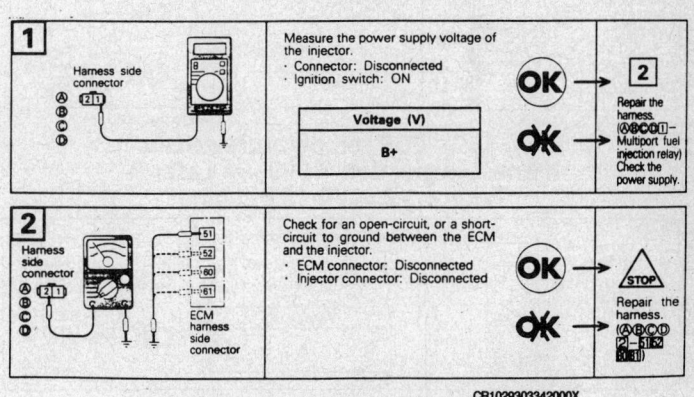

Fig. 147 Injector harness inspection. 1993–94 Laser & Talon w/1.8L/4-107 engine

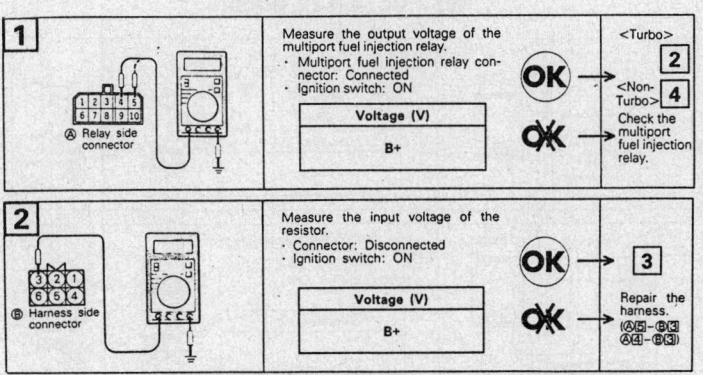

Fig. 148 Injector harness inspection (Part 1 of 2). 1993–94 Laser & Talon w/2.0L/4-122 engine

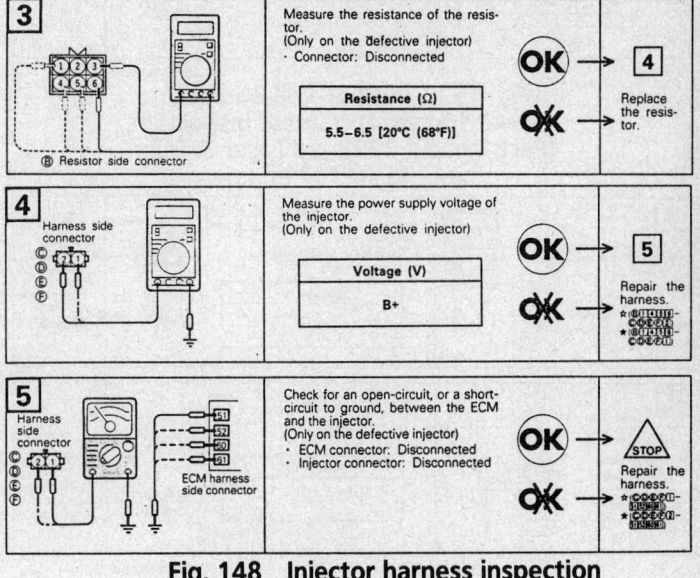

Fig. 148 Injector harness inspection (Part 2 of 2). 1993–94 Laser & Talon w/2.0L/4-122 engine

MULTI-POINT FUEL INJECTION (MODELS w/1.8L/4-107, 1.8L/4-110 & 2.4L/4-143 ENGINES, 1993-94 MODELS w/2.0L/4-122 ENGINE & 1995 TALON w/2.0L/4-122 TURBOCHARGED ENGINE)

7-113

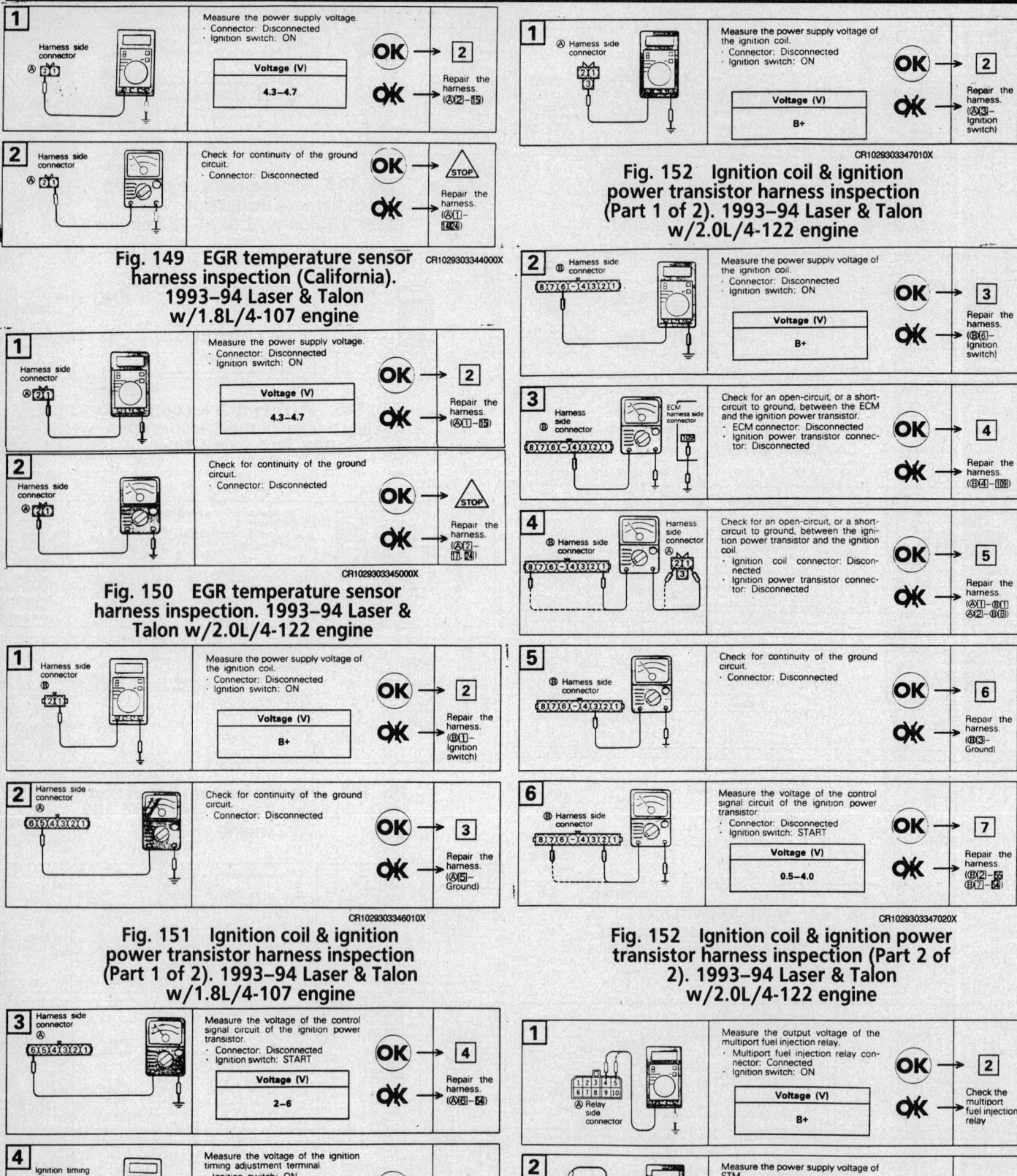

Fig. 149 EGR temperature sensor harness inspection (California). 1993–94 Laser & Talon w/1.8L/4-107 engine

Fig. 150 EGR temperature sensor harness inspection. 1993–94 Laser & Talon w/2.0L/4-122 engine

Fig. 151 Ignition coil & ignition power transistor harness inspection (Part 1 of 2). 1993–94 Laser & Talon w/1.8L/4-107 engine

Fig. 151 Ignition coil & ignition power transistor harness inspection (Part 2 of 2). 1993–94 Laser & Talon w/1.8L/4-107 engine

Fig. 152 Ignition coil & ignition power transistor harness inspection (Part 1 of 2). 1993–94 Laser & Talon w/2.0L/4-122 engine

Fig. 152 Ignition coil & ignition power transistor harness inspection (Part 2 of 2). 1993–94 Laser & Talon w/2.0L/4-122 engine

Fig. 153 Idle air control motor harness inspection (Part 1 of 2). 1993–94 Laser & Talon w/2.0L/4-122 engine

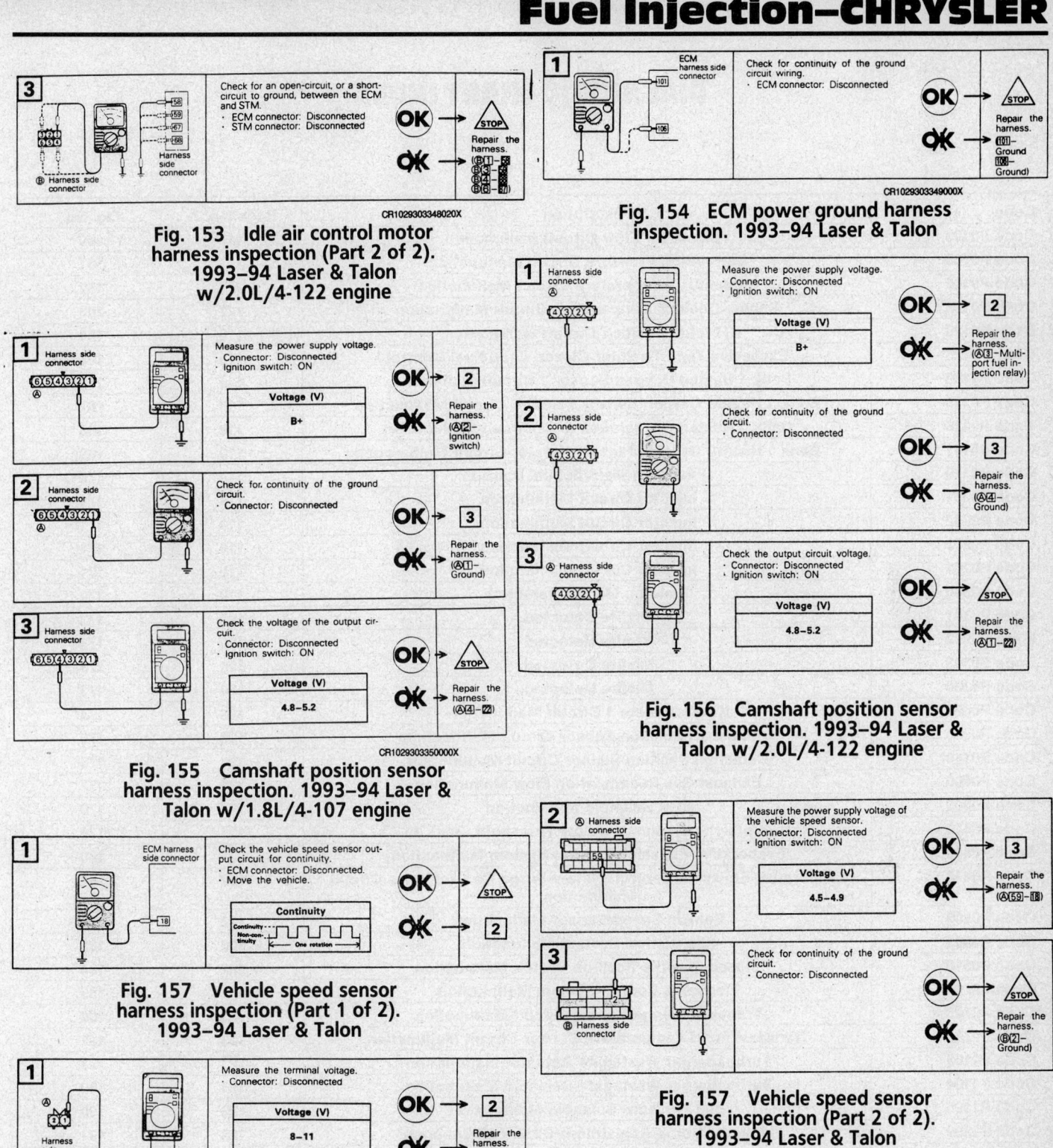

Fig. 153 Idle air control motor harness inspection (Part 2 of 2). 1993–94 Laser & Talon w/2.0L/4-122 engine

Fig. 154 ECM power ground harness inspection. 1993–94 Laser & Talon

Fig. 155 Camshaft position sensor harness inspection. 1993–94 Laser & Talon w/1.8L/4-107 engine

Fig. 156 Camshaft position sensor harness inspection. 1993–94 Laser & Talon w/2.0L/4-122 engine

Fig. 157 Vehicle speed sensor harness inspection (Part 1 of 2). 1993–94 Laser & Talon

Fig. 157 Vehicle speed sensor harness inspection (Part 2 of 2). 1993–94 Laser & Talon

Fig. 158 Knock sensor harness inspection. 1993–94 Laser & Talon w/2.0L/4-122 turbocharged engine

Fig. 159 Anti-lock braking signal harness inspection. 1993–94 Laser & Talon AWD w/2.0L/4-122 engine

MULTI-POINT FUEL INJECTION (MODELS w/1.8L/4-107, 1.8L/4-110 & 2.4L/4-143 ENGINES, 1993–94 MODELS w/2.0L/4-122 ENGINE & 1995 TALON w/2.0L/4-122 TURBOCHARGED ENGINE)

7-115

DIAGNOSTIC CHART INDEX

Code	Description	Page No. 7-	Fig. No.
Code P0100	Volume Air Flow Circuit Malfunction	117	160
Code P0105	Barometric Pressure Circuit Malfunction	117	161
Code P0110	Intake Air Temperature Circuit Malfunction	117	162
Code P0115	Engine Coolant Temperature Circuit Malfunction	117	163
Code P0120	Throttle Position Circuit Malfunction	118	164
Code P0125	Excessive Time To Enter Closed Loop Fuel Control	118	165
Code P0130	Bank 1 Heated Oxygen Sensor 1 Circuit Malfunction	118	166
Code P0135	Bank 1 Heated Oxygen Sensor 1 Heater Circuit Malfunction	118	167
Code P0136	Bank 1 Heated Oxygen Sensor 2 Circuit Malfunction	119	168
Code P0141	Bank 1 Heated Oxygen Sensor 2 Heater Circuit Malfunction	119	169
Code P0170	Fuel Trim Malfunction, Bank 1	119	170
Code P0201	Injector Circuit Malfunction	119	171
Code P0202	Injector Circuit Malfunction	119	171
Code P0203	Injector Circuit Malfunction	119	171
Code P0204	Injector Circuit Malfunction	119	171
Code P0300	Random Misfire Detected	120	172
Code P0301	Misfire Detected	120	173
Code P0302	Misfire Detected	120	173
Code P0303	Misfire Detected	120	173
Code P0304	Misfire Detected	120	173
Code P0325	Knock Sensor 1 Circuit Malfunction	120	174
Code P0335	Crankshaft Position Sensor Circuit Malfunction	120	175
Code P0340	Camshaft Position Sensor Circuit Malfunction	121	176
Code P0400	Exhaust Gas Recirculation Flow Malfunction	121	177
Code P0403	EGR Solenoid Malfunction	121	178
Code P0420	Catalytic Efficiency Below Threshold, Bank 1	121	179
Code P0440	Evaporative Emission Control System Malfunction	121	180
Code P0443	Evaporative Emission Control System Purge Control Valve Circuit Malfunction	122	181
Code P0500	Vehicle Speed Sensor Malfunction	122	182
Code P0505	Idle Control System Malfunction	122	183
Code P0510	Closed Throttle Position Switch Malfunction	122	184
Code P0700	Transaxle Control System Malfunction	123	185
Code P0705	Transaxle Range Sensor Circuit Malfunction	123	186
Code P0710	Transaxle Fluid Temperature Sensor Circuit Malfunction	123	187
Code P1103	Turbocharger Wastegate Actuator Malfunction	123	188
Code P1104	Turbocharger Wastegate Solenoid Malfunction	123	189
Code P1105	Fuel Pressure Solenoid Malfunction	123	190
Code P1300	Ignition Timing Adjustment Circuit Malfunction	123	191
Code P1400	Manifold Differential Pressure Sensor Circuit Malfunction	124	192
Code P1500	Generator FR Terminal Circuit Malfunction	124	193
Code P1715	PG Assembly Malfunction	124	194
Code P1750	Solenoid Assembly Malfunction	124	195

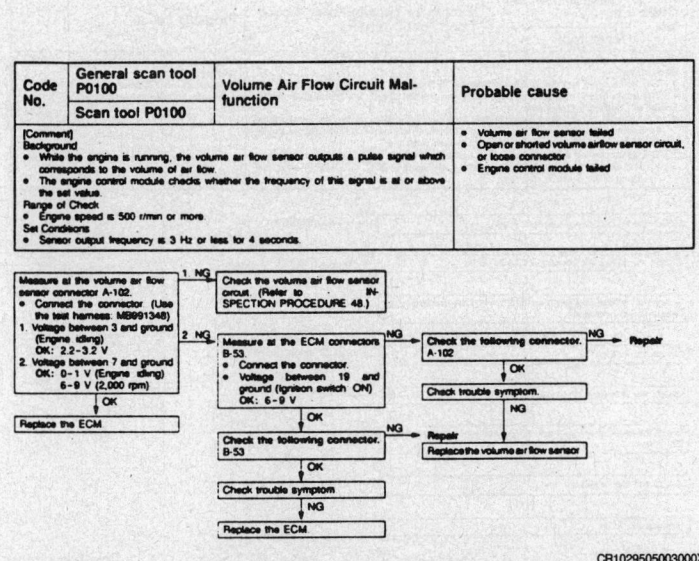

Fig. 160 Code P0100: Volume Air Flow Circuit Malfunction. 1995–96 Talon

CR1029505003000X

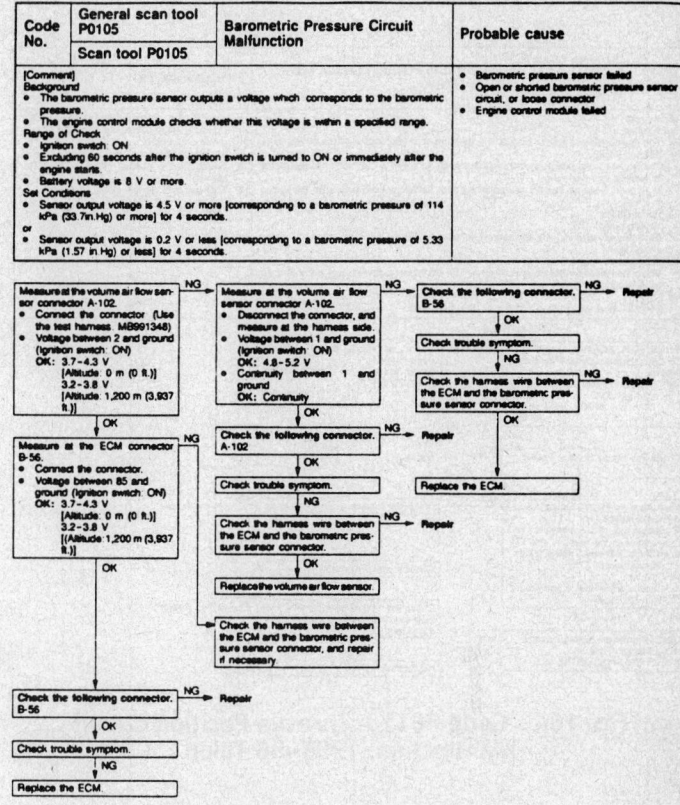

Fig. 161 Code P0105: Barometric Pressure Circuit Malfunction. 1995–96 Talon

CR1029505004000X

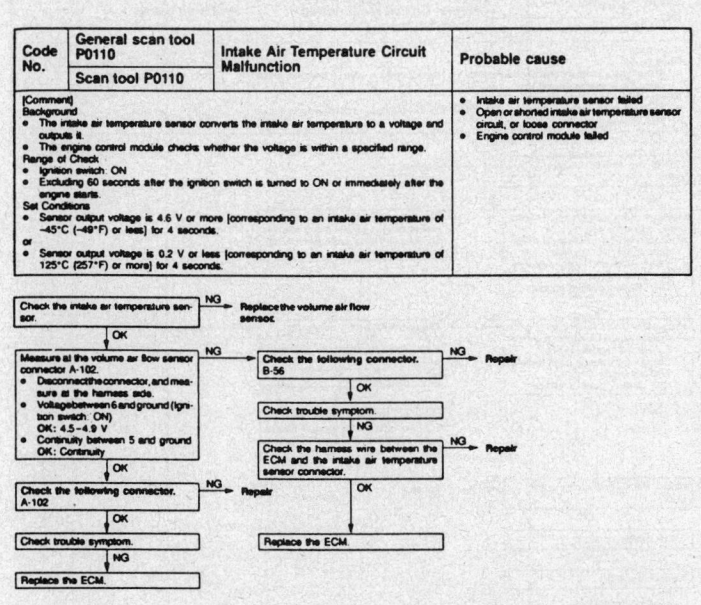

Fig. 162 Code P0110: Intake Air Temperature Circuit Malfunction. 1995–96 Talon

CR1029506473000X

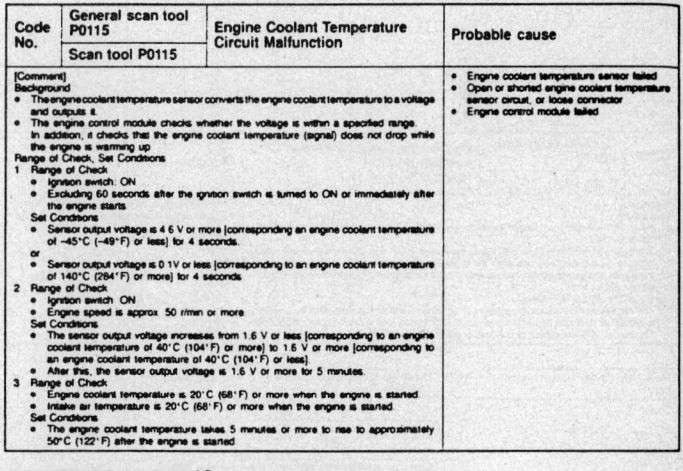

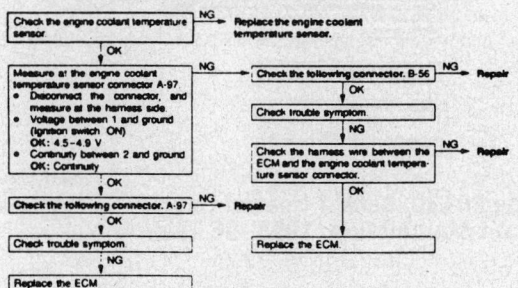

CR1029505005000X

Fig. 163 Code P0115: Engine Coolant Temperature Circuit Malfunction. 1995–96 Talon

CHRYSLER–Fuel Injection

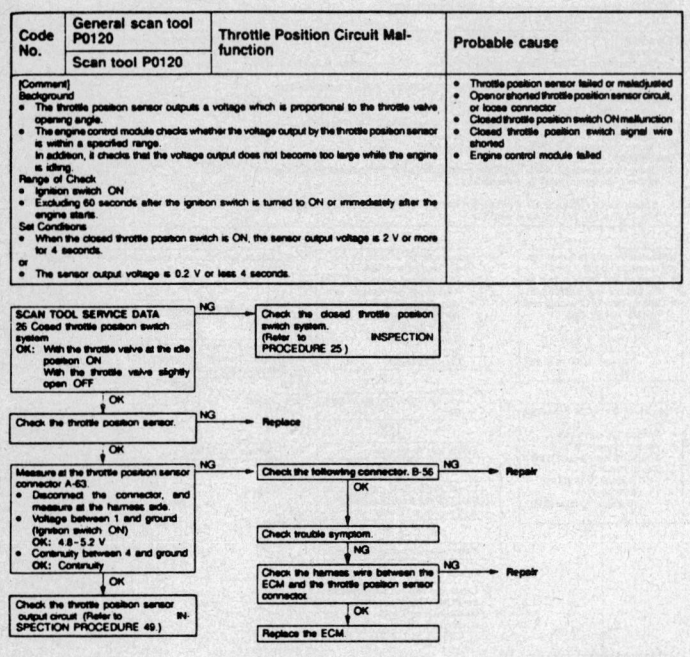

Fig. 164   Code P0120: Throttle Position Circuit Malfunction. 1995–96 Talon

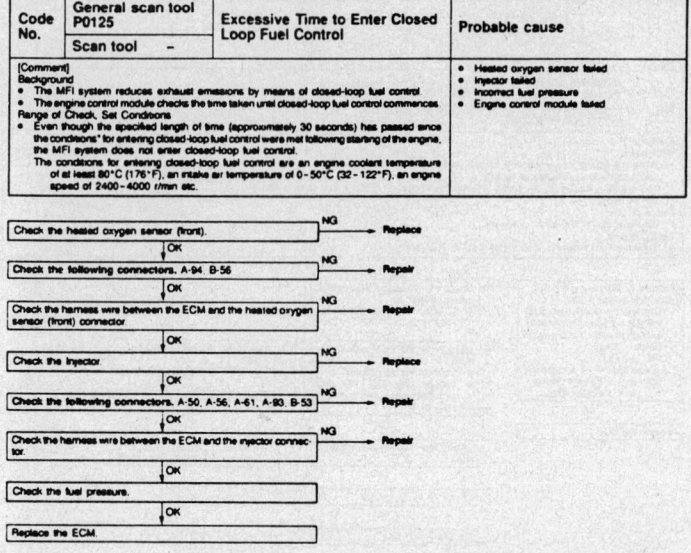

Fig. 165   Code P0125: Excessive Time To Enter Closed Loop Fuel Control. 1995–96 Talon

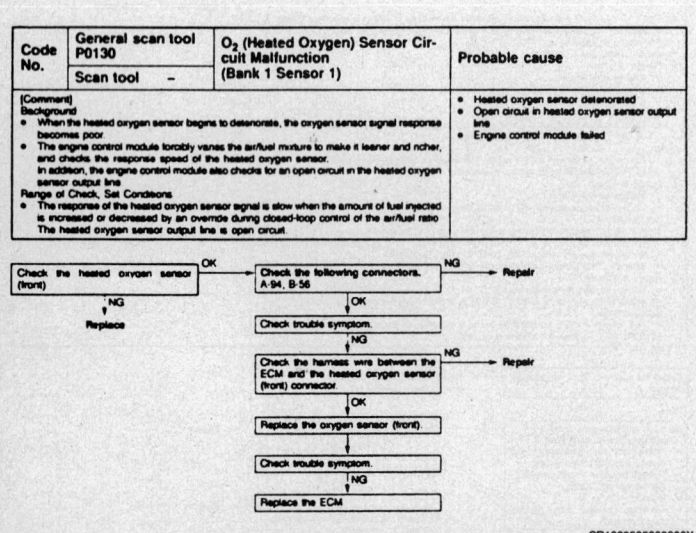

Fig. 166   Code P0130: Bank 1 Heated Oxygen Sensor 1 Circuit Malfunction. 1995–96 Talon

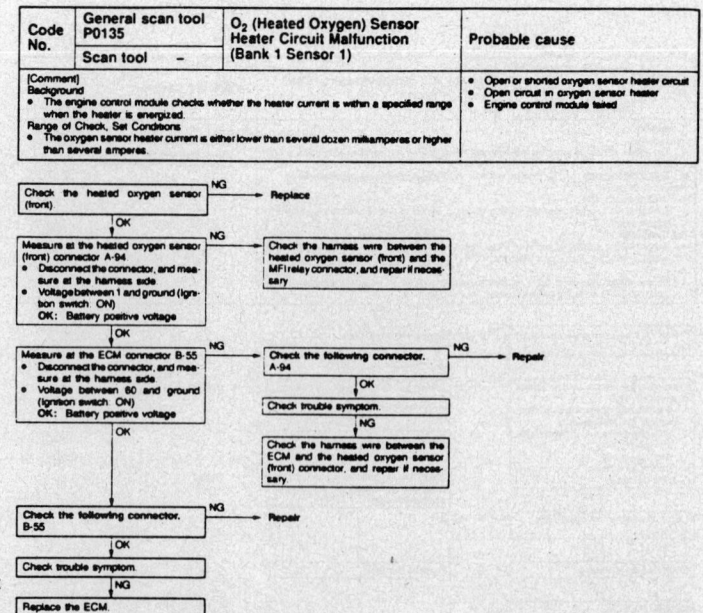

Fig. 167   Code P0135: Bank 1 Heated Oxygen Sensor 1 Heater Circuit Malfunction. 1995–96 Talon

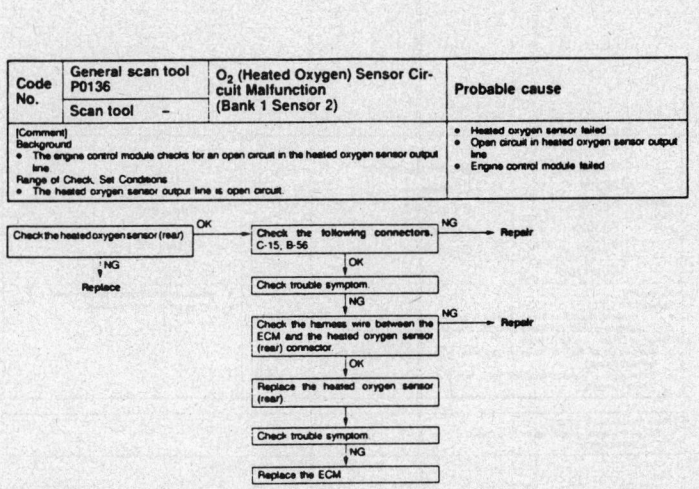

Fig. 168   Code P0136: Bank 1 Heated Oxygen Sensor 2
Circuit Malfunction. 1995–96 Talon

CR1029505010000X

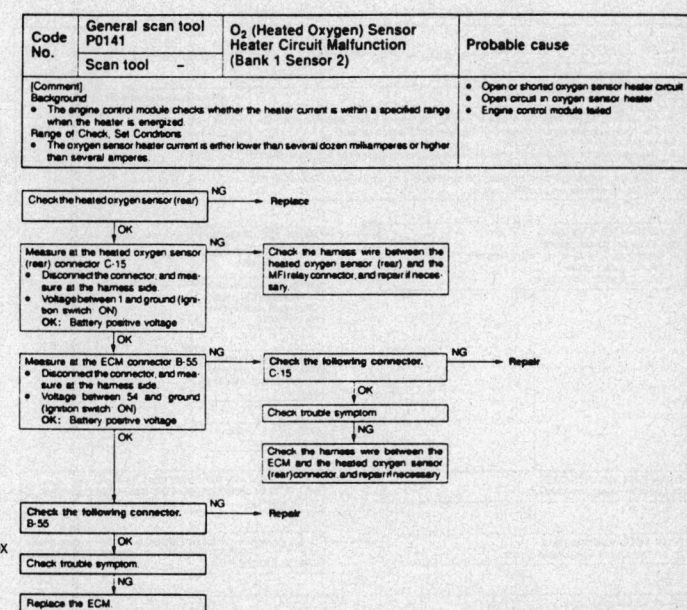

CR1029505011000X

Fig. 169   Code P0141: Bank 1 Heated Oxygen Sensor 2
Heater Circuit Malfunction. 1995–96 Talon

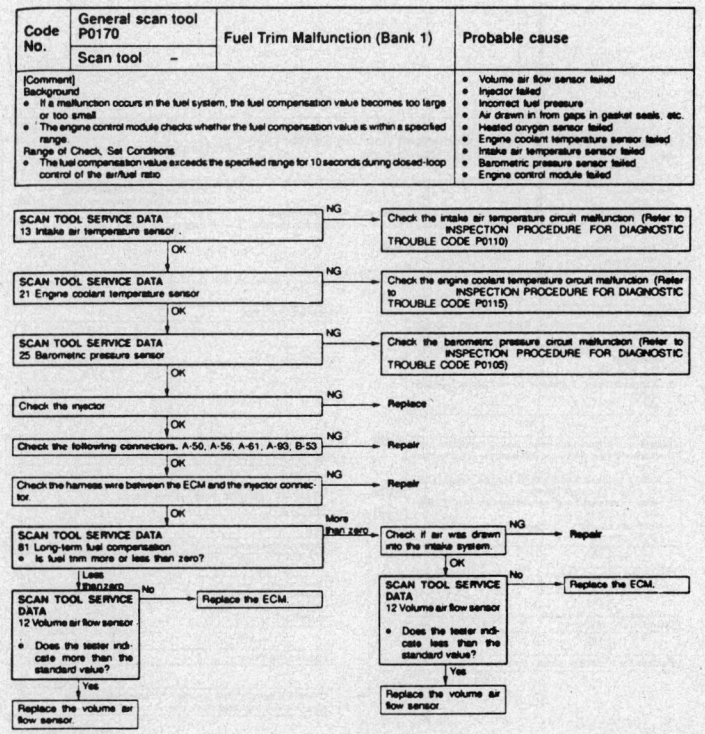

CR1029505012000X

Fig. 170   Code P0170: Fuel Trim Malfunction, Bank 1.
1995–96 Talon

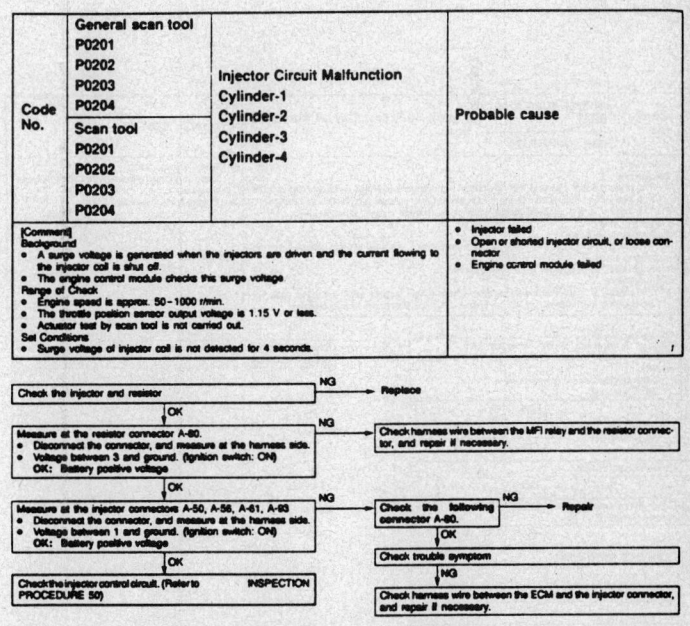

CR1029505013000X

Fig. 171   Codes P0201, P0202, P0203 & P0204: Injector
Circuit Malfunction. 1995–96 Talon

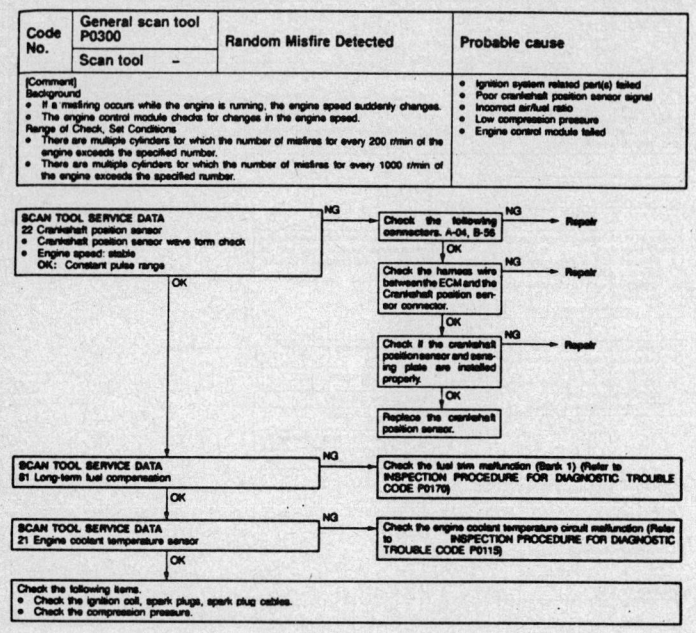

Fig. 172   Code P0300: Random Misfire Detected.
1995–96 Talon

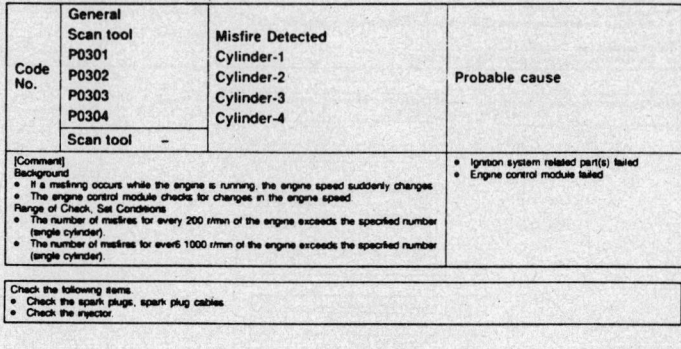

Fig. 173   Codes P0301, P0302, P0303 & P0304: Misfire
Detected. 1995–96 Talon

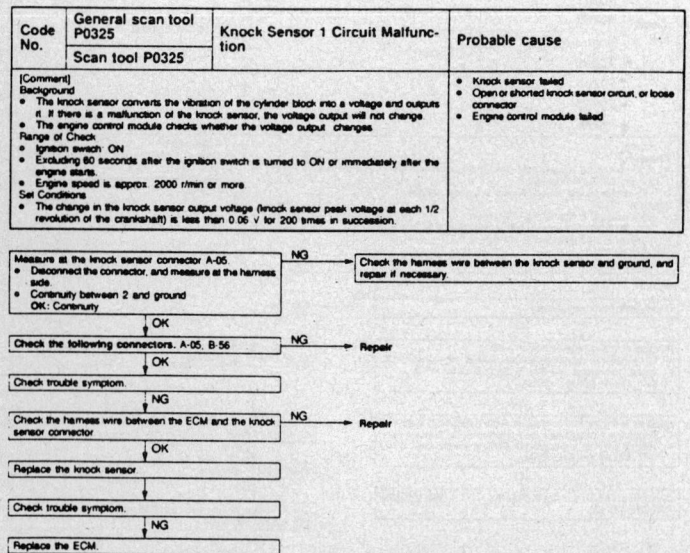

Fig. 174   Code P0325: Knock Sensor 1 Circuit
Malfunction. 1995–96 Talon

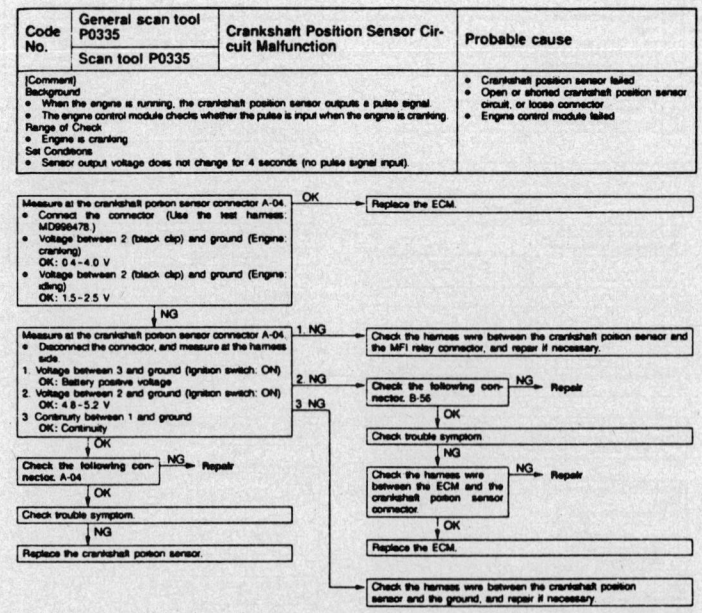

Fig. 175   Code P0335: Crankshaft Position Sensor Circuit
Malfunction. 1995–96 Talon

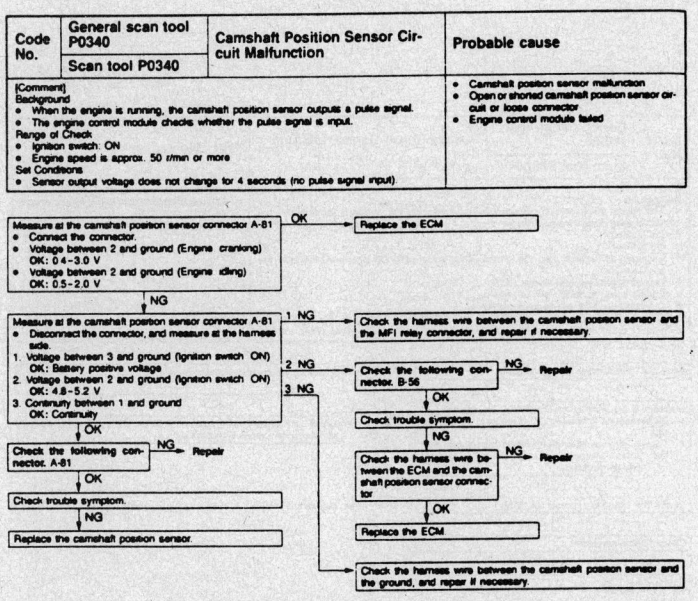

Fig. 176   Code P0340: Camshaft Position Sensor Circuit Malfunction. 1995–96 Talon

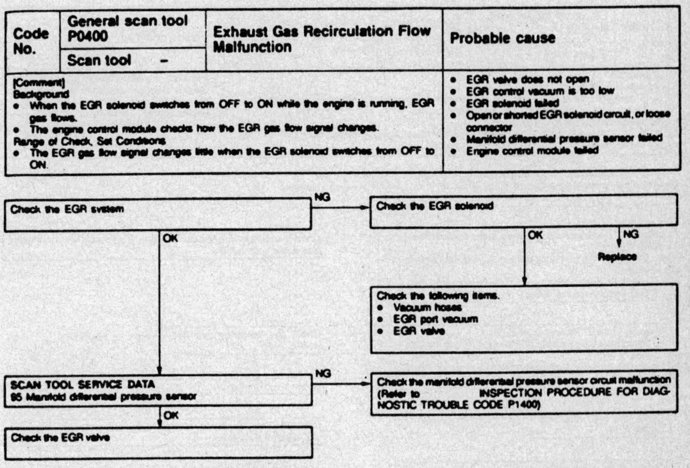

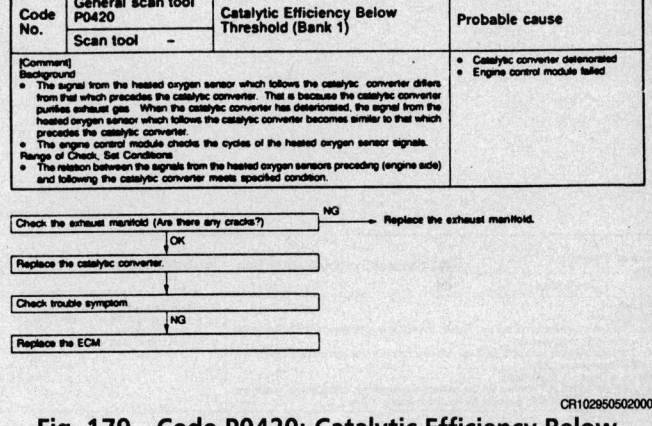

Fig. 177   Code P0400: Exhaust Gas Recirculation Flow Malfunction. 1995–96 Talon

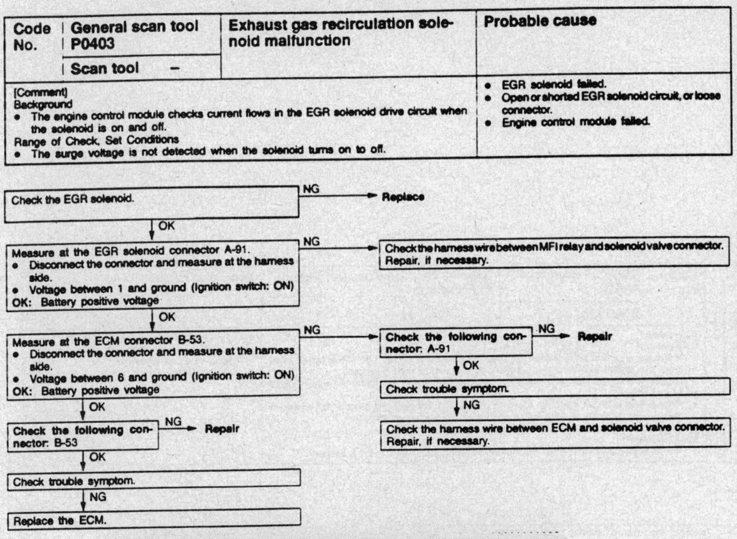

Fig. 178   Code P0403: EGR Solenoid Malfunction. 1996 Talon

Fig. 179   Code P0420: Catalytic Efficiency Below Threshold, Bank 1. 1995–96 Talon

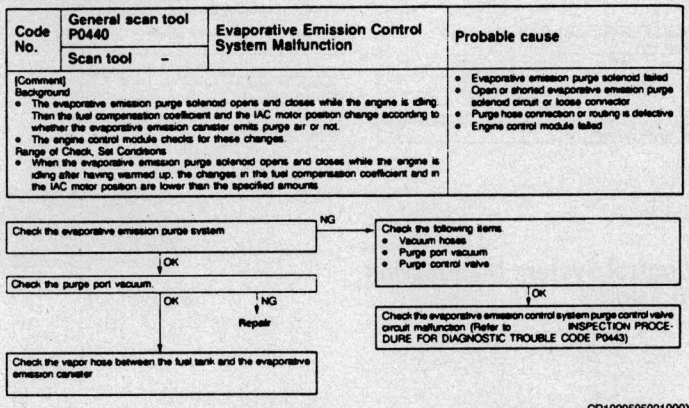

Fig. 180   Code P0440: Evaporative Emission Control System Malfunction. 1995–96 Talon

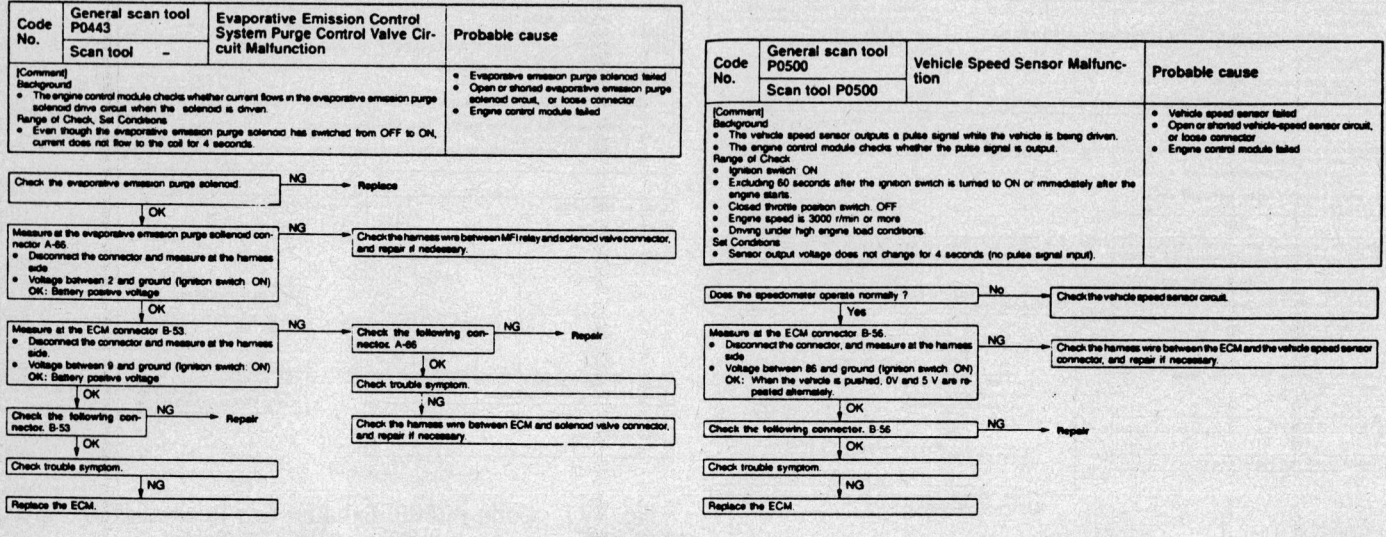

Fig. 181 Code P0443: Evaporative Emission Control System Purge Control Valve Circuit Malfunction. 1995–96 Talon

Fig. 182 Code P0500: Vehicle Speed Sensor Malfunction. 1995–96 Talon

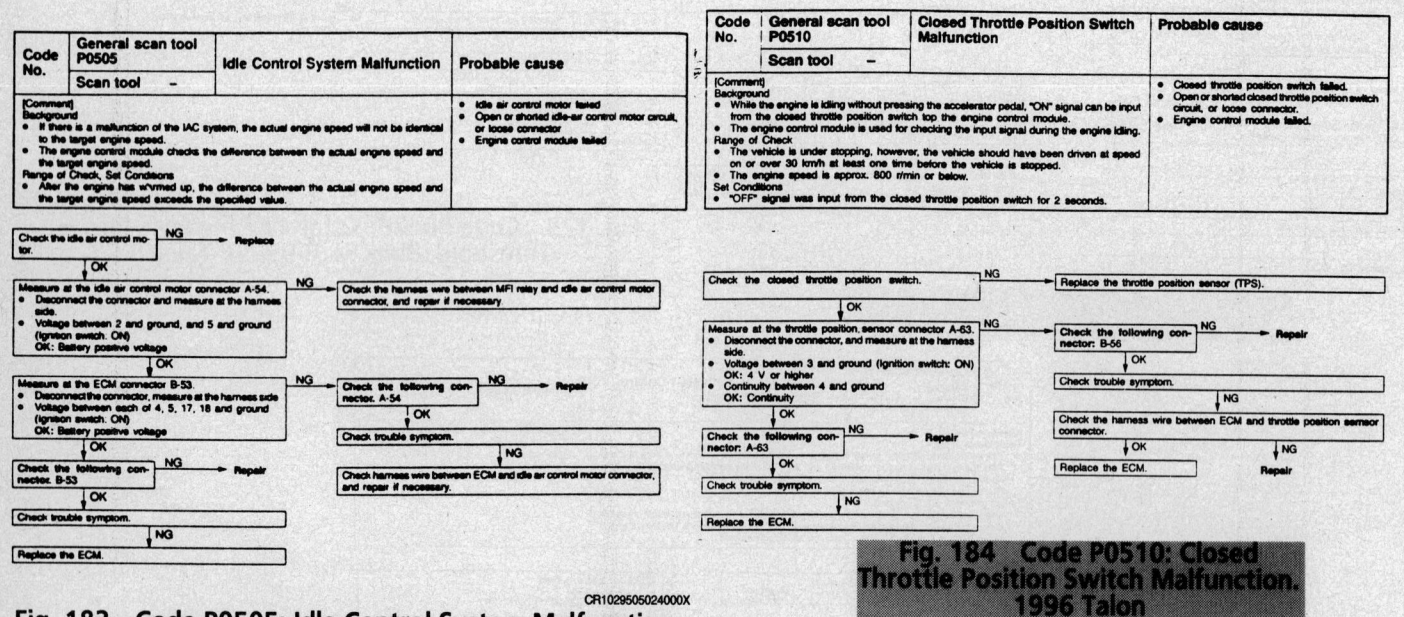

Fig. 183 Code P0505: Idle Control System Malfunction. 1995–96 Talon

Fig. 184 Code P0510: Closed Throttle Position Switch Malfunction. 1996 Talon

Code No.	General scan tool P0700	Transmission	Probable cause
	Scan tool –		
[Comment] Background • When a malfunction of the transaxle control system is detected, the transaxle control module outputs a malfunction signal to the engine control module. Range of Check, Set Conditions • The signal is input to the ECM.			• Automatic transaxle control system failed • Open or shorted communication line between the engine control module and the transaxle control module • Engine control module failed

Check the TCM

Fig. 185   Code P0700: Transaxle Control System Malfunction. 1995 Talon

Code No.	General scan tool P0705	Transaxle range sensor circuit malfunction (RPNDL Input)	Probable cause
	Scan tool –		
[Comment] Background • When a malfunction of the park/neutral position switch is detected, the transaxle control module outputs a malfunction signal to the engine control module. Range of Check, Set Conditions • Malfunction occurrence signal of the park/neutral position switch is input to the engine control module.			• Park/neutral position switch failed • Open or shorted park/neutral position switch circuit, or loose connector. • Engine control module failed.

Check the TCM.

Fig. 186   Code P0705: Transaxle Range Sensor Circuit Malfunction. 1996 Talon

Code No.	General scan tool P0710	Transaxle fluid temperature sensor circuit malfunction	Probable cause
	Scan tool –		
[Comment] Background • When a malfunction of the fluid temperature sensor is detected, the transaxle control module outputs a malfunction signal to the engine control module. Range of Check, Set Conditions • Malfunction occurrence signal of the fluid temperature sensor is input to the engine control module.			• Fluid temperature sensor failed. • Open or shorted fluid temperature sensor circuit, or loose connector. • Engine control module failed

Check the TCM.

Fig. 187   Code P0710: Transaxle Fluid Temperature Sensor Circuit Malfunction. 1996 Talon

Code No.	General scan tool P1103	Turbocharger waste gate actuator malfunction	Probable cause
	Scan tool –		
[Comment] Background • The engine control module checks that the engine is not overcharged by always monitoring intake air volume. • The engine control module protects the engine by shutting off fuel when an overcharged condition is detected. Range of Check, Set Conditions • The overcharged condition, which requires fuel shut off, is detected.			• Turbocharger waste gate actuator failed. • Charging pressure control system failed. • Engine control module failed.

Check the turbocharger supercharging.

Fig. 188   Code P1103: Turbocharger Wastegate Actuator Malfunction. 1996 Talon

Code No.	General scan tool P1104	Turbocharger waste gate solenoid malfunction	Probable cause
	Scan tool –		
[Comment] Background • The engine control module checks current flows in the turbocharger waste gate solenoid drive circuit when the solenoid is ON and OFF. Range of Check, Set Conditions • The surge voltage is not detected when the solenoid turns from on to off.			• Turbocharger waste gate solenoid failed. • Open or shorted turbocharger waste gate solenoid circuit, or loose connector. • Engine control module failed.

Check the turbocharger waste gate pressure solenoid. →NG→ Replace

OK↓

Measure at the turbocharger waste gate pressure solenoid connector A-100. • Disconnect the connector and measure at the harness side. • Voltage between 2 and ground (Ignition switch: ON) OK: Battery positive voltage →NG→ Check the harness wire between MFI relay and solenoid valve connector. Repair, if necessary.

OK↓

Measure at the ECM connector B-53. • Disconnect the connector and measure at the harness side. • Voltage between 11 and ground (Ignition switch: ON) OK: Battery positive voltage →NG→ Check the following connector: A-100 →OK→ Check trouble symptom. →OK→ Check the harness wire between ECM and solenoid valve connector. Repair, if necessary.
→NG→ Repair

OK↓

Check the following connector: B-53 →NG→ Repair

OK↓

Check trouble symptom.

NG↓

Replace the ECM.

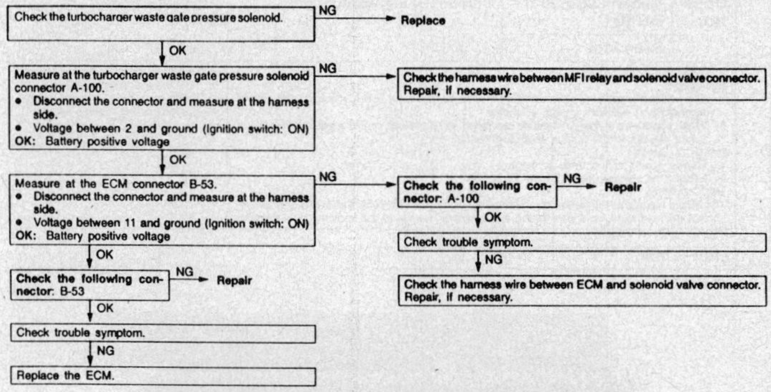

Fig. 189   Code P1104: Turbocharger Wastegate Solenoid Malfunction. 1996 Talon

Code No.	General scan tool P1105	Fuel pressure solenoid malfunction	Probable cause
	Scan tool –		
[Comment] Background • The engine control module checks current flows in the fuel pressure solenoid drive circuit when the solenoid is ON and off. Range of Check, Set Conditions • The surge voltage is not detected when the solenoid turns from on to off.			• Fuel pressure solenoid failed. • Open or shorted fuel pressure solenoid circuit, or loose connector • Engine control module failed.

Check the fuel pressure solenoid. →NG→ Replace

OK↓

Measure at the fuel pressure solenoid connector A-79. • Disconnect the connector and measure at the harness side. • Voltage between 1 and ground (Ignition switch: ON) OK: Battery positive voltage →NG→ Check the harness wire between MFI relay and solenoid valve connector. Repair, if necessary.

OK↓

Measure at the ECM connector B-53. • Disconnect the connector and measure at the harness side. • Voltage between 3 and ground (Ignition switch: ON) OK: Battery positive voltage →NG→ Check the following connector: A-79 →OK→ Check trouble symptom. →OK→ Check the harness wire between ECM and solenoid valve connector. Repair, if necessary.
→NG→ Repair

OK↓

Check the following connector: B-53 →NG→ Repair

OK↓

Check trouble symptom.

NG↓

Replace the ECM.

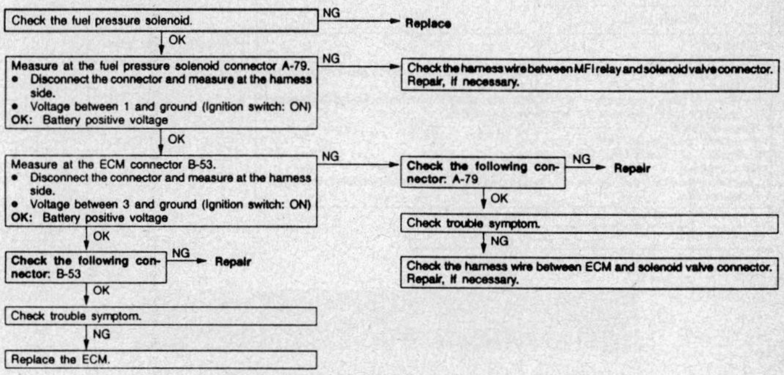

Fig. 190   Code P1105: Fuel Pressure Solenoid Malfunction. 1996 Talon

Code No.	General scan tool P1300	Ignition Timing Adjustment Circuit Malfunction	Probable cause
	Scan tool P1300		
[Comment] Background • If there is a short circuit in the line between the engine control module and the ignition timing adjustment terminal, the sync voltage will become low. • The engine control module checks whether this occurs. Range of Check Set Conditions • Ignition switch: ON • The ignition timing adjustment signal wire is shorted to the ground.			• Ignition timing adjustment signal wire circuit is shorted to ground • Engine control module failed

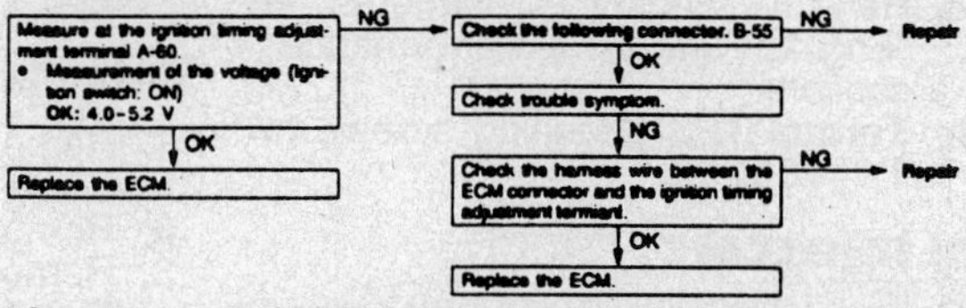

Measure at the ignition timing adjustment terminal A-80. • Measurement of the voltage (Ignition switch: ON) OK: 4.0–5.2 V →NG→ Check the following connector: B-55 →NG→ Repair →OK→ Check trouble symptom. →NG→ Check the harness wire between the ECM connector and the ignition timing adjustment terminal. →NG→ Repair →OK→ Replace the ECM.

OK↓

Replace the ECM.

Fig. 191   Code P1300: Ignition Timing Adjustment Circuit Malfunction. 1995–96 Talon

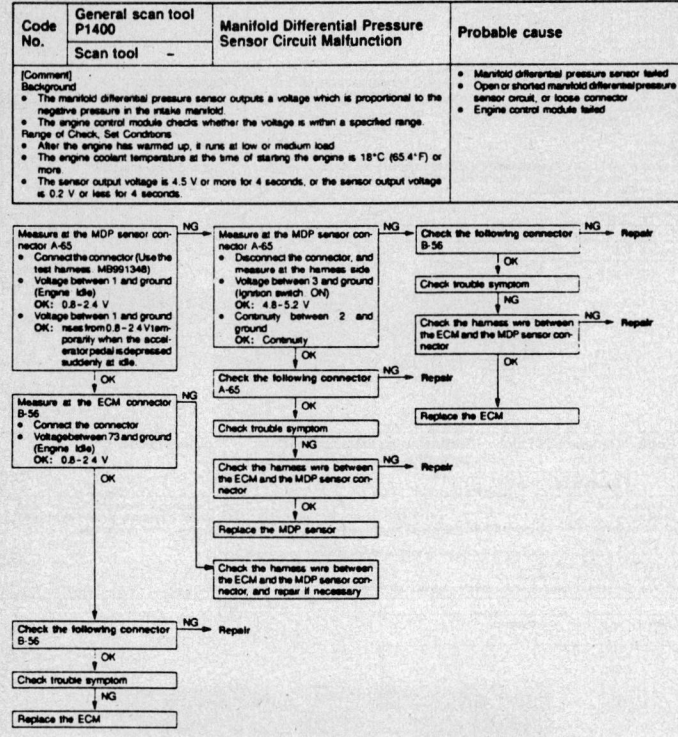

Fig. 192 Code P1400: Manifold Differential Pressure Sensor Circuit Malfunction. 1995–96 Talon

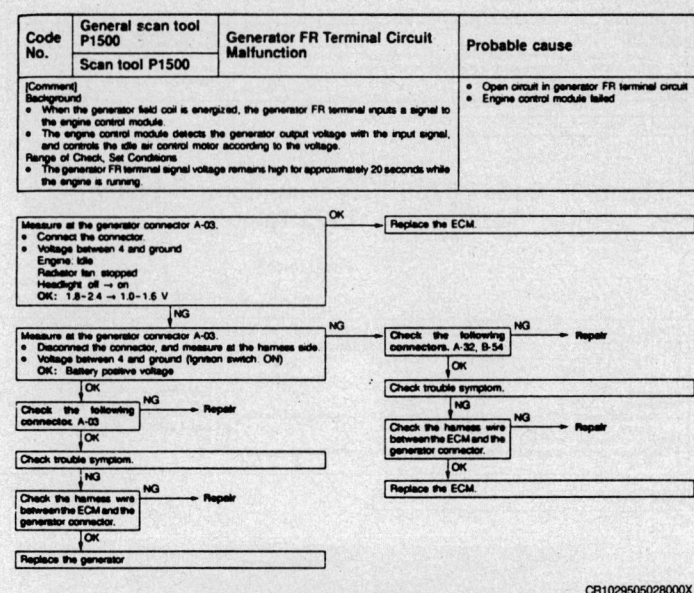

CR1029505028000X

Fig. 193 Code P1500: Generator FR Terminal Circuit Malfunction. 1995–96 Talon

Code No.	General scan tool P1715	PG Assy Malfunction	Probable cause
	Scan tool –		

[Comment]
Background
- The transaxle control module monitors the pulse signals of the pulse generators "A" and "B".
- When the pulse generators "A" and "B" fails, the transaxle control module inputs the pulse generator failure signal to the engine control module.
Range of Check
- Engine speed is 500 r/min or more.
- Position of selector lever: Except "P" or "N"
Set Conditions
The pulse generator failure signals were input from the transaxle control module to the engine control module.

Probable cause:
- Pulse generator failed.
- Engine control module failed.

Check the TCM.

Fig. 194 Code P1715: PG Assembly Malfunction. 1996 Talon

Code No.	General scan tool P1750	Solenoid Assy Malfunction	Probable cause
	Scan tool		

[Comment]
Background
- The transaxle control module monitors the torque converter clutch solenoid, shift control solenoid and pressure control solenoid.
- When some one of these solenoids has failed, the transaxle control module inputs these failure signals to the engine control module.
Range of Check
- Engine speed is 500 r/min or more.
- Position of selector lever: Except "P" or "N"
Set Conditions
The failure signals of the torque converter clutch solenoid, shift control solenoid or pressure control solenoid were input from the transaxle control module to the engine control module.

Probable cause:
- Converter clutch solenoid failed.
- Shift control solenoid failed.
- Pressure control solenoid failed.
- Engine control module failed.

Check the TCM.

Fig. 195 Code P1750: Solenoid Assembly Malfunction. 1996 Talon

SYSTEM SERVICE

Fuel System Pressure Relief

To avoid personal injury and vehicle damage, it is necessary to relieve fuel system pressure prior to servicing any fuel-related component. Refer to "Precautions" for pressure relief procedure.

Component Replacement

Oxygen Sensor (O₂S)

1. Disconnect O₂S electrical connector.
2. Remove O₂S from exhaust manifold.
3. Reverse procedure to install. **Torque** O₂S to 29–36 ft. lbs.

Throttle Position Sensor (TPS)

1. Remove TPS electrical connector.
2. Remove TPS attaching screws from throttle body, then TPS.
3. Reverse procedure to install, noting the following:
   a. Refer to "Sensor Adjustments" in "Engine Tune Up & Performance" section.
   b. **Torque** TPS attaching screws to 1.1–1.8 ft. lbs.

Fuel Injectors

1. Relieve fuel pressure as described under "Precautions."
2. Disconnect fuel injector electrical connectors.
3. Remove delivery pipe with injectors attached.
4. Install new grommets and O-rings and lubricate O-rings with a light oil.
5. Install injector into fuel delivery pipe by turning back and forth. Once injector are installed ensure they turn smoothly.
6. Install fuel delivery rail with injectors installed.

Throttle Body

1. Remove necessary throttle body electrical and throttle cable connections.
2. Remove air intake hose, if necessary.
3. Remove throttle body attaching bolts, then the throttle body.
4. Reverse procedure to install.

CR1029303358000X

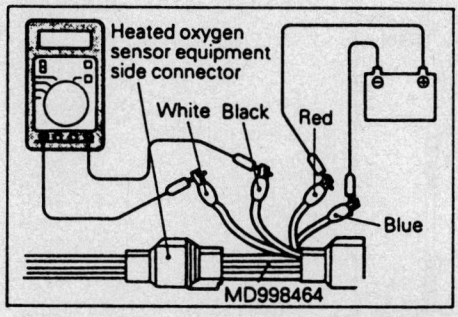

Fig. 196 Heated oxygen sensor inspection. 1993 Colt, Colt Vista, Summit & Summit Wagon w/California emissions, 1994 Colt & Colt Vista, 1994–96 Summit & Summit Wagon & 1995–96 Talon

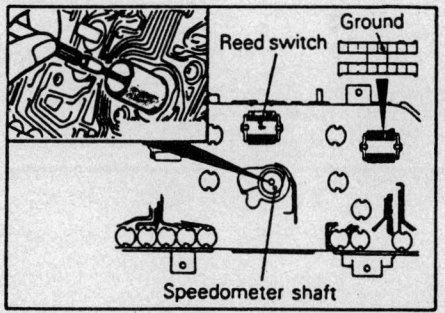

Inspection terminals	Continuity
③-⑤	Yes (approx. 95Ω)
②-⑤	
⑥-⑦	Yes (approx. 35Ω)
⑥-⑧	Yes in 1 direction only

CR1029103359000X

Fig. 197 Control relay inspection chart. Laser & Talon w/1.8L/4-107 engine

Battery voltage		Result
Non-Turbo	When applied	Vacuum leaks
	When discontinued	Vacuum is maintained
Turbo	When applied	Vacuum is maintained
	When discontinued	Vacuum leaks

CR1029100592000X

Fig. 198 Purge control solenoid valve inspection chart

CR1029200593000A

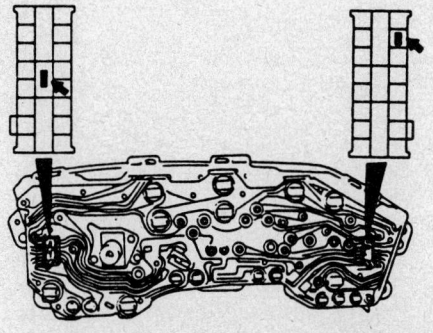

Fig. 199 Reed switch inspection chart. 1993 Colt Vista & Summit Wagon

CR1029100594000A

Fig. 200 Reed switch inspection chart. Laser & Talon

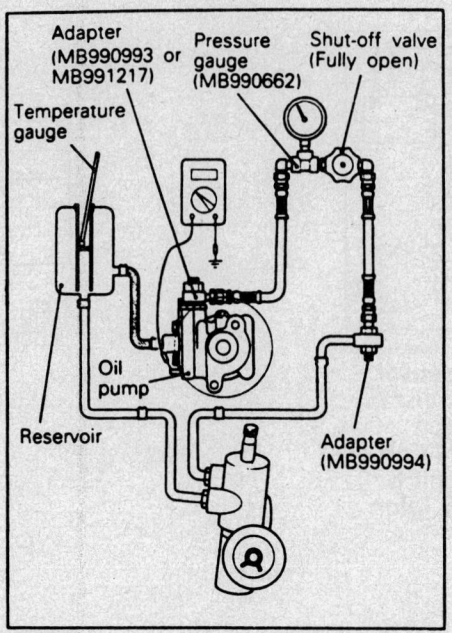

CR1029103360000X

**Fig. 201   Power steering pressure
switch inspection**

1995 AVENGER, CIRRUS, NEON, SEBRING, STRATUS & TALON w/2.0L/4-122 NON-TURBOCHARGED ENGINE

INDEX

	Page No.		Page No.		Page No.
Body Code Identification	8-1	Inactive Diagnostic Trouble Code Condition	8-4	Diagnostic Chart Index	8-11
Description	8-2	System & Component Diagnosis	8-4	Precautions:	8-2
Diagnosis & Testing:	8-2	Charging System Test	8-4	Fuel System Pressure Relief	8-2
Accessing Diagnostic Trouble Codes.	8-2	Diagnostic Trouble Code Tests	8-4	Scan Tool Safety	8-2
Using Malfunction Indicator Lamp (MIL)	8-2	No Diagnostic Trouble Code Tests.	8-4	Sensor Specifications	8-1
Using Scan Tool	8-2	No Start Tests	8-4	System Service:	8-4
Clearing Diagnostic Trouble Codes	8-4	Speed Control Tests	8-4	Component Replacement	8-80
Diagnostic Trouble Code Interpretation	8-2	Verification Tests	8-4	Fuel System Pressure Relief	8-4
		Visual Inspection	8-2	Troubleshooting:	8-2
				Fuel Injectors	8-2

SENSOR SPECIFICATIONS

	Resistance, Ohms	
Component	@68°F	@176°F
Engine Coolant Temperature Sensor	7000—13000	700—1000
Fuel Injector	12	—
Intake Air Temperature Sensor	7000—13000	700—1000

BODY CODE IDENTIFICATION

Model	Code
Avenger	FJ
Cirrus	JA
Neon	PL
Sebring	FJ
Stratus	JA
Talon	F24S

CHRYSLER–Fuel Injection

PRECAUTIONS

FUEL SYSTEM PRESSURE RELIEF

In order to avoid personal injury or vehicle damage, it is important to relieve fuel system pressure prior to servicing any fuel related component. Refer to "Fuel System Pressure Relief" under "System Service" for relief procedure.

SCAN TOOL SAFETY

It is important to note the following when using a DRB III or other scan tool:
1. Do not use scan tool or test leads if tool damage has occurred.
2. Do not touch test leads, tips or circuit components being tested as electrical shock may result.
3. Do not attempt to measure current or voltage that may exceed tool capacity.
4. When disconnecting tool, disconnect "live" or "hot" lead prior to disconnecting common test lead.
5. When measuring current, connect tool in series with load.

DESCRIPTION

The 2.0L/4-122 engine used on these models employs a sequential multi-port electronic fuel injection system. This system is computer controlled and is designed to provide precise air/fuel ratios under all driving conditions.

The Powertrain Control Module (PCM) regulates ignition timing, emission control devices, cooling fan(s), charging system, A/C compressor clutch and torque converter clutch engagement, idle speed, speed control and the air/fuel ratio. Input for operation of these components is provided by various sensors and switches.

Fuel is injected into the intake port above the intake valve through electrically operated injectors. This provides a precise metered injection in a specific sequence that is controlled by the PCM. Primary determinants of injector behavior are engine speed and manifold absolute pressure.

TROUBLESHOOTING

FUEL INJECTORS

Refer to **Fig. 1** for fuel injector troubleshooting procedure.

DIAGNOSIS & TESTING

Visual Inspection

All diagnostic procedures must start with a visual inspection of the vehicle as follows:
1. Inspect all electrical connections and harnesses for damage, loose terminals or terminals that are pushed out of connectors.
2. Look for any added accessories that may affect normal operation of MPI system.
3. Ensure all vacuum lines are connected and in good condition.
4. Ensure intake hoses and air cleaner housing are in place and secured for normal operation.
5. Battery must be fully charged. **Do not disconnect battery until all diagnostic trouble codes are retrieved from MPI system.**
6. The following items cannot be overlooked as possible driveability problems:
   a. Dirt buildup at throttle valve area.
   b. Improper engine timing.
   c. Improper engine vacuum.
   d. Improper engine valve timing.
   e. Improper engine compression.
   f. Incorrect idle speed.
   g. Restricted PCV system.
   h. Restricted exhaust system.
   i. Internal vacuum leaks at power brake booster.
   j. Incorrect fuel pressure.
7. Inspect fuel system components including fuel lines, fuel filter and fuel pump.
8. Inspect ignition system components including spark plugs, high tension cable, crank angle sensor and ignition coil.
9. Inspect emission control devices, including crankcase ventilation system and exhaust gas recirculation systems.

Accessing Diagnostic Trouble Codes

USING SCAN TOOL

Refer to "Precautions" for related safety information.
1. Connect scan tool to diagnostic connector, **Figs. 2 through 4**, then turn ignition switch to On position and access diagnostic trouble code reading screen on tool.
2. Record all diagnostic trouble codes indicated by scan tool. Ensure malfunction indicator lamp (MIL) on instrument panel lights for approximately 2 seconds as a bulb check.
3. Scan tool displays should appear as follows:
   a. **On DRB III scan tool,** screen should display a brief statement of a specific diagnostic trouble code, such as "PCM Failure SRI Mile Not Stored."
   b. **On general scan tools,** diagnostic trouble codes should be displayed as a five character string, such as "P1390."
4. Refer to Diagnostic Chart Index for location of diagnostic procedures corresponding to scan tool diagnostic trouble codes.
5. After repairing condition indicated by tool, erase diagnostic trouble codes as described under "Clearing Diagnostic Trouble Codes."

USING MALFUNCTION INDICATOR LAMP (MIL)

1. Cycle ignition key through an On, Off, On, Off On position sequence within five seconds, then observe MIL flash pattern. Diagnostic trouble codes may be read as follows:
   a. Initial flashes indicate "tens" digit of a diagnostic trouble code; these are followed by a brief pause, after which subsequent flashes indicate "ones" digit. For example, six flashes, followed by a brief pause and two additional flashes, indicates MIL diagnostic trouble code 62 is present.
   b. A longer pause will occur between trouble codes if multiple codes have been logged.
   c. Refer to Diagnostic Chart Index for location of diagnostic procedures corresponding to MIL diagnostic trouble codes.
2. After repairing condition indicated by tool, erase diagnostic trouble codes as described under "Clearing Diagnostic Trouble Codes."

Diagnostic Trouble Code Interpretation

Refer to the Diagnostic Chart Index for diagnostic trouble codes as referenced by the Malfunction Indicator Lamp (MIL), the DRB III scan tool or a general scan tool.

CODE 11—Indicates intermittent loss of crankshaft or camshaft position sensor signal, timing belt has skipped one or more teeth from initial learned value or no crank reference signal was detected during cranking.

CODE 12—Indicates that direct battery input to PCM was disconnected within the last 50 key On cycles.

CODE 13—Indicates that no difference has been recognized between MAP sensor reading and atmospheric pressure from start-up.

CODE 14—Indicates that MAP sensor input voltage is not within acceptable range or that output voltage is too low after key has been placed in Off position.

CODE 15—Indicates that no vehicle speed sensor signal was detected during road load conditions.

CODE 16—Indicates that there is no knock sensor input.

CODE 17—Indicates that closed loop operation temperature was not reached after ten minutes or that engine did not reach operating temperature within twenty minutes of a vehicle speed signal.

CODE 21—Indicates that upstream or downstream oxygen sensor input voltage is maintained above normal operating range or is shorted to ground, upstream oxygen sensor response was slower than minimum required switching frequency, upstream or downstream oxygen sensor input did not indicate rich or lean condition, upstream or downstream oxygen sensor heating element circuit has malfunctioned or downstream oxygen sensor did not

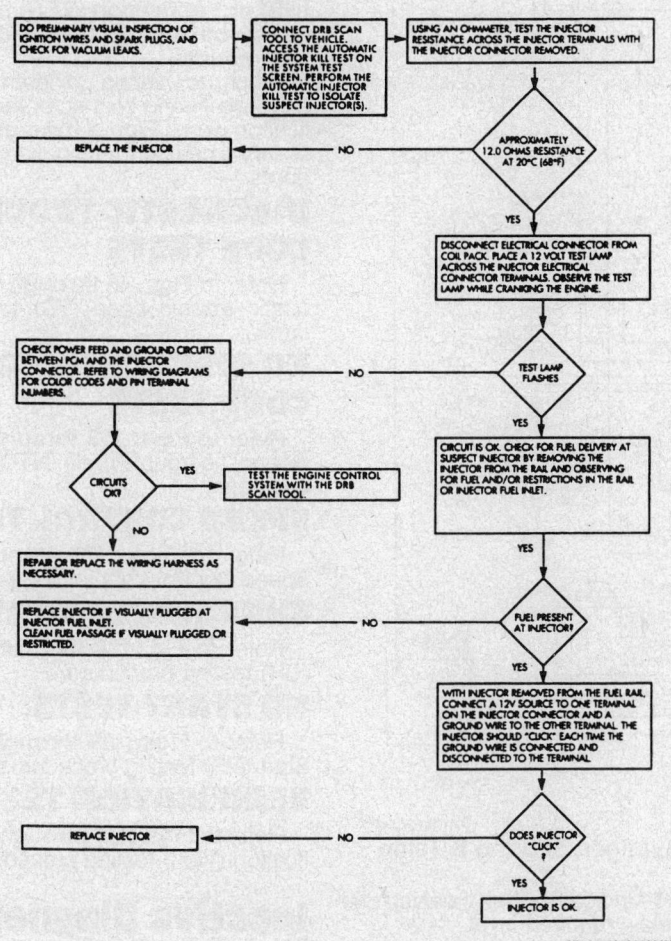

Fig. 1 Fuel injector troubleshooting chart

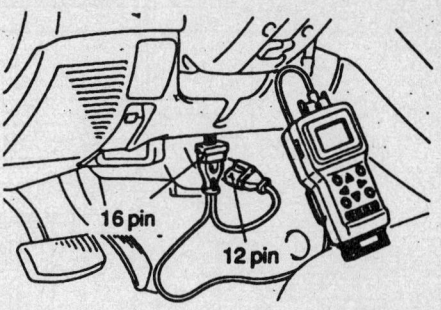

Fig. 2 Diagnostic connector location. Avenger, Sebring & Talon

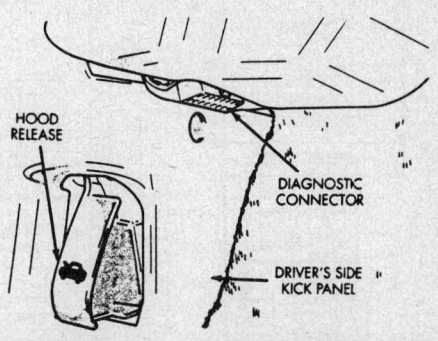

Fig. 3 Diagnostic connector location. Cirrus & Stratus

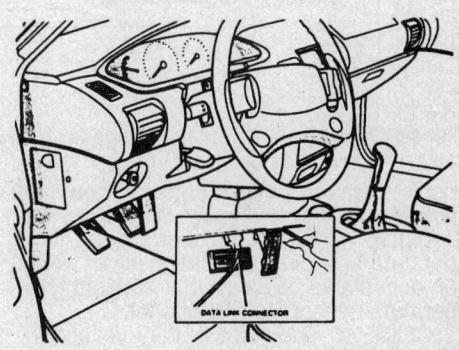

Fig. 4 Diagnostic connector location. Neon

match required response (rich at wide open throttle or lean at fuel shutoff).

CODE 22—Indicates that engine coolant temperature sensor input voltage is not within acceptable range.

CODE 23—Indicates that intake air temperature sensor input voltage is not within acceptable range.

CODE 24—Indicates that TPS signal does not correlate with that of MAP sensor, throttle voltage is too low during part throttle operation or TPS input voltage is not within acceptable range.

CODE 25—Indicates that a short or open has been detected in idle air control motor circuit(s), idle air control motor has remained at zero for more than twenty minutes, a vacuum leak has been detected or engine speed does not correlate with control speed.

CODE 27—Indicates that an injector does not respond electrically to its control signal.

CODE 31—Indicates insufficient vapor flow during evaporative emission system operation at idle or that an open or short exists in duty cycle purge solenoid circuit.

CODE 32—Indicates that a required change in air/fuel ratio was not detected during a diagnostic test.

CODE 33—Indicates an open or short in A/C clutch relay circuit or that pressure transducer input voltage is not within acceptable parameters.

CODE 34—Indicates an open or short in speed control vacuum or vent solenoid circuits or that speed control switch input voltage is not within acceptable parameters.

CODE 35—Indicates an open or short in high or low speed fan control relay circuit.

CODE 41—Indicates an open or short in alternator field control circuit.

CODE 42—Indicates an open or short in fuel pump relay control circuit or in auto shutdown relay circuit, absence of ASD output voltage when ASD relay is energized, open or short between body controller and fuel gauge sending unit or that no movement of fuel level sender was detected.

CODE 43—Indicates that one or more cylinders has misfired or that ignition coil

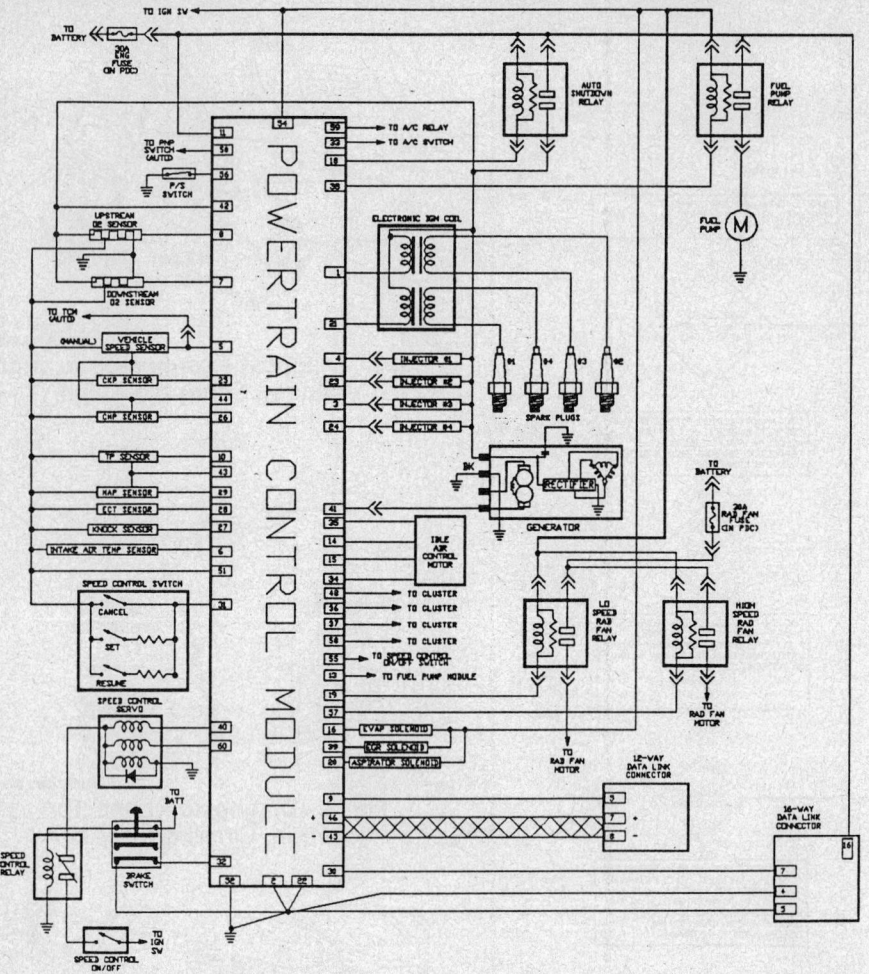

Fig. 5 Fuel injection system wiring diagram. Avenger, Sebring & Talon

peak primary circuit current was not achieved within maximum dwell time.

CODE 44—Indicates that battery temperature sensor input voltage is not within an acceptable range or that ambient temperature sensor input is absent.

CODE 46—Indicates battery voltage input was above target charging voltage during engine operation.

CODE 47—Indicates battery voltage input was below target charging voltage during engine operation and that a significant change was detected in battery voltage during active test of alternator output circuit.

CODE 51—Indicates lean fuel/air mixture by sensing an abnormally rich correction factor.

CODE 52—Indicates rich fuel/air mixture by sensing an abnormally lean correction factor.

CODE 53—Indicates PCM internal fault.

CODE 54—Indicates an absence of camshaft signal during cranking.

CODE 55—Indicates completion of MIL diagnostic trouble code display.

CODE 62—Indicates that an unsuccessful attempt was made to update EMR mileage in PCM EEPROM.

CODE 63—Indicates that an unsuccessful attempt was made by PCM to write to an EEPROM location.

CODE 64—Indicates that catalyst efficiency is below required level.

CODE 65—Indicates that power steering high pressure has been sensed at high speed.

CODE 66—Indicates an absence of communication from body control module.

CODE 71—Indicates that an internal PCM check for 5 volts is being performed.

CODE 77—Indicates that a speed control servo solenoid power feed malfunction has been detected.

Clearing Diagnostic Trouble Codes

Diagnostic trouble codes can be erased using the "Erase Trouble Code Data" screen on the DRB III scan tool or by disconnecting the battery ground cable for at least two minutes.

System & Component Diagnosis

The following tests are used to further diagnose systems and components monitored by the vehicle's on-board diagnostic system and also to test those which are not monitored as such. Prior to performing

any of these tests, inspect electrical and vacuum connections as described under "Visual Inspection."

Always start at the first Diagnostic Trouble Code (TC), No Diagnostic Trouble Code (NTC), Speed Control (SC), Charging System (CH), No Start (NS) or Verification (VER) test. Starting at any other test may yield inaccurate test results.

Refer to wiring diagrams, **Figs. 5 through 7**, and connector terminal identification views, **Figs. 8 through 44**, as necessary when performing diagnostic procedures.

DIAGNOSTIC TROUBLE CODE TESTS

Refer to **Figs. 45 through 152** for diagnostic trouble code (TC) testing procedures.

NO DIAGNOSTIC TROUBLE CODE TESTS

Refer to **Figs. 153 through 174** for no diagnostic trouble code (NTC) testing procedures.

SPEED CONTROL TESTS

Refer to **Figs. 175 through 187** for Speed Control (SC) testing procedures.

CHARGING SYSTEM TEST

Refer to **Fig. 188** for charging system (CH) testing procedure.

NO START TESTS

Refer to **Figs. 189 through 203** for No Start (NS) testing procedures.

VERIFICATION TESTS

Refer to **Figs. 204 through 207** for verification (VER) testing procedures.

Inactive Diagnostic Trouble Code Condition

Performing diagnostic tests as described under "System & Component Diagnosis" should simulate the condition that initially logged the diagnostic trouble code. However, the following may be helpful in identifying an intermittent problem:

1. Visually inspect wire harness connectors that are related to particular diagnostic item. These may exhibit broken, bent, pushed out or corroded terminals.
2. Visually inspect related wiring harnesses for wire chafing, piercing or breakage.

SYSTEM SERVICE

Fuel System Pressure Relief

In order to avoid personal injury or vehicle damage, it is important to relieve fuel system pressure prior to servicing any fuel related component. Proceed as follows:

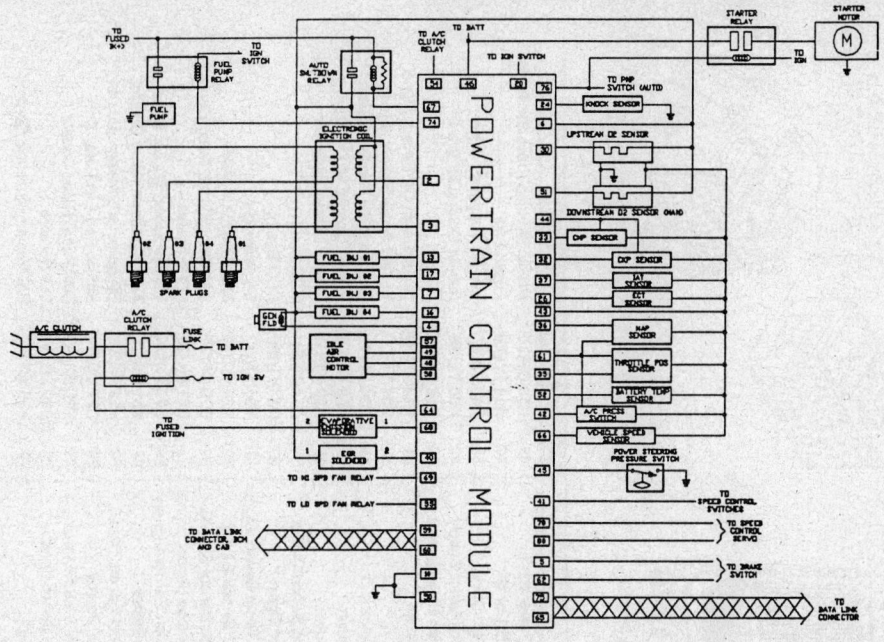

Fig. 6 Fuel injection system wiring diagram. Cirrus & Stratus

CR1029505034000X

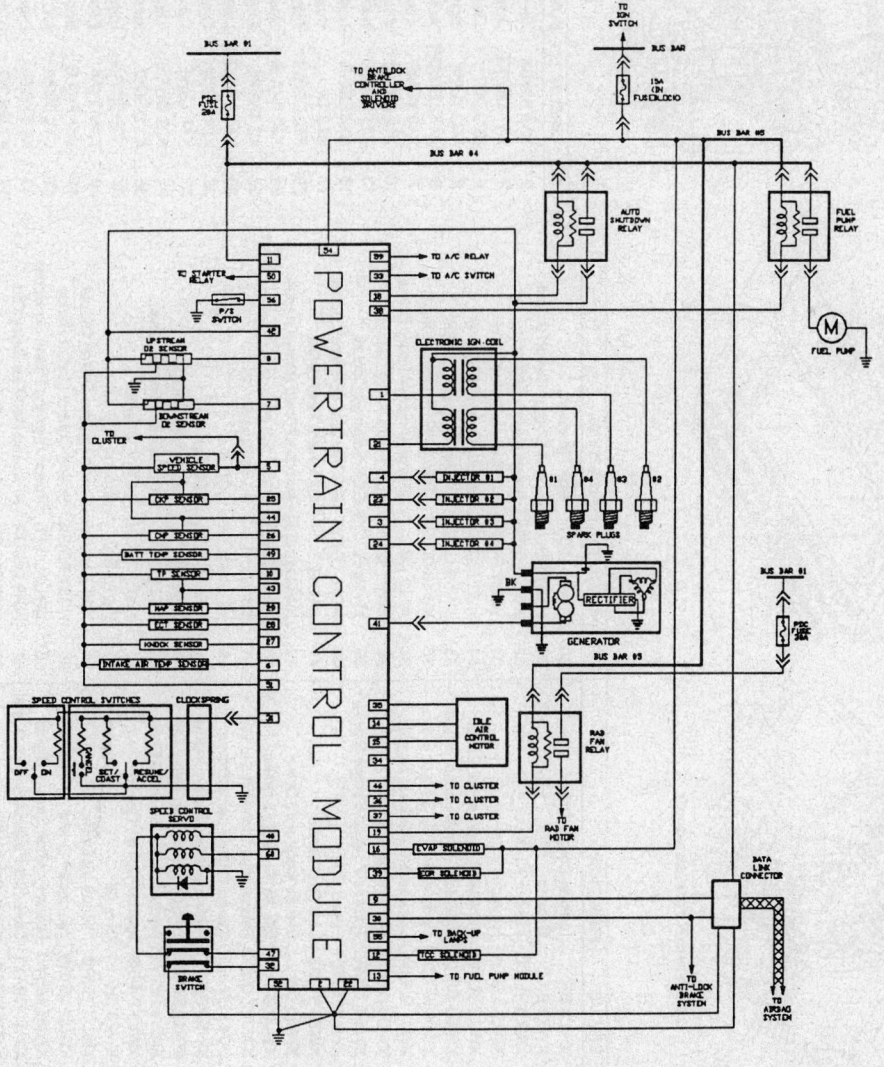

Fig. 7 Fuel injection system wiring diagram. Neon

CR1029505035000X

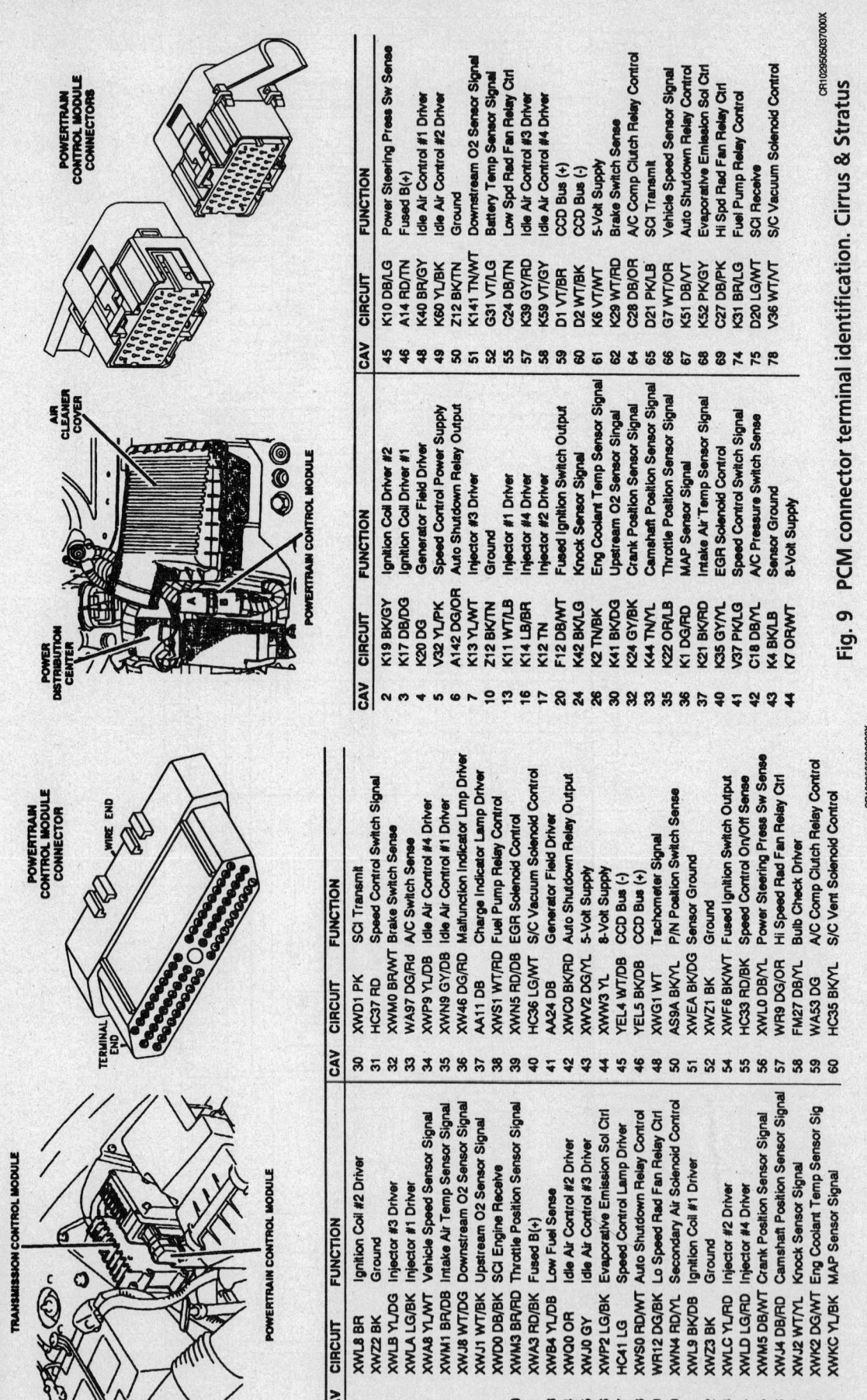

F24S AND FJ22 BODIES

Fig. 8 PCM connector terminal identification. Avenger, Sebring & Talon

CAV	CIRCUIT	FUNCTION
1	XWLB BR	Ignition Coil #2 Driver
2	XWZ2 BK	Ground
3	XWLB YL/DG	Injector #3 Driver
4	XWLA YL/BK	Injector #1 Driver
5	XWA8 YL/WT	Vehicle Speed Sensor Signal
6	XWM1 BR/DB	Intake Air Temp Sensor Signal
7	XWJ8 WT/DG	Downstream O2 Sensor Signal
8	XWJ1 WT/BK	Upstream O2 Sensor Signal
9	XWD0 DB/BK	SCI Engine Receive
10	XWM3 BR/RD	Throttle Position Sensor Signal
11	XWA3 RD/BK	Fused B(+)
13	XWB4 YL/DB	Low Fuel Sense
14	XWQ0 OR	Idle Air Control #2 Driver
15	XWJ0 GY	Idle Air Control #3 Driver
16	XWP2 LG/BK	Evaporative Emission Sol Ctrl
17	HC41 LG	Speed Control Lamp Driver
18	XWS0 RD/WT	Auto Shutdown Relay Control
19	WR12 DG/BK	Lo Speed Rad Fan Relay Ctrl
20	XWN4 RD/YL	Secondary Air Solenoid Control
21	XWL9 BK/DB	Ignition Coil #1 Driver
22	XWZ3 BK	Ground
23	XWLC YL/RD	Injector #2 Driver
24	XWLD LG/RD	Injector #4 Driver
25	XWM5 DB/WT	Crank Position Sensor Signal
26	XWJ4 DB/RD	Camshaft Position Sensor Signal
27	XWJ2 WT/YL	Knock Sensor Signal
28	XWK2 DG/WT	Eng Coolant Temp Sensor Sig
29	XWKC YL/BK	MAP Sensor Signal
30	XWD1 PK	SCI Transmit
31	HC37 RD	Speed Control Switch Signal
32	XWM0 BR/WT	Brake Switch Sense
33	WA97 DG/Rd	A/C Switch Sense
34	XWP9 YL/DB	Idle Air Control #4 Driver
35	XWN9 GY/DB	Idle Air Control #1 Driver
36	XW46 DG/RD	Malfunction Indicator Lmp Driver
37	AA11 DB	Charge Indicator Lamp Driver
38	XWS1 WT/RD	Fuel Pump Relay Driver
39	XWN5 RD/DB	EGR Solenoid Control
40	HC36 LG/WT	S/C Vacuum Solenoid Control
41	AA24 DB	Generator Field Driver
42	XWC0 BK/RD	Auto Shutdown Relay Output
43	XWV2 DG/YL	5-Volt Supply
44	XWW3 YL	8-Volt Supply
45	YEL4 WT/DB	CCD Bus (-)
46	YEL5 BK/DB	CCD Bus (+)
48	AS91 WT	Tachometer Signal
50	AS9A BK/YL	P/N Position Switch Sense
51	XWEA BK/DG	Sensor Ground
52	XWZ1 BK	Ground
54	XWF6 BK/WT	Fused Ignition Switch Output
55	HC33 RD/BK	Speed Control On/Off Sense
56	XWL0 DB/YL	Power Steering Press Sw Sense
57	WR9 DG/OR	Hi Speed Rad Fan Relay Ctrl
58	FM27 DB/YL	Bulb Check Driver
59	WA53 DG	A/C Comp Clutch Relay Control
60	HC35 BK/YL	S/C Vent Solenoid Control

CR102950503000X

Fig. 9 PCM connector terminal identification. Cirrus & Stratus

CAV	CIRCUIT	FUNCTION
2	K19 BK/GY	Ignition Coil Driver #2
3	K17 DB/DG	Ignition Coil Driver #1
4	K20 DG	Generator Field Driver
5	V32 YL/PK	Speed Control Power Supply
6	A142 DG/OR	Auto Shutdown Relay Output
7	K13 YL/WT	Injector #3 Driver
10	Z12 BK/TN	Ground
13	K11 WT/LB	Injector #1 Driver
16	K14 LB/BR	Injector #4 Driver
17	K12 TN	Injector #2 Driver
20	F12 DB/WT	Fused Ignition Switch Output
24	K42 BK/LG	Knock Sensor Signal
26	K2 TN/BK	Eng Coolant Temp Sensor Signal
30	K41 BK/DG	Upstream O2 Sensor Singal
32	K24 GY/BK	Crank Position Sensor Signal
33	K44 TN/YL	Camshaft Position Sensor Signal
35	K22 OR/LB	Throttle Position Sensor Signal
36	K1 DG/RD	MAP Sensor Signal
37	K21 BK/RD	Intake Air Temp Sensor Signal
40	K35 GY/YL	EGR Solenoid Control
41	V37 PK/LG	Speed Control Switch Signal
42	C18 DB/YL	A/C Pressure Switch Sense
43	K4 BK/LB	Sensor Ground
44	K7 OR/WT	8-Volt Supply
45	K10 DB/LG	Power Steering Press Sw Sense
46	A14 RD/TN	Fused B(+)
48	K40 BR/GY	Idle Air Control #1 Driver
49	K60 YL/BK	Idle Air Control #2 Driver
50	Z12 BK/TN	Ground
51	K141 TN/WT	Downstream O2 Sensor Signal
52	G31 VT/LG	Battery Temp Sensor Signal
55	C24 DB/TN	Low Spd Rad Fan Relay Ctrl
57	K39 GY/RD	Idle Air Control #3 Driver
58	K59 VT/GY	Idle Air Control #4 Driver
59	D1 VT/BR	CCD Bus (+)
60	D2 WT/BK	CCD Bus (-)
61	K6 VT/WT	5-Volt Supply
62	K29 WT/RD	Brake Switch Sense
64	C28 DB/OR	A/C Comp Clutch Relay Control
65	D21 PK/LB	SCI Transmit
66	G7 WT/OR	Vehicle Speed Sensor Signal
67	K51 DB/VT	Auto Shutdown Relay Control
68	K52 PK/GY	Evaporative Emission Sol Ctrl
69	C27 DB/PK	Hi Spd Rad Fan Relay Ctrl
74	K31 BR/LG	Fuel Pump Relay Control
75	D20 LG/WT	SCI Receive
78	V36 WT/VT	S/C Vacuum Solenoid Control

CR102950503700X

CAV	WIRE COLOR	DESCRIPTION
1	BK/GY*	IGNITION COIL DRIVER #2
2	BK/TN*	POWER GROUND
3	YL/WT*	FUEL INJECTOR #3
4	WT/DB*	FUEL INJECTOR #1
5	WT/OR*	VEHICLE SPEED SENSOR
6	BK/RD*	INTAKE AIR TEMPERATURE SENSOR
7	DG/BK*	DOWNSTREAM HEATED OXYGEN SENSOR
8	BK/DG*	UPSTREAM HEATED OXYGEN SENSOR
9	LG	DATA LINK
10	OR/DB*	THROTTLE POSITION SENSOR
11	RD/WT*	DIRECT BATTERY VOLTAGE
12		
13		
14	YL/BK*	IDLE AIR CONTROL MOTOR DRIVER #2
15	GY/RD*	IDLE AIR CONTROL MOTOR DRIVER #3
16	PK/BK*	DUTY CYCLE EVAP PURGE SOLENOID
17	OR/BK*	TORQUE CONVERTOR CLUTCH SOLENOID (AUTO. TRANS.)
18	DB/YL*	AUTOMATIC SHUTDOWN RELAY
19	DB/PK*	RADIATOR FAN RELAY
20		
21	DB/YL*	IGNITION COIL DRIVER #1
22	BK/TN*	POWER GROUND
23	TN	FUEL INJECTOR #2
24	LB/BR*	FUEL INJECTOR #4
25	GY/BK*	CRANKSHAFT POSITION SENSOR
26	TN/YL*	CAMSHAFT POSITION SENSOR
27	BK/LG*	KNOCK SENSOR
28	TN/BK*	ENGINE COOLANT TEMPERATURE SENSOR
29	DG/RD*	MAP SENSOR
30	PK	DATA LINK
31	RD/LG*	SPEED CONTROL SELECT SIGNAL
32	WT/PK*	BRAKE SWITCH
33	BR/OR*	A/C PRESSURE SWITCH
34	VT/BK*	IDLE AIR CONTROL MOTOR DRIVER #4
35	BR/WT*	IDLE AIR CONTROL MOTOR DRIVER #1
36	BK/PK*	MALFUNCTION INDICATOR LAMP

CAV	WIRE COLOR	DESCRIPTION
37	TN/BK*	CHARGING SYSTEM INDICATOR LAMP
38	BR	FUEL PUMP RELAY
39	GY/YL*	EGR SOLENOID
40	TN/RD*	SPEED CONTROL VACUUM SOLENOID
41	DG	GENERATOR FIELD
42	DG/OR*	IGNITION SENSE
43	VT/WT*	5 VOLT SUPPLY (FOR MAP AND TPS)
44	OR	9 VOLT SUPPLY
45		
46		
47	YL/RD*	SPEED CONTROL SERVO
48	GY/LB*	TACHOMETER
49	VT/LG	BATTERY TEMPERATURE SENSOR SIGNAL
50	BR/YL*	PARK/NEUTRAL SWITCH
51	BK/LB*	SENSOR GROUND
52	BK/WT*	SIGNAL GROUND
53		
54	LG/BK*	IGNITION SWITCH
55		
56	WT	POWER STEERING PRESSURE SWITCH
57		
58		
59	DB/OR*	A/C COMPRESSOR CLUTCH RELAY
60	LG/RD*	SPEED CONTROL VENT SOLENOID

WIRE COLOR CODES			
LB	LIGHT BLUE	VT	VIOLET
BK	BLACK	LG	LIGHT GREEN	WT	WHITE
BR	BROWN	OR	ORANGE	YL	YELLOW
DB	DARK BLUE	PK	PINK	*	WITH TRACER
DG	DARK GREEN	RD	RED		
GY	GRAY	TN	TAN		

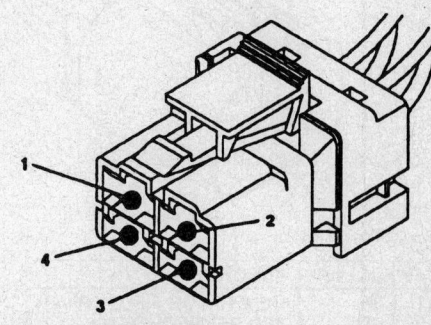

CAV	COLOR	FUNCTION
1	RD/BK	B(+)
2	BR/WT	BRAKE SWITCH SENSE
3	DG	SPEED CONTROL RELAY CONTROL
4	BK	GROUND

CR1029505039000X

Fig. 11 Brake switch connector terminal identification. Avenger, Sebring & Talon

CONNECTOR TERMINAL SIDE SHOWN

CR1029505038000X

Fig. 10 PCM connector terminal identification. Neon

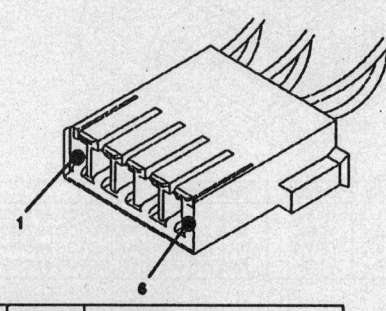

CAV	COLOR	FUNCTION
1	WT/RD	BRAKE SWITCH SENSE
2	BK/LG	GROUND
3	YL/PK	SC POWER SUPPLY
4	DB/RD	SWITCHED SC POWER SUPPLY
5	WT/TN	BRAKE LAMP SWITCH OUTPUT
6	RD/BK	FUSED B(+)

CR1029505040000X

Fig. 12 Brake switch connector terminal identification. Cirrus & Stratus

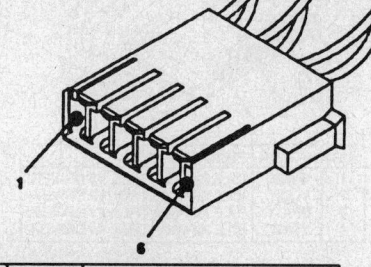

CAV	COLOR	FUNCTION
1	WT/PK	BRAKE SWITCH SENSE
2	BK/TN	GROUND
3	YL/RD	SC POWER SUPPLY
4	WT/BR	SWITCHED SC POWER SUPPLY
5	WT/TN	BRAKE LAMP SWITCH OUTPUT
6	PK/DB	FUSED B(+)

CR1029505041000X

Fig. 13 Brake switch connector terminal identification. Neon

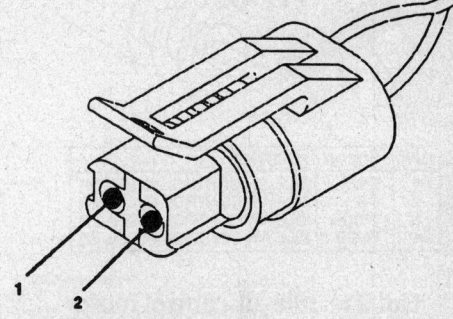

CAV	COLOR	FUNCTION
1	BK/WT	FUSED IGNITION SWITCH OUTPUT
2	RD/DB	EGR SOLENOID CONTROL

CR1029505042000X

Fig. 14 EGR solenoid connector terminal identification. Avenger, Sebring & Talon

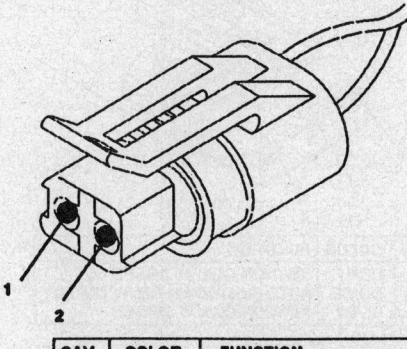

CAV	COLOR	FUNCTION
1	LG/BK	FUSED IGN SW OUTPUT
2	GY/YL	EGR SOLENOID CONTROL

CR1029505043000X

Fig. 15 EGR solenoid connector terminal identification. Neon

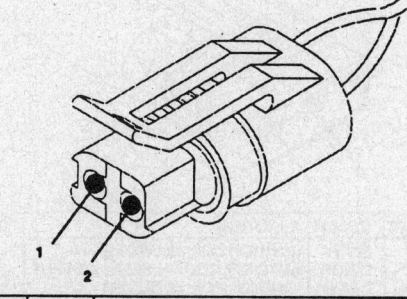

CAV	COLOR	FUNCTION
1	LG/BK	EVAPORATIVE EMISSION SOLENOID CONTROL
2	BK/WT	FUSED IGNITION SWITCH OUTPUT

CR1029505044000X

Fig. 16 Evaporative solenoid connector terminal identification. Avenger, Sebring & Talon

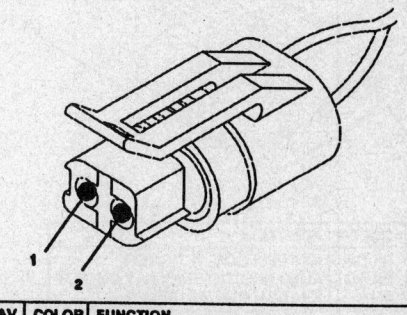

CAV	COLOR	FUNCTION
1	LG/BK	FUSED IGNITION SWITCH OUTPUT
2	PK/BK	EVAPORATIVE EMISSION SOLENOID CONTROL

CR1029505045000X

Fig. 17 Evaporative solenoid connector terminal identification. Cirrus, Neon & Stratus

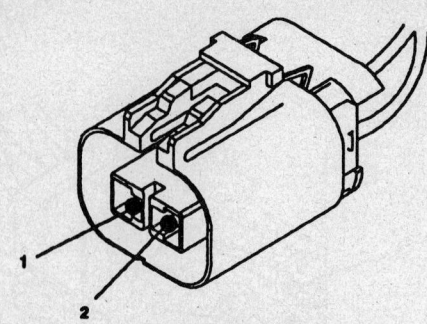

CAV	COLOR	FUNCTION
1	DB	GENERATOR FIELD DRIVER
2	RD	ASD RELAY OUTPUT

CR1029505046000X

Fig. 18 Generator field connector terminal identification. Avenger, Sebring & Talon

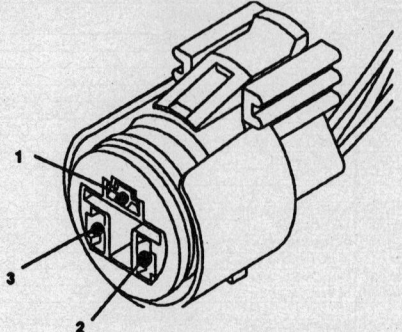

CAV	COLOR	FUNCTION
1	DG/OR	ASD RELAY OUTPUT
2	DG	GENERATOR FIELD DRIVER

CR1029505047000X

Fig. 19 Generator field connector terminal identification. Cirrus & Stratus

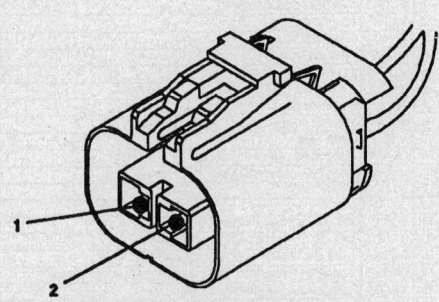

CAV	COLOR	FUNCTION
1	DG	GENERATOR FIELD DRIVER
2	DG/OR	ASD RELAY OUTPUT

CR1029505048000X

Fig. 20 Generator field connector terminal identification. Neon

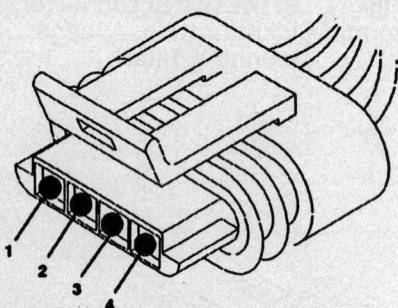

CAV	COLOR	FUNCTION
1	DG	IDLE AIR CONTROL #3 DRIVER
2	OR	IDLE AIR CONTROL #2 DRIVER
3	GY/DB	IDLE AIR CONTROL #1 DRIVER
4	YL/DB	IDLE AIR CONTROL #4 DRIVER

CR1029505049000X

Fig. 21 Idle air control motor connector terminal identification. Avenger, Sebring & Talon

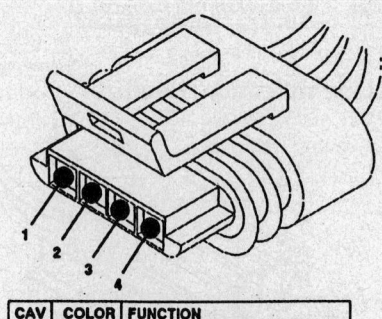

CAV	COLOR	FUNCTION
1	GY/RD	IDLE AIR CONTROL #3 DRIVER
2	YL/BK	IDLE AIR CONTROL #2 DRIVER
3	BR/GY	IDLE AIR CONTROL #1 DRIVER
4	VT/GY	IDLE AIR CONTROL #4 DRIVER

CR1029505050000X

Fig. 22 Idle air control motor connector terminal identification. Cirrus & Stratus

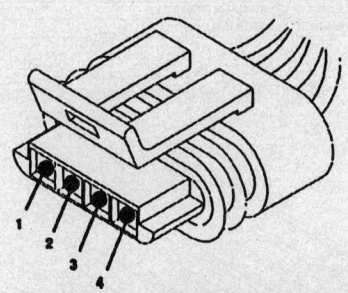

CAV	COLOR	FUNCTION
1	GY/RD	IDLE AIR CONTROL MOTOR #3 DRIVER
2	YL/BK	IDLE AIR CONTROL MOTOR #2 DRIVER
3	BR/WT	IDLE AIR CONTROL MOTOR #1 DRIVER
4	VT/BK	IDLE AIR CONTROL MOTOR #4 DRIVER

CR1029505051000X

Fig. 23 Idle air control motor connector terminal identification. Neon

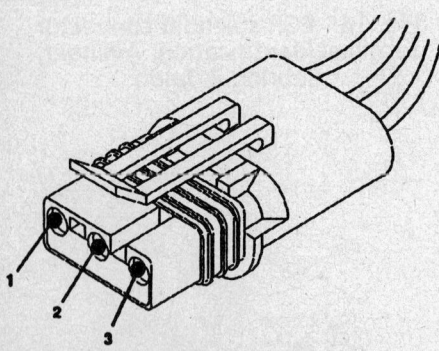

CAV	COLOR	FUNCTION
1	BK/DB	IGNITION COIL #1 DRIVER
2	BK/RD	AUTO SHUTDOWN RELAY OUTPUT
3	BR	IGNITION COIL #2 DRIVER

CR1029505052000X

Fig. 24 Ignition coil connector terminal identification. Avenger, Sebring & Talon

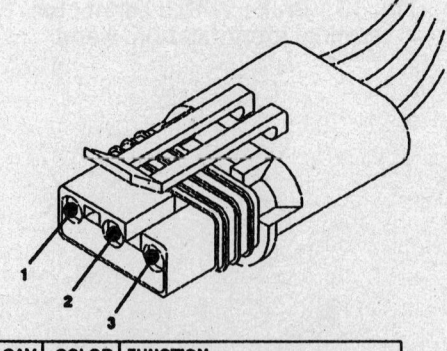

CAV	COLOR	FUNCTION
1	BK/GY	IGNITION COIL #2 DRIVER
2	DG/OR	AUTO SHUTDOWN RELAY OUTPUT
3	DB/DG	IGNITION COIL #1 DRIVER

CR1029505053000X

Fig. 25 Ignition coil connector terminal identification. Cirrus & Stratus

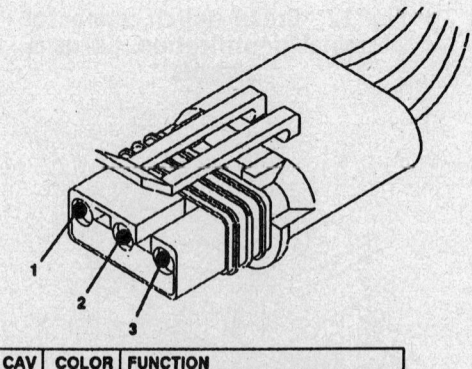

CAV	COLOR	FUNCTION
1	DB/*	IGNITION COIL #1 DRIVER
2	DG/OR	AUTO SHUTDOWN RELAY OUTPUT
3	BK/GY	IGNITION COIL #2 DRIVER

CR1029505054000X

Fig. 26 Ignition coil connector terminal identification. Neon

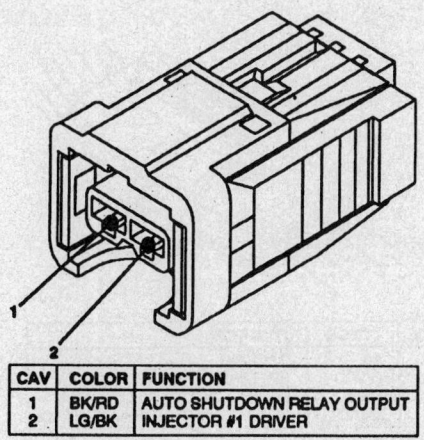

CAV	COLOR	FUNCTION
1	BK/RD	AUTO SHUTDOWN RELAY OUTPUT
2	LG/BK	INJECTOR #1 DRIVER

CR1029505055000X

Fig. 27 Injector No. 1 connector terminal identification. Avenger, Sebring & Talon

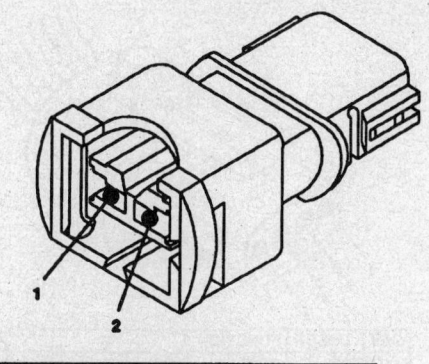

CAV	COLOR	FUNCTION
1	WT/LB	INJECTOR #1 DRIVER
2	DG/OR	AUTO SHUTDOWN RELAY OUTPUT

CR1029505056000X

Fig. 28 Injector No. 1 connector terminal identification. Cirrus, Neon & Stratus

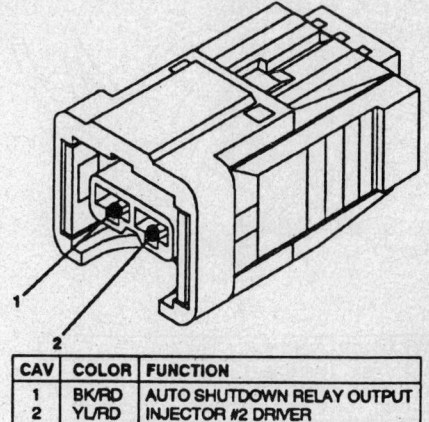

CAV	COLOR	FUNCTION
1	BK/RD	AUTO SHUTDOWN RELAY OUTPUT
2	YL/RD	INJECTOR #2 DRIVER

CR1029505057000X

Fig. 29 Injector No. 2 connector terminal identification. Avenger, Sebring & Talon

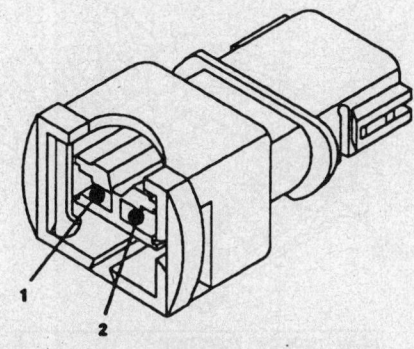

CAV	COLOR	FUNCTION
1	DG/OR	AUTO SHUTDOWN RELAY OUTPUT
2	TN	INJECTOR #2 DRIVER

CR1029505058000X

Fig. 30 Injector No. 2 connector terminal identification. Cirrus, Neon & Stratus

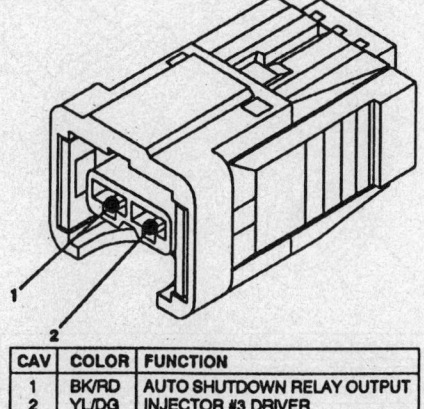

CAV	COLOR	FUNCTION
1	BK/RD	AUTO SHUTDOWN RELAY OUTPUT
2	YL/DG	INJECTOR #3 DRIVER

CR1029505059000X

Fig. 31 Injector No. 3 connector terminal identification. Avenger, Sebring & Talon

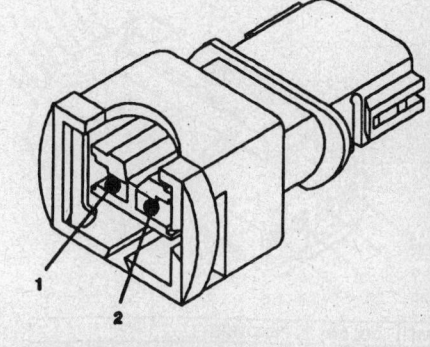

CAV	COLOR	FUNCTION
1	YL/WT	INJECTOR #3 DRIVER
2	DG/OR	AUTO SHUTDOWN RELAY OUTPUT

CR1029505060000X

Fig. 32 Injector No. 3 connector terminal identification. Cirrus, Neon & Stratus

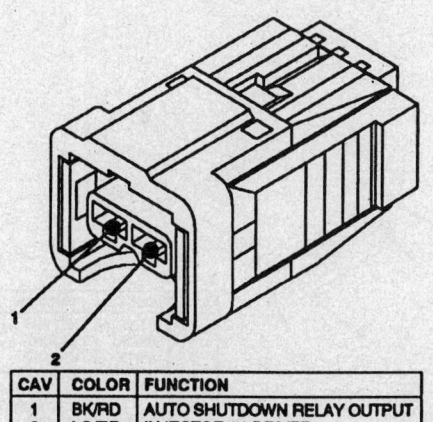

CAV	COLOR	FUNCTION
1	BK/RD	AUTO SHUTDOWN RELAY OUTPUT
2	LG/RD	INJECTOR #4 DRIVER

CR1029505061000X

Fig. 33 Injector No. 4 connector terminal identification. Avenger, Sebring & Talon

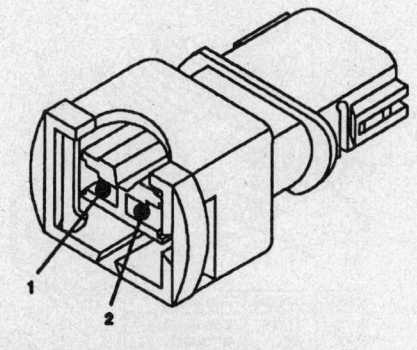

CAV	COLOR	FUNCTION
1	DG/OR	AUTO SHUTDOWN RELAY OUTPUT
2	LB/BR	INJECTOR #4 DRIVER

CR1029505062000X

Fig. 34 Injector No. 4 connector terminal identification. Cirrus, Neon & Stratus

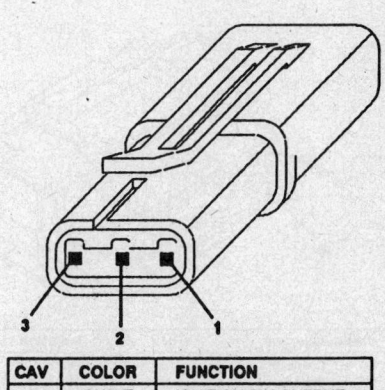

CAV	COLOR	FUNCTION
1	BK/WT	IGNITION SW OUTPUT
2	BK/YL	PNP SIGNAL
3	RD	TRANS RANGE SWITCH

CR1029505063000X

Fig. 35 Park/neutral position switch connector terminal identification. Avenger, Sebring & Talon

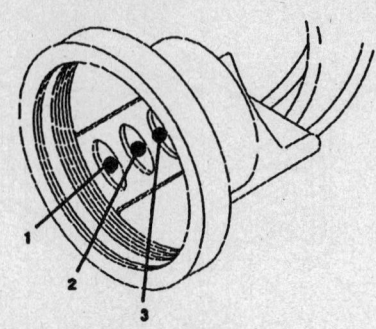

CAV	COLOR	FUNCTION
1	VT/BK	REVERSE LAMP SENSE
2	BR/YL	PARK/NEUTRAL POSITION SW SENSE
3	WT	FUSED IGNITION SWITCH OUTPUT

CR1029505064000X

Fig. 36   Park/neutral position switch connector terminal identification. Neon

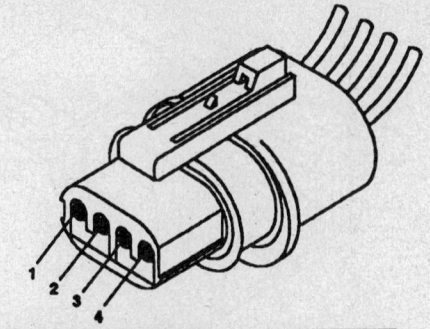

CAV	COLOR	FUNCTION
1	BK	GROUND
2	DB/WT	SC RELAY OUTPUT
3	BK/YL	SC VENT SEOLNOID CONTROL
4	LG/WT	SC VACUUM SOLENOID CONTROL

CR1029505065000X

Fig. 37   Speed control servo connector terminal identification. Avenger, Sebring & Talon

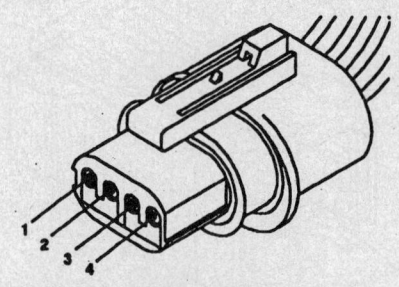

CAV	COLOR	FUNCTION
1	BK	GROUND
2	DB/RD	SWITCHED SC POWER SUPPLY
3	LG/RD	SC VENT SOLENOID CONTROL
4	WT/VT	SC VACUUM SOLENOID CONTROL

CR1029505066000X

Fig. 38   Speed control servo connector terminal identification. Cirrus & Stratus

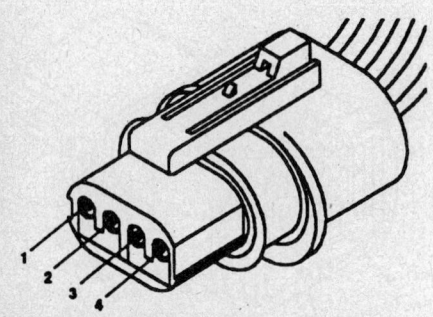

CAV	COLOR	FUNCTION
1	BK	GROUND
2	WT/BR	SWITCHED SC POWER SUPPLY
3	LG/RD	SC VENT SOLENOID CONTROL
4	TN/RD	SC VACUUM SOLENOID CONTROL

CR1029505067000X

Fig. 39   Speed control servo connector terminal identification. Neon

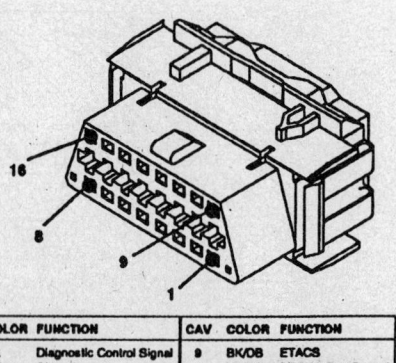

CAV	COLOR	FUNCTION
1	OR/BK	TCC SOLENOID CONTROL
2	LG/BK	FUSED IGNITION SWITCH OUTPUT

CR1029505068000X

Fig. 40   TCC solenoid connector terminal identification. Neon

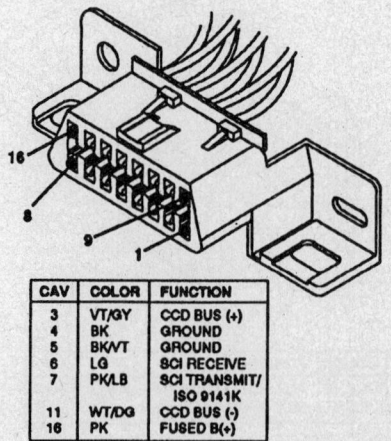

CAV	COLOR	FUNCTION
5	DB/BK	SCI - II ENG RECEIVE
6	DB/RD	SCI - II EATX RECEIVE
7	BK/DB	CCD BUS (+)
8	WT/DB	CCD BUS (-)

CR1029505069000X

Fig. 41   12-way diagnostic connector terminal identification. Avenger, Sebring & Talon

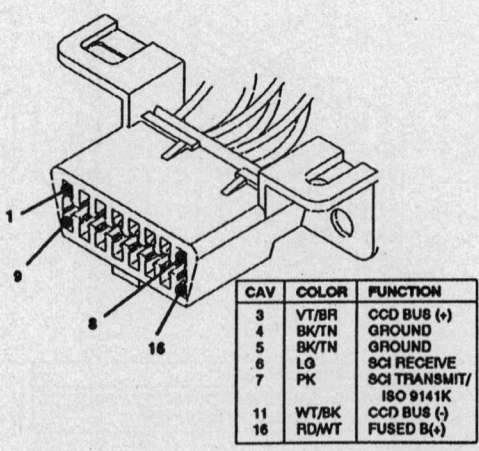

CAV	COLOR	FUNCTION	CAV	COLOR	FUNCTION
1	YL	Diagnostic Control Signal	9	BK/DB	ETACS
4	BK	Ground	12	YL/DG	SRS Air Bag Control
5	BK/WT	Ground	13	YL/BK	Speed Control Ctrl
6	YL/RD	Transmission Control	14	YL/WT	Simulated VSS
7	PK	SCI - II Transmit	16	RD/BK	Fused B(+)
8	YL/RD	Brake Control			

CR1029505070000X

Fig. 42   16-way diagnostic connector terminal identification. Avenger, Sebring & Talon

CAV	COLOR	FUNCTION
3	VT/GY	CCD BUS (+)
4	BK	GROUND
5	BK/VT	GROUND
6	LG	SCI RECEIVE
7	PK/LB	SCI TRANSMIT/ ISO 9141K
11	WT/DG	CCD BUS (-)
16	PK	FUSED B(+)

CR1029505071000X

Fig. 43   Diagnostic connector terminal identification. Cirrus & Stratus

CAV	COLOR	FUNCTION
3	VT/BR	CCD BUS (+)
4	BK/TN	GROUND
5	BK/TN	GROUND
6	LG	SCI RECEIVE
7	PK	SCI TRANSMIT/ ISO 9141K
11	WT/BK	CCD BUS (-)
16	RD/WT	FUSED B(+)

CR1029505072000X

Fig. 44   Diagnostic connector terminal identification. Neon

DIAGNOSTIC CHART INDEX

Test	Description	MIL Code	Scan Tool Code	Model	Page No. 8-	Fig. No.
TC-1A	Checking System For Diagnostic Trouble Codes	—	—	All	14	45
TC-2A	No Crank Reference Signal At PCM	11	—	All	15	46
TC-2B	No Crank Reference Signal At PCM	11	—	All	16	47
TC-3A	No Cam Signal At PCM	54	P0340	All	16	48
TC-4A	No Change In MAP From Start To Run	13	P1297	All	16	49
TC-5A	MAP Sensor Voltage Too Low	14	P0107	All	17	50
TC-6A	MAP Sensor Voltage Too High	14	P0108	All	17	51
TC-7A	No 5 Volts To MAP Sensor	14	P1296	Cirrus & Stratus	18	52
TC-8A	5 Volt Supply Output Too Low	71	P1496	Cirrus & Stratus	18	53
TC-8B	5 Volt Supply Output Too Low	71	P1496	All	19	54
TC-9A	No Vehicle Speed Sensor Signal	15	P0500	All	19	55
TC-9B	No Vehicle Speed Sensor Signal	15	P0500	All	20	56
TC-9C	No Vehicle Speed Sensor Signal	15	P0500	All	20	57
TC-10A	Upstream O2 Sensor Shorted To Voltage	21	P0132	All	21	58
TC-11A	Upstream O2 Sensor Stays At Center	21	P0134	All	21	59
TC-12A	Upstream O2 Sensor Heater Failure	21	P0135	All	21	60
TC-13A	Upstream O2 Sensor Slow Response	21	P0133	All	22	61
TC-14A	Upstream O2 Sensor Voltage Shorted To Ground	21	P0131	Cirrus & Stratus	22	62
TC-15A	Fuel System Rich	52	P0172	All	22	63
TC-16A	Fuel System Lean	51	P0171	All	23	64
TC-17A	Downstream O2 Sensor Shorted To Voltage	21	P0138	All	23	65
TC-18A	Downstream O2 Sensor Stays At Center	21	P0140	Cirrus & Stratus	23	66
TC-19A	Downstream O2 Sensor Heater Failure	21	P0141	All	24	67
TC-20A	Downstream O2 Sensor Slow Response	21	P0139	All	24	68
TC-21A	Downstream O2 Sensor Voltage Shorted To Ground	21	P0137	Cirrus & Stratus	24	69
TC-22A	Catalytic Converter Efficiency Failure	64	P0422	All	25	70
TC-23A	ECT Sensor Voltage Too Low	22	P0117	All	25	71
TC-24A	ECT Sensor Voltage Too High	22	P0118	All	25	72
TC-25A	Closed Loop Temp Not Reached	17	P0125	All	26	73
TC-26A	Intake Air Temp Sensor Voltage Low	23	P0112	All	26	74
TC-27A	Intake Air Temp Sensor Voltage High	23	P0113	All	26	75
TC-28A	Park/Neutral Switch Failure	37	P1899	All	27	76
TC-29A	Knock Sensor No. 1 Circuit	16	—	All	27	77
TC-30A	TPS Voltage Low	24	P0122	All	28	78
TC-31A	TPS Voltage High	24	P0123	All	29	79
TC-32A	TPS Voltage Does Not Agree With MAP	24	P0121	All	29	80
TC-33A	No 5 Volts To TPS	24	P1295	Cirrus & Stratus	30	81
TC-34A	Idle Air Control Motor Circuits	25	P0505	All	30	82
TC-34B	Idle Air Control Motor Circuits	25	P0505	All	31	83
TC-34C	Idle Air Control Motor Circuits	25	P0505	All	31	84
TC-34D	Idle Air Control Motor Circuits	25	P0505	All	31	85
TC-34E	Idle Air Control Motor Circuits	25	P0505	All	31	86
TC-35A	Target Idle Not Reached	25	P1294	All	32	87
TC-35B	Target Idle Not Reached	25	P1294	All	32	88
TC-36A	Vacuum Leak Found, IAC Fully Seated	25	P1299	All	32	89
TC-37A	Air Switching Solenoid Circuit	36	P0412	Avenger, Sebring & Talon	33	90
TC-38A	Injector No. 1 Control Circuit	27	P0201	All	33	91
TC-38B	Injector No. 1 Control Circuit	27	P0201	All	33	92
TC-39A	Injector No. 2 Control Circuit	27	P0202	All	34	93
TC-40A	Injector No. 3 Control Circuit	27	P0203	All	34	94
TC-41A	Injector No. 4 Control Circuit	27	P0204	All	34	95
TC-42A	Timing Belt Skipped 1 Tooth Or More	11	P1390	All	35	96

Continued

MULTI-POINT FUEL INJECTION (1995 AVENGER, CIRRUS, NEON, SEBRING, STRATUS & TALON w/NON-TURBOCHARGED 2.0L/4-122 ENGINE)

DIAGNOSTIC CHART INDEX—Continued

Test	Description	MIL Code	Scan Tool Code	Model	Page No. 8-	Fig. No.
TC-43A	PCM Failure SRI Mile Not Stored	62	—	All	35	97
TC-44A	PCM Failure EEPROM Write Denied	63	—	All	35	98
TC-45A	EGR Solenoid Circuit	32	P0403	All	35	99
TC-46A	EGR System Failure	32	P0401	All	36	100
TC-47A	Evap Solenoid Circuit	31	P0443	All	36	101
TC-48A	Evap Purge Flow Monitor Failure	31	P0441	All	37	102
TC-48B	Evap Purge Flow Monitor Failure	31	P0441	All	38	103
TC-49A	Torque Converter Clutch Solenoid Circuit	37	P0743	Neon	38	104
TC-50A	Torque Converter Clutch, No RPM Drop At Lockup	37	P0740	Neon	38	105
TC-51A	Too Little Secondary Air, Or Too Much Secondary Air	36	—	Avenger, Sebring & Talon	39	106
TC-52A	A/C Clutch Relay Circuit	33	—	All	39	107
TC-53A	A/C Pressure Sensor Volts Too Low	33	—	Cirrus & Stratus	40	108
TC-54A	A/C Pressure Sensor Volts Too High	33	—	Cirrus & Stratus	40	109
TC-55A	No 5 Volts To A/C Pressure Sensor	33	—	Cirrus & Stratus	41	110
TC-56A	Radiator Fan Control Relay Circuit	35	P1491	Neon	41	111
TC-57A	High Speed Fan Control Relay Circuit	35	P1489	All	42	112
TC-58A	Low Speed Fan Control Relay Circuit	35	P1490	All	42	113
TC-59A	Auto Shutdown Relay Control Circuit	42	—	All	42	114
TC-60A	No ASD Relay Output Voltage At PCM	42	—	All	43	115
TC-61A	Fuel Pump Relay Control Circuit	42	—	All	44	116
TC-62A	Fuel Level Sending Unit Volts Too Low	42	—	All	44	117
TC-62B	Fuel Level Sending Unit Volts Too Low	42	—	All	45	118
TC-62C	Fuel Level Sending Unit Volts Too Low	42	—	All	45	119
TC-63A	Fuel Level Sending Unit Volts Too High	42	—	All	45	120
TC-63B	Fuel Level Sending Unit Volts Too High	42	—	All	46	121
TC-63C	Fuel Level Sending Unit Volts Too High	42	—	All	46	122
TC-64A	Fuel Level Unit No Change Over Miles	42	—	All	47	123
TC-64B	Fuel Level Unit No Change Over Miles	42	—	All	47	124
TC-64C	Fuel Level Unit No Change Over Miles	42	—	All	47	125
TC-65A	Ignition Coil No. 1 Primary Circuit	43	P0351	All	48	126
TC-65B	Ignition Coil No. 1 Primary Circuit	43	P0351	All	48	127
TC-66A	Ignition Coil No. 2 Primary Circuit	43	P0352	All	48	128
TC-66B	Ignition Coil No. 2 Primary Circuit	43	P0352	All	49	129
TC-67A	Battery Temp Sensor Volts Out Of Limit	44	—	All	49	130
TC-67B	Battery Temp Sensor Volts Out Of Limit	44	—	All	49	131
TC-67C	Battery Temp Sensor Volts Out Of Limit	44	—	All	50	132
TC-68A	Generator Field Not Switching Properly	41	—	All	50	133
TC-69A	Charging System Voltage Too Low	47	—	All	50	134
TC-70A	Charging System Voltage Too High	46	—	All	51	135
TC-70B	Charging System Voltage Too High	46	—	All	51	136
TC-71A	Speed Control Solenoid Circuits	34	—	All	52	137
TC-71B	Speed Control Solenoid Circuits	34	—	All	52	138
TC-71C	Speed Control Solenoid Circuits	34	—	All	52	139
TC-72A	Speed Control Switch Always Low	34	—	All	53	140
TC-73A	Speed Control Switch Always High	34	—	All	53	141
TC-73B	Speed Control Switch Always High	34	—	All	53	142
TC-74A	Power Steering Switch Failure	65	P0551	All	54	143
TC-74B	Power Steering Switch Failure	65	P0551	All	54	144
TC-75A	Multiple Cylinder Misfire	43	P0300	All	54	145
TC-76A	Cylinder No. 1 Misfire	43	P0301	All	55	146
TC-76A	Cylinder No. 2 Misfire	43	P0302	All	55	146

Continued

DIAGNOSTIC CHART INDEX–Continued

Test	Description	MIL Code	Scan Tool Code	Model	Page No. 8-	Fig. No.
TC-76A	Cylinder No. 3 Misfire	43	P0303	All	55	146
TC-76A	Cylinder No. 4 Misfire	43	P0304	All	55	146
TC-77A	Intermittent Loss Of CMP Or CKP	11	P1391	All	56	147
TC-77B	Intermittent Loss Of CMP Or CKP	11	P1391	All	56	148
TC-77C	Intermittent Loss Of CMP Or CKP	11	P1391	All	57	149
TC-78A	Brake Switch Circuit	65	P0703	All	57	150
TC-79A	No CCD Messages From TCM	66	P1698	All	58	151
TC-80A	No CCD Message From Body Control Module	66	—	Cirrus & Stratus	58	152
NTC-1A	No Trouble Code Test Menu	—	—	All	59	153
NTC-2A	Checking Secondary Ignition & Timing	—	—	All	59	154
NTC-3A	Checking Fuel Pressure	—	—	All	59	155
NTC-3B	Checking Fuel Pressure	—	—	All	60	156
NTC-3C	Checking Fuel Pressure	—	—	All	60	157
NTC-4A	Checking Coolant Sensor Calibration & Radiator Fan Operation	—	—	All	61	158
NTC-5A	Checking Throttle Position Sensor Calibration	—	—	All	61	159
NTC-6A	Checking MAP Sensor Calibration	—	—	All	61	160
NTC-7A	Checking For Oxygen Sensor Switching	—	—	All	61	161
NTC-7B	Checking For Oxygen Sensor Switching	—	—	All	62	162
NTC-8A	Checking Oxygen Sensor Heater	—	—	All	62	163
NTC-9A	Checking Idle Air Control Motor	—	—	All	63	164
NTC-10A	Checking Solenoid Operation	—	—	All	63	165
NTC-11A	Checking Park/Neutral Position Switch	—	—	All	63	166
NTC-12A	Checking PCM Power And Ground Circuits	—	—	All	63	167
NTC-13A	Checking Evaporative Emission System	—	—	All	64	168
NTC-14A	Checking EGR System	—	—	All	64	169
NTC-15A	Checking Engine Vacuum	—	—	All	64	170
NTC-16A	Checking Intake Air Temperature Sensor	—	—	All	64	171
NTC-17A	Checking Timing Belt Alignment	—	—	All	65	172
NTC-18A	Checking Minimum Idle Air Flow	—	—	All	65	173
NTC-19A	Checking Engine Mechanical Systems	—	—	All	65	174
SC-1A	Checking Speed Control Operation	—	—	Cirrus, Neon & Stratus	65	175
SC-1B	Checking Speed Control Operation	—	—	Cirrus, Neon & Stratus	66	176
SC-2A	Checking Speed Control On/Off Switch	—	—	Cirrus, Neon & Stratus	66	177
SC-3A	Checking Speed Control Brake Switch Output	—	—	Cirrus, Neon & Stratus	67	178
SC-4A	Checking Park/Neutral Position Switch	—	—	Cirrus, Neon & Stratus	67	179
SC-5A	Checking For A Speed Control Denied Message	—	—	Cirrus, Neon & Stratus	67	180
SC-6A	Checking Speed Control Set/Resume Switch	—	—	Avenger, Sebring & Talon	67	181
SC-6B	Checking Speed Control Set/Resume Switch	—	—	Avenger, Sebring & Talon	68	182
SC-6C	Checking Speed Control Set/Resume Switch	—	—	Avenger, Sebring & Talon	68	183
SC-7A	Checking Speed Control On/Off Switch	—	—	Avenger, Sebring & Talon	68	184
SC-8A	Checking Brake Switch Sense	—	—	Avenger, Sebring & Talon	69	185
SC-9A	Checking Park/Neutral Position Switch	—	—	Avenger, Sebring & Talon	69	186

Continued

DIAGNOSTIC CHART INDEX–Continued

Test	Description	MIL Code	Scan Tool Code	Model	Page No. 8-	Fig. No.
SC-10A	Checking Speed Control Relay Output	—	—	Avenger, Sebring & Talon	69	187
CH-1A	Charging System No Code Test	—	—	All	70	188
NS-1A	Qualifying A No Start Condition	—	—	All	70	189
NS-2A	Checking Fuel System	—	—	All	71	190
NS-3A	Checking Engine Mechanical Systems	—	—	All	72	191
NS-4A	Repairing Low Fuel Pressure	—	—	All	72	192
NS-4B	Repairing High Fuel Pressure	—	—	All	73	193
NS-4C	Repairing High Fuel Pressure	—	—	All	73	194
NS-5A	Checking Fuel Pump	—	—	All	73	195
NS-6A	Repairing A "No Response" Condition	—	—	All	74	196
NS-6B	Repairing A "No Response" Condition	—	—	All	76	197
NS-6C	Repairing A "No Response" Condition	—	—	All	76	198
NS-6D	Repairing A "No Response" Condition	—	—	All	77	199
NS-7A	Checking Idle Air Control Motor	—	—	All	78	200
NS-8A	Repairing A Start & Stall Condition	—	—	All	78	201
NS-9A	Repairing A No Crank Condition	—	—	All	78	202
NS-9B	Repairing A No Crank Condition	—	—	All	79	203
VER-1A	No Start Verification	—	—	All	79	204
VER-2A	Road Test Verification	—	—	All	79	205
VER-3A	Charging Verification	—	—	All	80	206
VER-4A	Speed Control Verification	—	—	All	80	207

NOTE: The battery must be fully charged for any test.

Attempt to start the engine. Crank for up to 10 seconds if necessary.

Connect the DRB to the engine diagnostic connector. Write down the trouble codes that are displayed.

If the DRB screen displays "No Response", go to TEST NS-6A.

If trouble code messages are displayed, refer to the trouble code list for the appropriate test.

If there are no trouble codes displayed, refer to one of the following:

For Driveability problems NTC-1A
For No Start problems NS-1A
For Speed Control problems SC-1A
For Charging problems CH-1A

DRB TROUBLE CODE (DTC) DISPLAYED	SCAN TOOL	MIL CODE	DIAGNOSTIC TEST
NO CRANK REFERENCE SIGNAL AT PCM	N/A	11	TC- 2A
NO CAM SIGNAL AT PCM	P0340	54	TC- 3A
NO CHANGE IN MAP FROM START TO RUN	P1297	13	TC- 4A
MAP SENSOR VOLTAGE TOO LOW	P0107	14	TC- 5A
MAP SENSOR VOLTAGE TOO HIGH	P0108	14	TC- 6A
NO 5 VOLTS TO MAP SENSOR	P1296	14	TC- 7A
5-VOLT SUPPLY OUTPUT TOO LOW	P1496	71	TC- 8A
NO VEHICLE SPEED SENSOR SIGNAL	P0500	15	TC- 9A
UPSTREAM O2 SENSOR SHORTED TO VOLTAGE	P0132	21	TC-10A
UPSTREAM O2 SENSOR STAYS AT CENTER	P0134	21	TC-11A
UPSTREAM O2 SENSOR HEATER FAILURE	P0135	21	TC-12A
UPSTREAM O2 SENSOR SLOW RESPONSE	P0133	21	TC-13A
UPSTREAM O2S VOLTAGE SHORTED TO GROUND	P0131	21	TC-14A
FUEL SYSTEM RICH	P0172	52	TC-15A
FUEL SYSTEM LEAN	P0171	51	TC-16A
DOWNSTREAM O2 SENSOR SHORTED TO VOLTAGE	P0138	21	TC-17A
DOWNSTREAM O2 SENSOR STAYS AT CENTER	P0140	21	TC-18A
DOWNSTREAM O2 SENSOR HEATER FAILURE	P0141	21	TC-19A
DOWNSTREAM O2 SENSOR SLOW RESPONSE	P0139	21	TC-20A
DOWNSTREAM O2S VOLTAGE SHORTED TO GROUND	P0137	21	TC-21A
CATALYTIC CONVERTER EFFICIENCY FAILURE	P0422	64	TC-22A
ECT SENSOR VOLTAGE TOO LOW	P0117	22	TC-23A
ECT SENSOR VOLTAGE TOO HIGH	P0118	22	TC-24A
CLOSED LOOP TEMP NOT REACHED	P0125	17	TC-25A
INTAKE AIR TEMP SENSOR VOLTAGE LOW	P0112	23	TC-26A
INTAKE AIR TEMP SENSOR VOLTAGE HIGH	P0113	23	TC-27A

CR1029505073010X

Fig. 45 Test TC-1A: Checking System For Diagnostic Trouble Codes (Part 1 of 3)

DRB TROUBLE CODE (DTC) DISPLAYED	SCAN TOOL	MIL CODE	DIAGNOSTIC TEST
PARK/NEUTRAL SWITCH FAILURE	P1899	37	TC-28A
KNOCK SENSOR #1 CIRCUIT	N/A	16	TC-29A
THROTTLE POSITION SENSOR VOLTAGE LOW	P0122	24	TC-30A
THROTTLE POSITION SENSOR VOLTAGE HIGH	P0123	24	TC-31A
TPS VOLTAGE DOES NOT AGREE WITH MAP	P0121	24	TC-32A
NO 5 VOLTS TO TP SENSOR	P1295	24	TC-33A
IDLE AIR CONTROL MOTOR CIRCUITS	P0505	25	TC-34A
TARGET IDLE NOT REACHED	P1294	25	TC-35A
VACUUM LEAK FOUND (IAC FULLY SEATED)	P1299	25	TC-36A
AIR SWITCHING SOLENOID CIRCUIT	P0412	36	TC-37A
INJECTOR #1 CONTROL CIRCUIT	P0201	27	TC-38A
INJECTOR #2 CONTROL CIRCUIT	P0202	27	TC-39A
INJECTOR #3 CONTROL CIRCUIT	P0203	27	TC-40A
INJECTOR #4 CONTROL CIRCUIT	P0204	27	TC-41A
TIMING BELT SKIPPED 1 TOOTH OR MORE	P1390	11	TC-42A
PCM FAILURE SRI MILE NOT STORED	N/A	62	TC-43A
PCM FAILURE EEPROM WRITE DENIED	N/A	63	TC-43A
EGR SOLENOID CIRCUIT	P0403	32	TC-45A
EGR SYSTEM FAILURE	P0401	32	TC-46A
EVAP SOLENOID CIRCUIT	P0443	31	TC-47A
EVAP PURGE FLOW MONITOR FAILURE	P0441	31	TC-48A
TORQUE CONVERTER CLUTCH SOLENOID CIRCUIT	P0743	37	TC-49A
TORQ CONV CLU, NO RPM DROP AT LOCKUP	P0740	37	TC-50A
TOO LITTLE SEC AIR, OR TOO MUCH SEC AIR	N/A	36	TC-51A
A/C CLUTCH RELAY CIRCUIT	N/A	33	TC-52A
A/C PRESSURE SENSOR VOLTS TOO LOW	N/A	33	TC-53A
A/C PRESSURE SENSOR VOLTS TOO HIGH	N/A	33	TC-54A
NO 5 VOLTS TO A/C PRESSURE SENSOR	N/A	33	TC-55A
RAD FAN CONTROL RELAY CIRCUIT	P1491	35	TC-56A
HIGH SPEED FAN CTRL RELAY CIRCUIT	P1489	35	TC-57A
LOW SPEED FAN CTRL RELAY CIRCUIT	P1490	35	TC-58A
AUTO SHUTDOWN RELAY CONTROL CIRCUIT	N/A	42	TC-59A
NO ASD RELAY OUTPUT VOLTAGE AT PCM	N/A	42	TC-60A
FUEL PUMP RELAY CONTROL CIRCUIT	N/A	42	TC-61A
FUEL LEVEL SENDING UNIT VOLTS TOO LOW	N/A	42	TC-62A
FUEL LEVEL SENDING UNIT VOLTS TOO HIGH	N/A	42	TC-63A
FUEL LEVEL UNIT NO CHANGE OVER MILES	N/A	42	TC-64A
IGNITION COIL #1 PRIMARY CIRCUIT	P0351	43	TC-65A
IGNITION COIL #2 PRIMARY CIRCUIT	P0352	43	TC-66A
BATTERY TEMP SENSOR VOLTS OUT OF LIMIT	N/A	44	TC-67A
GENERATOR FIELD NOT SWITCHING PROPERLY	N/A	41	TC-68A
CHARGING SYSTEM VOLTAGE TOO LOW	N/A	47	TC-69A
CHARGING SYSTEM VOLTAGE TOO HIGH	N/A	46	TC-70A
SPEED CONTROL SOLENOID CIRCUITS	N/A	34	TC-71A
SPEED CONTROL POWER RELAY CIRCUIT	N/A	77	TC-71A
SPEED CONTROL SWITCH ALWAYS LOW	N/A	34	TC-72A
SPEED CONTROL SWITCH ALWAYS HIGH	N/A	34	TC-73A
POWER STEERING SWITCH FAILURE	P0551	65	TC-74A

CR1029505073020X

Fig. 45 Test TC-1A: Checking System For Diagnostic Trouble Codes (Part 2 of 3)

DRB TROUBLE CODE (DTC) DISPLAYED	SCAN TOOL	MIL CODE	DIAGNOSTIC TEST
MULTIPLE CYLINDER MISFIRE	P0300	43	TC-75A
CYLINDER #1 MISFIRE	P0301	43	TC-76A
CYLINDER #2 MISFIRE	P0302	43	TC-76A
CYLINDER #3 MISFIRE	P0301	43	TC-76A
CYLINDER #4 MISFIRE	P0304	43	TC-76A
INTERMITTENT LOSS OF CMP OR CKP	P1391	11	TC-77A
BRAKE SWITCH CIRCUIT	P0703	65	TC-78A
NO CCD MESSAGES FROM TCM	P1698	66	TC-79A
NO CCD MESSAGE FROM BODY CONTROL MODULE	N/A	66	TC-80A

For an **ENGINE IS COLD TOO LONG** trouble code, the engine does not warm to 176°F while driving for 20 minutes after start. See the service manual for cooling system repair (thermostat).

For an **INTERNAL CONTROLLER FAILURE** trouble code, replace the powertrain control module and go to **Verification TEST VER-2A.**

For a **PCM FAILURE SPI COMMUNICATIONS** trouble code, replace the powertrain control module and go to **Verification TEST VER-2A.**

CR1029505073030X

Fig. 45   Test TC-1A: Checking System For Diagnostic Trouble Codes (Part 3 of 3)

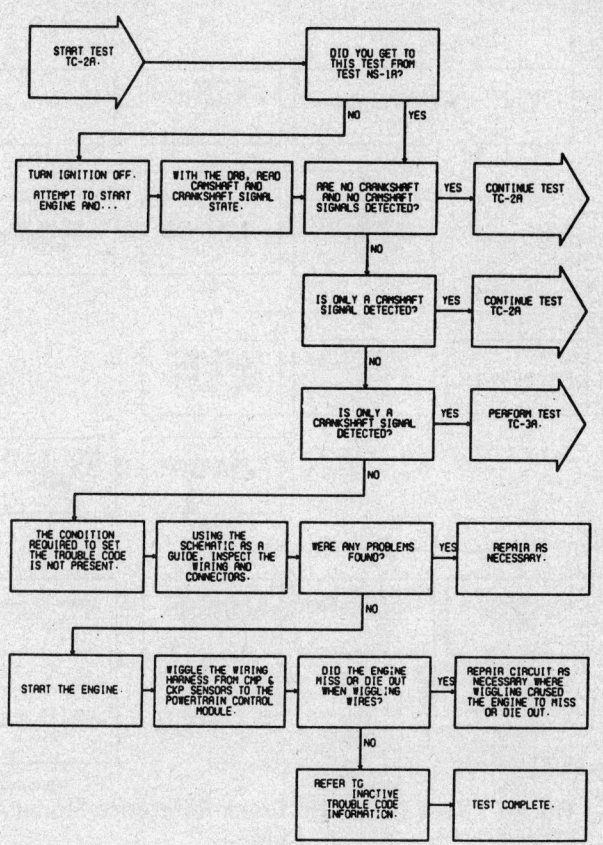

CR1029505074010X

Fig. 46   Test TC-2A: No Crank Reference Signal At PCM (Part 1 of 3)

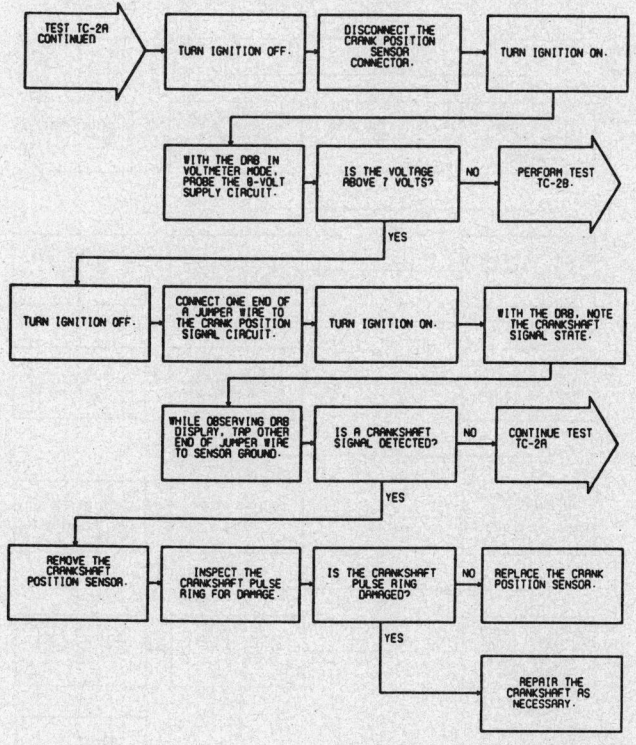

CR1029505074020X

Fig. 46   Test TC-2A: No Crank Reference Signal At PCM (Part 2 of 3)

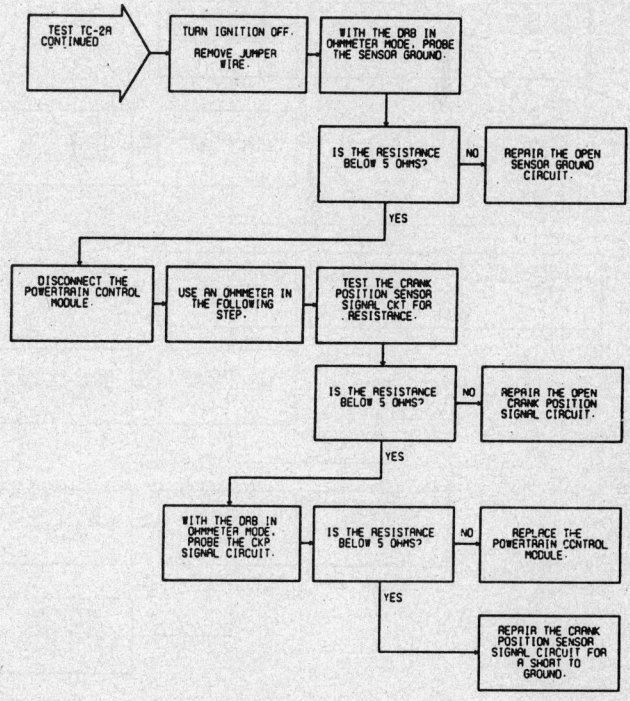

CR1029505074030X

Fig. 46   Test TC-2A: No Crank Reference Signal At PCM (Part 3 of 3)

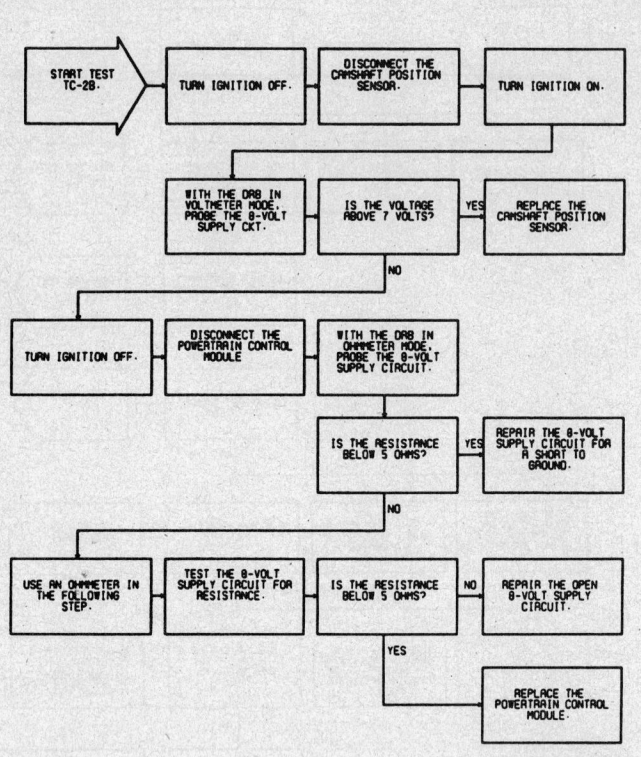

Fig. 47 Test TC-2B: No Crank Reference Signal At PCM

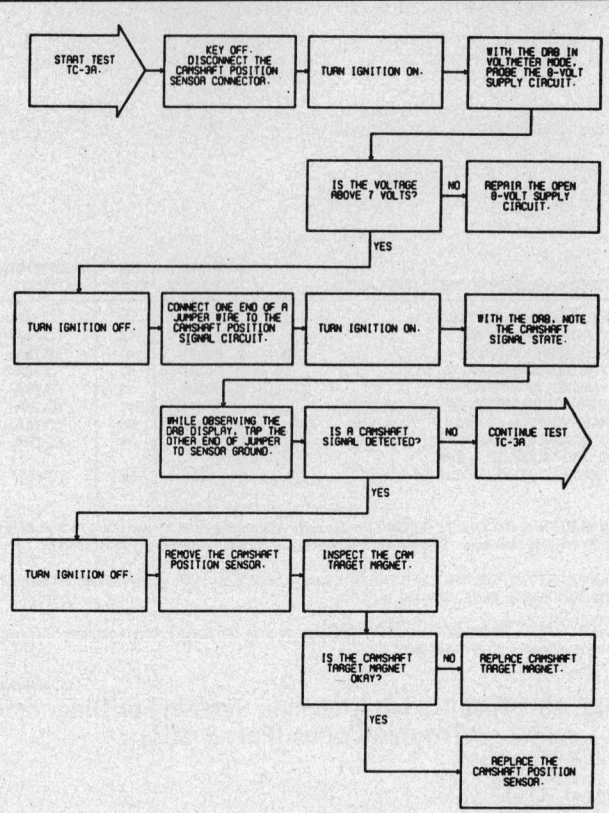

Fig. 48 Test TC-3A: No Cam Signal At PCM (Part 1 of 2)

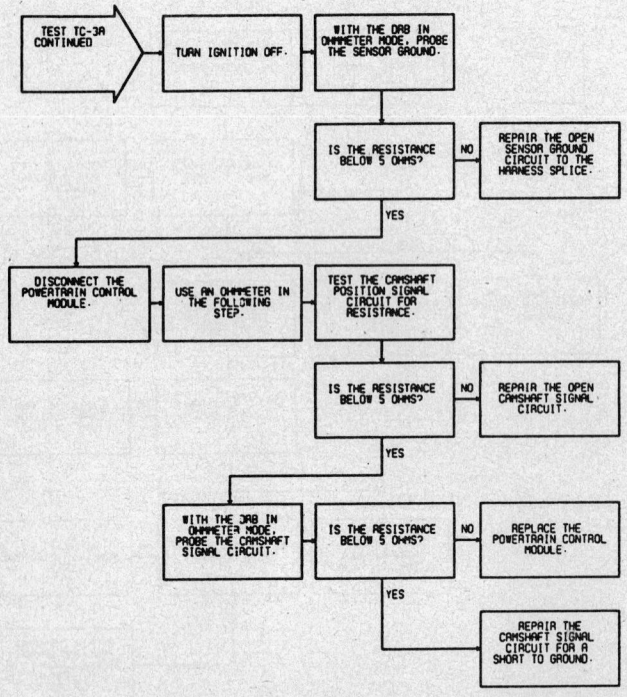

Fig. 48 Test TC-3A: No Cam Signal At PCM (Part 2 of 2)

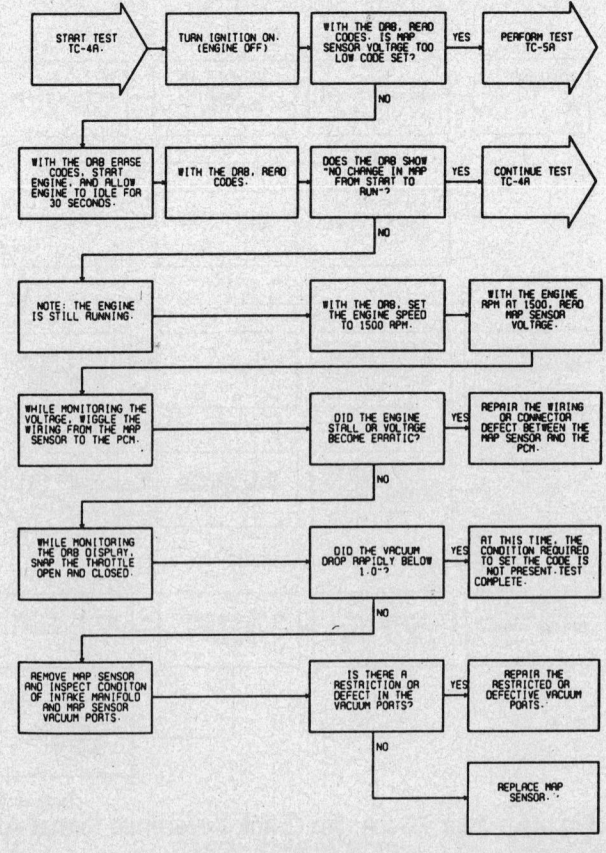

Fig. 49 Test TC-4A: No Change In MAP From Start To Run (Part 1 of 2)

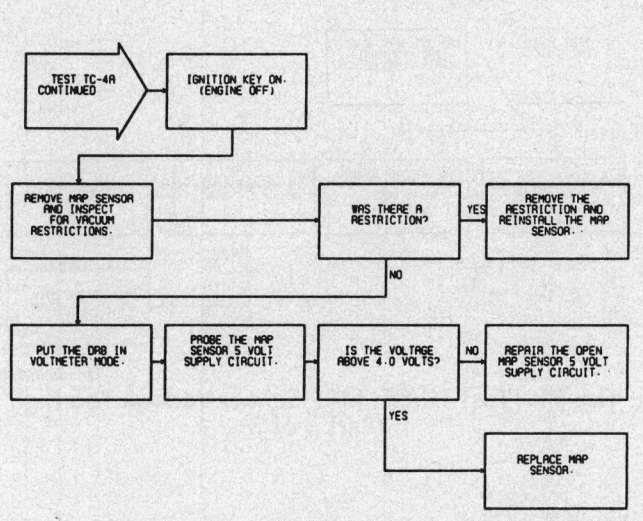

CR1029505077020X

Fig. 49   Test TC-4A: No Change In MAP From Start To Run (Part 2 of 2)

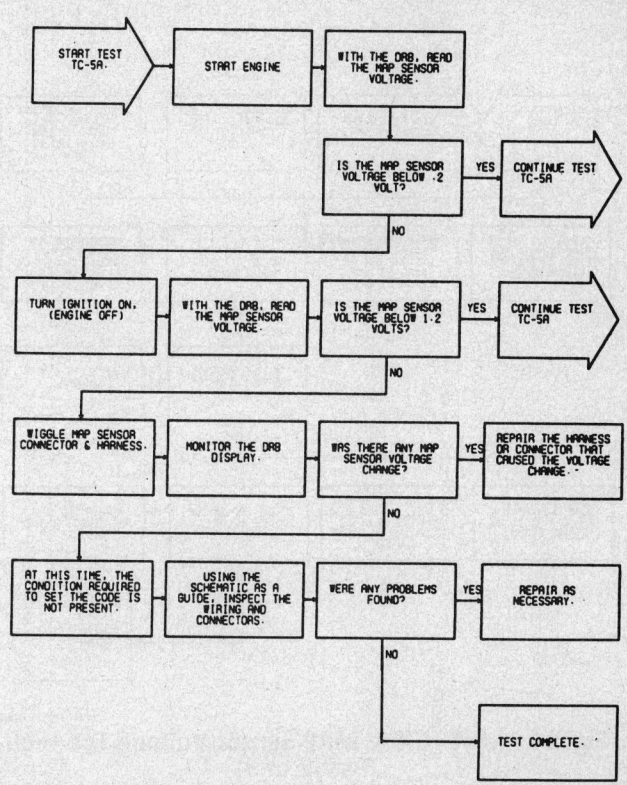

CR1029505078010X

Fig. 50   Test TC-5A: MAP Sensor Voltage Too Low (Part 1 of 2)

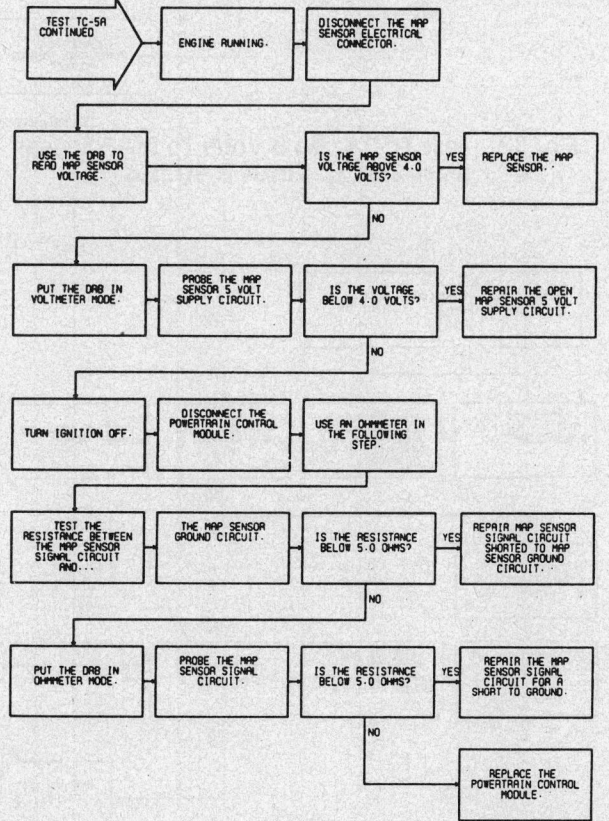

CR1029505078020X

Fig. 50   Test TC-5A: MAP Sensor Voltage Too Low (Part 2 of 2)

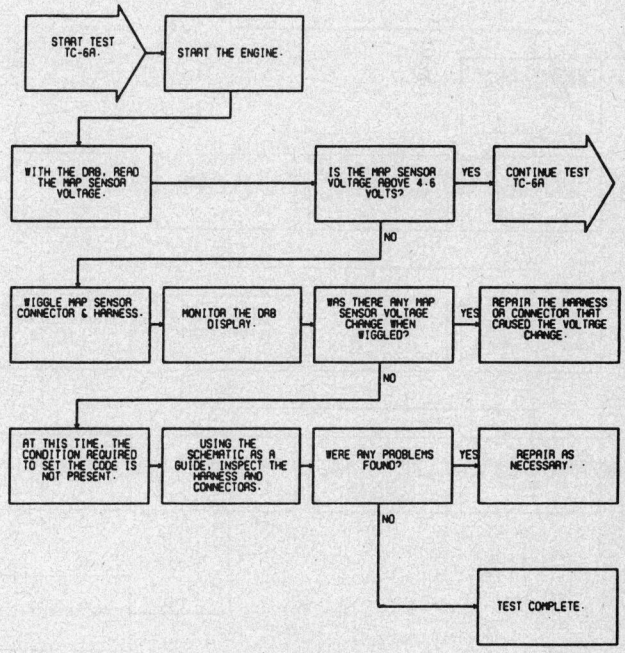

CR1029505079010X

Fig. 51   Test TC-6A: MAP Sensor Voltage Too High (Part 1 of 3)

CHRYSLER–Fuel Injection

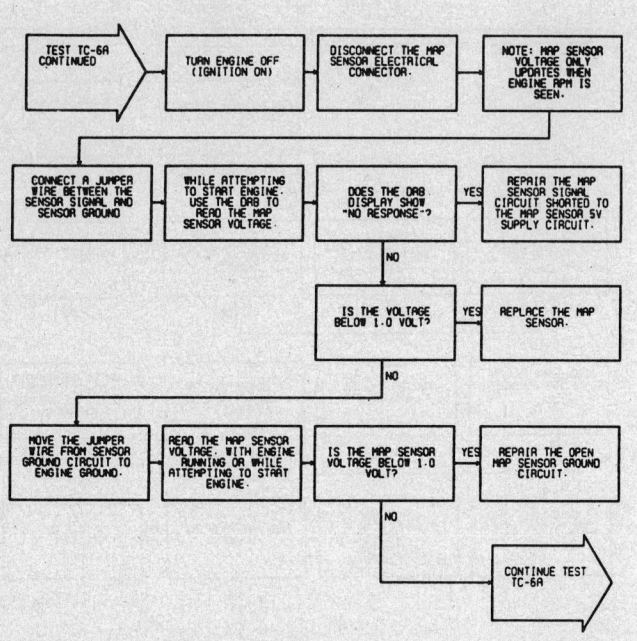

Fig. 51   Test TC-6A: MAP Sensor Voltage Too High (Part 2 of 3)

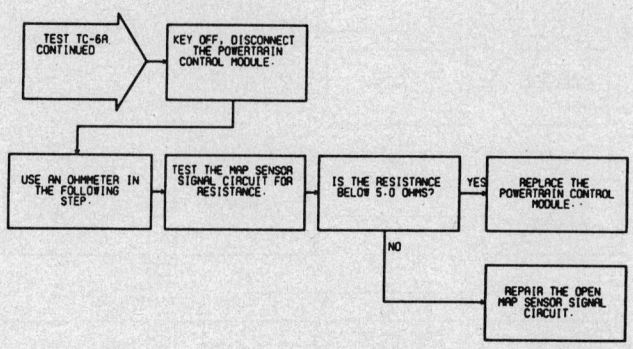

Fig. 51   Test TC-6A: MAP Sensor Voltage Too High (Part 3 of 3)

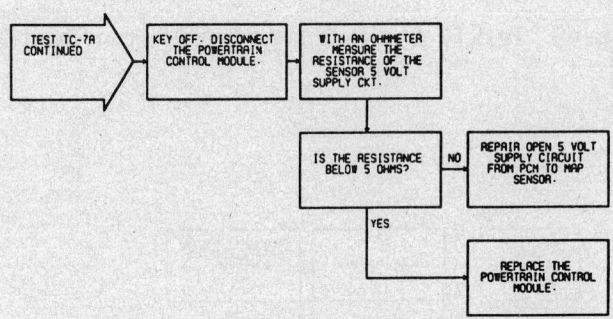

Fig. 52   Test TC-7A: No 5 Volts To MAP Sensor (Part 2 of 2). Cirrus & Stratus

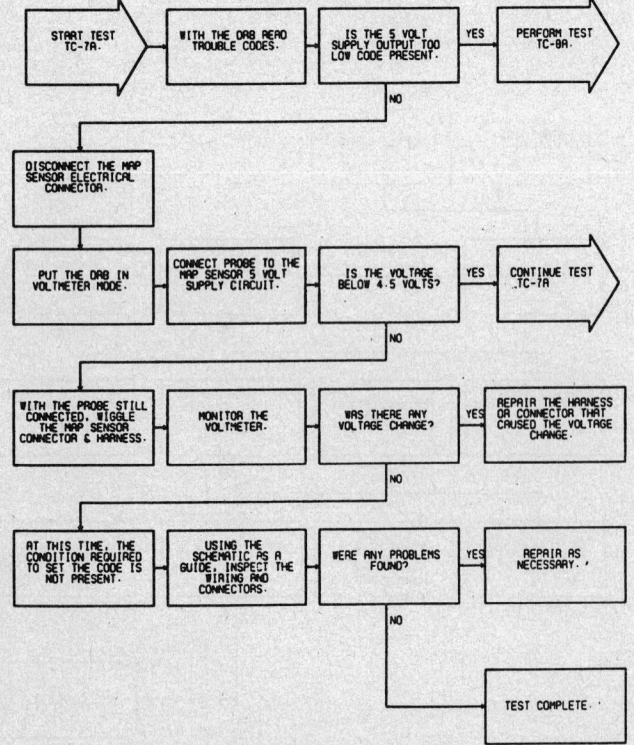

Fig. 52   Test TC-7A: No 5 Volts To MAP Sensor (Part 1 of 2). Cirrus & Stratus

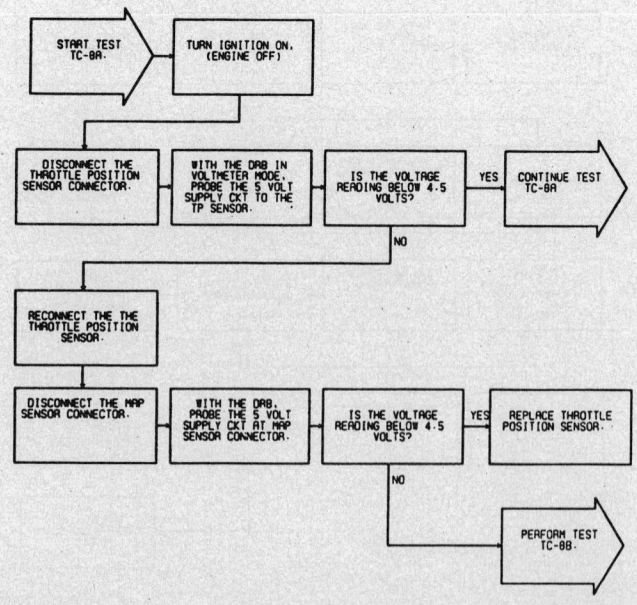

Fig. 53   Test TC-8A: 5 Volt Supply Output Too Low (Part 1 of 2). Cirrus & Stratus

Fuel Injection—CHRYSLER

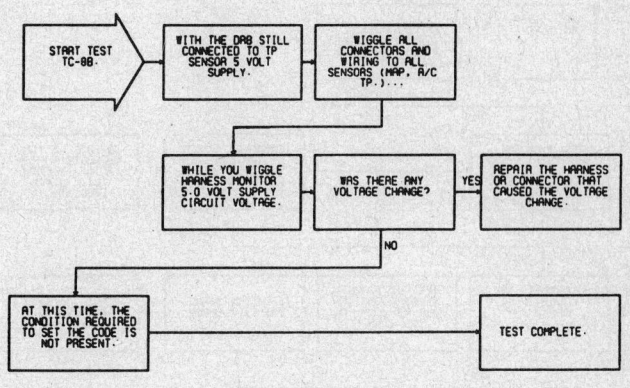

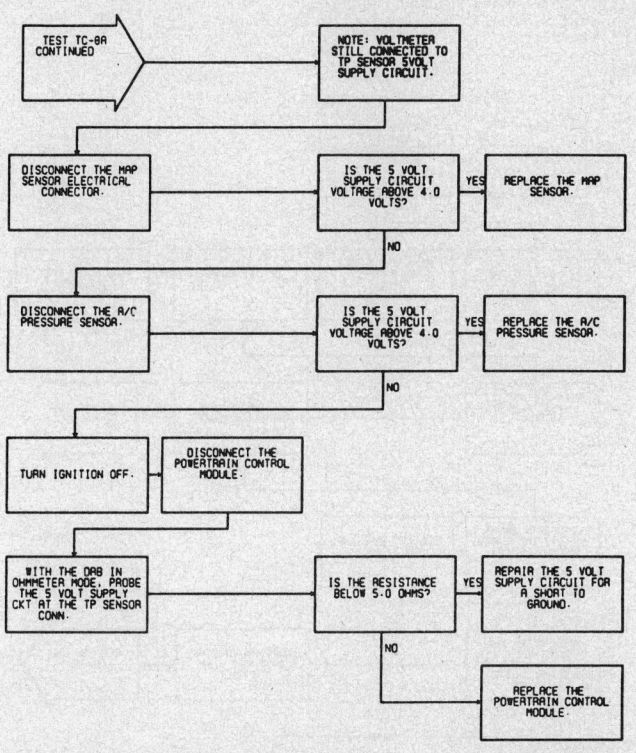

Fig. 53   Test TC-8A: 5 Volt Supply Output Too Low (Part 2 of 2). Cirrus & Stratus

Fig. 54   Test TC-8B: 5 Volt Supply Output Too Low

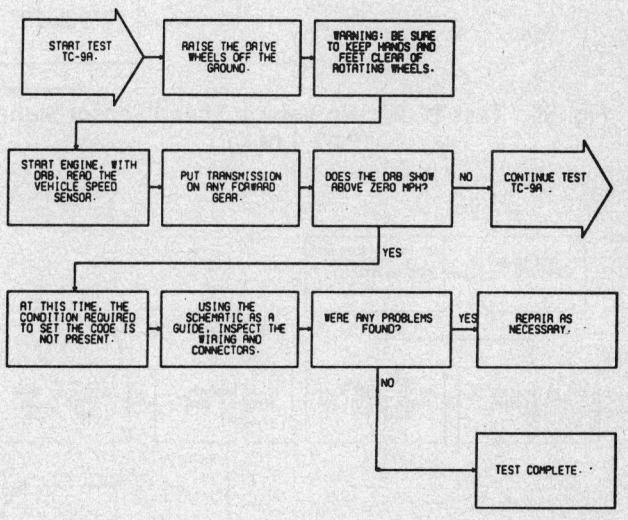

Fig. 55   Test TC-9A: No Vehicle Speed Sensor Signal (Part 1 of 4)

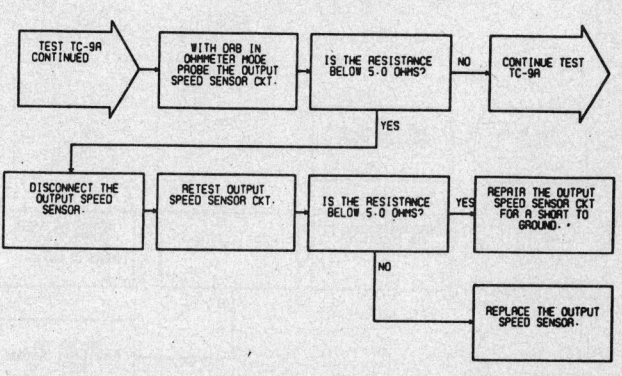

Fig. 55   Test TC-9A: No Vehicle Speed Sensor Signal (Part 3 of 4)

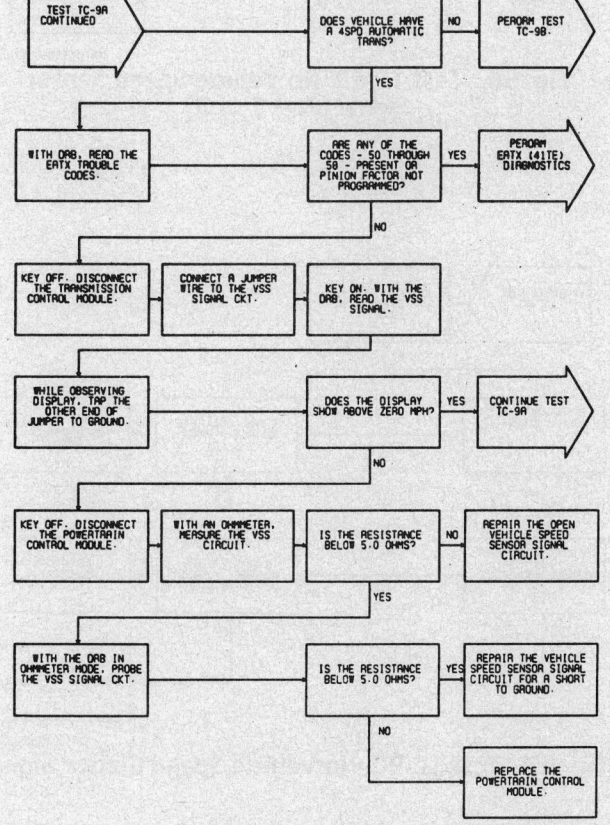

Fig. 55   Test TC-9A: No Vehicle Speed Sensor Signal (Part 2 of 4)

MULTI-POINT FUEL INJECTION (1995 AVENGER, CIRRUS, NEON, SEBRING, STRATUS & TALON w/NON-TURBOCHARGED 2.0L/4-122 ENGINE)

8-19

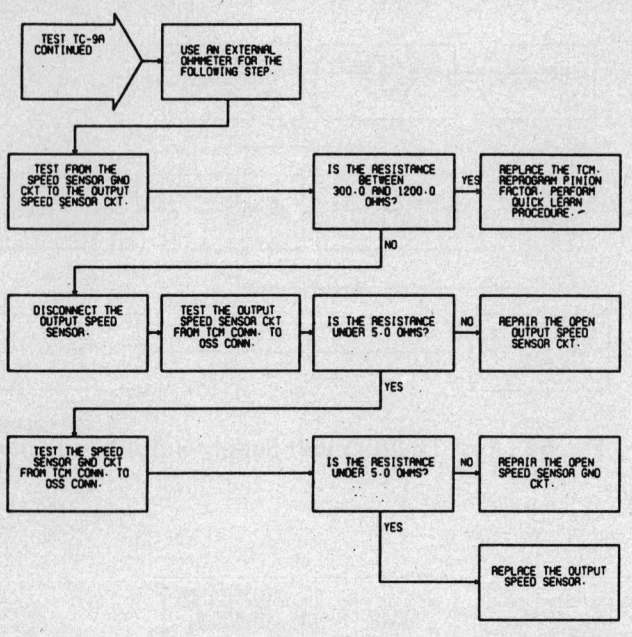

Fig. 55 Test TC-9A: No Vehicle Speed Sensor Signal (Part 4 of 4)

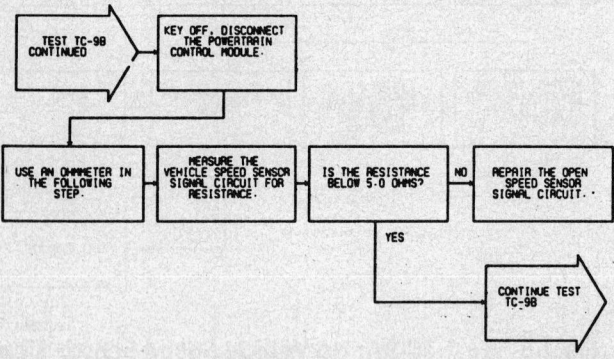

Fig. 56 Test TC-9B: No Vehicle Speed Sensor Signal (Part 2 of 3)

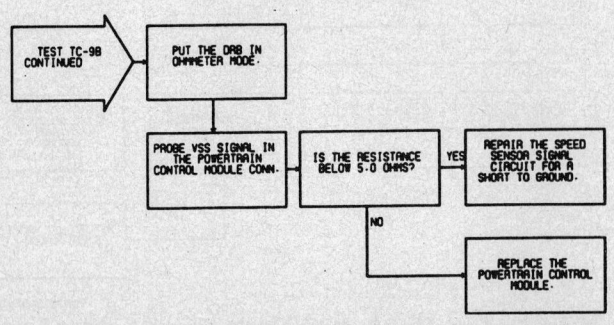

Fig. 56 Test TC-9B: No Vehicle Speed Sensor Signal (Part 3 of 3)

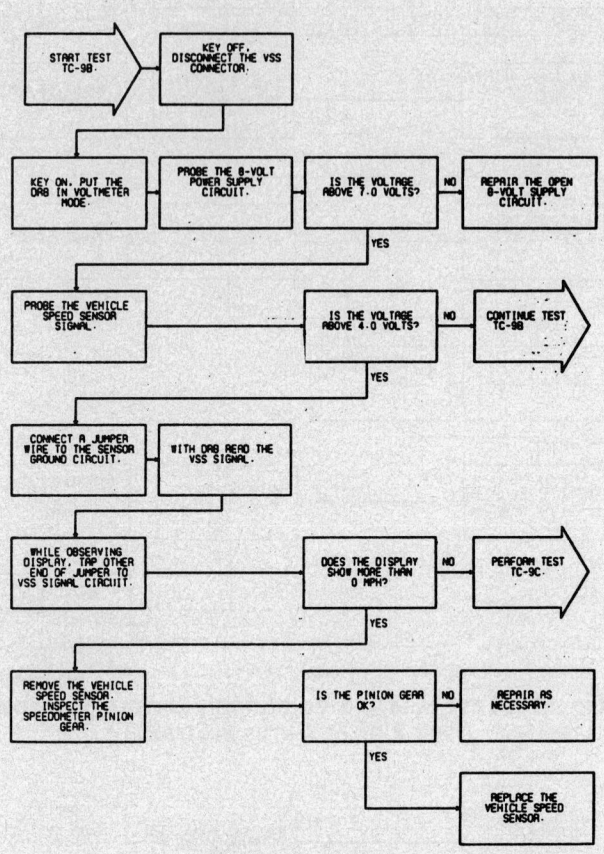

Fig. 56 Test TC-9B: No Vehicle Speed Sensor Signal (Part 1 of 3)

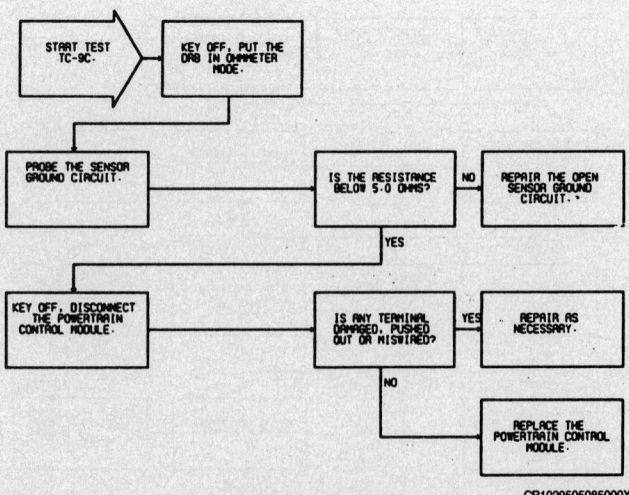

Fig. 57 Test TC-9C: No Vehicle Speed Sensor Signal

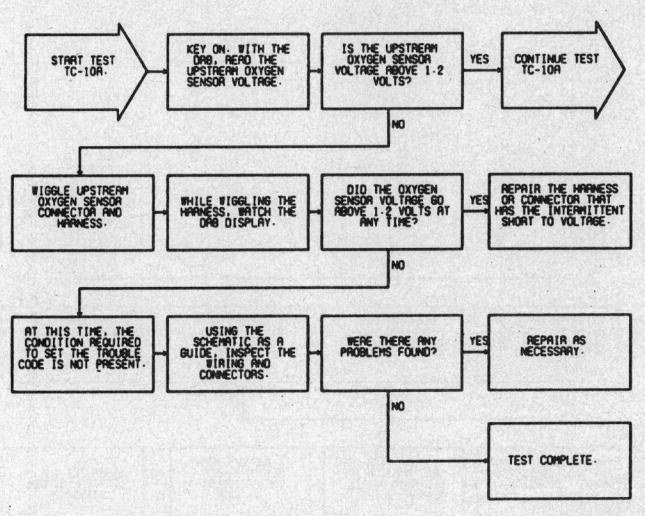

Fig. 58 Test TC-10A: Upstream O2S Shorted To Voltage (Part 1 of 2)

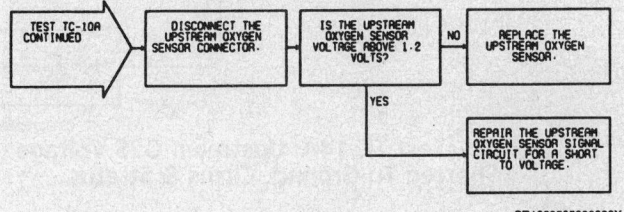

Fig. 58 Test TC-10A: Upstream O2S Shorted To Voltage (Part 2 of 2)

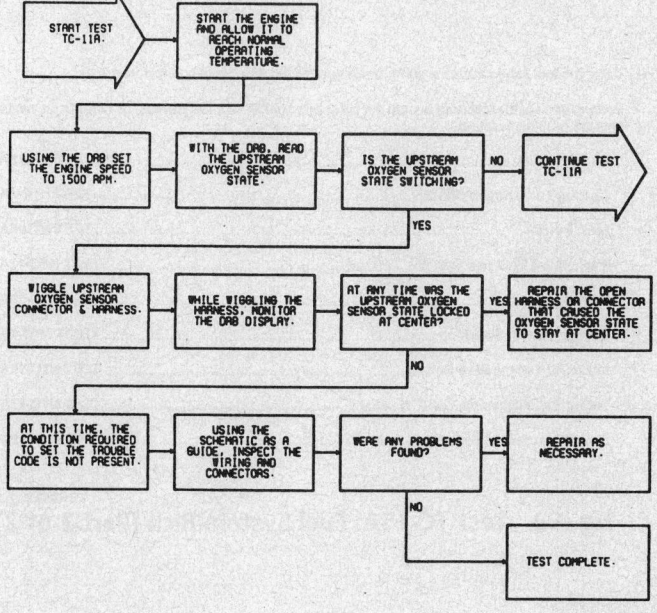

Fig. 59 Test TC-11A: Upstream O2S Stays At Center (Part 1 of 2)

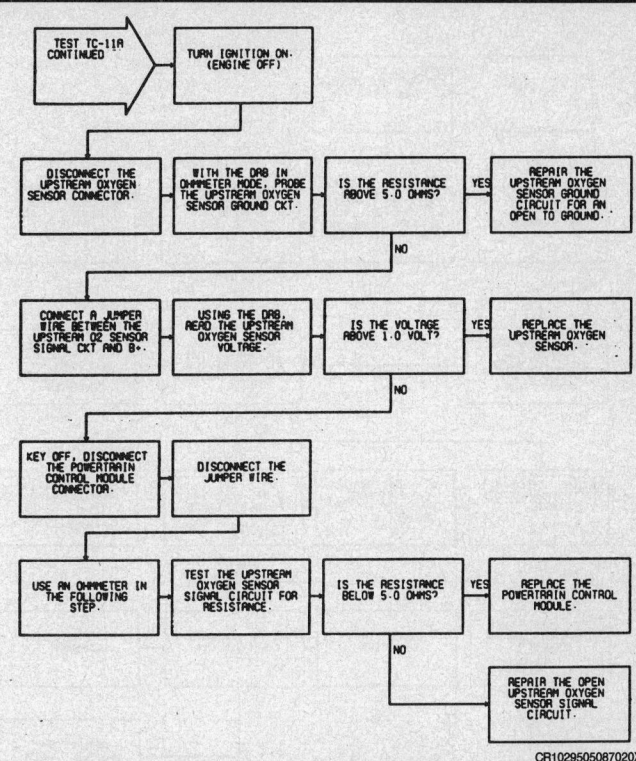

Fig. 59 Test TC-11A: Upstream O2S Stays At Center (Part 2 of 2)

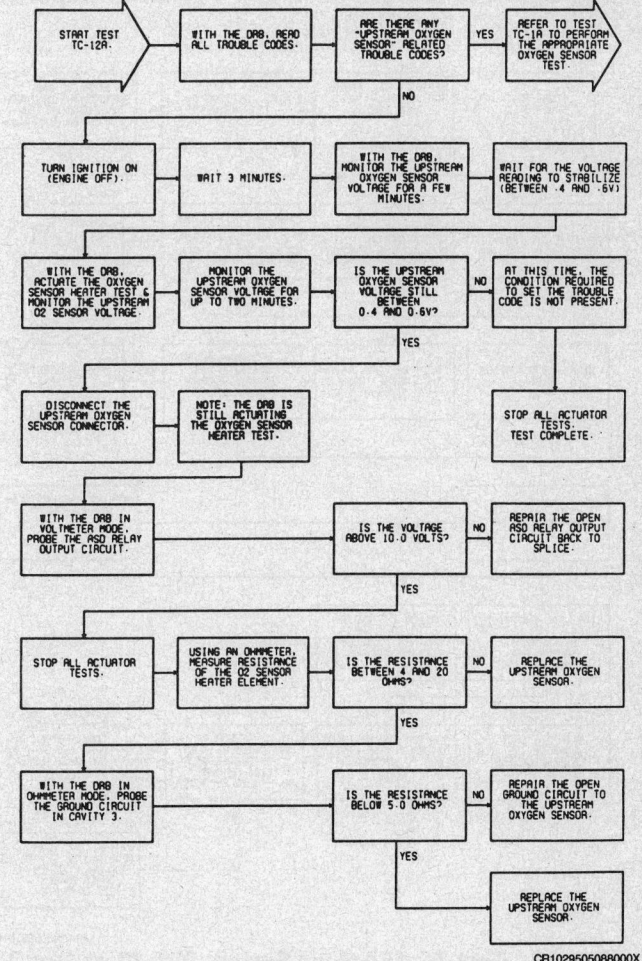

Fig. 60 Test TC-12A: Upstream O2S Heater Failure

MULTI-POINT FUEL INJECTION (1995 AVENGER, CIRRUS, NEON, SEBRING, STRATUS & TALON w/NON-TURBOCHARGED 2.0L/4-122 ENGINE)

8-21

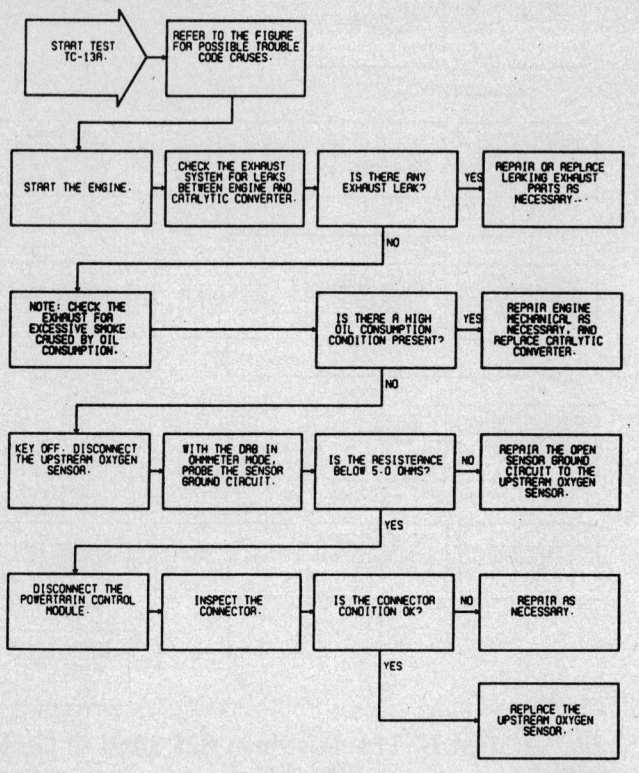

Fig. 61 Test TC-13A: Upstream O2S Slow Response

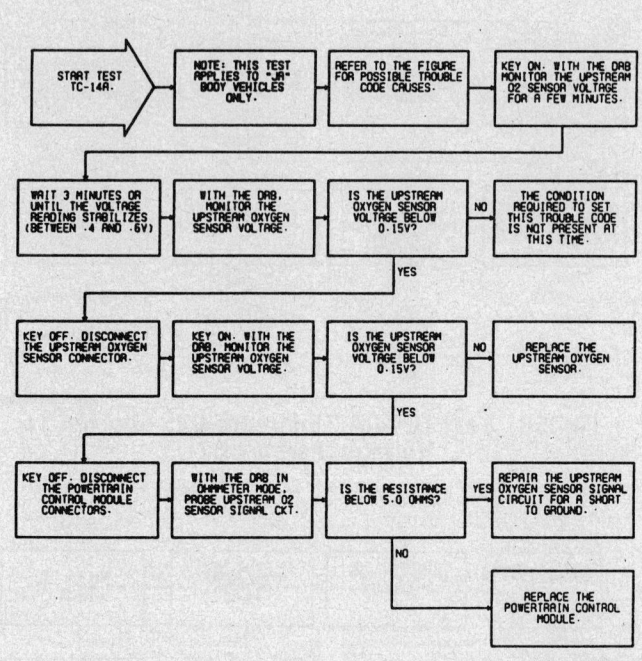

Fig. 62 Test TC-14A: Upstream O2S Voltage Shorted To Ground. Cirrus & Stratus

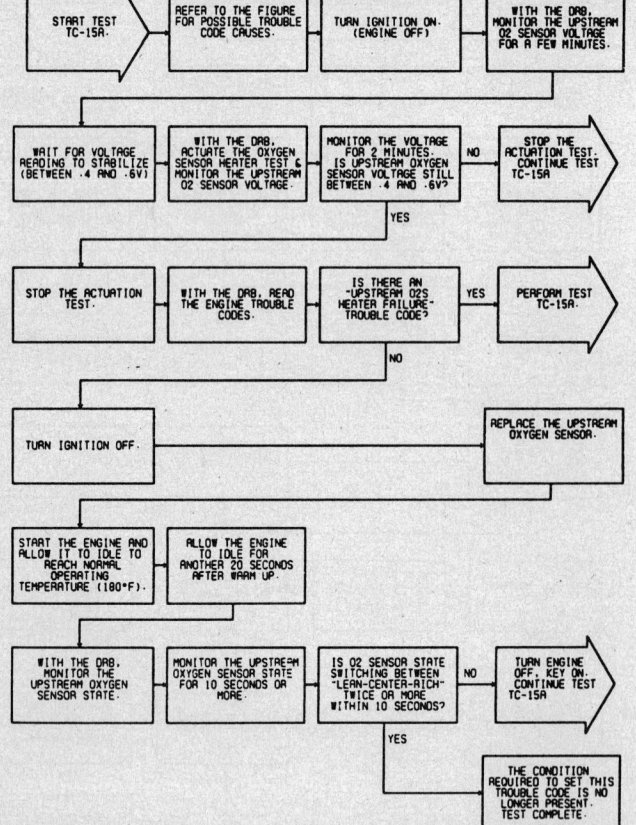

Fig. 63 Test TC-15A: Fuel System Rich (Part 1 of 2)

Using the test schematic as a guide, make sure all the wiring and connectors are ok.

Perform each of the following tests in the order listed below. If a test passes, continue to the next test until the problem is found.

Fuel Pressure	TEST NTC-3A
Coolant Temperature Sensor	TEST NTC-4A
MAP Sensor	TEST NTC-6A
Evaporative Emission System	TEST NTC-13A
EGR System	TEST NTC-14A
Oxygen Sensor Switching	TEST NTC-7A
Intake Air Temperature Sensor	TEST NTC-16A
Timing Belt Alignment	TEST NTC-17A
Engine Mechanical Systems	TEST NTC-19A

CR1029505091020X

Fig. 63 Test TC-15A: Fuel System Rich (Part 2 of 2)

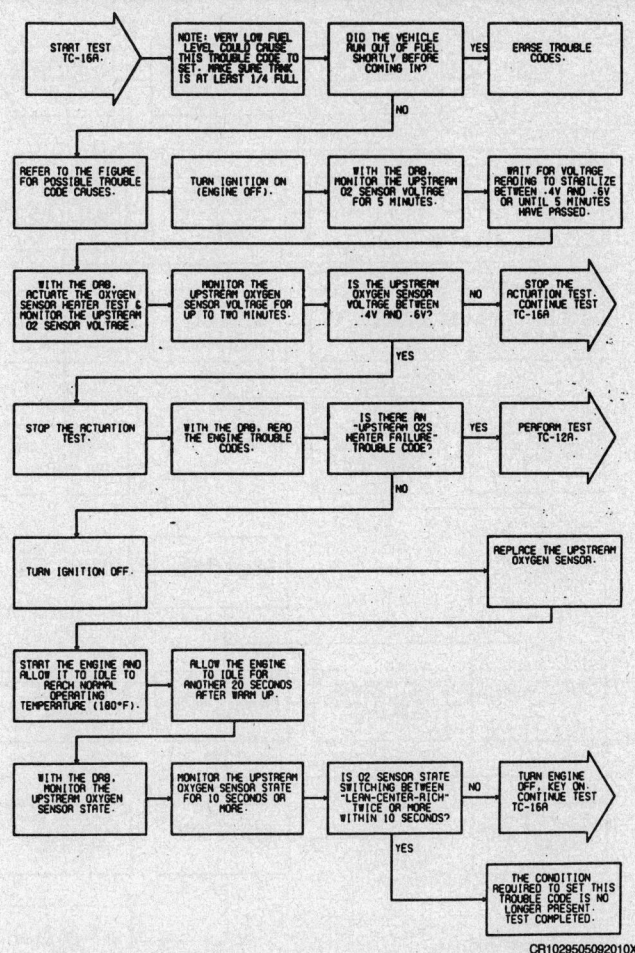

Fig. 64   Test TC-16A: Fuel System Lean (Part 1 of 3)

CR1029505092010X

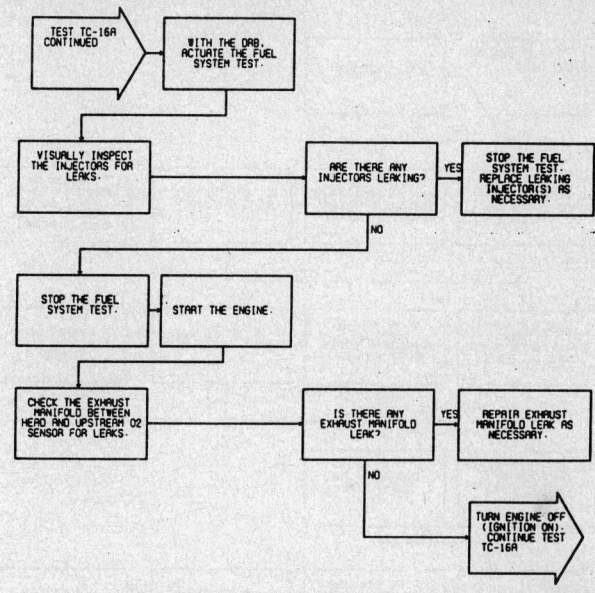

Fig. 64   Test TC-16A: Fuel System Lean (Part 2 of 3)

CR1029505092020X

Using the test schematic as a guide, make sure all the wiring and connectors are ok.

Perform each of the following tests in the order listed below. If a test passes, continue to the next test until the problem is found.

Fuel Pressure .... TEST NTC-3A

Ignition System .... TEST NTC-2A

Coolant Temperature Sensor .... TEST NTC-4A

MAP Sensor .... TEST NTC-6A

Oxygen Sensor Switching .... TEST NTC-7A

Engine Mechanical Systems .... TEST NTC-19A

CR1029505092030X

Fig. 64   Test TC-16A: Fuel System Lean (Part 3 of 3)

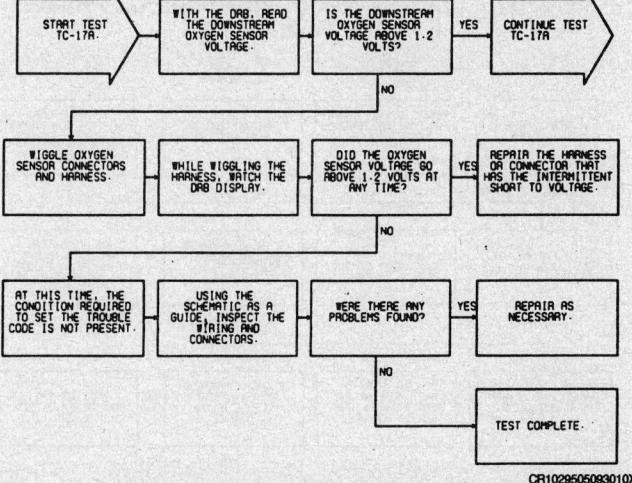

Fig. 65   Test TC-17A: Downstream O2S Shorted To Voltage (Part 1 of 2)

CR1029505093010X

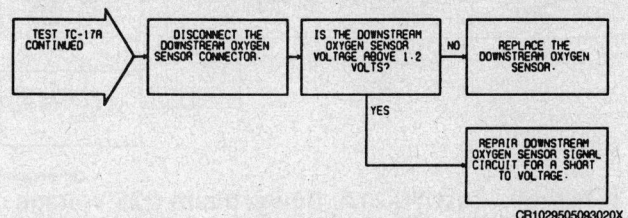

CR1029505093020X

Fig. 65   Test TC-17A: Downstream O2S Shorted To Voltage (Part 2 of 2)

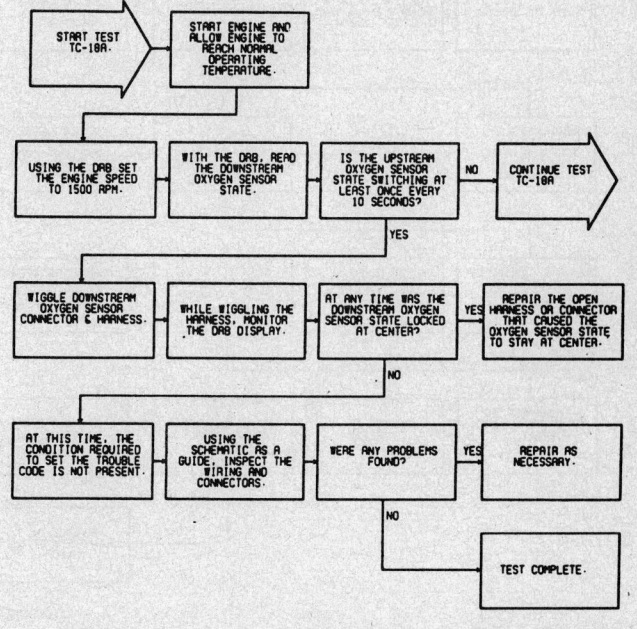

CR1029505094010X

Fig. 66   Test TC-18A: Downstream O2S Stays At Center (Part 1 of 2). Cirrus & Stratus

MULTI-POINT FUEL INJECTION (1995 AVENGER, CIRRUS, NEON, SEBRING, STRATUS & TALON w/NON-TURBOCHARGED 2.0L/4-122 ENGINE)

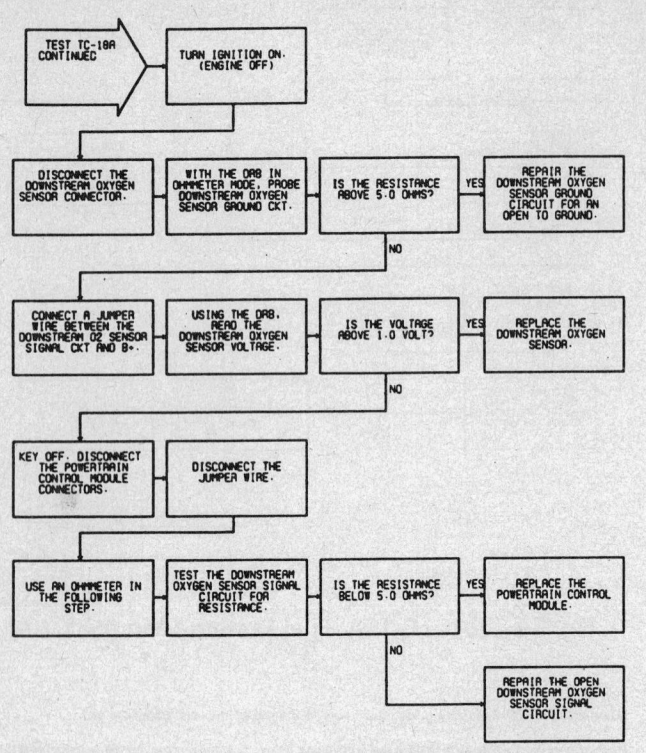

Fig. 66   Test TC-18A: Downstream O2S Stays At Center (Part 2 of 2). Cirrus & Stratus

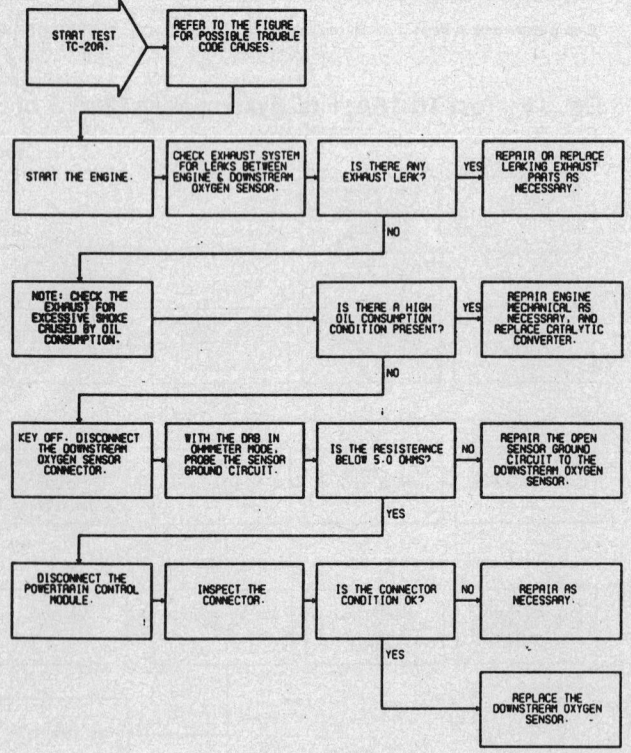

Fig. 68   Test TC-20A: Downstream O2S Slow Response

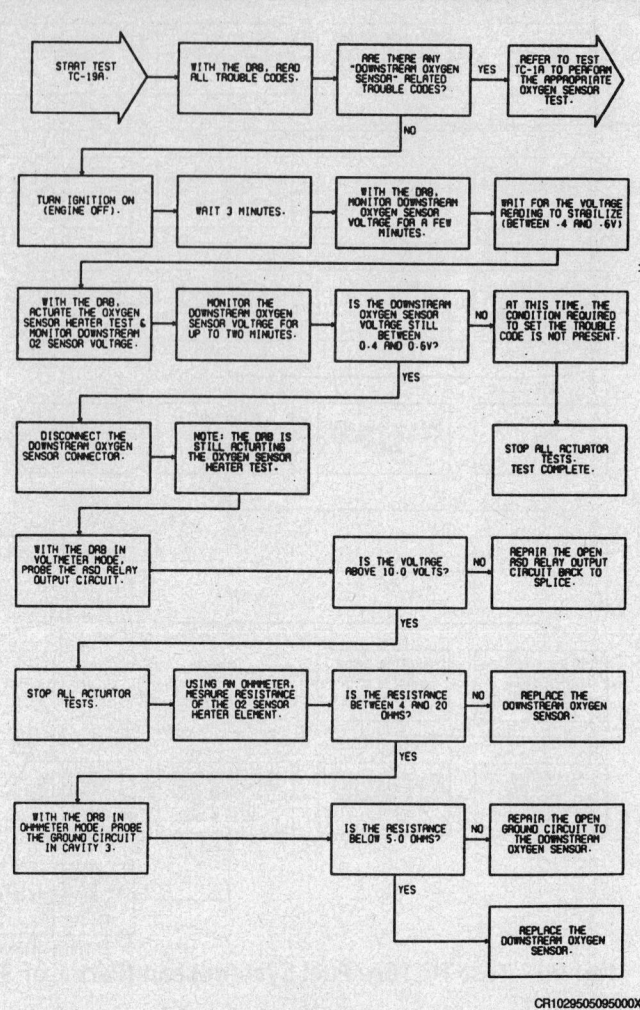

Fig. 67   Test TC-19A: Downstream O2S Heater Failure

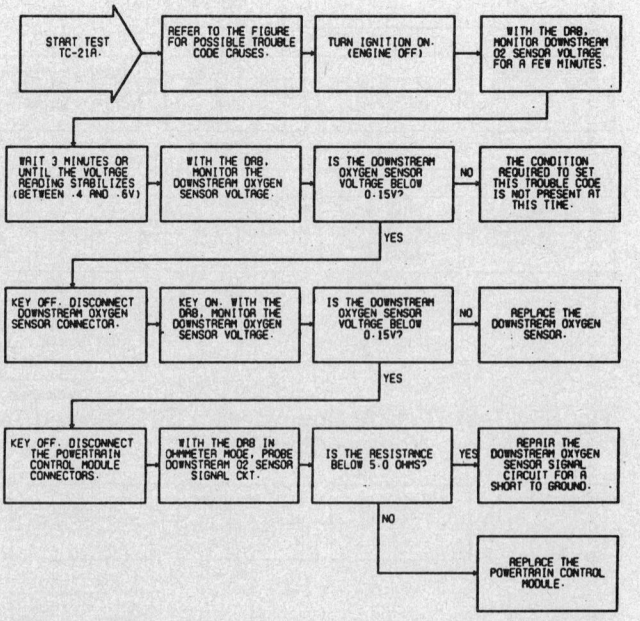

Fig. 69   Test TC-21A: Downstream O2S Voltage Shorted To Ground. Cirrus & Stratus

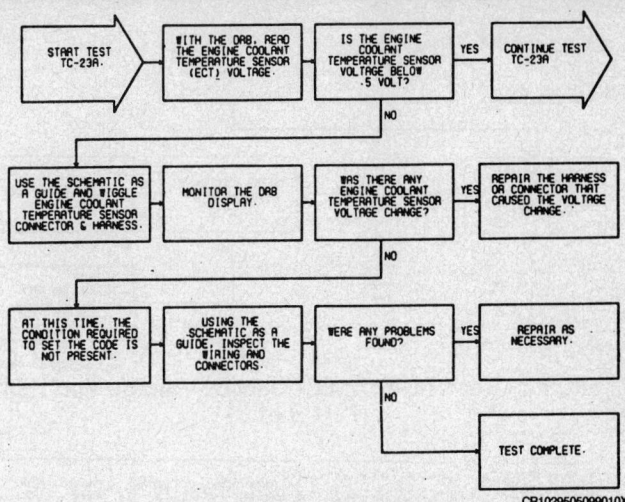

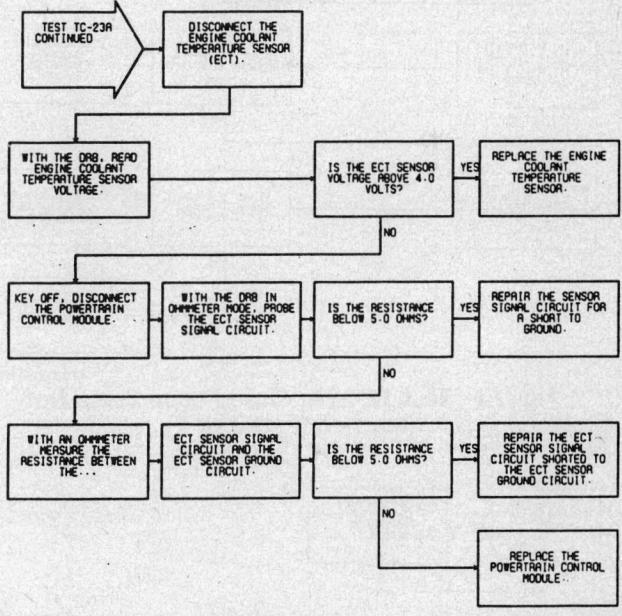

Fig. 71 Test TC-23A: ECT Sensor Voltage Too Low (Part 1 of 2)

CR1029505099010X

Fig. 71 Test TC-23A: ECT Sensor Voltage Too Low (Part 2 of 2)

CR1029505099020X

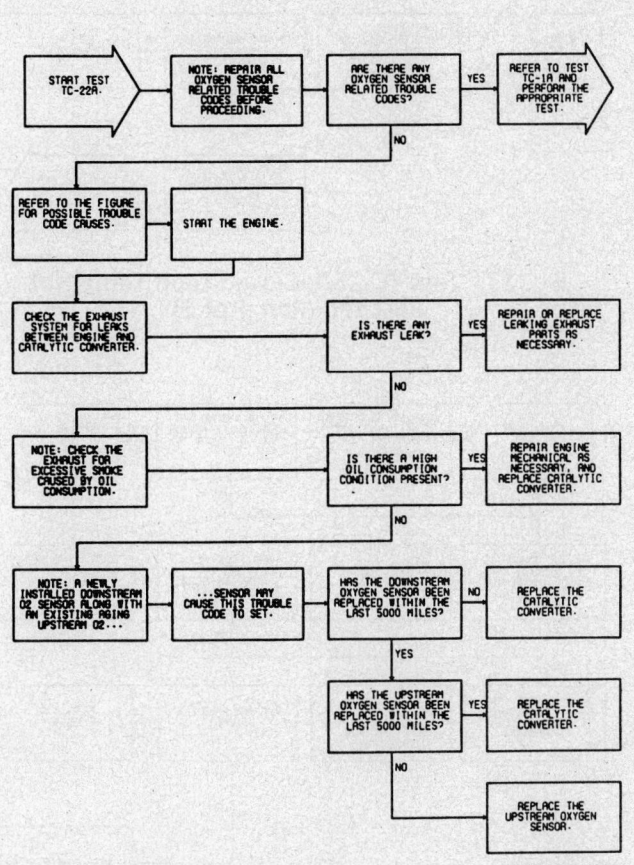

Fig. 70 Test TC-22A: Catalytic Converter Efficiency Failure

CR1029505098000X

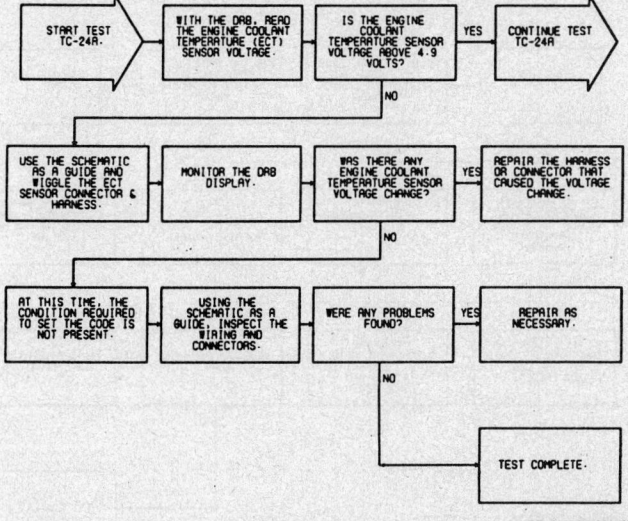

Fig. 72 Test TC-24A: ECT Sensor Voltage Too High (Part 1 of 3)

CR1029505100010X

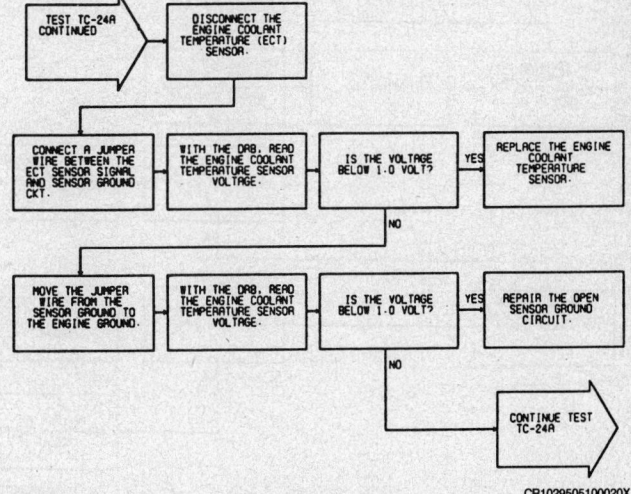

Fig. 72 Test TC-24A: ECT Sensor Voltage Too High (Part 2 of 3)

CR1029505100020X

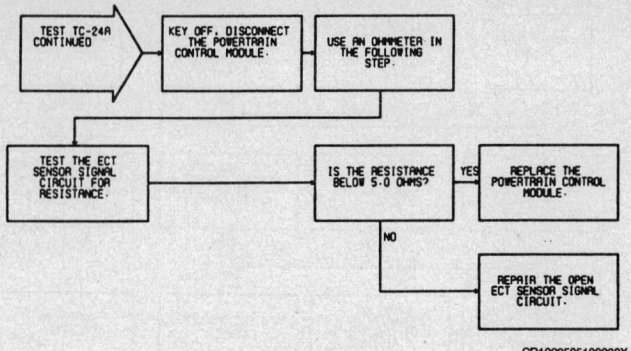

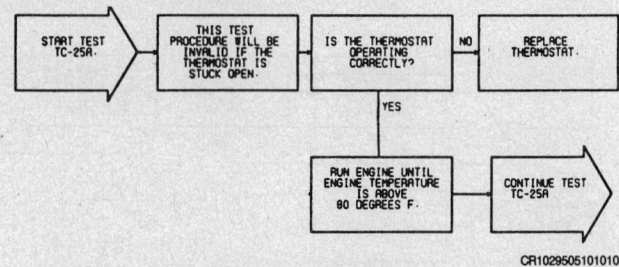

Fig. 72   Test TC-24A: ECT Sensor Voltage Too High
(Part 3 of 3)

Fig. 73   Test TC-25A: Closed Loop Temp Not
Reached (Part 1 of 2)

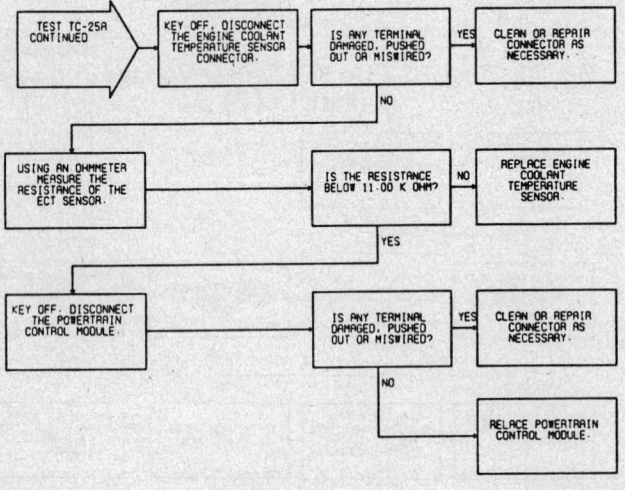

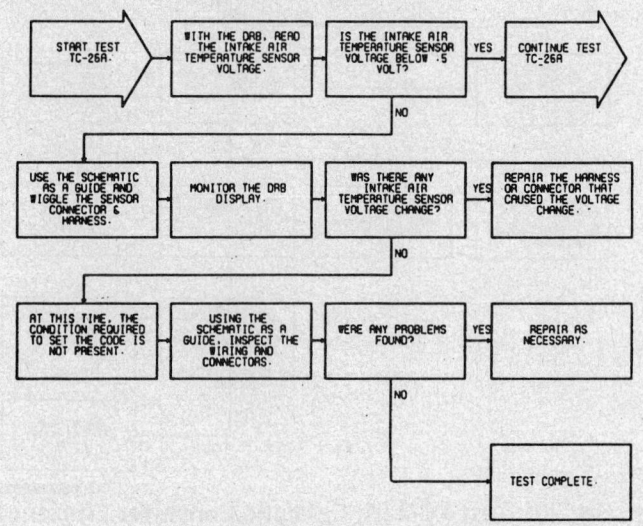

Fig. 73   Test TC-25A: Closed Loop Temp Not
Reached (Part 2 of 2)

Fig. 74   Test TC-26A: Intake Air Temperature
Sensor Voltage Low (Part 1 of 2)

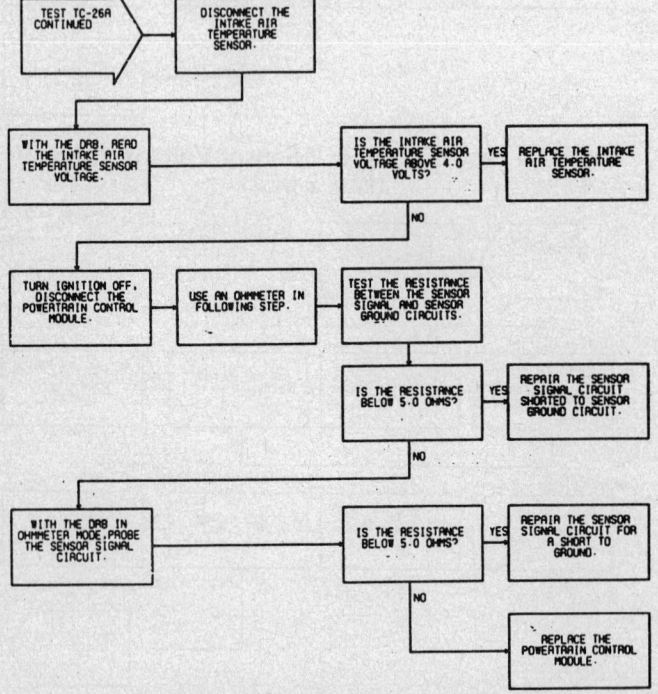

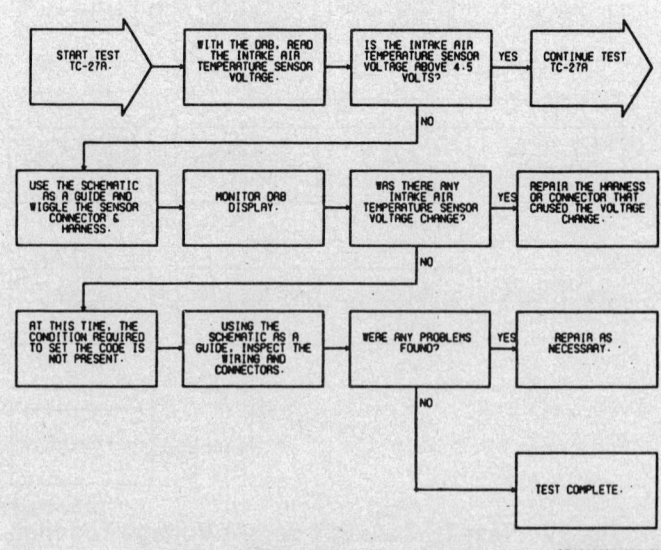

Fig. 74   Test TC-26A: Intake Air Temperature Sensor
Voltage Low (Part 2 of 2)

Fig. 75   Test TC-27A: Intake Air Temperature Sensor
Voltage High (Part 1 of 3)

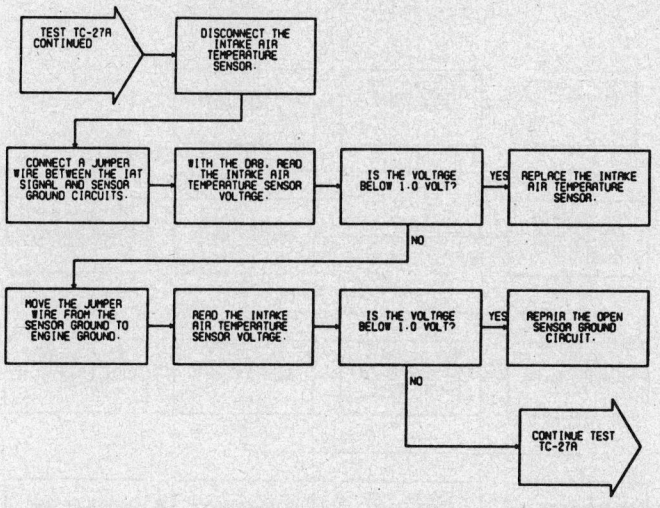

Fig. 75 Test TC-27A: Intake Air Temperature Sensor Voltage High (Part 2 of 3)

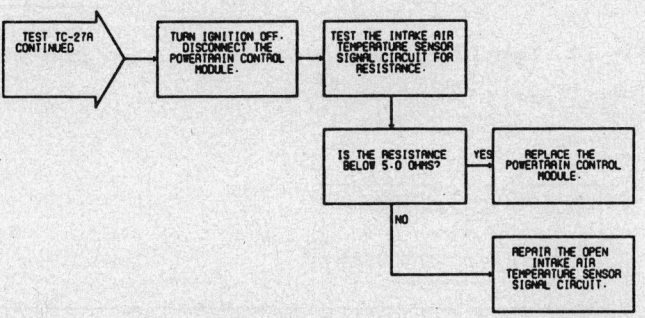

Fig. 75 Test TC-27A: Intake Air Temperature Sensor Voltage High (Part 3 of 3)

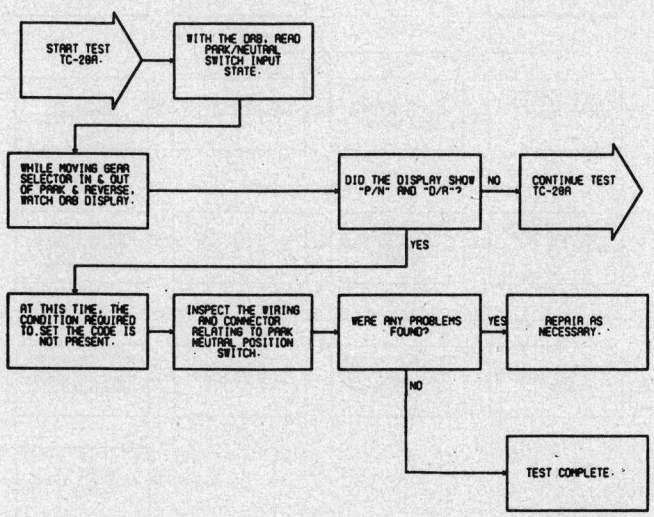

Fig. 76 Test TC-28A: Park/Neutral Switch Failure (Part 1 of 2)

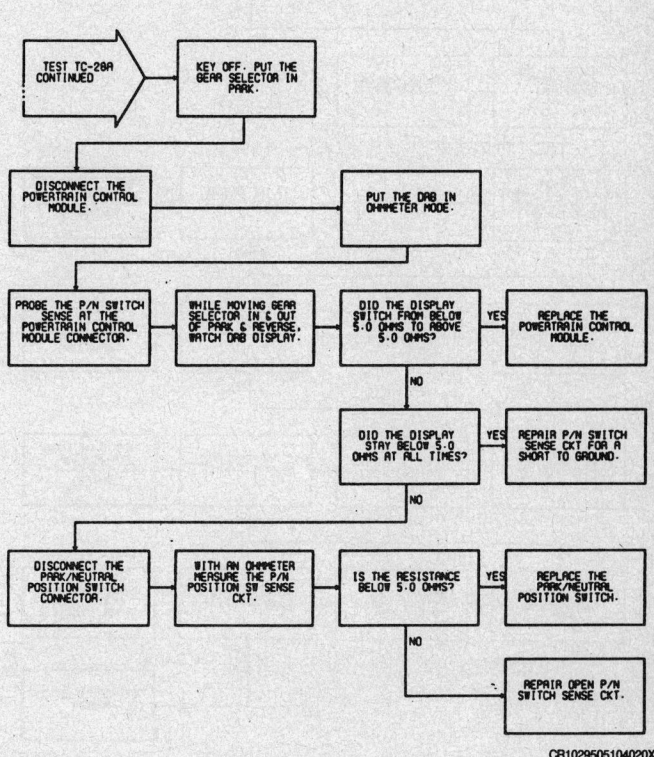

Fig. 76 Test TC-28A: Park/Neutral Switch Failure (Part 2 of 2)

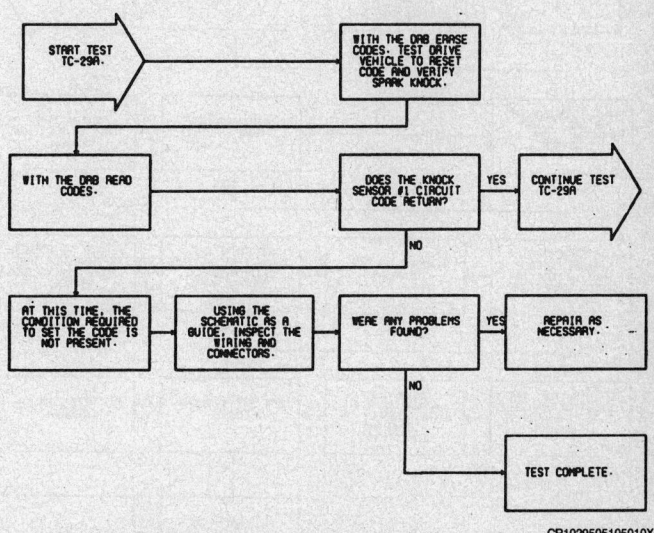

Fig. 77 Test TC-29A: Knock Sensor No. 1 Circuit (Part 1 of 3)

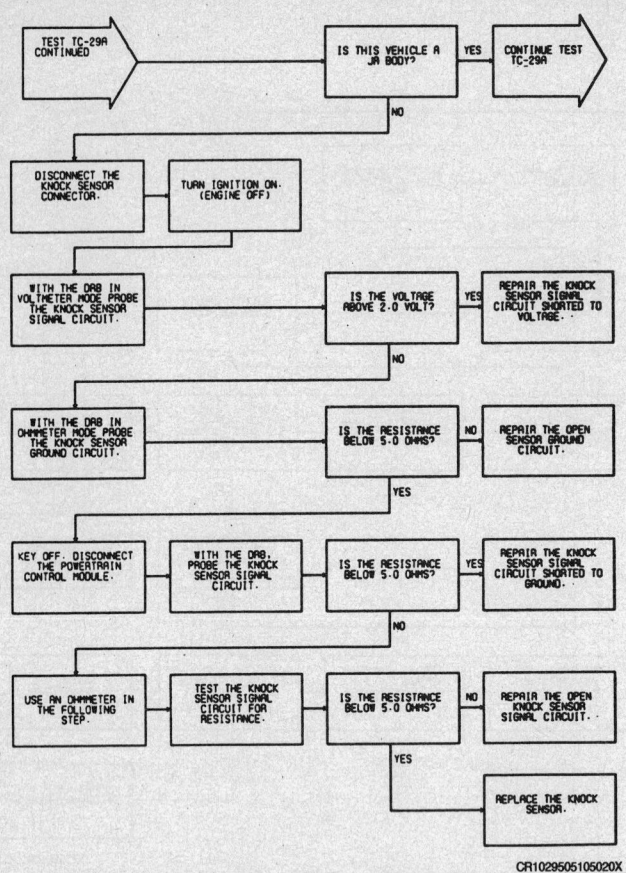

Fig. 77 Test TC-29A: Knock Sensor No. 1 Circuit (Part 2 of 3)

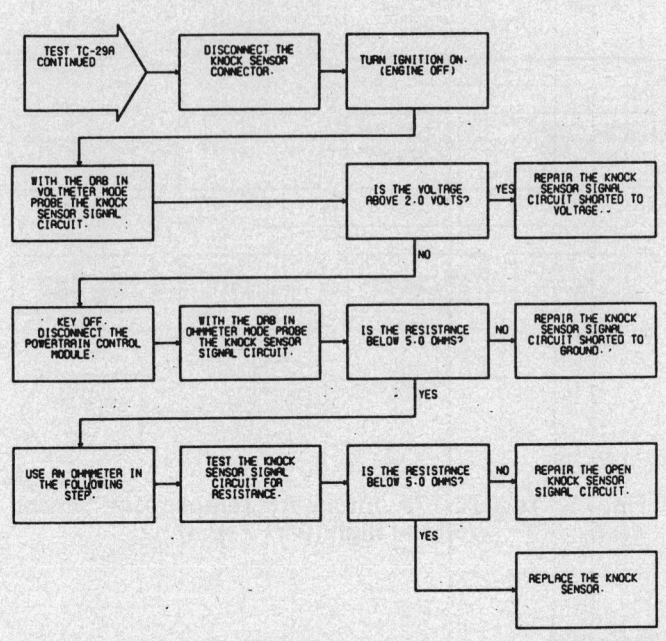

Fig. 77 Test TC-29A: Knock Sensor No. 1 Circuit (Part 3 of 3)

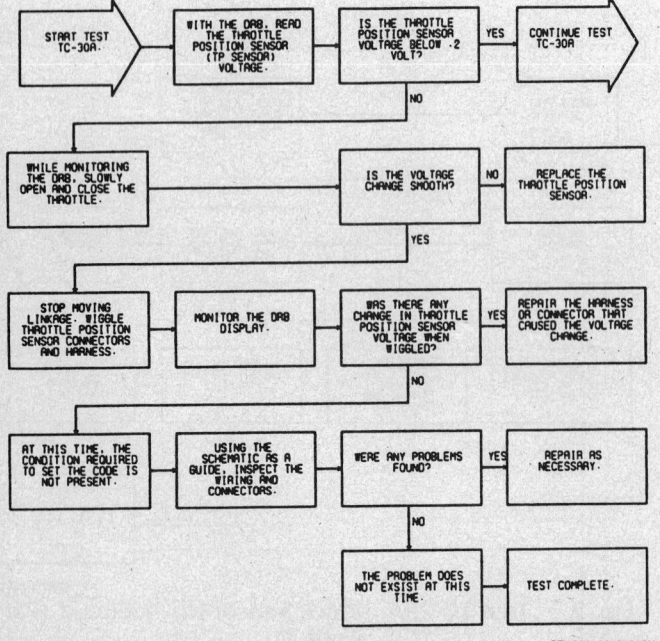

Fig. 78 Test TC-30A: TPS Voltage Low (Part 1 of 2)

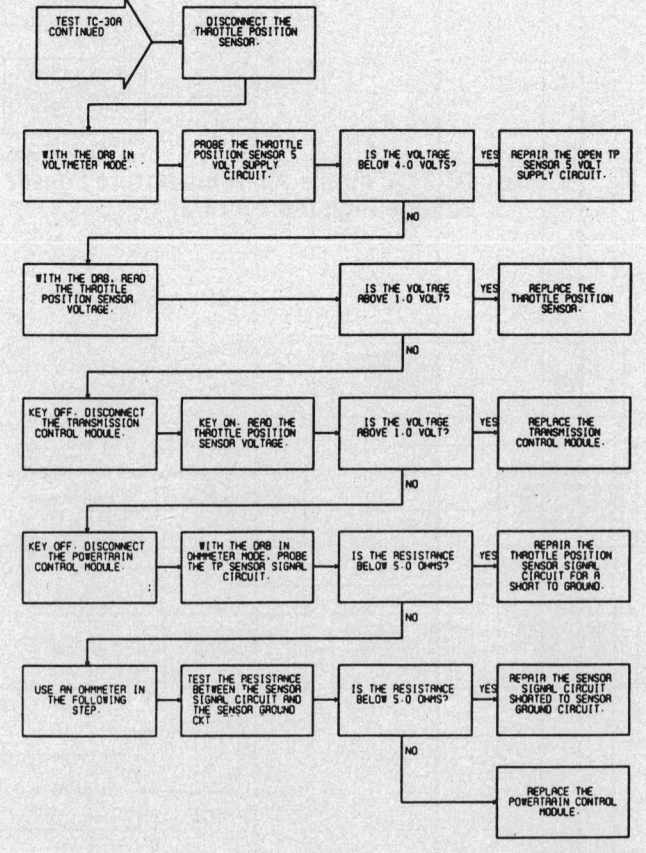

Fig. 78 Test TC-30A: TPS Voltage Low (Part 2 of 2)

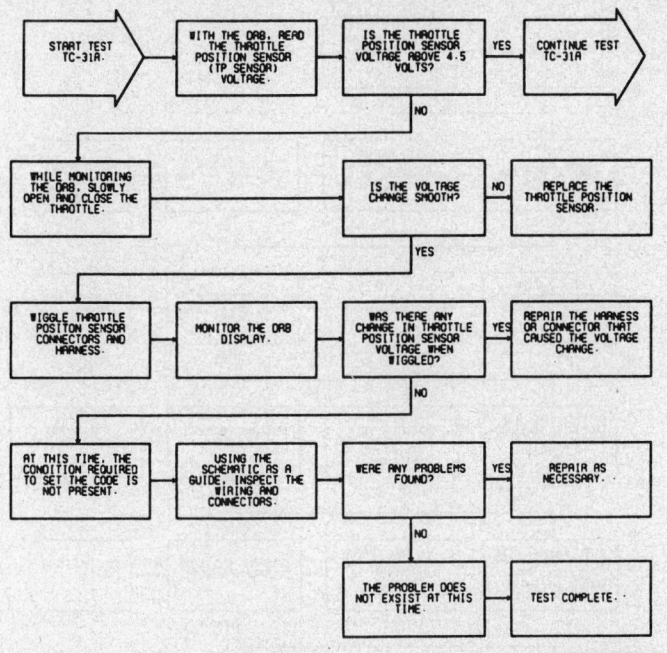

Fig. 79   Test TC-31A: TPS Voltage High (Part 1 of 3)

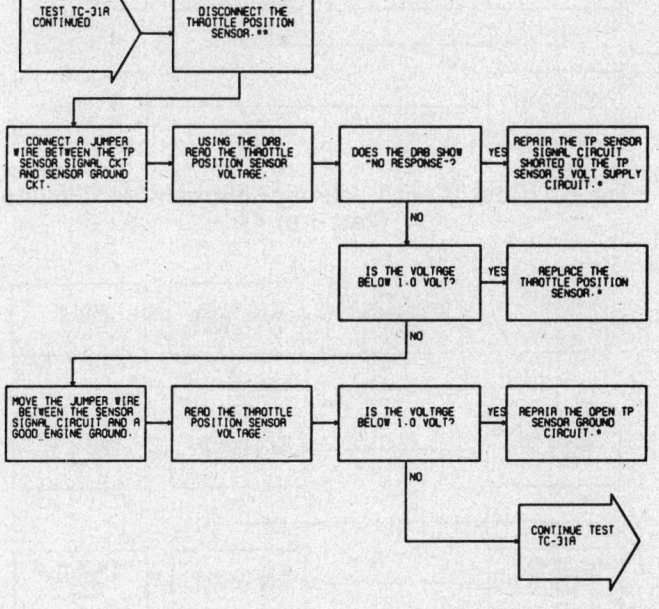

Fig. 79   Test TC-31A: TPS Voltage High (Part 2 of 3)

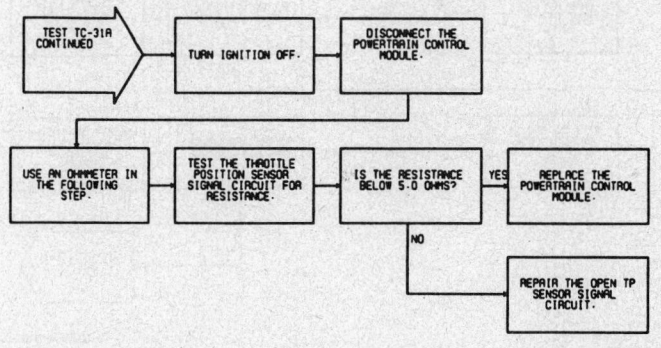

Fig. 79   Test TC-31A: TPS Voltage High (Part 3 of 3)

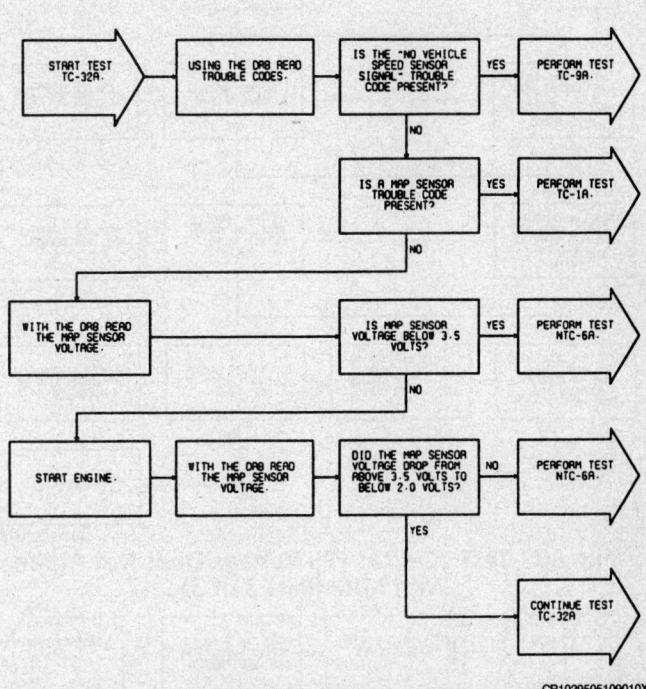

Fig. 80   Test TC-32A: TPS Voltage Does Not Agree With MAP (Part 1 of 3)

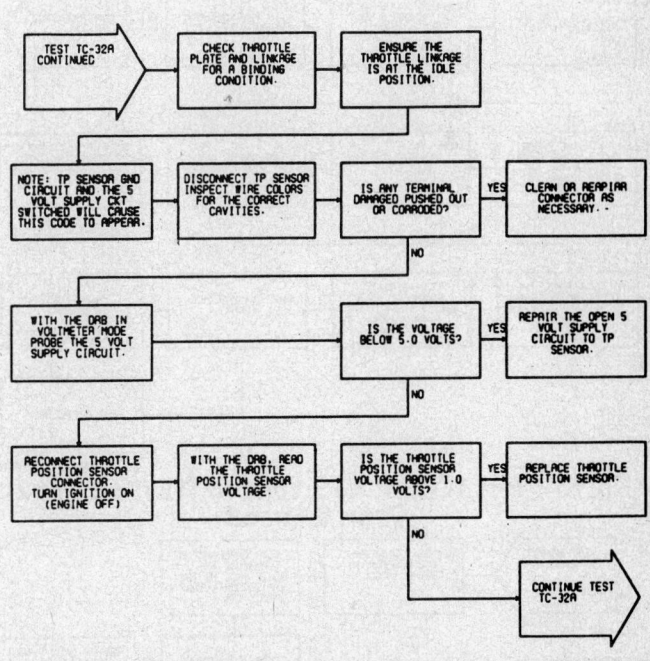

Fig. 80   Test TC-32A: TPS Voltage Does Not Agree With MAP (Part 2 of 3)

MULTI-POINT FUEL INJECTION (1995 AVENGER, CIRRUS, NEON, SEBRING, STRATUS & TALON w/NON-TURBOCHARGED 2.0L/4-122 ENGINE)

8-29

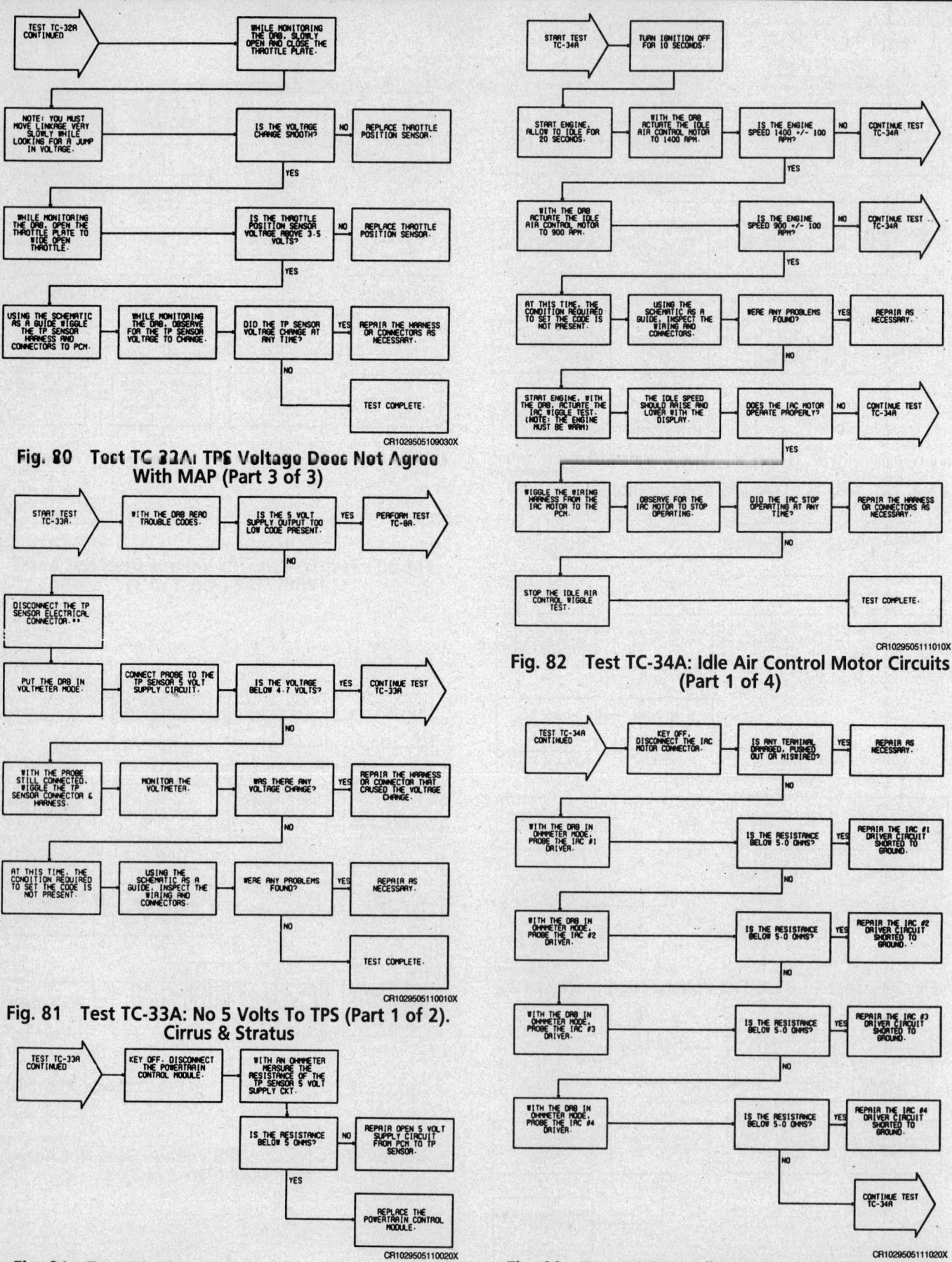

Fig. 80   Test TC-32A: TPS Voltage Does Not Agree With MAP (Part 3 of 3)

Fig. 81   Test TC-33A: No 5 Volts To TPS (Part 1 of 2). Cirrus & Stratus

Fig. 81   Test TC-33A: No 5 Volts To TPS (Part 2 of 2). Cirrus & Stratus

Fig. 82   Test TC-34A: Idle Air Control Motor Circuits (Part 1 of 4)

Fig. 82   Test TC-34A: Idle Air Control Motor Circuits (Part 2 of 4)

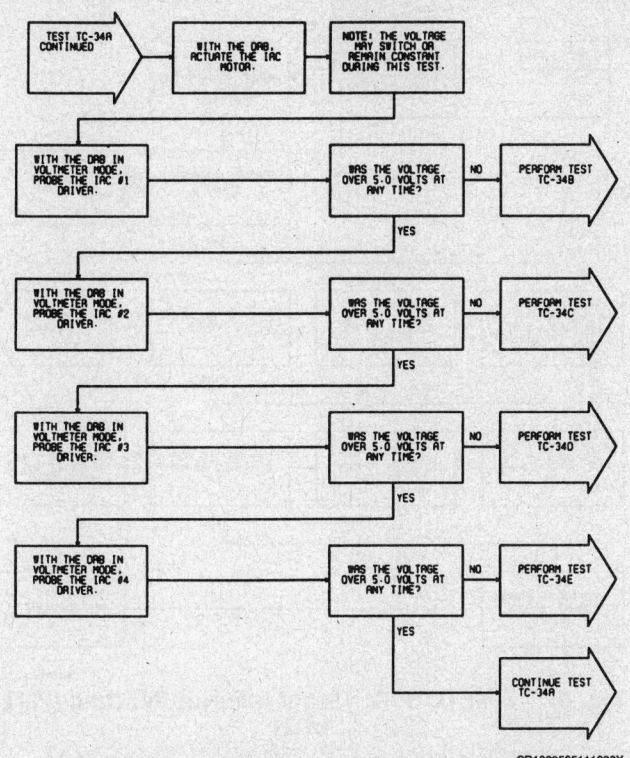

Fig. 82   Test TC-34A: Idle Air Control Motor Circuits (Part 3 of 4)

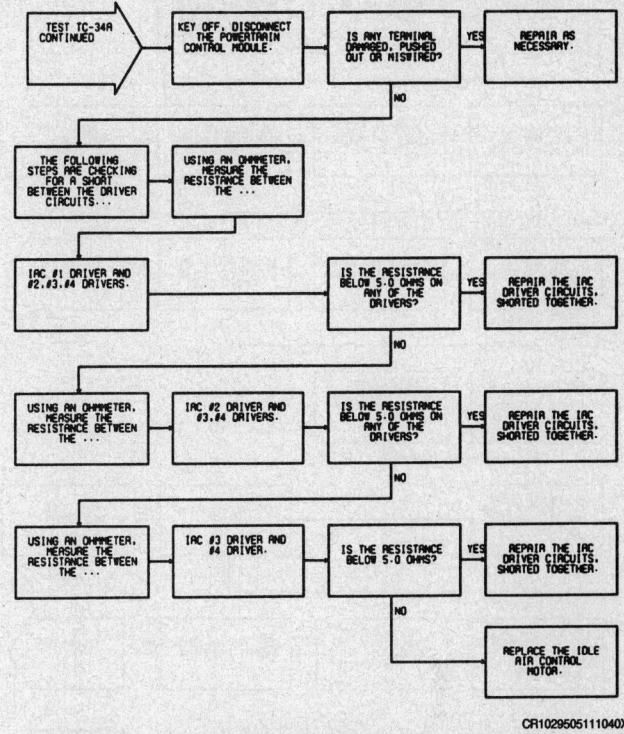

Fig. 82   Test TC-34A: Idle Air Control Motor Circuits (Part 4 of 4)

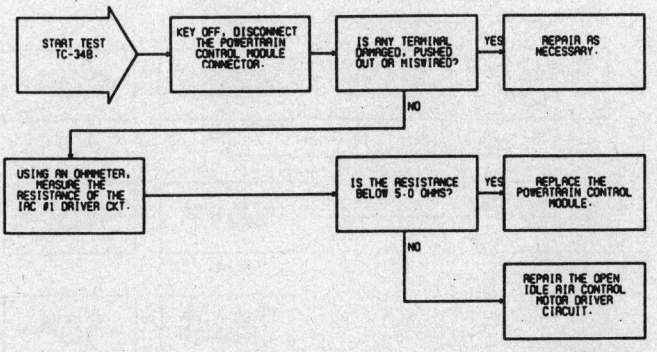

Fig. 83   Test TC-34B: Idle Air Control Motor Circuits

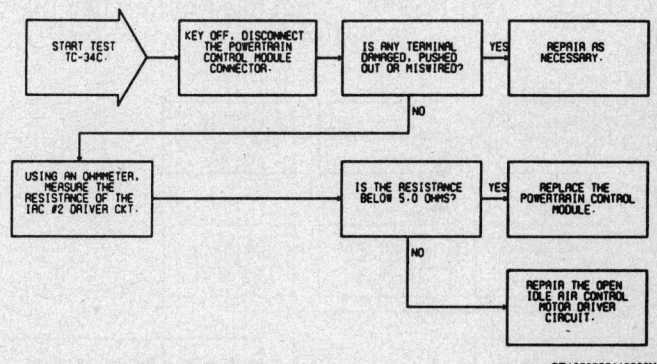

Fig. 84   Test TC-34C: Idle Air Control Motor Circuits

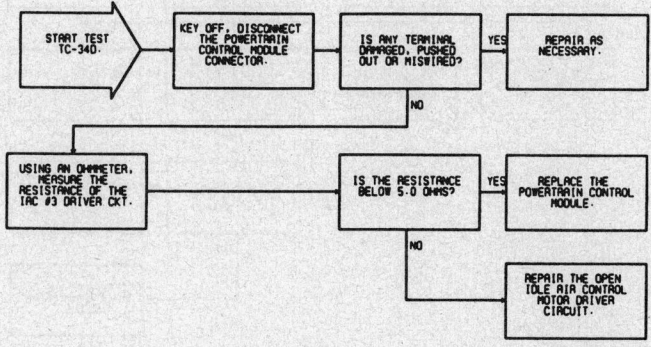

Fig. 85   Test TC-34D: Idle Air Control Motor Circuits

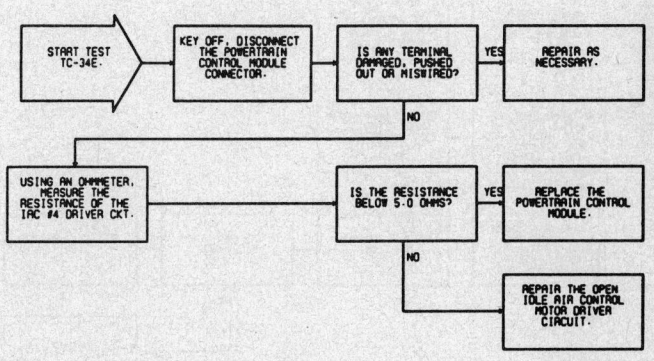

Fig. 86   Test TC-34E: Idle Air Control Motor Circuits

MULTI-POINT FUEL INJECTION (1995 AVENGER, CIRRUS, NEON, SEBRING, STRATUS & TALON w/NON-TURBOCHARGED 2.0L/4-122 ENGINE)

8-31

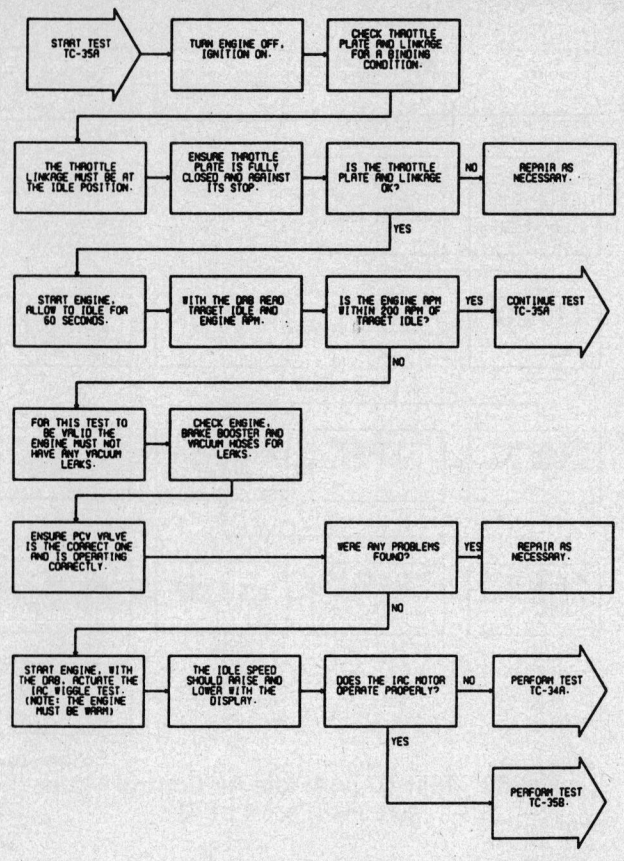

Fig. 87   Test TC-35A: Target Idle Not Reached (Part 1 of 2)

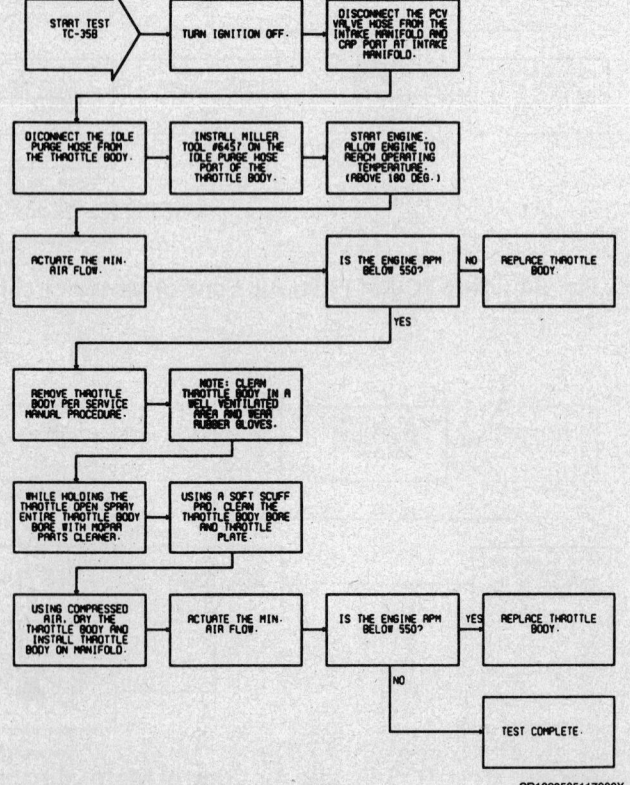

Fig. 88   Test TC-35B: Target Idle Not Reached

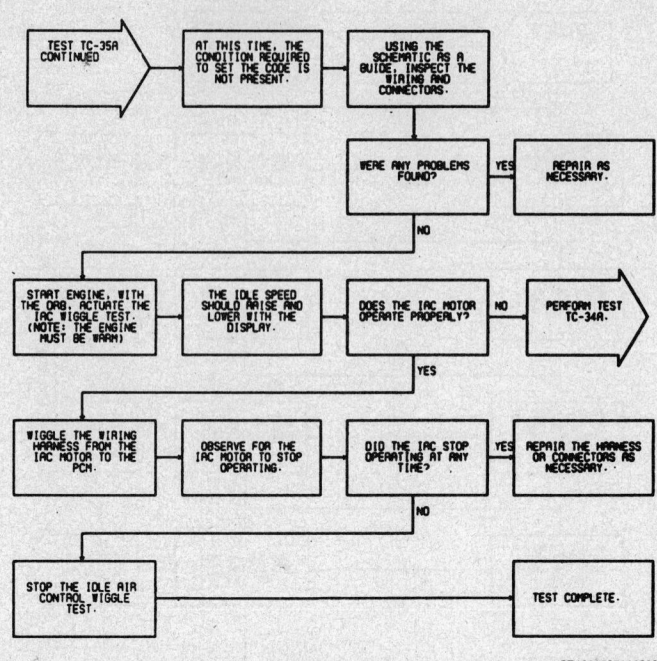

Fig. 87   Test TC-35A: Target Idle Not Reached (Part 2 of 2)

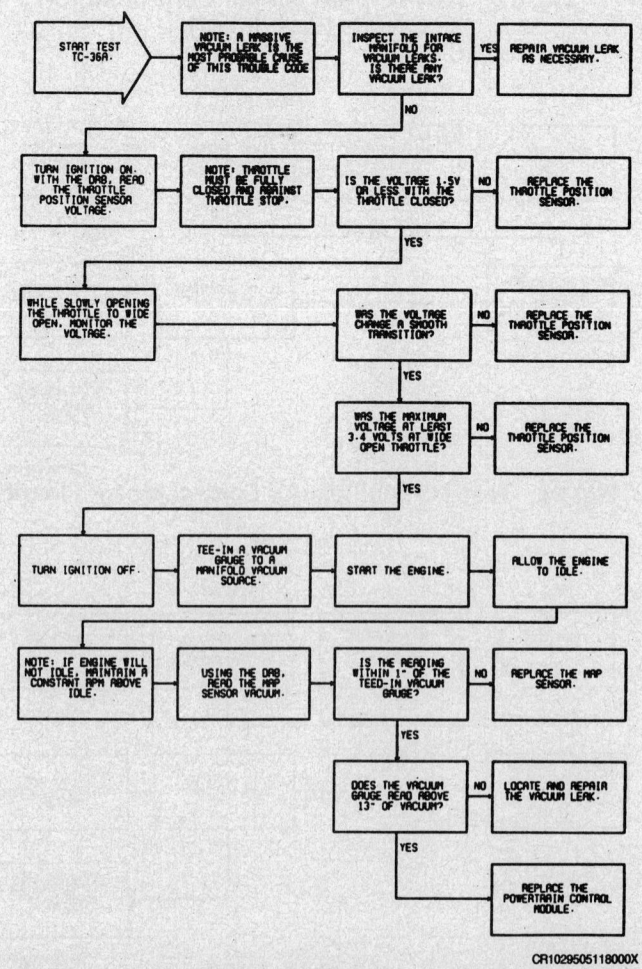

Fig. 89   Test TC-36A: Vacuum Leak Found, IAC Fully Seated

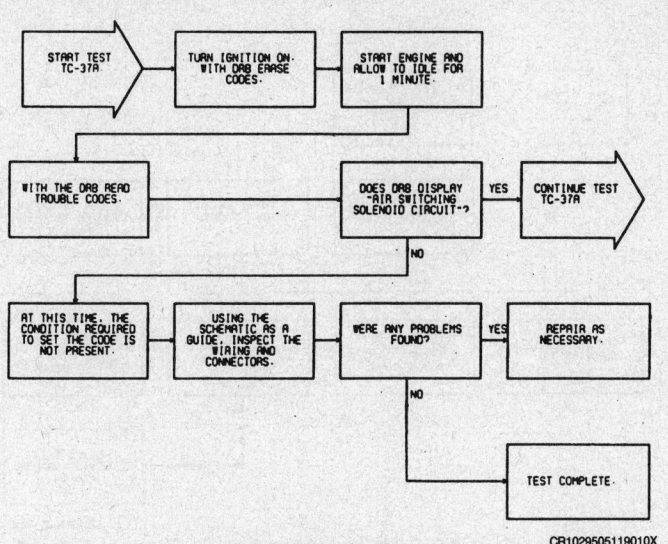

Fig. 90   Air Switching Solenoid Circuit (Part 1 of 3).
Avenger, Sebring & Talon

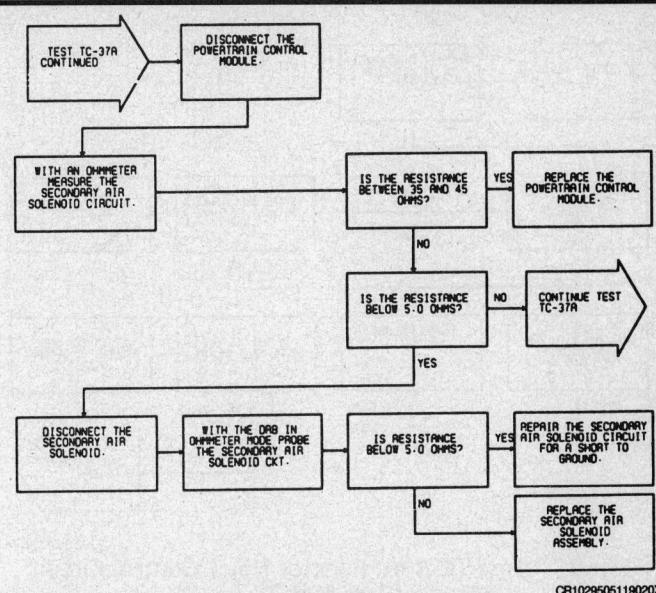

Fig. 90   Air Switching Solenoid Circuit (Part 2 of 3).
Avenger, Sebring & Talon

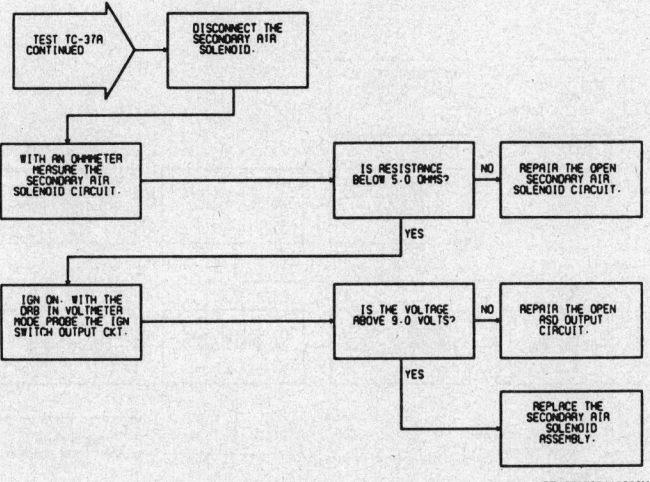

Fig. 90   Air Switching Solenoid Circuit (Part 3 of 3).
Avenger, Sebring & Talon

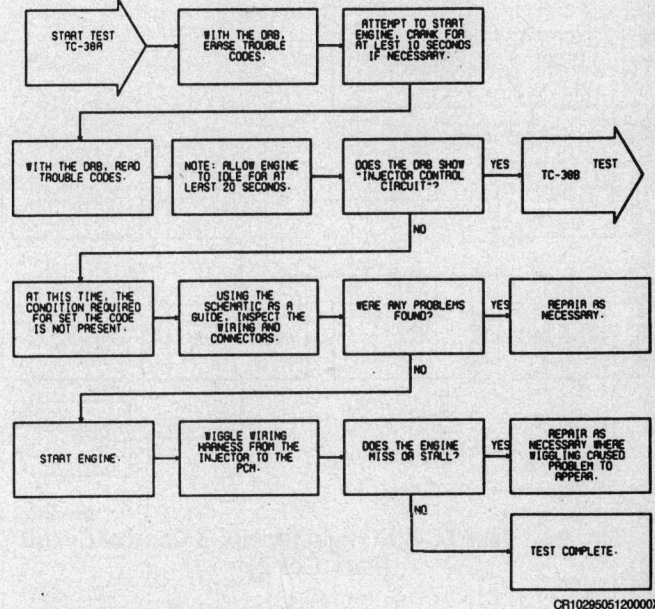

Fig. 91   Test TC-38A: Injector No. 1 Control Circuit

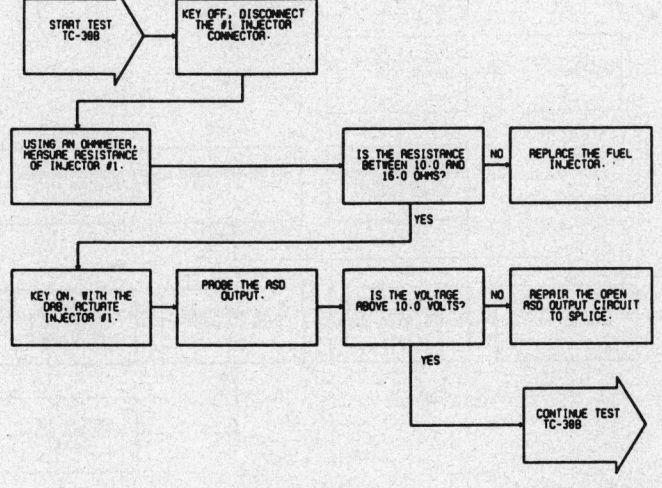

Fig. 92   Test TC-38B: Injector No. 1 Control Circuit
(Part 1 of 2)

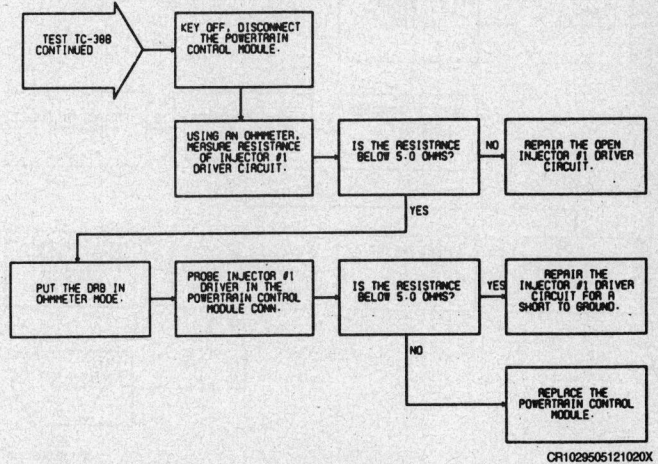

Fig. 92   Test TC-38B: Injector No. 1 Control Circuit
(Part 2 of 2)

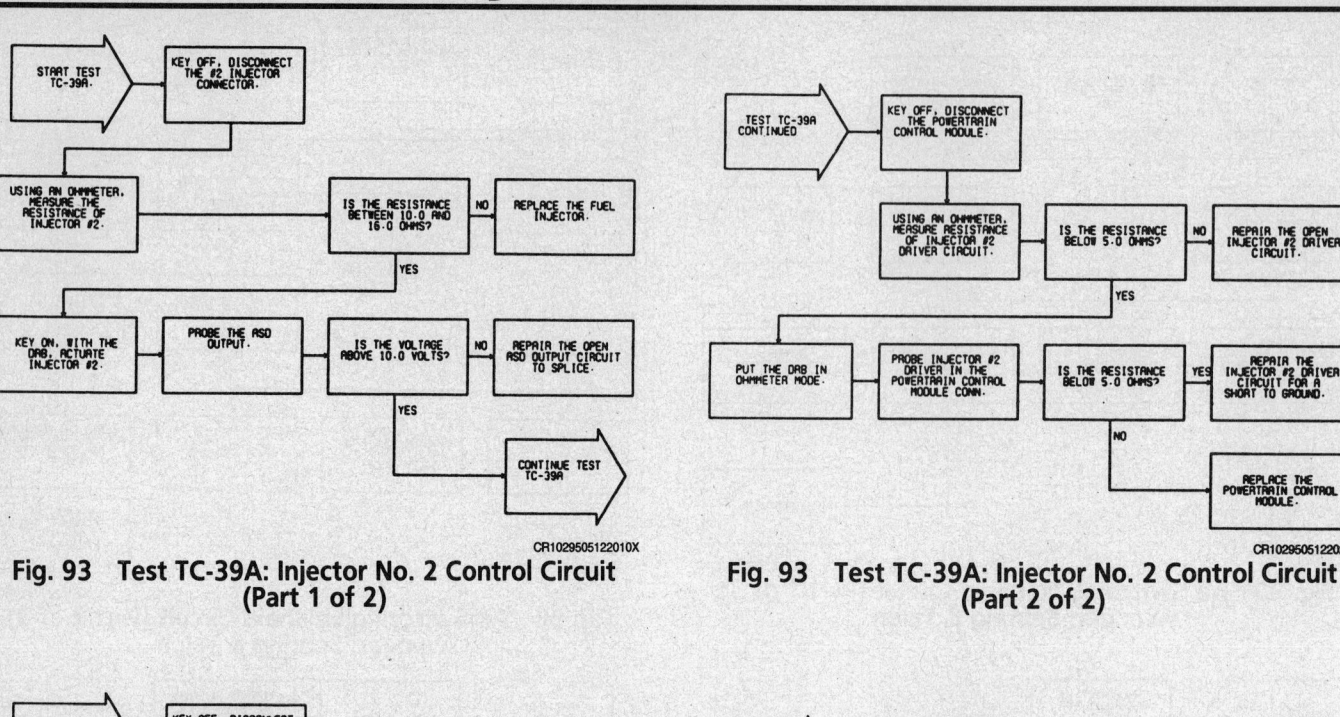

Fig. 93   Test TC-39A: Injector No. 2 Control Circuit (Part 1 of 2)

Fig. 93   Test TC-39A: Injector No. 2 Control Circuit (Part 2 of 2)

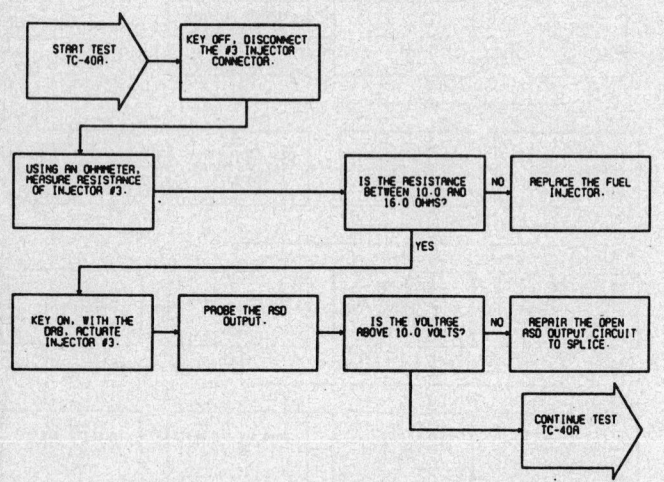

Fig. 94   Test TC-40A: Injector No. 3 Control Circuit (Part 1 of 2)

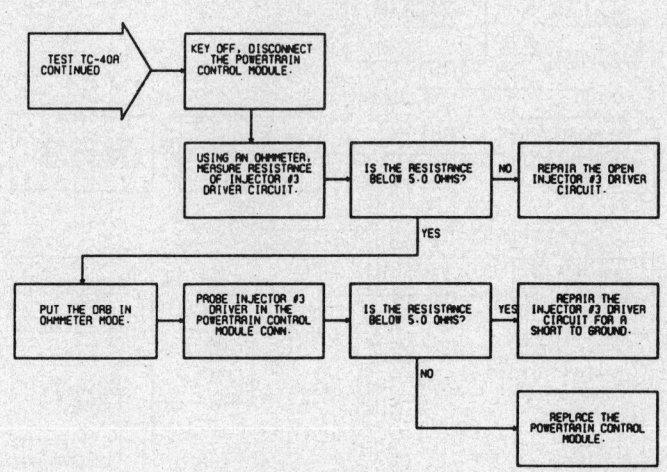

Fig. 94   Test TC-40A: Injector No. 3 Control Circuit (Part 2 of 2)

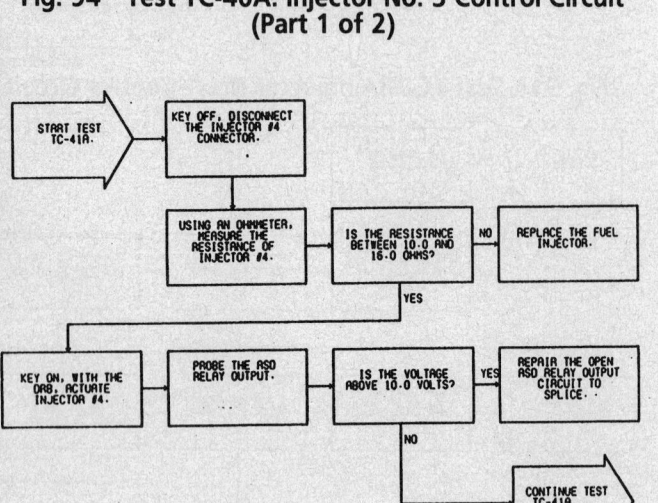

Fig. 95   Test TC-41A: Injector No. 4 Control Circuit (Part 1 of 2)

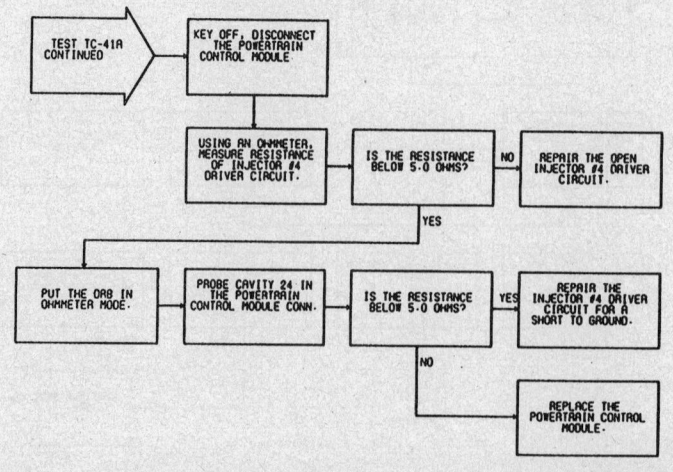

Fig. 95   Test TC-41A: Injector No. 4 Control Circuit (Part 2 of 2)

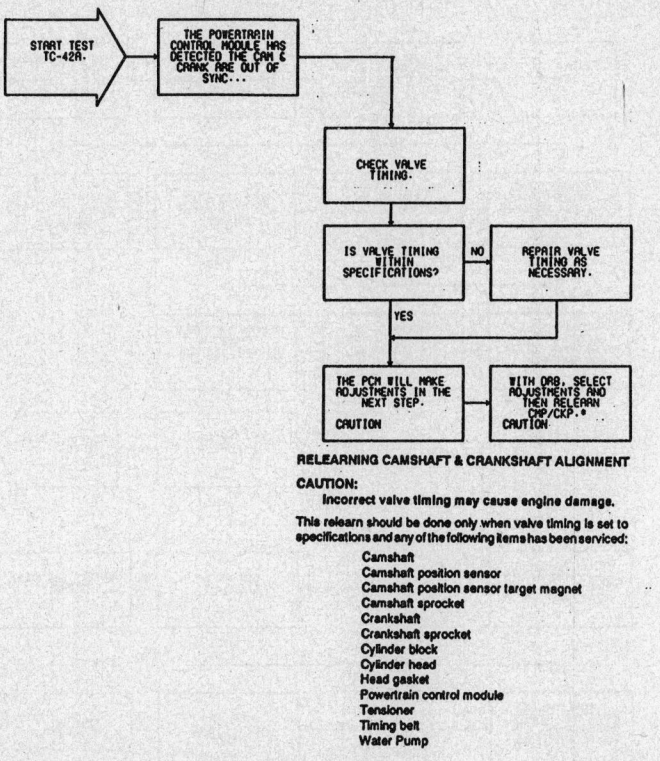

Fig. 96   Test TC-42A: Timing Belt Skipped 1 Tooth Or More

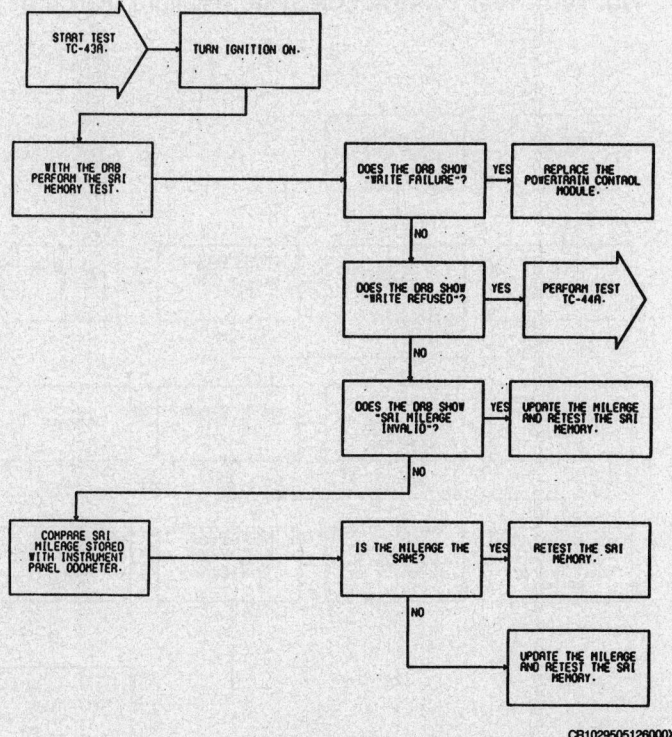

Fig. 97   Test TC-43A: PCM Failure SRI Mile Not Stored

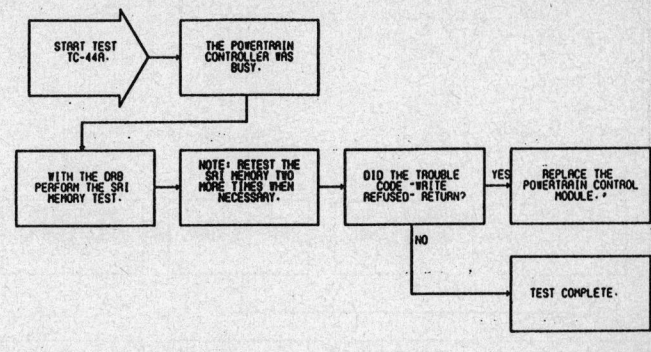

Fig. 98   Test TC-44A: PCM Failure EEPROM Write Denied

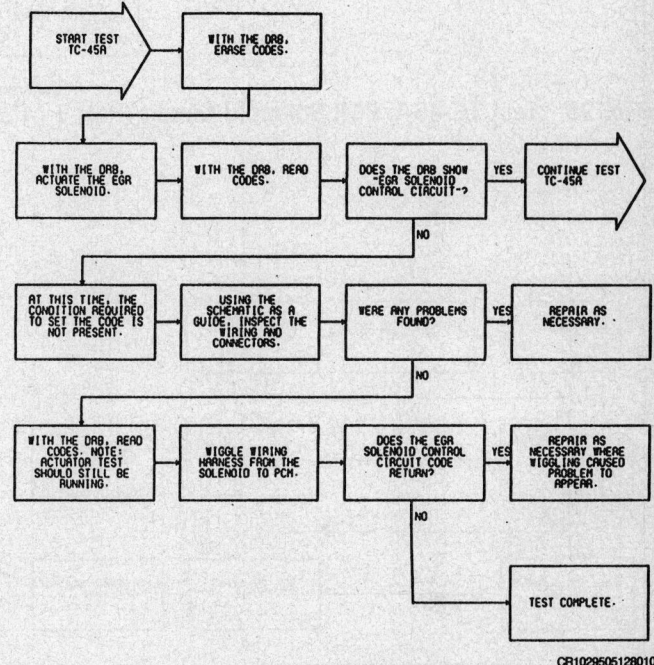

Fig. 99   Test TC-45A: EGR Solenoid Circuit (Part 1 of 3)

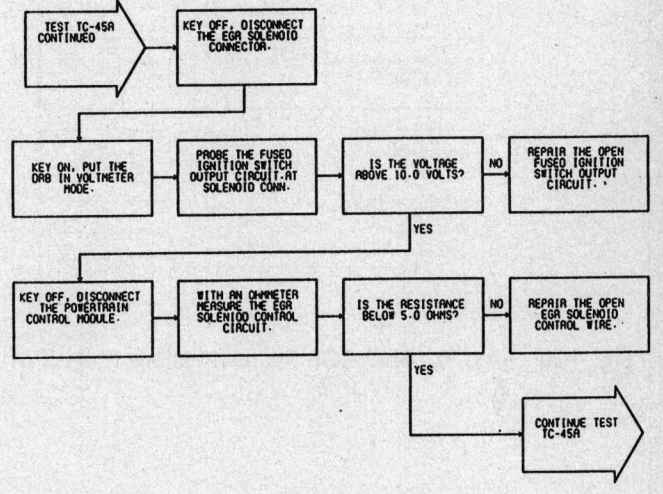

Fig. 99   Test TC-45A: EGR Solenoid Circuit (Part 2 of 3)

MULTI-POINT FUEL INJECTION (1995 AVENGER, CIRRUS, NEON, SEBRING, STRATUS & TALON w/NON-TURBOCHARGED 2.0L/4-122 ENGINE)

8-35

CHRYSLER--Fuel Injection

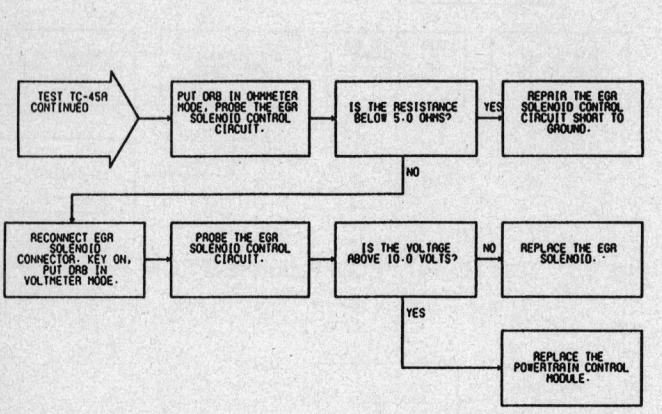

Fig. 99   Test TC-45A: EGR Solenoid Circuit (Part 3 of 3)

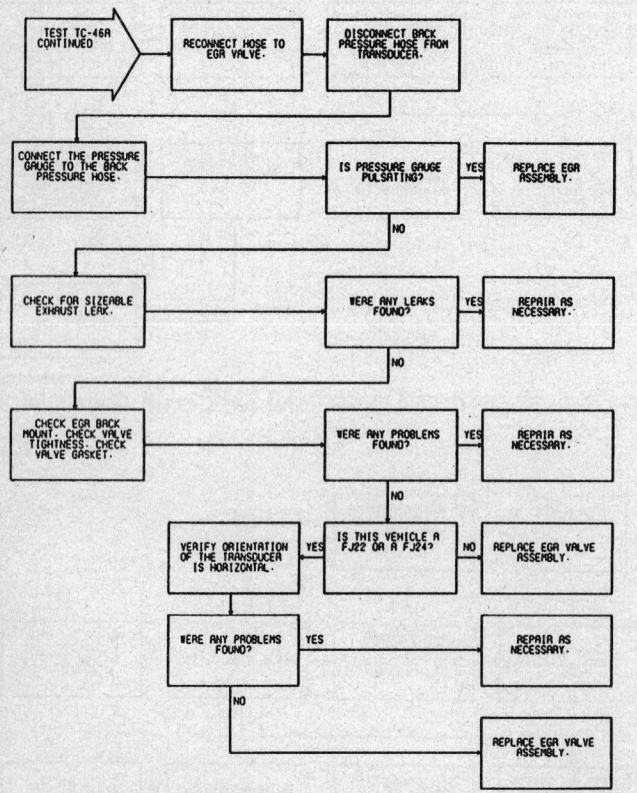

Fig. 100   Test TC-46A: EGR System Failure (Part 2 of 2)

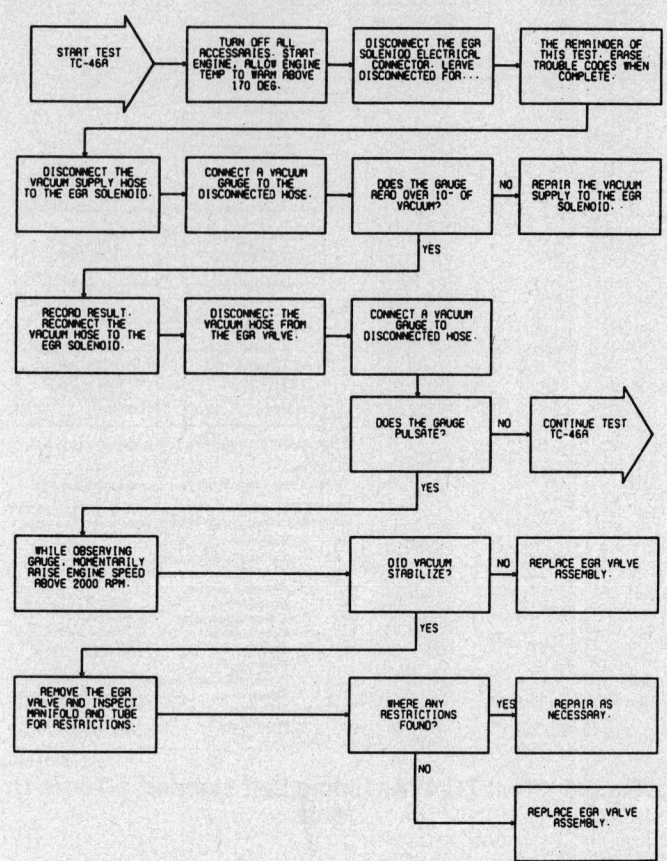

Fig. 100   Test TC-46A: EGR System Failure (Part 1 of 2)

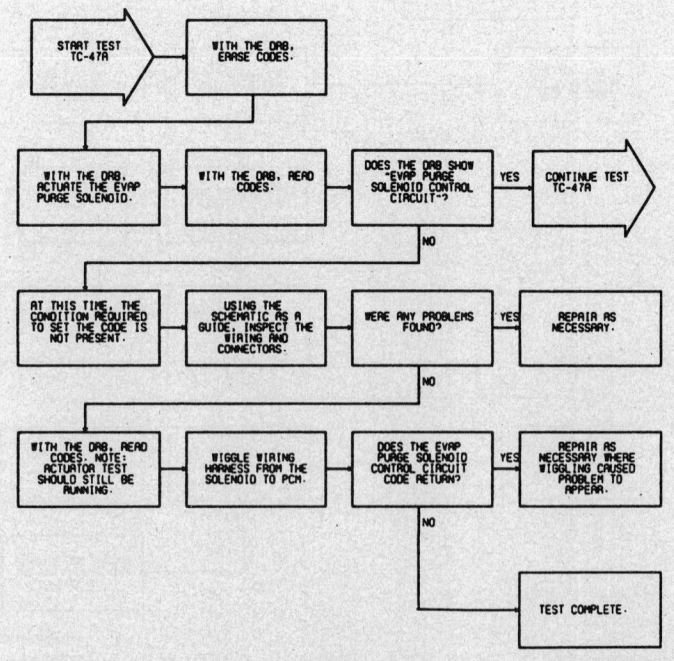

Fig. 101   Test TC-47A: Evap Solenoid Circuit(Part 1 of 3)

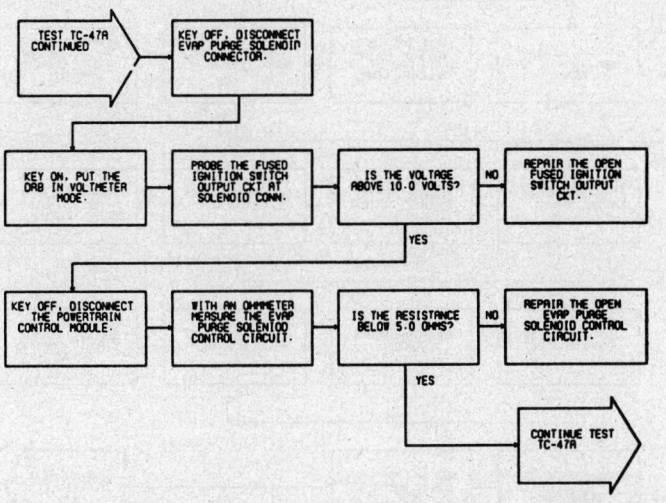

CR1029505130020X

Fig. 101   Test TC-47A: Evap Solenoid Circuit(Part 2 of 3)

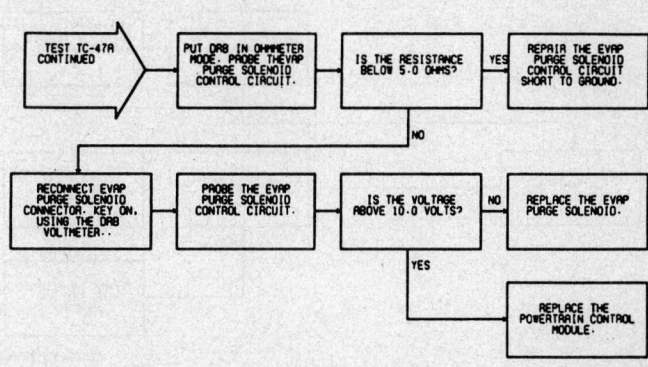

CR1029505130030X

Fig. 101   Test TC-47A: Evap Solenoid Circuit(Part 3 of 3)

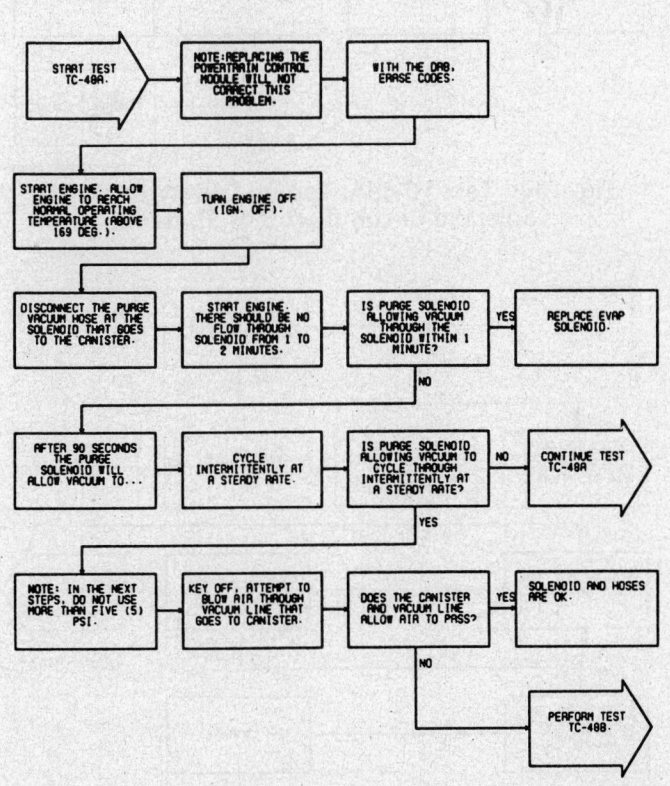

CR1029505131010X

Fig. 102   Test TC-48A: Evap Purge Flow Monitor Failure (Part 1 of 2)

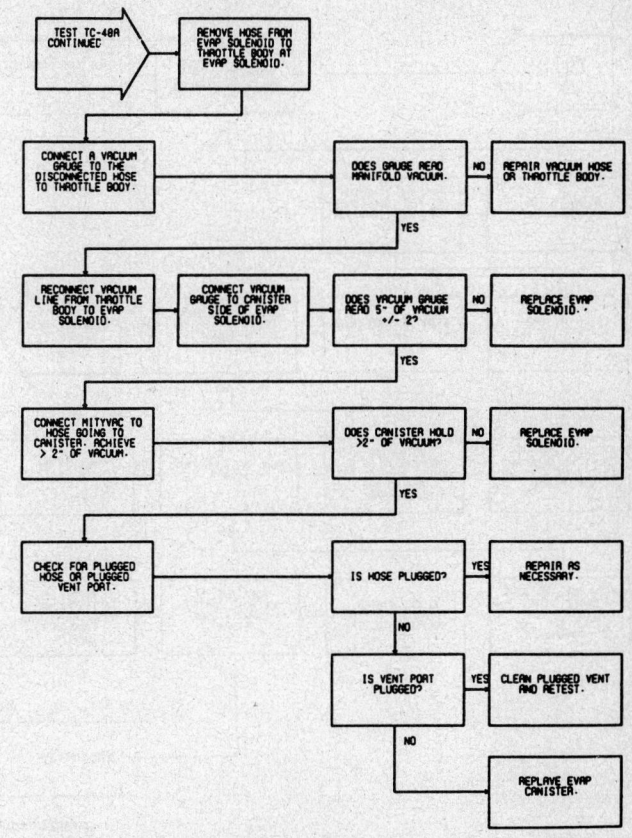

CR1029505131020X

Fig. 102   Test TC-48A: Evap Purge Flow Monitor Failure (Part 2 of 2)

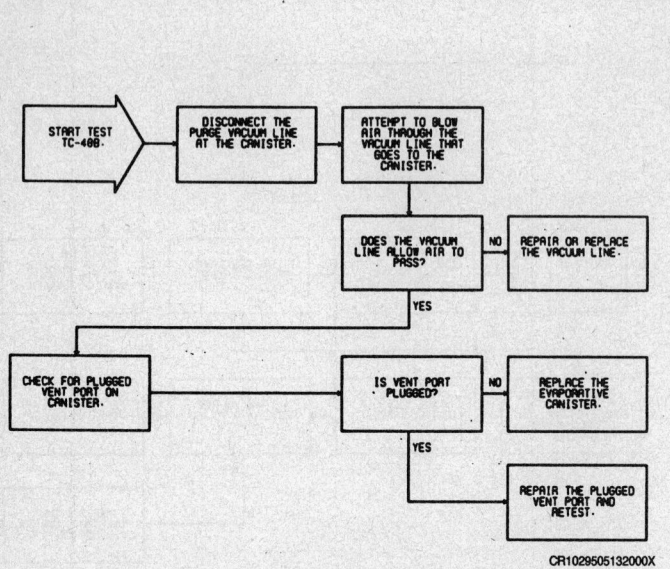

Fig. 103   Test TC-48B: Evap Purge Flow Monitor Failure

CR1029505132000X

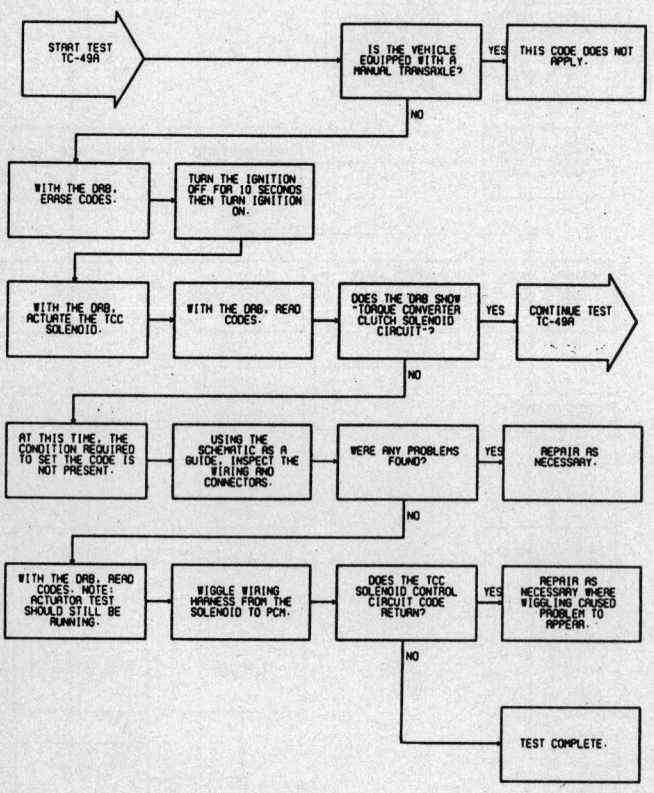

Fig. 104   Test TC-49A: Torque Converter Clutch Solenoid Circuit (Part 1 of 3). Neon

CR1029505133010X

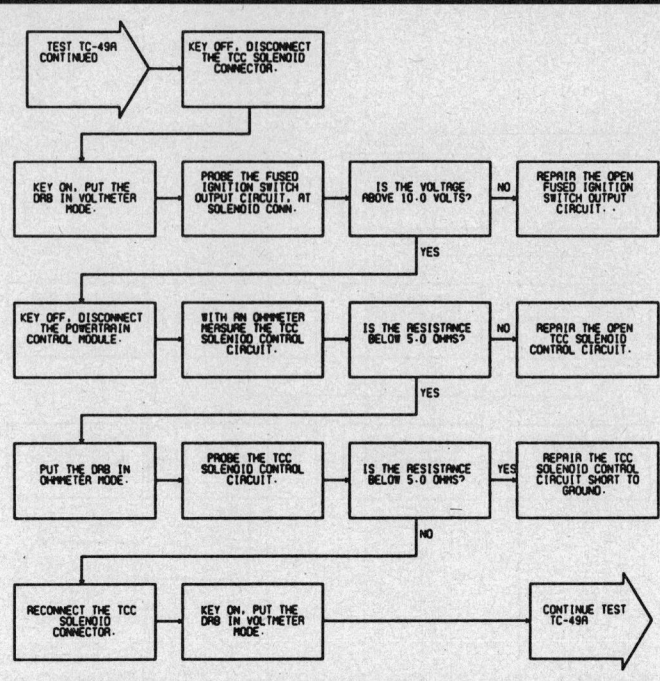

Fig. 104   Test TC-49A: Torque Converter Clutch Solenoid Circuit (Part 2 of 3). Neon

CR1029505133020X

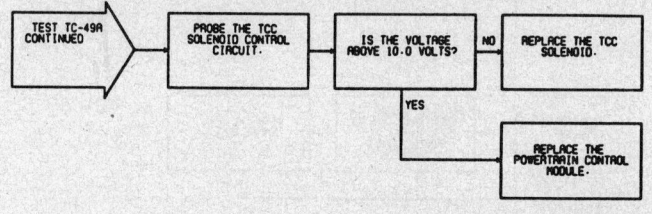

Fig. 104   Test TC-49A: Torque Converter Clutch Solenoid Circuit (Part 3 of 3). Neon

CR1029505133030X

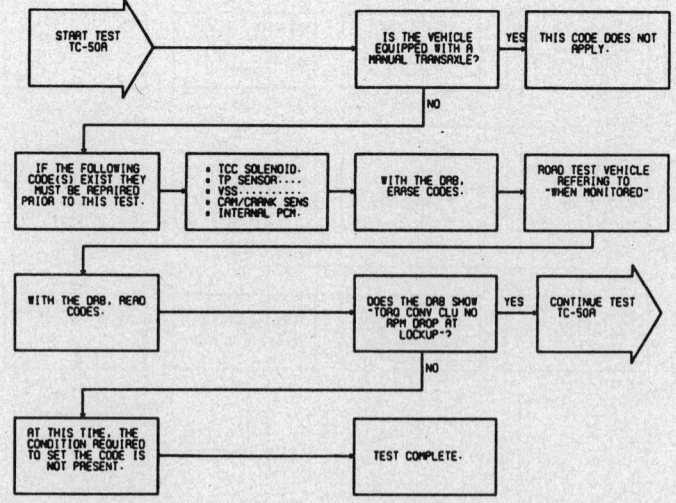

When monitored:

Vehicle speed < 60 mph
Run vehicle in third gear at about 40 mph with torque converter unlocked for at least 10 seconds.
Apply 1/3 throttle while making sure transmission does not downshift.   Back off on the throttle slightly until
the torque converter locks.   Keep the torque converter locked for at least 5 seconds by holding the throttle
and vehicle speed constant.

CR1029505134010X

Fig. 105   Test TC-50A: Torque Converter Clutch RPM Drop At Lockup (Part 1 of 3). Neon

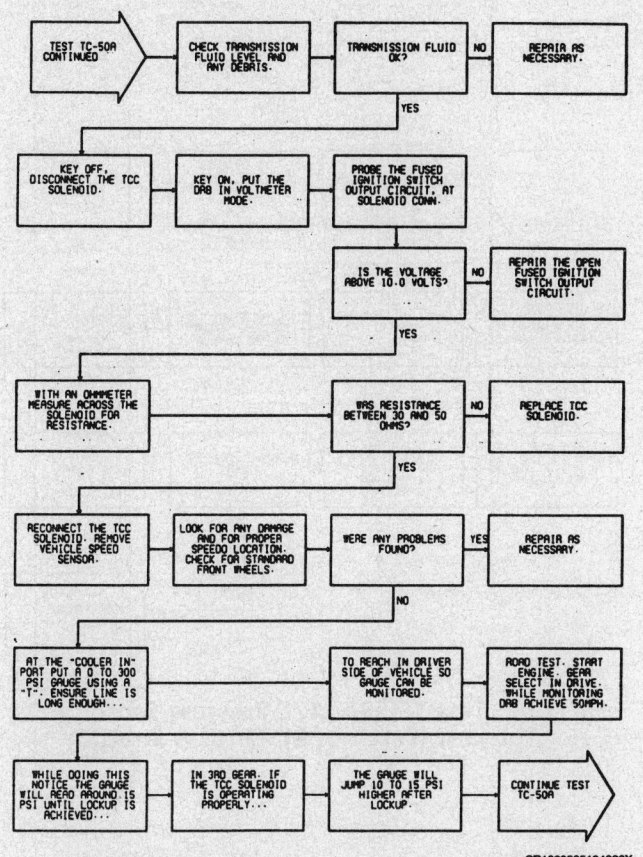

Fig. 105   Test TC-50A: Torque Converter Clutch RPM Drop At Lockup (Part 2 of 3). Neon

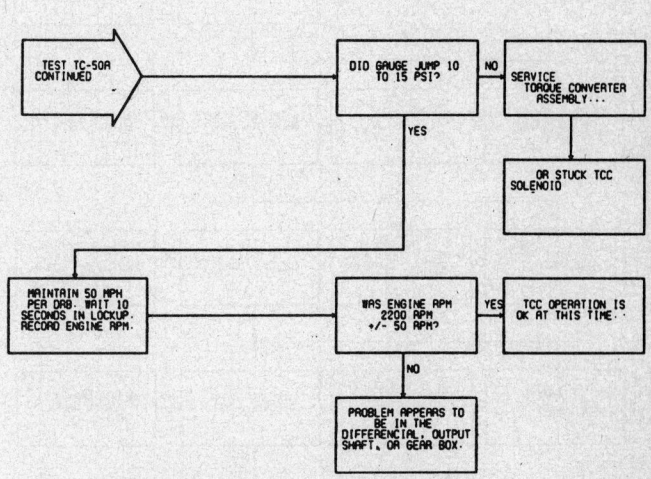

Fig. 105   Test TC-50A: Torque Converter Clutch RPM Drop At Lockup (Part 3 of 3). Neon

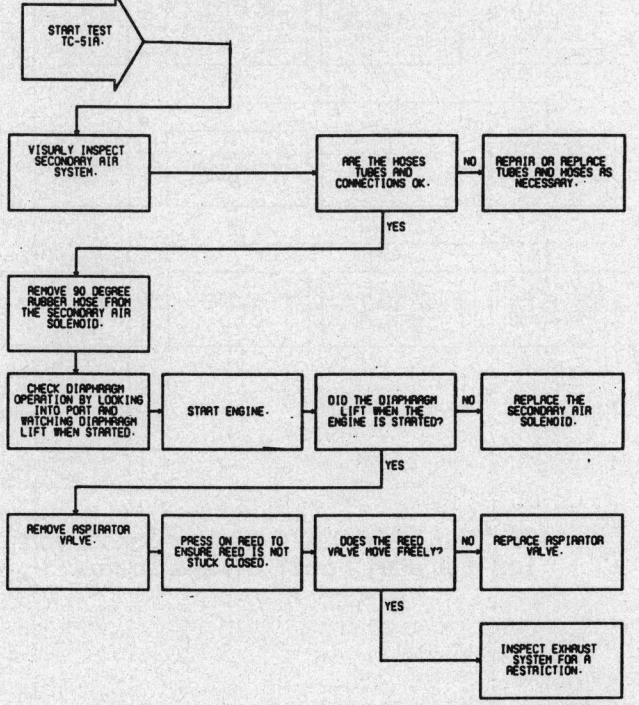

Fig. 106   Test TC-51A: Too Little Secondary Air Or Too Much Secondary Air. Avenger, Sebring & Talon

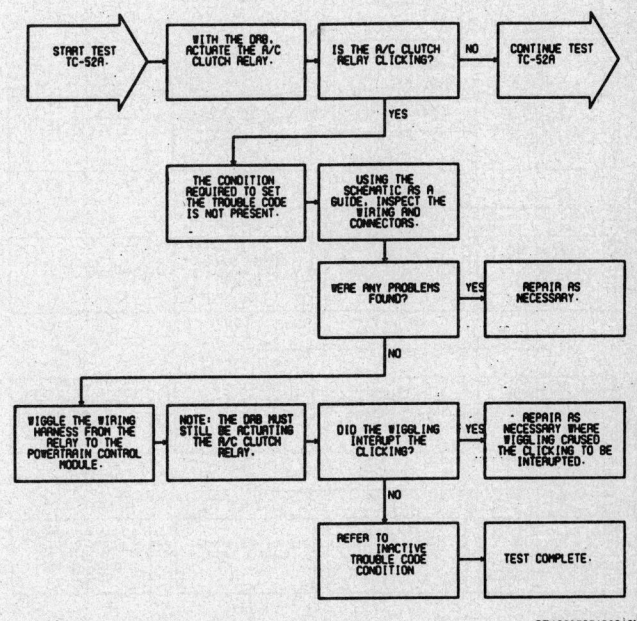

Fig. 107   Test TC-52A: A/C Clutch Relay Circuit (Part 1 of 2)

CHRYSLER–Fuel Injection

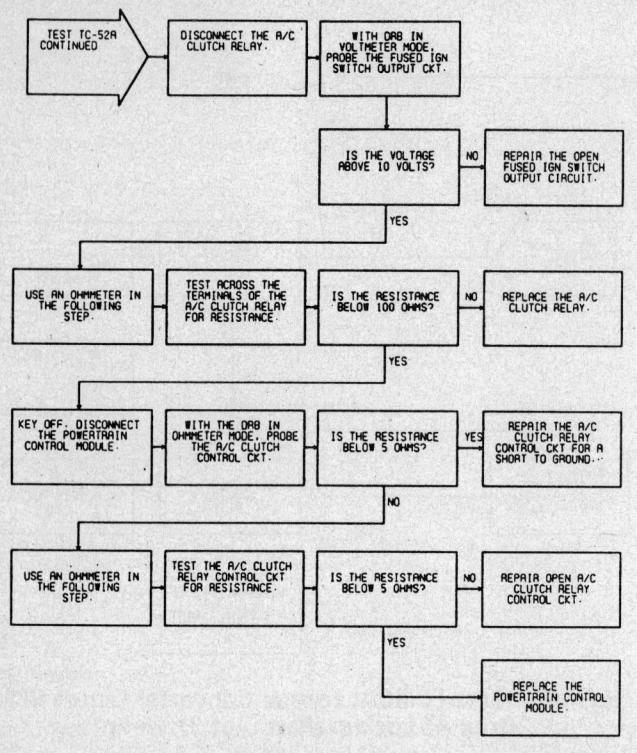

Fig. 107   Test TC-52A: A/C Clutch Relay Circuit (Part 2 of 2)

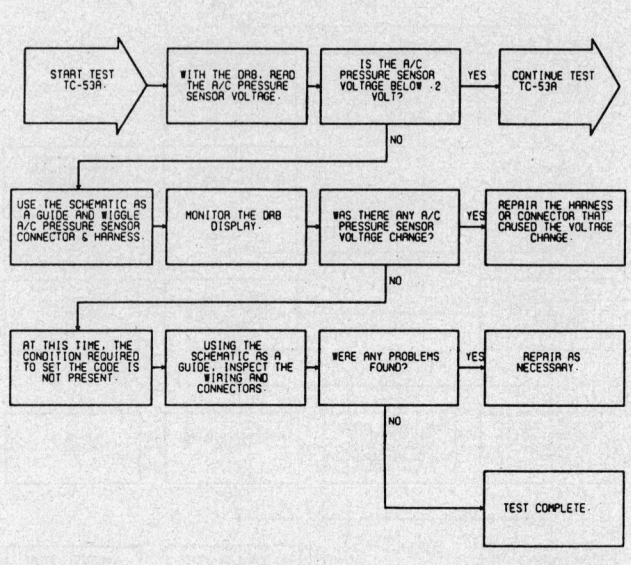

Fig. 108   Test TC-53A: A/C Pressure Sensor Volts Too Low (Part 1 of 2). Cirrus & Stratus

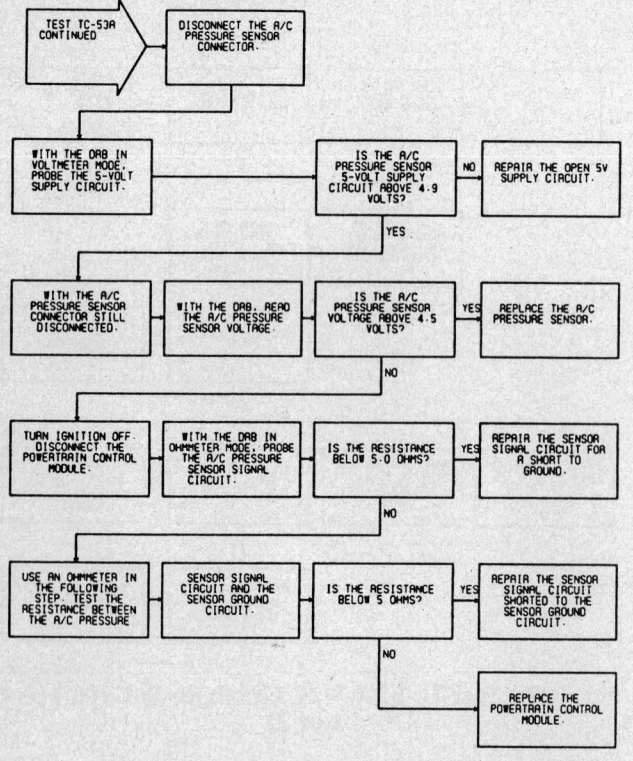

Fig. 108   Test TC-53A: A/C Pressure Sensor Volts Too Low (Part 2 of 2). Cirrus & Stratus

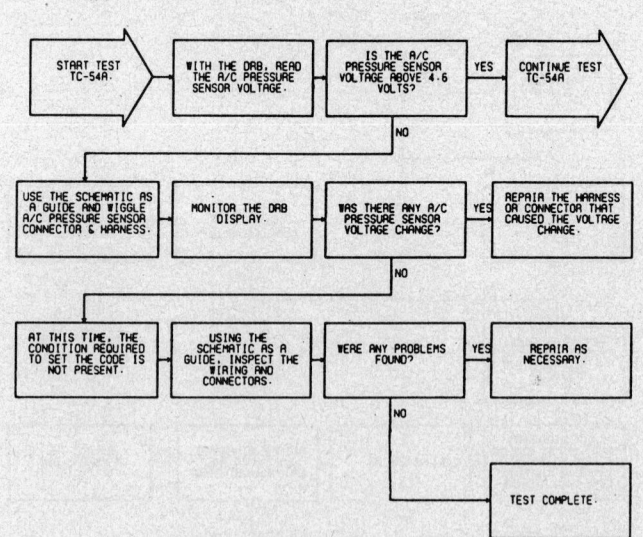

Fig. 109   Test TC-54A: A/C Pressure Sensor Volts Too High (Part 1 of 2). Cirrus & Stratus

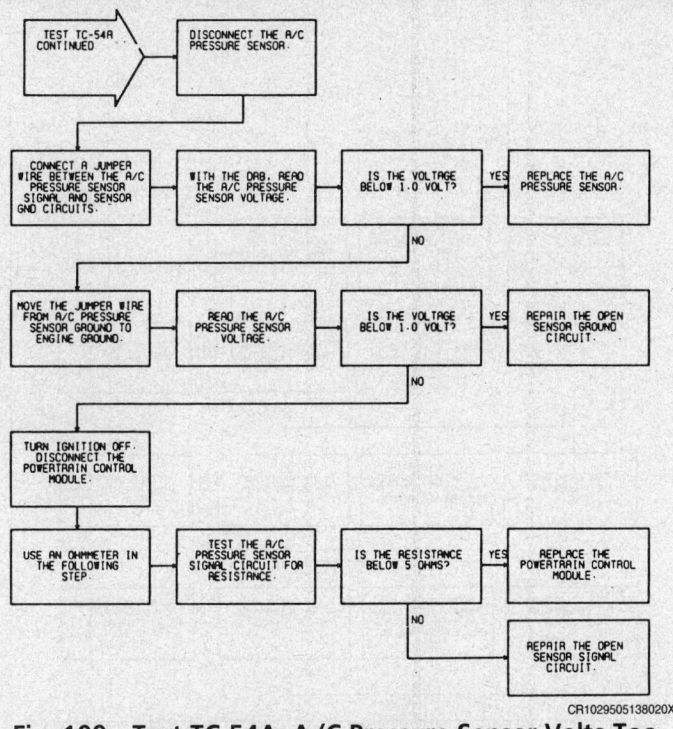

Fig. 109 Test TC-54A: A/C Pressure Sensor Volts Too
High (Part 2 of 2). Cirrus & Stratus

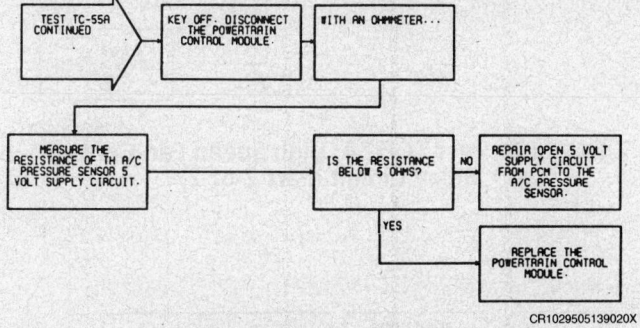

Fig. 110 Test TC-55A: No 5 Volts To A/C Pressure
Sensor (Part 2 of 2). Cirrus & Stratus

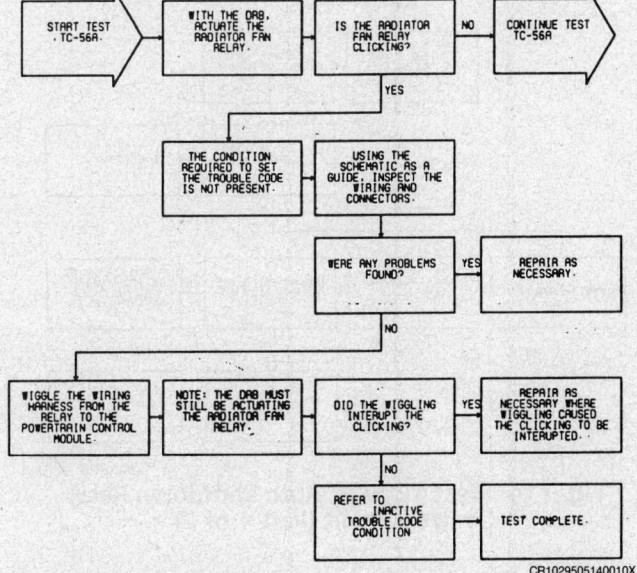

Fig. 111 Test TC-56A: Radiator Fan Control Relay
Circuit (Part 1 of 2). Neon

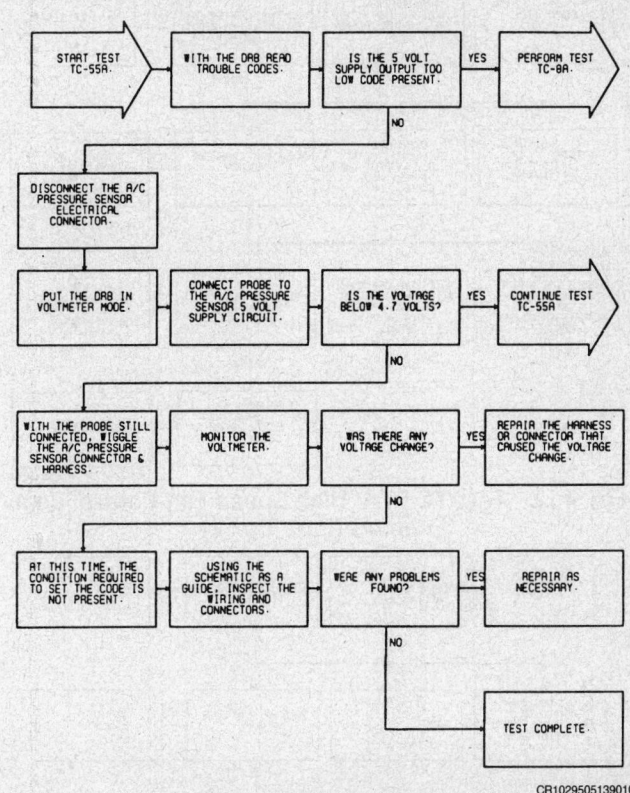

Fig. 110 Test TC-55A: No 5 Volts To A/C Pressure
Sensor (Part 1 of 2). Cirrus & Stratus

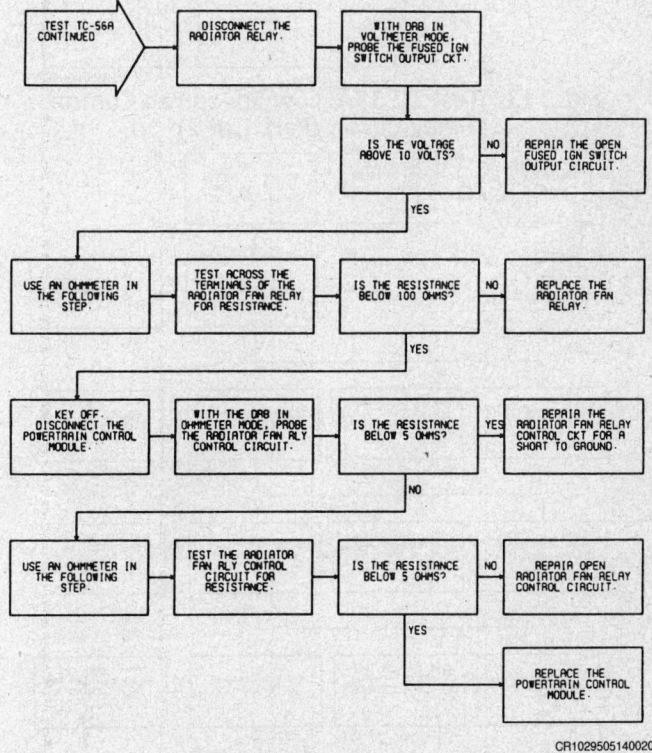

Fig. 111 Test TC-56A: Radiator Fan Control Relay
Circuit (Part 2 of 2). Neon

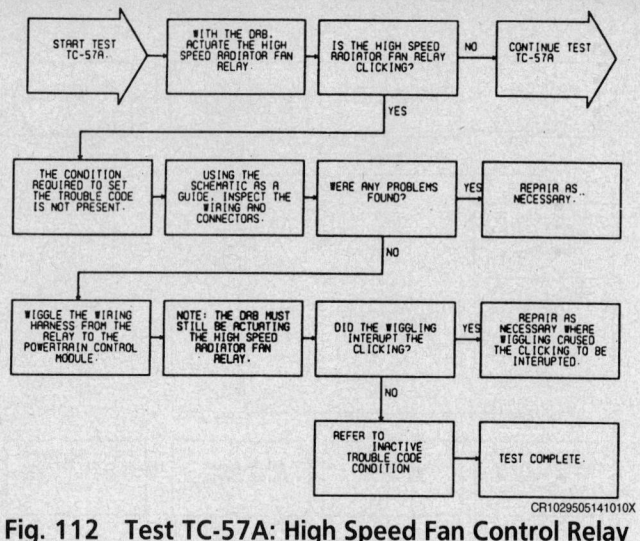

Fig. 112   Test TC-57A: High Speed Fan Control Relay Circuit (Part 1 of 2)

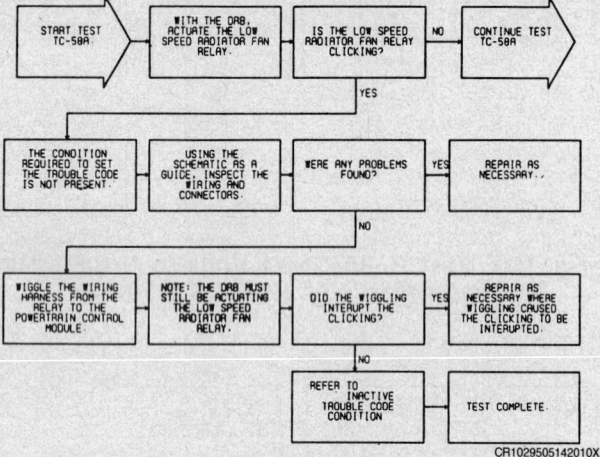

Fig. 113   Test TC-58A: Low Speed Fan Control Relay Circuit (Part 1 of 2)

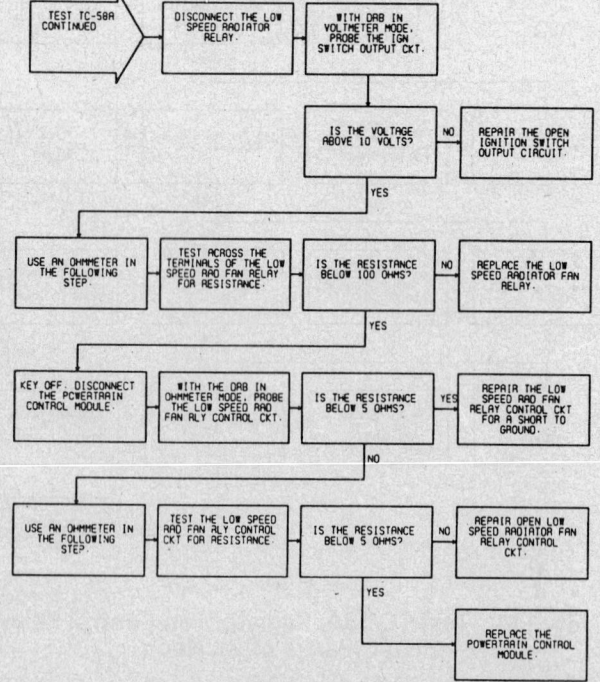

Fig. 113   Test TC-58A: Low Speed Fan Control Relay Circuit (Part 2 of 2)

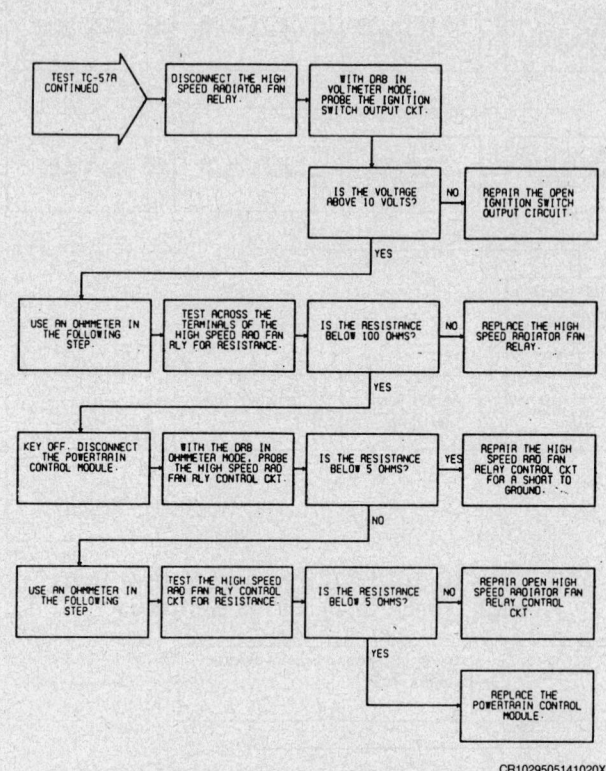

Fig. 112   Test TC-57A: High Speed Fan Control Relay Circuit (Part 2 of 2)

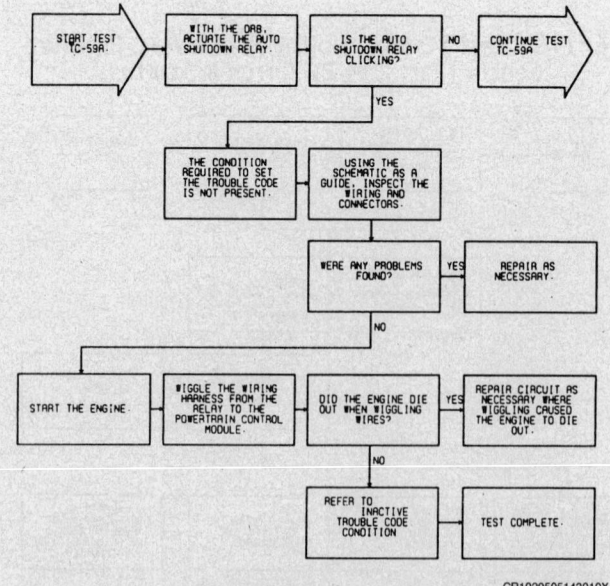

Fig. 114   Test TC-59A: Auto Shutdown Relay Control Circuit (Part 1 of 2)

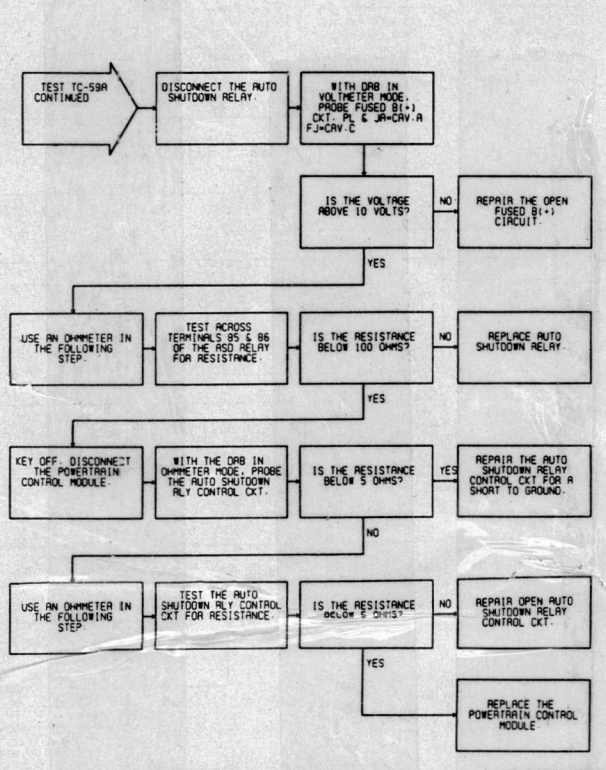

Fig. 114   Test TC-59A: Auto Shutdown Relay Control Circuit (Part 2 of 2)

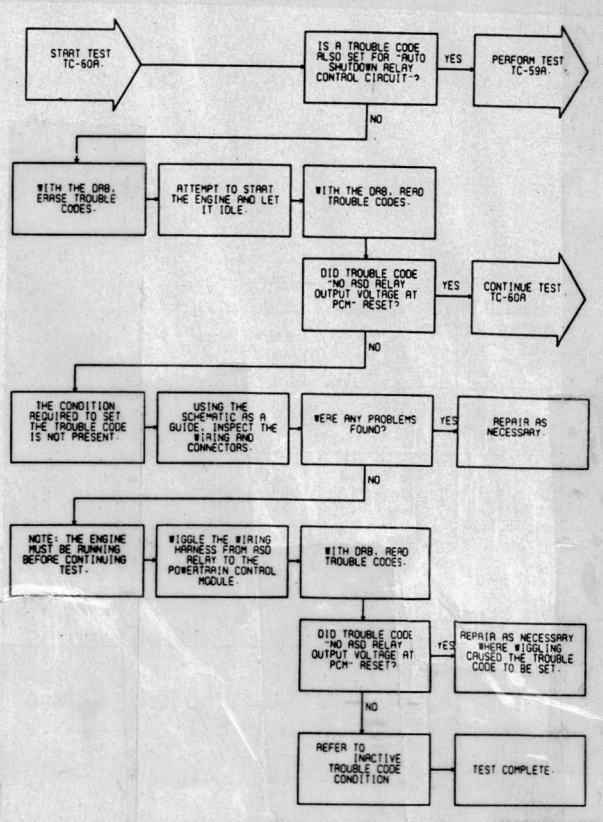

Fig. 115   Test TC-60A: No ASD Relay Output Voltage At PCM (Part 1 of 3)

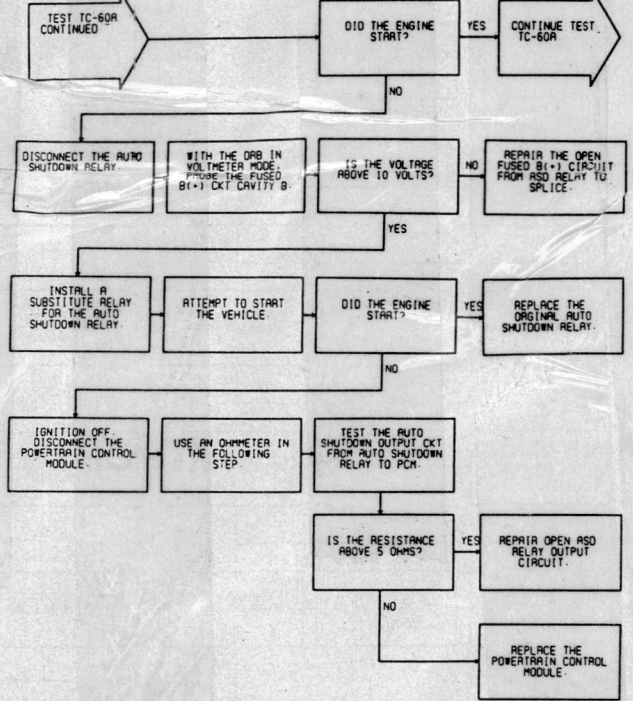

Fig. 115   Test TC-60A: No ASD Relay Output Voltage At PCM (Part 2 of 3)

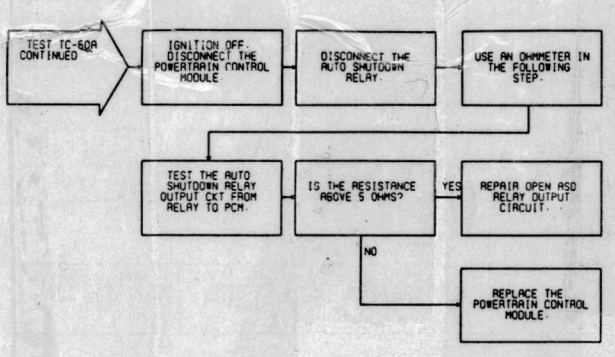

Fig. 115   Test TC-60A: No ASD Relay Output Voltage At PCM (Part 3 of 3)

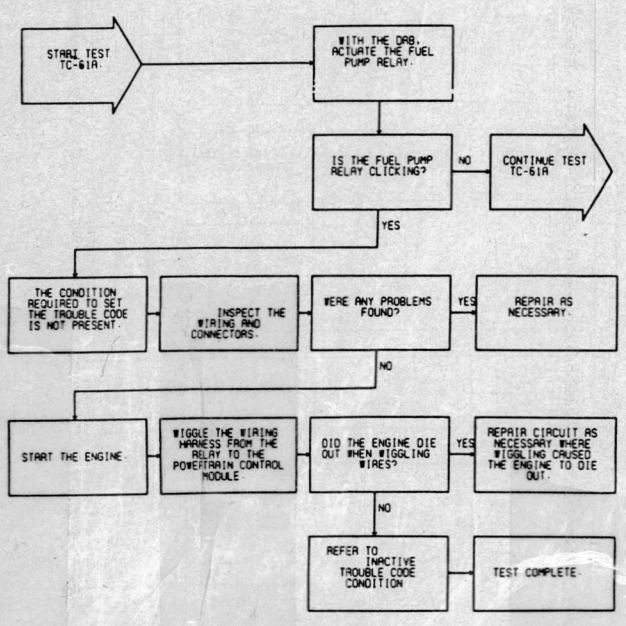

Fig. 116   Test TC-61A: Fuel Pump Relay Control Circuit (Part 1 of 2)

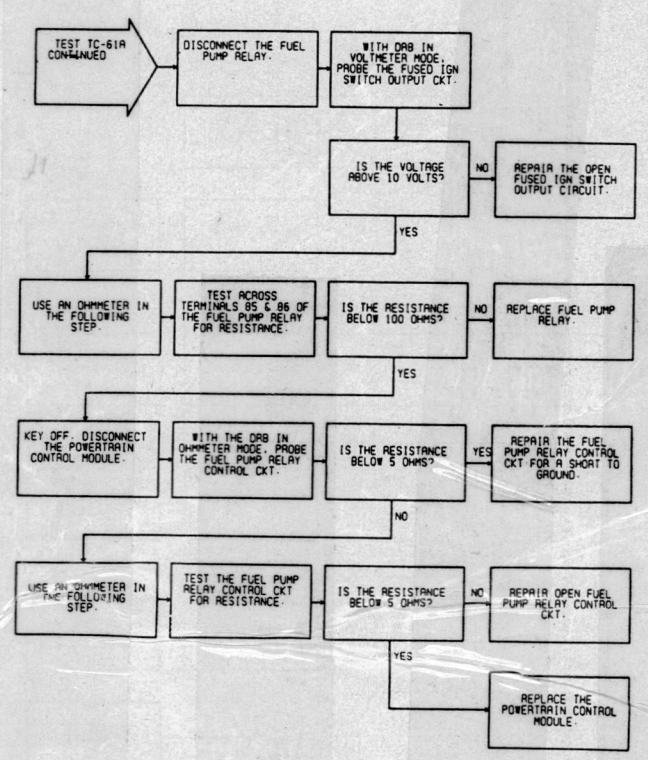

Fig. 116   Test TC-61A: Fuel Pump Relay Control Circuit (Part 2 of 2)

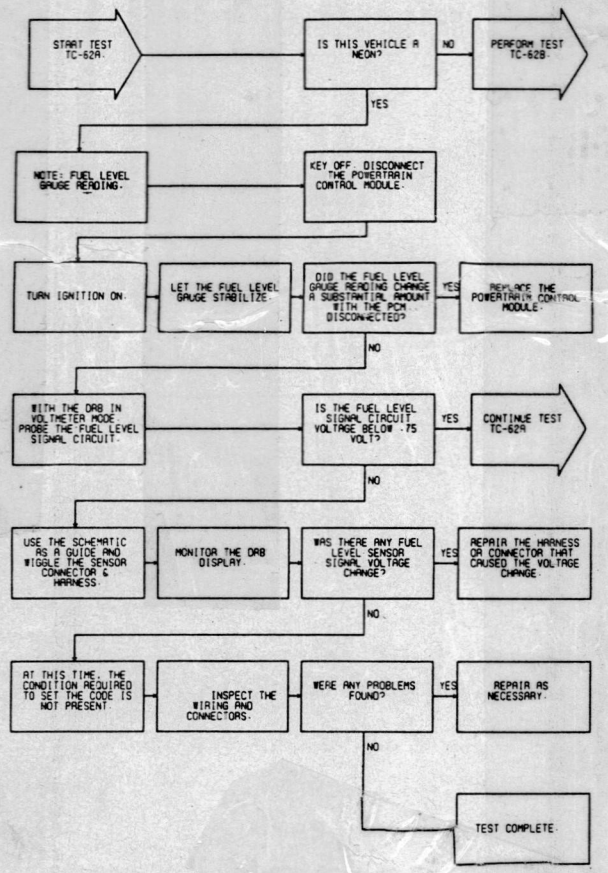

Fig. 117   Test TC-62A: Fuel Level Sending Unit Volts Too Low (Part 1 of 2)

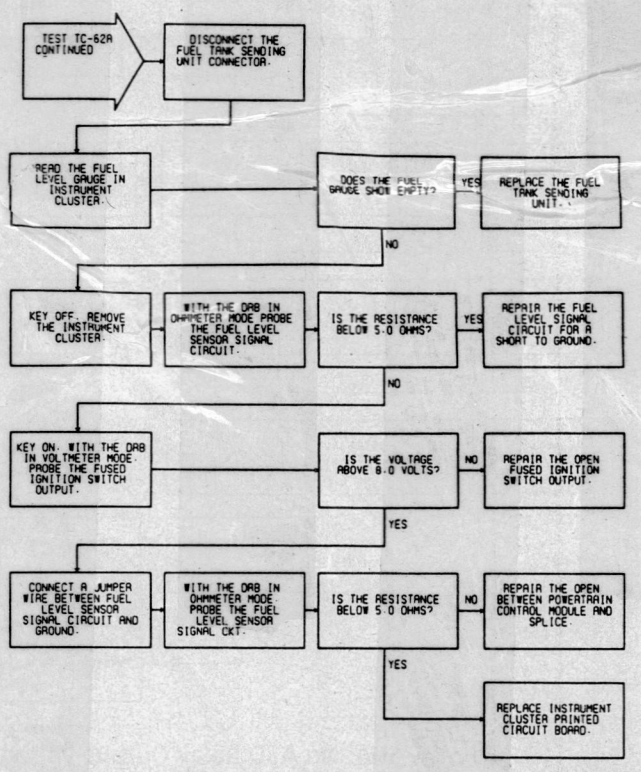

Fig. 117   Test TC-62A: Fuel Level Sending Unit Volts Too Low (Part 2 of 2)

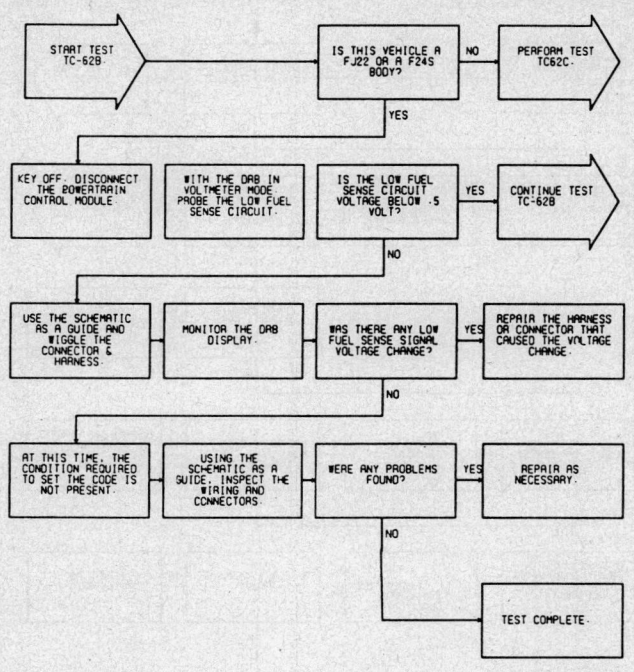

Fig. 118   Test TC-62B: Fuel Level Sending Unit Volts Too Low (Part 1 of 2)

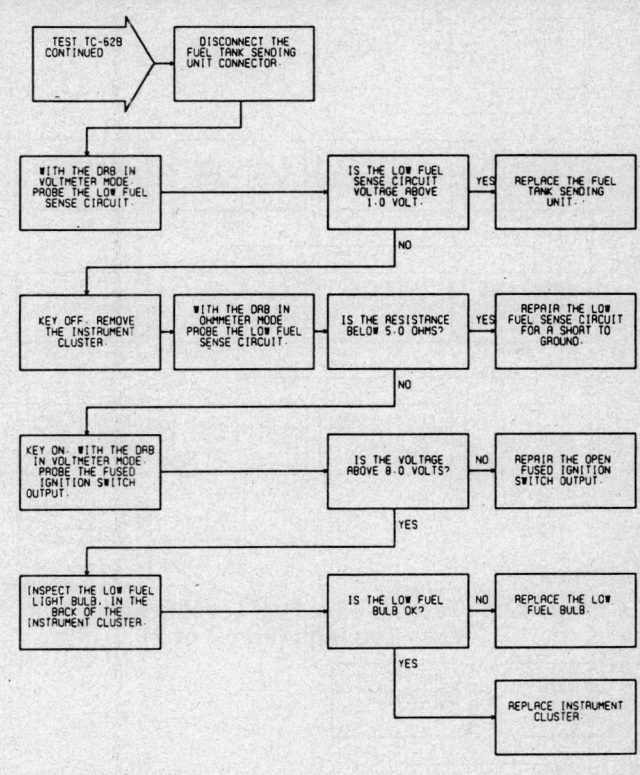

Fig. 118   Test TC-62B: Fuel Level Sending Unit Volts Too Low (Part 2 of 2)

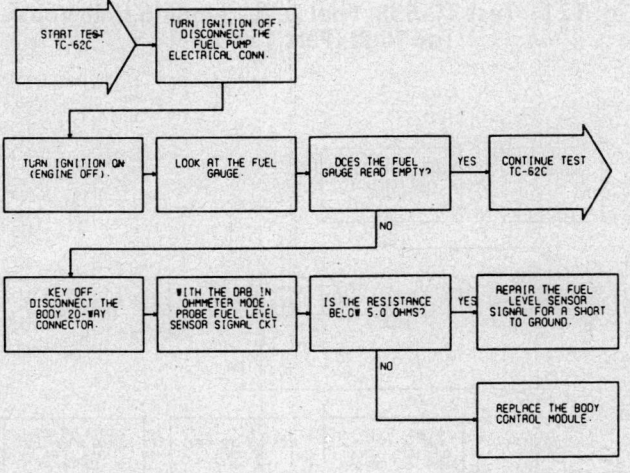

Fig. 119   Test TC-62C: Fuel Level Sending Unit Volts Too Low (Part 1 of 2)

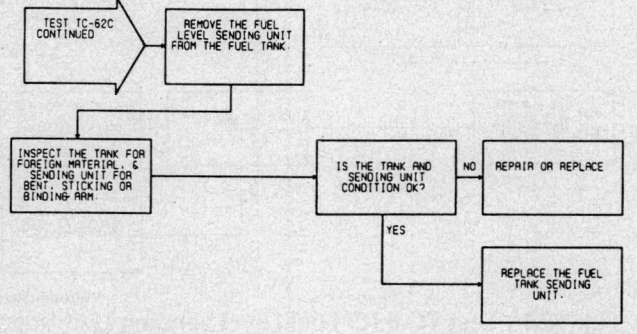

Fig. 119   Test TC-62C: Fuel Level Sending Unit Volts Too Low (Part 2 of 2)

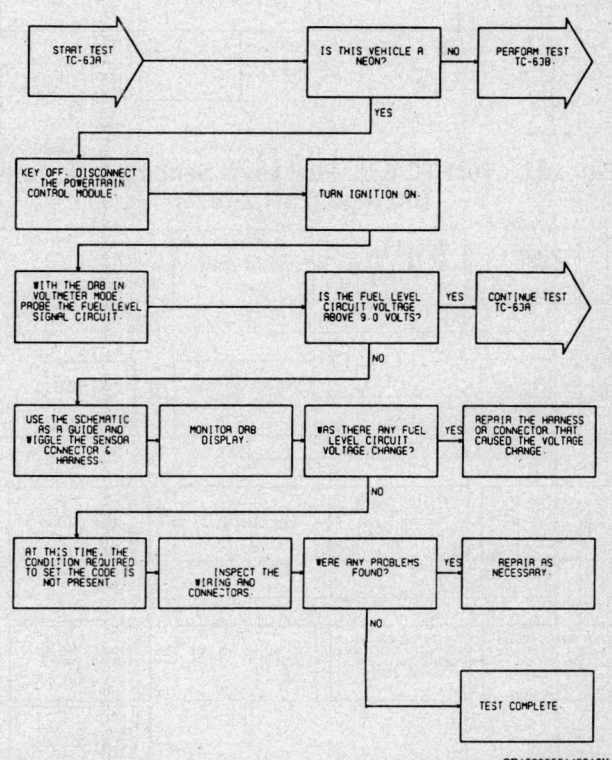

Fig. 120   Test TC-63A: Fuel Level Sending Unit Volts Too High (Part 1 of 2)

MULTI-POINT FUEL INJECTION (1995 AVENGER, CIRRUS, NEON, SEBRING, STRATUS & TALON w/NON-TURBOCHARGED 2.0L/4-122 ENGINE)

8-45

CHRYSLER–Fuel Injection

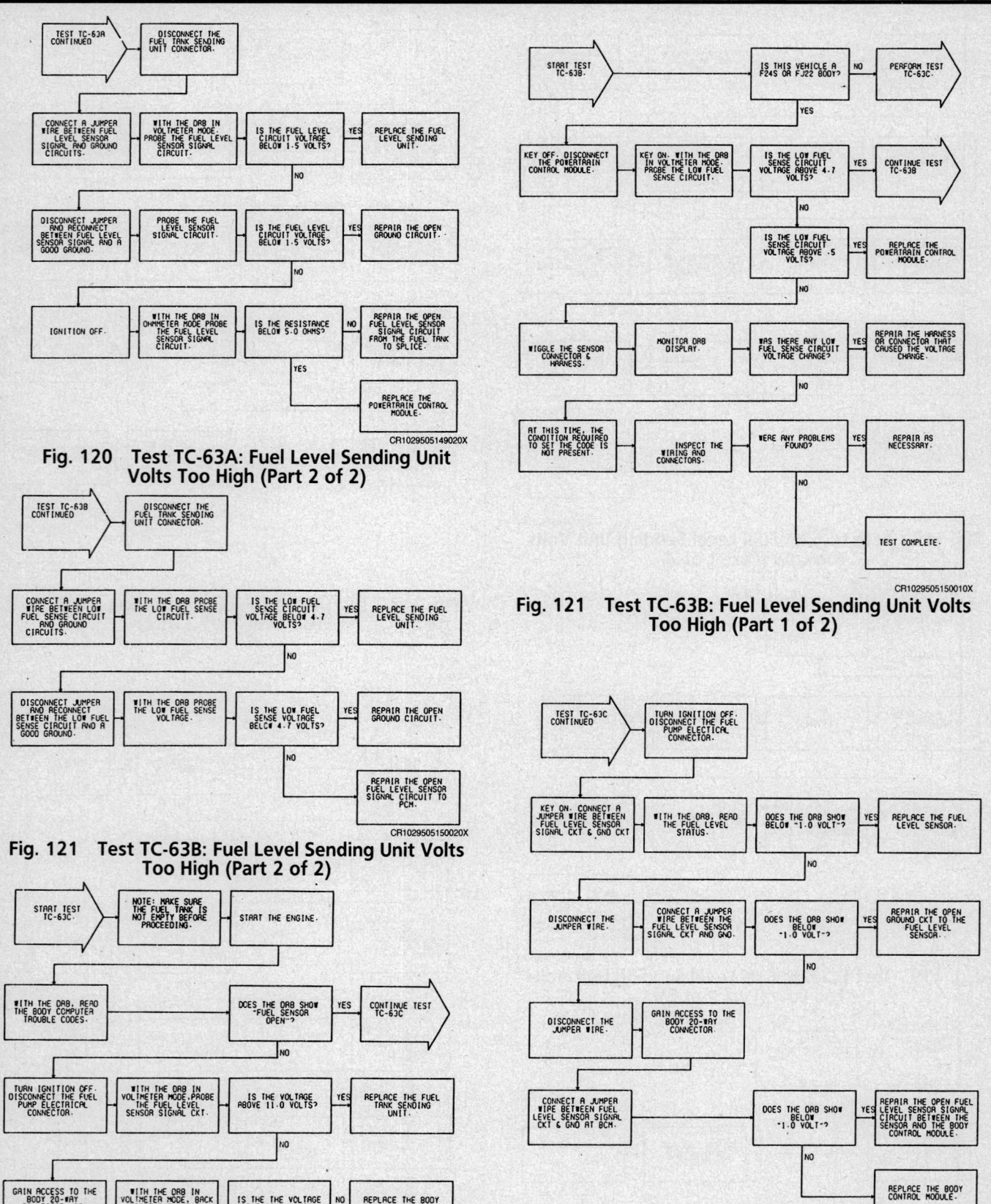

Fig. 120   Test TC-63A: Fuel Level Sending Unit Volts Too High (Part 2 of 2)

Fig. 121   Test TC-63B: Fuel Level Sending Unit Volts Too High (Part 2 of 2)

Fig. 121   Test TC-63B: Fuel Level Sending Unit Volts Too High (Part 1 of 2)

Fig. 122   Test TC-63C: Fuel Level Sending Unit Volts Too High (Part 1 of 2)

Fig. 122   Test TC-63C: Fuel Level Sending Unit Volts Too High (Part 2 of 2)

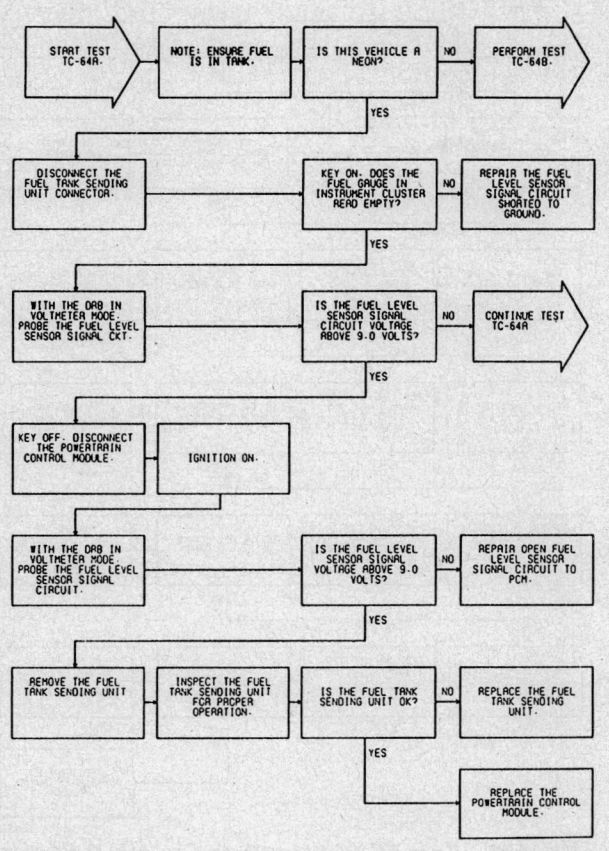

Fig. 123   Test TC-64A: Fuel Level Unit No Change Over Miles (Part 1 of 2)

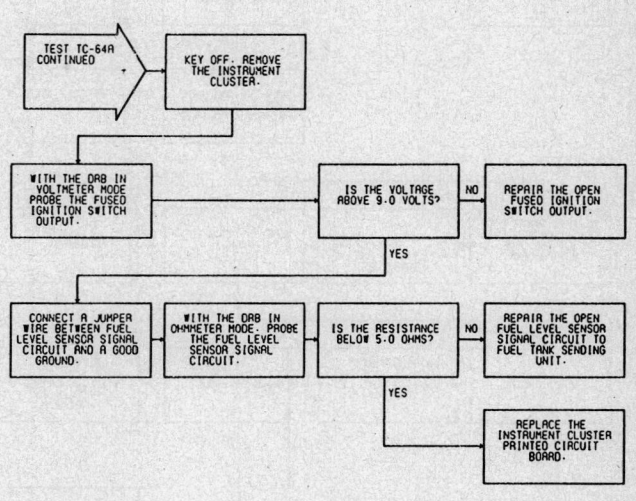

Fig. 123   Test TC-64A: Fuel Level Unit No Change Over Miles (Part 2 of 2)

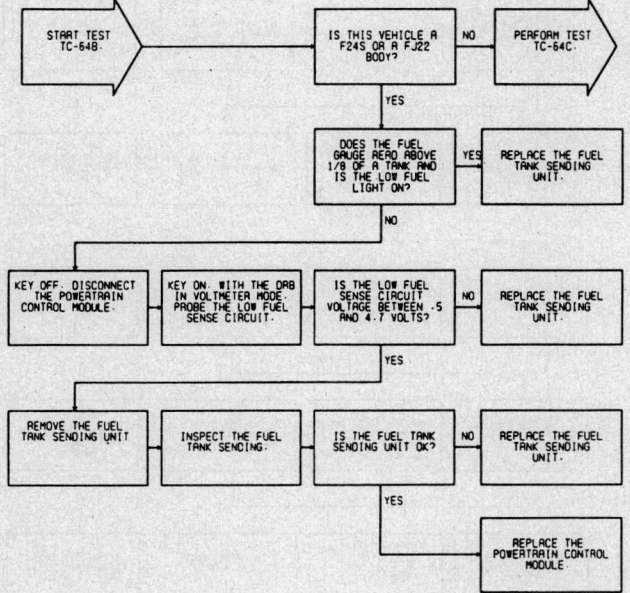

Fig. 124   Test TC-64B: Fuel Level Unit No Change Over Miles

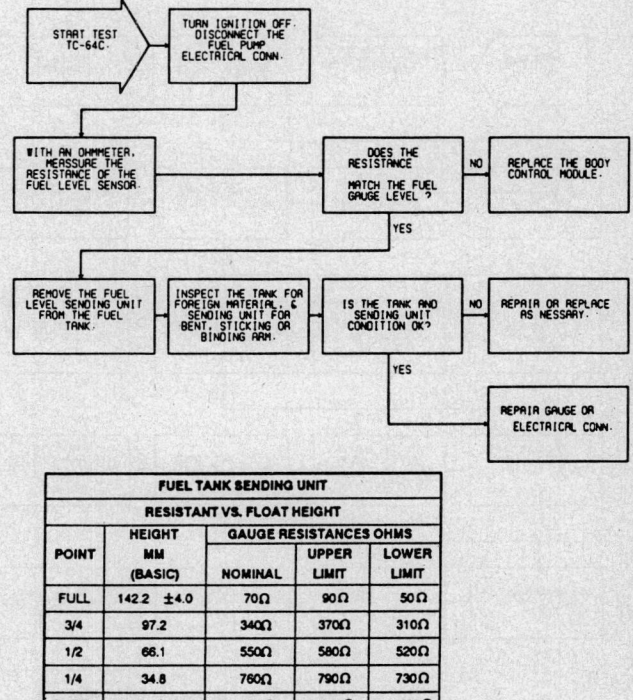

FUEL TANK SENDING UNIT				
RESISTANT VS. FLOAT HEIGHT				
POINT	**HEIGHT MM (BASIC)**	**GAUGE RESISTANCES OHMS**		
		NOMINAL	**UPPER LIMIT**	**LOWER LIMIT**
FULL	142.2 ±4.0	70Ω	90Ω	50Ω
3/4	97.2	340Ω	370Ω	310Ω
1/2	66.1	550Ω	580Ω	520Ω
1/4	34.8	760Ω	790Ω	730Ω
EMPTY	0.5 ±4.0	1050Ω	1080Ω	1020Ω

Fig. 125   Test TC-64C: Fuel Level Unit No Change Over Miles

MULTI-POINT FUEL INJECTION (1995 AVENGER, CIRRUS, NEON, SEBRING, STRATUS & TALON w/NON-TURBOCHARGED 2.0L/4-122 ENGINE)

8-47

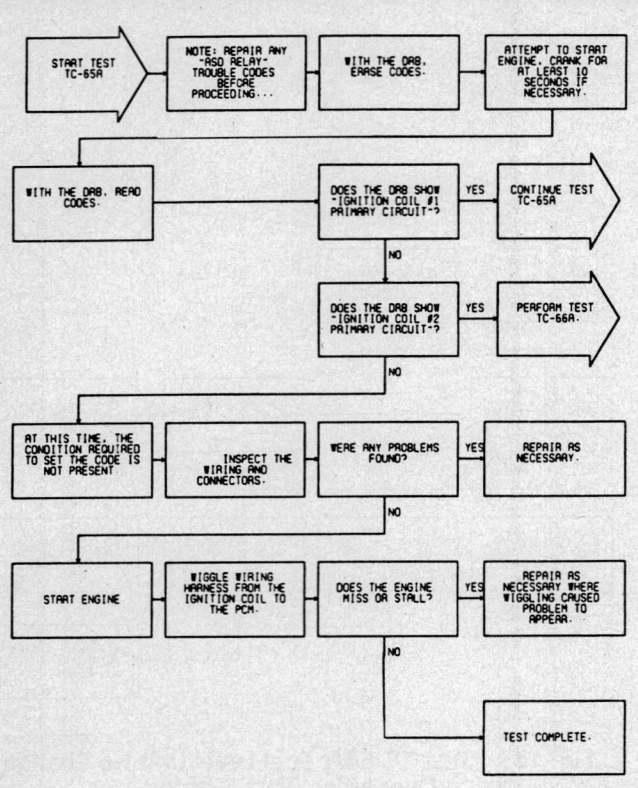

Fig. 126   Test TC-65A: Ignition Coil No. 1 Primary Circuit (Part 1 of 2)

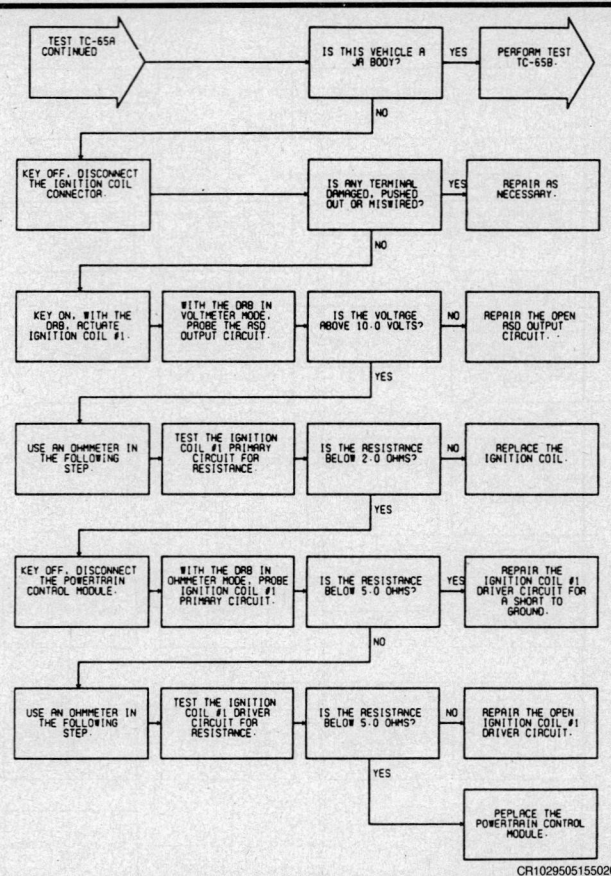

Fig. 126   Test TC-65A: Ignition Coil No. 1 Primary Circuit (Part 2 of 2)

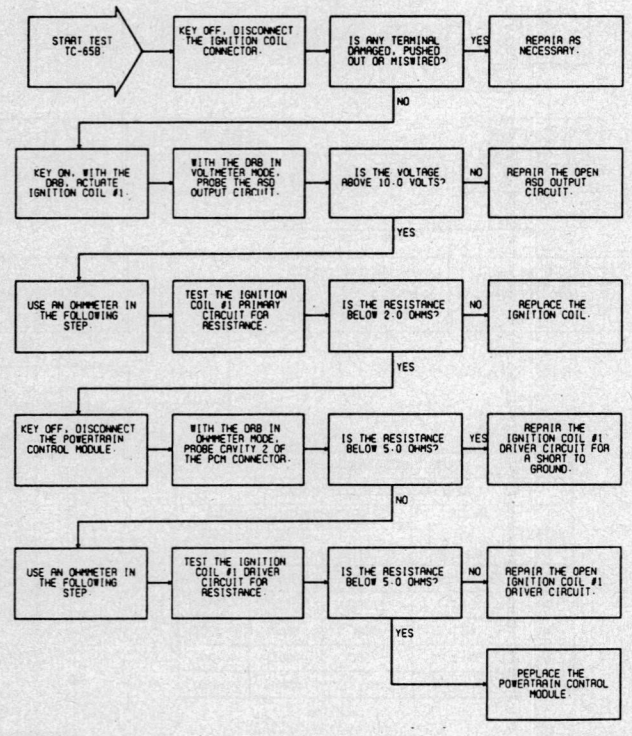

Fig. 127   Test TC-65B: Ignition Coil No. 1 Primary Circuit

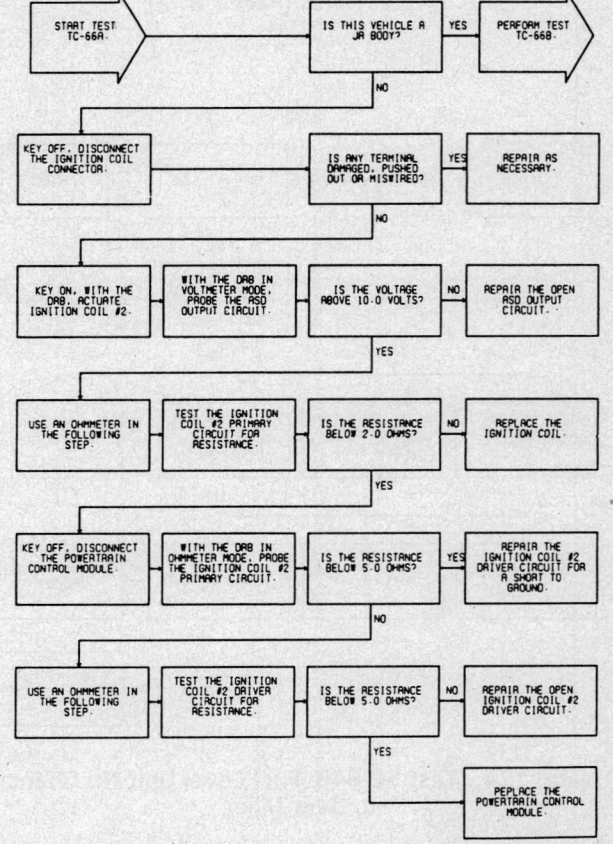

Fig. 128   Test TC-66A: Ignition Coil No. 2 Primary Circuit

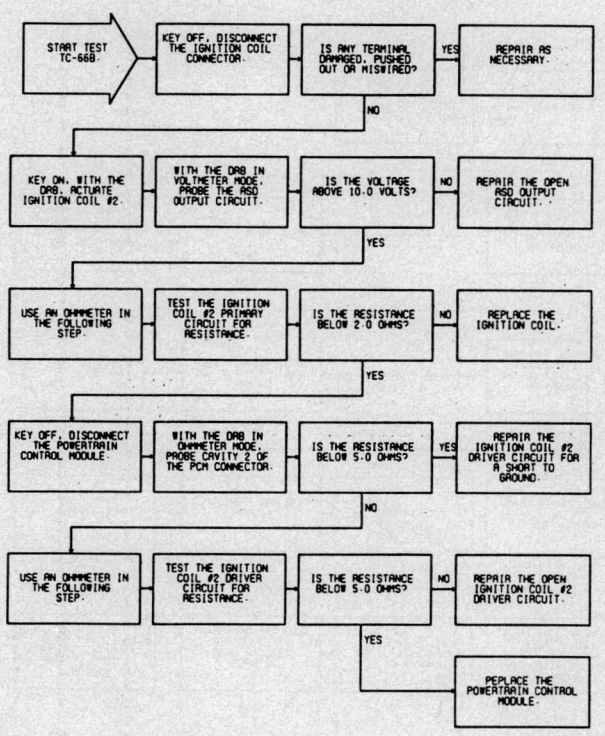

Fig. 129   Test TC-66B: Ignition Coil No. 2 Primary Circuit

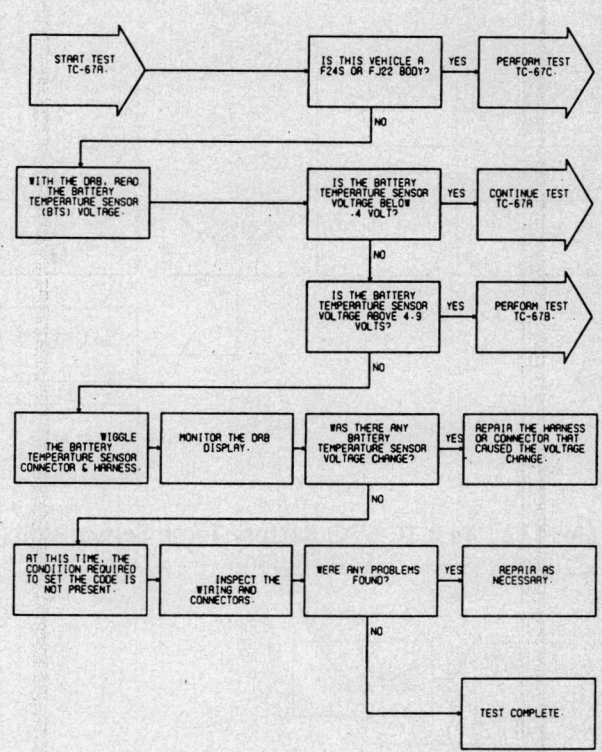

Fig. 130   Test TC-67A: Battery Temp Sensor Volts Out Of Limit (Part 1 of 2)

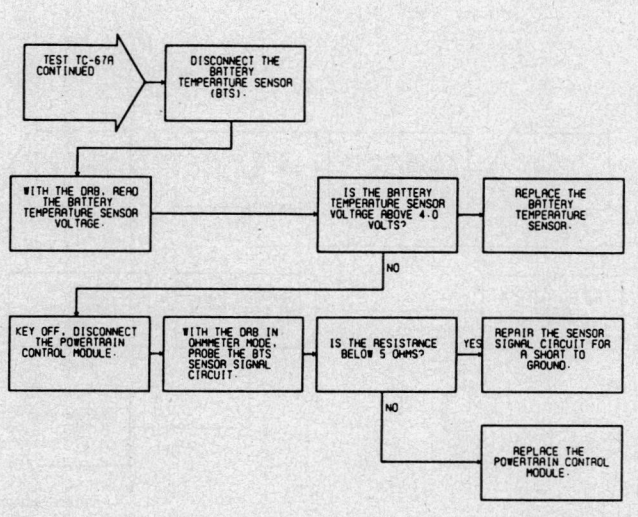

Fig. 130   Test TC-67A: Battery Temp Sensor Volts Out Of Limit (Part 2 of 2)

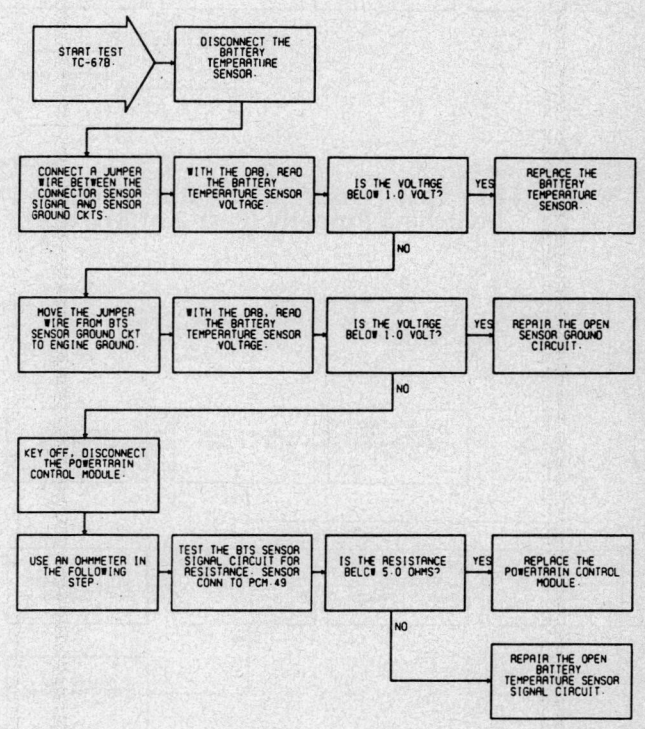

Fig. 131   Test TC-67B: Battery Temp Sensor Volts Out Of Limit

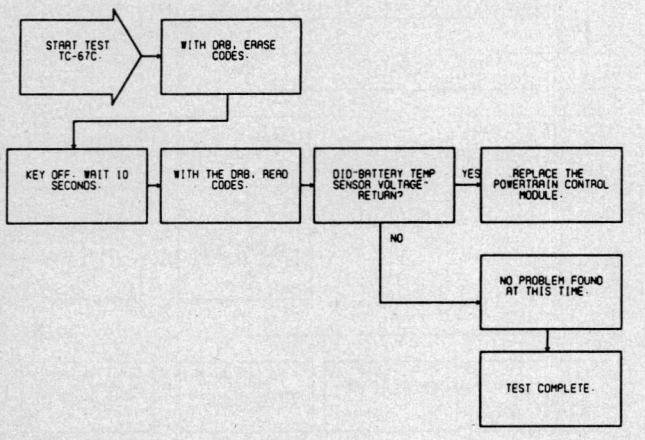

Fig. 132   Test TC-67C: Battery Temp Sensor Volts Out Of Limit

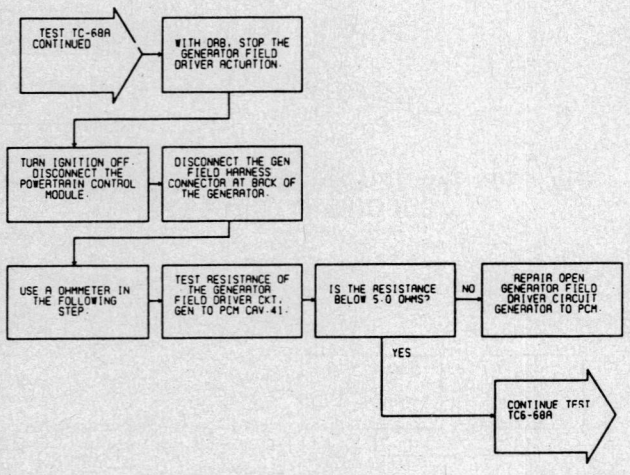

Fig. 133   Test TC-68A: Generator Field Not Switching Properly (Part 2 of 3)

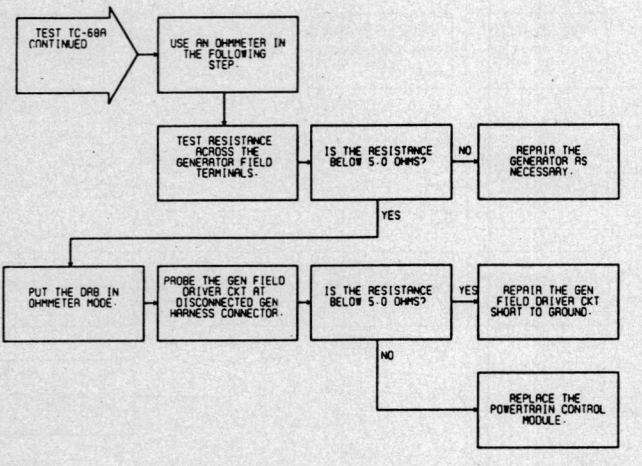

Fig. 133   Test TC-68A: Generator Field Not Switching Properly (Part 3 of 3)

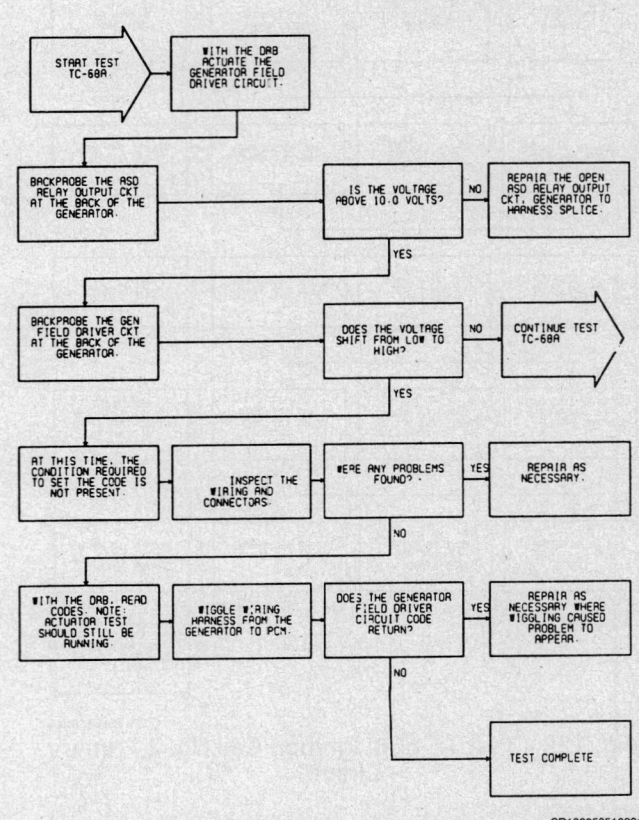

Fig. 133   Test TC-68A: Generator Field Not Switching Properly (Part 1 of 3)

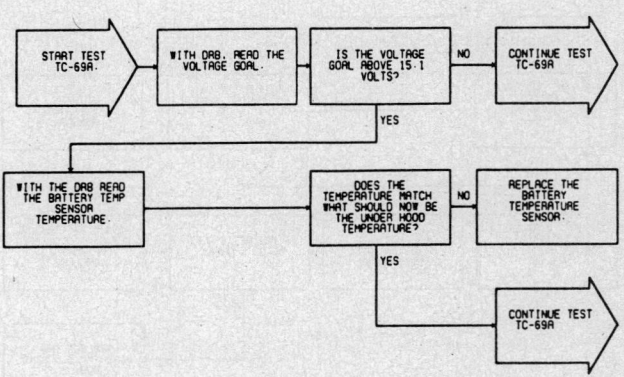

Fig. 134   Test TC-69A: Charging System Voltage Too Low (Part 1 of 2)

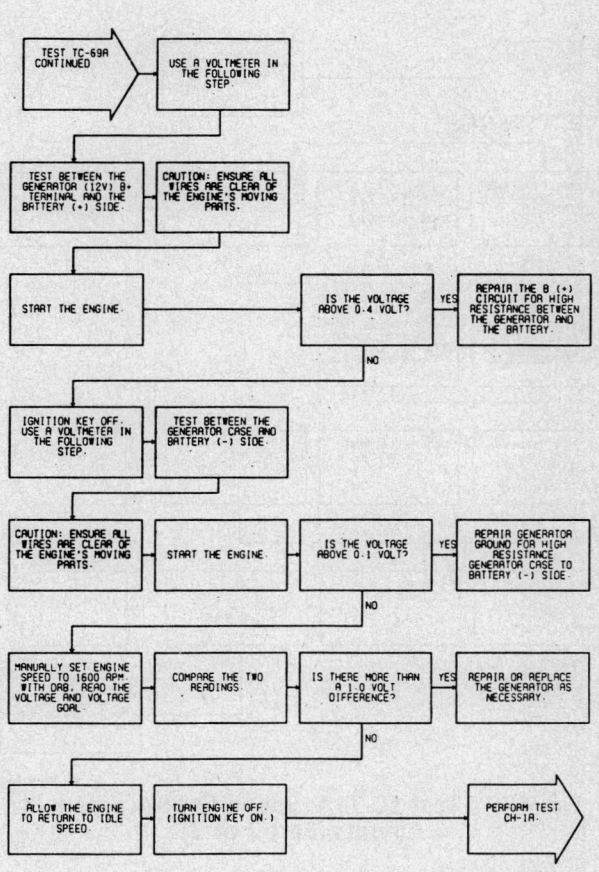

Fig. 134   Test TC-69A: Charging System Voltage Too Low (Part 2 of 2)

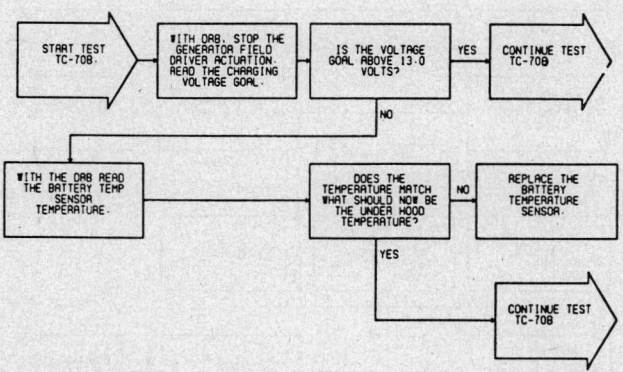

Fig. 136   Test TC-70B: Charging System Voltage Too High (Part 1 of 2)

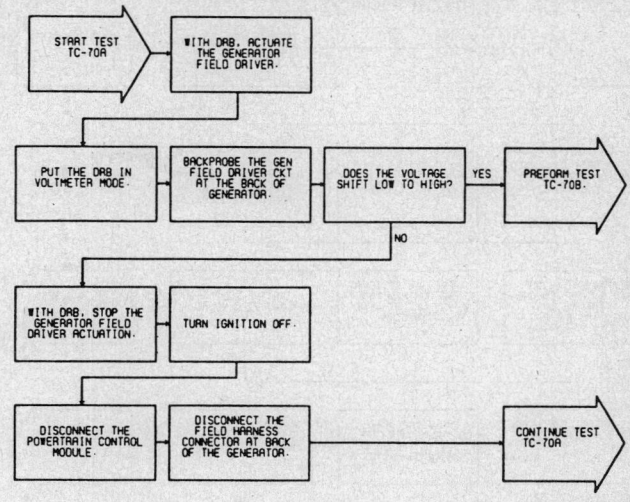

Fig. 135   Test TC-70A: Charging System Voltage Too High (Part 1 of 2)

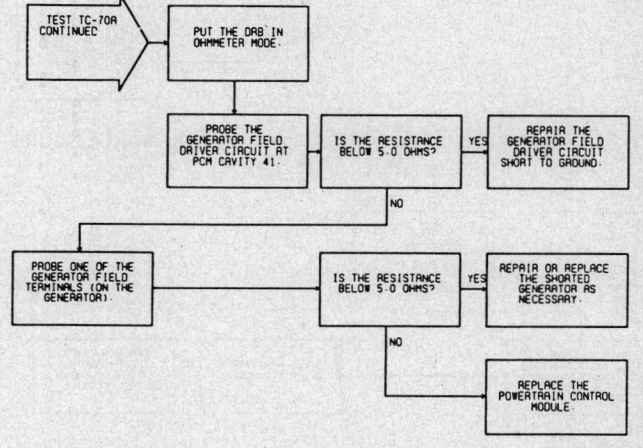

Fig. 135   Test TC-70A: Charging System Voltage Too High (Part 2 of 2)

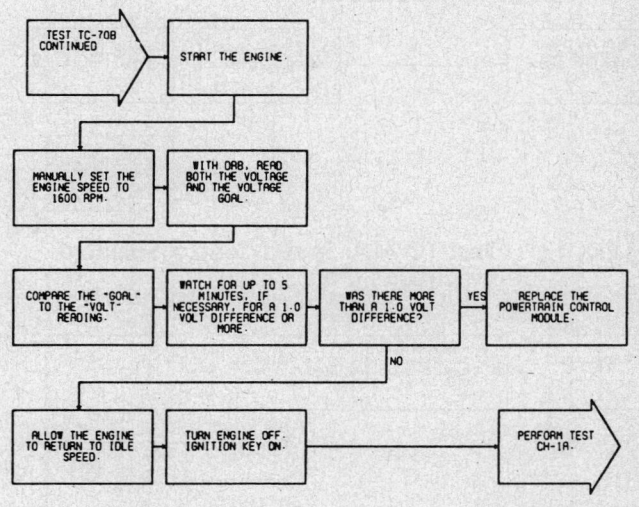

Fig. 136   Test TC-70B: Charging System Voltage Too High (Part 2 of 2)

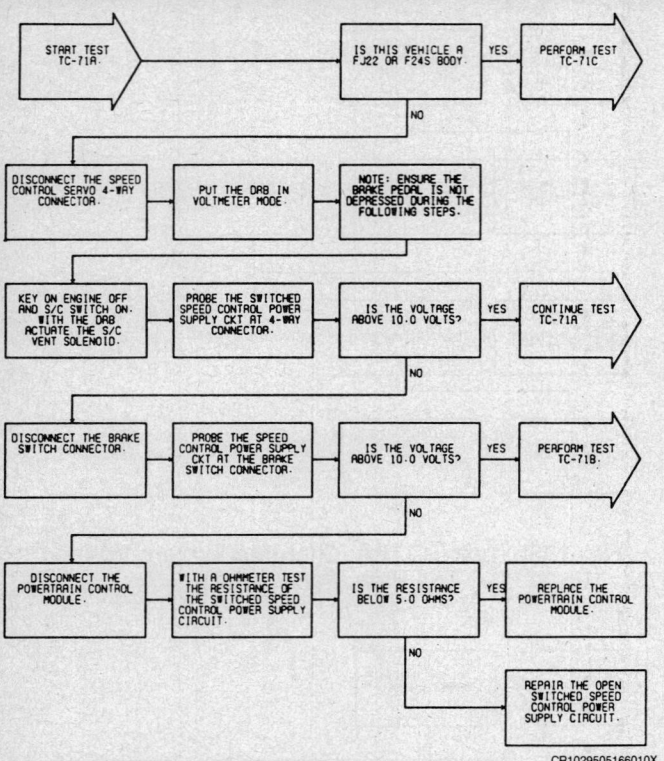

Fig. 137   Test TC-71A: Speed Control Solenoid Circuits (Part 1 of 3)

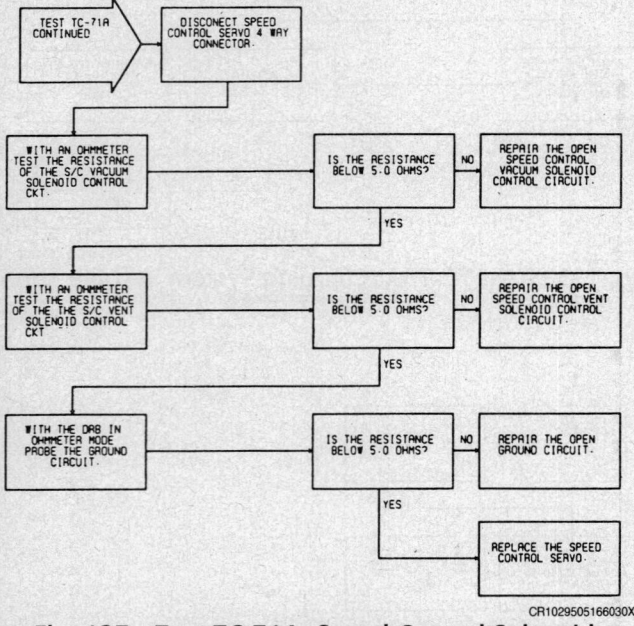

Fig. 137   Test TC-71A: Speed Control Solenoid Circuits (Part 3 of 3)

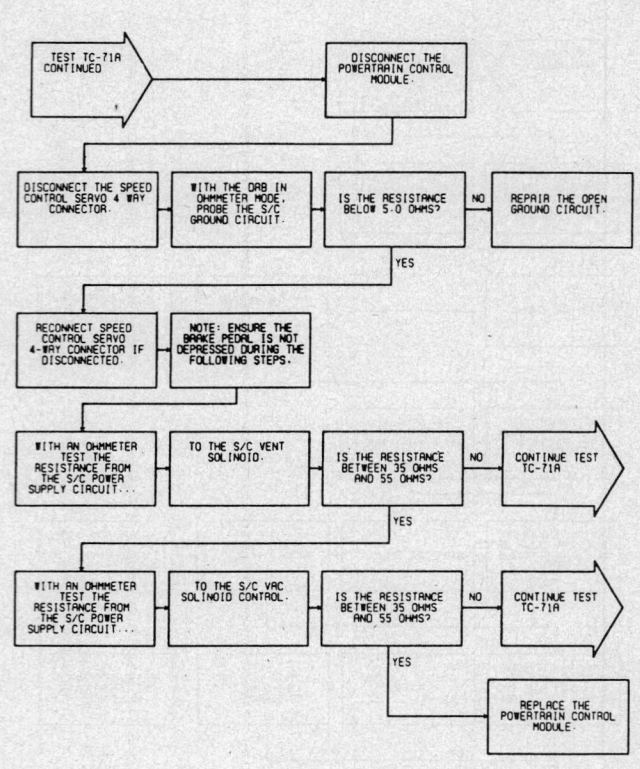

Fig. 137   Test TC-71A: Speed Control Solenoid Circuits (Part 2 of 3)

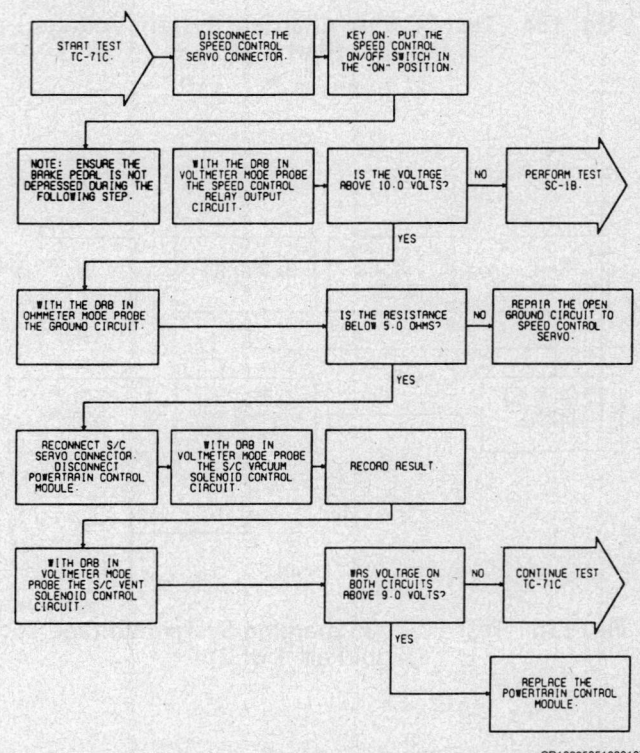

Fig. 139   Test TC-71C: Speed Control Solenoid Circuits (Part 1 of 2)

Fig. 138   Test TC-71B: Speed Control Solenoid Circuits

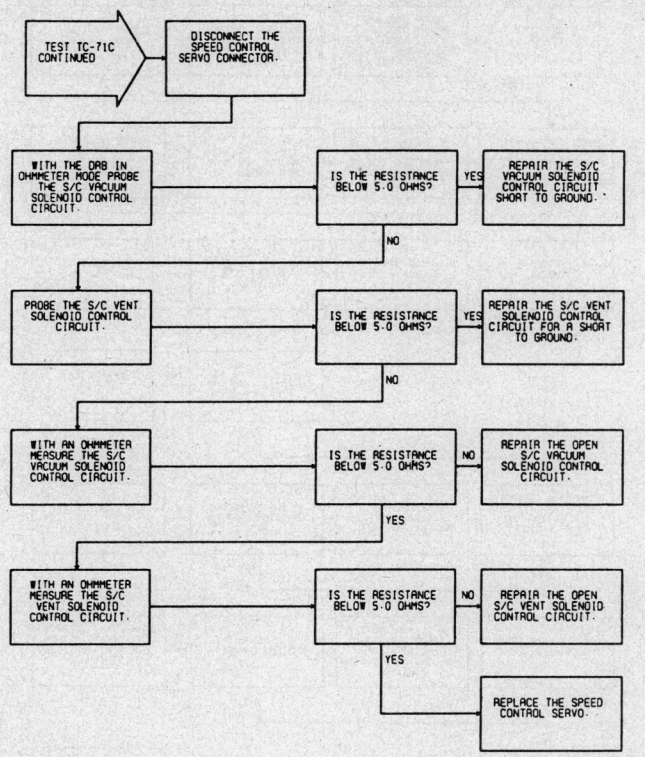

Fig. 139   Test TC-71C: Speed Control Solenoid Circuits (Part 2 of 2)

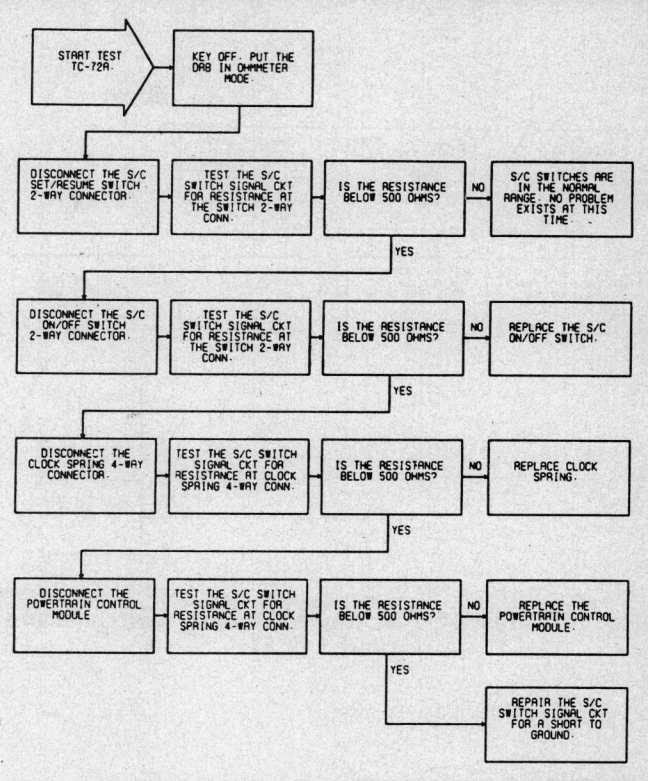

Fig. 140   Test TC-72A: Speed Control Switch Always Low

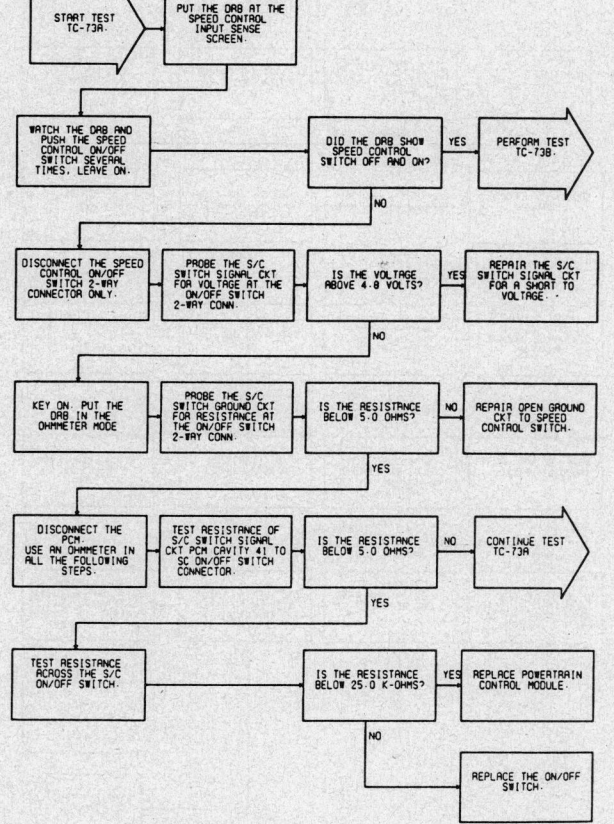

Fig. 141   Test TC-73A: Speed Control Switch Always High (Part 1 of 2)

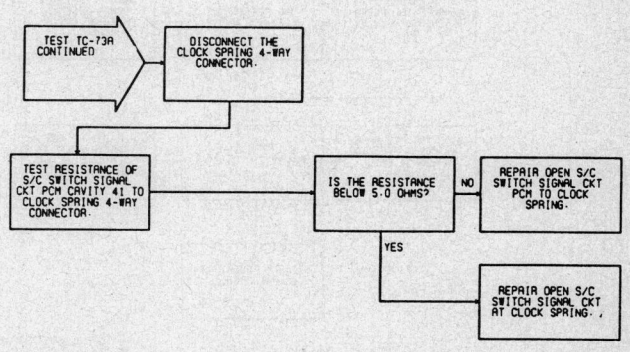

Fig. 141   Test TC-73A: Speed Control Switch Always High (Part 2 of 2)

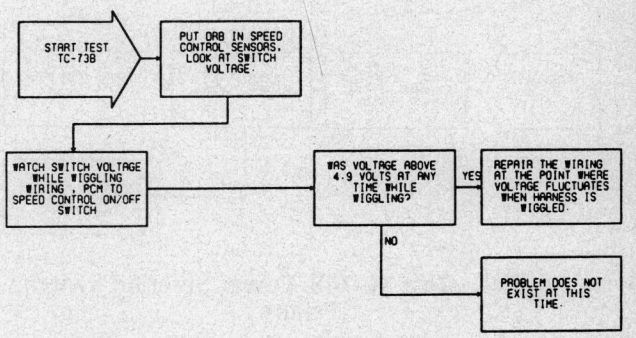

Fig. 142   Test TC-73B: Speed Control Switch Always High

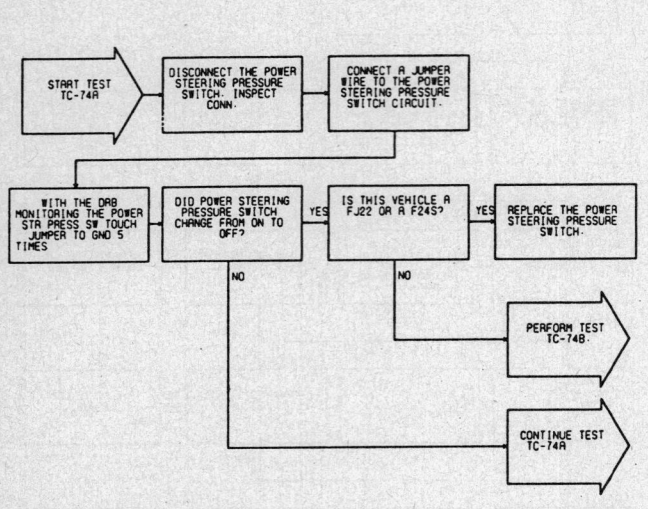

Fig. 143   Test TC-74A: Power Steering Switch Failure (Part 1 of 2)

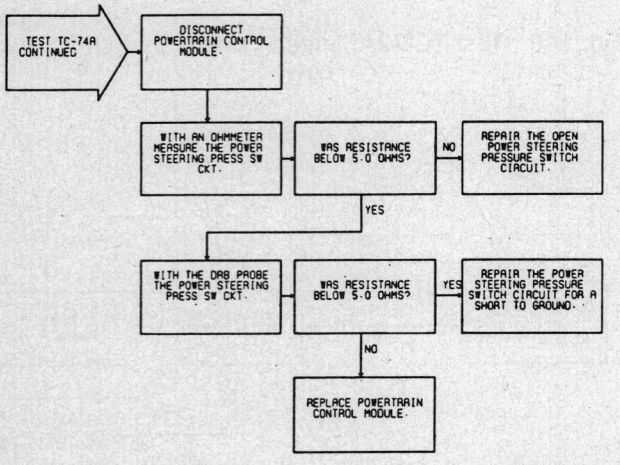

Fig. 143   Test TC-74A: Power Steering Switch Failure (Part 2 of 2)

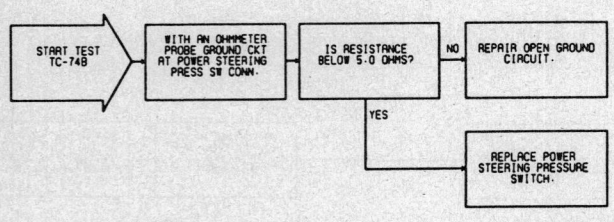

Fig. 144   Test TC-74B: Power Steering Switch Failure

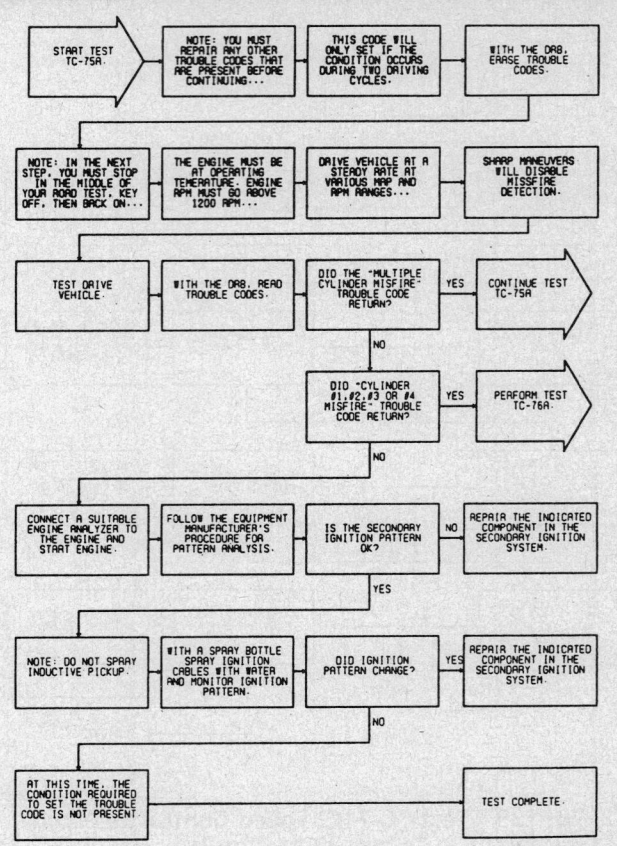

Fig. 145   Test TC-75A: Multiple Cylinder Misfire (Part 1 of 4)

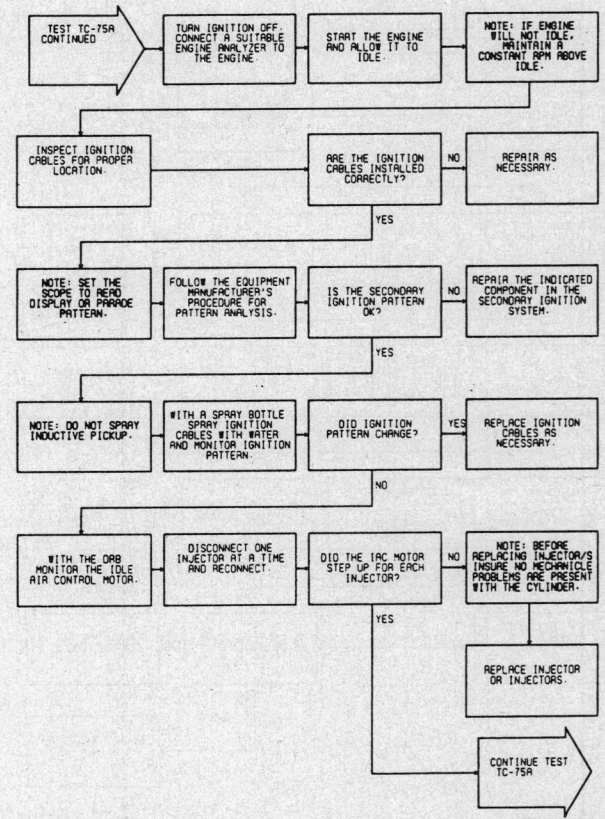

Fig. 145   Test TC-75A: Multiple Cylinder Misfire (Part 2 of 4)

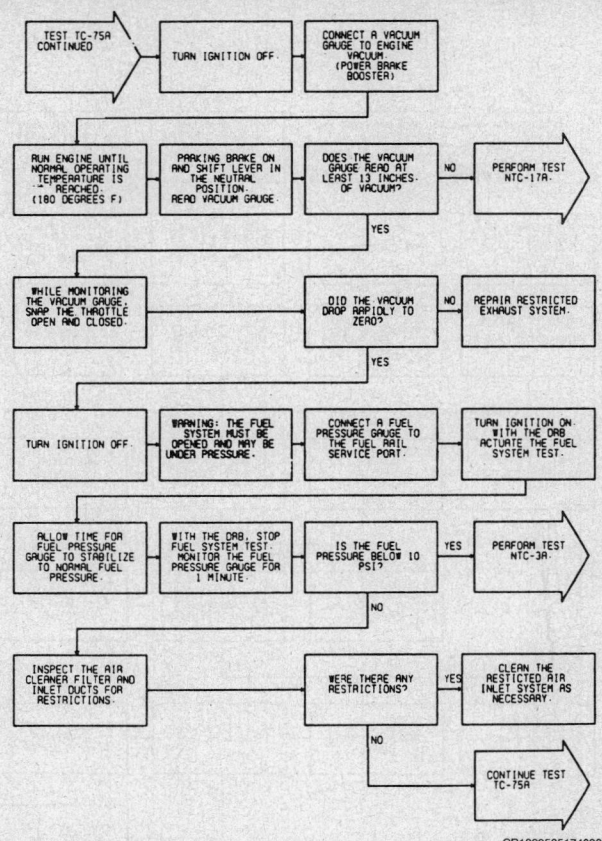

Make sure all the wiring and connectors are ok.

Perform each of the following tests in the order listed below. If a test passes, continue to the next test until the problem is found:

Secondary Ignition Patterns .... TEST NTC-2A

Fuel Pressure .... TEST NTC-3A

PCM Grounds and Power Circuit .... TEST NTC-12A

EGR System .... TEST NTC-14A

No Trouble Code Mechanical .... TEST NTC-19A

CR1029505174040X

Fig. 145 Test TC-75A: Multiple Cylinder Misfire (Part 4 of 4)

CR1029505174030X

Fig. 145 Test TC-75A: Multiple Cylinder Misfire (Part 3 of 4)

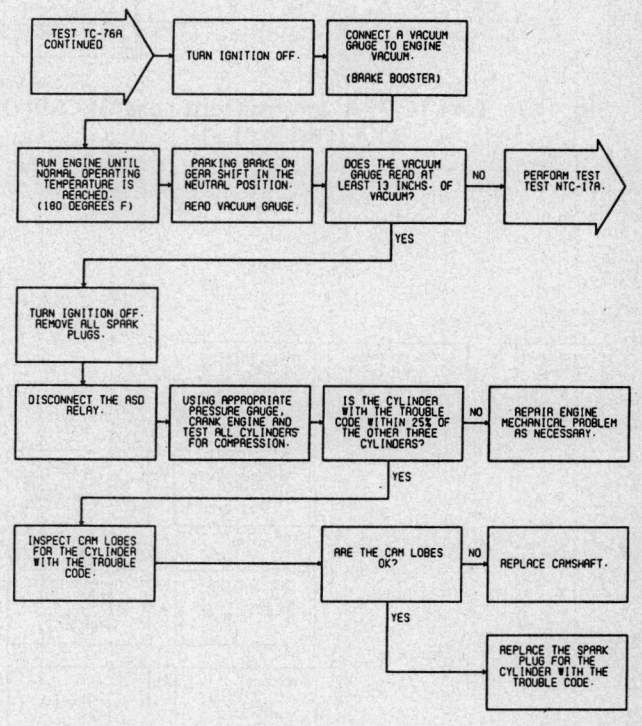

CR1029505175020X

Fig. 146 Test TC-76A: Cylinder No. 1, No. 2, No. 3 Or No. 4 Misfire (Part 2 of 2)

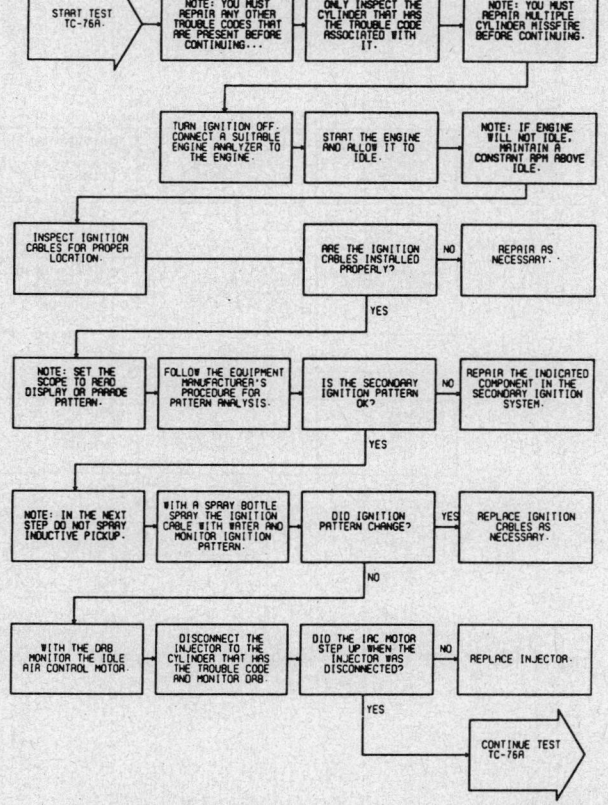

CR1029505175010X

Fig. 146 Test TC-76A: Cylinder No. 1, No. 2, No. 3 Or No. 4 Misfire (Part 1 of 2)

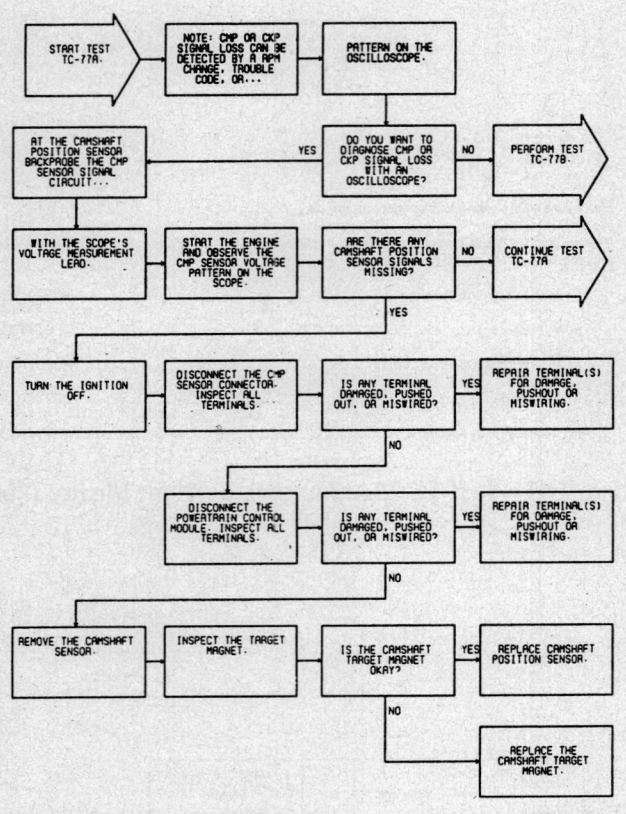

Fig. 147 Test TC-77A: Intermittent Loss Of CMP Or CKP (Part 1 of 3)

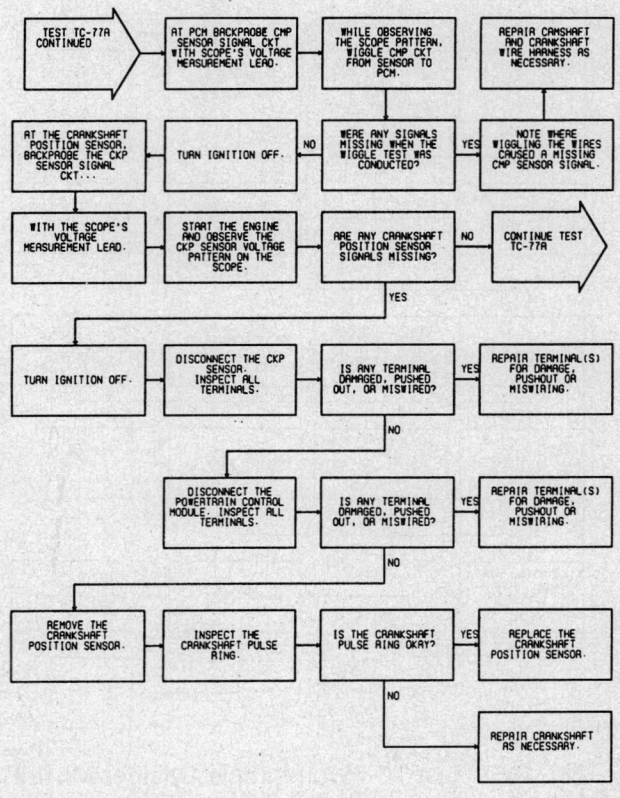

Fig. 147 Test TC-77A: Intermittent Loss Of CMP Or CKP (Part 2 of 3)

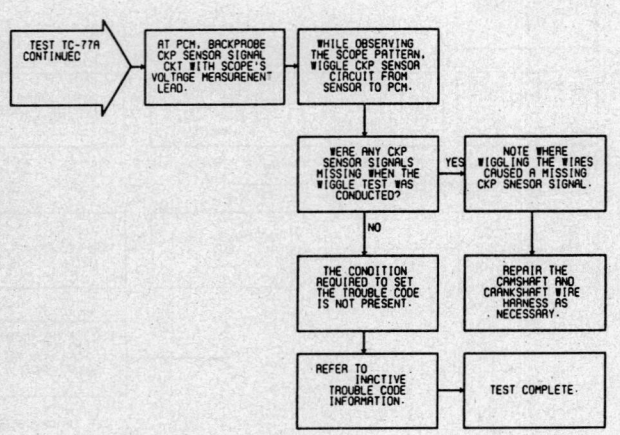

Fig. 147 Test TC-77A: Intermittent Loss Of CMP Or CKP (Part 3 of 3)

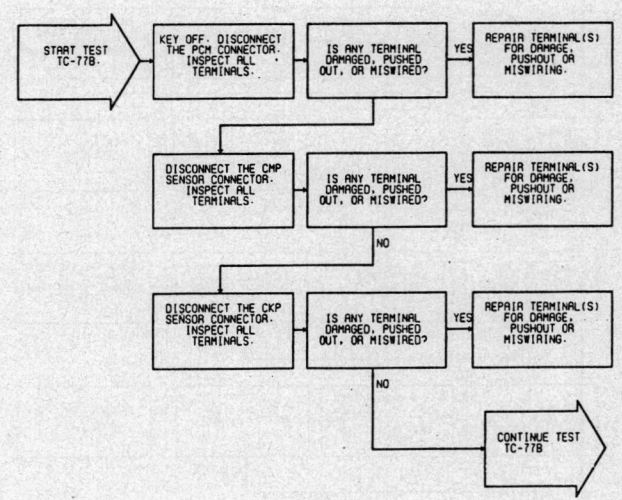

Fig. 148 Test TC-77B: Intermittent Loss Of CMP Or CKP (Part 1 of 3)

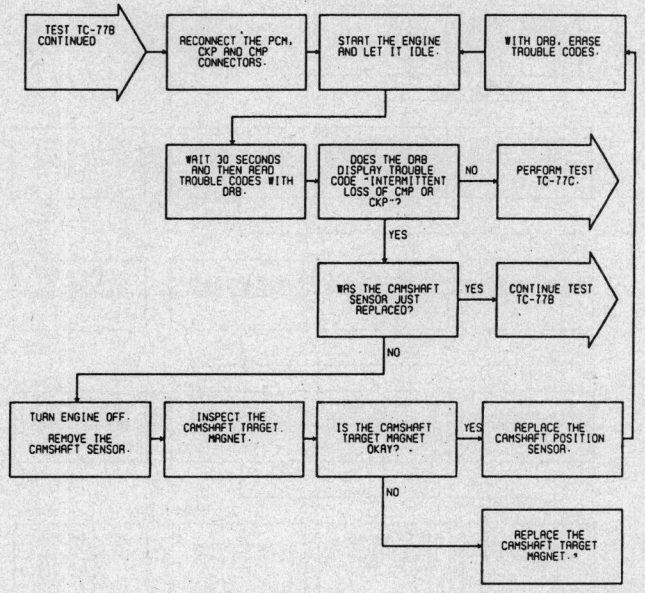

Fig. 148   Test TC-77B: Intermittent Loss Of CMP Or CKP (Part 2 of 3)

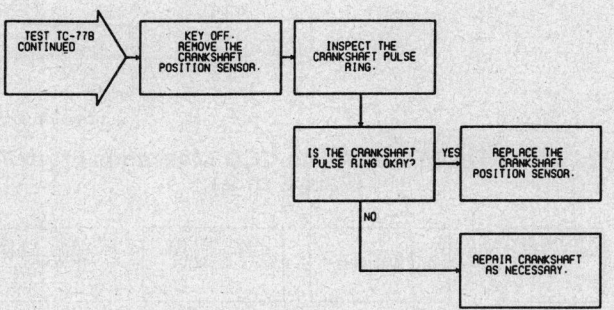

Fig. 148   Test TC-77B: Intermittent Loss Of CMP Or CKP (Part 3 of 3)

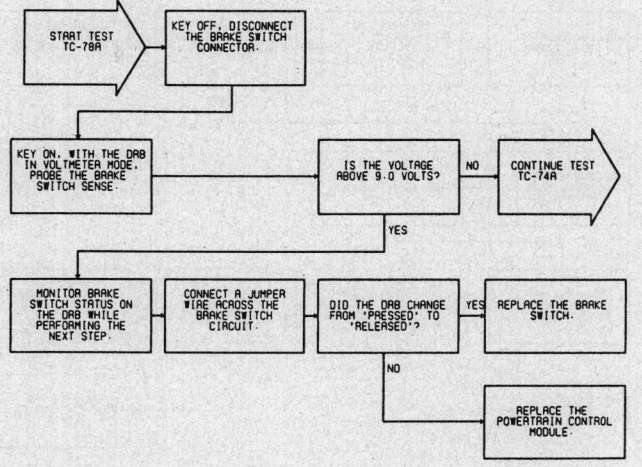

Fig. 150   Test TC-78A: Brake Switch Circuit (Part 1 of 2)

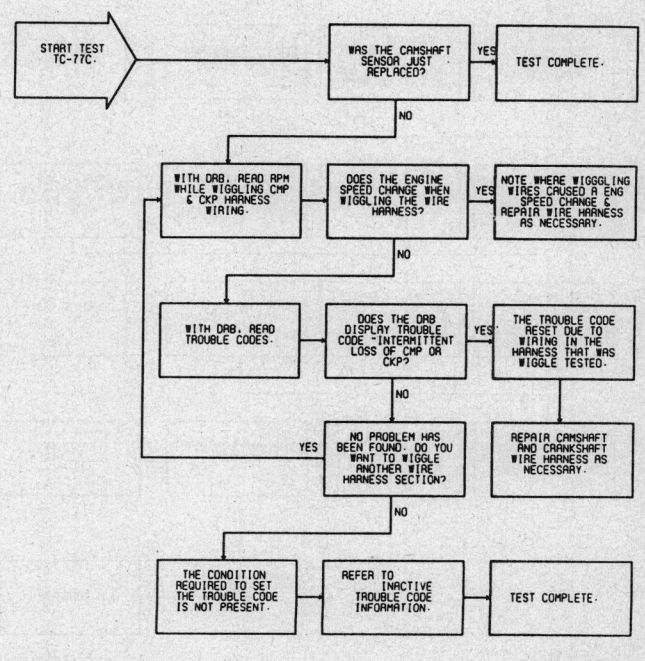

Fig. 149   Test TC-77C: Intermittent Loss Of CMP Or CKP

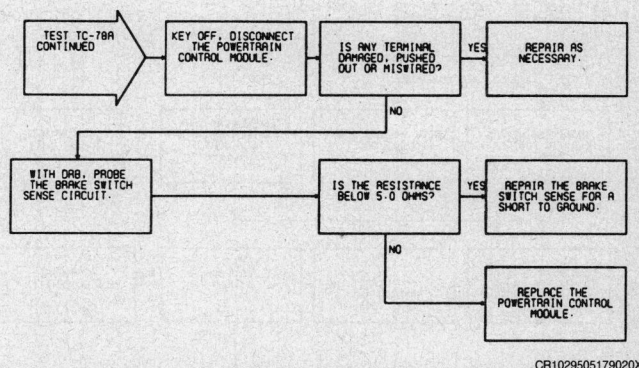

Fig. 150   Test TC-78A: Brake Switch Circuit (Part 2 of 2)

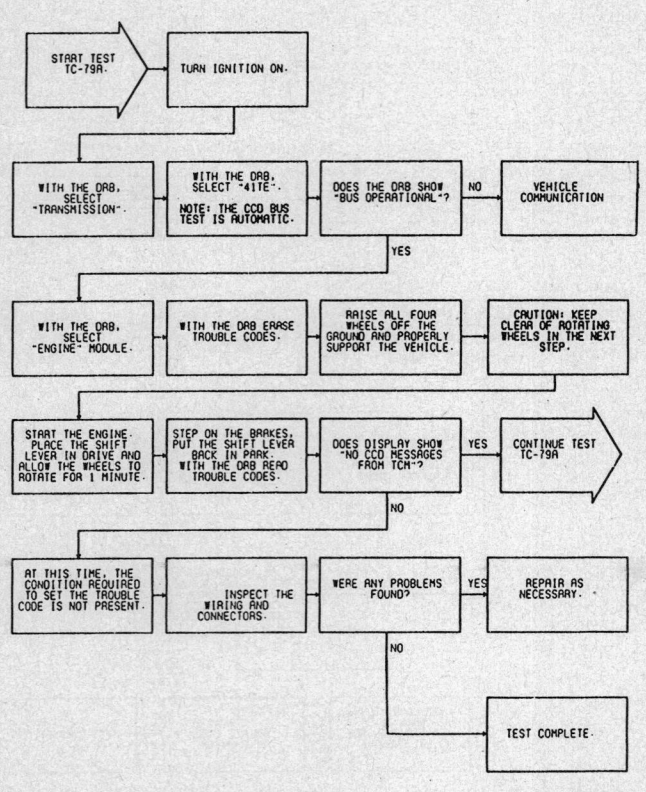

**Fig. 151   Test TC-79A: No CCD Messages From TCM
(Part 1 of 2)**

CR1029505180010X

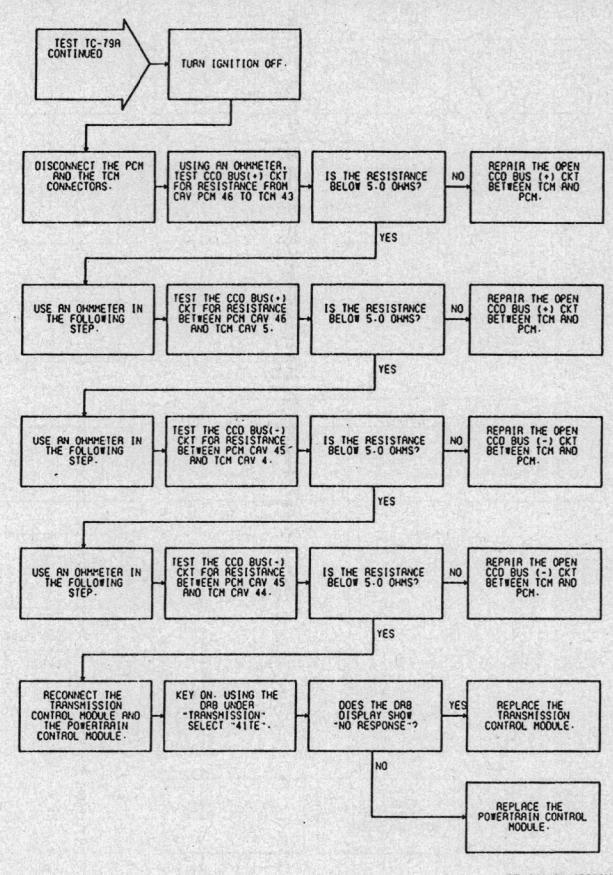

CR1029505180020X

**Fig. 151   Test TC-79A: No CCD Messages From TCM
(Part 2 of 2)**

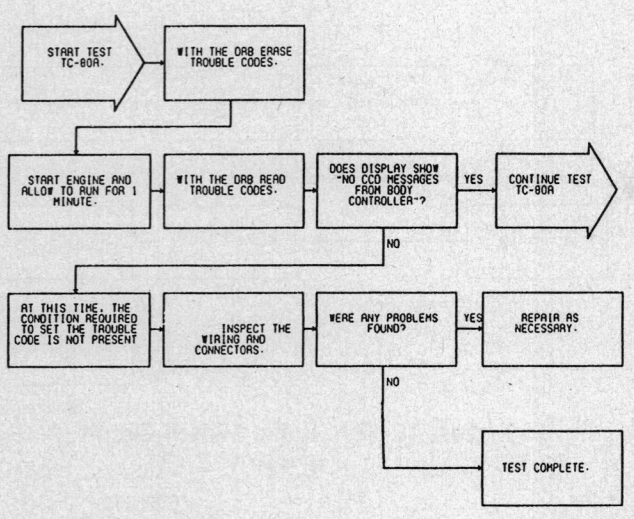

CR1029505181010X

**Fig. 152   Test TC-80A: No CCD Message From Body
Control Module (Part 1 of 2). Cirrus & Stratus**

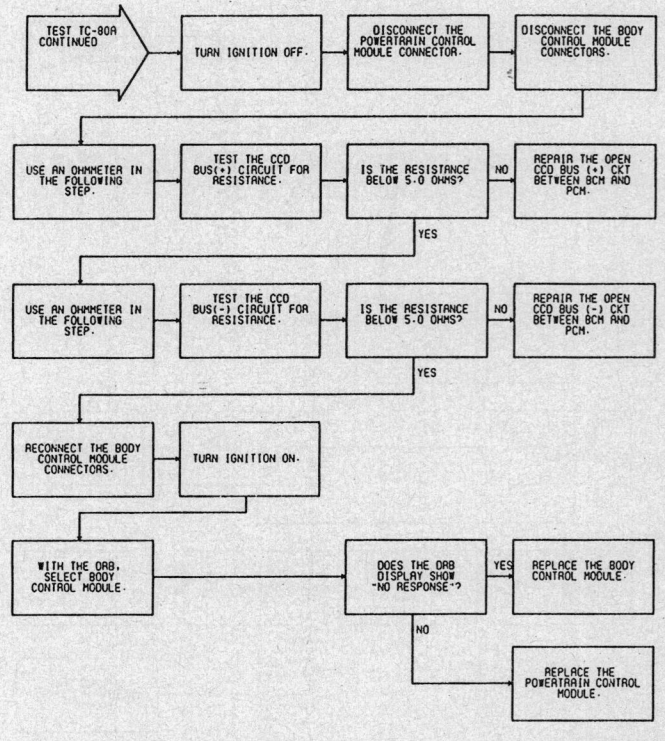

CR1029505181020X

**Fig. 152   Test TC-80A: No CCD Message From Body
Control Module (Part 2 of 2). Cirrus & Stratus**

First, check all Technical Service Bulletins _____ that relate to this driveability problem. Perform corrective actions if indicated; otherwise continue.

1. NO TROUBLE CODE COMPLETE TEST (non-monitored & monitored circuits)

Perform **TESTS NTC-2A** through **NTC-19A** in sequence until the driveability problem is found.

NO TROUBLE CODE MENU

CHECKING SECONDARY IGNITION AND TIMING	NTC-2A
CHECKING THE FUEL PRESSURE	NTC-3A
CHECKING COOLANT SENSOR CALIBRATION AND RADIATOR FAN OPERATION	NTC-4A
CHECKING THROTTLE POSITION SENSOR CALIBRATION	NTC-5A
CHECKING MAP SENSOR CALIBRATION	NTC-6A
CHECKING FOR OXYGEN SENSOR SWITCHING	NTC-7A
CHECKING THE OXYGEN SENSOR HEATER	NTC-8A
CHECKING THE IDLE AIR CONTROL MOTOR	NTC-9A
CHECKING SOLENOID OPERATIONS	NTC-10A
CHECKING THE PARK/NEUTRAL POSITION SWITCH	NTC-11A
CHECKING THE PCM POWER AND GROUND CIRCUITS	NTC-12A
CHECKING THE EVAPORATIVE EMISSION SYSTEM	NTC-13A
CHECKING THE EGR SYSTEM	NTC-14A
CHECKING THE ENGINE VACUUM	NTC-15A
CHECKING THE INTAKE AIR TEMPERATURE SENSOR	NTC-16A
CHECKING THE TIMING BELT ALIGNMENT	NTC-17A
CHECKING THE MINIMUM IDLE AIR FLOW	NTC-18A
CHECKING THE ENGINE MECHANICAL SYSTEMS	NTC-19A

2. NO TROUBLE CODE QUICK INDIVIDUAL TEST (individual test only)

If you suspect any of the above items to be the cause of the vehicle's driveability problem, perform the associated test(s) individually. Return to No Trouble Code Menu if driveability problem still exists, or perform No Trouble Code Complete Test.

3. NO TROUBLE CODE QUICK SYMPTOM TEST (symptom test only)

Symptom checks cannot be used properly unless the driveability problem characteristic actually happens while the vehicle is being tested. To reduce diagnostic time, ensure that TC-1A and appropriate sections have been reviewed before attempting to diagnose a symptom.

Select the symptom that most accurately describes the vehicle's driveability problem and then perform the test routine that pertains to this symptom. Perform each routine test in sequence until the problem is found.

SYMPTOM	DIAGNOSTIC TEST ROUTINE
HARD START	NTC-2A, 3A, 4A, 5A, 6A, 7A, 9A, 13A, 14A, 15A, 16A, 17A, 18A, 19A
START AND STALL	NTC-2A, 3A, 4A, 5A, 6A, 9A, 12A, 18A
HESITATION/SAG/STUMBLE	NO TROUBLE CODE COMPLETE TEST (STEP 1)
SURGE	NTC-2A, 3A, 4A, 5A, 6A, 7A, 9A, 12A, 13A, 18A
LACK OF POWER/SLUGGISH	NTC-2A, 3A, 4A, 5A, 6A, 7A, 9A, 12A, 14A, 17A, 18A
SPARK KNOCK/DETONATION	NTC-2A, 4A, 5A, 6A, 7A, 9A, 10A, 12A, 13A, 17A, 18A
CUTS OUT/MISSES	NTC-2A, 3A, 7A, 10A, 12A, 14A, 18A
BACKFIRE/POPBACK	NTC-2A, 3A, 6A, 7A, 12A, 14A, 17A, 18A
RUNS ROUGH/UNSTABLE/ERRATIC IDLE	NO TROUBLE CODE COMPLETE TEST (STEP 1)
POOR FUEL ECONOMY	NO TROUBLE CODE COMPLETE TEST (STEP 1)

CR1029505182020X

Fig. 153 Test NTC-1A: No Trouble Code Test Menu (Part 2 of 2)

Fig. 153 Test NTC-1A: No Trouble Code Test Menu (Part 1 of 2)

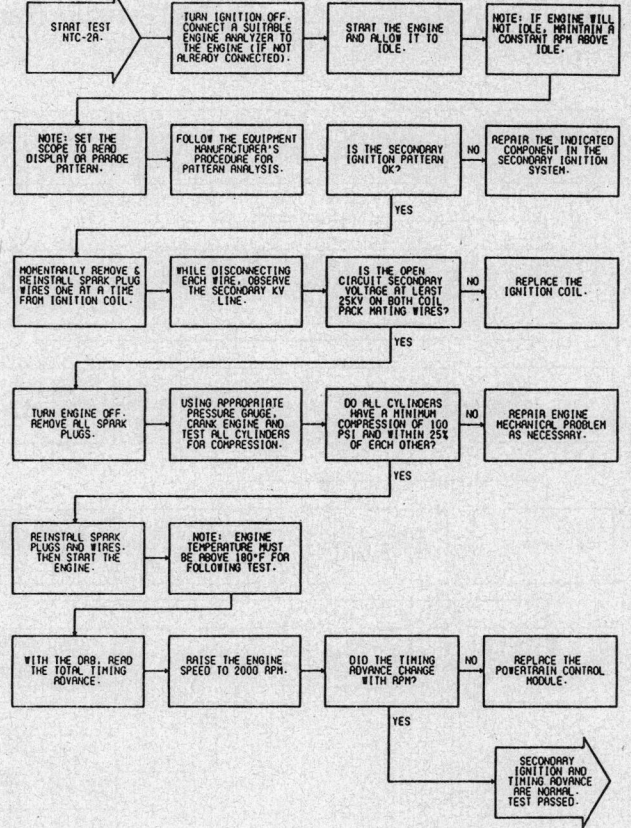

CR1029505183000X

Fig. 154 Test NTC-2A: Checking Secondary Ignition & Timing

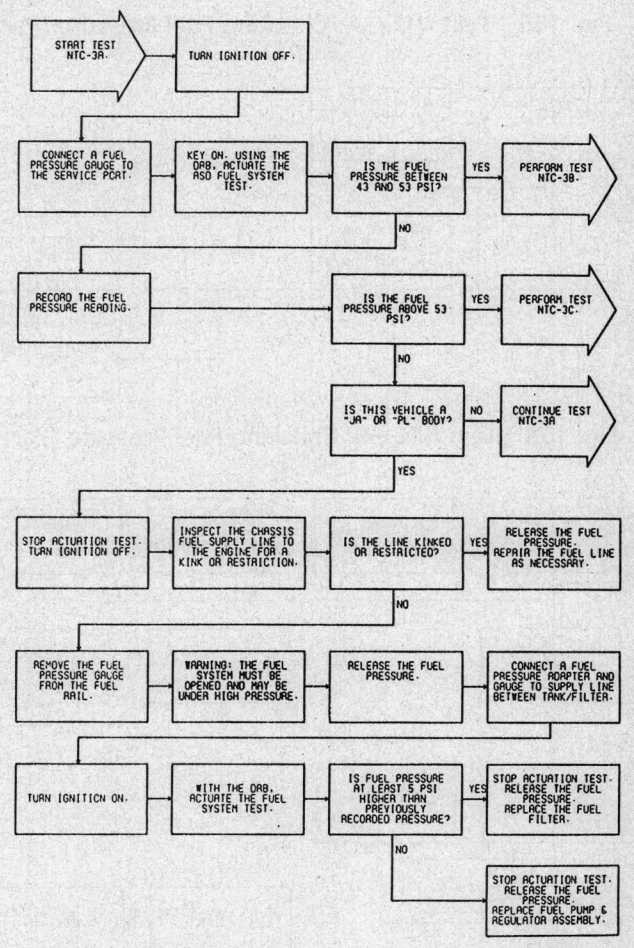

CR1029505184010X

Fig. 155 Test NTC-3A: Checking Fuel Pressure (Part 1 of 2)

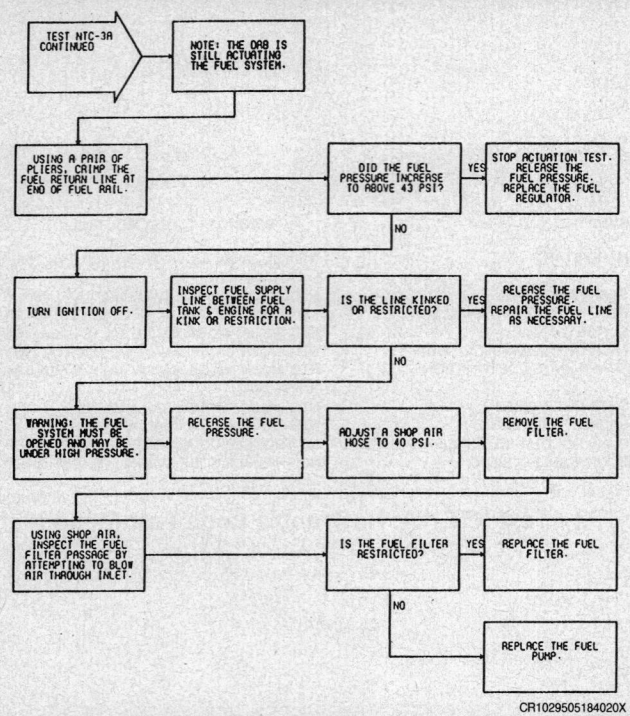

Fig. 155   Test NTC-3A: Checking Fuel Pressure (Part 2 of 2)

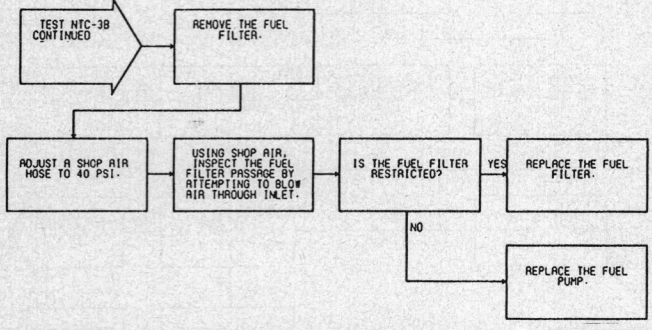

Fig. 156   Test NTC-3B: Checking Fuel Pressure (Part 2 of 2)

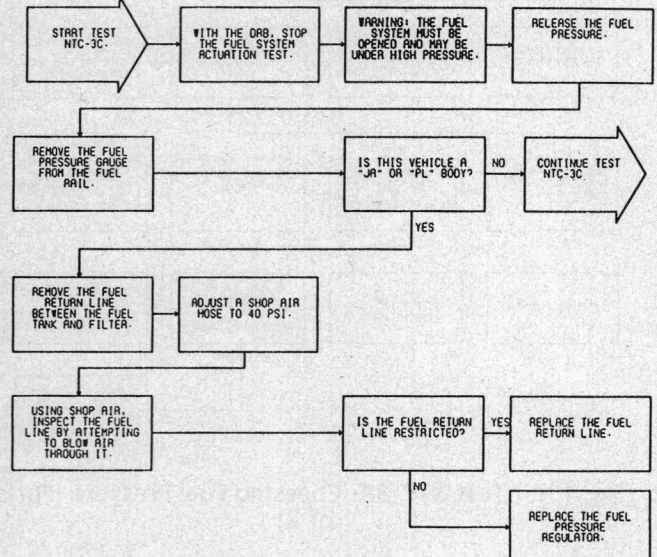

Fig. 157   Test NTC-3C: Checking Fuel Pressure (Part 1 of 2)

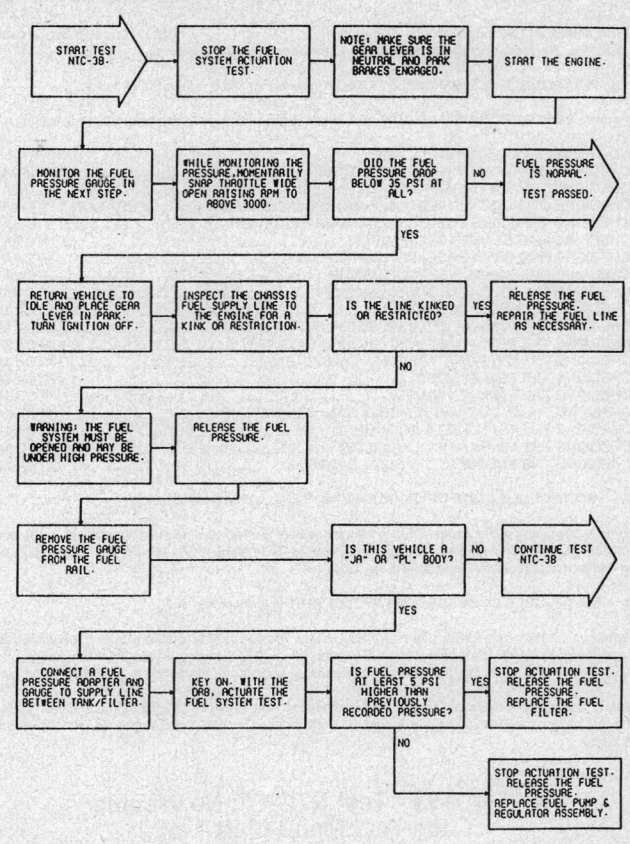

Fig. 156   Test NTC-3B: Checking Fuel Pressure (Part 1 of 2)

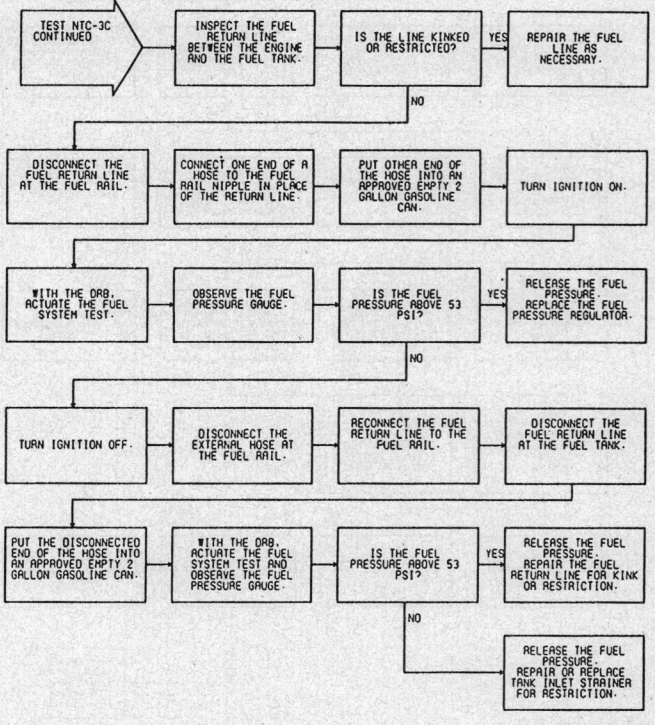

Fig. 157   Test NTC-3C: Checking Fuel Pressure (Part 2 of 2)

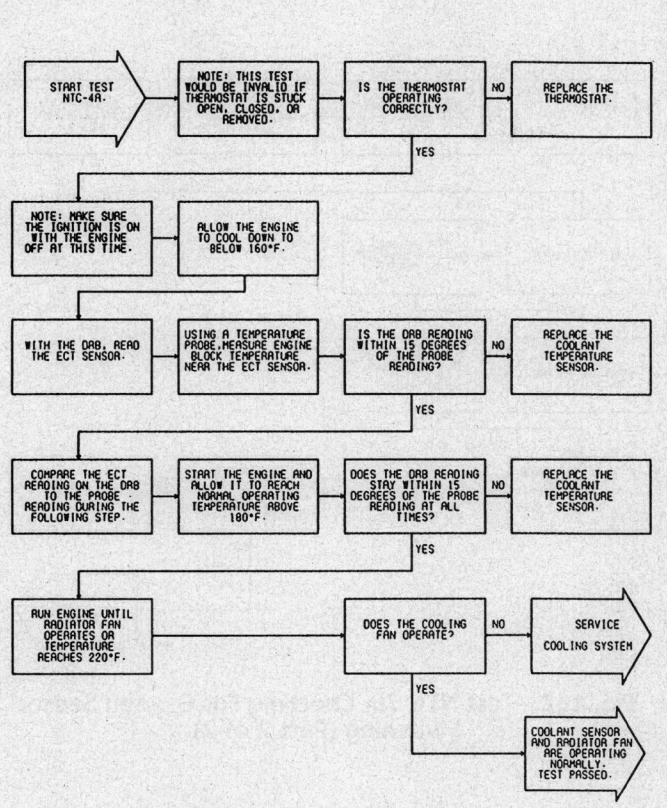

Fig. 158   Test NTC-4A: Checking Coolant Sensor Calibration & Radiator Fan Operation

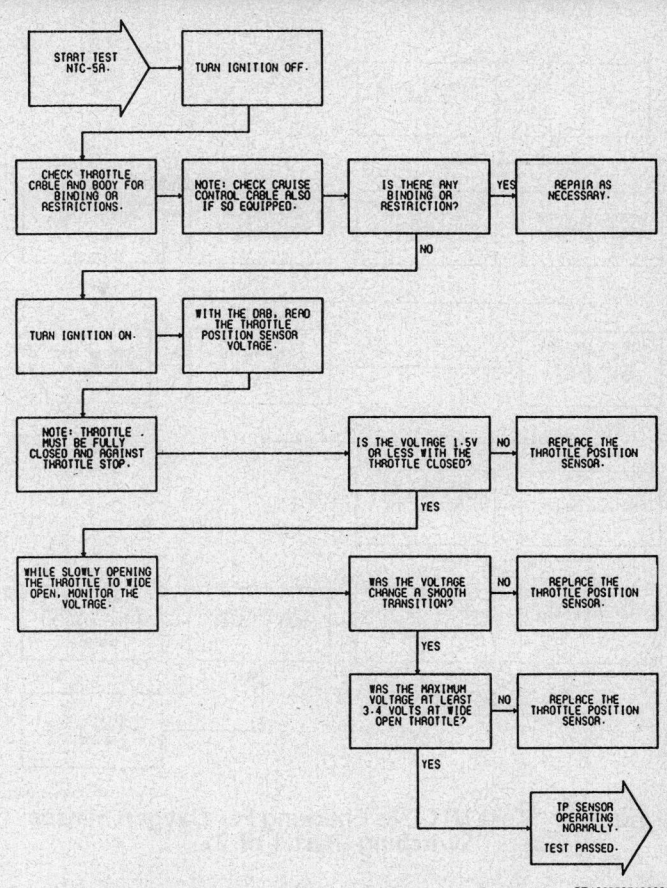

Fig. 159   Test NTC-5A: Checking TPS Calibration

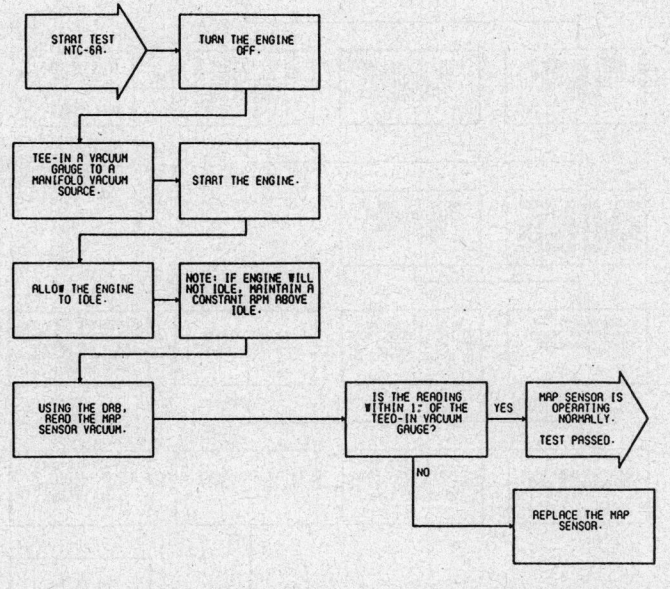

Fig. 160   Test NTC-6A: Checking MAP Sensor Calibration

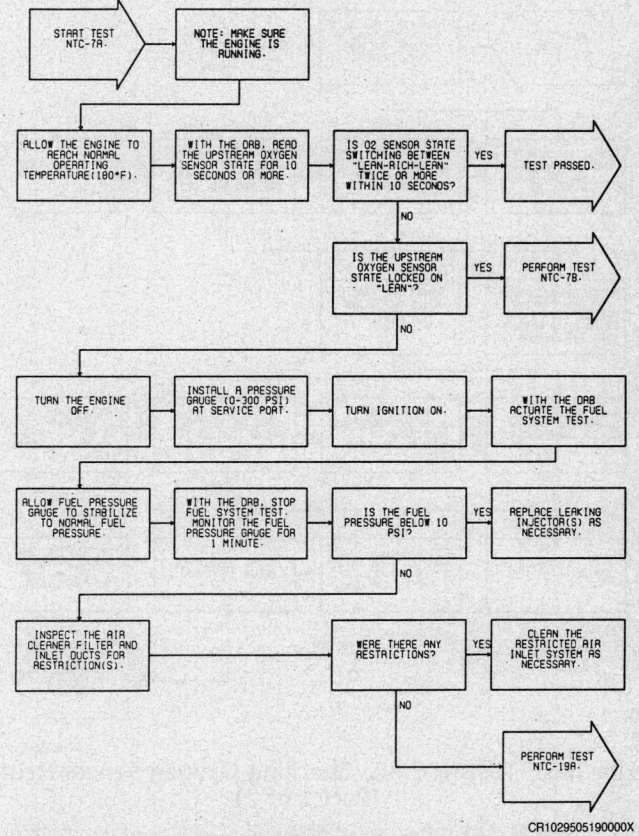

Fig. 161   Test NTC-7A: Checking For Oxygen Sensor Switching

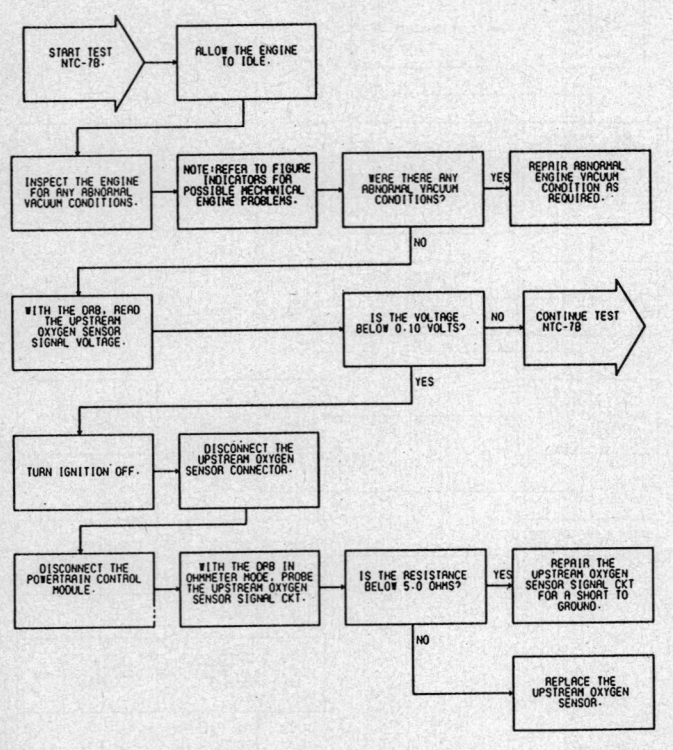

Fig. 162   Test NTC-7B: Checking For Oxygen Sensor Switching (Part 1 of 2)

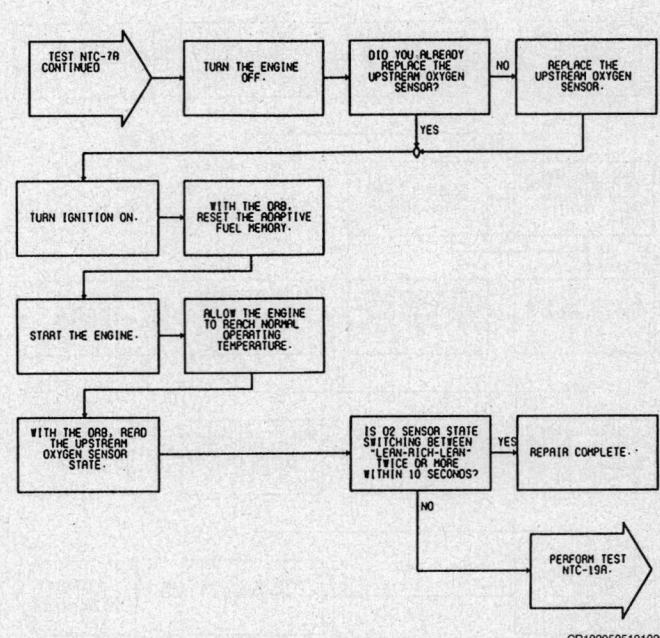

Fig. 162   Test NTC-7B: Checking For Oxygen Sensor Switching (Part 2 of 2)

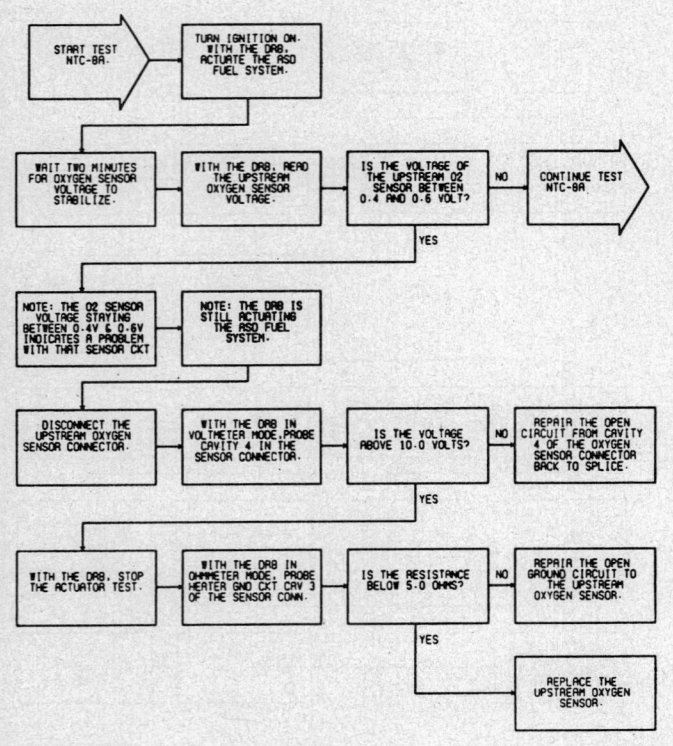

Fig. 163   Test NTC-8A: Checking Oxygen Sensor Heater (Part 1 of 2)

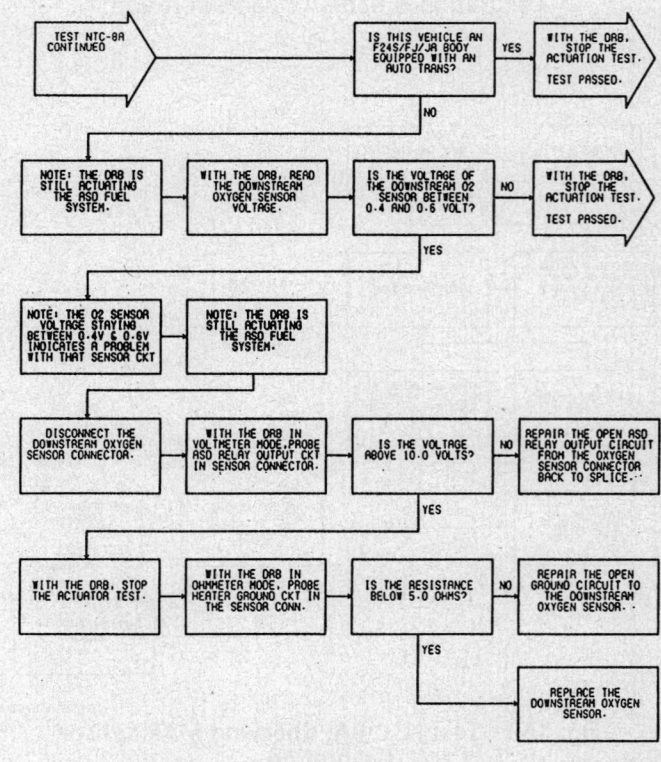

Fig. 163   Test NTC-8A: Checking Oxygen Sensor Heater (Part 2 of 2)

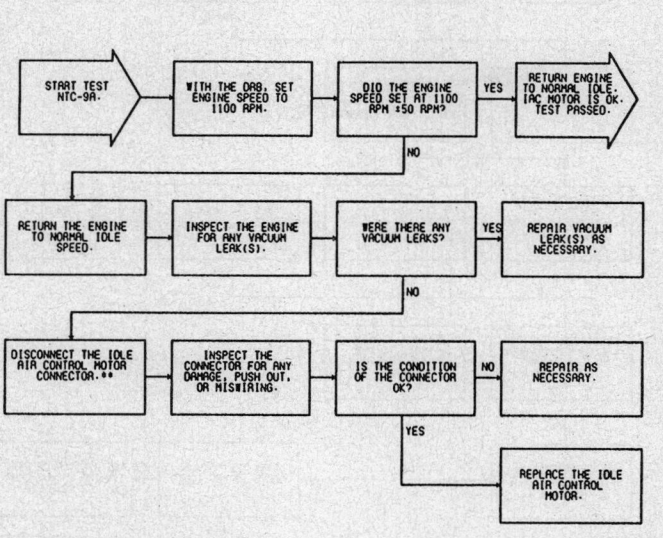

Fig. 164   Test NTC-9A: Checking Idle Air Control Motor

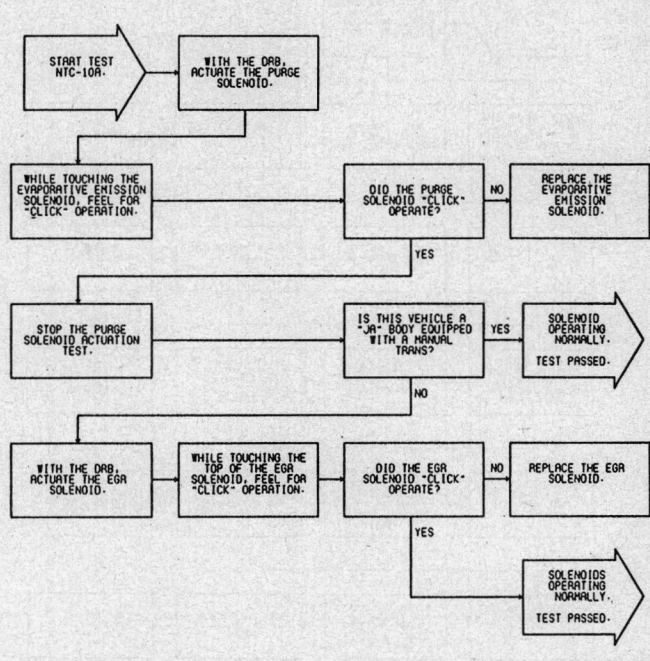

Fig. 165   Test NTC-10A: Checking Solenoid Operation

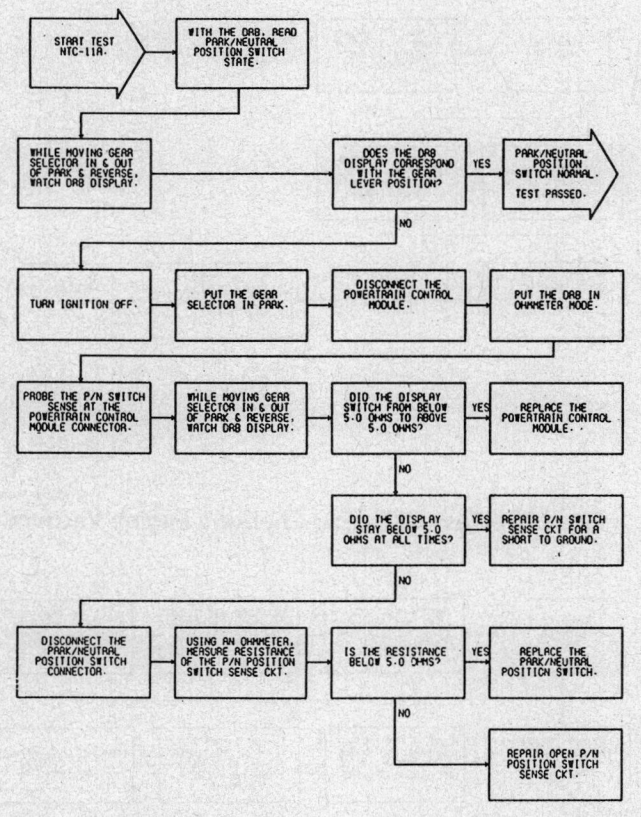

Fig. 166   Test NTC-11A: Checking Park/Neutral Position Switch

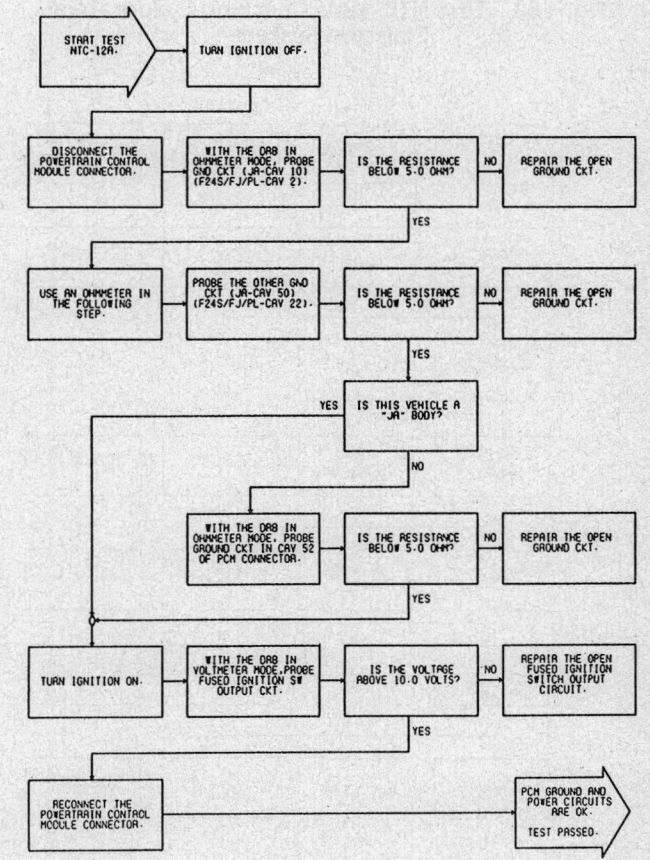

Fig. 167   Test NTC-12A: Checking PCM Power And Ground Circuits

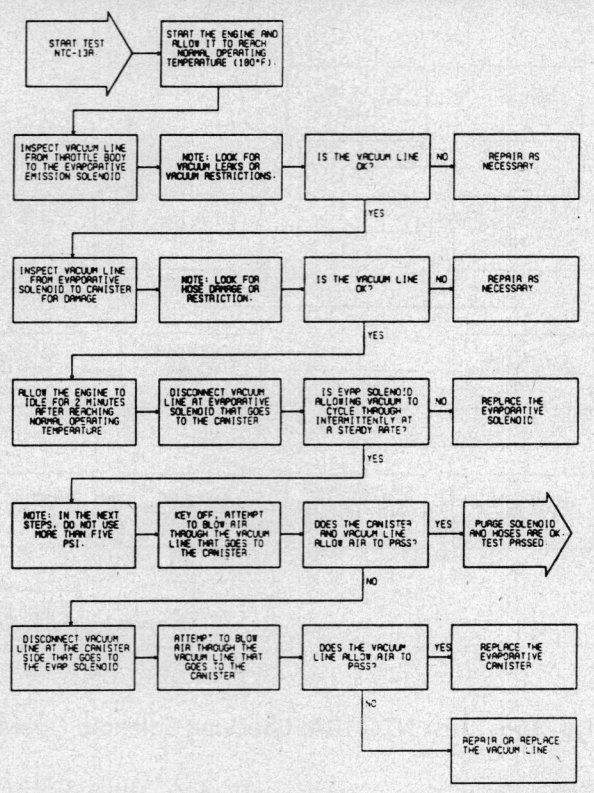

Fig. 168   Test NTC-13A: Checking Evaporative Emission System

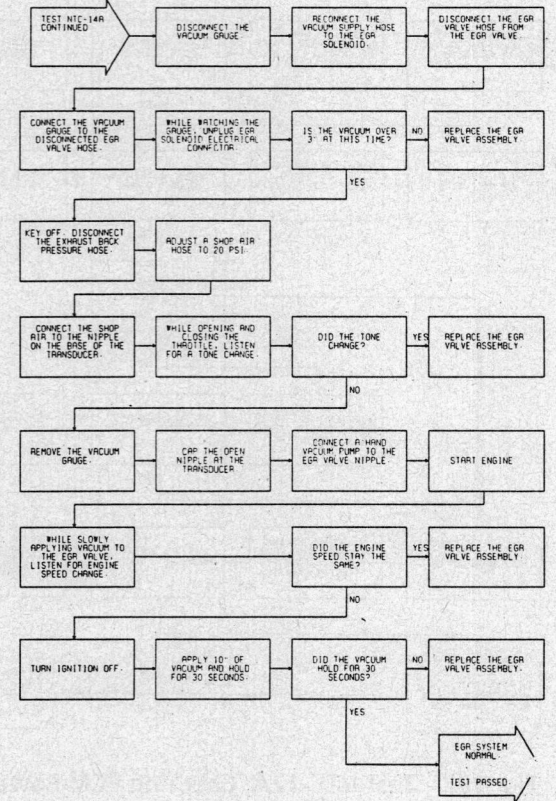

Fig. 169   Test NTC-14A: Checking EGR System (Part 2 of 2)

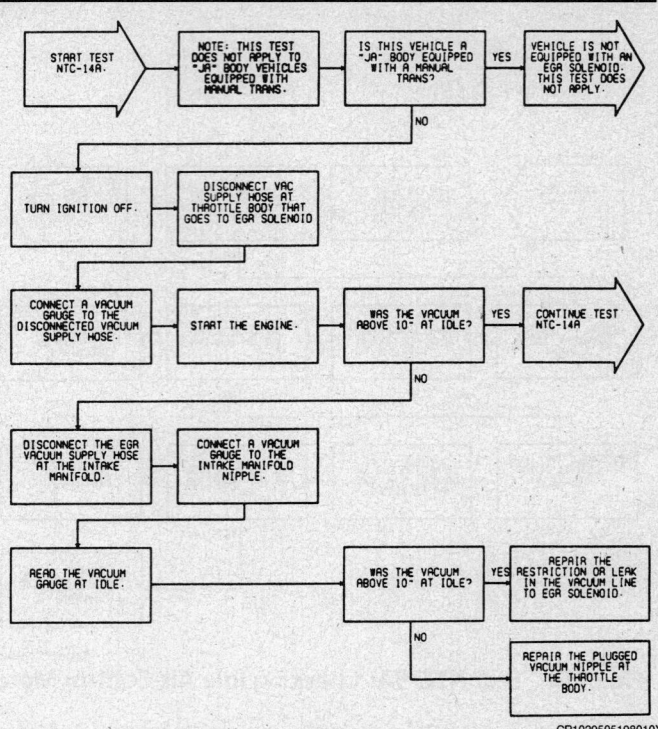

Fig. 169   Test NTC-14A: Checking EGR System (Part 1 of 2)

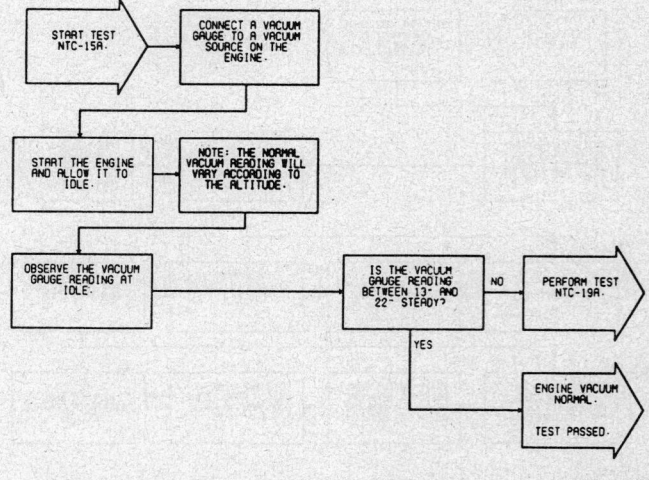

Fig. 170   Test NTC-15A: Checking Engine Vacuum

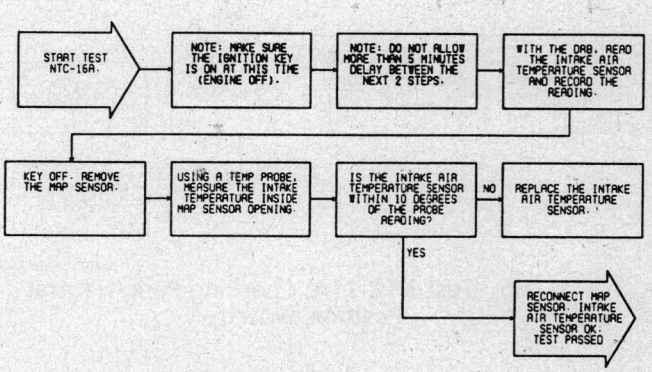

Fig. 171   Test NTC-16A: Checking Intake Air Temperature Sensor

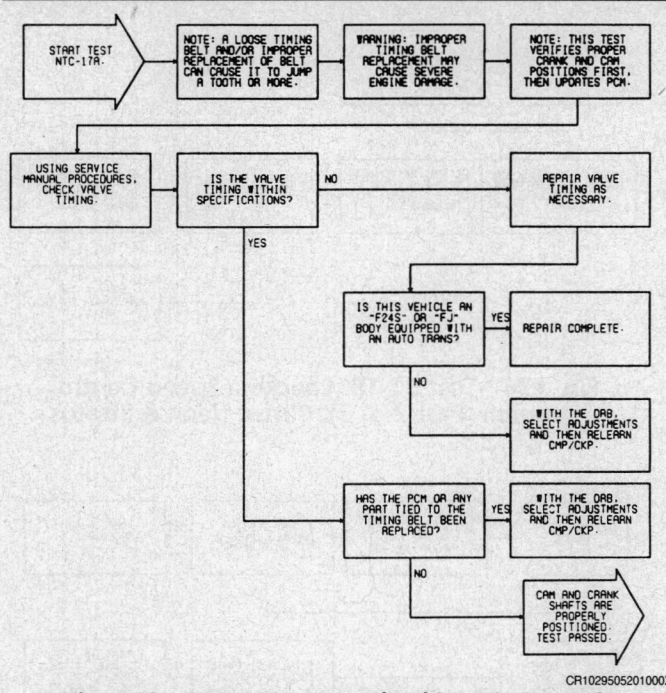

Fig. 172   Test NTC-17A: Checking Timing Belt Alignment

At this point in the diagnostic test procedure, you have determined that all of the **engine electrical systems** are operating as designed; therefore, they **are not the cause of the driveability problem.** The following additional items should be checked as possible mechanical causes of the problem:

1. **ENGINE VACUUM** - must be at least 13 inches in neutral *(see below)* †
2. **ENGINE VALVE TIMING** - must be within specifications
3. **ENGINE COMPRESSION** - must be within specifications
4. **CAMSHAFT LOBES** - check for abnormal wear
5. **CRANK SENSOR PICK-UP** - check crankshaft slots for debris/deterioration
6. **ENGINE EXHAUST SYSTEM** - must be free of any restrictions
7. **ENGINE PCV SYSTEM** - must flow freely
8. **ENGINE DRIVE SPROCKET** - must be properly positioned
9. **TORQUE CONVERTER STALL SPEED** - must be within specifications
10. **POWER BRAKE BOOSTER** - no internal vacuum leaks
11. **FUEL** - must be free of contamination
12. **FUEL INJECTOR** - plugged or restricted injector; control wire not connected to correct injector

NOTE: If you came to this test from the oxygen sensor, and the rich or lean condition is not caused by one of the first items above, replace the powertrain control module and perform TEST VER-2A (Road Test Verification).

Always look for any Technical Service Bulletins that may relate to the problem.

† The readings are only indicators of possible mechanical engine problems.

Fig. 174   Test NTC-19A: Checking Engine Mechanical Systems (Part 1 of 2)

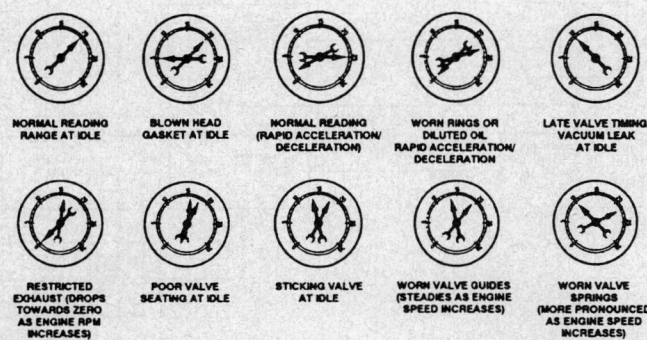

Fig. 174   Test NTC-19A: Checking Engine Mechanical Systems (Part 2 of 2)

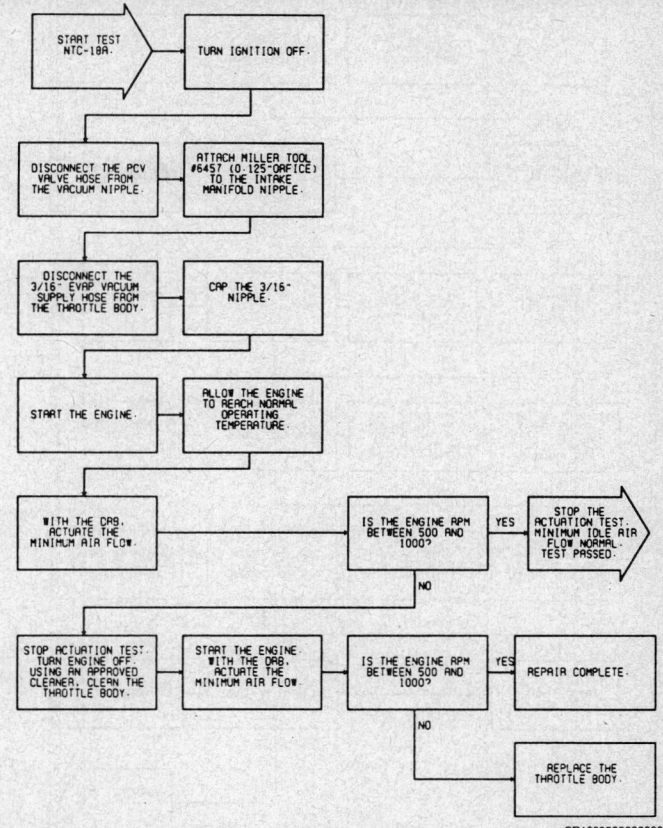

Fig. 173   Test NTC-18A: Checking Minimum Idle Air Flow

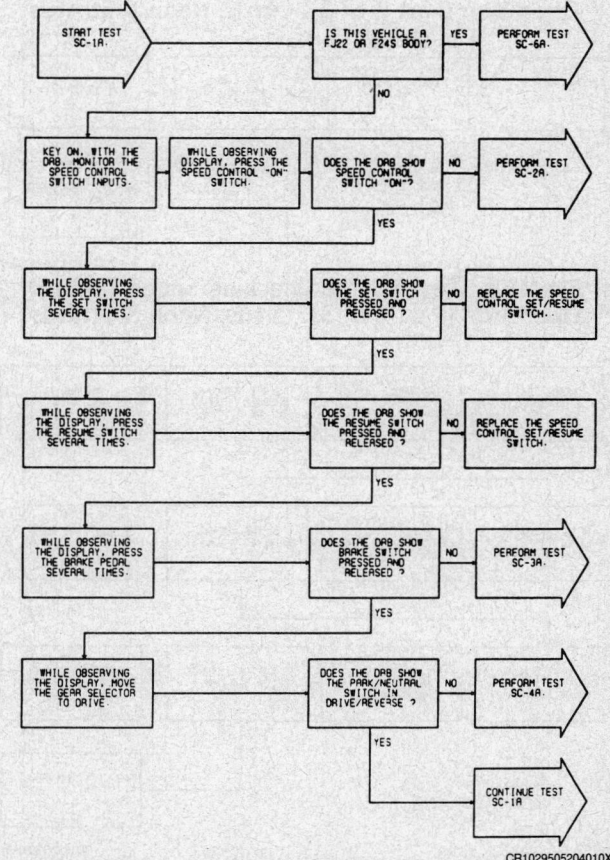

Fig. 175   Test SC-1A: Checking Speed Control Operation (Part 1 of 3). Cirrus, Neon & Stratus

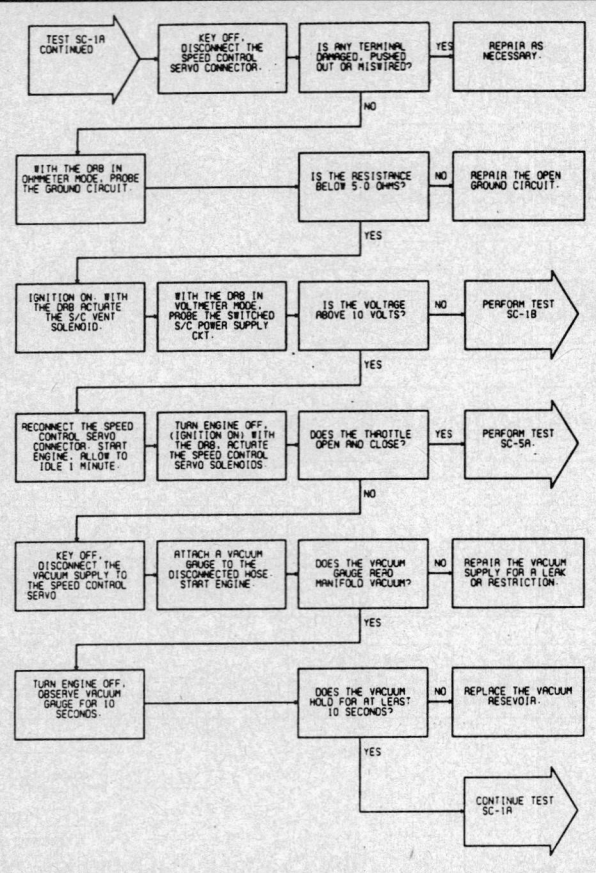

Fig. 175   Test SC-1A: Checking Speed Control Operation (Part 2 of 3). Cirrus, Neon & Stratus

CR1029505204020X

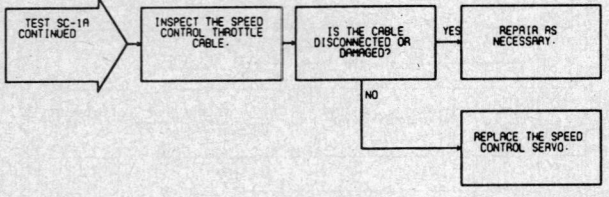

Fig. 175   Test SC-1A: Checking Speed Control Operation (Part 3 of 3). Cirrus, Neon & Stratus

CR1029505204030X

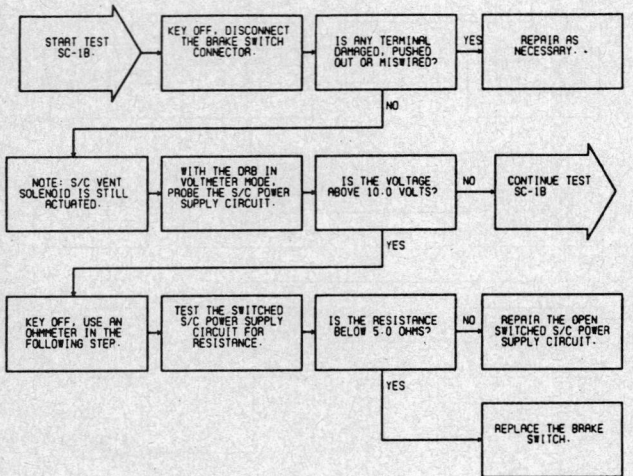

CR1029505205010X

Fig. 176   Test SC-1B: Checking Speed Control Operation (Part 1 of 2). Cirrus, Neon & Stratus

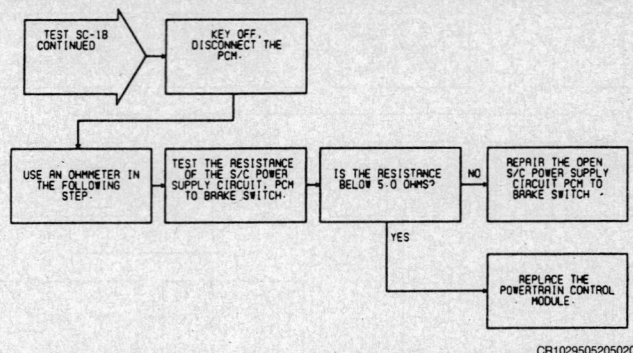

CR1029505205020X

Fig. 176   Test SC-1B: Checking Speed Control Operation (Part 2 of 2). Cirrus, Neon & Stratus

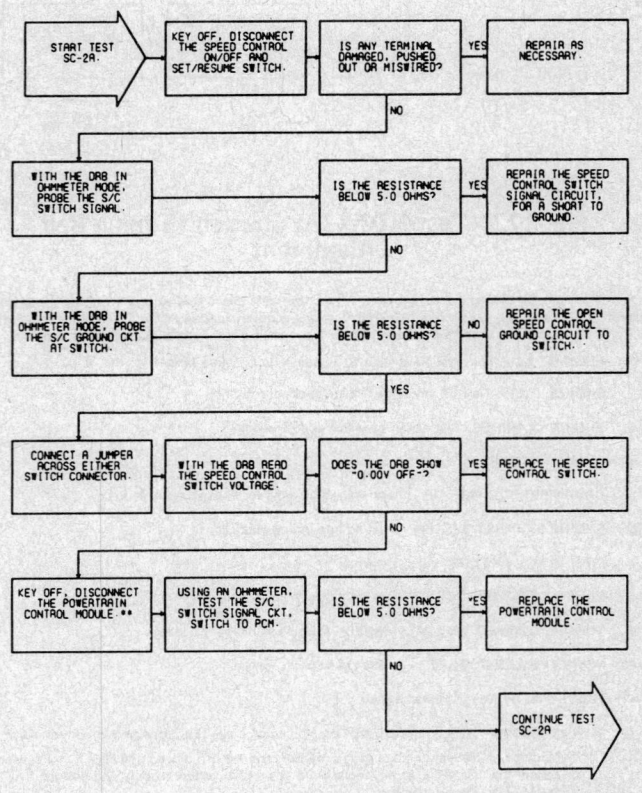

CR1029505206010X

Fig. 177   Test SC-2A: Checking Speed Control On/Off Switch (Part 1 of 2). Cirrus, Neon & Stratus

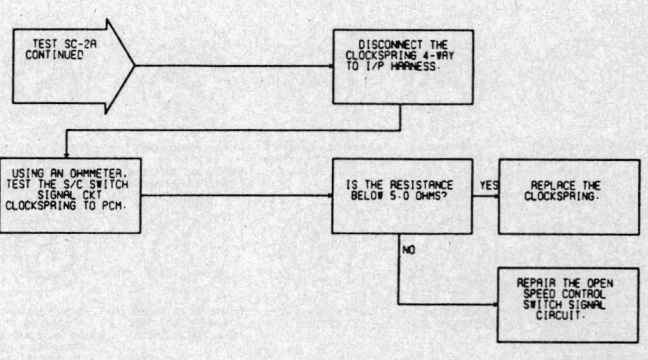

CR1029505206020X

Fig. 177   Test SC-2A: Checking Speed Control On/Off Switch (Part 2 of 2). Cirrus, Neon & Stratus

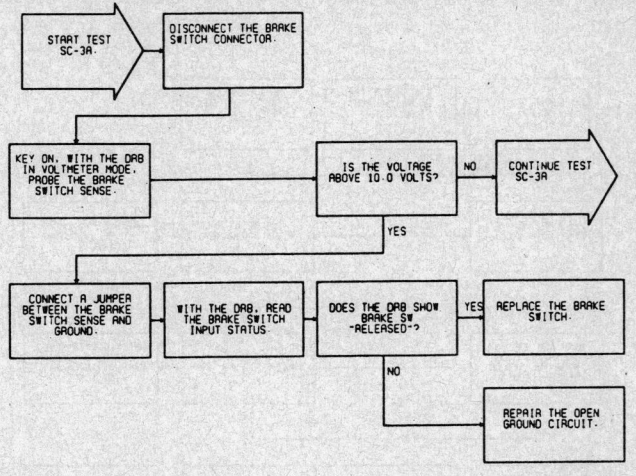

Fig. 178   Test SC-3A: Checking Speed Control Brake Switch Output (Part 1 of 2). Cirrus, Neon & Stratus

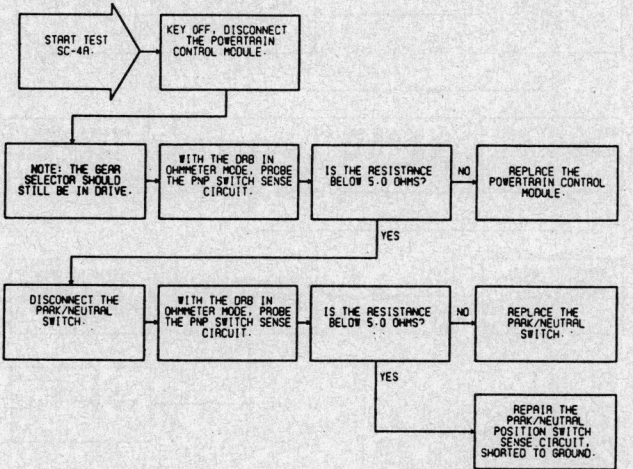

Fig. 178   Test SC-3A: Checking Speed Control Brake Switch Output (Part 2 of 2). Cirrus, Neon & Stratus

At this time the speed control switch and servo functions appear to operate properly. Using the DRB, monitor the speed control "cutout" status. Road test the vehicle at speeds over 30 mph and attempt to set the speed control. The following items will not allow the speed control to set. The last or most recent cause for speed control not to set is indicated by the "Denied" status.

Denied Message

ON/OFF	The powertrain control module does not see an "ON" signal from the switch at cavity 23.
SPEED	The vehicle speed as seen by the powertrain control module at cavity 29 is not greater than 36 mph.
RPM	The engine rpm is excessively high.
BRAKE	The brake switch sense circuit is open indicating to the powertrain control module that the brakes are applied. The sense circuit, cavity 29 of the PCM, is grounded through the brake pedal switch when the brakes are released.
P/N	The park/neutral switch sense circuit is grounded indicating to the powertrain control module that the transmission is not in gear. The sense circuit, cavity 30 of the PCM, is grounded through the park/neutral switch when the transmission is in park or neutral.
RPM/SPD	The PCM senses excessive engine rpm for a given vehicle speed.
SOL FLT	The powertrain control module senses a servo solenoid circuit trouble code that is maturing or set in memory.

Fig. 180   Test SC-5A: Checking For A Speed Control Denied Message. Cirrus, Neon & Stratus

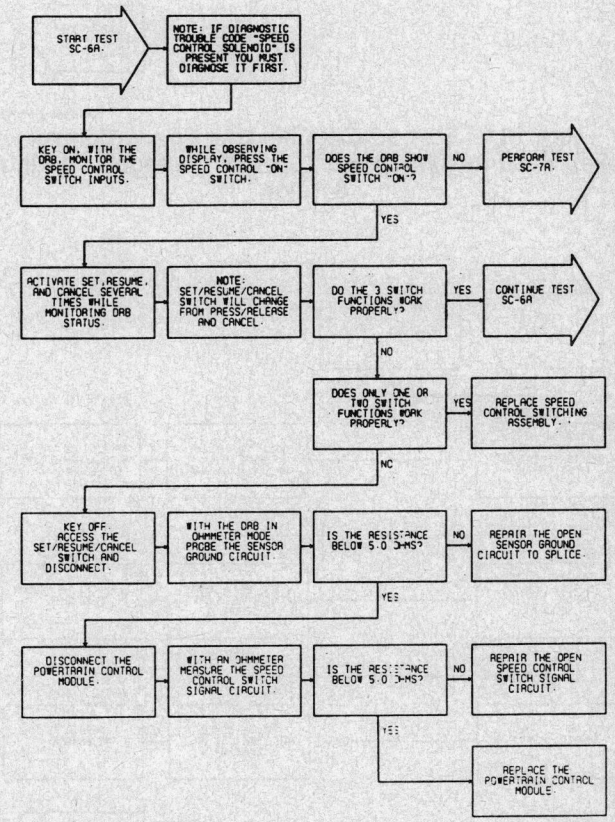

Fig. 181   Test SC-6A: Checking Speed Control Set/Resume Switch (Part 1 of 2). Avenger, Sebring & Talon

Fig. 179   Test SC-4A: Checking Park/Neutral Position Switch. Cirrus, Neon & Stratus

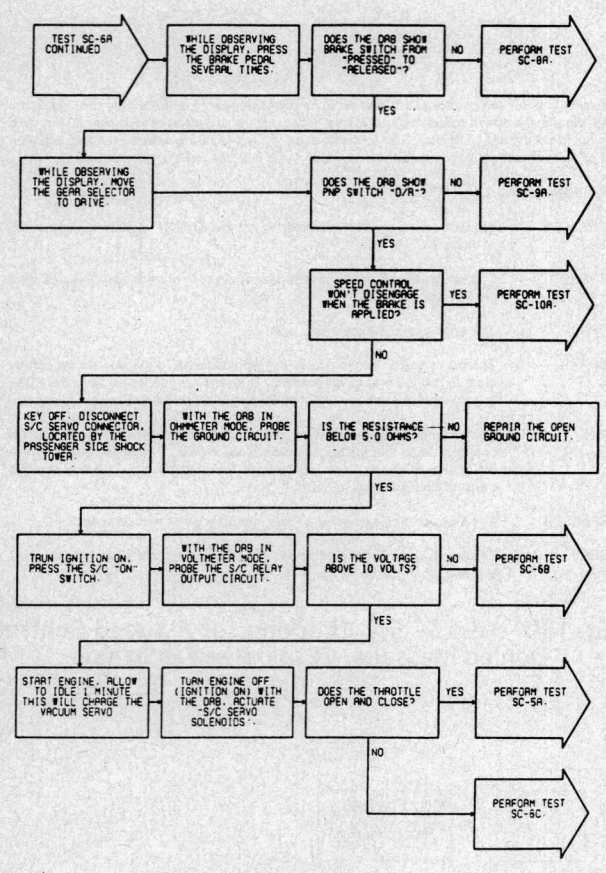

Fig. 181 Test SC-6A: Checking Speed Control Set/Resume Switch (Part 2 of 2). Avenger, Sebring & Talon

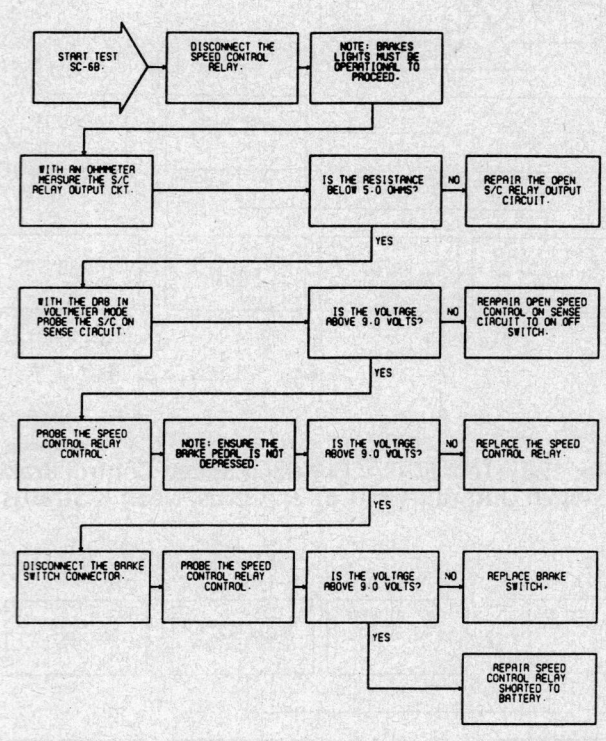

Fig. 182 Test SC-6B: Checking Speed Control Set/Resume Switch. Avenger, Sebring & Talon

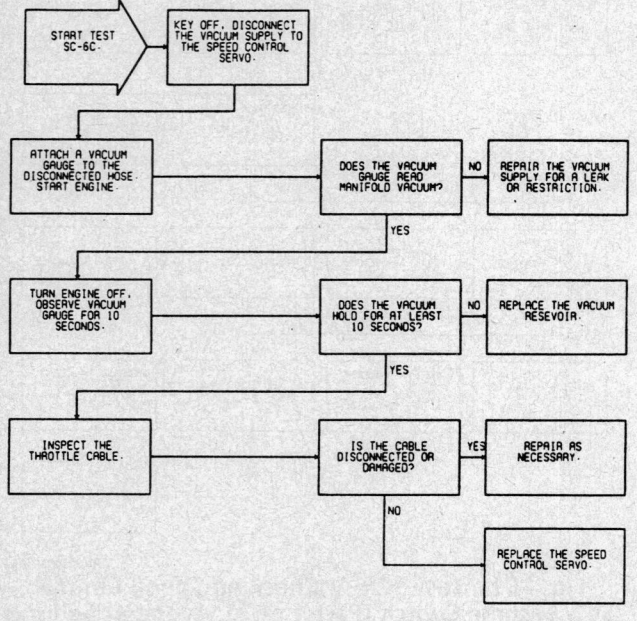

Fig. 183 Test SC-6C: Checking Speed Control Set/Resume Switch. Avenger, Sebring & Talon

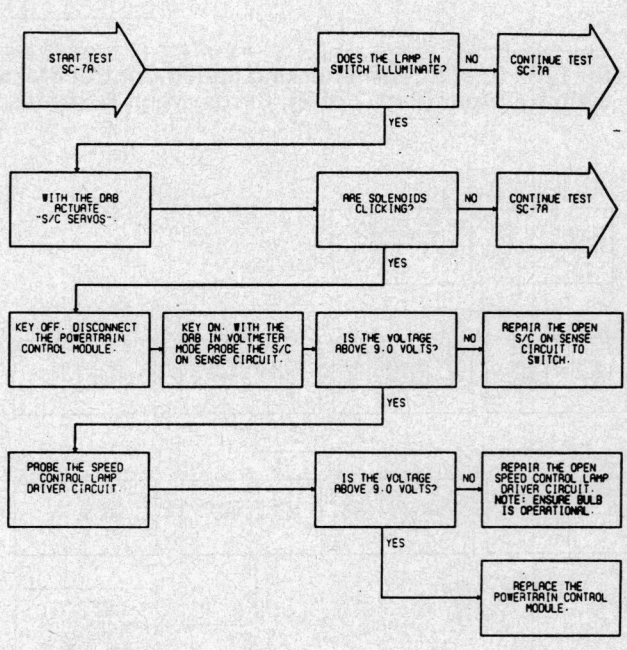

Fig. 184 Test SC-7A: Checking Speed Control On/Off Switch (Part 1 of 2). Avenger, Sebring & Talon

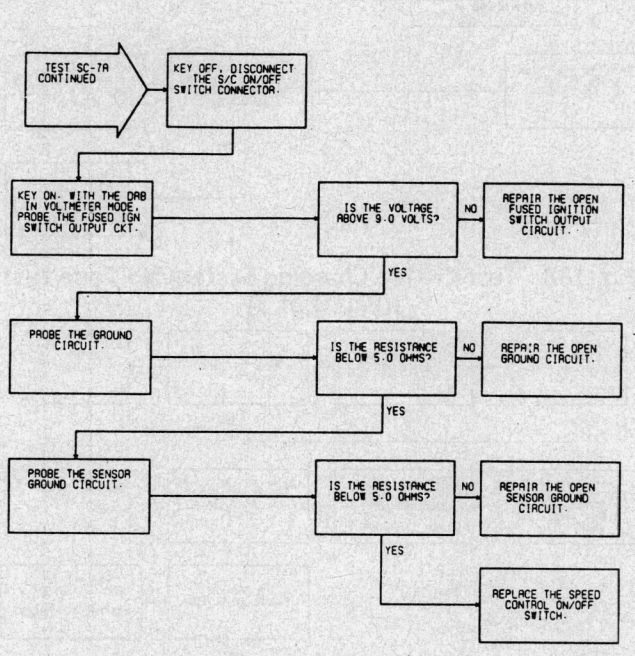

Fig. 184 Test SC-7A: Checking Speed Control On/Off Switch (Part 2 of 2). Avenger, Sebring & Talon

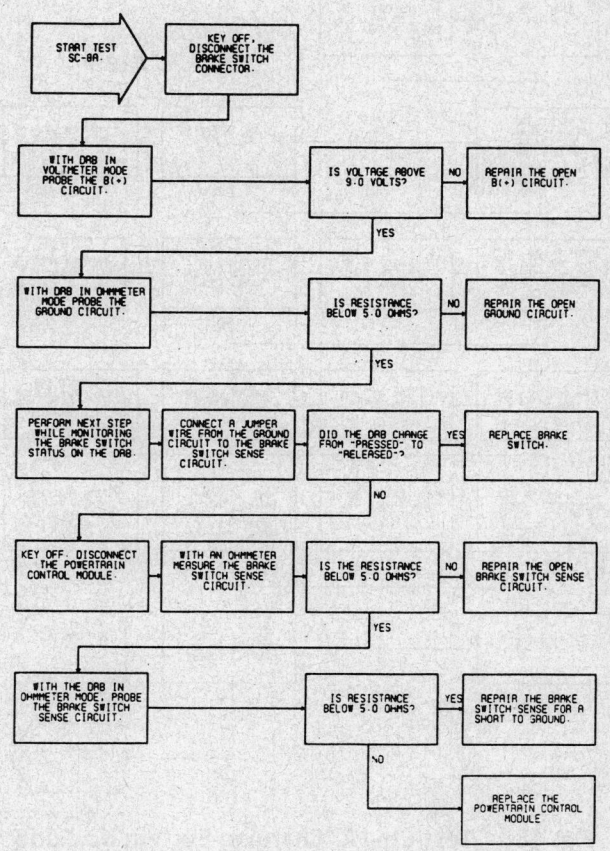

Fig. 185 Test SC-8A: Checking Brake Switch Sense. Avenger, Sebring & Talon

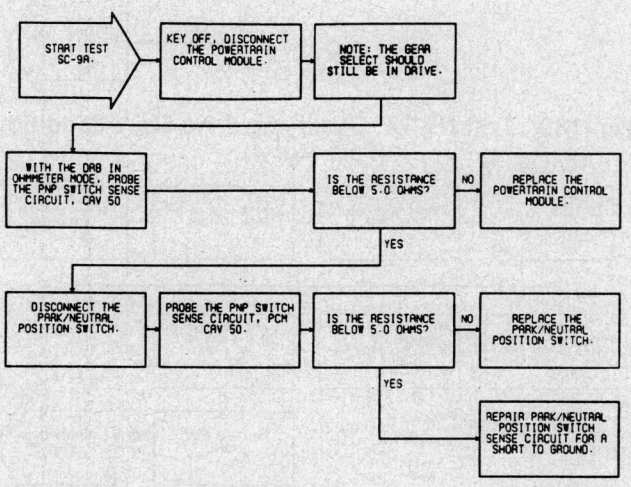

Fig. 186 Test SC-9A: Checking Park/Neutral Position Switch. Avenger, Sebring & Talon

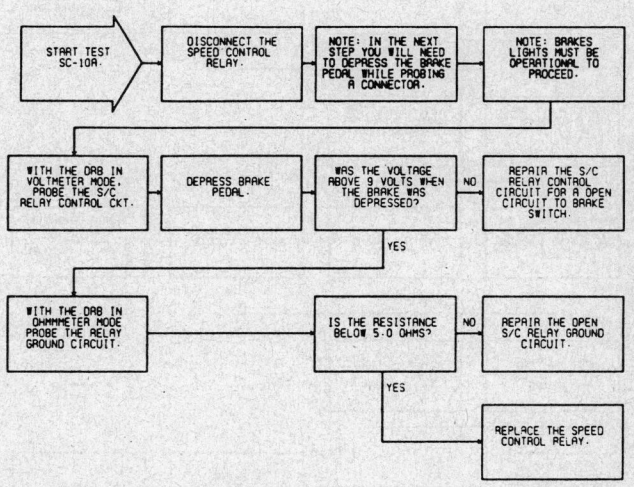

Fig. 187 Test SC-10A: Checking Speed Control Relay Output. Avenger, Sebring & Talon

CHRYSLER-Fuel Injection

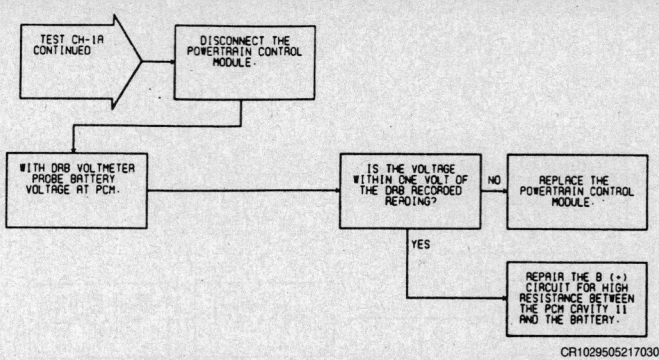

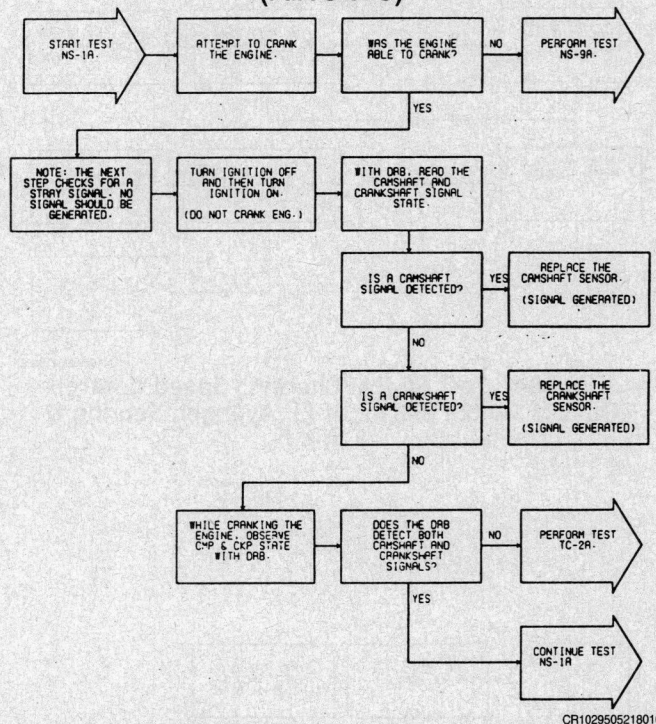

Fig. 188   Test CH-1A: Charging System No Code Test (Part 3 of 3)

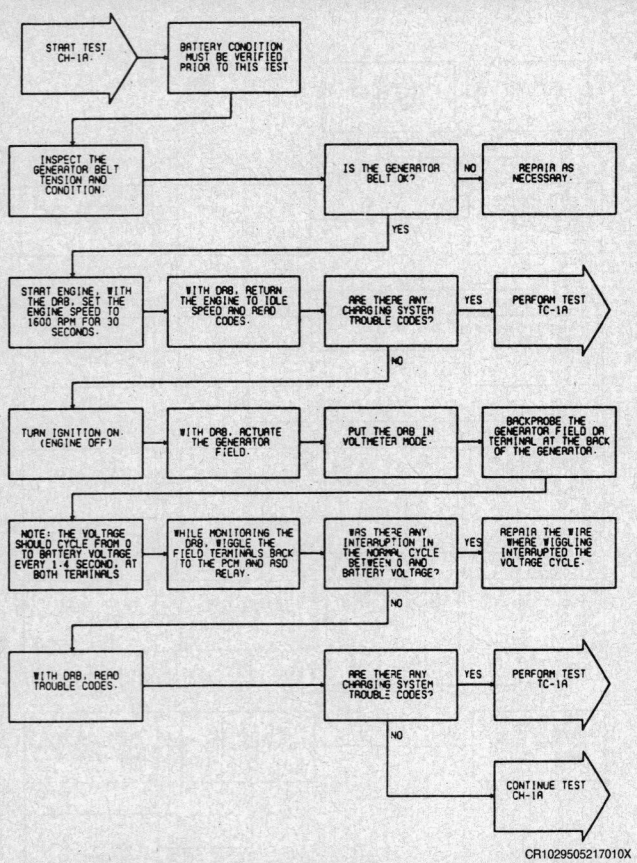

Fig. 188   Test CH-1A: Charging System No Code Test (Part 1 of 3)

Fig. 189   Test NS-1A: Qualifying A No Start Condition (Part 1 of 4)

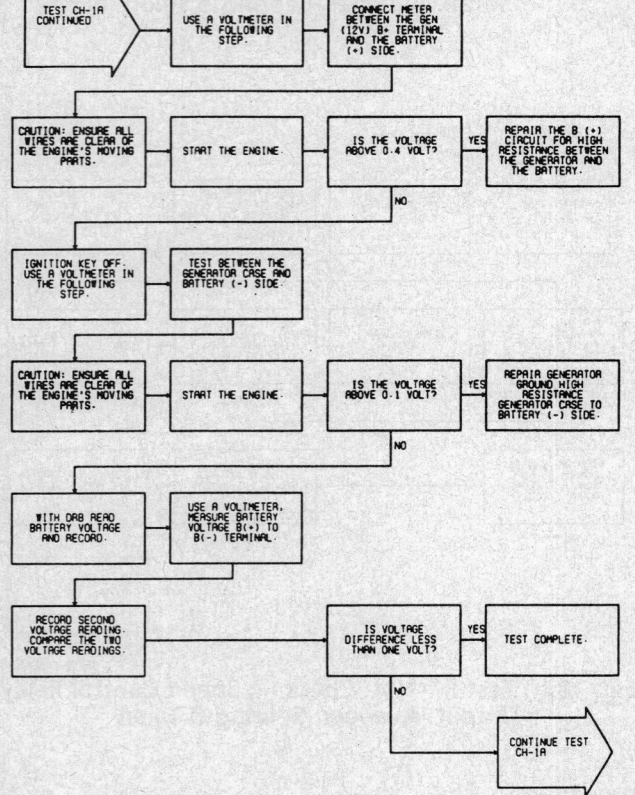

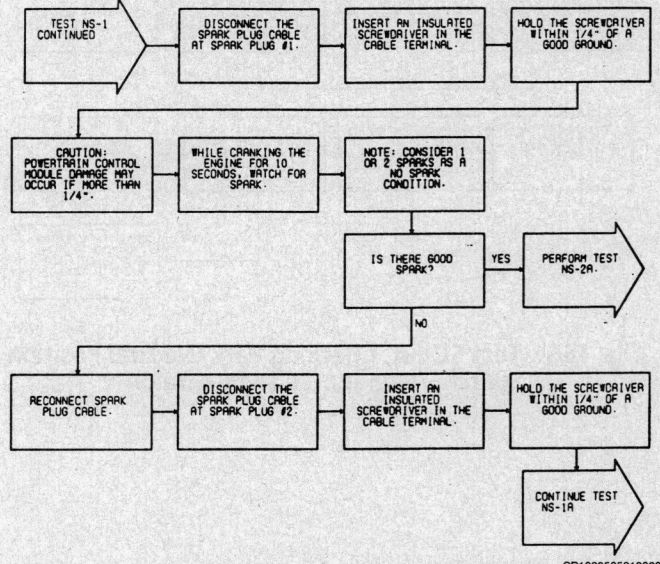

Fig. 188   Test CH-1A: Charging System No Code Test (Part 2 of 3)

Fig. 189   Test NS-1A: Qualifying A No Start Condition (Part 2 of 4)

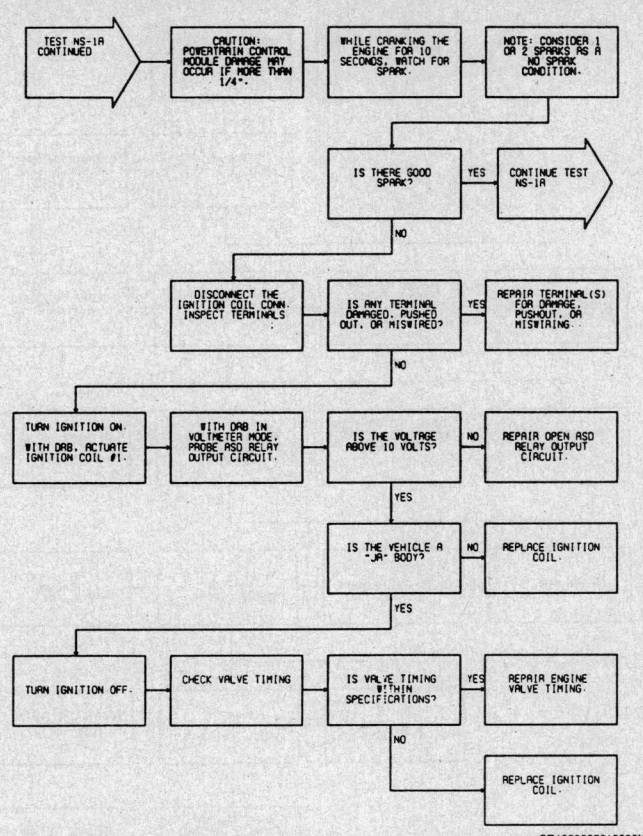

Fig. 189   Test NS-1A: Qualifying A No Start Condition
(Part 3 of 4)

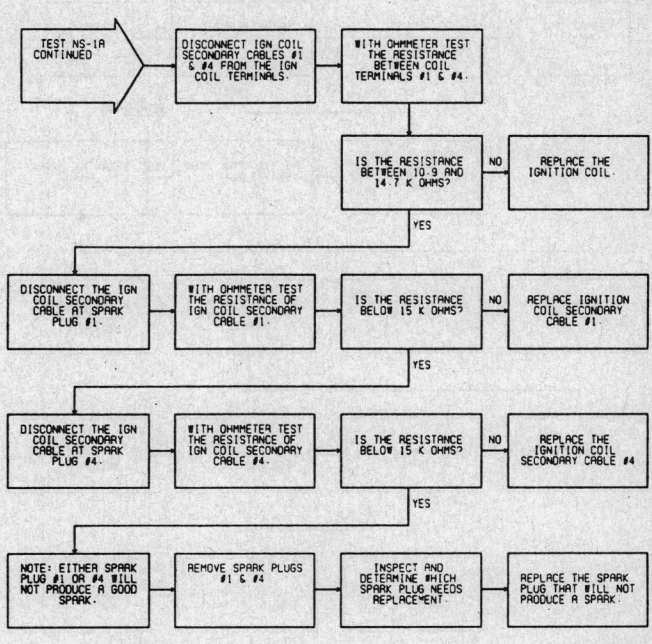

Fig. 189   Test NS-1A: Qualifying A No Start Condition
(Part 4 of 4)

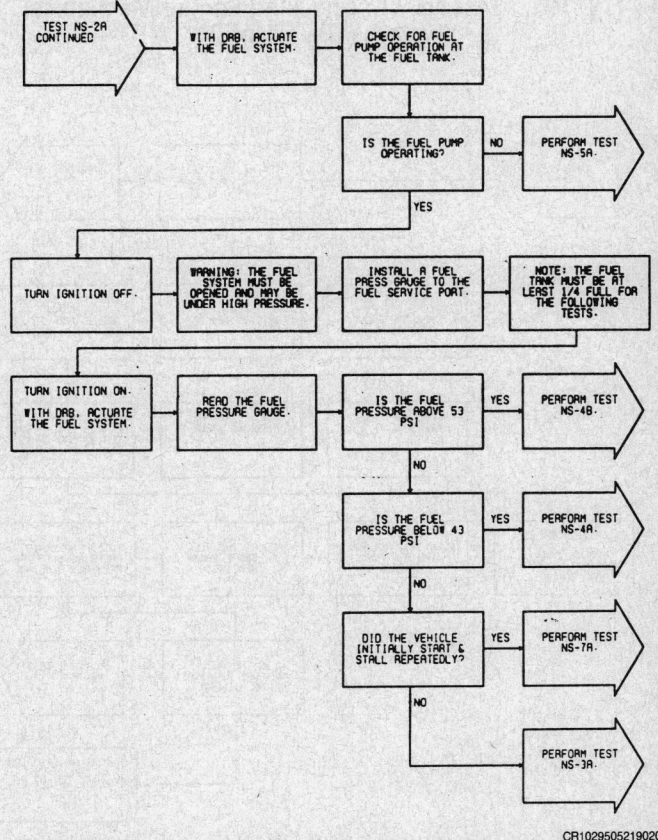

Fig. 190   Test NS-2A: Checking Fuel System (Part 2 of 2)

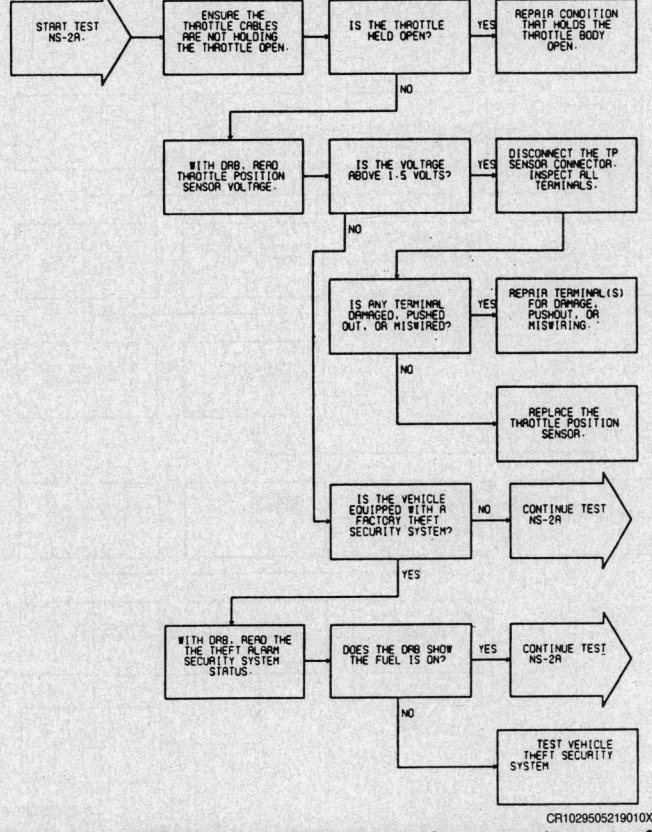

Fig. 190   Test NS-2A: Checking Fuel System (Part 1 of 2)

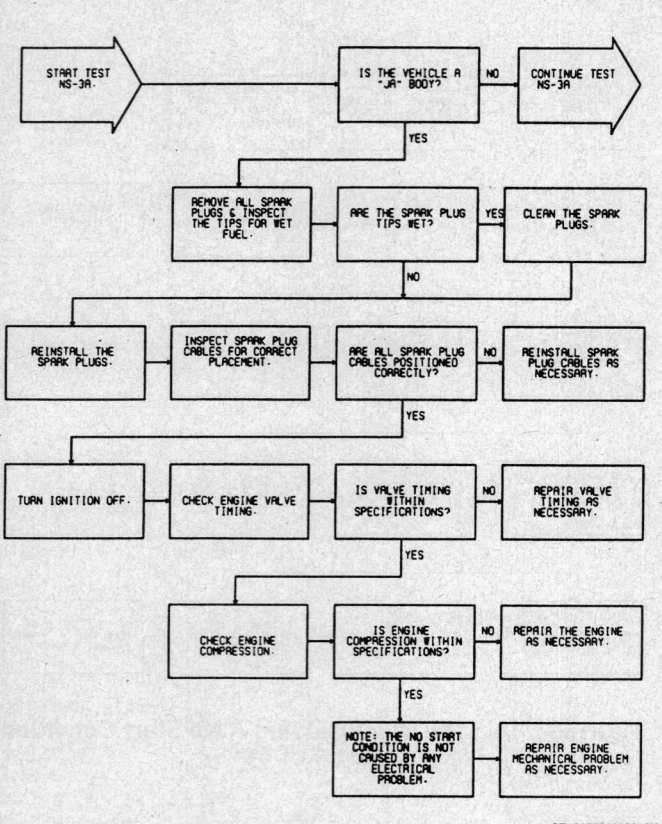

Fig. 191   Test NS-3A: Checking Engine Mechanical Systems (Part 1 of 2)

CR1029505220010X

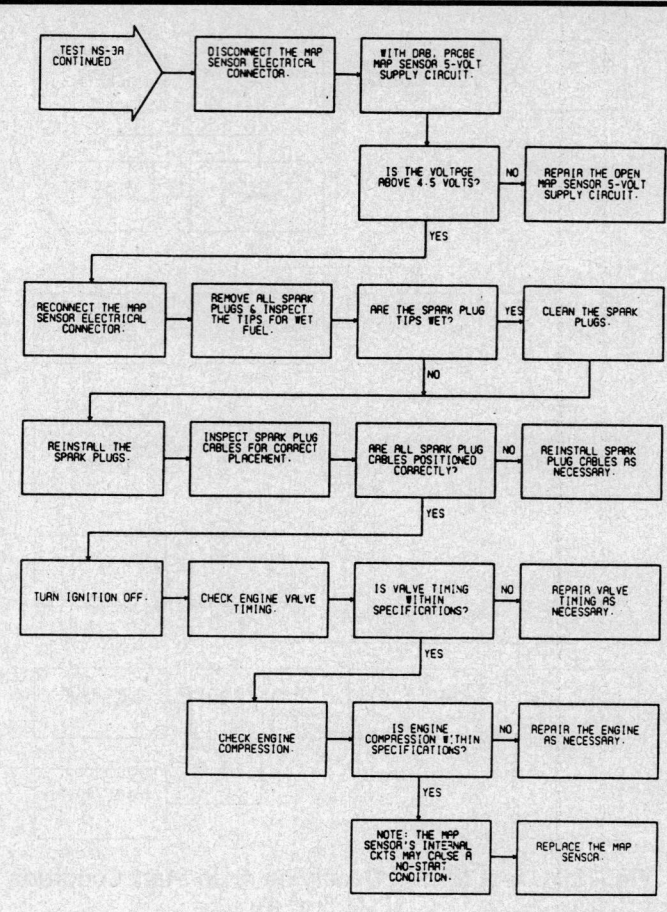

Fig. 191   Test NS-3A: Checking Engine Mechanical Systems (Part 2 of 2)

CR1029505220020X

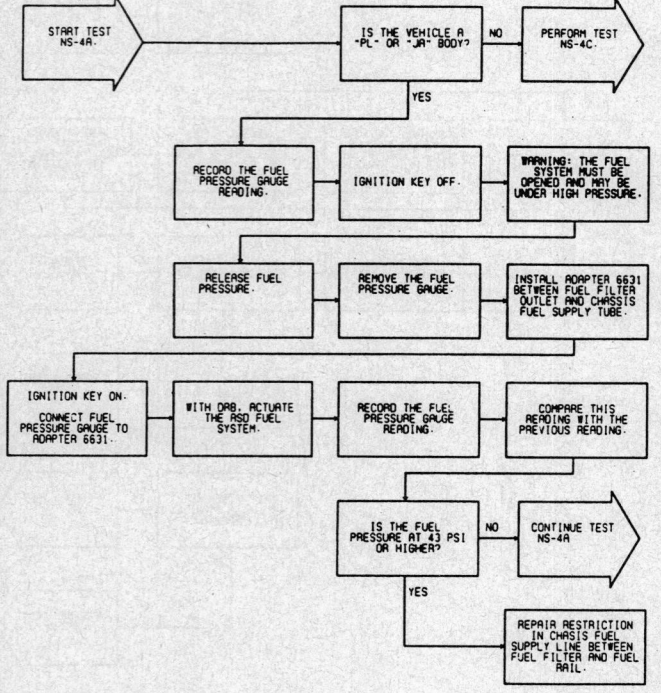

Fig. 192   Test NS-4A: Repairing Low Fuel Pressure (Part 1 of 2)

CR1029505221010X

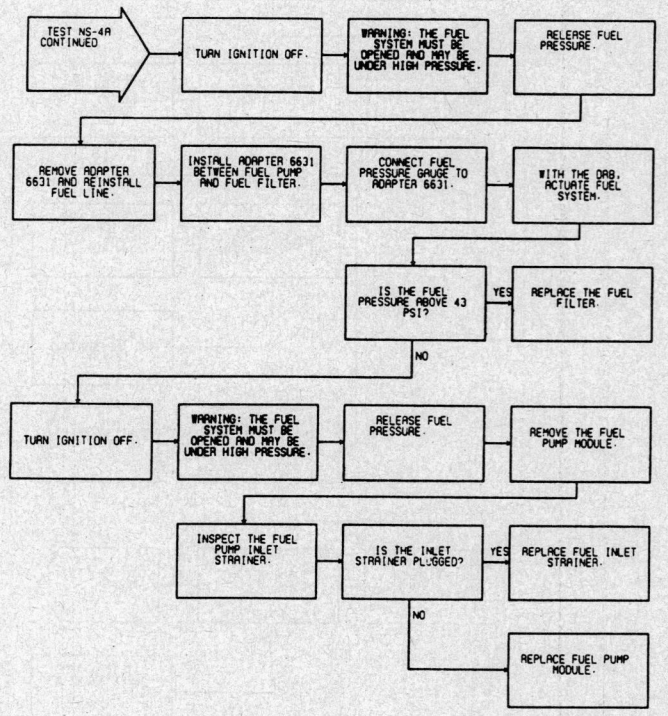

Fig. 192   Test NS-4A: Repairing Low Fuel Pressure (Part 2 of 2)

CR1029505221020X

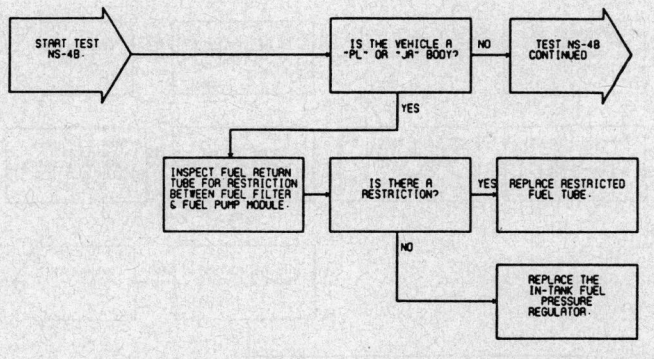

Fig. 193   Test NS-4B: Repairing High Fuel Pressure (Part 1 of 2)

CR1029505222010X

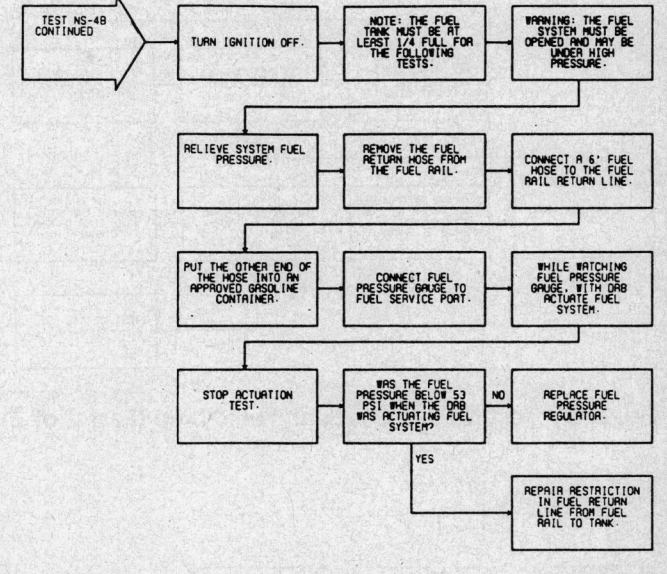

Fig. 193   Test NS-4B: Repairing High Fuel Pressure (Part 2 of 2)

CR1029505222020X

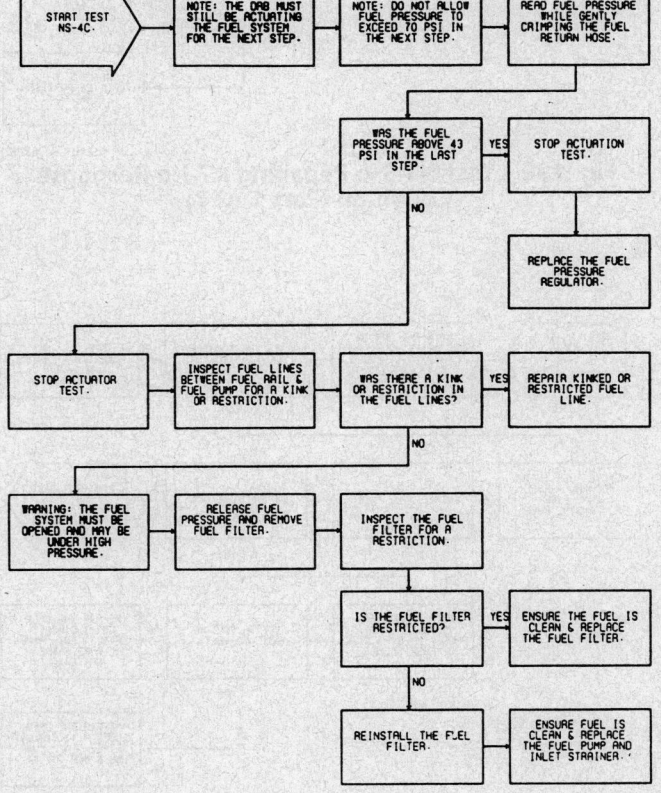

Fig. 194   Test NS-4C: Repairing High Fuel Pressure

CR1029505223000X

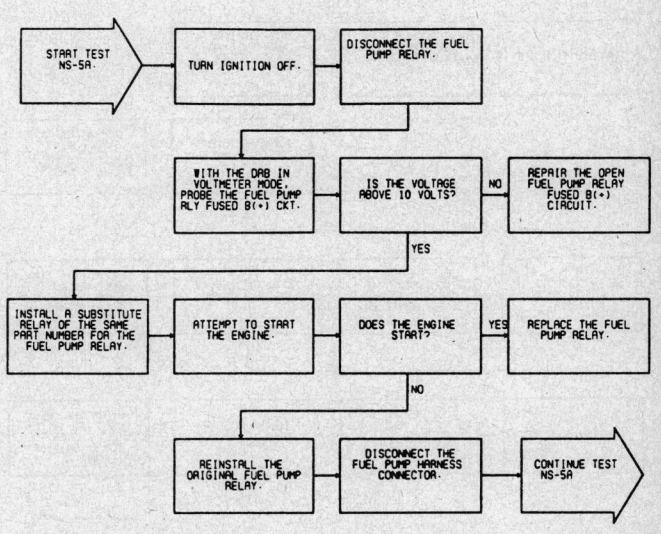

Fig. 195   Test NS-5A: Checking Fuel Pump (Part 1 of 2)

CR1029505224010X

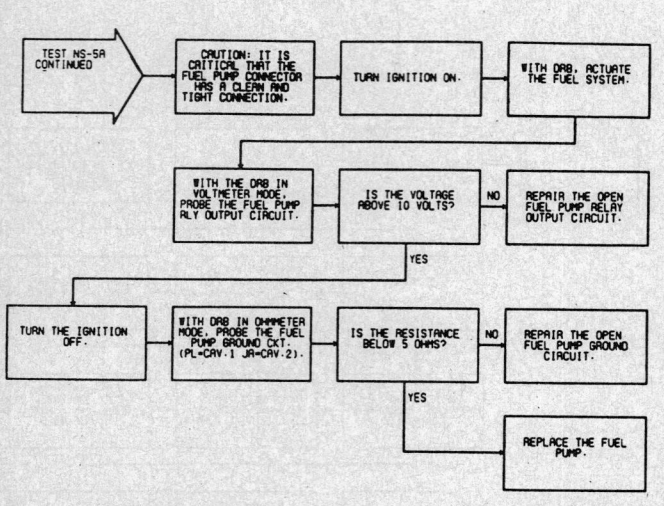

Fig. 195   Test NS-5A: Checking Fuel Pump (Part 2 of 2)

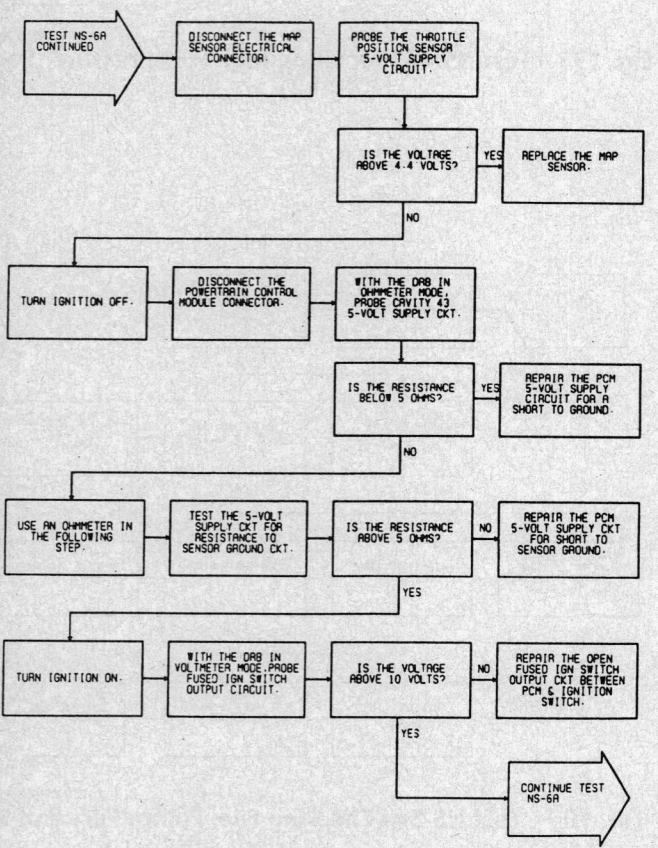

Fig. 196   Test NS-6A: Repairing A "No Response" Condition (Part 2 of 7)

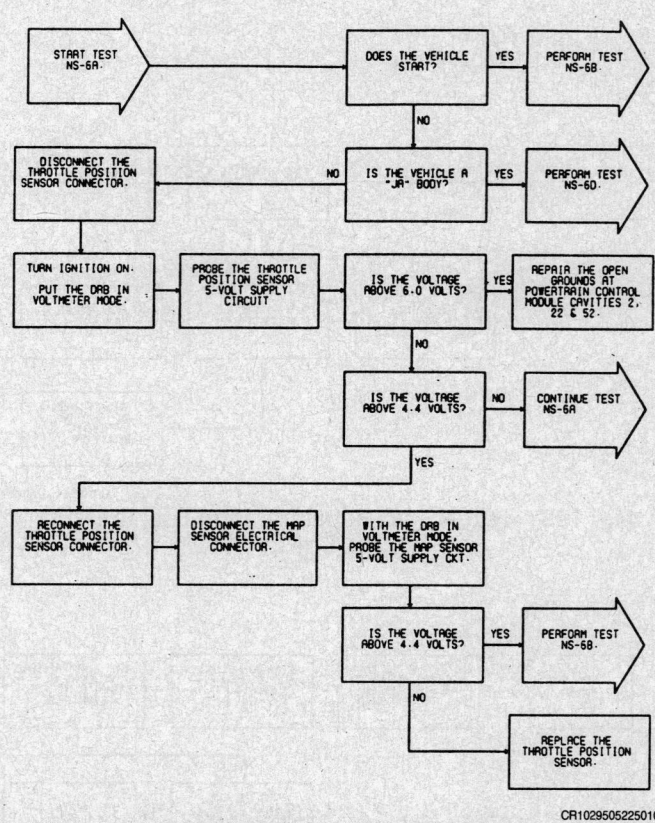

Fig. 196   Test NS-6A: Repairing A "No Response" Condition (Part 1 of 7)

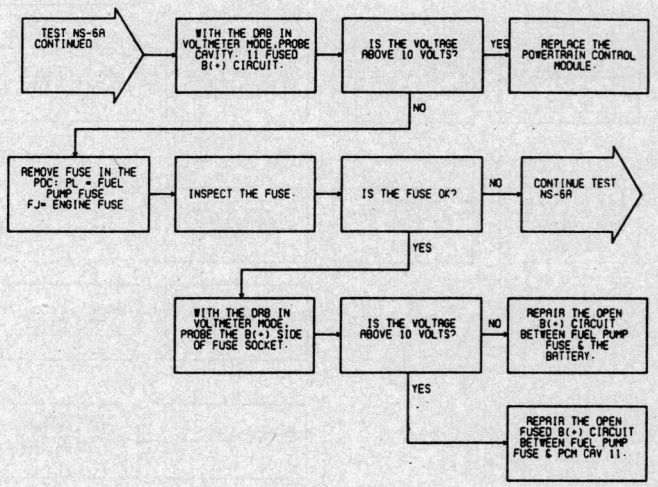

Fig. 196   Test NS-6A: Repairing A "No Response" Condition (Part 3 of 7)

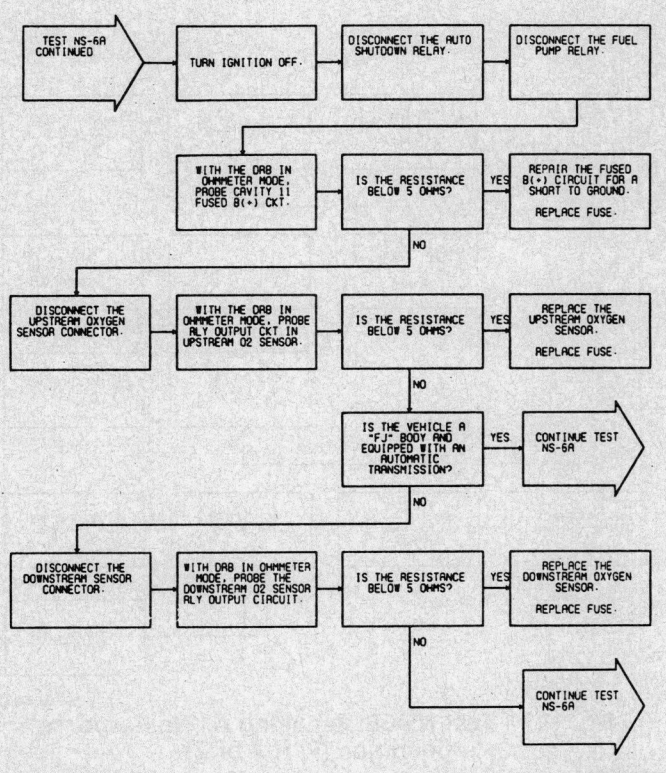

Fig. 196   Test NS-6A: Repairing A "No Response" Condition (Part 4 of 7)

CR1029505225040X

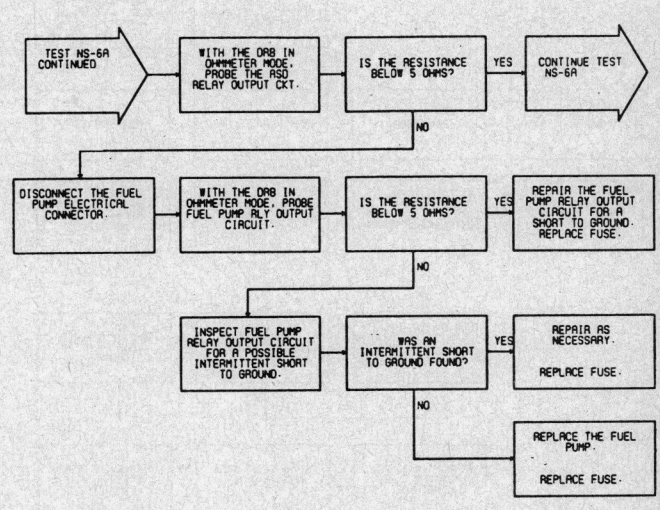

Fig. 196   Test NS-6A: Repairing A "No Response" Condition (Part 5 of 7)

CR1029505225050X

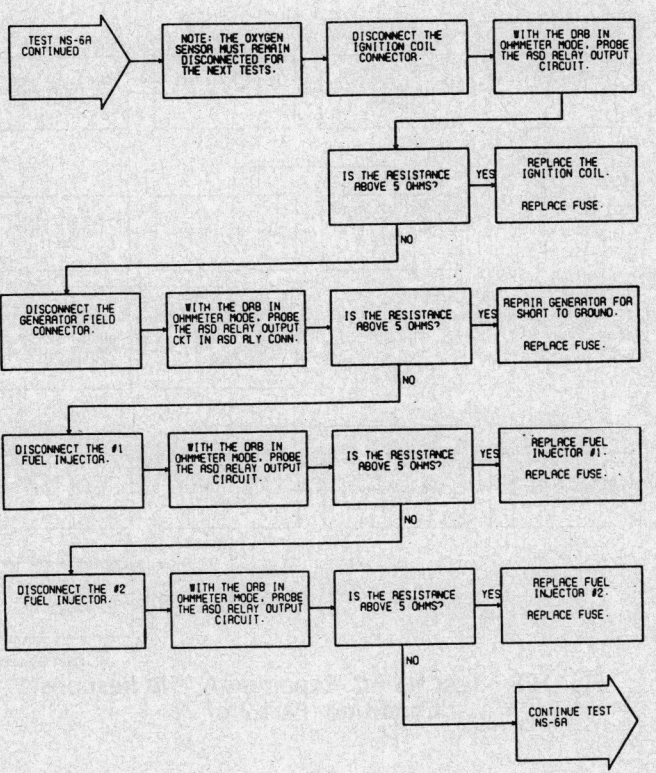

Fig. 196   Test NS-6A: Repairing A "No Response" Condition (Part 6 of 7)

CR1029505225060X

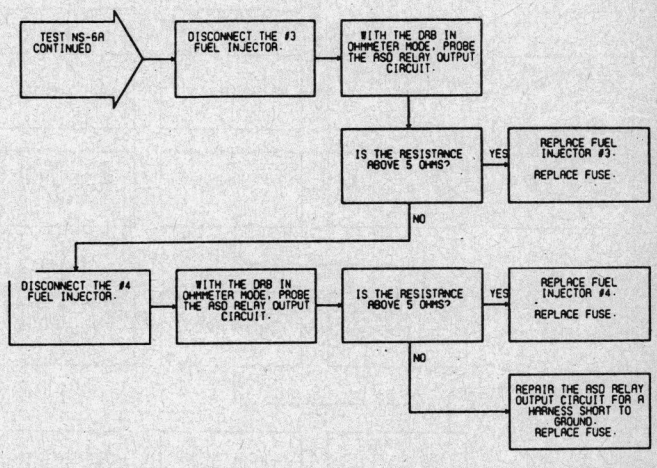

Fig. 196   Test NS-6A: Repairing A "No Response" Condition (Part 7 of 7)

CR1029505225070X

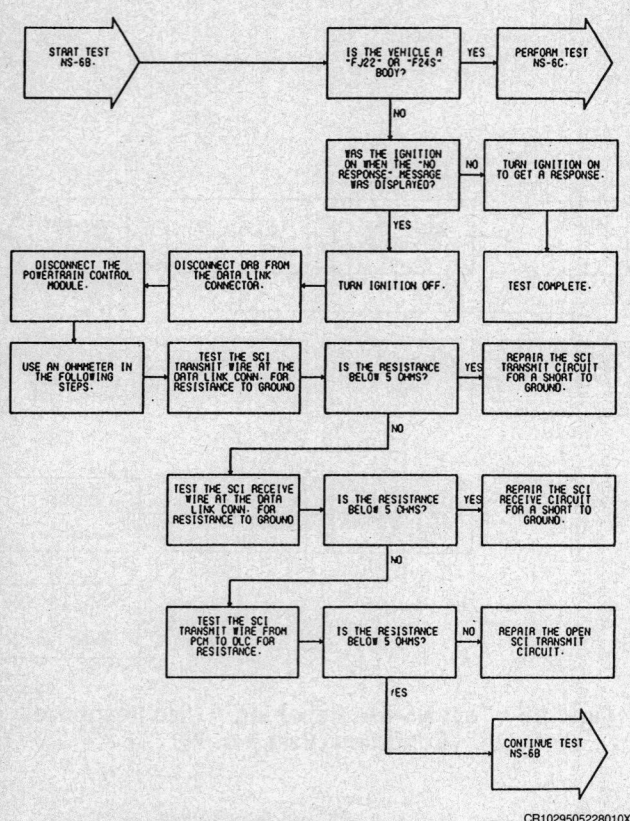

**Fig. 197   Test NS-6B: Repairing A "No Response"
Condition (Part 1 of 2)**

CR1029505228010X

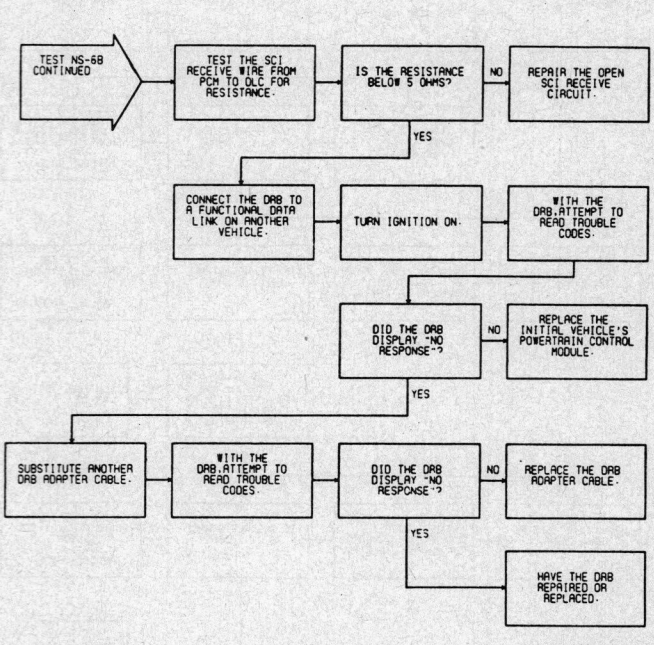

**Fig. 197   Test NS-6B: Repairing A "No Response"
Condition (Part 2 of 2)**

CR1029505228020X

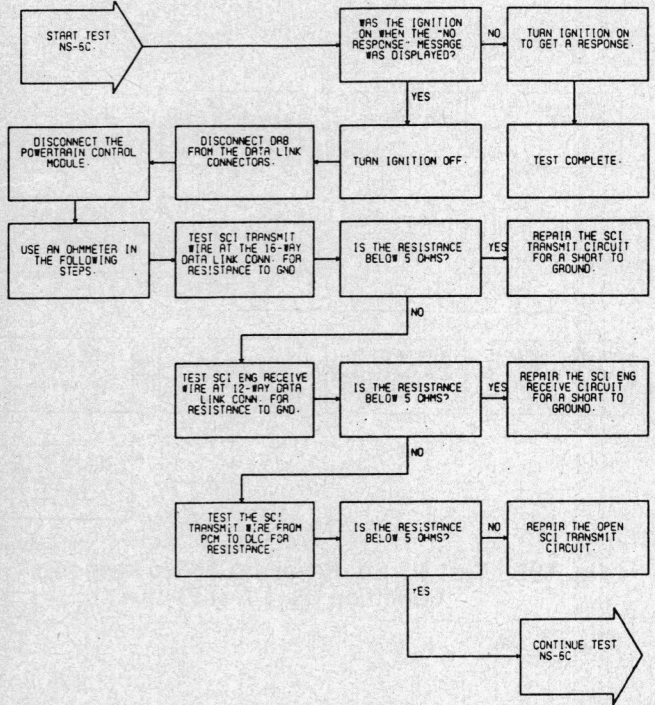

**Fig. 198   Test NS-6C: Repairing A "No Response"
Condition (Part 1 of 2)**

CR1029505229010X

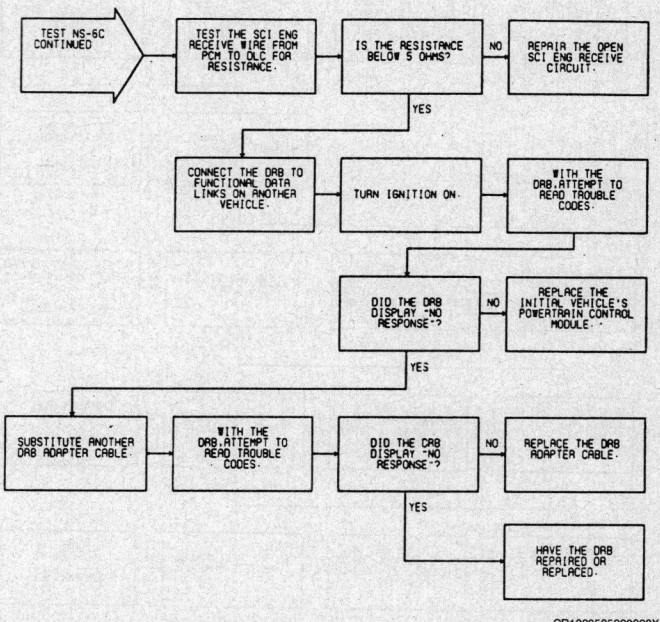

**Fig. 198   Test NS-6C: Repairing A "No Response"
Condition (Part 2 of 2)**

CR1029505229020X

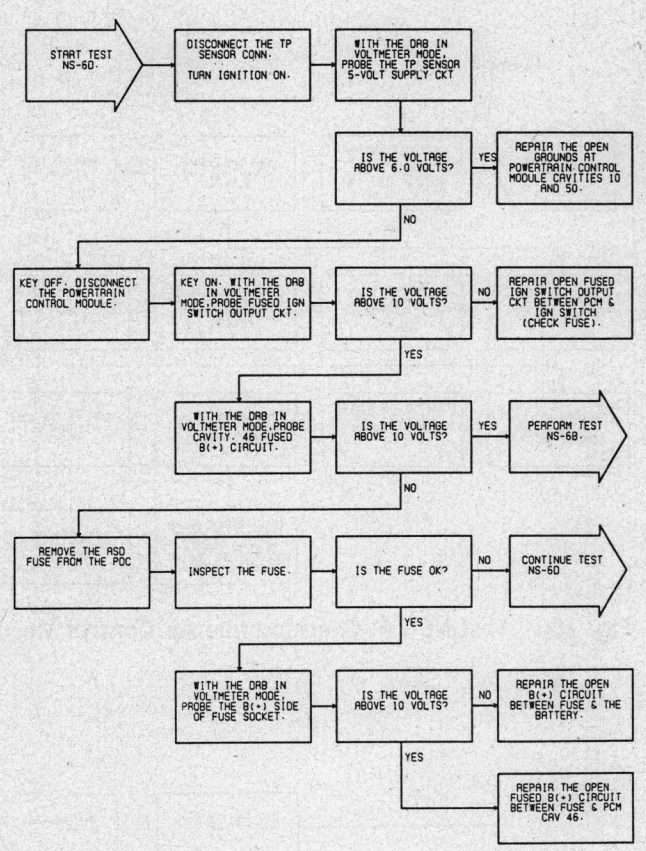

Fig. 199   Test NS-6D: Repairing A "No Response" Condition (Part 1 of 5)

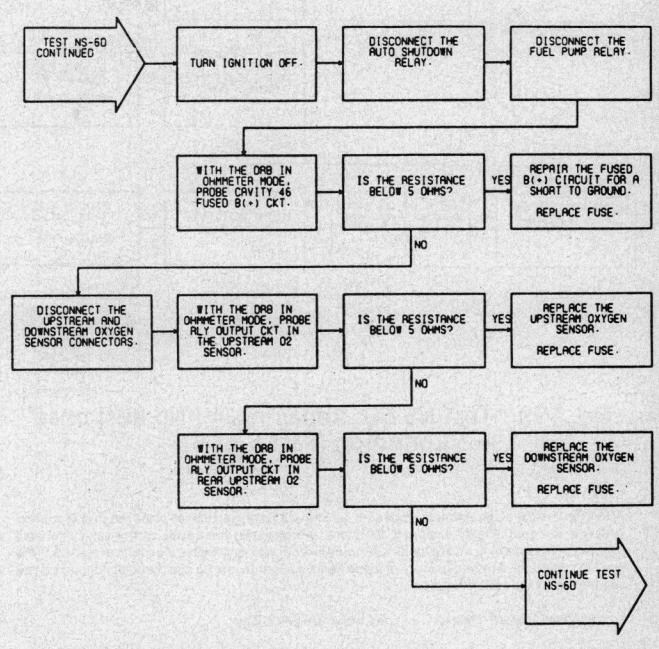

Fig. 199   Test NS-6D: Repairing A "No Response" Condition (Part 2 of 5)

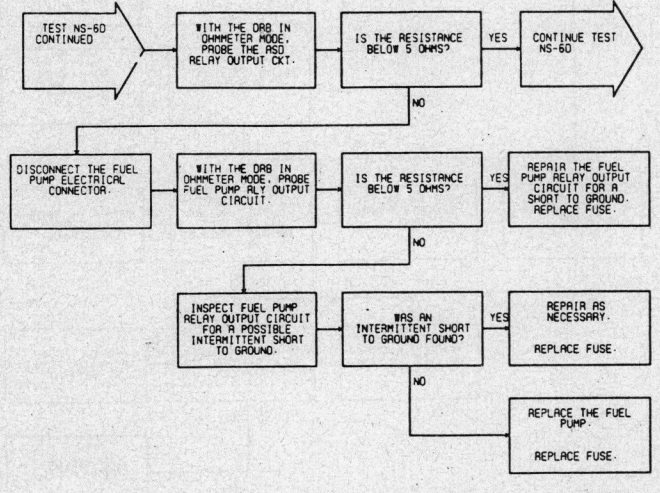

Fig. 199   Test NS-6D: Repairing A "No Response" Condition (Part 3 of 5)

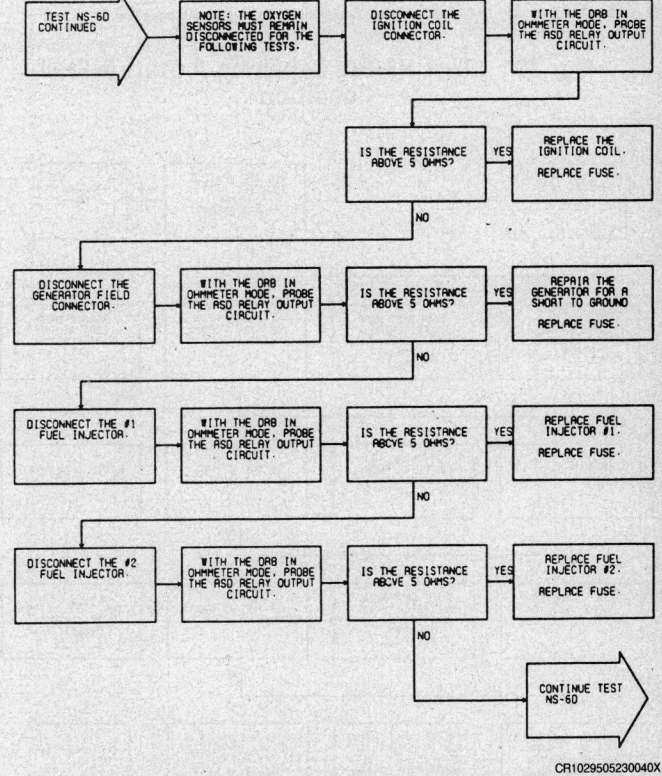

Fig. 199   Test NS-6D: Repairing A "No Response" Condition (Part 4 of 5)

MULTI-POINT FUEL INJECTION (1995 AVENGER, CIRRUS, NEON, SEBRING, STRATUS & TALON w/NON-TURBOCHARGED 2.0L/4-122 ENGINE)

8-77

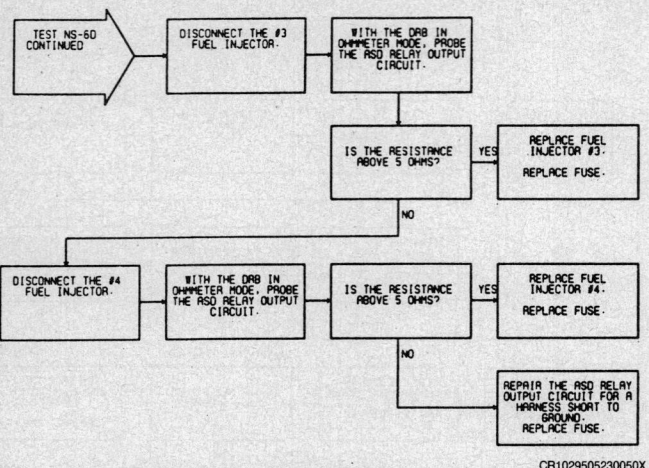

Fig. 199   Test NS-6D: Repairing A "No Response" Condition (Part 5 of 5)

At this point in the diagnostic test procedure, you have determined that all of the **engine electrical systems** are operating as designed; therefore, they are **not the cause of the start and stall problem.** The following additional items should be checked as possible mechanical causes of the no start condition. Any one or more of these items can produce a no start condition; none can be overlooked as a possible cause.

1. **ENGINE VALVE TIMING** - must be within specifications

2. **ENGINE COMPRESSION** - must be within specifications

3. **ENGINE EXHAUST SYSTEM** - must be free of any restrictions

4. **ENGINE PCV SYSTEM** - must flow freely

5. **FUEL** - must be free of contamination

6. **ENGINE SECONDARY IGNITION CHECK** - must exhibit a normal scope pattern

Always look for any Technical Service Bulletins that may relate to this condition.

Fig. 201   Test NS-8A: Repairing A Start & Stall Condition

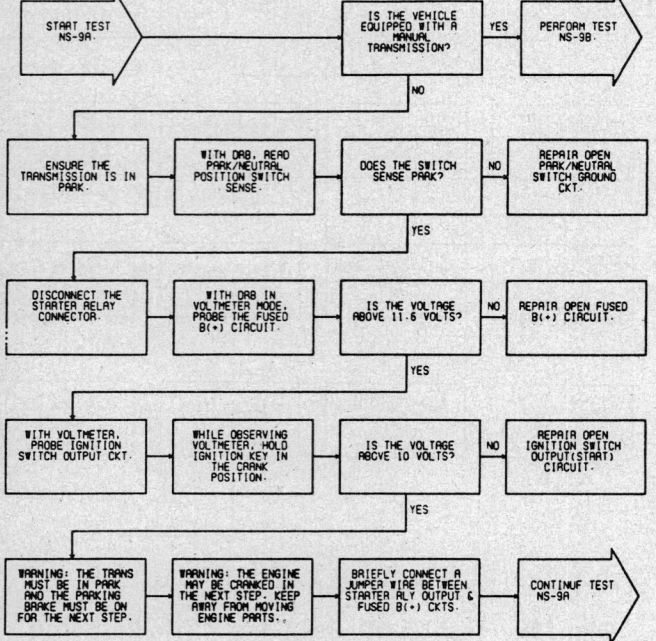

Fig. 202   Test NS-9A: Repairing A No Crank Condition (Part 1 of 3)

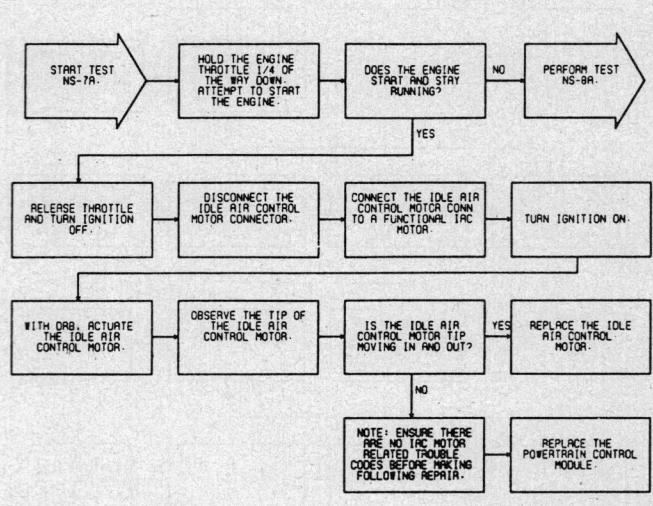

Fig. 200   Test NS-7A: Checking Idle Air Control Motor

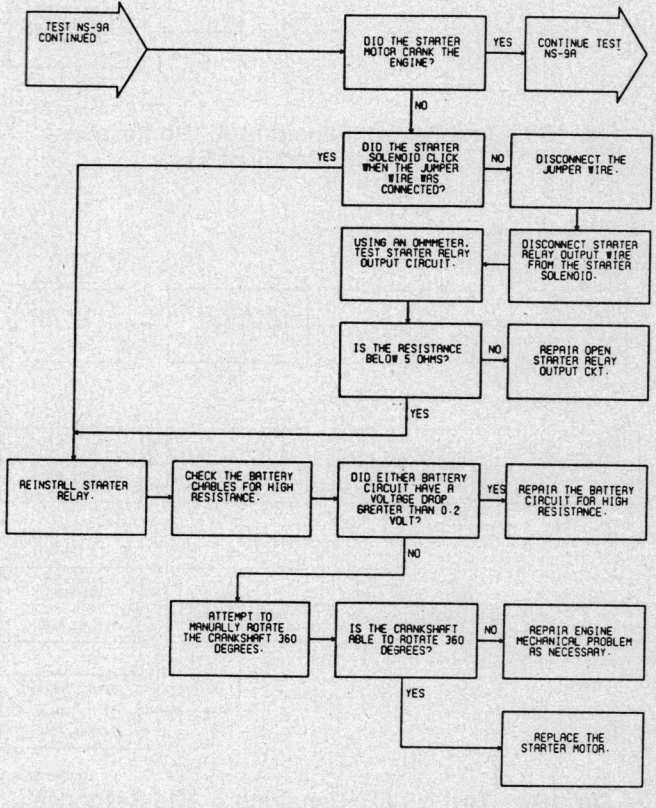

Fig. 202   Test NS-9A: Repairing A No Crank Condition (Part 2 of 3)

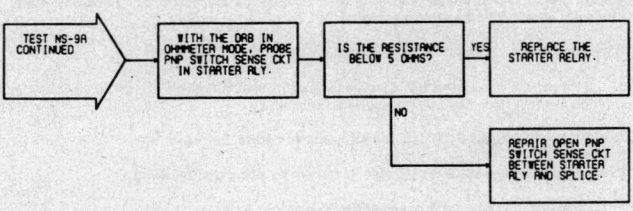

Fig. 202 Test NS-9A: Repairing A No Crank Condition (Part 3 of 3)

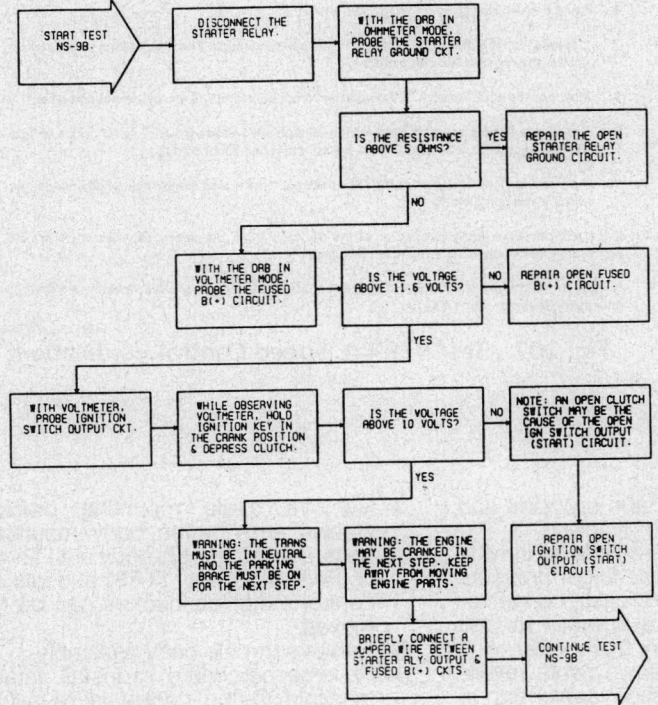

Fig. 203 Test NS-9B: Repairing A No Crank Condition (Part 1 of 2)

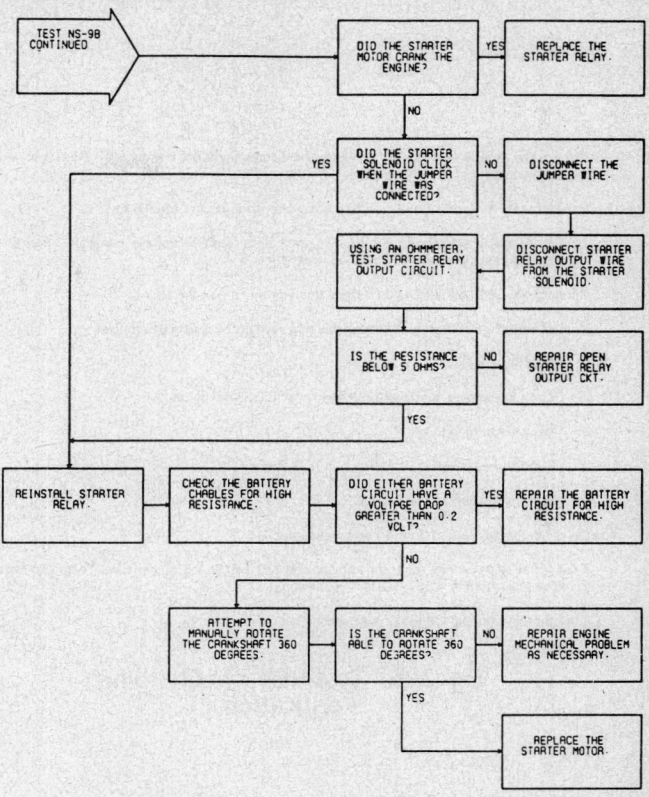

Fig. 203 Test NS-9B: Repairing A No Crank Condition (Part 2 of 2)

Inspect the vehicle to ensure that all engine components are connected. Reassemble and reconnect components as necessary.

Inspect the engine for contamination. If it is contaminated, change the oil and filter.

Attempt to start the engine.

If the engine is **unable** to start, look for any Technical Service Bulletins that may relate to this condition. Return to **TEST TC-1A** if necessary.

The repair is now complete.

Fig. 204 Test VER-1A: No Start Verification

Inspect the vehicle to ensure that all engine components are connected. Reassemble and reconnect all components as necessary.

If this verification procedure is being performed after a NO TROUBLE CODE test, do the following:

1. Check to see if the initial symptom still exists.

2. If the initial or another symptom exists, the repair is not complete. Check all pertinent Technical Service Bulletins and return to **TEST NTC-1A** if necessary.

If this verification procedure is being performed after a TROUBLE CODE test, do the following:

For previously read trouble codes that have not been dealt with, return to **TEST TC-1A** and follow the path specified. Otherwise, continue.

If the powertrain control module has not been changed:

1. Connect the DRB to the PCM data link connector and erase trouble codes.

2. With the DRB, reset all values in the adaptive memory.

3. Disconnect the DRB.

Ensure no trouble code remains by doing the following:

1. If the repair was for one of the following trouble codes, turn the A/C off and start the trouble code test again to ensure the code has not returned. For all others, go to step 2 below.

   – No Change In MAP From Start To Run   – Multiple Cylinder Misfire
   – Fuel System Rich   – Single Cylinder Misfire
   – Fuel System Lean   – Throttle Position Sensor Voltage Low
   – Catalytic Converter Efficiency Failure – Throttle Position Sensor Voltage High
   – Closed Loop Temp Not Reached   – TPS Does Not Agree With Map
   – EGR System Failure   – Target Idle Not Reached (+/- 200 rpm)
   – Evap System Failure   – Vacuum Leak Found (IAC Fully Seated)

2. If this test is for an **A/C Relay Control Circuit Code**, drive the vehicle for at least five minutes with the A/C on. For some of the drive, go at least 40 mph; at some point stop the car and turn the engine off for 10 seconds or more; then restart and continue. Ensure the transmission shifts through all gears. Upon completion of the road test, turn the engine off, and read trouble codes with the DRB.

3. If the repaired code has reset, the repair is not complete. Check all related Technical Service Bulletins and return to **TEST TC-1A** if necessary. If another trouble code has set, return to **TEST TC-1A** and follow the path specified for that trouble code. If there are no trouble codes, the repair was successful and is now complete.

Fig. 205 Test VER-2A: Road Test Verification

Inspect the vehicle to ensure that all engine components are connected. Reassemble and reconnect components as necessary.

If the powertrain control module has been changed, do the following:

1. If the vehicle is equipped with a factory theft alarm, start the vehicle at least 20 times so that the alarm system may be activated when desired.

Connect the DRB to the PCM data link connector and erase the codes.

Ensure no other charging system problems remain by doing the following:

1. Start the engine.
2. Raise the engine speed to 2000 rpm for at least 30 seconds.
3. Allow the engine to idle.
4. Turn the engine off.
5. Turn the ignition key on.
6. With the DRB, read trouble code messages.

If the repaired code has reset, or another one has set, check all pertinent Technical Service Bulletins and return to **TEST TC-1A** if necessary.

If there are no codes, the repair is now complete.

Fig. 206   Test VER-3A: Charging Verification

Inspect the vehicle to ensure that all engine components are connected. Reassemble and reconnect all components as necessary.

If the powertrain control module has been changed, do the following:

1. If the vehicle is equipped with a factory theft alarm, start the vehicle at least 20 times so that the alarm system may be activated when desired.

Connect the DRB to the PCM data link connector and erase the codes.

Ensure no other speed control problems remain by doing the following:

1. Road test the vehicle at a speed above 35 mph.
2. Turn the speed control ON/OFF switch to the ON position.
3. Depress and release the SET switch. If the speed control did not engage, the repair is not complete.*
4. For stalk switch equipped vehicles, quickly depress and release the SET switch. For steering wheel switch equipped vehicles, quickly depress and release the RESUME/ACCEL switch. If the vehicle speed did not increase by 2 mph, the repair is not complete.*
5. Using caution, depress and release the brake pedal. If the speed control did not disengage, the repair is not complete.*
6. Bring the vehicle speed back up to 35 mph.
7. Depress the RESUME/ACCEL switch. If the speed control did not resume the previously set speed, the repair is not complete.*
8. Hold down the SET switch. If the vehicle did not decelerate, the repair is not complete.*
9. Ensure the vehicle speed is greater than 35 mph and release the SET switch. If the vehicle did not adjust and set a new vehicle speed, the repair is not complete.*
10. Turn on the ON/OFF switch to the OFF position. If the speed control did not disengage, the repair is not complete.*

If the vehicle successfully passed all of the previous tests, the speed control system is now functioning as designed. The repair is now complete.

*Check for Technical Service Bulletins that pertain to this speed control problem and then, if necessary, return to **TEST TC-1A**.

CR1029505238000X

Fig. 207   Test VER-4A: Speed Control Verification

1. Disconnect battery ground cable, then loosen fuel filler cap and ensure ignition key is in Off position.
2. Remove protective cap from fuel pressure test port, then connect end of fuel pressure release hose tool No. C-4799-1 or equivalent to port and place other end in a suitable container.
3. Allow fuel pressure to bleed off through hose and into container, then remove hose from port.

Component Replacement

THROTTLE BODY

Neon

1. Relieve fuel system pressure as described under "Precautions."
2. **On models with manual transaxle,** proceed as follows:
   a. Remove throttle cable from throttle body lever, **Fig. 208**, then compress retaining tabs on cable and slide cable out of bracket.
   b. Slide clasp out from throttle cable hole to remove speed control cable from throttle lever.
3. **On models with automatic transaxle,** proceed as follows:
   a. Remove throttle cable from throttle body cam, **Fig. 209**, then compress retaining tabs on cable and slide cable out of bracket.
   b. While holding throttle lever in wide open position, use finger pressure to push kickdown cable connector off pivot. **Do not attempt to pull connector away from lever.**
   c. Compress kickdown cable retaining tabs and slide cable out of bracket; then, while holding throttle lever in wide open position, use finger pressure to push speed control cable connector off pivot. **Do not attempt to pull connector away from lever.**
   d. Compress speed control cable retaining tabs and slide cable out of bracket.
4. **On all models,** remove cable mounting bracket screws and throttle body mounting bolts, then remove throttle body.
5. Reverse procedure to install.

Cirrus & Stratus

1. Relieve fuel system pressure as described under "Precautions."
2. Remove air inlet resonator and disconnect throttle cable at throttle body lever, **Fig. 208**, then compress cable retaining tabs and slide cable out of bracket.
3. Slide speed control cable clasp out through throttle cable hole to remove cable, then disconnect evap purge hose at throttle body nipple.
4. Remove cable mounting bracket screws and throttle body mounting bolts, then lift throttle body until Throttle Position Sensor (TPS) and idle air control motor connectors can be removed.
5. Remove throttle body assembly.
6. Reverse procedure to install. Intake manifold O-ring gasket is reusable, but should be wiped clean prior to throttle body installation.

Talon

1. Release fuel system pressure as described under "Precautions."
2. Remove throttle body from intake manifold plenum as shown, **Fig. 210**.
3. Reverse procedure to install.

FUEL INJECTORS

Neon

1. Disconnect battery ground cable, then relieve fuel system pressure as described under "Precautions."
2. Disconnect fuel supply tube from fuel rail, then disconnect fuel injector electrical connectors.
3. Remove fuel rail mounting screws, then lift rail off intake manifold and cap manifold injector openings to prevent entry of foreign matter.
4. Remove fuel injector retainer, **Fig. 211**, then pull injector out of fuel rail.
5. Reverse procedure to install. Use new injector O-rings lightly coated with clean engine oil.

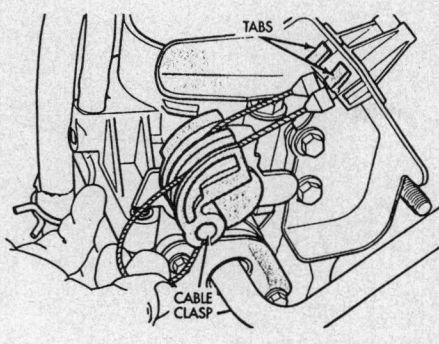

Fig. 208   Throttle cable removal from throttle body. Neon w/manual transaxle, Cirrus & Stratus

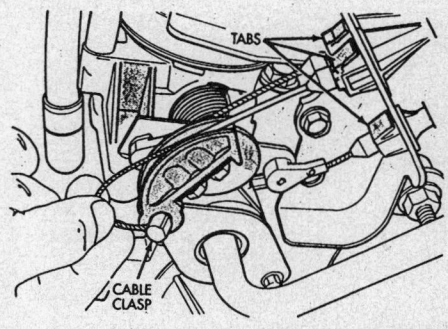

Fig. 209   Throttle cable removal from throttle body. Neon w/automatic transaxle

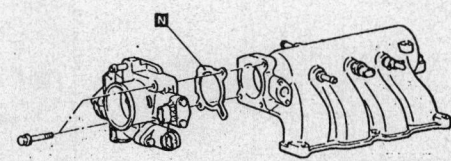

Fig. 210   Throttle body replacement. Talon

Cirrus & Stratus

1. Disconnect battery ground cable at auxiliary jumper terminal, then relieve fuel system pressure as described under "Precautions."
2. Disconnect fuel supply tube at fuel rail, keeping a shop towel wrapped around tube to prevent fuel spillage, then disconnect fuel injector electrical connectors.
3. Remove fuel rail mounting screws and lift rail off manifold, then cap manifold injector openings to prevent entry of foreign matter.
4. Remove fuel injector clip, **Fig. 212**, then pull injector out of fuel rail.
5. Reverse procedure to install. Use new injector O-rings.

Talon

1. Relieve fuel system pressure as described under "Precautions," then remove battery and air intake hose.
2. Remove injectors in numbered sequence shown in **Fig. 213**. Fuel rail may be removed with injectors attached.
3. Reverse procedure to install, noting the following:
   a. Install new fuel pressure regulator O-rings with a light coating of clean engine oil. **Do not allow oil to enter fuel rail assembly.**
   b. Ensure regulator can be rotated smoothly after installation; if not, O-ring may be folded and binding. Correct as necessary.
   c. Install injector O-rings with a light coating of clean engine oil. **Do not allow oil to enter fuel rail assembly.**
   d. Ensure injector can be rotated smoothly after installation; if not, O-ring may be trapped. Remove injector and correct as necessary.

IDLE AIR CONTROL MOTOR

1. Disconnect evap purge hose from throttle body, then disconnect throttle position sensor and idle air control motor electrical connectors.
2. Remove throttle body as described under "Throttle Body" in this section, then remove idle air control motor mounting screws and motor. **Ensure O-ring is removed with motor.**
3. Reverse procedure to install, noting the following:
   a. If installing a new idle air control motor, replacement unit will already have an O-ring in place.
   b. If pintle on new idle air control motor measures more than one inch, it must be retracted prior to installation using a DRB III to perform an AIS Motor Open/Close Test. Battery must be connected for this procedure.

CAMSHAFT POSITION SENSOR

1. Disconnect filtered air tube from throttle body, air cleaner housing and oil separator hose, then remove tube.
2. Remove air cleaner inlet tube, then disconnect engine coolant sensor and camshaft position sensor electrical connectors.
3. Remove brake booster hose and electrical connector from retainers at end of cylinder head cover, then remove camshaft position sensor mounting screws and sensor.
4. Remove target magnet from rear of camshaft.
5. Reverse procedure to install.

CRANKSHAFT POSITION SENSOR

1. Disconnect electrical connector from crankshaft position sensor.

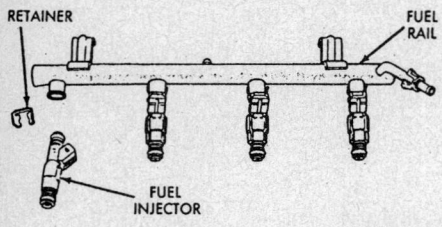

Fig. 211 Fuel injector & retainer replacement. Neon

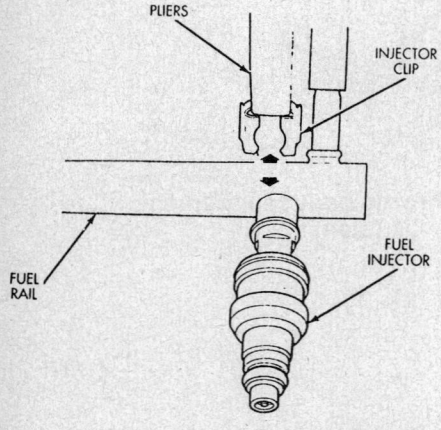

Fig. 212 Fuel injector & clip replacement. Cirrus & Stratus

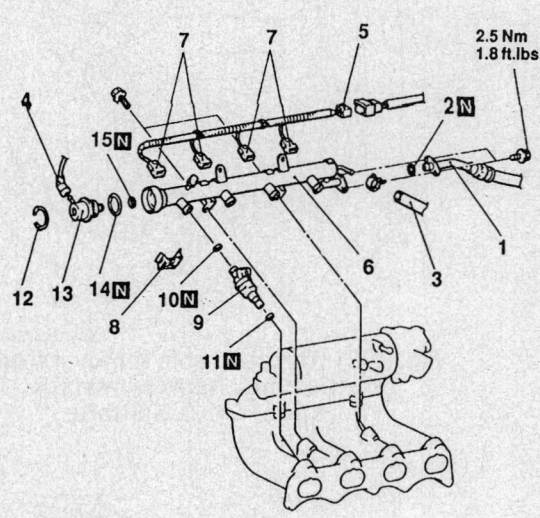

Engine oil

Removal steps
1. High-pressure fuel hose connection
2. O-ring
3. Fuel return hose connection
4. Vacuum hose connection
5. Injector harness connector
6. Fuel rail
7. Injector connectors
8. Retainers
9. Injectors
10. O-rings
11. O-rings
12. Snap ring
13. Fuel pressure regulator
14. O-ring
15. O-ring

Fig. 213 Fuel injector replacement. Talon

2. Remove sensor mounting screw, then the sensor.
3. Reverse procedure to install.

INTAKE AIR TEMPERATURE SENSOR

1. Remove engine cover and disconnect electrical connector from sensor, then remove sensor from intake manifold plenum.
2. Reverse procedure to install.

ENGINE COOLANT TEMPERATURE SENSOR

1. With engine cold and with a suitable container positioned below draincock, drain coolant until level drops below cylinder head.
2. Disconnect coolant temperature sensor electrical sensor, then remove sensor from cylinder head.
3. Reverse procedure to install. Refill cooling system.

MANIFOLD ABSOLUTE PRESSURE (MAP) SENSOR

1. Disconnect MAP sensor electrical connector and remove sensor mounting screws, then remove sensor from intake manifold plenum.

2. Reverse procedure to install. Ensure O-ring seal is not damaged during installation.

THROTTLE POSITION SENSOR

1. Disconnect evap purge hose from throttle body, then disconnect idle air control motor and throttle position sensor electrical connectors.
2. Remove throttle body as described under "Throttle Body" in this section, then remove throttle position sensor screws and sensor.
3. Reverse procedure to install.

Fuel Injection—CHRYSLER

MODELS w/2.5L/4-153 FLEXIBLE FUEL, 2.2L/4-135 TURBO & 2.5L/4-153 ENGINES

If Uncertain About The Proper Use Of Information Contained In This Section, Please Refer To "How To Use This Manual" Located In The Front Of This Manual.

On Air Bag Equipped Models, Refer To "Air Bag System Precautions" Located In The Front Of This Manual For System Disarming & Arming Procedures.

Electrical Symbol & Wire Color Code Identification Located In The Front Of This Manual May Be Used As An Aid When Using Wiring Circuits Found In This Section.

INDEX

	Page No.
Body Code Identification	9-1
Description:	9-2
Components	9-2
Operation	9-2
Diagnosis & Testing:	9-4
Accessing Diagnostic Trouble Codes:	9-4
Using Diagnostic Readout Box (DRB)	9-4
Using Malfunction Indicator Lamp (MIL) (Check Engine Lamp)	9-4
Clearing Diagnostic Trouble Codes	9-5
Diagnostic Trouble Code Interpretation:	9-5
Inactive Fault Condition	9-5
On Board Diagnosis:	9-5
Circuit Actuation Test Mode	9-5

	Page No.
Fuel System Pressure Test	9-6
Switch & Sensor Test Mode	9-5
Throttle Body Minimum Air Flow Test	9-5
System & Component Diagnosis:	9-6
1993 2.2L/4-135 Turbocharged Engines	9-6
2.5L/4-153 Non-Turbocharged Engines	9-6
Visual Inspection	9-4
Diagnostic Chart Index	9-17
Precautions:	9-1
Air Bag Systems	9-1
Flexible Fuel Vehicle Service	9-1
Fuel System Pressure Relief	9-1
Sensor Specifications	9-1

	Page No.
System Service:	9-97
Component Replacement:	9-97
Fuel Filter	9-98
Fuel Injector	9-98
Fuel Injector Rail Assembly	9-97
Idle Air Control (IAC) Motor	9-98
Manifold Absolute Pressure (MAP) Sensor	9-98
Methanol Concentration Sensor	9-98
Oxygen Sensor (O2S)	9-98
Powertrain Control Module (PCM)	9-98
Pressure Regulator	9-97
Throttle Body	9-97
Throttle Position Sensor (TPS)	9-98
Fuel System Pressure Relief	9-97

SENSOR SPECIFICATIONS

	Resistance, Ohms	
Sensor	@ 70°F	@ 200°F
Coolant Temp.	7000—13,000	700—1000
Charge Temp.	7000—13,000	700—1000
Throttle Body	5600—14,600	400—1500

BODY CODE IDENTIFICATION

Body Code	Vehicle Line
1993	
AA	Acclaim/LeBaron Landau/Spirit
AC	Dynasty/New Yorker Salon

Body Code	Vehicle Line
1993	
AG	Daytona
AJ	LeBaron Coupe/Convertible
AP	Shadow/Sundance
AY	Imperial/New Yorker Fifth Avenue
1994—95	
AA	Acclaim/LeBaron Sedan/Spirit
AP	Shadow/Sundance
AJ	LeBaron Convertible

PRECAUTIONS
AIR BAG SYSTEMS

Refer to "Air Bag System Precautions" in the front of this manual for system disarming and arming procedures.

FUEL SYSTEM PRESSURE RELIEF

In order to prevent personal injury and vehicle damage, fuel system pressure must be relieved prior to servicing any fuel-related component. Refer to "System Service" for fuel system pressure relief procedure.

FLEXIBLE FUEL VEHICLE SERVICE

Some vehicles are designed to operate on a mixture of gasoline and methanol. These flexible fuel vehicles can operate on a mixture of up to 85 percent methanol, 15 percent unleaded gasoline. These vehicles also operate on mixtures containing a lower percentage of methanol or just pure unleaded gasoline.

Methanol is more toxic than gasoline. Always release fuel system pressure before servicing fuel system components and wear methanol resistant gloves and eye protection.

Avoid breathing methanol vapors or ingesting methanol. Headaches, dizziness and even unconsciousness could result from breathing these vapors. Serious injury, blindness and even death could result from ingesting methanol.

Methanol vapors are extremely flammable and can travel along the ground. Service vehicles in well ventilated areas and avoid ignition sources. Never smoke while servicing the vehicle.

Do not allow methanol to contact skin. Prolonged contact with methanol can cause dry skin or an allergic skin reaction. Also, prolonged contact could result in absorption through the skin.

DESCRIPTION

OPERATION

2.2L/4-135 Turbo III Engine

This system, **Fig. 1**, combines an electronic fuel and spark advance control system with a turbocharged intake system. The fuel injection system is controlled by the Powertrain Control Module (PCM).

The PCM, or engine controller, regulates ignition timing, air-fuel ratio, emission control devices, cooling fan, charging system, speed control, turbocharger wastegate and idle speed.

Various sensors provide inputs necessary for the PCM to correctly regulate fuel flow at the fuel injector. These include the manifold absolute pressure, throttle position, oxygen sensor, coolant temperature, detonation and vehicle distance sensors. In addition to the sensors, the air conditioning clutch switch and various relays provide important information and system control. The outputs include the auto shutdown relay and fuel pump relay.

The PCM adjusts the air-fuel ratio by changing injector pulse width. Injector pulse width is the time an injector is energized.

2.5L/4-153 Engine

The multi-port fuel injection system, **Fig. 2**, is designed for flexible fuel vehicles. These vehicles have unique methanol compatible fuel system components. Methanol compatible components that could be mistakenly interchanged with gasoline only parts are colored green or have a green label or tag on them. **Even though they may appear physically identical, components for gasoline only vehicles must not be used on flexible fuel vehicles.**

The Powertrain Control Module (PCM) operates the electronic fuel injection system through various controls. The PCM regulates the air-fuel ratio, ignition coil dwell and idle speed. It also operates the high speed and low speed cooling fans, charging system, speed control system and various emission control devices.

Various sensors and switches provide inputs to the PCM. The PCM uses the inputs to adjust the systems it controls to meet the changing operating conditions.

Fuel is injected into the intake port above the intake valve in precise metered amounts through electrically operated injectors. The PCM operates the injectors in a specific sequence. The PCM adjusts the air/fuel ratio based on the percentage of methanol in the fuel. The PCM constantly adjusts injector pulse width to obtain the ideal air/fuel ratio for the current percentage of methanol in the fuel. Injector pulse width refers to the amount of time an injector operates. The PCM adjusts injector pulse width by opening and closing the ground path to the injectors. Engine RPM,

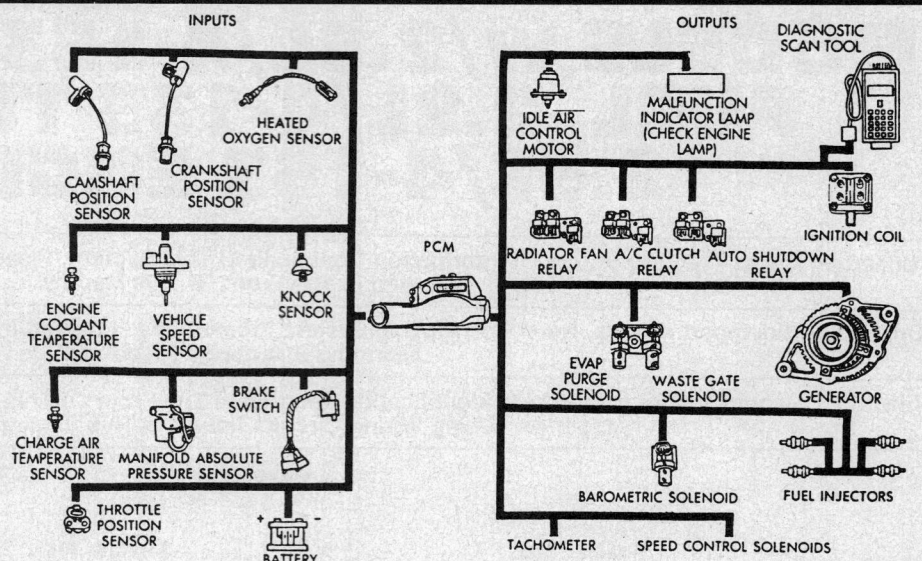

Fig. 1   Multi-point electronic fuel injection system components. 2.2L/4-135 Turbo III engine

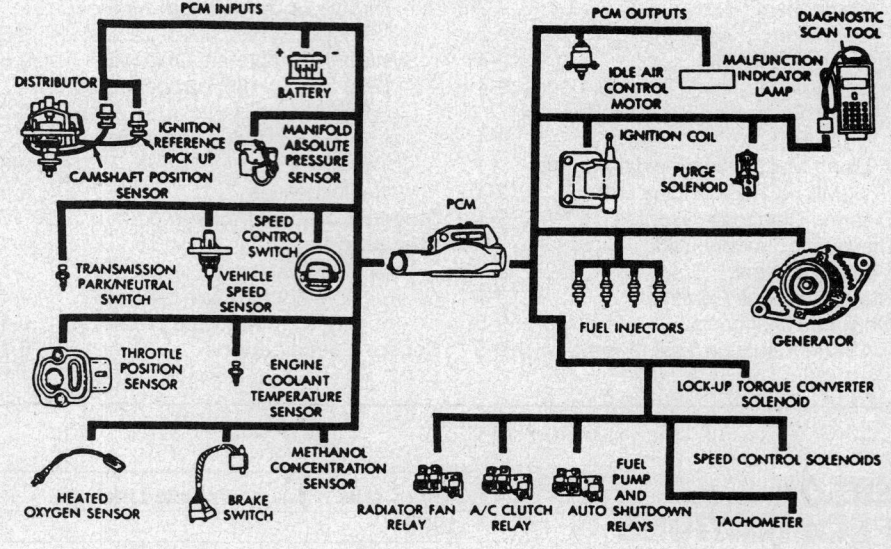

Fig. 2   Multi-point electronic fuel injection system components. 2.5L/4-153 engine

manifold absolute pressure and the percentage of methanol in the fuel are the primary inputs that determine injector pulse width.

COMPONENTS

Powertrain Control Module (PCM)

The PCM is an engine controller used to control the fuel injection system.

The controller receives input signals from various switches, sensors and components. This data is used to compute the fuel injector pulse width and control various other outputs, **Figs. 1 and 2.**

Manifold Absolute Pressure (MAP) Sensor

The MAP sensor, located in the right side passenger compartment or in engine compartment on right shock tower, monitors manifold vacuum. The sensor is connected to a vacuum nipple on the throttle

body or intake manifold and electrically to the controller. This device relays information on manifold vacuum and barometric pressure to the controller which is used in determining the proper air/fuel mixture.

Methanol Concentration Sensor (Flex Fuel)

The methanol concentration sensor contains a microprocessor that determines the percentage of gasoline and methanol in the fuel system. The PCM determines the amount of methanol in the fuel from the methanol concentration sensor input. The vehicle can operate on mixtures up to 80 percent methanol, 15 percent gasoline.

The PCM supplies 8 volts to the methanol concentration sensor. The methanol concentration sensor output voltage varies with the percent of methanol in the fuel system. The sensor output voltage (input

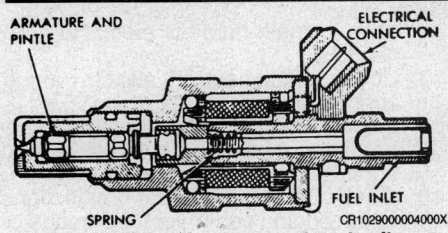

Fig. 3 Fuel injector (typical)

for PCM) ranges from 0.5 volts for pure gasoline to 4.5 volts for 85 percent methanol. At the first two seconds when the vehicle is started, the sensor calibrates the PCM. During this calibration period, the sensor sends 4.45 volts to the PCM as a correction factor.

The methanol concentration sensor has a built-in shutdown capability. If the sensor shuts down, the PCM starts with the previous learned value and can adapt to different methanol concentrations based on oxygen sensor input. This is a limp-in condition.

The methanol concentration sensor attaches to a bracket at the rear of the fuel tank, next to the fuel filler tube.

Oxygen Sensor (O₂S)

The oxygen sensor, located in the exhaust manifold or turbo outlet, produces voltage when exposed to oxygen in exhaust gasses. The sensor produces a low voltage when the air/fuel mixture is lean and a high voltage when the mixture is rich. Voltage is transmitted to the controller, triggering the fuel injector. The injector adjusts the air/fuel mixture accordingly.

Engine Coolant Temperature (ECT) Sensor

The ECT sensor, located in the thermostat housing, provides the controller with engine operating temperature information. This data, in conjunction with data provided by the charge temperature sensor, permits the controller to provide slightly richer air/fuel mixtures and higher idle speeds until the engine reaches normal operating temperature.

Throttle Position Sensor (TPS)

The TPS, located on the throttle body, is an electric resistor activated by the movement of the throttle shaft. The sensor produces a voltage which increases or decreases according to the throttle valve opening. The voltage signal is transmitted to the controller where it is used with data from other sensors to adjust the air/fuel mixture accordingly.

Switch Input

Various switches located throughout the vehicle provide information to the controller. These switches include neutral safety, A/C clutch, speed control and brake light switches. When one or more of these switches is in the On position, the controller signals the IAC (AIS) motor to increase idle speed to a specified RPM.

When air conditioning is on and the throttle valve is above a preset angle, the wide open throttle cut out relay prevents the air conditioning clutch from engaging until the throttle valve is below this angle.

Idle Air Control (IAC) Motor

The IAC motor, operated by the PCM, adjusts the air portion of the air/fuel mixture through an air bypass on the back of the throttle body. Base idle is determined by the minimum air flow through the throttle body. The IAC motor opens or closes off the air bypass as needed according to engine loads or ambient conditions. The engine controller senses the change in air/fuel mixture and increases or decreases fuel accordingly to change engine idle. The IAC motor also prevents stalling during deceleration by increasing engine idle when the throttle is closed quickly.

Automatic Shutdown (ASD) & Fuel Pump Relays

When no ignition signal is present with ignition key in Run position, there is no need for fuel delivery. When this condition occurs, the ASD relay interrupts power to the electric fuel pump, fuel injectors and ignition coil.

Malfunction Indicator (Power Loss/Check Engine) Lamp

The malfunction indicator (power loss/check engine) lamp on the instrument panel will illuminate if the controller receives an incorrect signal or no signal from the ECT sensor, charge temperature sensor, MAP sensor, TPS or battery voltage sensor input depending on vehicle application. This lamp indicates that the controller has gone into the "limp in mode" to keep the system operational, and indicates an immediate need for service.

The malfunction indicator (power loss/check engine) lamp will also light for several seconds each time the ignition key is turned on as a bulb check.

Throttle Body

The throttle body houses the TPS and IAC motor. Air flow through the throttle body is controlled by a cable operated throttle blade located in the base of the throttle body.

Fuel Injector

The fuel injector, **Fig. 3,** is a solenoid operated valve driven by the PCM.

Fuel Pressure Regulator

The fuel pressure regulator, **Fig. 4,** located downstream of the fuel injector on the throttle body, maintains a constant fuel pressure across the injector tip. The spring-loaded diaphragm in the regulator is assisted by vacuum in the throttle body above the throttle valve. As venturi vacuum increases, less pressure is needed to supply the same amount of fuel into the air flow. In order to fine tune the fuel pressure under all operating conditions, the vacuum assists in opening the fuel port during high vacuum conditions.

Fuel Pump

The fuel pump used in the MPI system is a positive displacement, roller vane, immersible pump with a permanent magnet electric motor. Operating voltage is supplied to the pump through the ASD relay.

The pump uses three check valves: one

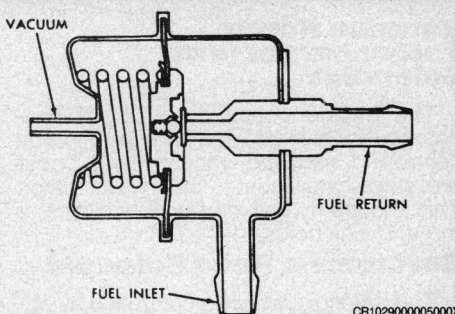

Fig. 4 Fuel pressure regulator

valve relieves internal pump pressure and regulates maximum pump output, the second valve, located near the pump outlet, restricts fuel flow in either direction when the pump is not operational, a third is located inside the pump assembly in the fuel return circuit to prevent fuel tank leakage if the line is damaged during an accident.

Fuel Reservoir

The fuel reservoir is located in the fuel tank and houses the fuel pump. The reservoir provides fuel at the pump intake under all driving conditions. The fuel return line directs fuel to a container on the side of the reservoir. The flow of fuel into this container creates a low pressure area and causes additional fuel from the main tank to flow into the reservoir. This combination of return fuel and fuel from the main tank maintains a full fuel condition in the reservoir even if fuel level is below the reservoir walls.

Charge Temperature Sensor

The charge temperature sensor, located in the intake manifold, measures the temperature of the air/fuel mixture. The engine controller uses this information to determine air/fuel mixture.

Knock (Detonation) Sensor

The knock (detonation) sensor generates a signal when spark knock occurs. It is mounted on the intake manifold in a position where detonation is each cylinder can be detected. The engine controller uses information from the knock sensor to modify spark advance and boost schedules to eliminate detonation.

Purge Solenoid

The purge solenoid is energized by the engine controller when engine temperature is below 70°F or is above 70°F for less than 7 seconds. This closes the solenoid and prevents manifold vacuum or pressure from reaching the charcoal canister valve. When predetermined time and engine temperature are reached, the solenoid is de-energized and vacuum will flow to the canister purge valve and purge vapors through the throttle body.

When in boost, the solenoid is energized which prevents canister purge operation.

Wastegate Control Solenoid

The wastegate control solenoid allows the engine controller to adjust maximum boost by varying the duty cycle of the solenoid.

Variable Nozzle Turbocharger (VNT) Solenoids

The engine controller adjusts turbocharger boost levels and vane position by controlling manifold vacuum and boost pressure signals sent to the VNT actuator. This is done by varying the duty cycles of the VNT solenoids.

Barometric Read Solenoid

This solenoid, which is controlled by engine controller, is located in the MAP sensor line. The solenoid measures barometric pressure at closed throttle, once per throttle closure, but no more than once every 3 minutes below a specified RPM. The barometric information is used primarily for boost control.

Air Conditioning Clutch Relay

This relay is powered by the radiator fan relay, A/C switch and the engine controller. When the engine controller senses wide open throttle through the throttle position sensor, or low engine RPM, it will de-energize the relay. This prevents air conditioning clutch engagement.

Distributor (Hall Effect) Pick-Up

The distributor pick-up supplies an engine speed signal to the engine controller. The distributor pick-up is a Hall Effect device.

A shutter, containing four blades, is attached to the distributor shaft and a switch plate containing the distributor pick-up, is attached to the distributor housing. As the shutter blades pass through the pick-up, they interrupt the magnetic field. The pick-up senses the change of the magnetic field and switches on and off, generating the input signal to the engine controller. The engine controller calculates engine speed through the number of pulses generated.

Part Throttle Unlock Solenoid

Three speed automatic transaxles use a part throttle unlock solenoid. The engine controller controls the lock-up of the torque convertor through the part throttle unlock solenoid. The transaxle is locked up only in direct drive mode.

Camshaft Position (CMP) Sensor

Fuel injection synchronization and cylinder identification are provided through the CMP. The CMP pulse is an input sent to the engine controller. The engine controller interprets the CMP and Crankshaft Position (CKP) Sensor inputs to determine crankshaft position. The engine controller uses CKP sensor to determine injector sequence and ignition timing.

Crankshaft Position (CKP) Sensor

The CKP senses slots cut into the flywheel. There are two sets of slots each set containing four slots. When the engine controller senses the last slot of a set, it determines crankshaft position. The en-

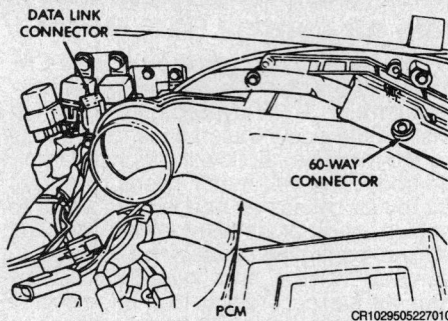

Fig. 5 Diagnostic data link connector (Part 1 of 2). Except LeBaron

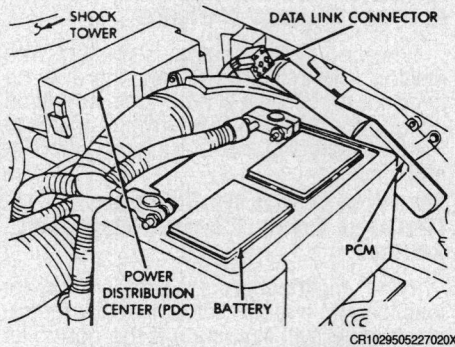

Fig. 5 Diagnostic data link connector (Part 2 of 2). LeBaron

gine controller uses the CKP input to determine injector sequence and ignition timing.

DIAGNOSIS & TESTING
Visual Inspection

Most fuel injection system problems can be traced to poor vacuum hose or wiring connections. Before proceeding with system tests or diagnosis, inspect the following:

1. Check ignition coil electrical connections.
2. Verify harness connector is attached to the canister purge solenoid.
3. Verify harness connector is attached to the wastegate solenoid.
4. Verify harness connector is attached to the MAP sensor.
5. Check vacuum hose connections between vacuum source and canister purge, wastegate and barometric read solenoids.
6. Verify hoses are securely attached to vapor canister.
7. Verify generator wiring and belt are correctly installed.
8. Check ignition cable routing and attachment.
9. Check oil pressure sending unit electrical connections.
10. Check distributor electrical connectors.
11. Check CMP and CKP sensor connections.
12. Check radiator fan electrical connector.
13. Inspect ECT sensor connection.
14. Check power brake booster and speed control connections.
15. Inspect engine and fuel injector har-

ness to main harness electrical connection.
16. Check park/neutral switch wiring connections.
17. Inspect relay conditions and ensure battery connections are clean and tight.
18. Check 60-way electrical connections at the engine controller for damage or spread terminals. Verify the 60-way connector is fully inserted into socket on engine controller. Ensure wires are not stretched or pulled out of connector.
19. Verify harness connector is attached to IAC motor.
20. Verify harness connector is attached to TPS.
21. Verify hose connections at intake manifold are secure.
22. Check vacuum hose connection between vacuum source and fuel pressure regulator.
23. Inspect charge air temperature sensor electrical connections.
24. Inspect fuel injector wiring connectors.
25. Inspect knock (detonation) sensor electrical connector.
26. Inspect oxygen sensor electrical connector.
27. Verify engine ground strap is attached to engine and dash panel.
28. Verify hose connections on turbocharger.
29. Verify 2-way connector is attached to vehicle speed sensor, then ensure sensor and connector are not damaged.
30. Check hose connections at fuel pump.
31. Ensure wiring connections at fuel pump are making contact with terminals on pump.
32. Inspect electrical connections at methanol concentration sensor.

Accessing Diagnostic Trouble Codes

USING DIAGNOSTIC READOUT BOX (DRB)

1. Connect DRB to diagnostic connector located in engine compartment near strut tower, **Fig. 5.**
2. If possible, start engine and cycle A/C switch, then turn off engine.
3. Start engine if possible, then cycle transmission selector and air conditioning switch.
4. Shut engine off.
5. Turn ignition switch to On position and record all diagnostic trouble codes displayed on DRB screen within 5 seconds. Note that the malfunction indicator (power loss/check engine) lamp should light for 2 seconds as a bulb check.

USING MALFUNCTION INDICATOR LAMP (MIL) (CHECK ENGINE LAMP)

If a suitable diagnostic read-out tool is not available, stored diagnostic trouble codes and be accessed directly through the MIL. To call up diagnostic trouble codes, cycle ignition switch on, off, on, off and on within 5 seconds. Stored codes will be indicated by flashes of the malfunction indicator (power loss/check engine) lamp. The codes will be indicated as two digit numbers, with a four second pause between codes. An example of a diagnostic trouble code output is as follows:

1. MIL illuminates for approximately 2 to 3 seconds as a bulb check, then turns off.
2. Lamp flashes two times, pauses, then flashes six times.
3. Lamp pauses for approximately four seconds.
4. Lamp flashes three times, pauses, then flashes one time.

This would indicate that diagnostic trouble codes 26 and 31 are stored. The lamp will continue to flash until all stored codes have been displayed.

Once the lamp starts flashing the stored diagnostic trouble codes, it cannot be stopped. If a code is missed, the entire procedure must be repeated. The lamp will not indicate if oxygen feedback system is switching lean-rich or if idle motor system is operational. The lamp also cannot be used to perform actuation test mode, sensor test mode or engine running test mode.

Diagnostic Trouble Code Interpretation

Diagnostic trouble codes indicate a failure, but do not identify the failed component. The diagnostic charts do not use diagnostic trouble codes for diagnosis. Instead, diagnosis is performed in a symptom driven format.

Prior to performing any procedure in the diagnostic charts, check electrical and vacuum component connections as described under "Visual Inspection." **Always start at the first No Start, Driveability, No Fault or Verification test. Starting at any other test may give inaccurate results.** After completing the test, perform verification test.

If using the Malfunction Indicator Lamp (MIL) (Check Engine lamp) to retrieve diagnostic trouble codes, refer to the Diagnostic Chart Index for flowcharts and scan tool information corresponding to MIL diagnostic trouble code output. The MIL cannot provide as much information as the DRB scan tool, and many of the flowcharts require the use of such a tool.

INACTIVE FAULT CONDITION

This section should only be used when referred to by the diagnostic charts.

You have just attempted to simulate the condition that initially set the fault message. The following additional checks may assist in identifying a possible intermittent problem:

1. Visually inspect related wire harness connectors. Look for broken, bent, pushed out or corroded terminals.

2. Visually inspect related harnesses. Look for chafed, pierced or partially broken wires.

Clearing Diagnostic Trouble Codes

Clearing diagnostic trouble codes can be accomplished in one of two ways. First is by selecting Erase Faults under the Read Faults display, or by disconnecting the battery ground cable for more than two minutes.

On Board Diagnosis

After performing the On-Board Diagnosis procedures, refer to "System & Component Diagnosis" to test systems indicated by the diagnostic trouble codes. Also refer to "System & Component Diagnosis" when testing systems not monitored by the On-Board Diagnosis System.

The engine controller is programmed to monitor various circuits in the MPI system. If a problem is sensed often enough to indicate an actual fault, its diagnostic trouble code is stored in the engine controller display. If the problem ceases to exist or is repaired, the diagnostic trouble code will be cancelled by the engine controller after 50-100 ignition key on/off cycles.

SWITCH & SENSOR TEST MODE

The switch inputs used by the engine controller have only two recognized states, High and Low. For this reason, the engine controller cannot recognize the difference between a switch position versus an open circuit, a short circuit or a defective switch. If the change is displayed, it can be assumed that the entire switch circuit to the engine controller is functioning normally.

Connect the DRB II tool to the vehicle and access the State Display Screen. Access Inputs and Outputs or Sensor to obtain the list of available components to be tested.

CIRCUIT ACTUATION TEST MODE

The circuit actuation test mode check for proper operation of output circuits or components which the engine controller cannot internally recognize. The engine controller can attempt to activate these outputs and allow an observer to verify proper operation. Most of the tests provide an audible or visual indication of operation. With the exception of an intermittent condition, if a component functions properly during its test, it can be assumed that the component, its associated wiring and its driver circuit are working properly.

Connect the DRB II tool to the vehicle and access the Actuators screen to obtain the list of available components to be tested.

THROTTLE BODY MINIMUM AIR FLOW TEST

1993

1. Connect DRB II scan tool.
2. Remove air cleaner assembly, then plug heated air door vacuum hose.

3. Start engine and allow cooling fan to cycle on and off at least once.
4. Connect suitable timing light, then disconnect coolant thermistor and set basic timing to 12° BTDC.
5. Stop engine and reconnect coolant thermistor wire.
6. Disconnect PCV valve hose from intake manifold nipple.
7. Attach air metering fitting tool No. 6457 or equivalent (.125 inch orifice in attached hose), to intake manifold PCV nipple.
8. Start engine and allow to idle for at least 1 minute.
9. Using read-out tool, access Min Airflow Idle Spd in sensor read test mode, then the following should occur:
   a. IAC (AIS) motor fully closes.
   b. Idle spark advance becomes fixed.
   c. Idle fuel becomes enriched.
   d. Engine RPM will be displayed on diagnostic read-out tool in units of RPM x 10. For example, display 95 equals 95 x 10 which indicates 950 RPM.
10. Check idle RPM with tachometer. Engine RPM should be 650-1150 RPM.
11. If idle RPM is within specification, then throttle body minimum air flow is satisfactory. If idle RPM is not as specified, replace throttle body.
12. Turn off engine, then remove air metering fitting tool No. 6457 from intake manifold PCV nipple.
13. Install PVC valve hose.
14. Remove read-out tool, then install air cleaner assembly and heated air door vacuum hose.

1994—95

1. Warm engine in park or neutral until cooling fan has cycled on and off at least once.
2. Hook up timing check device and tachometer.
3. Disconnect coolant temperature sensor and set basic timing to 10-12° BTDC.
4. Turn off engine, then connect harness connector to coolant temperature sensor.
5. Disconnect PCV valve hose from nipple on intake manifold PCV nipple.
6. Attach air metering fitting tool No. 6457 (0.1125 in. orifice) or equivalent, to intake manifold PCV nipple.
7. Connect DRB scan tool to data link connector located next to PCM.
8. Restart engine, then idle for at least one minute.
9. Using DRB scan tool, access Min. Airflow Idle Speed. The following will then occur:
   a. Idle air control motor will fully close.
   b. Idle spark advance will become fixed.
   c. DRB scan tool will display engine RPM.
10. Check idle RPM with tachometer. RPM should be as follows:
    a. 650-1400 RPM for odometer reading below 1000 miles.
    b. 600-1400 RPM for odometer reading above 1000 miles.

11. If idle RPM is within specification, then throttle body minimum air flow is satisfactory. If idle RPM is not as specified, replace throttle body.
12. Turn off engine.
13. Remove air metering fitting tool No. 6457 from intake manifold PCV nipple.
14. Install PCV valve hose.
15. Remove DRB scan tool.
16. Disconnect timing light and tachometer.

FUEL SYSTEM PRESSURE TEST

1. Release fuel system pressure as outlined under "Fuel System Pressure Relief" under "System Service."
2. Remove vacuum hose from pressure regulator before checking fuel pressure.
3. Connect fuel pressure gauge tool No. C-4799, or equivalent, to service port on fuel rail.
4. Turn ignition switch to On position.
5. Using DRB II, access ASD fuel system test to activate fuel pump and pressurize system.
6. If gauge reads 55 psi, system is operating normally.
7. If pressure is lower than 55 psi, record pressure and remove gauge tool.
8. Ensure system is not leaking, then proceed as follows:
   a. Release fuel system pressure as outlined under "Fuel System Pressure Relief" under "System Service."
   b. Install fuel pressure gauge tool and pressure test adapter tool Nos. C-4799 and 6539 or equivalents, in the fuel supply line between fuel tank and fuel filter.
   c. Turn ignition switch to On position, then using DRB II tester, access ASD fuel system test to activate fuel pump and pressurize system.
   d. If gauge reads 55 psi, system is operating normally. If pressure is at least 5 psi higher than first reading, replace fuel filter.
   e. If pressure is same as first reading, squeeze return hose.
   f. If fuel pressure increases after squeezing return hose, replace regulator. If pressure does not change, problem is either plugged inlet strainer or defective fuel pump.
9. If pressure is higher than 55 psi, record pressure and remove gauge tool.
10. Ensure system is not leaking, then proceed as follows:
    a. Release fuel system pressure as outlined under "Fuel System Pressure Relief" under "System Service."
    b. Remove fuel return line hose at fuel tank.
    c. Connect fuel pressure test adapter tool No. 6541, or equivalent, to return line. Place other end of adapter into approved gasoline container.
    d. Turn ignition switch to On position, then using DRB II tester, access ASD fuel system test to activate fuel pump and pressurize system.
    e. If pressure is now correct, replace fuel pump assembly. If pressure is not correct, remove fuel return hose from chassis fuel tubes at engine.
    f. Connect fuel pressure test adapter tool No. 6541, or equivalent, to return line. Place other end of adapter into approved gasoline container.
    g. Turn ignition switch to On position, then using DRB II tester, access ASD fuel system test to activate fuel pump and pressurize system.
    h. If pressure is now correct, check for restricted fuel return line. If no change in pressure is observed, replace fuel pressure regulator.

System & Component Diagnosis

Refer to "Accessing Diagnostic Trouble Codes" to obtain diagnostic trouble codes and "On-Board Diagnostics" to place the system in the various test modes. Refer to **Figs. 6 through 11** for wiring diagrams and engine controller connector terminal identification.

The following tests are used to further diagnose systems monitored by the On-Board Diagnosis System and to also test systems or parts of a system which are not monitored by the On-Board diagnosis system. Prior to performing any of the following tests, check electrical and vacuum component connections as described under "Visual Inspection." **Always start at the first No Start, Driveability, No Fault or Verification test. Starting at any other test may give inaccurate results.** After completing the test, perform appropriate verification test. Also check electrical connector terminal blades or pins for alignment and damage prior to replacing any component.

1993 2.2L/4-135 TURBOCHARGED ENGINES

Diagnostic Trouble Code Tests

Refer to the first Diagnostic Trouble (Fault) Code diagnosis chart, **Fig. 12**, and the remaining Diagnostic Trouble Code charts, **Figs. 13 through 47**, for trouble code diagnosis and testing.

No Diagnostic Trouble Code Tests

Refer to the first No Diagnostic Trouble Code (NF) diagnosis chart, **Fig. 48**, and the remaining No Diagnostic Trouble charts, **Figs. 49 through 64**, when no diagnostic trouble codes are set and a malfunction exists.

No Start Tests

Refer to the first No Start diagnosis chart **Fig. 65**, and the remaining No Start charts, **Figs. 66 through 79**, for no start diagnosis and testing.

Verification Tests

After completing diagnosis operations, perform verification tests, **Figs. 80 and 81**.

2.5L/4-153 NON-TURBOCHARGED ENGINES

Diagnostic Trouble Code Tests

Refer to the first Diagnostic Trouble Code diagnosis chart, **Fig. 82**, and the remaining Diagnostic Trouble Code charts, **Figs. 83 through 139**, for diagnostic trouble code diagnosis and testing.

Charging System Test

Refer to Checking Charging System diagnosis chart, **Figs. 140**.

Speed Control Tests

Refer to the first Speed Control diagnosis chart, **Fig. 141**, and the remaining Speed Control charts, **Figs. 142 through 146**, for speed control diagnosis and testing.

No Diagnostic Trouble Code Tests

Refer to the first No Diagnostic Trouble Code (NTC) diagnosis chart, **Fig. 147**, and the remaining No Diagnostic Trouble Code charts, **Figs. 148 through 164**, when no diagnostic trouble codes are set and a malfunction exists.

No Start Tests

Refer to the first No Start (NS) diagnosis chart, **Fig. 165**, and the remaining No Start charts, **Figs. 166 through 187**, for no start diagnosis and testing.

Verification Tests

After completing diagnosis operations, perform verification tests, **Figs. 188 through 191**.

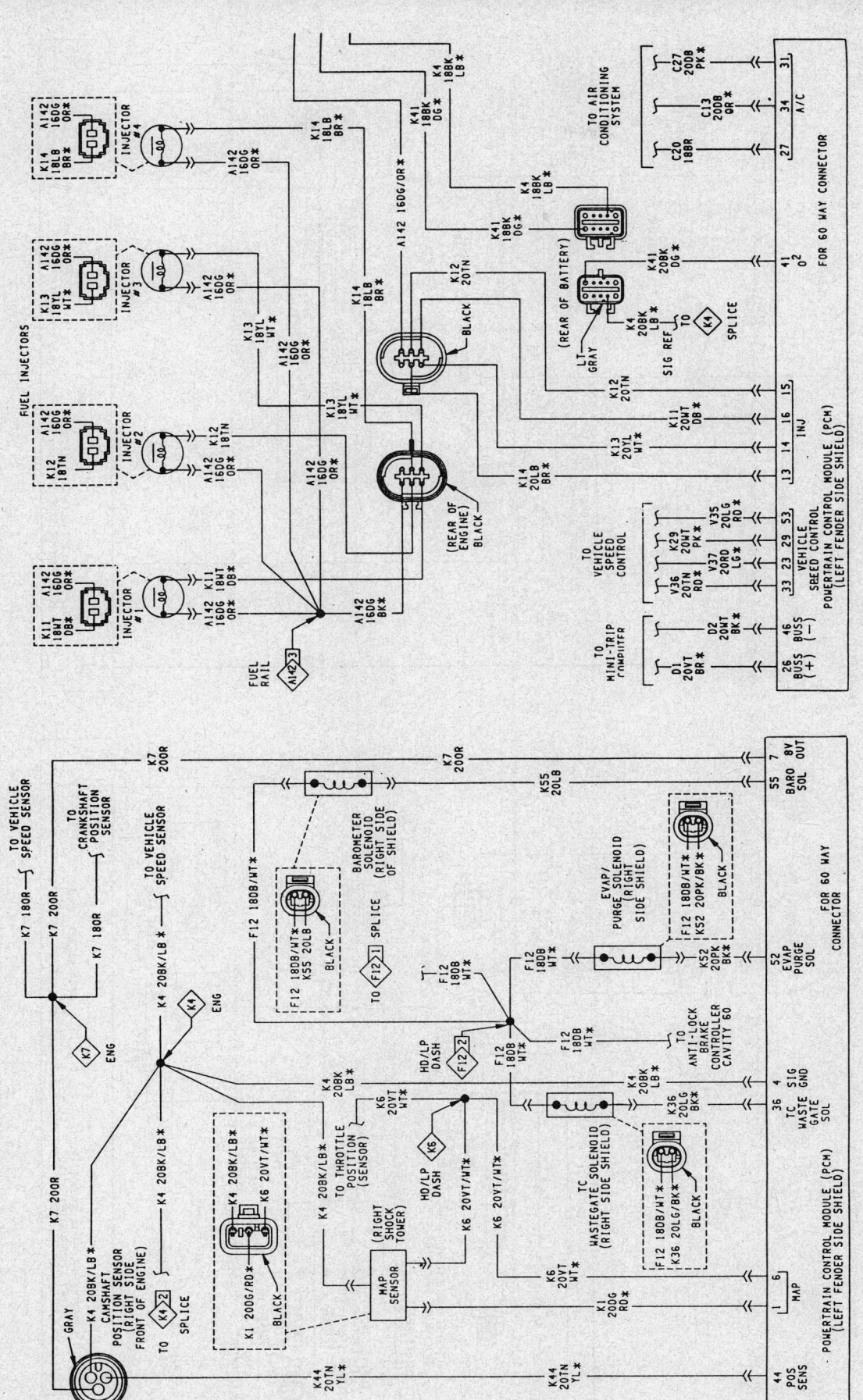

Fig. 6 MFI system wiring diagram (Part 2 of 6). 1993 2.2L/4-135 engine

Fig. 6 MFI system wiring diagram (Part 1 of 6). 1993 2.2L/4-135 engine

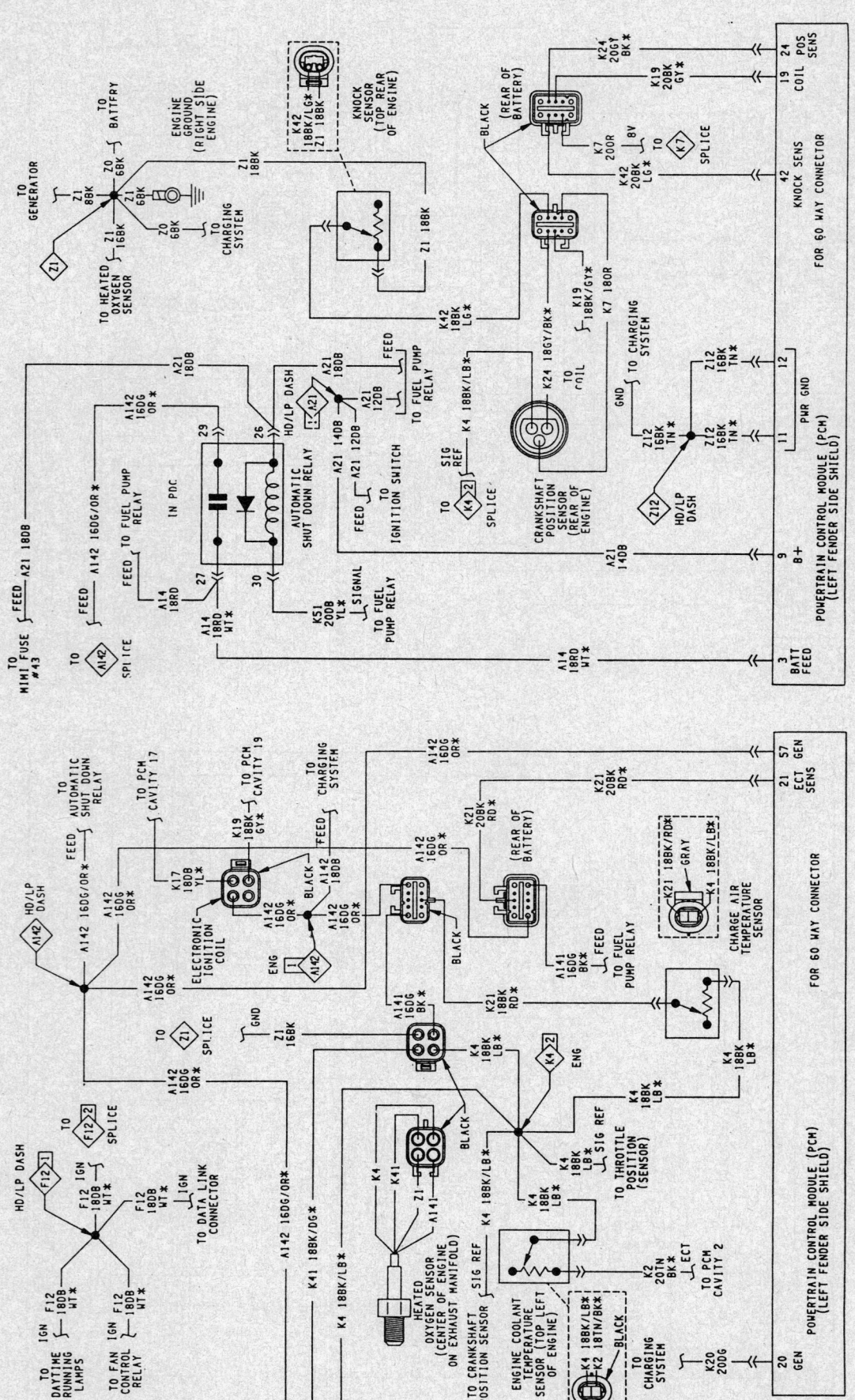

Fig. 6 MFI system wiring diagram (Part 4 of 6). 1993 2.2L/4-135 engine

Fig. 6 MFI system wiring diagram (Part 3 of 6). 1993 2.2L/4-135 engine

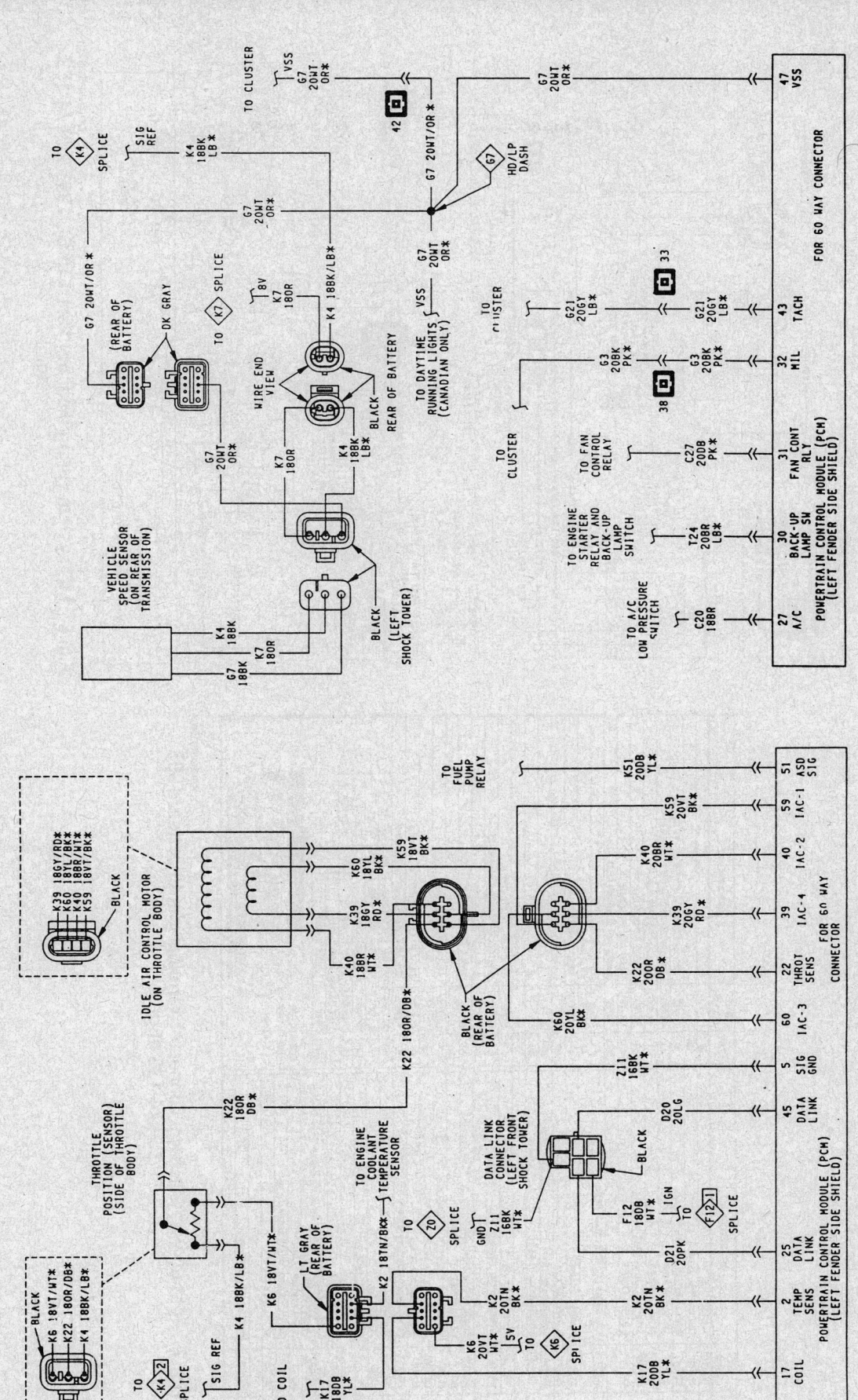

Fig. 6   MFI system wiring diagram (Part 6 of 6). 1993 2.2L/4-135 engine

Fig. 6   MFI system wiring diagram (Part 5 of 6). 1993 2.2L/4-135 engine

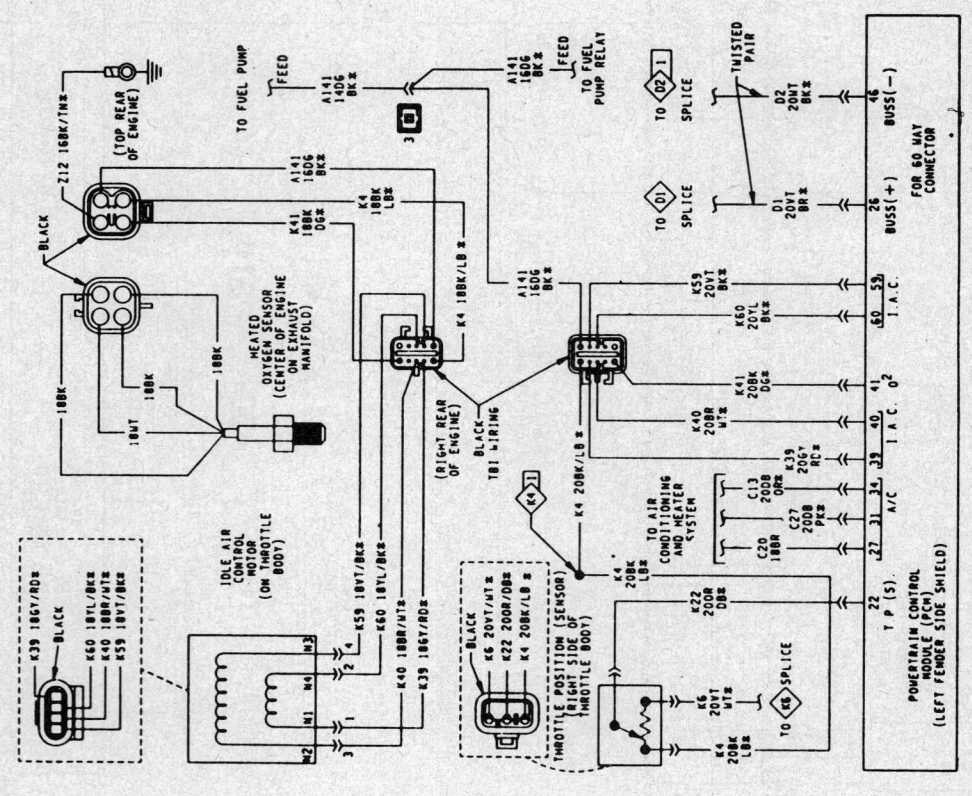

Fig. 8 MFI system wiring diagram (Part 1 of 6). 1993 2.5L/4-153 engine

CAV	WIRE COLOR	DESCRIPTION
1	DG/RD*	MAP SENSOR
2	TN/BK*	COOLANT SENSOR
3	RD/WT*	DIRECT BATTERY VOLTAGE
4	BK/LB*	SENSOR RETURN
5	BK/WT*	SIGNAL GROUND
6	VT/WT*	5.0 VOLT OUTPUT (MAP AND TPS)
7	OR	8.0 VOLT OUTPUT
8		
9	DB	A21 SUPPLY (IGNITION START/RUN)
10		
11	BK/TN*	POWER GROUND
12	BK/TN*	POWER GROUND
13	LB/OR	INJECTOR DRIVER #4
14	YL/WT*	INJECTOR DRIVER #3
15	TN	INJECTOR DRIVER #2
16	WT/DB*	INJECTOR DRIVER #1
17	DB/YL*	IGNITION COIL DRIVER #2
18		
19	BK/GY*	IGNITION COIL DRIVER #1
20	DG	GENERATOR FIELD CONTROL
21	BK/LB*	CHARGE AIR TEMPERATURE SENSOR
22	OR/DB*	THROTTLE POSITION SENSOR (TPS)
23	RD/DG*	SPEED CONTROL SET
24	GY/BK*	CRANKSHAFT POSITION SENSOR
25	PK	SCI TRANSMIT
26	WT/OR*	CCD BUS (+)
27	VT/BK*	A/C SWITCH SENSE
28		
29	WT/TN*	BRAKE SWITCH
30	RD/WT*	BACK UP LAMP SWITCH
31	DB/YL*	RADIATOR FAN RELAY
32.	DB/YL*	CHECK ENGINE LAMP
33	TN/RD*	SPEED CONTROL VACUUM SOLENOID
34	DB/OR*	A/C CLUTCH RELAY
35	LG/BK*	WASTEGATE SOLENOID
36		
37		
38		
39	GY/RD*	IDLE AIR CONTROL MOTOR DRIVER #3
40	BK/LB*	IDLE AIR CONTROL MOTOR DRIVER #1
41	BK/DG*	OXYGEN SENSOR SIGNAL
42	BK/LG*	KNOCK SENSOR SIGNAL
43	GY/LB*	TACHOMETER SIGNAL OUTPUT
44	TN/YL*	CAMSHAFT POSITION SENSOR
45	LG	SCI RECEIVE
46	WT/BK*	CCD BUS (-)
47	WT/OR*	SPEED SENSOR SIGNAL
48		
49		
50		
51	DB/YL*	AUTO SHUTDOWN (ASD) RELAY
52	PK/BK*	EVAP PURGE SOLENOID
53	LG/RD*	SPEED CONTROL VENT SOLENOID
54		
55	LB	BARO. PRESS. READ SOLENOID
56		
57	DG/OR*	A14.2 CIRCUIT VOLTAGE SENSE
58		
59	VT/BK*	IDLE AIR CONTROL MOTOR DRIVER #4
60	YL/BK*	IDLE AIR CONTROL MOTOR DRIVER #2

WIRE COLOR CODES

BK BLACK	LB LIGHT BLUE	VT VIOLET
BR BROWN	LG LIGHT GREEN	WT WHITE
DB DARK BLUE	OR ORANGE	YL YELLOW
DG DARK GREEN	PK PINK	* WITH TRACER
GY GRAY	RD RED	
	TN TAN	

CONNECTOR TERMINAL SIDE SHOWN

Fig. 7 PCM 60-way electrical connector terminal identification. 1993 2.2L/4-135 engine

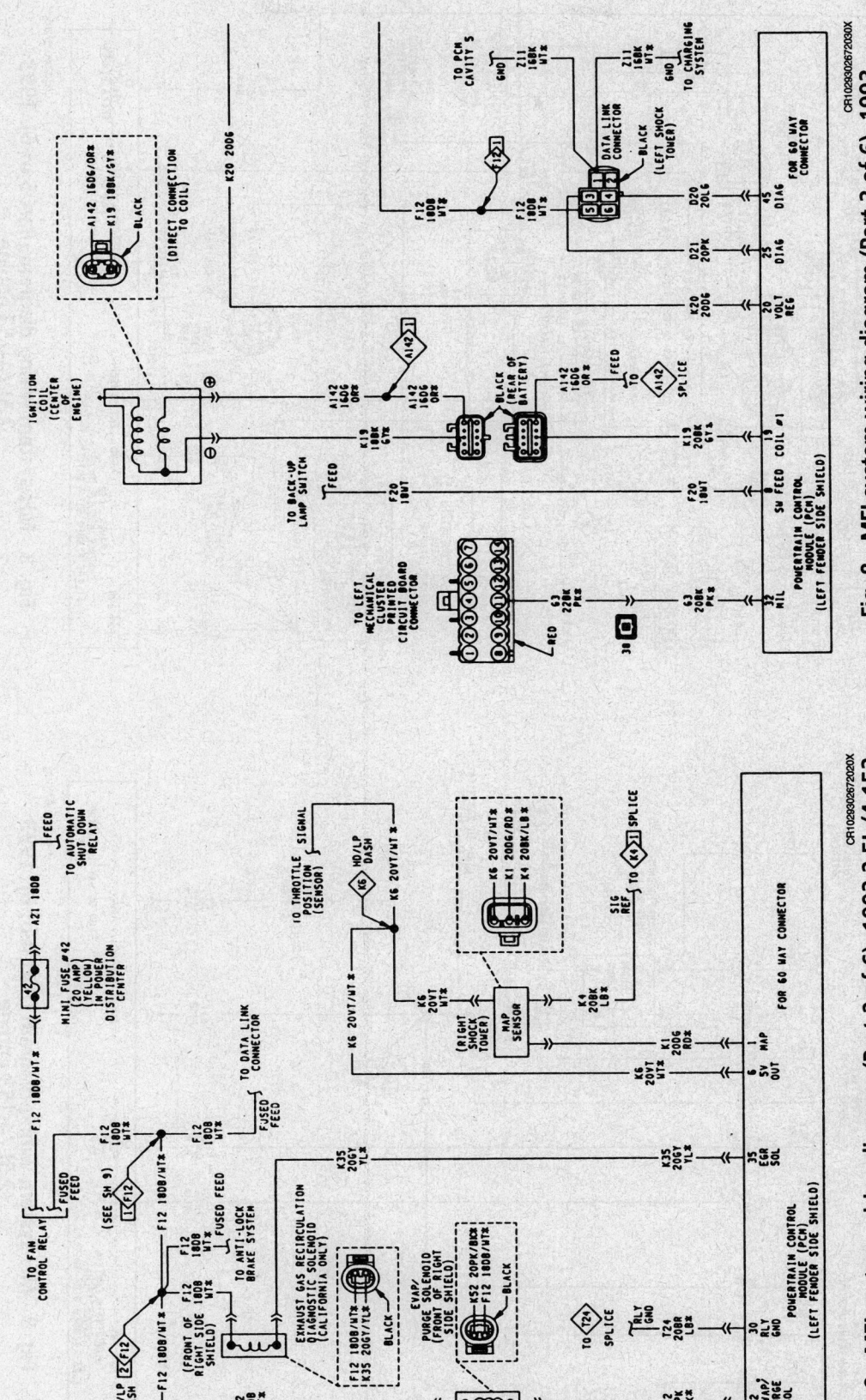

Fig. 8 MFI system wiring diagram (Part 3 of 6). 1993 2.5L/4-153 engine

Fig. 8 MFI system wiring diagram (Part 2 of 6). 1993 2.5L/4-153 engine

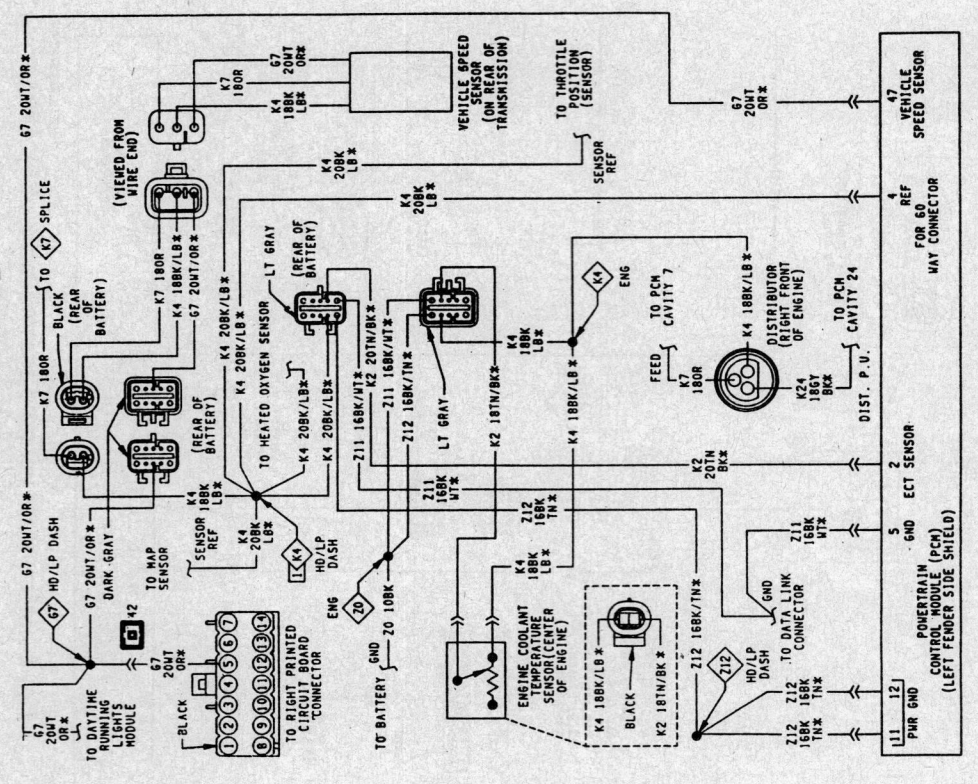

Fig. 8 MFI system wiring diagram (Part 5 of 6). 1993 2.5L/4-153 engine

Fig. 8 MFI system wiring diagram (Part 4 of 6). 1993 2.5L/4-153 engine

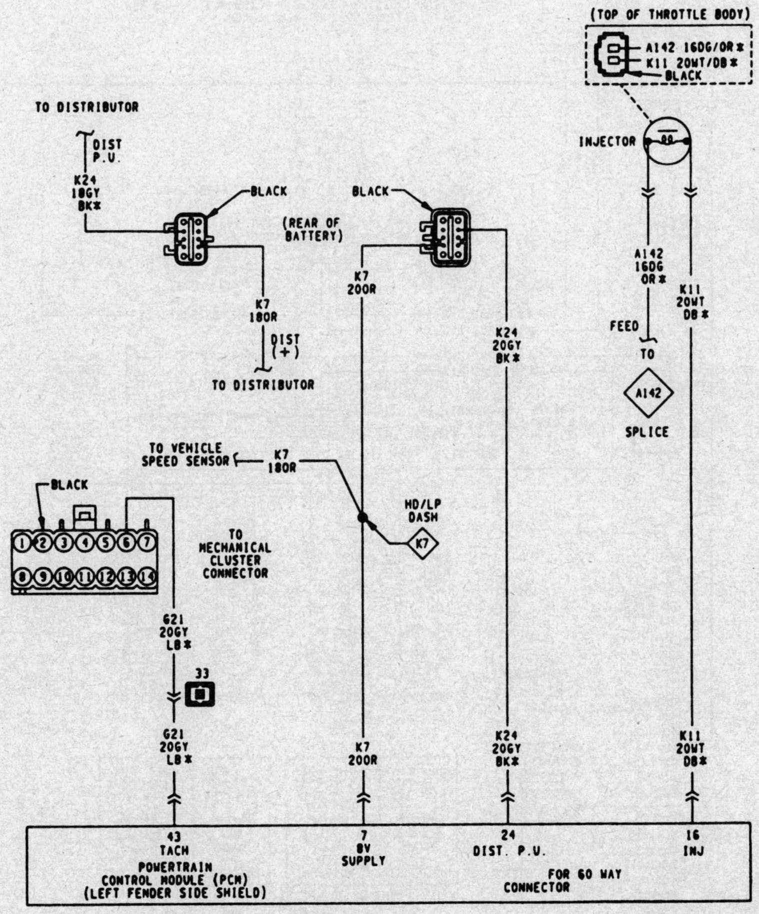

CAV	WIRE COLOR	DESCRIPTION
1	DG/RD*	MAP SENSOR
2	TN/BK*	ENGINE COOLANT TEMPERATURE SENSOR
3	RD/WT*	DIRECT BATTERY VOLTAGE
4	BK/LB*	SENSOR RETURN
5	BK/WT*	SIGNAL GROUND
6	VT/WT*	5-VOLT OUTPUT (MAP AND TPS)
7	OR	8-VOLT OUTPUT
8		
9	DB	A21 SUPPLY (IGNITION START/RUN)
10		
11	BK/TN*	POWER GROUND
12	BK/TN*	POWER GROUND
13	LB/BR	INJECTOR DRIVER #4
14	YL/WT*	INJECTOR DRIVER #3
15	TN	INJECTOR DRIVER #2
16	WT/DB*	INJECTOR DRIVER #1
17		
18		
19	BK/GY*	IGNITION COIL DRIVER #1
20	DG	GENERATOR FIELD CONTROL
21	BK/RD*	METHANOL CONCENTRATION SENSOR
22	RD/LG*	THROTTLE POSITION SENSOR (TPS)
23	OR/DB*	SPEED CONTROL SENSE
24	GY/BK*	IGNITION REFERENCE PICK-UP
25	PK	SCI TRANSMIT
26	VT/BR*	CCD BUS (+)
27	BR	A/C SWITCH SENSE
28		
29	WT/PK*	BRAKE SWITCH
30	BR/YL*	PARK/NEUTRAL SWITCH (AUTO TRANS.)
31	DB/PK*	RADIATOR FAN RELAY
32	BK/PK*	CHECK ENGINE LAMP
33	TN/RD*	SPEED CONTROL VACUUM SOLENOID
34	DB/OR*	A/C CLUTCH RELAY
35		
36		

CAV	WIRE COLOR	DESCRIPTION
37		
38		
39	GY/RD*	IDLE AIR CONTROL MOTOR TERMINAL #3
40	BR/WT*	IDLE AIR CONTROL MOTOR TERMINAL #1
41	BK/DG*	HEATED OXYGEN SENSOR SIGNAL
42		
43	GY/LB*	TACHOMETER SIGNAL OUTPUT
44	TN/YL*	CAMSHAFT POSITION SENSOR
45	LG	SCI RECEIVE
46		CCD BUS (-)
47	WT/BK*	..
48	WT/OR*	VEHICLE SPEED SENSOR
49		
50		
51	DB/YL*	AUTO SHUTDOWN (ASD) RELAY AND FUEL PUMP RELAY
52	PK/BK*	EVAP PURGE SOLENOID
53	LG/RD*	SPEED CONTROL VENT SOLENOID
54	LG/WT*	TORQUE CONVERTER CLUTCH SOLENOID
55		
56		
57	DG/OR*	A142 CIRCUIT VOLTAGE SENSE
58	VT/BK*	IDLE AIR CONTROL MOTOR TERMINAL #4
59	YL/LB*	IDLE AIR CONTROL MOTOR TERMINAL #2
60	LB	IDLE AIR CONTROL MOTOR TERMINAL #1

WIRE COLOR CODES					
BK	BLACK	LB	LIGHT BLUE	VT	VIOLET
BR	BROWN	LG	LIGHT GREEN	WT	WHITE
DB	DARK BLUE	OR	ORANGE	YL	YELLOW
DG	DARK GREEN	PK	PINK	*	WITH TRACER
GY	GRAY	RD	RED	TN	TAN

CONNECTOR TERMINAL SIDE SHOWN

CR1028302673000X

Fig. 9 PCM 60-way electrical connector terminal identification. 1993 2.5L/4-153 engine

CR1028302672060X

Fig. 8 MFI system wiring diagram (Part 6 of 6). 1993 2.5L/4-153 engine

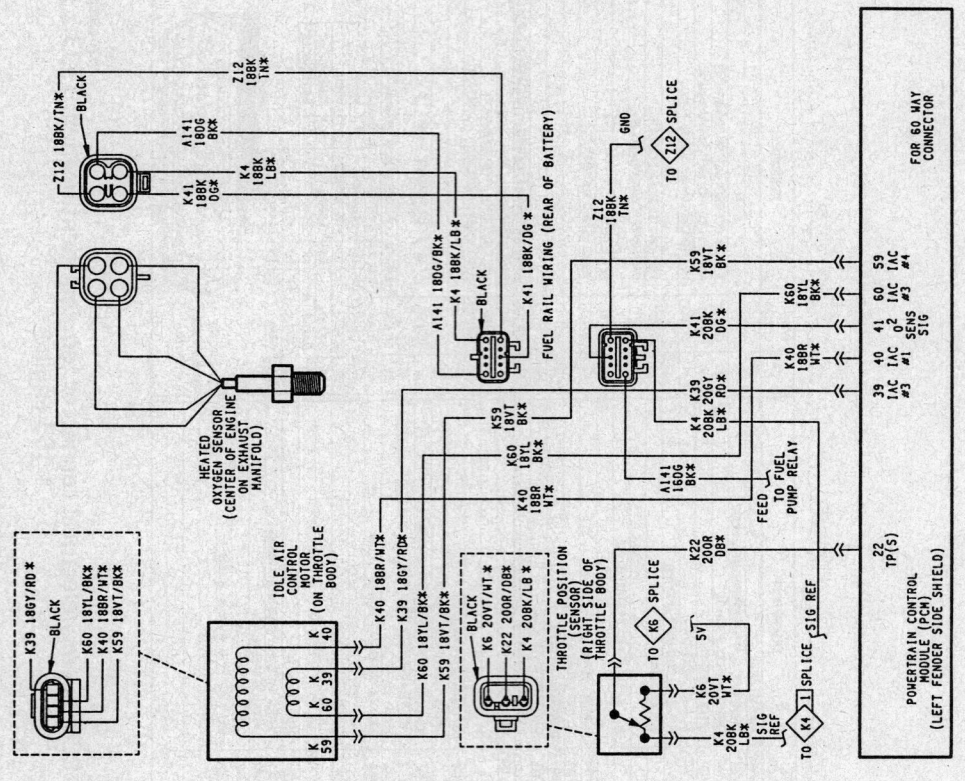

Fig. 10 MFI system wiring diagram (Part 2 of 6). 1994–95 2.5L/4-153 engine

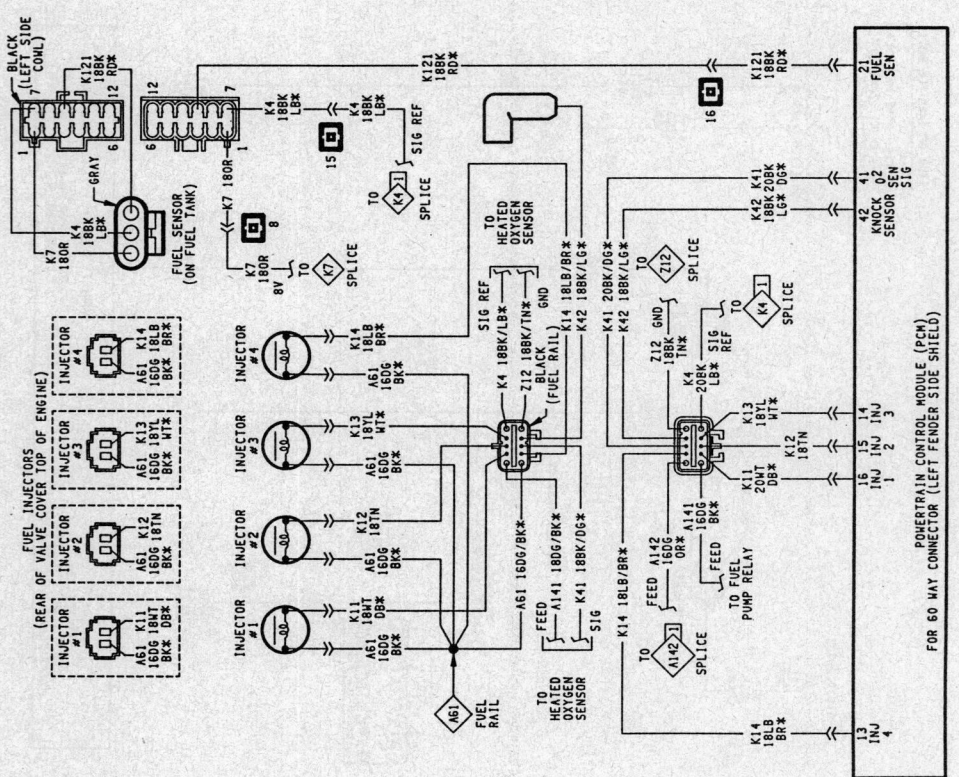

Fig. 10 MFI system wiring diagram (Part 1 of 6). 1994–95 2.5L/4-153 engine

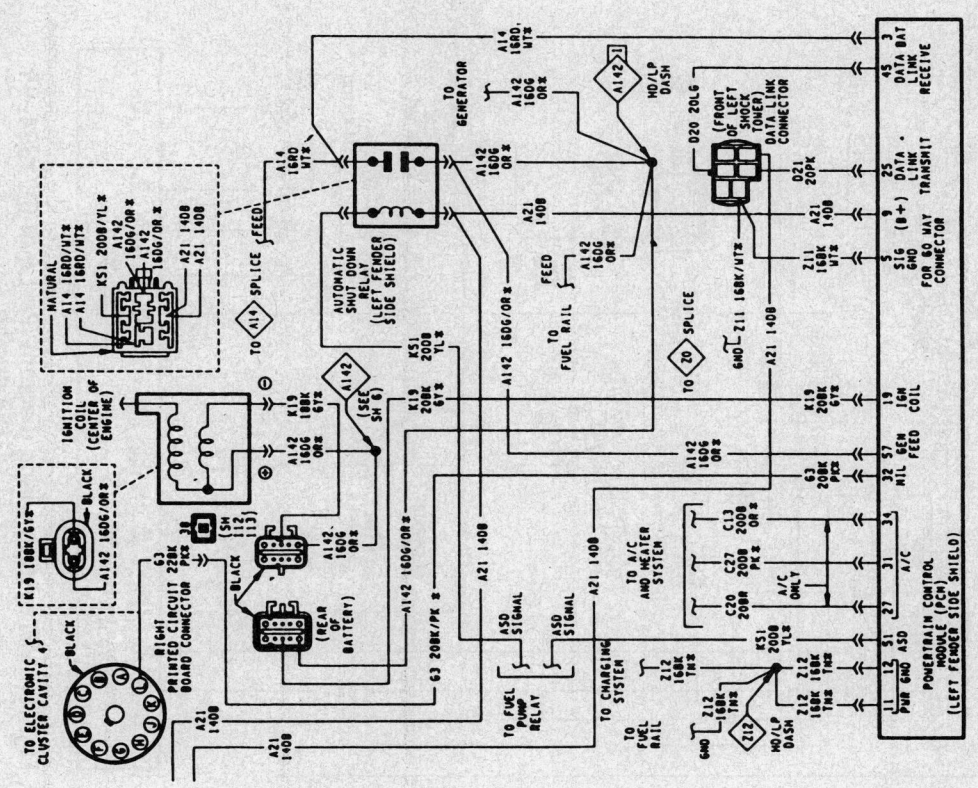

Fig. 10 MFI system wiring diagram (Part 4 of 6). 1994-95 2.5L/4-153 engine

Fig. 10 MFI system wiring diagram (Part 3 of 6). 1994-95 2.5L/4-153 engine

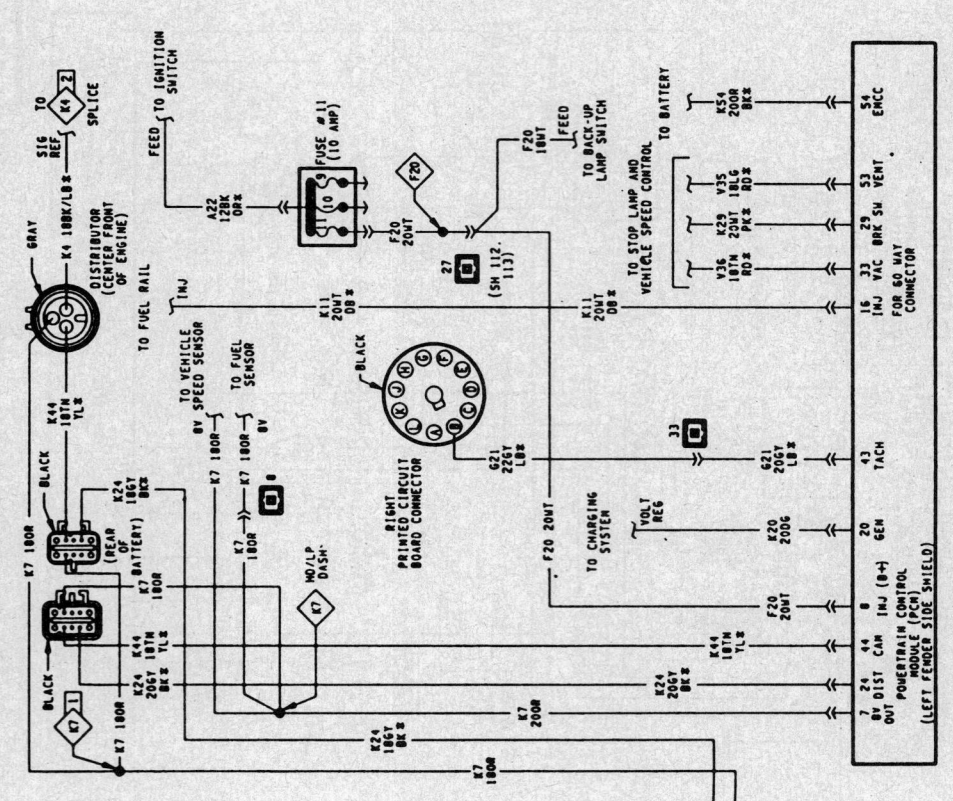

Fig. 10 MFI system wiring diagram (Part 6 of 6). 1994-95 2.5L/4-153 engine

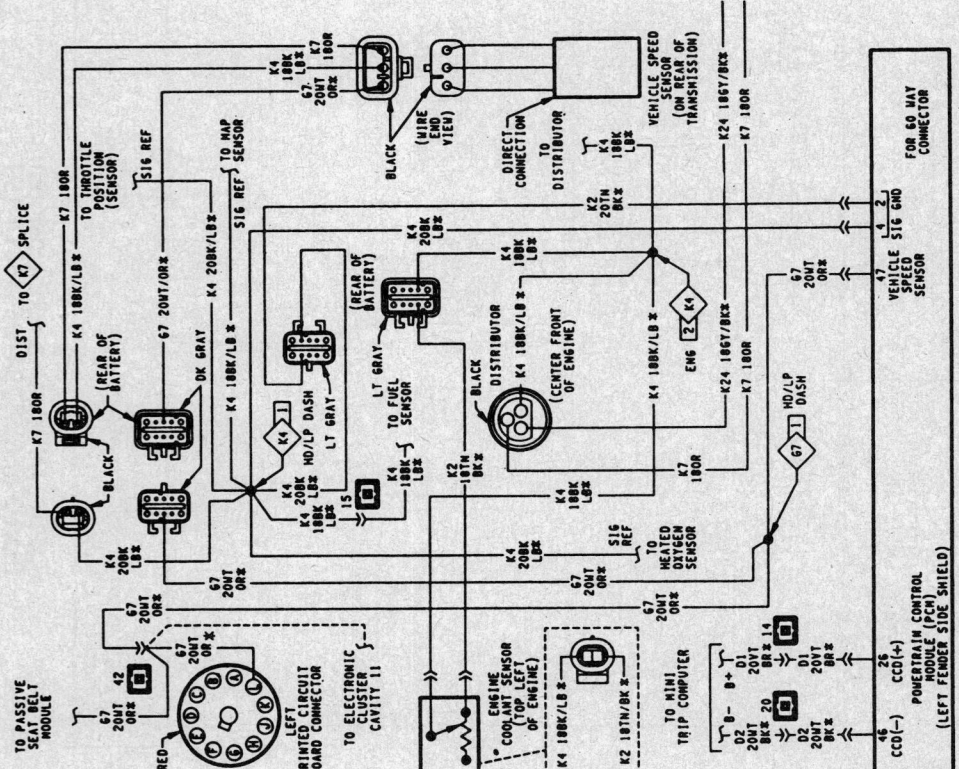

Fig. 10 MFI system wiring diagram (Part 5 of 6). 1994-95 2.5L/4-153 engine

CAV	WIRE COLOR	DESCRIPTION	CAV	WIRE COLOR	DESCRIPTION
1	BG/RD*	MAP SENSOR	37		
2	TN/BK*	ENGINE COOLANT TEMPERATURE SENSOR	38		
3	RD/WT*	DIRECT BATTERY VOLTAGE	39	GY/RD*	IDLE AIR CONTROL MOTOR TERMINAL #3
4	BK/LB*	SENSOR RETURN	40	BR/WT*	IDLE AIR CONTROL MOTOR TERMINAL #1
5	BK/WT*	SIGNAL GROUND	41	BK/DG*	HEATED OXYGEN SENSOR SIGNAL
6	VT/WT*	5-VOLT OUTPUT (MAP AND TPS)	42		
7	OR	8-VOLT OUTPUT	43	GY/LB*	TACHOMETER SIGNAL OUTPUT
8	WT	INJECTOR DRIVER	44	TN/YL*	CAMSHAFT POSITION SENSOR
9	DB	A21 SUPPLY (IGNITION START/RUN)	45	LG	SCI RECEIVE
10			46	WT/BK*	CCD BUS (-)
11	BK/TN*	POWER GROUND	47	WT/OR*	VEHICLE SPEED SENSOR
12	BK/TN*	POWER GROUND	48		
13	LB/BR	INJECTOR DRIVER #4	49		
14	YL/WT*	INJECTOR DRIVER #3	50		
15	TN	INJECTOR DRIVER #2	51	DB/YL*	AUTOMATIC SHUTDOWN RELAY AND FUEL PUMP RELAY
16	WT/DB*	INJECTOR DRIVER #1	52	PK/BK*	DUTY CYCLE EVAP PURGE SOLENOID
17			53	LG/RD*	SPEED CONTROL VENT SOLENOID
18			54	OR/BK*	TORQUE CONVERTER CLUTCH SOLENOID
19	BK/GY*=	IGNITION COIL DRIVER #1	55		
20	DG	GENERATOR FIELD CONTROL	56		
21	BK/RD*	METHANOL CONCENTRATION SENSOR	57	DG/OR*	A142 CIRCUIT VOLTAGE SENSE
22	OR/DB*	THROTTLE POSITION SENSOR (TPS)	58		
23	RD/LG*	SPEED CONTROL SENSE	59	VT/BK*	IDLE AIR CONTROL MOTOR TERMINAL #4
24	GY/BK*	IGNITION REFERENCE PICK-UP (DISTRIBUTOR PICK-UP)	60	YL/BK*	IDLE AIR CONTROL MOTOR TERMINAL #2
25	PK	SCI TRANSMIT			
26	VT/BR*	CCD BUS (+)			
27	BR	A/C SWITCH SENSE			
28					
29	WT/PK*	BRAKE SWITCH			
30	BR/YL*	PARK/NEUTRAL SWITCH (AUTO TRANS.)			
31	DB/PK*	RADIATOR FAN RELAY			
32	BK/PK*	MALFUNCTION INDICATOR LAMP			
33	TN/RD*	SPEED CONTROL VACUUM SOLENOID			
34	DB/OR*	A/C CLUTCH RELAY			
35					
36					

WIRE COLOR CODES

LB	LIGHT BLUE	VT	VIOLET
BK	BLACK	LG	LIGHT GREEN	WT	WHITE
BR	BROWN	OR	ORANGE	YL	YELLOW
DB	DARK BLUE	PK	PINK	*	WITH TRACER
DG	DARK GREEN	RD	RED		
GY	GRAY	TN	TAN		

CR1029402675000X

Fig. 11 PCM 60-way electrical connector terminal identification. 1994–95 2.5L/4-153 engine

DIAGNOSTIC CHART INDEX

Test	MIL Code	Description	Page No. 9-	Fig. No.
2.2L/4-135 ENGINE				
Test FC-1A	—	Checking The System For Fault Codes	21	12
Test FC-2A	11	Repairing Fault " No Crank Reference Signal At PCM"	21	13
Test FC-2B	11	Repairing Fault " No Crank Reference Signal At PCM"	22	14
Test FC-3A	—	Repairing Fault " No Cam Sync Signal At PCM"	22	15
Test FC-4A	13	Repairing Fault " Slow Change In Idle MAP Sensor Signal & No Change In MAP From Start To Run"	23	16
Test FC-5A	14	Repairing Fault " MAP Sensor Voltage Too Low"	24	17
Test FC-6A	14	Repairing Fault " MAP Sensor Voltage Too High"	24	18
Test FC-7A	15	Repairing Fault " No Vehicle Speed Sensor Signal"	25	19
Test FC-7B	15	Repairing Fault " No Vehicle Speed Sensor Signal"	25	20
Test FC-8A	21	Repairing Fault " O₂S Stays At Center"	26	21
Test FC-9A	52	Repairing Fault " O₂S Stays Above Center (Rich)"	26	22
Test FC-10A	51	Repairing Fault " O₂S Stays Below Center (Lean)"	26	23
Test FC-11A	21	Repairing Fault " O₂S Shorted To Voltage"	27	24
Test FC-12A	22	Repairing Fault " ECT Sensor Voltage Too Low"	27	25
Test FC-13A	22	Repairing Fault " ECT Sensor Voltage Too High"	28	26
Test FC-14A	—	Repairing Fault " Intake Air Temp Sensor Voltage Low"	28	27
Test FC-15A	—	Repairing Fault " Intake Air Temp Sensor Voltage High"	29	28
Test FC-16A	24	Repairing Fault " Throttle Position Sensor Voltage Low"	29	29
Test FC-17A	24	Repairing Fault " Throttle Position Sensor Voltage High"	30	30
Test FC-18A	25	Repairing Fault " Idle Air Control Motor Circuits"	30	31
Test FC-19A	27	Repairing Fault " Injector No. 1 Control Circuit"	31	32
Test FC-20A	27	Repairing Fault " Injector No. 2 Control Circuit"	31	33
Test FC-21A	27	Repairing Fault " Injector No. 3 Control Circuit"	32	34
Test FC-22A	27	Repairing Fault " Injector No. 4 Control Circuit"	32	35
Test FC-23A	—	Repairing Fault " Ignition Coil No. 1 Primary Circuit"	33	36
Test FC-24A	—	Repairing Fault " Ignition Coil No. 2 Primary Circuit"	33	37

Continued

DIAGNOSTIC CHART INDEX—Continued

Test	MIL Code	Description	Page No. 9-	Fig. No.
2.2L/4-135 ENGINE				
Test FC-25A	31	Repairing Fault " EVAP Purge Solenoid Circuit"	34	38
Test FC-26A	—	Repairing Fault " TC Wastegate Solenoid Circuit"	35	39
Test FC-27A	—	Repairing Fault " BARO Read Solenoid Circuit"	35	40
Test FC-28A	—	Repairing Fault " Turbo Boost Limit Exceeded"	36	41
Test FC-29A	42	Repairing Fault " Auto Shutdown Relay Control Circuit"	36	42
Test FC-30A	—	Repairing Fault " No ASD Relay Volt Sense At PCM"	37	43
Test FC-31A	35	Repairing Fault " RAD Fan Control Relay Circuit"	37	44
Test FC-32A	33	Repairing Fault " A/C Clutch Relay Circuit"	38	45
Test FC-33A	—	Repairing Fault " Knock Sensor No. 1 Circuit"	38	46
Test FC-34A	63	Repairing Fault " PCM Failure SPI Communications & EEPROM Write Denied"	39	47
Test NF-1A	—	No Fault Code Test Menu	39	48
Test NF-2A	—	Checking Secondary Ignition & Timing	40	49
Test NF-3A	—	Checking Fuel Pressure	40	50
Test NF-3B	—	Checking Fuel Pressure	40	51
Test NF-4A	—	Checking Coolant Sensor Calibration & Radiator Fan Operation	41	52
Test NF-5A	—	Checking TP Sensor Calibration	41	53
Test NF-6A	—	Checking MAP Sensor Calibration	41	54
Test NF-7A	—	Checking Oxygen Sensor Switching	42	55
Test NF-7B	—	Checking Oxygen Sensor Switching	42	56
Test NF-8A	—	Checking Idle Air Control Motor	43	57
Test NF-8A	—	Checking Idle Air Control Motor	43	58
Test NF-9A	—	Checking Solenoid Operations	43	59
Test NF-10A	—	Checking PCM Grounds & Power Circuit	44	60
Test NF-11A	—	Checking Engine Vacuum	44	61
Test NF-12A	—	Checking Minimum Idle Air Flow	44	62
Test NF-13A	—	Checking Knock Sensor	45	63
Test NF-14A	—	No Fault Code Mechanical Test	45	64
Test NS-1A	—	Qualifying No Start Condition	45	65
Test NS-2A	—	Inspecting Fuel System	46	66
Test NS-3A	—	Inspecting Mechanical System	46	67
Test NS-4A	—	Correcting Fuel Delivery	47	68
Test NS-4B	—	Correcting Fuel Delivery	47	69
Test NS-5A	—	Inspecting Fuel Pump	48	70
Test NS-5B	—	Inspecting Fuel Pump	48	71
Test NS-6A	—	Correcting " No Response" Condition	48	72
Test NS-6B	—	Correcting " No Response" Condition	49	73
Test NS-7A	—	Inspecting Idle Air Control Motor Operation	50	74
Test NS-7B	—	Inspecting Idle Air Control Motor Operation	50	75
Test NS-7C	—	Inspecting Idle Air Control Motor Operation	51	76
Test NS-7D	—	Inspecting Idle Air Control Motor Operation	51	77
Test NS-7E	—	Inspecting Idle Air Control Motor Operation	51	78
Test NS-8A	—	Correcting Start & Stall Condition	51	79
Test VER-1	—	Verification Test 1	51	80
Test VER-2	—	Road Test Verification	51	81
2.5L/4-153 ENGINE				
Test TC-1A	—	Checking The System For Trouble Codes	52	82
Test TC-2A	11	Repairing No Crank Reference Signal At PCM	52	83
Test TC-2B	11	Repairing No Crank Reference Signal At PCM	53	84
Test TC-2C	11	Repairing No Crank Reference Signal At PCM	53	85
Test TC-2D	11	Repairing No Crank Reference Signal At PCM	54	86
Test TC-3A	—	Repairing No Cam Sync Signal At PCM	54	87
Test TC-4A	14	Repairing MAP Sensor Voltage Too Low	55	88

Continued

DIAGNOSTIC CHART INDEX—Continued

Test	MIL Code	Description	Page No. 9-	Fig. No.
2.5L/4-153 ENGINE -CONTINUED				
Test TC-5A	14	Repairing MAP Sensor Voltage Too High	55	89
Test TC-6A	13	Repairing No Change In MAP From Start To Run Or Slow Change In Idle MAP Sensor Signal	56	90
Test TC-7A	21	Repairing O₂S Stays At Center	56	91
Test TC-8A	52	Repairing O₂S Stays Above Center, Rich	57	92
Test TC-9A	51	Repairing O₂S Stays Below Center, Lean	57	93
Test TC-10A	21	Repairing O₂S Shorted To Voltage	57	94
Test TC-11A	15	Repairing No Vehicle Speed Sensor Signal	58	95
Test TC-11B	15	Repairing No Vehicle Speed Sensor Signal	58	96
Test TC-11C	15	Repairing No Vehicle Speed Sensor Signal	58	97
Test TC-11D	15	Repairing No Vehicle Speed Sensor Signal	59	98
Test TC-11E	15	Repairing No Vehicle Speed Sensor Signal	59	99
Test TC-12A	25	Repairing Idle Air Control Motor Circuits	59	100
Test TC-12B	25	Repairing Idle Air Control Motor Circuits	60	101
Test TC-12C	25	Repairing Idle Air Control Motor Circuits	60	102
Test TC-12D	25	Repairing Idle Air Control Motor Circuits	60	103
Test TC-12E	25	Repairing Idle Air Control Motor Circuits	60	104
Test TC-13A	27	Repairing Injector Control Circuits	61	105
Test TC-13B	27	Repairing Injector Control Circuits	61	106
Test TC-13C	27	Repairing Injector Control Circuits	61	107
Test TC-14A	27	Repairing Injector No. 2 Control Circuit	62	108
Test TC-15A	27	Repairing Injector No. 3 Control Circuit	62	109
Test TC-16A	27	Repairing Injector No. 4 Control Circuit	62	110
Test TC-17A	32	Repairing EGR System Failure	62	111
Test TC-18A	32	Repairing EGR Solenoid Circuit	63	112
Test TC-19A	31	Repairing EVAP Solenoid Circuit	64	113
Test TC-20A	37	Repairing Torque Converter Clutch Solenoid Circuit	64	114
Test TC-21A	24	Repairing Throttle Position Sensor Voltage Low	65	115
Test TC-22A	24	Repairing Throttle Position Sensor Voltage High	65	116
Test TC-23A	—	Repairing Throttle Body Temp Sensor Voltage Low	66	117
Test TC-24A	—	Repairing Throttle Body Temp Sensor Voltage High	66	118
Test TC-25A	22	Repairing ECT Sensor Voltage Too Low	67	119
Test TC-26A	22	Repairing ECT Sensor Voltage Too High	67	120
Test TC-27A	—	Repairing No ASD Relay Output Voltage At PCM	68	121
Test TC-28A	42	Repairing Auto Shutdown Relay Control Circuit	69	122
Test TC-29A	35	Repairing RAD Fan Control Relay Circuit	69	123
Test TC-30A	—	Repairing Low Speed Fan Control Relay Circuit	70	124
Test TC-31A	—	Repairing High Speed Fan Control Relay Circuit	70	125
Test TC-32A	33	Repairing A/C Clutch Relay Circuit	71	126
Test TC-33A	64	Repairing Flex Fuel Sensor Volts Too High	72	127
Test TC-34A	64	Repairing Flex Fuel Sensor Volts Too Low	72	128
Test TC-35A	—	Repairing Loss Of Flex Fuel Calibration Signal	73	129
Test TC-36A	62	Repairing PCM Failure SRI Mile Not Stored	73	130
Test TC-37A	—	Repairing Battery Temp Sensor Volts Out Of Limit	73	131
Test TC-38A	47	Repairing Charging System Voltage Too Low	73	132
Test TC-39A	46	Repairing Charging System Voltage Too High	74	133
Test TC-39B	—	Checking Powertrain Control Module Regulating Circuit	74	134
Test TC-40A	41	Repairing Generator Field Not Switching Properly	74	135
Test TC-40B	41	Repairing Generator Field Not Switching Properly	75	136
Test TC-41A	34	Repairing Speed Control Solenoid Circuits	75	137
Test TC-41B	34	Repairing Speed Control Solenoid Circuits	76	138
Test TC-41C	34	Repairing Speed Control Solenoid Circuits	76	139

Continued

DIAGNOSTIC CHART INDEX—Continued

Test	MIL Code	Description	Page No. 9-	Fig. No.
2.5L/4-153 ENGINE-CONTINUED				
Test CH-1A	—	Checking Charging System No Trouble Codes	76	140
Test SC-1A	—	Checking Speed Control System	77	141
Test SC-1B	—	Checking Speed Control Brake Switch Output	77	142
Test SC-2A	—	Checking Speed Control On/Off Switch	78	143
Test SC-3A	—	Checking Speed Control Brake Switch Sense	78	144
Test SC-4A	—	Checking Speed Control Park/Neutral Circuit	78	145
Test SC-5A	—	Checking Speed Control System For Denied Messages	79	146
Test NTC-1A	—	No Trouble Code Test Menu	79	147
Test NTC-2A	—	Checking Secondary Ignition & Timing	79	148
Test NTC-3A	—	Checking Fuel Pressure	80	149
Test NTC-3B	—	Checking Fuel Pressure	80	150
Test NTC-4A	—	Checking Coolant Sensor Calibration & Radiator Fan Operation	80	151
Test NTC-5A	—	Checking Throttle Position Sensor Calibration	81	152
Test NTC-6A	—	Checking MAP Sensor Calibration	81	153
Test NTC-7A	—	Checking Oxygen Sensor Switching	81	154
Test NTC-7B	—	Checking Oxygen Sensor Switching	82	155
Test NTC-8A	—	Checking Idle Air Control Motor	82	156
Test NTC-8B	—	Checking Idle Air Control Motor	82	157
Test NTC-9A	—	Checking Solenoid Operations	83	158
Test NTC-10A	—	Checking Park/Neutral Position Switch	83	159
Test NTC-11A	—	Checking PCM Grounds & Power Circuit	83	160
Test NTC-12A	—	Checking EGR System	84	161
Test NTC-13A	—	Checking Engine Vacuum	84	162
Test NTC-14A	—	Checking Minimum Idle Air Flow	85	163
Test NTC-15A	—	No Trouble Code Mechanical Test	85	164
Test NS-1A	—	Qualifying No Start Condition	85	165
Test NS-2A	—	Inspecting Fuel System	86	166
Test NS-3A	—	Inspecting mechanical system	87	167
Test NS-4A	—	Correcting Fuel Delivery	88	168
Test NS-4B	—	Correcting Fuel Delivery	88	169
Test NS-4C	—	Correcting Fuel Delivery	89	170
Test NS-5A	—	Inspecting Fuel Pump	89	171
Test NS-5B	—	Inspecting Fuel Pump	90	172
Test NS-5C	—	Inspecting Fuel Pump	90	173
Test NS-6A	—	Correcting " No Response" Condition	90	174
Test NS-6B	—	Correcting " No Response" Condition	91	175
Test NS-6C	—	Correcting " No Response" Condition	92	176
Test NS-6D	—	Correcting " No Response" Condition	92	177
Test NS-6E	—	Correcting " No Response" Condition	93	178
Test NS-7A	—	Inspecting Idle Air Control Motor Operation	93	179
Test NS-7B	—	Inspecting Idle Air Control Motor Operation	93	180
Test NS-7C	—	Inspecting Idle Air Control Motor Operation	94	181
Test NS-7D	—	Inspecting Idle Air Control Motor Operation	94	182
Test NS-7E	—	Inspecting Idle Air Control Motor Operation	94	183
Test NS-8A	—	Correcting Start & Stall Condition	94	184
Test NS-9A	—	Repairing " No Crank" Condition	95	185
Test NS-9B	—	Repairing " No Crank" Condition	95	186
Test NS-9C	—	Repairing " No Crank" Condition	96	187
Test VER-1	—	No Start Verification	96	188
Test VER-2	—	Road Test Verification	96	189
Test CH-VER	—	Charging Verification	97	190
Test SC-VER	—	Speed Control Verification	97	191

NOTE: The battery must be fully charged for any test in this manual.

1. Attempt to start the engine. Crank for up to 10 seconds if necessary.

2. Connect the DRBII to the engine diagnostic connector. Write down fault messages that are displayed.

3. If the DRBII screen has a no response message, go to TEST NS-6A.

4. If the DRBII has an error message or blank screen, go to Introduction

5. If fault messages are displayed, refer to the fault code list below

6. If there are no faults displayed refer to TEST NS-1A for no-start tests or NF-1A for no-fault code tests.

DRBII MESSAGE	DIAGNOSTIC TEST
NO CRANK REFERENCE SIGNAL AT PCM	FC- 2A
NO CAM SYNC SIGNAL AT PCM	FC- 3A
SLOW CHANGE IN IDLE MAP SENSOR SIGNAL AND NO CHANGE IN MAP FROM START TO RUN	FC- 4A
MAP SENSOR VOLTAGE TOO LOW	FC- 5A
MAP SENSOR VOLTAGE TOO HIGH	FC- 6A
NO VEHICLE SPEED SENSOR SIGNAL	FC- 7A
O2S STAYS AT CENTER	FC- 8A
O2S STAYS ABOVE CENTER (RICH)	FC- 9A
O2S STAYS BELOW CENTER (LEAN)	FC-10A
O2S SHORTED TO VOLTAGE	FC-11A
ECT SENSOR VOLTAGE TOO LOW	FC-12A
ECT SENSOR VOLTAGE TOO HIGH	FC-13A
INTAKE AIR TEMP SENSOR VOLTAGE LOW	FC-14A
INTAKE AIR TEMP SENSOR VOLTAGE HIGH	FC-15A
THROTTLE POSITION SENSOR VOLTAGE LOW	FC-16A
THROTTLE POSITION SENSOR VOLTAGE HIGH	FC-17A
IDLE AIR CONTROL MOTOR CIRCUITS	FC-18A
INJECTOR #1 CONTROL CIRCUIT	FC-19A
INJECTOR #2 CONTROL CIRCUIT	FC-20A
INJECTOR #3 CONTROL CIRCUIT	FC-21A
INJECTOR #4 CONTROL CIRCUIT	FC-22A
IGNITION COIL #1 PRIMARY CIRCUIT	FC-23A
IGNITION COIL #2 PRIMARY CIRCUIT	FC-24A
EVAP PURGE SOLENOID CIRCUIT	FC-25A
TC WASTEGATE SOLENOID CIRCUIT	FC-26A
BARO READ SOLENOID CIRCUIT	FC-27A
TURBO BOOST LIMIT EXCEEDED	FC-28A
AUTO SHUTDOWN RELAY CONTROL CIRCUIT	FC-29A
NO ASD RELAY VOLT SENSE AT PCM	FC-30A
RAD FAN CONTROL RELAY CIRCUIT	FC-31A
A/C CLUTCH RELAY CIRCUIT	FC-32A
KNOCK SENSOR #1 CIRCUIT	FC-33A
PCM FAILURE SRI MILES NOT STORED AND PCM FAILURE EEPROM WRITE DENIED	FC-34A

CR1029302714010X

Fig. 12 Test FC-1A: Checking The System For Fault Codes (Part 1 of 2). 1993 2.2L/4-135 engine

Engine is cold too long - engine does not warm to 176°F while driving 20 minutes after start. See service manual for cooling system repair (thermostat). This fault may set in error during very cold slow speed driving.

For an internal PCM failure, replace the PCM and go to Verification TEST VER-1.

For No Start problems .... see page 214
For Driveability problems .... see page 168
For Verification Test .... see page 268

Refer to the Charging and Speed Control Diagnostic Manual for the following messages:

- Generator field not switching properly
- Battery temp sensor voltage out of limit
- Charging system voltage too low
- Charging system voltage too high
- Speed control solenoid circuits
- Speed control switch always high
- Speed control switch always low
- Speed control power relay circuit

CR1029302714020X

Fig. 12 Test FC-1A: Checking The System For Fault Codes (Part 2 of 2). 1993 2.2L/4-135 engine

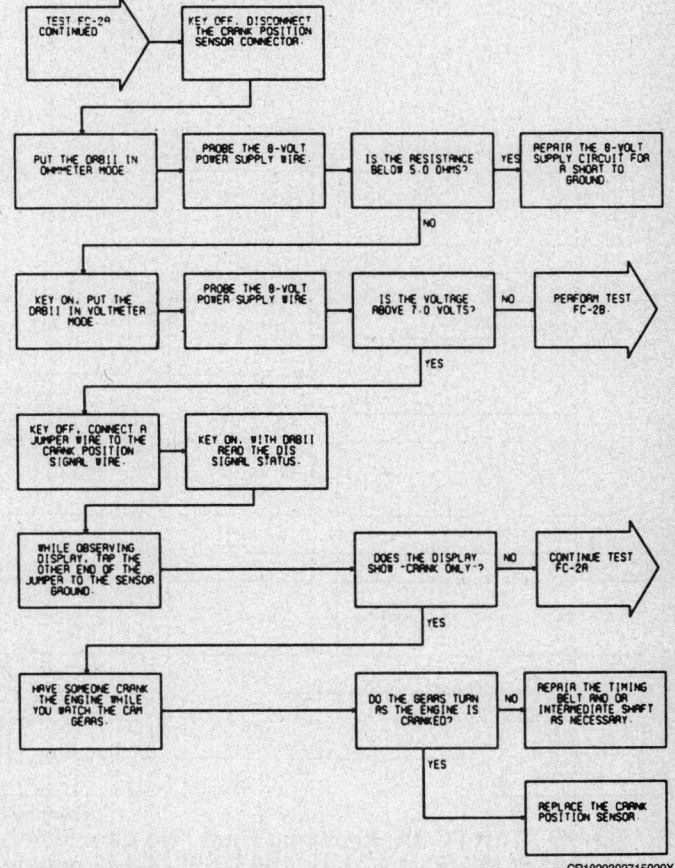

CR1029302715010X

Fig. 13 Test FC-2A: Repairing Fault "No Crank Reference Signal At PCM" (Part 1 of 3). 1993 2.2L/4-135 engine

CR1029302715020X

Fig. 13 Test FC-2A: Repairing Fault "No Crank Reference Signal At PCM" (Part 2 of 3). 1993 2.2L/4-135 engine

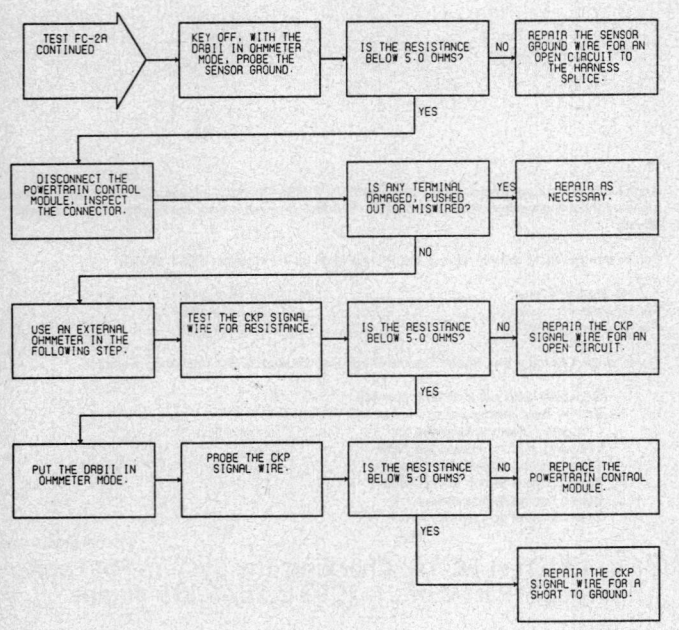

Fig. 13   Test FC-2A: Repairing Fault "No Crank Reference Signal At PCM" (Part 3 of 3). 1993 2.2L/4-135 engine

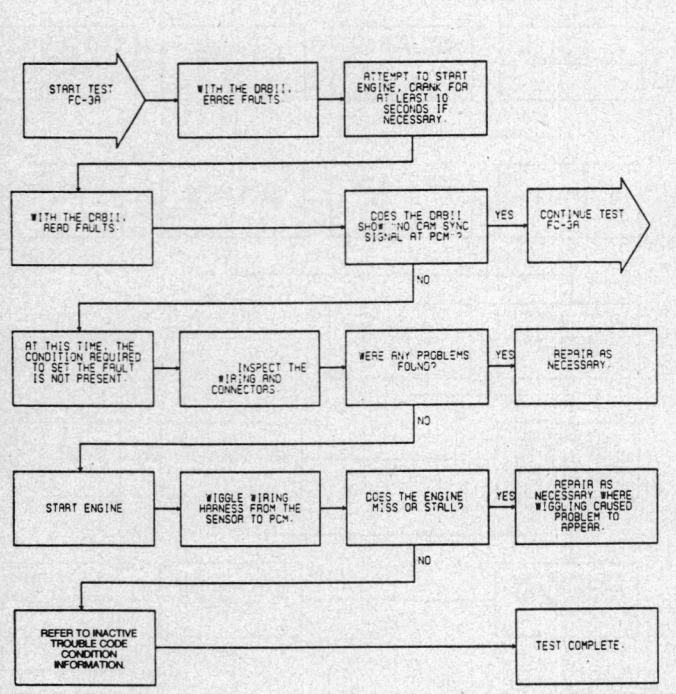

Fig. 15   Test FC-3A: Repairing Fault "No Cam Sync Signal At PCM" (Part 1 of 3). 1993 2.2L/4-135 engine

Fig. 14   Test FC-2B: Repairing Fault "No Crank Reference Signal At PCM." 1993 2.2L/4-135 engine

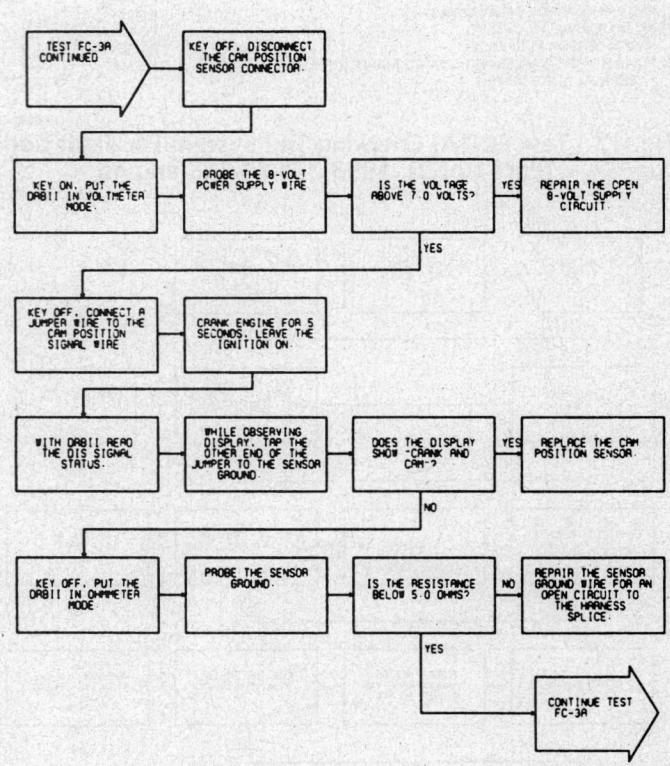

Fig. 15   Test FC-3A: Repairing Fault "No Cam Sync Signal At PCM" (Part 2 of 3). 1993 2.2L/4-135 engine

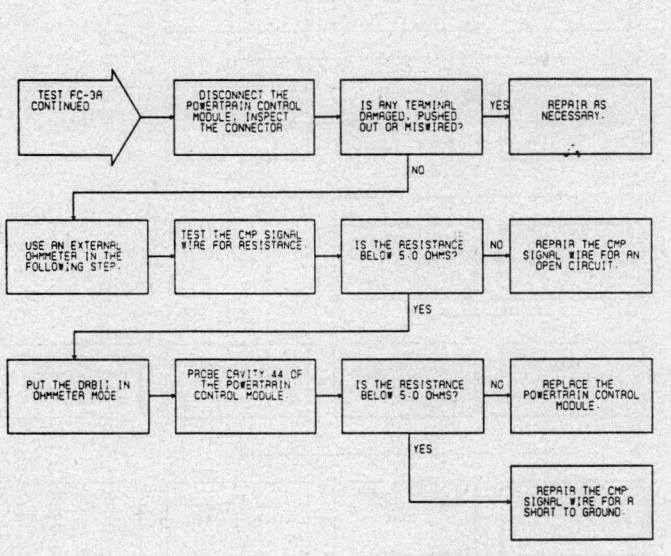

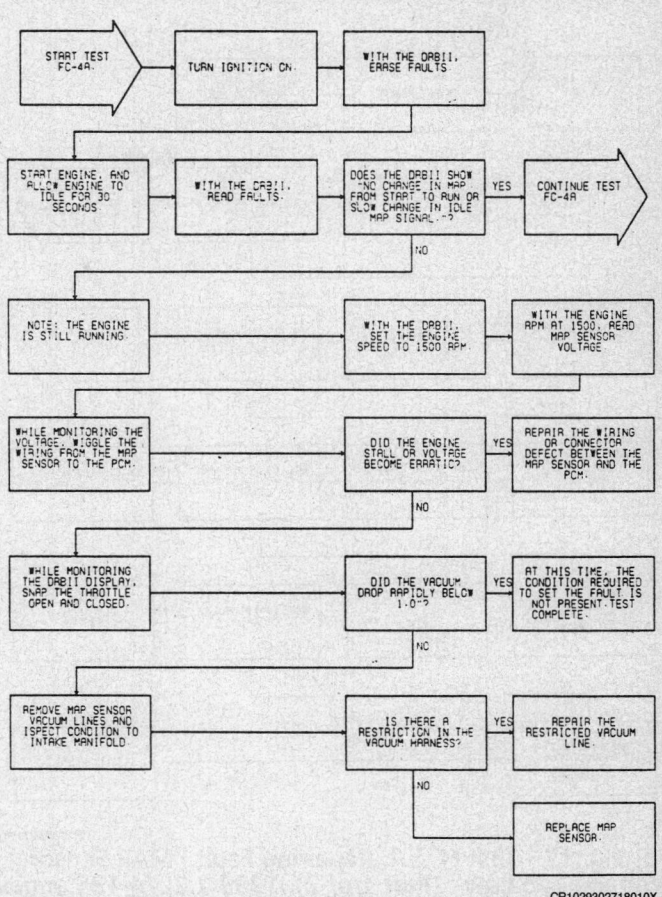

Fig. 15   Test FC-3A: Repairing Fault "No Cam Sync Signal At PCM" (Part 3 of 3). 1993 2.2L/4-135 engine

CR1029302717030X

CR1029302718010X

Fig. 16   Test FC-4A: Repairing Fault "Slow Change In Idle MAP Sensor Signal & No Change In MAP From Start To Run" (Part 1 of 3). 1993 2.2L/4-135 engine

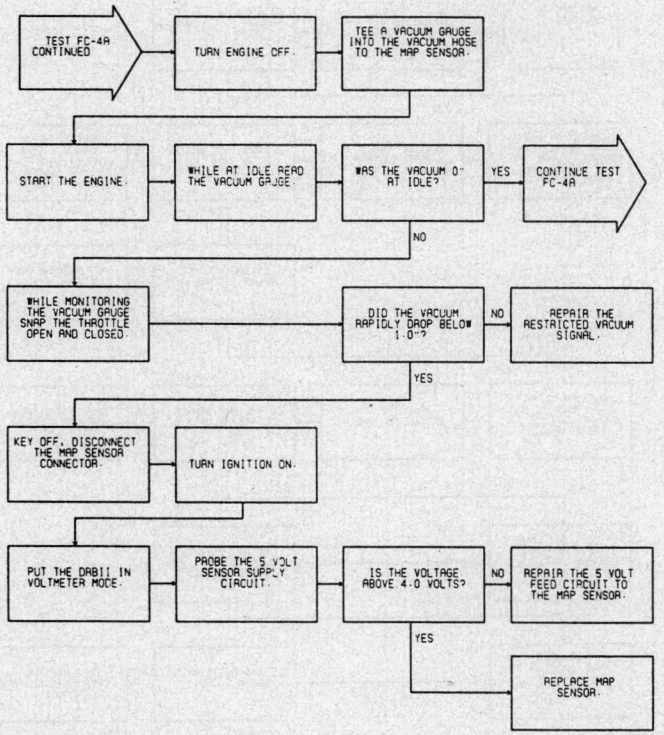

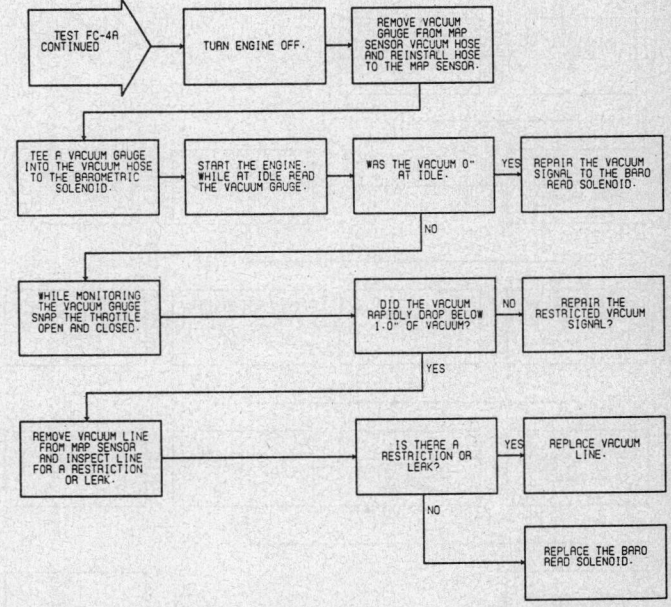

CR1029302718020X

Fig. 16   Test FC-4A: Repairing Fault "Slow Change In Idle MAP Sensor Signal & No change In MAP From Start To Run" (Part 2 of 3). 1993 2.2L/4-135 engine

CR1029302718030X

Fig. 16   Test FC-4A: Repairing Fault "Slow Change In Idle MAP Sensor Signal & No change In MAP From Start To Run" (Part 3 of 3). 1993 2.2L/4-135 engine

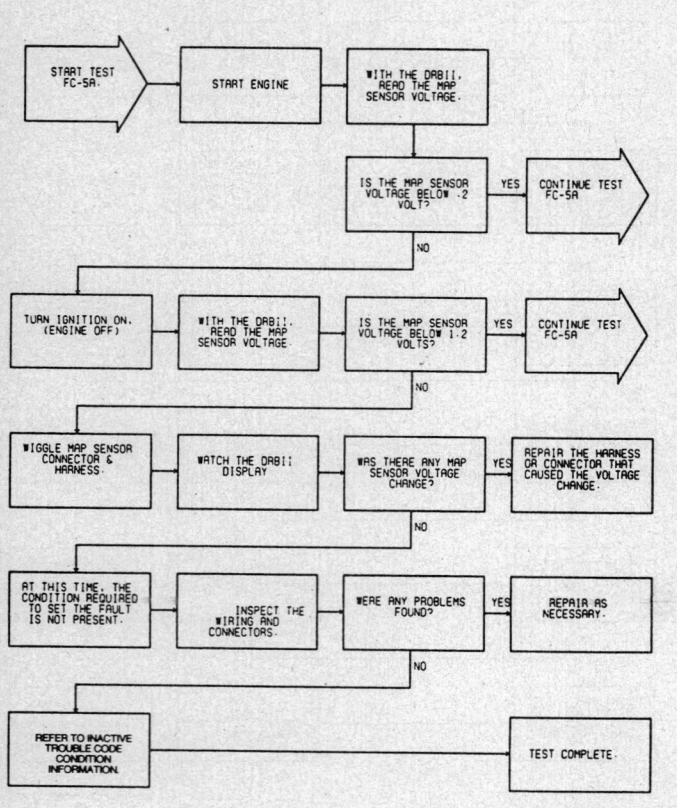

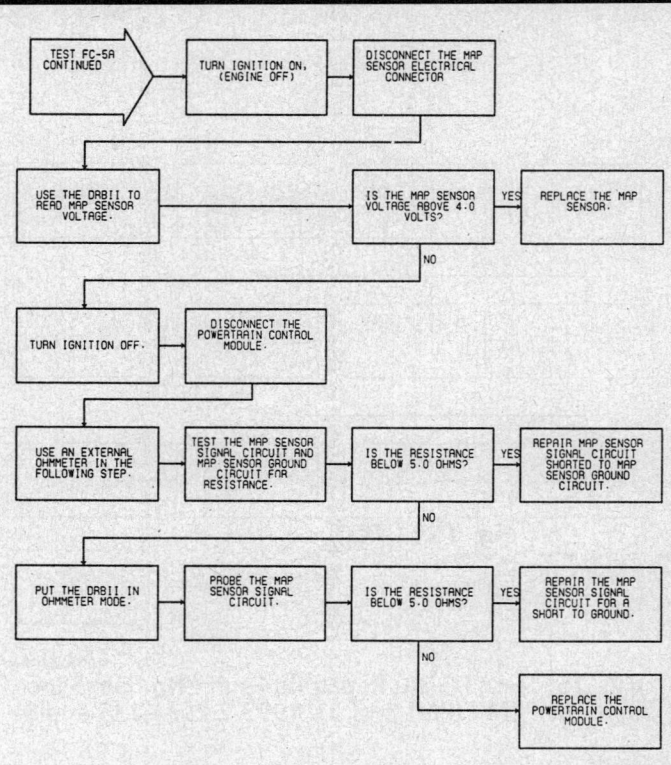

Fig. 17 Test FC-5A: Repairing Fault "MAP Sensor Voltage Too Low" (Part 1 of 2). 1993 2.2L/4-135 engine

Fig. 17 Test FC-5A: Repairing Fault "MAP Sensor Voltage Too Low" (Part 2 of 2). 1993 2.2L/4-135 engine

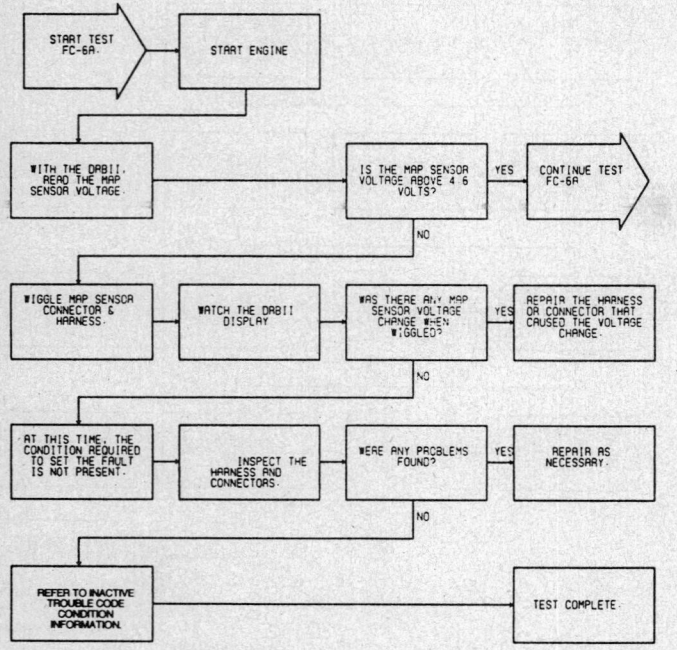

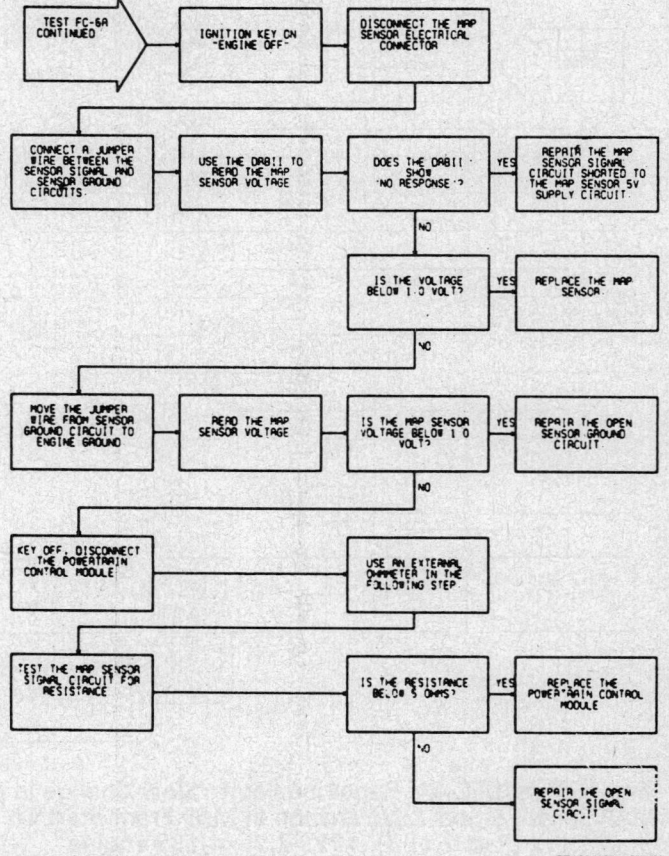

Fig. 18 Test FC-6A: Repairing Fault "MAP Sensor Voltage Too High" (Part 1 of 2). 1993 2.2L/4-135 engine

Fig. 18 Test FC-6B: Repairing Fault "MAP Sensor Voltage Too High" (Part 2 of 2). 1993 2.2L/4-135 engine

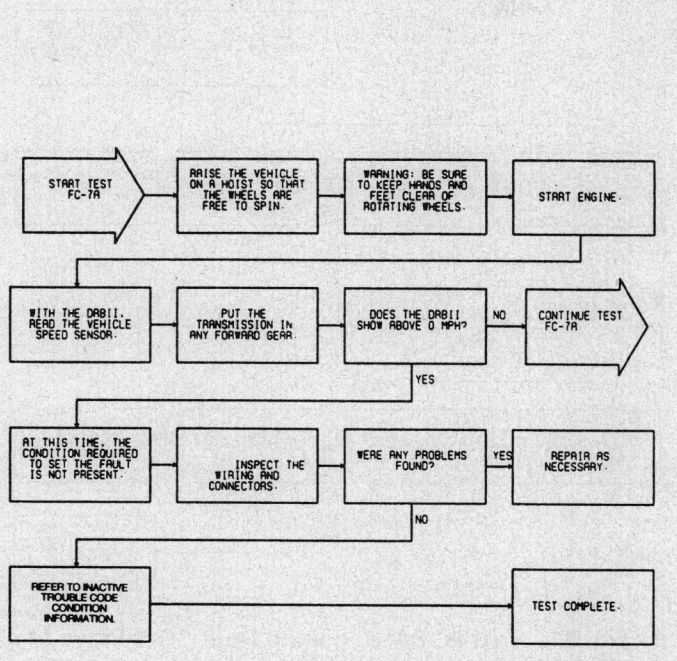

Fig. 19   Test FC-7A: Repairing Fault "No Vehicle Speed Sensor Signal" (Part 1 of 3). 1993 2.2L/4-135 engine

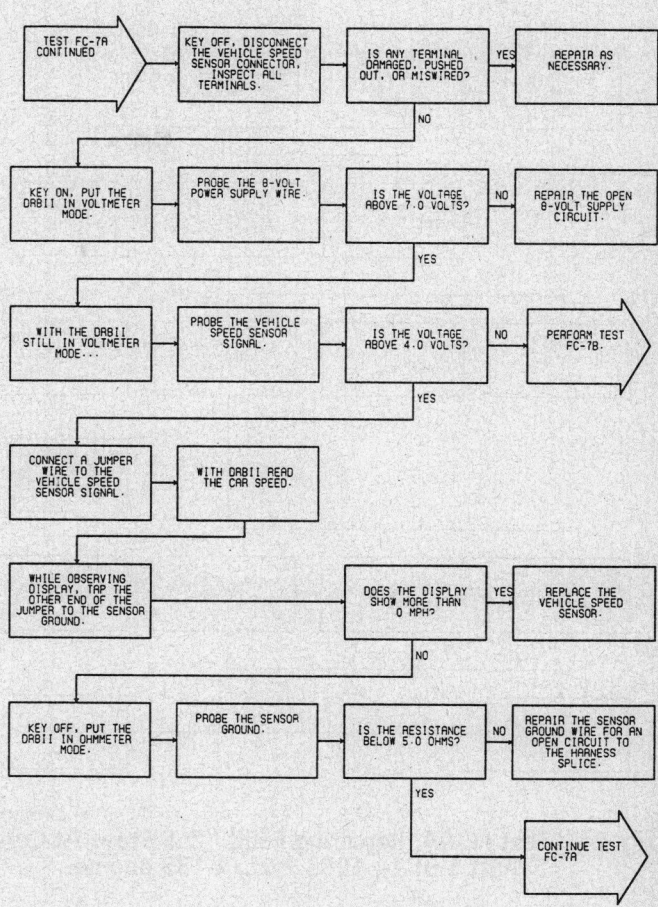

Fig. 19   Test FC-7A: Repairing Fault "No Vehicle Speed Sensor Signal" (Part 2 of 3). 1993 2.2L/4-135 engine

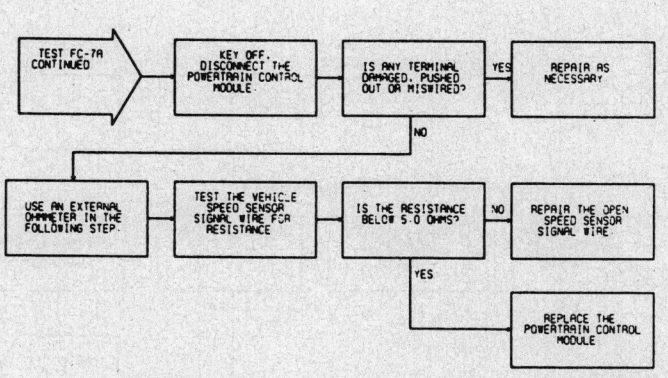

Fig. 19   Test FC-7A: Repairing Fault "No Vehicle Speed Sensor Signal" (Part 3 of 3). 1993 2.2L/4-135 engine

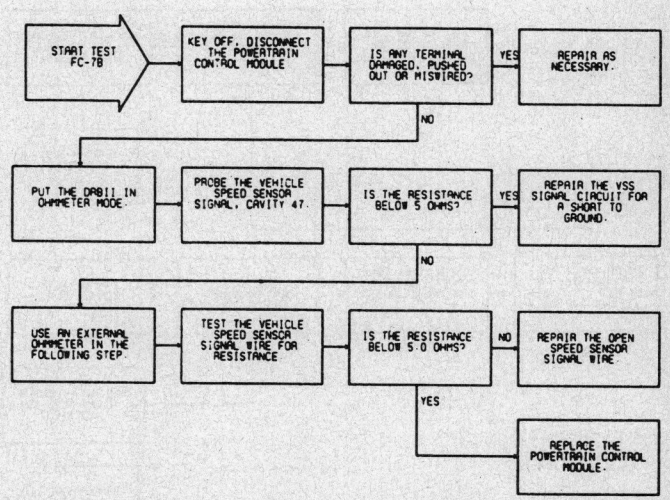

Fig. 20   Test FC-7B: Repairing Fault "No Vehicle Speed Sensor Signal." 1993 2.2L/4-135 engine

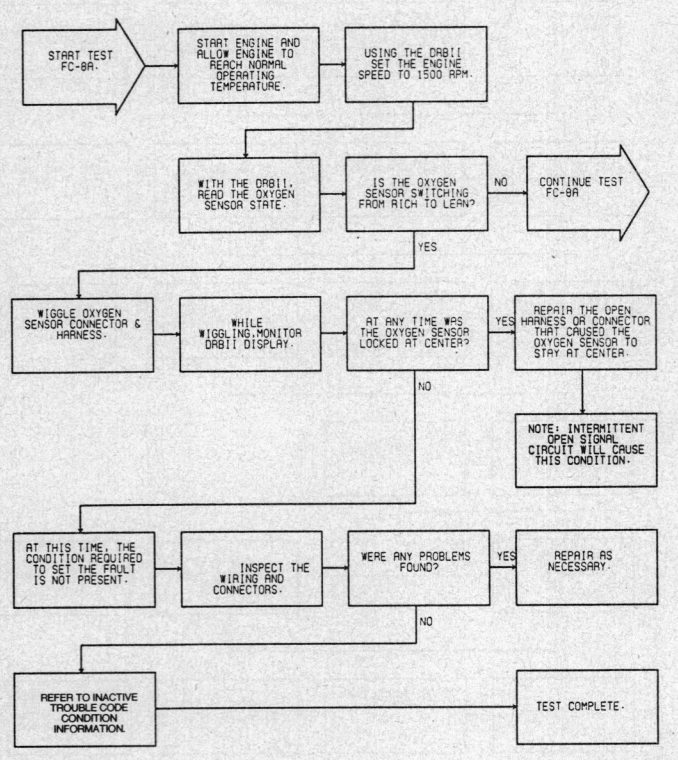

Fig. 21 Test FC-8A: Repairing Fault "O₂S Stays At Center " (Part 1 of 2). 1993 2.2L/4-135 engine

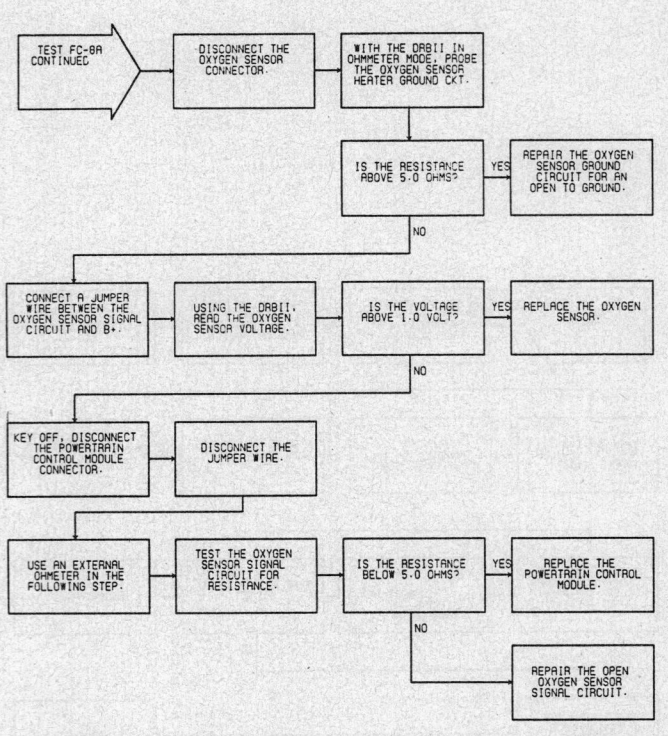

Fig. 21 Test FC-8A: Repairing Fault "O₂S Stays At Center" (Part 2 of 2). 1993 2.2L/4-135 engine

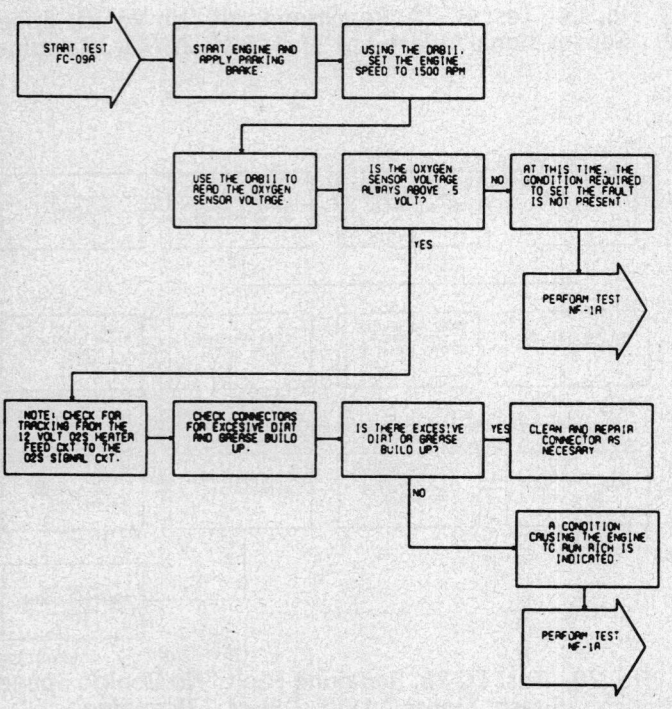

Fig. 22 Test FC-9A: Repairing Fault "O₂S Stays Above Center (Rich)." 1993 2.2L/4-135 engine

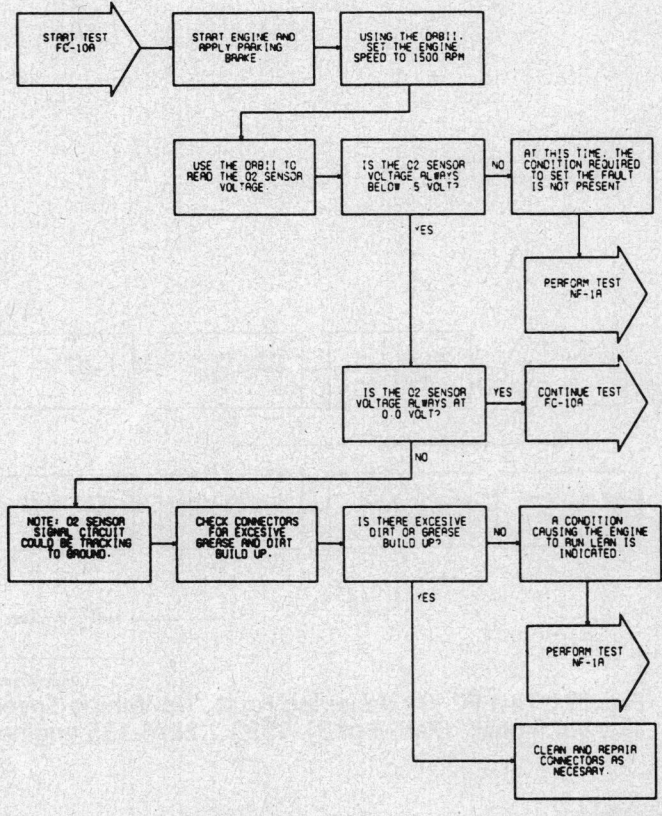

Fig. 23 Test FC-10A: Repairing Fault "O₂S Stays Below Center (Lean)" (Part 1 of 2). 1993 2.2L/4-135 engine

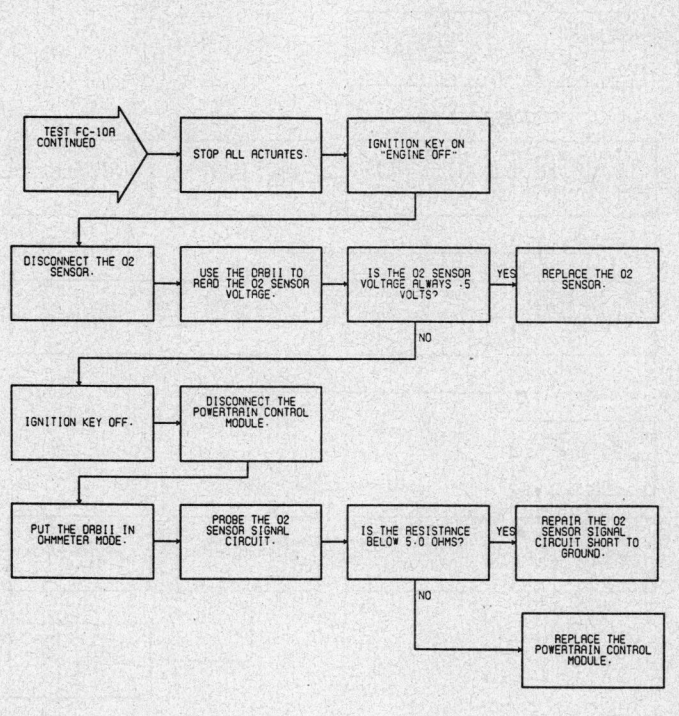

Fig. 23   Test FC-10A: Repairing Fault "O₂S Stays Below Center (Lean)" (Part 2 of 2). 1993 2.2L/4-135 engine

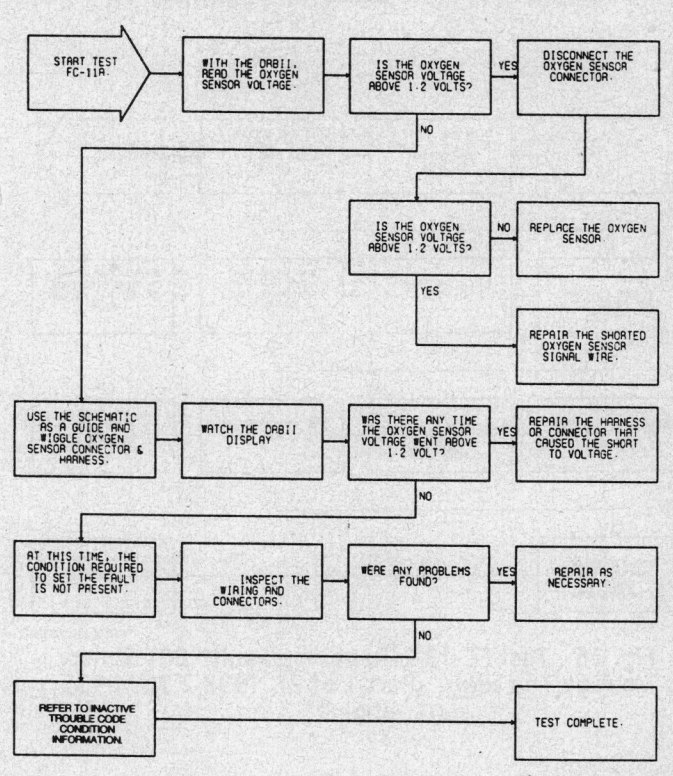

Fig. 24   Test FC-11A: Repairing Fault "O₂S Shorted To Voltage." 1993 2.2L/4-135 engine

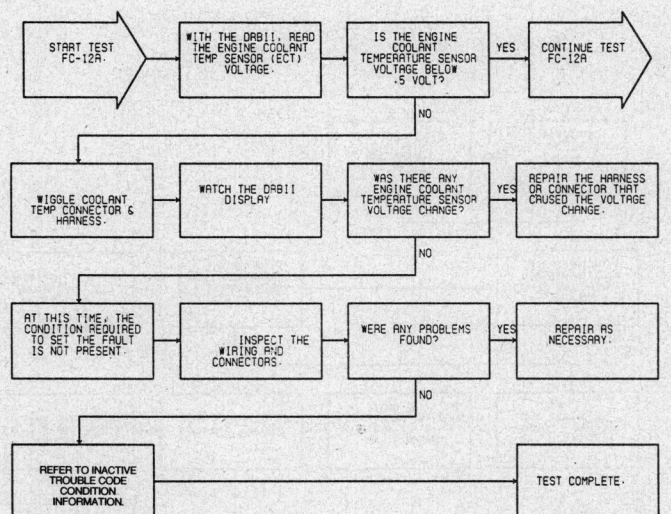

Fig. 25   Test FC-12A: Repairing Fault "ECT Sensor Voltage Too Low" (Part 1 of 2). 1993 2.2L/4-135 engine

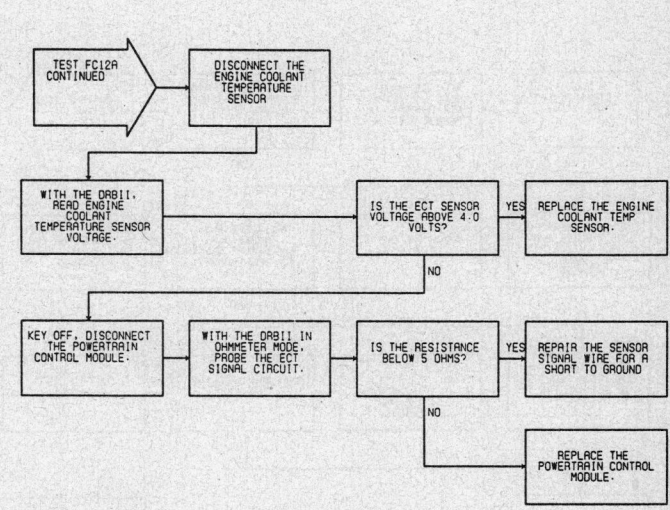

Fig. 25   Test FC-12A: Repairing Fault "ECT Sensor Voltage Too Low" (Part 2 of 2). 1993 2.2L/4-135 engine

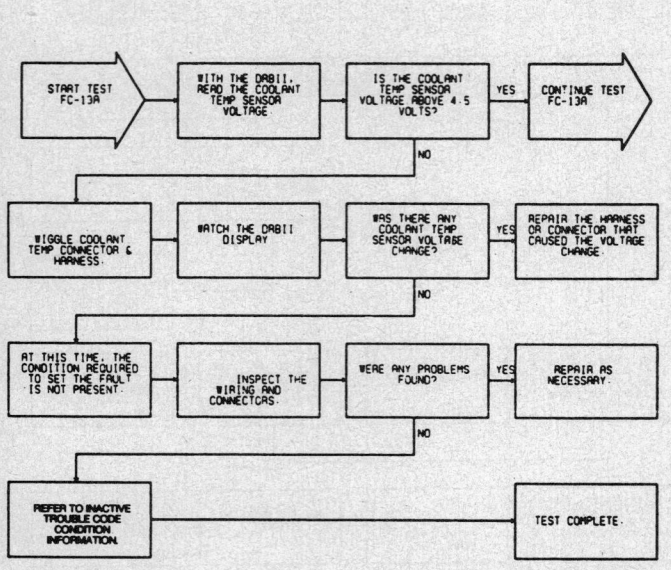

Fig. 26 Test FC-13A: Repairing Fault "ECT Sensor Voltage Too High" (Part 1 of 2). 1993 2.2L/4-135 engine

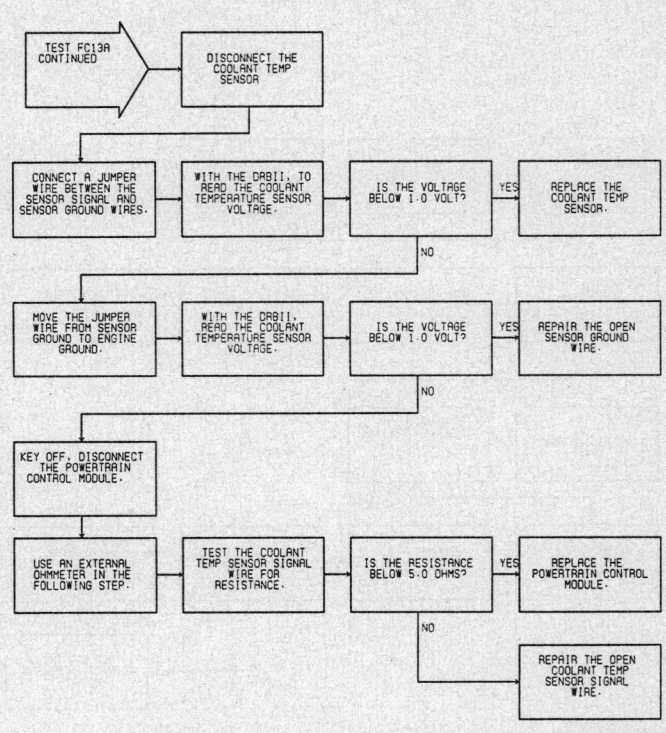

Fig. 26 Test FC-13A: Repairing Fault "ECT Sensor Voltage Too High" (Part 2 of 2). 1993 2.2L/4-135 engine

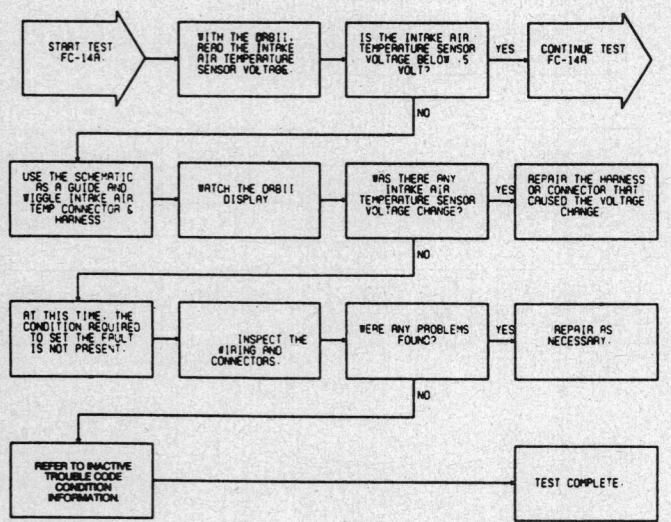

Fig. 27 Test FC-14A: Repairing Fault "Intake Air Temp Sensor Voltage Low" (Part 1 of 2). 1993 2.2L/4-135 engine

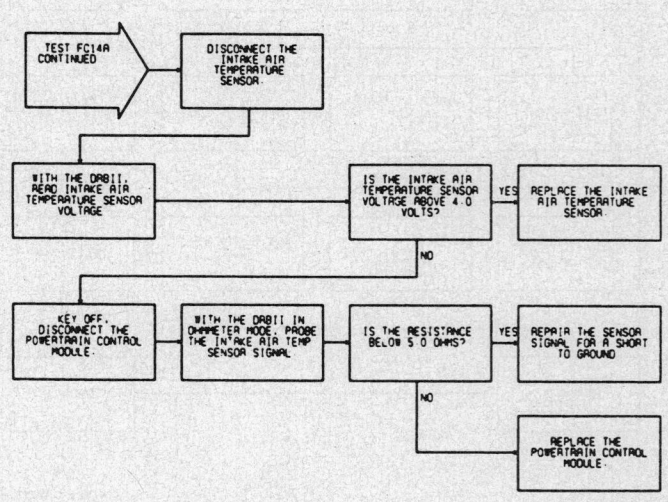

Fig. 27 Test FC-14A: Repairing Fault "Intake Air Temp Sensor Voltage Low" (Part 2 of 2). 1993 2.2L/4-135 engine

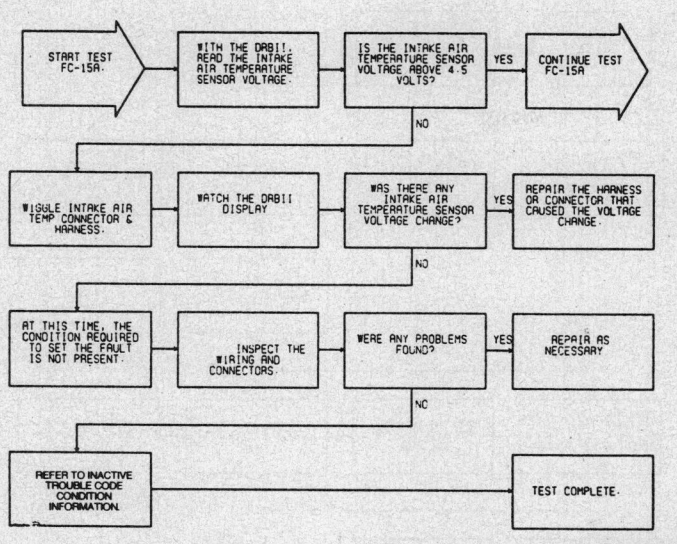

Fig. 28 Test FC-15A: Repairing Fault "Intake Air Temp Sensor Voltage High" (Part 1 of 2). 1993 2.2L/4-135 engine

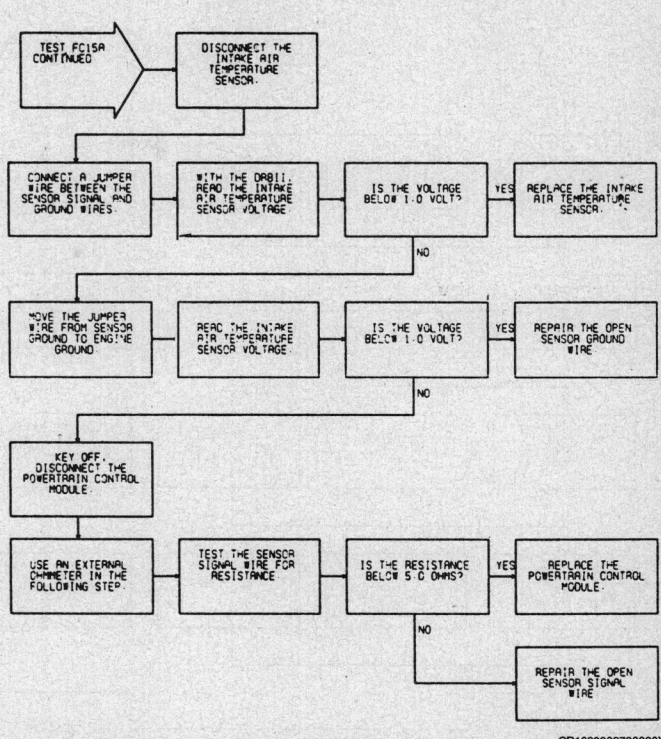

Fig. 28 Test FC-15A: Repairing Fault "Intake Air Temp Sensor Voltage High" (Part 2 of 2). 1993 2.2L/4-135 engine

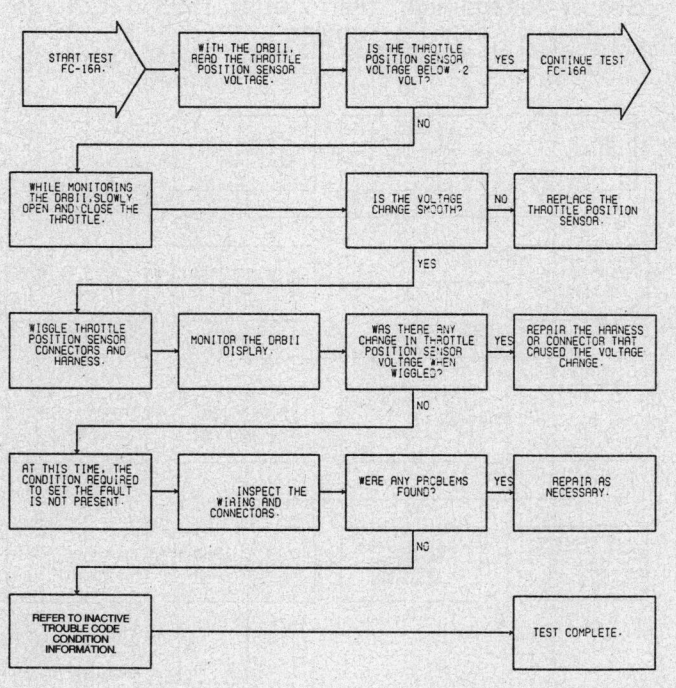

Fig. 29 Test FC-16A: Repairing Fault "Throttle Position Sensor Voltage Low" (Part 1 of 2). 1993 2.2L/4-135 engine

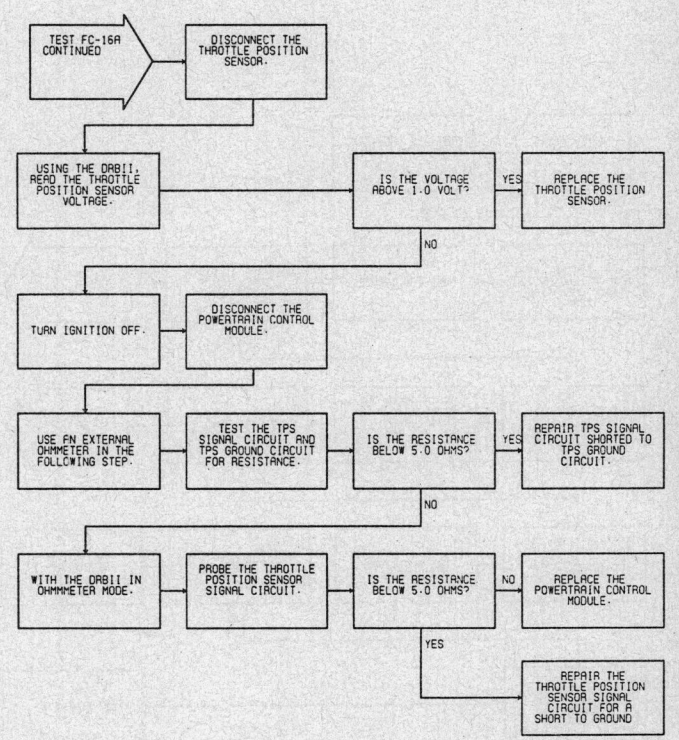

Fig. 29 Test FC-16A: Repairing Fault "Throttle Position Sensor Voltage Low" (Part 2 of 2). 1993 2.2L/4-135 engine

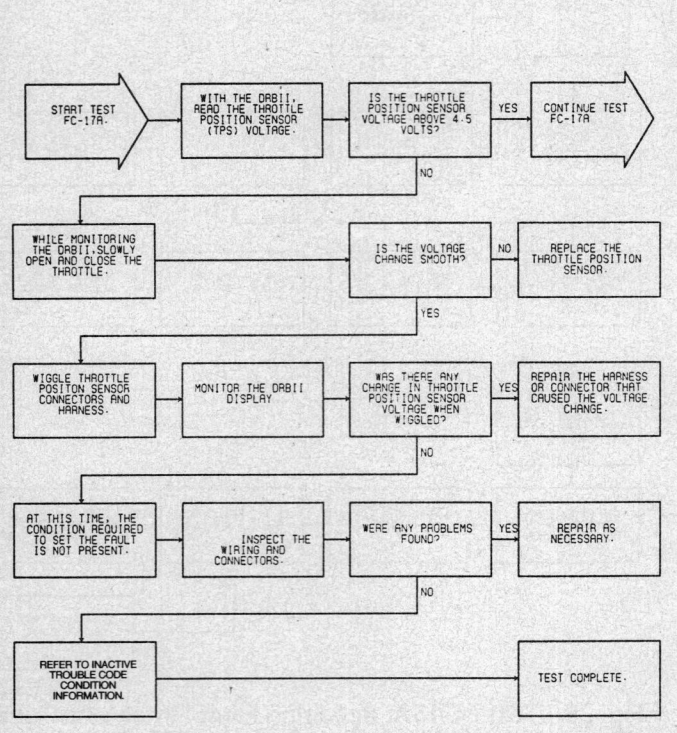

Fig. 30   Test FC-17A: Repairing Fault "Throttle Position Sensor Voltage High" (Part 1 of 2). 1993 2.2L/4-135 engine

CR1029302732010X

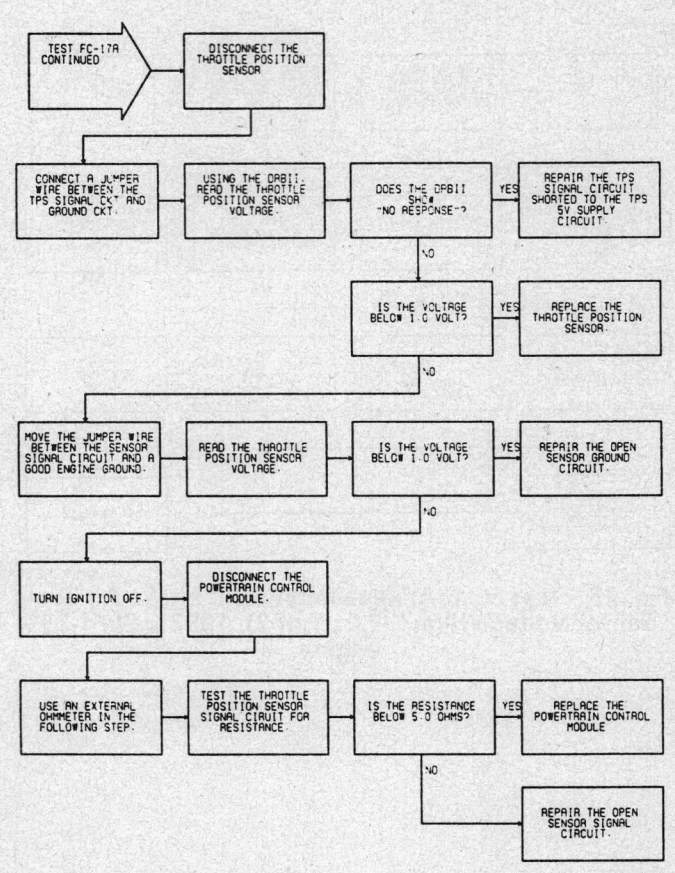

Fig. 30   Test FC-17A: Repairing Fault "Throttle Position Sensor Voltage High" (Part 2 of 2). 1993 2.2L/4-135 engine

CR1029302732020X

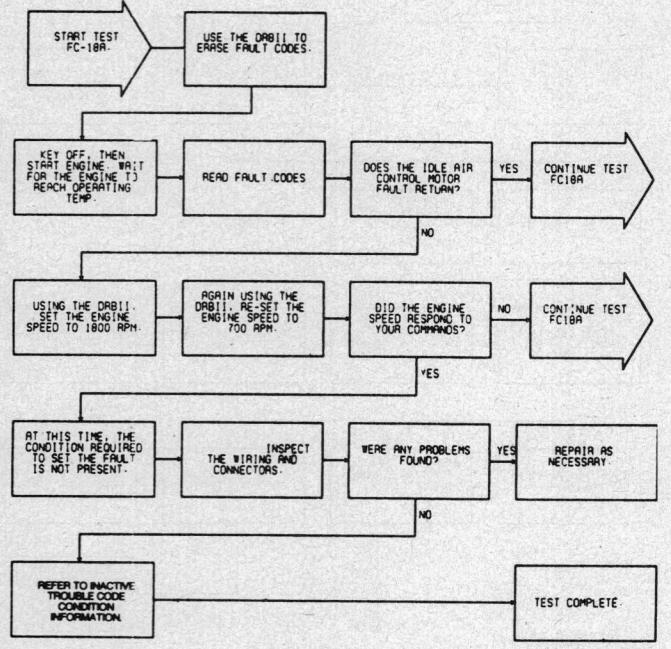

Fig. 31   Test FC-18A: Repairing Fault "Idle Air Control Motor Circuits" (Part 1 of 3). 1993 2.2L/4-135 engine

CR1029302733010X

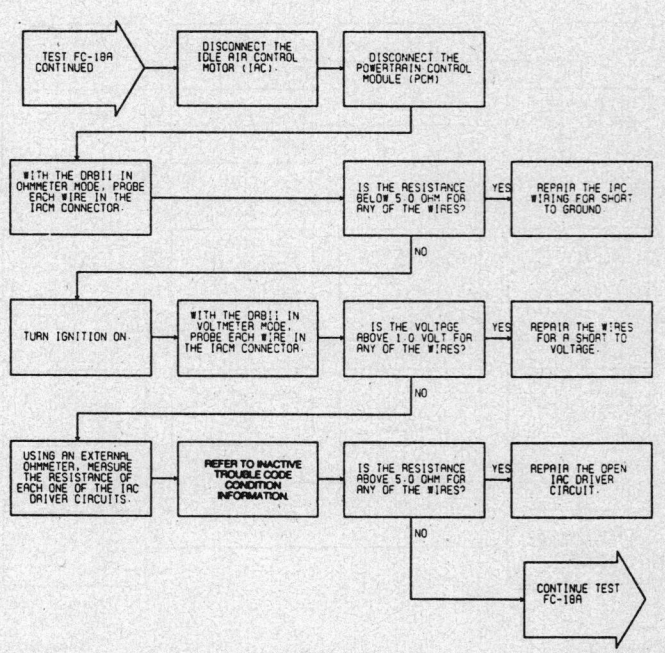

Fig. 31   Test FC-18A: Repairing Fault "Idle Air Control Motor Circuits" (Part 2 of 3). 1993 2.2L/4-135 engine

CR1029302733020X

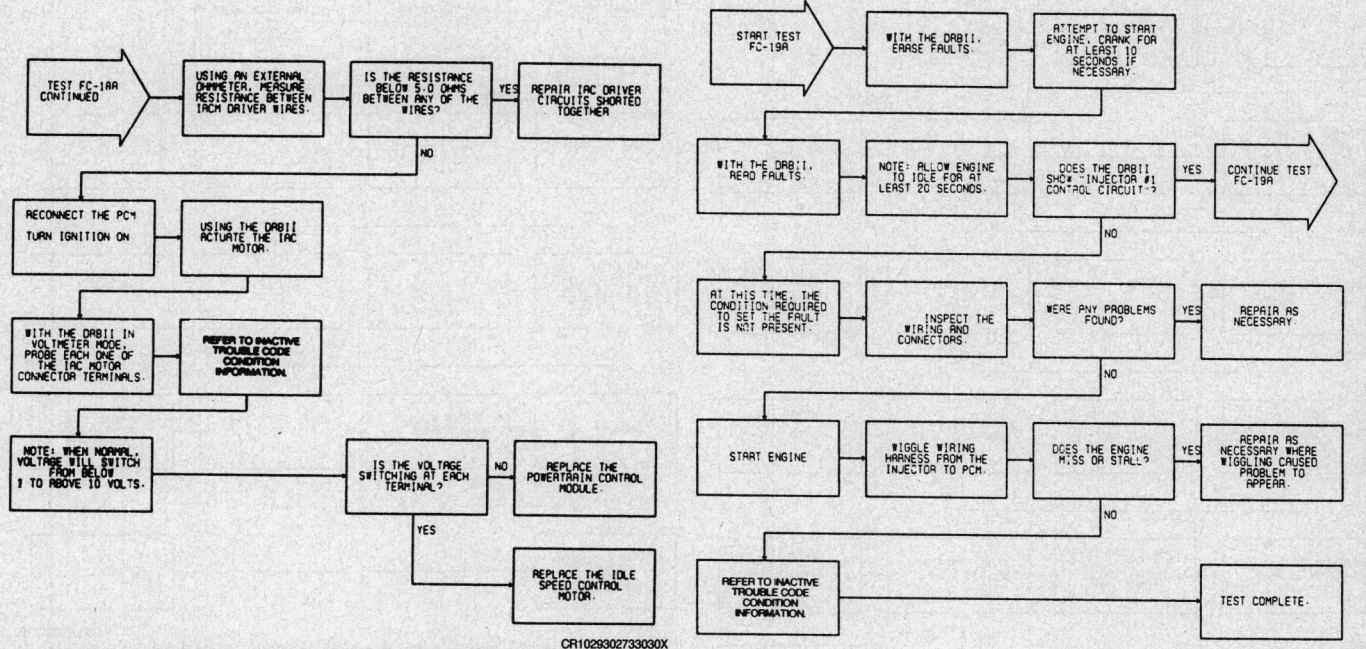

Fig. 31   Test FC-18A: Repairing Fault "Idle Air Control Motor Circuits" (Part 3 of 3). 1993 2.2L/4-135 engine

CR1029302733030X

Fig. 32   Test FC-19A: Repairing Fault "Injector No. 1 Control Circuit" (Part 1 of 2). 1993 2.2L/4-135 engine

CR1029302734010X

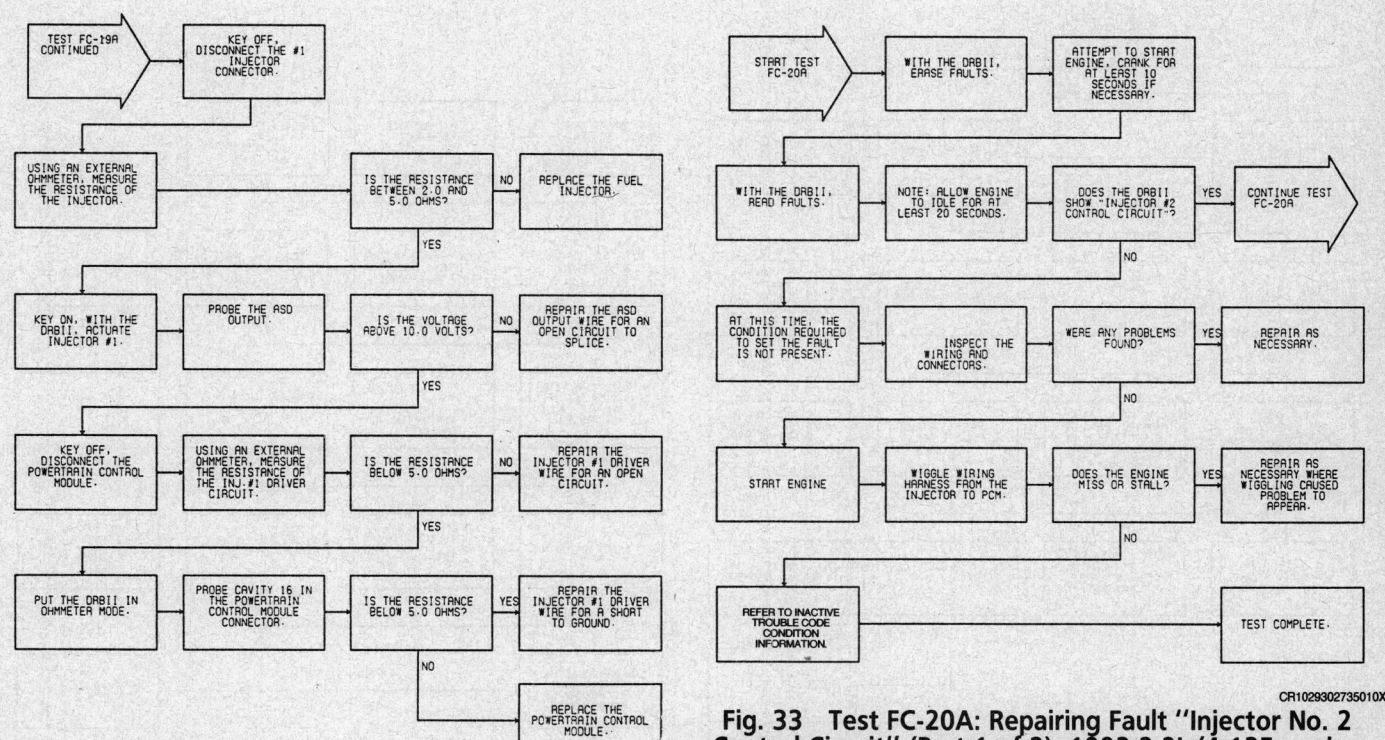

Fig. 33   Test FC-20A: Repairing Fault "Injector No. 2 Control Circuit" (Part 1 of 2). 1993 2.2L/4-153 engine

CR1029302735010X

CR1029302734020X

Fig. 32   Test FC-19A: Repairing Fault "Injector No. 1 Control Circuit" (Part 2 of 2). 1993 2.2L/4-135 engine

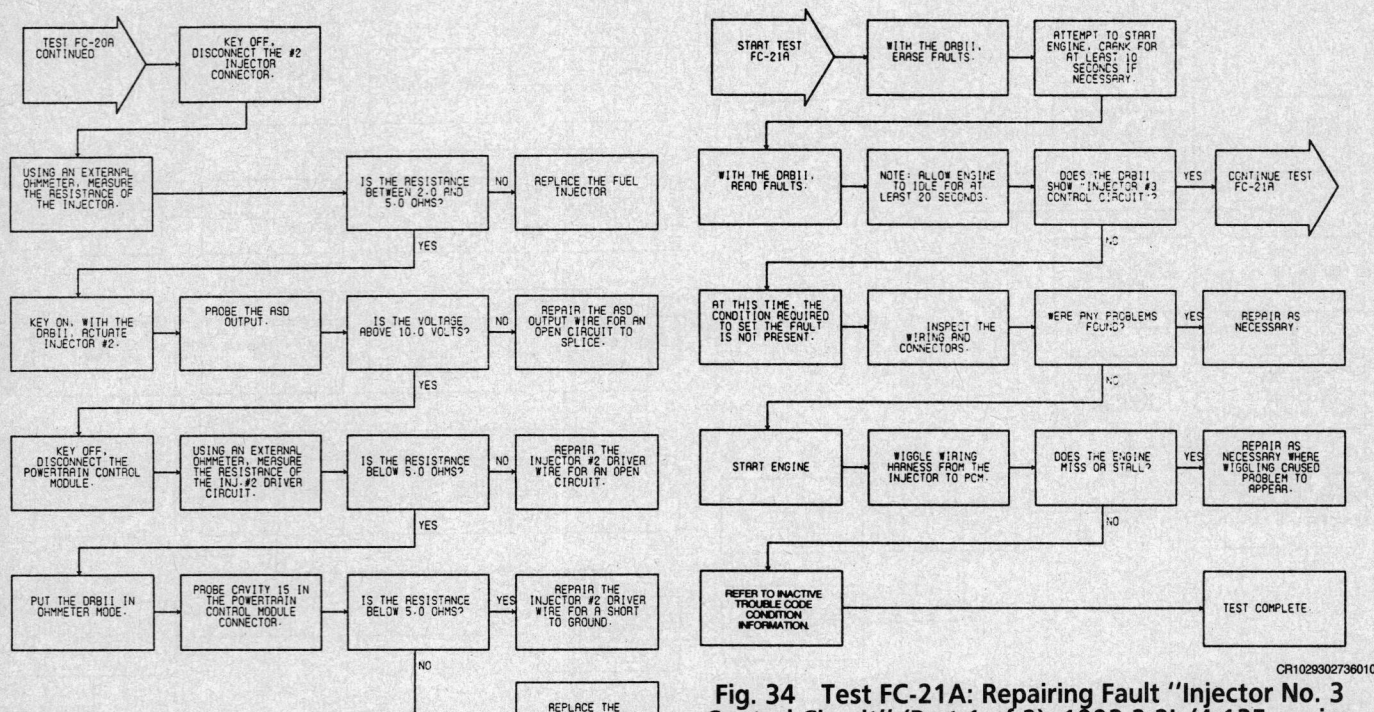

Fig. 33 Test FC-20A: Repairing Fault "Injector No. 2 Control Circuit" (Part 2 of 2). 1993 2.2L/4-135 engine

Fig. 34 Test FC-21A: Repairing Fault "Injector No. 3 Control Circuit" (Part 1 of 2). 1993 2.2L/4-135 engine

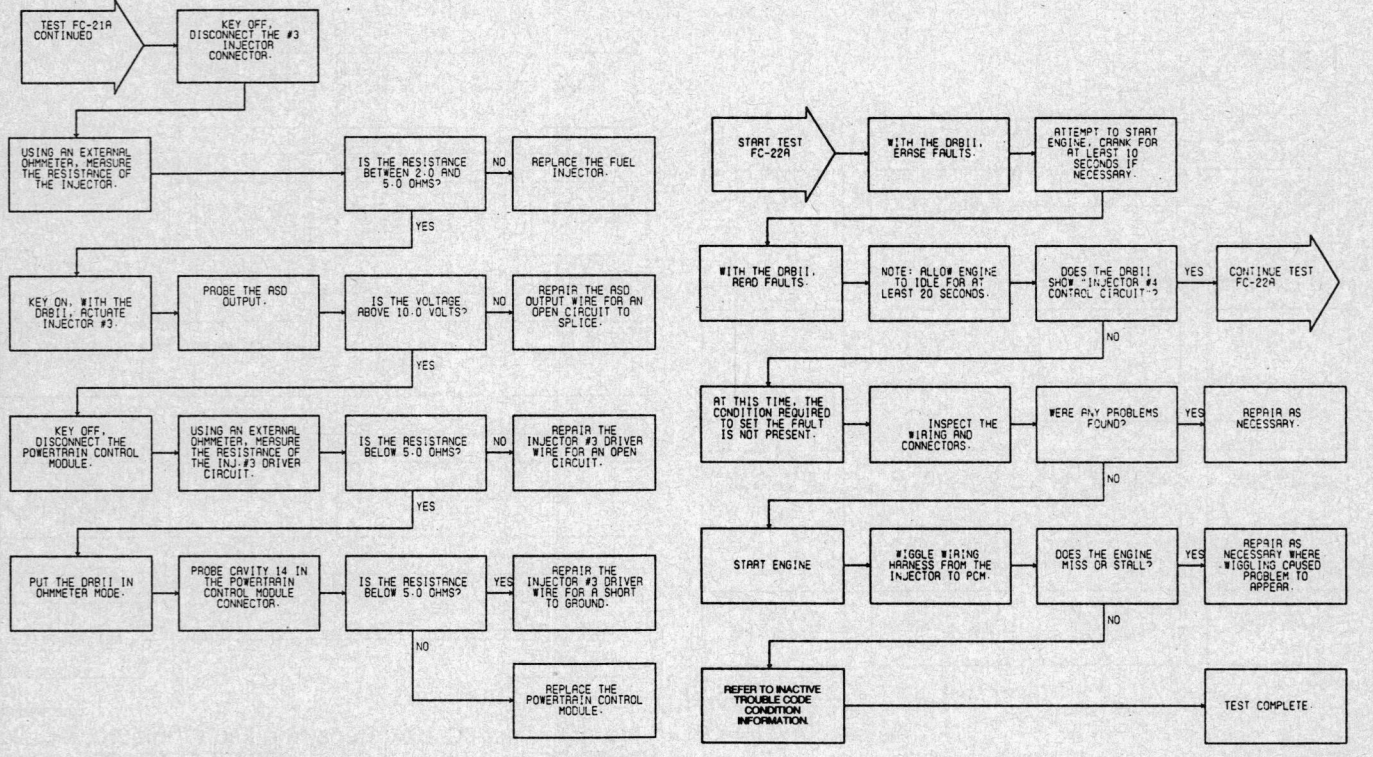

Fig. 34 Test FC-21A: Repairing Fault "Injector No. 3 Control Circuit" (Part 2 of 2). 1993 2.2L/4-135 engine

Fig. 35 Test FC-22A: Repairing Fault "Injector No. 4 Control Circuit" (Part 1 of 2). 1993 2.2L/4-135 engine

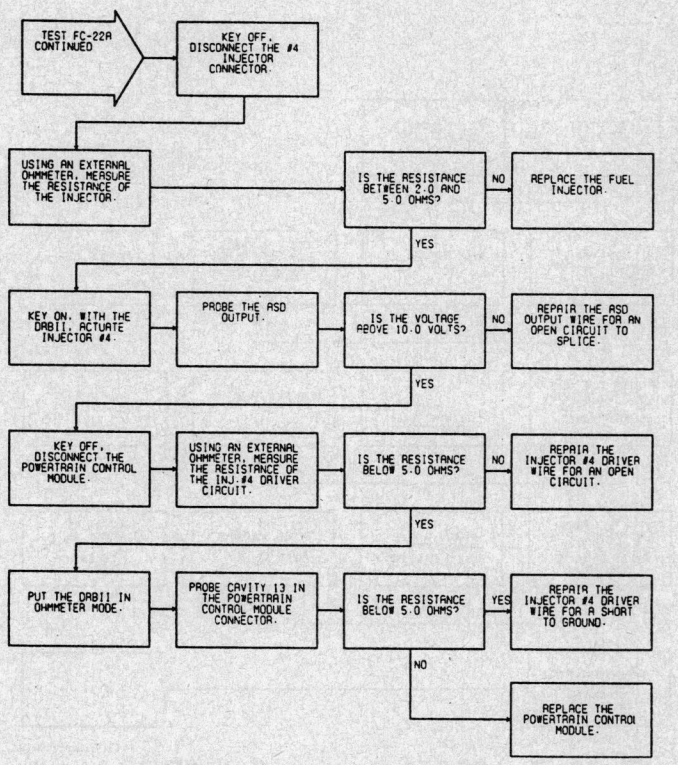

Fig. 35 Test FC-22A: Repairing Fault "Injector No. 4 Control Circuit" (Part 2 of 2). 1993 2.2L/4-135 engine

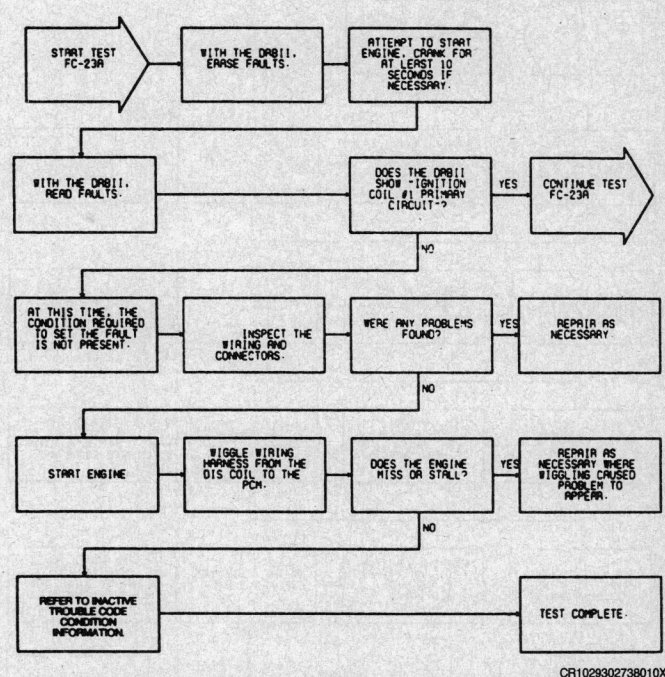

Fig. 36 Test FC-23A: Repairing Fault "Ignition Coil No. 1 Primary Circuit" (Part 1 of 2). 1993 2.2L/4-135 engine

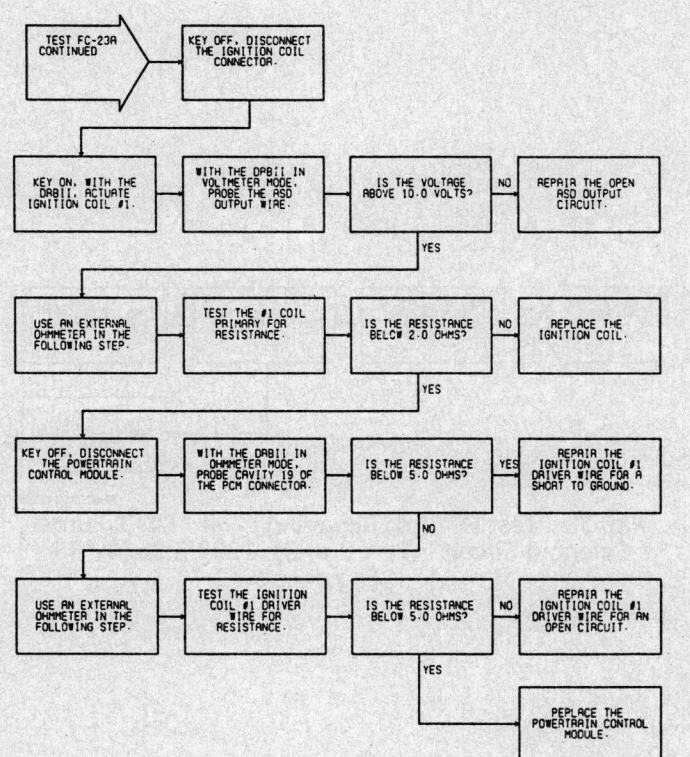

Fig. 36 Test FC-23A: Repairing Fault "Ignition Coil No. 1 Primary Circuit" (Part 2 of 2). 1993 2.2L/4-135 engine

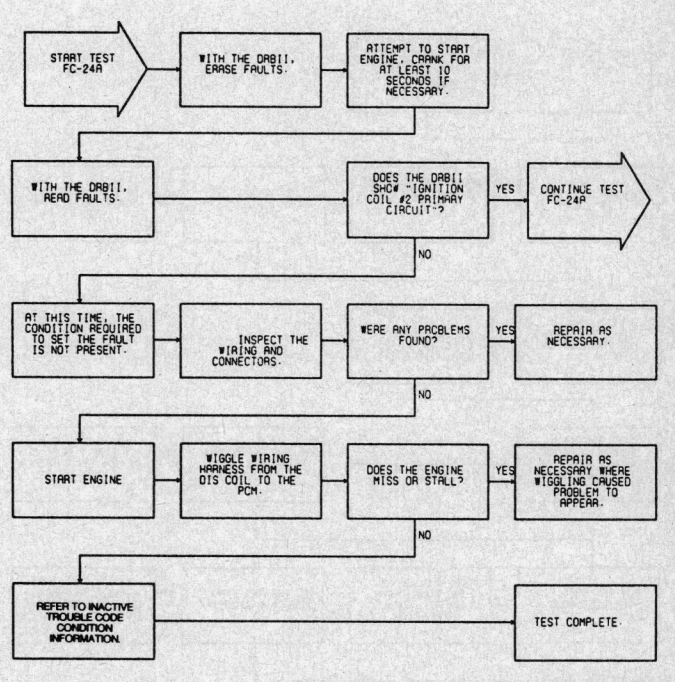

Fig. 37 Test FC-24A: Repairing Fault "Ignition Coil No. 2 Primary Circuit" (Part 1 of 2). 1993 2.2L/4-135 engine

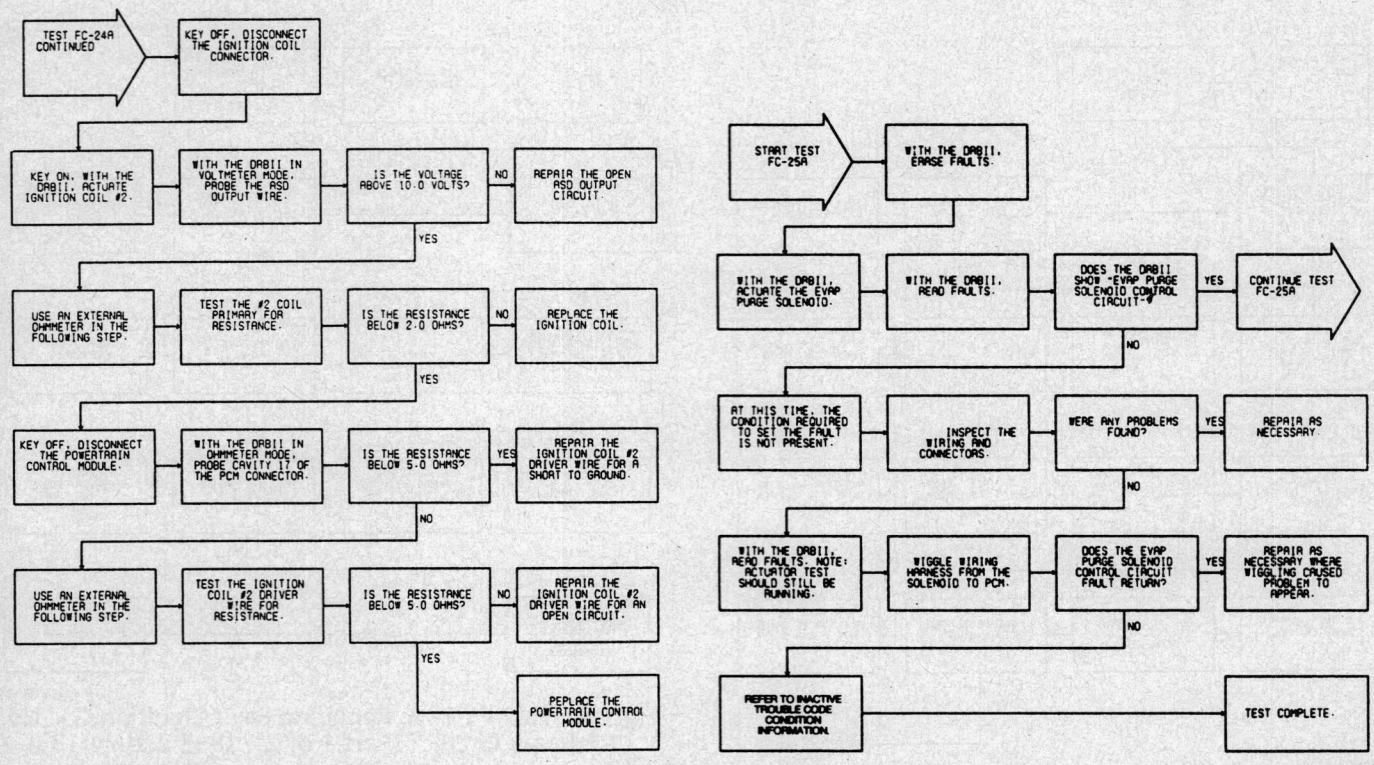

Fig. 37   Test FC-24A: Repairing Fault "Ignition Coil No. 2 Primary Circuit" (Part 2 of 2). 1993 2.2L/4-135 engine

Fig. 38   Test FC-25A: Repairing Fault "EVAP Purge Solenoid Circuit" (Part 1 of 3). 1993 2.2L/4-135 engine

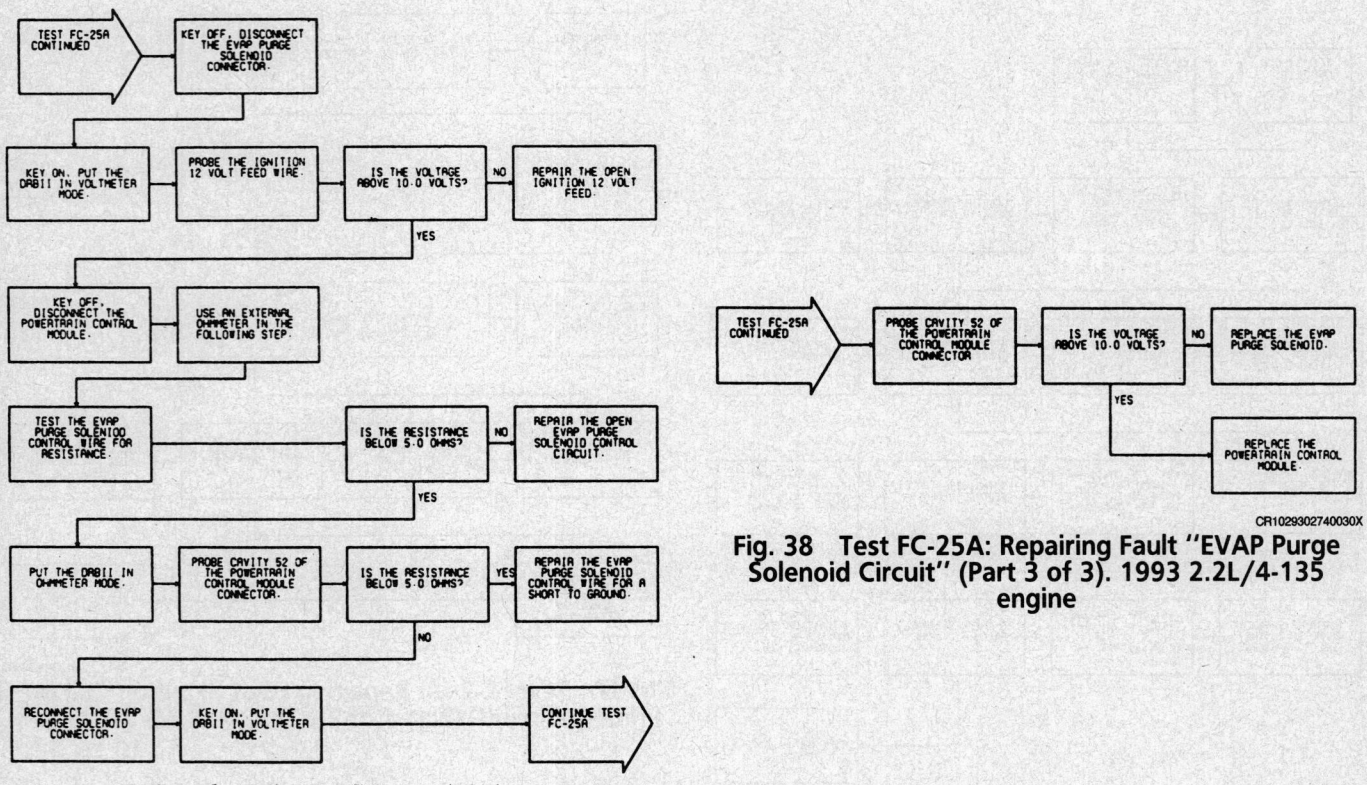

Fig. 38   Test FC-25A: Repairing Fault "EVAP Purge Solenoid Circuit" (Part 3 of 3). 1993 2.2L/4-135 engine

Fig. 38   Test FC-25A: Repairing Fault "EVAP Purge Solenoid Circuit" (Part 2 of 3). 1993 2.2L/4-135 engine

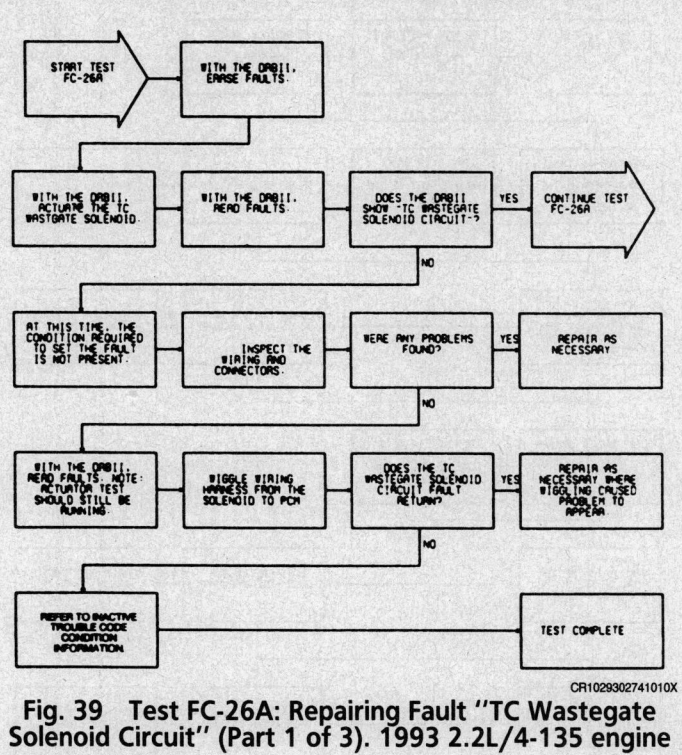

Fig. 39   Test FC-26A: Repairing Fault "TC Wastegate Solenoid Circuit" (Part 1 of 3). 1993 2.2L/4-135 engine

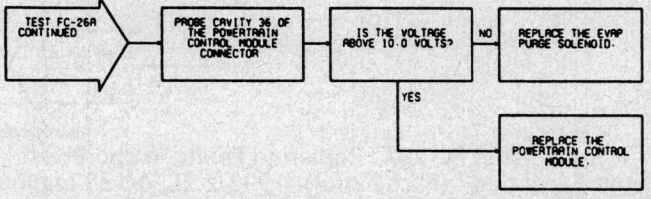

Fig. 39   Test FC-26A: Repairing Fault "TC Wastegate Solenoid Circuit" (Part 3 of 3). 1993 2.2L/4-135 engine

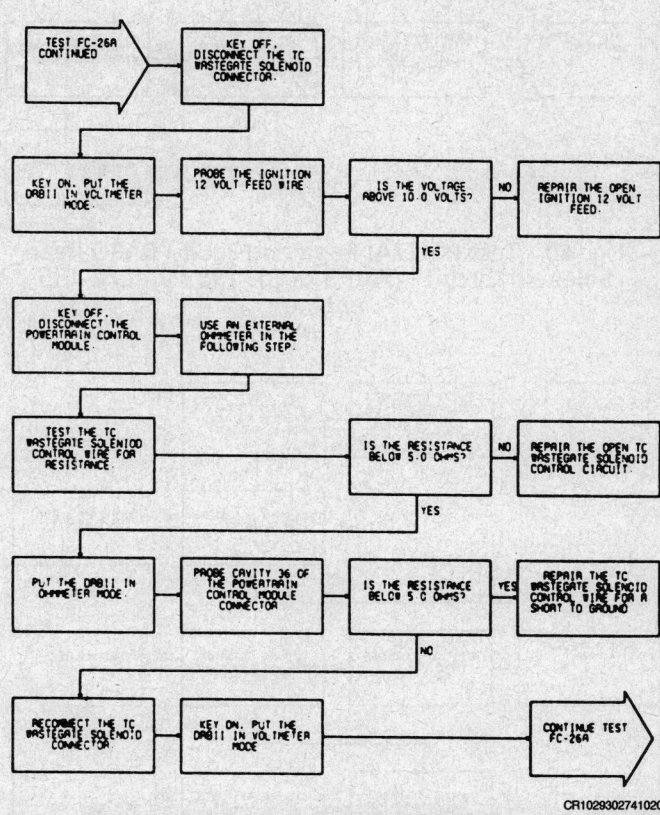

Fig. 39   Test FC-26A: Repairing Fault "TC Wastegate Solenoid Circuit" (Part 2 of 3). 1993 2.2L/4-135 engine

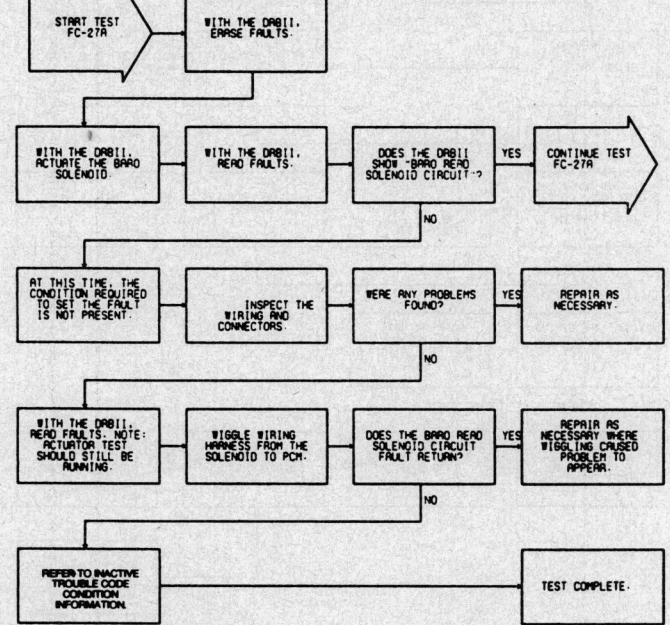

Fig. 40   Test FC-27A: Repairing Fault "BARO Read Solenoid Circuit" (Part 1 of 3). 1993 2.2L/4-135 engine

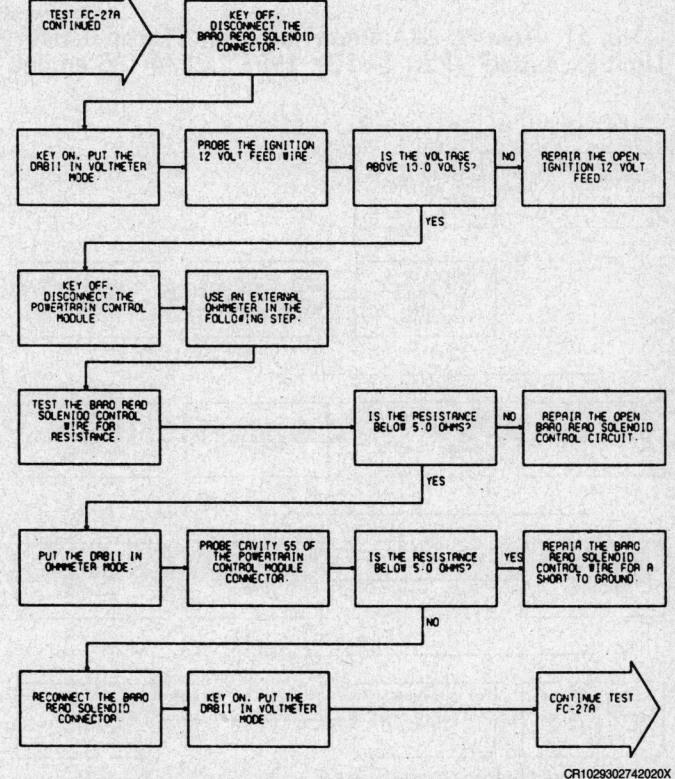

Fig. 40   Test FC-27A: Repairing Fault "BARO Read Solenoid Circuit" (Part 2 of 3). 1993 2.2L/4-135

CR1029302742030X

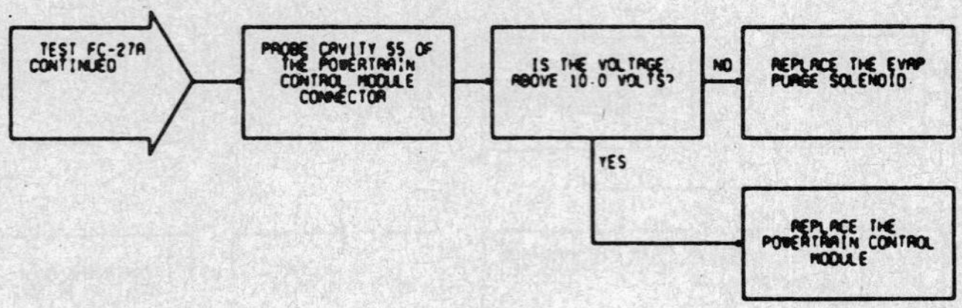

Fig. 40 Test FC-27A: Repairing Fault "BARO Read Solenoid Circuit" (Part 3 of 3). 1993 2.2L/4-135 engine

CR1029302743010X

Fig. 41 Test FC-28A: Repairing Fault "Turbo Boost Limit Exceeded" (Part 1 of 3). 1993 2.2L/4-135 engine

CR1029302743030X

Fig. 41 Test FC-28A: Repairing Fault "Turbo Boost Limit Exceeded" (Part 3 of 3). 1993 2.2L/4-135 engine

CR1029302743020X

Fig. 41 Test FC-28A: Repairing Fault "Turbo Boost Limit Exceeded" (Part 2 of 3). 1993 2.2L/4-135 engine

CR1029302744010X

Fig. 42 Test FC-29A: Repairing Fault "Auto Shutdown Relay Control Circuit" (Part 1 of 2). 1993 2.2L/4-135 engine

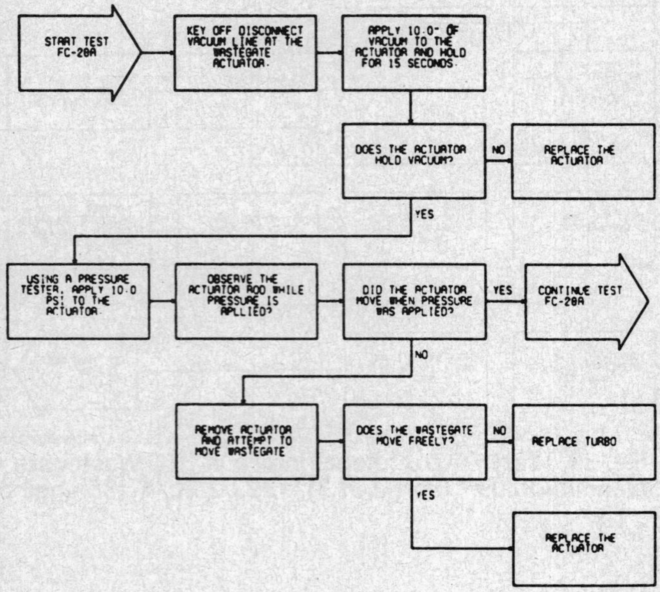

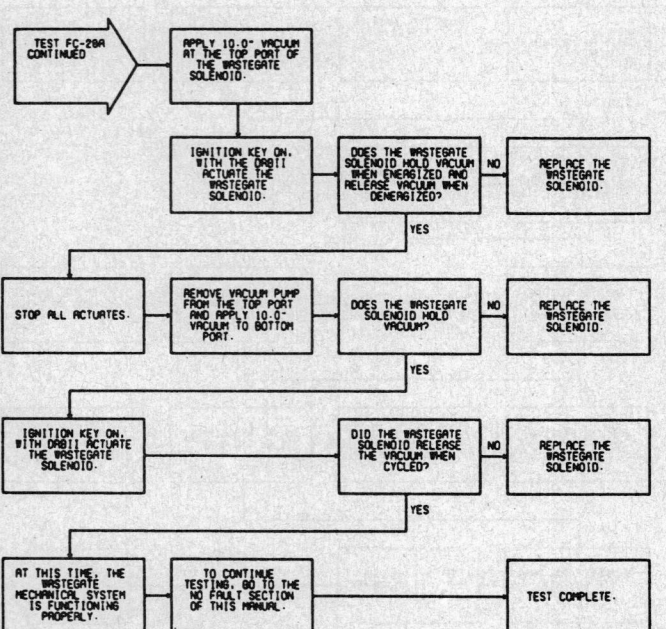

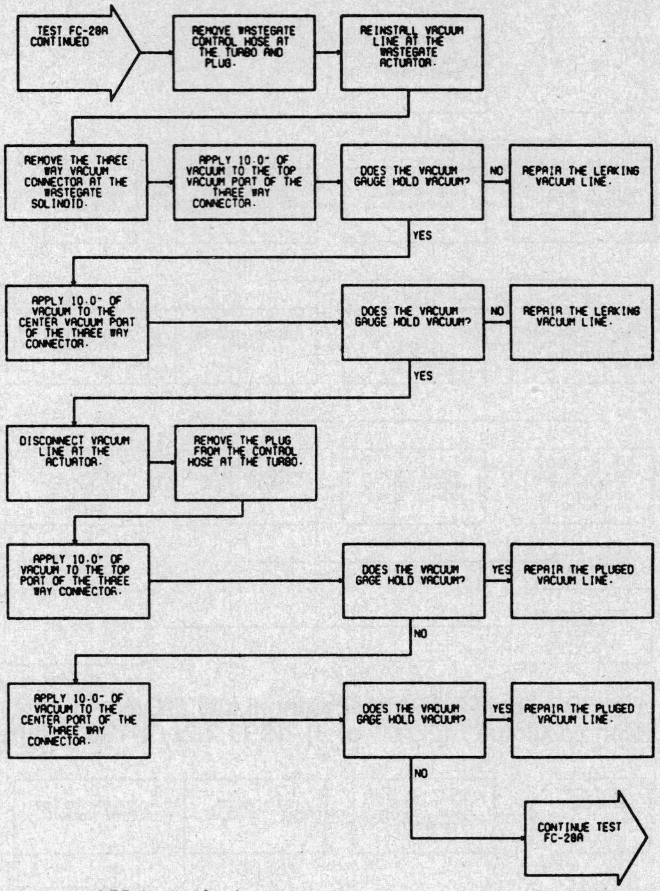

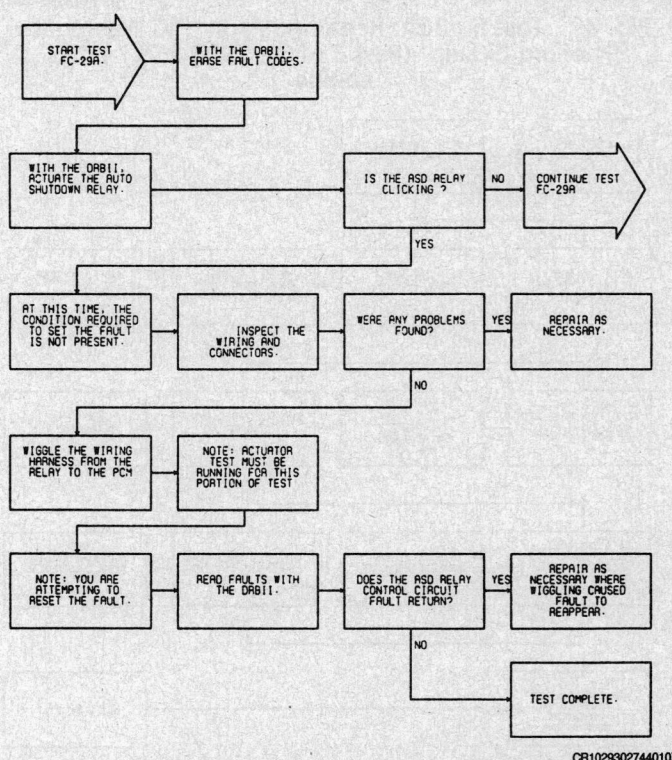

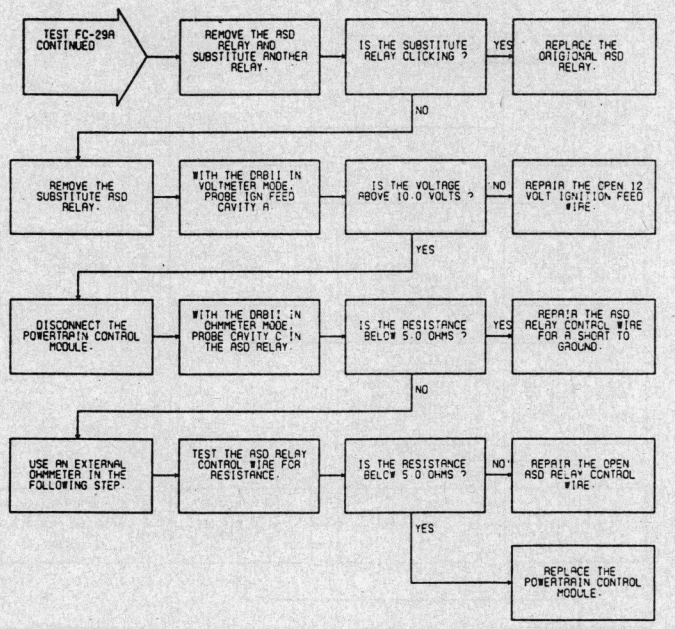

Fig. 42   Test FC-29A: Repairing Fault "Auto Shutdown Relay Control Circuit" (Part 2 of 2). 1993 2.2L/4-135 engine

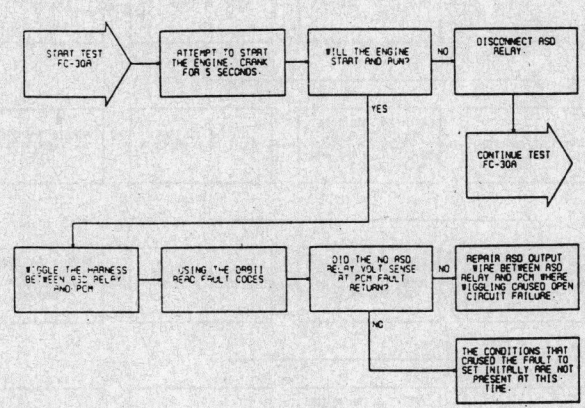

Fig. 43   Test FC-30A: Repairing Fault "No ASD Relay Volt Sense At PCM" (Part 1 of 2). 1993 2.2L/4-135 engine

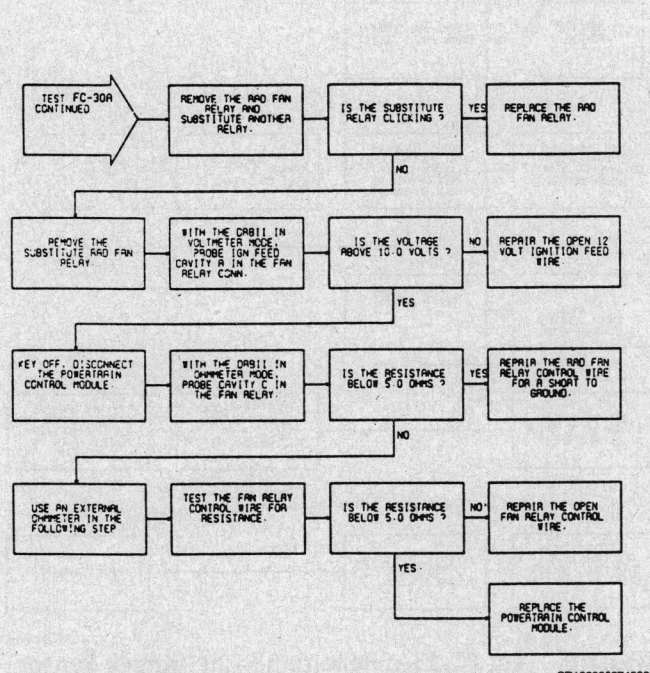

Fig. 43   Test FC-30A: Repairing Fault "No ASD Relay Volt Sense At PCM" (Part 2 of 2). 1993 2.2L/4-135 engine

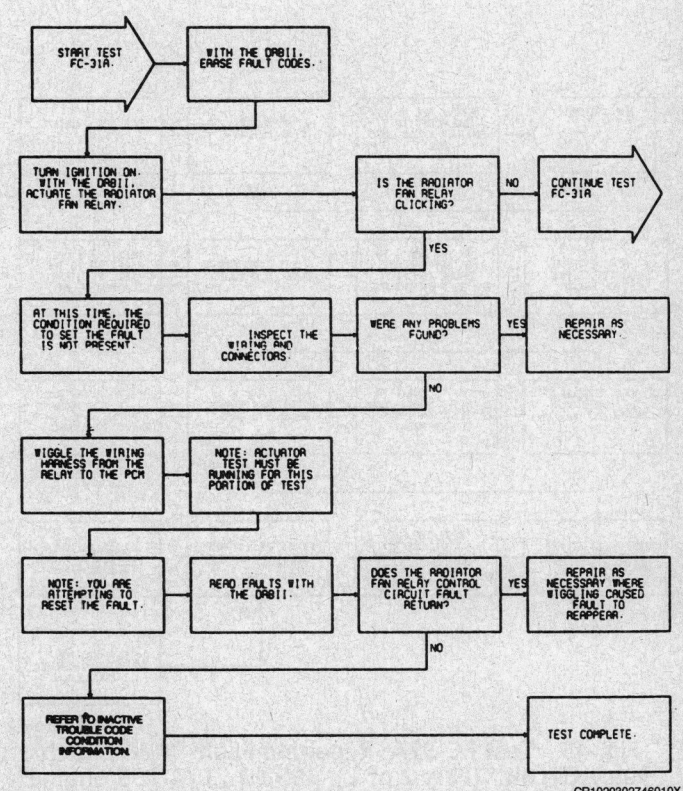

Fig. 44   Test FC-31A: Repairing Fault "RAD Fan Control Relay Circuit" (Part 1 of 2). 1993 2.2L/4-135 engine

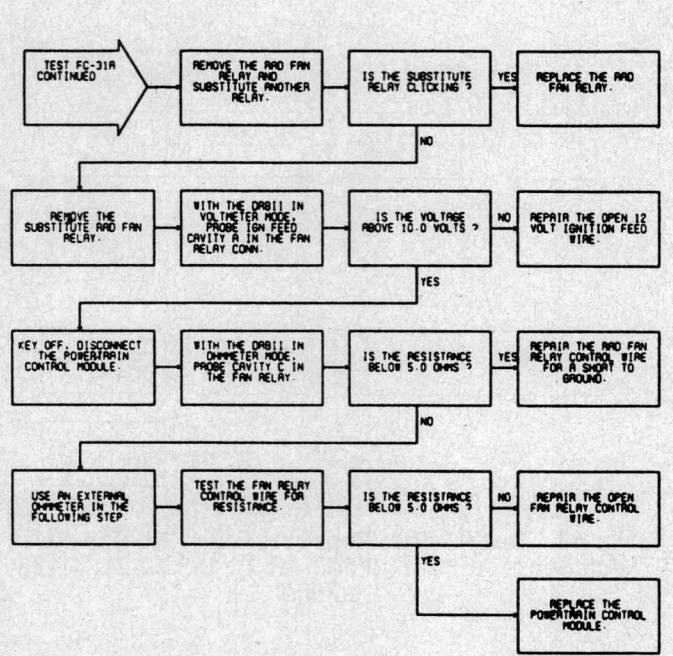

Fig. 44   Test FC-31A: Repairing Fault "RAD Fan Control Relay Circuit" (Part 2 of 2). 1993 2.2L/4-135 engine

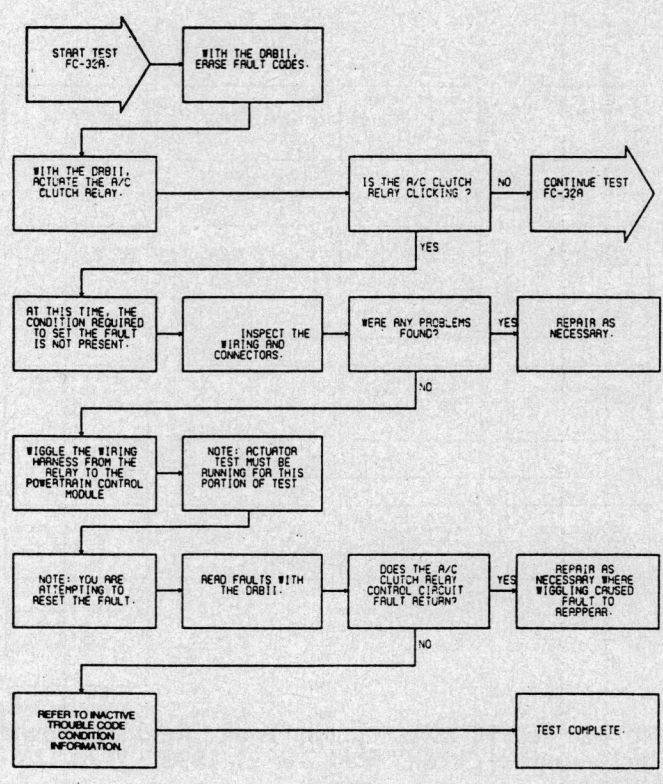

Fig. 45   Test FC-32A: Repairing Fault "A/C Clutch Relay Circuit" (Part 1 of 2). 1993 2.2L/4-135 engine

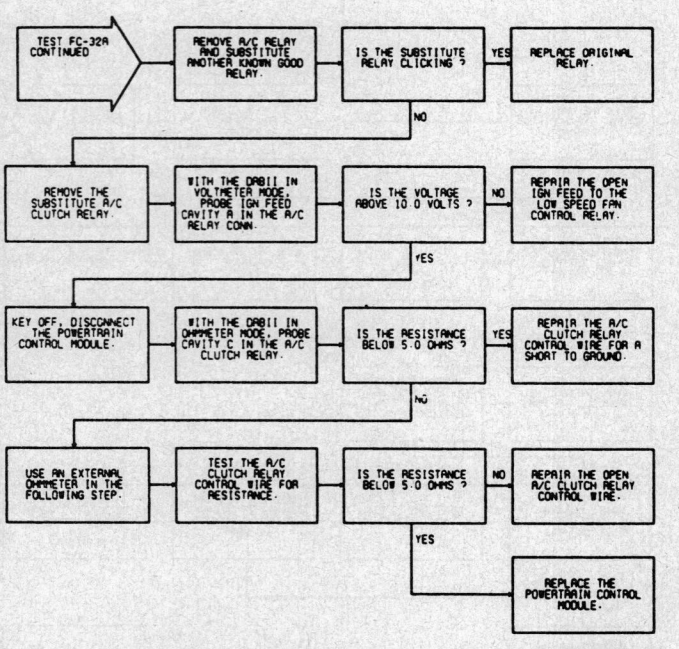

Fig. 45   Test FC-32A: Repairing Fault "A/C Clutch Relay Circuit" (Part 2 of 2). 1993 2.2L/4-135 engine

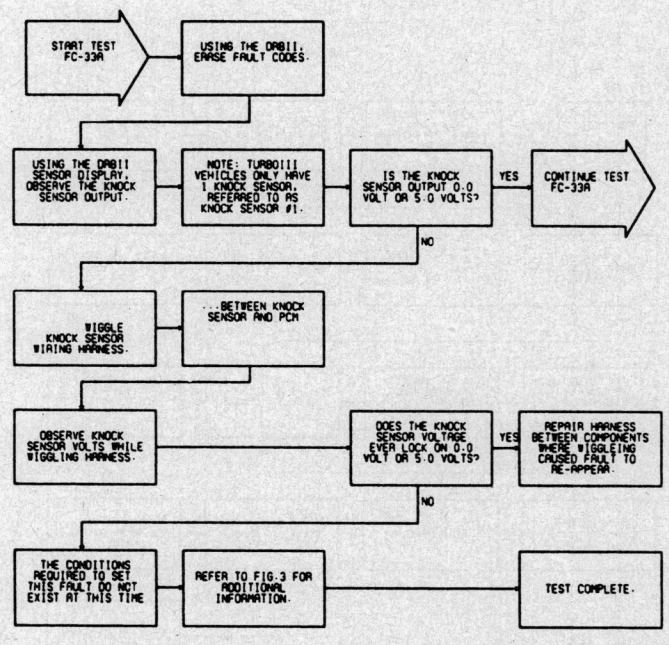

Fig. 46   Test FC-33A: Repairing Fault "Knock Sensor No. 1 Circuit" (Part 1 of 2). 1993 2.2L/4-135 engine

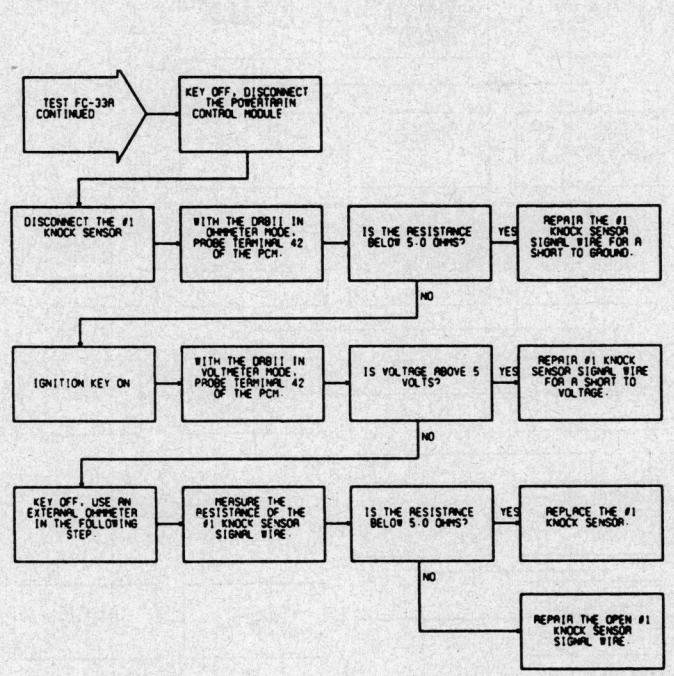

Fig. 46   Test FC-33A: Repairing Fault "Knock Sensor No.1 Circuit" (Part 2 of 2). 1993 2.2L/4-135 engine

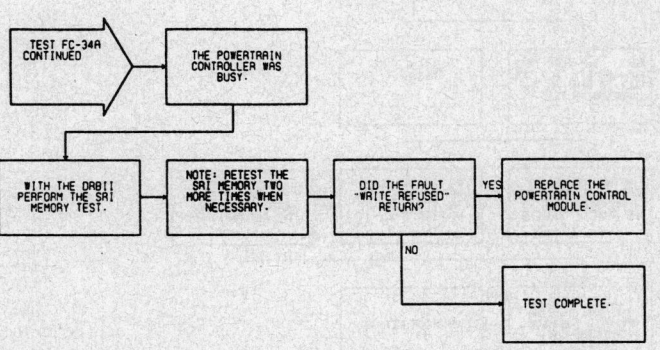

Fig. 47   Test FC-34A: Repairing Fault "PCM Failure SPI Communications & EEPROM Write Denied" (Part 2 of 2). 1993 2.2L/4-135 engine

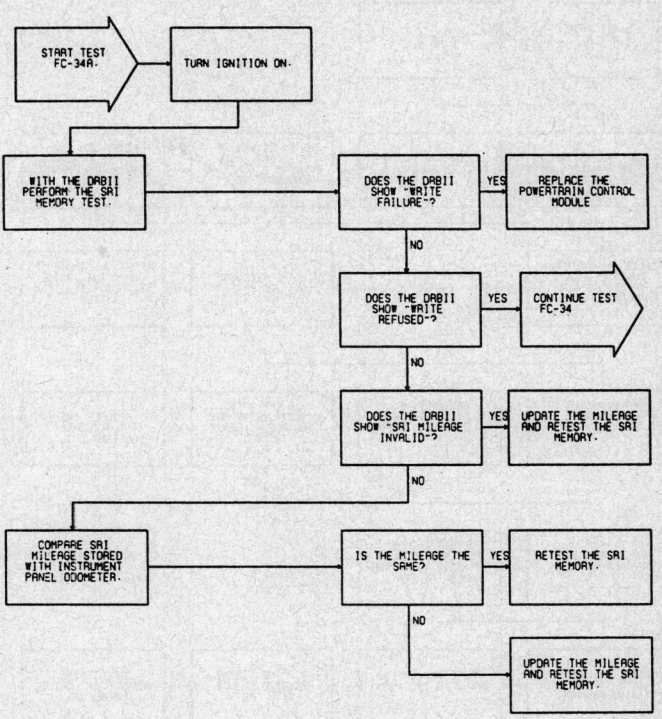

Fig. 47   Test FC-34A: Repairing Fault "PCM Failure SPI Communications & EEPROM Write Denied" (Part 1 of 2). 1993 2.2L/4-135 engine

First, check all Technical Service Bulletins and Hotline Newsletters that relate to this driveability problem. Perform corrective actions if indicated; otherwise continue.

1.   NO FAULT COMPLETE TEST (non-monitored & monitored circuits)

Perform **TESTS NF-2A** through **NF-15A** in sequence until the driveability problem is found.

NO FAULT MENU
CHECKING SECONDARY IGNITION AND TIMING	NF-2A
CHECKING FUEL PRESSURE	NF-3A
CHECKING COOLANT SENSOR CALIBRATION AND RADIATOR FAN OPERATION	NF-4A
CHECKING TPS SENSOR CALIBRATION	NF-5A
CHECKING MAP SENSOR CALIBRATION	NF-6A
CHECKING OXYGEN SENSOR SWITCHING	NF-7A
CHECKING IDLE AIR CONTROL MOTOR	NF-8A
CHECKING SOLENOID OPERATIONS	NF-9A
CHECKING PCM GROUNDS AND POWER CIRCUIT	NF-10A
CHECKING ENGINE VACUUM	NF-11A
CHECKING MINIMUM IDLE AIR FLOW	NF-12A
CHECKING KNOCK SENSOR	NF-13A
PERFORMING NO FAULT CODE MECHANICAL TEST	NF-14A

2.   NO FAULT QUICK INDIVIDUAL TEST (individual test only)

If you suspect any of the above items to be the cause of the vehicle's driveability problem, perform the associated test(s) individually. Return to No Fault Menu if driveability problem still exists, or perform No Fault Complete Test.

3.   NO FAULT QUICK SYMPTOM TEST (symptom test only)

Symptom checks cannot be used properly unless the driveability problem characteristic actually happens while the vehicle is being tested. To reduce diagnostic time, ensure that FC-1A and appropriate INTRODUCTION sections have been reviewed before attempting to diagnose a symptom.

Select the symptom that most accurately describes the vehicle's driveability problem and then perform the test routine that pertains to this symptom. Perform each routine test in sequence until the problem is found. For definitions, see Section 12.0 in the INTRODUCTION section in this manual.

SYMPTOM	DIAGNOSTIC TEST ROUTINE
HARD START	NF-2A, 3A, 4A, 5A, 6A, 7A, 8A, 10A, 11A, 12A, 14A
START AND STALL	NF-2A, 3A, 4A, 5A, 6A, 8A, 10A, 14A
HESITATION/SAG/STUMBLE	NO FAULT COMPLETE TEST (3)
SURGE	NF-2A, 3A, 4A, 5A, 6A, 7A, 8A, 9A, 10A, 14A
LACK OF POWER/SLUGGISH	NF-2A, 3A, 4A, 5A, 6A, 7A, 8A, 10A, 11A, 14A
SPARK KNOCK/DETONATION	NF-2A, 3A, 4A, 5A, 6A, 7A, 8A, 9A, 10A, 13A, 14A
CUTS OUT/MISSES	NF-2A, 3A, 7A, 9A, 10A, 11A, 14A
BACKFIRE/POPBACK	NF-2A, 3A, 6A, 7A, 10A, 11A, 14A
RUNS ROUGH/UNSTABLE/ERRATIC IDLE	NO FAULT COMPLETE TEST (3)
POOR FUEL ECONOMY	NO FAULT COMPLETE TEST (3)

Fig. 48   Test NF-1A: No Fault Code Test Menu. 1993 2.2L/4-135 engine

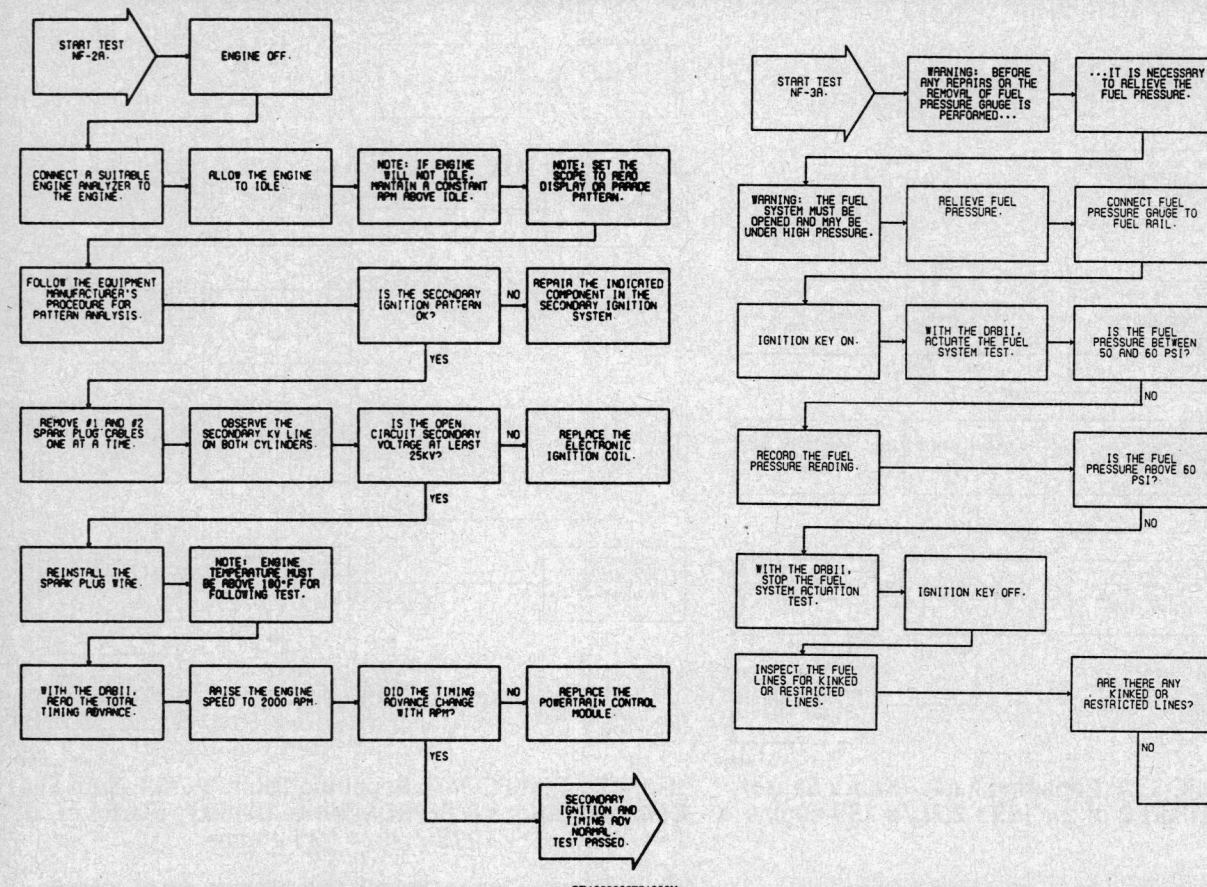

Fig. 49   Test NF-2A: Checking Secondary Ignition & Timing. 1993 2.2L/4-135 engine

CR1029302751000X

Fig. 50   Test NF-3A: Checking Fuel Pressure (Part 1 of 2). 1993 2.2L/4-135 engine

CR1029302752010X

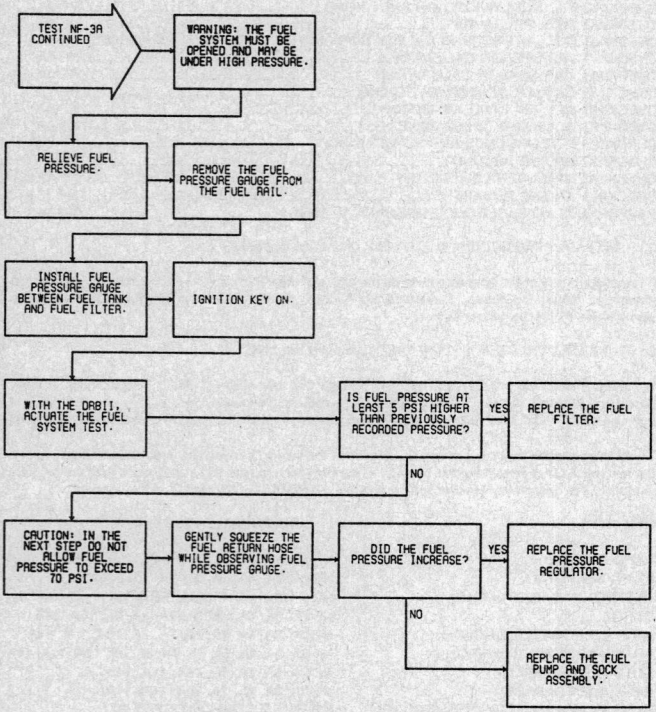

Fig. 50   Test NF-3A: Checking Fuel Pressure (Part 2 of 2). 1993 2.2L/4-135 engine

CR1029302752020X

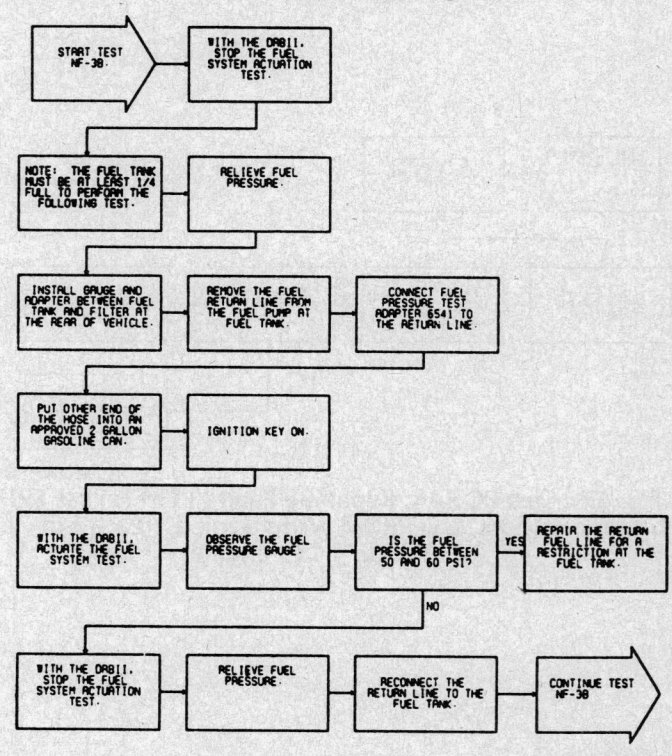

Fig. 51   Test NF-3B: Checking Fuel Pressure (Part 1 of 2). 1993 2.2L/4-135 engine

CR1029302753010X

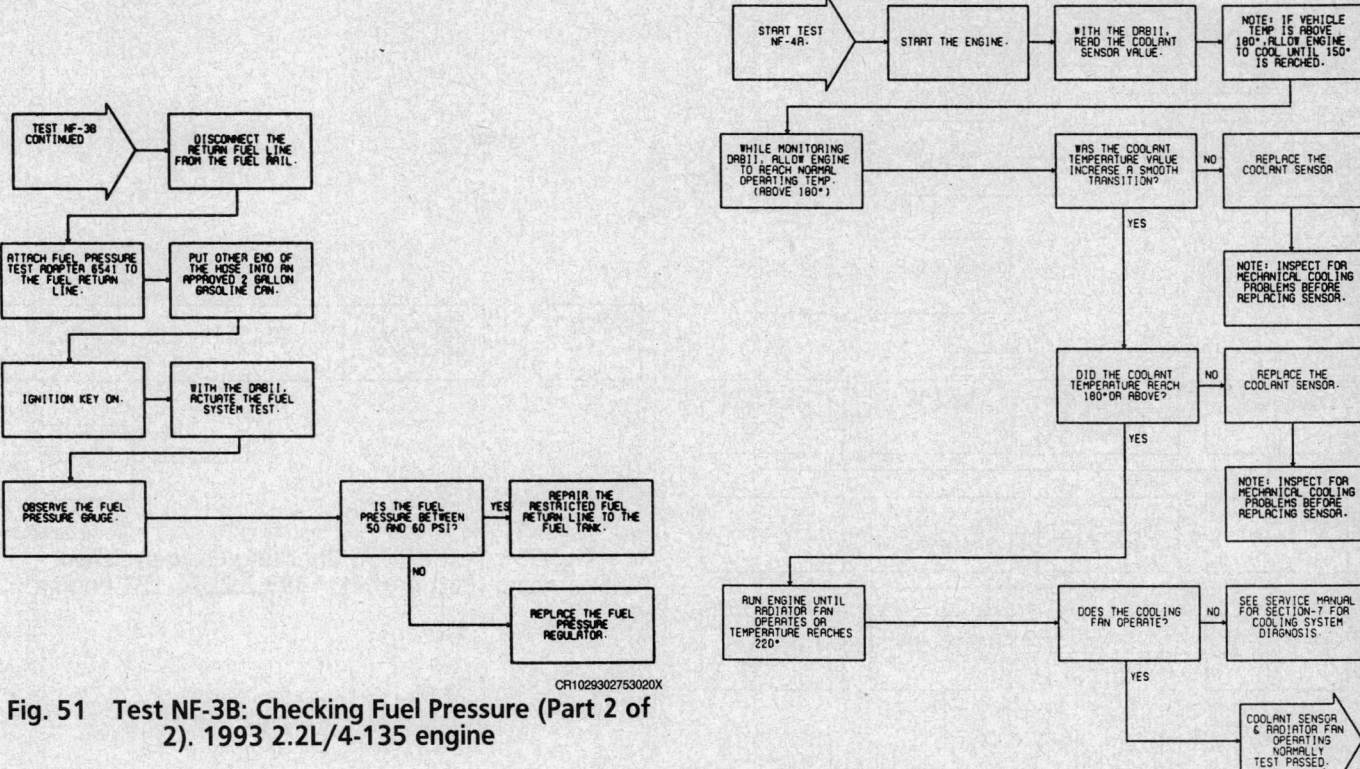

Fig. 51   Test NF-3B: Checking Fuel Pressure (Part 2 of 2). 1993 2.2L/4-135 engine

CR1029302753020X

Fig. 52   Test NF-4A: Checking Coolant Sensor Calibration & Radiator Fan Operation. 1993 2.2L/4-135 engine

CR1029302754000X

Fig. 53   Test NF-5A: Checking TP Sensor Calibration. 1993 2.2L/4-135 engine

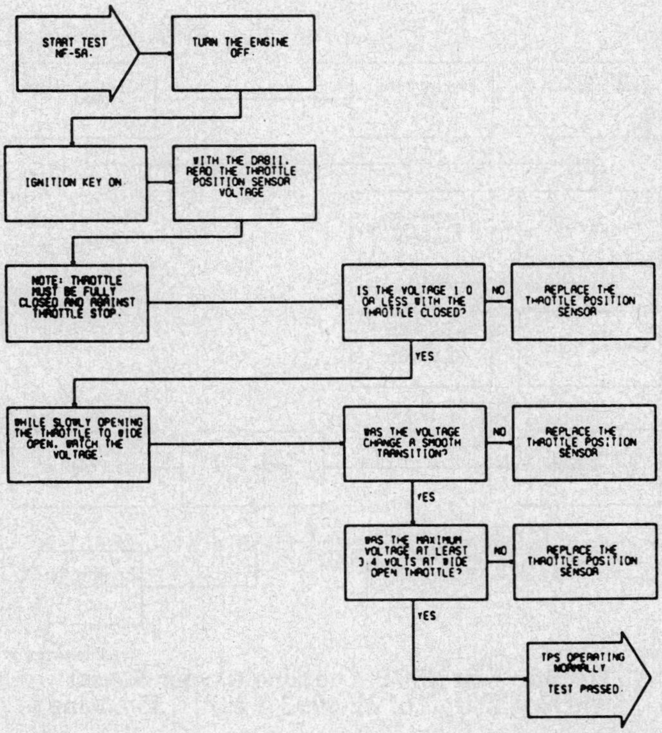

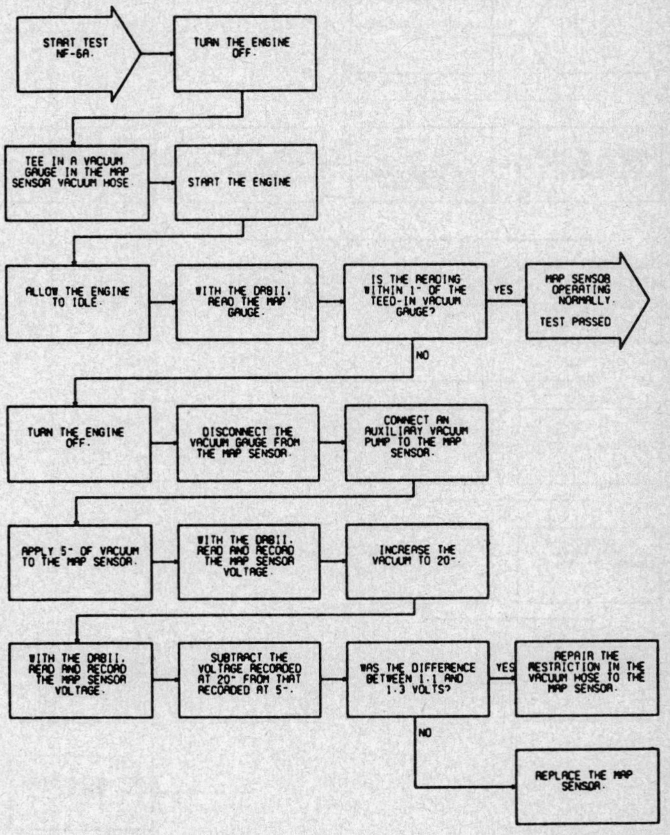

CR1029302755000X

Fig. 54   Test NF-6A: Checking MAP Sensor Calibration. 1993 2.2L/4-135 engine

CR1029302756000X

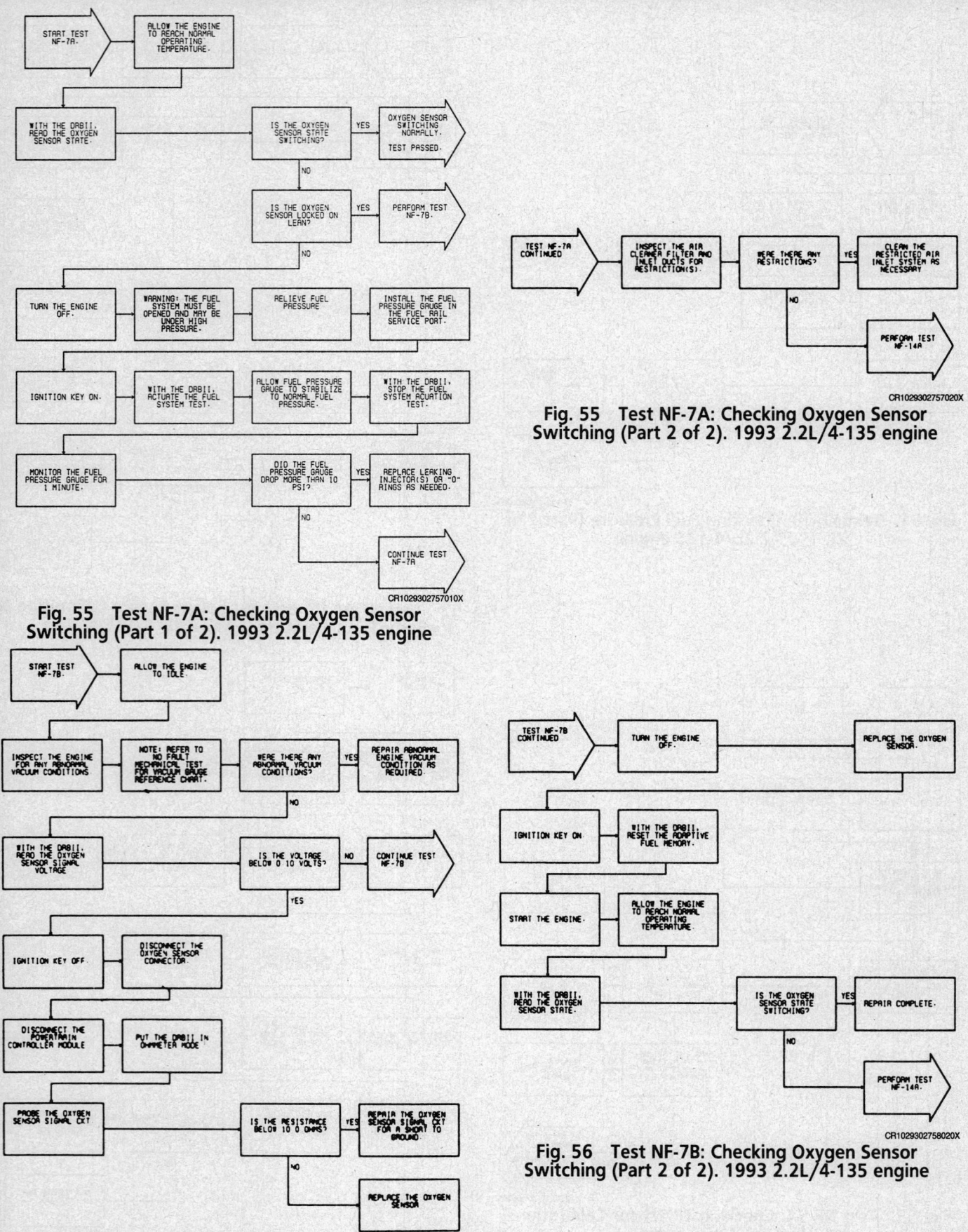

Fig. 55   Test NF-7A: Checking Oxygen Sensor Switching (Part 2 of 2). 1993 2.2L/4-135 engine

Fig. 55   Test NF-7A: Checking Oxygen Sensor Switching (Part 1 of 2). 1993 2.2L/4-135 engine

Fig. 56 Test NF-7B: Checking Oxygen Sensor Switching (Part 1 of 2). 1993 2.2L/4-135 engine

Fig. 56   Test NF-7B: Checking Oxygen Sensor Switching (Part 2 of 2). 1993 2.2L/4-135 engine

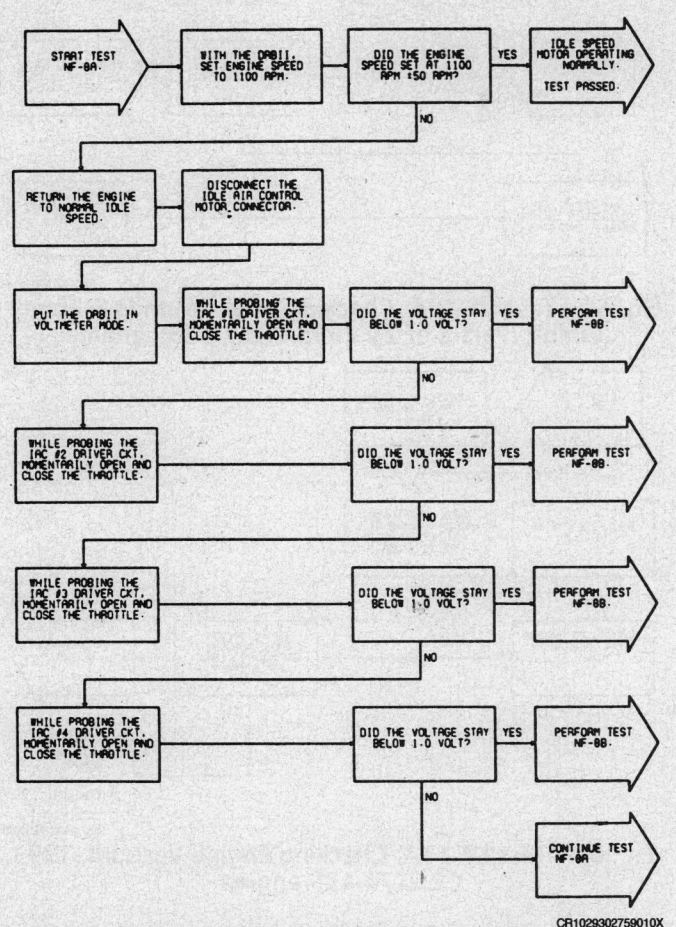

Fig. 57   Test NF-8A: Checking Idle Air Control Motor
(Part 1 of 2). 1993 2.2L/4-135 engine

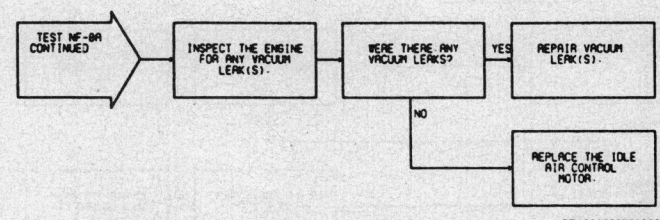

Fig. 57   Test NF-8A: Checking Idle Air Control Motor
(Part 2 of 2). 1993 2.2L/4-135 engine

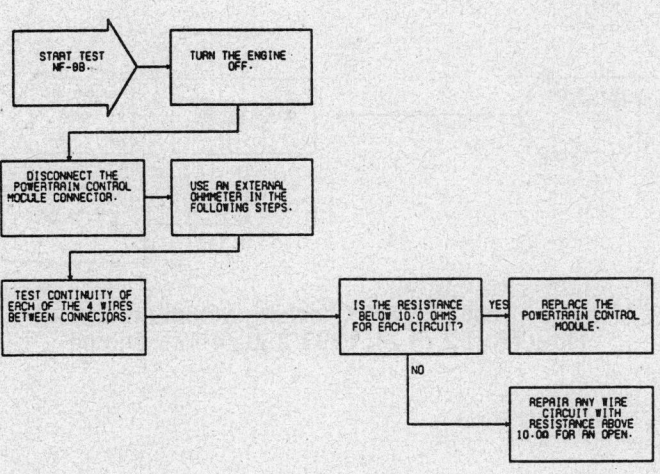

Fig. 58   Test NF-8A: Checking Idle Air Control Motor.
1993 2.2L/4-135 engine

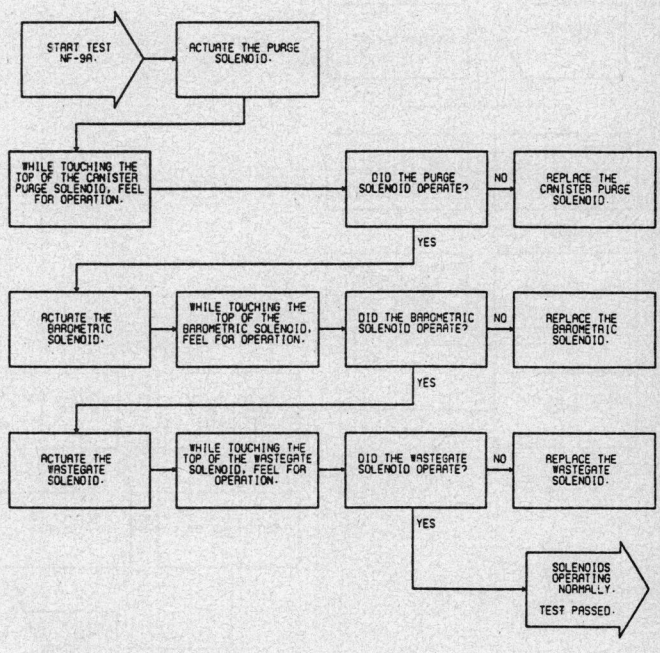

Fig. 59   Test NF-9A: Checking Solenoid Operations.
1993 2.2L/4-135 engine

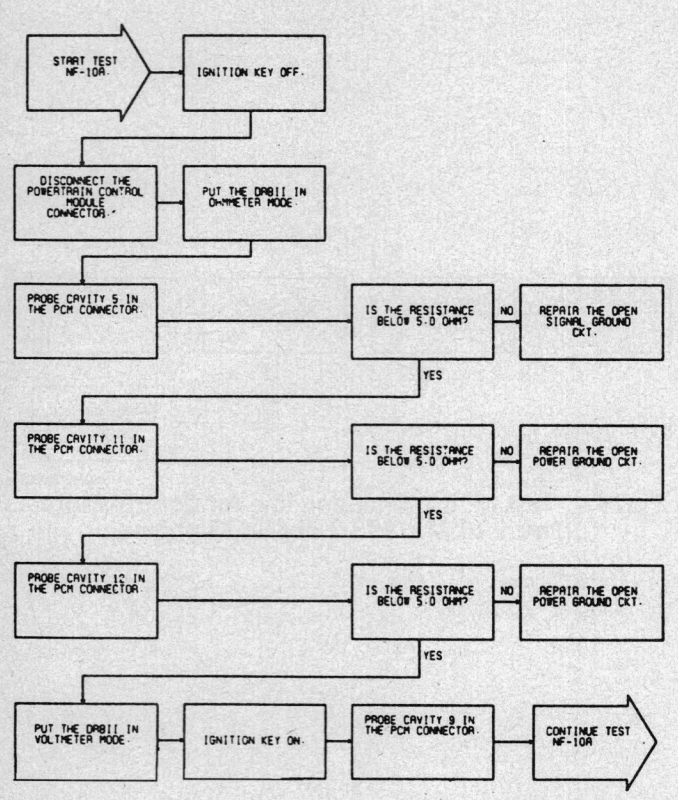

Fig. 60   Test NF-10A: Checking PCM Grounds & Power Circuit (Part 1 of 2). 1993 2.2L/4-135 engine

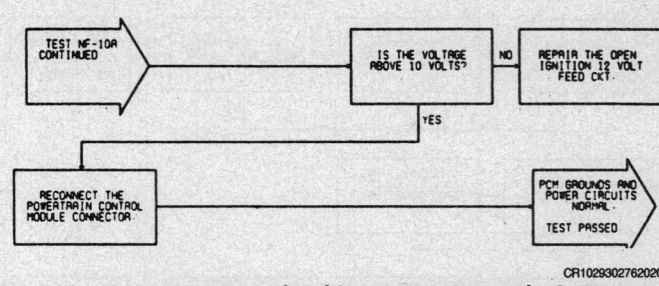

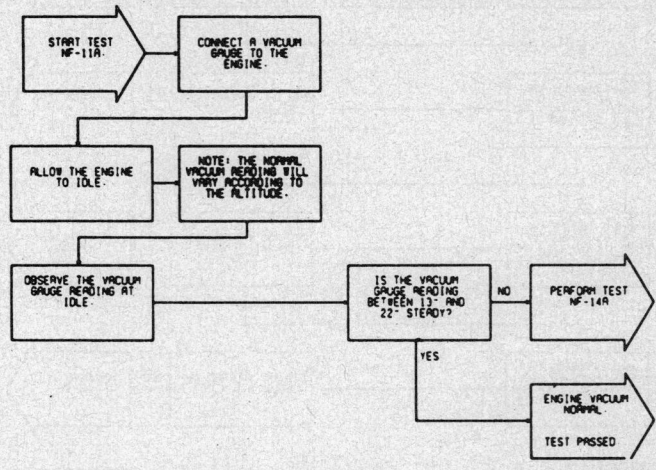

Fig. 60   Test NF-10A: Checking PCM Grounds & Power Circuit (Part 2 of 2). 1993 2.2L/4-135 engine

Fig. 61   Test NF-11A: Checking Engine Vacuum. 1993 2.2L/4-135 engine

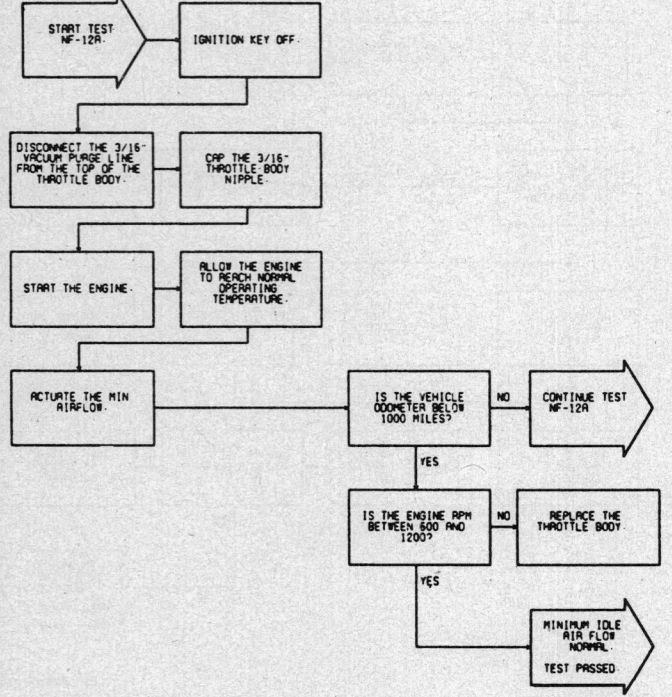

Fig. 62   Test NF-12A: Checking Minimum Idle Air Flow (Part 1 of 2). 1993 2.2L/4-135 engine

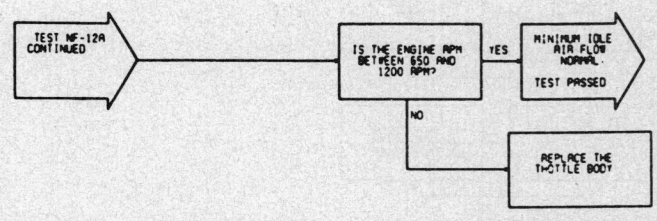

Fig. 62   Test NF-12A: Checking Minimum Idle Air Flow (Part 2 of 2). 1993 2.2L/4-135 engine

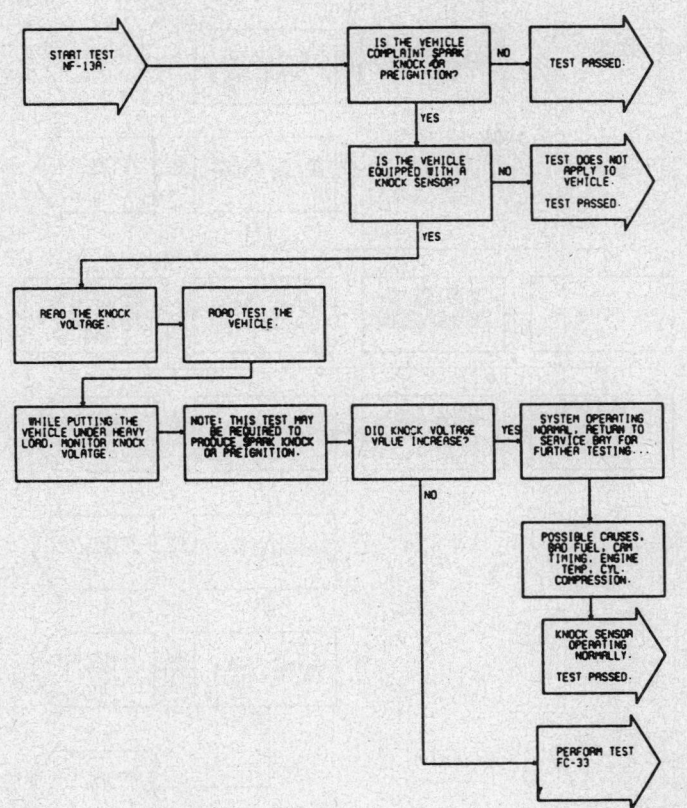

Fig. 63   Test NF-13A: Checking Knock Sensor. 1993 2.2L/4-135 engine

At this point in the diagnostic test procedure, you have determined that all of the engine controller systems are operating as designed and are not the cause of the driveability problem. Therefore, the following additional items should be checked as possible mechanical causes of the problem:

1. **ENGINE VACUUM** - must be at least 13 inches in neutral *(see below)**

2. **ENGINE VALVE TIMING** - must be within specifications

3. **ENGINE COMPRESSION** - must be within specifications

4. **ENGINE EXHAUST SYSTEM** - must be free of any restrictions

5. **ENGINE PVC SYSTEM** - must flow freely

6. **ENGINE DRIVE SPROCKET** - must be properly positioned

7. **TORQUE CONVERTER STALL SPEED** - must be within specifications (auto only)

8. **POWER BRAKE BOOSTER** - no internal vacuum leaks

9. **FUEL** - must be free of contamination

10. **FUEL INJECTOR** - plugged or restricted injector; control wire not connected to correct injector

NOTE: If you came to this test from the oxygen sensor, and the rich or lean condition is not caused by one of the first items above, replace the powertrain control module.*

* The readings below are only indicators of possible mechanical engine problems.

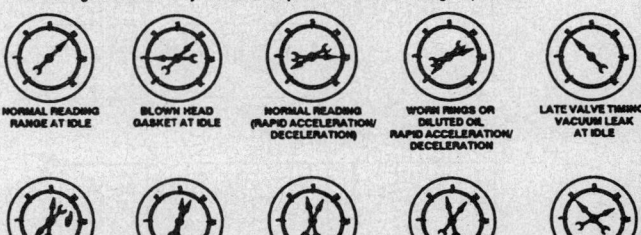

Fig. 64   Test NF-14A: No Fault Code Mechanical Test. 1993 2.2L/4-135 engine

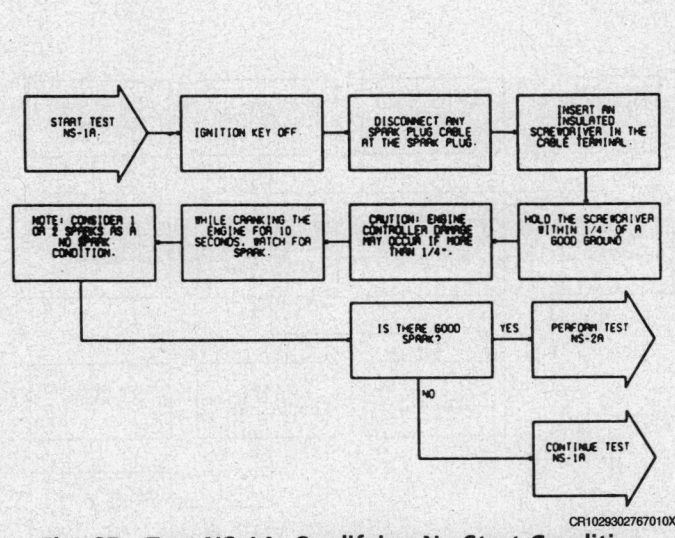

Fig. 65   Test NS-1A: Qualifying No Start Condition (Part 1 of 2). 1993 2.2L/4-135 engine

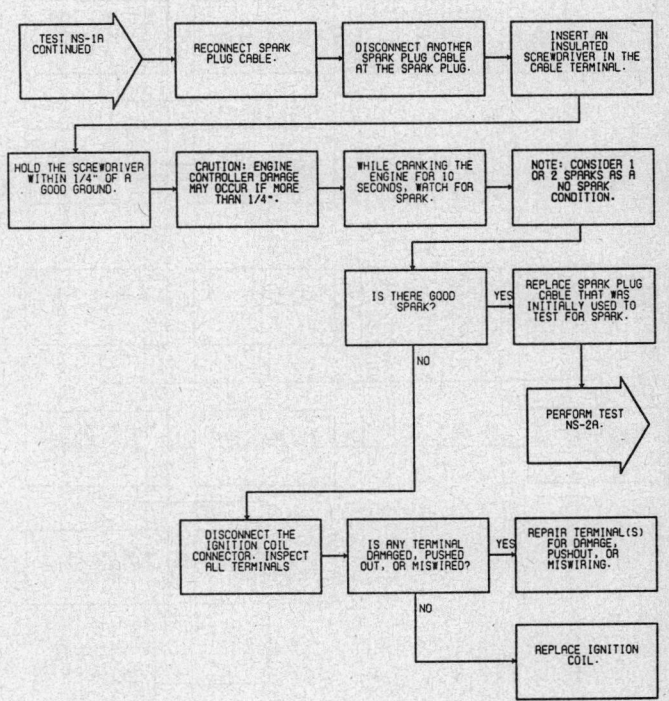

Fig. 65   Test NS-1A: Qualifying No Start Condition (Part 2 of 2). 1993 2.2L/4-135 engine

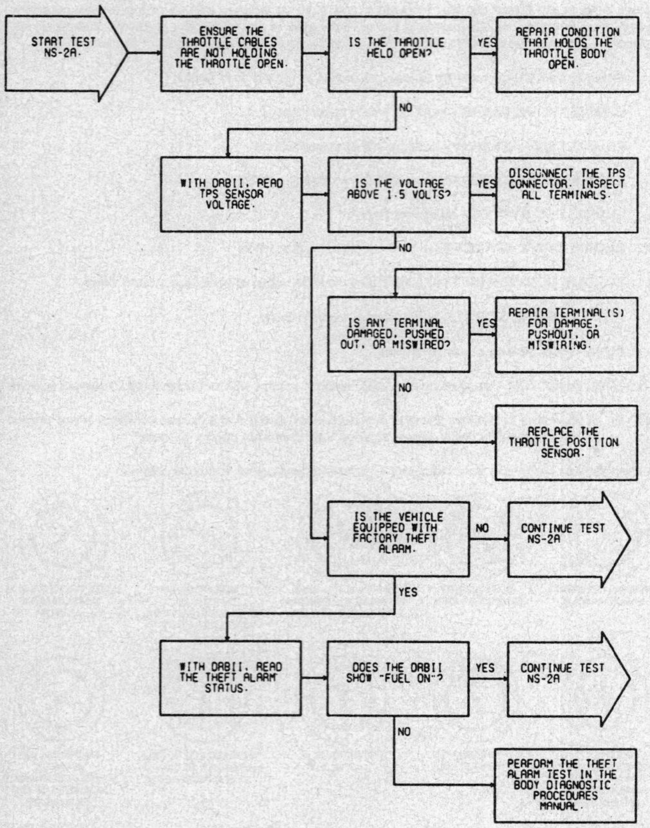

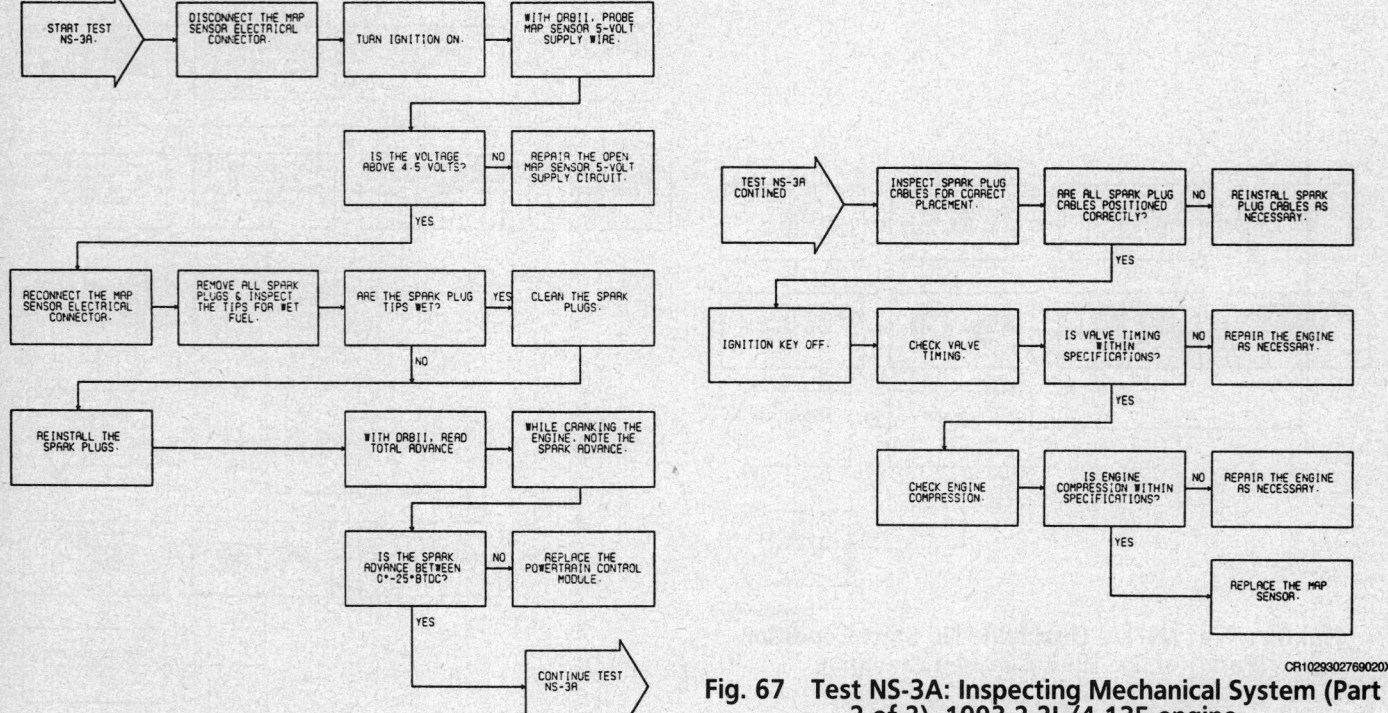

Fig. 66   Test NS-2A: Inspecting Fuel System (Part 1 of 2). 1993 2.2L/4-135 engine

CR1029302768010X

Fig. 66   Test NS-2A: Inspecting Fuel System (Part 2 of 2). 1993 2.2L/4-135 engine

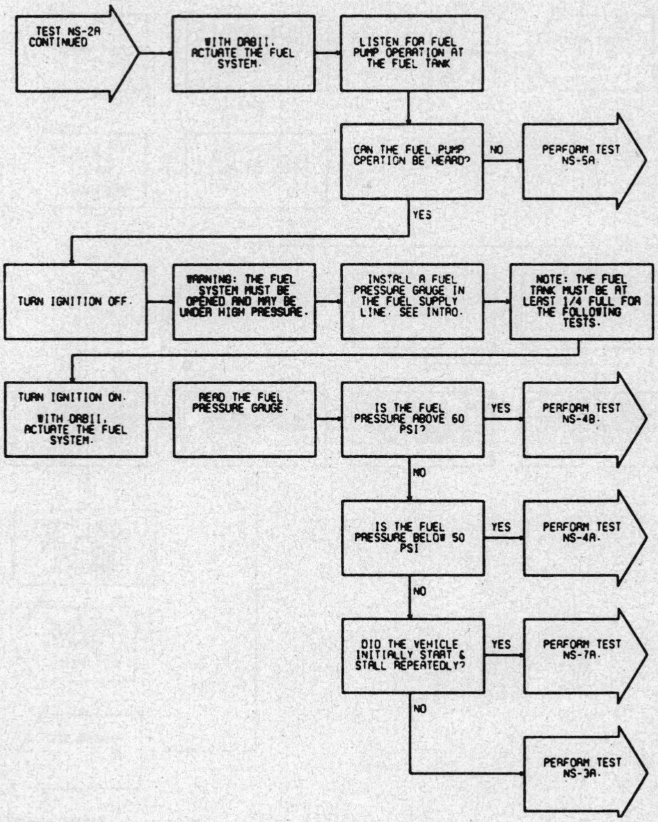

CR1029302768020X

Fig. 67   Test NS-3A: Inspecting Mechanical System (Part 2 of 2). 1993 2.2L/4-135 engine

CR1029302769020X

CR1029302769010X

Fig. 67   Test NS-3A: Inspecting Mechanical System (Part 1 of 2). 1993 2.2L/4-135 engine

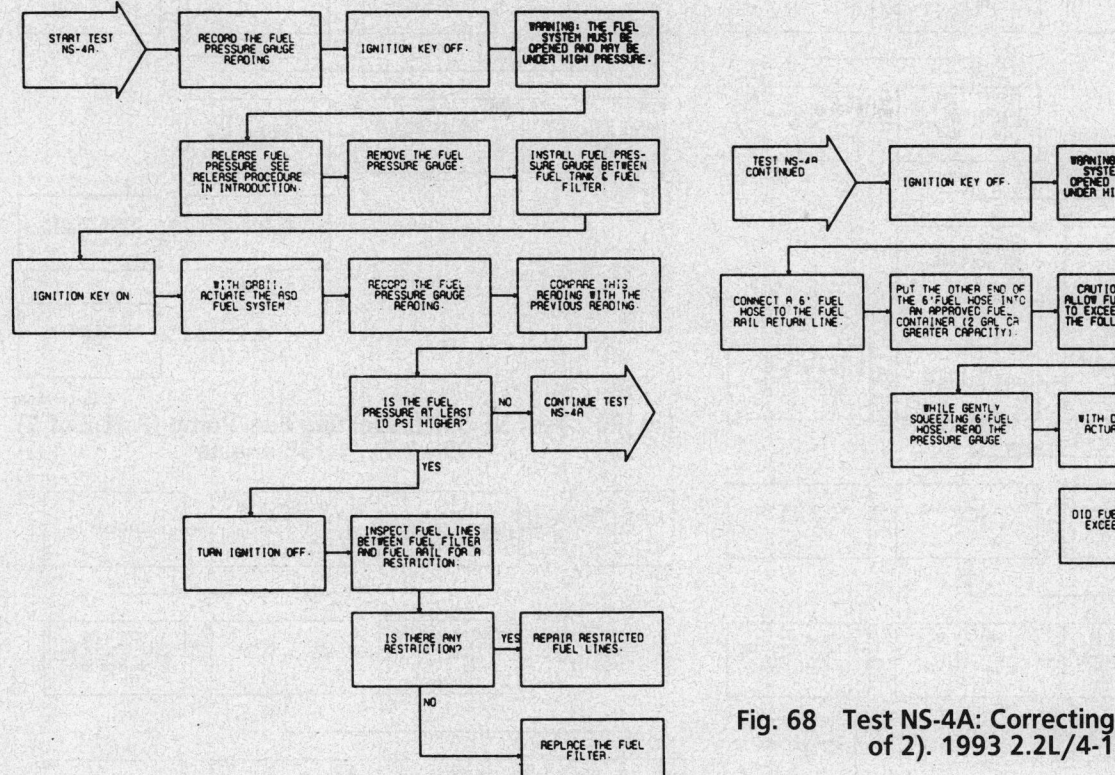

Fig. 68 Test NS-4A: Correcting Fuel Delivery (Part 1 of 2). 1993 2.2L/4-135 engine

CR1029302770010X

Fig. 68 Test NS-4A: Correcting Fuel Delivery (Part 2 of 2). 1993 2.2L/4-135 engine

CR1029302770020X

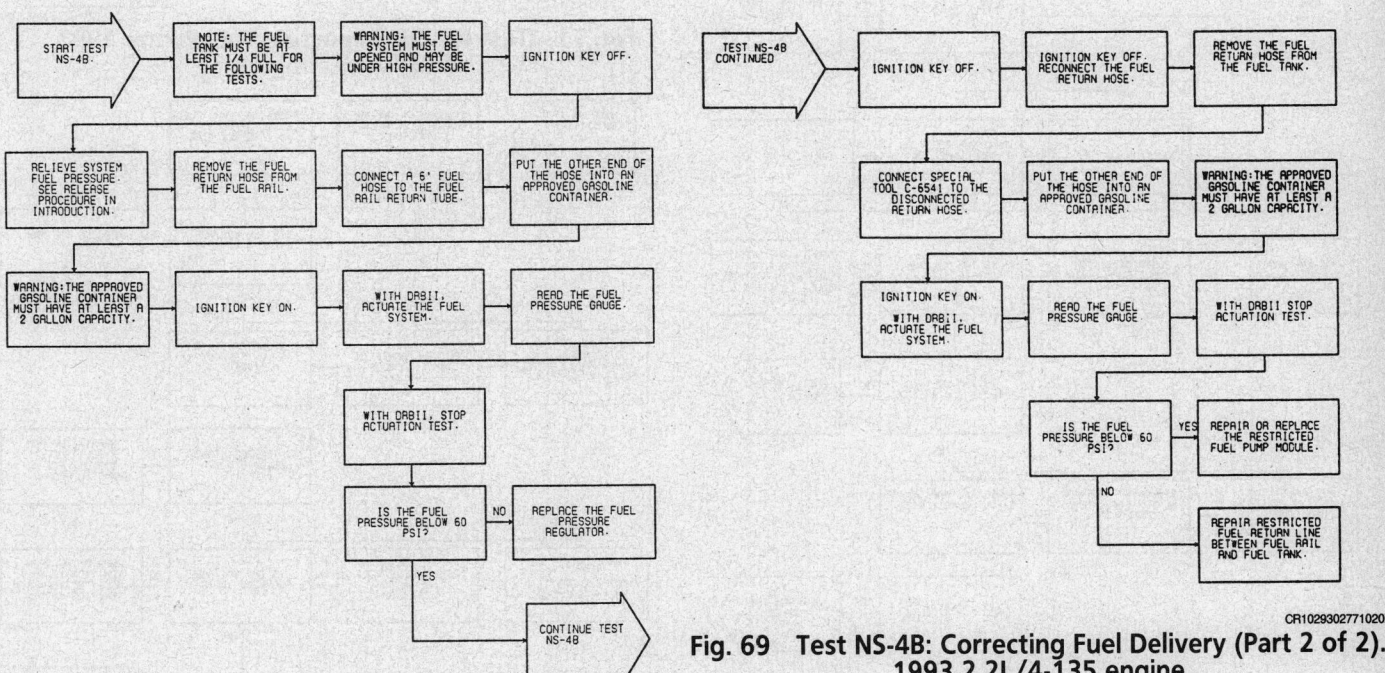

Fig. 69 Test NS-4B: Correcting Fuel Delivery (Part 1 of 2). 1993 2.2L/4-135 engine

CR1029302771010X

Fig. 69 Test NS-4B: Correcting Fuel Delivery (Part 2 of 2). 1993 2.2L/4-135 engine

CR1029302771020X

CHRYSLER–Fuel Injection

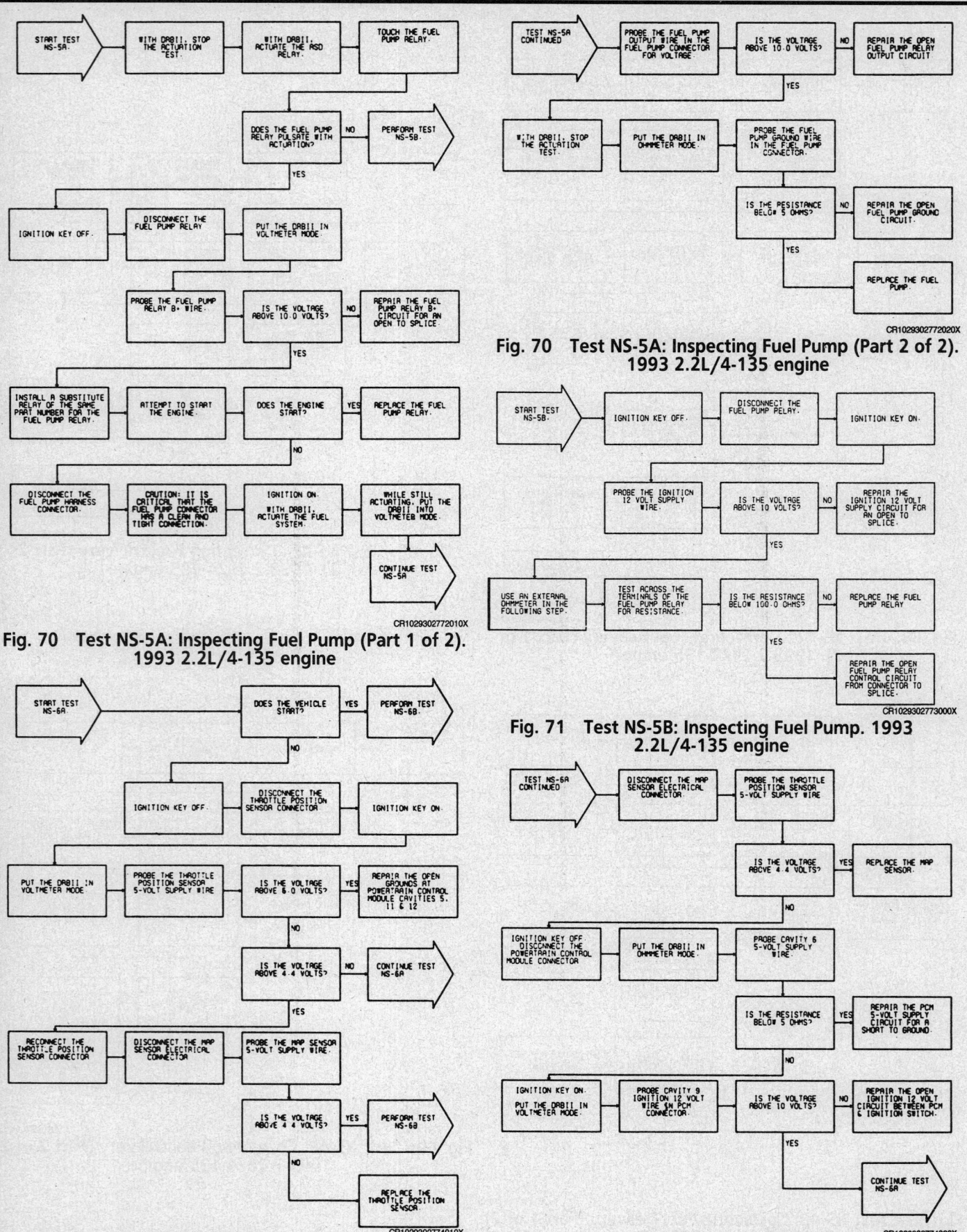

Fig. 70 Test NS-5A: Inspecting Fuel Pump (Part 1 of 2). 1993 2.2L/4-135 engine

Fig. 70 Test NS-5A: Inspecting Fuel Pump (Part 2 of 2). 1993 2.2L/4-135 engine

Fig. 71 Test NS-5B: Inspecting Fuel Pump. 1993 2.2L/4-135 engine

Fig. 72 Test NS-6A: Correcting "No Response" Condition (Part 1 of 5). 1993 2.2L/4-135 engine

Fig. 72 Test NS-6A: Correcting "No Response" Condition (Part 2 of 5). 1993 2.2L/4-135 engine

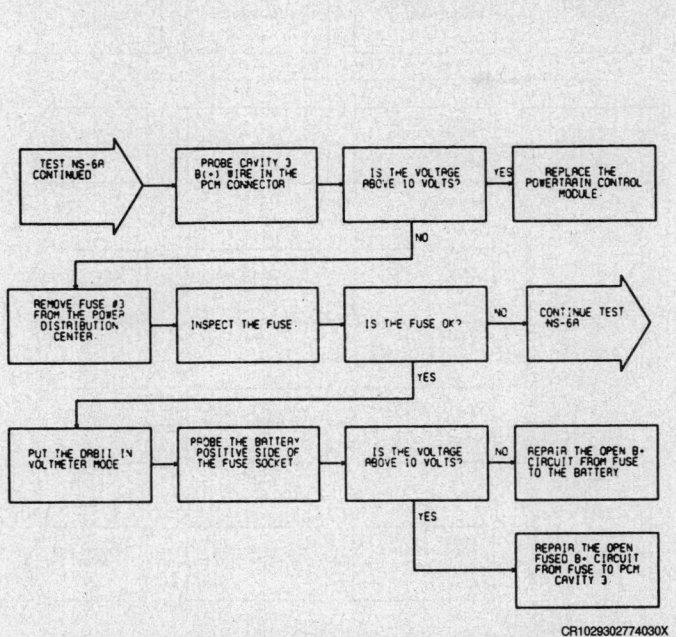

Fig. 72 Test NS-6A: Correcting "No Response" Condition (Part 3 of 5). 1993 2.2L/4-135 engine

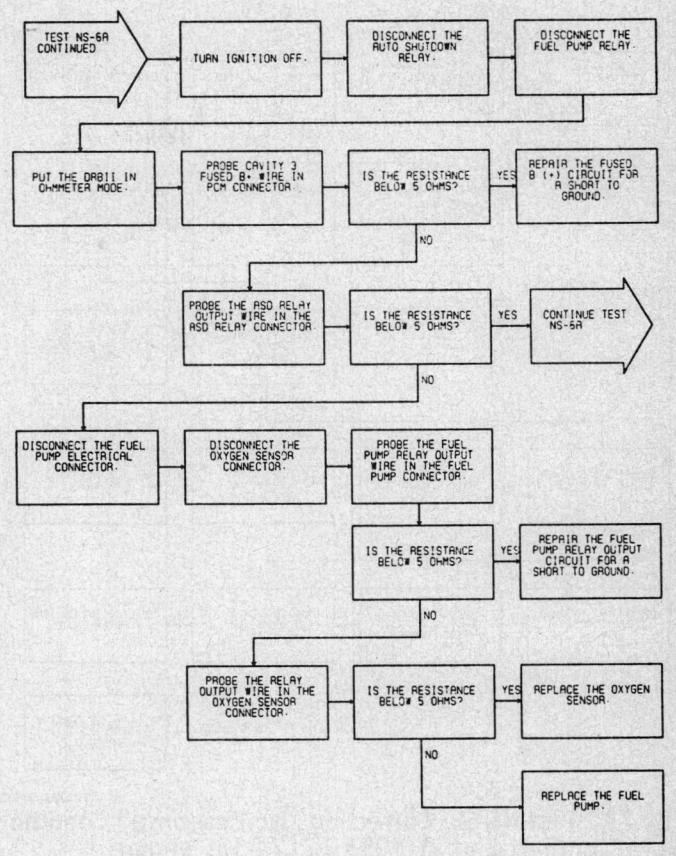

Fig. 72 Test NS-6A: Correcting "No Response" Condition (Part 4 of 5). 1993 2.2L/4-135 engine

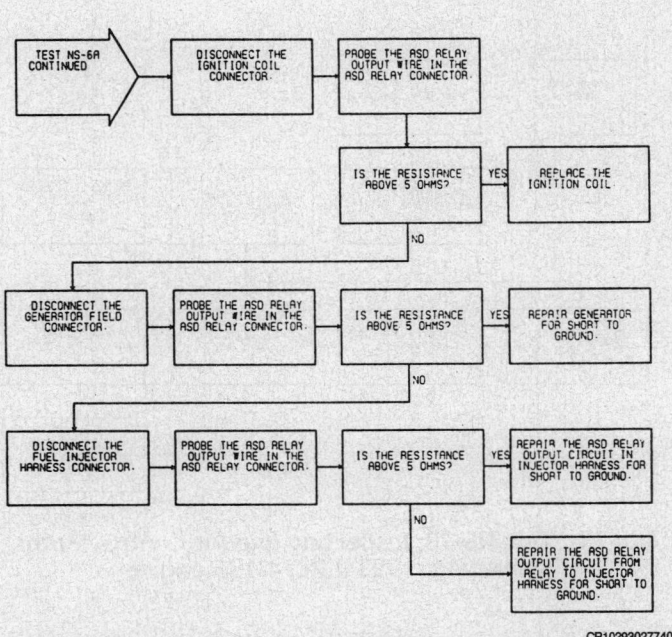

Fig. 72 Test NS-6A: Correcting "No Response" Condition (Part 5 of 5). 1993 2.2L/4-135 engine

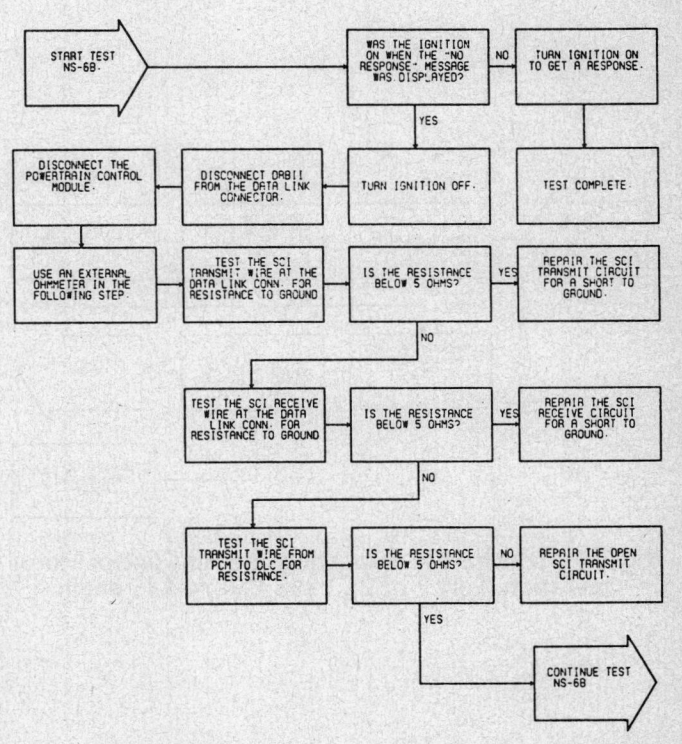

Fig. 73 Test NS-6B: Correcting "No Response" Condition (Part 1 of 2). 1993 2.2L/4-135 engine

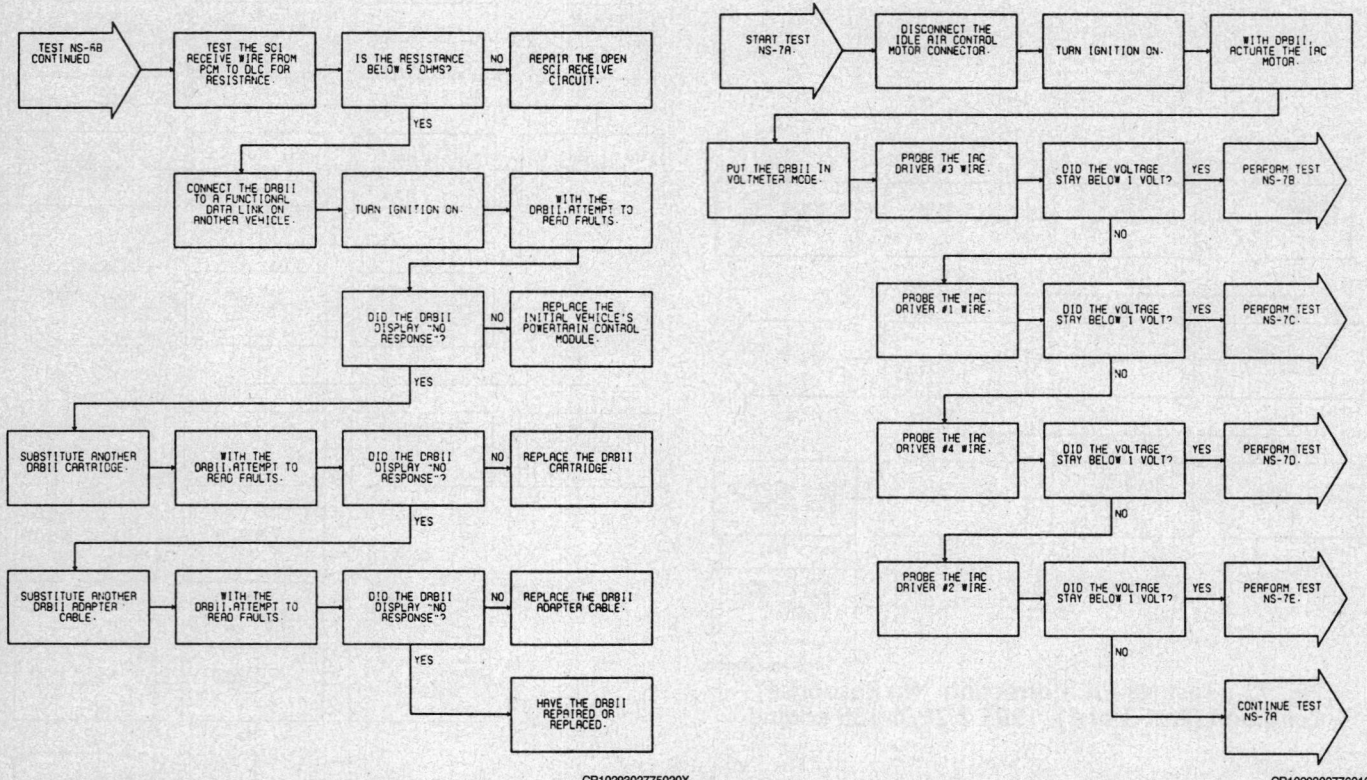

Fig. 73   Test NS-6B: Correcting "No Response" Condition (Part 2 of 2). 1993 2.2L/4-135 engine

Fig. 74   Test NS-7A: Inspecting Idle Air Control Motor Operation (Part 1 of 2). 1993 2.2L/4-135 engine

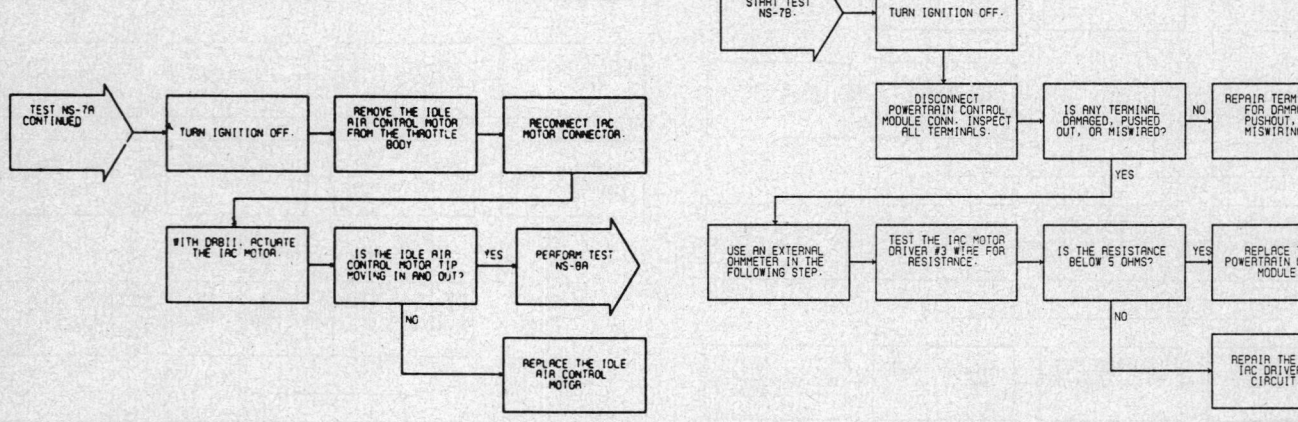

Fig. 74   Test NS-7A: Inspecting Idle Air Control Motor Operation (Part 2 of 2). 1993 2.2L/4-135 engine

Fig. 75   Test NS-7B: Inspecting Idle Air Control Motor Operation. 1993 2.2L/4-135 engine

CR1029302778000X

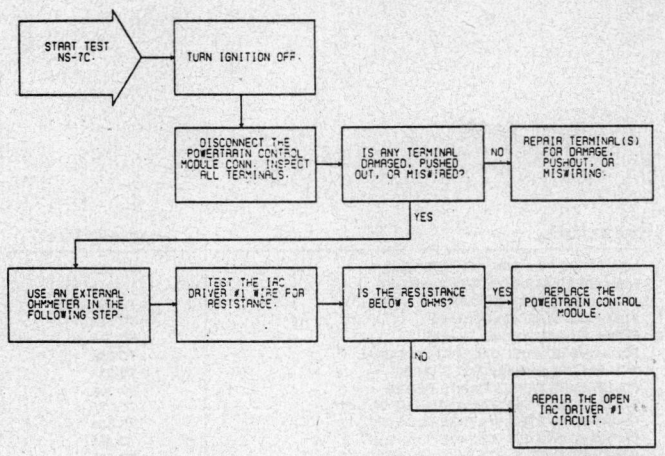

Fig. 76 Test NS-7C: Inspecting Idle Air Control Motor Operation. 1993 2.2L/4-135 engine

CR1029302779000X

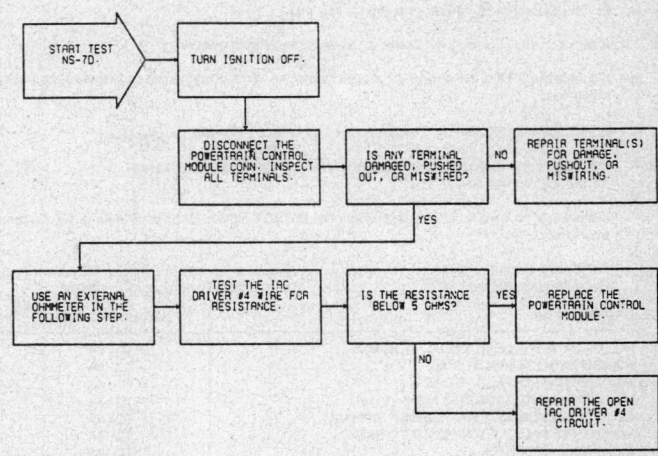

Fig. 77 Test NS-7D: Inspecting Idle Air Control Motor Operation. 1993 2.2L/4-135 engine

CR1029302780000X

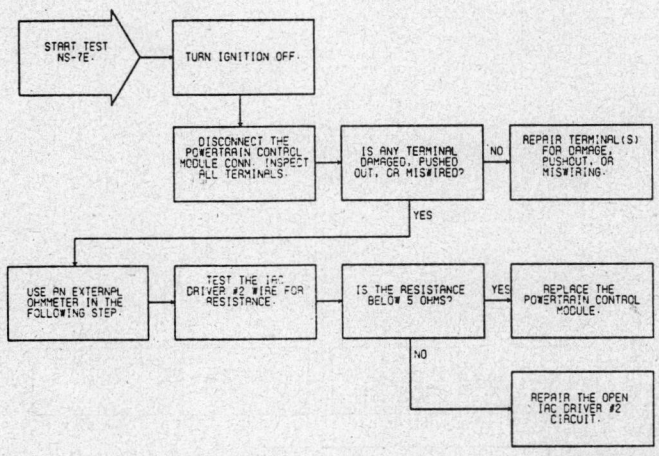

Fig. 78 Test NS-7E: Inspecting Idle Air Control Motor Operation. 1993 2.2L/4-135 engine

At this point in the diagnostic procedure, you have determined that all of the engine controller systems are operating as designed. Therefore, they are not the cause of the start and stall problem.

The following potential causes of a no start condition should also be checked:

1. **ENGINE VALVE TIMING** - must be within specifications
2. **ENGINE COMPRESSION** - must be within specifications
3. **ENGINE EXHAUST** - must be unrestricted
4. **ENGINE PCV SYSTEM** - must flow freely
5. **ENGINE DRIVE SPROCKETS** - must be properly positioned
6. **FUEL** - must be free of contamination
7. **ENGINE SECONDARY IGNITION CHECK** - must exhibit a normal scope pattern

Any one or more of these items can produce a no start condition; none of them can be overlooked as possible causes.

Also, look for any Technical Service Bulletins that may relate to this condition.

CR1029302781000X

Fig. 79 Test NS-8A: Correcting Start & Stall Condition. 1993 2.2L/4-135 engine

Inspect the vehicle to ensure that all engine components are connected. Reassemble and reconnect components as necessary.

Inspect the engine oil for fuel contamination. If it is contaminated, change the oil and filter.

Attempt to start the engine.

If the engine is unable to start, check all pertinent Technical Service Bulletins and return to **TEST FC-1A** if necessary.

If the engine is able to start and the powertrain control module has been changed, the repair is now complete.

If the engine is able to start and the powertrain control module has not been changed, connect the DRBII to the data link connector and erase faults. The repair is now complete.

CR1029302782000X

Fig. 80 Test VER-1: Verification Test 1. 1993 2.2L/4-135 engine

Inspect the vehicle to ensure that all engine components are connected. Reassemble and reconnect components as necessary.

If another fault was read previously that has not been dealt with, return to **TEST FC-1A** and follow the path specified by the other fault.

If the powertrain control module has not been changed, do the following:

1. Connect the DRBII to the data link connector and erase faults.
2. With DRBII, reset all values in adaptive memory.
3. Disconnect the DRBII.

Ensure no other fault remains by doing the following:

1. If the vehicle is equipped with air conditioning, turn on the air conditioning and blower.
2. Drive the vehicle for at least five minutes and at some point attain a speed of 40 mph. Ensure the transmission shifts through all gears. Upon the completion of the road test, turn the engine off.

1. Start the engine. Allow the engine to idle for at least two minutes.
2. Turn the engine off.
3. Connect the DRBII to the data link connector.
4. With the DRBII, read all fault messages.

If the repaired fault has reset, the repair is not complete. Check all pertinent Technical Service Bulletins and return to **TEST FC-1A** if necessary.

If there is another fault, return to **TEST FC-1A** and follow the path specified by the other fault.

If there are no faults, the repair is now complete.

CR1029302783000X

Fig. 81 Test VER-2: Road Test Verification. 1993 2.2L/4-135 engine

NOTE: The battery must be fully charged for any test

1. Attempt to start the engine. Crank for up to 10 seconds if necessary.

2. Connect the DRB to the engine diagnostic connector. Write down trouble code messages that are displayed.

3. If the DRB screen displays "No Response," go to TEST NS-6A.

4. If trouble code messages are displayed, refer to the trouble code list below for the appropriate test.

5. If there are no trouble codes displayed refer to TEST NS-1A for no start tests or NF-1A for no trouble code tests.

For Speed Control problems SC-1A
For Charging problems CH-1A

DRB MESSAGE	DIAGNOSTIC TEST
NO CRANK REFERENCE SIGNAL AT PCM	TC- 2A
NO CAM SYNC SIGNAL AT PCM	TC- 3A
MAP SENSOR VOLTAGE TOO LOW	TC- 4A
MAP SENSOR VOLTAGE TOO HIGH	TC- 5A
SLOW CHANGE IN IDLE MAP SENSOR SIGNAL	TC- 6A
NO CHANGE IN MAP FROM START TO RUN	TC- 6A
O2S STAYS AT CENTER	TC- 7A
O2S STAYS ABOVE CENTER (RICH)	TC- 8A
O2S STAYS BELOW CENTER (LEAN)	TC- 9A
O2S SHORTED TO VOLTAGE	TC-10A
NO VEHICLE SPEED SENSOR SIGNAL	TC-11A
IDLE AIR CONTROL MOTOR CIRCUITS	TC-12A
INJECTOR CONTROL CIRCUIT	TC-13A
INJECTOR #1 CONTROL CIRCUIT	TC-13A
INJECTOR #2 CONTROL CIRCUIT	TC-13A
INJECTOR #3 CONTROL CIRCUIT	TC-13A
INJECTOR #4 CONTROL CIRCUIT	TC-13A
EGR SYSTEM FAILURE	TC-17A
EGR SOLENOID CIRCUIT	TC-18A
EVAP SOLENOID CIRCUIT	TC-19A
TORQUE CONVERTER CLUTCH SOLENOID CKT	TC-20A
THROTTLE POSITION SENSOR VOLTAGE LOW	TC-21A
THROTTLE POSITION SENSOR VOLTAGE HIGH	TC-22A
THROTTLE BODY TEMP SENSOR VOLTAGE LOW	TC-23A
THROTTLE BODY TEMP SENSOR VOLTAGE HIGH	TC-24A
ECT SENSOR VOLTAGE TOO LOW	TC-25A
ECT SENSOR VOLTAGE TOO HIGH	TC-26A
NO ASD RELAY OUTPUT VOLTAGE AT PCM	TC-27A
AUTO SHUTDOWN RELAY CONTROL CIRCUIT	TC-28A
RAD FAN CONTROL RELAY CIRCUIT	TC-29A

CR1029302784010X

Fig. 82   Test TC-1A: Checking The System For Trouble Codes (Part 1 of 2). 2.5L/4-153 engine

DRB MESSAGE	DIAGNOSTIC TEST
LOW SPEED FAN CTRL RELAY CIRCUIT	TC-30A
HIGH SPEED FAN CTRL RELAY CIRCUIT	TC-31A
A/C CLUTCH RELAY CIRCUIT	TC-32A
FLEX FUEL SENSOR VOLTS HIGH	TC-33A
FLEX FUEL SENSOR VOLTS LOW	TC-34A
LOSS OF FLEX FUEL CALIBRATION SIGNAL	TC-35A
PCM FAILURE SRI MILE NOT STORED	TC-36A
PCM FAILURE EEPROM WRITE DENIED	TC-36A
BATTERY TEMP SENSOR VOLTS OUT OF LIMIT	TC-37A
CHARGING SYSTEM VOLTAGE TOO LOW	TC-38A
CHARGING SYSTEM VOLTAGE TOO HIGH	TC-39A
GENERATOR FIELD NOT SWITCHING PROPERLY	TC-40A
SPEED CONTROL SOLENOID CIRCUITS	TC-41A

Engine is cold too long - engine does not warm to 176°F while driving 20 minutes after start. See Service Manual for cooling system repair (thermostat). This code may set in error during very cold slow speed driving.

For an internal PCM failure, replace the PCM and go to Verfication TEST VER-1.

CR1029302784020X

Fig. 82   Test TC-1A: Checking The System For Trouble Codes (Part 2 of 2). 2.5L/4-153 engine

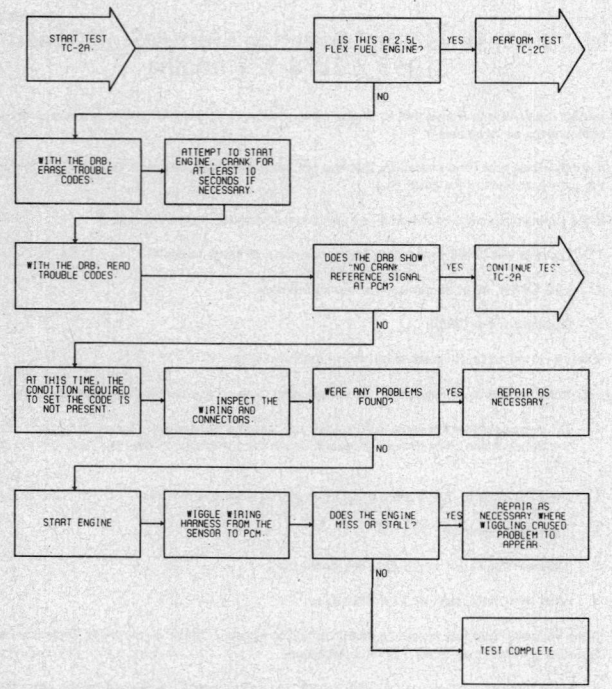

CR1029302785010X

Fig. 83   Test TC-2A: Repairing No Crank Reference Signal At PCM (Part 1 of 3). 2.5L/4-153 engine

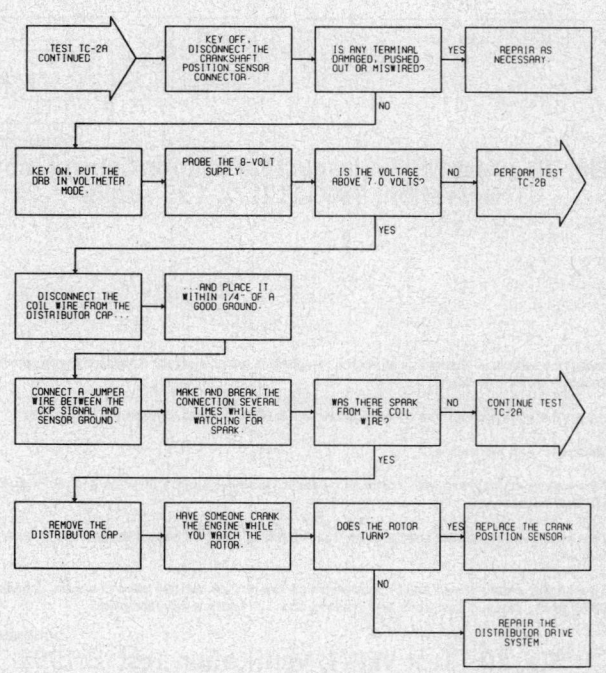

CR1029302785020X

Fig. 83   Test TC-2A: Repairing No Crank Reference Signal At PCM (Part 2 of 3). 2.5L/4-153 engine

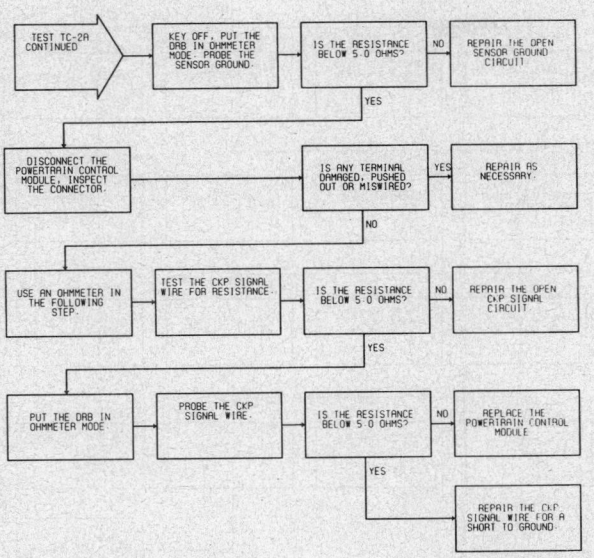

CR1029302785030X

Fig. 83 Test TC-2A: Repairing No Crank Reference Signal At PCM (Part 3 of 3). 2.5L/4-153 engine

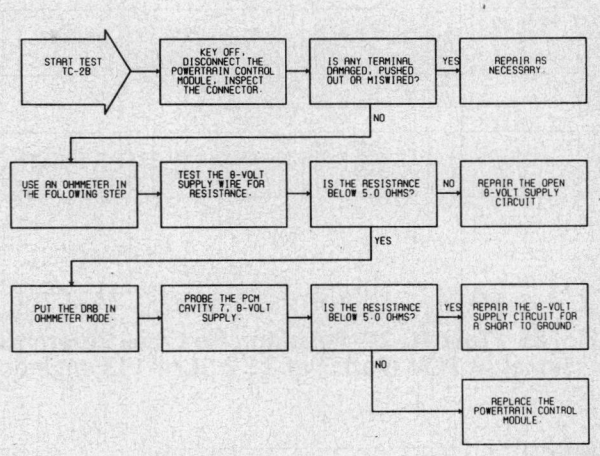

CR1029302786000X

Fig. 84 Test TC-2B: Repairing No Crank Reference Signal At PCM. 2.5L/4-153 engine

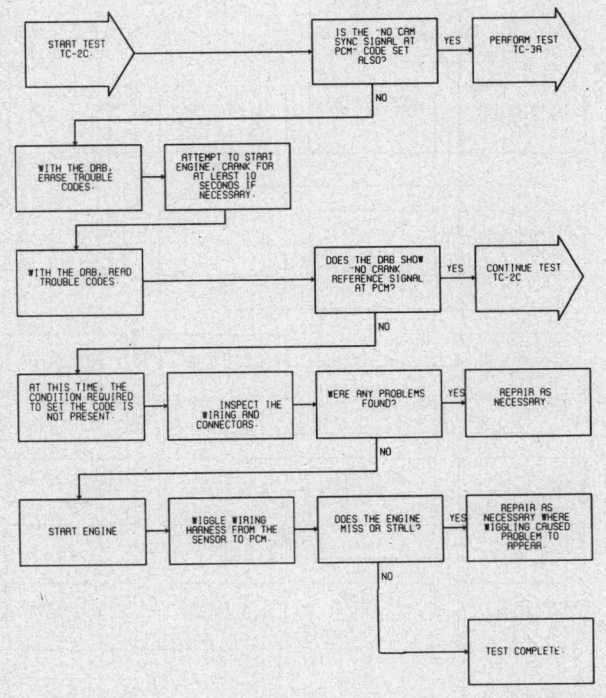

CR1029302787010X

Fig. 85 Test TC-2C: Repairing No Crank Reference Signal At PCM (Part 1 of 3). 2.5L/4-153 engine

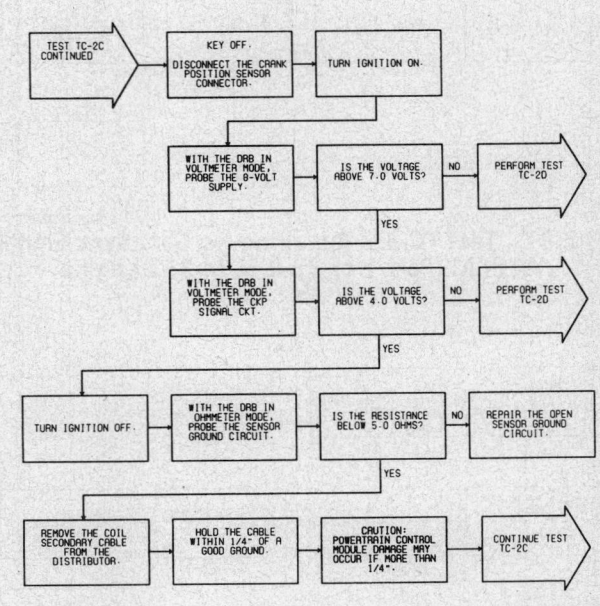

CR1029302787020X

Fig. 85 Test TC-2C: Repairing No Crank Reference Signal At PCM (Part 2 of 3). 2.5L/4-153 engine

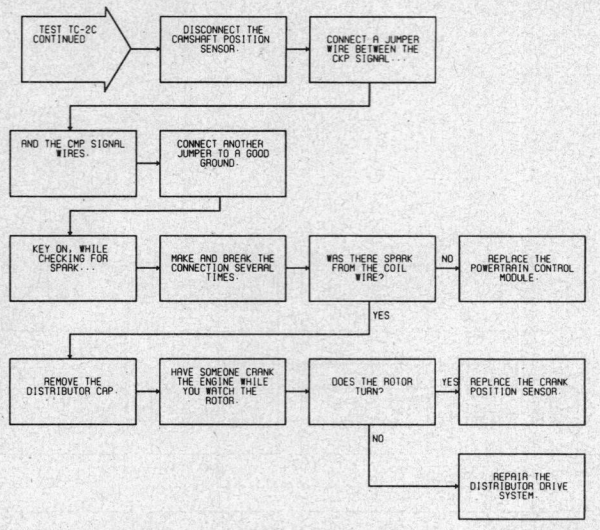

Fig. 85   Test TC-2C: Repairing No Crank Reference Signal At PCM (Part 3 of 3). 2.5L/4-153 engine

CR1029302787030X

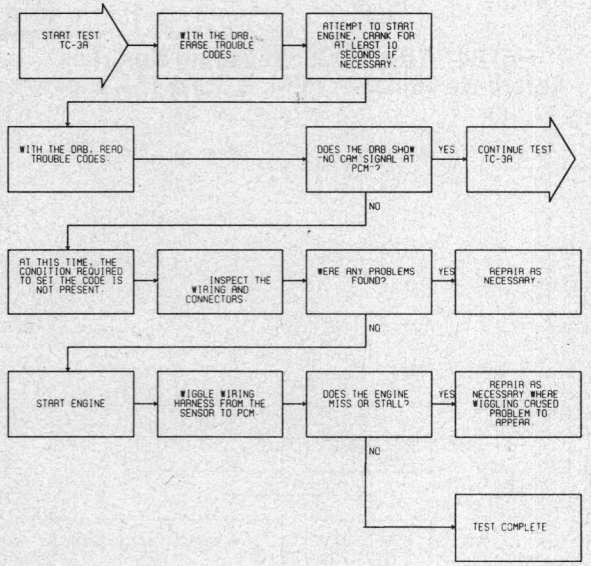

Fig. 87   Test TC-3A: Repairing No Cam Sync Signal At PCM (Part 1 of 3). 2.5L/4-153 engine

CR1029302789010X

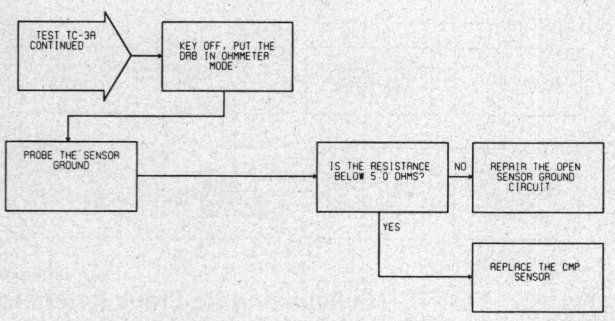

Fig. 87   Test TC-3A: Repairing No Cam Sync Signal At PCM (Part 3 of 3). 2.5L/4-153 engine

CR1029302789030X

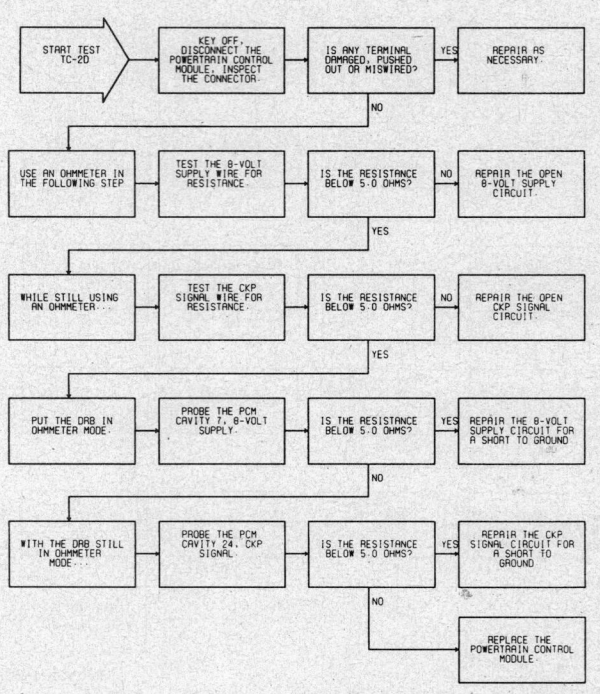

Fig. 86   Test TC-2D: Repairing No Crank Reference Signal At PCM. 2.5L/4-153 engine

CR1029302788000X

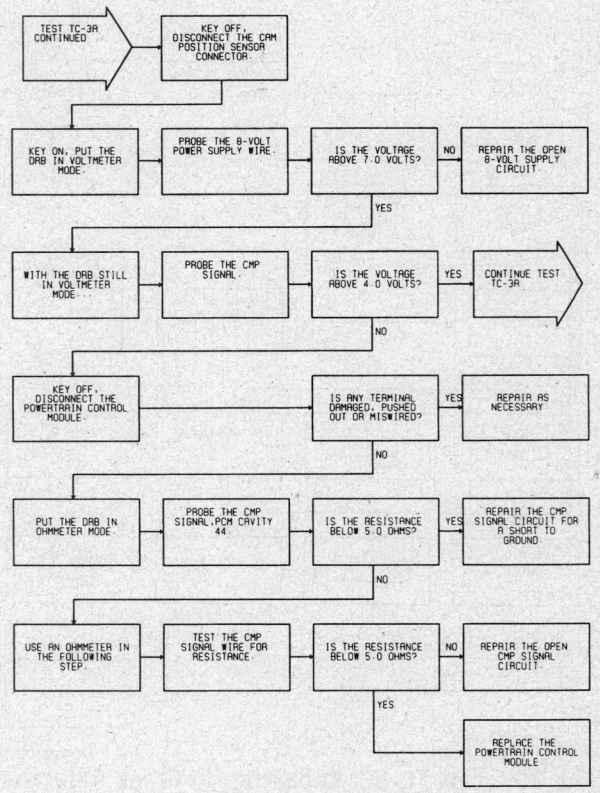

Fig. 87   Test TC-3A: Repairing No Cam Sync Signal At PCM (Part 2 of 3). 2.5L/4-153 engine

CR1029302789020X

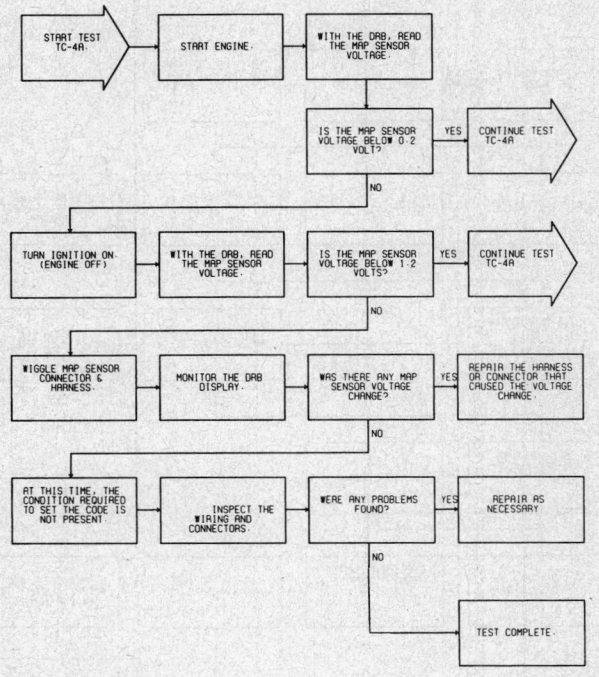

Fig. 88   Test TC-4A: Repairing MAP Sensor Voltage Too Low (Part 1 of 2). 2.5L/4-153 engine

CR1029302790010X

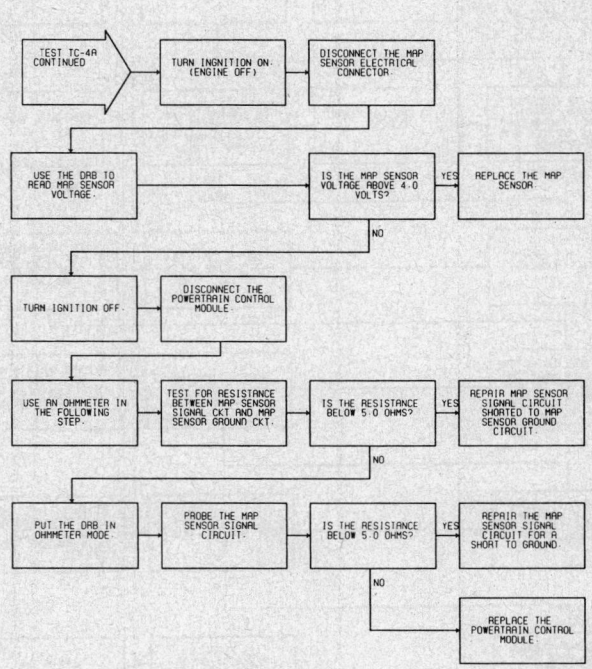

Fig. 88   Test TC-4A: Repairing MAP Sensor Voltage Too Low (Part 2 of 2). 2.5L/4-153 engine

CR1029302790020X

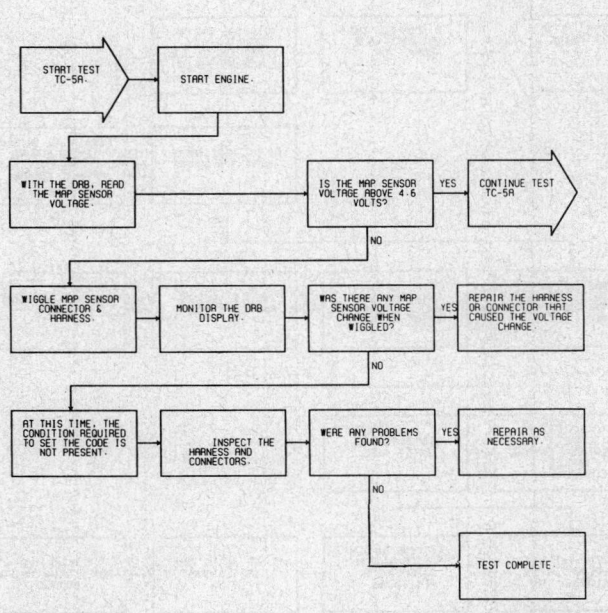

Fig. 89   Test TC-5A: Repairing MAP Sensor Voltage Too High (Part 1 of 2). 2.5L/4-153 engine

CR1029302791010X

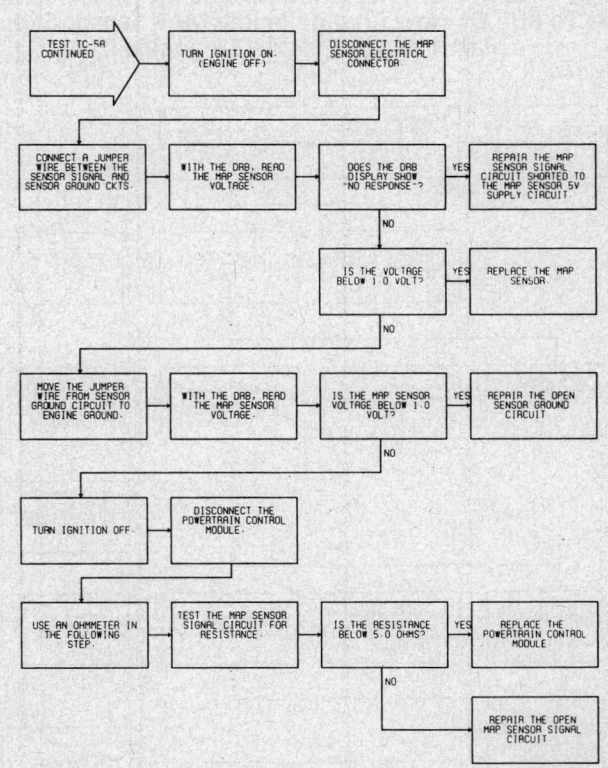

Fig. 89   Test TC-5A: Repairing MAP Sensor Voltage Too High (Part 2 of 2). 2.5L/4-153 engine

CR1029302791020X

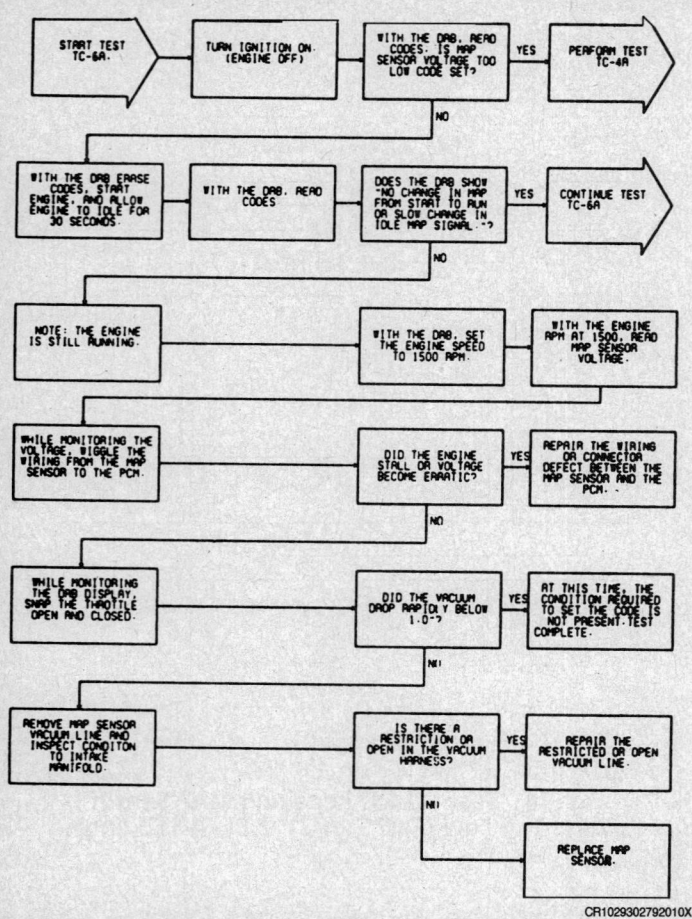

Fig. 90 Test TC-6A: Repairing No Change In MAP From Start To Run Or Slow Change In Idle MAP Sensor Signal (Part 1 of 2). 2.5L/4-153 engine

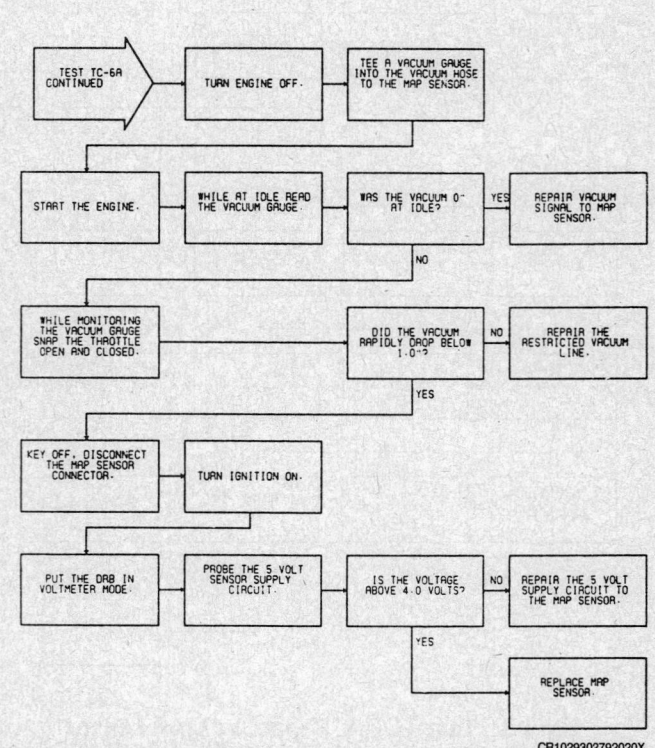

Fig. 90 Test TC-6A: Repairing No Change In MAP From Start To Run Or Slow Change In Idle MAP Sensor Signal (Part 2 of 2). 2.5L/4-153 engine

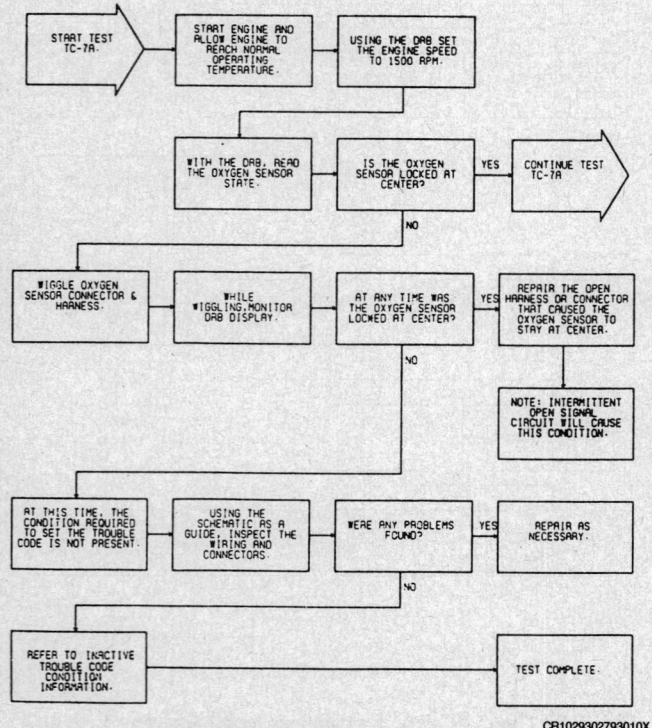

Fig. 91 Test TC-7A: Repairing O₂S Stays At Center (Part 1 of 2). 2.5L/4-153 engine

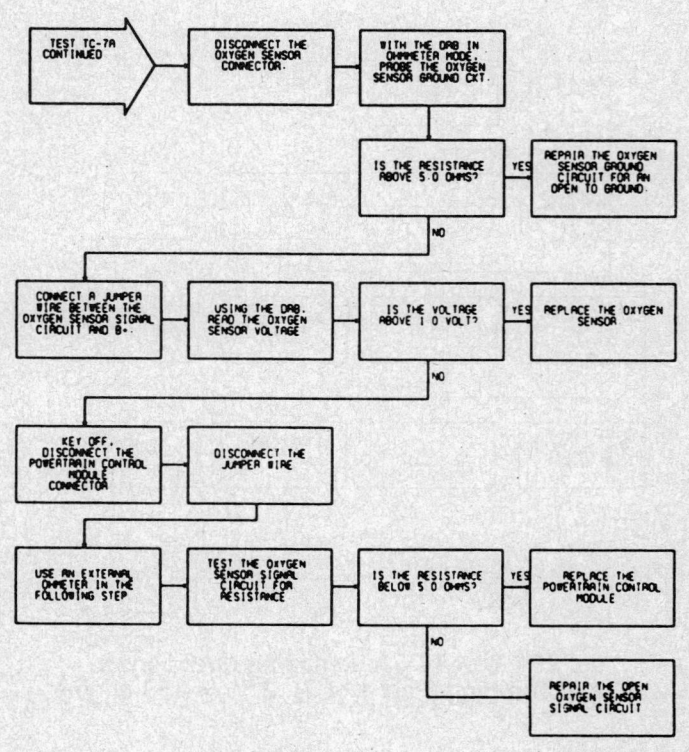

Fig. 91 Test TC-7A: Repairing O₂S Stays At Center (Part 2 of 2). 2.5L/4-153 engine

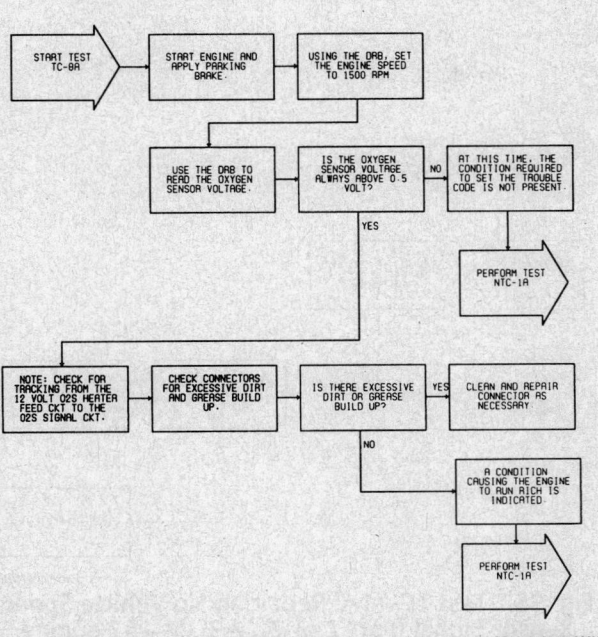

Fig. 92   Test TC-8A: Repairing O2S Stays Above Center, Rich. 2.5L/4-153 engine

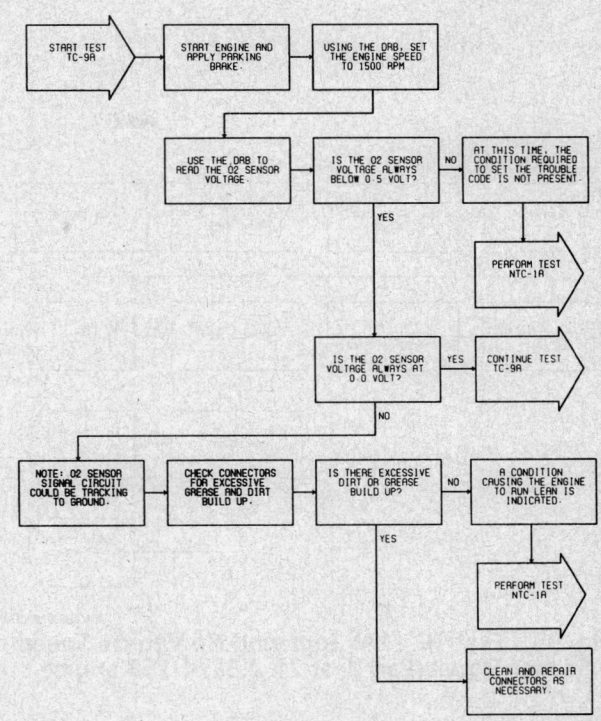

Fig. 93   Test TC-9A: Repairing O2S Stays Below Center, Lean (Part 1 of 2). 2.5L/4-153 engine

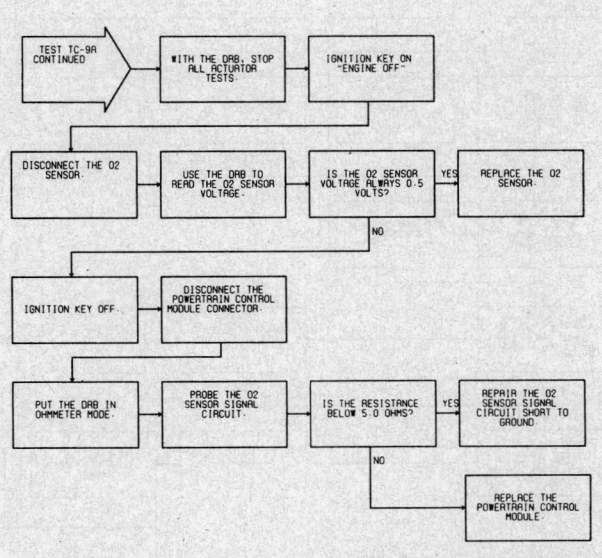

Fig. 93   Test TC-9A: Repairing O2S Stays Below Center, Lean (Part 2 of 2). 2.5L/4-153 engine

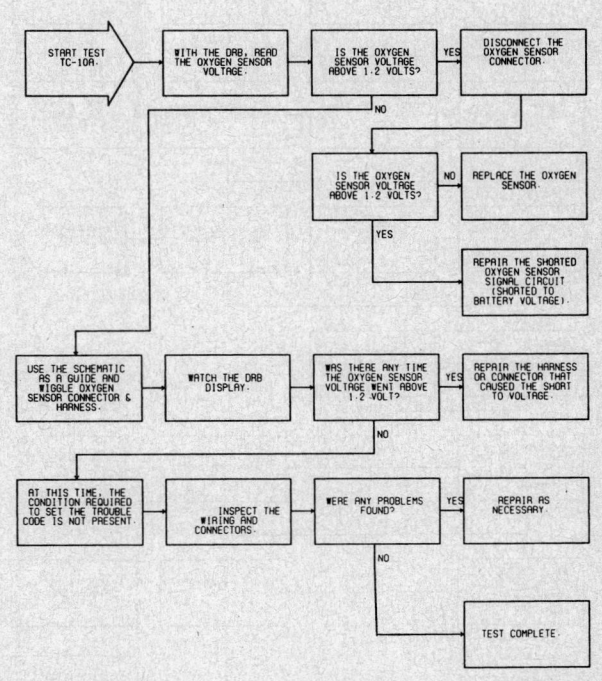

Fig. 94   Test TC-10A: Repairing O2S Shorted To Voltage. 2.5L/4-153 engine

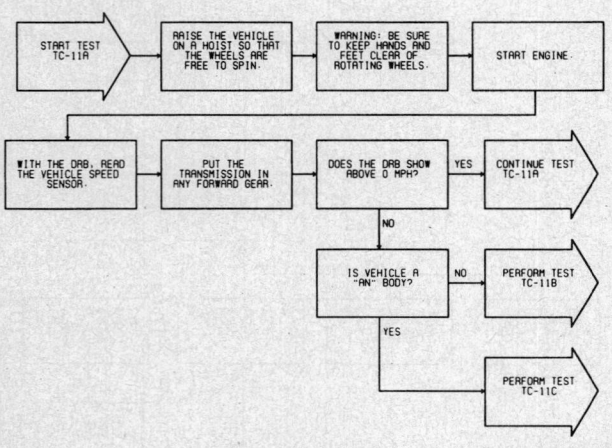

Fig. 95 Test TC-11A: Repairing No Vehicle Speed Sensor Signal (Part 1 of 2). 2.5L/4-153 engine

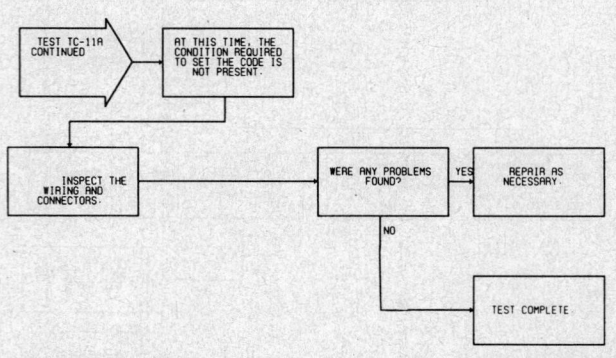

Fig. 95 Test TC-11A: Repairing No Vehicle Speed Sensor Signal (Part 2 of 2). 2.5L/4-153 engine

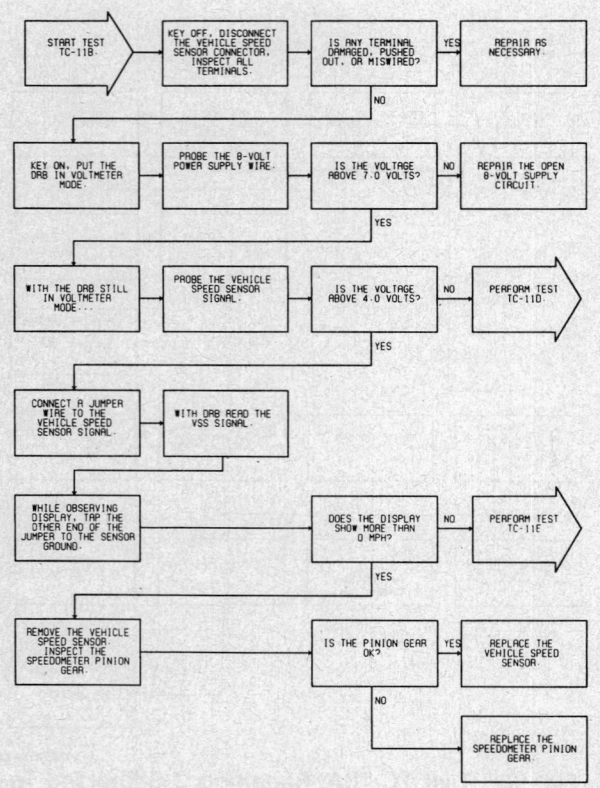

Fig. 96 Test TC-11B: Repairing No Vehicle Speed Sensor Signal. 2.5L/4-153 engine

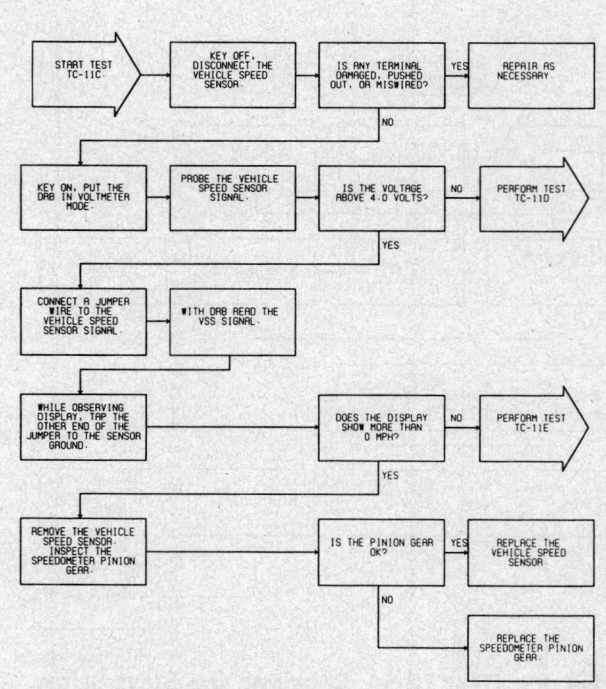

Fig. 97 Test TC-11C: Repairing No Vehicle Speed Sensor Signal. 2.5L/4-153 engine

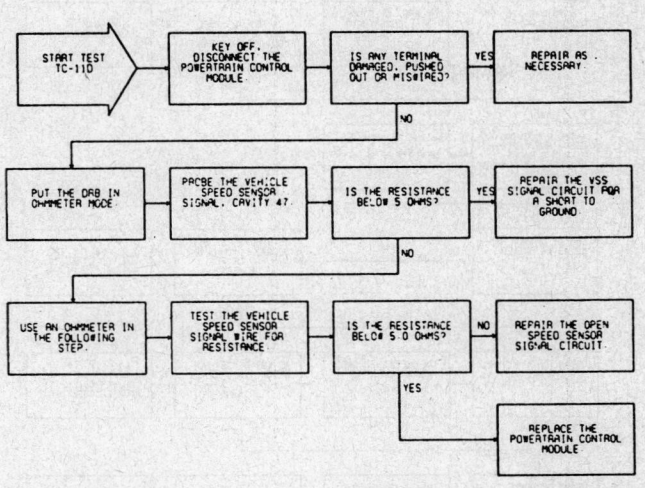

Fig. 98   Test TC-11D: Repairing No Vehicle Speed Sensor Signal. 2.5L/4-153 engine

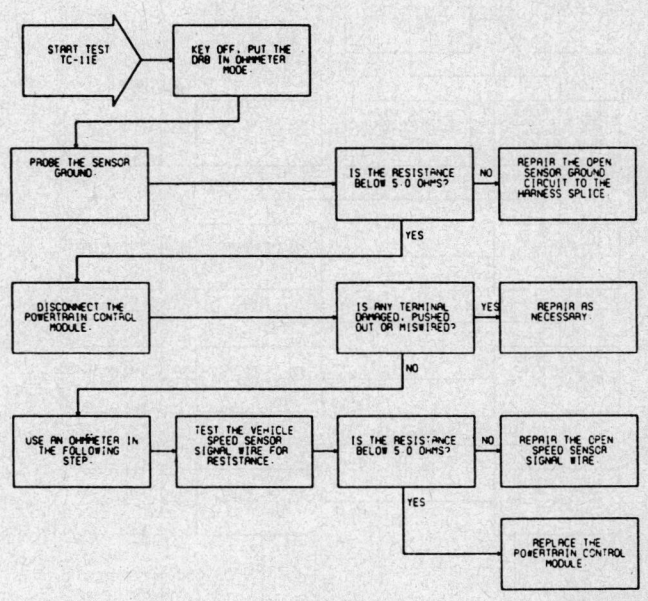

Fig. 99   Test TC-11E: Repairing No Vehicle Speed Sensor Signal. 2.5L/4-153 engine

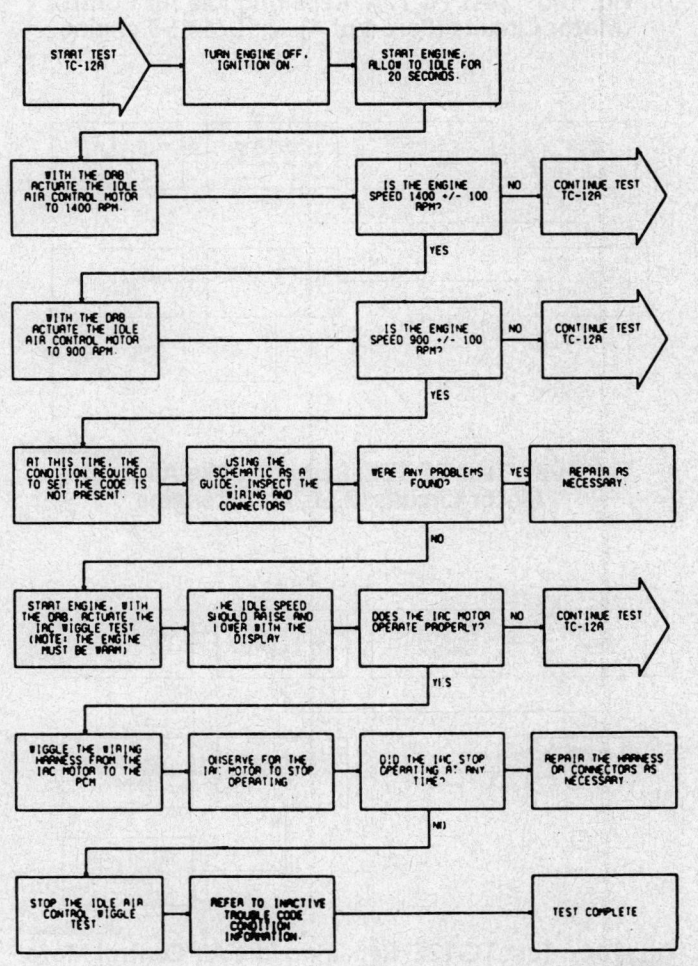

Fig. 100   Test TC-12A: Repairing Idle Air Control Motor Circuits (Part 1 of 4). 2.5L/4-153 engine

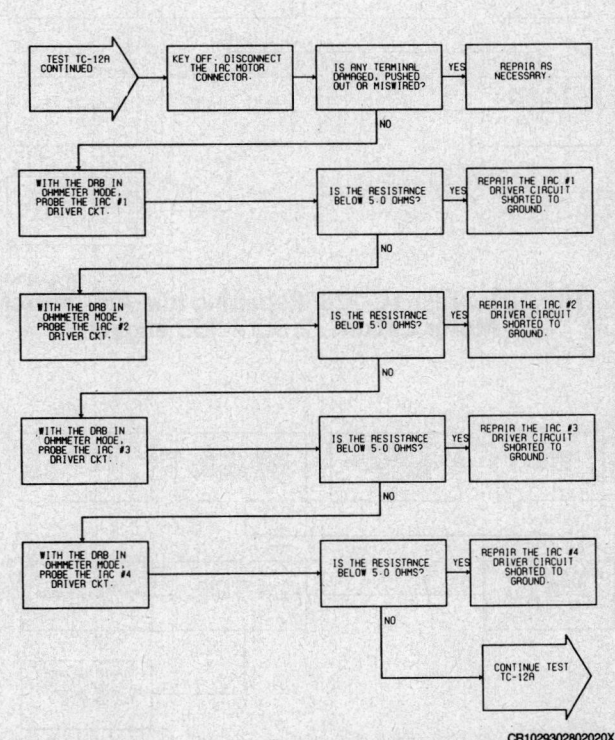

Fig. 100   Test TC-12A: Repairing Idle Air Control Motor Circuits (Part 2 of 4). 2.5L/4-153 engine

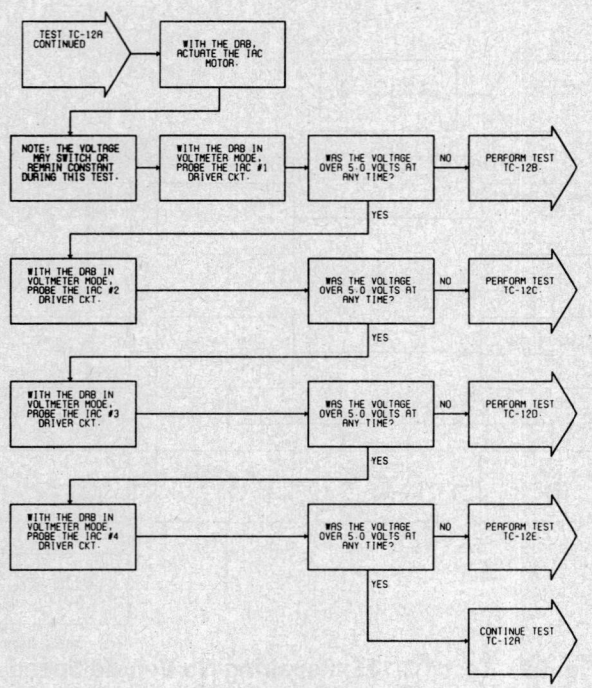

Fig. 100   Test TC-12A: Repairing Idle Air Control Motor Circuits (Part 3 of 4). 2.5L/4-153 engine

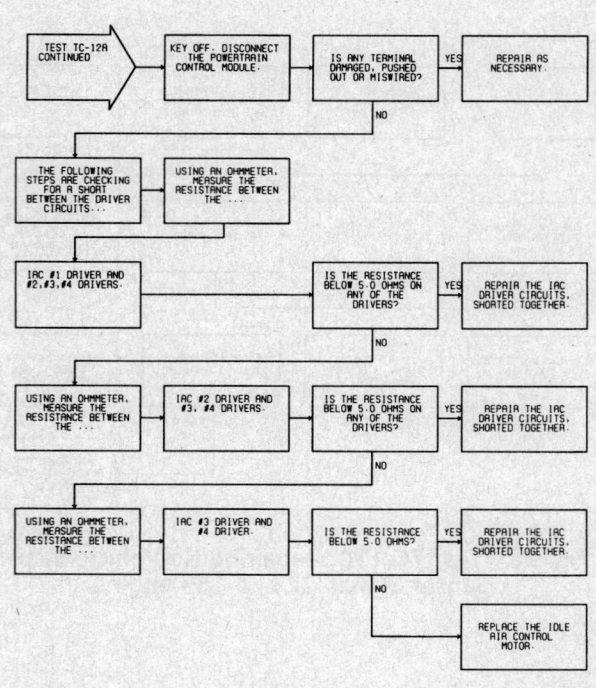

Fig. 100   Test TC-12A: Repairing Idle Air Control Motor Circuits (Part 4 of 4). 2.5L/4-153 engine

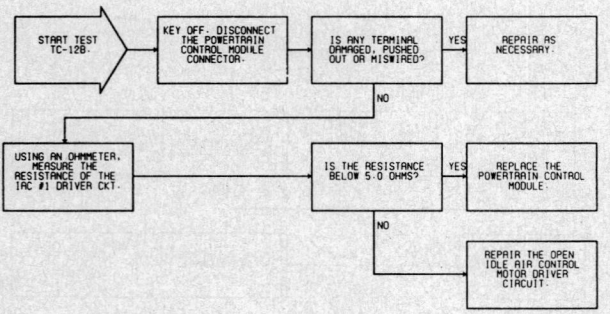

Fig. 101   Test TC-12B: Repairing Idle Air Control Motor Circuits. 2.5L/4-153 engine

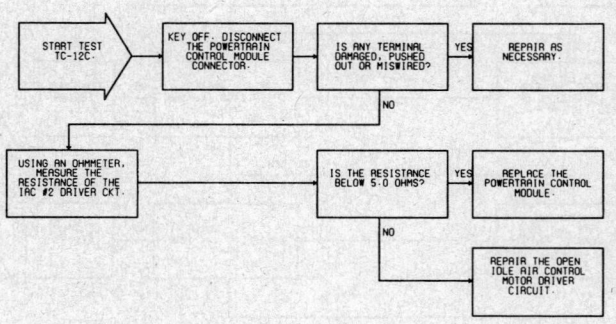

Fig. 102   Test TC-12C: Repairing Idle Air Control Motor Circuits. 2.5L/4-153 engine

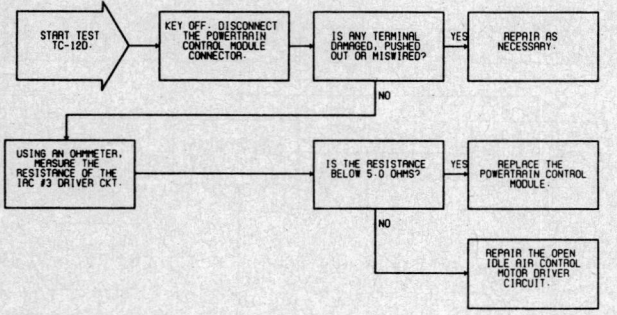

Fig. 103   Test TC-12D: Repairing Idle Air Control Motor Circuits. 2.5L/4-153 engine

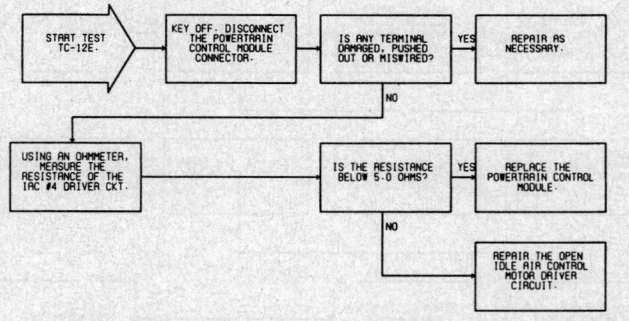

Fig. 104   Test TC-12E: Repairing Idle Air Control Motor Circuits. 2.5L/4-153 engine

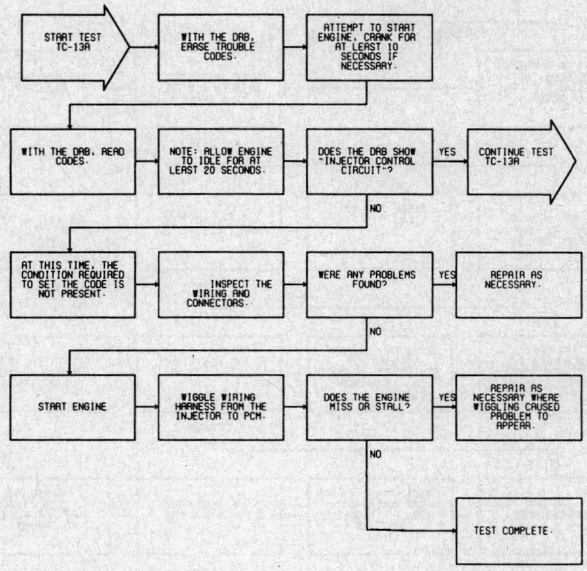

Refer to the chart below and perform the diagnostic test that corresponds to the trouble code displayed on the DRB.

TROUBLE CODE	DIAGNOSTIC TEST	
	2.5 TBI	2.5 FLEX FUEL
INJECTOR #1 CONTROL CIRCUIT	TC-13B	TC-13C
INJECTOR #2 CONTROL CIRCUIT		TC-14A
INJECTOR #3 CONTROL CIRCUIT		TC-15A
INJECTOR #4 CONTROL CIRCUIT		TC-16A

CR1029302807020X

Fig. 105 Test TC-13A: Repairing Injector Control Circuits (Part 2 of 2). 2.5L/4-153 engine

Fig. 105 Test TC-13A: Repairing Injector Control Circuits (Part 1 of 2). 2.5L/4-153 engine

CR1029302807010X

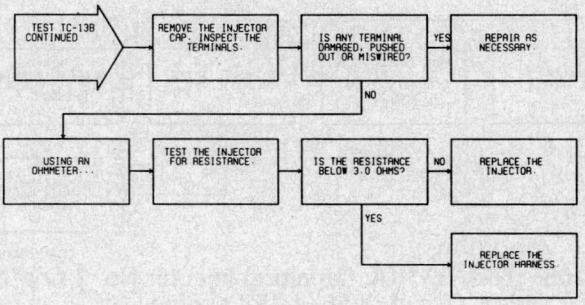

CR1029302808020X

Fig. 106 Test TC-13B: Repairing Injector Control Circuits (Part 2 of 2). 2.5L/4-153 engine

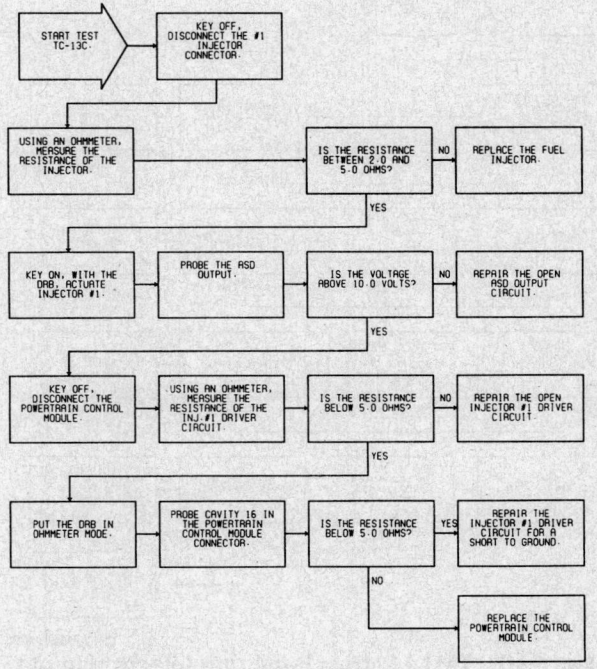

Fig. 106 Test TC-13B: Repairing Injector Control Circuits (Part 1 of 2). 2.5L/4-153 engine

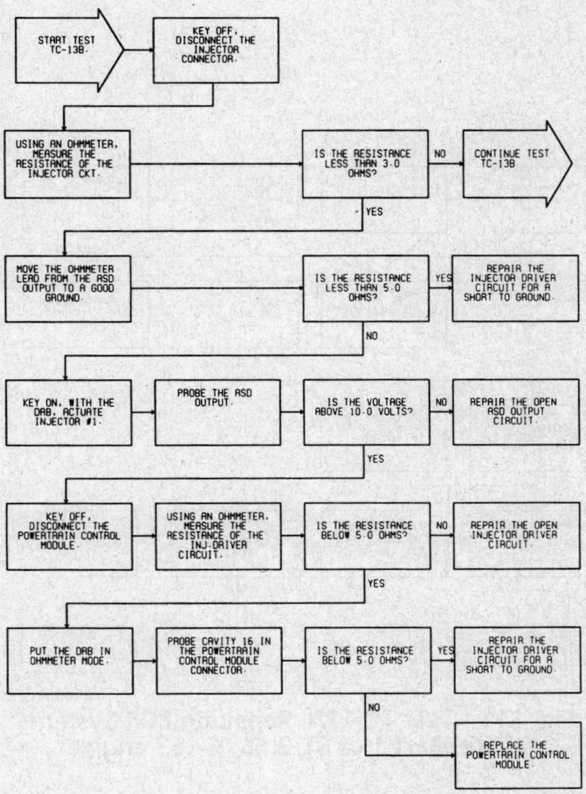

CR1029302808010X

Fig. 107 Test TC-13C: Repairing Injector Control Circuits. 2.5L/4-153 engine

CR1029302809000X

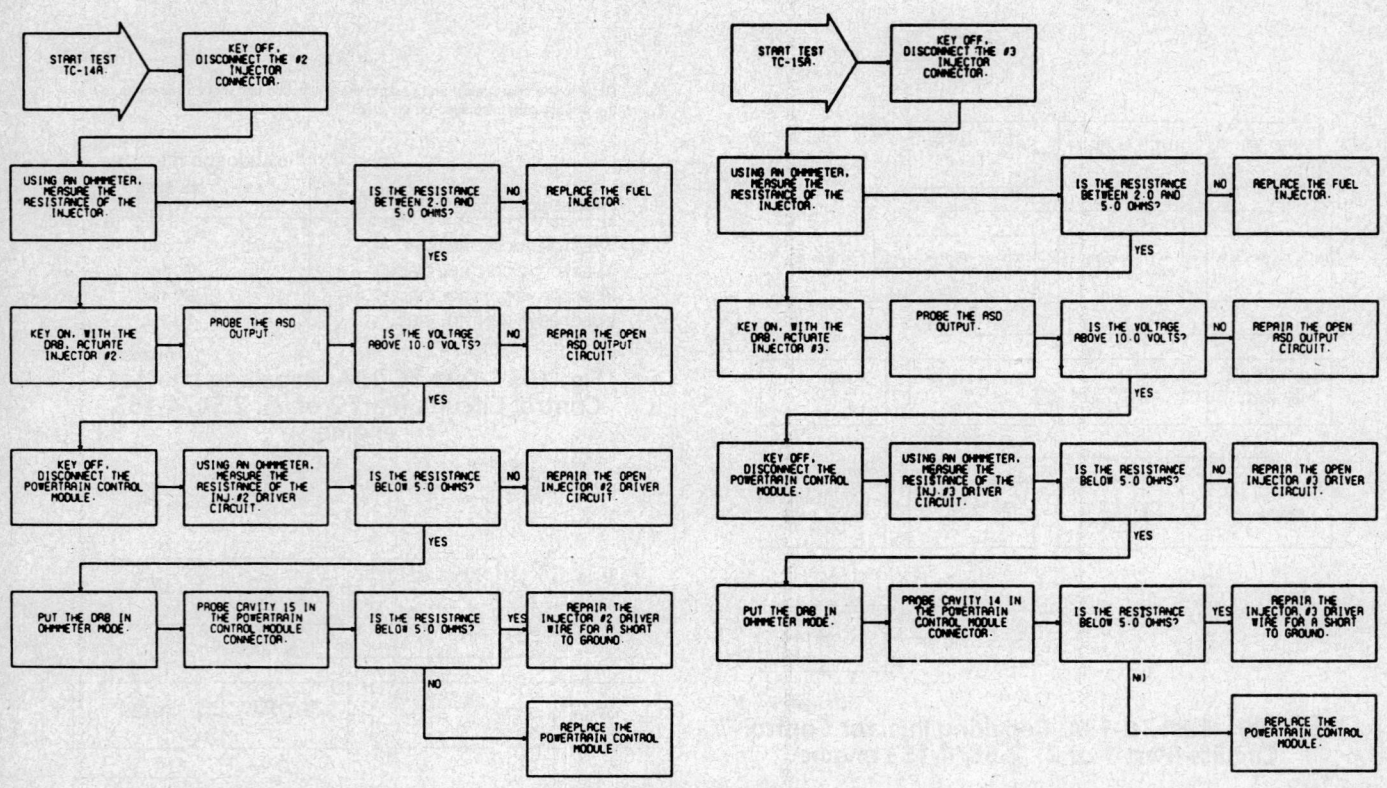

Fig. 108   Test TC-14A: Repairing Injector No. 2 Control Circuit. 2.5L/4-153 engine

Fig. 109   Test TC-15A: Repairing Injector No. 3 Control Circuit. 2.5L/4-153 engine

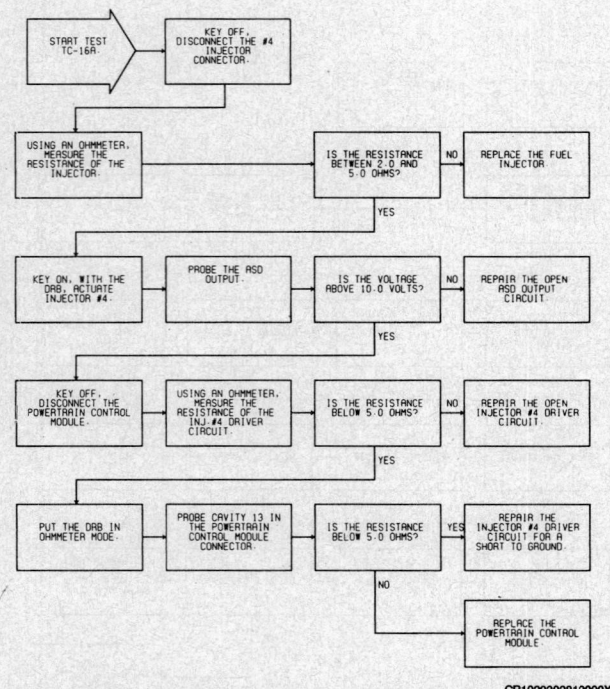

Fig. 110   Test TC-16A: Repairing Injector No. 4 Control Circuit. 2.5L/4-153 engine

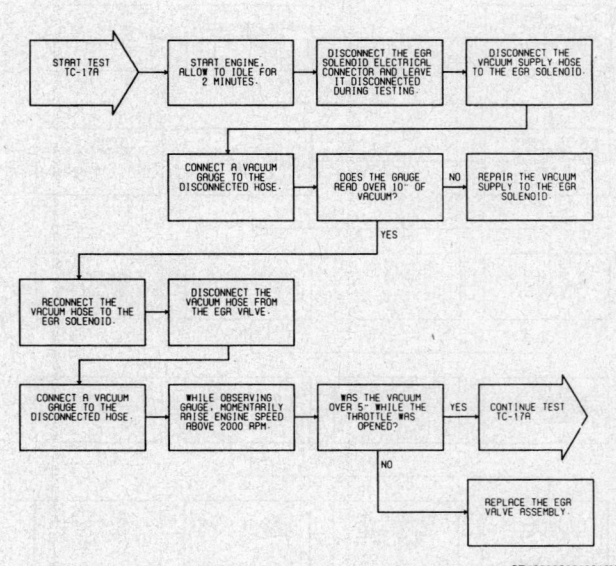

Fig. 111   Test TC-17A: Repairing EGR System Failure (Part 1 of 3). 2.5L/4-153 engine

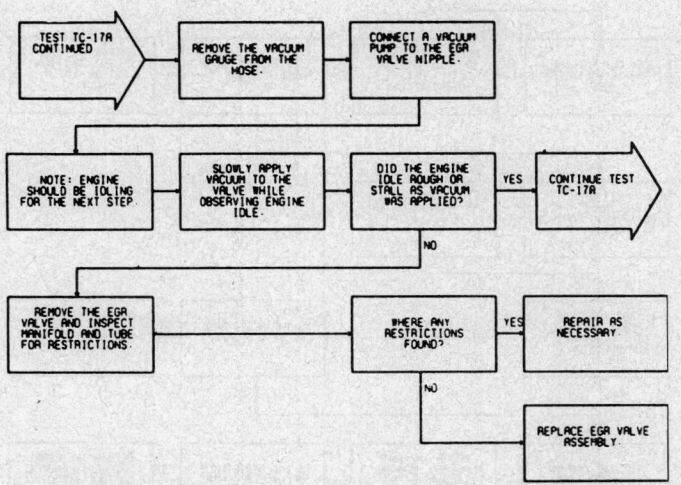

Fig. 111 Test TC-17A: Repairing EGR System Failure (Part 2 of 3). 2.5L/4-153 engine

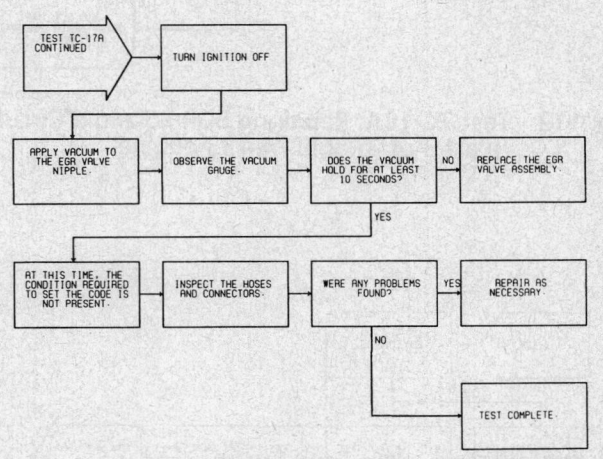

Fig. 111 Test TC-17A: Repairing EGR System Failure (Part 3 of 3). 2.5L/4-153 engine

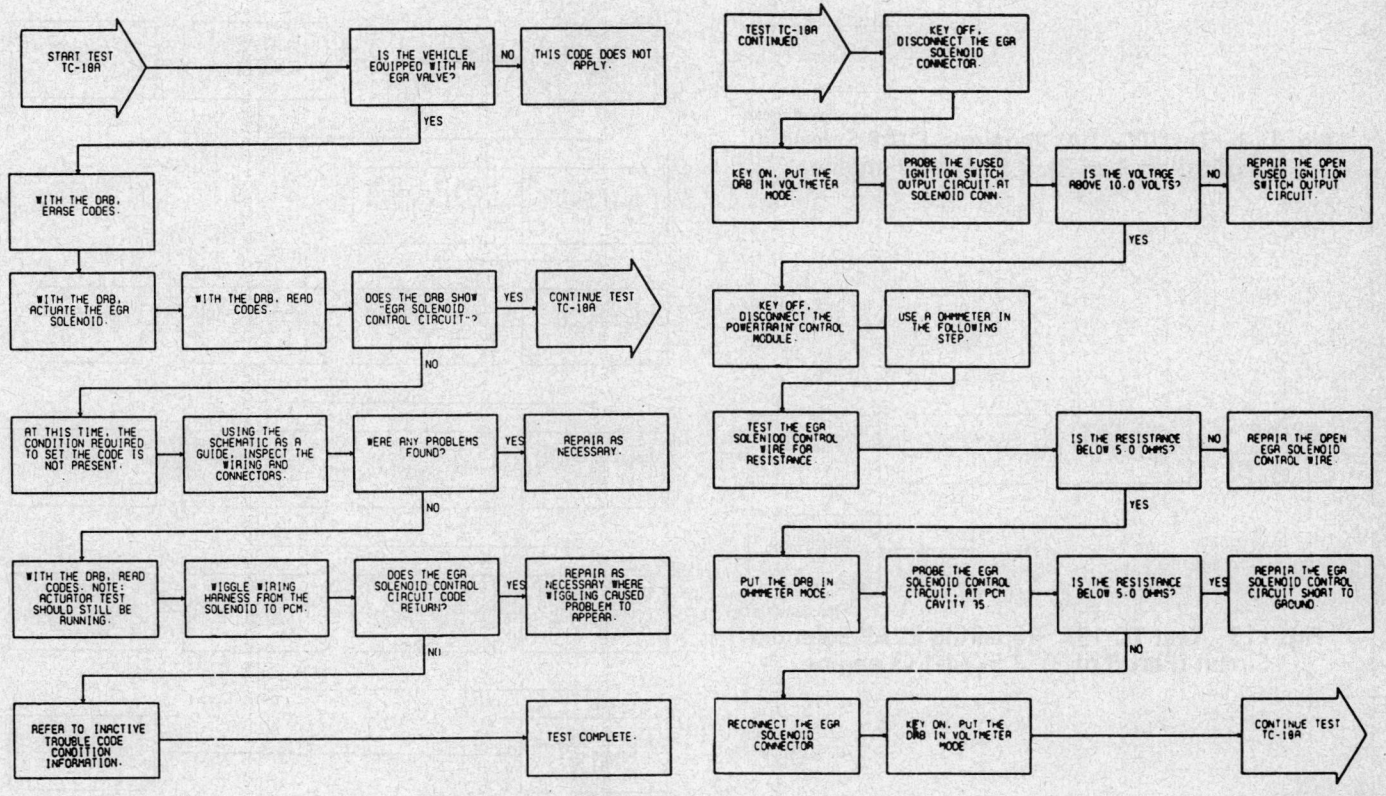

Fig. 112 Test TC-18A: Repairing EGR Solenoid Circuit (Part 1 of 3). 2.5L/4-153 engine

Fig. 112 Test TC-18A: Repairing EGR Solenoid Circuit (Part 2 of 3). 2.5L/4-153 engine

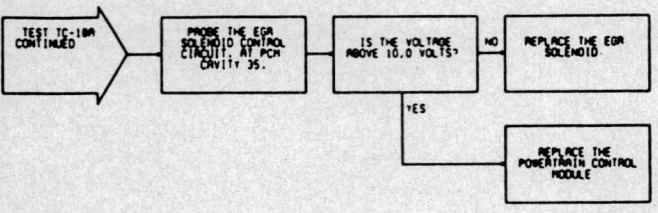

Fig. 112 Test TC-18A: Repairing EGR Solenoid Circuit (Part 3 of 3). 2.5L/4-153 engine

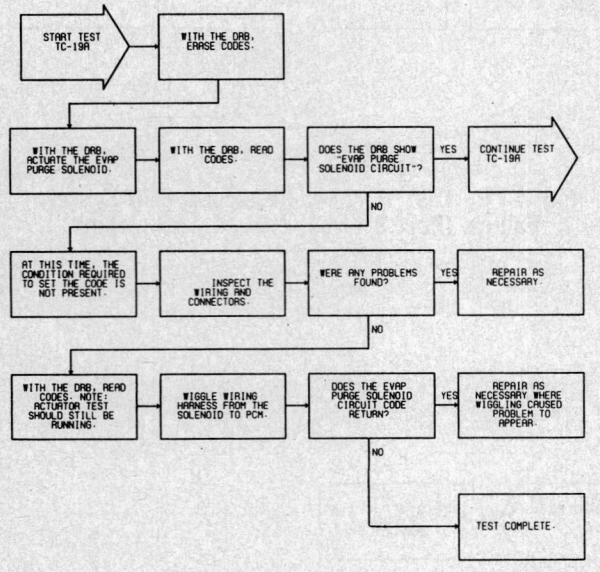

Fig. 113 Test TC-19A: Repairing EVAP Solenoid Circuit (Part 1 of 3). 2.5L/4-153 engine

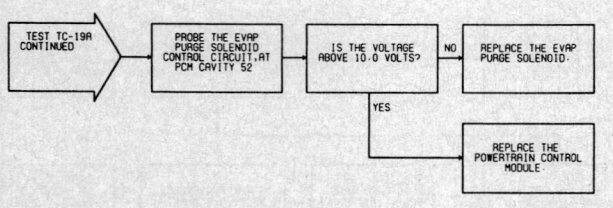

Fig. 113 Test TC-19A: Repairing EVAP Solenoid Circuit (Part 3 of 3). 2.5L/4-153 engine

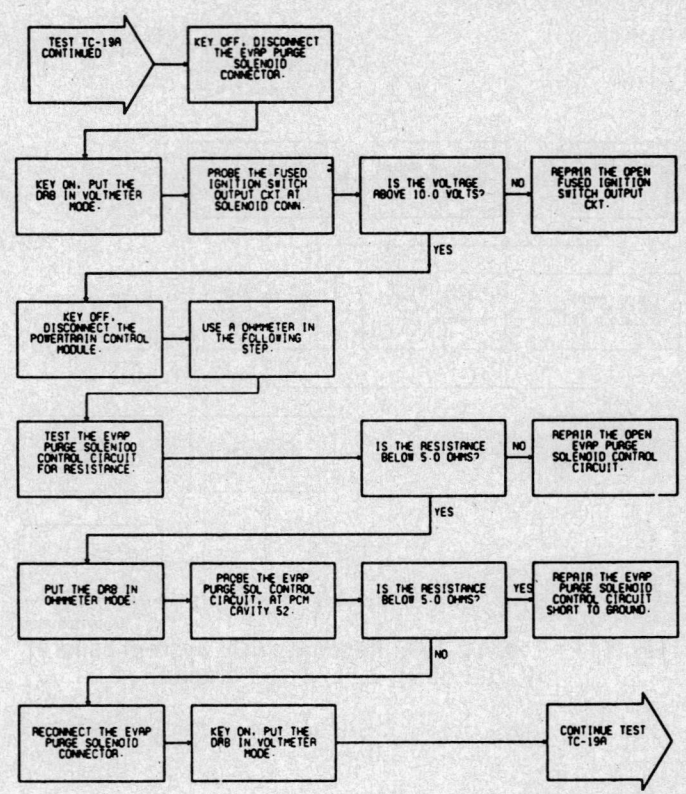

Fig. 113 Test TC-19A: Repairing EVAP Solenoid Circuit (Part 2 of 3). 2.5L/4-153 engine

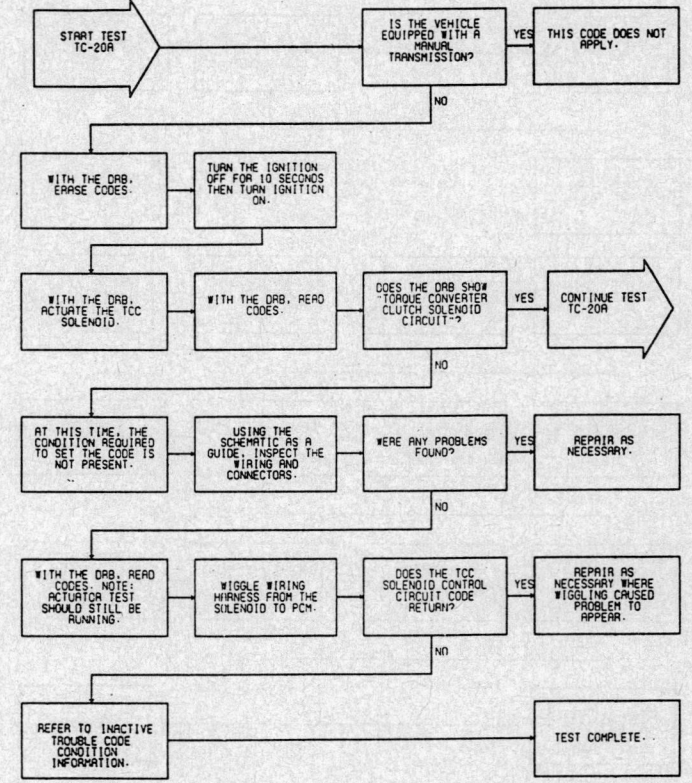

Fig. 114 Test TC-20A: Repairing Torque Converter Clutch Solenoid Circuit (Part 1 of 3). 2.5L/4-153 engine

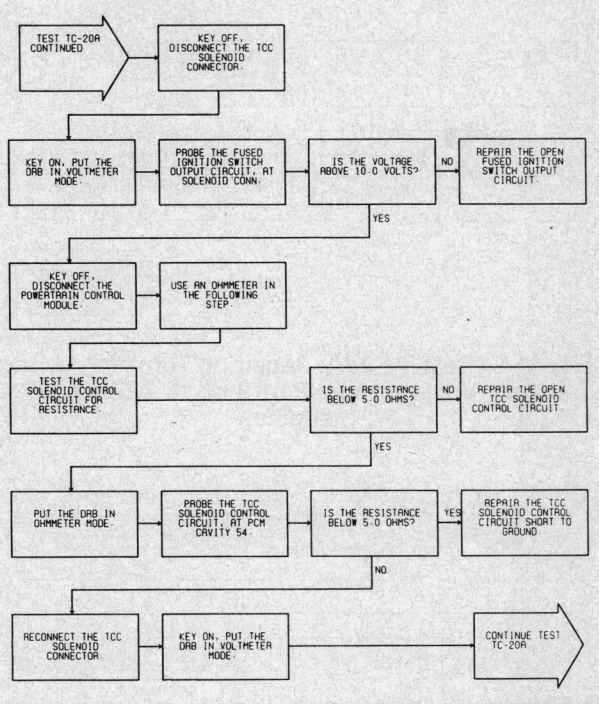

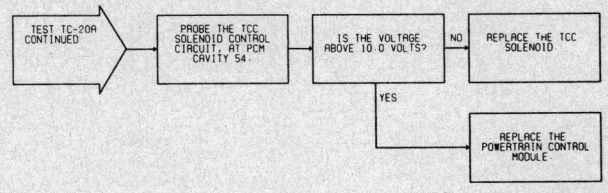

Fig. 114 Test TC-20A: Repairing Torque Converter Clutch Solenoid Circuit (Part 3 of 3). 2.5L/4-153 engine

Fig. 114 Test TC-20A: Repairing Torque Converter Clutch Solenoid Circuit (Part 2 of 3). 2.5L/4-153 engine

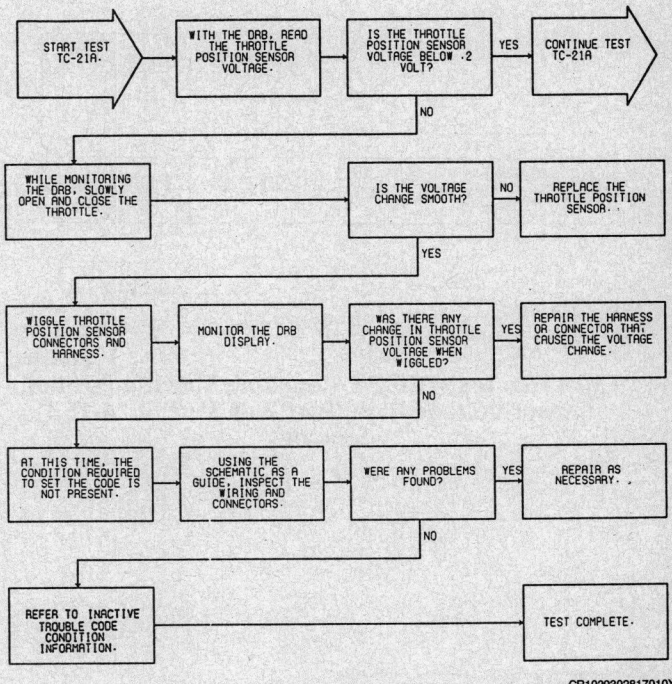

Fig. 115 Test TC-21A: Repairing Throttle Position Sensor Voltage Low (Part 1 of 2). 2.5L/4-153 engine

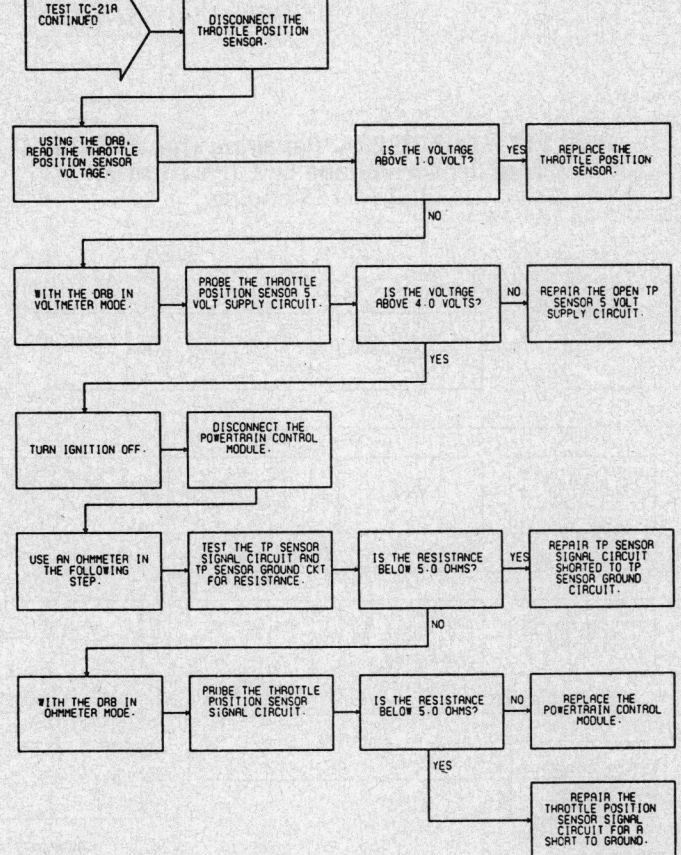

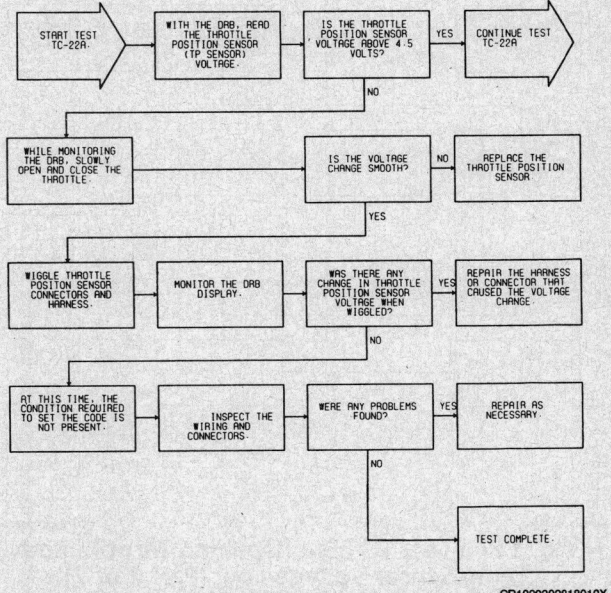

Fig. 115 Test TC-21A: Repairing Throttle Position Sensor Voltage Low (Part 2 of 2). 2.5L/4-153 engine

Fig. 116 Test TC-22A: Repairing Throttle Position Sensor Voltage High (Part 1 of 3). 2.5L/4-153 engine

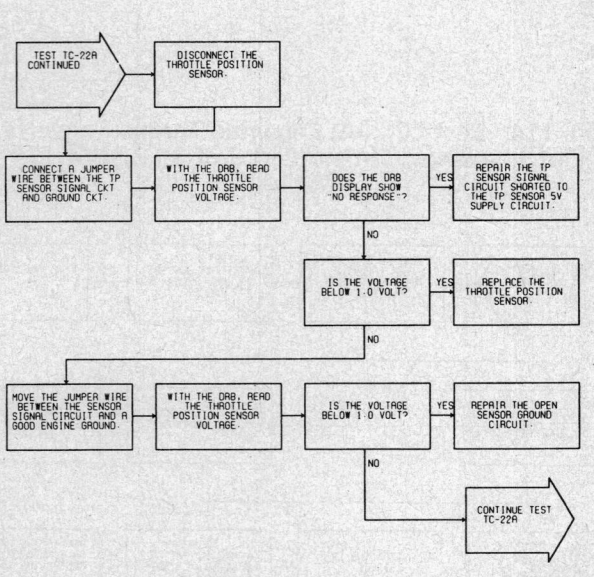

Fig. 116 Test TC-22A: Repairing Throttle Position Sensor Voltage High (Part 2 of 3). 2.5L/4-153 engine

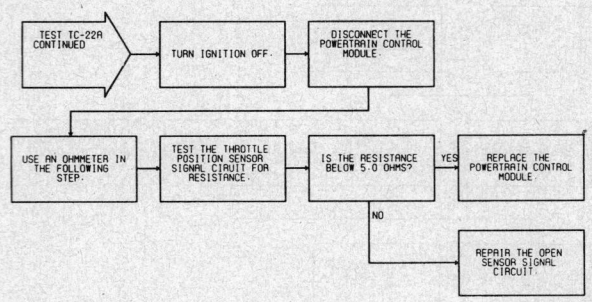

Fig. 116 Test TC-22A: Repairing Throttle Position Sensor Voltage High (Part 3 of 3). 2.5L/4-153 engine

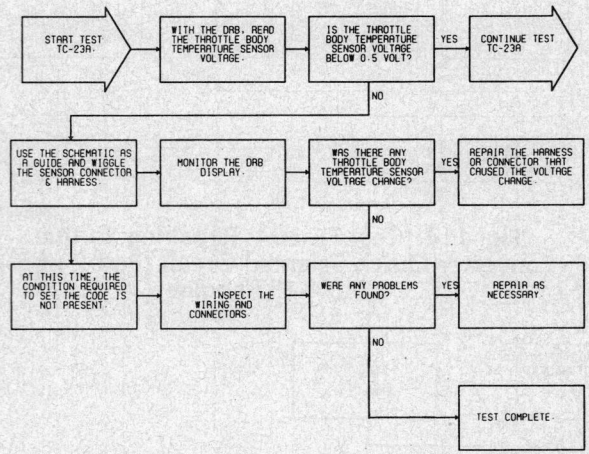

Fig. 117 Test TC-23A: Repairing Throttle Body Temp Sensor Voltage Low (Part 1 of 2). 2.5L/4-153 engine

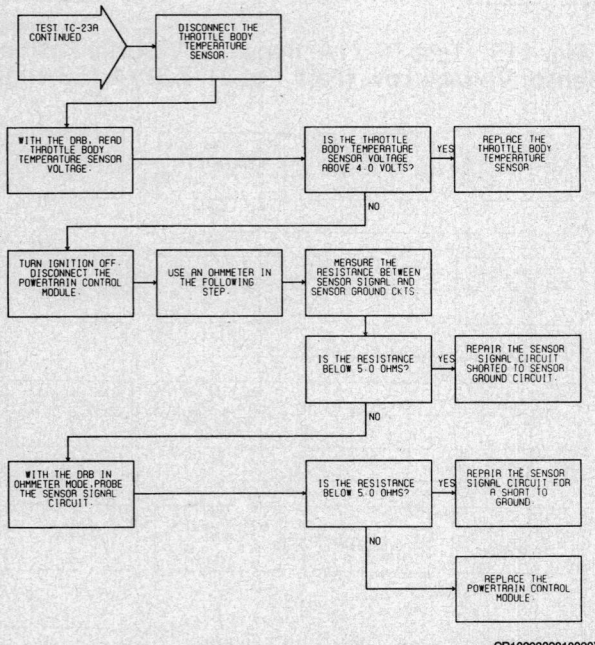

Fig. 117 Test TC-23A: Repairing Throttle Body Temp Sensor Voltage Low (Part 2 of 2). 2.5L/4-153 engine

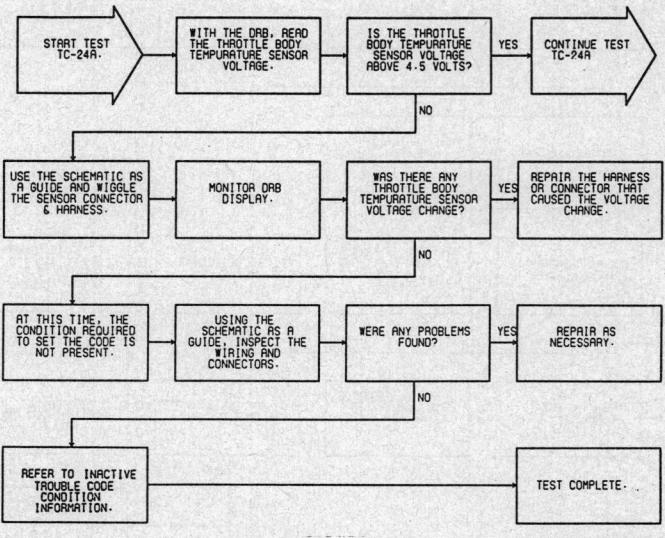

Fig. 118 Test TC-24A: Repairing Throttle Body Temp Sensor Voltage High (Part 1 of 2). 2.5L/4-153 engine

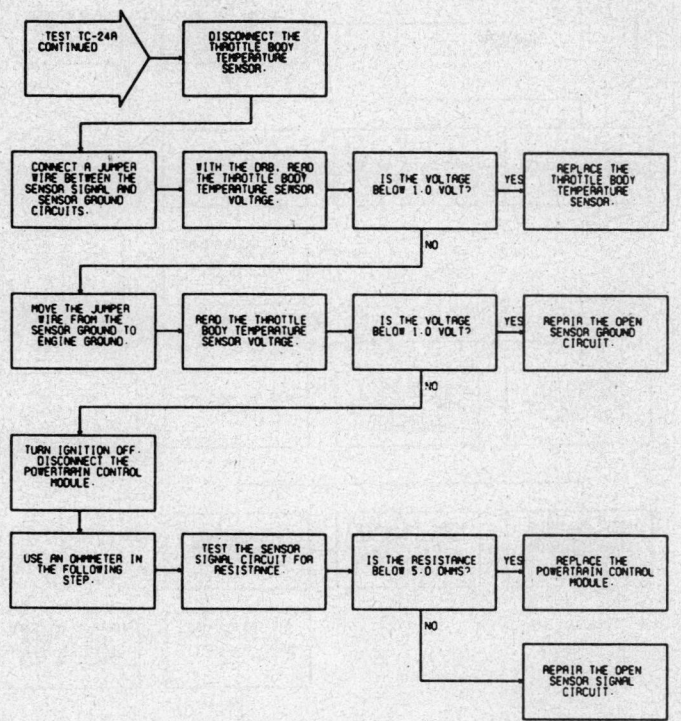

Fig. 118   Test TC-24A: Repairing Throttle Body Temp Sensor Voltage High (Part 2 of 2). 2.5L/4-153 engine

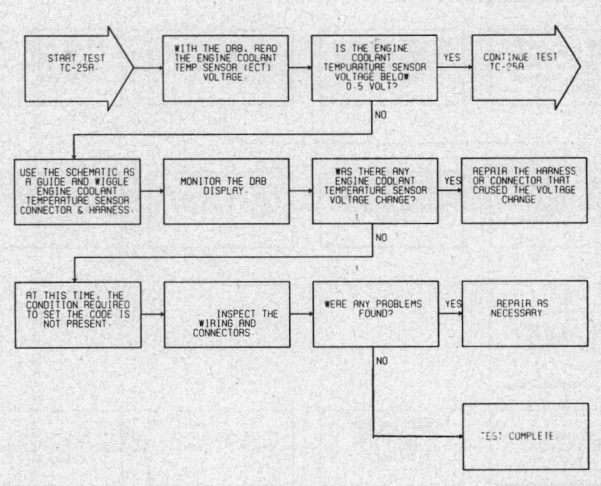

Fig. 119   Test TC-25A: Repairing ECT Sensor Voltage Too Low (Part 1 of 2). 2.5L/4-153 engine

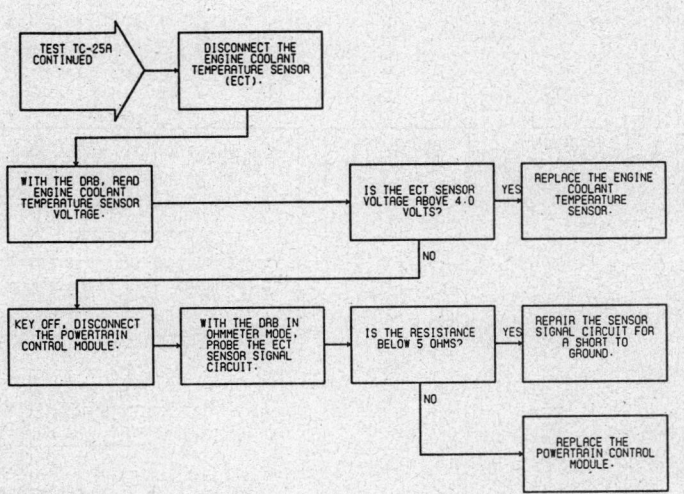

Fig. 119   Test TC-25A: Repairing ECT Sensor Voltage Too Low (Part 2 of 2). 2.5L/4-153 engine

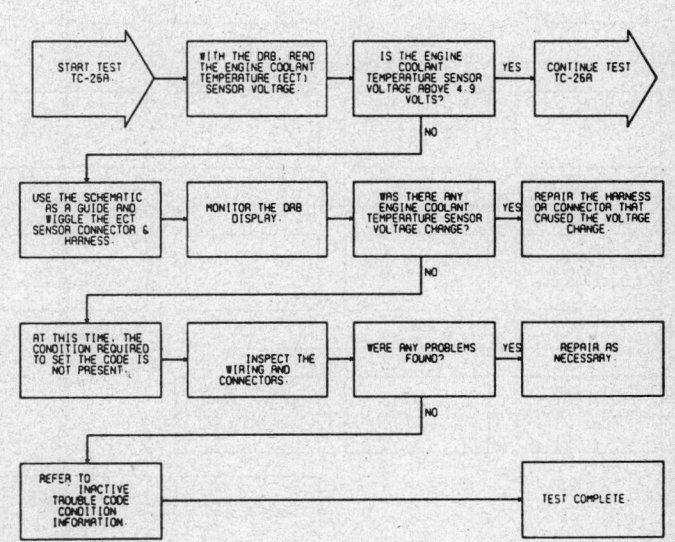

Fig. 120   Test TC-26A: Repairing ECT Sensor Voltage Too High (Part 1 of 2). 2.5L/4-153 engine

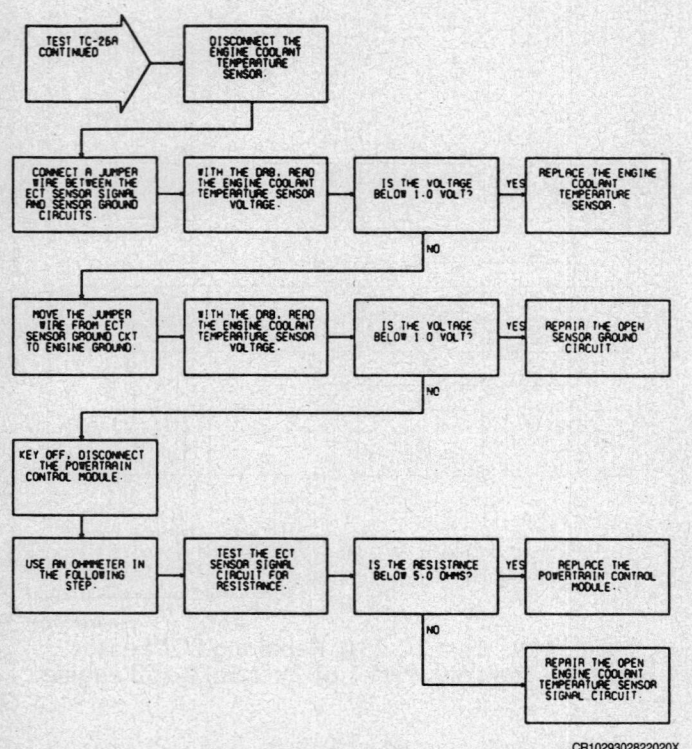

Fig. 120   Test TC-26A: Repairing ECT Sensor Voltage Too High (Part 2 of 2). 2.5L/4-153 engine

CR1029302822020X

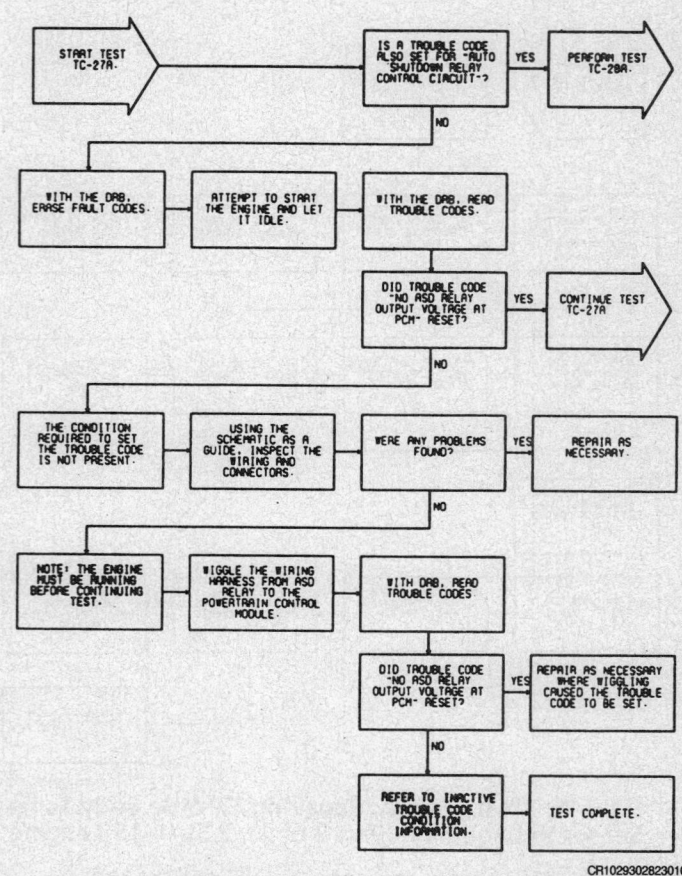

Fig. 121   Test TC-27A: Repairing No ASD Relay Output Voltage At PCM (Part 1 of 3). 2.5L/4-153 engine

CR1029302823010X

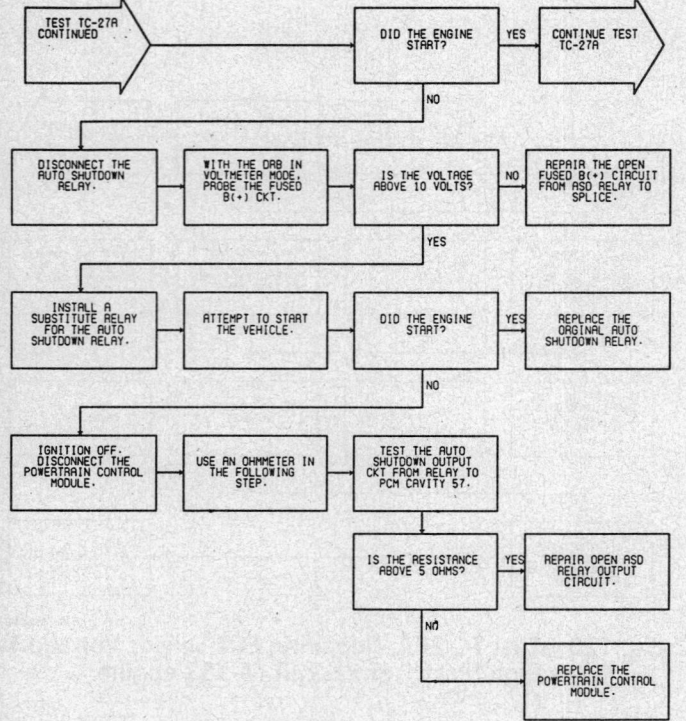

Fig. 121   Test TC-27A: Repairing No ASD Relay Output Voltage At PCM (Part 2 of 3). 2.5L/4-153 engine

CR1029302823020X

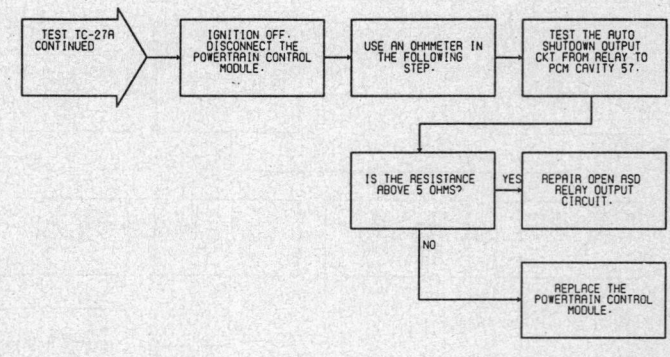

Fig. 121   Test TC-27A: Repairing No ASD Relay Output Voltage At PCM (Part 3 of 3). 2.5L/4-153 engine

CR1029302823030X

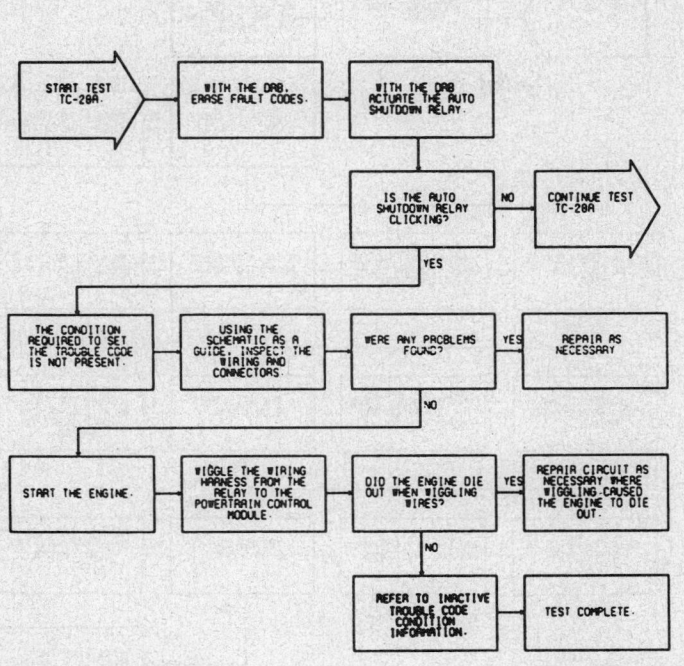

Fig. 122   Test TC-28A: Repairing Auto Shutdown Relay Control Circuit (Part 1 of 2). 2.5L/4-153 engine

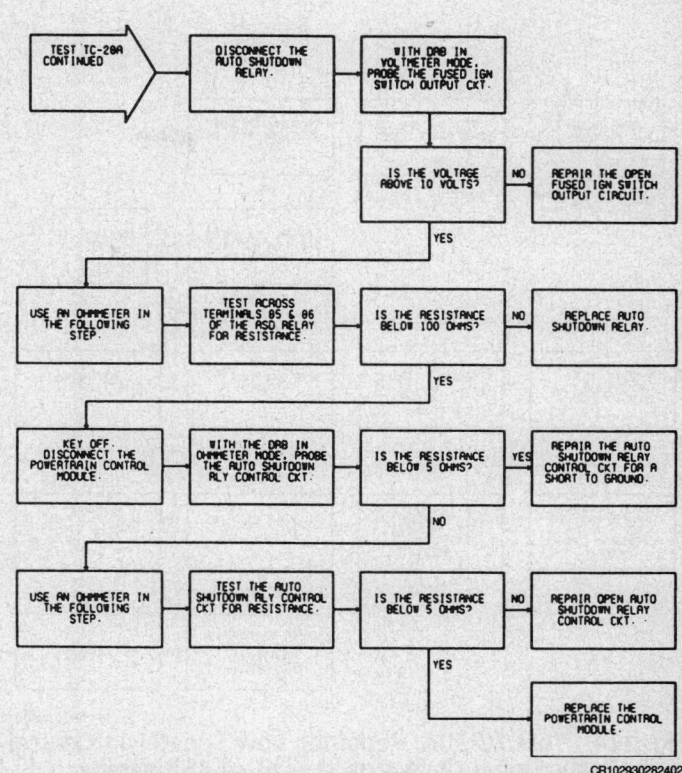

Fig. 122   Test TC-28A: Repairing Auto Shutdown Relay Control Circuit (Part 2 of 2). 2.5L/4-153 engine

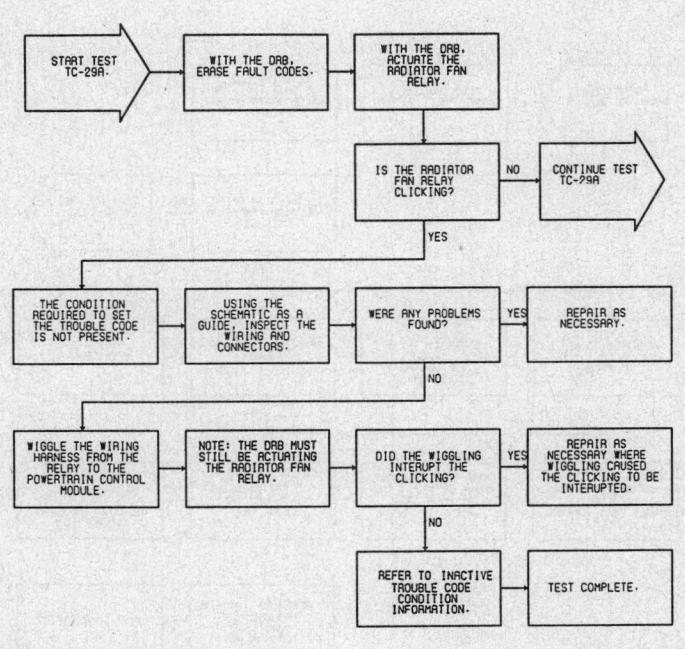

Fig. 123   Test TC-29A: Repairing RAD Fan Control Relay Circuit (Part 1 of 2). 2.5L/4-153 engine

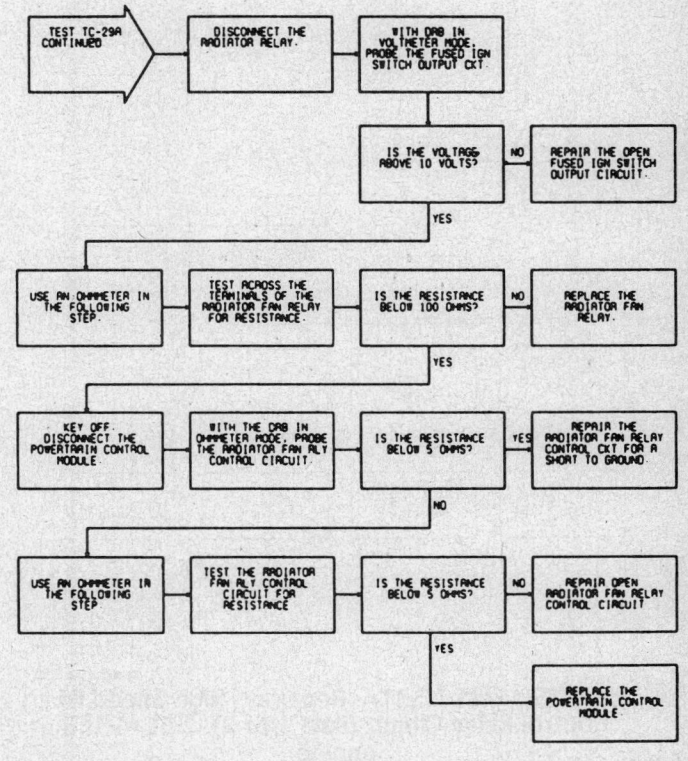

Fig. 123   Test TC-29A: Repairing RAD Fan Control Relay Circuit (Part 2 of 2). 2.5L/4-153 engine

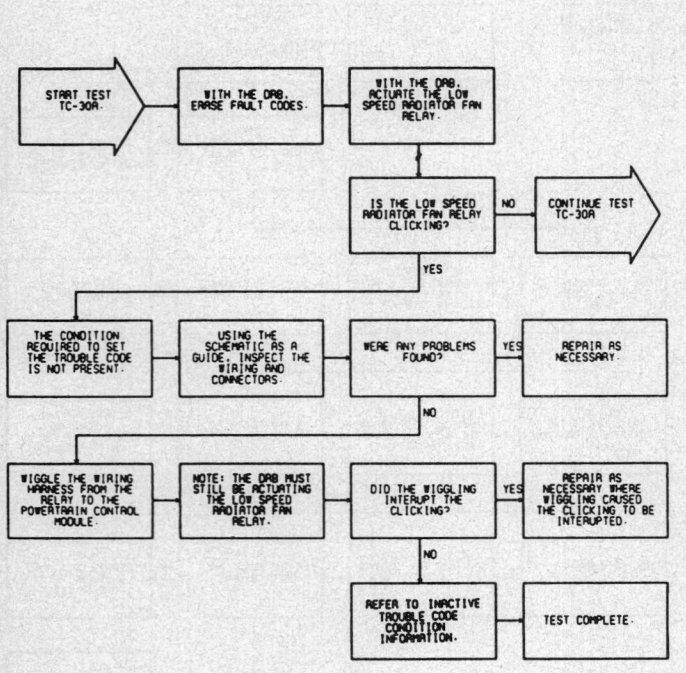

Fig. 124   Test TC-30A: Repairing Low Speed Fan Control Relay Circuit (Part 1 of 2). 2.5L/4-153 engine

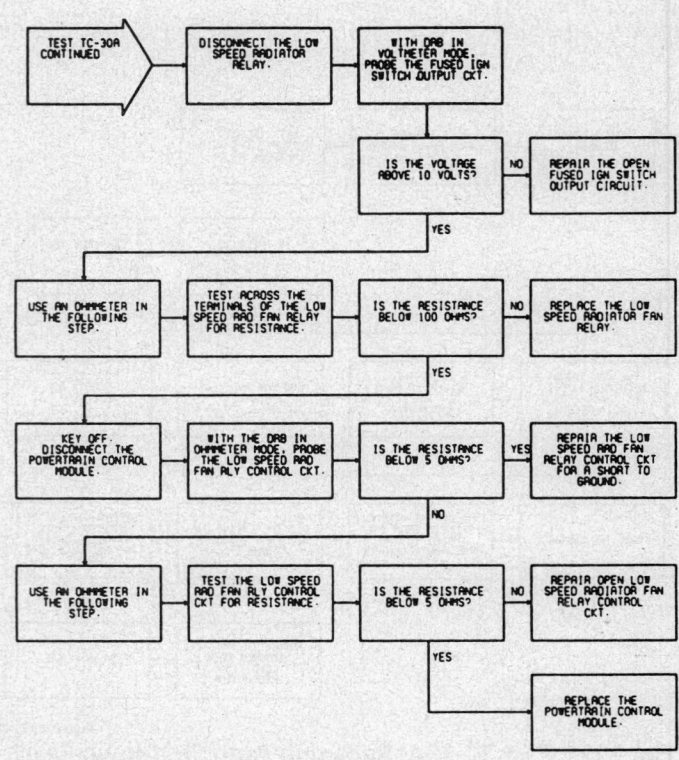

Fig. 124   Test TC-30A: Repairing Low Speed Fan Control Relay Circuit (Part 2 of 2). 2.5L/4-153 engine

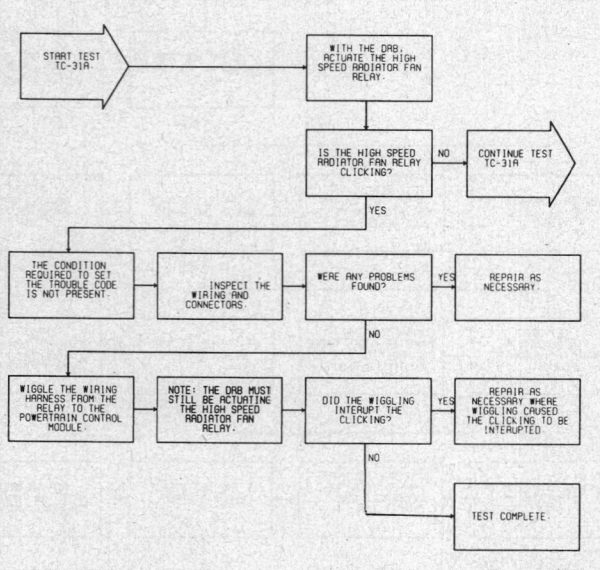

Fig. 125   Test TC-31A: Repairing High Speed Fan Control Relay Circuit (Part 1 of 2). 2.5L/4-153 engine

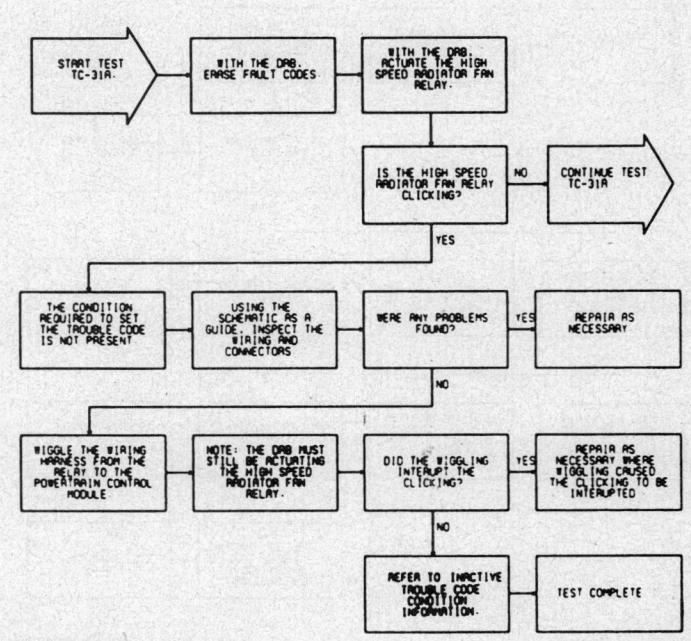

Fig. 125   Test TC-31A: Repairing High Speed Fan Control Relay Circuit (Part 2 of 2). 2.5L/4-153 engine

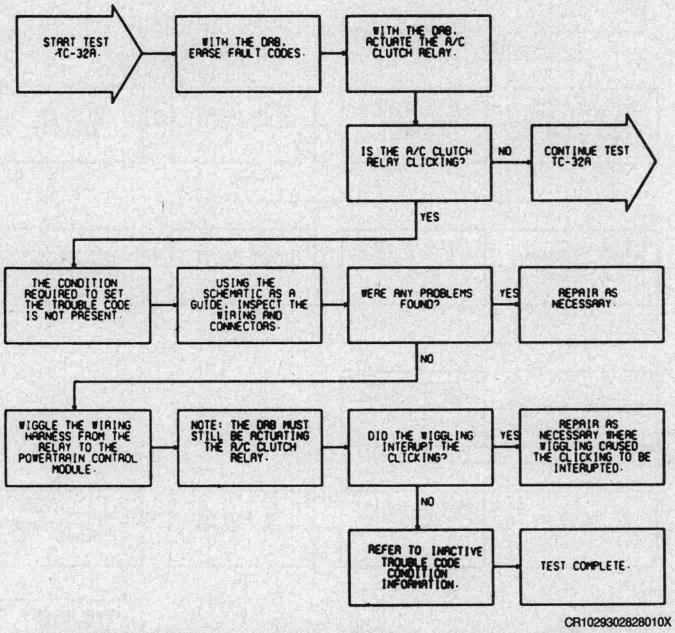

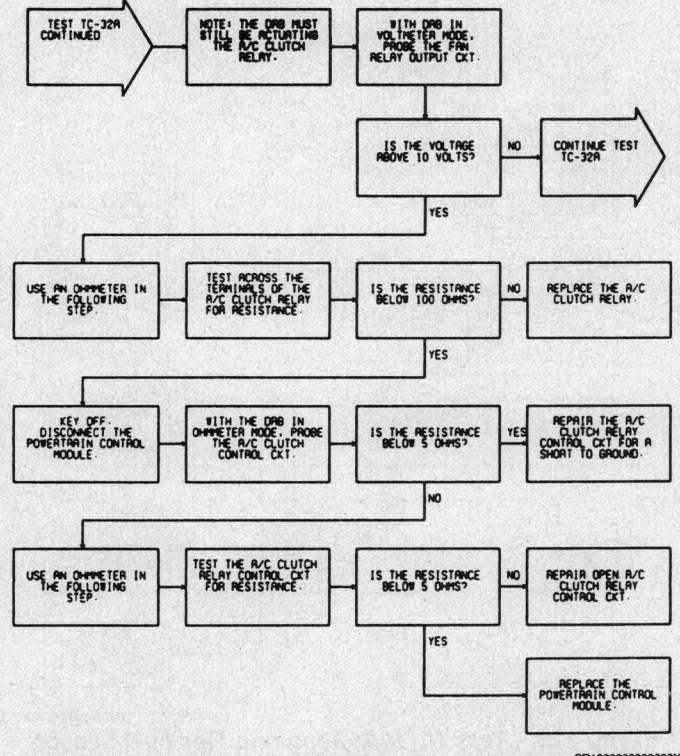

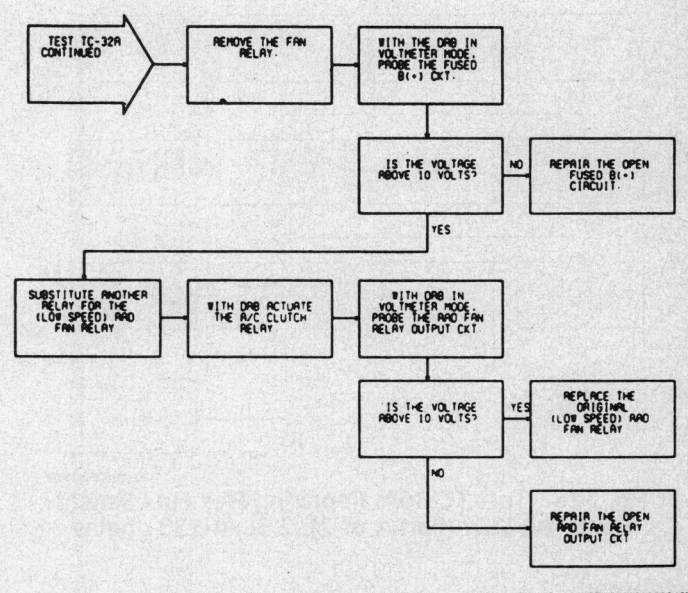

Fig. 126   Test TC-32A: Repairing A/C Clutch Relay Circuit (Part 1 of 4). 2.5L/4-153 engine

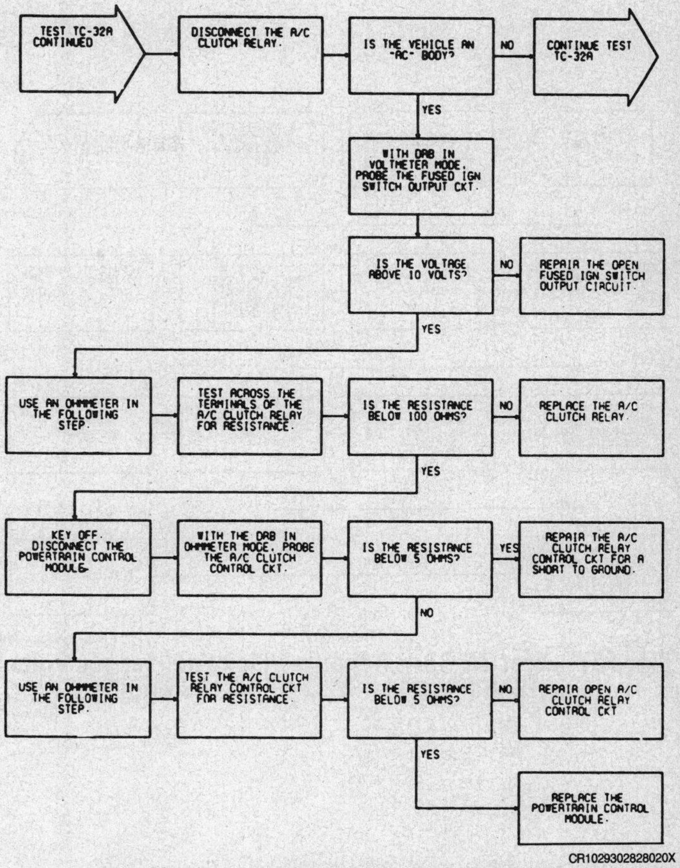

Fig. 126   Test TC-32A: Repairing A/C Clutch Relay Circuit (Part 2 of 4). 2.5L/4-153 engine

Fig. 126   Test TC-32A: Repairing A/C Clutch Relay Circuit (Part 3 of 4). 2.5L/4-153 engine

Fig. 126   Test TC-32A: Repairing A/C Clutch Relay Circuit (Part 4 of 4). 2.5L/4-153 engine

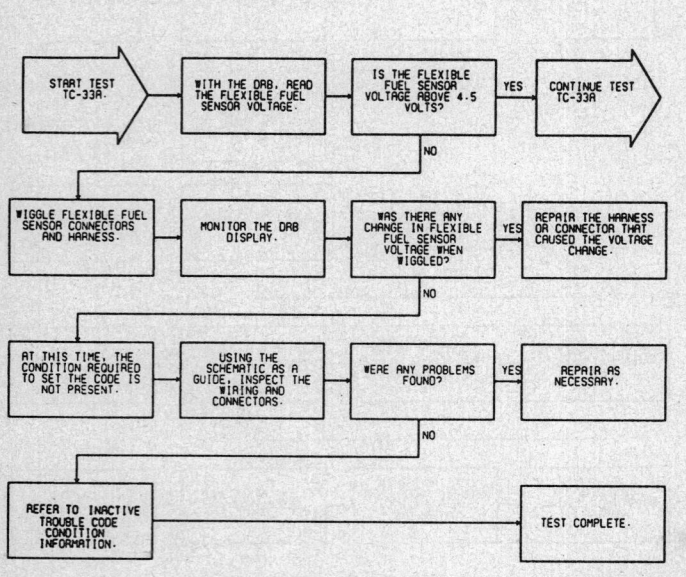

Fig. 127 Test TC-33A: Repairing Flex Fuel Sensor Volts Too High (Part 1 of 2). 2.5L/4-153 engine

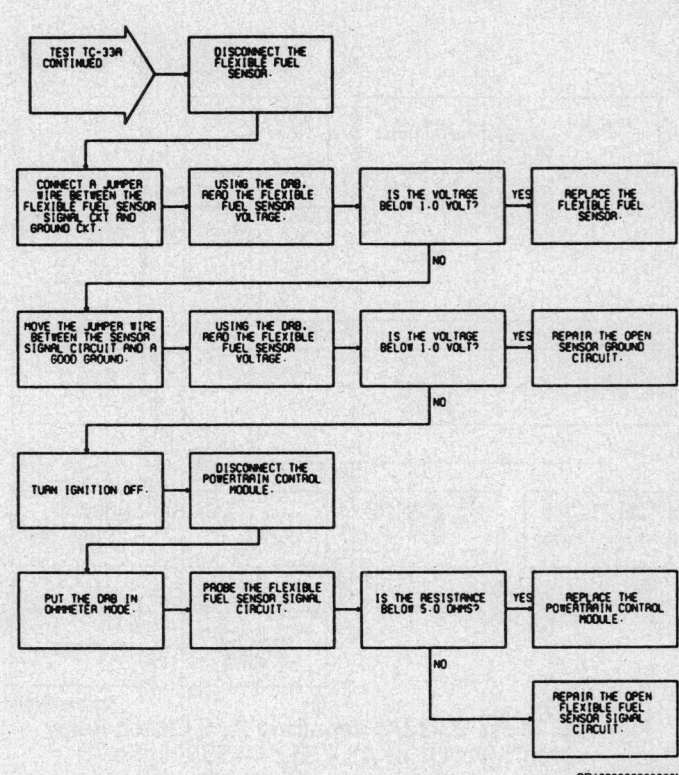

Fig. 127 Test TC-33A: Repairing Flex Fuel Sensor Volts Too High (Part 2 of 2). 2.5L/4-153 engine

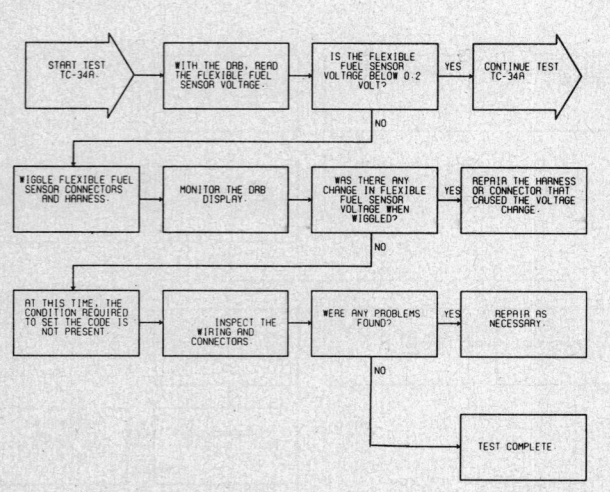

Fig. 128 Test TC-34A: Repairing Flex Fuel Sensor Volts Too Low (Part 1 of 2). 2.5L/4-153 engine

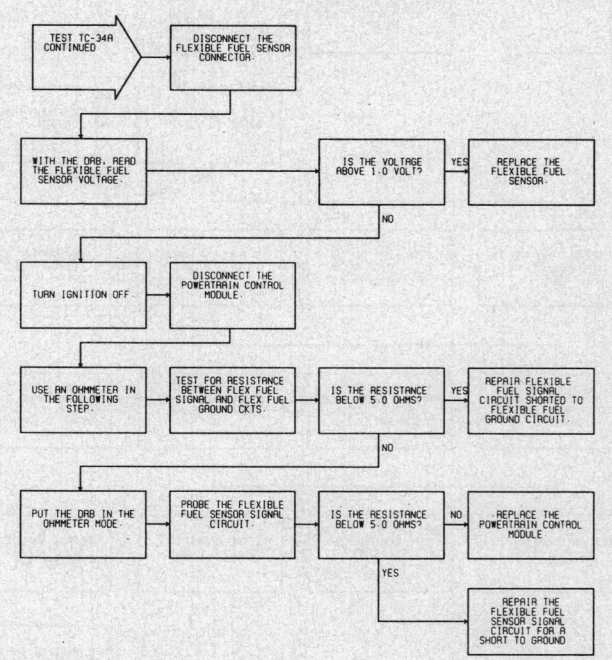

Fig. 128 Test TC-34A: Repairing Flex Fuel Sensor Volts Too Low (Part 2 of 2). 2.5L/4-153 engine

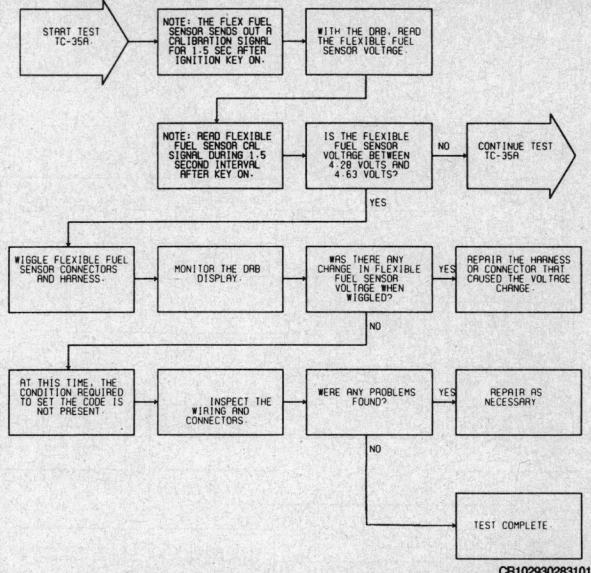

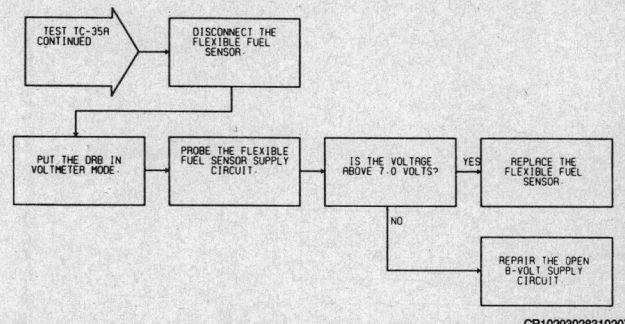

Fig. 129 Test TC-35A: Repairing Loss Of Flex Fuel Calibration Signal (Part 1 of 2). 2.5L/4-153 engine

Fig. 129 Test TC-35A: Repairing Loss Of Flex Fuel Calibration Signal (Part 2 of 2). 2.5L/4-153 engine

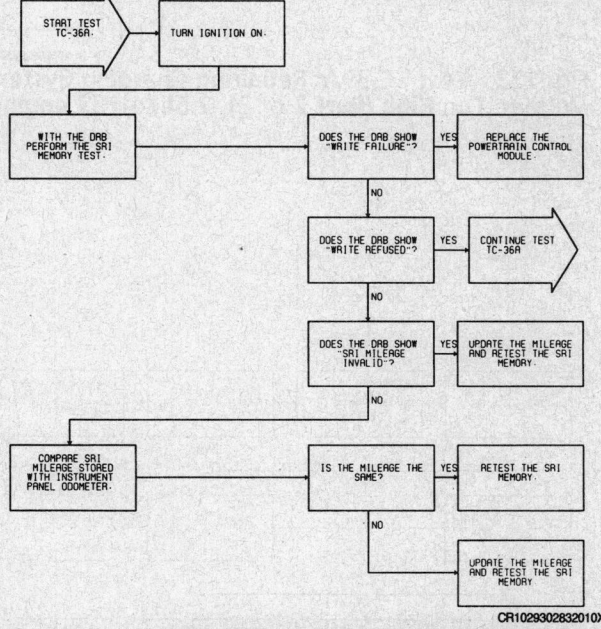

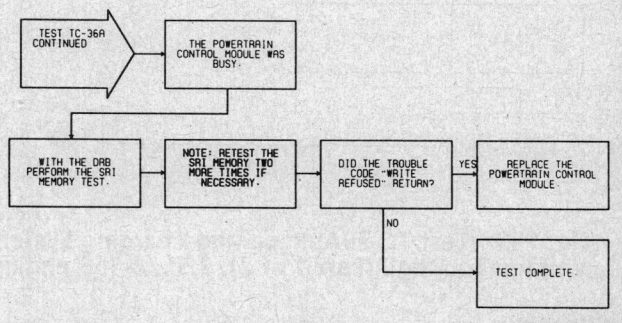

Fig. 130 Test TC-36A: Repairing PCM Failure SRI Mile Not Stored (Part 1 of 2). 2.5L/4-153 engine

Fig. 130 Test TC-36A: Repairing PCM Failure SRI Mile Not Stored (Part 2 of 2). 2.5L/4-153 engine

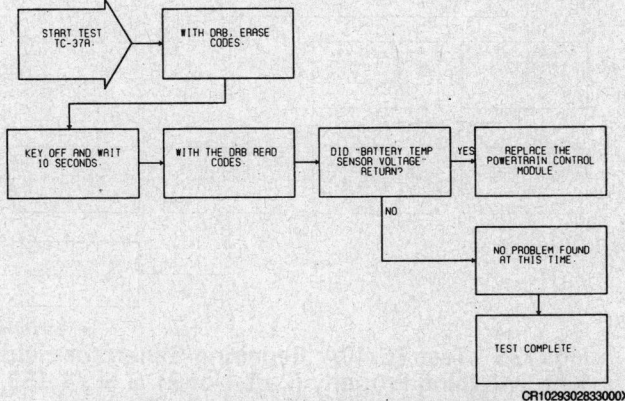

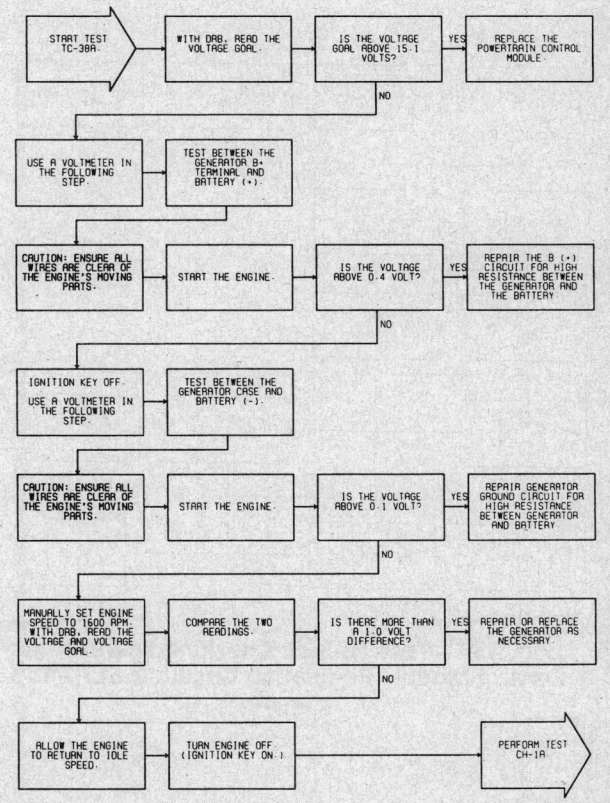

Fig. 131 Test TC-37A: Repairing Battery Temp Sensor Volts Out Of Limit. 2.5L/4-153 engine

Fig. 132 Test TC-38A: Repairing Charging System Voltage Too Low. 2.5L/4-153 engine

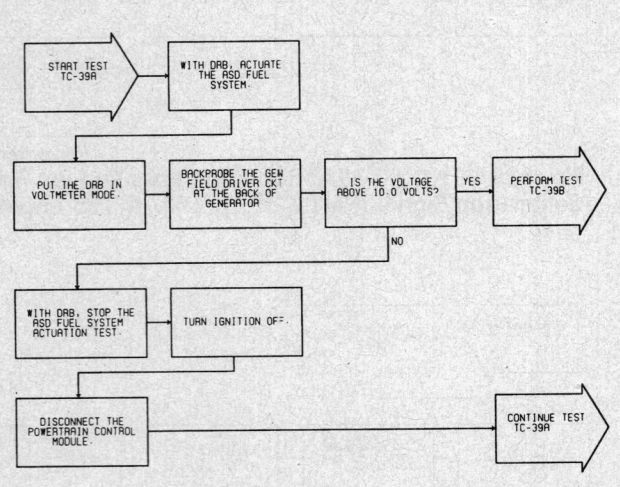

Fig. 133   Test TC-39A: Repairing Charging System
Voltage Too High (Part 1 of 2). 2.5L/4-153 engine

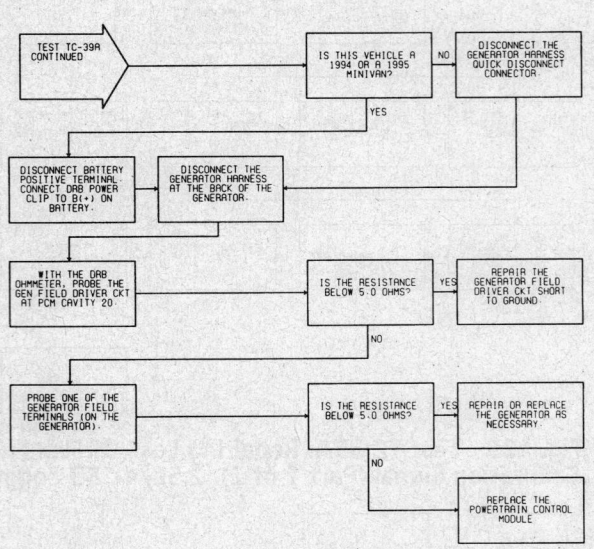

Fig. 133   Test TC-39A: Repairing Charging System
Voltage Too High (Part 2 of 2). 2.5L/4-153 engine

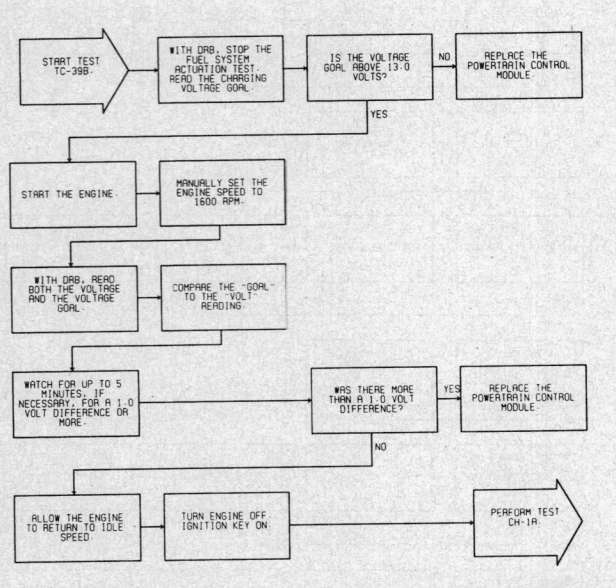

Fig. 134   Test TC-39B: Checking Powertrain
Control Module Regulating Circuit. 2.5L/4-153
engine

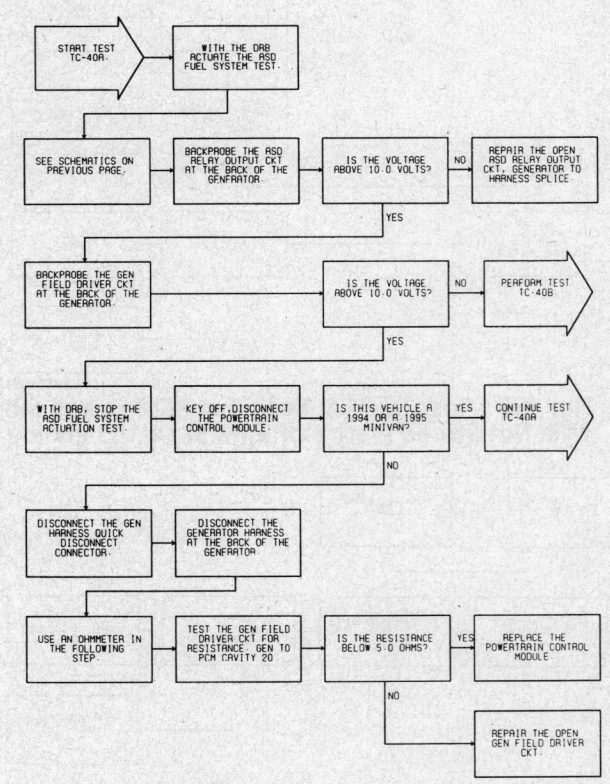

Fig. 135   Test TC-40A: Repairing Generator Field
Not Switching Properly (Part 1 of 2). 2.5L/4-153
engine

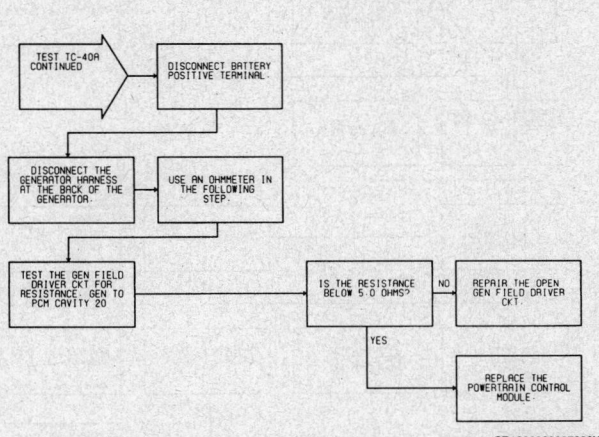

Fig. 135   Test TC-40A: Repairing Generator Field Not Switching Properly (Part 2 of 2). 2.5L/4-153 engine

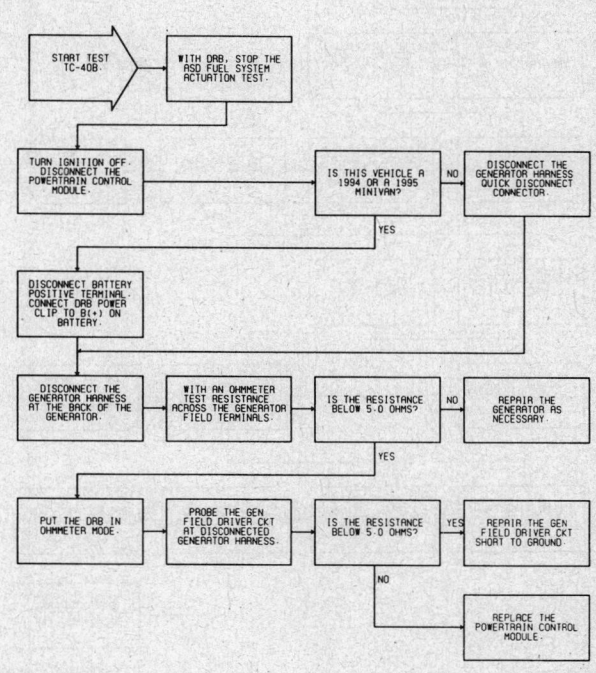

Fig. 136   Test TC-40B: Repairing Generator Field Not Switching Properly. 2.5L/4-153 engine

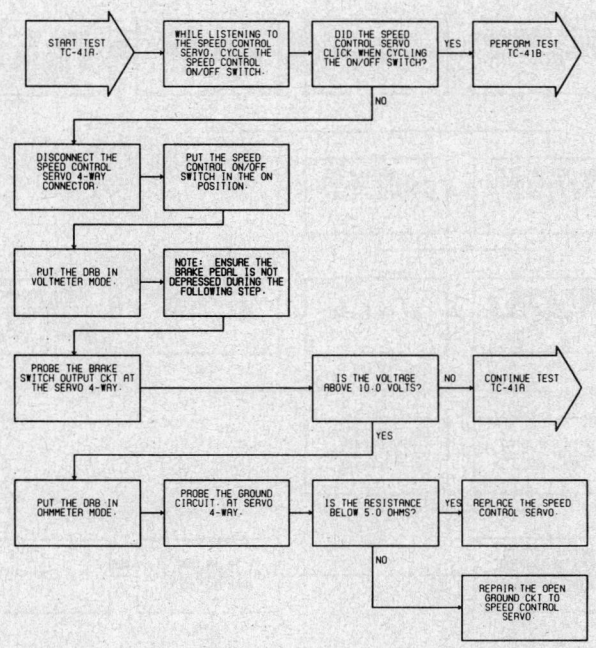

Fig. 137   Test TC-41A: Repairing Speed Control Solenoid Circuits (Part 1 of 2). 2.5L/4-153 engine

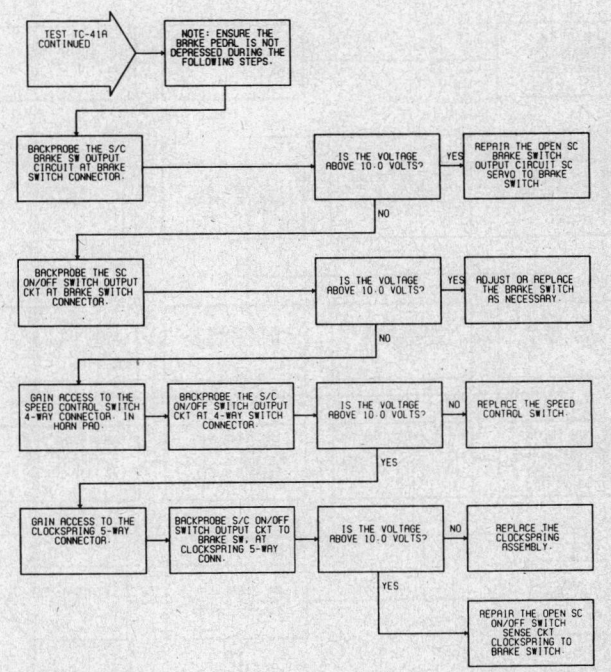

Fig. 137   Test TC-41A: Repairing Speed Control Solenoid Circuits (Part 2 of 2). 2.5L/4-153 engine

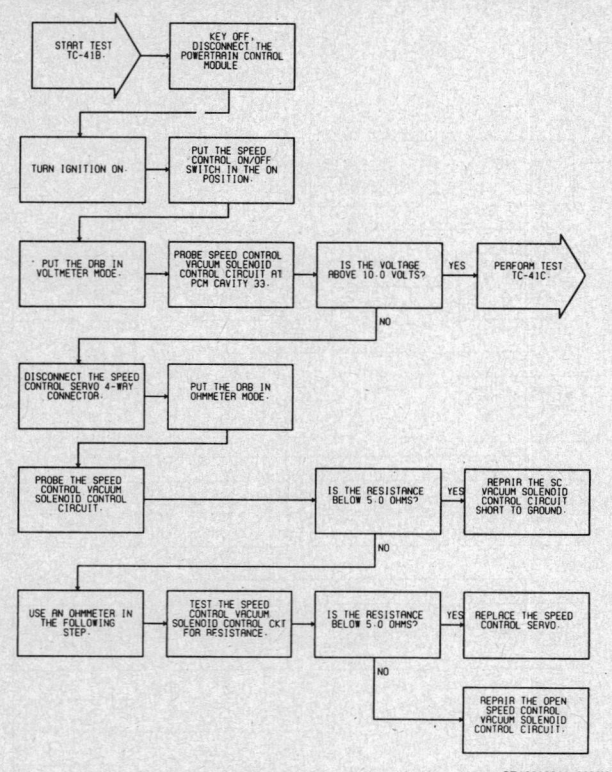

Fig. 138 Test TC-41B: Repairing Speed Control Solenoid Circuits. 2.5L/4-153 engine

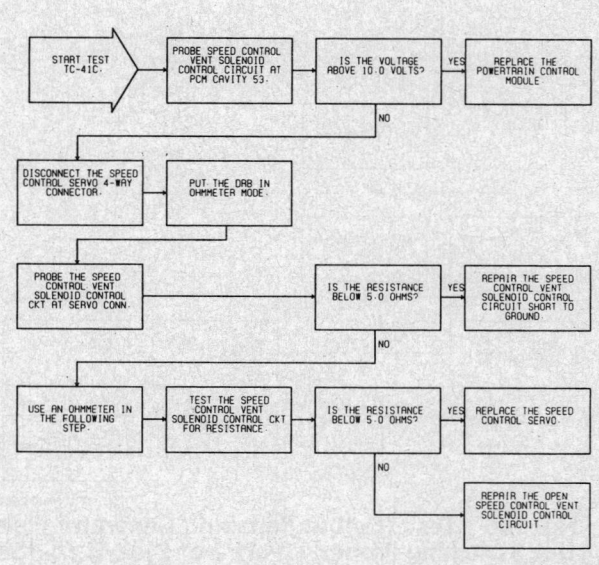

Fig. 139 Test TC-41C: Repairing Speed Control Solenoid Circuits. 2.5L/4-153 engine

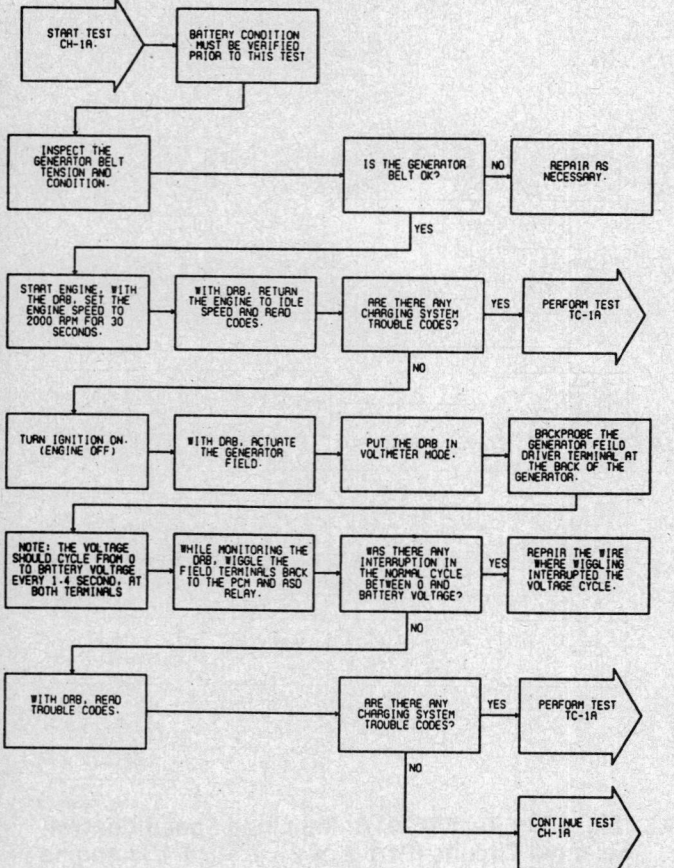

Fig. 140 Test CH-1A: Checking Charging System No Trouble Codes (Part 1 of 3). 2.5L/4-153 engine

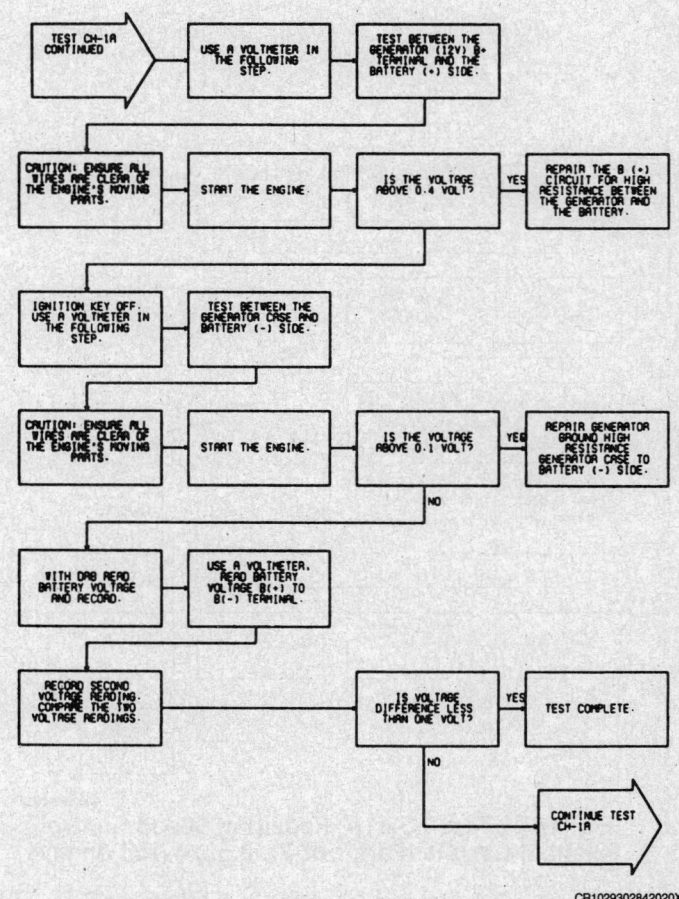

Fig. 140 Test CH-1A: Checking Charging System No Trouble Codes (Part 2 of 3). 2.5L/4-153 engine

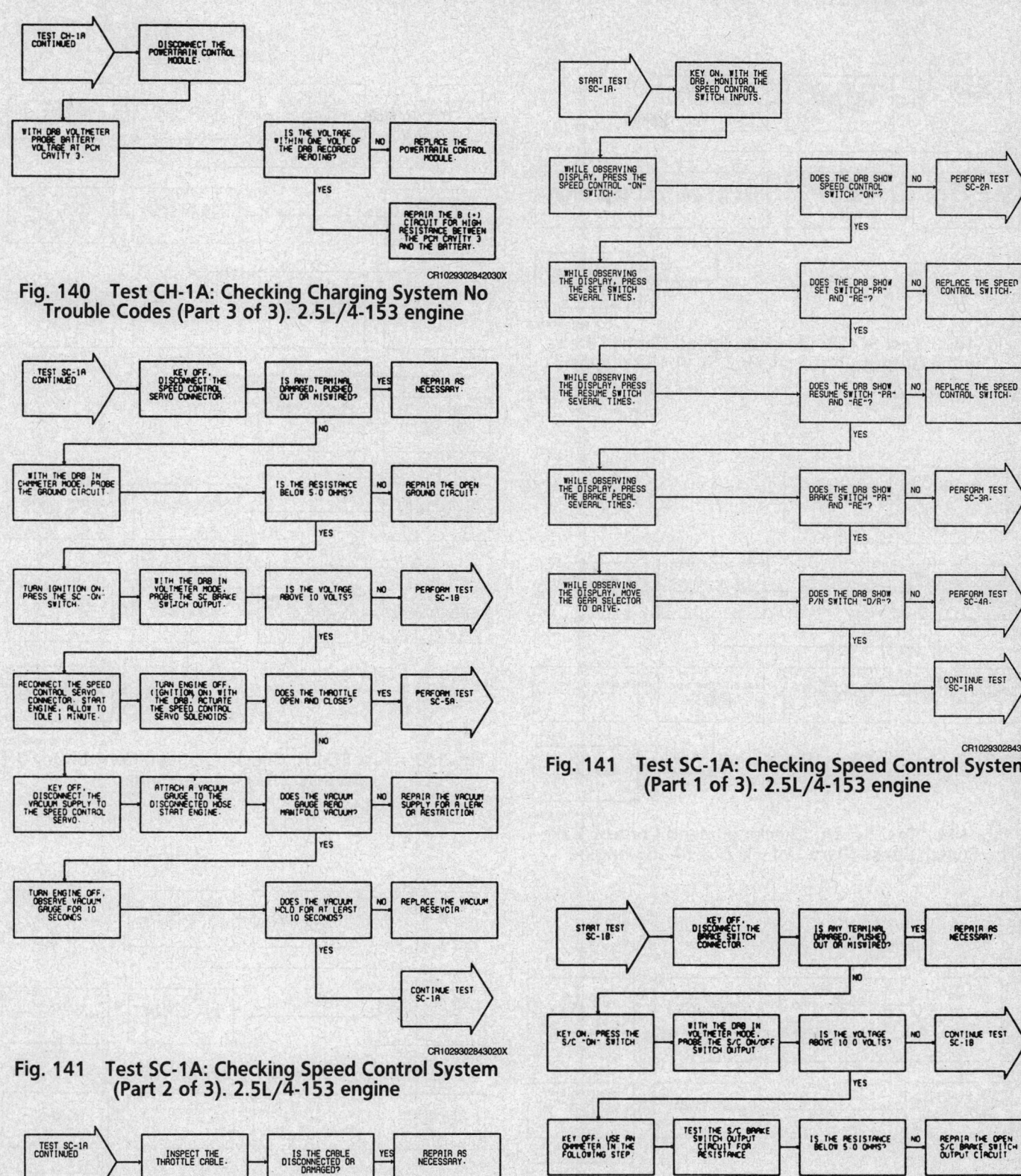

Fig. 140 Test CH-1A: Checking Charging System No Trouble Codes (Part 3 of 3). 2.5L/4-153 engine

Fig. 141 Test SC-1A: Checking Speed Control System (Part 2 of 3). 2.5L/4-153 engine

Fig. 141 Test SC-1A: Checking Speed Control System (Part 3 of 3). 2.5L/4-153 engine

Fig. 141 Test SC-1A: Checking Speed Control System (Part 1 of 3). 2.5L/4-153 engine

Fig. 142 Test SC-1B: Checking Speed Control Brake Switch Output (Part 1 of 2). 2.5L/4-153 engine

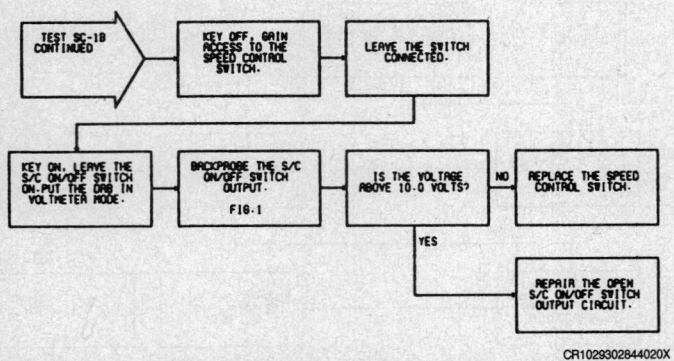

Fig. 142   Test SC-1B: Checking Speed Control Brake Switch Output (Part 2 of 2). 2.5L/4-153 engine

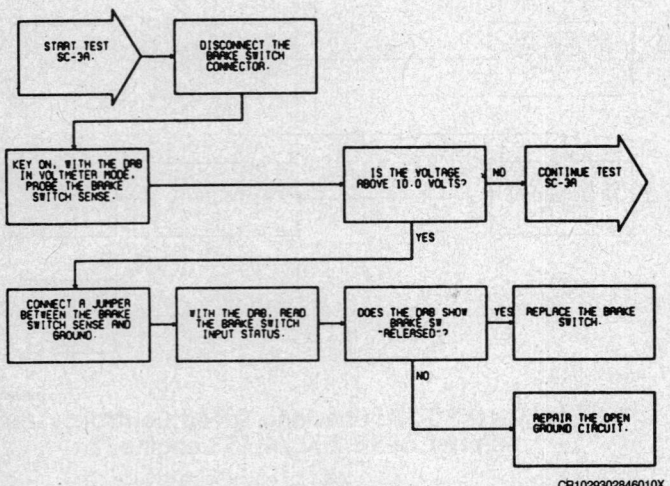

Fig. 144   Test SC-3A: Checking Speed Control Brake Switch Sense (Part 1 of 2). 2.5L/4-153 engine

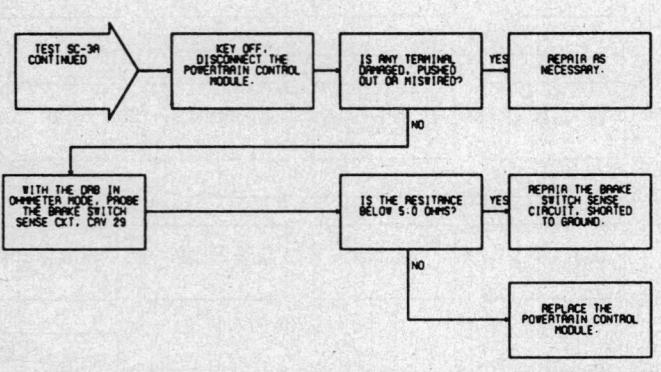

Fig. 144   Test SC-3A: Checking Speed Control Brake Switch Sense (Part 2 of 2). 2.5L/4-153 engine

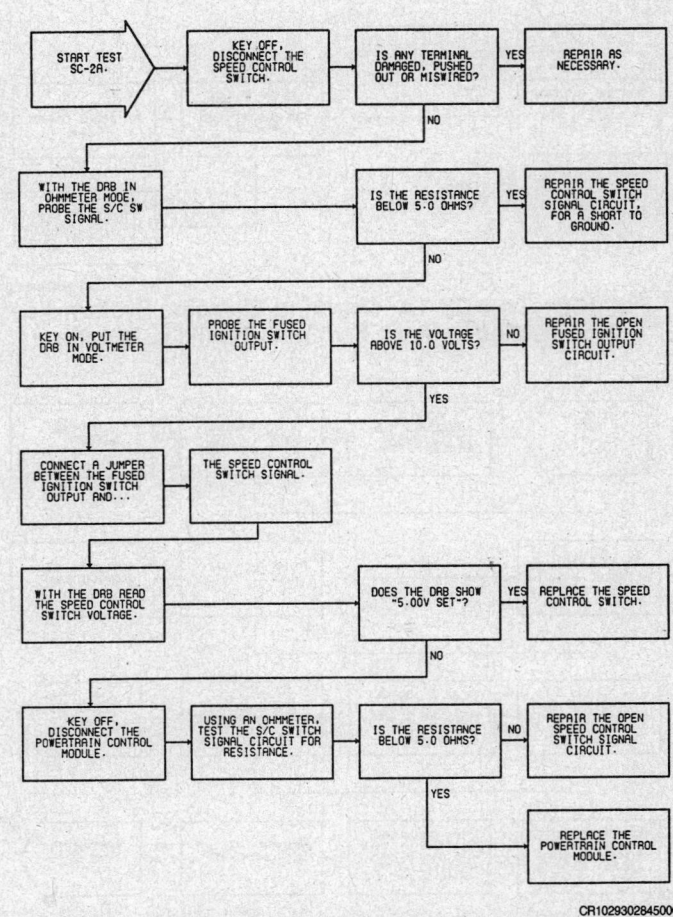

Fig. 143   Test SC-2A: Checking Speed Control On/Off Switch. 2.5L/4-153 engine

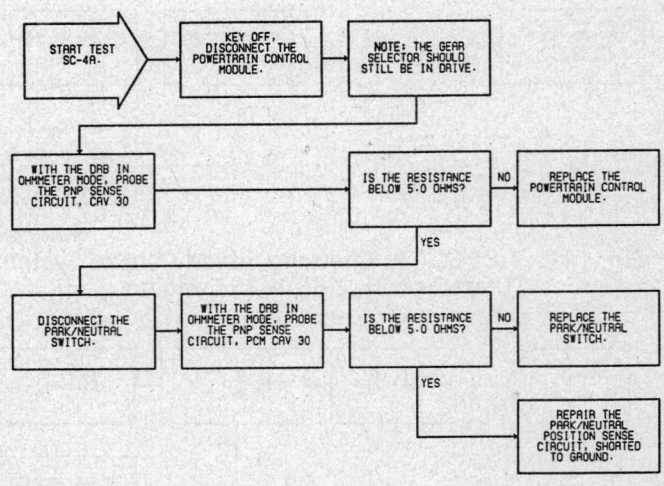

Fig. 145   Test SC-4A: Checking Speed Control Park/Neutral Circuit. 2.5L/4-153 engine

At this time, the speed control switch and servo functions appear to operate properly. Using the DRB, monitor the speed control "cutout" status. Road test the vehicle at speeds over 35 mph and attempt to set the speed control. The following items will not allow the speed control to set. The last or most recent cause for speed control not to set indicated by the "Denied" status.

Denied Message

ON/OFF - The powertrain control module does not see an "on" signal from the switch at cavity 23.

SPEED - The vehicle speed as seen by the powertrain control module at cavity 47 is not greater than 36 mph.

RPM - The engine rpm is excessively high.

BRAKE - The brake switch sense circuit is open indicating to the powertrain control module that the brakes are applied. The sense circuit, cavity 29 of the PCM, is grounded through the brake pedal switch when the brakes are released.

P/N - The park/neutral (p/n) switch sense circuit is grounded indicating to the powertrain control module that the transmission is not in gear. The sense circuit, cavity 30 of the PCM, is grounded through the park/neutral switch when the transmission is in park or neutral.

RPM/SPD - The PCM senses excessive engine rpm for a given vehicle speed.

SOL FLT - The powertrain control module senses a servo solenoid circuit trouble code that is maturing or set in memory.

CR1029302848000X

Fig. 146 Test SC-5A: Checking Speed Control System For Denied Messages. 2.5L/4-153 engine

1. **NO TROUBLE CODE COMPLETE TEST** (non-monitored & monitored circuits)

Perform TESTS NTC-2A through NTC-15A in sequence until the driveability problem is found.

NO TROUBLE CODE MENU
CHECKING SECONDARY IGNITION AND TIMING NTC-2A
CHECKING FUEL PRESSURE NTC-3A
CHECKING COOLANT SENSOR CALIBRATION AND RADIATOR FAN OPERATION ... NTC-4A
CHECKING THROTTLE POSITION SENSOR CALIBRATION NTC-5A
CHECKING MAP SENSOR CALIBRATION NTC-6A
CHECKING OXYGEN SENSOR SWITCHING NTC-7A
CHECKING IDLE AIR CONTROL MOTOR NTC-8A
CHECKING SOLENOID OPERATIONS NTC-9A
CHECKING PARK/NEUTRAL POSITION SWITCH NTC-10A
CHECKING PCM GROUNDS AND POWER CIRCUIT NTC-11A
CHECKING EGR SYSTEM NTC-12A
CHECKING ENGINE VACUUM NTC-13A
CHECKING MINIMUM IDLE AIR FLOW NTC-14A
PERFORMING NO TROUBLE CODE MECHANICAL TEST NTC-15A

2. **NO TROUBLE CODE QUICK INDIVIDUAL TEST** (individual test only)

If you suspect any of the above items to be the cause of the vehicle's driveability problem, perform the associated test(s) individually. Return to No Fault Menu if driveability problem still exists, or perform No Trouble Code Complete Test.

3. **NO TROUBLE CODE QUICK SYMPTOM TEST** (symptom test only)

Symptom checks cannot be used properly unless the driveability problem characteristic actually happens while the vehicle is being tested. To reduce diagnostic time, ensure that FC-1A and appropriate GENERAL INFORMATION sections have been reviewed before attempting to diagnose a symptom.

Select the symptom that most accurately describes the vehicle's driveability problem and then perform the test routine that pertains to this symptom. Perform each routine test in sequence until the problem is found.

SYMPTOM	DIAGNOSTIC TEST ROUTINE
HARD START	NTC-2A, 3A, 4A, 5A, 6A, 7A, 8A, 11A, 14A, 15A
START AND STALL	NTC-2A, 3A, 4A, 5A, 6A, 8A, 11A, 15A
HESITATION/SAG/STUMBLE	NO TROUBLE CODE COMPLETE TEST (3)
SURGE	NTC-2A, 3A, 4A, 5A, 6A, 7A, 8A, 11A, 12A, 15A
LACK OF POWER/SLUGGISH	NTC-2A, 3A, 4A, 5A, 6A, 7A, 8A, 11A, 13A, 15A
SPARK KNOCK/DETONATION	NTC-2A, 3A, 4A, 5A, 6A, 7A, 8A, 9A, 11A, 12A, 15A
CUTS OUT/MISSES	NTC-2A, 3A, 7A, 9A, 11A, 13A, 15A
BACKFIRE/POPBACK	NTC-2A, 3A, 6A, 7A, 11A, 13A, 15A
RUNS ROUGH/UNSTABLE/ERRATIC IDLE	NO TROUBLE CODE COMPLETE TEST (3)
POOR FUEL ECONOMY	NO TROUBLE CODE COMPLETE TEST (3)

CR1029302849000X

Fig. 147 Test NTC-1A: No Trouble Code Test Menu. 2.5L/4-153 engine

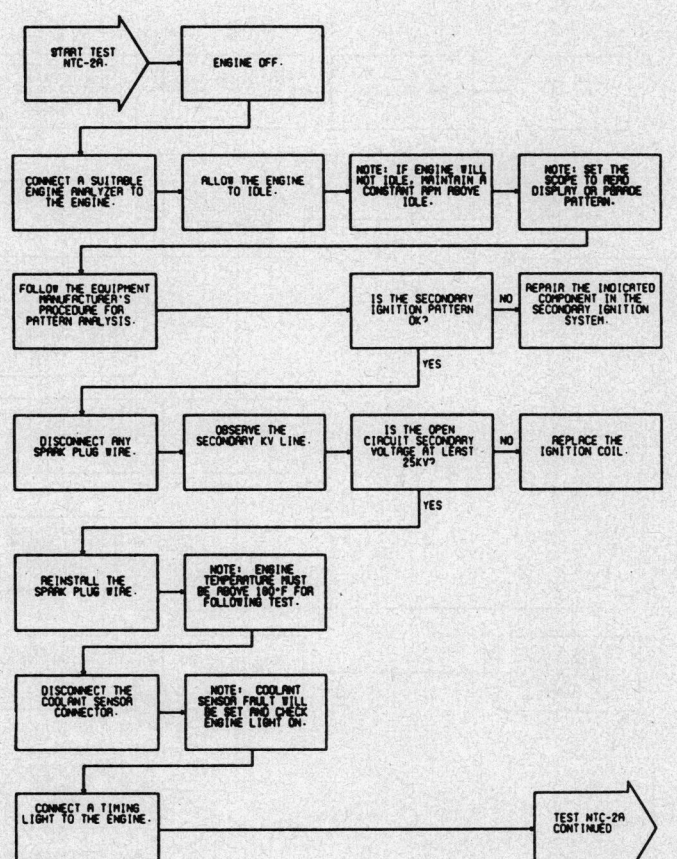

CR1029302850010X

Fig. 148 Test NTC-2A: Checking Secondary Ignition & Timing (Part 1 of 2). 2.5L/4-153 engine

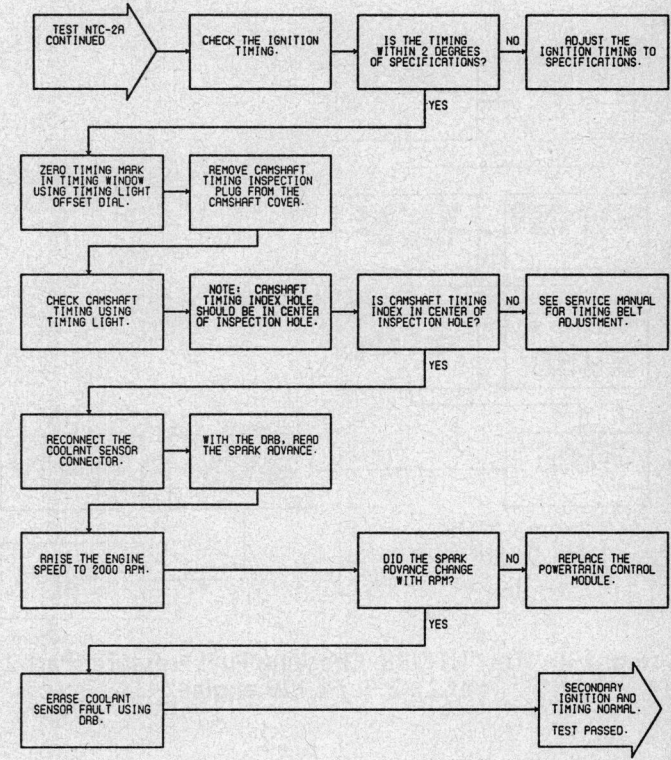

CR1029302850020X

Fig. 148 Test NTC-2A: Checking Secondary Ignition & Timing (Part 2 of 2). 2.5L/4-153 engine

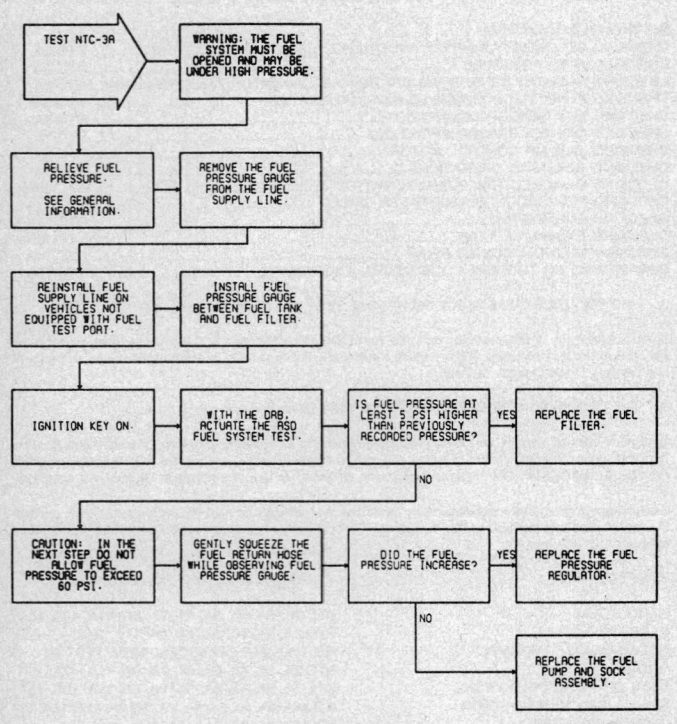

Fig. 149   Test NTC-3A: Checking Fuel Pressure. 2.5L/4-153 engine

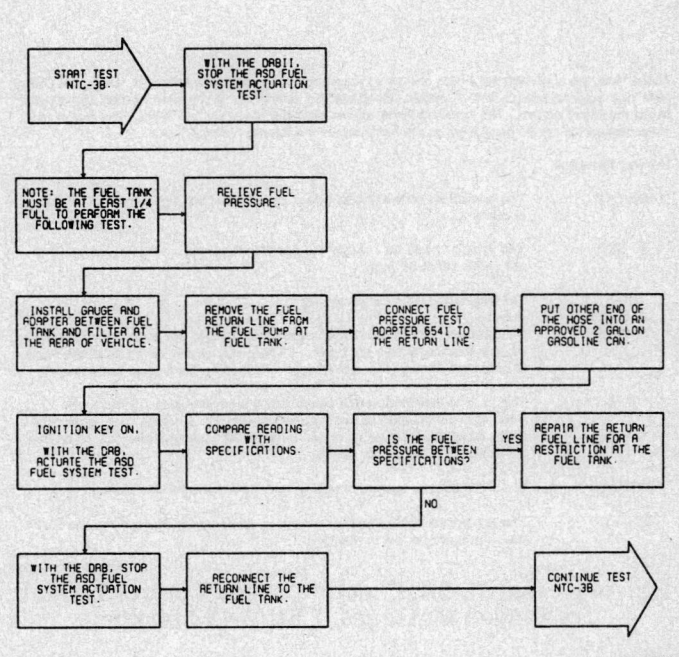

Fig. 150   Test NTC-3B: Checking Fuel Pressure (Part 1 of 2). 2.5L/4-153 engine

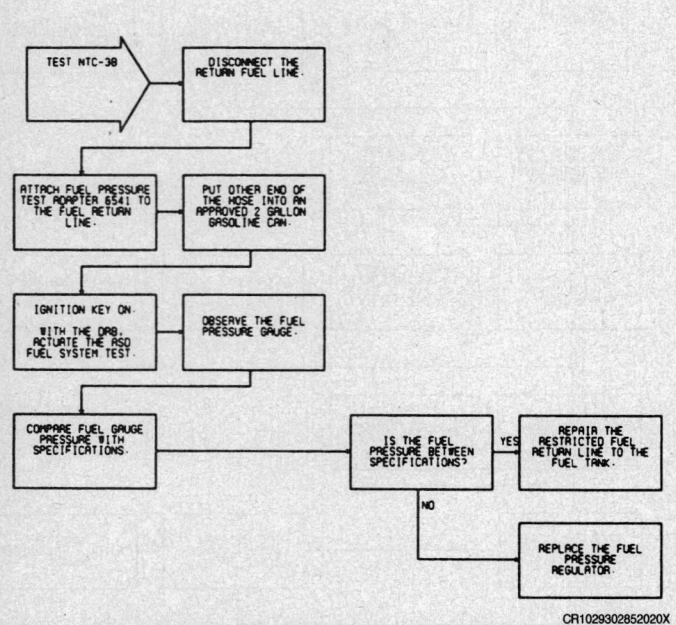

Fig. 150   Test NTC-3B: Checking Fuel Pressure (Part 2 of 2). 2.5L/4-153 engine

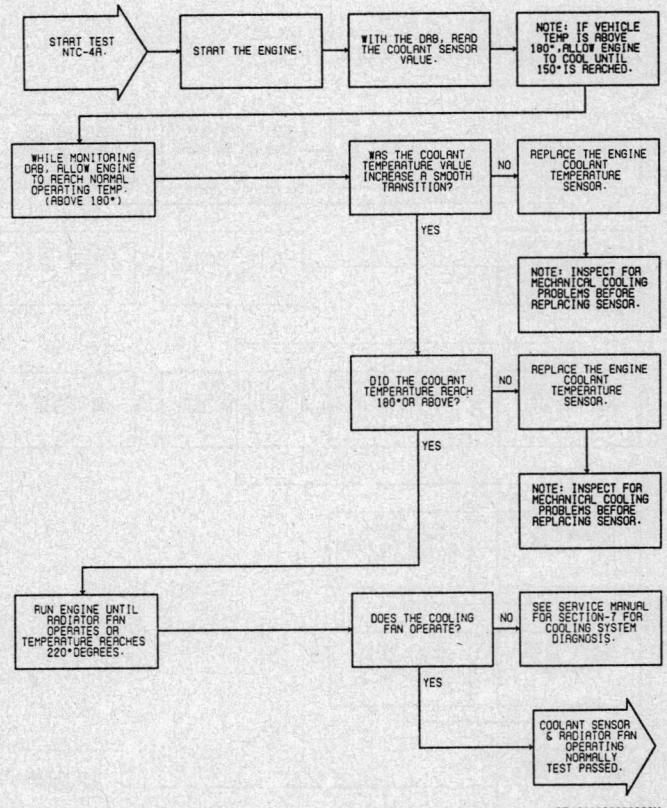

Fig. 151   Test NTC-4A: Checking Coolant Sensor Calibration & Radiator Fan Operation. 2.5L/4-153 engine

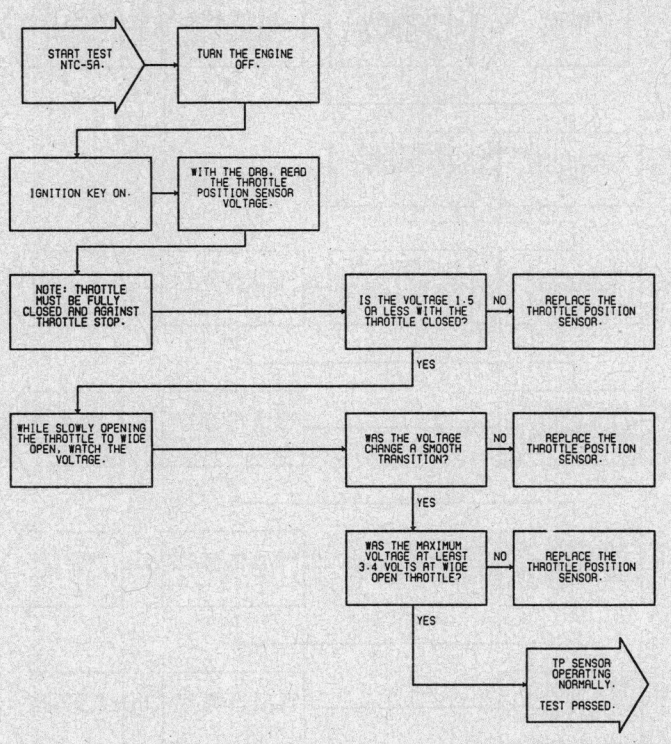

Fig. 152   Test NTC-5A: Checking Throttle Position Sensor Calibration. 2.5L/4-153 engine

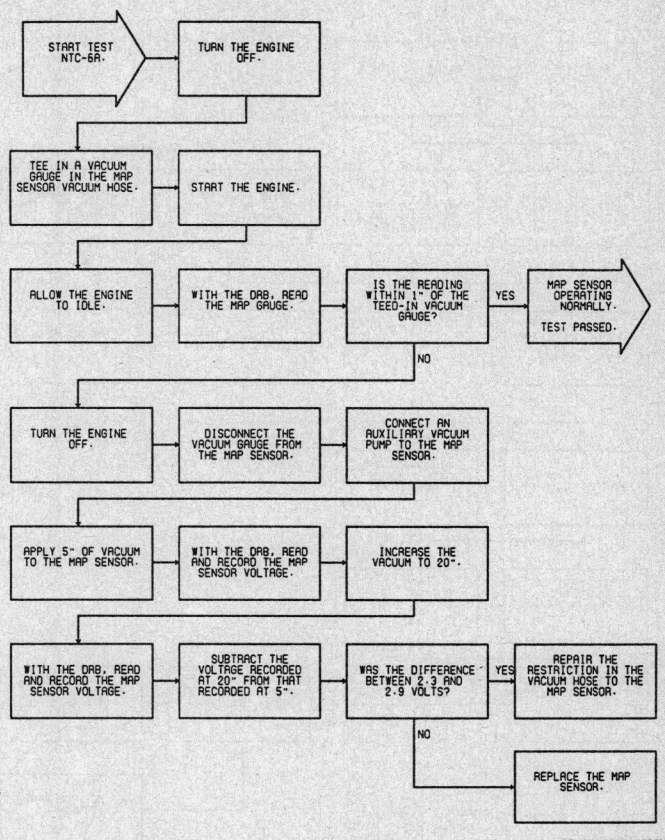

Fig. 153   Test NTC-6A: Checking MAP Sensor Calibration. 2.5L/4-153 engine

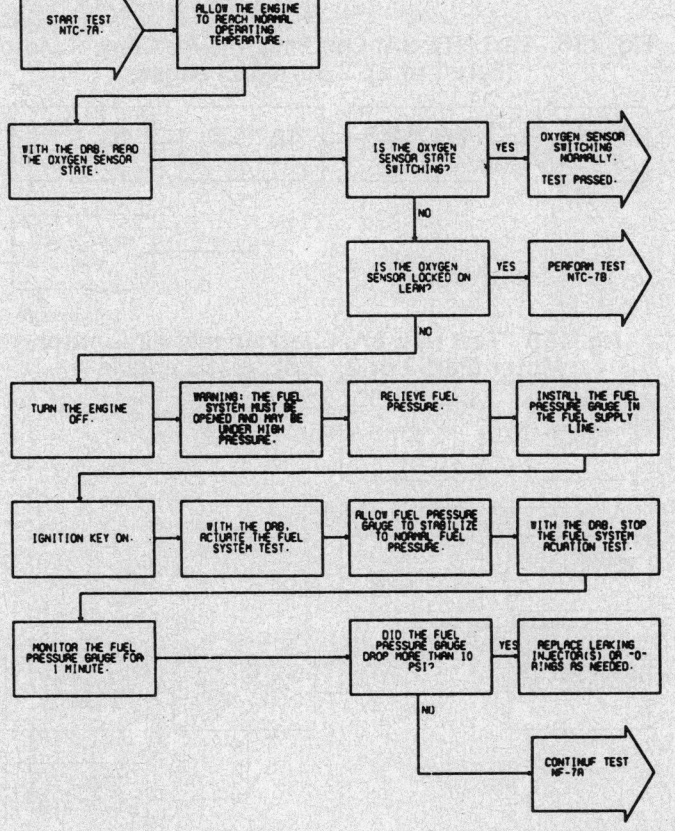

Fig. 154   Test NTC-7A: Checking Oxygen Sensor Switching (Part 1 of 2). 2.5L/4-153 engine

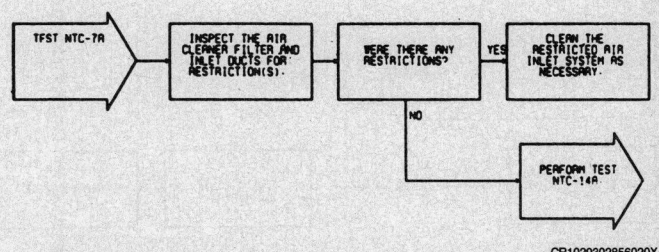

Fig. 154   Test NTC-7A: Checking Oxygen Sensor Switching (Part 2 of 2). 2.5L/4-153 engine

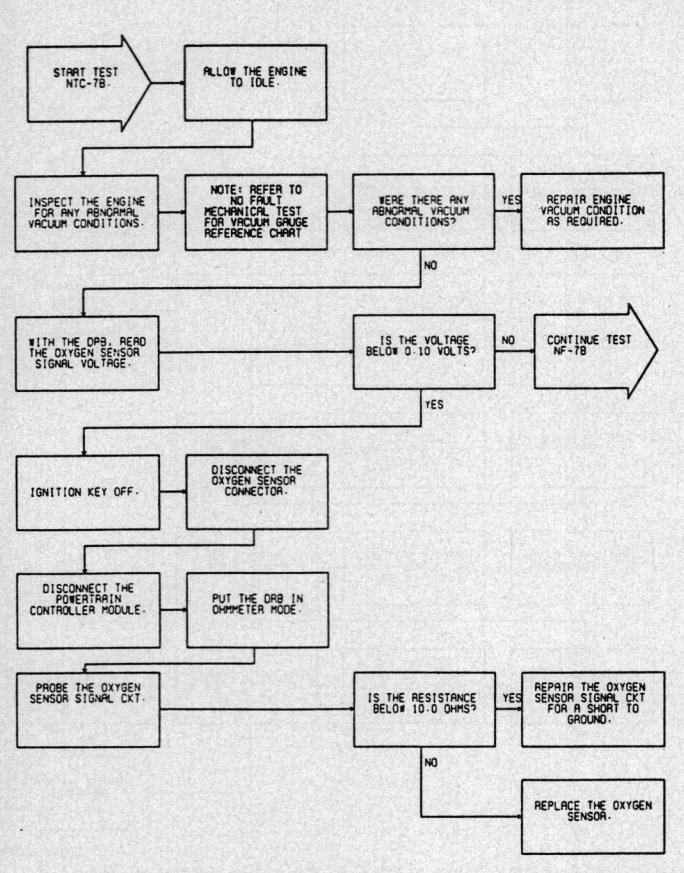

Fig. 155   Test NTC-7B: Checking Oxygen Sensor Switching (Part 1 of 2). 2.5L/4-153 engine

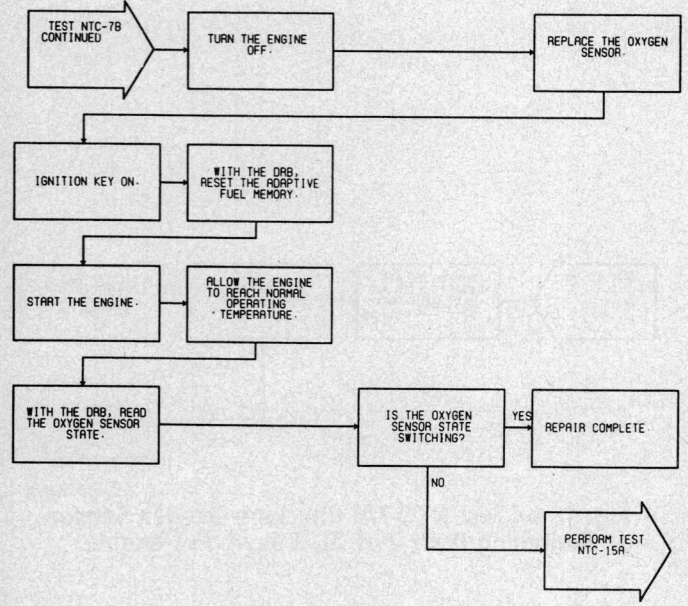

Fig. 155   Test NTC-7B: Checking Oxygen Sensor Switching (Part 2 of 2). 2.5L/4-153 engine

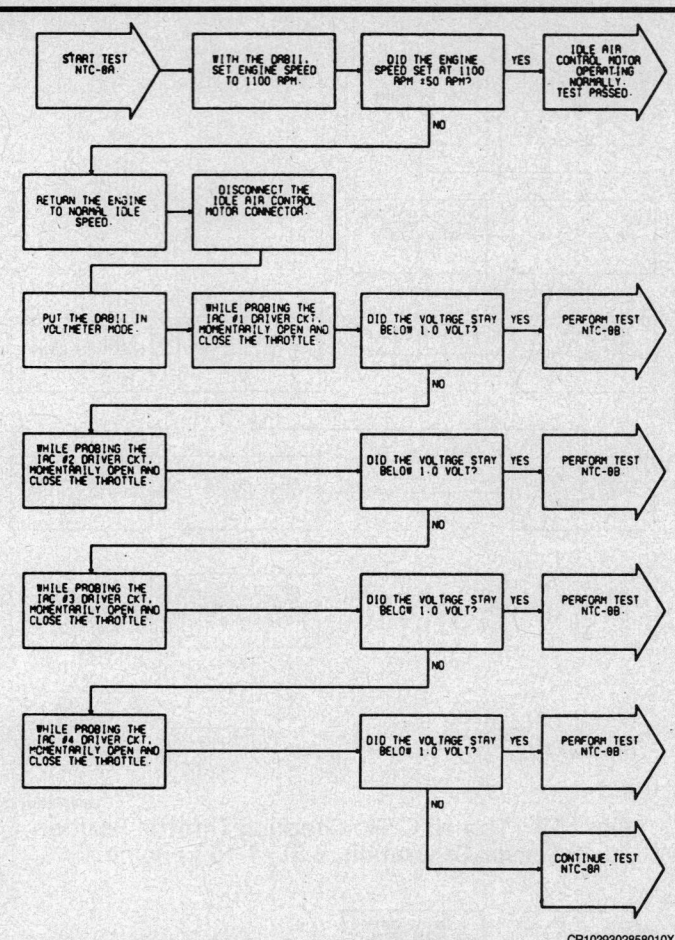

Fig. 156   Test NTC-8A: Checking Idle Air Control Motor (Part 1 of 2). 2.5L/4-153 engine

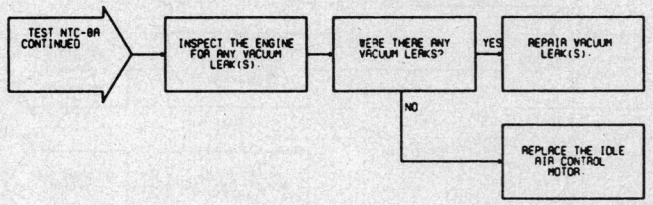

Fig. 156   Test NTC-8A: Checking Idle Air Control Motor (Part 2 of 2). 2.5L/4-153 engine

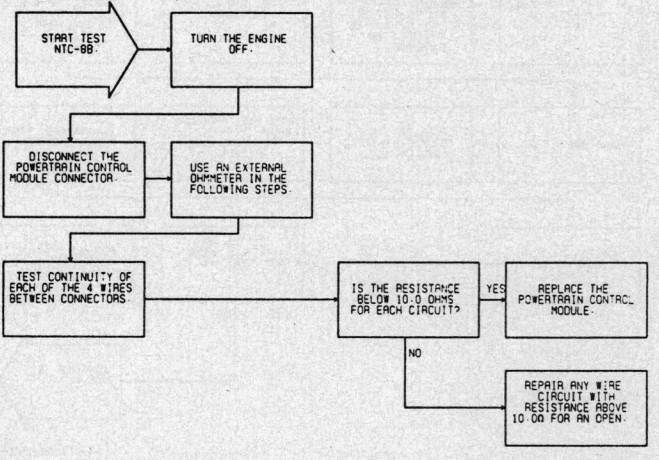

Fig. 157   Test NTC-8B: Checking Idle Air Control Motor. 2.5L/4-153 engine

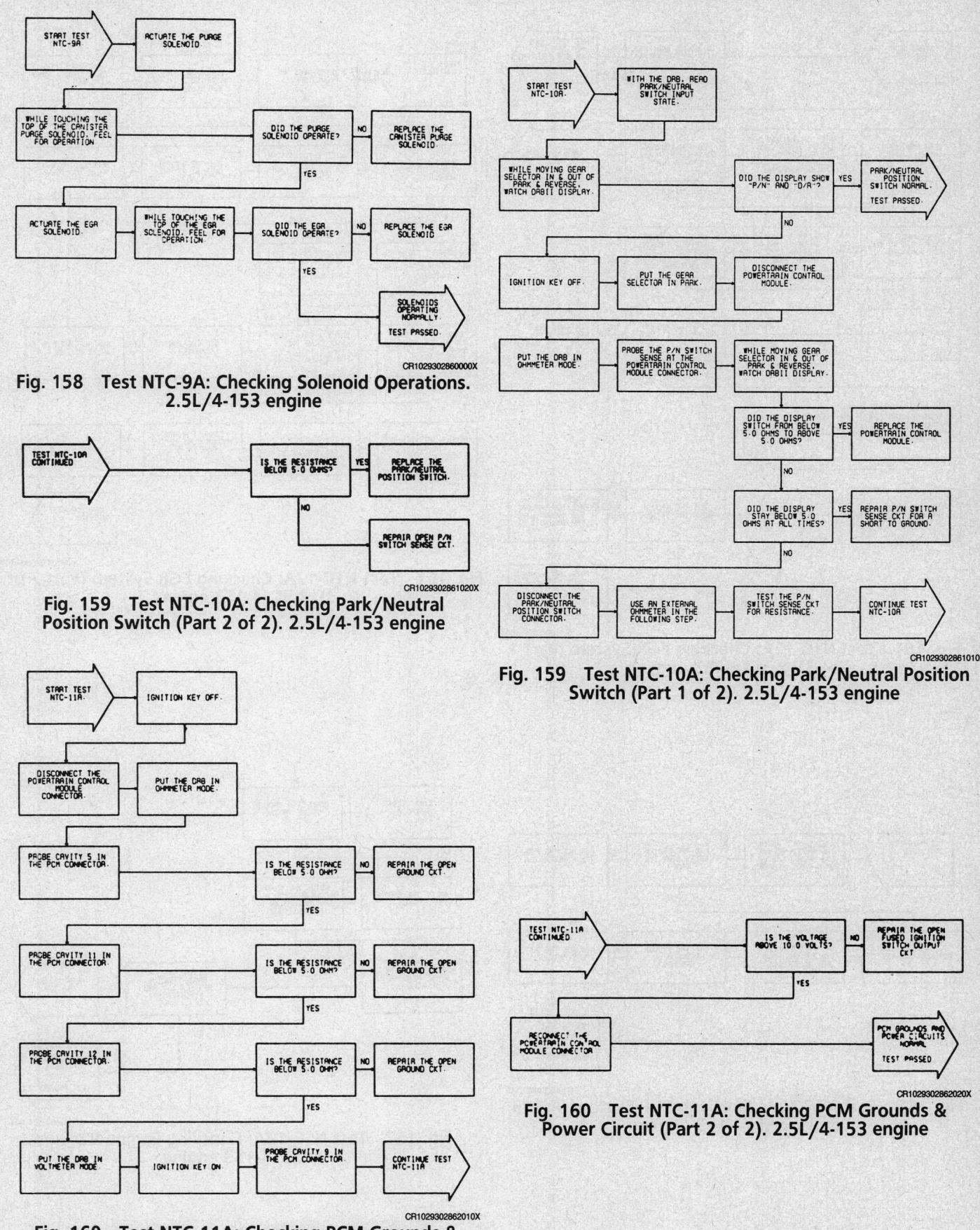

Fig. 158   Test NTC-9A: Checking Solenoid Operations. 2.5L/4-153 engine

Fig. 159   Test NTC-10A: Checking Park/Neutral Position Switch (Part 2 of 2). 2.5L/4-153 engine

Fig. 159   Test NTC-10A: Checking Park/Neutral Position Switch (Part 1 of 2). 2.5L/4-153 engine

Fig. 160   Test NTC-11A: Checking PCM Grounds & Power Circuit (Part 1 of 2). 2.5L/4-153 engine

Fig. 160   Test NTC-11A: Checking PCM Grounds & Power Circuit (Part 2 of 2). 2.5L/4-153 engine

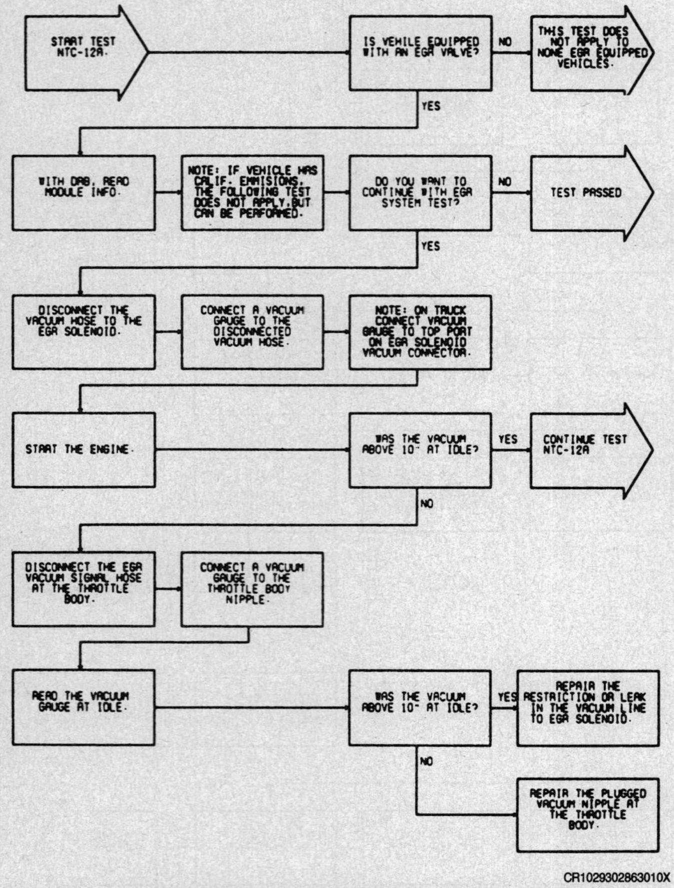

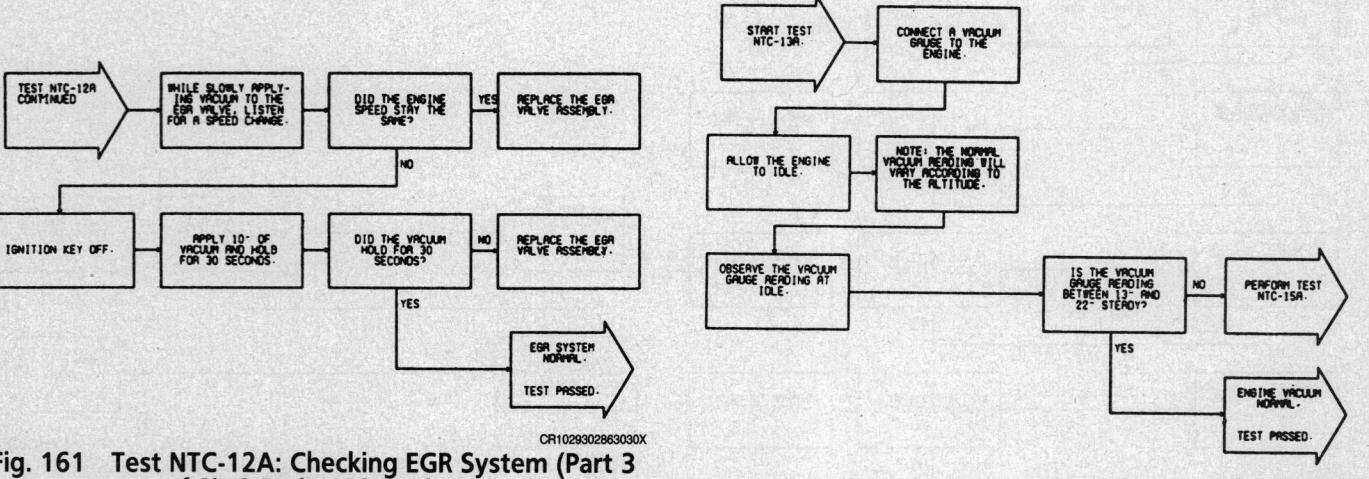

Fig. 161   Test NTC-12A: Checking EGR System (Part 1 of 3). 2.5L/4-153 engine

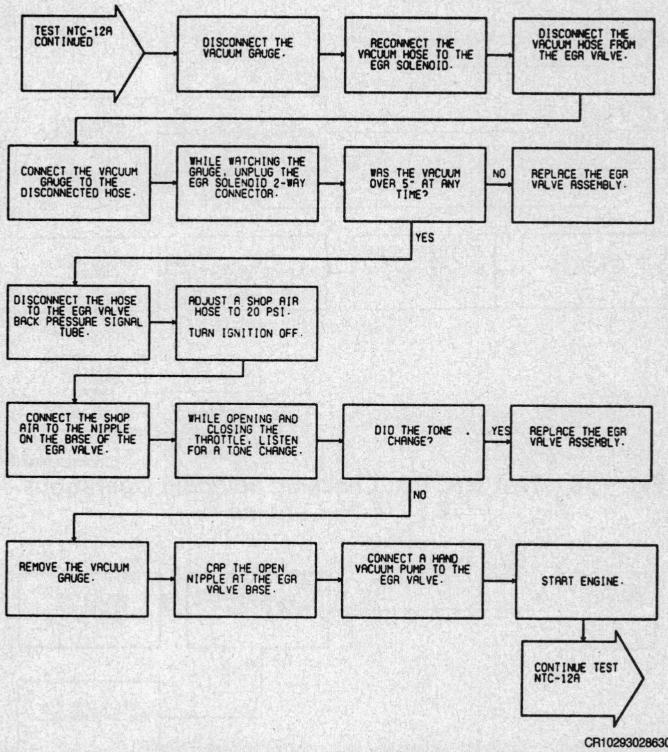

Fig. 161   Test NTC-12A: Checking EGR System (Part 2 of 3). 2.5L/4-153 engine

Fig. 161   Test NTC-12A: Checking EGR System (Part 3 of 3). 2.5L/4-153 engine

Fig. 162   Test NTC-13A: Checking Engine Vacuum. 2.5L/4-153 engine

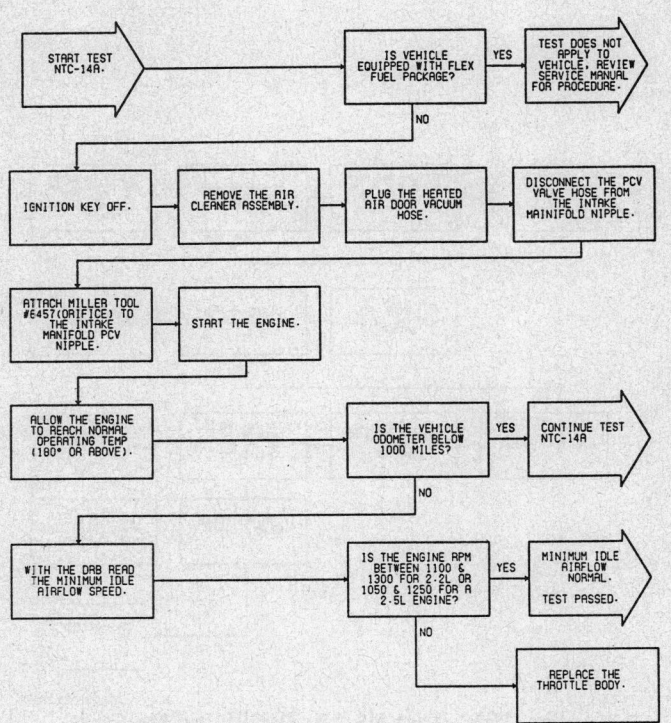

CR1029302865010X

Fig. 163   Test NTC-14A: Checking Minimum Idle Air Flow (Part 1 of 2). 2.5L/4-153 engine

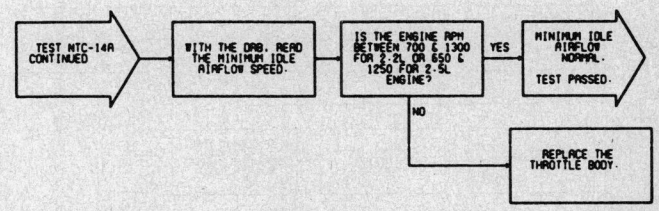

CR1029302865020X

Fig. 163   Test NTC-14A: Checking Minimum Idle Air Flow (Part 2 of 2). 2.5L/4-153 engine

At this point in the diagnostic test procedure, you have determined that all of the engine controller systems are operating as designed and are not the cause of the driveability problem. Therefore, the following additional items should be checked as possible mechanical causes of the problem:

1. **ENGINE VACUUM** - must be at least 13 inches in neutral *(see below)**

2. **ENGINE VALVE TIMING** - must be within specifications

3. **ENGINE COMPRESSION** - must be within specifications

4. **ENGINE EXHAUST SYSTEM** - must be free of any restrictions

5. **ENGINE PVC SYSTEM** - must flow freely

6. **ENGINE DRIVE SPROCKET** - must be properly positioned

7. **TORQUE CONVERTER STALL SPEED** - must be within specifications

8. **POWER BRAKE BOOSTER** - no internal vacuum leaks

9. **FUEL** - must be free of contamination

10. **FUEL INJECTOR** - plugged or restricted injector; control wire not connected to correct injector

NOTE: If you came to this test from the oxygen sensor, and the rich or lean condition is not caused by one of the first items above, replace the powertrain control module.*

* The readings below are only indicators of possible mechanical engine problems.

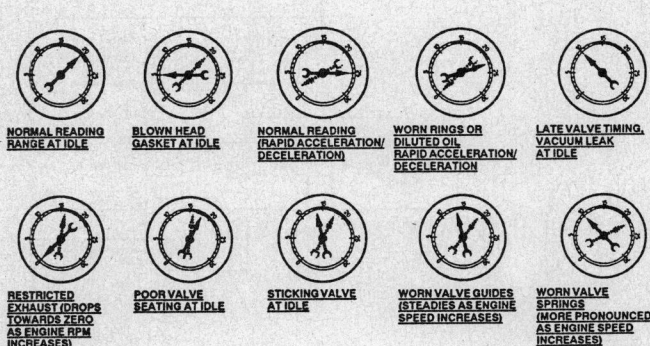

CR1029302866000X

Fig. 164   Test NTC-15A: No Trouble Code Mechanical Test. 2.5L/4-153 engine

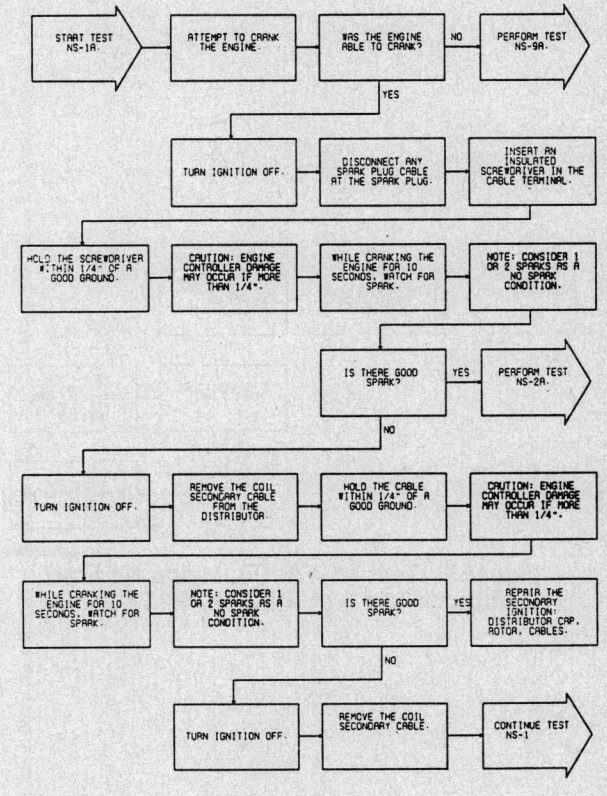

CR1029302867010X

Fig. 165   Test NS-1A: Qualifying No Start Condition (Part 1 of 4). 2.5L/4-153 engine

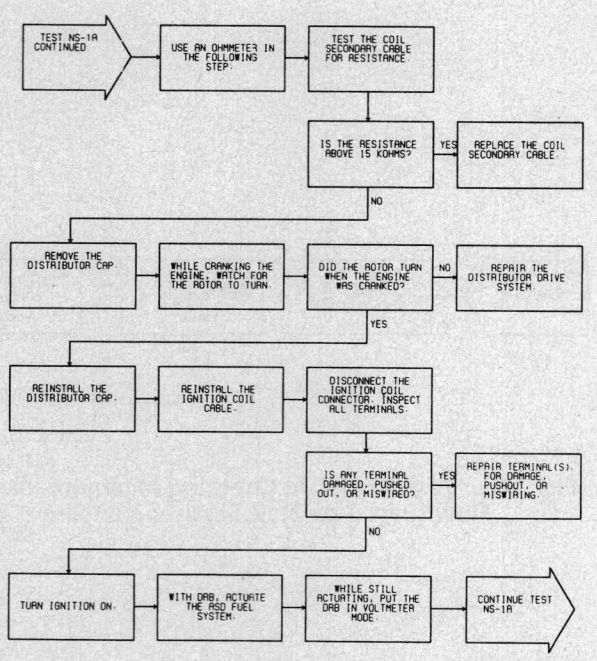

Fig. 165   Test NS-1A: Qualifying No Start Condition (Part 2 of 4). 2.5L/4-153 engine

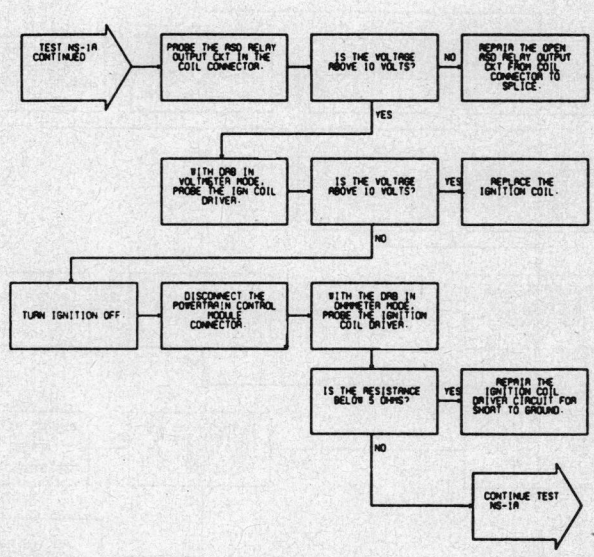

Fig. 165   Test NS-1A: Qualifying No Start Condition (Part 3 of 4). 2.5L/4-153 engine

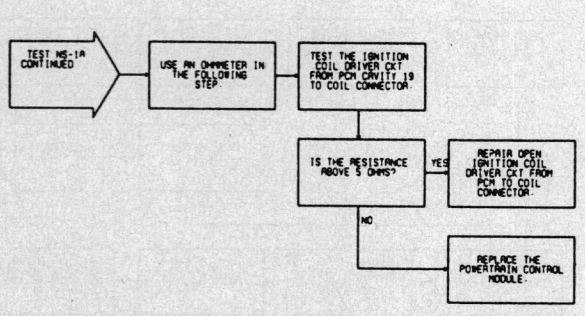

Fig. 165   Test NS-1A: Qualifying No Start Condition (Part 4 of 4). 2.5L/4-153 engine

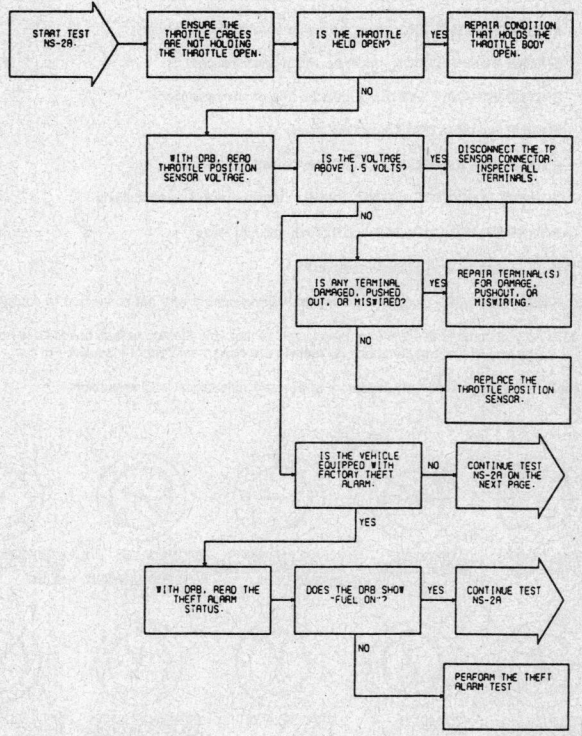

Fig. 166   Test NS-2A: Inspecting Fuel System (Part 1 of 3). 2.5L/4-153 engine

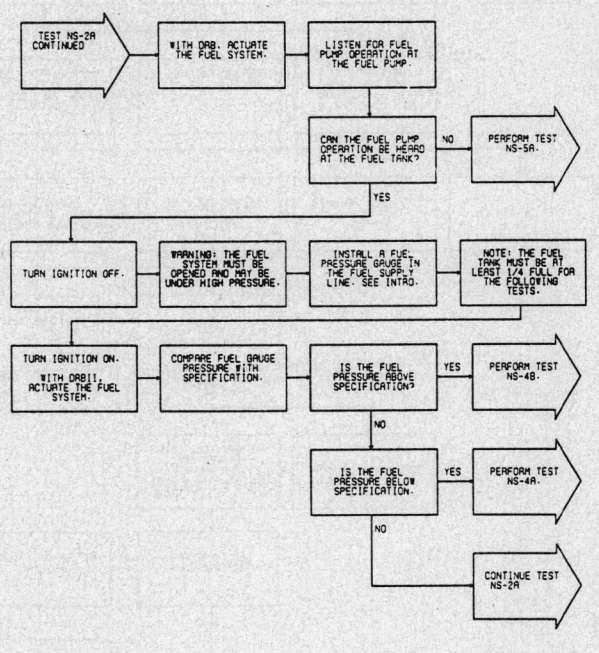

Fig. 166   Test NS-2A: Inspecting Fuel System
(Part 2 of 3). 2.5L/4-153 engine

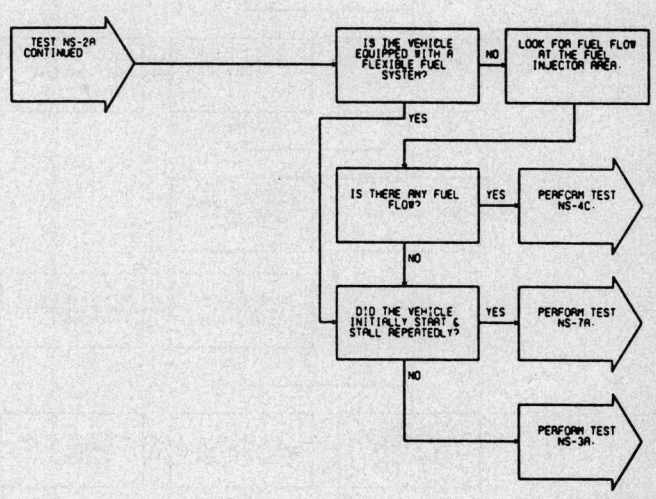

Fig. 166   Test NS-2A: Inspecting Fuel System (Part 3
of 3). 2.5L/4-153 engine

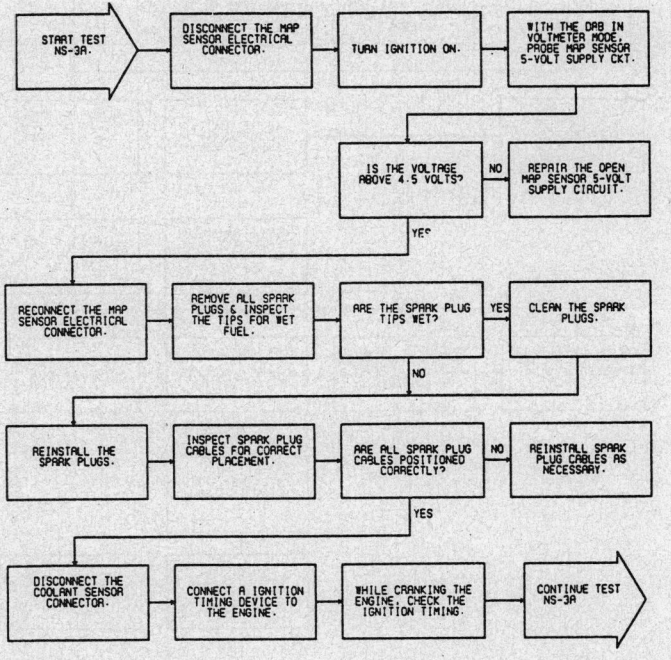

Fig. 167   Test NS-3A: Inspecting Mechanical System
(Part 1 of 3). 2.5L/4-153 engine

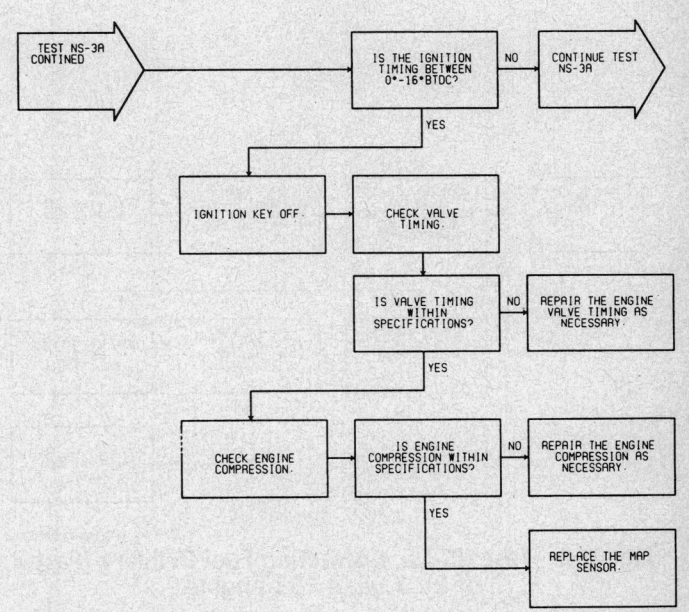

Fig. 167   Test NS-3A: Inspecting Mechanical System (Part
2 of 3). 2.5L/4-153 engine

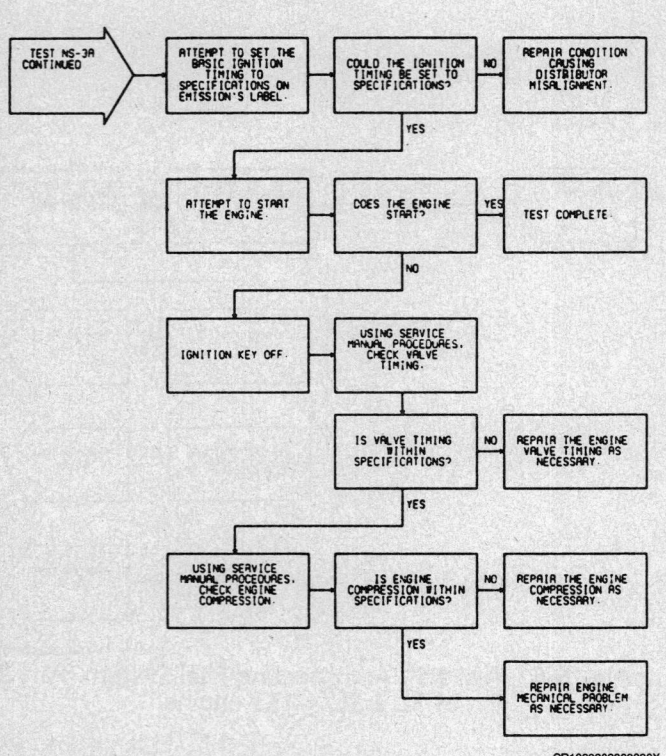

Fig. 167   Test NS-3A: Inspecting Mechanical System (Part 3 of 3). 2.5L/4-153 engine

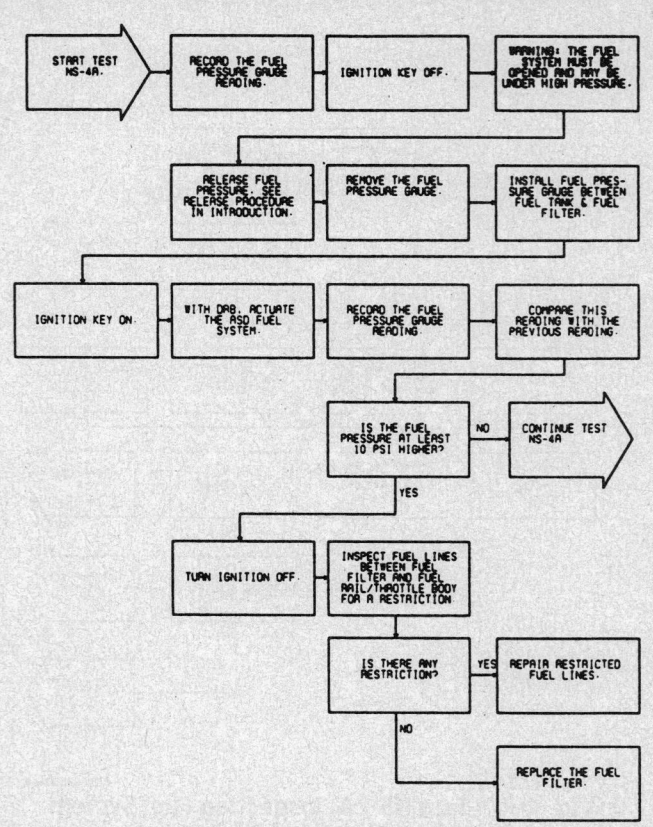

Fig. 168   Test NS-4A: Correcting Fuel Delivery (Part 1 of 2). 2.5L/4-153 engine

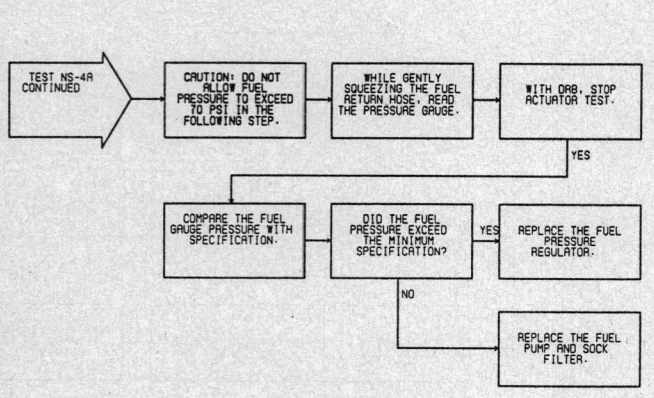

Fig. 168   Test NS-4A: Correcting Fuel Delivery (Part 2 of 2). 2.5L/4-153 engine

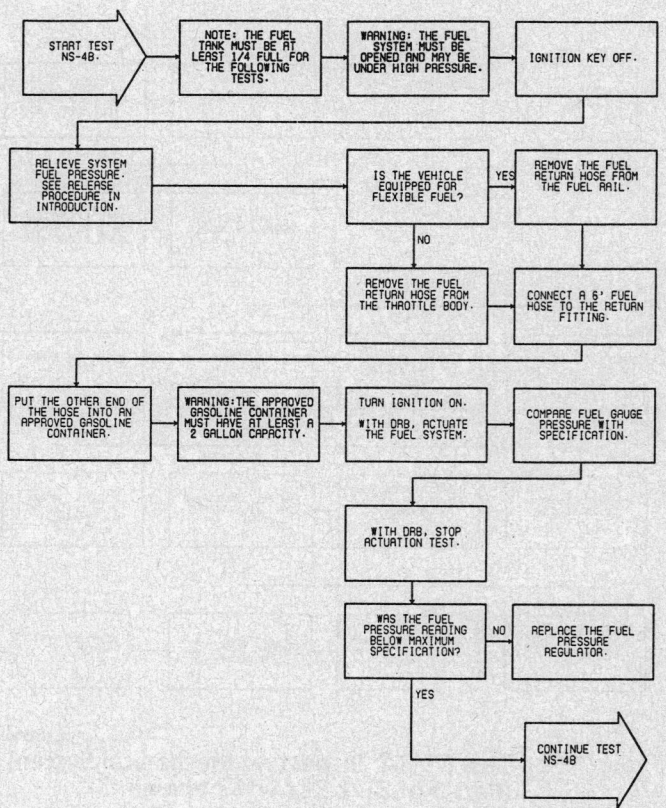

Fig. 169   Test NS-4B: Correcting Fuel Delivery (Part 1 of 2). 2.5L/4-153 engine

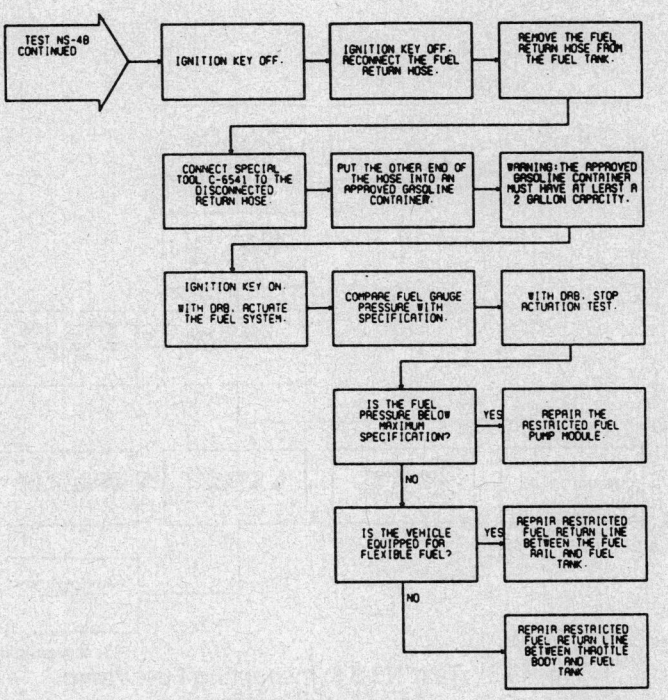

Fig. 169   Test NS-4B: Correcting Fuel Delivery (Part 2 of 2). 2.5L/4-153 engine

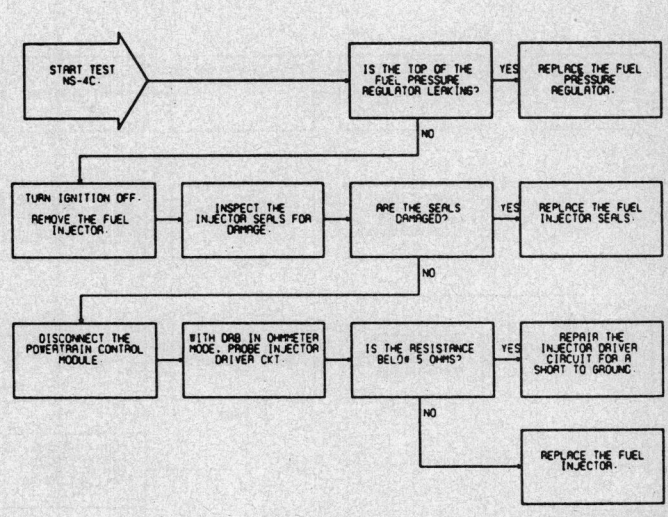

Fig. 170   Test NS-4C: Correcting Fuel Delivery. 2.5L/4-153 engine

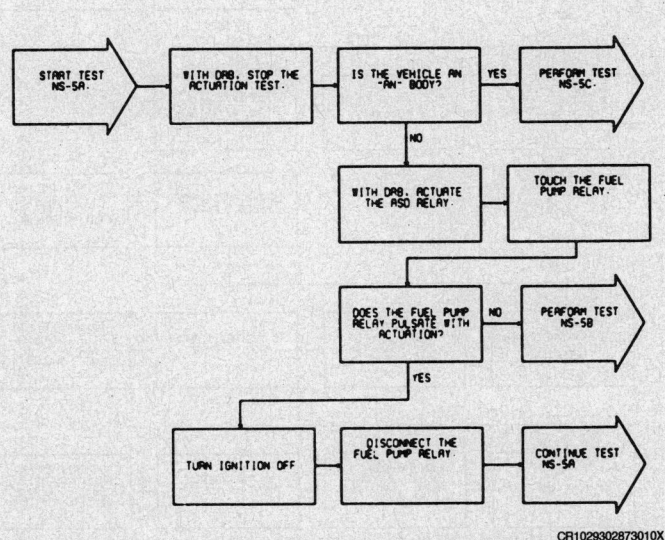

Fig. 171   Test NS-5A: Inspecting Fuel Pump (Part 1 of 2). 2.5L/4-153 engine

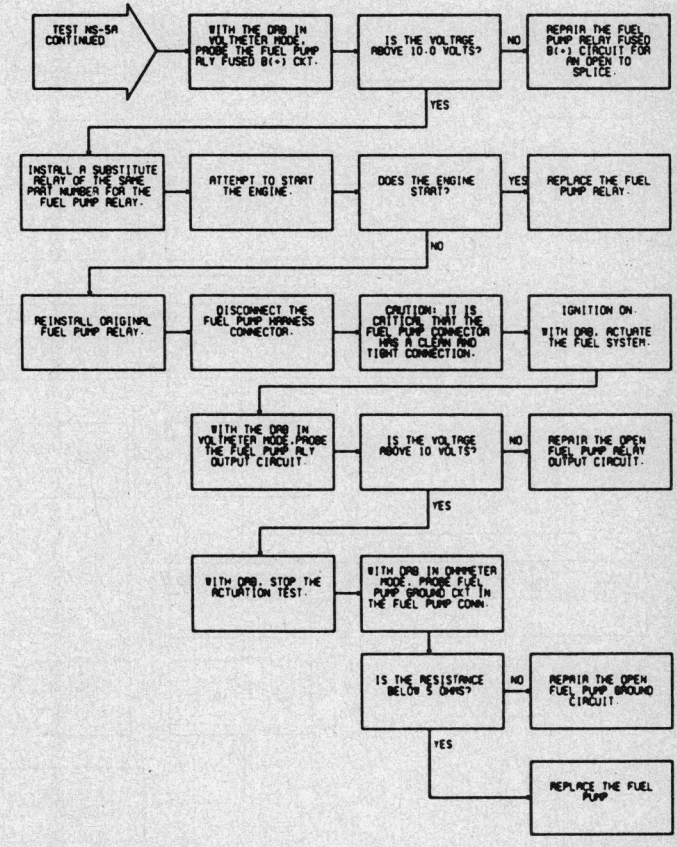

Fig. 171   Test NS-5A: Inspecting Fuel Pump (Part 2 of 2). 2.5L/4-153 engine

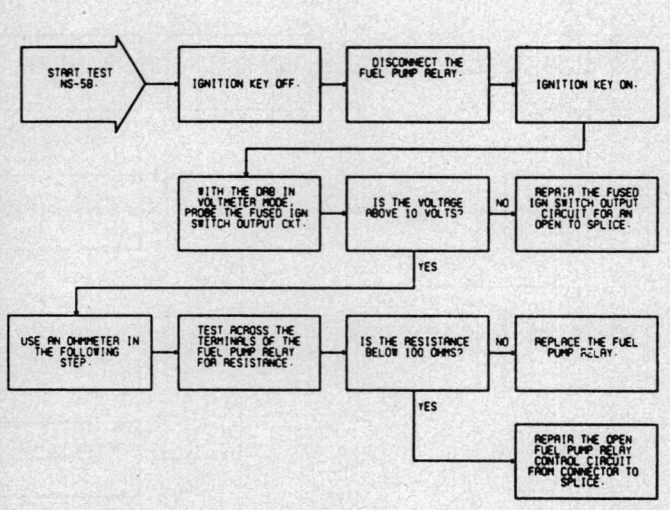

Fig. 172   Test NS-5B: Inspecting Fuel Pump. 2.5L/4-153 engine

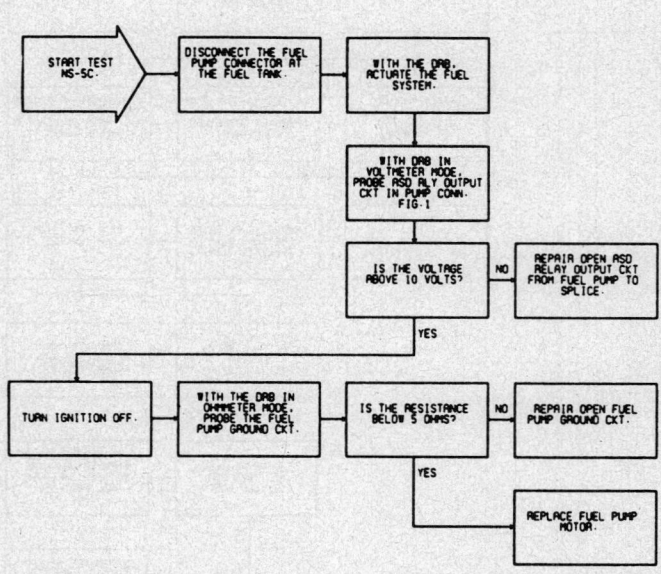

Fig. 173   Test NS-5C: Inspecting Fuel Pump. 2.5L/4-153 engine

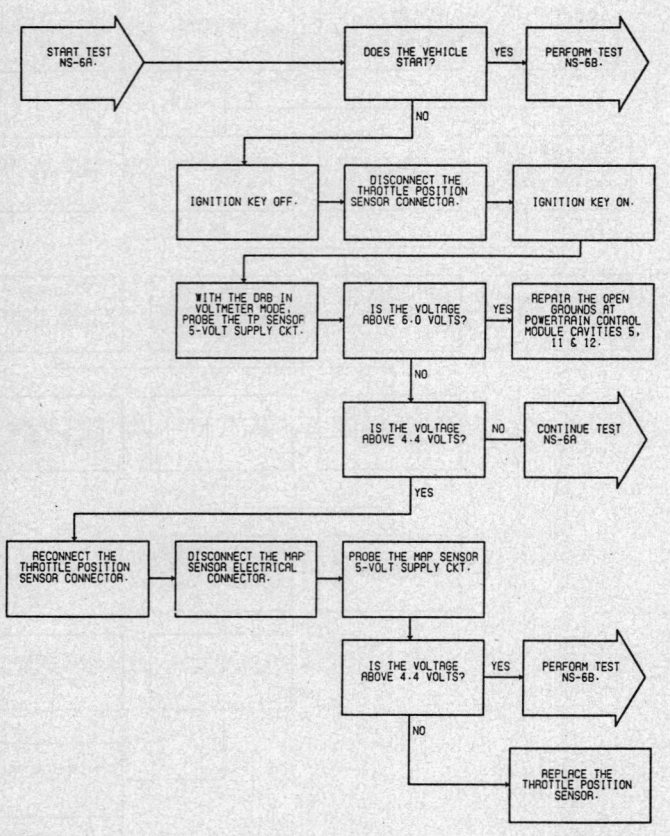

Fig. 174   Test NS-6A: Correcting "No Response" Condition (Part 1 of 5). 2.5L/4-153 engine

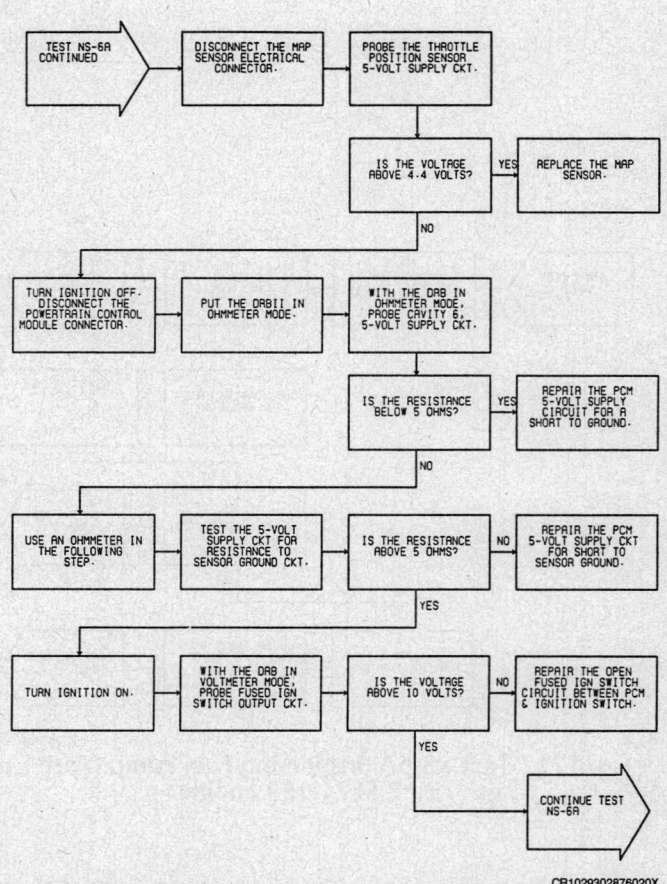

Fig. 174   Test NS-6A: Correcting "No Response" Condition (Part 2 of 5). 2.5L/4-153 engine

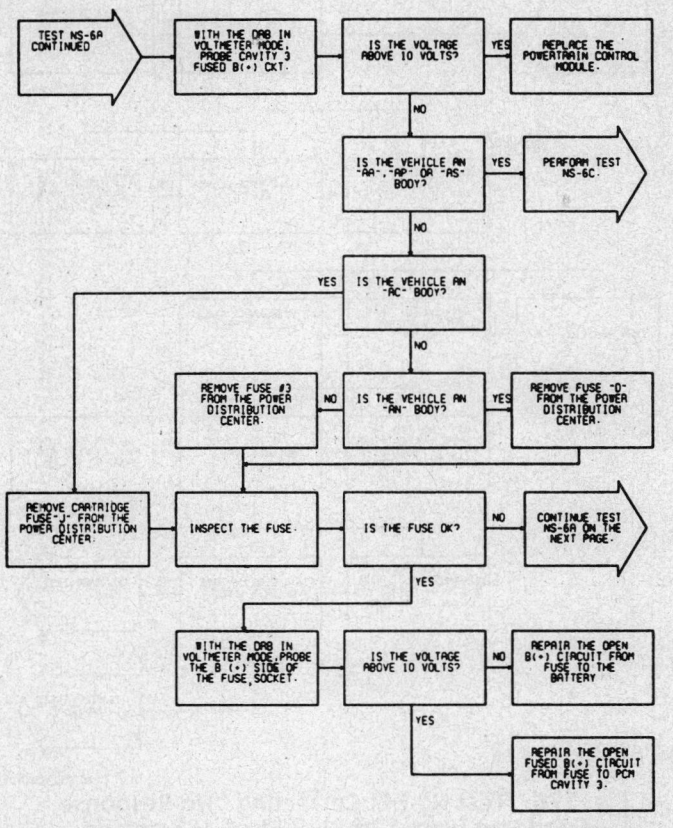

Fig. 174   Test NS-6A: Correcting "No Response" Condition (Part 3 of 5). 2.5L/4-153 engine

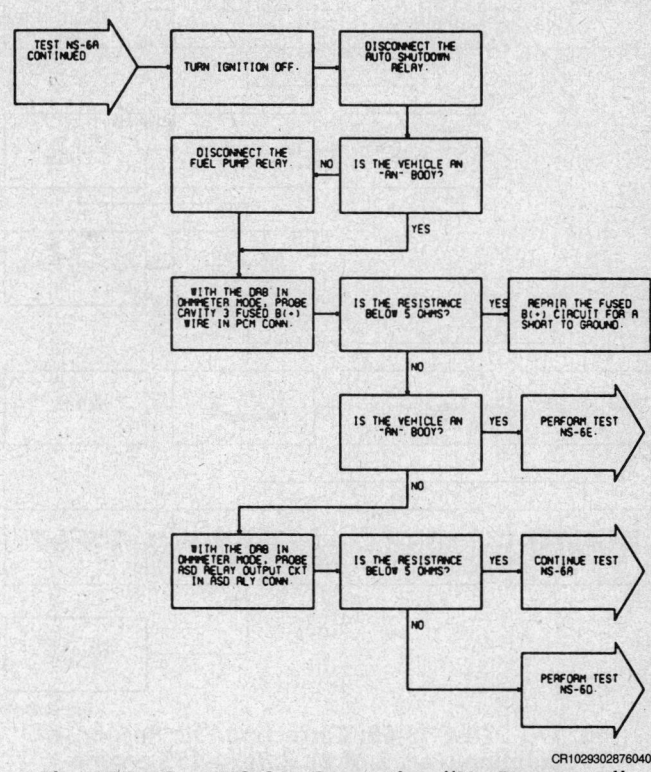

Fig. 174   Test NS-6A: Correcting "No Response" Condition (Part 4 of 5). 2.5L/4-153 engine

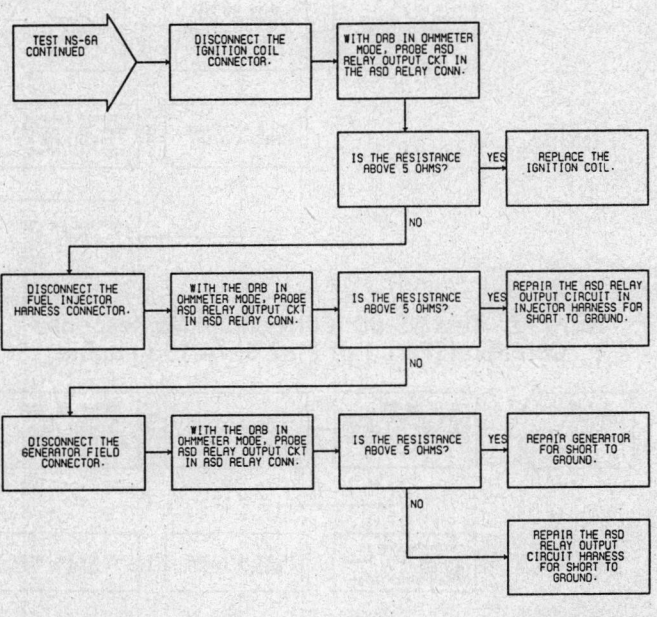

Fig. 174   Test NS-6A: Correcting "No Response" Condition (Part 5 of 5). 2.5L/4-153 engine

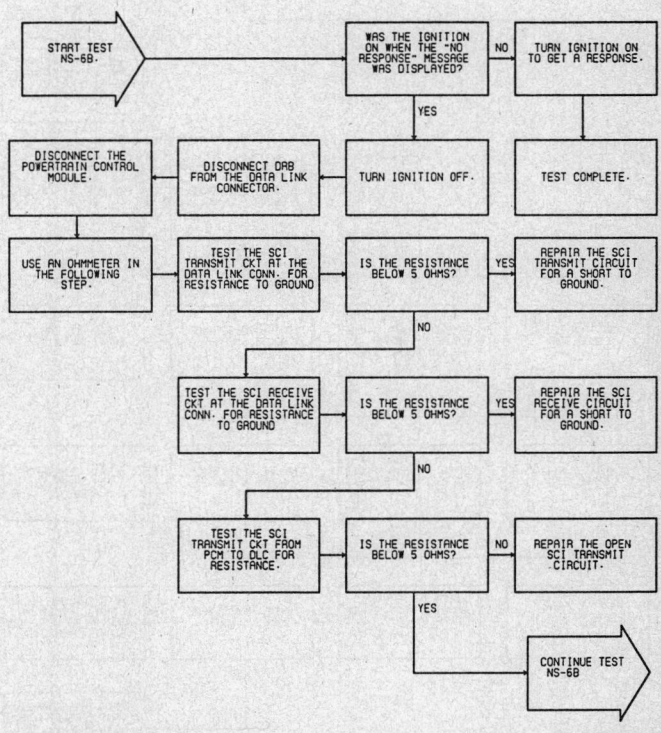

Fig. 175   Test NS-6B: Correcting "No Response" Condition (Part 1 of 2). 2.5L/4-153 engine

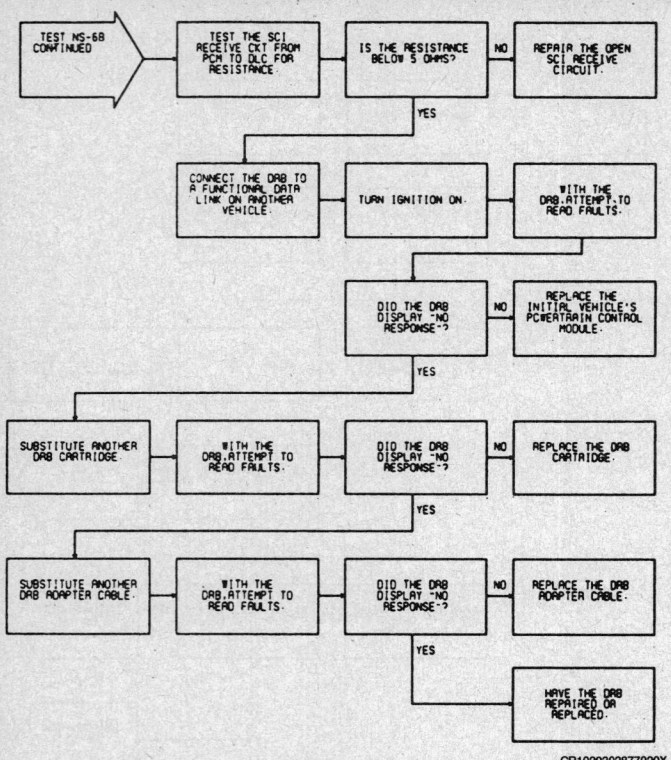

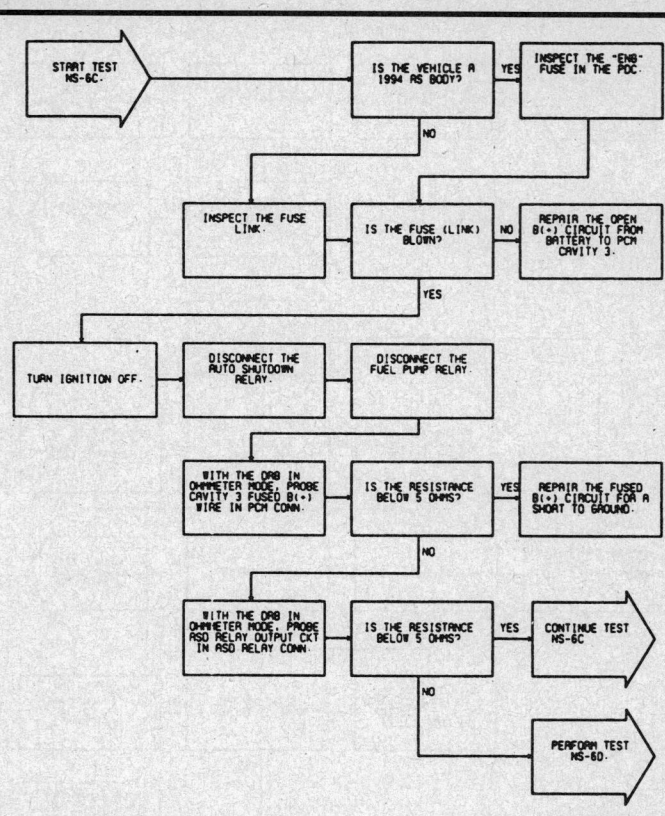

Fig. 175   Test NS-6B: Correcting "No Response" Condition (Part 2 of 2). 2.5L/4-153 engine

Fig. 176   Test NS-6C: Correcting "No Response" Condition (Part 1 of 2). 2.5L/4-153 engine

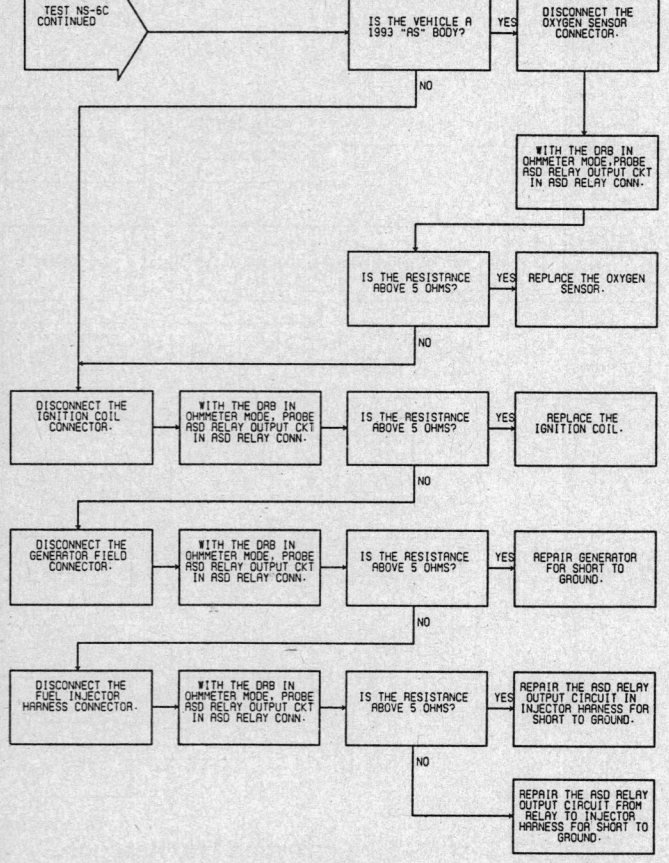

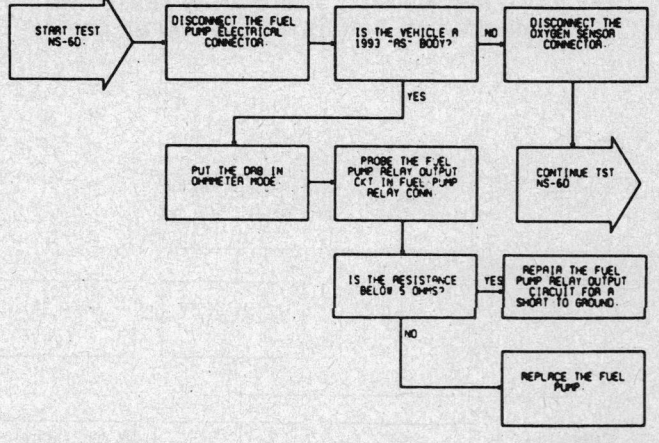

Fig. 177   Test NS-6D: Correcting "No Response" Condition (Part 1 of 2). 2.5L/4-153 engine

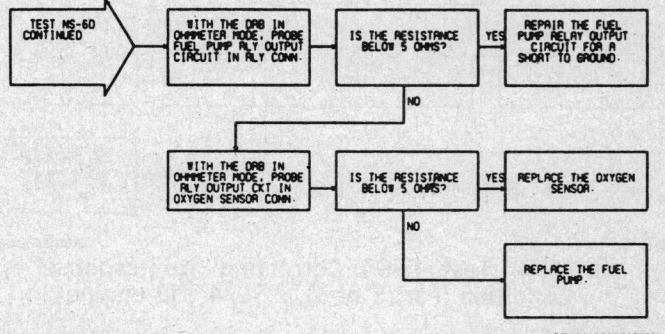

Fig. 176   Test NS-6C: Correcting "No Response" Condition (Part 2 of 2). 2.5L/4-153 engine

Fig. 177   Test NS-6D: Correcting "No Response" Condition (Part 2 of 2). 2.5L/4-153 engine

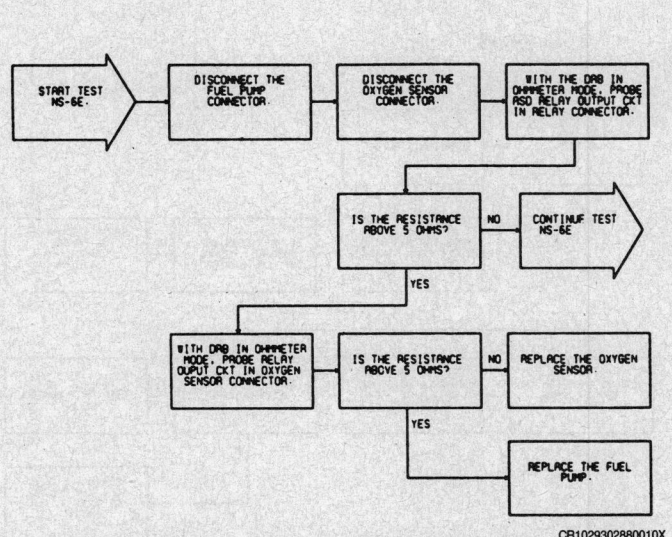

Fig. 178 Test NS-6E: Correcting "No Response" Condition (Part 1 of 2). 2.5L/4-153 engine

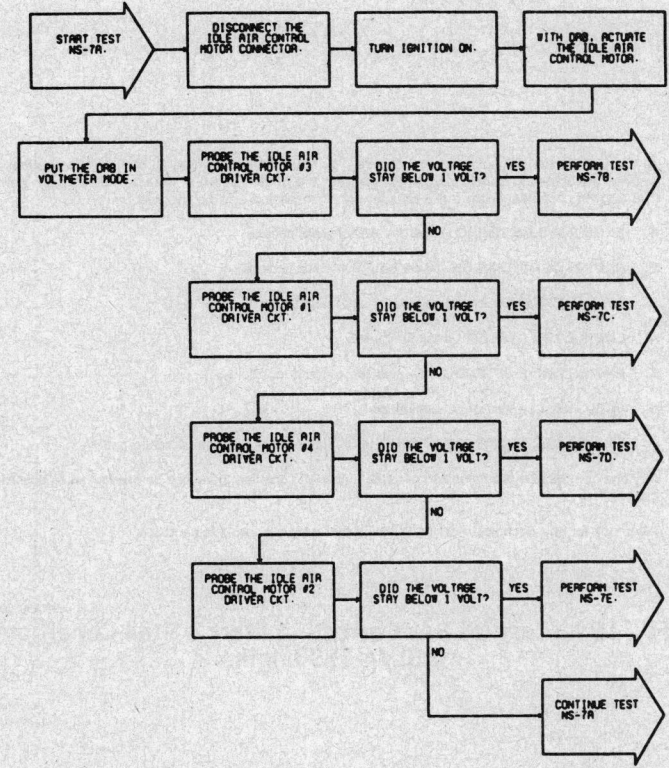

Fig. 179 Test NS-7A: Inspecting Idle Air Control Motor Operation (Part 1 of 2). 2.5L/4-153 engine

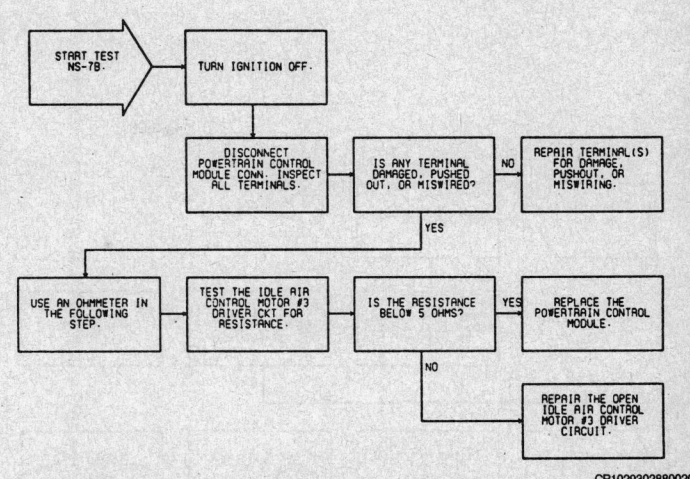

Fig. 178 Test NS-6E: Correcting "No Response" Condition (Part 2 of 2). 2.5L/4-153 engine

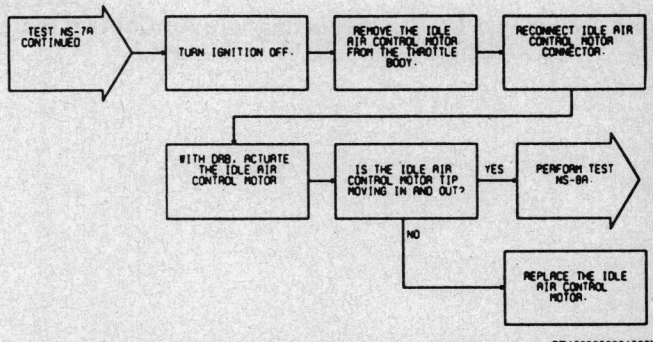

Fig. 179 Test NS-7A: Inspecting Idle Air Control Motor Operation (Part 2 of 2). 2.5L/4-153 engine

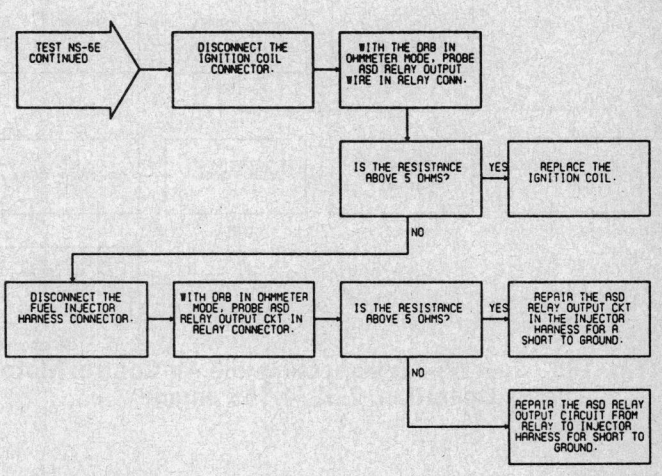

Fig. 180 Test NS-7B: Inspecting Idle Air Control Motor Operation. 2.5L/4-153 engine

CR1029302883000X

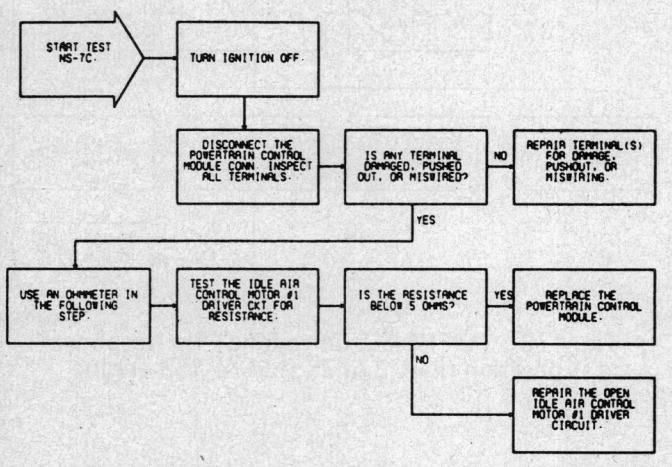

Fig. 181 Test NS-7C: Inspecting Idle Air Control Motor Operation. 2.5L/4-153 engine

CR1029302884000X

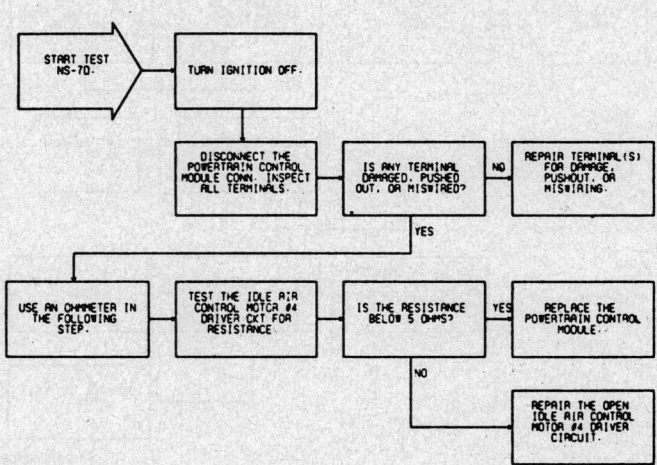

Fig. 182 Test NS-7D: Inspecting Idle Air Control Motor Operation. 2.5L/4-153 engine

CR1029302885000X

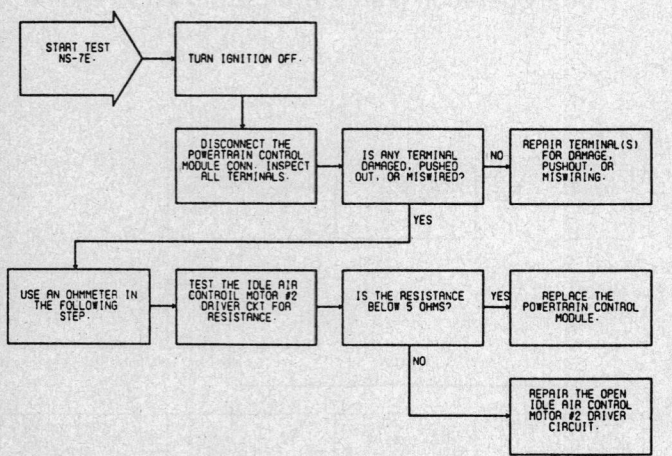

Fig. 183 Test NS-7E: Inspecting Idle Air Control Motor Operation. 2.5L/4-153 engine

At this point in the diagnostic test procedure, you have determined that all of the engine controller systems are operating as designed. Therefore, they are **not the cause of the start and stall problem.** The following potential causes of a no start condition should also be checked:

1. **ENGINE VALVE TIMING** - must be within specifications
2. **ENGINE COMPRESSION** - must be within specifications
3. **ENGINE EXHAUST** - must be free of any restrictions
4. **ENGINE PCV SYSTEM** - must flow freely
5. **ENGINE DRIVE SPROCKETS** - must be properly positioned
6. **FUEL** - must be free of contamination
7. **ENGINE SECONDARY IGNITION CHECK** - must exhibit a normal scope pattern

Any one or more of these items can produce a no start condition; none can be overlooked as possible causes.

Also, look for any Technical Service Bulletins that may relate to this condition.

CR1029302886000X

Fig. 184 Test NS-8A: Correcting Start & Stall Condition. 2.5L/4-153 engine

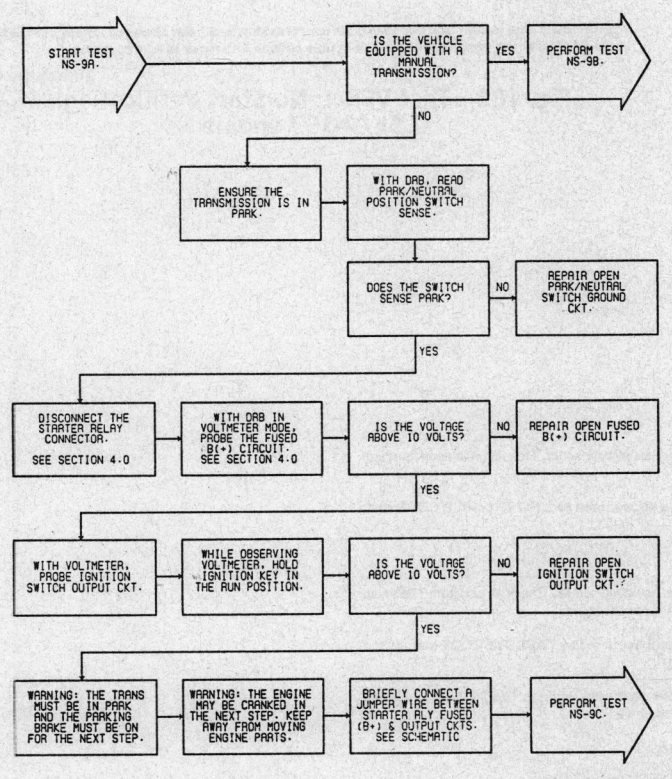

Fig. 185   Test NS-9A: Repairing "No Crank" Condition.
2.5L/4-153 engine

CR1029302887000X

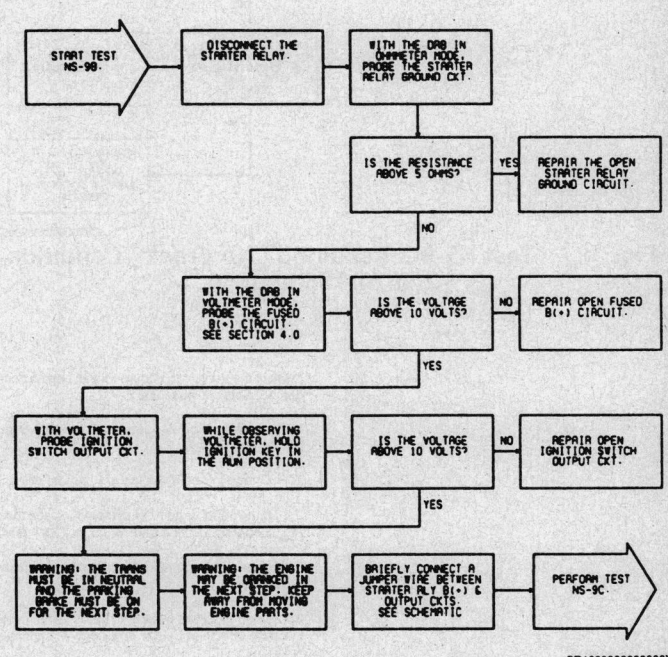

Fig. 186   Test NS-9B: Repairing "No Crank" Condition.
2.5L/4-153 engine

CR1029302888000X

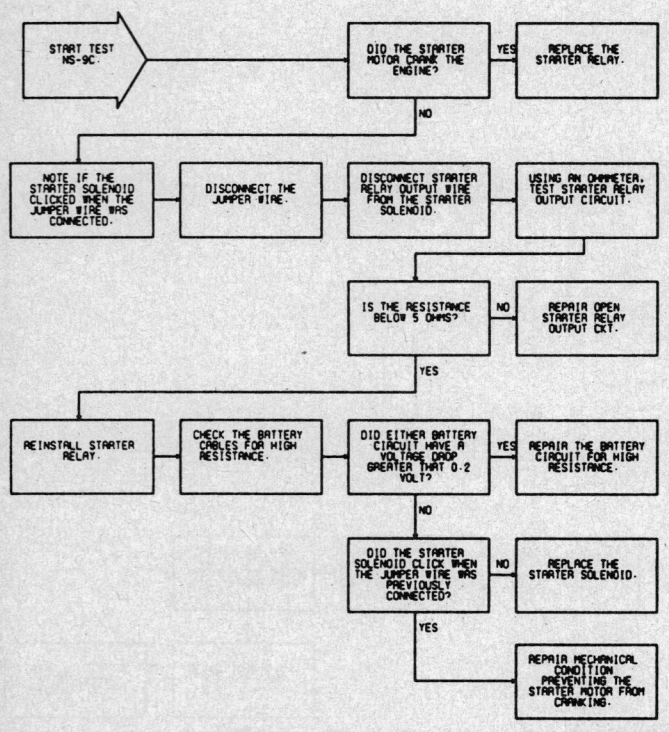

**Fig. 187 Test NS-9C: Repairing "No Crank" Condition.
2.5L/4-153 engine**

Inspect the vehicle to ensure that all engine components are connected. Reassemble and reconnect components as necessary.

Inspect the engine for contamination. If it is contaminated, change the oil and filter.

Attempt to start the engine.

If the engine is unable to start, check all pertinent Technical Service Bulletins, and return to TEST TC-1A if necessary.

If the engine is able to start, and the powertrain control module has been changed, connect the DRB to the PCM data link connector and erase trouble codes. The repair is now complete.

**Fig. 188 Test VER-1: No Start Verification.
2.5L/4-153 engine**

Inspect the vehicle to ensure that all engine components are connected. Reassemble and reconnect components as necessary.

If this verification procedure is being performed subsequent to a NO TROUBLE CODE test, do the following:

1. Check to see if the initial symptom still exists.

2. If the initial or another symptom exists, the repair is not complete. Check all pertinent Technical Service Bulletins and return to TEST NTC-1A if necessary.

If this verification procedure is being performed subsequent to a TROUBLE CODE test, do the following:

For previously read trouble codes that have not been dealt with, return to TEST TC-1A and follow the path specified by the other code. Otherwise, continue.

If the powertrain control module has not been changed:

> Connect the DRB to the PCM data link connector and erase trouble codes.

> With the DRB, reset all values in the adaptive memory.

> Disconnect the DRB.

Ensure no other trouble code remains by doing the following:

1. If the vehicle is equipped with air conditioning, turn on the air conditioning and blower.

2. Drive the vehicle for at least five minutes and at some point attain a speed of 40 mph. Ensure the transmission shifts through all gears. Upon completion of the road test, turn the engine off.

3. Start the engine. Allow the engine to idle for at least two minutes.

4. Turn the engine off.

5. Connect the DRB to the PCM data link connector, and with the DRB, read all trouble codes.

If the repaired code has reset, the repair is not complete. Check all pertinent Technical Service Bulletins and return to TEST TC-1A if necessary.

If another trouble code has set, return to TEST TC-1A and follow the path specified by the other trouble code.

If there are no trouble codes, the repair is now complete.

**Fig. 189 Test VER-2: Road Test Verification.
2.5L/4-153 engine**

Inspect the vehicle to ensure that all engine components are connected. Reassemble and reconnect components as necessary.

If the powertrain control module has been changed, do the following:

1. If the vehicle is equipped with a factory theft alarm, start the vehicle at least 20 times so that the alarm system may be activated when desired.

Connect the DRB to the PCM data link connector and erase the codes.

Ensure no other charging system problems remain by doing the following:

1. Start the engine.
2. Raise the engine speed to 2000 rpm for at least 30 seconds.
3. Allow the engine to idle.
4. Turn the engine off.
5. Turn the ignition key on.
6. With the DRB, read trouble code messages.

If the repaired code has reset, or another one has set, check all pertinent Technical Service Bulletins and return to TEST TC-1A if necessary.

If there are no codes, the repair is now complete.

CR1029302892000X

Fig. 190 Test CH-VER: Charging Verification. 2.5L/4-153 engine

SYSTEM SERVICE
Fuel System Pressure Relief

In order to prevent personal injury and vehicle damage, fuel system pressure must be relieved prior to servicing any fuel-related component. Proceed as follows:

1. Disconnect battery ground cable.
2. Remove fuel filler cap.
3. Remove protective cap from fuel pressure test port on fuel rail.
4. Place open end of fuel pressure release hose tool No. C-4799-91, or equivalent, into suitable container.
5. Connect other end of hose tool to test port on fuel rail to release fuel pressure.
6. Remove hose tool.

Component Replacement

THROTTLE BODY

1. Disconnect battery ground cable.
2. Remove air cleaner hose clamp from hose, then the hose.
3. Remove accelerator cable, then disconnect IAC (AIS) motor and TPS electrical connectors.
4. **On 1993 models,** disconnect vacuum hoses from throttle body.
5. **On all models,** remove throttle body to intake manifold attaching nuts, then the throttle body and gasket.
6. Reverse procedure to install.

PRESSURE REGULATOR
2.2L/4-135 Turbo III Engine

1. Release fuel system pressure as described in this section, then disconnect battery ground cable.
2. Remove vacuum hose harness and wire harness from valve cover bracket.
3. Loosen fuel supply hose clamp at fuel rail inlet, then remove hose.
4. Loosen fuel return hose clamp at fuel pressure regulator, then remove hose.
5. Remove pressure regulator attaching nuts, then fuel pressure regulator.
6. Reverse procedure to install. **Torque** fuel pressure regulator attaching nuts to 65 inch lbs.

2.5L/4-153 Engine

1. Release fuel system pressure as described in this section, then disconnect battery ground cable.
2. **On 1993 models,** remove vacuum hose harness and wire harness from valve cover bracket.
3. **On 1994-95 models,** disconnect vacuum hose from fuel pressure regulator.
4. **On all models,** loosen fuel return tube nut using two open end wrenches. **Two wrenches are necessary or damage will occur.**
5. Remove pressure regulator attaching nuts, then the fuel pressure regulator.
6. Reverse procedure to install. **Torque** fuel pressure regulator attaching nuts to 65 inch lbs. and return tube nut to 150 inch lbs.

FUEL INJECTOR RAIL ASSEMBLY
1993

1. Release fuel system pressure as described in this section, then disconnect battery ground cable.
2. Disconnect fuel injector electrical connectors.
3. Loosen supply hose clamp at fuel rail inlet, then remove hose.

Inspect the vehicle to ensure that all engine components are connected. Reassemble and reconnect all components as necessary.

If the powertrain control module has been changed, do the following:

1. If the vehicle is equipped with a factory theft alarm, start the vehicle at least 20 times so that the alarm system may be activated when desired.

Connect the DRB to the PCM data link connector and erase the codes.

Ensure no other speed control problems remain by doing the following:

1. Road test the vehicle at a speed above 35 mph.
2. Turn the speed control ON/OFF switch to the ON position.
3. Depress and release the SET switch. If the speed control did not engage, the repair is not complete.*
4. For stalk switch equipped vehicles, quickly depress and release the SET switch. For steering wheel switch equipped vehicles, quickly depress and release the RESUME/ACCEL switch. If the vehicle speed did not increase by 2 mph, the repair is not complete.*
5. Using caution, depress and release the brake pedal. If the speed control did not disengage, the repair is not complete.*
6. Bring the vehicle speed back up to 35 mph.
7. Depress the RESUME/ACCEL switch. If the speed control did not resume the previously set speed, the repair is not complete.*
8. Hold down the SET switch. If the vehicle did not decelerate, the repair is not complete.*
9. Ensure the vehicle speed is greater than 35 mph and release the SET switch. If the vehicle did not adjust and set a new vehicle speed, the repair is not complete.*
10. Turn on the ON/OFF switch to the OFF position. If the speed control did not disengage, the repair is not complete.*

If the vehicle successfully passed all of the previous tests, the speed control system is now functioning as designed. The repair is now complete.

*Check for Technical Service Bulletins that pertain to this speed control problem and then, if necessary, return to TEST TC-1A.

CR1029302893000X

Fig. 191 Test SC-VER: Speed Control Verification. 2.5L/4-153 engine

4. Loosen fuel return hose clamp at fuel pressure regulator, then remove hose.
5. Disconnect vacuum and vapor hoses.
6. Disconnect fuel pressure regulator vacuum hose from regulator.
7. Remove fuel rail to valve cover bracket attaching screws, then fuel rail to intake manifold attaching screws.
8. Remove fuel rail and injector assembly by pulling rail so injectors come straight out of their ports. **Use caution to prevent damage to injector O-rings during removal.**
9. Remove fuel rail assembly from vehicle.
10. Reverse procedure to install, noting the following:
   a. Lubricate injector and fuel pressure regulator O-ring with clean oil to facilitate installation.
   b. **Torque** fuel rail attaching screws to 16-17 ft. lbs.

1994—95

1. Release fuel system pressure as described in this section, then disconnect battery ground cable.
2. Disconnect fuel injector harness from engine harness.
3. Remove fittings from chassis fuel tubes.
4. Disconnect vacuum hose from top of intake manifold, then the vacuum hose from pressure regulator.
5. Remove fuel tube clamp screw, then the fuel rail mounting screws.
6. Remove fuel rail and injector assembly by pulling rail so injectors come straight out of their ports. **Use caution to prevent damage to injector O-rings during removal.**

7. Reverse procedure to install, noting the following:
   a. Lubricate injector and fuel pressure regulator O-ring with clean oil.
   b. **Torque** fuel rail attaching screws to 16-17 ft. lbs.

FUEL INJECTOR

1. Release fuel system pressure as described in this section.
2. Disconnect electrical connector from injector.
3. Remove fuel rail assembly and position so injectors are easily accessible.
4. Remove injector clip from injector and fuel rail.
5. Pull injector straight out of fuel rail receiver cup.
6. Check injector O-ring for damage. Replace O-ring if damaged. If injector will be reused, install protective cap on injector tip to prevent damage.
7. Reverse procedure to install. Install injector clip by sliding open end into top slot of injector and onto receiver cup ridge, then into side slots of clip.

FUEL FILTER

1. Release pressure from fuel system as described in this section.
2. Remove fuel filter attaching screw, then the filter from mounting plate, **Fig. 192.**
3. Remove quick disconnect fitting. **Wrap a clean towel around fuel lines to prevent leakage of residual fuel.**
4. Remove filter assembly from vehicle.
5. Reverse procedure to install. **Torque** filter attaching screw to 75 inch lbs.

THROTTLE POSITION SENSOR (TPS)

1. Disconnect battery ground cable.
2. Disconnect throttle position sensor electrical connector.

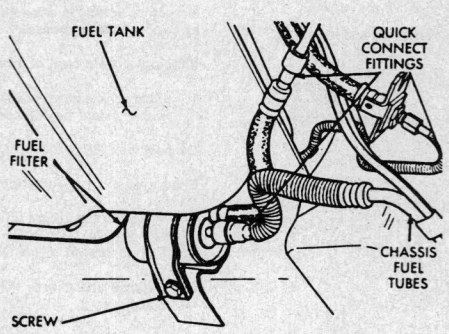

Fig. 192 Fuel filter assembly

3. Remove throttle position sensor to throttle body attaching screws, then lift throttle position sensor off throttle shaft.
4. Reverse procedure to install. **Torque** sensor attaching screws to 17 inch lbs.

MANIFOLD ABSOLUTE PRESSURE (MAP) SENSOR

1. Disconnect vacuum hose and wiring harness from sensor.
2. Remove sensor attaching screws, then the sensor.
3. Reverse procedure to install.

METHANOL CONCENTRATION SENSOR

Flex Fuel Engine

1. Release fuel system pressure as described in this section.
2. Disconnect fuel tubes and electrical connector from sensor.
3. Remove mounting nuts, then the sensor from bracket.
4. Reverse procedure to install.

POWERTRAIN CONTROL MODULE (PCM)

1. Remove air cleaner duct from engine controller.
2. Remove battery.
3. Disconnect 60-way module electrical connector.
4. Remove two attaching screws, then the PCM.
5. Reverse procedure to install.

OXYGEN SENSOR (O₂S)

1. **On 1993 models,** remove sensor from exhaust manifold using oxygen sensor socket tool No. C-4907, or equivalent.
2. **On 1994-95 models,** remove sensor from exhaust manifold using socket tool No. YA8875, or equivalent.
3. **On all models,** clean threads in manifold using 18 mm X 1.5 X 6E tap.
4. Install new sensor and **torque** to 20 ft. lbs. If original sensor is to be reinstalled, coat threads with suitable anti-seize compound. New sensors are pre-coated and need no additional compound.

IDLE AIR CONTROL (IAC) MOTOR

1. Disconnect battery ground cable.
2. Disconnect IAC motor electrical connector.
3. Remove IAC motor to throttle body attaching screws, then the IAC motor from throttle body. Ensure O-ring in on IAC motor during removal.
4. Reverse procedure to install, noting the following:
   a. If pintle measures more than 1 inch, it must be retracted using a Diagnostic Readout Box (DRB) scan tool in IAC Open/Close mode.
   b. **Torque** mounting screws to 17 inch lbs.

1995 AVENGER, CIRRUS, SEBRING & STRATUS w/2.5L/V6-152 ENGINE

If Unsure Of The System Used On The Vehicle Being Serviced, Refer To The "Engine Systems Identification Chart." Further Assistance For The Proper Use Of Information Contained In This Section Can Also Be Found In The Front Of This Tabbed Section Under "How To Use This Manual."

Prior To Performing Any Service Operations Listed In This Section, Consult The Technical Service Bulletin Section For Related Information.

Electrical Symbol & Wire Color Code Identification Located In The Front Of This Manual May Be Used As An Aid When Using Wiring Circuits Found In This Section.

INDEX

Page No.	Page No.	Page No.
Description: 10-2	Speed Control Tests 10-7	Sensor Specifications.............. 10-1
Components 10-2	Trouble Code Tests............. 10-4	System Service: 10-56
Diagnosis & Testing: 10-4	Verification Tests 10-7	Component Replacement......... 10-56
Accessing Diagnostic Trouble Codes 10-4	Diagnostic Trouble Code	Air Inlet Resonator............. 10-56
Using Drb Scan Tool............ 10-4	Interpretation 10-4	Fuel Injectors.................. 10-56
Using Mil 10-4	Diagnostic Chart Index: 10-7	Fuel Rail...................... 10-56
Clearing Diagnostic Trouble Codes . 10-4	Precautions:...................... 10-2	Intake Air Temperature Sensor . . 10-58
Diagnostic Tests.................. 10-4	DRB Safety Information......... 10-2	Oxygen Sensor................. 10-58
Charging Test 10-7	Electronic Pinion Factor Warning . 10-2	Throttle Body 10-56
Inactive Trouble Code Condition.. 10-7	Fuel System Pressure Relief 10-2	Throttle Position Sensor (TPS) .. 10-58
No Start Tests................. 10-7	Servicing Subassemblies 10-2	Fuel System Pressure Relief 10-56
No Trouble Code Tests......... 10-7	Vehicle Damage Warnings....... 10-2	Troubleshooting 10-4

SENSOR SPECIFICATIONS

Component	Voltage	Resistance
Engine Coolant Temperature Sensor	—	①
Heated Oxygen Sensor	—	5—7
Intake Air Temperature Sensor	—	7000—13,000 ②
Manifold Absolute Pressure Sensor	③	—
Throttle Position Sensor	④	—

①—At normal operating temperature of 200°F, 700—1000 ohms; at room temperature of 70°F, 7000—13,000 ohms.
②—At 70°F.
③—Ignition switch ON & engine not running, 4—5 volts; engine hot at neutral idle speed, 1.5—2.1 volts
④—Idle speed, .5 volts; wide open throttle, 3.7 volts.

FUNCTION	INPUT LIMIT
Volts	0 - 500 peak volts AC 0 - 500 volts DC
Ohms (resistance)*	0 - 1.12 megohms
Frequency Measured Frequency Generated	0 - 10 kHz
Temperature	-58 - 1100° F -50 - 600° C

* Ohms cannot be measured if voltage is present. Ohms can be measured only in a non-powered circuit.

CR1029505248000X

Fig. 1   DRB testing limits

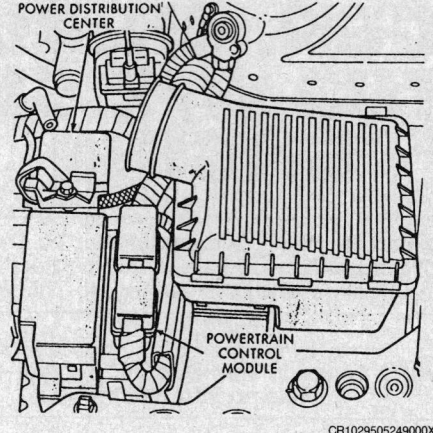

CR1029505249000X

Fig. 2   Power Distribution Center (PDC) & Powertrain Control Module (PCM)

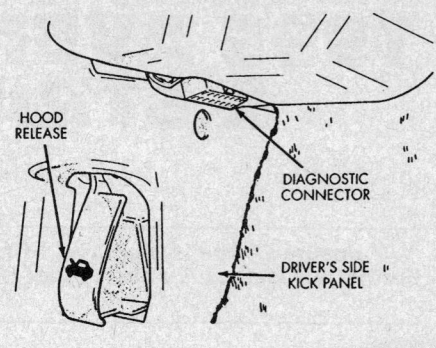

CR1029505250000X

Fig. 3   Data link (diagnostic) connector

PRECAUTIONS

FUEL SYSTEM PRESSURE RELIEF

To relieve fuel system pressure, refer to "Fuel System Pressure Relief" under "System Service" prior to performing any fuel system component.

SERVICING SUBASSEMBLIES

Some powertrain system components are intended to be serviced in assembly only. Attempting to remove or repair certain system sub-components may result in personal injury and/or improper system operation. Only those components with approved repair and installation procedures in this manual should be serviced.

DRB SAFETY INFORMATION

Exceeding the limits of the DRB multimeter is dangerous. It can expose you to serious or possibly fatal injury. Carefully read and understand the following cautions and specification limits.
1. Follow vehicle manufacturer's service specifications at all times.
2. Do not use DRB if it is damaged, or the test leads if the insulation is damaged or if metal is exposed.
3. To avoid electrical shock, do not touch test leads, tips or circuit being tested.
4. Choose proper range and function for measurement. Do not try voltage or current measurements which may exceed rated capacity.
.5. Do not exceed specified limits, **Fig. 1.**

VEHICLE DAMAGE WARNINGS

Before disconnecting any control module, ensure ignition switch is in Off position. Failure to do so could damage the module.

When testing voltage or continuity at any control module, use the terminal side (not the wire end) of the connector. Do not probe a wire through the insulation, as this will damage it and eventually cause it to fail due to corrosion.

When performing electrical tests, use caution to prevent accidental shorting of terminals. Such mistakes can damage fuses or components. Also, a second code could be set, making diagnosis of the original problem more difficult.

ELECTRONIC PINION FACTOR WARNING

The pinion factor must be set for all new transmission control modules. If the pinion factor is not set or if it is set incorrectly, any speed-related accessories will not operate or will operate inaccurately. This includes the speedometer, speed control, rolling door locks and other devices that are operated by the powertrain and body controllers.

DESCRIPTION

The Avenger, Cirrus, Sebring and Stratus all use a sequential Multi-Port Electronic Fuel Injection System (MPI). The MPI system is computer regulated and provides precise air/fuel ratios for all driving conditions. The Powertrain Control Module (PCM) operates the fuel injection system.

Various switches and sensors provide the inputs necessary for the PCM to correctly operate the MPI system. All sensor and switch inputs to the PCM are converted into signals. The PCM can adapt its programming to meet changing operating conditions.

The PCM adjusts injector pulse width (length of time the injector is open) by opening and closing the ground path to the injector.

COMPONENTS

Power Distribution Center (PDC)

The PDC, **Fig. 2,** is located next to the battery. The PDC contains the starter relay, radiator fan relay, A/C compressor clutch relay, auto shutdown relay, fuel pump relay and several fuses.

Powertrain Control Module (PCM)

The PCM, **Fig. 2,** is a digital computer with a microprocessor which receives input signals from various switches and sensors. Based on these inputs, the PCM adjusts various engine and vehicle operations through PCM outputs.

Data Link Circuits

The data link receive and transmit circuits allow the Powertrain Control Module (PCM) to communicate with the DRB scan tool. Data link connector terminal 6 is the data link engine receive circuit, while the data link connector terminal 7 is the data link engine transmit circuit.

Data Link Connector (DLC)

The DLC, **Fig. 3,** links the DRB scan tool with the Powertrain Control Module (PCM). The data link connector is located inside the vehicle, under the instrument panel, at the driver's kick panel.

ASD Sense Circuit (PCM Input)

The Automatic Shutdown (ASD) sense circuit informs the Powertrain Control Module (PCM) when then ASD relay energizes. When energized, the ASD relay supplies battery voltage to the fuel injectors, ignition coils and the heating element in each oxygen sensor. If the PCM does not receive 12 volts from this input after grounding the ASD relay, it sets a diagnostic trouble code.

Battery Voltage (PCM Input)

The Powertrain Control Module (PCM) monitors battery voltage input to determine fuel injector pulse width and generator field control. If battery voltage is low, the PCM will increase injector pulse width (period of time injector is energized).

Battery Temperature Sensor

The Powertrain Control Module (PCM) uses the temperature of the battery area to control the charge rate. The signal is used to regulate the system voltage. The system voltage is higher at cold temperatures and is gradually reduced as temperature is increased.

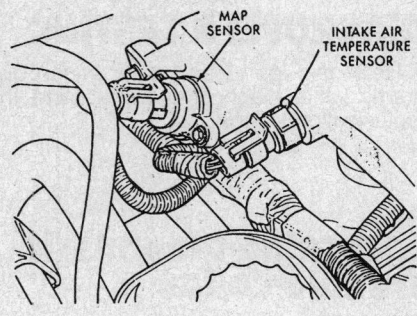

Fig. 4 Intake Air Temperature (IAT) sensor & Manifold Absolute Pressure (MAP) sensor

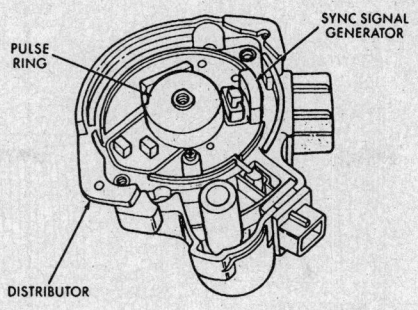

Fig. 5 Camshaft position sensor

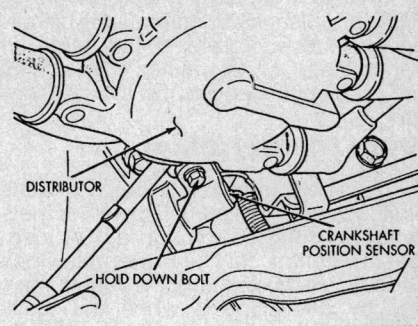

Fig. 6 Crankshaft position sensor

Intake Air Temperature Sensor (PCM Input)

The Intake Air Temperature (IAT) sensor measures the temperature of the intake air as it enters the engine. The sensor supplies one of the inputs the PCM uses to determine injector pulse width and spark advance. The IAT sensor threads into the intake manifold, **Fig. 4.**

Camshaft Position Sensor (PCM Input)

The Powertrain Control Module (PCM) determines fuel injection synchronization and cylinder identification from inputs provided by the camshaft position sensor and crankshaft position sensor. From two inputs, the PCM determines the crankshaft position.

The engine is equipped with a camshaft driven mechanical distributor. The distributor is also equipped with an internal camshaft position (fuel synch) sensor, **Fig. 5.**

Crankshaft Position Sensor (PCM Input)

The Powertrain Control Module (PCM) determines what cylinder to fire from the crankshaft and camshaft position sensor input. It is also used to synchronize the fuel injectors with their respective cylinders.

The sensor is a hall effect device which detects notches in the flexplate. The sensor is located in the transaxle housing, above the vehicle speed sensor, **Fig. 6.**

Manifold Absolute Pressure (MAP) Sensor (PCM Input)

The Powertrain Control Module (PCM) supplies 5 volts of direct current to the Manifold Absolute Pressure (MAP) sensor. The MAP sensor converts intake manifold pressure into voltage. The PCM monitors the MAP sensor output voltage. As vacuum increases, MAP sensor voltage decreases proportionately. Also, as vacuum decreases, MAP sensor voltage increases proportionately. The MAP sensor mounts to the intake manifold, **Fig. 4.**

Heated Oxygen Sensors

As vehicles accumulate mileage, the catalytic convertor deteriorates. The deterioration results in a less efficient catalyst.

To monitor convertor deterioration, the fuel injection system uses heated oxygen sensors. The Powertrain Control Module (PCM) compares the readings from the sensors to calculate the catalytic converter oxygen storage capacity and converter efficiency.

Park/Neutral Position Switch (PCM Input)

The park/neutral position switch is located on the automatic transaxle housing. Manual transaxles do not use park/neutral switches. The switch provides an input to the Powertrain Control Module (PCM) to indicate whether the automatic transaxle is in Park/Neutral, or a drive gear selection. This input is used to determine idle speed (varying with gear selection) and ignition timing advance. The park/neutral input is also used to cancel vehicle speed control. The park/neutral switch is sometimes referred to as the neutral safety switch.

Power Steering Pressure Switch (PCM Input)

A pressure sensing switch is located on the power steering gear. The switch provides an input to the PCM during periods of high pump load and low engine RPM, such as during parking maneuvers.

When power steering pump pressure exceeds 600 psi, the switch opens and the PCM increases idle air flow through the IAC motor to prevent engine stalling. When the pump pressure is low, the switch is closed.

Sensor Return (PCM Input)

The sensor return circuit provides a low electrical noise ground reference for all of the system sensors. The sensor return circuit connects to the internal ground circuits within the Powertrain Control Module (PCM).

Speed Control (PCM Input)

The speed control system provides 5 voltage levels to the PCM. The voltages correspond to the On/Off, Set, Resume and Cancel.

The Throttle Position Sensor (TPS) mounts to the side of the throttle body. The TPS connects to the throttle blade shaft. The TPS is a variable resistor providing the PCM with an input signal. This signal represents the throttle blade position. As the position of the throttle blade changes, the resistance of the TPS changes.

Along with inputs from other sensors, the Powertrain Control Module (PCM) uses TPS input to determine current engine operating conditions. The PCM also adjusts fuel injector pulse width and ignition timing based on these inputs.

Automatic Shutdown Relay (PCM Output)

The Automatic Shutdown (ASD) Relay supplies battery voltage to the fuel injectors, electronic ignition coil and the heating elements in the oxygen sensors.

Charging System Indicator Lamp (PCM Output)

The Powertrain Control Module (PCM) sends a message over the CCD Bus to the Body Control Module (BCM). The BCM turns on the instrument panel Charging System Lamp.

Duty Cycle EVAP Purge Solenoid (PCM Output)

The duty cycle EVAP purge solenoid regulates the rate of vapor flow from the EVAP canister to the throttle body. The Powertrain Control Module (PCM) operates the solenoid.

Electric EGR Transducer (PCM Output)

The electric EGR transducer, contains an electrically operated solenoid and a backpressure controlled vacuum transducer. The PCM operates the solenoid based on inputs from the multi-port fuel injection system. The solenoid/transducer and EGR valve are serviced as an assembly.

Fuel Injectors (PCM Output)

This engine uses electrically operated top feed injectors. The Automatic Shutdown (ASD) relay supplies battery voltage to the fuel injectors. The Powertrain Control Module (PCM) controls the ground path for each injector in sequence. By switching the ground paths on and off, the PCM fine-tunes injector pulse width. Injector pulse width refers to the amount of time an injector operates.

The PCM determines injector synchronization from the camshaft position sensor and crankshaft position sensor inputs. Then, the PCM energizes the injectors in a sequential order during all engine operating conditions except start-up. For the first injector pulse width during start-up, all injectors are energized at the same time. Once the PCM determines crankshaft position, it begins energizing the injectors in sequence.

Fuel Pump Relay

The fuel pump relay supplies battery voltage to the fuel pump. Power for the solenoid is supplied through a 10A fuse in the junction block. The Powertrain Control Module (PCM) controls the fuel pump relay by energizing it when the ignition switch is placed in the On position, then de-energizing it when the ignition switch is placed in the Off position.

Idle Air Control Motor (PCM Output)

The Idle Air Control (IAC) motor is mounted on the throttle body. The Powertrain Control Module (PCM) operates the idle air control motor.

The PCM adjusts engine idle speed through the idle air control motor to compensate for engine load, coolant temperature or barometric pressure changes. The PCM adjusts engine idle speed by moving the IAC motor pintle in and out of the bypass passage. The adjustments are based on inputs the PCM receives from the throttle position sensor, crankshaft position sensor, coolant temperature sensor, MAP sensor, vehicle speed sensor and various switch operations (brake, park/neutral, air conditioning and power steering).

Malfunction Indicator Lamp (MIL) (PCM Output)

If a problem is detected, the PCM sends a message over the CCD Bus to the Body Control Module (BCM). The BCM interprets this message and sends a signal to the instrument cluster to illuminate a malfunction indicator (Check Engine) lamp. The lamp comes on each time the ignition key is placed in On position and stays on for a three second bulb test.

TROUBLESHOOTING

Before diagnosing or servicing the fuel injection system, perform visual inspection for loose, disconnected or misrouted wires and hoses. A thorough visual inspection which includes the following checks saves unnecessary test and diagnostic time.

1. Inspect remote battery cable connections. Ensure they are clean and tight. Clean corroded terminals, **Fig. 7.**
2. Verify PCM 40-way connectors are fully inserted into their sockets on PCM.
3. Open Power Distribution Center (PDC). Check for blown fuses and ensure relays and fuses are fully seated in the PDC. Label on underside of PDC cover shows locations of each relay and fuse.
4. Inspect accelerator cable and cruise control cable connections. Check connections to throttle arm of throttle body for any binding or restrictions.

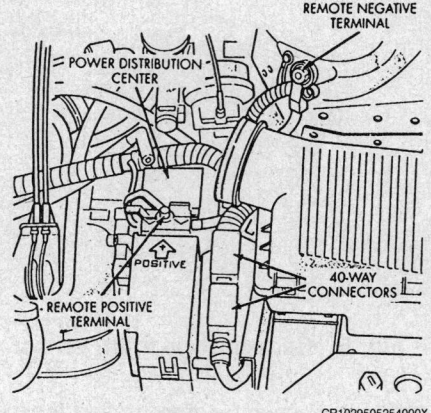

Fig. 7   Remote battery terminals

5. Check electrical connections at idle air control motor and throttle position sensor.
6. Check hose connections between PCV valve, vacuum port - intake manifold and oil separator.
7. Inspect electrical connections at intake air temperature sensor and MAP sensor.
8. Inspect fuel injector electrical connections. Use DRB scan tool to verify connection on engine.
9. Inspect distributor connectors and spark plug cables at distributor.
10. Inspect distributor connectors and spark plug cables at distributor.
11. Check electrical connection to radiator fan, then inspect system body grounds for loose or dirty connections.
12. Inspect air cleaner filter element and replace as necessary. Check air induction system for restrictions.
13. Check electrical connections at camshaft position sensor, then at engine coolant temperature sensor.
14. Check electrical connector at electronic EGR transducer. Inspect vacuum and backpressure hoses at solenoid and transducer for leaks.
15. Inspect electrical connections at generator. Check generator belt for glazing or damage.
16. Inspect electrical connector at crankshaft position sensor, then at vehicle speed sensor.
17. Check electrical connection at power steering pressure switch on power steering gear housing.
18. **On models equipped with automatic transaxle,** check electrical connections at park/neutral switch.
19. **On all models,** inspect electrical connections at upstream and downstream heated oxygen sensors.
20. Inspect fuel pump module electrical connection in trunk for corrosion or damage.
21. Inspect connections to speed control servo.

DIAGNOSIS & TESTING

Refer to **Figs. 8 and 9** for wiring diagrams while diagnosing and testing the fuel injection system.

Accessing Diagnostic Trouble Codes

USING DRB SCAN TOOL

1. Connect DRB scan tool to data link connector located in the passenger's compartment below the center of the instrument panel on the driver's side, **Fig. 3.**
2. Place ignition switch in On position, then access Read Fault Screen.
3. Record all Diagnostic Trouble Codes (DTCs) shown on DRB scan tool, then observe malfunction (check engine) indicator lamp on instrument panel. Lamp should light for two seconds, then go out.

USING MIL

1. Cycle ignition key On-Off-On-Off-On within five seconds.
2. Count number of times malfunction indicator lamp on instrument panel flashes on and off. Number of flashes represents diagnostic trouble code.
3. There is a slight pause between flashes representing first and second digits of code. Longer pauses separate individual diagnostic trouble codes.

Diagnostic Trouble Code Interpretation

Refer to **Fig. 10** for diagnostic trouble code definitions.

Clearing Diagnostic Trouble Codes

To clear the diagnostic trouble codes, use the Erase Trouble Code data screen on the DRB scan tool.

Diagnostic Tests

TROUBLE CODE TESTS

Refer to **Figs. 11 through 80** for Trouble Code Tests.

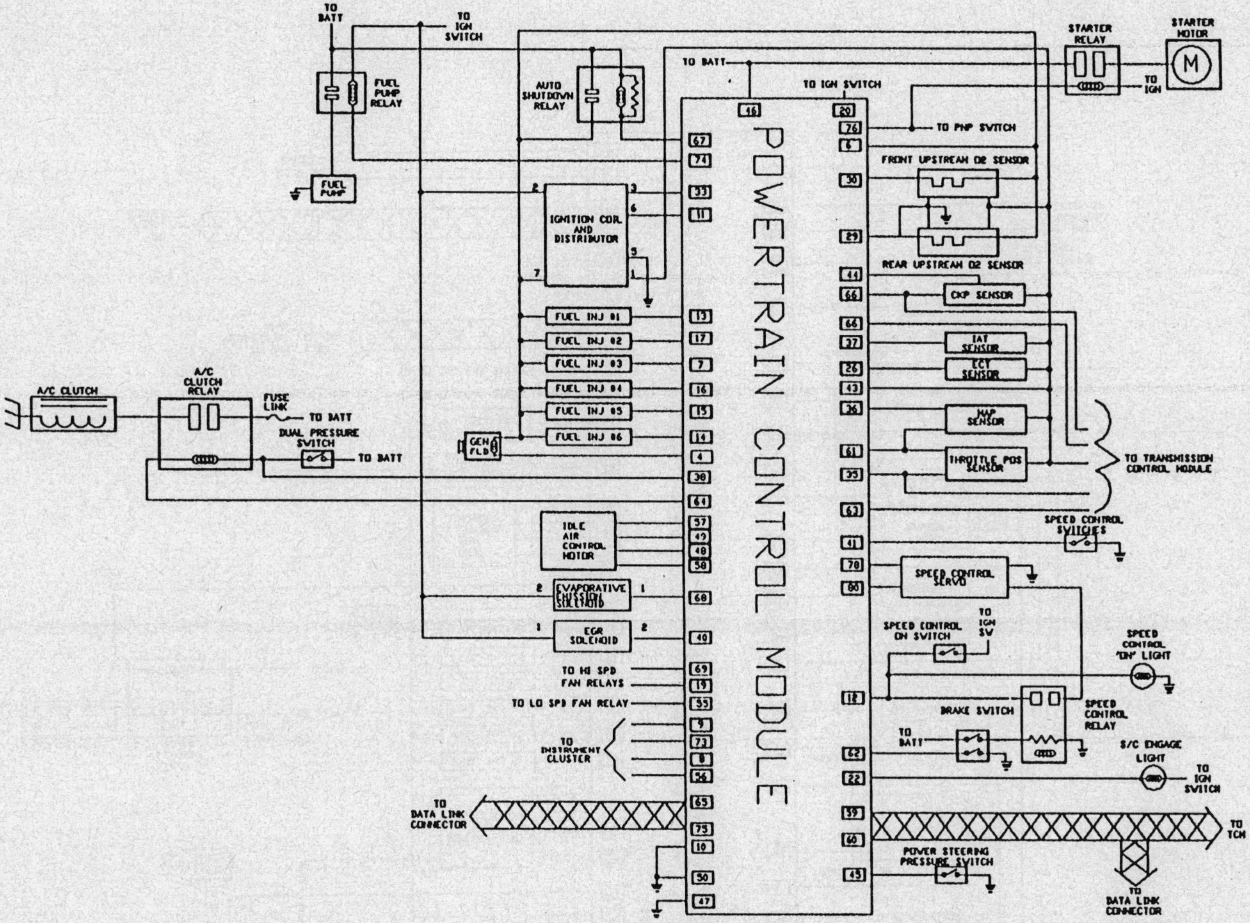

CAV	CIRCUIT	FUNCTION
1	K19 BK/GY	Ignition Coil #2 Driver
2	Z12 BK/TN	Ground
3	K13 YL/WT	Injector #3 Driver
4	K11 WT/DB	Injector #1 Driver
5	G7 WT/OR	Vehicle Speed Sensor Sig
6	K21 BK/RD	Intake Air Temp Sensor Sig
7	K141 TN/WT	Downstream O2 Sensor Sig
8	K41 BK/DG	Upstream O2 Sensor Sig
9	D20 LG	SCI Receive
10	K22 OR/DB	Throttle Pos Sensor Sig
11	A14 RD/WT	Fused B(+)
13	G4 DB	Fuel Level Sensor Sig
14	K60 YL/BK	Idle Air Ctrl Motor #2 Driver
15	K39 GY/RD	Idle Air Ctrl Motor #3 Driver
16	K52 PK/BK	Evap Emission Solenoid Ctrl
17	K54 OR/BK	Torque Conv Clutch Sol Ctrl
18	K51 DB/YL	Auto Shutdown Relay Ctrl
19	C27 DB/PK	Radiator Fan Relay Ctrl
21	K17 DB/TN	Ignition Coil #1 Driver
22	Z12 BK/TN	Ground
23	K12 TN	Injector #2 Driver
24	K14 LB/BR	Injector #4 Driver
25	K24 GY/BK	Crank Pos Sensor Sig
26	K44 TN/YL	Camshaft Pos Sensor Sig
27	K42 DB/LG	Knock Sensor Sig
28	K2 TN/DB	Engine Coolant Temp Sensor Sig
29	K1 DG/RD	MAP Sensor Sig
30	D21 PK	SCI Transmit
31	V37 RD/LG	Speed Control Switch Sig
32	K29 WT/PK	Brake Switch Sense
33	C20 BR/OR	A/C Switch Sense
34	K59 VT/BK	Idle Air Control #4 Driver
35	K40 BR/WT	Idle Air Control #1 Driver
36	G3 BK/PK	Malfunction Indicator Lmp Driver
37	G12 TN/BK	Charge Indicator Lamp Driver
38	K31 BR	Fuel Pump Relay Ctrl
39	K35 GY/YL	EGR Solenoid Ctrl
40	V36 TN/RD	SC Vacuum Solenoid Ctrl
41	K20 DG	Generator Field Driver
42	A142 DG/OR	Auto Shutdown Relay Output
43	K6 VT/WT	5-Volt Supply
44	K7 OR	8-Volt Supply
47	V32 YL/RD	Speed Control Power Supply
48	G21 GY/LB	Tachometer Sig
49	G31 VT/LG	Battery Temp Sensor Sig
50	T41 BR/YL	Park/Neutral Pos Sw Sense
51	K4 BK/LB	Sensor Ground
52	Z11 BK/WT	Ground
54	F18 LG/BK	Fused Ignition Switch Output
55	L1 VT/BK	Reverse Lamp Sense
56	K10 WT	Pwr Steering Press Sw Sense
59	C28 DB/OR	A/C Comp Clutch Relay Ctrl
60	V35 LG/RD	SC Vent Solenoid Ctrl

CR1029508255000X

Fig. 8 Wiring diagram. Avenger & Sebring

POWERTRAIN CONTROL MODULE

CAV	Circuit	FUNCTION
4	K20 DG	Generator Field Driver
5	V32 YL/PK	S/C Power Supply
6	A142 DG/OR	Auto Shutdown Relay Output
7	K13 YL/WT	Injector #3 Driver
10	Z12 BK/TN	Ground
11	K19 BK/GY	Ignition Coil Driver
13	K11 WT/LB	Injector #1 Driver
14	K58 BR/DG	Injector #6 Driver
15	K38 GY	Injector #5 Driver
16	K14 LB/BR	Injector #4 Driver
17	K12 TN	Injector #2 Driver
20	F12 DB/WT	Fused Ignition Switch Output
26	K2 TN/BK	Engine Coolant Temp
29	K141 TN/WT	Sensor Signal
30	K41 BK/DG	Rear Upstream O2 Sensor Sig
32	K24 GY/BK	Front Upstream O2Sensor Sig
33	K44 TN/YL	Crank Position Sensor Sig
35	K22 OR/LB	Camshaft Position Sensor Sig
36	K1 DG/RD	TP Sensor Signal
37	K21 BK/RD	MAP Sensor Signal
40	K35 GY/YL	Intake Air Temp Sensor Signal
41	V37 PK/LG	EGR Solenoid Control
42	C18 DB/YL	S/C Switch Sensor Signal
43	K4 BK/LB	A/C Pressure Sw Sense
44	K7 OR/WT	Sensor Ground
45	K10 DB/LG	8-Volt Supply
46	A14 RD/TN	Power Steer Press Sw Sense
48	K40 BR/GY	Fused B(+)
49	K60 YL/BK	Idle Air Ctrl Motor #1 Driver
50	Z12 BK/TN	Idle Air Ctrl Motor #2 Driver
52	G31 VT/LG	Ground
55	C24 DB/TN	Batt Temp Sensor Signal
57	K39 GY/RD	Lo Spd Rad Fan Rly Ctrl
58	K59 VT/GY	Idle Air Ctrl Motor #3 Driver
59	D1 VT/BR	Idle Air Ctrl Motor #4 Driver
60	D2 WT/BK	CCD Bus (+)
61	K6 VT/WT	CCD Bus (-)
62	K29 WT/RD	5-Volt Supply
63	T10 YL/DG	Brake Switch Sense
64	C28 DB/OR	Torq Mgmt Request Sense
65	D21 PK/LB	A/C Comp Clutch Rly Ctrl
66	G7 WT/OR	SCI Transmit
67	K51 DB/VT	Vehicle Spd Sensor Signal
68	K52 PK/GY	Auto Shutdown Relay Ctrl
69	C27 DB/PK	Evap Emission Sol Ctrl
74	K31 BR/LG	Hi Spd Rad Fan Rly Ctrl
75	D20 LG/WT	Fuel Pump Relay Control
76	T41 BK/WT	SCI Receive
78	V38 WT/VT	P/N Position Switch Sense
80	V35 LG/RD	S/C Vacuum Solenoid Control
		S/C Vent Solenoid Control

CR10295C5256000X

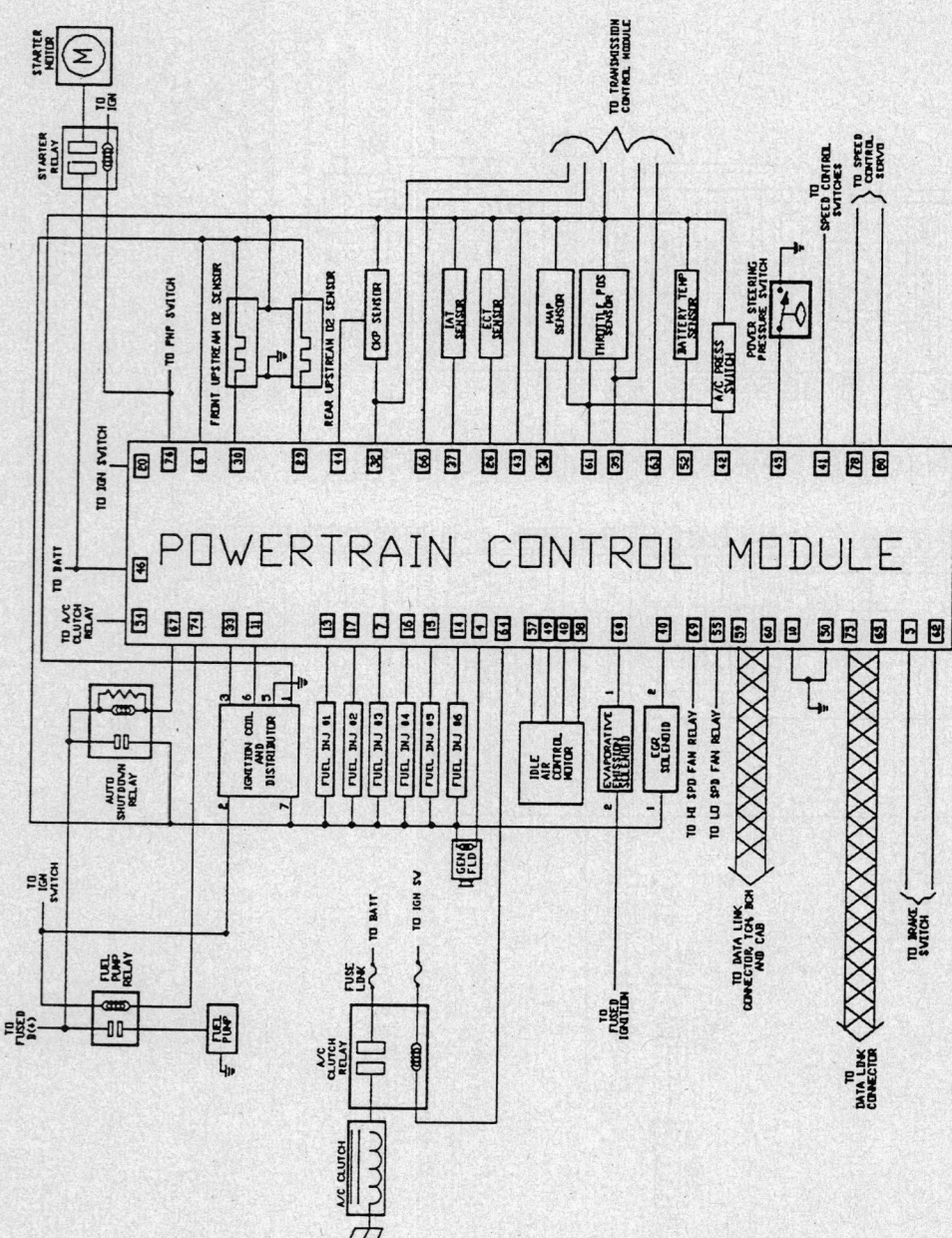

Fig. 9 Wiring diagram. Cirrus & Stratus

INACTIVE TROUBLE CODE CONDITION

Refer to **Fig. 13** for Inactive Trouble Code Condition.

NO TROUBLE CODE TESTS

Refer to **Figs. 81 through 100** for No Trouble Code Tests.

SPEED CONTROL TESTS

Refer to **Figs. 101 through 113** for Speed Control Tests.

CHARGING TEST

Refer to **Fig. 114** for Charging Test.

NO START TESTS

Refer to **Figs. 115 through 126** for No Start Tests.

VERIFICATION TESTS

Refer to **Figs. 127 through 130** for Verification Tests.

DIAGNOSTIC CHART INDEX

Test	Description	Page No. 10-	Fig. No.
—	Diagnostic Trouble Code Descriptions	9	10
—	Inactive Trouble Code Condition	12	13
Test TC-1A	Checking System For Diagnostic Trouble Codes (DTCs)	11	11
Test TC-2A	Repairing No Crank Reference Signal At PCM	11	12
Test TC-2B	Repairing No Crank Reference Signal At PCM	12	14
Test TC-3A	Repairing No Cam Signal At PCM	12	15
Test TC-4A	Repairing No Change In MAP From Start To Run	13	16
Test TC-5A	Repairing MAP Sensor Voltage Too Low	13	17
Test TC-6A	Repairing MAP Sensor Voltage Too High	14	18
Test TC-7A	Repairing No 5 Bolts To MAP Sensor	14	19
Test TC-8A	Repairing 5-Volt Supply Output Too Low	14	20
Test TC-8A	Repairing 5-Volt Supply Output Too Low	15	21
Test TC-9A	Repairing No Vehicle Speed Sensor Signal	15	22
Test TC-9B	Repairing No Vehicle Speed Sensor Signal	16	23
Test TC-10A	Repairing Front Upstream (Bank) O2S Shorted To Voltage	16	24
Test TC-11A	Repairing Front Upstream (Bank) O2S Stays At Center	16	25
Test TC-12A	Repairing Rear Upstream (Bank) O2S Shorted To Voltage	17	26
Test TC-13A	Repairing Rear Upstream (Bank) O2S Stays At Center	17	27
Test TC-14A	Repairing Front Upstream (Bank) O2S Stays Below Center (Lean)	18	28
Test TC-15A	Repairing Rear Upstream (Bank) O2S Stays Below Center (Lean)	18	29
Test TC-16A	Repairing Front Upstream (Bank) O2S Stays Above Center (Rich)	19	30
Test TC-17A	Repairing Rear Upstream (Bank) O2S Stays Above Center (Rich)	19	31
Test TC-18A	Repairing ECT Sensor Voltage Too Low	19	32
Test TC-19A	Repairing ECT Sensor Voltage Too High	20	33
Test TC-20A	Repairing Intake Air Temperature Sensor Voltage Low	20	34
Test TC-21A	Repairing Intake Air Temperature Sensor Voltage High	21	35
Test TC-22A	Repairing Throttle Position Sensor Voltage Low	21	36
Test TC-23A	Repairing Throttle Position Sensor Voltage High	22	37
Test TC-24A	Repairing No 5 Volts To TP sensor	22	38
Test TC-25A	Repairing Idle Air Control Motor Circuits	22	39
Test TC-25B	Repairing Idle Air Control Motor Circuits	23	40
Test TC-25B	Repairing Idle Air Control Motor Circuits	24	41
Test TC-25D	Repairing Idle Air Control Motor Circuits	24	42
Test TC-25E	Repairing Idle Air Control Motor Circuits	24	43
Test TC-26A	Repairing Injector Control Circuit	24	44
Test TC-26B	Repairing Injector Control Circuit	24	45
Test TC-26C	Repairing Injector Control Circuit	25	46
Test TC-27A	Repairing Injector No. 2 Control Circuit	25	47
Test TC-28A	Repairing Injector No. 3 Control Circuit	25	48
Test TC-28B	Repairing Injector No. 3 Control Circuit	25	49

Continued

DIAGNOSTIC CHART INDEX–Continued

Test	Description	Page No. 10-	Fig. No.
Test TC-29A	Repairing Injector No. 4 Control Circuit	26	50
Test TC-30A	Repairing Injector No. 5 Control Circuit	26	51
Test TC-30B	Repairing Injector No. 5 Control Circuit	26	52
Test TC-31A	Repairing Injector No. 6 Control Circuit	26	53
Test TC-32A	Repairing PCM Failure SRI Mile Not Stored Or PCM Failure EEPROM Write Denied	27	54
Test TC-33A	Repairing EGR Solenoid Circuit	27	55
Test TC-34A	Repairing EGR Solenoid Circuit	27	56
Test TC-35A	Repairing EVAP Purge Solenoid Circuit	28	57
Test TC-36A	Repairing A/C Clutch Relay Circuit	28	58
Test TC-37A ②	Repairing A/C Pressure Sensor Volts Too Low	29	59
Test TC-38A ②	Repairing A/C Pressure Sensor Volts Too High	29	60
Test TC-39A ②	Repairing No 5 Volts To A/C Pressure Sensor	30	61
Test TC-40A	Repairing High Speed Fan Control Relay Circuit	30	62
Test TC-41A	Repairing Low Speed Fan Control Relay Circuit	31	63
Test TC-42A	Repairing Auto Shutdown Relay Control Circuit	31	64
Test TC-43A	Repairing No ASD Relay Output Voltage At PCM	32	65
Test TC-44A	Repairing Fuel Pump Relay Control Circuit	32	65
Test TC-45A	Repairing Generator Field Not Switching Properly	33	66
Test TC-46A	Repairing Charging System Voltage Too Low	33	67
Test TC-47A	Repairing Charging System Voltage Too High	34	68
Test TC-48A	Repairing Speed Control Solenoid Circuits Or Speed Control Power Relay Circuit	34	69
Test TC-48B	Repairing Speed Control Solenoid Circuits Or Speed Control Power Relay Circuit	35	70
Test TC-48C	Repairing Speed Control Solenoid Circuits Or Speed Control Power Relay Circuit	35	71
Test TC-49A ②	Repairing Speed Control Switch Always Low	35	72
Test TC-50A	Repairing Speed Control Switch Always High ②	36	73
Test TC-50B ②	Repairing Speed Control Switch Always High	36	74
Test TC-51A	Repairing Battery Temp Sensor Volts Out Of Limit	36	75
Test TC-51B	Repairing Battery Temp Sensor Volts Out Of Limit	37	76
Test TC-51C ①	Repairing Battery Temp Sensor Volts Out Of Limit	37	77
Test TC-52A	Repairing No CCD Messages From TCM	37	78
Test TC-53A ②	Repairing No CCD Message From Body Control Module	38	79
Test TC-54A ①	Repairing High Speed Condenser Fan Control Relay Circuit	38	80
Test NTC-1A	No Trouble Code Test Menu	39	81
Test NTC-2A	Checking Secondary ignition & Timing	39	82
Test NTC-3A	Checking Fuel Pressure	40	83
Test NTC-3B	Checking Fuel Pressure	40	84
Test NTC-3C	Checking Fuel Pressure	40	85
Test NTC-4A	Checking Coolant Sensor Calibration & Radiator Fan Operation	41	86
Test NTC-5A	Checking Throttle Position Sensor Calibration	41	87
Test NTC-6A	Checking MAP Sensor Calibration	41	88
Test NTC-7A	Checking For Oxygen Sensor Switching	42	89
Test NTC-8A	Checking Oxygen Sensor Heater	42	90
Test NTC-9A	Checking Idle Air Conditioning Control Motor	43	91
Test NTC-10A	Checking Solenoid Operation	43	92
Test NTC-11A	Checking Park/Neutral Position Switch	43	93
Test NTC-12A	Checking PCM Power & Ground Circuits	43	94
Test NTC-13A	Checking Evaporative Emission System	44	95
Test NTC-14A	Checking EGR System	44	96
Test NTC-15A	Checking Engine Vacuum	44	97
Test NTC-16A	Checking Intake Air Temperature Sensor	44	98
Test NTC-17A	Checking Minimum Idle Air Flow	45	99
Test NTC-18A	Checking Engine Mechanical Systems	45	100
Test SC-1A	Checking Speed Control Operation	45	101

Continued

DIAGNOSTIC CHART INDEX–Continued

Test	Description	Page No. 10-	Fig. No.
Test SC-1B	Checking Speed Control Operation	46	102
Test SC-2A	Checking Speed Control On/Off Switch	46	103
Test SC-3A	Checking Speed Control Brake Switch Output	46	104
Test SC-4A	Checking Park/Neutral Position Switch	47	105
Test SC-5A	Checking For A Speed Control Denied Message	47	106
Test SC-6A	Checking Speed Control Operation	47	107
Test SC-6B	Checking Speed Control Operation	48	108
Test SC-6C	Checking Speed Control Operation	48	109
Test SC-7A	Checking Speed Control On/Off Switch	48	110
Test SC-8A	Checking Speed Control Brake Switch Output	49	111
Test SC-9A	Checking Park/Neutral Position Switch	49	112
Test SC-10A	Checking Speed Control Relay Output	49	113
Test CH-1A	Charging System No Code Test	49	114
Test NS-1A	Qualifying A No Start Condition	50	115
Test NS-2A	Checking Fuel System	51	116
Test NS-3A	Checking Engine Mechanical Systems	51	117
Test NS-4A	Repairing Low Fuel Pressure	51	118
Test NS-4B	Repairing Low Fuel Pressure	51	119
Test NS-4C	Repairing Low Pressure	51	120
Test NS-5A	Checking Fuel Pump	51	121
Test NS-6A	Repairing A "No Response" Condition	53	122
Test NS-6B	Repairing A "No Response" Condition	54	123
Test NS-7A	Checking Idle Air Control Motor	54	124
Test NS-8A	Repairing A Start & Stall Condition	54	125
Test NS-9A	Repairing A No Crank Condition	54	126
Test VER-1A	No Start Verification	55	127
Test VER-2A	Road Test Verification	55	128
Test VER-3A	Charging Verification	55	129
Test VER-4A	Speed Control Verification	56	130

①—Avenger & Sebring.
②—Cirrus & Stratus.

MIL Code	DRB Scan Tool Display	Description of Diagnostic Trouble Code
11**	No Crank Reference Signal at PCM	No crank reference signal detected during engine cranking.
12*	Battery Disconnect	Direct battery input to PCM was disconnected within the last 50 Key-on cycles.
13**	No Change in MAP From Start to Run	No difference recognized between the engine MAP reading and the barometric (atmospheric) pressure reading from start-up.
14**	MAP Sensor Voltage Too Low	MAP sensor input below minimum acceptable voltage.
	or	
	MAP Sensor Voltage Too High	MAP sensor input above maximum acceptable voltage.
	or	
	No 5 Volts to MAP Sensor	MAP sensor output voltage too low for barometric pressure after key off.
15**	No Vehicle Speed Sensor Signal	No vehicle speed sensor signal detected during road load conditions.
17**	Engine Cold Too Long	Engine does not reach operating temperature within 20 minutes with a vehicle speed signal.
21**	Front O2S Shorted to Voltage	Upstream oxygen sensor input voltage maintained above the normal operating range.
	or	
	Front O2S Stays at Center	Neither rich or lean condition detected from the upstream oxygen sensor input.
	or	

* Check Engine Lamp will not illuminate at all times if this Diagnostic Trouble Code was recorded. Cycle Ignition key as described in manual and observe code flashed by Check Engine lamp.

** Check Engine Lamp will illuminate during engine operation if this Diagnostic Trouble Code was recorded.

***Generator Lamp Illuminated

CR1029505257010X

Fig. 10 Diagnostic Trouble Code Descriptions (Part 1 of 5)

MIL Code	DRB Scan Tool Display	Description of Diagnostic Trouble Code
	Rear O2S Shorted to Voltage	Right upstream oxygen sensor input voltage maintained above the normal operating range.
	or	
	Rear O2S Stays at Center	Neither rich or lean condition detected from the upstream oxygen sensor input.
22**	ECT Sensor Voltage Too Low	Engine coolant temperature sensor input below minimum acceptable voltage.
	or	
	ECT Sensor Voltage Too High	Engine coolant temperature sensor input above maximum acceptable voltage.
23**	Intake Air Temp Sensor Voltage Low	Intake air temperature sensor input below the maximum acceptable voltage.
	or	
	Intake Air Temp Sensor Voltage High	Intake air temperature sensor input above the minimum acceptable voltage.
24**	Throttle Position Sensor Voltage Low	Throttle position sensor input below the minimum acceptable voltage.
	or	
	Throttle Position Sensor Voltage High	Throttle position sensor input above the maximum acceptable voltage.
	or	
	No 5 volts to TPS Sensor	Throttle voltage too low while operating at part throttle.
25**	Idle Air Control Motor Circuits	A shorted or open condition detected in one or more of the idle air control motor circuits.
27**	Injector #1 Control Circuit	Injector #1 does not respond electrically to the control signal.
	or	
	Injector #2 Control Circuit	Injector #2 does not respond electrically to the control signal.
	or	
	Injector #3 Control Circuit	Injector #3 does not respond electrically to the control signal.

* Check Engine Lamp will not illuminate at all times if this Diagnostic Trouble Code was recorded. Cycle Ignition key as described in manual and observe code flashed by Check Engine lamp.
** Check Engine Lamp will illuminate during engine operation if this Diagnostic Trouble Code was recorded.
***Generator Lamp illuminated

CR1029505257020X

Fig. 10 Diagnostic Trouble Code Descriptions (Part 2 of 5)

MIL Code	DRB Scan Tool Display	Description of Diagnostic Trouble Code
	or	
	Injector #4 Control Circuit	Injector #4 does not respond electrically to the control signal.
	or	
	Injector #5 Control Circuit	Injector #5 does not respond electrically to the control signal.
	or	
	Injector #6 Control Circuit	Injector #6 does not respond electrically to the control signal.
31**	EVAP Solenoid Circuit	An open or shorted condition detected in the duty cycle purge solenoid circuit.
32**	EGR System Failure	Insufficient or excessive change in air/fuel ratio not detected during diagnostic test.
	or	
	EGR Solenoid Circuit	An open or shorted condition detected in the EGR transducer solenoid circuit.
33*	A/C Clutch Relay Circuit	An open or shorted condition detected in the A/C clutch relay circuit.
	or	
	A/C Pressure Sensor Volts Too High	A/C pressure transducer input above the maximum acceptable voltage.
	or	
	A/C Pressure Sensor Volts Too Low	A/C pressure transducer input below the minimum acceptable voltage.
34*	Speed Control Solenoid Circuits	An open or shorted condition detected in the Speed Control vacuum or vent solenoid circuits.
	or	
	Speed Control Switch Always Low	Speed Control switch input below the minimum acceptable voltage.
	or	
	Speed Control Switch Always High	Speed Control switch input above the maximum acceptable voltage.

* Check Engine Lamp will not illuminate at all times if this Diagnostic Trouble Code was recorded. Cycle Ignition key as described in manual and observe code flashed by Check Engine lamp.
** Check Engine Lamp will illuminate during engine operation if this Diagnostic Trouble Code was recorded.
***Generator Lamp illuminated

CR1029505257030X

Fig. 10 Diagnostic Trouble Code Descriptions (Part 3 of 5)

MIL Code	DRB Scan Tool Display	Description of Diagnostic Trouble Code
	or	
	Injector #4 Control Circuit	Injector #4 does not respond electrically to the control signal.
	or	
	Injector #5 Control Circuit	Injector #5 does not respond electrically to the control signal.
	or	
	Injector #6 Control Circuit	Injector #6 does not respond electrically to the control signal.
31**	EVAP Solenoid Circuit	An open or shorted condition detected in the duty cycle purge solenoid circuit.
32**	EGR System Failure	Insufficient or excessive change in air/fuel ratio not detected during diagnostic test.
	or	
	EGR Solenoid Circuit	An open or shorted condition detected in the EGR transducer solenoid circuit.
33*	A/C Clutch Relay Circuit	An open or shorted condition detected in the A/C clutch relay circuit.
	or	
	A/C Pressure Sensor Volts Too High	A/C pressure transducer input above the maximum acceptable voltage.
	or	
	A/C Pressure Sensor Volts Too Low	A/C pressure transducer input below the minimum acceptable voltage.
34*	Speed Control Solenoid Circuits	An open or shorted condition detected in the Speed Control vacuum or vent solenoid circuits.
	or	
	Speed Control Switch Always Low	Speed Control switch input below the minimum acceptable voltage.
	or	
	Speed Control Switch Always High	Speed Control switch input above the maximum acceptable voltage.

* Check Engine Lamp will not illuminate at all times if this Diagnostic Trouble Code was recorded. Cycle Ignition key as described in manual and observe code flashed by Check Engine lamp.

Fig. 10 Diagnostic Trouble Code Descriptions (Part 4 of 5)

MIL Code	DRB Scan Tool Display	Description of Diagnostic Trouble Code
53****	Internal Controller Failure	PCM Internal fault condition detected.
	or	
	PCM Failure SPI Communications	PCM Internal fault condition detected.
54*	No Cam Signal at PCM	No camshaft signal detected during engine cranking.
55*		Completion of fault code display on Check Engine lamp.
62*	PCM Failure SRI Mile Not Stored	Unsuccessful attempt to update EMR mileage in the PCM EEPROM.
63*	PCM Failure EEPROM Write Denied	Unsuccessful attempt to write to an EEPROM location by the PCM.
66*	No CCD Message From TCM	No communication from transmission control module (2.4L & 2.5L only).
	or	
	No CCD Message From Body Controller	No communication from body control module.
71**	5 Volt Output Low	Internal PCM check for 5 volts.
77*	Speed Control Power Circuit	Malfunction detected with power feed to speed control servo solenoids.

* Check Engine Lamp will not illuminate at all times if this Diagnostic Trouble Code was recorded. Cycle Ignition key as described in manual and observe code flashed by Check Engine lamp.
** Check Engine Lamp will illuminate during engine operation if this Diagnostic Trouble Code was recorded.
***Generator Lamp illuminated

CR1029505257050X

Fig. 10 Diagnostic Trouble Code Descriptions (Part 5 of 5)

NOTE: The battery must be fully charged for any test in this manual.

1. Attempt to start the engine. Crank for up to 10 seconds if necessary.

2. Connect the DRB to the engine diagnostic connector. Write down the trouble codes that are displayed.

3. If the DRB screen displays "No Response", go to TEST NS-6A.

4. If trouble code messages are displayed, refer to the trouble code list below for the appropriate test.

5. If there are no trouble codes displayed, refer to one of the following:
   For Driveability problems NTC-1A
   For No Start problems NS-1A
   For Speed Control problems SC-1A
   For Charging problems CH-1A

DIAGNOSTIC TROUBLE CODE (DTC) DISPLAYED	MIL CODE	DIAGNOSTIC TEST
NO CRANK REFERENCE SIGNAL AT PCM	11	TC- 2A
NO CAM SIGNAL AT PCM	54	TC- 3A
NO CHANGE IN MAP FROM START TO RUN	13	TC- 4A
MAP SENSOR VOLTAGE TOO LOW	14	TC- 5A
MAP SENSOR VOLTAGE TOO HIGH	14	TC- 6A
NO 5 VOLTS TO MAP SENSOR	14	TC- 7A
5 VOLT SUPPLY OUTPUT TOO LOW	71	TC- 8A
NO VEHICLE SPEED SENSOR SIGNAL	15	TC- 9A
FRONT UPSTREAM (BANK) O2S SHORTED TO VOLTAGE	21	TC-10A
FRONT UPSTREAM (BANK) O2S STAYS AT CENTER	21	TC-11A
REAR UPSTREAM (BANK) O2S SHORTED TO VOLTAGE	21	TC-12A
REAR UPSTREAM (BANK) O2S STAYS AT CENTER	21	TC-13A
FRONT UPSTREAM (BANK) O2S STAYS BELOW CENTER (LEAN)	51	TC-14A
REAR UPSTREAM (BANK) O2S STAYS BELOW CENTER (LEAN)	51	TC-15A
FRONT UPSTREAM (BANK) O2S STAYS ABOVE CENTER (RICH)	52	TC-16A
REAR UPSTREAM (BANK) O2S STAYS ABOVE CENTER (RICH)	52	TC-17A
ECT SENSOR VOLTAGE TOO LOW	22	TC-18A
ECT SENSOR VOLTAGE TOO HIGH	22	TC-19A
INTAKE AIR TEMP SENSOR VOLTAGE LOW	23	TC-20A
INTAKE AIR TEMP SENSOR VOLTAGE HIGH	23	TC-21A
THROTTLE POSITION SENSOR VOLTAGE LOW	24	TC-22A
THROTTLE POSITION SENSOR VOLTAGE HIGH	24	TC-23A
NO 5 VOLTS TO TP SENSOR	24	TC-24A
IDLE AIR CONTROL MOTOR CIRCUITS	25	TC-25A

CR1029505258010X

Fig. 11 Test TC-1A: Checking System For Diagnostic Trouble Codes (DTCs) (Part 1 of 2)

DIAGNOSTIC TROUBLE CODE (DTC) DISPLAYED	MIL CODE	DIAGNOSTIC TEST
INJECTOR CONTROL CIRCUIT	27	TC-26A
PCM FAILURE SRI MILE NOT STORED	62	TC-32A
PCM FAILURE EEPROM WRITE DENIED	63	TC-32A
EGR SOLENOID CIRCUIT	32	TC-33A
EGR SYSTEM FAILURE	32	TC-34A
EVAP PURGE SOLENOID CIRCUIT	31	TC-35A
A/C CLUTCH RELAY CIRCUIT	33	TC-36A
A/C PRESSURE SENSOR VOLTS TOO LOW	33	TC-37A
A/C PRESSURE SENSOR VOLTS TOO HIGH	33	TC-38A
NO 5 VOLTS TO A/C PRESSURE SENSOR	33	TC-39A
HIGH SPEED FAN CTRL RELAY CIRCUIT	35	TC-40A
LOW SPEED FAN CTRL RELAY CIRCUIT	35	TC-41A
AUTO SHUTDOWN RELAY CONTROL CIRCUIT	42	TC-42A
NO ASD RELAY OUTPUT VOLTAGE AT PCM	42	TC-43A
FUEL PUMP RELAY CONTROL CIRCUIT	42	TC-44A
GENERATOR FIELD NOT SWITCHING PROPERLY	41	TC-45A
CHARGING SYSTEM VOLTAGE TOO LOW	47	TC-46A
CHARGING SYSTEM VOLTAGE TOO HIGH	46	TC-47A
SPEED CONTROL SOLENOID CIRCUITS	34	TC-48A
SPEED CONTROL POWER RELAY CIRCUIT	77	TC-48A
SPEED CONTROL SWITCH ALWAYS LOW	34	TC-49A
SPEED CONTROL SWITCH ALWAYS HIGH	34	TC-50A
BATTERY TEMP SENSOR VOLTS OUT OF LIMIT	44	TC-51A
NO CCD MESSAGES FROM TCM	66	TC-52A
NO CCD MESSAGE FROM BODY CONTROL MODULE	66	TC-53A
HIGH SPEED CONDENSER FAN CTRL RELAY CKT	N/A	TC-54A
PCM FAILURE SPI COMMUNICATIONS	53	See Below
INTERNAL CONTROLLER FAILURE	53	See Below
ENGINE IS COLD TOO LONG	17	See Below

For an ENGINE IS COLD TOO LONG trouble code, the engine does not warm to 176°F while driving for 20 minutes after start. See the service manual for cooling system repair (thermostat).

For an INTERNAL CONTROLLER FAILURE trouble code, replace the powertrain control module and go to Verification TEST VER-2A.

For a PCM FAILURE SPI COMMUNICATIONS trouble code, replace the powertrain control module and go to Verification TEST VER-2A.

CR1029505258020X

Fig. 11 Test TC-1A: Checking System For Diagnostic Trouble Codes (DTCs) (Part 2 of 2)

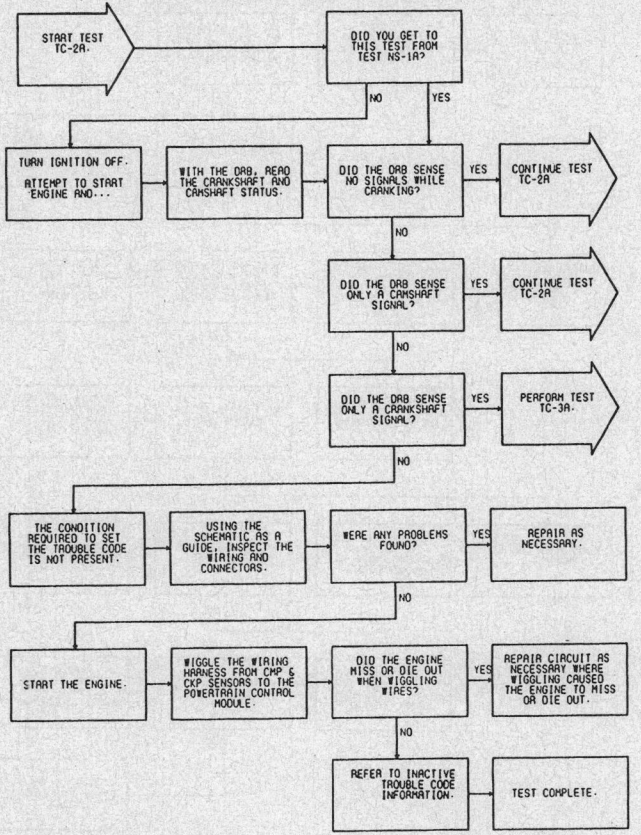

CR1029505259010X

Fig. 12 Test TC-2A: Repairing No Crank Reference Signal At PCM (Part 1 of 3)

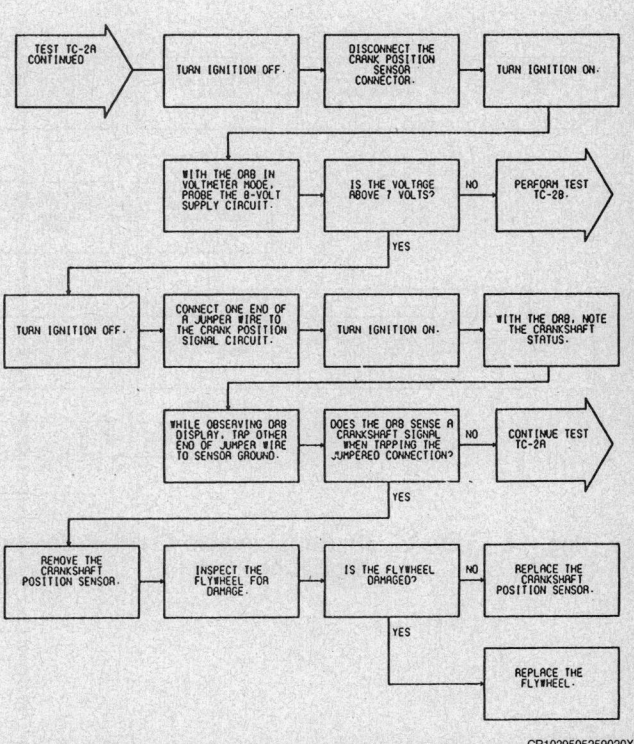

CR1029505259020X

Fig. 12 Test TC-2A: Repairing No Crank Reference Signal At PCM (Part 2 of 3)

MULTI-POINT FUEL INJECTION (1995 AVENGER, CIRRUS, SEBRING & STRATUS w/2.5L/V6-152)

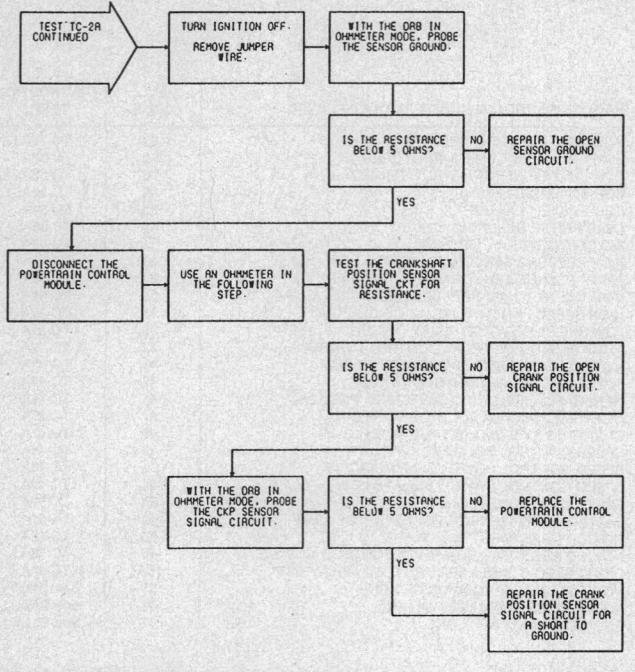

Fig. 12 Test TC-2A: Repairing No Crank Reference Signal At PCM (Part 3 of 3)

You have just attempted to simulate the condition that initially set the trouble code message. The following additional checks may assist you in identifying a possible intermittent problem:

— Visually inspect related wire harness connectors. Look for broken, bent, pushed out, or corroded terminals.

— Visually inspect the related harnesses. Look for chafed, pierced, or partially broken wire.

— Refer to any hotlines or technical service bulletins that may apply.

Fig. 13 Inactive Trouble Code Condition

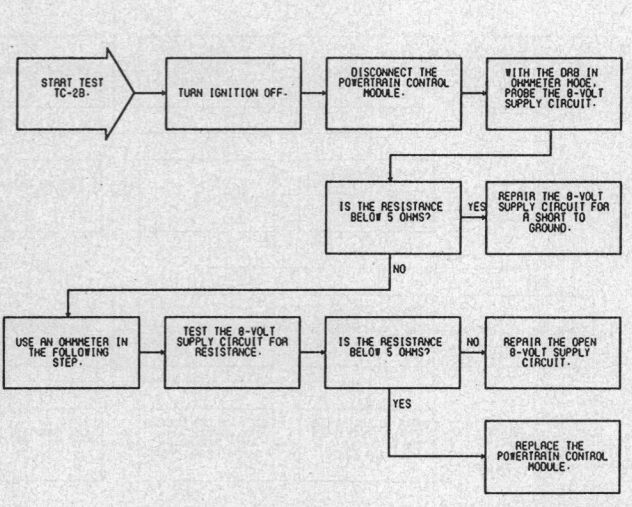

Fig. 14 Test TC-2B: Repairing No Crank Reference Signal At PCM

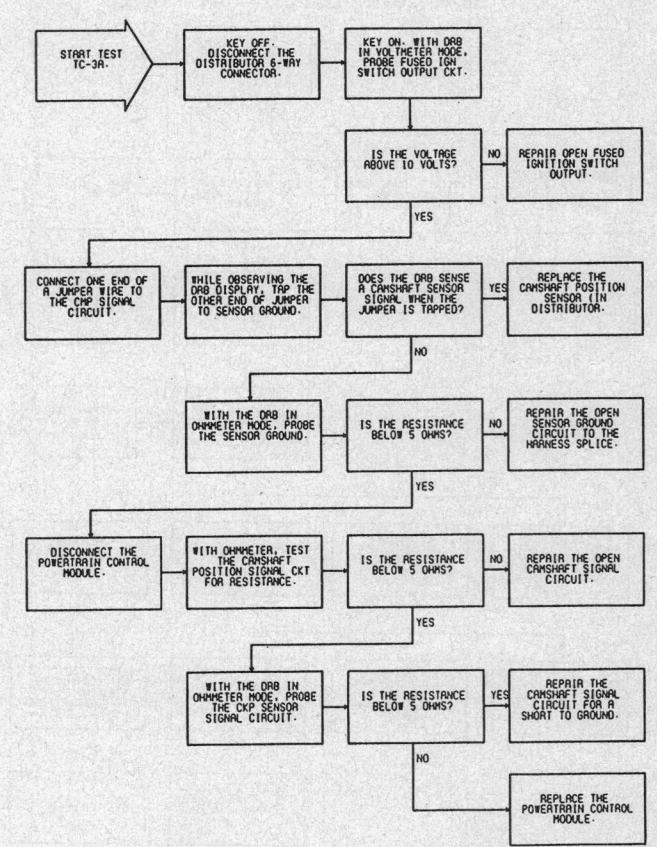

Fig. 15 Test TC-3A: Repairing No Cam Signal At PCM

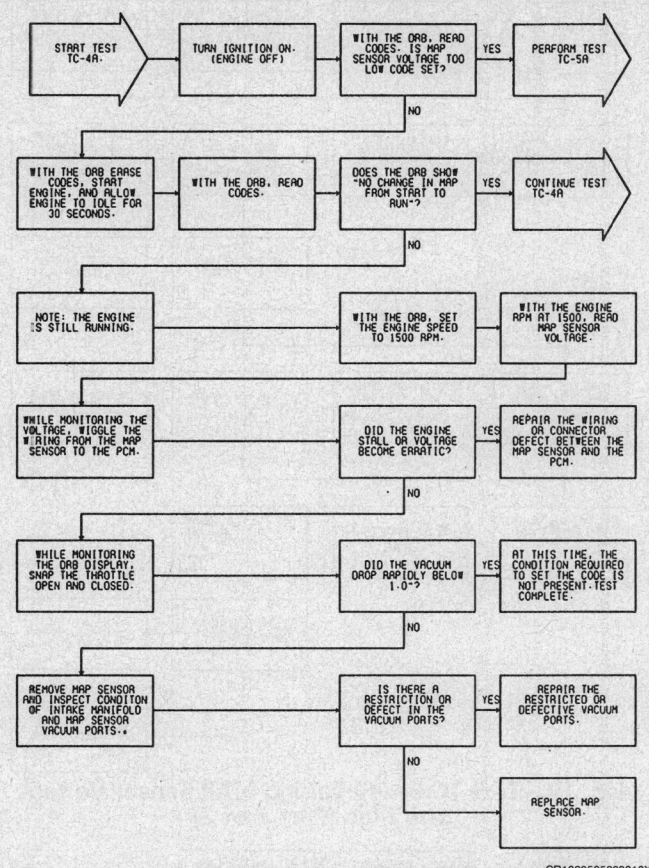

Fig. 16   Test TC-4A: Repairing No Change In MAP
From Start To Run (Part 1 of 2)

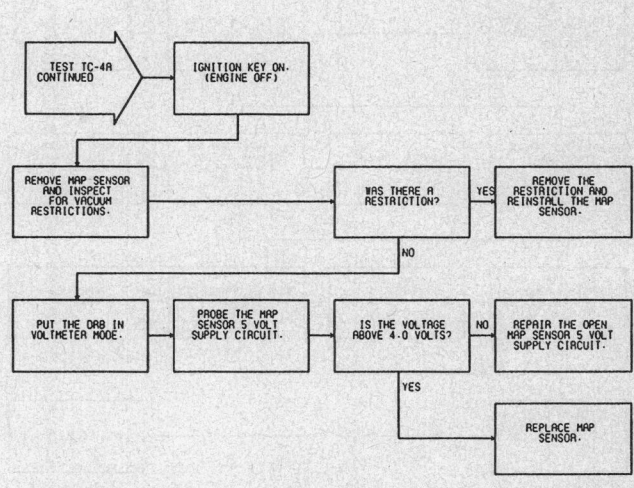

Fig. 16   Test TC-4A: Repairing No Change In MAP
From Start To Run (Part 2 of 2)

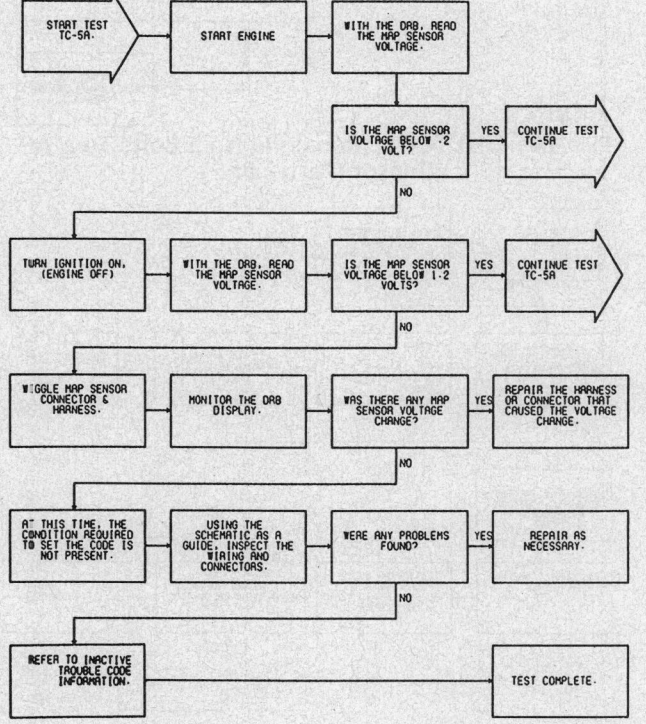

Fig. 17   Test TC-5A: Repairing MAP Sensor Voltage
Too Low (Part 1 of 2)

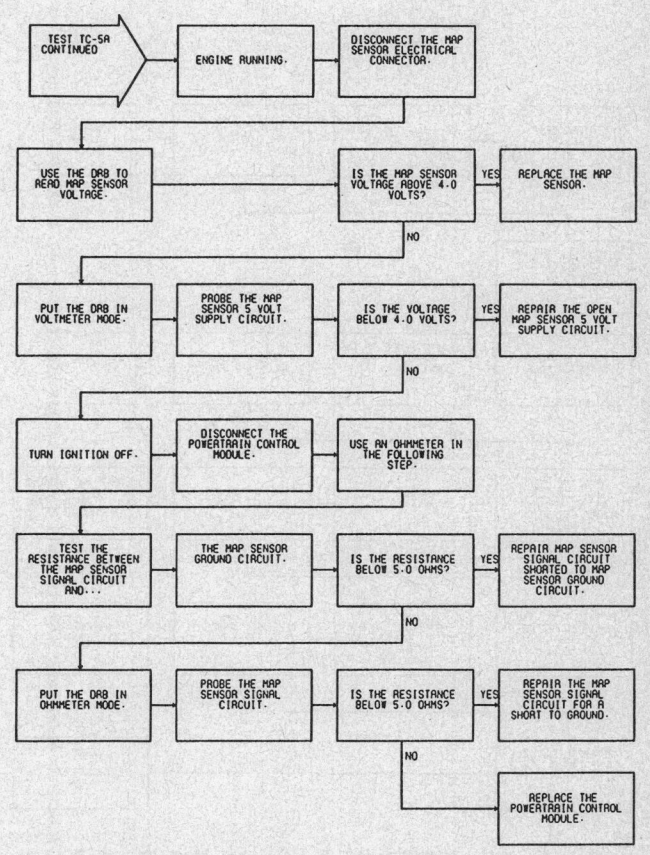

Fig. 17   Test TC-5A: Repairing MAP Sensor Voltage
Too Low (Part 2 of 2)

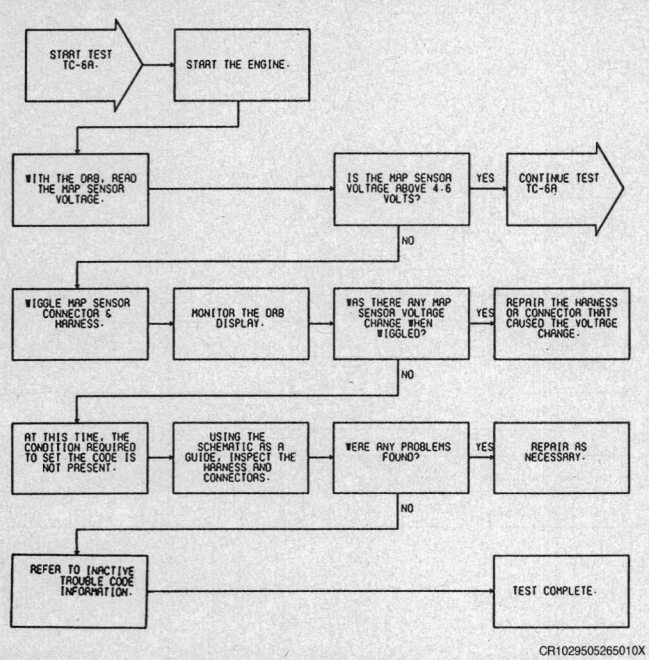

Fig. 18   Test TC-6A: Repairing MAP Sensor Voltage Too High (Part 1 of 2)

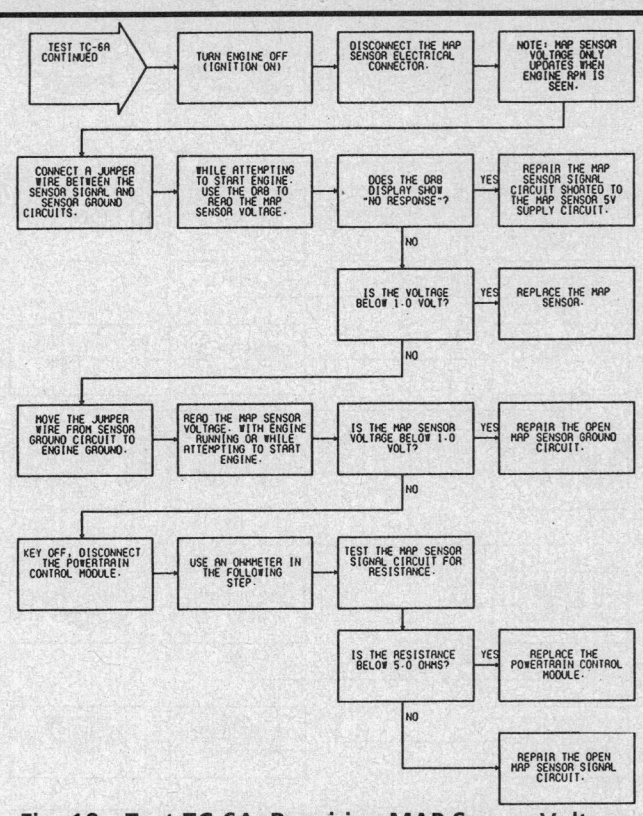

Fig. 18   Test TC-6A: Repairing MAP Sensor Voltage Too High (Part 2 of 2)

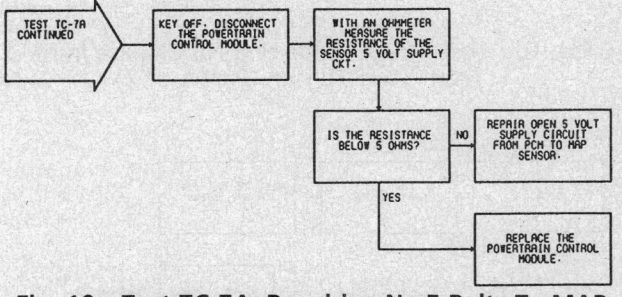

Fig. 19   Test TC-7A: Repairing No 5 Bolts To MAP Sensor (Part 2 of 2)

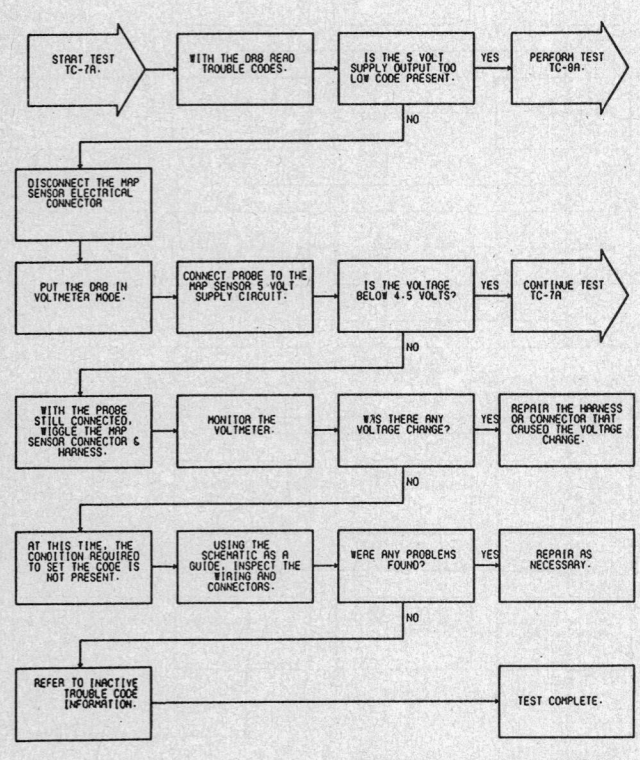

Fig. 19   Test TC-7A: Repairing No 5 Bolts To MAP Sensor (Part 1 of 2)

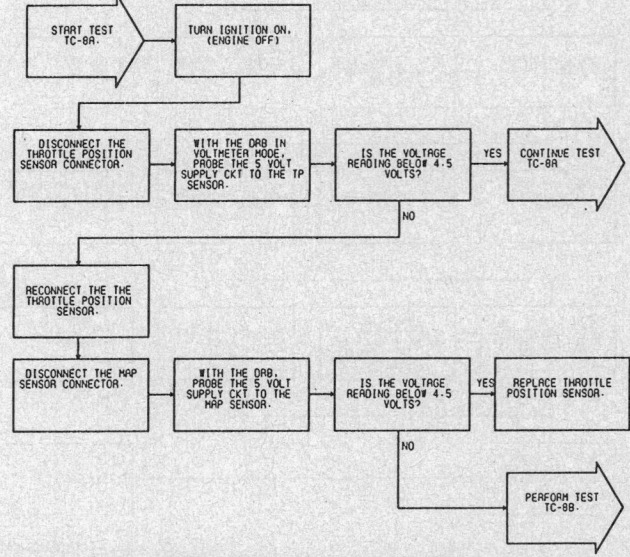

Fig. 20   Test TC-8A: Repairing 5-Volt Supply Output Too Low (Part 1 of 3)

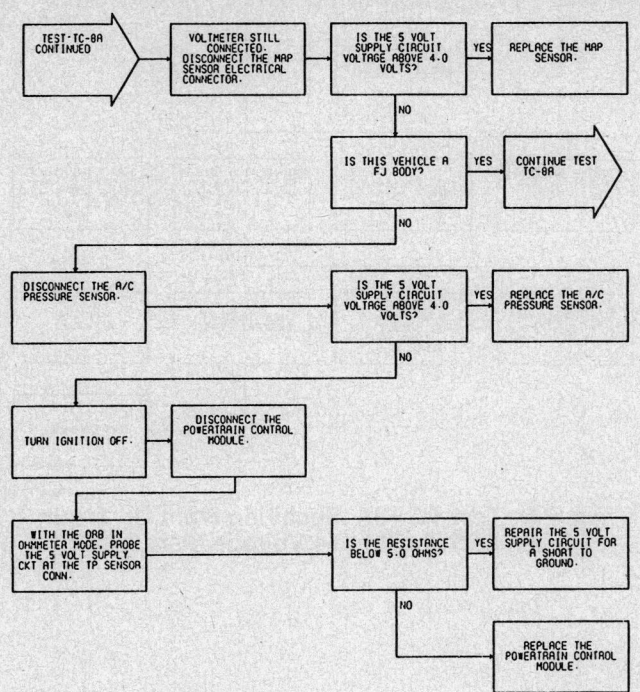

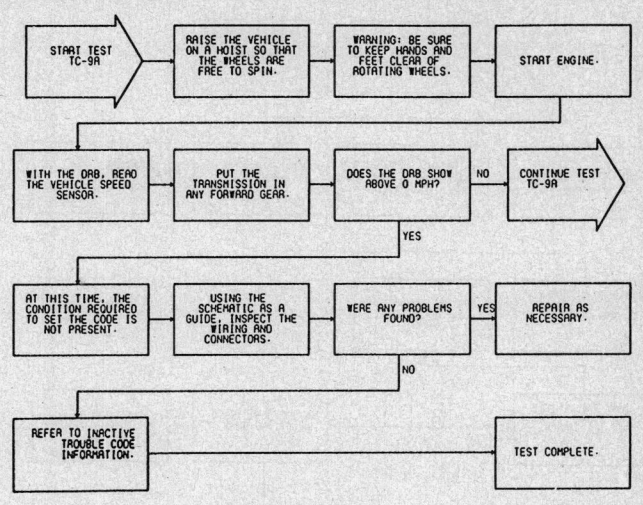

Fig. 22   Test TC-9A: Repairing No Vehicle Speed Sensor Signal (Part 1 of 3)

Fig. 20   Test TC-8A: Repairing 5-Volt Supply Output Too Low (Part 2 of 3)

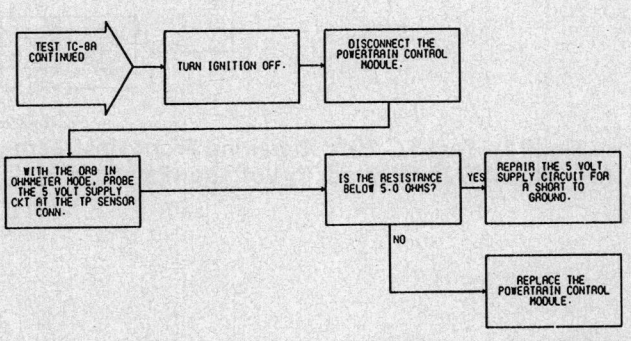

Fig. 20   Test TC-8A: Repairing 5-Volt Supply Output Too Low (Part 3 of 3)

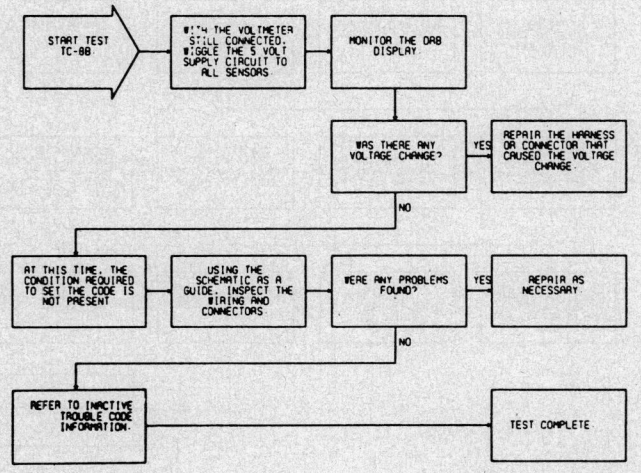

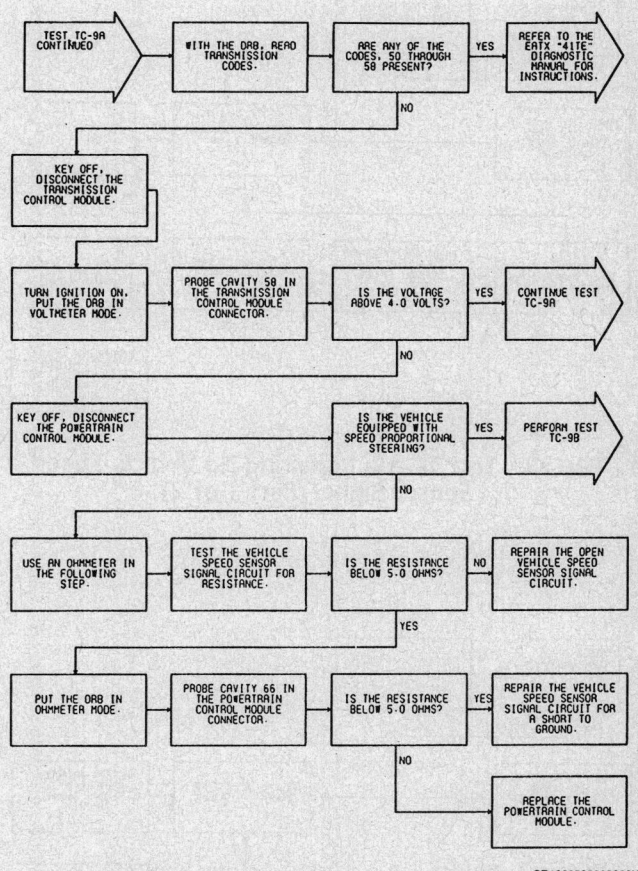

Fig. 21   Test TC-8A: Repairing 5-Volt Supply Output Too Low

Fig. 22   Test TC-9A: Repairing No Vehicle Speed Sensor Signal (Part 2 of 3)

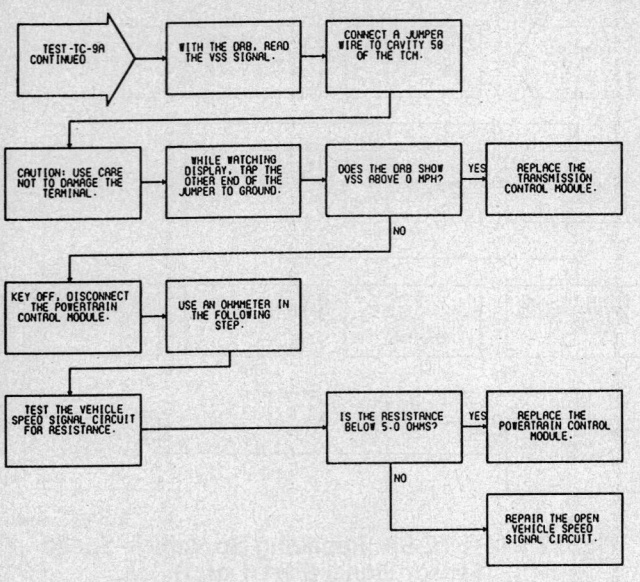

Fig. 22   Test TC-9A: Repairing No Vehicle Speed
Sensor Signal (Part 3 of 3)

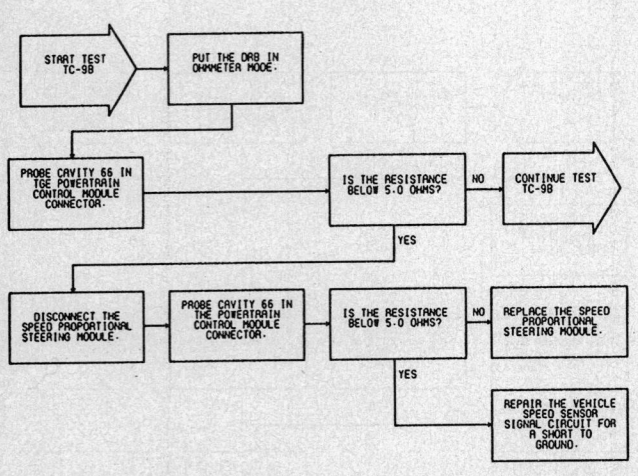

Fig. 23   Test TC-9B: Repairing No Vehicle Speed
Sensor Signal (Part 1 of 2)

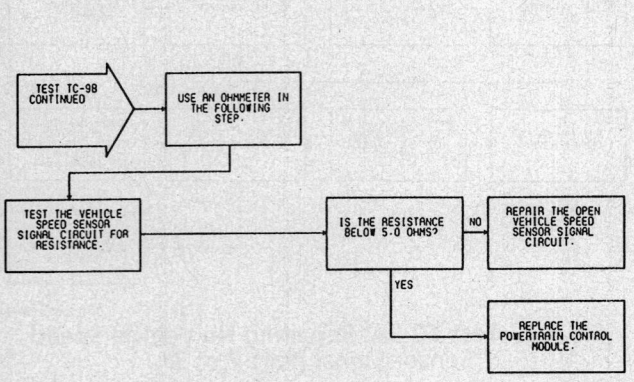

Fig. 23   Test TC-9B: Repairing No Vehicle Speed
Sensor Signal (Part 2 of 2)

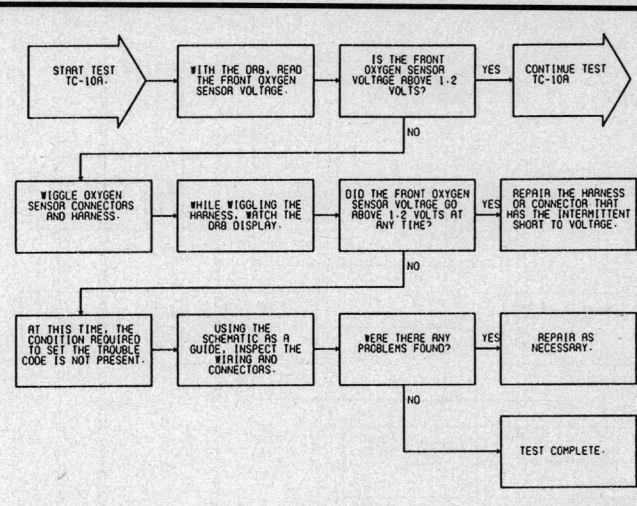

Fig. 24   Test TC-10A: Repairing Front Upstream
(Bank) O2S Shorted To Voltage (Part 1 of 2)

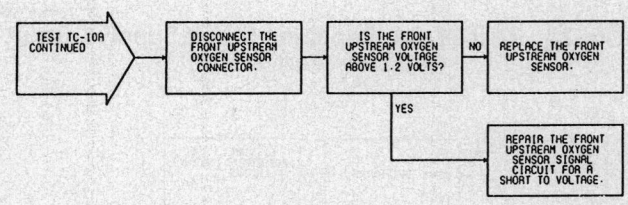

Fig. 24   Test TC-10A: Repairing Front Upstream
(Bank) O2S Shorted To Voltage (Part 2 of 2)

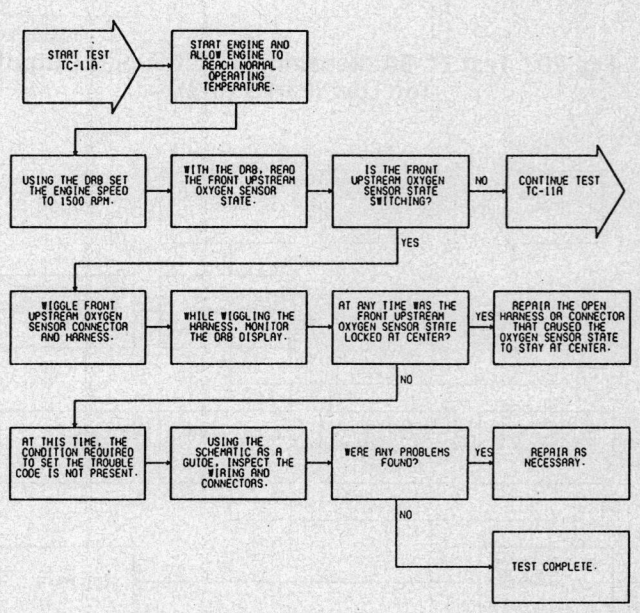

Fig. 25   Test TC-11A: Repairing Front Upstream
(Bank) O2S Stays At Center (Part 1 of 2)

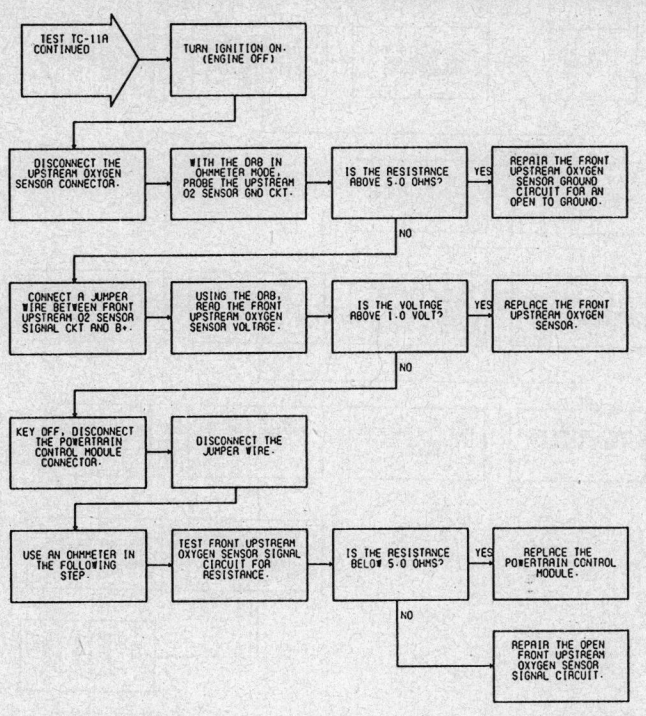

Fig. 25   Test TC-11A: Repairing Front Upstream (Bank) O2S Stays At Center (Part 2 of 2)

CR1029505271020X

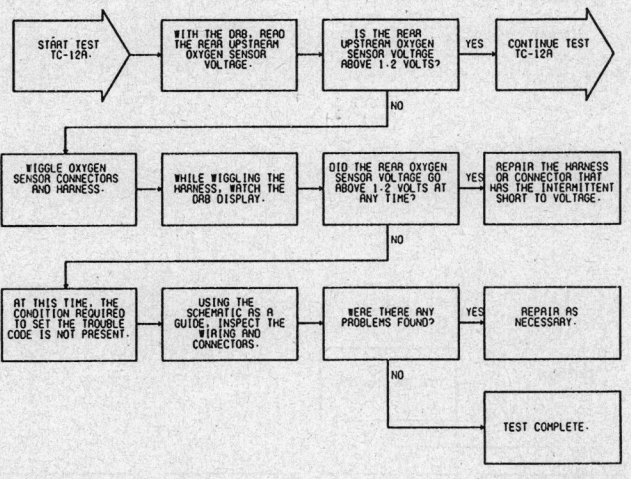

Fig. 26   Test TC-12A: Repairing Rear Upstream (Bank) O2S Shorted To Voltage (Part 1 of 2)

CR1029505272010X

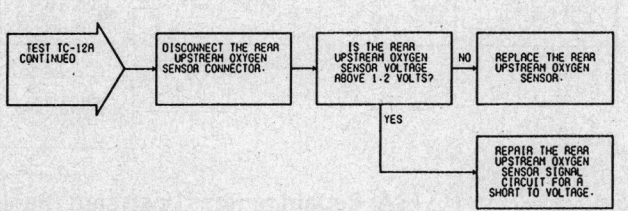

Fig. 26   Test TC-12A: Repairing Rear Upstream (Bank) O2S Shorted To Voltage (Part 2 of 2)

CR1029505272020X

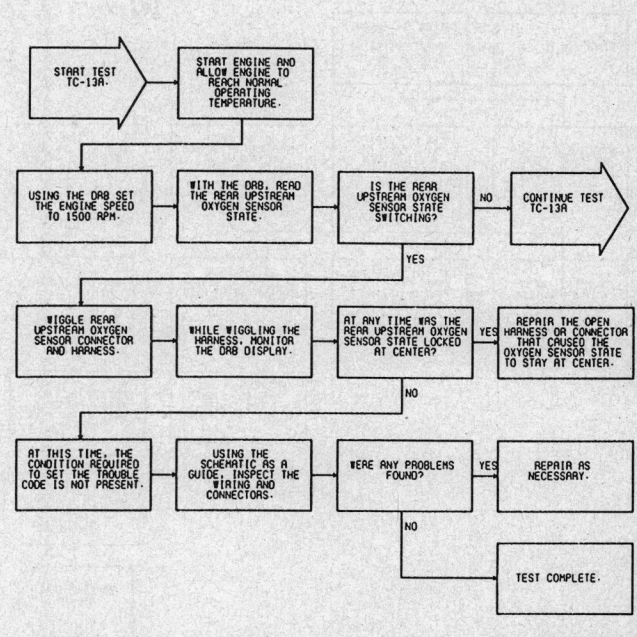

Fig. 27   Test TC-13A: Repairing Rear Upstream (Bank) O2S Stays At Center (Part 1 of 2)

CR1029505273010X

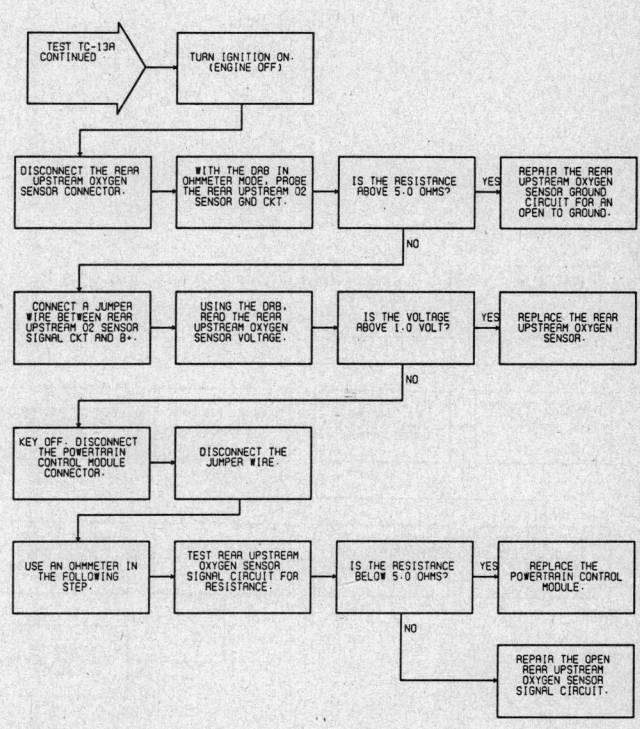

Fig. 27   Test TC-13A: Repairing Rear Upstream (Bank) O2S Stays At Center (Part 2 of 2)

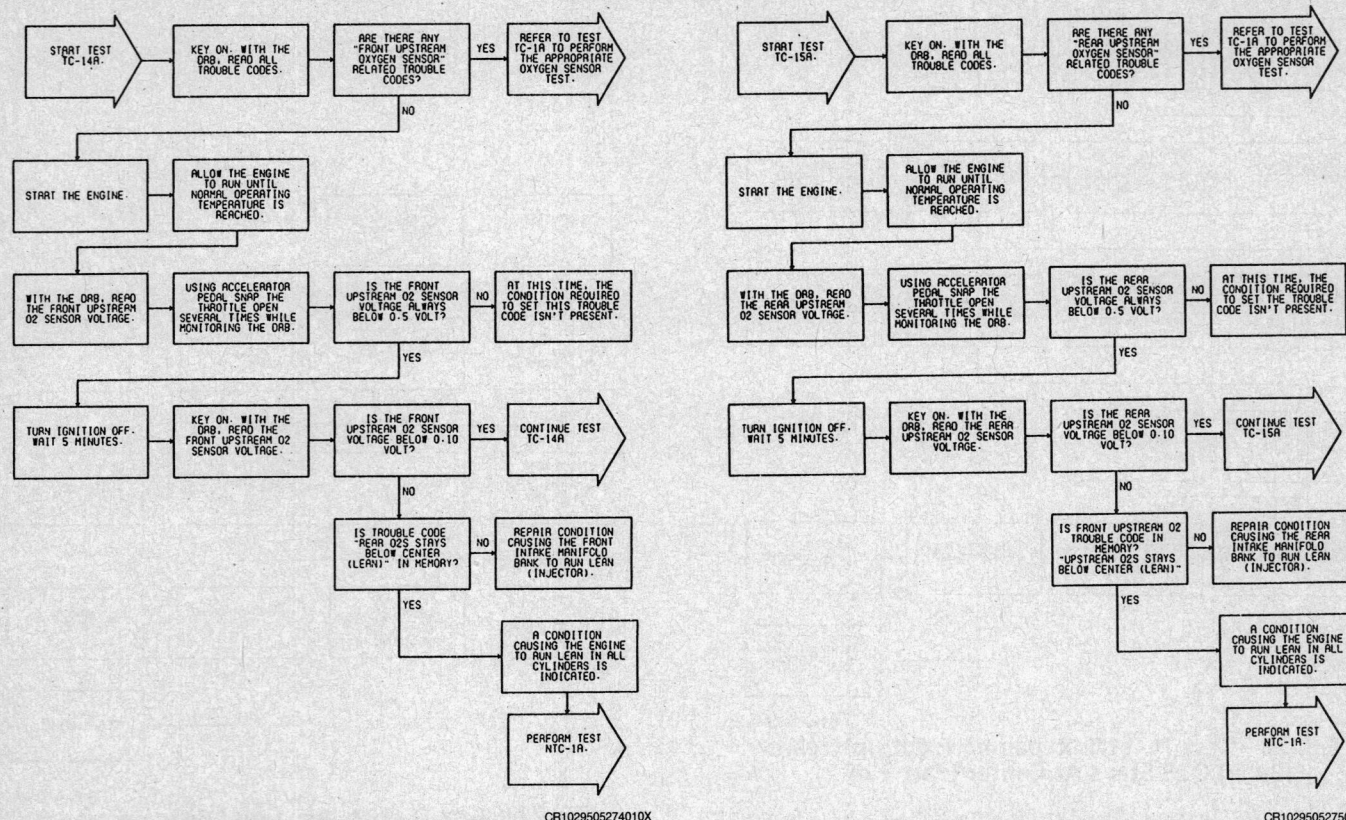

Fig. 28   Test TC-14A: Repairing Front Upstream (Bank) O2S Stays Below Center (Lean) (Part 1 of 2)

CR1029505274010X

Fig. 29   Test TC-15A: Repairing Rear Upstream (Bank) O2S Stays Below Center (Lean) (Part 1 of 2)

CR1029505275010X

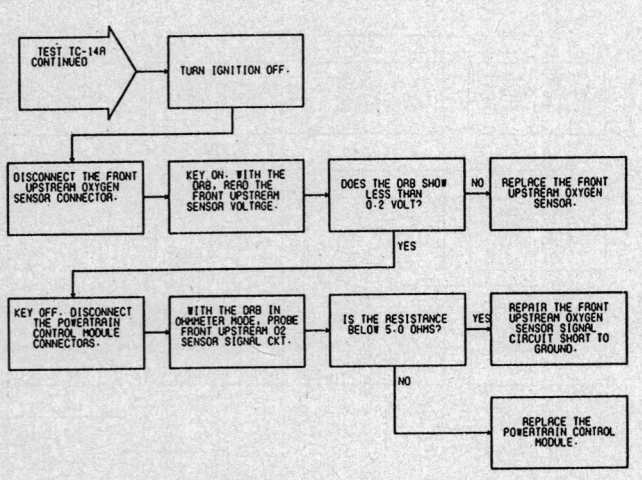

CR1029505274020X

Fig. 28   Test TC-14A: Repairing Front Upstream (Bank) O2S Stays Below Center (Lean) (Part 2 of 2)

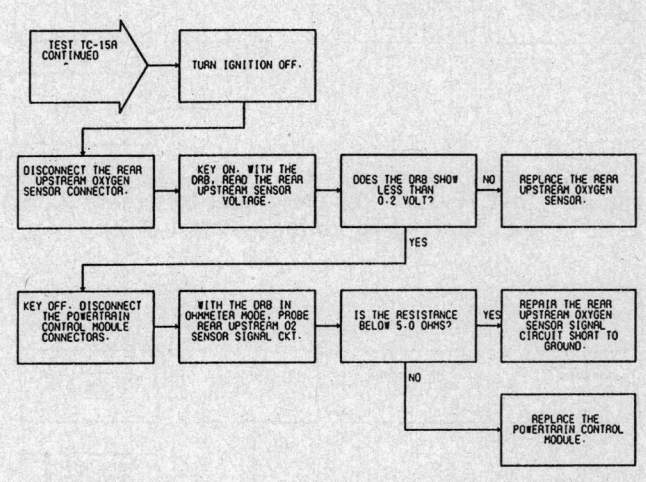

CR1029505275020X

Fig. 29   Test TC-15A: Repairing Rear Upstream (Bank) O2S Stays Below Center (Lean) (Part 2 of 2)

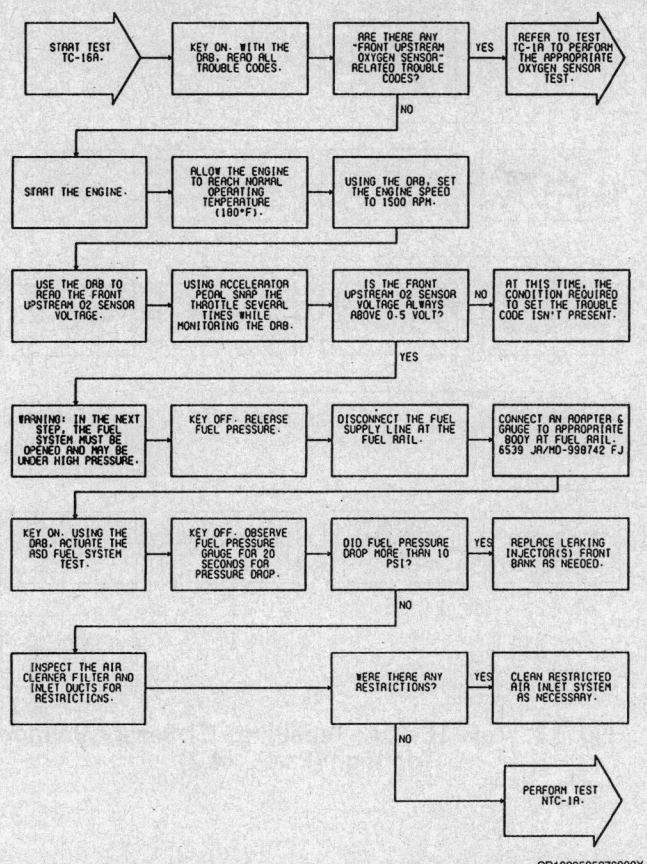

Fig. 30 Test TC-16A: Repairing Front Upstream (Bank) O2S Stays Above Center (Rich)

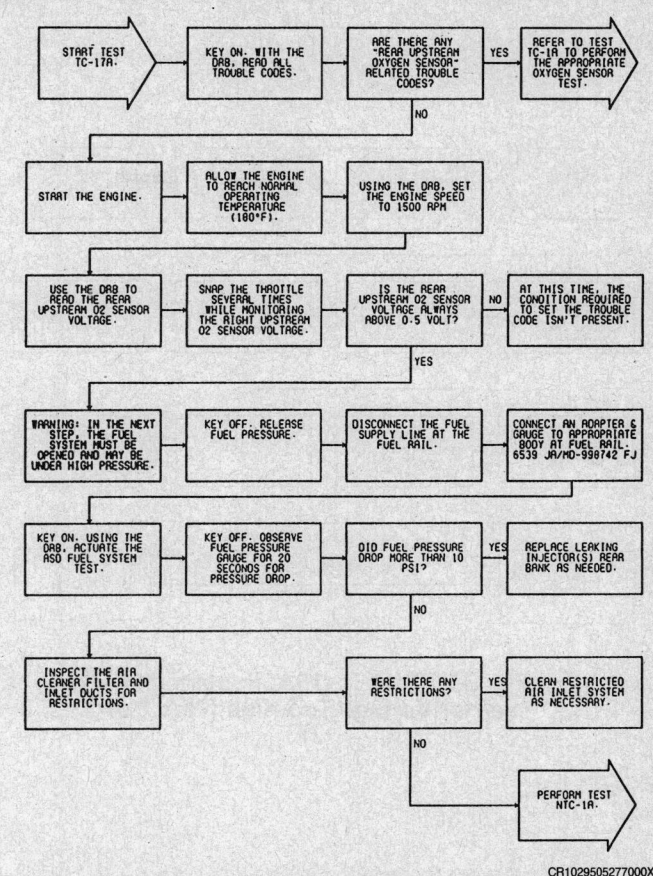

Fig. 31 Test TC-17A: Repairing Rear Upstream (Bank) O2S Stays Above Center (Rich)

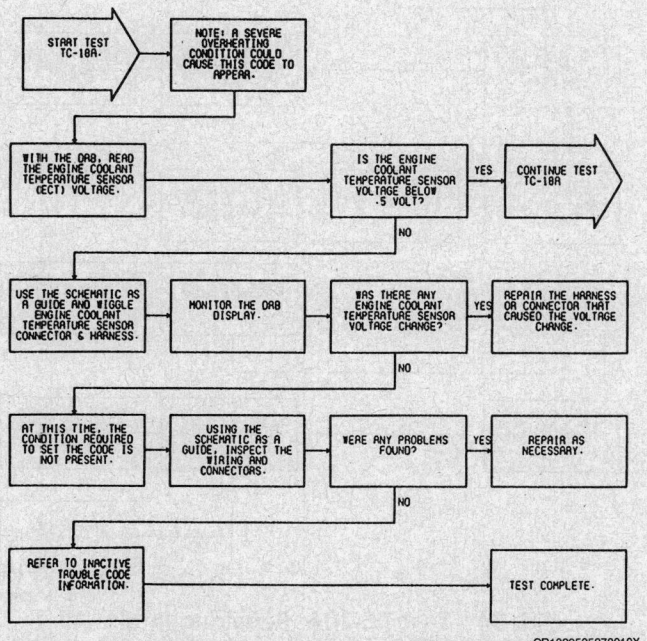

Fig. 32 Test TC-18A: Repairing ECT Sensor Voltage Too Low (Part 1 of 2)

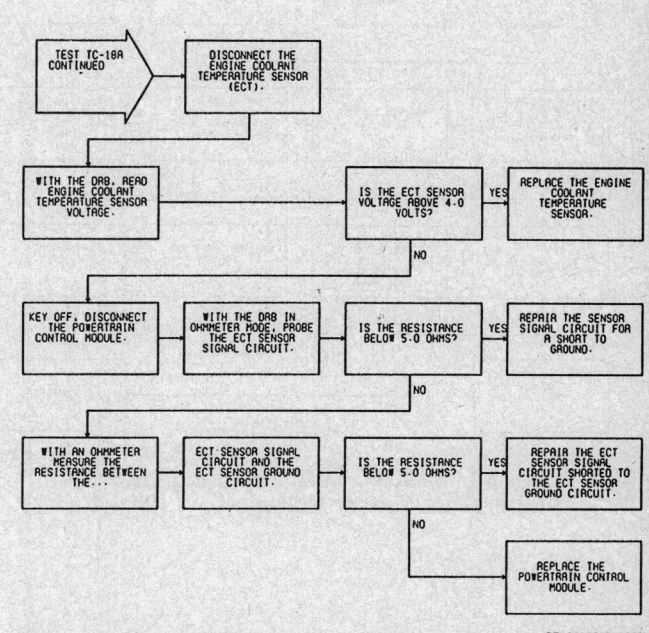

Fig. 32 Test TC-18A: Repairing ECT Sensor Voltage Too Low (Part 2 of 2)

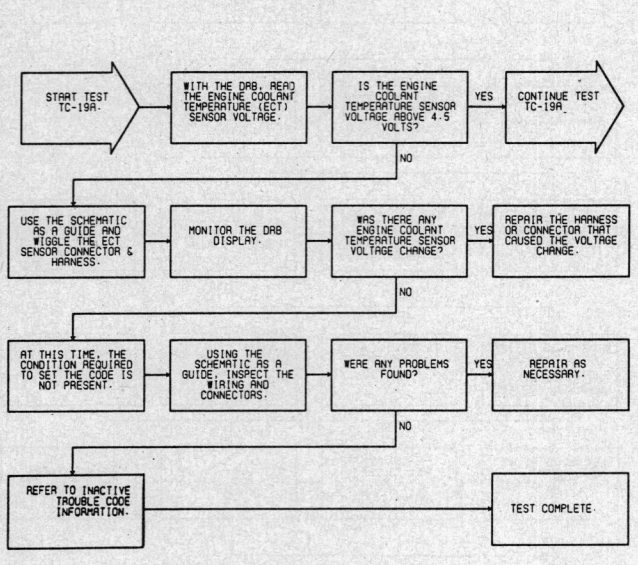

Fig. 33   Test TC-19A: Repairing ECT Sensor Voltage Too High (Part 1 of 2)

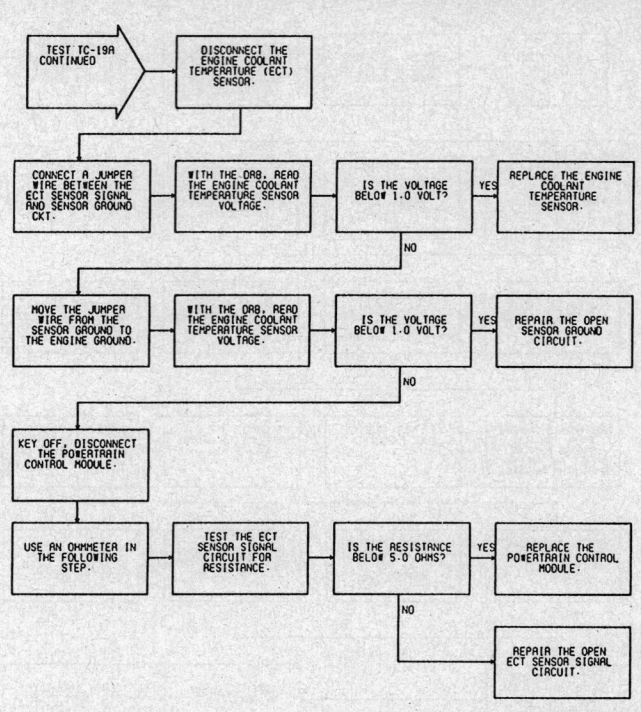

CR1029505279020X

Fig. 33   Test TC-19A: Repairing ECT Sensor Voltage Too High (Part 2 of 2)

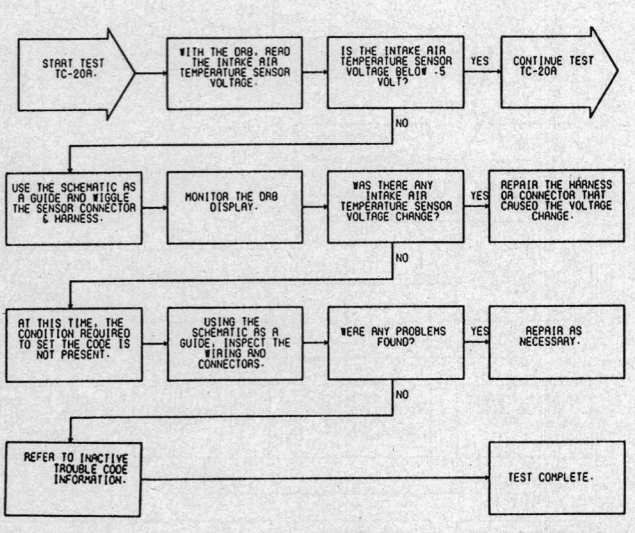

CR1029505280010X

Fig. 34   Test TC-20A: Repairing Intake Air Temperature Sensor Voltage Low (Part 1 of 2)

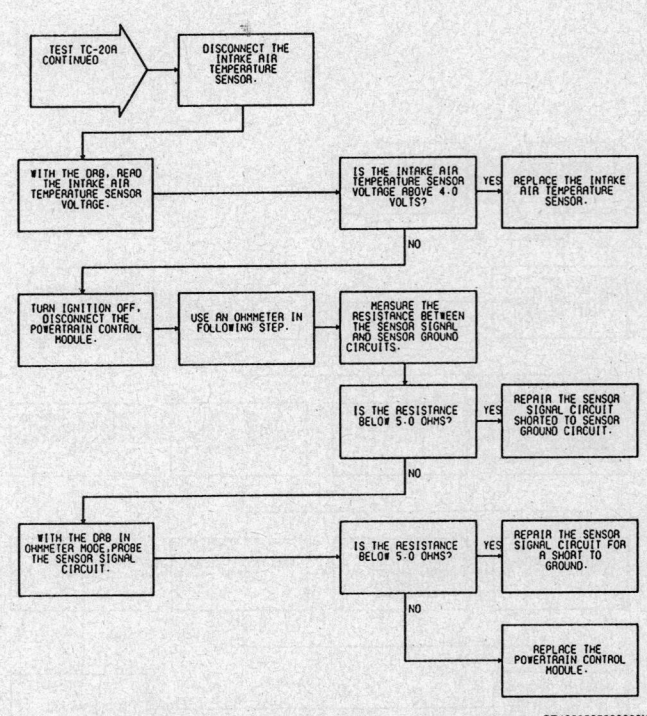

CR1029505280020X

Fig. 34   Test TC-20A: Repairing Intake Air Temperature Sensor Voltage Low (Part 2 of 2)

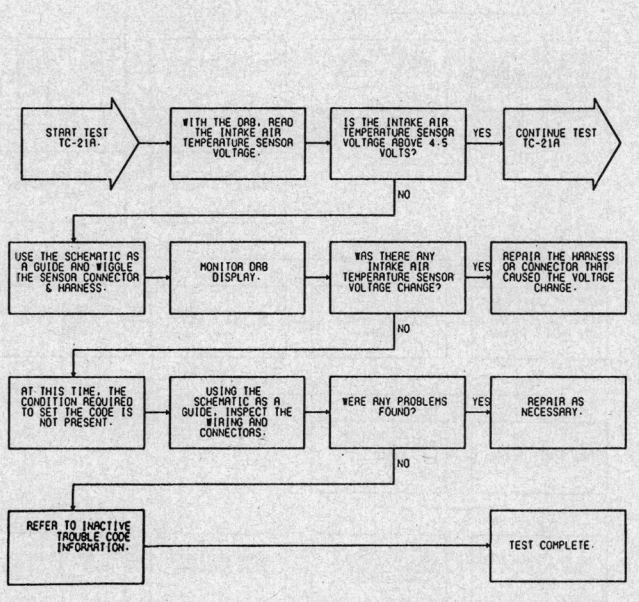

Fig. 35   Test TC-21A: Repairing Intake Air Temperature Sensor Voltage High (Part 1 of 2)

CR1029505282010X

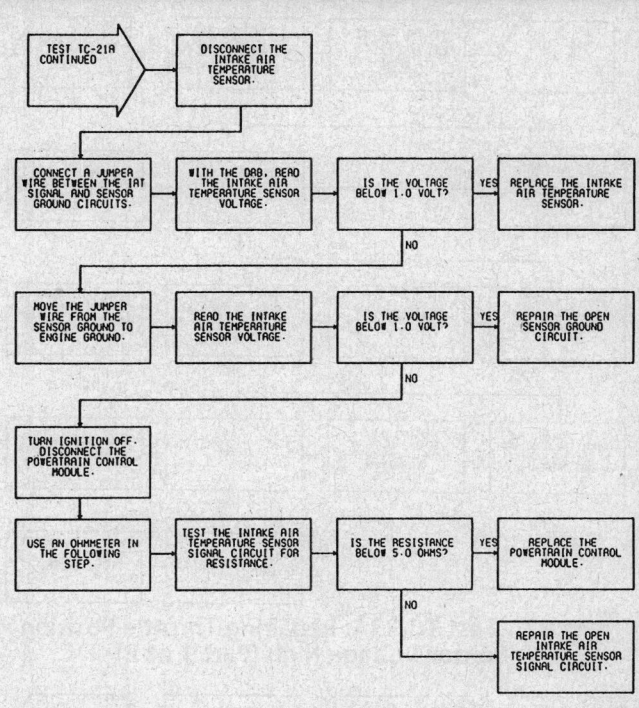

Fig. 35   Test TC-21A: Repairing Intake Air Temperature Sensor Voltage High (Part 2 of 2)

CR1029505282020X

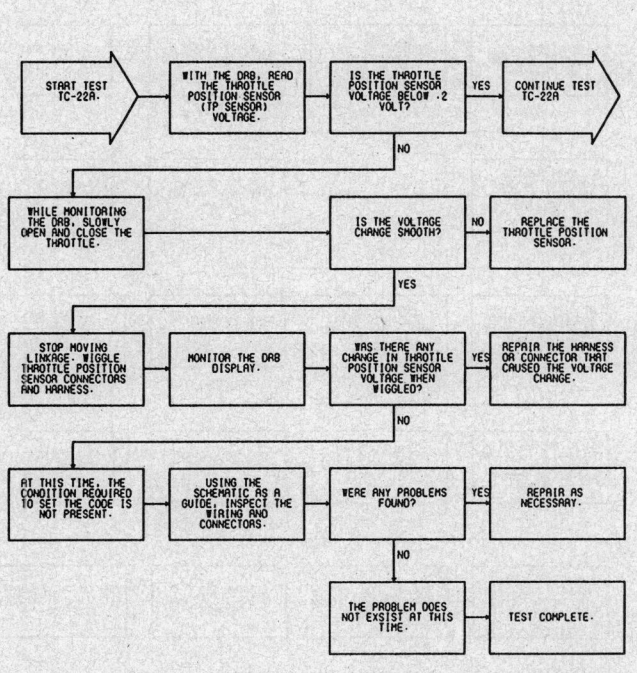

Fig. 36   Test TC-22A: Repairing Throttle Position Sensor Voltage Low (Part 1 of 2)

CR1029505283010X

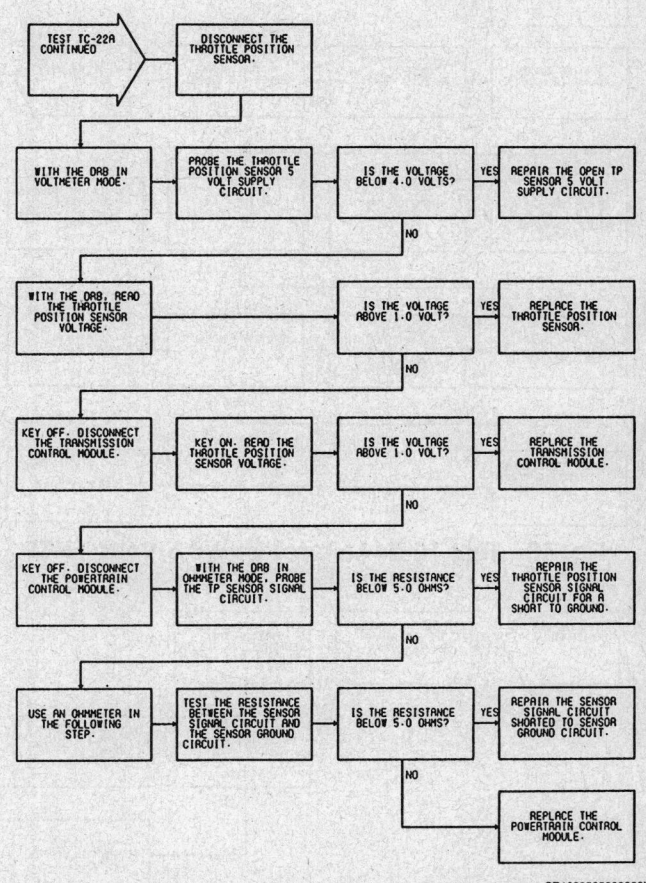

Fig. 36   Test TC-22A: Repairing Throttle Position Sensor Voltage Low (Part 2 of 2)

CR1029505283020X

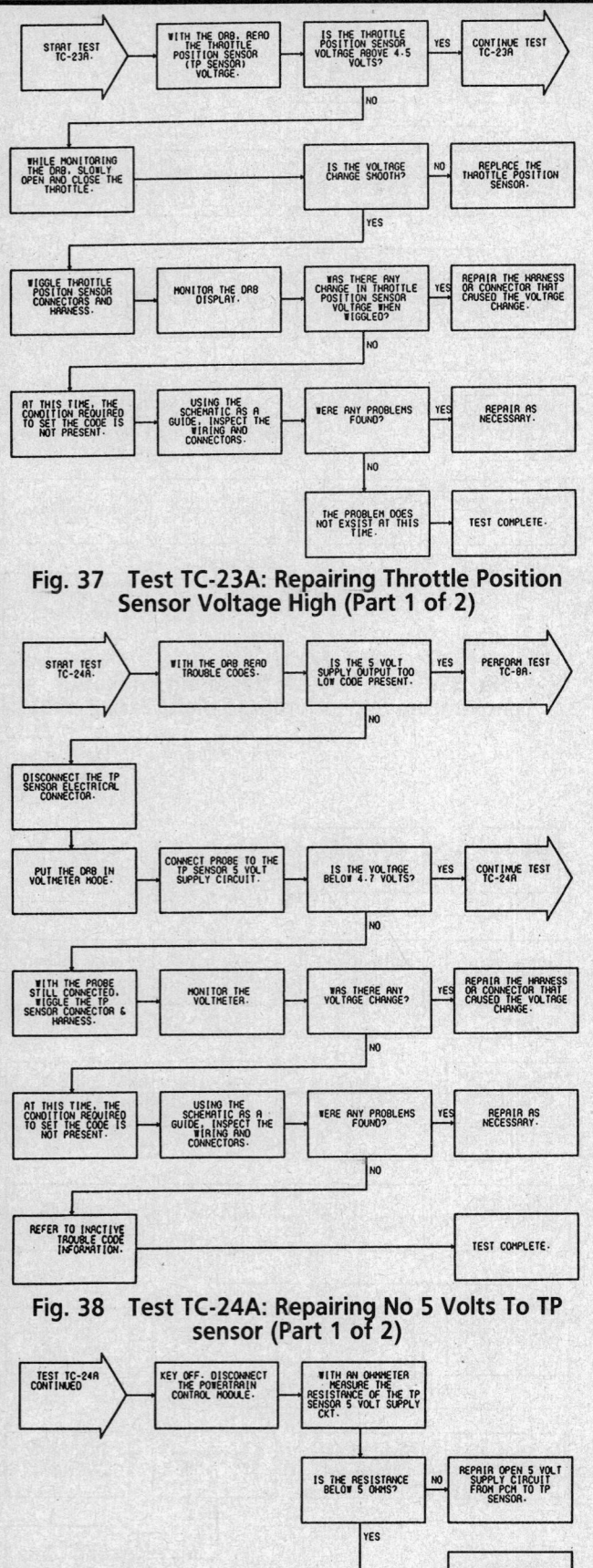

Fig. 37   Test TC-23A: Repairing Throttle Position
Sensor Voltage High (Part 1 of 2)

Fig. 38   Test TC-24A: Repairing No 5 Volts To TP
sensor (Part 1 of 2)

Fig. 38   Test TC-24A: Repairing No 5 Volts To TP
sensor (Part 2 of 2)

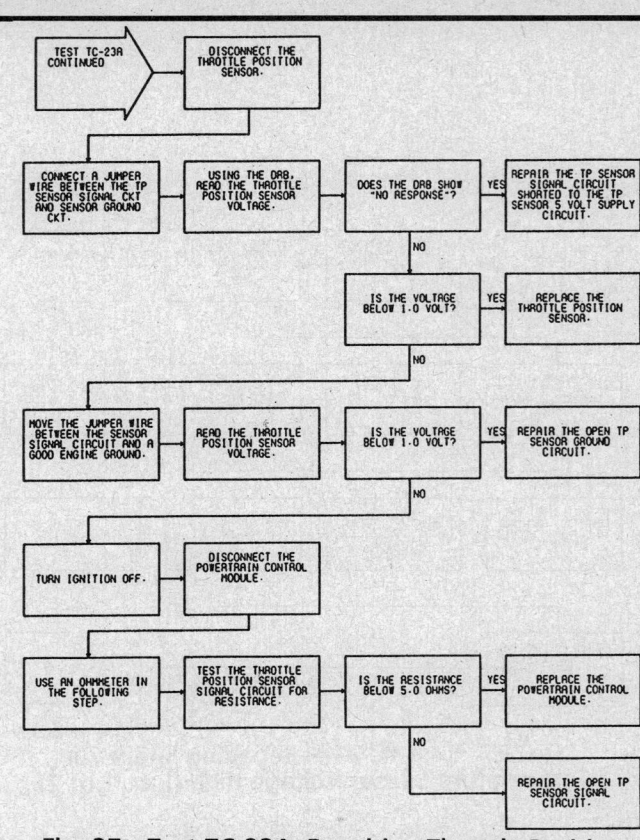

Fig. 37   Test TC-23A: Repairing Throttle Position
Sensor Voltage High (Part 2 of 2)

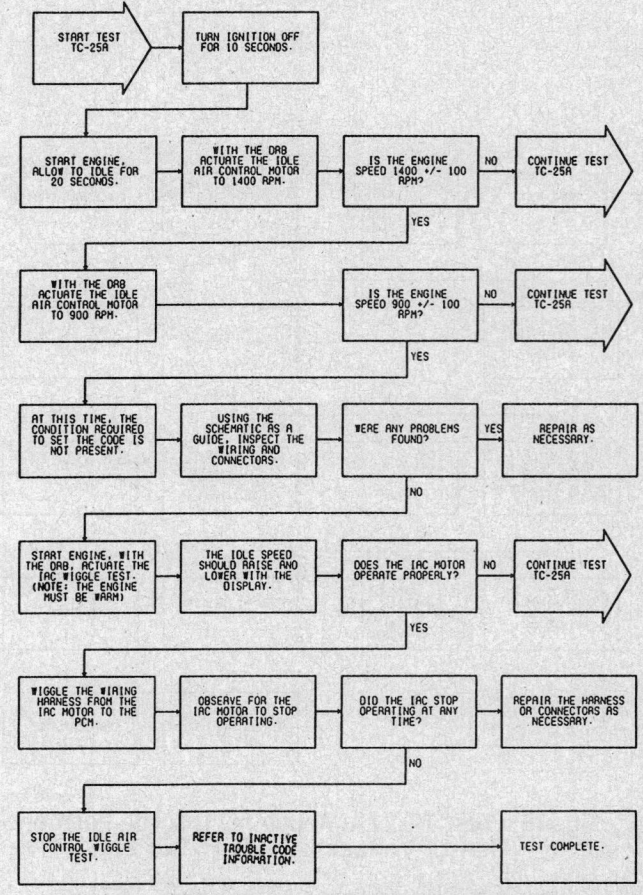

Fig. 39   Test TC-25A: Repairing Idle Air Control
Motor Circuits (Part 1 of 4)

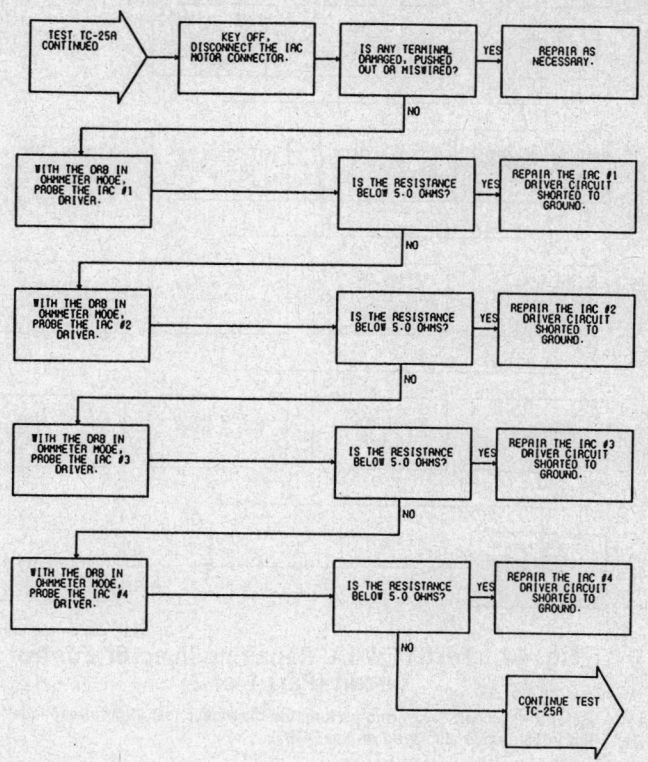

Fig. 39   Test TC-25A: Repairing Idle Air Control Motor Circuits (Part 2 of 4)

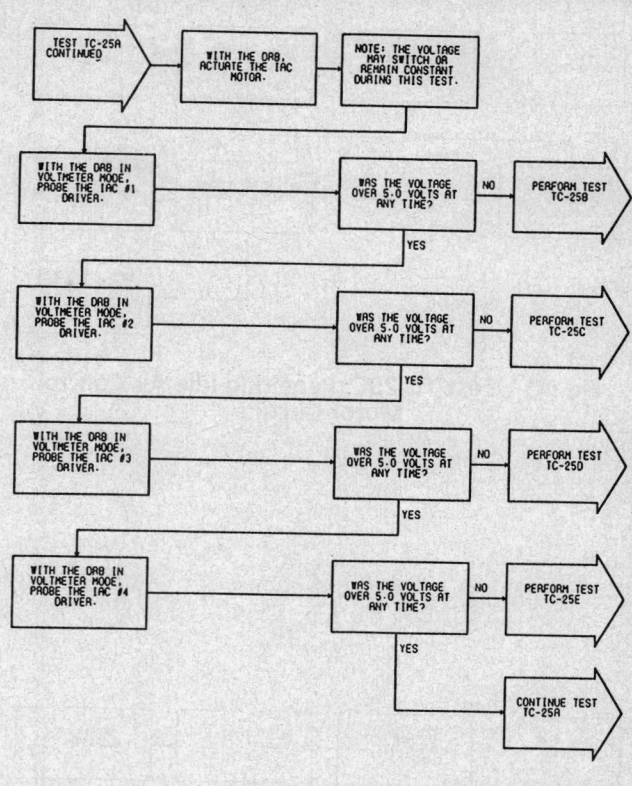

Fig. 39   Test TC-25A: Repairing Idle Air Control Motor Circuits (Part 3 of 4)

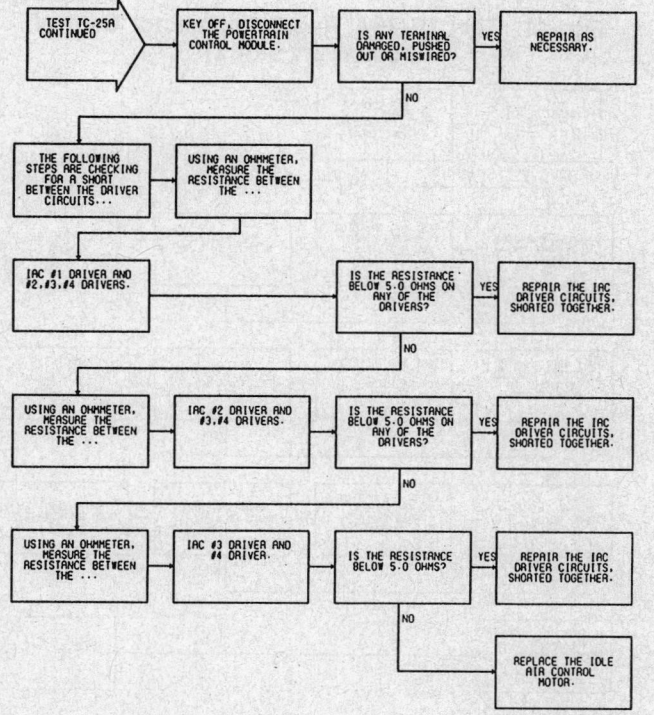

Fig. 39   Test TC-25A: Repairing Idle Air Control Motor Circuits (Part 4 of 4)

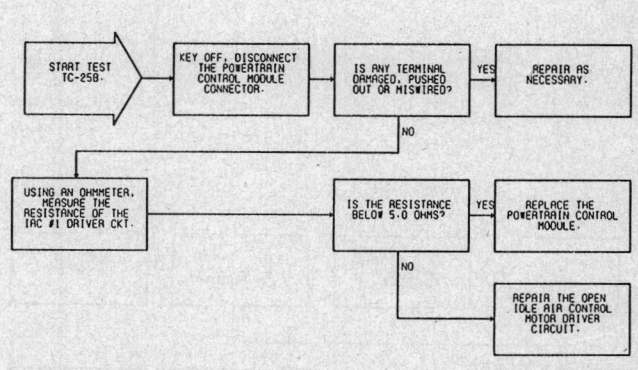

Fig. 40   Test TC-25B: Repairing Idle Air Control Motor Circuits

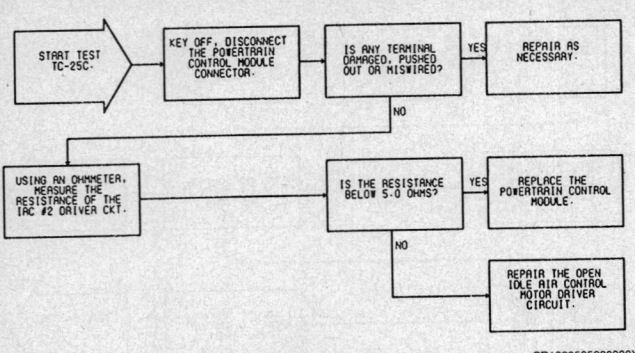

Fig. 41 Test TC-25C: Repairing Idle Air Control Motor Circuits

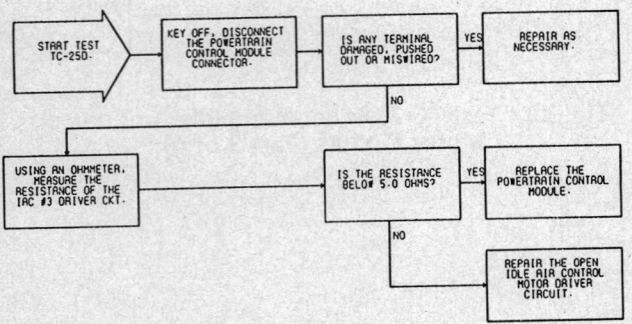

Fig. 42 Test TC-25D: Repairing Idle Air Control Motor Circuits

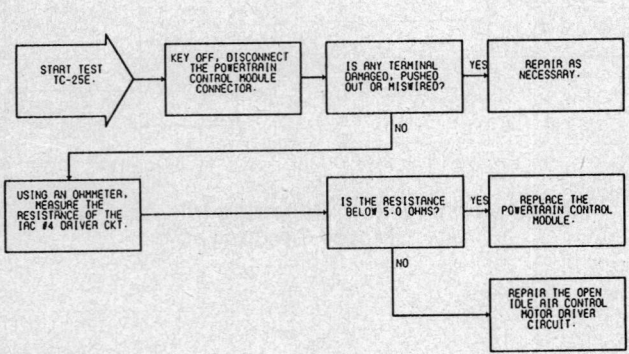

Fig. 43 Test TC-25E: Repairing Idle Air Control Motor Circuits

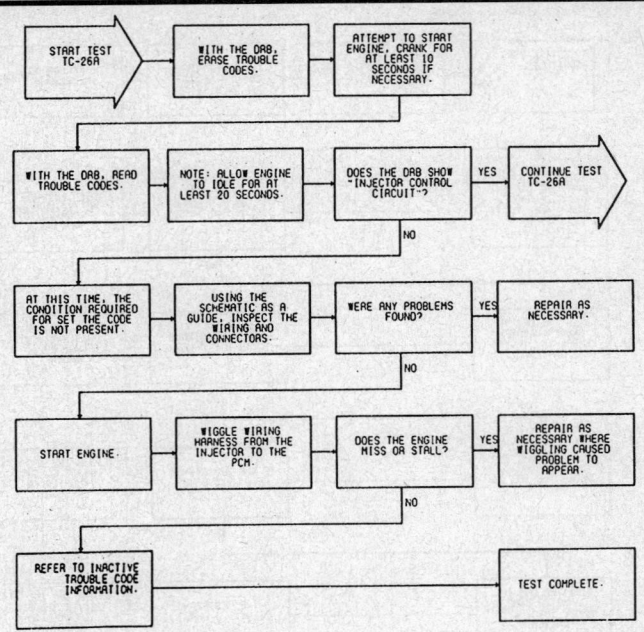

Fig. 44 Test TC-26A: Repairing Injector Control Circuit (Part 1 of 2)

Refer to the chart below and perform the diagnostic test that corresponds to the trouble code displayed on the DRB.

TROUBLE CODE	DIAGNOSTIC TEST
INJECTOR #1 CONTROL CIRCUIT	TC-26B
INJECTOR #2 CONTROL CIRCUIT	TC-27A
INJECTOR #3 CONTROL CIRCUIT	TC-28A
INJECTOR #4 CONTROL CIRCUIT	TC-29A
INJECTOR #5 CONTROL CIRCUIT	TC-30A
INJECTOR #6 CONTROL CIRCUIT	TC-31A

Fig. 44 Test TC-26A: Repairing Injector Control Circuit (Part 2 of 2)

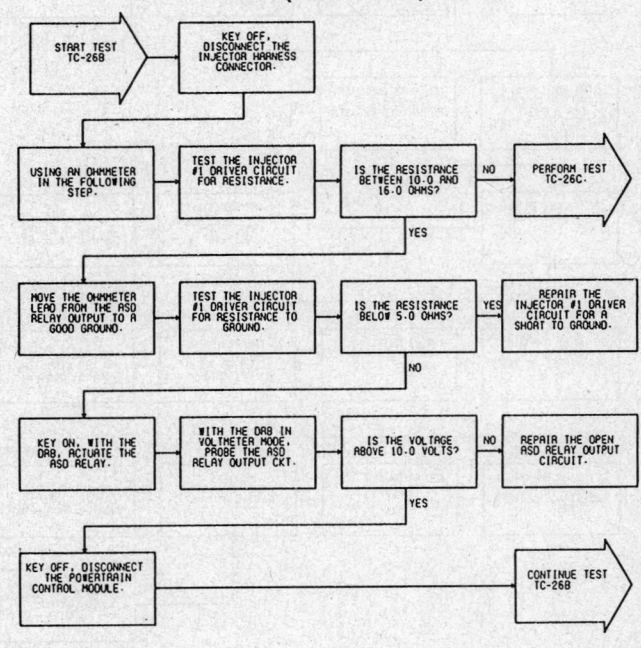

Fig. 45 Test TC-26B: Repairing Injector Control Circuit (Part 1 of 2)

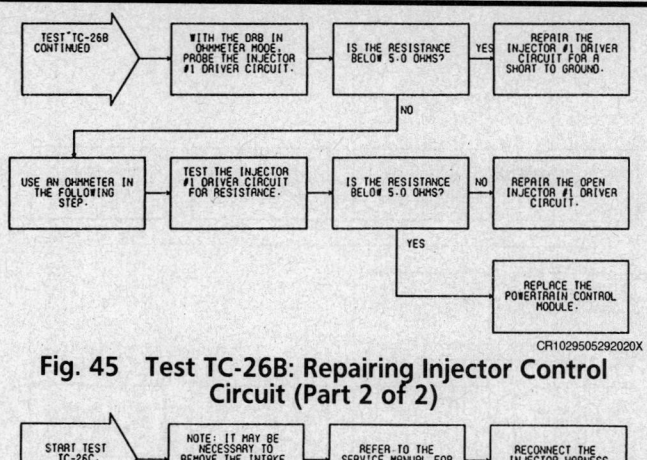

Fig. 45 Test TC-26B: Repairing Injector Control Circuit (Part 2 of 2)

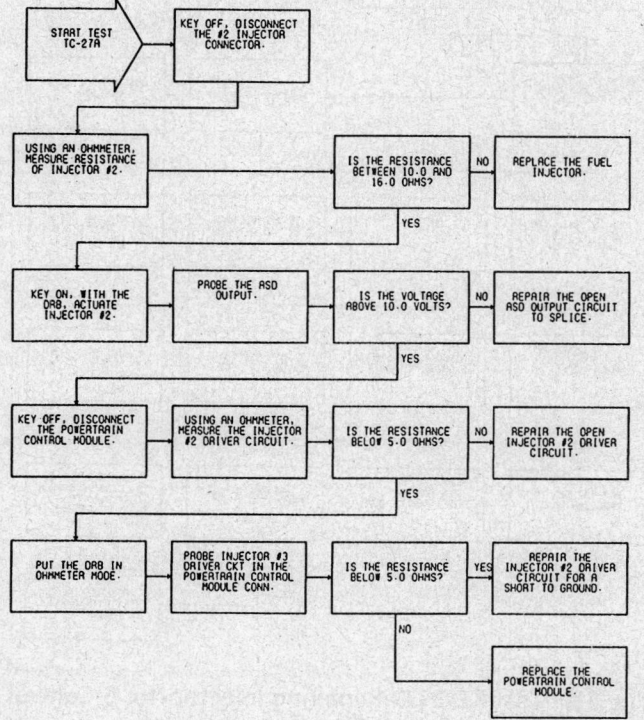

Fig. 46 Test TC-26C: Repairing Injector Control Circuit

Fig. 47 Test TC-27A: Repairing Injector No. 2 Control Circuit

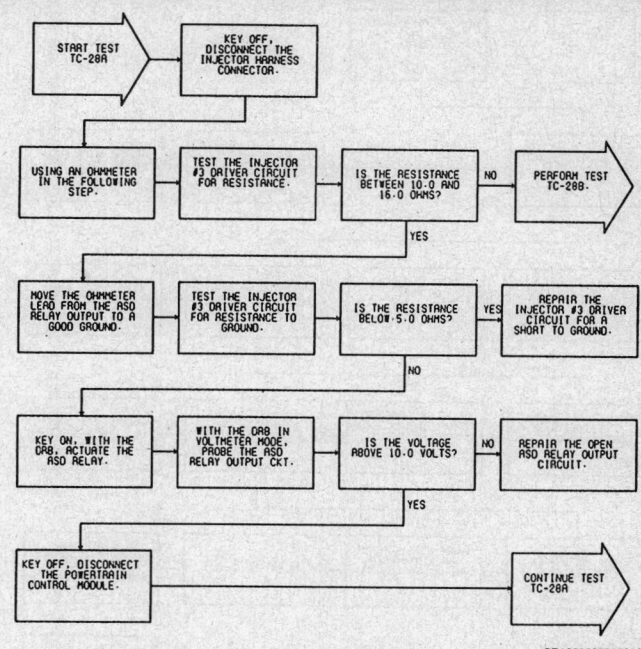

Fig. 48 Test TC-28A: Repairing Injector No. 3 Control Circuit (Part 1 of 2)

Fig. 48 Test TC-28A: Repairing Injector No. 3 Control Circuit (Part 2 of 2)

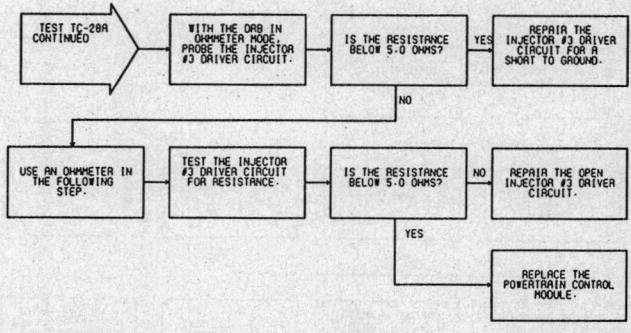

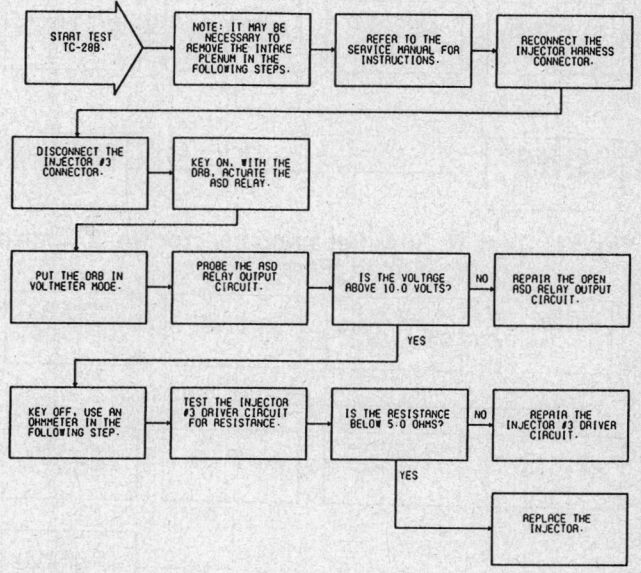

Fig. 49 Test TC-28B: Repairing Injector No. 3 Control Circuit

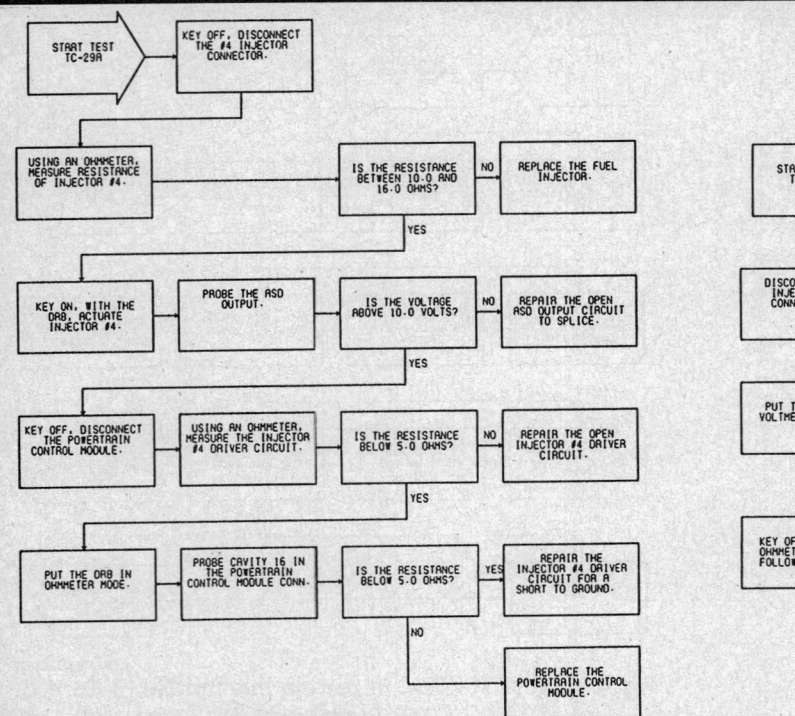

Fig. 50   Test TC-29A: Repairing Injector No. 4 Control Circuit

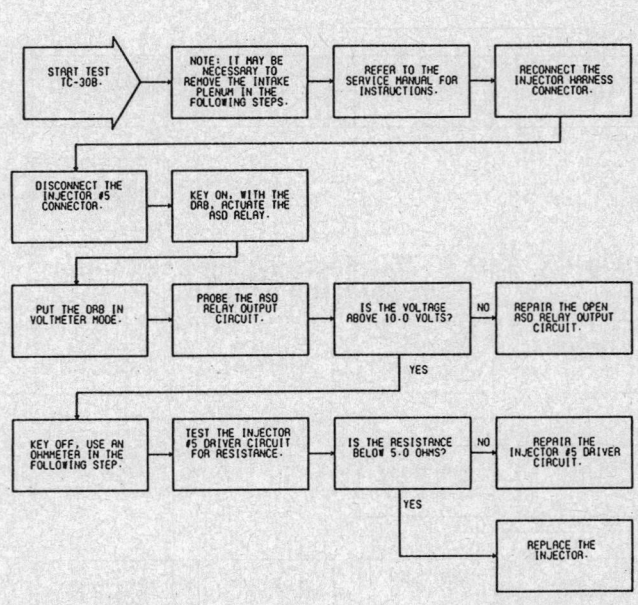

CR1029505299000X

Fig. 52   Test TC-30B: Repairing Injector No. 5 Control Circuit

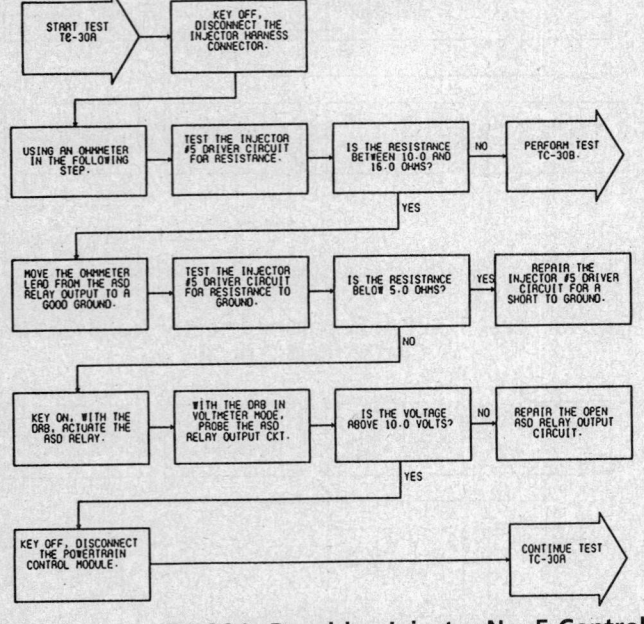

Fig. 51   Test TC-30A: Repairing Injector No. 5 Control Circuit (Part 1 of 2)

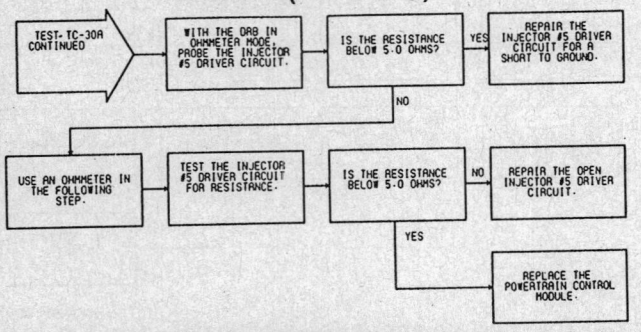

Fig. 51   Test TC-30A: Repairing Injector No. 5 Control Circuit (Part 2 of 2)

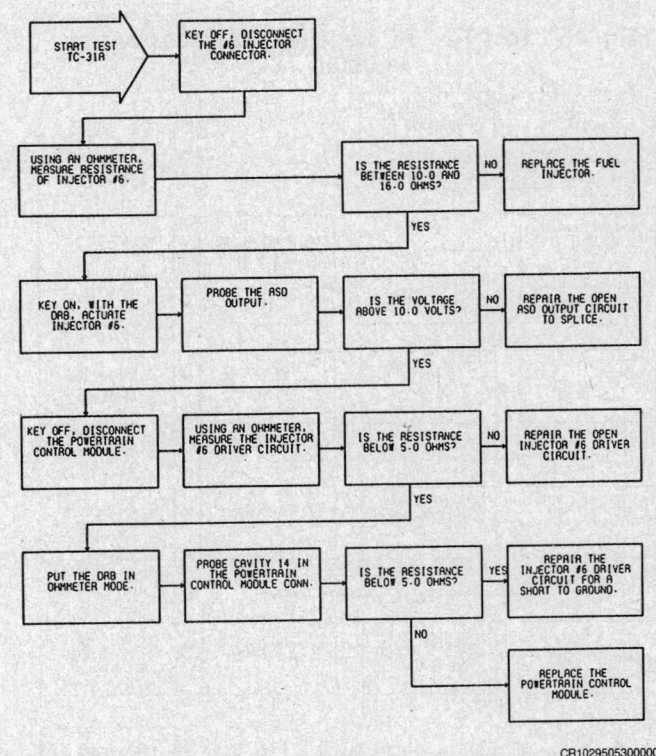

CR1029505300000X

Fig. 53   Test TC-31A: Repairing Injector No. 6 Control Circuit

MULTI-POINT FUEL INJECTION (1995 AVENGER, CIRRUS, SEBRING & STRATUS w/2.5L/V6-152)

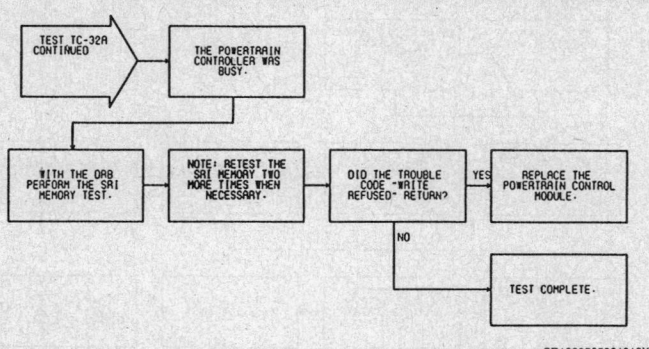

Fig. 54   Test TC-32A: Repairing PCM Failure SRI Mile Not Stored Or PCM Failure EEPROM Write Denied (Part 1 of 2)

CR1029505301010X

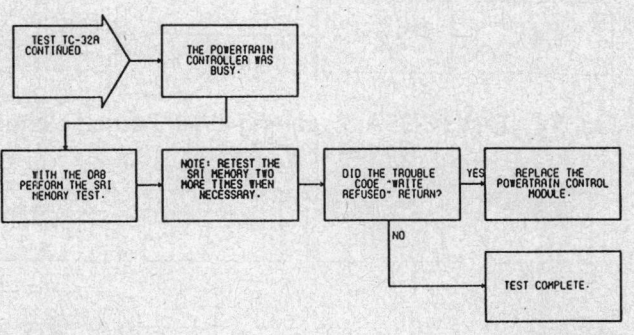

Fig. 54   Test TC-32A: Repairing PCM Failure SRI Mile Not Stored Or PCM Failure EEPROM Write Denied (Part 2 of 2)

CR102950530102 0X

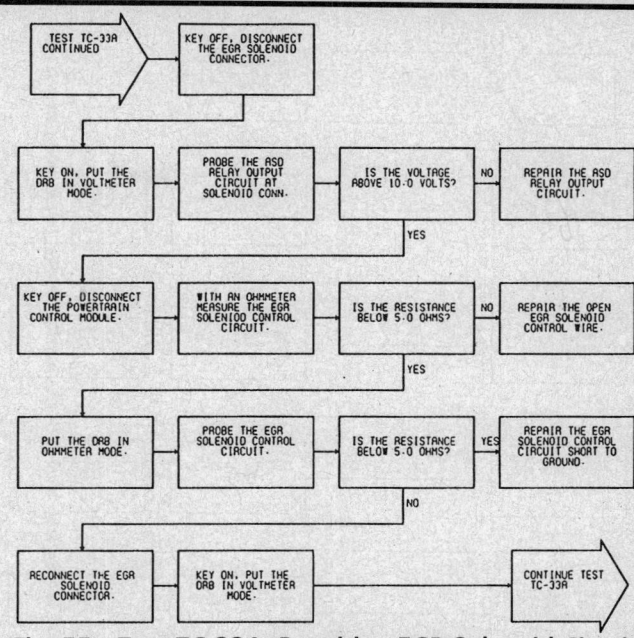

Fig. 55   Test TC-33A: Repairing EGR Solenoid Circuit (Part 2 of 3)

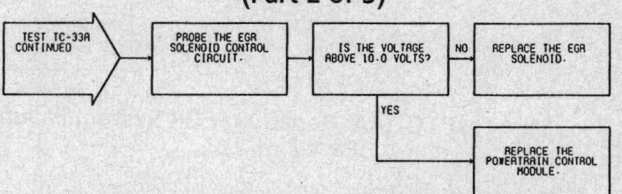

Fig. 55   Test TC-33A: Repairing EGR Solenoid Circuit (Part 3 of 3)

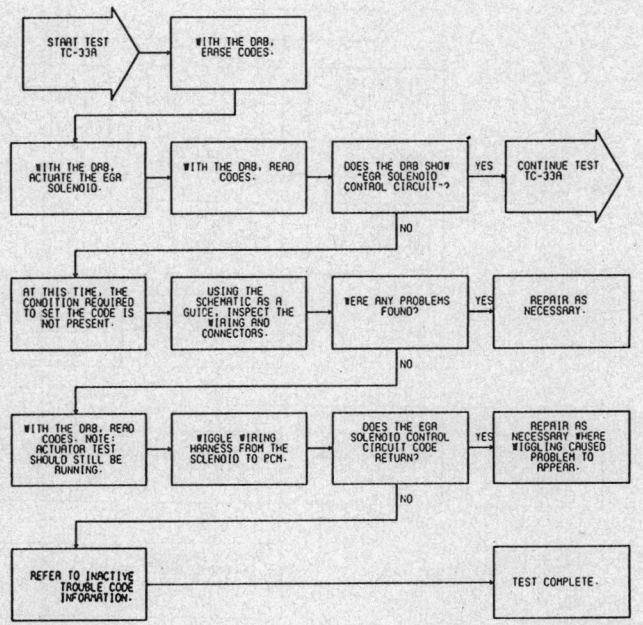

CR102950530 2010X

Fig. 55   Test TC-33A: Repairing EGR Solenoid Circuit (Part 1 of 3)

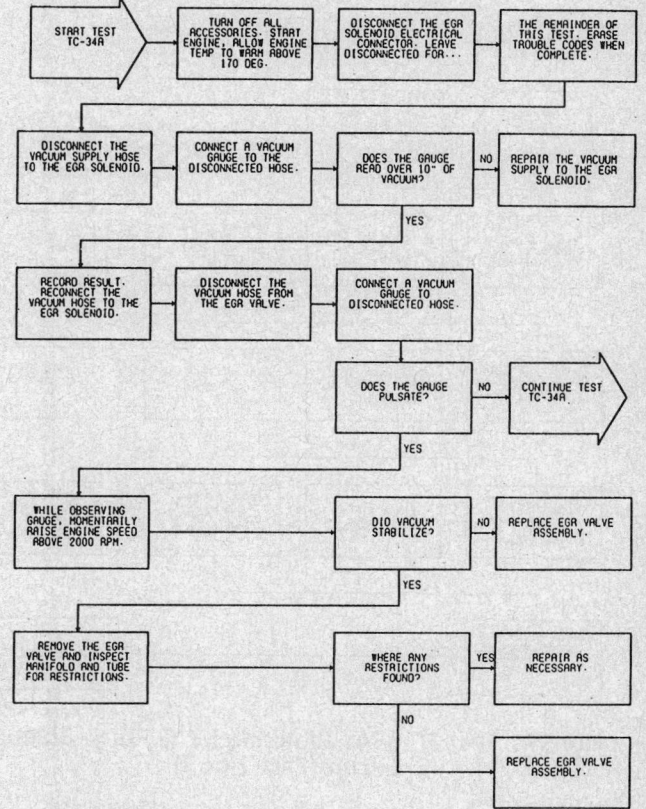

CR1029505303010X

Fig. 56   Test TC-34A: Repairing EGR System Failure (Part 1 of 2)

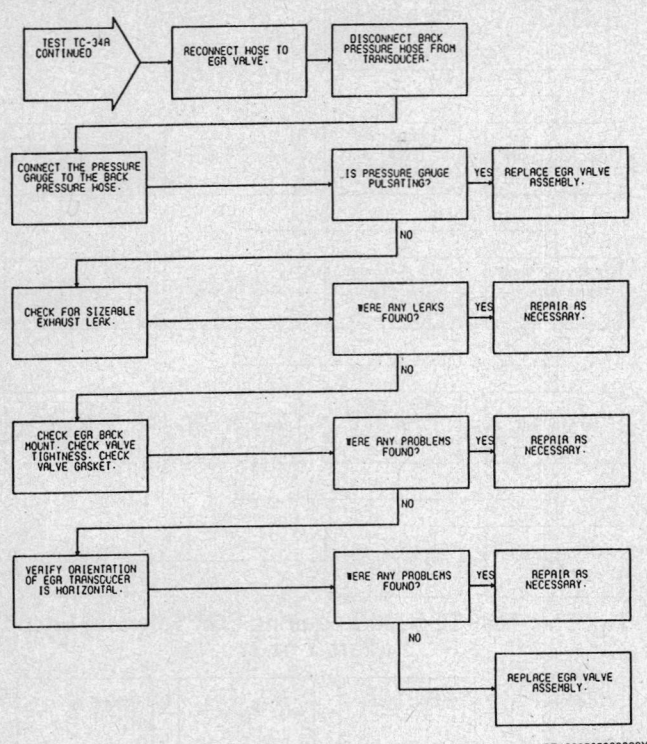

Fig. 56 Test TC-34A: Repairing EGR System Failure
(Part 2 of 2)

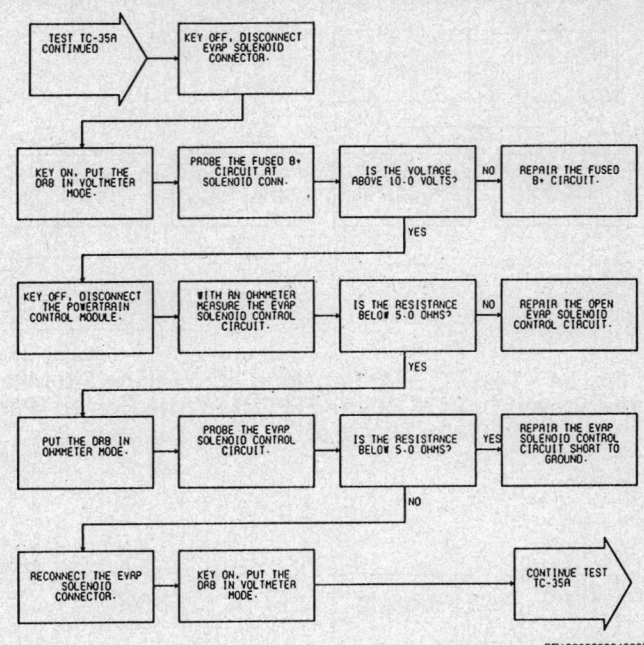

Fig. 57 Test TC-35A: Repairing EVAP Purge Solenoid
Circuit (Part 2 of 3)

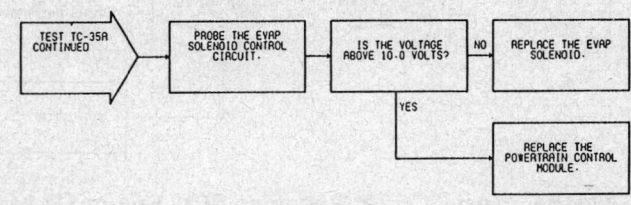

Fig. 57 Test TC-35A: Repairing EVAP Purge
Solenoid Circuit (Part 3 of 3)

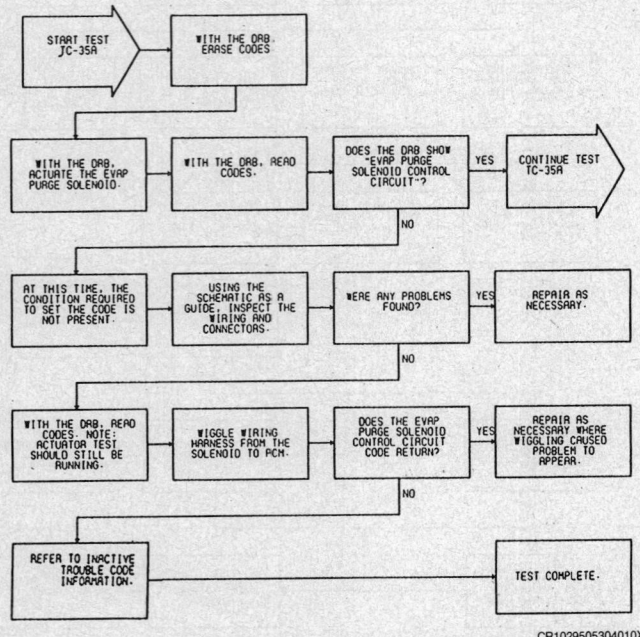

Fig. 57 Test TC-35A: Repairing EVAP Purge Solenoid
Circuit (Part 1 of 3)

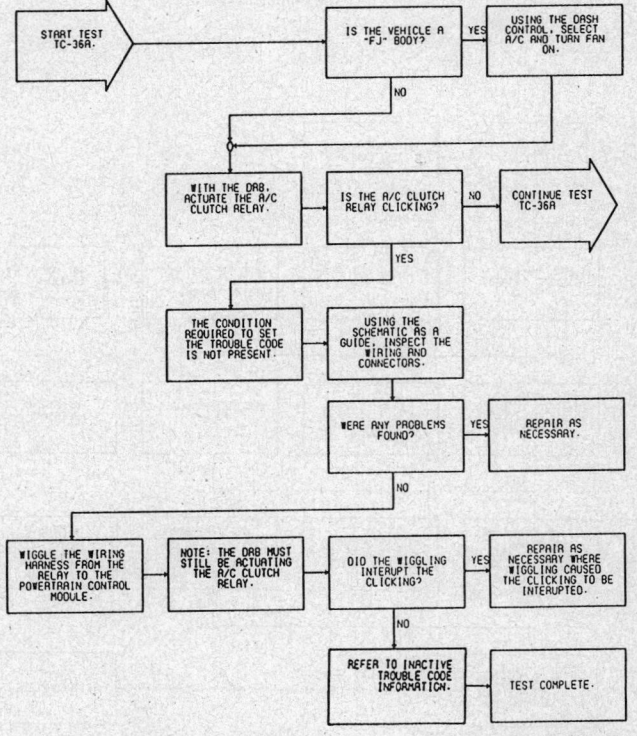

Fig. 58 Test TC-36A: Repairing A/C Clutch Relay
Circuit (Part 1 of 2)

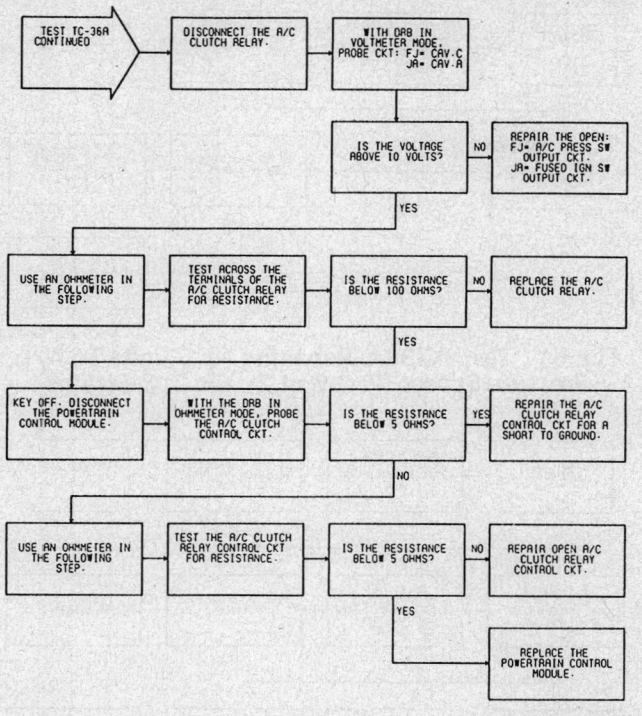

Fig. 58 Test TC-36A: Repairing A/C Clutch Relay Circuit (Part 2 of 2)

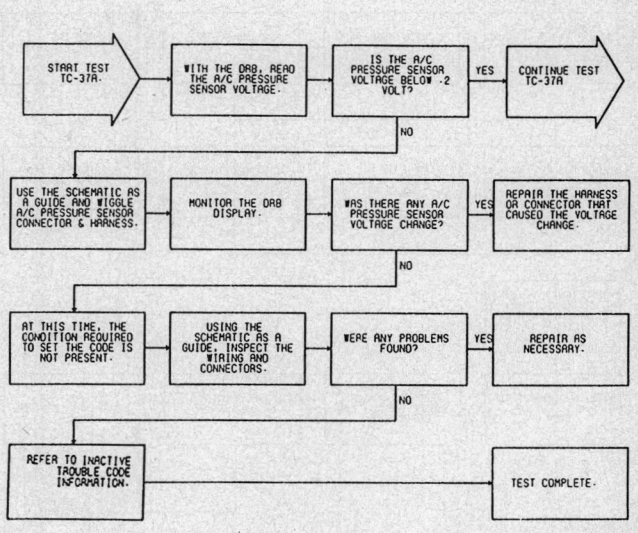

Fig. 59 Test TC-37A: Repairing A/C Pressure Sensor Volts Too Low (Part 1 of 2). Cirrus & Stratus

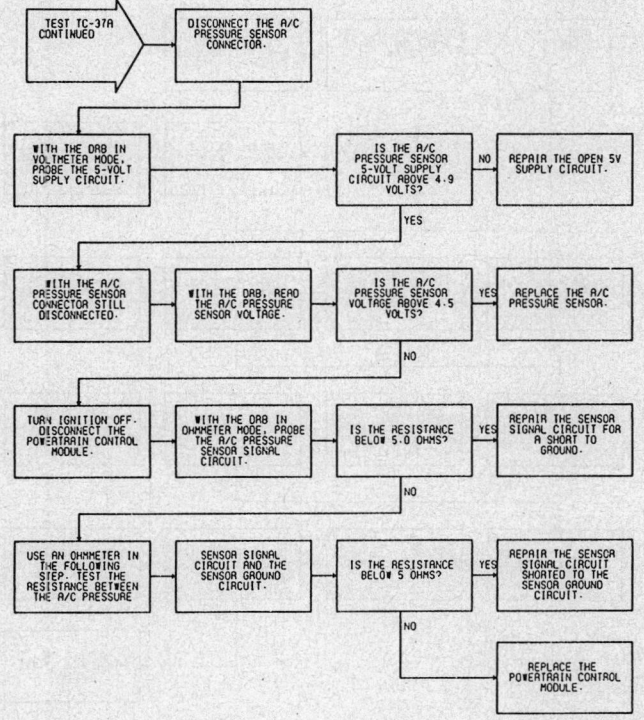

Fig. 59 Test TC-37A: Repairing A/C Pressure Sensor Volts Too Low (Part 2 of 2). Cirrus & Stratus

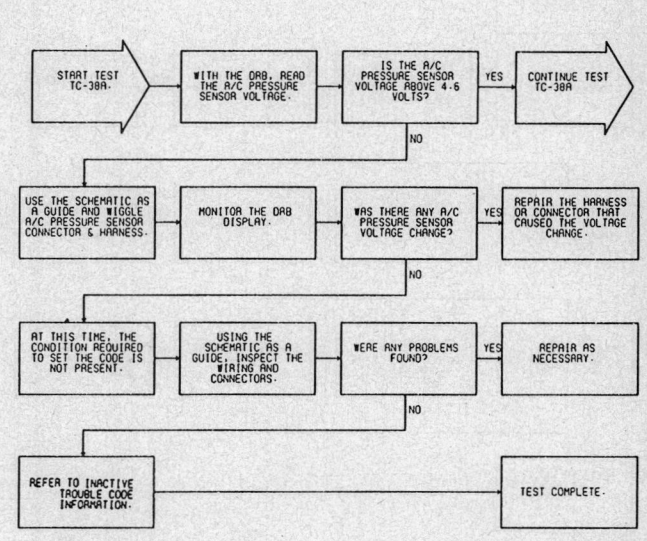

Fig. 60 Test TC-38A: Repairing A/C Pressure Sensor Volts Too High (Part 1 of 2). Cirrus & Stratus

CHRYSLER–Fuel Injection

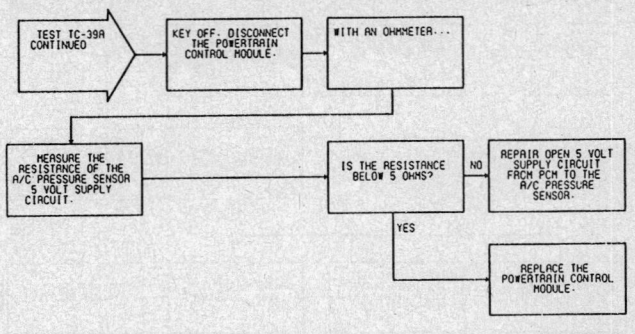

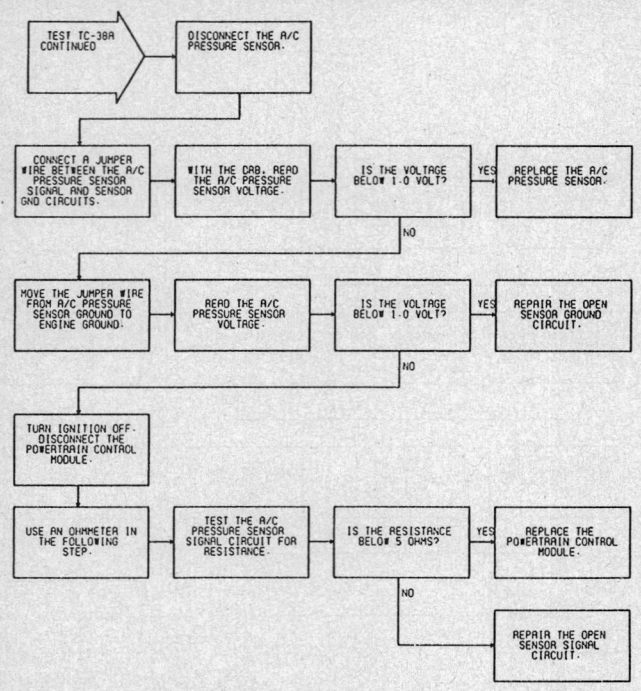

Fig. 60   Test TC-38A: Repairing A/C Pressure Sensor Volts Too High (Part 2 of 2). Cirrus & Stratus

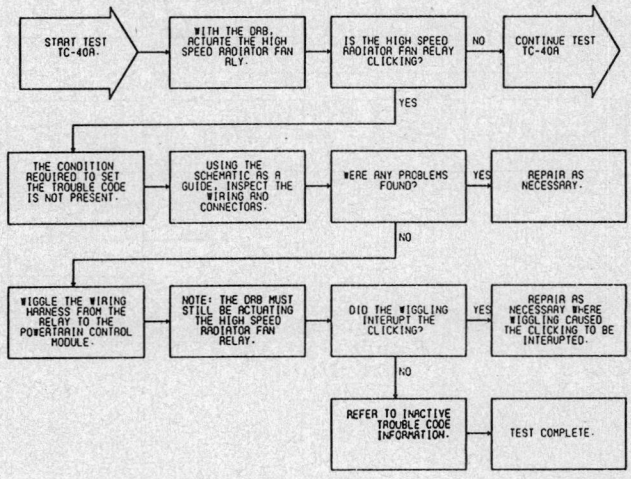

Fig. 61   Test TC-39A: Repairing No 5 Volts To A/C Pressure Sensor (Part 2 of 2). Cirrus & Stratus

Fig. 62   Test TC-40A: Repairing High Speed Fan Control Relay Circuit (Part 1 of 2)

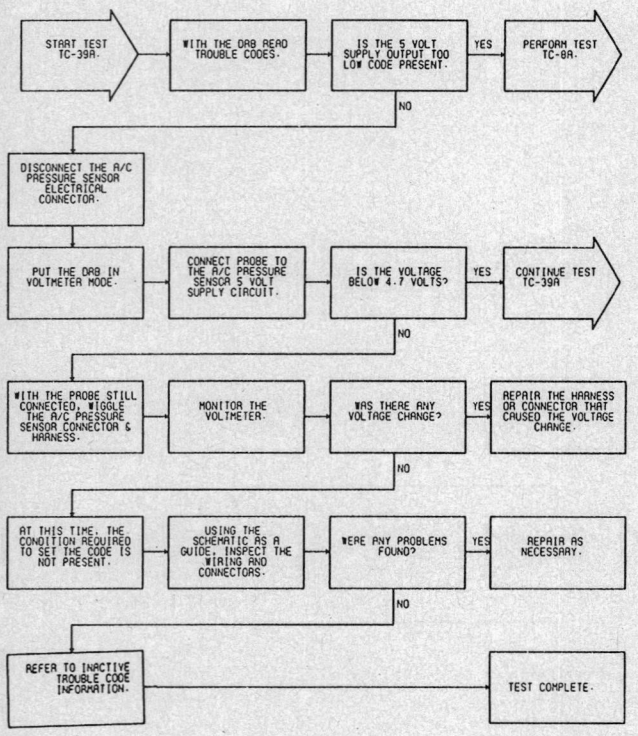

Fig. 61   Test TC-39A: Repairing No 5 Volts To A/C Pressure Sensor (Part 1 of 2). Cirrus & Stratus

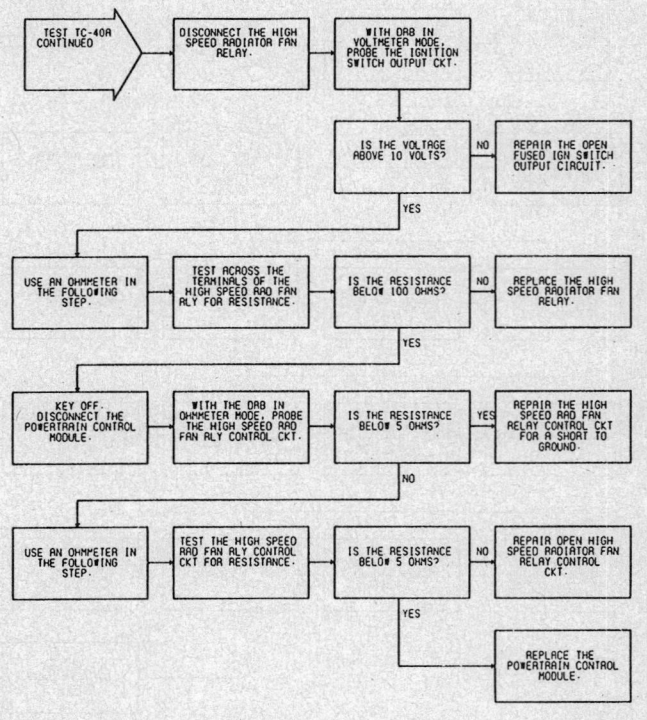

Fig. 62   Test TC-40A: Repairing High Speed Fan Control Relay Circuit (Part 2 of 2)

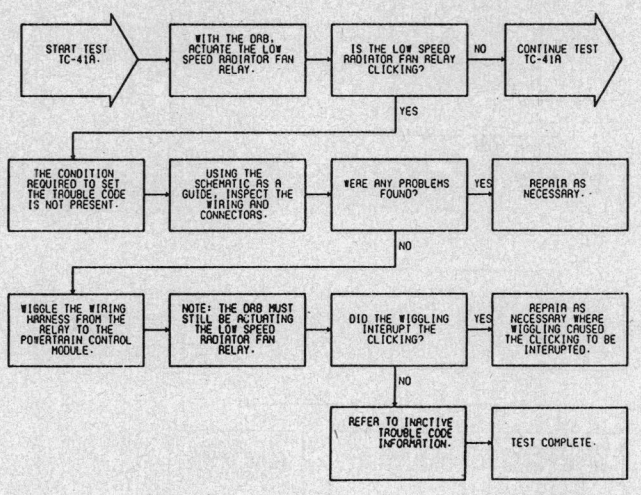

Fig. 63   Test TC-41A: Repairing Low Speed Fan Control Relay Circuit (Part 1 of 2)

CR1029505310010X

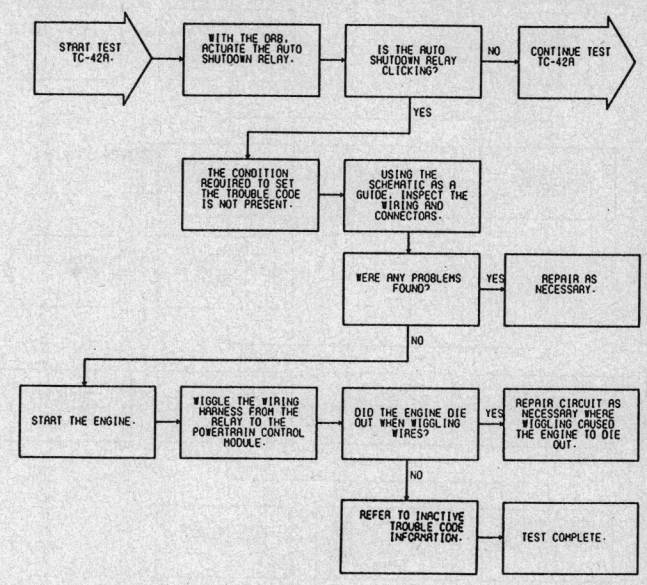

Fig. 64   Test TC-42A: Repairing Auto Shutdown Relay Control Circuit (Part 1 of 2)

CR1029505311010X

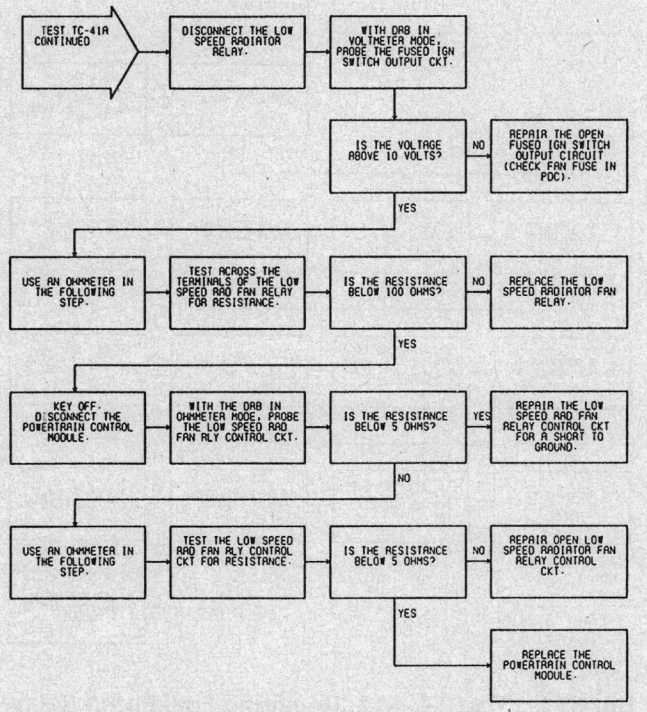

CR1029505310020X

Fig. 63   Test TC-41A: Repairing Low Speed Fan Control Relay Circuit (Part 2 of 2)

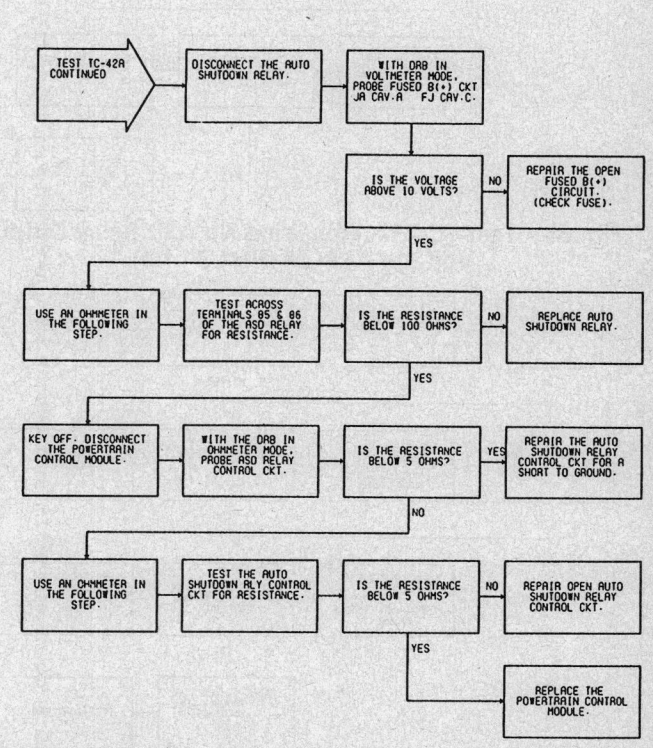

CR1029505311020X

Fig. 64   Test TC-42A: Repairing Auto Shutdown Relay Control Circuit (Part 2 of 2)

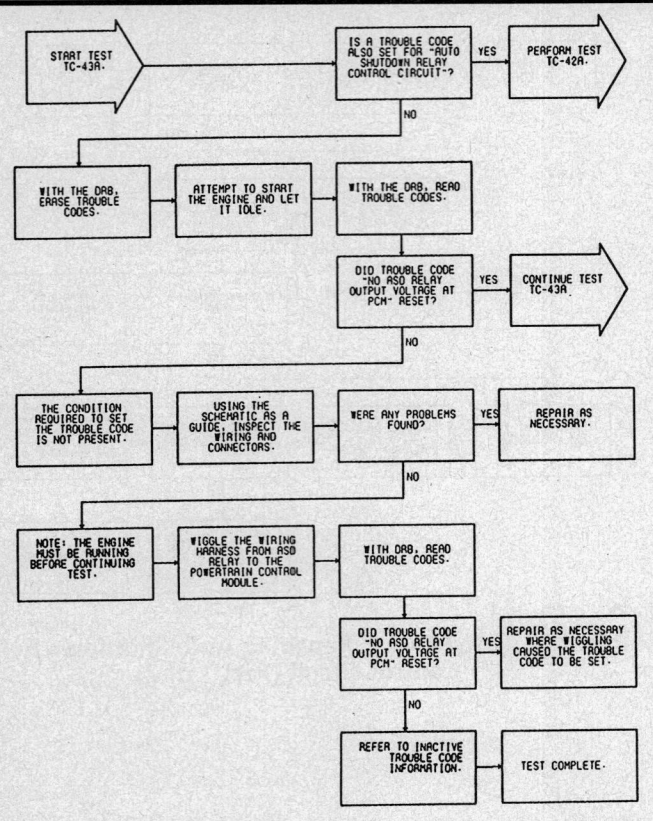

Fig. 65   Test TC-43A: Repairing No ASD Relay Output Voltage At PCM (Part 1 of 3)

Fig. 65   Test TC-43A: Repairing No ASD Relay Output Voltage At PCM (Part 2 of 3)

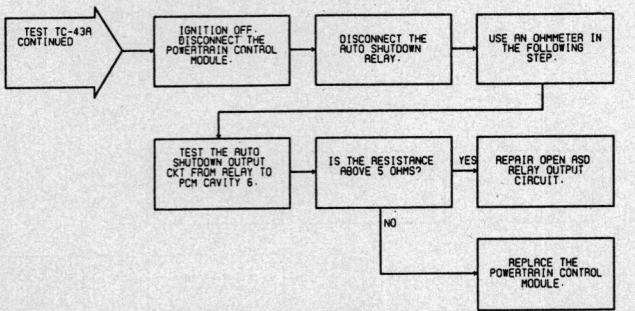

Fig. 65   Test TC-43A: Repairing No ASD Relay Output Voltage At PCM (Part 3 of 3)

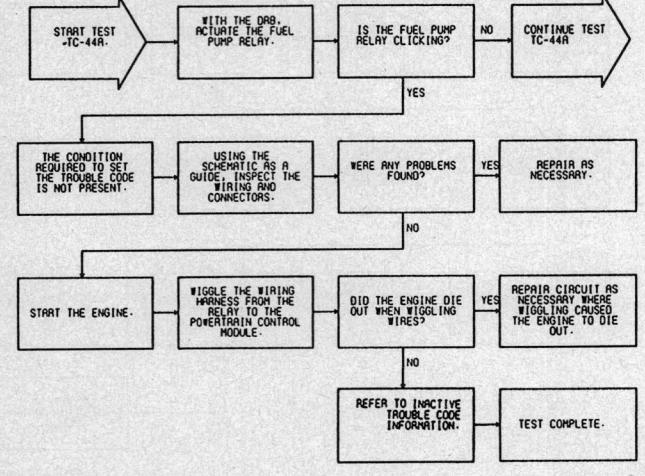

Fig. 65A   Test TC-44A: Repairing Fuel Pump Relay Control Circuit (Part 1 of 2)

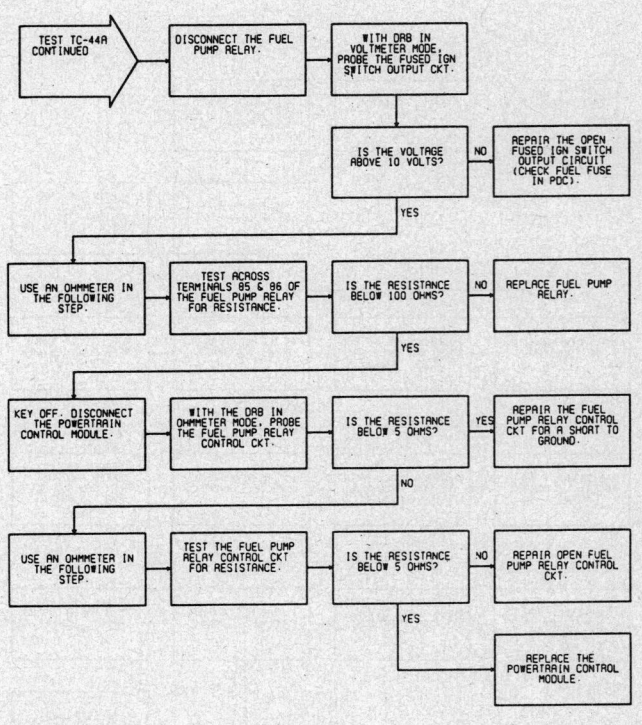

Fig. 65A   Test TC-44A: Repairing Fuel Pump Relay Control Circuit (Part 2 of 2)

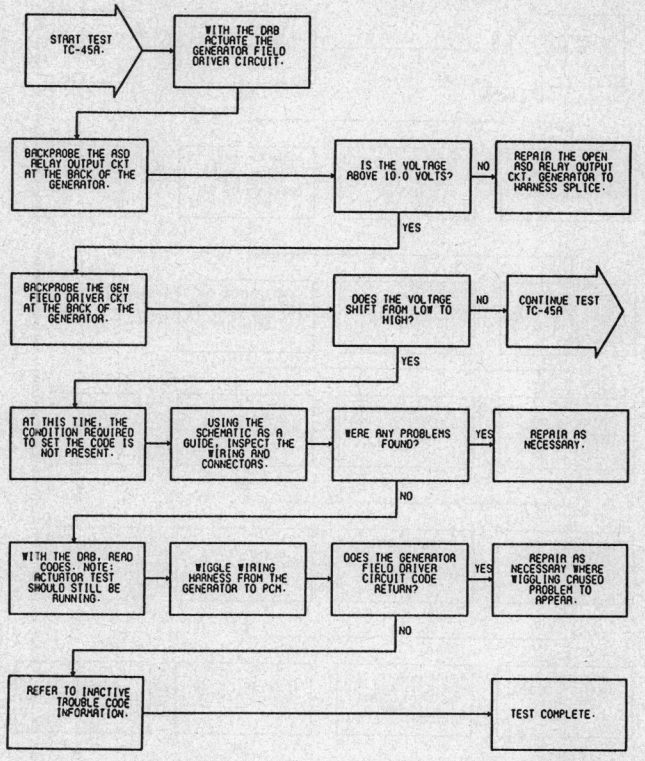

Fig. 66   Test TC-45A: Repairing Generator Field Not Switching Properly (Part 1 of 2)

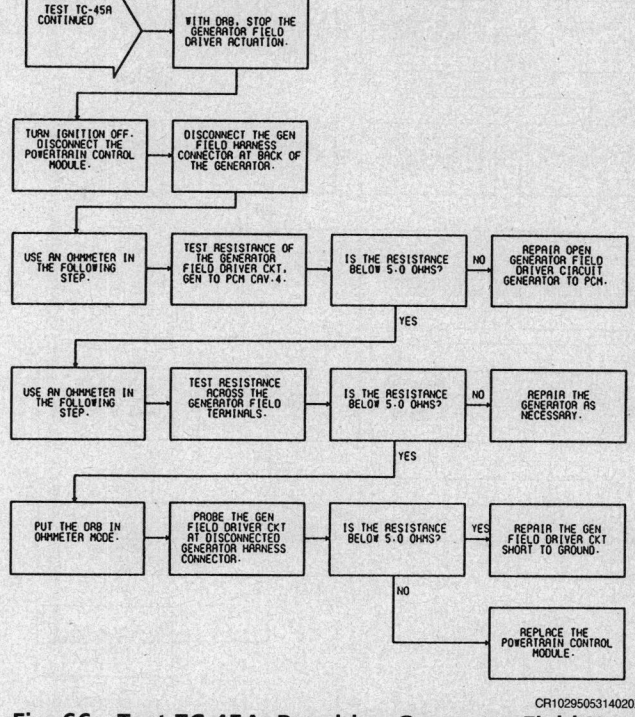

Fig. 66   Test TC-45A: Repairing Generator Field Not Switching Properly (Part 2 of 2)

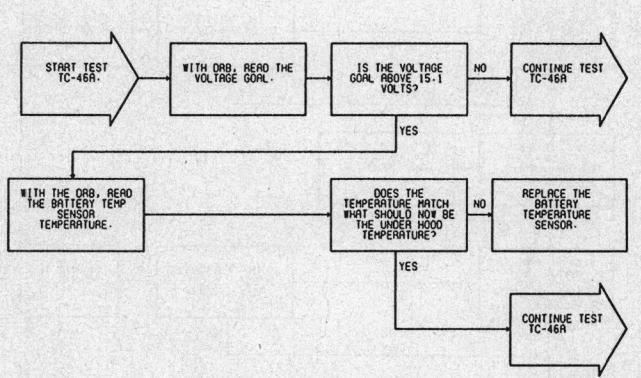

Fig. 67   Test TC-46A: Repairing Charging System Voltage Too Low (Part 1 of 2)

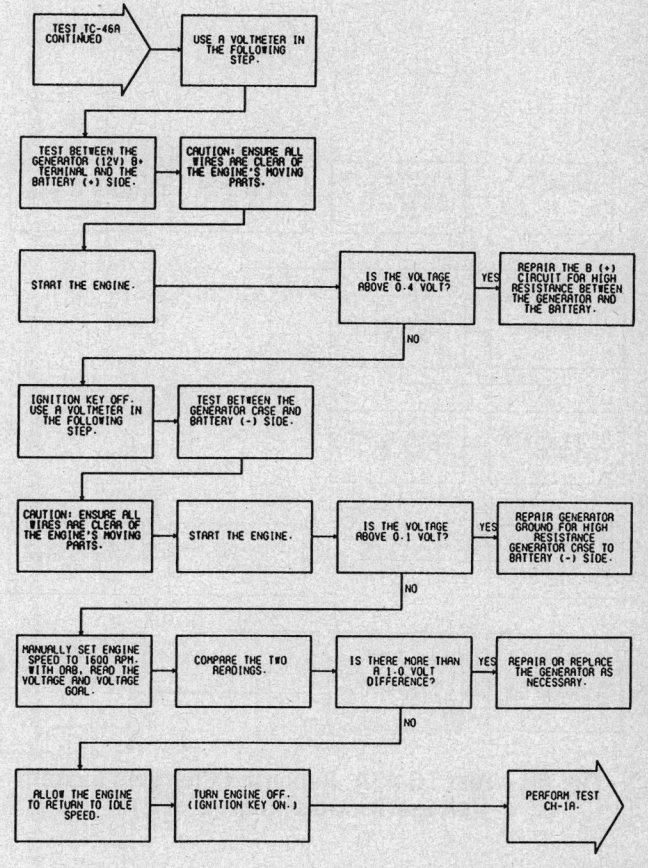

Fig. 67   Test TC-46A: Repairing Charging System Voltage Too Low (Part 2 of 2)

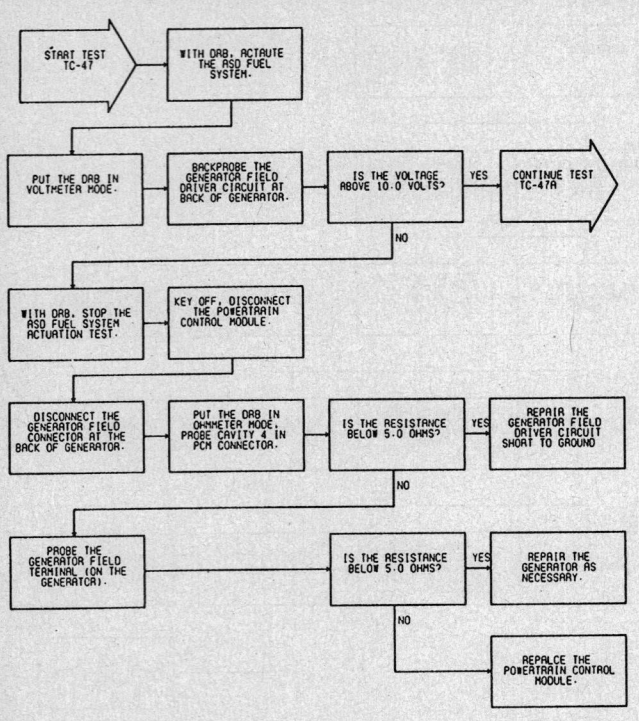

Fig. 68   Test TC-47A: Repairing Charging System Voltage Too High (Part 1 of 2)

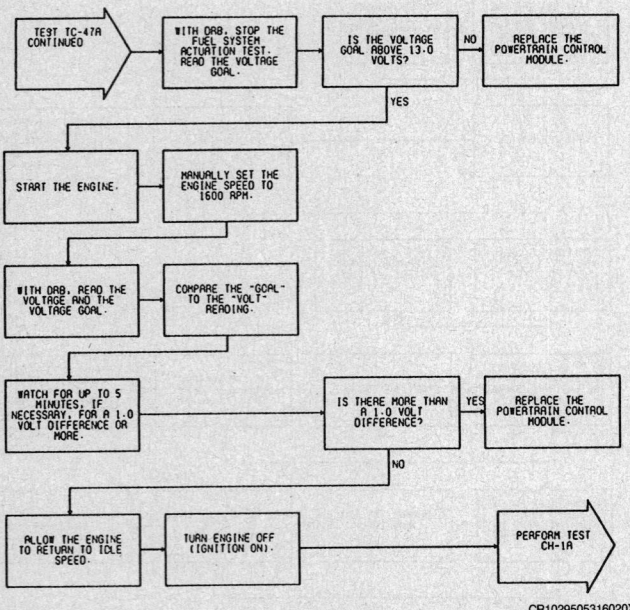

Fig. 68   Test TC-47A: Repairing Charging System Voltage Too High (Part 2 of 2)

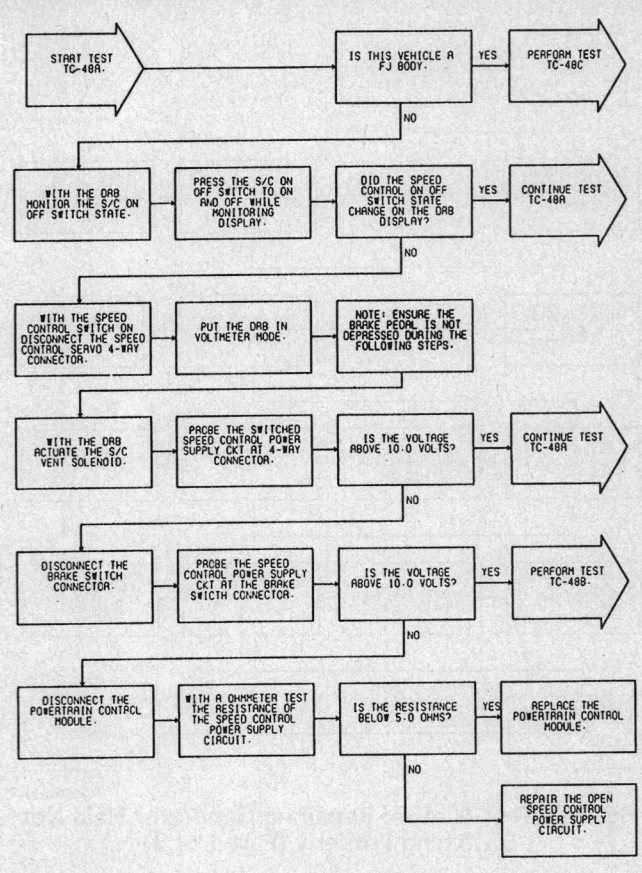

Fig. 69   Test TC-48A: Repairing Speed Control Solenoid Circuits Or Speed Control Power Relay Circuit (Part 1 of 3)

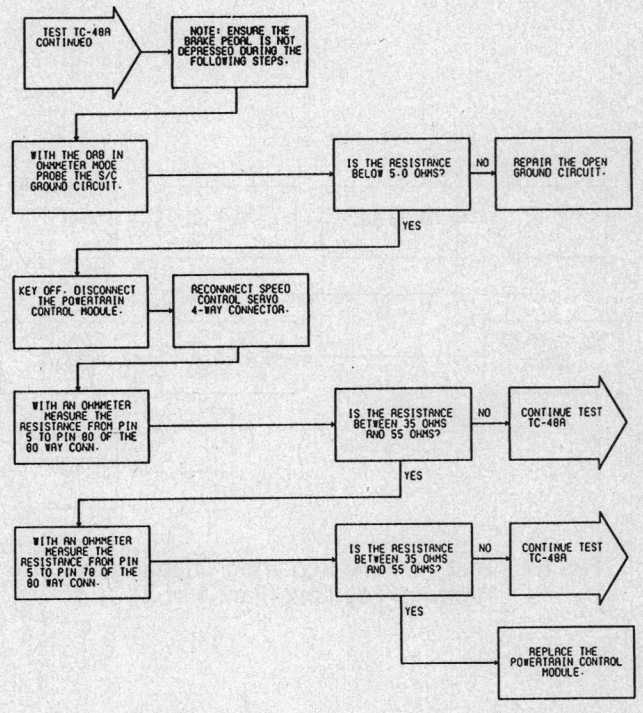

Fig. 69   Test TC-48A: Repairing Speed Control Solenoid Circuits Or Speed Control Power Relay Circuit (Part 2 of 3)

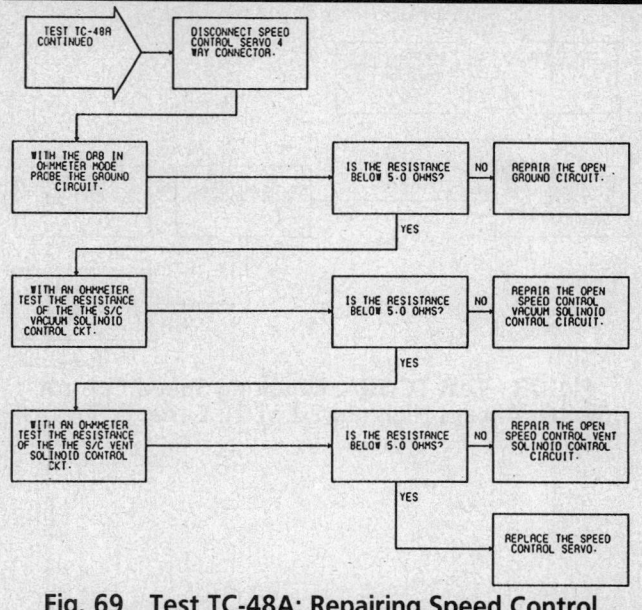

Fig. 69   Test TC-48A: Repairing Speed Control Solenoid Circuits Or Speed Control Power Relay Circuit (Part 3 of 3)

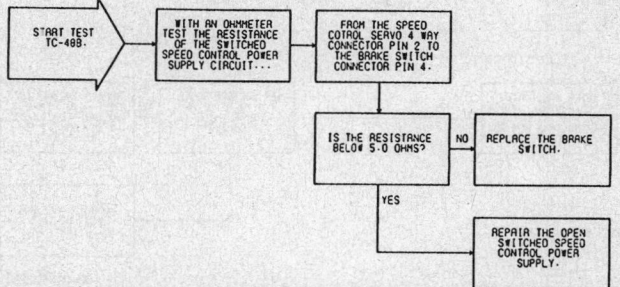

Fig. 70   Test TC-48B: Repairing Speed Control Solenoid Circuits Or Speed Control Power Relay Circuit

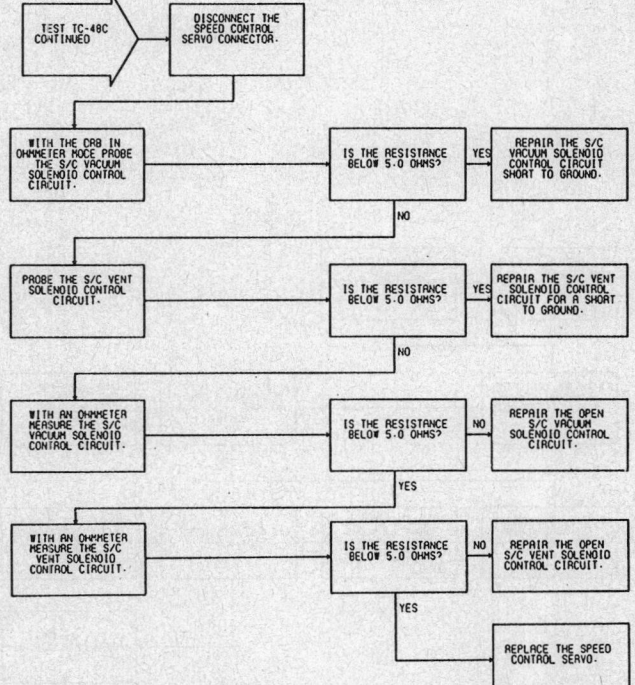

Fig. 71   Test TC-48C: Repairing Speed Control Solenoid Circuits Or Speed Control Power Relay Circuit (Part 2 of 2)

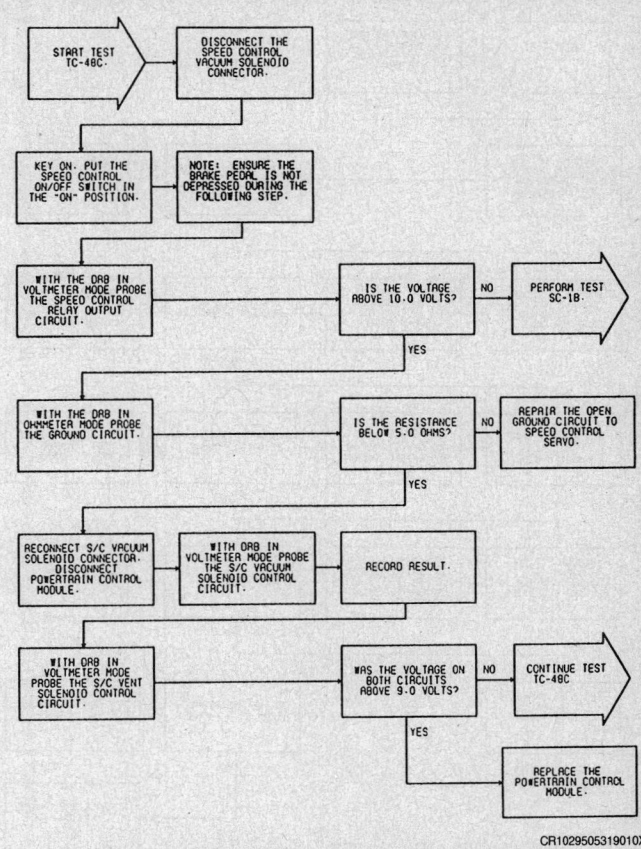

CR1029505319010X

Fig. 71   Test TC-48C: Repairing Speed Control Solenoid Circuits Or Speed Control Power Relay Circuit (Part 1 of 2)

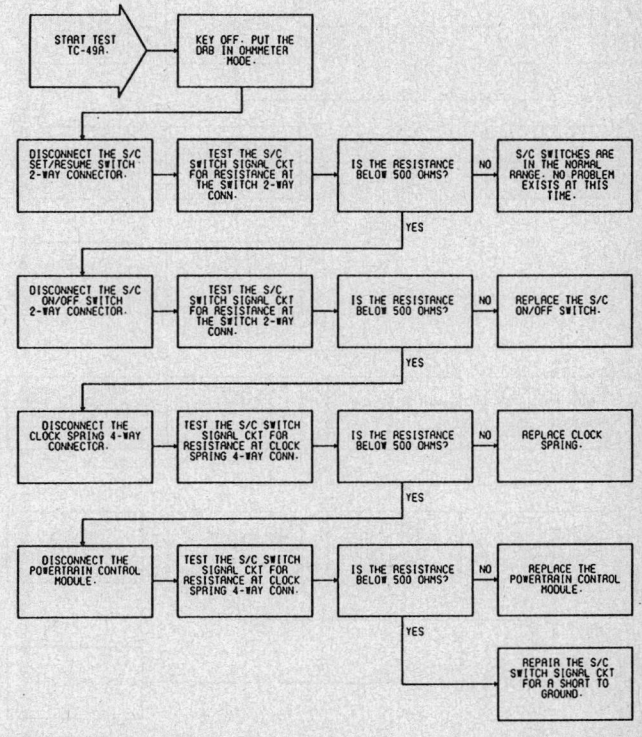

CR1029505320000X

Fig. 72   Test TC-49A: Repairing Speed Control Switch Always Low. Cirrus & Stratus

CHRYSLER–Fuel Injection

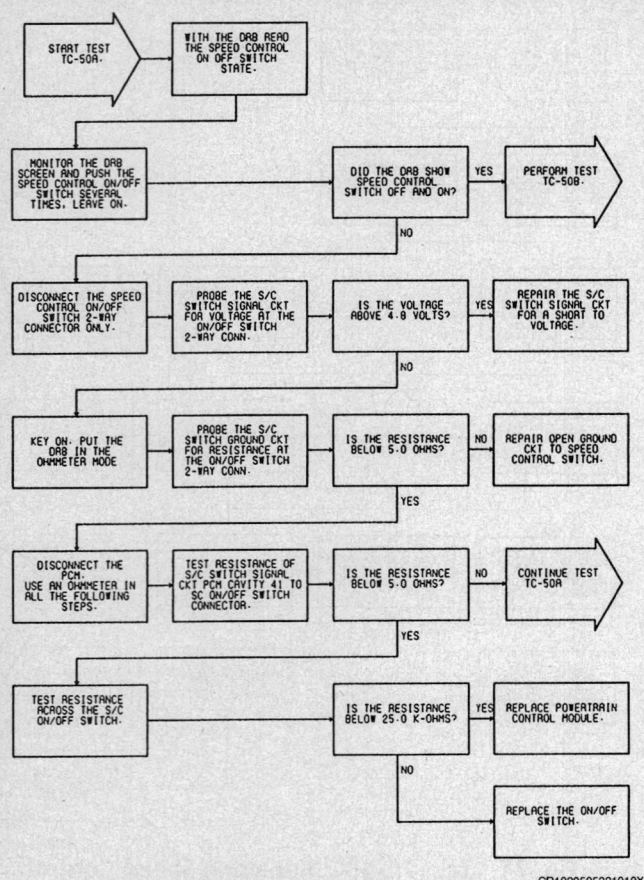

Fig. 73   Test TC-50A: Repairing Speed Control Switch Always High (Part 1 of 2). Cirrus & Stratus

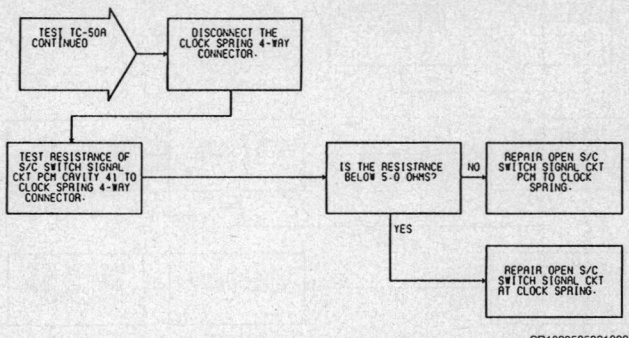

Fig. 73   Test TC-50A: Repairing Speed Control Switch Always High (Part 2 of 2). Cirrus & Stratus

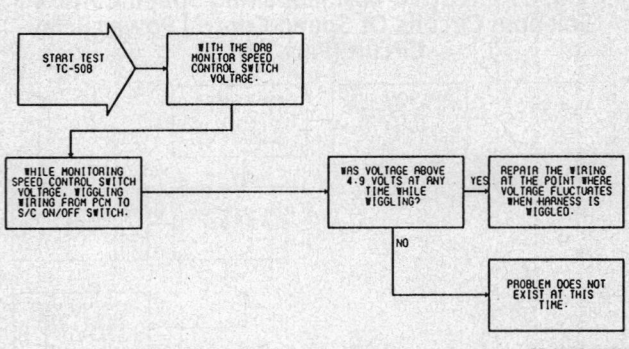

Fig. 74   Test TC-50B: Repairing Speed Control Switch Always High. Cirrus & Stratus

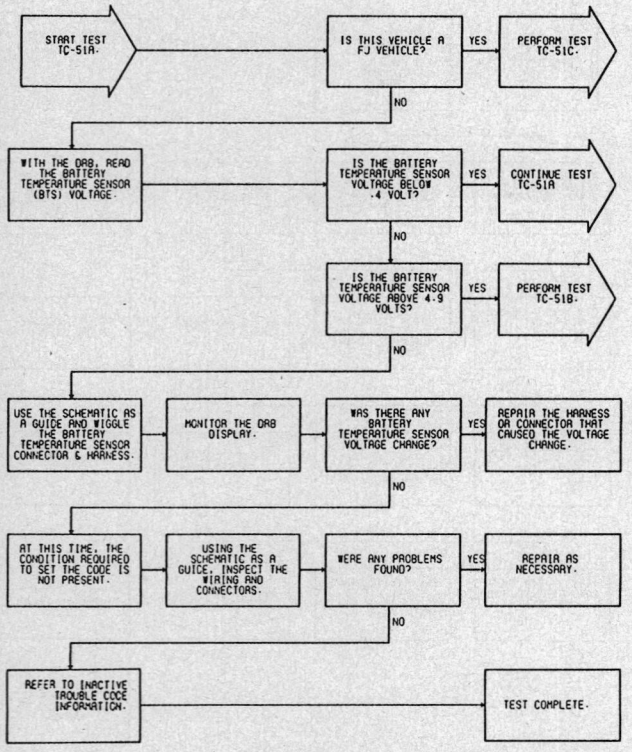

Fig. 75   Test TC-51A: Repairing Battery Temp Sensor Volts Out Of Limit (Part 1 of 2)

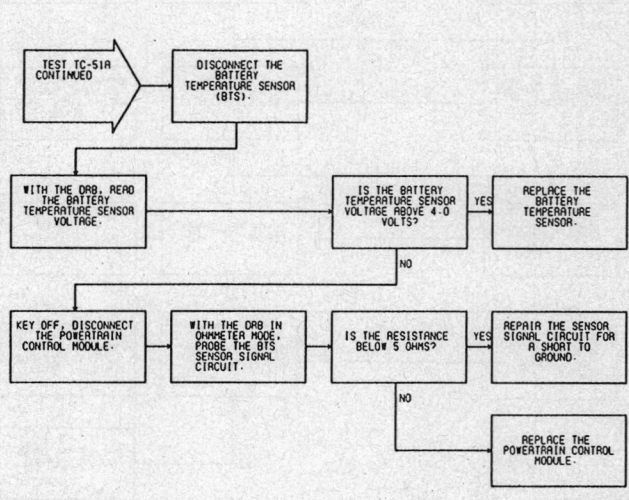

Fig. 75   Test TC-51A: Repairing Battery Temp Sensor Volts Out Of Limit (Part 2 of 2)

MULTI-POINT FUEL INJECTION (1995 AVENGER, CIRRUS, SEBRING & STRATUS w/2.5L/V6-152)

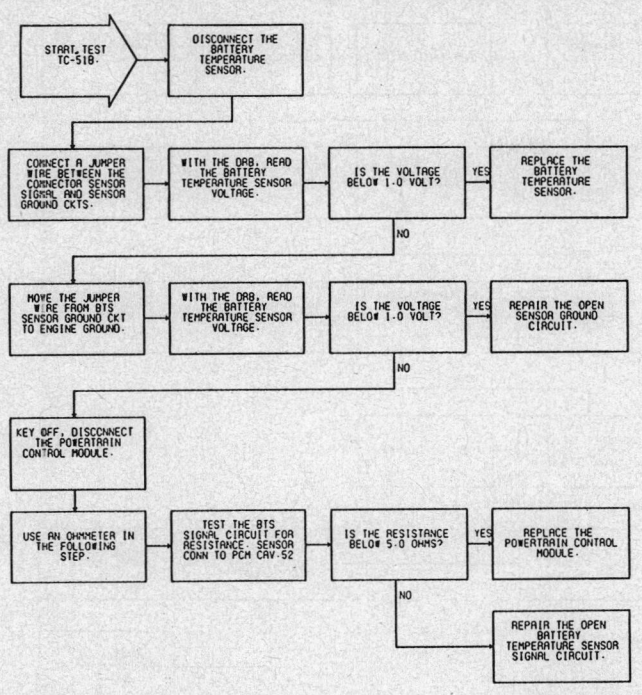

Fig. 76   Test TC-51B: Repairing Battery Temp Sensor
Volts Out Of Limit

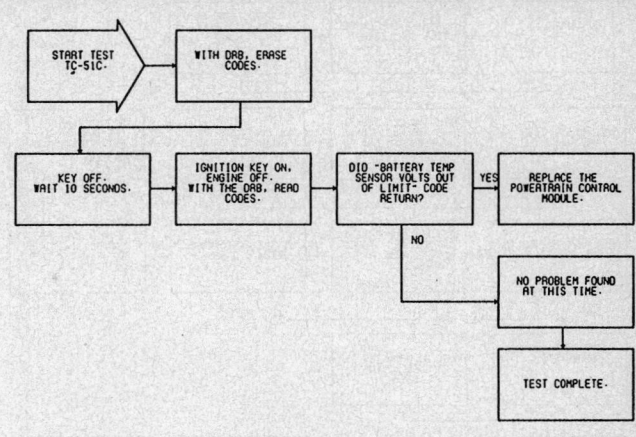

Fig. 77   Test TC-51C: Repairing Battery Temp Sensor
Volts Out Of Limit. Avenger & Sebring

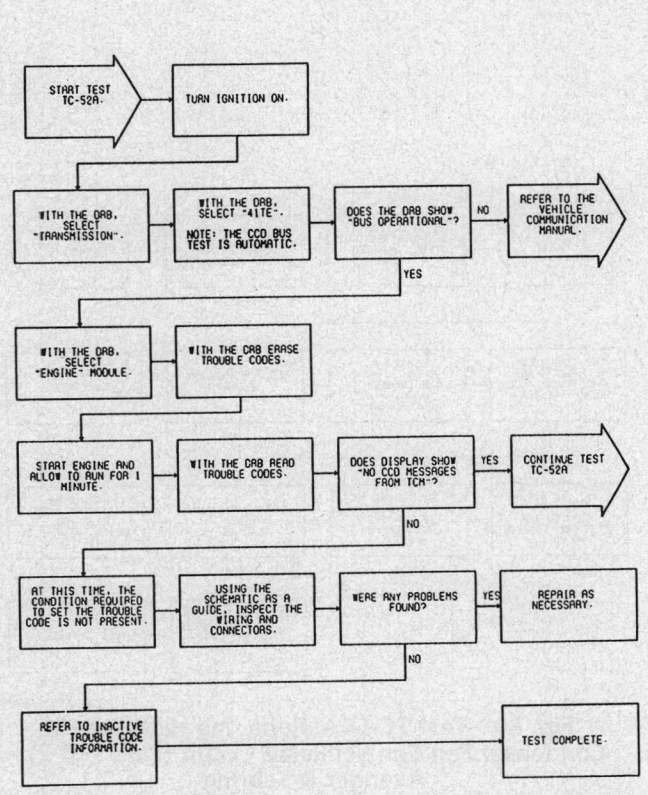

Fig. 78   Test TC-52A: Repairing No CCD Messages
From TCM (Part 1 of 4)

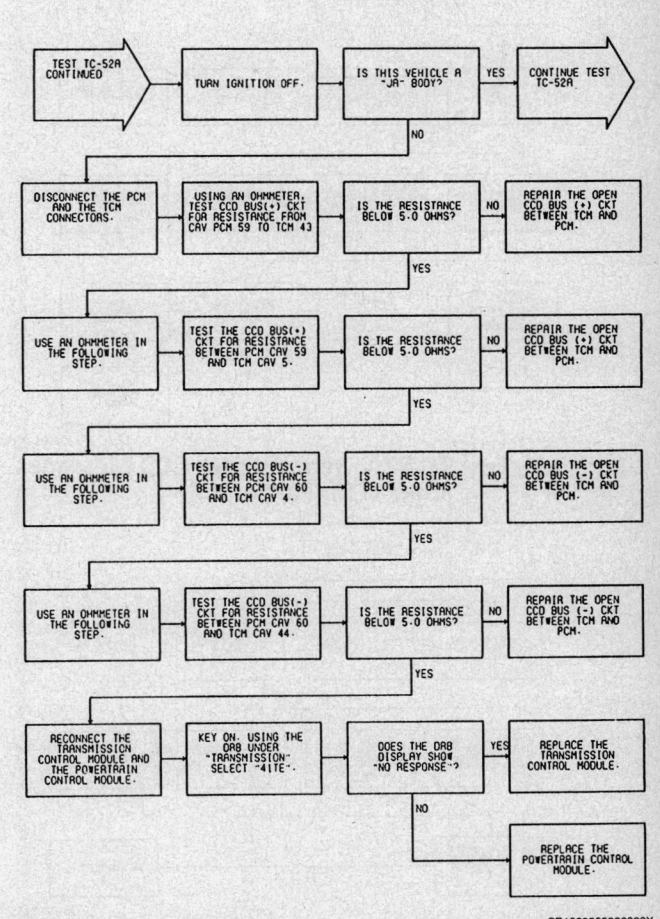

Fig. 78   Test TC-52A: Repairing No CCD Messages
From TCM (Part 2 of 4)

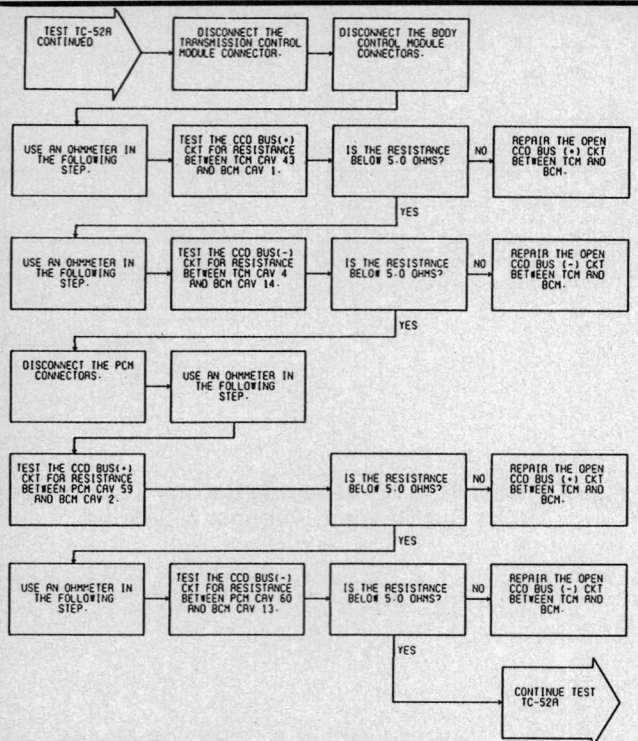

Fig. 78   Test TC-52A: Repairing No CCD Messages From TCM (Part 3 of 4)

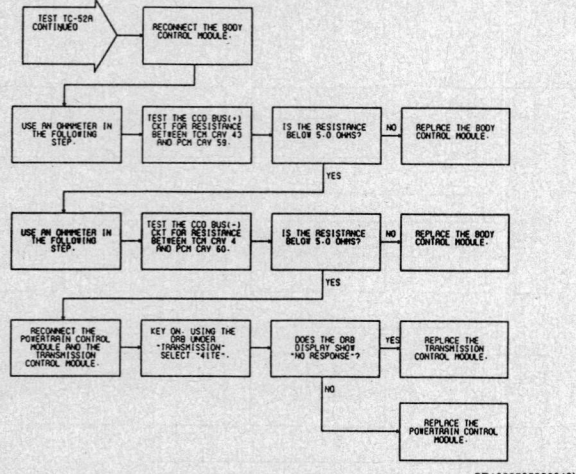

Fig. 78   Test TC-52A: Repairing No CCD Messages From TCM (Part 4 of 4)

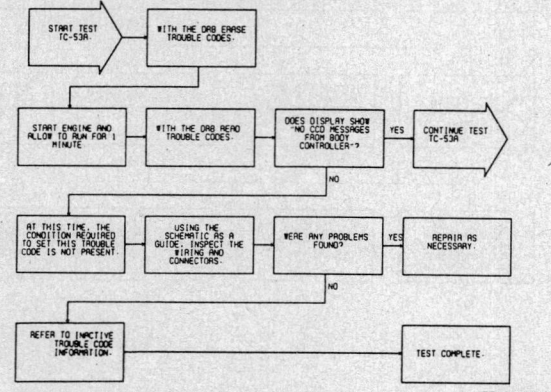

Fig. 79   Test TC-53A: Repairing No CCD Message From Body Control Module (Part 1 of 2). Cirrus & Stratus

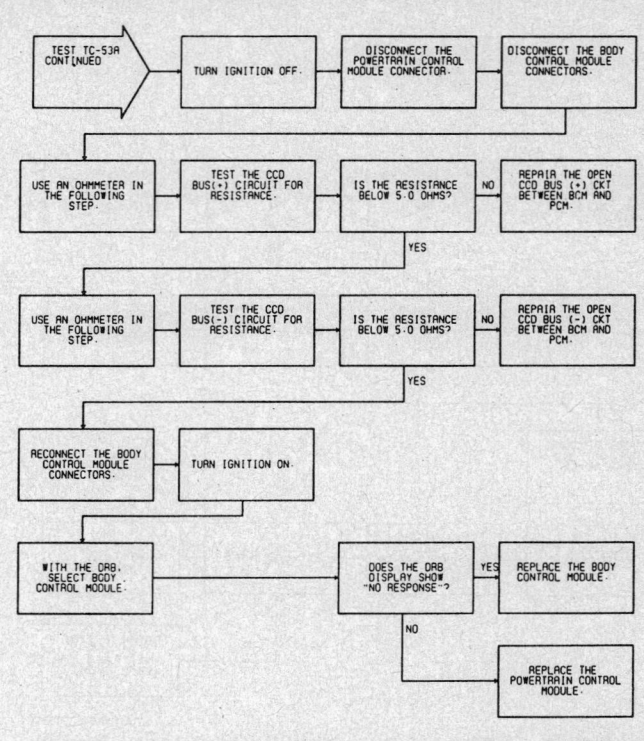

Fig. 79   Test TC-53A: Repairing No CCD Message From Body Control Module (Part 2 of 2). Cirrus & Stratus

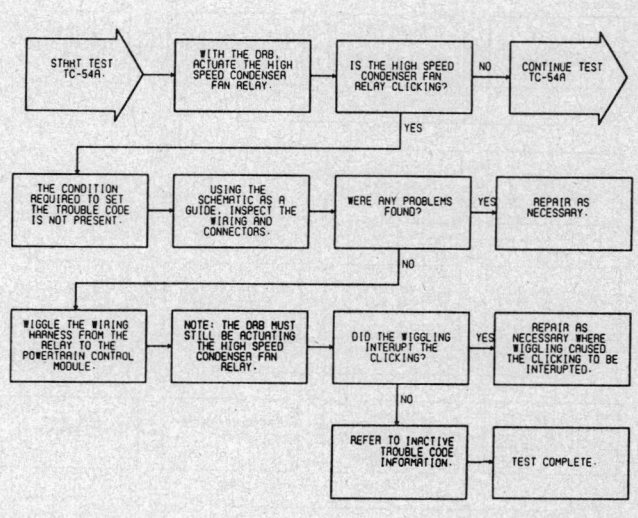

Fig. 80   Test TC-54A: Repairing High Speed Condenser Fan Control Relay Circuit (Part 1 of 2). Avenger & Sebring

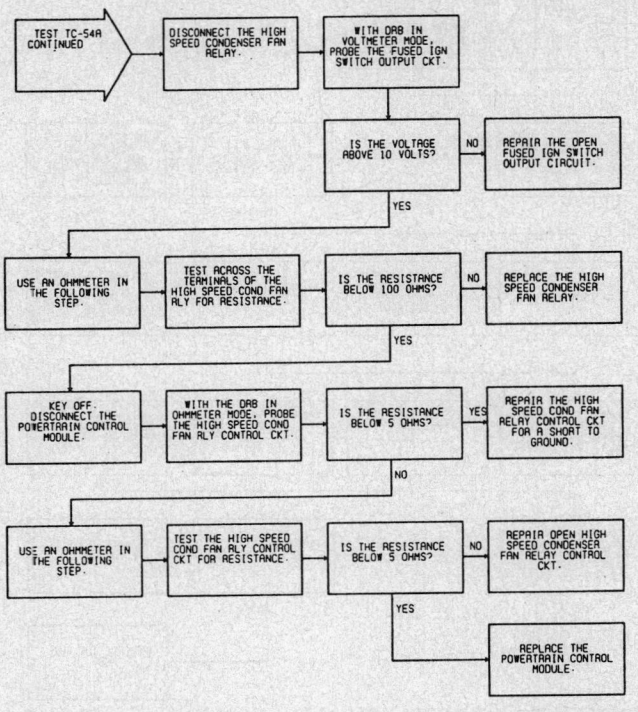

Fig. 80   Test TC-54A: Repairing High Speed Condenser Fan Control Relay Circuit (Part 2 of 2). Avenger & Sebring

Select the symptom that most accurately describes the vehicle's driveability problem and then perform the test routine that pertains to this symptom. Perform each routine test in sequence until the problem is found.

SYMPTOM	DIAGNOSTIC TEST ROUTINE
HARD START	NTC-2A, 3A, 4A, 5A, 6A, 7A, 9A, 12A, 15A, 17A, 18A
START AND STALL	NTC-2A, 3A, 4A, 5A, 6A, 9A, 12A, 17A, 18A
HESITATION/SAG/STUMBLE	NO TROUBLE CODE COMPLETE TEST (STEP 1)
SURGE	NTC-2A, 3A, 4A, 5A, 6A, 7A, 9A, 12A, 13A, 17A, 18A
LACK OF POWER/SLUGGISH	NTC-2A, 3A, 4A, 5A, 6A, 7A, 9A, 12A, 14A, 17A, 18A
SPARK KNOCK/DETONATION	NTC-2A, 3A, 4A, 5A, 6A, 7A, 9A, 10A, 12A, 13A, 17A, 18A
CUTS OUT/MISSES	NTC-2A, 3A, 7A, 10A, 12A, 14A, 17A, 18A
BACKFIRE/POPBACK	NTC-2A, 3A, 6A, 7A, 12A, 14A, 17A, 18A
RUNS ROUGH/UNSTABLE/ERRATIC IDLE	NO TROUBLE CODE COMPLETE TEST (STEP 1)
POOR FUEL ECONOMY	NO TROUBLE CODE COMPLETE TEST (STEP 1)

CR1029505329020X

Fig. 81   Test NTC-1A: No Trouble Code Test Menu (Part 2 of 2)

Perform **TEST TC-1A** Before Proceeding

First, check all Technical Service Bulletins and Hotline Newsletters that relate to this driveability problem. Perform corrective actions if indicated; otherwise continue.

1. **NO TROUBLE CODE COMPLETE TEST** (non-monitored & monitored circuits)

Perform **TESTS NTC-2A** through **NTC-18A** in sequence until the driveability problem is found.

NO TROUBLE CODE MENU

CHECKING SECONDARY IGNITION AND TIMING	NTC-2A
CHECKING THE FUEL PRESSURE	NTC-3A
CHECKING COOLANT SENSOR CALIBRATION	NTC-4A
CHECKING THROTTLE POSITION SENSOR CALIBRATION	NTC-5A
CHECKING MAP SENSOR CALIBRATION	NTC-6A
CHECKING FOR OXYGEN SENSOR SWITCHING	NTC-7A
CHECKING THE OXYGEN SENSOR HEATER	NTC-8A
CHECKING THE IDLE AIR CONTROL MOTOR	NTC-9A
CHECKING SOLENOID OPERATION	NTC-10A
CHECKING THE PARK/NEUTRAL POSITION SWITCH	NTC-11A
CHECKING THE PCM POWER AND GROUND CIRCUITS	NTC-12A
CHECKING THE EVAPORATIVE EMISSION SYSTEM	NTC-13A
CHECKING THE EGR SYSTEM	NTC-14A
CHECKING THE ENGINE VACUUM	NTC-15A
CHECKING THE INTAKE AIR TEMPERATURE SENSOR	NTC-16A
CHECKING THE MINIMUM IDLE AIR FLOW	NTC-17A
CHECKING THE ENGINE MECHANICAL SYSTEMS	NTC-18A

2. **NO TROUBLE CODE QUICK INDIVIDUAL TEST** (individual test only)

If you suspect any of the above items to be the cause of the vehicle's driveability problem, perform the associated test(s) individually. Return to No Trouble Code Menu if driveability problem still exists, or perform No Trouble Code Complete Test.

3. **NO TROUBLE CODE QUICK SYMPTOM TEST** (symptom test only)

Symptom checks cannot be used properly unless the driveability problem characteristic actually happens while the vehicle is being tested.

CR1029505329010X

Fig. 81   Test NTC-1A: No Trouble Code Test Menu (Part 1 of 2)

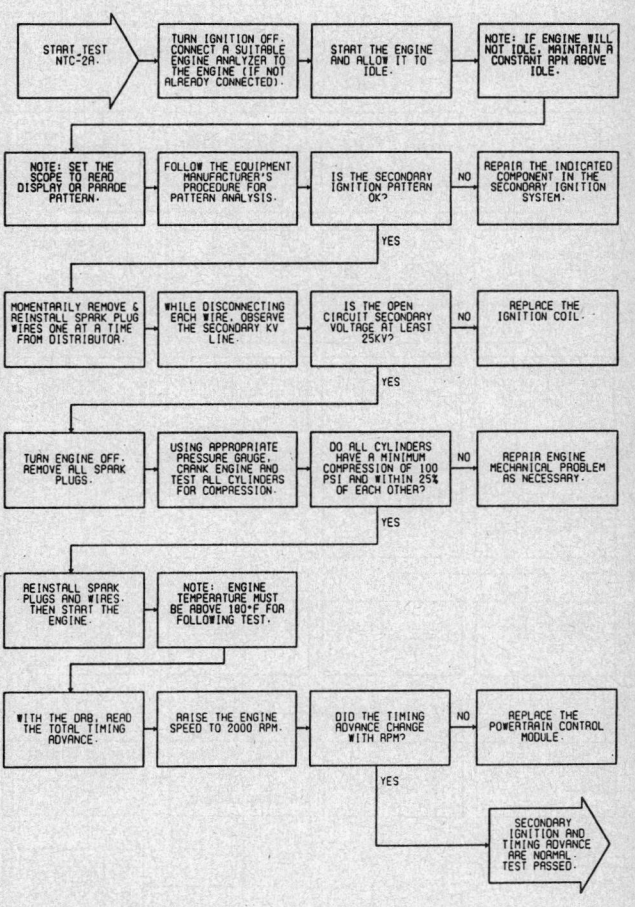

CR1029505330000X

Fig. 82   Test NTC-2A: Checking Secondary Ignition & Timing

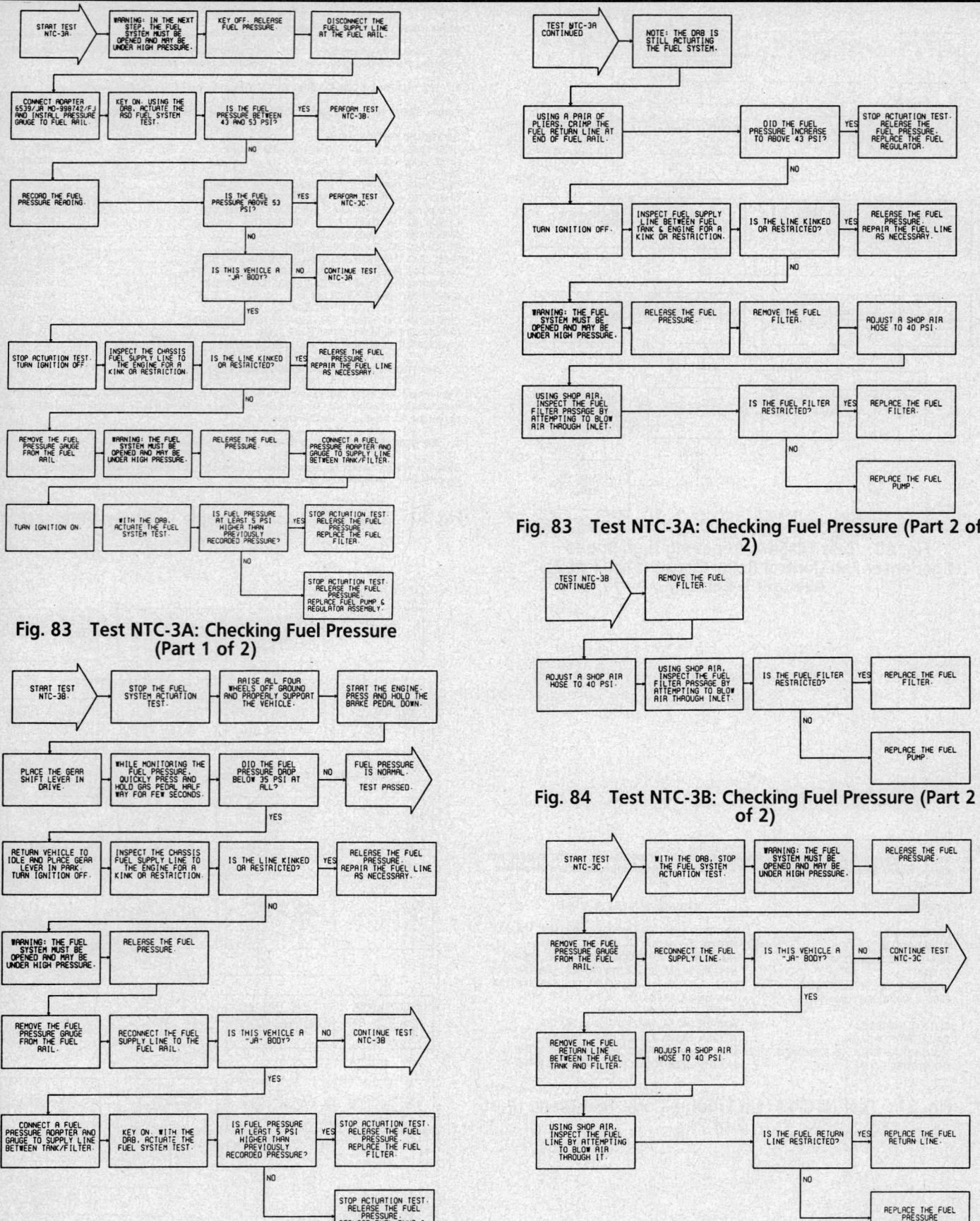

Fig. 83 Test NTC-3A: Checking Fuel Pressure (Part 1 of 2)

Fig. 83 Test NTC-3A: Checking Fuel Pressure (Part 2 of 2)

Fig. 84 Test NTC-3B: Checking Fuel Pressure (Part 2 of 2)

Fig. 84 Test NTC-3B: Checking Fuel Pressure (Part 1 of 2)

Fig. 85 Test NTC-3C: Checking Fuel Pressure (Part 1 of 2)

CR1029505333010X

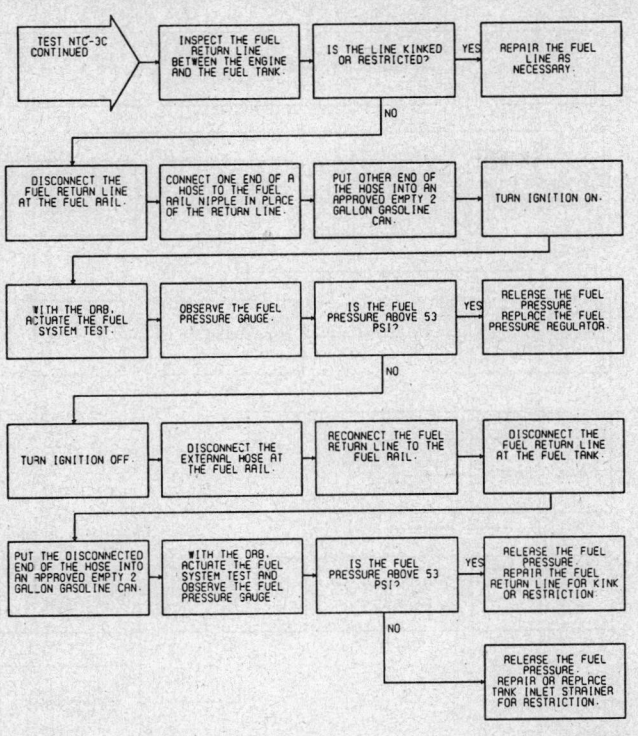

Fig. 85   Test NTC-3C: Checking Fuel Pressure (Part 2 of 2)

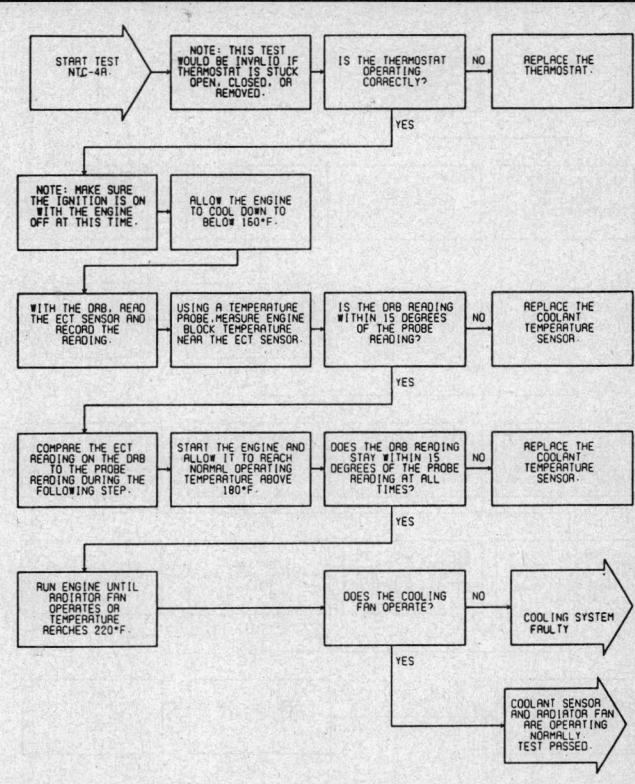

Fig. 86   Test NTC-4A: Checking Coolant Sensor Calibration & Radiator Fan Operation

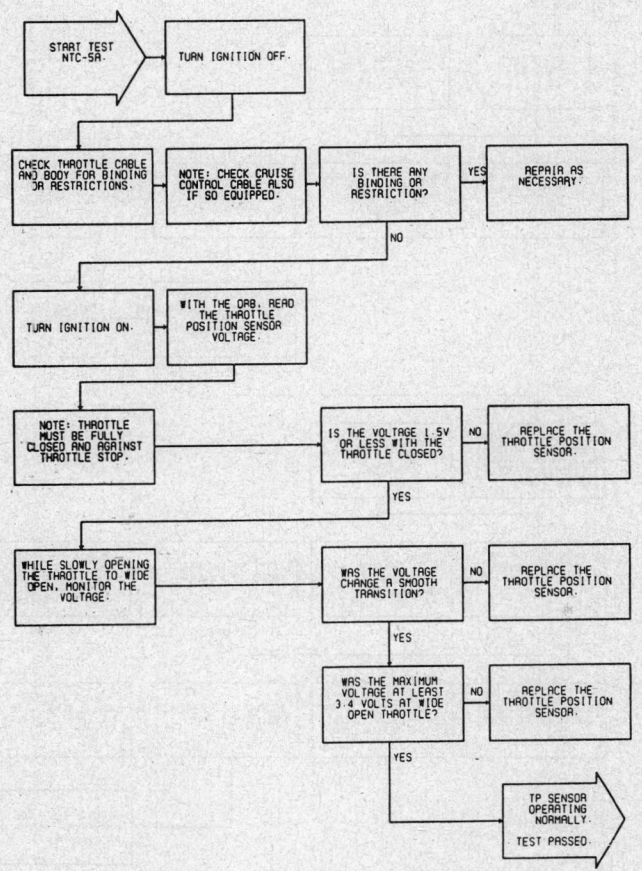

Fig. 87   Test NTC-5A: Checking Throttle Position Sensor Calibration

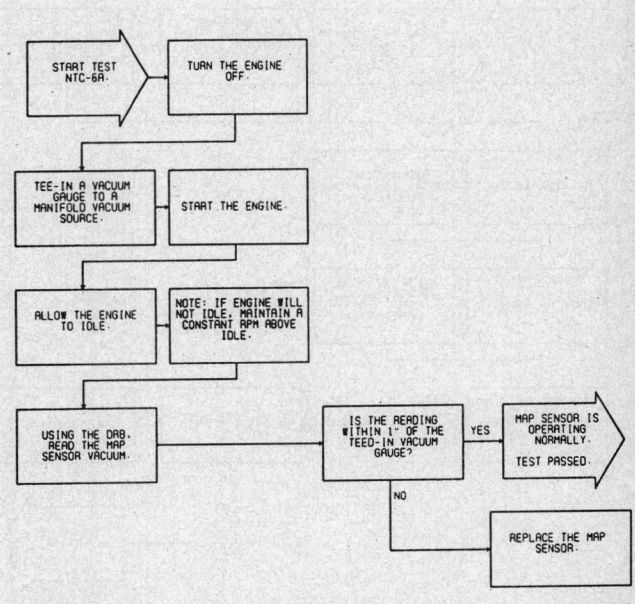

Fig. 88   Test NTC-6A: Checking MAP Sensor Calibration

MULTI-POINT FUEL INJECTION (1995 AVENGER, CIRRUS, SEBRING & STRATUS w/2.5L/V6-152)

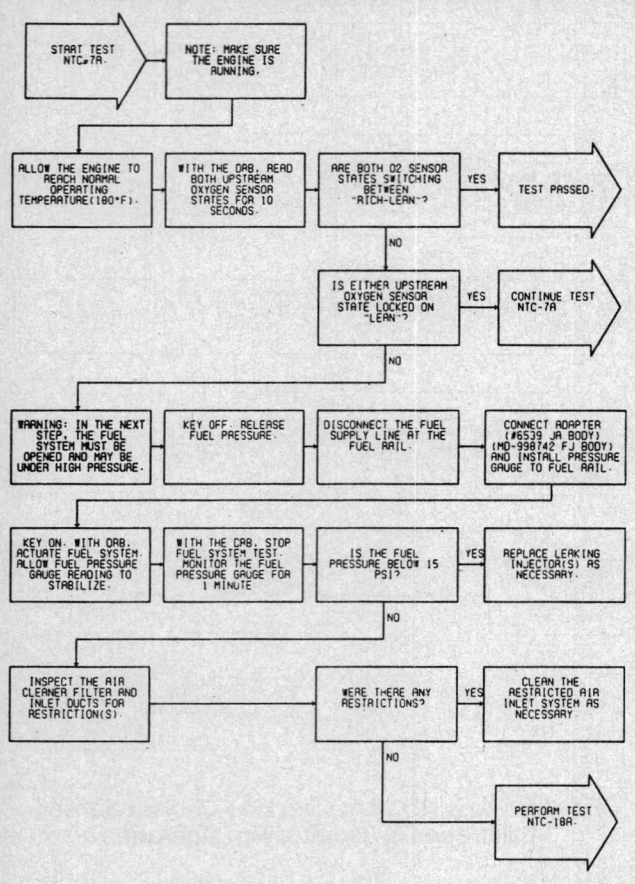

Fig. 89   Test NTC-7A: Checking For Oxygen Sensor Switching (Part 1 of 3)

CR1029505337010X

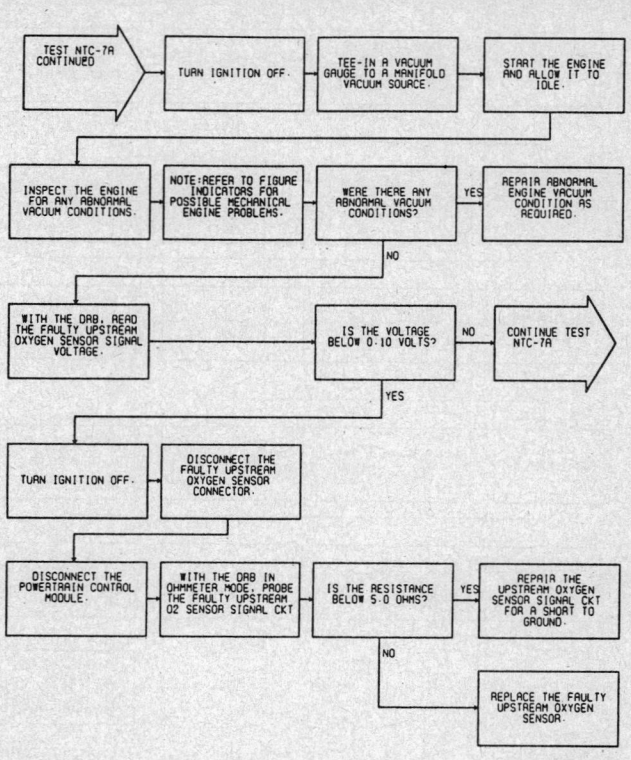

CR1029505337020X

Fig. 89   Test NTC-7A: Checking For Oxygen Sensor Switching (Part 2 of 3)

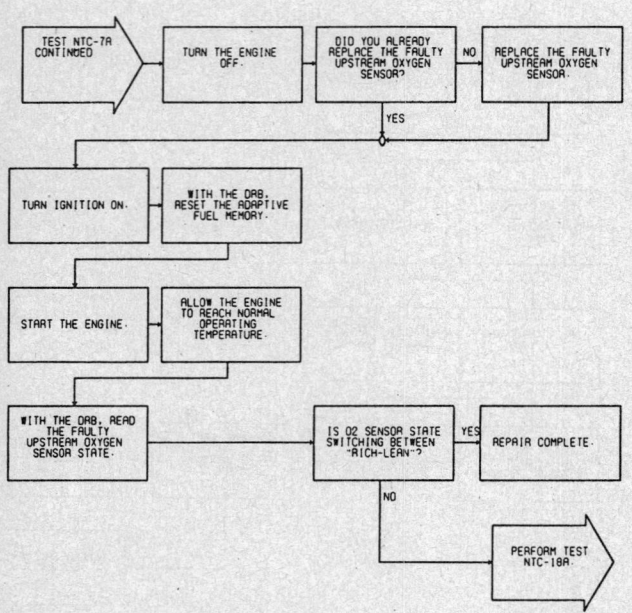

Fig. 89   Test NTC-7A: Checking For Oxygen Sensor Switching (Part 3 of 3)

CR1029505337030X

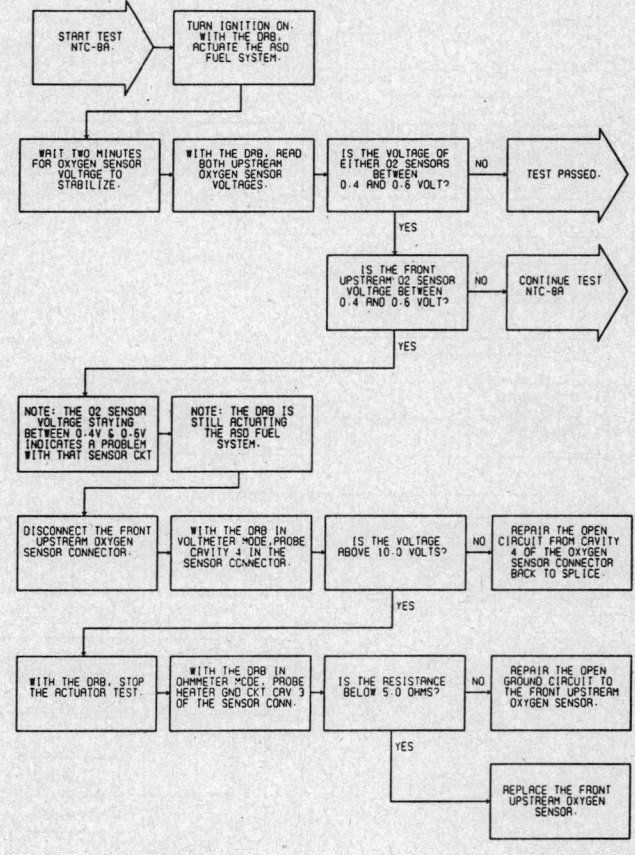

CR1029505339010X

Fig. 90   Test NTC-8A: Checking Oxygen Sensor Heater (Part 1 of 2)

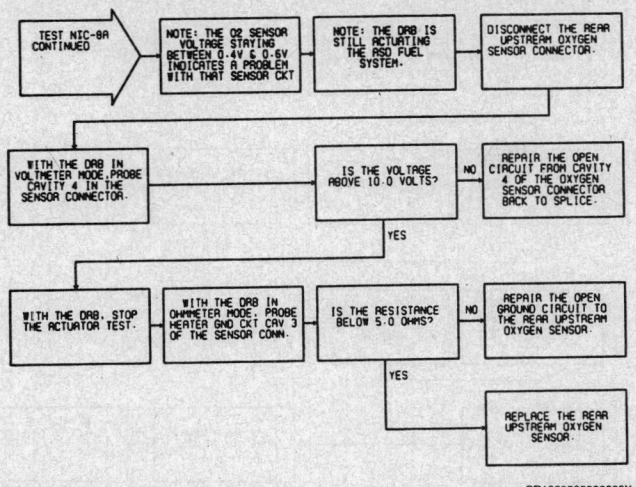

Fig. 90 Test NTC-8A: Checking Oxygen Sensor Heater (Part 2 of 2)

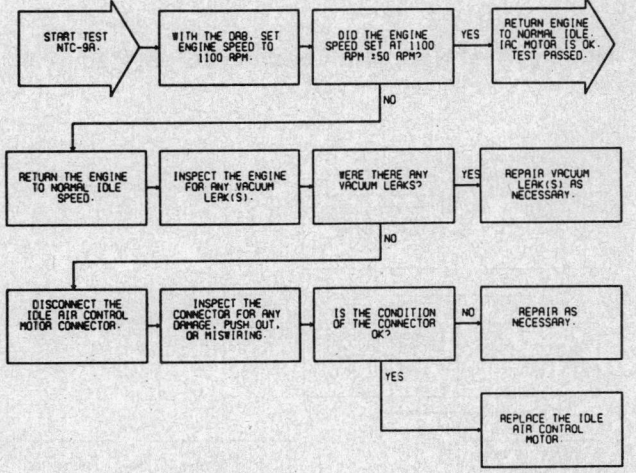

Fig. 91 Test NTC-9A: Checking Idle Air Conditioning Control Motor

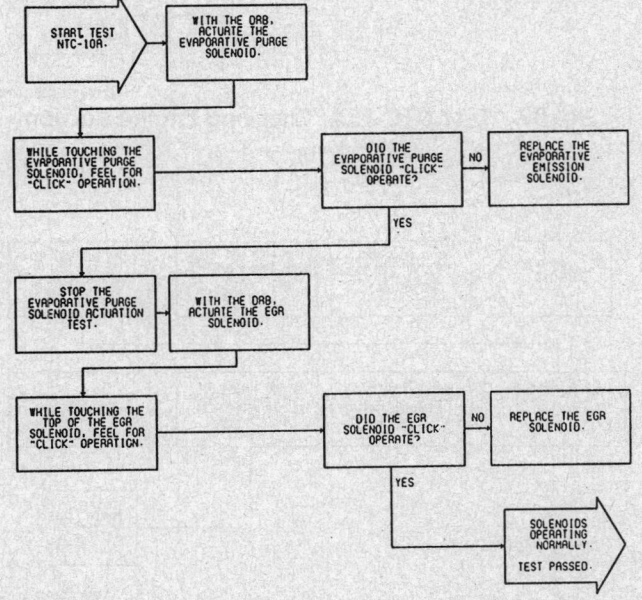

Fig. 92 Test NTC-10A: Checking Solenoid Operation

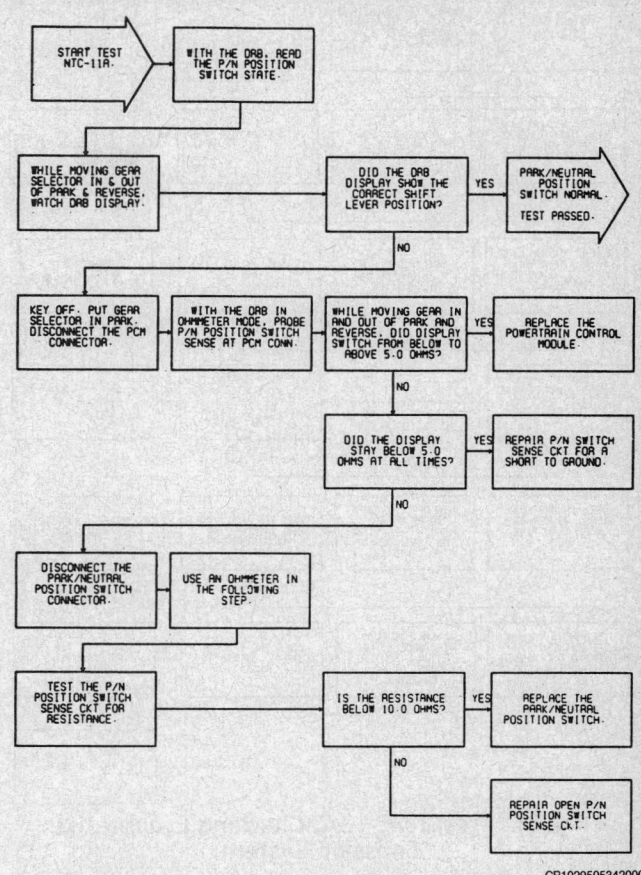

Fig. 93 Test NTC-11A: Checking Park/Neutral Position Switch

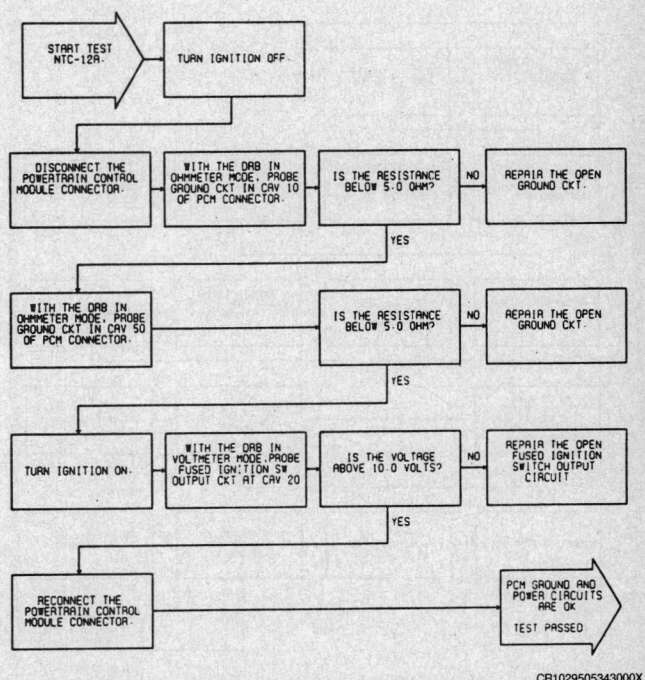

Fig. 94 Test NTC-12A: Checking PCM Power & Ground Circuits

MULTI-POINT FUEL INJECTION (1995 AVENGER, CIRRUS, SEBRING & STRATUS w/2.5L/V6-152)

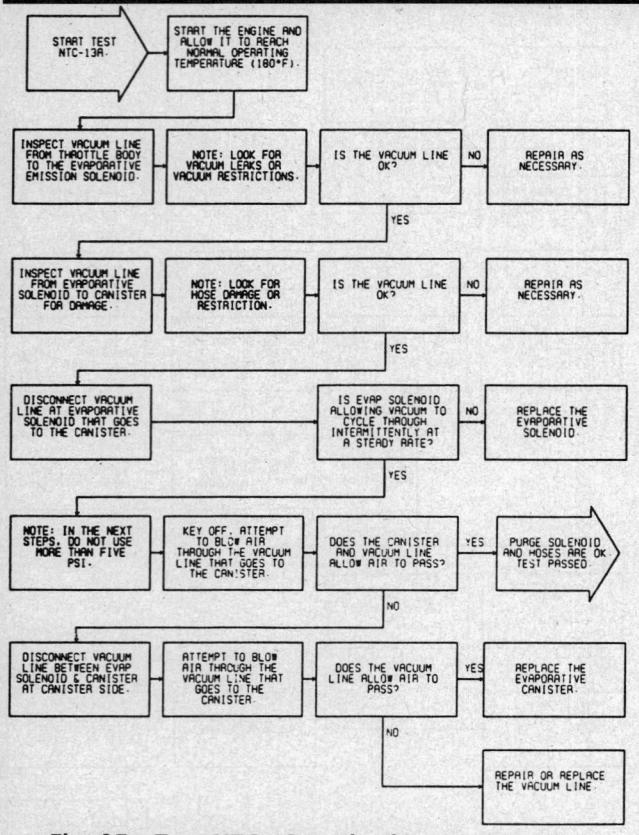

Fig. 95   Test NTC-13A: Checking Evaporative Emission System

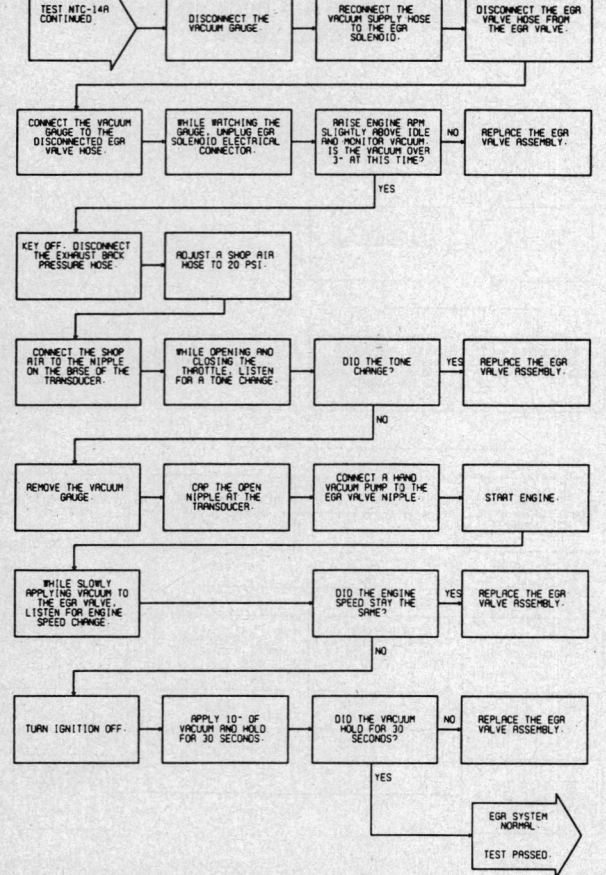

Fig. 96   Test NTC-14A: Checking EGR System (Part 2 of 2)

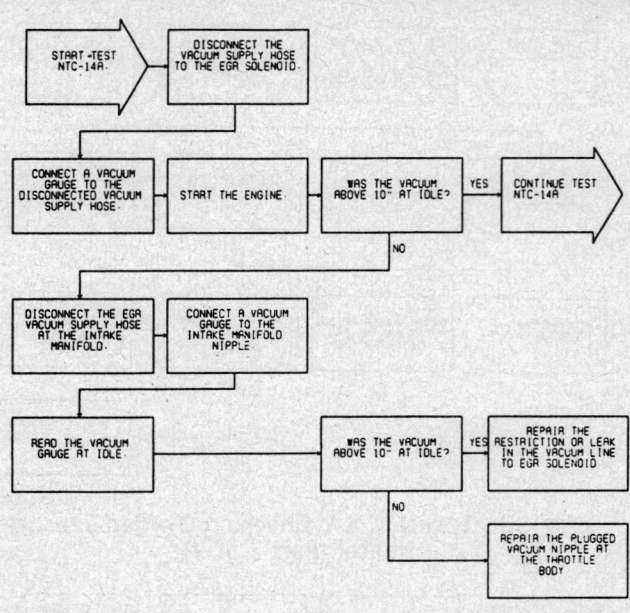

CR1029505345010X

Fig. 96   Test NTC-14A: Checking EGR System (Part 1 of 2)

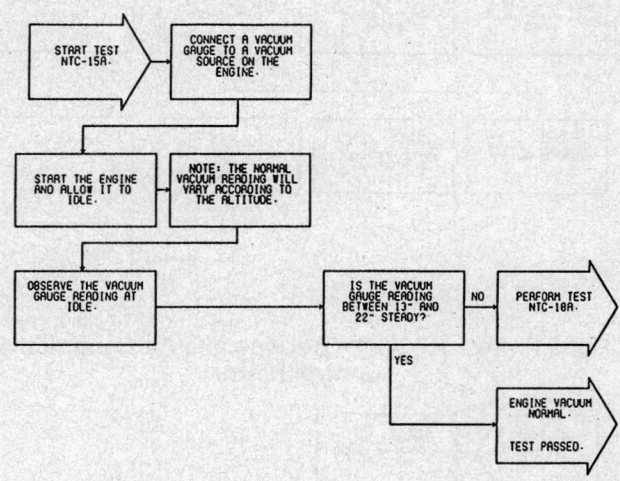

CR1029505346000X

Fig. 97   Test NTC-15A: Checking Engine Vacuum

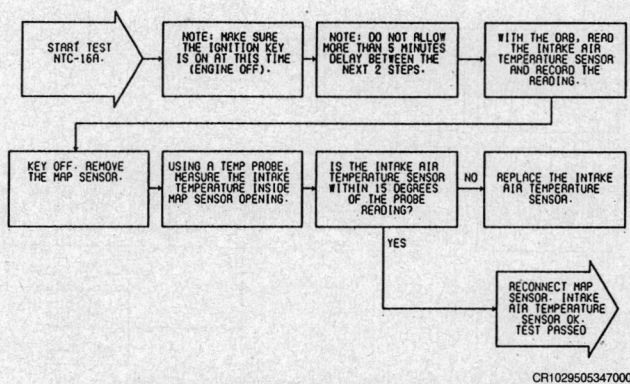

CR1029505347000X

Fig. 98   Test NTC-16A: Checking Intake Air Temperature Sensor

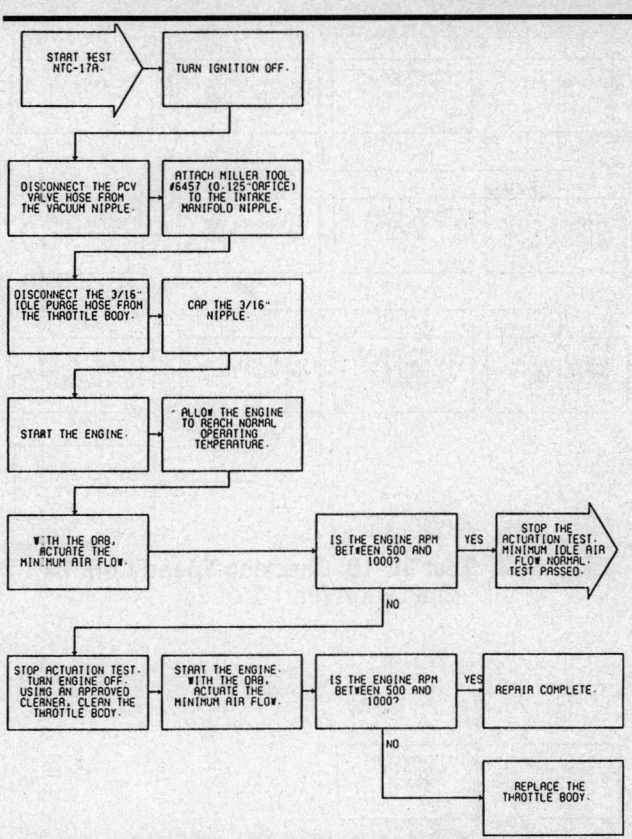

Fig. 99   Test NTC-17A: Checking Minimum Idle Air Flow

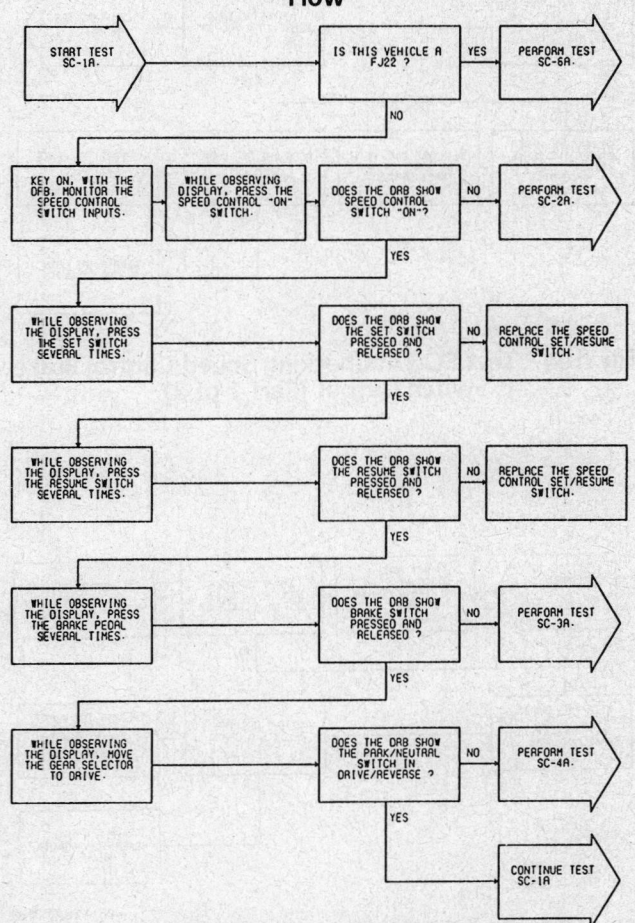

Fig. 101   Test SC-1A: Checking Speed Control Operation (Part 1 of 3)

Perform TEST NTC-1A, NTC-7A, NTC-15A or NTC-17A Before Proceeding

At this point in the diagnostic test procedure, you have determined that all of the engine electrical systems are operating as designed; therefore, they are not the cause of the driveability problem. The following additional items should be checked as possible mechanical causes of the problem:

1. **ENGINE VACUUM** - must be at least 13 inches in neutral *(see below)* †

2. **ENGINE VALVE TIMING** - must be within specifications

3. **ENGINE COMPRESSION** - must be within specifications

4. **ENGINE EXHAUST SYSTEM** - must be free of any restrictions

5. **ENGINE PCV SYSTEM** - must flow freely

6. **ENGINE DRIVE SPROCKET** - must be properly positioned

7. **TORQUE CONVERTER STALL SPEED** - must be within specifications

8. **POWER BRAKE BOOSTER** - no internal vacuum leaks

9. **FUEL** - must be free of contamination

10. **FUEL INJECTOR** - leaky or restricted injector; control wire not connected to correct injector

NOTE: If you came to this test from the oxygen sensor, and the rich or lean condition is not caused by one of the first items above, replace the powertrain control module and perform TEST VER-2A (Road Test Verification).

Always look for any Technical Service Bulletins that may relate to the problem.

† The readings below are only indicators of possible mechanical engine problems.

CR1029505349000X

Fig. 100   Test NTC-18A: Checking Engine Mechanical Systems

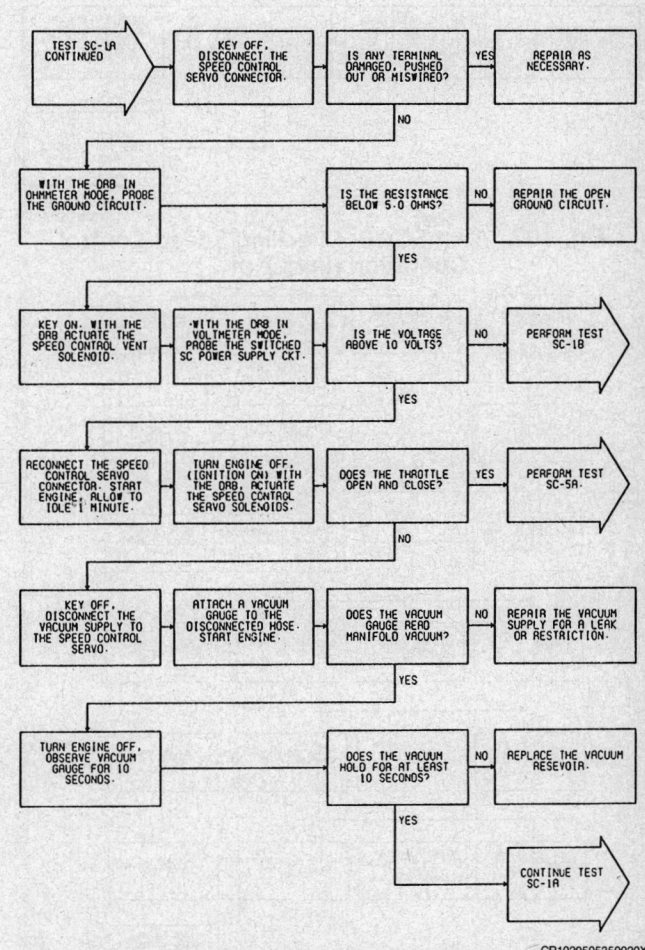

CR1029505350020X

Fig. 101   Test SC-1A: Checking Speed Control Operation (Part 2 of 3)

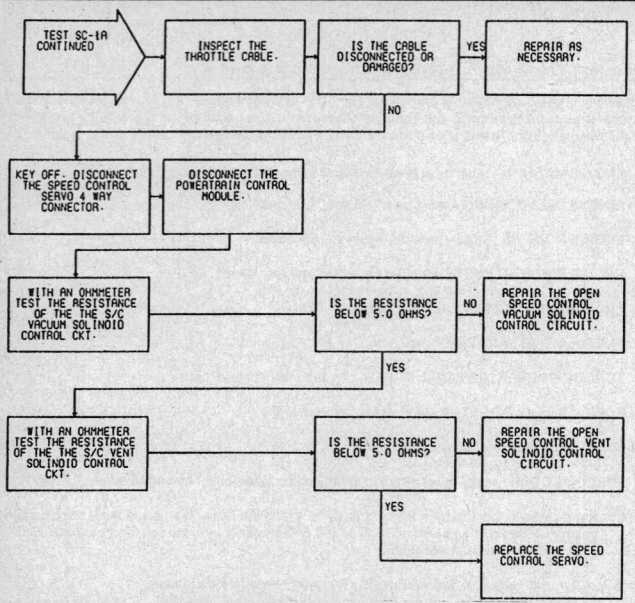

Fig. 101 Test SC-1A: Checking Speed Control Operation (Part 3 of 3)

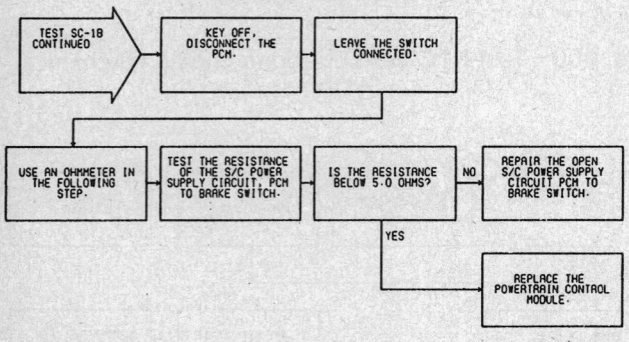

CR1029505351020X

Fig. 102 Test SC-1B: Checking Speed Control Operation (Part 2 of 2)

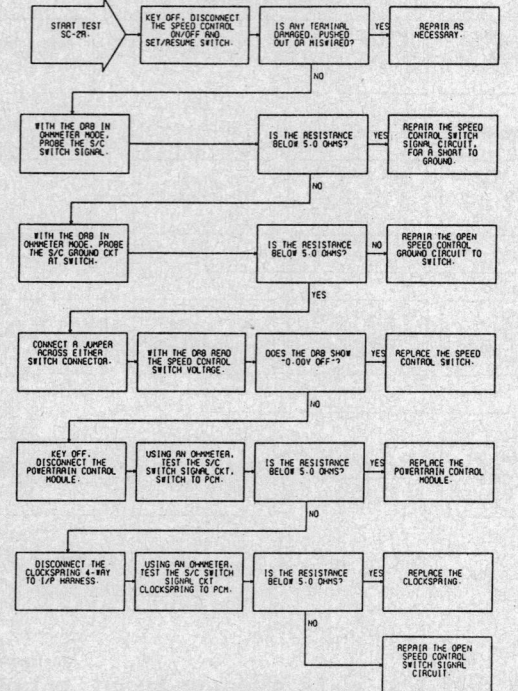

Fig. 103 Test SC-2A: Checking Speed Control On/Off Switch

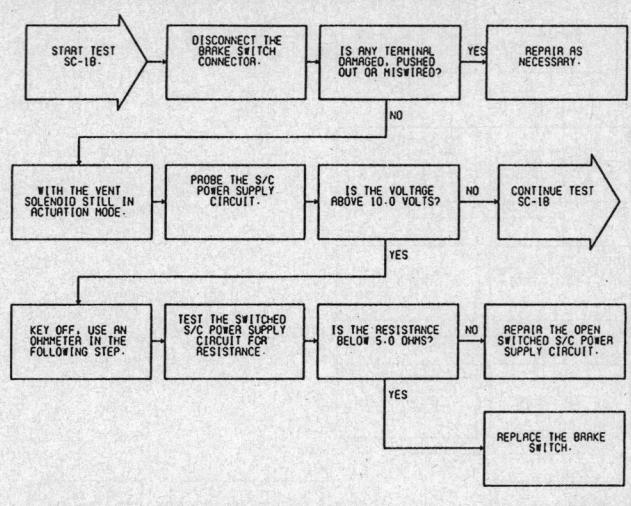

CR1029505351010X

Fig. 102 Test SC-1B: Checking Speed Control Operation (Part 1 of 2)

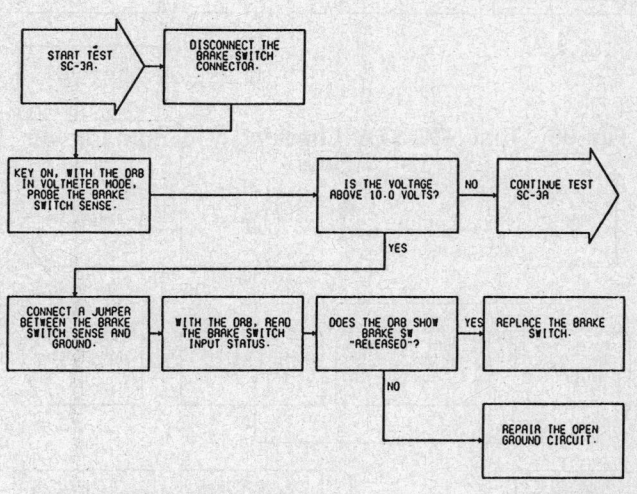

CR1029505353010X

Fig. 104 Test SC-3A: Checking Speed Control Brake Switch Output (Part 1 of 2)

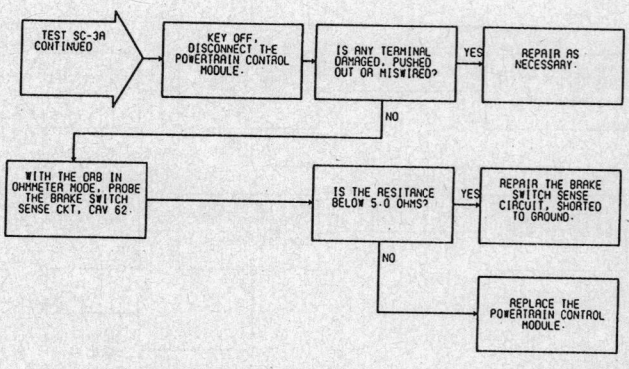

CR1029505353020X

Fig. 104 Test SC-3A: Checking Speed Control Brake Switch Output (Part 2 of 2)

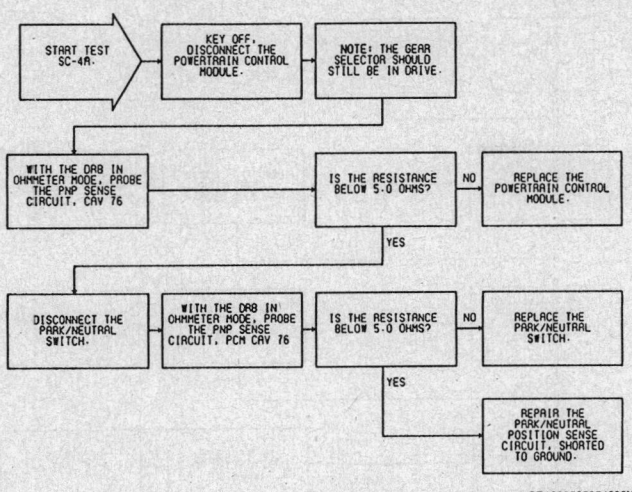

Fig. 105 Test SC-4A: Checking Park/Neutral Position Switch

CR1029505354000X

Perform TEST SC-1A Before Proceeding

At this time the speed control switch and servo functions appear to operate properly. Using the DRB, monitor the speed control "cutout" status. Road test the vehicle at speeds over 35 mph and attempt to set the speed control. The following items will not allow the speed control to set. The last or most recent cause for speed control not to set is indicated by the "Denied" status.

Denied Message

ON/OFF	The powertrain control module does not see an "ON" signal from the switch at cavity 41.
SPEED	The vehicle speed as seen by the powertrain control module at cavity 66 is not greater than 36 mph.
RPM	The engine rpm is excessively high.
BRAKE	The brake switch sense circuit is open indicating to the powertrain control module that the brakes are applied. The sense circuit, cavity 62 of the PCM, is grounded through the brake pedal switch when the brakes are released.
P/N	The park/neutral switch sense circuit is grounded indicating to the powertrain control module that the transmission is not in gear. The sense circuit, cavity 76 of the PCM, is grounded through the park/neutral switch when the transmission is in park or neutral.
RPM/SPD	The PCM senses excessive engine rpm for a given vehicle speed.
SOL FLT	The powertrain control module senses a servo solenoid circuit trouble code that is maturing or set in memory.

CR1029505355000X

Fig. 106 Test SC-5A: Checking For A Speed Control Denied Message

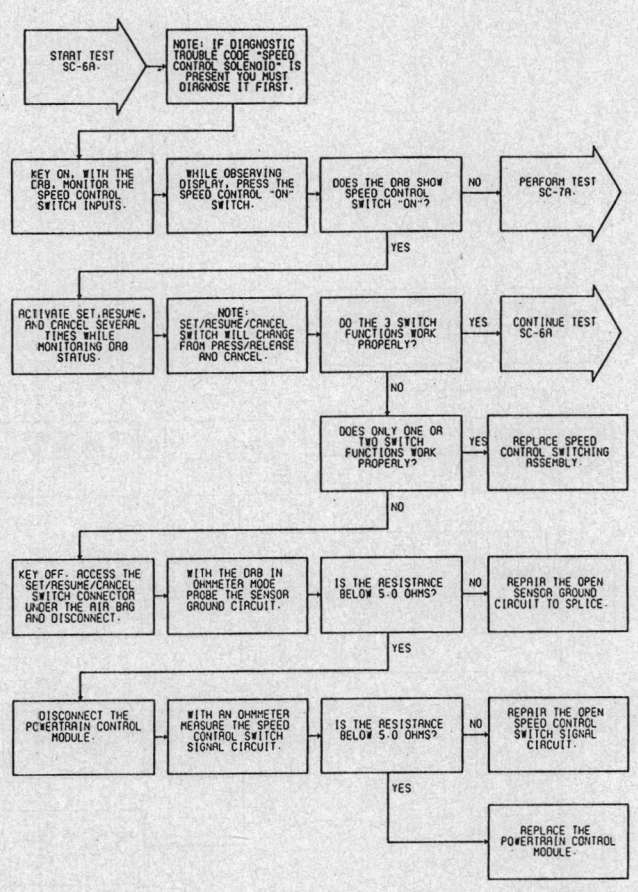

Fig. 107 Test SC-6A: Checking Speed Control Operation (Part 1 of 2)

CR1029505356010X

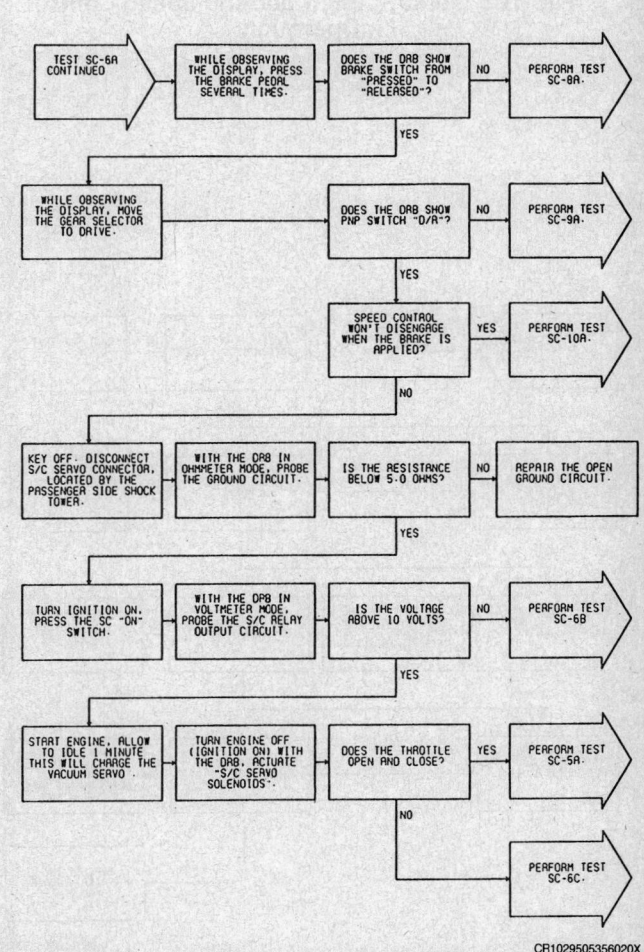

Fig. 107 Test SC-6A: Checking Speed Control Operation (Part 2 of 2)

CR1029505356020X

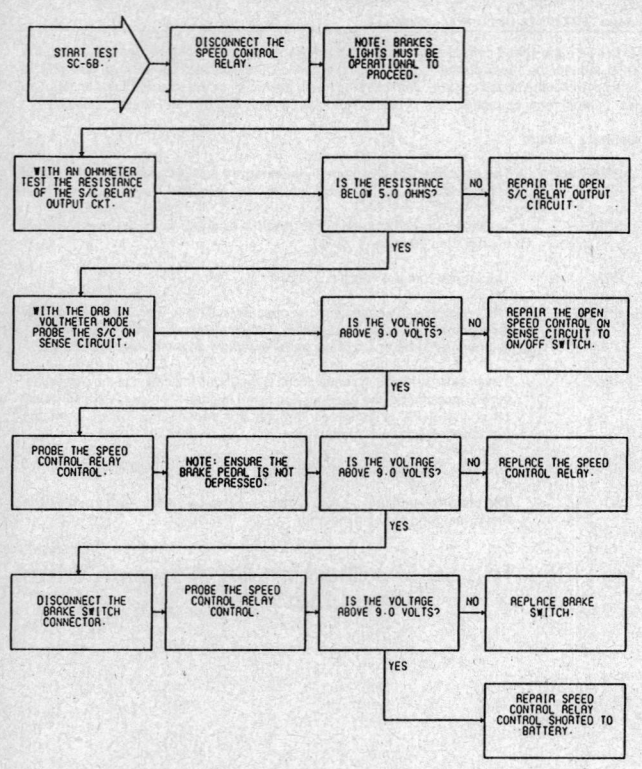

Fig. 108   Test SC-6B: Checking Speed Control Operation

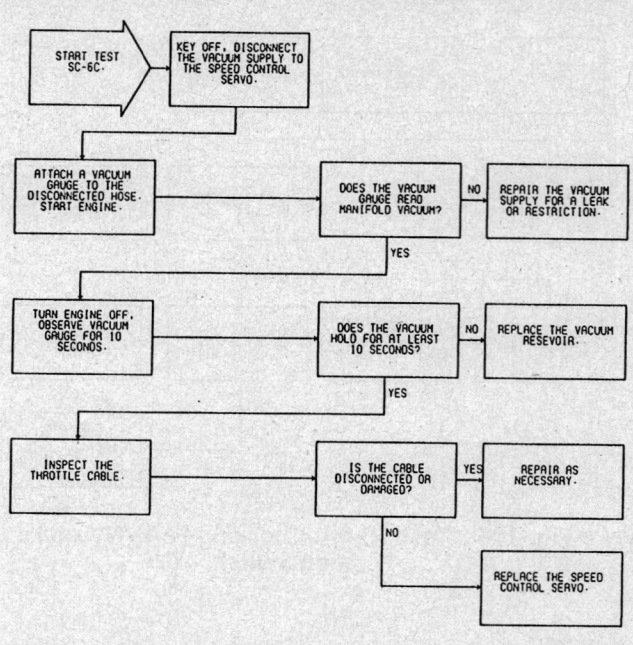

Fig. 109   Test SC-6C: Checking Speed Control Operation

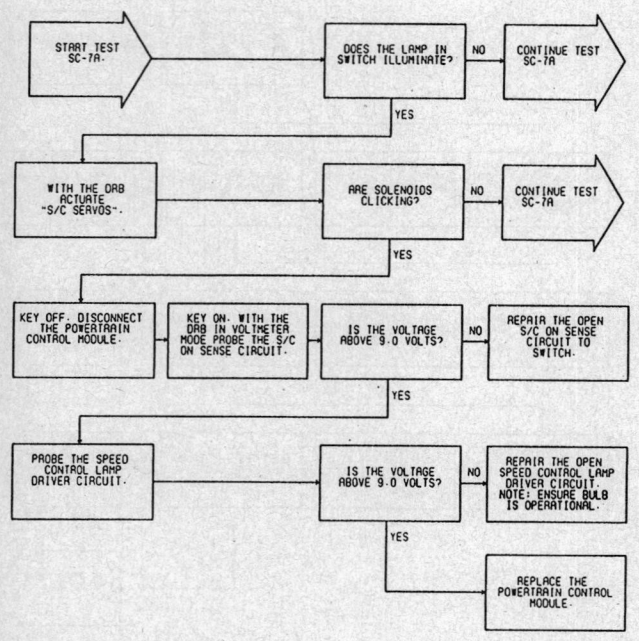

Fig. 110   Test SC-7A: Checking Speed Control On/Off Switch (Part 1 of 2)

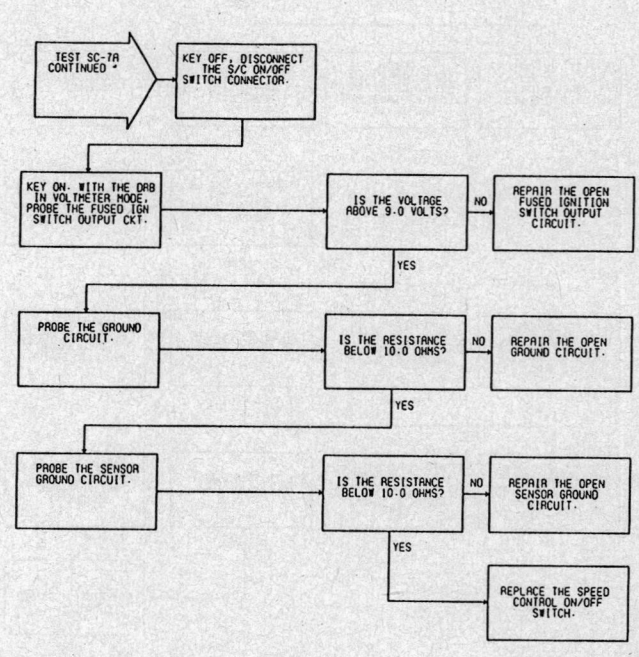

Fig. 110   Test SC-7A: Checking Speed Control On/Off Switch (Part 2 of 2)

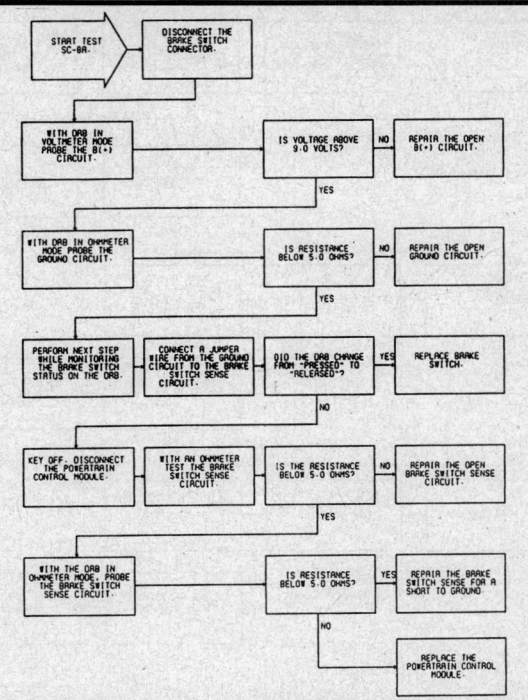

Fig. 111   Test SC-8A: Checking Speed Control Brake Switch Output

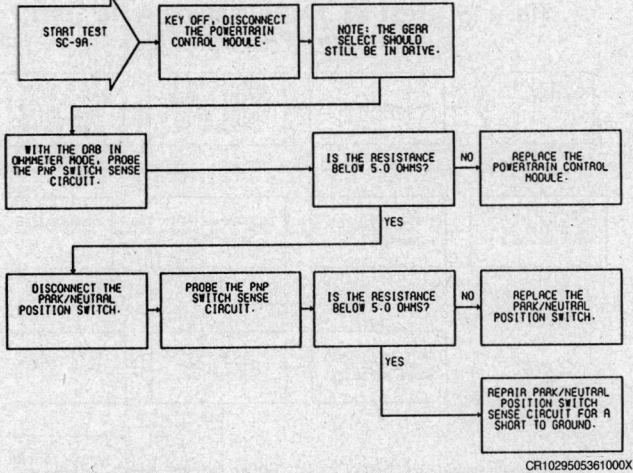

Fig. 112   Test SC-9A: Checking Park/Neutral Position Switch

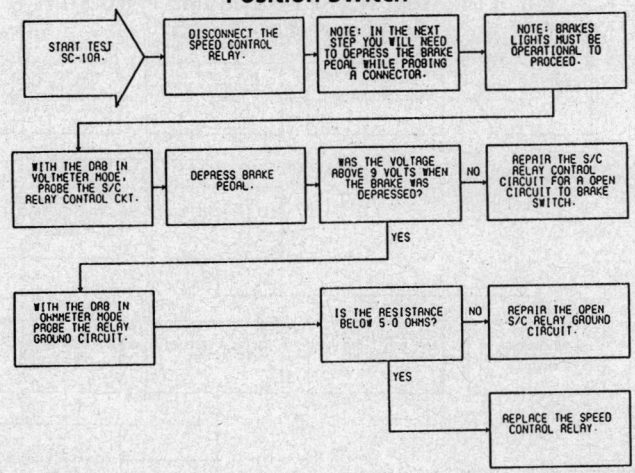

Fig. 113   Test SC-10A: Checking Speed Control Relay Output

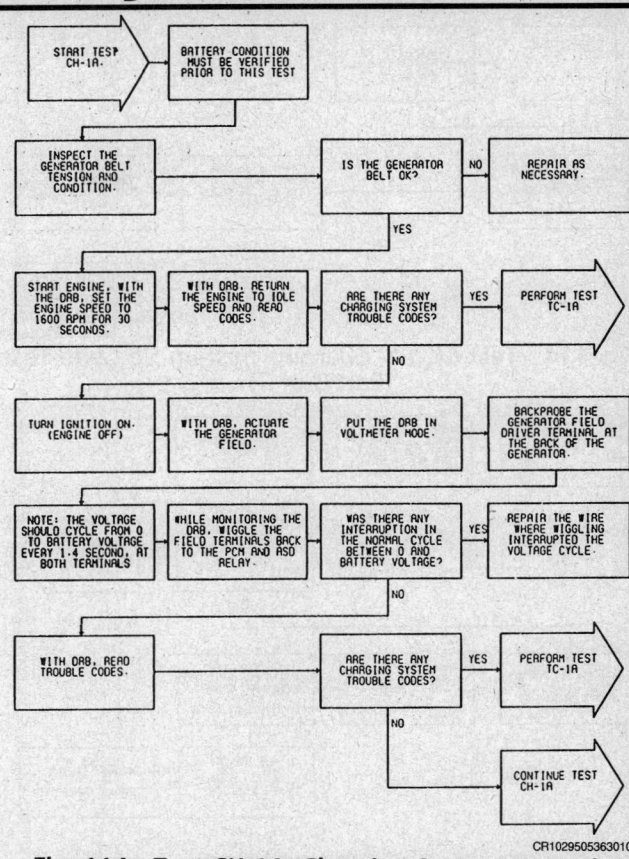

Fig. 114   Test CH-1A: Charging System No Code Test (Part 1 of 3)

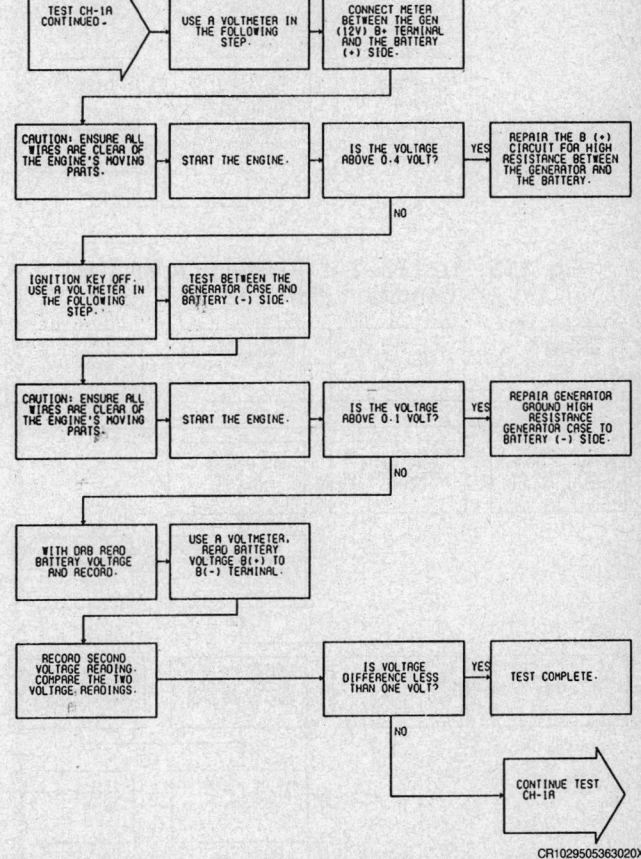

Fig. 114   Test CH-1A: Charging System No Code Test (Part 2 of 3)

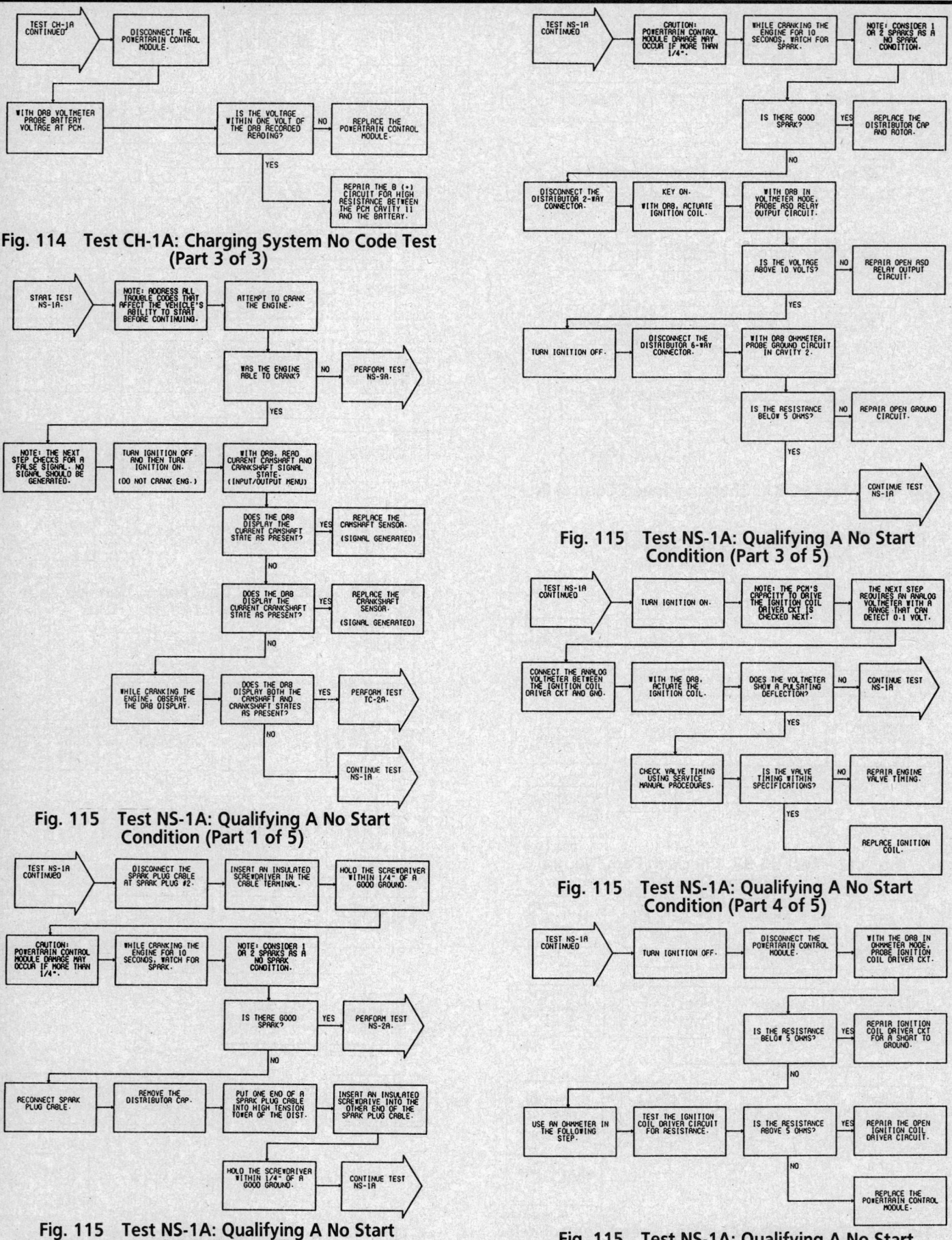

Fig. 114   Test CH-1A: Charging System No Code Test
(Part 3 of 3)

Fig. 115   Test NS-1A: Qualifying A No Start
Condition (Part 1 of 5)

Fig. 115   Test NS-1A: Qualifying A No Start
Condition (Part 2 of 5)

Fig. 115   Test NS-1A: Qualifying A No Start
Condition (Part 3 of 5)

Fig. 115   Test NS-1A: Qualifying A No Start
Condition (Part 4 of 5)

Fig. 115   Test NS-1A: Qualifying A No Start
Condition (Part 5 of 5)

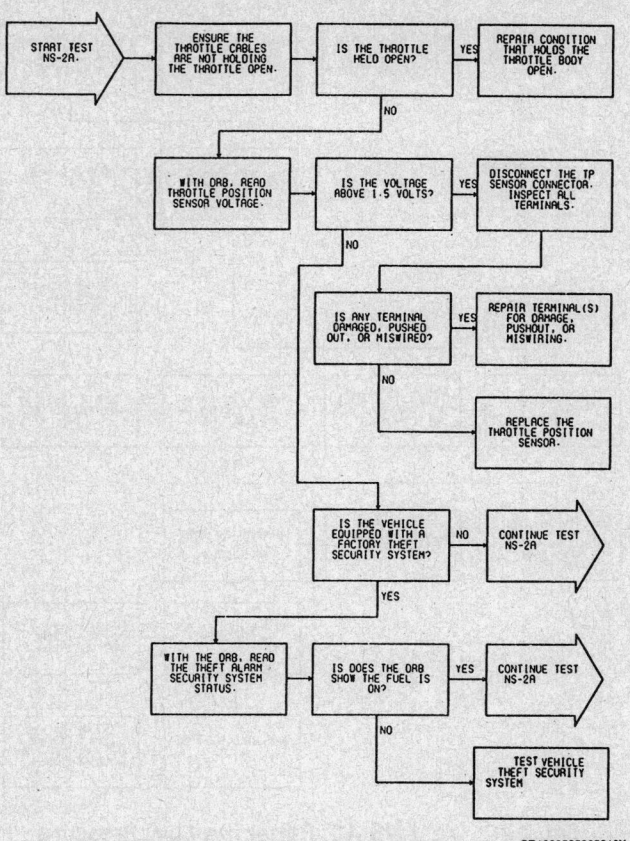

Fig. 116   Test NS-2A: Checking Fuel System (Part 1
of 2)

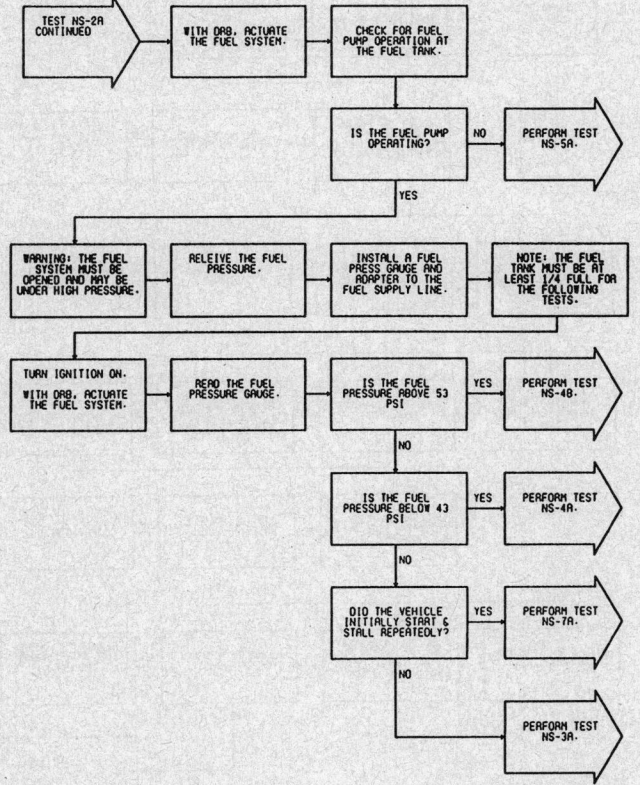

Fig. 116   Test NS-2A: Checking Fuel System (Part 2
of 2)

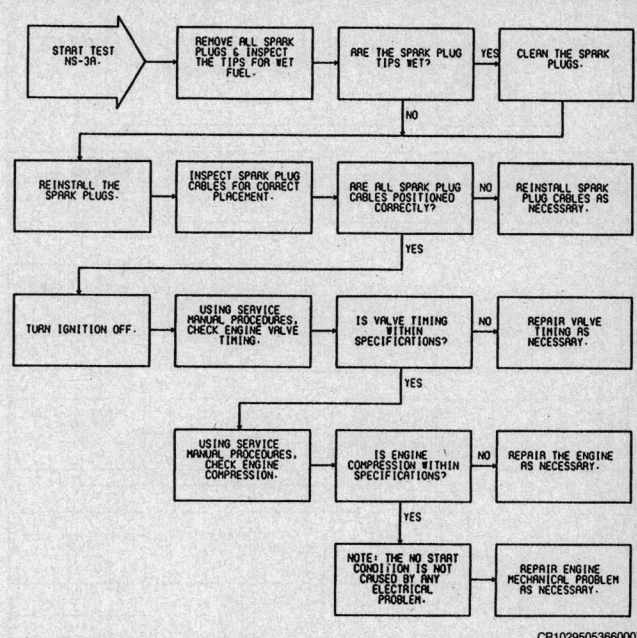

Fig. 117   Test NS-3A: Checking Engine Mechanical
Systems

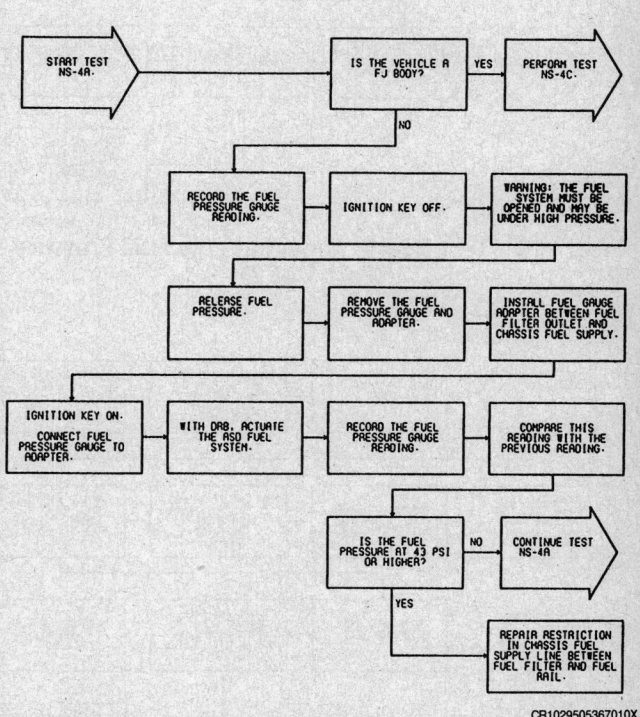

Fig. 118   Test NS-4A: Repairing Low Fuel Pressure
(Part 1 of 2)

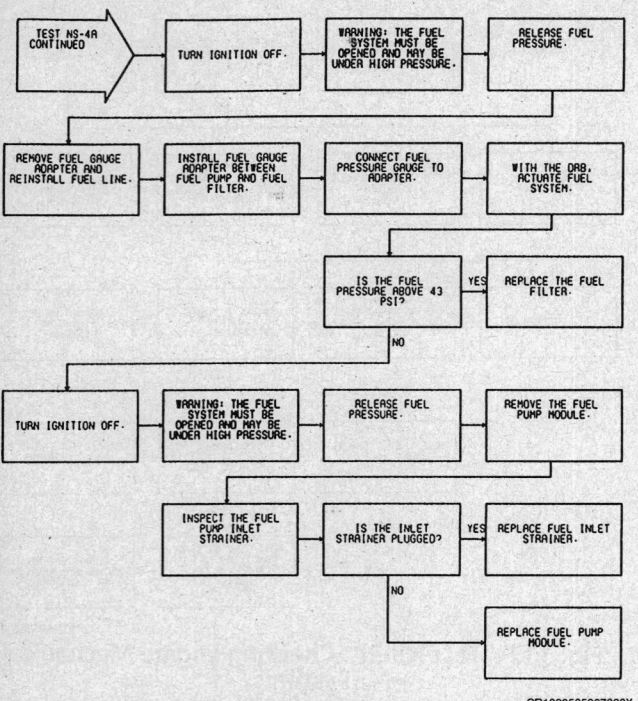

Fig. 118   Test NS-4A: Repairing Low Fuel Pressure
(Part 2 of 2)

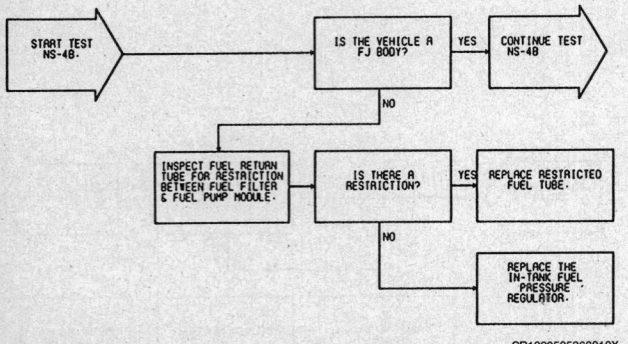

Fig. 119   Test NS-4B: Repairing Low Fuel Pressure
(Part 1 of 2)

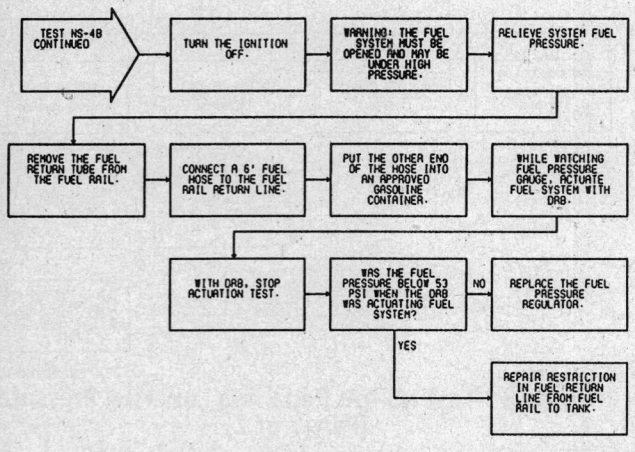

Fig. 119   Test NS-4B: Repairing Low Fuel Pressure
(Part 2 of 2)

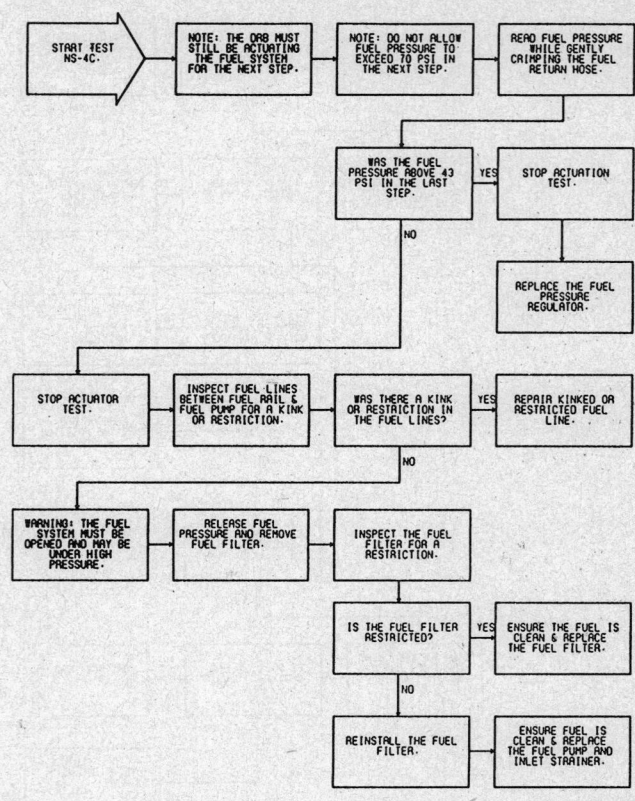

Fig. 120   Test NS-4C: Repairing Low Pressure

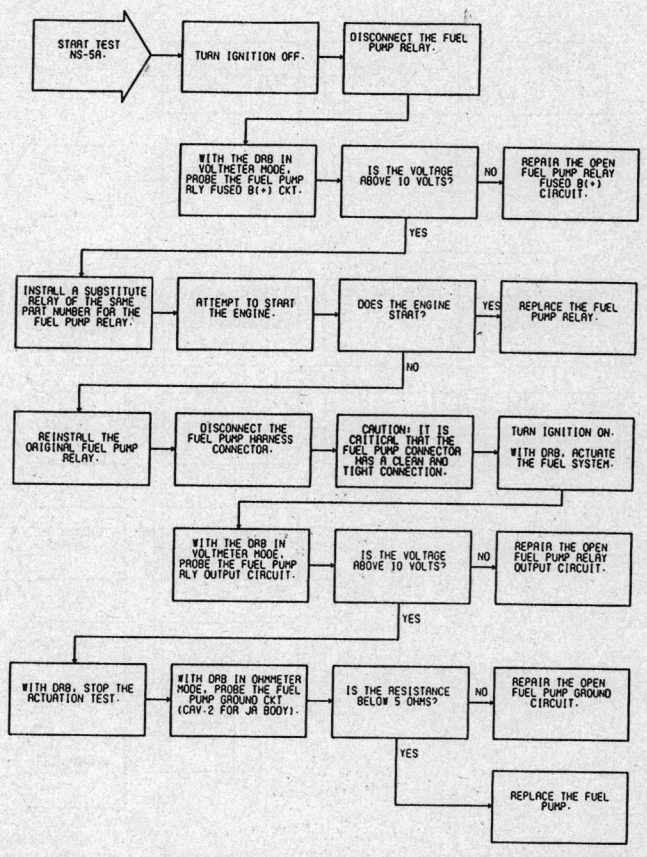

Fig. 121   Test NS-5A: Checking Fuel Pump

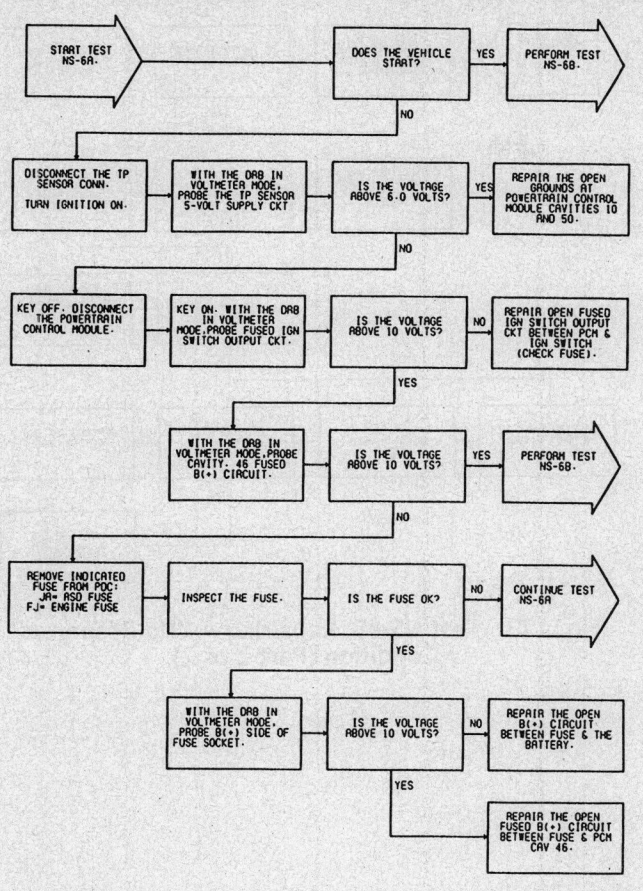

Fig. 122   Test NS-6A: Repairing A "No Response" Condition (Part 1 of 4)

CR1029505371010X

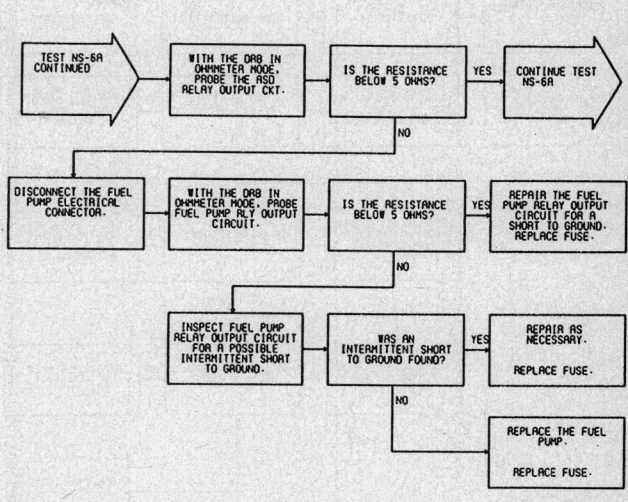

CR1029505371030X

Fig. 122   Test NS-6A: Repairing A "No Response" Condition (Part 3 of 4)

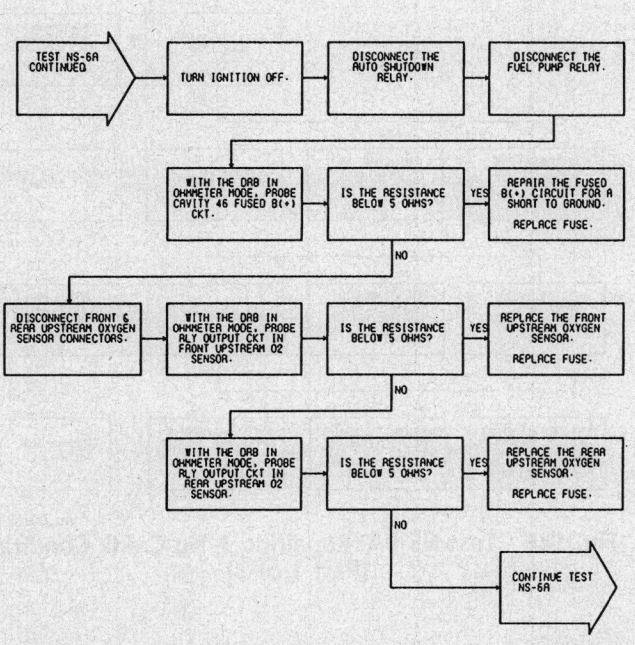

CR1029505371020X

Fig. 122   Test NS-6A: Repairing A "No Response" Condition (Part 2 of 4)

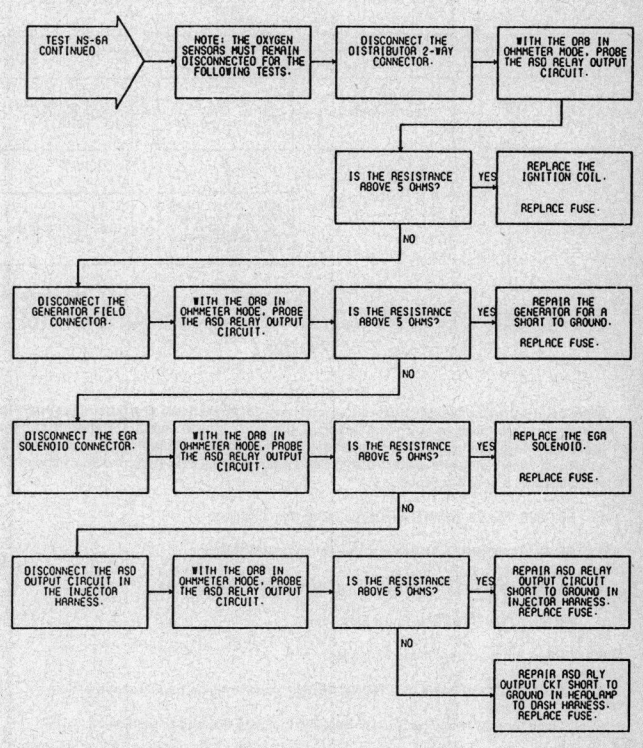

CR1029505371040X

Fig. 122   Test NS-6A: Repairing A "No Response" Condition (Part 4 of 4)

CHRYSLER–Fuel Injection

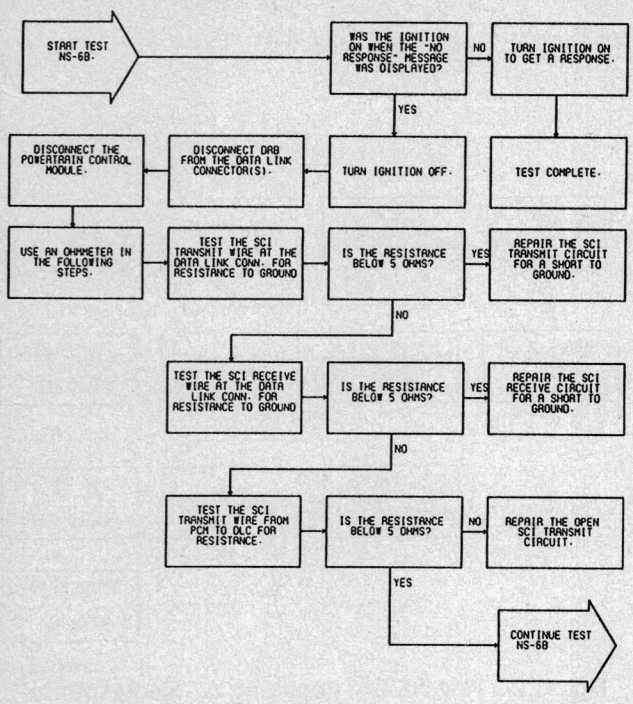

Fig. 123 Test NS-6B: Repairing A "No Response" Condition (Part 1 of 2)

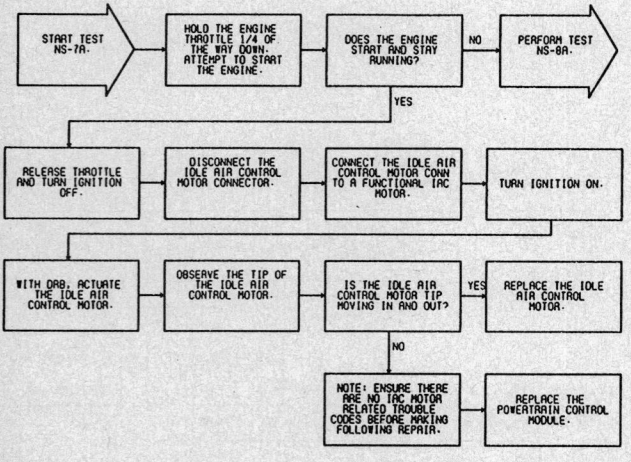

Fig. 124 Test NS-7A: Checking Idle Air Control Motor

At this point in the diagnostic test procedure, you have determined that all of the engine electrical systems are operating as designed; therefore, they are not the cause of the start and stall problem. The following additional items should be checked as possible mechanical causes of the no start condition. Any one or more of these items can produce a no start condition; none can be overlooked as a possible cause.

1. **ENGINE VALVE TIMING** - must be within specifications
2. **ENGINE COMPRESSION** - must be within specifications
3. **ENGINE EXHAUST SYSTEM** - must be free of any restrictions
4. **ENGINE PCV SYSTEM** - must flow freely
5. **FUEL** - must be free of contamination
6. **ENGINE SECONDARY IGNITION CHECK** - must exhibit a normal scope pattern

Always look for any Technical Service Bulletins that may relate to this condition.

Fig. 125 Test NS-8A: Repairing A Start & Stall Condition

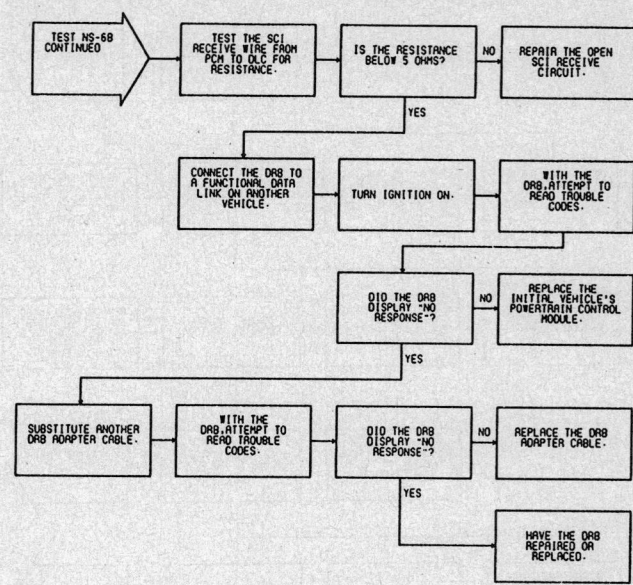

Fig. 123 Test NS-6B: Repairing A "No Response" Condition (Part 2 of 2)

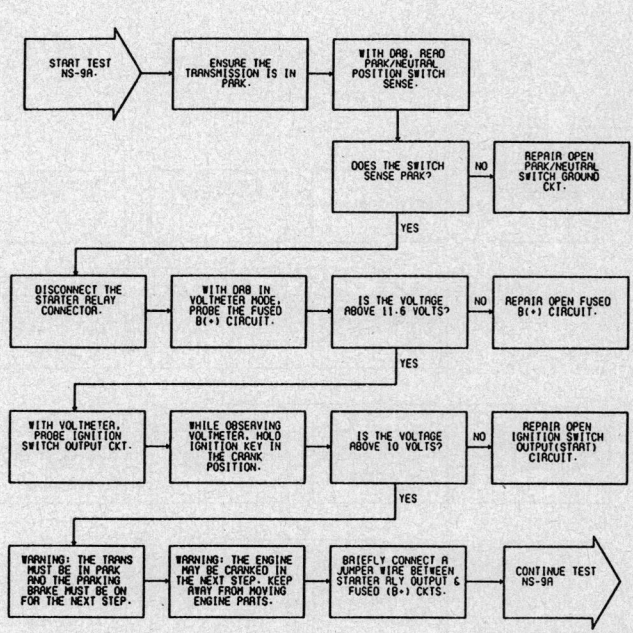

Fig. 126 Test NS-9A: Repairing A No Crank Condition (Part 1 of 3)

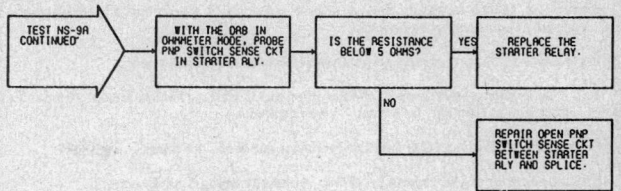

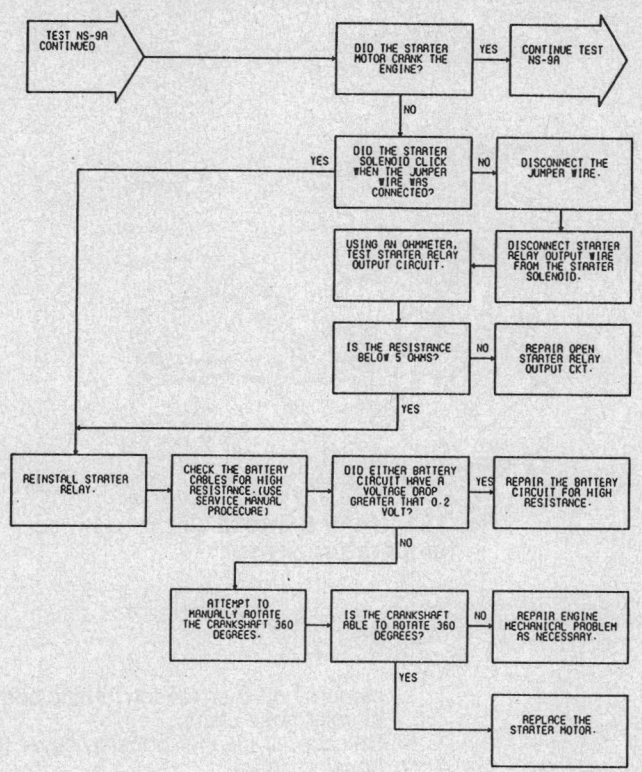

Fig. 126   Test NS-9A: Repairing A No Crank Condition (Part 2 of 3)

CR1029505375020X

Fig. 126   Test NS-9A: Repairing A No Crank Condition (Part 3 of 3)

CR1029505375030X

Inspect the vehicle to ensure that all engine components are connected. Reassemble and reconnect components as necessary.

Inspect the engine for contamination. If it is contaminated, change the oil and filter.

Attempt to start the engine.

If the engine is unable to start, look for any Technical Service Bulletins that may relate to this condition. Return to **TEST TC-1A** if necessary.

The repair is now complete.

CR1029505376000X

Fig. 127   Test VER-1A: No Start Verification

Inspect the vehicle to ensure that all engine components are connected. Reassemble and reconnect all components as necessary.

If this verification procedure is being performed after a **NO TROUBLE CODE** test, do the following:

1. Check to see if the initial symptom still exists.

2. If the initial or another symptom exists, the repair is not complete. Check all pertinent Technical Service Bulletins and return to **TEST NTC-1A** if necessary.

If this verification procedure is being performed after a **TROUBLE CODE** test, do the following:

For previously read trouble codes that have not been dealt with, return to **TEST TC-1A** and follow the path specified. Otherwise, continue.

If the powertrain control module has not been changed:

1. Connect the DRB to the PCM data link connector and erase trouble codes.

2. With the DRB, reset all values in the adaptive memory.

3. Disconnect the DRB.

Ensure no trouble code remains by doing the following:

1. If the vehicle is equipped with air conditioning, turn on the air conditioning and blower.

2. Drive the vehicle for at least five minutes and at some point reach a speed of 40 mph. Ensure the transmission shifts through all gears. Upon completion of the road test, turn the engine off.

3. Start the engine. Allow the engine to idle for at least two minutes.

4. Turn the engine off.

5. Connect the DRB to the PCM data link connector, and read all trouble code messages.

If the repaired code has reset, the repair is not complete. Check all pertinent Technical Service Bulletins and return to **TEST TC-1A** if necessary.

If another trouble code has set, return to **TEST TC-1A** and follow the path specified by the other trouble code.

If there are no trouble codes, the repair is now complete.

CR1029505377000X

Fig. 128   Test VER-2A: Road Test Verification

Inspect the vehicle to ensure that all engine components are connected. Reassemble and reconnect all components as necessary.

If the powertrain control module has been changed, do the following:

1. If the vehicle is equipped with a factory theft alarm, start the vehicle at least 20 times so that the alarm system may be activated when desired.

Connect the DRB to the PCM data link connector and erase the codes.

Ensure no other speed control problems remain by doing the following:

1. Road test the vehicle at a speed above 35 mph.

2. Turn the speed control ON/OFF switch to the ON position.

3. Depress and release the SET switch. If the speed control did not engage, the repair is not complete.*

4. For stalk switch equipped vehicles, quickly depress and release the SET switch. For steering wheel switch equipped vehicles, quickly depress and release the RESUME/ACCEL switch. If the vehicle speed did not increase by 2 mph, the repair is not complete.*

5. Using caution, depress and release the brake pedal. If the speed control did not disengage, the repair is not complete.*

6. Bring the vehicle speed back up to 35 mph.

7. Depress the RESUME/ACCEL switch. If the speed control did not resume the previously set speed, the repair is not complete.*

8. Hold down the SET switch. If the vehicle did not decelerate, the repair is not complete.*

9. Ensure the vehicle speed is greater than 35 mph and release the SET switch. If the vehicle did not adjust and set a new vehicle speed, the repair is not complete.*

10. Turn on the ON/OFF switch to the OFF position. If the speed control did not disengage, the repair is not complete.*

If the vehicle successfully passed all of the previous tests, the speed control system is now functioning as designed. The repair is now complete.

*Check for Technical Service Bulletins that pertain to this speed control problem and then, if necessary, return to **TEST TC-1A**.

CR1029505378000X

Fig. 129   Test VER-3A: Charging Verification

Inspect the vehicle to ensure that all engine components are connected. Reassemble and reconnect all components as necessary.

If the powertrain control module has been changed, do the following:

1. If the vehicle is equipped with a factory theft alarm, start the vehicle at least 20 times so that the alarm system may be activated when desired.

Connect the DRB to the PCM data link connector and erase the codes.

Ensure no other speed control problems remain by doing the following:

1. Road test the vehicle at a speed above 35 mph.
2. Turn the speed control ON/OFF switch to the ON position.
3. Depress and release the SET switch. If the speed control did not engage, the repair is not complete.*
4. For stalk switch equipped vehicles, quickly depress and release the SET switch. For steering wheel switch equipped vehicles, quickly depress and release the RESUME/ACCEL switch. If the vehicle speed did not increase by 2 mph, the repair is not complete.*
5. Using caution, depress and release the brake pedal. If the speed control did not disengage, the repair is not complete.*
6. Bring the vehicle speed back up to 35 mph.
7. Depress the RESUME/ACCEL switch. If the speed control did not resume the previously set speed, the repair is not complete.*
8. Hold down the SET switch. If the vehicle did not decelerate, the repair is not complete.*
9. Ensure the vehicle speed is greater than 35 mph and release the SET switch. If the vehicle did not adjust and set a new vehicle speed, the repair is not complete.*
10. Turn on the ON/OFF switch to the OFF position. If the speed control did not disengage, the repair is not complete.*

If the vehicle successfully passed all of the previous tests, the speed control system is now functioning as designed. The repair is now complete.

*Check for Technical Service Bulletins that pertain to this speed control problem and then, if necessary, return to **TEST TC-1A.**

CR1029505379000X

Fig. 130   Test VER-4A: Speed Control Verification

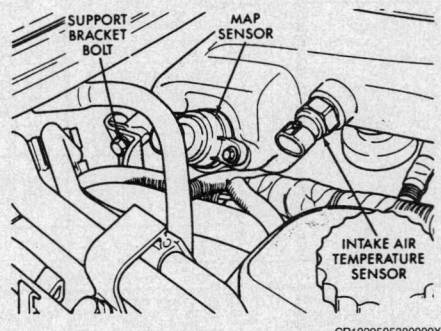

Fig. 131   MAP & intake air temperature sensor

CR1029505380000X

SYSTEM SERVICE

Fuel System Pressure Relief

Do not attempt to start the engine for several minutes to avoid hydrostatic lock.

1. Disconnect fuel rail electrical harness from engine harness, then connect one end of jumper wire to A142 circuit terminal of fuel rail harness connector and other end of jumper wire to 12 volt power source.
2. Connect one end of jumper wire to good ground source, then momentarily ground one of injectors by connecting other end of jumper wire to an injector terminal in the harness connector.
3. Repeat procedure for two to three injectors.

Component Replacement

AIR INLET RESONATOR

1. Remove resonator to intake manifold bolt.
2. Loosen resonator to air inlet tube clamp, then remove resonator.
3. Reverse procedure to install. **Torque** resonator to intake manifold bolt to 40-50 inch lbs.

THROTTLE BODY

1. Remove air tube from throttle body, then the throttle cable from throttle body lever.
2. Pry retainer tab back on throttle cable and slide cable out of bracket.
3. **On models equipped with speed control,** slide speed control cable out of bracket.
4. **On all models,** remove EVAP purge hose from nipple on throttle body, then the connectors from throttle position sensor and idle air control motor.
5. Remove throttle body to intake manifold bolts, then the throttle body.
6. Reverse procedure to install. **Torque** throttle body to intake manifold bolts to 250 inch lbs., then the clamps to 20-25 inch lbs.

FUEL RAIL

1. Disconnect battery ground cable from auxiliary jumper terminal.
2. Relieve fuel system pressure as described under "System Service."
3. Disconnect fuel supply tube from rail, then disconnect connectors from MAP and intake air temperature sensors, **Fig. 131.**
4. Remove air inlet resonator to intake

plenum bolt, then loosen throttle body air inlet hose clamp.
5. Release air cleaner housing cover to housing snaps.
6. Remove air cleaner cover and inlet hoses from engine.
7. Disconnect TPS and idle air control motor connectors.
8. Pry retainer tab back on throttle cable and slide cable out of bracket, **Fig. 132.**
9. **On models equipped with speed control,** slide speed control cable out of bracket.
10. **On all models,** remove EGR tube from intake plenum, then the plenum support bracket bolt located rearward of EGR tube.
11. Remove upper intake plenum bolts, then the plenum.
12. Disconnect electrical connectors from fuel injectors.
13. Remove fuel rail bolts, then the fuel rail off engine. There are spacers under each fuel rail bolt.
14. Reverse procedure to install, noting the following:
    a. Apply light coating of clean engine oil to O-ring on nozzle end of each injector.
    b. **Torque** fuel rail bolts to 8 ft. lbs.
    c. Install new intake plenum gasket. **Torque** plenum bolts to 13 ft. lbs.
    d. **Torque** plenum support bracket bolts to 13 ft. lbs.
    e. **Torque** air inlet tube clamps to 20-30 inch lbs.

FUEL INJECTORS

1. Remove fuel rail as previously described.
2. Remove fuel injector clip, **Fig. 133,** then pull injector out of fuel rail.
3. Reverse procedure to install. Replace fuel injector O-rings.

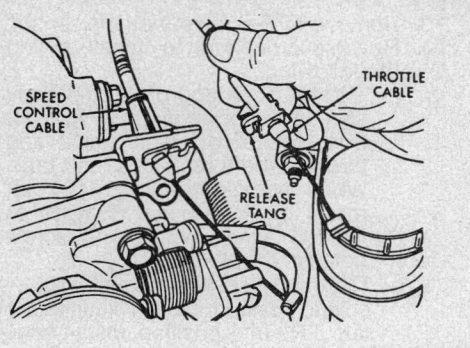

Fig. 132   Throttle cable removal

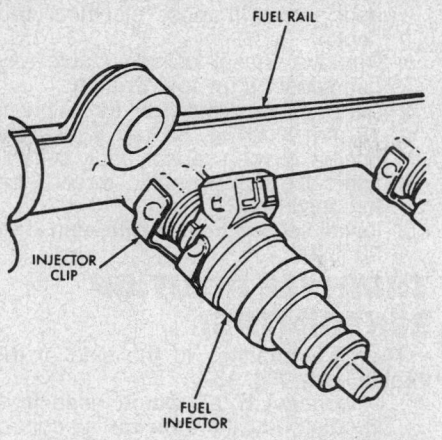

Fig. 133   Fuel injector replacement

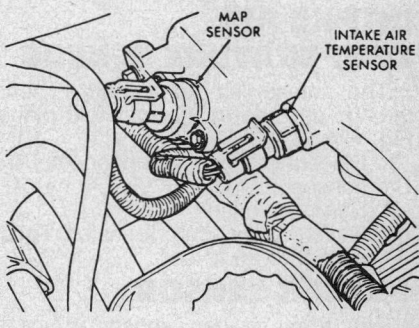

Fig. 134   Intake air temperature sensor

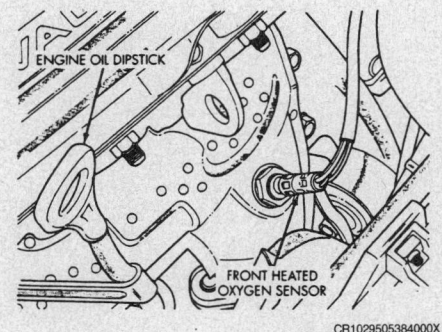

Fig. 135   Front oxygen sensor

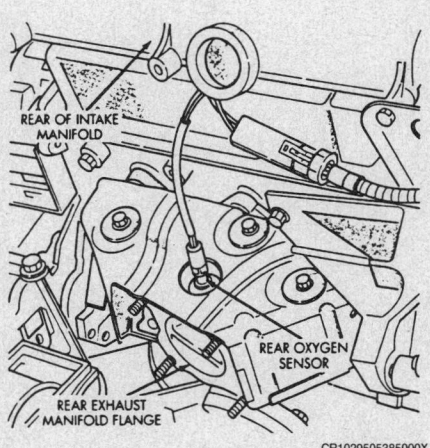

Fig. 136   Rear oxygen sensor

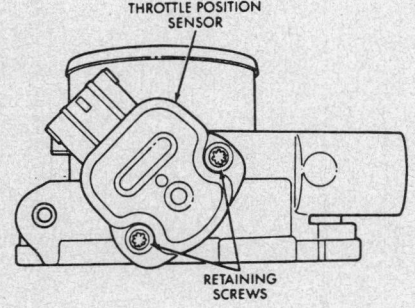

Fig. 137   Throttle Position Sensor (TPS)

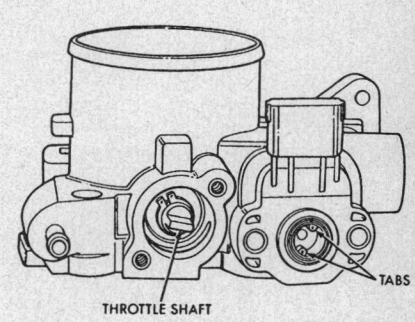

Fig. 138   Throttle Position Sensor (TPS) indexing

MULTI-POINT FUEL INJECTION (1995 AVENGER, CIRRUS, SEBRING & STRATUS w/2.5L/V6-152)

CHRYSLER–Fuel Injection

INTAKE AIR TEMPERATURE SENSOR

The intake air temperature sensor threads into the intake manifold plenum, **Fig. 134.**

1. Disconnect electrical connector from sensor.
2. Remove sensor.
3. Reverse procedure to install. **Torque** sensor to 20 ft. lbs.

OXYGEN SENSOR

The front oxygen sensor is located above the outlet flange of the forward exhaust manifold, **Fig. 135.** The rear oxygen sensor is located below the rear exhaust manifold flange, **Fig. 136.**

1. **For rear oxygen sensor,** raise and support vehicle.
2. **For both oxygen sensors,** disconnect sensor harness electrical connector.
3. Remove sensor using suitable oxygen sensor crow foot wrench.
4. Clean exhaust manifold threads with 18 mm X 1.5 + 6E tap. If installing original oxygen sensor, apply suitable anti-seize compound to threads before installing.
5. Install sensor, then **torque** sensor to 20 ft. lbs.

THROTTLE POSITION SENSOR (TPS)

The TPS attaches to the side of the throttle body, **Fig. 137.**

1. Disconnect EVAP purge hose from throttle body, then the idle air control motor and TPS electrical connector.
2. Remove throttle body as previously described.
3. Remove TPS screws, then the sensor.
4. Reverse procedure to install, noting the following:
   a. Throttle shaft end of throttle body slides into socket in TPS, **Fig. 138.** Socket has two tabs inside and throttle shaft rests against tabs. When indexed correctly, TPS can rotate clockwise few degrees to line up screw holes with screw holes in throttle body.
   b. TPS has slight tension when rotated into position. If it is difficult to rotate TPS into position, install sensor with throttle shaft on other side of tabs in socket.
   c. **Torque** screws to 17 inch lbs.
   d. After installing TPS, throttle plate should be closed. If plate is open, install sensor on other side of tabs in socket.

FUEL INJECTION
Stealth

INDEX

If Uncertain About The Proper Use Of Information Contained In This Section, Please Refer To "How To Use This Manual" Located In The Front Of This Manual.

On Air Bag Equipped Models, Refer To "Air Bag System Precautions" Located In The Front Of This Manual For System Disarming & Arming Procedures.

Electrical Symbol & Wire Color Code Identification Located In The Front Of This Manual May Be Used As An Aid When Using Wiring Circuits Found In This Section.

Page No.	Page No.	Page No.
Description: 11-1	Diagnostic Trouble Code	**Specifications** 11-1
System Components 11-2	Interpretation 11-34	**System Service:** 11-45
Diagnosis & Testing: **11-2**	System & Component Testing: 11-34	Component Replacement: 11-48
Accessing Diagnostic Trouble	Component Inspections 11-42	Injector 11-48
Codes: 11-2	Harness Inspections 11-34	Throttle Body 11-48
Using Analog Voltmeter 11-2	**Precautions:** 11-1	Component Service: 11-45
Using Diagnostic Scan Tool 11-34	Air Bag Systems 11-1	Throttle Body 11-45
Using Malfunction Indicator Lamp	Fuel System Pressure Relief 11-1	Fuel System Pressure Relief 11-45
(MIL) 11-2	**Sensor & Fuel Injector**	**Troubleshooting** 11-2
Clearing Diagnostic Trouble Codes 11-34		

SENSOR & FUEL INJECTOR SPECIFICATIONS

Component	Voltage	Resistance, Ohms
Intake Air Temp. Sensor	—	①
Engine Coolant Temp. Sensor	—	②
Throttle Position Sensor	—	3500-6500
Oxygen Sensor	.6—1.0	20③
Resistor	—	5.5-6.5③
Injector	—	13-16④ ③
		2-3⑤ ③
Idle Speed Control	—	28-33③
Fuel Pump Resistor⑤	—	.6—.9
Vehicle Speed Sensor	—	3000-10,000

①—**Resistance is 6000 ohms @ 32°F,** **2400 ohms @ 68°F, 1100 ohms @**
2700 ohms @ 68°F & 400 ohms @ **104°F & 300 ohms @ 176°F.**
176°F. ③—**At 68°F.**
②—**Resistance is 5800 ohms @ 32°F,** ④—**Non-turbocharged engines.**
⑤—**DOHC turbocharged engines.**

PRECAUTIONS
AIR BAG SYSTEMS

Refer to "Air Bag System Precautions" in the front of this manual for system disarming and arming procedures.

FUEL SYSTEM PRESSURE RELIEF

Bleed fuel pipe residual pressure as follows:

1. Remove fuel gauge cover, located in luggage compartment.
2. Disconnect fuel pump electrical connector.
3. Start engine, allow to idle until stalls, turn ignition switch to "Off" position.
4. Carefully bleed fuel pipe line residual pressure. **Cover hose connection with suitable rag to prevent fuel spray by residual pressure in fuel pipe line.**

DESCRIPTION

The multi-point fuel injection system is controlled by the Engine Control Module (ECM) (Engine Control Unit (ECU)) for precision air/fuel ratios under all driving conditions. The ECM/ECU accepts information from various sensors and switches to control idle speed, ignition timing, air conditioning power relay, fuel pump drive, purge air and EGR requirements. This system also uses a self diagnostic function which monitors various parameters for proper operation.

SYSTEM COMPONENTS

Volume Air Flow Sensor (Air Flow Sensor)

The volume air flow sensor (air flow sensor) inputs information to the ECM (ECU) for control of air/fuel mixture, ignition timing and purge air control.

Barometric Pressure Sensor

The barometric pressure sensor, senses the ambient barometric pressure and converts this pressure into a voltage which is sent the ECU or ECM. The ECU or ECM uses this signal to compute the altitude at which the vehicle is operating. This information is sent the ECM (ECU) for controlling the air/fuel mixture and ignition timing.

Intake Air Temperature Sensor

The intake air temperature sensor measures intake air temperature density and inputs it to the ECM (ECU) for control of the air/fuel mixture, ignition timing, purge air and EGR requirements.

Engine Coolant Temperature Sensor

The engine coolant temperature sensor is located in the engine coolant passage. The ECM (ECU) judges the warm up state by the sensor output voltage and provides fuel amount and ignition timing advance.

Throttle Position Sensor

The throttle position sensor, which also incorporates the idle position switch outputs information to the ECM (ECU). This information is used for the control of air/fuel mixture, idle speed and ignition timing requirements.

Idle Position Switch

The idle position switch which is incorporated in the throttle position sensor. The switch detects that the throttle valve is open and sends that information to the ECM (ECU) for control of air/fuel mixture, ignition timing and idle speed requirements.

Crank Position (CKP) (Crank Angle) Sensor

The slots on the outer circumference of the disc serve to detect the position of the crankshaft and piston relative to top dead center. The ECM (ECU) uses this information to control the air/fuel mixture, ignition timing, idle speed, air conditioning power relay and fuel pump drive requirements.

Camshaft Position (CMP) (Top Dead Center) Sensor

The CMP (top dead center) sensor sends information to the ECM (ECU) for the control for air/fuel mixture requirements.

Park/Neutral Position (Inhibitor) Switch

On models equipped with automatic transaxle, the inhibitor switch detects whether the selector lever is currently po-

sitioned in Neutral or Park. Based on this information, the ECM (ECU) senses the automatic transaxle load and drives the idle speed control servo to ensure optimum idle speed.

Power Steering Oil Pressure Switch

The power steering oil pressure switch is used to supply power steering load information to the ECM (ECU) for idle speed control.

Ignition Switch

The ignition switch supplies "On" and "Start" information to the ECM (ECU) to position idle speed control components and control fuel pump drive.

Air Conditioning Switch

On models equipped with air conditioning, when the A/C switch is engaged, an "A/C On" signal is sent to the ECM (ECU) and based on this signal, the ECM (ECU) drives the idle speed control servo to maintain ideal idle speed.

Vehicle Speed Sensor

The vehicle speed sensor or, on models less turbocharger, a reed switch, produces pulses in accordance with the vehicle speed. These are then input to the ECM (ECU) for ignition timing control and idle speed control.

TROUBLESHOOTING

Refer to **Figs. 1 through 9** for multipoint fuel injection system wiring diagrams and connector terminal identification.

Refer to **Figs. 10 and 11** for troubleshooting procedures.

DIAGNOSIS & TESTING

Refer to **Figs. 1 through 9** for multipoint fuel injection system wiring diagrams and connector terminal identification.

The "Check Engine" light on the instrument cluster will be illuminated whenever the ECM (ECU) detects a system irregularity. The lamp will remain illuminated until the ECM (ECU) determines the system has returned to normal operation. The lamp will be illuminated for approximately five seconds when the ignition switch is placed in the On position to indicate the system is functioning. The following items are indicated by illumination of the "Check Engine" lamp:

1. Engine Control Unit (ECU) and Engine Control Module (ECM).
2. Heated oxygen sensor.
3. Volume Air Flow Sensor (Air flow sensor).
4. Intake air temperature sensor.
5. Throttle position sensor.
6. Engine coolant temperature sensor.
7. Crankshaft position sensor (CKP) (Crank angle sensor).
8. CMP (Top dead center) sensor.
9. Barometric pressure sensor.
10. Detonation sensor (DOHC).
11. Ignition timing adjustment signal (DOHC).
12. Injector.

13. EGR system (California models only).
14. Ignition coil (DOHC).
15. Power transistor unit (DOHC).

All diagnostic procedures must start with a thorough visual inspection of the vehicle.

1. Verify all fuel system electrical connections and harness condition.
   a. Connectors must lock together.
   b. Look for terminals that are pushed out, loose or corroded.
   c. Ensure wiring between connectors is not pinched behind other components or screws.
2. Look for any added accessories that may affect normal operation of the MPI system.
3. All hoses and vacuum lines connections must be secure and hoses must not be pinched.
4. All vehicle with an air flow meter, intake hoses and air cleaner housings must be in placed and secure.
5. Vehicle battery must be fully charged.

Accessing Diagnostic Trouble Codes

USING ANALOG VOLTMETER

1993

The presence or absence of diagnostic trouble codes can be established by reading voltmeter needle deflections. For example, the "tens" digit of Diagnostic Trouble Code 24 would be indicated by two initial 1.5 second deflections separated by a .5 second pause. This would be followed by the "ones" digit, which would be indicated by four .5 second deflections separated by .5 second pauses.

To access diagnostic trouble codes, proceed as follows:

1. Turn ignition switch to Off position.
2. Connect suitable analog voltmeter between MPI terminal and ground, **Fig. 12.**
3. Turn ignition switch to On position and observe voltmeter needle. Refer to "Diagnostic Trouble Code Interpretation" for further information regarding specific diagnostic trouble codes indicated by needle deflections.

USING MALFUNCTION INDICATOR LAMP (MIL)

1994–95

Flashes of the MIL or "Check Engine" lamp may be used to establish the presence or absence of stored diagnostic trouble codes. For example, in order to indicate the presence of Diagnostic Trouble Code 24, the lamp would first illuminate in two 1.5 second pulses separated by a .5 second pause ("tens" digit), then would illuminate in four .5 second pulses separated by .5 second pauses ("ones" digit).

To access diagnostic trouble codes, proceed as follows:

1. Connect diagnostic check harness

Continued on page 11-34

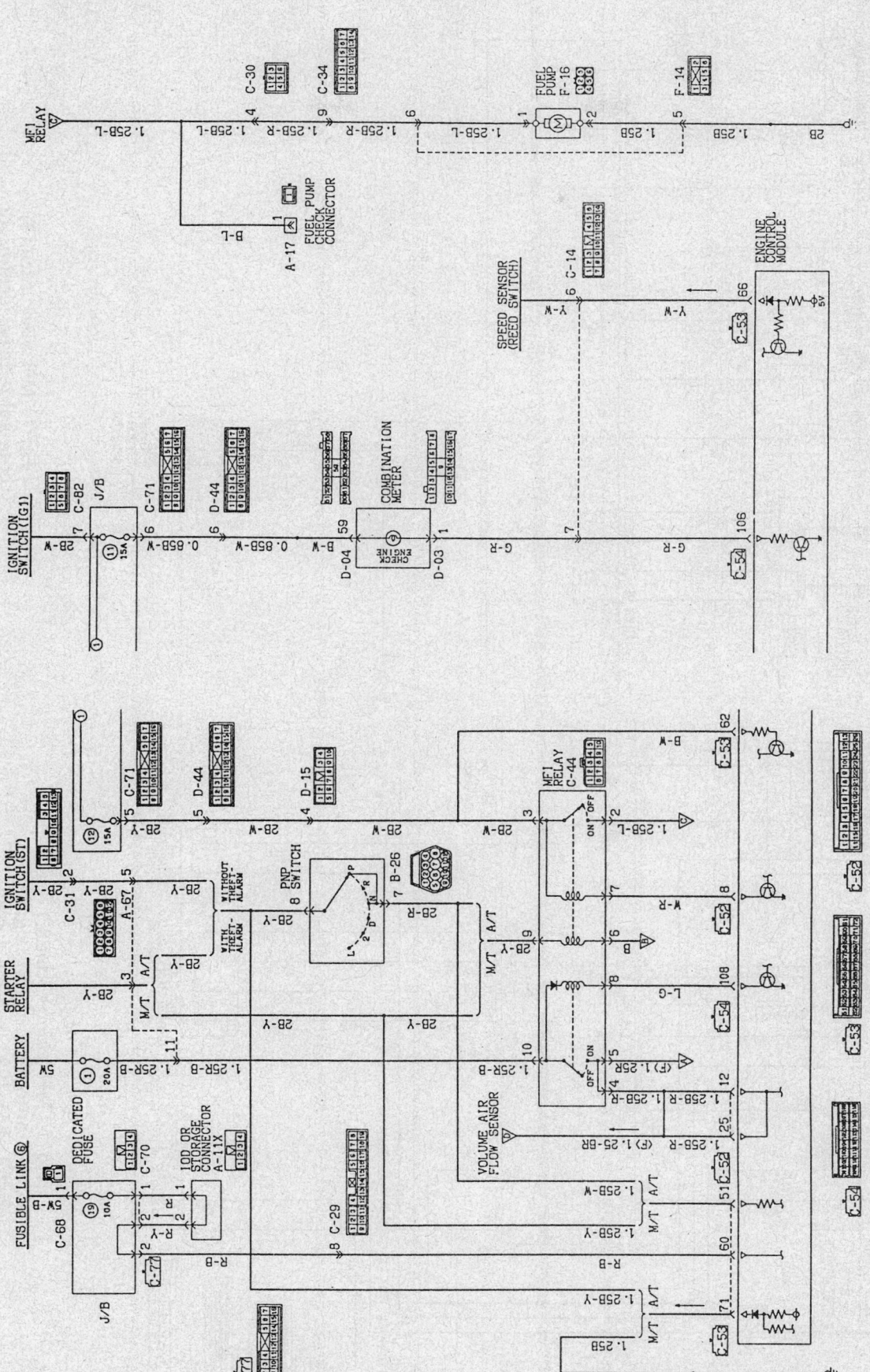

Fig. 1 MPI wiring circuit & connector terminal identification (Part 2 of 6). 1993 w/SOHC engine

Fig. 1 MPI wiring circuit & connector terminal identification (Part 1 of 6). 1993 w/SOHC engine

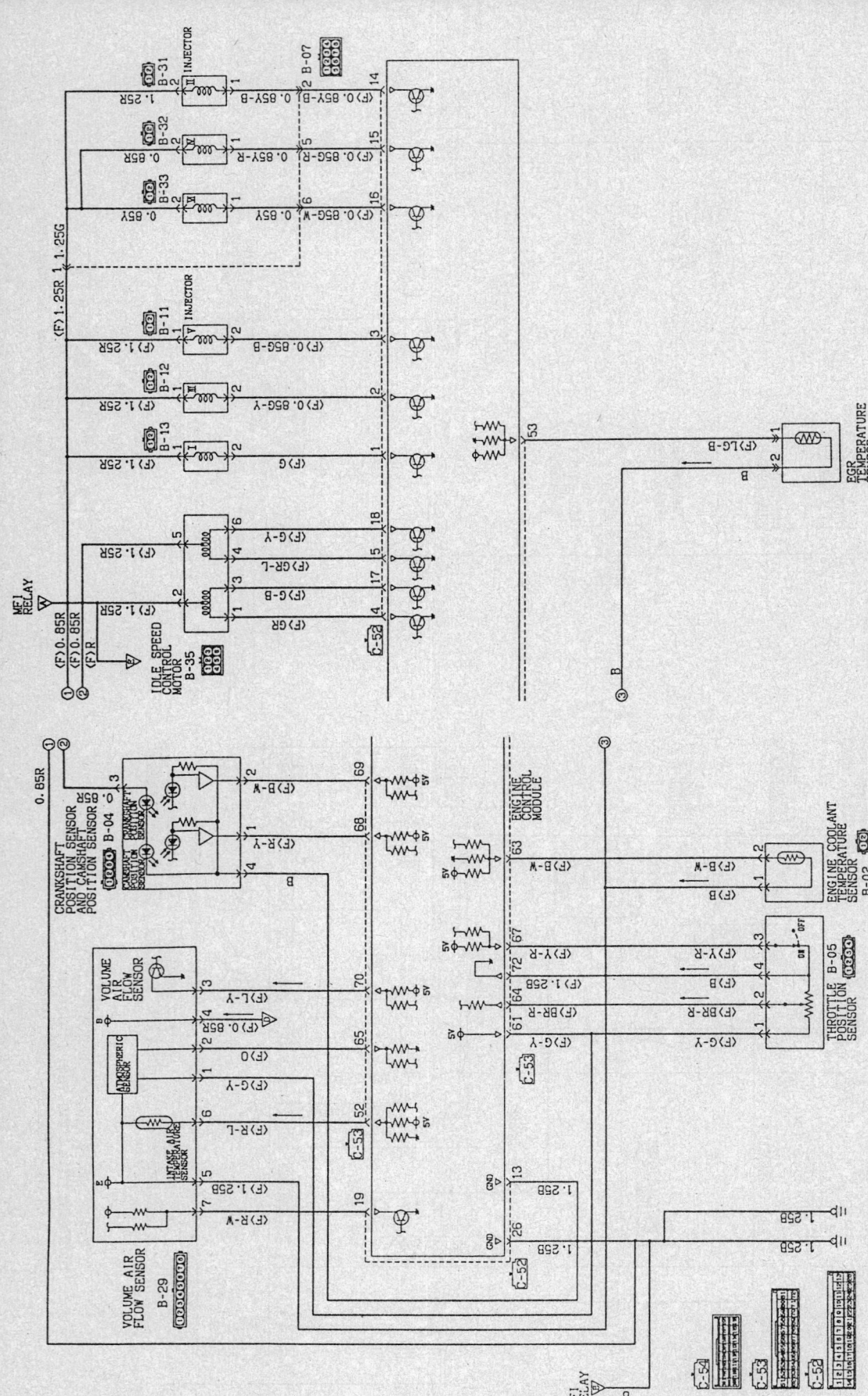

Fig. 1 MPI wiring circuit &
connector terminal identification
(Part 4 of 6). 1993 w/SOHC engine

Fig. 1 MPI wiring circuit &
connector terminal identification
(Part 3 of 6). 1993 w/SOHC engine

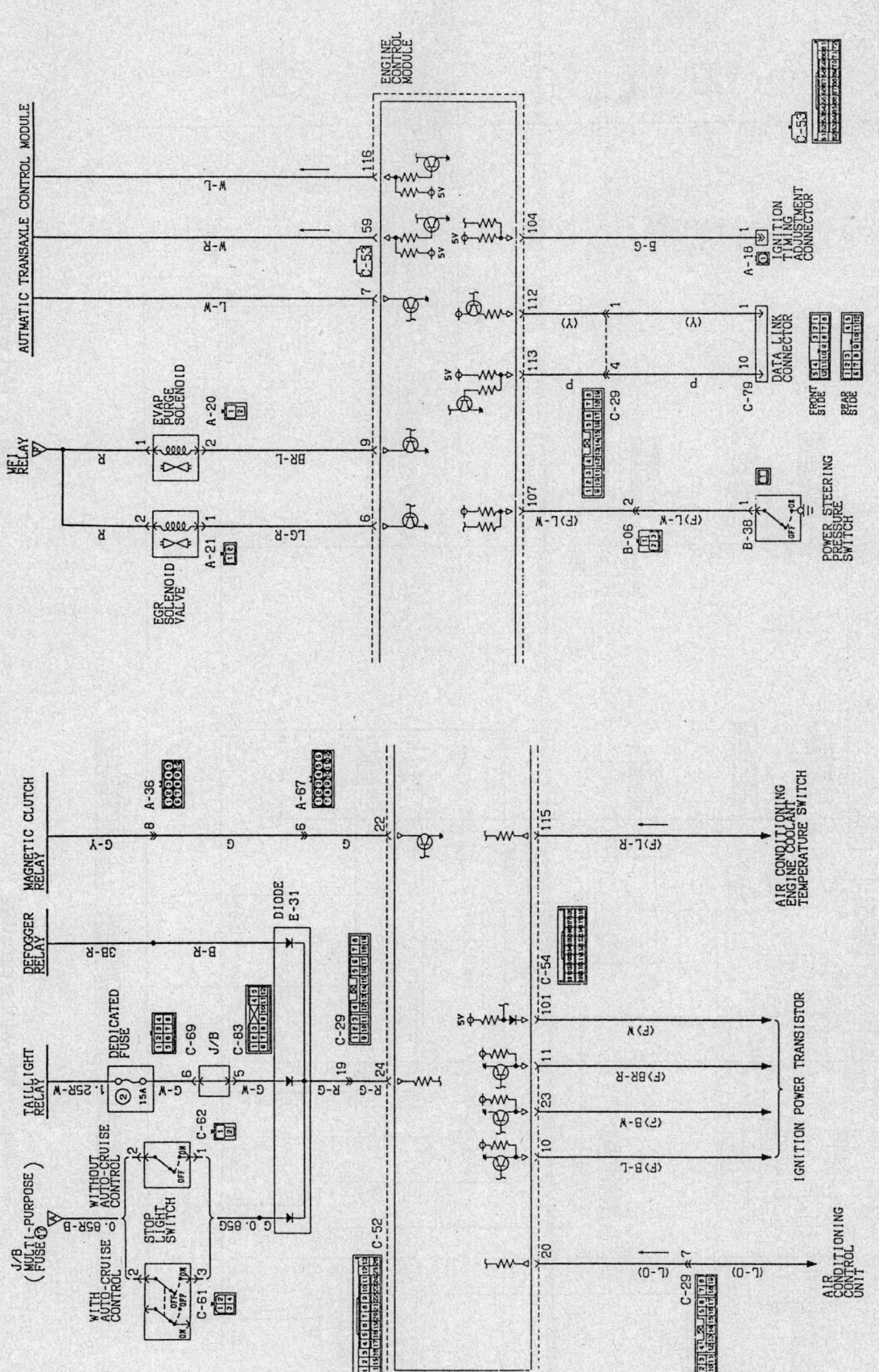

Fig. 1 MPI wiring circuit & connector terminal identification (Part 6 of 6). 1993 w/SOHC engine

Fig. 1 MPI wiring circuit & connector terminal identification (Part 5 of 6). 1993 w/SOHC engine

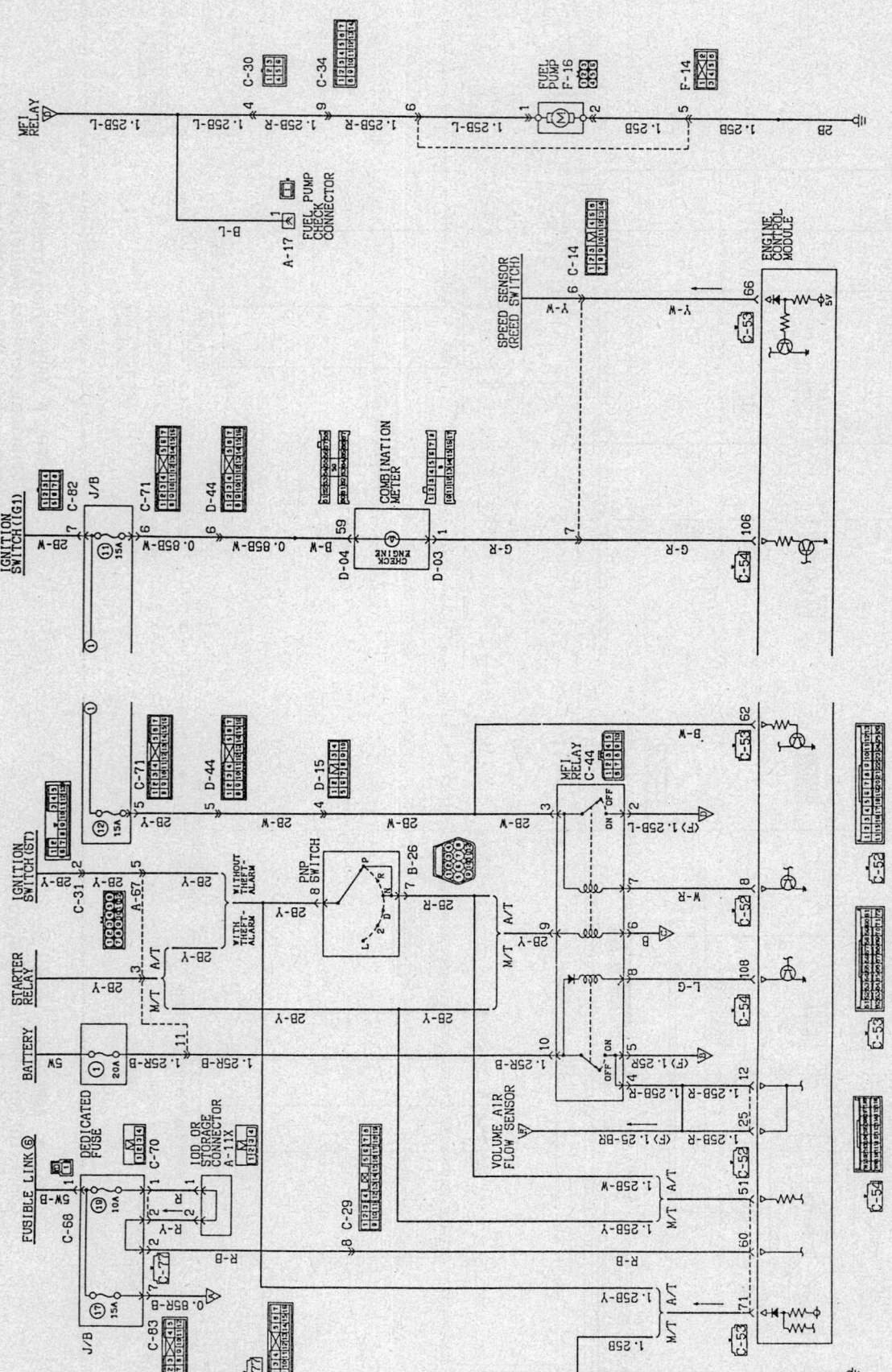

Fig. 2 MPI wiring circuit & connector terminal identification (Part 2 of 6). 1993 w/DOHC non-turbocharged engine

Fig. 2 MPI wiring circuit & connector terminal identification (Part 1 of 6). 1993 w/DOHC non-turbocharged engine

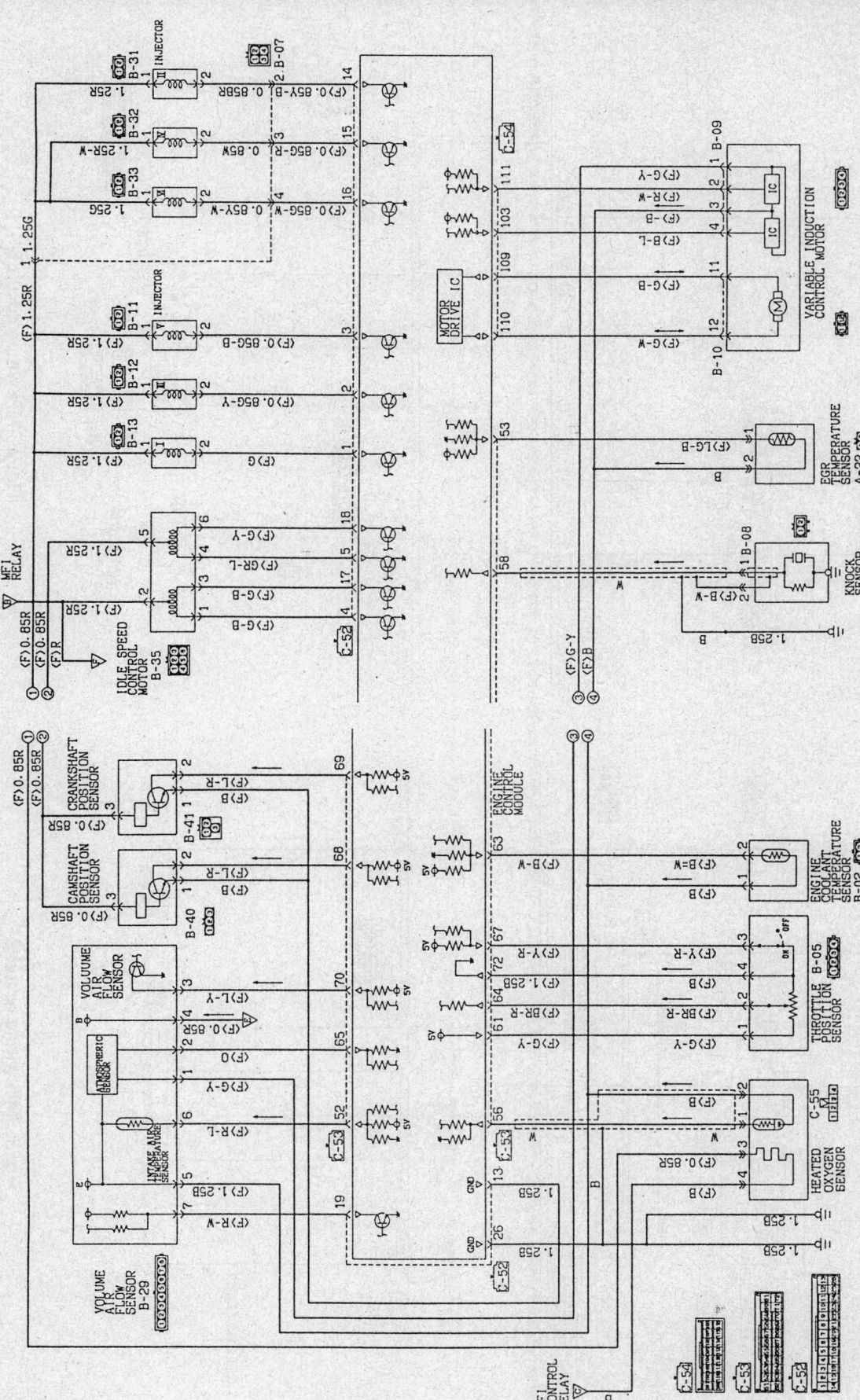

Fig. 2 MPI wiring circuit & connector terminal identification (Part 4 of 6), 1993 w/DOHC non-turbocharged engine

Fig. 2 MPI wiring circuit & connector terminal identification (Part 3 of 6), 1993 w/DOHC non-turbocharged engine

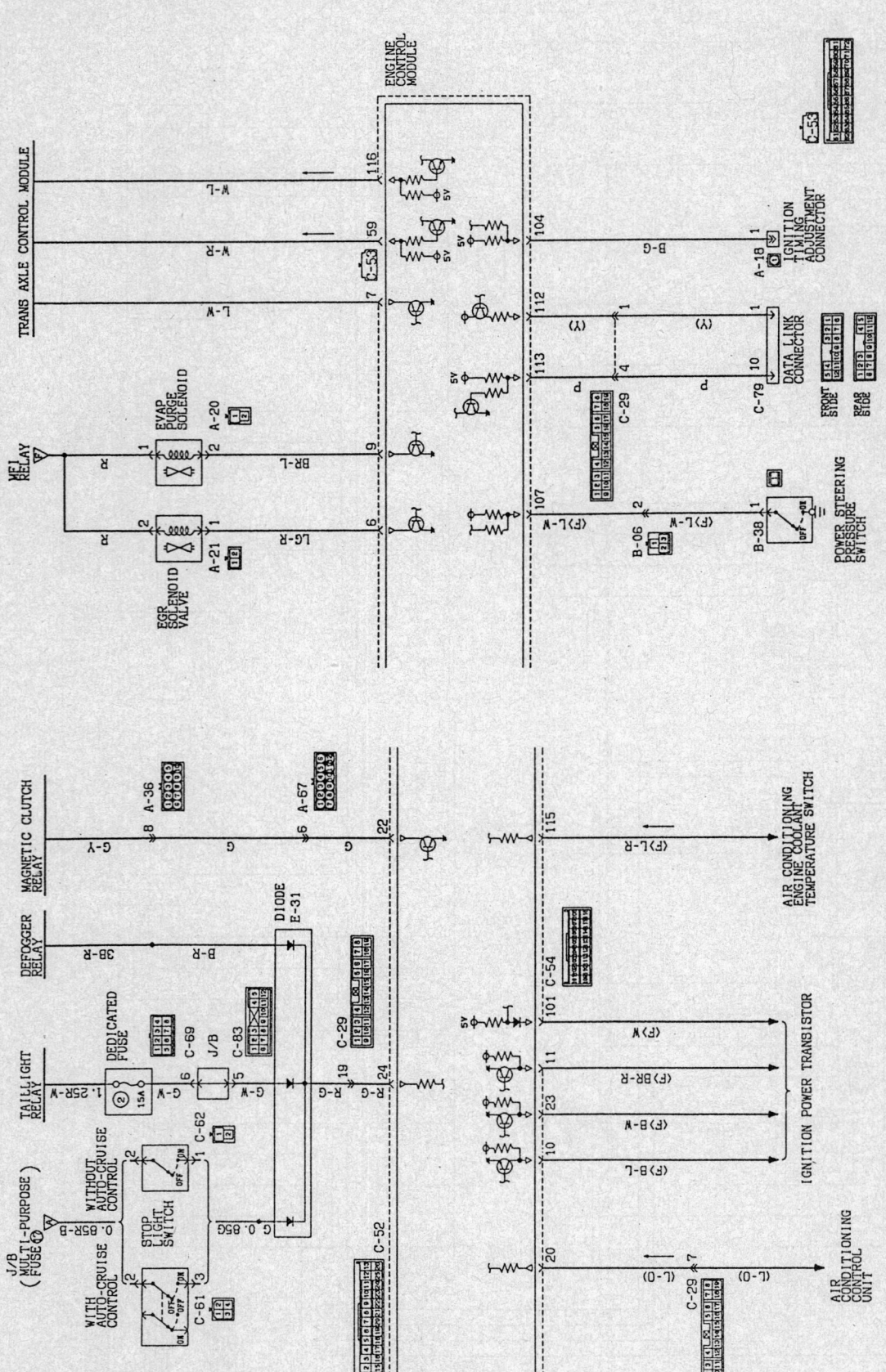

Fig. 2   MPI wiring circuit &
connector terminal identification
(Part 6 of 6). 1993 w/DOHC
non-turbocharged engine

Fig. 2   MPI wiring circuit &
connector terminal identification
(Part 5 of 6). 1993 w/DOHC
non-turbocharged engine

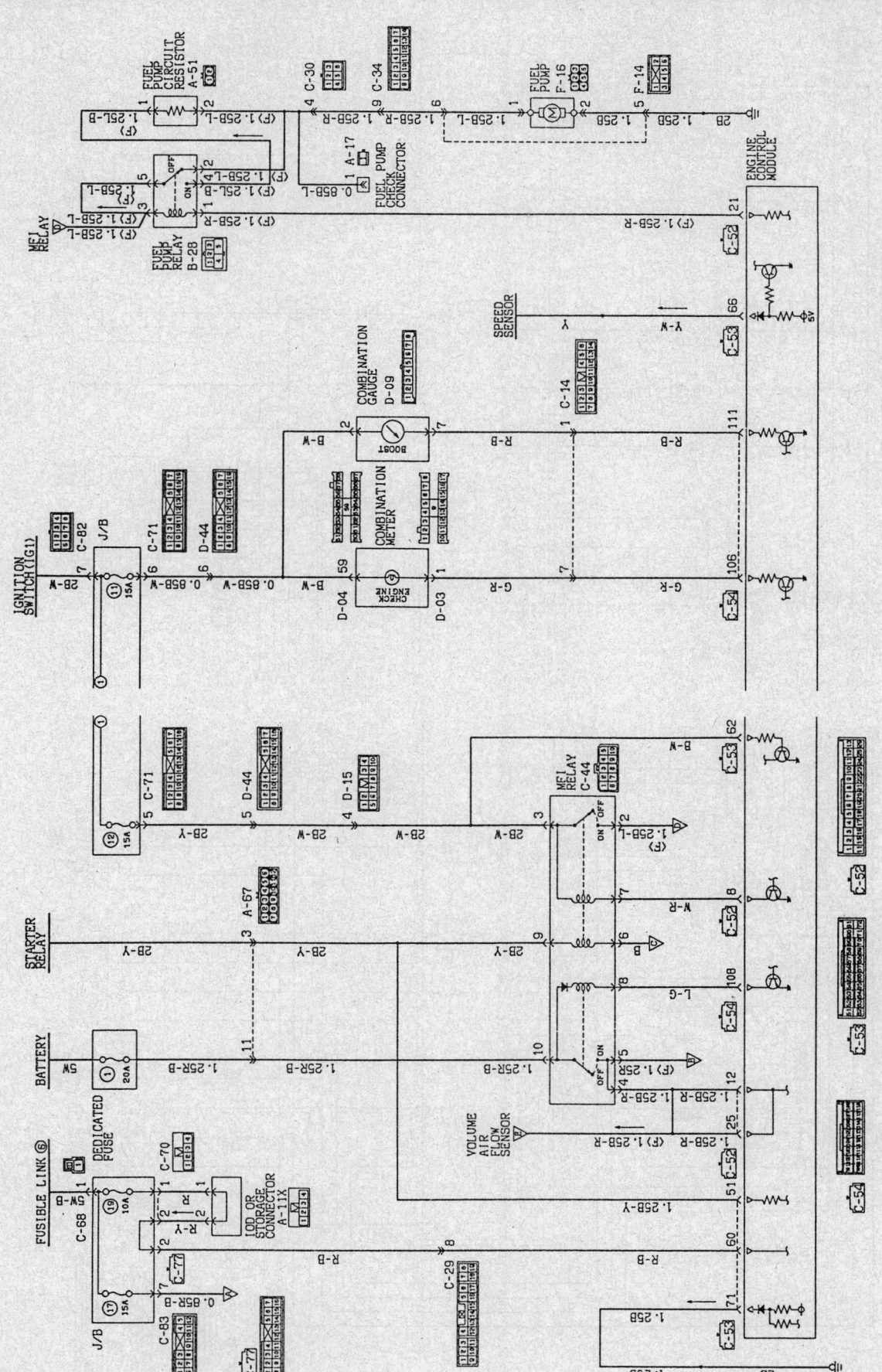

Fig. 3 MPI wiring circuit & connector terminal identification (Part 2 of 6). 1993 w/DOHC turbocharged engine

Fig. 3 MPI wiring circuit & connector terminal identification (Part 1 of 6). 1993 w/DOHC turbocharged engine

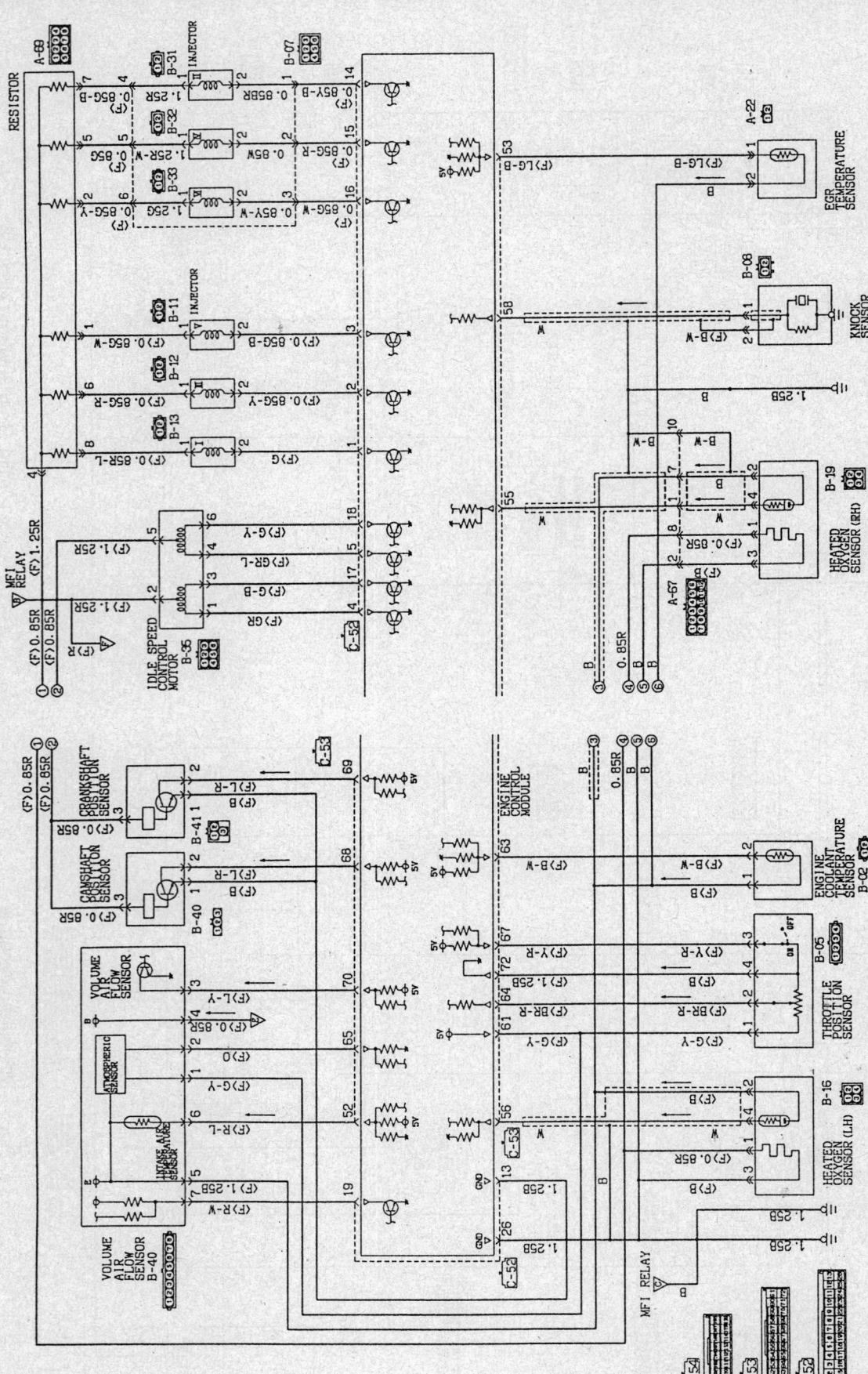

Fig. 3 MPI wiring circuit & connector terminal identification (Part 4 of 6). 1993 w/DOHC turbocharged engine

Fig. 3 MPI wiring circuit & connector terminal identification (Part 3 of 6). 1993 w/DOHC turbocharged engine

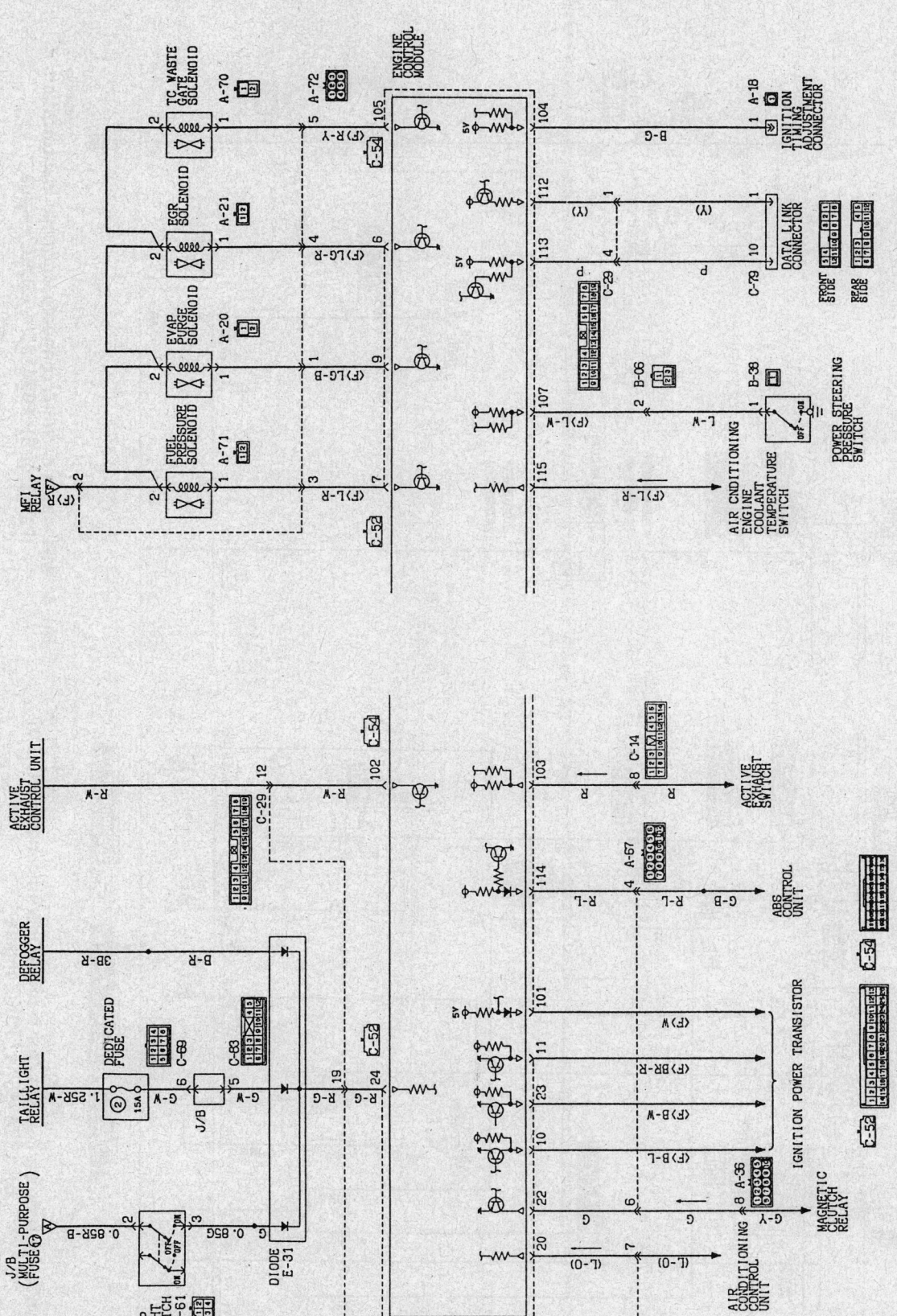

Fig. 3 MPI wiring circuit & connector terminal identification (Part 6 of 6). 1993 w/DOHC turbocharged engine

Fig. 3 MPI wiring circuit & connector terminal identification (Part 5 of 6). 1993 w/DOHC turbocharged engine

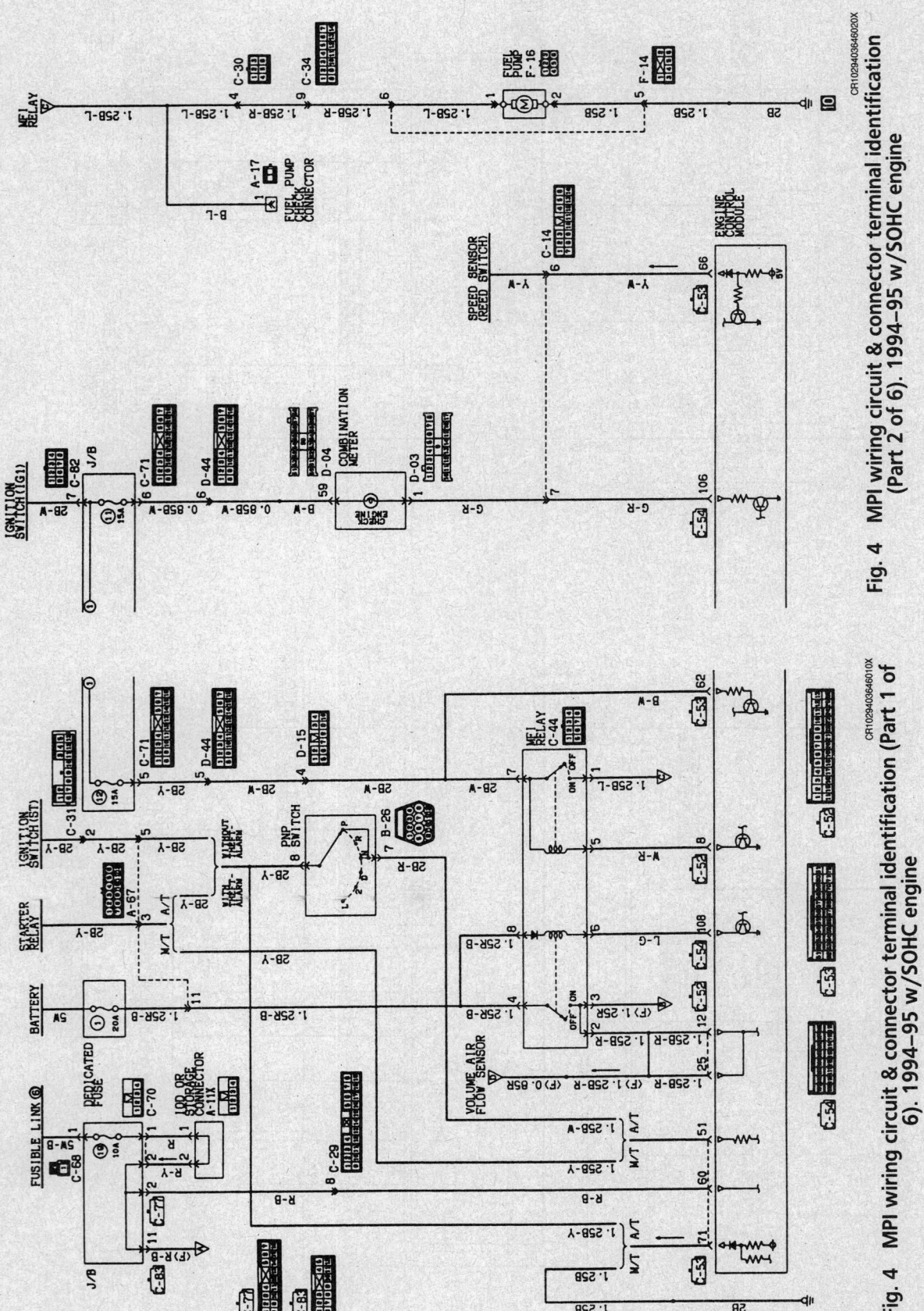

Fig. 4   MPI wiring circuit & connector terminal identification (Part 2 of 6). 1994–95 w/SOHC engine

Fig. 4   MPI wiring circuit & connector terminal identification (Part 1 of 6). 1994–95 w/SOHC engine

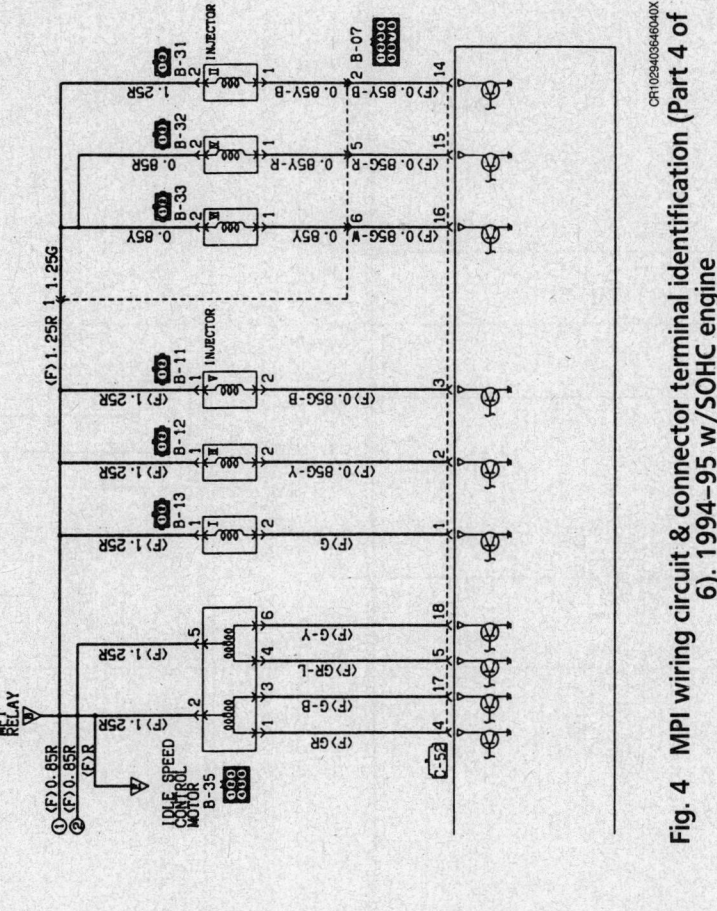

Fig. 4 MPI wiring circuit & connector terminal identification (Part 4 of 6). 1994-95 w/SOHC engine

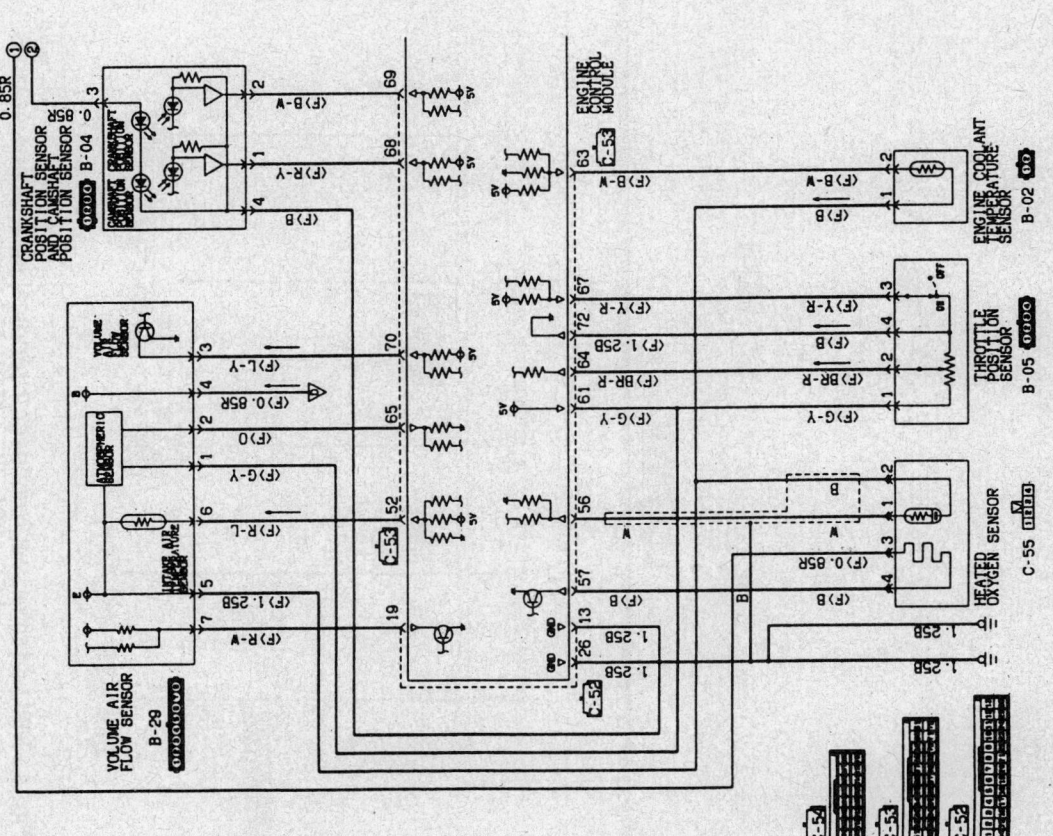

Fig. 4 MPI wiring circuit & connector terminal identification (Part 3 of 6). 1994-95 w/SOHC engine

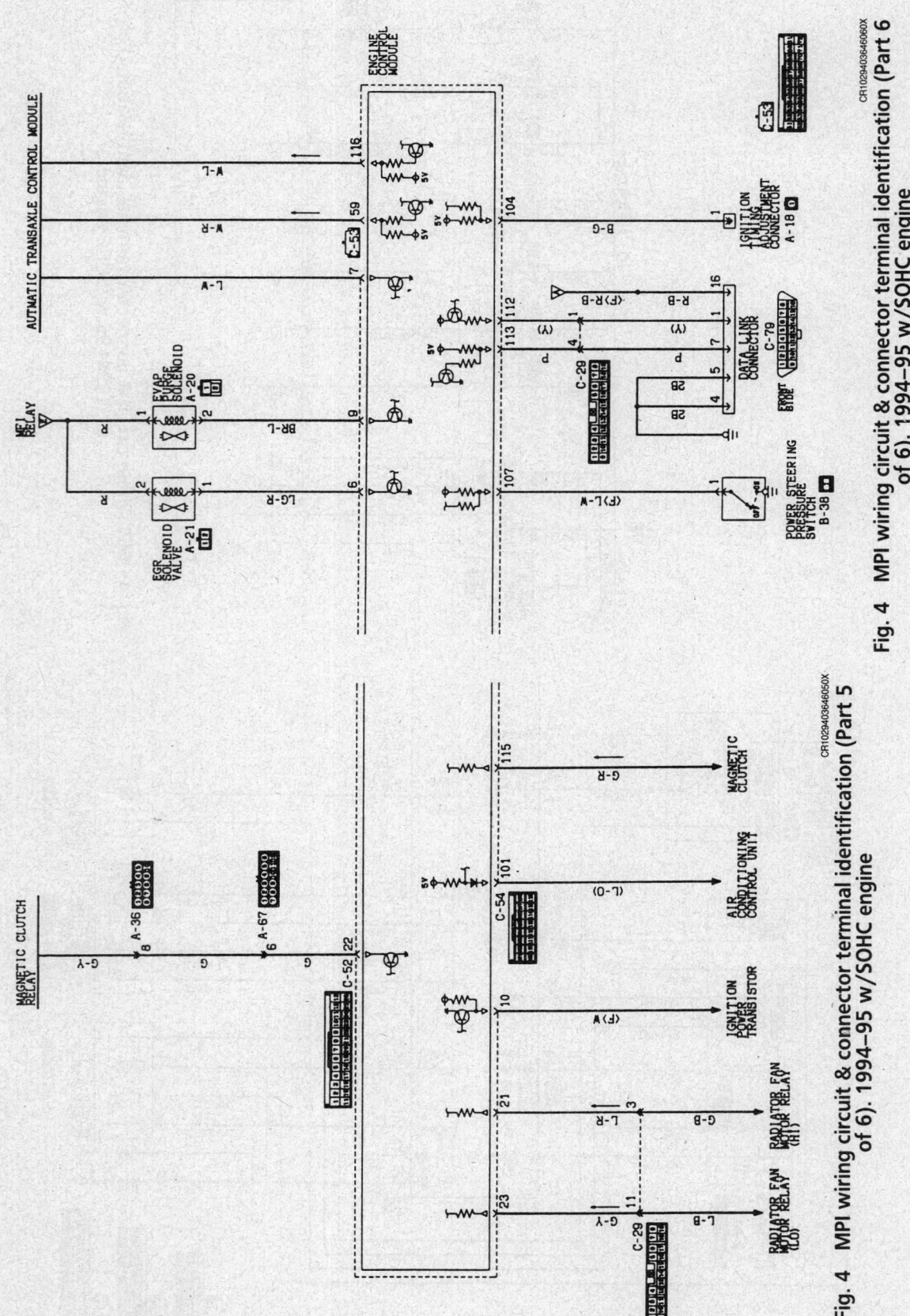

Fig. 4 MPI wiring circuit & connector terminal identification (Part 6 of 6). 1994–95 w/SOHC engine

Fig. 4 MPI wiring circuit & connector terminal identification (Part 5 of 6). 1994–95 w/SOHC engine

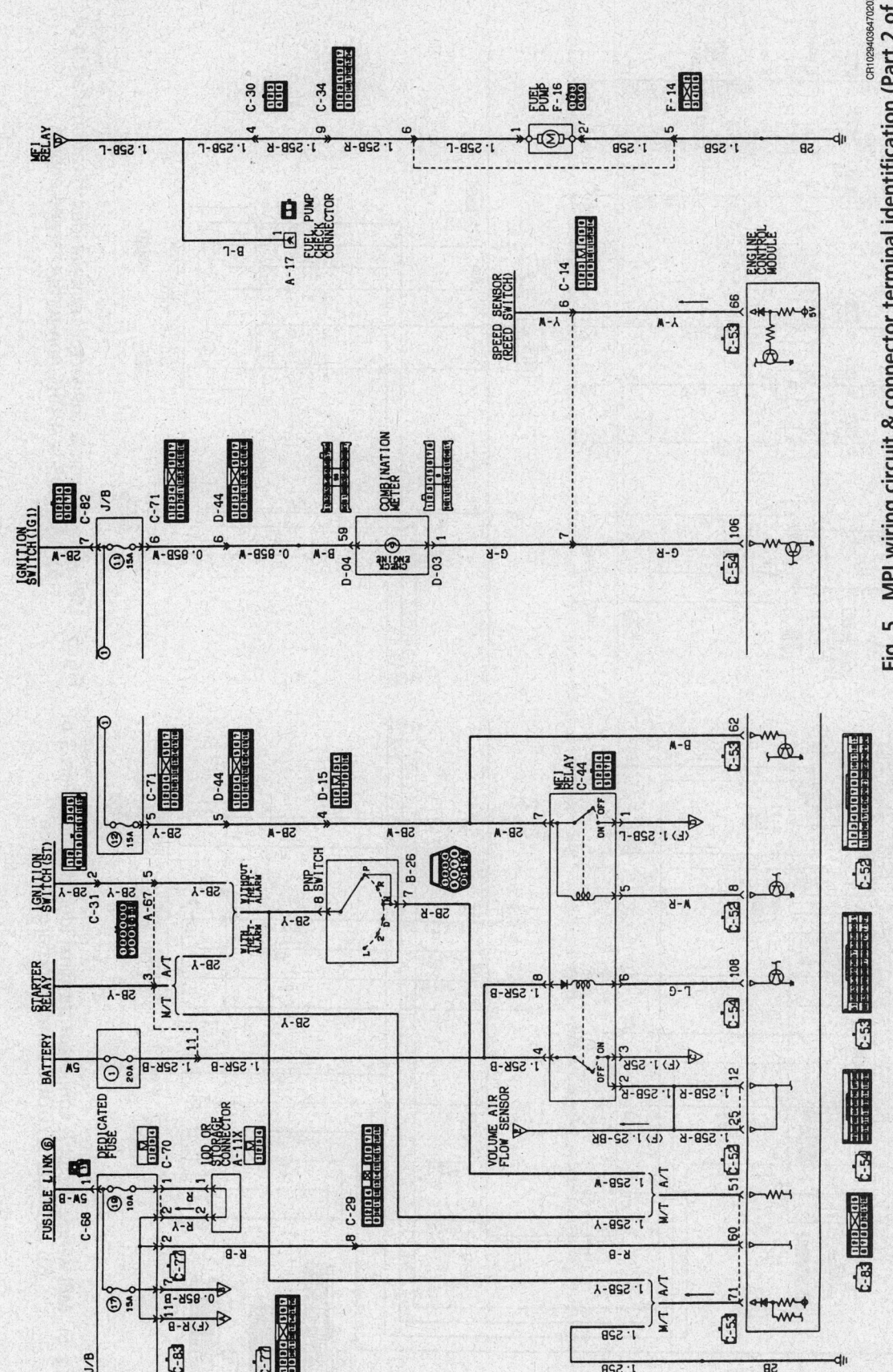

Fig. 5 MPI wiring circuit & connector terminal identification (Part 2 of 6). 1994–95 w/DOHC non-turbocharged engine

Fig. 5 MPI wiring circuit & connector terminal identification (Part 1 of 6). 1994–95 w/DOHC non-turbocharged engine

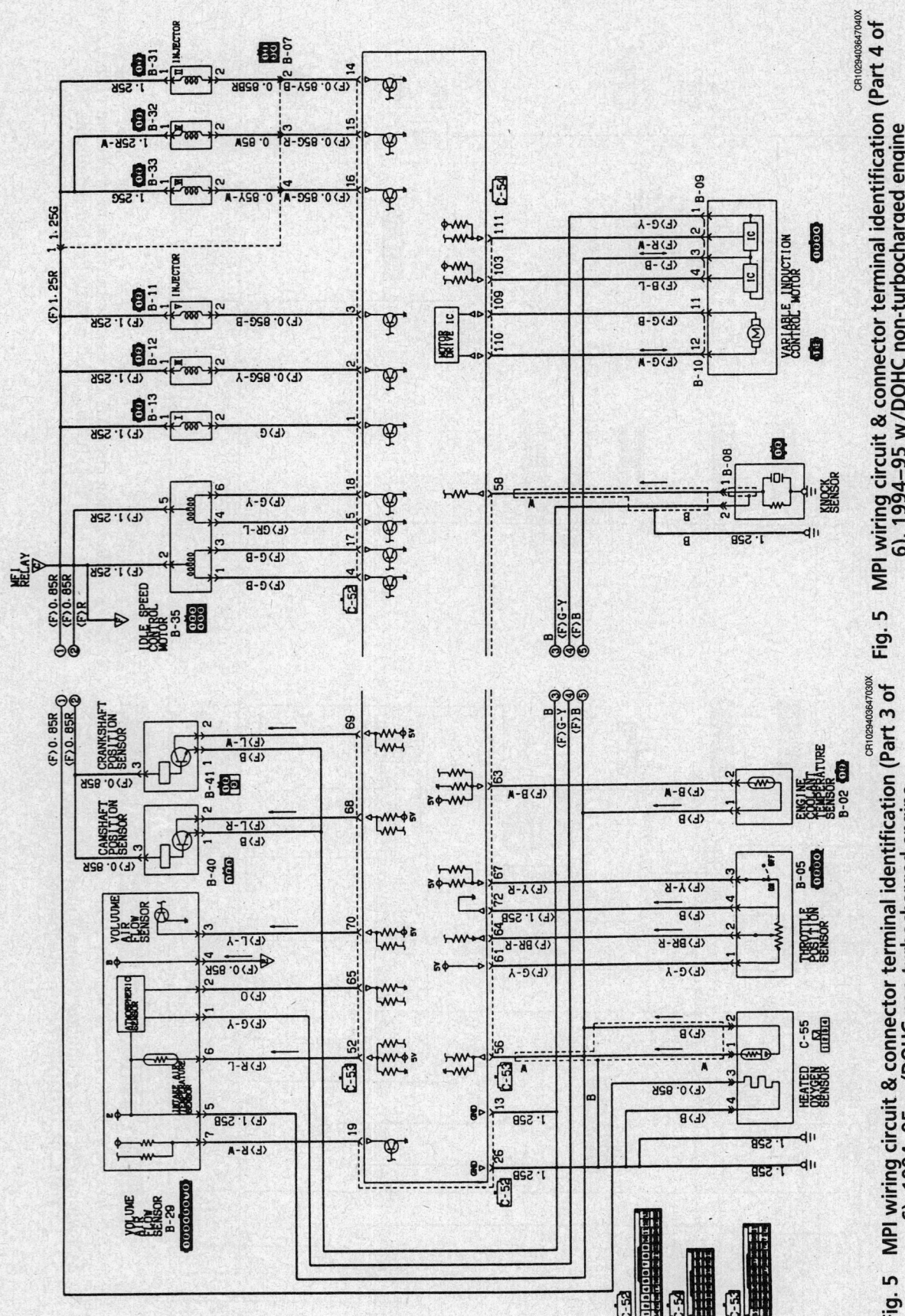

Fig. 5   MPI wiring circuit & connector terminal identification (Part 4 of 6). 1994–95 w/DOHC non-turbocharged engine

Fig. 5   MPI wiring circuit & connector terminal identification (Part 3 of 6). 1994–95 w/DOHC non-turbocharged engine

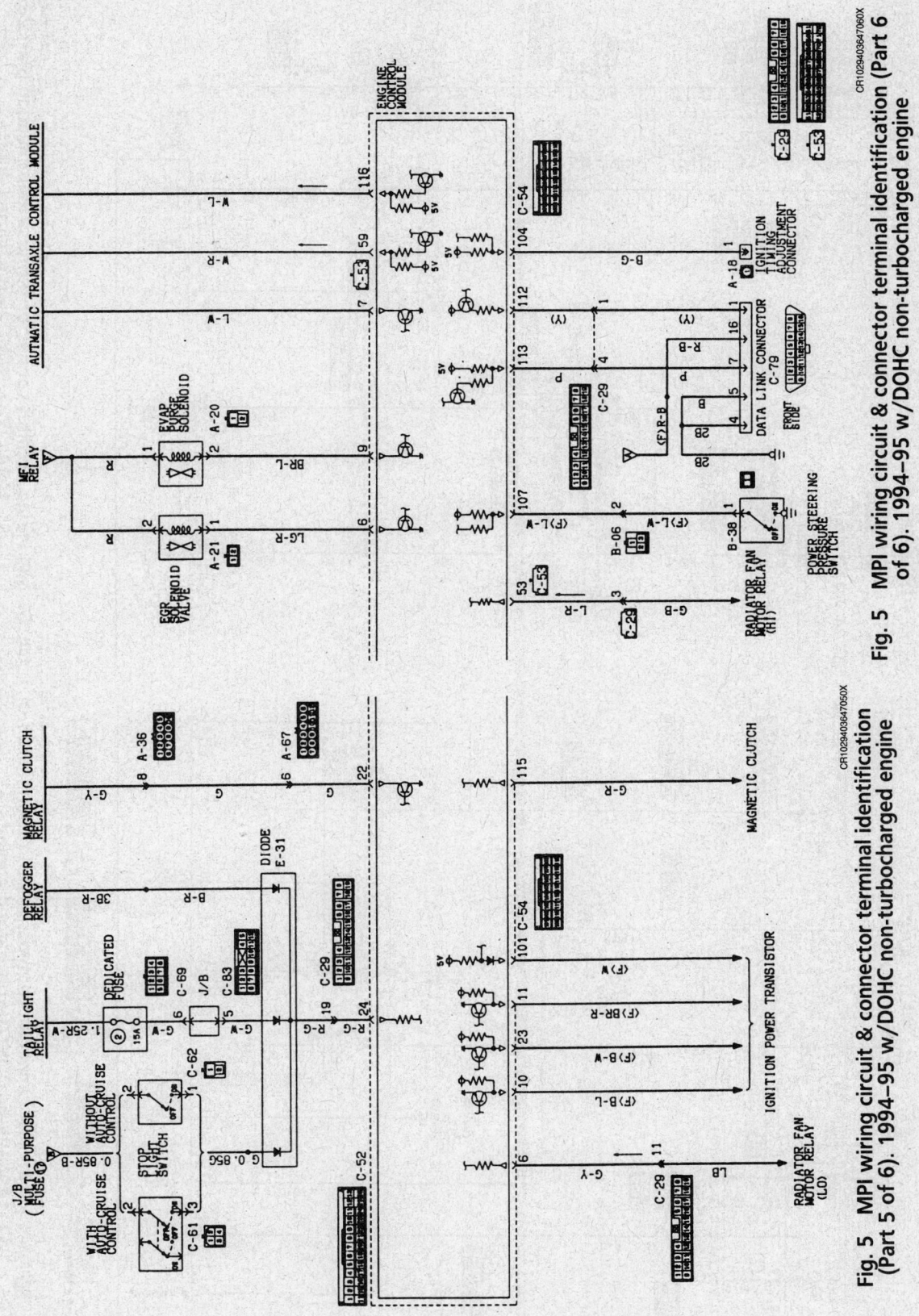

Fig. 5   MPI wiring circuit & connector terminal identification (Part 6 of 6). 1994–95 w/DOHC non-turbocharged engine

Fig. 5   MPI wiring circuit & connector terminal identification (Part 5 of 6). 1994–95 w/DOHC non-turbocharged engine

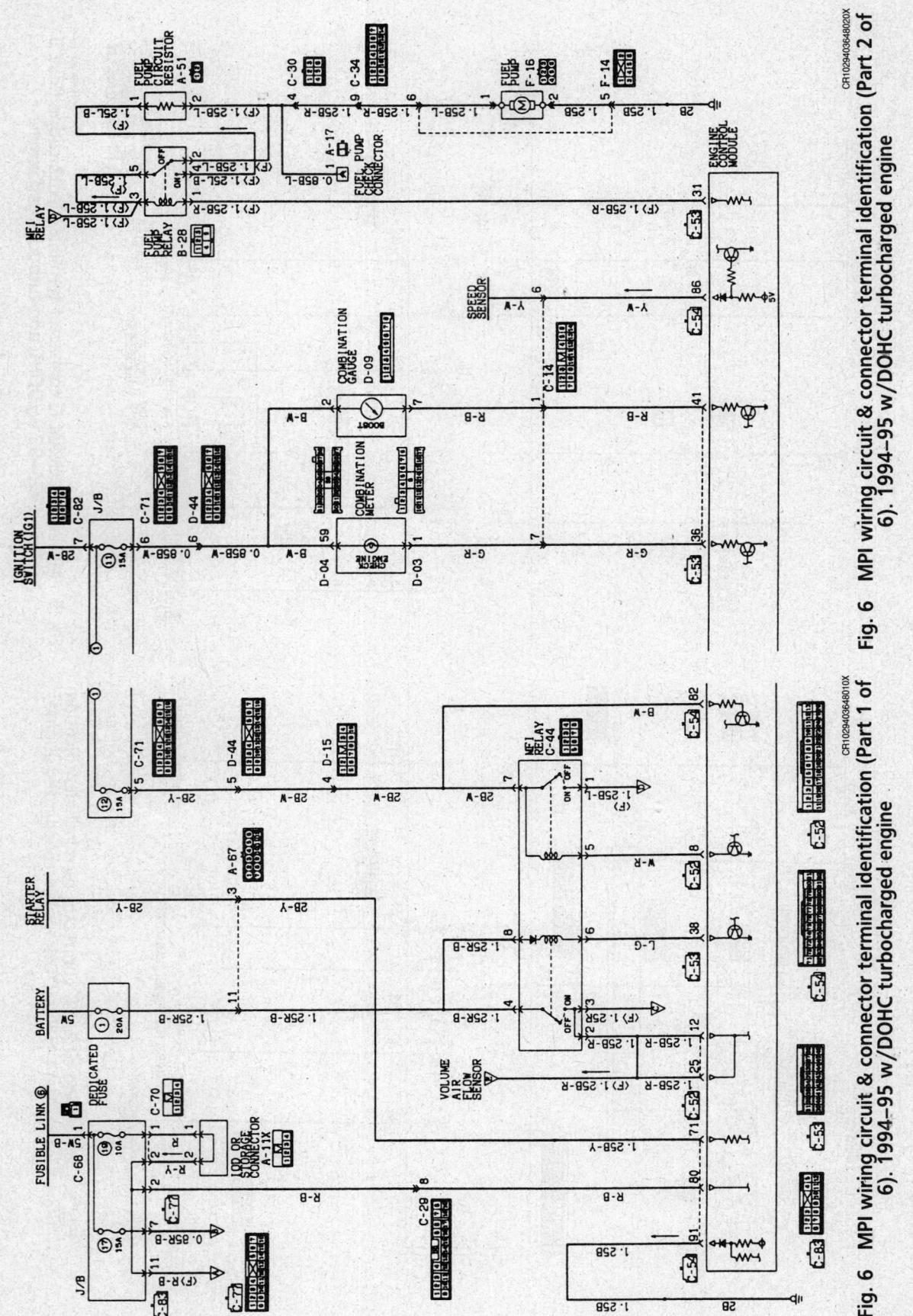

Fig. 6   MPI wiring circuit & connector terminal identification (Part 2 of 6). 1994-95 w/DOHC turbocharged engine

Fig. 6   MPI wiring circuit & connector terminal identification (Part 1 of 6). 1994-95 w/DOHC turbocharged engine

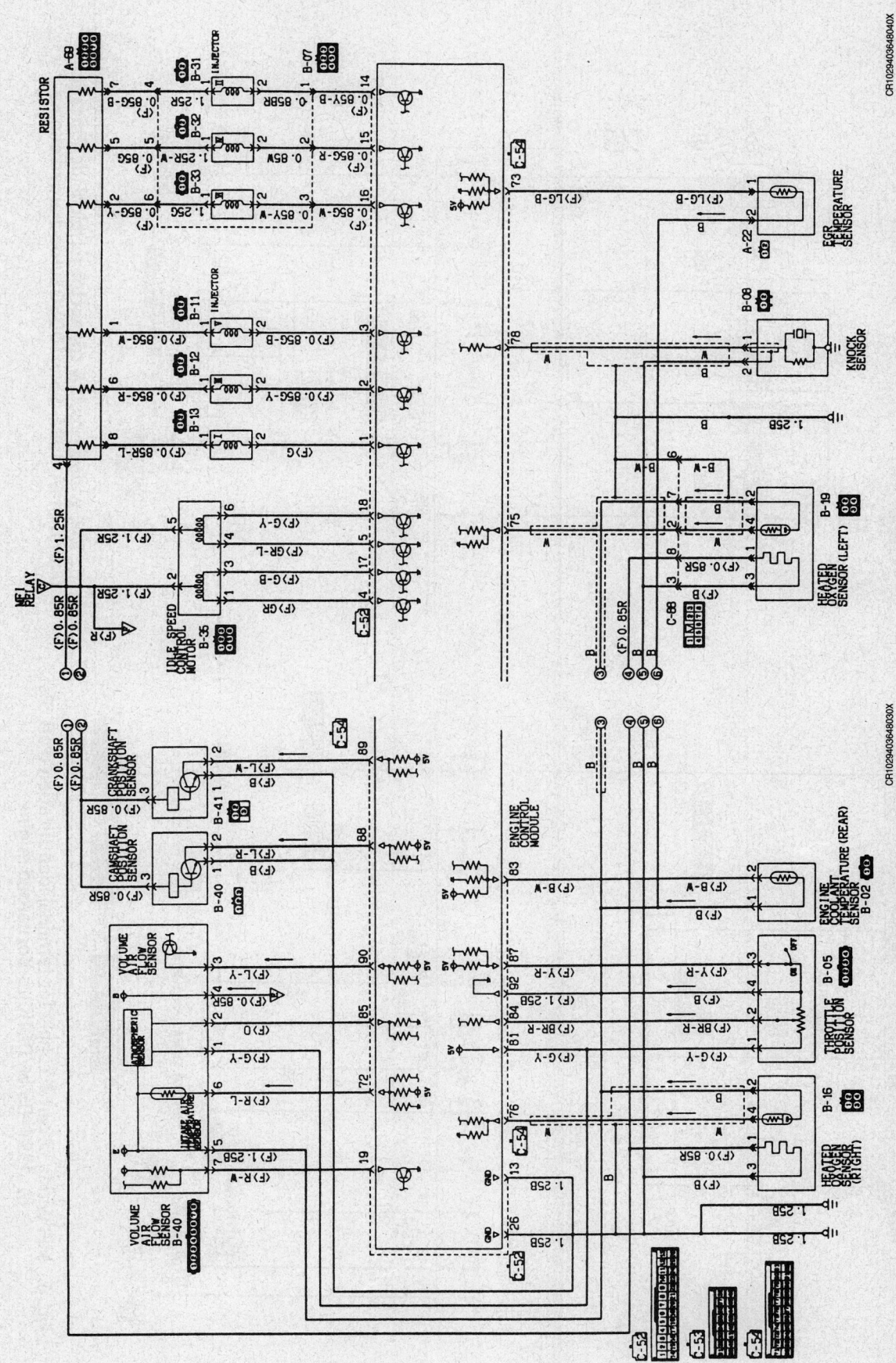

Fig. 6 MPI wiring circuit & connector terminal identification (Part 4 of 6). 1994-95 w/DOHC turbocharged engine

Fig. 6 MPI wiring circuit & connector terminal identification (Part 3 of 6). 1994-95 w/DOHC turbocharged engine

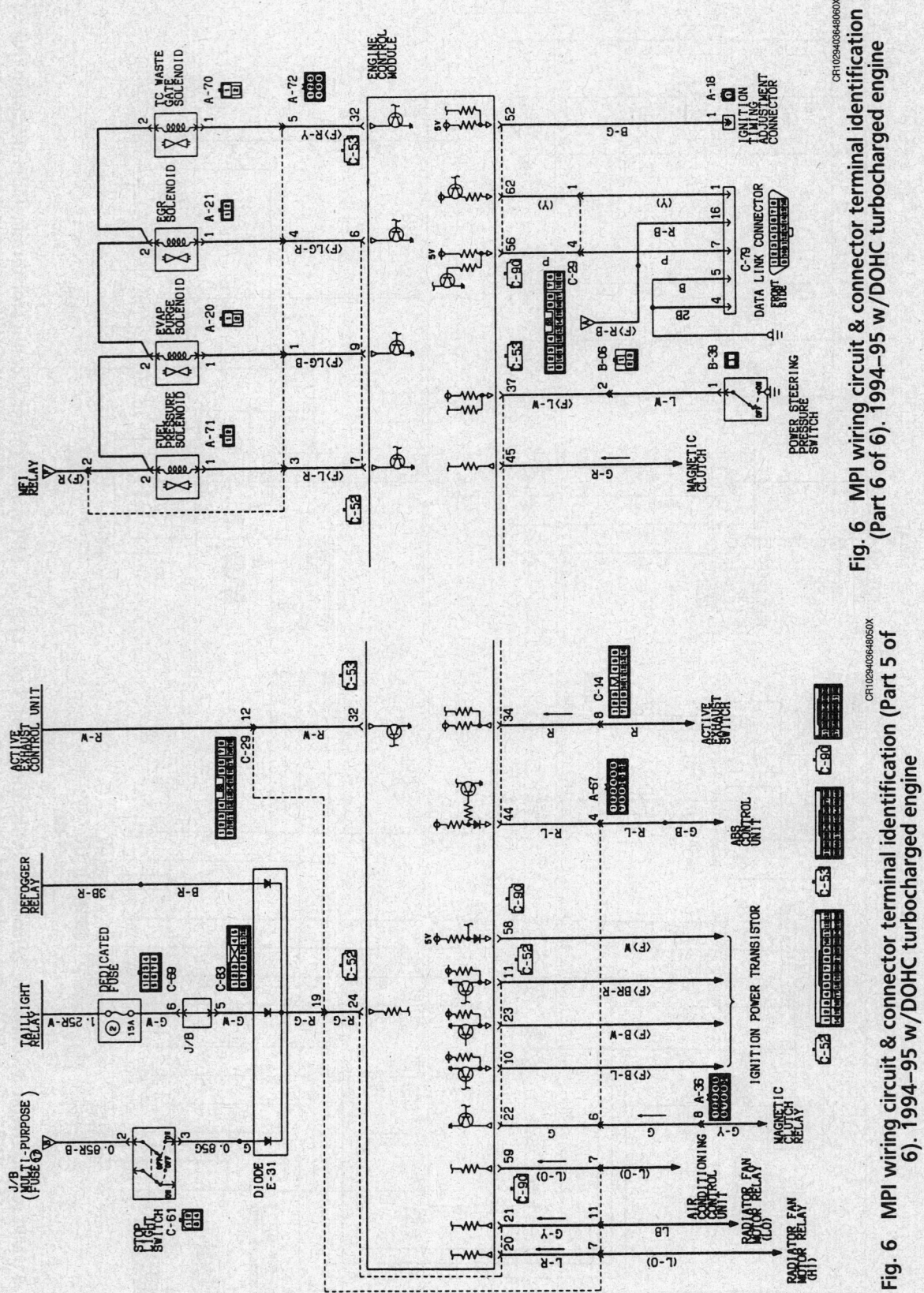

Fig. 6 MPI wiring circuit & connector terminal identification (Part 6 of 6). 1994–95 w/DOHC turbocharged engine

Fig. 6 MPI wiring circuit & connector terminal identification (Part 5 of 6). 1994–95 w/DOHC turbocharged engine

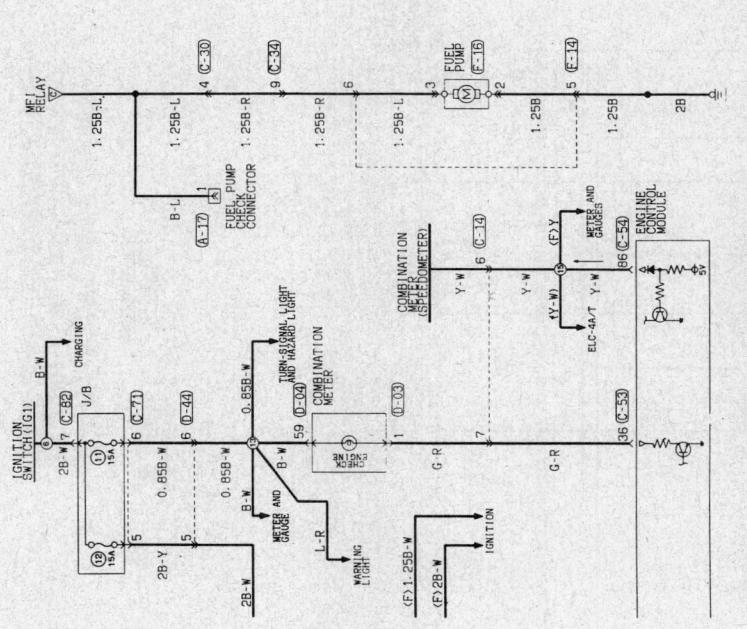

Fig. 7 MPI wiring circuit & connector terminal identification (Part 2 of 8). 1996 w/SOHC engine

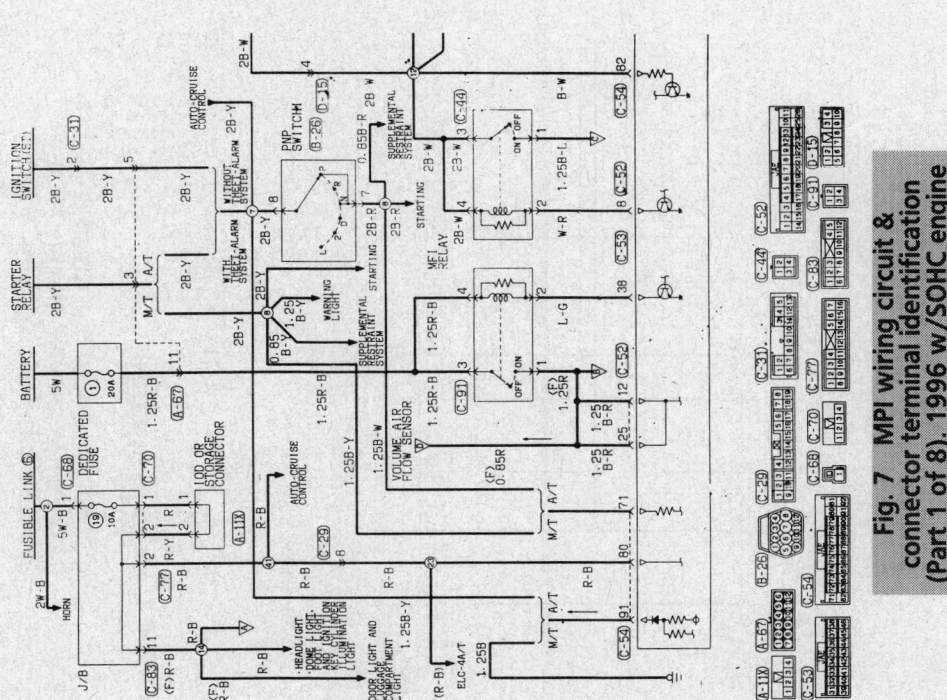

Fig. 7 MPI wiring circuit & connector terminal identification (Part 1 of 8). 1996 w/SOHC engine

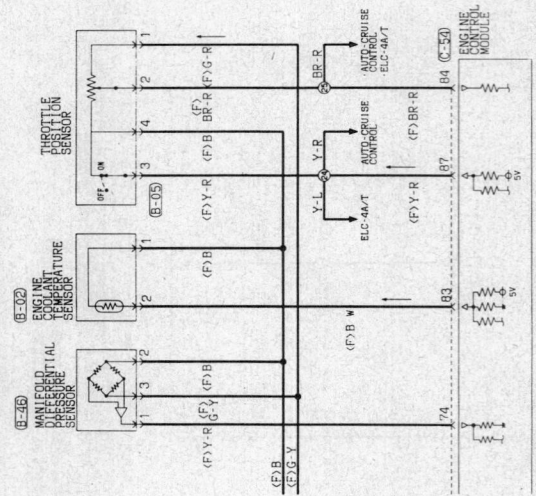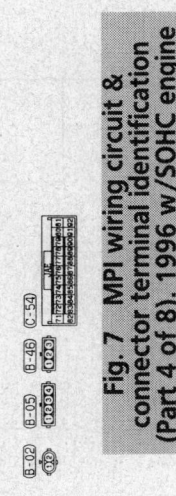

Fig. 7 MPI wiring circuit & connector terminal identification (Part 4 of 8). 1996 w/SOHC engine

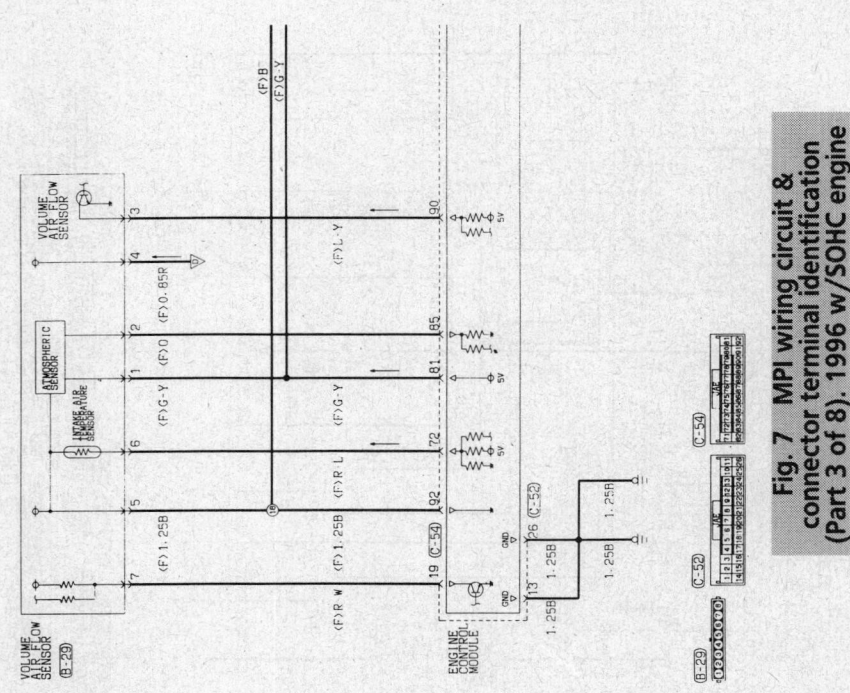

Fig. 7 MPI wiring circuit & connector terminal identification (Part 3 of 8). 1996 w/SOHC engine

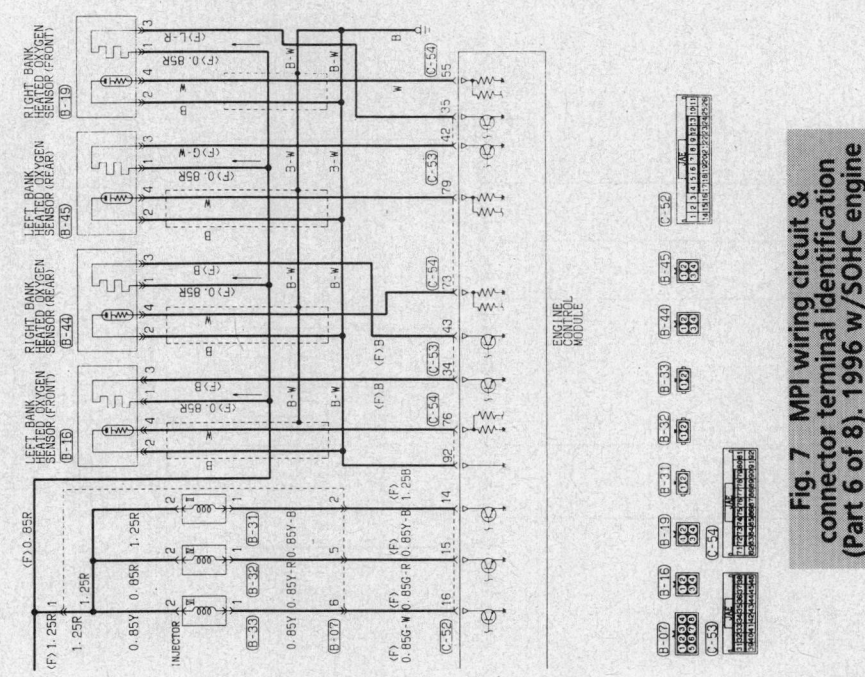

Fig. 7 MPI wiring circuit & connector terminal identification (Part 6 of 8). 1996 w/SOHC engine

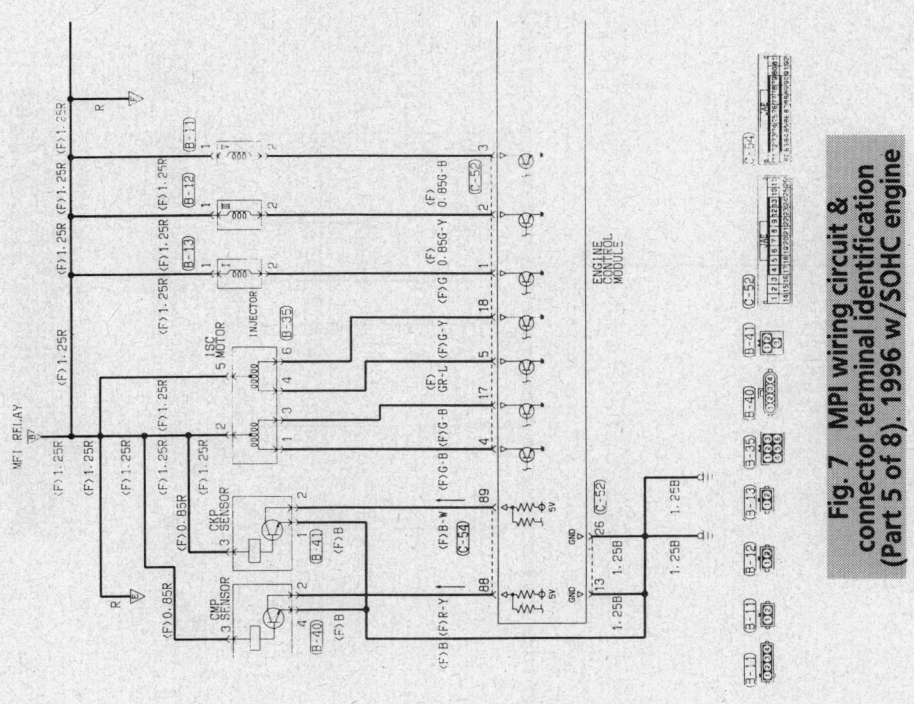

Fig. 7 MPI wiring circuit & connector terminal identification (Part 5 of 8). 1996 w/SOHC engine

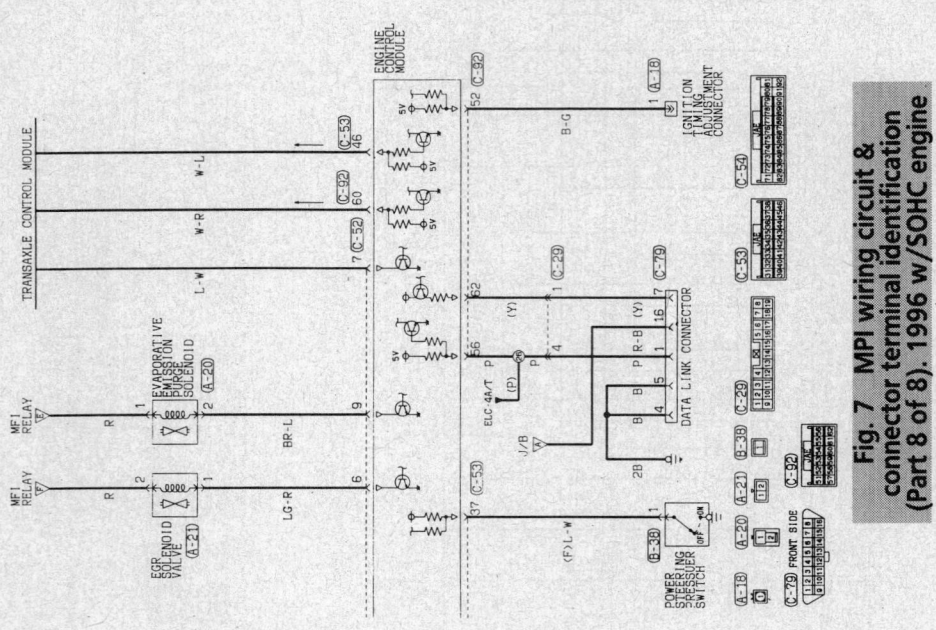

Fig. 7 MPI wiring circuit & connector terminal identification (Part 8 of 8). 1996 w/SOHC engine

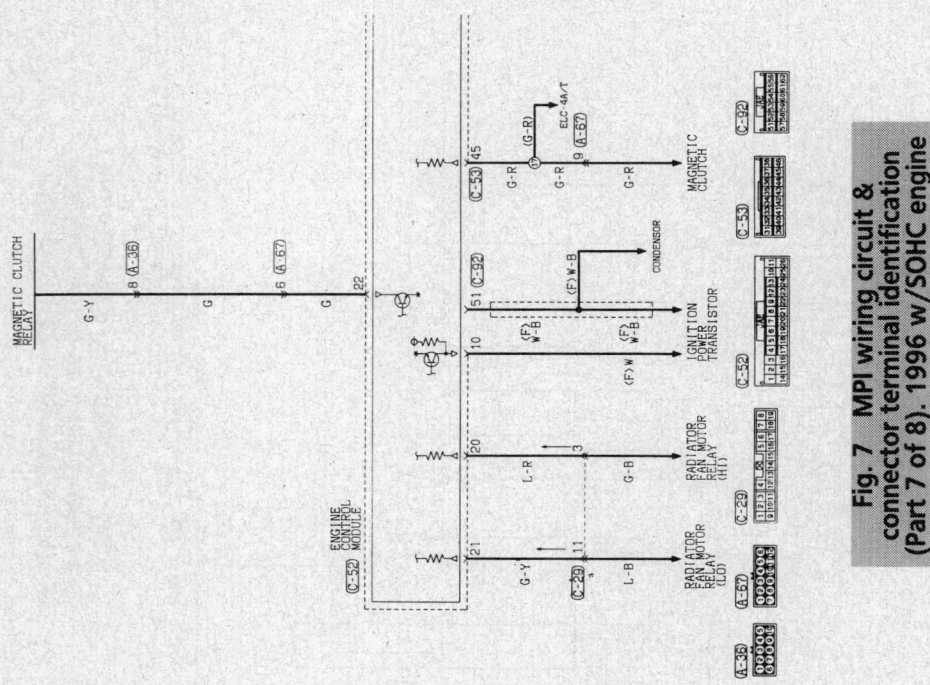

Fig. 7 MPI wiring circuit & connector terminal identification (Part 7 of 8). 1996 w/SOHC engine

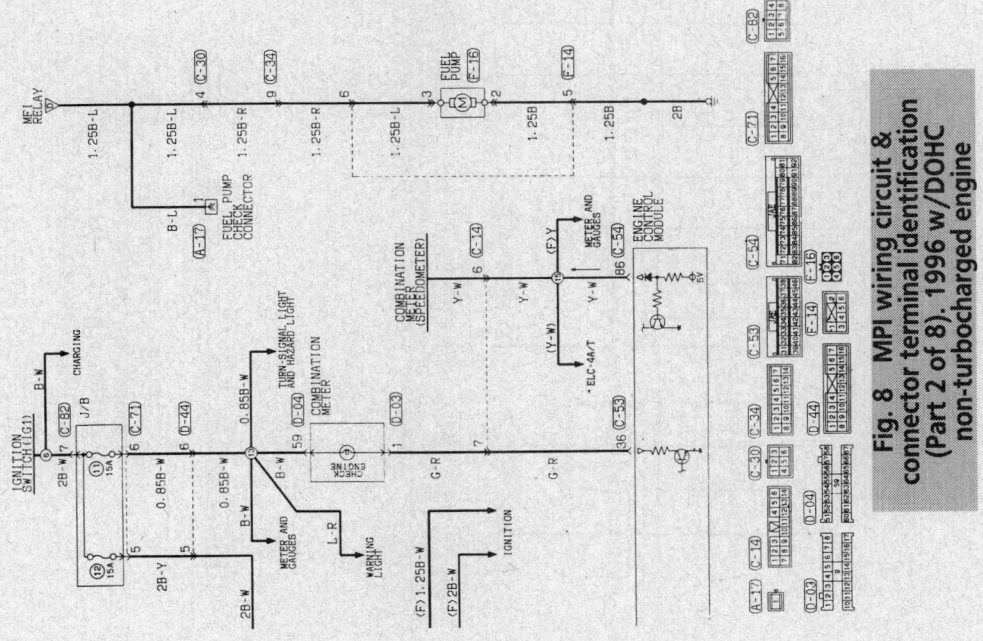

Fig. 8 MPI wiring circuit & connector terminal identification (Part 2 of 8). 1996 w/DOHC non-turbocharged engine

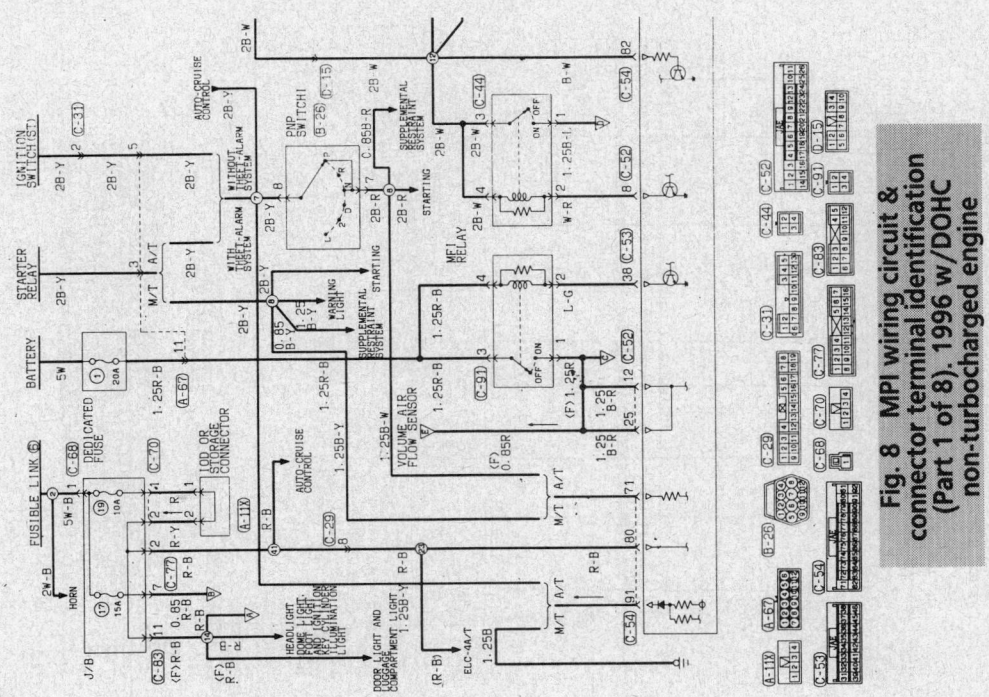

Fig. 8 MPI wiring circuit & connector terminal identification (Part 1 of 8). 1996 w/DOHC non-turbocharged engine

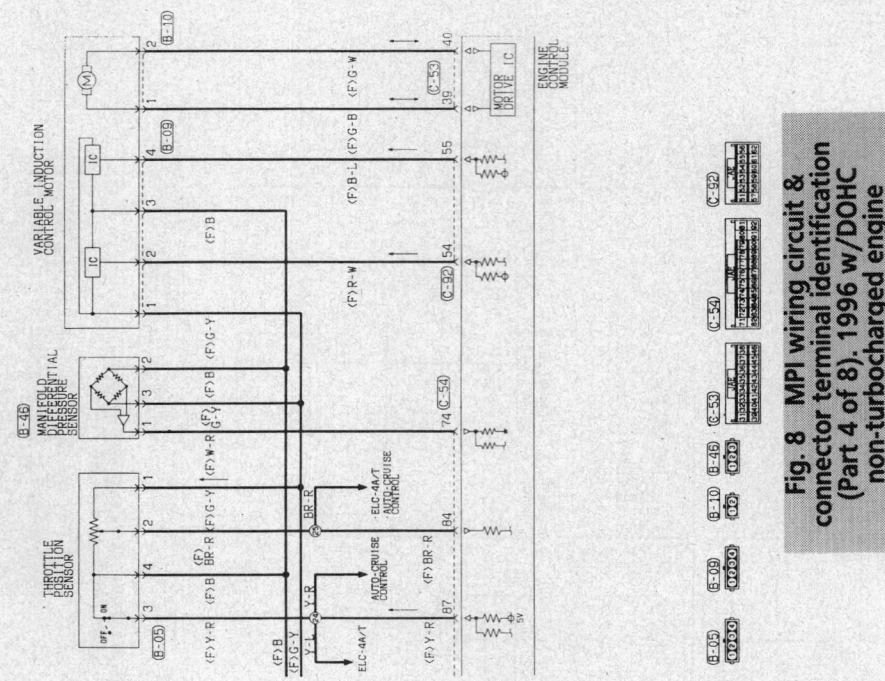

Fig. 8 MPI wiring circuit & connector terminal identification (Part 4 of 8). 1996 w/DOHC non-turbocharged engine

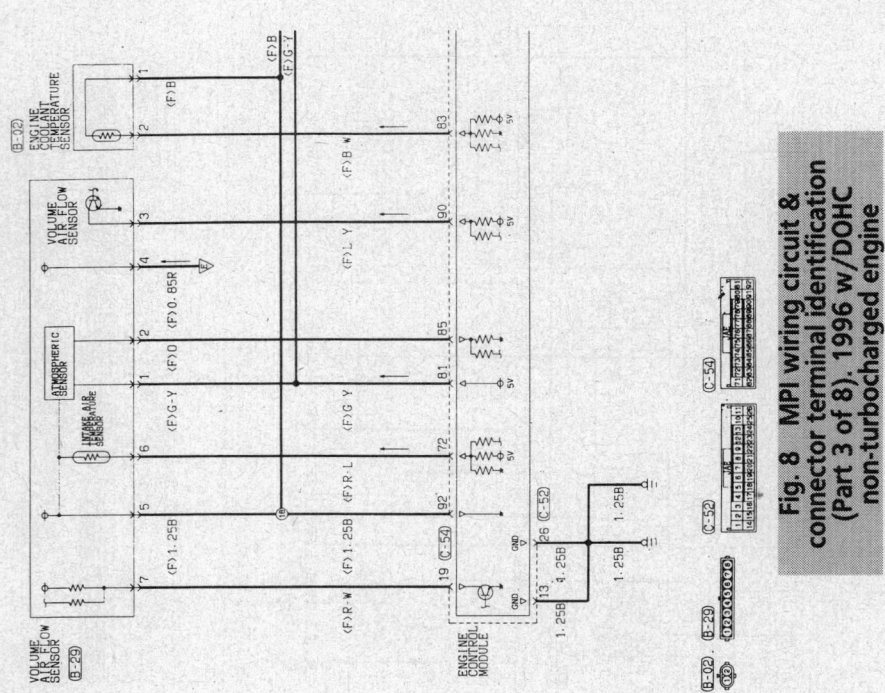

Fig. 8 MPI wiring circuit & connector terminal identification (Part 3 of 8). 1996 w/DOHC non-turbocharged engine

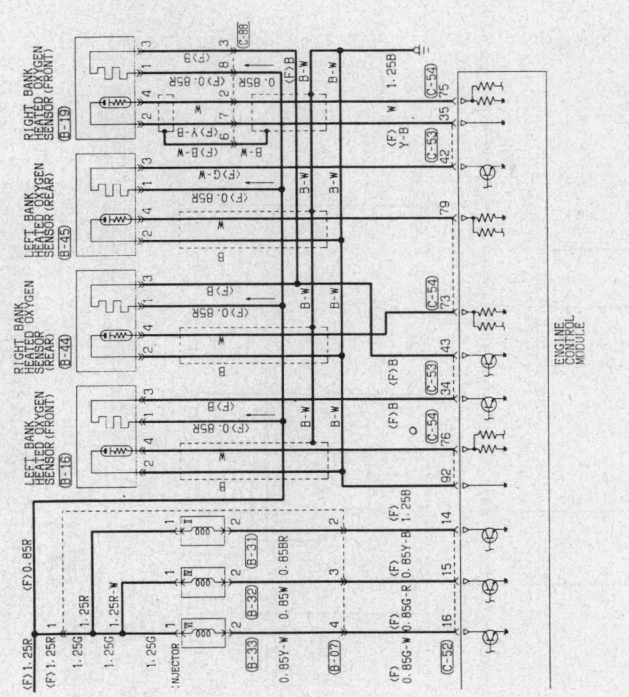
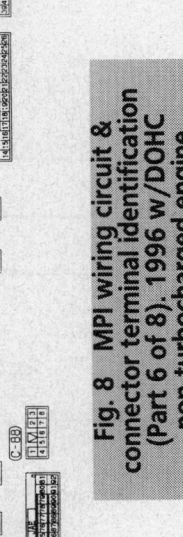

Fig. 8 MPI wiring circuit & connector terminal identification (Part 6 of 8). 1996 w/DOHC non-turbocharged engine

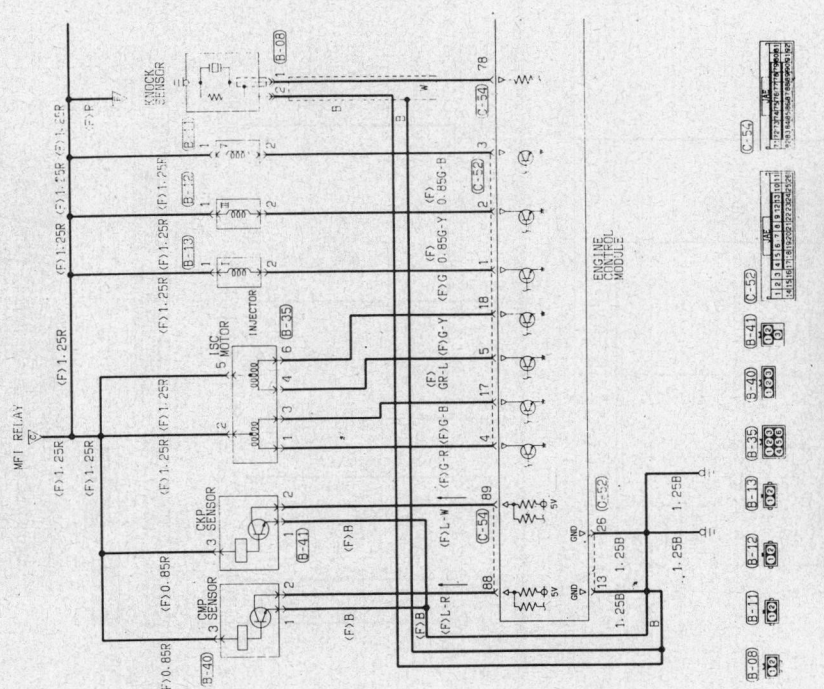

Fig. 8 MPI wiring circuit & connector terminal identification (Part 5 of 8). 1996 w/DOHC non-turbocharged engine

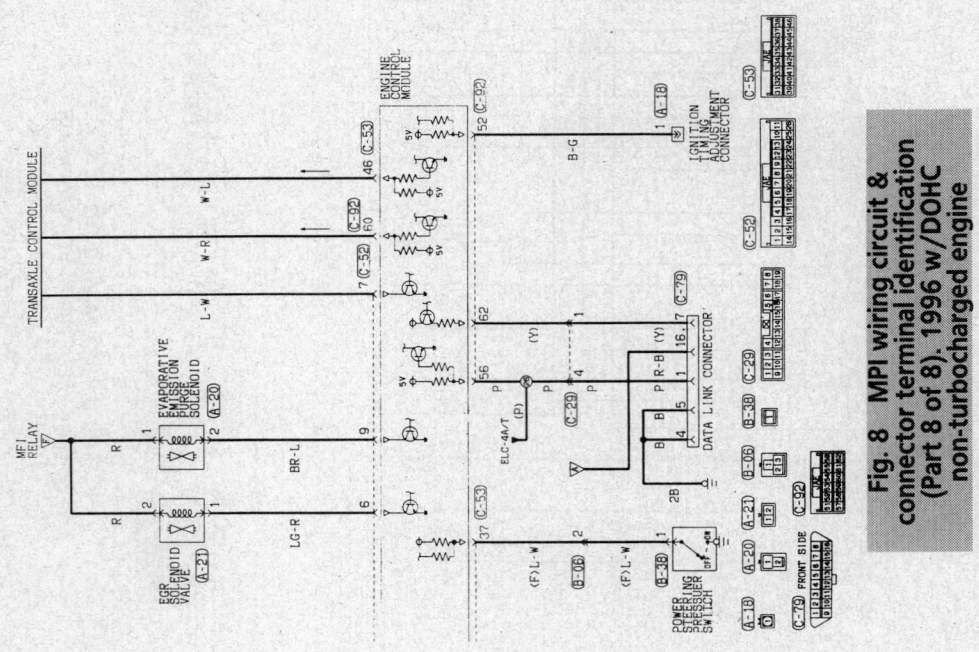

Fig. 8 MPI wiring circuit & connector terminal identification (Part 8 of 8). 1996 w/DOHC non-turbocharged engine

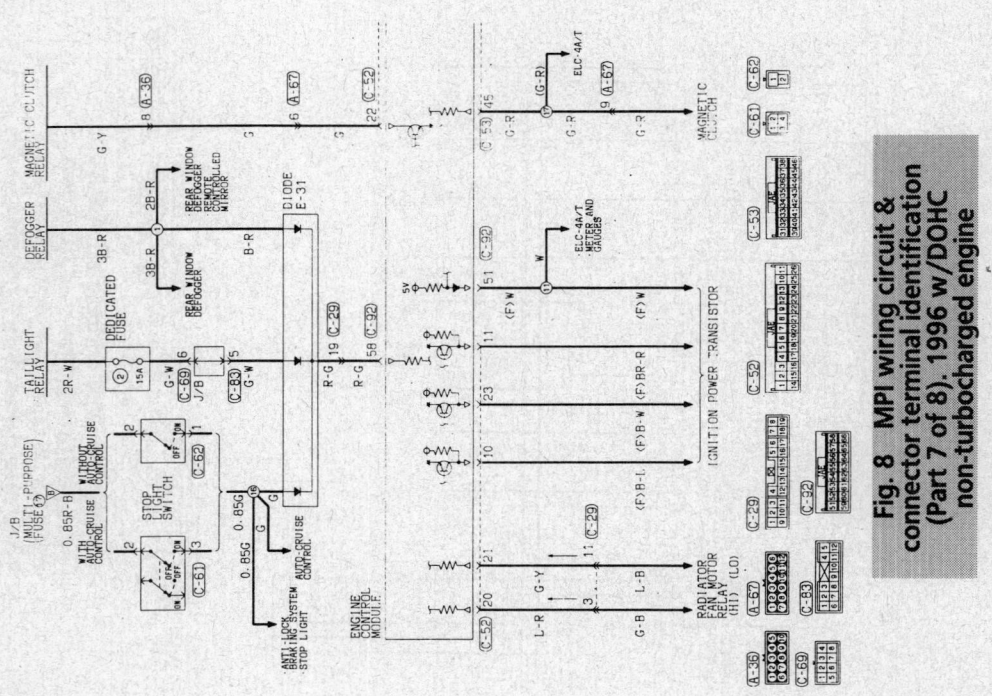

Fig. 8 MPI wiring circuit & connector terminal identification (Part 7 of 8). 1996 w/DOHC non-turbocharged engine

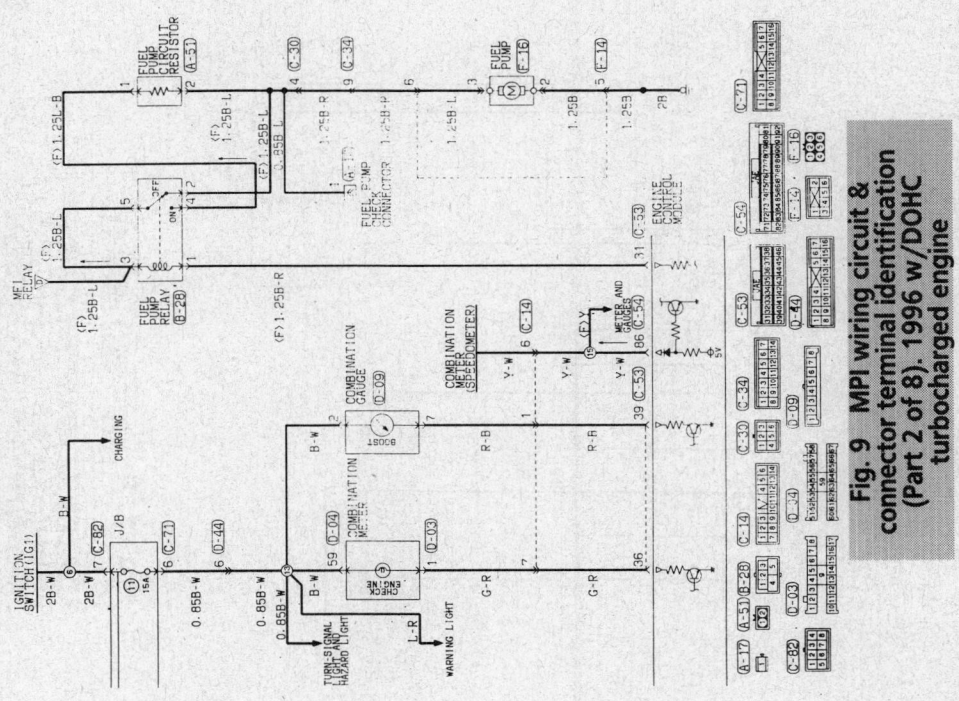

Fig. 9 MPI wiring circuit & connector terminal identification (Part 2 of 8). 1996 w/DOHC turbocharged engine

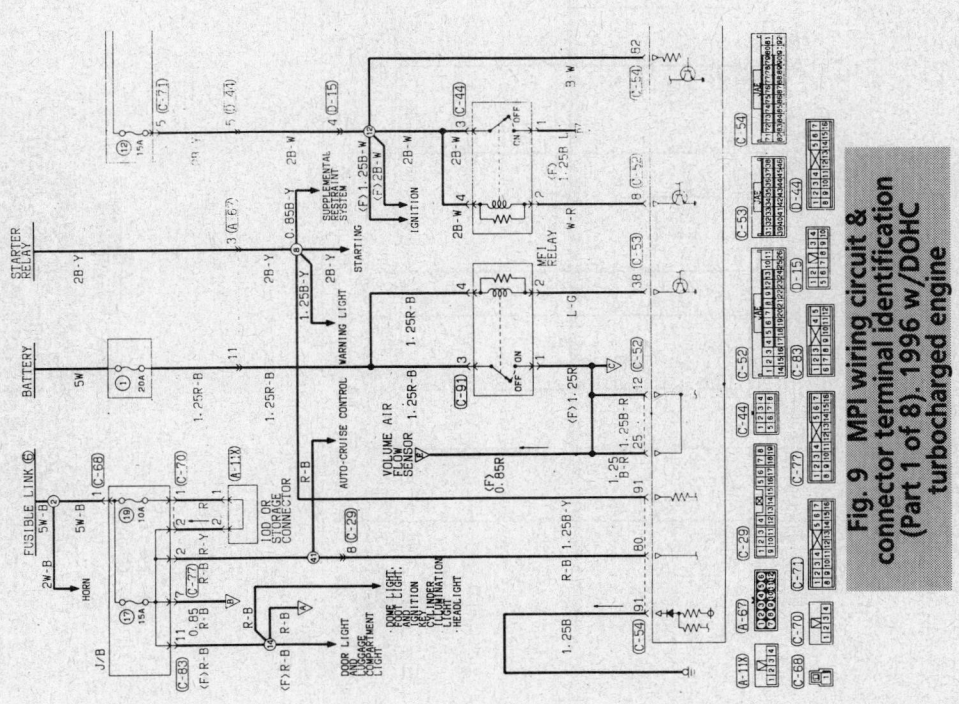

Fig. 9 MPI wiring circuit & connector terminal identification (Part 1 of 8). 1996 w/DOHC turbocharged engine

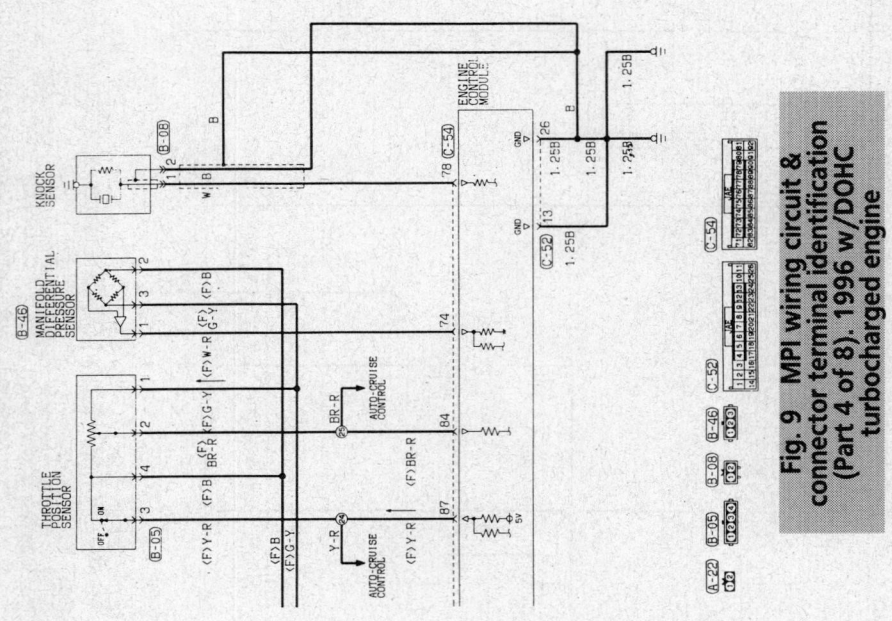

Fig. 9 MPI wiring circuit &
connector terminal identification
(Part 4 of 8). 1996 w/DOHC
turbocharged engine

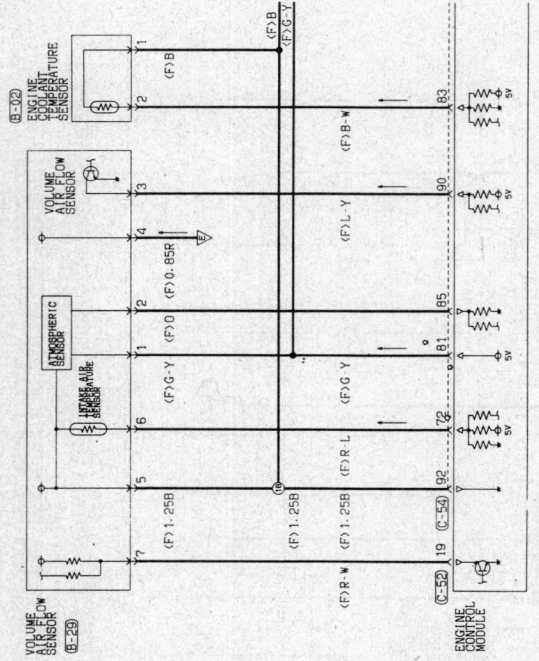

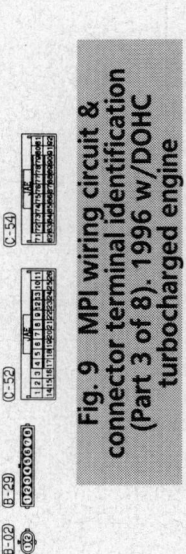

Fig. 9 MPI wiring circuit &
connector terminal identification
(Part 3 of 8). 1996 w/DOHC
turbocharged engine

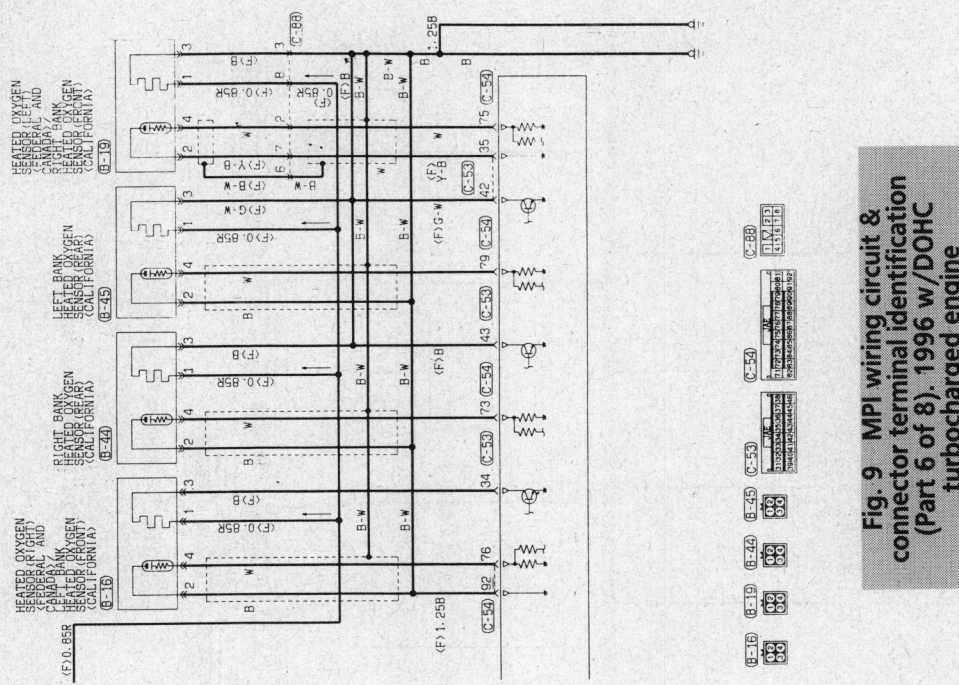

Fig. 9   MPI wiring circuit & connector terminal identification (Part 6 of 8). 1996 w/DOHC turbocharged engine

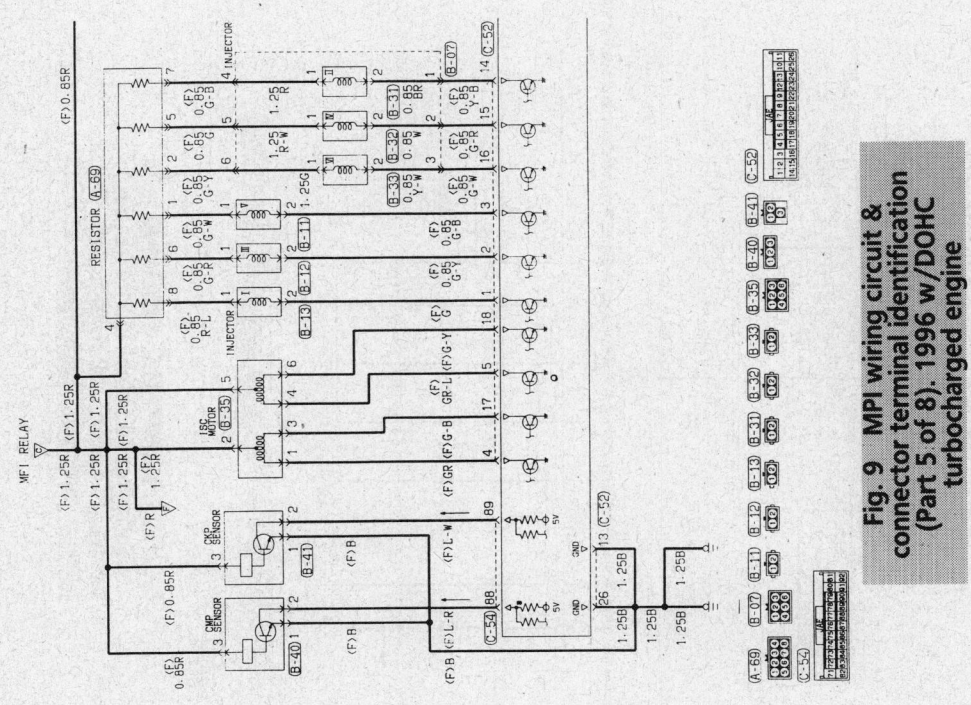

Fig. 9   MPI wiring circuit & connector terminal identification (Part 5 of 8). 1996 w/DOHC turbocharged engine

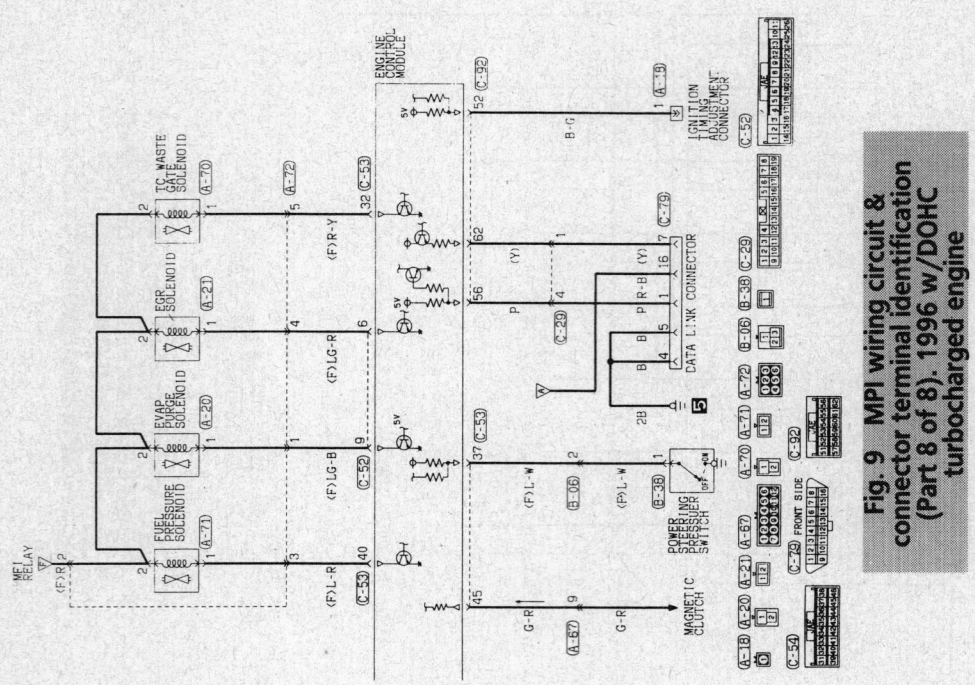

Fig. 9   MPI wiring circuit & connector terminal identification (Part 8 of 8). 1996 w/DOHC turbocharged engine

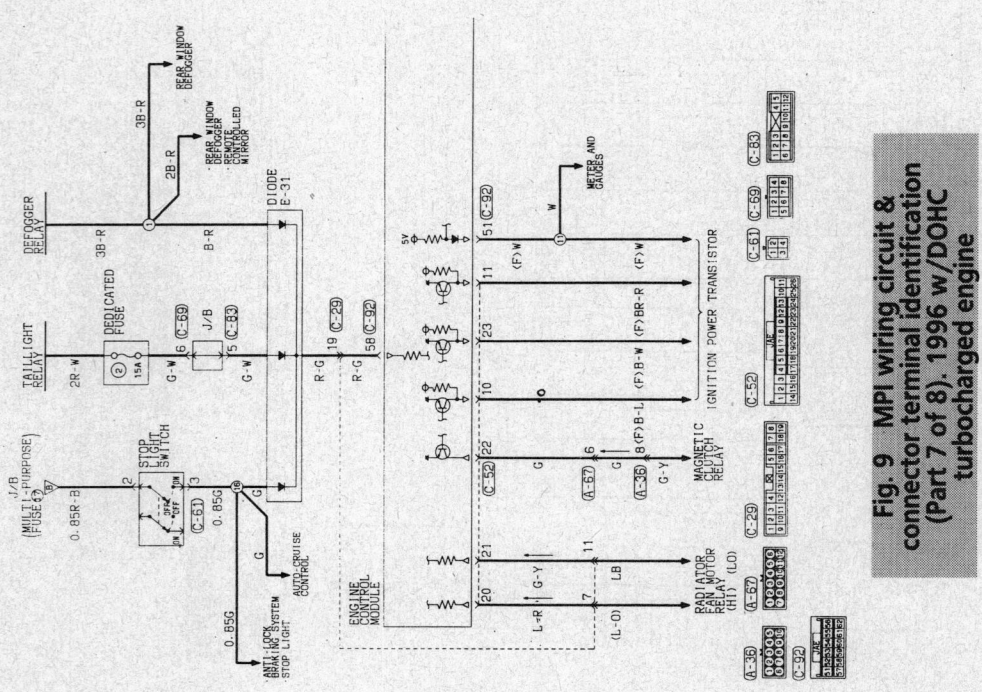

Fig. 9   MPI wiring circuit & connector terminal identification (Part 7 of 8). 1996 w/DOHC turbocharged engine

Fig. 11 Troubleshooting symptom chart (Part 1 of 2). 1995–96

Items	Starting Will not start	Starting Fires up and dies / Hard starting	Idling stability Idling instability (rough idling)	Idling stability Incorrect idle speed	Engine stall
Power supply and ignition switch-IG	1 (1)				
Engine control module power ground	2 (2)				
Fuel pump	3 (3)	1 (1)			1 (1)
Volume air flow sensor					13 (11)
Intake air temperature sensor			5		
Barometric pressure sensor			7		
Engine coolant temperature sensor		(3)	6 (5)	1 (1)	5 (5)
Throttle position sensor			3 (3)	2 (2)	4 (4)
Closed throttle position switch					8 (7)
Camshaft position sensor		8 (8)			9 (8)
Crankshaft position sensor		3 (4)			
Ignition switch-ST <M/T>	5 (5)	7 (7)			
Ignition switch-ST and Park/Neutral position switch <A/T>	4 (4)	8 (8)			
Vehicle speed sensor				7	
Power steering pressure switch				3	6
Air conditioning switch and compressor clutch relay				4	
Knock sensor <DOHC>					
Electrical load switch <DOHC>				5	
Fan motor relay				6	11 (10)
Induction control valve position sensor <DOHC – Non Turbo>					
Heated oxygen sensor			10		
Injectors	8 (8)	2 (2)	2 (2)	8 (3)	3 (3)
Idle air control motor (stepper motor type)		4 (5)	1 (1)		2 (2)
Ignition coil and ignition power transistor	7 (7)				10 (9)
Evaporative emission purge solenoid			8		
EGR solenoid		6	9		12
Fuel pressure solenoid <Turbo>					
Turbocharger waste gate control solenoid <Turbo>					
Variable induction control motor (DC motor) <DOHC – Non Turbo>					
Anti-lock braking signal <Turbo>					
Engine and transaxle total control signal <A/T>					
Fuel pressure		5 (6)	4 (4)		7 (6)

NOTE
The numbers in the table indicate the check order for warm engine. (Numbers in ( ) are for cold engine.)

*1: SOHC
*2: DOHC

Fig. 10 Troubleshooting symptom chart. 1993–94

O: Warm engine (number inside indicates check order)
☐: Cold engine (number inside indicates check order)

*: Non Turbo
*: Turbo
*: SOHC
*: DOHC

CR102930363800 00X

tool to diagnostic connector, **Fig. 13.**
2. Place ignition switch in On position.
3. Observe MIL Lamp should begin to flash any diagnostic trouble codes after an initial three second pause.
4. Record MIL output signal patterns, then refer to "Diagnostic Trouble Code Interpretation" for further information regarding specific diagnostic trouble codes indicated by MIL output.

USING DIAGNOSTIC SCAN TOOL

Scan tools should always be connected and disconnected with the ignition switch in the Off position.

Diagnostic trouble codes may be accessed using a Diagnostic Readout Box (DRB) scan tool, **Fig. 14,** a Multi-Use Tester (MUT) or a generic scan tool. Proceed as follows:
1. With ignition switch in Off position, connect scan tool to data link connector, **Figs. 12 and 13.**
2. Place ignition switch in On position, then note scan tool diagnostic output. Refer to "Diagnostic Trouble Code Interpretation" for further information regarding specific diagnostic trouble code messages.

Diagnostic Trouble Code Interpretation

Refer to **Figs. 15 and 16** for diagnostic trouble code indications, then proceed to "System & Component Testing" as necessary to address problem areas indicated by diagnostic trouble codes.

Clearing Diagnostic Trouble Codes

After repairs have been completed, diagnostic trouble codes may be erased by disconnecting the battery ground cable for 10 seconds or more, or by instructing a diagnostic scan tool to erase diagnostic trouble codes from memory.

System & Component Testing

The vehicle battery must be at full charge whenever a test in this section is performed. Partial or complete battery discharge will result in inaccurate measurements and unnecessary diagnosis or repair.

HARNESS INSPECTIONS

When testing a harness, always use a suitable voltmeter. Follow procedures exactly as described to pinpoint malfunction.

MFI RELAY (POWER SUPPLY)

1993–95

1. Measure ignition switch terminal input voltage at ECM connector terminal No. 62 with engine control module (ECM) disconnected. If voltage is 0-1V with ignition switch in Off position or battery (B+) voltage with switch in On position, proceed to next step; if not, repair harness to ignition switch or check ignition switch.
2. Measure power supply voltage of MFI relay at harness connector terminal Nos. A4 and A8 with ignition switch in Off position and MFI relay connector disconnected. If B+ voltage is present, proceed to next step; if not, repair harness.
3. Check for open-circuit or short to ground between ECM and MFI relay. Test at harness connector terminal No. 6 and ECM connector terminal No. 108. If satisfactory, proceed to next step. If an open circuit or short is found, repair harness. Then test harness connector No. 2 and ECM connector Nos. 12 and 25. Repair harness as needed.
4. Measure power voltage to actuator with MFI relay and ECM connected. Test at harness connector terminal No. A3. If voltage is not at least 8V during cranking or if B+ voltage is not present with engine racing, replace MFI relay or defective ECM.

1996

1. Measure ignition switch terminal input voltage at ECM connector terminal No. 82 with engine control module (ECM) disconnected. If voltage is 0-1V with ignition switch in Off position or B+ voltage with switch in On position, proceed to next step; if not, repair harness to ignition switch or check ignition switch.

Items	Driving						Stopping
	Hesitation Sag	Poor acceleration	Stumble	Shock	Surge	Knocking	Run-on (Dieseling)
Power supply and ignition switch-IG							
Engine control module power ground							
Fuel pump	1 (1)	1 (1)					
Volume air flow sensor	11 (11)		5 (5)	5 (5)		4 (4)	
Intake air temperature sensor	7 (7)	8 (8)				2 (2)	
Barometric pressure sensor	10 (10)	10 (10)				3 (3)	
Engine coolant temperature sensor	9 (9)	9 (9)	4 (4)		3 (3)		
Throttle position sensor	8 (8)		3 (3)	4 (4)			
Closed throttle position switch							
Camshaft position sensor			2 (2)				
Crankshaft position sensor			3 (3)				
Ignition switch-ST <M/T>							
Ignition switch-ST and Park/Neutral position switch <A/T>							
Vehicle speed sensor				6			
Power steering pressure switch							
Air conditioning switch and compressor clutch relay							
Knock sensor <DOHC>						1 (1)	
Electrical load switch <DOHC>							
Fan motor relay							
Induction control valve position sensor <DOHC – Non Turbo>	4 (4)	6 (6)					
Heated oxygen sensor							
Injectors	2 (2)	2 (2)	1 (1)		1 (1)		1
Idle air control motor (stepper motor type)				9 (7)			
Ignition coil and ignition power transistor		11 (11)		1 (1)		5 (5)	
Evaporative emission purge solenoid							
EGR solenoid	6 (6)		6 (6)		4 (4)		
Fuel pressure solenoid <Turbo>		4 (4)					
Turbocharger waste gate control solenoid <Turbo>		5 (5)					
Variable induction control motor (DC motor) <DOHC – Non Turbo>	5 (5)	7 (7)					
Anti-lock braking signal <Turbo>					7		
Engine and transaxle total control signal <A/T>				8 (6)	5 (5)		
Fuel pressure	3 (3)	3 (3)	2 (2)		2 (2)		

NOTE
The numbers in the table indicates the check order for warm engine. [Numbers in ( ) are for cold engine.]
•1: SOHC
•2: DOHC

Fig. 11 Troubleshooting symptom chart (Part 2 of 2). 1995–96

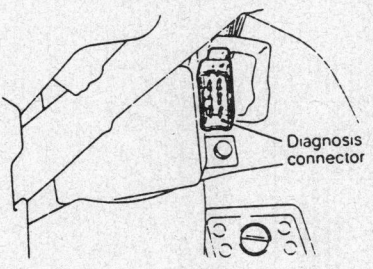

Fig. 12   Diagnostic connector location. 1993

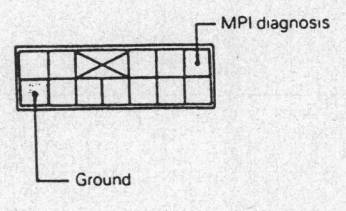

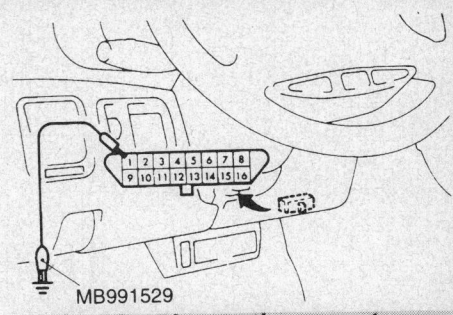

Fig. 13   Diagnostic connector terminal identification. 1994–96

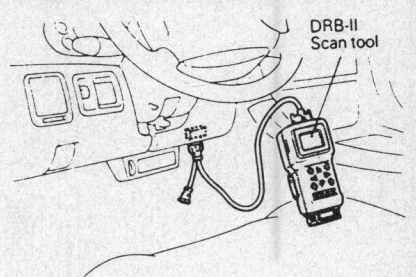

Fig. 14   DRB scan tool

2. Measure power supply voltage of MFI relay at harness connector Nos. A3 and A4 with ignition switch in Off position and MFI relay connector disconnected. If battery voltage is present, proceed to next step; if not, repair harness.

3. Check for an open circuit or short to ground between ECM and MFI relay. Test harness between MFI relay connector terminal No. A2 and ECM connector terminal No. 38. If satisfactory, proceed to next step. If an open circuit or short is found, repair harness.

4. Test harness between MFI relay connector terminal No. A1 and ECM connector terminal Nos. 12 and 25. Repair harness as needed.

5. Measure power voltage to actuator with MFI relay and ECM connected. Test at harness connector terminal No. A1. If voltage is not at least 8V during cranking or if B+ voltage is not present with engine racing, replace MFI relay or defective ECM.

ENGINE CONTROL MODULE (ECM) POWER GROUND

Check for continuity of ground circuit with ECM disconnected. Test ECM connector terminal Nos. 13 and 26. If ground is not sufficient, repair harness.

FUEL PUMP

Non-Turbocharged Engine

1. Apply battery voltage to checking terminal and operate pump. If pump is functioning correctly, proceed to next step; if pump is not functioning correctly, proceed as follows:
   a. Check ground circuit of fuel pump with harness disconnected. Test harness connector terminal No. B2. If ground circuit is satisfactory, proceed to next step; if not, repair harness.
   b. Check continuity between fuel pump connector C1 and harness connector B1. If continuity exists, continue to next step; if not, repair harness.

2. Check continuity between fuel pump checking terminal and MFI relay with MFI relay disconnected. Test harness between harness side connector terminal No. A1 and fuel pump connector terminal No. C1. If continuity exists, continue to next step; if not, repair harness.

3. Disconnect control relay connector.

4. **On 1993-95 models,** measure power supply voltage at MFI relay harness connector terminal A7.

5. **On 1996 models,** measure power supply voltage at MFI relay harness connector terminals A3 and A4.

6. **On all models,** if voltage is 0-1V with ignition switch in Off position or if B+ voltage is present with ignition switch in On position, continue with next step. If not, repair harness.

7. Check for open or short to ground between MFI relay and ECM with both disconnected, noting the following:
   a. **On 1993-95 models,** test harness between MFI relay connector terminal No. A5 and ECM connector terminal No. 8.
   b. **On 1996 models,** test harness between MFI relay connector terminal No. A2 and ECM connector terminal No. 8.

8. If circuit between MFI relay and ECM is satisfactory, continue with next step. If an open or short is found, repair harness.

9. Check for open or short to ground between MFI relay (for fuel pump) and fuel pump. Test harness between connector terminal Nos. A1 and B1. If satisfactory, continue with next step. If an open or short is found, repair harness.

10. Measure power supply voltage of fuel pump with MFI relay and ECM connected. If voltage is not at least 8V with engine cranking or B+ with engine racing, replace defective MFI relay or ECM.

Turbocharged Engine

1. Apply battery voltage to checking terminal and operate pump. If pump is functioning correctly, proceed to next step; if pump is not functioning correctly, proceed as follows:
   a. Check ground circuit of fuel pump with harness disconnected. Test harness connector terminal No. B2. If ground circuit is satisfactory, proceed to next step; if not, repair harness.
   b. Check continuity between fuel pump connector C1 and harness connector B1. If continuity exists, continue to next step; if not, repair harness.

2. Check continuity between fuel pump checking terminal C1 and fuel pump relay II terminal D2 with relay disconnected, then check between checking

terminal C1 and fuel pump resistor terminal E2 with resistor disconnected. If continuity exists, continue to next step. If not, repair faulty harness.

3. Check for an open or short to ground between fuel pump relay II terminal D1 and ECM terminal 31 with fuel pump relay II and ECM connectors disconnected. If satisfactory, proceed to next step; if not, repair harness as necessary.

4. Check for continuity between fuel pump relay II terminal D4 and fuel pump resistor terminal E1 with relay and resistor connectors disconnected. If continuity exists, proceed to next step; if not, repair harness as necessary.

5. **On 1993-95 models,** measure power supply voltage at MFI relay harness connector terminal A7.

6. **On 1996 models,** measure power supply voltage at MFI relay harness connector terminals A3 and A4.

7. **On all models,** if voltage is 0V with ignition switch in Off position or if B+ voltage is present with ignition switch in On position, continue with next step. If not, repair faulty harness.

8. Check for open or short to ground between MFI relay and ECM with both disconnected, noting the following:
   a. **On 1993-95 models,** test harness between MFI relay connector terminal No. A5 and ECM connector terminal No. 8.
   b. **On 1996 models,** test harness between MFI relay connector terminal No. A2 and ECM connector terminal No. 8.

9. If circuit between MFI relay and ECM is satisfactory, continue to next step. If an open or short is found, repair harness.

10. Disconnect fuel pump relay II and MFI relay connectors.

Fig. 15 Diagnostic trouble code interpretation (Part 1 of 3). 1993-95

Code No.	Output signal pattern	Diagnostic item	Check Item (Remedy)	Memory
11	(signal pattern)	Engine control module	• Fuse • Harness and connector • Ground (Replace ECM (power + ground available)	
12	(signal pattern)	Heated oxygen sensor <Except California model> Left bank heated oxygen sensor (front) <California>	• Harness and connector • Heated oxygen sensor • Fuel pressure • Injector (Replace if defective) • Intake air leaks	Retained
13	(signal pattern)	Volume air flow sensor	• Harness and connector (If harness and connector are normal, replace volume air flow sensor assembly.)	Retained
14	(signal pattern)	Intake air temperature sensor	• Harness and connector • Intake air temperature sensor	Retained
21	(signal pattern)	Throttle position sensor	• Harness and connector • Throttle position sensor • Closed throttle position switch	Retained
22	(signal pattern)	Engine coolant temperature sensor	• Harness and connector • Engine coolant temperature sensor	Retained
23	(signal pattern)	Crankshaft position sensor	• Harness and connector (If harness and connector are normal, replace crankshaft position sensor assembly.)	Retained
24	(signal pattern)	Camshaft position sensor	• Harness and connector (If harness and connector are normal, replace camshaft position sensor.)	Retained
25	(signal pattern)	Vehicle speed sensor	• Harness and connector • Vehicle speed sensor	Retained
31	(signal pattern)	Barometric pressure sensor	• Harness and connector (If harness and connector are normal, replace barometric pressure sensor assembly.)	Retained
31	(signal pattern)	Knock sensor <DOHC>	• Harness and connector (If harness and connector are normal, replace knock sensor.)	Retained

NOTE
Do not replace the ECM until a thorough terminal check reveals are no short/open circuits.

Fig. 15 Diagnostic trouble code interpretation (Part 2 of 3). 1993-95

Code No.	Output signal pattern	Diagnostic item	Check Item (Remedy)	Memory
36	(signal pattern)	Ignition timing adjustment signal <DOHC>	• Harness and connector	
39	(signal pattern)	Heated oxygen sensor <Turbo other than California models> Right bank heated oxygen sensor (front) <California>	• Harness and connector • Heated oxygen sensor • Fuel pressure • Injectors (Replace if defective) • Intake air leaks	Retained
41	(signal pattern)	Injector	• Harness and connector • Injector coil resistance	Retained
43	(signal pattern)	EGR <California – Non Turbo, Turbo>	• Harness and connector • EGR thermo-sensor • EGR valve • EGR solenoid • EGR valve control vacuum	Retained
44	(signal pattern)	Ignition coil, Ignition power transistor unit (No. 1-4 cylinder) <DOHC>	• Harness and connector • Ignition coil • Ignition power transistor unit	Retained
52	(signal pattern)	Ignition coil, Ignition power transistor unit (No. 2-5 cylinder) <DOHC>	• Harness and connector • Ignition coil • Ignition power transistor unit	Retained
53	(signal pattern)	Ignition coil, Ignition power transistor unit (No. 3-6 cylinder) <DOHC>	• Harness and connector • Ignition coil • Ignition power transistor unit	Retained
59	(signal pattern)	Left bank heated oxygen sensor (Rear) <California>	• Harness and connector • Heated oxygen sensor • Fuel pressure • Injectors (Replace if defective) • Intake air leaks	Retained
61	(signal pattern)	A cable from transaxle control module, for transmission of torque reduction signal <A/T>	• Harness and connector (If harness and connector are normal, replace only transaxle control module.)	Retained
62	(signal pattern)	Induction control valve position sensor <Non Turbo, DOHC>	• Harness and connector (If harness and connector and induction control valve are normal, replace air intake plenum assembly.)	Retained

NOTE
Do not replace the ECM until a thorough terminal check reveals are no short/open circuits.

DTC No. <General scan tool mode>	DTC No. <Scan tool (MUT-II) mode>	Diagnostic Item	Check item (Remedy)	Memory
P0100	P0100	Volume Air Flow Circuit Malfunction	• Harness and connector (If harness and connector are normal, replace volume air flow sensor assembly.)	Retained
P0105	P0105	Barometric Pressure Circuit Malfunction	• Harness and connector (If harness and connector are normal, replace volume air flow sensor assembly.)	Retained
P0110	P0110	Intake Air Temperature Circuit Malfunction	• Harness and connector • Intake air temperature sensor	Retained
P0115	P0115	Engine Coolant Temperature Circuit Malfunction	• Harness and connector • Engine coolant temperature sensor	Retained
P0120	P0120	Throttle Position Circuit Malfunction	• Harness and connector • Throttle position sensor • Closed throttle position switch	Retained
P0125	-	Excessive Time to Enter Closed Loop Fuel Control	• O_2 sensor (front) • O_2 sensor harness and connector • Injector	Retained
P0130	-	O_2 Sensor Circuit Malfunction (Bank 1 Sensor 1)	• Harness and connector (If harness and connector are normal, replace Right bank O_2 sensor front.)	Retained
P0135	-	O_2 Sensor Heater Circuit Malfunction (Bank 1 Sensor 1)	• Harness and connector • Right bank O_2 sensor (front) heater	Retained
P0136	-	O_2 Sensor Circuit Malfunction (Bank 1 Sensor 2)	• Harness and connector • Right bank O_2 sensor (rear)	Retained
P0141	-	O_2 Sensor Heater Circuit Malfunction (Bank 1 Sensor 2)	• Harness and connector • Right bank O_2 sensor (rear) heater	Retained
P0150	-	O_2 Sensor Circuit Malfunction (Bank 2 Sensor 1)	• Harness and connector (If harness and connector are normal, replace Left bank O_2 sensor front.)	Retained
P0155	-	O_2 Sensor Heater Circuit Malfunction (Bank 2 Sensor 1)	• Harness and connector • Left bank O_2 sensor (front) heater	Retained
P0156	-	O_2 Sensor Circuit Malfunction (Bank 2 Sensor 2)	• Harness and connector • Left bank O_2 sensor (rear)	Retained
P0161	-	O_2 Sensor Heater Circuit Malfunction (Bank 2 Sensor 2)	• Harness and connector • Left bank O_2 sensor (rear) heater	Retained
P0170	-	Fuel Trim Malfunction (Bank 1)	• Volume air flow sensor output frequency • Injector • Fuel pressure • Intake air leaks • Engine coolant temperature sensor • Intake air temperature sensor • Barometric pressure sensor • O_2 sensor • Exhaust manifold cracked	Retained
P0173	-	Fuel Trim Malfunction (Bank 2)		

Fig. 16 Diagnostic trouble code interpretation (Part 1 of 3). 1996

Code No.	Output signal pattern	Diagnostic Item	Check item (Remedy)	Memory
69	H ⎍⎍⎍⎍ L ⎍⎍⎍	Right bank heated oxygen sensor (Rear) <California>	• Harness and connector • Heated oxygen sensor • Fuel pressure • Injectors (Replace if defective) • Intake air leaks	Retained
-	H ⎍⎍⎍⎍ L (Continuous)	Normal state		

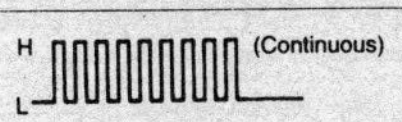

NOTE
Do not replace the ECM until a thorough terminal check reveals are no short/open circuits.

Fig. 15 Diagnostic trouble code interpretation (Part 3 of 3). 1993–95

DTC No. \<General scan tool mode\>	DTC No. \<Scan tool (MUT-II) mode\>	Diagnostic item	Check item (Remedy)	Memory
P0500	P0500	Vehicle Speed Sensor Malfunction	• Harness and connector • Vehicle speed sensor	Retained
P0505	P0505	Idle Control System Malfunction	• Harness and connector • Idle air control motor	Retained
P0510	—	Closed Throttle Position Switch Malfunction	• Harness and connector • Closed throttle position switch	Retained
P0705	—	Transmission Range Sensor Circuit Malfunction (RPNDL Input)	• Harness and connector • Park/Neutral position switch	Retained
P0710	—	Transmission Fluid Temperature Sensor Circuit Malfunction	• Harness and connector • Transaxle oil temperature sensor	Retained
P1103	—	Turbocharger Waste Gate Actuator Malfunction	• Harness and connector • Turbocharger waste gate solenoid • Turbocharger waste gate actuator • Vacuum hoses routing	Retained
P1104	—	Turbocharger Waste Gate Solenoid Malfunction	• Harness and connector • Turbocharger waste gate solenoid	Retained
P1105	—	Fuel Pressure Solenoid Malfunction	• Harness and connector • Fuel pressure solenoid	Retained
P1300	P1300	Ignition Timing Adjustment Circuit Malfunction	• Harness and connector	Retained
P1400	—	Manifold Differential Pressure (MDP) Sensor Circuit Malfunction	• Harness and connector • MDP sensor	Retained
P1715	—	PG Assy Malfunction	• Harness and connector • Pulse generator	Retained
P1750	*	Solenoid Assy Malfunction	• Harness and connector • Converter clutch solenoid • Shift control solenoid • Pressure control solenoid	Retained

Fig. 16 Diagnostic trouble code interpretation (Part 3 of 3). 1996

NOTE
1. Do not replace the engine control module (ECM) until a through terminal check reveals there are no short/open circuits.
2. After the ECM detects a malfunction, a diagnostic trouble code is recorded when the engine is next started and the same malfunction is re-detected. However, for items marked with a "*", the diagnostic trouble code is recorded on the first detection of the malfunction.
3. O_2: Heated oxygen sensor
4. Sensor 1: indicates sensors which are mounted closest to the engine.
5. Sensor 2: indicates sensors which are mounted next-closest to the engine.

DTC No. \<General scan tool mode\>	DTC No. \<Scan tool (MUT-II) mode\>	Diagnostic item	Check item (Remedy)	Memory
P0201	P0201	Injector Circuit Malfunction – Cylinder 1	• Harness and connector • Injector	Retained
P0202	P0202	Injector Circuit Malfunction – Cylinder 2		
P0203	P0203	Injector Circuit Malfunction – Cylinder 3		
P0204	P0204	Injector Circuit Malfunction – Cylinder 4		
P0205	P0205	Injector Circuit Malfunction – Cylinder 5		
P0206	P0206	Injector Circuit Malfunction – Cylinder 6		
P0300	—	Random Misfire Detected*	• Ignition coil • Ignition power transistor • Spark plug • Ignition circuit • Injector • O_2 sensor • Compression pressure • Timing belt • Crankshaft position sensor • Air intake • Fuel pressure • Crankshaft position sensor circuit and connector	Retained
P0301	—	Cylinder 1 Misfire Detected*		
P0302	—	Cylinder 2 Misfire Detected*		
P0303	—	Cylinder 3 Misfire Detected*		
P0304	—	Cylinder 4 Misfire Detected*		
P0305	—	Cylinder 5 Misfire Detected*		
P0306	—	Cylinder 6 Misfire Detected*		
P0325	P0325	Knock Sensor 1 Circuit Malfunction (DOHC)	• Harness and connector (If harness and connector are not defective, replace knock sensor.)	Retained
P0335	P0335	Crankshaft Position Sensor Circuit Malfunction	• Harness and connector (If harness and connector are normal, replace crankshaft position sensor.)	Retained
P0340	P0340	Camshaft Position Sensor Circuit Malfunction	• Harness and connector (If harness and connector are normal, replace camshaft position sensor.)	Retained
P0400	—	Exhaust Gas Recirculation Flow Malfunction	• Harness and connector • EGR valve • EGR solenoid • EGR valve control vacuum • Manifold differential pressure sensor	Retained
P0403	—	Exhaust Gas Recirculation Solenoid Malfunction	• Harness and connector • EGR solenoid	Retained
P0421	—	Warm Up Catalyst Efficiency Below Threshold (Bank 1)	• Exhaust manifold (Replace the catalytic converter if there is no cracks, etc.)	Retained
P0431	—	Warm Up Catalyst Efficiency Below Threshold (Bank 2)	• Exhaust manifold (Replace the catalytic converter if there is no cracks, etc.)	Retained
P0440	—	Evaporative Emission Control System Malfunction	• Harness and connector • Evaporative emission purge solenoid • Purge control valve • Vacuum hoses routing	Retained
P0443	—	Evaporative Emission Control System Purge Control Valve Circuit Malfunction	• Harness and connector • Evaporative emission purge solenoid (No. 1)	Retained

Fig. 16 Diagnostic trouble code interpretation (Part 2 of 3). 1996

11. **On 1993-95 models,** check for continuity between MFI relay terminal A2 and fuel pump relay II terminals D3 and D5.
12. **On 1996 models,** check for continuity between MFI relay terminal A1 and fuel pump relay II terminals D3 and D5.
13. **On all models,** proceed to next step if continuity exists. If it does not, repair harness as necessary.
14. Check for an open or short to ground between fuel pump relay II connector terminal D2 and fuel pump connector terminal B1 with both disconnected. If an open or short exists, repair harness as necessary.

VOLUME AIR FLOW SENSOR

1. Measure power supply voltage at harness side connector terminal A4 with harness connector disconnected and ignition switch in On position. If B + voltage is present, continue with next step, if not, repair harness to control relay or check control relay.
2. Measure voltage at harness connector terminal A3 with connector disconnected and ignition switch in On position. If voltage is 4.8-5.2V, continue with next step; if not, repair harness.
3. Check for continuity to ground at harness side connector terminal A5 with connector disconnected. If ground is satisfactory, proceed to next step; if not, repair harness.
4. Check for continuity between volume air flow sensor harness side connector terminal A7 and ECM connector No. 19 with sensor and ECM disconnected. If continuity is not present, repair harness.

INTAKE AIR TEMPERATURE SENSOR

1. Check continuity of ground circuit at harness connector terminal A5 with connector disconnected. If ground is satisfactory, continue with next step; if not, repair harness.
2. Measure power supply voltage at harness connector terminal A6 with connector disconnected and ignition switch in On position. If voltage is not 4.5-4.9V, repair harness.

BAROMETRIC PRESSURE SENSOR

1. Check continuity of ground circuit at harness side connector terminal A5 with sensor disconnected. If ground is satisfactory, continue with next step; if not, repair harness.
2. Measure power supply voltage to sensor harness side connector terminal A1 with ignition switch in On position. If voltage is 4.8-5.2V, continue with next step; if not, repair harness.
3. Check for open or short to ground between ECM and barometric pressure sensor harness side connector terminal A2 with volume air flow sensor and ECM disconnected. If an open or short is found, repair harness.

ENGINE COOLANT TEMPERATURE SENSOR

1. Check for continuity to ground at harness side connector terminal A2 with sensor disconnected. If ground is satisfactory, continue with next step; if not, repair harness.
2. Measure power supply voltage at harness side connector terminal A1 with sensor disconnected and ignition switch in On position. If voltage is not 4.5-4.9V, repair harness.

THROTTLE POSITION SENSOR

1. Measure power supply voltage at sensor harness side connector terminal A1 with sensor disconnected and ignition switch in On position. If voltage is 4.8-5.2V, continue with next step; if not, repair harness.
2. Check harness connector terminal A4 for continuity to ground with sensor disconnected. If ground is satisfactory, continue with next step; if not, repair harness.
3. Disconnect electrical connectors of any modules which, like ECM, utilize throttle position sensor input.
4. **On 1993-95 models,** check for an open or short to ground between ECM terminal 64 and throttle position sensor harness side connector terminal A2 with throttle position sensor and ECM disconnected.
5. **On 1996 models,** check for an open or short to ground between ECM terminal 84 and throttle position sensor harness side connector terminal A2 with throttle position sensor and ECM disconnected.
6. **On all models,** repair harness if an open or short to ground is found.

CLOSED THROTTLE POSITION SWITCH

1. Measure power supply voltage to switch while disconnected and ignition switch on. Test at harness connector terminal No. A3. If voltage is 4.0V or more, continue with next step; if not, repair harness.
2. Check for continuity of ground circuit at harness connector A4. If ground is not satisfactory, repair harness.

CAMSHAFT POSITION SENSOR

1. Measure power supply voltage to sensor with sensor disconnected and ignition switch on. Test harness connector No. A3. If voltage is correct, continue with next step, if not, repair harness to MFI relay.
2. **On models equipped with SOHC engine,** check for continuity to ground at harness connector terminal A4 with sensor disconnected.
3. **On models equipped with DOHC engine,** check for continuity to ground at harness connector terminal A1 with sensor disconnected.
4. **On all models,** if ground is satisfactory, continue with next step; if not, repair harness to ground.
5. Check voltage of output circuit at har-

ness connector terminal A2 while connector is disconnected and ignition switch is in On position. If voltage is 4.8-5.2V, problem has been solved; if not, repair harness.

CRANKSHAFT POSITION SENSOR

1. Measure power supply voltage at sensor harness side connector terminal A3 with connector disconnected and ignition switch in On position. If battery voltage is present, proceed to next step; if not, repair harness between terminal A3 and MFI relay.
2. **On 1993-95 models equipped with DOHC engine and 1996 models,** check for ground circuit continuity at sensor harness side connector terminal A1. If ground is satisfactory, proceed to next step; if not, repair harness between terminal A1 and ground.
3. **On 1993-95 models equipped with SOHC engine,** check for ground circuit continuity at sensor harness side connector terminal A4. If ground is satisfactory, proceed to next step; if not, repair harness between terminal A4 and ground.
4. **On all models,** measure voltage at sensor harness side connector terminal A2 with ignition switch in On position and connector disconnected. If voltage is 4.8-5.2V, sensor harness is satisfactory; if not, repair harness between terminal A2 and ECM.

IGNITION SWITCH
Manual Transaxle

1. **On 1993-95 models,** measure input voltage at ECM connector terminal 51 while disconnected and ignition switch in Start position.
2. **On 1996 models,** measure input voltage at ECM connector terminal 71 while disconnected and ignition switch in Start position.
3. **On all models,** continue to next step if voltage is 8V or more; if not, repair harness.
4. **On 1993-95 models,** check ground circuit continuity at ECM harness side connector terminal 71.
5. **On 1996 models,** check ground circuit continuity at ECM harness side connector terminal 91.
6. **On all models,** harness is satisfactory if ground is satisfactory; if not, repair ground circuit.

Automatic Transaxle

1. Measure power supply voltage at Park/Neutral Position (PNP) switch harness connector terminal A8 with switch and ECM disconnected and ignition switch in Start position. If battery voltage is present, continue with next step; if not, check power supply circuit.
2. Check for continuity between PNP switch and ECM with both disconnected, noting the following:
   a. **On 1993-95 models,** test between harness connector terminal A8 and ECM connector No. 71, then between terminal A7 and

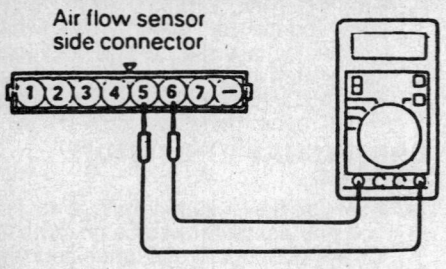

Fig. 17 Intake air temperature sensor connector

ECM connector No. 51.
b. **On 1996 models,** test between harness connector terminal A8 and ECM connector No. 91, then between terminal A7 and ECM connector No. 71.
3. If continuity is satisfactory, continue with next step, if not, repair harness.
4. Measure voltage to PNP switch at harness connector terminal A8 with ECM connected and PNP switch disconnected and ignition switch in On position. If battery voltage is not present, replace ECM.

PARK/NEUTRAL POSITION SWITCH
Automatic Transaxle

Refer to "Ignition Switch" in this section for park/neutral position switch inspection procedure.

VEHICLE SPEED SENSOR

1. Measure sensor line voltage at harness side connector terminal A1 with connector disconnected and ignition switch in On position. If battery voltage is present, proceed to next step; if not, repair harness between terminal A1 and ignition switch.
2. Check vehicle speed sensor output circuit for continuity with ECM disconnected, ignition switch in On position and vehicle in motion. **Although vehicle cannot be driven, movement must take place in order to generate sensor output. Perform this step in a safe environment.** Note the following:
   a. **On 1993-95 models,** check continuity at ECM connector terminal 66.
   b. **On 1996 models,** check continuity at ECM connector terminal 86.
3. Problem is not in sensor if continuity is distinctly intermittent (four pulses per rotation); proceed to next step. If continuity is not as described, replace sensor.
4. **On 1993-94 models,** measure power supply voltage to sensor at harness connector terminal A109 with connector disconnected and ignition switch in On position.
5. **On 1995-96 models,** measure power supply voltage to sensor at harness connector terminal A3 with connector disconnected and ignition switch in On position.
6. **On all models,** if voltage is 4.5-4.9V, continue with next step; if not, repair harness.

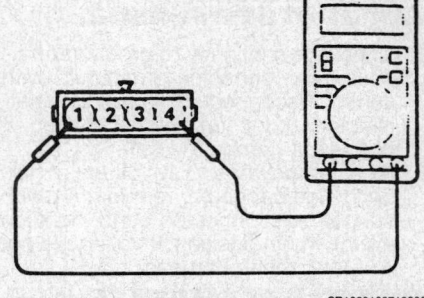

Fig. 18 Throttle position sensor connector

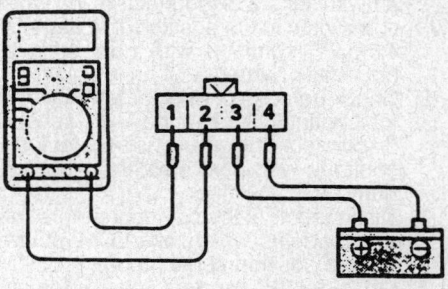

Fig. 20 HO2S connector. 1993 w/non-turbocharged engine & 1994–95 w/DOHC & Federal SOHC engines

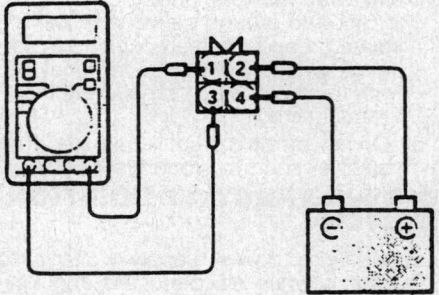

Fig. 21 Oxygen sensor connector. 1993 w/Turbocharged Engine & 1994–95 w/California SOHC Engine

7. Check for continuity to ground with sensor disconnected, noting the following:
8. **On 1993-94 models,** check at harness connector terminal B64.
9. **On 1995-96 models,** check at harness connector terminal A2.
10. **On all models,** if ground is not satisfactory, repair harness to ground.

POWER STEERING PRESSURE SWITCH

1. Measure power supply voltage at switch harness connector terminal A1 with switch disconnected and ignition switch in On position.
2. If battery voltage is not present, repair harness.

A/C SWITCH & COMPRESSOR CLUTCH RELAY

1. Measure A/C circuit power supply voltage with A/C, dual A/C and igni-

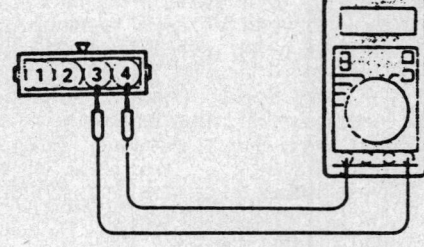

Fig. 19 Idle position switch connector

tion switches in On position and ECM disconnected, noting the following:
a. **On 1993-95 models equipped with SOHC engine,** measure voltage at ECM connector terminals 22, 115 and 101.
b. **On 1993-95 models equipped with DOHC non-turbocharged engine,** measure voltage at ECM connector terminals 22, 115 and 20.
c. **On 1993-95 models equipped with DOHC turbocharged engine,** measure voltage at ECM connector terminals 22, 115 and 59.
d. **On 1996 models equipped with non-turbocharged engine,** measure voltage at ECM connector terminals 22, 45 and 61.
e. **On 1996 models equipped with turbocharged engine,** measure voltage at ECM connector terminals 22, 45 and 59.
2. If battery voltage is not present, check and repair A/C circuits as necessary.

KNOCK SENSOR
DOHC Engine

1. Check at knock sensor harness connector terminal A1 for open or short to ground between sensor and ECM with sensor and ECM disconnected. If no such abnormalities are found, continue with next step. If open or short circuits are found, repair harness.
2. Check for continuity to ground at sensor harness connector terminal A2. If ground is not satisfactory, repair harness.

ELECTRICAL LOAD SWITCH
DOHC Engine

1. Measure input voltage of ECM while disconnected and with lighting switch (tail light relay) on, noting the following:
   a. **On 1993-95 models,** measure voltage at ECM connector terminal 24.
   b. **On 1996 models,** measure voltage at ECM connector terminal 58.
2. If battery voltage is present, continue with next step; if not, check circuit related to tail light relay.
3. Measure input voltage of ECM while disconnected and with defogger switch (defogger relay) on. If battery voltage is present, continue with next step; if not, check circuit related to defogger relay.

4. Measure input voltage of ECM while disconnected and with brake pedal depressed (stop light switch and relay). If battery voltage is not present, check circuit related to stop light switch and relay.

FAN MOTOR RELAY

Measure input voltage to ECM at connector terminals 20 and 21 with connector disconnected and ignition switch in On position. If battery voltage is not present, check fan motor relay circuit.

INDUCTION CONTROL VALVE POSITION SENSOR

DOHC Engine

1. Measure power supply voltage to sensor at connector terminal A1 with connector disconnected and ignition switch in On position. If voltage is 4.8-5.2V, continue with next step; if not, repair harness.
2. Check for continuity to ground at harness connector terminal A3. If ground is satisfactory, continue with next step; if not, repair harness.
3. Measure voltage at terminals A2 and A4 with sensor disconnected and ignition switch in On position. If voltage is not 4.8-5.2V, repair harness.

MANIFOLD DIFFERENTIAL PRESSURE (MDP) SENSOR

1996

1. Check ground circuit continuity at MDP sensor harness connector terminal A2 with connector disconnected. If satisfactory, proceed to next step; if not, repair ground circuit harness.
2. Check for open or short circuit between ECM terminal 74 and MDP sensor harness connector terminal A1 with sensor and ECM connectors disconnected. If circuit is satisfactory, proceed to next step; if not, repair harness between terminal 74 and MDP sensor connector terminal A1.
3. Measure voltage to MDP sensor at harness connector terminal A3 with sensor disconnected, ECM connected and ignition switch in On position. If voltage is 4.8-5.2V, MDP sensor harness is satisfactory; if not, repair ECM.

HEATED OXYGEN SENSOR (HO₂S)

1993 w/Non-Turbocharged Engine & 1994–95 w/Federal Emissions

1. Measure power supply voltage to sensor while disconnected and ignition switch on. Test harness connector No. A3. If voltage is correct, continue with next step, if not, repair harness.
2. Check for open or short to ground between ECM and sensor with both disconnected. Test harness connector No. A1 and ECM connector No. 56. If none is found, continue with next step, if an open or short is found, repair harness.

3. Check for continuity to ground. Test harness connector Nos. A2 and A4. If ground is not satisfactory, repair harness.

1993 w/Turbocharged Engine

1. Measure heated oxygen sensor power supply voltage at terminals A1 and B1 with sensor disconnected and ignition switch in On position. If battery voltage is present, proceed to next step; if not, repair harness between terminal A1 or B1 and MFI relay.
2. With heated oxygen sensor and ECM connectors disconnected, check for an open or short circuit between ECM connector terminal 56 and sensor connector terminal A4, then between ECM connector terminal 55 and sensor connector terminal B4. If circuits are satisfactory, proceed to next step; if not, repair them as necessary.
3. Check ground circuit continuity at sensor connectors A2, B2, A3 and B3 with connector disconnected. If satisfactory, sensor harness is not at fault; if not satisfactory, repair harness as necessary.

1994–95 w/California Emissions & 1996

1. Measure power supply voltage at sensor connector terminals A1, B1, C1 and D1 with connector disconnected and ignition switch in On position. If battery voltage is present, proceed to next step; if not, repair harness between connector terminals and MFI relay.
2. With ECM and oxygen sensor connectors disconnected, check for an open or short circuit between ECM connector terminal 73 and sensor connector terminal A4, then between ECM connector terminal 75 and sensor connector terminal B4, between ECM connector terminal 76 and sensor connector terminal C4 and, finally, between ECM connector terminal 79 and sensor connector terminal D4.
3. If no open or short circuits were found in preceding step, continue to next step; if opens or shorts are indicated, repair harness.
4. With ECM and oxygen sensor connectors disconnected, check for an open or short circuit between ECM connector terminal 43 and sensor connector terminal A3, then between ECM connector terminal 35 and sensor connector terminal B3, between ECM connector terminal 34 and sensor connector terminal C3 and, finally, between ECM connector terminal 42 and sensor connector terminal D3.
5. If no open or short circuits were found in preceding step, continue to next step; if opens or shorts are indicated, repair harness.
6. Check ground circuit continuity at sensor connector terminals A2, B2, C2 and D2 with connector disconnected. If satisfactory, sensor harness is not at fault; if not satisfactory, repair harness.

INJECTORS

1. Measure power supply voltage of front bank injector while disconnected and ignition switch on. Test harness connector terminals A1, B1 and C1. If battery voltage is present, continue with next step; if not, repair harness.
2. Measure power supply voltage to rear bank injector while disconnected and ignition switch on. Test harness connector Nos. D1 and E1. If battery voltage is present, continue with next step; if not, repair harness.
3. Check for open or short between front bank injector and ECM with both disconnected. Test harness connector terminals A2, B2 and C2 and ECM connector terminals 1, 2 and 3. If no opens or shorts are found, continue with next step. If open or short is found, repair harness.
4. Check for open or short between rear bank injector and ECM with both disconnected, noting the following:
   a. **On 1993-95 models,** test between harness connector terminals D2, D5, D6, E2, E3 and E4 and ECM connector terminals 14, 15 and 16.
   b. **On 1996 models,** test between harness connector terminals D2, D5 and D6 and ECM connector terminals 14, 15 and 16.
5. If open or short is found, repair harness.

IDLE AIR CONTROL MOTOR

1. Measure power supply voltage to motor while disconnected and ignition switch in On position. Test harness connector terminals A2 and A5. If battery voltage is present, continue with next step; if not, repair harness.
2. Check for open or short between ECM and motor with both disconnected. Test harness connector terminal A1 to ECM connector terminal 4 , A3 to 17, A4 to 5 and A6 to 18. If an open or short is found, repair harness.

IGNITION COIL & IGNITION POWER TRANSISTOR

SOHC Engine

1. Measure power supply voltage of ignition coil at harness connector terminal A2 with coil disconnected and ignition switch in On position. If battery voltage is present, continue with next step; if not, repair harness.
2. Check continuity between ignition power transistor and ignition coil with both disconnected. Test at ignition coil harness connector No. A1 and ignition power transistor harness connector No. B3. If continuity is satisfactory, continue with next step; if not, repair harness.
3. **On 1996 models,** check for open or short to ground between ignition coil connector terminal A2 and ECM connector terminal 51 with ignition coil and ECM connectors disconnected. If no opens or shorts are found, proceed to next step; if an open or short exists, repair harness between coil connector and ECM.

4. **On all models,** check continuity of ignition power transistor ground circuit while transistor and ECM are disconnected. Test at harness connector terminal B2. If continuity is satisfactory, continue with next step; if not, repair harness.
5. Measure control signal voltage of ignition power transistor while disconnected and ignition switch in Start position. Test at harness connector terminal B1. If signal voltage is 2.0-6.0V, continue with next step; if not, repair harness.
6. Measure voltage of ignition timing adjustment terminal with ignition switch in On position. Test at harness connector terminal C1. If voltage is not 4.0-5.2V, repair harness.

DOHC Engine

1. Measure power supply voltage to ignition coil with coil disconnected and ignition switch in On position. Test at harness connector terminals A3 and B6. If battery voltage is present, continue with next step; if not, repair harness.
2. Check for open or short circuit to ground between ECM and ignition power transistor with both disconnected, noting the following:
   a. **On 1993-95 models,** test between harness connector terminal B5 and ECM connector terminal 101.
   b. **On 1996 models,** test between harness connector terminal B5 and ECM connector terminal 58.
3. If no opens or shorts are found, continue with next step. If an open or short is found, repair harness.
4. Check for open or short to ground between ignition power transistor and ignition coil with both disconnected. Test harnesses between connector terminals A2 and B13, A1 and B12 and A4 and B11. If no trouble is found, continue with next step. If an open or short is found, repair harness.
5. Check continuity of ground circuit at harness connector terminal B4. If ground is satisfactory, continue with next step; if not, repair harness.
6. Measure voltage of control signal circuit of ignition power transistor with transistor disconnected and ignition switch in Start position. Test at connector terminals B1, B2 and B3. If voltage is 0.5-4.0V, continue with next step; if not, repair harness.
7. Measure voltage at ignition timing adjustment terminal C1 with ignition switch in On position. If voltage is not 4.0-5.2V, repair harness.

EVAPORATIVE EMISSION PURGE SOLENOID

1. Measure power supply voltage to solenoid with solenoid disconnected and ignition switch in On position. Test at harness connector terminal A1. If battery voltage is present, continue with next step; if not, repair harness.

2. Check for open or short to ground between solenoid and ECM with both disconnected. Test harness between solenoid connector terminal A2 and ECM connector terminal 9. If an open or short is found, repair harness.

EGR SOLENOID

1. Measure power supply voltage at solenoid harness side connector terminal A1 with connector disconnected and ignition switch in On position. If battery voltage is present, proceed to next step; if not, repair harness between terminal A1 and MFI relay.
2. Check for an open or short circuit to ground between EGR solenoid connector terminal A2 and ECM connector terminal 6 with solenoid and ECM connectors disconnected. If an open or short is found, repair harness.

VARIABLE INDUCTION CONTROL MOTOR

DOHC Engine

1. **On 1993-95 models,** proceed as follows:
   a. Check for an open or short to ground between ECM connector terminal 109 and control motor connector terminal A1 with both disconnected.
   b. Check for an open or short to ground between ECM connector terminal 110 and control motor connector terminal A2 with both disconnected.
2. **On 1996 models,** proceed as follows:
   a. Check for an open or short to ground between ECM connector terminal 39 and control motor connector terminal A1 with both disconnected.
   b. Check for an open or short to ground between ECM connector terminal 40 and control motor connector terminal A2 with both disconnected.
3. **On all models,** if an open or short exists, repair harness.

ENGINE & TRANSAXLE TOTAL CONTROL SIGNAL

Automatic Transaxle

1. **On 1993-95 models,** proceed as follows:
   a. Check for an open or short to ground between transaxle control module connector terminal A7 and ECM connector terminal 116.
   b. Check for an open or short to ground between transaxle control module connector terminal A9 and ECM connector terminal 59.
   c. Check for an open or short to ground between transaxle control module connector terminal A108 and ECM connector terminal 7.
2. **On 1996 models,** proceed as follows:
   a. Check for an open or short to ground between transaxle control module connector terminal A7 and ECM connector terminal 46.

   b. Check for an open or short to ground between transaxle control module connector terminal A9 and ECM connector terminal 60.
   c. Check for an open or short to ground between transaxle control module connector terminal A108 and ECM connector terminal 7.
3. **On all models,** repair harness if any shorts or opens are found.

COMPONENT INSPECTIONS

INTAKE AIR TEMPERATURE SENSOR

1. Disconnect volume air flow sensor electrical connector.
2. Using a suitable ohmmeter, measure resistance between terminals 5 and 6, **Fig. 17.**
3. Resistance should be 6000 ohms at 32°F, 2700 ohms at 68°F and 400 ohms at 176°F.
4. While heating intake air temperature sensor with a suitable hair dryer, measure resistance again. If resistance does not vary inversely with temperature, replace volume air flow sensor.

ENGINE COOLANT TEMPERATURE SENSOR

1. Remove engine coolant temperature sensor at intake manifold assembly.
2. Place sensing portion or sensor in hot water, then measure resistance.
3. Resistance should be 5800 ohms at 32°F, 2400 ohms at 68°F, 1100 ohms at 104°F and 300 ohms at 176°F.
4. If resistances is not as indicated, replace engine coolant temperature sensor.

THROTTLE POSITION SENSOR

1. Disconnect throttle position sensor electrical connector.
2. Using suitable ohmmeter, measure resistance between terminals 1 and 4, **Fig. 18.** Resistance should be 3500-6500 ohms.
3. Connect ohmmeter to terminals 2 and 4, then slowly cycle throttle from idle position to full throttle position. Resistance should be as indicated in preceding step.
4. If resistance is not as indicated, replace throttle position sensor.

IDLE POSITION SWITCH

1. With accelerator pedal released, ensure throttle valve lever is depressed.
2. Disconnect idle position switch electrical connector.
3. Using a suitable ohmmeter, measure continuity between throttle position sensor connector terminals 4 and 3, **Fig. 19.**
4. With the accelerator pedal depressed, ohmmeter should indicate an infinite reading. With accelerator pedal released, ohmmeter should indicate 0 ohms.
5. If no continuity is indicated with accel-

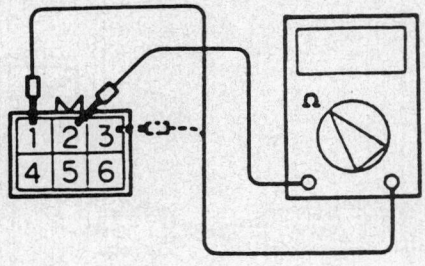

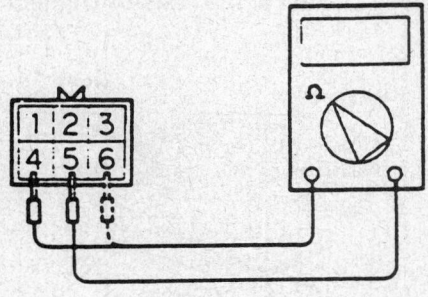

Fig. 22 Idle speed control servo connector

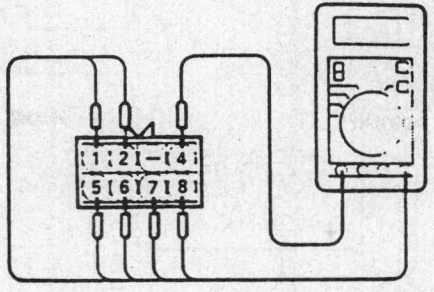

Fig. 23 Resistor terminal connector

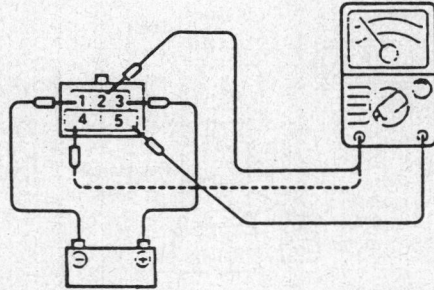

Fig. 25 Fuel pump relay II connector

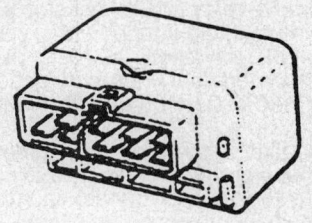

Fig. 24 Control relay connector

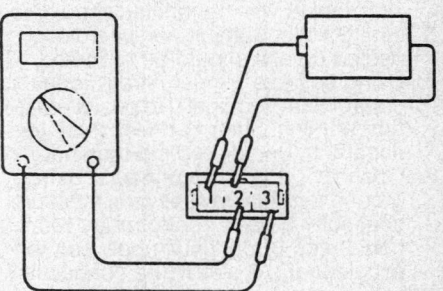

Fig. 26 Power transistor connector. SOHC engine

erator pedal released, loosen throttle position sensor attaching screw, then after turning in counterclockwise direction, measure again for continuity.
6. If continuity is not as indicated, replace throttle position sensor incorporating idle position switch.

HEATED OXYGEN SENSOR (HO₂S)

1993 w/Non-Turbocharged Engine & 1994–95 w/DOHC & Federal SOHC Engines

1. Disconnect HO₂S electrical connector.
2. Ensure continuity between terminals 3 and 4 of approximately 20 ohms at 68°F.
3. If continuity is not as indicated, replace HO₂S.
4. Start engine and allow coolant temperature to reach 176°F or higher.
5. Using suitable jumper wires, connect HO₂S terminal 3 to battery positive terminal, then connect terminal 4 to negative battery terminal, **Fig. 20. Ensure when applying voltage that correct terminals are used. Damage or short circuits may result if incorrect terminals are connected.**
6. Connect suitable digital voltmeter to HO₂S terminals 1 and 2.
7. While racing engine, measure HO₂S output voltage. Voltage should be .6-1.0 volt.
8. If voltage is not as indicated, replace HO₂S.

1993 w/Turbocharged Engine & 1994–95 w/California SOHC Engine

Test both front and rear heated oxygen sensors using the following procedure.
1. Disconnect HO₂S electrical connector.

2. Ensure continuity between terminals 2 and 4 of approximately 20 ohms at 68°F.
3. If continuity is not as indicated, replace HO₂S.
4. Start engine, allow coolant temperature to reach 176°F or higher.
5. Using suitable jumper wires, connect HO₂S terminal 2 to battery positive terminal, then connect terminal 4 to negative battery terminal, **Fig. 21. Ensure when applying voltage that correct terminals are used. Damage or short circuits may result if incorrect terminals are connected.**
6. Connect suitable digital voltmeter to HO₂S terminals 1 and 3.
7. While racing engine, measure HO₂S output voltage. Voltage should be .6-1.0 volt.
8. If voltage is not as indicated, replace HO₂S.

1996

1. Inspect front sensor as described under "1993 w/Turbocharged Engine & 1994-95 w/California SOHC Engine" in this section.
2. Inspect rear sensor as follows:
   a. Disconnect rear sensor electrical connector and connect test harness tool No. MD998464, or equivalent, to sensor side connector.
   b. Ensure resistance measures approximately 12 ohms at 68°F between terminals 2 and 4 (between red and blue clips on harness tool). If continuity does not exist, replace rear heted oxygen sensor.

INJECTORS

1. Disconnect injector electrical connector.

2. Using suitable circuit tester, measure resistance between injector terminals. Resistance should be as specified under "Sensor & Fuel Injector Specifications."
3. If resistance is not as indicated, replace injector.

IDLE SPEED CONTROL SERVO

1. Disconnect idle speed control servo electrical connector.
2. Using a suitable ohmmeter, measure resistance between control servo terminal 2 and terminals 1 or 3, **Fig. 22,** then measure resistance between terminal 5 and terminals 6 or 4.
3. Resistance should be 28-33 ohms at 68°F.
4. If resistance is not as indicated, replace idle speed control servo.

RESISTOR

DOHC Turbocharged Engine

1. Disconnect resistor electrical connectors.
2. Using a suitable ohmmeter, measure resistance between resistor terminals 1 and 4, 2 and 4, 5 and 4, 6 and 4, 7 and 4 and 8 and 4, **Fig. 23.**
3. Resistance should be 5.5-6.5 ohms at 68°F.
4. If resistance is not as indicated, replace resistor assembly.

CONTROL RELAY

Ensure battery voltage is applied to correct terminal, or relay may be damaged.

1. Remove relay control assembly.
2. Using suitable jumper wires, connect control relay terminal 10 to positive battery terminal, then connect terminal 8 to battery ground terminal, **Fig. 24.**
3. Connect suitable digital voltmeter to battery ground terminal and control relay terminal 4. Connect and disconnect battery ground terminal jumper wire, measuring voltage at control relay terminal 4. Voltage at terminal 4 with jumper wire connected should be 11-13 volts, with jumper wire disconnected 0 volts should be indicated.
4. Connect suitable digital voltmeter to battery ground terminal and control relay terminal 5. Connect and disconnect battery ground terminal jumper wire, measuring voltage at control relay terminal 5. Voltage at terminal 5 with jumper wire connected should be 11-13 volts, with jumper wire disconnected 0 volts should be indicated.
5. Using suitable jumper wires, connect control relay terminal 9 to positive battery terminal, then connect relay terminal 6 to battery ground terminal.
6. Connect and disconnect battery ground terminal jumper wire, measure continuity across control relay terminals 2 and 3. Continuity between terminals 2 and 3 should be conductive with jumper wire connected and non-conductive with jumper wire disconnected.
7. Using suitable jumper wires, connect control relay terminal 3 to positive battery terminal, then connect relay terminal 7 to battery ground terminal.
8. Connect suitable digital voltmeter to battery ground terminal and control relay terminal 2. Connect and disconnect battery ground terminal jumper wire, measuring voltage at control relay terminal 2. Voltage at terminal 2 with jumper wire connected should be 11-13 volts, with jumper wire disconnected 0 volts should be indicated.
9. If control relay values are not as indicated, replace relay.

FUEL PUMP RELAY II

DOHC Turbocharged Engine

1. Remove fuel pump relay.
2. Using suitable jumper wires, connect fuel pump relay terminal 3 to positive battery terminal, then connect terminal 1 to battery ground terminal, **Fig. 25.**
3. Connect and disconnect battery ground terminal jumper wire, measure continuity across fuel pump relay terminals 2 and 5. Continuity between terminals 2 and 5 should not be indicated with jumper wire connected and should be indicated with jumper wire disconnected.
4. Connect and disconnect battery ground terminal jumper wire, measure continuity across fuel pump relay terminals 4 and 5. Continuity between terminals 4 and 5 should be indicated with jumper wire connected and

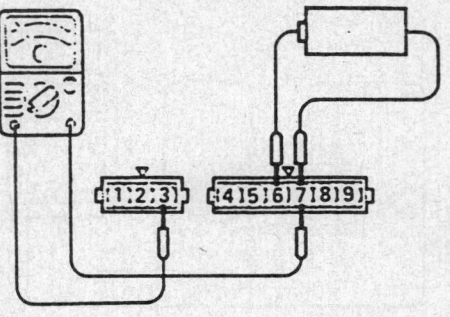

Fig. 27 Power transistor connector. DOHC

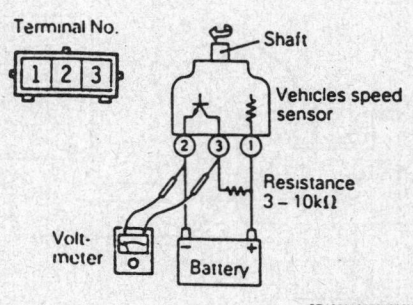

Fig. 29 Vehicle speed sensor connections

should not be indicated with jumper wire disconnected.
5. If continuity is not as indicated, replace fuel pump relay.

POWER TRANSISTOR

SOHC Engine

1. Disconnect power transistor electrical connector.
2. Using a suitable 1.5 volt power supply, connect power supply negative terminal to power transistor terminal 2, **Fig. 26.**
3. Using a suitable analog circuit tester, connect tester negative probe to power transistor terminal 3 and positive probe to terminal 2.
4. Test for continuity between terminals 2 and 3 while connecting and disconnecting power transistor terminal 1 and power supply positive terminal.
5. Continuity should be indicated when terminal 1 and power supply positive terminal are connected, continuity should not be indicated when terminal 1 and power supply are disconnected.
6. If continuity is not as indicated, replace power transistor.

DOHC Engine

1. Disconnect power transistor electrical connector.
2. Test power transistor coil side No. 1 and No. 4 as follows:
   a. Using a suitable 1.5 volt power supply, connect power supply negative terminal to power transistor terminal 7, **Fig. 27.**
   b. Using a suitable analog circuit tester, connect tester negative probe

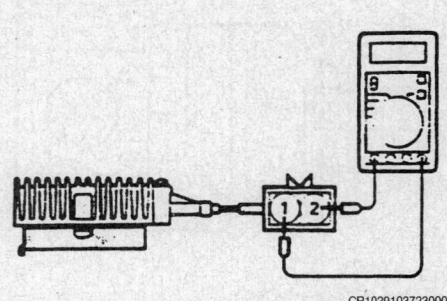

Fig. 28 Fuel pump resistor connector

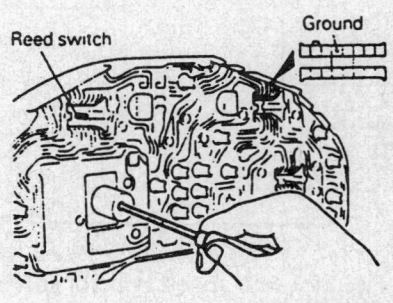

Fig. 30 Reed switch inspection

to power transistor terminal 3 and positive probe to terminal 7.
   c. Test for continuity between terminals 3 and 7 while connecting and disconnecting power transistor terminal 6 and power supply positive terminal.
   d. Continuity should be indicated when terminal 6 and power supply positive terminal are connected, continuity should not be indicated when terminal 6 and power supply are disconnected.
3. Test power transistor coil side No. 2 and No. 5 as follows:
   a. Using a suitable 1.5 volt power supply, connect power supply negative terminal to power transistor terminal 7, **Fig. 23.**
   b. Using a suitable analog circuit tester, connect tester negative probe to power transistor terminal 2 and positive probe to terminal 7.
   c. Test for continuity between terminals 2 and 7 while connecting and disconnecting power transistor terminal 5 and power supply positive terminal.
   d. Continuity should be indicated when terminal 5 and power supply positive terminal are connected, continuity should not be indicated when terminal 5 and power supply are disconnected.
4. Test power transistor coil side No. 3 and No. 6 as follows:
   a. Using a suitable 1.5 volt power supply, connect power supply negative terminal to power transistor terminal 7, **Fig. 27.**
   b. Using a suitable analog circuit tester, connect tester negative probe to power transistor terminal 1 and

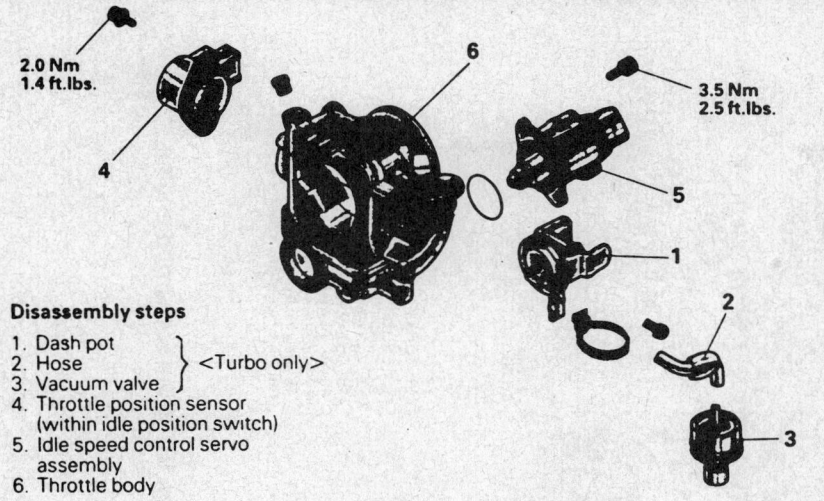

2.0 Nm
1.4 ft.lbs.

6

3.5 Nm
2.5 ft.lbs.

4

5

1

2

3

Disassembly steps

1. Dash pot ⎫
2. Hose ⎬ <Turbo only>
3. Vacuum valve ⎭
4. Throttle position sensor
   (within idle position switch)
5. Idle speed control servo
   assembly
6. Throttle body

CR1029103732000X

Fig. 31 Throttle body assembly

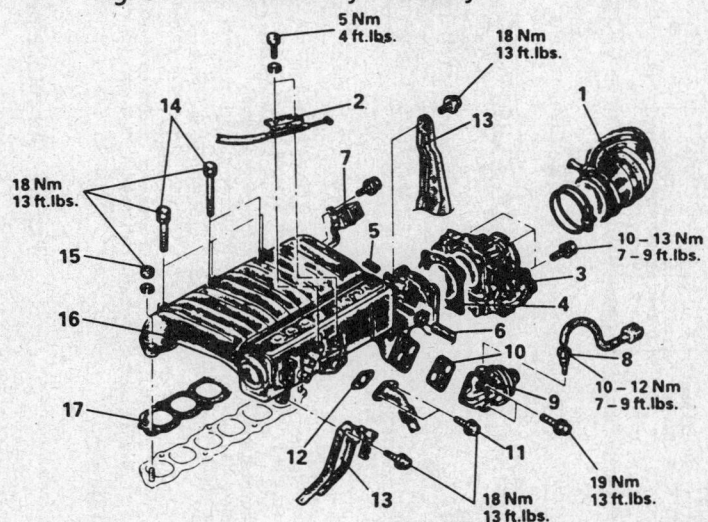

5 Nm
4 ft.lbs.

18 Nm
13 ft.lbs.

14

2

13

18 Nm
13 ft.lbs.

7

1

15

5

10 – 13 Nm
7 – 9 ft.lbs.

16

3

4

6

10

8

9

10 – 12 Nm
7 – 9 ft.lbs.

17

11

12

13

18 Nm
13 ft.lbs.

19 Nm
13 ft.lbs.

1. Connection of air intake hose
2. Connection of accelerator cable
3. Throttle body assembly
4. Throttle body gasket
5. Connection of vacuum hose
6. Connection of brake booster vacuum hose
7. Harness connector
8. EGR temperature sensor ⎫ <Vehicles for
9. EGR valve ⎬ California>

10. EGR valve gasket ⎫
11. EGR pipe installation bolts ⎬ <Vehicles for
12. EGR pipe gasket ⎭ California>
13. Connection of air intake plenum stay
14. Air intake plenum installation bolts
15. Air intake plenum installation nuts
16. Air intake plenum
17. Air intake plenum gasket

CR1029103726000X

Fig. 34 Air intake plenum. SOHC engine

positive probe to terminal 7.
c. Test for continuity between terminals 1 and 7 while connecting and disconnecting power transistor terminal 4 and power supply positive terminal.
d. Continuity should be indicated when terminal 4 and power supply positive terminal are connected, continuity should not be indicated when terminal 4 and power supply are disconnected.
5. If continuity is not as indicated, replace power transistor.

FUEL PUMP RESISTOR

DOHC Turbocharged Engine

1. Disconnect fuel pump resistor electrical connectors.

2. Using suitable ohmmeter, measure resistance between terminals 1 and 2, **Fig. 28.**
3. Resistance should be .6-.9 ohms.
4. If resistance is not as indicated, replace fuel pump resistor.

VEHICLE SPEED SENSOR

1. Remove vehicle speed sensor.
2. Connect test equipment as shown, **Fig. 29.**
3. Using suitable voltmeter, ensure voltage at terminals 2 and 3 when pulse generator shaft is turned, one revolution is four pulses.

REED SWITCH

Using a suitable circuit tester, check circuit off/on between terminals when speedometer shaft is turned several times, **Fig. 30.**

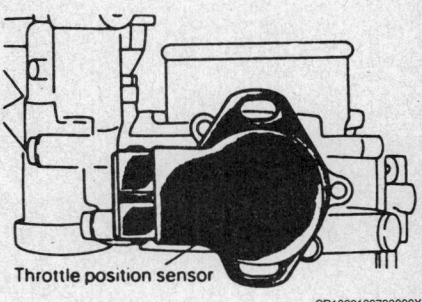

Throttle position sensor

CR1029103733000X

Fig. 32 Throttle position sensor replacement

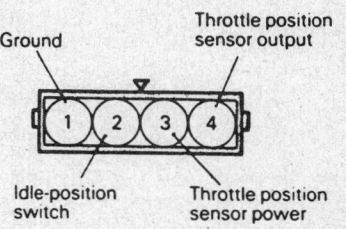

Ground

Throttle position sensor output

1 2 3 4

Idle-position switch

Throttle position sensor power

CR1029103734000X

Fig. 33 Throttle position sensor connector

SYSTEM SERVICE

Fuel System Pressure Relief

To relieve fuel system pressure, refer to "Fuel System Pressure Relief" under "Precautions."

Component Service

THROTTLE BODY

1. Disassemble throttle body as shown, **Fig. 31.**
2. Inspect and clean all throttle body parts. **Do not immerse the throttle position sensor (idle position switch) assembly and idle speed control servo in solvent, wipe with suitable cloth only, or damage may result.**
3. Inspect dash pot diaphragm for damage. Pull dash pot rod up fully, close nipple, then release rod. If rod does not return to initial position with nipple held closed, operation is normal. If rod does return to initial position, replace dash pot.
4. Inspect vacuum valve as follows:
   a. Remove vacuum valve filter.
   b. Connect suitable hand held vacuum pump to vacuum valve black nipple.
   c. Close other nipple with finger, then apply negative pressure of 19.7 inches Hg, ensuring negative pressure is maintained.
   d. Open nipple, ensuring negative pressure gradually leaks out.
   e. Connect hand held vacuum pump to vacuum valve green nipple.

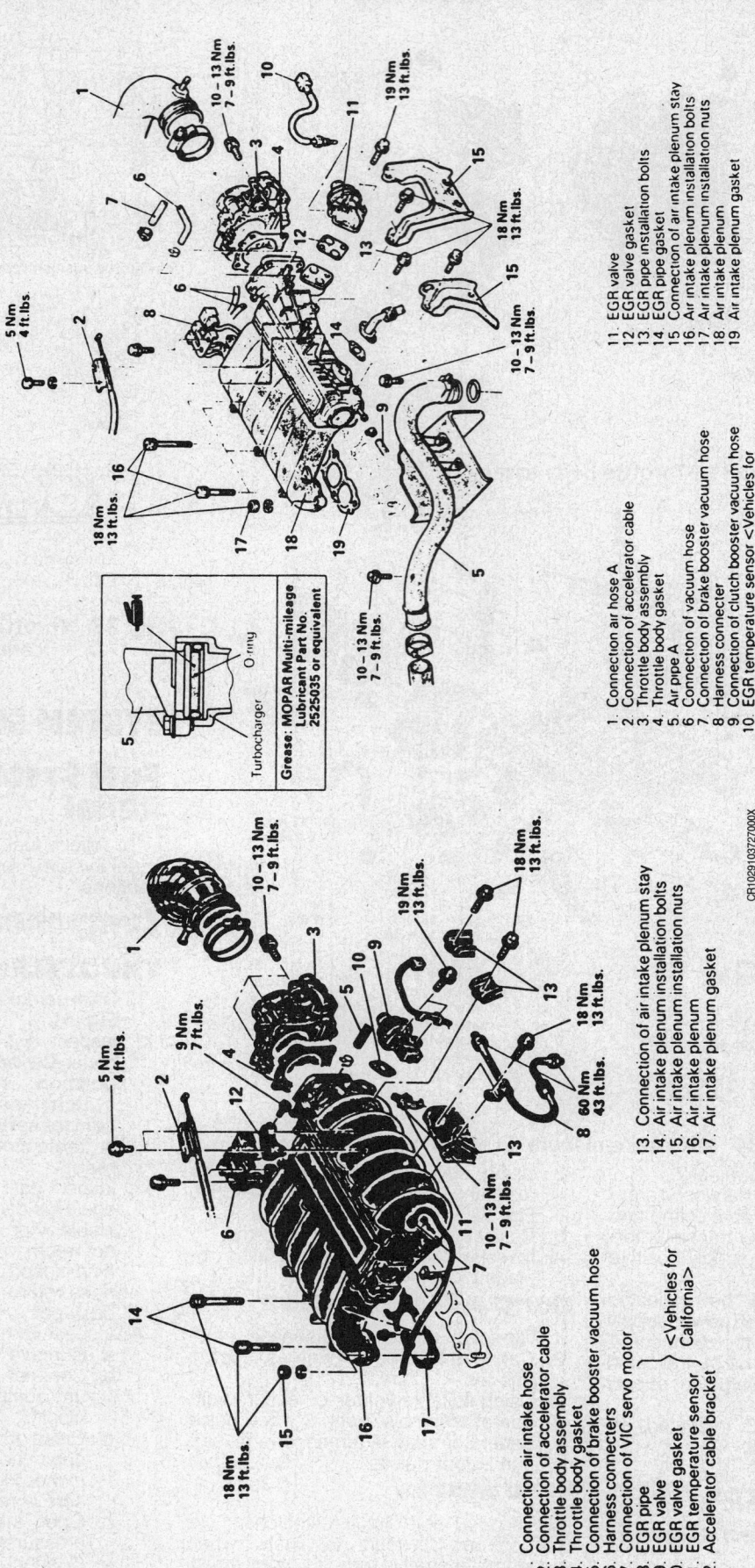

Fig. 36 Air intake plenum. DOHC turbocharged engine

1. Connection air intake hose
2. Connection of accelerator cable
3. Throttle body assembly
4. Throttle body gasket
5. Air pipe A
6. Connection of vacuum hose
7. Connection of brake booster vacuum hose
8. Harness connecter
9. Connection of clutch booster vacuum hose
10. EGR temperature sensor <Vehicles for California>
11. EGR valve
12. EGR valve gasket
13. EGR pipe installation bolts
14. EGR pipe gasket
15. Connection of air intake plenum stay
16. Air intake plenum installation bolts
17. Air intake plenum installation nuts
18. Air intake plenum
19. Air intake plenum gasket

Fig. 35 Air intake plenum. DOHC non-turbocharged engine

1. Connection air intake hose
2. Connection of accelerator cable
3. Throttle body assembly
4. Throttle body gasket
5. Connection of brake booster vacuum hose
6. Harness connecters
7. Connection of VIC servo motor
8. EGR pipe
9. EGR valve
10. EGR valve gasket
11. EGR temperature sensor <Vehicles for California>
12. Accelerator cable bracket
13. Connection of air intake plenum stay
14. Air intake plenum installation bolts
15. Air intake plenum installation nuts
16. Air intake plenum
17. Air intake plenum gasket

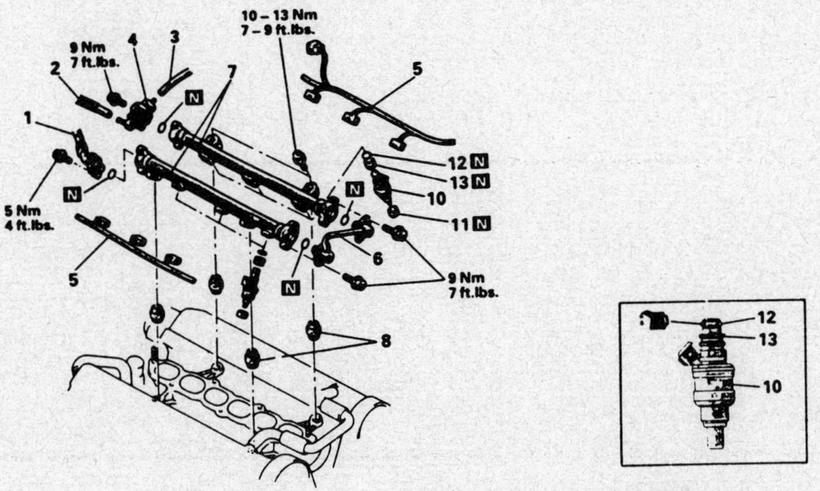

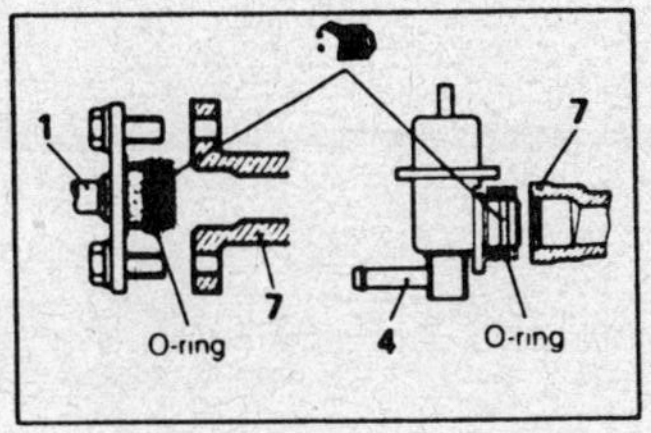

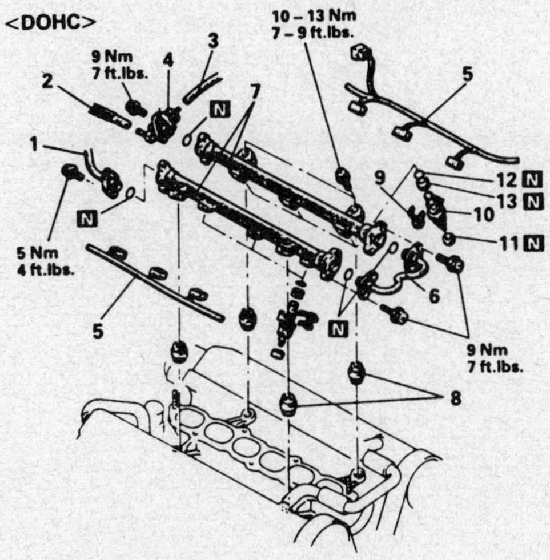

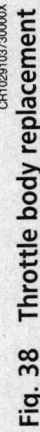

\<DOHC (Non Turbol) – California\>

\<DOHC (Turbo)\>

\<DOHC (Non Turbol) – Federal, Canada\>

\<SOHC – California\>

10 – 13 Nm
7 – 9 ft.lbs.

5 Nm
4 ft.lbs.

CR1029103730000X

Removal steps

1. Connection of accelerator cable
2. Connection of air intake hose
3. Connection of vacuum hose
4. Connection of TPS connector
5. Connection of ISC motor connector
6. Connection of water hose
7. Vacuum pipe assembly
8. Throttle body
9. Gasket

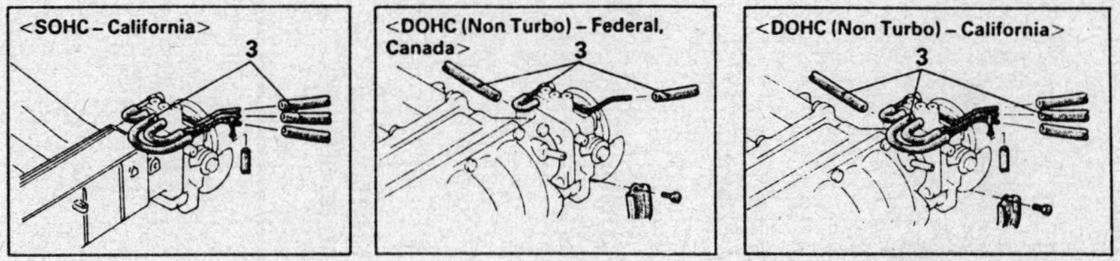

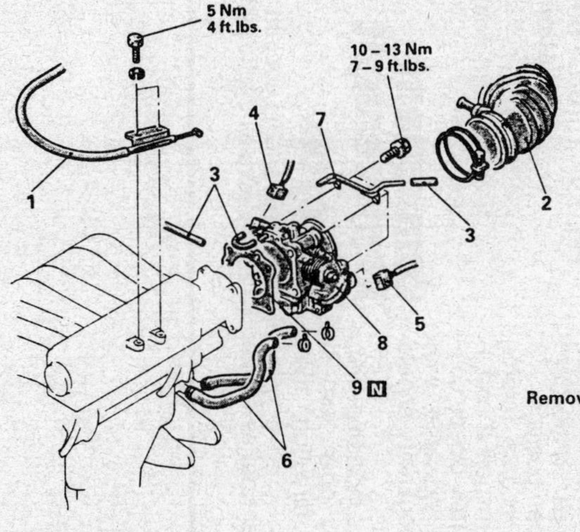

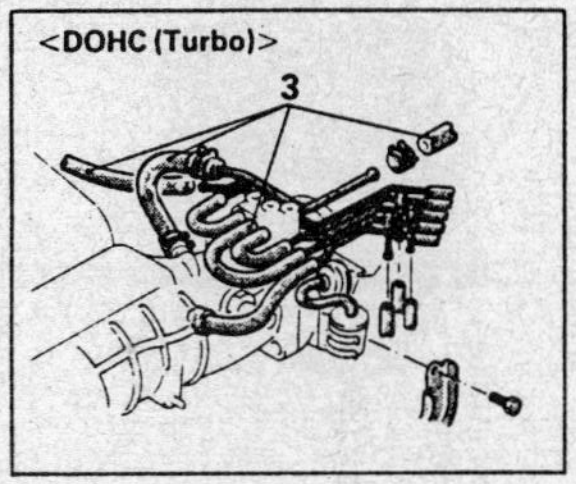

NOTE:
The layout of vacuum hoses (No. 3) of the construction drawing
is for the SOHC – Federal, Canada.

Fig. 38   Throttle body replacement

CR1029103729000X

12
13
10

5

12 N
13 N
11 N

9 Nm
7 ft.lbs.

10 – 13 Nm
7 – 9 ft.lbs.

9

6

8

7

3

4

9 Nm
7 ft.lbs.

2

1

5 Nm
4 ft.lbs.

5

Fig. 37   Injector replacement

12 N
13 N
11 N

9 Nm
7 ft.lbs.

10 – 13 Nm
7 – 9 ft.lbs.

3

4

9 Nm
7 ft.lbs.

2

1

5 Nm
4 ft.lbs.

5

8

7

7

O-ring

4

7

O-ring

O-ring

1

Removal steps

1. Connection of high pressure fuel hose
2. Connection of fuel return hose
3. Connection of vacuum hose
4. Fuel pressure regulator
5. Connection of control harness
6. Fuel pipe
7. Delivery pipe
8. Insulator
9. Injector support
10. Injector
11. Insulator
12. O-ring
13. Grommet

CHRYSLER–Fuel Injection

f. Apply negative pressure, ensuring pressure leaks immediately.
5. Reverse procedure to assemble throttle body, noting the following:
   a. Install throttle position sensor to throttle body assembly as shown in **Fig. 32.**
   b. Turn throttle position sensor 90° clockwise to set sensor, then tighten attaching screws.
   c. Using suitable circuit tester, test resistance between throttle position sensor terminals 1 and 3 or 3 and 4, **Fig. 33,** ensuring resistance changes smoothly as throttle valve is moved to full open position.
   d. Check continuity across throttle position sensor terminals 2 and 1, with throttle valve fully closed continuity should be indicated, with valve fully open continuity should not be indicated.
   e. If no continuity is indicated with throttle valve fully open, turn in counterclockwise direction, then retest.
   f. If measurements are not as speci-

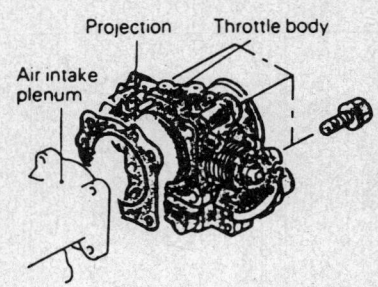

CR1029103731000X

Fig. 39   Throttle body gasket installation

fied, replace throttle position sensor.

Component Replacement

INJECTOR

1. Drain engine coolant system.
2. Remove air intake plenum as outlined in **Figs. 34 through 36.**
3. Relieve fuel pressure as outlined under "Precautions."
4. Refer to **Fig. 37** for injector removal procedure.
5. Reverse procedure to install, noting the following:
   a. Install injector to delivery pipe, turning right and left, ensuring injector turns smoothly. **If injector does not turn smoothly, the O-ring may be trapped. Remove injector, then reinstall, ensuring smooth turning.**
   b. Apply light oil to fuel pressure regulator O-ring, then install.

THROTTLE BODY

1. Drain engine coolant system.
2. Refer to **Fig. 38** for throttle body removal.
3. Reverse to install, noting the following:
   a. Install throttle body gasket as shown in **Fig. 39. Improper gasket installation may result in poor idling.**

MODELS w/3.0L/V6-181, 3.3L/V6-201 & 3.8L/V6-231 ENGINES EXCEPT CONCORDE, INTREPID, LHS, STEALTH, VISION & 1994–96 NEW YORKER

If Unsure Of The System Used On The Vehicle Being Serviced, Refer To The "Engine Systems Identification Chart." Further Assistance For The Proper Use Of Information Contained In This Section Can Also Be Found In The Front Of This Tabbed Section Under "How To Use This Manual."

On Air Bag Equipped Models, Refer To "Air Bag System Precautions" Located In The Front Of This Manual For System Disarming & Arming Procedures.

Prior To Performing Any Service Operations Listed In This Section, Consult The "Technical Service Bulletins" Section For Related Information.

Electrical Symbol & Wire Color Code Identification Located In The Front Of This Manual May Be Used As An Aid When Using Wiring Circuits Found In This Section.

INDEX

	Page No.		Page No.		Page No.
Body Code Identification	12-2	On-Board Diagnosis	12-5	Canister Purge & EGR Diagnostic Solenoid	12-112
Description:	12-2	Circuit Actuation Test Mode	12-5	Crankshaft Position (CKP) Sensor	12-112
Components	12-2	Fuel System Pressure Test	12-5	Fuel Injector	12-112
Diagnosis & Testing:	12-3	Switch & Sensor Test Mode	12-5	Fuel Injector Rail Assembly	12-111
Accessing Diagnostic Trouble Codes	12-3	Throttle Body Minimum Air Flow Test	12-5	Fuel Pressure Regulator	12-112
Using Diagnostic Readout Tool (DRB)	12-3	System & Component Diagnosis	12-5	Heated Oxygen Sensor (O2S)	12-112
Using Malfunction Indicator (Power Loss/Check Engine) Lamp	12-4	3.0L/V6-181 Engine	12-5	Idle Air Control (IAC) (Automatic Idle Speed (AIS)) Motor	12-111
Clearing Diagnostic Trouble Codes	12-4	3.3L/V6-201 & 3.8L/V6-231 Engines	12-6	Manifold Absolute Pressure (MAP) Sensor	12-112
Diagnostic Trouble Code Interpretation	12-4	Visual Inspection	12-3	Powertrain Control Module (PCM)	12-112
DRB Problems & Error Messages	12-4	**Diagnostic Chart Index**	12-23	Throttle Body	12-111
""High Or Low Battery" Message	12-5	**Precautions:**	12-2	Throttle Position Sensor (TPS)	12-111
""Key Pad Test Failure" Message	12-4	Fuel System Pressure Relief	12-2	Fuel System Pressure Relief	12-111
""No Response" Message	12-4	**Sensor Specifications**	12-1	3.0L/V6-181 Engine	12-111
""Ram Test Failure" & ""Cartridge Error" Message	12-4	**System Service:**	12-111	3.3L/V6-201 & 3.8L/V6-231 Engines	12-111
Blank Message Screen	12-4	Adjustments	12-112		
Inactive Trouble Condition	12-4	Ignition Timing	12-112		
		Component Replacement	12-111		
		Camshaft Position (CMP) Sensor	12-112		

SENSOR SPECIFICATIONS

Sensor	Resistance (Ohms)	
	70°F	200°F
Coolant Temp.	7000—13,000	700—1000
Charge Temp.	7000—13,000	700—1000
Throttle Body Temp.	5600—14,600	400—1500

MODELS w/3.0L/V6-181, 3.3L/V6-201 & 3.8L/V6-231 ENGINES EXCEPT CONCORDE, INTREPID, LHS, STEALTH, VISION & 1994-96 NEW YORKER

12-1

BODY CODE IDENTIFICATION

Body Code	Year	Vehicle Line	Body Code	Year	Vehicle Line
AA	1993-95	Spirit/Acclaim/LeBaron Landau	AJ	1993-95	LeBaron Coupe/Convertible
AC	1993	Dynasty/New Yorker Salon	AP	1993-94	Shadow/Sundance
AG	1993	Daytona	AY	1993	Imperial/New Yorker Fifth Avenue

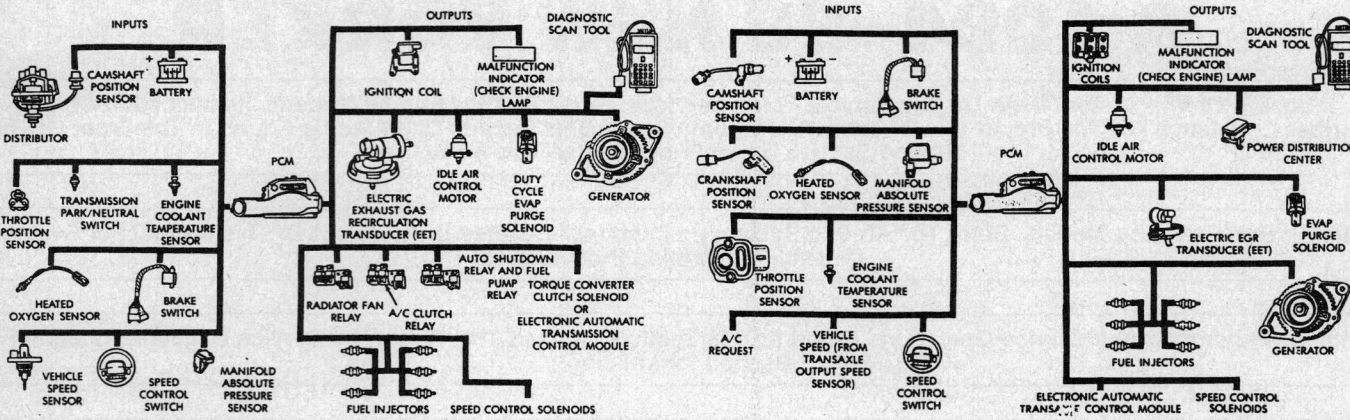

Fig. 1   MPFI system components. 3.0L/V6-181 engine

Fig. 2   MPFI system components. 3.3L/V6-201 & 3.8L/V6-231 engines

PRECAUTIONS
FUEL SYSTEM PRESSURE RELIEF

Prior to servicing any fuel system component, refer to "Fuel System Pressure Relief" under "System Service" to relieve fuel system pressure.

DESCRIPTION

This system combines an electronic fuel and spark advance control system with a cross type intake system to provide a precise air/fuel ratio under all driving conditions. These systems use a digital preprogrammed computer to regulate ignition timing, air/fuel ratio, emission control devices, cooling fan, charging system, idle speed and speed control.

Various sensors provide the input necessary for the engine controller to correctly regulate fuel flow at the fuel injectors, **Figs. 1 and 2**. These include manifold absolute pressure, throttle position, oxygen feedback, coolant temperature, charge temperature and vehicle speed sensors. In addition to the sensors, various switches also provide important information. These include transmission neutral safety, brake, speed control and A/C clutch switches. These signals cause the engine controller to change the fuel flow at the injector, the ignition timing or both.

The engine controller tests many of its own input and output circuits. If a problem is detected in a major system, the information is stored in the memory. This information can be displayed by a instrument panel malfunction indicator (check engine) lamp, or by connecting a diagnostic readout tool and reading a numbered display which corresponds to a specific problem.

COMPONENTS
Powertrain Control Module (PCM)

The PCM contains circuits necessary to power the ignition coil, alternator field and fuel injector and to energize the automatic shutdown (ASD) relay. The unit also receives a signal from the distributor. If no distributor signal is received, the ASD relay is not activated and power is discontinued to the fuel pump and ignition coil. A voltage converter in the unit reduces battery voltage to a regulated 8 volt output which powers the distributor.

The engine controller is a digital computer which contains a microprocessor. Input signals from various switches, sensors and components are sent to the engine controller, which then computes the fuel injector pulse width, spark advance, ignition coil dwell, idle speed, purge, cooling fan turn on and alternator charge rate.

Manifold Absolute Pressure (MAP) Sensor

The MAP sensor, located in engine compartment on the bulkhead (depending on application), monitors manifold absolute pressure. The sensor is connected to a vacuum nipple on the intake plenum and is tied electrically to the engine controller. This device relays information on manifold pressure conditions to the engine controller which is used in determining the proper air/fuel mixture.

Oxygen Sensor

The oxygen sensor, located in the rear exhaust manifold, produces voltage when exposed to oxygen present in exhaust gases. The sensor produces a low voltage when the air/fuel mixture is lean and a high voltage when the mixture is rich. The voltage is transmitted to the engine controller, triggering the fuel injector. On all models, the injector adjusts the mixture accordingly.

Charge Temperature Sensor

The charge temperature sensor, located in the intake manifold, measures the temperature of the air/fuel mixture. The engine controller uses this information to determine air/fuel mixture.

Coolant Temperature Sensor

The coolant temperature sensor, located in the thermostat housing, provides the engine controller with information on engine operating temperature. This data, in conjunction with data provided by the charge temperature sensor, permits the engine controller to provide slightly richer air/fuel mixtures and higher idle speeds until normal operating temperatures are reached.

Electric Exhaust Gas Recirculation Transducer (EET)

The EET combines a backpressure transducer and an electric vacuum solenoid. Using signals from the engine controller, the vacuum solenoid regulates vacuum to the transducer of the EET. The transducer uses backpressure to provide correct amounts of exhaust gas recirculation under all conditions.

Cam Reference Sensor

The cam reference sensor is located on top of engine timing chain cover. This sensor reads cam shaft position, then sends a signal to the engine controller. The engine controller uses this signal in combination with the Crank Timing Sensor signal to determine if fuel injectors and ignition coils are sequenced properly.

Crank Timing Sensor

The crank timing sensor is located on the transmission bellhousing. This sensor reads crank shaft position, then sends a signal to the engine controller. The engine controller uses this signal in combination with the Cam Reference Sensor signal to determine if fuel injectors and ignition coils are sequenced properly.

Knock Sensor

The knock sensor is located on the engine block where detonation in each cylinder can be detected. This sensor provides information used by the engine controller to modify spark advance in order to eliminate detonation.

Switch Input

Various switches located throughout the vehicle provide information to the engine controller. These switches include neutral safety, A/C clutch, speed control and brake light switches.

Malfunction Indicator (Check Engine) Lamp

The malfunction indicator (check engine) lamp on the instrument panel will illuminate if the engine controller receives an incorrect signal or no signal from the coolant temperature sensor, charge temperature sensor, MAP sensor, throttle position sensor, battery voltage sensor input or a emission related system (Calif. models) depending on vehicle application. This lamp indicates that the engine controller has gone into the "limp in mode" to keep the system operational, and indicates an immediate need for service.

The malfunction indicator (check engine) lamp will also light for several seconds each time the ignition key is turned on as a bulb check.

Canister Purge Solenoid

The purge solenoid controls vapor canister purge and fuel pressure regulator. When the solenoid is energized, it blocks flow of fuel vapor. Depending on data received by the coolant temperature sensor and charge temperature sensor at engine start-up, the solenoid will be energized for a controlled time or when a predetermined temperature is reached.

Air Conditioning Cut Out Relay

The air-conditioning cut out relay is wired in series with the A/C dampened pressure switch and A/C switch. When the throttle position sensor sends a wide open throttle signal to the engine controller or low engine RPM is detected, the relay is energized and air conditioning clutch engagement is prevented.

Air Conditioning Clutch Relay

The air conditioning clutch relay is controlled by the engine controller and pow-

ered by the fan relay, A/C switch and engine controller. When the throttle position sensor sends a wide open throttle signal to the engine controller or low engine RPM is detected, the relay is energized and air conditioning clutch engagement is prevented.

Automatic Shutdown (ASD) Relay & Fuel Pump Relay

The PCM operates the auto shutdown (ASD) relay and fuel pump relay through one ground path. The PCM operates the relays by switching the ground path on and off. Both relays turn on and off at the same time. The ASD relay connects battery voltage to the fuel injector and ignition coil. The fuel pump relay connects battery voltage to the fuel pump and oxygen sensor heating element.

The PCM turns the ground path off when the ignition switch is in the Off position. Both relays are off. When the ignition witch is in the On or crank position, the PCM monitors the distributor pickup signal to determine engine speed and ignition timing (coil dwell). If the PCM does not receive a distributor signal when the ignition switch is in the Run position, it will de-energize both relays. When the relays are de-energized, battery voltage is not supplied to the fuel injector, ignition coil, fuel pump and oxygen sensor heating element.

Throttle Body

The throttle body houses the TPS and AIS motor. Air flow through the throttle body is controlled by a cable operated throttle blade located in the base of the throttle body.

Throttle Position Sensor (TPS)

The TPS, located on the throttle body, is an electric resistor which is activated by the movement of the throttle blade. The sensor produces a voltage which increases or decreases according to the throttle blade opening. The voltage signal is transmitted to the engine controller where it is used with data from other sensors to adjust the air/fuel mixture accordingly.

Automatic Idle Speed (AIS) Motor

The AIS motor, operated by the engine controller, adjusts the air portion of the air/fuel mixture through an air bypass on the back of the throttle body. Base idle is determined by the minimum air flow through the throttle body. The AIS motor opens or closes off the air bypass as needed according to engine loads or ambient conditions. The engine controller senses the change in air/fuel mixture and increases or decreases fuel accordingly to change engine idle. The AIS motor also prevents stalling during deceleration by increasing engine idle when the throttle is closed quickly.

Fuel Pump

Fuel is pumped to the fuel rail by an electric pump which is mounted in the fuel tank. The pump inlet is fitted with a filter to prevent water and other contaminants from entering fuel supply circuit.

Fuel Injector

The fuel injector is an electric solenoid which is powered by the engine controller. The engine controller determines when and how long the injector should operate.

Fuel Pressure Regulator

The fuel pressure regulator, located downstream of the fuel injector on the fuel rail, maintains a constant fuel pressure of 48 psi across the injector tip. The spring-loaded diaphragm in the regulator is used to uncover a fuel return port. When the fuel pump operates, fuel flows past the injector into the regulator, and is restricted from flowing any further by the blocked return port. When fuel pressure reaches a predetermined value, it pushes on the diaphragm, compressing the spring and uncovers the fuel return port. The diaphragm and spring will constantly move from an open to closed position to keep fuel pressure constant.

DIAGNOSIS & TESTING
Visual Inspection

Many problems with the multi-point fuel injection system can be traced to poor hose or wiring connections. Before proceeding with system tests or diagnosis, inspect the following:

1. Check ignition cable and ignition coil electrical connections.
2. Ensure purge solenoid, EGR diagnostic solenoid, MAP sensor, torque lock-up solenoid and alternator electrical connectors are secure.
3. Ensure purge solenoid, EGR diagnostic solenoid, MAP sensor, vapor canister, fuel pressure regulator and EGR system vacuum connections are secure.
4. Ensure engine ground strap is attached at engine and dash panel.
5. Ensure oxygen sensor, distributor, charge temperature sensor, coolant temperature sensor, oil pressure sending unit, throttle body, fuel injector, neutral safety switch and distance sensor connectors are secure.
6. Ensure power brake booster and speed control connections are secure.
7. Ensure engine harness to main harness electrical connections are secure.
8. Ensure engine controller 60-way electrical connections are secure.

Accessing Diagnostic Trouble Codes
USING DIAGNOSTIC READOUT TOOL (DRB)

1. Connect the DRB to diagnostic connector located in engine compartment near the strut tower.
2. Start the engine if possible, then cycle the transmission selector and air conditioning switch.
3. Shutoff the engine.
4. Turn ignition on and record all diagnostic trouble codes displayed on the DRB screen within 5 seconds. Note

that the malfunction indicator (power loss/check engine) lamp should light for 2 seconds as a bulb check.

USING MALFUNCTION INDICATOR (POWER LOSS/CHECK ENGINE) LAMP

If suitable diagnostic readout tool is not available, stored diagnostic trouble codes and be accessed directly through the malfunction indicator (power loss/check engine) lamp. To call up diagnostic trouble codes, cycle ignition switch on, off, on, off and on within 5 seconds. Stored diagnostic trouble codes will be indicated by flashes of the malfunction indicator (power loss/check engine) lamp. The diagnostic trouble codes will be indicated as two digit numbers, with a four second pause between diagnostic trouble codes. An example of such a diagnostic trouble code output is as follows:

1. Malfunction Indicator (Power Loss/Check Engine) Lamp illuminated for approximately 2 to 3 seconds as a bulb check, then turns off.
2. Lamp flashes two times, pauses, then flashes six times.
3. Lamp pauses for approximately four seconds.
4. Lamp flashes three times, pauses, then flashes one time.
5. This would indicate that Diagnostic Trouble Codes 26 and 31 are stored. The lamp will continue to flash until all stored diagnostic trouble codes have been displayed.

Once the lamp starts flashing the stored diagnostic trouble codes, it cannot be stopped. If a diagnostic trouble code is missed, the entire procedure must be repeated. The lamp will not indicate if oxygen feedback system is switching lean-rich or if idle motor system is operational. The lamp also cannot be used to perform actuation test mode, sensor test mode or engine running test mode.

Diagnostic Trouble Code Interpretation

Diagnostic trouble codes can be displayed either by flashes of the malfunction indicator (check engine) lamp or by connecting Diagnostic Readout Box (DRB) to the system.

Diagnostic trouble codes indicate the results of a failure, but do not identify the failed component. The diagnostic charts do not use diagnostic trouble codes for diagnosis. Instead, diagnosis is performed in a symptom driven format.

Prior to performing any procedure in the diagnostic charts, check electrical and vacuum component connections as described under "Visual Inspection." **Always start at the first No Start, Driveability, No Fault or Verification test. Starting at any other test may give inaccurate results.** After completing the test, perform verification test.

CODE 11—Indicates no reference signal during engine cranking.

CODE 12—Indicates No. of key On since last fault or since faults were erased.

CODE 13—Indicates a fault in the MAP sensor pneumatic circuit.

CODE 14—Indicates a fault in the MAP sensor electrical circuit.

CODE 15—Indicates a fault in the vehicle distance sensor circuit.

CODE 17—Indicates engine running too cool.

CODE 21—Indicates a problem in the oxygen feedback circuit.

CODE 22—Indicates a fault in the coolant temperature sensor circuit.

CODE 23—Indicates a fault in the charge temperature sensor circuit.

CODE 24—Indicates a fault in the throttle position sensor circuit.

CODE 25—Indicates a fault in the AIS motor drive circuit.

CODE 26—Indicates injector current limit not achieved.

CODE 27—Indicates a fault in injector driver interface circuit.

CODE 31—Indicates a fault in the purge solenoid circuit.

CODE 32—Indicates a fault in EGR Diagnostics (Calif. models).

CODE 33—Indicates a fault in air conditioning cutout relay circuit or air conditioning clutch relay circuit.

CODE 34—Indicates a fault in speed control solenoid driver circuit.

CODE 35—Indicates a fault in fan relay circuit.

CODE 37—Indicates a fault in the torque converter unlock solenoid circuit.

CODE 41—Indicates a fault in the charging system or no field current.

CODE 42—Indicates a fault in the ASD relay driver circuit.

CODE 43—Indicates fault in ignition coil control circuit.

CODE 44—Indicates battery temperature voltage is incorrect.

CODE 46—Indicates battery voltage is too high.

CODE 47—Indicates battery voltage is too low.

CODE 51—Indicates a lean condition is indicated.

CODE 52—Indicates a rich condition is indicated.

CODE 53—Indicates internal problem in Module.

CODE 54—Indicates a fault in the distributor high data rate pickup circuit.

CODE 55—Indicates end of message. This diagnostic trouble code will appear after all other diagnostic trouble codes have been displayed.

CODE 62—Indicates unsuccessful attempt to update EMR mileage.

CODE 63—Indicates controller failure.

Diagnostic trouble codes indicated by an will cause the malfunction indicator (check engine) lamp to remain illuminated when set in the engine controller memory.

After all diagnostic trouble codes have been displayed and Diagnostic Trouble Code 55 has been received, refer to On-Board Diagnosis for test mode activation and make sure that the display changes when the switch is activated and released: brake pedal, gearshift selector and A/C switch.

Inactive Trouble Condition

This section should only be used when referred to by the diagnostic charts.

You have just attempted to simulate the condition that initially set the fault message. The following additional checks may assist in identifying a possible intermittent problem:

1. Visually inspect related wire harness connectors. Look for broken, bent, pushed out or corroded terminals.
2. Visually inspect the related harnesses. Look for chafed, pierced or partially broken wires.

Clearing Diagnostic Trouble Codes

Clearing diagnostic trouble codes can be accomplished in one of two ways. First is by selecting Erase Faults under the Read Faults display, or by disconnecting the battery ground cable for more than two minutes.

DRB Problems & Error Messages

BLANK MESSAGE SCREEN

1. Connect the DRB to a different vehicle.
2. If screen remains blank, the DRB or its adapter are at fault. Substitute parts to determine which.
3. If screen is no longer blank, proceed to step 4.
4. Inspect diagnostic connector for proper wire placement, flared terminals or push outs.
5. If connector is in good condition, ensure black/white wire is connected to ground.

"NO RESPONSE" MESSAGE

1. Ensure ignition switch in On position.
2. Test pink and light green wires for continuity between diagnostic connector and cavities 25 and 26 of the engine controller 60-way connector.
3. Install a different DRB with a different set of cables and check for a "No Response" message.
4. If steps 1 through 3 do not correct "No Response" message, replace engine controller.

"RAM TEST FAILURE" & "CARTRIDGE ERROR" MESSAGE

If this message is displayed on the DRB, replace the DRB unit or cartridge.

"KEY PAD TEST FAILURE" MESSAGE

If this message is displayed on the DRB, power the DRB up again with fingers off key pad. If message persists, replace the DRB.

12-4 *MODELS w/3.0L/V6-181, 3.3L/V6-201 & 3.8L/V6-231 ENGINES EXCEPT CONCORDE, INTREPID, LHS, STEALTH, VISION & 1994-96*

NEW YORKER

"HIGH OR LOW BATTERY" MESSAGE

If this message is displayed, correct condition and reconnect the DRB.

On-Board Diagnosis

After performing the On-Board Diagnosis procedures, refer to "System and Component Diagnosis" to test systems indicated by the diagnostic trouble codes. Also refer to "System and Component Diagnosis" when testing systems not monitored by the On-Board Diagnosis System.

The engine controller is programmed to monitor various circuits in the MPI system. If a problem is sensed often enough to indicate an actual fault, its diagnostic trouble code is stored in the engine controller display. If the problem ceases to exist or is repaired, the diagnostic trouble code will be cancelled by the engine controller after 50-100 ignition key on/off cycles.

SWITCH & SENSOR TEST MODE

The switch inputs used by the engine controller have only two recognized states, High and Low. For this reason, the engine controller cannot recognize the difference between a switch position versus an open circuit, a short circuit or a defective switch. If the change is displayed, it can be assumed that the entire switch circuit to the engine controller is functioning normally.

Connect the DRB tool to the vehicle and access the State Display Screen. Access Inputs and Outputs or Sensor to obtain the list of available components to be tested.

CIRCUIT ACTUATION TEST MODE

The circuit actuation test mode check for proper operation of output circuits or components which the engine controller cannot internally recognize. The engine controller can attempt to activate these outputs and allow an observer to verify proper operation. Most of the tests provide an audible or visual indication or operation. With the exception of an intermittent condition, if a component functions properly during its test, it can be assumed that the component, its associated wiring and its driver circuit are working properly.

Connect the DRB tool to the vehicle and access the Actuators screen to obtain the list of available components to be tested.

THROTTLE BODY MINIMUM AIR FLOW TEST

1. Connect the DRB scan tool.
2. Remove air cleaner assembly, then plug heated air door vacuum hose.
3. Start engine and allow cooling fan to cycle on and off at least once.
4. Connect suitable timing light, then disconnect coolant thermistor and set basic timing to 12° BTDC.
5. Stop engine and reconnect coolant thermistor wire.
6. Disconnect PCV valve hose from intake manifold nipple.
7. Attach tool No. C-6457 or equivalent (.125 inch orifice in attached hose) to intake manifold PCV nipple.
8. Start engine and allow to idle for at least 1 minute.
9. Using readout tool, access Min Airflow Idle Speed in the sensor read test mode, then the following should occur:
   a. IAC (AIS) motor will fully close.
   b. Idle spark advance will become fixed.
   c. Idle fuel will become enriched.
   d. Engine RPM will be displayed on diagnostic readout tool in units of RPM x 10. For example, display 95 equals 95 x 10 which indicates 950 RPM.
10. Check idle RPM. Engine speed should be as follows:
    a. **On models with Turbo I engine,** engine speed should be 700-1400 RPM.
    b. **On models with Turbo III engine,** engine speed should be 650-1150 RPM.
11. **On all models,** if idle RPM is within specification, then throttle body minimum air flow is satisfactory. If idle RPM is not as specified, replace throttle body.
12. Shutoff engine, then remove tool No. C-6457 or equivalent, from intake manifold PCV nipple. Install PVC valve hose.
13. Remove readout tool, then install air cleaner assembly and heated air door vacuum hose.

FUEL SYSTEM PRESSURE TEST

Fuel system pressure must be released any time a fuel line is to be disconnected.

1. Remove protective cover from service valve on fuel rail on 3.3L/V6-201 and 3.8L/V6-231 or remove fuel hose quick connector from chassis lines on 3.0L/V6-181.
2. Connect fuel pressure gauge tool No. C-4799 or equivalent to fuel rail service valve or to fuel pressure test adapter tool, No. C-6539 or equivalent between fuel supply hose and chassis fuel line assembly.
3. Using diagnostic tester and key in run position, use ASD fuel system test. This will activate fuel pump and pressurize the system.
4. If gauge reads correct fuel pressure specification, further testing in not required.
5. If pressure is not correct, record pressure and remove gauge tool.
6. Use ASD fuel system test to activate fuel pump. Ensure fuel does not leak from fuel rail service valve or fuel connection point.
7. If fuel pressure is below specification, proceed as follows:
   a. Install fuel pressure gauge tool and adapter in fuel supply line between fuel tank and fuel filter at rear of vehicle.
   b. Repeat step 3. If pressure is at least 5 psi higher than previously recorded, gently squeeze return hose.
   c. If pressure increases, replace pressure regulator.
   d. If pressure does not change, problem is either a plugged pump filter or defective fuel pump.
8. If pressure is above specification, proceed as follows:
   a. Remove fuel return line hose from fuel tank.
   b. Connect fuel pressure test adapter to the return line.
   c. Put other end into a suitable two gallon container.
   d. Repeat step 3. If pressure is now correct, replace fuel pump assembly.
   e. If pressure is still high, remove fuel return hose from chassis fuel tubes. Connect adapter tool to return hose and place other end into a suitable container.
   f. Repeat step 3. If pressure is now correct, check for restricted fuel return line.
   g. If no change in pressure is observed, replace fuel pressure regulator.

System & Component Diagnosis

The following tests are used to further diagnose systems monitored by the On-Board Diagnosis System and to also test systems or parts of a system which are not monitored by the On-Board diagnosis system. Prior to performing any of the following tests, check electrical and vacuum component connections as described under "Visual Inspection." **Always start at the first No Start, Driveability, No Fault or Verification test. Starting at any other test may give inaccurate results.** After completing the test, perform appropriate verification test. Also check electrical connector terminal blades or pins for alignment and damage prior to replacing any component.

Refer to "On-Board Diagnosis" for procedures on placing system in the various test modes. Refer to **Figs. 3 through 10** for wiring diagrams and connector terminal identification.

3.0L/V6-181 ENGINE
Driveability Tests

Refer to the first Driveability diagnosis chart, **Fig. 11,** and the remaining Driveability charts, **Figs. 12 through 67,** for driveability diagnosis and testing.

No Fault Tests

Refer to the first No Fault diagnosis chart, **Fig. 68,** and the remaining No Fault charts, **Figs. 69 through 91,** when no diagnostic trouble codes are set and a malfunction exists.

No Start Test

Refer to the first No Start diagnosis chart, **Fig. 92,** and the remaining No Start charts, **Figs. 93 through 111,** for no start diagnosis and testing.

Verification Tests

After completing diagnosis operations, perform verification tests, **Figs. 112 through 115.**

MODELS w/3.0L/V6-181, 3.3L/V6-201 & 3.8L/V6-231 ENGINES EXCEPT CONCORDE, INTREPID, LHS, STEALTH, VISION & 1994-96 NEW YORKER

12-5

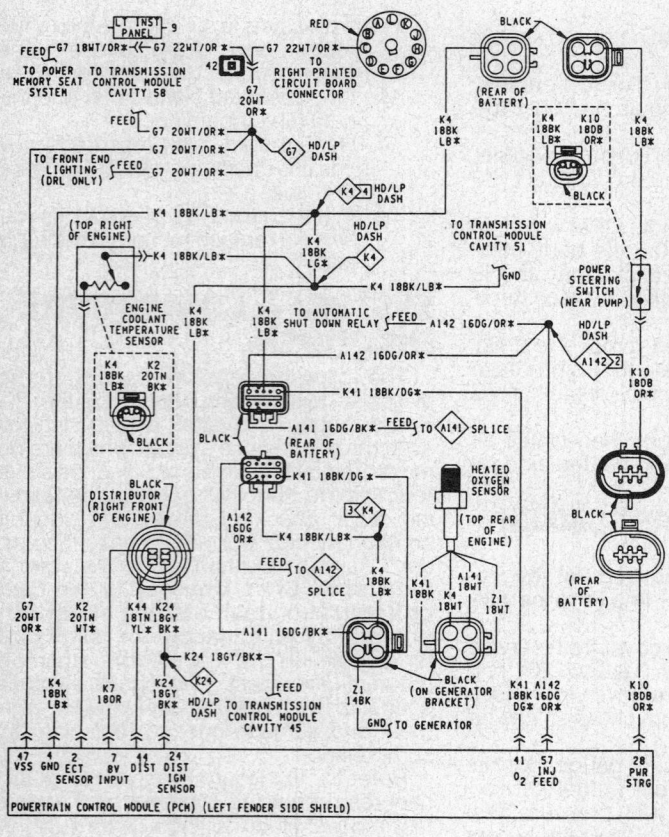

Fig. 3   MPFI wiring circuit (Part 1 of 5). 1993 3.0L/V6-181 engine

CR1029302899010X

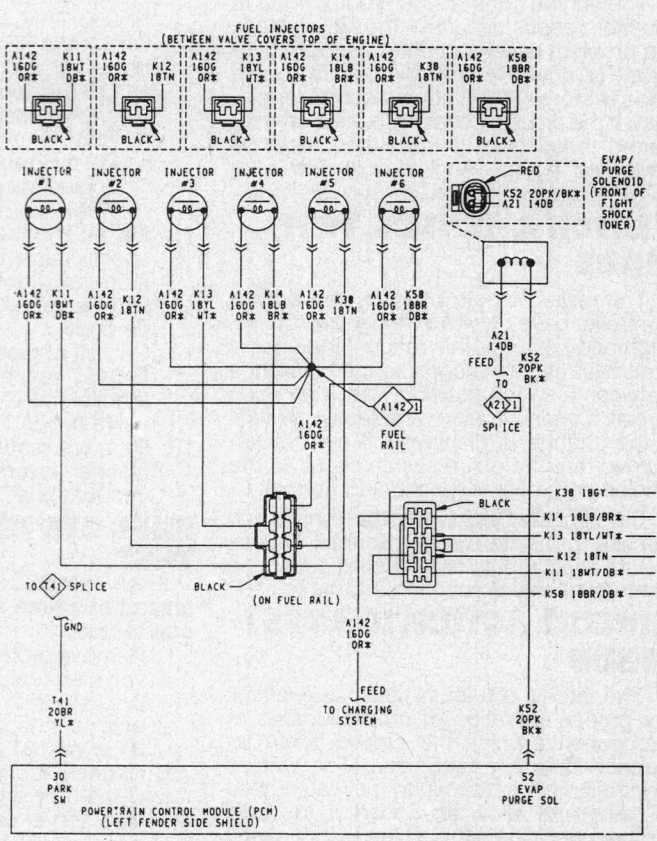

Fig. 3   MPFI wiring circuit (Part 2 of 5). 1993 3.0L/V6-181 engine

CR1029302899020X

3.3L/V6-201 & 3.8L/V6-231 ENGINES

Driveability Tests

Refer to the first Driveability diagnosis chart, **Fig. 116**, and the remaining Driveability charts, **Figs. 117 through 179**, for driveability diagnosis and testing.

No Fault Tests

Refer to the first No Fault diagnosis chart, **Fig. 180**, and the remaining No Fault charts, **Figs. 181 through 198**, when no diagnostic trouble codes are set and a malfunction exists.

No Start Test

Refer to the first No Start diagnosis chart, **Fig. 199**, and the remaining No Start charts, **Figs. 200 through 215**, for no start diagnosis and testing.

Verification Tests

After completing diagnosis operations, perform verification tests, **Figs. 216 through 219**.

12-6   *MODELS w/3.0L/V6-181, 3.3L/V6-201 & 3.8L/V6-231 ENGINES EXCEPT CONCORDE, INTREPID, LHS, STEALTH, VISION & 1994-96*

NEW YORKER

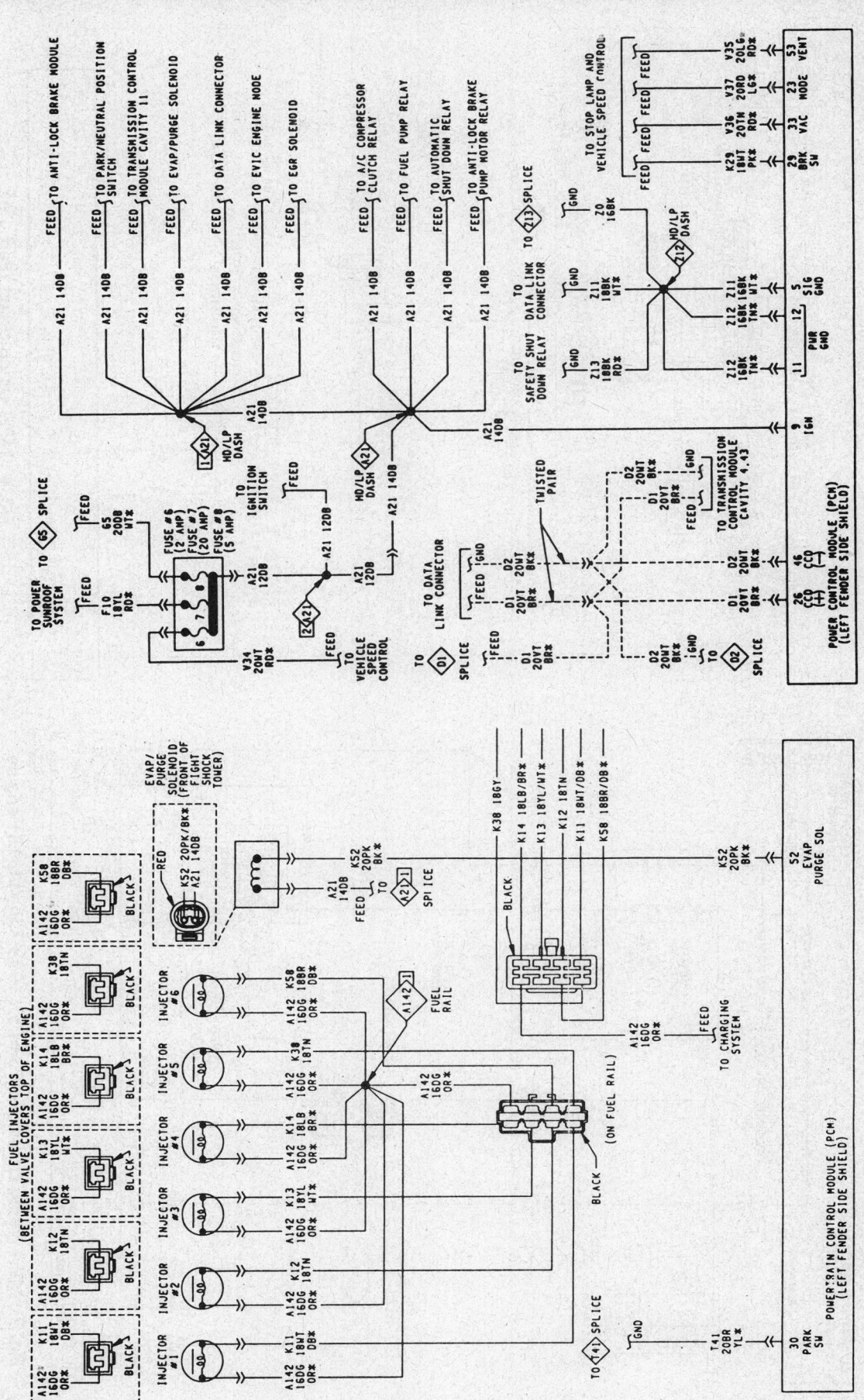

Fig. 3 MPFI wiring circuit (Part 4 of 5). 1993 3.0L/V6-181 engine

Fig. 3 MPFI wiring circuit (Part 3 of 5). 1993 3.0L/V6-181 engine

MODELS w/3.0L/V6-181, 3.3L/V6-201 & 3.8L/V6-231 ENGINES EXCEPT CONCORDE, INTREPID, LHS, STEALTH, VISION &
1994-96 NEW YORKER

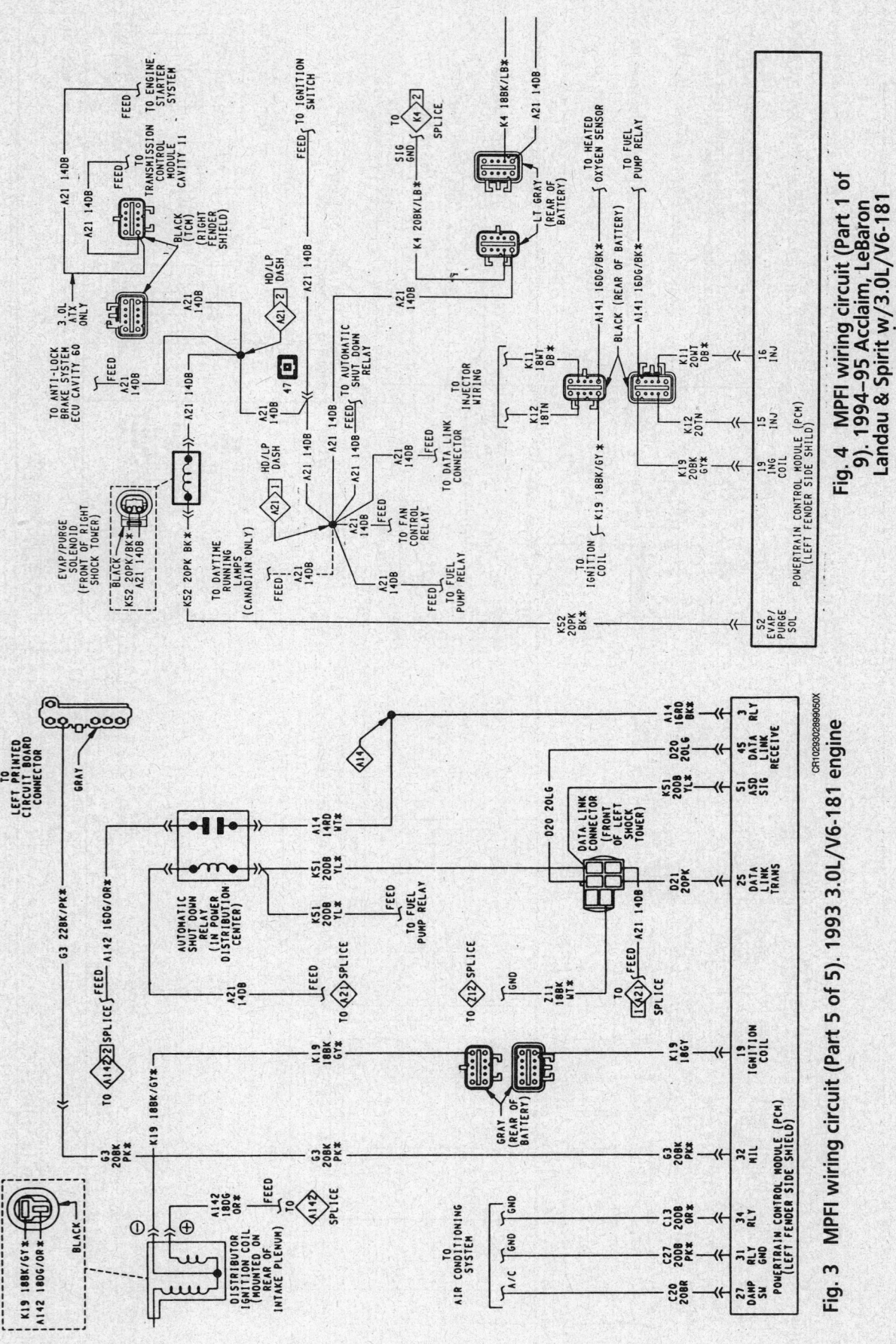

Fig. 4 MPFI wiring circuit (Part 1 of 9). 1994–95 Acclaim, LeBaron Landau & Spirit w/3.0L/V6-181 engine

Fig. 3 MPFI wiring circuit (Part 5 of 5). 1993 3.0L/V6-181 engine

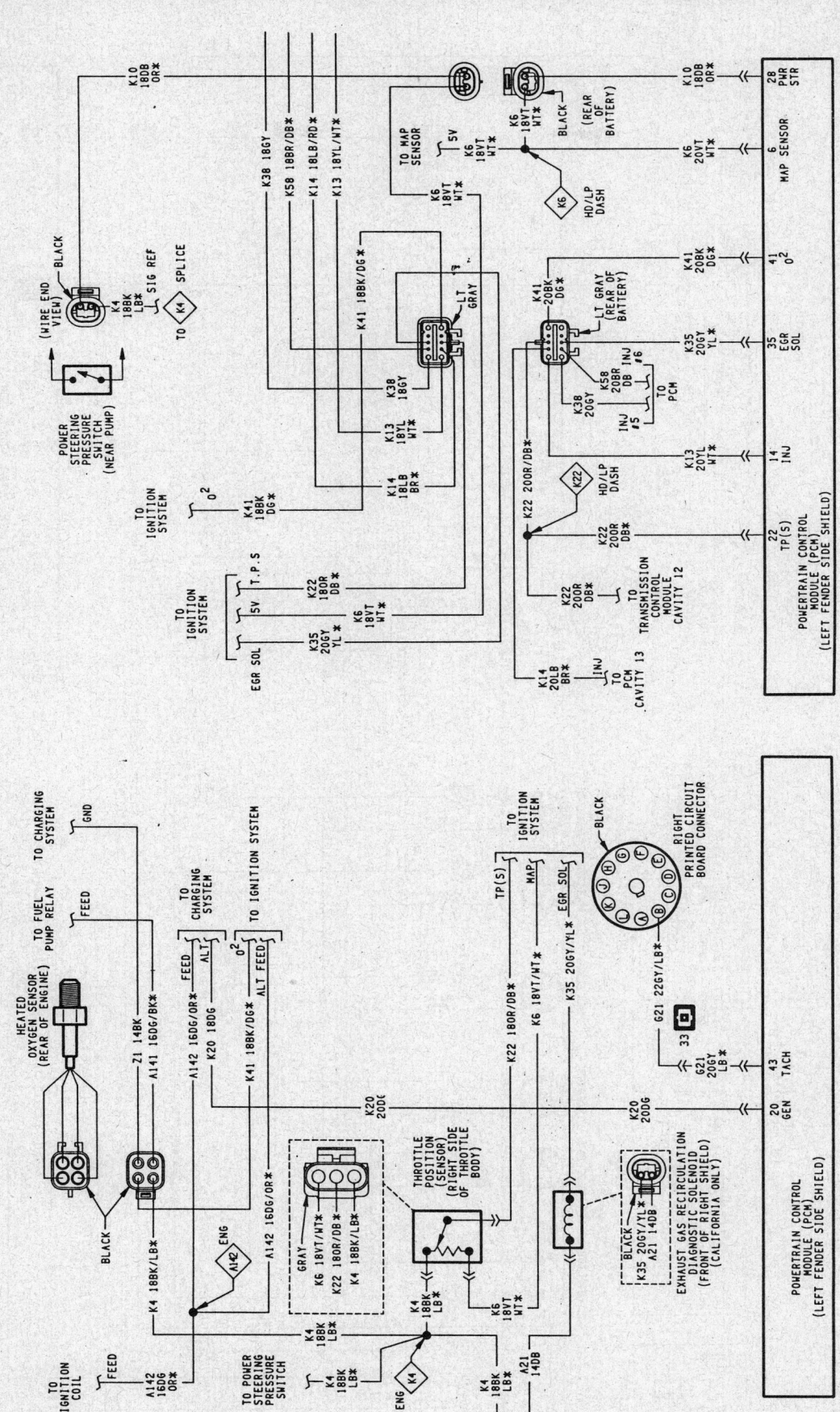

Fig. 4 MPFI wiring circuit (Part 3 of 9). 1994-95 Acclaim, LeBaron Landau & Spirit w/3.0L/V6-181 engine

Fig. 4 MPFI wiring circuit (Part 2 of 9). 1994-95 Acclaim, LeBaron Landau & Spirit w/3.0L/V6-181 engine

MODELS w/3.0L/V6-181, 3.3L/V6-201 & 3.8L/V6-231 ENGINES EXCEPT CONCORDE, INTREPID, LHS, STEALTH, VISION & 1994-96 NEW YORKER

12-9

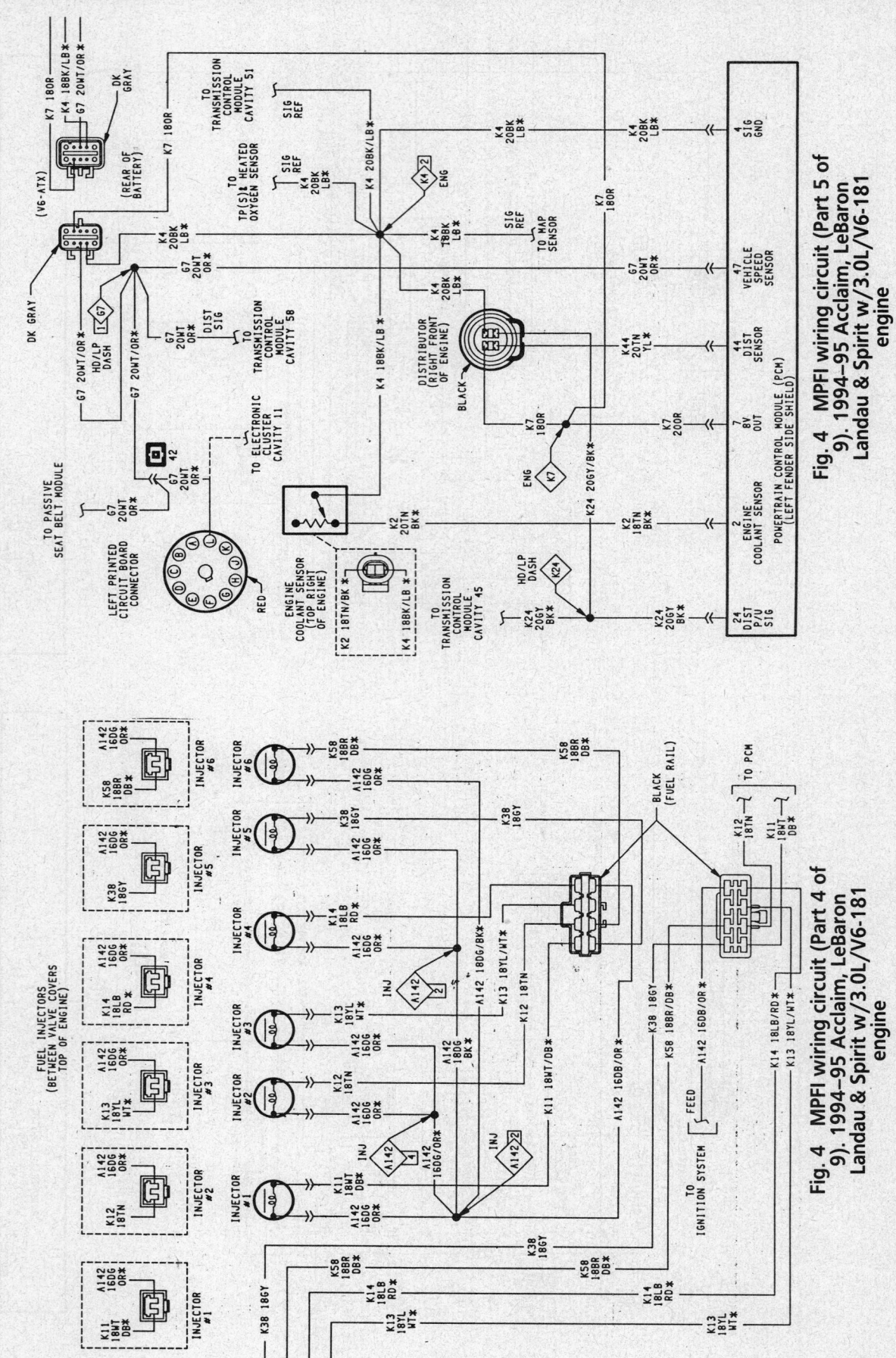

Fig. 4 MPFI wiring circuit (Part 5 of 9). 1994–95 Acclaim, LeBaron Landau & Spirit w/3.0L/V6-181 engine

Fig. 4 MPFI wiring circuit (Part 4 of 9). 1994–95 Acclaim, LeBaron Landau & Spirit w/3.0L/V6-181 engine

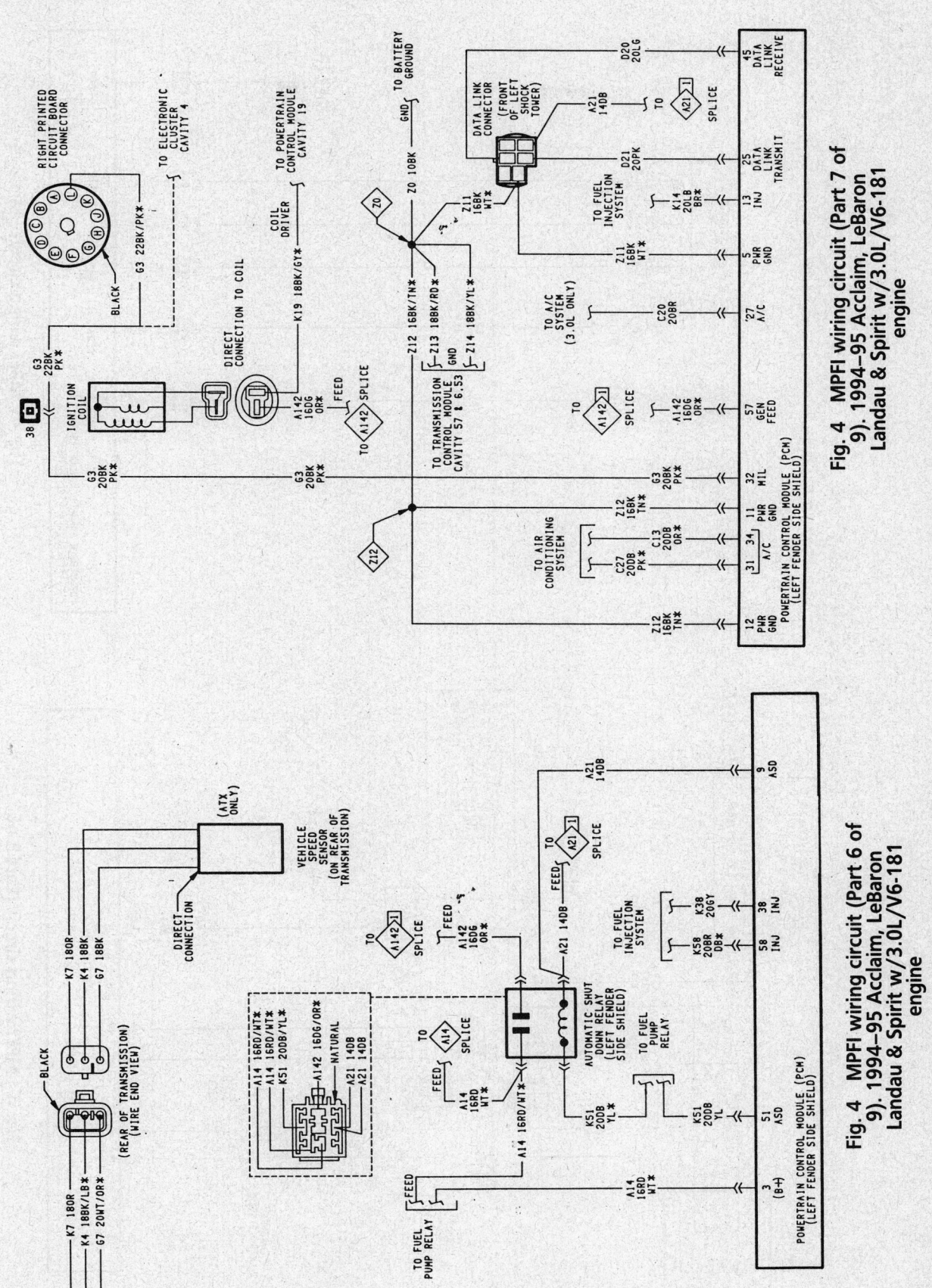

Fig. 4 MPFI wiring circuit (Part 7 of 9). 1994-95 Acclaim, LeBaron Landau & Spirit w/3.0L/V6-181 engine

Fig. 4 MPFI wiring circuit (Part 6 of 9). 1994-95 Acclaim, LeBaron Landau & Spirit w/3.0L/V6-181 engine

MODELS w/3.0L/V6-181, 3.3L/V6-201 & 3.8L/V6-231 ENGINES EXCEPT CONCORDE, INTREPID, LHS, STEALTH, VISION & 1994-96 NEW YORKER

12-11

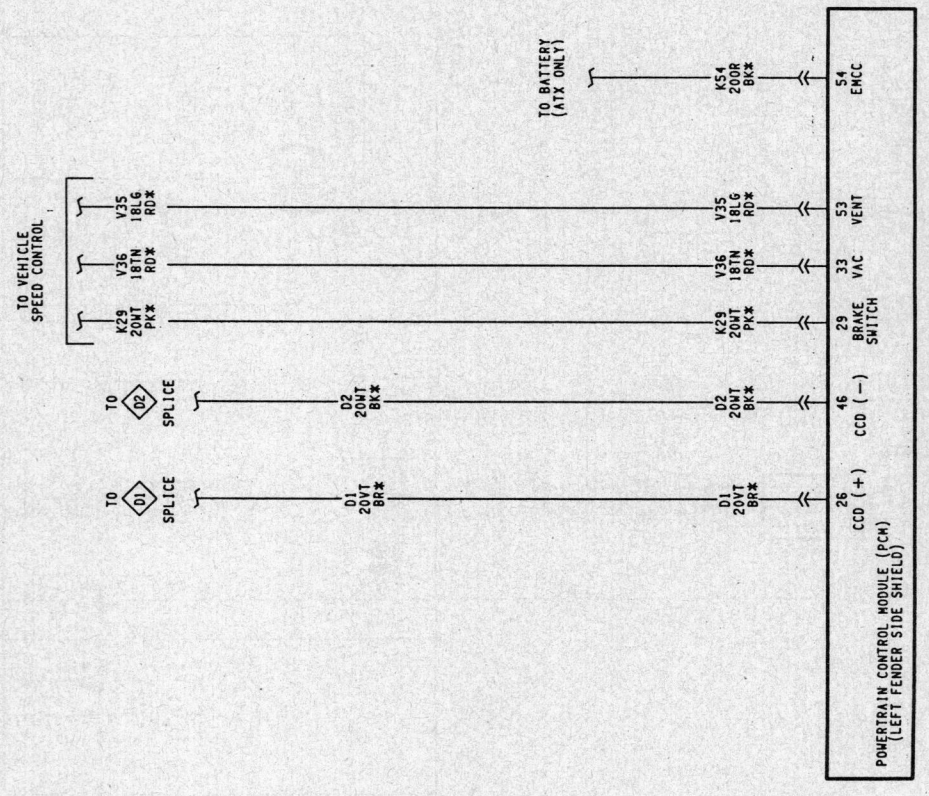

Fig. 4   MPFI wiring circuit (Part 9 of 9). 1994–95 Acclaim, LeBaron Landau & Spirit w/3.0L/V6-181 engine

Fig. 4   MPFI wiring circuit (Part 8 of 9). 1994–95 Acclaim, LeBaron Landau & Spirit w/3.0L/V6-181 engine

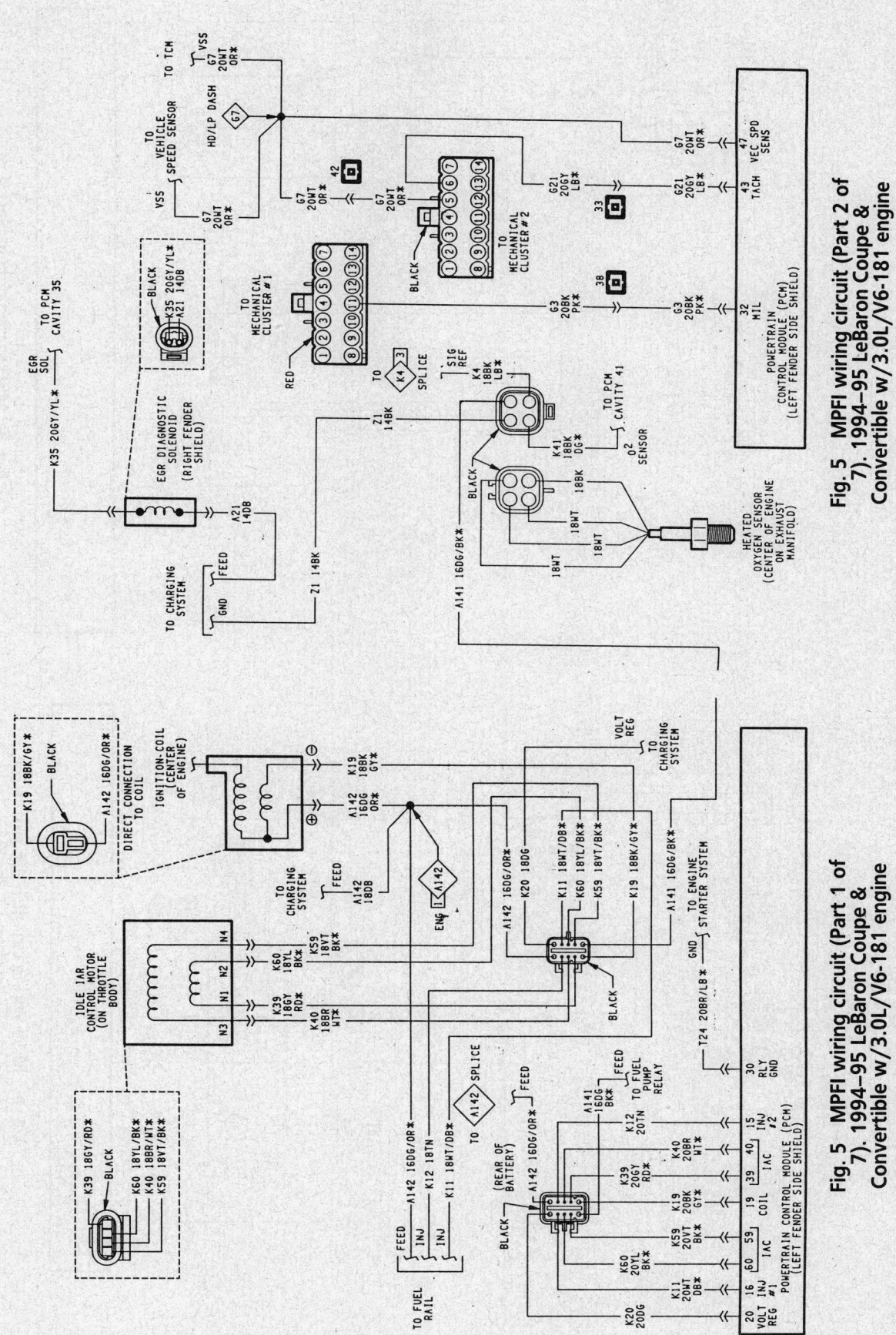

Fig. 5   MPFI wiring circuit (Part 2 of 7). 1994-95 LeBaron Coupe & Convertible w/3.0L/V6-181 engine

Fig. 5   MPFI wiring circuit (Part 1 of 7). 1994-95 LeBaron Coupe & Convertible w/3.0L/V6-181 engine

MODELS w/3.0L/V6-181, 3.3L/V6-201 & 3.8L/V6-231 ENGINES EXCEPT CONCORDE, INTREPID, LHS, STEALTH, VISION & 1994-96 NEW YORKER

12-13

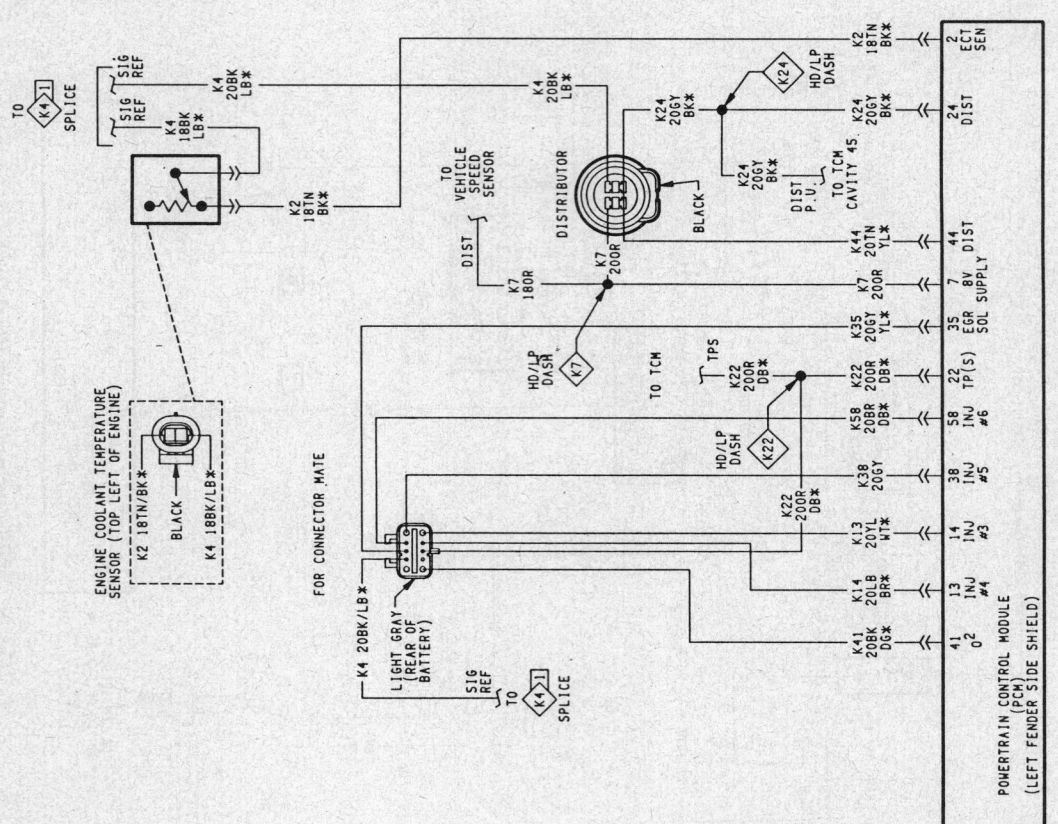

Fig. 5 MPFI wiring circuit (Part 4 of 7). 1994–95 LeBaron Coupe & Convertible w/3.0L/V6-181 engine

Fig. 5 MPFI wiring circuit (Part 3 of 7). 1994–95 LeBaron Coupe & Convertible w/3.0L/V6-181 engine

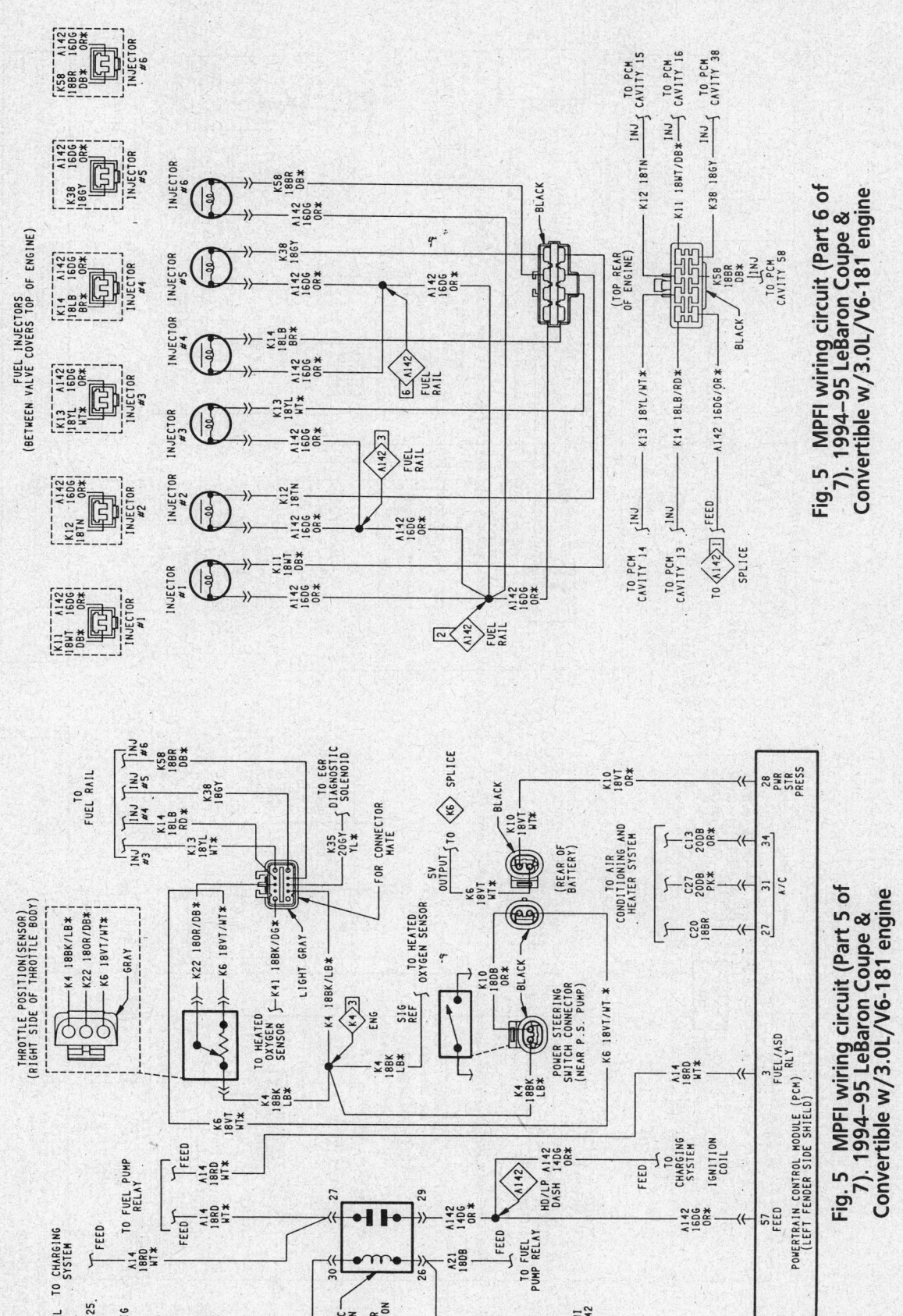

Fig. 5 MPFI wiring circuit (Part 6 of 7). 1994-95 LeBaron Coupe & Convertible w/3.0L/V6-181 engine

Fig. 5 MPFI wiring circuit (Part 5 of 7). 1994-95 LeBaron Coupe & Convertible w/3.0L/V6-181 engine

MODELS w/3.0L/V6-181, 3.3L/V6-201 & 3.8L/V6-231 ENGINES EXCEPT CONCORDE, INTREPID, LHS, STEALTH, VISION & 1994-96 NEW YORKER

12-15

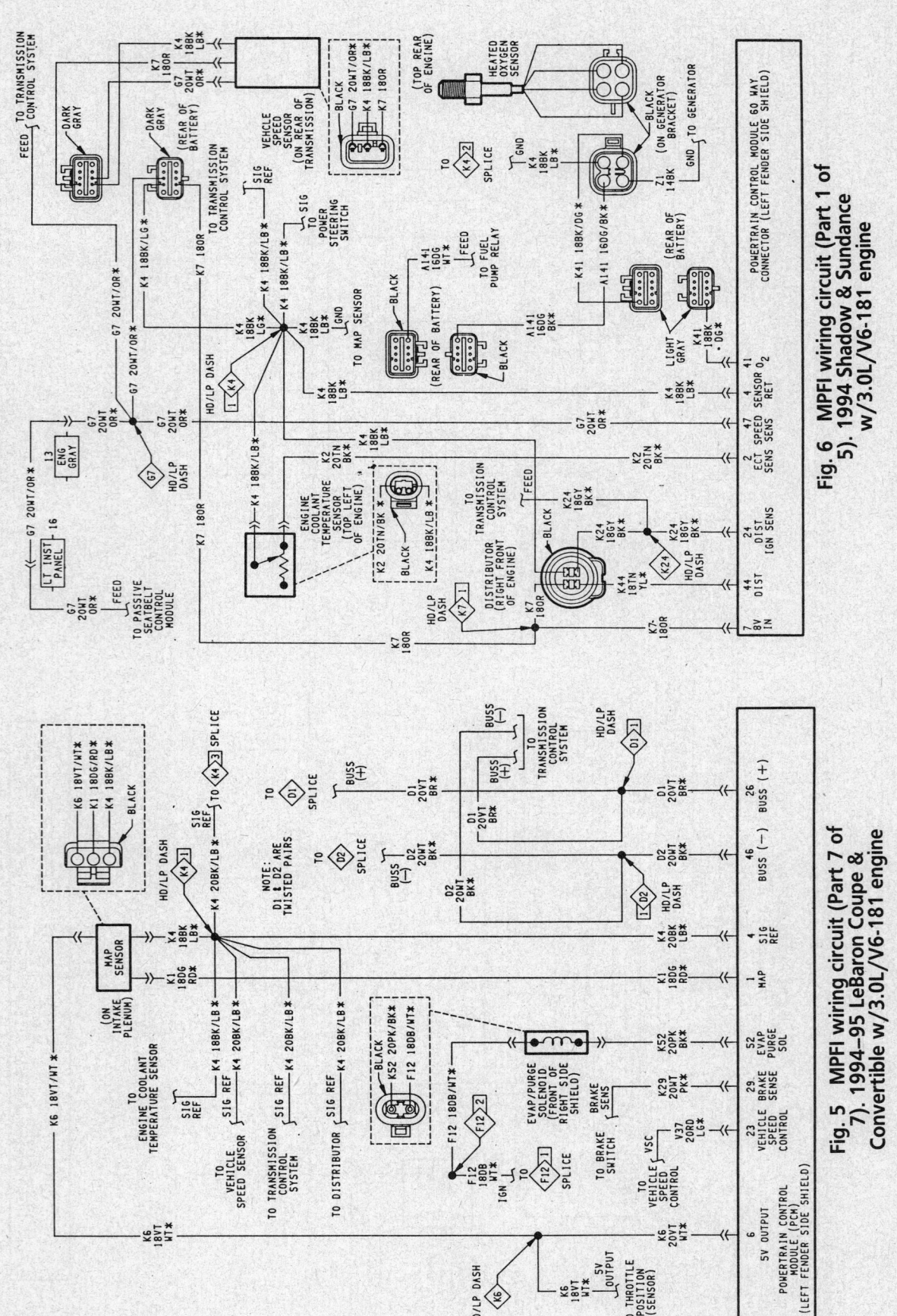

Fig. 6 MPFI wiring circuit (Part 1 of 5). 1994 Shadow & Sundance w/3.0L/V6-181 engine

Fig. 5 MPFI wiring circuit (Part 7 of 7). 1994-95 LeBaron Coupe & Convertible w/3.0L/V6-181 engine

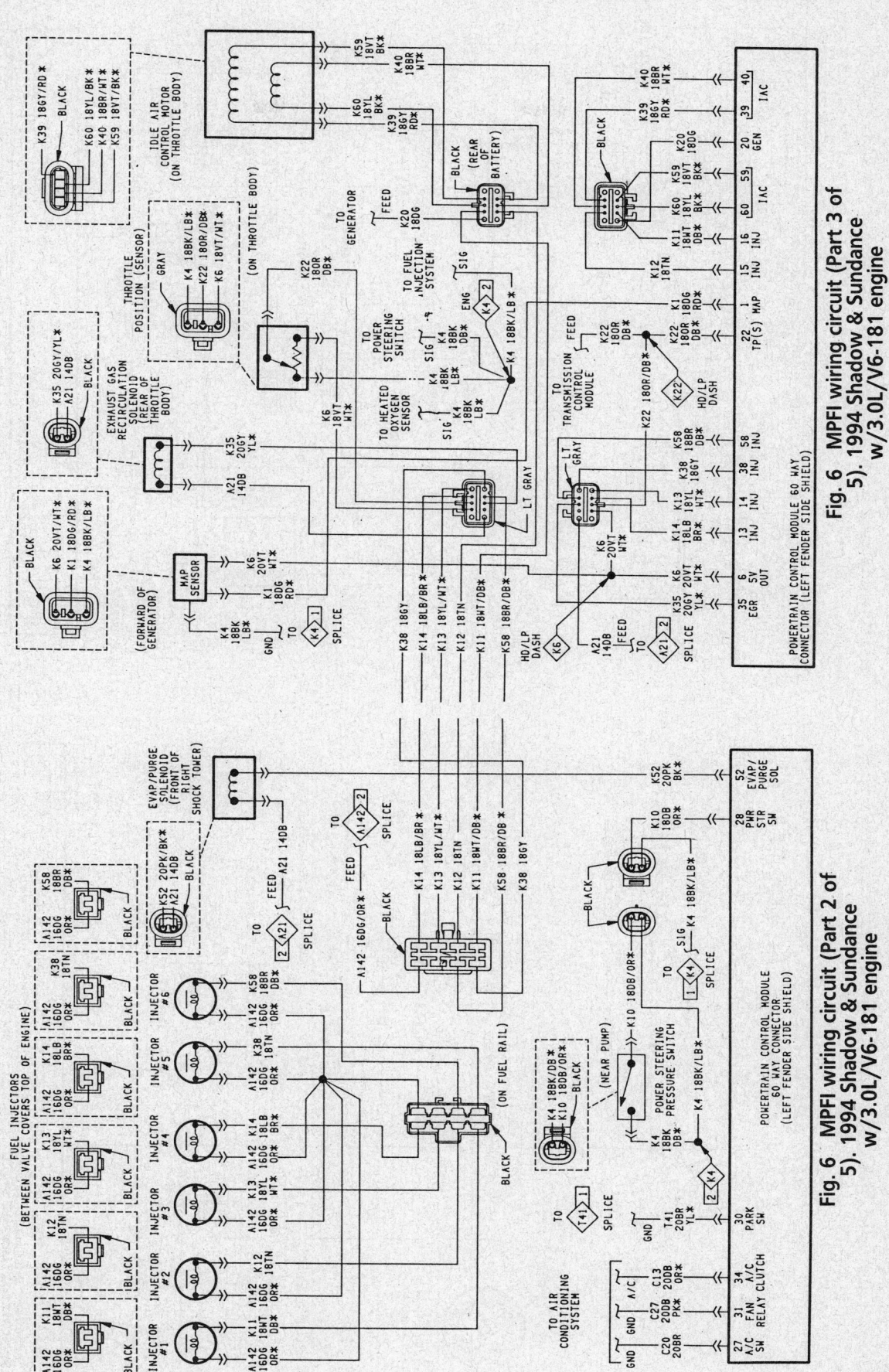

Fig. 6 MPFI wiring circuit (Part 3 of 5). 1994 Shadow & Sundance w/3.0L/V6-181 engine

Fig. 6 MPFI wiring circuit (Part 2 of 5). 1994 Shadow & Sundance w/3.0L/V6-181 engine

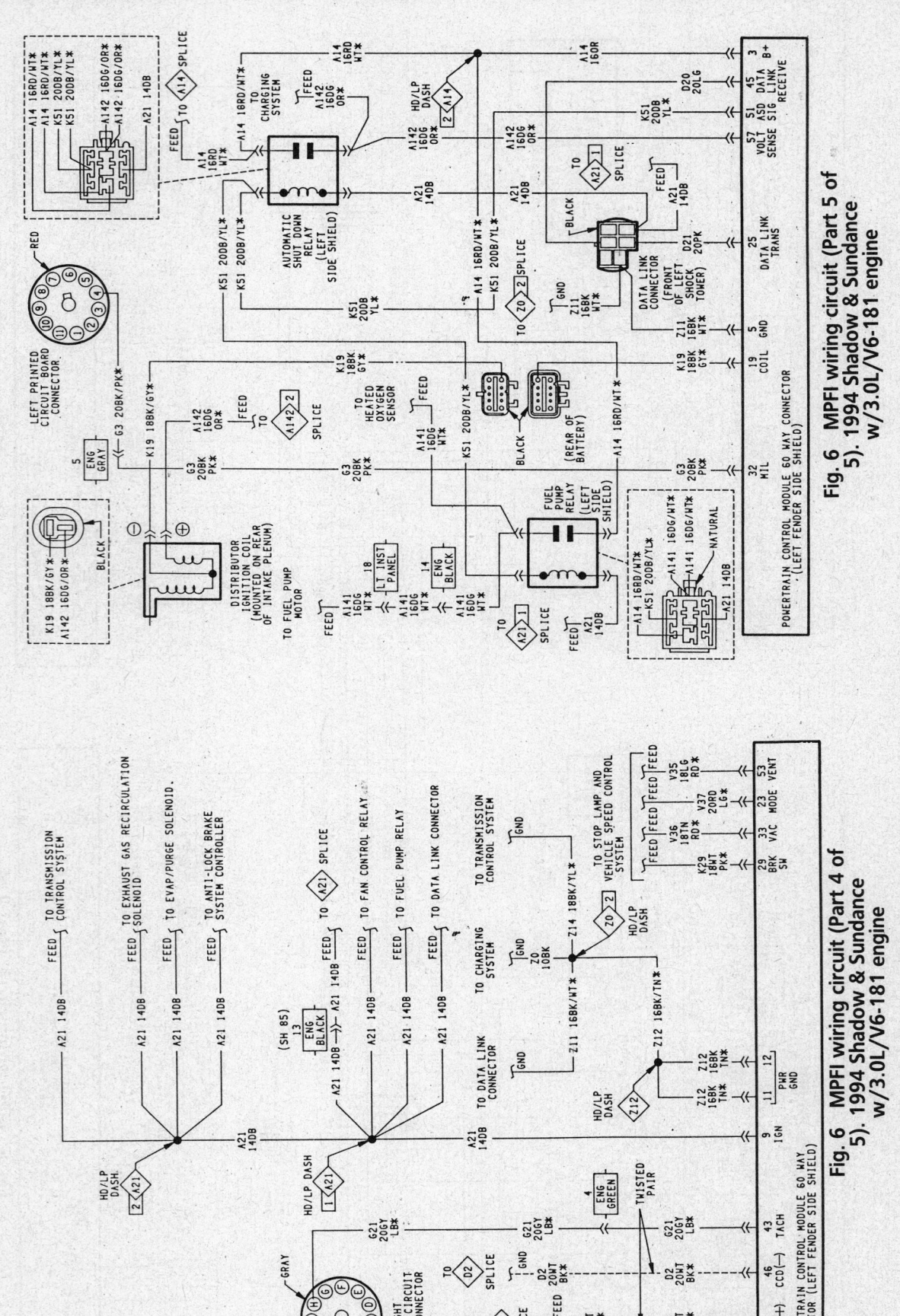

Fig. 6 MPFI wiring circuit (Part 5 of 5). 1994 Shadow & Sundance w/3.0L/V6-181 engine

Fig. 6 MPFI wiring circuit (Part 4 of 5). 1994 Shadow & Sundance w/3.0L/V6-181 engine

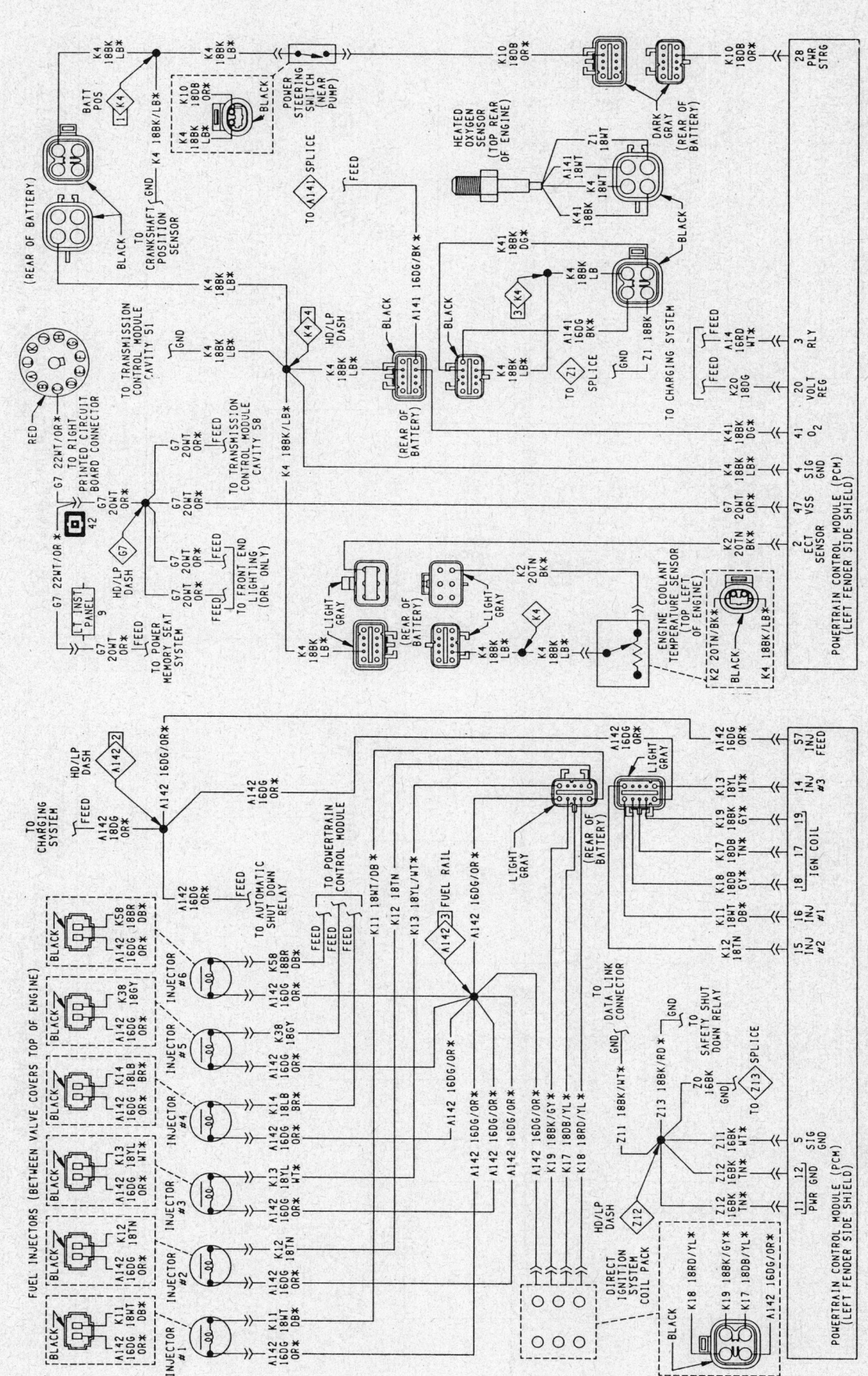

Fig. 7 MPFI wiring circuit (Part 2 of 6). 3.3L/V6-201 & 3.8L/V6-231 engines

Fig. 7 MPFI wiring circuit (Part 1 of 6). 3.3L/V6-201 & 3.8L/V6-231 engines

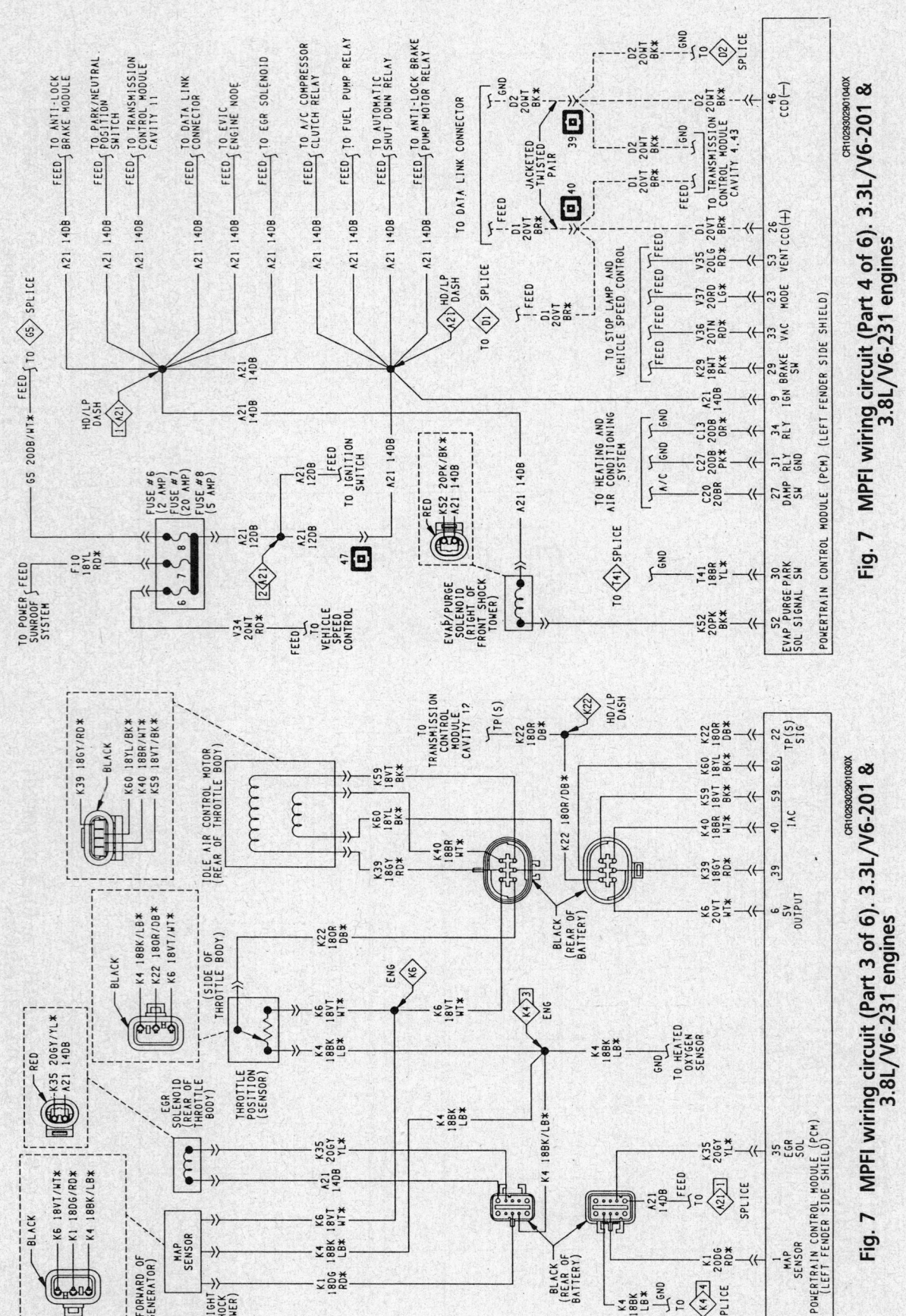

Fig. 7   MPFI wiring circuit (Part 4 of 6). 3.3L/V6-201 & 3.8L/V6-231 engines

Fig. 7   MPFI wiring circuit (Part 3 of 6). 3.3L/V6-201 & 3.8L/V6-231 engines

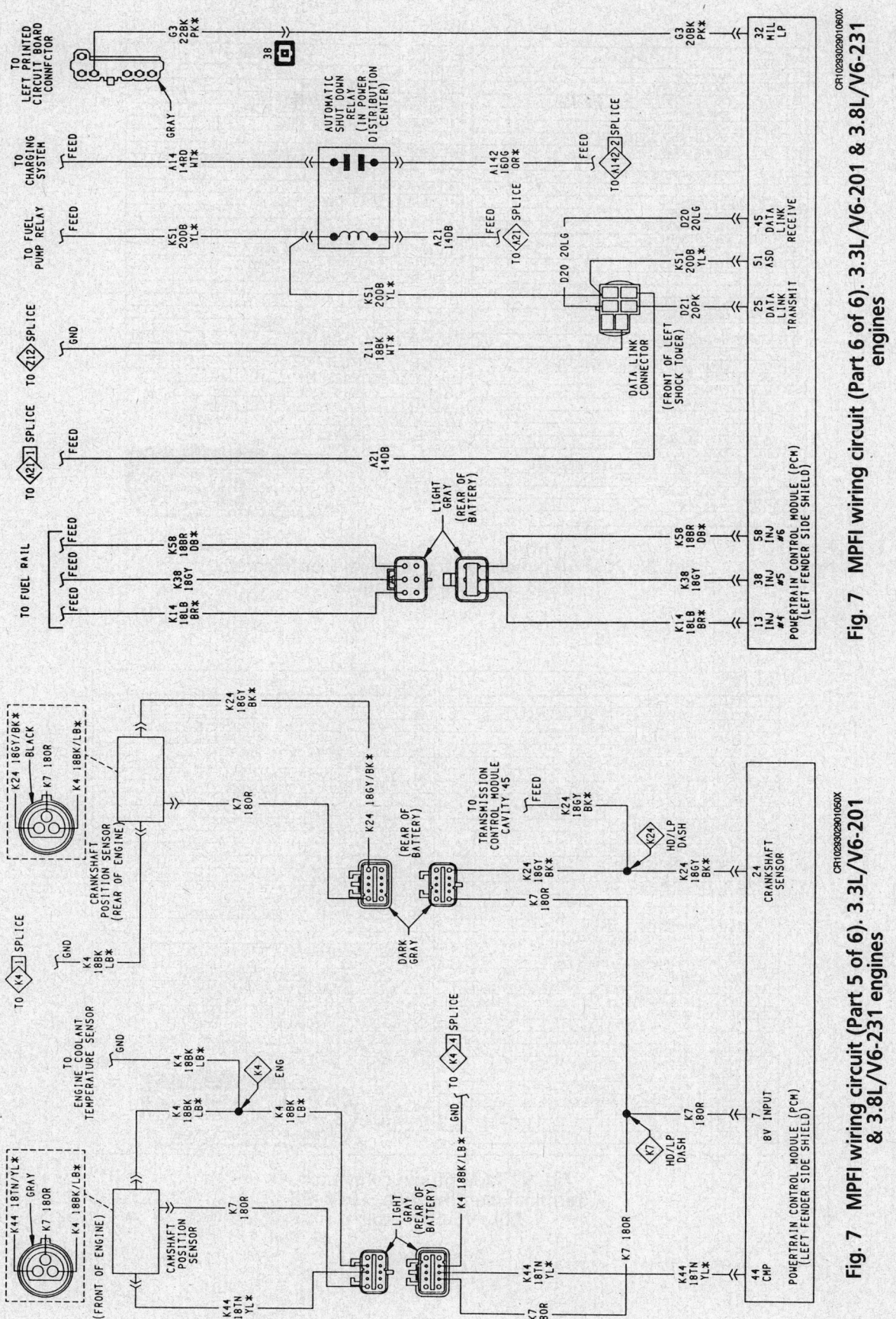

Fig. 7 MPFI wiring circuit (Part 6 of 6). 3.3L/V6-201 & 3.8L/V6-231 engines

Fig. 7 MPFI wiring circuit (Part 5 of 6). 3.3L/V6-201 & 3.8L/V6-231 engines

MODELS w/3.0L/V6-181, 3.3L/V6-201 & 3.8L/V6-231 ENGINES EXCEPT CONCORDE, INTREPID, LHS, STEALTH, VISION & 1994-96 NEW YORKER

12-21

CHRYSLER–Fuel Injection

CAV	WIRE COLOR	DESCRIPTION
1	DG/RD*	MAP SENSOR
2	TN/BK*	COOLANT SENSOR
3	RD/WT*	DIRECT BATTERY VOLTAGE
4	BK/LB*	SENSOR RETURN
5	BK/WT*	SIGNAL GROUND
6	VT/WT*	5.0 VOLT OUTPUT (MAP AND TPS)
7	OR	8.0 VOLT OUTPUT
8		
9	DB	A21 SUPPLY (IGNITION START/RUN)
10		
11	BK/TN*	POWER GROUND
12	BK/TN*	POWER GROUND
13	LB/BR*	INJECTOR DRIVER #4
14	YL/WT*	INJECTOR DRIVER #3
15	TN	INJECTOR DRIVER #2
16	WT/DB*	INJECTOR DRIVER #1
17		
18		
19	BK/GY*	IGNITION COIL DRIVER #1
20	DG	GENERATOR FIELD CONTROL
21		
22	OR/DB*	THROTTLE POSITION SENSOR (TPS)
23	RD/LG*	SPEED CONTROL SENSE
24	GY/BK*	CAMSHAFT POSITION SENSOR (IGNITION PICK-UP)
25	PK	SCI TRANSMIT
26	VT/BR*	CCD BUS (+)
27	BR	A/C SWITCH SENSE
28		
29	WT/PK*	BRAKE SWITCH
30	BR/LB*	PARK/NEUTRAL SWITCH
31	DB/PK*	RADIATOR FAN RELAY
32	BK/PK*	MALFUNCTION INDICATOR LAMP (CHECK ENGINE)
33	TN/RD*	SPEED CONTROL VACUUM SOLENOID
34	DB/OR*	A/C CLUTCH RELAY
35	GY/YL*	EGR SOLENOID
36		

CAV	WIRE COLOR	DESCRIPTION
37		
38	GY	INJECTOR DRIVER #5
39	GY/RD*	IDLE AIR CONTROL MOTOR #3 DRIVER
40	BR/WT*	IDLE AIR CONTROL MOTOR #1 DRIVER
41	BK/DG*	OXYGEN SENSOR SIGNAL
42		
43	GY/LB*	TACHOMETER SIGNAL OUTPUT
44	TN/YL*	CAMSHAFT POSITION SENSOR (INJECTOR SYNC.)
45	LG	SCI RECEIVE
46	WT/BK	CCD BUS (-)
47	WT/OR*	VEHICLE SPEED SIGNAL
48		
49		
50		
51	DB/YL*	AUTO SHUTDOWN (ASD) RELAY
52	PK/BK*	DUTY CYCLE EVAP PURGE SOLENOID
53	LG/RD*	SPEED CONTROL VENT SOLENOID
54		
55		
56		
57	DG/OR*	A142 CIRCUIT VOLTAGE SENSE
58	BR/DB*	INJECTOR DRIVER #6
59	VT/BK*	IDLE AIR CONTROL MOTOR #4 DRIVER
60	YL/BK*	IDLE AIR CONTROL MOTOR #2 DRIVER

WIRE COLOR CODES				
BK	BLACK	LG	LIGHT GREEN	WT WHITE
BR	BROWN	OR	ORANGE	YL YELLOW
DB	DARK BLUE	PK	PINK	* WITH TRACER
DG	DARK GREEN	RD	RED	
GY	GRAY	TN	TAN	
		LB	LIGHT BLUE	VT VIOLET

CONNECTOR TERMINAL SIDE SHOWN

CR1029302903000X

Fig. 8   PCM 60 pin connector terminal identification.
1993 3.0L/V6-181 engine

CAV	WIRE COLOR	DESCRIPTION
1	DG/RD*	MAP SENSOR
2	TN/BK*	ENGINE COOLANT TEMPERATURE SENSOR
3	RD/WT*	DIRECT BATTERY VOLTAGE
4	BK/LB*	SENSOR RETURN
5	BK/WT*	SIGNAL GROUND
6	VT/WT*	5-VOLT OUTPUT (MAP AND TPS)
7	OR	8-VOLT OUTPUT
8	WT	INJECTOR DRIVER
9	DB	A21 SUPPLY (IGNITION START/RUN)
10		
11	BK/TN*	POWER GROUND
12	BK/TN*	POWER GROUND
13	LB/BR	INJECTOR DRIVER #4
14	YL/WT*	INJECTOR DRIVER #3
15	TN	INJECTOR DRIVER #2
16	WT/DB*	INJECTOR DRIVER #1
17		
18		
19	BK/GY*	IGNITION COIL DRIVER #1
20	DG	GENERATOR FIELD CONTROL
21	BK/RD*	METHANOL CONCENTRATION SENSOR
22	OR/DB*	THROTTLE POSITION SENSOR (TPS)
23	RD/LG*	SPEED CONTROL SENSE
24	GY/BK*	IGNITION REFERENCE PICK-UP (DISTRIBUTOR PICK-UP)
25	PK	SCI TRANSMIT
26	VT/BR*	CCD BUS (+)
27	BR	A/C SWITCH SENSE
28		
29	WT/PK*	BRAKE SWITCH
30	BR/YL*	PARK/NEUTRAL SWITCH (AUTO TRANS.)
31	DB/PK*	RADIATOR FAN RELAY
32	BK/PK*	MALFUNCTION INDICATOR LAMP
33	TN/RD*	SPEED CONTROL VACUUM SOLENOID
34	DB/OR*	A/C CLUTCH RELAY
35		
36		

CAV	WIRE COLOR	DESCRIPTION
37		
38		
39	GY/RD*	IDLE AIR CONTROL MOTOR TERMINAL #3
40	BR/WT*	IDLE AIR CONTROL MOTOR TERMINAL #1
41	BK/DG*	HEATED OXYGEN SENSOR SIGNAL
42		
43	GY/LB*	TACHOMETER SIGNAL OUTPUT
44	TN/YL*	CAMSHAFT POSITION SENSOR
45	LG	SCI RECEIVE
46	WT/BK*	CCD BUS (-)
47	WT/OR*	VEHICLE SPEED SENSOR
48		
49		
50		
51	DB/YL*	AUTOMATIC SHUTDOWN RELAY AND FUEL PUMP RELAY
52	PK/BK*	DUTY CYCLE EVAP PURGE SOLENOID
53	LG/RD*	SPEED CONTROL VENT SOLENOID
54	OR/BK*	TORQUE CONVERTER CLUTCH SOLENOID
55		
56		
57	DG/OR*	A142 CIRCUIT VOLTAGE SENSE
58		
59	VT/BK*	IDLE AIR CONTROL MOTOR TERMINAL #4
60	YL/BK*	IDLE AIR CONTROL MOTOR TERMINAL #2

WIRE COLOR CODES				
BK	BLACK	LG	LIGHT GREEN	WT WHITE
BR	BROWN	OR	ORANGE	YL YELLOW
DB	DARK BLUE	PK	PINK	* WITH TRACER
DG	DARK GREEN	RD	RED	
GY	GRAY	TN	TAN	
		LB	LIGHT BLUE	VT VIOLET

CONNECTOR TERMINAL SIDE SHOWN

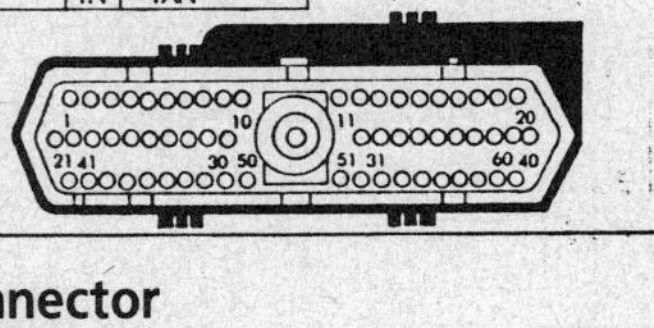

Fig. 9   PCM 60 pin connector
terminal identification. 1994–95
3.0L/V6-181 engine

CAV	WIRE COLOR	DESCRIPTION
1	DG/RD*	MAP SENSOR
2	TN/BK*	COOLANT SENSOR
3	RD/WT*	DIRECT BATTERY
4	BK/LB*	SENSOR RETURN
5	BK/WT*	SIGNAL GROUND
6	VT/WT*	5.0 VOLT OUTPUT (MAP AND TPS)
7	OR	8.0 VOLT OUTPUT
8		
9	DB	A21 SUPPLY (IGNITION START/RUN)
10		
11	BK/TN*	POWER GROUND
12	BK/TN*	POWER GROUND
13	LB/BR*	INJECTOR DRIVER #4
14	YL/WT*	INJECTOR DRIVER #3
15	TN	INJECTOR DRIVER #2
16	WT/DB*	INJECTOR DRIVER #1
17	DB/TN*	IGNITION COIL DRIVER #2
18	DB/GY*	IGNITION COIL DRIVER #3
19	BK/GY*	IGNITION COIL DRIVER #1
20	DG	GENERATOR FIELD CONTROL
21		
22	OR/DB*	THROTTLE POSITION SENSOR (TPS)
23		
24	GY/BK*	CRANKSHAFT POSITION SENSOR
25	PK	SCI TRANSMIT
26	VT/BR*	CCD BUS (+)
27	BR	A/C SWITCH SENSE
28		
29	WT/PK*	BRAKE SWITCH
30	BR/YL*	PARK/NEUTRAL SWITCH
31	DB/PK*	RADIATOR FAN RELAY
32	BK/PK*	MALFUNCTION INDICATOR LAMP (CHECK ENGINE)
33	TN/RD*	SPEED CONTROL VACUUM SOLENOID
34	DB/OR*	A/C CLUTCH RELAY
35	GY/YL*	EGR SOLENOID
36		

CAV	WIRE COLOR	DESCRIPTION
37		
38	GY	INJECTOR DRIVER #5
39	GY/RD*	IDLE AIR CONTROL MOTOR #3 DRIVER
40	BR/WT*	IDLE AIR CONTROL MOTOR #1 DRIVER
41	BK/DG*	OXYGEN SENSOR SIGNAL
42		
43	GY/LB*	TACHOMETER SIGNAL OUTPUT
44	TN/YL*	CAMSHAFT POSITION SENSOR
45	LG	SCI RECEIVE
46	WT/BK	CCD BUS (-)
47	WT/OR*	VEHICLE SPEED SIGNAL
48		
49		
50		
51	DB/YL*	AUTO SHUTDOWN (ASD) RELAY
52	PK/BK*	EVAP PURGE SOLENOID
53	LG/RD*	SPEED CONTROL VENT SOLENOID
54		
55		
56		
57	DG/OR*	A142 CIRCUIT VOLTAGE SENSE
58	BR/DB*	INJECTOR DRIVER #6
59	VT/BK*	IDLE AIR CONTROL MOTOR #4 DRIVER
60	YL/BK*	IDLE AIR CONTROL MOTOR #2 DRIVER

WIRE COLOR CODES					
BK	BLACK	LG	LIGHT GREEN	WT	WHITE
BR	BROWN	OR	ORANGE	YL	YELLOW
DB	DARK BLUE	PK	PINK	*	WITH TRACER
DG	DARK GREEN	RD	RED		
GY	GRAY	TN	TAN		

LB | LIGHT BLUE
VT | VIOLET

CONNECTOR TERMINAL SIDE SHOWN

Fig. 10   PCM 60 pin connector
terminal identification. 3.3L/V6-201
& 3.8L/V6-231 engines

DIAGNOSTIC CHART INDEX

Test	Description	Page No. 12-	Fig. No.
3.0L/V6-181 ENGINE			
CH-1A	Inspecting Charging System No Trouble Codes	57	86
NS-1A	Qualifying No Start Condition	60	92
NS-2A	Inspecting Fuel System	61	93
NS-3A	Inspecting Mechanical System	62	94
NS-4A	Correcting Fuel Delivery	62	95
NS-4B	Correcting Fuel Delivery	63	96
NS-5A	Inspecting Fuel Pump	63	97
NS-5B	Inspecting Fuel Pump	63	98
NS-6A	Correcting No Response Condition	64	99
NS-6B	Correcting No Response Condition	65	100
NS-6C	Correcting No Response Condition	65	101
NS-6D	Correcting No Response Condition	66	102
NS-7A	Inspecting Idle Air Control Motor Operation	66	103
NS-7B	Inspecting Idle Air Control Motor Operation	67	104
NS-7C	Inspecting Idle Air Control Motor Operation	67	105
NS-7D	Inspecting Idle Air Control Motor Operation	67	106
NS-7E	Inspecting Idle Air Control Motor Operation	67	107
NS-8A	Correcting Start & Stall Condition	67	108
NS-9A	Repairing No Crank Condition	67	109
NS-9B	Repairing No Crank Condition	68	110
NS-9C	Repairing No Crank Condition	68	111
NTC-1A	No Trouble Code Test Menu	51	68
NTC-2A	Inspecting Secondary Ignition & Timing	51	69
NTC-3A	Inspecting Fuel Pressure	52	70
NTC-3B	Inspecting Fuel Pressure	52	71
NTC-4A	Inspecting Coolant Sensor Calibration & Radiator Fan Operation	53	72

Continued

MODELS w/3.0L/V6-181, 3.3L/V6-201 & 3.8L/V6-231 ENGINES EXCEPT CONCORDE, INTREPID, LHS, STEALTH, VISION & 1994-96 NEW YORKER

12-23

DIAGNOSTIC CHART INDEX–Continued

Test	Description	Page No. 12-	Fig. No.
3.0L/V6-181 ENGINE-CONTINUED			
NTC-5A	Inspecting TP Sensor Calibration	53	73
NTC-6A	Inspecting MAP Sensor Calibration	53	74
NTC-7A	Inspecting Oxygen Sensor Switching	53	75
NTC-7B	Inspecting Oxygen Sensor Switching	54	76
NTC-8A	Inspecting Oxygen Sensor Heater	54	77
NTC-9A	Inspecting Idle Air Control Motor	55	78
NTC-9B	Inspecting Idle Air Control Motor	55	79
NTC-10A	Inspecting Solenoid Operations	55	80
NTC-11A	Inspecting Park/Neutral Position Switch	56	81
NTC-12A	Inspecting PCM Grounds & Power Circuits	56	82
NTC-13A	Inspecting Engine Vacuum	56	83
NTC-14A	Inspecting Minimum Idle Air Flow	57	84
NTC-15A	Performing No Trouble Code Mechanical Test	57	85
TC-1A	Inspecting The System For Trouble Codes	28	11
TC-2A	No Crank Reference Signal At PCM	28	12
TC-2B	No Crank Reference Signal At PCM	29	13
TC-3A	No Cam SYNC Signal At PCM	29	14
TC-4A	No Change In MAP From Start To Run	30	15
TC-5A	MAP Sensor Voltage Too Low	30	16
TC-6A	MAP Sensor Voltage Too High	31	17
TC-7A	No Vehicle Speed Sensor Signal	31	18
TC-7B	No Vehicle Speed Sensor Signal	32	19
TC-7C	No Vehicle Speed Sensor Signal	32	20
TC-7D	No Vehicle Speed Sensor Signal	33	21
TC-8A	O2S Stays At Center	33	22
TC-9A	O2S Stays Above Center, Rich	33	23
TC-10A	O2S Stays Above Center, Lean	34	24
TC-11A	O2S Shorted To Voltage	34	25
TC-12A	O2S Shorted To Voltage	34	26
TC-13A	ECT Sensor Voltage Too High	35	27
TC-14A	Throttle Position Sensor Voltage Too Low	35	28
TC-15A	Throttle Position Sensor Voltage Too High	36	29
TC-16A	Idle Air Control Motor Circuits	36	30
TC-16B	Idle Air Control Motor Circuits	37	31
TC-16C	Idle Air Control Motor Circuits	37	32
TC-16D	Idle Air Control Motor Circuits	37	33
TC-16E	Idle Air Control Motor Circuits	37	34
TC-17A	Injector Control Circuit	38	35
TC-17B	Injector No. 1 Control Circuit	38	36
TC-17C	Injector No. 1 Control Circuit	38	37
TC-18A	Injector No 2 Control Circuit	39	38
TC-18B	Injector No 2 Control Circuit	39	39
TC-19A	Injector No. 3 Control Circuit	39	40
TC-19B	Injector No. 3 Control Circuit	40	41
TC-20A	Injector No 4 Control Circuit	40	42
TC-20B	Injector No 4 Control Circuit	40	43
TC-21A	Injector No 5 Control Circuit	40	44
TC-21B	Injector No 5 Control Circuit	41	45
TC-22A	Injector No 6 Control Circuit	41	46
TC-22B	Injector No 6 Control Circuit	41	47
TC-23A	PCM Failure SRI Mile Not Stored	41	48

Continued

DIAGNOSTIC CHART INDEX–Continued

Test	Description	Page No. 12-	Fig. No.
3.0L/V6-181 ENGINE-CONTINUED			
TC-24A	EGR System Failure	42	49
TC-25A	EGR Solenoid Circuit	42	50
TC-26A	EVAP Solenoid Circuit	43	51
TC-27A	Torque Converter Clutch Solenoid Circuit	44	52
TC-28A	No ASD Relay Output Voltage At PCM	44	53
TC-29A	Auto Shutdown Relay Control Circuit	45	54
TC-30A	A/C Clutch Relay Circuit	45	55
TC-31A	Radiator Fan Control Relay Circuit	46	56
TC-32A	Low Speed Fan Control Relay Circuit	47	57
TC-33A	High Speed Fan Control Relay Circuit	47	58
TC-34A	Generator Field Not Switching Properly	48	59
TC-34B	Inspecting Field Driver Circuit For Shorts	48	60
TC-35A	Charging System Voltage Too Low	49	61
TC-36A	Charging System Voltage Too High	49	62
TC-36B	Powertrain Control Module Regulating Circuit	49	63
TC-37A	Speed Control Solenoid Circuits	50	64
TC-37B	Speed Control Solenoid Circuits	50	65
TC-37C	Speed Control Solenoid Circuits	50	66
TC-38A	Battery Temperature Sensor Circuit	51	67
SC-1A	Inspecting Speed Control System	58	87
SC-1B	Inspecting Speed Control System	59	88
SC-2A	Inspecting Speed Control Switch Signal Circuit	59	89
SC-3A	Inspecting Speed Control Brake Switch	60	90
SC-4A	Inspecting Speed Control Park/Neutral Circuit	60	91
VER-1A	No Start Verification	68	112
VER-2A	Road Test Verification	68	113
VER-3A	Charging Verification	68	114
VER-4A	Speed Control Verification	69	115
3.3L/V6-201 & 3.8L/V6-231 ENGINES			
CH-VER	Charging Verification	110	218
CH-1A	Inspecting Charging System No Trouble Codes	93	173
NS-1A	Qualifying No Start Condition	102	199
NS-2A	Inspecting Fuel System	103	200
NS-3A	Inspecting Mechanical System	104	201
NS-4A	Correcting Fuel Delivery	104	202
NS-4B	Correcting Fuel Delivery	104	203
NS-5A	Inspecting Fuel Pump	105	204
NS-5B	Inspecting Fuel Pump	105	205
NS-6A	Correcting No Response Condition	106	206
NS-6B	Correcting No Response Condition	107	207
NS-6C	Correcting No Response Condition	107	208
NS-7A	Inspecting Idle Air Control Motor Operation	108	209
NS-7B	Inspecting Idle Air Control Motor Operation	108	210
NS-7C	Inspecting Idle Air Control Motor Operation	109	211
NS-7D	Inspecting Idle Air Control Motor Operation	109	212
NS-7E	Inspecting Idle Air Control Motor Operation	109	213
NS-8A	Correcting Start & Stall Condition	109	214
NS-9A	No Crank Condition	109	215
NTC-1A	No Trouble Code Test Menu	96	180
NTC-2A	Inspecting Secondary Ignition & Timing	96	181
NTC-3A	Inspecting Fuel Pressure	96	182
NTC-3B	Inspecting Fuel Pressure	97	183
NTC-4A	Inspecting Coolant Sensor Calibration & Radiator Fan Operation	97	184

Continued

MODELS w/3.0L/V6-181, 3.3L/V6-201 & 3.8L/V6-231 ENGINES EXCEPT CONCORDE, INTREPID, LHS, STEALTH, VISION & 1994-96 NEW YORKER

12-25

CHRYSLER–Fuel Injection

DIAGNOSTIC CHART INDEX–Continued

Test	Description	Page No. 12-	Fig. No.
3.3L/V6-201 & 3.8L/V6-231 ENGINES-CONTINUED			
NTC-5A	Inspecting TP Sensor Calibration	98	185
NTC-6A	Inspecting MAP Sensor Calibration	98	186
NTC-7A	Inspecting Oxygen Sensor Switching	98	187
NTC-7B	Inspecting Oxygen Sensor Switching	99	188
NTC-8A	Inspecting Oxygen Sensor Heater	99	189
NTC-9A	Inspecting Idle Air Control Motor	99	190
NTC-9B	Inspecting Idle Air Control Motor	100	191
NTC-10A	Inspecting Solenoid Operations	100	192
NTC-11A	Inspecting Park/Neutral Position Switch	100	193
NTC-12A	Inspecting PCM Grounds & Power Circuit	101	194
NTC-13A	Inspecting EGR System	101	195
NTC-14A	Inspecting Engine Vacuum	102	196
NTC-15A	Inspecting Minimum Idle Air Flow	102	197
NTC-16A	Performing No Trouble Code Mechanical Test	102	198
TC-1A	Inspecting The System For Trouble Codes	69	116
TC-2A	No Crank Reference Signal At PCM	69	117
TC-2B	No Crank Reference Signal At PCM	70	118
TC-3A	No Cam Sync Signal At PCM	70	119
TC-4A	No Change In MAP From Start To Run	71	120
TC-5A	MAP Sensor Voltage Too Low	71	121
TC-6A	MAP Sensor Voltage Too High	72	122
TC-7A	No Vehicle Speed Sensor Signal	72	123
TC-8A	O₂S Shorted To Voltage	73	124
TC-9A	O₂S Stays At Center	73	125
TC-10A	O₂S Stays Above Center, Rich	74	126
TC-11A	O₂S Stays Above Center, Lean	74	127
TC-12A	ECT Sensor Voltage Too High	75	128
TC-13A	ECT Sensor Voltage Too Low	75	129
TC-14A	Throttle Position Sensor Voltage High	76	130
TC-15A	Throttle Position Sensor Voltage Low	76	131
TC-16A	Idle Air Control Motor Circuits	77	132
TC-16B	Idle Air Control Motor Circuits	77	133
TC-16C	Idle Air Control Motor Circuits	78	134
TC-16D	Idle Air Control Motor Circuits	78	135
TC-16E	Idle Air Control Motor Circuits	78	136
TC-17A	Injector Control Circuit	79	137
TC-17B	Injector No. 1 Control Circuit	79	138
TC-17C	Injector No. 1 Control Circuit	80	139
TC-18A	Injector No. 2 Control Circuit	80	140
TC-18B	Injector No. 2 Control Circuit	80	141
TC-19A	Injector No. 3 Control Circuit	80	142
TC-19B	Injector No. 3 Control Circuit	81	143
TC-20A	Injector No. 4 Control Circuit	81	144
TC-20B	Injector No. 4 Control Circuit	81	145
TC-21A	Injector No. 5 Control Circuit	81	146
TC-21B	Injector No. 5 Control Circuit	82	147
TC-22A	Injector No. 6 Control Circuit	82	148
TC-22B	Injector No. 6 Control Circuit	82	149
TC-23A	EVAP Solenoid Circuit	83	150
TC-24A	EGR Solenoid Circuit	83	151
TC-25A	EGR System Failure	84	152
TC-26A	A/C Clutch Relay Circuit	84	153
TC-27A	Radiator Fan Control Relay Circuit	85	154

Continued

DIAGNOSTIC CHART INDEX—Continued

Test	Description	Page No. 12-	Fig. No.
3.3L/V6-201 & 3.8L/V6-231 ENGINES-CONTINUED			
TC-28A	Low Speed Fan Control Relay Circuit	86	155
TC-29A	High Speed Fan Control Relay Circuit	86	156
TC-30A	Auto Shutdown Control Circuit	87	157
TC-31A	No ASD Relay Output Voltage At PCM	87	158
TC-32A	Ignition Coil Primary Circuit	88	159
TC-32B	Ignition Coil No. 1 Primary Circuit	88	160
TC-33A	Ignition Coil No. 2 Primary Circuit	88	161
TC-34A	Ignition Coil No. 3 Primary Circuit	89	162
TC-35A	PCM Failure SRI Mile Not Stored	89	163
TC-36A	Battery Temperature Sensor Volts Out Of Limit	89	164
TC-37A	Generator Field Not Switching Properly	90	165
TC-37B	Generator Field Not Switching Properly	90	166
TC-38A	Charging System Voltage Too Low	90	167
TC-39A	Charging System Voltage Too High	91	168
TC-39B	Charging System Voltage Too High	91	169
TC-40A	Speed Control Solenoid Circuits	91	170
TC-40B	Speed Control Solenoid Circuits	92	171
TC-40C	Speed Control Solenoid Circuits	92	172
SC-1A	Inspecting Speed Control System	94	174
SC-1B	Inspecting Speed Control Brake Switch	94	175
SC-2A	Inspecting Speed Control On/Off Switch	95	176
SC-3A	Inspecting Speed Control Brake Sense	95	177
SC-4A	Inspecting Speed Control Park/Neutral Sense	95	178
SC-5A	Inspecting A Speed Control Denied Message	96	179
SC-VER	Speed Control Verification	110	219
VER-1	No Start Verification	110	216
VER-2	Road Test Verification	110	217

MODELS w/3.0L/V6-181, 3.3L/V6-201 & 3.8L/V6-231 ENGINES EXCEPT CONCORDE, INTREPID, LHS, STEALTH, VISION & 1994-96 NEW YORKER

12-27

TEST TC-1A CHECKING THE SYSTEM FOR DIAGNOSTIC TROUBLE CODES (DTCs)

NOTE: The battery must be fully charged for any test

Attempt to start the engine. Crank for up to 10 seconds if necessary.

Connect the DRB to the engine diagnostic connector. Write down the trouble codes that are displayed.

If the DRB screen displays "No Response", go to **TEST NS-6A.**

If **trouble code messages** are displayed, refer to the trouble code list below and on the next page for the appropriate test.

If there are **no trouble codes** displayed, refer to one of the following:
For Driveability problems...NTC-1A
For No Start problems NS-1A
For Speed Control problems SC-1A
For Charging problems CH-1A

DIAGNOSTIC TROUBLE CODE (DTC) DISPLAYED	DIAGNOSTIC TEST
NO CRANK REFERENCE SIGNAL AT PCM	TC- 2A
NO CAM SIGNAL AT PCM	TC- 3A
NO CHANGE IN MAP FROM START TO RUN	TC- 4A
MAP SENSOR VOLTAGE TOO LOW	TC- 5A
MAP SENSOR VOLTAGE TOO HIGH	TC- 6A
NO VEHICLE SPEED SENSOR SIGNAL	TC- 7A
O2S STAYS AT CENTER	TC- 8A
O2S STAYS ABOVE CENTER (RICH)	TC- 9A
O2S STAYS BELOW CENTER (LEAN)	TC-10A
O2S SHORTED TO VOLTAGE	TC-11A
ECT SENSOR VOLTAGE TOO LOW	TC-12A
ECT SENSOR VOLTAGE TOO HIGH	TC-13A
THROTTLE POSITION SENSOR VOLTAGE LOW	TC-14A
THROTTLE POSITION SENSOR VOLTAGE HIGH	TC-15A
IDLE AIR CONTROL MOTOR CIRCUITS	TC-16A
INJECTOR CONTROL CIRCUIT	TC-17A
PCM FAILURE SRI MILE NOT STORED	TC-23A
PCM FAILURE EEPROM WRITE DENIED	TC-23A
EGR SYSTEM FAILURE	TC-24A
EGR SOLENOID CIRCUIT	TC-25A
EVAP SOLENOID CIRCUIT	TC-26A
TORQUE CONVERTER CLUTCH SOLENOID CKT	TC-27A
NO ASD RELAY OUTPUT VOLTAGE AT PCM	TC-28A
AUTO SHUTDOWN RELAY CONTROL CIRCUIT	TC-29A
A/C CLUTCH RELAY CIRCUIT	TC-30A

Fig. 11   Test TC-1A: Inspecting The System For Trouble Codes (Part 1 of 2). 3.0L/V6-181 Engine

TEST TC-1A CHECKING THE SYSTEM FOR DIAGNOSTIC TROUBLE CODES (DTCs)

DIAGNOSTIC TROUBLE CODE (DTC) DISPLAYED	DIAGNOSTIC TEST
NO ASD RELAY OUTPUT VOLTAGE AT PCM	TC-28A
AUTO SHUTDOWN RELAY CONTROL CIRCUIT	TC-29A
A/C CLUTCH RELAY CIRCUIT	TC-30A
RAD FAN CONTROL RELAY CIRCUIT	TC-31A
LOW SPEED FAN CTRL RELAY CIRCUIT (AS BODY ONLY)	TC-32A
HIGH SPEED FAN CTRL RELAY CIRCUIT (AS BODY ONLY)	TC-33A
GENERATOR FIELD NOT SWITCHING PROPERLY	TC-34A
CHARGING SYSTEM VOLTAGE TOO LOW	TC-35A
CHARGING SYSTEM VOLTAGE TOO HIGH	TC-36A
SPEED CONTROL SOLENOID CIRCUITS	TC-37A
BATTERY TEMP SENSOR VOLTS OUT OF LIMIT	TC-38A

For an ENGINE IS COLD TOO LONG trouble code, the engine does not warm to 176°F while driving for 20 minutes after start.

For an INTERNAL CONTROLLER FAILURE trouble code, replace the powertrain control module and go to **Verification TEST VER-2A.**

For a PCM FAILURE SPI COMMUNICATIONS trouble code, replace the powertrain control module and go to **Verification TEST VER-2A.**

Fig. 11   Test TC-1A: Inspecting The System For Trouble Codes (Part 2 of 2). 3.0L/V6-181 Engine

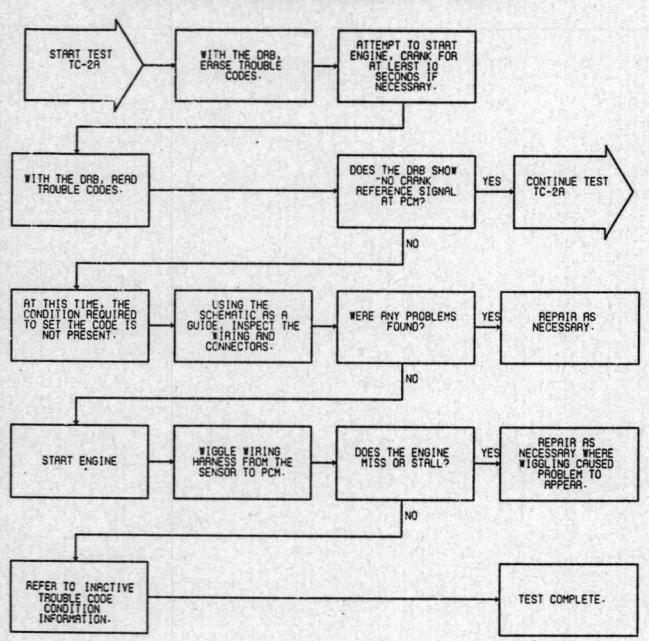

Fig. 12   Test TC-2A: No Crank Reference Signal At PCM (Part 1 of 3). 3.0L/V6-181 Engine

CR1029302983010X

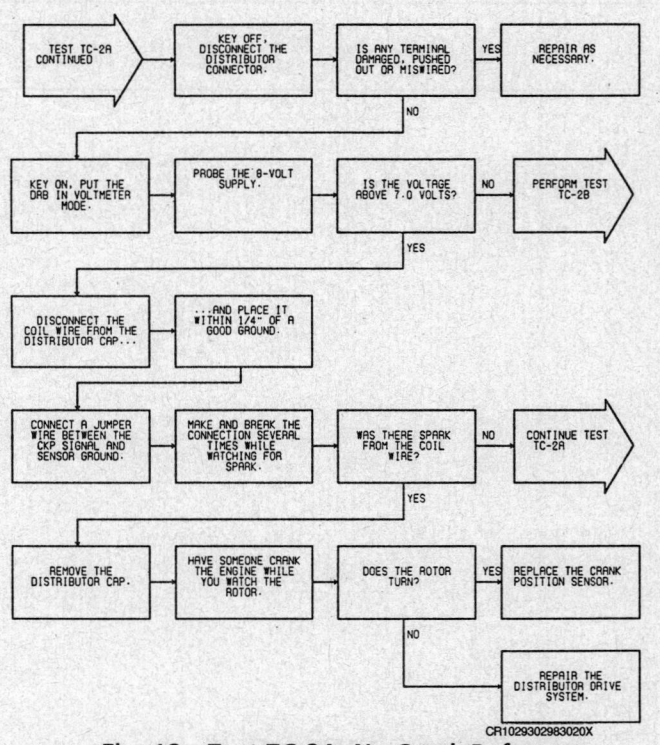

Fig. 12   Test TC-2A: No Crank Reference Signal At PCM (Part 2 of 3). 3.0L/V6-181 Engine

CR1029302983020X

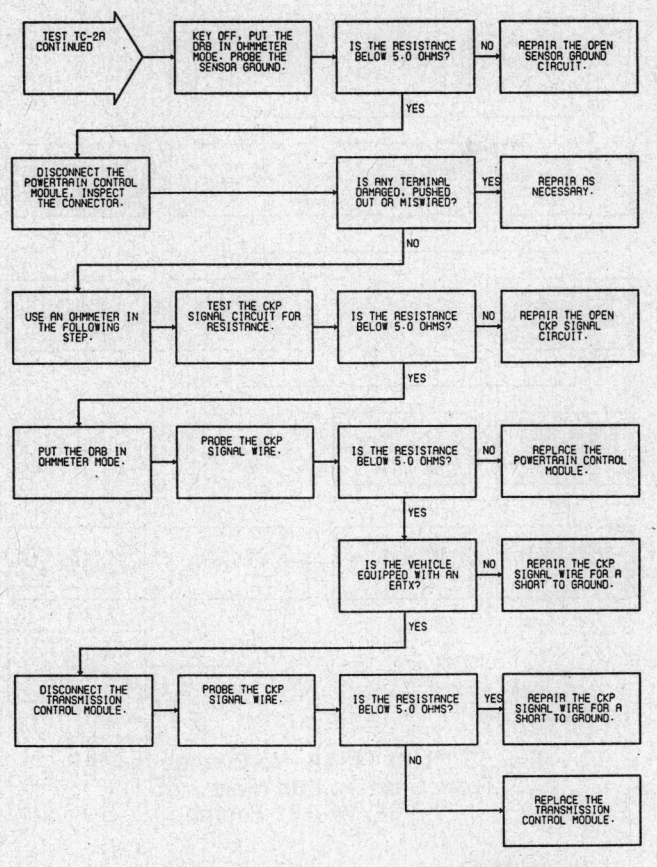

Fig. 12   Test TC-2A: No Crank Reference Signal At PCM (Part 3 of 3). 3.0L/V6-181 Engine

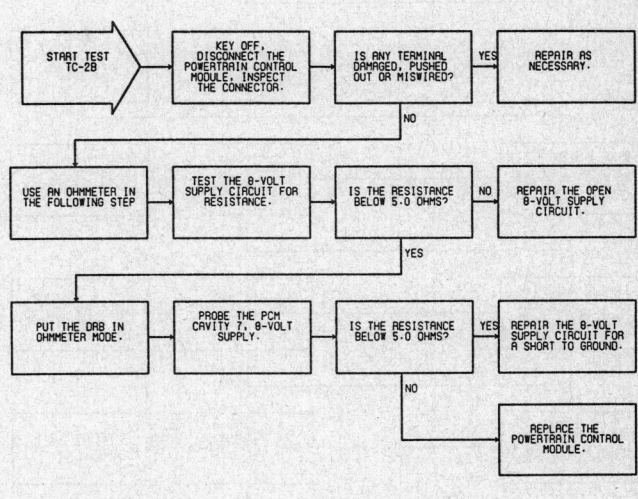

Fig. 13   Test TC-2B: No Crank Reference Signal At PCM. 3.0L/V6-181 Engine

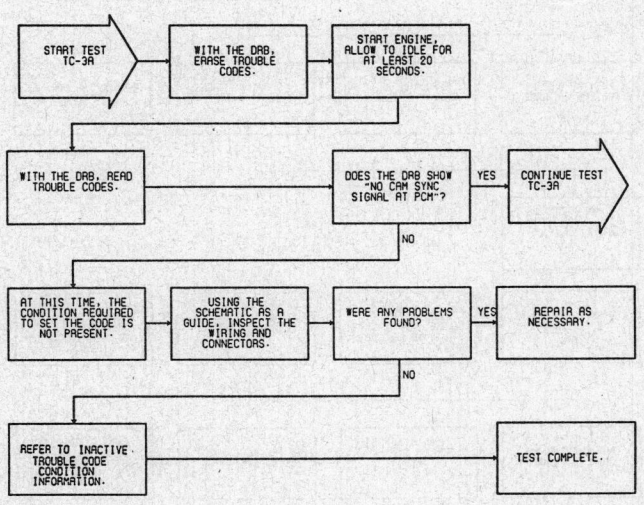

Fig. 14   Test TC-3A: No Cam SYNC Signal At PCM (Part 1 of 2). 3.0L/V6-181 Engine

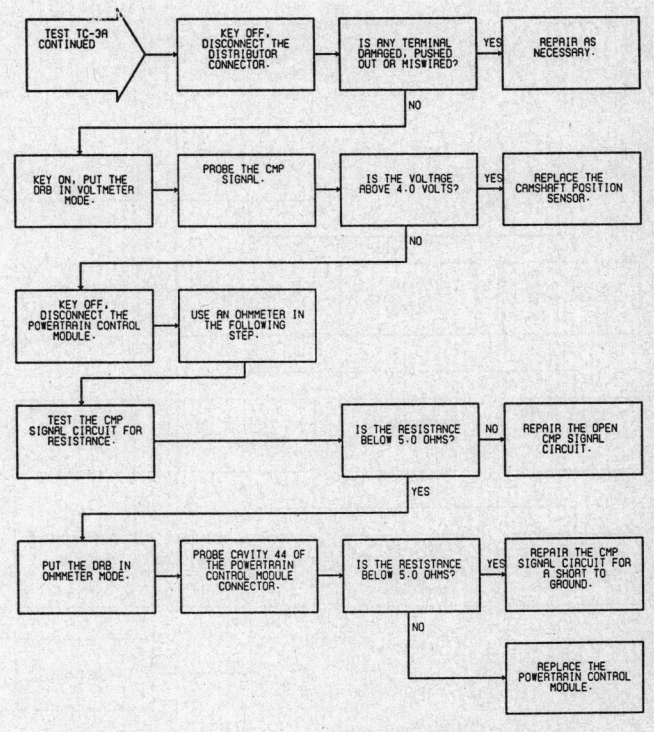

Fig. 14   Test TC-3A: No Cam SYNC Signal At PCM (Part 2 of 2). 3.0L/V6-181 Engine

MODELS w/3.0L/V6-181, 3.3L/V6-201 & 3.8L/V6-231 ENGINES EXCEPT CONCORDE, INTREPID, LHS, STEALTH, VISION & 1994-96 NEW YORKER

12-29

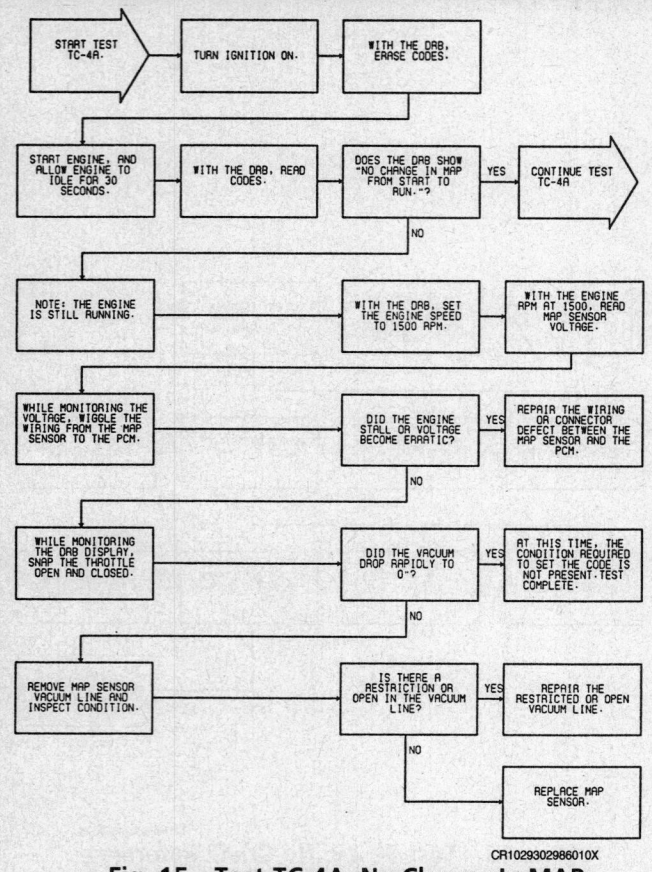

Fig. 15   Test TC-4A: No Change In MAP
From Start To Run (Part 1 of 2).
3.0L/V6-181 Engine

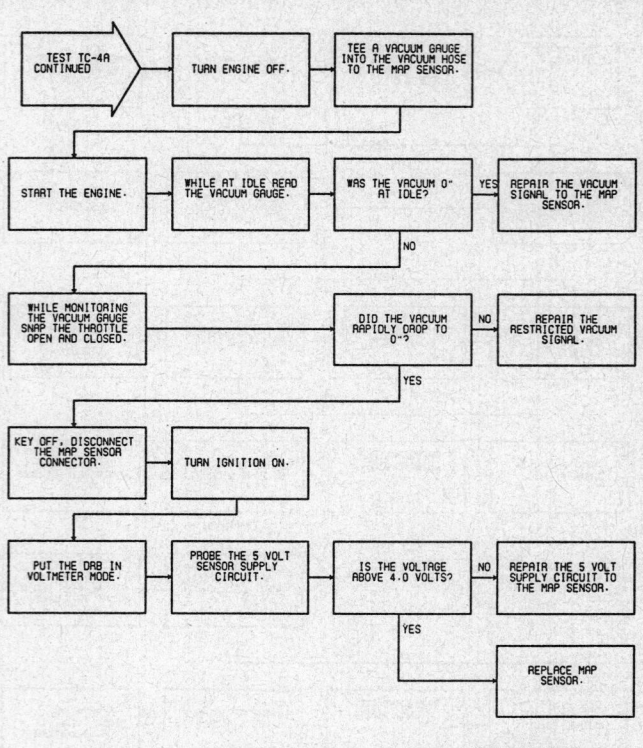

Fig. 15   Test TC-4A: No Change In MAP
From Start To Run (Part 2 of 2).
3.0L/V6-181 Engine

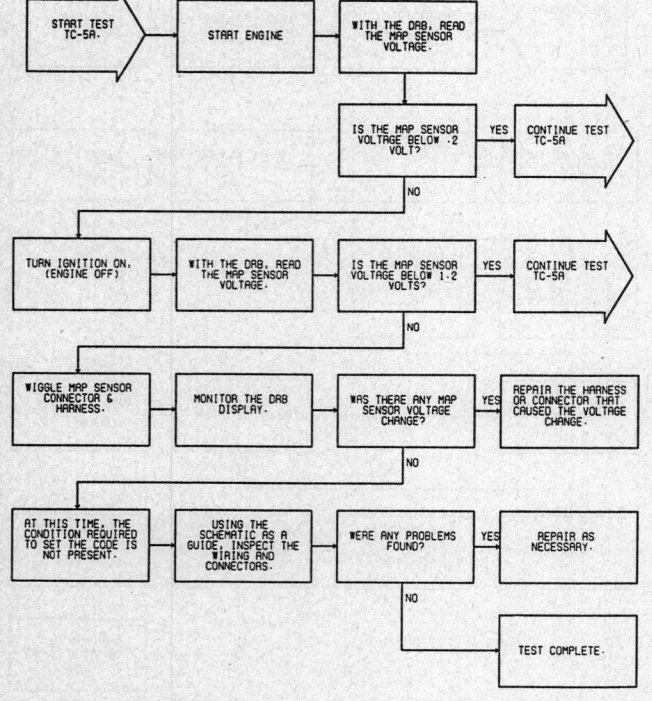

Fig. 16   Test TC-5A: MAP Sensor
Voltage Too Low (Part 1 of 2).
3.0L/V6-181 Engine

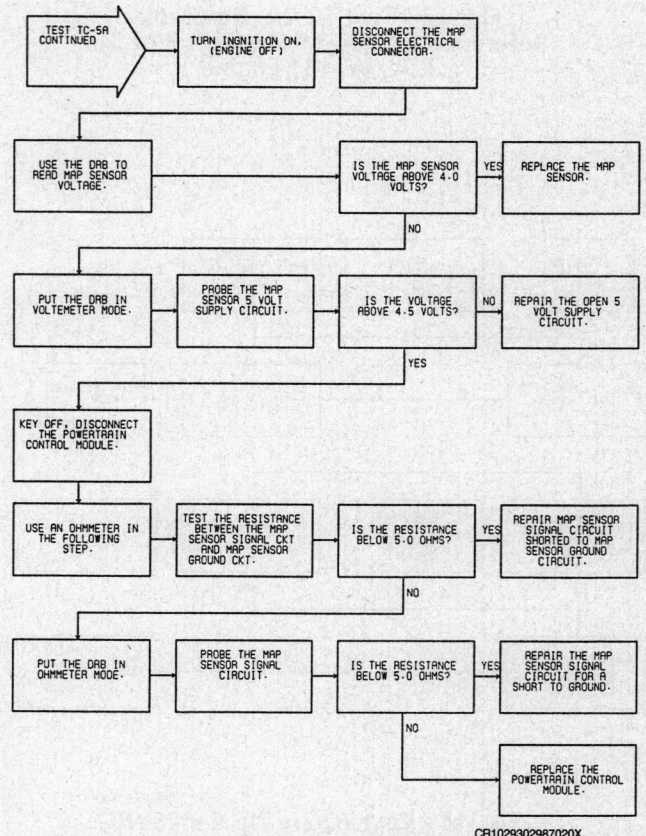

Fig. 16   Test TC-5A: MAP Sensor
Voltage Too Low (Part 2 of 2).
3.0L/V6-181 Engine

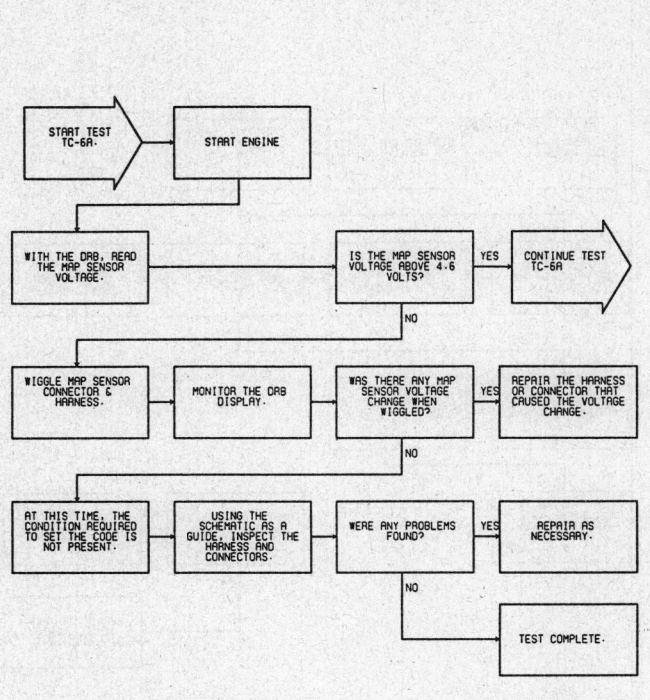

Fig. 17   Test TC-6A: MAP Sensor Voltage Too High (Part 1 of 2). 3.0L/V6-181 Engine

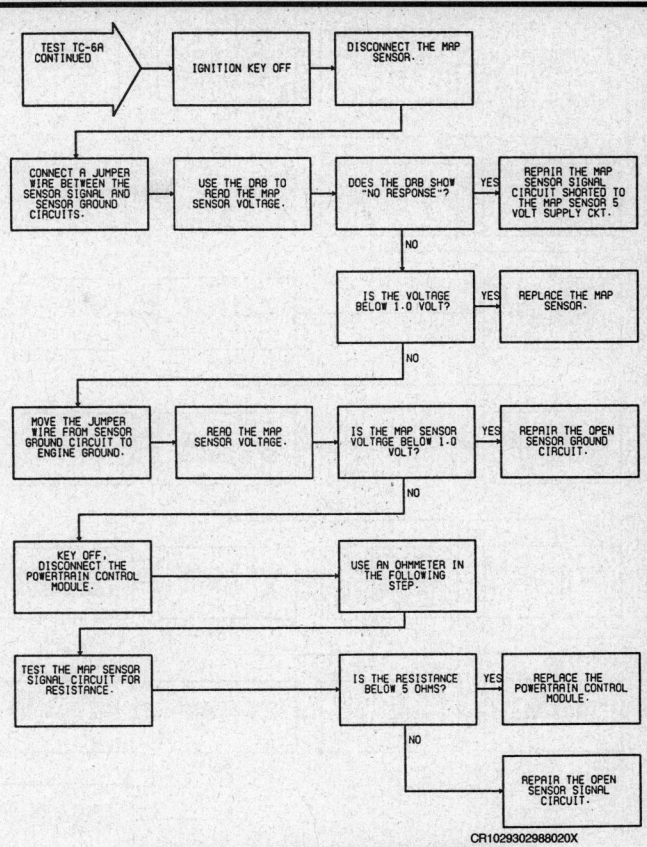

Fig. 17   Test TC-6A: MAP Sensor Voltage Too High (Part 2 of 2). 3.0L/V6-181 Engine

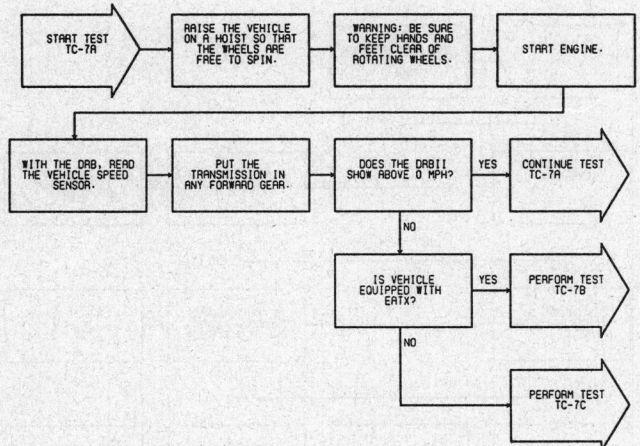

Fig. 18   Test TC-7A: No Vehicle Speed Sensor Signal (Part 1 of 2). 3.0L/V6-181 Engine

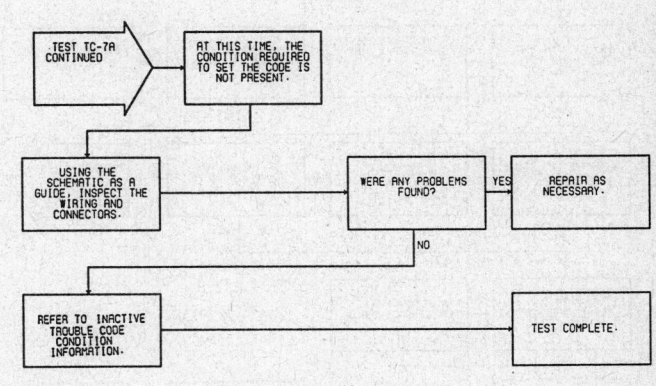

Fig. 18   Test TC-7A: No Vehicle Speed Sensor Signal (Part 2 of 2). 3.0L/V6-181 Engine

MODELS w/3.0L/V6-181, 3.3L/V6-201 & 3.8L/V6-231 ENGINES EXCEPT CONCORDE, INTREPID, LHS, STEALTH, VISION & 1994-96 NEW YORKER

12-31

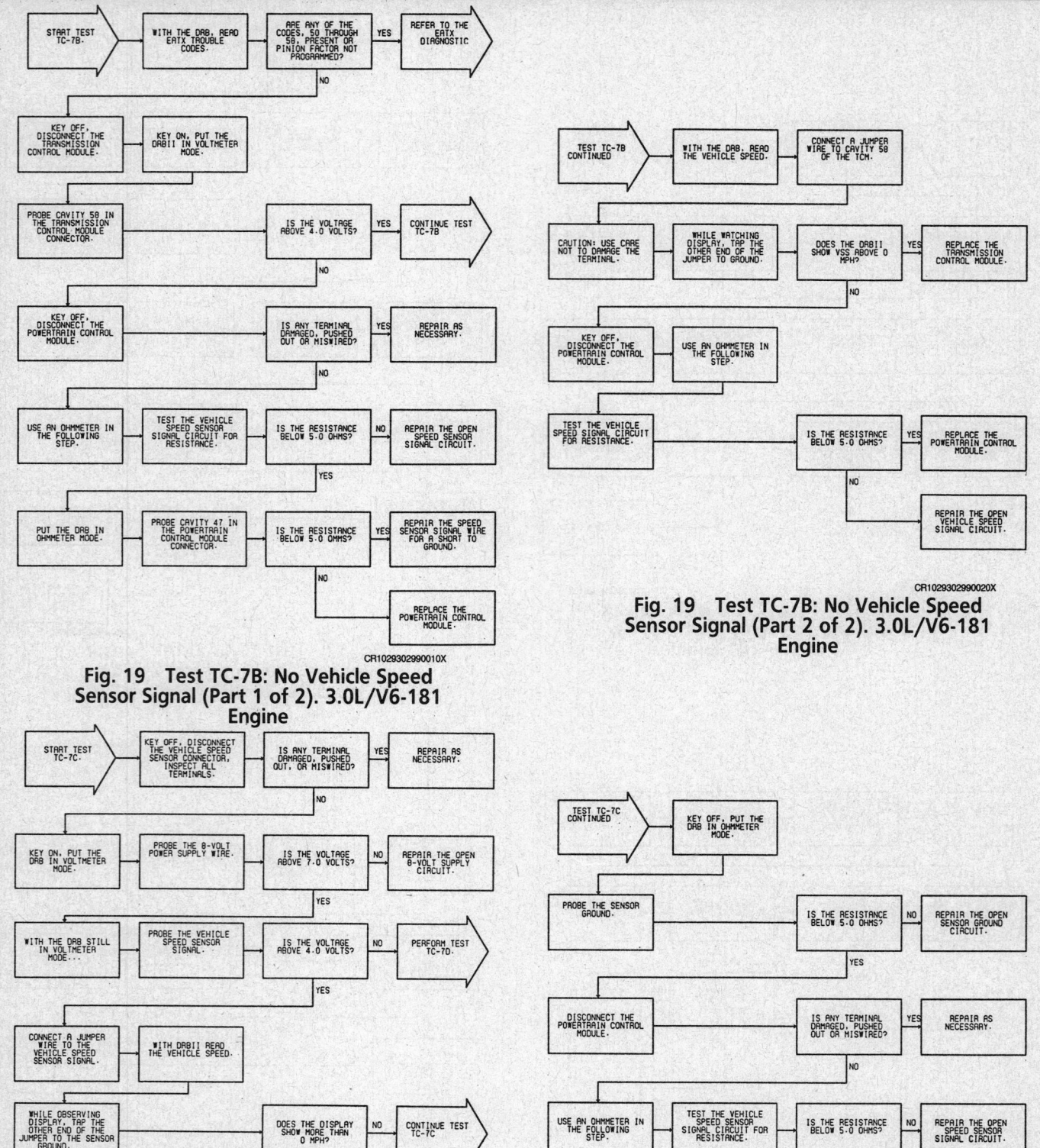

Fig. 19   Test TC-7B: No Vehicle Speed
Sensor Signal (Part 1 of 2). 3.0L/V6-181
Engine

Fig. 19   Test TC-7B: No Vehicle Speed
Sensor Signal (Part 2 of 2). 3.0L/V6-181
Engine

Fig. 20   Test TC-7C: No Vehicle Speed
Sensor Signal (Part 1 of 2). 3.0L/V6-181
Engine

Fig. 20   Test TC-7C: No Vehicle Speed Sensor Signal
(Part 2 of 2). 3.0L/V6-181 Engine

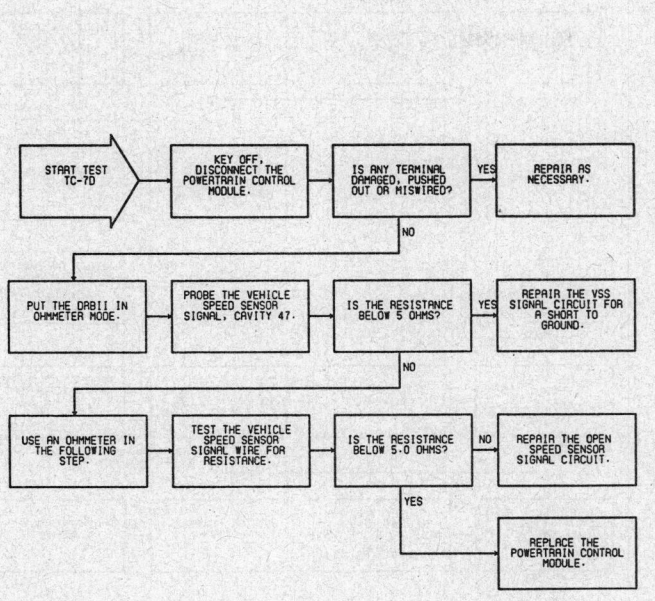

Fig. 21 Test TC-7D: No Vehicle Speed Sensor Signal. 3.0L/V6-181 Engine

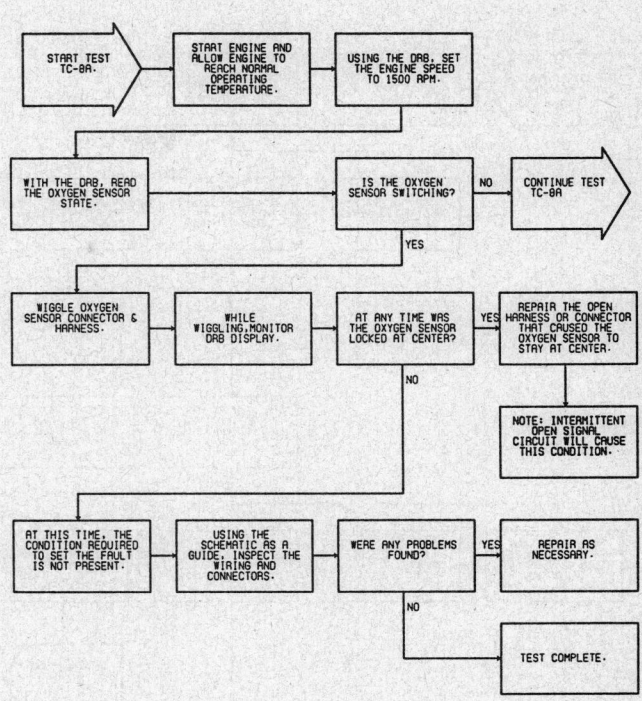

Fig. 22 Test TC-8A: O₂S Stays At Center (Part 1 of 2). 3.0L/V6-181 Engine

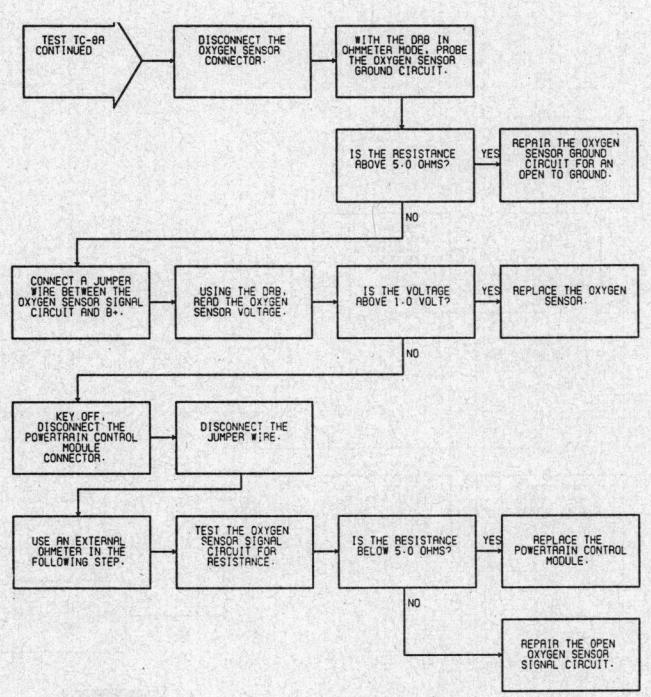

Fig. 22 Test TC-8A: O₂S Stays At Center (Part 2 of 2). 3.0L/V6-181 Engine

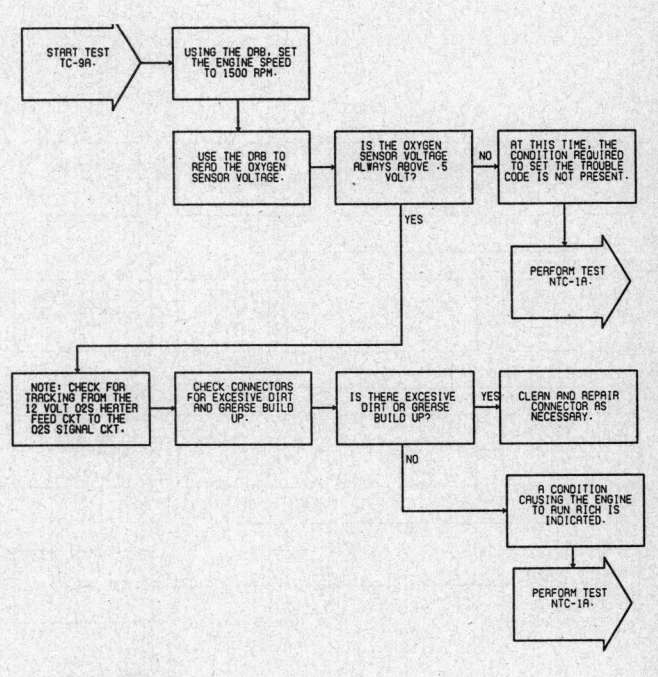

Fig. 23 Test TC-9A: O₂S Stays Above Center, Rich. 3.0L/V6-181 Engine

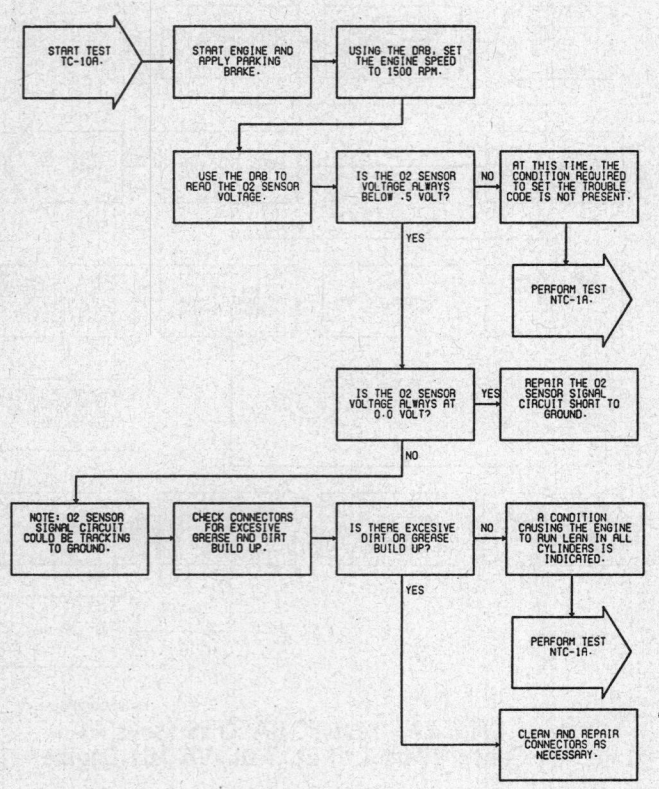

Fig. 24   Test TC-10A: O 2S Stays Above Center, Lean. 3.0L/V6-181 Engine

CR1029302995000X

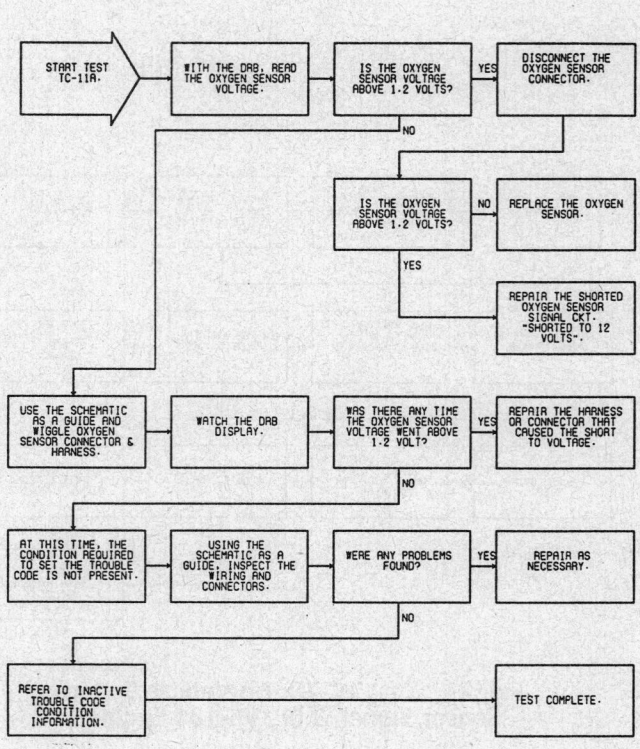

Fig. 25   Test TC-11A: O 2S Shorted To Voltage. 3.0L/V6-181 Engine

CR1029302996000X

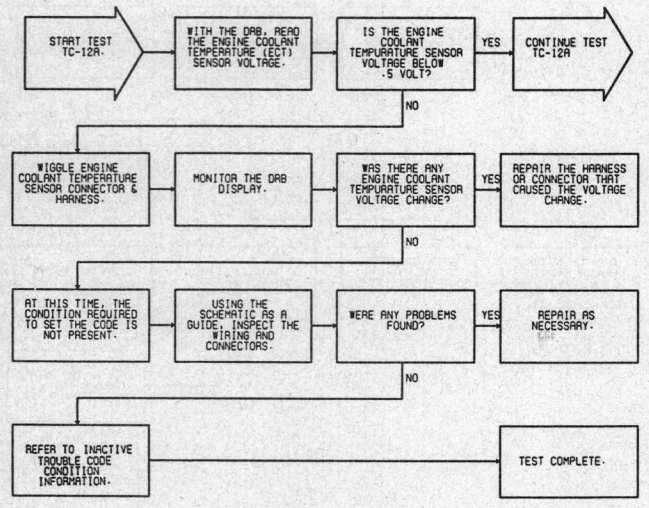

Fig. 26   Test TC-12A: O 2S Shorted To Voltage (Part 1 of 2). 3.0L/V6-181 Engine

CR1029302997010X

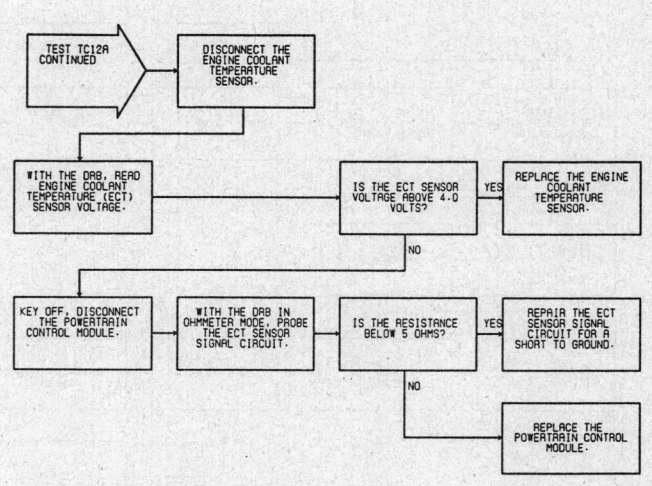

Fig. 26   Test TC-12A: O 2S Shorted To Voltage (Part 2 of 2). 3.0L/V6-181 Engine

CR1029302997020X

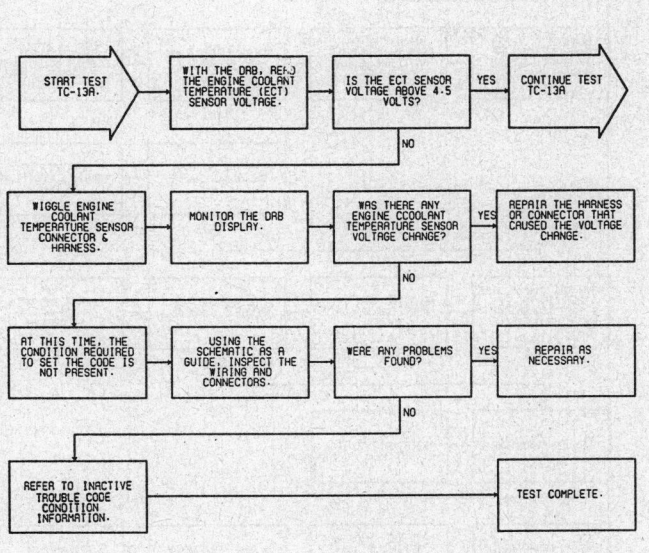

Fig. 27   Test TC-13A: ECT Sensor Voltage Too High (Part 1 of 2). 3.0L/V6-181 Engine

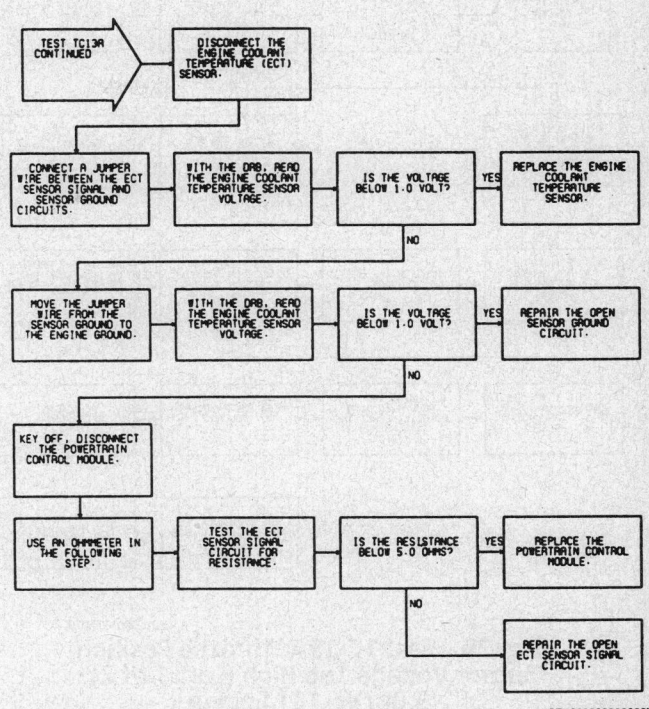

Fig. 27   Test TC-13A: ECT Sensor Voltage Too High (Part 2 of 2). 3.0L/V6-181 Engine

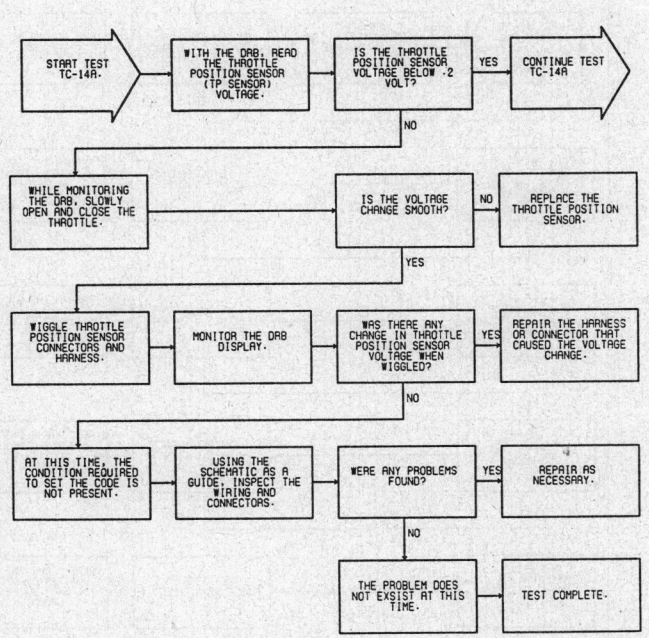

Fig. 28   Test TC-14A: Throttle Position Sensor Voltage Too Low (Part 1 of 2). 3.0L/V6-181 Engine

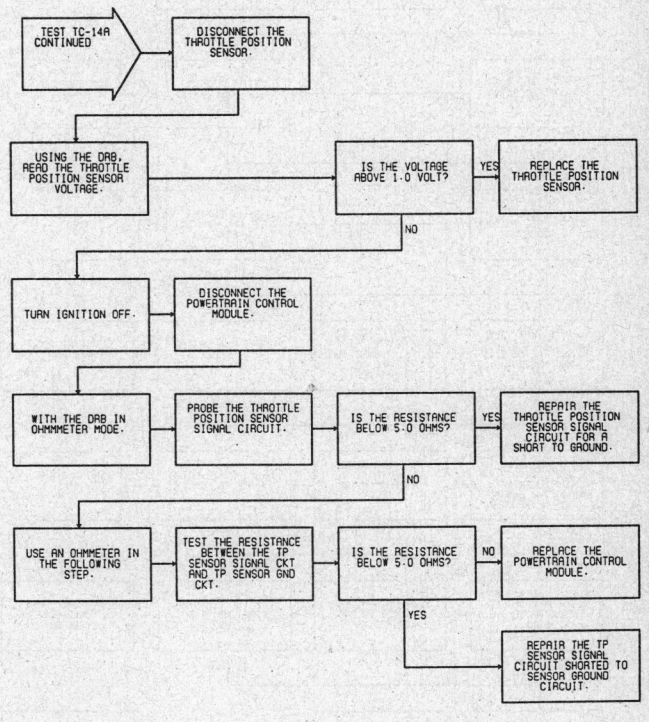

Fig. 28   Test TC-14A: Throttle Position Sensor Voltage Too Low (Part 2 of 2). 3.0L/V6-181 Engine

MODELS w/3.0L/V6-181, 3.3L/V6-201 & 3.8L/V6-231 ENGINES EXCEPT CONCORDE, INTREPID, LHS, STEALTH, VISION & 1994-96 NEW YORKER

12-35

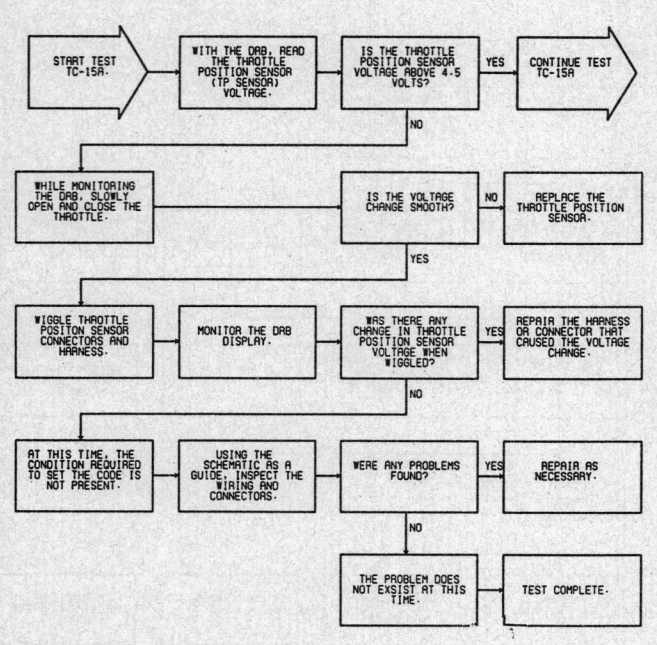

Fig. 29 Test TC-15A: Throttle Position Sensor Voltage Too High (Part 1 of 2). 3.0L/V6-181 Engine

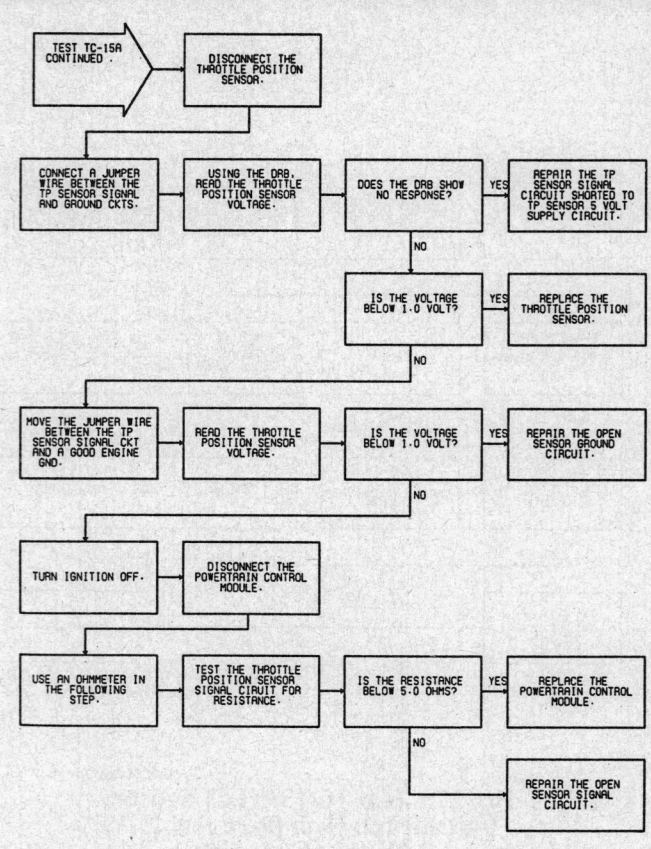

Fig. 29 Test TC-15A: Throttle Position Sensor Voltage Too High (Part 2 of 2). 3.0L/V6-181 Engine

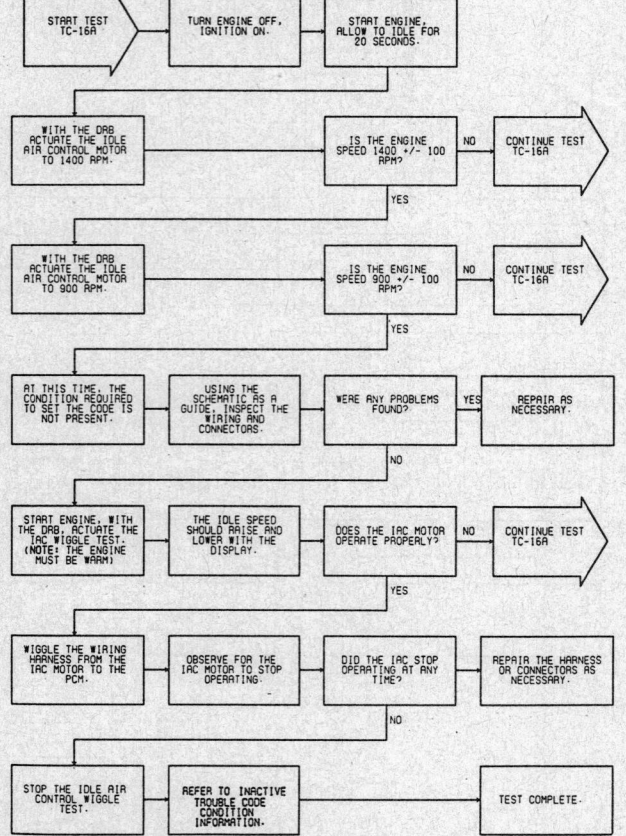

Fig. 30 Test TC-16A: Idle Air Control Motor Circuits (Part 1 of 4). 3.0L/V6-181 Engine

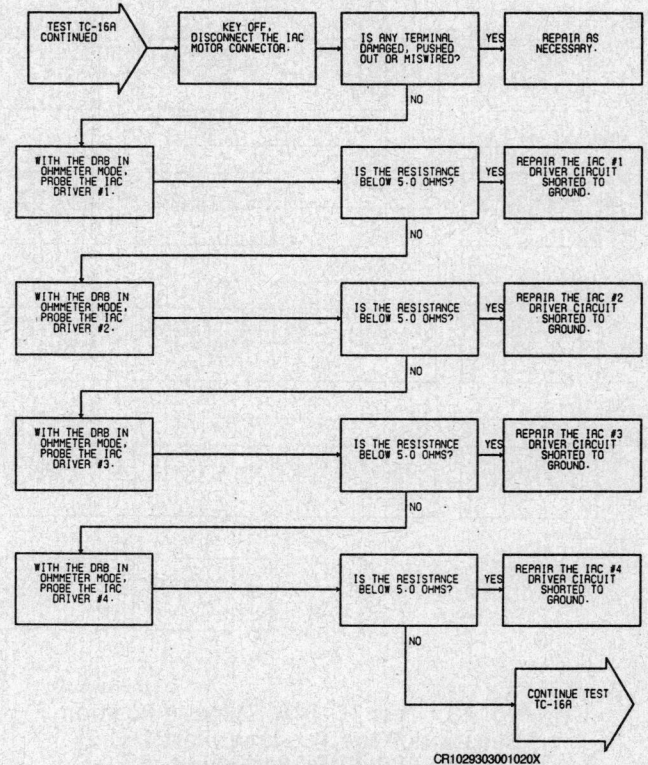

Fig. 30 Test TC-16A: Idle Air Control Motor Circuits (Part 2 of 4). 3.0L/V6-181 Engine

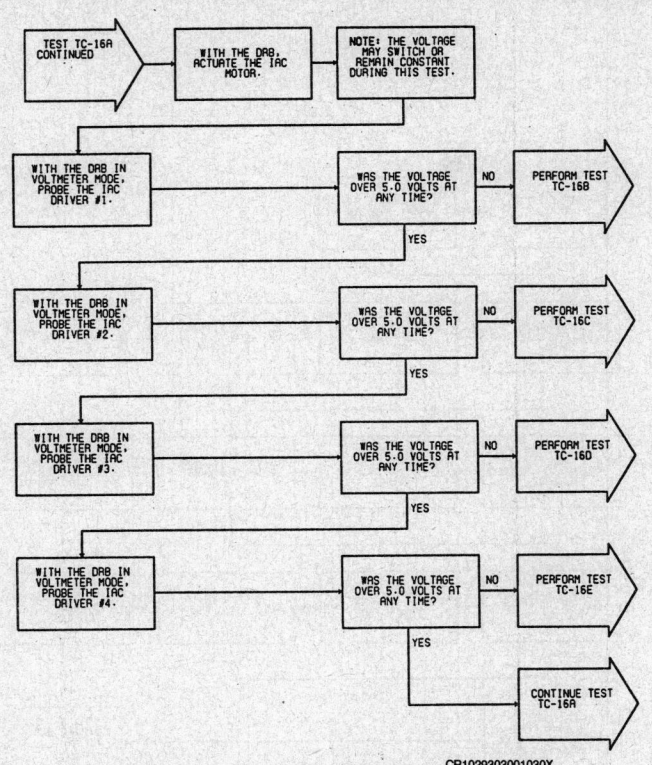

Fig. 30 Test TC-16A: Idle Air Control Motor Circuits (Part 3 of 4). 3.0L/V6-181 Engine

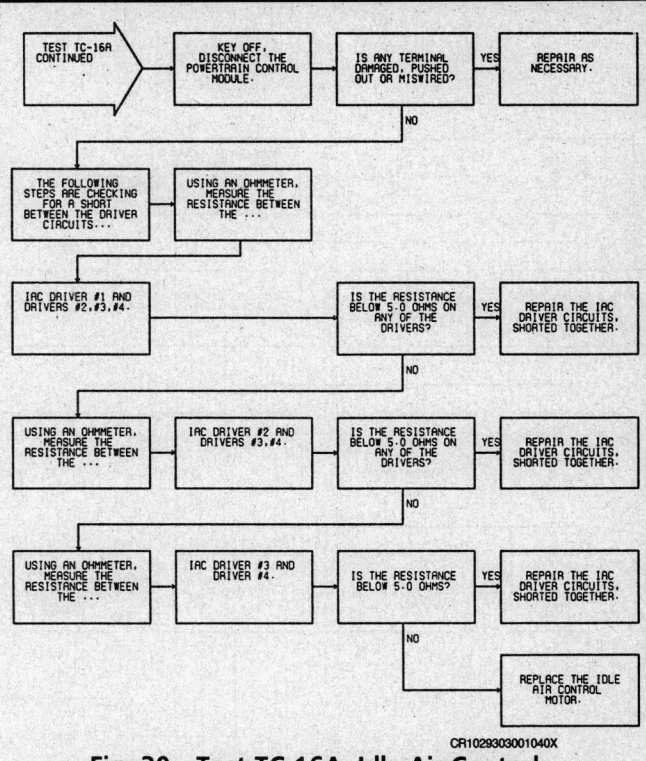

Fig. 30 Test TC-16A: Idle Air Control Motor Circuits (Part 4 of 4). 3.0L/V6-181 Engine

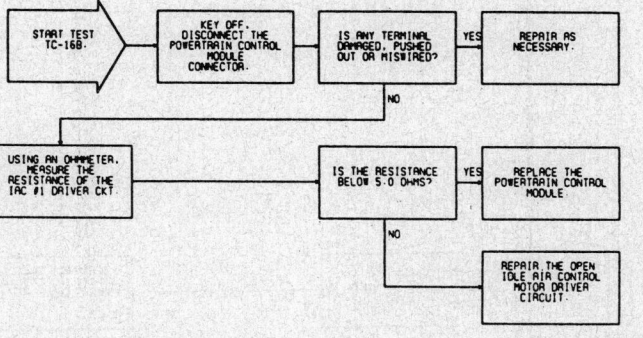

Fig. 31 Test TC-16B: Idle Air Control Motor Circuits. 3.0L/V6-181 Engine

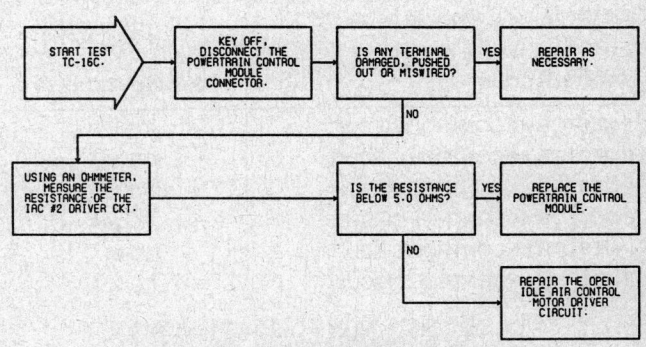

Fig. 32 Test TC-16C: Idle Air Control Motor Circuits. 3.0L/V6-181 Engine

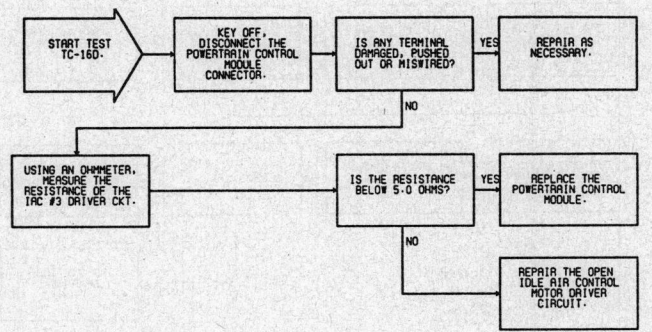

Fig. 33 Test TC-16D: Idle Air Control Motor Circuits. 3.0L/V6-181 Engine

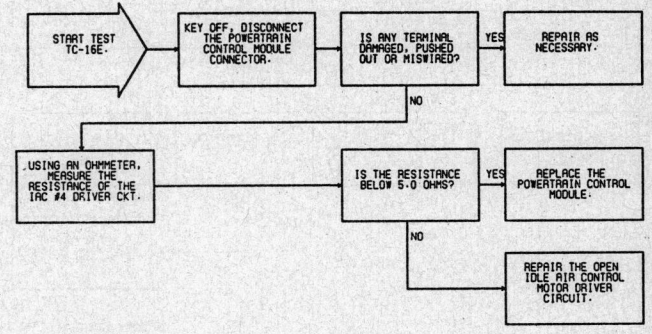

Fig. 34 Test TC-16E: Idle Air Control Motor Circuits. 3.0L/V6-181 Engine

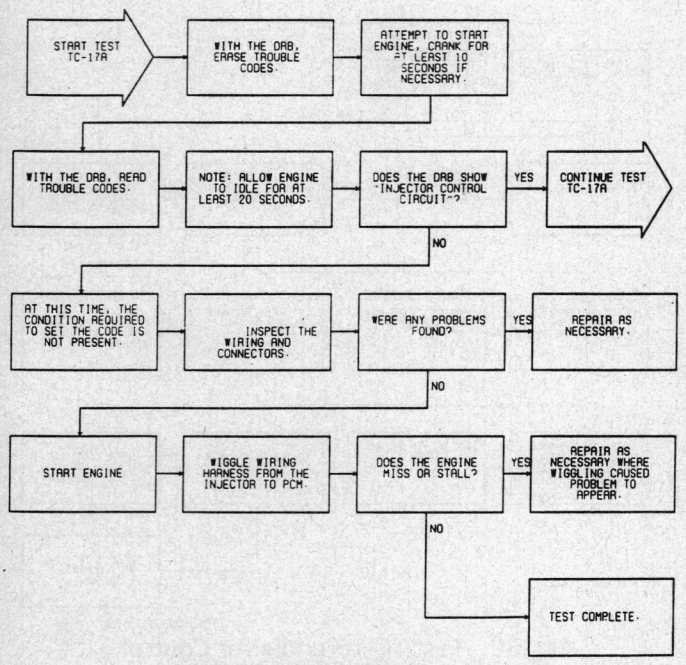

Fig. 35   Test TC-17A: Injector Control Circuit (Part 1 of 2). 3.0L/V6-181 Engine

Refer to the chart below and perform the diagnostic test that corresponds to the trouble code displayed on the DRB.

TROUBLE CODE	DIAGNOSTIC TEST
INJECTOR #1 CONTROL CIRCUIT	TC-17B
INJECTOR #2 CONTROL CIRCUIT	TC-18A
INJECTOR #3 CONTROL CIRCUIT	TC-19A
INJECTOR #4 CONTROL CIRCUIT	TC-20A
INJECTOR #5 CONTROL CIRCUIT	TC-21A
INJECTOR #6 CONTROL CIRCUIT	TC-22A

Fig. 35   Test TC-17A: Injector Control Circuit (Part 2 of 2). 3.0L/V6-181 Engine

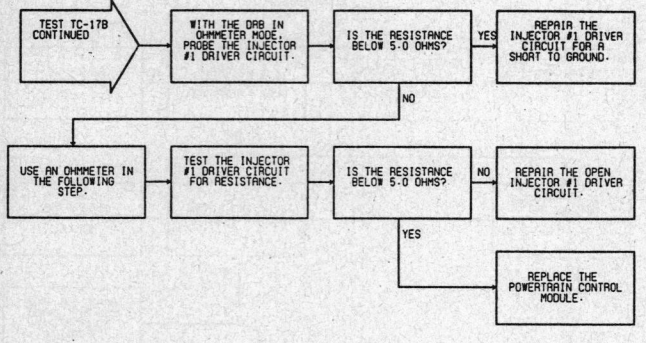

CR1029303006020X

Fig. 36   Test TC-17B: Injector No. 1 Control Circuit (Part 2 of 2). 3.0L/V6-181 Engine

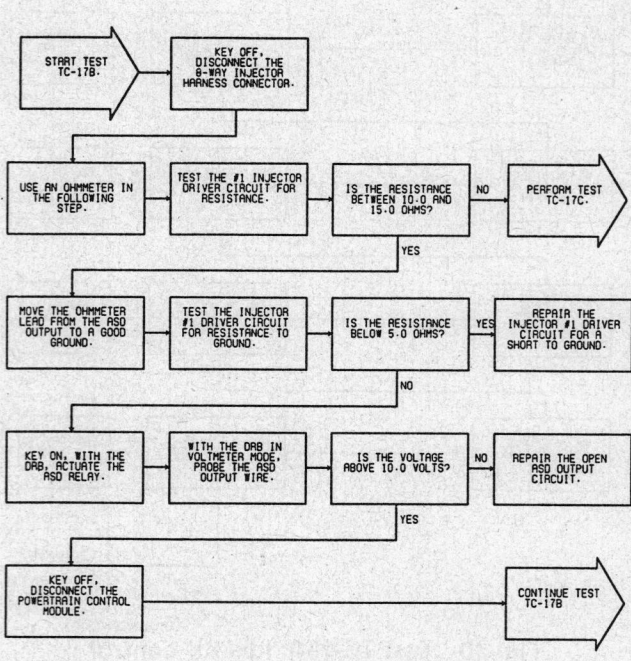

CR1029303006010X

Fig. 36   Test TC-17B: Injector No. 1 Control Circuit (Part 1 of 2). 3.0L/V6-181 Engine

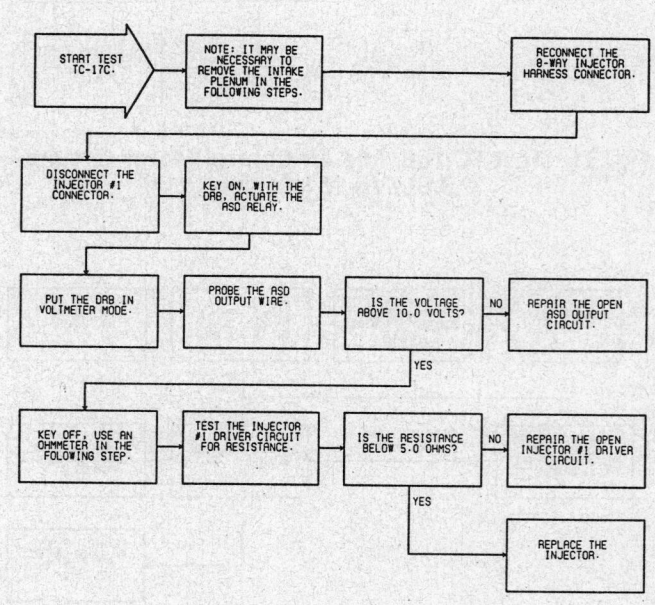

CR1029303007000X

Fig. 37   Test TC-17C: Injector No. 1 Control Circuit. 3.0L/V6-181 Engine

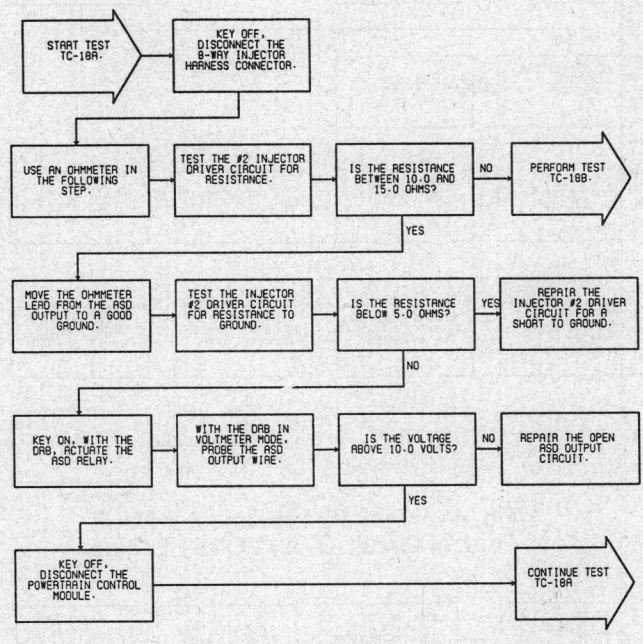

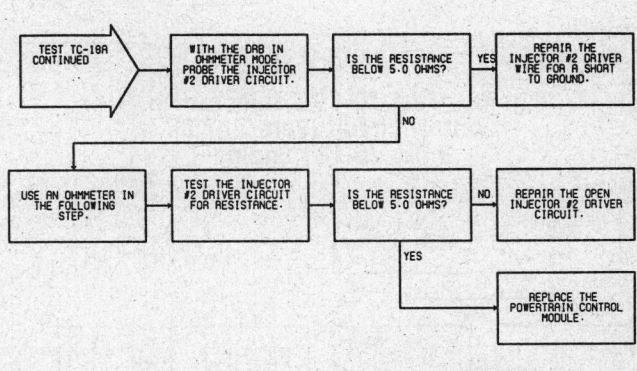

Fig. 38   Test TC-18A: Injector No. 2 Control Circuit (Part 1 of 2). 3.0L/V6-181 Engine

Fig. 38   Test TC-18A: Injector No. 2 Control Circuit (Part 2 of 2). 3.0L/V6-181 Engine

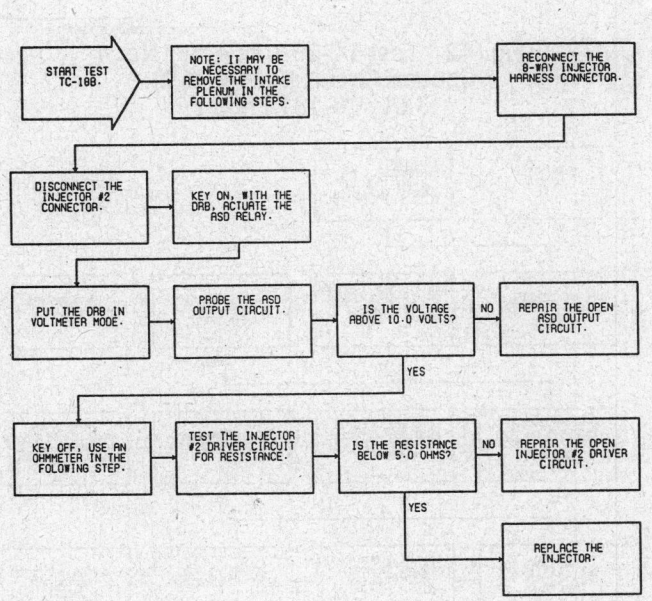

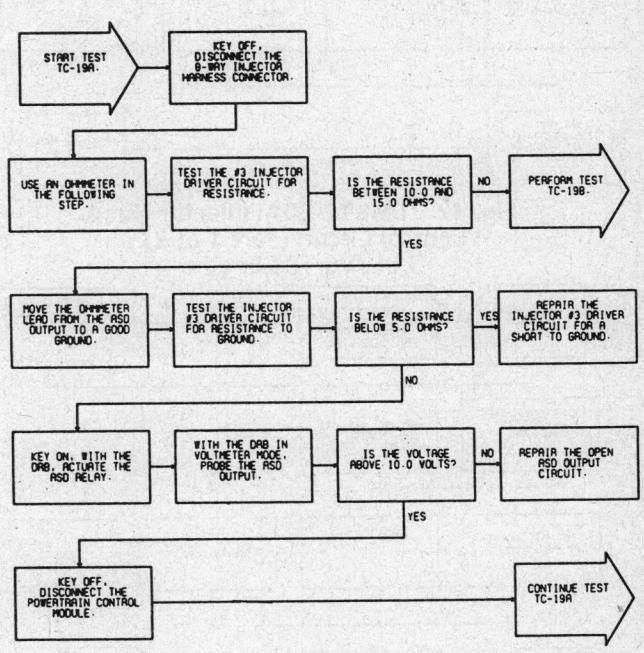

Fig. 39   Test TC-18B: Injector No. 2 Control Circuit. 3.0L/V6-181 Engine

Fig. 40   Test TC-19A: Injector No. 3 Control Circuit (Part 1 of 2). 3.0L/V6-181 Engine

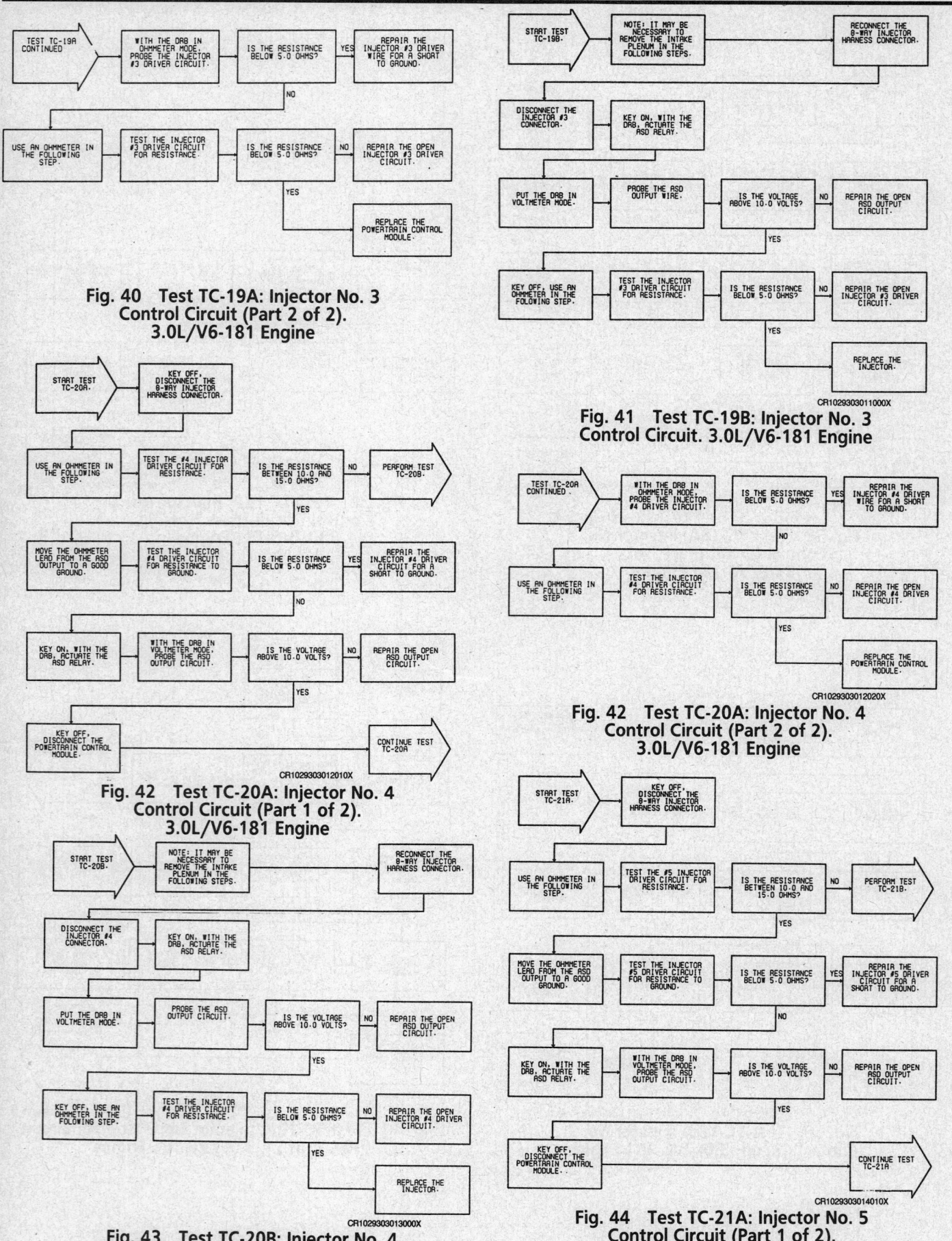

Fig. 40   Test TC-19A: Injector No. 3 Control Circuit (Part 2 of 2). 3.0L/V6-181 Engine

Fig. 42   Test TC-20A: Injector No. 4 Control Circuit (Part 1 of 2). 3.0L/V6-181 Engine

Fig. 43   Test TC-20B: Injector No. 4 Control Circuit. 3.0L/V6-181 Engine

Fig. 41   Test TC-19B: Injector No. 3 Control Circuit. 3.0L/V6-181 Engine

Fig. 42   Test TC-20A: Injector No. 4 Control Circuit (Part 2 of 2). 3.0L/V6-181 Engine

Fig. 44   Test TC-21A: Injector No. 5 Control Circuit (Part 1 of 2). 3.0L/V6-181 Engine

12-40

MODELS w/3.0L/V6-181, 3.3L/V6-201 & 3.8L/V6-231 ENGINES EXCEPT CONCORDE, INTREPID, LHS, STEALTH, VISION & 1994-96 NEW YORKER

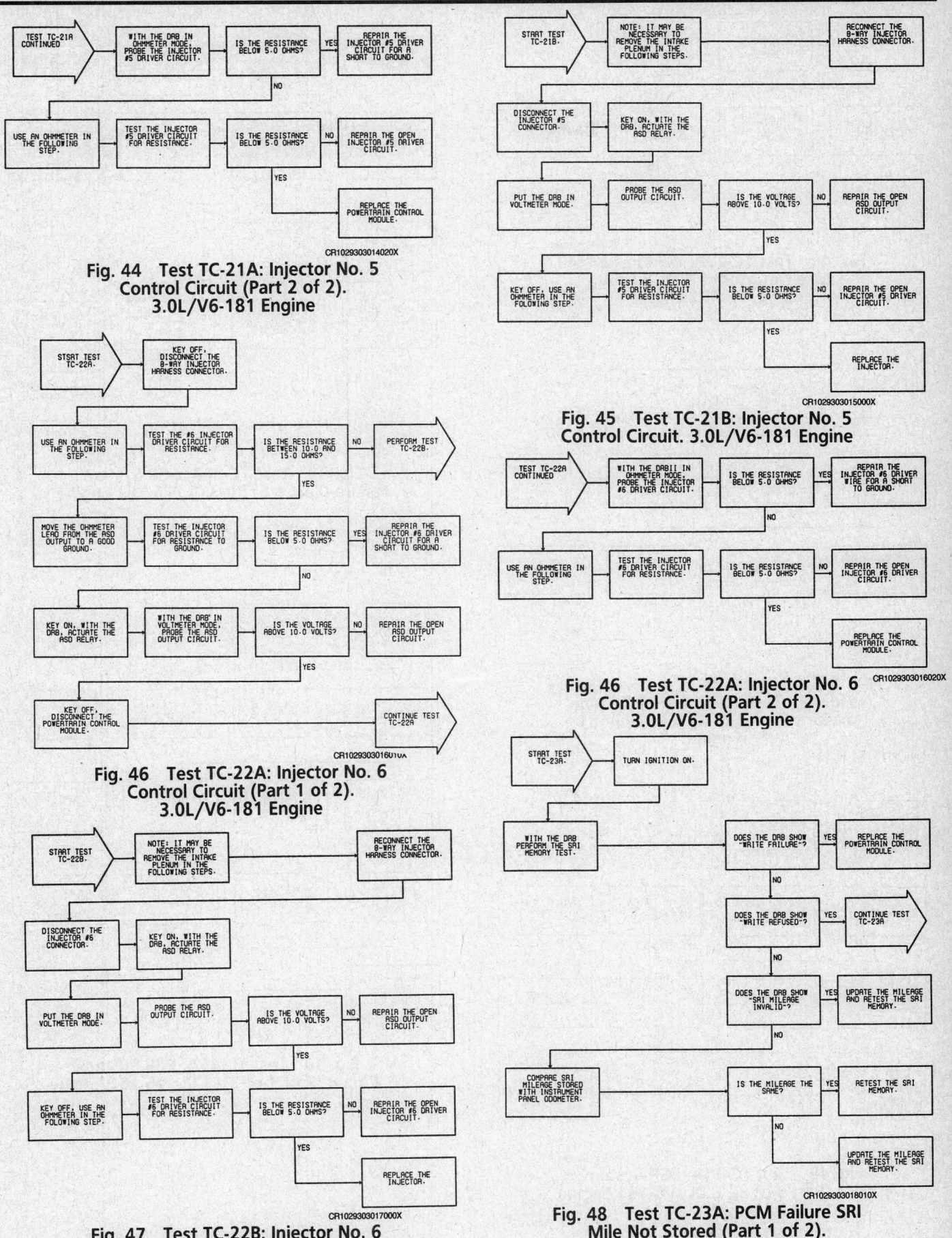

Fig. 44   Test TC-21A: Injector No. 5
Control Circuit (Part 2 of 2).
3.0L/V6-181 Engine

CR1029303014020X

Fig. 45   Test TC-21B: Injector No. 5
Control Circuit. 3.0L/V6-181 Engine

CR1029303015000X

Fig. 46   Test TC-22A: Injector No. 6
Control Circuit (Part 1 of 2).
3.0L/V6-181 Engine

CR1029303016010X

Fig. 46   Test TC-22A: Injector No. 6
Control Circuit (Part 2 of 2).
3.0L/V6-181 Engine

CR1029303016020X

Fig. 47   Test TC-22B: Injector No. 6
Control Circuit. 3.0L/V6-181 Engine

CR1029303017000X

Fig. 48   Test TC-23A: PCM Failure SRI
Mile Not Stored (Part 1 of 2).
3.0L/V6-181 Engine

CR1029303018010X

*MODELS w/3.0L/V6-181, 3.3L/V6-201 & 3.8L/V6-231 ENGINES EXCEPT CONCORDE, INTREPID, LHS, STEALTH, VISION &
1994-96 NEW YORKER*

12-41

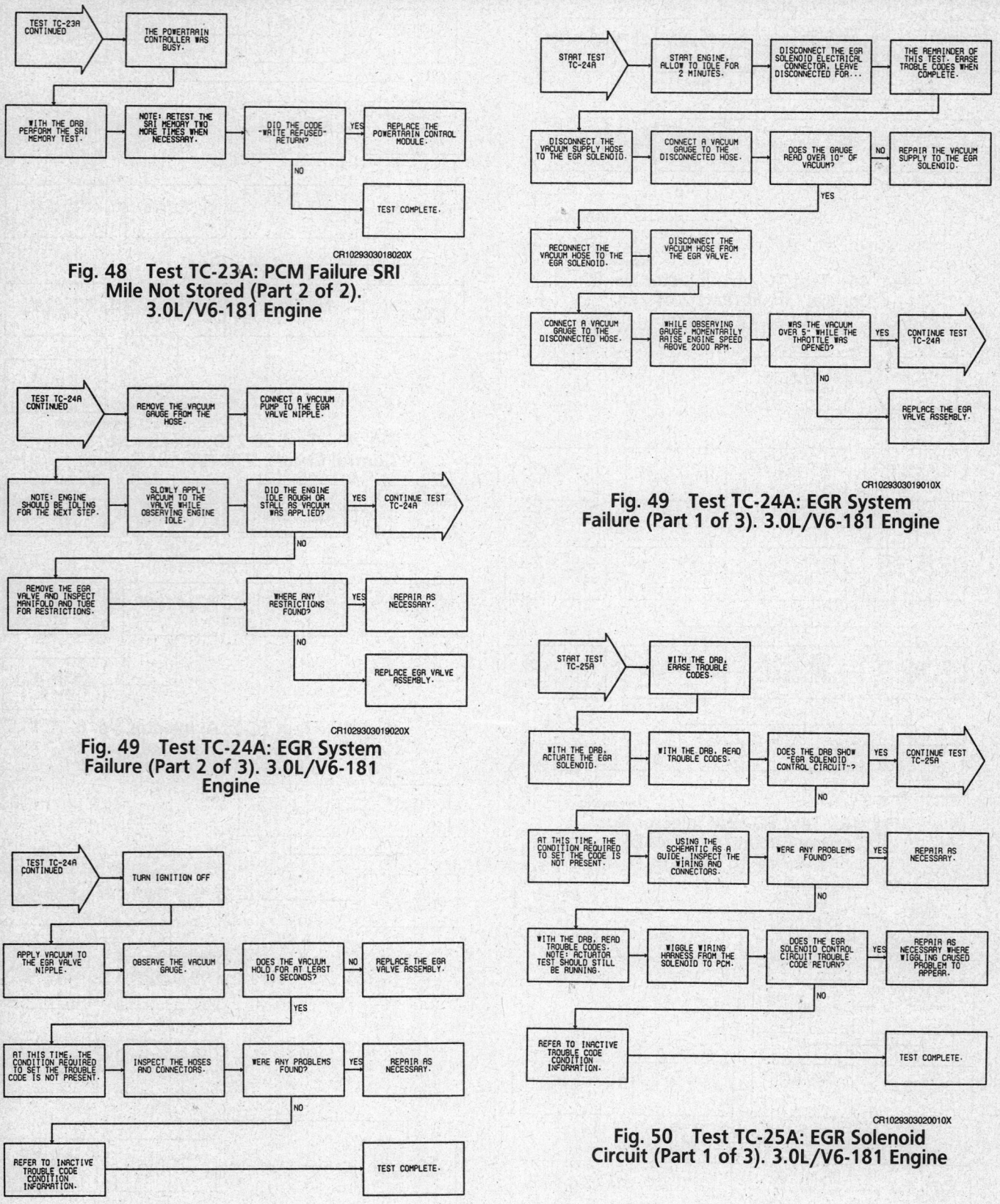

Fig. 48 Test TC-23A: PCM Failure SRI
Mile Not Stored (Part 2 of 2).
3.0L/V6-181 Engine

Fig. 49 Test TC-24A: EGR System
Failure (Part 2 of 3). 3.0L/V6-181
Engine

Fig. 49 Test TC-24A: EGR System
Failure (Part 3 of 3). 3.0L/V6-181 Engine

Fig. 49 Test TC-24A: EGR System
Failure (Part 1 of 3). 3.0L/V6-181 Engine

Fig. 50 Test TC-25A: EGR Solenoid
Circuit (Part 1 of 3). 3.0L/V6-181 Engine

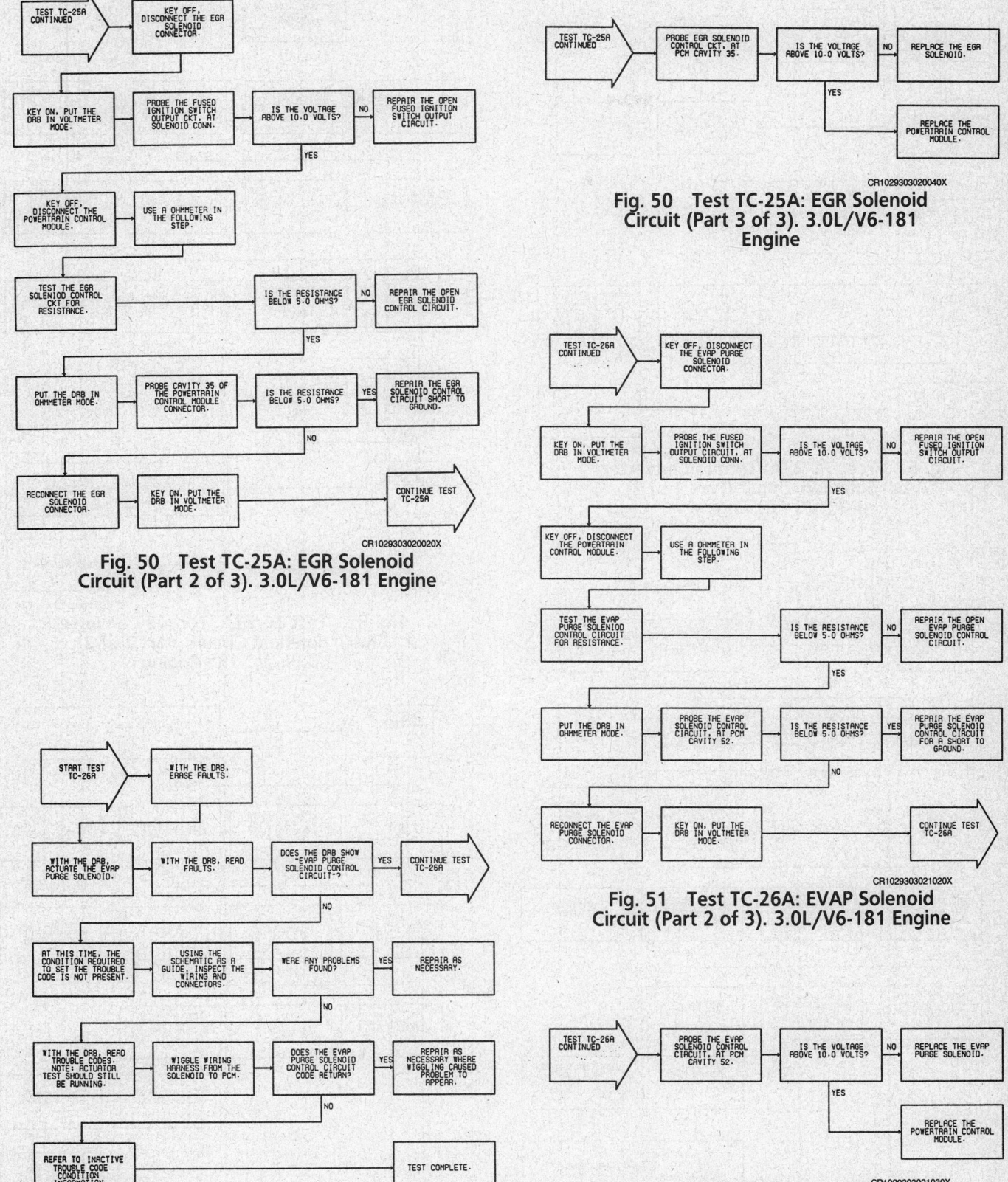

Fig. 50   Test TC-25A: EGR Solenoid Circuit (Part 2 of 3). 3.0L/V6-181 Engine

Fig. 50   Test TC-25A: EGR Solenoid Circuit (Part 3 of 3). 3.0L/V6-181 Engine

Fig. 51   Test TC-26A: EVAP Solenoid Circuit (Part 2 of 3). 3.0L/V6-181 Engine

Fig. 51   Test TC-26A: EVAP Solenoid Circuit (Part 1 of 3). 3.0L/V6-181 Engine

Fig. 51   Test TC-26A: EVAP Solenoid Circuit (Part 3 of 3). 3.0L/V6-181 Engine

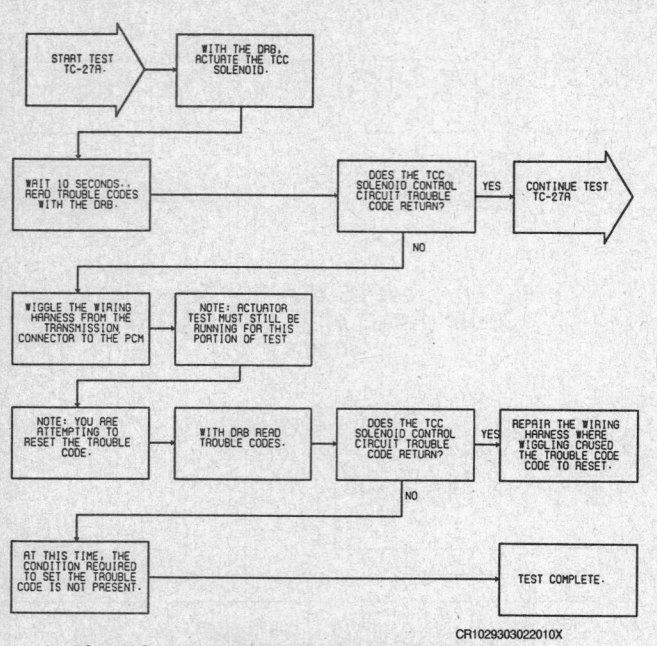

Fig. 52 Test TC-27A: Torque Converter Clutch Solenoid Circuit (Part 1 of 2). 3.0L/V6-181 Engine

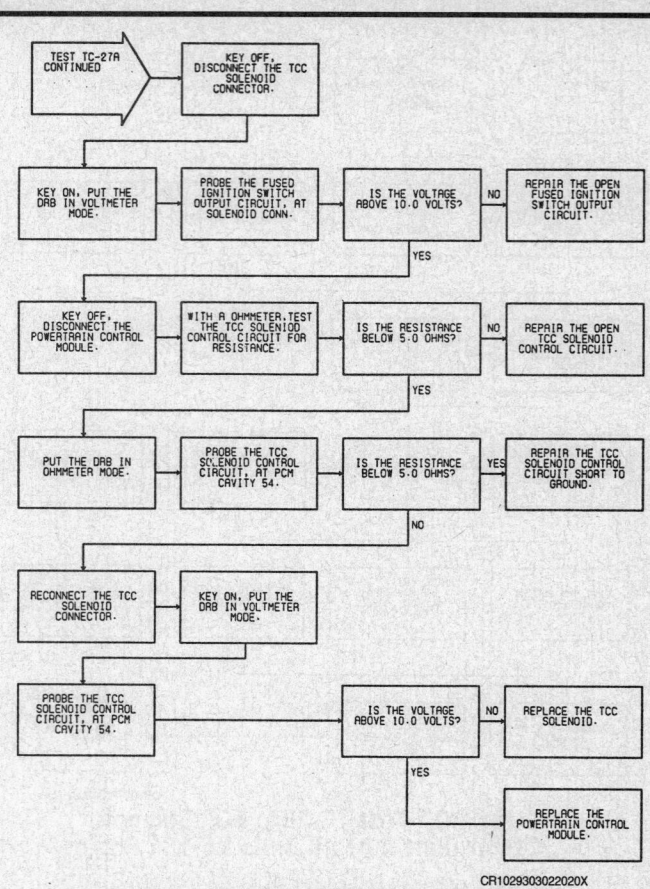

Fig. 52 Test TC-27A: Torque Converter Clutch Solenoid Circuit (Part 2 of 2). 3.0L/V6-181 Engine

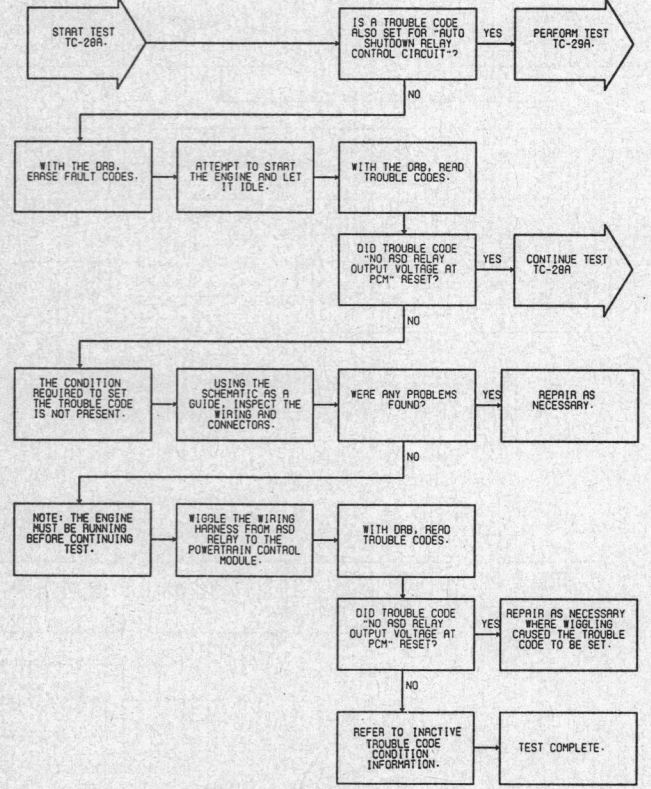

Fig. 53 Test TC-28A: No ASD Relay Output Voltage At PCM (Part 1 of 3). 3.0L/V6-181 Engine

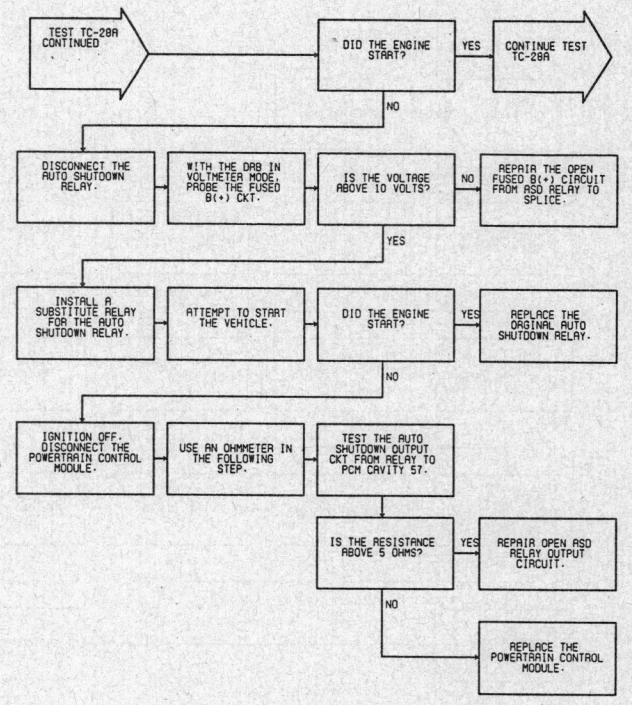

Fig. 53 Test TC-28A: No ASD Relay Output Voltage At PCM (Part 2 of 3). 3.0L/V6-181 Engine

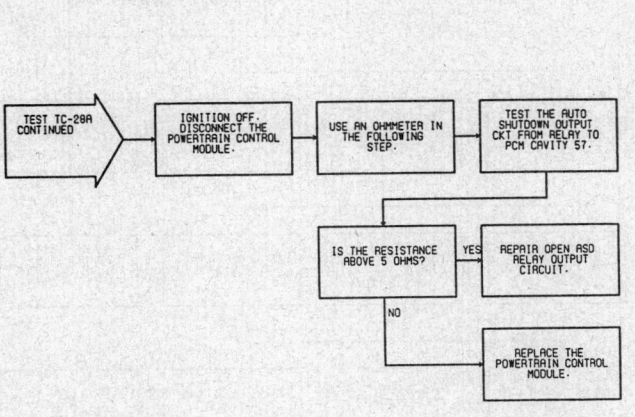

Fig. 53 Test TC-28A: No ASD Relay Output Voltage At PCM (Part 3 of 3). 3.0L/V6-181 Engine

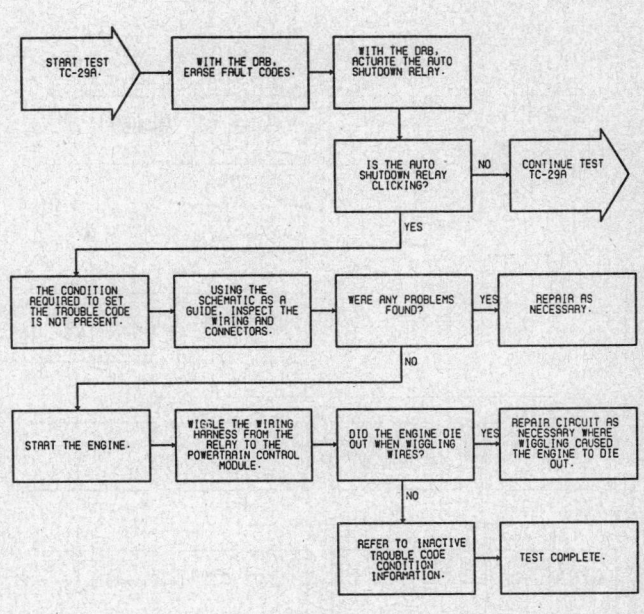

Fig. 54 Test TC-29A: Auto Shutdown Relay Control Circuit (Part 1 of 2). 3.0L/V6-181 Engine

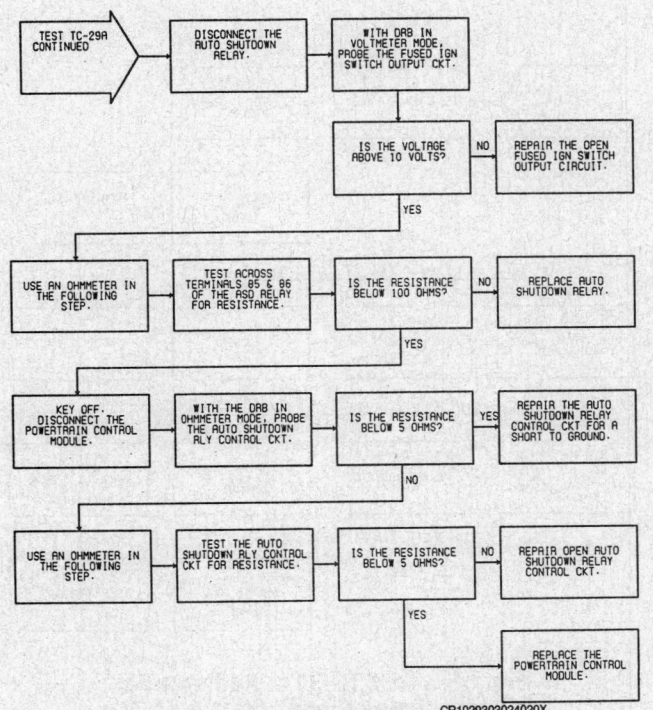

Fig. 54 Test TC-29A: Auto Shutdown Relay Control Circuit (Part 2 of 2). 3.0L/V6-181 Engine

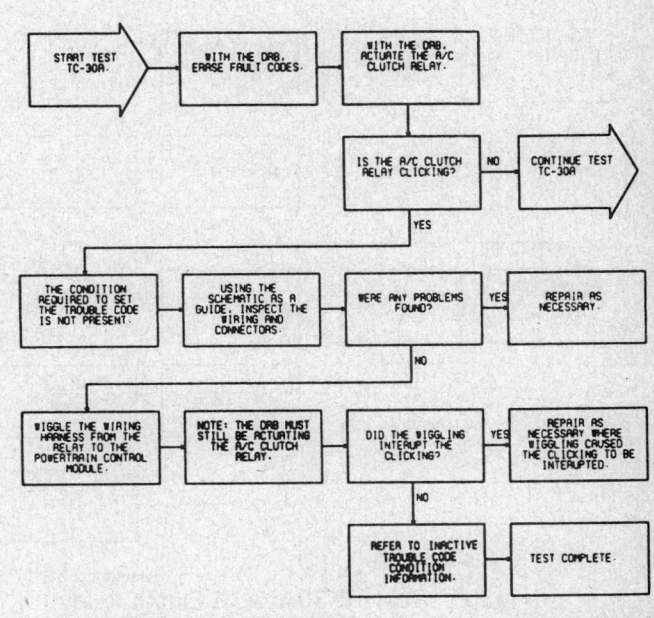

Fig. 55 Test TC-30A: A/C Clutch Relay Circuit (Part 1 of 4). 3.0L/V6-181 Engine

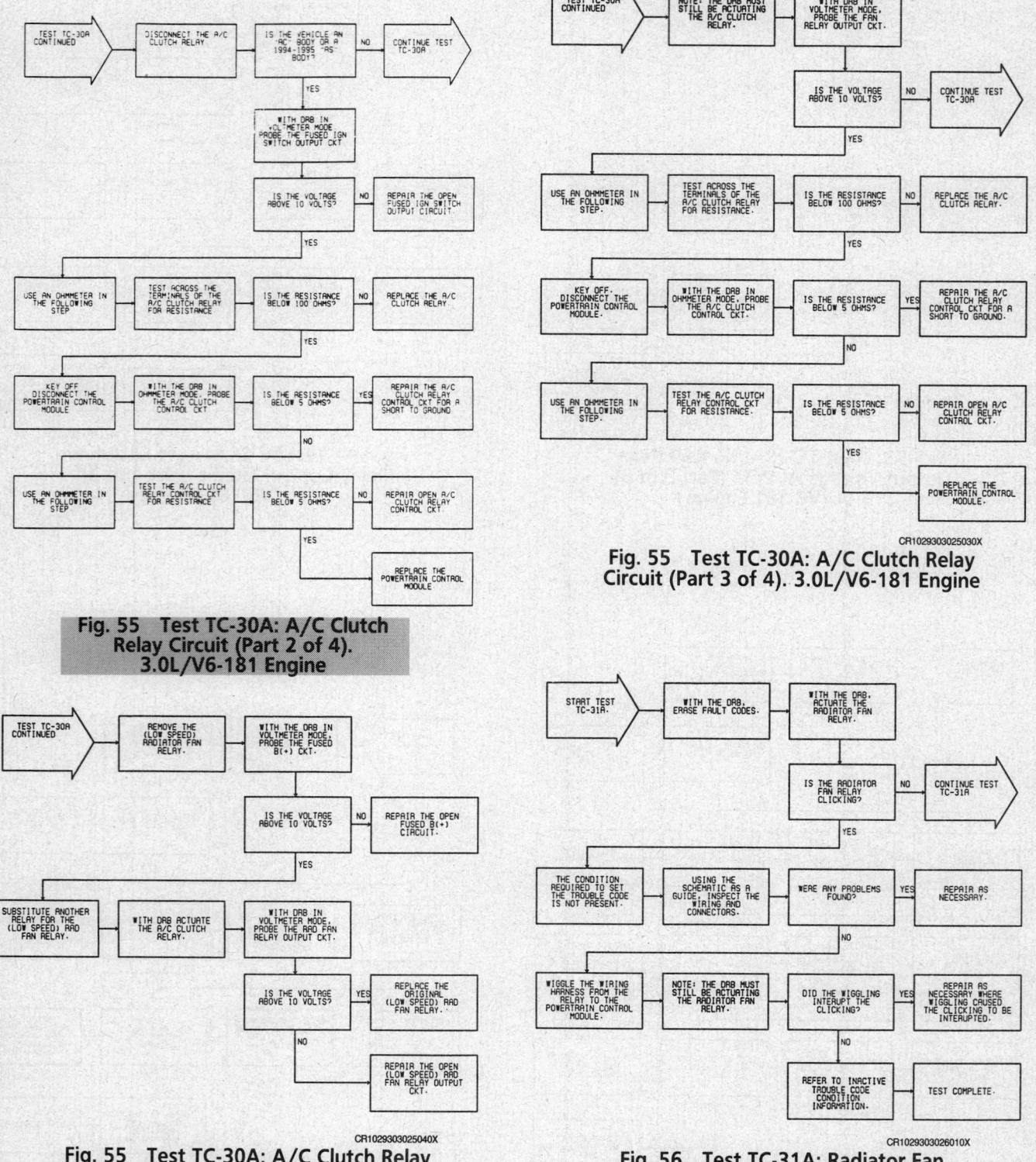

Fig. 55   Test TC-30A: A/C Clutch Relay Circuit (Part 2 of 4). 3.0L/V6-181 Engine

Fig. 55   Test TC-30A: A/C Clutch Relay Circuit (Part 3 of 4). 3.0L/V6-181 Engine

CR1029303025030X

CR1029303025040X

Fig. 55   Test TC-30A: A/C Clutch Relay Circuit (Part 4 of 4). 3.0L/V6-181 Engine

CR1029303026010X

Fig. 56   Test TC-31A: Radiator Fan Control Relay Circuit (Part 1 of 2). 3.0L/V6-181 Engine

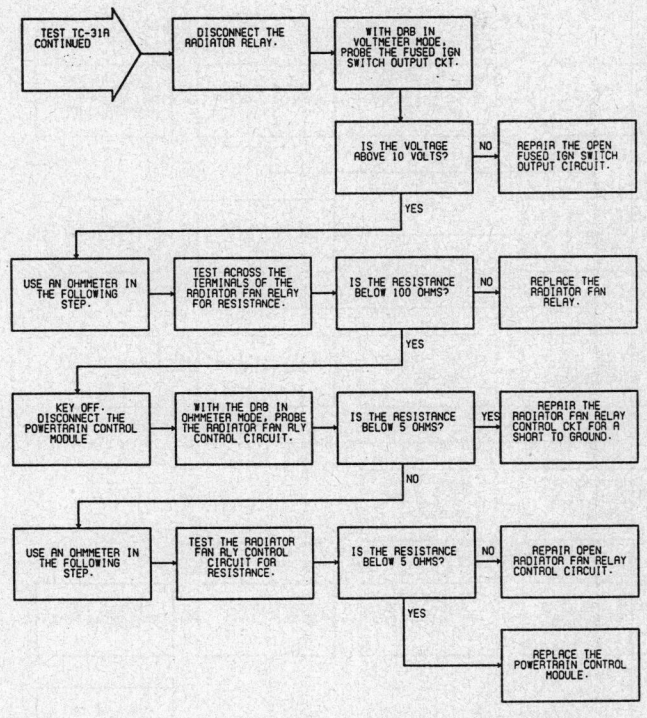

CR1029303026020X

Fig. 56   Test TC-31A: Radiator Fan Control Relay Circuit (Part 2 of 2). 3.0L/V6-181 Engine

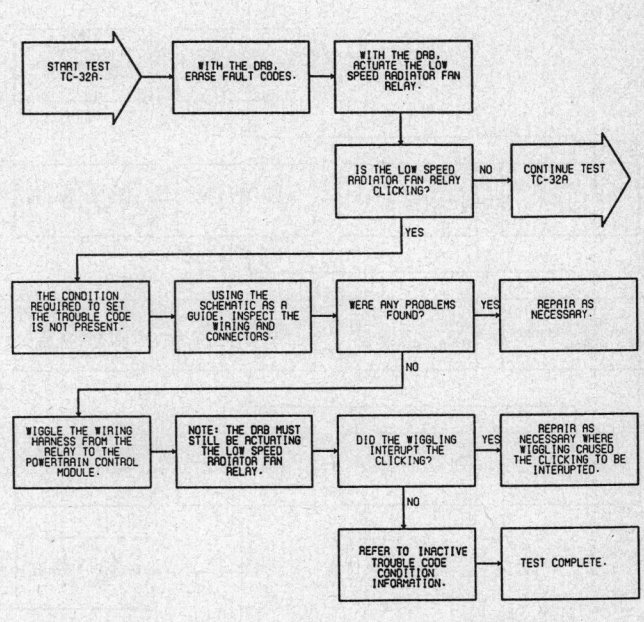

CR1029303027010X

Fig. 57   Test TC-32A: Low Speed Fan Control Relay Circuit (Part 1 of 2). 3.0L/V6-181 Engine

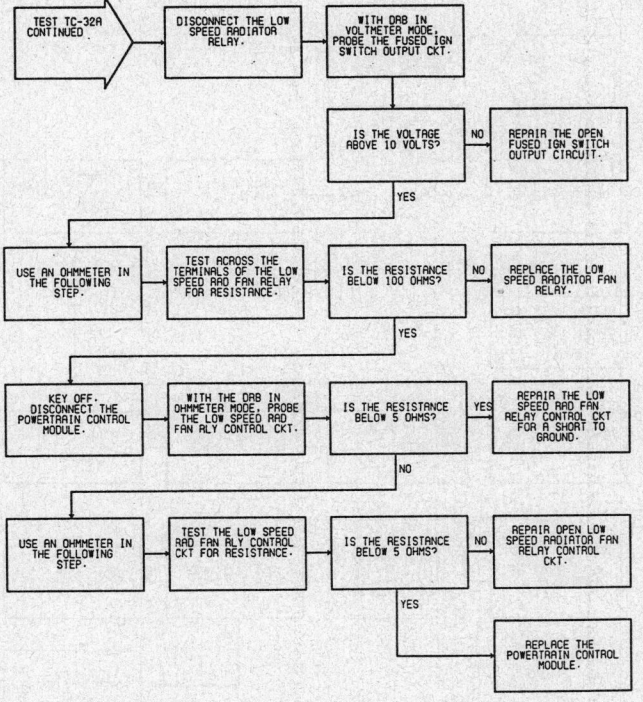

CR1029303027020X

Fig. 57   Test TC-32A: Low Speed Fan Control Relay Circuit (Part 2 of 2). 3.0L/V6-181 Engine

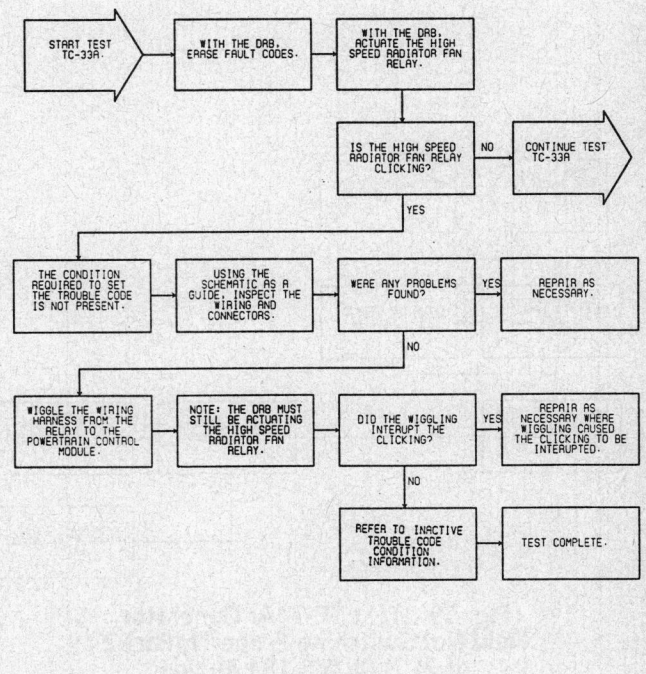

CR1029303028010X

Fig. 58   Test TC-33A: High Speed Fan Control Relay Circuit (Part 1 of 2). 3.0L/V6-181 Engine

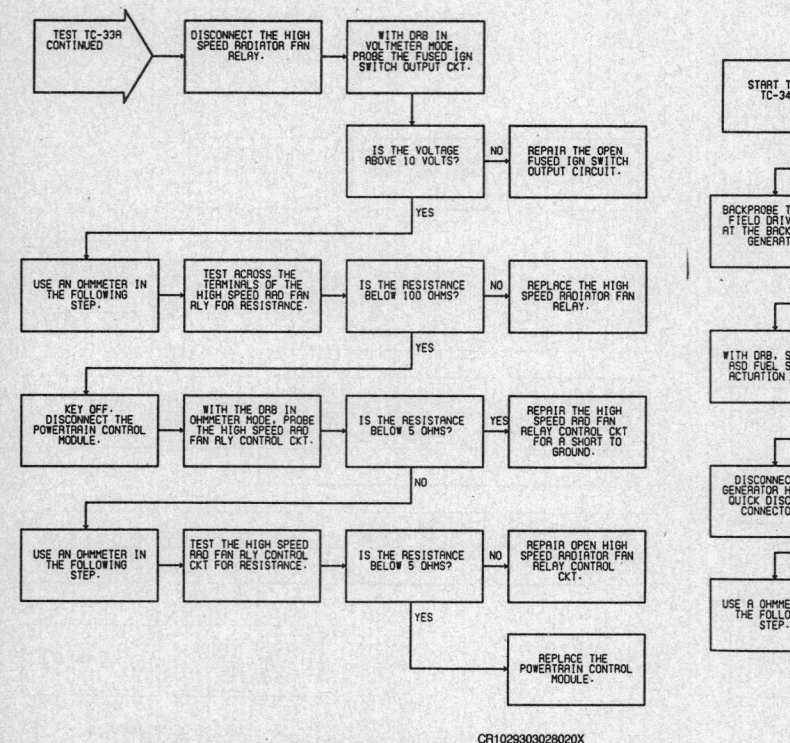

Fig. 58   Test TC-33A: High Speed Fan Control Relay Circuit (Part 2 of 2). 3.0L/V6-181 Engine

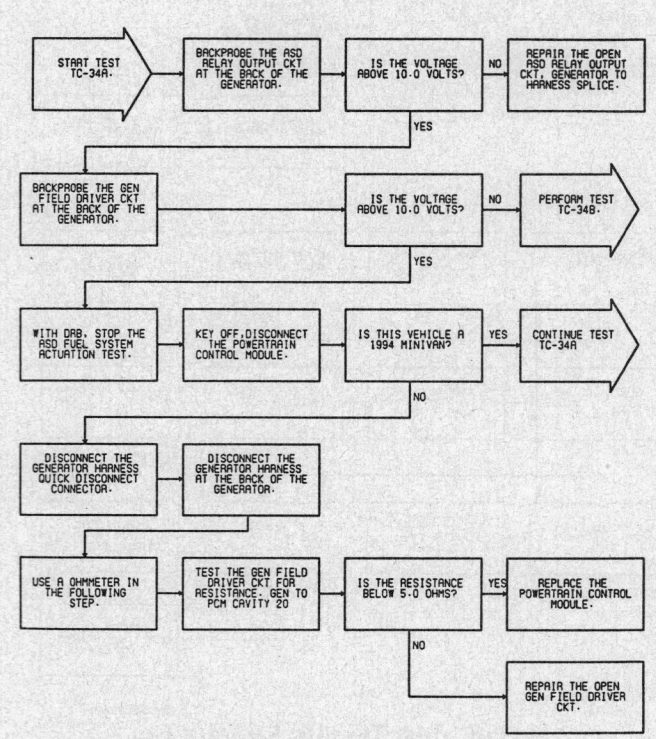

Fig. 59   Test TC-34A: Generator Field Not Switching Properly (Part 1 of 2). 3.0L/V6-181 Engine

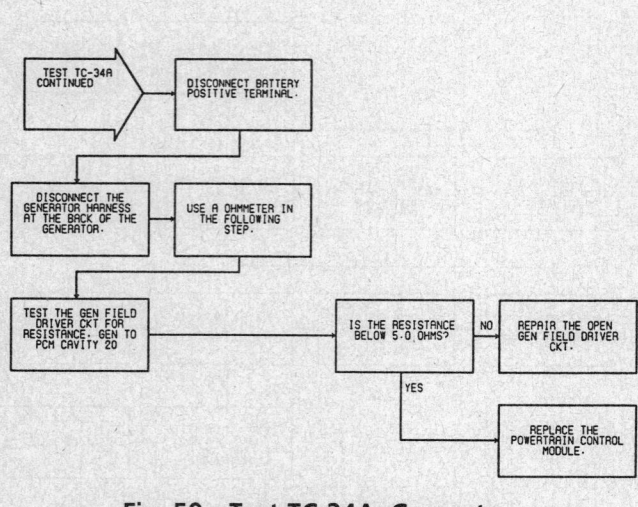

Fig. 59   Test TC-34A: Generator Field Not Switching Properly (Part 2 of 2). 3.0L/V6-181 Engine

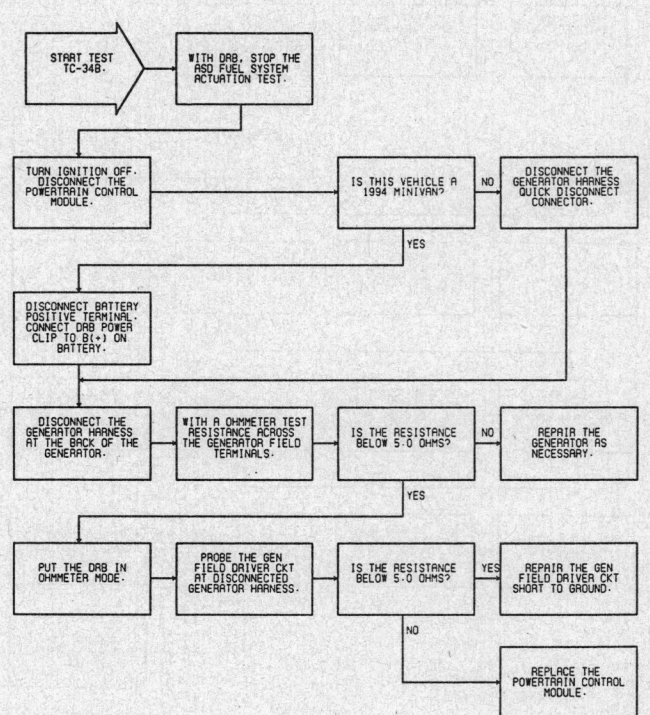

Fig. 60   Test TC-34B: Inspecting Field Driver Circuit For Shorts. 3.0L/V6-181 Engine

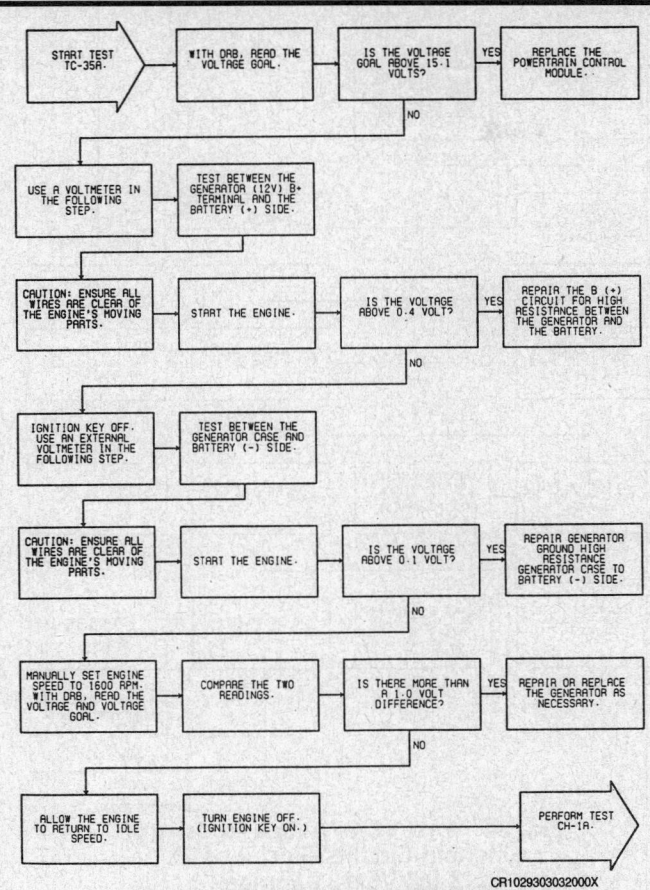

Fig. 61   Test TC-35A: Charging System Voltage Too Low. 3.0L/V6-181 Engine

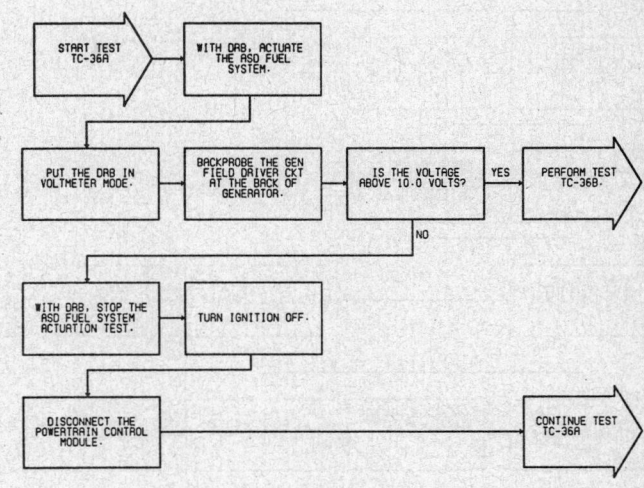

Fig. 62   Test TC-36A: Charging System Voltage Too High (Part 1 of 2). 3.0L/V6-181 Engine

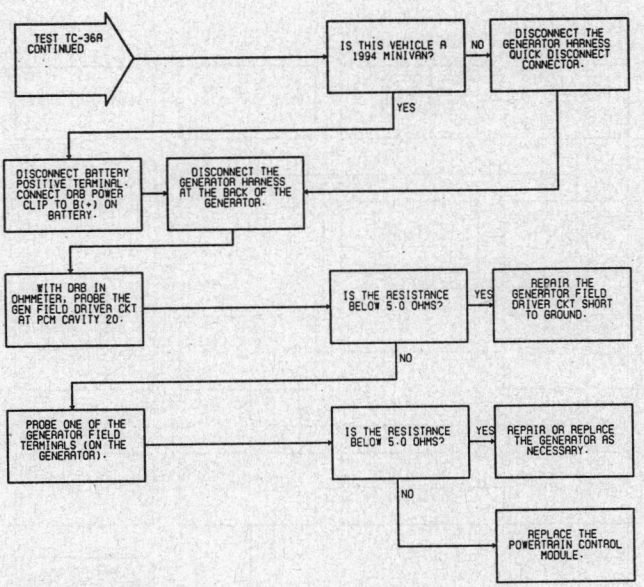

Fig. 62   Test TC-36A: Charging System Voltage Too High (Part 2 of 2). 3.0L/V6-181 Engine

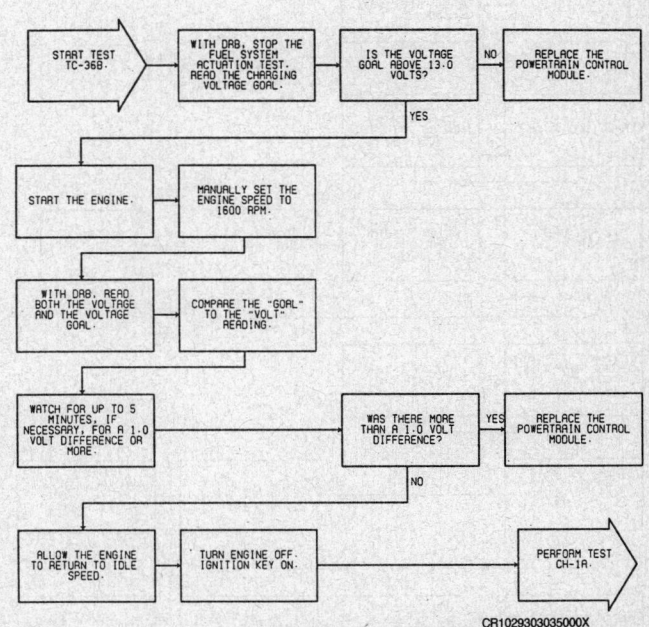

Fig. 63   Test TC-36B: Powertrain Control Module Regulating Circuit. 3.0L/V6-181 Engine

MODELS w/3.0L/V6-181, 3.3L/V6-201 & 3.8L/V6-231 ENGINES EXCEPT CONCORDE, INTREPID, LHS, STEALTH, VISION & 1994-96 NEW YORKER

12-49

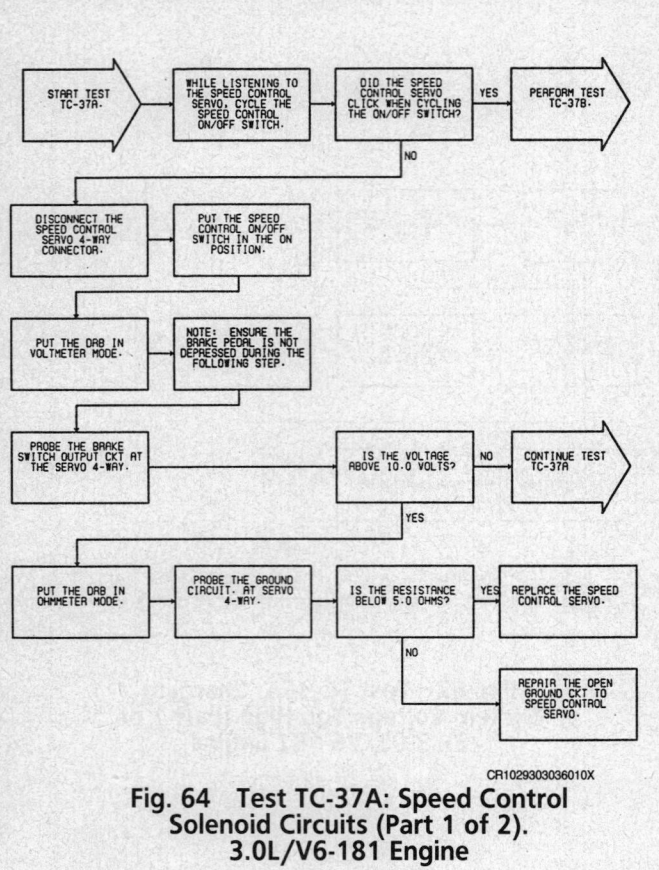

Fig. 64   Test TC-37A: Speed Control
Solenoid Circuits (Part 1 of 2).
3.0L/V6-181 Engine

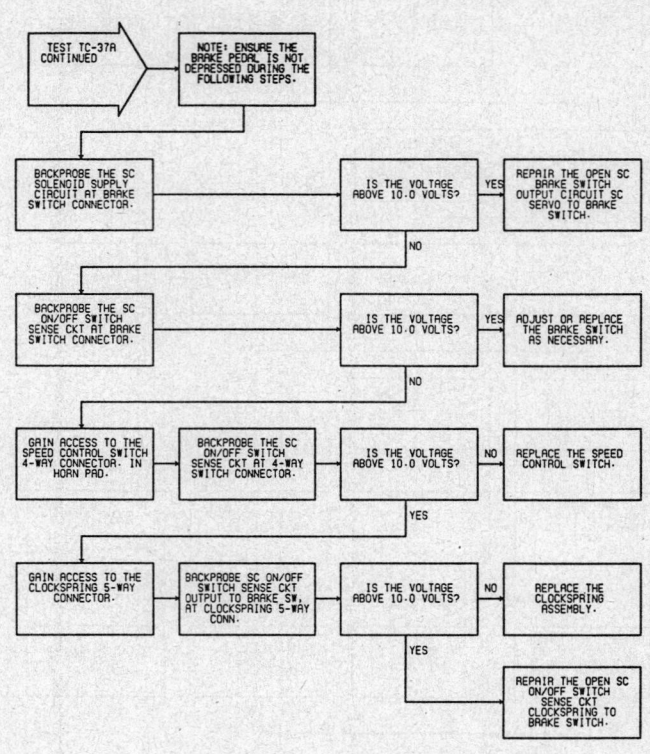

Fig. 64   Test TC-37A: Speed Control
Solenoid Circuits (Part 2 of 2).
3.0L/V6-181 Engine

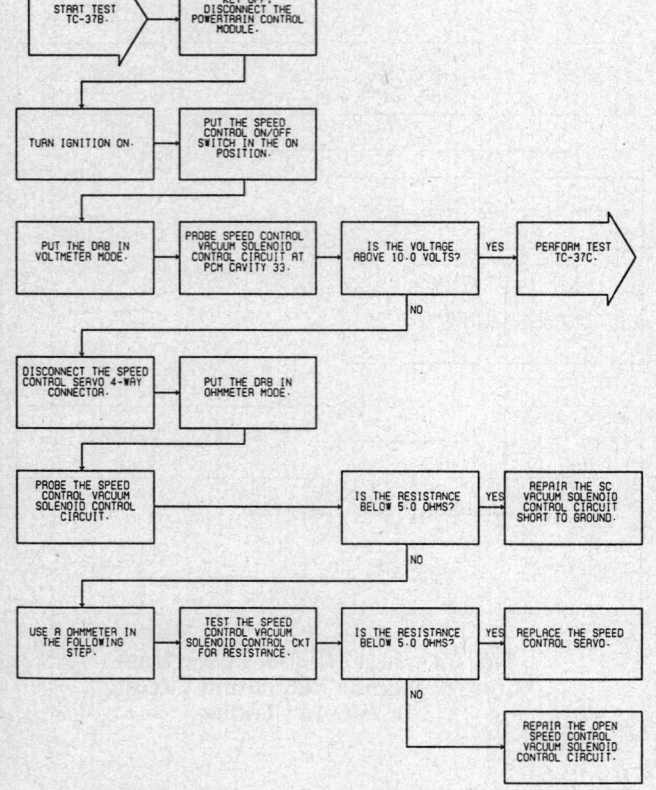

Fig. 65   Test TC-37B: Speed Control
Solenoid Circuits. 3.0L/V6-181 Engine

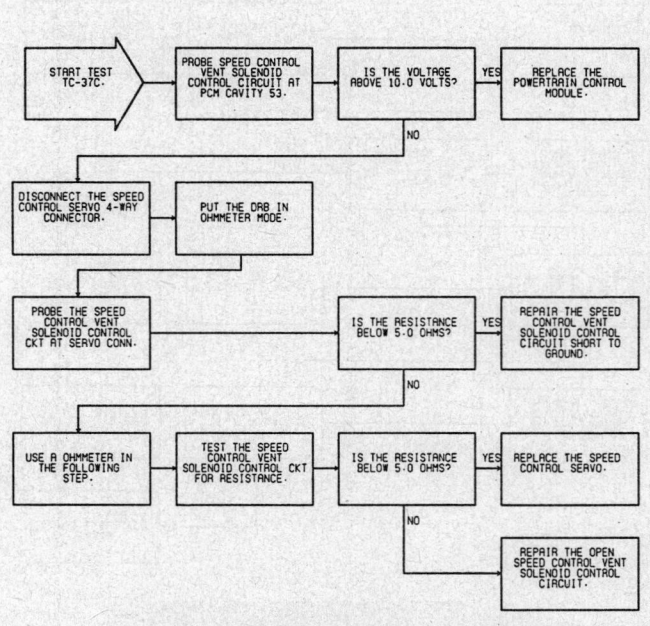

Fig. 66   Test TC-37C: Speed Control
Solenoid Circuits. 3.0L/V6-181 Engine

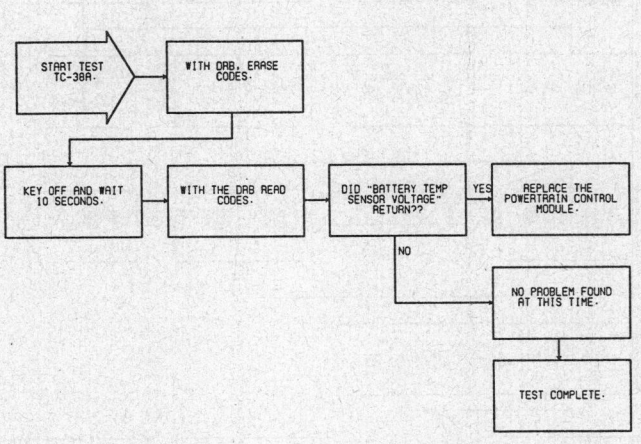

Fig. 67   Test TC-38A: Battery Temperature Sensor Circuit. 3.0L/V6-181 Engine

CR1029303039000X

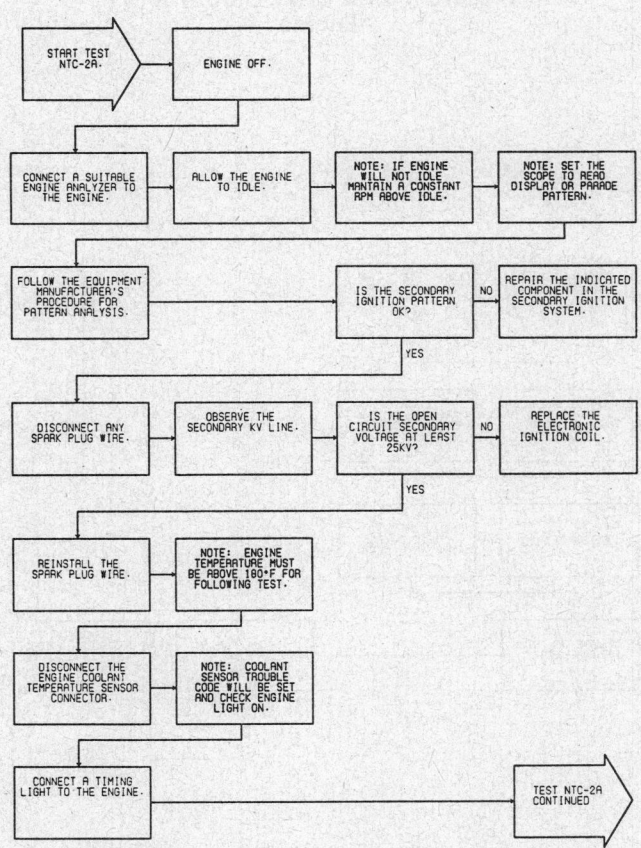

CR1029303041010X

Fig. 69   Test NTC-2A: Inspecting Secondary Ignition & Timing (Part 1 of 2). 3.0L/V6-181 Engine

---

TEST NTC-1A	NO TROUBLE CODE TEST MENU

Perform TEST TC-1A or TC-9A or TC-10A Before Proceeding

First, check all Technical Service Bulletins that relate to this driveability problem. Perform corrective actions if indicated; otherwise continue.

1. **NO TROUBLE CODE COMPLETE TEST** (non-monitored & monitored circuits)

Perform **TESTS NTC-2A** through **NTC-15A** in sequence until the driveability problem is found.

NO FAULT MENU

CHECKING SECONDARY IGNITION AND TIMING	NTC-2A
CHECKING THE FUEL PRESSURE	NTC-3A
CHECKING COOLANT SENSOR CALIBRATION AND RADIATOR FAN OPERATION	NTC-4A
CHECKING THROTTLE POSITION SENSOR CALIBRATION	NTC-5A
CHECKING MAP SENSOR CALIBRATION	NTC-6A
CHECKING FOR OXYGEN SENSOR SWITCHING	NTC-7A
CHECKING THE OXYGEN SENSOR HEATER	NTC-8A
CHECKING THE IDLE AIR CONTROL MOTOR	NTC-9A
CHECKING SOLENOID OPERATION	NTC-10A
CHECKING THE PARK/NEUTRAL POSITION SWITCH	NTC-11A
CHECKING THE PCM POWER AND GROUND CIRCUITS	NTC-12A
CHECKING THE ENGINE VACUUM	NTC-13A
CHECKING THE MINIMUM IDLE AIR FLOW	NTC-14A
CHECKING THE ENGINE MECHANICAL SYSTEMS	NTC-15A

2. **NO TROUBLE CODE QUICK INDIVIDUAL TEST** (individual test only)

If you suspect any of the above items to be the cause of the vehicle's driveability problem, perform the associated test(s) individually. **Return to No Trouble Code Menu if driveability problem still exists, or perform No Trouble Code Complete Test.**

3. **NO TROUBLE CODE QUICK SYMPTOM TEST** (symptom test only)

Symptom checks cannot be used properly unless the driveability problem characteristic actually happens while the vehicle is being tested. To reduce diagnostic time, ensure that TC-1A and appropriate sections have been reviewed before attempting to diagnose a symptom.

Select the symptom that most accurately describes the vehicle's driveability problem and then perform the test routine that pertains to this symptom. Perform each routine test in sequence until the problem is found.

SYMPTOM	DIAGNOSTIC TEST ROUTINE
HARD START	NTC-2A, 3A, 4A, 5A, 6A, 7A, 9A, 12A, 13A, 14A, 15A
START AND STALL	NTC-2A, 3A, 4A, 5A, 6A, 9A, 12A, 15A
HESITATION/SAG/STUMBLE	NO TROUBLE CODE COMPLETE TEST (STEP 1)
SURGE	NTC-2A, 3A, 4A, 5A, 6A, 7A, 9A, 12A, 15A
LACK OF POWER/SLUGGISH	NTC-2A, 3A, 4A, 5A, 6A, 7A, 9A, 12A, 14A, 15A
SPARK KNOCK/DETONATION	NTC-2A, 3A, 4A, 5A, 6A, 7A, 9A, 10A, 12A, 15A
CUTS OUT/MISSES	NTC-2A, 3A, 7A, 10A, 12A, 14A, 15A
BACKFIRE/POPBACK	NTC-2A, 3A, 6A, 7A, 12A, 14A, 15A
RUNS ROUGH/UNSTABLE/ERRATIC IDLE	NO TROUBLE CODE COMPLETE TEST (STEP 1)
POOR FUEL ECONOMY	NO TROUBLE CODE COMPLETE TEST (STEP 1)

Fig. 68   Test NTC-1A: No Trouble Code Test Menu. 3.0L/V6-181 Engine

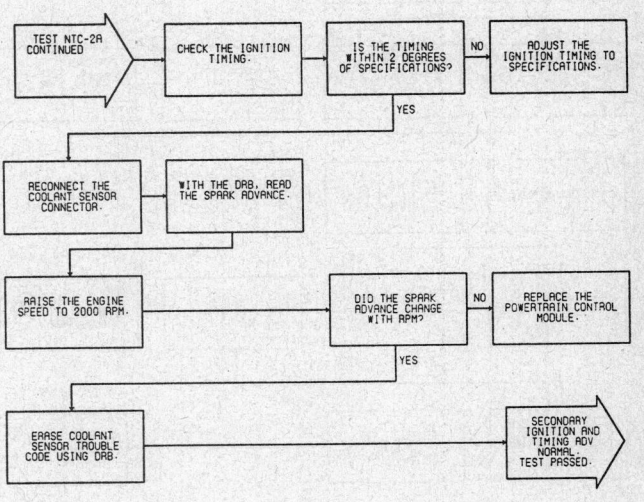

CR1029303041020X

Fig. 69   Test NTC-2A: Inspecting Secondary Ignition & Timing (Part 2 of 2). 3.0L/V6-181 Engine

---

MODELS w/3.0L/V6-181, 3.3L/V6-201 & 3.8L/V6-231 ENGINES EXCEPT CONCORDE, INTREPID, LHS, STEALTH, VISION & 1994-96 NEW YORKER

12-51

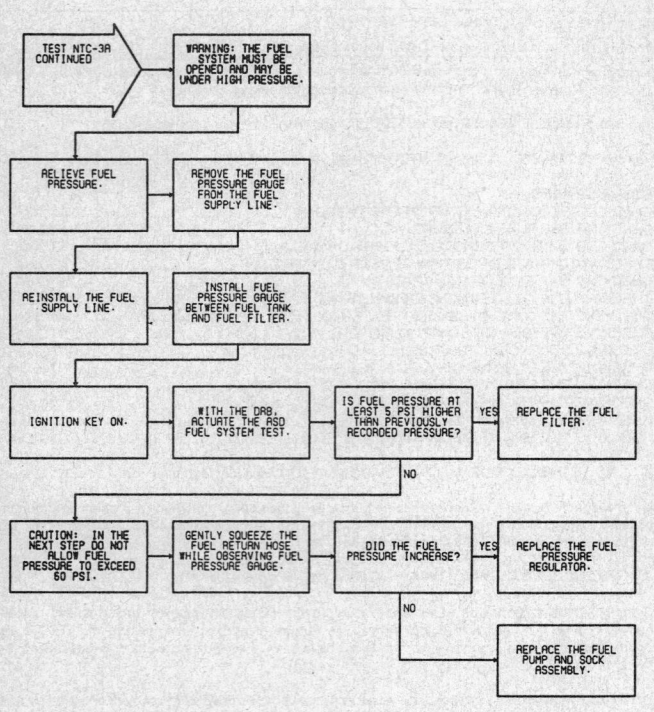

Fig. 70   Test NTC-3A: Inspecting Fuel Pressure (Part 1 of 2). 3.0L/V6-181 Engine

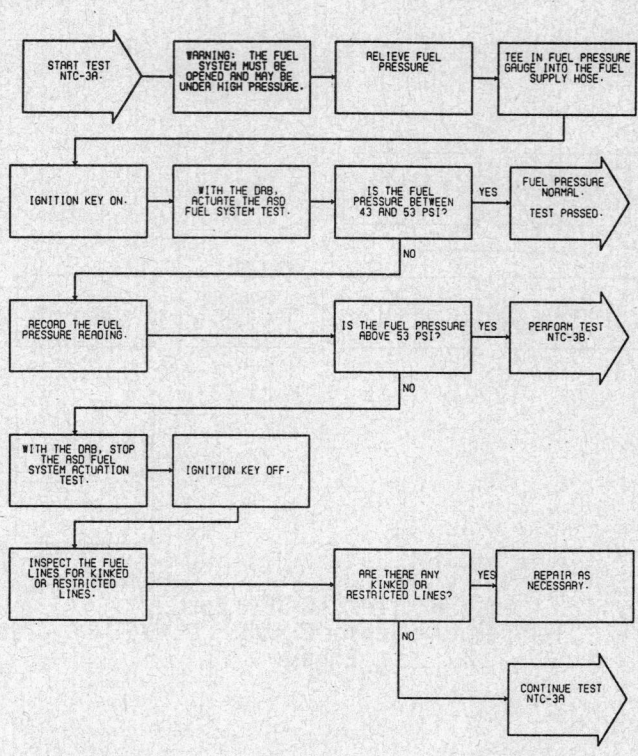

Fig. 70   Test NTC-3A: Inspecting Fuel Pressure (Part 2 of 2). 3.0L/V6-181 Engine

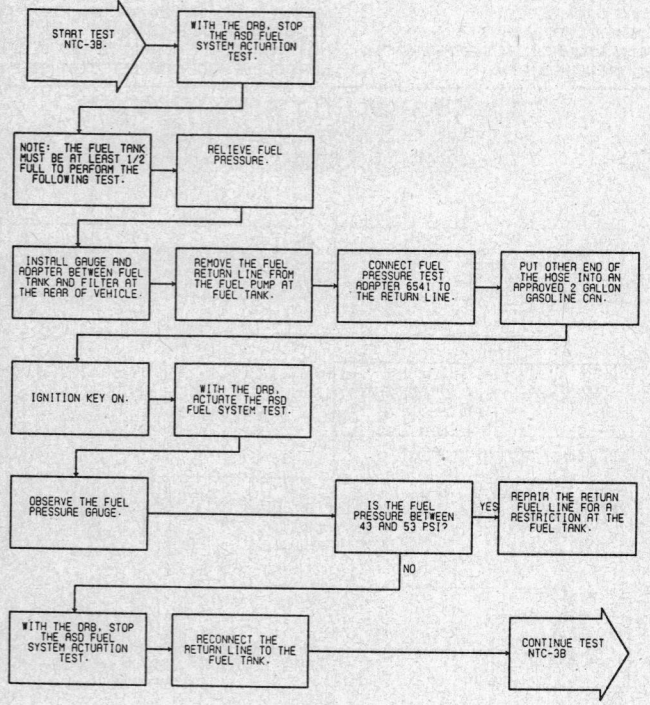

Fig. 71   Test NTC-3B: Inspecting Fuel Pressure (Part 1 of 2). 3.0L/V6-181 Engine

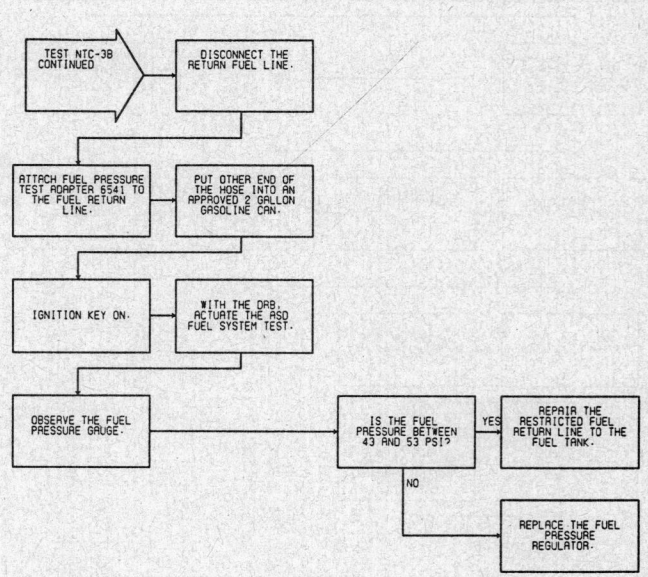

Fig. 71   Test NTC-3B: Inspecting Fuel Pressure (Part 2 of 2). 3.0L/V6-181 Engine

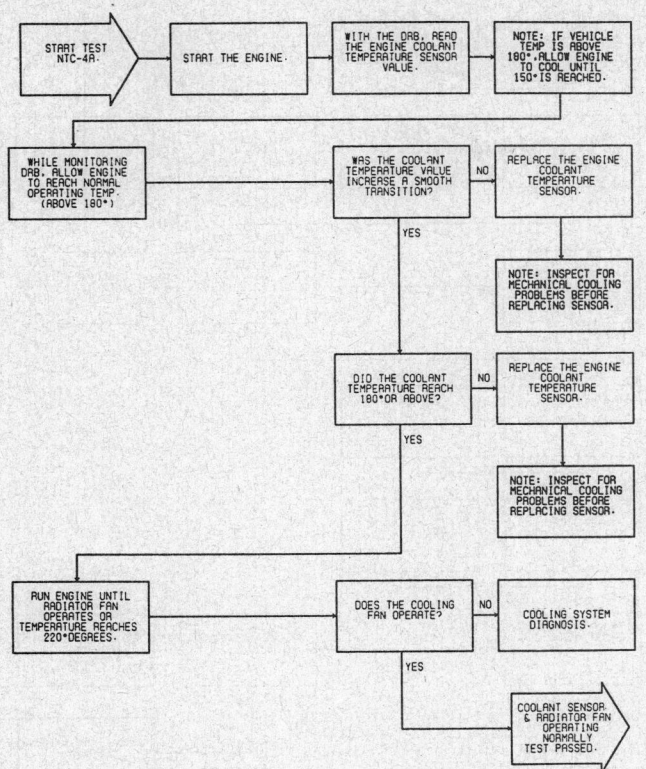

Fig. 72   Test NTC-4A: Inspecting Coolant Sensor Calibration & Radiator Fan Operation. 3.0L/V6-181 Engine

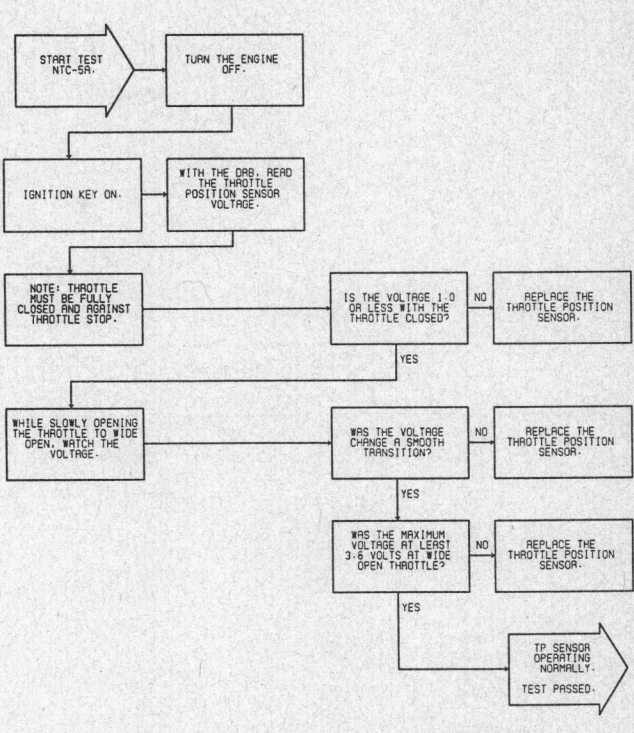

Fig. 73   Test NTC-5A: Inspecting TP Sensor Calibration. 3.0L/V6-181 Engine

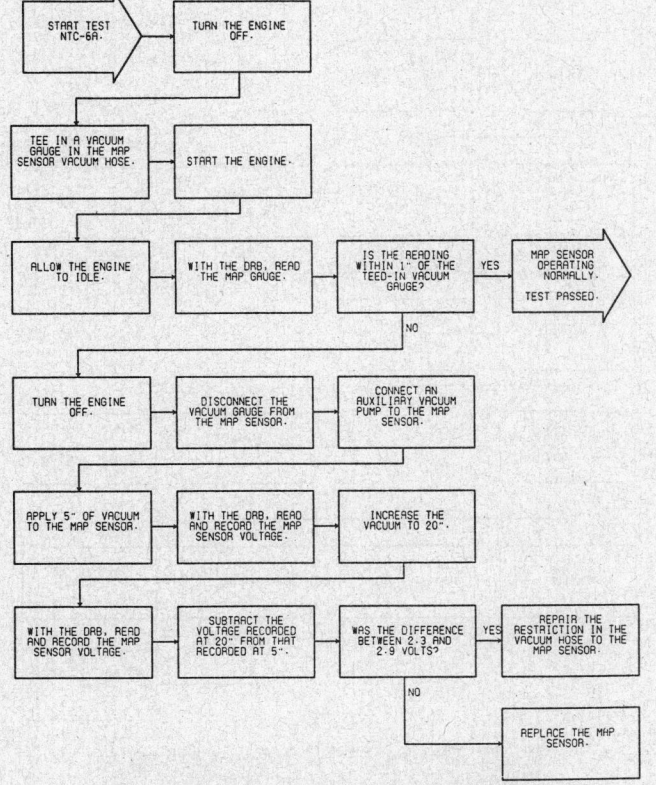

Fig. 74   Test NTC-6A: Inspecting MAP Sensor Calibration. 3.0L/V6-181 Engine

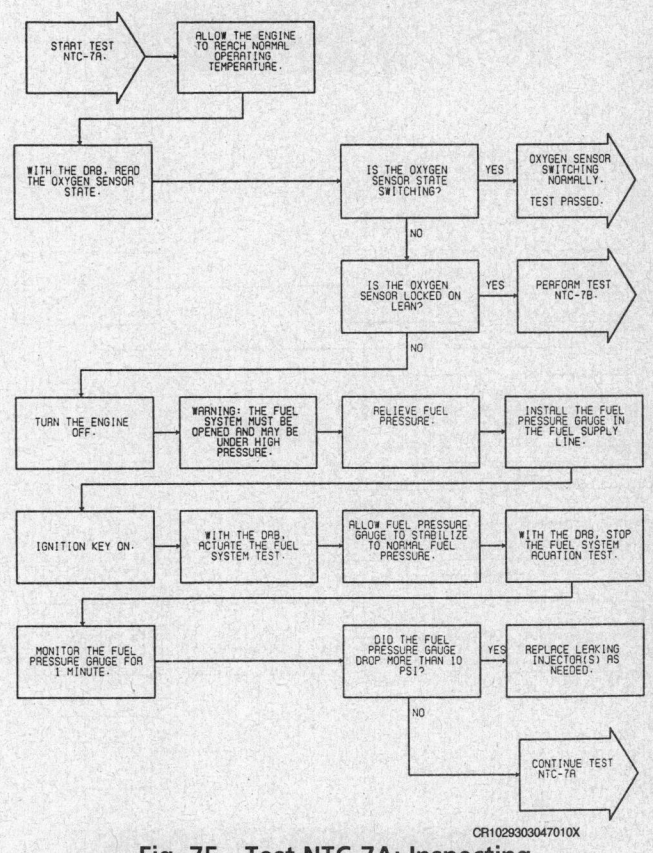

Fig. 75   Test NTC-7A: Inspecting Oxygen Sensor Switching (Part 1 of 2). 3.0L/V6-181 Engine

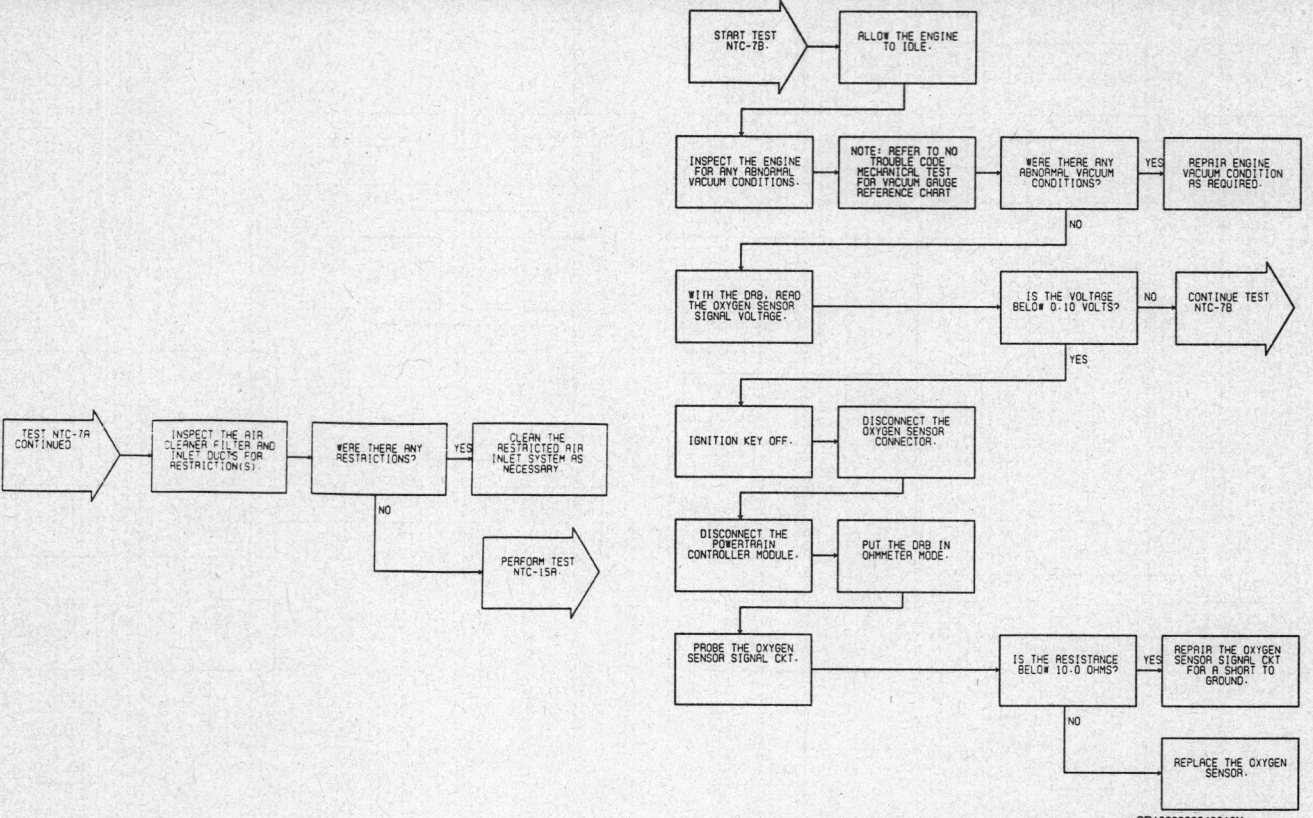

Fig. 76   Test NTC-7B: Inspecting Oxygen Sensor Switching (Part 1 of 2). 3.0L/V6-181 Engine

Fig. 75   Test NTC-7A: Inspecting Oxygen Sensor Switching (Part 2 of 2). 3.0L/V6-181 Engine

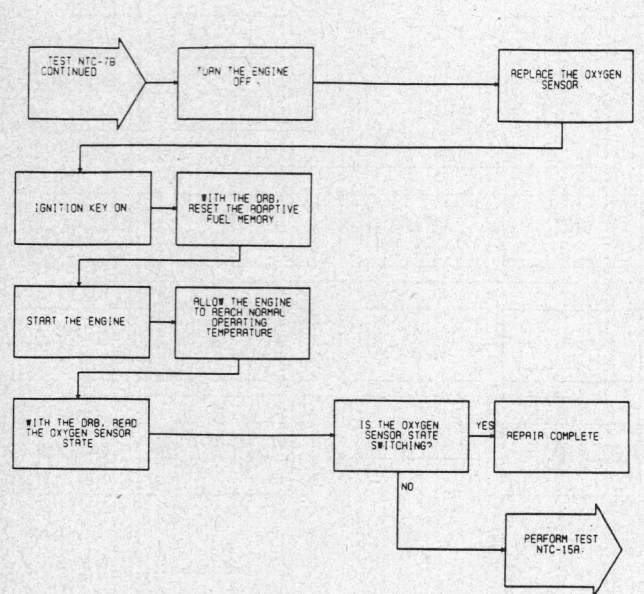

Fig. 76   Test NTC-7B: Inspecting Oxygen Sensor Switching (Part 2 of 2). 3.0L/V6-181 Engine

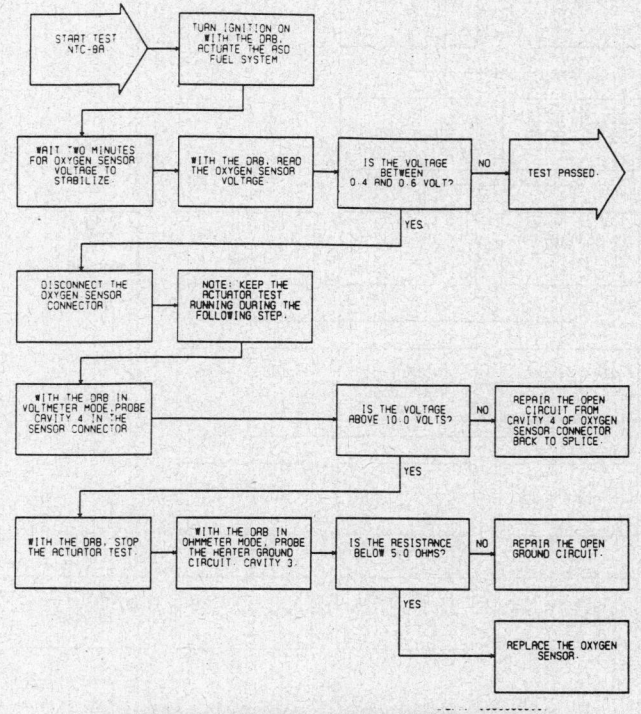

Fig. 77   Test NTC-8A: Inspecting Oxygen Sensor Heater. 3.0L/V6-181 Engine

12-54

MODELS w/3.0L/V6-181, 3.3L/V6-201 & 3.8L/V6-231 ENGINES EXCEPT CONCORDE, INTREPID, LHS, STEALTH, VISION & 1994-96 NEW YORKER

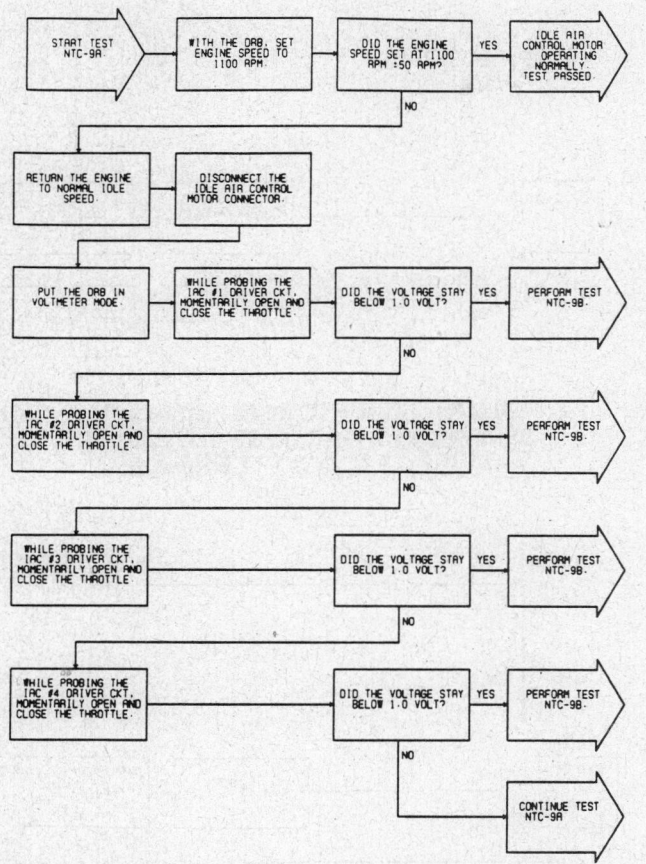

Fig. 78   Test NTC-9A: Inspecting Idle Air Control Motor (Part 1 of 2). 3.0L/V6-181 Engine

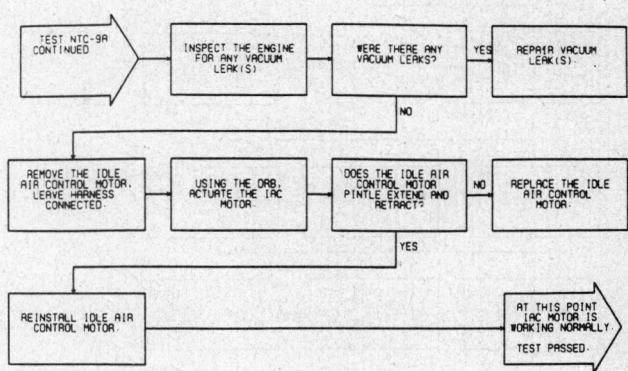

Fig. 78   Test NTC-9A: Inspecting Idle Air Control Motor (Part 2 of 2). 3.0L/V6-181 Engine

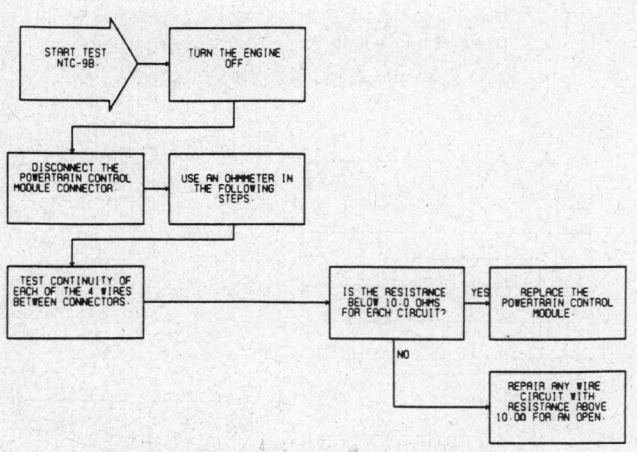

Fig. 79   Test NTC-9B: Inspecting Idle Air Control Motor. 3.0L/V6-181 Engine

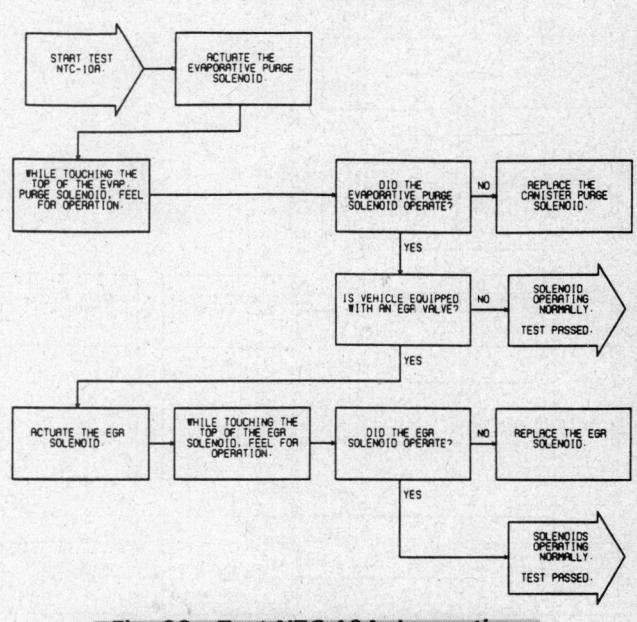

Fig. 80   Test NTC-10A: Inspecting Solenoid Operations. 3.0L/V6-181 Engine

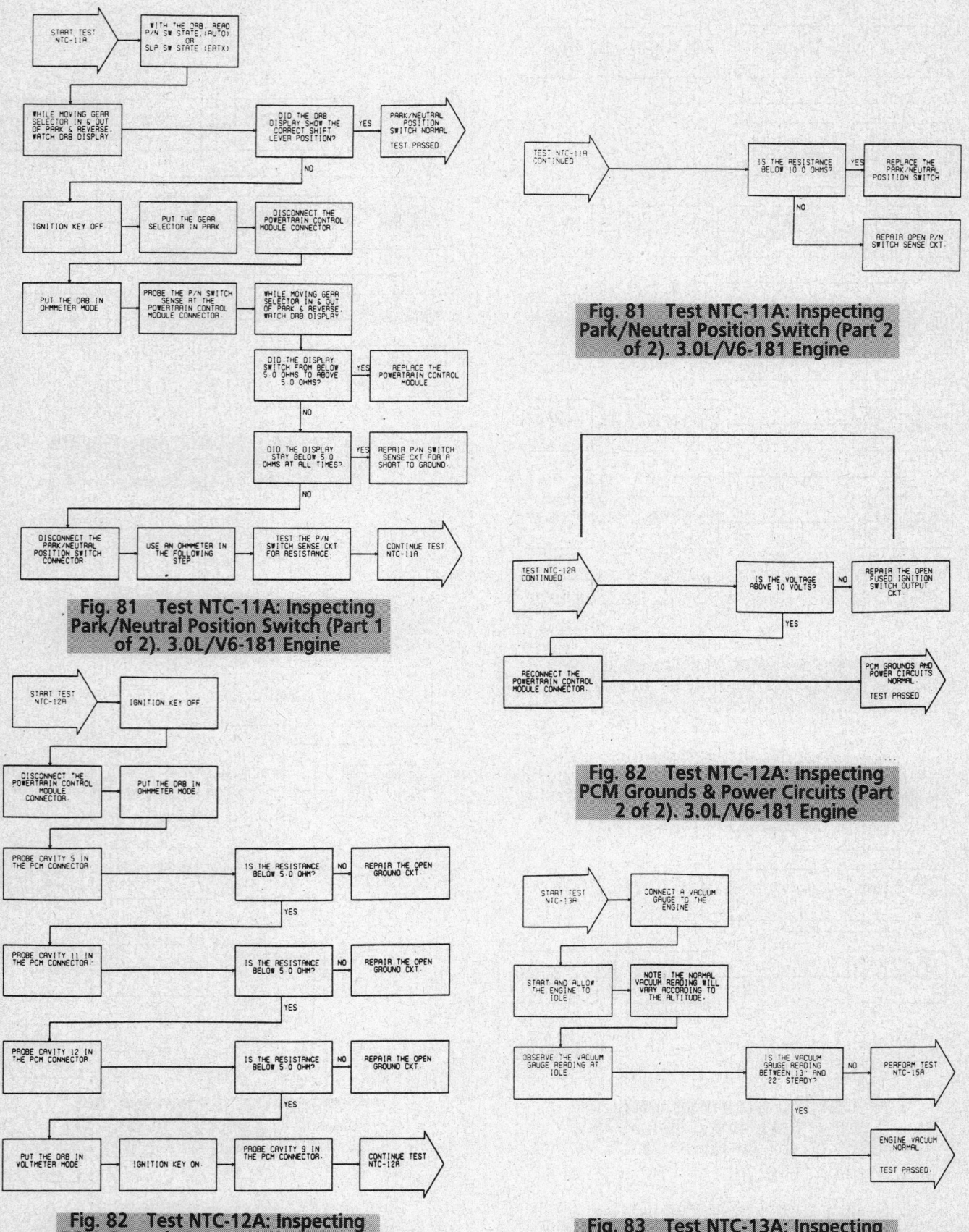

Fig. 81 Test NTC-11A: Inspecting Park/Neutral Position Switch (Part 1 of 2). 3.0L/V6-181 Engine

Fig. 81 Test NTC-11A: Inspecting Park/Neutral Position Switch (Part 2 of 2). 3.0L/V6-181 Engine

Fig. 82 Test NTC-12A: Inspecting PCM Grounds & Power Circuits (Part 1 of 2). 3.0L/V6-181 Engine

Fig. 82 Test NTC-12A: Inspecting PCM Grounds & Power Circuits (Part 2 of 2). 3.0L/V6-181 Engine

Fig. 83 Test NTC-13A: Inspecting Engine Vacuum. 3.0L/V6-181 Engine

12-56

MODELS w/3.0L/V6-181, 3.3L/V6-201 & 3.8L/V6-231 ENGINES EXCEPT CONCORDE, INTREPID, LHS, STEALTH, VISION &
1994-96 NEW YORKER

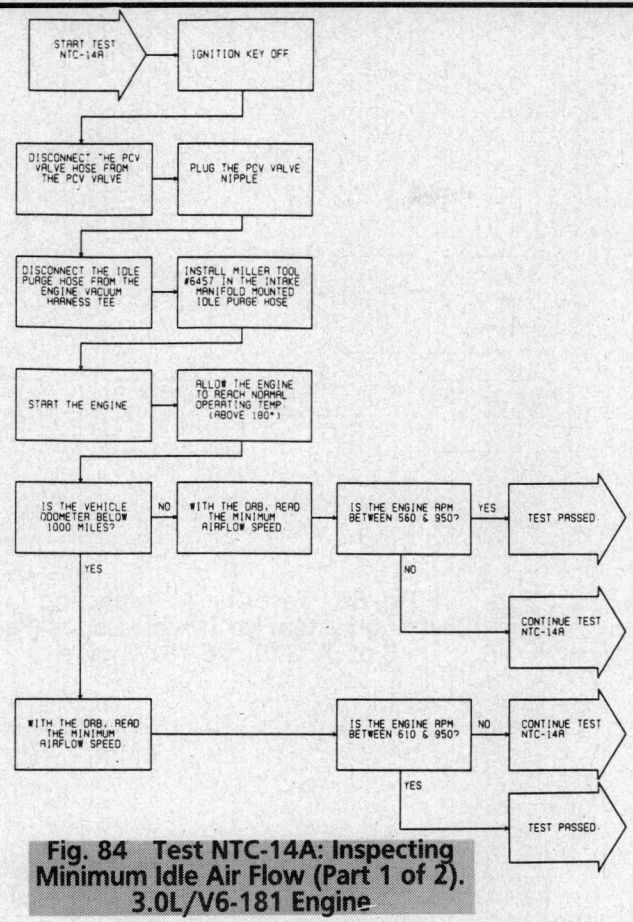

Fig. 84 Test NTC-14A: Inspecting Minimum Idle Air Flow (Part 1 of 2). 3.0L/V6-181 Engine

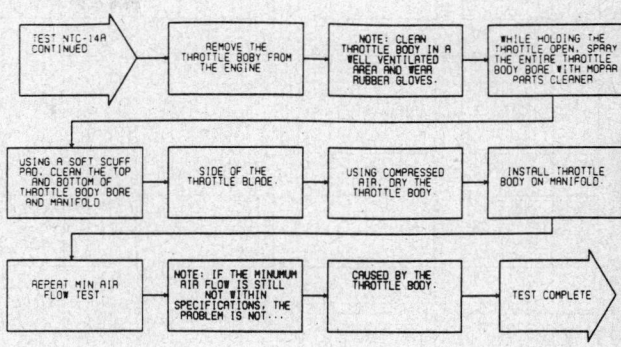

Fig. 84 Test NTC-14A: Inspecting Minimum Idle Air Flow (Part 2 of 2). 3.0L/V6-181 Engine

At this point in the diagnostic test procedure, you have determined that all of the **engine electrical systems** are operating as designed; therefore, they **are not the cause of the driveability problem.** The following additional items should be checked as possible mechanical causes of the problem:

1. **ENGINE VACUUM** - must be at least 13 inches in neutral *(see below)* †

2. **ENGINE VALVE TIMING** - must be within specifications

3. **ENGINE COMPRESSION** - must be within specifications

4. **ENGINE EXHAUST SYSTEM** - must be free of any restrictions

5. **ENGINE PCV SYSTEM** - must flow freely

6. **ENGINE DRIVE SPROCKET** - must be properly positioned

7. **TORQUE CONVERTER STALL SPEED** - must be within specifications

8. **POWER BRAKE BOOSTER** - no internal vacuum leaks

9. **FUEL** - must be free of contamination

10. **FUEL INJECTOR** - plugged or restricted injector; control wire not connected to correct injector

NOTE: If you came to this test from the oxygen sensor, and the rich or lean condition is not caused by one of the first items above, replace the powertrain control module and perform TEST VER-2A (Road Test Verification).

† The readings below are only indicators of possible mechanical engine problems.

NORMAL READING RANGE AT IDLE

BLOWN HEAD GASKET AT IDLE

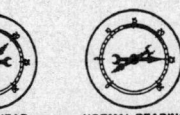
NORMAL READING (RAPID ACCELERATION/ DECELERATION)

WORN RINGS OR DILUTED OIL RAPID ACCELERATION/ DECELERATION

LATE VALVE TIMING, VACUUM LEAK AT IDLE

RESTRICTED EXHAUST (DROPS TOWARDS ZERO AS ENGINE RPM INCREASES)

POOR VALVE SEATING AT IDLE

STICKING VALVE AT IDLE

WORN VALVE GUIDES (STEADIES AS ENGINE SPEED INCREASES)

WORN VALVE SPRINGS (MORE PRONOUNCED AS ENGINE SPEED INCREASES)

Fig. 85 Test NTC-15A: Performing No Trouble Code Mechanical Test. 3.0L/V6-181 Engine

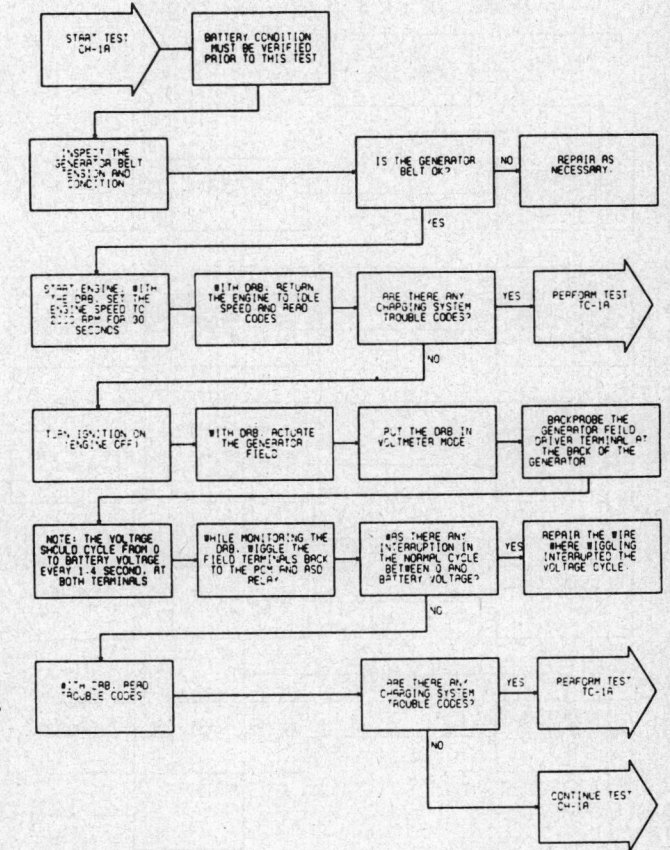

CR1029303057010X

Fig. 86 Test CH-1A: Inspecting Charging System No Trouble Codes (Part 1 of 3). 3.0L/V6-181 Engine

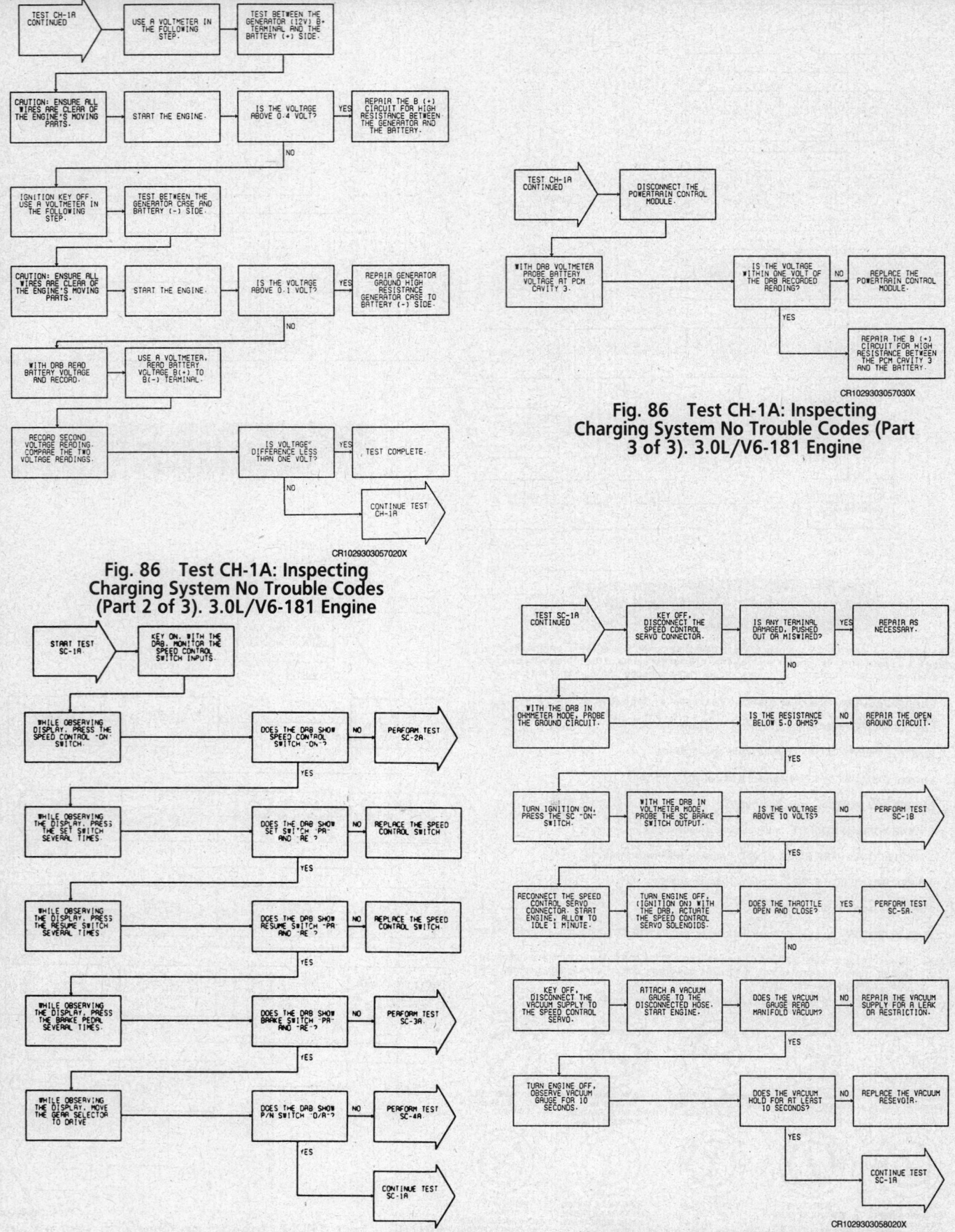

Fig. 86 Test CH-1A: Inspecting Charging System No Trouble Codes (Part 3 of 3). 3.0L/V6-181 Engine

Fig. 86 Test CH-1A: Inspecting Charging System No Trouble Codes (Part 2 of 3). 3.0L/V6-181 Engine

Fig. 87 Test SC-1A: Inspecting Speed Control System (Part 1 of 3). 3.0L/V6-181 Engine

Fig. 87 Test SC-1A: Inspecting Speed Control System (Part 2 of 3). 3.0L/V6-181 Engine

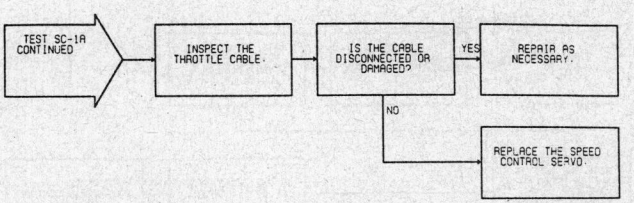

Fig. 87   Test SC-1A: Inspecting Speed Control System (Part 3 of 3). 3.0L/V6-181 Engine

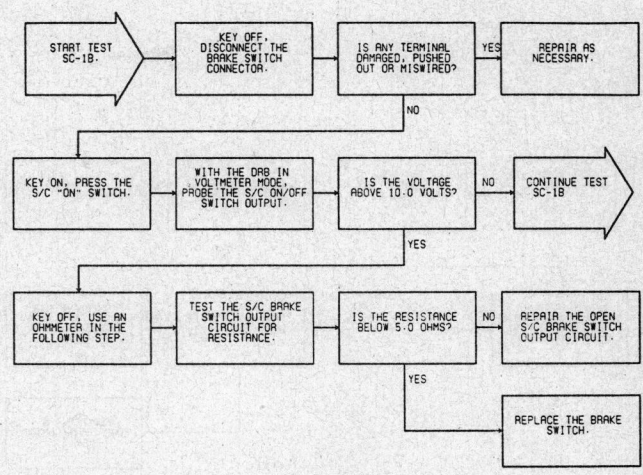

Fig. 88   Test SC-1B: Inspecting Speed Control System (Part 1 of 2). 3.0L/V6-181 Engine

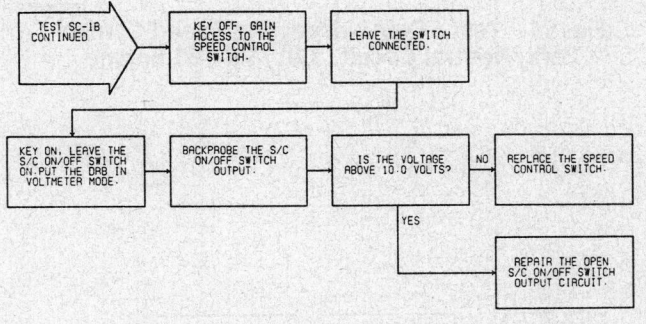

Fig. 88   Test SC-1B: Inspecting Speed Control System (Part 2 of 2). 3.0L/V6-181 Engine

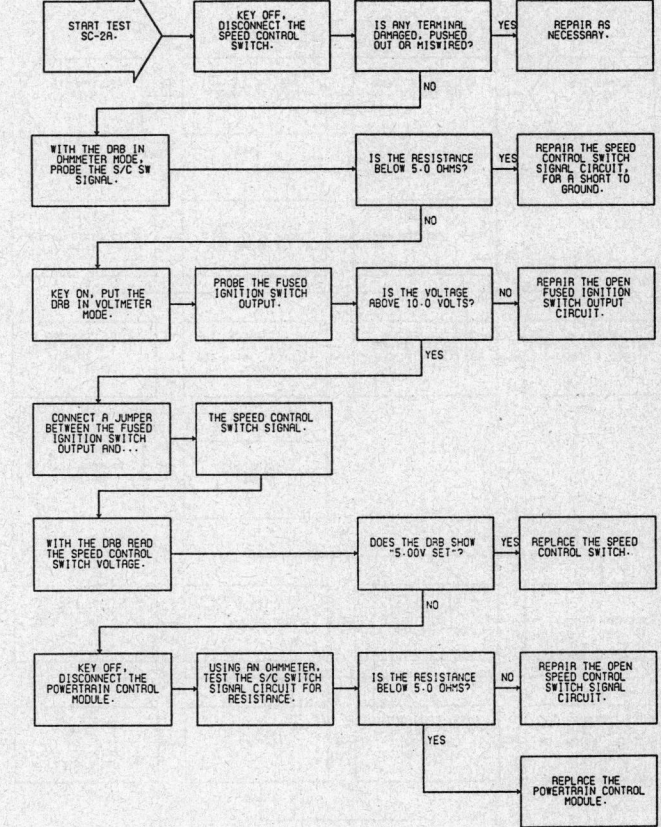

Fig. 89   Test SC-2A: Inspecting Speed Control Switch Signal Circuit. 3.0L/V6-181 Engine

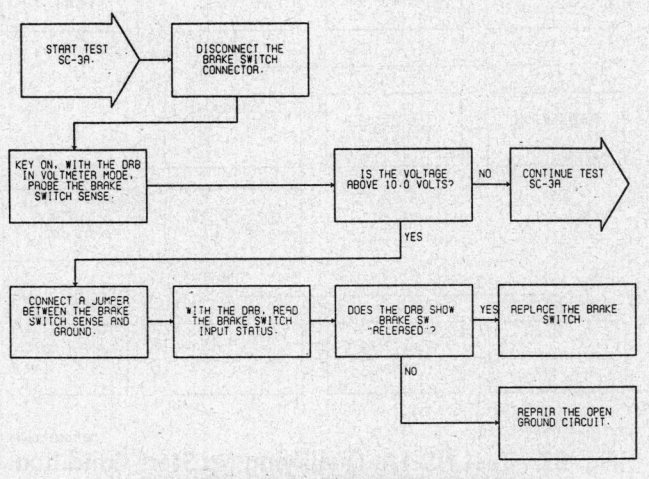

Fig. 90   Test SC-3A: Inspecting Speed Control Brake Switch (Part 1 of 2). 3.0L/V6-181 Engine

MODELS w/3.0L/V6-181, 3.3L/V6-201 & 3.8L/V6-231 ENGINES EXCEPT CONCORDE, INTREPID, LHS, STEALTH, VISION & 1994-96 NEW YORKER

12-59

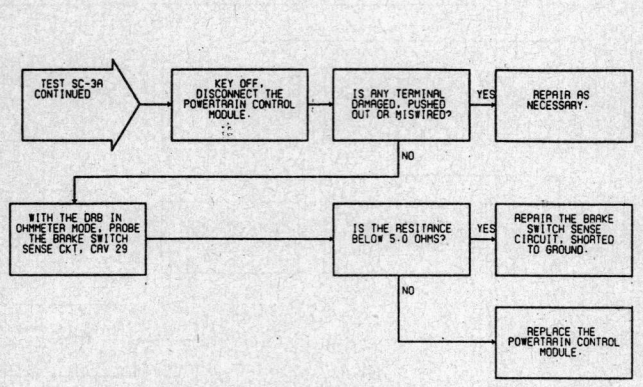

Fig. 90 Test SC-3A: Inspecting Speed Control Brake Switch (Part 2 of 2). 3.0L/V6-181 Engine

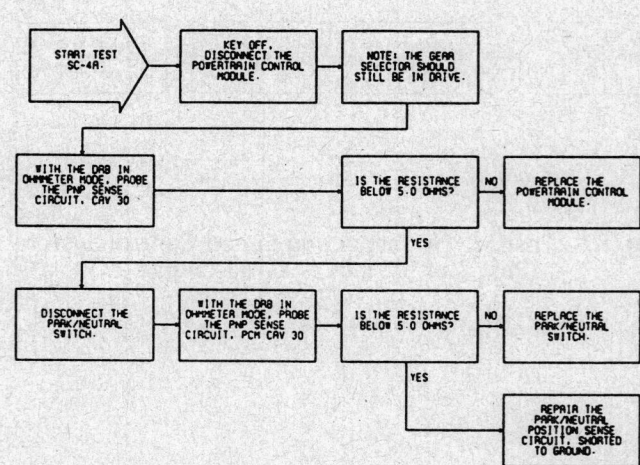

CR1029303063000X

Fig. 91 Test SC-4A: Inspecting Speed Control Park/Neutral Circuit. 3.0L/V6-181 Engine

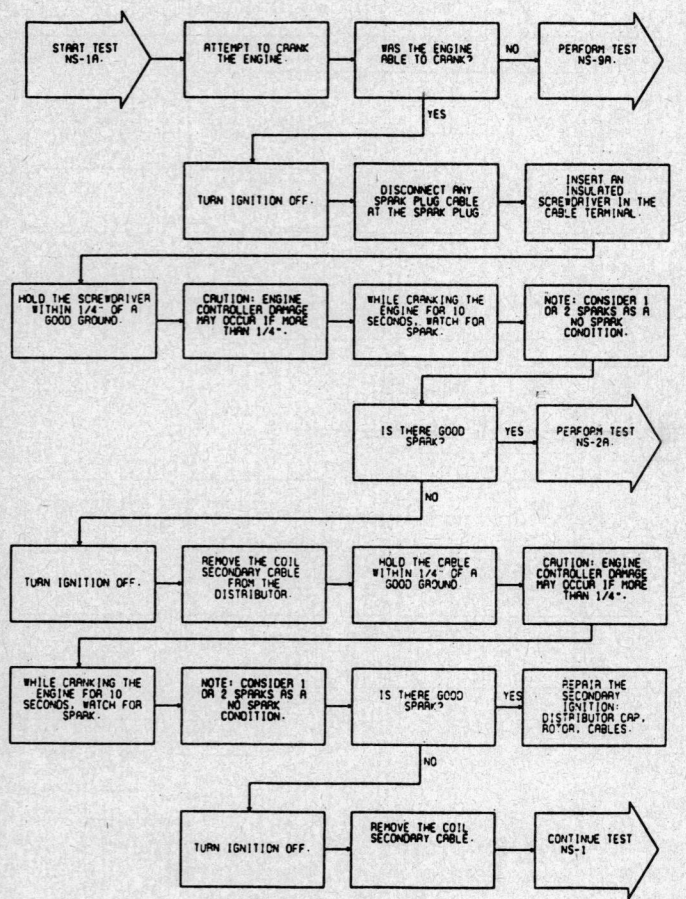

CR1029303064010X

Fig. 92 Test NS-1A: Qualifying No Start Condition (Part 1 of 4). 3.0L/V6-181 Engine

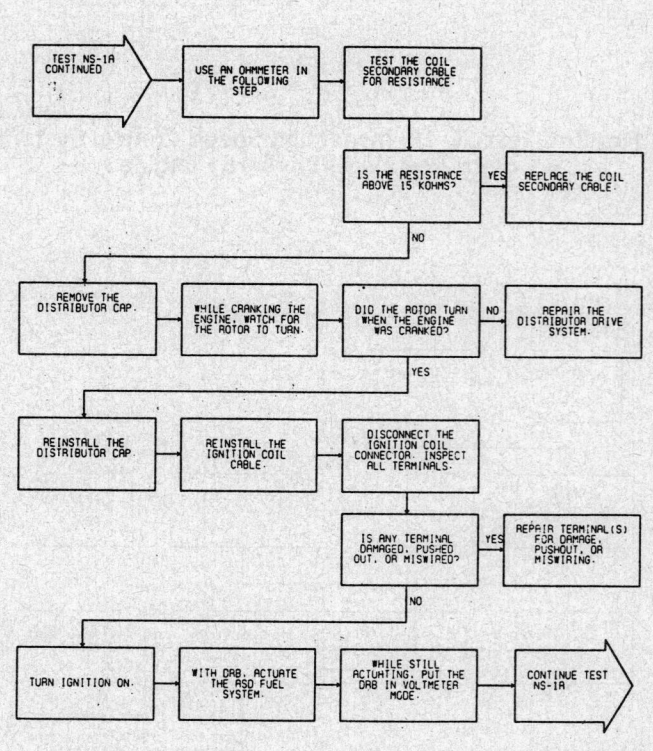

CR1029303064020X

Fig. 92 Test NS-1A: Qualifying No Start Condition (Part 2 of 4). 3.0L/V6-181 Engine

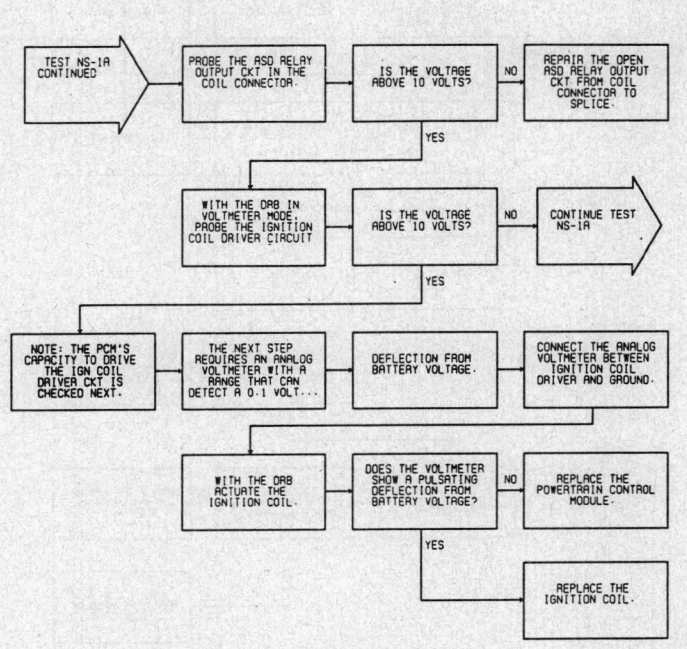

Fig. 92   Test NS-1A: Qualifying No Start Condition (Part 3 of 4). 3.0L/V6-181 Engine

Fig. 92   Test NS-1A: Qualifying No Start Condition (Part 4 of 4). 3.0L/V6-181 Engine

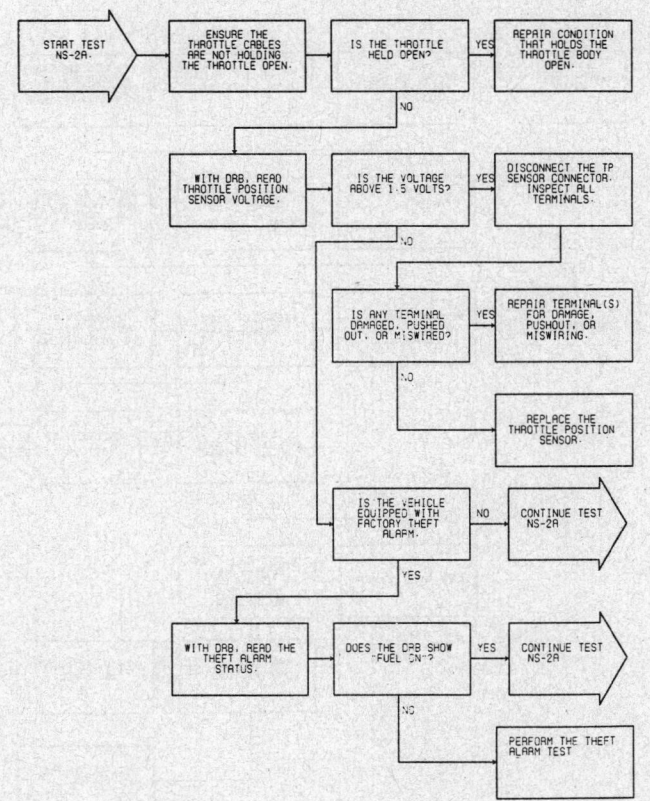

Fig. 93   Test NS-2A: Inspecting Fuel System (Part 1 of 2). 3.0L/V6-181 Engine

CR1029303065010X

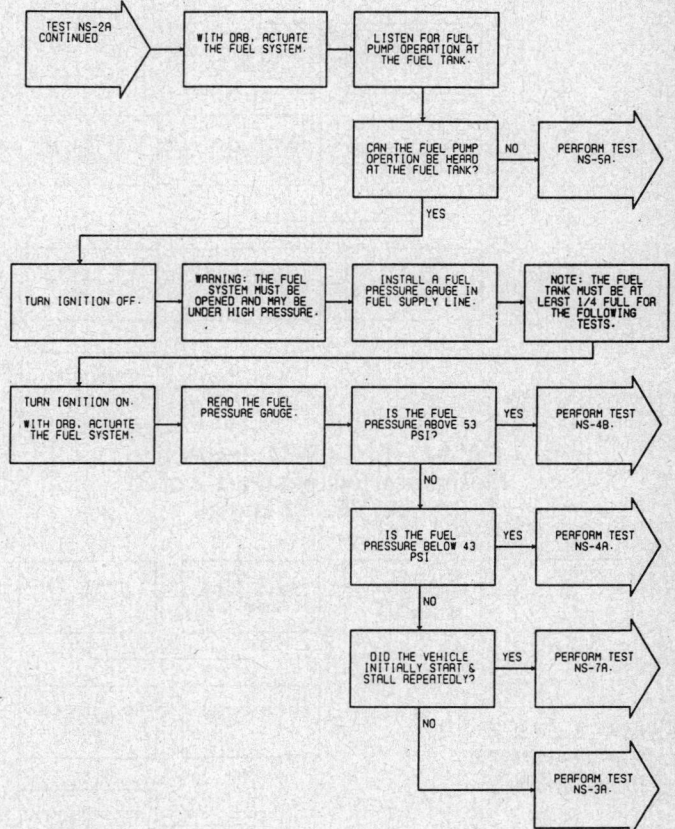

Fig. 93   Test NS-2A: Inspecting Fuel System (Part 2 of 2). 3.0L/V6-181 Engine

MODELS w/3.0L/V6-181, 3.3L/V6-201 & 3.8L/V6-231 ENGINES EXCEPT CONCORDE, INTREPID, LHS, STEALTH, VISION & 1994-96 NEW YORKER

12-61

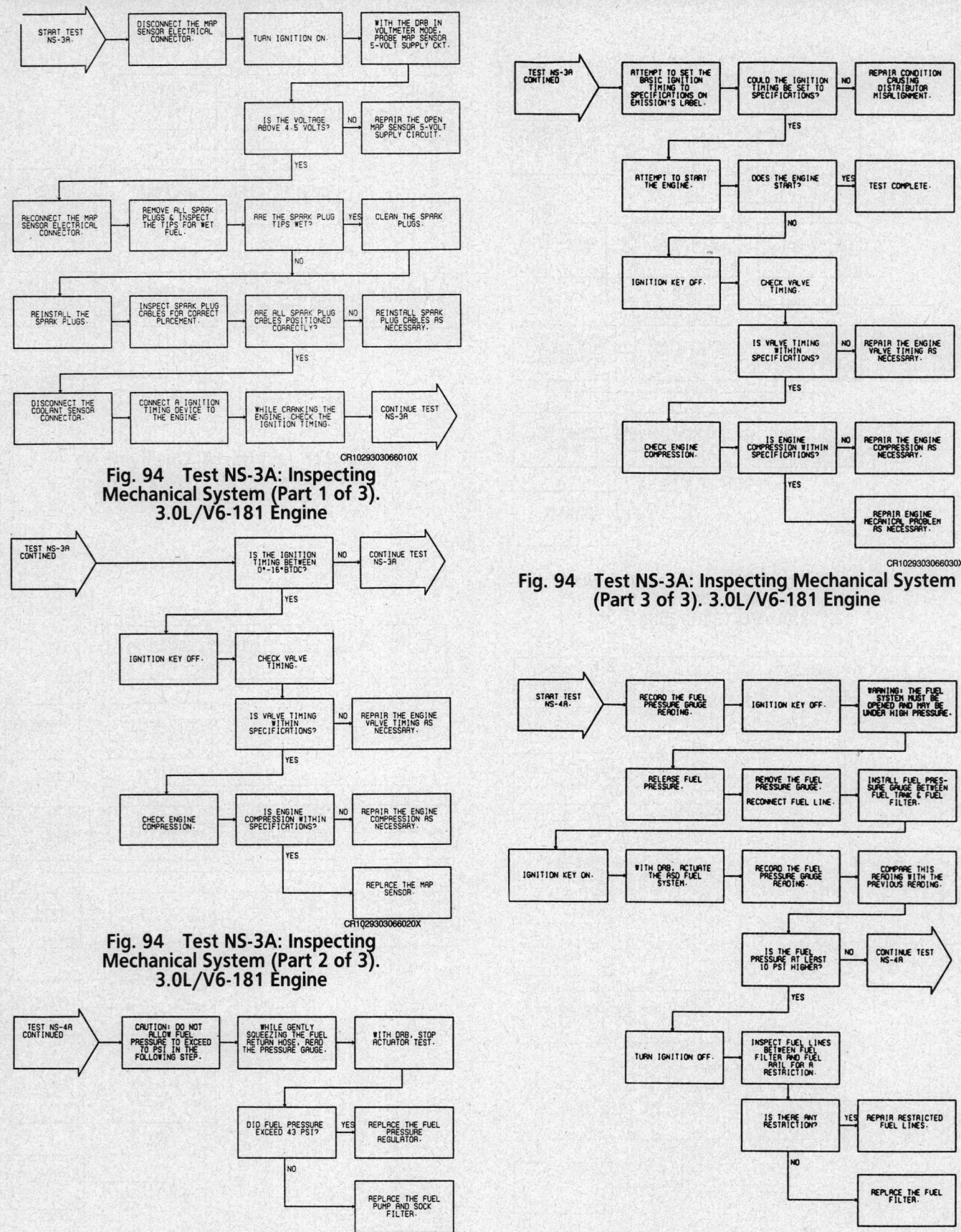

Fig. 94   Test NS-3A: Inspecting
Mechanical System (Part 1 of 3).
3.0L/V6-181 Engine

Fig. 94   Test NS-3A: Inspecting
Mechanical System (Part 2 of 3).
3.0L/V6-181 Engine

Fig. 94   Test NS-3A: Inspecting Mechanical System
(Part 3 of 3). 3.0L/V6-181 Engine

Fig. 95   Test NS-4A: Correcting Fuel
Delivery (Part 2 of 2). 3.0L/V6-181
Engine

Fig. 95   Test NS-4A: Correcting Fuel Delivery (Part 1
of 2). 3.0L/V6-181 Engine

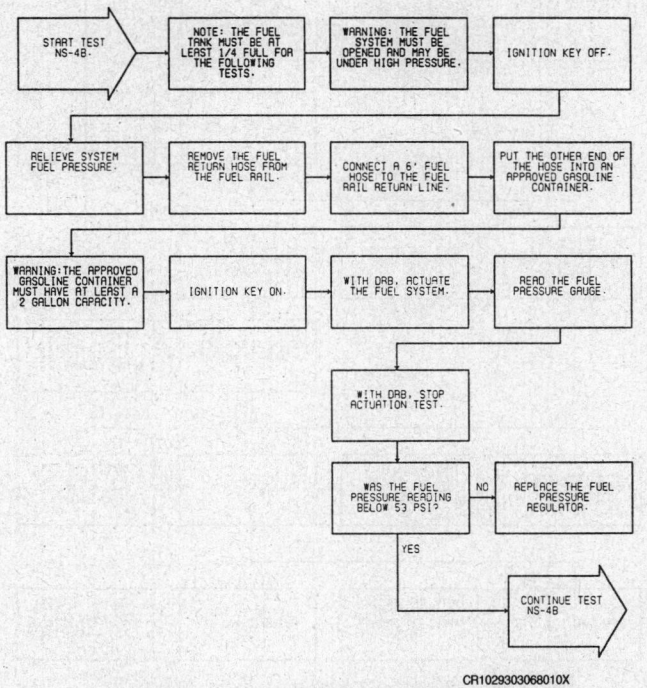

Fig. 96   Test NS-4B: Correcting Fuel
Delivery (Part 1 of 2). 3.0L/V6-181
Engine

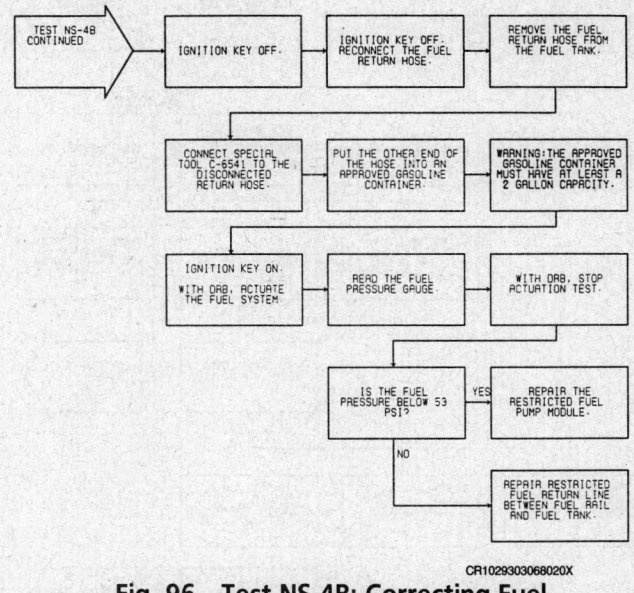

CR1029303068020X

Fig. 96   Test NS-4B: Correcting Fuel
Delivery (Part 2 of 2). 3.0L/V6-181
Engine

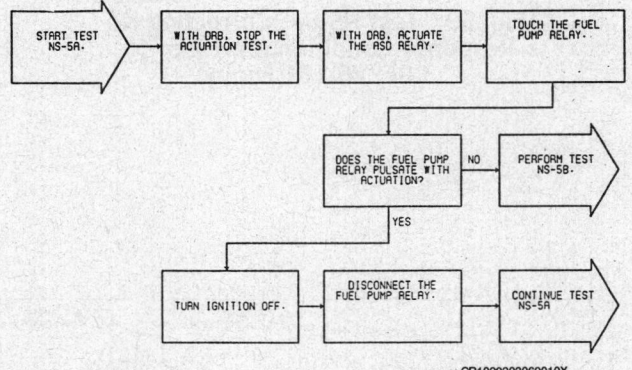

CR1029303069010X

Fig. 97   Test NS-5A: Inspecting Fuel
Pump (Part 1 of 2). 3.0L/V6-181 Engine

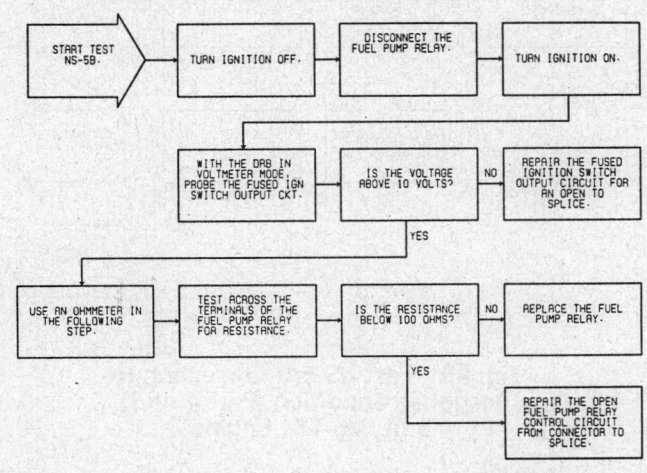

CR1029303070000X

Fig. 98   Test NS-5B: Inspecting Fuel
Pump. 3.0L/V6-181 Engine

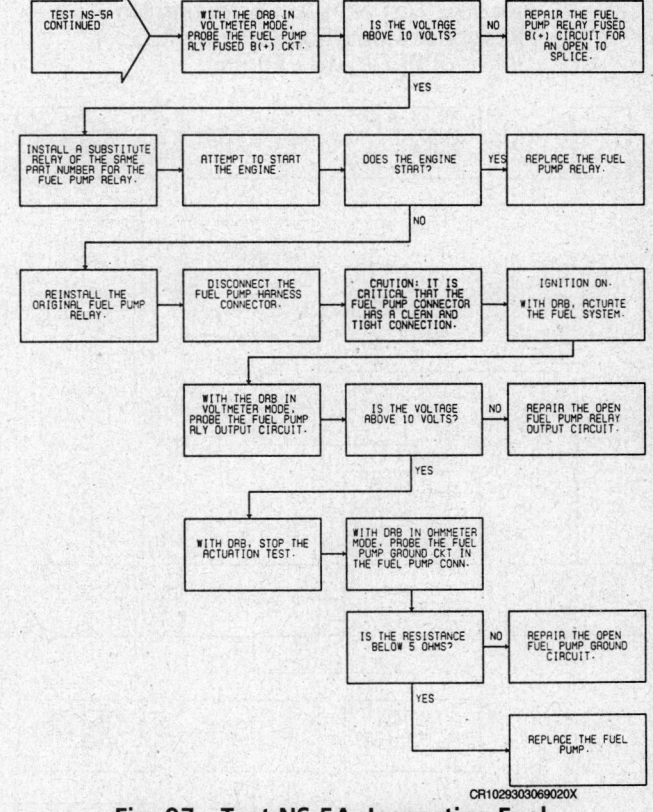

CR1029303069020X

Fig. 97   Test NS-5A: Inspecting Fuel
Pump (Part 2 of 2). 3.0L/V6-181 Engine

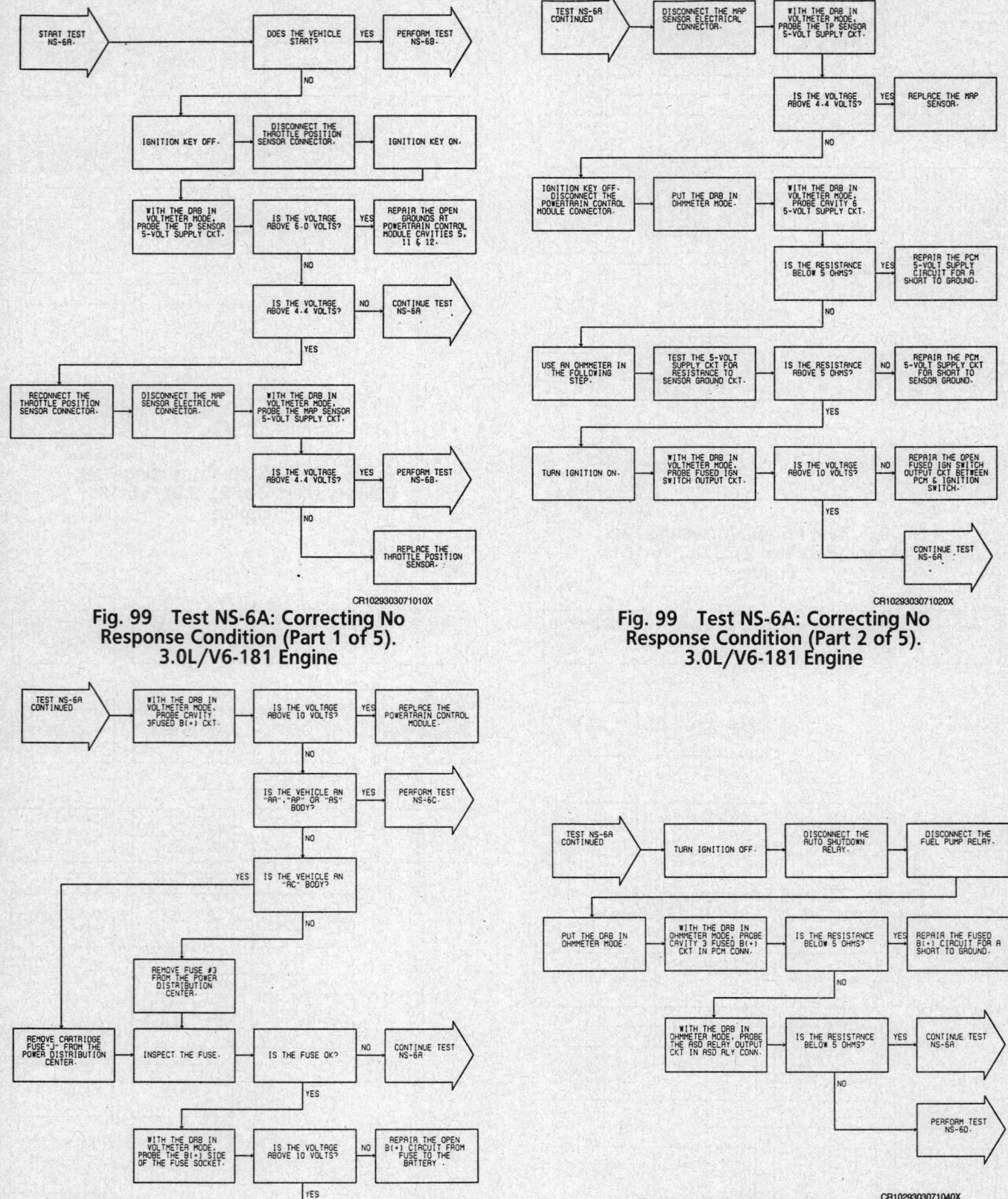

Fig. 99   Test NS-6A: Correcting No
Response Condition (Part 1 of 5).
3.0L/V6-181 Engine

Fig. 99   Test NS-6A: Correcting No
Response Condition (Part 2 of 5).
3.0L/V6-181 Engine

Fig. 99   Test NS-6A: Correcting No
Response Condition (Part 4 of 5).
3.0L/V6-181 Engine

Fig. 99   Test NS-6A: Correcting No
Response Condition (Part 3 of 5).
3.0L/V6-181 Engine

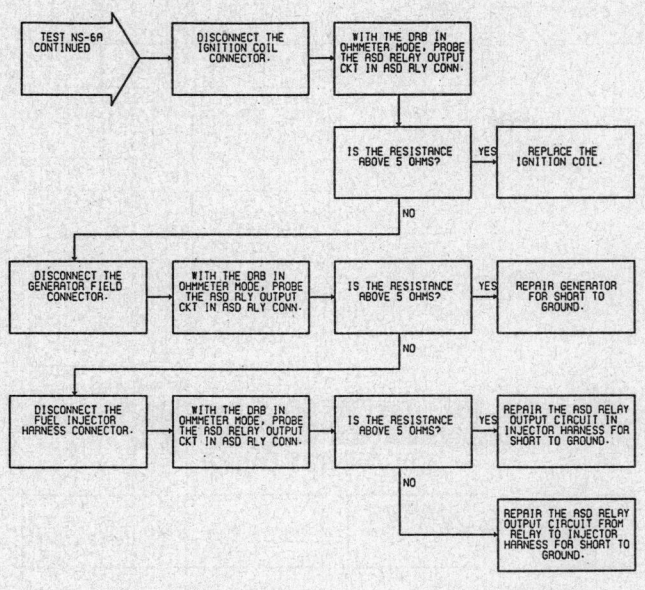

Fig. 99   Test NS-6A: Correcting No Response Condition (Part 5 of 5). 3.0L/V6-181 Engine

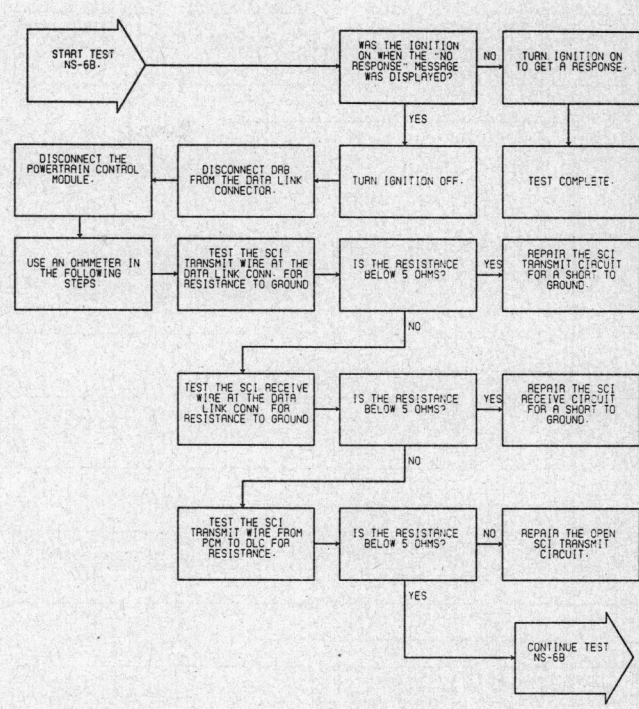

Fig. 100   Test NS-6B: Correcting No Response Condition (Part 1 of 2). 3.0L/V6-181 Engine

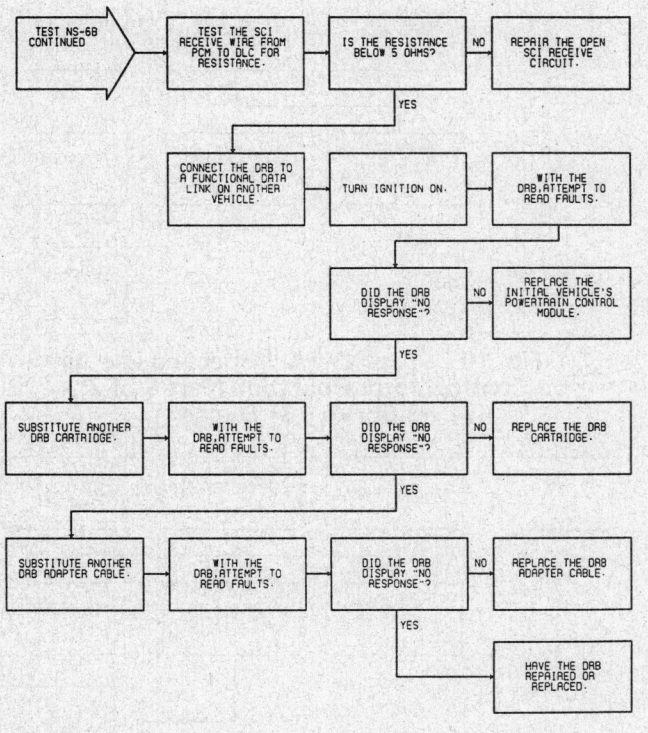

Fig. 100   Test NS-6B: Correcting No Response Condition (Part 2 of 2). 3.0L/V6-181 Engine

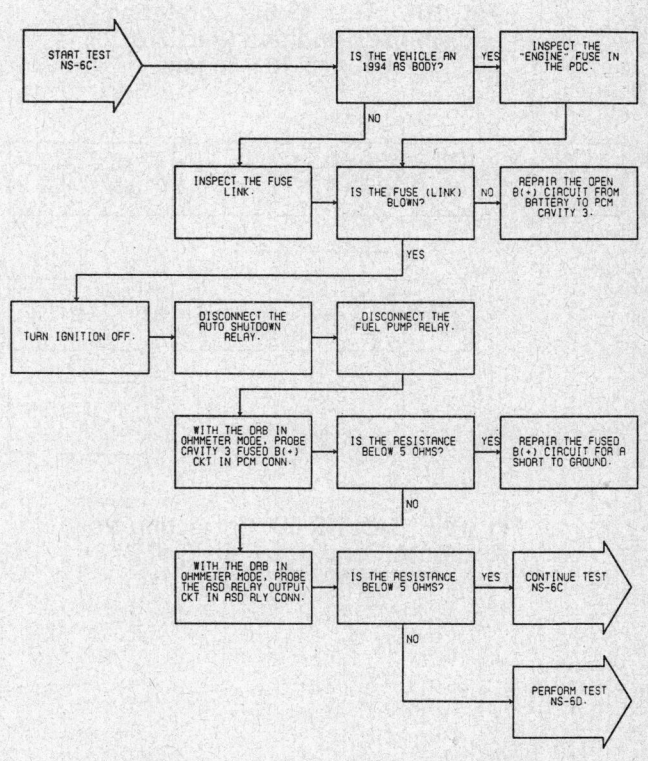

Fig. 101   Test NS-6C: Correcting No Response Condition (Part 1 of 2). 3.0L/V6-181 Engine

MODELS w/3.0L/V6-181, 3.3L/V6-201 & 3.8L/V6-231 ENGINES EXCEPT CONCORDE, INTREPID, LHS, STEALTH, VISION & 1994-96 NEW YORKER

12-65

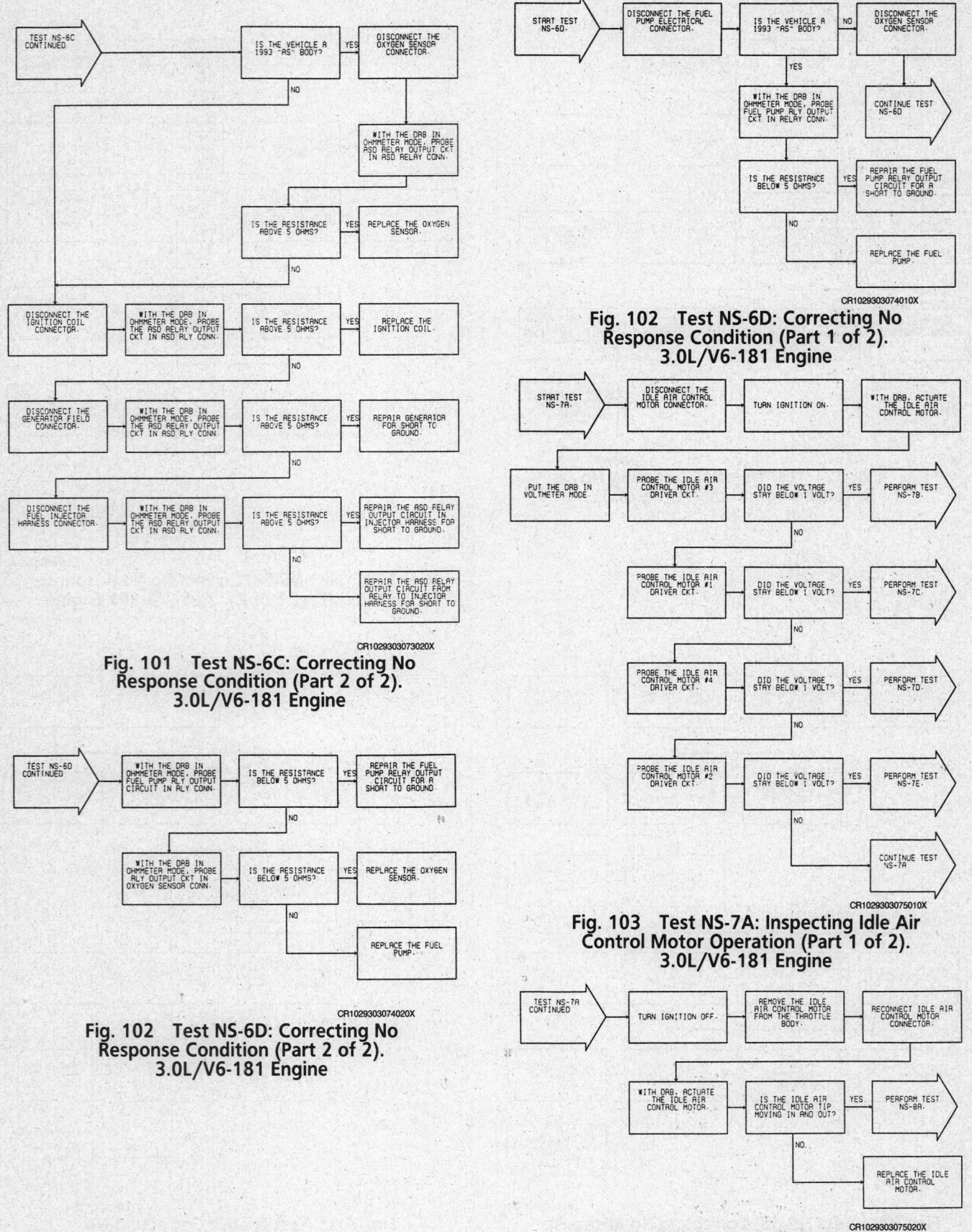

Fig. 101 Test NS-6C: Correcting No Response Condition (Part 2 of 2). 3.0L/V6-181 Engine

Fig. 102 Test NS-6D: Correcting No Response Condition (Part 2 of 2). 3.0L/V6-181 Engine

Fig. 102 Test NS-6D: Correcting No Response Condition (Part 1 of 2). 3.0L/V6-181 Engine

Fig. 103 Test NS-7A: Inspecting Idle Air Control Motor Operation (Part 1 of 2). 3.0L/V6-181 Engine

Fig. 103 Test NS-7A: Inspecting Idle Air Control Motor Operation (Part 2 of 2). 3.0L/V6-181 Engine

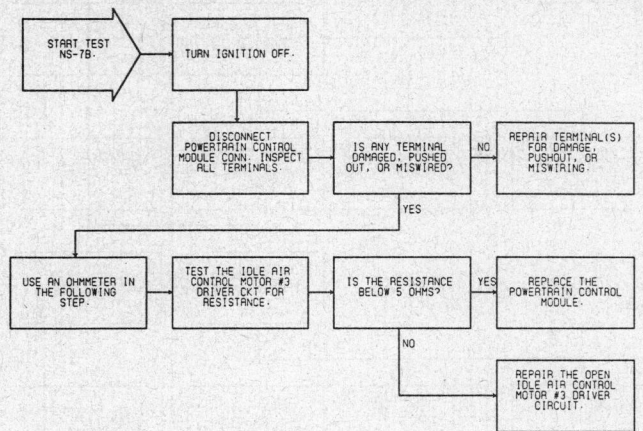

Fig. 104 Test NS-7B: Inspecting Idle Air Control Motor Operation. 3.0L/V6-181 Engine

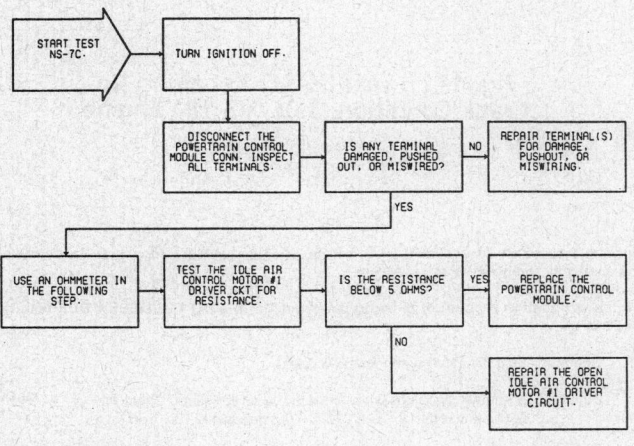

Fig. 105 Test NS-7C: Inspecting Idle Air Control Motor Operation. 3.0L/V6-181 Engine

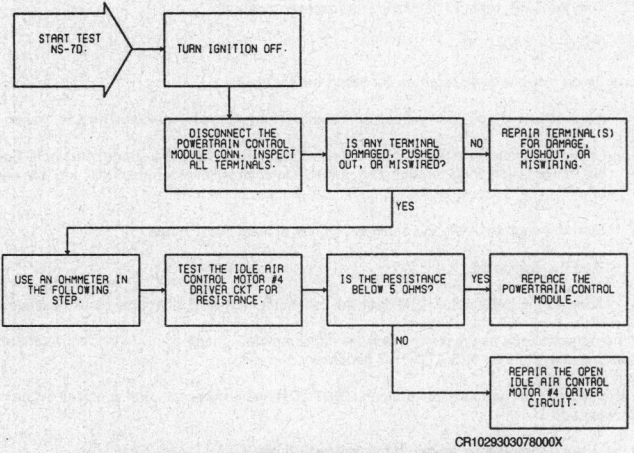

Fig. 106 Test NS-7D: Inspecting Idle Air Control Motor Operation. 3.0L/V6-181 Engine

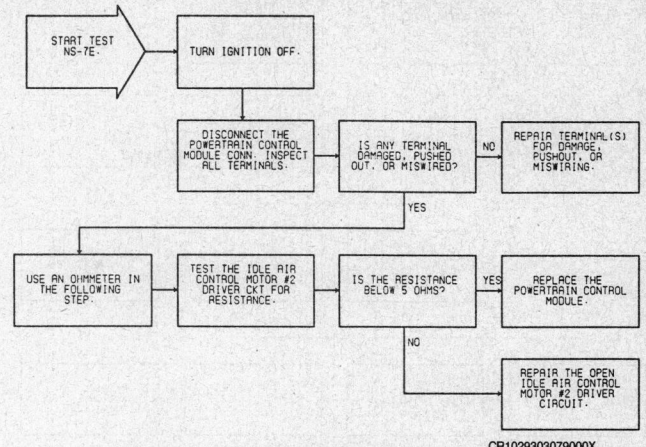

Fig. 107 Test NS-7E: Inspecting Idle Air Control Motor Operation. 3.0L/V6-181 Engine

At this point in the diagnostic procedure, you have determined that all of the engine control module systems are operating as designed. Therefore, they are **not the cause of the start and stall problem.**

The following potential causes of a no start condition should also be checked:

1. **ENGINE VALVE TIMING** - must be within specifications
2. **ENGINE COMPRESSION** - must be within specifications
3. **ENGINE EXHAUST** - must be unrestricted
4. **ENGINE PCV SYSTEM** - must flow freely
5. **ENGINE DRIVE SPROCKETS** - must be properly positioned
6. **FUEL** - must be free of contamination
7. **ENGINE SECONDARY IGNITION CHECK** - must exhibit a normal scope pattern

Any one or more of these items can produce a no start condition; none of them can be overlooked as possible causes.

Also, look for any Technical Service Bulletins that may relate to this condition.

Fig. 108 Test NS-8A: Correcting Start & Stall Condition. 3.0L/V6-181 Engine

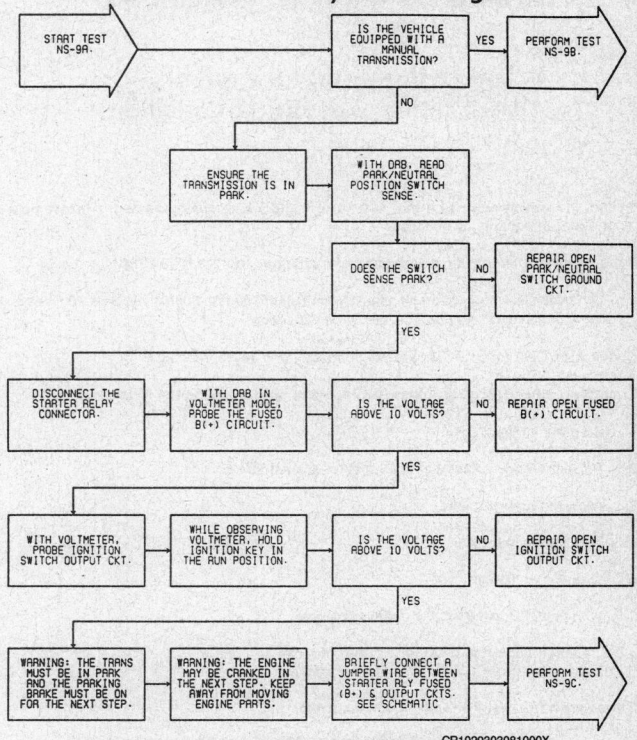

Fig. 109 Test NS-9A: Repairing No Crank Condition. 3.0L/V6-181 Engine

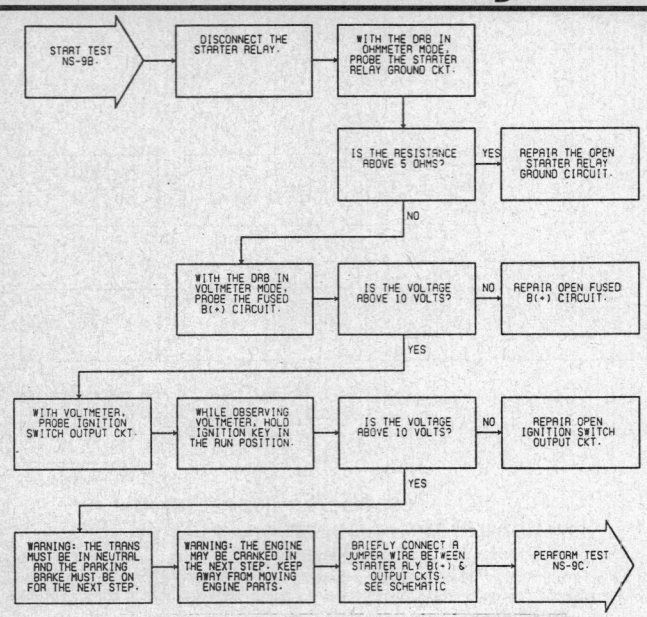

Fig. 110 Flowchart (Test NS-9B):
- START TEST NS-9B.
- DISCONNECT THE STARTER RELAY.
- WITH THE DRB IN OHMMETER MODE, PROBE THE STARTER RELAY GROUND CKT.
- IS THE RESISTANCE ABOVE 5 OHMS? — YES → REPAIR THE OPEN STARTER RELAY GROUND CIRCUIT.
- NO → WITH THE DRB IN VOLTMETER MODE, PROBE THE FUSED B(+) CIRCUIT.
- IS THE VOLTAGE ABOVE 10 VOLTS? — NO → REPAIR OPEN FUSED B(+) CIRCUIT.
- YES → WITH VOLTMETER, PROBE IGNITION SWITCH OUTPUT CKT.
- WHILE OBSERVING VOLTMETER, HOLD IGNITION KEY IN THE RUN POSITION.
- IS THE VOLTAGE ABOVE 10 VOLTS? — NO → REPAIR OPEN IGNITION SWITCH OUTPUT CKT.
- YES → WARNING: THE TRANS MUST BE IN NEUTRAL AND THE PARKING BRAKE MUST BE ON FOR THE NEXT STEP.
- WARNING: THE ENGINE MAY BE CRANKED IN THE NEXT STEP. KEEP AWAY FROM MOVING ENGINE PARTS.
- BRIEFLY CONNECT A JUMPER WIRE BETWEEN STARTER RLY B(+) & OUTPUT CKTS. SEE SCHEMATIC.
- PERFORM TEST NS-9C.

CR1029303082000X

Fig. 110 Test NS-9B: Repairing No Crank Condition. 3.0L/V6-181 Engine

Fig. 111 Flowchart (Test NS-9C):
- START TEST NS-9C.
- DID THE STARTER MOTOR CRANK THE ENGINE? — YES → REPLACE THE STARTER RELAY.
- NO → NOTE IF THE STARTER SOLENOID CLICKED WHEN THE JUMPER WIRE WAS CONNECTED.
- DISCONNECT THE JUMPER WIRE.
- DISCONNECT STARTER RELAY OUTPUT WIRE FROM THE STARTER SOLENOID.
- USING AN OHMMETER, TEST STARTER RELAY OUTPUT CIRCUIT.
- IS THE RESISTANCE BELOW 5 OHMS? — NO → REPAIR OPEN STARTER RELAY OUTPUT CKT.
- YES → REINSTALL STARTER RELAY.
- CHECK THE BATTERY CABLES FOR HIGH RESISTANCE.
- DID EITHER BATTERY CIRCUIT HAVE A VOLTAGE DROP GREATER THAT 0.2 VOLT? — YES → REPAIR THE BATTERY CIRCUIT FOR HIGH RESISTANCE.
- NO → DID THE STARTER SOLENOID CLICK WHEN THE JUMPER WIRE WAS PREVIOUSLY CONNECTED? — NO → REPLACE THE STARTER SOLENOID.
- YES → REPAIR MECHANICAL CONDITION PREVENTING THE STARTER MOTOR FROM CRANKING.

CR1029303083000X

Fig. 111 Test NS-9C: Repairing No Crank Condition. 3.0L/V6-181 Engine

Inspect the vehicle to ensure that all engine components are connected. Reassemble and reconnect components as necessary.

Inspect the engine for contamination. If it is contaminated, change the oil and filter.

Attempt to start the engine.

If the engine is unable to start, look for any Technical Service Bulletins that may relate to this condition. Return to **TEST TC-1A** if necessary.

The repair is now complete.

Fig. 112 Test VER-1A: No Start Verification. 3.0L/V6-181 Engine

Inspect the vehicle to ensure that all engine components are connected. Reassemble and reconnect components as necessary.

If the powertrain control module has been changed, do the following:

1. If the vehicle is equipped with a factory theft alarm, start the vehicle at least 20 times so that the alarm system may be activated when desired.

Connect the DRB to the PCM data link connector and erase the codes.

Ensure no other charging system problems remain by doing the following:

1. Start the engine.
2. Raise the engine speed to 2000 rpm for at least 30 seconds.
3. Allow the engine to idle.
4. Turn the engine off.
5. Turn the ignition key on.
6. With the DRB, read trouble code messages.

If the repaired code has reset, or another one has set, check Technical Service Bulletins and return to **TEST TC-1A** if necessary.

If there are no codes, the repair is now complete.

Fig. 114 Test VER-3A: Charging Verification. 3.0L/V6-181 Engine

Inspect the vehicle to ensure that all engine components are connected. Reassemble and reconnect all components as necessary.

If this verification procedure is being performed after a NO TROUBLE CODE test, do the following:

1. Check to see if the initial symptom still exists.
2. If the initial or another symptom exists, the repair is not complete. Check all Technical Service Bulletins and return to **TEST NTC-1A** if necessary.

If this verification procedure is being performed after a TROUBLE CODE test, do the following:

For previously read trouble codes that have not been dealt with, return to **TEST TC-1A** and follow the path specified. Otherwise, continue.

If the powertrain control module has not been changed:

1. Connect the DRB to the PCM data link connector and erase trouble codes.
2. With the DRB, reset all values in the adaptive memory.
3. Disconnect the DRB.

Ensure no trouble code remains by doing the following:

1. If the vehicle is equipped with air conditioning, turn on the air conditioning and blower.
2. Drive the vehicle for at least five minutes and at some point reach a speed of 40 mph. Ensure the transmission shifts through all gears. Upon completion of the road test, turn the engine off.
3. Start the engine. Allow the engine to idle for at least two minutes.
4. Turn the engine off.
5. Connect the DRB to the PCM data link connector, and read all trouble code messages.

If the repaired code has reset, the repair is not complete. Check all Technical Service Bulletins and return to **TEST TC-1A** if necessary.

If another trouble code has set, return to **TEST TC-1A** and follow the path specified by the other trouble code.

If there are no trouble codes, the repair is now complete.

Fig. 113 Test VER-2A: Road Test Verification. 3.0L/V6-181 Engine

Inspect the vehicle to ensure that all engine components are connected. Reassemble and reconnect all components as necessary.

If the powertrain control module has been changed, do the following:

1. If the vehicle is equipped with a factory theft alarm, start the vehicle at least 20 times so that the alarm system may be activated when desired.

Connect the DRB to the PCM data link connector and erase the codes.

Ensure no other speed control problems remain by doing the following:

1. Road test the vehicle at a speed above 35 mph.

2. Turn the speed control ON/OFF switch to the ON position.

3. Depress and release the SET switch. If the speed control did not engage, the repair is not complete.*

4. For stalk switch equipped vehicles, quickly depress and release the SET switch. For steering wheel switch equipped vehicles, quickly depress and release the RESUME/ACCEL switch. If the vehicle speed did not increase by 2 mph, the repair is not complete.*

5. Using caution, depress and release the brake pedal. If the speed control did not disengage, the repair is not complete.*

6. Bring the vehicle speed back up to 35 mph.

7. Depress the RESUME/ACCEL switch. If the speed control did not resume the previously set speed, the repair is not complete.*

8. Hold down the SET switch. If the vehicle did not decelerate, the repair is not complete.*

9. Ensure the vehicle speed is greater than 35 mph and release the SET switch. If the vehicle did not adjust and set a new vehicle speed, the repair is not complete.*

10. Turn on the ON/OFF switch to the OFF position. If the speed control did not disengage, the repair is not complete.*

If the vehicle successfully passed all of the previous tests, the speed control system is now functioning as designed. The repair is now complete.

*Check for Technical Service Bulletins and then, if necessary, return to **TEST TC-1A.**

Fig. 115   Test VER-4A: Speed Control Verification. 3.0L/V6-181 Engine

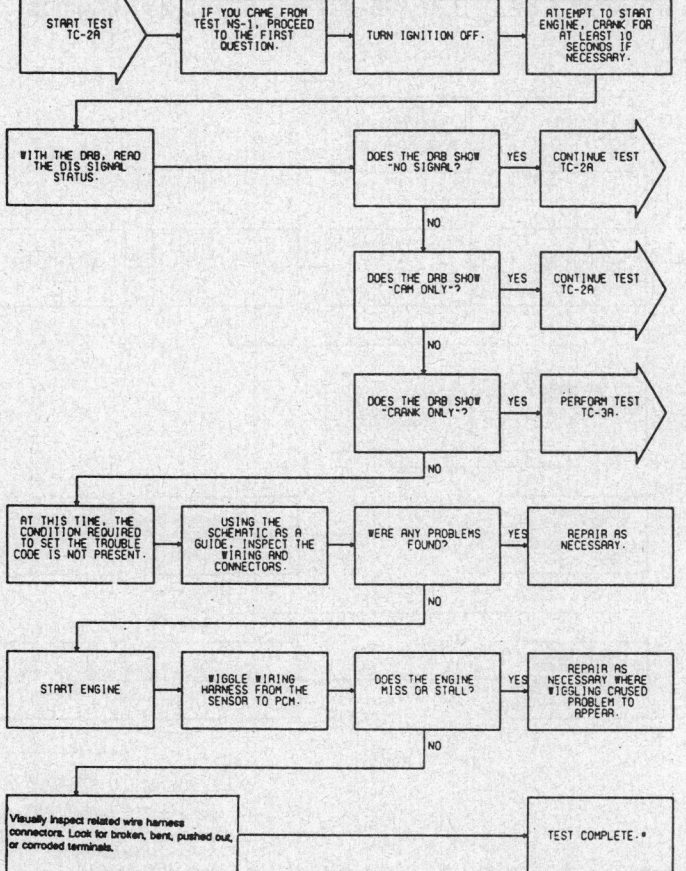

Fig. 117   Test TC-2A: No Crank Reference Signal At PCM (Part 1 of 3). 3.3L/V6-201 & 3.8L/V6-231 Engines

CR1029303110010)

NOTE: The battery must be fully charged for any test in this manual.

1. Attempt to start the engine. Crank for up to 10 seconds if necessary.

2. Connect the DRB to the engine diagnostic connector. Write down trouble code messages that are displayed.

3. If the DRB screen displays "No Response", go to **TEST NS-6A.**

4. If the DRB screen is blank, do the following: — Ensure there is a good body ground at cavity 1 of the data link connector.   substitute another cable, cartridge, and DRB until the condition is corrected.

5. If trouble code messages are displayed, refer to the trouble code list below and on the next page for the appropriate test.

6. If there are no trouble codes displayed, refer to one of the following:
   For Driveability problems NTC-1A
   For No Start problems NS-1A
   For Speed Control problems SC-1A
   For Charging problems CH-1A

DRB MESSAGE	DIAGNOSTIC TEST
NO CRANK REFERENCE SIGNAL AT PCM	TC- 2A
NO CAM SYNC SIGNAL AT PCM	TC- 3A
NO CHANGE IN MAP FROM START TO RUN	TC- 4A
MAP SENSOR VOLTAGE TOO LOW	TC- 5A
MAP SENSOR VOLTAGE TOO HIGH	TC- 6A
NO VEHICLE SPEED SENSOR SIGNAL	TC- 7A
O2S SHORTED TO VOLTAGE	TC- 8A
O2S STAYS AT CENTER	TC- 9A
O2S STAYS ABOVE CENTER (RICH)	TC-10A
O2S STAYS BELOW CENTER (LEAN)	TC-11A
ECT SENSOR VOLTAGE TOO HIGH	TC-12A
ECT SENSOR VOLTAGE TOO LOW	TC-13A
THROTTLE POSITION SENSOR VOLTAGE LOW	TC-14A
THROTTLE POSITION SENSOR VOLTAGE HIGH	TC-15A
IDLE AIR CONTROL MOTOR CIRCUITS	TC-16A
INJECTOR #1 CONTROL CIRCUIT	TC-17A
INJECTOR #2 CONTROL CIRCUIT	TC-17A
INJECTOR #3 CONTROL CIRCUIT	TC-17A
INJECTOR #4 CONTROL CIRCUIT	TC-17A
INJECTOR #5 CONTROL CIRCUIT	TC-17A
INJECTOR #6 CONTROL CIRCUIT	TC-17A
EVAP SOLENOID CIRCUIT	TC-23A
EGR SOLENOID CIRCUIT	TC-24A
EGR SYSTEM FAILURE	TC-25A
A/C CLUTCH RELAY CIRCUIT	TC-26A
RAD FAN CONTROL RELAY CIRCUIT (AC/AY ONLY)	TC-27A
LOW SPEED FAN CTRL RELAY CIRCUIT (AS ONLY)	TC-28A
HIGH SPEED FAN CTRL RELAY CIRCUIT (AS ONLY)	TC-29A
AUTO SHUTDOWN RELAY CONTROL CIRCUIT	TC-30A

CR1029303109010X

Fig. 116   Test TC-1A: Inspecting The System For Trouble Codes (Part 1 of 2). 3.3L/V6-201 & 3.8L/V6-231 Engines

DRB MESSAGE	DIAGNOSTIC TEST
NO ASD RELAY OUTPUT VOLTAGE AT PCM	TC-31A
IGNITION COIL #1 PRIMARY CIRCUIT	TC-32A
IGNITION COIL #2 PRIMARY CIRCUIT	TC-32A
IGNITION COIL #3 PRIMARY CIRCUIT	TC-32A
PCM FAILURE SRI MILE NOT STORED	TC-35A
PCM FAILURE EEPROM WRITE DENIED	TC-35A
BATTERY TEMP SENSOR VOLTS OUT OF LIMIT	TC-36A
GENERATOR FIELD NOT SWITCHING PROPERLY	TC-37A
CHARGING SYSTEM VOLTAGE TOO LOW	TC-38A
CHARGING SYSTEM VOLTAGE TOO HIGH	TC-39A
SPEED CONTROL SOLENOID CIRCUITS	TC-40A

For an Internal Controller Failure trouble code, replace the PCM and go to **Verification TEST VER-1.**

For a PCM Failure SPI Communications trouble code, replace the PCM and perform **Verification TEST VER-2.**

CR1029303109020X

Fig. 116   Test TC-1A: Inspecting The System For Trouble Codes (Part 2 of 2). 3.3L/V6-201 & 3.8L/V6-231 Engines

MODELS w/3.0L/V6-181, 3.3L/V6-201 & 3.8L/V6-231 ENGINES EXCEPT CONCORDE, INTREPID, LHS, STEALTH, VISION & 1994-96 NEW YORKER

12-69

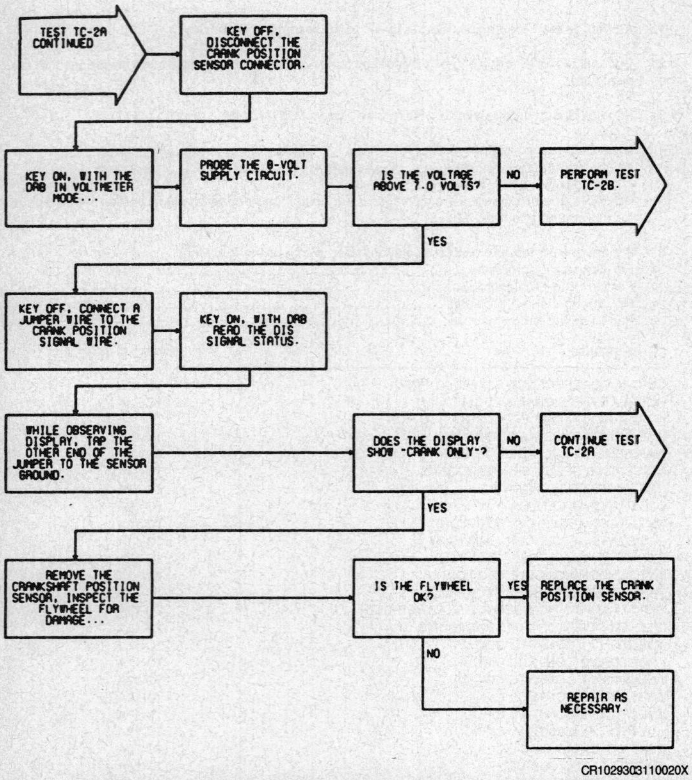

Fig. 117 (Part 2 of 3) — Test TC-2A flowchart:

TEST TC-2A CONTINUED → KEY OFF, DISCONNECT THE CRANK POSITION SENSOR CONNECTOR.

KEY ON, WITH THE DRB IN VOLTMETER MODE... → PROBE THE 8-VOLT SUPPLY CIRCUIT. → IS THE VOLTAGE ABOVE 7.0 VOLTS? — NO → PERFORM TEST TC-2B.

(YES)

KEY OFF, CONNECT A JUMPER WIRE TO THE CRANK POSITION SIGNAL WIRE. → KEY ON, WITH DRB READ THE DIS SIGNAL STATUS.

WHILE OBSERVING DISPLAY, TAP THE OTHER END OF THE JUMPER TO THE SENSOR GROUND. → DOES THE DISPLAY SHOW "CRANK ONLY"? — NO → CONTINUE TEST TC-2A

(YES)

REMOVE THE CRANKSHAFT POSITION SENSOR, INSPECT THE FLYWHEEL FOR DAMAGE... → IS THE FLYWHEEL OK? — YES → REPLACE THE CRANK POSITION SENSOR.

(NO) → REPAIR AS NECESSARY.

Fig. 117 (Part 3 of 3) — Test TC-2A flowchart:

TEST TC-2A CONTINUED → KEY OFF, WITH THE DRB IN OHMMETER MODE, PROBE THE SENSOR GROUND. → IS THE RESISTANCE BELOW 5.0 OHMS? — NO → REPAIR THE OPEN SENSOR GROUND CIRCUIT.

(YES)

DISCONNECT THE POWERTRAIN CONTROL MODULE, INSPECT THE CONNECTOR. → IS ANY TERMINAL DAMAGED, PUSHED OUT OR MISWIRED? — YES → REPAIR AS NECESSARY.

(NO)

USE AN OHMMETER IN THE FOLLOWING STEP. → TEST THE CKP SIGNAL CIRCUIT FOR RESISTANCE. → IS THE RESISTANCE BELOW 5.0 OHMS? — NO → REPAIR THE OPEN CKP SIGNAL CIRCUIT.

(YES)

PUT THE DRB IN OHMMETER MODE. → PROBE THE CKP SIGNAL CIRCUIT. → IS THE RESISTANCE BELOW 5.0 OHMS? — NO → REPLACE THE POWERTRAIN CONTROL MODULE.

(YES)

DISCONNECT THE TRANSMISSION CONTROL MODULE. → PROBE THE CKP SIGNAL CIRCUIT. → IS THE RESISTANCE BELOW 5.0 OHMS? — NO → REPLACE THE TRANSMISSION CONTROL MODULE.

(YES) → REPAIR THE CKP SIGNAL CIRCUIT FOR A SHORT TO GROUND.

CR1029303110020X

CR1029303110030X

Fig. 117 Test TC-2A: No Crank Reference Signal At PCM (Part 2 of 3). 3.3L/V6-201 & 3.8L/V6-231 Engines

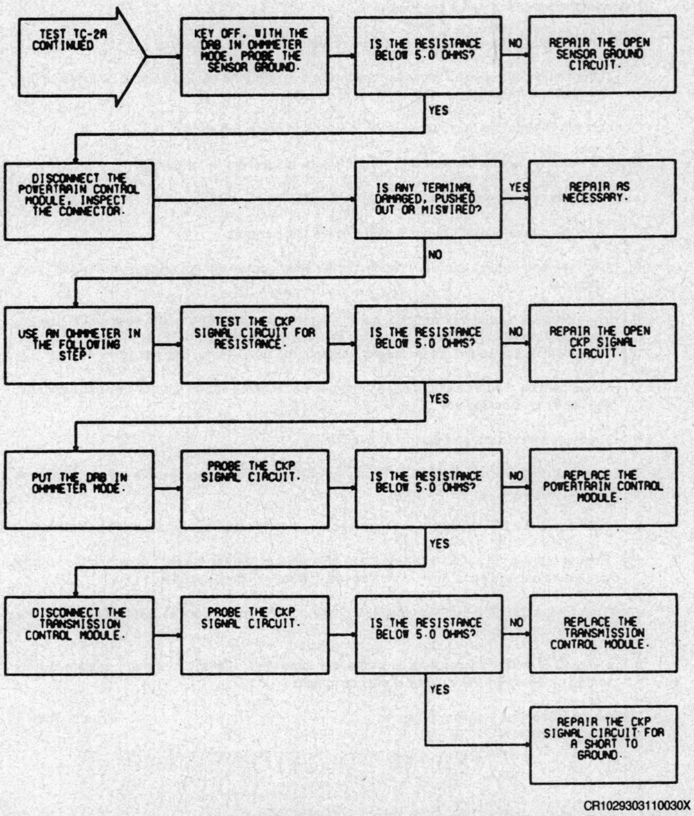

Fig. 117 Test TC-2A: No Crank Reference Signal At PCM (Part 3 of 3). 3.3L/V6-201 & 3.8L/V6-231 Engines

Fig. 118 — Test TC-2B flowchart:

START TEST TC-2B → DISCONNECT THE CAMSHAFT POSITION SENSOR. → IS ANY TERMINAL DAMAGED, PUSHED OUT OR MISWIRED? — YES → REPAIR AS NECESSARY.

(NO)

WITH THE DRB IN VOLTMETER MODE, PROBE THE CKP 8-VOLT SUPPLY CIRCUIT. → IS THE VOLTAGE ABOVE 7.0 VOLTS? — YES → REPLACE THE CAMSHAFT POSITION SENSOR.

(NO)

KEY OFF, DISCONNECT THE POWERTRAIN CONTROL MODULE, INSPECT THE CONNECTOR. → IS ANY TERMINAL DAMAGED, PUSHED OUT OR MISWIRED? — YES → REPAIR AS NECESSARY.

(NO)

PUT THE DRB IN OHMMETER MODE... → PROBE THE 8-VOLT SUPPLY CIRCUIT. → IS THE RESISTANCE BELOW 5.0 OHMS? — YES → REPAIR THE 8-VOLT SUPPLY CIRCUIT FOR A SHORT TO GROUND.

(NO)

USE AN OHMMETER IN THE FOLLOWING STEP... → TEST THE 8-VOLT SUPPLY CIRCUIT FOR RESISTANCE. → IS THE RESISTANCE BELOW 5.0 OHMS? — NO → REPAIR THE OPEN 8-VOLT SUPPLY CIRCUIT.

(YES) → REPLACE THE POWERTRAIN CONTROL MODULE.

Fig. 119 — Test TC-3A flowchart:

START TEST TC-3A → KEY OFF, DISCONNECT THE CAMSHAFT POSITION SENSOR CONNECTOR.

KEY ON, WITH THE DRB IN VOLTMETER MODE... → PROBE THE 8-VOLT SUPPLY CIRCUIT. → IS THE VOLTAGE ABOVE 7.0 VOLTS? — NO → REPAIR THE OPEN 8-VOLT SUPPLY CIRCUIT.

(YES)

KEY OFF, CONNECT A JUMPER WIRE TO THE CMP SIGNAL CIRCUIT. → KEY ON, WITH DRB READ THE DIS SIGNAL STATUS.

WHILE OBSERVING DISPLAY, TAP THE OTHER END OF THE JUMPER TO THE SENSOR GROUND. → DOES THE DISPLAY SHOW "CAM ONLY"? — NO → CONTINUE TEST TC-3A

(YES)

KEY OFF, REMOVE THE CAMSHAFT POSITION SENSOR, INSPECT THE CAM SPROCKET... → IS THE CAM SPROCKET OK? — YES → REPLACE THE CAMSHAFT POSITION SENSOR.

(NO) → REPAIR AS NECESSARY.

CR1029303111000X

CR1029303112010X

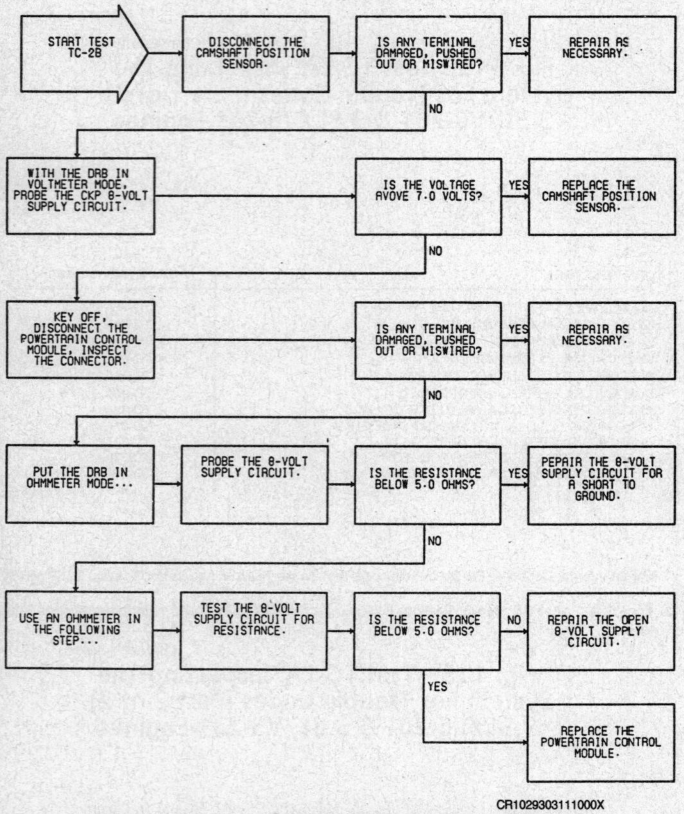

Fig. 118 Test TC-2B: No Crank Reference Signal At PCM. 3.3L/V6-201 & 3.8L/V6-231 Engines

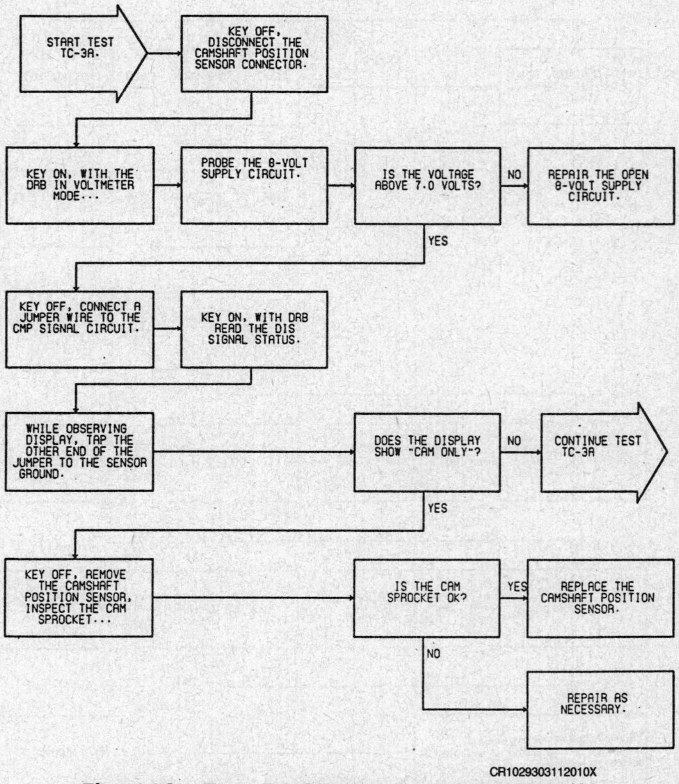

Fig. 119 Test TC-3A: No Cam Sync Signal At PCM (Part 1 of 2). 3.3L/V6-201 & 3.8L/V6-231 Engines

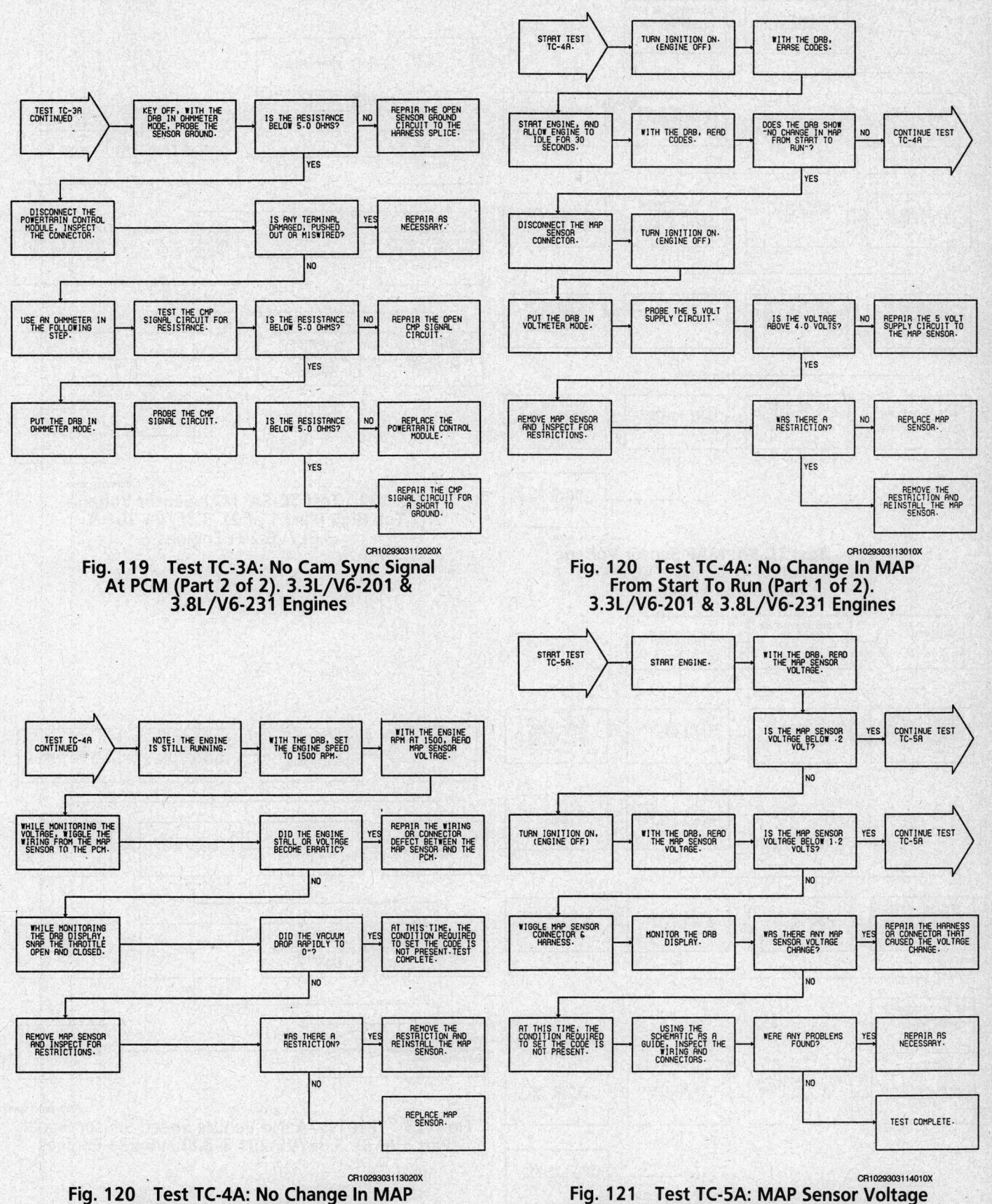

Fig. 119   Test TC-3A: No Cam Sync Signal At PCM (Part 2 of 2). 3.3L/V6-201 & 3.8L/V6-231 Engines

Fig. 120   Test TC-4A: No Change In MAP From Start To Run (Part 1 of 2). 3.3L/V6-201 & 3.8L/V6-231 Engines

Fig. 120   Test TC-4A: No Change In MAP From Start To Run (Part 2 of 2). 3.3L/V6-201 & 3.8L/V6-231 Engines

Fig. 121   Test TC-5A: MAP Sensor Voltage Too Low (Part 1 of 2). 3.3L/V6-201 & 3.8L/V6-231 Engines

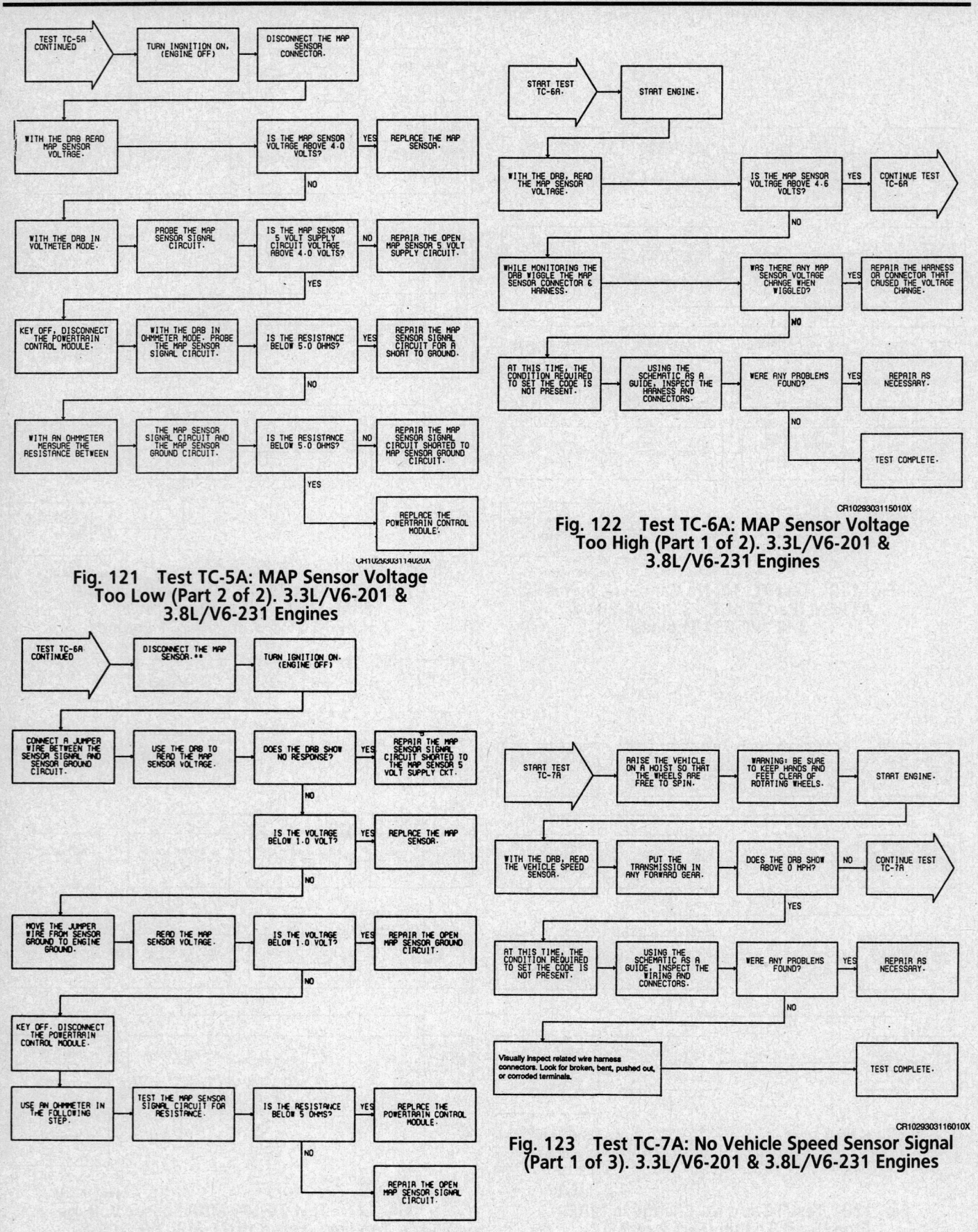

Fig. 121 Test TC-5A: MAP Sensor Voltage Too Low (Part 2 of 2). 3.3L/V6-201 & 3.8L/V6-231 Engines

Fig. 122 Test TC-6A: MAP Sensor Voltage Too High (Part 1 of 2). 3.3L/V6-201 & 3.8L/V6-231 Engines

Fig. 122 Test TC-6A: MAP Sensor Voltage Too High (Part 2 of 2). 3.3L/V6-201 & 3.8L/V6-231 Engines

Fig. 123 Test TC-7A: No Vehicle Speed Sensor Signal (Part 1 of 3). 3.3L/V6-201 & 3.8L/V6-231 Engines

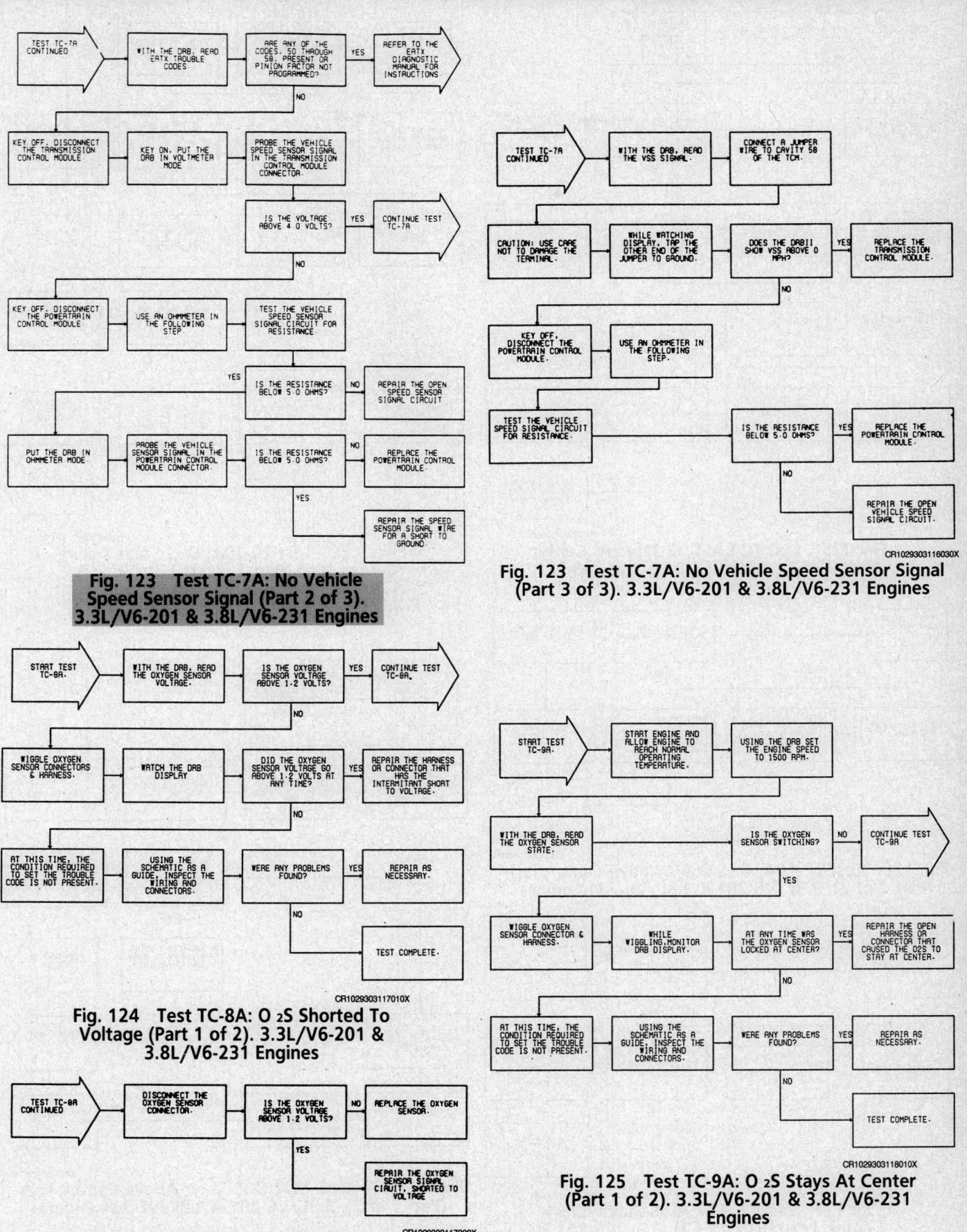

Fig. 123   Test TC-7A: No Vehicle Speed Sensor Signal (Part 2 of 3). 3.3L/V6-201 & 3.8L/V6-231 Engines

Fig. 123   Test TC-7A: No Vehicle Speed Sensor Signal (Part 3 of 3). 3.3L/V6-201 & 3.8L/V6-231 Engines

CR1029303116030X

Fig. 124   Test TC-8A: O₂S Shorted To Voltage (Part 1 of 2). 3.3L/V6-201 & 3.8L/V6-231 Engines

CR1029303117010X

Fig. 124   Test TC-8A: O₂S Shorted To Voltage (Part 2 of 2). 3.3L/V6-201 & 3.8L/V6-231 Engines

CR1029303117020X

Fig. 125   Test TC-9A: O₂S Stays At Center (Part 1 of 2). 3.3L/V6-201 & 3.8L/V6-231 Engines

CR1029303118010X

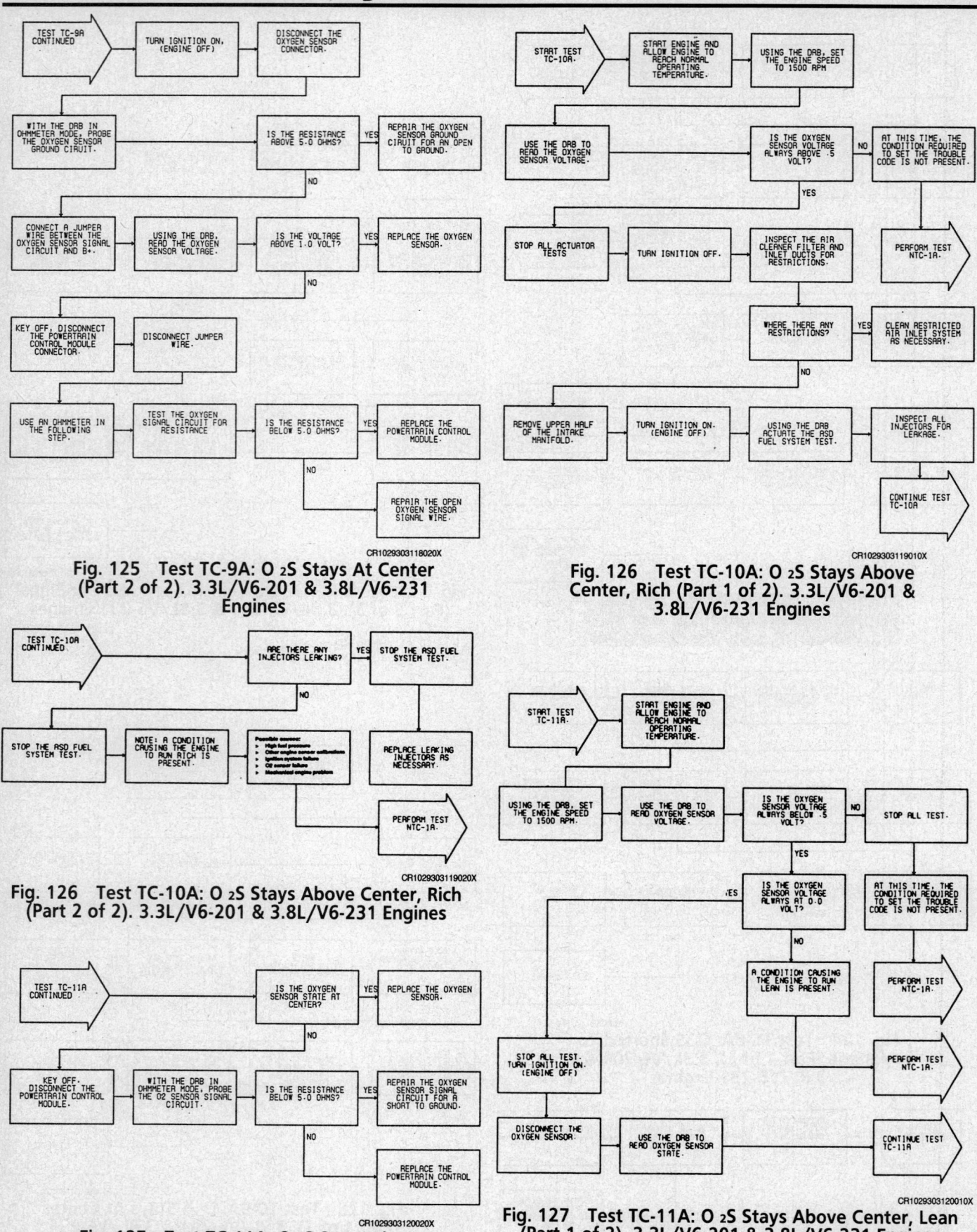

Fig. 125   Test TC-9A: O₂S Stays At Center (Part 2 of 2). 3.3L/V6-201 & 3.8L/V6-231 Engines

Fig. 126   Test TC-10A: O₂S Stays Above Center, Rich (Part 1 of 2). 3.3L/V6-201 & 3.8L/V6-231 Engines

Fig. 126   Test TC-10A: O₂S Stays Above Center, Rich (Part 2 of 2). 3.3L/V6-201 & 3.8L/V6-231 Engines

Fig. 127   Test TC-11A: O₂S Stays Above Center, Lean (Part 2 of 2). 3.3L/V6-201 & 3.8L/V6-231 Engines

Fig. 127   Test TC-11A: O₂S Stays Above Center, Lean (Part 1 of 2). 3.3L/V6-201 & 3.8L/V6-231 Engines

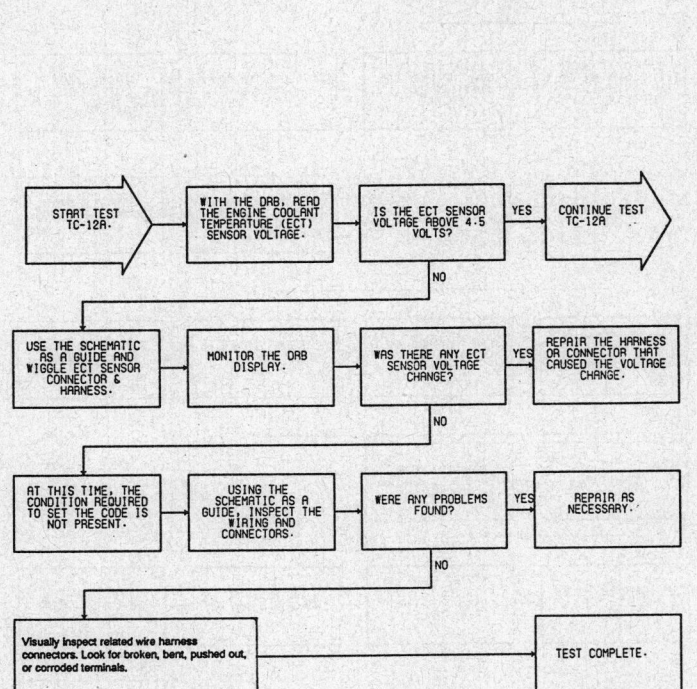

Fig. 128   Test TC-12A: ECT Sensor Voltage Too High (Part 1 of 2). 3.3L/V6-201 & 3.8L/V6-231 Engines

CR1029303121010X

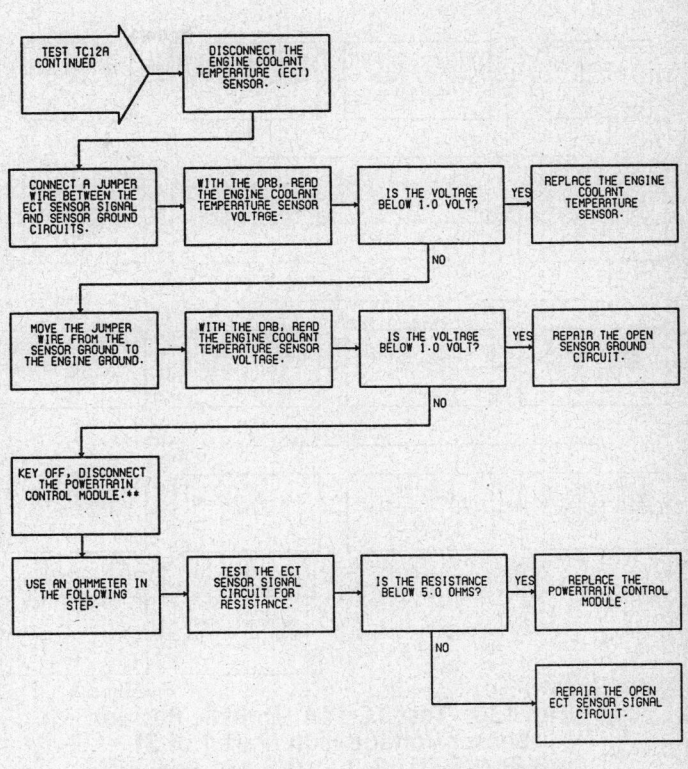

Fig. 128   Test TC-12A: ECT Sensor Voltage Too High (Part 2 of 2). 3.3L/V6-201 & 3.8L/V6-231 Engines

CR1029303121020X

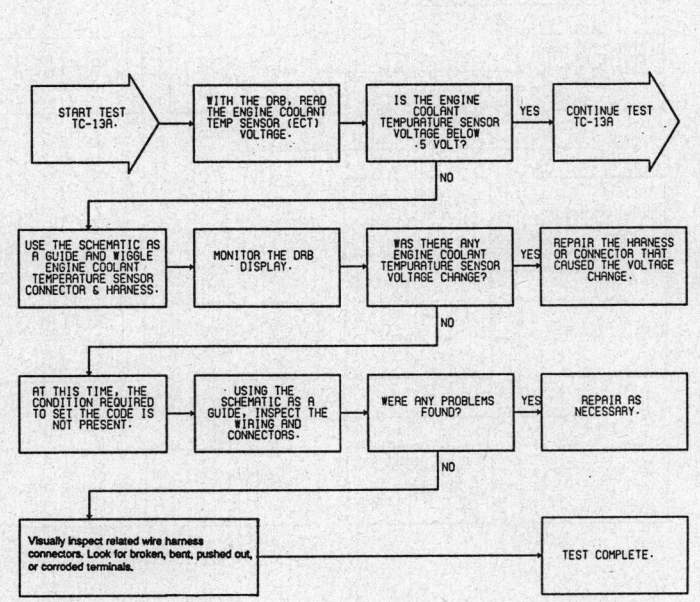

Fig. 129   Test TC-13A: ECT Sensor Voltage Too Low (Part 1 of 2). 3.3L/V6-201 & 3.8L/V6-231 Engines

CR1029303122010X

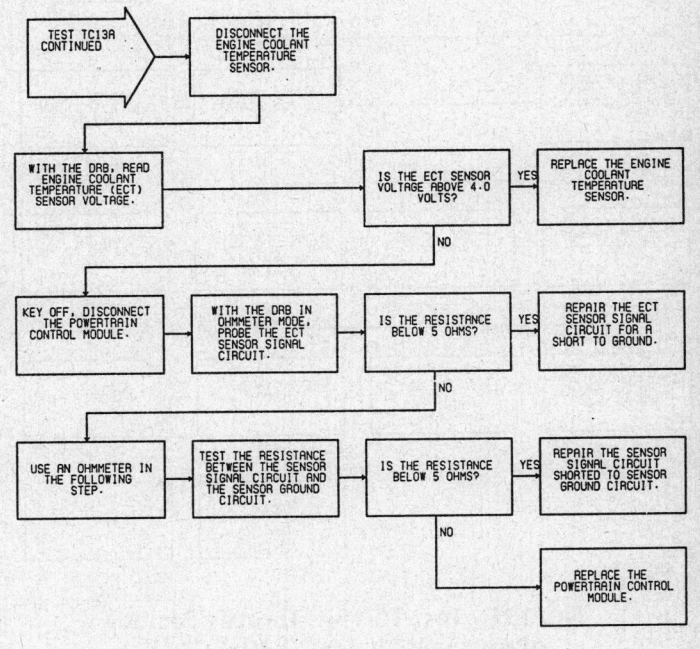

Fig. 129   Test TC-13A: ECT Sensor Voltage Too Low (Part 2 of 2). 3.3L/V6-201 & 3.8L/V6-231 Engines

CR1029303122020X

MODELS w/3.0L/V6-181, 3.3L/V6-201 & 3.8L/V6-231 ENGINES EXCEPT CONCORDE, INTREPID, LHS, STEALTH, VISION & 1994-96 NEW YORKER

12-75

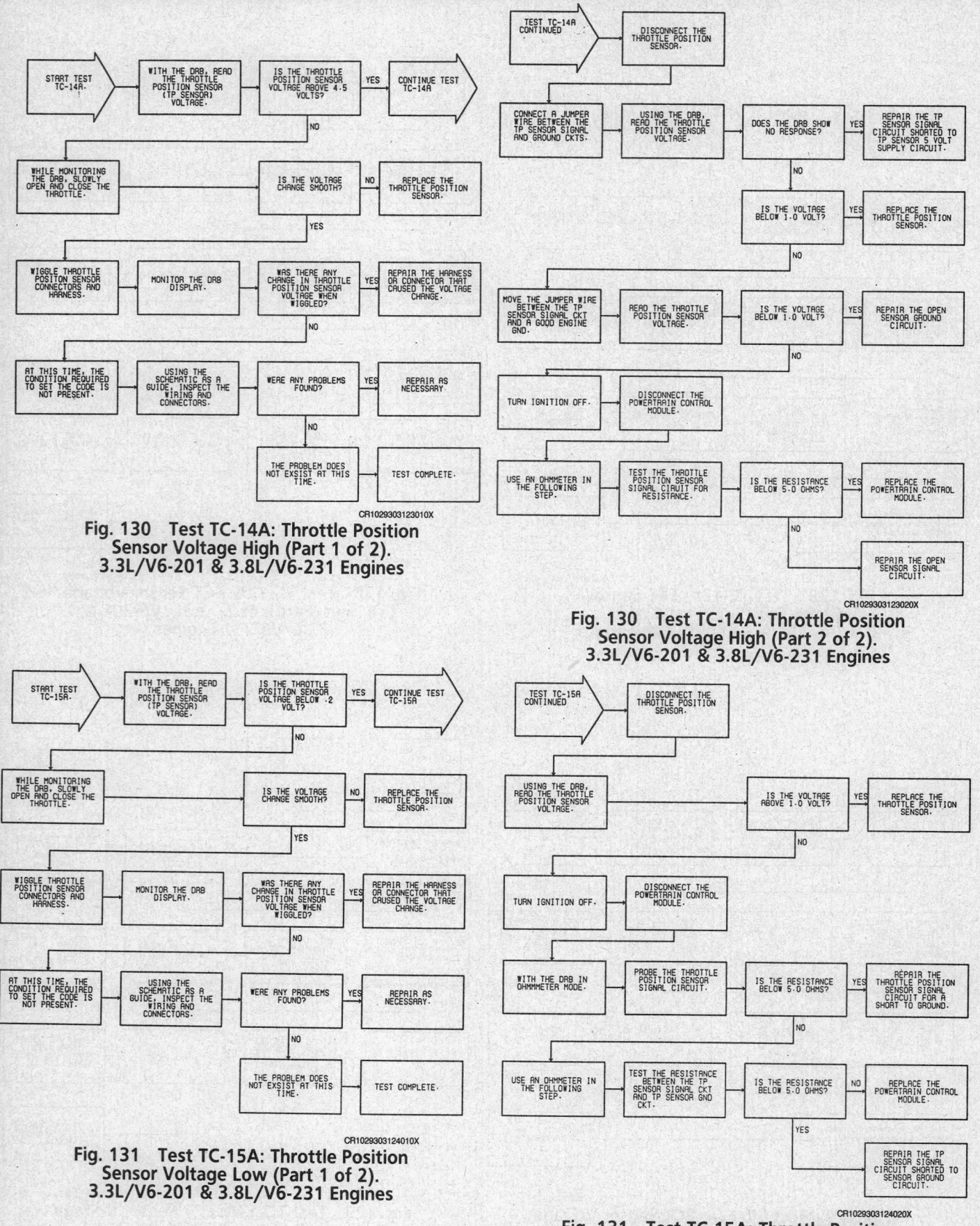

Fig. 130   Test TC-14A: Throttle Position Sensor Voltage High (Part 1 of 2). 3.3L/V6-201 & 3.8L/V6-231 Engines

Fig. 130   Test TC-14A: Throttle Position Sensor Voltage High (Part 2 of 2). 3.3L/V6-201 & 3.8L/V6-231 Engines

Fig. 131   Test TC-15A: Throttle Position Sensor Voltage Low (Part 1 of 2). 3.3L/V6-201 & 3.8L/V6-231 Engines

Fig. 131   Test TC-15A: Throttle Position Sensor Voltage Low (Part 2 of 2). 3.3L/V6-201 & 3.8L/V6-231 Engines

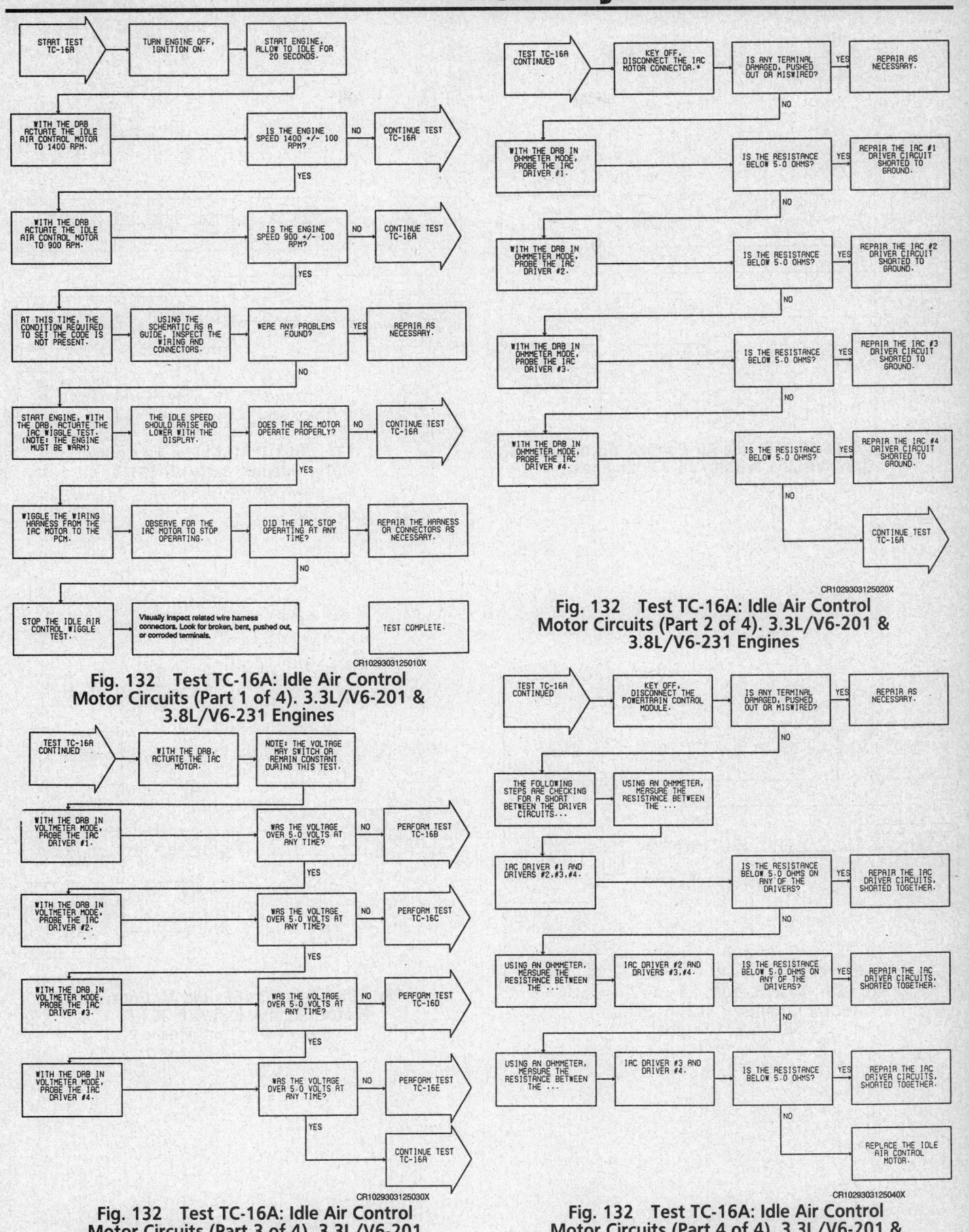

Fig. 132   Test TC-16A: Idle Air Control Motor Circuits (Part 1 of 4). 3.3L/V6-201 & 3.8L/V6-231 Engines

Fig. 132   Test TC-16A: Idle Air Control Motor Circuits (Part 2 of 4). 3.3L/V6-201 & 3.8L/V6-231 Engines

Fig. 132   Test TC-16A: Idle Air Control Motor Circuits (Part 3 of 4). 3.3L/V6-201 & 3.8L/V6-231 Engines

Fig. 132   Test TC-16A: Idle Air Control Motor Circuits (Part 4 of 4). 3.3L/V6-201 & 3.8L/V6-231 Engines

MODELS w/3.0L/V6-181, 3.3L/V6-201 & 3.8L/V6-231 ENGINES EXCEPT CONCORDE, INTREPID, LHS, STEALTH, VISION & 1994-96 NEW YORKER

12-77

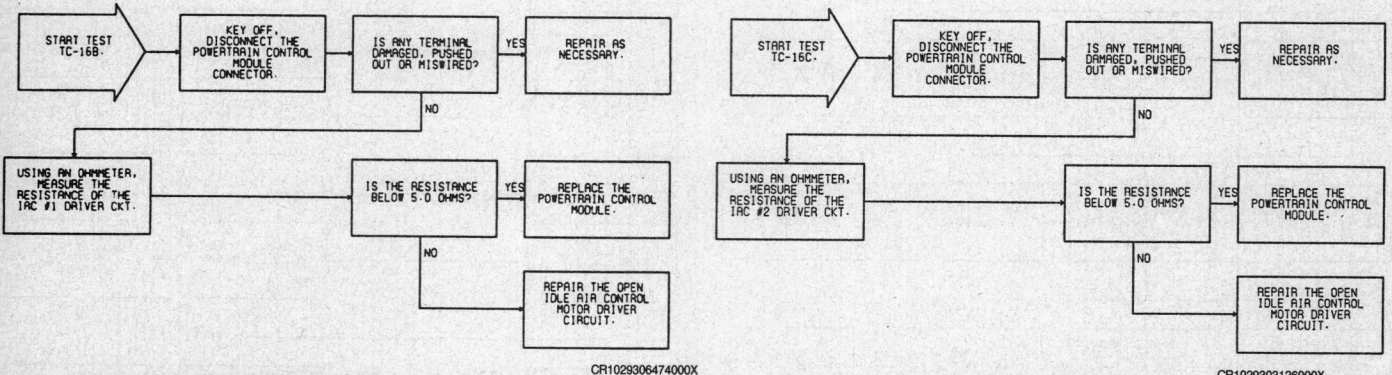

Fig. 133   Test TC-16B: Idle Air Control Motor Circuits. 3.3L/V6-201 & 3.8L/V6-231 Engines

Fig. 134   Test TC-16C: Idle Air Control Motor Circuits. 3.3L/V6-201 & 3.8L/V6-231 Engines

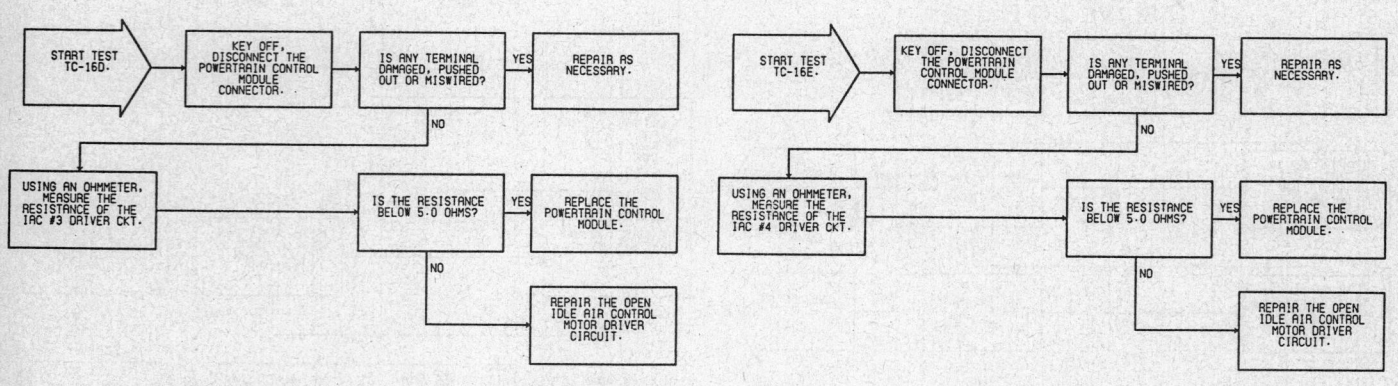

Fig. 135   Test TC-16D: Idle Air Control Motor Circuits. 3.3L/V6-201 & 3.8L/V6-231 Engines

Fig. 136   Test TC-16E: Idle Air Control Motor Circuits. 3.3L/V6-201 & 3.8L/V6-231 Engines

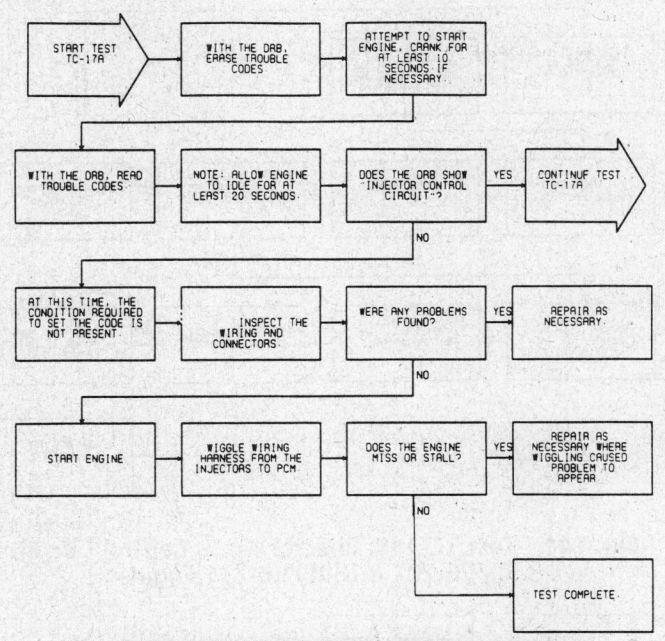

Fig. 137   Test TC-17A: Injector Control Circuit (Part 1 of 2). 3.3L/V6-201 & 3.8L/V6-231 Engines

Refer to the chart below and perform the diagnostic test that corresponds to the trouble code displayed on the DRB.

TROUBLE CODE	DIAGNOSTIC TEST
INJECTOR #1 CONTROL CIRCUIT	TC-17B
INJECTOR #2 CONTROL CIRCUIT	TC-18A
INJECTOR #3 CONTROL CIRCUIT	TC-19A
INJECTOR #4 CONTROL CIRCUIT	TC-20A
INJECTOR #5 CONTROL CIRCUIT	TC-21A
INJECTOR #6 CONTROL CIRCUIT	TC-22A

Fig. 137   Test TC-17A: Injector Control Circuit (Part 2 of 2). 3.3L/V6-201 & 3.8L/V6-231 Engines

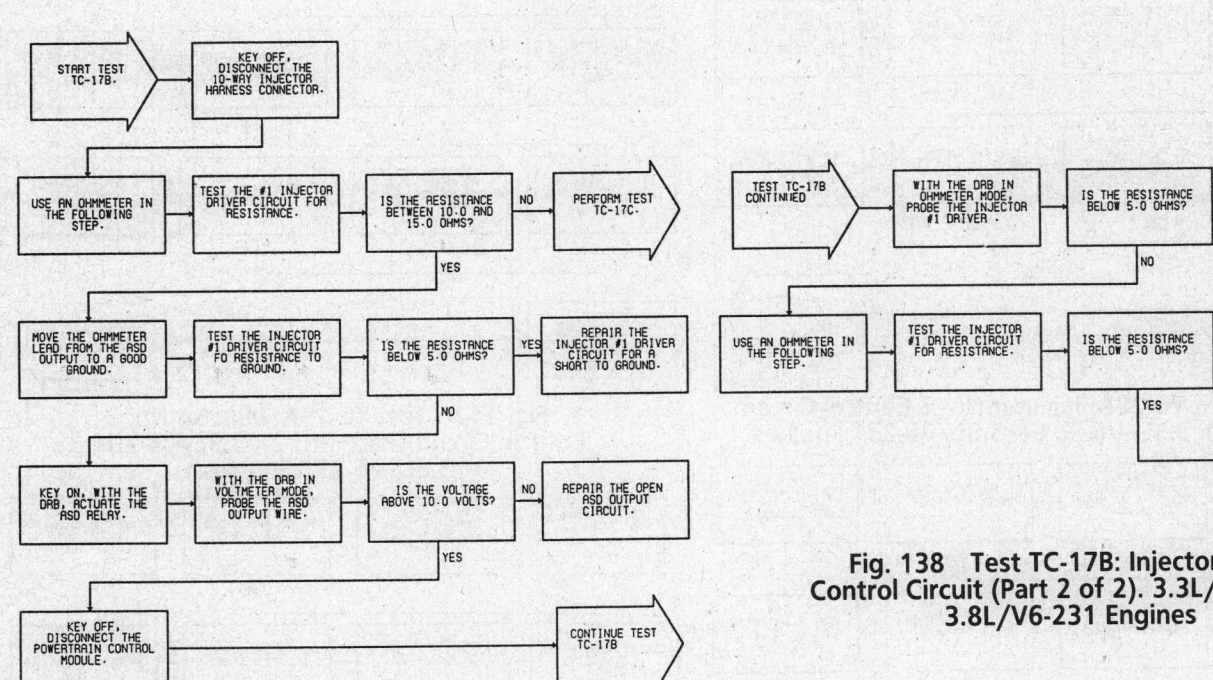

CR1029303130010X

Fig. 138   Test TC-17B: Injector No. 1 Control Circuit (Part 1 of 2). 3.3L/V6-201 & 3.8L/V6-231 Engines

CR1029303130020X

Fig. 138   Test TC-17B: Injector No. 1 Control Circuit (Part 2 of 2). 3.3L/V6-201 & 3.8L/V6-231 Engines

MODELS w/3.0L/V6-181, 3.3L/V6-201 & 3.8L/V6-231 ENGINES EXCEPT CONCORDE, INTREPID, LHS, STEALTH, VISION & 1994-96 NEW YORKER

12-79

CHRYSLER–Fuel Injection

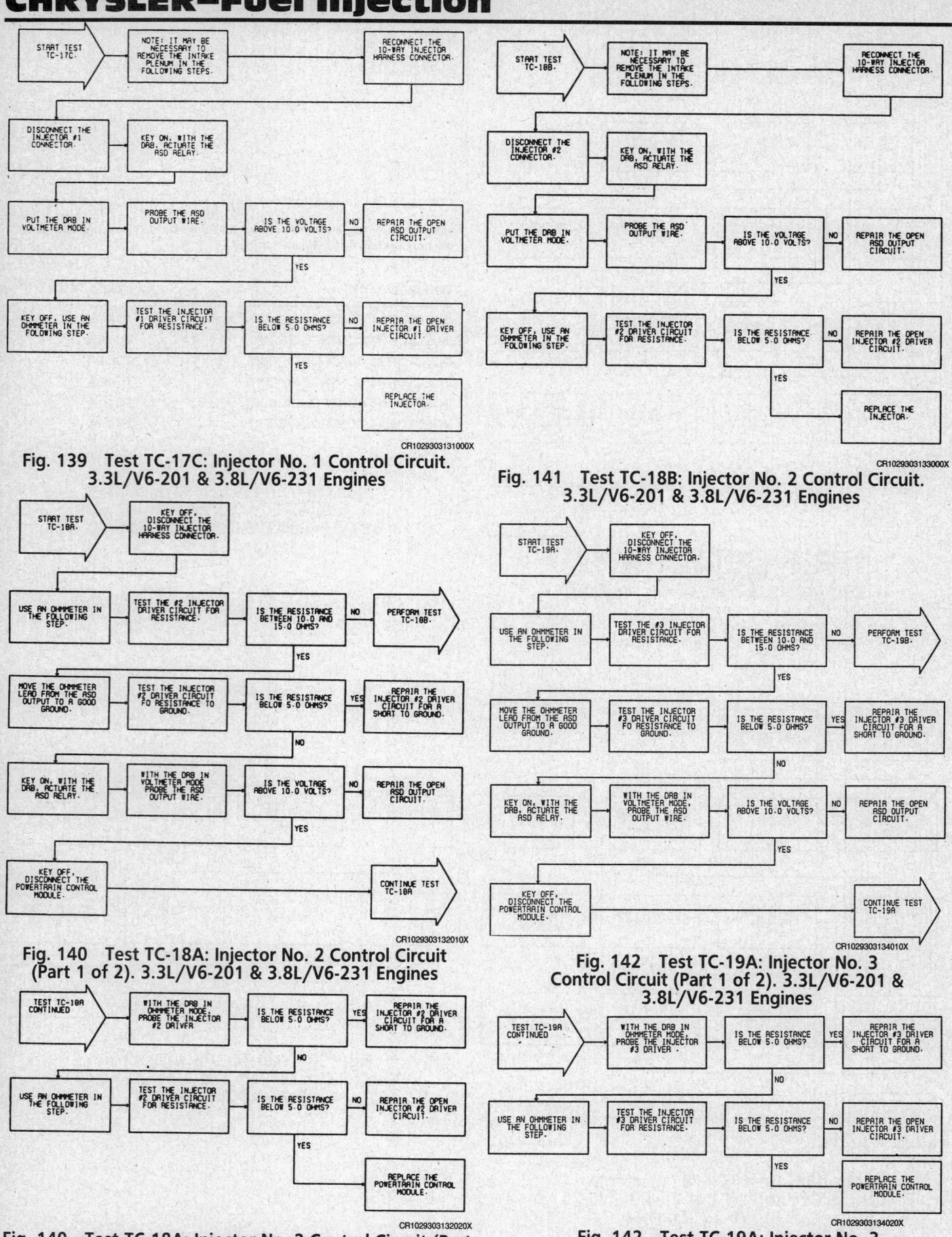

Fig. 139   Test TC-17C: Injector No. 1 Control Circuit.
3.3L/V6-201 & 3.8L/V6-231 Engines

Fig. 141   Test TC-18B: Injector No. 2 Control Circuit.
3.3L/V6-201 & 3.8L/V6-231 Engines

Fig. 140   Test TC-18A: Injector No. 2 Control Circuit
(Part 1 of 2). 3.3L/V6-201 & 3.8L/V6-231 Engines

Fig. 142   Test TC-19A: Injector No. 3
Control Circuit (Part 1 of 2). 3.3L/V6-201 &
3.8L/V6-231 Engines

Fig. 140   Test TC-18A: Injector No. 2 Control Circuit (Part
2 of 2). 3.3L/V6-201 & 3.8L/V6-231 Engines

Fig. 142   Test TC-19A: Injector No. 3
Control Circuit (Part 2 of 2). 3.3L/V6-201
& 3.8L/V6-231 Engines

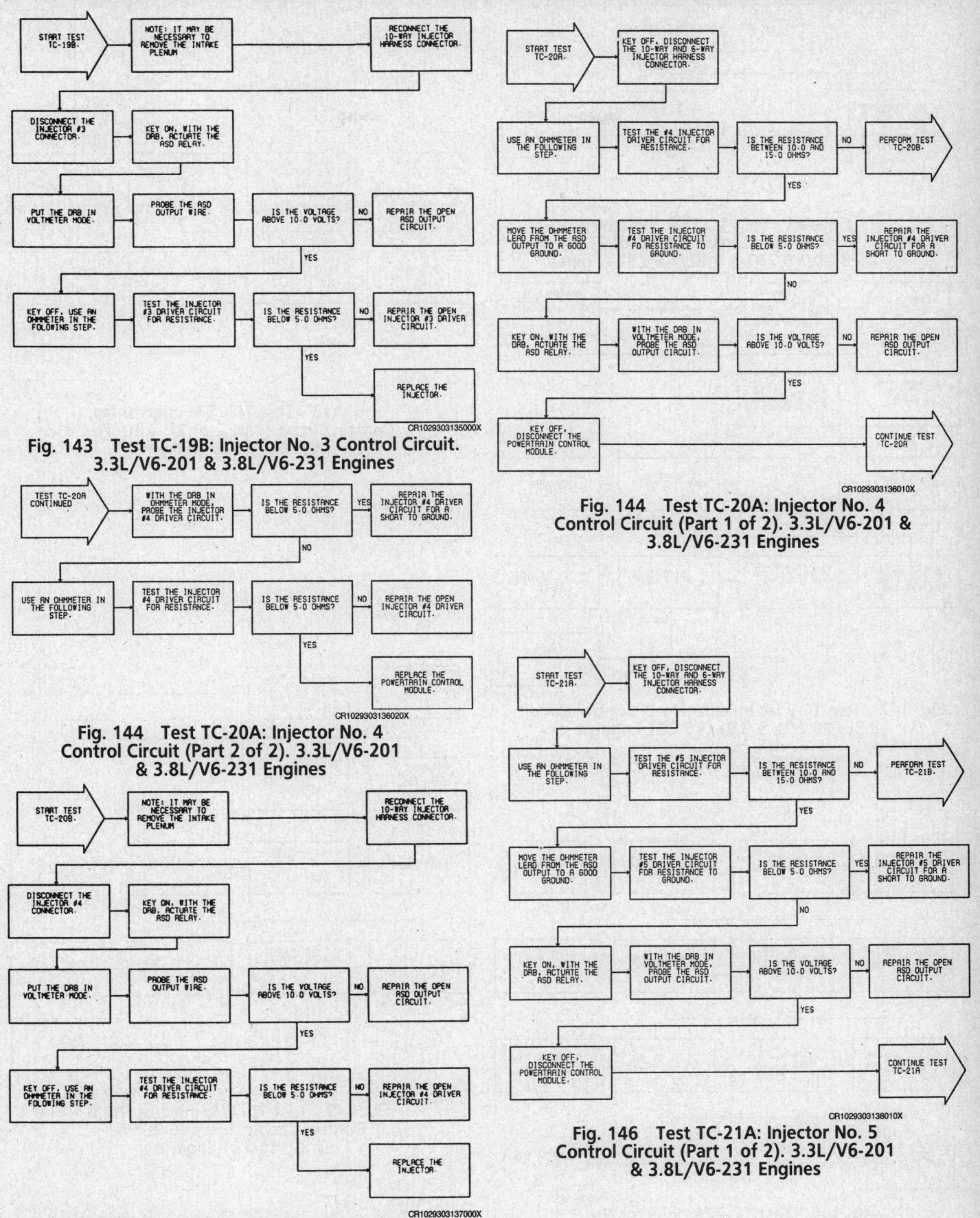

Fig. 143   Test TC-19B: Injector No. 3 Control Circuit. 3.3L/V6-201 & 3.8L/V6-231 Engines

Fig. 144   Test TC-20A: Injector No. 4 Control Circuit (Part 2 of 2). 3.3L/V6-201 & 3.8L/V6-231 Engines

Fig. 144   Test TC-20A: Injector No. 4 Control Circuit (Part 1 of 2). 3.3L/V6-201 & 3.8L/V6-231 Engines

Fig. 145   Test TC-20B: Injector No. 4 Control Circuit. 3.3L/V6-201 & 3.8L/V6-231 Engines

Fig. 146   Test TC-21A: Injector No. 5 Control Circuit (Part 1 of 2). 3.3L/V6-201 & 3.8L/V6-231 Engines

MODELS w/3.0L/V6-181, 3.3L/V6-201 & 3.8L/V6-231 ENGINES EXCEPT CONCORDE, INTREPID, LHS, STEALTH, VISION & 1994-96 NEW YORKER

12-81

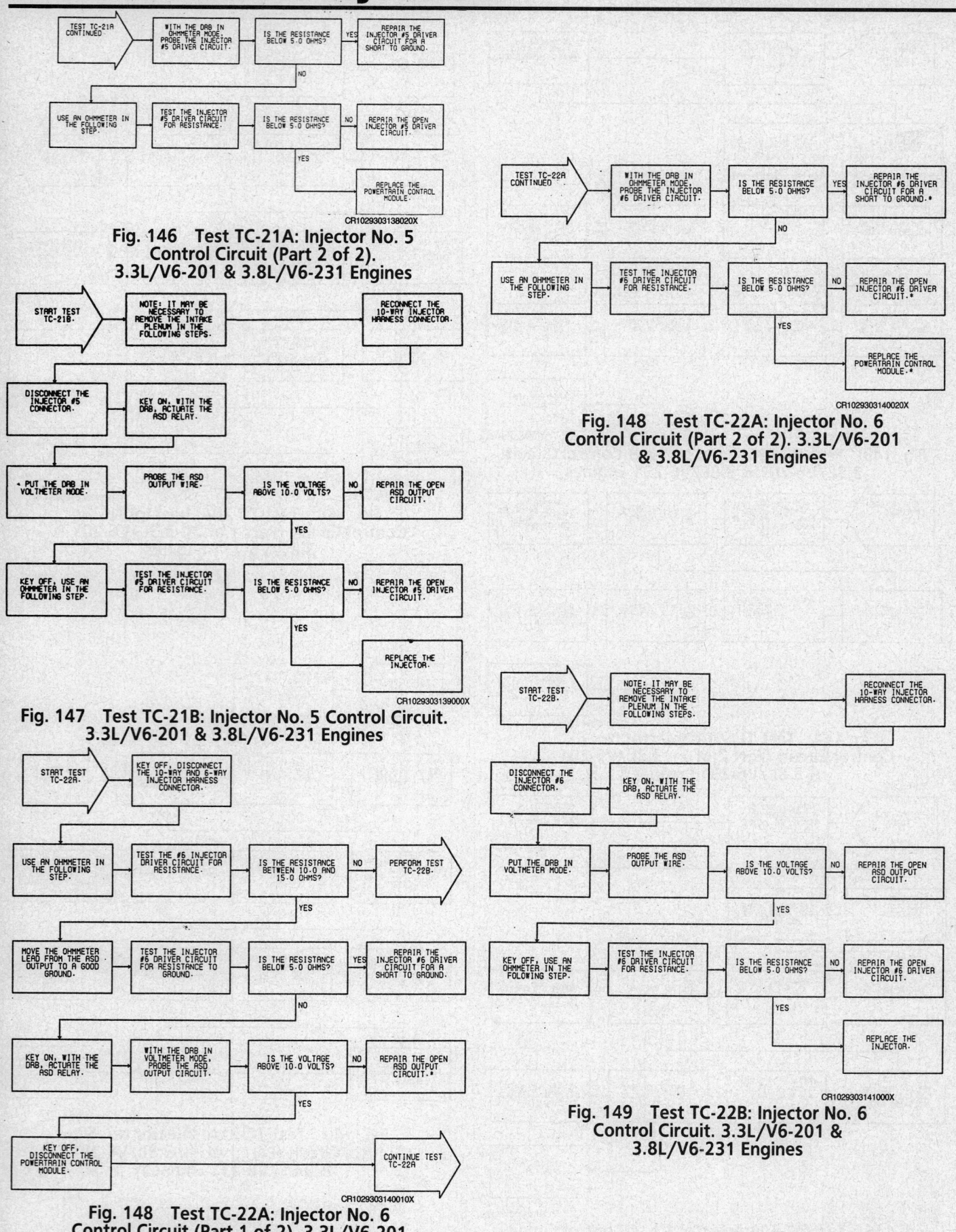

Fig. 146   Test TC-21A: Injector No. 5 Control Circuit (Part 2 of 2). 3.3L/V6-201 & 3.8L/V6-231 Engines

Fig. 147   Test TC-21B: Injector No. 5 Control Circuit. 3.3L/V6-201 & 3.8L/V6-231 Engines

Fig. 148   Test TC-22A: Injector No. 6 Control Circuit (Part 1 of 2). 3.3L/V6-201 & 3.8L/V6-231 Engines

Fig. 148   Test TC-22A: Injector No. 6 Control Circuit (Part 2 of 2). 3.3L/V6-201 & 3.8L/V6-231 Engines

Fig. 149   Test TC-22B: Injector No. 6 Control Circuit. 3.3L/V6-201 & 3.8L/V6-231 Engines

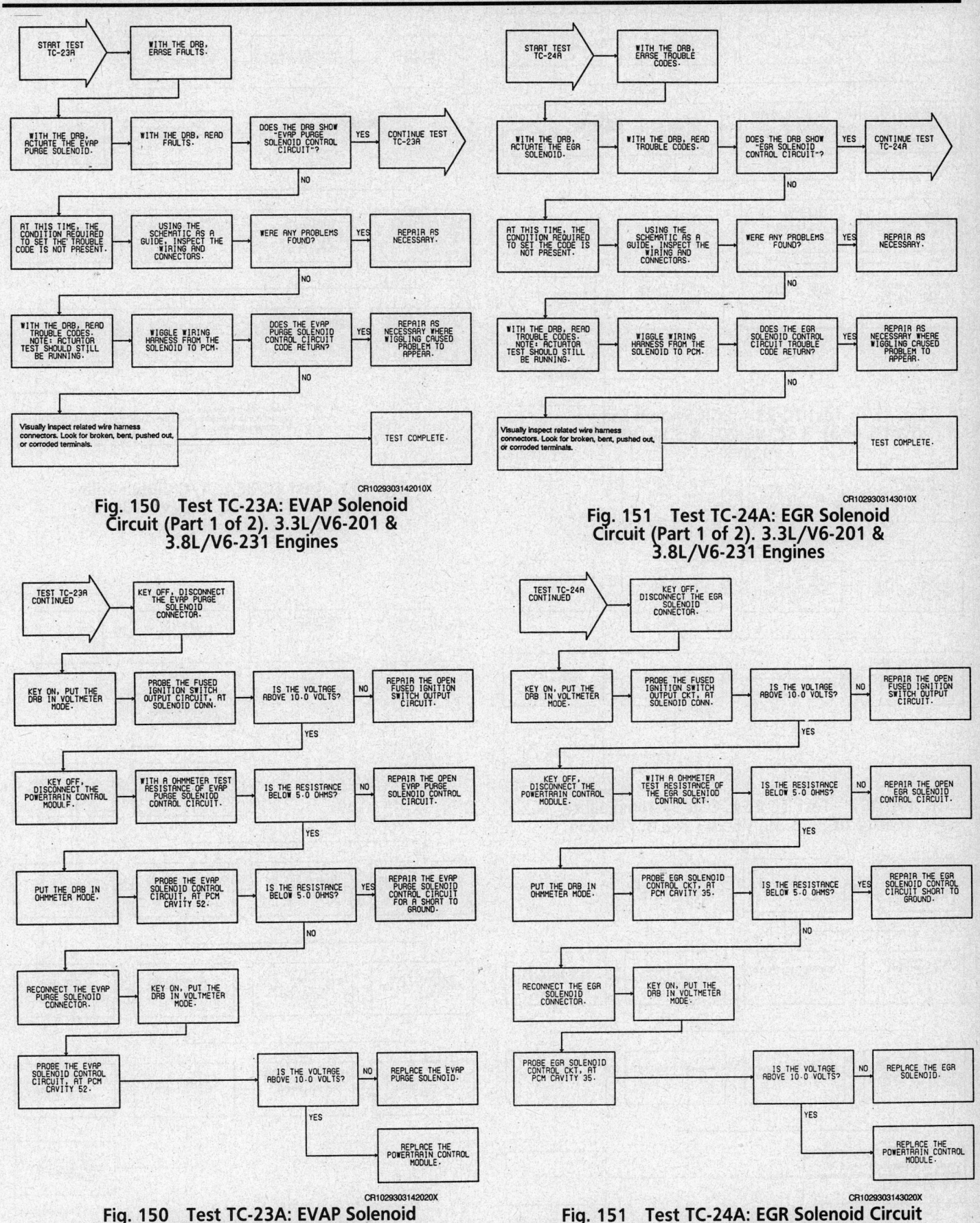

CR1029303142010X

Fig. 150   Test TC-23A: EVAP Solenoid Circuit (Part 1 of 2). 3.3L/V6-201 & 3.8L/V6-231 Engines

CR1029303143010X

Fig. 151   Test TC-24A: EGR Solenoid Circuit (Part 1 of 2). 3.3L/V6-201 & 3.8L/V6-231 Engines

CR1029303142020X

Fig. 150   Test TC-23A: EVAP Solenoid Circuit (Part 2 of 2). 3.3L/V6-201 & 3.8L/V6-231 Engines

CR1029303143020X

Fig. 151   Test TC-24A: EGR Solenoid Circuit (Part 2 of 2). 3.3L/V6-201 & 3.8L/V6-231 Engines

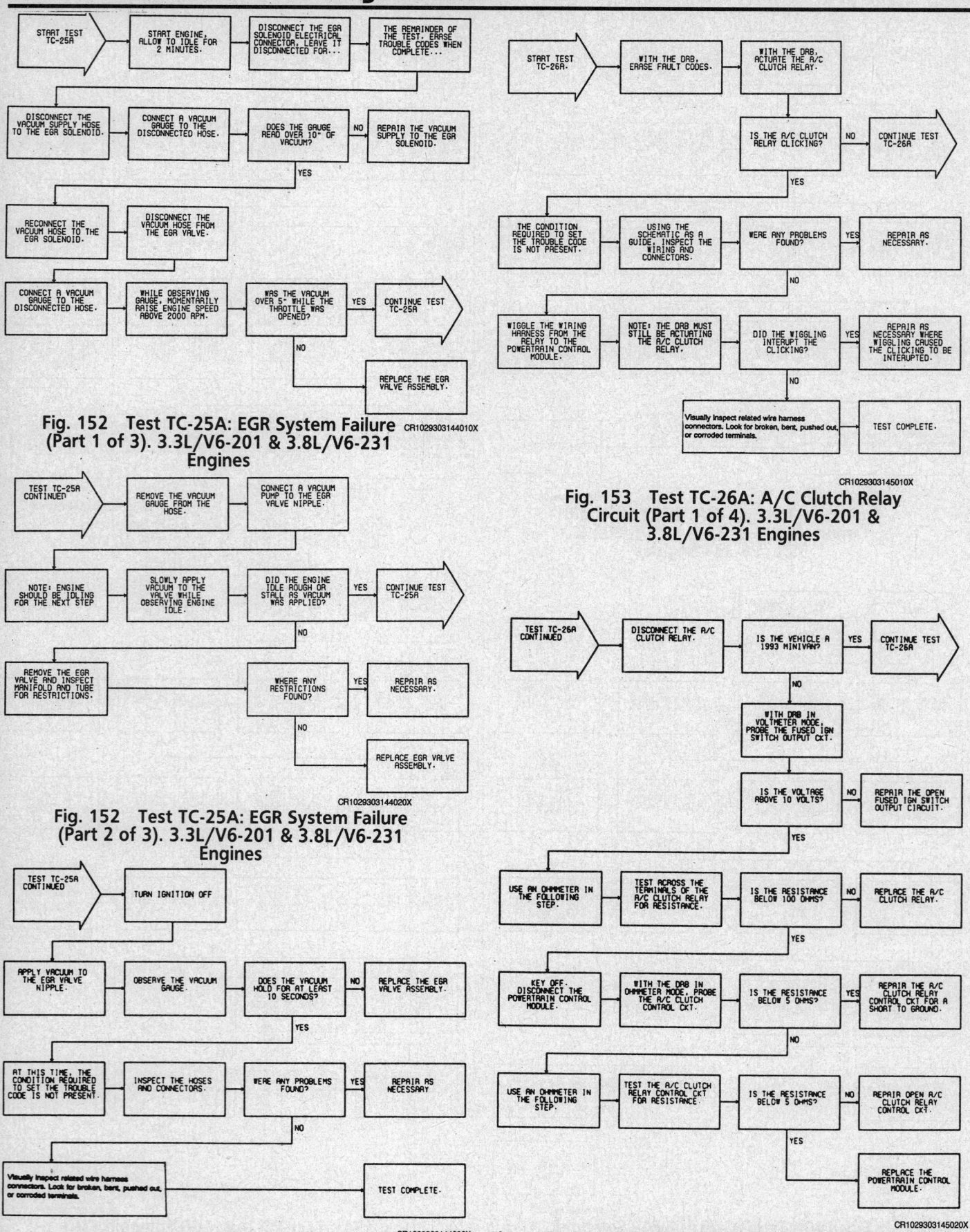

Fig. 152   Test TC-25A: EGR System Failure (Part 1 of 3). 3.3L/V6-201 & 3.8L/V6-231 Engines

CR1029303144010X

Fig. 152   Test TC-25A: EGR System Failure (Part 2 of 3). 3.3L/V6-201 & 3.8L/V6-231 Engines

CR1029303144020X

Fig. 152   Test TC-25A: EGR System Failure (Part 3 of 3). 3.3L/V6-201 & 3.8L/V6-231 Engines

CR1029303144030X

Fig. 153   Test TC-26A: A/C Clutch Relay Circuit (Part 1 of 4). 3.3L/V6-201 & 3.8L/V6-231 Engines

CR1029303145010X

Fig. 153   Test TC-26A: A/C Clutch Relay Circuit (Part 2 of 4). 3.3L/V6-201 & 3.8L/V6-231 Engines

CR1029303145020X

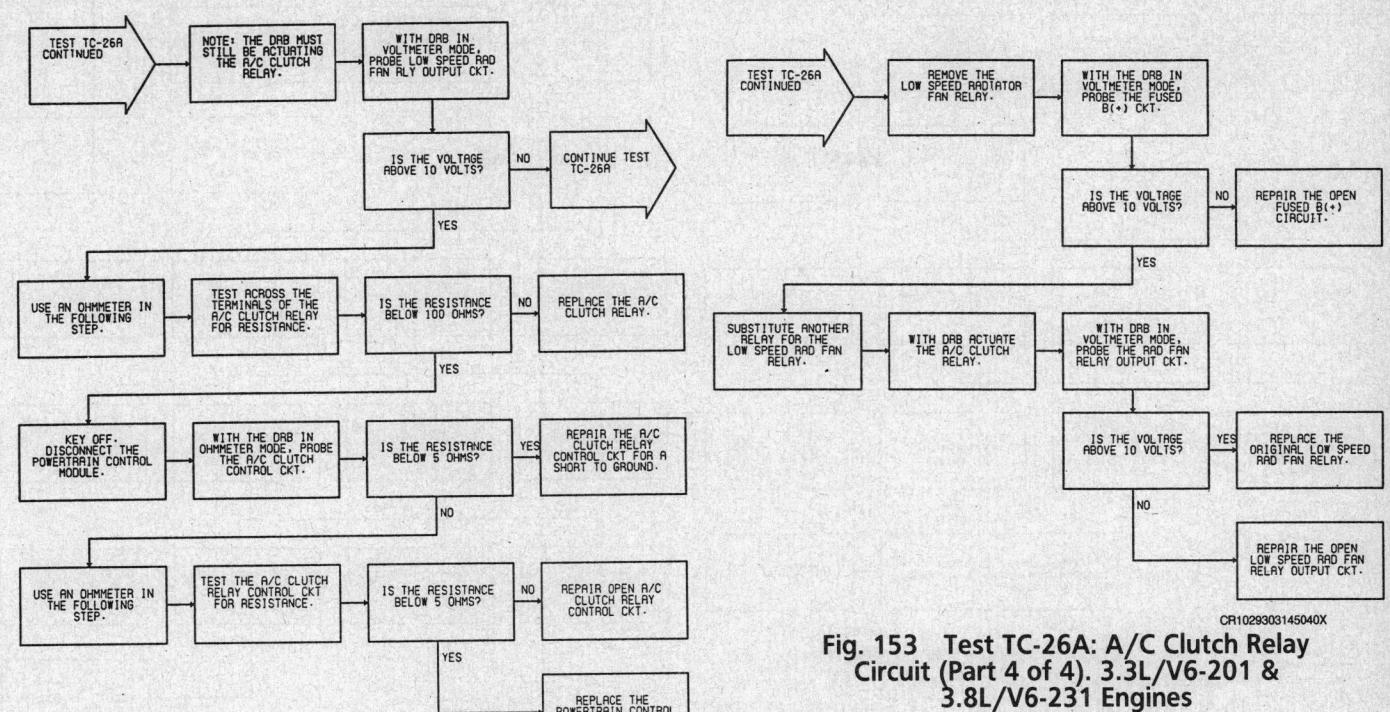

Fig. 153   Test TC-26A: A/C Clutch Relay
Circuit (Part 3 of 4). 3.3L/V6-201 &
3.8L/V6-231 Engines

Fig. 153   Test TC-26A: A/C Clutch Relay
Circuit (Part 4 of 4). 3.3L/V6-201 &
3.8L/V6-231 Engines

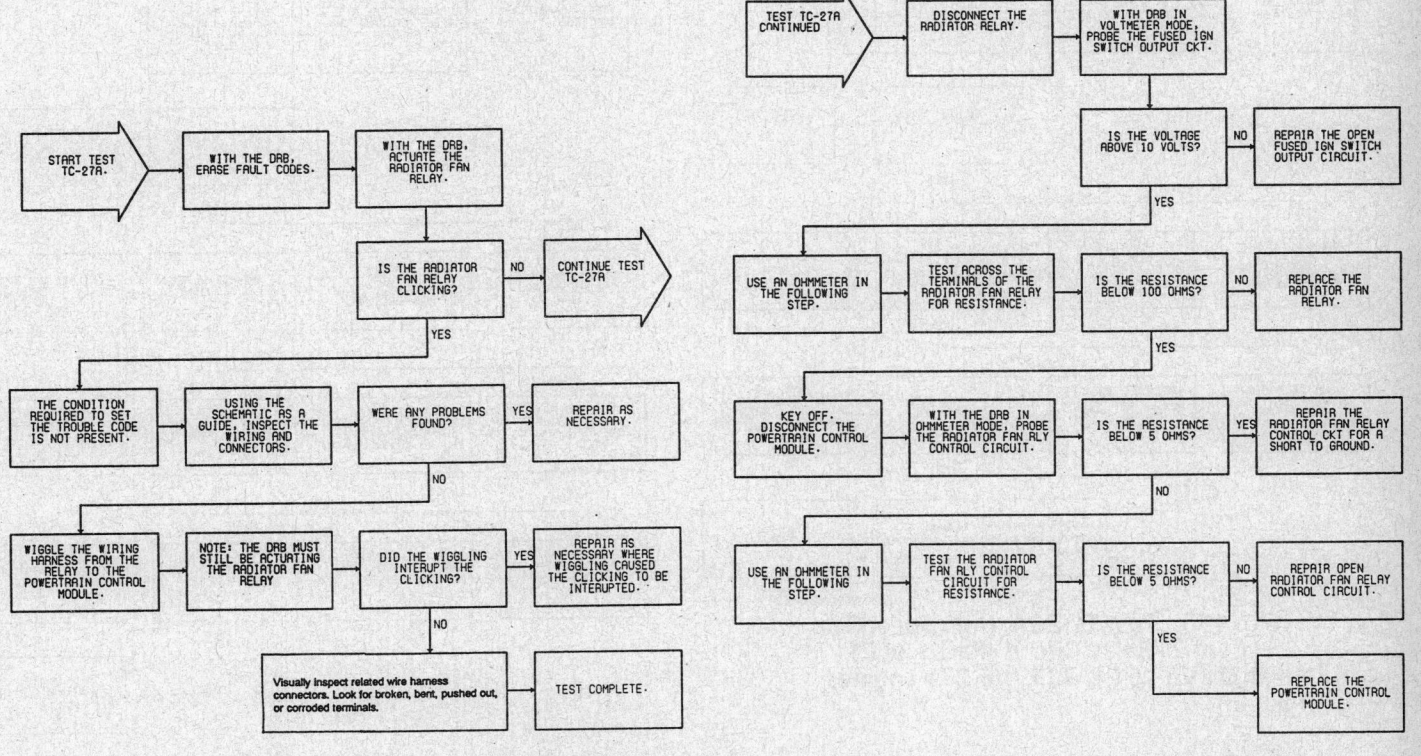

Fig. 154   Test TC-27A: Radiator Fan Control
Relay Circuit (Part 1 of 2). 3.3L/V6-201 &
3.8L/V6-231 Engines

Fig. 154   Test TC-27A: Radiator Fan
Control Relay Circuit (Part 2 of 2).
3.3L/V6-201 & 3.8L/V6-231 Engines

*MODELS w/3.0L/V6-181, 3.3L/V6-201 & 3.8L/V6-231 ENGINES EXCEPT CONCORDE, INTREPID, LHS, STEALTH, VISION &
1994-96 NEW YORKER*

12-85

CHRYSLER—Fuel Injection

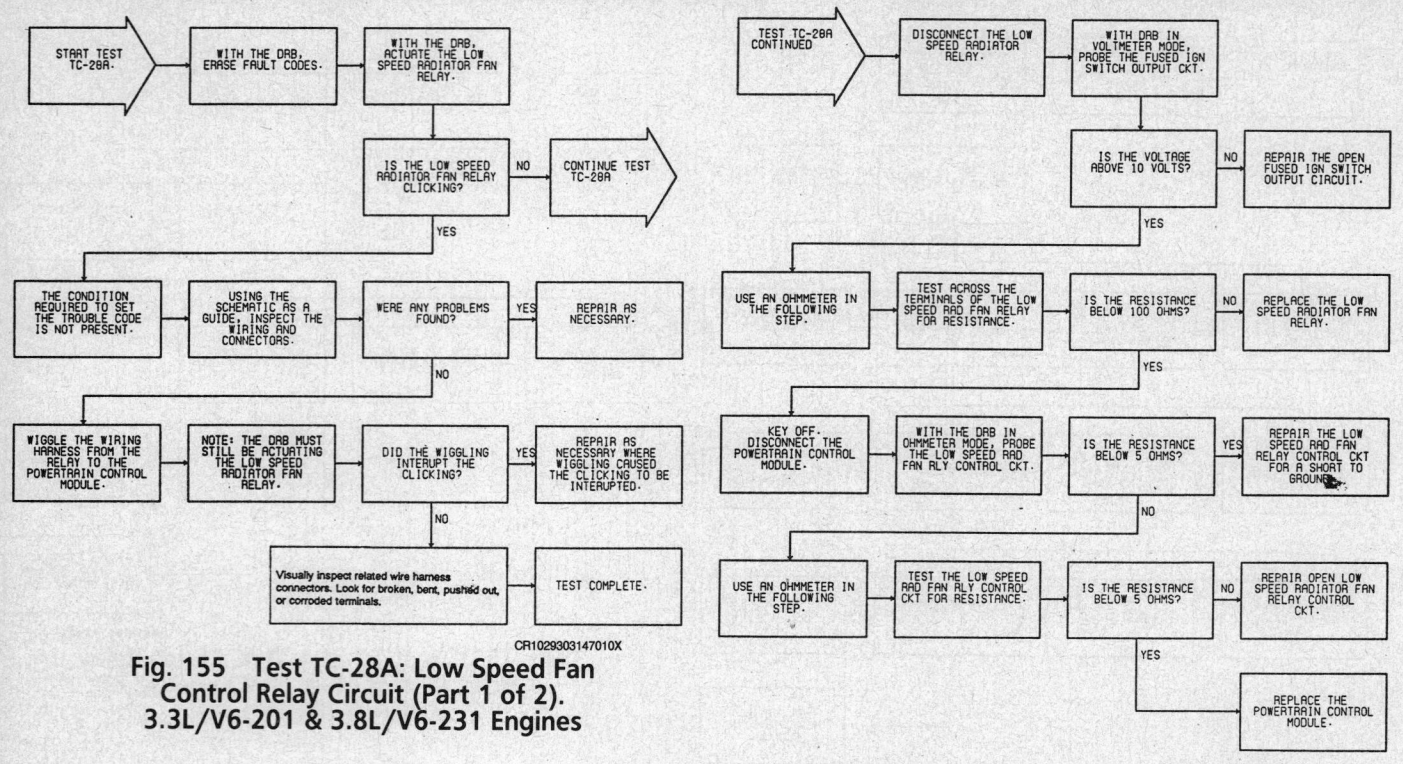

Fig. 155 Test TC-28A: Low Speed Fan
Control Relay Circuit (Part 1 of 2).
3.3L/V6-201 & 3.8L/V6-231 Engines

CR1029303147010X

Fig. 155 Test TC-28A: Low Speed Fan
Control Relay Circuit (Part 2 of 2).
3.3L/V6-201 & 3.8L/V6-231 Engines

CR1029303147020X

Fig. 156 Test TC-29A: High Speed Fan
Control Relay Circuit (Part 1 of 2).
3.3L/V6-201 & 3.8L/V6-231 Engines

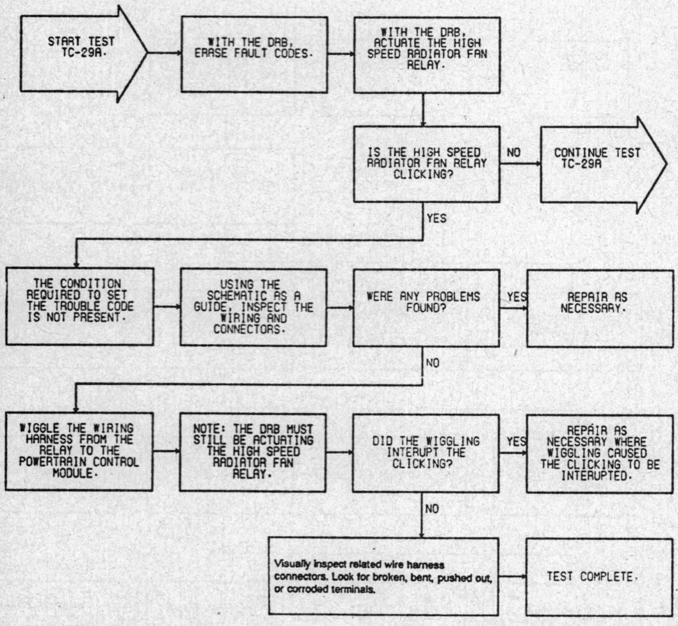

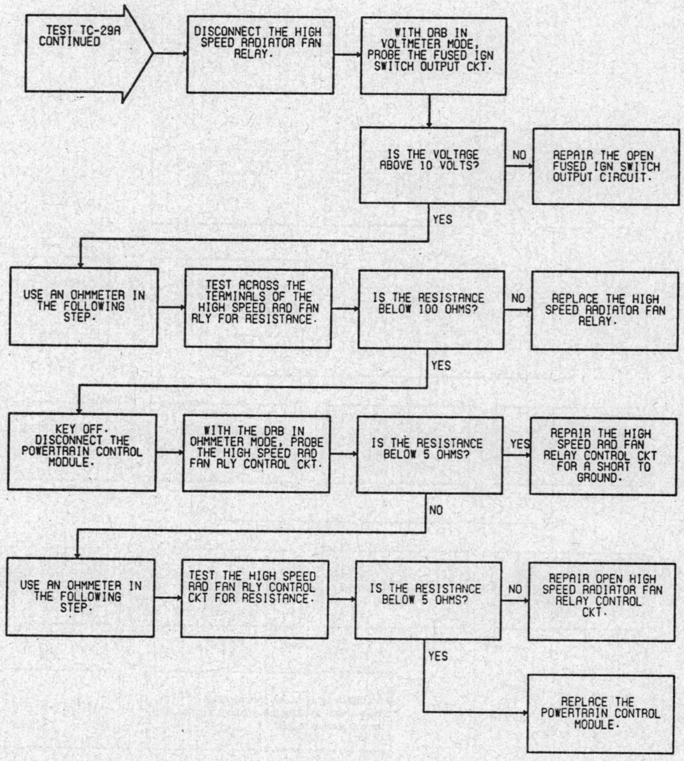

CR1029303148010X

Fig. 156 Test TC-29A: High Speed Fan
Control Relay Circuit (Part 2 of 2).
3.3L/V6-201 & 3.8L/V6-231 Engines

CR1029303148020X

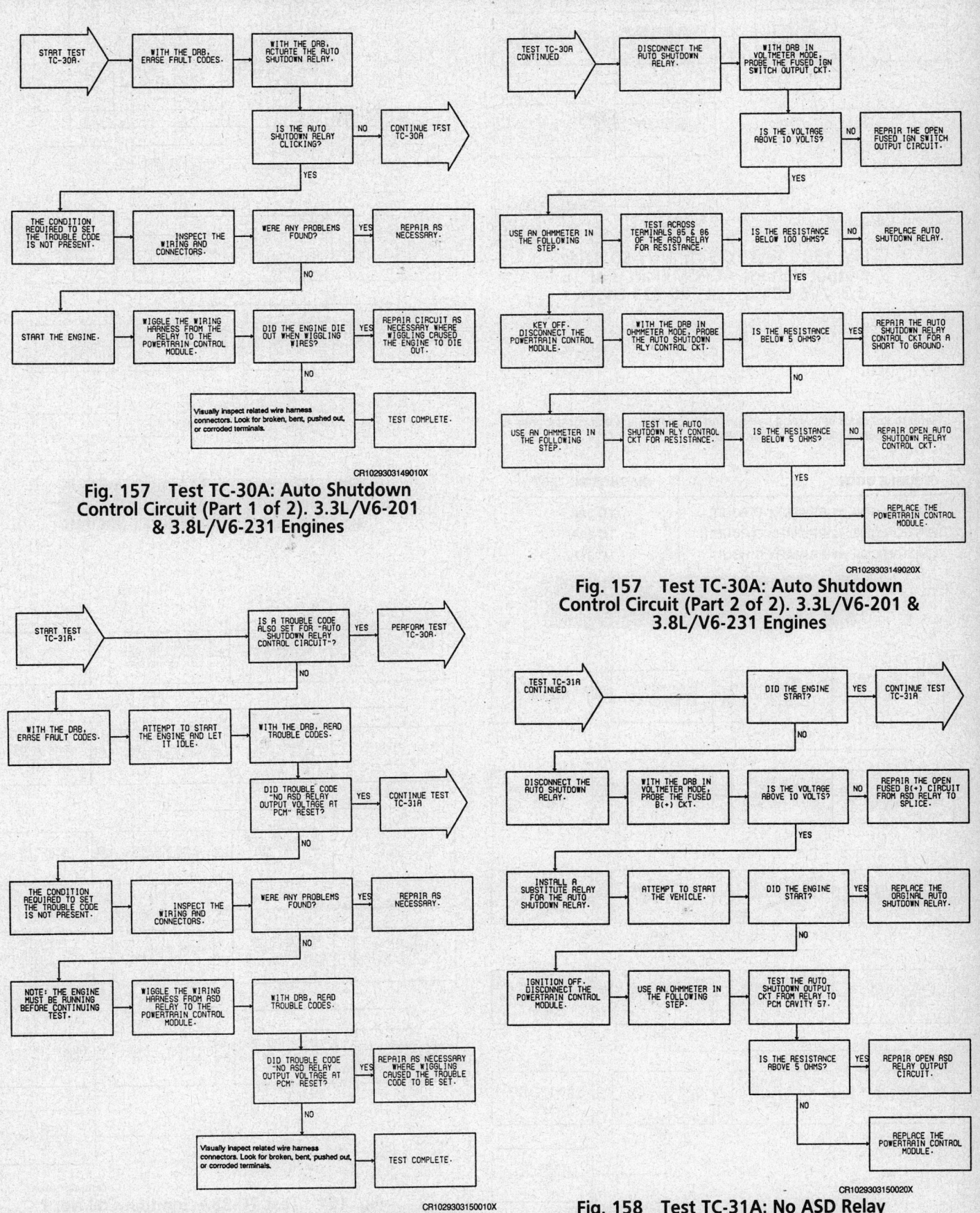

Fig. 157   Test TC-30A: Auto Shutdown Control Circuit (Part 1 of 2). 3.3L/V6-201 & 3.8L/V6-231 Engines

Fig. 157   Test TC-30A: Auto Shutdown Control Circuit (Part 2 of 2). 3.3L/V6-201 & 3.8L/V6-231 Engines

Fig. 158   Test TC-31A: No ASD Relay Output Voltage At PCM (Part 1 of 3). 3.3L/V6-201 & 3.8L/V6-231 Engines

Fig. 158   Test TC-31A: No ASD Relay Output Voltage At PCM (Part 2 of 3). 3.3L/V6-201 & 3.8L/V6-231 Engines

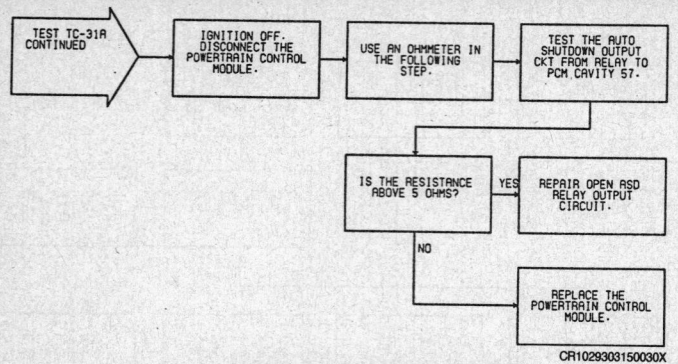

Fig. 158 Test TC-31A: No ASD Relay Output Voltage At PCM (Part 3 of 3). 3.3L/V6-201 & 3.8L/V6-231 Engines

Refer to the chart below and perform the diagnostic test that corresponds to the trouble code displayed on the DRB.

TROUBLE CODE	DIAGNOSTIC TEST
IGNITION COIL #1 PRIMARY CIRCUIT	TC-32B
IGNITION COIL #2 PRIMARY CIRCUIT	TC-33A
IGNITION COIL #3 PRIMARY CIRCUIT	TC-34A

Fig. 159 Test TC-32A: Ignition Coil Primary Circuit (Part 1 of 2). 3.3L/V6-201 & 3.8L/V6-231 Engines

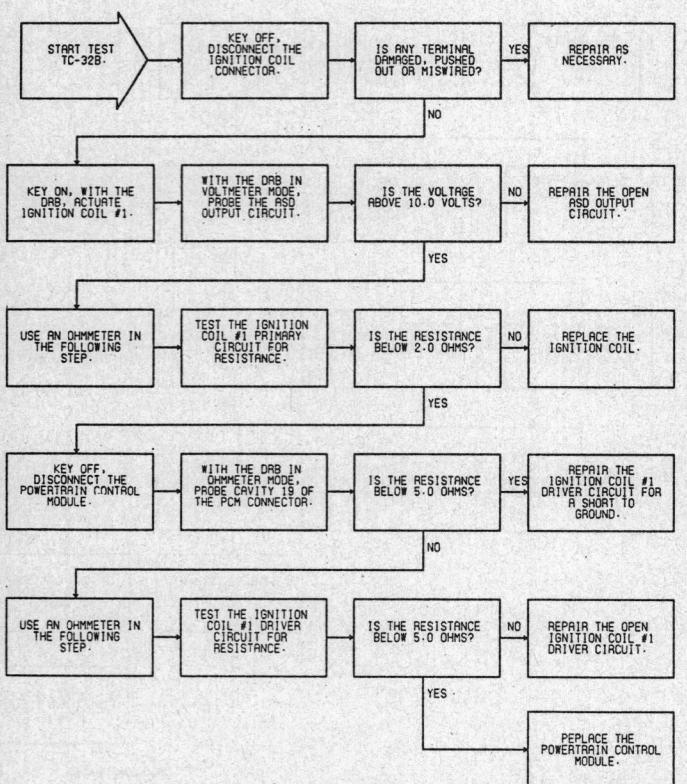

CR1029303152000X

Fig. 160 Test TC-32B: Ignition Coil No. 1 Primary Circuit. 3.3L/V6-201 & 3.8L/V6-231 Engines

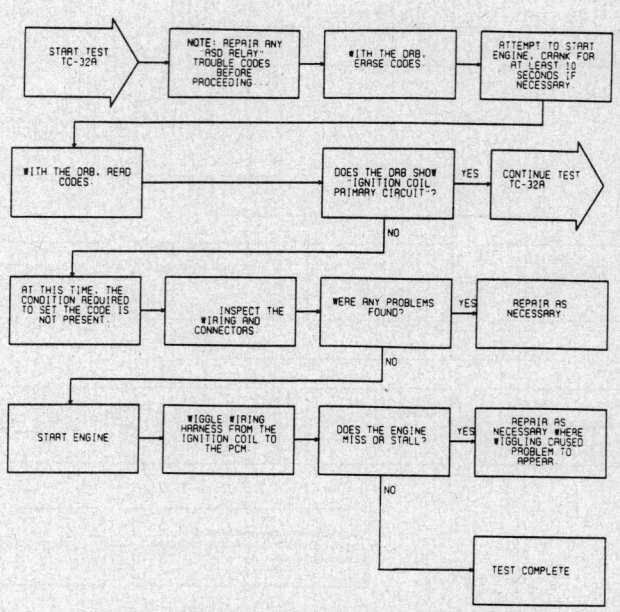

Fig. 159 Test TC-32A: Ignition Coil Primary Circuit (Part 2 of 2). 3.3L/V6-201 & 3.8L/V6-231 Engines

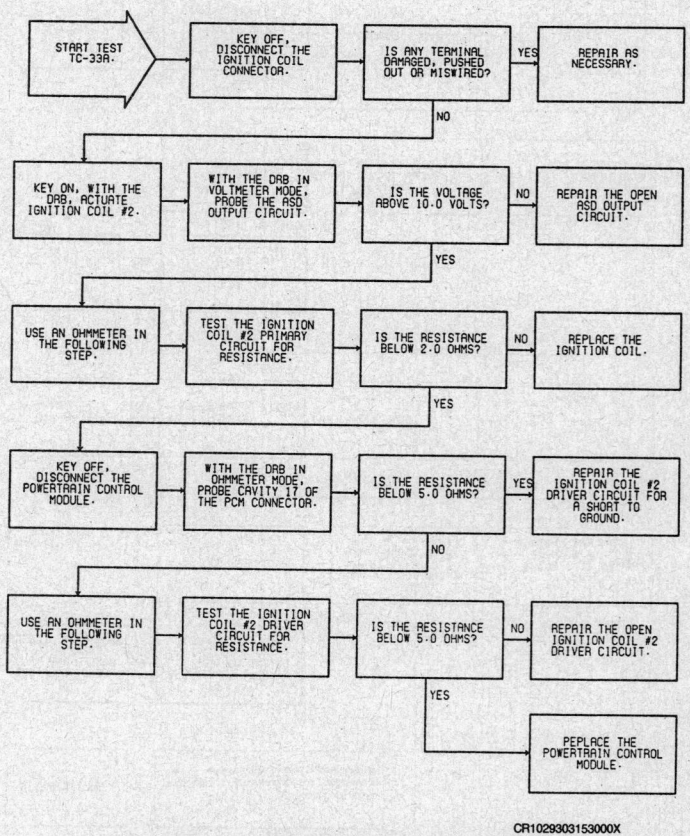

CR1029303153000X

Fig. 161 Test TC-33A: Ignition Coil No. 2 Primary Circuit. 3.3L/V6-201 & 3.8L/V6-231 Engines

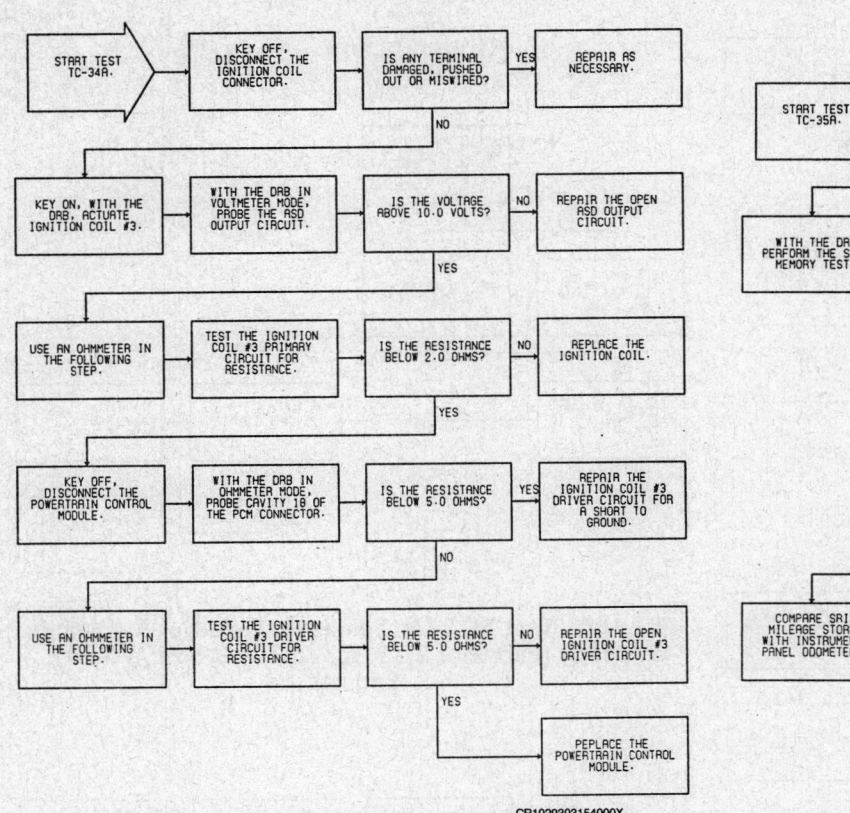

Fig. 162   Test TC-34A: Ignition Coil No. 3 Primary Circuit. 3.3L/V6-201 & 3.8L/V6-231 Engines

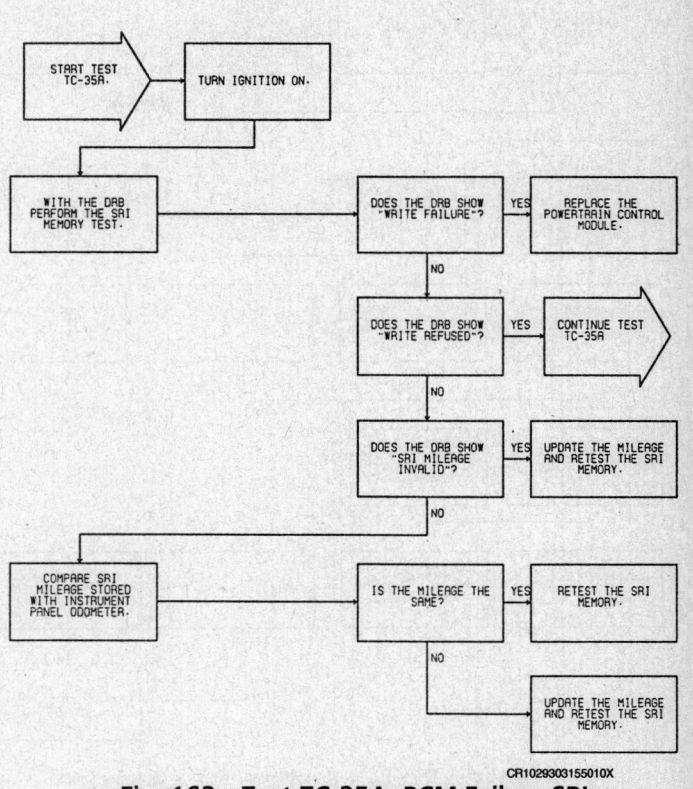

Fig. 163   Test TC-35A: PCM Failure SRI Mile Not Stored (Part 1 of 2). 3.3L/V6-201 & 3.8L/V6-231 Engines

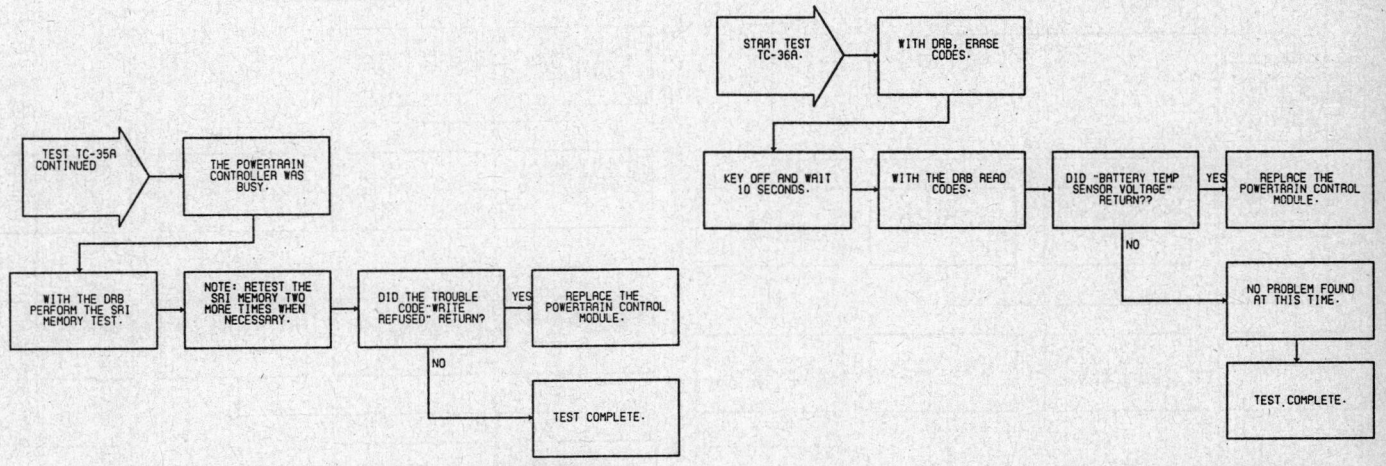

Fig. 163   Test TC-35A: PCM Failure SRI Mile Not Stored (Part 2 of 2). 3.3L/V6-201 & 3.8L/V6-231 Engines

Fig. 164   Test TC-36A: Battery Temperature Sensor Volts Out Of Limit. 3.3L/V6-201 & 3.8L/V6-231 Engines

MODELS w/3.0L/V6-181, 3.3L/V6-201 & 3.8L/V6-231 ENGINES EXCEPT CONCORDE, INTREPID, LHS, STEALTH, VISION & 1994-96 NEW YORKER

12-89

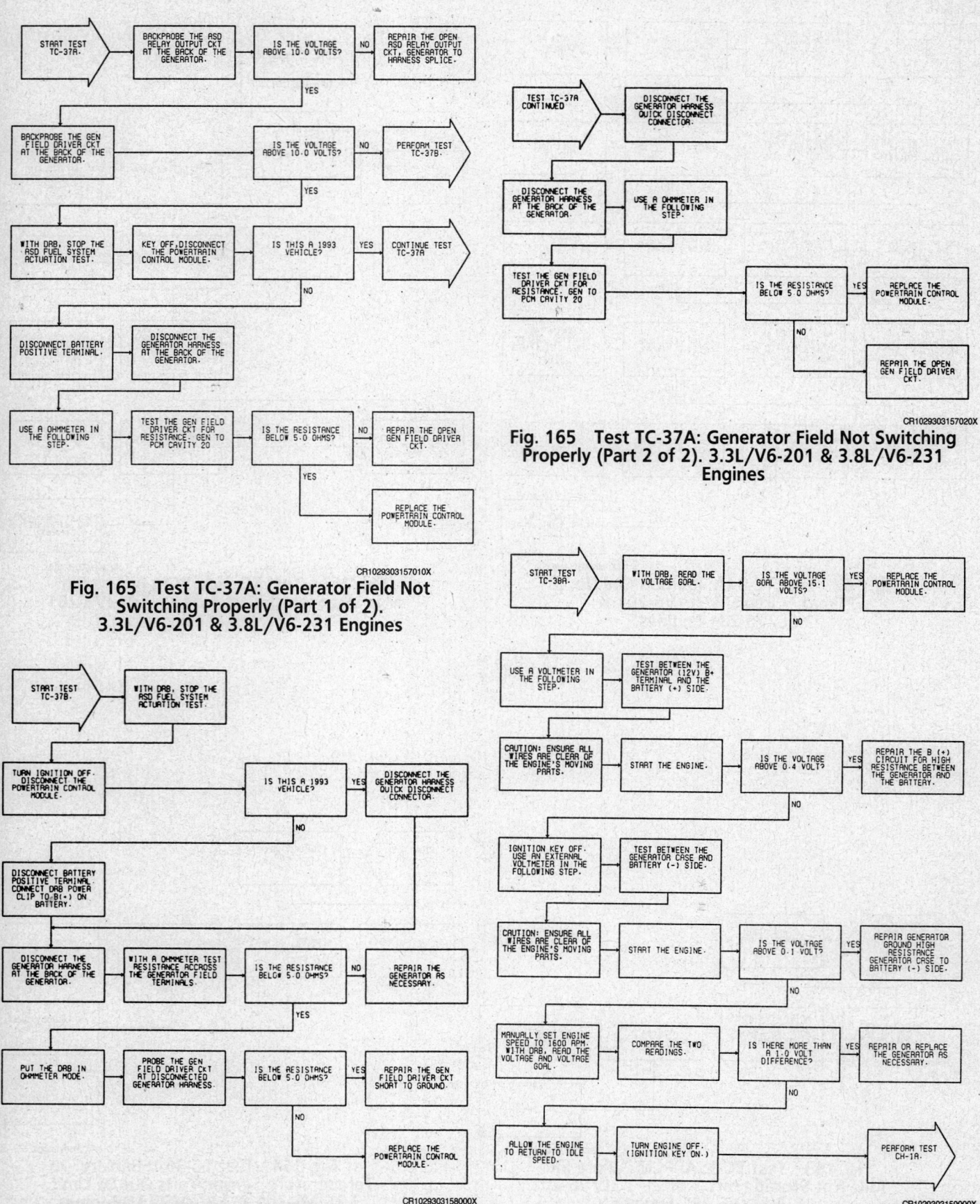

Fig. 165 Test TC-37A: Generator Field Not Switching Properly (Part 1 of 2). 3.3L/V6-201 & 3.8L/V6-231 Engines

Fig. 165 Test TC-37A: Generator Field Not Switching Properly (Part 2 of 2). 3.3L/V6-201 & 3.8L/V6-231 Engines

Fig. 166 Test TC-37B: Generator Field Not Switching Properly. 3.3L/V6-201 & 3.8L/V6-231 Engines

Fig. 167 Test TC-38A: Charging System Voltage Too Low. 3.3L/V6-201 & 3.8L/V6-231 Engines

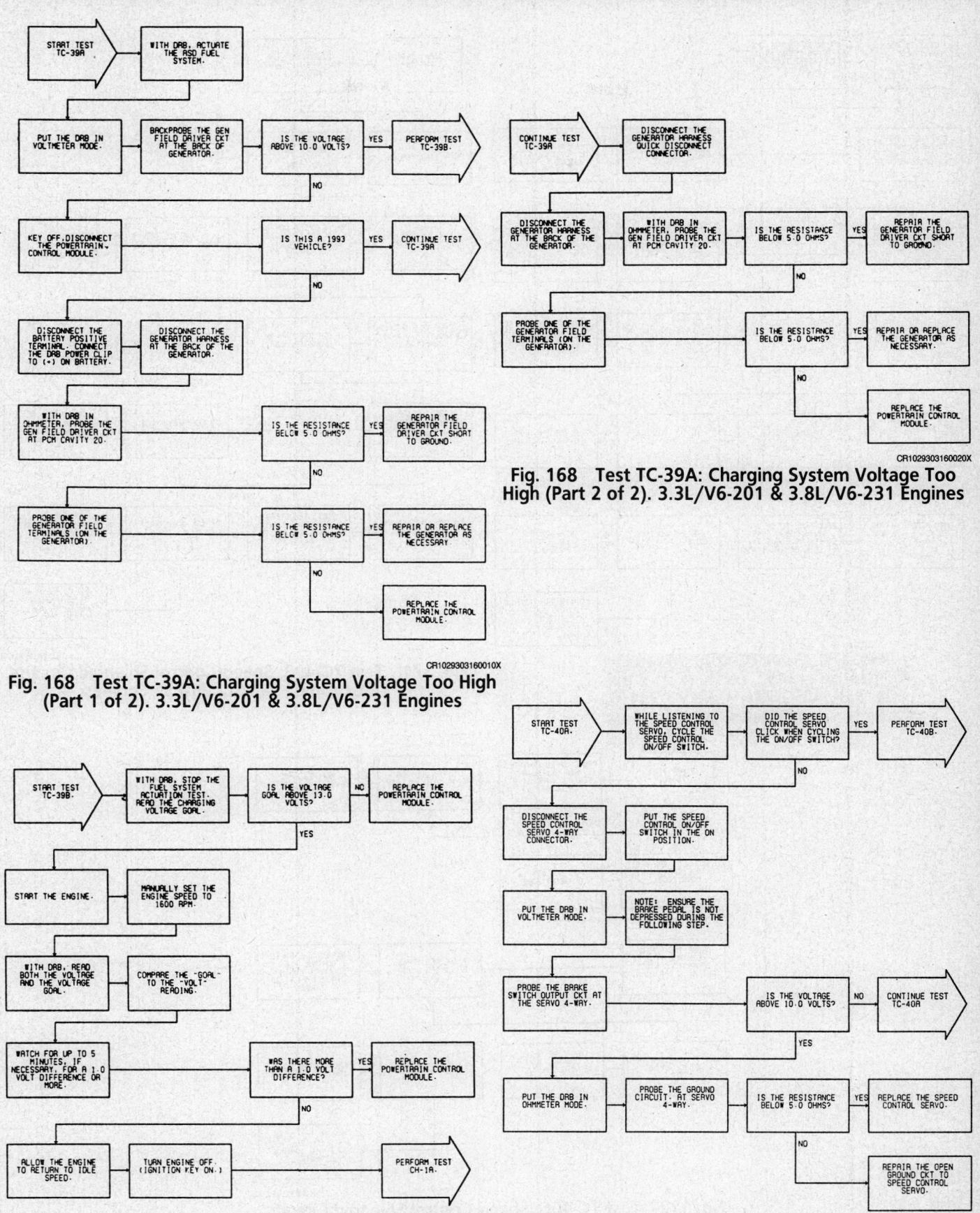

Fig. 168   Test TC-39A: Charging System Voltage Too High (Part 2 of 2). 3.3L/V6-201 & 3.8L/V6-231 Engines

Fig. 168   Test TC-39A: Charging System Voltage Too High (Part 1 of 2). 3.3L/V6-201 & 3.8L/V6-231 Engines

Fig. 169   Test TC-39B: Charging System Voltage Too High. 3.3L/V6-201 & 3.8L/V6-231 Engines

Fig. 170   Test TC-40A: Speed Control Solenoid Circuits (Part 1 of 2). 3.3L/V6-201 & 3.8L/V6-231 Engines

MODELS w/3.0L/V6-181, 3.3L/V6-201 & 3.8L/V6-231 ENGINES EXCEPT CONCORDE, INTREPID, LHS, STEALTH, VISION & 1994-96 NEW YORKER

12-91

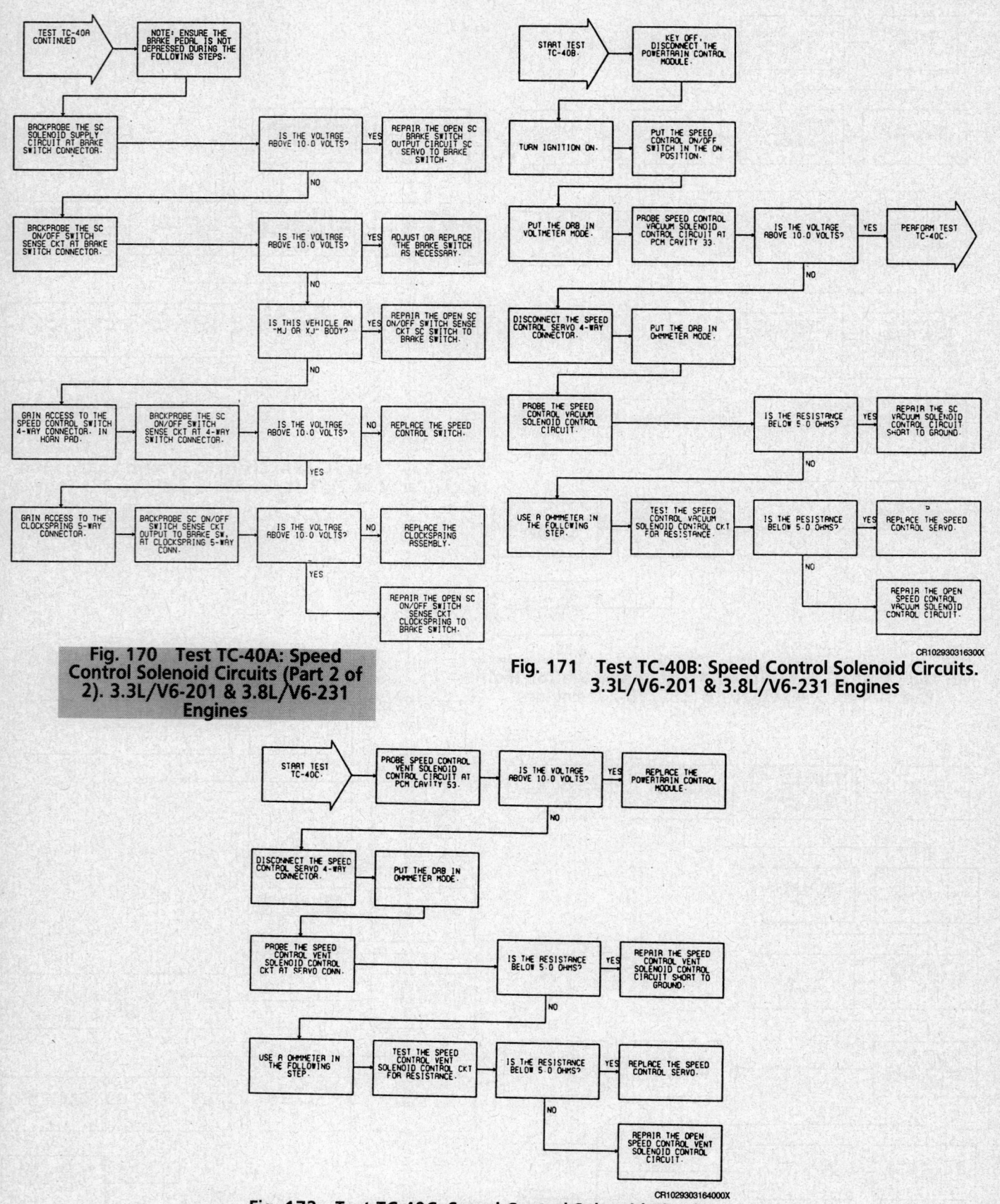

Fig. 170 Test TC-40A: Speed Control Solenoid Circuits (Part 2 of 2). 3.3L/V6-201 & 3.8L/V6-231 Engines

Fig. 171 Test TC-40B: Speed Control Solenoid Circuits. 3.3L/V6-201 & 3.8L/V6-231 Engines

Fig. 172 Test TC-40C: Speed Control Solenoid Circuits. 3.3L/V6-201 & 3.8L/V6-231 Engines

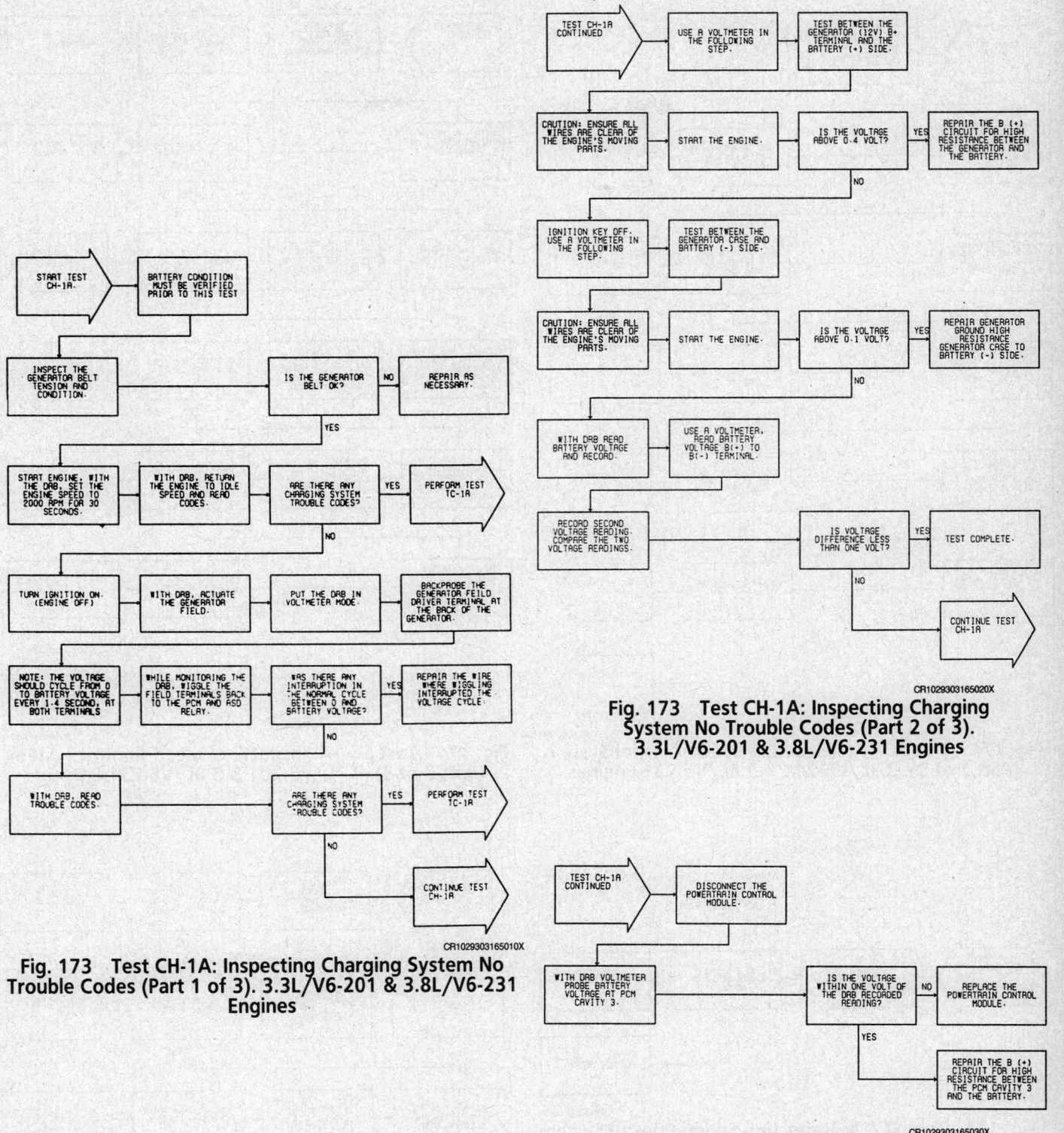

Fig. 173   Test CH-1A: Inspecting Charging System No Trouble Codes (Part 1 of 3). 3.3L/V6-201 & 3.8L/V6-231 Engines

CR1029303165010X

Fig. 173   Test CH-1A: Inspecting Charging System No Trouble Codes (Part 2 of 3). 3.3L/V6-201 & 3.8L/V6-231 Engines

CR1029303165020X

Fig. 173   Test CH-1A: Inspecting Charging System No Trouble Codes (Part 3 of 3). 3.3L/V6-201 & 3.8L/V6-231 Engines

CR1029303165030X

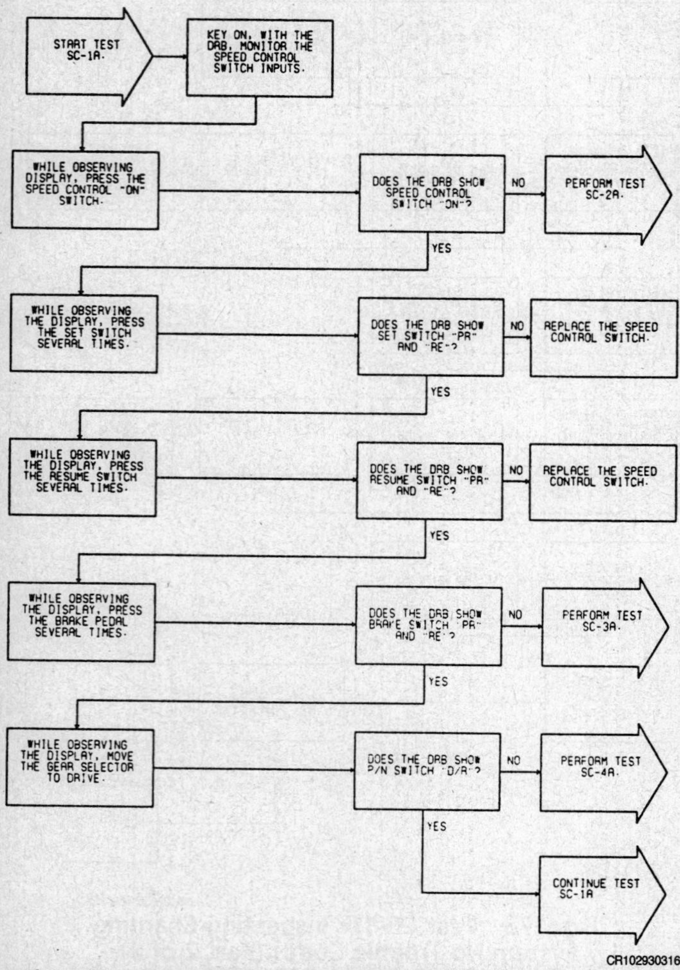

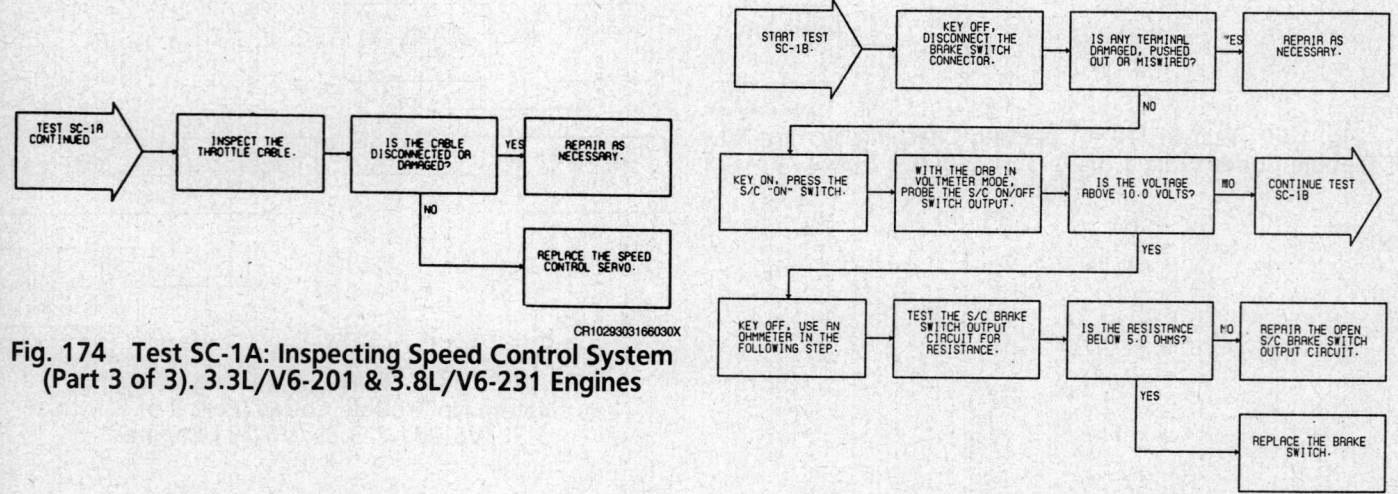

Fig. 174   Test SC-1A: Inspecting Speed Control System
(Part 1 of 3). 3.3L/V6-201 & 3.8L/V6-231 Engines

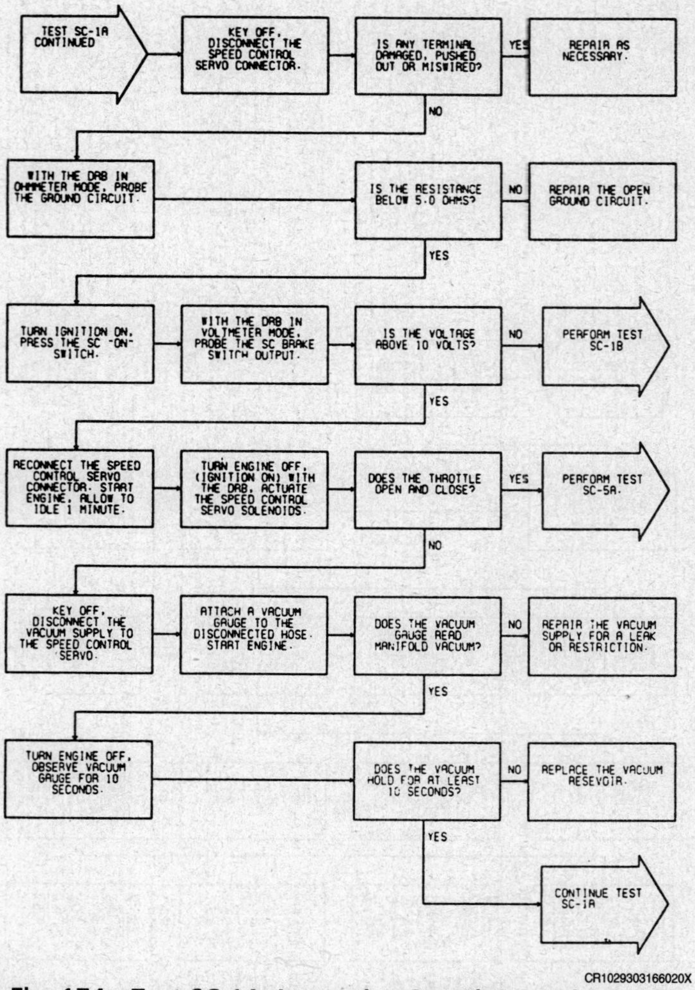

Fig. 174   Test SC-1A: Inspecting Speed Control System
(Part 2 of 3). 3.3L/V6-201 & 3.8L/V6-231 Engines

Fig. 174   Test SC-1A: Inspecting Speed Control System
(Part 3 of 3). 3.3L/V6-201 & 3.8L/V6-231 Engines

Fig. 175   Test SC-1B: Inspecting Speed
Control Brake Switch (Part 1 of 2).
3.3L/V6-201 & 3.8L/V6-231 Engines

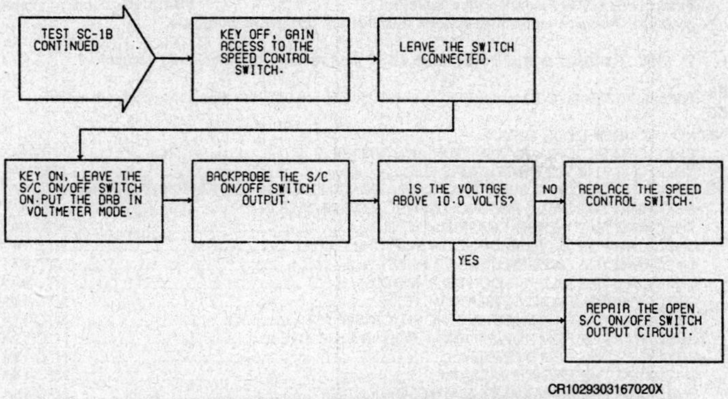

TEST SC-1B CONTINUED
KEY OFF, GAIN ACCESS TO THE SPEED CONTROL SWITCH.
LEAVE THE SWITCH CONNECTED.
KEY ON, LEAVE THE S/C ON/OFF SWITCH ON. PUT THE DRB IN VOLTMETER MODE.
BACKPROBE THE S/C ON/OFF SWITCH OUTPUT.
IS THE VOLTAGE ABOVE 10.0 VOLTS?
NO
REPLACE THE SPEED CONTROL SWITCH.
YES
REPAIR THE OPEN S/C ON/OFF SWITCH OUTPUT CIRCUIT.
CR1029303167020X

Fig. 175 Test SC-1B: Inspecting Speed Control Brake Switch (Part 2 of 2). 3.3L/V6-201 & 3.8L/V6-231 Engines

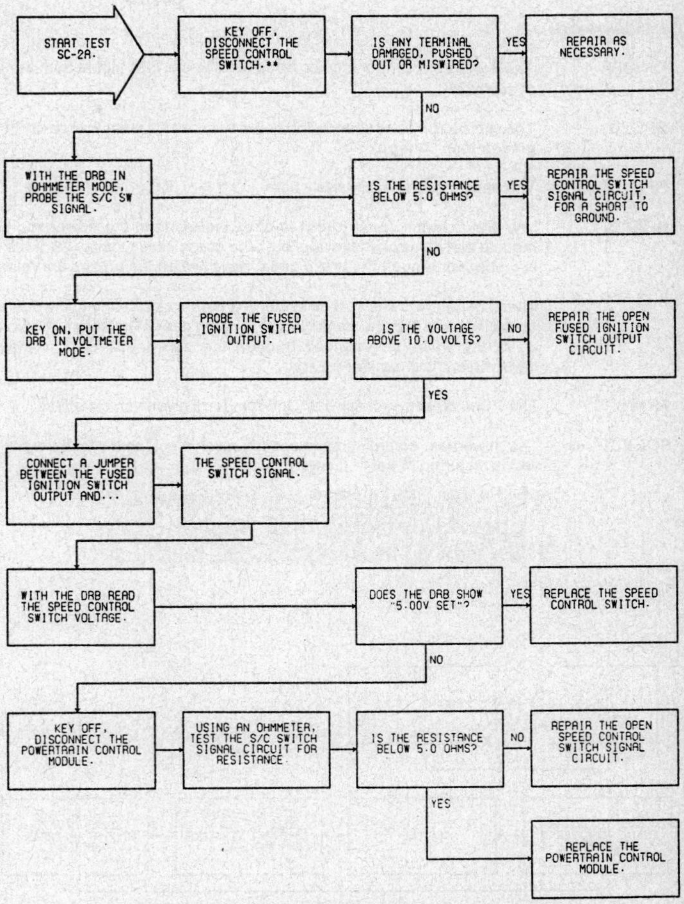

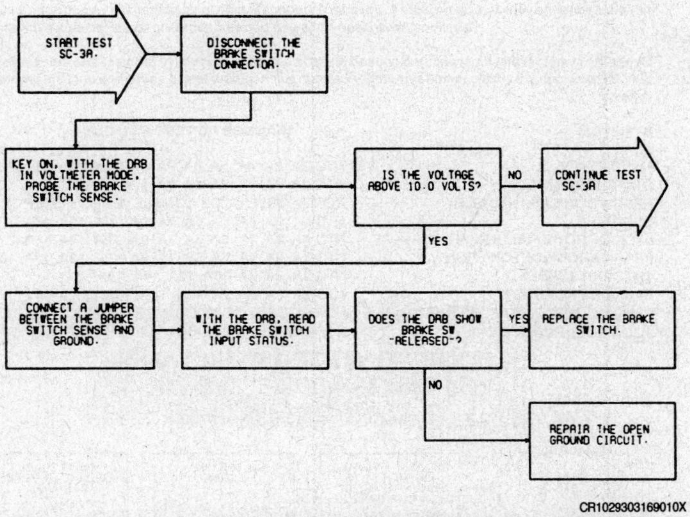

START TEST SC-3A.
DISCONNECT THE BRAKE SWITCH CONNECTOR.
KEY ON, WITH THE DRB IN VOLTMETER MODE, PROBE THE BRAKE SWITCH SENSE.
IS THE VOLTAGE ABOVE 10.0 VOLTS?
NO
CONTINUE TEST SC-3A
YES
CONNECT A JUMPER BETWEEN THE BRAKE SWITCH SENSE AND GROUND.
WITH THE DRB, READ THE BRAKE SWITCH INPUT STATUS.
DOES THE DRB SHOW BRAKE SW "RELEASED"?
YES
REPLACE THE BRAKE SWITCH.
NO
REPAIR THE OPEN GROUND CIRCUIT.
CR1029303169010X

Fig. 177 Test SC-3A: Inspecting Speed Control Brake Sense (Part 1 of 2). 3.3L/V6-201 & 3.8L/V6-231 Engines

START TEST SC-2A.
KEY OFF, DISCONNECT THE SPEED CONTROL SWITCH.**
IS ANY TERMINAL DAMAGED, PUSHED OUT OR MISWIRED?
YES
REPAIR AS NECESSARY.
NO
WITH THE DRB IN OHMMETER MODE, PROBE THE S/C SW SIGNAL.
IS THE RESISTANCE BELOW 5.0 OHMS?
YES
REPAIR THE SPEED CONTROL SWITCH SIGNAL CIRCUIT, FOR A SHORT TO GROUND.
NO
KEY ON, PUT THE DRB IN VOLTMETER MODE.
PROBE THE FUSED IGNITION SWITCH OUTPUT.
IS THE VOLTAGE ABOVE 10.0 VOLTS?
NO
REPAIR THE OPEN FUSED IGNITION SWITCH OUTPUT CIRCUIT.
YES
CONNECT A JUMPER BETWEEN THE FUSED IGNITION SWITCH OUTPUT AND...
THE SPEED CONTROL SWITCH SIGNAL.
WITH THE DRB READ THE SPEED CONTROL SWITCH VOLTAGE.
DOES THE DRB SHOW "5.00V SET"?
YES
REPLACE THE SPEED CONTROL SWITCH.
NO
KEY OFF, DISCONNECT THE POWERTRAIN CONTROL MODULE.
USING AN OHMMETER, TEST THE S/C SWITCH SIGNAL CIRCUIT FOR RESISTANCE.
IS THE RESISTANCE BELOW 5.0 OHMS?
NO
REPAIR THE OPEN SPEED CONTROL SWITCH SIGNAL CIRCUIT.
YES
REPLACE THE POWERTRAIN CONTROL MODULE.

Fig. 176 Test SC-2A: Inspecting Speed Control On/Off Switch. 3.3L/V6-201 & 3.8L/V6-231 Engines

TEST SC-3A CONTINUED
KEY OFF, DISCONNECT THE POWERTRAIN CONTROL MODULE.
IS ANY TERMINAL DAMAGED, PUSHED OUT OR MISWIRED?
YES
REPAIR AS NECESSARY.
NO
WITH THE DRB IN OHMMETER MODE, PROBE THE BRAKE SWITCH SENSE CKT, CAV 29
IS THE RESITANCE BELOW 5.0 OHMS?
YES
REPAIR THE BRAKE SWITCH SENSE CIRCUIT, SHORTED TO GROUND.
NO
USE AN OHMMETER IN THE FOLLOWING STEP.
TEST RESISTANCE OF THE BRAKE SWITCH SENSE CKT. PCM TO BRAKE SWITCH.
IS THE RESITANCE BELOW 5.0 OHMS?
YES
REPLACE THE POWERTRAIN CONTROL MODULE.
NO
REPAIR THE OPEN BRAKE SWITCH SENSE CIRCUIT. BRAKE SWITCH TO PCM.

Fig. 177 Test SC-3A: Inspecting Speed Control Brake Sense (Part 2 of 2). 3.3L/V6-201 & 3.8L/V6-231 Engines

START TEST SC-4A.
KEY OFF, DISCONNECT THE POWERTRAIN CONTROL MODULE.
NOTE: THE GEAR SELECTOR SHOULD STILL BE IN DRIVE.
WITH THE DRB IN OHMMETER MODE, PROBE THE PNP SENSE CIRCUIT, CAV 30
IS THE RESISTANCE BELOW 5.0 OHMS?
NO
REPLACE THE POWERTRAIN CONTROL MODULE.
YES
DISCONNECT THE PARK/NEUTRAL SWITCH.
WITH THE DRB IN OHMMETER MODE, PROBE THE PNP SENSE CIRCUIT, PCM CAV 30
IS THE RESISTANCE BELOW 5.0 OHMS?
NO
REPLACE THE PARK/NEUTRAL SWITCH.
YES
REPAIR THE PARK/NEUTRAL POSITION SENSE CIRCUIT, SHORTED TO GROUND.
CR1029303170000X

Fig. 178 Test SC-4A: Inspecting Speed Control Park/Neutral Sense. 3.3L/V6-201 & 3.8L/V6-231 Engines

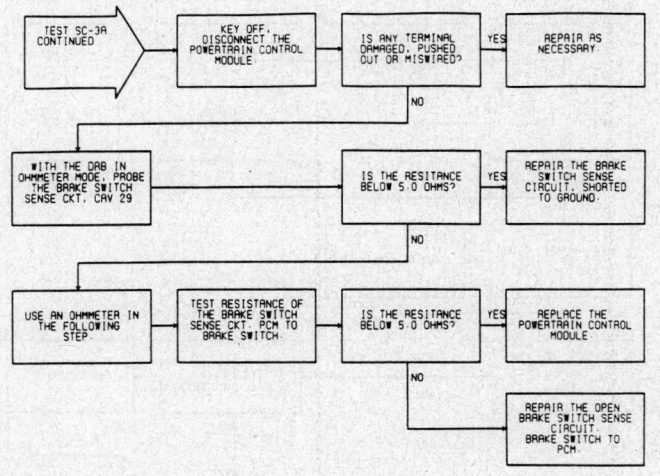

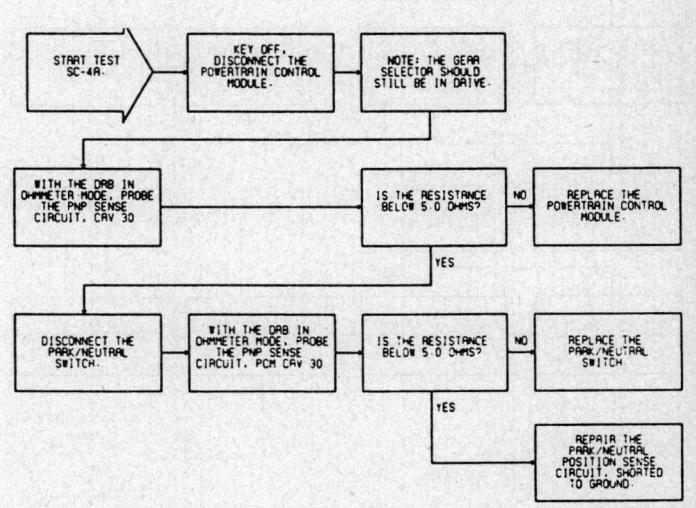

At this time the speed control switch and servo functions appear to operate properly. Using the DRB, monitor the speed control "cutout" status. Road test the vehicle at speeds over 35 mph and attempt to set the speed control. The following items will not allow the speed control to set. The last or most recent cause for speed control not to set is indicated by the "Denied" status.

Denied Message

ON/OFF — The powertrain control module does not see an "ON" signal from the switch at cavity 23.

SPEED — The vehicle speed as seen by the powertrain control module at cavity 29 is not greater than 36 mph.

RPM — The engine rpm is excessively high.

BRAKE — The brake switch sense circuit is open indicating to the powertrain control module that the brakes are applied. The sense circuit, cavity 29 of the PCM, is grounded through the brake pedal switch when the brakes are released.

P/N — The park/neutral switch sense circuit is grounded indicating to the powertrain control module that the transmission is not in gear. The sense circuit, cavity 30 of the PCM, is grounded through the park/neutral switch when the transmission is in park or neutral.

RPM/SPD — The PCM senses excessive engine rpm for a given vehicle speed.

SOL FLT — The powertrain control module senses a servo solenoid circuit trouble code that is maturing or set in memory.

Fig. 179 Test SC-5A: Inspecting A Speed Control Denied Message. 3.3L/V6-201 & 3.8L/V6-231 Engines

First, check all Technical Service Bulletins that relate to this driveability problem. Perform corrective actions if indicated; otherwise continue.

1. **NO TROUBLE CODE COMPLETE TEST** (non-monitored & monitored circuits)

Perform **TESTS NTC-2A** through **NTC-16A** in sequence until the driveability problem is found.

NO TROUBLE CODE MENU

CHECKING SECONDARY IGNITION AND TIMING	NTC-2A
CHECKING THE FUEL PRESSURE	NTC-3A
CHECKING COOLANT SENSOR CALIBRATION AND RADIATOR FAN OPERATION	NTC-4A
CHECKING THROTTLE POSITION SENSOR CALIBRATION	NTC-5A
CHECKING MAP SENSOR CALIBRATION	NTC-6A
CHECKING FOR OXYGEN SENSOR SWITCHING	NTC-7A
CHECKING THE OXYGEN SENSOR HEATER	NTC-8A
CHECKING THE IDLE AIR CONTROL MOTOR	NTC-9A
CHECKING SOLENOID OPERATION	NTC-10A
CHECKING THE PARK/NEUTRAL POSITION SWITCH	NTC-11A
CHECKING THE PCM POWER AND GROUND CIRCUITS	NTC-12A
CHECKING THE EGR SYSTEM	NTC-13A
CHECKING THE ENGINE VACUUM	NTC-14A
CHECKING THE MINIMUM IDLE AIR FLOW	NTC-15A
CHECKING THE ENGINE MECHANICAL SYSTEMS	NTC-16A

2. **NO TROUBLE CODE QUICK INDIVIDUAL TEST** (individual test only)

If you suspect any of the above items to be the cause of the vehicle's driveability problem, perform the associated test(s) individually. **Return to No Trouble Code Menu if driveability problem still exists, or perform No Trouble Code Complete Test.**

3. **NO TROUBLE CODE QUICK SYMPTOM TEST** (symptom test only)

Symptom checks cannot be used properly unless the driveability problem characteristic actually happens while the vehicle is being tested. To reduce diagnostic time, ensure that TC-1A and appropriate sections have been reviewed before attempting to diagnose a symptom.

Select the symptom that most accurately describes the vehicle's driveability problem and then perform the test routine that pertains to this symptom. Perform each routine test in sequence until the problem is found.

SYMPTOM	DIAGNOSTIC TEST ROUTINE
HARD START	NTC-2A, 3A, 4A, 5A, 6A, 7A, 9A, 12A, 15A, 16A
START AND STALL	NTC-2A, 3A, 4A, 5A, 6A, 9A, 12A, 16A
HESITATION/SAG/STUMBLE	NO TROUBLE CODE COMPLETE TEST (STEP 1)
SURGE	NTC-2A, 3A, 4A, 5A, 6A, 7A, 9A, 12A, 13A, 16A
LACK OF POWER/SLUGGISH	NTC-2A, 3A, 4A, 5A, 6A, 7A, 9A, 12A, 14A, 16A
SPARK KNOCK/DETONATION	NTC-2A, 3A, 4A, 5A, 6A, 7A, 9A, 10A, 12A, 13A, 16A
CUTS OUT/MISSES	NTC-2A, 3A, 7A, 10A, 12A, 14A, 16A
BACKFIRE/POPBACK	NTC-2A, 3A, 6A, 7A, 12A, 14A, 16A
RUNS ROUGH/UNSTABLE/ERRATIC IDLE	NO TROUBLE CODE COMPLETE TEST (STEP 1)
POOR FUEL ECONOMY	NO TROUBLE CODE COMPLETE TEST (STEP 1)

Fig. 180 Test NTC-1A: No Trouble Code Test Menu. 3.3L/V6-201 & 3.8L/V6-231 Engines

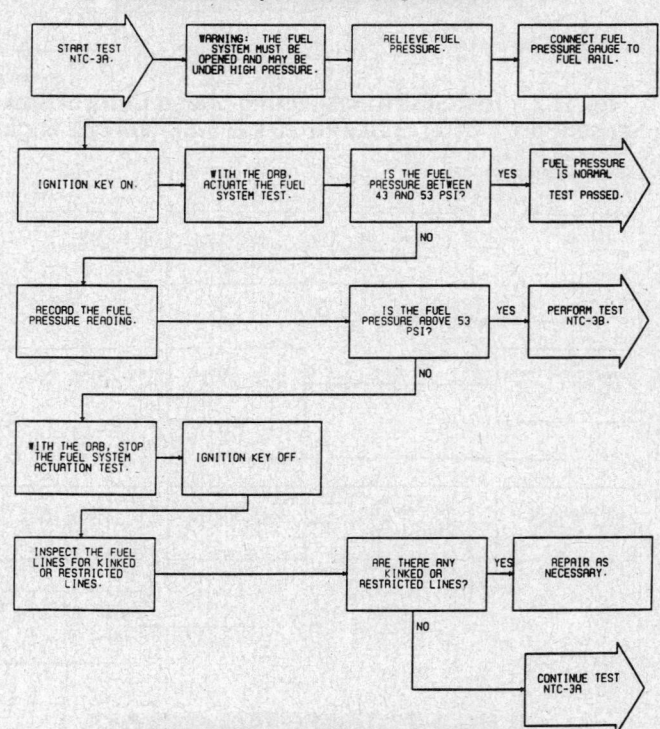

CR1029303172000X

Fig. 181   Test NTC-2A: Inspecting Secondary Ignition & Timing. 3.3L/V6-201 & 3.8L/V6-231 Engines

Fig. 182   Test NTC-3A: Inspecting Fuel Pressure (Part 1 of 2). 3.3L/V6-201 & 3.8L/V6-231 Engines

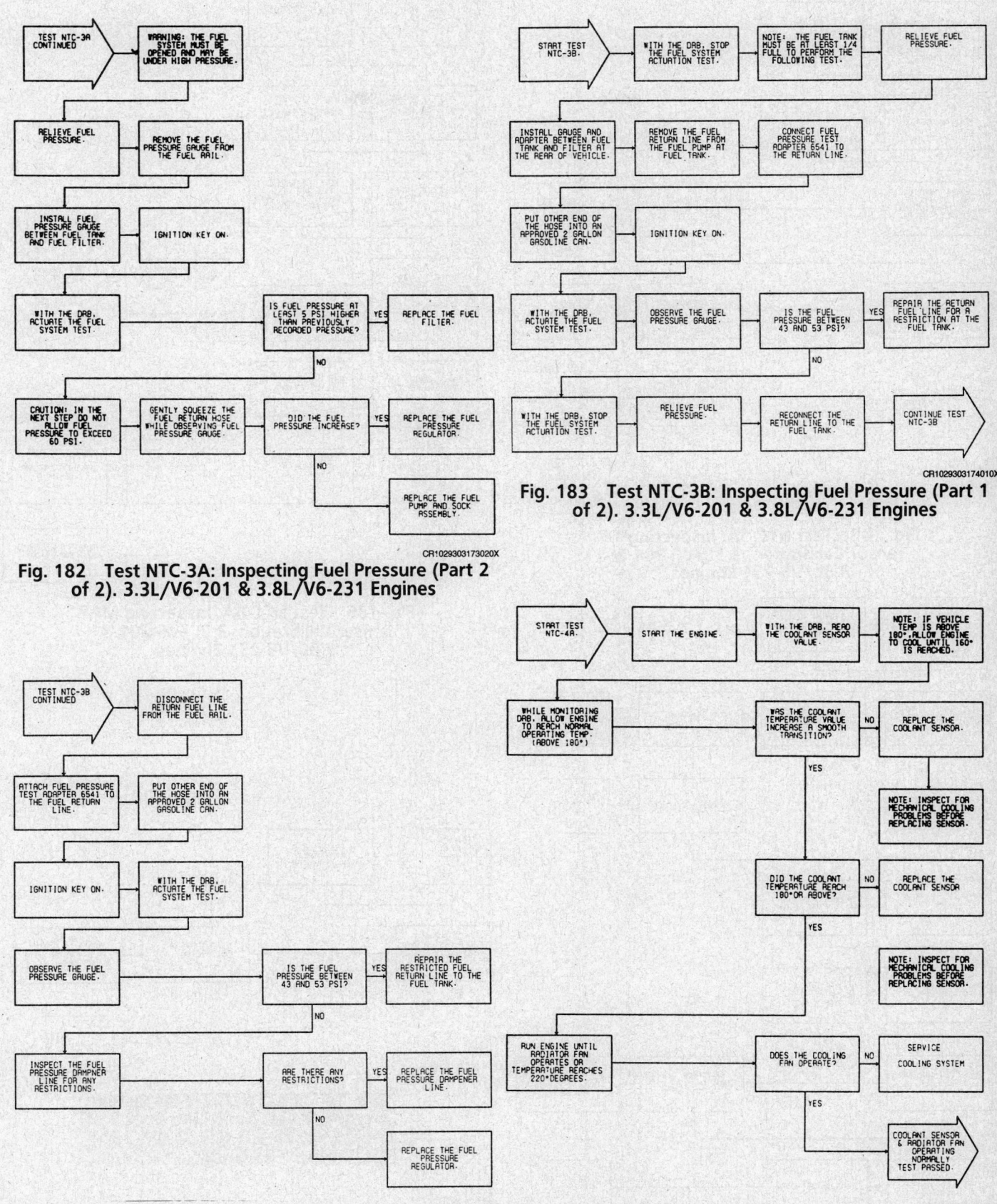

Fig. 182   Test NTC-3A: Inspecting Fuel Pressure (Part 2 of 2). 3.3L/V6-201 & 3.8L/V6-231 Engines

Fig. 183   Test NTC-3B: Inspecting Fuel Pressure (Part 1 of 2). 3.3L/V6-201 & 3.8L/V6-231 Engines

Fig. 183   Test NTC-3B: Inspecting Fuel Pressure (Part 2 of 2). 3.3L/V6-201 & 3.8L/V6-231 Engines

Fig. 184   Test NTC-4A: Inspecting Coolant Sensor Calibration & Radiator Fan Operation. 3.3L/V6-201 & 3.8L/V6-231 Engines

MODELS w/3.0L/V6-181, 3.3L/V6-201 & 3.8L/V6-231 ENGINES EXCEPT CONCORDE, INTREPID, LHS, STEALTH, VISION & 1994-96 NEW YORKER

12-97

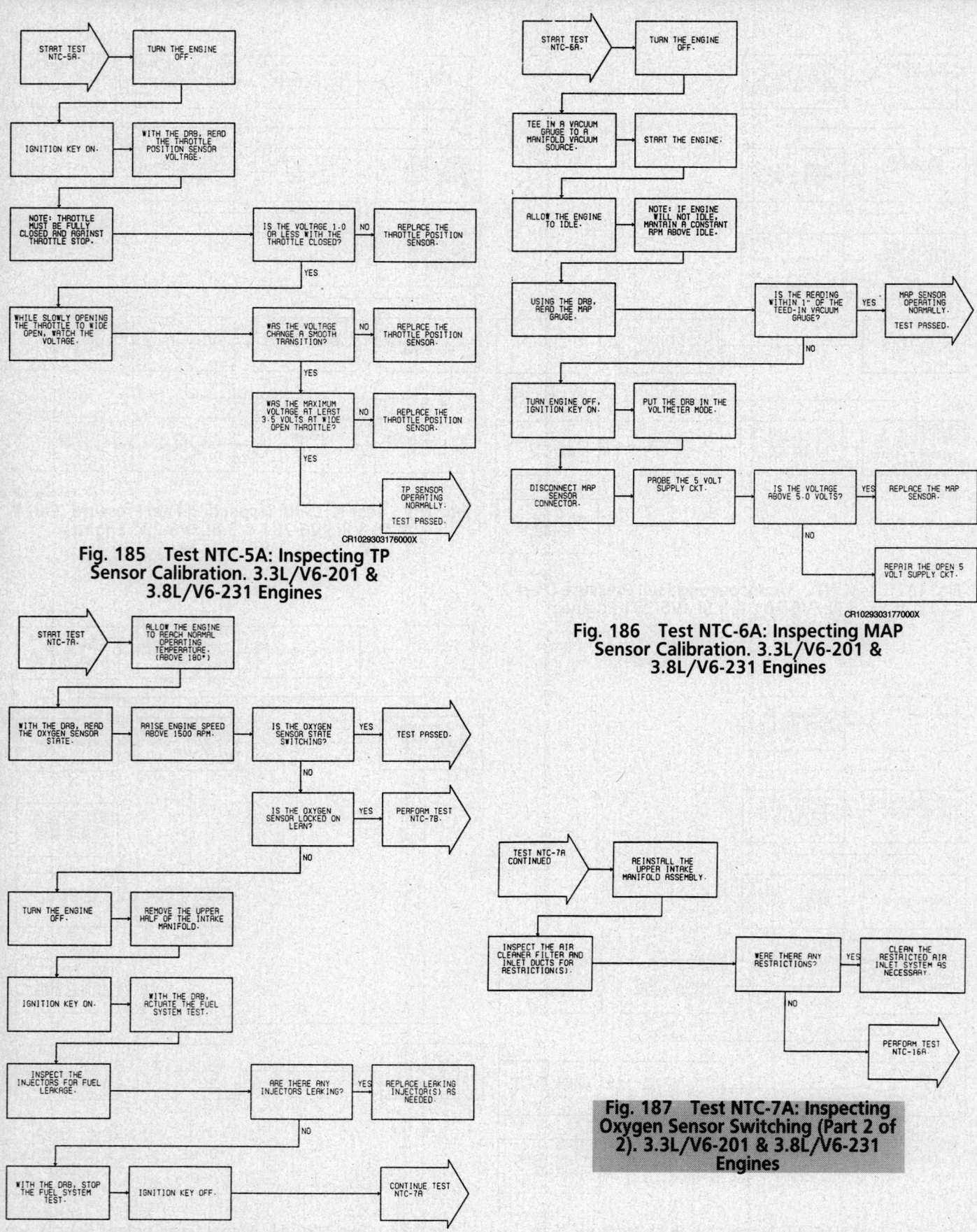

Fig. 185   Test NTC-5A: Inspecting TP Sensor Calibration. 3.3L/V6-201 & 3.8L/V6-231 Engines

Fig. 186   Test NTC-6A: Inspecting MAP Sensor Calibration. 3.3L/V6-201 & 3.8L/V6-231 Engines

Fig. 187   Test NTC-7A: Inspecting Oxygen Sensor Switching (Part 2 of 2). 3.3L/V6-201 & 3.8L/V6-231 Engines

Fig. 187   Test NTC-7A: Inspecting Oxygen Sensor Switching (Part 1 of 2). 3.3L/V6-201 & 3.8L/V6-231 Engines

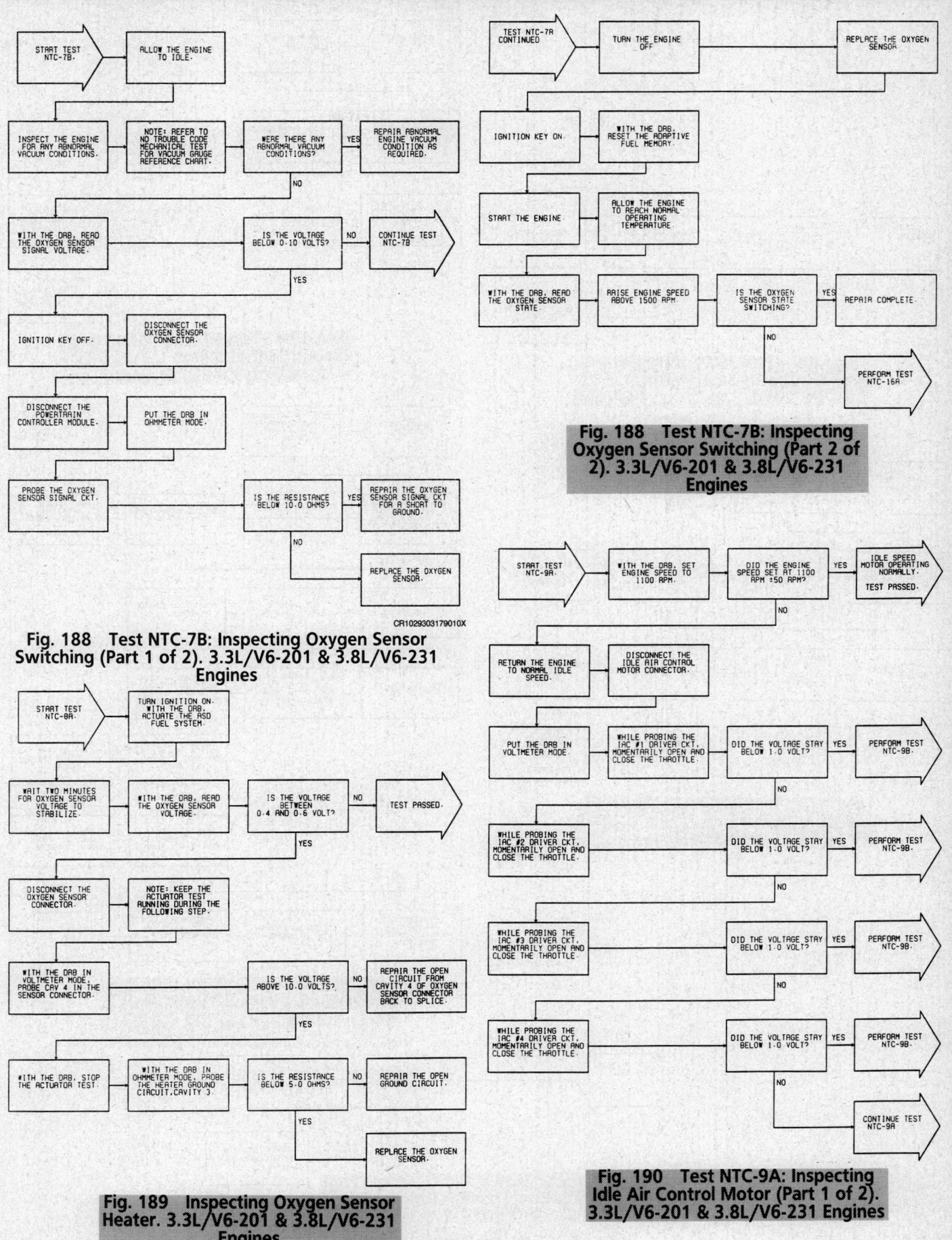

Fig. 188   Test NTC-7B: Inspecting Oxygen Sensor Switching (Part 1 of 2). 3.3L/V6-201 & 3.8L/V6-231 Engines

CR1029303179010X

Fig. 188   Test NTC-7B: Inspecting Oxygen Sensor Switching (Part 2 of 2). 3.3L/V6-201 & 3.8L/V6-231 Engines

Fig. 189   Inspecting Oxygen Sensor Heater. 3.3L/V6-201 & 3.8L/V6-231 Engines

Fig. 190   Test NTC-9A: Inspecting Idle Air Control Motor (Part 1 of 2). 3.3L/V6-201 & 3.8L/V6-231 Engines

MODELS w/3.0L/V6-181, 3.3L/V6-201 & 3.8L/V6-231 ENGINES EXCEPT CONCORDE, INTREPID, LHS, STEALTH, VISION & 1994-96 NEW YORKER

12-99

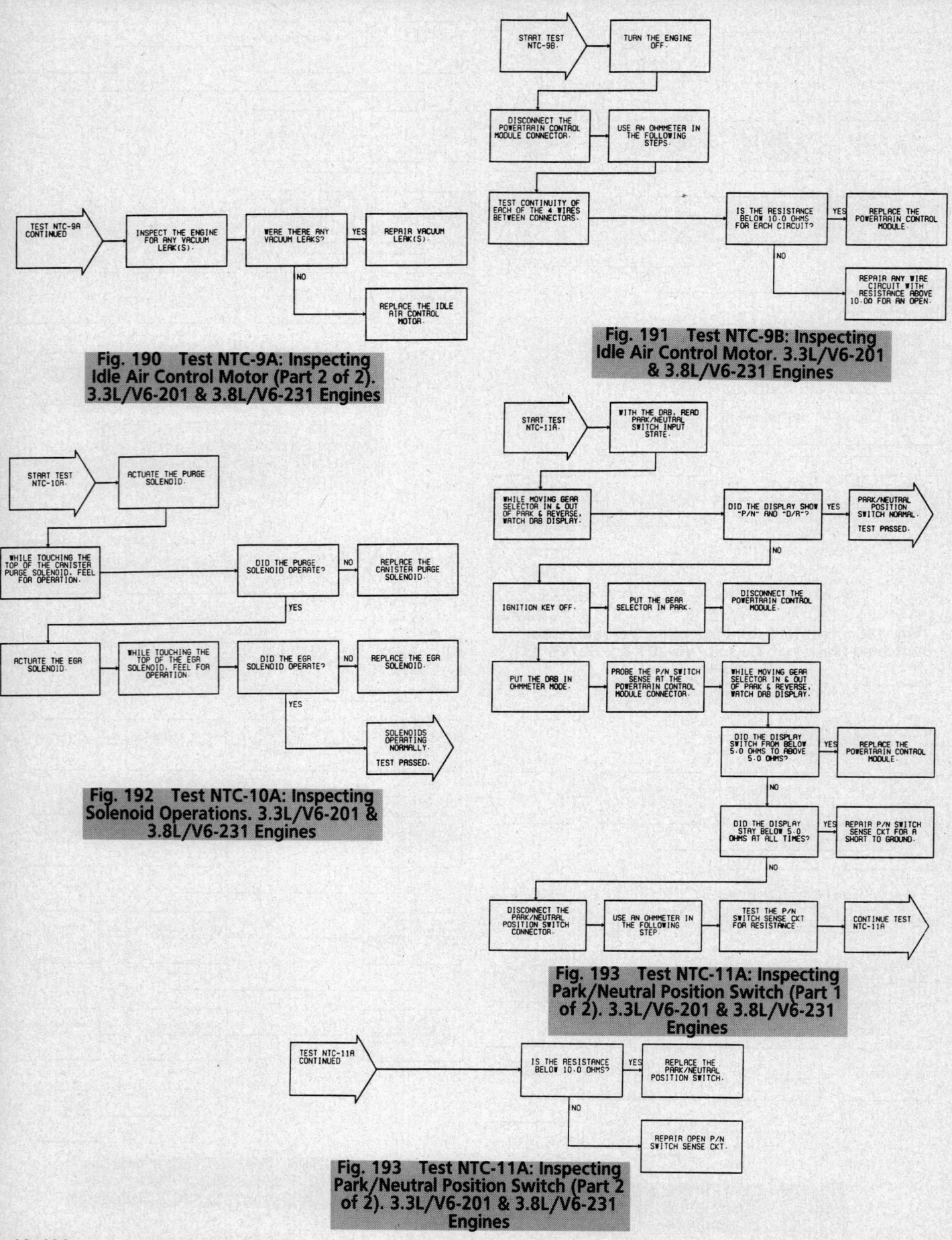

Fig. 190   Test NTC-9A: Inspecting Idle Air Control Motor (Part 2 of 2). 3.3L/V6-201 & 3.8L/V6-231 Engines

Fig. 191   Test NTC-9B: Inspecting Idle Air Control Motor. 3.3L/V6-201 & 3.8L/V6-231 Engines

Fig. 192   Test NTC-10A: Inspecting Solenoid Operations. 3.3L/V6-201 & 3.8L/V6-231 Engines

Fig. 193   Test NTC-11A: Inspecting Park/Neutral Position Switch (Part 1 of 2). 3.3L/V6-201 & 3.8L/V6-231 Engines

Fig. 193   Test NTC-11A: Inspecting Park/Neutral Position Switch (Part 2 of 2). 3.3L/V6-201 & 3.8L/V6-231 Engines

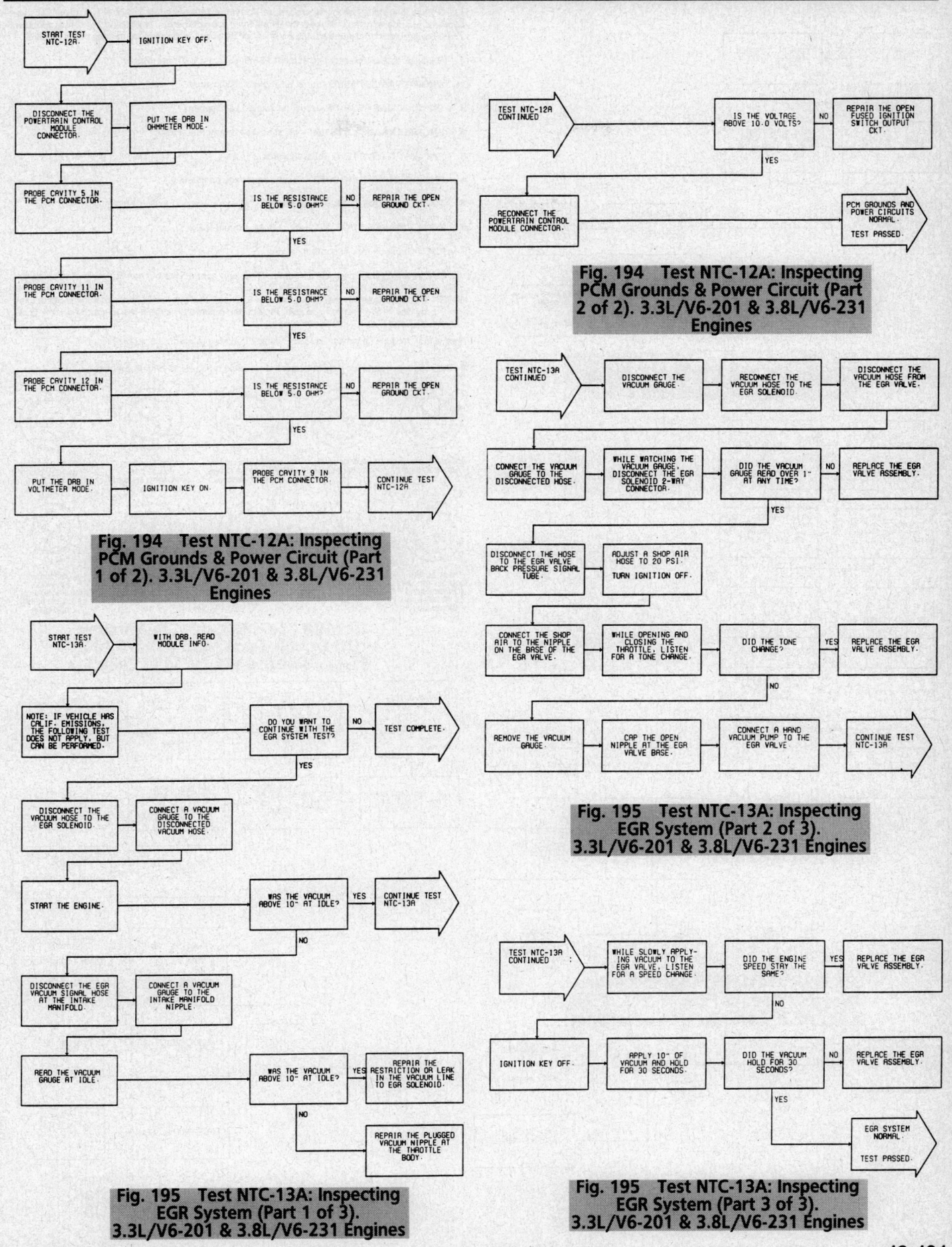

Fig. 194   Test NTC-12A: Inspecting PCM Grounds & Power Circuit (Part 1 of 2). 3.3L/V6-201 & 3.8L/V6-231 Engines

Fig. 195   Test NTC-13A: Inspecting EGR System (Part 1 of 3). 3.3L/V6-201 & 3.8L/V6-231 Engines

Fig. 194   Test NTC-12A: Inspecting PCM Grounds & Power Circuit (Part 2 of 2). 3.3L/V6-201 & 3.8L/V6-231 Engines

Fig. 195   Test NTC-13A: Inspecting EGR System (Part 2 of 3). 3.3L/V6-201 & 3.8L/V6-231 Engines

Fig. 195   Test NTC-13A: Inspecting EGR System (Part 3 of 3). 3.3L/V6-201 & 3.8L/V6-231 Engines

MODELS w/3.0L/V6-181, 3.3L/V6-201 & 3.8L/V6-231 ENGINES EXCEPT CONCORDE, INTREPID, LHS, STEALTH, VISION & 1994-96 NEW YORKER

12-101

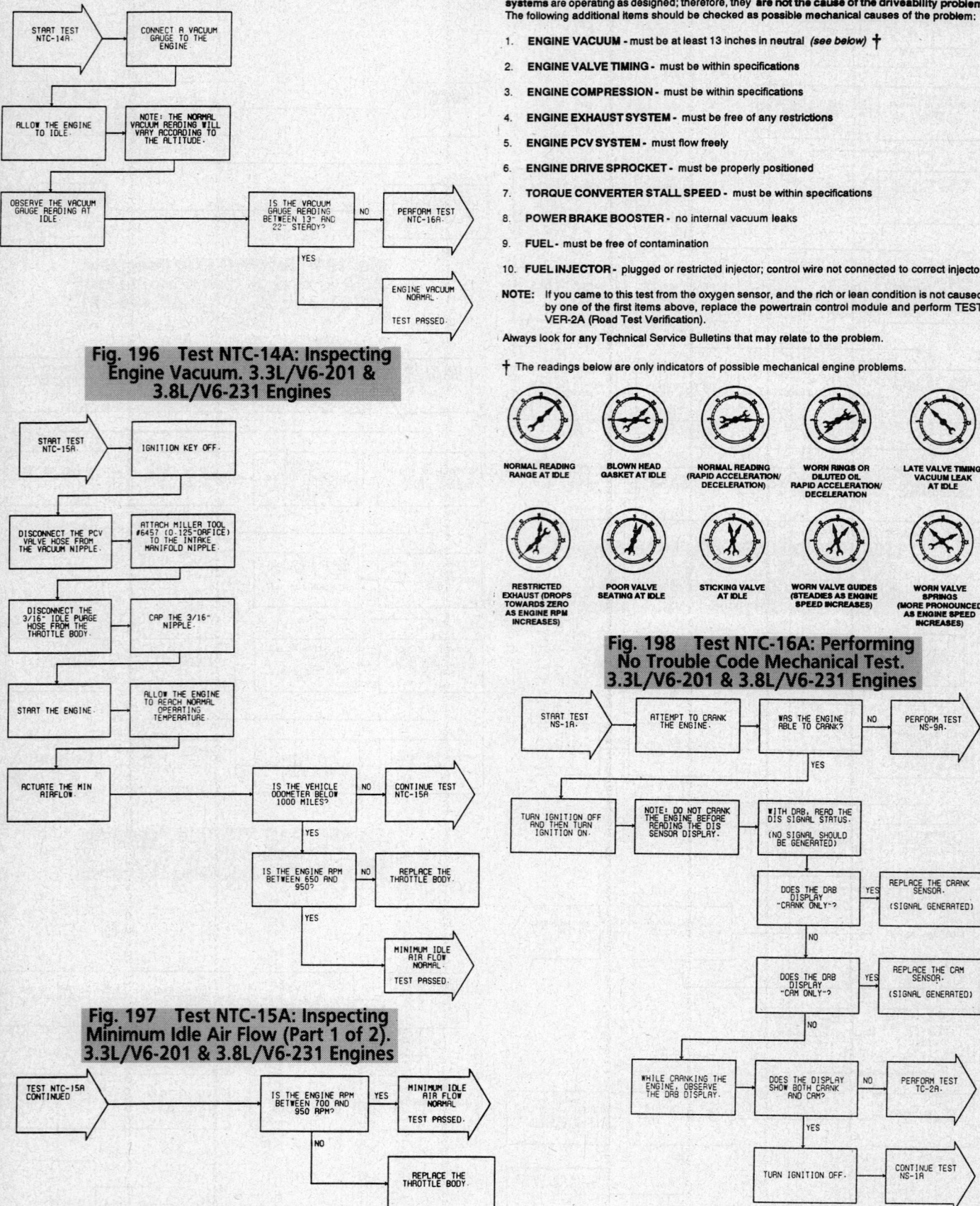

At this point in the diagnostic test procedure, you have determined that all of the **engine electrical systems** are operating as designed; therefore, they **are not the cause of the driveability problem.** The following additional items should be checked as possible mechanical causes of the problem:

1. **ENGINE VACUUM** - must be at least 13 inches in neutral *(see below)* †

2. **ENGINE VALVE TIMING** - must be within specifications

3. **ENGINE COMPRESSION** - must be within specifications

4. **ENGINE EXHAUST SYSTEM** - must be free of any restrictions

5. **ENGINE PCV SYSTEM** - must flow freely

6. **ENGINE DRIVE SPROCKET** - must be properly positioned

7. **TORQUE CONVERTER STALL SPEED** - must be within specifications

8. **POWER BRAKE BOOSTER** - no internal vacuum leaks

9. **FUEL** - must be free of contamination

10. **FUEL INJECTOR** - plugged or restricted injector; control wire not connected to correct injector

NOTE: If you came to this test from the oxygen sensor, and the rich or lean condition is not caused by one of the first items above, replace the powertrain control module and perform TEST VER-2A (Road Test Verification).

Always look for any Technical Service Bulletins that may relate to the problem.

† The readings below are only indicators of possible mechanical engine problems.

Fig. 196   Test NTC-14A: Inspecting Engine Vacuum. 3.3L/V6-201 & 3.8L/V6-231 Engines

Fig. 197   Test NTC-15A: Inspecting Minimum Idle Air Flow (Part 1 of 2). 3.3L/V6-201 & 3.8L/V6-231 Engines

Fig. 197   Test NTC-15A: Inspecting Minimum Idle Air Flow (Part 2 of 2). 3.3L/V6-201 & 3.8L/V6-231 Engines

Fig. 198   Test NTC-16A: Performing No Trouble Code Mechanical Test. 3.3L/V6-201 & 3.8L/V6-231 Engines

Fig. 199   Test NS-1A: Qualifying No Start Condition (Part 1 of 3). 3.3L/V6-201 & 3.8L/V6-231 Engines

CR1029303188010X

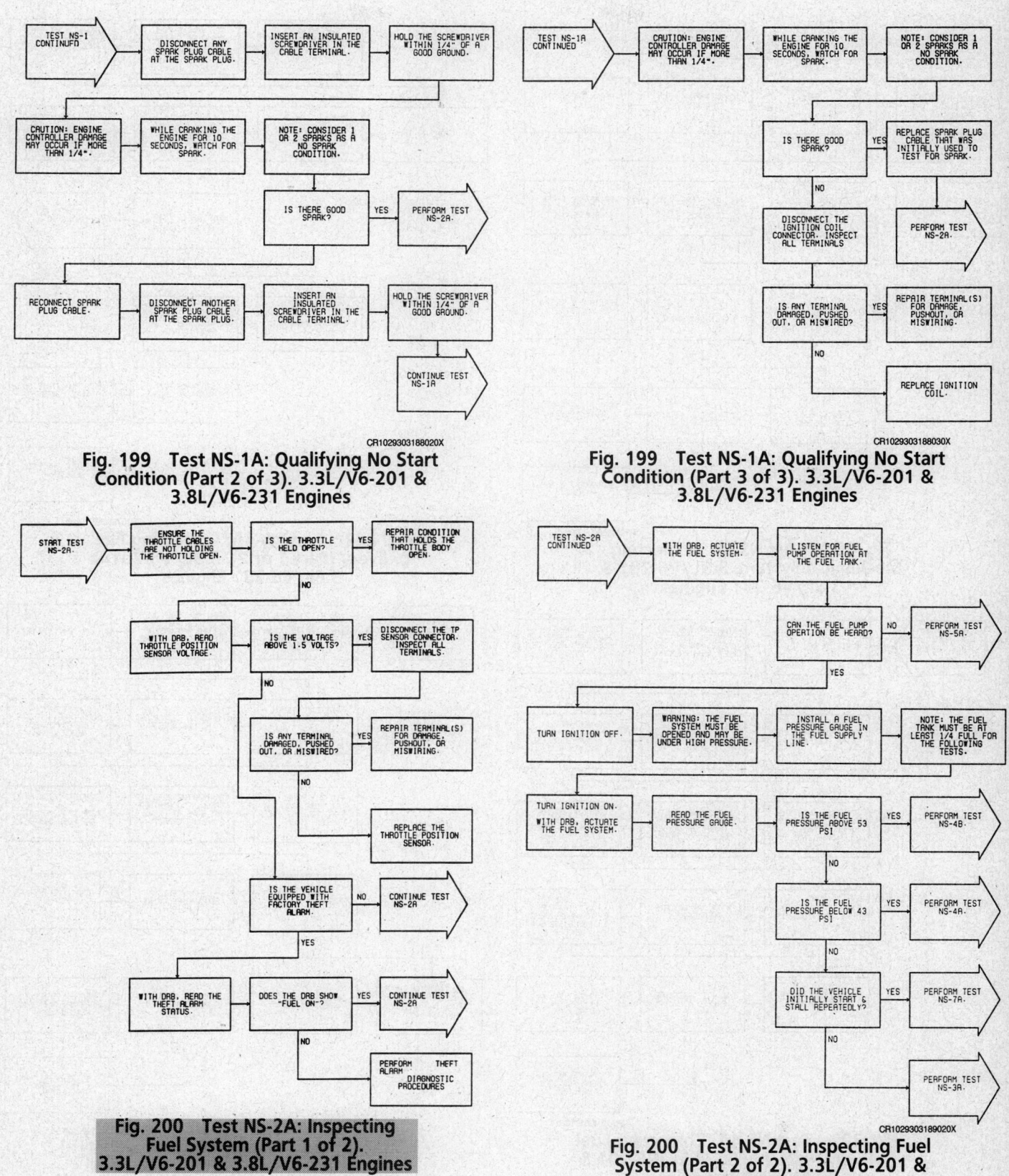

Fig. 199   Test NS-1A: Qualifying No Start
Condition (Part 2 of 3). 3.3L/V6-201 &
3.8L/V6-231 Engines

Fig. 199   Test NS-1A: Qualifying No Start
Condition (Part 3 of 3). 3.3L/V6-201 &
3.8L/V6-231 Engines

Fig. 200   Test NS-2A: Inspecting
Fuel System (Part 1 of 2).
3.3L/V6-201 & 3.8L/V6-231 Engines

Fig. 200   Test NS-2A: Inspecting Fuel
System (Part 2 of 2). 3.3L/V6-201 &
3.8L/V6-231 Engines

*MODELS w/3.0L/V6-181, 3.3L/V6-201 & 3.8L/V6-231 ENGINES EXCEPT CONCORDE, INTREPID, LHS, STEALTH, VISION &
1994-96 NEW YORKER*

12-103

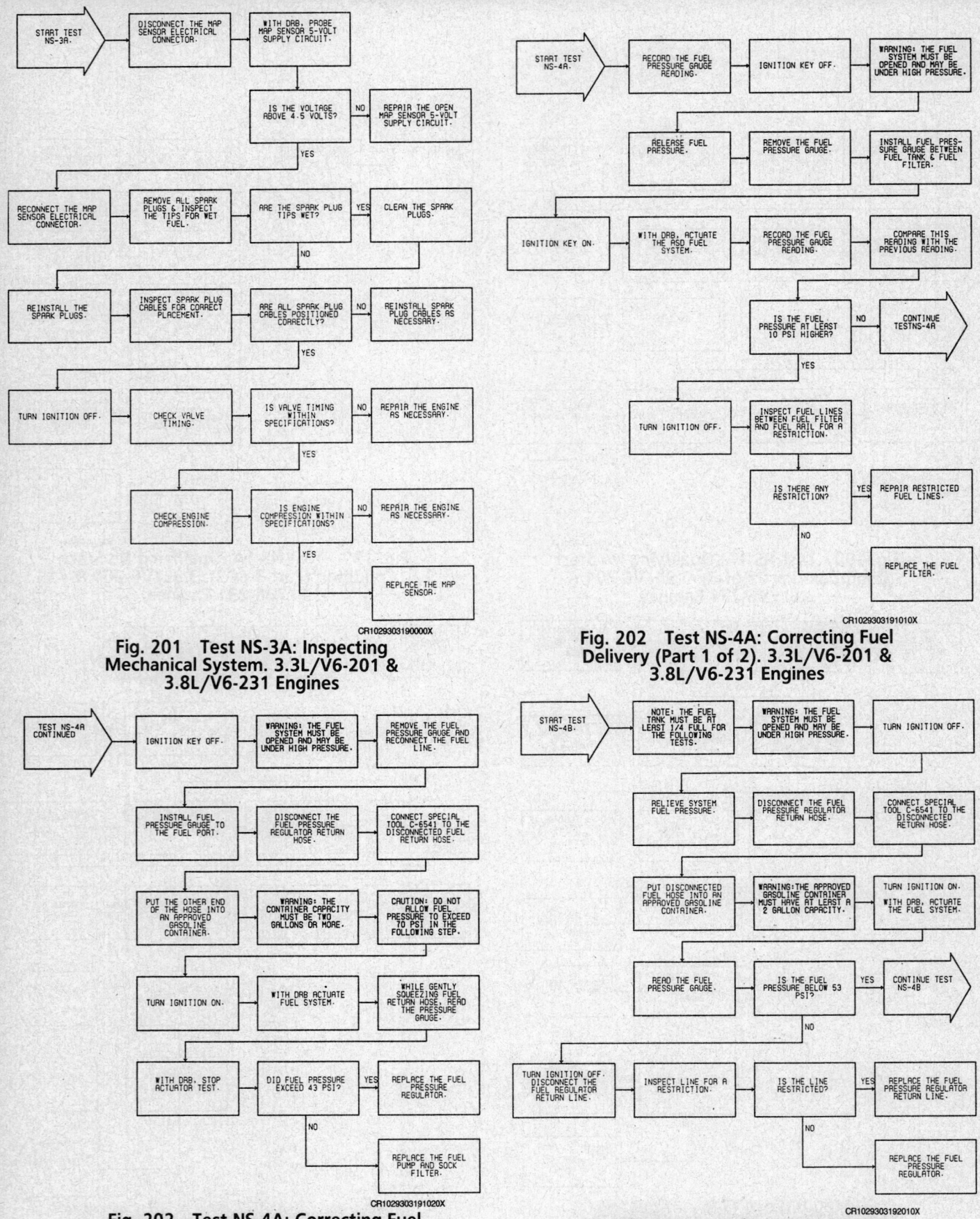

Fig. 201   Test NS-3A: Inspecting
Mechanical System. 3.3L/V6-201 &
3.8L/V6-231 Engines

Fig. 202   Test NS-4A: Correcting Fuel
Delivery (Part 1 of 2). 3.3L/V6-201 &
3.8L/V6-231 Engines

Fig. 202   Test NS-4A: Correcting Fuel
Delivery (Part 2 of 2). 3.3L/V6-201 &
3.8L/V6-231 Engines

Fig. 203   Test NS-4B: Correcting Fuel
Delivery (Part 1 of 2). 3.3L/V6-201 &
3.8L/V6-231 Engines

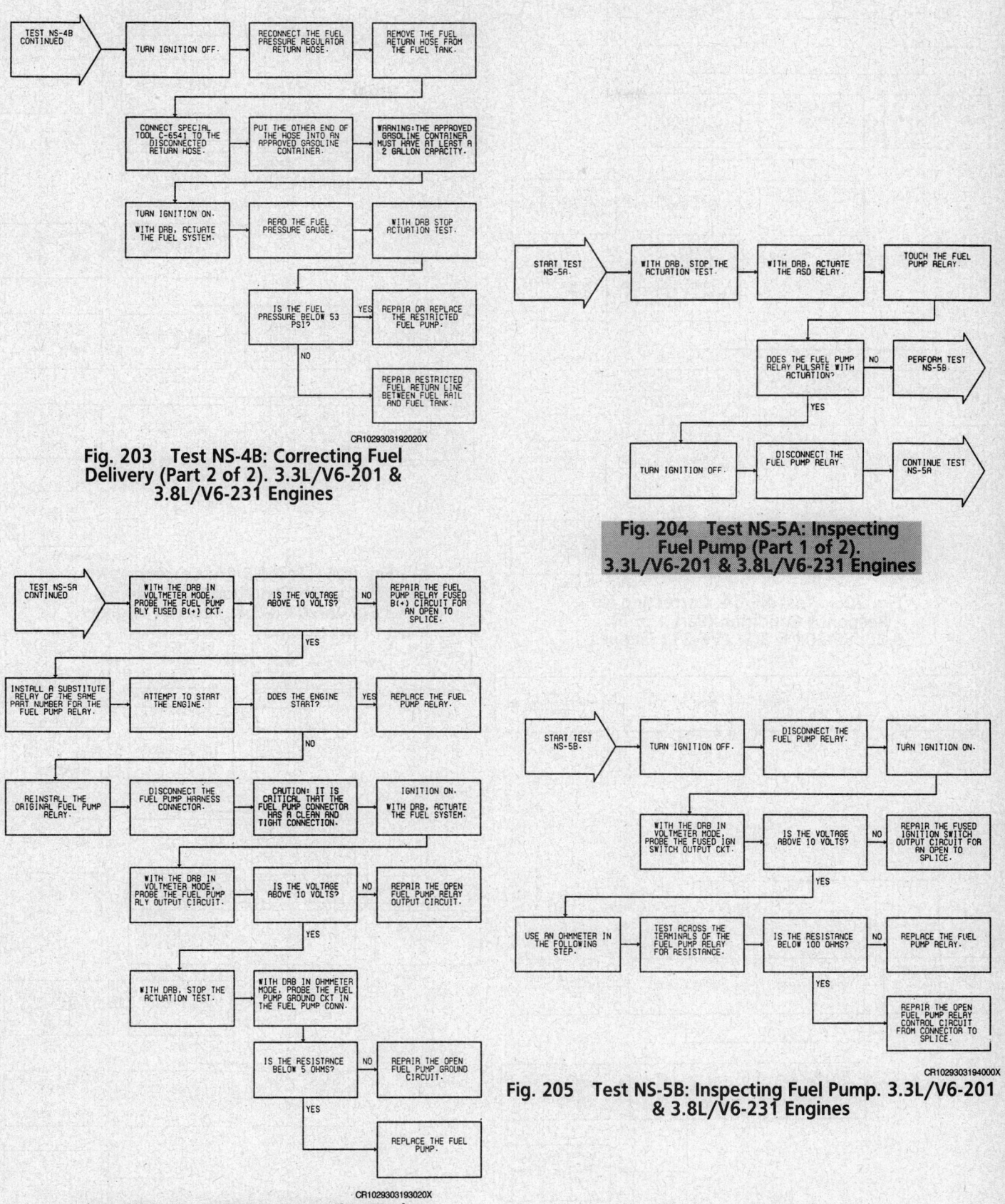

Fig. 203   Test NS-4B: Correcting Fuel Delivery (Part 2 of 2). 3.3L/V6-201 & 3.8L/V6-231 Engines

CR1029303192020X

Fig. 204   Test NS-5A: Inspecting Fuel Pump (Part 1 of 2). 3.3L/V6-201 & 3.8L/V6-231 Engines

Fig. 204   Test NS-5A: Inspecting Fuel Pump (Part 2 of 2). 3.3L/V6-201 & 3.8L/V6-231 Engines

CR1029303193020X

Fig. 205   Test NS-5B: Inspecting Fuel Pump. 3.3L/V6-201 & 3.8L/V6-231 Engines

CR1029303194000X

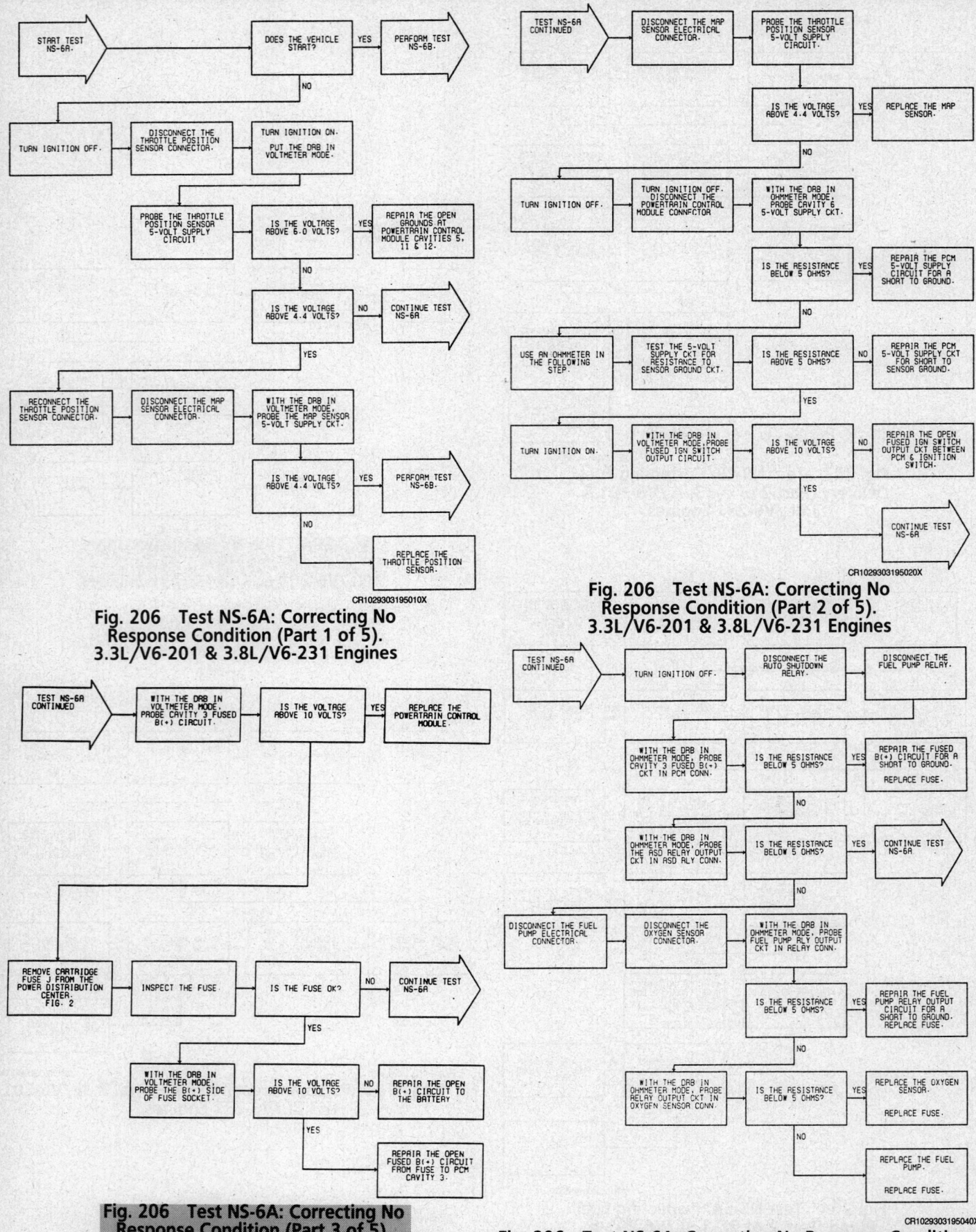

Fig. 206 Test NS-6A: Correcting No Response Condition (Part 1 of 5). 3.3L/V6-201 & 3.8L/V6-231 Engines

CR1029303195010X

Fig. 206 Test NS-6A: Correcting No Response Condition (Part 2 of 5). 3.3L/V6-201 & 3.8L/V6-231 Engines

CR1029303195020X

Fig. 206 Test NS-6A: Correcting No Response Condition (Part 3 of 5). 3.3L/V6-201 & 3.8L/V6-231 Engines

Fig. 206 Test NS-6A: Correcting No Response Condition (Part 4 of 5). 3.3L/V6-201 & 3.8L/V6-231 Engines

CR1029303195040X

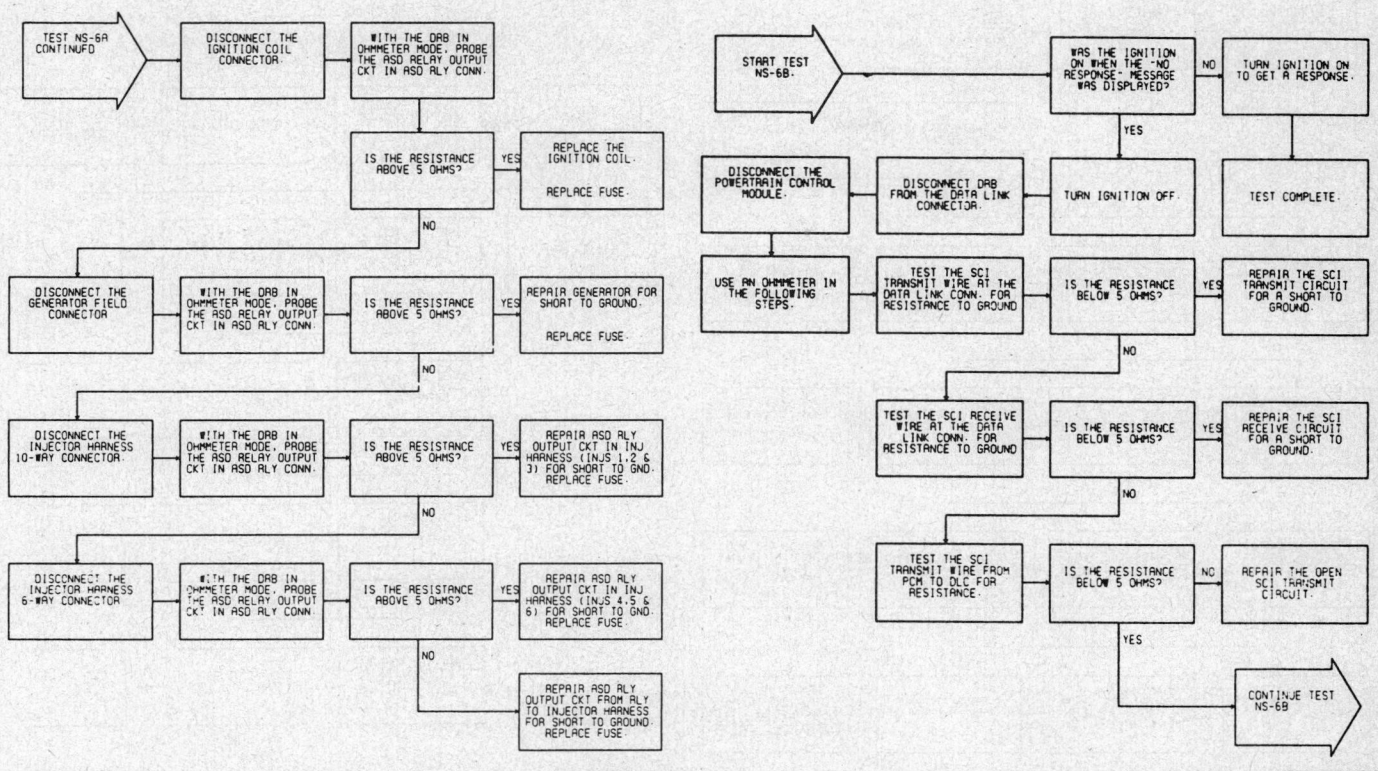

Fig. 206   Test NS-6A: Correcting No Response Condition (Part 5 of 5). 3.3L/V6-201 & 3.8L/V6-231 Engines

Fig. 207   Test NS-6B: Correcting No Response Condition (Part 1 of 2). 3.3L/V6-201 & 3.8L/V6-231 Engines

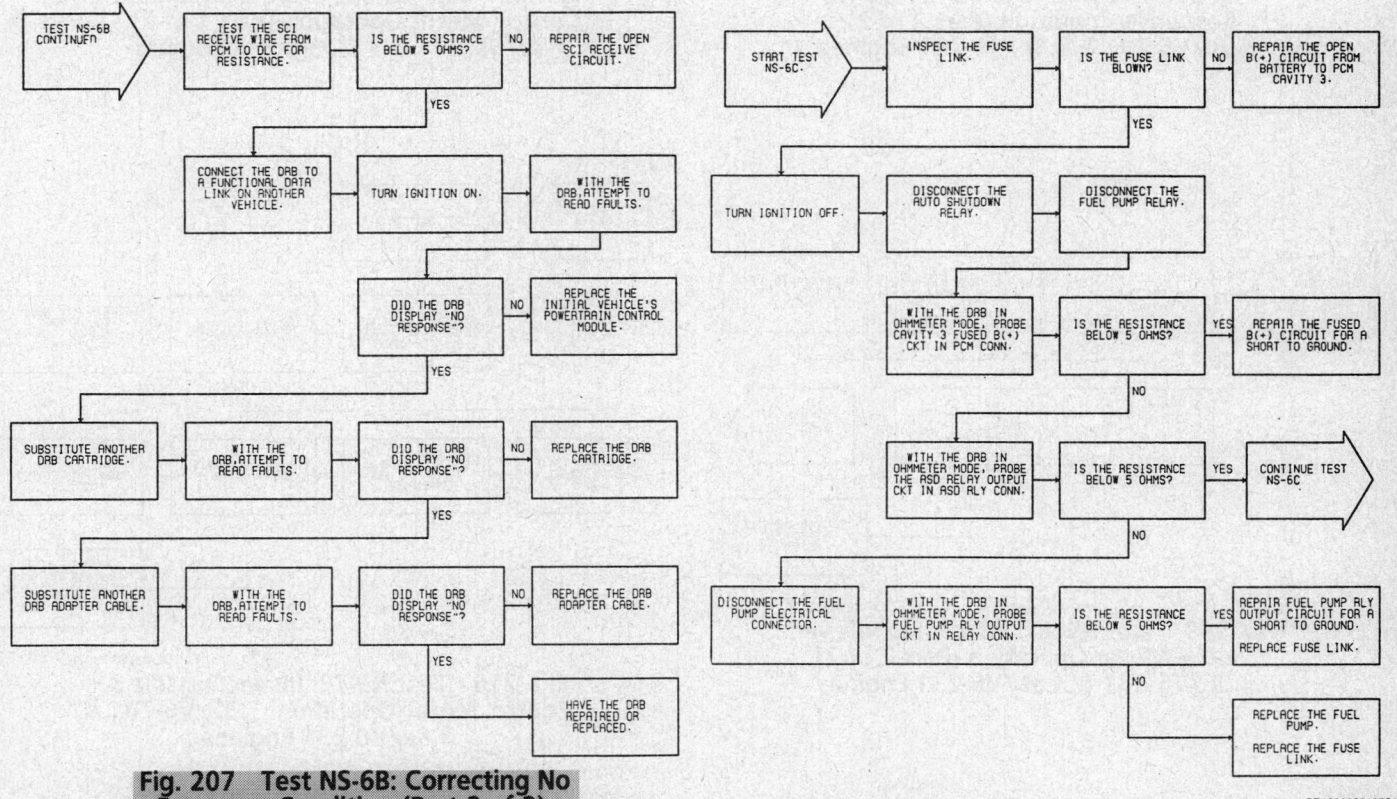

Fig. 207   Test NS-6B: Correcting No Response Condition (Part 2 of 2). 3.3L/V6-201 & 3.8L/V6-231 Engines

Fig. 208   Test NS-6C: Correcting No Response Condition (Part 1 of 2). 3.3L/V6-201 & 3.8L/V6-231 Engines

MODELS w/3.0L/V6-181, 3.3L/V6-201 & 3.8L/V6-231 ENGINES EXCEPT CONCORDE, INTREPID, LHS, STEALTH, VISION & 1994-96 NEW YORKER

12-107

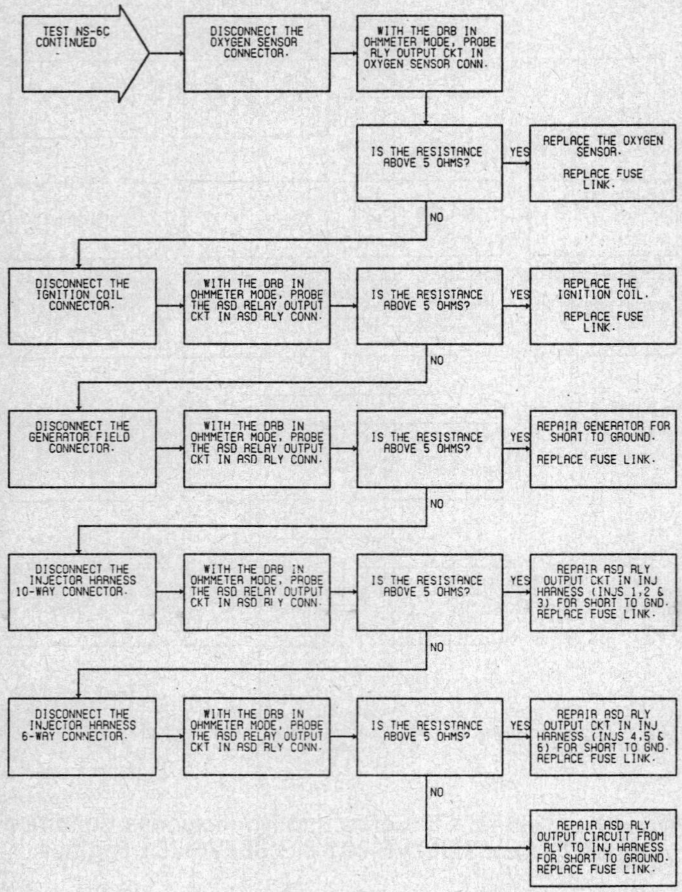

Fig. 208 (left top flowchart)

TEST NS-6C CONTINUED → DISCONNECT THE OXYGEN SENSOR CONNECTOR. → WITH THE DRB IN OHMMETER MODE, PROBE RLY OUTPUT CKT IN OXYGEN SENSOR CONN.

IS THE RESISTANCE ABOVE 5 OHMS? → YES → REPLACE THE OXYGEN SENSOR. REPLACE FUSE LINK.

NO

DISCONNECT THE IGNITION COIL CONNECTOR. → WITH THE DRB IN OHMMETER MODE, PROBE THE ASD RELAY OUTPUT CKT IN ASD RLY CONN. → IS THE RESISTANCE ABOVE 5 OHMS? → YES → REPLACE THE IGNITION COIL. REPLACE FUSE LINK.

NO

DISCONNECT THE GENERATOR FIELD CONNECTOR. → WITH THE DRB IN OHMMETER MODE, PROBE THE ASD RELAY OUTPUT CKT IN ASD RLY CONN. → IS THE RESISTANCE ABOVE 5 OHMS? → YES → REPAIR GENERATOR FOR SHORT TO GROUND. REPLACE FUSE LINK.

NO

DISCONNECT THE INJECTOR HARNESS 10-WAY CONNECTOR. → WITH THE DRB IN OHMMETER MODE, PROBE THE ASD RELAY OUTPUT CKT IN ASD RLY CONN. → IS THE RESISTANCE ABOVE 5 OHMS? → YES → REPAIR ASD RLY OUTPUT CKT IN INJ HARNESS (INJS 1,2 & 3) FOR SHORT TO GND. REPLACE FUSE LINK.

NO

DISCONNECT THE INJECTOR HARNESS 6-WAY CONNECTOR. → WITH THE DRB IN OHMMETER MODE, PROBE THE ASD RELAY OUTPUT CKT IN ASD RLY CONN. → IS THE RESISTANCE ABOVE 5 OHMS? → YES → REPAIR ASD RLY OUTPUT CKT IN INJ HARNESS (INJS 4,5 & 6) FOR SHORT TO GND. REPLACE FUSE LINK.

NO

REPAIR ASD RLY OUTPUT CIRCUIT FROM RLY TO INJ HARNESS FOR SHORT TO GROUND. REPLACE FUSE LINK.

CR1029303197020X

Fig. 208   Test NS-6C: Correcting No Response Condition (Part 2 of 2). 3.3L/V6-201 & 3.8L/V6-231 Engines

Fig. 209 (right top flowchart)

START TEST NS-7A → DISCONNECT THE IDLE AIR CONTROL MOTOR CONNECTOR. → TURN IGNITION ON. → WITH DRB, ACTUATE THE IDLE AIR CONTROL MOTOR.

PUT THE DRB IN VOLTMETER MODE. → PROBE THE IDLE AIR CONTROL MOTOR #3 DRIVER CKT. → DID THE VOLTAGE STAY BELOW 1 VOLT? → YES → PERFORM TEST NS-7B.

NO

PROBE THE IDLE AIR CONTROL MOTOR #1 DRIVER CKT. → DID THE VOLTAGE STAY BELOW 1 VOLT? → YES → PERFORM TEST NS-7C.

NO

PROBE THE IDLE AIR CONTROL MOTOR #4 DRIVER CKT. → DID THE VOLTAGE STAY BELOW 1 VOLT? → YES → PERFORM TEST NS-7D.

NO

PROBE THE IDLE AIR CONTROL MOTOR #2 DRIVER CKT. → DID THE VOLTAGE STAY BELOW 1 VOLT? → YES → PERFORM TEST NS-7E.

NO

CONTINUE TEST NS-7A

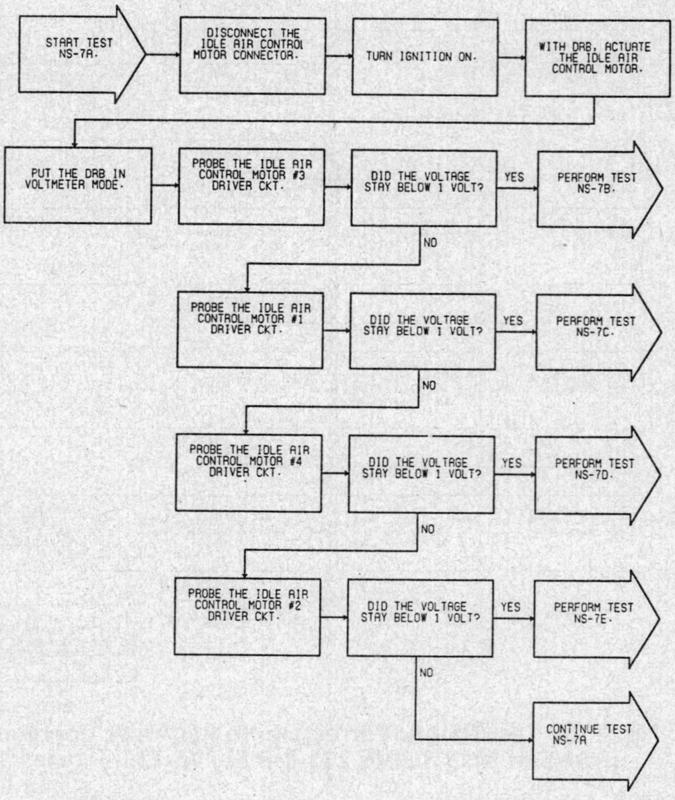

CR1029303198010X

Fig. 209   Test NS-7A: Inspecting Idle Air Control Motor Operation (Part 1 of 2). 3.3L/V6-201 & 3.8L/V6-231 Engines

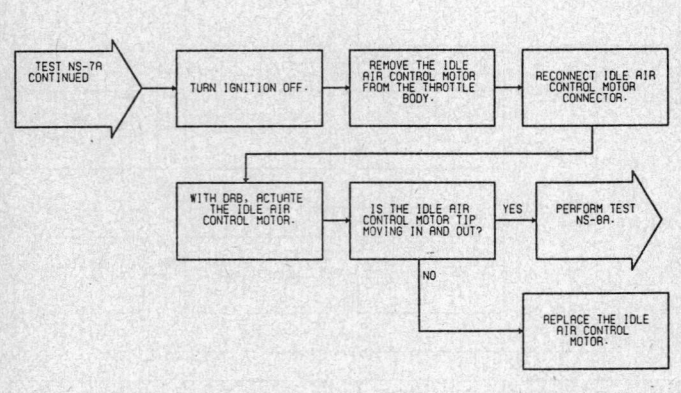

Fig. 209 (Part 2)

TEST NS-7A CONTINUED → TURN IGNITION OFF. → REMOVE THE IDLE AIR CONTROL MOTOR FROM THE THROTTLE BODY. → RECONNECT IDLE AIR CONTROL MOTOR CONNECTOR.

WITH DRB, ACTUATE THE IDLE AIR CONTROL MOTOR. → IS THE IDLE AIR CONTROL MOTOR TIP MOVING IN AND OUT? → YES → PERFORM TEST NS-8A.

NO

REPLACE THE IDLE AIR CONTROL MOTOR.

CR1029303198020X

Fig. 209   Test NS-7A: Inspecting Idle Air Control Motor Operation (Part 2 of 2). 3.3L/V6-201 & 3.8L/V6-231 Engines

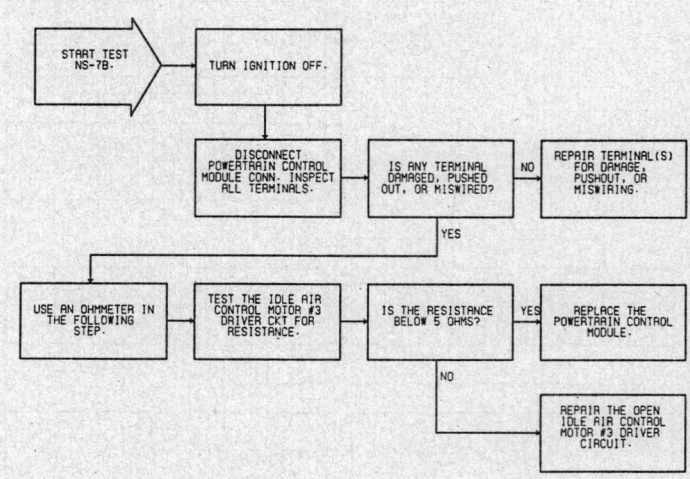

Fig. 210

START TEST NS-7B → TURN IGNITION OFF.

DISCONNECT POWERTRAIN CONTROL MODULE CONN. INSPECT ALL TERMINALS. → IS ANY TERMINAL DAMAGED, PUSHED OUT, OR MISWIRED? → NO → REPAIR TERMINAL(S) FOR DAMAGE, PUSHOUT, OR MISWIRING.

YES

USE AN OHMMETER IN THE FOLLOWING STEP. → TEST THE IDLE AIR CONTROL MOTOR #3 DRIVER CKT FOR RESISTANCE. → IS THE RESISTANCE BELOW 5 OHMS? → YES → REPLACE THE POWERTRAIN CONTROL MODULE.

NO

REPAIR THE OPEN IDLE AIR CONTROL MOTOR #3 DRIVER CIRCUIT.

CR1029303199000X

Fig. 210   Test NS-7B: Inspecting Idle Air Control Motor Operation. 3.3L/V6-201 & 3.8L/V6-231 Engines

CR1029303200000X

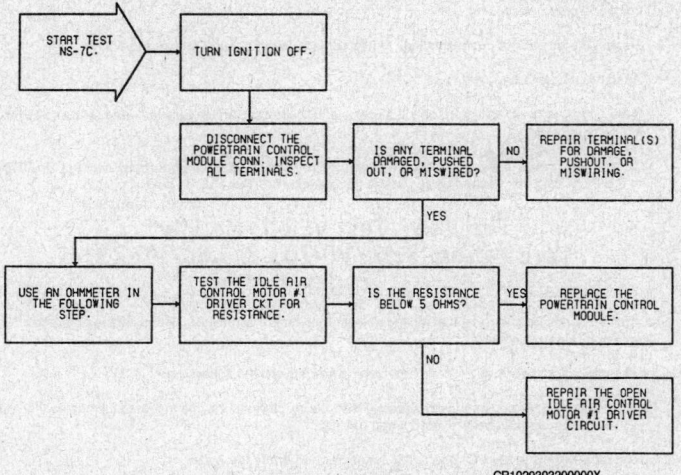

Fig. 211 Test NS-7C: Inspecting Idle Air Control Motor Operation. 3.3L/V6-201 & 3.8L/V6-231 Engines

CR1029303201000X

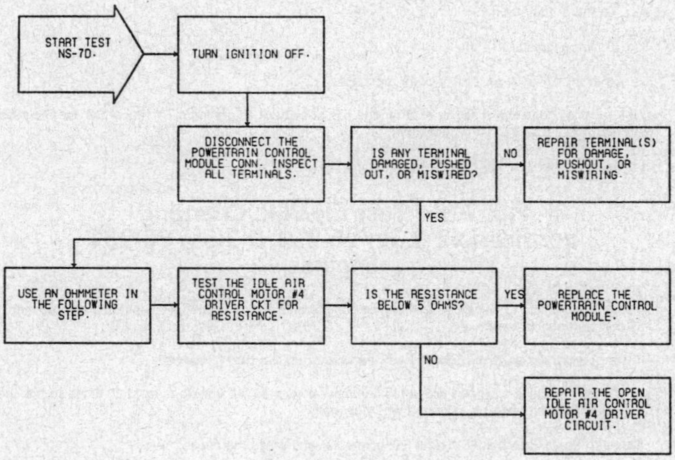

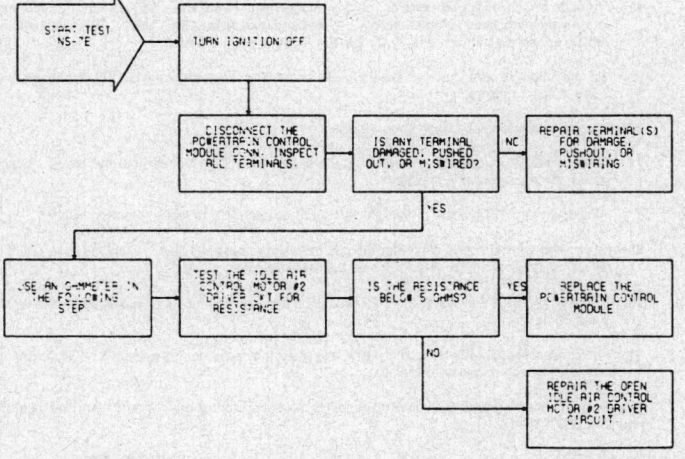

Fig. 212 Test NS-7D: Inspecting Idle Air Control Motor Operation. 3.3L/V6-201 & 3.8L/V6-231 Engines

CR1029303202000X

Fig. 213 Test NS-7E: Inspecting Idle Air Control Motor Operation. 3.3L/V6-201 & 3.8L/V6-231 Engines

At this point in the diagnostic test procedure, you have determined that all of the engine controller systems are operating as designed. Therefore, they are **not the cause of the start and stall problem.** The following potential causes of a no start condition should also be checked:

1. **ENGINE VALVE TIMING** - must be within specifications
2. **ENGINE COMPRESSION** - must be within specifications
3. **ENGINE EXHAUST** - must be unrestricted
4. **ENGINE PCV SYSTEM** - must flow freely
5. **ENGINE DRIVE SPROCKETS** - must be properly positioned
6. **FUEL** - must be free of contamination
7. **ENGINE SECONDARY IGNITION CHECK** - must exhibit a normal scope pattern

Any one or more of these items can produce a no start condition; none can be overlooked as possible causes.

Also, look for any Technical Service Bulletins that may relate to this condition.

CR1029303203000X

Fig. 214 Test NS-8A: Correcting Start & Stall Condition. 3.3L/V6-201 & 3.8L/V6-231 Engines

CR1029303204010X

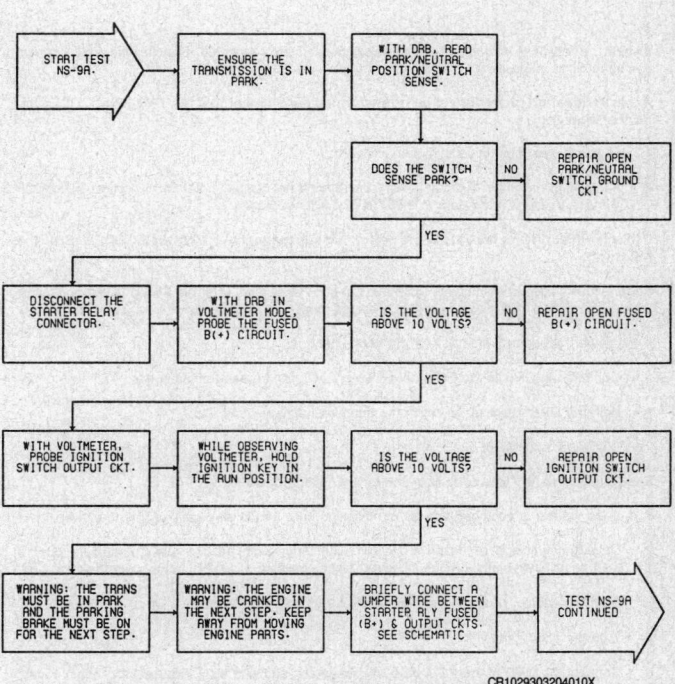

Fig. 215 Test NS-9A: No Crank Condition (Part 1 of 2). 3.3L/V6-201 & 3.8L/V6-231 Engines

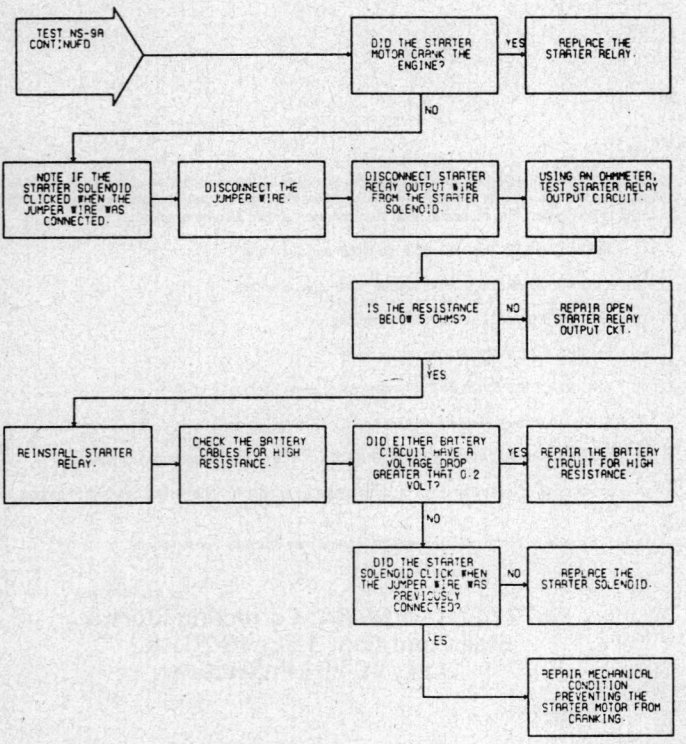

Fig. 215 Test NS-9A: No Crank Condition (Part 2 of 2). 3.3L/V6-201 & 3.8L/V6-231 Engines

Inspect the vehicle to ensure that all engine components are connected. Reassemble and reconnect components as necessary.

If this verification procedure is being performed subsequent to a NO TROUBLE CODE test, do the following:

1. Check to see if the initial symptom still exists.

2. If the initial or another symptom exists, the repair is not complete. Check all pertinent Technical Service Bulletins and return to **TEST NTC-1A** if necessary.

If this verification procedure is being performed subsequent to a TROUBLE CODE test, do the following:

For previously read trouble codes that have not been dealt with, return to **TEST TC-1A** and follow the path specified by the other code. Otherwise, continue.

If the powertrain control module has not been changed:

> Connect the DRB to the PCM data link connector and erase trouble codes.

> With the DRB, reset all values in the adaptive memory.

> Disconnect the DRB.

Ensure no other trouble code remains by doing the following:

1. If the vehicle is equipped with air conditioning, turn on the air conditioning and blower.

2. Drive the vehicle for at least five minutes and at some point attain a speed of 40 mph. Ensure the transmission shifts through all gears. Upon completion of the road test, turn the engine off.

3. Start the engine. Allow the engine to idle for at least two minutes.

4. Turn the engine off.

5. Connect the DRB to the PCM data link connector, and with the DRB, read all trouble codes.

If the repaired code has reset, the repair is not complete. Check all pertinent Technical Service Bulletins and return to **TEST TC-1A** if necessary.

If another trouble code has set, return to **TEST TC-1A** and follow the path specified by the other trouble code.

If there are no trouble codes, the repair is now complete.

CR1029303206000X

Fig. 217 Test VER-2: Road Test Verification. 3.3L/V6-201 & 3.8L/V6-231 Engines

Inspect the vehicle to ensure that all engine components are connected. Reassemble and reconnect components as necessary.

Inspect the engine for contamination. If it is contaminated, change the oil and filter.

Attempt to start the engine.

If the engine is **unable** to start, check all pertinent Technical Service Bulletins, and return to **TEST TC-1A** if necessary.

If the engine is **able** to start, and the powertrain control module **has been changed**, connect the DRB to the PCM data link connector and erase trouble codes. The repair is now complete.

CR1029303205000X

Fig. 216 Test VER-1: No Start Verification. 3.3L/V6-201 & 3.8L/V6-231 Engines

Inspect the vehicle to ensure that all engine components are connected. Reassemble and reconnect components as necessary.

If the powertrain control module has been changed, do the following:

1. If the vehicle is equipped with a factory theft alarm, start the vehicle at least 20 times so that the alarm system may be activated when desired.

Connect the DRB to the PCM data link connector and erase the codes.

Ensure no other charging system problems remain by doing the following:

1. Start the engine.

2. Raise the engine speed to 2000 rpm for at least 30 seconds.

3. Allow the engine to idle.

4. Turn the engine off.

5. Turn the ignition key on.

6. With the DRB, read trouble code messages.

If the repaired code has reset, or another one has set, check all pertinent Technical Service Bulletins and return to **TEST TC-1A** if necessary.

If there are no codes, the repair is now complete.

CR1029303207000X

Fig. 218 Test CH-VER: Charging Verification. 3.3L/V6-201 & 3.8L/V6-231 Engines

Inspect the vehicle to ensure that all engine components are connected. Reassemble and reconnect all components as necessary.

If the powertrain control module has been changed, do the following:

1. If the vehicle is equipped with a factory theft alarm, start the vehicle at least 20 times so that the alarm system may be activated when desired.

Connect the DRB to the PCM data link connector and erase the codes.

Ensure no other speed control problems remain by doing the following:

1. Road test the vehicle at a speed above 35 mph.

2. Turn the speed control ON/OFF switch to the ON position.

3. Depress and release the SET switch. If the speed control did not engage, the repair is not complete.*

4. For stalk switch equipped vehicles, quickly depress and release the SET switch. For steering wheel switch equipped vehicles, quickly depress and release the RESUME/ACCEL switch. If the vehicle speed did not increase by 2 mph, the repair is not complete.*

5. Using caution, depress and release the brake pedal. If the speed control did not disengage, the repair is not complete.*

6. Bring the vehicle speed back up to 35 mph.

7. Depress the RESUME/ACCEL switch. If the speed control did not resume the previously set speed, the repair is not complete.*

8. Hold down the SET switch. If the vehicle did not decelerate, the repair is not complete.*

9. Ensure the vehicle speed is greater than 35 mph and release the SET switch. If the vehicle did not adjust and set a new vehicle speed, the repair is not complete.*

10. Turn on the ON/OFF switch to the OFF position. If the speed control did not disengage, the repair is not complete.*

If the vehicle successfully passed all of the previous tests, the speed control system is now functioning as designed. The repair is now complete.

*Check for Technical Service Bulletins that pertain to this speed control problem and then, if necessary, return to **TEST TC-1A.**

CR1029303208000X

Fig. 219 Test SH-VER: Speed Control Verification. 3.3L/V6-201 & 3.8L/V6-231 Engines

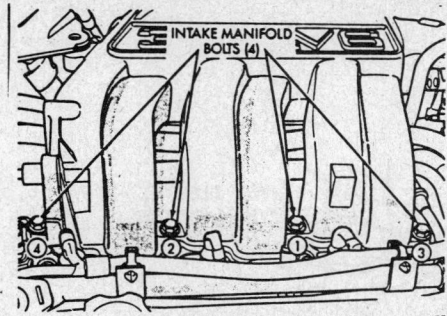

Fig. 220 Intake manifold tightening sequence. 3.3L/V6-201 & 3.8L/V6-231 Engines

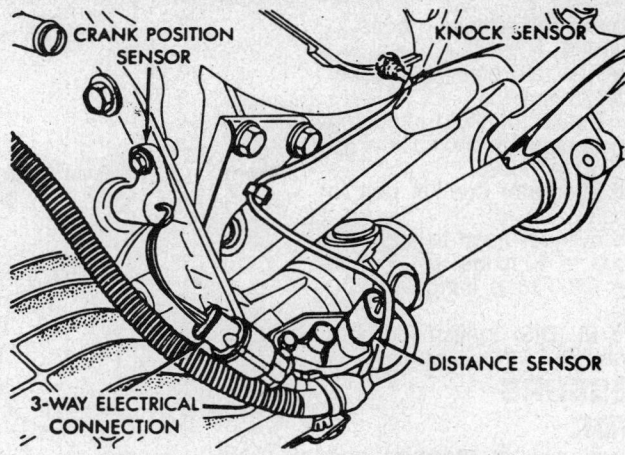

Fig. 221 CKP sensor replacement

SYSTEM SERVICE

Fuel System Pressure Relief

The EFI system is under a constant fuel pressure of approximately 48 psi. Fuel system pressure must be released prior to servicing fuel tank, fuel pump, fuel lines, fuel filter or fuel components of the throttle body.

3.0L/V6-181 ENGINE

1. Loosen gas cap to release any residual pressure in the fuel tank.
2. Disconnect electrical connector from fuel injector.
3. Using a suitable jumper wire, ground one injector terminal, then connect another jumper wire to other injector terminal and touch battery positive post for no more than 10 seconds.
4. Remove jumper wires from injector terminals. shutoff engine and remove tools.

3.3L/V6-201 & 3.8L/V6-231 ENGINES

1. Disconnect battery ground cable.
2. Remove fuel filler cap.
3. Remove protective cap from fuel pressure test port on the fuel rail.
4. Place open end of hose tool No. C-4799-1 or equivalent into a suitable container.
5. Connect other end of hose tool to test port on fuel rail to release fuel pressure.
6. Remove hose tool.
7. Continue fuel system service.

Component Replacement

THROTTLE BODY

1. Disconnect battery ground cable.
2. Remove air cleaner hose clamp to throttle body, then the hose.
3. Remove throttle cable and transaxle linkage, then disconnect IAC (AIS) motor and TPS electrical connectors.
4. Disconnect vacuum hoses from throttle body.
5. Remove throttle body to intake manifold attaching nuts, then the throttle body and gasket.
6. Reverse procedure to install.

THROTTLE POSITION SENSOR (TPS)

1. Disconnect battery ground cable.
2. Disconnect throttle position sensor electrical connector.
3. Remove throttle position sensor to throttle body attaching screws, then lift throttle position sensor off throttle shaft.
4. Reverse procedure to install. Torque sensor attaching screws to 17 inch lbs.

IDLE AIR CONTROL (IAC) (AUTOMATIC IDLE SPEED (AIS)) MOTOR

1. Disconnect battery ground cable.
2. Disconnect IAC (AIS) motor electrical connector.
3. Remove AIS motor to throttle body attaching screws, then the AIS motor from throttle body. Ensure O-ring in on AIS motor during removal.
4. Reverse procedure to install. If pintle measures more than one inches it must be retracted by using the DRB II in the IAC (AIS) Open/Close mode.

FUEL INJECTOR RAIL ASSEMBLY

3.0L/V6-181 Engine

1. Release fuel system pressure and disconnect battery ground cable.
2. Remove air cleaner hose then the throttle cable.
3. Disconnect IAC (AIS) motor and TPS sensors.
4. Remove vacuum harness from throttle body and intake plenum.
5. Remove EGR tube flange from intake plenum.
6. Disconnect ECT (coolant temperature) sensor.
7. Remove vacuum connections from air intake plenum vacuum connector.
8. Disconnect fuel hoses from fuel rail.
9. Remove intake plenum to intake manifold bolts.
10. Remove ignition coil.
11. Remove air intake plenum and cover intake manifold.
12. Remove vacuum hose from fuel rail.
13. Disconnect fuel injector wiring harness from engine harness.
14. Remove fuel rail mounting bolts, lift fuel rail assembly off intake manifold.
15. Reverse procedure to install, noting the following:
   a. **Torque** fuel rail attaching bolts to 115 inch lbs.
   b. **Torque** fuel supply and return tube hold-down bolts to 95 inch lbs.
   c. Install intake manifold gaskets with beaded seal facing up on lower manifold. **Torque** attaching bolts to 115 inch lbs.
   d. **Torque** EGR tube flange to 200 inch lbs.

3.3L/V6-201 & 3.8L/V6-231 Engines

1. Release fuel system pressure and disconnect battery ground cable.
2. Remove air cleaner hose then the throttle cable.
3. Remove wiring harness from throttle cable bracket and intake manifold water tube.
4. Disconnect IAC (AIS) motor and TPS sensors.
5. Remove vacuum harness from throttle body and intake plenum.
6. Remove PCV and brake booster vacuum hoses intake plenum.
7. Remove EGR tube flange from intake plenum.
8. Remove cylinder head to intake plenum strut.
9. Disconnect MAP and O₂S (oxygen) sensors.
10. Remove engine ground strap.
11. Disconnect fuel hoses from fuel rail.
12. Remove EI (DIS) ignition coil.
13. Remove intake manifold bolts and rotate manifold back over rear valve cover.
14. Cover intake manifold.
15. Remove vacuum harness connection from pressure regulator.
16. Remove fuel tube retainer bracket screw and fuel rail attaching bolts.
17. Remove fuel rail injector wiring clip from alternator bracket.
18. Disconnect CMP (camshaft position) and ECT (coolant temperature) sensors.
19. Remove fuel rail.
20. Reverse procedure to install, noting the following:

a. **Torque** fuel rail attaching bolts to 200 inch lbs.
b. **Torque** fuel rail retaining bracket screw to 35 inch lbs.
c. **Torque** intake manifold attaching bolts in sequence shown in **Fig. 220** to 250 inch lbs.
d. **Torque** alternator bracket bolt to 40 ft. lbs.
e. **Torque** cylinder head to manifold strut bolts to 40 ft. lbs.
f. **Torque** EGR tube flange to 200 inch lbs.
g. **Torque** El (DIS) ignition coils to 105 inch lbs.

FUEL PRESSURE REGULATOR

1. Release fuel system pressure and disconnect battery ground cable.
2. If necessary, remove fuel rail.
3. **On models equipped with 3.0L/V6-181 engine,** loosen hose clamps and remove fuel return hose from regulator.
4. **On all models,** remove vacuum hose from regulator.
5. Remove pressure regulator mounting screws then the regulator.
6. Reverse procedure to install, noting the following:
   a. **On 3.0L/V6-181 engine, torque** regulator screws to 90 inch lbs. and fuel return tube clamp to 95 inch lbs.
   b. **On 3.3L/V6-201 and 3.8L/V6-231 engines, torque** regulator screws to 60 inch lbs.

FUEL INJECTOR

1. Remove fuel injector rail assembly, then disconnect wiring connector from injector.
2. Position fuel rail assembly so that fuel injectors are easily accessible.
3. Remove injector clip from injector and fuel rail.
4. Pull injector straight out of fuel rail receiver cup.
5. Check injector O-ring for damage. Replace O-ring if damaged. If injector will be reused, install protective cap on injector tip to prevent damage.
6. Reverse procedure to install. Install injector clip by sliding open end into top slot of injector and on to receiver cup ridge into side slots of clip.

MANIFOLD ABSOLUTE PRESSURE (MAP) SENSOR

1. Disconnect battery ground cable.
2. Remove sensor vacuum hose and electrical connector.
3. Remove sensor attaching bolts, then the sensor.
4. Reverse procedure to install.

CANISTER PURGE & EGR DIAGNOSTIC SOLENOID

1. Disconnect battery ground cable.
2. Remove solenoid vacuum hose and electrical connector.
3. Remove solenoid attaching nuts, the solenoid assembly.
4. Reverse procedure to install.

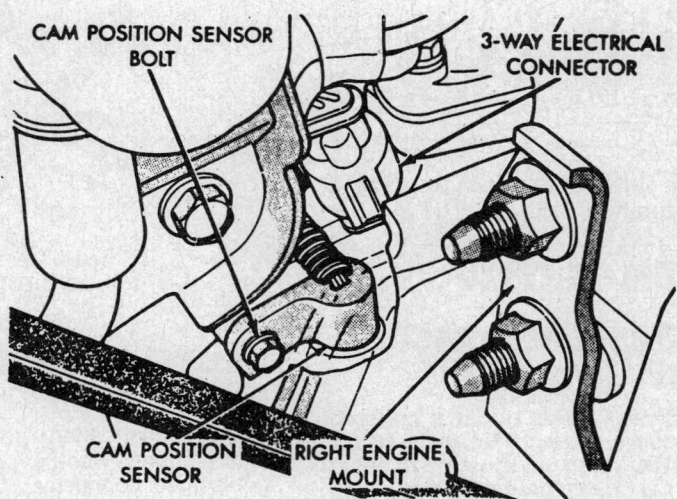

Fig. 222   CMP sensor replacement

POWERTRAIN CONTROL MODULE (PCM)

1. Remove air cleaner duct from engine controller.
2. Disconnect battery ground cable.
3. Disconnect 60-way module electrical connectors.
4. Remove two module attaching screws, then the module.
5. Reverse procedure to install.

HEATED OXYGEN SENSOR (O₂S)

1. Remove sensor from exhaust manifold using tool No. C-4589, or equivalent.
2. Clean threads in manifold using an 18 mm X 1.5 X 6E tap.
3. Install new sensor and **torque** to 20 ft. lbs. If original sensor is to be reinstalled, coat threads with a suitable anti-seize compound. New sensors are pre-coated and need no additional compound.

CRANKSHAFT POSITION (CKP) SENSOR

1. Disconnect electrical connector from sensor, then remove sensor attaching bolts, **Fig. 221.**
2. Pull sensor straight up out of transaxle housing.

3. Reverse procedure to install, noting the following:
   a. If old sensor is reused, a new spacer must be attached to sensor face.
   b. **Torque** retaining bolt to 105 inch lbs.

CAMSHAFT POSITION (CMP) SENSOR

1. Disconnect electrical connector from sensor, then loosen sensor retaining bolt, **Fig. 222.** Ensure slot in sensor will slide past bolt.
2. Remove sensor from chain case cover.
3. Reverse procedure to install, noting the following:
   a. If old sensor is reused, a new spacer must be attached to sensor face.
   b. Apply lubricant to O-ring before installation.
   c. **Torque** retaining bolt to 105 inch lbs.

Adjustments

IGNITION TIMING

Refer to "Ignition Timing" in the "Engine Tune Up & Performance" section for ignition timing procedures.

1993–95 CONCORDE, INTREPID & VISION & 1994–95 LHS & NEW YORKER

If Unsure Of The System Used On The Vehicle Being Serviced, Refer To The "Engine Systems Identification Chart." Further Assistance For The Proper Use Of Information Contained In This Section Can Also Be Found In The Front Of This Tabbed Section Under "How To Use This Manual."

Electrical Symbol & Wire Color Code Identification Located In The Front Of This Manual May Be Used As An Aid When Using Wiring Circuits Found In This Section.

INDEX

Page No.

Description: 13-2
  Components 13-2
Diagnosis & Testing: 13-3
  Accessing Diagnostic Trouble Codes 13-4
  Using Diagnostic Read-Out Tool
    DRB II 13-4
  Using Malfunction Indicator
    (Power Loss/Check Engine)
    Lamp 13-4
  Clearing Diagnostic Trouble Codes . 13-4
  Component Testing 13-5
    ASD & Fuel Pump Relays 13-6
    Fuel Injectors 13-6
    Heated Oxygen Sensor 13-6
    Throttle Position Sensor 13-6
    Transaxle Driveplate 13-6
  Diagnostic Trouble Code
    Interpretation 13-4
  DRB II Problems & Error Messages . 13-4
  "High Or Low Battery" Message . . 13-5
  "Key Pad Test Failure" Message . 13-5
  "No Response" Message 13-4
  "Ram Test Failure" & "Cartridge
    Error" Message 13-5
  Blank Message Screen 13-4

Page No.

Inactive Trouble Condition 13-4
On-Board Diagnosis 13-5
  Circuit Actuation Test Mode 13-5
  Fuel System Pressure Test 13-5
  Switch & Sensor Test Mode 13-5
  Throttle Body Minimum Air Flow
    Test 13-5
System Diagnosis 13-6
  Checking Charging System
    Controls 13-7
  Diagnostic Trouble Code Test 13-7
  No Fault Tests 13-7
  No Start Tests 13-7
  Verification Tests 13-7
Visual Inspection 13-3
Diagnostic Chart Index 13-24
Precautions: 13-1
  Fuel System Pressure Relief 13-1
  Subassembly Service 13-1
  Vehicle Damage Warning 13-1
Sensor Specifications 13-1
System Service: 13-75
  Adjustments 13-78
  Ignition Timing 13-78
  Throttle Body Synchronization . . 13-78

Page No.

Component Replacement 13-75
  Camshaft Position (CMP) Sensor 13-77
  Charge Air Temperature Sensor . 13-77
  Crankshaft Position (CKP)
    Sensor 13-77
  Engine Coolant Temperature
    (ECT) Sensor 13-77
  EVAP Purge Solenoid 13-77
  Fuel Injectors 13-76
  Fuel Rail 13-76
  Heated Oxygen Sensor (O2S) . . . 13-77
  Idle Air Control (IAC) Motor 13-77
  Intake Manifold Plenum 13-76
  Knock Sensor 13-77
  Manifold Absolute Pressure
    (MAP) Sensor 13-77
  Manifold Tuning Valve 13-78
  Manifold Tuning Valve Solenoid . 13-77
  Powertrain Control Module
    (PCM) 13-78
  Throttle Body 13-75
  Throttle Position Sensor (TPS) . . 13-78
Component Service 13-75
  Throttle Body Cleaning 13-75
  Fuel System Pressure Relief 13-75

SENSOR SPECIFICATIONS

Component	Resistance, Ohms
Heated Oxygen Sensor	5—7

PRECAUTIONS

FUEL SYSTEM PRESSURE RELIEF

To relieve fuel system pressure, refer to "Fuel System Pressure Relief" under "System Service" prior to servicing any fuel system component.

SUBASSEMBLY SERVICE

Some components are intended to be serviced as an assembly only. Attempting to remove or repair certain system subcomponents may result in personal injury and/or improper system operation.

VEHICLE DAMAGE WARNING

When testing voltage or continuity at the Powertrain Control Module (PCM), use the terminal side (not the wire end) of the connector. Do not probe a wire through the insulation, as this will damage it and eventually cause it to fail due to corrosion.

Use care when performing electrical tests so as to prevent accidental shorting of terminals. Mistakes during testing can cause damage to fuses or components and may set a second diagnostic trouble code, making diagnosis of original condition more difficult.

DESCRIPTION

The 3.3L/V6-201 and 3.5L/V6-215 engines use a multi-port electronic fuel injection system, **Fig. 1**. The Powertrain Control Module (PCM) operates the fuel injection system providing the engine with precise air/fuel ratios and ignition timing for all driving conditions.

Various sensors and switches provide input to the PCM which converts these inputs into signals and regulates various systems based on the inputs. The PCM adjusts the system it controls to meet changing operating conditions.

COMPONENTS

POWERTRAIN CONTROL MODULE (PCM)

The PCM is a digital computer containing a microprocessor. The PCM receives input signals from various switches and sensor references. Based on these inputs, the PCM adjusts various engine and vehicle operations through devices referred to as PCM outputs, **Fig. 1**.

The PCM contains a voltage converter that changes battery voltage to a regulated 8 volts for certain circuits and 5 volts for others.

TRANSAXLE CONTROL MODULE (TCM)

The TCM provides the PCM with two input signals: road speed and, on models with 3.5L/V6-215 engine, torque management.

Road Speed

The TCM supplies the road speed and distance traveled inputs to the PCM. From these inputs and the throttle position sensor input, the PCM determines when a deceleration condition occurs.

Torque Management

On models with 3.5L/V6-215 engine, the PCM receives torque management input from the transaxle control module when the transaxle shifts gears. In response, the PCM shuts off a number of fuel injectors when the transaxle shifts gears.

CAMSHAFT POSITION (CMP) SENSOR

The CMP provides cylinder identification to the PCM. The sensor generates pulses as groups of notches on the camshaft sprocket pass underneath it. The PCM keeps track of camshaft rotation and identifies each cylinder by the pulses gen-

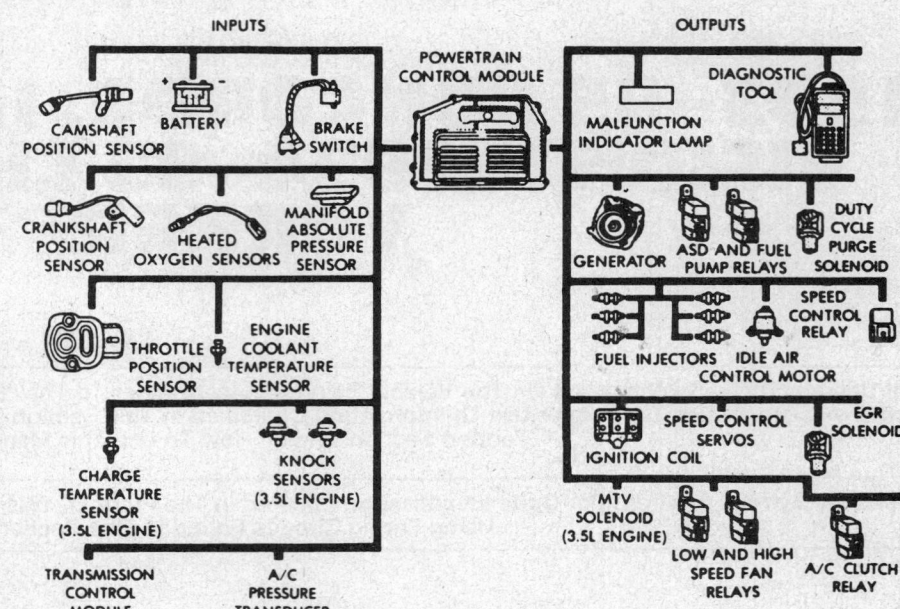

Fig. 1 Multi-point fuel injection system components

erated by the notches. Four crankshaft pulses follow each group of camshaft pulses.

CHARGE AIR TEMPERATURE SENSOR

The charge air temperature sensor is used on the 3.5L/V6-215 engine. The sensor is located in the intake manifold plenum and measures air temperature. The sensor provides one of the inputs the PCM monitors when it adjusts injector pulse width and spark advance.

CRANKSHAFT POSITION (CKP) SENSOR

The CKP detects slots cut into transaxle driveplate extension. There are three sets of slots each containing four slots. Basic timing is set by the position of the last slot in each group. Once the PCM senses the last slot, it determines crankshaft position from the camshaft position sensor input. The four pulses of the CKP represent the 60°, 49°, 29° and 9° BTDC marks. It may take the PCM one revolution to determine crankshaft position.

ENGINE COOLANT TEMPERATURE (ECT) SENSOR

The ECT sensor is located in the water jacket next to the thermostat housing. As coolant temperature varies, the sensor resistance changes resulting in a different input signal to the PCM. When the engine is cold, the PCM will demand a slightly richer air-fuel mixture and higher idle speed until normal operating temperature is reached.

The ECT also determines operation of the low and high speed cooling fans.

KNOCK SENSOR

3.5L/V6-215 Engine

Two knock sensors are used, one for each bank of cylinders and are located in the top of the cylinder block below the cylinder heads. When an engine knock is de-

tected, the knock sensor sends an input signal to the PCM which responds by retarding the ignition timing by a scheduled amount.

The knock sensor contains a crystal which constantly vibrates and sends an input voltage (signal) to the PCM while the engine operates. As the intensity of the crystal's vibration increases, the knock sensor output voltage also increases.

MANIFOLD ABSOLUTE PRESSURE (MAP) SENSOR

The MAP sensor converts intake manifold pressure into voltage. The PCM monitors the MAP sensor output voltage. As vacuum increases, MAP sensor voltage drops. Also, as vacuum drops, MAP sensor voltage increases.

HEATED OXYGEN SENSOR (O2S)

Fuel injector system uses two heated oxygen sensors, one in each exhaust manifold. Both sensors monitor the amount of oxygen in the exhaust gas stream. The inputs from the O2S tell the PCM the oxygen content of the exhaust gas. Based on this input the PCM fine tunes the air/fuel ratio in each cylinder by adjusting injector pulse width.

The oxygen sensors are equipped with heating elements keeping the sensor at the correct operating temperature under all driving conditions.

THROTTLE POSITION SENSOR (TPS)

The throttle position sensor is a variable resistor that is mounted to the throttle body. Although the 3.5L/V6-215 engine uses two throttle bodies only one TPS is used. The sensor provides the PCM with an input signal that represents throttle blade position. As the position of the throttle blade changes, the resistance of the TPS changes.

AUTO SHUTDOWN (ASD) & FUEL PUMP RELAYS

The ASD relay connects battery voltage to the fuel injectors and ignition coil. The fuel pump relay connects battery voltage to the fuel pump. The PCM operates the ASD and fuel pump relays by switching the ground path for the solenoid side of the relays On and Off. Both relays turn On and Off at the same time. The ASD and fuel pump relays are located in the power distribution center near the battery.

MANIFOLD TUNING VALVE (MTV) SOLENOID

3.5L/V6-215 Engine

The MTV solenoid regulates the supply of vacuum to the manifold tuning valve and is controlled by the PCM. The manifold tuning valve optimizes acoustical tuning of the intake system during wide open throttle operation throughout the RPM range. The valve opens a crossover passage that connects both sides of the intake manifold plenum.

When energized, the MTV solenoid allows vacuum to close the manifold tuning valve. When not energized, the solenoid closes and vacuum is bled off from the manifold tuning valve vacuum motor. The manifold tuning valve opens the crossover when the solenoid de-energizes.

ELECTRONIC EXHAUST GAS RECIRCULATION TRANSDUCER (EET)

The EET transducer contains an electrically operated solenoid and a backpressure transducer. The PCM operates the solenoid and exhaust system backpressure controls the transducer. When exhaust system backpressure becomes high enough, it fully closes a bleed valve in the transducer. When the PCM de-energizes the solenoid and backpressure closes the transducer bleed valve, vacuum flows through the transducer to operate the EGR valve.

De-energizing the solenoid varies the strength of vacuum applied to the EGR valve. Varying the strength of vacuum changes the EGR supplied to the engine. This provides the correct amount of exhaust gas recirculation for different operating conditions.

DUTY CYCLE EVAP PURGE SOLENOID

The duty cycle EVAP purge solenoid regulates the rate of vapor flow from the EVAP canister to the throttle body. The PCM controls the solenoid.

FUEL INJECTOR

The 3.3L/V6-201 engine uses a top feed type fuel injector. The 3.5L/V6-215 engine uses a bottom feed type fuel injector. The PCM energizes the injector in a sequence order during all engine operating conditions except start-up. During start-up when coolant temperature is below 60°F, all injectors are energized at the same time.

IGNITION COIL

The coil assembly consists of three coils molded together. The coil assembly is mounted on the intake manifold and high tension wires connect the coil to each spark plug. The PCM determines which of the coils are to fire and at what time.

IDLE AIR CONTROL (IAC) MOTOR

3.3L/V6-201 Engine

The IAC motor attaches to the throttle body and is controlled by the PCM. The PCM adjusts engine idle speed through the IAC motor to compensate for engine load or ambient conditions. The throttle body has an air bypass passage that provides air for the engine at idle. The PCM adjusts engine idle speed by moving the IAC motor pintle in and out of the air bypass to regulate air flow.

3.5L/V6-215 Engine

The IAC motor and housing attaches to the rear of the intake manifold plenum. The housing opens to the rear runner in the intake manifold plenum. A hose from the air cleaner supplies filtered air to the IAC motor housing. The PCM adjusts engine idle speed by moving the IAC motor pintle in and out of the housing to regulate air flow.

MALFUNCTION INDICATOR LAMP

The PCM transmits the malfunction indicator lamp signal over the CCD bus. The lamp comes on each time the ignition key is turned On, and it will stay on for 3 seconds as a bulb test. The malfunction indicator lamp warns the operator that the PCM has entered its "Limp-In" mode. While in this mode, the PCM attempts to keep the system operational by compensating for the failure of certain components that send incorrect signals.

THROTTLE BODY

3.3L/V6-201 Engine

The throttle body assembly is located on the right side of the intake manifold plenum. The throttle body houses the TPS sensor and IAC motor. Air flow is controlled by a cable operated throttle blade.

3.5L/V6-215 Engine

The 3.5L/V6-215 engine has two throttle bodies. A shaft connects both throttle bodies and a single TPS sensor together to maintain synchronization. The throttle bodies connect to the rear of the intake manifold plenum. The TPS attaches to the right throttle body.

If either throttle body is removed or replaced, the Throttle Body Synchronization procedure must be performed as outlined under "System Service."

FUEL PRESSURE REGULATOR

The PCM does not control the fuel pressure regulator. The regulator is a mechanical device that maintains fuel system pressure.

DIAGNOSIS & TESTING

The on-board diagnostics incorporated with the Single Board Engine Controller II (SBEC II) are intended to assist the technician in repairing vehicle problems by the shortest means.

The PCM has been programed to monitor many different circuits of the fuel injection system. If a problem is sensed with a monitored circuit, and all criteria (arming conditions) are met, a diagnostic trouble code will be stored in the PCM.

Visual Inspection

Prior to diagnosing or servicing the fuel injection system, perform a visual inspection for loose, disconnected or misrouted wires and hoses. A complete visual inspection, including the following, saves unnecessary diagnostic time.

1. Remove power distribution cover. Check for blown fuses and ensure all relays are properly installed.
2. Check battery terminal connections for looseness and corrosion.
3. Check MAP sensor electrical connection.
4. Ensure spark plug cables are firmly connected and installed correctly on the coil pack.
5. Check IAC motor, TPS and ECT sensor electrical connections.
6. **On models with 3.5L/V6-215 engine,** check the following:
   a. Ensure air plenum hoses are attached to the IAC motor and the make up air nipple for the PCV system.
   b. Ensure PCV hose is connected to the PCV valve, not the IAC control motor.
   c. Ensure vacuum hose is attached to the manifold tuning valve and the vacuum harness.
7. **On all models,** ensure purge hose is connected to throttle bodies.
8. Ensure vacuum hose is attached to the fuel pressure regulator. Check hose for cracks or leaks.
9. Check EVAP solenoid and MTV solenoid electrical connections.
10. Inspect the air cleaner element and replace if necessary.
11. Inspect hose connections at the EVAP canister for leaks.
12. Ensure the 60-way connector is fully inserted into the PCM. Check for stretched or pulled out wires.
13. Ensure accessory drive belt tension is correct.
14. Check for loose or corroded connections at the generator.
15. Inspect fuel supply and return tube connections for leaks.
16. Check CKP and O2S sensor electrical connections.
17. Check for loose or corroded electrical connections at the starter motor.

CHRYSLER—Fuel Injection

Accessing Diagnostic Trouble Codes

USING DIAGNOSTIC READ-OUT TOOL DRB II

1. Connect the DRB II scan tool to the data link connector located in the passenger compartment, below the center of the instrument panel on the driver's side.
2. If possible, start engine and cycle the air conditioning switch, then turn Off engine.
3. Turn ignition switch to On position, access Read Fault Screen and record all diagnostic trouble codes shown on DRB II screen.
4. The malfunction indicator lamp on the instrument panel should light for two seconds as a bulb test, then go out.

USING MALFUNCTION INDICATOR (POWER LOSS/CHECK ENGINE) LAMP

If suitable diagnostic read-out tool is not available, stored diagnostic trouble codes can be accessed directly through the malfunction indicator (power loss/check engine) lamp. To call up diagnostic trouble codes, cycle ignition switch to On, Off, On, Off and then to On position within 5 seconds. Stored diagnostic trouble codes will be indicated by flashes of the malfunction indicator lamp. The diagnostic trouble codes will be indicated as two digit numbers, with a four second pause between diagnostic trouble codes. An example of a diagnostic trouble code is as follows:
1. Malfunction Indicator Lamp illuminated for approximately 2 to 3 seconds as a bulb check, then turns off.
2. Lamp flashes two times, pauses, then flashes seven times.
3. Lamp pauses for approximately four seconds.
4. Lamp flashes three times, pauses, then flashes one time.
5. This would indicate that Diagnostic Trouble Codes 27 and 31 are stored. The lamp will continue to flash until all stored diagnostic trouble codes have been displayed.

Once the lamp starts flashing the stored diagnostic trouble codes, it cannot be stopped. If a diagnostic trouble code is missed, the entire procedure must be repeated. The lamp will not indicate if oxygen feedback system is switching lean-rich or if idle motor system is operational. The lamp also cannot be used to perform actuation test mode, sensor test mode or engine running test mode.

Diagnostic Trouble Code Interpretation

Diagnostic trouble codes can be displayed either by flashes of the malfunction indicator lamp or by connecting Diagnostic Read-out Box II (DRB II) to the system.

Diagnostic trouble codes indicate the results of a failure, but do not identify the failed component. The diagnostic charts do not use diagnostic trouble codes for diagnosis. Instead, diagnosis is performed in a symptom driven format.

Prior to performing any procedure in the diagnostic charts, check electrical and vacuum component connections as described under "Visual Inspection." **Always start at the first No Start, Driveability, No Fault or Verification test. Starting at any other test may give inaccurate results.** After completing the test, perform verification test.

CODE 11—Indicates no reference signal during engine cranking.
CODE 13—Indicates a fault in the MAP sensor pneumatic circuit.
CODE 14—Indicates a fault in the MAP sensor electrical circuit.
CODE 15—Indicates a fault in the vehicle speed sensor circuit.
CODE 17—Indicates engine running too cool too long.
CODE 21—Indicates a problem in the oxygen feedback circuit.
CODE 22—Indicates a fault in the coolant temperature sensor circuit.
CODE 23—Indicates a fault in the charge temperature sensor circuit.
CODE 24—Indicates a fault in the throttle position sensor circuit.
CODE 25—Indicates a fault in the IAC motor drive circuit.
CODE 27—Indicates a fault in injector control circuit.
CODE 31—Indicates a fault in the purge solenoid circuit.
CODE 32—Indicates a fault in EGR system.
CODE 33—Indicates a fault in air conditioning clutch relay circuit.
CODE 34—Indicates a fault in speed control solenoid circuit.
CODE 35—Indicates a fault in fan relay circuit.
CODE 41—Indicates a fault in the charging system or no field current.
CODE 42—Indicates a fault in the ASD relay driver circuit.
CODE 43—Indicates fault in ignition coil control circuit.
CODE 44—Indicates battery temperature voltage is incorrect.
CODE 46—Indicates battery voltage is too high.
CODE 47—Indicates battery voltage is too low.
CODE 51—Indicates a lean condition is indicated.
CODE 52—Indicates a rich condition is indicated.
CODE 53—Indicates internal controller problem in module.
CODE 54—Indicates no sync pick-up signal.
CODE 55—Indicates end of message. This code will appear after all other diagnostic trouble codes have been displayed.
CODE 62—Indicates unsuccessful attempt to update EMR mileage.
CODE 63—Indicates controller failure. EEPROM write denied.
CODE 65—Indicates a fault in the manifold tuning valve.
CODE 66—Indicates a fault in the CCD bus system.
CODE 77—Indicates a fault in the speed control relay circuit.
Diagnostic trouble codes indicated by an will cause the malfunction indicator lamp to remain illuminated when set in the engine controller memory.

Inactive Trouble Condition

This section should only be used when referred to by the diagnostic charts.

You have just attempted to simulate the condition that initially set the fault message. The following additional checks may assist in identifying a possible intermittent problem:
1. Visually inspect related wire harness connectors. Look for broken, bent, pushed out or corroded terminals.
2. Visually inspect the related harnesses. Look for chafed, pierced or partially broken wires.
3. Refer to any technical service bulletins that may apply.

Clearing Diagnostic Trouble Codes

Diagnostic trouble codes can be cleared in one of two ways. First is by selecting Erase Faults under the Read Faults display, or by disconnecting the battery ground cable for at least two minutes.

DRB II Problems & Error Messages

BLANK MESSAGE SCREEN

1. Connect the DRB II to a different vehicle.
2. If screen remains blank, the DRB II or its adapter are at fault. Substitute parts to determine which.
3. If screen is no longer blank, proceed to step 4.
4. Inspect diagnostic connector for proper wire placement, flared terminals or push outs.
5. If connector is in good condition, ensure black/white wire is connected to ground.

"NO RESPONSE" MESSAGE

1. Ensure ignition switch in On position.
2. Test pink and light green wires for continuity between diagnostic connector and cavities 25 and 26 of the engine controller 60-way connector.
3. Install a different DRB II with a different set of cables and check for a "No Response" message.
4. If steps 1 through 3 do not correct "No Response" message, replace engine controller.

"RAM TEST FAILURE" & "CARTRIDGE ERROR" MESSAGE

If this message is displayed on the DRB II, replace the DRB II unit or cartridge.

"KEY PAD TEST FAILURE" MESSAGE

If this message is displayed on the DRB II, power the DRB II up again with fingers off key pad. If message persists, replace the DRB II.

"HIGH OR LOW BATTERY" MESSAGE

If this message is displayed, correct condition and reconnect the DRB II.

On-Board Diagnosis

SWITCH & SENSOR TEST MODE

The switch inputs used by the engine controller have only two recognized states: High and Low. For this reason, the engine controller cannot recognize the difference between a switch position versus an open circuit, a short circuit or a defective switch. If the change is displayed, it can be assumed that the entire switch circuit to the engine controller is functioning normally.

Connect the DRB II tool to the vehicle and access the State Display Screen. Access Inputs and Outputs or Sensor to obtain the list of available components to be tested.

CIRCUIT ACTUATION TEST MODE

The circuit actuation test mode check for proper operation of output circuits or components which the engine controller cannot internally recognize. The engine controller can attempt to activate these outputs and allow an observer to verify proper operation. Most of the tests provide an audible or visual indication or operation. With the exception of an intermittent condition, if a component functions properly during its test, it can be assumed that the component, its associated wiring and its driver circuit are working properly.

Connect the DRB II tool to the vehicle and access the Actuators screen to obtain the list of available components to be tested.

THROTTLE BODY MINIMUM AIR FLOW TEST

3.3L/V6-201 Engine

1. Warm engine in park or neutral until cooling fan has cycled On and Off at least once.
2. Place all accessories in the Off position.
3. Turn ignition switch to Off position.
4. Disconnect PCV valve hose from in-

take manifold nipple and cap valve.
5. Disconnect purge hose from nipple on throttle body.
6. Install air metering orifice tool No. 6457 or equivalent to the purge nipple on the throttle body.
7. Connect the DRB II scan tool to the data link connector inside the passenger compartment.
8. Start engine and allow to idle for at lease one minute.
9. Using DRB II, access Min. Airflow Idle Spd. screen.
10. After accessing, the following will occur:
    a. IAC motor will fully close.
    b. Idle spark advance will become fixed.
    c. DRB II scan tool displays engine RPM.
11. If idle RPM is within 600-840 RPM, throttle body minimum airflow is set correctly.
12. If idle RPM is above specification, use the DRB II to check IAC motor operation.
13. If idle RPM is below specification, shutoff engine and clean throttle body as outlined under "System Service."
14. Repeat procedure after cleaning throttle body. If air flow is still not within specifications, problem is not caused by the throttle body.

3.5L/V6-215 Engine

If the vehicle has a low idle speed condition, first use the DRB II to check for proper operation of the IAC motor. If the IAC motor operates normally, clean the throttle bodies referring to "System Service."

1. Warm engine in park or neutral until cooling fan has cycled On and Off at least once.
2. Place all accessories in the Off position.
3. Turn ignition switch to Off position.
4. Disconnect PCV valve hose from intake manifold nipple and cap valve.
5. Disconnect purge hose from nipple on throttle body.
6. Install air metering orifice tool No. 6457 or equivalent to the purge nipple on the throttle body.
7. Connect the DRB II scan tool to the data link connector inside the passenger compartment.
8. Start engine and allow to idle for at least one minute.
9. Using DRB II, access Min. Airflow Idle Spd. screen.
10. After accessing, the following will occur:
    a. IAC motor will fully close.
    b. Idle spark advance will become fixed.
    c. DRB II scan tool displays engine RPM.
11. If idle RPM is within 750-1100 RPM, throttle body minimum airflow is set correctly.
12. If idle RPM is below specification even though the IAC motor operates correctly and the throttle bodies were cleaned and then synchronized, replace the throttle bodies.
13. If idle RPM is above specification, re-

set throttle body synchronization. Also recheck IAC motor operation. If idle RPM is still above specification check for leaking intake manifold plenum or gaskets.

FUEL SYSTEM PRESSURE TEST

Fuel system pressure must be released any time a fuel line is to be disconnected.

1. Remove protective cover from service valve on fuel rail.
2. Connect fuel pressure gauge tool No. C-4799B or equivalent to fuel rail service valve.
3. Using diagnostic tester with ignition switch in Run position, perform ASD fuel system test. This will activate fuel pump and pressurize the system.
4. If gauge reads correct fuel pressure specification, further testing in not required.
5. If pressure is not correct, record pressure and remove gauge tool.
6. Use ASD fuel system test to activate fuel pump. Ensure fuel does not leak from fuel rail service valve or fuel connection point.
7. If fuel pressure is below specification, proceed as follows:
    a. Install fuel pressure gauge tool and adapter in fuel supply line between fuel tank and fuel filter at rear of vehicle.
    b. Repeat step 3. If pressure is at least 5 psi higher than previously recorded, replace fuel filter.
    c. If no chance is recorded, gently squeeze return hose.
    d. If pressure increases, replace pressure regulator.
    e. If pressure does not change, problem is either a plugged pump filter or defective fuel pump.
8. If pressure is above specification, proceed as follows:
    a. Remove fuel return line hose from fuel tank.
    b. Connect fuel pressure test adapter to the return line.
    c. Put other end into a suitable two gallon container.
    d. Repeat step 3. If pressure is now correct, replace fuel pump assembly.
    e. If pressure is still high, remove fuel return hose from chassis fuel tubes. Connect adapter tool to return hose and place other end into a suitable container.
    f. Repeat step 3. If pressure is now correct, check for restricted fuel return line.
    g. If no change in pressure is observed, replace fuel pressure regulator.

Component Testing

For components not found in this section, refer to the appropriate diagnostic chart under "System Diagnosis."

CHRYSLER–Fuel Injection

FUEL INJECTORS

Refer to **Figs. 2 and 3** for fuel injector testing procedures.

TRANSAXLE DRIVEPLATE

A cracked transaxle driveplate could cause poor fuel economy and an engine miss. If the driveplate cracks, the CMP and CKP sensors could get out of synchronization and retard ignition timing. In worst cases, a cracked driveplate may cause a no-start condition.

ASD & FUEL PUMP RELAYS

The following test is for the ASD or fuel pump relay. Refer to **Fig. 4** for relay terminal identification and relay operation.

1. Remove relay from connector prior to testing.
2. Use an ohmmeter to check the resistance between terminals 85 and 86. Resistance should be 70-80 ohms.
3. Connect ohmmeter between terminals 30 and 87A. Ohmmeter should show continuity.
4. Connect ohmmeter between terminals 87 and 30. Ohmmeter should not show continuity.
5. Connect a wire between terminal 87 and ground.
6. Connect a second wire to battery voltage.
7. Connect an ohmmeter to terminals 87 and 30 then connect second wire to terminal 86. Ohmmeter should show continuity when second wire is attached to terminal 86.
8. If relay did not perform as specified, replace the relay.
9. If relay performed as specified, check remainder of the ASD and fuel pump circuit.

THROTTLE POSITION SENSOR

The throttle position sensor can be tested with a digital voltmeter. The center terminal of the sensor is the output terminal. With ignition switch in On position, check output voltage at center terminal wire of connector. Check output voltage at idle and at wide open throttle. At idle, TPS output voltage should be greater than .6 millivolts. At wide open throttle, TPS output voltage should be less than 4.5 volts. Output voltage should gradually increase as throttle plate moves slowly from idle to wide open throttle.

HEATED OXYGEN SENSOR

Use an ohmmeter to test the heating element of the O2S sensor. Disconnect electrical connection from each sensor. The white wires in the sensor connector are the power and ground circuits for the sensor. Connect the ohmmeter to terminals of white wires in the O2S connector. Replace the O2S sensor if resistance is not between 5 and 7 ohms.

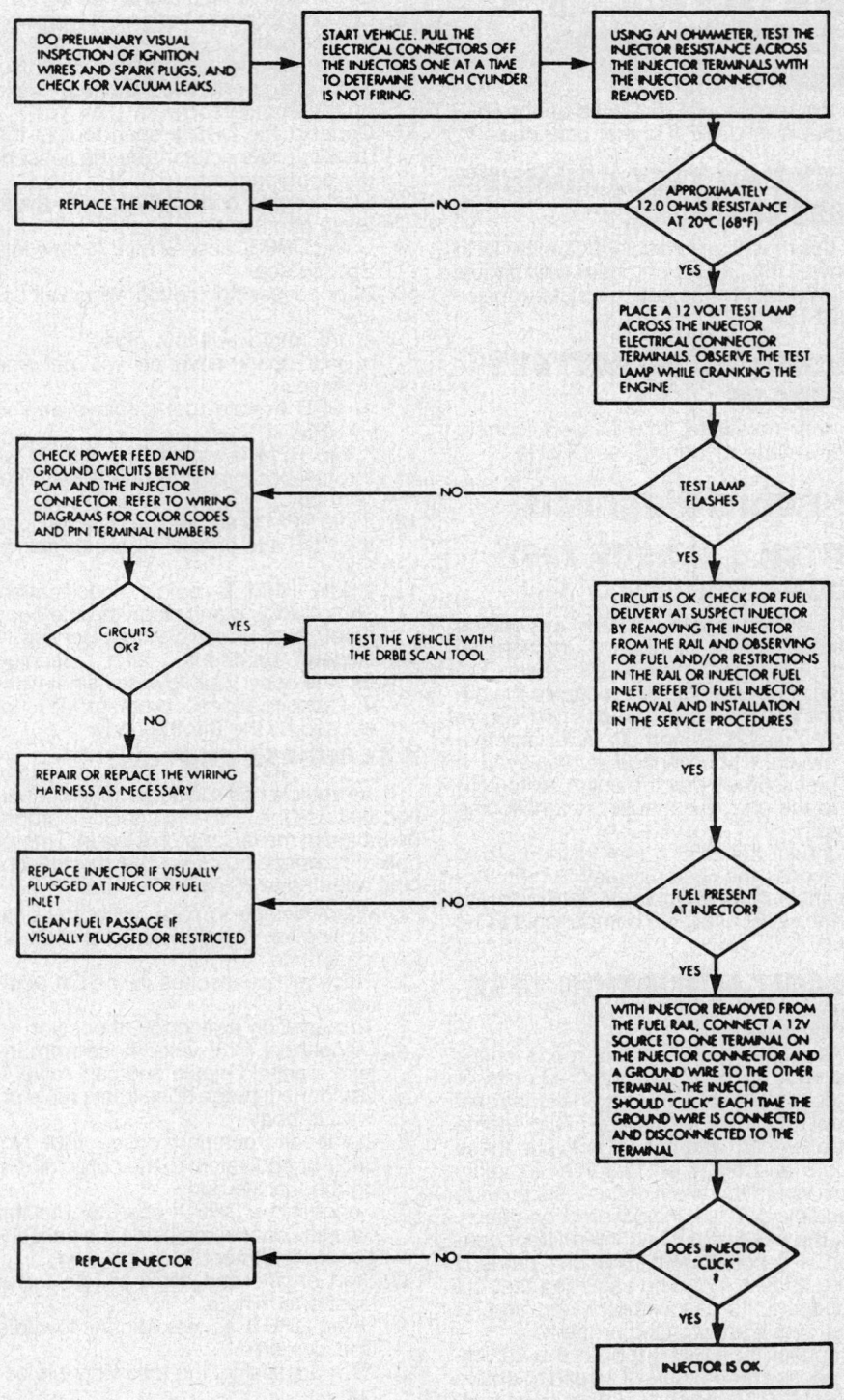

Fig. 2   Fuel injector diagnosis. 3.3L/V6-201 engine

System Diagnosis

The following tests are used to further diagnose systems monitored by the On-Board Diagnosis System and to also test systems or parts of a system which are not monitored by the On-Board diagnosis system. Prior to performing any of the following tests, check electrical and vacuum component connections as described under "Visual Inspection." **Always start with the first Diagnostic Trouble Code, No Fault, No Start or Verification Test. Starting at any other test may give inaccurate results.** After completing the test, perform appropriate verification test. Also check electrical connector terminal blades or pins for alignment and damage prior to replacing any component.

Refer to **Figs. 5 through 8** for wiring diagrams and connector terminal identification.

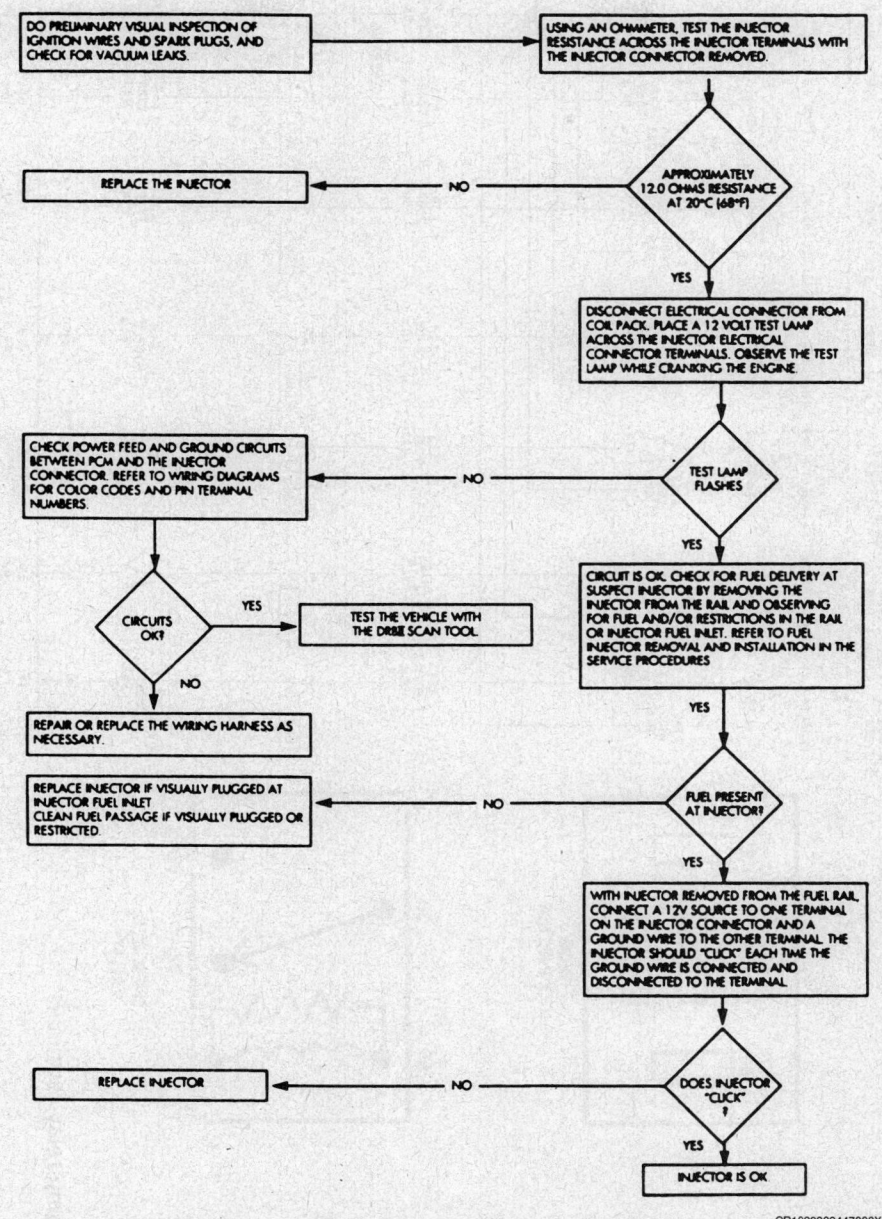

Fig. 3   Fuel injector diagnosis. 3.5L/V6-215 engine

CR1029303447000X

DIAGNOSTIC TROUBLE CODE TEST

Refer to the first Diagnostic Trouble Code diagnosis chart, **Fig. 9,** and the remaining Diagnostic Trouble Code charts, **Figs. 10 through 94,** for no start diagnosis and testing.

NO FAULT TESTS

Refer to the first Driveability diagnosis chart, **Fig. 95,** and the remaining Drivea-bility charts, **Figs. 96 through 120,** for driveability diagnosis and testing.

NO START TESTS

Refer to the first No Start diagnosis chart, **Fig. 121,** and the remaining No Start charts, **Figs. 122 through 136,** when no diagnostic trouble codes are set and a malfunction exists.

CHECKING CHARGING SYSTEM CONTROLS

Refer to **Fig. 137** when checking charging system controls.

VERIFICATION TESTS

After completing diagnosis operations, perform verification tests, **Figs. 138 through 141.**

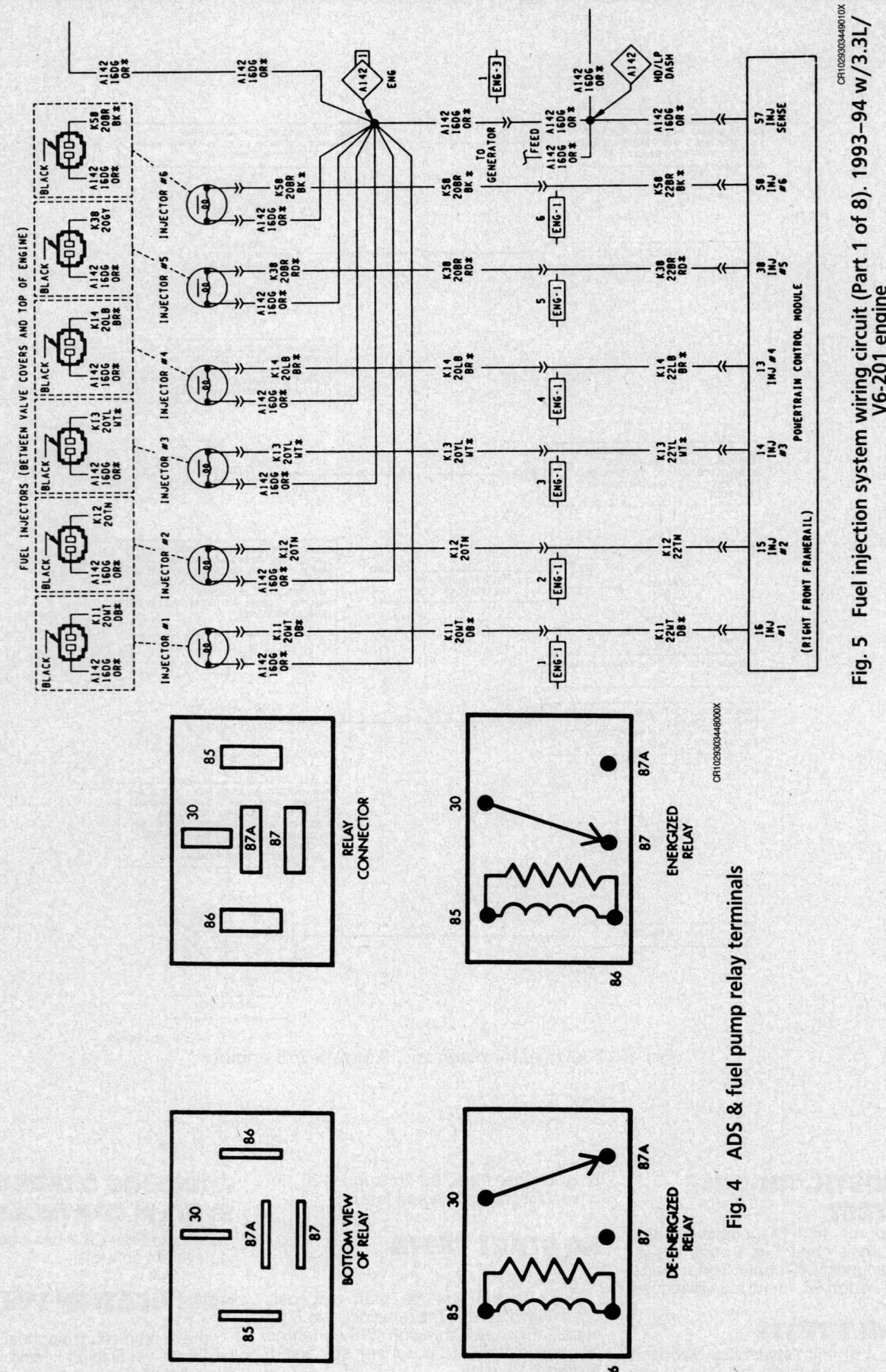

Fig. 5 Fuel injection system wiring circuit (Part 1 of 8). 1993–94 w/3.3L/V6-201 engine

Fig. 4 ADS & fuel pump relay terminals

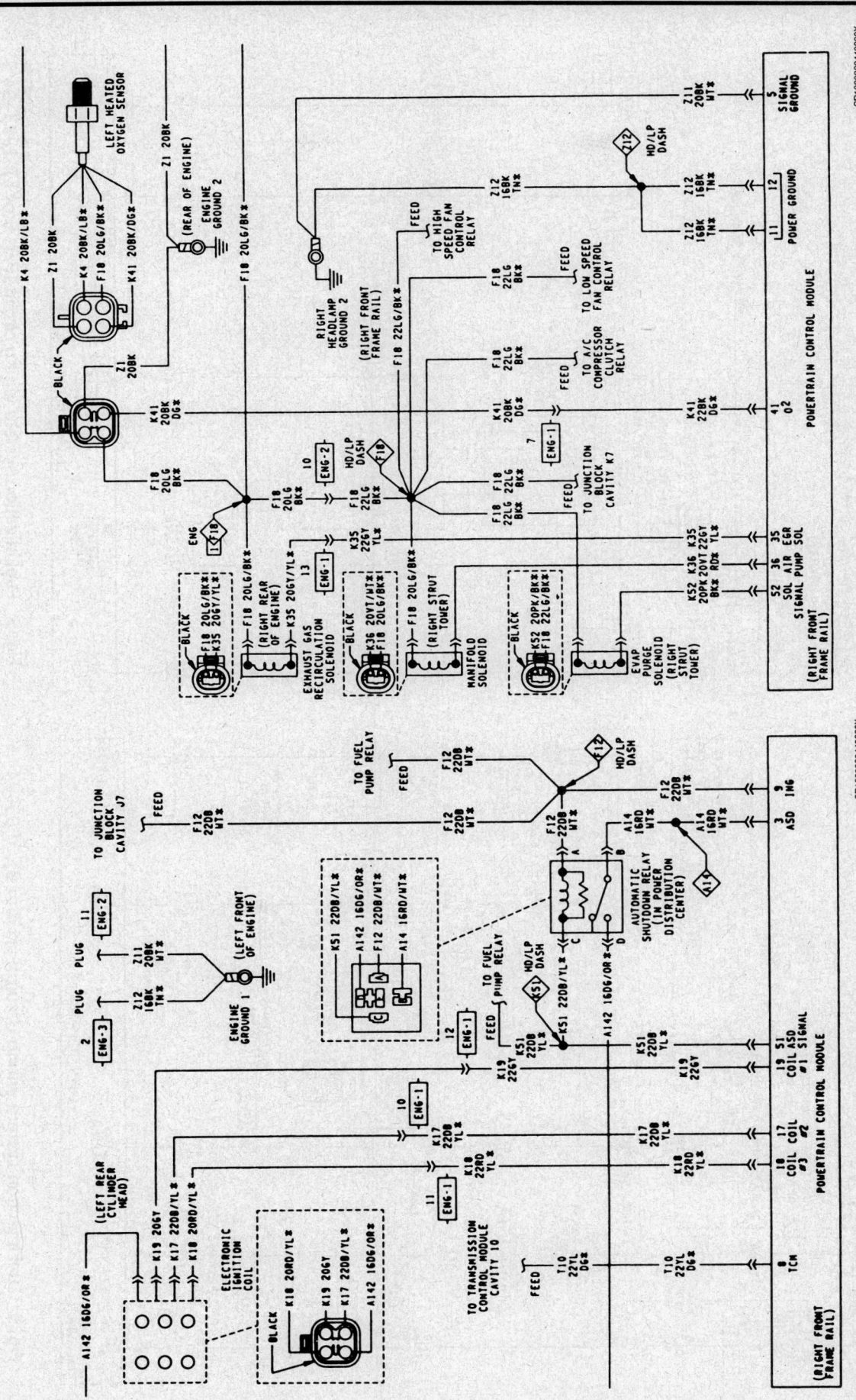

Fig. 5   Fuel injection system wiring circuit (Part 3 of 8). 1993–94 w/3.3L/V6-201 engine

Fig. 5   Fuel injection system wiring circuit (Part 2 of 8). 1993–94 w/3.3L/V6-201 engine

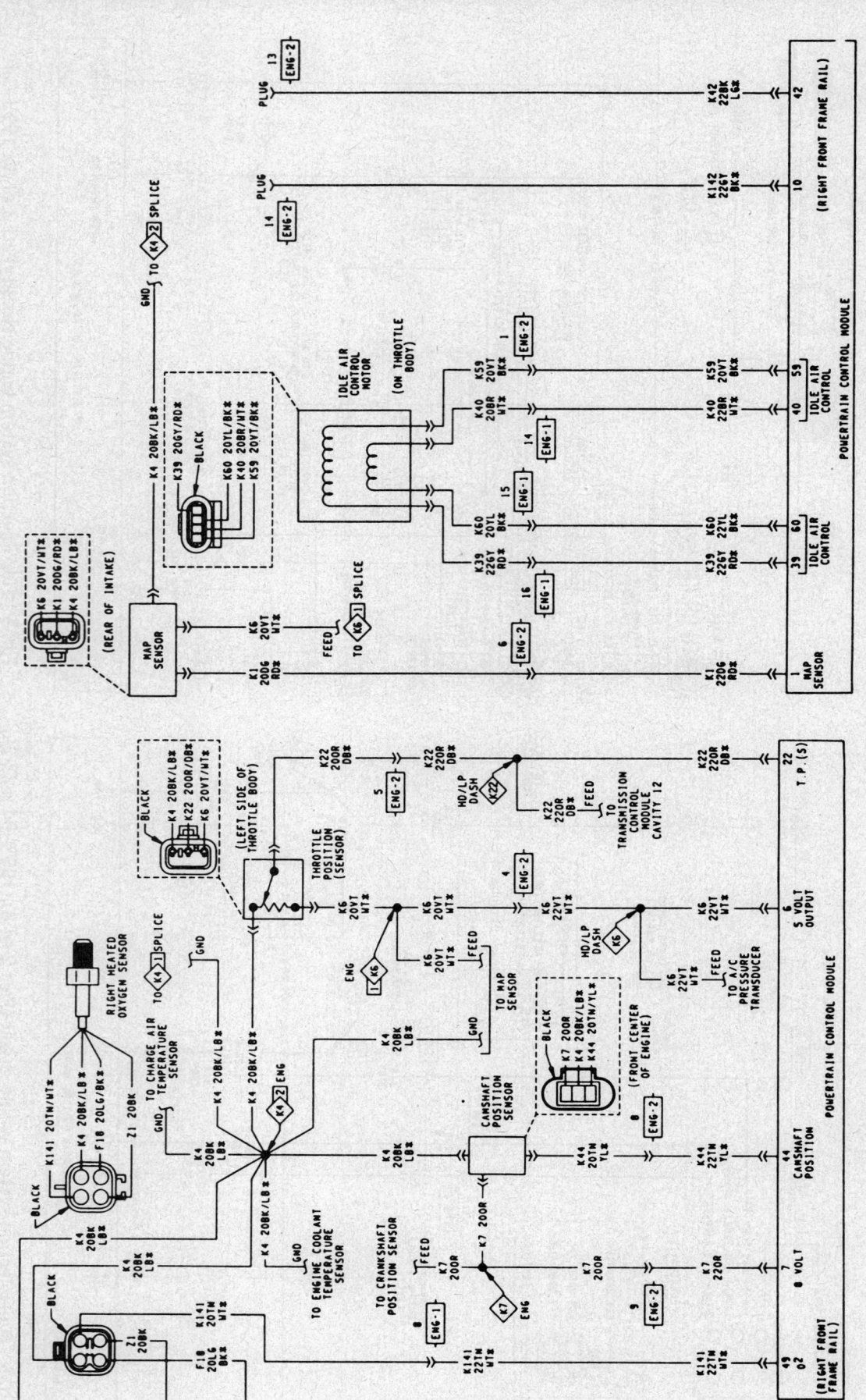

Fig. 5 Fuel injection system wiring circuit (Part 5 of 8). 1993-94 w/3.3L/V6-201 engine

Fig. 5 Fuel injection system wiring circuit (Part 4 of 8). 1993-94 w/3.3L/V6-201 engine

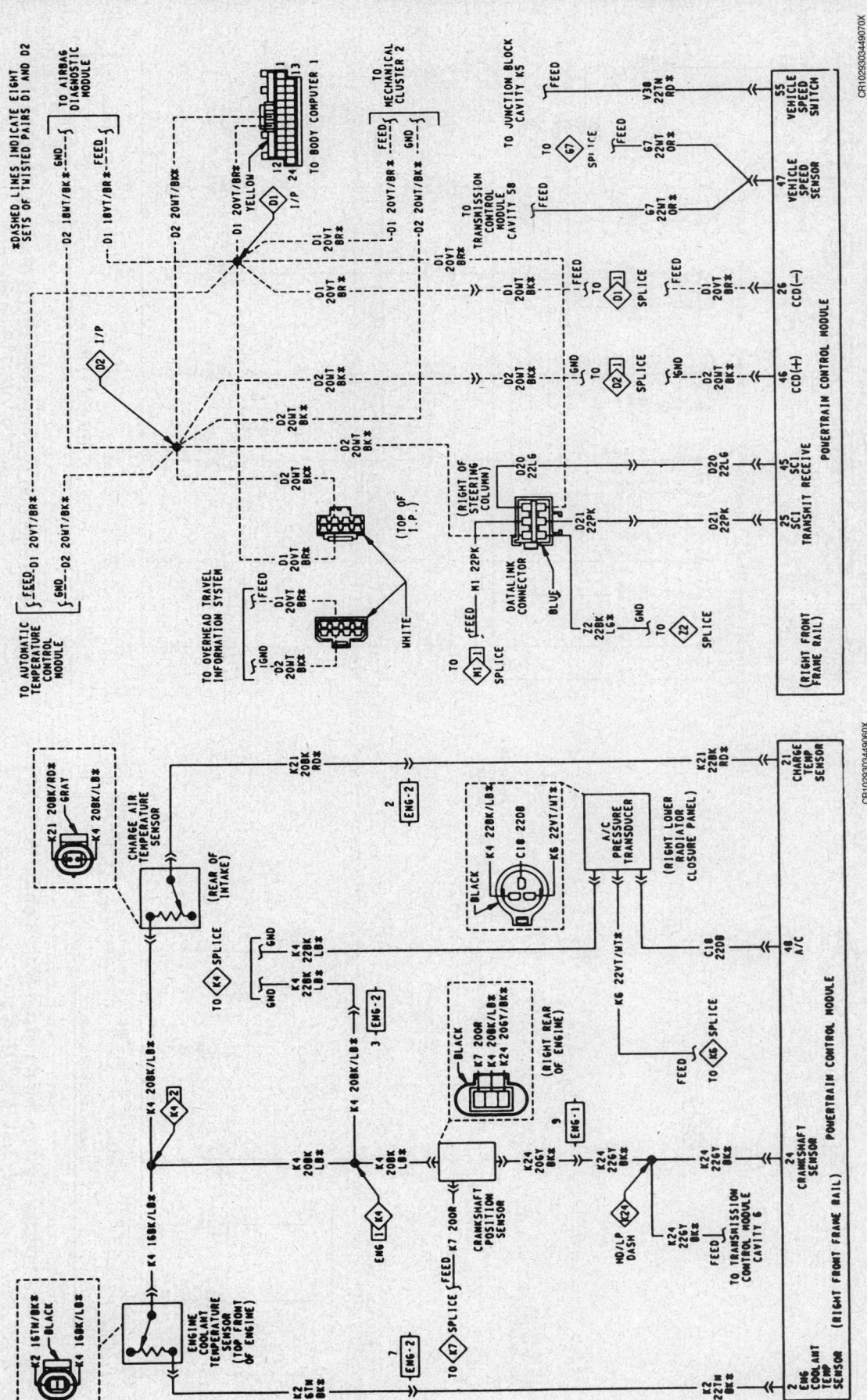

Fig. 5 Fuel injection system wiring circuit (Part 7 of 8). 1993-94 w/3.3L/V6-201 engine

Fig. 5 Fuel injection system wiring circuit (Part 6 of 8). 1993-94 w/3.3L/V6-201 engine

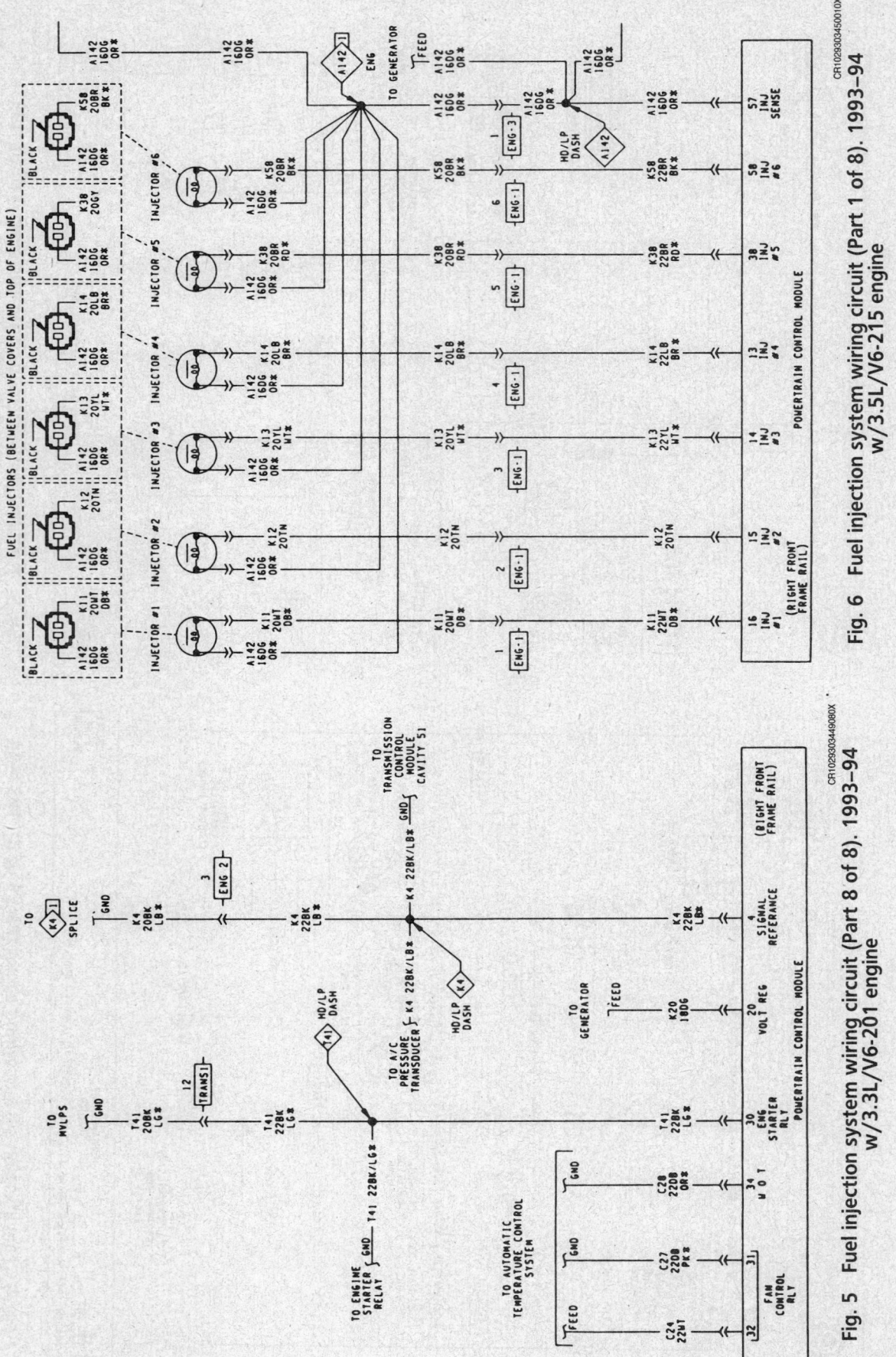

Fig. 6 Fuel injection system wiring circuit (Part 1 of 8). 1993-94 w/3.5L/V6-215 engine

Fig. 5 Fuel injection system wiring circuit (Part 8 of 8). 1993-94 w/3.3L/V6-201 engine

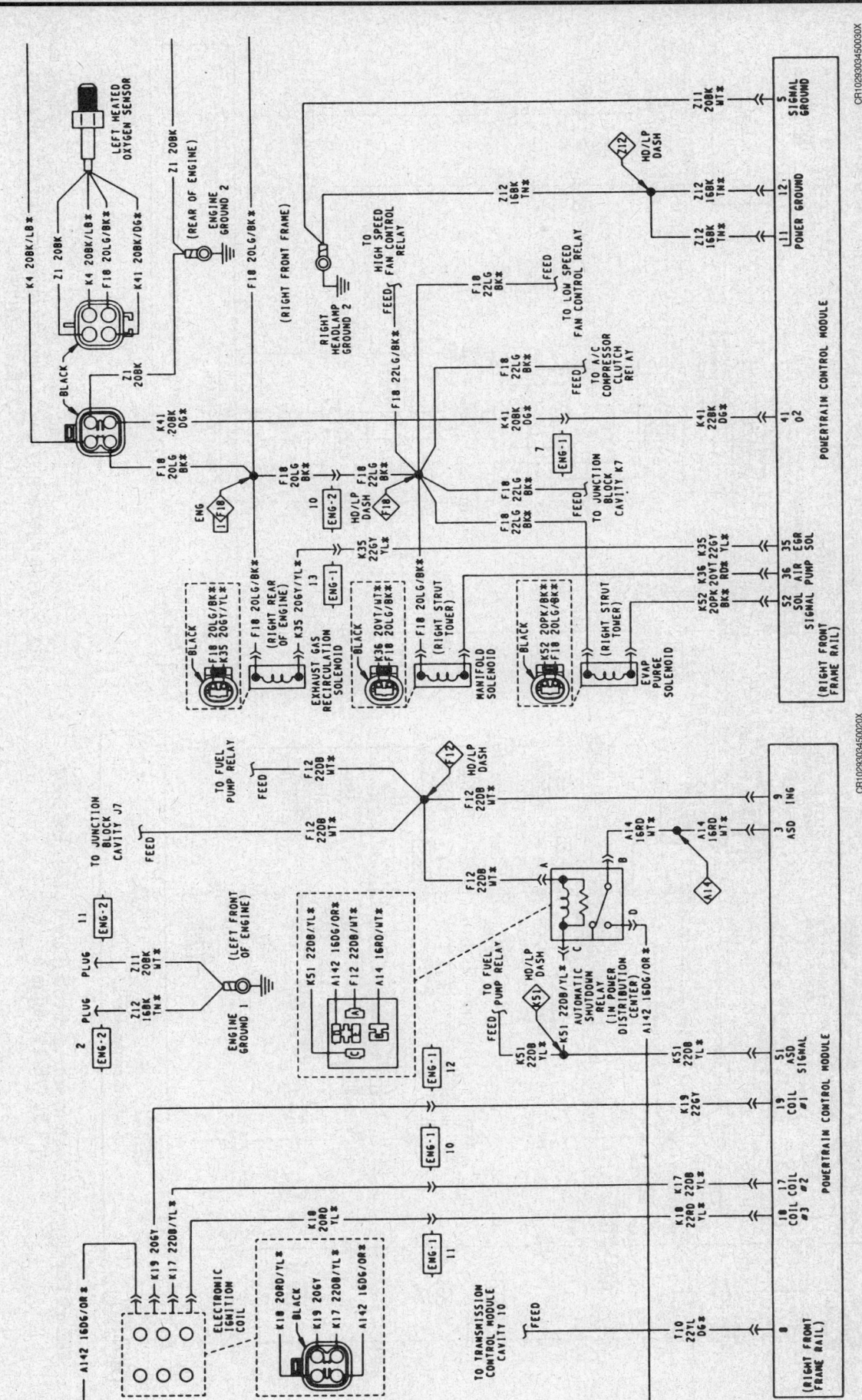

Fig. 6   Fuel injection system wiring circuit (Part 3 of 8). 1993–94 w/3.5L/V6-215 engine

Fig. 6   Fuel injection system wiring circuit (Part 2 of 8). 1993–94 w/3.5L/V6-215 engine

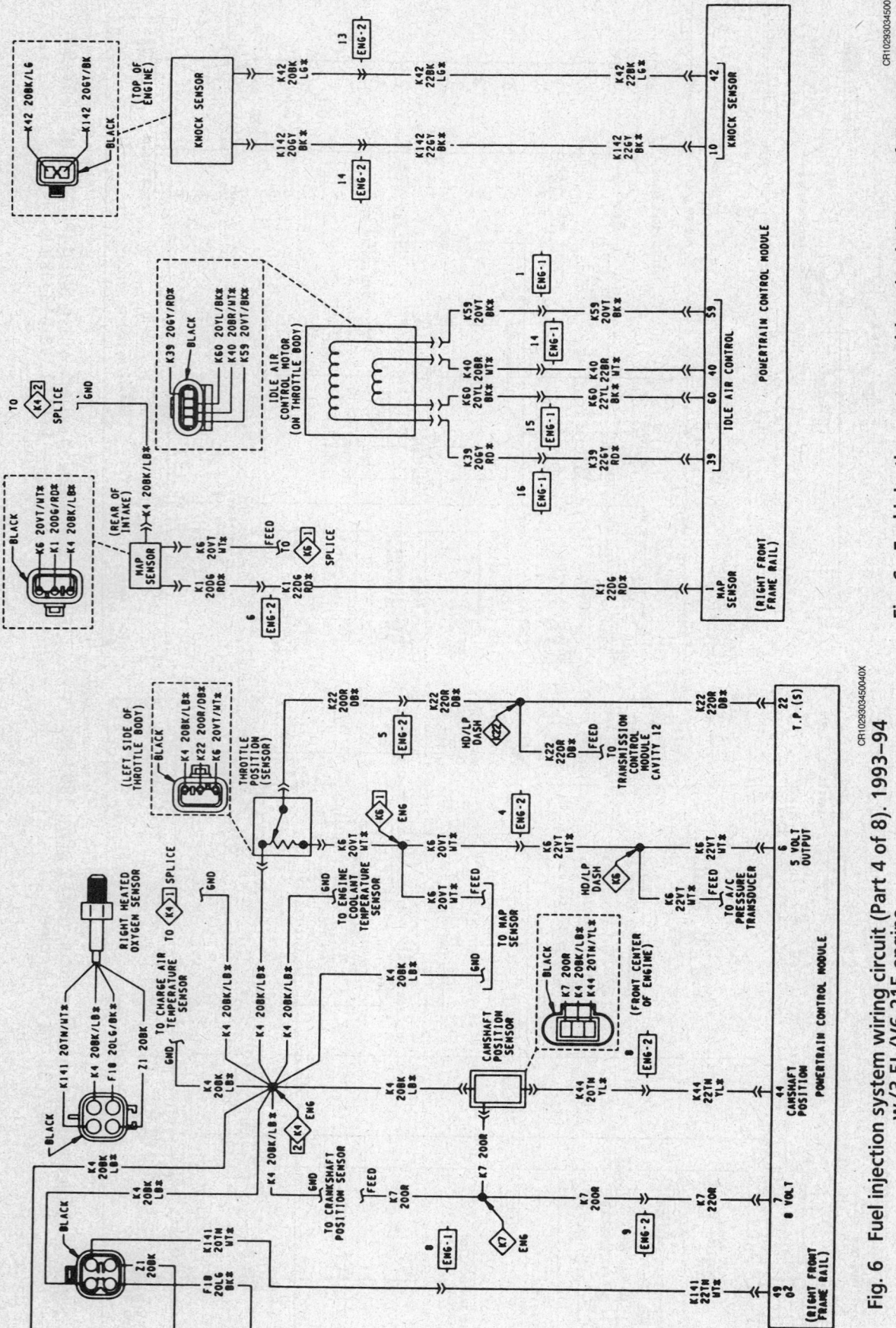

Fig. 6 Fuel injection system wiring circuit (Part 5 of 8). 1993-94 w/3.5L/V6-215 engine

Fig. 6 Fuel injection system wiring circuit (Part 4 of 8). 1993-94 w/3.5L/V6-215 engine

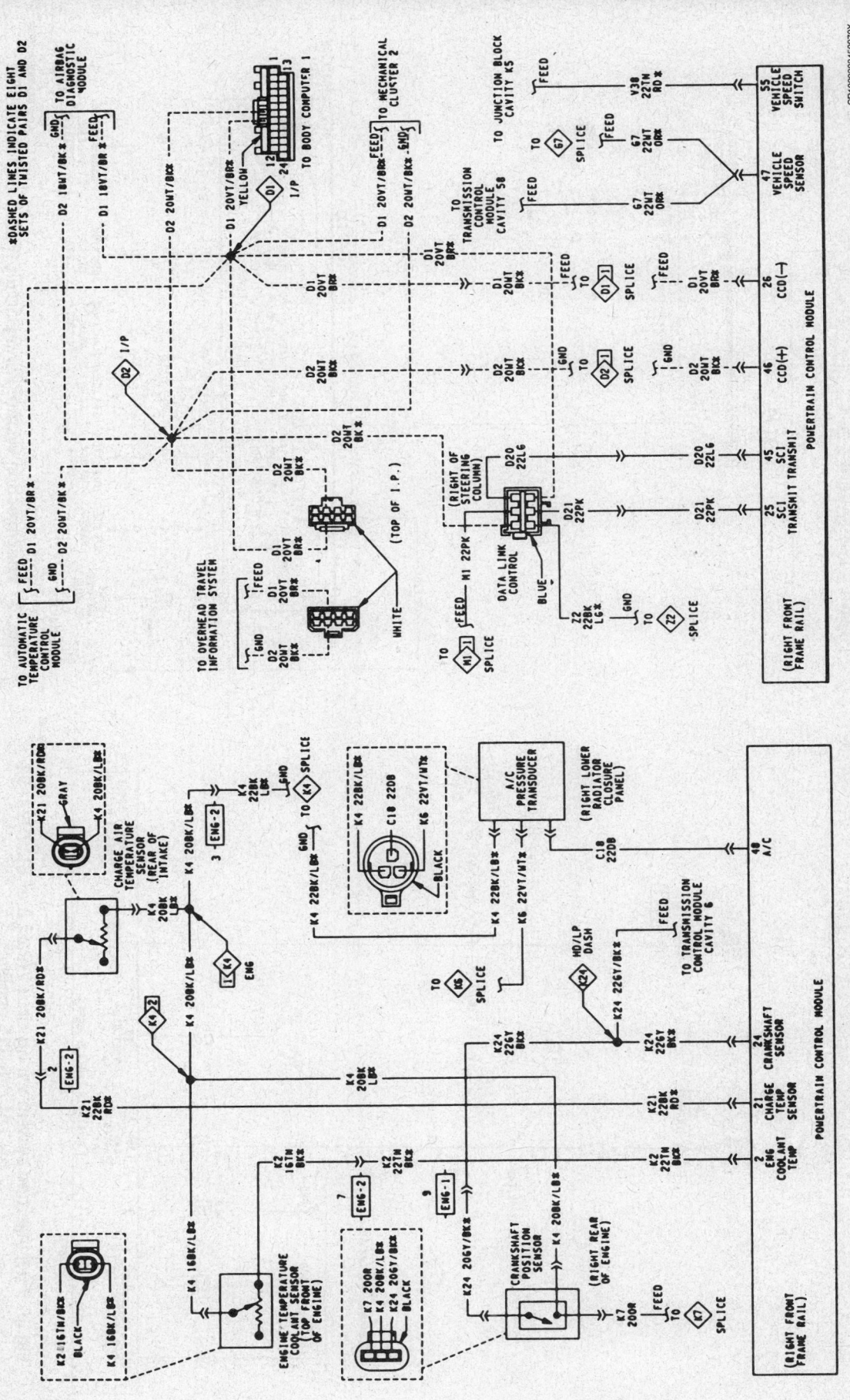

Fig. 6 Fuel injection system wiring circuit (Part 7 of 8). 1993–94 w/3.5L/V6-215 engine

Fig. 6 Fuel injection system wiring circuit (Part 6 of 8). 1993–94 w/3.5L/V6-215 engine

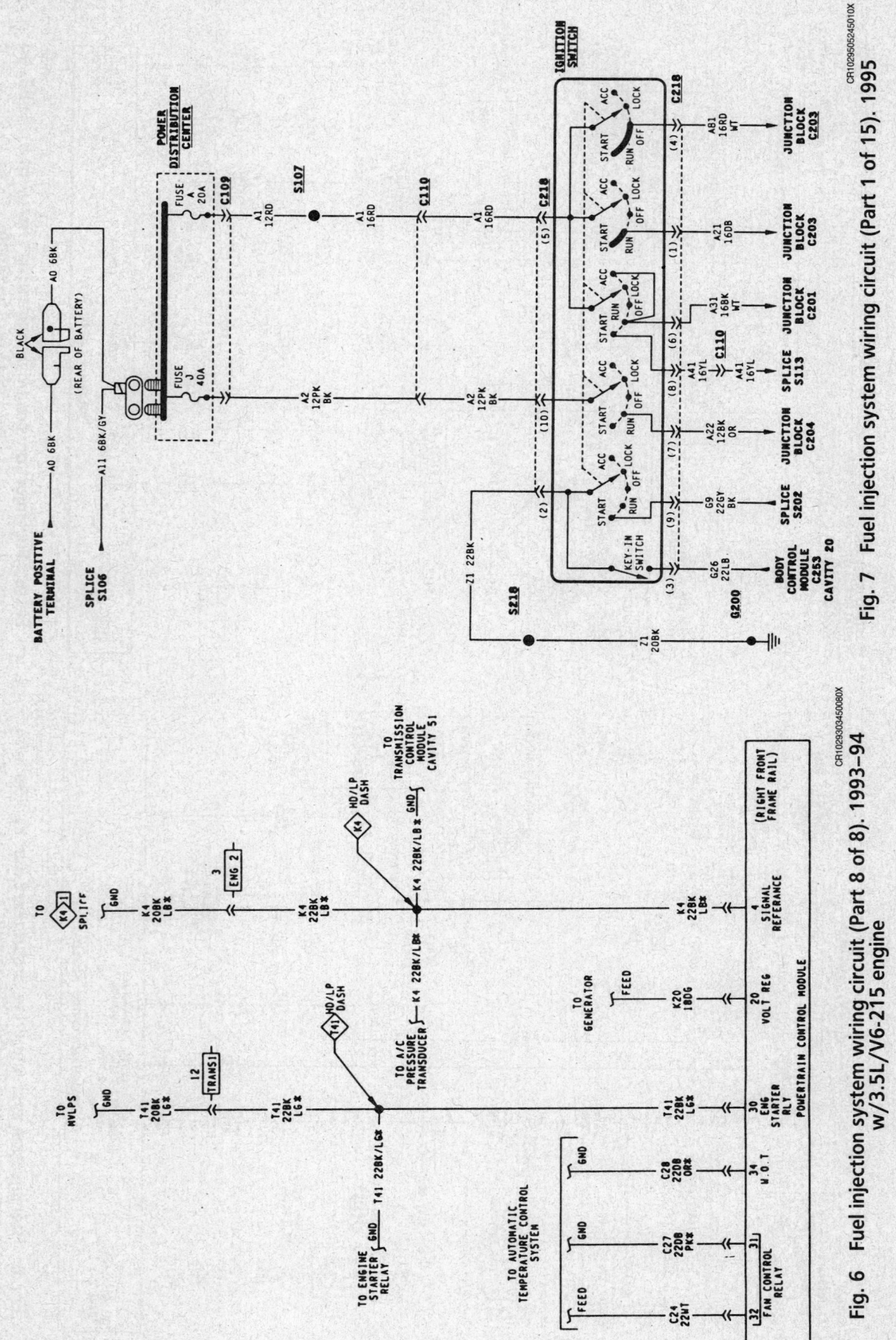

Fig. 7 Fuel injection system wiring circuit (Part 1 of 15). 1995

Fig. 6 Fuel injection system wiring circuit (Part 8 of 8). 1993–94 w/3.5L/V6-215 engine

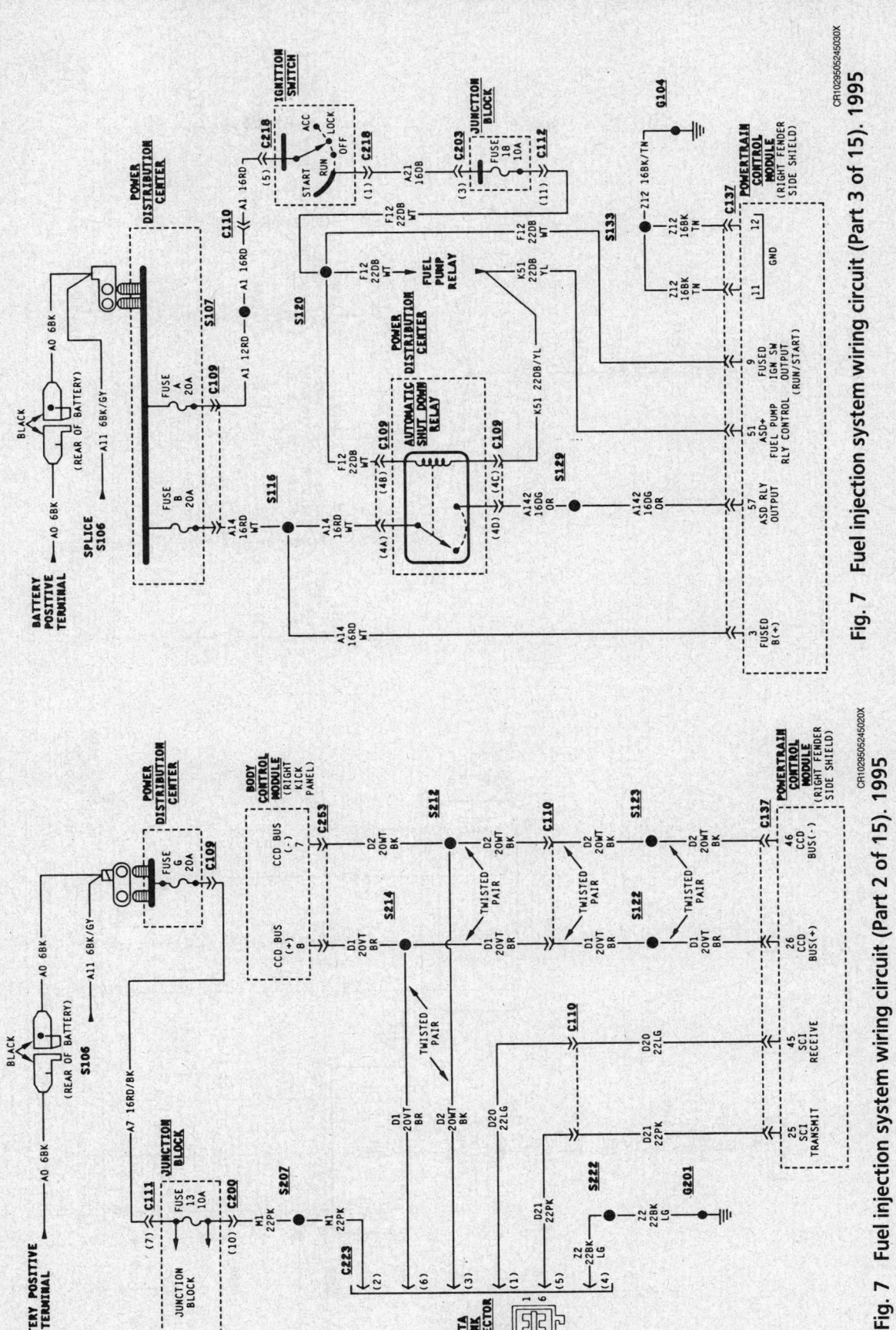

Fig. 7 Fuel injection system wiring circuit (Part 3 of 15). 1995

Fig. 7 Fuel injection system wiring circuit (Part 2 of 15). 1995

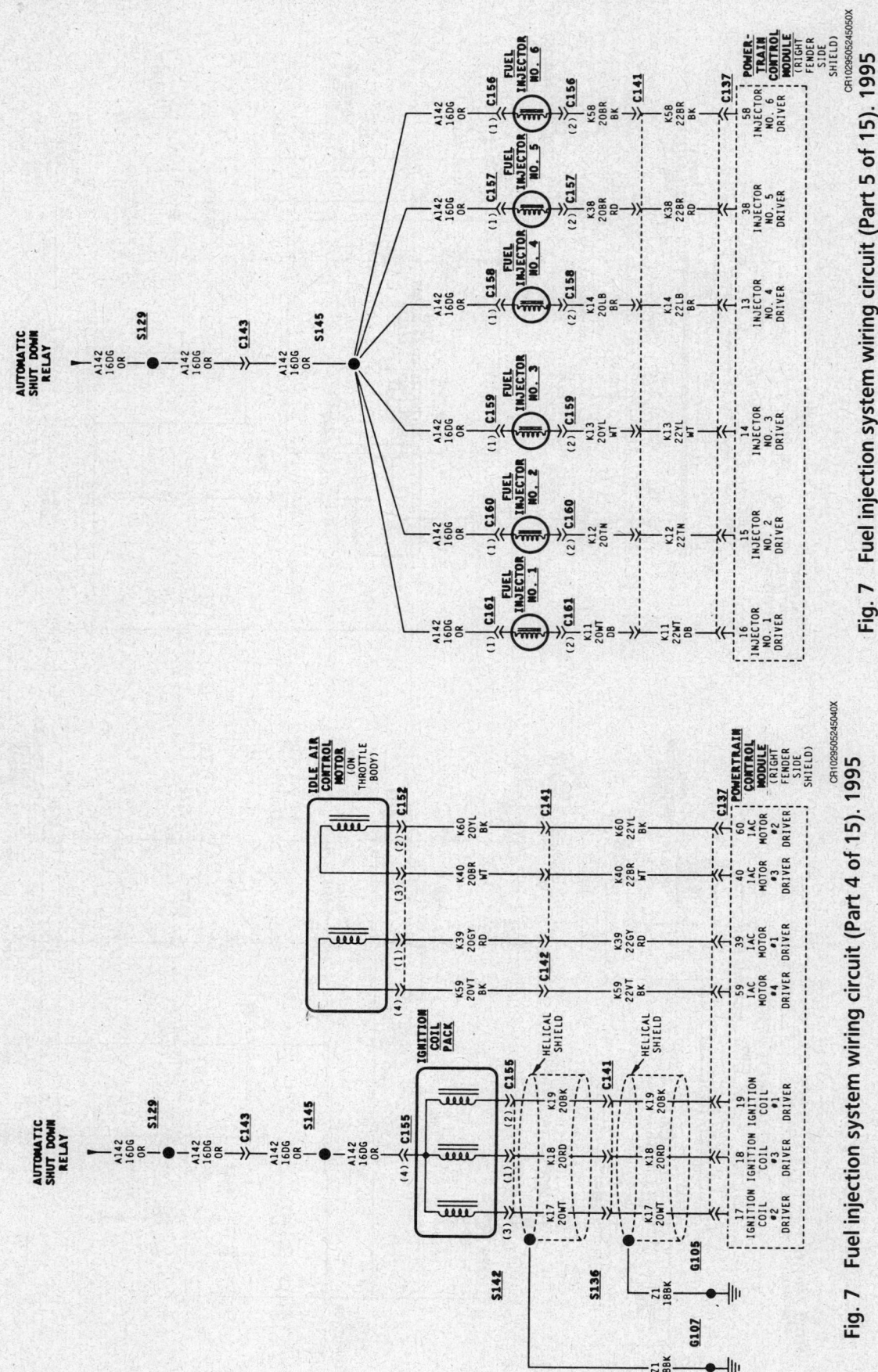

Fig. 7 Fuel injection system wiring circuit (Part 5 of 15). 1995

Fig. 7 Fuel injection system wiring circuit (Part 4 of 15). 1995

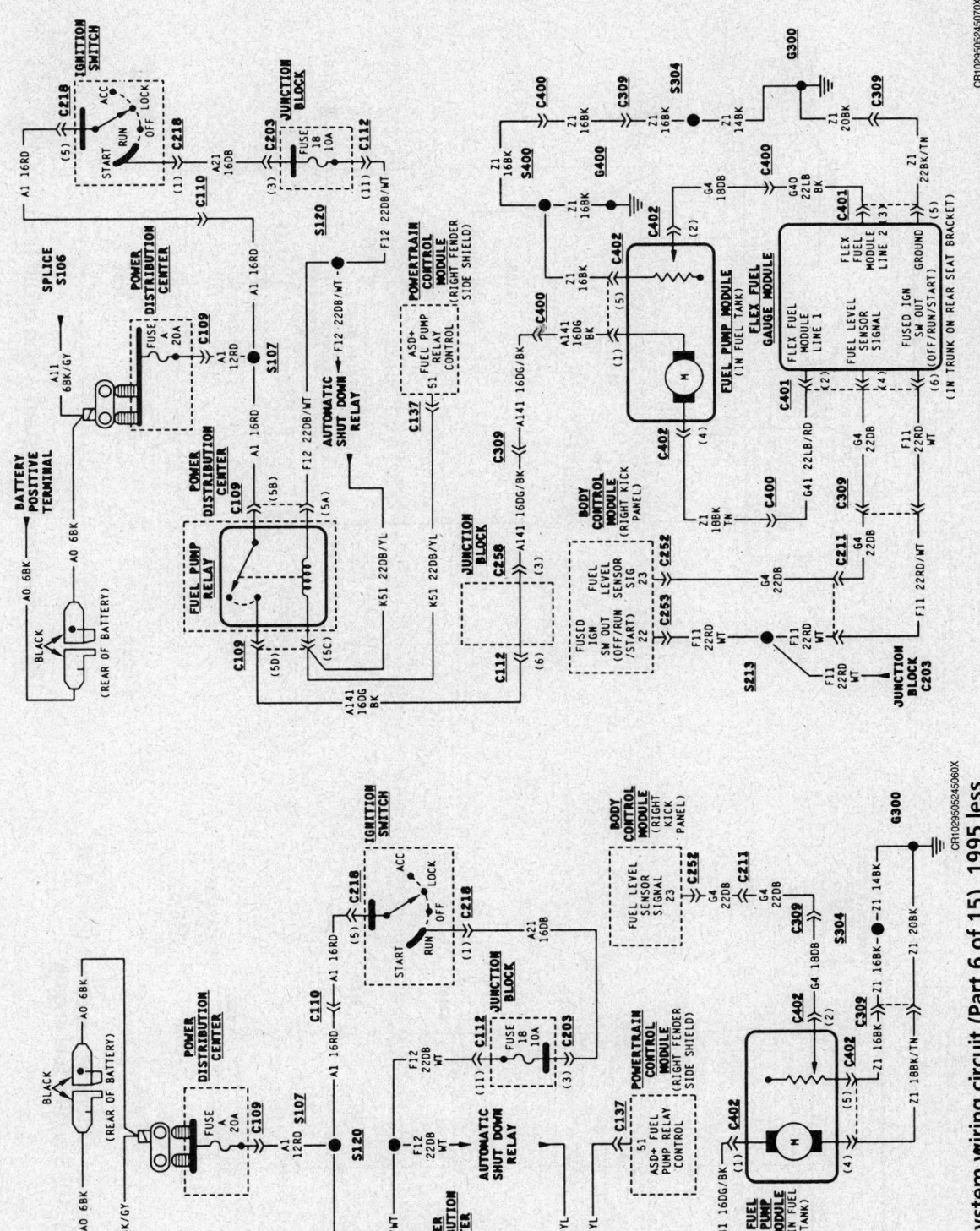

Fig. 7 Fuel injection system wiring circuit (Part 7 of 15). 1995 w/flex fuel engine

Fig. 7 Fuel injection system wiring circuit (Part 6 of 15). 1995 less flex fuel engine

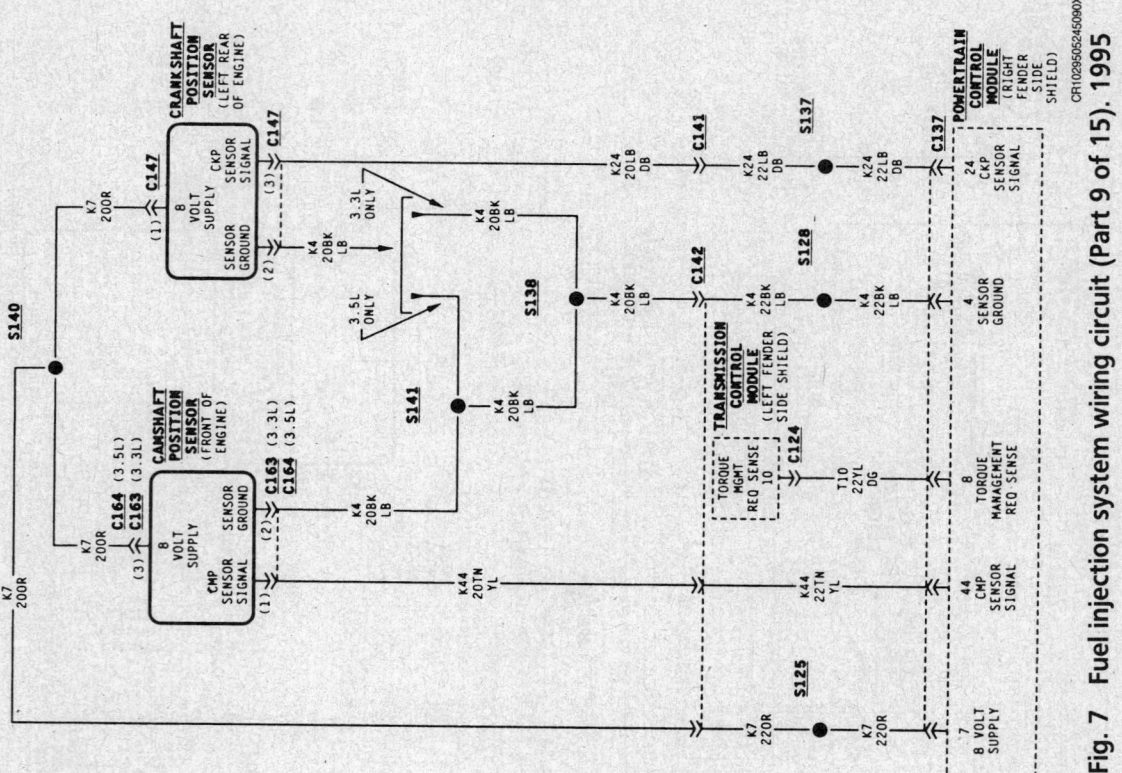

Fig. 7 Fuel injection system wiring circuit (Part 9 of 15). 1995

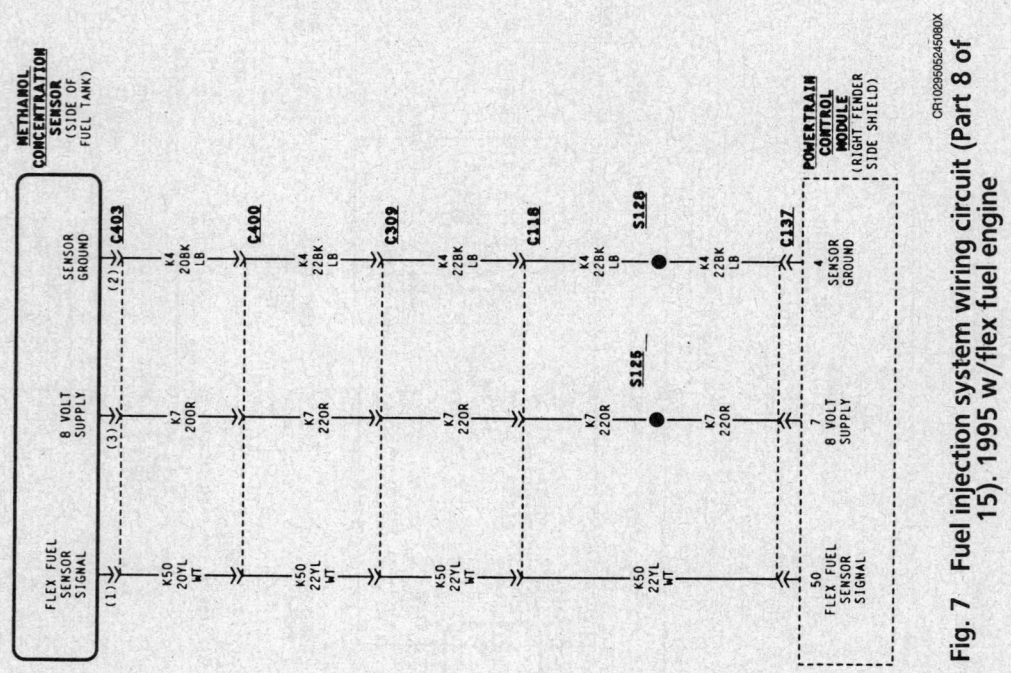

Fig. 7 Fuel injection system wiring circuit (Part 8 of 15). 1995 w/flex fuel engine

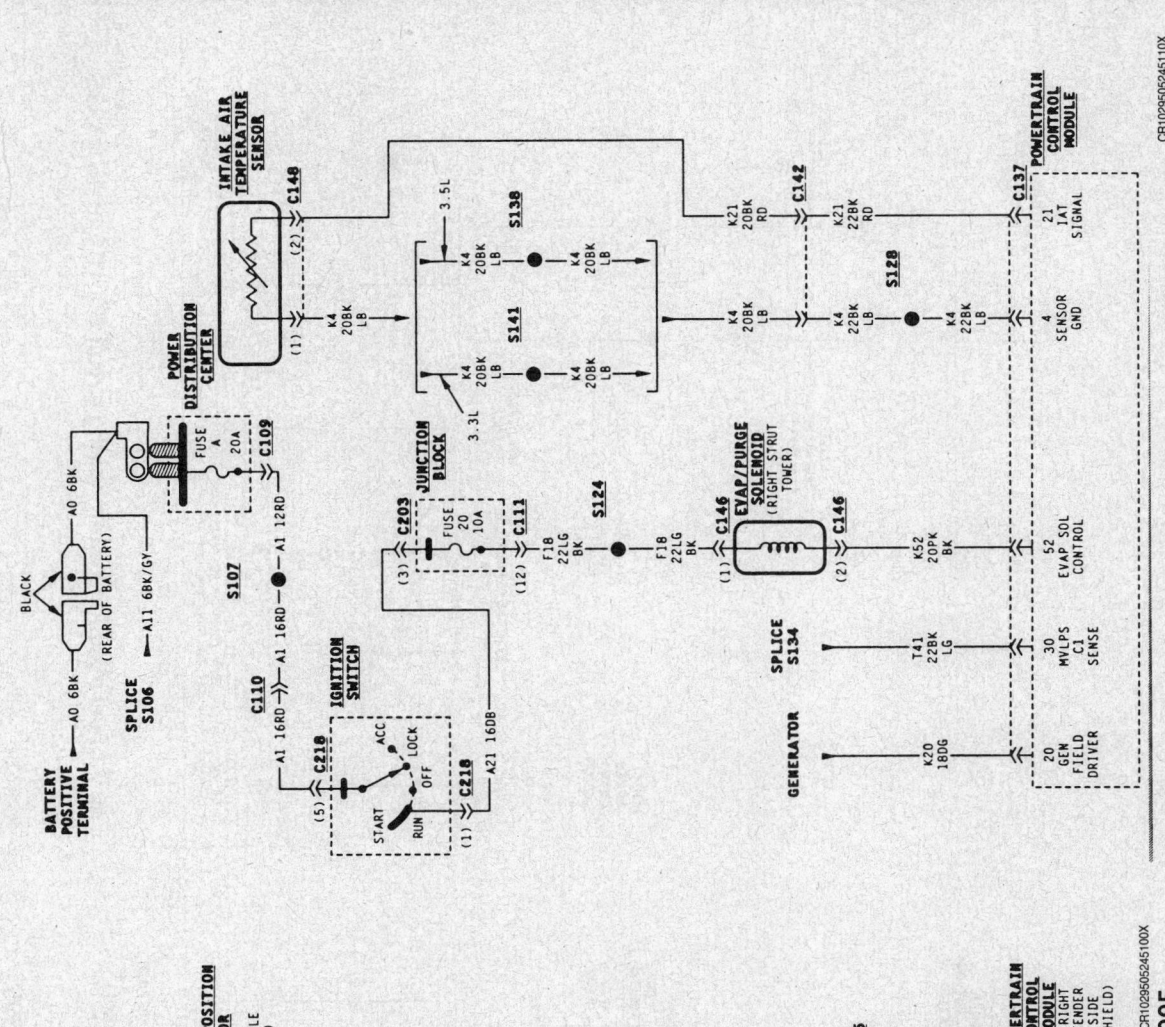

Fig. 7 Fuel injection system wiring circuit (Part 11 of 15). 1995

Fig. 7 Fuel injection system wiring circuit (Part 10 of 15). 1995

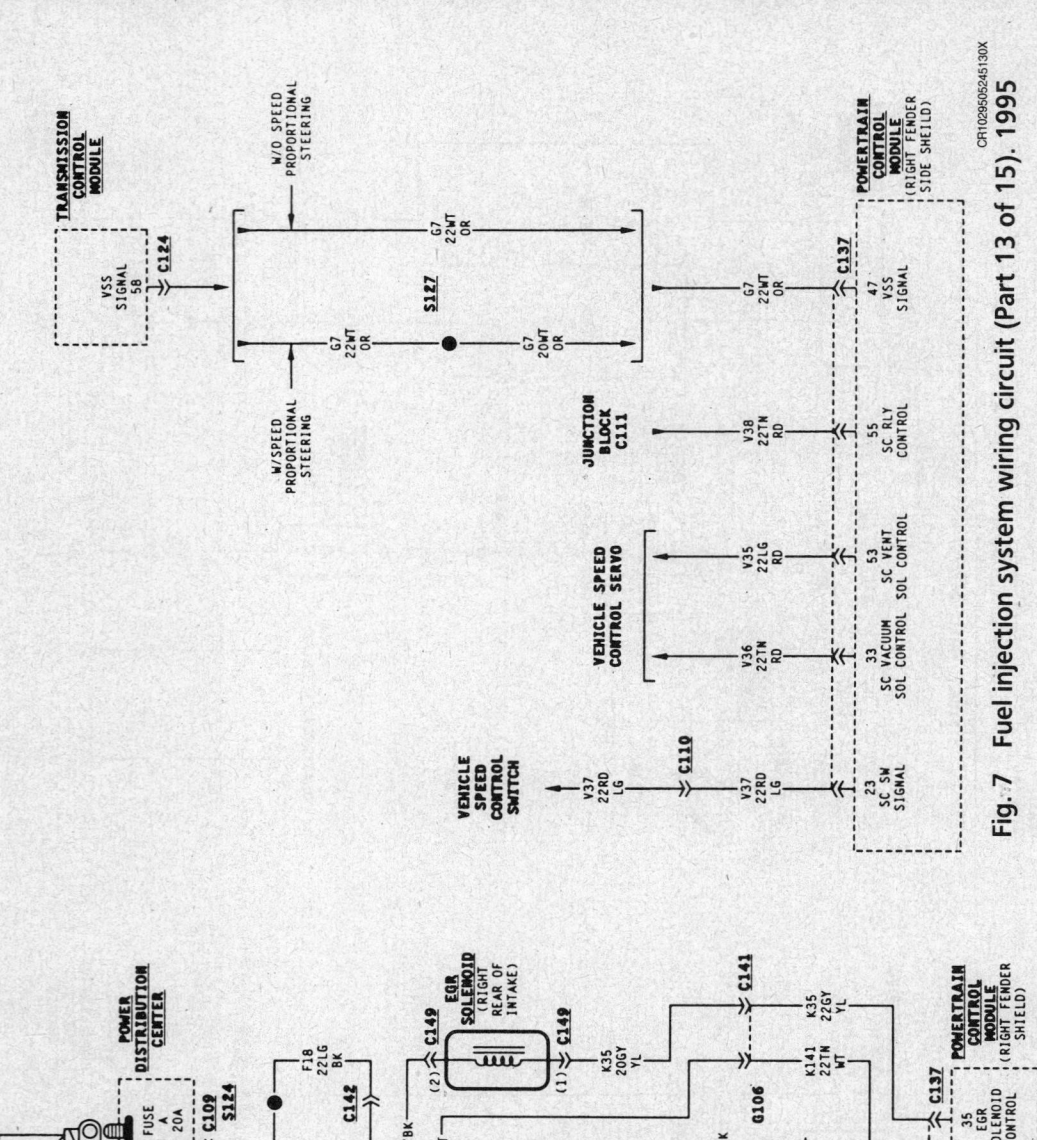

Fig. 7 Fuel injection system wiring circuit (Part 13 of 15). 1995

Fig. 7 Fuel injection system wiring circuit (Part 12 of 15). 1995

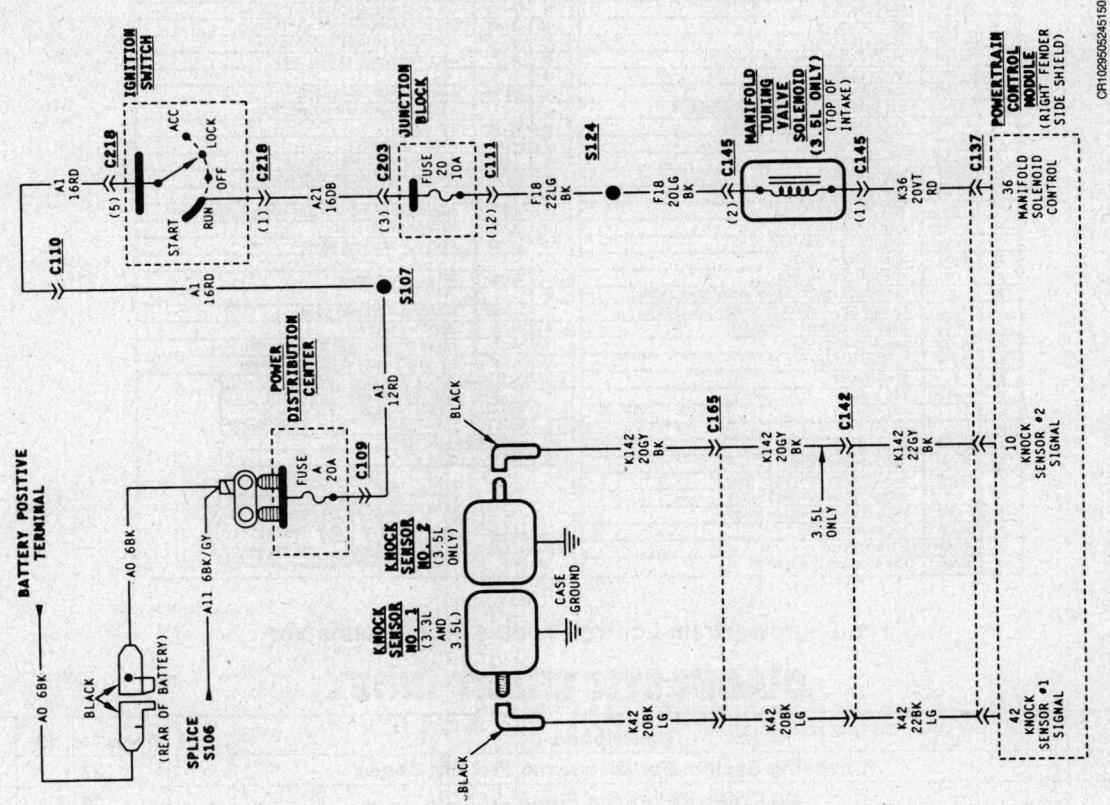

Fig. 7 Fuel injection system wiring circuit (Part 15 of 15). 1995

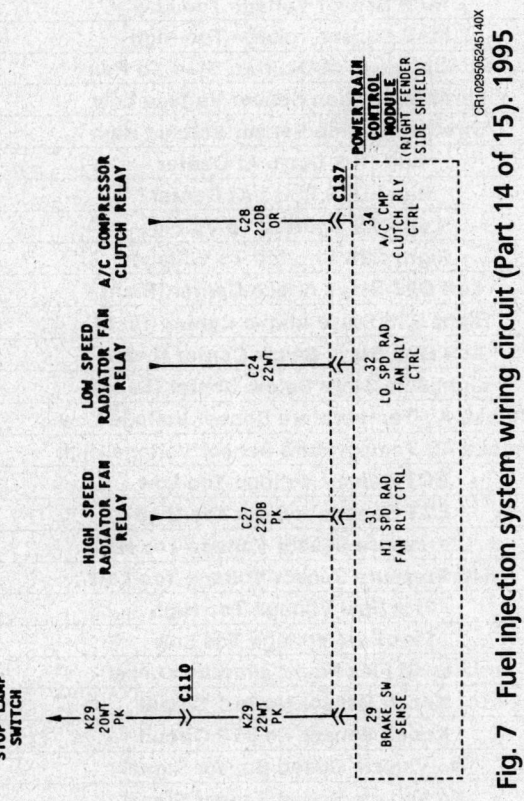

Fig. 7 Fuel injection system wiring circuit (Part 14 of 15). 1995

CAV	WIRE COLOR	DESCRIPTION
1	DG/RD*	MAP SENSOR
2	TN/BK*	ENGINE COOLANT TEMPERATURE SENSOR
3	RD/WT*	DIRECT BATTERY
4	BK/LB*	SENSOR RETURN
5	BK/WT*	SIGNAL GROUND
6	VT/WT*	5-VOLT OUTPUT (MAP AND TPS)
7	OR	8-VOLT OUTPUT
8	YL/DG*	TORQUE MANAGEMENT
9	DB/WT*	A21 SUPPLY (IGNITION START/RUN SENSE)
10	GY/BK*	KNOCK SENSOR #2 (3.5L ENGINE)
11	BK/TN*	POWER GROUND
12	BK/TN*	POWER GROUND
13	LB/BR*	INJECTOR DRIVER #4
14	YL/WT*	INJECTOR DRIVER #3
15	TN	INJECTOR DRIVER #2
16	WT/DB*	INJECTOR DRIVER #1
17	DB/YL*	IGNITION COIL DRIVER #2
18	RD/YL*	IGNITION COIL DRIVER #3
19	GY	IGNITION COIL DRIVER #1
20	DG	GENERATOR FIELD CONTROL (VOLTAGE REGULATOR)
21	BK/RD*	CHARGE AIR TEMPERATURE SENSOR (3.5L ENGINE)
22	OR/DB*	THROTTLE POSITION SENSOR (TPS)
23	RD/LG*	SPEED CONTROL SELECT
24	GY/BK*	CRANKSHAFT REF. PICK-UP
25	PK	SCI TRANSMIT
26	VT/BR*	CCD BUS (+)
27		
28		
29	WT/PK*	BRAKE SWITCH
30	BR/YL*	PARK/NEUTRAL SIGNAL
31	DB/PK*	RADIATOR FAN HIGH SPEED RELAY
32	WT	RADIATOR FAN LOW SPEED RELAY
33	TN/RD*	SPEED CONTROL VACUUM SERVO
34	DB/OR*	A/C CLUTCH RELAY
35	GY/YL*	EGR SOLENOID
36	VT/WT*	MTV SOLENOID (3.5L ENGINE)
37		
38	GY	INJECTOR DRIVER #5
39	GY/RD*	IDLE AIR CONTROL MOTOR (#1 TERMINAL)
40	BR/WT*	IDLE AIR CONTROL MOTOR (#3 TERMINAL)
41	BK/DG*	LEFT HEATED OXYGEN SENSOR SIGNAL
42	BK/LG*	KNOCK SENSOR #1 (3.5L ENGINE)
43		
44	TN/YL*	CAMSHAFT POSITION SENSOR
45	LG	SCI RECEIVE (DATA LINK CONNECTOR)
46	WT/BK*	CCD BUS (-)
47	WT/OR*	VEHICLE SPEED INPUT
48	DB	A/C PRESSURE TRANSDUCER
49	TN/WT*	RIGHT HEATED OXYGEN SENSOR SIGNAL
50		
51	DB/YL*	AUTO SHUTDOWN (ASD) RELAY AND FUEL PUMP RELAY
52	PK/BK*	PURGE SOLENOID
53	LG/RD*	SPEED CONTROL VENT SERVO
54		
55	TN/RD*	SPEED CONTROL RELAY
56		
57	DG/OR*	A142 CIRCUIT VOLTAGE SENSE
58	BR/DB*	INJECTOR DRIVER #6
59	VT/BK*	IDLE AIR CONTROL MOTOR (#4 TERMINAL)
60	YL/BK*	IDLE AIR CONTROL MOTOR (#2 TERMINAL)

WIRE COLOR CODES

BK	BLACK	LG	LIGHT GREEN
BR	BROWN	OR	ORANGE
DB	DARK BLUE	PK	PINK
DG	DARK GREEN	RD	RED
GY	GRAY	TN	TAN
LB	LIGHT BLUE	VT	VIOLET
WT	WHITE	YL	YELLOW
*	WITH TRACER		

CONNECTOR TERMINAL SIDE SHOWN

CR1029303451000X

Fig. 8 Powertrain Control Module (PCM) connector

DIAGNOSTIC CHART INDEX

Test	Description	Page No. 13-	Fig. No.
TC-1A	Checking System For Diagnostic Trouble Codes	27	9
TC-2A	No Crank Reference Signal At PCM	28	10
TC-2B	No Crank Reference Signal At PCM	28	11
TC-3A	No Cam SYNC Signal At PCM	29	12
TC-4A	MAP Sensor Voltage Too Low	29	13
TC-5A	MAP Sensor Voltage Too High	30	14
TC-6A	No Change In MAP From Start To Run	30	15
TC-7A	Throttle Position Sensor Voltage Low	31	16
TC-8A	Throttle Position Sensor Voltage High	31	17
TC-9A	Left O2S Stays At Center	32	18
TC-10A	Right O2S Stays At Center	32	19
TC-11A	Left O2S Shorted To Voltage	33	20
TC-12A	Right O2S Shorted To Voltage	33	21
TC-13A	Left O2S Stays Above Center (Rich)	33	22
TC-14A	Right O2S Stays Above Center (Rich)	34	23
TC-15A	Left O2S Stays Below Center (Lean)	34	24
TC-16A	Right O2S Stays Below Center (Lean)	34	25
TC-17A	Intake Air Temperature Sensor Voltage Low	34	26
TC-18A	Intake Air Temperature Sensor Voltage High	35	27
TC-19A	ECT Sensor Voltage Too Low	35	28
TC-20A	ECT Sensor Voltage Too High	36	29
TC-21A	A/C Pressure Sensor Voltage Too High	36	30
TC-22A	A/C Pressure Sensor Voltage Too Low	36	31
TC-23A	Flex Fuel Voltage Too High	37	32
TC-23B	Flex Fuel Voltage Too Low	37	33
TC-24A	Loss Of Flex Fuel Calibration Level	38	34
TC-25A	Knock Sensor No.34 1 Circuit	38	35
TC-26A	Knock Sensor No.36 2 Circuit	38	36
TC-27A	No Vehicle Speed Sensor Signal	39	37
TC-27B	No Vehicle Speed Sensor Signal	39	38
TC-28A	Idle Air Control Motor Circuits	40	39

Continued

DIAGNOSTIC CHART INDEX–Continued

Test	Description	Page No. 13-	Fig. No.
TC-28B	Idle Air Control Motor Circuits	40	40
TC-28C	Idle Air Control Motor Circuits	41	41
TC-28D	Idle Air Control Motor Circuits	41	42
TC-28E	Idle Air Control Motor Circuits	41	43
TC-29A	Injector Control Circuits	41	44
TC-29B	Injector No. 1 Control Circuit	41	45
TC-29C	Injector No. 1 Control Circuit	42	46
TC-29D	Injector No. 1 Control Circuit	42	47
TC-30A	Injector No. 2 Control Circuit	42	48
TC-30B	Injector No. 2 Control Circuit	42	49
TC-30C	Injector No. 2 Control Circuit	43	50
TC-31A	Injector No. 3 Control Circuit	43	51
TC-31B	Injector No. 3 Control Circuit	43	52
TC-31C	Injector No. 3 Control Circuit	43	53
TC-32A	Injector No. 4 Control Circuit	44	54
TC-32B	Injector No. 4 Control Circuit	44	55
TC-32C	Injector No. 4 Control Circuit	44	56
TC-33A	Injector No. 5 Control Circuit	44	57
TC-33B	Injector No. 5 Control Circuit	45	58
TC-33C	Injector No. 5 Control Circuit	45	59
TC-34A	Injector No. 6 Control Circuit	45	60
TC-34B	Injector No. 6 Control Circuit	46	61
TC-34C	Injector No. 6 Control Circuit	46	62
TC-35A	Ignition Coil Primary Circuit	46	63
TC-35B	Ignition Coil No. 1 Primary Circuit	46	64
TC-36A	Ignition Coil No. 2 Primary Circuit	47	65
TC-37A	Ignition Coil No. 3 Primary Circuit	47	66
TC-37B	Ignition Coil No. 3 Primary Circuit	47	67
TC-38A	EGR System Failure	47	68
TC-39A	EGR Solenoid Circuit	48	69
TC-39B	EGR Solenoid Circuit	48	70
TC-40A	EVAP Solenoid Circuit	49	71
TC-40B	EVAP Solenoid Circuit	49	72
TC-41A	Manifold Tune Valve Solenoid Circuit	49	73
TC-41B	Manifold Tune Valve Solenoid Circuit	50	74
TC-42A	Low Speed Fan Control Relay Circuit	50	75
TC-43A	High Speed Fan Control Relay Circuit	51	76
TC-44A	Auto Shutdown Relay Control Circuit	51	77
TC-45A	A/C Clutch Relay Circuit	52	78
TC-46A	No CCD Bus Messages	52	79
TC-47A	No CCD Bus Messages	52	80
TC-47B	No CCD Bus Messages From TCM	53	81
TC-48A	No CCD Message From Body Control Module	53	82
TC-49A	Battery Temp Sensor Volts Out Of Limits	53	83
TC-50A	Alternator Field Not Switching Properly	53	84
TC-51A	Charging System Voltage Too Low	54	85
TC-52A	Charging System Voltage Too High	54	86
TC-53A	Speed Control Power Relay Circuit	55	87
TC-53B	Speed Control Power Relay Circuit	55	88
TC-54A	Speed Control Switch Always High	56	89
TC-54B	Speed Control Switch Always High	56	90
TC-55A	Speed Control Switch Always Low	56	91

Continued

DIAGNOSTIC CHART INDEX–Continued

Test	Description	Page No. 13-	Fig. No.
TC-56A	Speed Control Solenoid Circuits	56	92
TC-56B	Speed Control Solenoid Circuits	57	93
TC-56C	Speed Control Solenoid Circuits	57	94
NTC-1A	No Trouble Code Test Menu	58	95
NTC-2A	Checking Secondary Ignition & Timing	58	96
NTC-3A	Checking Fuel Pressure	58	97
NTC-3B	Checking Fuel Pressure	59	98
NTC-4A	Checking Coolant Sensor Calibration & Radiator Fan Operation	59	99
NTC-5A	Checking Throttle Position Sensor Calibration	59	100
NTC-6A	Checking MAP Sensor Calibration	60	101
NTC-7A	Checking Oxygen Sensor Switching	60	102
NTC-7B	Checking Oxygen Sensor Switching	60	103
NTC-8A	Checking Idle Air Control Motor	61	104
NTC-8B	Checking Idle Air Control Motor	61	105
NTC-9A	Checking Solenoid Operations	61	106
NTC-10A	Checking Park/Neutral Switch (MVLPS)	62	107
NTC-11A	Checking PCM Grounds & Power Circuit	62	108
NTC-12A	Checking EGR System	62	109
NTC-13A	Checking Engine Vacuum	63	110
NTC-14A	Checking Minimum Idle Air Flow	63	111
NTC-15A	Performing No Diagnostic Trouble Code Mechanical Test	64	112
CH-1A	Checking Charging System Controls	64	113
SC-1A	Checking Speed Control Relay Output	64	114
SC-1B	Checking Speed Control Relay Output	65	115
SC-2A	Checking Speed Control On/Off Switch	65	116
SC-3A	Checking Speed Control Set/Resume Switch	65	117
SC-4A	Checking Speed Control Brake Switch	66	118
SC-5A	Checking Park Neutral Switch	66	119
SC-6A	Checking Speed Control System For Denied Messages	66	120
NS-1A	Qualifying No Start Condition	66	121
NS-2A	Inspecting Fuel System	67	122
NS-3A	Inspecting Mechanical System	68	123
NS-4A	Correcting Fuel Delivery	68	124
NS-4B	Correcting Fuel Delivery	69	125
NS-5A	Inspecting Fuel Pump	69	126
NS-5B	Inspecting Fuel Pump	70	127
NS-6A	Correcting No Response Condition	70	128
NS-6B	Correcting No Response Condition	71	129
NS-7A	Inspecting Idle Air Control Motor Operation	72	130
NS-7B	Inspecting Idle Air Control Motor Operation	72	131
NS-7C	Inspecting Idle Air Control Motor Operation	73	132
NS-7D	Inspecting Idle Air Control Motor Operation	73	133
NS-7E	Inspecting Idle Air Control Motor Operation	73	134
NS-8A	Correcting Start & Stall Condition	73	135
NS-9A	Repairing No Crank Condition	73	136
VER-1	Verification Test 1	74	137
VER-2	Road Test Verification	74	138
VER-3A	Charging Verification	75	139
VER-4A	Speed Control Verification	75	140

NOTE: The battery must be fully charged for any test in this manual.

1. Attempt to start the engine. Crank for up to 10 seconds if necessary.
2. Connect the DRB to the engine diagnostic connector. Write down trouble code messages that are displayed.
3. If the DRB screen displays "No Response," go to TEST NS-6A.
4. If trouble code messages are displayed, refer to the trouble code list below and on the next page for the appropriate test.
5. If there are no trouble codes displayed, refer to one of the following:
   For Driveability problems NTC-1A
   For Charging problems CH-1A
   For Speed Control problems SC-1A
   For No Start problems NS-1A

DRB MESSAGE	DIAGNOSTIC TEST
NO CRANK REFERENCE SIGNAL AT PCM	TC- 2A
NO CAM SYNC SIGNAL AT PCM	TC- 3A
MAP SENSOR VOLTAGE TOO LOW	TC- 4A
MAP SENSOR VOLTAGE TOO HIGH	TC- 5A
NO CHANGE IN MAP FROM START TO RUN	TC- 6A
THROTTLE POSITION SENSOR VOLTAGE LOW	TC- 7A
THROTTLE POSITION SENSOR VOLTAGE HIGH	TC- 8A
LEFT O2S STAYS AT CENTER	TC- 9A
RIGHT O2S STAYS AT CENTER	TC-10A
LEFT O2S SHORTED TO VOLTAGE	TC-11A
RIGHT O2S SHORTED TO VOLTAGE	TC-12A
LEFT O2S STAYS ABOVE CENTER (RICH)	TC-13A
RIGHT O2S STAYS ABOVE CENTER (RICH)	TC-14A
LEFT O2S STAYS BELOW CENTER (LEAN)	TC-15A
RIGHT O2S STAYS BELOW CENTER (LEAN)	TC-16A
INTAKE AIR TEMP SENSOR VOLTAGE LOW	TC-17A
INTAKE AIR TEMP SENSOR VOLTAGE HIGH	TC-18A
ECT SENSOR VOLTAGE TOO LOW	TC-19A
ECT SENSOR VOLTAGE TOO HIGH	TC-20A
A/C PRESSURE SENSOR VOLTS TOO HIGH	TC-21A
A/C PRESSURE SENSOR VOLTS TOO LOW	TC-22A
FLEX FUEL SENSOR VOLTS TOO HIGH	TC-23A
FLEX FUEL SENSOR VOLTS TOO LOW	TC-23A
LOSS OF FLEX FUEL CALIBRATION SIGNAL	TC-24A
KNOCK SENSOR #1 CIRCUIT	TC-25A
KNOCK SENSOR #2 CIRCUIT	TC-26A
NO VEHICLE SPEED SENSOR SIGNAL	TC-27A
IDLE AIR CONTROL MOTOR CIRCUITS	TC-28A
INJECTOR #1 CONTROL CIRCUIT	TC-29A

CR102930345201OX

Fig. 9 Test TC-1A: Checking System For Diagnostic Trouble Codes (Part 1 of 2)

DRB MESSAGE	DIAGNOSTIC TEST
INJECTOR #2 CONTROL CIRCUIT	TC-29A
INJECTOR #3 CONTROL CIRCUIT	TC-29A
INJECTOR #4 CONTROL CIRCUIT	TC-29A
INJECTOR #5 CONTROL CIRCUIT	TC-29A
INJECTOR #6 CONTROL CIRCUIT	TC-29A
IGNITION COIL PRIMARY CIRCUIT	TC-35A
IGNITION COIL #2 PRIMARY CIRCUIT	TC-36A
IGNITION COIL #3 PRIMARY CIRCUIT	TC-37A
EGR SYSTEM FAILURE	TC-38A
EGR SOLENOID CIRCUIT	TC-39A
EVAP SOLENOID CIRCUIT	TC-40A
MANIFOLD TUNE VALVE SOLENOID CIRCUIT	TC-41A
LOW SPEED FAN CTRL RELAY CIRCUIT	TC-42A
HIGH SPEED FAN CTRL RELAY CIRCUIT	TC-43A
AUTO SHUTDOWN RELAY CONTROL CIRCUIT	TC-44A
A/C CLUTCH RELAY CIRCUIT	TC-45A
NO CCD BUS MESSAGES	TC-46A
NO CCD MESSAGE FROM TCM	TC-47A
NO CCD MESSAGE FROM BODY CONTROL MODULE	TC-48A
BATTERY TEMP SENSOR VOLTS OUT OF LIMIT	TC-49A
GENERATOR FIELD NOT SWITCHING PROPERLY	TC-50A
CHARGING SYSTEM VOLTAGE TOO LOW	TC-51A
CHARGING SYSTEM VOLTAGE TOO HIGH	TC-52A
SPEED CONTROL POWER RELAY CIRCUIT	TC-53A
SPEED CONTROL SWITCH ALWAYS HIGH	TC-54A
SPEED CONTROL SWITCH ALWAYS LOW	TC-55A
SPEED CONTROL SOLENOID CIRCUITS	TC-56A

Engine is cold too long-engine does not warm to 176°F while driving 20 minutes after start.
This fault may set in error during very cold slow speed driving.

Internal PCM failure - replace PCM and go to Verification TEST VER-1.
SPI Communications - replace PCM and perform Verification TEST VER-1.

CR102930345202OX

Fig. 9 Test TC-1A: Checking System For Diagnostic Trouble Codes (Part 2 of 2)

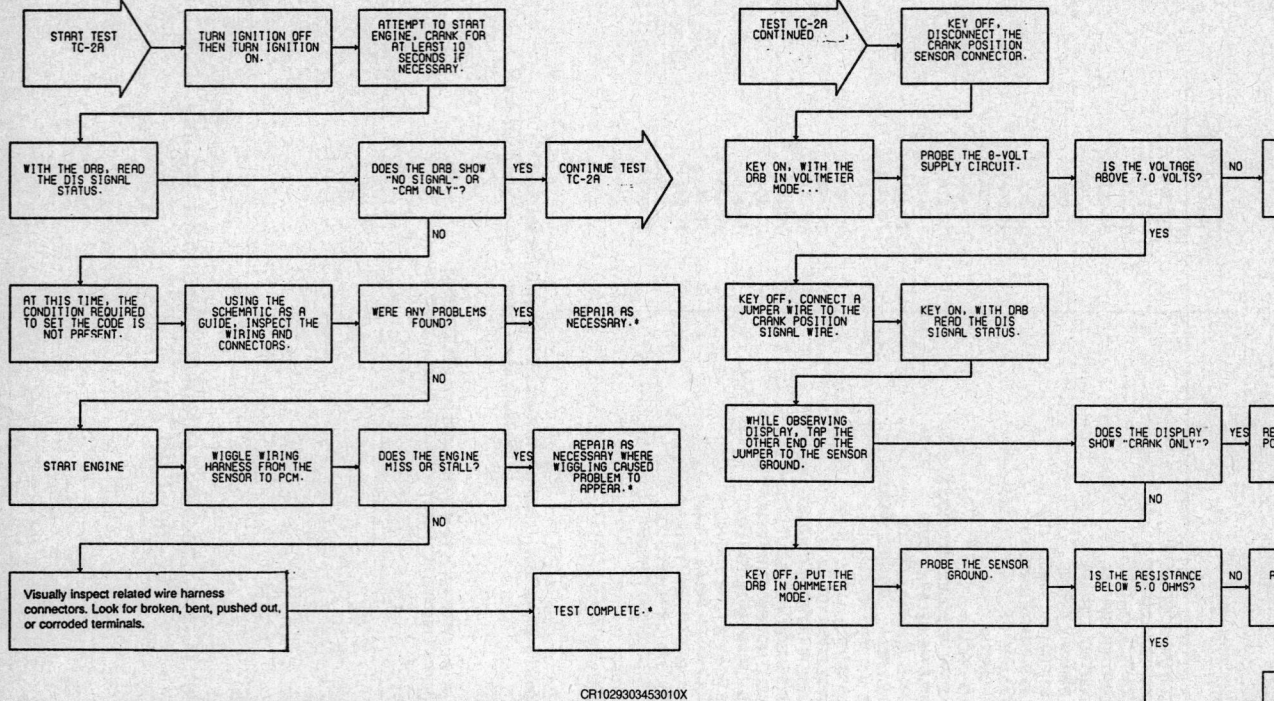

Fig. 10 Test TC-2A: No Crank Reference Signal At PCM (Part 1 of 3)

CR1029303453010X

Fig. 10 Test TC-2A: No Crank Reference Signal At PCM (Part 2 of 3)

CR1029303453020X

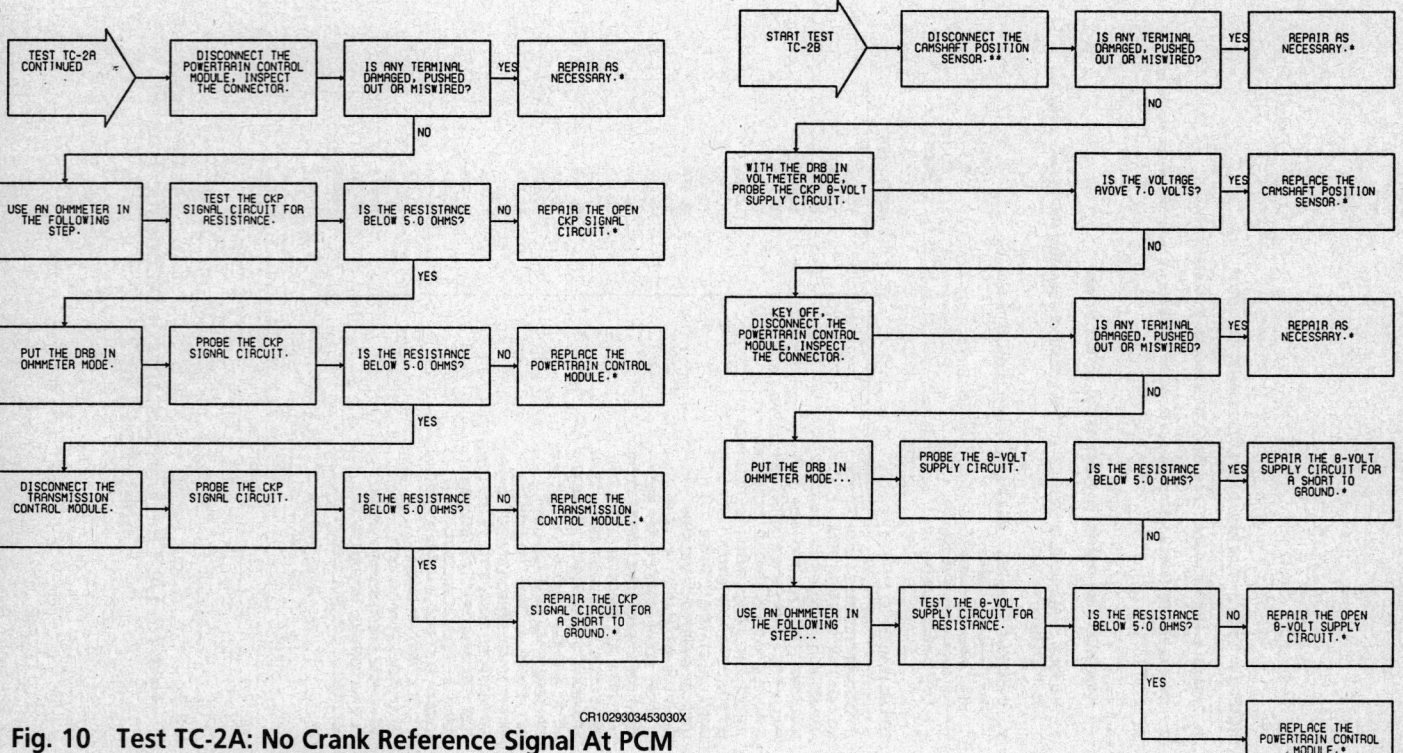

Fig. 10 Test TC-2A: No Crank Reference Signal At PCM (Part 3 of 3)

CR1029303453030X

Fig. 11 Test TC-2B: No Crank Reference Signal At PCM

CR1029303454000X

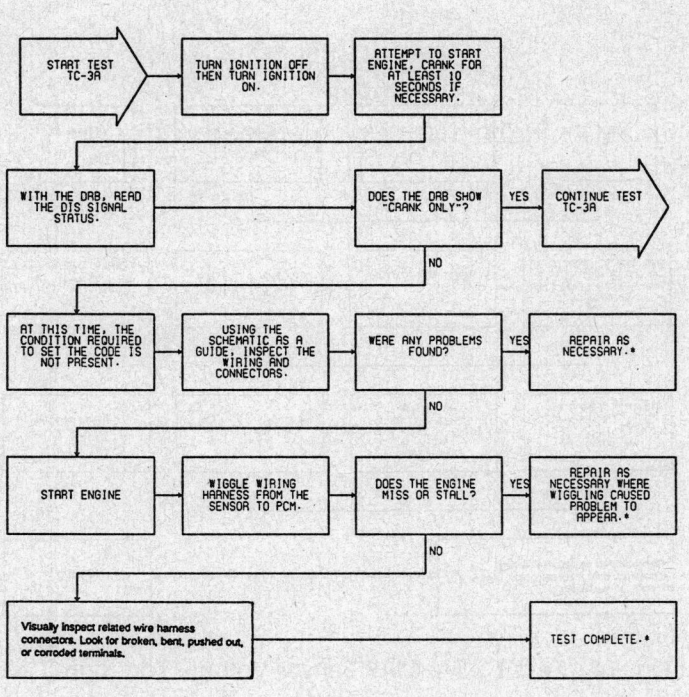

Fig. 12 Test TC-3A: No Cam SYNC Signal At PCM (Part 1 of 3)

CR1029303455010X

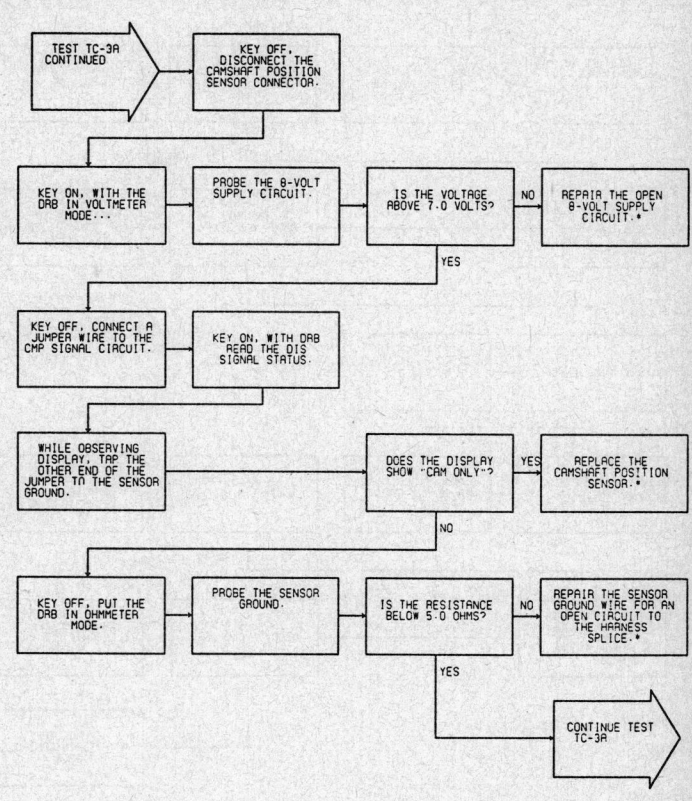

Fig. 12 Test TC-3A: No Cam SYNC Signal At PCM (Part 2 of 3)

CR1029303455020X

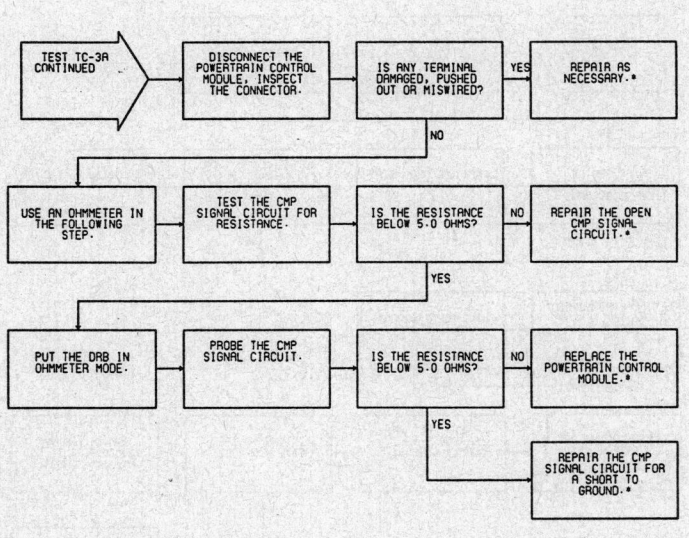

Fig. 12 Test TC-3A: No Cam SYNC Signal At PCM (Part 3 of 3)

CR1029303455030X

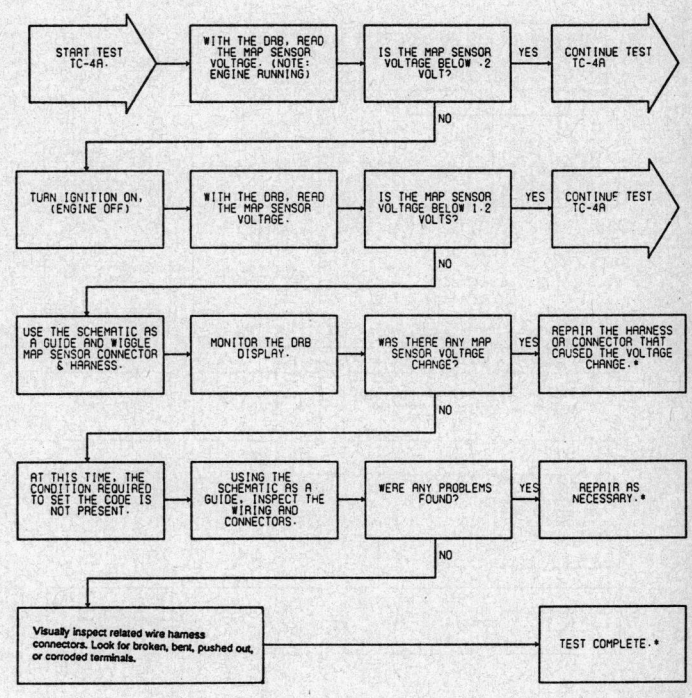

Fig. 13 Test TC-4A: MAP Sensor Voltage Too Low (Part 1 of 2)

CR1029303456010X

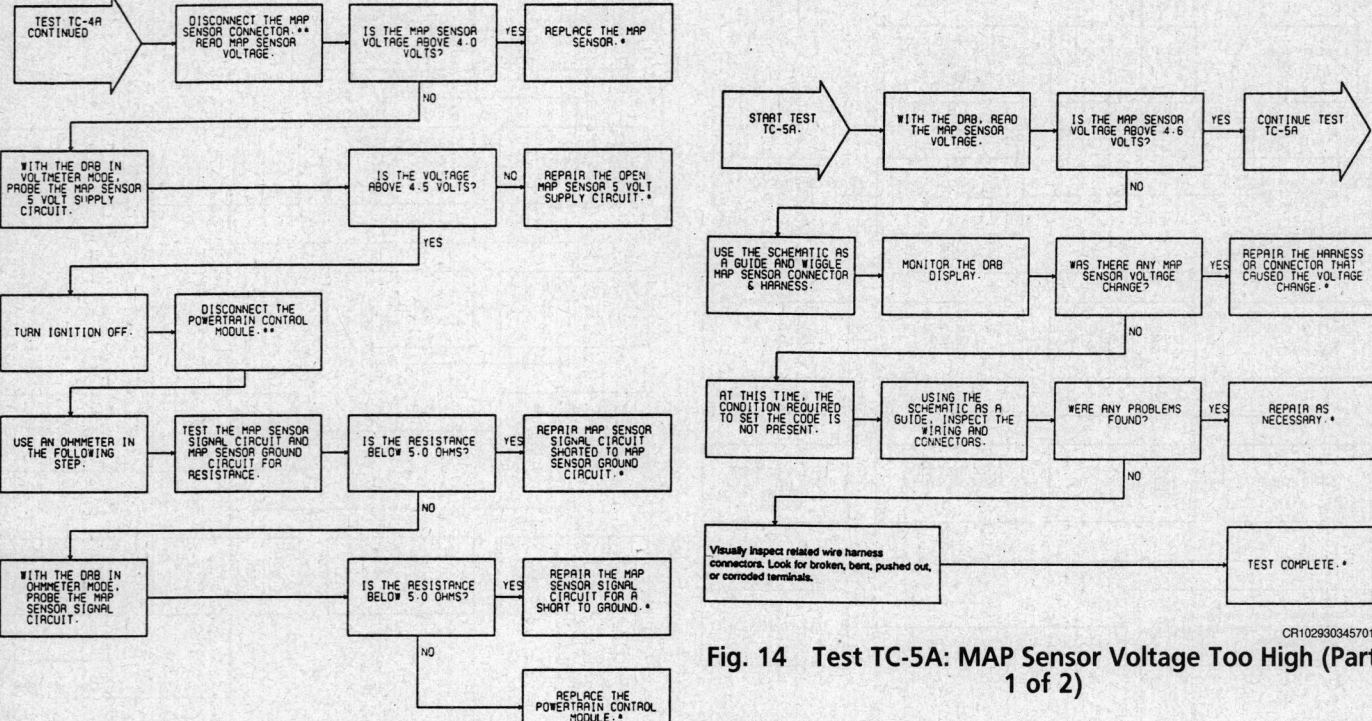

Fig. 13   Test TC-4A: MAP Sensor Voltage Too Low (Part 2 of 2)

Fig. 14   Test TC-5A: MAP Sensor Voltage Too High (Part 1 of 2)

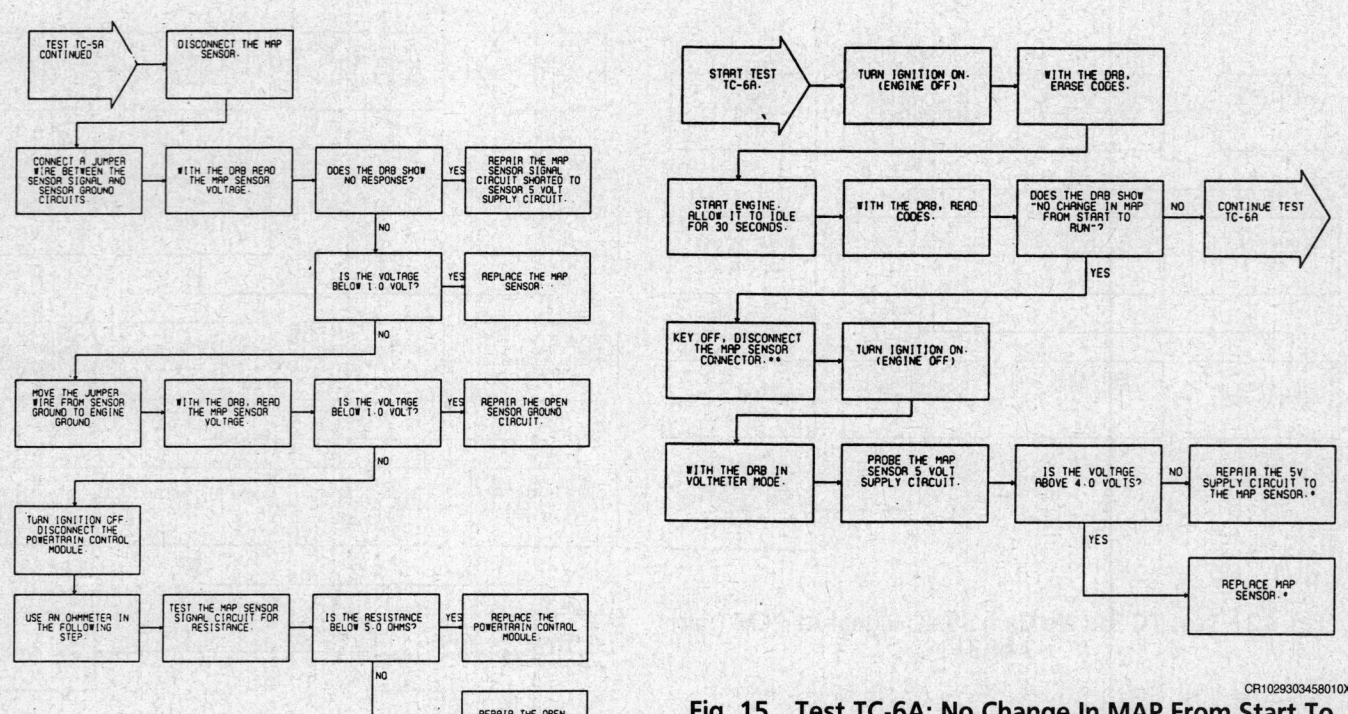

Fig. 14   Test TC-5A: MAP Sensor Voltage Too High (Part 2 of 2)

Fig. 15   Test TC-6A: No Change In MAP From Start To Run (Part 1 of 2)

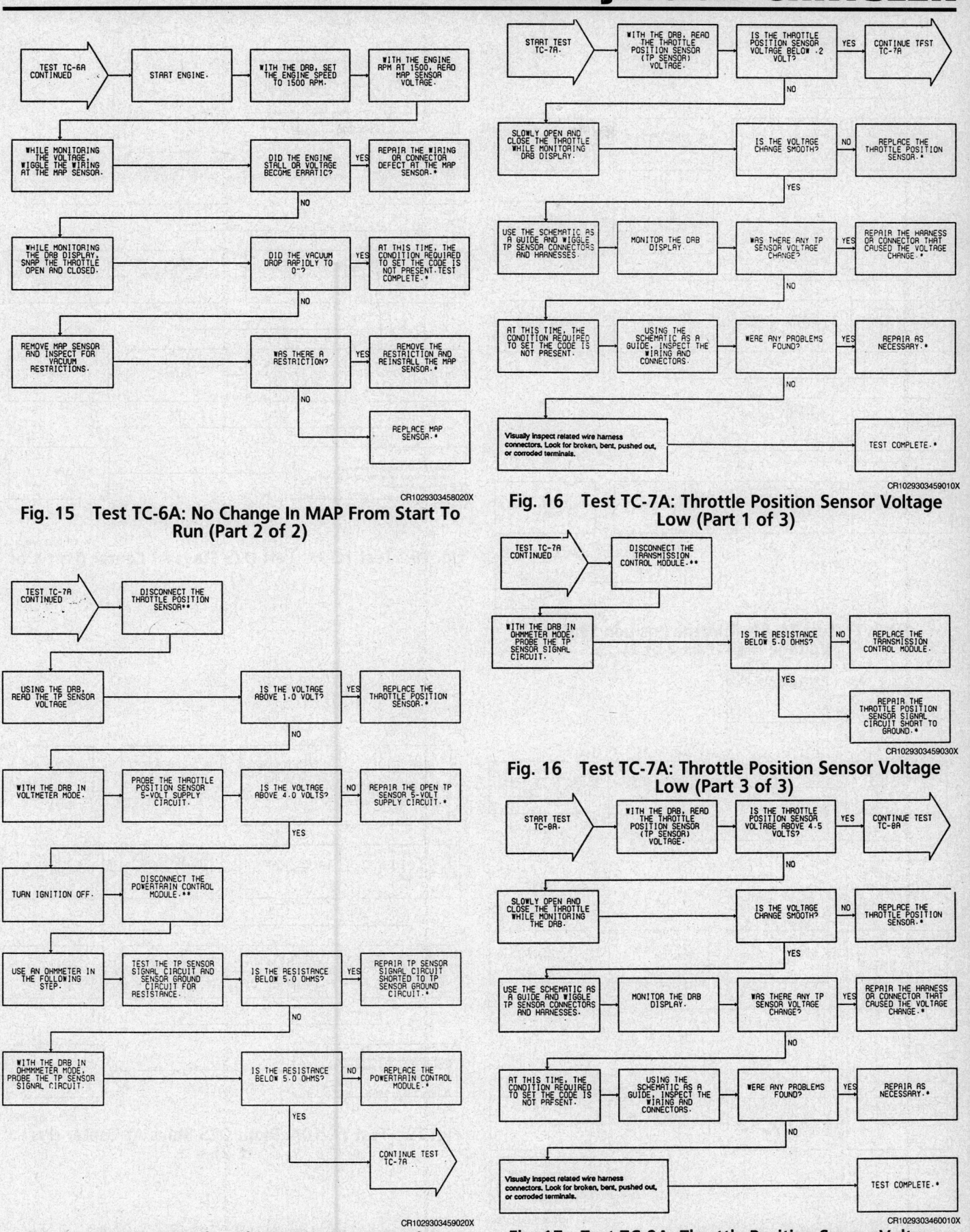

Fig. 15   Test TC-6A: No Change In MAP From Start To Run (Part 2 of 2)

Fig. 16   Test TC-7A: Throttle Position Sensor Voltage Low (Part 1 of 3)

Fig. 16   Test TC-7A: Throttle Position Sensor Voltage Low (Part 3 of 3)

Fig. 16   Test TC-7A: Throttle Position Sensor Voltage Low (Part 2 of 3)

Fig. 17   Test TC-8A: Throttle Position Sensor Voltage High (Part 1 of 2)

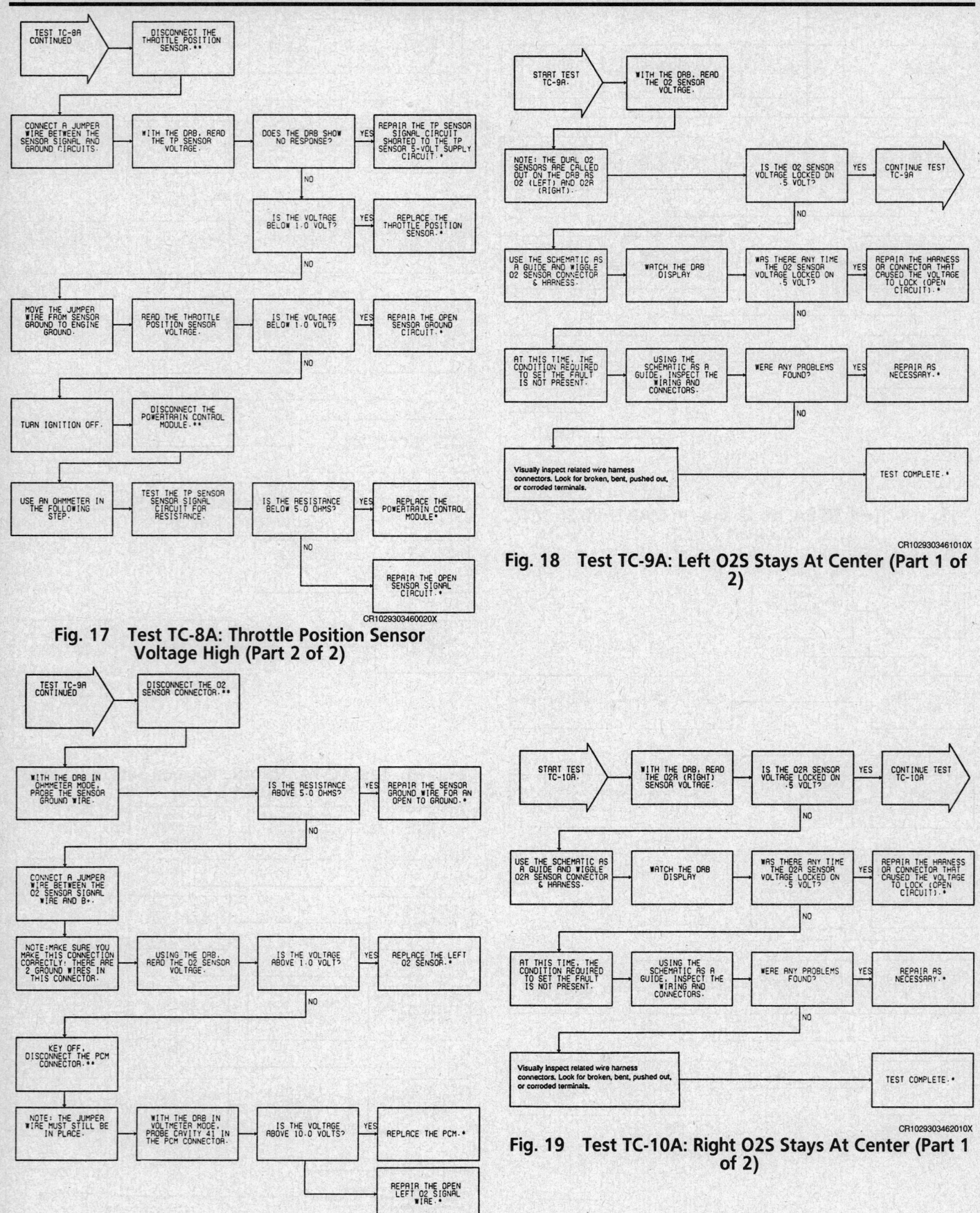

Fig. 17   Test TC-8A: Throttle Position Sensor Voltage High (Part 2 of 2)

CR1029303460020X

Fig. 18   Test TC-9A: Left O2S Stays At Center (Part 1 of 2)

CR1029303461010X

Fig. 18   Test TC-9A: Left O2S Stays At Center (Part 2 of 2)

CR1029303461020X

Fig. 19   Test TC-10A: Right O2S Stays At Center (Part 1 of 2)

CR1029303462010X

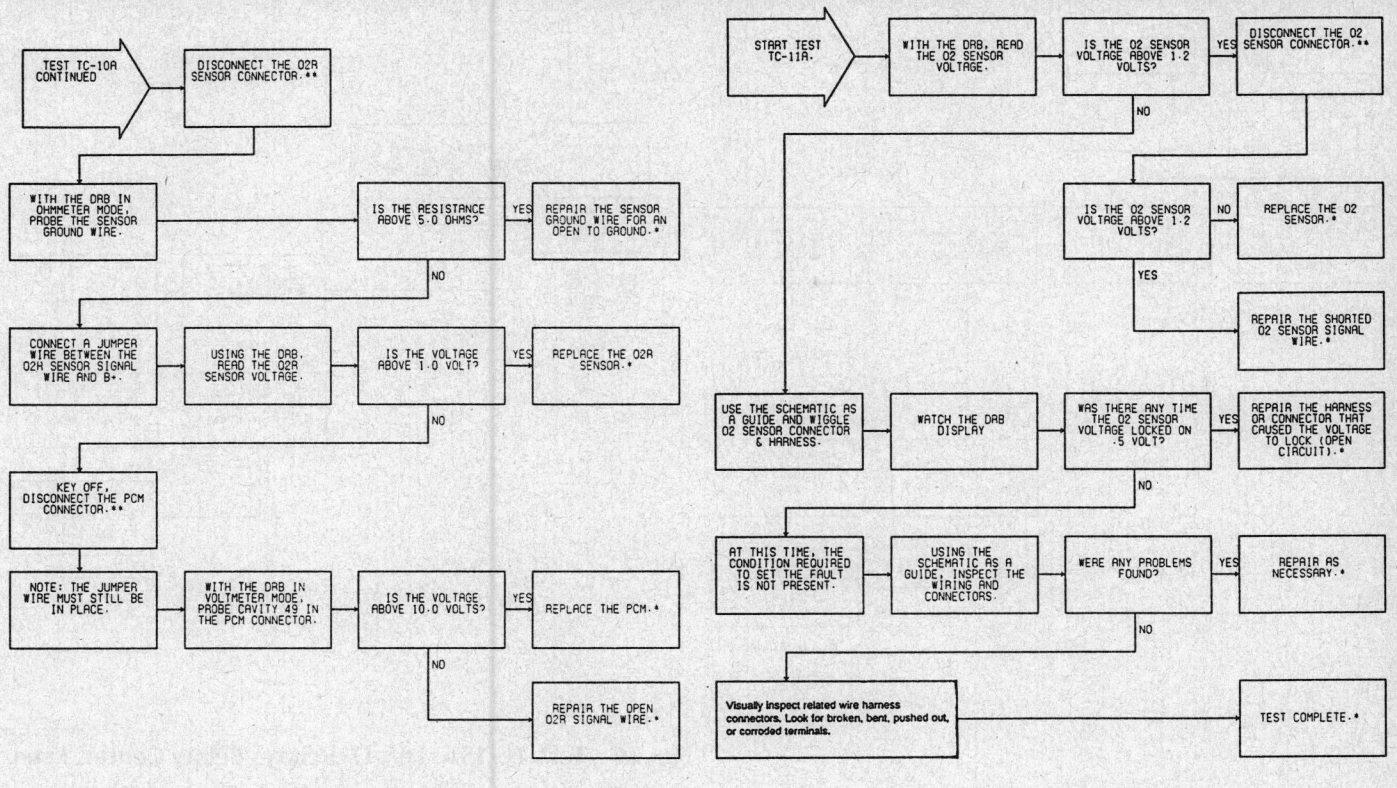

Fig. 19   Test TC-10A: Right O2S Stays At Center (Part 2 of 2)

CR1029303462020X

Fig. 20   Test TC-11A: Left O2S Shorted To Voltage

CR1029303463000X

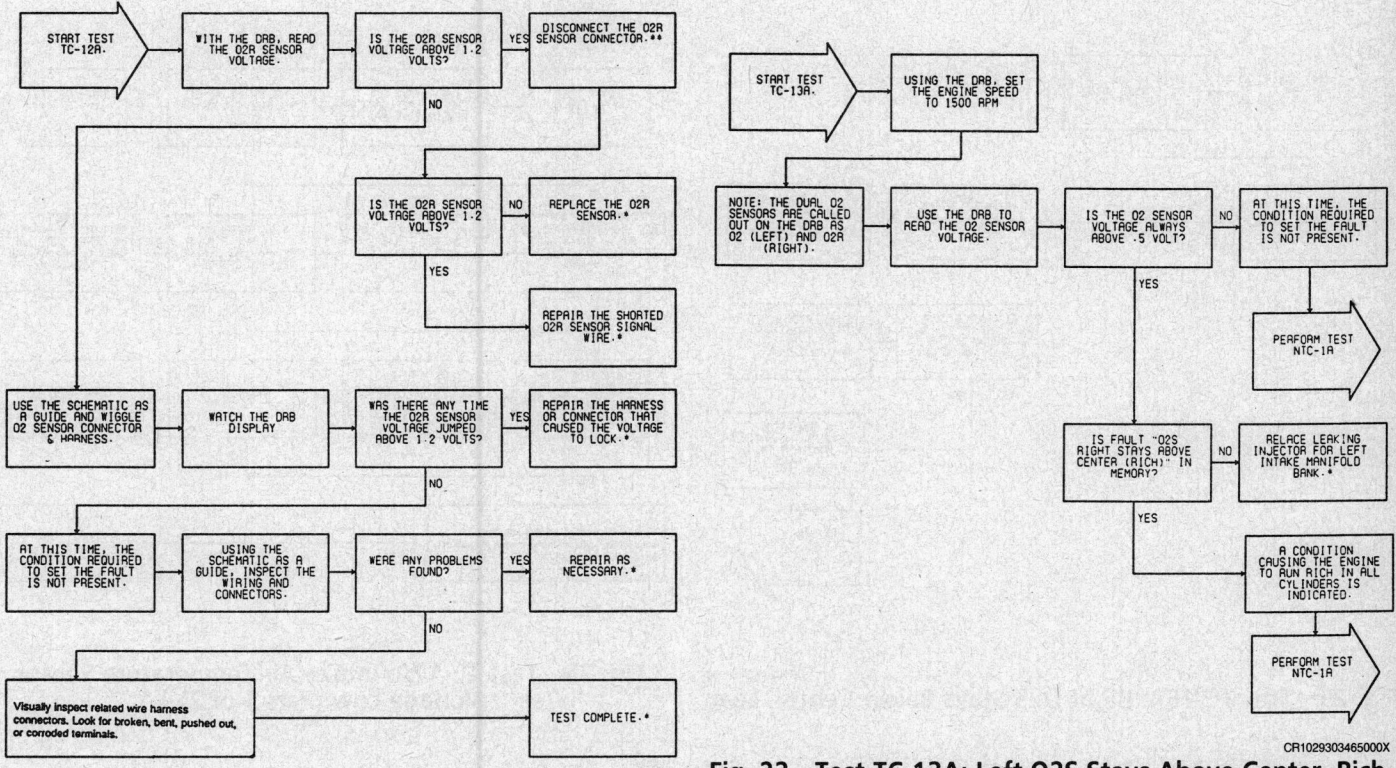

Fig. 21   Test TC-12A: Right O2S Shorted To Voltage

CR1029303464000X

Fig. 22   Test TC-13A: Left O2S Stays Above Center, Rich

CR1029303465000X

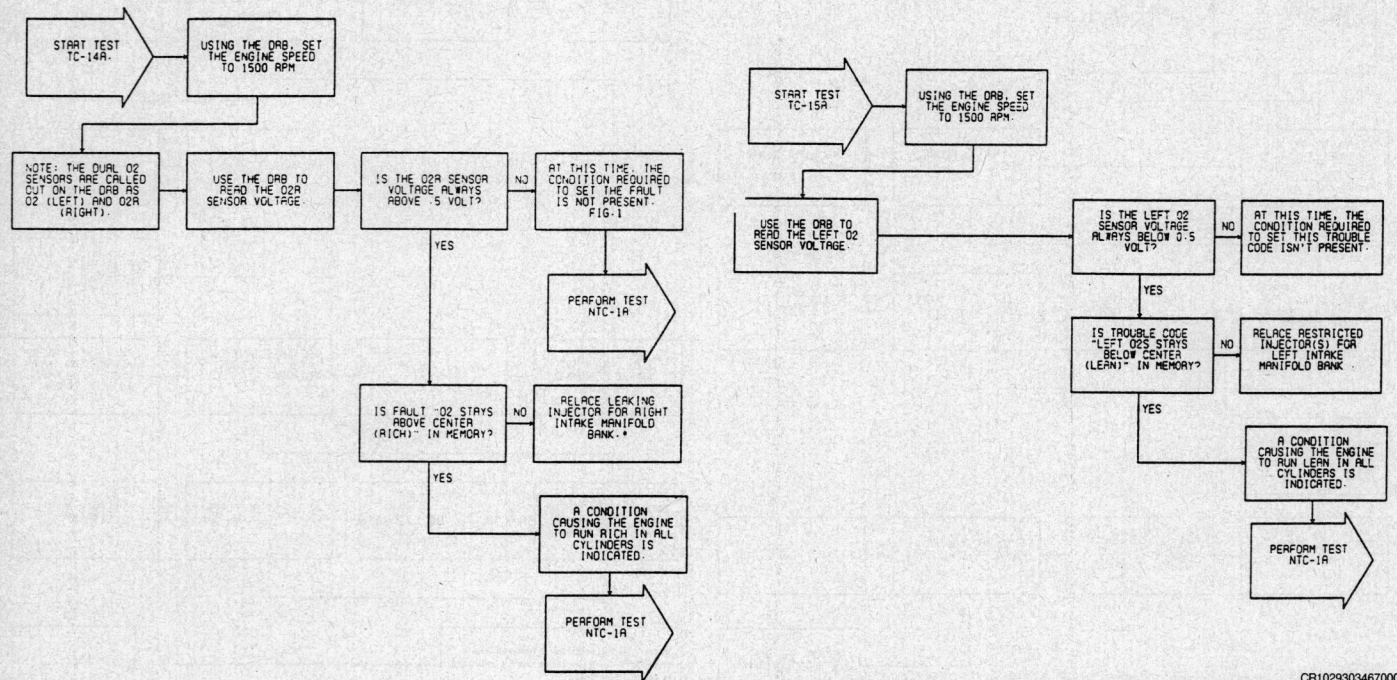

CR1029303466000X

Fig. 23 Test TC-14A: Right O2S Stays Above Center, Rich

CR1029303467000A

Fig. 24 Test TC-15A: Left O2S Stays Below Center, Lean

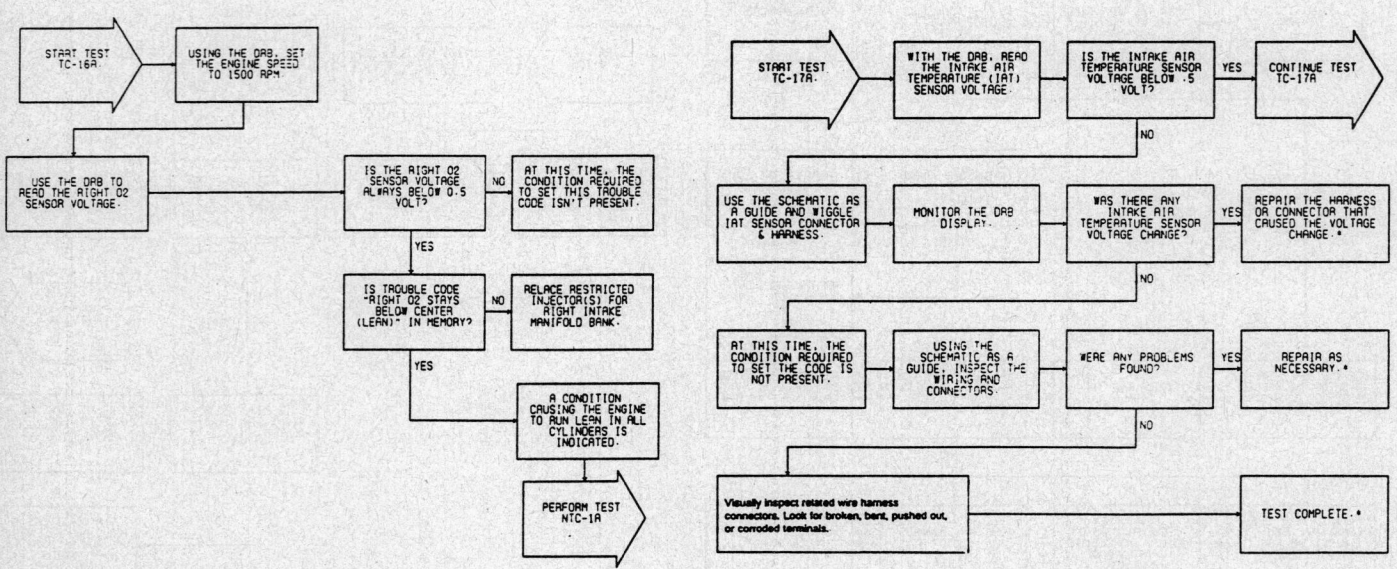

CR1029303468000A

Fig. 25 Test TC-16A: Right O2S Stays Below Center, Lean

CR1029303469010X

Fig. 26 Test TC-17A: Intake Air Temperature Sensor Voltage Low (Part 1 of 2)

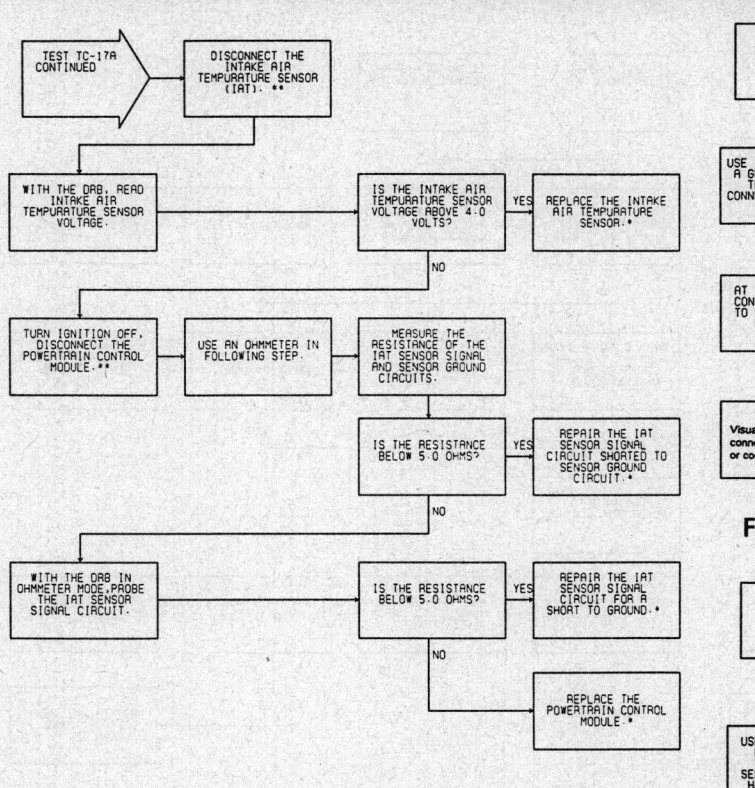

Fig. 26   Test TC-17A: Intake Air Temperature Sensor
Voltage Low (Part 2 of 2)

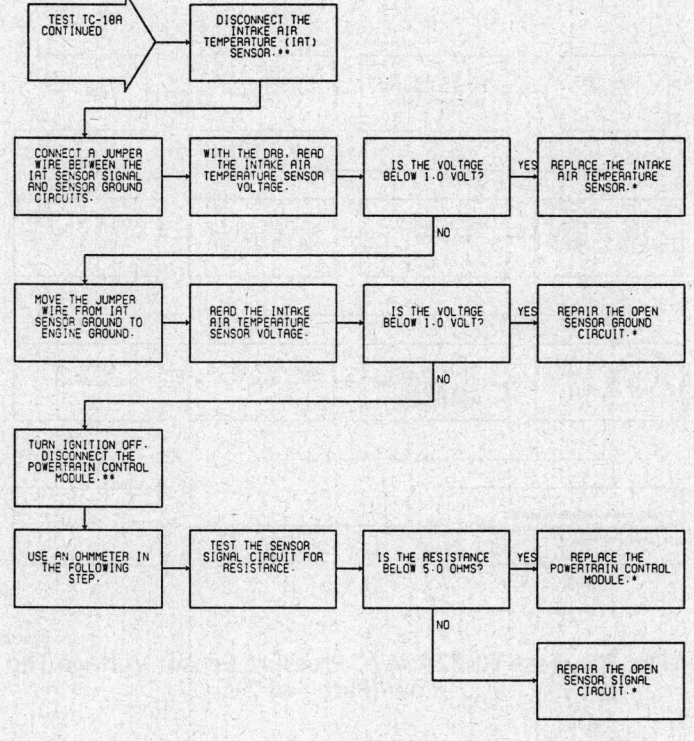

Fig. 27   Test TC-18A: Intake Air Temperature Sensor
Voltage High (Part 2 of 2)

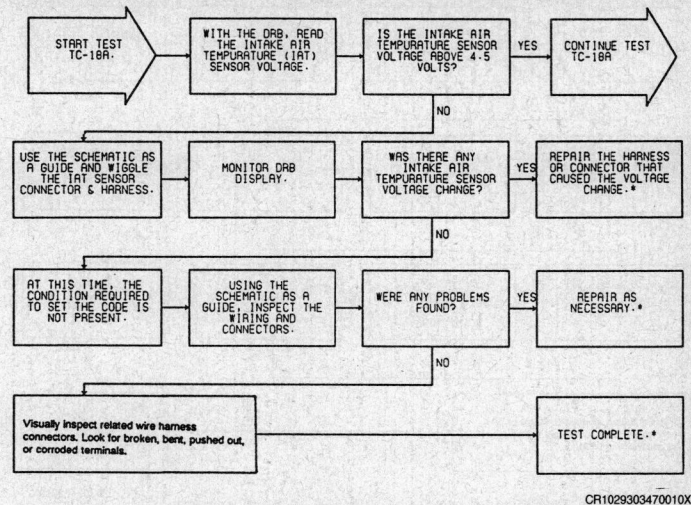

Fig. 27   Test TC-18A: Intake Air Temperature Sensor
Voltage High (Part 1 of 2)

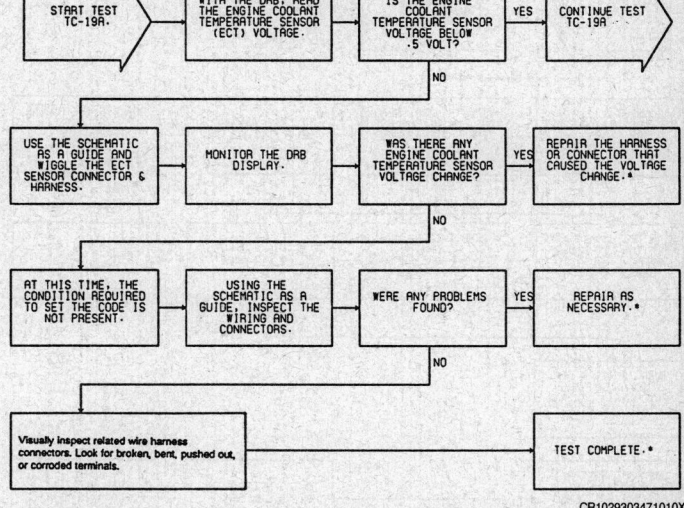

Fig. 28   Test TC-19A: ECT Sensor Voltage Too Low (Part
1 of 2)

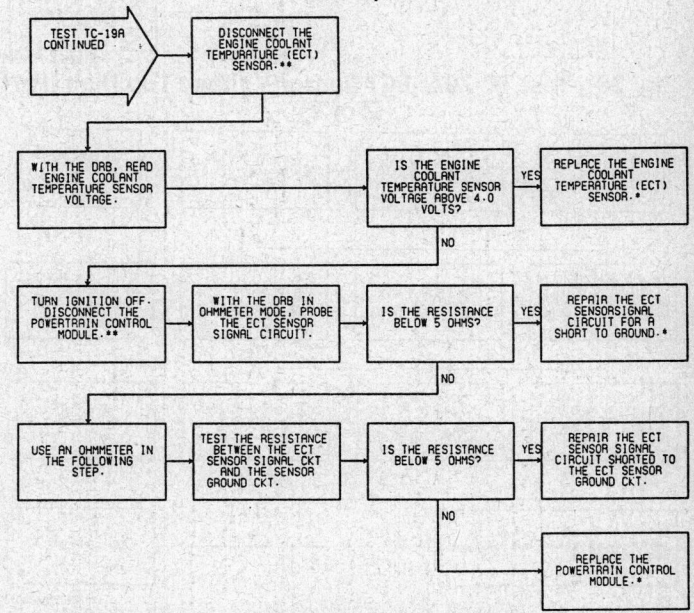

Fig. 28   Test TC-19A: ECT Sensor Voltage Too Low (Part
2 of 2)

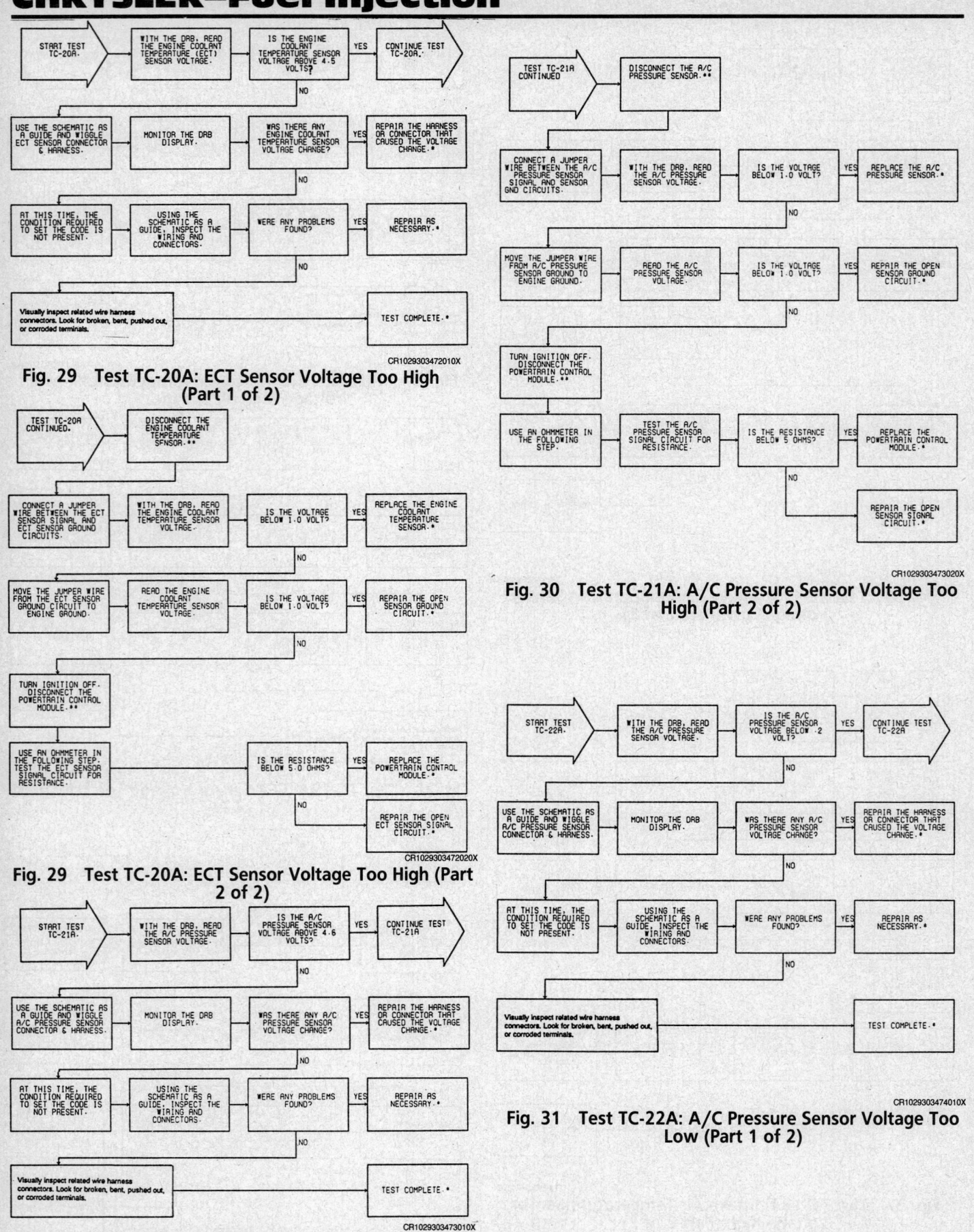

Fig. 29 Test TC-20A: ECT Sensor Voltage Too High (Part 1 of 2)

CR1029303472010X

Fig. 29 Test TC-20A: ECT Sensor Voltage Too High (Part 2 of 2)

CR1029303472020X

Fig. 30 Test TC-21A: A/C Pressure Sensor Voltage Too High (Part 1 of 2)

CR1029303473010X

Fig. 30 Test TC-21A: A/C Pressure Sensor Voltage Too High (Part 2 of 2)

CR1029303473020X

Fig. 31 Test TC-22A: A/C Pressure Sensor Voltage Too Low (Part 1 of 2)

CR1029303474010X

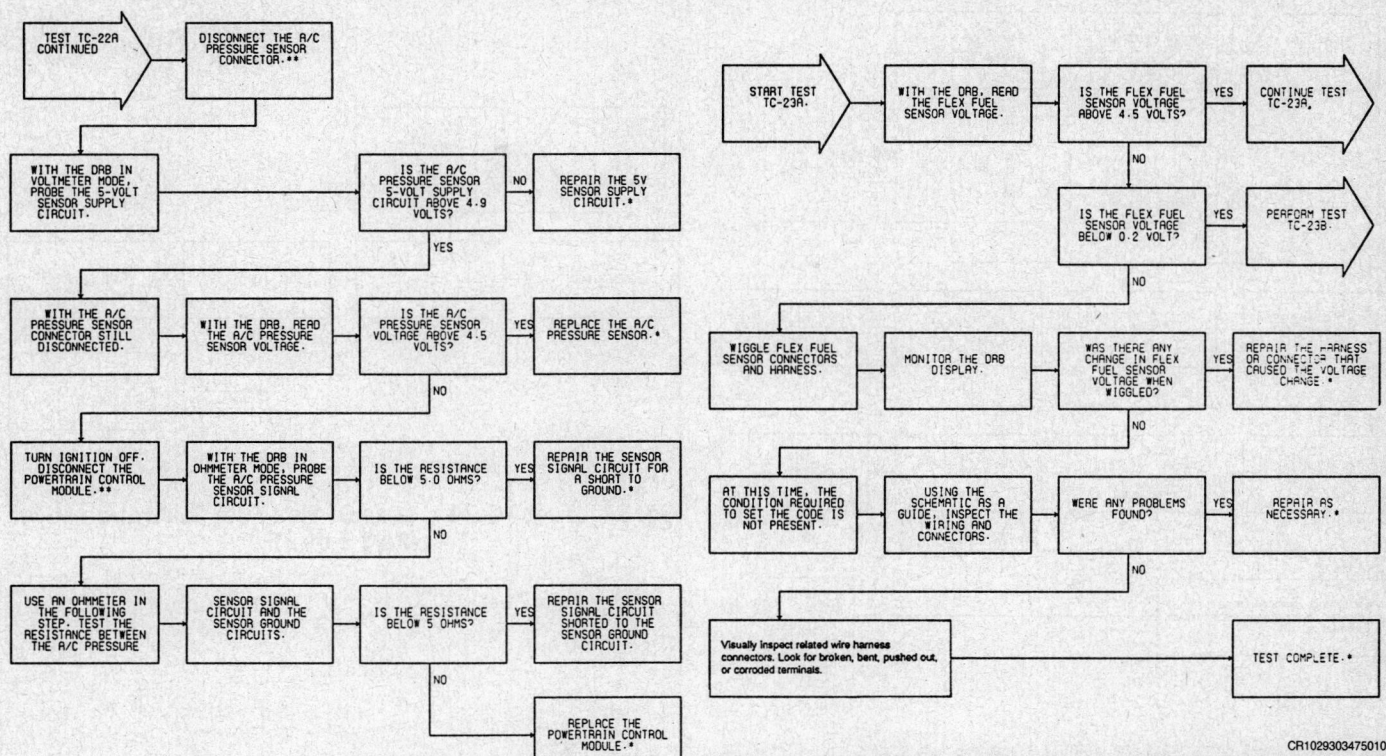

Fig. 31   Test TC-22A: A/C Pressure Sensor Voltage Too Low (Part 2 of 2)

Fig. 32   Test TC-23A: Flex Fuel Voltage Too High (Part 1 of 2)

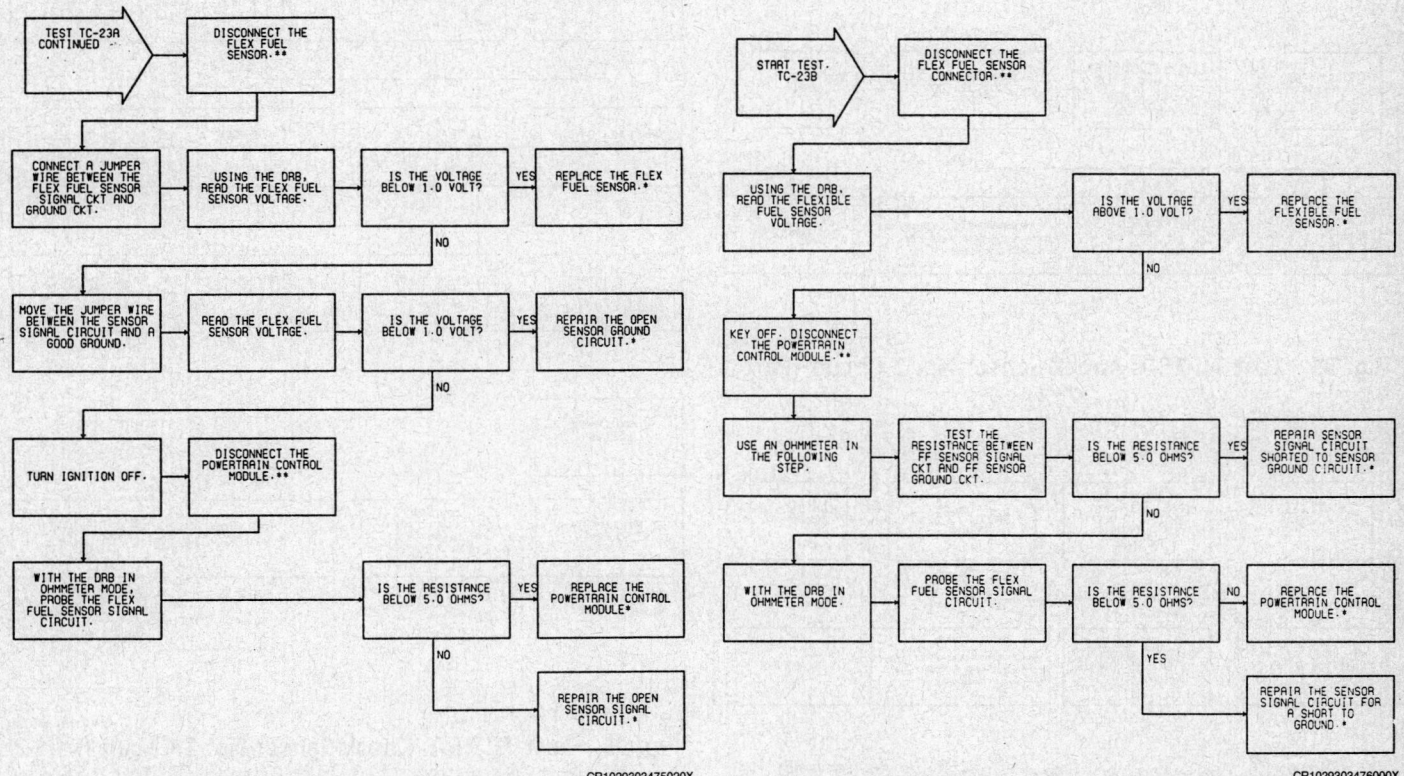

Fig. 32   Test TC-23A: Flex Fuel Voltage Too High (Part 2 of 2)

Fig. 33   Test TC-23B: Flex Fuel Voltage Too Low

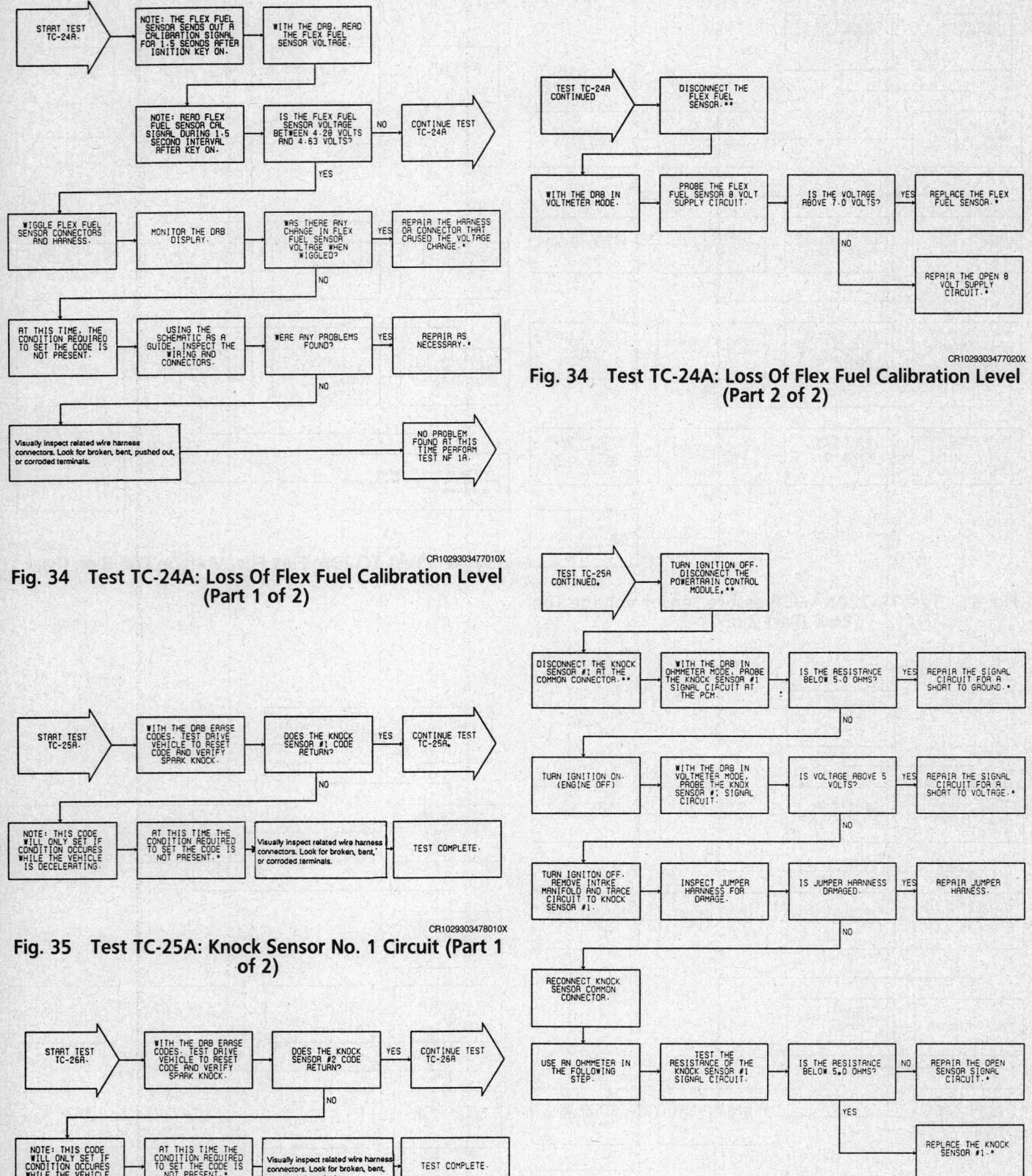

Fig. 34   Test TC-24A: Loss Of Flex Fuel Calibration Level
(Part 2 of 2)

CR1029303477010X

Fig. 34   Test TC-24A: Loss Of Flex Fuel Calibration Level
(Part 1 of 2)

CR1029303478010X

Fig. 35   Test TC-25A: Knock Sensor No. 1 Circuit (Part 1
of 2)

CR1029303478020X

Fig. 35   Test TC-25A: Knock Sensor No. 1 Circuit (Part 2
of 2)

CR1029303479010X

Fig. 36   Test TC-26A: Knock Sensor No. 2
Circuit (Part 1 of 2)

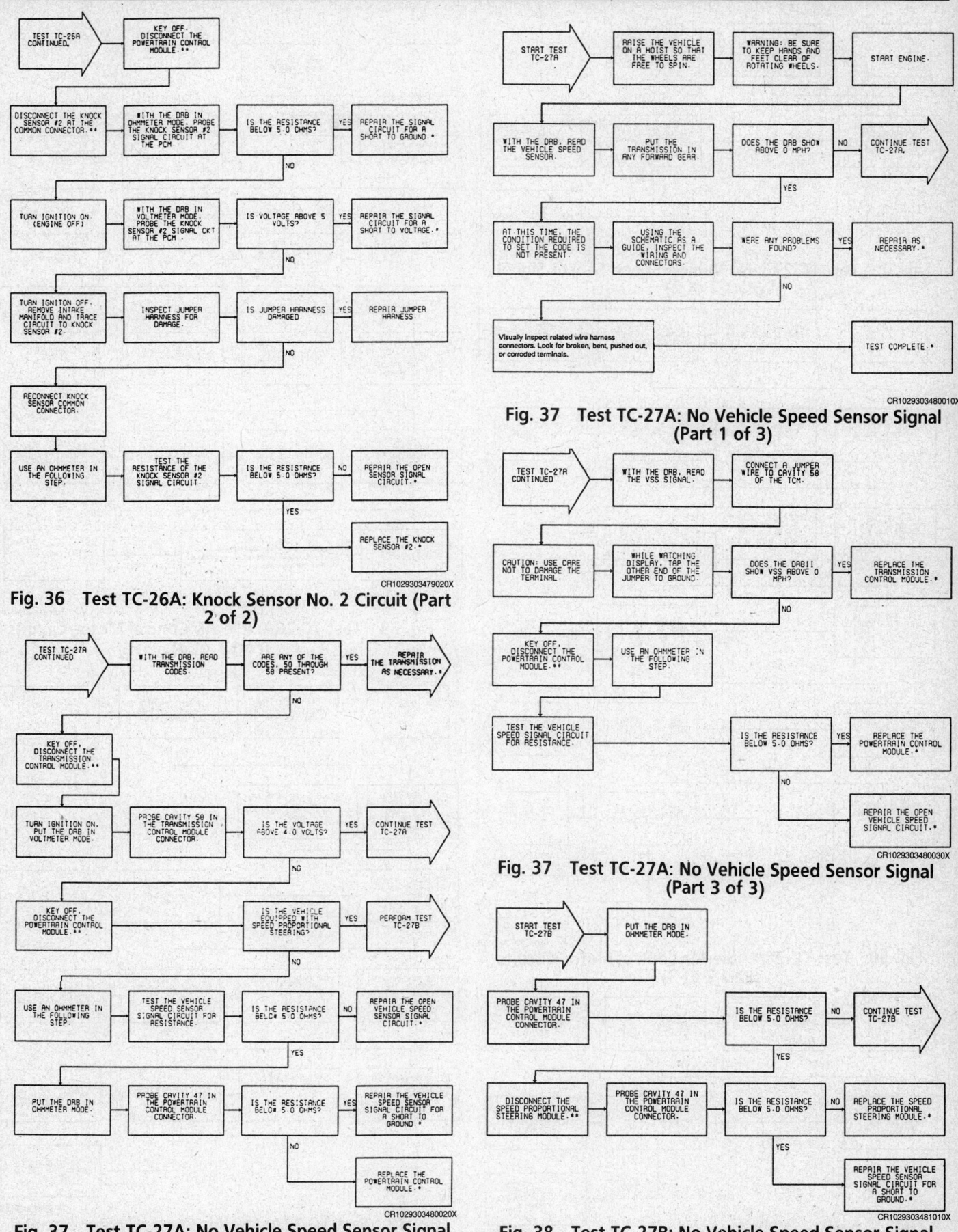

Fig. 36   Test TC-26A: Knock Sensor No. 2 Circuit (Part 2 of 2)

CR1029303479020X

Fig. 37   Test TC-27A: No Vehicle Speed Sensor Signal (Part 1 of 3)

CR1029303480010X

Fig. 37   Test TC-27A: No Vehicle Speed Sensor Signal (Part 3 of 3)

CR1029303480030X

Fig. 37   Test TC-27A: No Vehicle Speed Sensor Signal (Part 2 of 3)

CR1029303480020X

Fig. 38   Test TC-27B: No Vehicle Speed Sensor Signal (Part 1 of 2)

CR1029303481010X

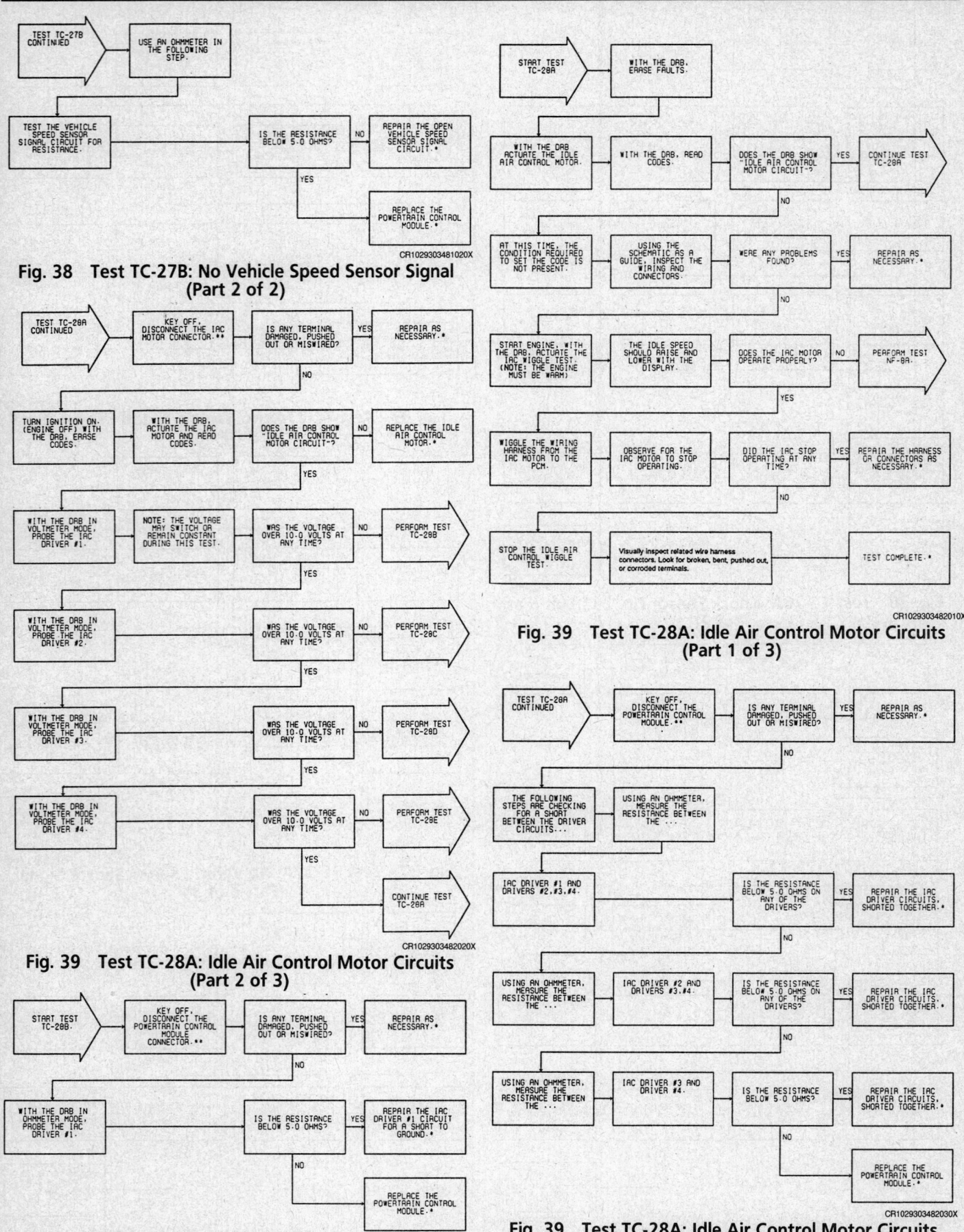

Fig. 38   Test TC-27B: No Vehicle Speed Sensor Signal (Part 2 of 2)

Fig. 39   Test TC-28A: Idle Air Control Motor Circuits (Part 2 of 3)

Fig. 39   Test TC-28A: Idle Air Control Motor Circuits (Part 1 of 3)

Fig. 40   Test TC-28B: Idle Air Control Motor Circuits

Fig. 39   Test TC-28A: Idle Air Control Motor Circuits (Part 3 of 3)

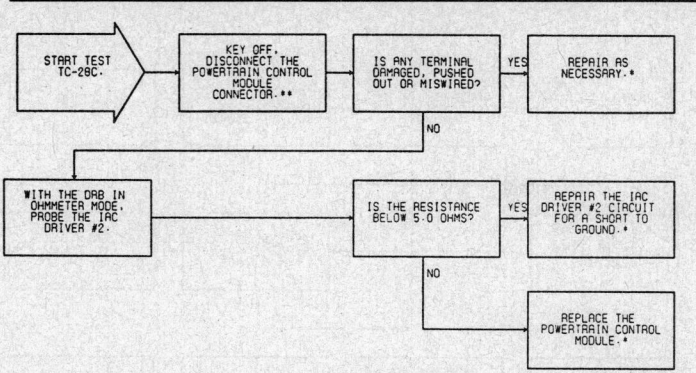

Fig. 41 Test TC-28C: Idle Air Control Motor Circuits

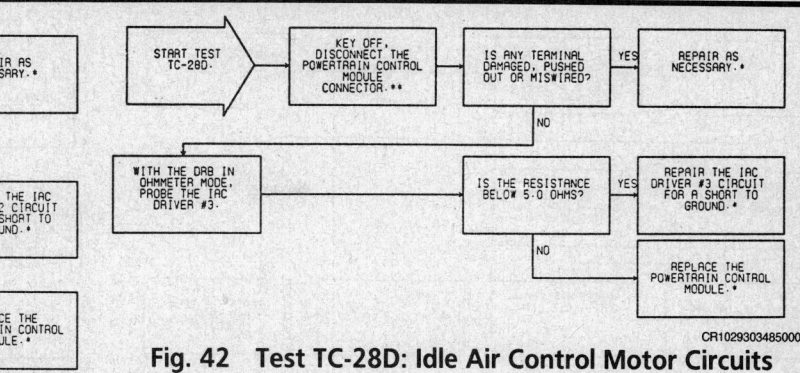

Fig. 42 Test TC-28D: Idle Air Control Motor Circuits

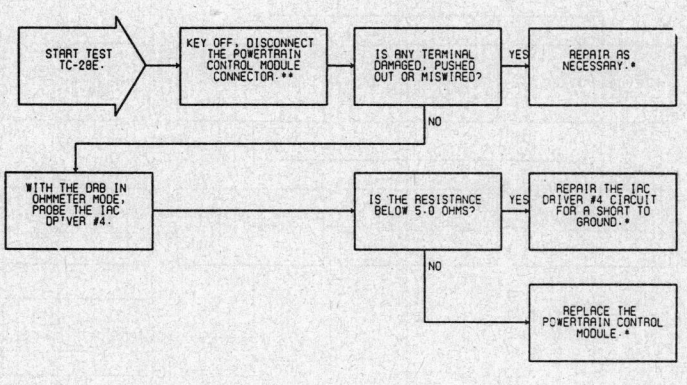

Fig. 43 Test TC-28E: Idle Air Control Motor Circuits

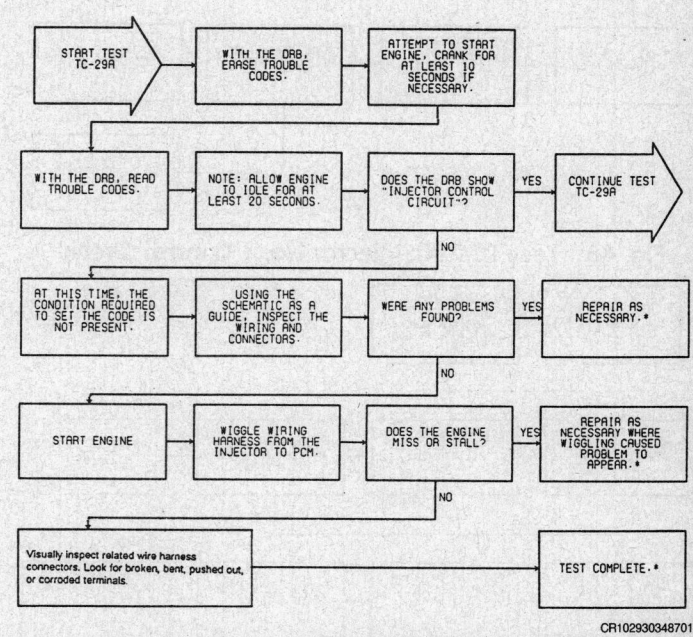

Fig. 44 Test TC-29A: Injector Control Circuits (Part 1 of 2)

PERFORM THE INJECTOR TEST AS FOLLOWS:

If the trouble code is:	Diagnostic Test	
	3.3L	3.5L
Injector #1 Control Circuit	TC-29B	TC-29D
Injector #2 Control Circuit	TC-30A	TC-30C
Injector #3 Control Circuit	TC-31A	TC-31C
Injector #4 Control Circuit	TC-32A	TC-32C
Injector #5 Control Circuit	TC-33A	TC-33C
Injector #6 Control Circuit	TC-34A	TC-34C

Fig. 44 Test TC-29A: Injector Control Circuits (Part 2 of 2)

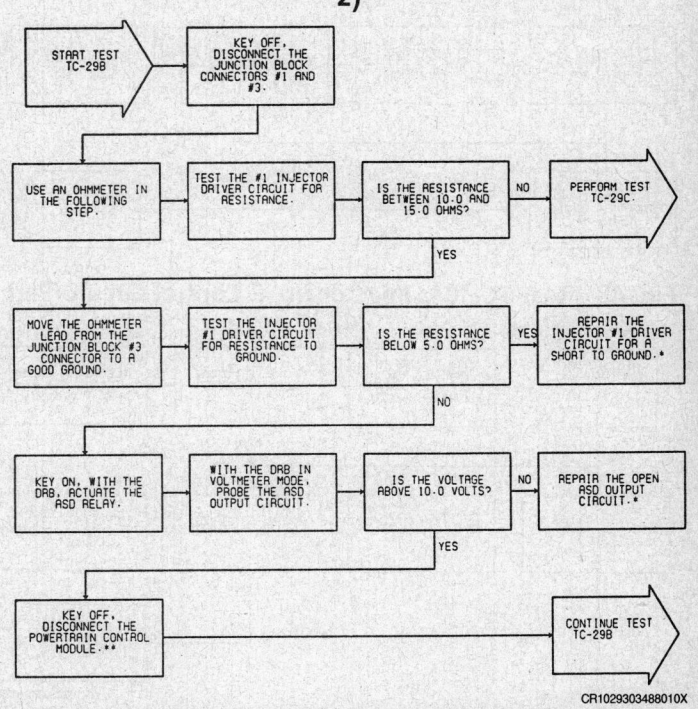

Fig. 45 Test TC-29B: Injector No. 1 Control Circuit (Part 1 of 2)

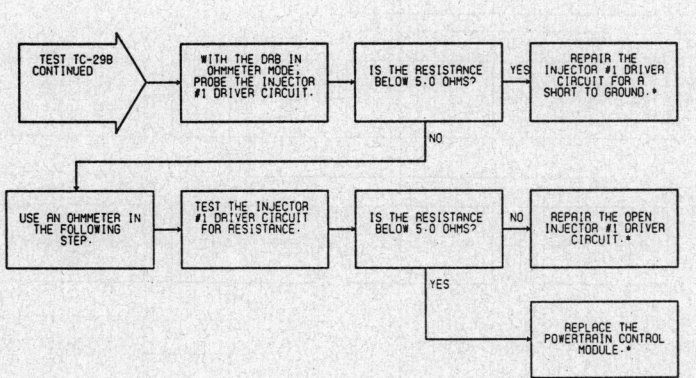

Fig. 45 Test TC-29B: Injector No. 1 Control Circuit (Part 2 of 2)

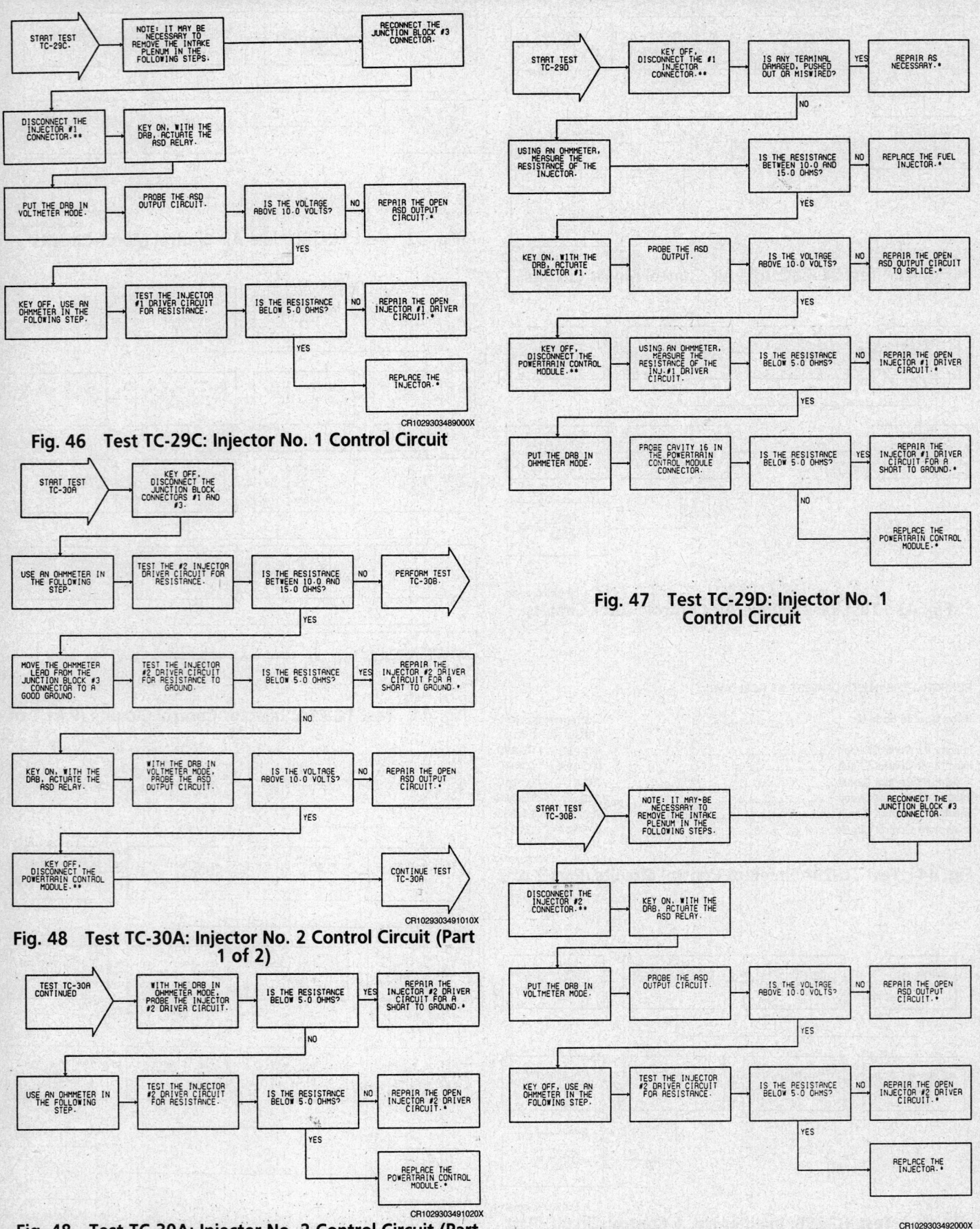

Fig. 46 Test TC-29C: Injector No. 1 Control Circuit

Fig. 47 Test TC-29D: Injector No. 1 Control Circuit

Fig. 48 Test TC-30A: Injector No. 2 Control Circuit (Part 1 of 2)

Fig. 48 Test TC-30A: Injector No. 2 Control Circuit (Part 2 of 2)

Fig. 49 Test TC-30B: Injector No. 2 Control Circuit

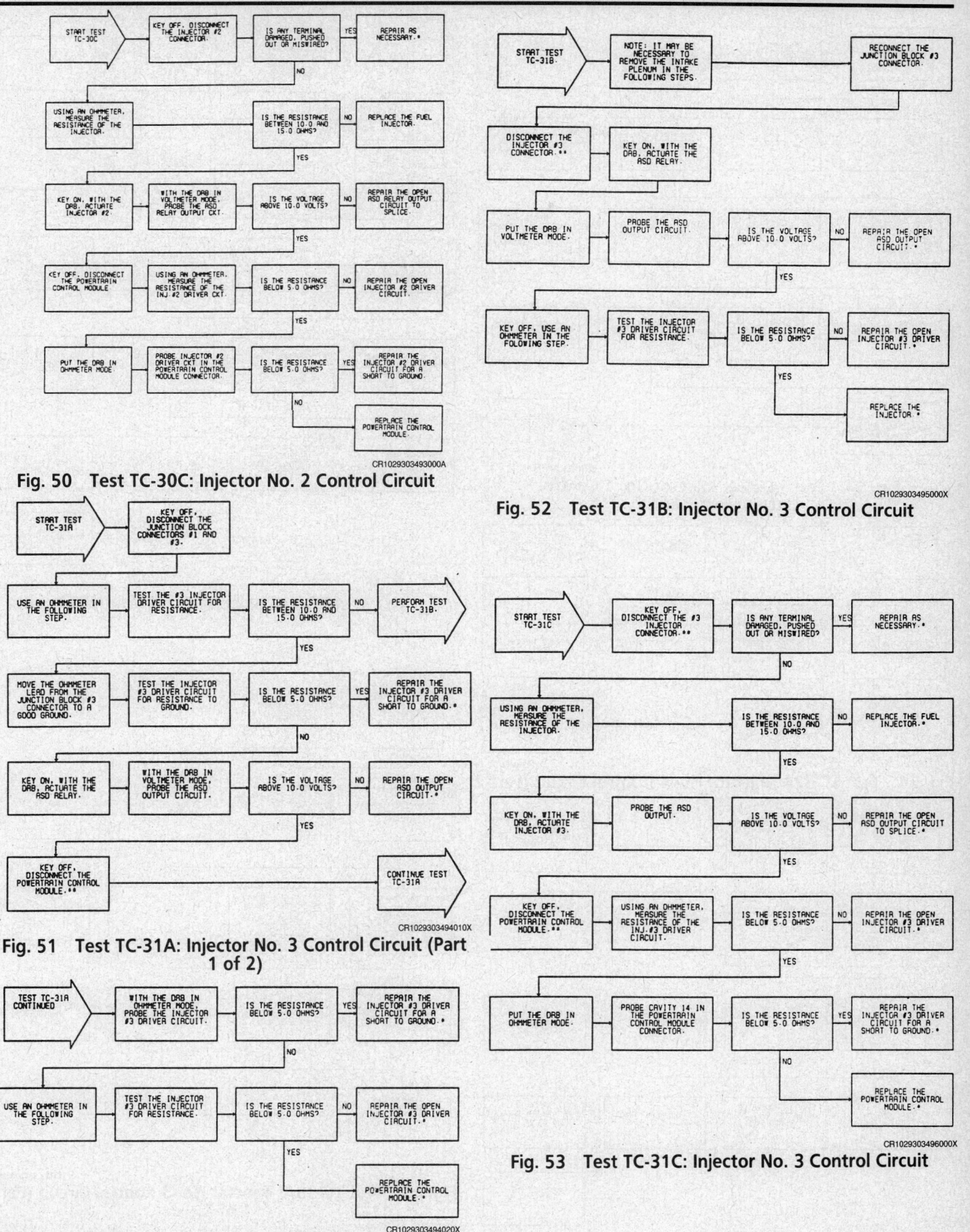

Fig. 50   Test TC-30C: Injector No. 2 Control Circuit

Fig. 52   Test TC-31B: Injector No. 3 Control Circuit

Fig. 51   Test TC-31A: Injector No. 3 Control Circuit (Part 1 of 2)

Fig. 51   Test TC-31A: Injector No. 3 Control Circuit (Part 2 of 2)

Fig. 53   Test TC-31C: Injector No. 3 Control Circuit

CHRYSLER–Fuel Injection

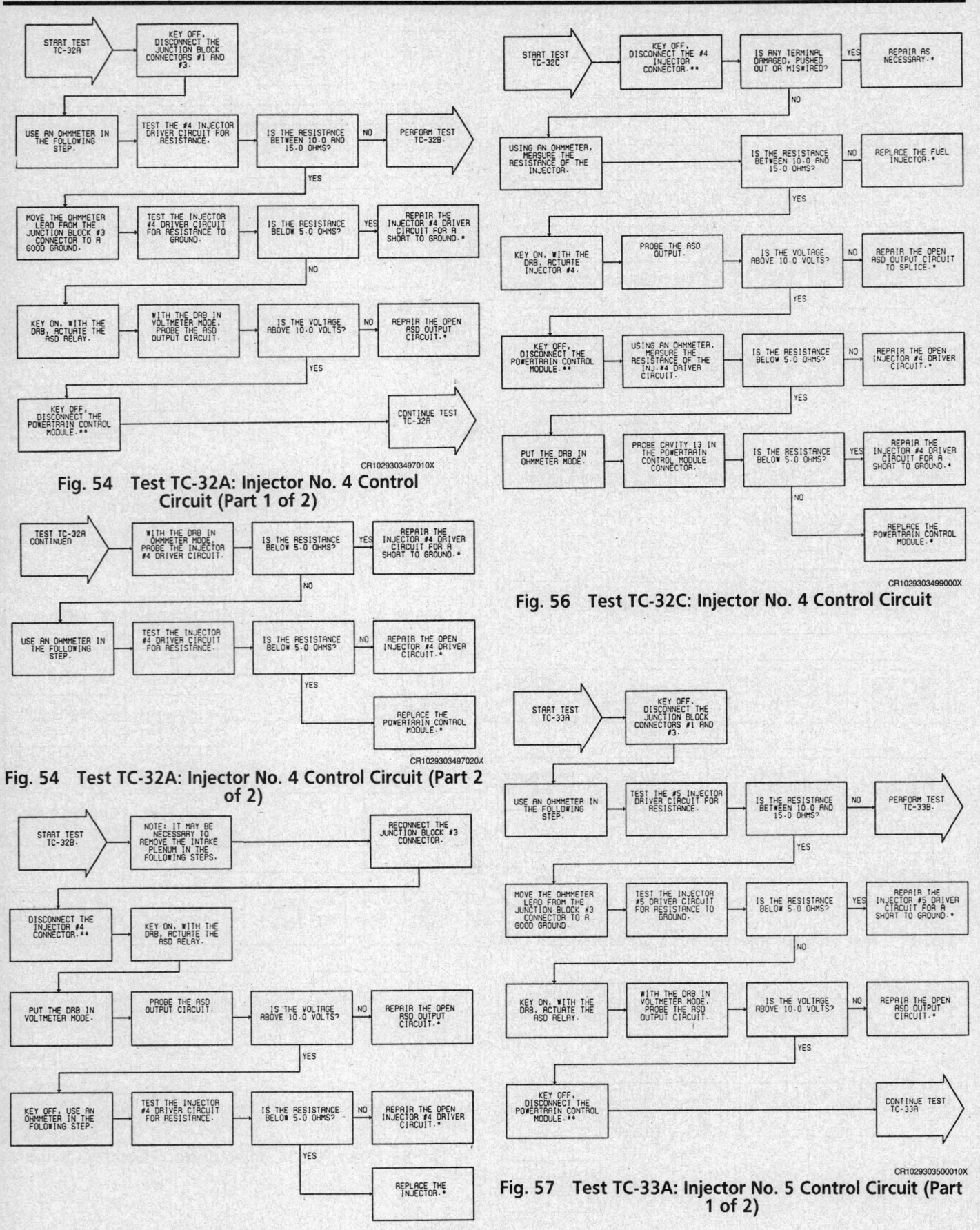

Fig. 54 Test TC-32A: Injector No. 4 Control Circuit (Part 1 of 2)

Fig. 54 Test TC-32A: Injector No. 4 Control Circuit (Part 2 of 2)

Fig. 55 Test TC-32B: Injector No. 4 Control Circuit

Fig. 56 Test TC-32C: Injector No. 4 Control Circuit

Fig. 57 Test TC-33A: Injector No. 5 Control Circuit (Part 1 of 2)

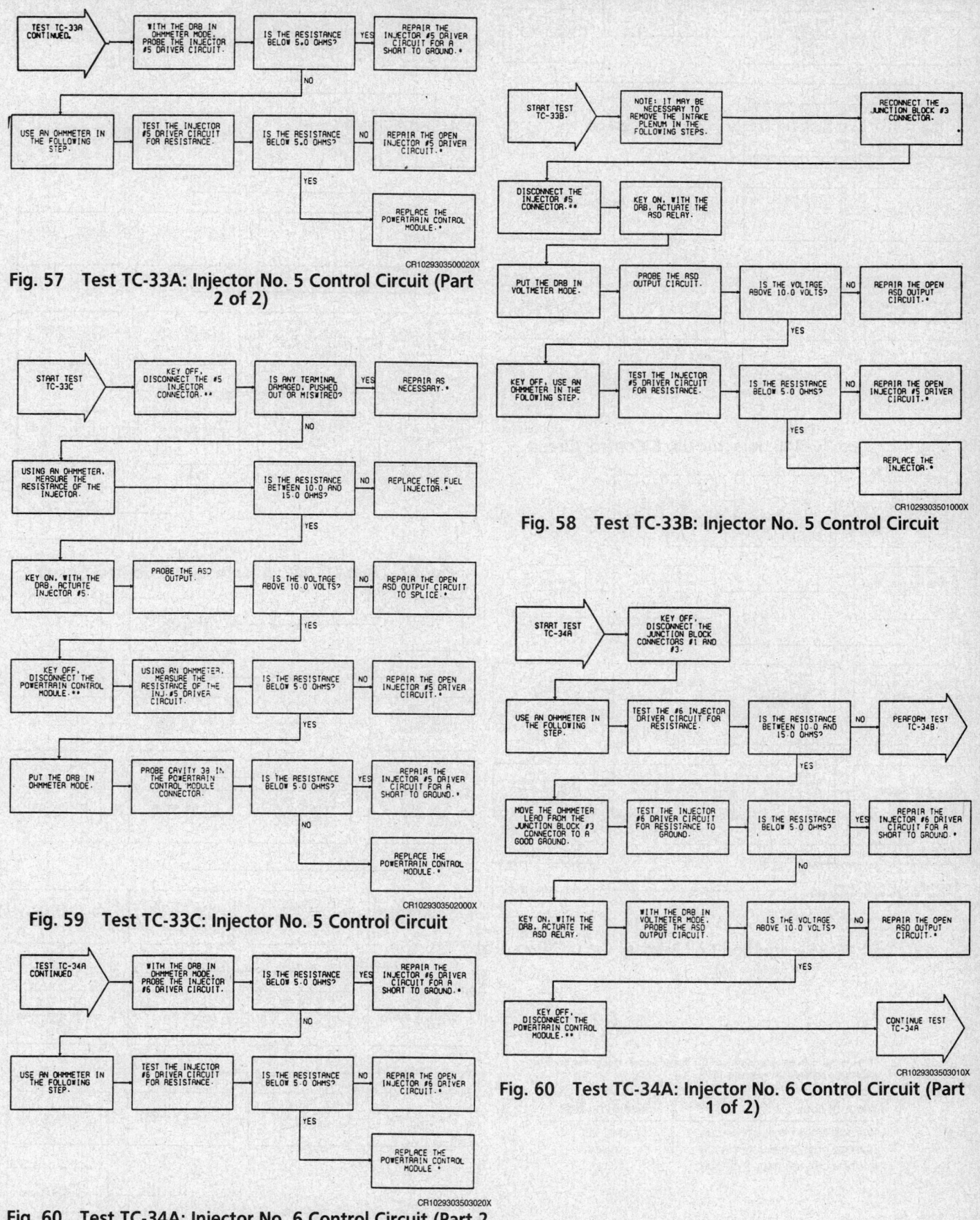

Fig. 57   Test TC-33A: Injector No. 5 Control Circuit (Part 2 of 2)

Fig. 58   Test TC-33B: Injector No. 5 Control Circuit

Fig. 59   Test TC-33C: Injector No. 5 Control Circuit

Fig. 60   Test TC-34A: Injector No. 6 Control Circuit (Part 1 of 2)

Fig. 60   Test TC-34A: Injector No. 6 Control Circuit (Part 2 of 2)

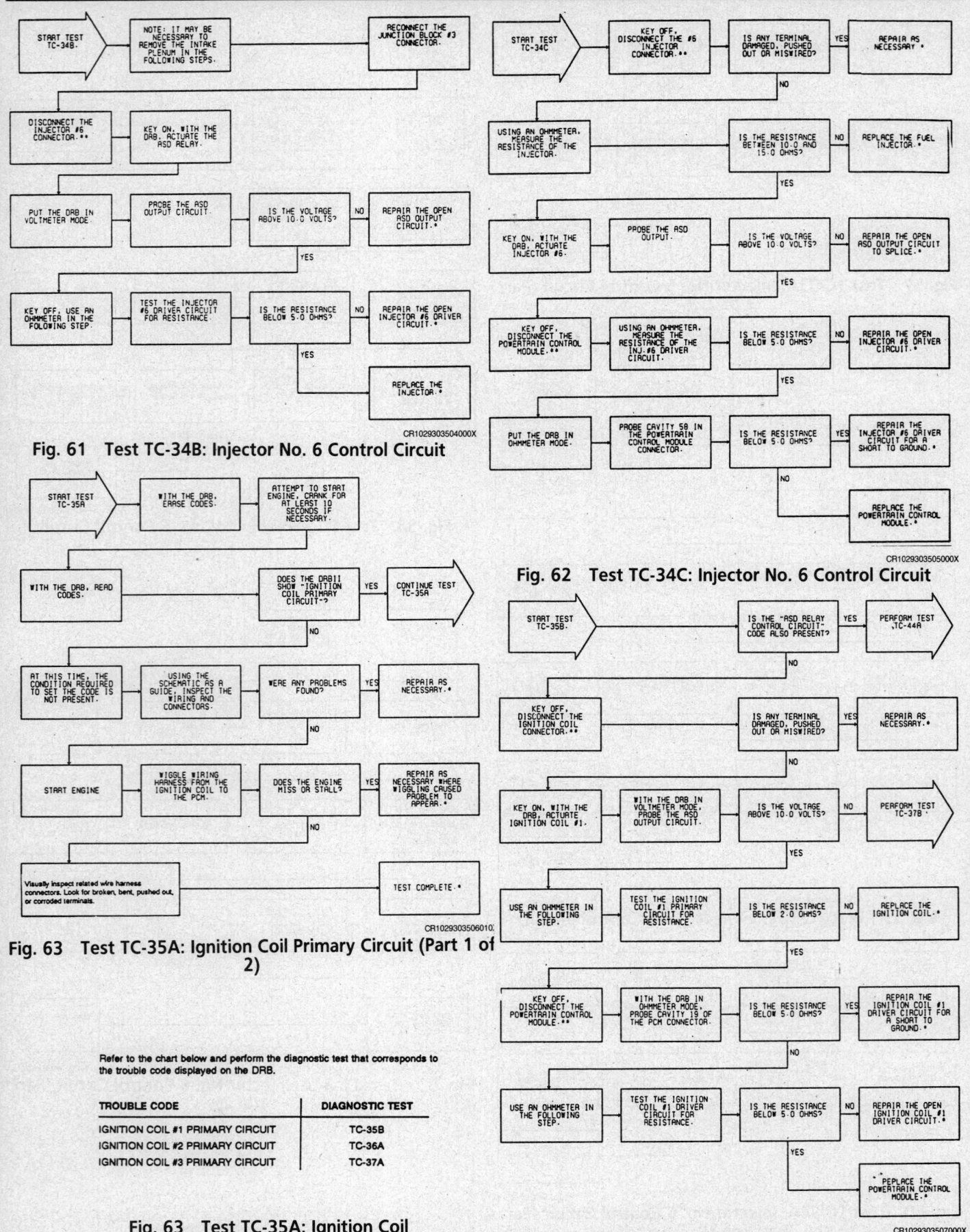

Fig. 61 Test TC-34B: Injector No. 6 Control Circuit

Fig. 62 Test TC-34C: Injector No. 6 Control Circuit

Fig. 63 Test TC-35A: Ignition Coil Primary Circuit (Part 1 of 2)

Fig. 63 Test TC-35A: Ignition Coil Primary Circuit (Part 2 of 2)

Fig. 64 Test TC-35B: Ignition Coil No. 1 Primary Circuit

Refer to the chart below and perform the diagnostic test that corresponds to the trouble code displayed on the DRB.

TROUBLE CODE	DIAGNOSTIC TEST
IGNITION COIL #1 PRIMARY CIRCUIT	TC-35B
IGNITION COIL #2 PRIMARY CIRCUIT	TC-36A
IGNITION COIL #3 PRIMARY CIRCUIT	TC-37A

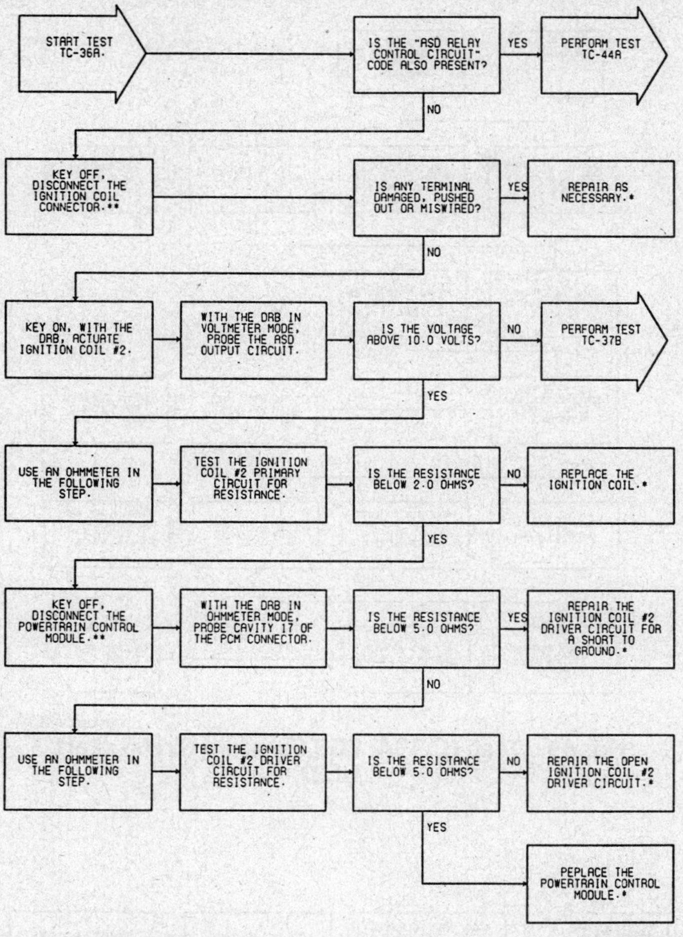

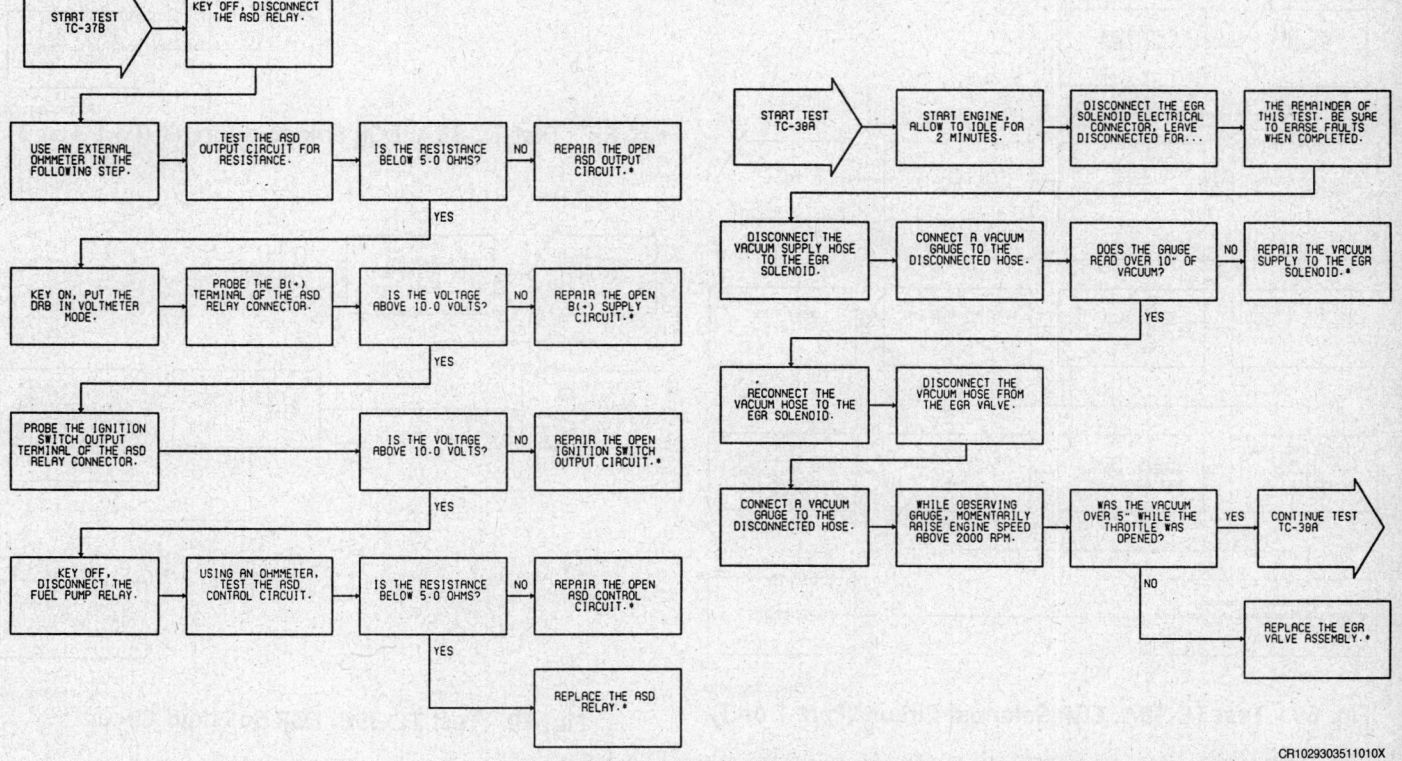

Fig. 65   Test TC-36A: Ignition Coil No. 2 Primary Circuit

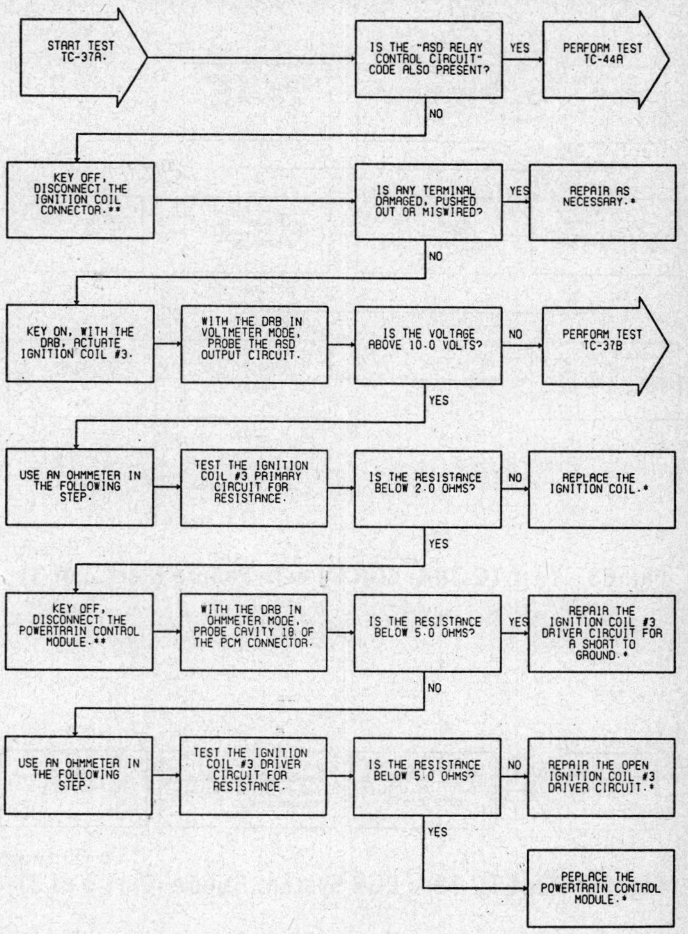

Fig. 66   Test TC-37A: Ignition Coil No. 3 Primary Circuit

Fig. 67   Test TC-37B: Ignition Coil No. 3 Primary Circuit

Fig. 68   Test TC-38A: EGR System Failure (Part 1 of 3)

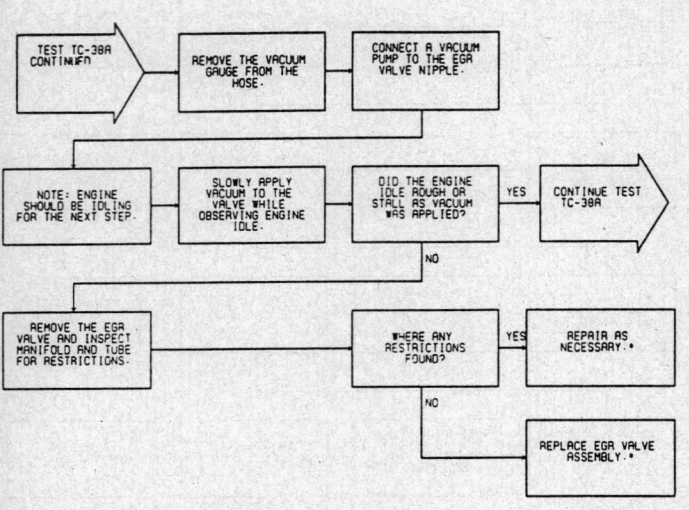

Fig. 68   Test TC-38A: EGR System Failure (Part 2 of 3)

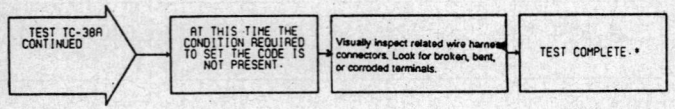

Fig. 68   Test TC-38A: EGR System Failure (Part 3 of 3)

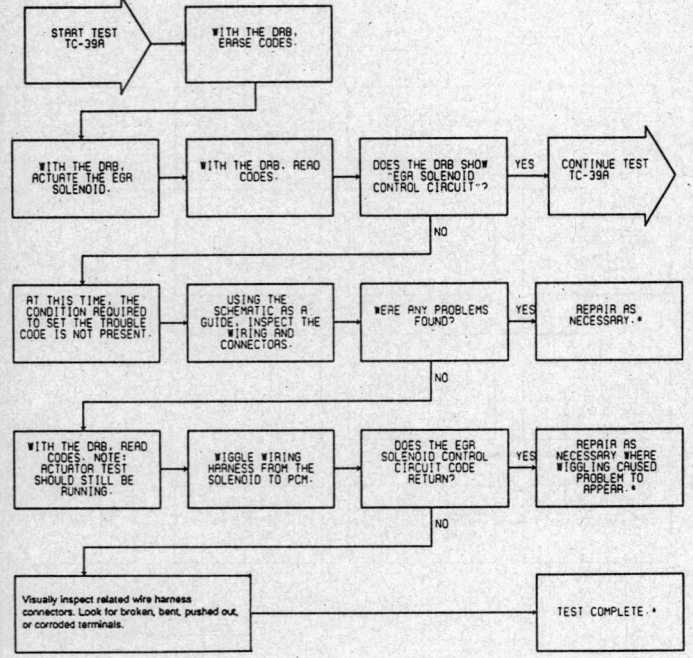

Fig. 69   Test TC-39A: EGR Solenoid Circuit (Part 1 of 3)

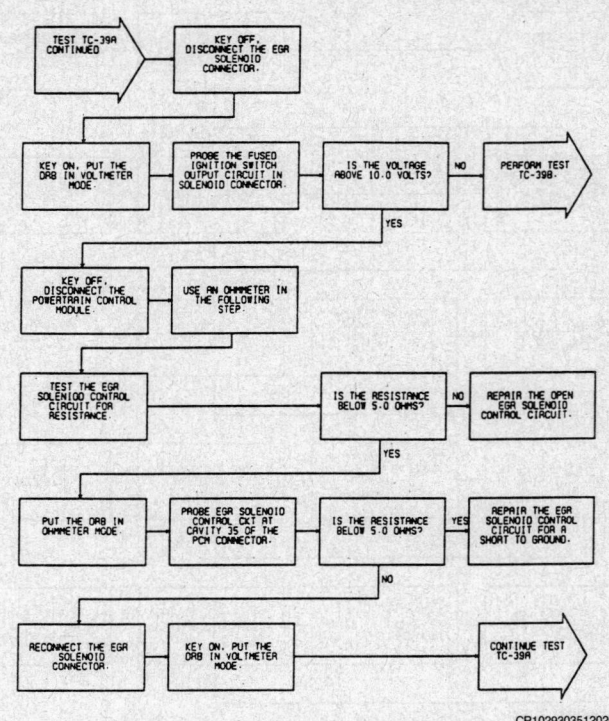

Fig. 69   Test TC-39A: EGR Solenoid Circuit (Part 2 of 3)

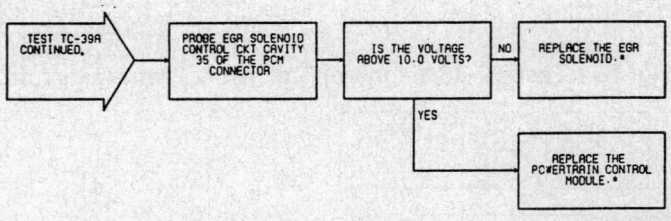

Fig. 69   Test TC-39A: EGR Solenoid Circuit (Part 3 of 3)

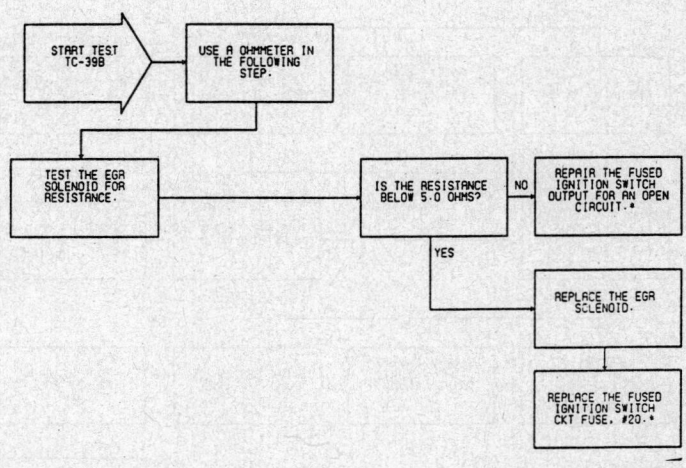

Fig. 70   Test TC-39B: EGR Solenoid Circuit

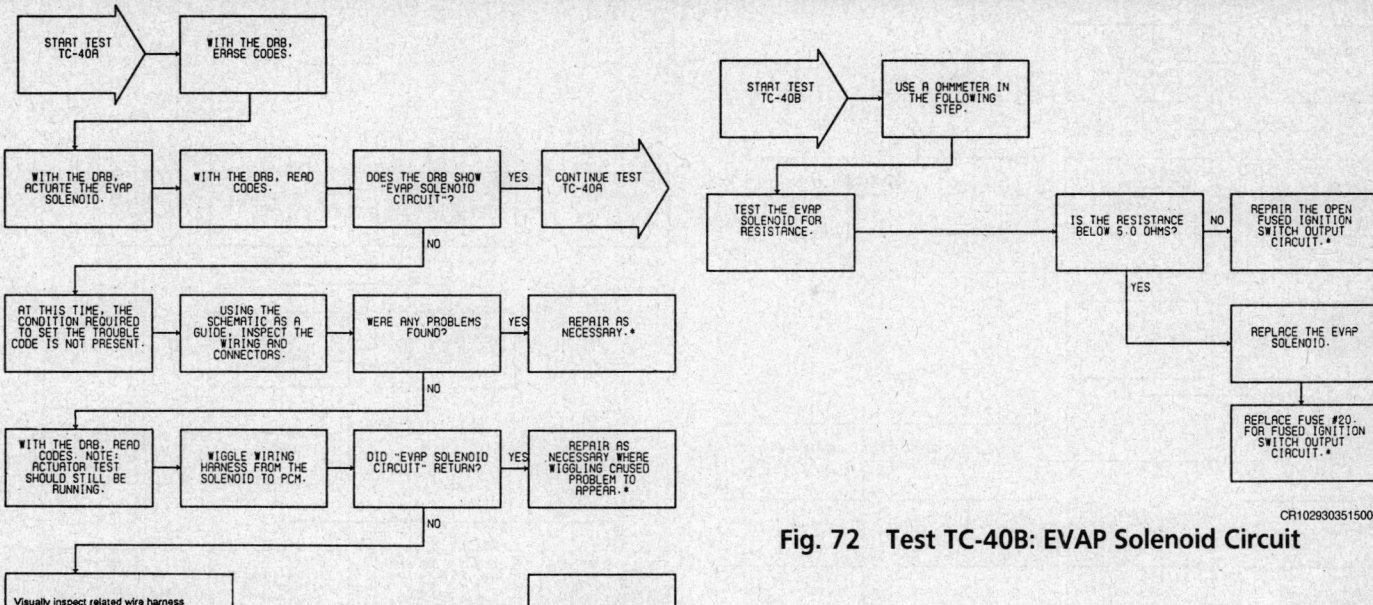

Fig. 71   Test TC-40A: EVAP Solenoid Circuit (Part 1 of 3)

Fig. 72   Test TC-40B: EVAP Solenoid Circuit

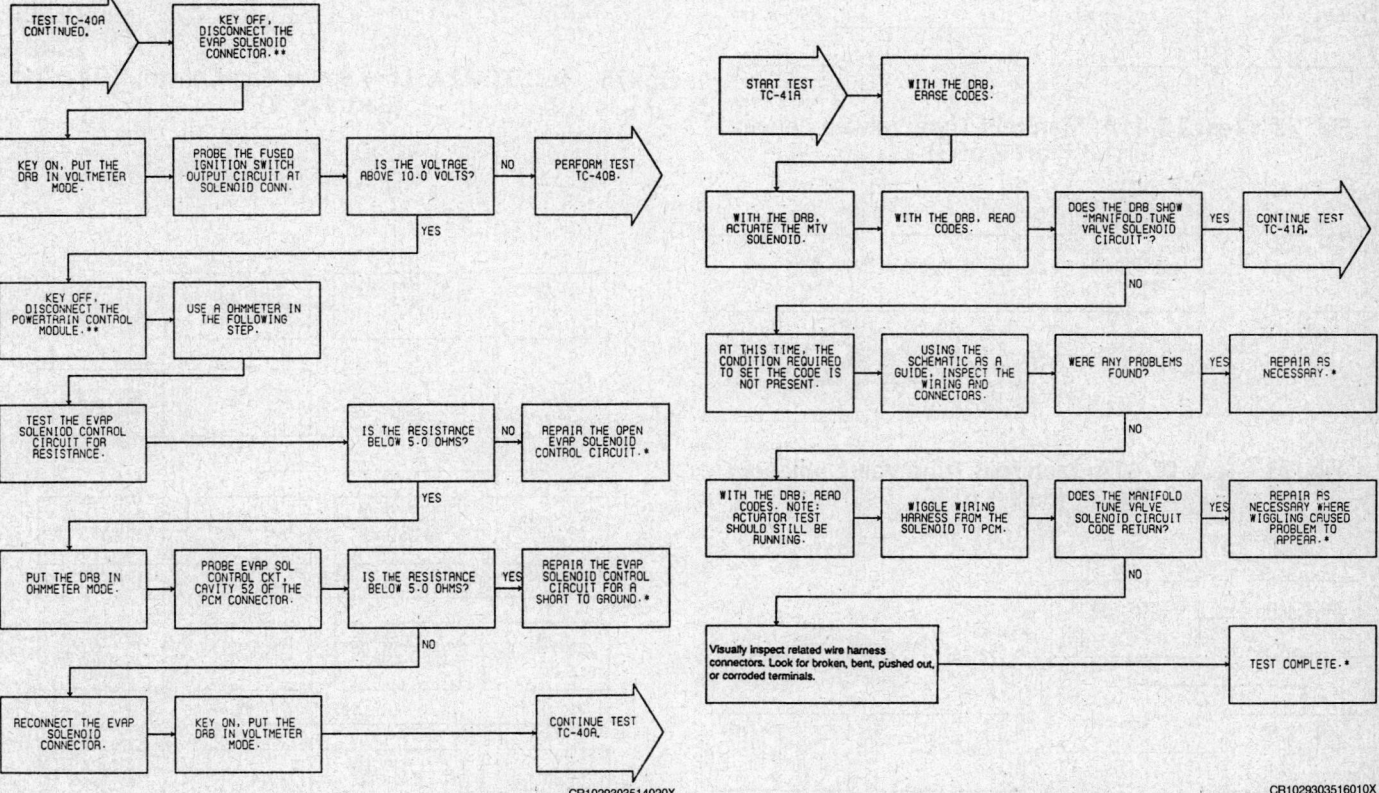

Fig. 71   Test TC-40A: EVAP Solenoid Circuit (Part 2 of 3)

Fig. 73   Test TC-41A: Manifold Tune Valve Solenoid Circuit (Part 1 of 3)

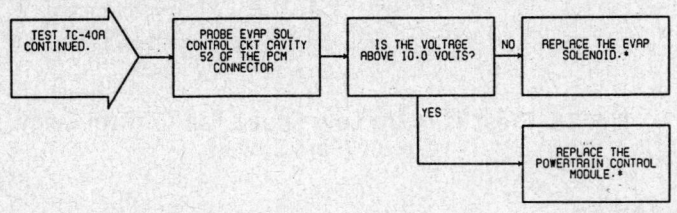

Fig. 71   Test TC-40A: EVAP Solenoid Circuit (Part 3 of 3)

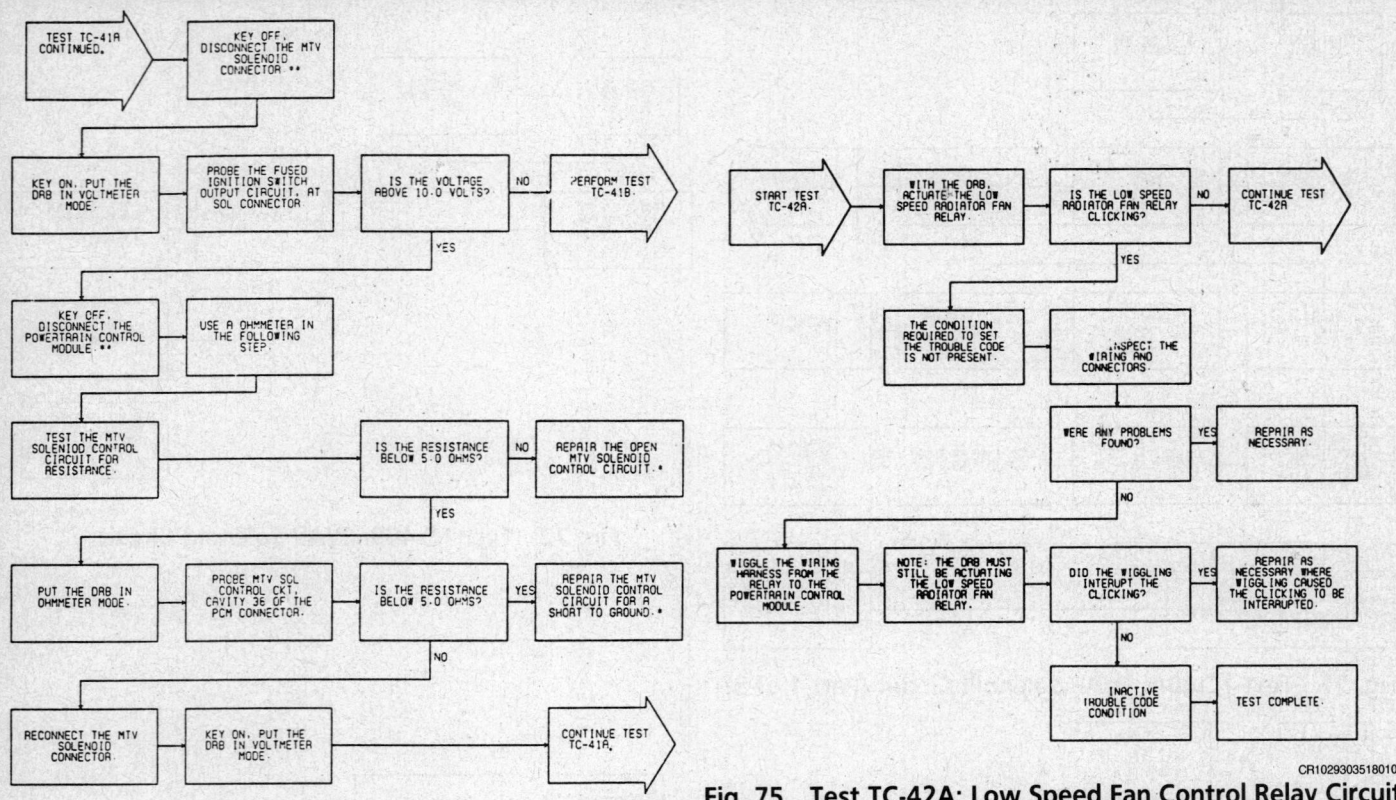

Fig. 73   Test TC-41A: Manifold Tune Valve Solenoid
Circuit (Part 2 of 3)

Fig. 75   Test TC-42A: Low Speed Fan Control Relay Circuit
(Part 1 of 2)

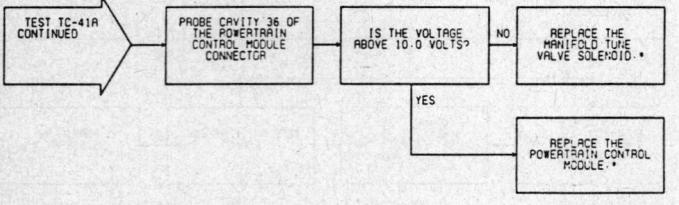

Fig. 73   Test TC-41A: Manifold Tune Valve Solenoid
Circuit (Part 3 of 3)

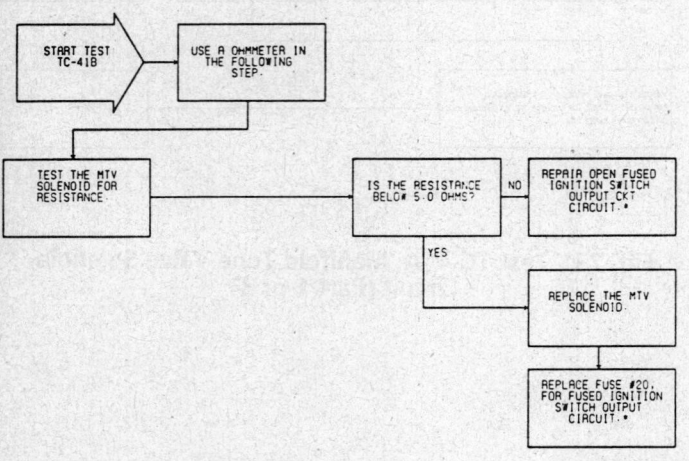

Fig. 74   Test TC-41B: Manifold Tune Valve Solenoid
Circuit

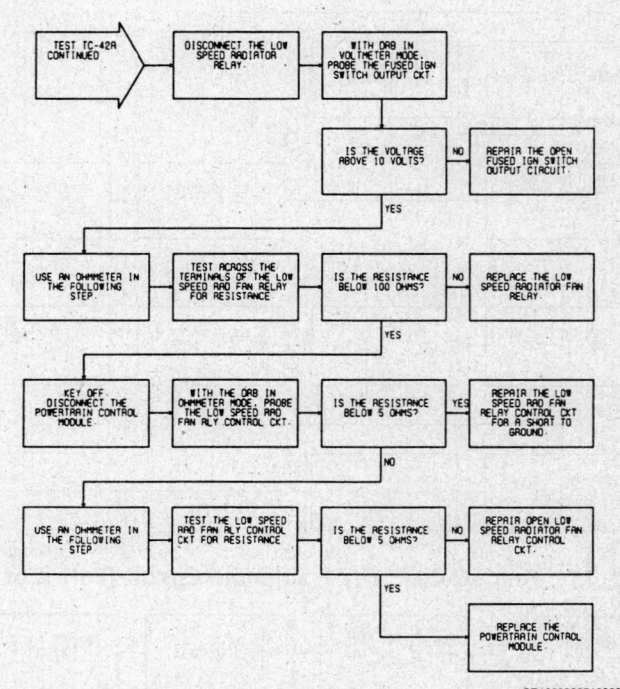

Fig. 75   Test TC-42A: Low Speed Fan Control Relay
Circuit (Part 2 of 2)

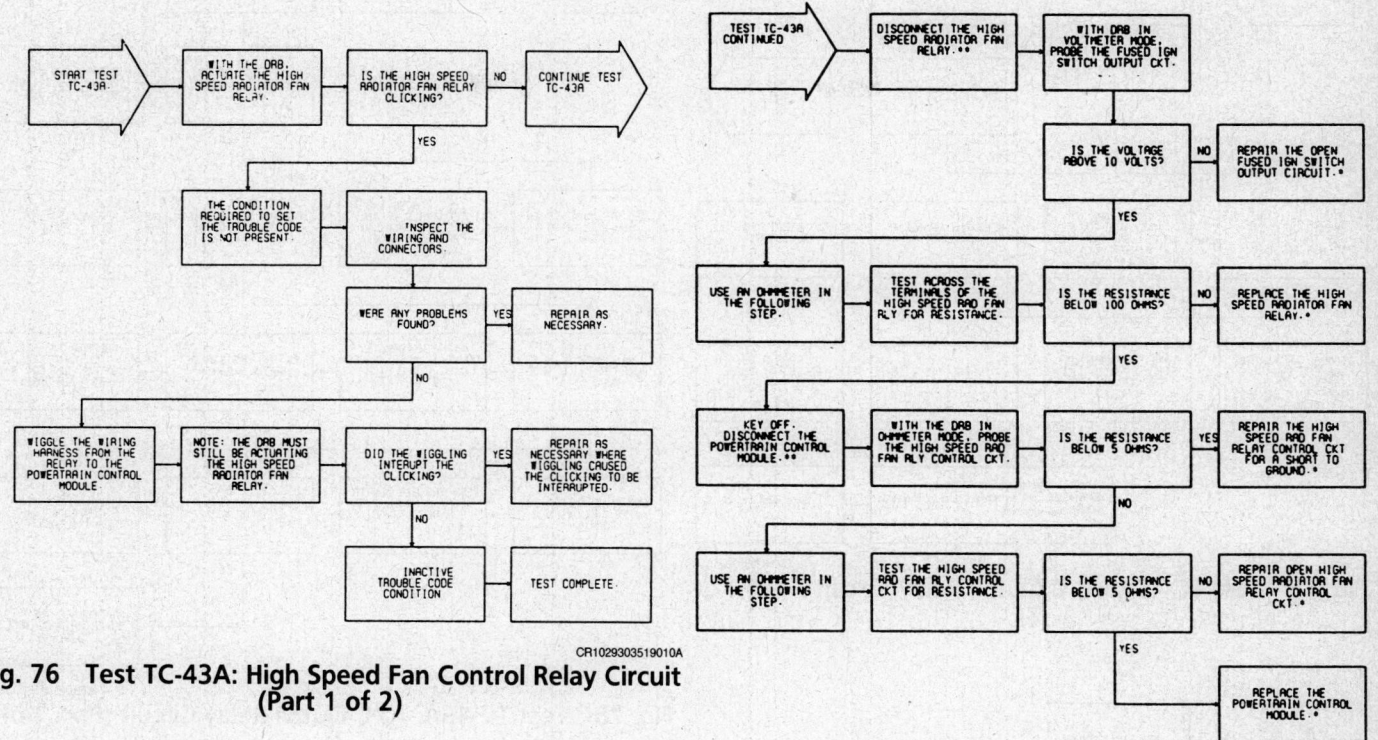

Fig. 76 Test TC-43A: High Speed Fan Control Relay Circuit (Part 1 of 2)

CR1029303519010A

CR1029303519020X

Fig. 76 Test TC-43A: High Speed Fan Control Relay Circuit (Part 2 of 2)

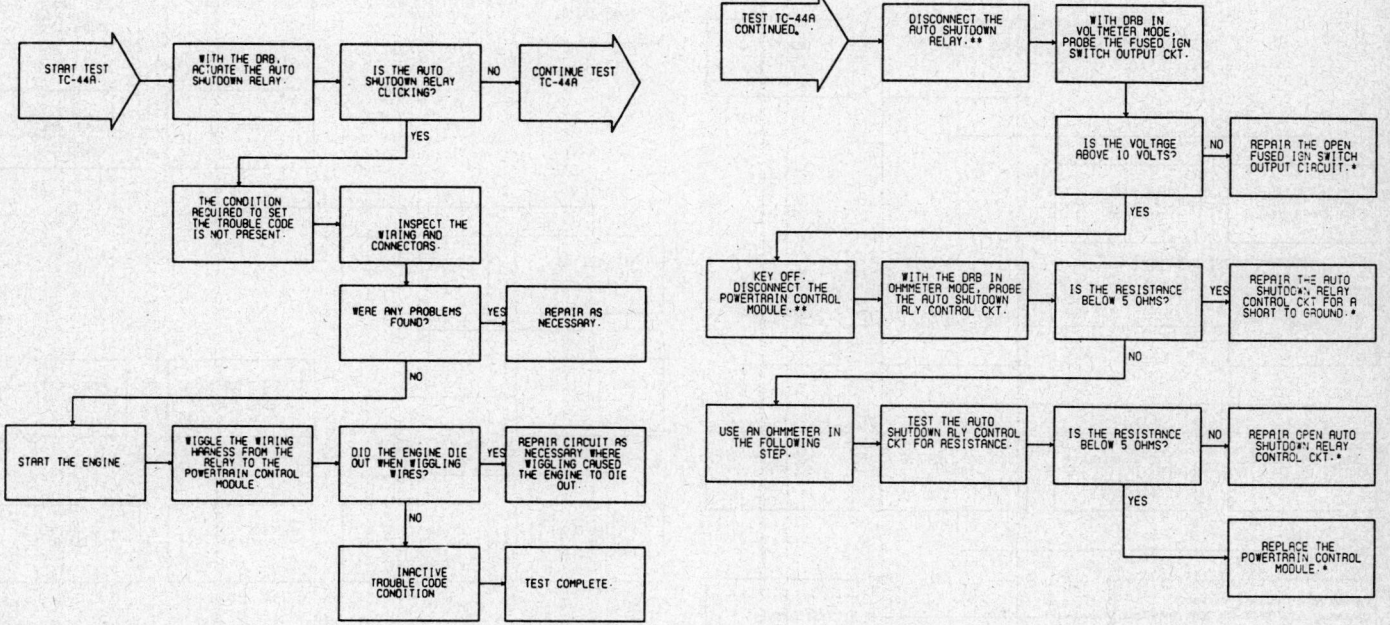

CR1029303520010A

Fig. 77 Test TC-44A: Auto Shutdown Relay Control Circuit (Part 1 of 2)

CR1029303520020X

Fig. 77 Test TC-44A: Auto Shutdown Relay Control Circuit (Part 2 of 2)

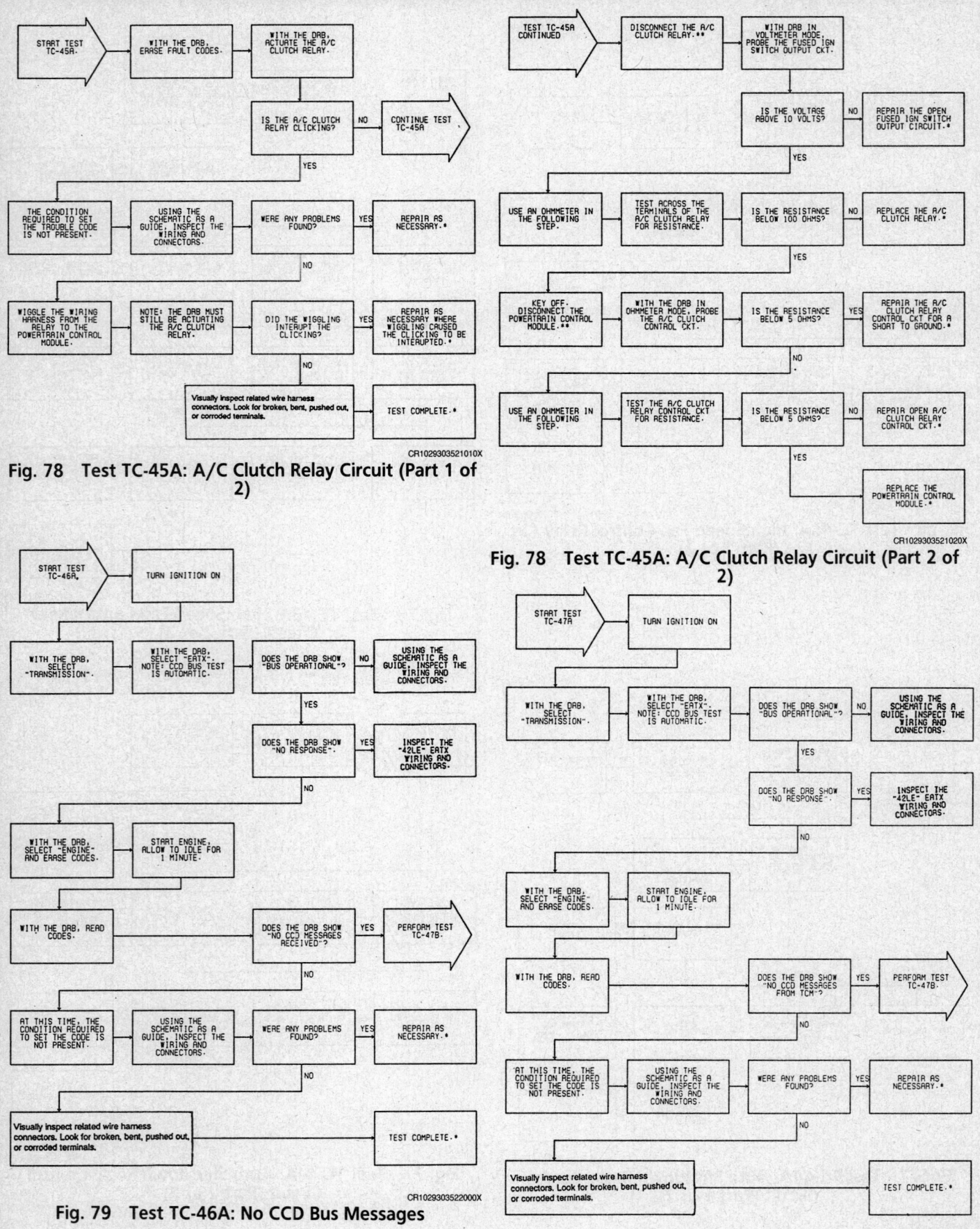

Fig. 78   Test TC-45A: A/C Clutch Relay Circuit (Part 1 of 2)

CR1029303521010X

Fig. 78   Test TC-45A: A/C Clutch Relay Circuit (Part 2 of 2)

CR1029303521020X

Fig. 79   Test TC-46A: No CCD Bus Messages

CR1029303522000X

Fig. 80   Test TC-47A: No CCD Bus Messages

CR1029303523000X

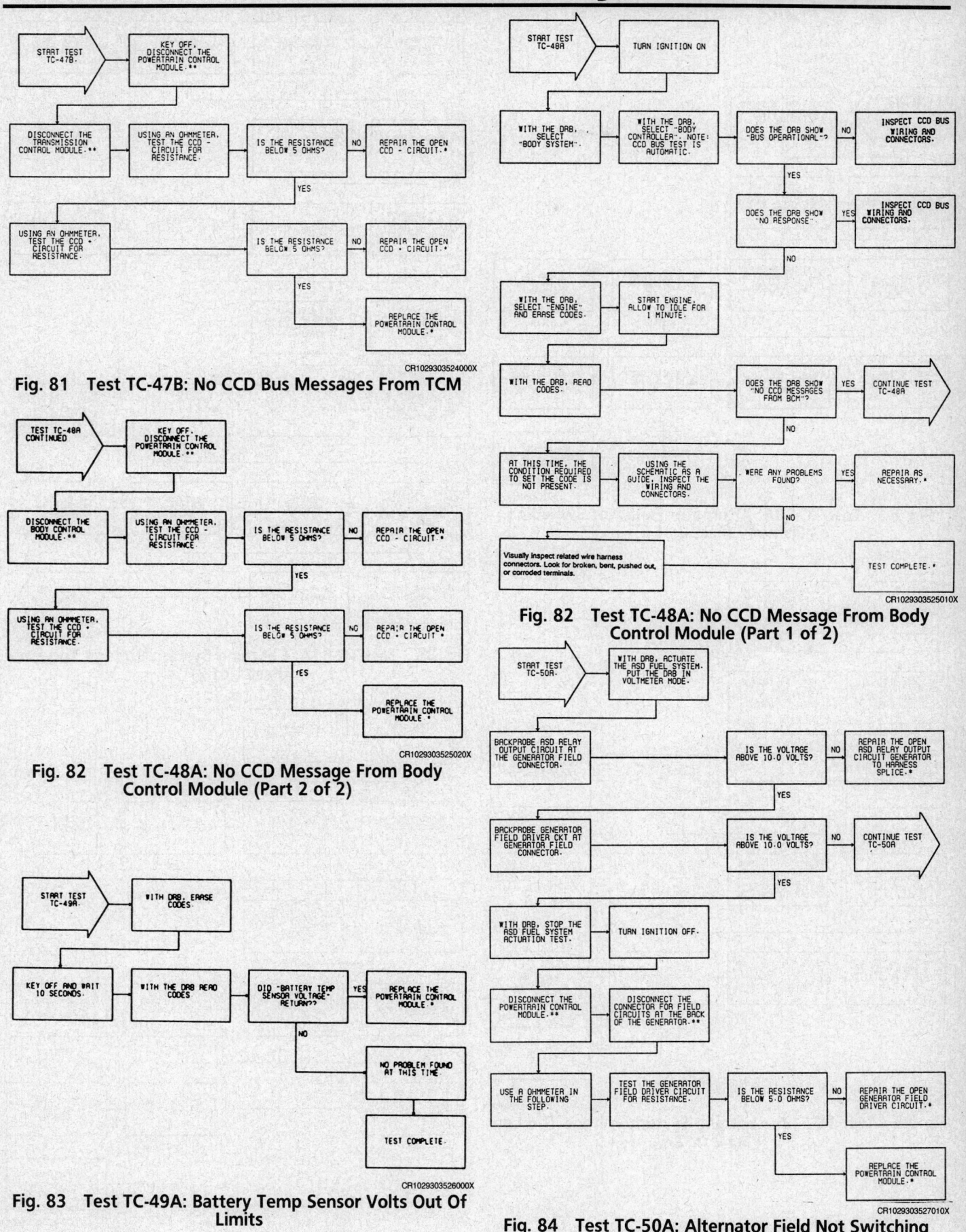

Fig. 81   Test TC-47B: No CCD Bus Messages From TCM

Fig. 82   Test TC-48A: No CCD Message From Body
Control Module (Part 2 of 2)

Fig. 83   Test TC-49A: Battery Temp Sensor Volts Out Of
Limits

Fig. 82   Test TC-48A: No CCD Message From Body
Control Module (Part 1 of 2)

Fig. 84   Test TC-50A: Alternator Field Not Switching
Properly (Part 1 of 2)

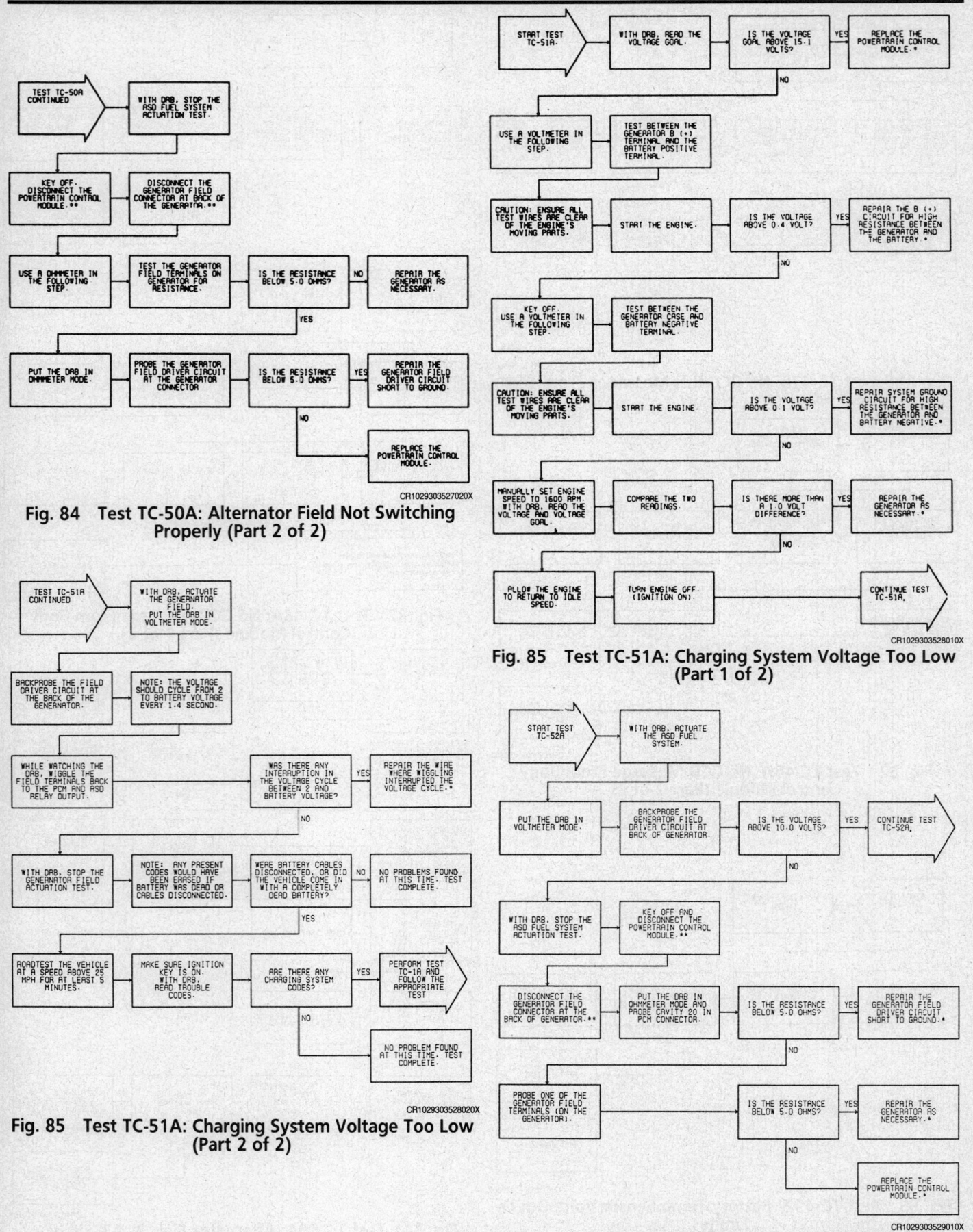

Fig. 84   Test TC-50A: Alternator Field Not Switching Properly (Part 2 of 2)

CR1029303527020X

Fig. 85   Test TC-51A: Charging System Voltage Too Low (Part 2 of 2)

CR1029303528020X

Fig. 85   Test TC-51A: Charging System Voltage Too Low (Part 1 of 2)

CR1029303528010X

Fig. 86   Test TC-52A: Charging System Voltage Too High (Part 1 of 2)

CR1029303529010X

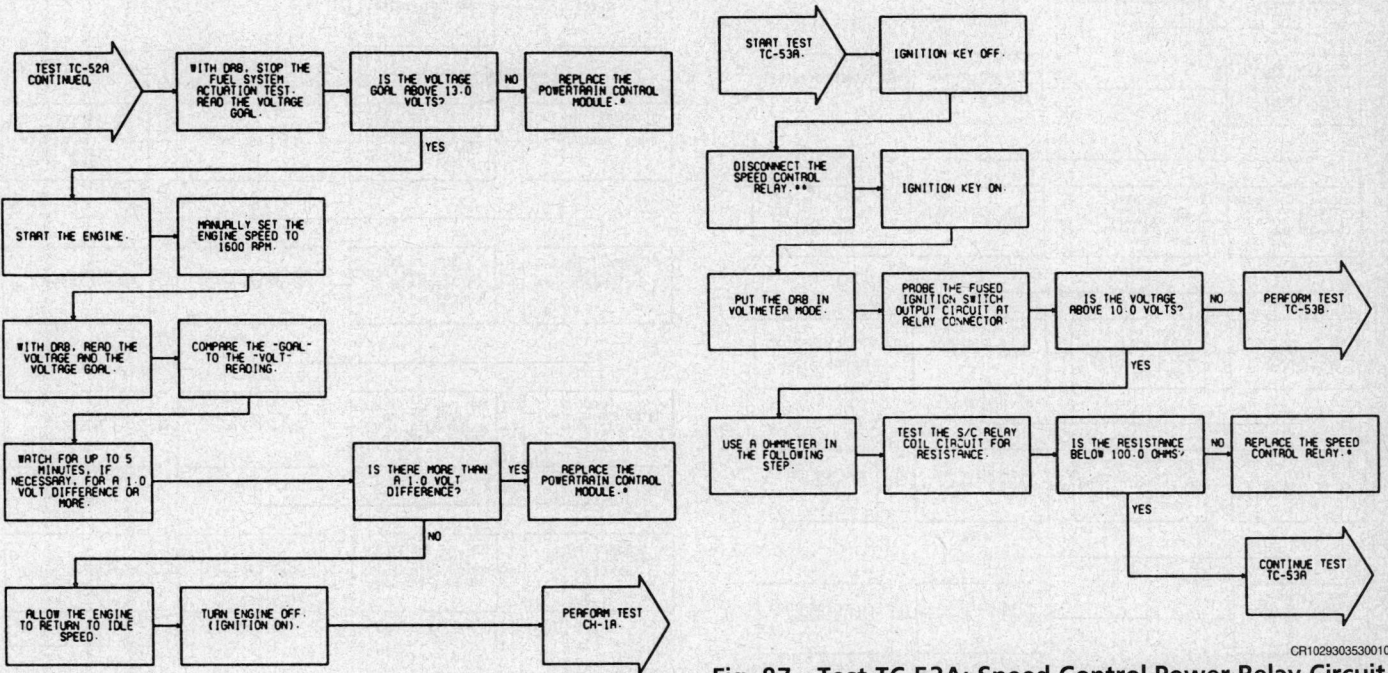

Fig. 86 Test TC-52A: Charging System Voltage Too High (Part 2 of 2)

CR1029303529020X

Fig. 87 Test TC-53A: Speed Control Power Relay Circuit (Part 1 of 2)

CR1029303530010X

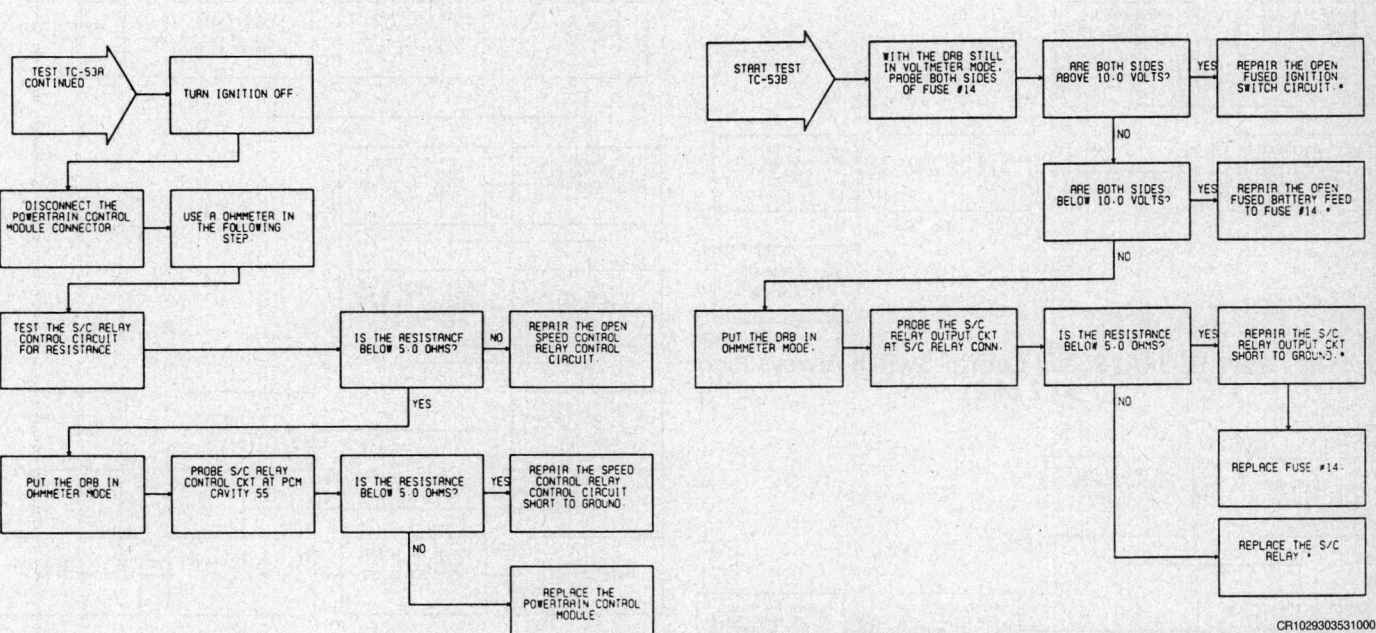

Fig. 87 Test TC-53A: Speed Control Power Relay Circuit (Part 2 of 2)

CR1029303530020A

Fig. 88 Test TC-53B: Speed Control Power Relay Circuit

CR1029303531000X

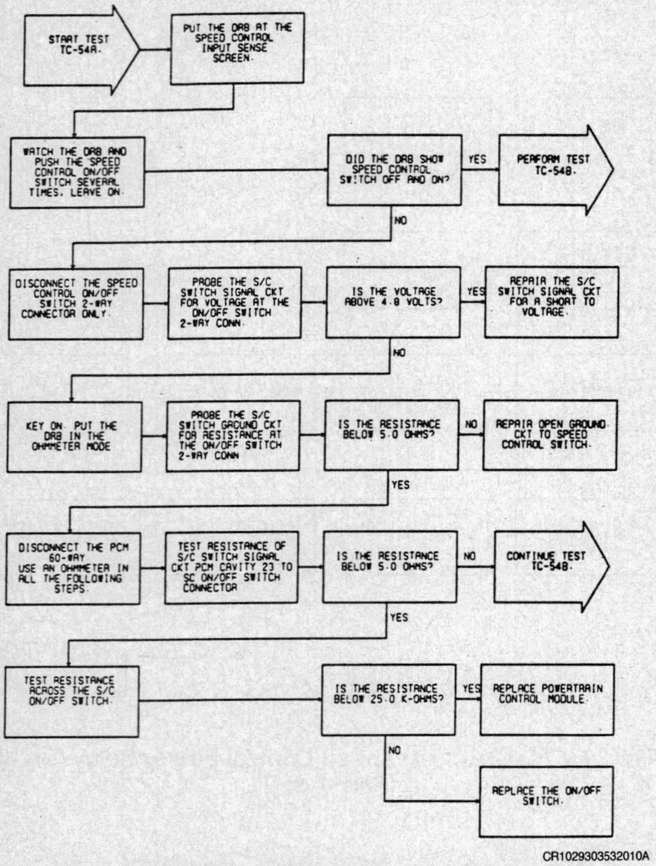

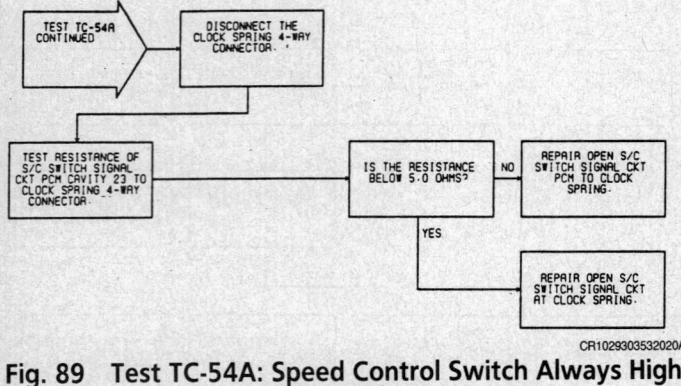

Fig. 89   Test TC-54A: Speed Control Switch Always High (Part 1 of 2)

Fig. 89   Test TC-54A: Speed Control Switch Always High (Part 2 of 2)

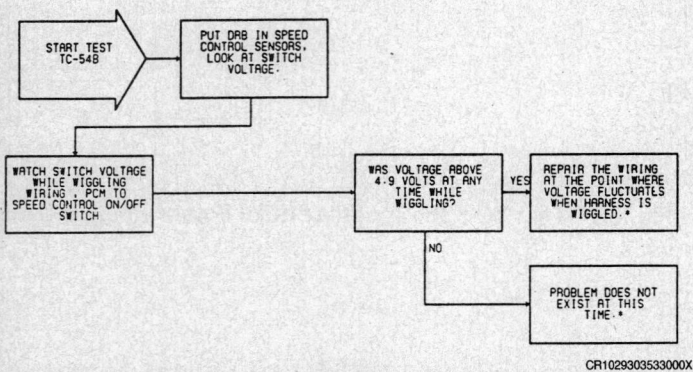

Fig. 90   Test TC-54B: Speed Control Switch Always High

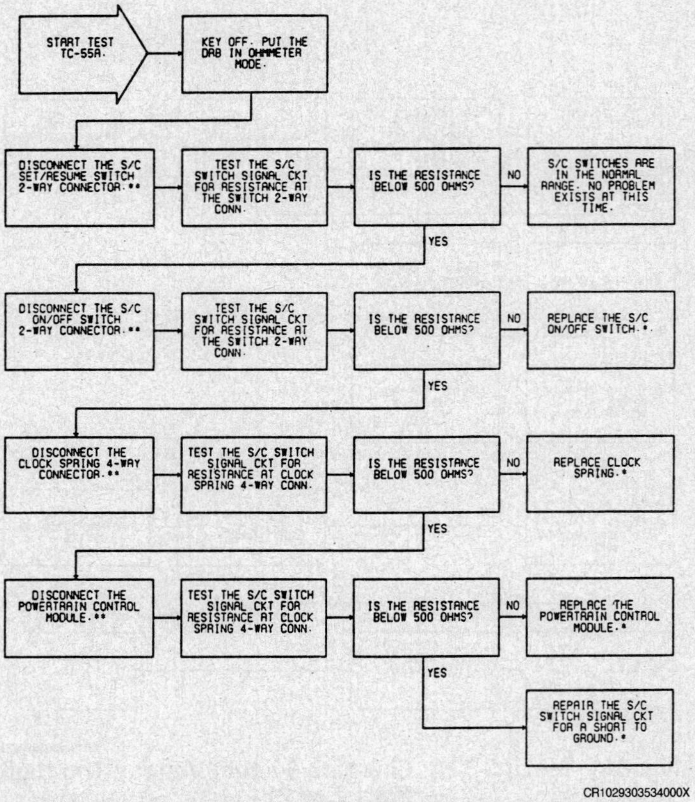

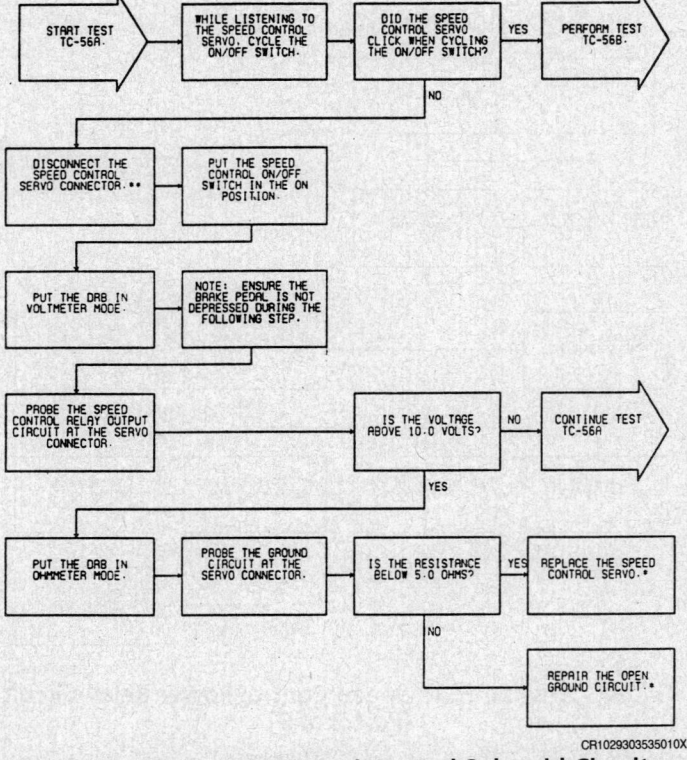

Fig. 91   Test TC-55A: Speed Control Switch Always Low

Fig. 92   Test TC-56A: Speed Control Solenoid Circuits (Part 1 of 2)

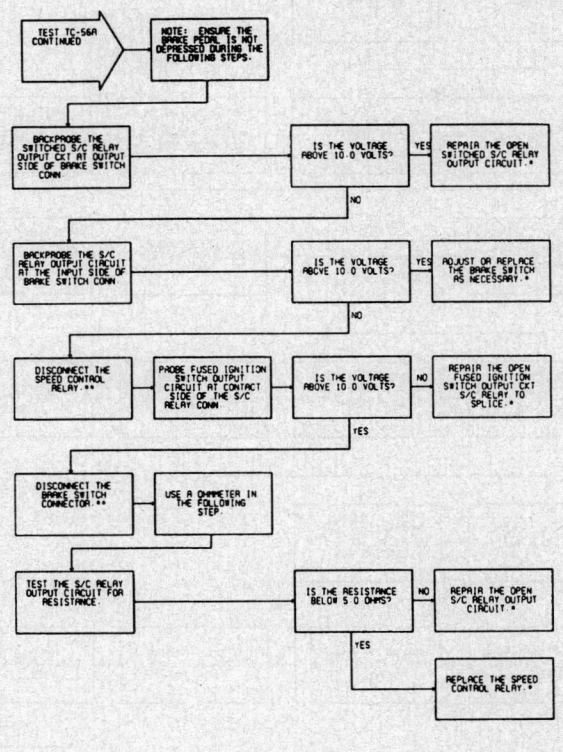

Fig. 92 Test TC-56A: Speed Control Solenoid Circuits (Part 2 of 2)

CR1029303535020X

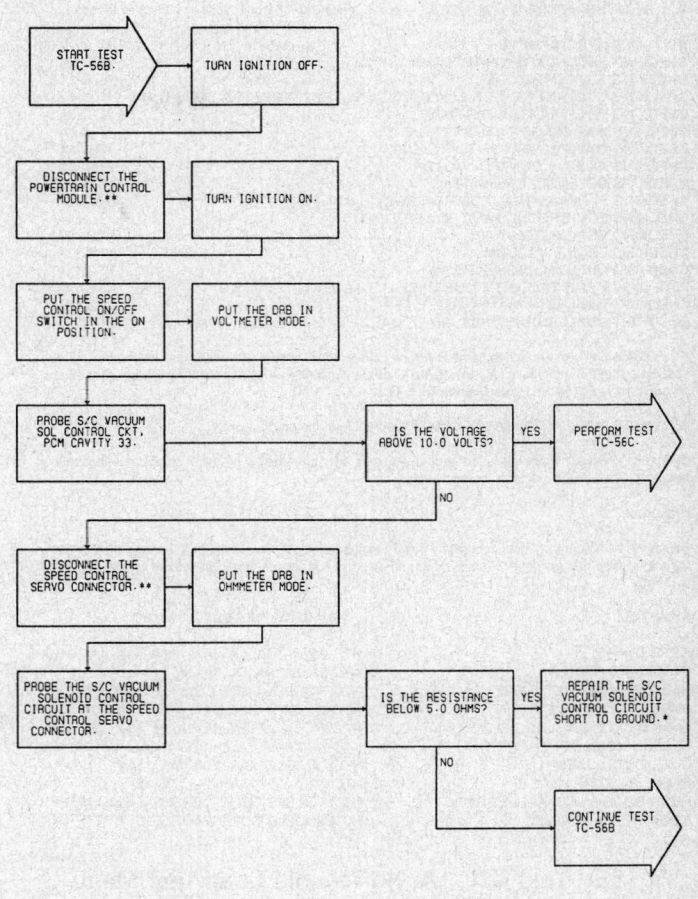

Fig. 93 Test TC-56B: Speed Control Solenoid Circuits (Part 1 of 2)

CR1029303536010X

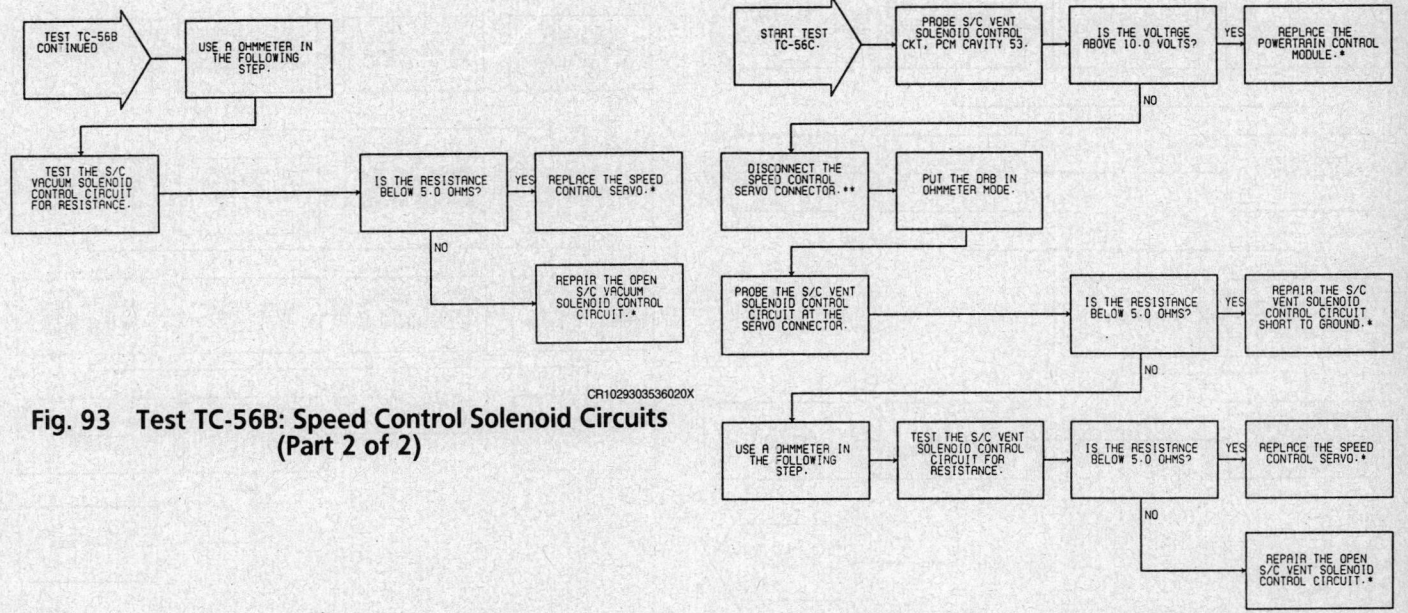

Fig. 93 Test TC-56B: Speed Control Solenoid Circuits (Part 2 of 2)

CR1029303536020X

Fig. 94 Test TC-56C: Speed Control Solenoid Circuits (Part 1 of 2)

Perform corrective actions if indicated; otherwise continue.

1. NO TROUBLE CODE COMPLETE TEST (non-monitored & monitored circuits)

Perform **TESTS NTC-2A** through **NTC-15A** in sequence until the driveability problem is found.

NO TROUBLE CODE MENU

CHECKING SECONDARY IGNITION AND TIMING	NTC-2A
CHECKING FUEL PRESSURE	NTC-3A
CHECKING COOLANT SENSOR CALIBRATION AND RADIATOR FAN OPERATION	NTC-4A
CHECKING TP SENSOR CALIBRATION	NTC-5A
CHECKING MAP SENSOR CALIBRATION	NTC-6A
CHECKING OXYGEN SENSOR SWITCHING	NTC-7A
CHECKING IDLE AIR CONTROL MOTOR	NTC-8A
CHECKING SOLENOID OPERATIONS	NTC-9A
CHECKING PARK/NEUTRAL POSITION SWITCH (MVLPS)	NTC-10A
CHECKING PCM GROUNDS AND POWER CIRCUIT	NTC-11A
CHECKING EGR SYSTEM	NTC-12A
CHECKING ENGINE VACUUM	NTC-13A
CHECKING MINIMUM IDLE AIR FLOW	NTC-14A
PERFORMING NO TROUBLE CODE MECHANICAL TEST	NTC-15A
CHECKING THE OXYGEN SENSOR HEATER	NTC-16A

2. NO TROUBLE CODE QUICK INDIVIDUAL TEST (individual test only)

If you suspect any of the above items to be the cause of the vehicle's driveability problem, perform the associated test(s) individually. **Return to No Trouble Code Menu if driveability problem still exists, or perform No Trouble Code Complete Test.**

3. NO TROUBLE CODE QUICK SYMPTOM TEST (symptom test only)

Symptom checks cannot be used properly unless the driveability problem characteristic actually happens while the vehicle is being tested.

symptom.

Select the symptom that most accurately describes the vehicle's driveability problem and then perform the test routine that pertains to this symptom. Perform each routine test in sequence until the problem is found.

SYMPTOM	DIAGNOSTIC TEST ROUTINE
HARD START	NTC-2A, 3A, 4A, 5A, 6A, 7A, 8A, 11A, 14A, 15A
START AND STALL	NTC-2A, 3A, 4A, 5A, 6A, 8A, 11A, 15A
HESITATION/SAG/STUMBLE	NO TROUBLE CODE COMPLETE TEST (STEP 1
SURGE	NTC-2A, 3A, 4A, 5A, 6A, 7A, 8A, 11A, 12A, 15A
LACK OF POWER/SLUGGISH	NTC-2A, 3A, 4A, 5A, 6A, 7A, 8A, 11A, 13A, 15A
SPARK KNOCK/DETONATION	NTC-2A, 3A, 4A, 5A, 6A, 7A, 8A, 9A, 11A, 12A, 15A
CUTS OUT/MISSES	NTC-2A, 3A, 7A, 9A, 11A, 13A, 15A
BACKFIRE/POPBACK	NTC-2A, 3A, 6A, 7A, 11A, 13A, 15A
RUNS ROUGH/UNSTABLE/ERRATIC IDLE	NO TROUBLE CODE COMPLETE TEST (STEP 1
POOR FUEL ECONOMY	NO TROUBLE CODE COMPLETE TEST (STEP 1

CR1029303538000A

Fig. 95 Test NTC-1A: No Trouble Code Test Menu

CR1029303539000X

Fig. 96 Test NTC-2A: Checking Secondary Ignition Timing

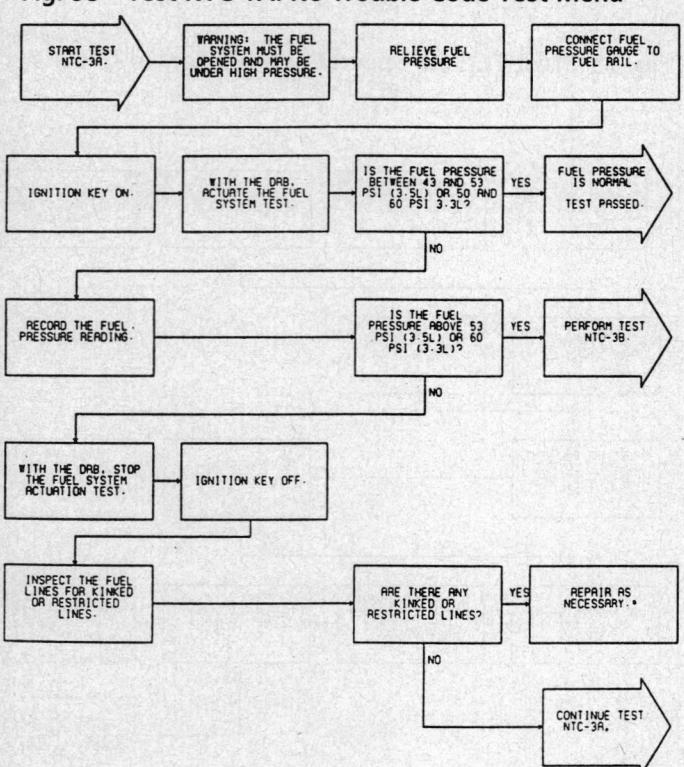

CR1029303540010X

Fig. 97   Test NTC-3A: Checking Fuel Pressure (Part 1 of 2)

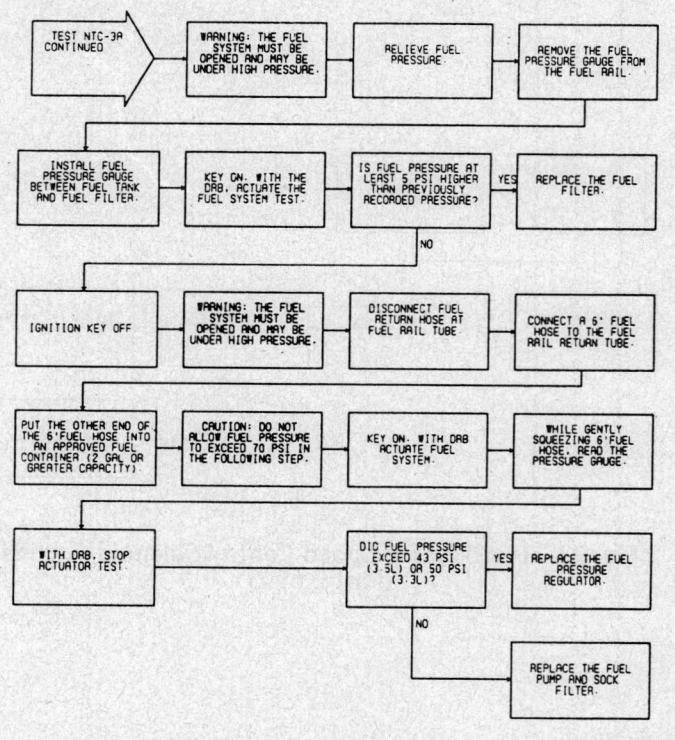

CR1029303540020A

Fig. 97   Test NTC-3A: Checking Fuel Pressure (Part 2 of 2)

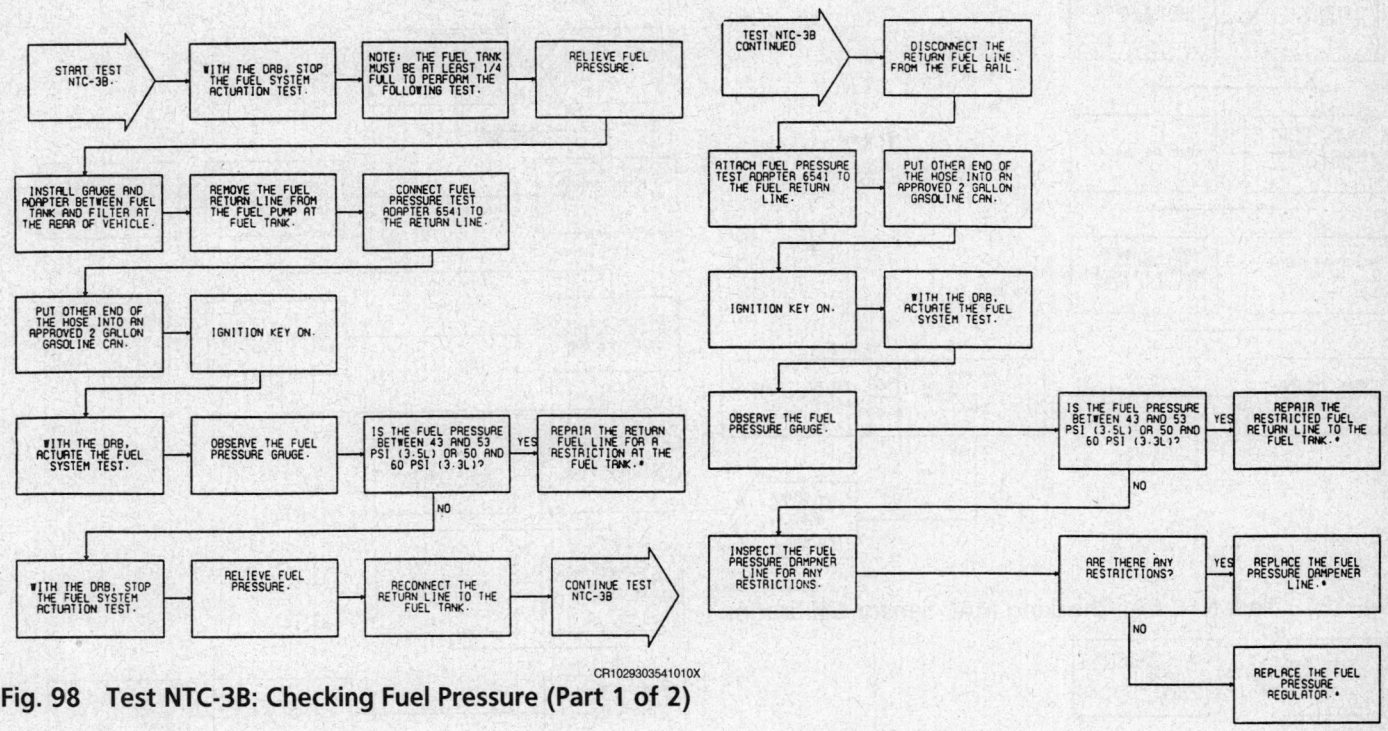

Fig. 98 Test NTC-3B: Checking Fuel Pressure (Part 1 of 2)

Fig. 98 Test NTC-3B: Checking Fuel Pressure (Part 2 of 2)

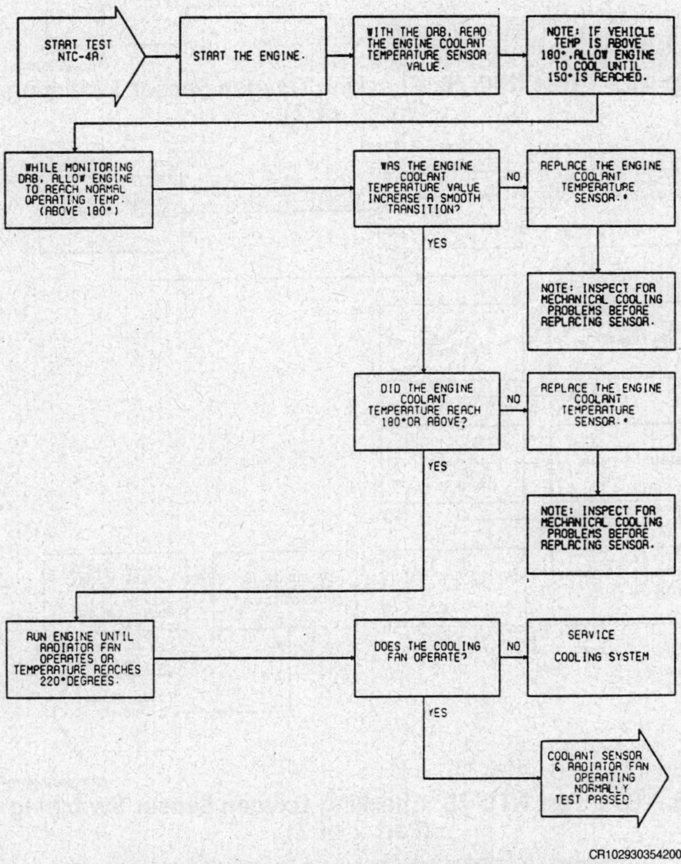

Fig. 99 Test NTC-4A: Checking Coolant Sensor
Calibration & Radiator Fan Operation

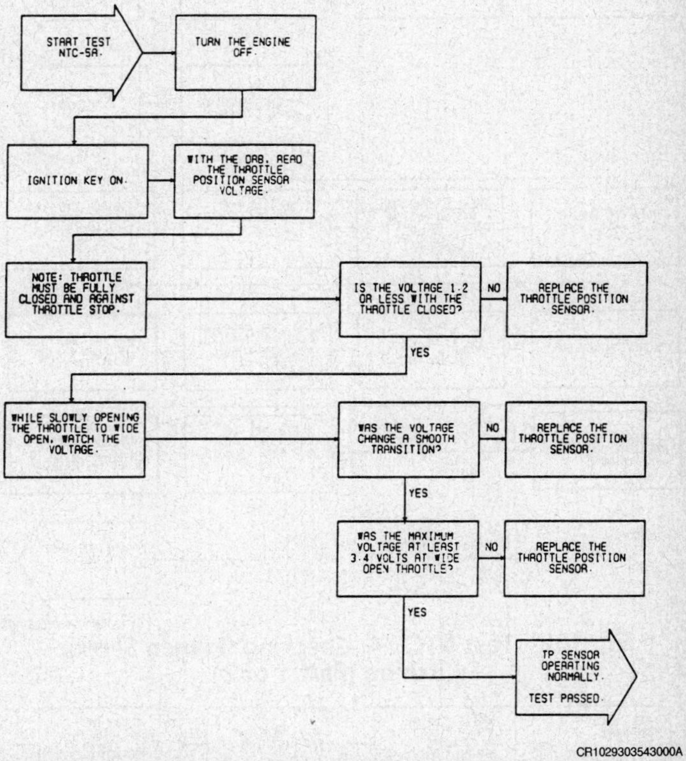

Fig. 100 Test NTC-5A: Checking Throttle Position Sensor
Calibration

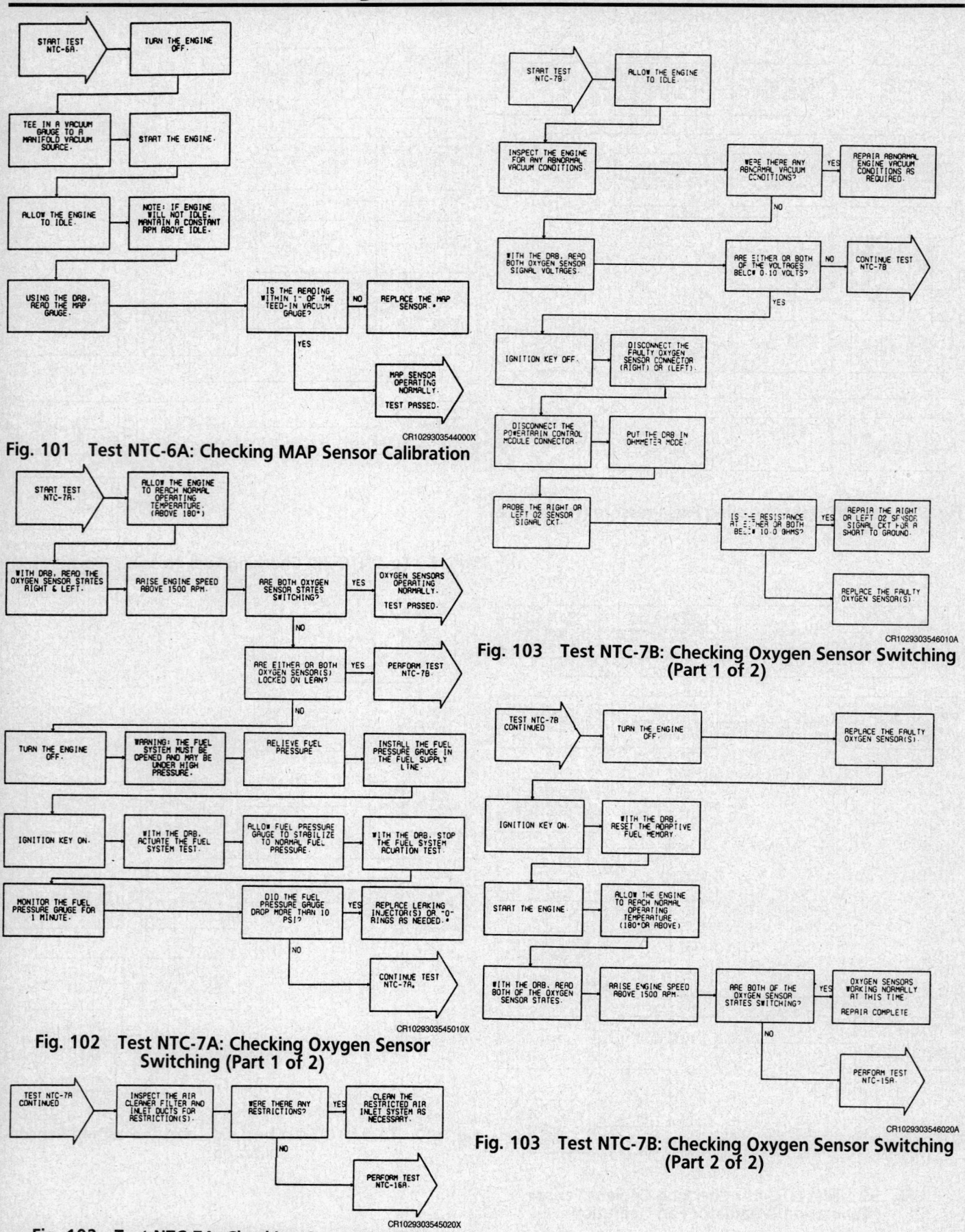

Fig. 101   Test NTC-6A: Checking MAP Sensor Calibration

Fig. 102   Test NTC-7A: Checking Oxygen Sensor Switching (Part 1 of 2)

Fig. 102   Test NTC-7A: Checking Oxygen Sensor Switching (Part 2 of 2)

Fig. 103   Test NTC-7B: Checking Oxygen Sensor Switching (Part 1 of 2)

Fig. 103   Test NTC-7B: Checking Oxygen Sensor Switching (Part 2 of 2)

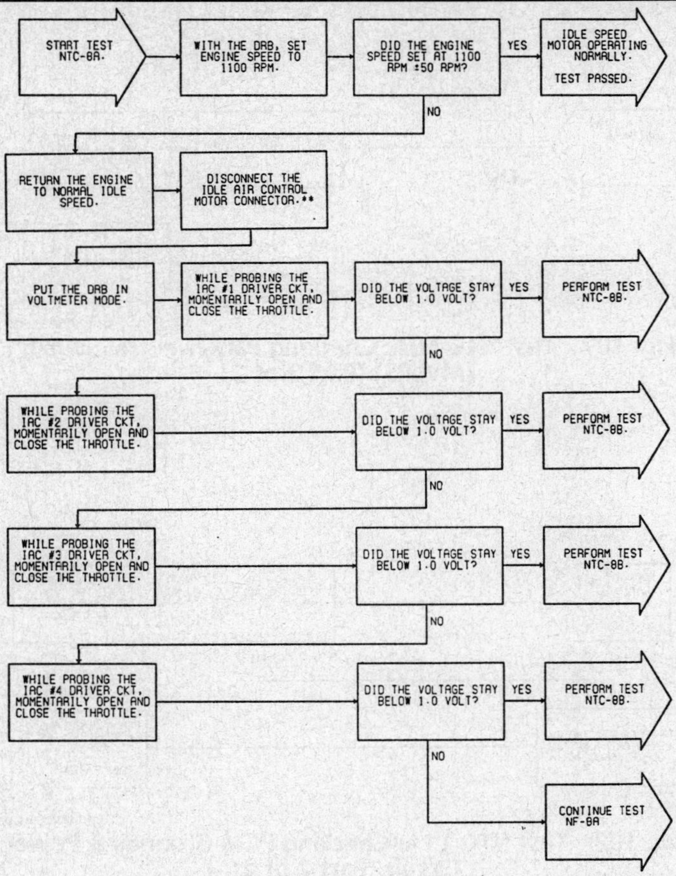

Fig. 104 Test NTC-8A: Checking Idle Air Control Motor (Part 1 of 2)

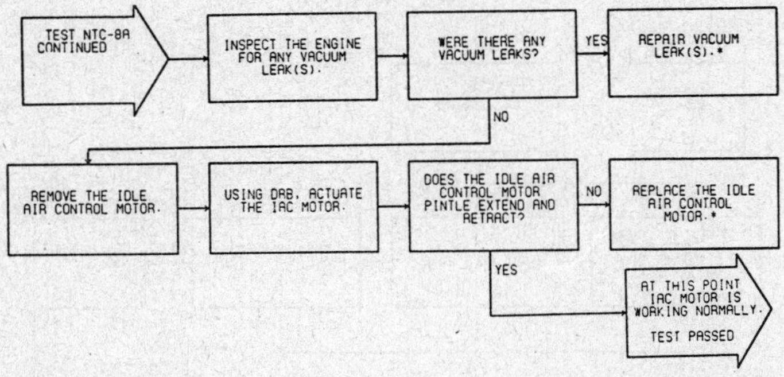

START TEST NTC-8A. → WITH THE DRB, SET ENGINE SPEED TO 1100 RPM. → DID THE ENGINE SPEED SET AT 1100 RPM ±50 RPM? → YES → IDLE SPEED MOTOR OPERATING NORMALLY. TEST PASSED.

NO ↓

RETURN THE ENGINE TO NORMAL IDLE SPEED. → DISCONNECT THE IDLE AIR CONTROL MOTOR CONNECTOR.**

PUT THE DRB IN VOLTMETER MODE. → WHILE PROBING THE IAC #1 DRIVER CKT, MOMENTARILY OPEN AND CLOSE THE THROTTLE. → DID THE VOLTAGE STAY BELOW 1.0 VOLT? → YES → PERFORM TEST NTC-8B.

NO ↓

WHILE PROBING THE IAC #2 DRIVER CKT, MOMENTARILY OPEN AND CLOSE THE THROTTLE. → DID THE VOLTAGE STAY BELOW 1.0 VOLT? → YES → PERFORM TEST NTC-8B.

NO ↓

WHILE PROBING THE IAC #3 DRIVER CKT, MOMENTARILY OPEN AND CLOSE THE THROTTLE. → DID THE VOLTAGE STAY BELOW 1.0 VOLT? → YES → PERFORM TEST NTC-8B.

NO ↓

WHILE PROBING THE IAC #4 DRIVER CKT, MOMENTARILY OPEN AND CLOSE THE THROTTLE. → DID THE VOLTAGE STAY BELOW 1.0 VOLT? → YES → PERFORM TEST NTC-8B.

NO ↓

CONTINUE TEST NF-8A

CR1029303547010X

Fig. 104 Test NTC-8A: Checking Idle Air Control Motor (Part 2 of 2)

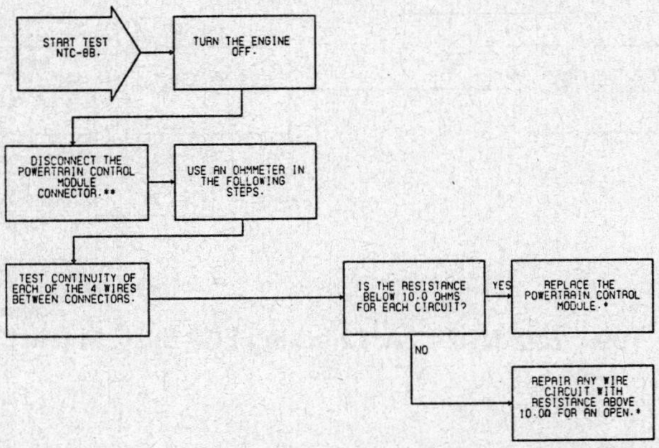

TEST NTC-8A CONTINUED → INSPECT THE ENGINE FOR ANY VACUUM LEAK(S). → WERE THERE ANY VACUUM LEAKS? → YES → REPAIR VACUUM LEAK(S).*

NO ↓

REMOVE THE IDLE AIR CONTROL MOTOR. → USING DRB, ACTUATE THE IAC MOTOR. → DOES THE IDLE AIR CONTROL MOTOR PINTLE EXTEND AND RETRACT? → NO → REPLACE THE IDLE AIR CONTROL MOTOR.*

YES ↓

AT THIS POINT IAC MOTOR IS WORKING NORMALLY. TEST PASSED.

CR1029303547020X

Fig. 105 Test NTC-8B: Checking Idle Air Control Motor

START TEST NTC-8B. → TURN THE ENGINE OFF.

DISCONNECT THE POWERTRAIN CONTROL MODULE CONNECTOR.** → USE AN OHMMETER IN THE FOLLOWING STEPS.

TEST CONTINUITY OF EACH OF THE 4 WIRES BETWEEN CONNECTORS. → IS THE RESISTANCE BELOW 10.0 OHMS FOR EACH CIRCUIT? → YES → REPLACE THE POWERTRAIN CONTROL MODULE.*

NO ↓

REPAIR ANY WIRE CIRCUIT WITH RESISTANCE ABOVE 10.0Ω FOR AN OPEN.*

CR1029303548000X

Fig. 106 Test NTC-9A: Checking Solenoid Operations (Part 1 of 2)

START TEST NTC-9A. → ACTUATE THE PURGE SOLENOID.

WHILE TOUCHING THE TOP OF THE CANISTER PURGE SOLENOID, FEEL FOR OPERATION. → DID THE PURGE SOLENOID OPERATE? → NO → REPLACE THE CANISTER PURGE SOLENOID.*

YES ↓

ACTUATE THE EGR SOLENOID. → WHILE TOUCHING THE TOP OF THE EGR SOLENOID, FEEL FOR OPERATION. → DID THE EGR SOLENOID OPERATE? → NO → REPLACE THE EGR SOLENOID.*

YES ↓

IS VEHICLE EQUIPPED WITH A 3.5L ENGINE? → NO → SOLENOIDS OPERATING NORMALLY. TEST PASSED.

YES ↓

ACTUATE THE MANIFOLD (MTV) SOLENOID. → WHILE TOUCHING THE TOP OF THE MANIFOLD SOLENOID, FEEL FOR OPERATION. → DID THE MANIFOLD SOLENOID OPERATE? → NO → REPLACE THE MANIFOLD (MTV) SOLENOID.*

YES ↓

START ENGINE LET IDLE FOR 1 MINUTE TO BUILD UP VACUUM, TURN ENGINE OFF (KEY ON). → ACTUATE THE MTV VALVE. → DID THE VALVE OPEN AND CLOSE FULLY WHEN ACTUATED? → YES → MTV SOLENOID & VALVE OPERATING NORMALLY. TEST PASSED.

NO ↓

CONTINUE TEST NTC-9A

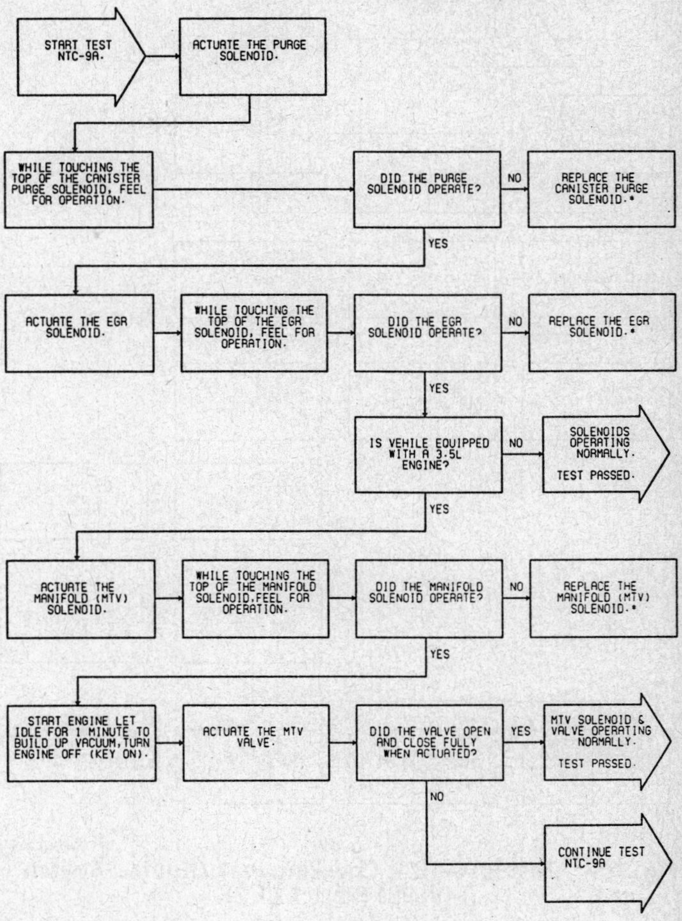

CR1029303549010X

Fig. 106 Test NTC-9A: Checking Solenoid Operations (Part 2 of 2)

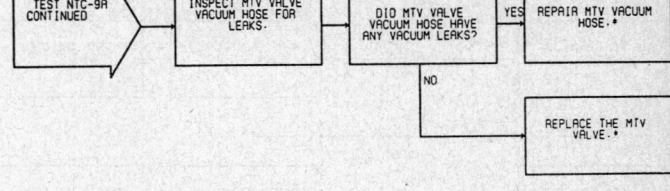

TEST NTC-9A CONTINUED → INSPECT MTV VALVE VACUUM HOSE FOR LEAKS. → DID MTV VALVE VACUUM HOSE HAVE ANY VACUUM LEAKS? → YES → REPAIR MTV VACUUM HOSE.*

NO ↓

REPLACE THE MTV VALVE.*

CR1029303549020X

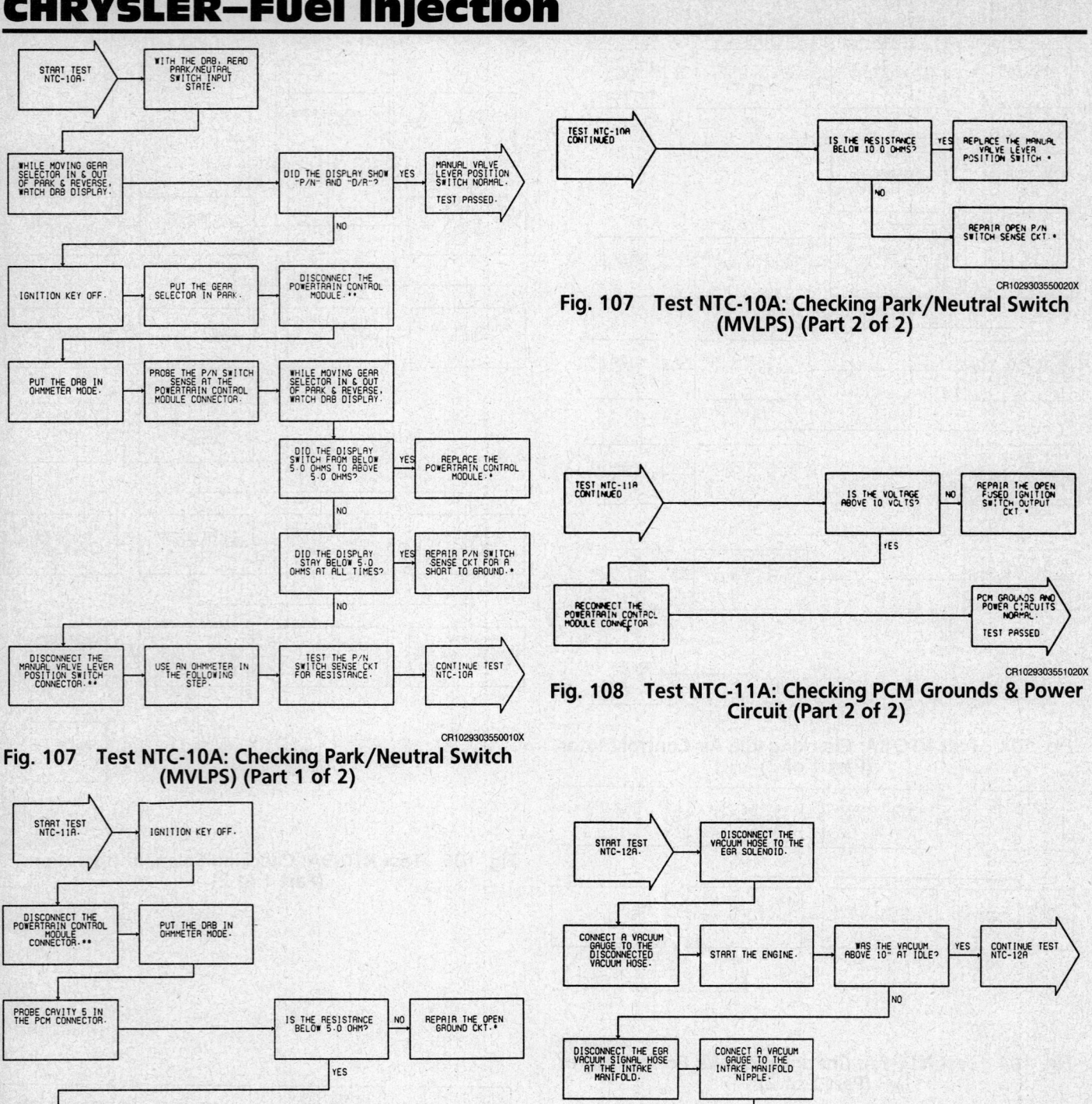

Fig. 107   Test NTC-10A: Checking Park/Neutral Switch (MVLPS) (Part 1 of 2)

Fig. 107   Test NTC-10A: Checking Park/Neutral Switch (MVLPS) (Part 2 of 2)

Fig. 108   Test NTC-11A: Checking PCM Grounds & Power Circuit (Part 2 of 2)

Fig. 108   Test NTC-11A: Checking PCM Grounds & Power Circuit (Part 1 of 2)

Fig. 109   Test NTC-12A: Checking EGR System (Part 1 of 3)

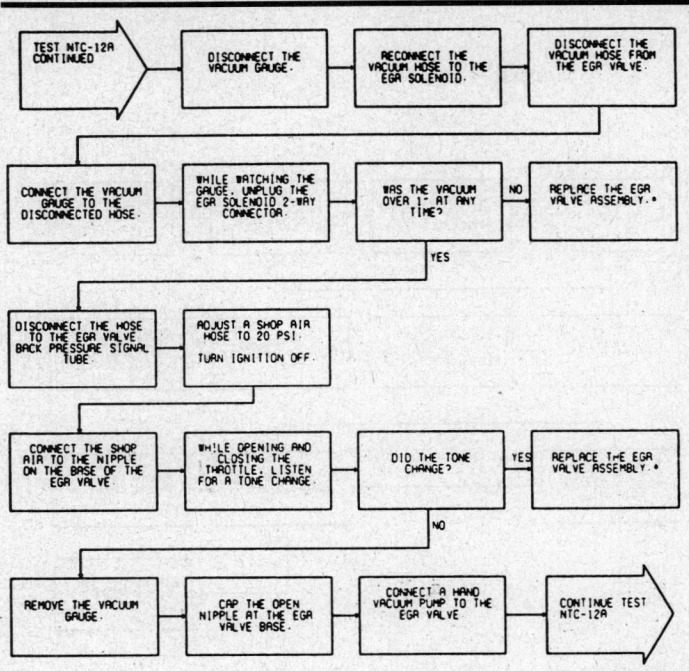

Fig. 109   Test NTC-12A: Checking EGR System (Part 2 of 3)

CR1029303552020X

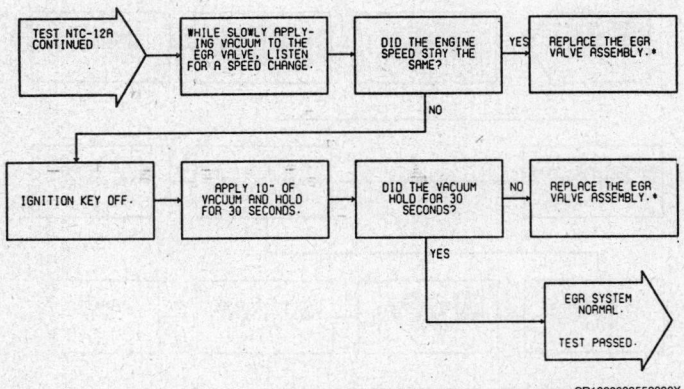

Fig. 109   Test NTC-12A: Checking EGR System (Part 3 of 3)

CR1029303552030X

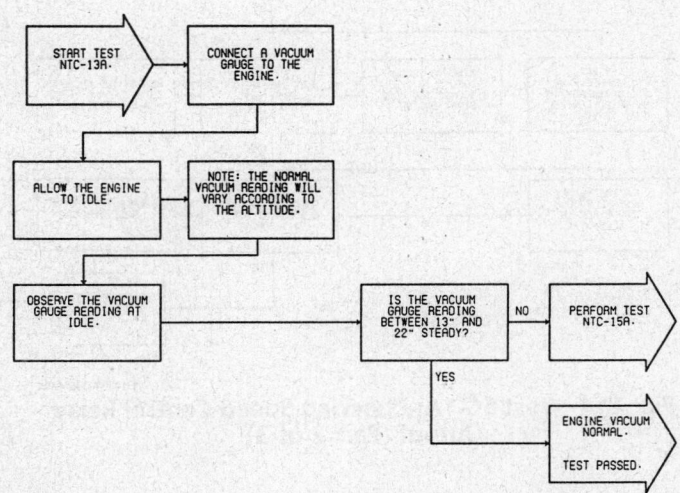

Fig. 110   Test NTC-13A: Checking Engine Vacuum

CR1029303553000X

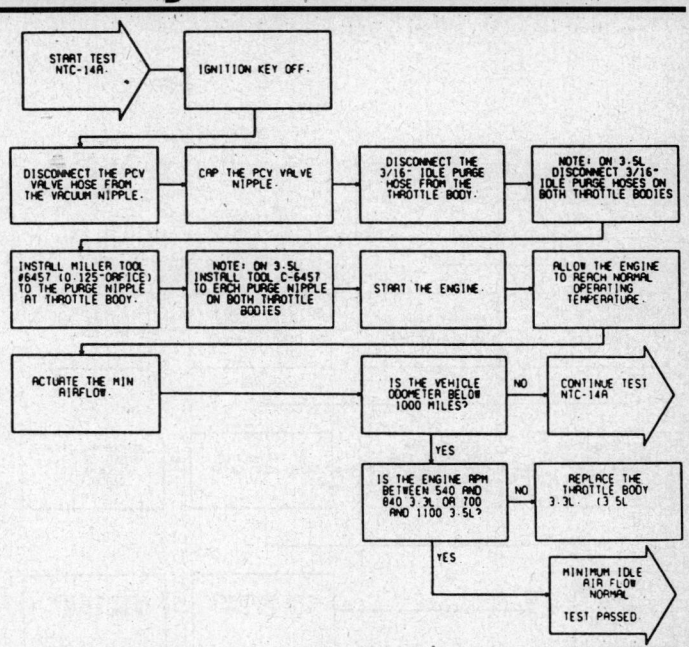

Fig. 111   Test NTC-14A: Checking Minimum Idle Air Flow (Part 1 of 2)

CR1029303554010X

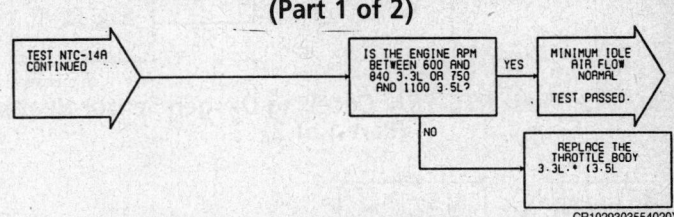

Fig. 111   Test NTC-14A: Checking Minimum Idle Air Flow (Part 2 of 2)

CR1029303554020X

At this point in the diagnostic test procedure, you have determined that all of the powertrain control module systems are operating as designed and are not the cause of the driveability problem. Therefore, the following additional items should be checked as possible mechanical causes of the problem:

1. **ENGINE VACUUM** - must be at least 13 inches in neutral *(see below)**

2. **ENGINE VALVE TIMING** - must be within specifications

3. **ENGINE COMPRESSION** - must be within specifications

4. **ENGINE EXHAUST SYSTEM** - must be free of any restrictions

5. **ENGINE PVC SYSTEM** - must flow freely

6. **ENGINE DRIVE SPROCKET** - must be properly positioned

7. **TORQUE CONVERTER STALL SPEED** - must be within specifications

8. **POWER BRAKE BOOSTER** - no internal vacuum leaks

9. **FUEL** - must be free of contamination

10. **FUEL INJECTOR** - plugged or restricted injector; control wire not connected to correct injector

NOTE: If you came to this test from the oxygen sensor, and the rich or lean condition is not caused by one of the first items above, replace the powertrain control module.*

* The readings below are only indicators of possible mechanical engine problems.

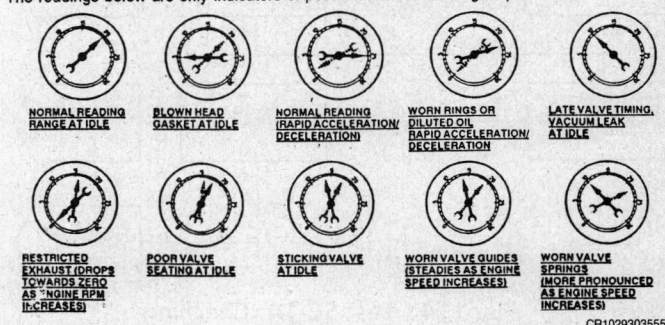

Fig. 112   Test NTC-15A: Performing No Diagnostic Trouble Code Mechanical Test

CR1029303555000X

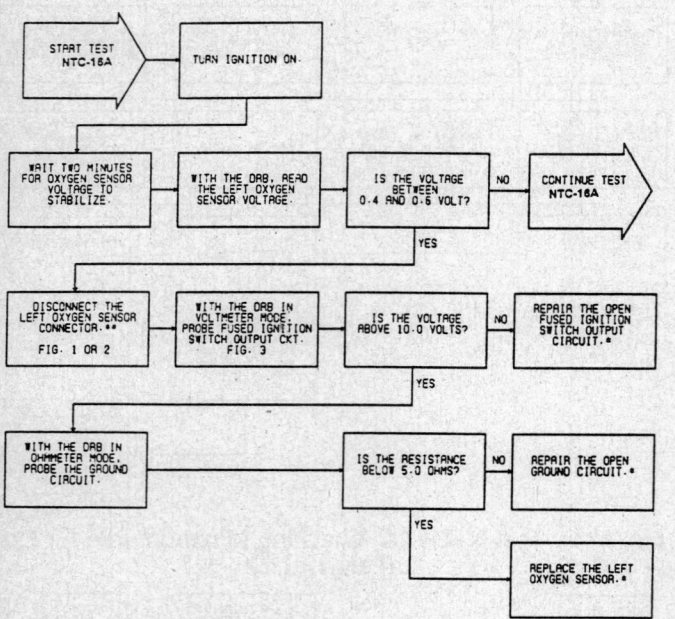

Fig. 113   Test NTC-16A: Checking Oxygen Sensor Heater (Part 1 of 2)

CR1029303556010A

Fig. 113   Test NTC-16A: Checking Oxygen Sensor Heater (Part 2 of 2)

CR1029303556020A

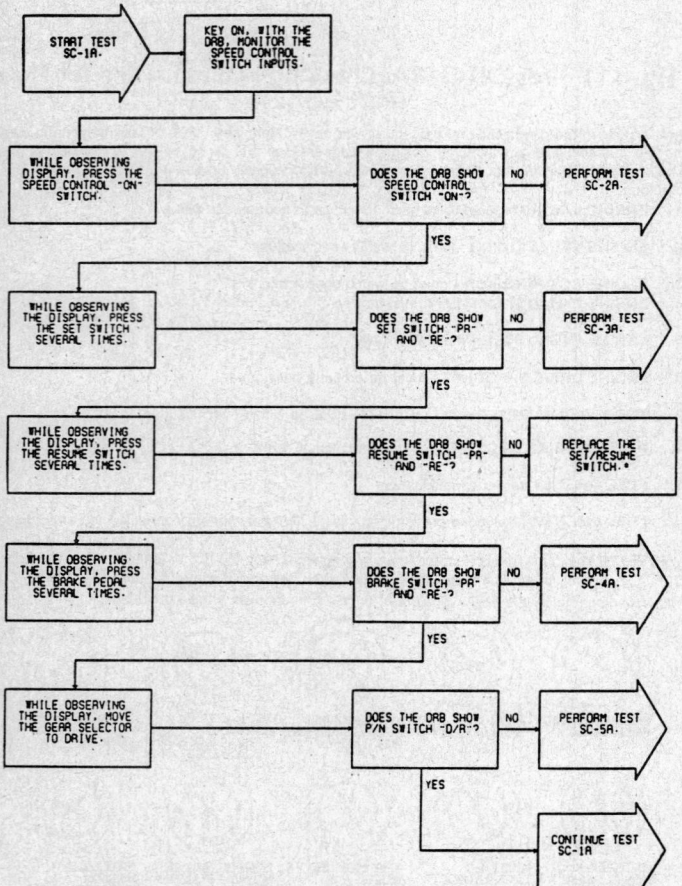

Fig. 114   Test SC-1A: Checking Speed Control Relay Output (Part 1 of 3)

Fig. 114   Test SC-1A: Checking Speed Control Relay Output (Part 2 of 3)

CR1029303557020X

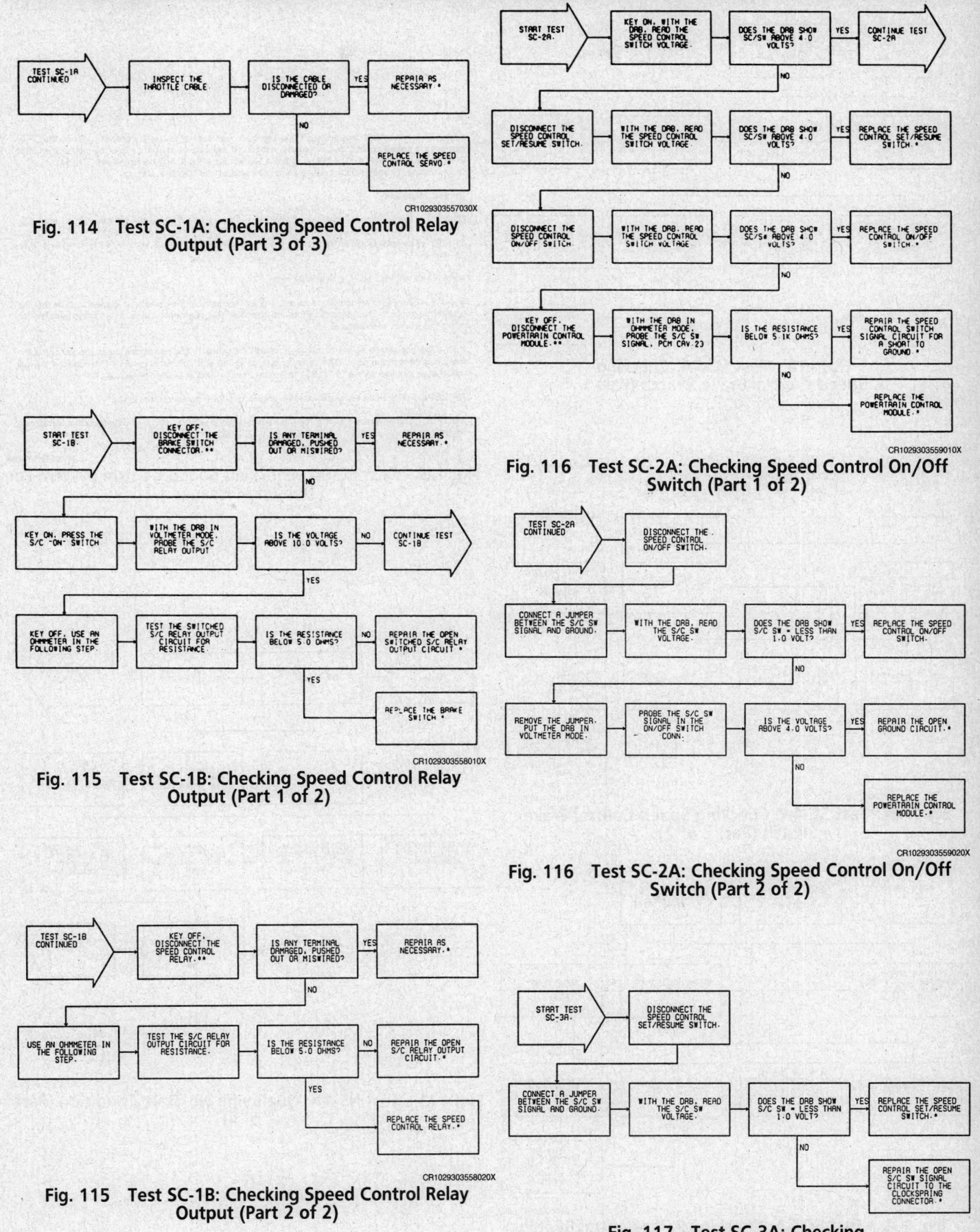

Fig. 114   Test SC-1A: Checking Speed Control Relay Output (Part 3 of 3)

Fig. 115   Test SC-1B: Checking Speed Control Relay Output (Part 1 of 2)

Fig. 115   Test SC-1B: Checking Speed Control Relay Output (Part 2 of 2)

Fig. 116   Test SC-2A: Checking Speed Control On/Off Switch (Part 1 of 2)

Fig. 116   Test SC-2A: Checking Speed Control On/Off Switch (Part 2 of 2)

Fig. 117   Test SC-3A: Checking Speed Control Set/Resume Switch

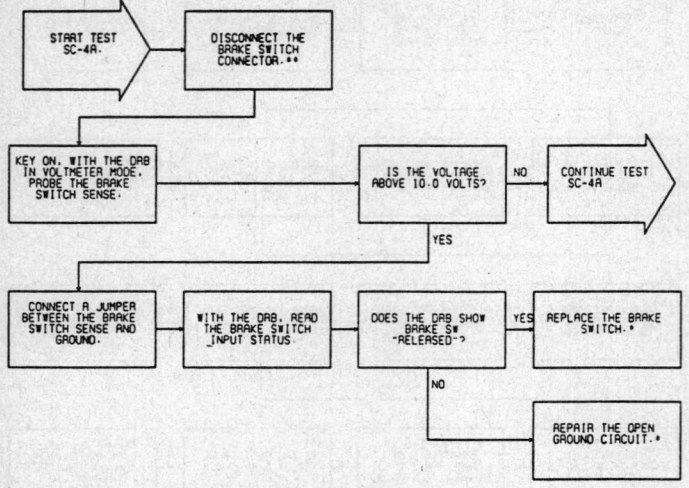

Fig. 118 Test SC-4A: Checking Speed Control Brake Switch (Part 1 of 2)

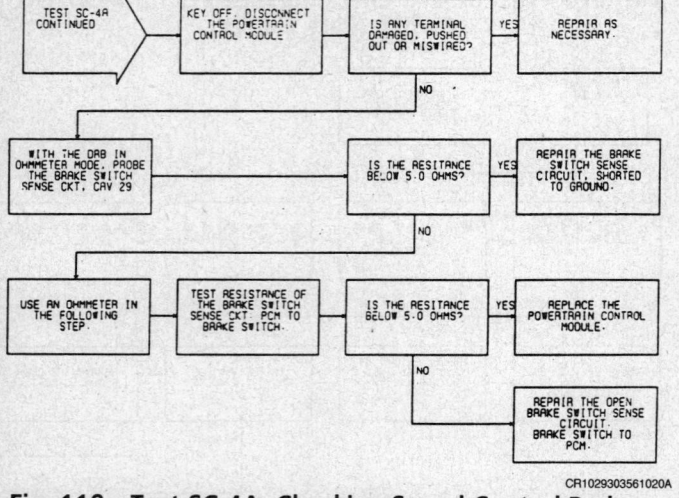

CR1029303561020A

Fig. 118 Test SC-4A: Checking Speed Control Brake Switch (Part 2 of 2)

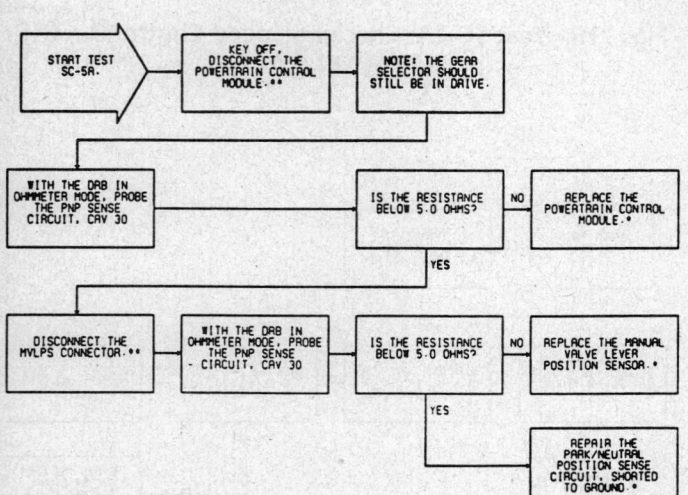

CR1029303562000X

Fig. 119 Test SC-5A: Checking Park/Neutral Switch

At this time, the speed control switch and servo function appear to operate properly. Using the DRB, monitor the speed control "cutout" status. Road test the vehicle at speeds over 35 mph and attempt to set the speed control. The following items will not allow the speed control to set. The last or most recent cause for speed control not to set is indicated by the "Denied" status.

Denied Message

ON/OFF – The powertrain control module does not see an "On" signal from the switch at cavity 23.

SPEED – The vehicle speed as seen by the powertrain control module at cavity 47 is not greater than 36 mph.

RPM – The engine rpm is excessively high.

BRAKE – The brake switch sense circuit is open indicating to the powertrain control module that the brakes are applied. The sense circuit, cavity 29 of the PCM, is grounded through the brake pedal switch when the brakes are released.

P/N – The p/n switch sense circuit is grounded indicating to the powertrain control module that the transmission is not in gear. The sense circuit, cavity 30 of the PCM, is grounded through the manual valve lever position sensor (MVLPS) when the transmission is in park or neutral.

RPM/SPD – The PCM senses excessive engine rpm for a given vehicle speed.

SOL FLT – The powertrain control module senses a servo solenoid circuit trouble code that is maturing or set in memory.

CR1029303563000X

Fig. 120 Test SC-6A: Checking Speed Control System For Denied Messages

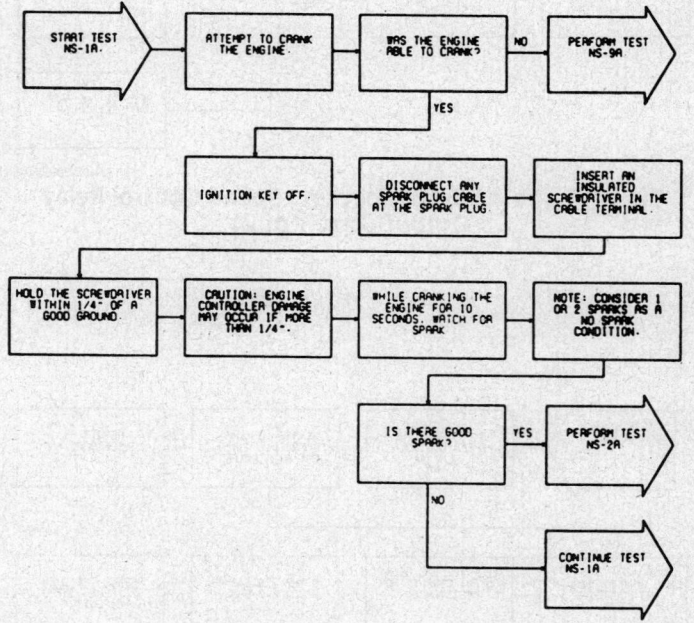

CR1029303564010X

Fig. 121 Test NS-1A: Qualifying No Start Condition (Part 1 of 4)

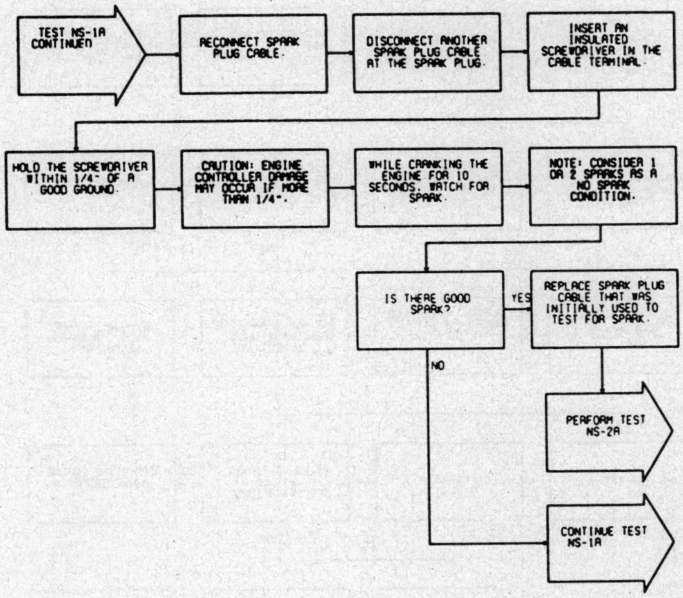

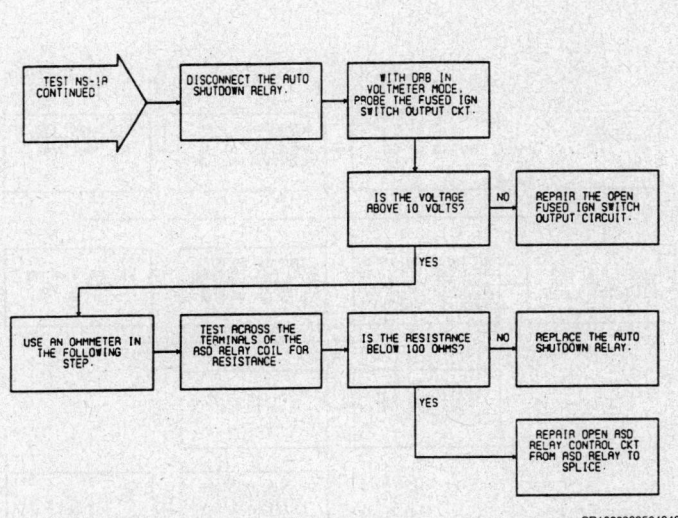

CR1029303564020X

Fig. 121 Test NS-1A: Qualifying No Start Condition (Part 2 of 4)

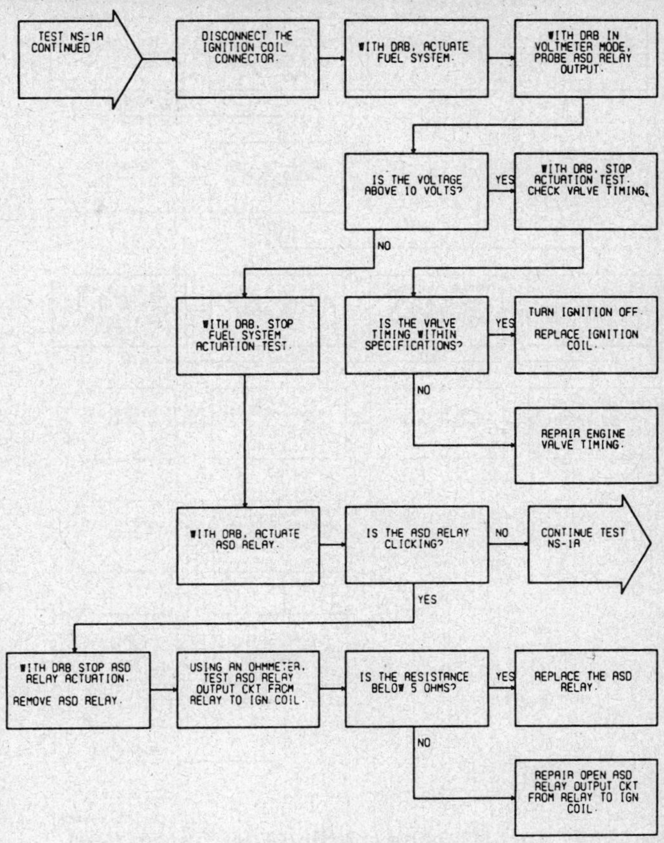

CR1029303564030A

Fig. 121 Test NS-1A: Qualifying No Start Condition (Part 3 of 4)

CR1029303564040A

Fig. 121 Test NS-1A: Qualifying No Start Condition (Part 4 of 4)

CR1029303565010A

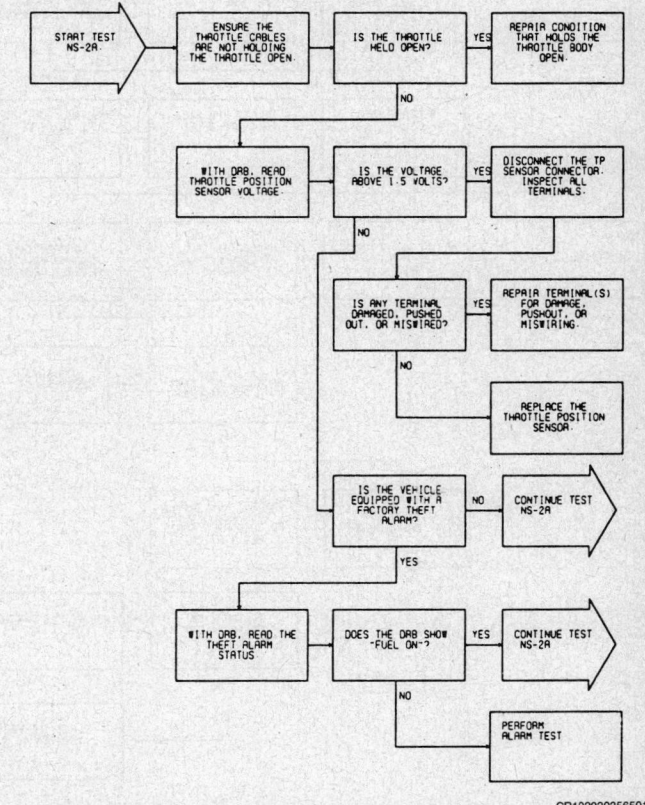

Fig. 122 Test NS-2A: Inspecting Fuel System (Part 1 of 2)

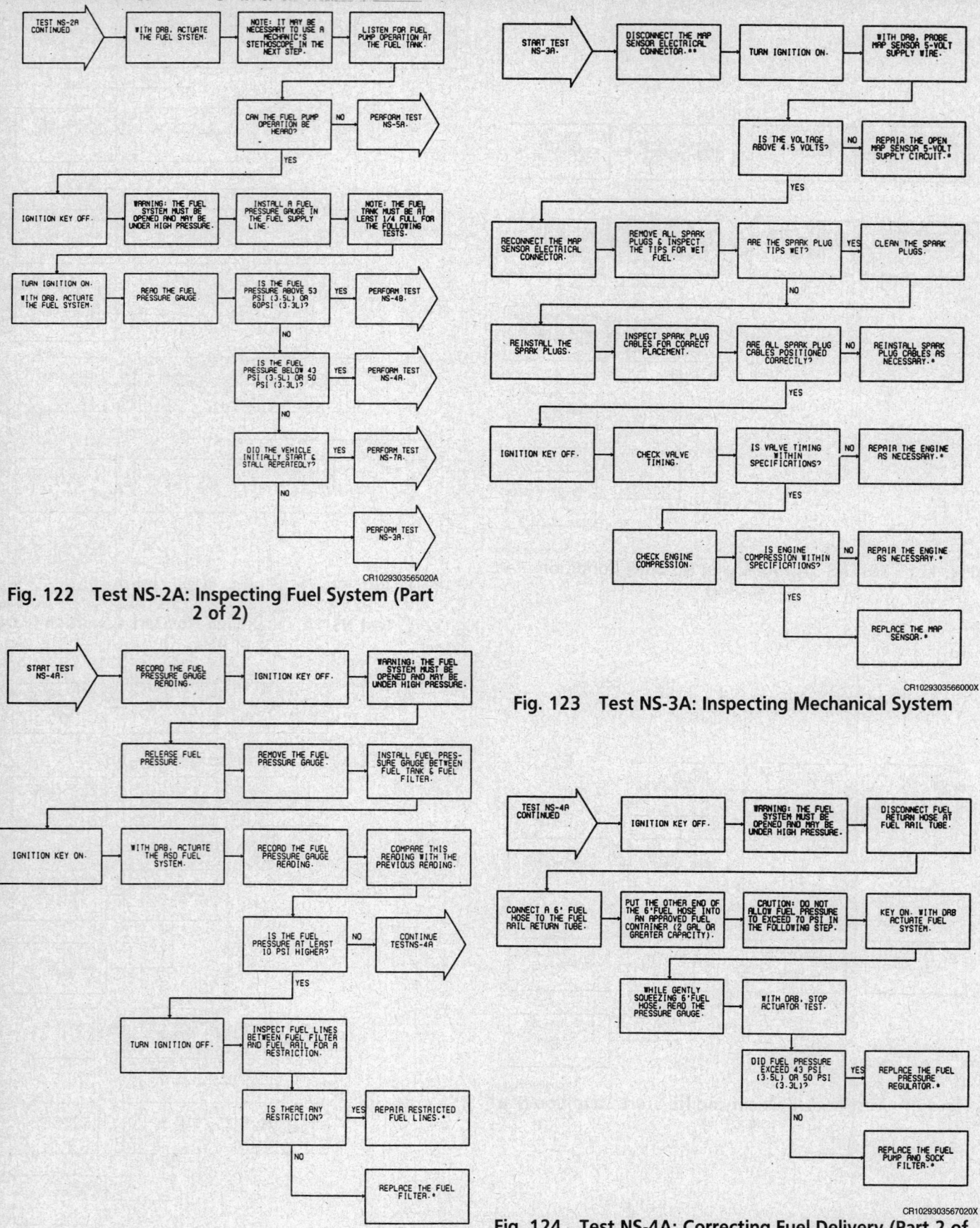

Fig. 122 Test NS-2A: Inspecting Fuel System (Part 2 of 2)

CR1029303565020A

Fig. 123 Test NS-3A: Inspecting Mechanical System

CR1029303566000X

Fig. 124 Test NS-4A: Correcting Fuel Delivery (Part 1 of 2)

CR1029303567010X

Fig. 124 Test NS-4A: Correcting Fuel Delivery (Part 2 of 2)

CR1029303567020X

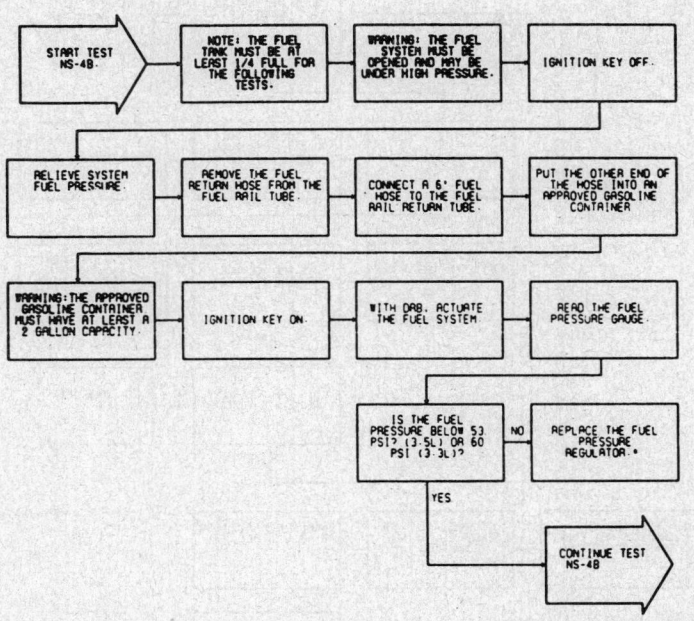

Fig. 125 Test NS-4B: Correcting Fuel Delivery (Part 1 of 2)

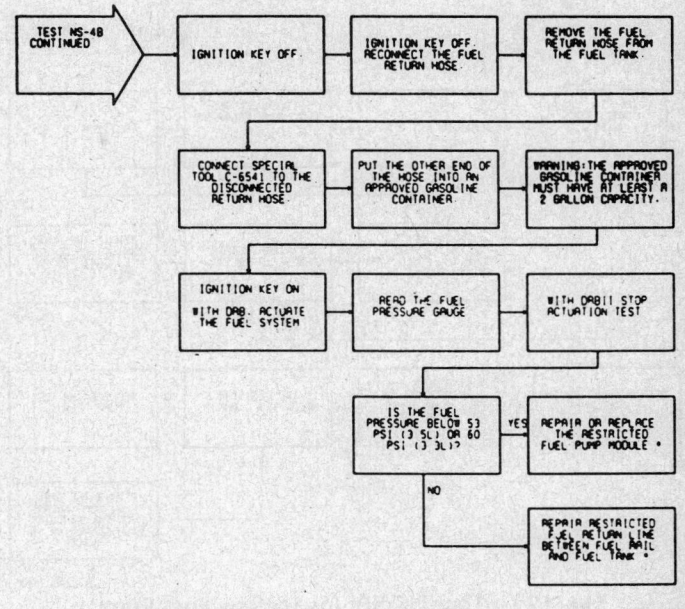

Fig. 125 Test NS-4B: Correcting Fuel Delivery (Part 2 of 2)

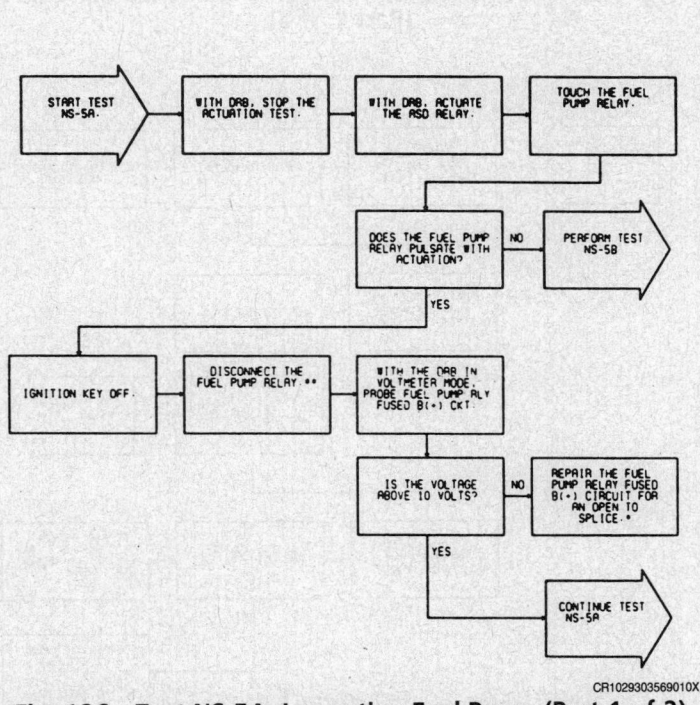

Fig. 126 Test NS-5A: Inspecting Fuel Pump (Part 1 of 2)

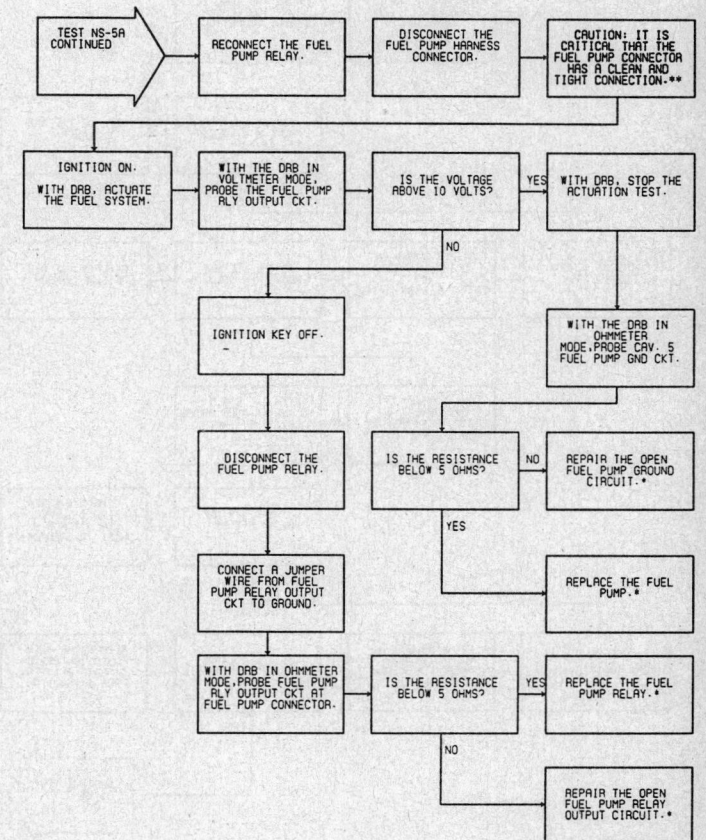

Fig. 126 Test NS-5A: Inspecting Fuel Pump (Part 2 of 2)

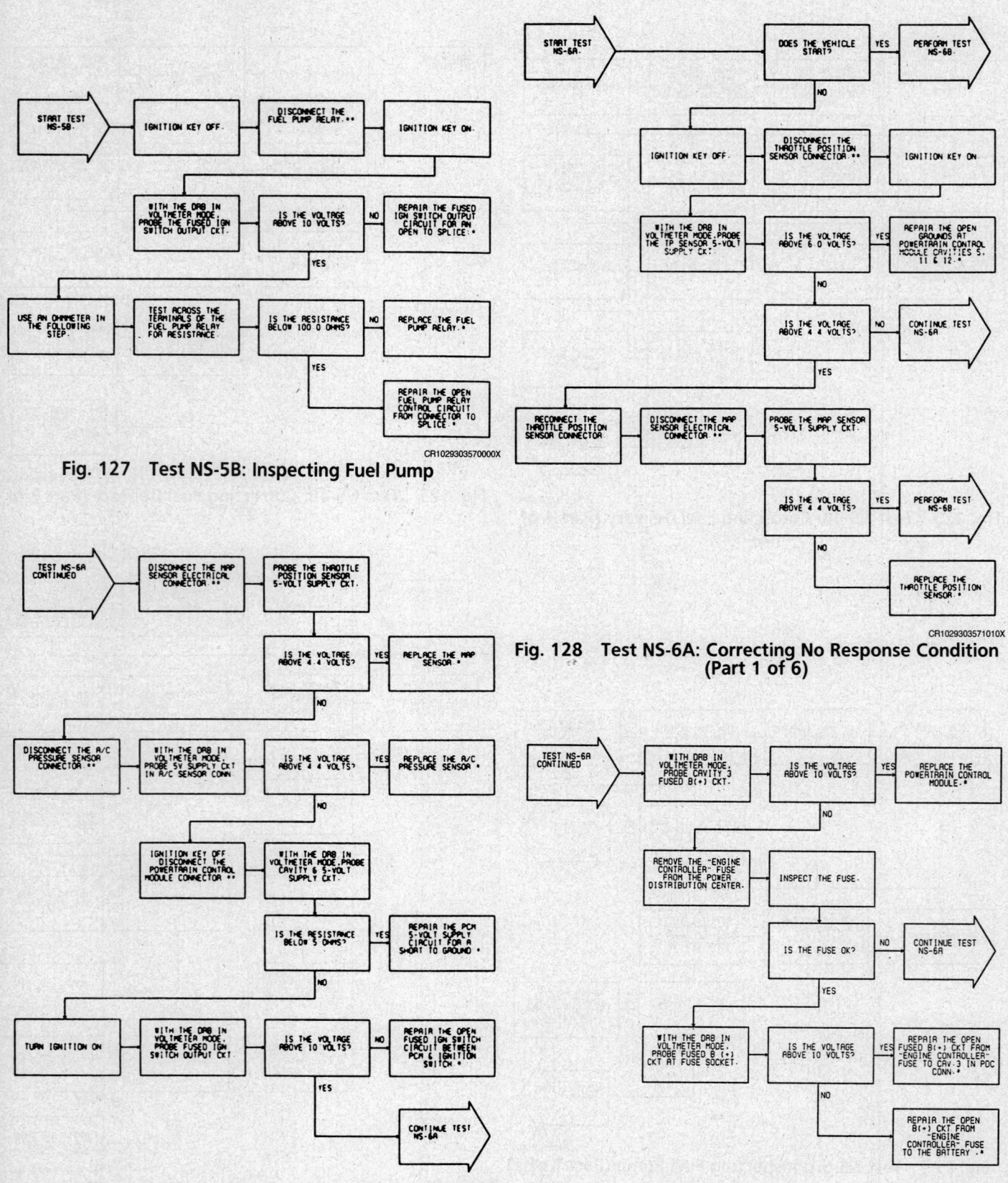

Fig. 127   Test NS-5B: Inspecting Fuel Pump

CR1029303570000X

Fig. 128   Test NS-6A: Correcting No Response Condition
(Part 1 of 6)

CR1029303571010X

Fig. 128   Test NS-6A: Correcting No Response Condition
(Part 2 of 6)

CR1029303571020X

Fig. 128   Test NS-6A: Correcting No Response Condition
(Part 3 of 6)

CR1029303571030X

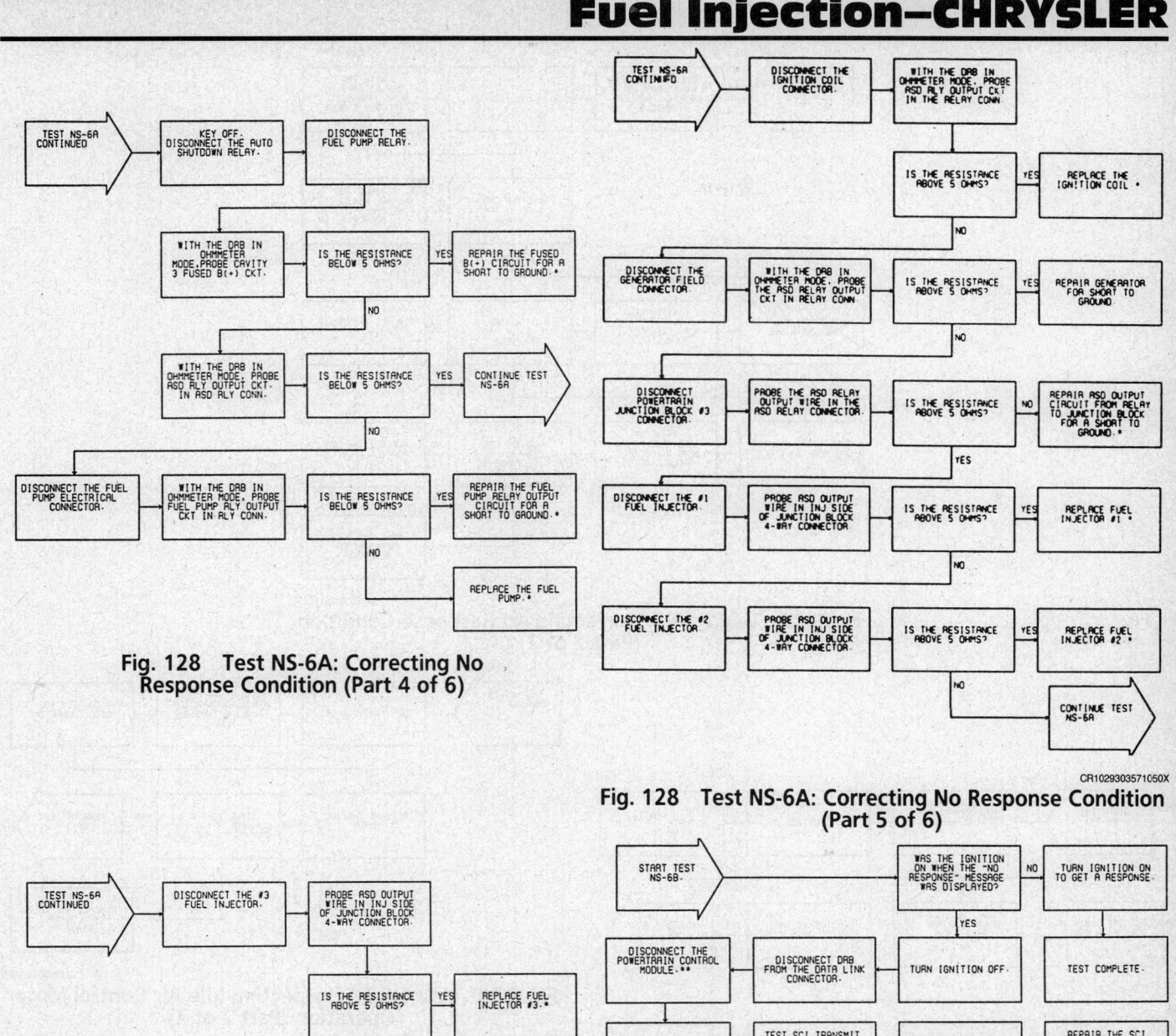

Fig. 128   Test NS-6A: Correcting No Response Condition (Part 4 of 6)

Fig. 128   Test NS-6A: Correcting No Response Condition (Part 5 of 6)

CR1029303571050X

Fig. 128   Test NS-6A: Correcting No Response Condition (Part 6 of 6)

CR1029303571060X

Fig. 129   Test NS-6B: Correcting No Response Condition (Part 1 of 2)

CR1029303572010X

CR1029303572020X

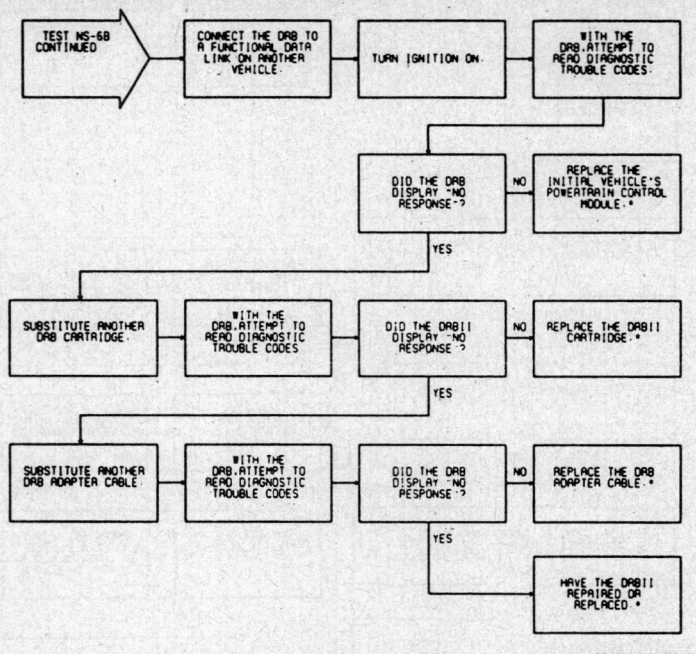

Fig. 129 Test NS-6B: Correcting No Response Condition (Part 2 of 2)

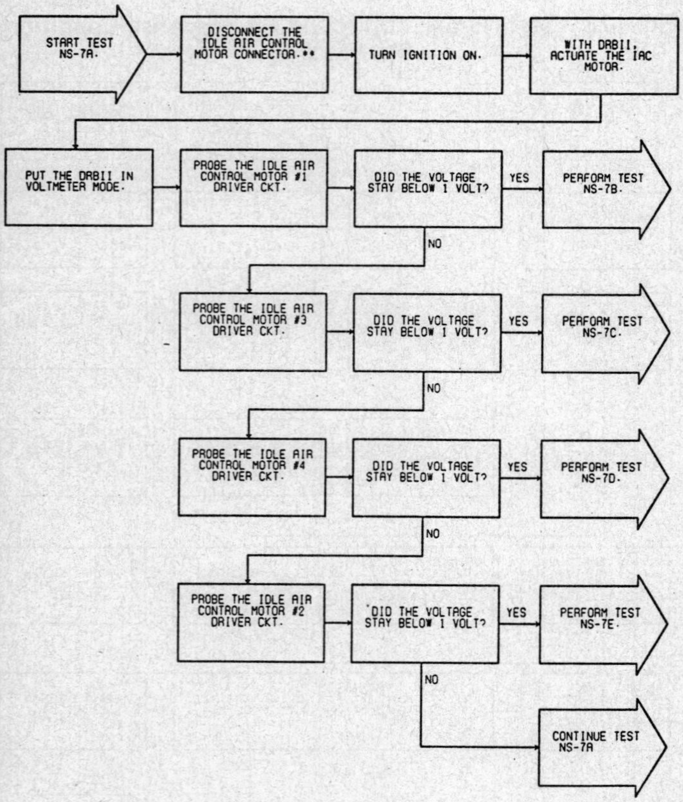

CR1029303573010X

Fig. 130 Test NS-7A: Inspecting Idle Air Control Motor Operation (Part 1 of 2)

CR1029303573020X

Fig. 130 Test NS-7A: Inspecting Idle Air Control Motor Operation (Part 2 of 2)

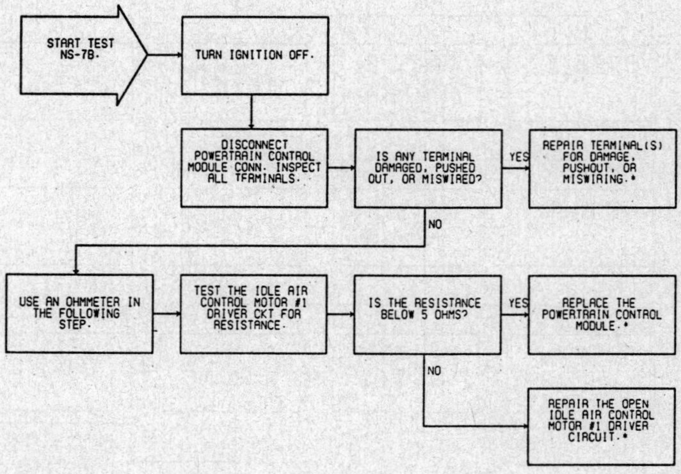

CR1029303574000X

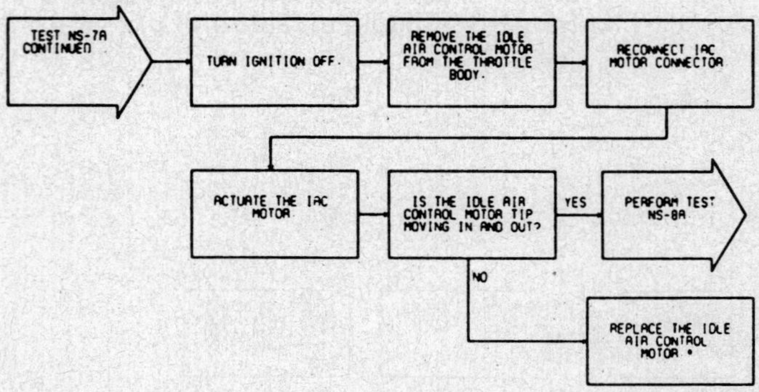

Fig. 131 Test NS-7B: Inspecting Idle Air Control Motor Operation

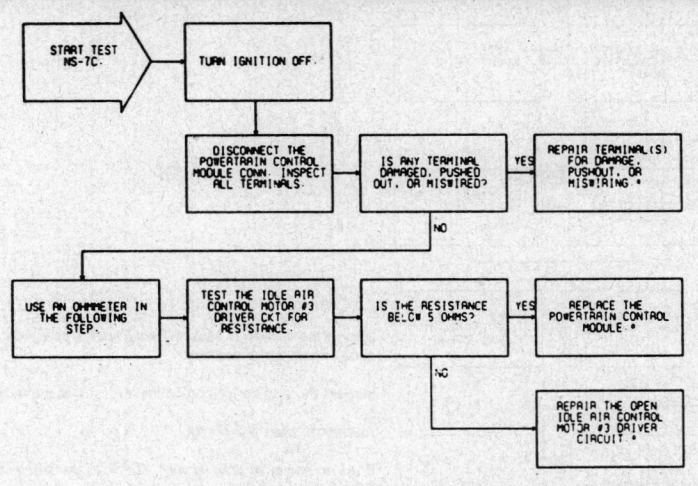

Fig. 132   Test NS-7C: Inspecting Idle Air Control Motor Operation

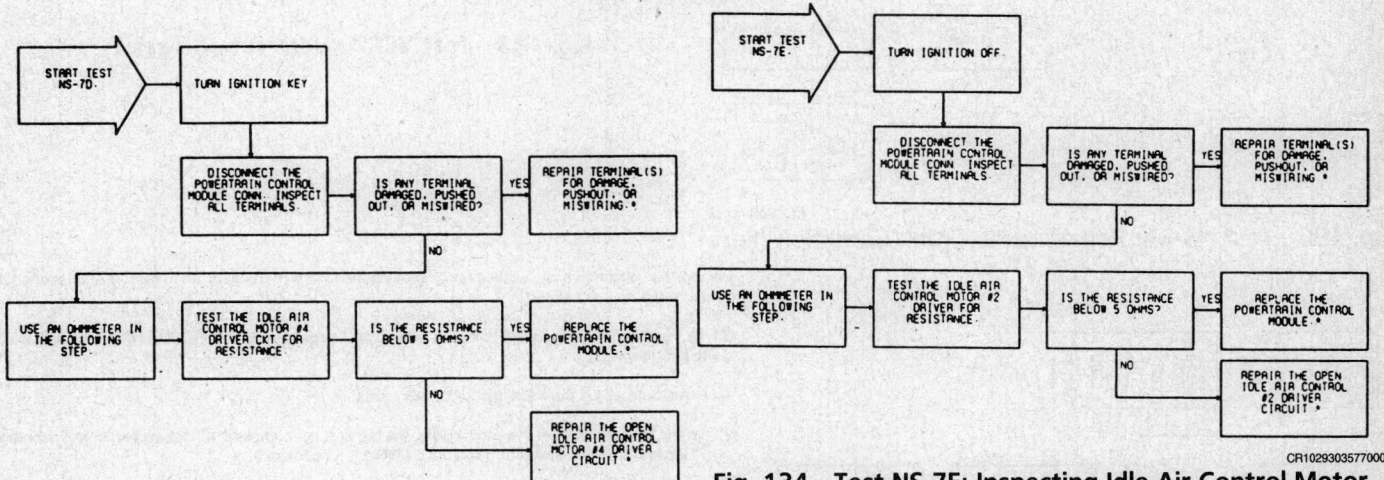

Fig. 133   Test NS-7D: Inspecting idle Air Control Motor Operation

Fig. 134   Test NS-7E: Inspecting Idle Air Control Motor Operation

At this point in the diagnostic test procedure, you have determined that all of the powertrain control module systems are operating as designed. Therefore, they are not the cause of the start and stall problem.

The following potential causes of a no start condition should also be checked.

1. **ENGINE VALVE TIMING** - must be within specifications

2. **ENGINE COMPRESSION** - must be within specifications

3. **ENGINE EXHAUST** - must be unrestricted

4. **ENGINE PCV SYSTEM** - must flow freely

5. **ENGINE DRIVE SPROCKETS** - must be properly positioned

6. **TORQUE CONVERTER STALL SPEED** - must be within specifications

7. **FUEL** - must be free of contamination

8. **ENGINE SECONDARY IGNITION CHECK** - must exhibit a normal scope pattern

Any one or more of these items can produce a no start condition; none of them can be overlooked as possible causes.

Fig. 135   Test NS-8A: Correcting Start & Stall Condition

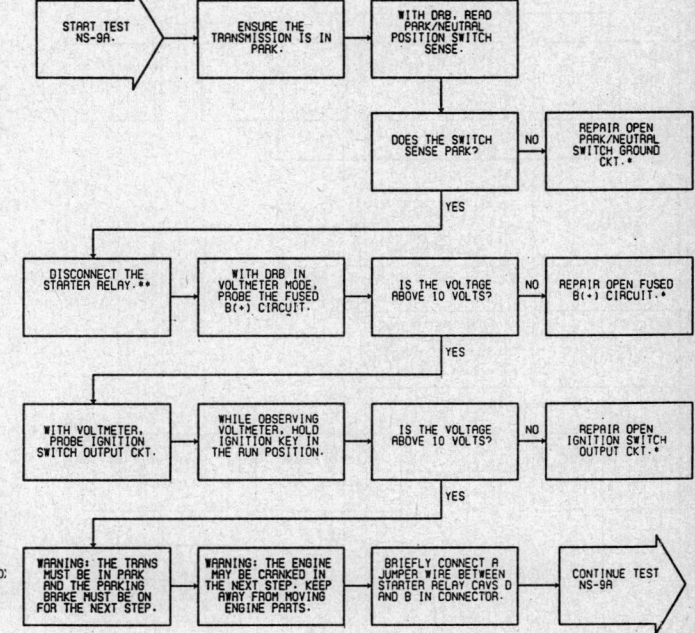

Fig. 136   Test NS-9A: Repairing No Crank Condition (Part 1 of 2)

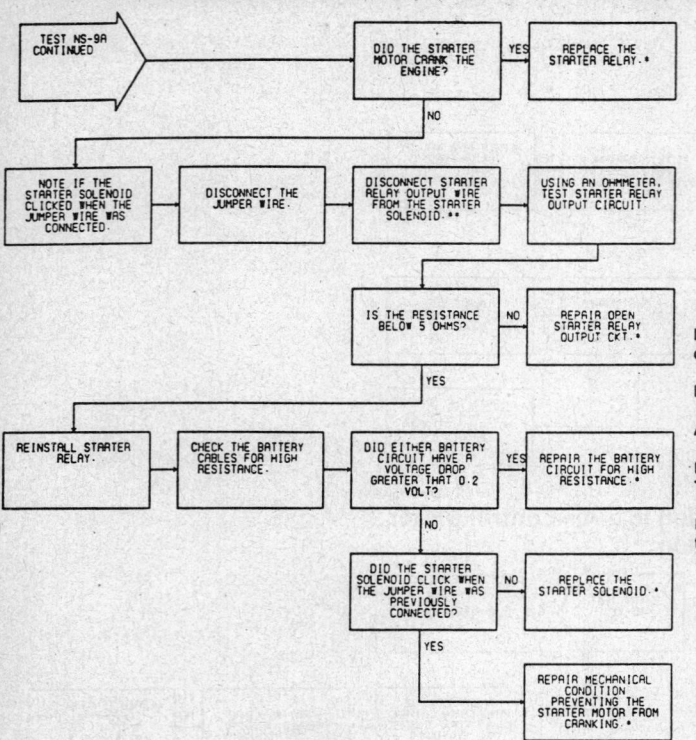

Fig. 136   Test NS-9A: Repairing No Crank Condition (Part 2 of 2)

Inspect the vehicle to ensure that all engine components are connected. Reassemble and reconnect components as necessary.

Inspect the engine for contamination. If it is contaminated, change the oil and filter.

Attempt to start the engine.

If the engine is unable to start, check all pertinent Technical Service Bulletins, and return to **TEST TC-1A** if necessary.

If the engine is able to start, and the powertrain control module has been changed, connect the DRB to the PCM data link connector and erase trouble codes. The repair is now complete.

CR1029303580000X

Fig. 138   Test VER-1: Verification Test 1

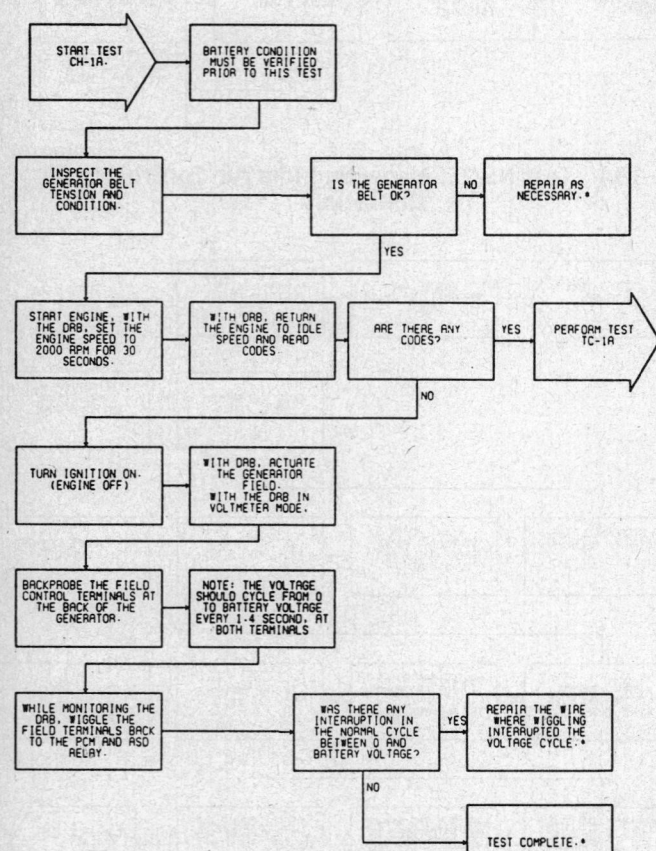

CR1029306472000X

Fig. 137   Test CH-1A: Checking Charging System Controls

Inspect the vehicle to ensure that all engine components are connected. Reassemble and reconnect components as necessary.

If this verification procedure is being performed subsequent to a NO TROUBLE CODE test, do the following:

1. Check to see if the initial symptom still exists.

2. If the initial or another symptom exists, the repair is not complete. Check all pertinent Technical Service Bulletins and return to **TEST NTC-1A** if necessary.

If this verification procedure is being performed subsequent to a TROUBLE CODE test, do the following:

For previously read trouble codes that have not been dealt with, return to **TEST TC-1A** and follow the path specified by the other code. Otherwise, continue.

If the powertrain control module has not been changed:

> Connect the DRB to the PCM data link connector and erase trouble codes.

> With the DRB, reset all values in the adaptive memory.

> Disconnect the DRB.

Ensure no other trouble code remains by doing the following:

1. If the vehicle is equipped with air conditioning, turn on the air conditioning and blower.

2. Drive the vehicle for at least five minutes and at some point attain a speed of 40 mph. Ensure the transmission shifts through all gears. Upon completion of the road test, turn the engine off.

3. Start the engine. Allow the engine to idle for at least two minutes.

4. Turn the engine off.

5. Connect the DRB to the PCM data link connector, and with the DRB, read all trouble codes.

If the repaired code has reset, the repair is not complete. Check all pertinent Technical Service Bulletins and return to **TEST TC-1A** if necessary.

If another trouble code has set, return to **TEST TC-1A** and follow the path specified by the other trouble code.

If there are no trouble codes, the repair is now complete.

CR1029303581000X

Fig. 139   Test VER-2: Road Test Verification

Inspect the vehicle to ensure that all engine components are connected. Reassemble and reconnect components as necessary.

If the powertrain control module has been changed, do the following:

1. If the vehicle is equipped with a vehicle theft security system, start the vehicle at least 20 times so that the alarm system may be activated when desired.

Connect the DRB to the PCM data link connector and erase the codes.

Ensure no other charging system problems remain by doing the following:

1. Start the engine.
2. Raise the engine speed to 2000 rpm for at least 30 seconds.
3. Allow the engine to idle.
4. Turn the engine off.
5. Turn the ignition key on.
6. With the DRB, read trouble code messages.

If the repaired code has reset, or another one has set, check all pertinent Technical Service Bulletins and return to **TEST TC-1A** if necessary.

If there are no codes, the repair is now complete.

CR1029305246000X

Fig. 140   Test VER-3A: Charging Verification

SYSTEM SERVICE

Fuel System Pressure Relief

1. Disconnect battery ground cable.
2. Remove fuel filler cap.
3. Remove protective cap from fuel pressure test port on fuel rail.
4. Place open end of fuel pressure release hose tool No. C-4799-1 or equivalent into an approved container.
5. Connect other end to the fuel pressure test port on the fuel rail. Fuel pressure will be bleed into the container.
6. Remove release tool. **Connect battery ground cable after all system repairs are complete.**

Component Service

THROTTLE BODY CLEANING

Clean throttle body in a well ventilated area. Wear rubber or butyl gloves, do not allow Mopar parts cleaner to come in contact with eyes or skin. Avoid ingesting the cleaner. Wash thoroughly after using cleaner.

3.3L/V6-201 Engine

1. Remove throttle body.
2. While holding throttle open, spray entire throttle body bore and manifold side of the throttle blade with Mopar Parts Cleaner or equivalent.
3. Using a soft scuff pad, clean the top and bottom of throttle body bore and edges and manifold side of throttle blade. **The edges of the throttle blade and portion of the throttle bore that are closest to the throttle blade when closed must be free of deposits.**
4. Use compressed air to dry the throttle body.
5. Inspect throttle body for foreign material.

6. Install throttle body on manifold.

3.5L/V6-215 Engine

Choked throttle bodies will cause low idle speed and poor idle quality. Clean both throttle bodies and synchronize them prior to checking minimum air flow.

1. Remove throttle bodies from engine.
2. While holding throttle open, spray entire throttle body bore and manifold side of the throttle blade with Mopar Parts Cleaner. **Use Only Mopar Parts Cleaner to clean throttle bodies.**
3. Using a soft scuff pad, clean the top and bottom of throttle body bore and edges and manifold side of throttle blade. **The edges of the throttle blade and portion of the throttle bore that are closest to the throttle blade when closed must be free of deposits.**
4. Use compressed air to dry the throttle bodies.
5. Inspect throttle bodies for foreign material.
6. Install throttle bodies on manifold.
7. Adjust throttle body synchronization as outlined under "Adjustments."

Component Replacement

THROTTLE BODY

3.3L/V6-201 ENGINE

1. Disconnect PCV make-up air hose from cylinder head cover.

Inspect the vehicle to ensure that all engine components are connected. Reassemble and reconnect all components as necessary.

If the powertrain control module has been changed, do the following:

1. If the vehicle is equipped with a factory theft alarm, start the vehicle at least 20 times so that the alarm system may be activated when desired.

Connect the DRB to the PCM data link connector and erase the codes.

Ensure no other speed control problems remain by doing the following:

1. Road test the vehicle at a speed above 35 mph.
2. Turn the speed control ON/OFF switch to the ON position.
3. Depress and release the SET switch. If the speed control did not engage, the repair is not complete.
4. For stalk switch equipped vehicles, quickly depress and release the SET switch. For steering wheel switch equipped vehicles, quickly depress and release the RESUME/ACCEL switch. If the vehicle speed did not increase by 2 mph, the repair is not complete.
5. Using caution, depress and release the brake pedal. If the speed control did not disengage, the repair is not complete.
6. Bring the vehicle speed back up to 35 mph.
7. Depress the RESUME/ACCEL switch. If the speed control did not resume the previously set speed, the repair is not complete.
8. Hold down the SET switch. If the vehicle did not decelerate, the repair is not complete.
9. Ensure the vehicle speed is greater than 35 mph and release the SET switch. If the vehicle did not adjust and set a new vehicle speed, the repair is not complete.
10. Turn on the ON/OFF switch to the OFF position. If the speed control did not disengage, the repair is not complete.

If the vehicle successfully passed all of the previous tests, the speed control system is now functioning as designed. The repair is now complete.

Check for Technical Service Bulletins that pertain to this speed control problem and then, if necessary, return to **TEST TC-1A**.

CR1029305247000X

Fig. 141   Test VER-4A: Speed Control Verification

2. Remove air cleaner tube from throttle body.
3. disconnect purge hose from throttle body.
4. Rotate throttle lever to wide open throttle position and remove throttle and speed control cables.
5. Remove throttle body mounting bolts then the throttle body.
6. Clean gasket surface on throttle body and intake manifold plenum.
7. Reverse procedure to install, **torquing** throttle body bolts to 19 ft. lbs.

3.5L/V6-215 ENGINE

Removal

1. Disconnect battery ground cable.
2. **For left throttle body replacement,** hold throttle lever in wide open position and remove throttle and speed control cables from throttle arm.
3. **For either throttle body replacement,** remove tube connecting air cleaner to air plenum.
4. Disconnect air plenum from throttle bodies, PCV make-up air tube and IAC motor.
5. Remove plenum from right side of vehicle.
6. Disconnect purge hose from throttle body.
7. **For right throttle body replacement,** disconnect electrical connector to the TPS sensor.
8. **For either throttle body replacement,** remove throttle body mounting nuts. The end throttle body shaft has a ball stud that fits into a socket in the synchronization shaft, **Fig. 142.** Also, the tang on the end of the throttle

Fig. 142 Left throttle body replacement

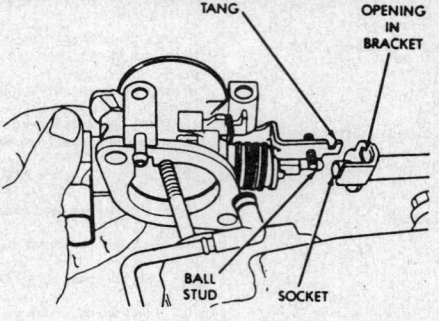

Fig. 143 Right throttle body replacement

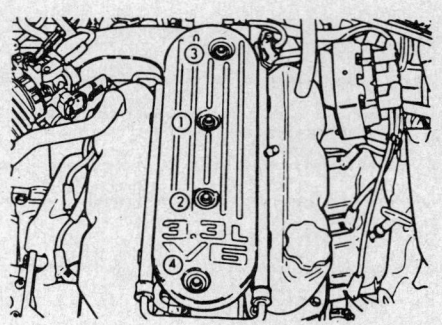

Fig. 144 Intake manifold plenum tightening sequence. 3.3L/V6-201 engine

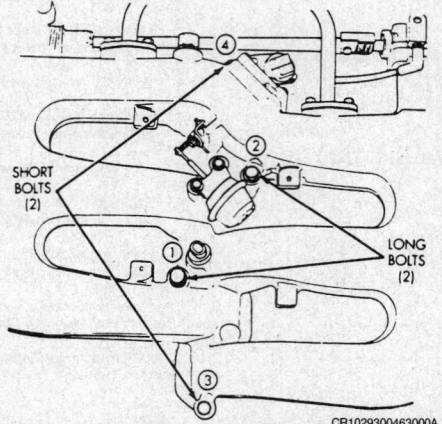

Fig. 145 Intake manifold plenum tightening sequence. 3.5L/V6-215 engine

body lever fits into an opening in the bracket on the synchronization shaft, **Fig. 143.**

9. Slide throttle body back off of mounting studs. Separate throttle body from the synchronization shaft. Remove throttle body.
10. Clean gasket mating surfaces.

Installation

Prior to installing either throttle body, remove and clean opposite throttle body.
1. Position new gasket over throttle body mounting studs.
2. Connect left throttle body synchronization shaft. ensure ball stud enters socket in the end of synchronization shaft, **Fig. 142.** ensure spring attaches to shaft and throttle body arm. Ensure spring does not bind when opening and closing the throttle blade.
3. Connect right throttle body synchronization shaft. Ensure ball stud on throttle shaft enters socket in end of synchronization shaft. At the same time, the tang on the throttle lever locks into the bracket on the synchronization shaft, **Fig. 143.**
4. Install left and/or throttle body over mounting studs and **torque** nuts to 19 ft. lbs.
5. Connect purge tube to nipple on throttle body.
6. Hold left throttle lever in wide open throttle position and install throttle and speed control cables.
7. Connect TPS sensor electrical connector to right throttle body.
8. Check throttle body synchronization as outlined under "Adjustments."
9. Install air plenum and air cleaner to plenum tube.
10. Connect battery ground cable.

FUEL RAIL

3.3L/V6-201 Engine

1. Release fuel system pressure as outlined under "Fuel System Pressure Relief."
2. Disconnect battery ground cable.
3. Disconnect air plenum from air cleaner and throttle body.
4. Hold throttle lever in wide open position and remove throttle and speed control cables.
5. Compress locking tabs on throttle and

speed control cable housings and remove from bracket.
6. Disconnect EET solenoid, IAC motor, TPS and MAP sensor connectors.
7. Disconnect PCV and brake booster hoses.
8. Disconnect vacuum line from pressure regulator.
9. Disconnect purge hose from throttle body.
10. Remove EGR tube mounting screws at intake manifold plenum.
11. Remove intake manifold plenum and cover intake manifold opening to prevent entry of foreign objects.
12. Disconnect fuel supply and return hoses at rear of manifold.
13. Remove screw from fuel tube clamp then separate fuel tubes from bracket.
14. Rotate injectors toward center of engine. Tag injector connectors with their cylinder number.
15. Remove fuel rail mounting bolts, lift fuel rail straight off engine.
16. Reverse procedure to install, noting the following:
   a. Apply a light coat of clean engine oil to O-rings of injectors.
   b. **Torque** fuel rail mounting screws to 16 ft. lbs.
   c. **Torque** intake manifold plenum bolts to 21 ft. lbs. in sequence shown in **Fig. 144.**

3.5L/V6-215 Engine

Refer to "Intake Manifold Plenum" and "Fuel Injector" for fuel rail replacement procedure.

INTAKE MANIFOLD PLENUM

3.5L/V6-215 Engine

1. Release fuel system pressure as outlined under "Fuel system Pressure Relief."
2. Disconnect battery ground cable.
3. Remove engine cover from top of intake manifold plenum.
4. Remove throttle and speed control cables from throttle arm.
5. Disconnect IAC motor, charge air temperature, MAP and TPS sensors.
6. Disconnect purge hose from throttle bodies.
7. Disconnect PCV make-up air and IAC motor hoses.
8. Remove air inlet tube from behind manifold.
9. Disconnect EGR tube from intake manifold plenum.
10. Disconnect support bracket from plenum.
11. Remove intake manifold plenum bolts. **Plenum uses two different length bolts. Mark locations when removing.**
12. Remove intake manifold plenum and cover intake opening to prevent entry of foreign objects.
13. Reverse procedure to install, **torquing** intake manifold plenum bolts to 250 inch lbs. in sequence shown in **Fig. 145.**

FUEL INJECTORS

3.3L/V6-201 Engine

1. Remove fuel rail as outlined under "Fuel Rail."
2. Remove fuel injector retaining clip.
3. Reverse procedure to install.

3.5L/V6-215 Engine

1. Release fuel system pressure as outlined under "Fuel System Pressure Relief."
2. Remove intake manifold plenum as outlined under "Intake Manifold Plenum."
3. Disconnect fuel supply and return tubes from fuel rail.
4. Connect fuel gauge adapter tool No. 6631 or equivalent to the fuel supply tube end of the fuel rail.

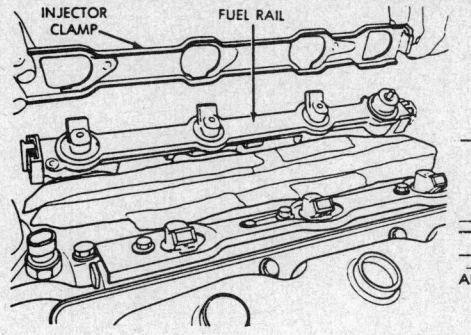

Fig. 146 Fuel injector clamp. 3.5L/V6-215 engine

Fig. 147 Fuel injector alignment. 3.5L/V6-215 engine

Fig. 148 Intake manifold tightening sequence. 3.5L/V6-215 engine

5. Connect fuel hose tool No. 6668 or equivalent to the return tube end of the fuel rail.
6. Place other end of fuel hose tool into a suitable container.
7. Purge fuel from fuel rail by spraying a maximum of 55 psi of compressed air into the fuel gauge adapter tool.
8. Tag injector connectors with their cylinder number.
9. Disconnect fuel injector electrical connector.
10. Remove vacuum tube from fuel pressure regulator.
11. Remove fuel rail mounting bolts.
12. Remove injector clamp screw, **Fig. 146.**
13. Slide injector clamp toward rear of engine, then lift clamp off the rail.
14. Install fuel rail mounting bolts finger tight.
15. Using a thin flat screwdriver, pry fuel injector out of fuel rail.
16. Ensure upper and lower O-rings were removed with injector.
17. Reverse procedure to install, noting the following:
    a. Lightly lubricate O-rings with clean engine oil.
    b. Index injector with tab in fuel, **Fig. 147.**
    c. **Torque** fuel rail bolts to 100 inch lbs.

CAMSHAFT POSITION (CMP) SENSOR

1. Disconnect CMP sensor connector.
2. Remove CMP sensor screw.
3. Pull sensor out of timing chain case cover.
4. Reverse procedure to install, noting the following:
    a. When reusing sensor, old paper spacer must be replaced. When a new sensor is being used, verify paper spacer is installed on sensor.
    b. **Torque** sensor screw to 9 ft. lbs.

CRANKSHAFT POSITION (CKP) SENSOR

1. Disconnect CKP sensor connector.
2. Remove sensor mounting screw.
3. Remove sensor.
4. Reverse procedure to install.

CHARGE AIR TEMPERATURE SENSOR

3.5L/V6-215 Engine

1. Remove engine cover.
2. Disconnect sensor connector.
3. Remove sensor from intake manifold plenum.
4. Reverse procedure to install, **torquing** sensor to 20 ft. lbs.

ENGINE COOLANT TEMPERATURE (ECT) SENSOR

1. Ensure engine temperature is cold.
2. Remove radiator pressure cap.
3. Disconnect ECT sensor connector.
4. Remove sensor from thermostat housing.
5. Reverse procedure to install, **torquing** sensor to 20 ft. lbs.

EVAP PURGE SOLENOID

1. Remove air cleaner tube.
2. Disconnect EVAP solenoid and MTV (if equipped) electrical connector.
3. Disconnect vacuum harness from solenoid(s).
4. Remove solenoid bracket and solenoid(s).
5. Lift solenoid up off bracket.
6. Reverse procedure to install, installing the solenoid(s) with the word TOP upward. **If solenoid is not installed with word TOP upward, solenoid will not operate correctly.**

HEATED OXYGEN SENSOR (O2S)

3.3L/V6-201 Engine

1. Raise and support vehicle.
2. Disconnect O2S sensor electrical connection.
3. Using a crow fool wrench, remove O2S sensor.
4. After removal, use a 18mm X 1.5 + 6E tap over threads in manifold.
5. Coat threads of O2S sensor with anti-seize compound and **torque** sensor to 20 ft. lbs.

3.5L/V6-215 Engine

1. Remove air cleaner tube.
2. Disconnect O2S sensor electrical connection.

3. Remove O2S using a crow foot wrench or socket tool No. C-4907.
4. After removal, use a 18mm X 1.5 + 6E tap over threads in manifold.
5. Coat threads of O2S sensor with anti-seize compound and **torque** sensor to 20 ft. lbs.

IDLE AIR CONTROL (IAC) MOTOR

1. Remove PCV make-up air hose.
2. Disconnect IAC motor electrical connector.
3. Remove IAC motor mounting screws then the IAC motor. Ensure O-ring is removed with engine.
4. Reverse procedure to install, noting the following:
    a. When installing, if the pintle is extended more than 1 inch in must be retracted using the DRB II scan tool in the AIS Motor Open/Close Test screen.
    b. **Torque** IAC motor screws to 25 inch lbs.

KNOCK SENSOR

3.5L/V6-215 Engine

1. Remove intake manifold plenum as outlined under "Intake Manifold Plenum."
2. Remove upper radiator hose from thermostat housing and heater hose from rear of intake manifold.
3. Remove intake manifold attaching bolts in reverse sequence shown in **Fig. 148,** then the intake manifold.
4. Disconnect knock sensor electrical connection.
5. Remove knock sensor using a suitable crows foot socket.
6. Reverse procedure to install, **torquing** knock sensor to 7 ft. lbs. and intake manifold bolts to 250 inch lbs.

MANIFOLD ABSOLUTE PRESSURE (MAP) SENSOR

1. Disconnect map electrical connection.
2. Remove MAP sensor.
3. Reverse procedure to install.

MANIFOLD TUNING VALVE SOLENOID

3.5L/V6-215 Engine

1. Remove air cleaner tube.
2. Remove electrical connectors from

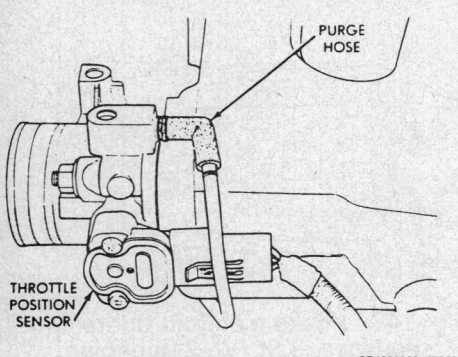

Fig. 149   TPS sensor installation

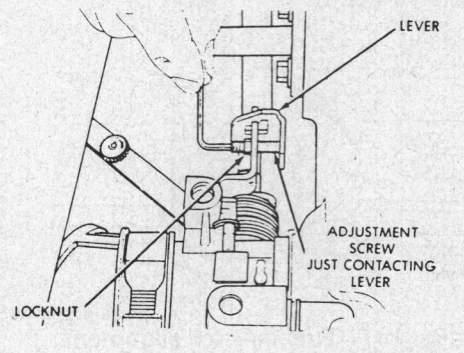

Fig. 150   Throttle body adjustment screw. 3.5L/V6-215 engine

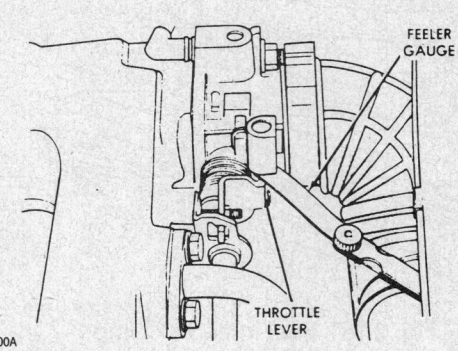

Fig. 151   Idle speed screw. 3.5L/V6-215 engine

EVAP purge solenoid and manifold tuning valve solenoid.
3. Disconnect vacuum harness from solenoids.
4. Remove solenoid mounting bracket and solenoids.
5. Lift MTV solenoid off bracket.
6. Reverse procedure to install.

MANIFOLD TUNING VALVE

3.5L/V6-215 Engine

1. Remove engine cover.
2. Disconnect vacuum hose from manifold tuning valve vacuum motor.
3. Remove retaining clip from manifold tuning valve arm.
4. Remove manifold tuning valve mounting screws then the valve vacuum motor.
5. Reverse procedure to install, **torquing** tuning valve screws to 8 ft. lbs.

POWERTRAIN CONTROL MODULE (PCM)

1. Remove air cleaner assembly.
2. Remove stud bolt and push pin attaching PCM to body. The push pin

has a center lock. Pull center lock up to remove the push pin.
3. Lift PCM up and disconnect 60-way connector.
4. Remove PCM.
5. Reverse procedure to install, **torquing** 60-way connector screw to 35 inch lbs and PCM stud bolt to 7 ft. lbs.

THROTTLE POSITION SENSOR (TPS)

1. Disconnect TPS sensor electrical connector.
2. Remove TPS sensor mounting screws then the TPS sensor.
3. Reverse procedure to install, noting the following:
   a. Align throttle shaft and tabs in TPS sensor so that shaft rests against the tabs, **Fig. 149.** When indexed correctly, the TPS can be rotated clockwise a few degrees to line up the mounting screw holes. If it is difficult to rotate the TPS sensor, install sensor with shaft on other side of tabs in the TPS.
   b. **Torque** TPS sensor screws to 25 inch lbs.

Adjustments

IGNITION TIMING

Ignition timing is controlled by the PCM and is not adjustable.

THROTTLE BODY SYNCHRONIZATION

3.5L/V6-215 Engine

Synchronize the throttle bodies if there is a gap between the adjustment screw and the linkage lever, **Fig. 150**, as follows:
1. Install a .004 inch feeler gauge between idle speed screw and the throttle lever on the right throttle body, **Fig. 151.**
2. Loosen adjustment screw locknut on synchronization shaft, **Fig. 150.**
3. Turn adjustment screw until it just contacts the lever on the synchronization shaft. **Torque** locknut to 36 inch lbs.
4. Check clearance between throttle lever and idle speed screw. the .004 inch feeler gauge should drag when removed and a .006 inch feeler gauge should not fit between throttle lever and isle speed screw.

1␣␣␣6 Models w/2.0L/4-122 Non-Turbo, 2.4L/4-148, 2.5L/V6-152, 3.3L/V6-201 & 3.5L/V6-215 Engines

NOTE: If Uncertain About The Proper Use Of Information Contained In This Section, Please Refer To "How To Use This Manual" Located In The Front Of This Manual.

NOTE: On Air Bag Equipped Models, Refer To "Air Bag System Precautions" Located In The Front Of This Manual For System Disarming & Arming Procedures.

NOTE: Electrical Symbol & Wire Color Code Identification Located In The Front Of This Manual May Be Used As An Aid When Using Wiring Circuits Found In This Section.

INDEX

Page No.

Body Code Identification 14-2
Description 14-2
Diagnosis & Testing: 14-3
  Accessing Diagnostic Trouble Codes 14-3
  Using Malfunction Indicator Lamp
    (MIL) 14-3
  Using Scan Tool 14-3
  Clearing Diagnostic Trouble Codes . 14-3
  Diagnostic Trouble Code
    Interpretation 14-3
  Inactive Diagnostic Trouble Code
    Condition 14-3
Diagnostic Chart Index 14-45
Precautions: 14-2
  Air Bag Systems 14-2
  Fuel System Pressure Relief 14-2
Sensor & Fuel Injector
  Specifications 14-1

Page No.

System Service: 14-137
  Adjustments 14-140
  Throttle Body Synchronization . 14-140
  Component Replacement 14-137
  Air Inlet Resonator 14-138
  Camshaft Position (CMP)
    Sensor 14-139
  Crankshaft Position (CKP)
    Sensor 14-140
  Engine Coolant Temperature
    Sensor 14-140
  Fuel Injectors 14-138
  Fuel Rail 14-138
  Idle Air Control Motor 14-139
  Intake Air Temperature Sensor . 14-140
  Intake Manifold Plenum 14-139
  Manifold Absolute Pressure
    (MAP) Sensor 14-140

Page No.

  Throttle Body 14-137
  Throttle Position Sensor 14-140
Fuel System Pressure Relief 14-137
  Avenger & Sebring Coupe 14-137
  Breeze, Cirrus, Sebring
    Convertible & Stratus
    w/2.0L/4-122 & 2.4L/4-148
    Engines, Concorde, Intrepid,
    LHS, Neon, New Yorker &
    Vision 14-137
  Breeze, Cirrus, Sebring
    Convertible & Stratus
    w/2.5L/V6-152 Engine 14-137
  Talon 14-137
Troubleshooting 14-2

SENSOR & FUEL INJECTOR SPECIFICATIONS

Component	Resistance, Ohms		Output Voltage
	@68°F	@176°F	
BREEZE, CIRRUS, CONCORDE, INTREPID, LHS, NEON, NEW YORKER, SEBRING CONVERTIBLE, STRATUS & VISION			
Camshaft Position Sensor	—	—	.30—5.00 ④
Crankshaft Position Sensor	—	—	.30—5.00 ④
Engine Coolant Temperature Sensor	7000—13,000	700—1000	—
Fuel Injector	12	—	—
Heated Oxygen Sensor	4—7	—	—
Intake Air Temperature Sensor	7000—13,000	700—1000	—
Knock Sensor	—	—	.08—4.00 ①
MAP Sensor	—	—	4.00—5.00 ②
Throttle Position Sensor	—	—	③

Continued

SENSOR & FUEL INJECTOR SPECIFICATIONS–Continued

Component	Resistance, Ohms		Output Voltage
	@68°F	@176°F	
AVENGER, SEBRING COUPE & TALON			
Engine Coolant Temperature Sensor	⑥	⑥	—
Fuel Injector	⑦	—	—
Heated Oxygen Sensor	—	—	.60—1.00 ⑧
IAC Motor	38—52	—	—
Intake Air Temperature Sensor	⑥	⑥	—
Throttle Position Sensor	3.5—6.5 ⑤	3.5—6.5 ⑤	—

①—Engine @ 576—2208 RPM.
②—Ignition switch in On position, engine stopped.
③—On Neon models, output voltage should be approximately .38—1.03V @ idle and 3.10—4.00V @ wide open throttle. On Breeze, Cirrus, Concorde, Intrepid, LHS, New Yorker, Sebring Convertible, Stratus & Vision models, output voltage should be at least .60V @ idle & below 4.5V @ wide open throttle. Voltage increase should be proportional to throttle opening throughout travel.
④—Voltage should switch between .30 and 5.00V.
⑤—Resistance should change smoothly as throttle valve opens.
⑥—At 77°F, 9000—11,000 ohms; @ 212°F, 600—800 ohms.
⑦—2.0L/4-122 engine, 11—15 ohms; 2.5L/V6-152 engine, 13—16 ohms.
⑧—With engine racing repeatedly @ normal operating temperature (176°F).

BODY CODE IDENTIFICATION

Body Code	Model
FJ22	Avenger
	Sebring Coupe
F24S	Talon
JA	Breeze
	Cirrus
	Stratus
JX	Sebring Convertible
LH	Concorde
	Intrepid
	LHS
	New Yorker
	Vision
PL	Neon

PRECAUTIONS
AIR BAG SYSTEMS

Refer to "Air Bag System Precautions" in the front of this manual for system disarming and arming procedures.

FUEL SYSTEM PRESSURE RELIEF

In order to avoid personal injury and vehicle damage, fuel system pressure must be released prior to servicing any fuel-related component. Refer to "System Service" for fuel system pressure relief procedures.

When releasing fuel pressure on Flexible Fuel Vehicles (FFV), use methanol resistant gloves and eye protection. Avoid prolonged skin contact with liquid or breathing of vapors.

Persons taking medications containing DISULFIRAM, such as ANTIBUSE, should avoid contact with liquids or vapors from methanol based fuels.

DESCRIPTION

The fuel injection system is comprised of several interactive circuits coordinated and monitored by the Powertrain Control Module (PCM). The PCM receives input from various sensors throughout these circuits and, in turn, provides output information to the devices it controls. For example, if the throttle position sensor indicates the throttle plate is closed, the PCM calculates optimum injector pulse width and ignition timing for idle speed conditions. Then, as the sensor's indications change, the PCM will revise its messages to output devices in order to maintain optimum performance for all driving conditions.

The PCM operates in either "open loop" or "closed loop" mode. During open loop operation, the PCM acts according to preset programming and ignores input from the heated oxygen sensors. Open loop optimizes start-up, warm-up and wide open throttle conditions. During closed loop operation, the PCM monitors the heated oxygen sensors and calculates an air-fuel ratio ideal for low emission levels and peak fuel economy. Closed loop modes occur when the engine is at normal operating temperature and driving conditions are not extreme.

The PCM, through constant monitoring of sensors, operating conditions and interactions between components, can perform on-board diagnoses and communicate its findings to the technician in the form of diagnostic trouble codes. Diagnostic trouble codes are stored in the PCM's memory when it is perceived that a malfunction has occurred. Refer to "Diagnosis & Testing" for diagnostic trouble code retrieval, interpretation and deletion procedures and for further information regarding specific diagnostic trouble codes.

TROUBLESHOOTING

Before diagnosing or servicing the fuel injection system, perform a visual inspection for loose, disconnected or improperly routed wires and hoses. A thorough visual inspection which includes the following checks will save unnecessary diagnostic time.

1. Inspect battery cable connections. Ensure they are clean and tight. Clean any corroded terminals.
2. Verify PCM 40-way connectors are fully inserted into their sockets on PCM.
3. Open Power Distribution Center (PDC). Check for blown fuses and ensure relays and fuses are fully seated in the PDC. Label on underside of PDC cover shows locations of each relay and fuse.
4. Inspect accelerator cable and cruise control cable connections. Check connections to throttle arm of throttle body for any binding or restrictions.
5. Check electrical connections at idle air control motor and throttle position sensor.
6. Check hose connections between PCV valve, vacuum port - intake manifold and oil separator.
7. Inspect electrical connections at intake air temperature sensor and MAP sensor.
8. Inspect fuel injector electrical connections. Use DRB scan tool to verify connection on engine.
9. Inspect distributor connectors and spark plug cables at distributor.
10. Inspect distributor connectors and spark plug cables at distributor.
11. Check electrical connection to radiator fan, then inspect system body grounds for loose or dirty connections.
12. Inspect air cleaner filter element and replace as necessary. Check air induction system for restrictions.
13. Check electrical connections at camshaft position sensor, then at engine coolant temperature sensor.
14. Check electrical connector at electronic EGR transducer. Inspect vacuum and backpressure hoses at solenoid and transducer for leaks.
15. Inspect electrical connections at generator. Check generator belt for glazing or damage.
16. Inspect electrical connector at crankshaft position sensor, then at vehicle speed sensor.
17. Check electrical connection at power steering pressure switch on power steering gear housing.

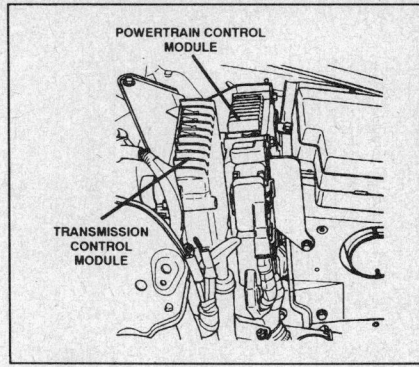

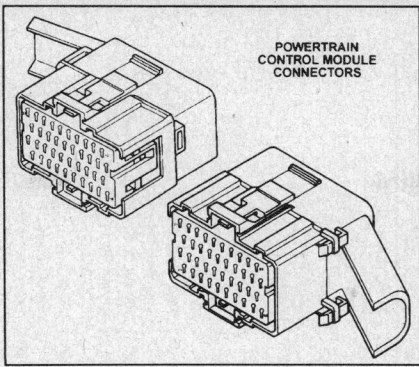

CAV	CKT/COLOR	FUNCTION
1	XWJ5 WT/RD	Downstream Left O2 Sensor Signal (2.5L)
2	XWL9 BK/DB	Ignition Coil Driver #1 (2.0L)
3	XWL8 BR	Ignition Coil Driver #2 (2.0L)
4	AA24 DB	Generator Field Driver
6	XWC0 BK/RD	Auto Shutdown Relay Output
7	XWLB YL/DG	Injector #3 Driver (2.0L)
7	XWL3 YL/DG	Injector #3 Driver (2.5L)
8	XW46 DG/RD	Check Engine Lamp (MIL) Driver
9	FM27 DB/YL	Lamp Check Driver
10	XWZ2 BK	Ground
11	XWT6 RD/DG	Ignition Coil Driver (2.5L)
12	HC33 RD/BK	Speed Control ON Switch Sense
13	XWLA LG/BK	Injector #1 Driver (2.0L)
13	XWL1 LG/BK	Injector #1 Driver (2.5L)
14	XWL6 BR/RD	Injector #6 Driver (2.5L)
15	XWL5 RD/WT	Injector #5 Driver (2.5L)
16	XWLD LG/RD	Injector #4 Driver (2.0L)
16	XWL4 LG/RD	Injector #4 Driver (2.5L)
17	XWLC YL/RD	Injector #2 Driver (2.0L)
17	XWL2 YL/RD	Injector #2 Driver (2.5L)
19	WA5G DG/OR	High Speed Rad Fan Relay Control (2.0L)
19	WR9 DG/OR	High Speed Rad Fan Relay Control (2.5L)
20	XWF6 BK/WT	Fused Ignition Switch Output
22	HC41 LG	Speed Control Lamp Driver
23	XWB4 YL/DB	Fuel Level Sensor Signal
24	XWJ2 WT/YL	Knock Sensor Signal (2.0L)
26	XWK2 DG/WT	Engine Coolant Temp Sensor Sig
28	WR16 DG/YL	High Spd Rad Fan Relay Control (2.5L)
29	XWJ9 DG/BK	Upstream Left O2 Sensor Signal (2.5L)
30	XWJ1 WT/BK	Upstream Oxygen Sensor Signal (2.0L)
30	XWJ1 WT/BK	Upstream Right O2 Sensor Signal (2.5L)
32	XWM5 DB/WT	Crank Position Sensor Signal
32	XWJ4 DB/RD	Camshaft Position Sensor Signal (2.0L)
33	XWL7 BR	Camshaft Position Sensor Signal (2.5L)
35	XWM3 BR/RD	Throttle Position Sensor Signal
36	XWK1 YL/BK	MAP Sensor Signal
37	XWM1 BR/DB	Intake Air Temp Sensor Signal
38	WA54 DG/RD	A/C Clutch Switch Sense

CAV	CKT/COLOR	FUNCTION
40	XWN5 RD/DB	EGR Solenoid Control (2.0L)
40	XWN6 RD/DB	EGR Solenoid Control (2.5L)
41	HC37 RD	Speed Control Switch Signal
43	XWEA BK/DG	Sensor Ground
44	XWW3	8-Volt Supply
45	XWL0 DB/YL	Power Steering Press Sw Sense
46	XWA3 RD/BK	Fused B(+)
47	XWZ1 BK	Signal Ground
48	XWN9 DG/DB	Idle Air Control Motor #3 Driver
49	XWQ0 OR	Idle Air Control Motor #2 Driver
50	XWZ3 BK	Ground
51	XWJ8	Downstream Right O2 Sensor Signal
55	WR12 DG/BK	Low Spd Rad Fan Relay Control
56	AA11 DB	Generator Lamp Driver
57	XWJ0 DG	Idle Air Control Motor #1 Driver
58	XWP9 YL/DB	Idle Air Control Motor #4 Driver
59	YEJ5 BK/DB	CCD Bus (+)
60	YEJ4 WT/DB	CCD Bus (-)
61	XWV2 DG/YL	5-Volt Supply
62	XWM0 BR/WT	Brake Switch Sense
63	YEA0 OR/BK	Torque Management Request Sense
64	WA53 DG	A/C Comp Clutch Relay Control
65	XWD1 PK	SCI Transmit
66	XWG8 YL/WT	Vehicle Speed Sensor Signal
67	XWS0 RD/WT	Auto Shutdown Sense
68	XWP2 LG/BK	Evaporative Emission Solenoid Control
69	WR9A DG/OR	High Speed Cond Fan Relay Control (2.0L)
69	WA5B DG/WT	High Speed Cond Fan Relay Control (2.5L)
72	XWP3 RD/DB	Leak Detection Pump Switch Sense
73	XWG1 WT	Tach Signal
74	XWB1 BK/DB	Fuel Pump Relay Control
75	XWD0 DB/BK	SCI Receive
76	AS19 BK/YL	P/N Position Switch Sense
77	XWN3 RD/YL	Leak Detection Pump Solenoid Control
78	HC36 LG/WT	SC Vacuum Solenoid Control
79	XWN4 RD/YL	Aspirator Solenoid Control (2.0L MTX)
80	HC35 BK/YL	SC Vent Solenoid Control

CR1029606800000X

Fig. 1 PCM connector terminal identification. Avenger, Sebring Coupe & Talon

18. **On models equipped with automatic transaxle,** check electrical connections at park/neutral switch.
19. **On all models,** inspect electrical connections at upstream and downstream heated oxygen sensors.
20. Inspect fuel pump module electrical connection in trunk for corrosion or damage.
21. Inspect connections to speed control servo.

DIAGNOSIS & TESTING

Refer to **Figs. 1 through 10** for connector terminal identification and fuel injection system wiring diagrams.

Accessing Diagnostic Trouble Codes
USING SCAN TOOL

1. Connect a DRB or generic scan tool to diagnostic connector, **Figs. 11**

through **14,** then turn ignition switch to On position and access diagnostic trouble codes by following tool screen prompts.
2. Record all diagnostic trouble codes indicated by scan tool. Ensure malfunction indicator lamp (MIL) on instrument panel lights for approximately 2 seconds as a bulb check.
3. If any diagnostic trouble codes are present, proceed to "Diagnostic Trouble Code Interpretation" for further information regarding specific diagnostic trouble codes.
4. Refer to Diagnostic Chart Index for location of diagnostic procedures corresponding to scan tool diagnostic trouble codes.

USING MALFUNCTION INDICATOR LAMP (MIL)

1. Cycle ignition key through an On, Off,

On, Off On position sequence within five seconds, then observe MIL flash pattern. Diagnostic trouble codes may be read as follows:
   a. Initial flashes indicate "tens" digit of a diagnostic trouble code; these are followed by a brief pause, after which subsequent flashes indicate "ones" digit. For example, six flashes, followed by a brief pause and two additional flashes, indicates MIL diagnostic trouble code 62 is present.
   b. A longer pause will occur between trouble codes if multiple codes have been logged.
   c. Refer to Diagnostic Chart Index for location of diagnostic procedures corresponding to MIL diagnostic trouble codes.
2. After repairing condition indicated by tool, erase diagnostic trouble codes as described under "Clearing Diagnostic Trouble Codes."

Diagnostic Trouble Code Interpretation

If a DRB scan tool was used to access diagnostic trouble codes, the display will provide a brief description of the problem area. If a generic scan tool was used, output will be in the form of a five-character code beginning with the letter "P." If the Malfunction Indicator Lamp (MIL) was used, interpret flashes as described under "Accessing Diagnostic Trouble Codes" in order to obtain the two-digit diagnostic trouble code number.

Refer to the Diagnostic Chart Index for locations of diagnostic flowcharts corresponding to specific diagnostic trouble codes that were displayed via the various retrieval methods. Proceed to the flowcharts, **Figs. 15 through 222,** as directed by the Diagnostic Chart Index.

Clearing Diagnostic Trouble Codes

Diagnostic trouble codes can be erased using the "Erase Trouble Code Data" screen on the DRB III scan tool or by disconnecting the battery ground cable for at least two minutes.

Inactive Diagnostic Trouble Code Condition

This section should only be used when referenced by the diagnostic charts in this section.

You have just attempted to simulate the condition that initially set the diagnostic trouble code. The following additional checks may assist in identifying a possible intermittent problem:
1. Visually inspect related wire harness connectors. Look for broken, bent, pushed out or corroded terminals.
2. Visually inspect the related harnesses. Look for chafed, pierced or partially broken wires.
3. Refer to any technical service bulletins that may apply.

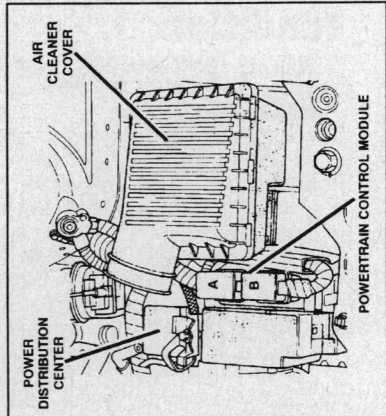

Fig. 3 PCM connector terminal identification. Concorde, Intrepid, LHS, New Yorker & Vision

CAV	CKT/COLOR	FUNCTION	CAV	CKT/COLOR	FUNCTION
1	K241 LG/RD	Downstream Left O2 Sensor Signal	42	C18 DB	A/C Pressure Signal
2	K18 RD	Ignition Coil Driver #3	43	K4 BK/LB	Sensor Ground
3	K17 WT	Ignition Coil Driver #2	44	K7 OR	8-Volt Supply
4	K20 DG	Generator Field Driver	46	A14 RD/WT	Fused B(+)
5	V32 YL/RD	Speed Control Power Supply	47	Z11 BK/WT	Ground
6	A142 DG/OR	Auto Shutdown Relay Output	48	K40 BR/WT	Idle Air Control Motor #1 Driver
7	K13 YL/WT	Injector #3 Driver	49	K60 YL/BK	Idle Air Control Motor #2 Driver
10	Z12 BK/TN	Ground	50	Z12 BK/TN	Ground
11	K19 BK	Ignition Coil Driver #1	51	K341 TN/WT	Downstream Right O2 Sensor Signal
13	K11 WT/LB	Injector #1 Driver	55	C24 WT	Low Spd Rad Fan Relay Control
14	K58 BR/BK	Injector #6 Driver	57	K39 GY/RD	Idle Air Control Motor #3 Driver
15	K38 BR/RD	Injector #5 Driver	58	K59 VT/BK	Idle Air Control Motor #4 Driver
16	K14 LB/BR	Injector #4 Driver	59	D1 VT/BR	CCD Bus (+)
17	K12 TN	Injector #2 Driver	60	D2 WT/BK	CCD Bus (–)
20	F12 DB/WT	Fused Ignition Switch Output	61	K6 VT/WT	5-Volt Supply
24	K42 BK/LG	Knock Sensor #1 Signal (3.5L)	62	K29 WT/PK	Brake Switch Sense
25	K142 GY/BK	Knock Sensor #2 Signal (3.5L)	63	T10 YL/DG	Torque Management Request Sense
26	K2 TN/BK	Engine Coolant Temp Sensor Sig	64	C28 DB/OR	A/C Comp Clutch Relay Control
29	K141 TN/WT	Upstream Left O2 Sensor Signal	65	D21 PK	SCI Transmit
30	K41 BK/DG	Upstream Right O2 Sensor Signal	66	G7 WT/OR	Vehicle Speed Sensor Signal
32	K24 LB/DB	Crank Position Sensor Signal	67	K51 DB/YL	Auto Shutdown Relay Control
33	K44 TN/YL	Camshaft Position Sensor Signal	68	K52 PK/BK	Evaporative Emission Solenoid Control
35	K22 OR/DB	Throttle Position Sensor Signal	69	C27 DB/PK	High Spd Rad Fan Relay Control
36	K1 DG/RD	MAP Sensor Signal	74	K31 BR	Fuel Pump Relay Control
37	K21 BK/RD	Intake Air Temp Sensor Signal	75	D20 LG	SCI Receive
39	K36 VT/RD	Manifold Solenoid Control	76	T41 BK/DG	P/N Position Switch Sense
40	K35 GY/YL	EGR Solenoid Control	78	V36 TN/RD	SC Vacuum Solenoid Control
41	V37 RD/LG	Speed Control Switch Signal	80	V35 LG/RD	SC Vent Solenoid Control

CR1029606679800X

Fig. 2 PCM connector terminal identification. Breeze, Cirrus, Sebring Convertible & Stratus

CAV	CIRCUIT	FUNCTION	CAV	CIRCUIT	FUNCTION
2	K19 BK/GY	Ignition Coil Driver #1 (2.0/2.4L)	48	K40 BR/GY	Idle Air Control Motor #1 Driver
3	K17 DB/DG	Ignition Coil Driver #2 (2.0/2.4L)	49	K60 YL/GY	Idle Air Control Motor #2 Driver
4	K20 DG	Generator Field Driver	50	Z12 BK/TN	Ground
5	V32 YL/PK	Speed Control Power Supply	51	K141 TN/WT	Downstream Oxygen Sensor Signal
6	A142 DG/OR	Auto Shutdown Relay Output	52	K25 VT/LG	Battery Temp Sensor Signal
7	K13 YL/WT	Injector #3 Driver	55	C24 DB/TN	Low Spd Rad Fan Relay Output
10	Z12 BK/TN	Ground	57	K39 GY/RD	Idle Air Control Motor #3 Driver
11	K19 BK/GY	Ignition Coil Driver (2.5L)	58	K59 VT/GY	Idle Air Control Motor #4 Driver
13	K11 WT/LB	Injector #1 Driver	59	D1 VT/BR	CCD Bus (+)
14	K58 BR/DG	Injector #6 Driver (2.5L)	60	D2 WT/BK	CCD Bus (–)
15	K38 GY	Injector #5 Driver (2.5L)	61	K6 VT/WT	5-Volt Supply
16	K14 LB/BR	Injector #4 Driver	62	K29 WT/RD	Brake Switch Sense
17	K12 TN	Injector #2 Driver	63	T10 YL/DG	Torque Management Request Sense (EATX)
20	F12 DB/WT	Fused Ignition Switch Output	64	C28 DB/OR	A/C Comp Clutch Relay Control
24	K24 GY/BK	Knock Sensor Signal	65	D21 PK/LB	SCI Transmit
26	K2 TN/BK	Engine Coolant Temp Sensor Sig	66	G7 WT/OR	Vehicle Speed Sensor Signal
30	K41 BK/DG	Front Upstream Oxygen Sensor Signal	67	K51 DB/VT	Auto Shutdown Relay Control
32	K24 GY/BK	Crank Position Sensor Signal	68	K52 PK/GY	Evaporative Emission Solenoid Control
33	K44 TN/YL	Camshaft Position Sensor Signal	69	C27 DB/PK	High Speed Rad Fan Relay Control
35	K22 OR/LB	Throttle Position Sensor Signal	72	K107 OR/DG	Leak Detection Pump Switch Sense
36	K1 DG/RD	MAP Sensor Signal	74	K31 BR/LG	Fuel Pump Relay Control
37	K21 BK/RD	Intake Air Temp Sensor Signal	75	D20 LG/WT	SCI Receive
40	K35 GY/YL	EGR Solenoid Circuit	76	T41 BK/WT	P/N Position Switch Sense (EATX)
41	V37 PK/LG	Speed Control Switch Signal	77	K106 WT/DG	Leak Detection Pump Solenoid Control
42	C18 DB/YL	A/C Pressure Switch Sense	78	V36 WT/VT	SC Vacuum Solenoid Control
43	K4 BK/LB	Sensor Ground	80	V35 LG/RD	SC Vent Solenoid Control
44	K7 OR/WT	8-Volt Supply			
45	K10 DB/LG	Power Steering Press Sw Sense			
46	A14 RD/TN	Fused B(+)			

CR1029606799000X

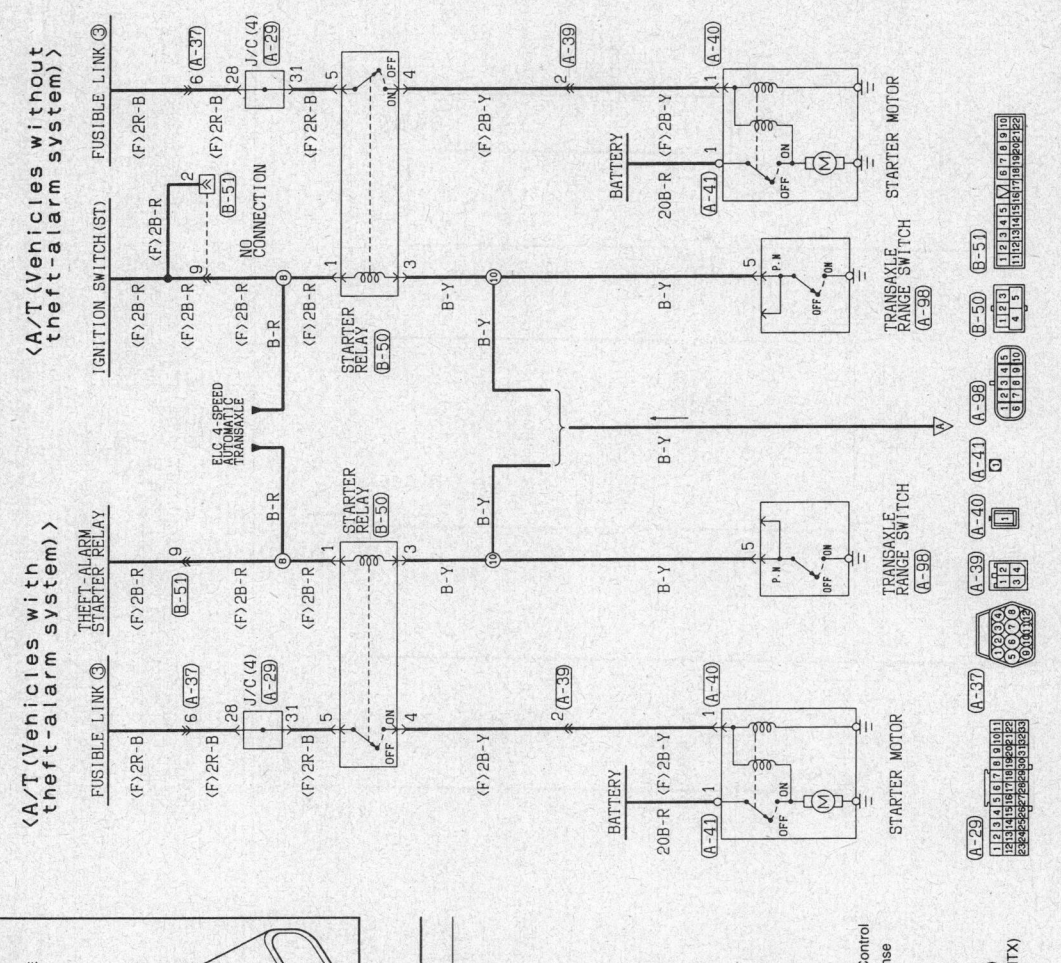

Fig. 5 MFI wiring diagram (Part 1 of 10). Avenger & Sebring Coupe w/2.0L/4-122 engine

CAV	CKT/COLOR	FUNCTION	CAV	CKT/COLOR	FUNCTION
2	K19 BK/GY	Ignition Coil Driver #1	45	K10 WT	Power Steering Press Sw Sense
3	K17 DB/TN	Ignition Coil Driver #2	46	A14 RD/WT	Fused B(+)
4	K20 DG	Generator Field Driver	47	Z11 BK/WT	Ground
5	V32 YL/RD	Speed Control Power Supply	48	K40 BR/WT	Idle Air Control Motor #3 Driver
6	A142 DG/OR	Auto Shutdown Relay Output	49	K60 YL/BK	Idle Air Control Motor #2 Driver
7	K13 YL/WT	Injector #3 Driver	50	Z12 BK/TN	Ground
8	G3 BK/PK	MIL Lamp Driver	51	K141 TN/WT	Downstream O2 Sensor
10	Z12 BK/TN	Ground	52	G31 VT/LG	Battery Temp Sensor Signal
13	K11 WT/LB	Injector #1 Driver	55	C27 DB/PK	Low Spd Rad Fan Relay Control
16	K14 LB/BR	Injector #4 Driver	56	G12 TN/BK	Generator Lamp Driver
17	K12 TN	Injector #2 Driver	57	K39 GY/RD	Idle Air Control Motor #1 Driver
20	F12 DB/WT	Fused Ignition Switch Output	58	K59 VT	Idle Air Control Motor #4 Driver
23	G4 DB	Fuel Level Sensor Signal	61	K6 VT/WT	5-Volt Supply
24	K42 BK/LG	Knock Sensor Signal (DOHC)	62	K29 WT/PK	Brake Switch Sense
24	K42 DB/LG	Knock Sensor Siganl (SOHC)	64	C28 DB/OR	A/C Comp Clutch Relay Control
26	K2 TN/BK	Engine Coolant Temp Sensor Signal (DOHC)	65	D21 PK	SCI Transmit
26	K2 TN/DB	Engine Coolant Temp Sensor Signal (SOHC)	66	G7 WT/OR	Vehicle Speed Sensor Signal
30	K41 BK/DG	Upstream Oxygen Sensor Signal	67	K51 DB/YL	Auto Shutdown Relay Control
32	K24 GY/BK	Crank Position Sensor Signal	68	K52 PK/BK	Evaporative Emission Solenoid Control
33	K44 TN/YL	Camshaft Position Sensor Signal	72	K107 OR	Leak Detection Pump Switch Sense (MTX)
35	K22 OR/LB	Throttle Position Sensor Signal	73	G21 GY/LB	Tachometer Signal
36	K1 DG/RD	MAP Sensor Signal	74	K31 BR	Fuel Pump Relay Control
37	K21 BK/RD	Intake Air Temp Sensor Signal	75	D20 LG	SCI Receive
38	C20 BR	A/C Switch Sense	76	T41 BR/YL	P/N Position Switch Sense (ATX)
40	K35 GY/YL	EGR Solenoid Control	77	K106 WT/LG	Leak Detection Pump Sol Ctrl (MTX)
41	V37 RD/LG	Speed Control Switch Signal	78	V36 TN/RD	SC Vacuum Solenoid Control
43	K4 BK/LB	Sensor Ground	79	K54 OR/BK	Torq Conv Clutch Sol Ctrl (ATX)
44	K7 OR	8-Volt Supply	80	V35 LG/RD	SC Vent Solenoid Control

Fig. 4 PCM connector terminal identification. Neon

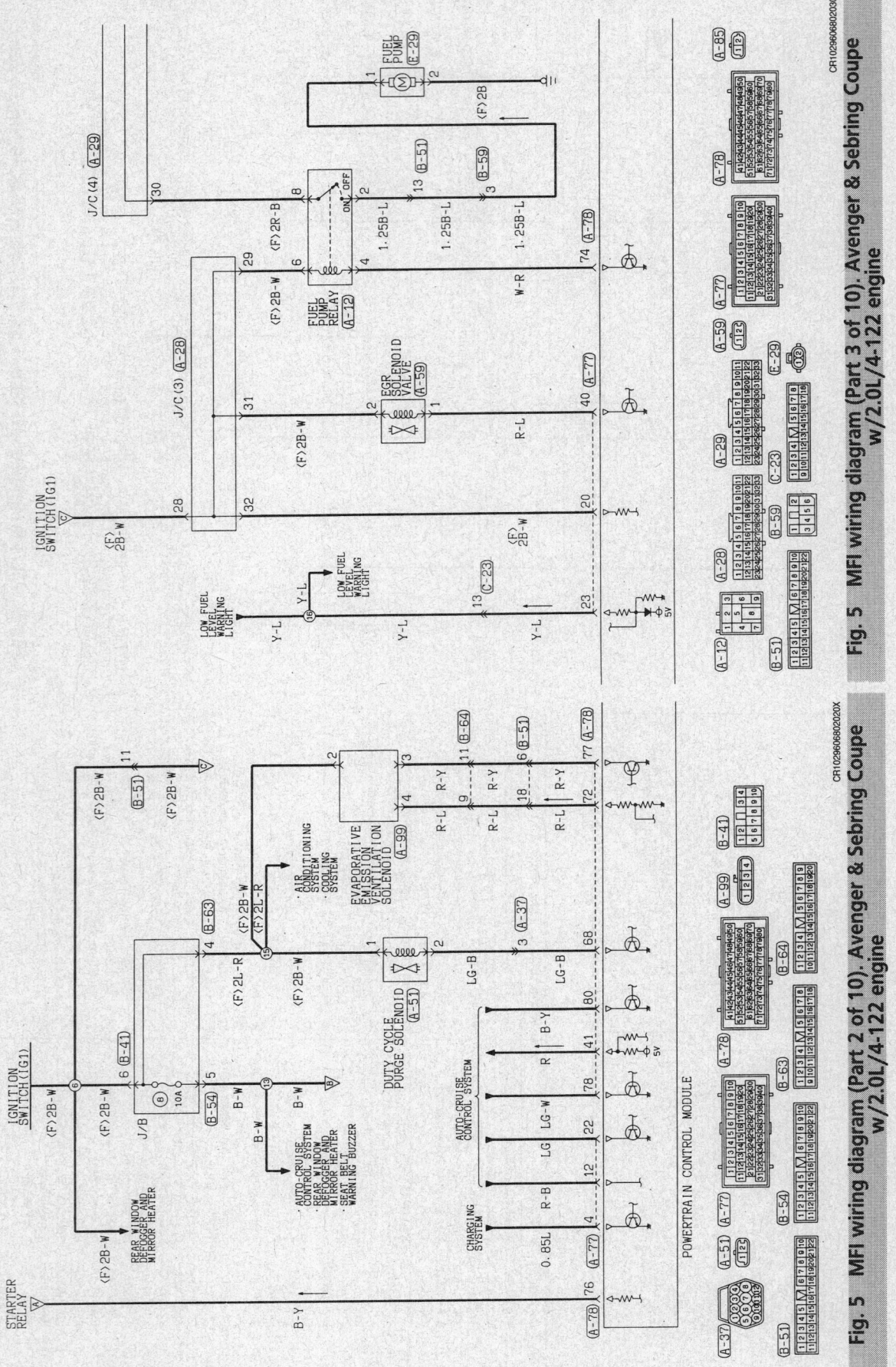

Fig. 5   MFI wiring diagram (Part 3 of 10), Avenger & Sebring Coupe w/2.0L/4-122 engine

Fig. 5   MFI wiring diagram (Part 2 of 10), Avenger & Sebring Coupe w/2.0L/4-122 engine

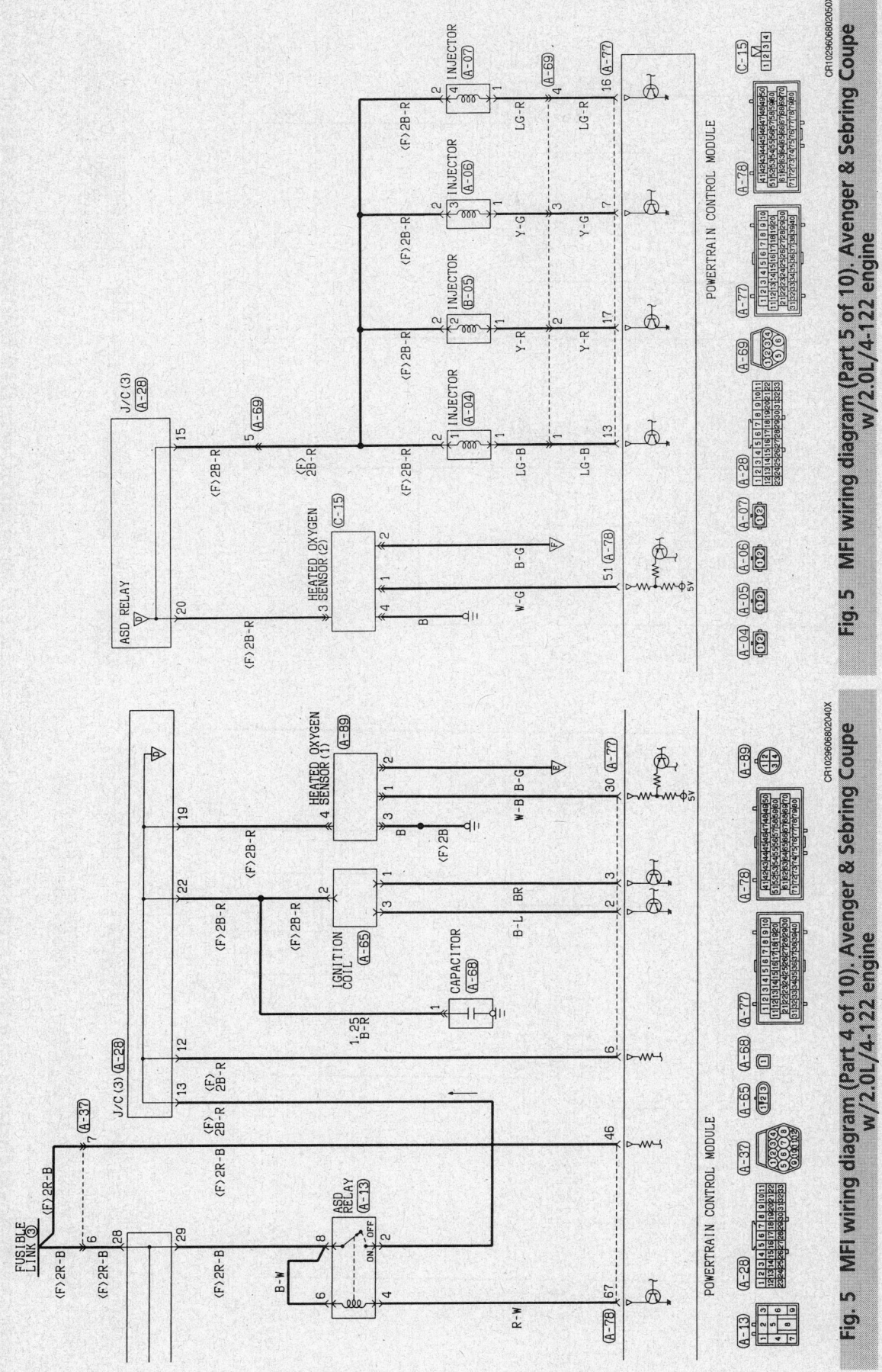

Fig. 5 MFI wiring diagram (Part 5 of 10), Avenger & Sebring Coupe w/2.0L/4-122 engine

Fig. 5 MFI wiring diagram (Part 4 of 10), Avenger & Sebring Coupe w/2.0L/4-122 engine

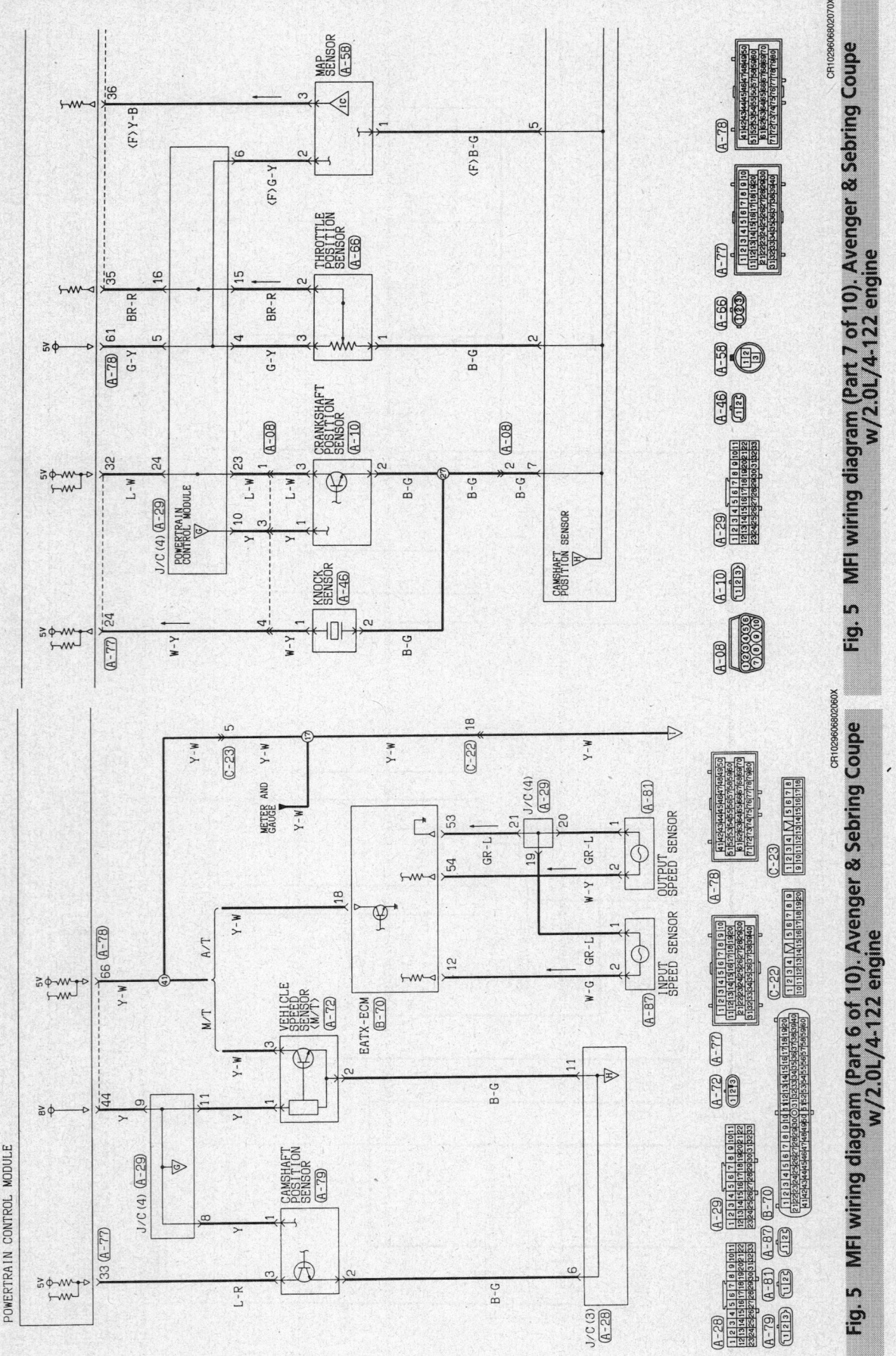

Fig. 5   MFI wiring diagram (Part 7 of 10). Avenger & Sebring Coupe w/2.0L/4-122 engine

Fig. 5   MFI wiring diagram (Part 6 of 10). Avenger & Sebring Coupe w/2.0L/4-122 engine

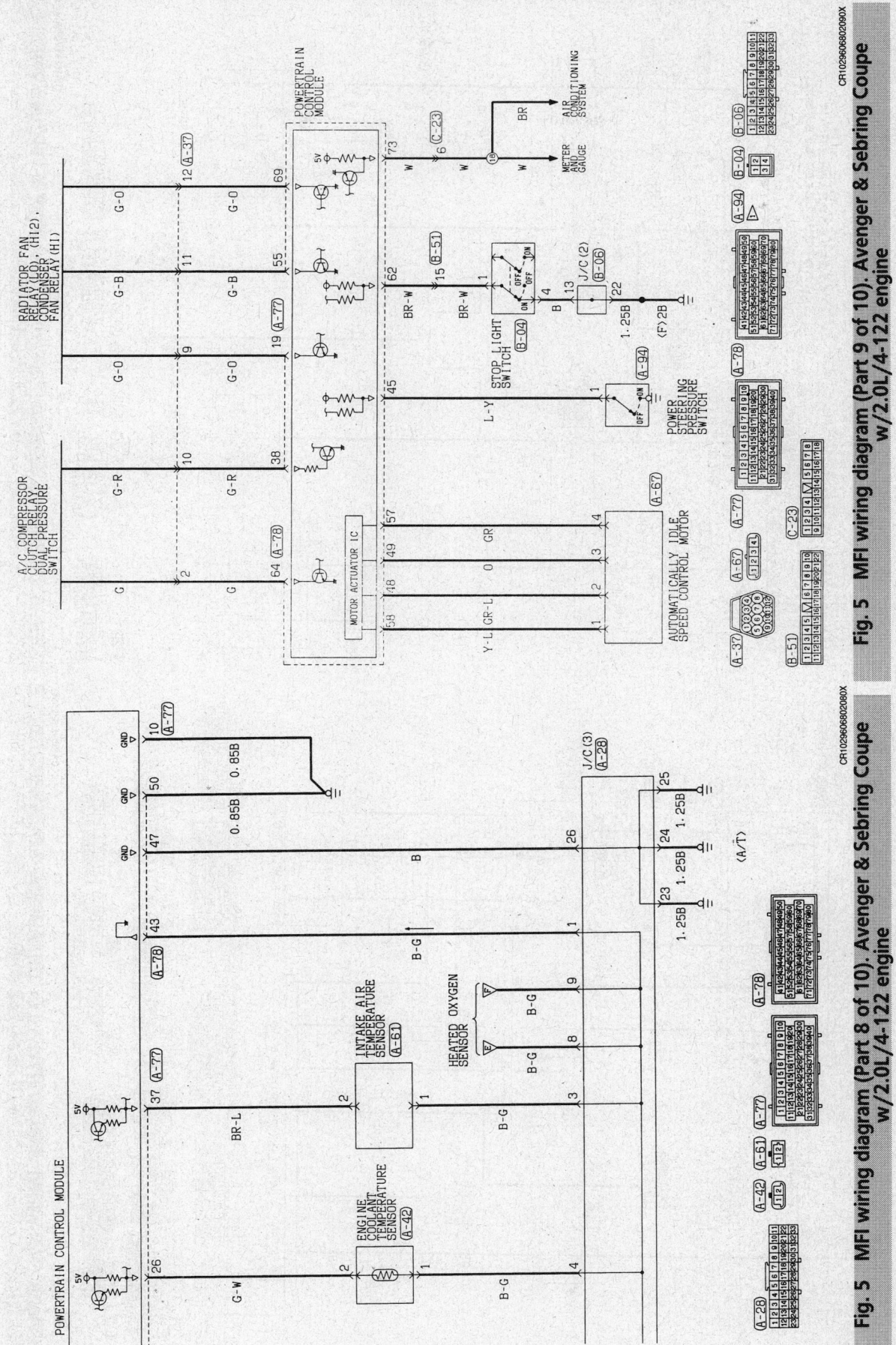

Fig. 5 MFI wiring diagram (Part 9 of 10). Avenger & Sebring Coupe w/2.0L/4-122 engine

Fig. 5 MFI wiring diagram (Part 8 of 10). Avenger & Sebring Coupe w/2.0L/4-122 engine

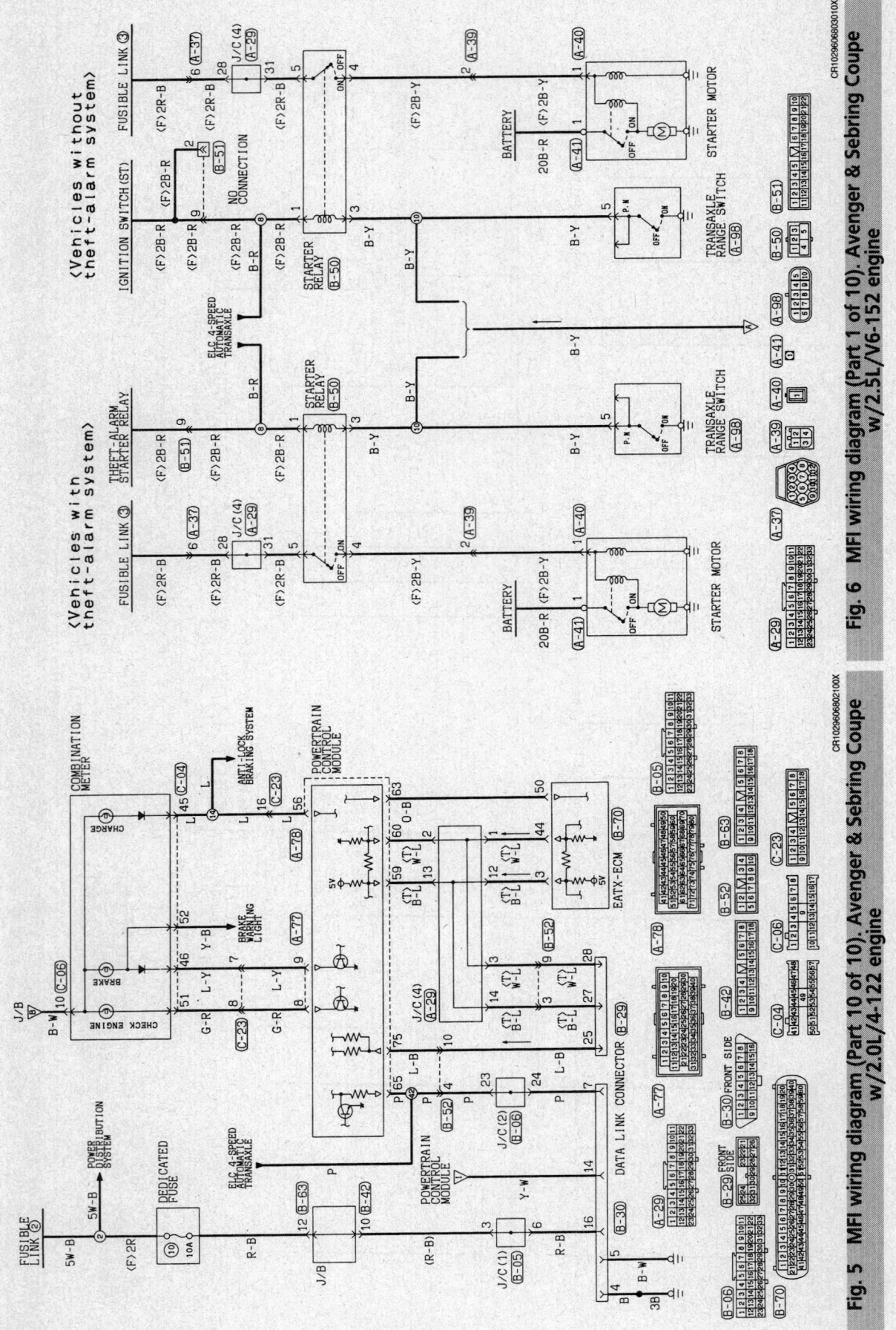

Fig. 6   MFI wiring diagram (Part 1 of 10). Avenger & Sebring Coupe w/2.5L/V6-152 engine

Fig. 5   MFI wiring diagram (Part 10 of 10). Avenger & Sebring Coupe w/2.0L/4-122 engine

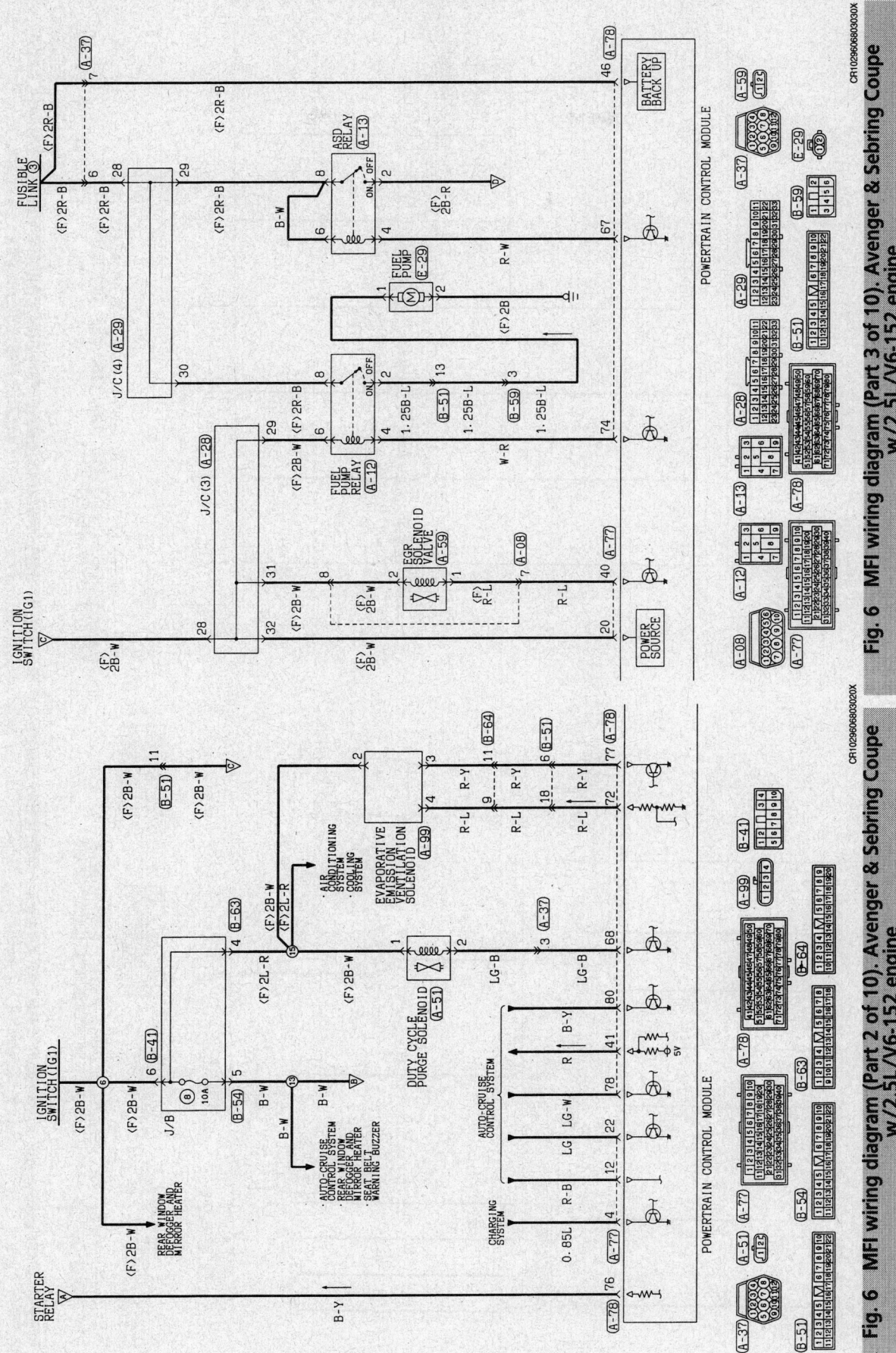

Fig. 6   MFI wiring diagram (Part 3 of 10). Avenger & Sebring Coupe w/2.5L/V6-152 engine

Fig. 6   MFI wiring diagram (Part 2 of 10). Avenger & Sebring Coupe w/2.5L/V6-152 engine

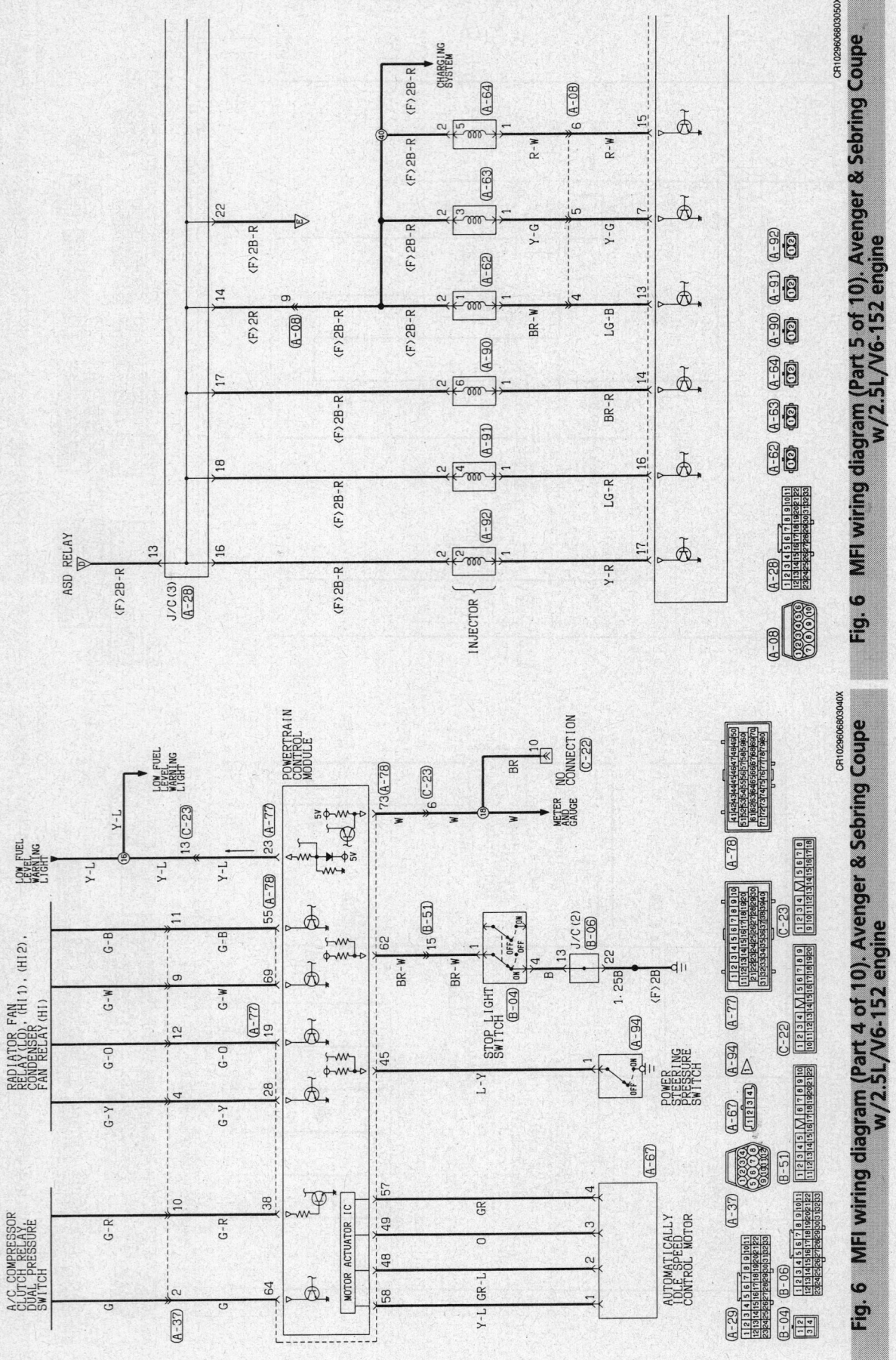

Fig. 6 MFI wiring diagram (Part 5 of 10). Avenger & Sebring Coupe w/2.5L/V6-152 engine

Fig. 6 MFI wiring diagram (Part 4 of 10). Avenger & Sebring Coupe w/2.5L/V6-152 engine

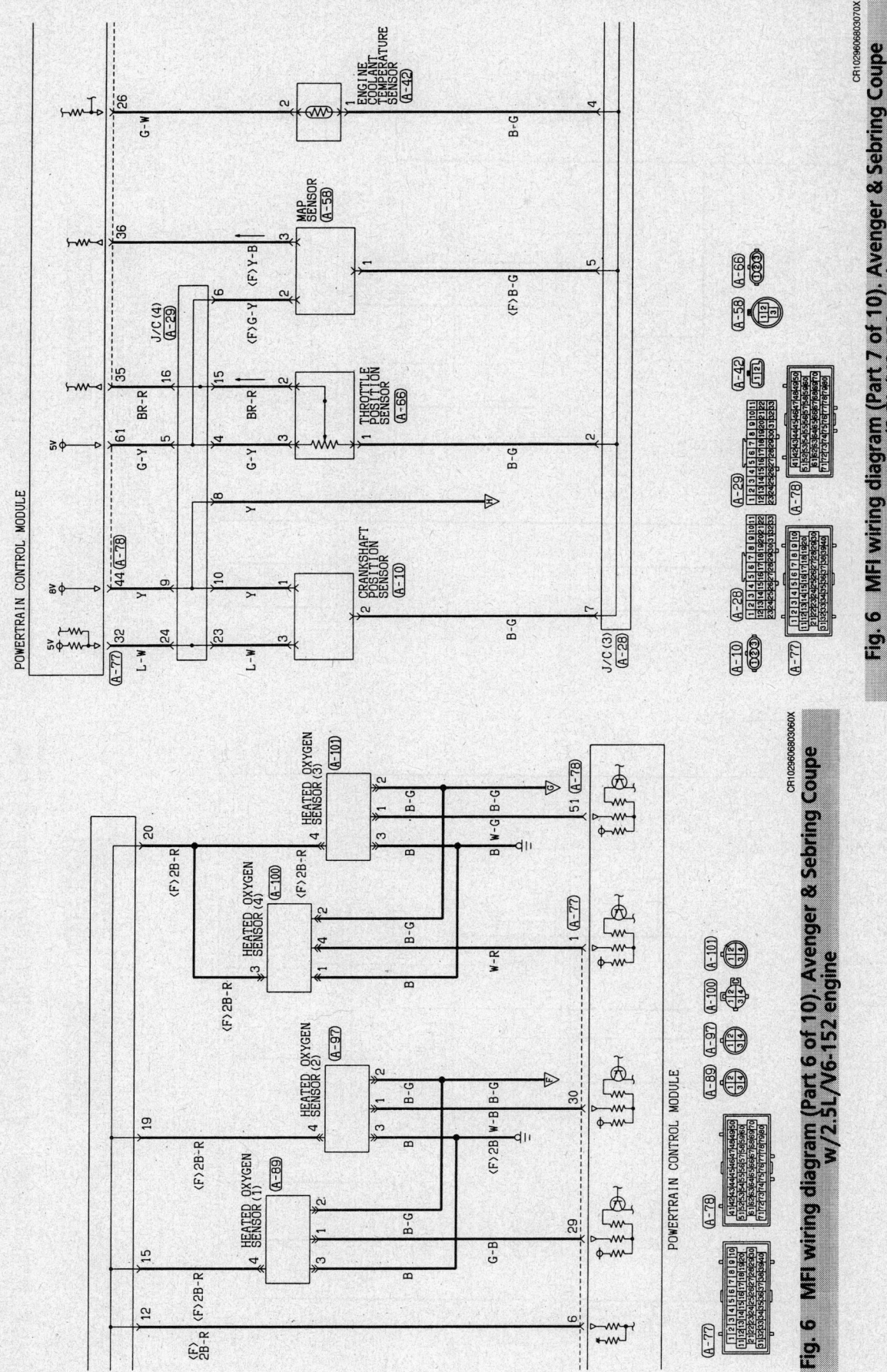

Fig. 6 MFI wiring diagram (Part 7 of 10). Avenger & Sebring Coupe w/2.5L/V6-152 engine

Fig. 6 MFI wiring diagram (Part 6 of 10). Avenger & Sebring Coupe w/2.5L/V6-152 engine

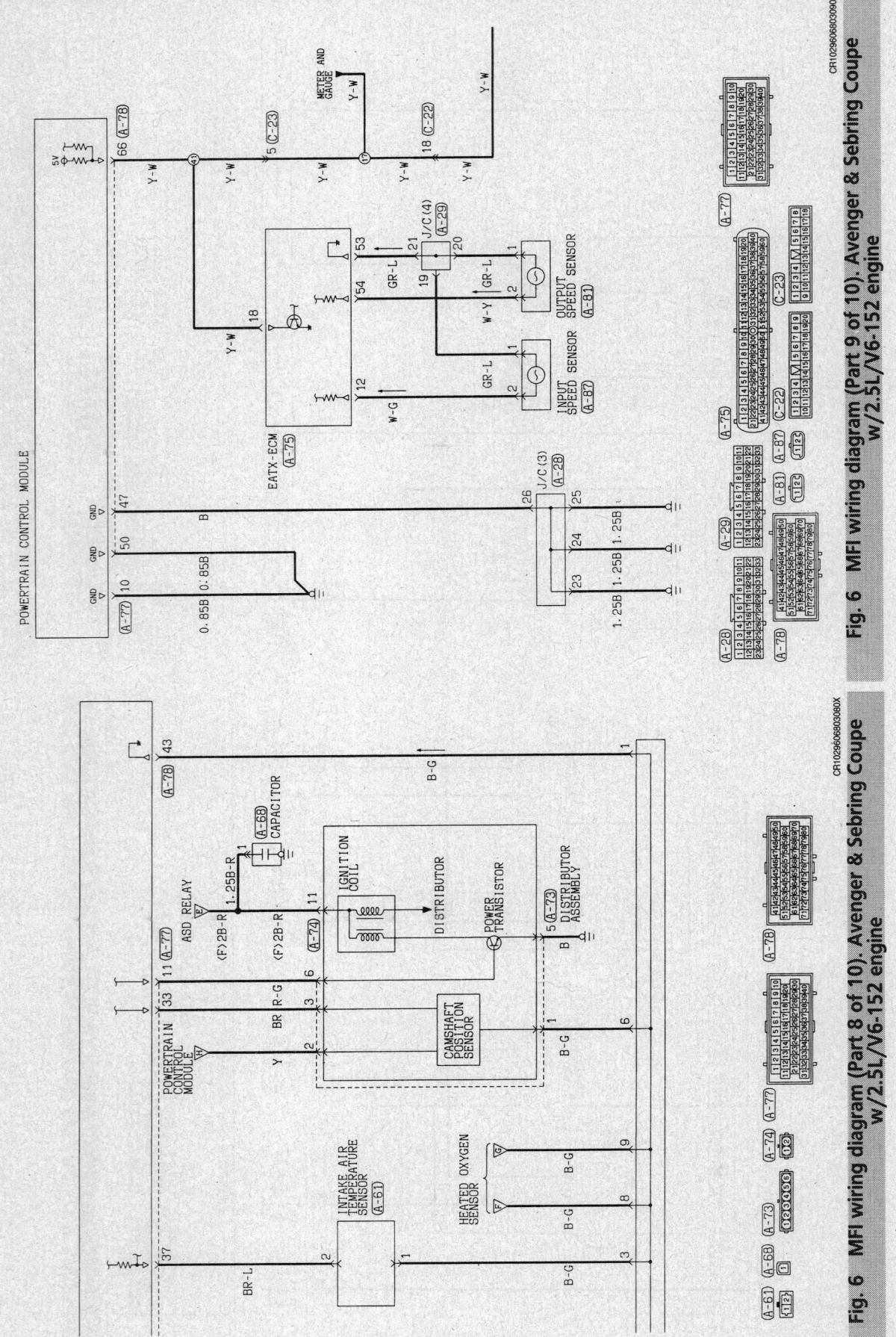

Fig. 6   MFI wiring diagram (Part 9 of 10). Avenger & Sebring Coupe w/2.5L/V6-152 engine

Fig. 6   MFI wiring diagram (Part 8 of 10). Avenger & Sebring Coupe w/2.5L/V6-152 engine

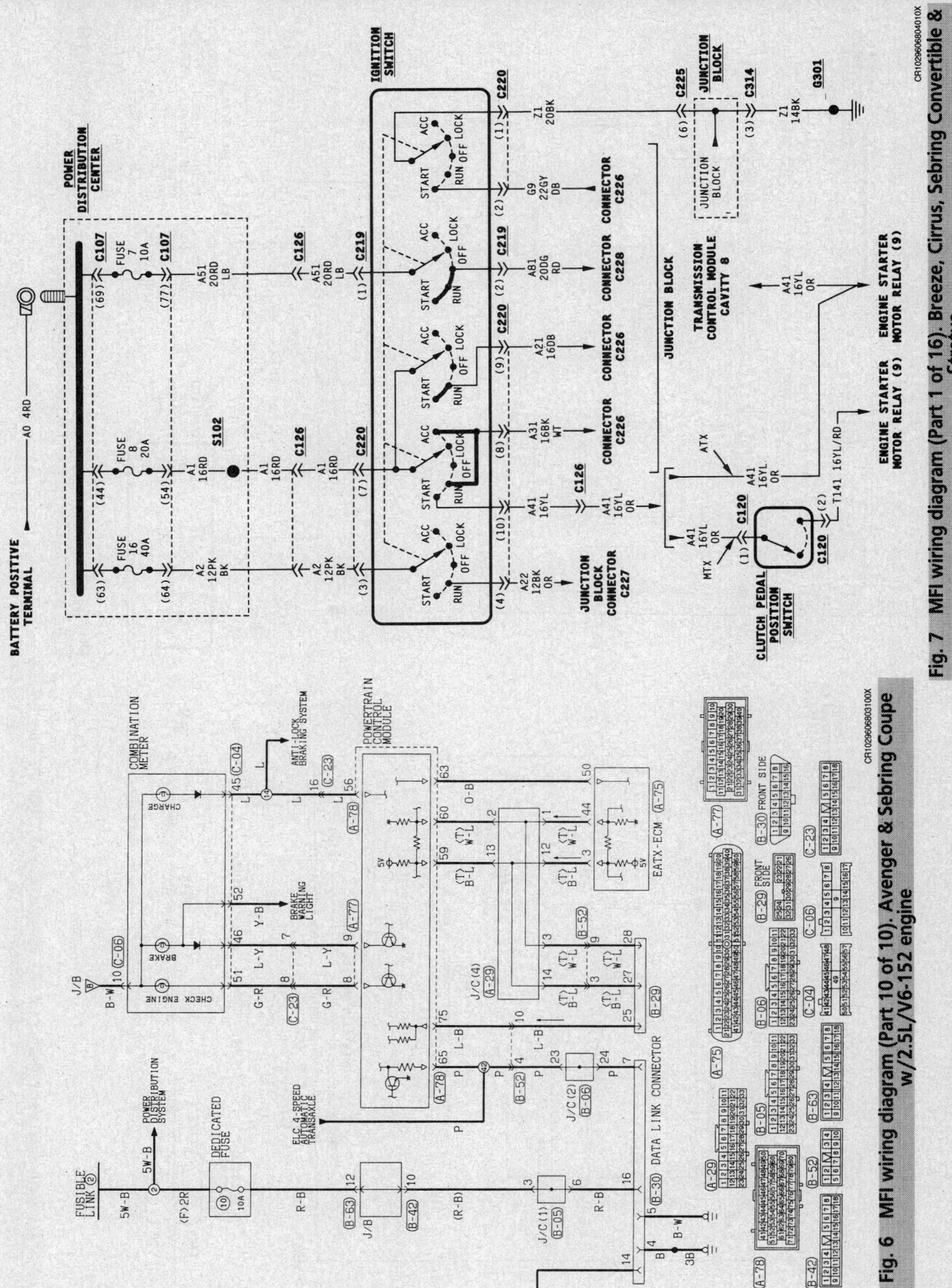

Fig. 7 MFI wiring diagram (Part 1 of 16). Breeze, Cirrus, Sebring Convertible & Stratus

Fig. 6 MFI wiring diagram (Part 10 of 10). Avenger & Sebring Coupe w/2.5L/V6-152 engine

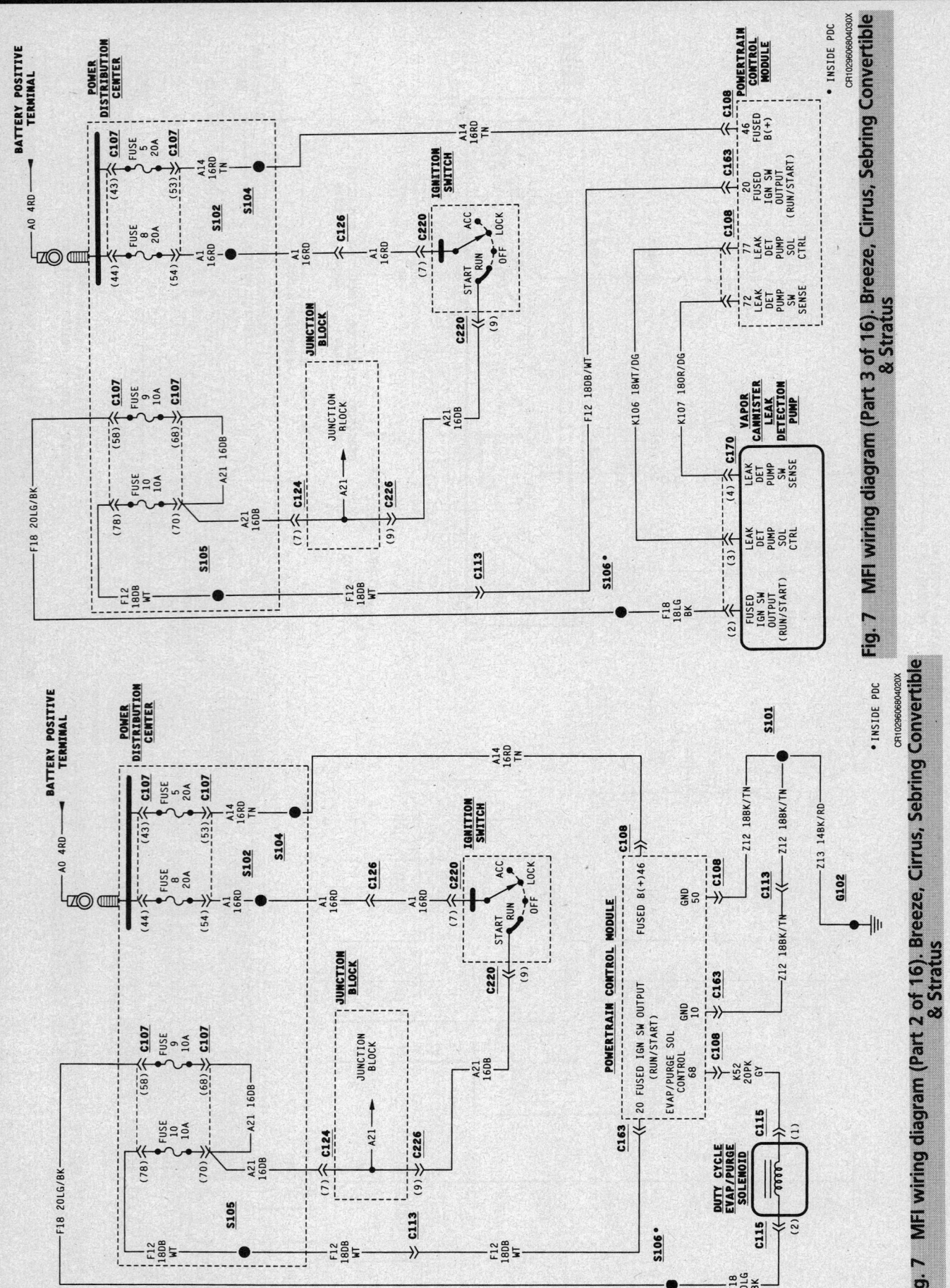

Fig. 7   MFI wiring diagram (Part 3 of 16). Breeze, Cirrus, Sebring Convertible & Stratus

Fig. 7   MFI wiring diagram (Part 2 of 16). Breeze, Cirrus, Sebring Convertible & Stratus

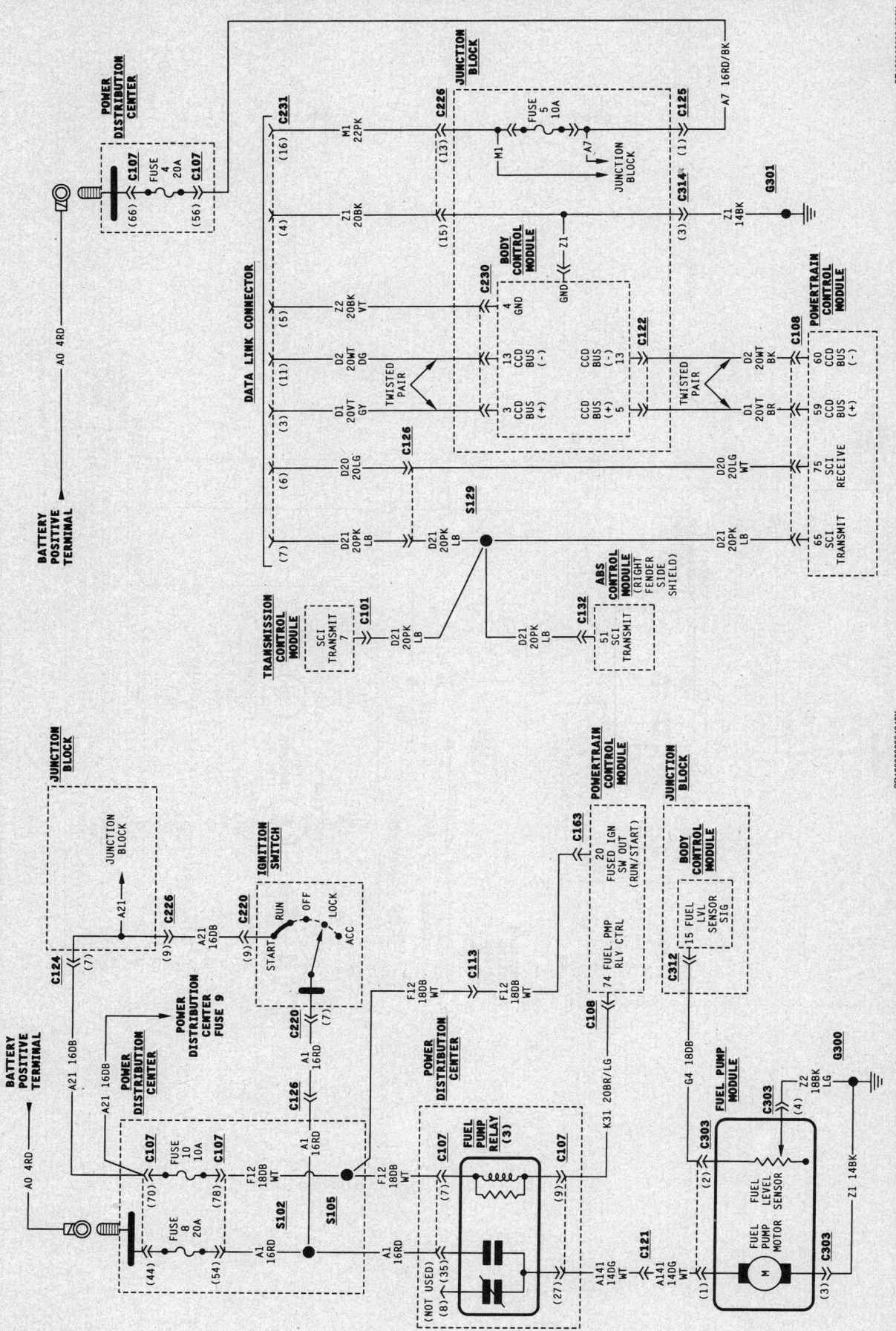

Fig. 7 MFI wiring diagram (Part 5 of 16). Breeze, Cirrus, Sebring Convertible & Stratus

Fig. 7 MFI wiring diagram (Part 4 of 16). Breeze, Cirrus, Sebring Convertible & Stratus

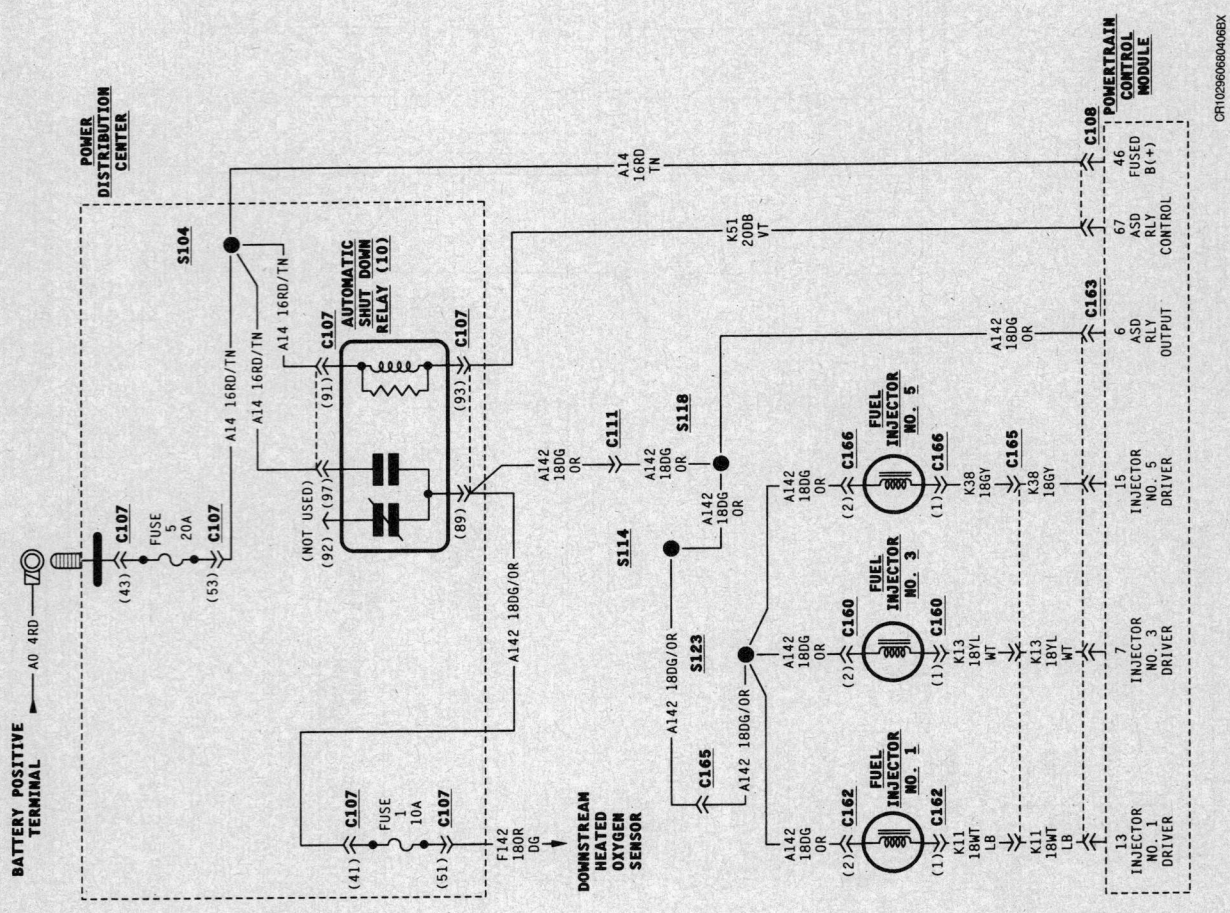

Fig. 7 MFI wiring diagram (Part 6 of 16). Breeze, Cirrus, Sebring Convertible & Stratus w/2.0L/4-122 & 2.4L/4-148 engines

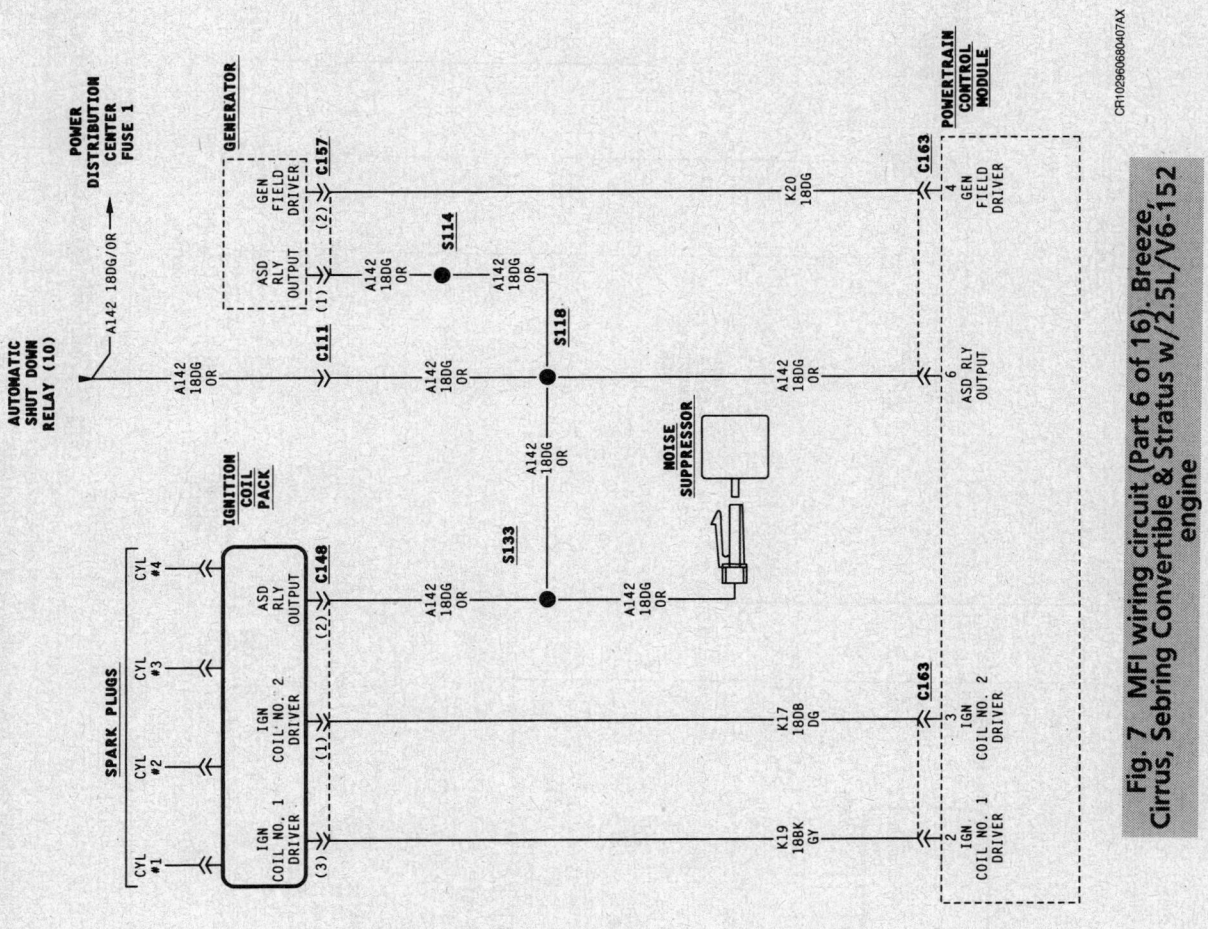

Fig. 7 MFI wiring circuit (Part 6 of 16). Breeze, Cirrus, Sebring Convertible & Stratus w/2.5L/V6-152 engine

CR102960680407AX

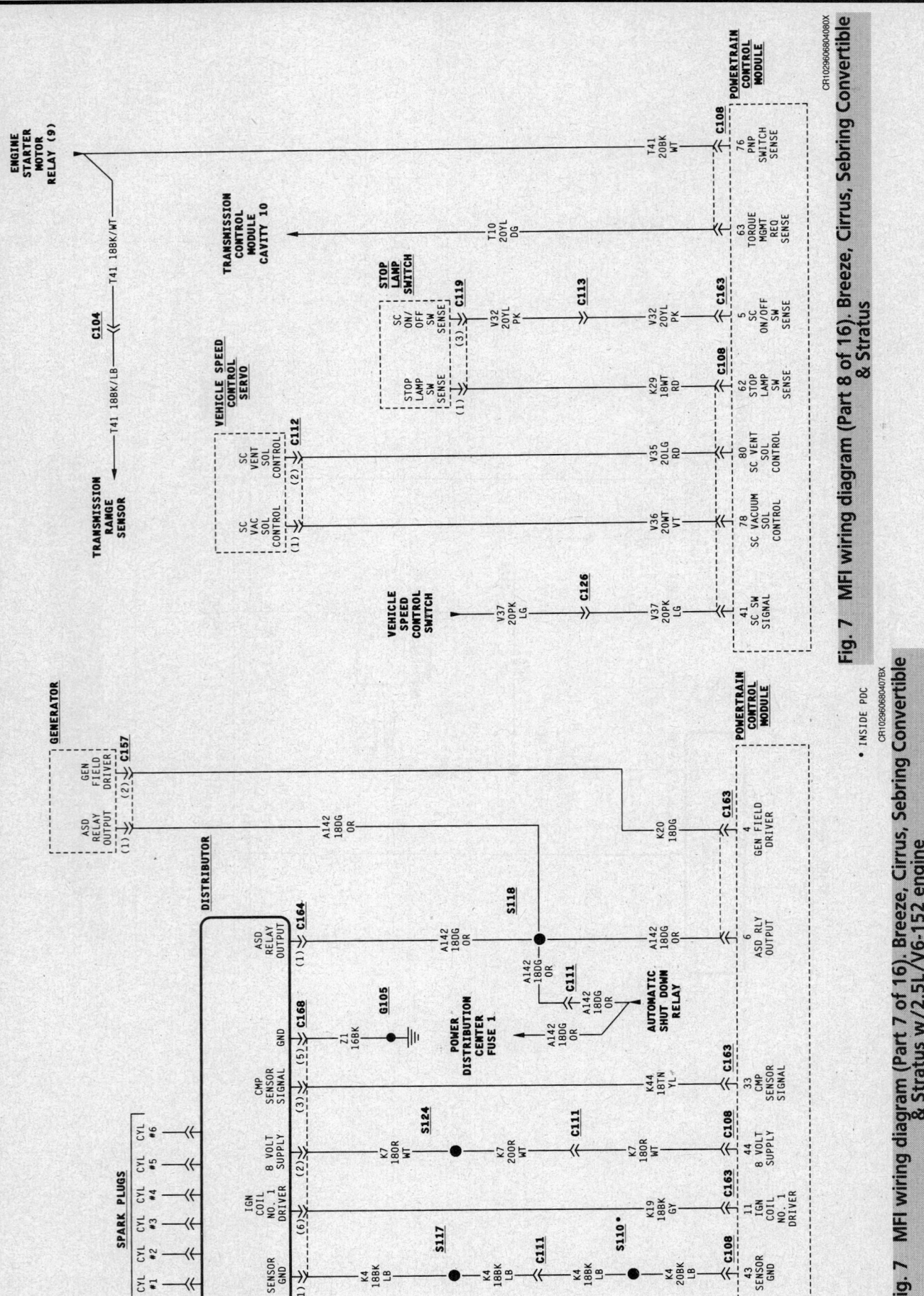

Fig. 7 MFI wiring diagram (Part 8 of 16). Breeze, Cirrus, Sebring Convertible & Stratus

Fig. 7 MFI wiring diagram (Part 7 of 16). Breeze, Cirrus, Sebring Convertible & Stratus w/2.5L/V6-152 engine

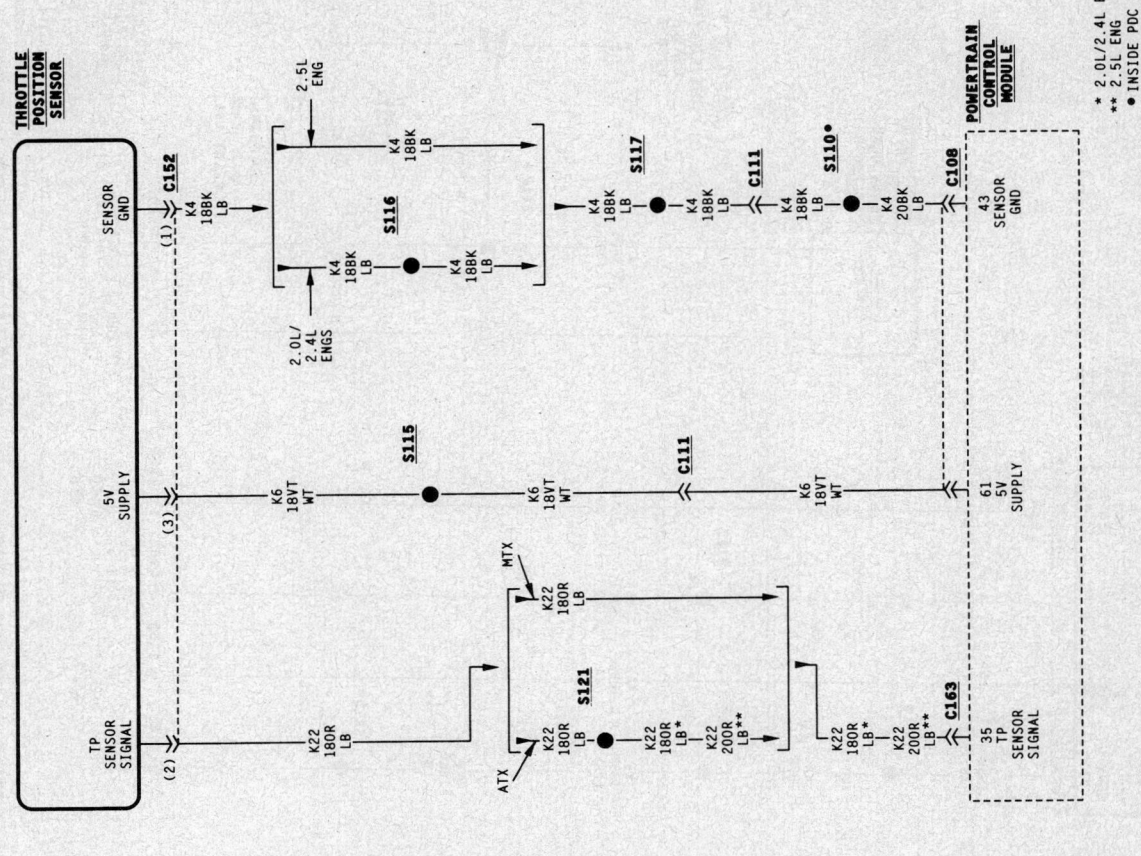

Fig. 7 MFI wiring diagram (Part 10 of 16). Breeze, Cirrus, Sebring Convertible & Stratus

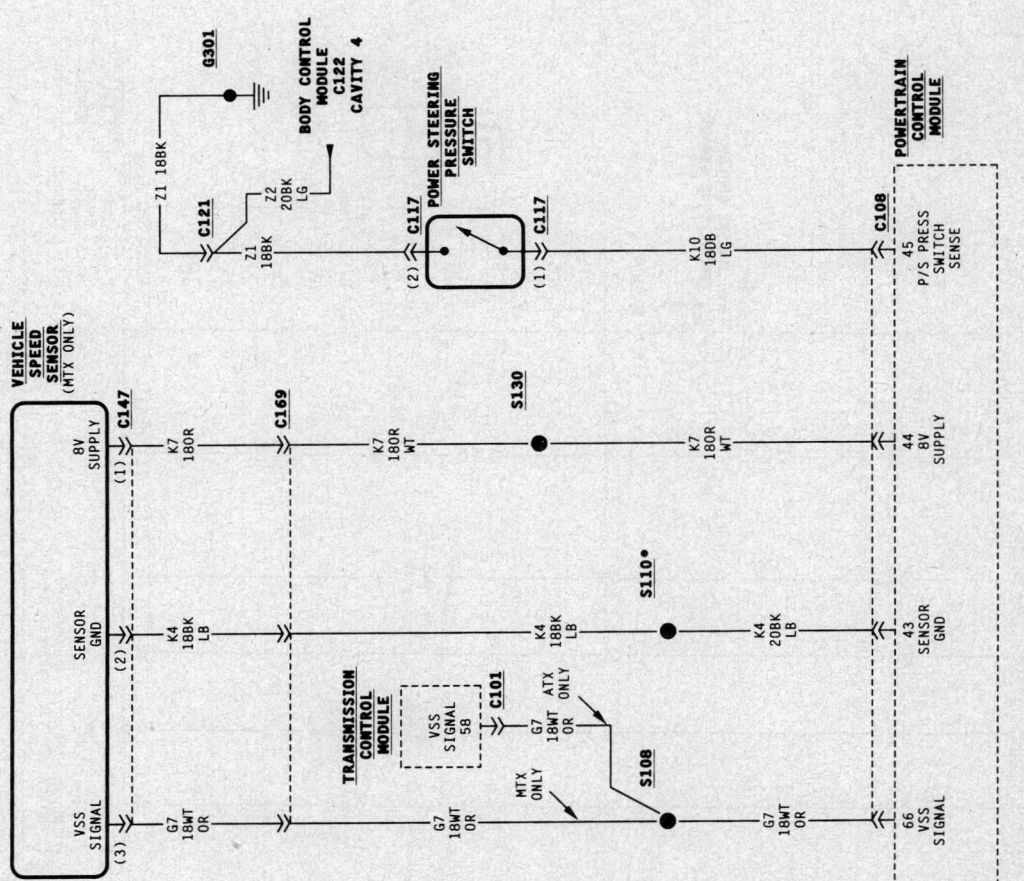

Fig. 7 MFI wiring diagram (Part 9 of 16). Breeze, Cirrus, Sebring Convertible & Stratus

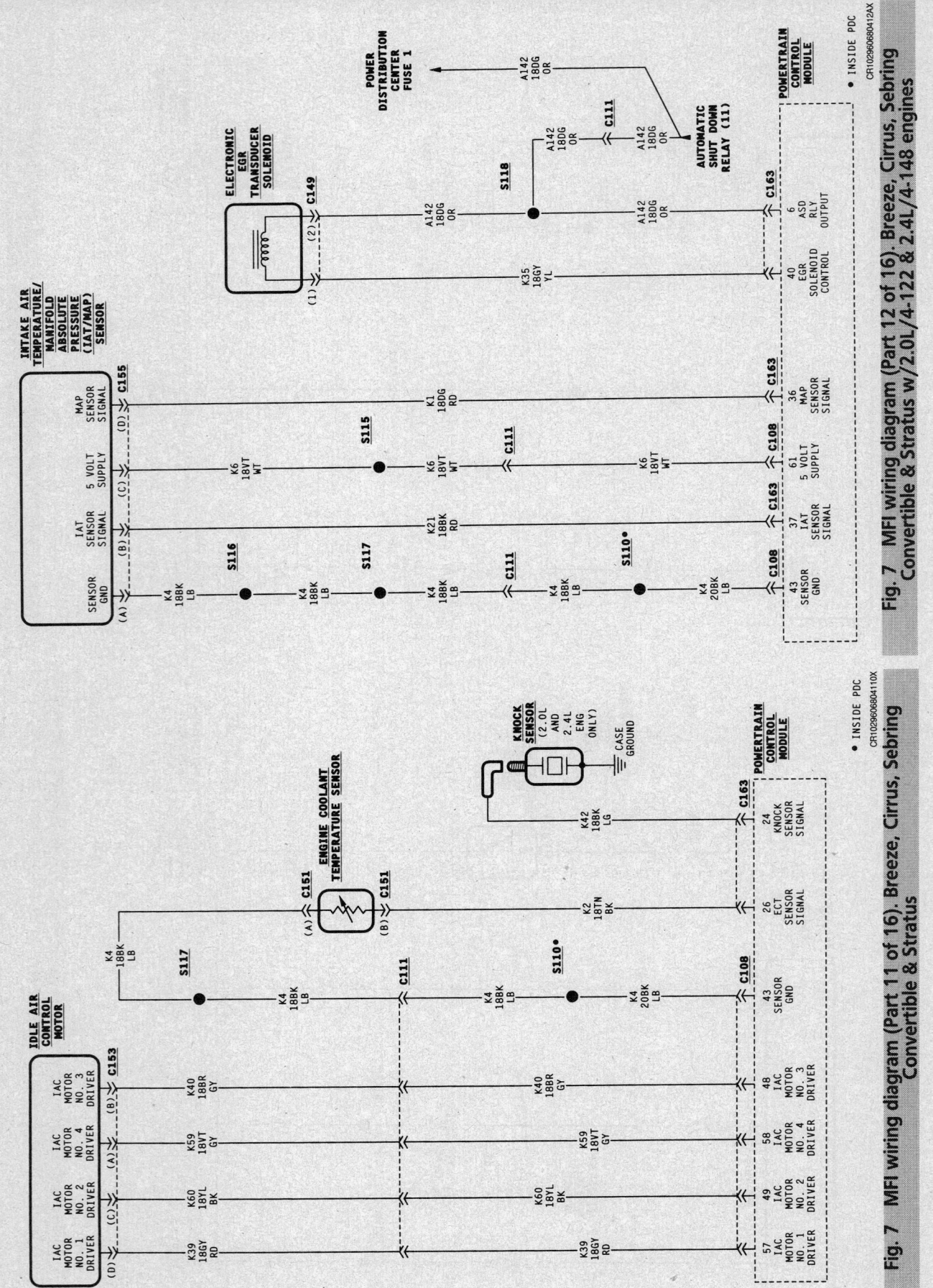

Fig. 7   MFI wiring diagram (Part 12 of 16). Breeze, Cirrus, Sebring Convertible & Stratus w/2.0L/4-122 & 2.4L/4-148 engines

Fig. 7   MFI wiring diagram (Part 11 of 16). Breeze, Cirrus, Sebring Convertible & Stratus

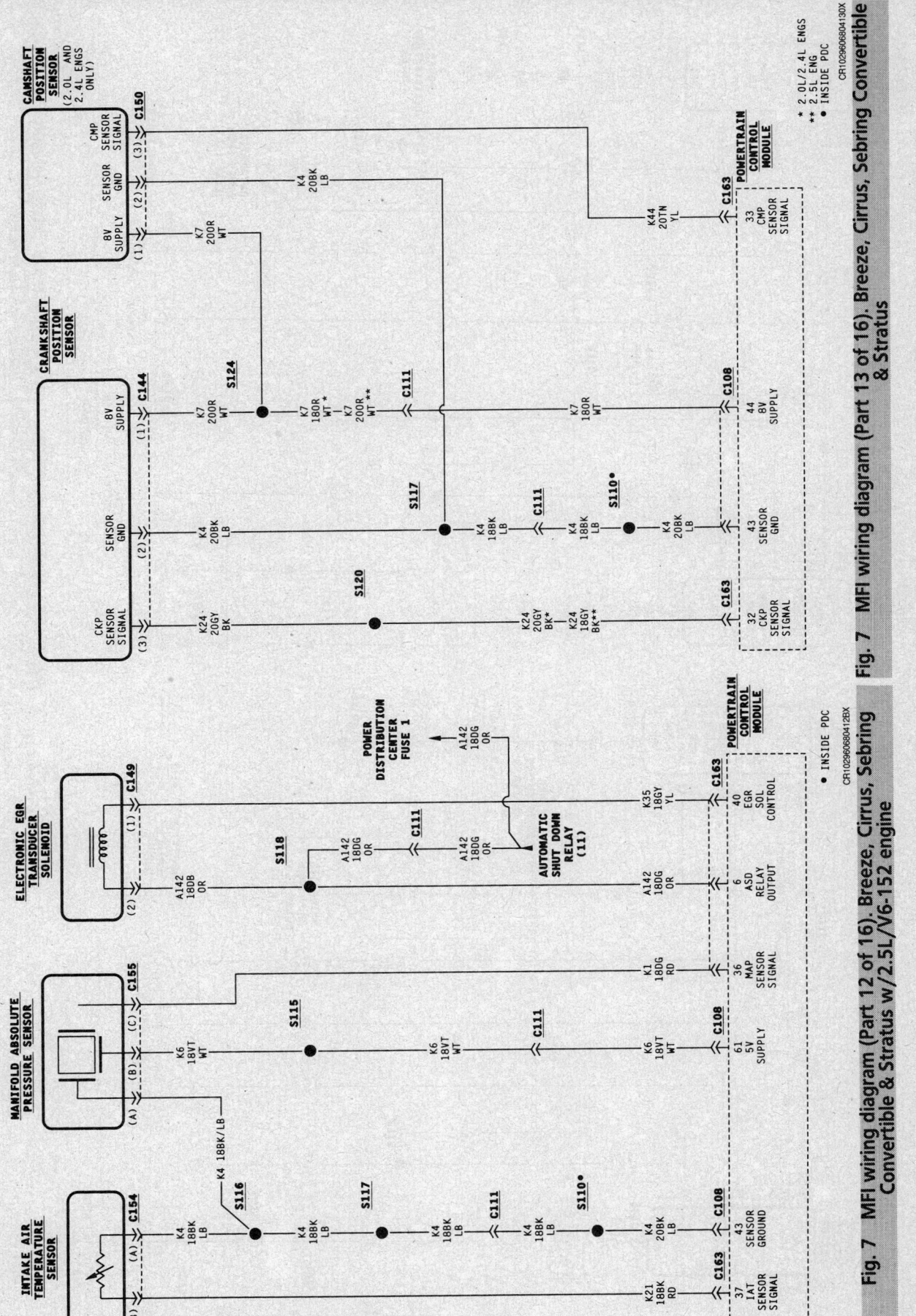

Fig. 7 MFI wiring diagram (Part 13 of 16), Breeze, Cirrus, Sebring Convertible & Stratus

Fig. 7 MFI wiring diagram (Part 12 of 16), Breeze, Cirrus, Sebring Convertible & Stratus w/2.5L/V6-152 engine

CHRYSLER—Fuel Injection

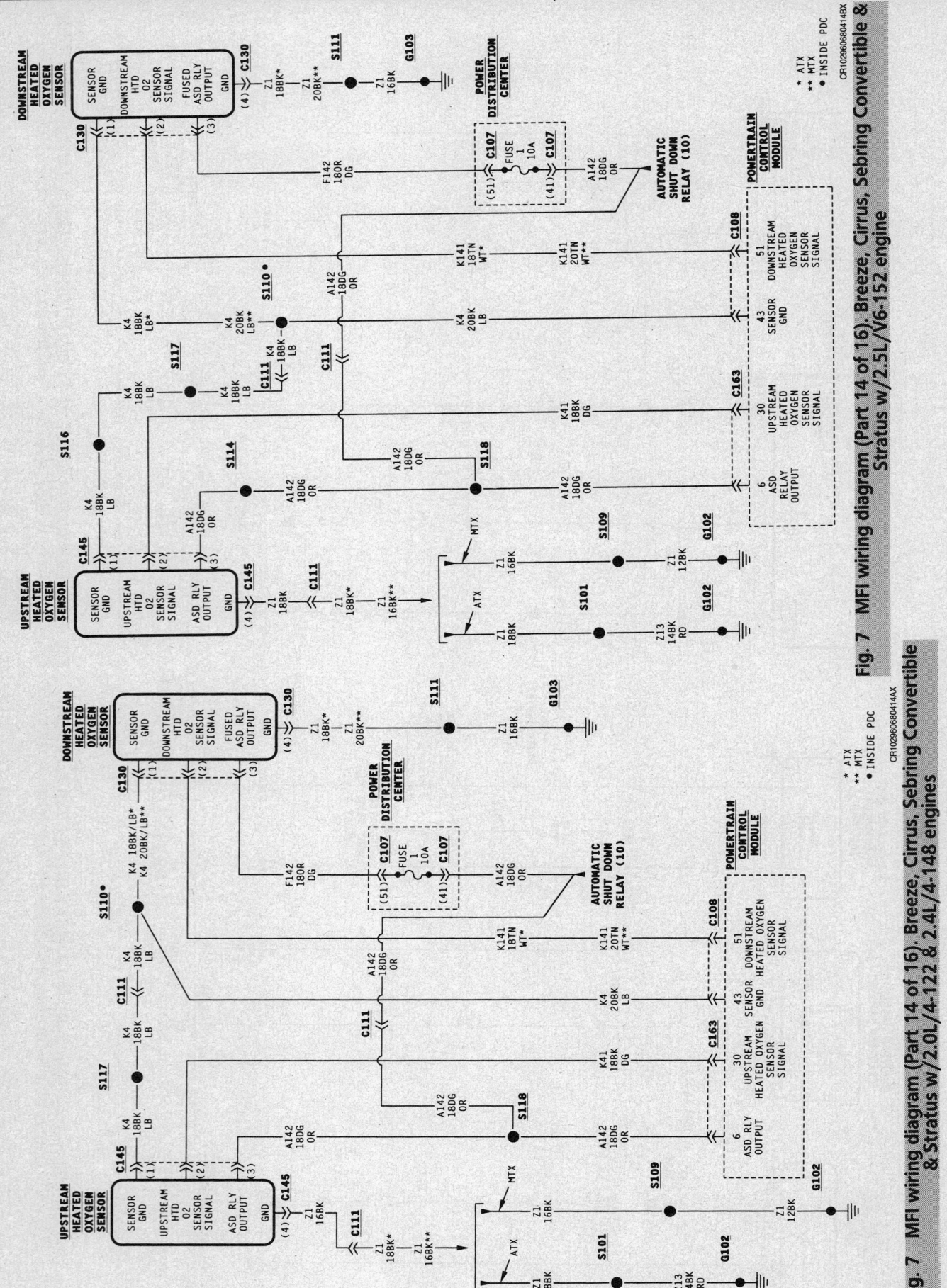

Fig. 7 MFI wiring diagram (Part 14 of 16). Breeze, Cirrus, Sebring Convertible & Stratus w/2.5L/V6-152 engine

Fig. 7 MFI wiring diagram (Part 14 of 16). Breeze, Cirrus, Sebring Convertible & Stratus w/2.0L/4-122 & 2.4L/4-148 engines

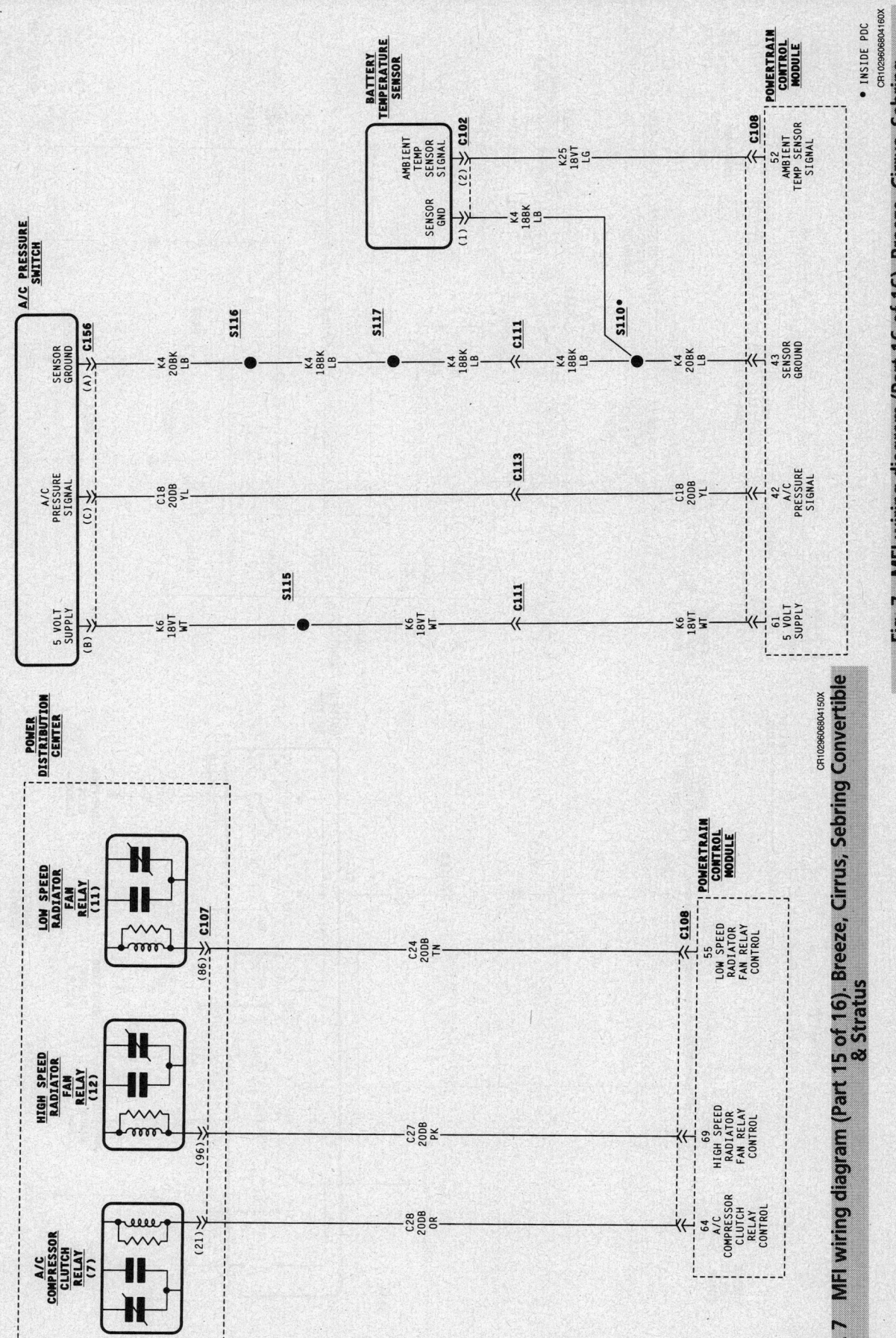

Fig. 7 MFI wiring diagram (Part 16 of 16). Breeze, Cirrus, Sebring Convertible & Stratus

Fig. 7 MFI wiring diagram (Part 15 of 16). Breeze, Cirrus, Sebring Convertible & Stratus

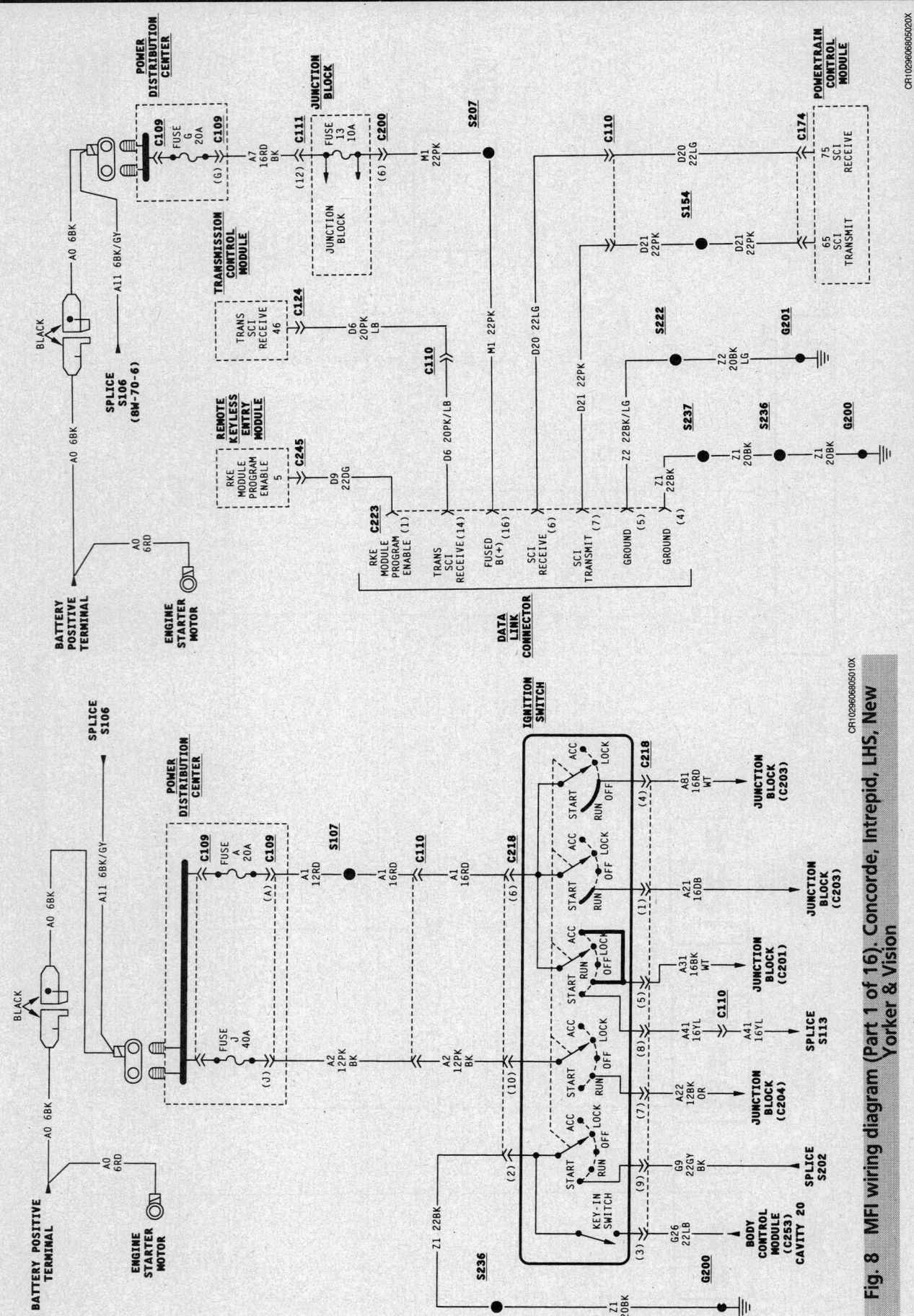

Fig. 8 MFI wiring diagram (Part 2 of 16). Concorde, Intrepid, LHS, New Yorker & Vision

Fig. 8 MFI wiring diagram (Part 1 of 16). Concorde, Intrepid, LHS, New Yorker & Vision

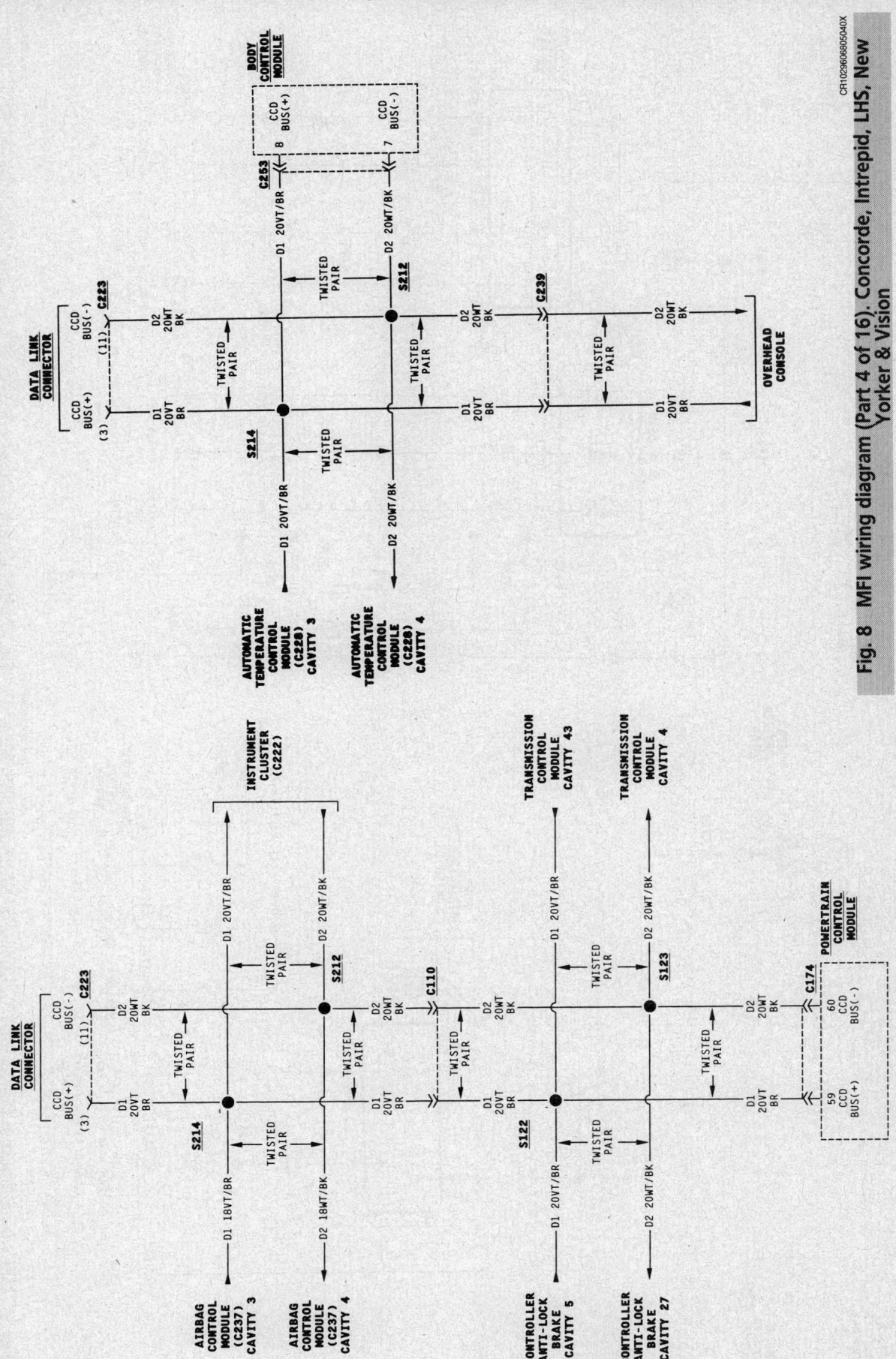

Fig. 8 MFI wiring diagram (Part 4 of 16). Concorde, Intrepid, LHS, New Yorker & Vision

Fig. 8 MFI wiring diagram (Part 3 of 16). Concorde, Intrepid, LHS, New Yorker & Vision

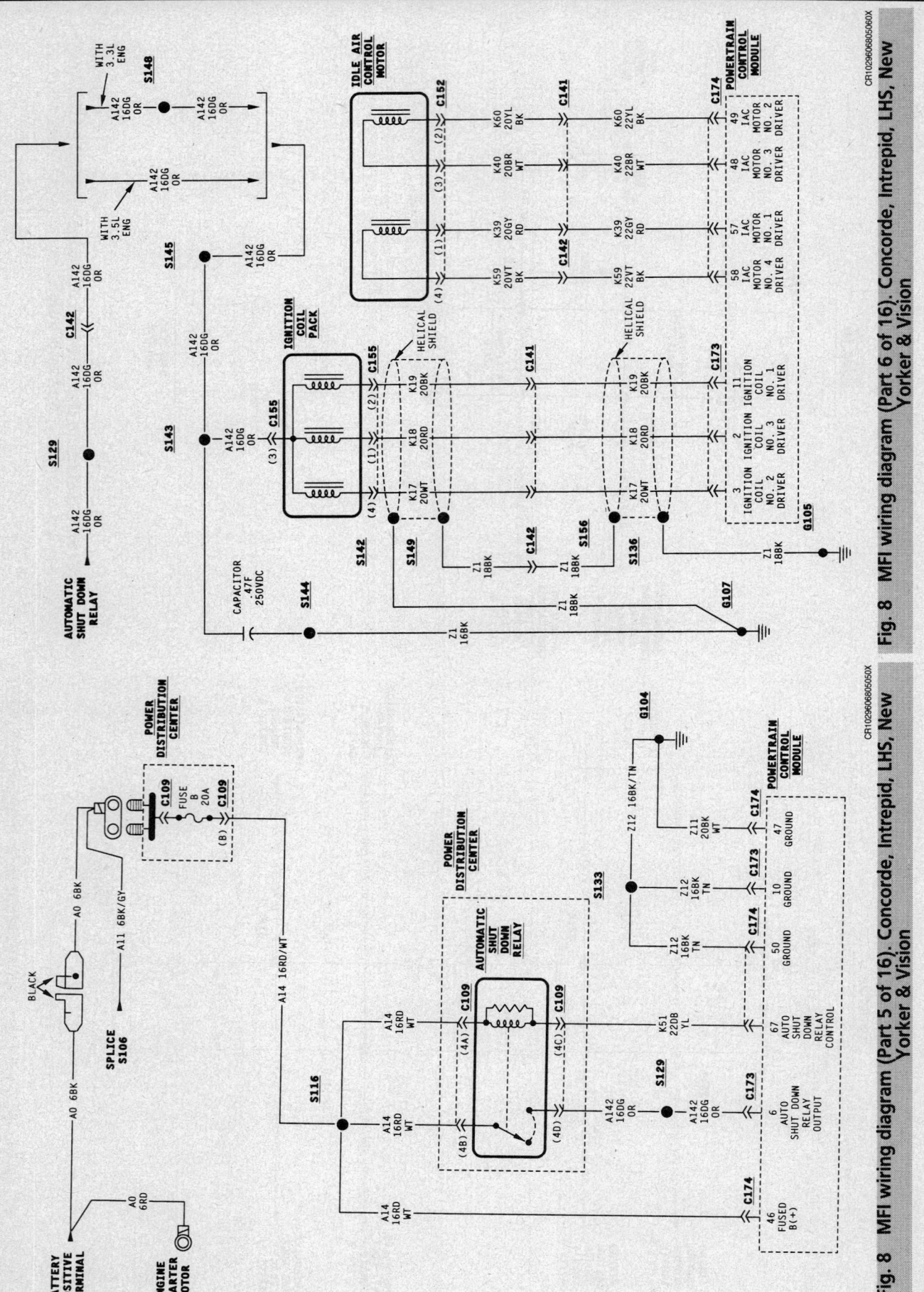

Fig. 8   MFI wiring diagram (Part 6 of 16). Concorde, Intrepid, LHS, New Yorker & Vision

Fig. 8   MFI wiring diagram (Part 5 of 16). Concorde, Intrepid, LHS, New Yorker & Vision

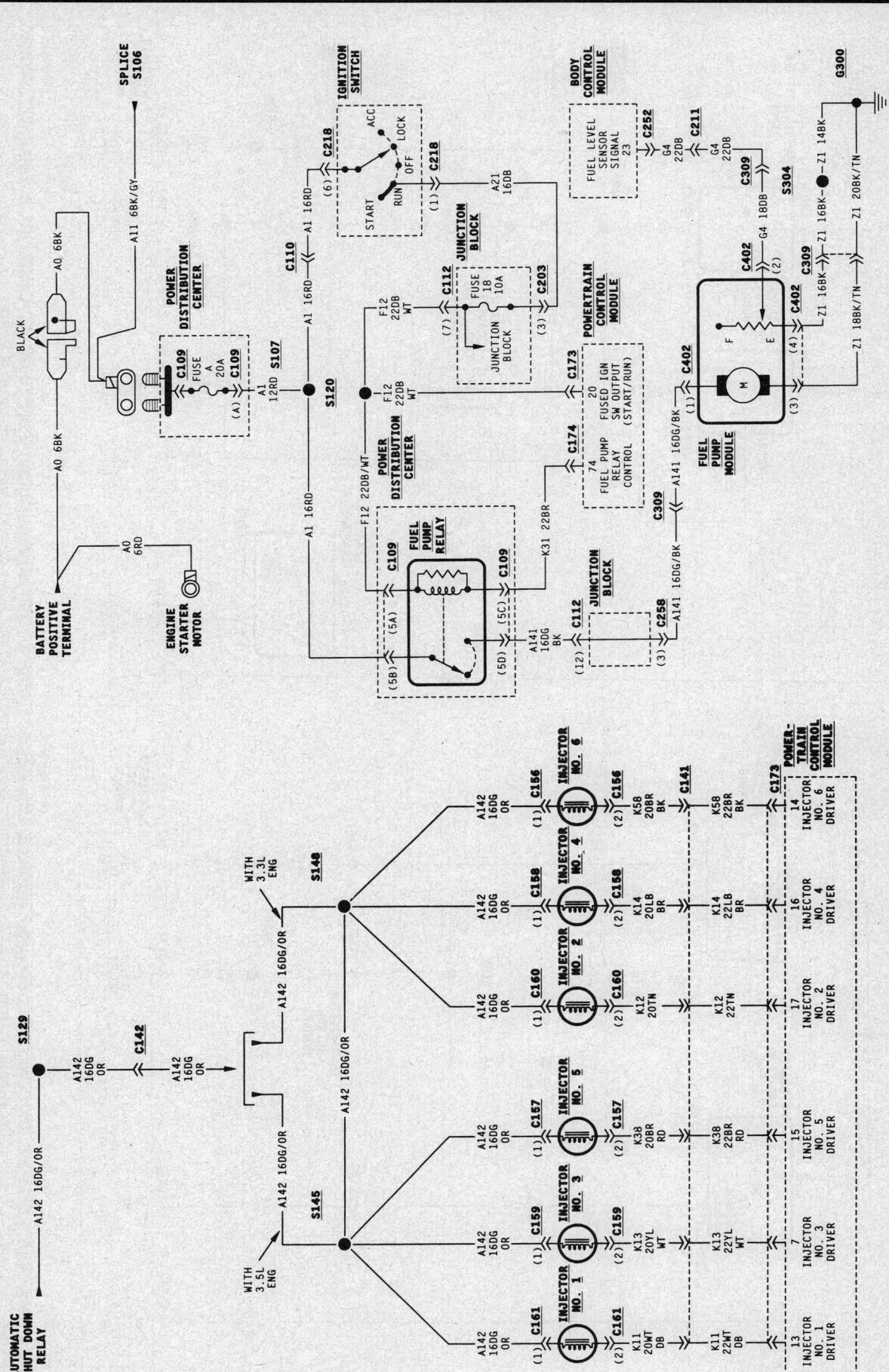

Fig. 8   MFI wiring diagram (Part 8 of 16). Concorde, Intrepid, LHS, New Yorker & Vision

Fig. 8   MFI wiring diagram (Part 7 of 16). Concorde, Intrepid, LHS, New Yorker & Vision

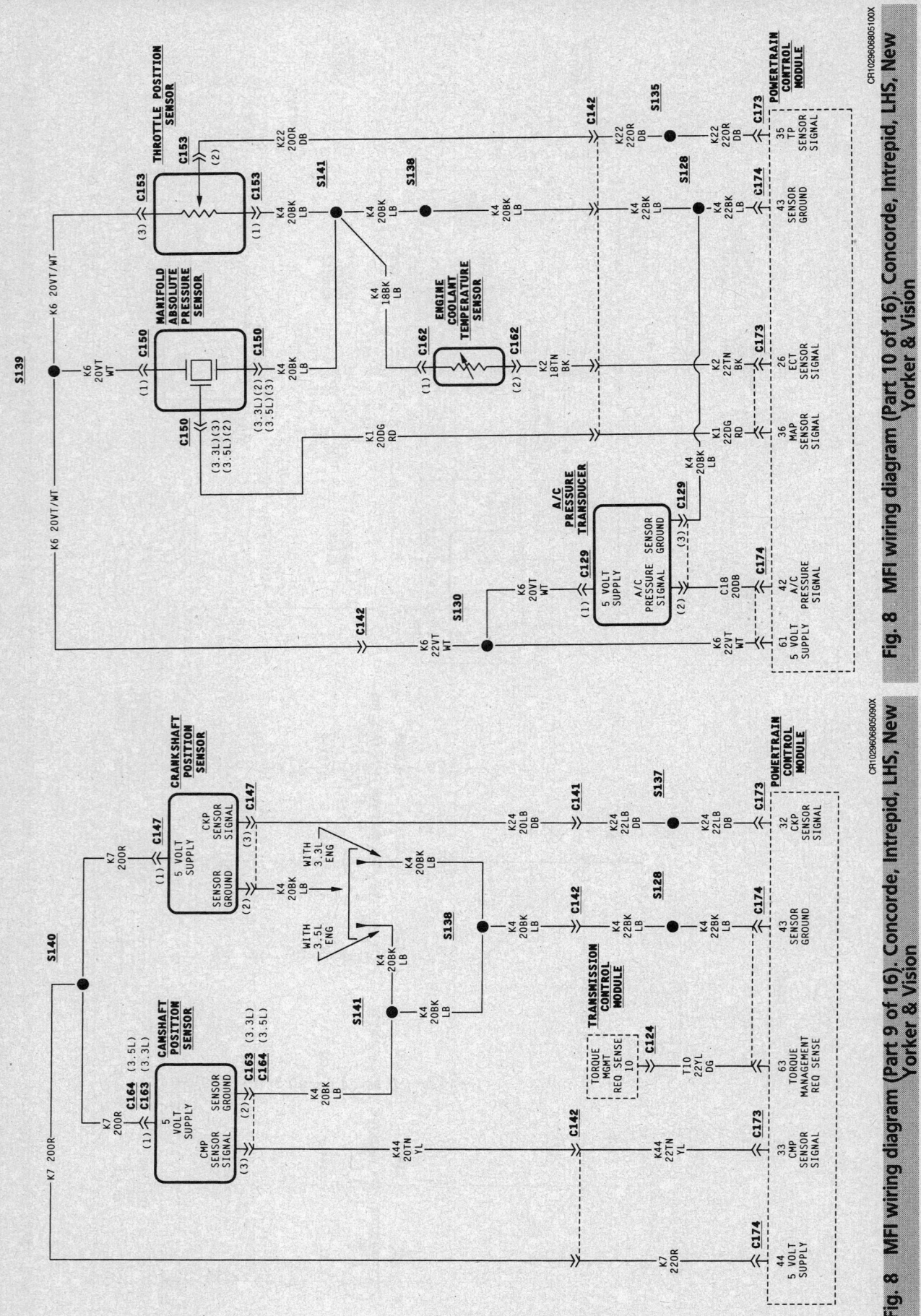

Fig. 8 MFI wiring diagram (Part 10 of 16). Concorde, Intrepid, LHS, New Yorker & Vision

Fig. 8 MFI wiring diagram (Part 9 of 16). Concorde, Intrepid, LHS, New Yorker & Vision

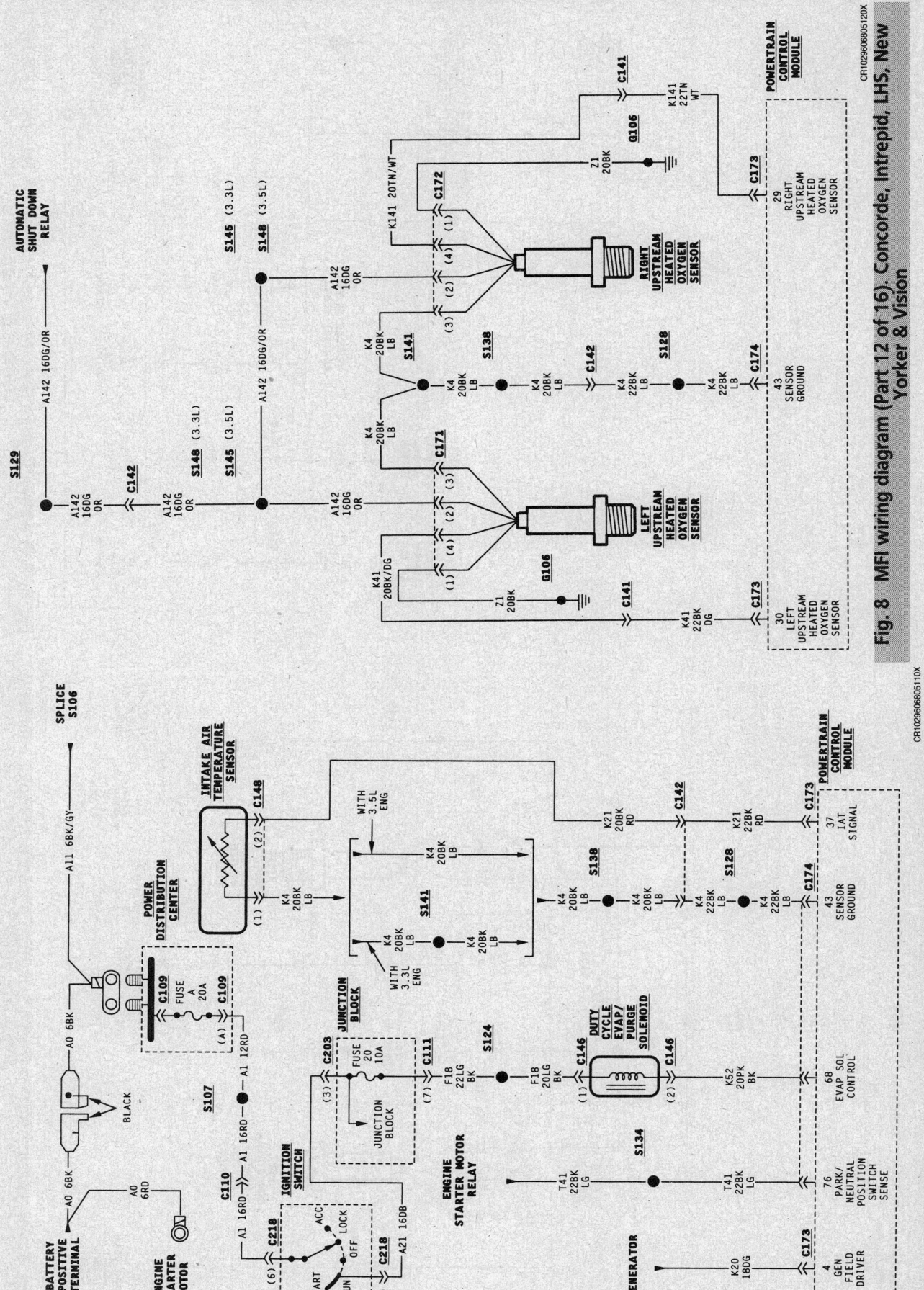

Fig. 8 MFI wiring diagram (Part 12 of 16). Concorde, Intrepid, LHS, New Yorker & Vision

Fig. 8 MFI wiring diagram (Part 11 of 16). Concorde, Intrepid, LHS, New Yorker & Vision

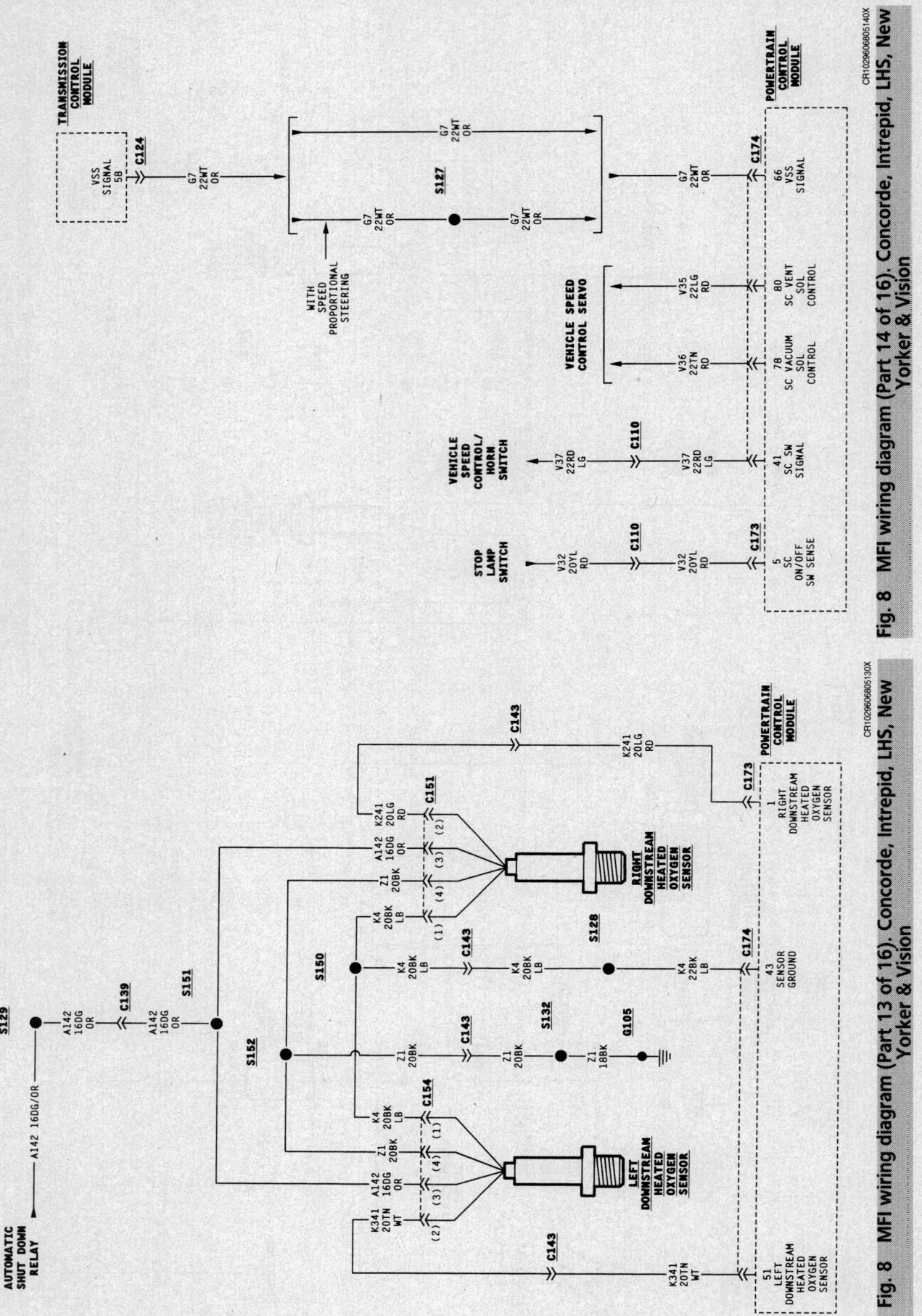

Fig. 8 MFI wiring diagram (Part 14 of 16). Concorde, Intrepid, LHS, New Yorker & Vision

Fig. 8 MFI wiring diagram (Part 13 of 16). Concorde, Intrepid, LHS, New Yorker & Vision

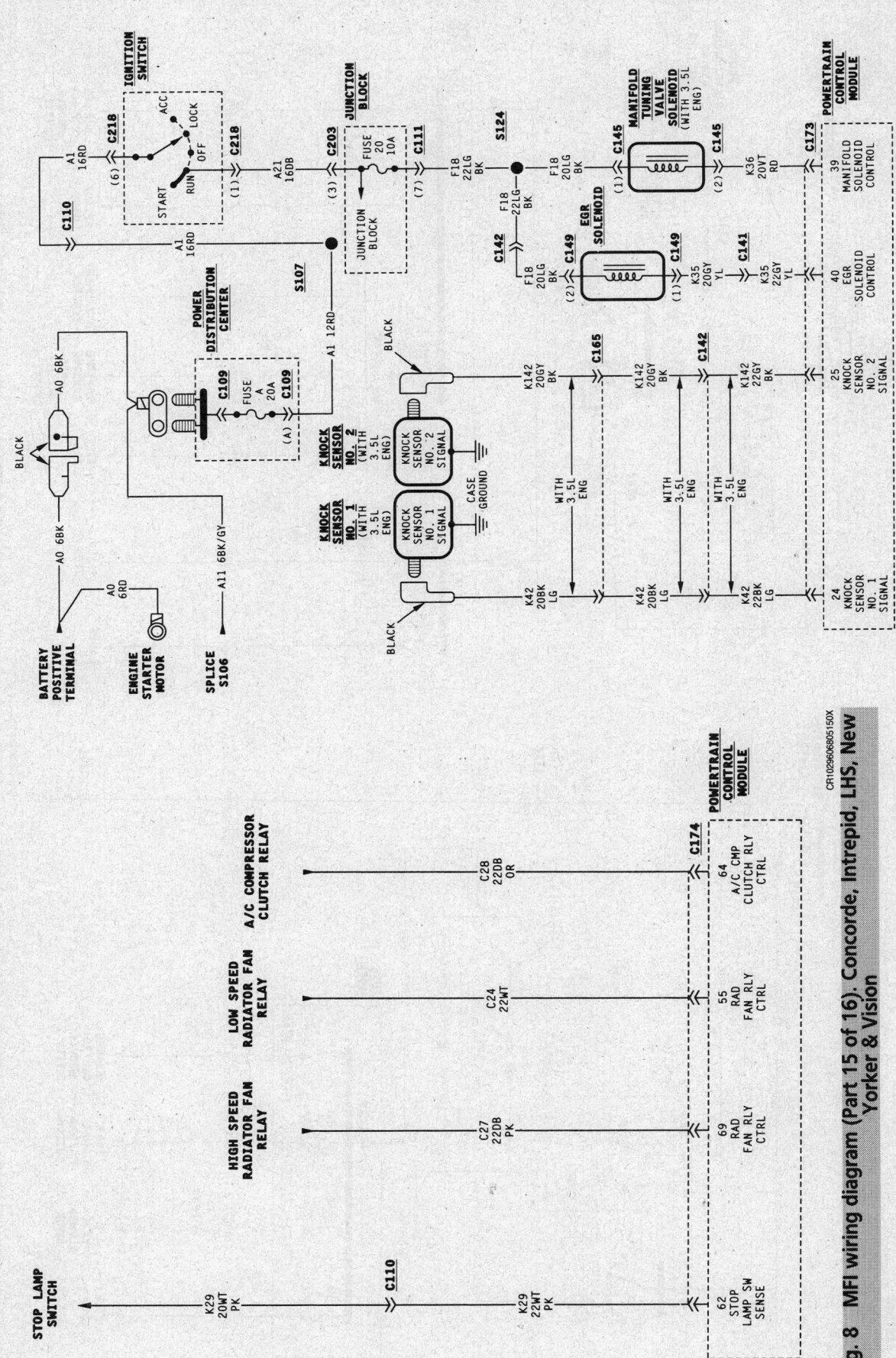

Fig. 8 MFI wiring diagram (Part 16 of 16). Concorde, Intrepid, LHS, New Yorker & Vision

Fig. 8 MFI wiring diagram (Part 15 of 16). Concorde, Intrepid, LHS, New Yorker & Vision

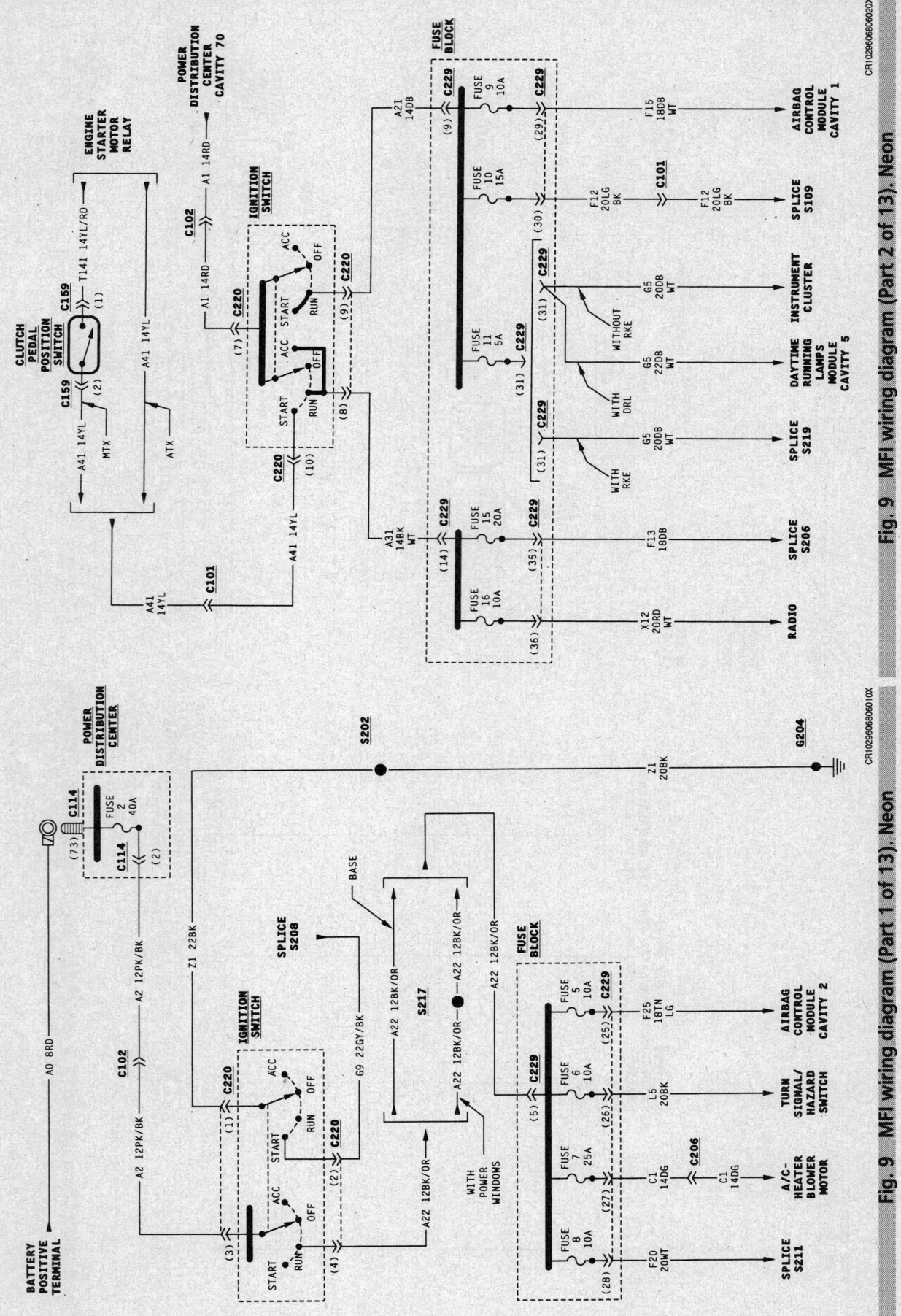

Fig. 9   MFI wiring diagram (Part 2 of 13). Neon

Fig. 9   MFI wiring diagram (Part 1 of 13). Neon

1996 MODELS w/2.0L/4-122 NON-TURBO, 2.4L/4-148, 2.5L/V6-152, 3.3L/V6-201 & 3.5L/V6-215 ENGINES

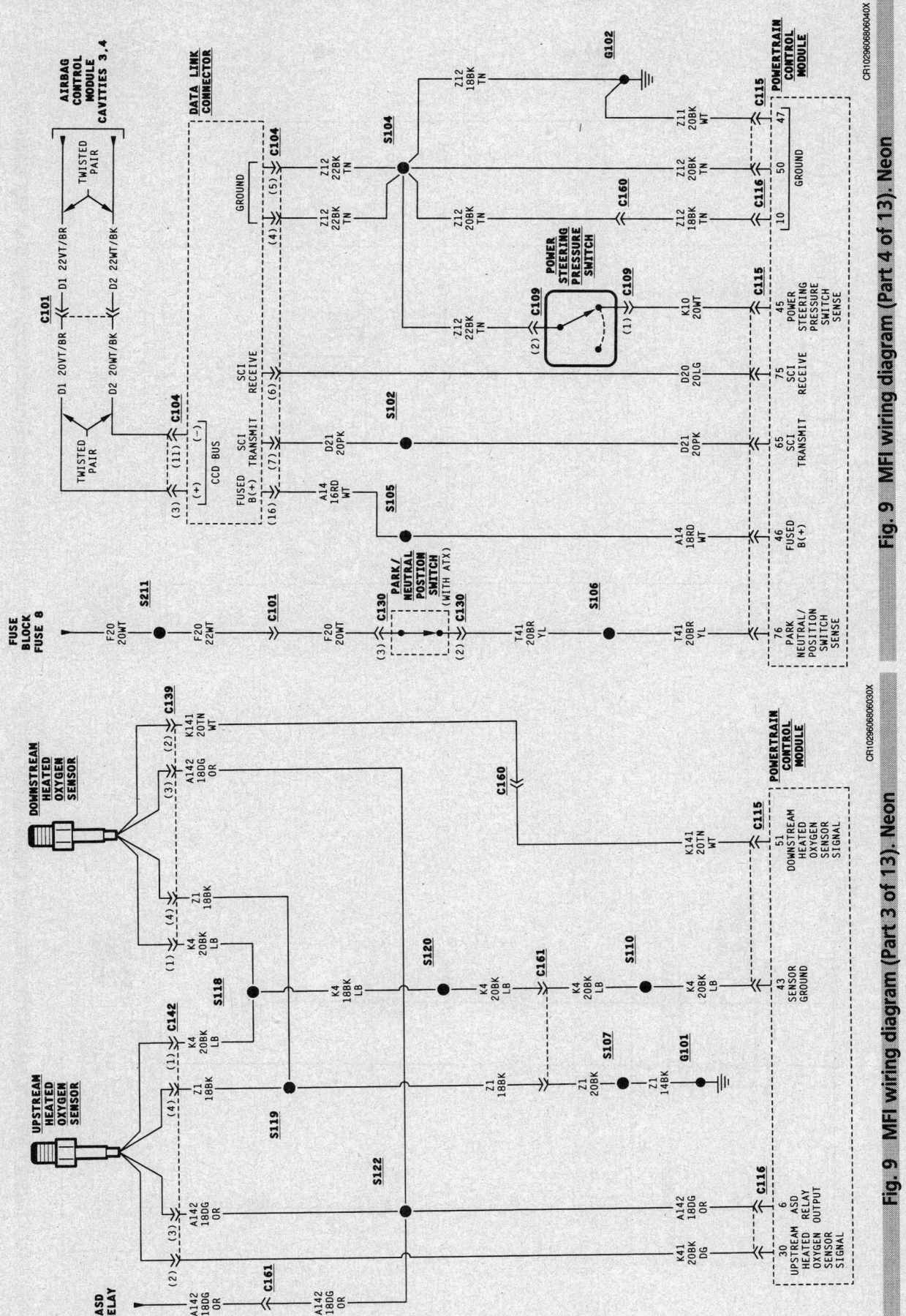

Fig. 9   MFI wiring diagram (Part 4 of 13). Neon

Fig. 9   MFI wiring diagram (Part 3 of 13). Neon

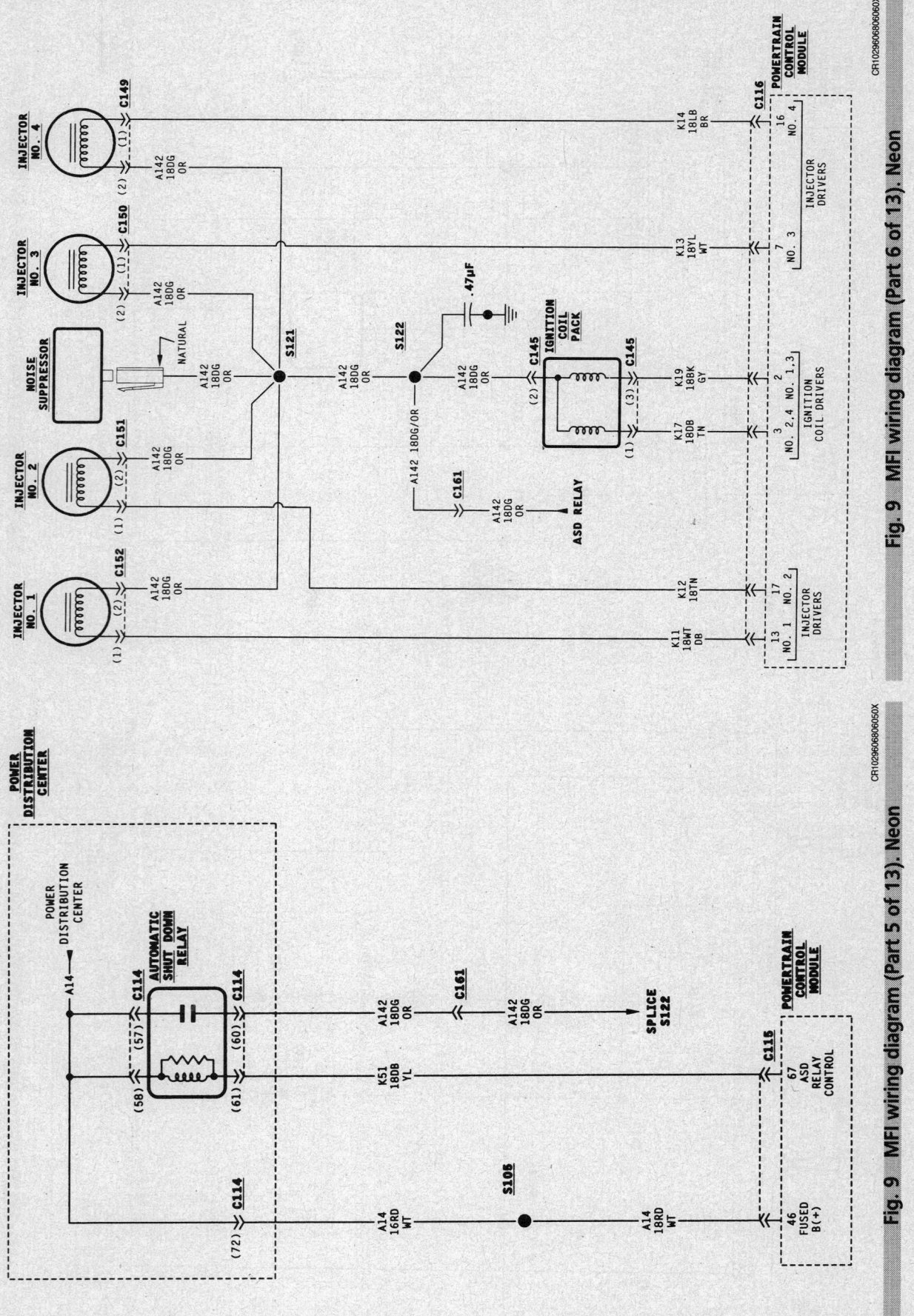

Fig. 9 MFI wiring diagram (Part 6 of 13). Neon

Fig. 9 MFI wiring diagram (Part 5 of 13). Neon

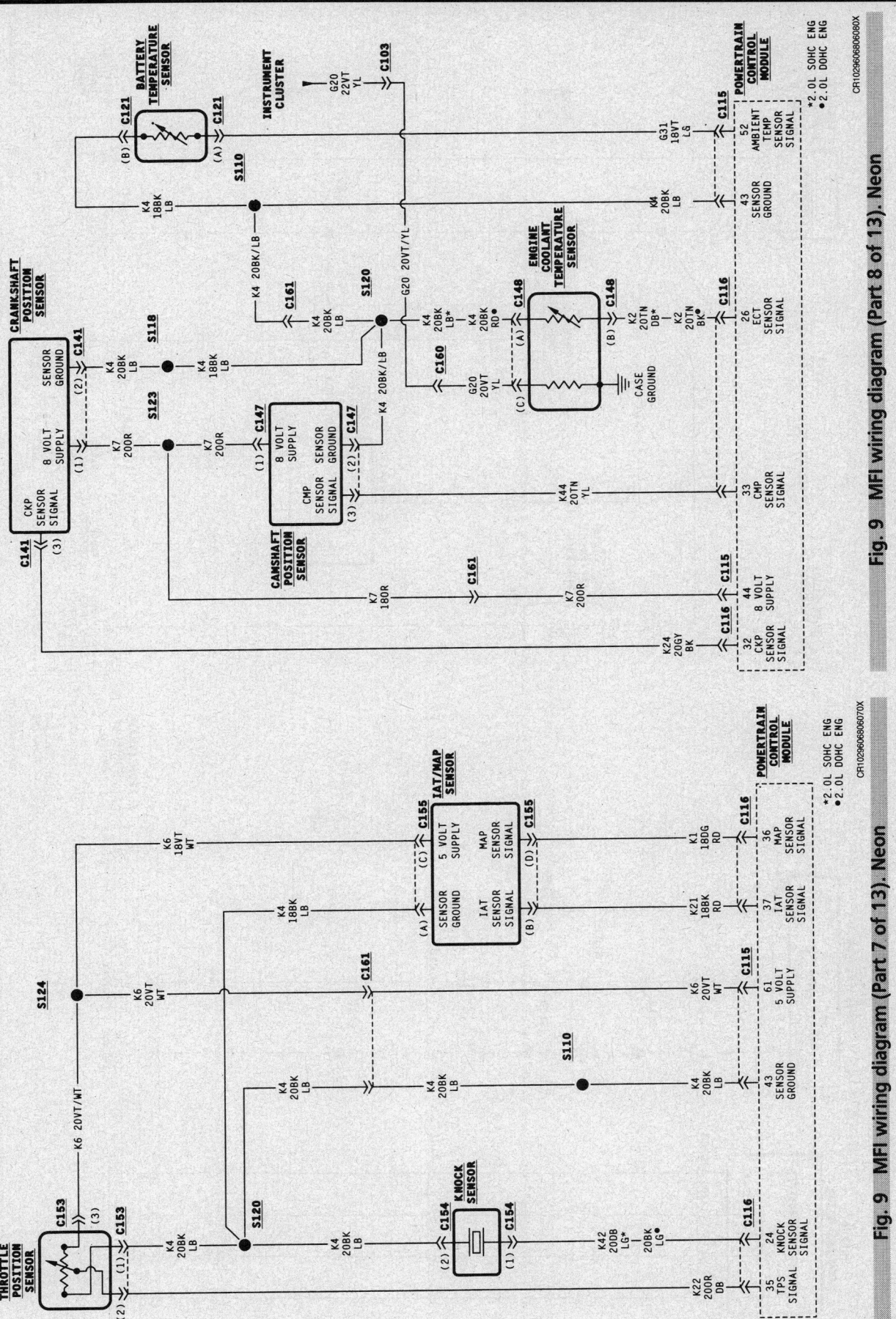

Fig. 9 MFI wiring diagram (Part 8 of 13). Neon

Fig. 9 MFI wiring diagram (Part 7 of 13). Neon

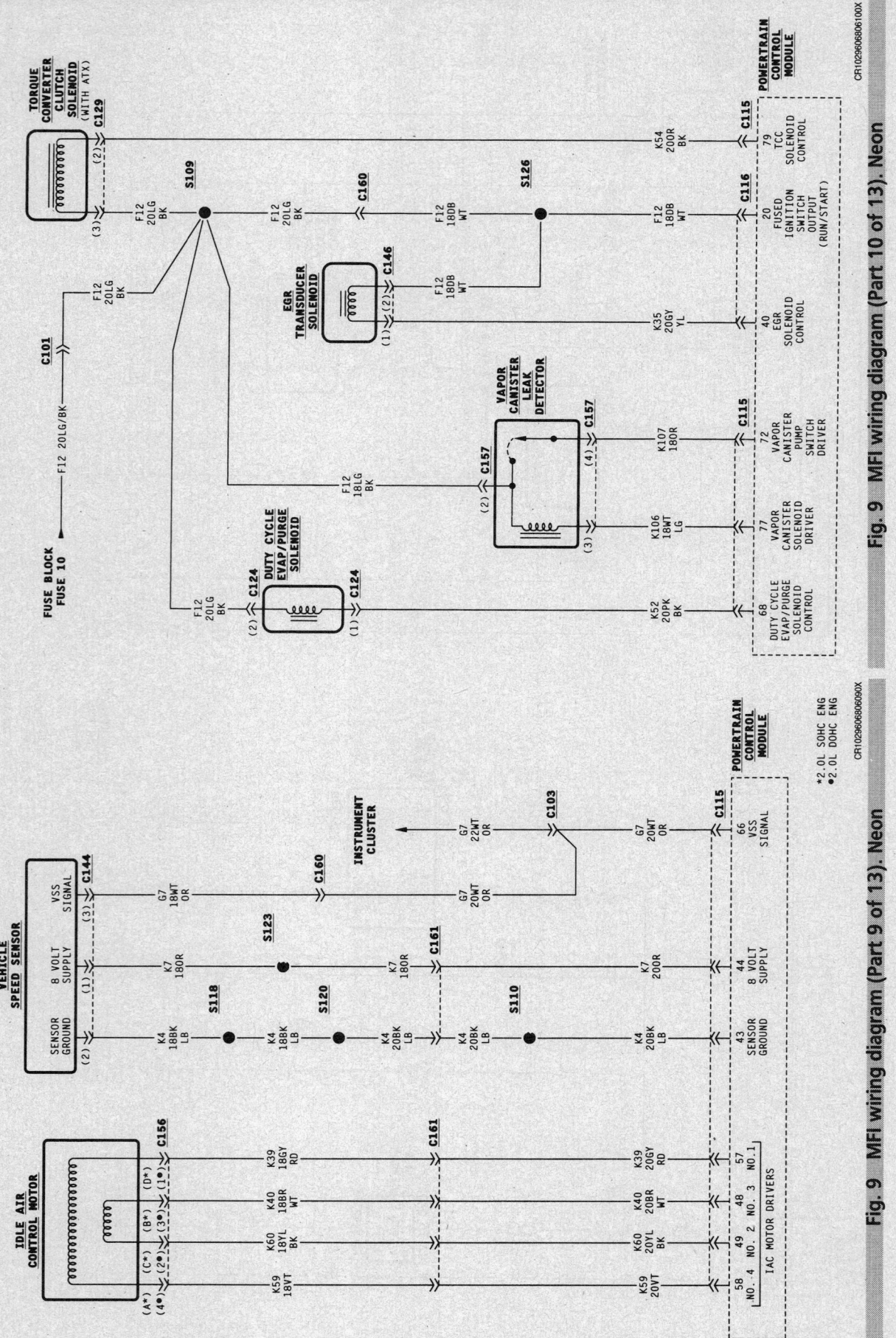

Fig. 9   MFI wiring diagram (Part 10 of 13). Neon

Fig. 9   MFI wiring diagram (Part 9 of 13). Neon

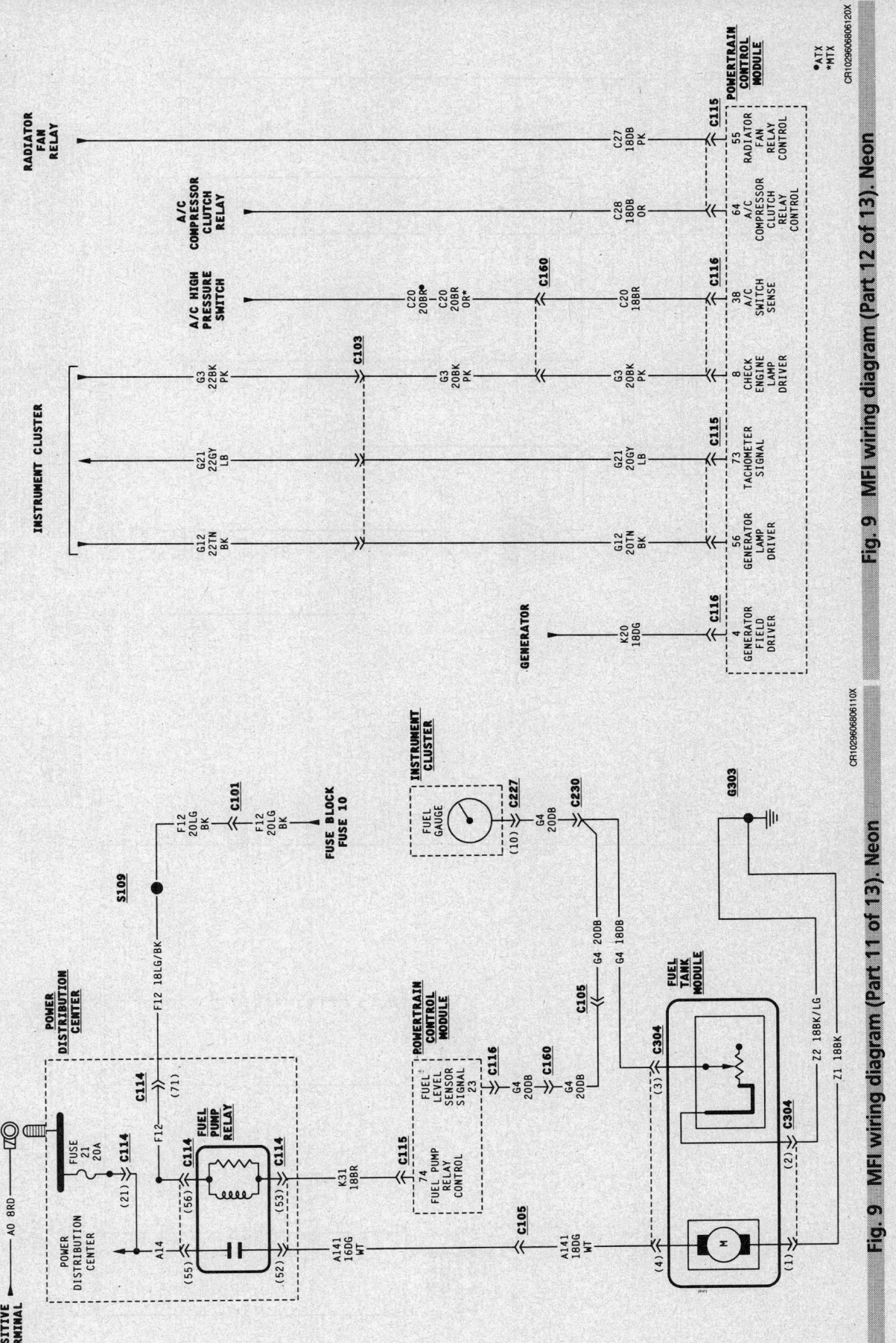

Fig. 9 MFI wiring diagram (Part 12 of 13). Neon

Fig. 9 MFI wiring diagram (Part 11 of 13). Neon

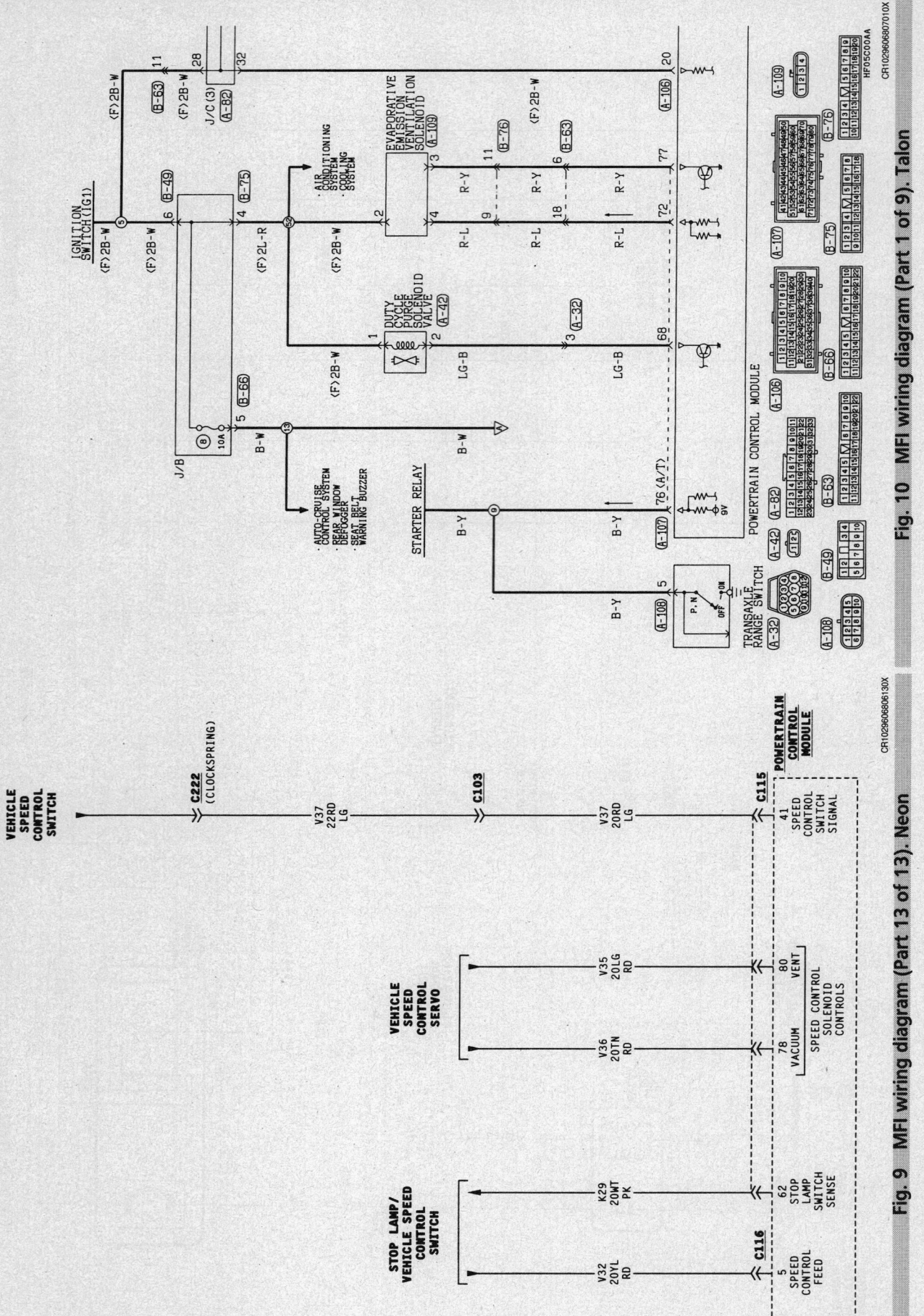

Fig. 10 MFI wiring diagram (Part 1 of 9). Talon

Fig. 9 MFI wiring diagram (Part 13 of 13). Neon

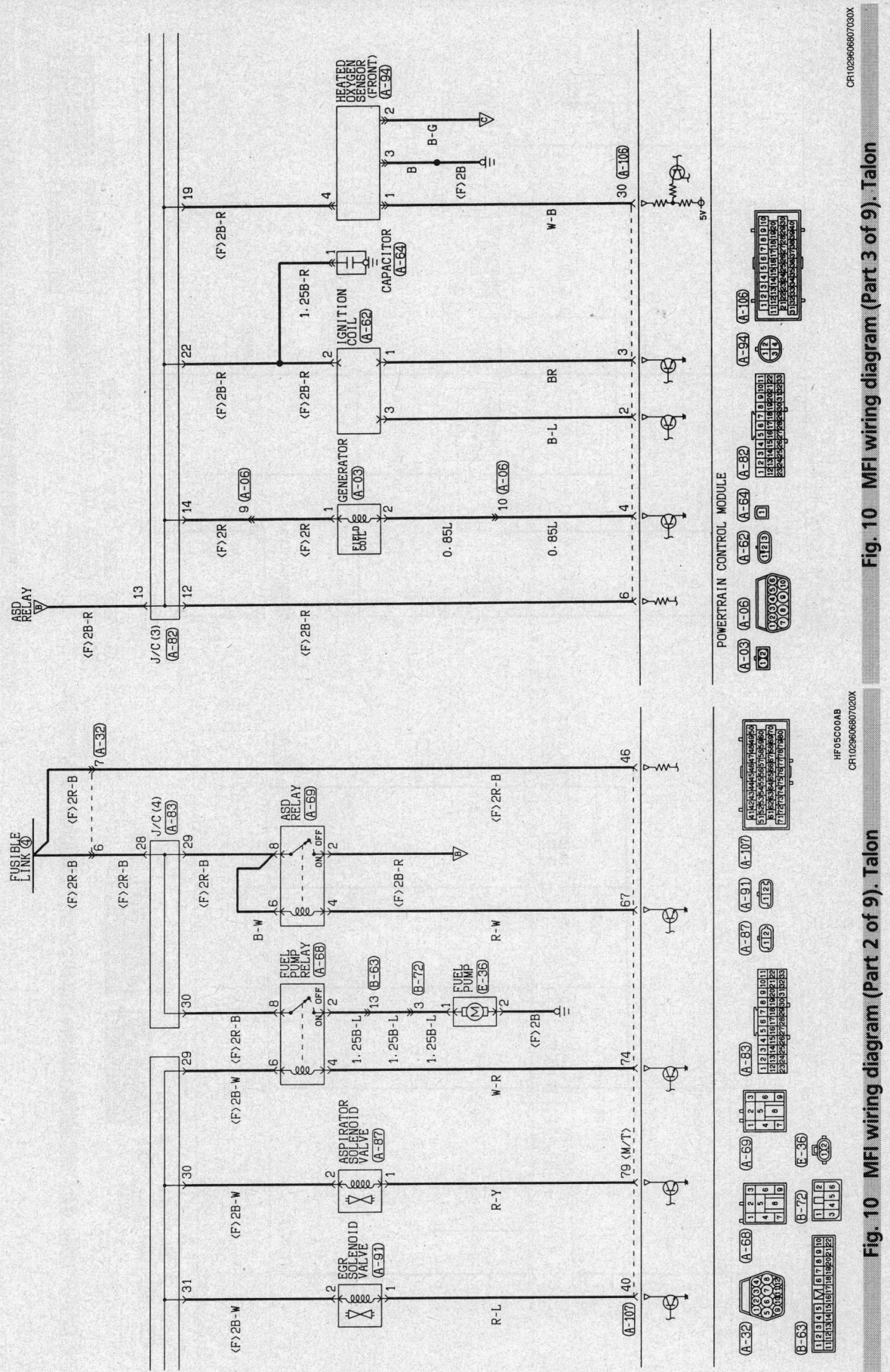

Fig. 10 MFI wiring diagram (Part 3 of 9). Talon

Fig. 10 MFI wiring diagram (Part 2 of 9). Talon

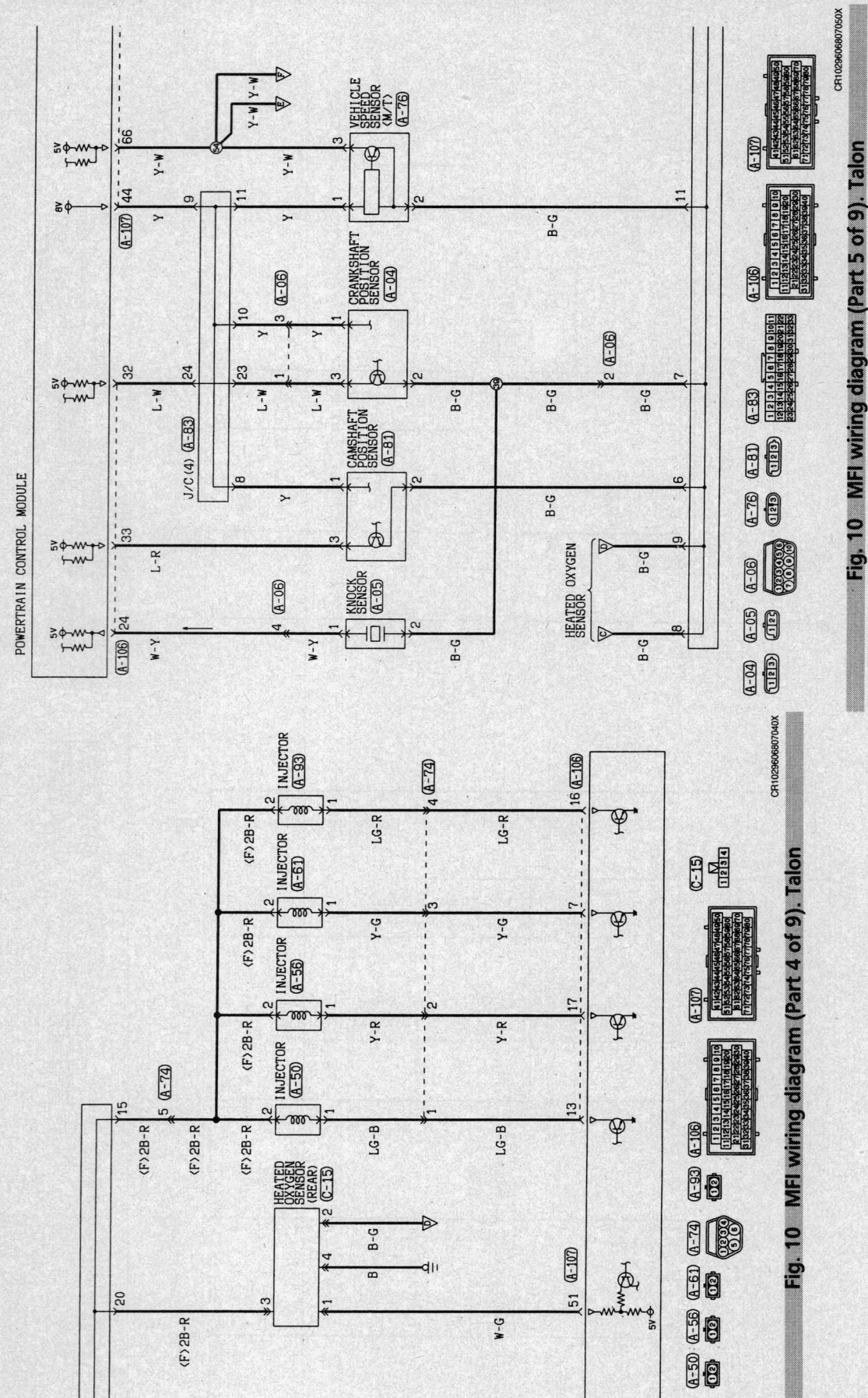

Fig. 10 MFI wiring diagram (Part 5 of 9). Talon

Fig. 10 MFI wiring diagram (Part 4 of 9). Talon

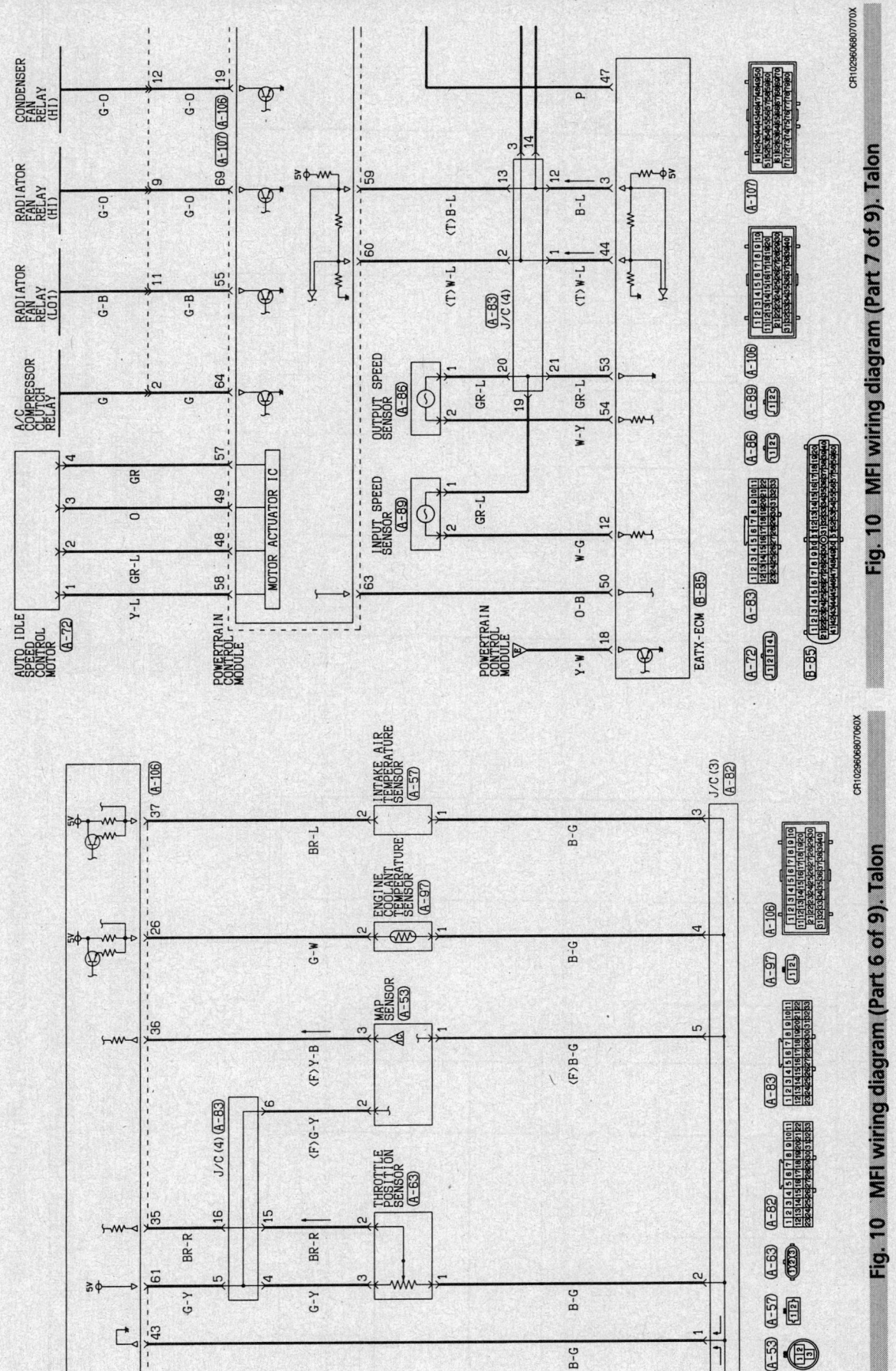

Fig. 10   MFI wiring diagram (Part 7 of 9). Talon

Fig. 10   MFI wiring diagram (Part 6 of 9). Talon

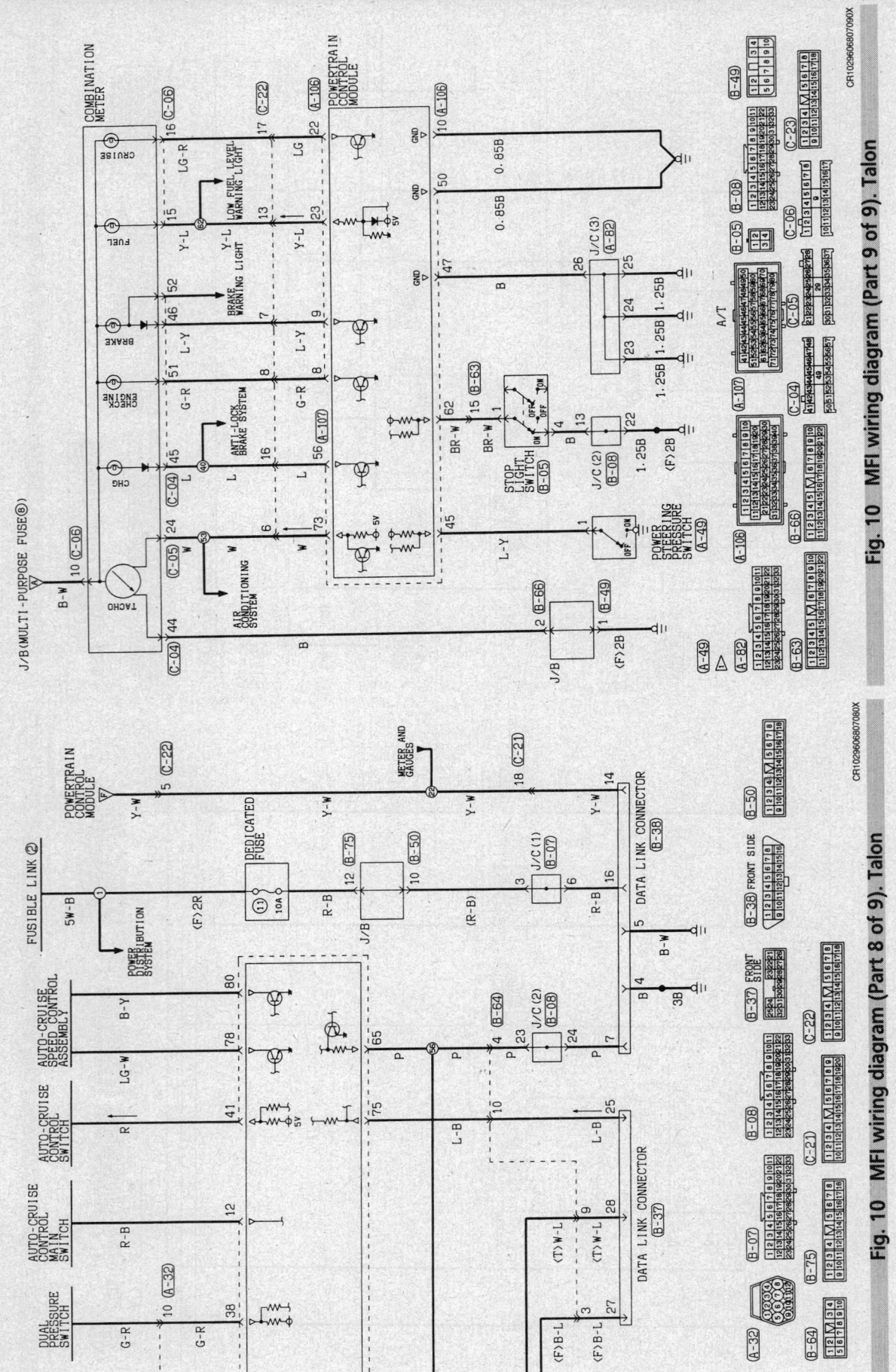

Fig. 10 MFI wiring diagram (Part 9 of 9). Talon

Fig. 10 MFI wiring diagram (Part 8 of 9). Talon

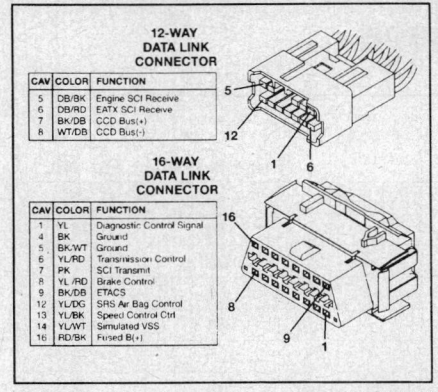

Fig. 11 Diagnostic connector location & terminal identification. Avenger, Sebring Coupe & Talon

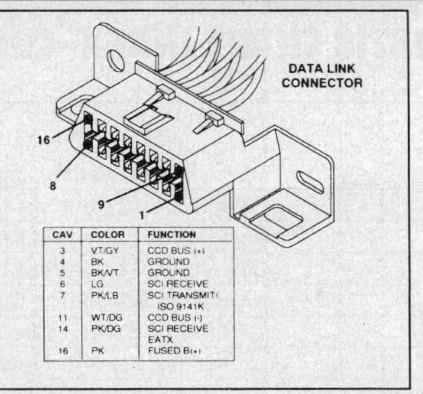

Fig. 12 Diagnostic connector location & terminal identification. Breeze, Cirrus, Sebring Convertible & Stratus

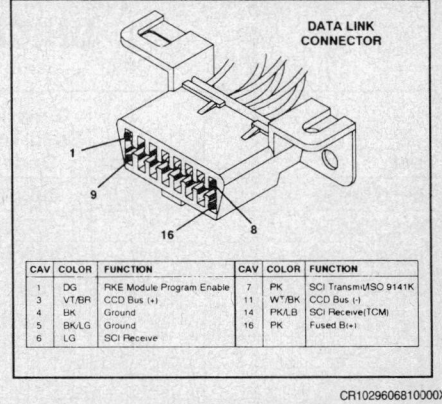

Fig. 13 Diagnostic connector location & terminal identification. Concorde, Intrepid, LHS, New Yorker & Vision

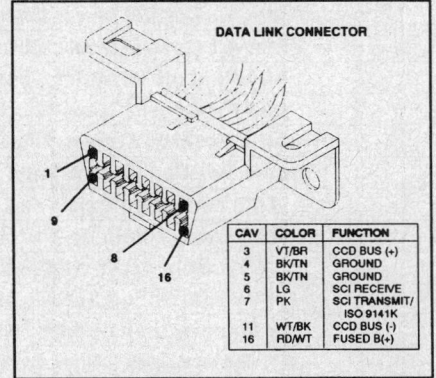

Fig. 14 Diagnostic connector location & terminal identification. Neon

DIAGNOSTIC CHART INDEX

Test	MIL Code	Generic Scan Tool Code	Description	Page No. 14-	Fig. No.
—	—	—	**Diagnostic Trouble Code Inspection**	50	15
Test TC-1A	54	P0340	**No Cam Signal At PCM**	51	16
Test TC-5A	47	—	**Charging System Voltage Low**	51	17
Test TC-6A	46	—	**Charging System Voltage High**	52	18
Test TC-6B	46	—	**Charging System Voltage High**	52	19
Test TC-10A	—	—	**Auto Shutdown Relay Control Circuit**	52	20
Test TC-11A	41	—	**Generator Field Not Switching Properly**	53	21
Test TC-12A	37	P0743	**Torque Converter Clutch Solenoid Circuit ①**	54	22
Test TC-15A	34	—	**Speed Control Power Circuit & Speed Control Solenoid Circuits**	54	23
Test TC-15B	34	—	**Speed Control Power Circuit & Speed Control Solenoid Circuits**	55	24
Test TC-15C	34	—	**Speed Control Power Circuit & Speed Control Solenoid Circuits**	55	25
Test TC-16A	33	—	**A/C Clutch Relay Circuit**	56	26
Test TC-17A	32	P0403	**EGR Solenoid Circuit**	56	27
Test TC-18A	31	P0443	**EVAP Purge Solenoid Circuit**	57	28
Test TC-19A	27	P0203	**Injector No. 3 Control Circuit**	58	29
Test TC-19B	27	P0203	**Injector No. 3 Control Circuit**	58	30
Test TC-19C	27	P0203	**Injector No. 3 Control Circuit**	58	31
Test TC-19D	27	P0203	**Injector No. 3 Control Circuit**	59	32

Continued

CHRYSLER–Fuel Injection

DIAGNOSTIC CHART INDEX–Continued

Test	MIL Code	Generic Scan Tool Code	Description	Page No. 14-	Fig. No.
Test TC-19E	27	P0203	Injector No. 3 Control Circuit	59	33
Test TC-20A	27	P0202	Injector No. 2 Control Circuit	60	34
Test TC-20B	27	P0202	Injector No. 2 Control Circuit	60	35
Test TC-20C	27	P0202	Injector No. 2 Control Circuit	61	36
Test TC-21A	27	P0201	Injector Control Circuit	61	37
Test TC-21B	27	P0201	Injector Control Circuit	61	38
Test TC-21C	27	P0201	Injector Control Circuit	62	39
Test TC-21D	27	P0201	Injector Control Circuit	62	40
Test TC-21E	27	P0201	Injector Control Circuit	62	41
Test TC-21F	27	P0201	Injector Control Circuit	63	42
Test TC-25A	25	P0505	Idle Air Control Motor Circuits	63	43
Test TC-25B	25	P0505	Idle Air Control Motor Circuits	64	44
Test TC-25C	25	P0505	Idle Air Control Motor Circuits	64	45
Test TC-25D	25	P0505	Idle Air Control Motor Circuits	64	46
Test TC-25E	25	P0505	Idle Air Control Motor Circuits	64	47
Test TC-26A	24	P0122	Throttle Position Sensor Voltage Low	65	48
Test TC-27A	24	P0123	Throttle Position Sensor Voltage High	65	49
Test TC-30A	22	P0117	ECT Sensor Voltage Too Low	66	50
Test TC-31A	22	P0118	ECT Sensor Voltage Too High	66	51
Test TC-32A	21	—	O₂ Sensor Stays At Center	67	52
Test TC-35A	15	P0500	No Vehicle Speed Sensor Signal	67	53
Test TC-35B	15	P0500	No Vehicle Speed Sensor Signal	68	54
Test TC-35C	15	P0500	No Vehicle Speed Sensor Signal	69	55
Test TC-36A	14	P0107	MAP Sensor Voltage Too Low	69	56
		P1296	No 5 Volts To MAP Sensor	69	56
Test TC-37A	14	P0108	MAP Sensor Voltage Too High	69	57
Test TC-39A	13	P1297	No Change In MAP Sensor From Start To Run	70	58
Test TC-40A	11	—	No Crank Reference Signal At PCM	71	59
Test TC-40B	11	—	No Crank Reference Signal At PCM	71	60
Test TC-41A	43	P0353	Ignition Coil No. 3 Primary Circuit	72	61
Test TC-42A	43	P0352	Ignition Coil No. 2 Primary Circuit	72	62
Test TC-43A	43	P0351	Ignition Coil No. 1 Primary Circuit	73	63
Test TC-44A	42	—	No ASD Relay Output Voltage At PCM	73	64
Test TC-46A	32	P0401	EGR System Failure	74	65
Test TC-57A	23	P0112	Intake Air Temperature Sensor Voltage Low	75	66
Test TC-58A	23	P0113	Intake Air Temperature Sensor Voltage High	75	67
Test TC-59A	16	P0325	Knock Sensor Circuit	76	68
Test TC-59B	16	P0325	Knock Sensor Circuit	76	69
Test TC-61A	27	P0204	Injector No. 4 Control Circuit	77	70
Test TC-61B	27	P0204	Injector No. 4 Control Circuit	77	71
Test TC-61C	27	P0204	Injector No. 4 Control Circuit	77	72
Test TC-62A	21	P0132	Left Upstream O₂ Sensor Shorted To Voltage	78	73
Test TC-65A	21	P0154	Right Upstream O₂ Sensor Stays At Center	78	74
Test TC-66A	21	P0152	Right Upstream O₂ Sensor Shorted To Voltage	78	75
Test TC-69A	27	P0205	Injector No. 5 Control Circuit	79	76
Test TC-69B	27	P0205	Injector No. 5 Control Circuit	79	77
Test TC-69C	27	P0205	Injector No. 5 Control Circuit	79	78
Test TC-69D	27	P0205	Injector No. 5 Control Circuit	80	79
Test TC-69E	27	P0205	Injector No. 5 Control Circuit	80	80
Test TC-70A	27	P0206	Injector No. 6 Control Circuit	80	81
Test TC-70B	27	P0206	Injector No. 6 Control Circuit	81	82

Continued

1996 MODELS w/2.0L/4-122 NON-TURBO, 2.4L/4-148, 2.5L/V6-152, 3.3L/V6-201 & 3.5L/V6-215 ENGINES

DIAGNOSTIC CHART INDEX–Continued

Test	MIL Code	Generic Scan Tool Code	Description	Page No. 14-	Fig. No.
Test TC-70C	27	P0206	Injector No. 6 Control Circuit	81	83
Test TC-83A	16	—	Knock Sensor No. 2 Circuit	82	84
Test TC-86A	34	—	Speed Control Switch Always High	82	85
Test TC-86B	34	—	Speed Control Switch Always High	82	86
Test TC-87A	34	—	Speed Control Switch Always Low	82	87
Test TC-88A	—	—	Manifold Tune Valve Solenoid Circuit	83	88
Test TC-88B	—	—	Manifold Tune Valve Solenoid Circuit	83	89
Test TC-90A	33	—	A/C Pressure Sensor Voltage Too High	84	90
Test TC-91A	33	—	A/C Pressure Sensor Voltage Too Low	84	91
Test TC-92A	35	P1489	Low Speed Fan Control Relay Circuit	85	92
Test TC-93A	35	P1490	High Speed Fan Control Relay Circuit	85	93
Test TC-96A	66	P1698	No CCD Messages From TCM	86	94
Test TC-97A	66	—	No CCD Message From Body Control Module	86	95
Test TC-101A	42	—	Fuel Pump Relay Control Circuit	87	96
Test TC-102A	21	P0133	Left Upstream O$_2$ Sensor Slow Response	87	97
Test TC-103A	21	P0135	Left Upstream O$_2$ Sensor Heater Failure	88	98
Test TC-105A	21	P0141	Left Downstream O$_2$ Sensor Heater Failure	88	99
Test TC-106A	43	P0300	Multiple Cylinder Misfire	88	100
Test TC-107A	43	P0301	Cylinder No. 1 Misfire	89	101
		P0302	Cylinder No. 2 Misfire	89	101
		P0303	Cylinder No. 3 Misfire	89	101
		P0304	Cylinder No. 4 Misfire	89	101
		P0305	Cylinder No. 5 Misfire	89	101
		P0306	Cylinder No. 6 Misfire	89	101
Test TC-112A	72	P0420	Catalytic Converter Efficiency Failure	90	102
Test TC-113A	31	P0441	EVAP Purge Flow Monitor Failure	90	103
Test TC-113B	31	P0441	EVAP Purge Flow Monitor Failure	90	104
Test TC-114A	37	P1899	Park/Neutral Position Switch Failure	91	105
Test TC-115A	65	P0551	Power Steering Switch Failure	91	106
Test TC-115B	65	P0551	Power Steering Switch Failure	91	107
Test TC-118A	52	P0172	Fuel System Rich	92	108
Test TC-118B	52	P0172	Fuel System Rich	92	109
Test TC-119A	51	P0171	Fuel System Lean	92	110
Test TC-119B	51	P0171	Fuel System Lean	92	111
Test TC-120A	52	P0172	Right Bank Fuel System Rich	93	112
Test TC-120B	52	P0172	Right Bank Fuel System Rich	93	113
Test TC-121A	52	P0174	Right Bank Fuel System Lean	93	114
Test TC-121B	52	P0174	Right Bank Fuel System Lean	93	115
Test TC-122A	21	P0153	Right Upstream O$_2$ Sensor Slow Response	94	116
Test TC-124A	21	P0155	Right Upstream O$_2$ Sensor Heater Failure	94	117
Test TC-125A	21	P0161	Right Downstream O$_2$ Sensor Heater Failure	94	118
Test TC-126A	21	P0138	Left Downstream O$_2$ Sensor Shorted To Voltage	95	119
Test TC-127A	21	P0158	Right Downstream O$_2$ Sensor Shorted To Voltage	95	120
Test TC-128A	17	P0125	Closed Loop Temperature Not Reached	95	121
Test TC-129A	21	P0140	Left Downstream O$_2$ Sensor Stays At Center	96	122
Test TC-130A	21	P0160	Right Downstream O$_2$ Sensor Stays At Center	96	123
Test TC-132A	24	P0121	TPS Voltage Does Not Agree w/MAP	97	124
Test TC-133A	11	P1390	Timing Belt Skipped One Tooth Or More	98	125
Test TC-135A	14	P1296	No Five Volts To MAP Sensor	98	126
Test TC-138A	25	P1294	Target Idle Not Reached	98	127
Test TC-138B	25	P1294	Target Idle Not Reached	99	128
Test TC-139A	35	P1489	High Speed Radiator Fan Control Relay Circuit	99	129

Continued

DIAGNOSTIC CHART INDEX–Continued

Test	MIL Code	Generic Scan Tool Code	Description	Page No. 14-	Fig. No.
Test TC-145A	25	P1299	Vacuum Leak Found; IAC Fully Seated	100	130
Test TC-146A	14	P1496	5 Volt Supply Output Too Low	100	131
Test TC-146B	14	P1496	5 Volt Supply Output Too Low	100	132
Test TC-148A	37	P0740	Torque Converter Clutch, No RPM Drop Lockup①	101	133
Test TC-149A	42	—	Fuel Level Sending Unit Voltage Too Low	101	134
Test TC-149B	42	—	Fuel Level Sending Unit Voltage Too Low	102	135
Test TC-150A	42	—	Fuel Level Sending Unit Voltage Too High	102	136
Test TC-150B	42	—	Fuel Level Sending Unit Voltage Too High	103	137
Test TC-151A	42	—	Fuel Level Unit No Change Over Miles	103	138
Test TC-151B	42	—	Fuel Level Unit No Change Over Miles	104	139
Test TC-152A	65	P0703	Brake Switch Sense Circuit	104	140
Test TC-153A	44	P1492	Battery Temperature Sensor Voltage Too High	105	141
	44	P1493	Battery Temperature Sensor Voltage Too Low	105	141
Test TC-153B	44	P1492	Battery Temperature Sensor Voltage Too High	105	142
	44	P1493	Battery Temperature Sensor Voltage Too Low	105	142
Test TC-153C	44	P1492	Battery Temperature Sensor Voltage Too High	105	143
	44	P1493	Battery Temperature Sensor Voltage Too Low	105	143
Test TC-155A	21	P0131	Left Upstream O2S Voltage Shorted To Ground	105	144
Test TC-156A	21	P0137	Left Downstream O2S Voltage Shorted To Ground	106	145
Test TC-157A	11	P1391	Intermittent Loss Of CMP Or CKP	106	146
Test TC-157B	11	P1391	Intermittent Loss Of CMP Or CKP	107	147
Test TC-157C	11	P1391	Intermittent Loss Of CMP Or CKP	107	148
Test TC-160A	—	—	EVAP Leak Monitor Small Leak Detected	108	149
Test TC-161A	—	—	EVAP Leak Monitor Large Leak Detected	108	150
Test TC-180A	72	P0432	Right Catalytic Converter Efficiency Failure	109	151
Test TC-181A	21	P0151	Right Upstream O2 Sensor Shorted To Ground	109	152
Test TC-182A	21	P0157	Right/Downstream Shorted To Ground	109	153
Test TC-183A	31	P1495	Leak Detection Pump Solenoid Circuit	110	154
Test TC-184A	31	P1494	Leak Detection Pump Switch Or Mechanical Fault	110	155
Test TC-186A	11	P1398	Misfire Adaptive Numerator At Limit	111	156
Test TC-187A	—	—	EVAP Leak Monitor Pinched Hose	111	157
Test TC-187B	—	—	EVAP Leak Monitor Pinched Hose	111	158
Test TC-187C	—	—	EVAP Leak Monitor Pinched Hose	111	159
Test TC-197A	—	—	High Speed Radiator Fan Ground Control Relay Circuit	112	160
Test NTC-1A	—	—	Checking The Engine Mechanical Systems	112	161
Test NTC-2A	—	—	Checking Secondary Ignition & Timing	113	162
Test NTC-3A	—	—	Checking Fuel Pressure & Injector Operation	113	163
Test NTC-3B	—	—	Checking Fuel Pressure & Injector Operation	113	164
Test NTC-3C	—	—	Checking Fuel Pressure & Injector Operation	114	165
Test NTC-3D	—	—	Checking Fuel Pressure & Injector Operation	114	166
Test NTC-3E	—	—	Checking Fuel Pressure & Injector Operation	115	167
Test NTC-4A	—	—	Checking Coolant Sensor Calibration	115	168
Test NTC-5A	—	—	Checking Throttle Position Sensor	116	169
Test NTC-6A	—	—	Checking MAP Sensor	116	170
Test NTC-7A	—	—	Checking The Oxygen Sensor Switching	116	171
Test NTC-7B	—	—	Checking The Oxygen Sensor Switching	117	172
Test NTC-8A	—	—	Checking The Oxygen Sensor Heater	117	173
Test NTC-9A	—	—	Checking Idle Air Control Motor	118	174
Test NTC-10A	—	—	Checking Park/Neutral Position Switch	118	175
Test NTC-11A	—	—	Checking The PCM Power & Grounds	118	176
Test NTC-12A	—	—	Checking The Evaporative Emissions Systems	119	177

Continued

DIAGNOSTIC CHART INDEX–Continued

Test	MIL Code	Generic Scan Tool Code	Description	Page No. 14-	Fig. No.
Test NTC-13A	—	—	Checking EGR Systems	119	178
Test NTC-14A	—	—	Checking The Engine Vacuum	119	179
Test NTC-15A	—	—	Checking The Intake Air Temperature Sensor	120	180
Test NTC-16A	—	—	Checking The Timing Belt Alignment	120	181
Test NTC-17A	—	—	Checking The Minimum Idle Air Flow	120	182
Test NTC-17B	—	—	Checking The Minimum Idle Air Flow	120	183
Test NTC-18A	—	—	Checking The Engine Mechanical Systems	121	184
Test SC-1A	—	—	Checking Speed Control Operation ②	121	185
Test SC-1B	—	—	Checking Speed Control Operation ②	122	186
Test SC-1C	—	—	Checking Speed Control Operation ②	122	187
Test SC-1D	—	—	Checking Speed Control Operation ②	122	188
Test SC-2A	—	—	Checking Speed Control On/Off Switch ②	123	189
Test SC-3A	—	—	Checking Speed Control Set/Resume Switch ②	123	190
Test SC-4A	—	—	Checking The Brake Switch Sense ②	123	191
Test SC-5A	—	—	Checking The Park/Neutral Position Switch ②	124	192
Test SC-6A	—	—	Checking For A Speed Control Denied Message	124	193
Test SC-7A	—	—	Checking Speed Control Operation ③	124	194
Test SC-7B	—	—	Checking Speed Control Operation ③	125	195
Test SC-7C	—	—	Checking Speed Control Operation ③	125	196
Test SC-8A	—	—	Checking Speed Control On/Off Switch ③	125	197
Test SC-10A	—	—	Checking The Park/Neutral Position Switch ③	126	198
Test SC-11A	—	—	Checking Speed Control Relay Output ③	126	199
Test CH-1A	—	—	Charging System No Code Test	126	200
Test NS-1A	—	—	Qualifying A No Start Condition	127	201
Test NS-1B	—	—	Qualifying A No Start Condition	128	202
Test NS-2A	—	—	Checking Fuel System	129	203
Test NS-3A	—	—	Checking The Engine Mechanical Systems	129	204
Test NS-4A	—	—	Repairing Low Fuel Pressure	130	205
Test NS-4B	—	—	Repairing Low Fuel Pressure	130	206
Test NS-4C	—	—	Repairing Low Fuel Pressure	131	207
Test NS-4D	—	—	Repairing Low Fuel Pressure	131	208
Test NS-4E	—	—	Repairing Low Fuel Pressure	131	209
Test NS-5A	—	—	Checking The Fuel Pump	132	210
Test NS-6A	—	—	Repairing A No Response Condition	132	211
Test NS-6B	—	—	Repairing A " No Response" Condition	133	212
Test NS-6C	—	—	Repairing A " No Response" Condition	134	213
Test NS-7A	—	—	Checking The Idle Air Control Motor Operation	134	214
Test NS-8A	—	—	Repairing A Start & Stall Condition	135	215
Test NS-9A	—	—	Repairing A No Crank Condition	135	216
Test NS-9B	—	—	Repairing A No Crank Condition	136	217
Test VER-1A	—	—	No Start Verification	136	218
Test VER-2A	—	—	Road Test Verification	136	219
Test VER-3A	—	—	Charging Verification	136	220
Test VER-4A	—	—	Speed Control Verification	136	221
Test VER-5A	—	—	Road Test For OBD II Trouble Codes	137	222

①—Neon.
②—Breeze, Cirrus, Concorde, Intrepid, LHS, Neon, New Yorker, Sebring Convertible, Stratus & Vision.
③—Avenger, Sebring Coupe & Talon.

NOTE: The battery must be fully charged for any test

Attempt to start the engine. Crank for up to 10 seconds if necessary.

Connect the DRB to the engine diagnostic connector. Write down the trouble codes that are displayed.

If the DRB screen displays "No Response", go to **TEST NS-6A.**

If the DRB screen is blank or has a DRB error message, go to **General Information**

If **trouble code messages** are displayed, refer to the trouble code list below for the appropriate test.

If there are **no trouble codes** displayed, refer to one of the following:

For Driveability problems NTC-1A
For No Start problems NS-1A
For Speed Control problems SC-1A
For Charging problems CH-1A

NOTE: The test numbers for these trouble codes were derived from the decimal codes as set in the PCM. Therefore, some test numbers will be missing because all codes are not applicable to the vehicles covered

DRB TROUBLE CODE (DTC) DISPLAYED	TEST #	MIL CODE	DTC HEX CODE	SCAN TOOL J2012 CODE
5 VOLT SUPPLY OUTPUT TOO LOW	TC-146	71	92	P1496
A/C CLUTCH RELAY CIRCUIT	TC-16	33	10	N/A
A/C PRESSURE SENSOR VOLTS TOO HIGH	TC-90	33	5A	N/A
A/C PRESSURE SENSOR VOLTS TOO LOW	TC-91	33	5B	N/A
AUTO SHUTDOWN RELAY CONTROL CIRCUIT	TC-10	42	0A	N/A
BATTERY TEMP SENSOR VOLTAGE TOO HIGH	TC-153	44	9A	P 1492
BATTERY TEMP SENSOR VOLTAGE TOO LOW	TC-153	44	99	P 1493
BRAKE SWITCH STUCK PRESSED OR RELEASED	TC-152	65	98	P 0703
CATALYTIC CONVERTER EFFICIENCY FAILURE	TC-112	72,64	70	P 0420
CHARGING SYSTEM VOLTAGE TOO HIGH	TC-6	46	06	N/A
CHARGING SYSTEM VOLTAGE TOO LOW	TC-5	47	05	N/A
CLOSED LOOP TEMP NOT REACHED	TC-128	17	80	P 0125
CYLINDER #1 MIS-FIRE	TC-107	43	6B	P 0301
CYLINDER #2 MIS-FIRE	TC-107	43	6C	P 0302
CYLINDER #3 MIS-FIRE	TC-107	43	6D	P 0303
CYLINDER #4 MIS-FIRE	TC-107	43	6E	P 0304
CYLINDER #5 MIS-FIRE	TC-107	43	AE	P 0305
CYLINDER #6 MIS-FIRE	TC-107	43	AF	P 0306
DOWNSTREAM O2 SENSOR HEATER FAILURE	TC-105	21	69	P 0141
DOWNSTREAM O2 SENSOR SHORTED TO VOLTAGE	TC-126	21	7E	P 0138
DOWNSTREAM O2 SENSOR STAYS AT CENTER	TC-129	21	81	P 0140
DOWNSTREAM O2S VOLTS SHORTED TO GROUND	TC-156	21	9C	P 0137
ECT SENSOR VOLTAGE TOO HIGH	TC-31	22	1F	P 0118

CR1029606590010X

Fig. 15 Diagnostic Trouble Code Inspection (Part 1 of 4)

DRB TROUBLE CODE (DTC) DISPLAYED	TEST #	MIL CODE	DTC HEX CODE	SCAN TOOL J2012 CODE
LEFT DOWNSTREAM O2S VOLTS SHORTED TO GROUND	TC-156	21	9C	P 0137
LEFT O2 SENSOR SHORTED TO VOLTAGE	TC-62	21	3E	P 0132
LEFT O2 SENSOR STAYS AT CENTER	TC-32	21	20	P 0134
LEFT UPSTREAM O2 SENSOR HEATER FAILURE	TC-103	21	67	P 0135
LEFT UPSTREAM O2 SENSOR SLOW RESPONSE	TC-102	21	66	P 0133
LOW SPEED FAN CTRL RELAY CIRCUIT	TC-92	35	5C	P 1490
MANIFOLD TUNE VALVE SOLENOID CIRCUIT	TC-88	65	58	P 1289
MAP SENSOR VOLTAGE TOO HIGH	TC-37	14	25	P 0108
MAP SENSOR VOLTAGE TOO LOW	TC-36	14	24	P 0107
MIS-FIRE ADAPTIVE NUMERATOR AT LIMIT	TC-186	11	BA	P 1398
MULTIPLE CYLINDER MIS-FIRE	TC-106	43	6A	P 0300
NO 5 VOLTS TO MAP SENSOR	TC-135	14	87	P 1296
NO ASD RELAY OUTPUT VOLTAGE AT PCM	TC-44	42	2C	N/A
NO CAM SIGNAL AT PCM	TC-1	54	01	P 0340
NO CCD MESSAGE FROM BODY CONTROL MODULE	TC-97	66	61	N/A
NO CCD MESSAGES FROM TCM	TC-96	66	60	P 1698
NO CHANGE IN MAP FROM START TO RUN	TC-39	13	27	P 1297
NO CRANK REFERENCE SIGNAL AT PCM	TC-40	11	28	N/A
NO VEHICLE SPEED SENSOR SIGNAL	TC-35	15	23	P 0500
O2 SENSOR STAYS AT CENTER	TC-32	21	20	P 0134
P/N SWITCH STUCK IN PARK OR IN GEAR	TC-114	37	72	P 1899
PCM FAILURE EEPROM WRITE DENIED	TC-49	63	31	P 1696
PCM FAILURE SPI COMMUNICATIONS	**	53	44	P 0600
PCM FAILURE SRI MILE NOT STORED	TC-48	62	30	P 1697
POWER STEERING SWITCH FAILURE	TC-115	65	73	P 0551
RIGHT BANK CATALYST EFFICIENCY FAILURE	TC-180	72	B4	P 0432
RIGHT BANK DWNSTR O2S SHORTED TO GROUND	TC-182	21	B6	P 0157
RIGHT BANK FUEL SYSTEM LEAN	TC-121	51	79	P 0174
RIGHT BANK FUEL SYSTEM RICH	TC-120	52	78	P 0175
RIGHT BANK UPSTRM O2S SHORTED TO GROUND	TC-181	21	B5	P 0151
RIGHT DOWNSTREAM O2S HEATER FAILURE	TC-125	21	7D	P 0161
RIGHT DOWNSTREAM O2S SHORTED TO VOLTAGE	TC-127	21	7F	P 0158
RIGHT DOWNSTREAM O2S STAYS AT CENTER	TC-130	21	82	P 0160
RIGHT O2 SENSOR SHORTED TO VOLTAGE	TC-66	21	42	P 0152
RIGHT O2 SENSOR STAYS AT CENTER	TC-65	21	41	P 0154
RIGHT UPSTREAM O2 SENSOR HEATER FAILURE	TC-124	21	7C	P 0155
RIGHT UPSTREAM O2 SENSOR SLOW RESPONSE	TC-122	21	7A	P 0153
SPEED CONTROL POWER RELAY CIRCUIT	TC-15	77	52	N/A
SPEED CONTROL SOLENOID CIRCUITS	TC-15	34	0F	N/A
SPEED CONTROL SWITCH ALWAYS HIGH	TC-86	34	56	N/A
SPEED CONTROL SWITCH ALWAYS LOW	TC-87	34	57	N/A
TARGET IDLE NOT REACHED	TC-138	25	8A	P 1294
THROTTLE POSITION SENSOR VOLTAGE HIGH	TC-27	24	1B	P 0123
THROTTLE POSITION SENSOR VOLTAGE LOW	TC-26	24	1A	P 0122
TIMING BELT SKIPPED 1 TOOTH OR MORE	TC-133	11	85	P 1390

** = Trouble code information on last page of DTC TEST.

Fig. 15 Diagnostic Trouble Code Inspection (Part 3 of 4)

DRB TROUBLE CODE (DTC) DISPLAYED	TEST #	MIL CODE	DTC HEX CODE	SCAN TOOL J2012 CODE
ECT SENSOR VOLTAGE TOO LOW	TC-30	22	1E	P 0117
EGR SOLENOID CIRCUIT	TC-17	32	11	P 0403
EGR SYSTEM FAILURE	TC-46	32	2E	P 0401
ENGINE IS COLD TOO LONG	**	17	21	N/A
EVAP LEAK MONITOR LARGE LEAK DETECTED	TC-161	31	A1	P 0455
EVAP LEAK MONITOR PINCHED HOSE FOUND	TC-187	31	BB	P 1486
EVAP LEAK MONITOR SMALL LEAK DETECTED	TC-160	31	A0	P 0442
EVAP PURGE FLOW MONITOR FAILURE	TC-113	31	71	P 0441
EVAP PURGE SOLENOID CIRCUIT	TC-18	31	12	P 0443
FUEL LEVEL SENDING UNIT VOLTS TOO HIGH	**	42	96	N/A
FUEL LEVEL SENDING UNIT VOLTS TOO LOW	**	42	95	N/A
FUEL LEVEL UNIT NO CHANGE OVER MILES	**	42	97	N/A
FUEL PUMP RELAY CONTROL CIRCUIT	TC-101	42	65	N/A
FUEL SYSTEM LEAN	TC-119	51	77	P 0171
FUEL SYSTEM RICH	TC-118	52	76	P 0172
GENERATOR FIELD NOT SWITCHING PROPERLY	TC-11	41	0B	N/A
GOV PRES ABOVE 3 PSI IN GEAR WITH 0 MPH	TC-142	45	8E	P 1757
GOV PRESS NOT EQUAL TO TARGET @ 15-20 PSI	TC-141	45	8D	P 1756
HI SPEED RAD FAN CTRL RELAY CIRCUIT	TC-139	35	8B	P 1487
HIGH SPEED RAD FAN CTRL RELAY CIRCUIT	TC-93	35	5D	P 1489
HIGH SPEED RAD FAN GROUND CTRL RLY CKT	TC-197	35	C5	P 1498
IDLE AIR CONTROL MOTOR CIRCUITS	TC-25	25	19	P 0505
IGNITION COIL #1 PRIMARY CIRCUIT	TC-43	43	2B	P 0351
IGNITION COIL #2 PRIMARY CIRCUIT	TC-42	43	2A	P 0352
IGNITION COIL #3 PRIMARY CIRCUIT	TC-41	43	29	P 0353
INJECTOR #1 CONTROL CIRCUIT	TC-21	27	15	P 0201
INJECTOR #2 CONTROL CIRCUIT	TC-21	27	14	P 0202
INJECTOR #3 CONTROL CIRCUIT	TC-21	27	13	P 0203
INJECTOR #4 CONTROL CIRCUIT	TC-21	27	3D	P 0204
INJECTOR #5 CONTROL CIRCUIT	TC-21	27	45	P 0205
INJECTOR #6 CONTROL CIRCUIT	TC-21	27	46	P 0206
INTAKE AIR TEMP SENSOR VOLTAGE HIGH	TC-58	23	3A	P 0113
INTAKE AIR TEMP SENSOR VOLTAGE LOW	TC-57	23	39	P 0112
INTERMITTENT LOSS OF CMP OR CKP	TC-157	11	9D	P 1391
INTERNAL CONTROLLER FAILURE	**	53	02	P 0601
KNOCK SENSOR #2 CIRCUIT	TC-83	16	53	N/A
KNOCK SENSOR CIRCUIT	TC-59	16	3B	N/A
LEAK DETECT PUMP SW OR MECHANICAL FAULT	TC-184	31	B8	P 1494
LEAK DETECTION PUMP SOLENOID CIRCUIT	TC-183	31	B7	P 1495
LEAK DETECTION PUMP SOLENOID CIRCUIT	TC-183	31	B7	P 1495
LEFT BANK CATALYTIC CONVERTER EFFICIENCY FAILURE	TC-112	72,64	70	P 0420
LEFT BANK UPSTREAM O2S VOLTAGE SHORTED TO GROUND	TC-155	21	9B	P 0131
LEFT DOWNSTREAM O2 SENSOR HEATER FAILURE	TC-105	21	69	P 0141
LEFT DOWNSTREAM O2 SENSOR STAYS AT CENTER	TC-129	21	81	P 0140

** = Trouble code information on last page of DTC TEST.

CR1029606590020X

Fig. 15 Diagnostic Trouble Code Inspection (Part 2 of 4)

DRB TROUBLE CODE (DTC) DISPLAYED	TEST #	MIL CODE	DTC HEX CODE	SCAN TOOL J2012 CODE
TORQ CONV CLU, NO RPM DROP AT LOCKUP	TC-148	37	94	P 0740
TORQUE CONVERTER CLUTCH SOLENOID/TRANS RELAY CKTS	TC-12	37	0C	P 0743
TPS VOLTAGE DOES NOT AGREE WITH MAP	TC-132	24	84	P 0121
UPSTREAM O2S VOLTAGE SHORTED TO GROUND	TC-155	21	9B	P 0131
UPSTREAM O2 SENSOR HEATER FAILURE	TC-103	21	67	P 0135
UPSTREAM O2 SENSOR SHORTED TO VOLTAGE	TC-62	21	3E	P 0132
UPSTREAM O2 SENSOR SLOW RESPONSE	TC-102	21	66	P 0133
VACUUM LEAK FOUND (IAC FULLY SEATED)	TC-145	25	91	P 1299

For an ENGINE IS COLD TOO LONG trouble code, the engine does not warm to 176°F while driving for 20 minutes after start.

For a FUEL LEVEL SENDING UNIT VOLTS TOO HIGH trouble code appropriate body diagnostics manual for repairs. For all other bodies, go to **TEST-150A.**

For a FUEL LEVEL SENDING UNIT VOLTS TOO LOW trouble code go to **TEST-149A.**

For a FUEL LEVEL UNIT NO CHANGE OVER MILES trouble code go to **TEST-151A.**

For an INTERNAL CONTROLLER FAILURE trouble code, replace the powertrain control module and go to **Verification TEST VER-2A.**

For a PCM FAILURE SPI COMMUNICATIONS trouble code, replace the powertrain control module and go to **Verification TEST VER-2A.**

Fig. 15 Diagnostic Trouble Code Inspection (Part 4 of 4)

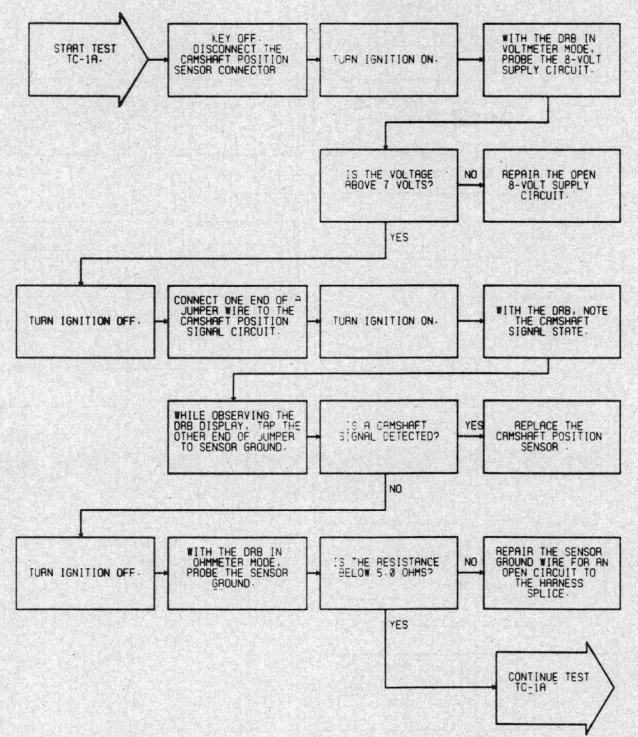

Fig. 16   Test TC-1A: No Cam Signal At PCM (Part 1 of 2)

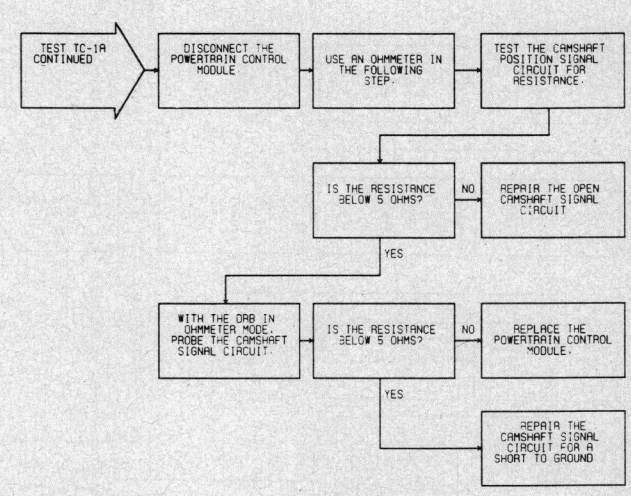

Fig. 16   Test TC-1A: No Cam Signal At PCM (Part 2 of 2)

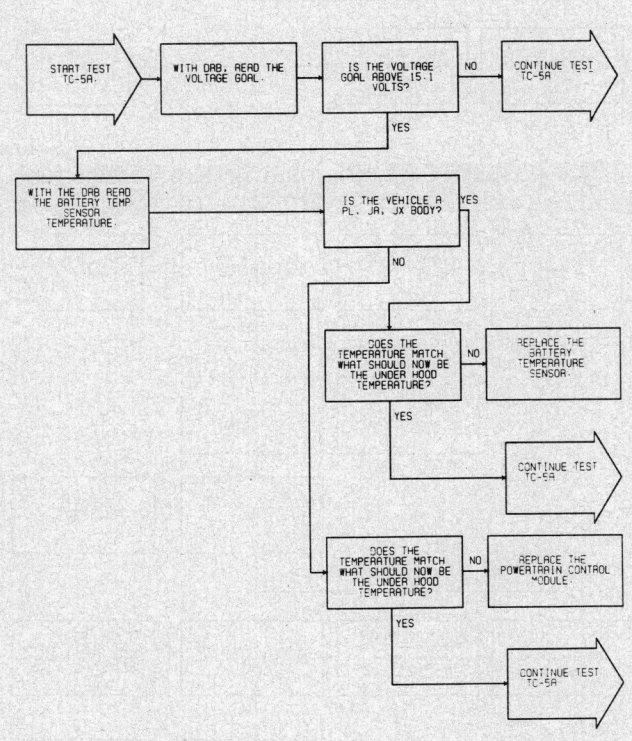

CR1029606592010X

Fig. 17   Test TC-5A: Charging System Voltage Low (Part 1 of 2)

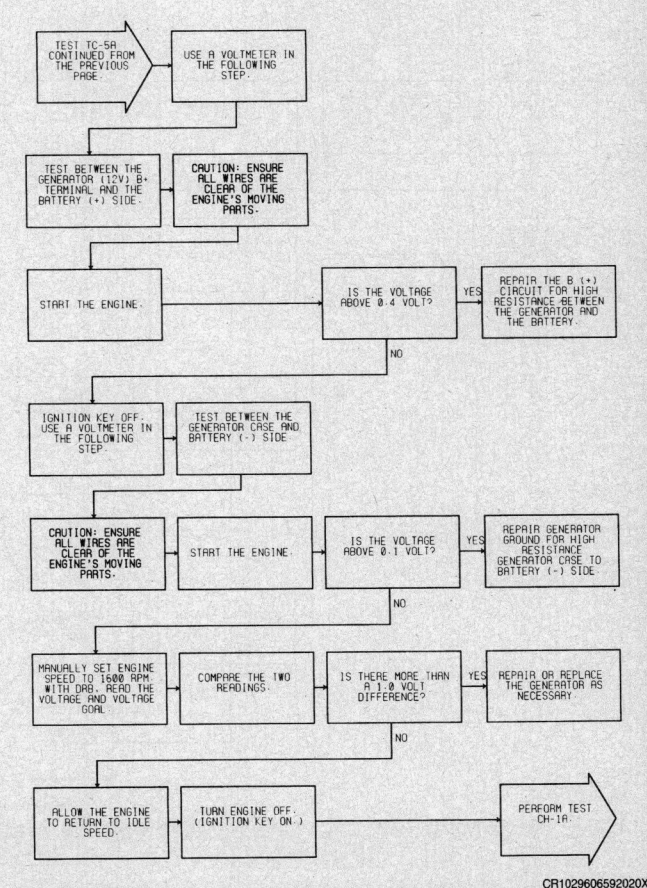

CR1029606592020X

Fig. 17   Test TC-5A: Charging System Voltage Low (Part 2 of 2)

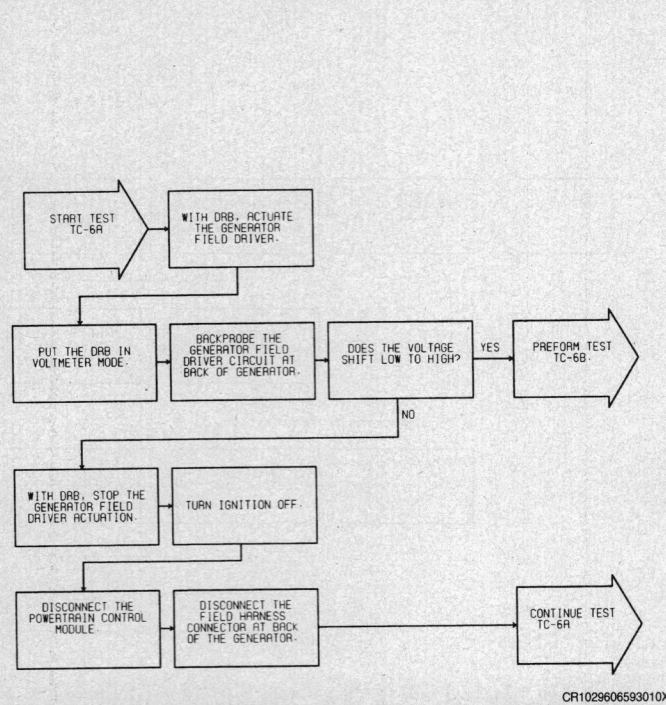

Fig. 18   Test TC-6A: Charging System Voltage High (Part 1 of 2)

CR1029606593010X

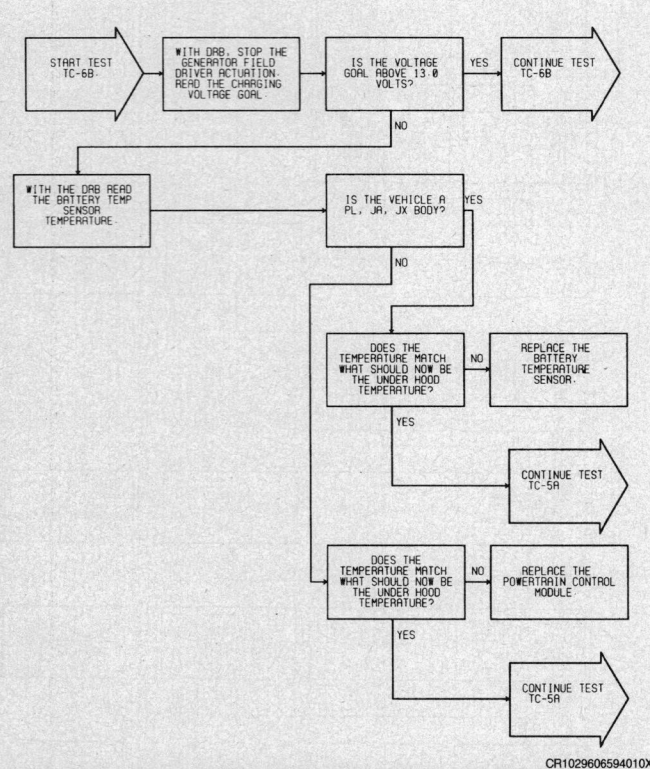

Fig. 19   Test TC-6B: Charging System Voltage High (Part 1 of 2)

CR1029606594010X

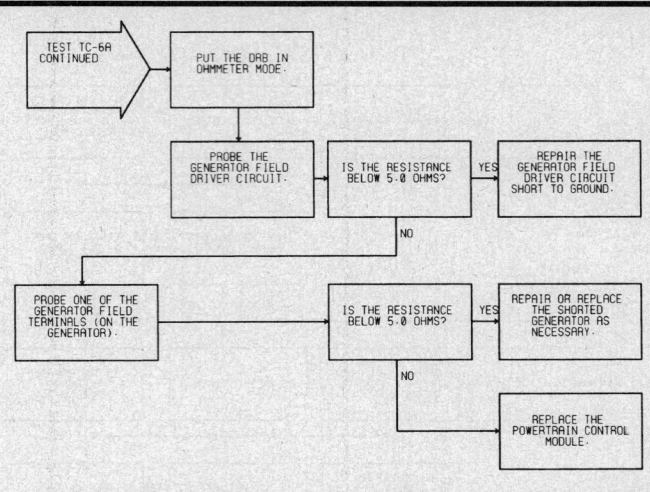

CR1029606593020X

Fig. 18   Test TC-6A: Charging System Voltage High (Part 2 of 2)

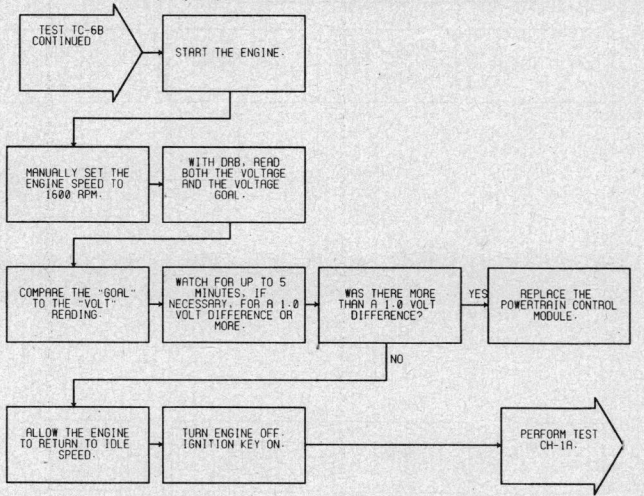

CR1029606594020X

Fig. 19   Test TC-6B: Charging System Voltage High (Part 2 of 2)

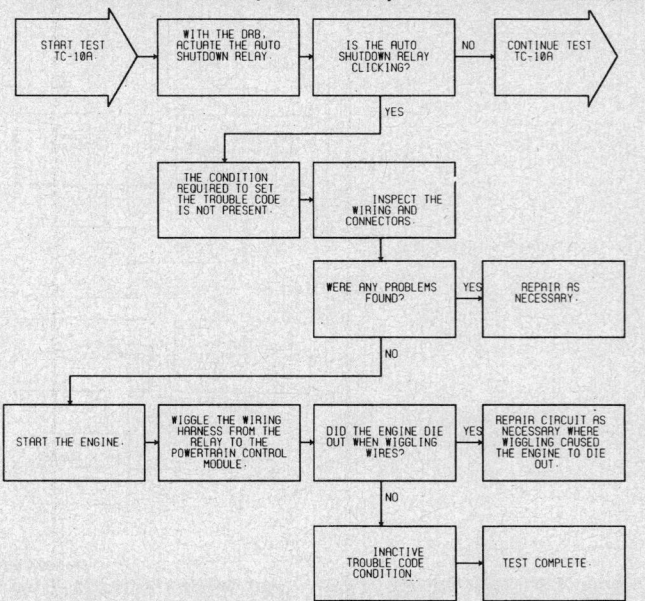

CR1029606595010X

Fig. 20   Test TC-10A: Auto Shutdown Relay Control Circuit (Part 1 of 3)

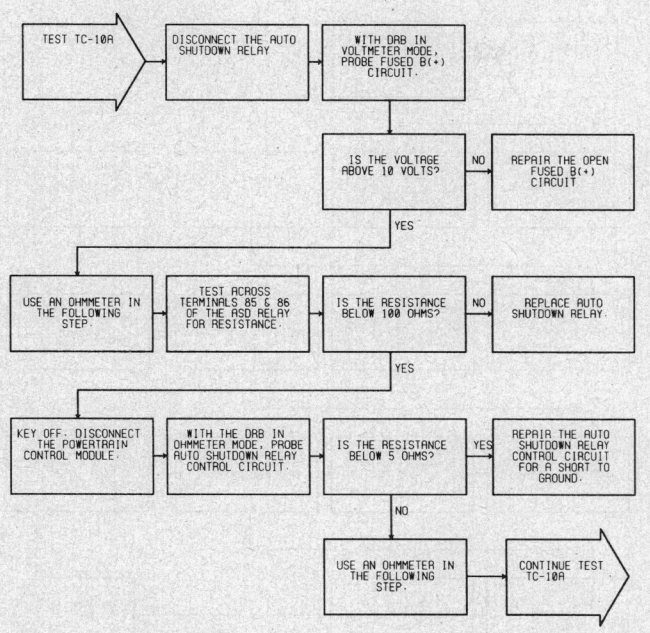

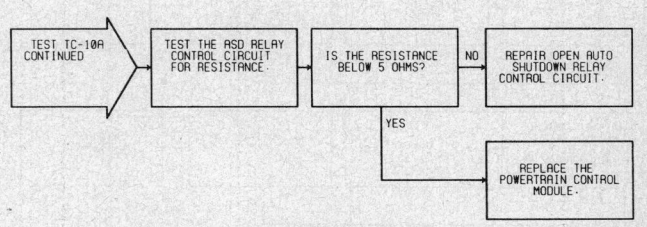

Fig. 20   Test TC-10A: Auto Shutdown Relay Control Circuit (Part 3 of 3)

Fig. 20   Test TC-10A: Auto Shutdown Relay Control Circuit (Part 2 of 3)

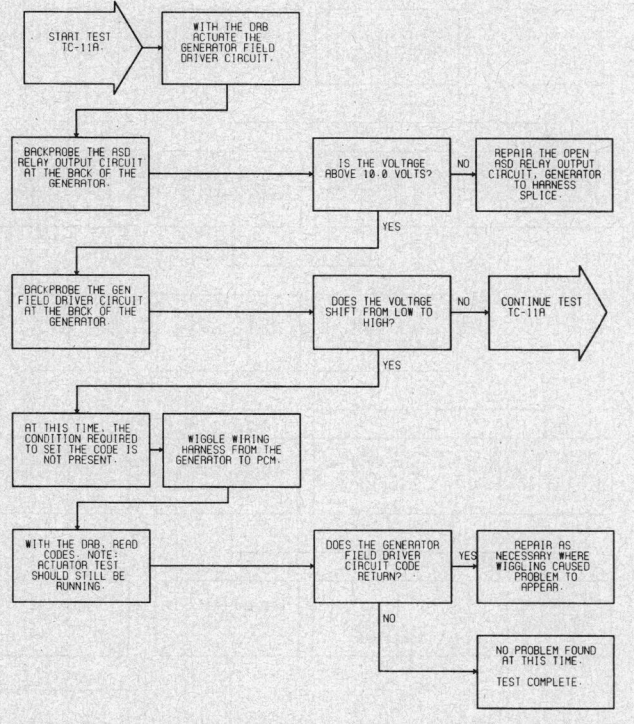

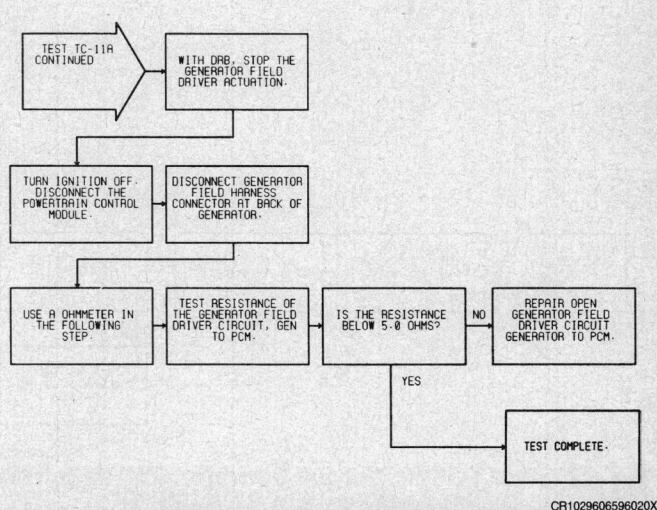

Fig. 21   Test TC-11A: Generator Field Not Switching Properly (Part 2 of 2)

Fig. 21   Test TC-11A: Generator Field Not Switching Properly (Part 1 of 2)

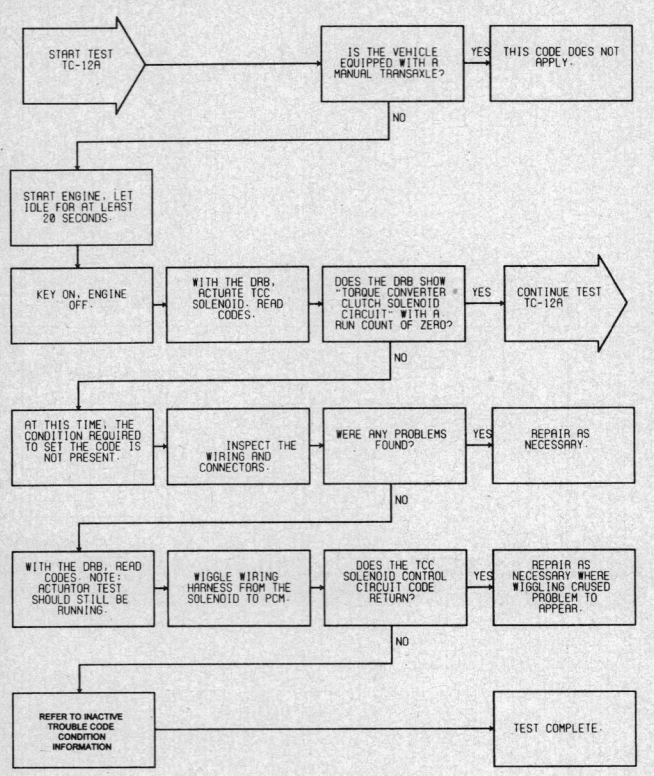

Fig. 22   Test TC-12A: Torque Converter Clutch Solenoid Circuit (Part 1 of 3). Neon

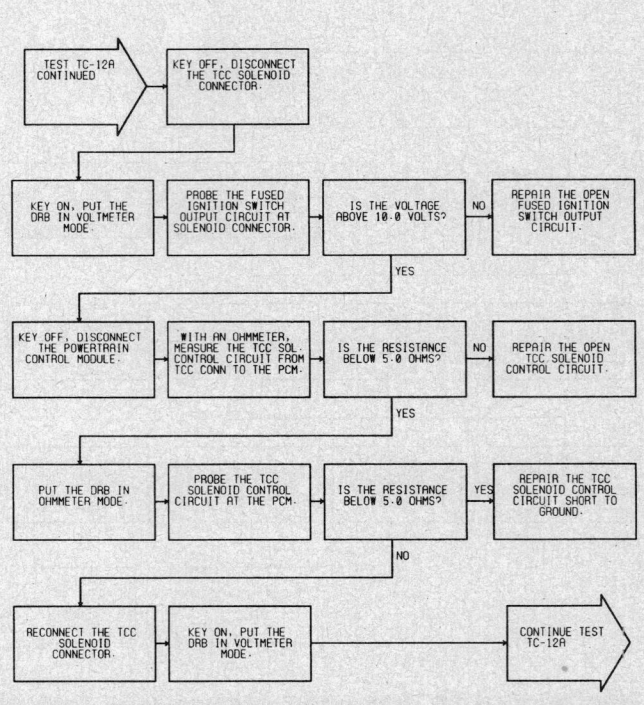

Fig. 22   Test TC-12A: Torque Converter Clutch Solenoid Circuit (Part 2 of 3). Neon

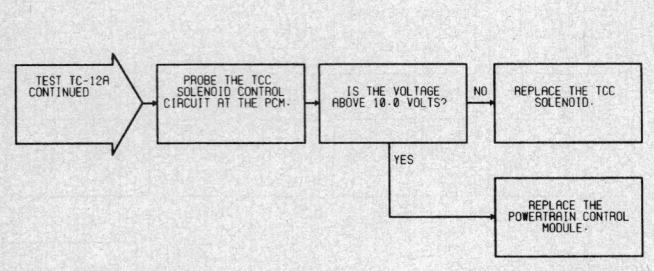

Fig. 22   Test TC-12A: Torque Converter Clutch Solenoid Circuit (Part 3 of 3). Neon

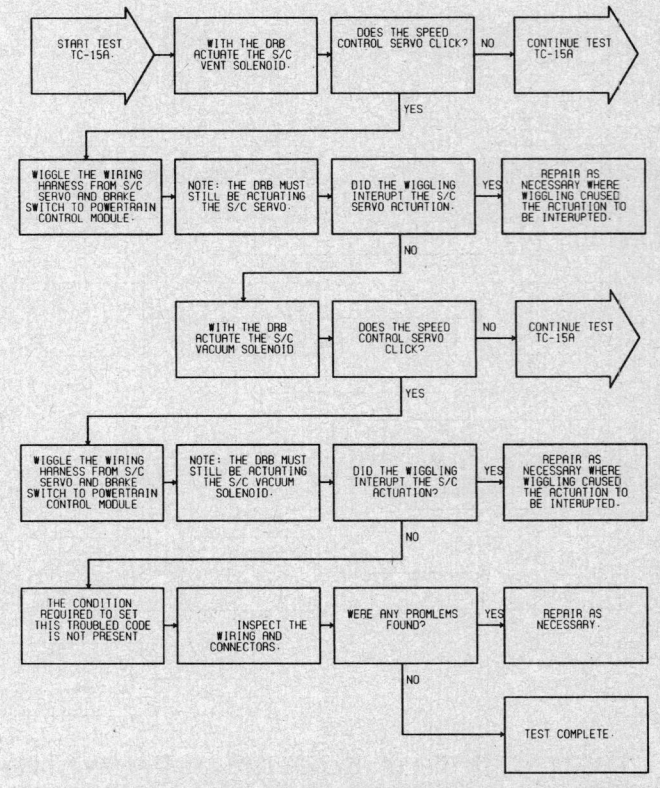

Fig. 23   Test TC-15A: Speed Control Power Circuit & Speed Control Solenoid Circuits (Part 1 of 4)

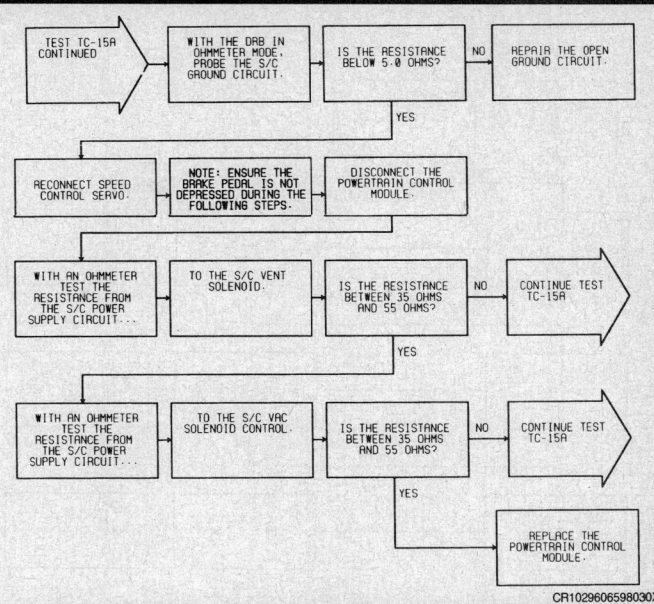

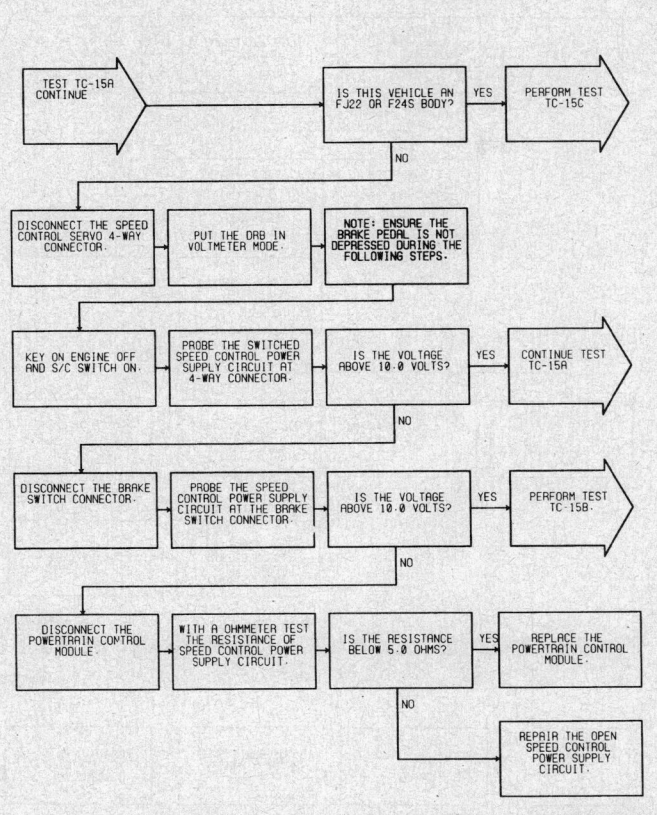

Fig. 23   Test TC-15A: Speed Control Power Circuit & Speed Control Solenoid Circuits (Part 2 of 4)

Fig. 23   Test TC-15A: Speed Control Power Circuit & Speed Control Solenoid Circuits (Part 3 of 4)

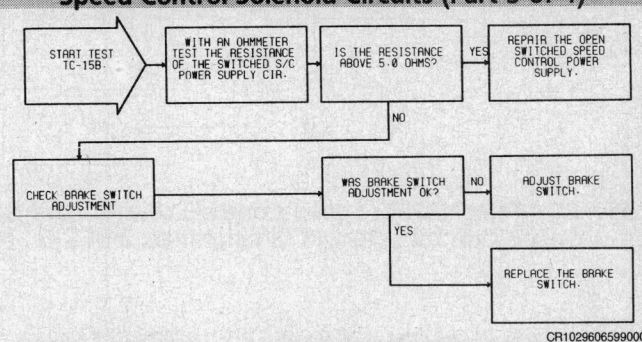

Fig. 24   Test TC-15B: Speed Control Power Circuit & Speed Control Solenoid Circuits

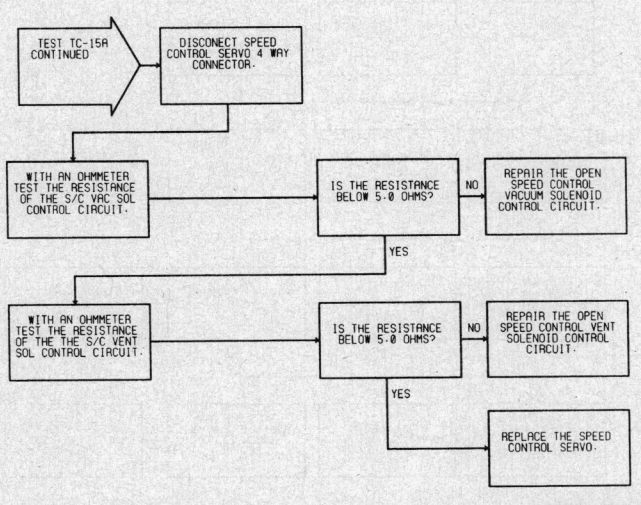

Fig. 23   Test TC-15A: Speed Control Power Circuit & Speed Control Solenoid Circuits (Part 4 of 4)

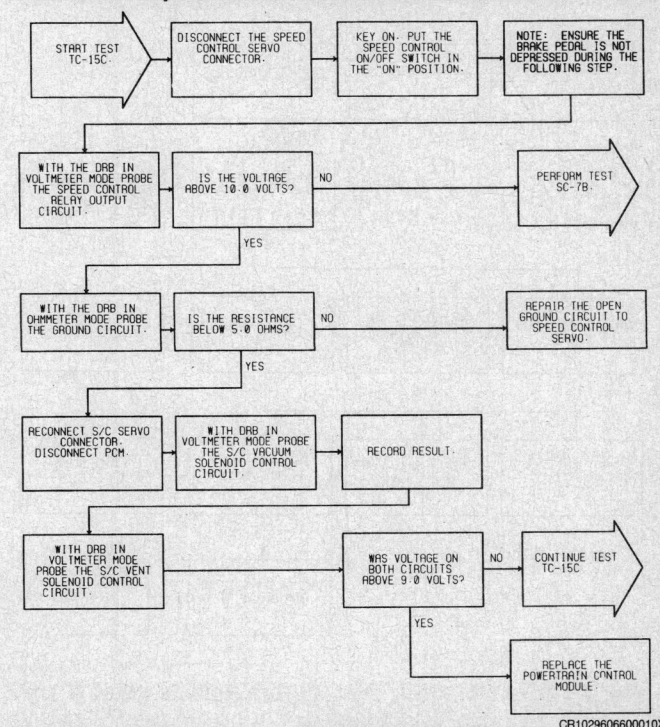

Fig. 25   Test TC-15C: Speed Control Power Circuit & Speed Control Solenoid Circuits (Part 1 of 2)

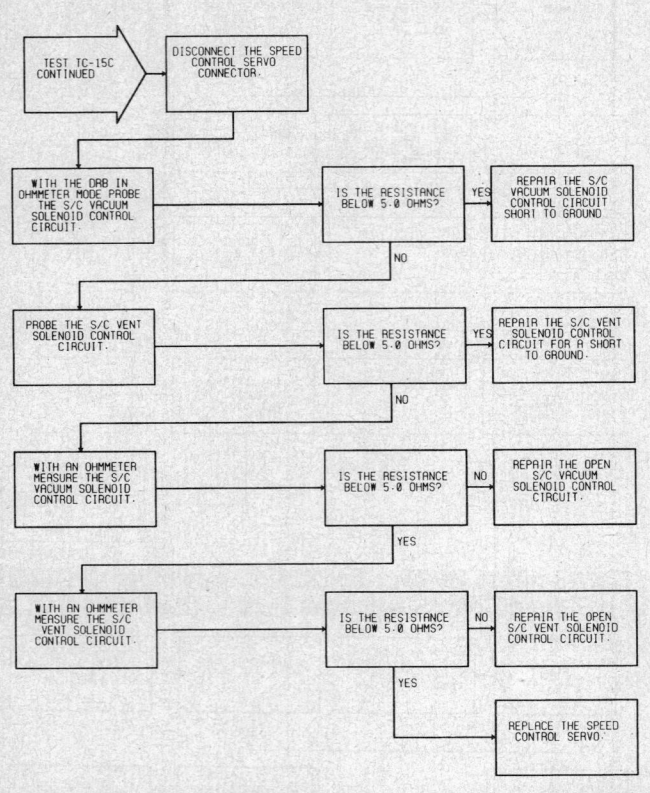

Fig. 25   Test TC-15C: Speed Control Power Circuit & Speed Control Solenoid Circuits (Part 2 of 2)

CR1029606600020X

Fig. 26   Test TC-16A: A/C Clutch Relay Circuit (Part 1 of 3)

CR1029606601010X

Fig. 26   Test TC-16A: A/C Clutch Relay Circuit (Part 3 of 3)

CR1029606601030X

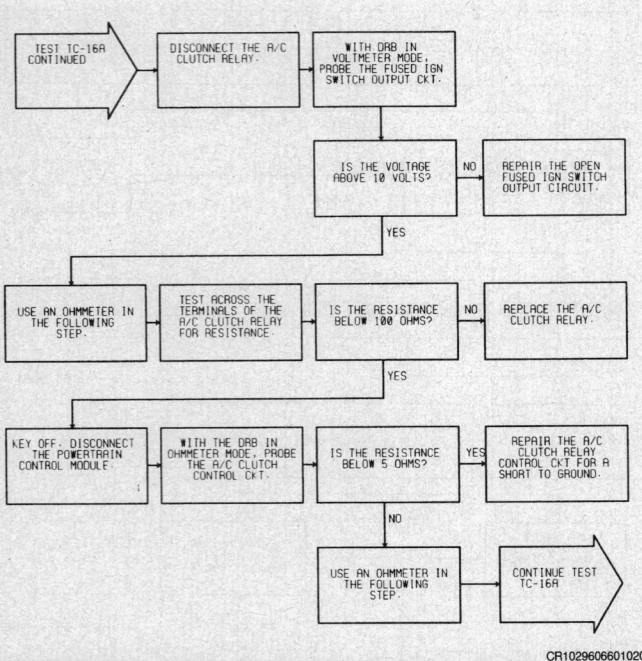

Fig. 26   Test TC-16A: A/C Clutch Relay Circuit (Part 2 of 3)

CR1029606601020X

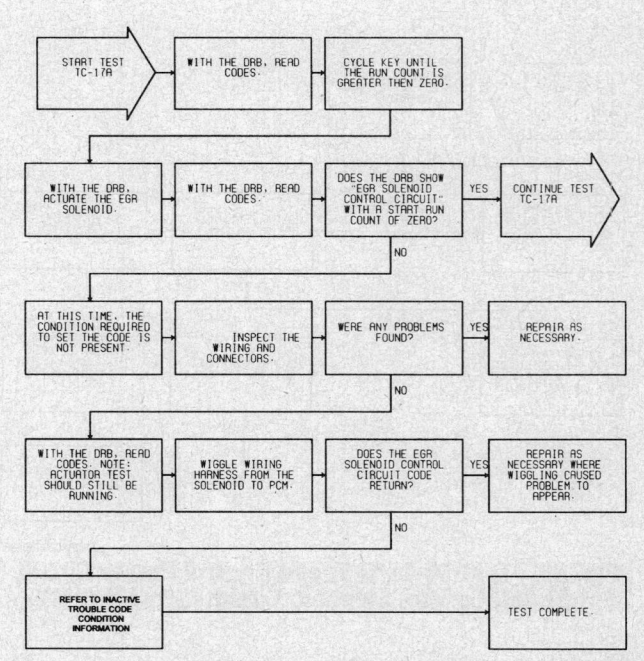

Fig. 27   Test TC-17A: EGR Solenoid Circuit (Part 1 of 3)

CR1029606602010X

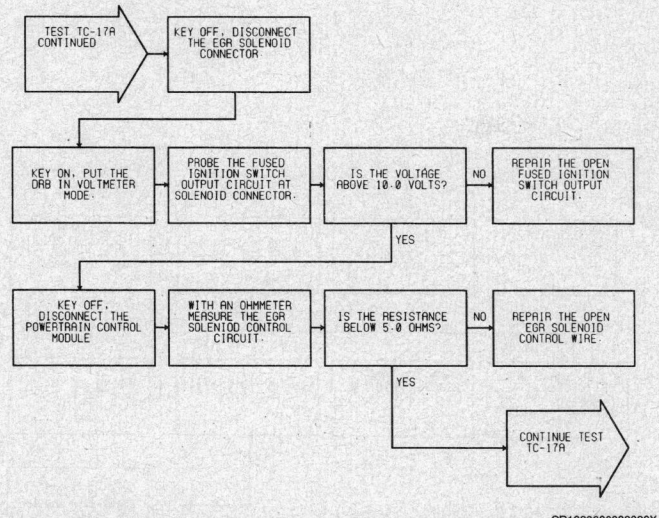

Fig. 27   Test TC-17A: EGR Solenoid Circuit (Part 2 of 3)

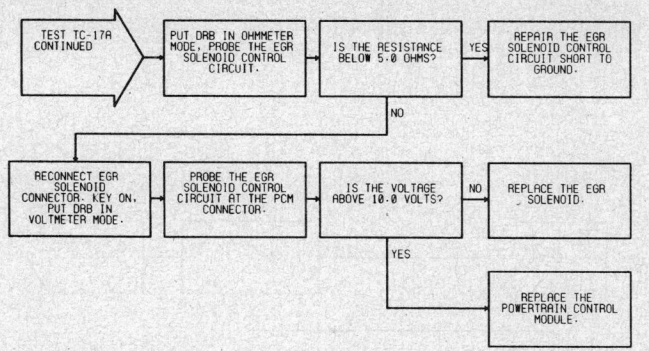

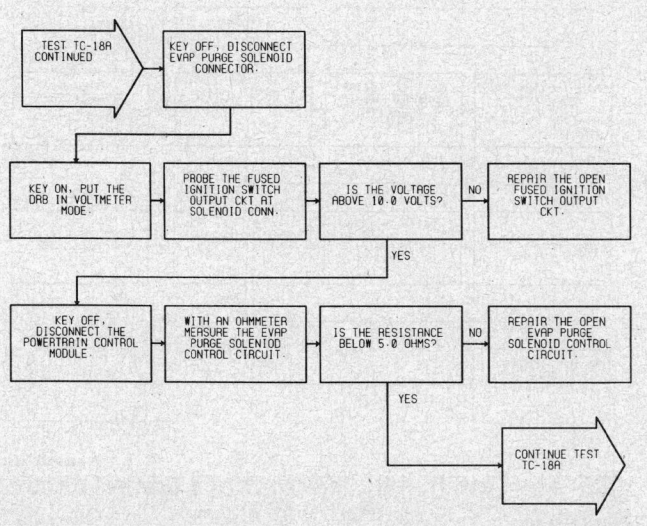

Fig. 27   Test TC-17A: EGR Solenoid Circuit (Part 3 of 3)

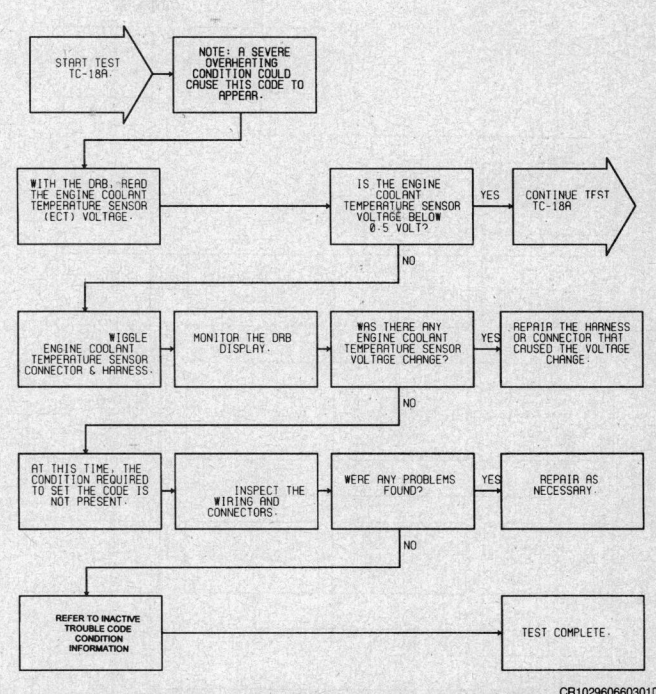

Fig. 28   Test TC-18A: EVAP Purge Solenoid Circuit (Part 1 of 3)

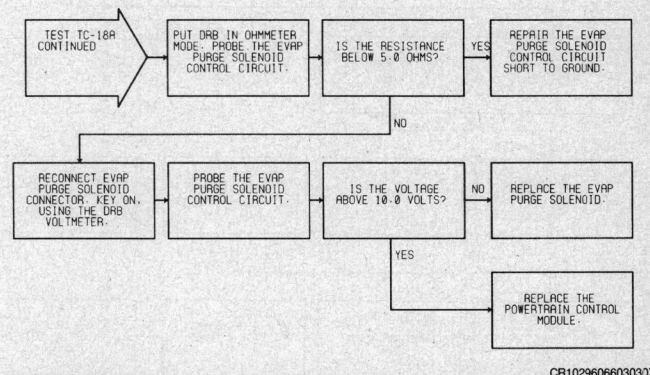

Fig. 28   Test TC-18A: EVAP Purge Solenoid Circuit (Part 3 of 3)

Fig. 28   Test TC-18A: EVAP Purge Solenoid Circuit (Part 2 of 3)

CHRYSLER–Fuel Injection

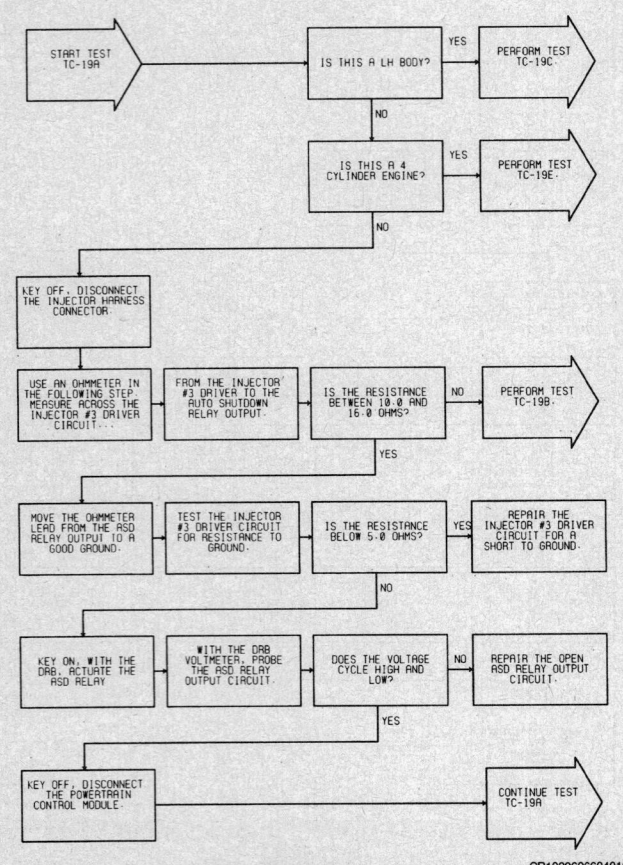

Fig. 29   Test TC-19A: Injector No. 3 Control Circuit (Part 1 of 2)

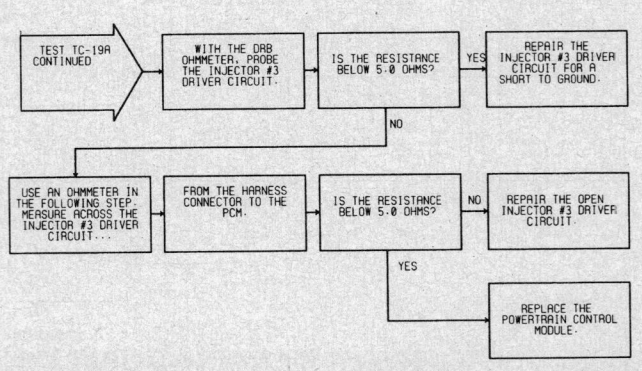

Fig. 29   Test TC-19A: Injector No. 3 Control Circuit (Part 2 of 2)

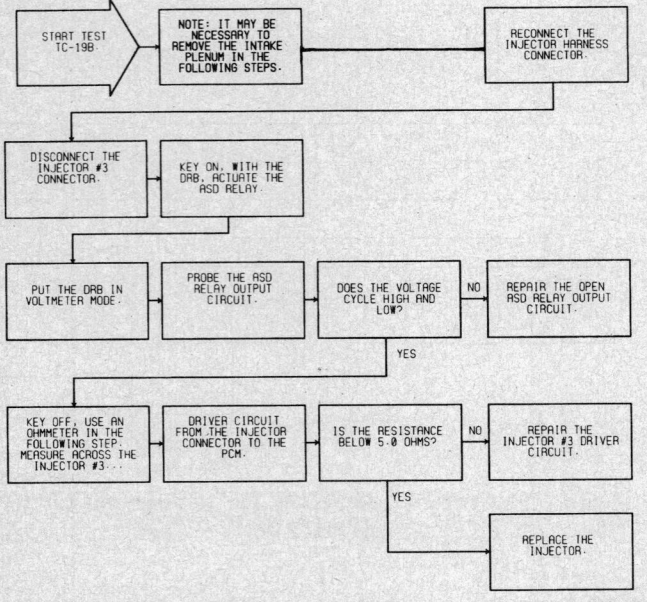

Fig. 30   Test TC-19B: Injector No. 3 Control Circuit

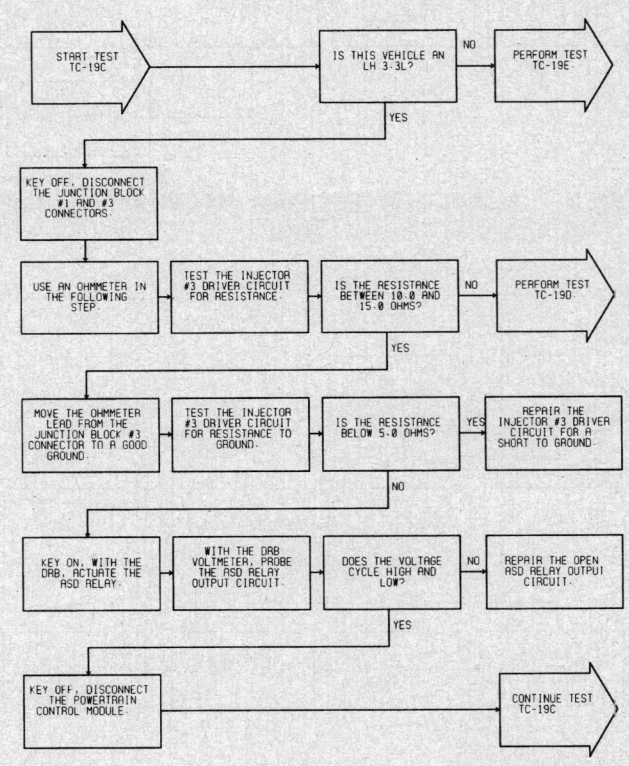

Fig. 31   Test TC-19C: Injector No. 3 Control Circuit (Part 1 of 2)

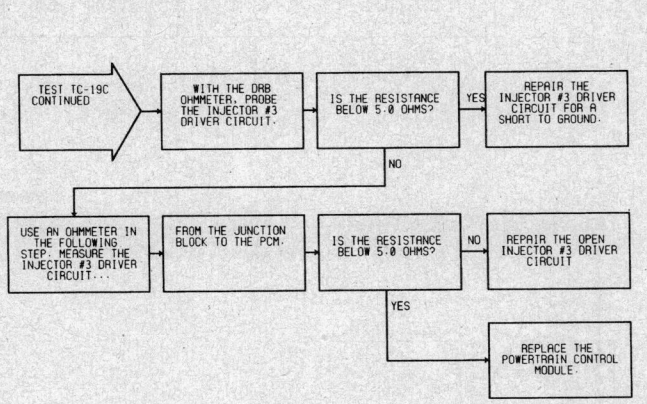

**Fig. 31 Test TC-19C: Injector No. 3 Control Circuit
(Part 2 of 2)**

CR1029606606020X

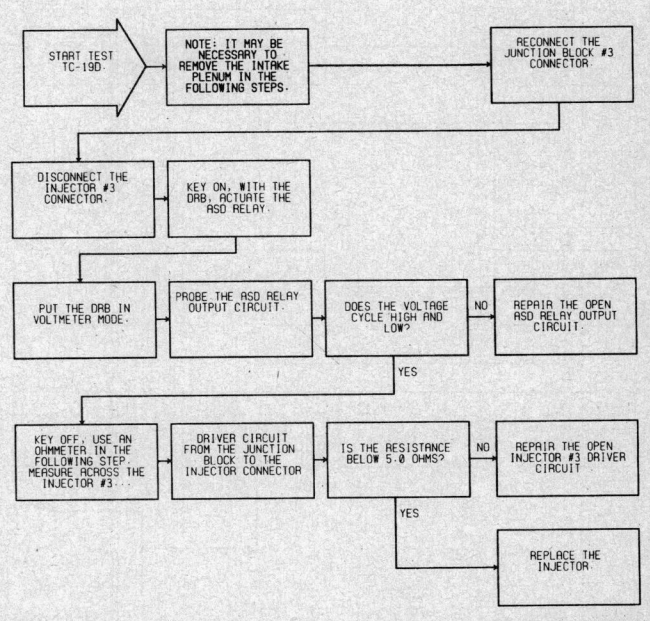

CR1029606607000X

Fig. 32 Test TC-19D: Injector No. 3 Control Circuit

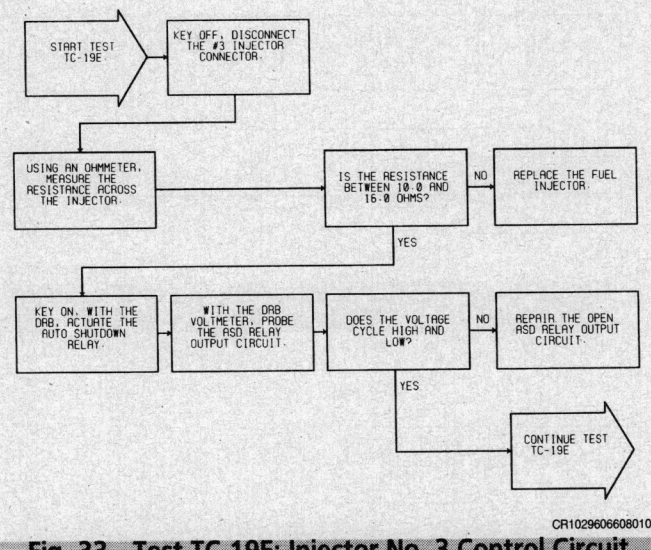

CR1029606608010X

**Fig. 33 Test TC-19E: Injector No. 3 Control Circuit
(Part 1 of 2)**

CR1029606608020X

**Fig. 33 Test TC-19E: Injector No. 3 Control Circuit
(Part 2 of 2)**

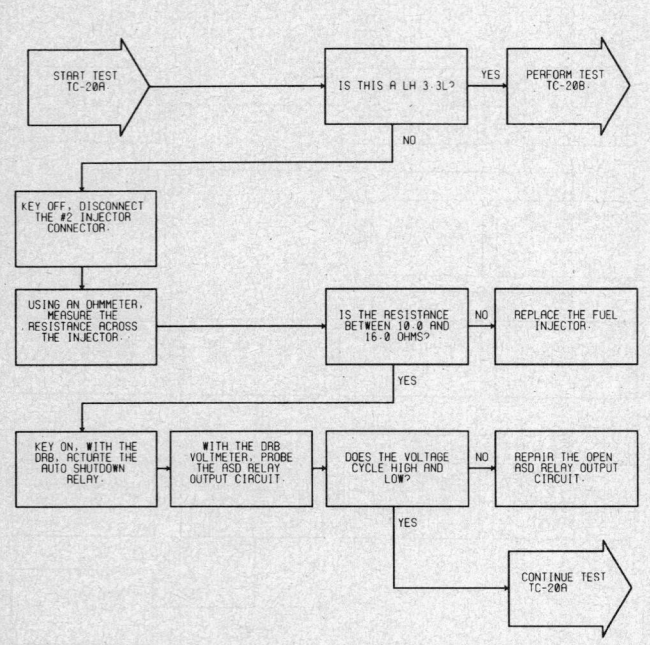

Fig. 34 Test TC-20A: Injector No. 2 Control Circuit (Part 1 of 3)

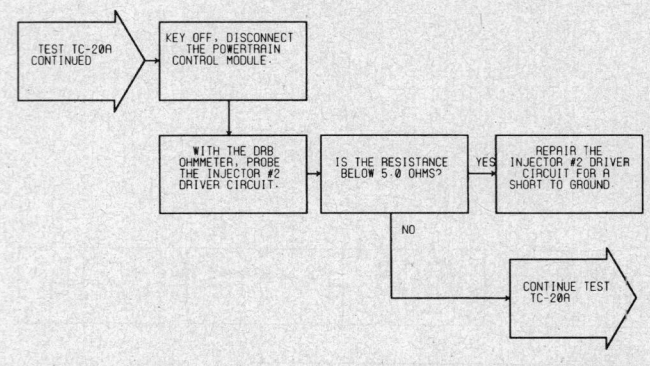

Fig. 34 Test TC-20A: Injector No. 2 Control Circuit (Part 2 of 3)

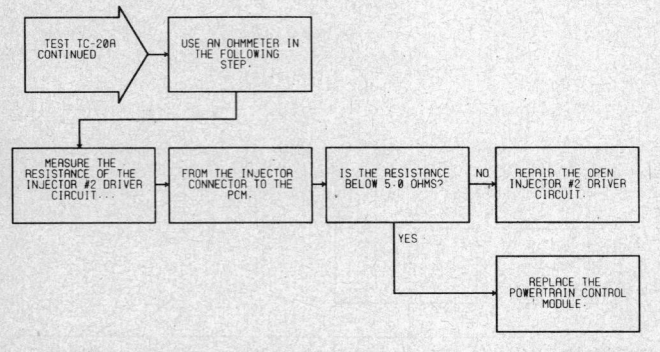

Fig. 34 Test TC-20A: Injector No. 2 Control Circuit (Part 3 of 3)

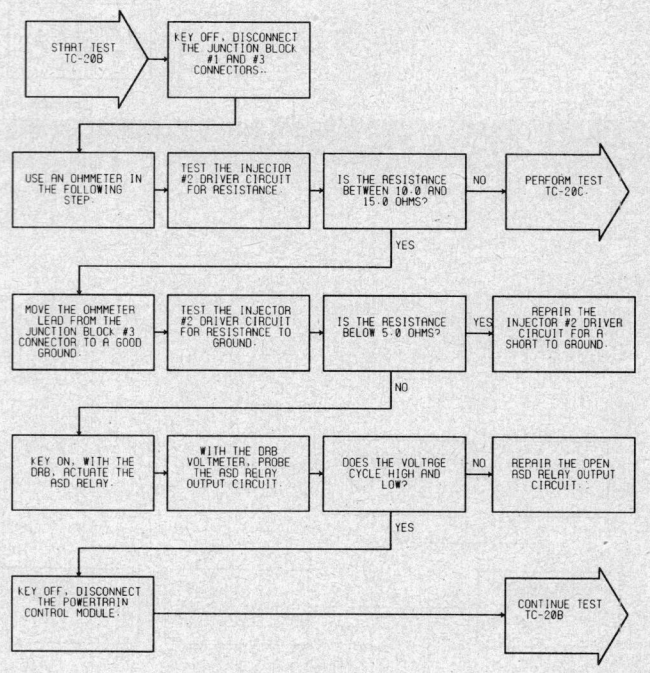

Fig. 35 Test TC-20B: Injector No. 2 Control Circuit (Part 1 of 2)

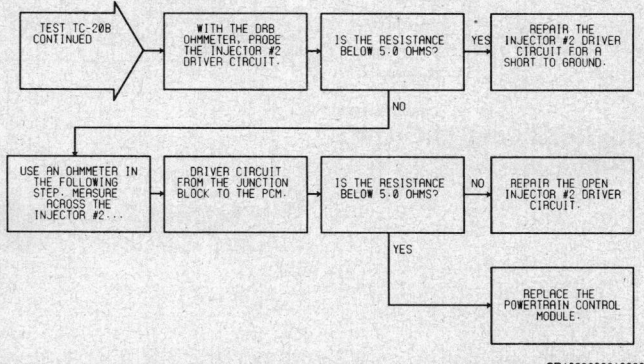

Fig. 35 Test TC-20B: Injector No. 2 Control Circuit (Part 2 of 2)

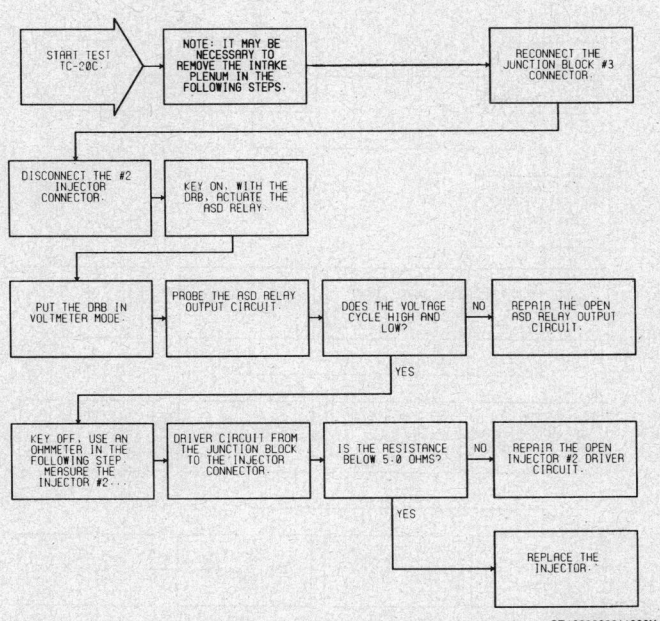

Fig. 36   Test TC-20C: Injector No. 2 Control Circuit

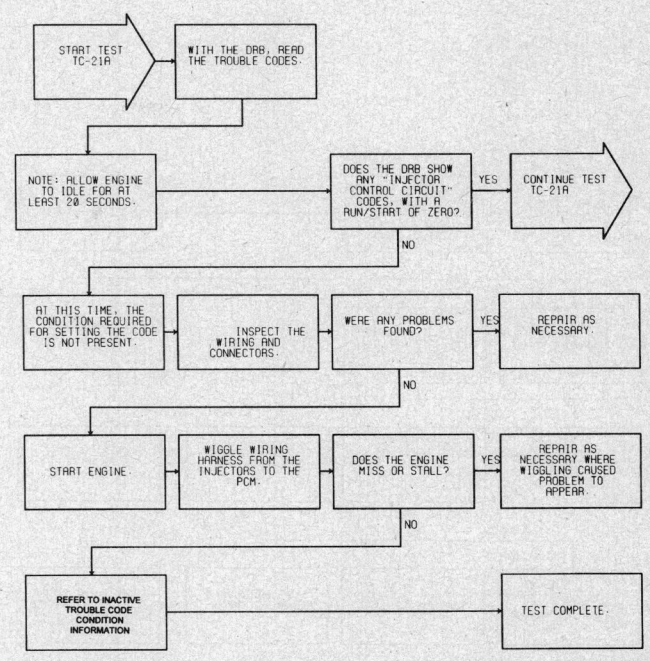

Fig. 37   Test TC-21A: Injector Control Circuit (Part 1 of 2)

Refer to the chart below and perform the diagnostic test that corresponds to the trouble code displayed on the DRB.

TROUBLE CODE	DIAGNOSTIC TEST
INJECTOR #1 CONTROL CIRCUIT	TC-21B
INJECTOR #2 CONTROL CIRCUIT	TC-20A
INJECTOR #3 CONTROL CIRCUIT	TC-19A
INJECTOR #4 CONTROL CIRCUIT	TC-61A
INJECTOR #5 CONTROL CIRCUIT	TC-69A
INJECTOR #6 CONTROL CIRCUIT	TC-70A

CR1029606612020X

Fig. 37   Test TC-21A: Injector Control Circuit (Part 2 of 2)

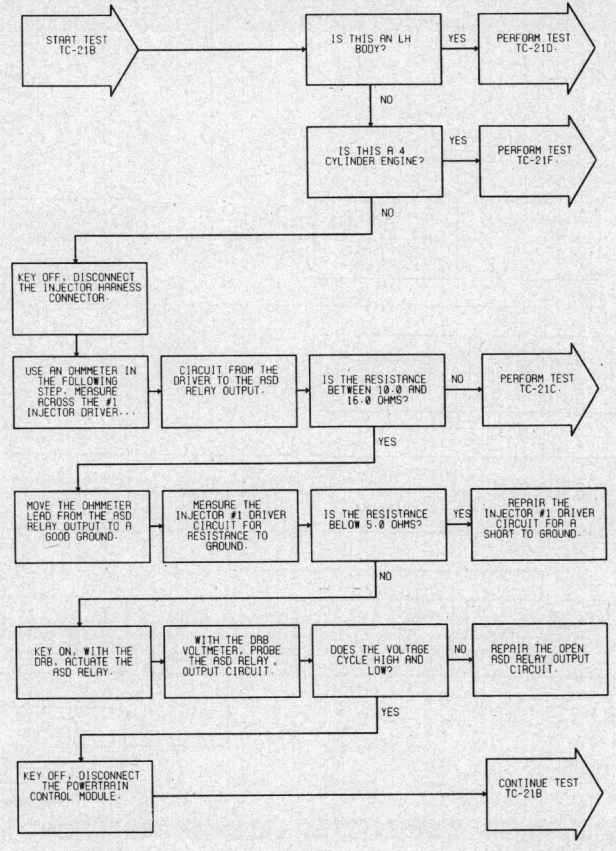

Fig. 38   Test TC-21B: Injector Control Circuit (Part 1 of 2)

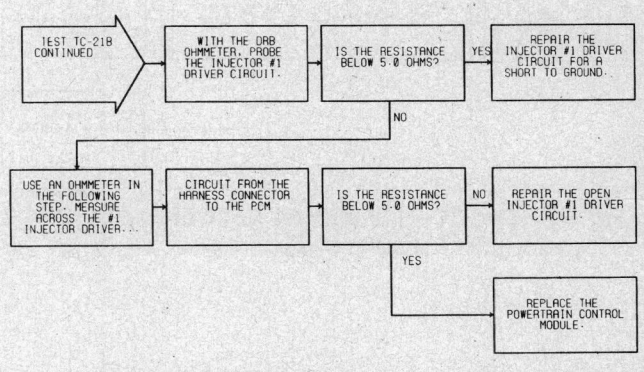

Fig. 38   Test TC-21B: Injector Control Circuit (Part 2 of 2)

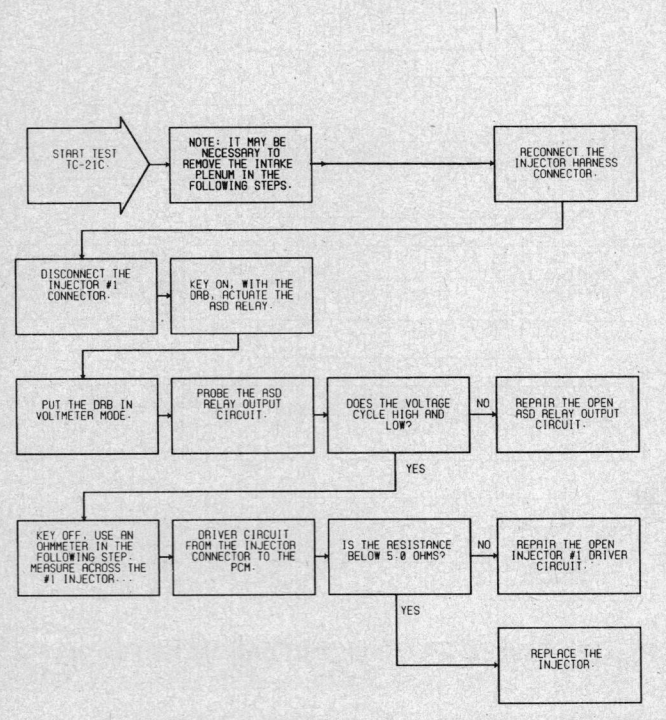

Fig. 39   Test TC-21C: Injector Control Circuit

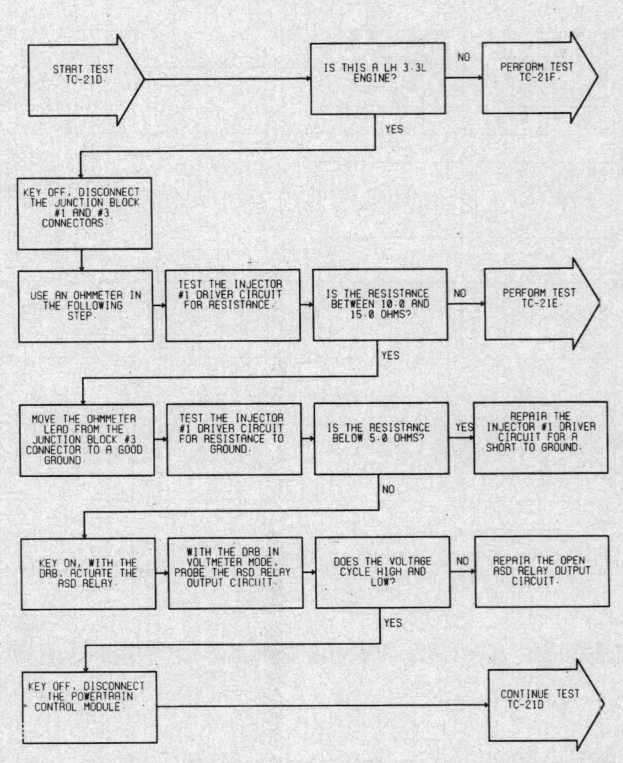

Fig. 40   Test TC-21D: Injector Control Circuit (Part 1 of 2)

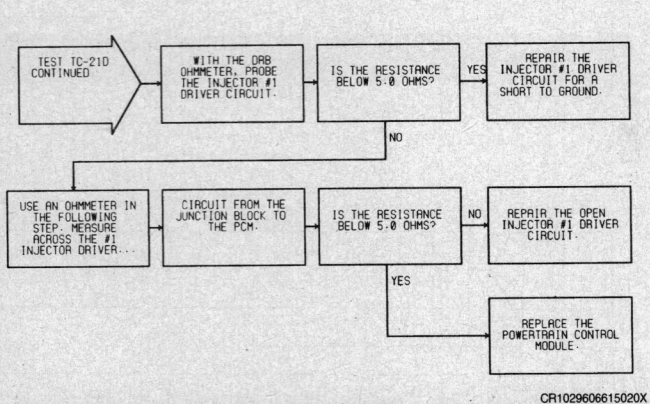

Fig. 40   Test TC-21D: Injector Control Circuit (Part 2 of 2)

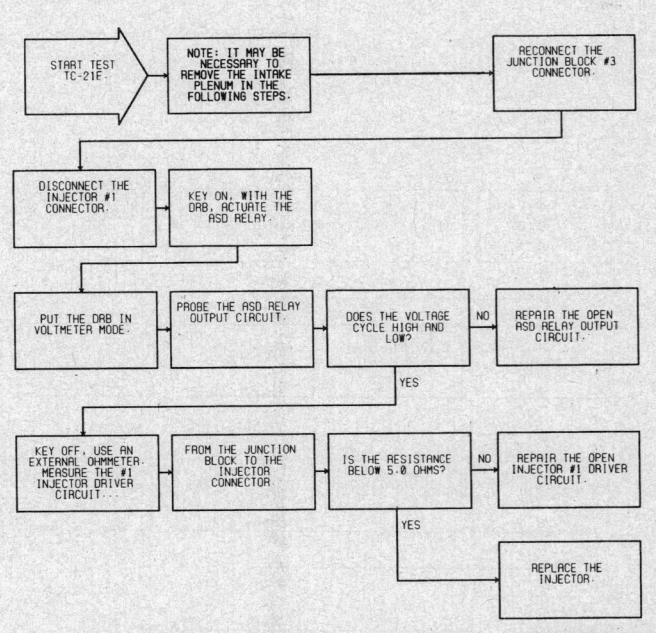

Fig. 41   Test TC-21E: Injector Control Circuit

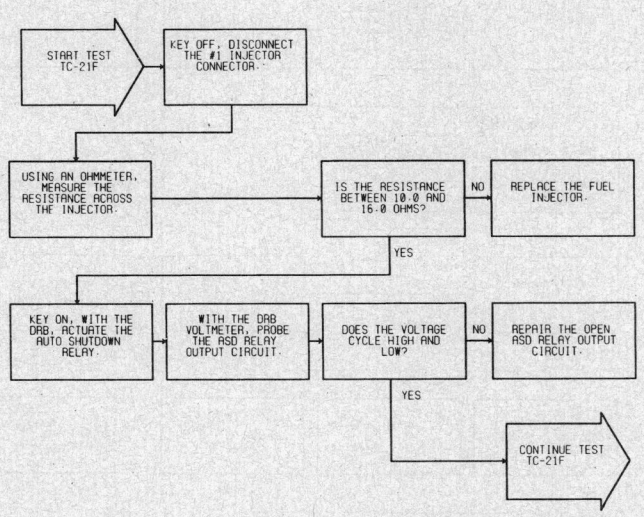

CR1029606617010X

Fig. 42   Test TC-21F: Injector Control Circuit (Part 1 of 3)

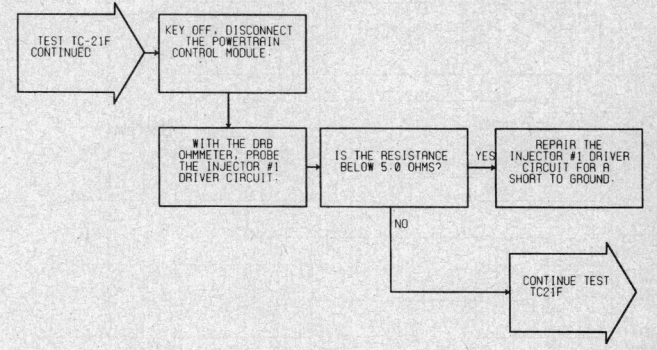

CR1029606617020X

Fig. 42   Test TC-21F: Injector Control Circuit (Part 2 of 3)

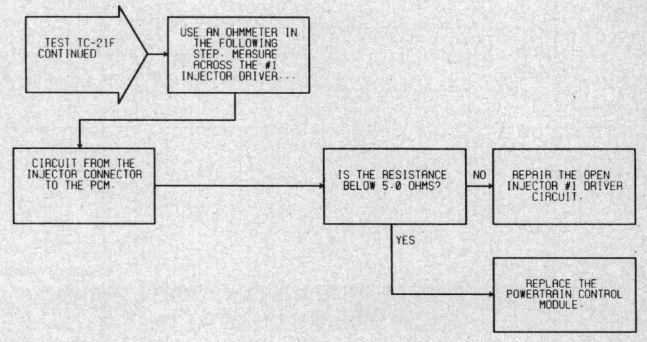

CR1029606617030X

Fig. 42   Test TC-21F: Injector Control Circuit (Part 3 of 3)

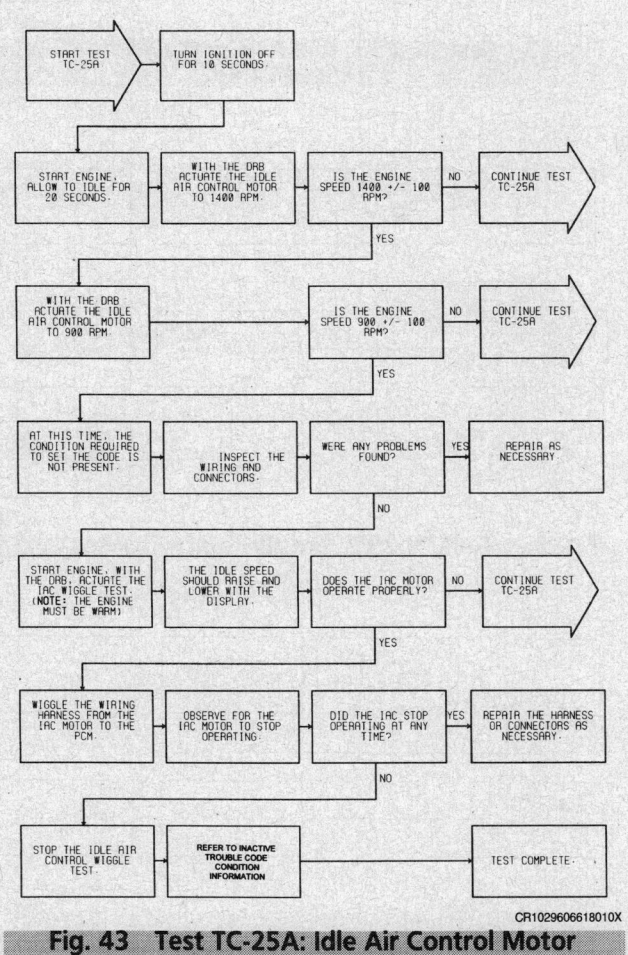

CR1029606618010X

Fig. 43   Test TC-25A: Idle Air Control Motor Circuits (Part 1 of 4)

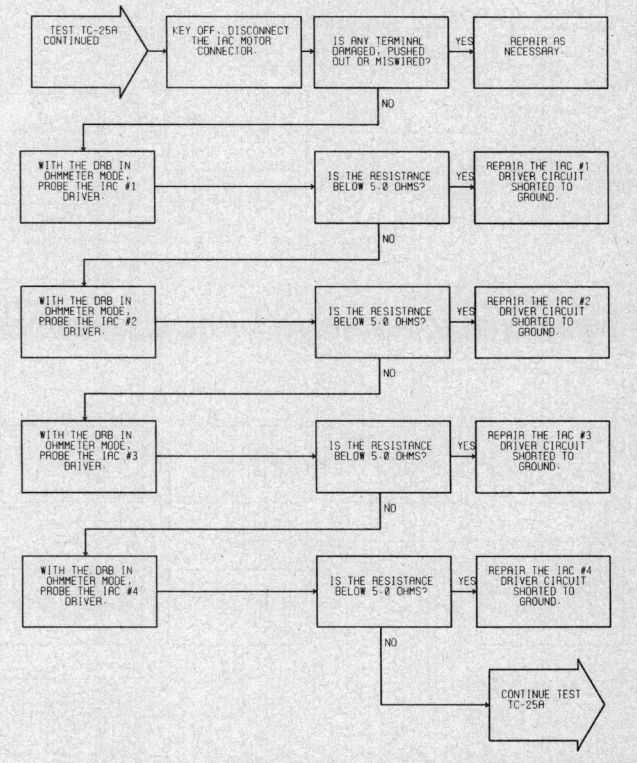

CR1029606618020X

Fig. 43   Test TC-25A: Idle Air Control Motor Circuits (Part 2 of 4)

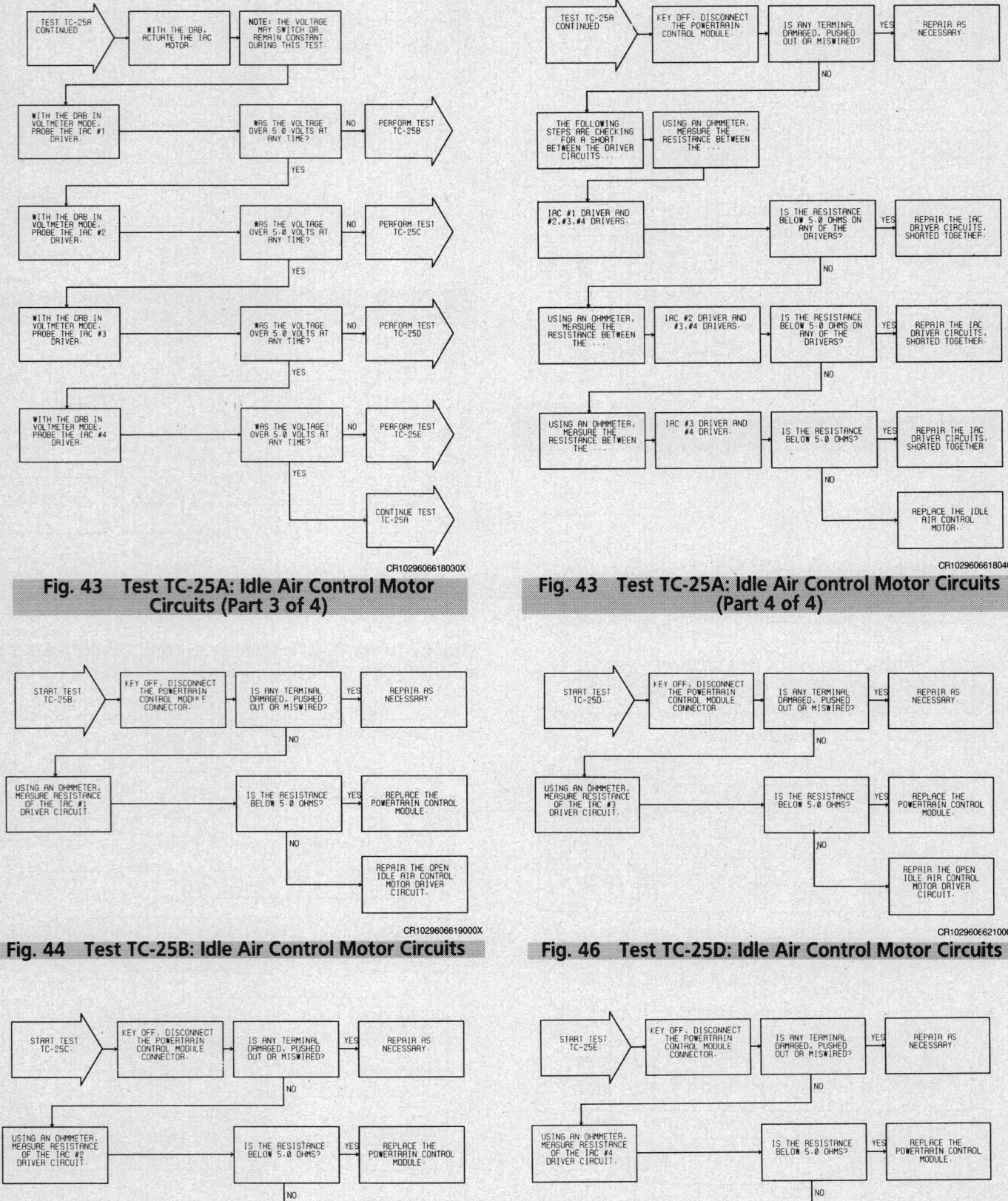

Fig. 43   Test TC-25A: Idle Air Control Motor Circuits (Part 3 of 4)

Fig. 43   Test TC-25A: Idle Air Control Motor Circuits (Part 4 of 4)

Fig. 44   Test TC-25B: Idle Air Control Motor Circuits

Fig. 46   Test TC-25D: Idle Air Control Motor Circuits

Fig. 45   Test TC-25C: Idle Air Control Motor Circuits

Fig. 47   Test TC-25E: Idle Air Control Motor Circuits

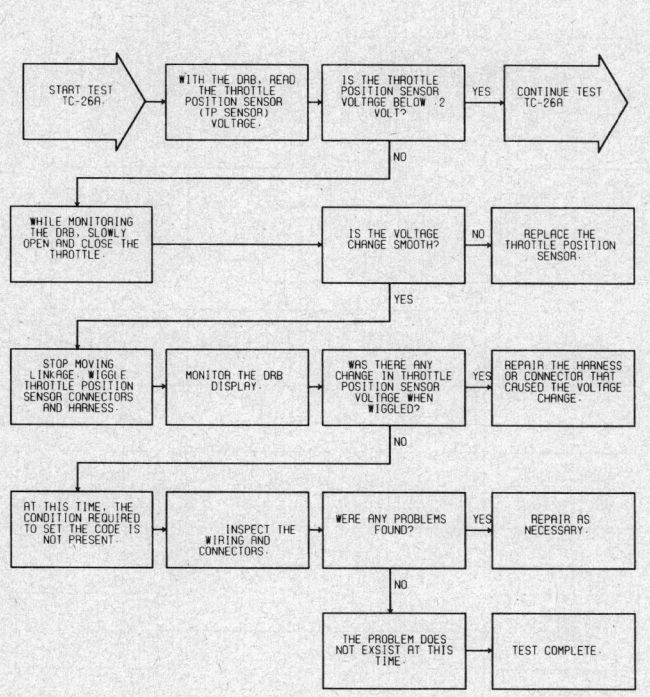

Fig. 48   Test TC-26A: Throttle Position Sensor Voltage Low (Part 1 of 2)

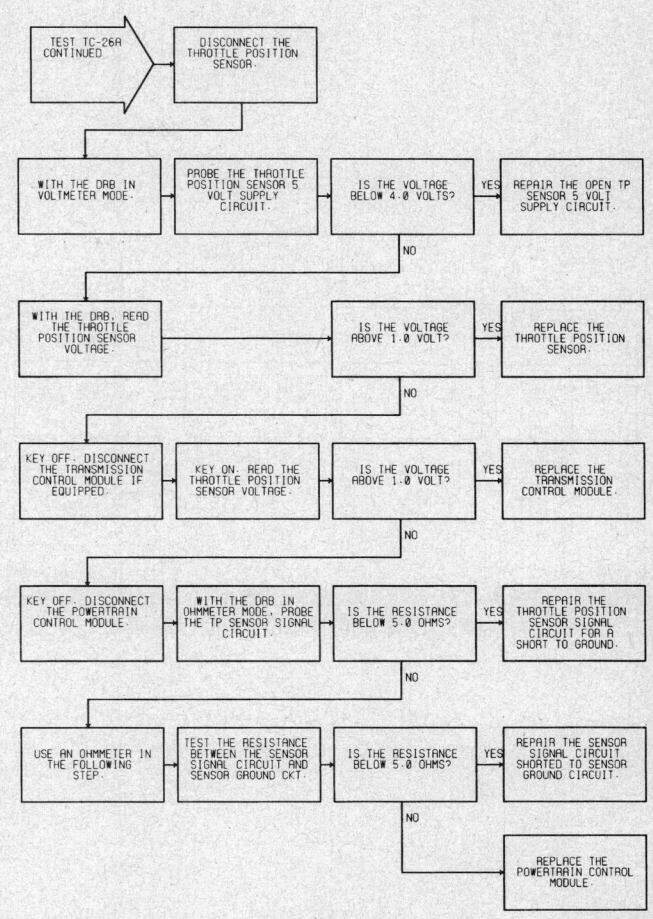

Fig. 48   Test TC-26A: Throttle Position Sensor Voltage Low (Part 2 of 2)

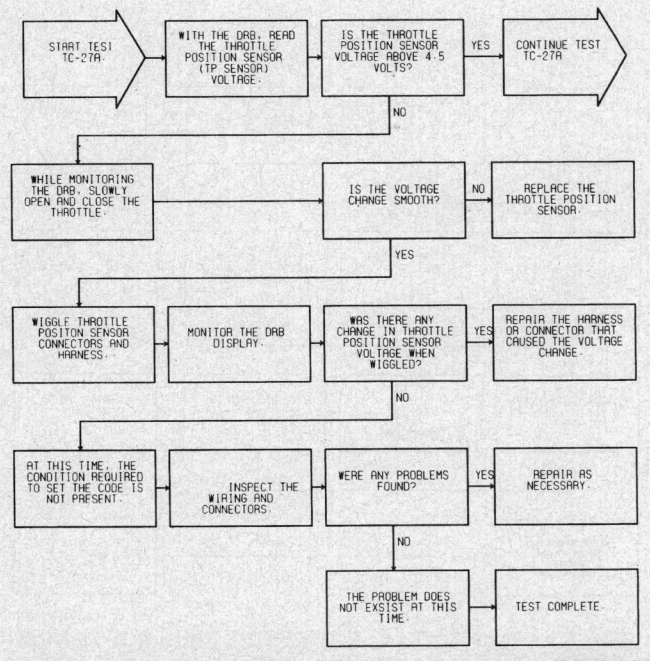

Fig. 49   Test TC-27A: Throttle Position Sensor Voltage High (Part 1 of 3)

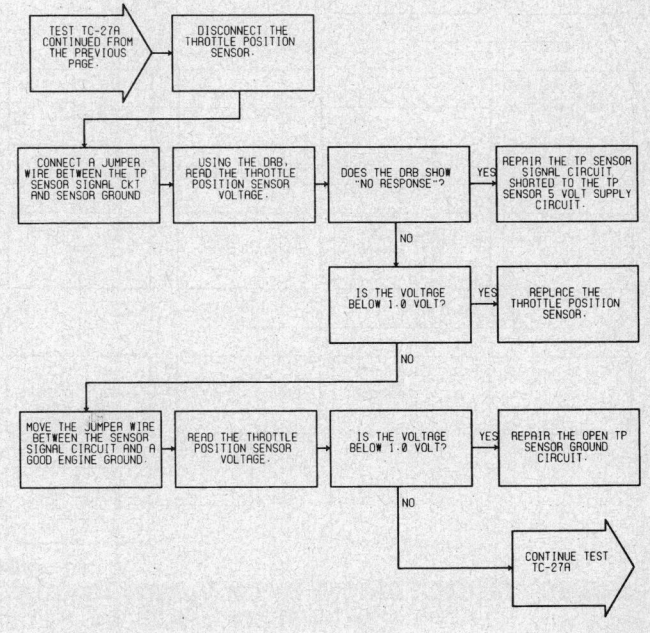

Fig. 49   Test TC-27A: Throttle Position Sensor Voltage High (Part 2 of 3)

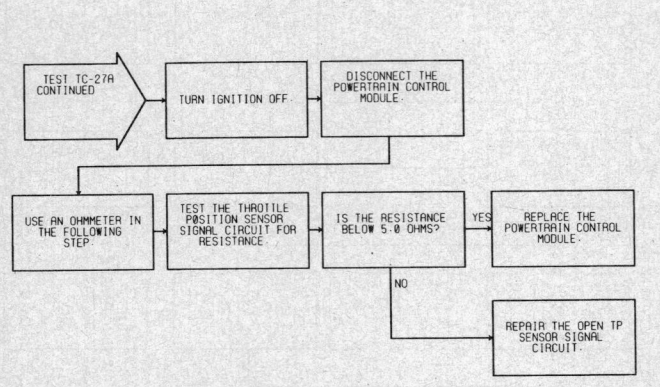

Fig. 49   Test TC-27A: Throttle Position Sensor Voltage High (Part 3 of 3)

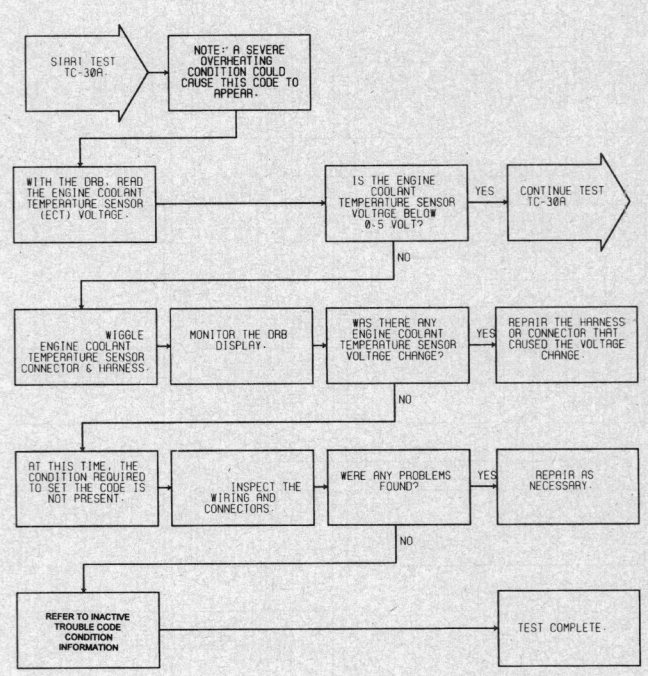

Fig. 50   Test TC-30A: ECT Sensor Voltage Too Low (Part 1 of 2)

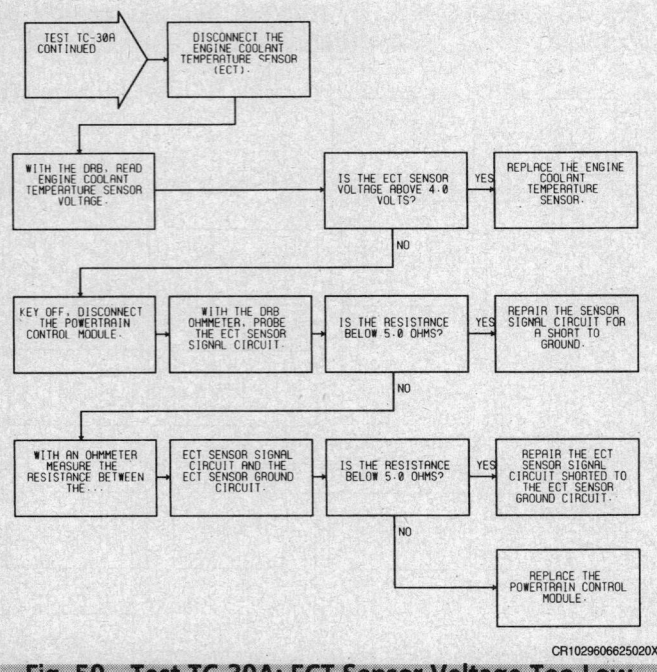

Fig. 50   Test TC-30A: ECT Sensor Voltage Too Low (Part 2 of 2)

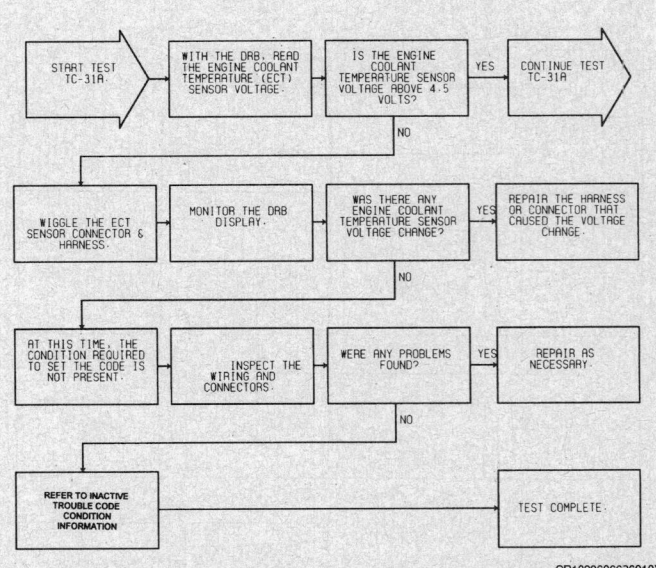

Fig. 51   Test TC-31A: ECT Sensor Voltage Too High (Part 1 of 3)

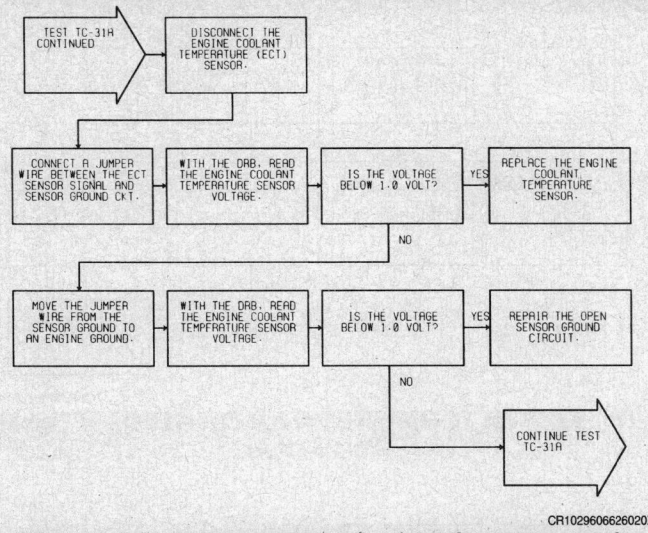

Fig. 51   Test TC-31A: ECT Sensor Voltage Too High (Part 2 of 3)

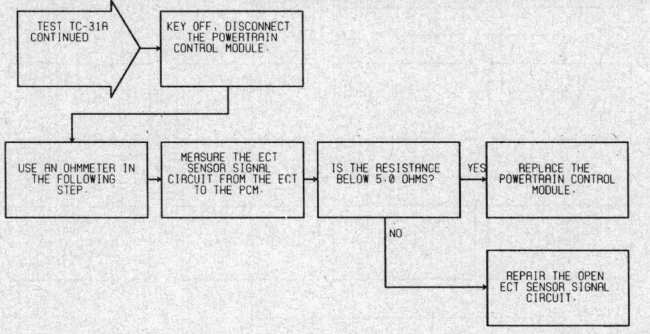

Fig. 51   Test TC-31A: ECT Sensor Voltage Too High (Part 3 of 3)

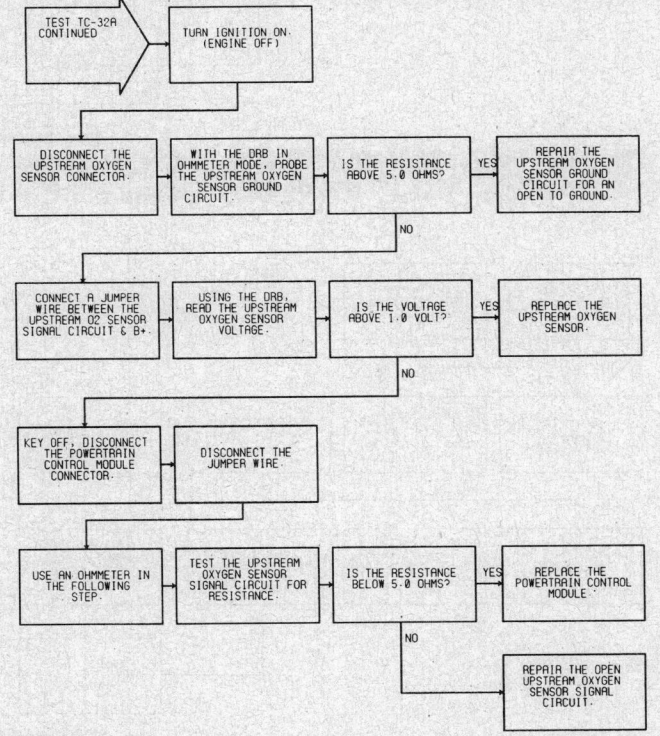

Fig. 52   Test TC-32A: O₂ Sensor Stays At Center (Part 2 of 2)

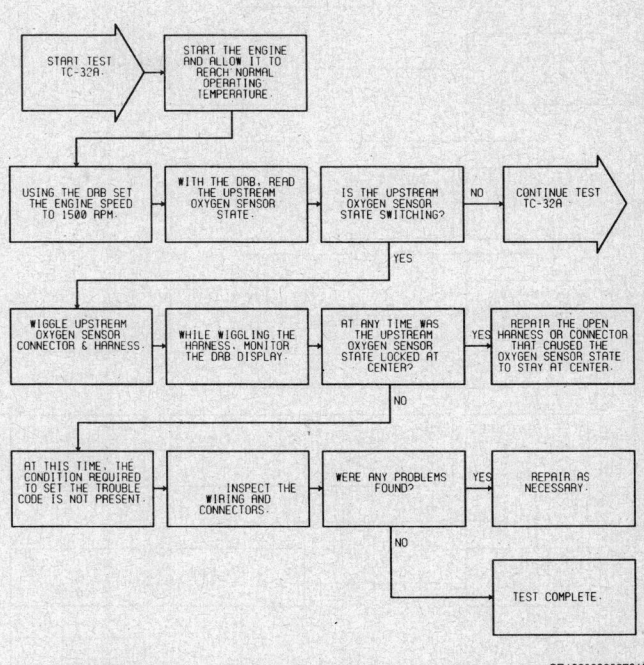

Fig. 52   Test TC-32A: O₂ Sensor Stays At Center (Part 1 of 2)

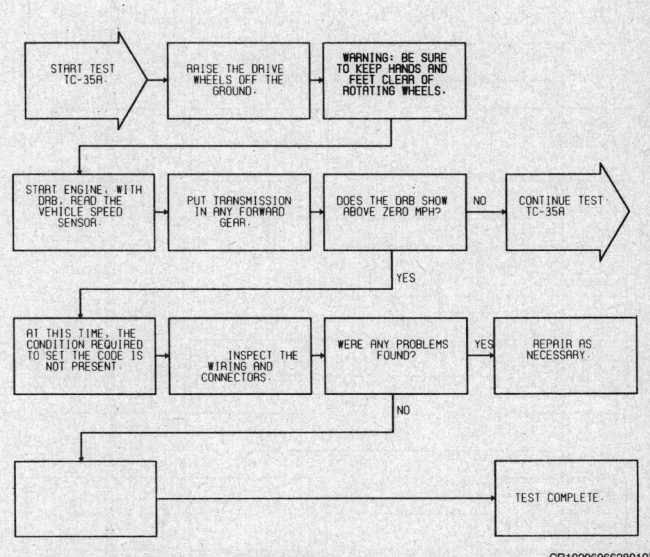

Fig. 53   Test TC-35A: No Vehicle Speed Sensor Signal (Part 1 of 4)

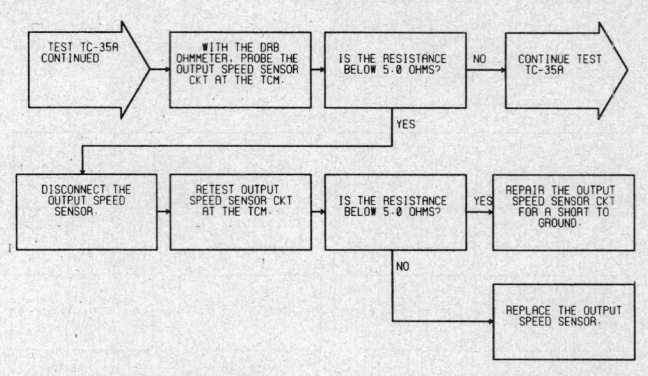

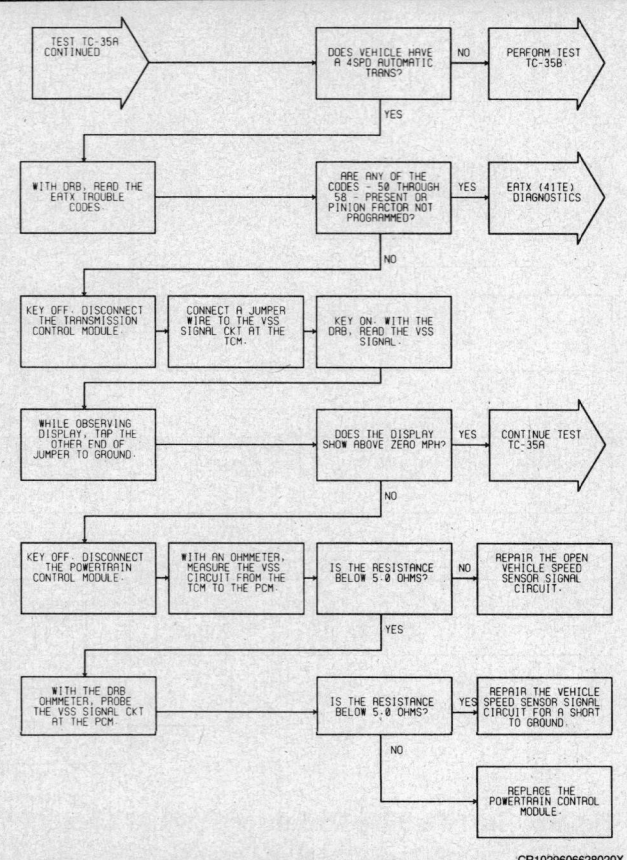

Fig. 53   Test TC-35A: No Vehicle Speed Sensor Signal (Part 2 of 4)

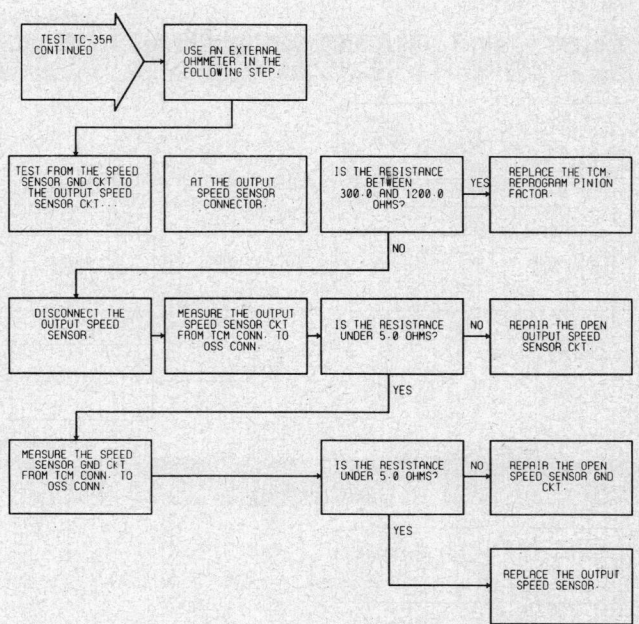

Fig. 53   Test TC-35A: No Vehicle Speed Sensor Signal (Part 3 of 4)

CR1029606628030X

Fig. 53   Test TC-35A: No Vehicle Speed Sensor Signal (Part 4 of 4)

CR1029606628040X

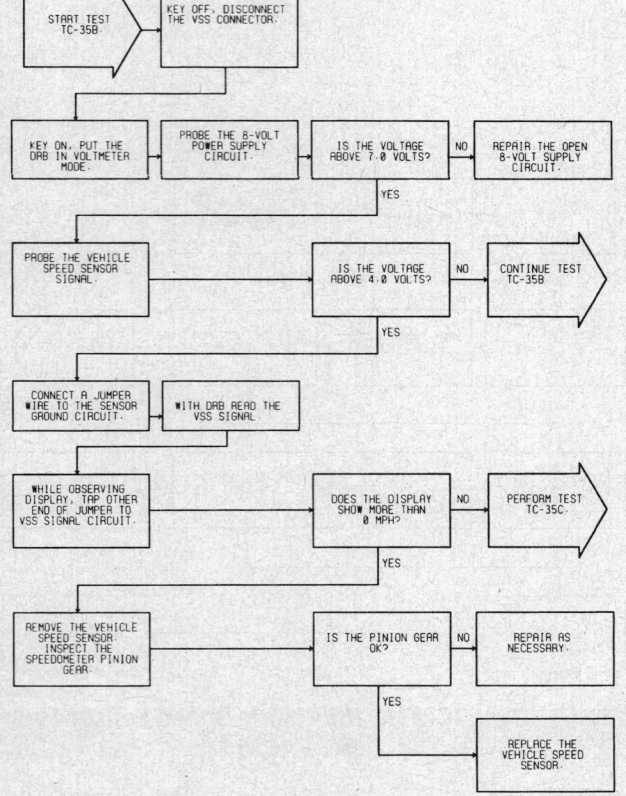

CR1029606629010X

Fig. 54   Test TC-35B: No Vehicle Speed Sensor Signal (Part 1 of 2)

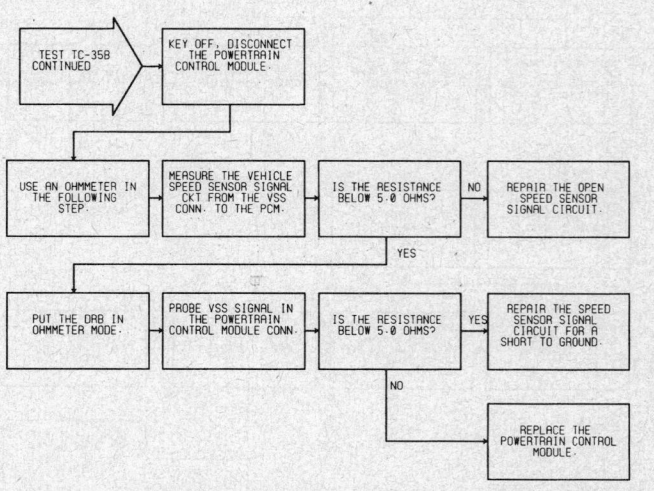

CR1029606629020X

Fig. 54   Test TC-35B: No Vehicle Speed Sensor Signal (Part 2 of 2)

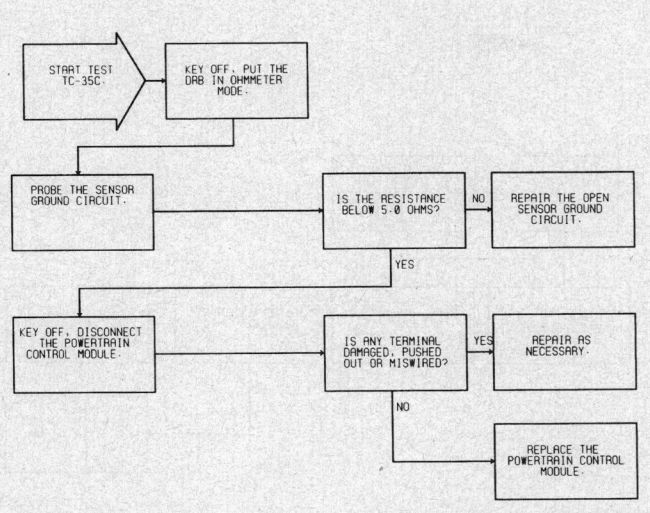

Fig. 55   Test TC-35C: No Vehicle Speed Sensor Signal

CR1029606630000X

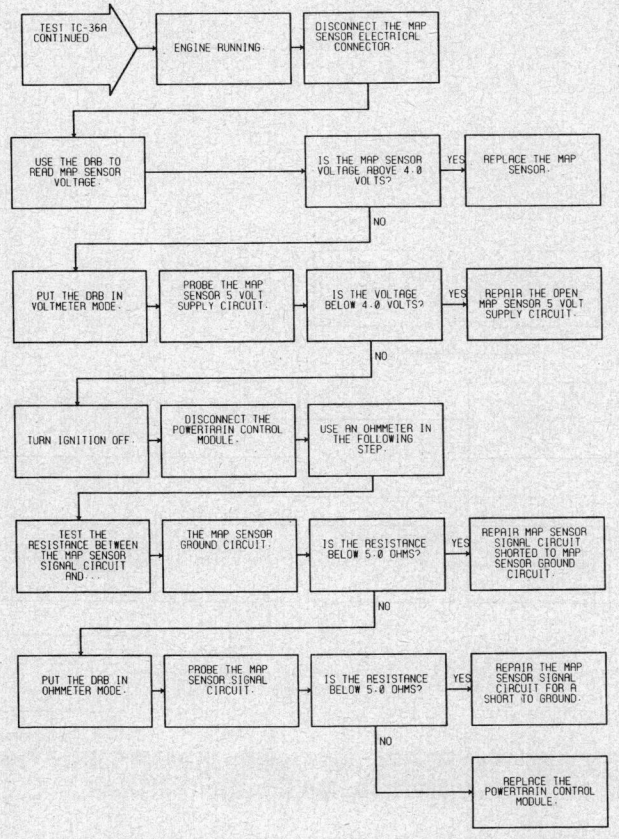

**Fig. 56   Test TC-36A: MAP Sensor Voltage Too Low;
No 5 Volts To MAP Sensor (Part 2 of 2)**

CR1029606631020X

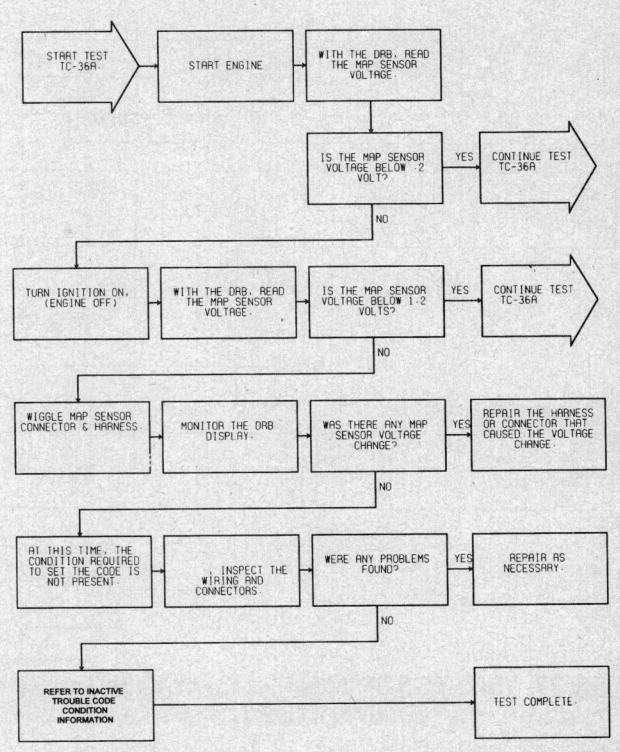

**Fig. 56   Test TC-36A: MAP Sensor Voltage Too Low;
No 5 Volts To MAP Sensor (Part 1 of 2)**

CR1029606631010X

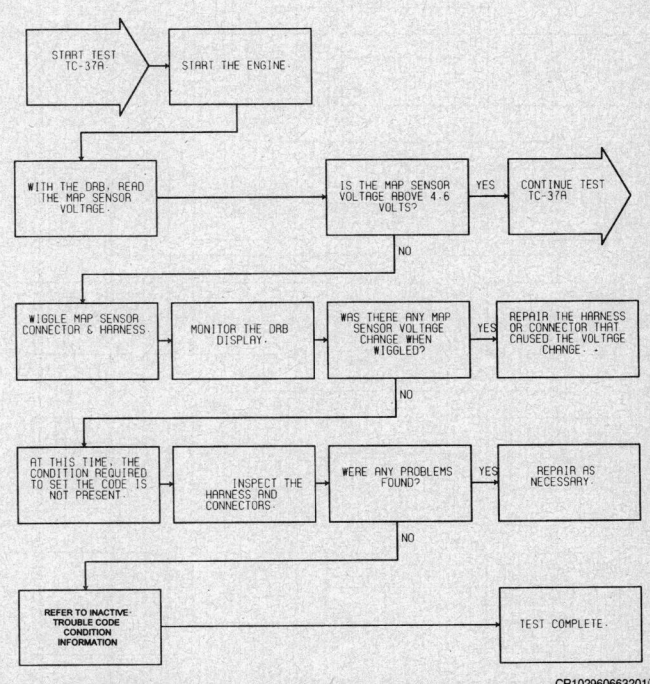

**Fig. 57   Test TC-37A: MAP Sensor Voltage Too High
(Part 1 of 3)**

CR1029606632010X

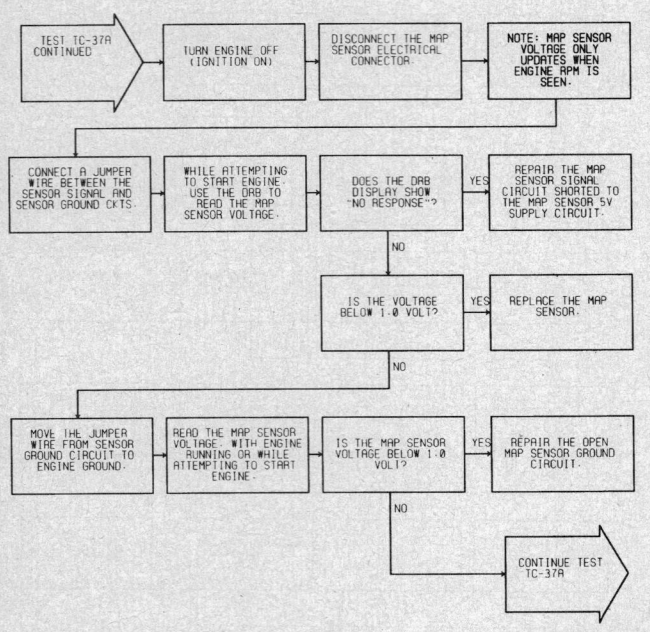

**Fig. 57   Test TC-37A: MAP Sensor Voltage Too High
(Part 2 of 3)**

CR1029606632020X

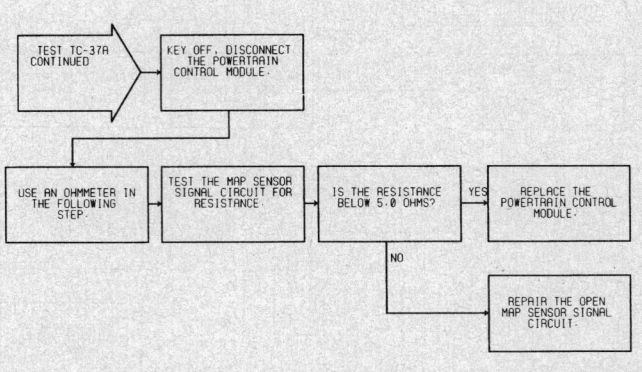

CR1029606632030X

**Fig. 57   Test TC-37A: MAP Sensor Voltage Too High
(Part 3 of 3)**

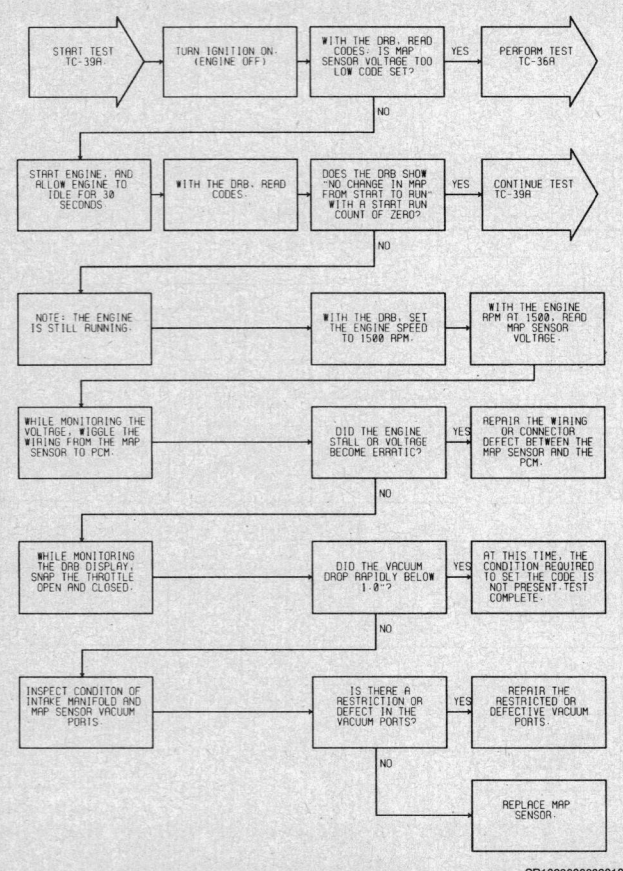

CR1029606633010X

**Fig. 58   Test TC-39A: No Change In MAP Sensor
From Start To Run (Part 1 of 2)**

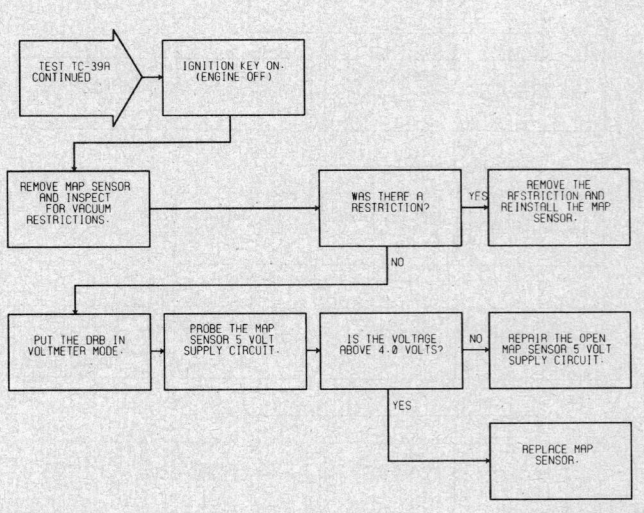

CR1029606633020X

**Fig. 58   Test TC-39A: No Change In MAP Sensor From
Start To Run (Part 2 of 2)**

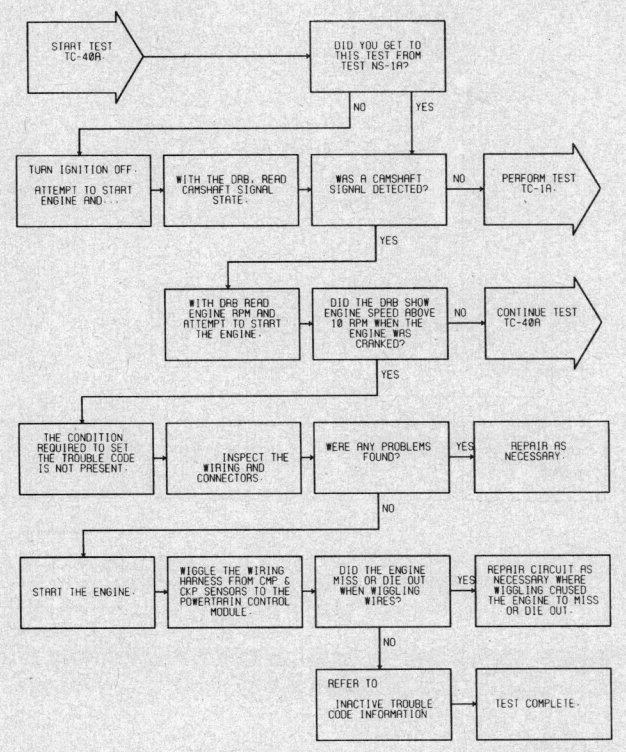

Fig. 59   Test TC-40A: No Crank Reference Signal At PCM (Part 1 of 3)

CR1029606634010X

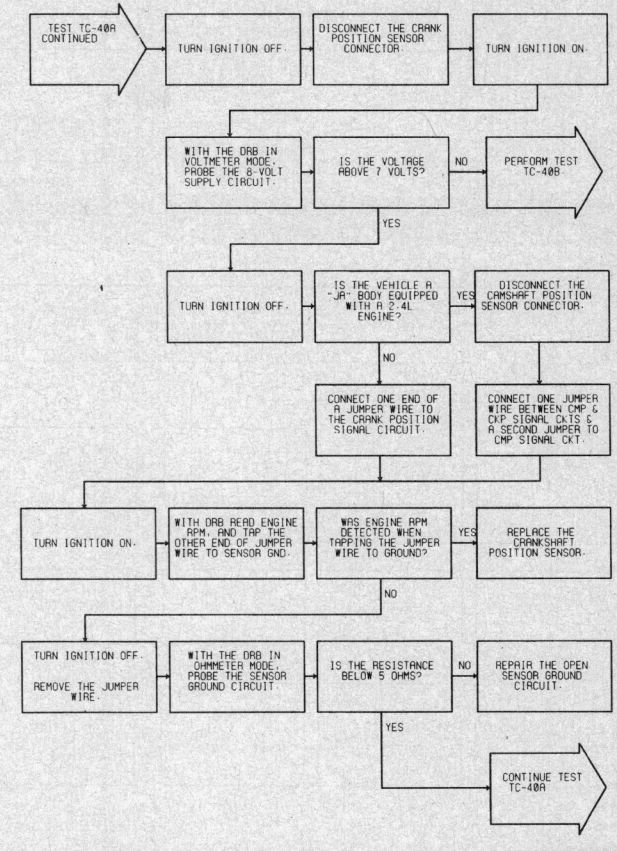

Fig. 59   Test TC-40A: No Crank Reference Signal At PCM (Part 2 of 3)

CR1029606634020X

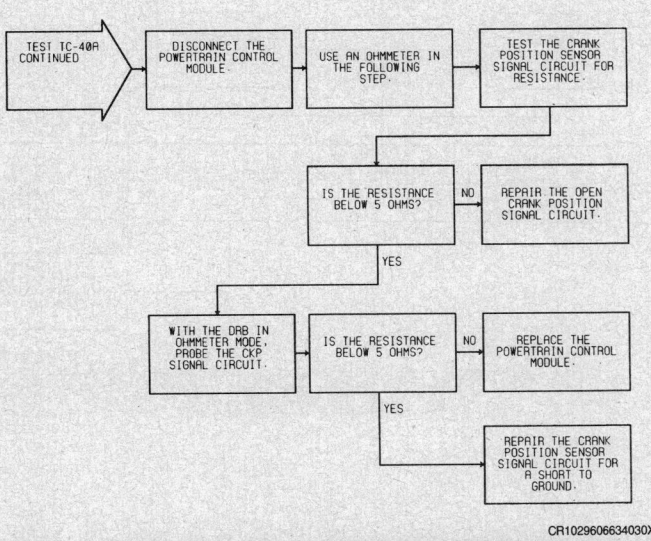

Fig. 59   Test TC-40A: No Crank Reference Signal At PCM (Part 3 of 3)

CR1029606634030X

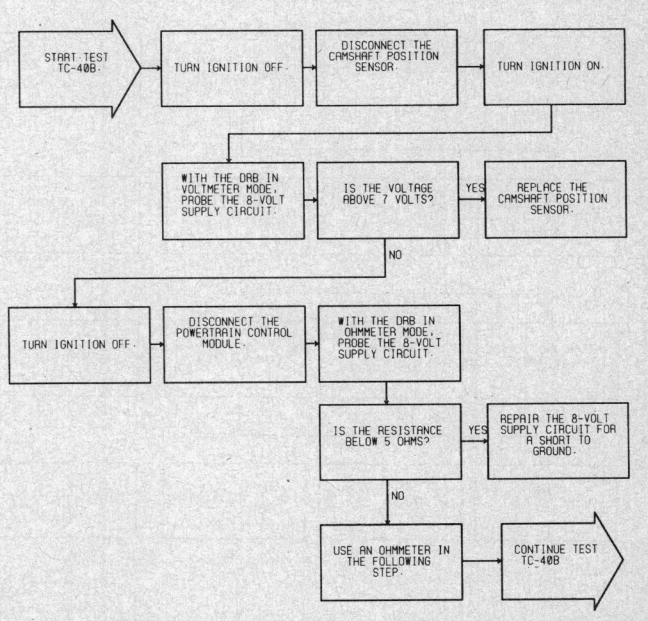

Fig. 60   Test TC-40B: No Crank Reference Signal At PCM (Part 1 of 2)

CR1029606635010X

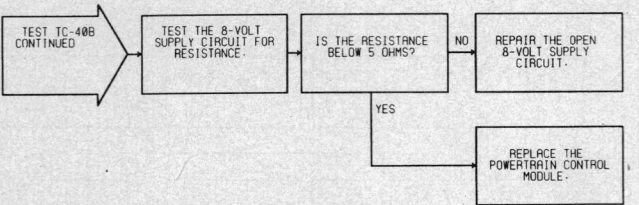

Fig. 60   Test TC-40B: No Crank Reference Signal At PCM (Part 2 of 2)

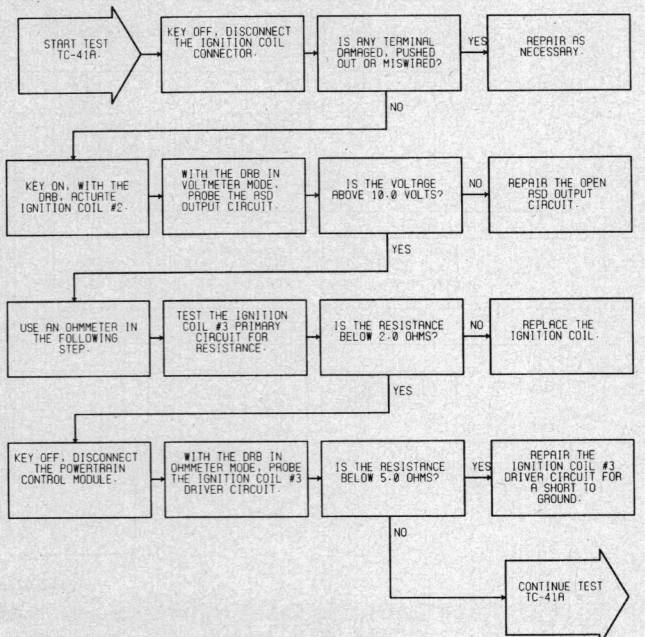

Fig. 61   Test TC-41A: Ignition Coil No. 3 Primary Circuit (Part 1 of 2)

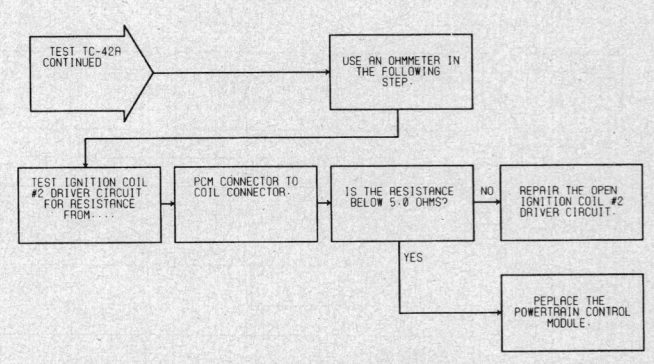

Fig. 61   Test TC-41A: Ignition Coil No. 3 Primary Circuit (Part 2 of 2)

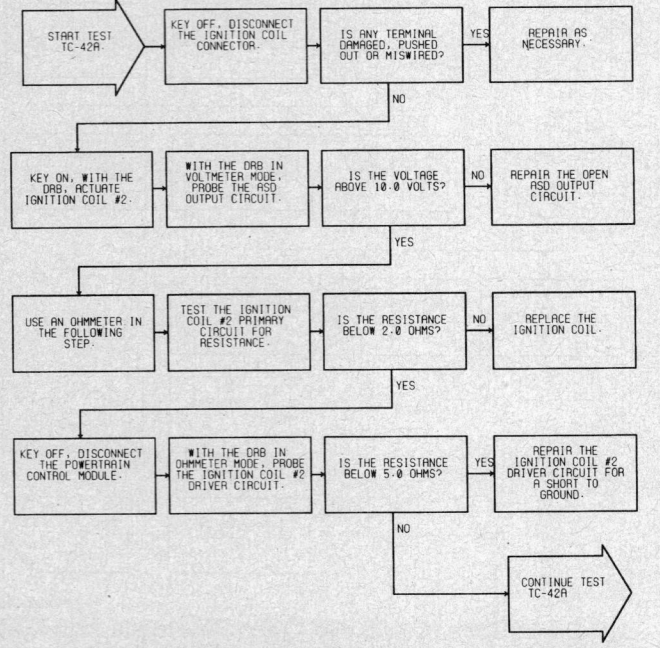

Fig. 62   Test TC-42A: Ignition Coil No. 2 Primary Circuit (Part 1 of 2)

Fig. 62   Test TC-42A: Ignition Coil No. 2 Primary Circuit (Part 2 of 2)

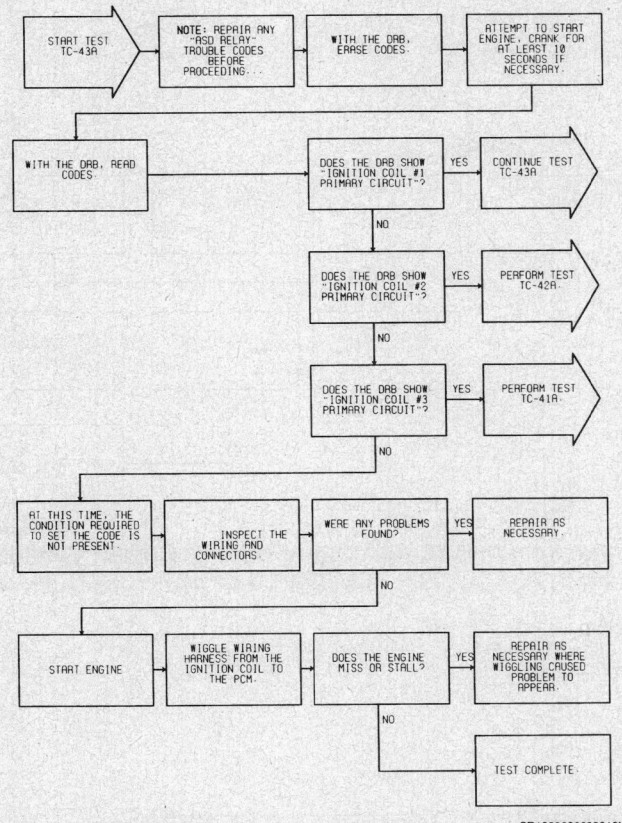

Fig. 63   Test TC-43A: Ignition Coil No. 1 Primary Circuit (Part 1 of 3)

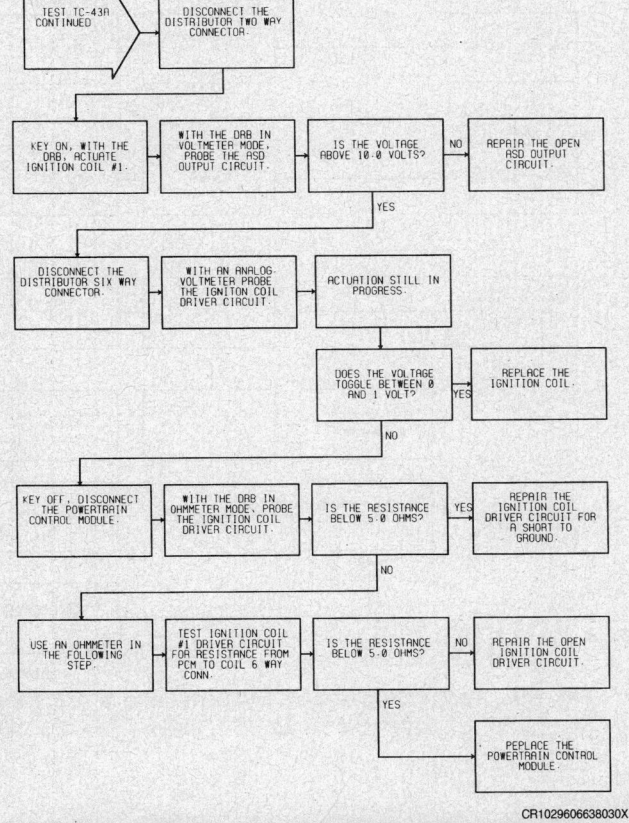

Fig. 63   Test TC-43A: Ignition Coil No. 1 Primary Circuit (Part 3 of 3)

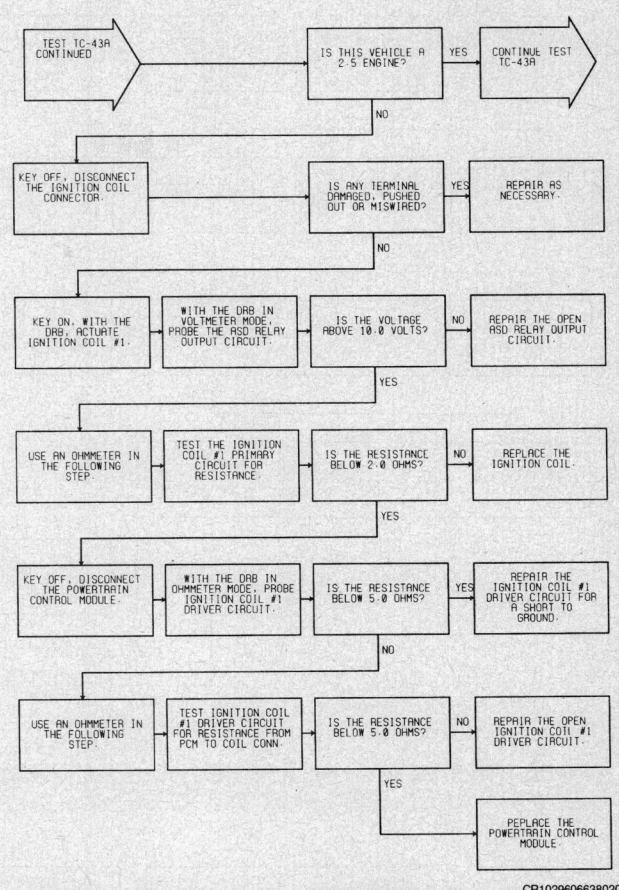

Fig. 63   Test TC-43A: Ignition Coil No. 1 Primary Circuit (Part 2 of 3)

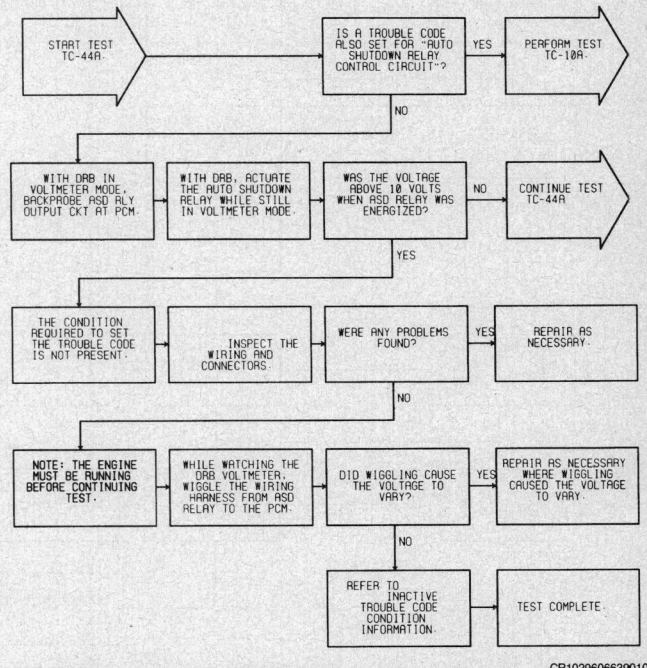

Fig. 64   Test TC-44A: No ASD Relay Output Voltage At PCM (Part 1 of 3)

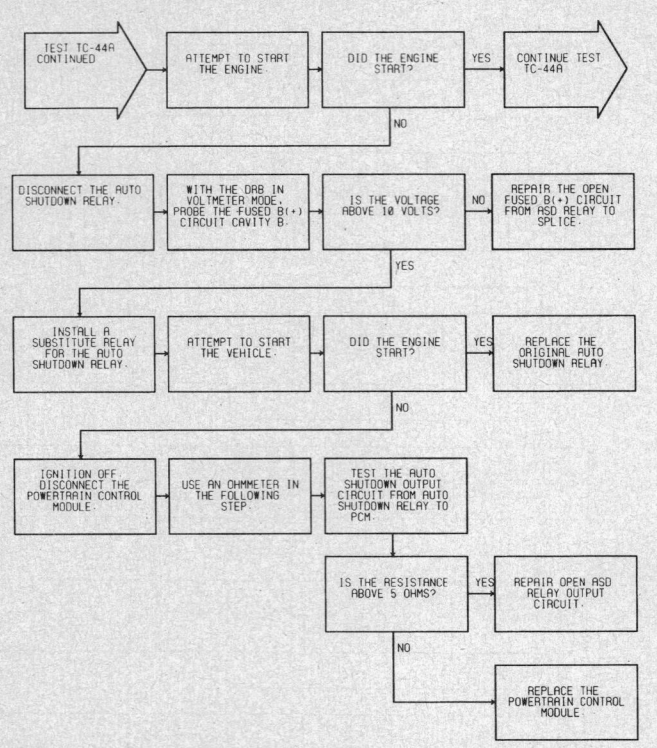

Fig. 64   Test TC-44A: No ASD Relay Output Voltage At PCM (Part 2 of 3)

CR1029606639020X

Fig. 64   Test TC-44A: No ASD Relay Output Voltage At PCM (Part 3 of 3)

CR1029606639030X

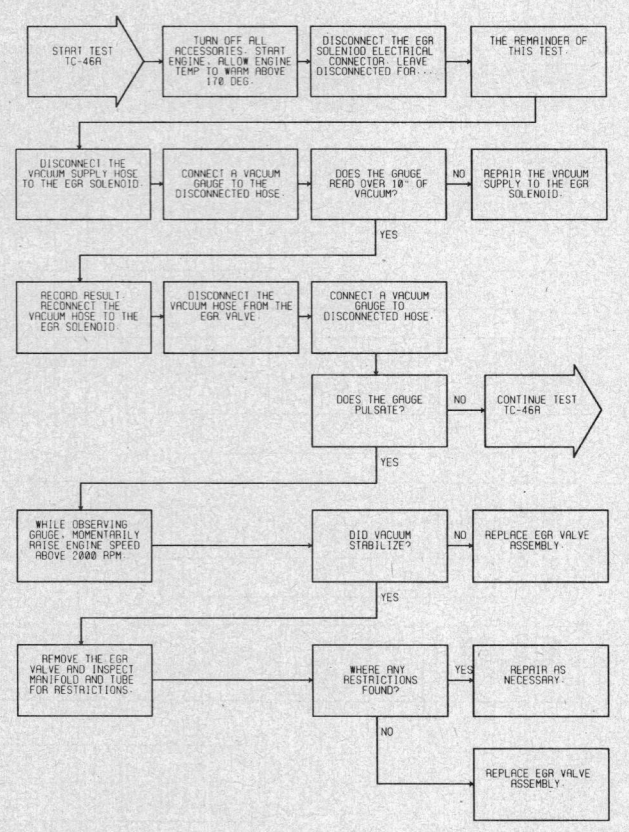

Fig. 65   Test TC-46A: EGR System Failure (Part 1 of 2)

CR1029606640010X

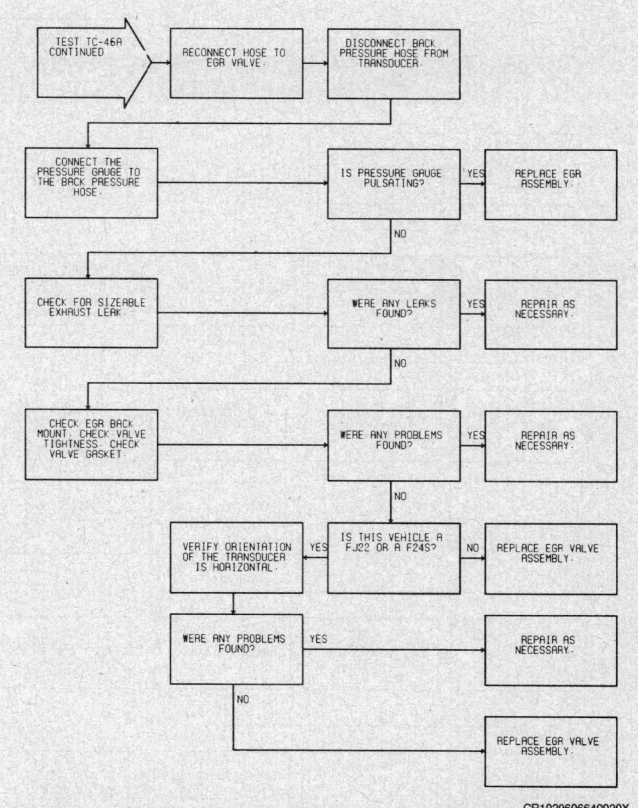

Fig. 65   Test TC-46A: EGR System Failure (Part 2 of 2)

CR1029606640020X

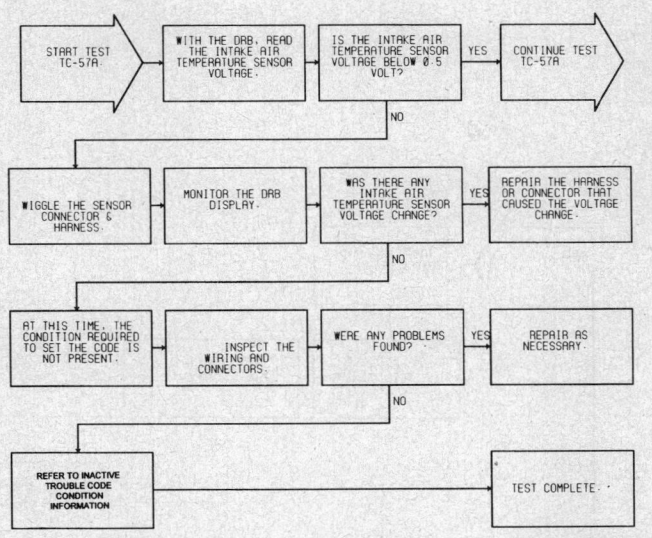

CR1029606641010X

Fig. 66   Test TC-57A: Intake Air Temperature Sensor Voltage Low (Part 1 of 2)

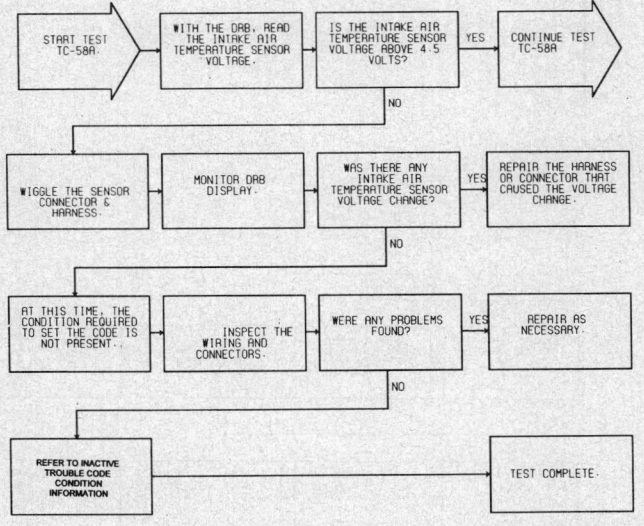

CR1029606642010X

Fig. 67   Test TC-58A: Intake Air Temperature Sensor Voltage High (Part 1 of 3)

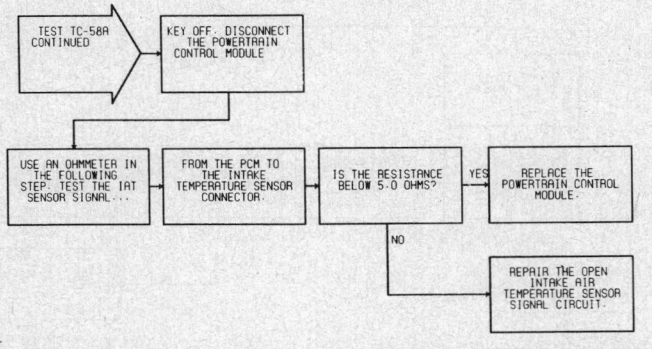

CR1029606642030X

Fig. 67   Test TC-58A: Intake Air Temperature Sensor Voltage High (Part 3 of 3)

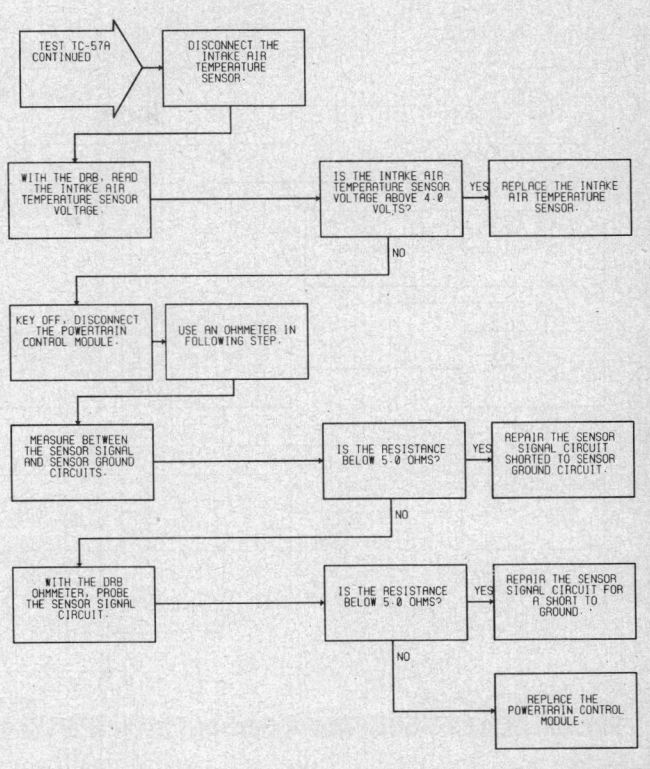

CR1029606641020X

Fig. 66   Test TC-57A: Intake Air Temperature Sensor Voltage Low (Part 2 of 2)

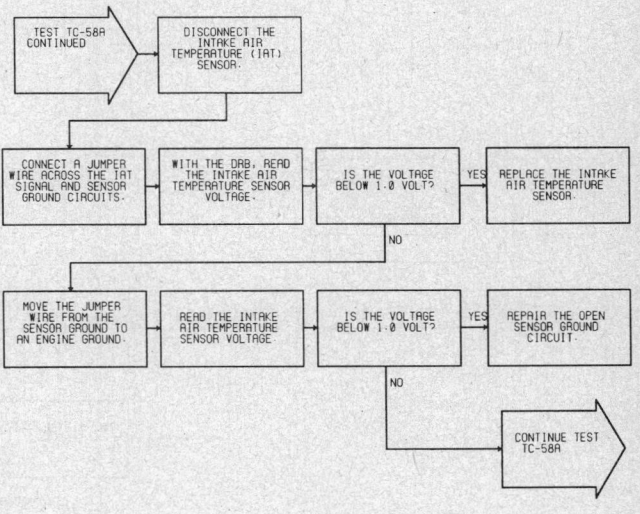

CR1029606642020X

Fig. 67   Test TC-58A: Intake Air Temperature Sensor Voltage High (Part 2 of 3)

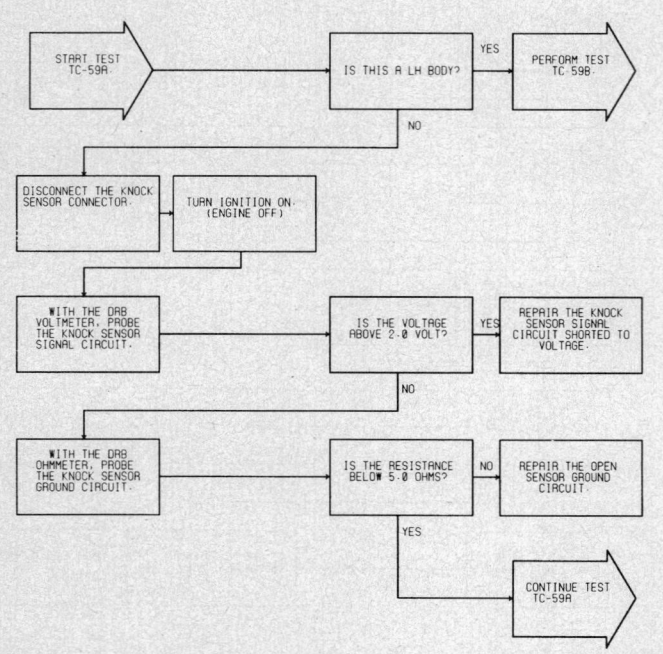

CR1029606643010X

Fig. 68   Test TC-59A: Knock Sensor Circuit (Part 1 of 3)

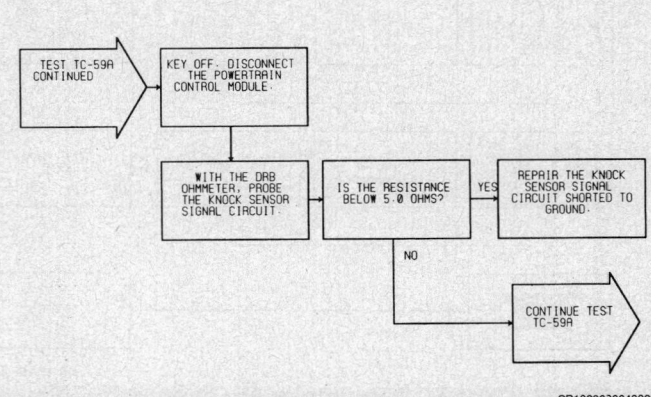

CR10296066643020X

Fig. 68   Test TC-59A: Knock Sensor Circuit (Part 2 of 3)

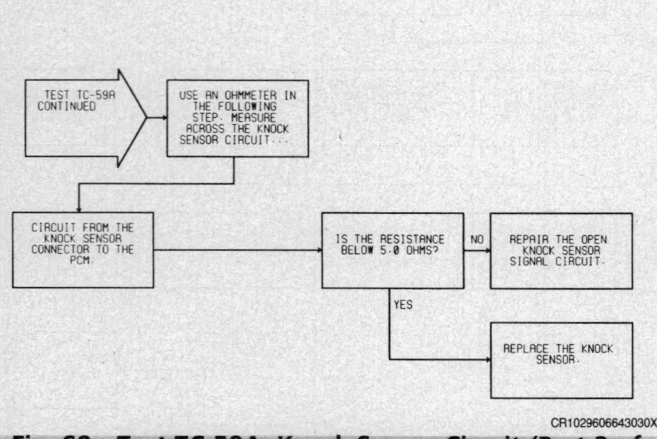

CR1029606643030X

Fig. 68   Test TC-59A: Knock Sensor Circuit (Part 3 of 3)

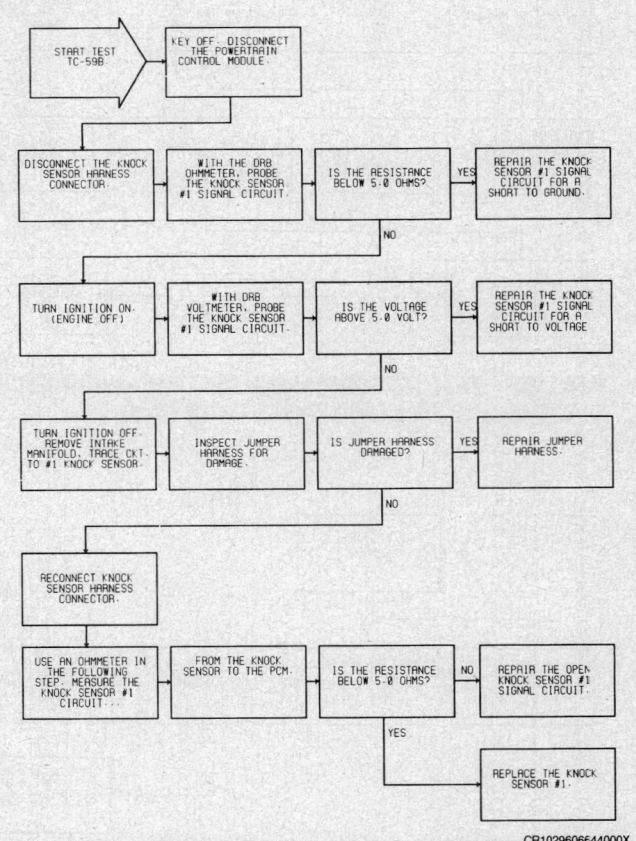

CR1029606644000X

Fig. 69   Test TC-59B: Knock Sensor Circuit

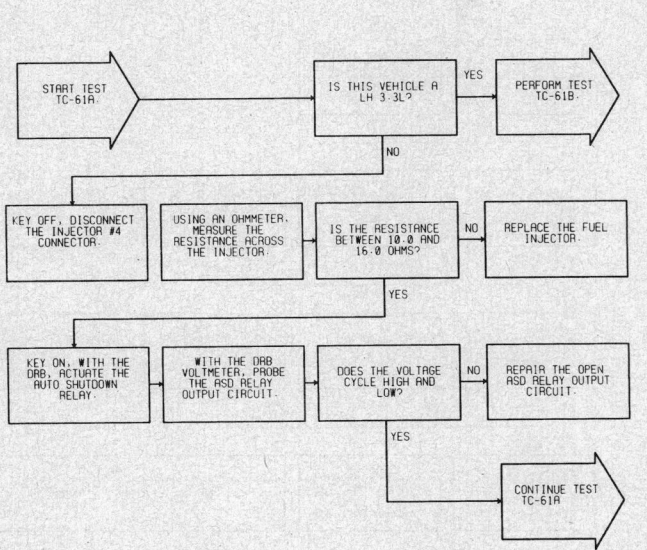

Fig. 70   Test TC-61A: Injector No. 4 Control Circuit (Part 1 of 2)

CR1029606645010X

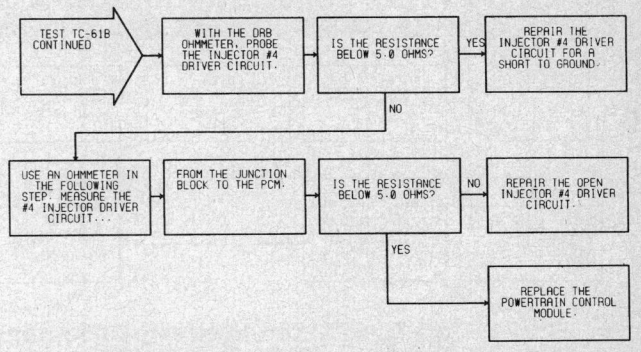

Fig. 70   Test TC-61A: Injector No. 4 Control Circuit (Part 2 of 2)

CR1029606645020X

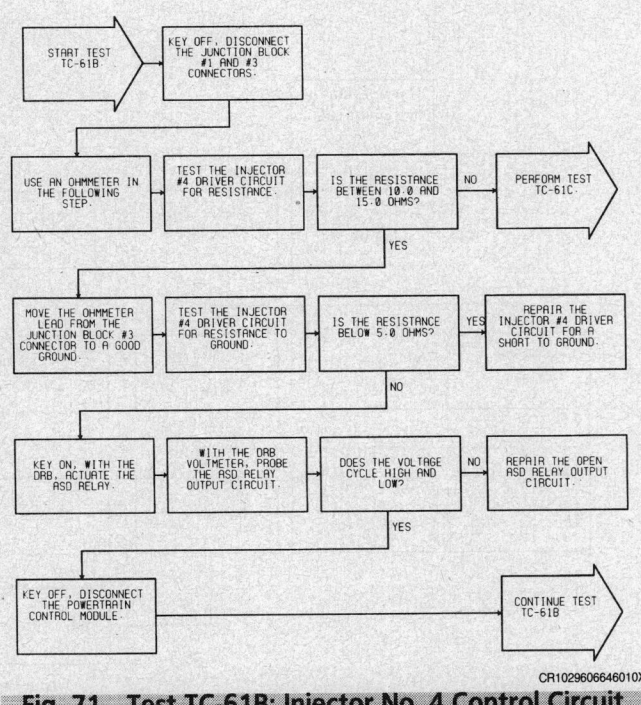

Fig. 71   Test TC-61B: Injector No. 4 Control Circuit (Part 1 of 2)

CR1029606646010X

Fig. 71   Test TC-61B: Injector No. 4 Control Circuit (Part 2 of 2)

CR1029606646020X

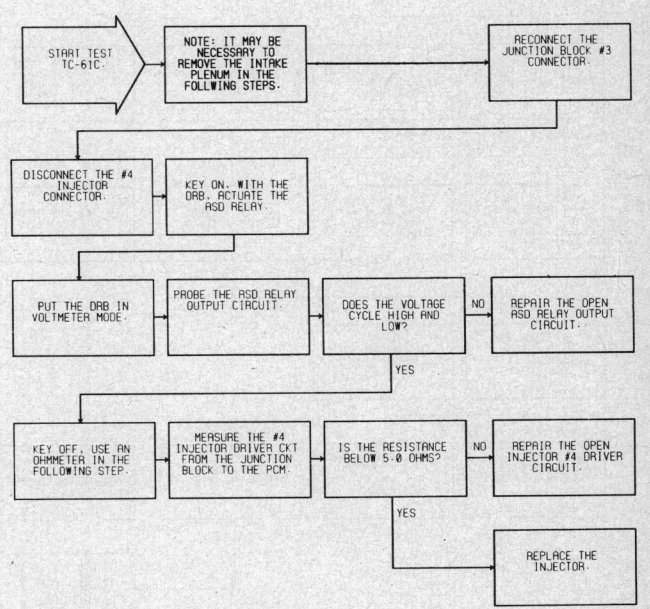

Fig. 72   Test TC-61C: Injector No. 4 Control Circuit

CR1029606647000X

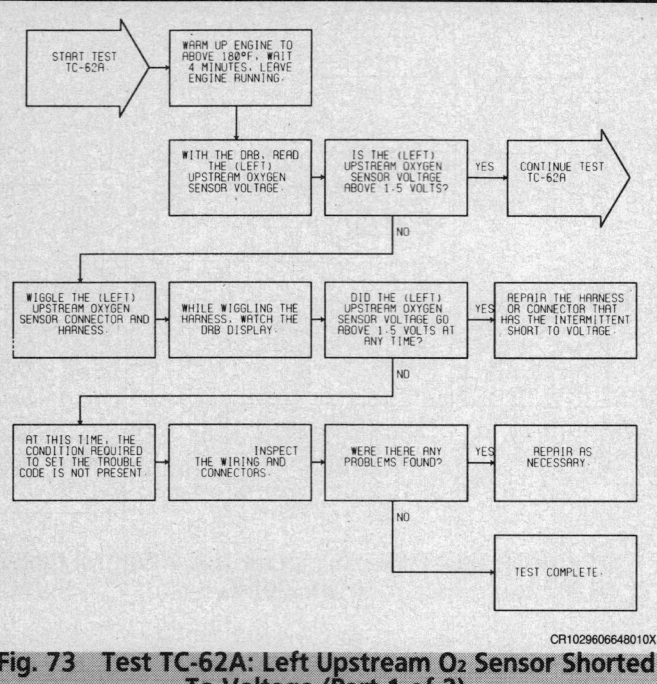

Fig. 73   Test TC-62A: Left Upstream O₂ Sensor Shorted To Voltage (Part 1 of 2)

CR1029606648010X

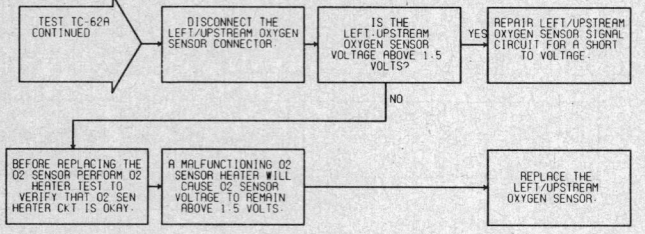

Fig. 73   Test TC-62A: Left Upstream O₂ Sensor Shorted To Voltage (Part 2 of 2)

CR1029606648020X

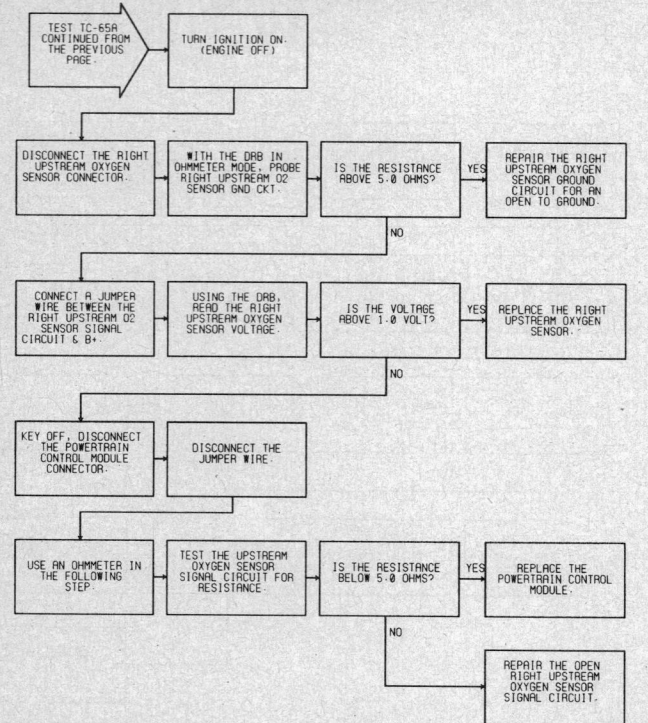

Fig. 74   Test TC-65A: Right Upstream O₂ Sensor Stays At Center (Part 2 of 2)

CR1029606649020X

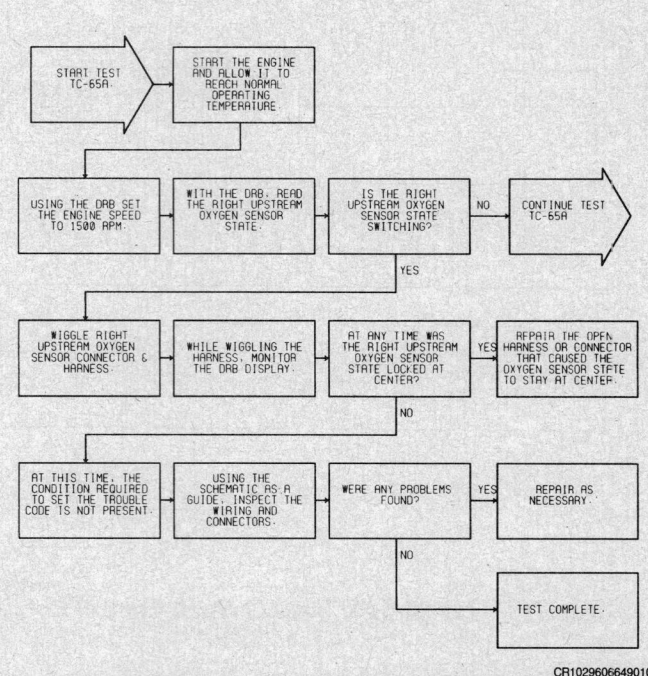

Fig. 74   Test TC-65A: Right Upstream O₂ Sensor Stays At Center (Part 1 of 2)

CR1029606649010X

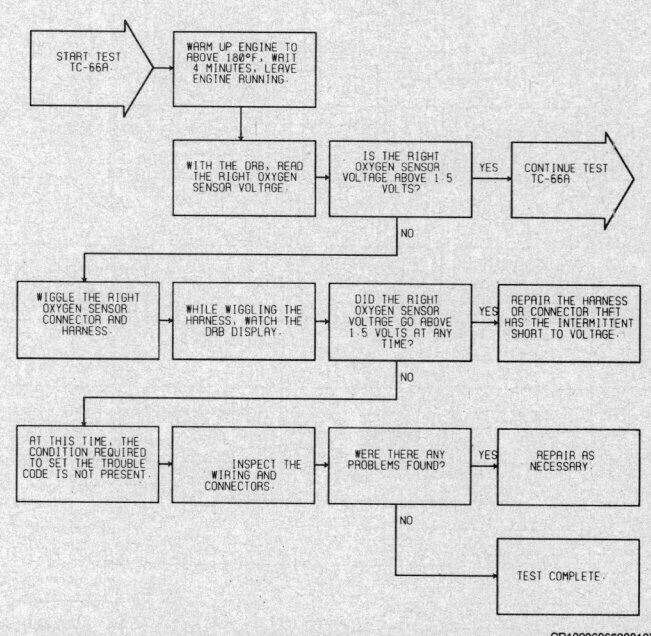

Fig. 75   Test TC-66A: Right Upstream O₂ Sensor Shorted To Voltage (Part 1 of 2)

CR1029606690010X

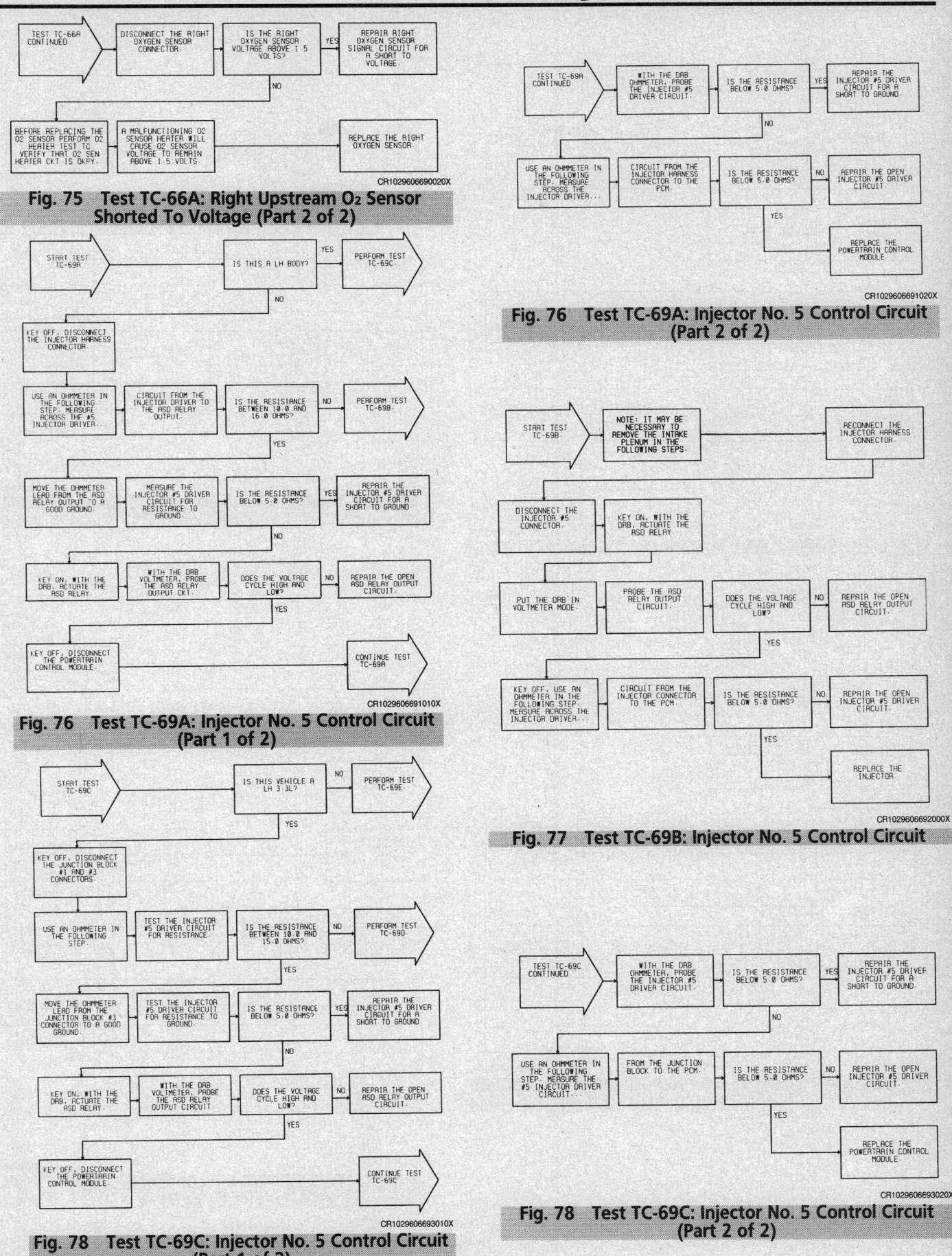

Fig. 75 Test TC-66A: Right Upstream O₂ Sensor Shorted To Voltage (Part 2 of 2)

CR1029606690020X

Fig. 76 Test TC-69A: Injector No. 5 Control Circuit (Part 1 of 2)

CR1029606691010X

Fig. 76 Test TC-69A: Injector No. 5 Control Circuit (Part 2 of 2)

CR1029606691020X

Fig. 77 Test TC-69B: Injector No. 5 Control Circuit

CR1029606692000X

Fig. 78 Test TC-69C: Injector No. 5 Control Circuit (Part 1 of 2)

CR1029606693010X

Fig. 78 Test TC-69C: Injector No. 5 Control Circuit (Part 2 of 2)

CR1029606693020X

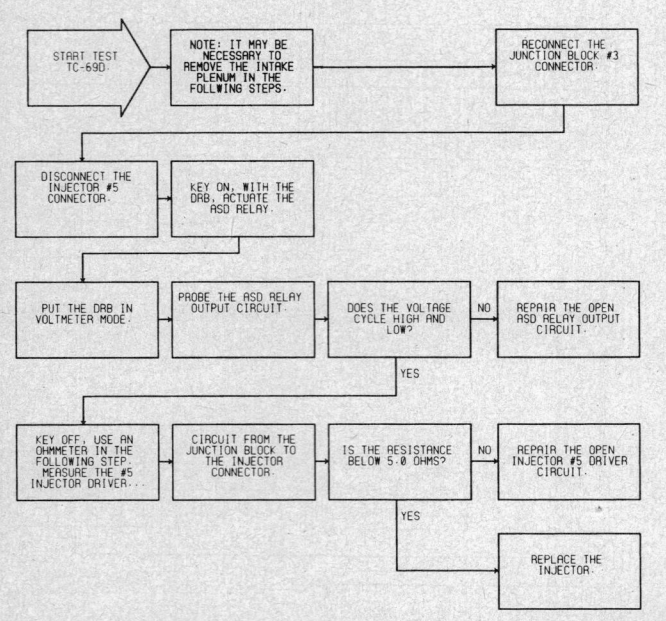

Fig. 79   Test TC-69D: Injector No. 5 Control Circuit

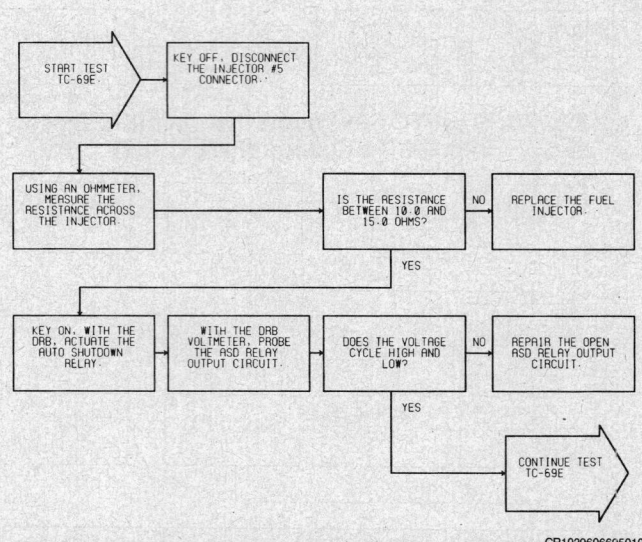

Fig. 80   Test TC-69E: Injector No. 5 Control Circuit (Part 1 of 2)

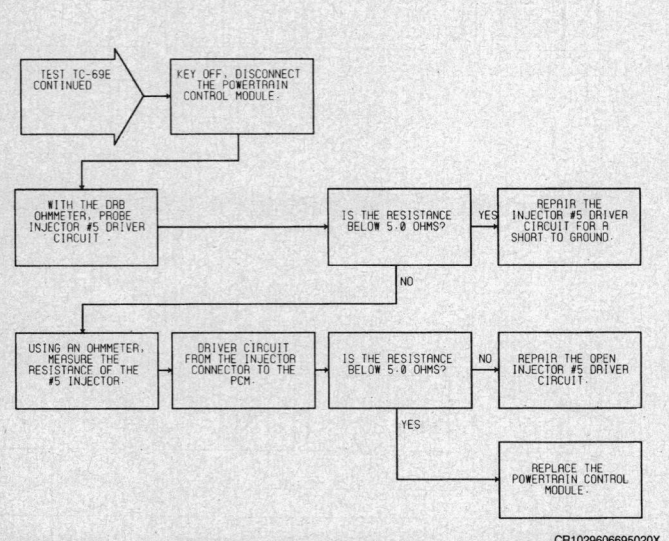

Fig. 80   Test TC-69E: Injector No. 5 Control Circuit (Part 2 of 2)

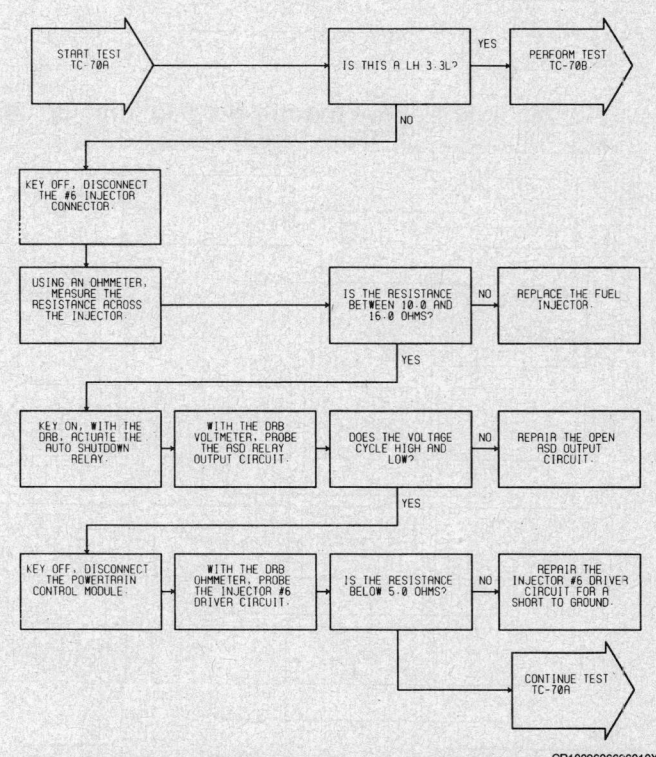

Fig. 81   Test TC-70A: Injector No. 6 Control Circuit (Part 1 of 3)

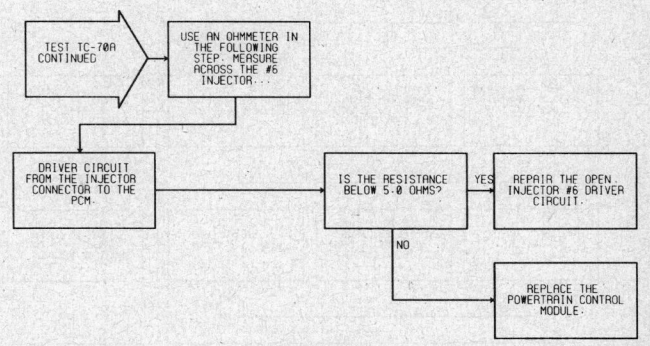

Fig. 81   Test TC-70A: Injector No. 6 Control Circuit (Part 3 of 3)

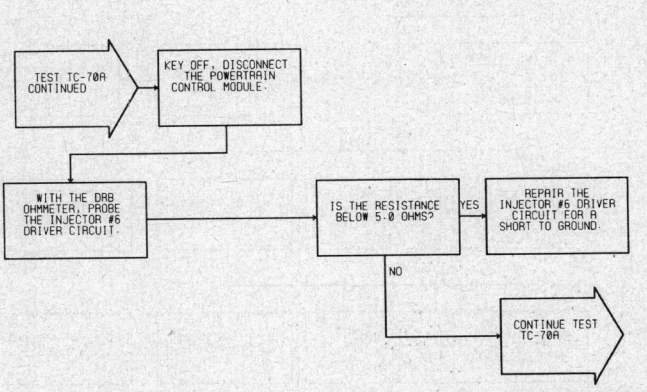

Fig. 81   Test TC-70A: Injector No. 6 Control Circuit (Part 2 of 3)

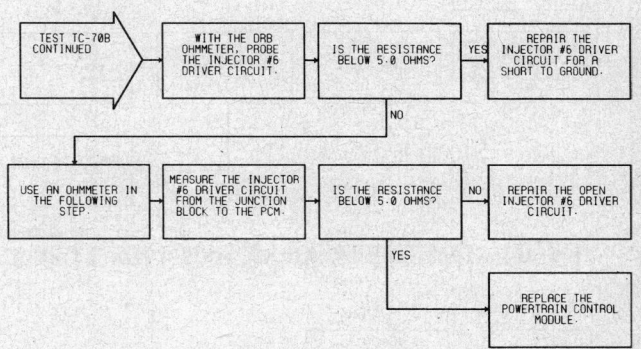

Fig. 82   Test TC-70B: Injector No. 6 Control Circuit (Part 2 of 2)

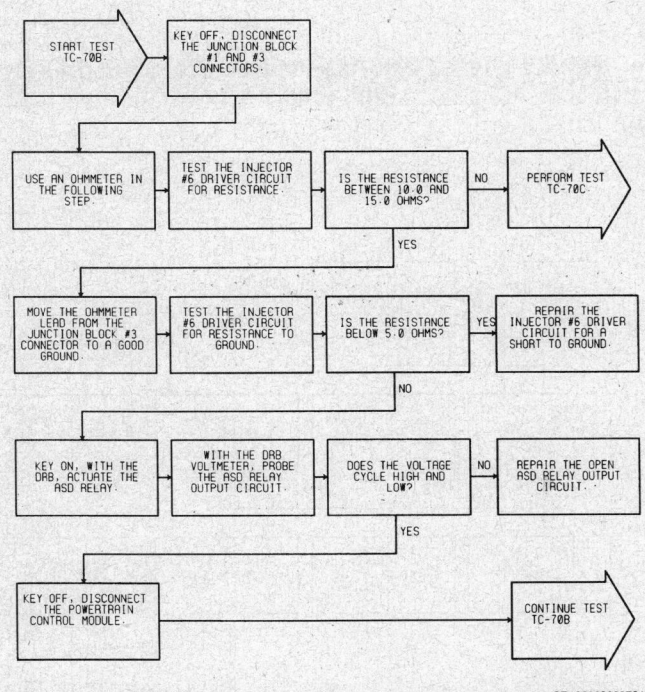

Fig. 82   Test TC-70B: Injector No. 6 Control Circuit (Part 1 of 2)

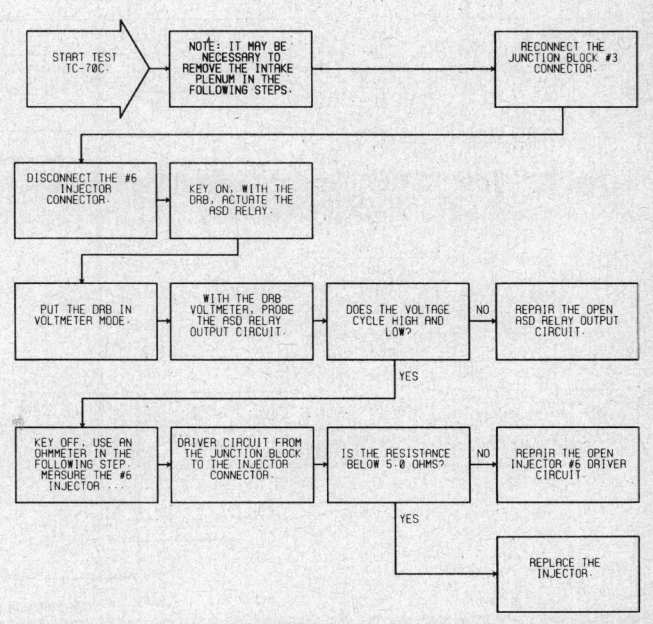

Fig. 83   Test TC-70C: Injector No. 6 Control Circuit

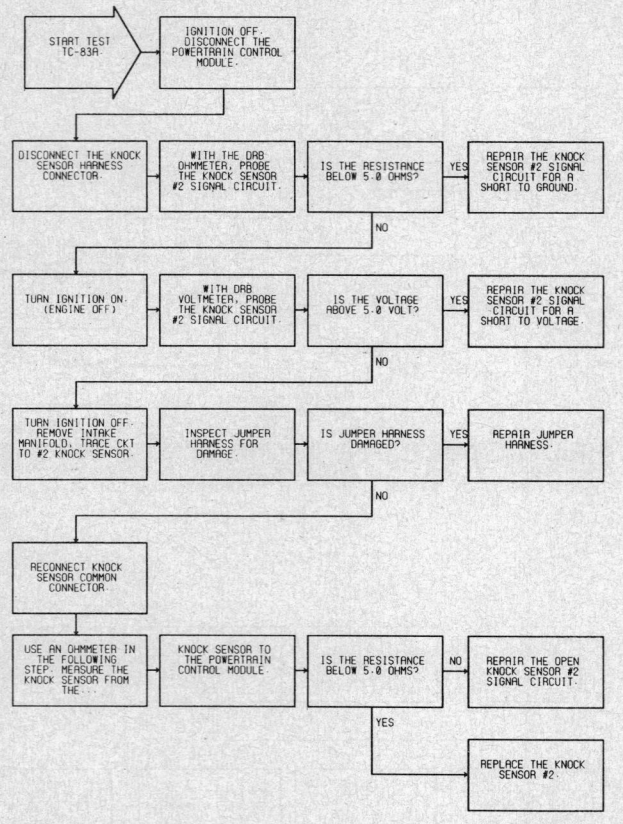

Fig. 84   Test TC-83A: Knock Sensor No. 2 Circuit

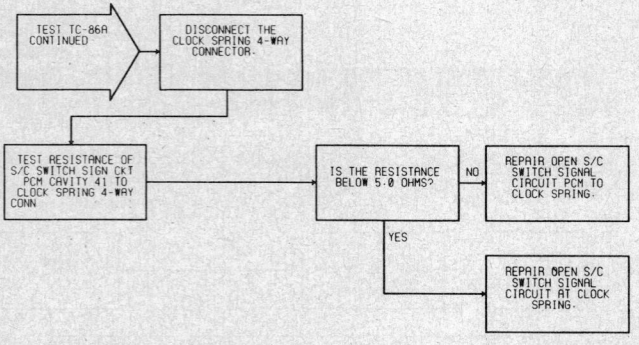

Fig. 85   Test TC-86A: Speed Control Switch Always High (Part 2 of 2)

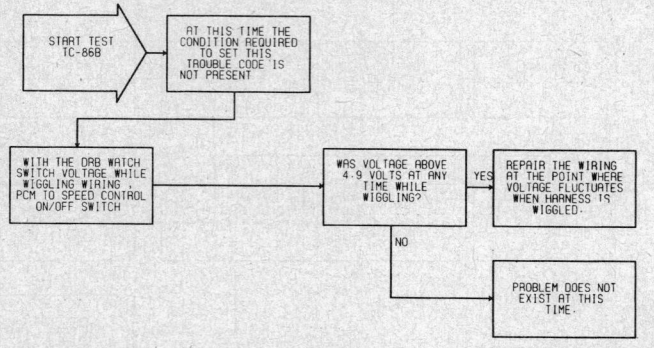

Fig. 86   Test TC-86B: Speed Control Switch Always High

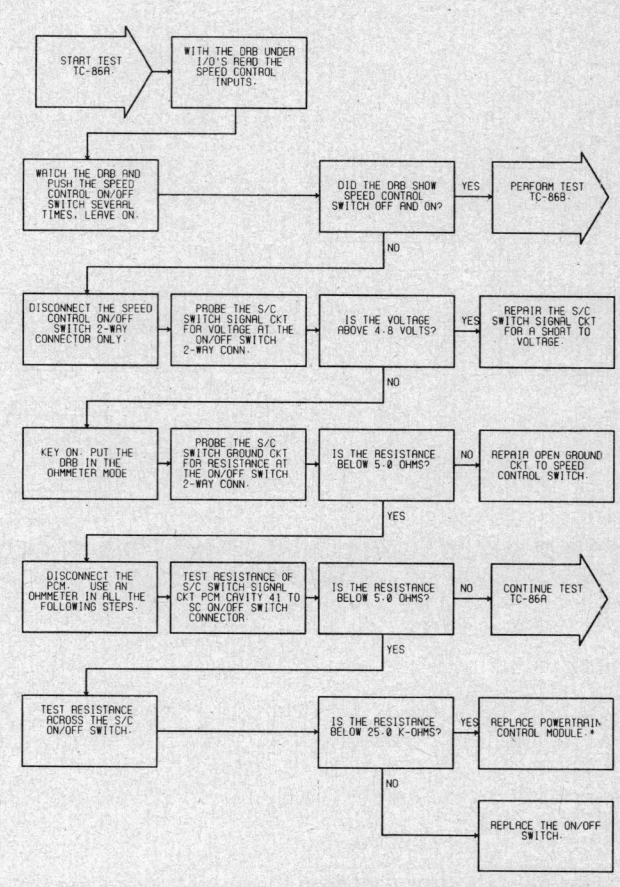

Fig. 85   Test TC-86A: Speed Control Switch Always High (Part 1 of 2)

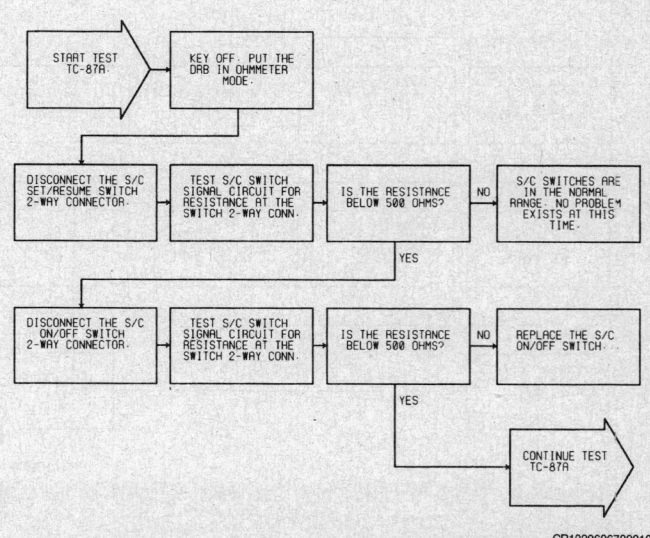

Fig. 87   Test TC-87A: Speed Control Switch Always Low (Part 1 of 2)

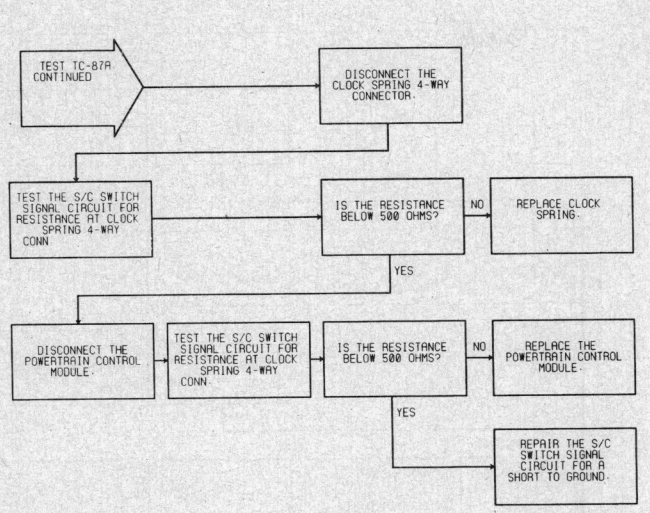

Fig. 87 Test TC-87A: Speed Control Switch Always Low (Part 2 of 2)

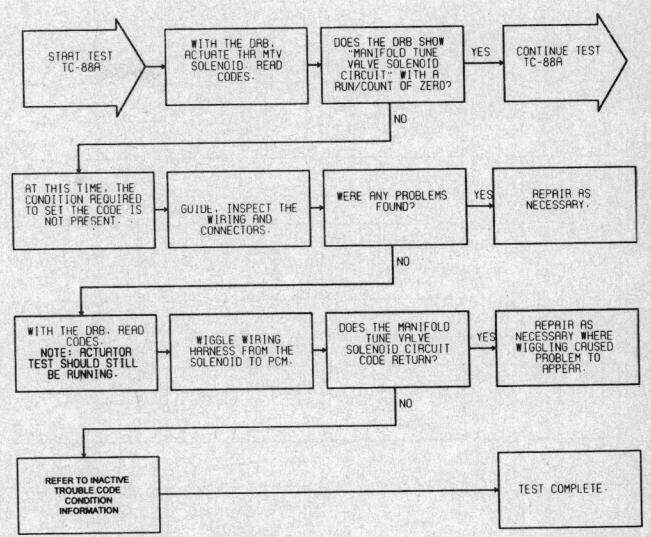

Fig. 88 Test TC-88A: Manifold Tune Valve Solenoid Circuit (Part 1 of 3)

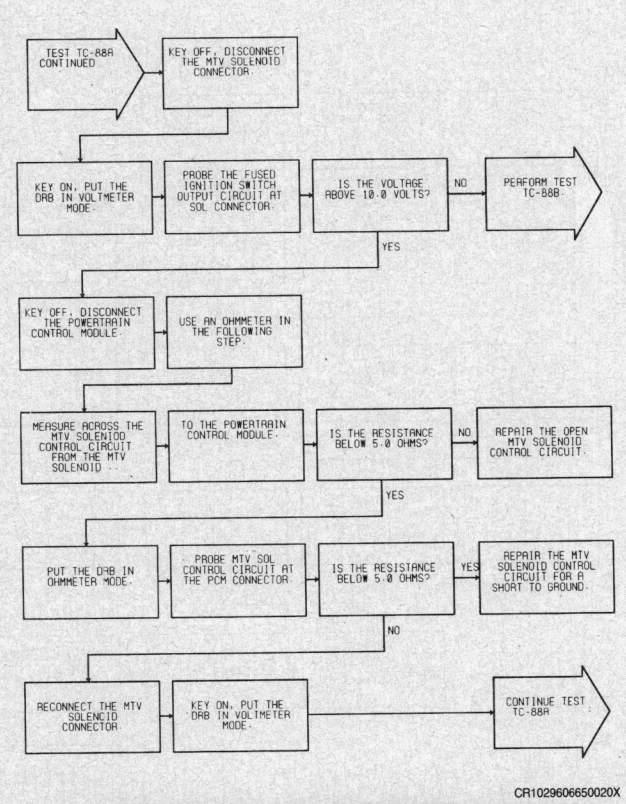

Fig. 88 Test TC-88A: Manifold Tune Valve Solenoid Circuit (Part 2 of 3)

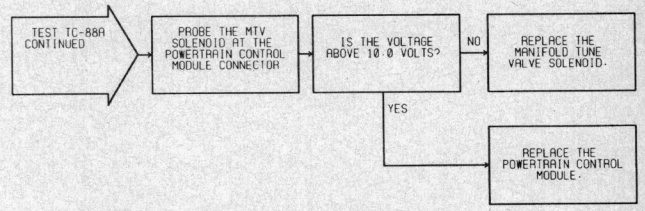

Fig. 88 Test TC-88A: Manifold Tune Valve Solenoid Circuit (Part 3 of 3)

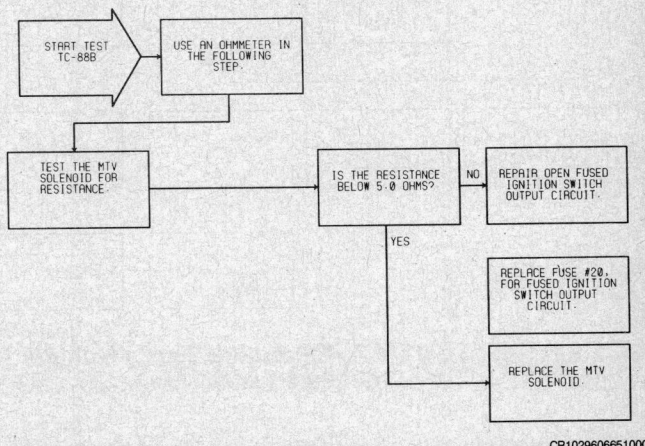

Fig. 89 Test TC-88B: Manifold Tune Valve Solenoid Circuit

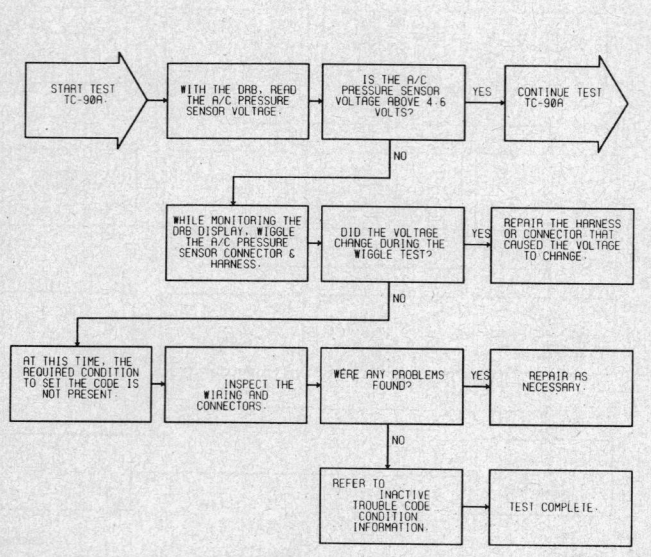

Fig. 90   Test TC-90A: A/C Pressure Sensor Voltage Too High (Part 1 of 2)

CR1029606652010X

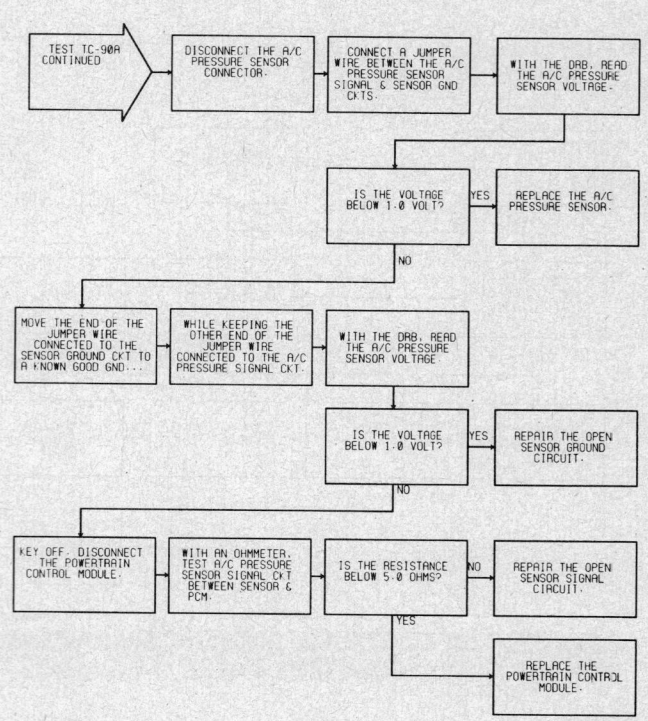

Fig. 90   Test TC-90A: A/C Pressure Sensor Voltage Too High (Part 2 of 2)

CR1029606652020X

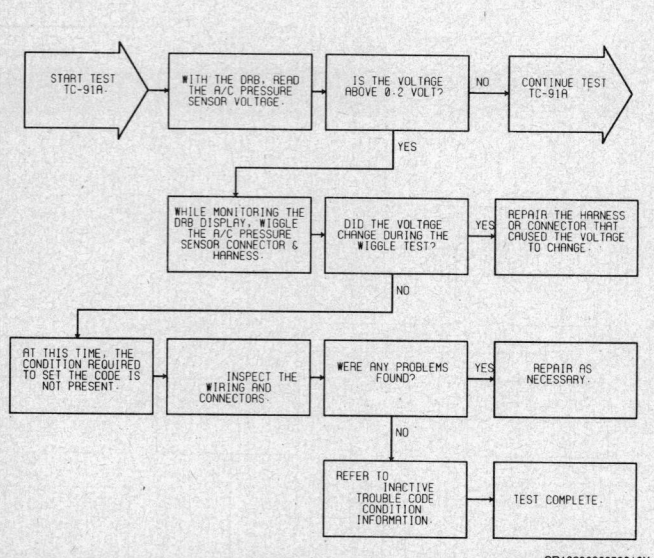

Fig. 91   Test TC-91A: A/C Pressure Sensor Voltage Too Low (Part 1 of 2)

CR1029606653010X

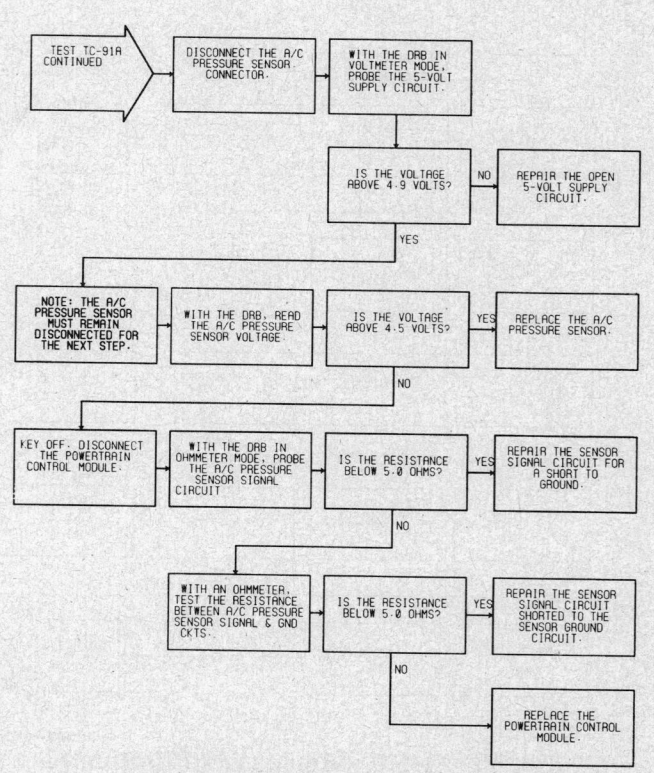

Fig. 91   Test TC-91A: A/C Pressure Sensor Voltage Too Low (Part 2 of 2)

CR1029606653020X

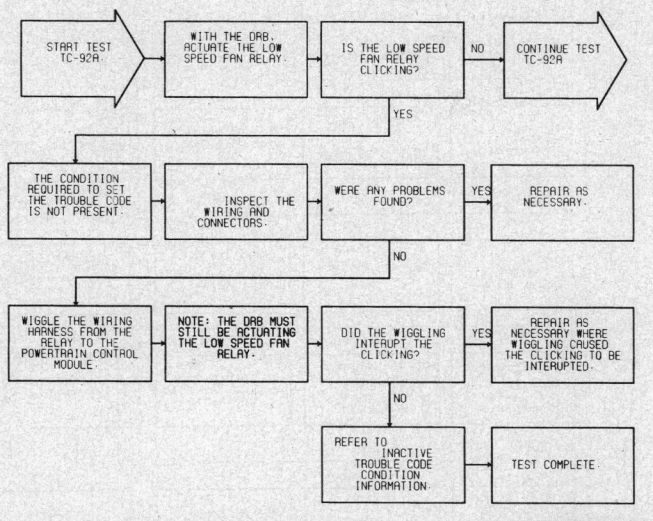

Fig. 92   Test TC-92A: Low Speed Fan Control Relay Circuit (Part 1 of 3)

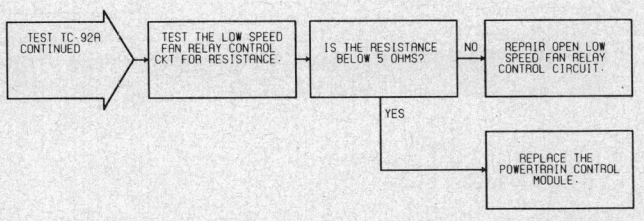

Fig. 92   Test TC-92A: Low Speed Fan Control Relay Circuit (Part 3 of 3)

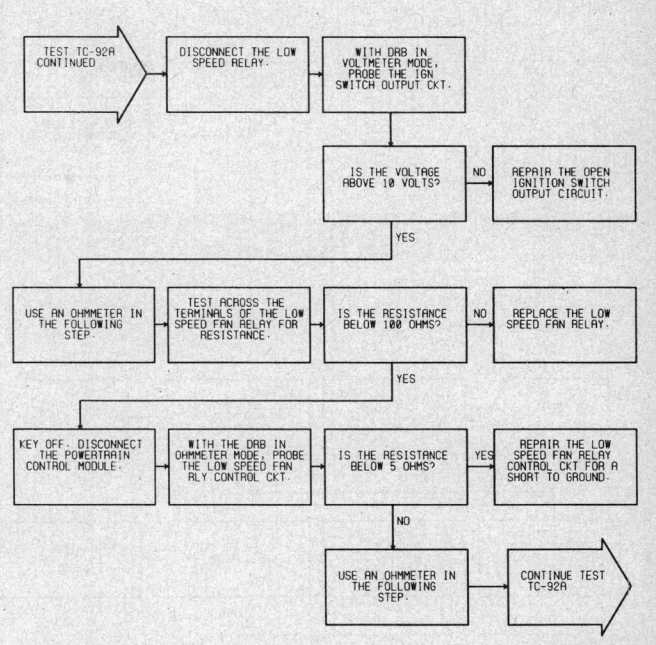

Fig. 92   Test TC-92A: Low Speed Fan Control Relay Circuit (Part 2 of 3)

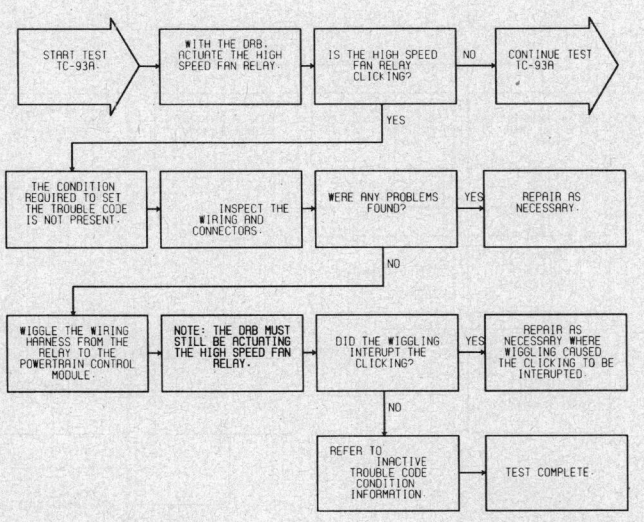

Fig. 93   Test TC-93A: High Speed Fan Control Relay Circuit (Part 1 of 3)

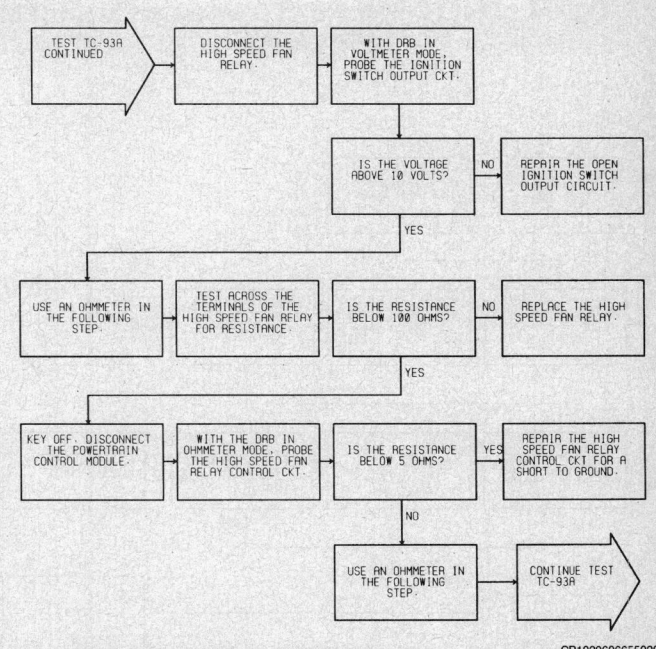

Fig. 93   Test TC-93A: High Speed Fan Control Relay Circuit (Part 2 of 3)

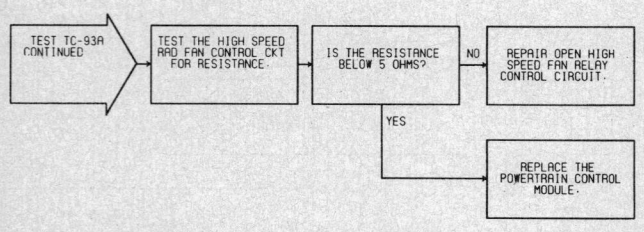

Fig. 93   Test TC-93A: High Speed Fan Control Relay Circuit (Part 3 of 3)

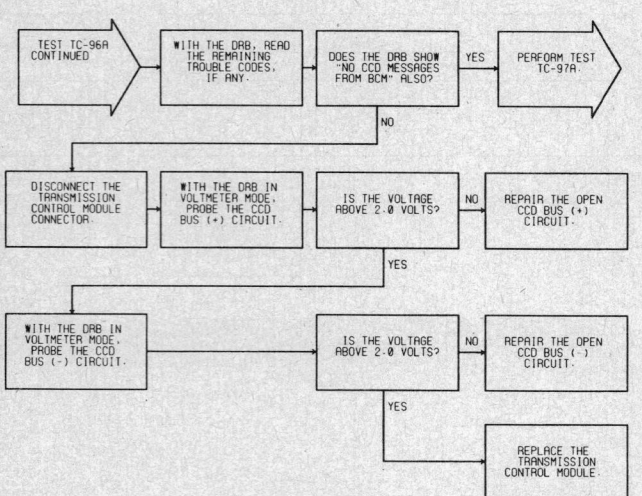

Fig. 94   Test TC-96A: No CCD Messages From TCM (Part 2 of 2)

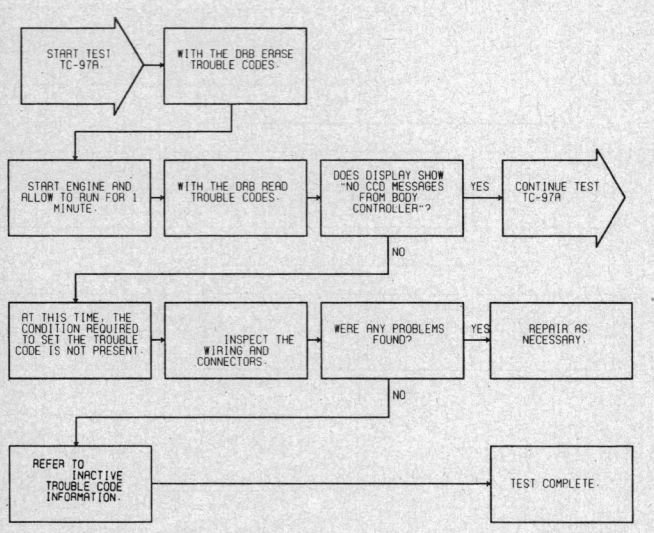

Fig. 95   Test TC-97A: No CCD Message From Body Control Module (Part 1 of 2)

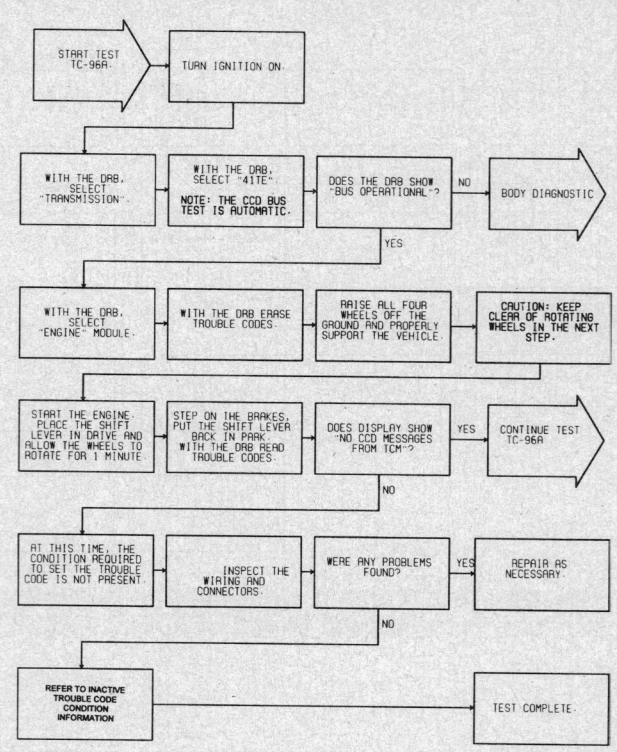

Fig. 94   Test TC-96A: No CCD Messages From TCM (Part 1 of 2)

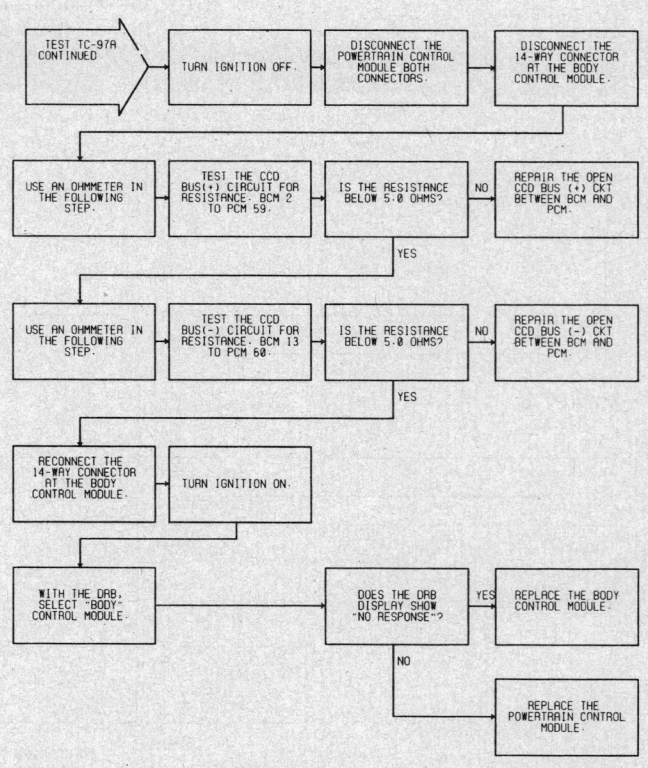

Fig. 95   Test TC-97A: No CCD Message From Body Control Module (Part 2 of 2)

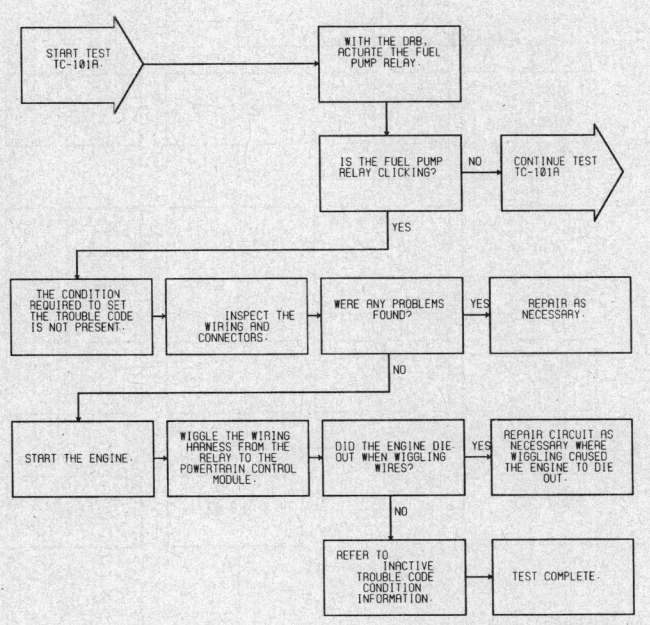

Fig. 96   Test TC-101A: Fuel Pump Relay Control Circuit (Part 1 of 3)

CR1029606658010X

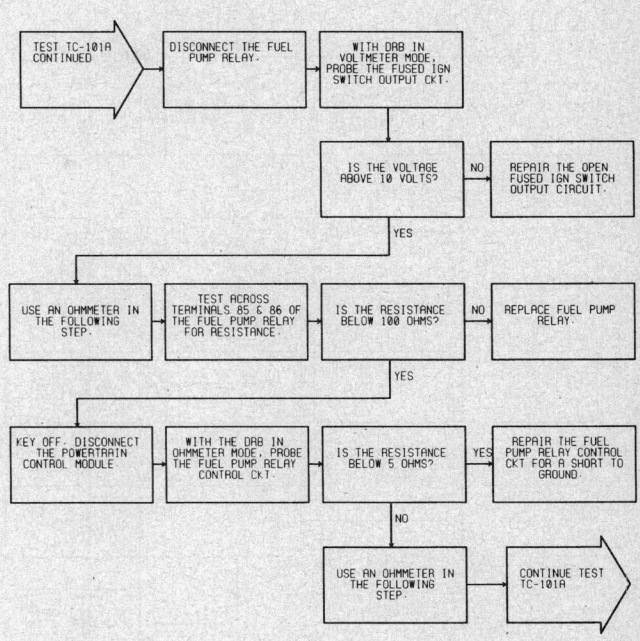

Fig. 96   Test TC-101A: Fuel Pump Relay Control Circuit (Part 2 of 3)

CR1029606658020X

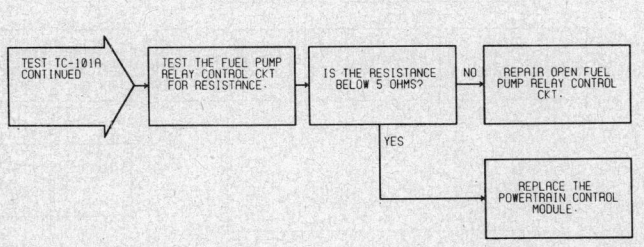

Fig. 96   Test TC-101A: Fuel Pump Relay Control Circuit (Part 3 of 3)

CR1029606658030X

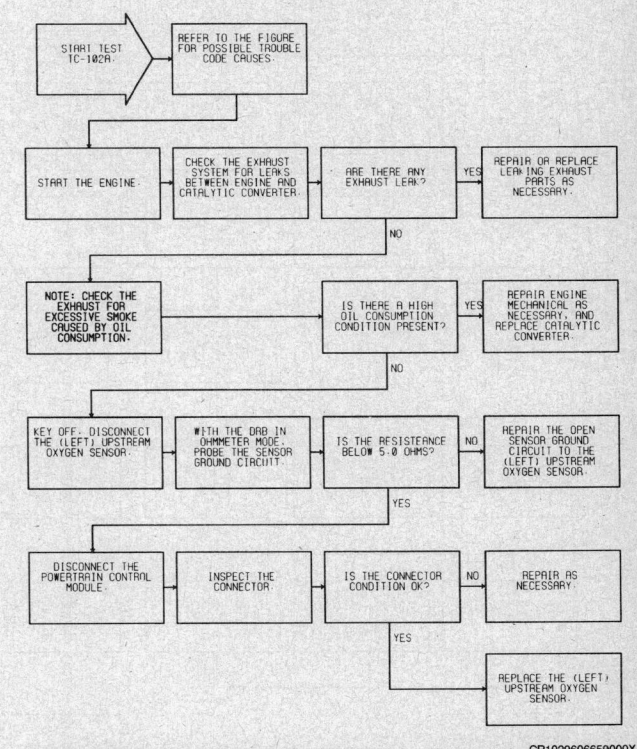

Fig. 97   Test TC-102A: Left Upstream O₂ Sensor Slow Response

CR1029606659000X

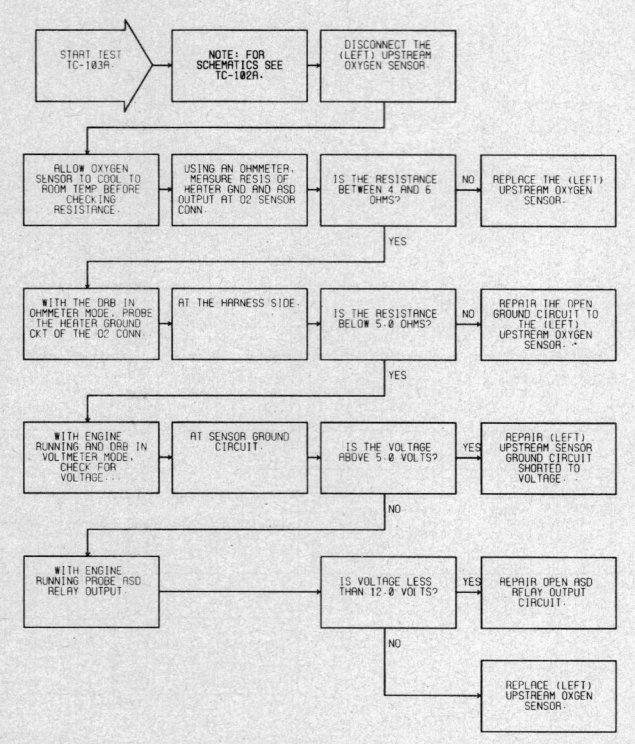

CR1029606660000X

Fig. 98   Test TC-103A: Left Upstream O₂ Sensor Heater Failure

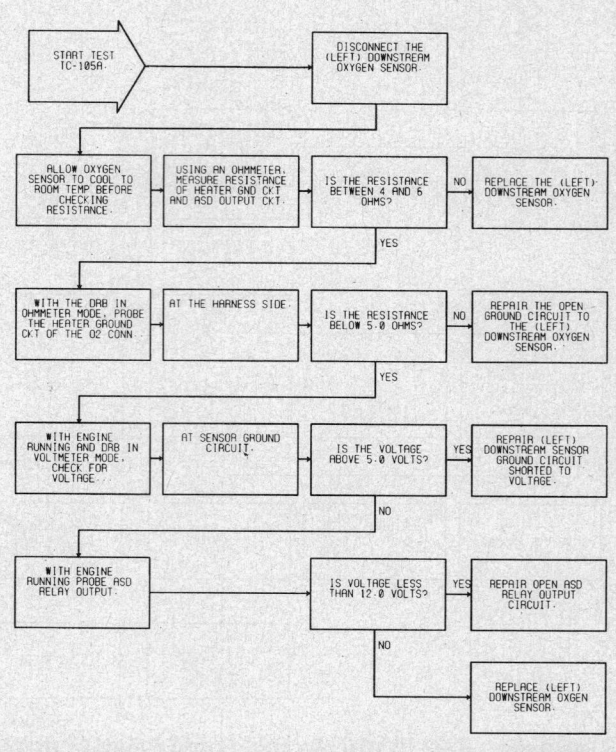

CR1029606661000X

Fig. 99   Test TC-105A: Left Downstream O₂ Sensor Heater Failure

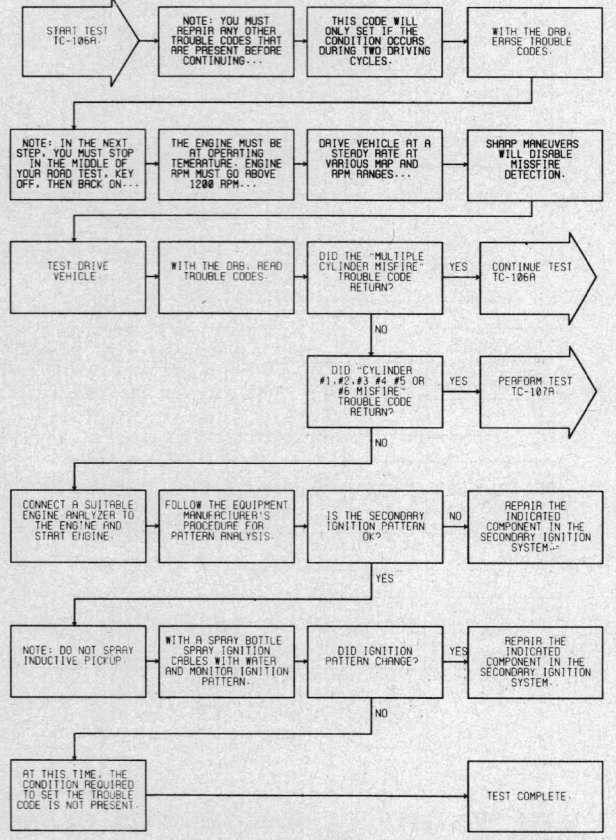

CR1029606662010X

Fig. 100   Test TC-106A: Multiple Cylinder Misfire (Part 1 of 4)

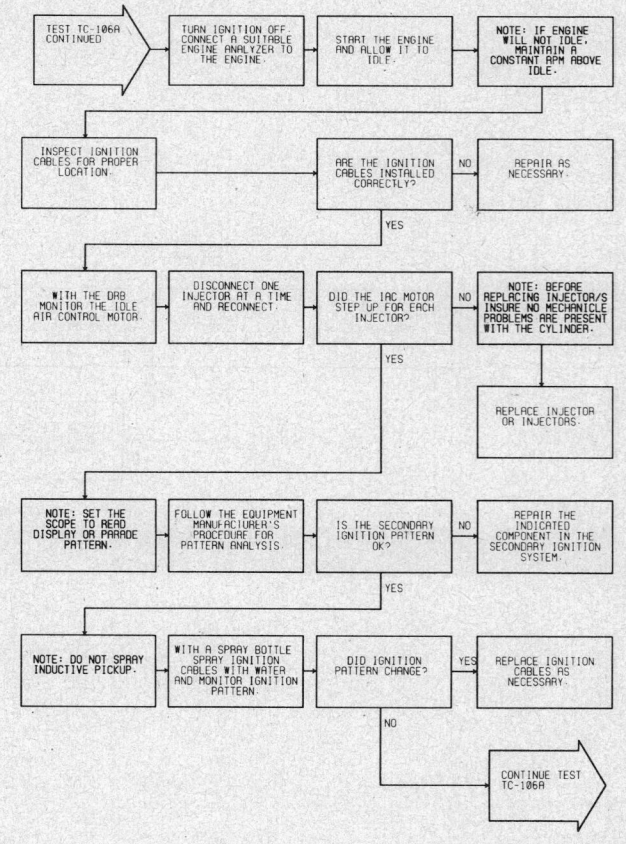

CR1029606662020X

Fig. 100   Test TC-106A: Multiple Cylinder Misfire (Part 2 of 4)

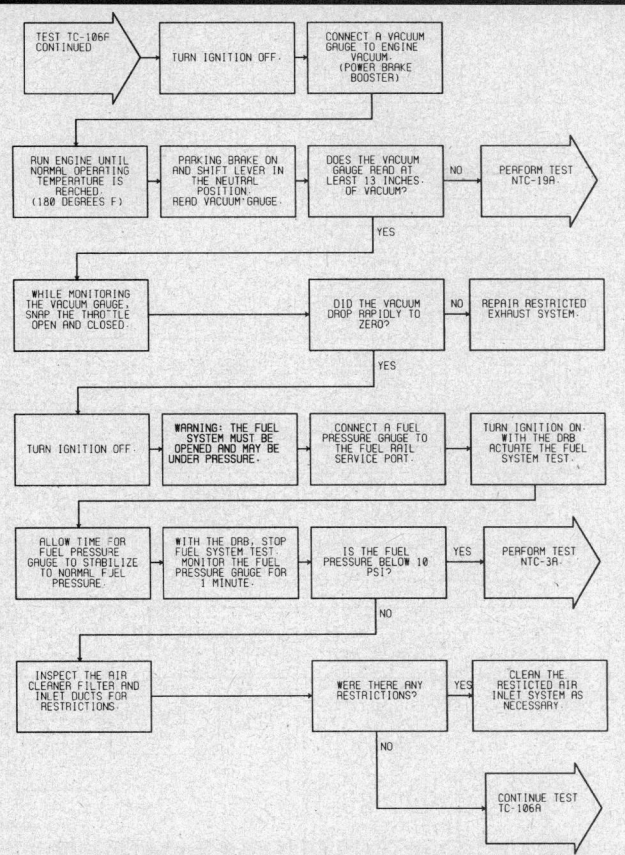

Make sure all the wiring and connectors are ok.

Perform each of the following tests in the order listed below. If a test passes, continue to the next test until the problem is found:

Secondary Ignition Patterns . . . . .TEST NTC-2A

Fuel Pressure. . . . . .TEST NTC-3A

PCM Grounds and Power Circuits . . . . .TEST NTC-11A

EGR System . . . . .TEST NTC-13A

No Trouble Code Mechanical . . . . .TEST NTC-18A

CR1029606662040X

Fig. 100   Test TC-106A: Multiple Cylinder Misfire (Part 4 of 4)

CR1029606662030X

Fig. 100   Test TC-106A: Multiple Cylinder Misfire (Part 3 of 4)

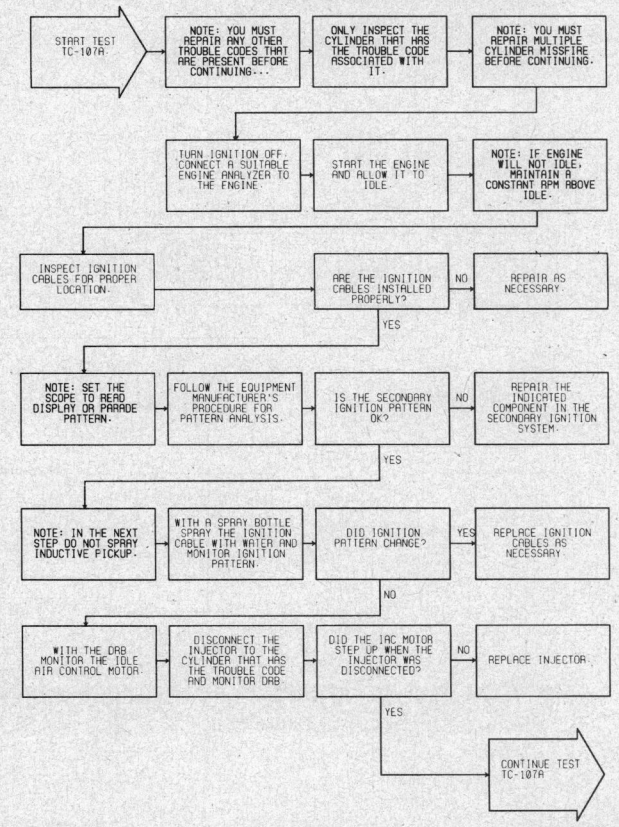

CR1029606663010X

Fig. 101   Test TC-107A: Cylinder Nos. 1, 2, 3, 4, 5 Or 6 Misfire (Part 1 of 2)

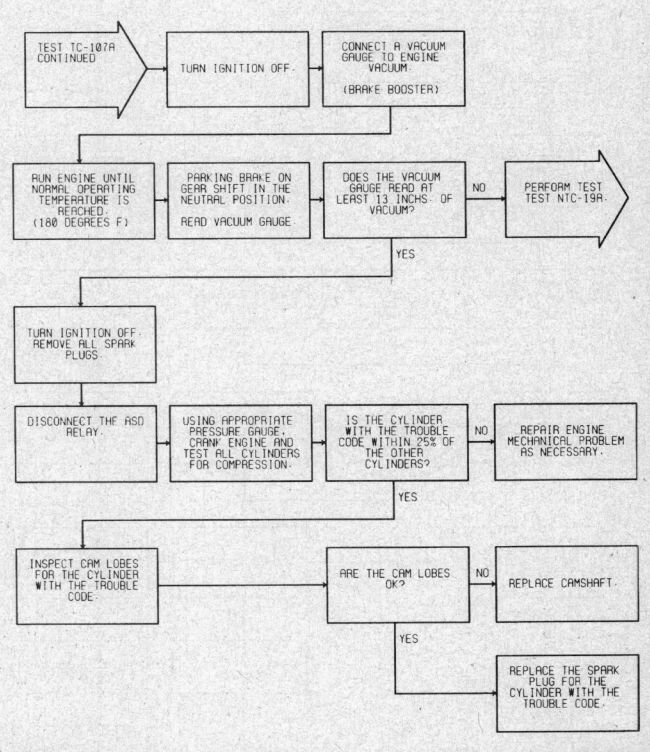

CR1029606663020X

Fig. 101   Test TC-107A: Cylinder Nos. 1, 2, 3, 4, 5 Or 6 Misfire (Part 2 of 2)

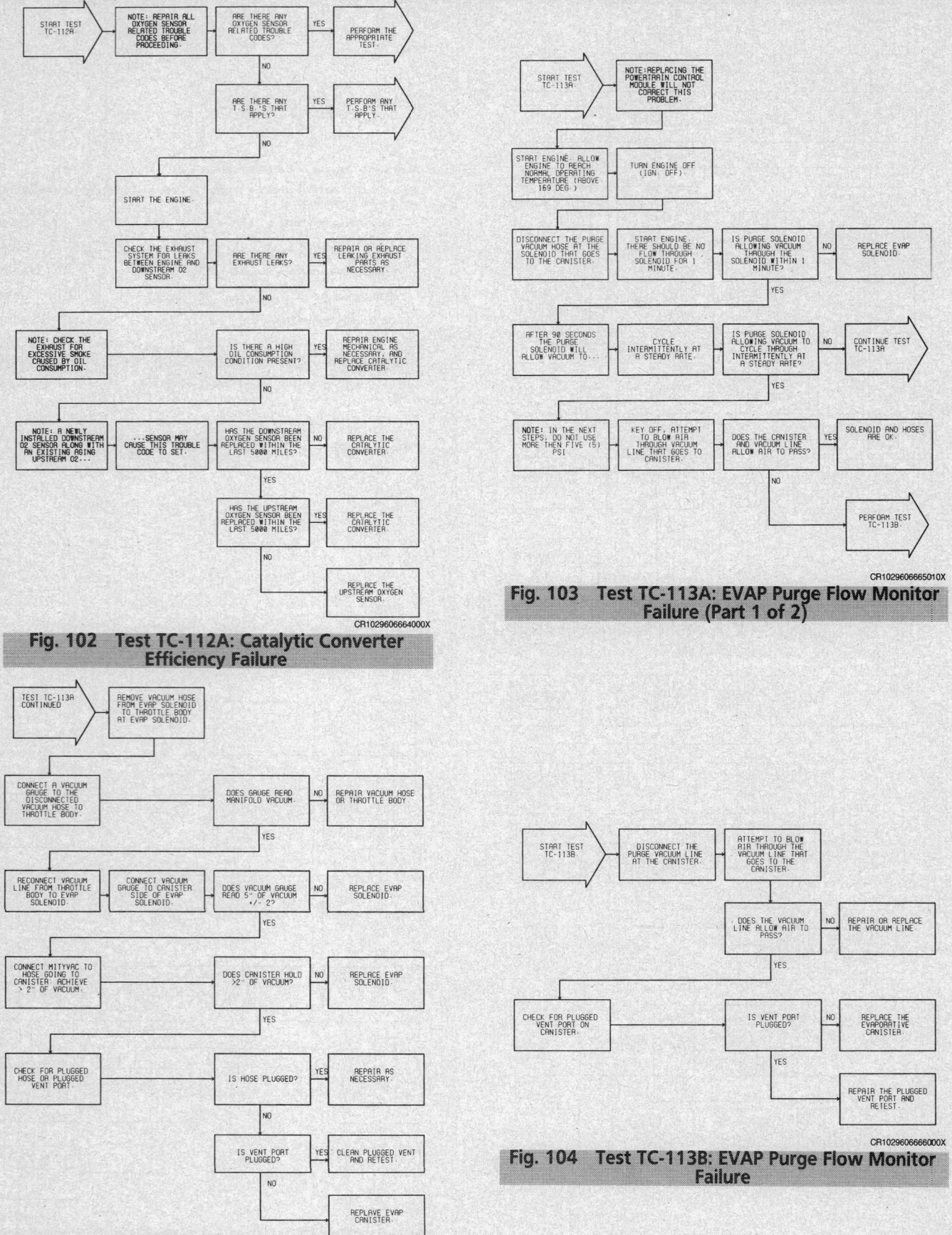

Fig. 102   Test TC-112A: Catalytic Converter
Efficiency Failure

Fig. 103   Test TC-113A: EVAP Purge Flow Monitor
Failure (Part 1 of 2)

Fig. 103   Test TC-113A: EVAP Purge Flow Monitor
Failure (Part 2 of 2)

Fig. 104   Test TC-113B: EVAP Purge Flow Monitor
Failure

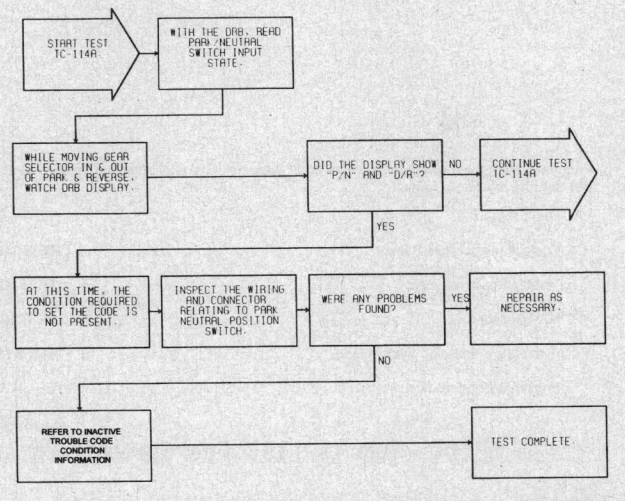

CR1029606667010X

Fig. 105   Test TC-114A: Park/Neutral Position Switch Failure (Part 1 of 3)

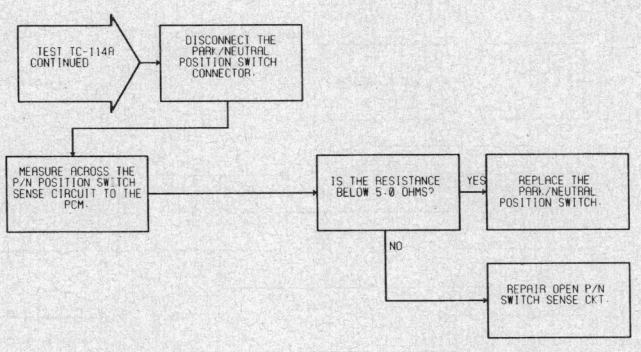

CR1029606667030X

Fig. 105   Test TC-114A: Park/Neutral Position Switch Failure (Part 3 of 3)

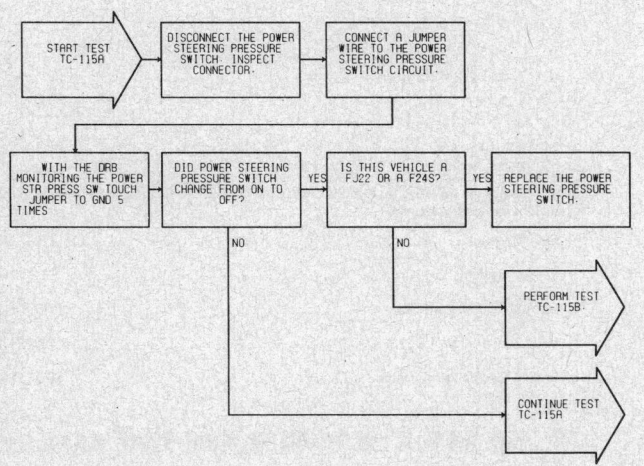

CR1029606668010X

Fig. 106   Test TC-115A: Power Steering Switch Failure (Part 1 of 2)

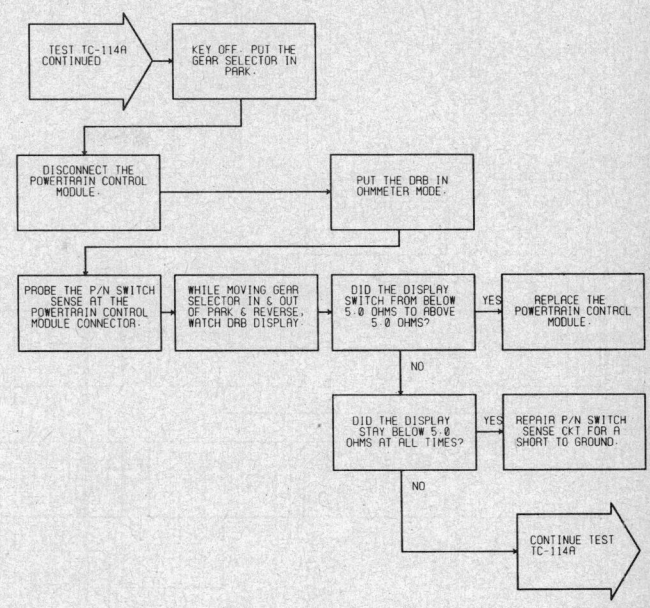

CR1029606667020X

Fig. 105   Test TC-114A: Park/Neutral Position Switch Failure (Part 2 of 3)

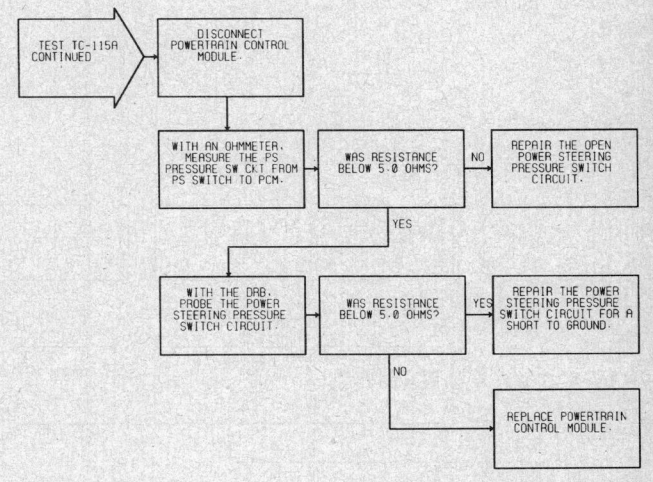

CR1029606668020X

Fig. 106   Test TC-115A: Power Steering Switch Failure (Part 2 of 2)

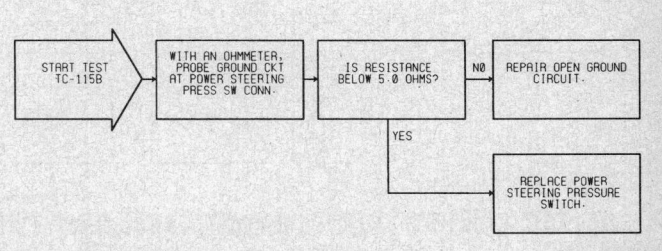

CR1029606669000X

Fig. 107   Test TC-115B: Power Steering Switch Failure

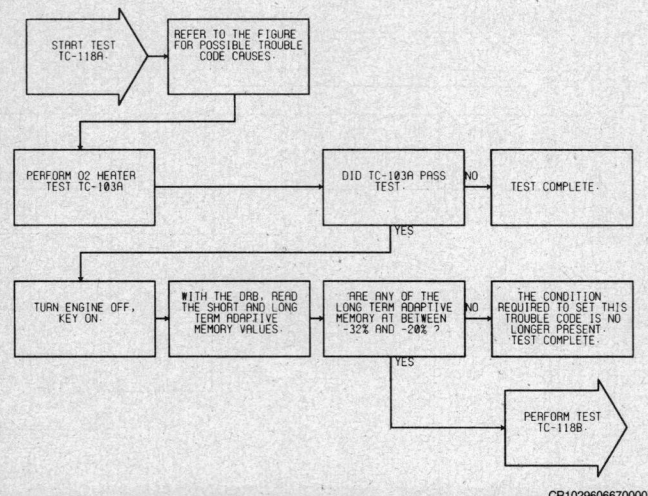

Fig. 108 Test TC-118A: Fuel System Rich

Perform each of the following tests in the order listed below. If a test passes, continue to the next test until the problem is found.

Fuel Pressure. . . . . .TEST NTC-3A

Coolant Temperature Sensor. . . . . .TEST NTC-4A

Throttle Position Sensor . . . . .TEST NTC-5A

MAP Sensor. . . . . .TEST NTC-6A

Evaporative Emission System. . . . . .TEST NTC-12A

Engine Mechanical Systems . . . . .TEST NTC-18A

CR1029606671000X

Fig. 109 Test TC-118B: Fuel System Rich

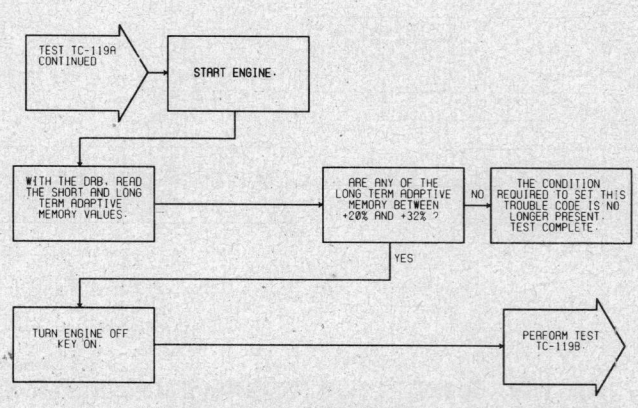

CR1029606672020X

Fig. 110 Test TC-119A: Fuel System Lean (Part 2 of 2)

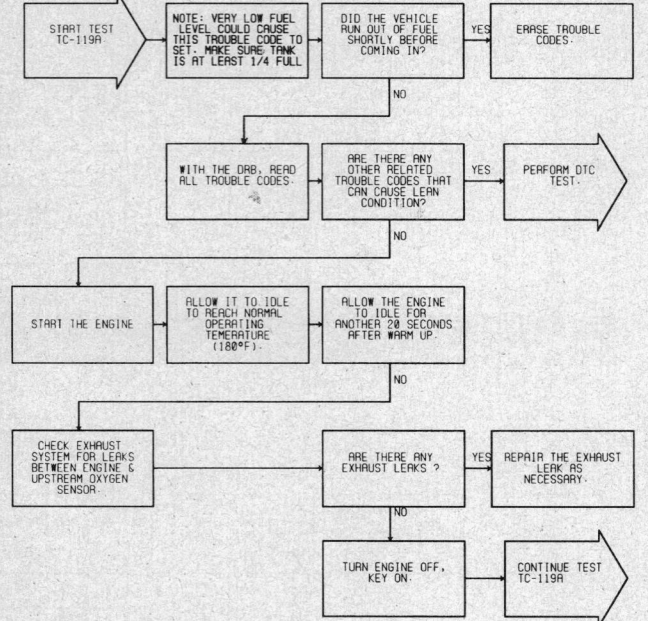

CR1029606672010X

Fig. 110 Test TC-119A: Fuel System Lean (Part 1 of 2)

Perform each of the following tests in the order listed below. If a test passes, continue to the next test until the problem is found.

Fuel Pressure. . . . . .TEST NTC-3A

Ignition System . . . . .TEST NTC-2A

Coolant Temperature Sensor. . . . . .TEST NTC-4A

MAP Sensor. . . . . .TEST NTC-6A

Engine Mechanical Systems . . . . .TEST NTC-18A

CR1029606673000X

Fig. 111 Test TC-119B: Fuel System Lean

CR1029606674000X

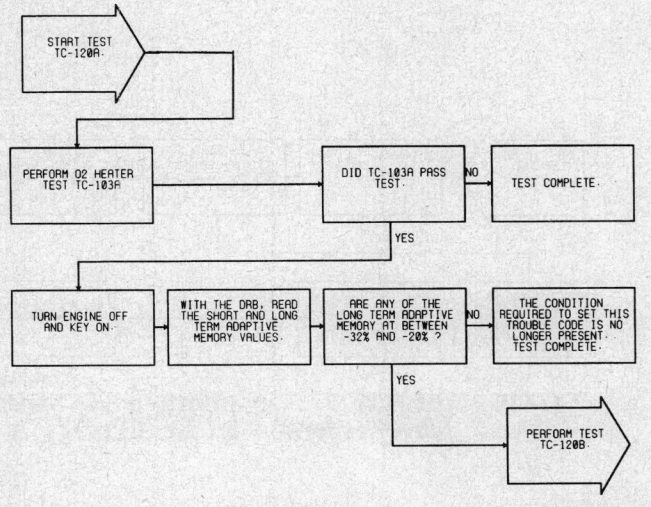

Fig. 112 Test TC-120A: Right Bank Fuel System Rich

Perform each of the following tests in the order listed below. If a test passes, continue to the next test until the problem is found.

Fuel Pressure....................TEST NTC-3A

Coolant Temperature Sensor....................TEST NTC-4A

Throttle Position Sensor....................TEST NTC-5A

MAP Sensor....................TEST NTC-6A

Evaporative Emission System....................TEST NTC-12A

Engine Mechanical Systems....................TEST NTC-18A

CR1029606675000X

Fig. 113 Test TC-120B: Right Bank Fuel System Rich

CR1029606676010X

Fig. 114 Test TC-121A: Right Bank Fuel System Lean (Part 1 of 2)

CR1029606676020X

Fig. 114 Test TC-121A: Right Bank Fuel System Lean (Part 2 of 2)

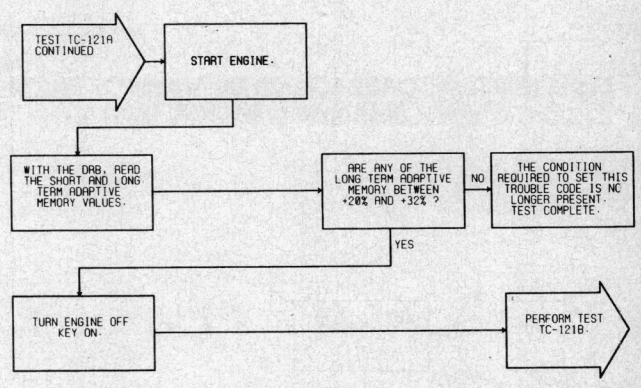

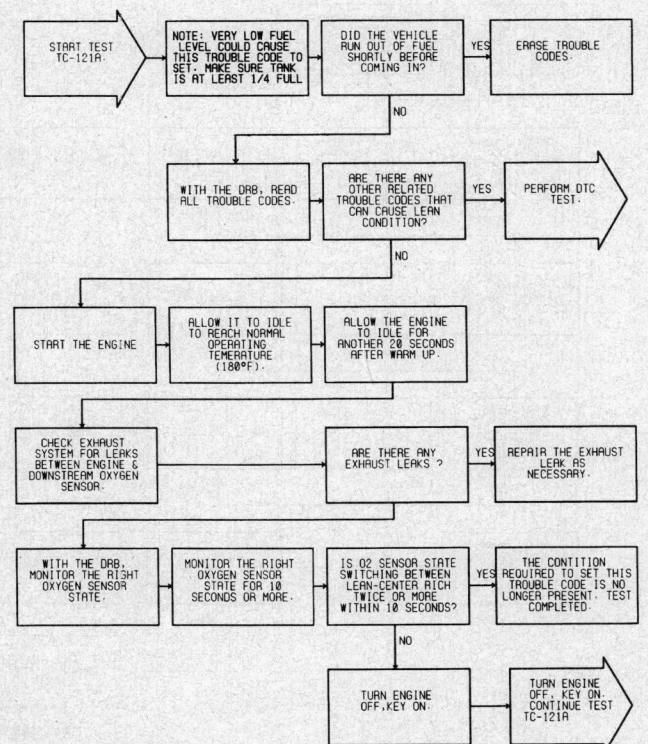

Perform each of the following tests in the order listed below. If a test passes, continue to the next test until the problem is found.

Fuel Pressure....................TEST NTC-3A

Ignition System....................TEST NTC-2A

Coolant Temperature Sensor....................TEST NTC-4A

MAP Sensor....................TEST NTC-6A

Engine Mechanical Systems....................TEST NTC-18A

CR1029606677000X

Fig. 115 Test TC-121B: Right Bank Fuel System Lean

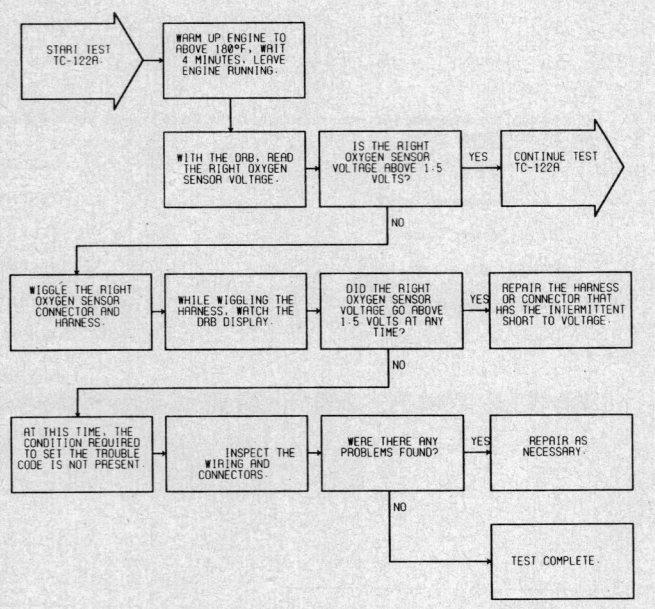

CR1029606678010X

Fig. 116   Test TC-122A: Right Upstream O₂ Sensor Slow Response (Part 1 of 2)

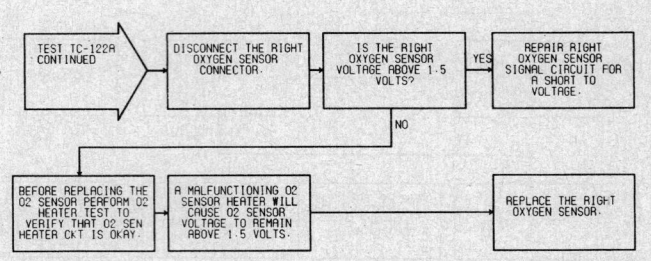

CR1029606678020X

Fig. 116   Test TC-122A: Right Upstream O₂ Sensor Slow Response (Part 2 of 2)

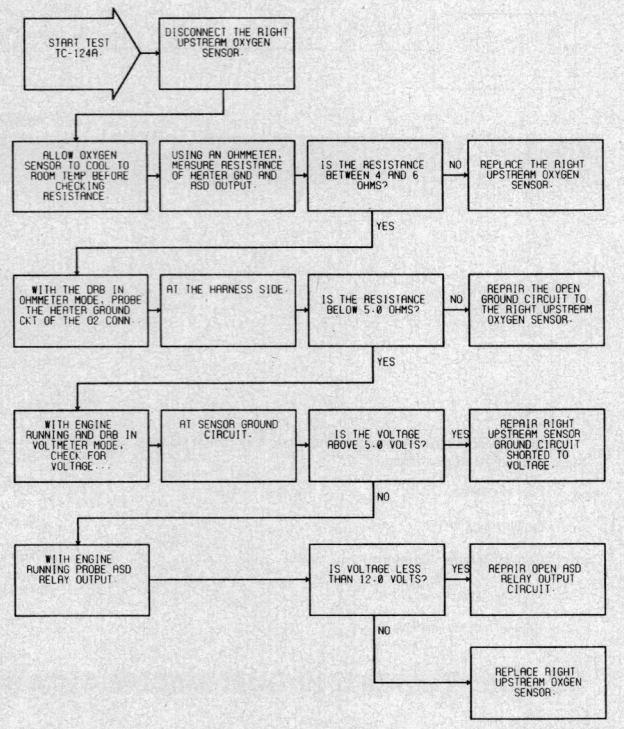

CR1029606679000X

Fig. 117   Test TC-124A: Right Upstream O₂ Sensor Heater Failure

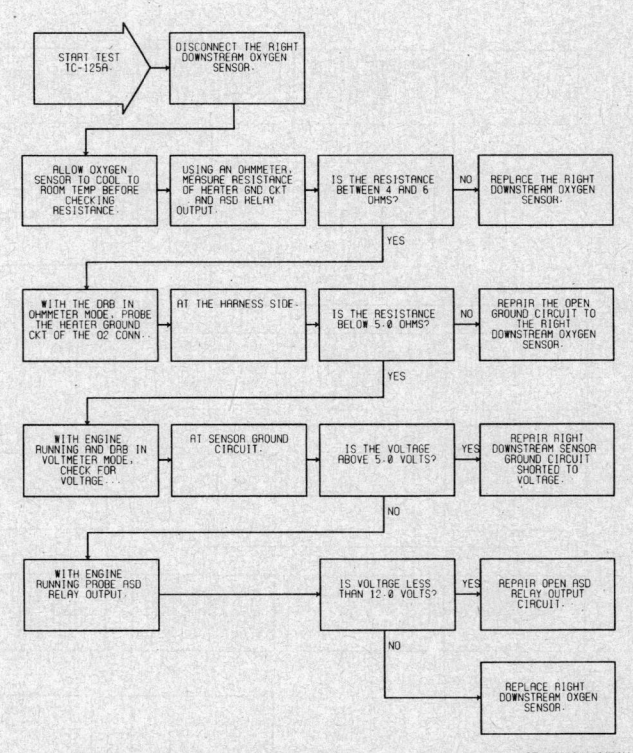

CR1029606680000X

Fig. 118   Test TC-125A: Right Downstream O₂ Sensor Heater Failure

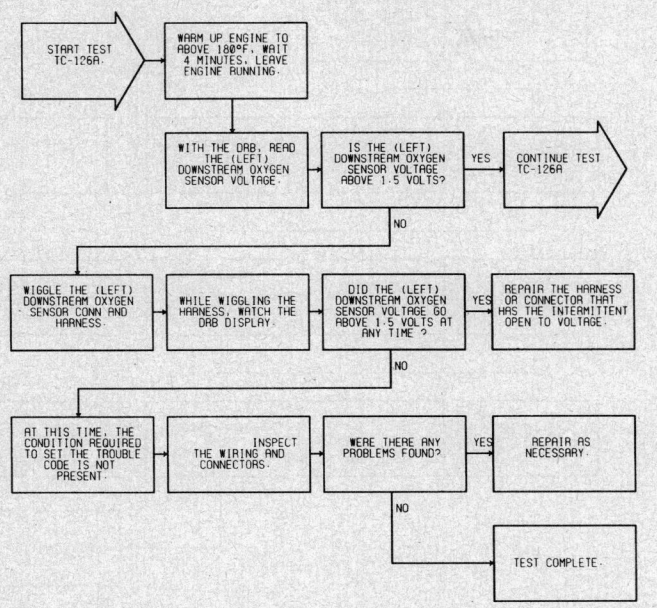

Fig. 119   Test TC-126A: Left Downstream O₂ Sensor
Shorted To Voltage (Part 1 of 2)

CR1029606681010X

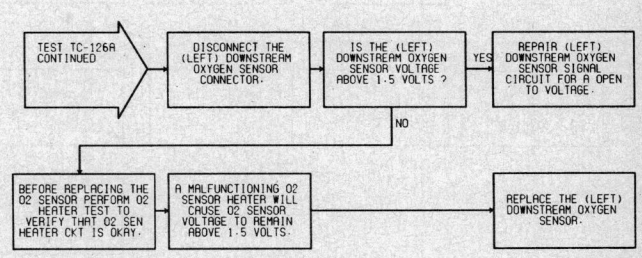

Fig. 119   Test TC-126A: Left Downstream O₂ Sensor
Shorted To Voltage (Part 2 of 2)

CR1029606681020X

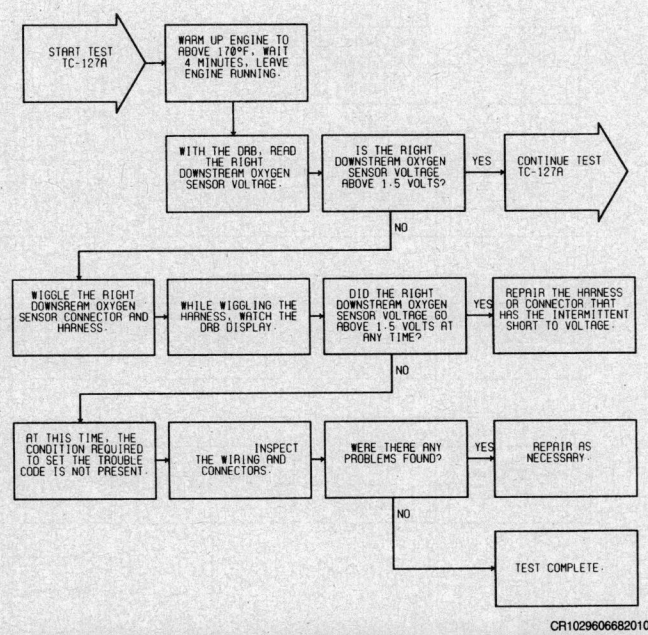

Fig. 120   Test TC-127A: Right Downstream O₂ Sensor
Shorted To Voltage (Part 1 of 2)

CR1029606682010X

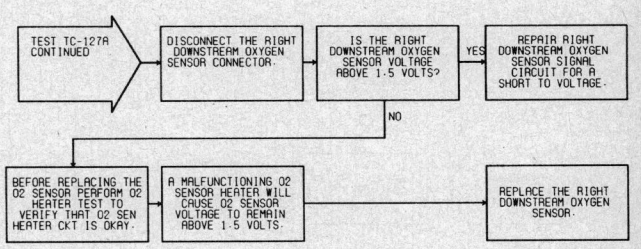

Fig. 120   Test TC-127A: Right Downstream O₂ Sensor
Shorted To Voltage (Part 2 of 2)

CR1029606682020X

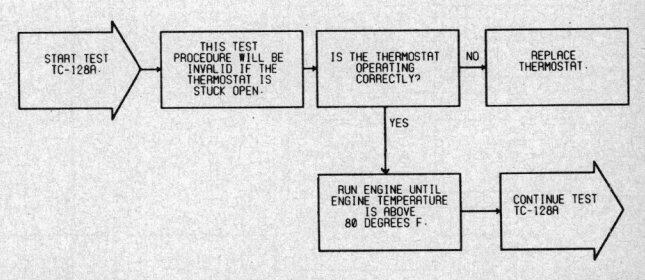

Fig. 121   Test TC-128A: Closed Loop Temperature Not
Reached (Part 1 of 2)

CR1029606683010X

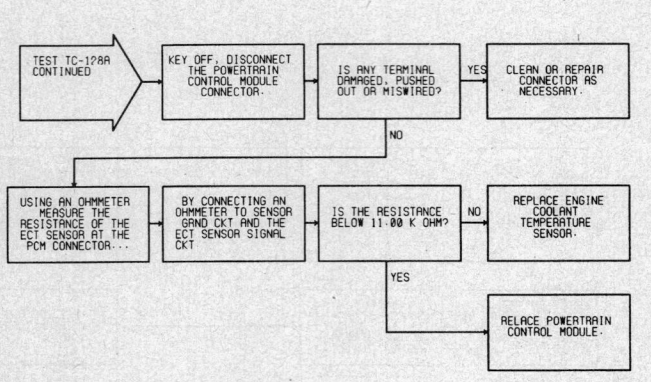

CR1029606683020X

Fig. 121 Test TC-128A: Closed Loop Temperature Not Reached (Part 2 of 2)

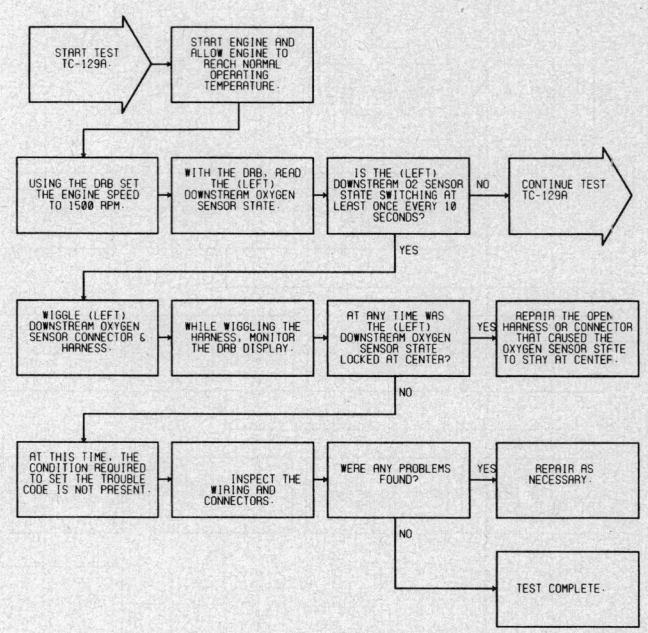

CR1029606684010X

Fig. 122 Test TC-129A: Left Downstream O₂ Sensor Stays At Center (Part 1 of 2)

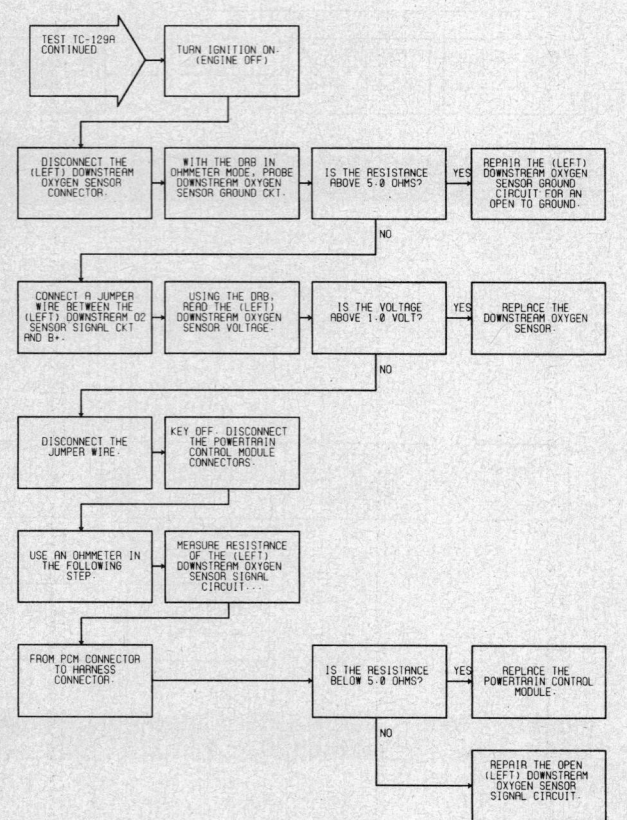

CR1029606684020X

Fig. 122 Test TC-129A: Left Downstream O₂ Sensor Stays At Center (Part 2 of 2)

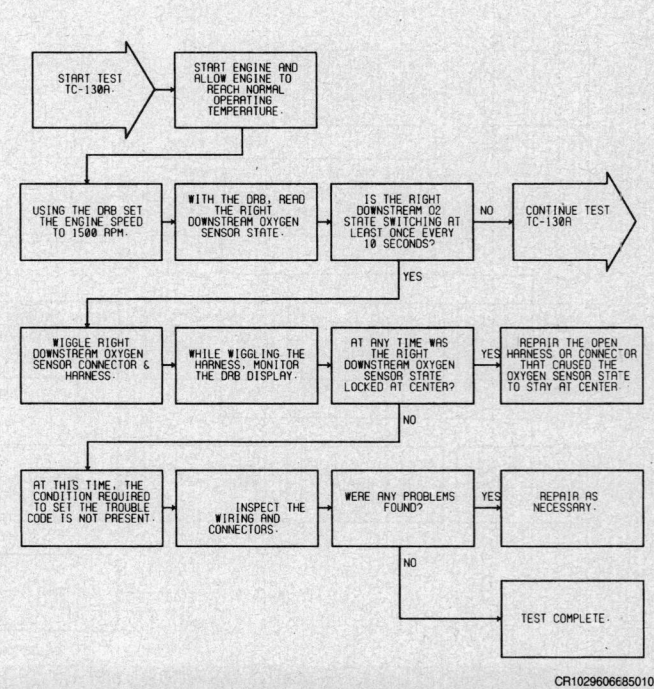

CR1029606685010X

Fig. 123 Test TC-130A: Right Downstream O₂ Sensor Stays At Center (Part 1 of 2)

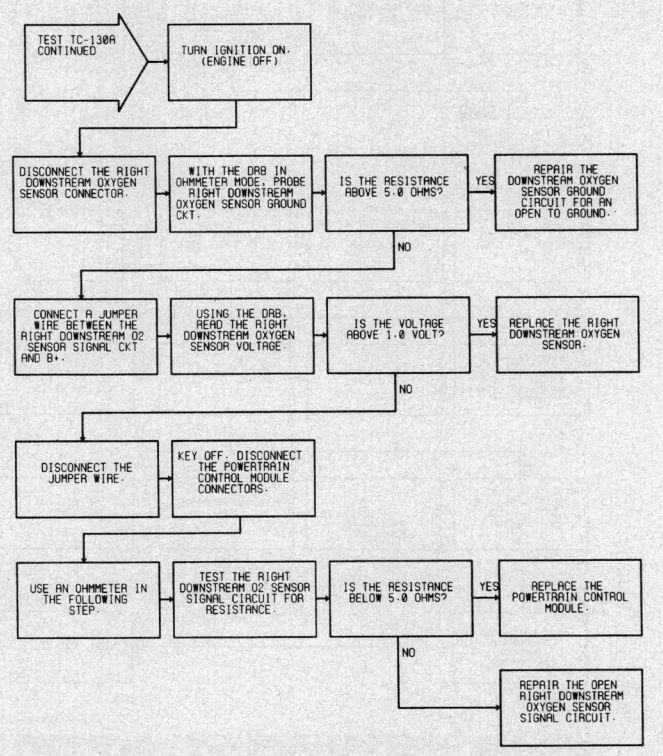

Fig. 123 Test TC-130A: Right Downstream O₂ Sensor Stays At Center (Part 2 of 2)

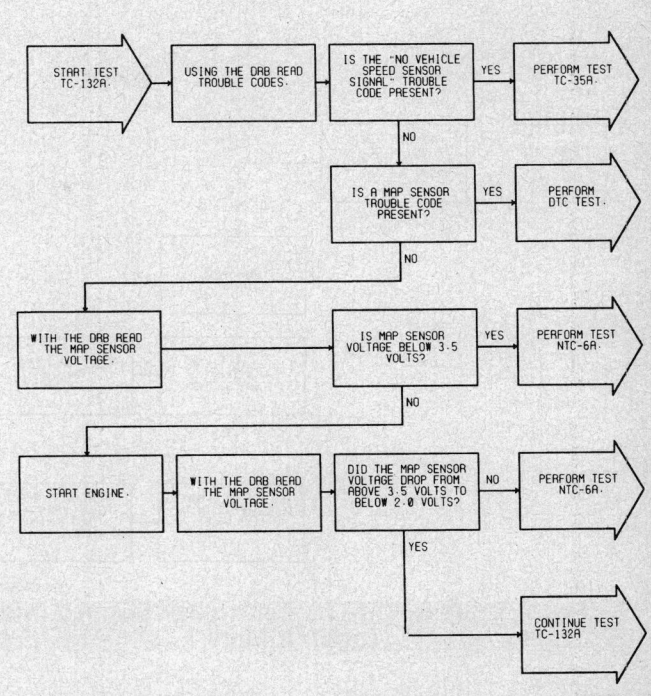

Fig. 124 Test TC-132A: TPS Voltage Does Not Agree w/MAP (Part 1 of 3)

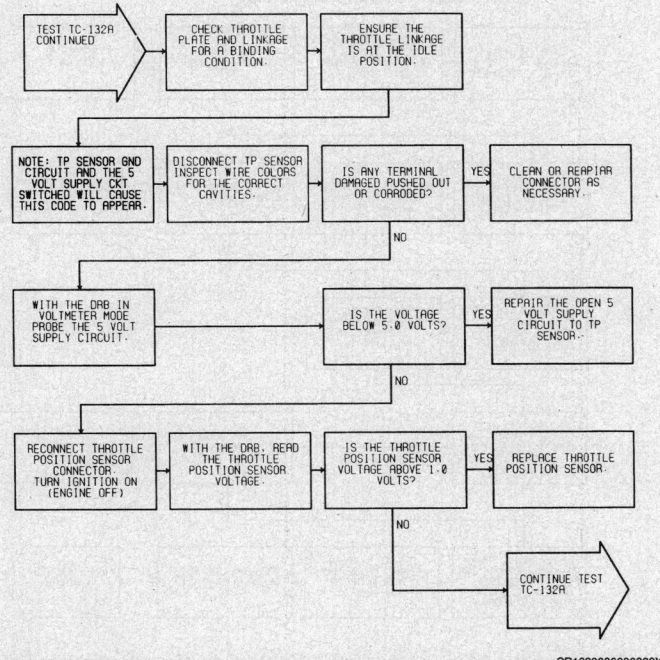

Fig. 124 Test TC-132A: TPS Voltage Does Not Agree w/MAP (Part 2 of 3)

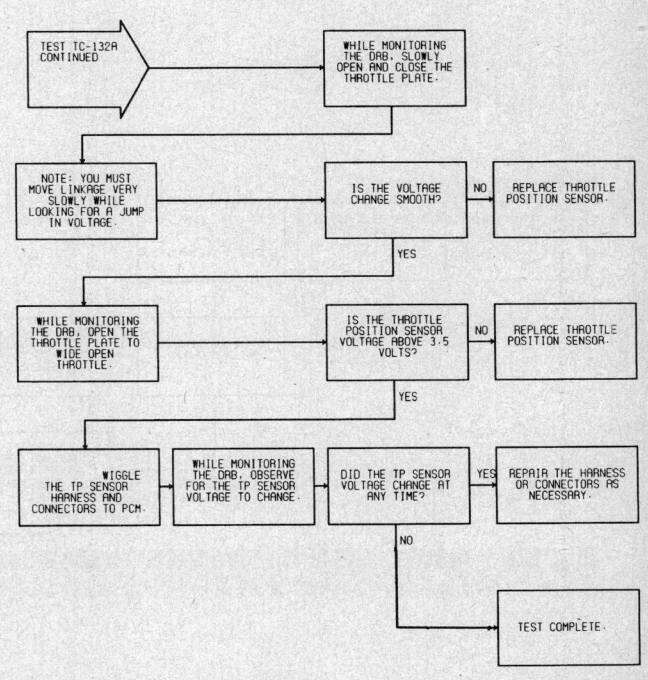

Fig. 124 Test TC-132A: TPS Voltage Does Not Agree w/MAP (Part 3 of 3)

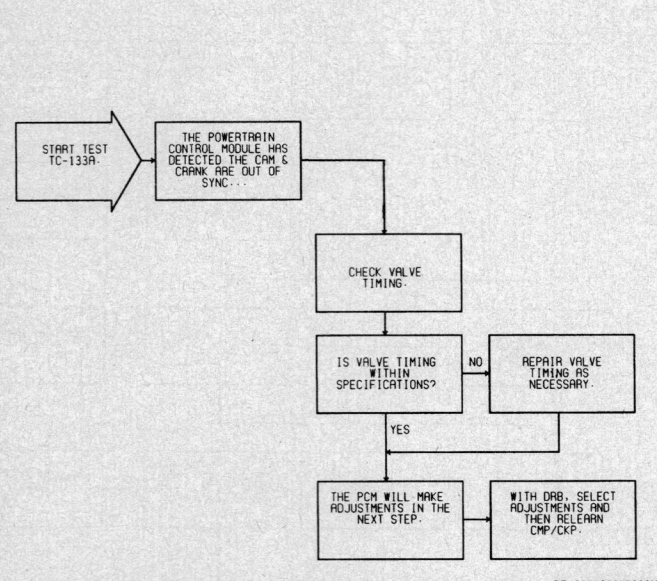

Fig. 125   Test TC-133A: Timing Belt Skipped One Tooth Or More

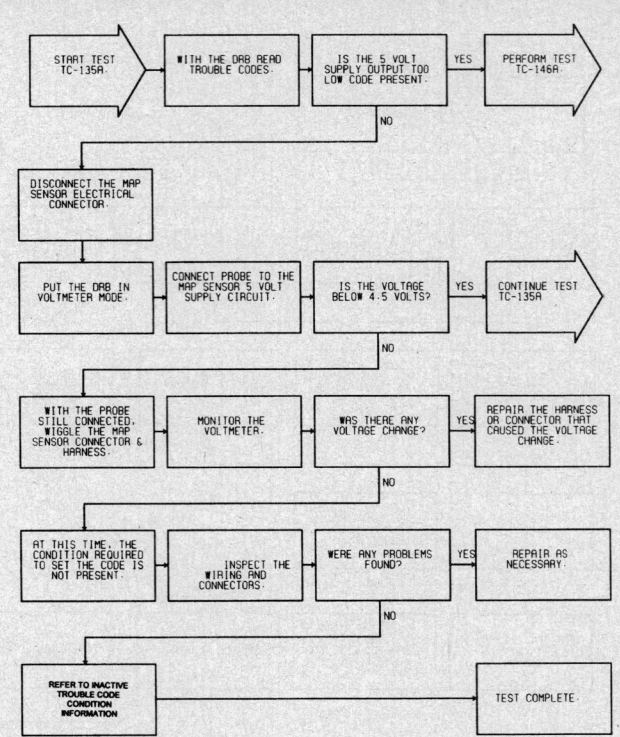

Fig. 126   Test TC-135A: No Five Volts To MAP Sensor (Part 1 of 2)

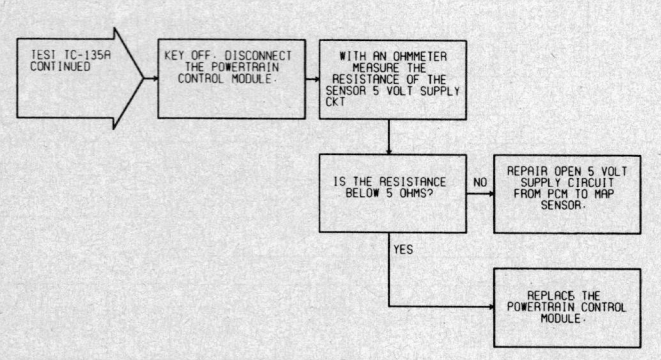

Fig. 126   Test TC-135A: No Five Volts To MAP Sensor (Part 2 of 2)

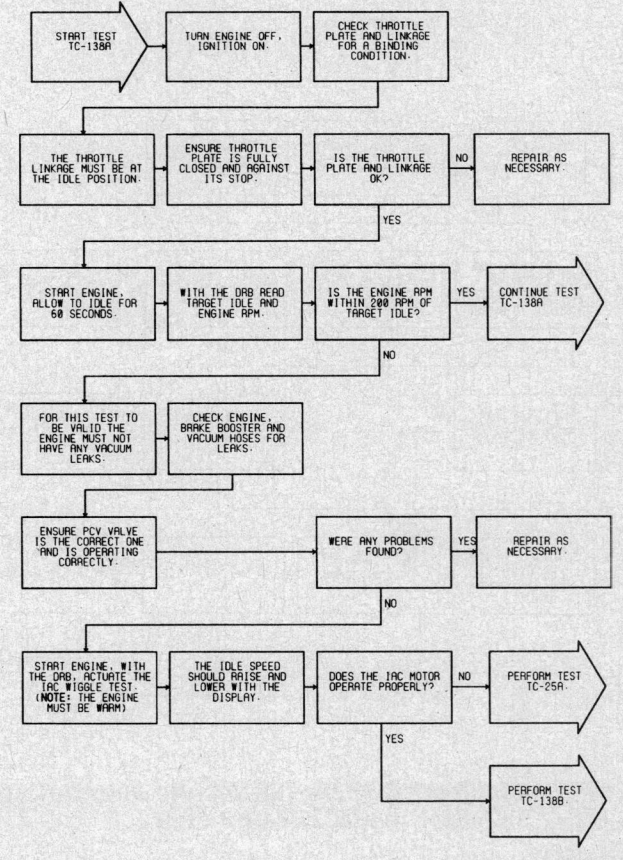

Fig. 127   Test TC-138A: Target Idle Not Reached (Part 1 of 2)

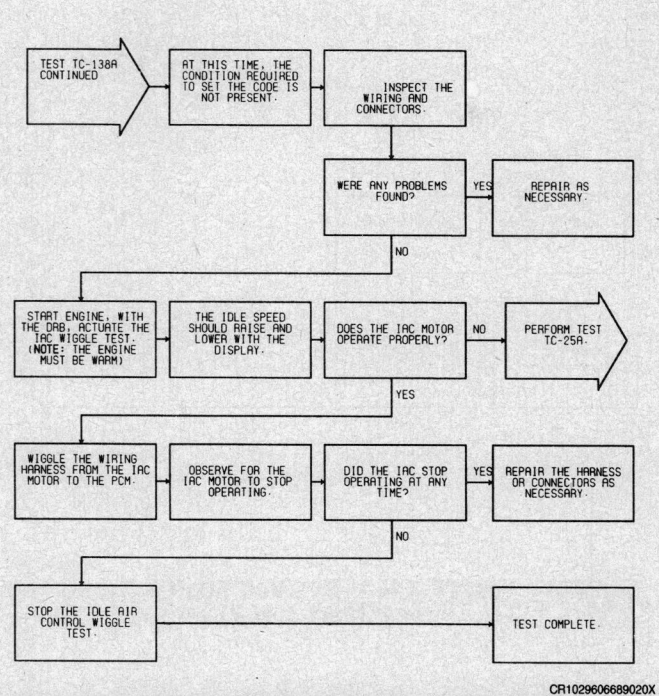

Fig. 127   Test TC-138A: Target Idle Not Reached (Part 2 of 2)

CR1029606689020X

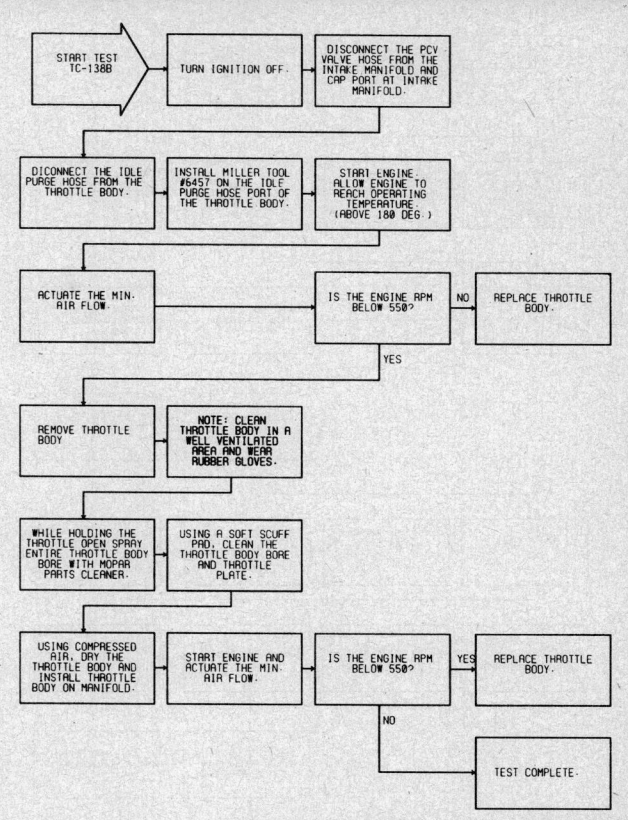

Fig. 128   Test TC-138B: Target Idle Not Reached

CR1029606703000X

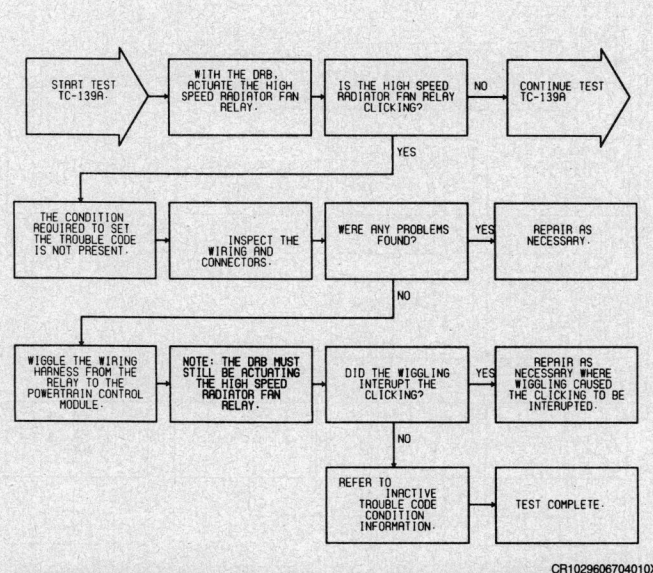

Fig. 129   Test TC-139A: High Speed Radiator Fan Control Relay Circuit (Part 1 of 2)

CR1029606704010X

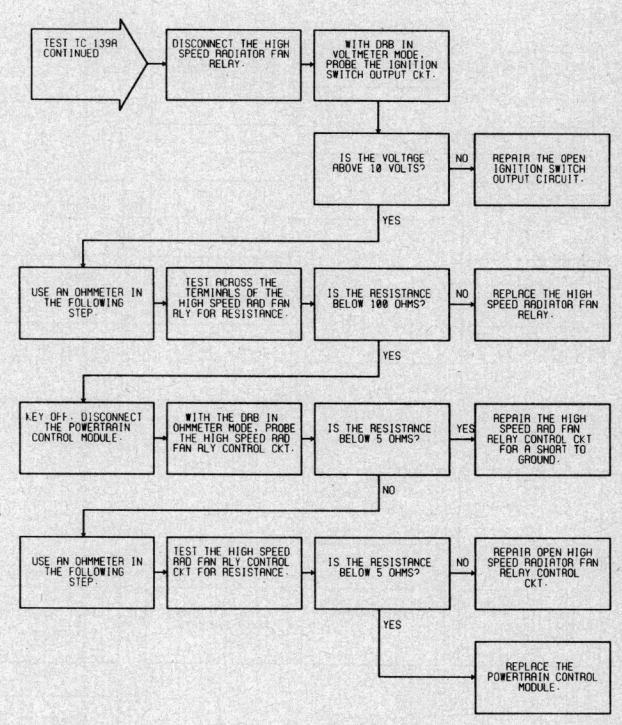

Fig. 129   Test TC-139A: High Speed Radiator Fan Control Relay Circuit (Part 2 of 2)

CR1029606704020X

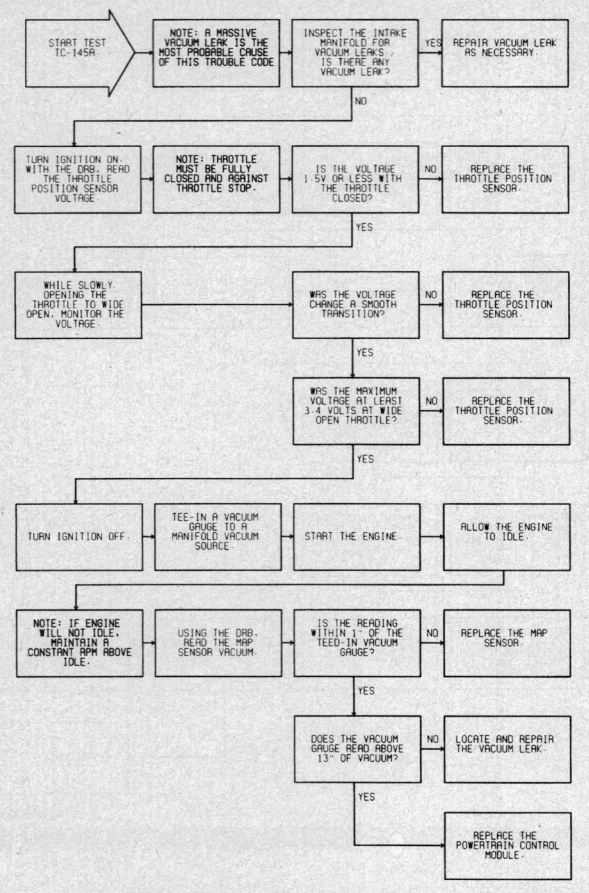

Fig. 130   Test TC-145A: Vacuum Leak Found, IAC Fully Seated

CR1029606705000X

Fig. 131   Test TC-146A: Five Volt Supply Output Too Low (Part 1 of 2)

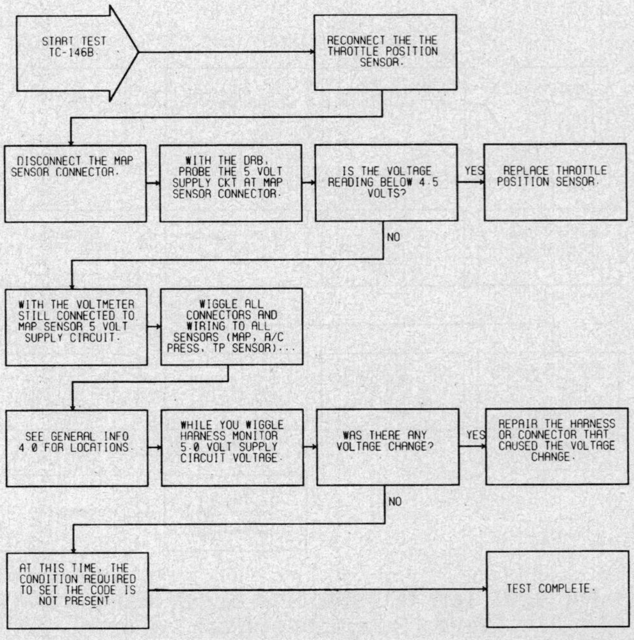

CR1029606706010X

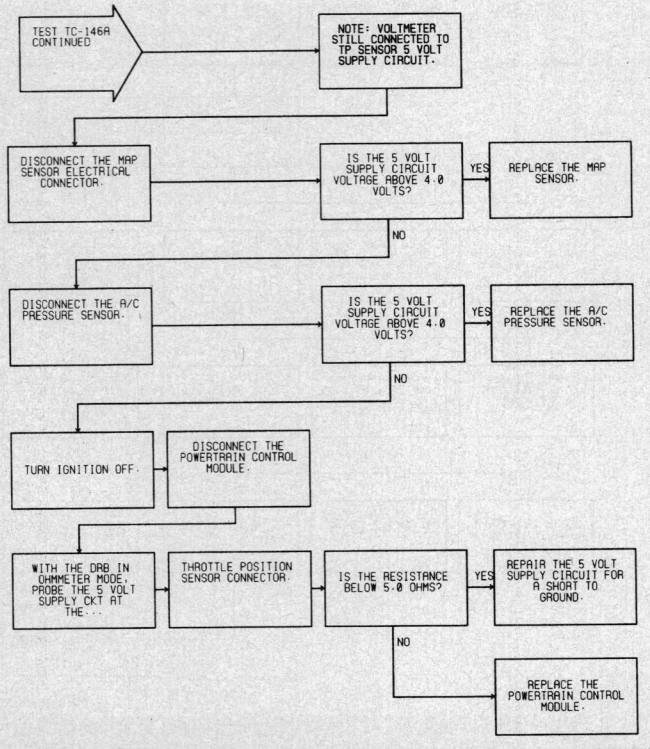

CR1029606706020X

Fig. 131   Test TC-146A: Five Volt Supply Output Too Low (Part 2 of 2)

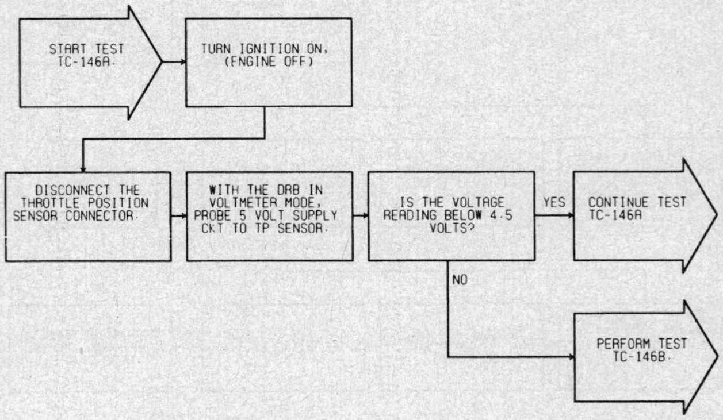

CR1029606707000X

Fig. 132   Test TC-146B: Five Volt Supply Output Too Low

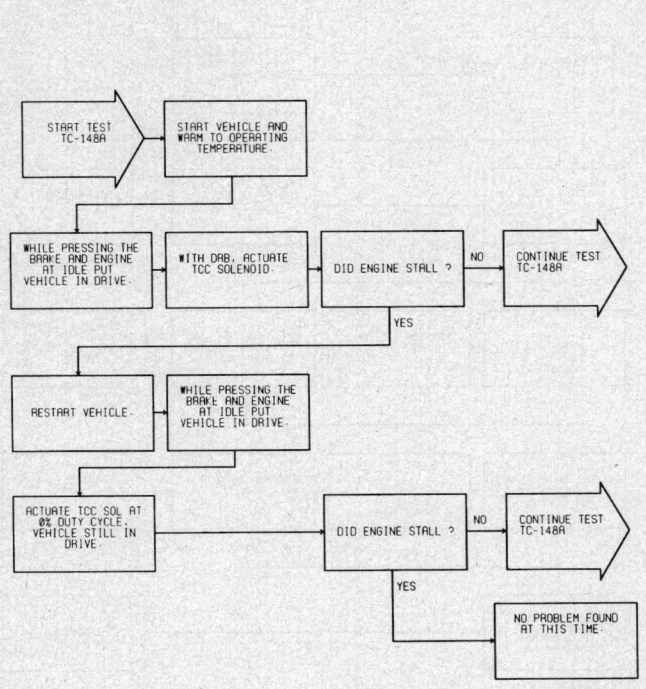

Fig. 133   Test TC-148A: Torque Converter Clutch, No RPM Drop Lockup (Part 1 of 3). Neon

CR1029606708010X

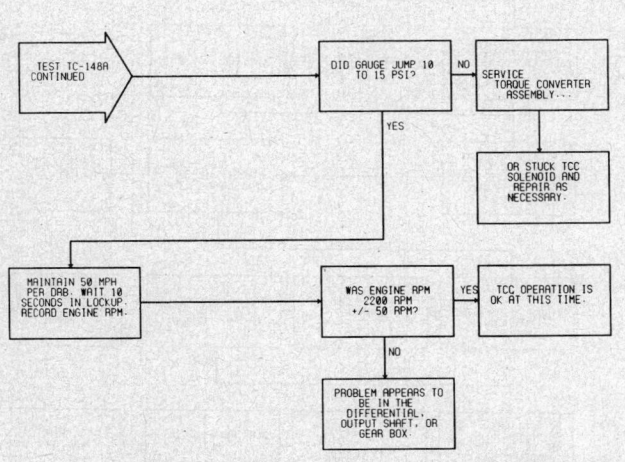

Fig. 133   Test TC-148A: Torque Converter Clutch, No RPM Drop Lockup (Part 3 of 3). Neon

CR1029606708030X

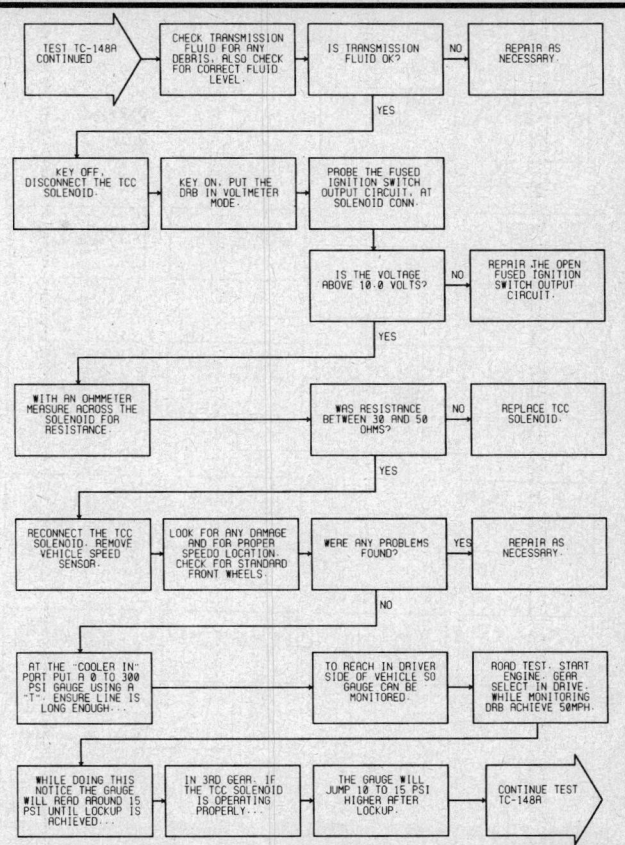

Fig. 133   Test TC-148A: Torque Converter Clutch, No RPM Drop Lockup (Part 2 of 3). Neon

CR1029606708020X

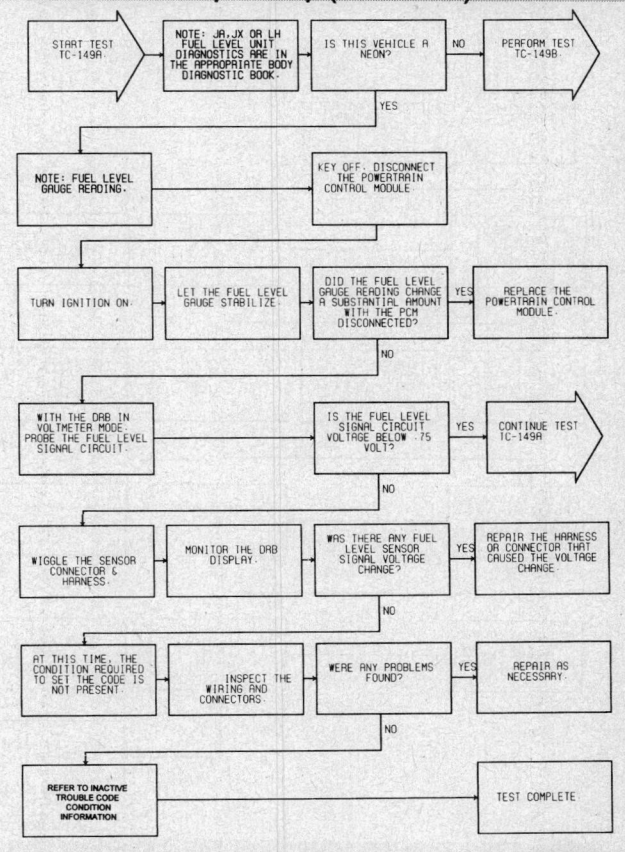

Fig. 134   Test TC-149A: Fuel Level Sending Unit Voltage Too Low (Part 1 of 2)

CR1029606709010X

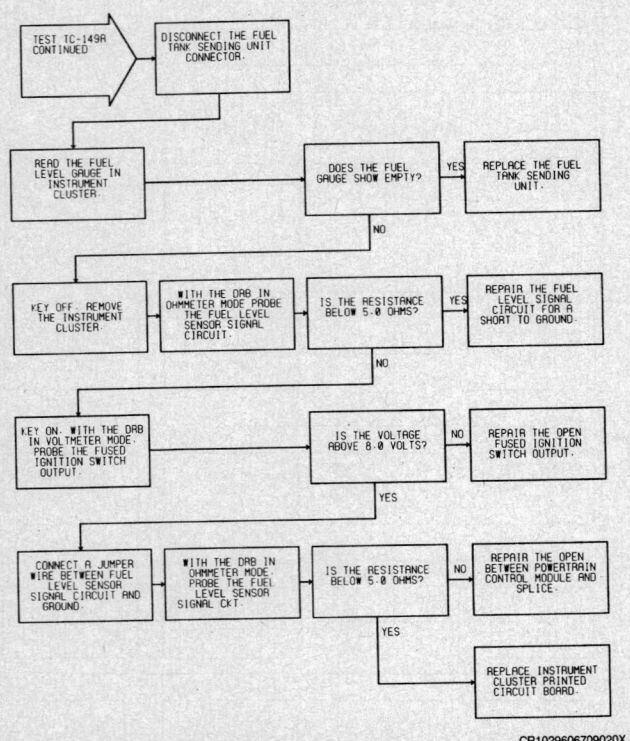

Fig. 134 Test TC-149A: Fuel Level Sending Unit Voltage Too Low (Part 2 of 2)

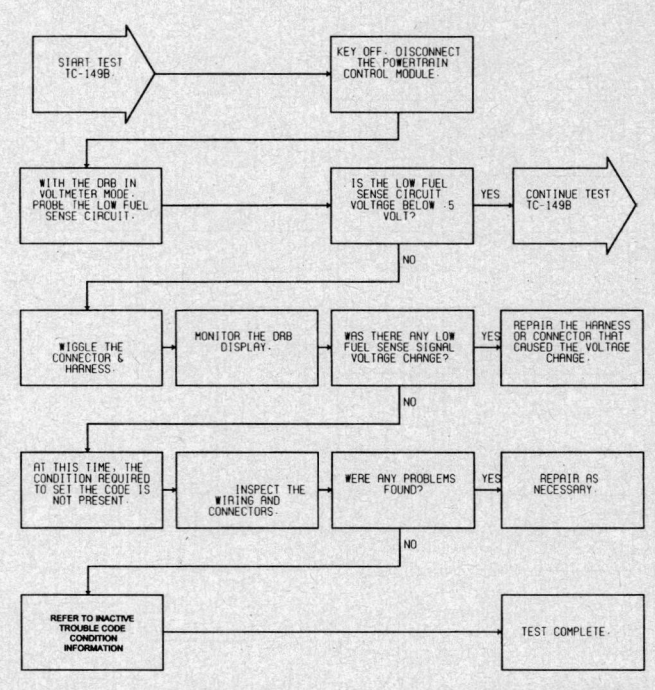

Fig. 135 Test TC-149B: Fuel Level Sending Unit Voltage Too Low (Part 1 of 2)

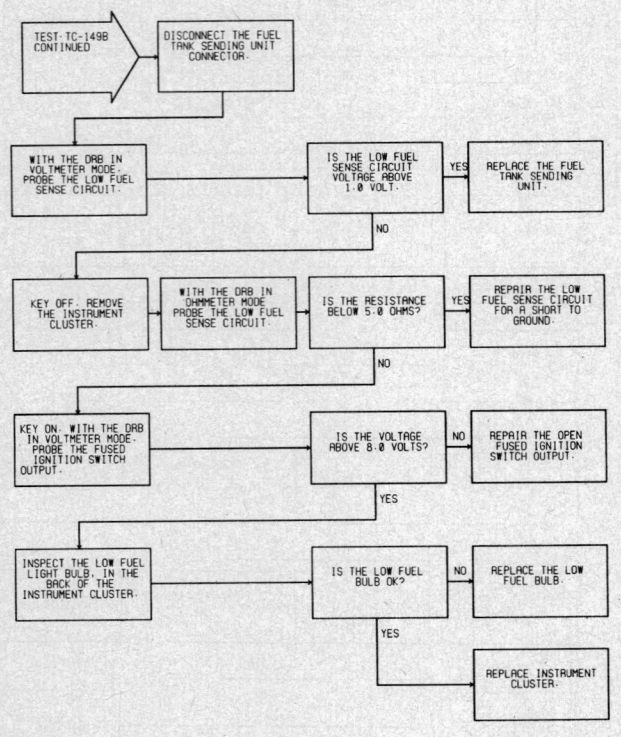

Fig. 135 Test TC-149B: Fuel Level Sending Unit Voltage Too Low (Part 2 of 2)

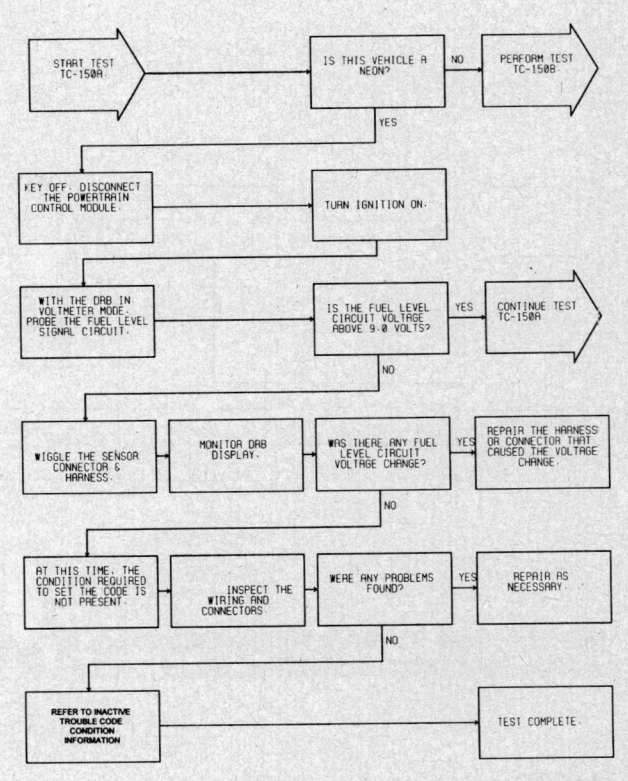

Fig. 136 Test TC-150A: Fuel Level Sending Unit Voltage Too High (Part 1 of 2)

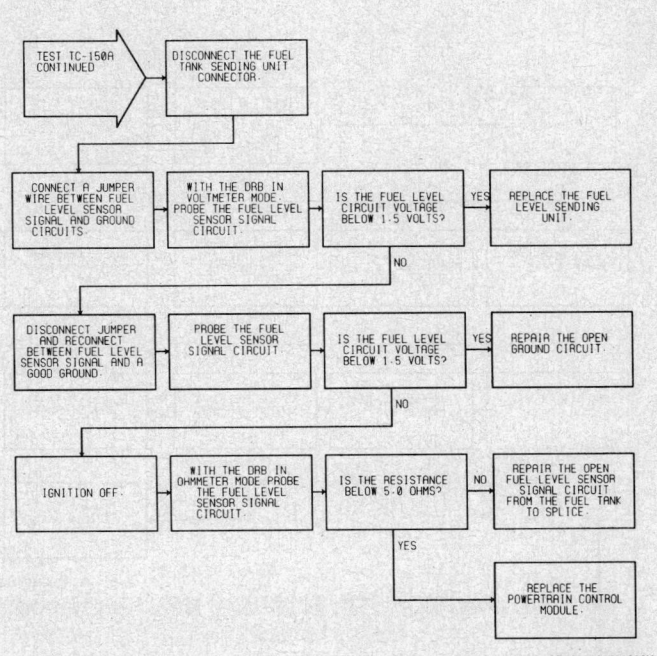

Fig. 136   Test TC-150A: Fuel Level Sending Unit Voltage Too High (Part 2 of 2)

CR1029606711020X

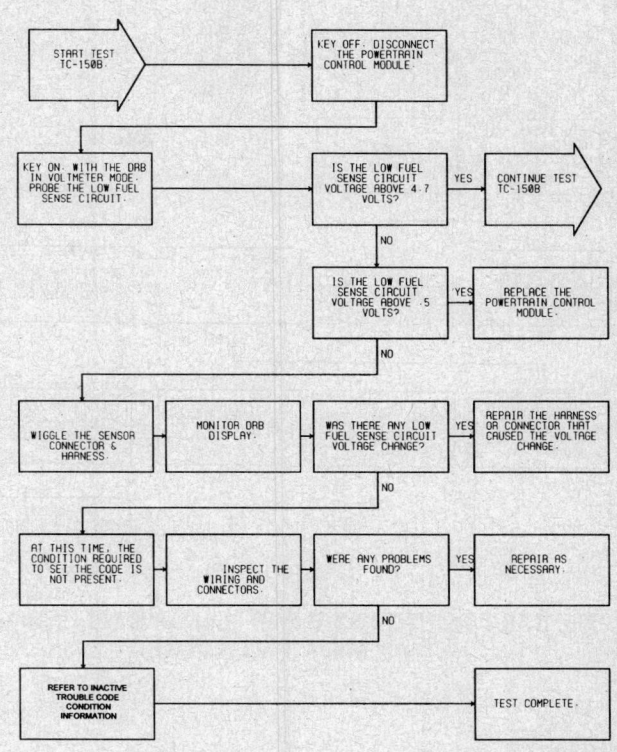

Fig. 137   Test TC-150B: Fuel Level Sending Unit Voltage Too High (Part 1 of 2)

CR1029606712010X

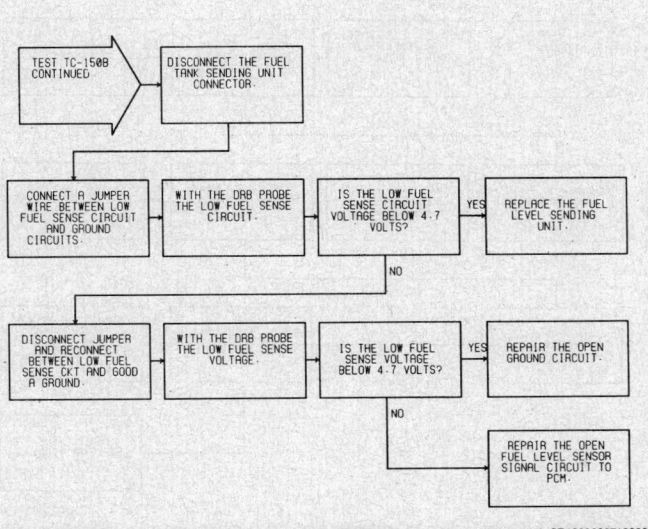

Fig. 137   Test TC-150B: Fuel Level Sending Unit Voltage Too High (Part 2 of 2)

CR1029606712020X

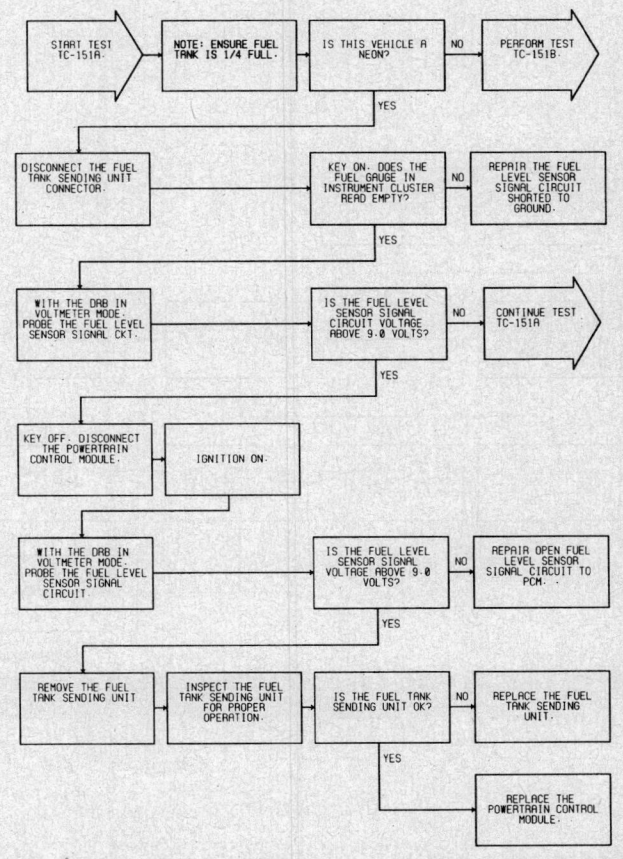

Fig. 138   Test TC-151A: Fuel Level Unit No Change Over Miles (Part 1 of 2)

CR1029606713010X

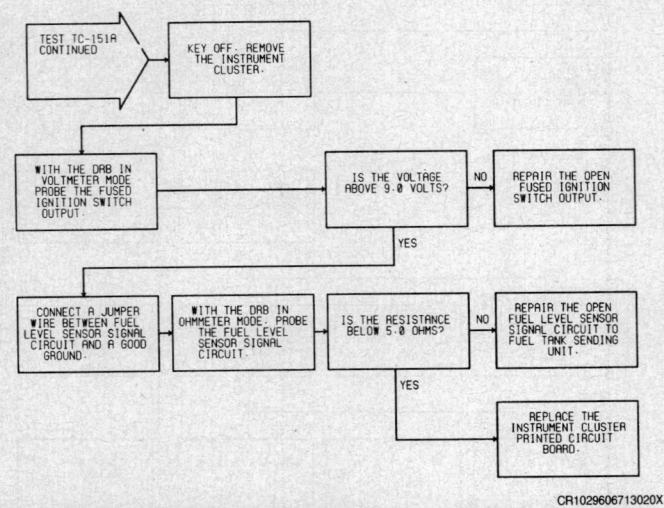

Fig. 138   Test TC-151A: Fuel Level Unit No Change Over Miles (Part 2 of 2)

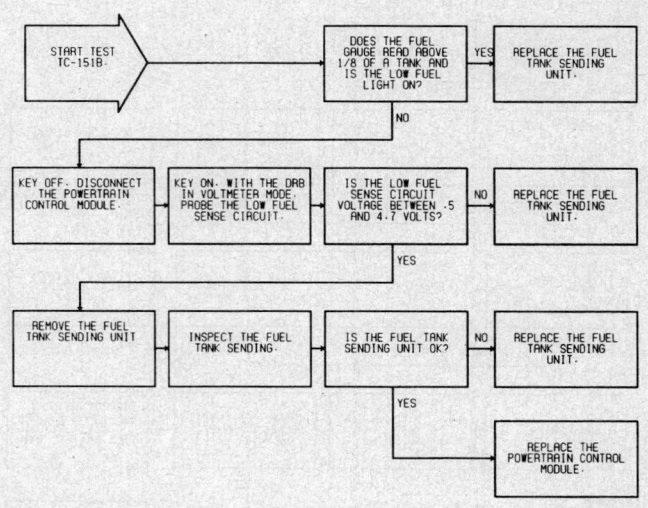

Fig. 139   Test TC-151B: Fuel Level Unit No Change Over Miles

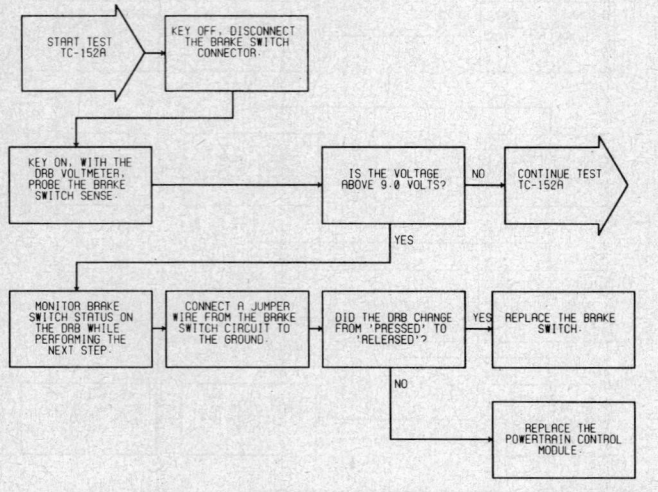

Fig. 140   Test TC-152A: Brake Switch Sense Circuit (Part 1 of 2)

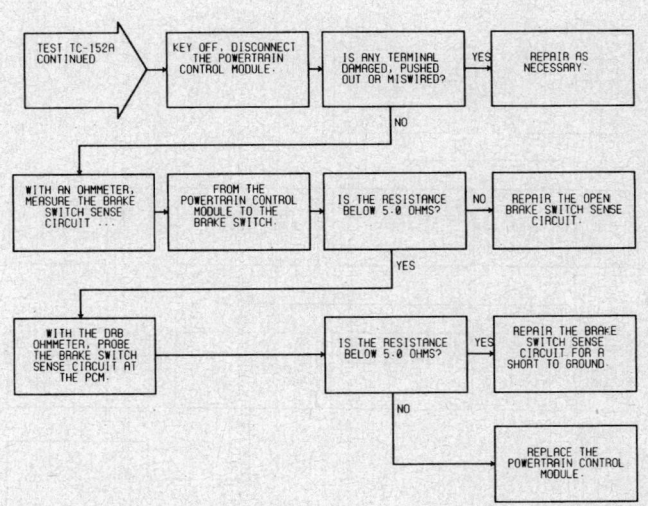

Fig. 140   Test TC-152A: Brake Switch Sense Circuit (Part 2 of 2)

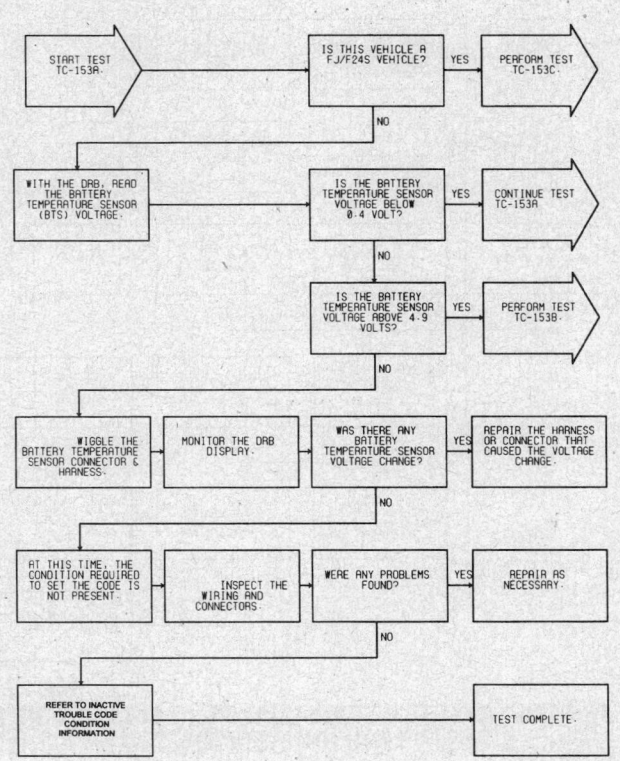

Fig. 141   Test TC-153A: Battery Temperature Sensor Voltage Too Low Or High (Part 1 of 2)

CR1029606716010X

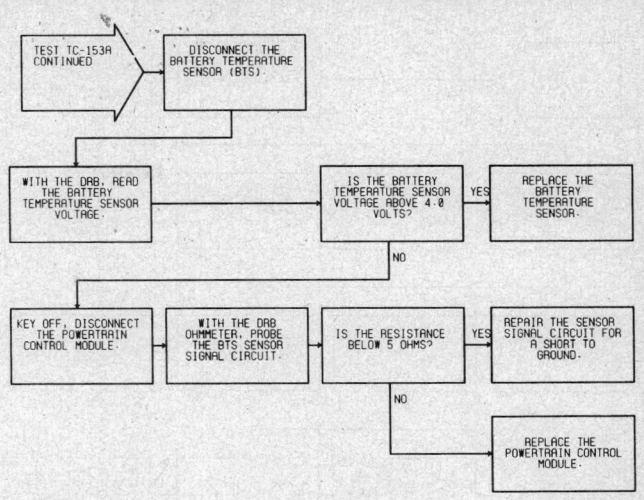

Fig. 141   Test TC-153A: Battery Temperature Sensor Voltage Too Low Or High (Part 2 of 2)

CR1029606716020X

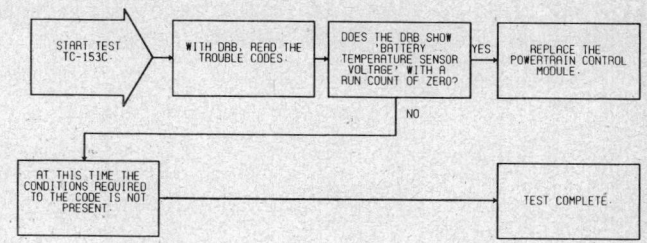

Fig. 143   Test TC-153C: Battery Temperature Sensor Voltage Too Low Or High

CR1029606718000X

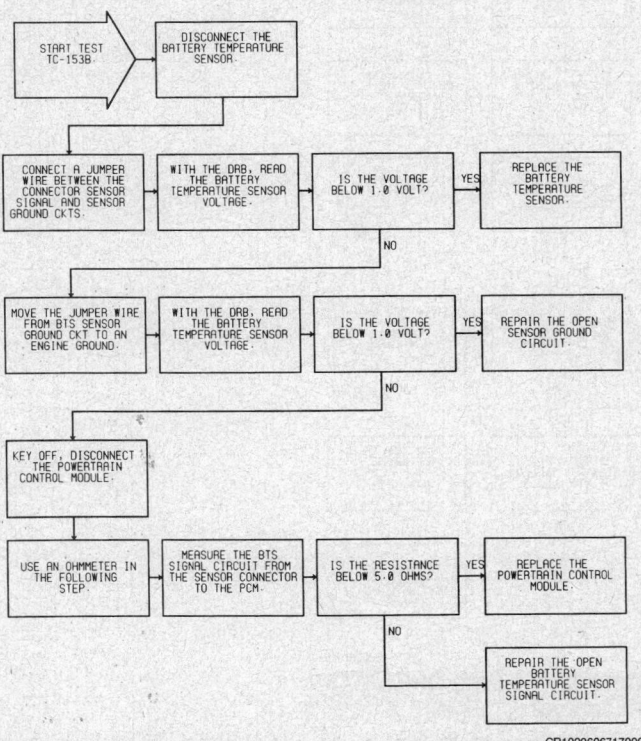

Fig. 142   Test TC-153B: Battery Temperature Sensor Voltage Too Low Or High

CR1029606717000X

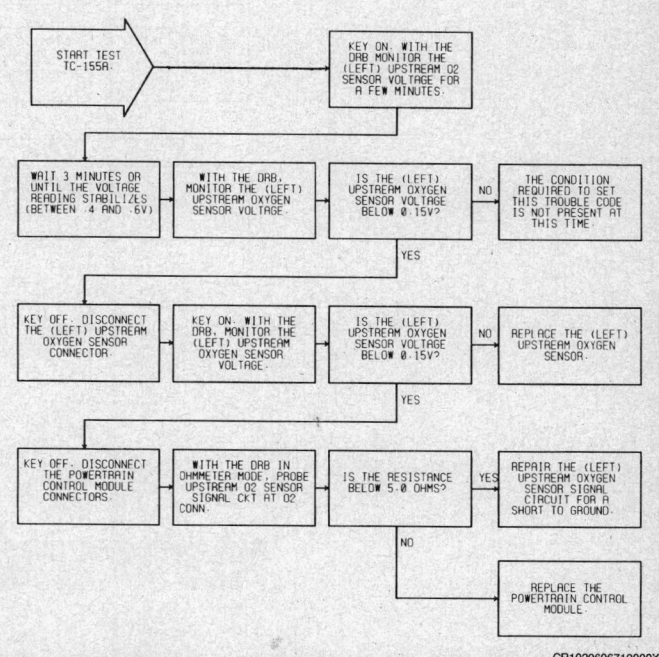

Fig. 144   Test TC-155A: Left Upstream O2S Voltage Shorted To Ground

CR1029606719000X

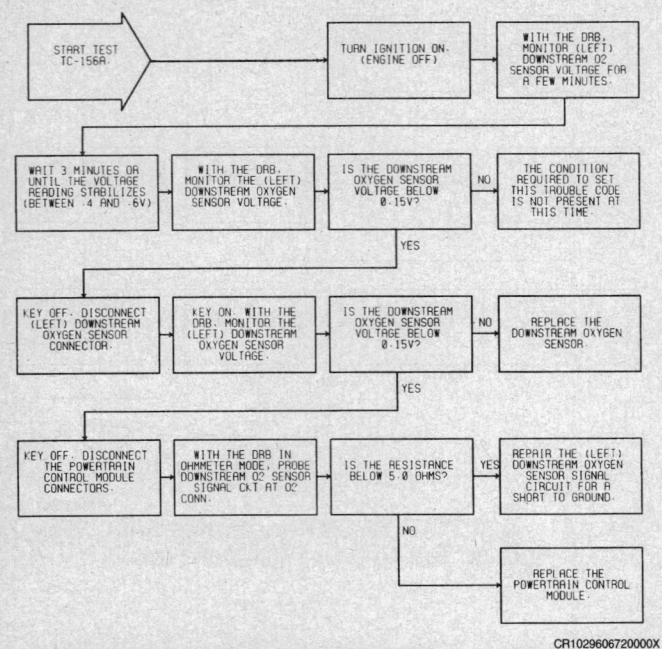

Fig. 145 Test TC-156A: Left Downstream O₂S Voltage Shorted To Ground

CR1029606720000X

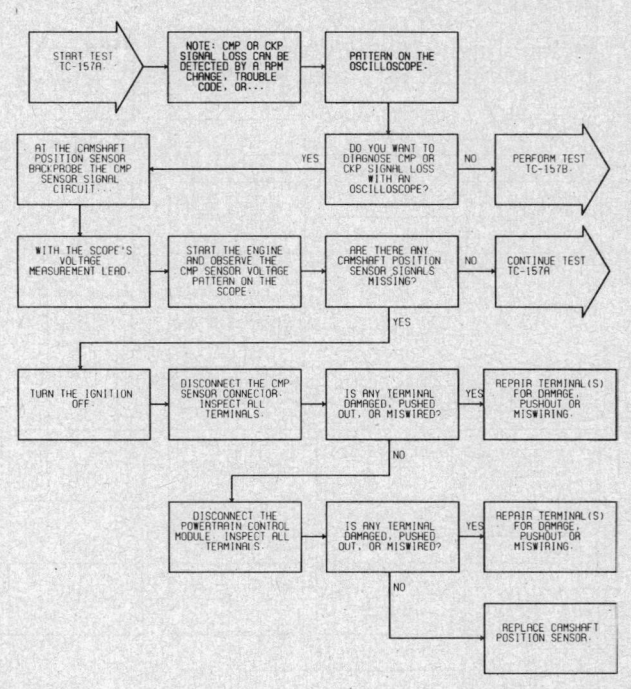

CR1029606721010X

Fig. 146 Test TC-157A: Intermittent Loss Of CMP Or CKP (Part 1 of 3)

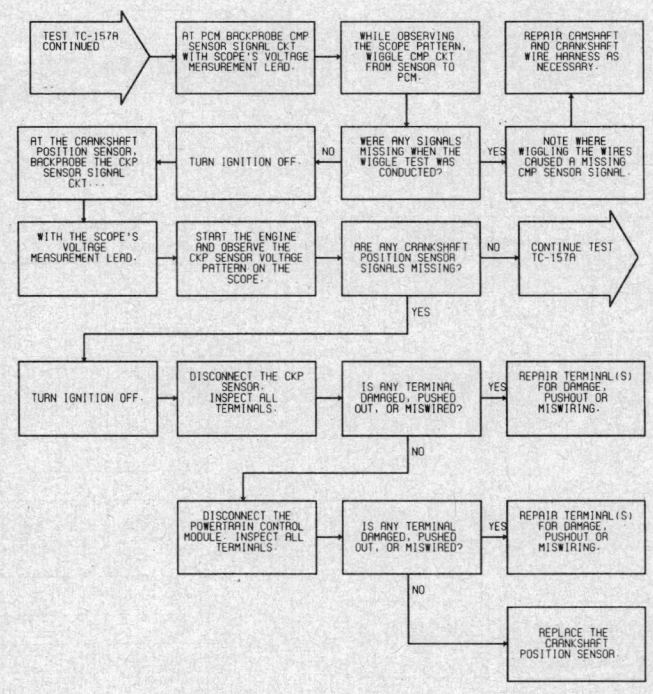

CR1029606721020X

Fig. 146 Test TC-157A: Intermittent Loss Of CMP Or CKP (Part 2 of 3)

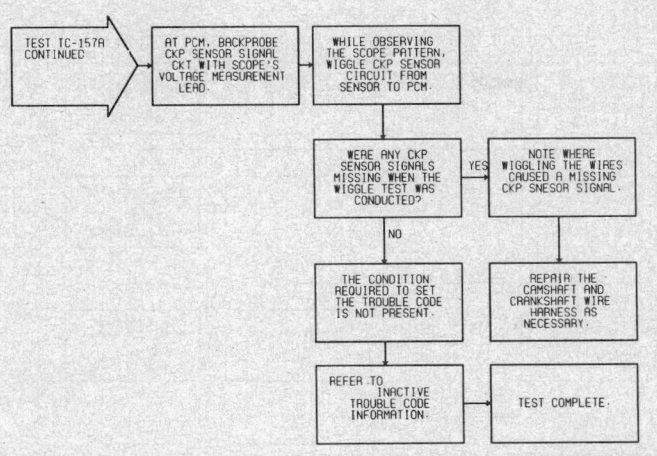

Fig. 146 Test TC-157A: Intermittent Loss Of CMP Or CKP (Part 3 of 3)

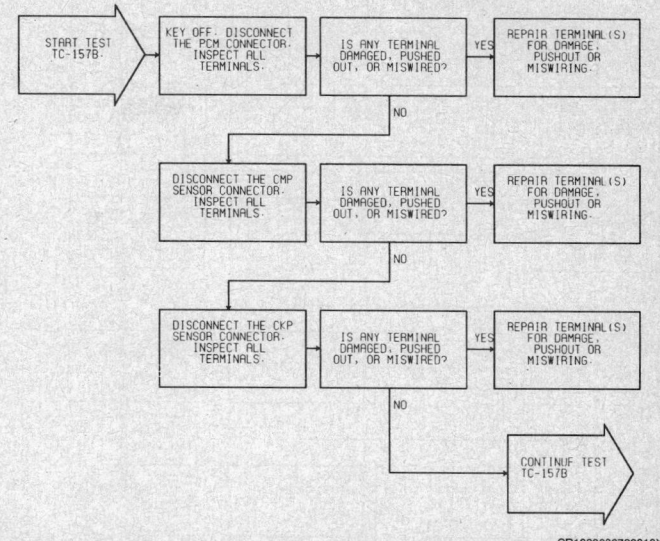

Fig. 147 Test TC-157B: Intermittent Loss Of CMP Or CKP (Part 1 of 2)

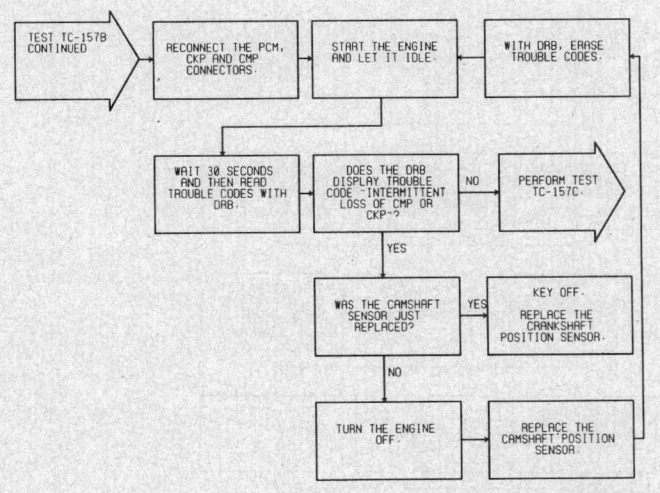

Fig. 147 Test TC-157B: Intermittent Loss Of CMP Or CKP (Part 2 of 2)

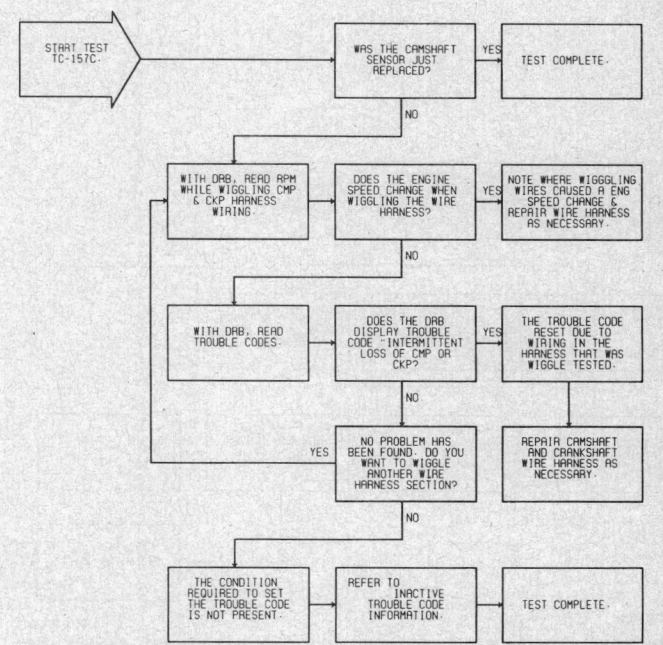

Fig. 148 Test TC-157C: Intermittent Loss Of CMP Or CKP

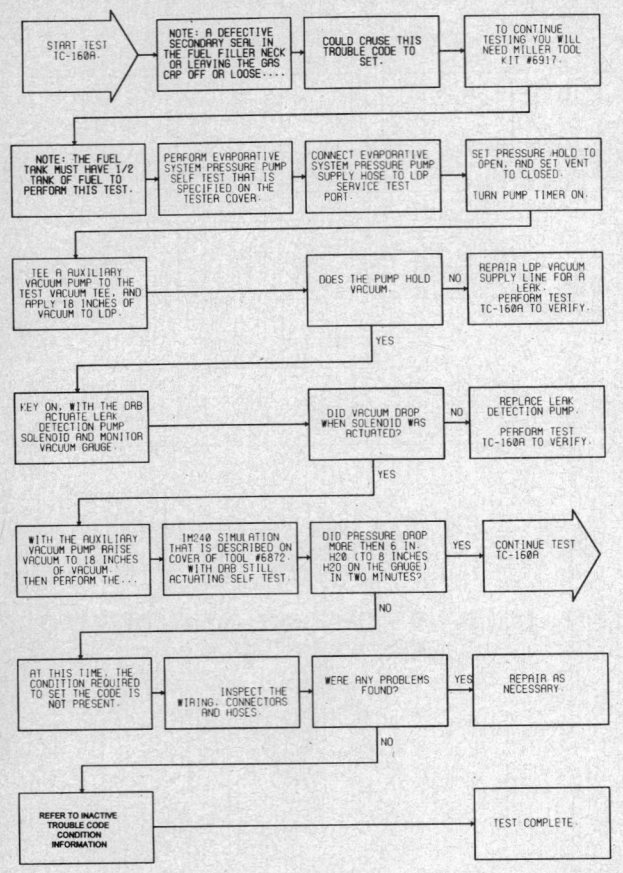

Fig. 149   Test TC-160A: EVAP Leak Monitor Small Leak Detected (Part 1 of 2)

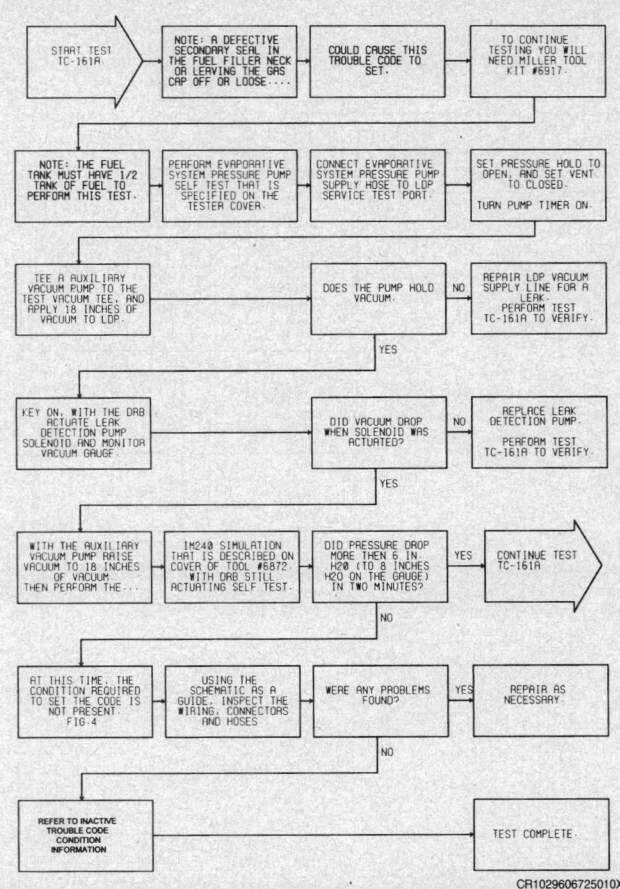

Fig. 150   Test TC-161A: EVAP Leak Monitor Large Leak Detected (Part 1 of 2)

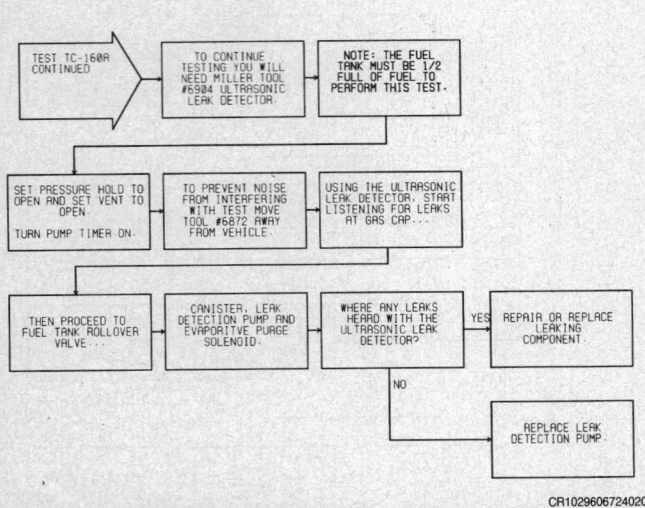

Fig. 149   Test TC-160A: EVAP Leak Monitor Small Leak Detected (Part 2 of 2)

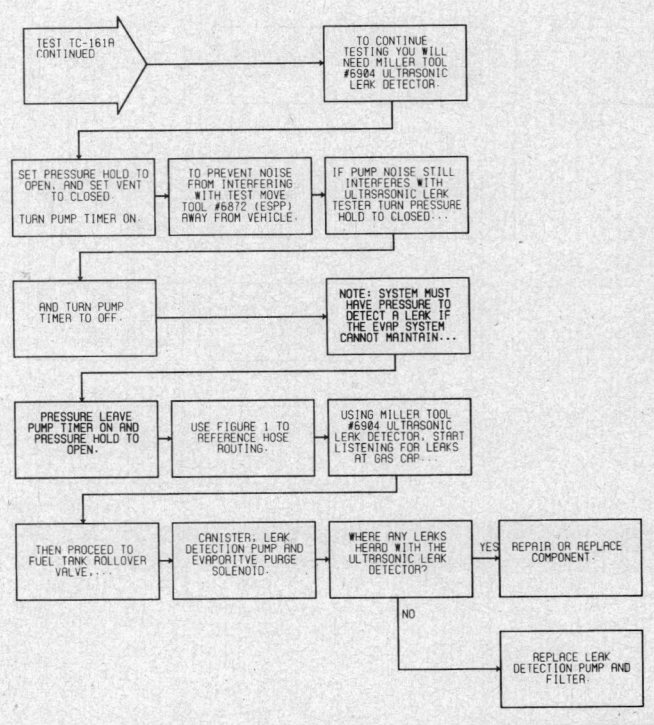

Fig. 150   Test TC-161A: EVAP Leak Monitor Large Leak Detected (Part 2 of 2)

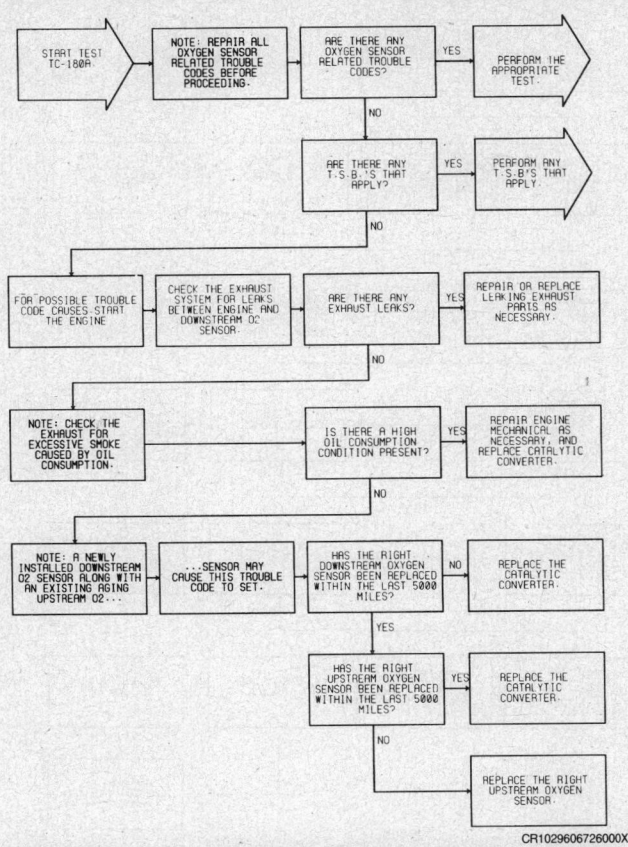

Fig. 151   Test TC-180A: Right Catalytic Converter Efficiency Failure

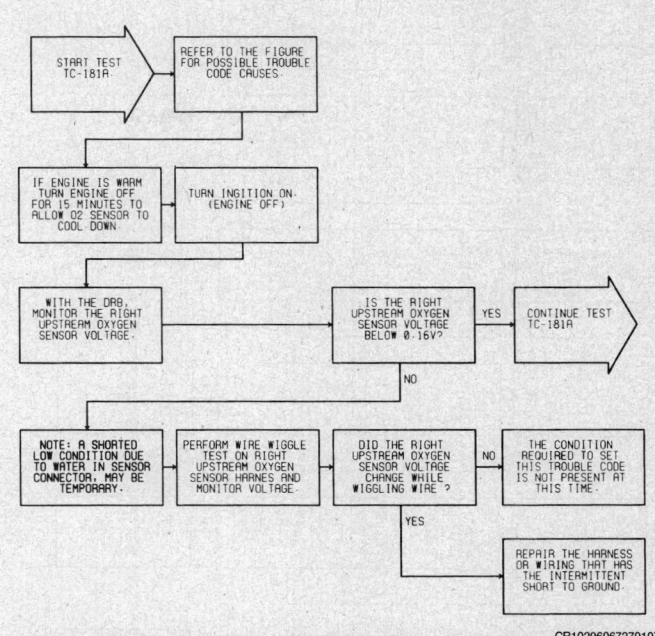

Fig. 152   Test TC-181A: Right Upstream O₂ Sensor Shorted To Ground (Part 1 of 2)

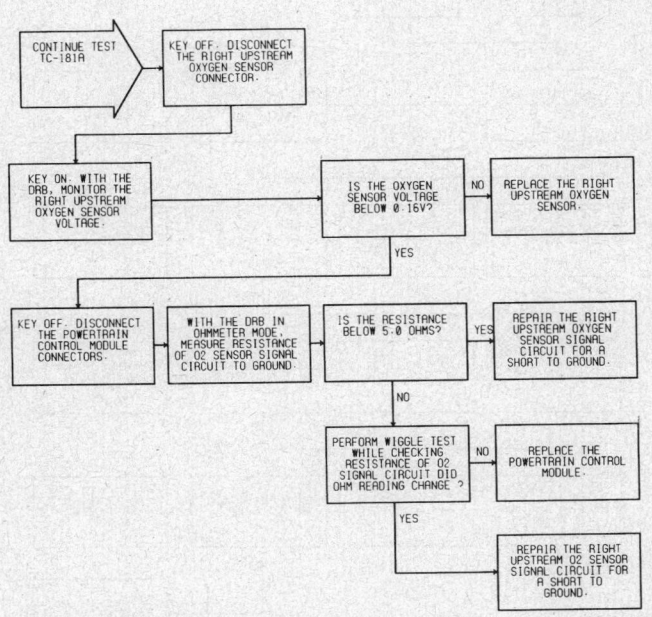

Fig. 152   Test TC-181A: Right Upstream O₂ Sensor Shorted To Ground (Part 2 of 2)

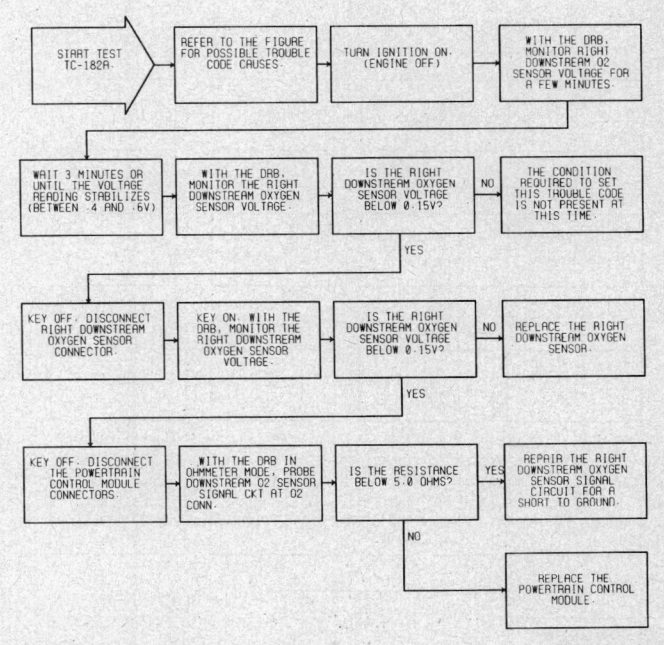

Fig. 153   Test TC-182A: Right/Downstream Shorted To Ground

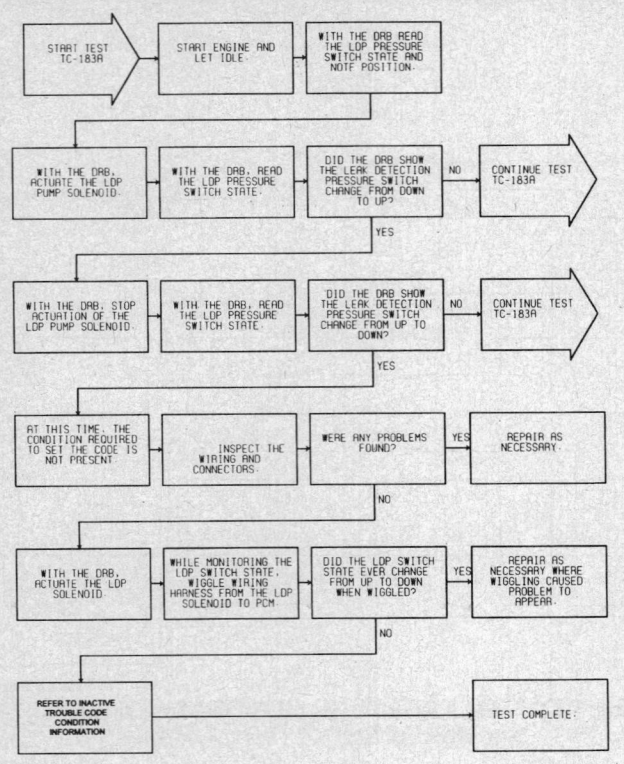

Fig. 154   Test TC-183A: Leak Detection Pump Solenoid Circuit (Part 1 of 2)

CR1029606729010X

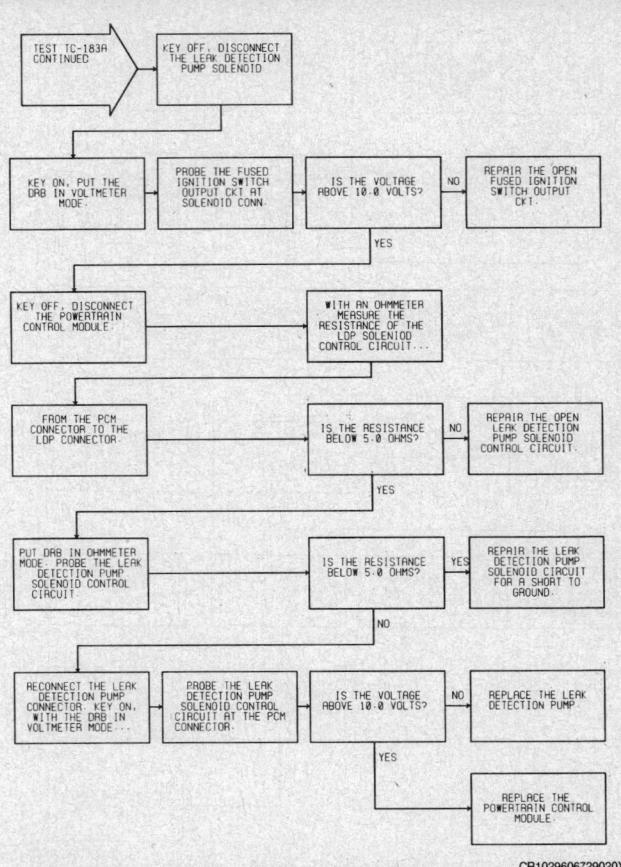

Fig. 154   Test TC-183A: Leak Detection Pump Solenoid Circuit (Part 2 of 2)

CR1029606729020X

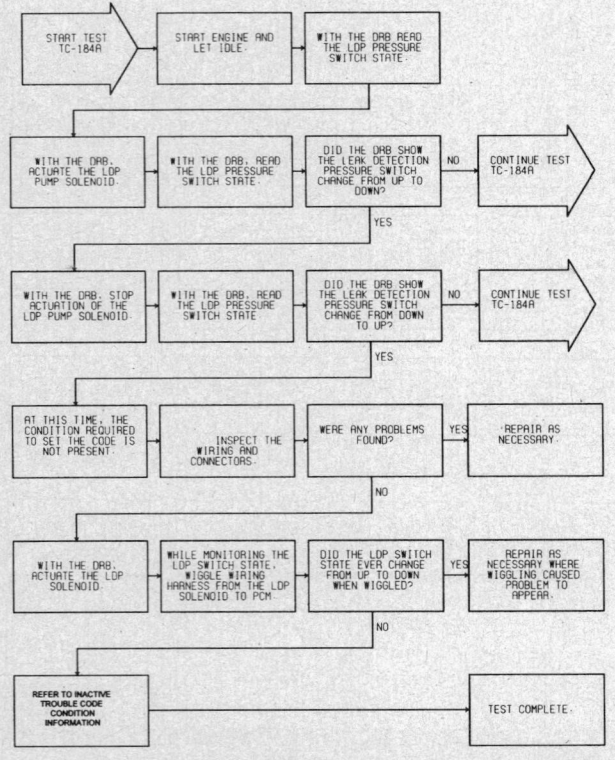

Fig. 155   Test TC-184A: Leak Detection Pump Switch Or Mechanical Fault (Part 1 of 2)

CR1029606730010X

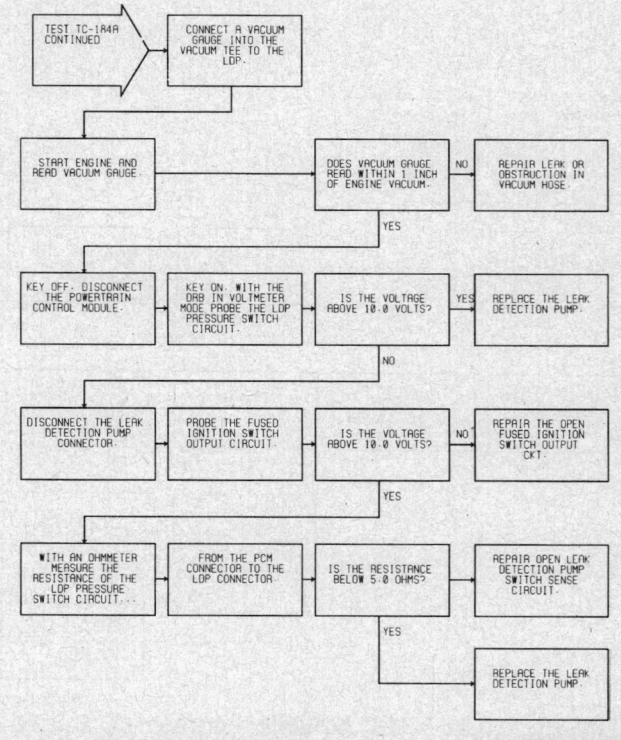

Fig. 155   Test TC-184A: Leak Detection Pump Switch Or Mechanical Fault (Part 2 of 2)

CR1029606730020X

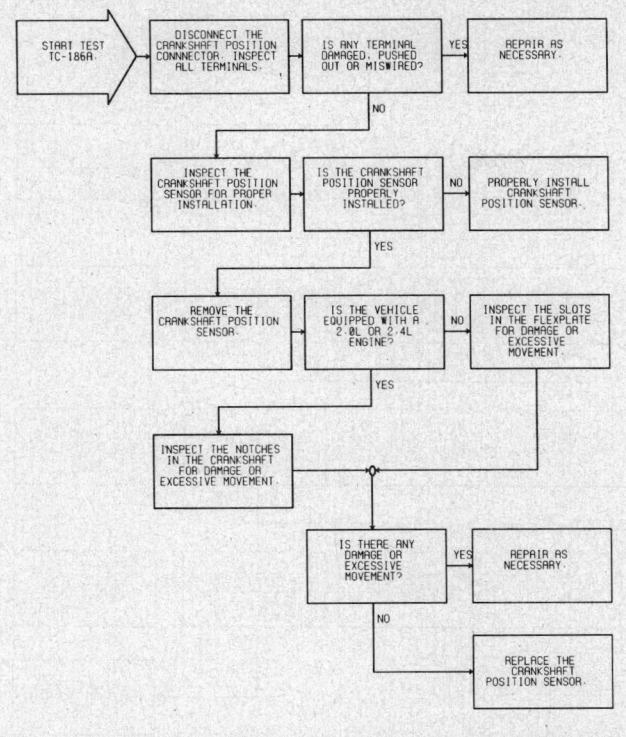

Fig. 156 Test TC-186A: Misfire Adaptive Numerator At Limit

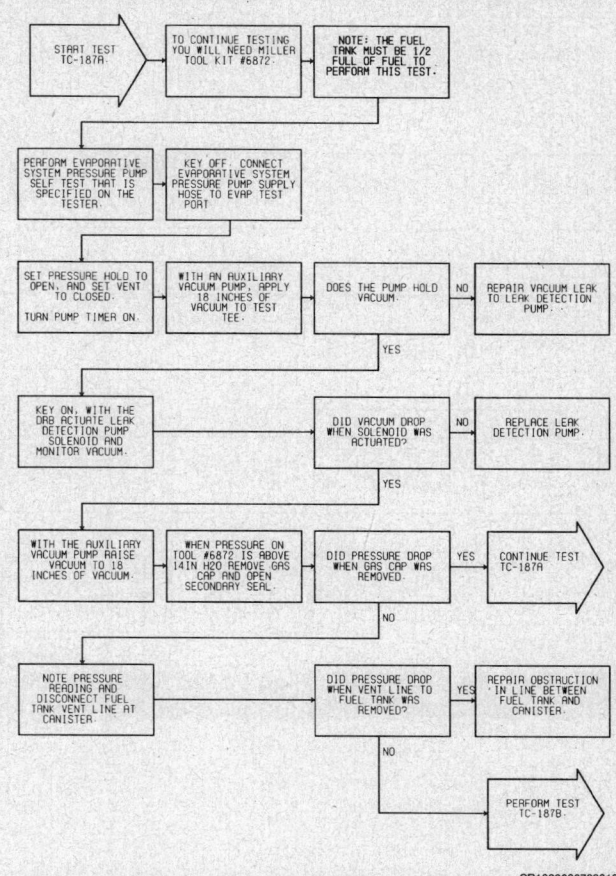

Fig. 157 Test TC-187A: EVAP Leak Monitor Pinched Hose (Part 1 of 2)

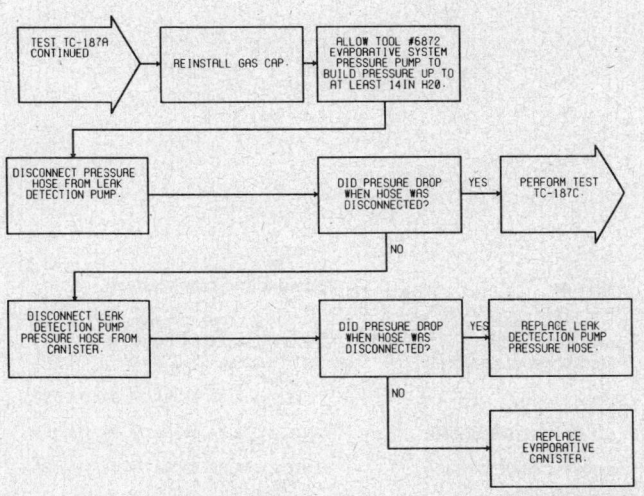

Fig. 157 Test TC-187A: EVAP Leak Monitor Pinched Hose (Part 2 of 2)

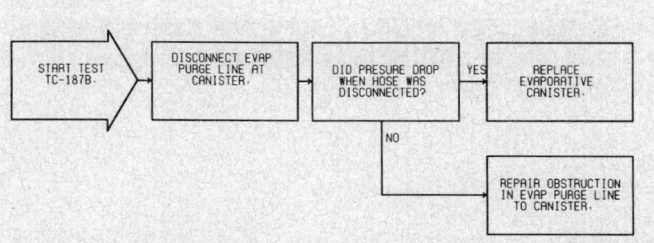

Fig. 158 Test TC-187B: EVAP Leak Monitor Pinched Hose

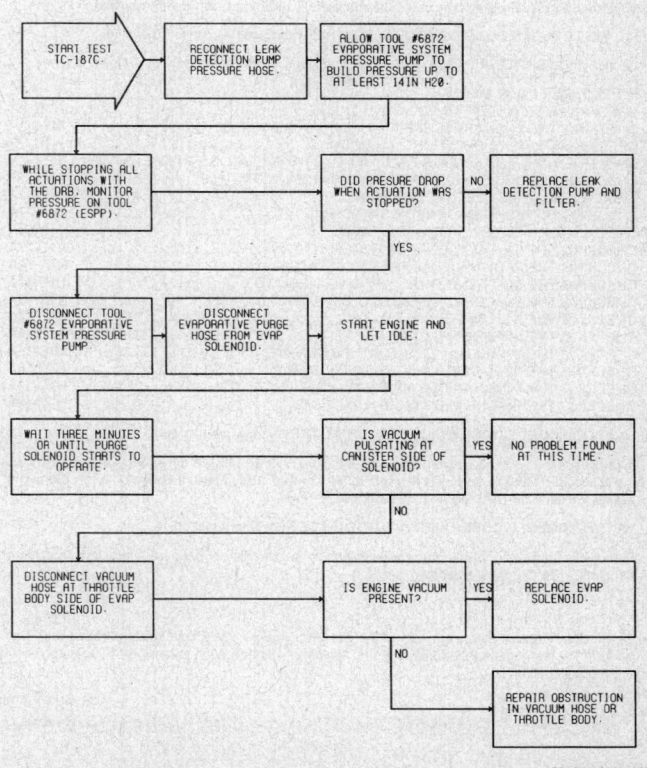

Fig. 159 Test TC-187C: EVAP Leak Monitor Pinched Hose

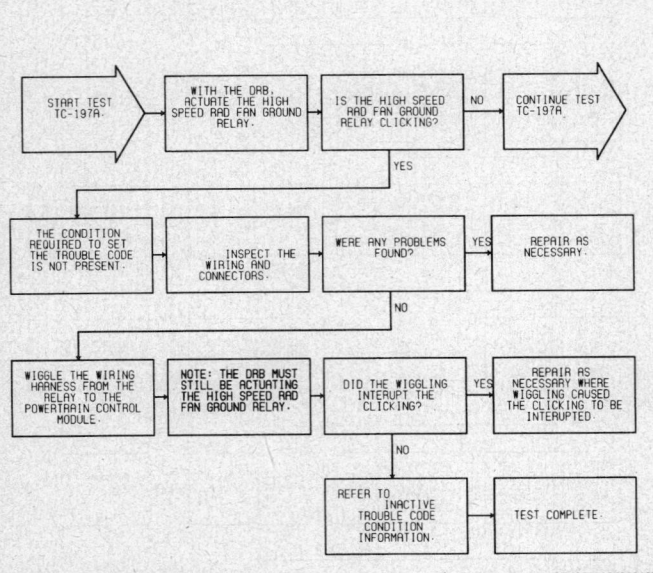

Fig. 160   Test TC-197A: High Speed Radiator Fan Ground Control Relay Circuit (Part 1 of 2)

CR1029606735010X

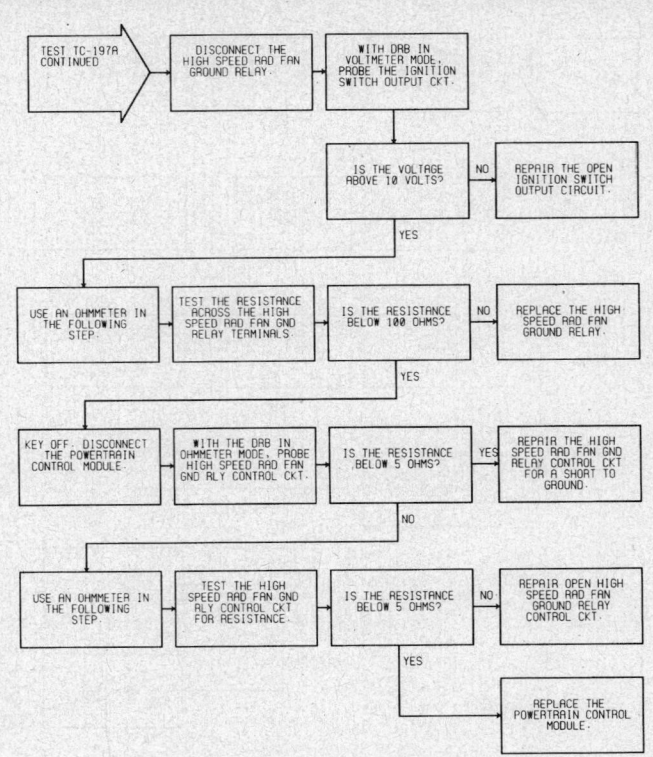

CR1029606735020X

Fig. 160   Test TC-197A: High Speed Radiator Fan Ground Control Relay Circuit (Part 2 of 2)

First, check all Technical Service Bulletins that relate to this driveability problem. Perform corrective actions if indicated; otherwise continue.

1. NO TROUBLE CODE COMPLETE TEST (non-monitored & monitored circuits)

Perform **TESTS NTC-2A** through **NTC-19A** in sequence until the driveability problem is found.

NO TROUBLE CODE MENU
CHECKING SECONDARY IGNITION AND TIMING NTC-2A
CHECKING THE FUEL PRESSURE (F24S, FJ, JA, JX AND PL) NTC-3A
CHECKING THE FUEL PRESSURE (LH BODY) NTC-3D
CHECKING COOLANT SENSOR CALIBRATION AND RADIATOR FAN OPERATION . . . NTC-4A
CHECKING THROTTLE POSITION SENSOR CALIBRATION NTC-5A
CHECKING MAP SENSOR CALIBRATION NTC-6A
CHECKING FOR OXYGEN SENSOR SWITCHING NTC-7A
CHECKING THE OXYGEN SENSOR HEATER NTC-8A
CHECKING THE IDLE AIR CONTROL MOTOR NTC-9A
CHECKING THE PARK/NEUTRAL POSITION SWITCH NTC-10A
CHECKING THE PCM POWER AND GROUND CIRCUITS NTC-11A
CHECKING THE EVAPORATIVE EMISSION SYSTEM NTC-12A
CHECKING THE EGR SYSTEM NTC-13A
CHECKING THE ENGINE VACUUM NTC-14A
CHECKING THE INTAKE AIR TEMPERATURE SENSOR NTC-15A
CHECKING THE TIMING BELT ALIGNMENT (PL ONLY) NTC-16A
CHECKING THE MINIMUM IDLE AIR FLOW NTC-17A
CHECKING THE ENGINE MECHANICAL SYSTEMS NTC-18A

2. NO TROUBLE CODE QUICK INDIVIDUAL TEST (individual test only)

If you suspect any of the above items to be the cause of the vehicle's driveability problem, perform the associated test(s) individually. **Return to No Trouble Code Menu if driveability problem still exists, or perform No Trouble Code Complete Test.**

3. NO TROUBLE CODE QUICK SYMPTOM TEST (symptom test only)

Symptom checks cannot be used properly unless the driveability problem characteristic actually happens while the vehicle is being tested.

SYMPTOM	DIAGNOSTIC TEST ROUTINE
HARD START	NTC-2A, 3A, 4A, 5A, 6A, 7A, 9A, 12A, 13A, 14A, 15A, 16A, 17A, 18A
START AND STALL	NTC-2A, 3A, 4A, 5A, 6A, 9A, 11A, 17A
HESITATION/SAG/STUMBLE	NO TROUBLE CODE COMPLETE TEST (STEP 1)
SURGE	NTC-2A, 3A, 4A, 5A, 6A, 7A, 9A, 11A, 12A, 17A
LACK OF POWER/SLUGGISH	NTC-2A, 3A, 4A, 5A, 6A, 7A, 9A, 11A, 13A, 16A, 17A
SPARK KNOCK/DETONATION	NTC-2A, 3A, 4A, 5A, 6A, 7A, 9A, 11A, 12A, 16A, 17A
CUTS OUT/MISSES	NTC-2A, 3A, 7A, 11A, 13A, 17A
BACKFIRE/POPBACK	NTC-2A, 3A, 6A, 7A, 11A, 13A, 16A, 17A
RUNS ROUGH/UNSTABLE/ERRATIC IDLE	NO TROUBLE CODE COMPLETE TEST (STEP 1)
POOR FUEL ECONOMY	NO TROUBLE CODE COMPLETE TEST (STEP 1)

CR1029606736020X

Fig. 161   Test NTC-1A: Engine Mechanical System Inspection (Part 2 of 2)

Select the symptom that most accurately describes the vehicle's driveability problem and then perform the test routine that pertains to this symptom. Perform each routine test in sequence until the problem is found.

CR1029606736010X

Fig. 161   Test NTC-1A: Engine Mechanical System Inspection (Part 1 of 2)

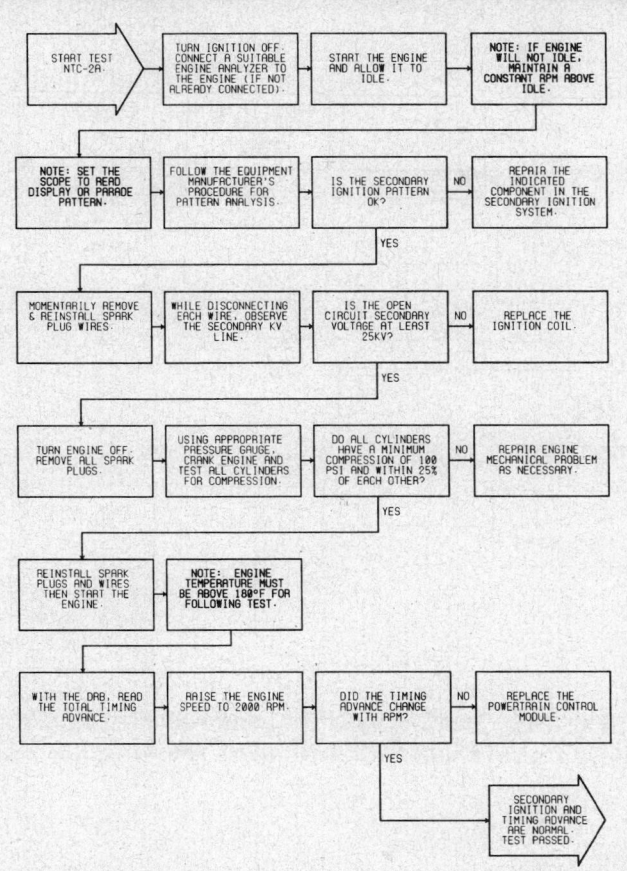

Fig. 162 Test NTC-2A: Checking Secondary Ignition & Timing

CR1029606737000X

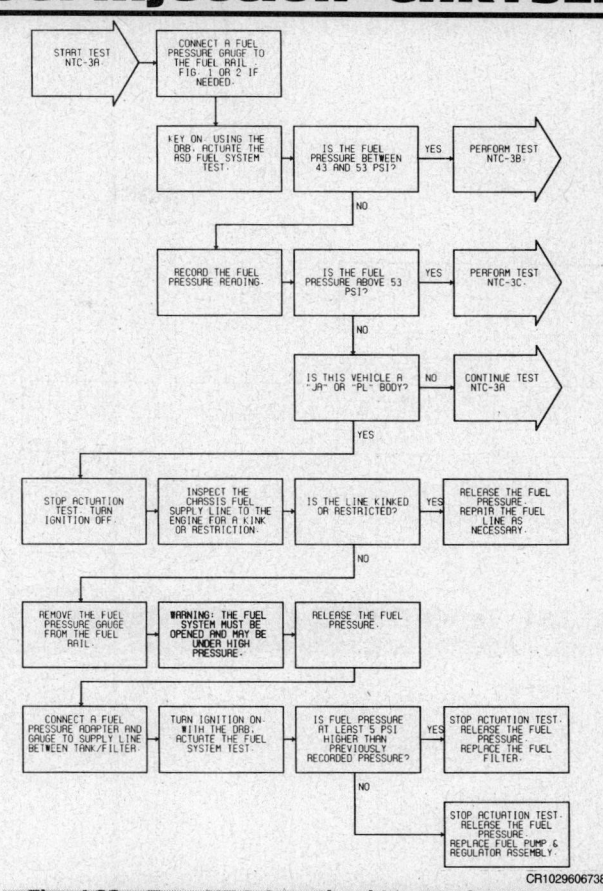

CR1029606738010X

Fig. 163 Test NTC-3A: Checking Fuel Pressure & Injector Operation (Part 1 of 2)

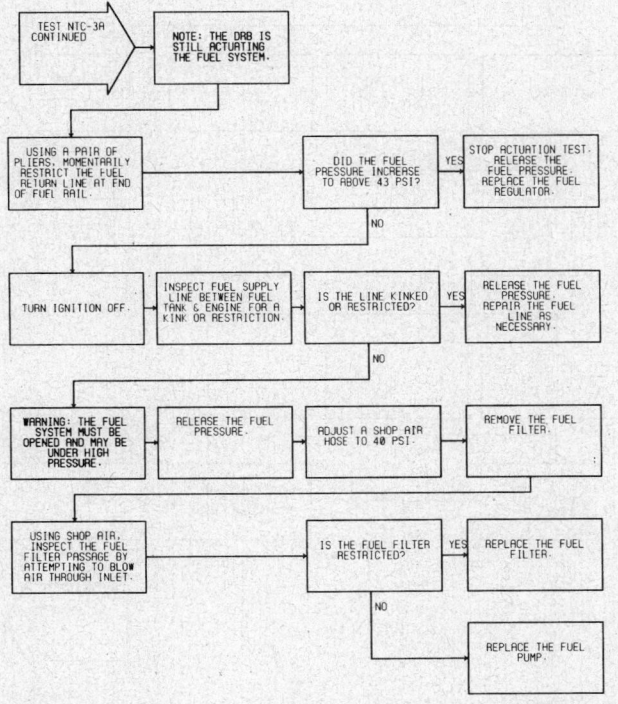

CR1029606738020X

Fig. 163 Test NTC-3A: Checking Fuel Pressure & Injector Operation (Part 2 of 2)

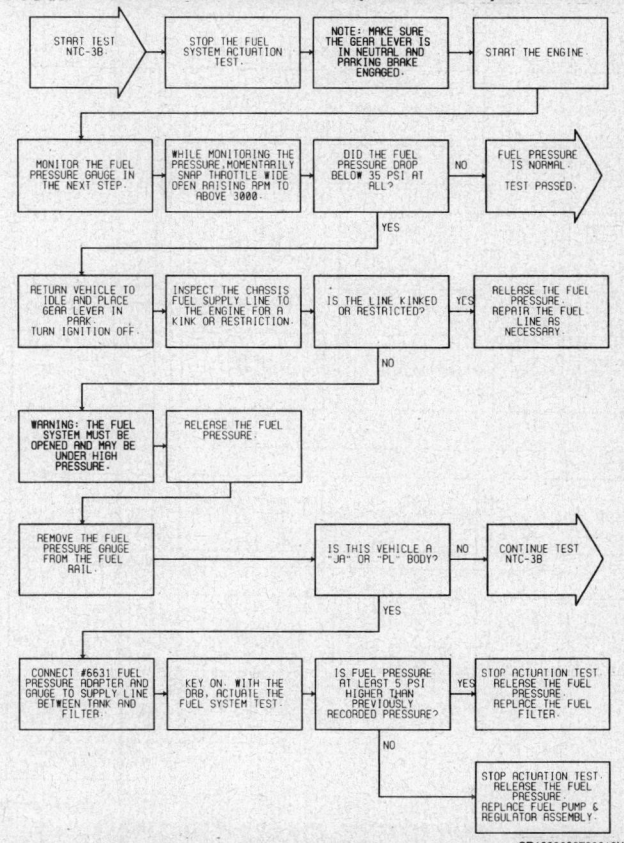

CR1029606739010X

Fig. 164 Test NTC-3B: Checking Fuel Pressure & Injector Operation (Part 1 of 2)

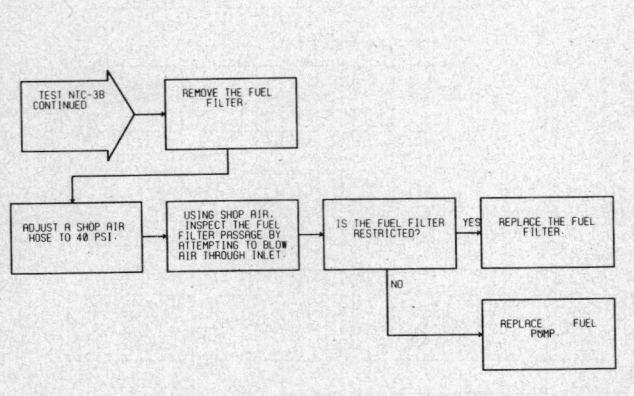

Fig. 164   Test NTC-3B: Checking Fuel Pressure & Injector Operation (Part 2 of 2)

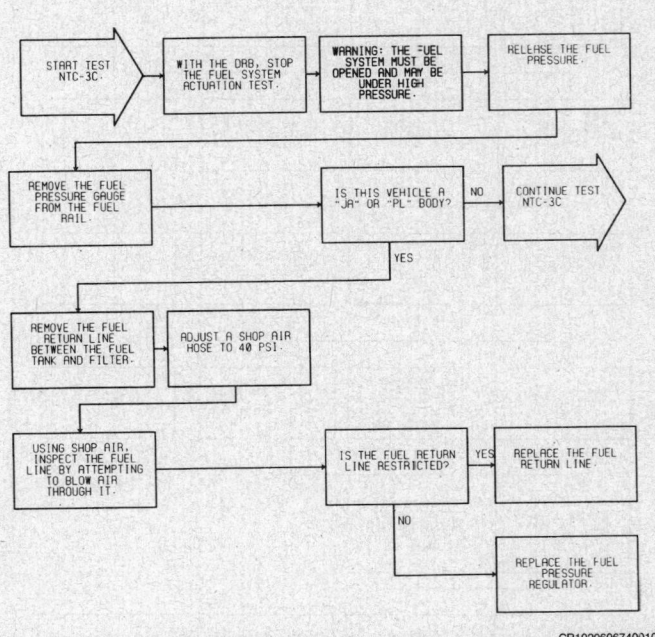

Fig. 165   Test NTC-3C: Checking Fuel Pressure & Injector Operation (Part 1 of 2)

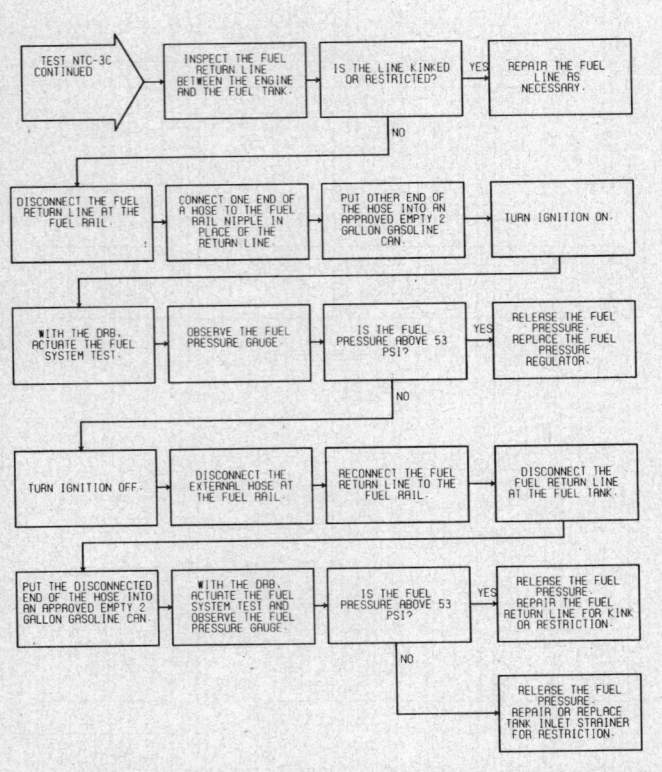

Fig. 165   Test NTC-3C: Checking Fuel Pressure & Injector Operation (Part 2 of 2)

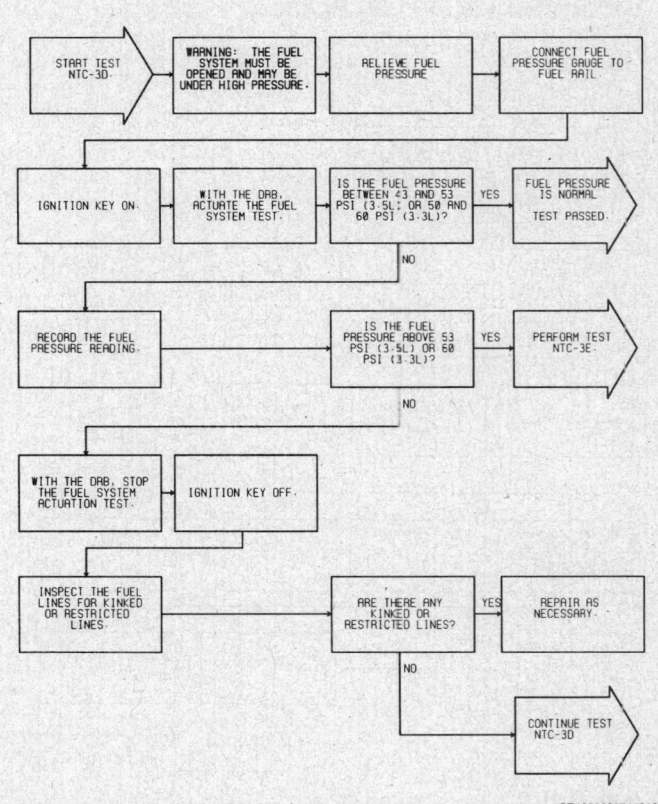

Fig. 166   Test NTC-3D: Checking Fuel Pressure & Injector Operation (Part 1 of 2)

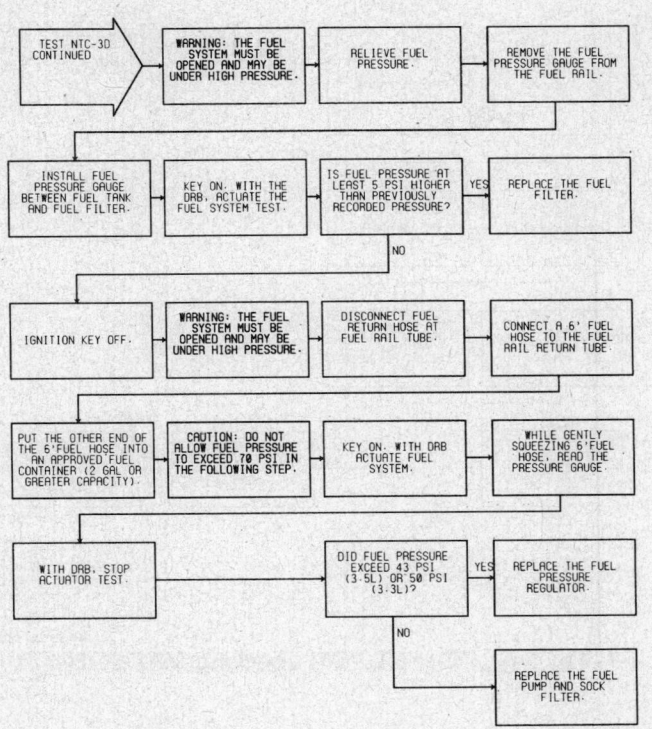

Fig. 166   Test NTC-3D: Checking Fuel Pressure & Injector Operation (Part 2 of 2)

CR1029606741020X

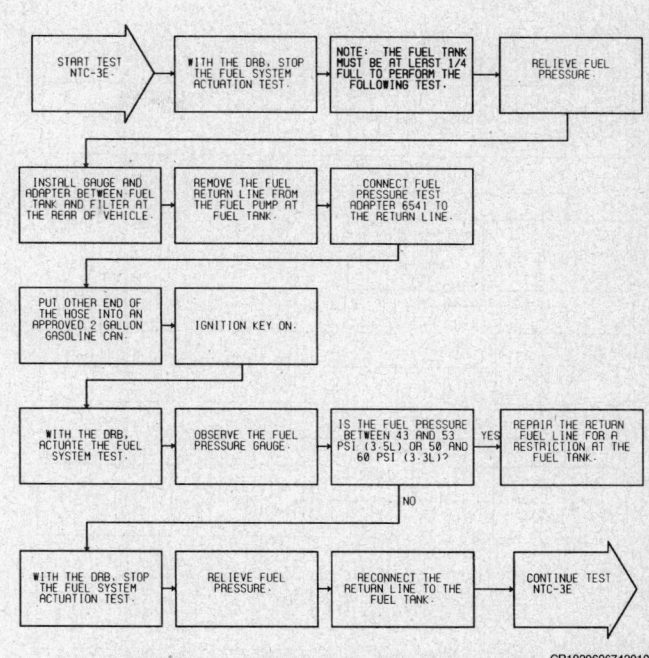

Fig. 167   Test NTC-3E: Checking Fuel Pressure & Injector Operation (Part 1 of 2)

CR1029606742010X

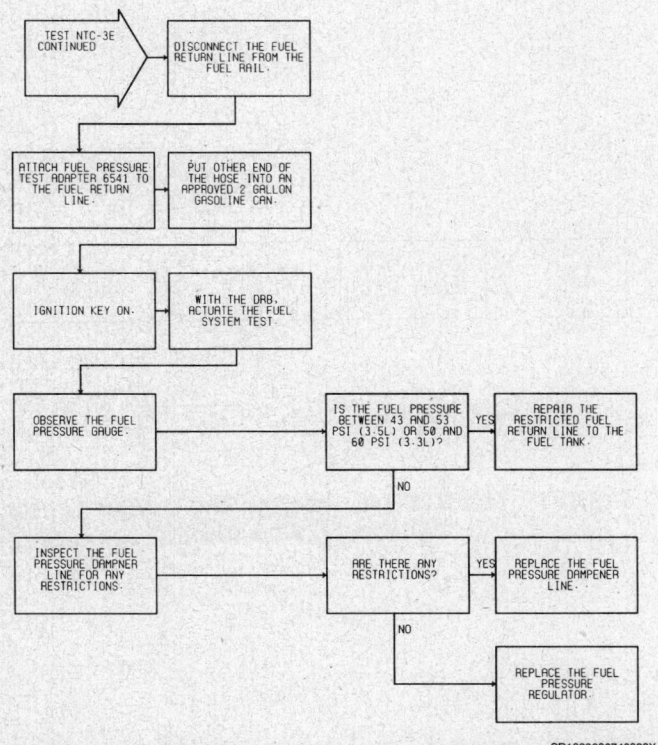

Fig. 167   Test NTC-3E: Checking Fuel Pressure & Injector Operation (Part 2 of 2)

CR1029606742020X

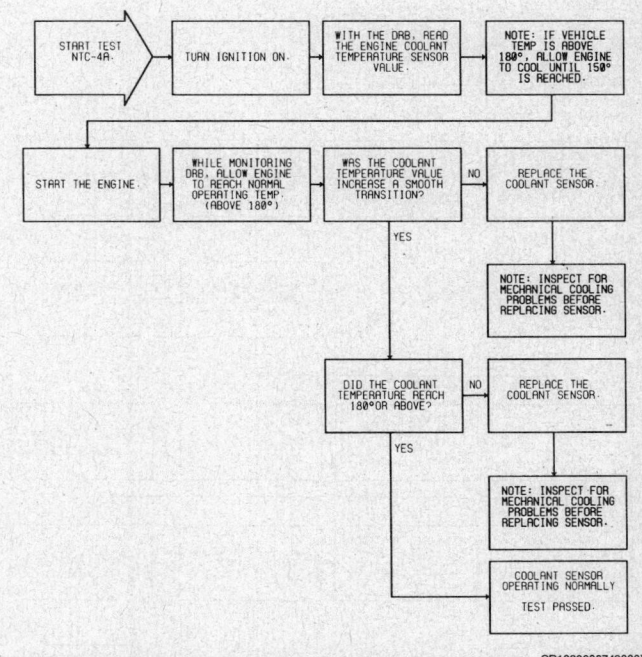

Fig. 168   Test NTC-4A: Checking Coolant Sensor Calibration

CR1029606743000X

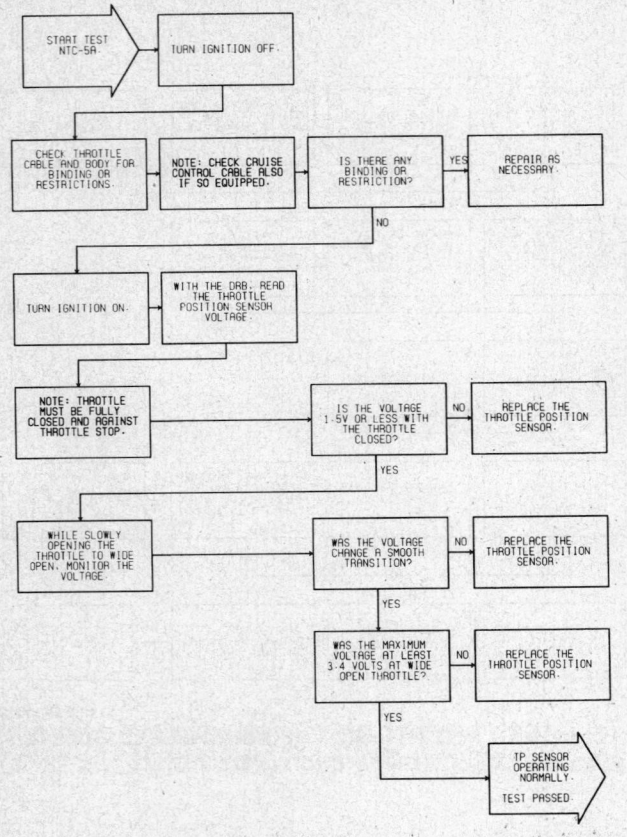

Fig. 169   Test NTC-5A: Checking Throttle Position
Sensor

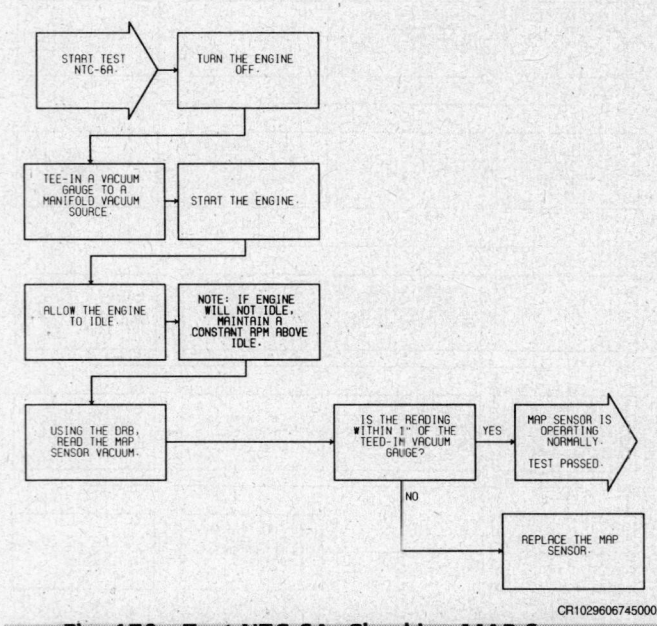

Fig. 170   Test NTC-6A: Checking MAP Sensor

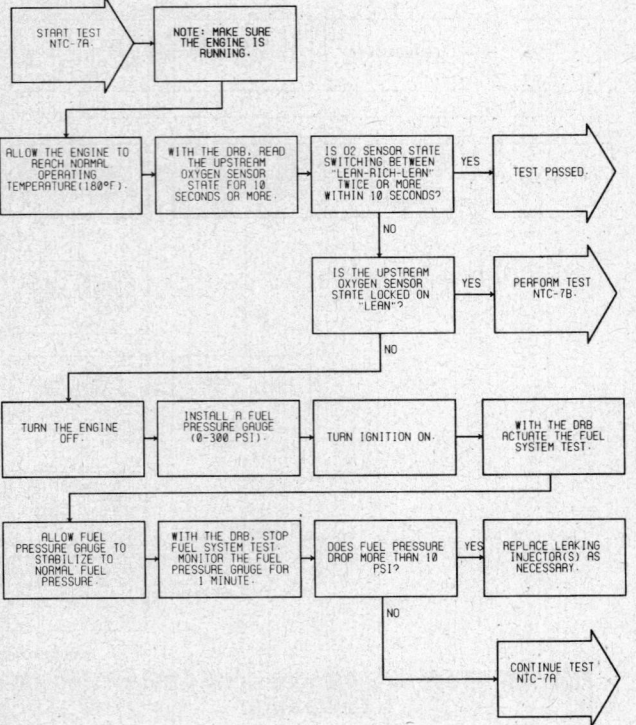

Fig. 171   Test NTC-7A: Checking The Oxygen Sensor
Switching (Part 2 of 2)

Fig. 171   Test NTC-7A: Checking The Oxygen Sensor
Switching (Part 1 of 2)

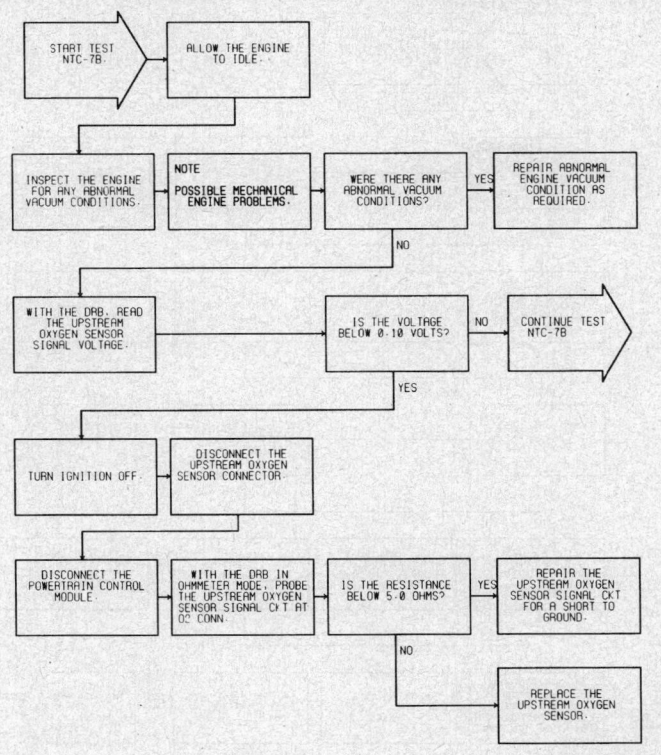

Fig. 172   Test NTC-7B: Checking The Oxygen Sensor Switching (Part 1 of 2)

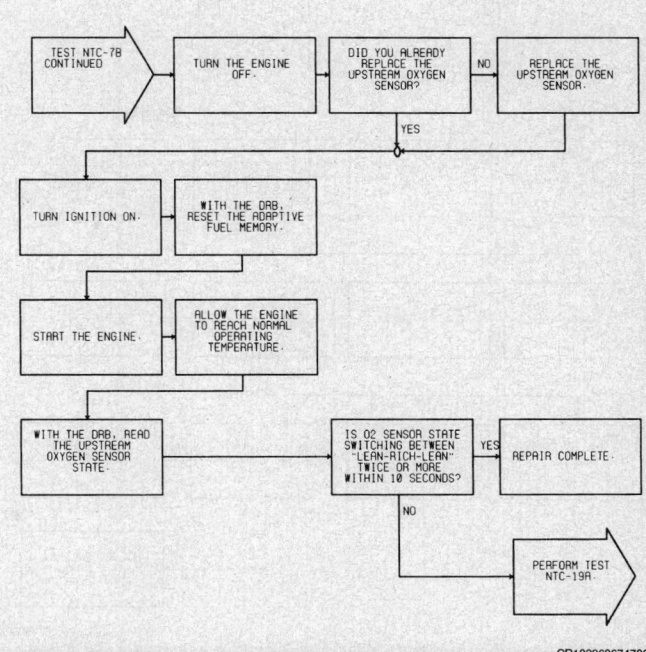

Fig. 172   Test NTC-7B: Checking The Oxygen Sensor Switching (Part 2 of 2)

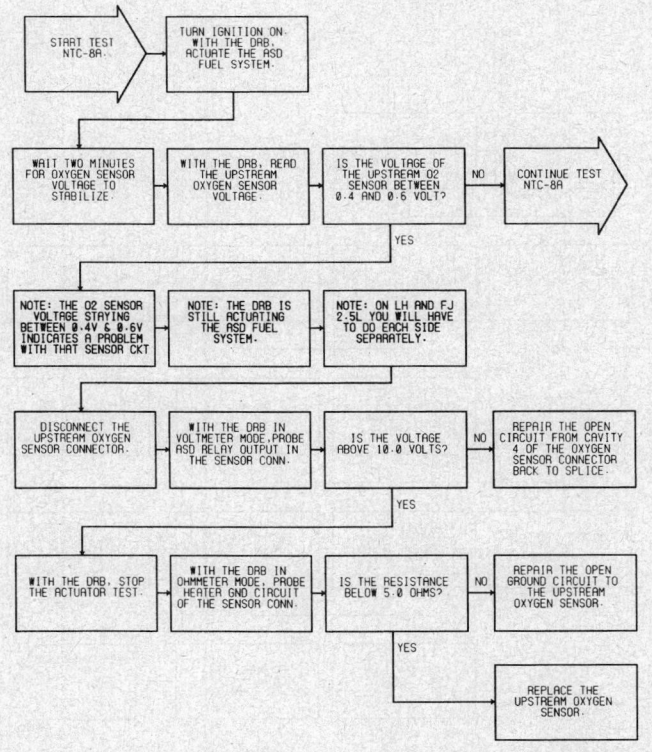

Fig. 173   Test NTC-8A: Checking The Oxygen Sensor Heater (Part 1 of 2)

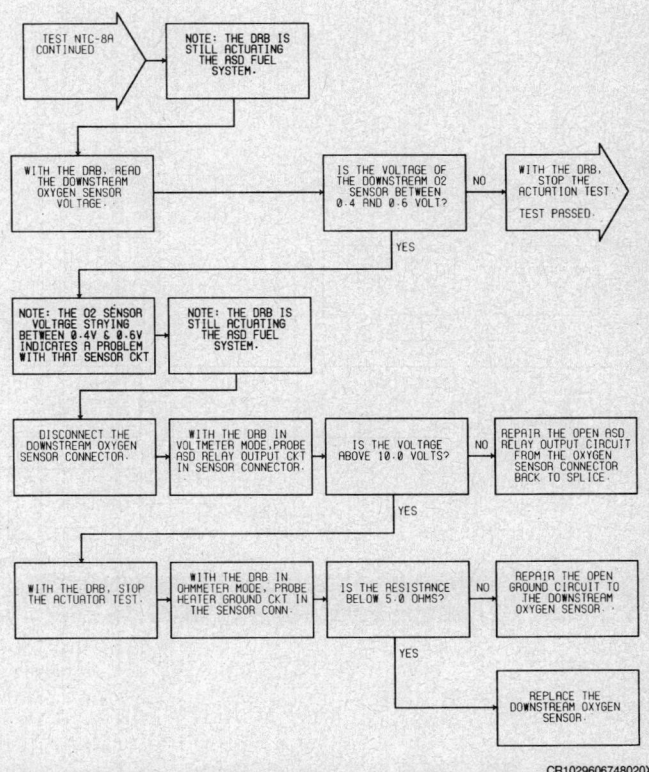

Fig. 173   Test NTC-8A: Checking The Oxygen Sensor Heater (Part 2 of 2)

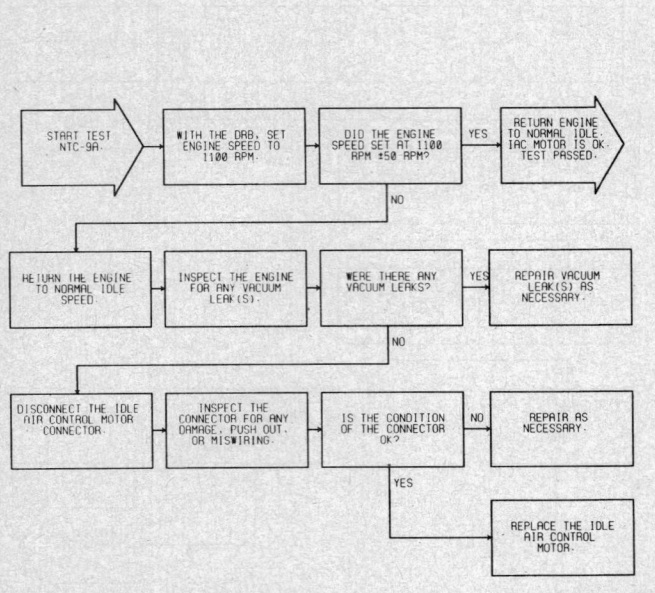

Fig. 174   Test NTC-9A: Checking Idle Air Control Motor

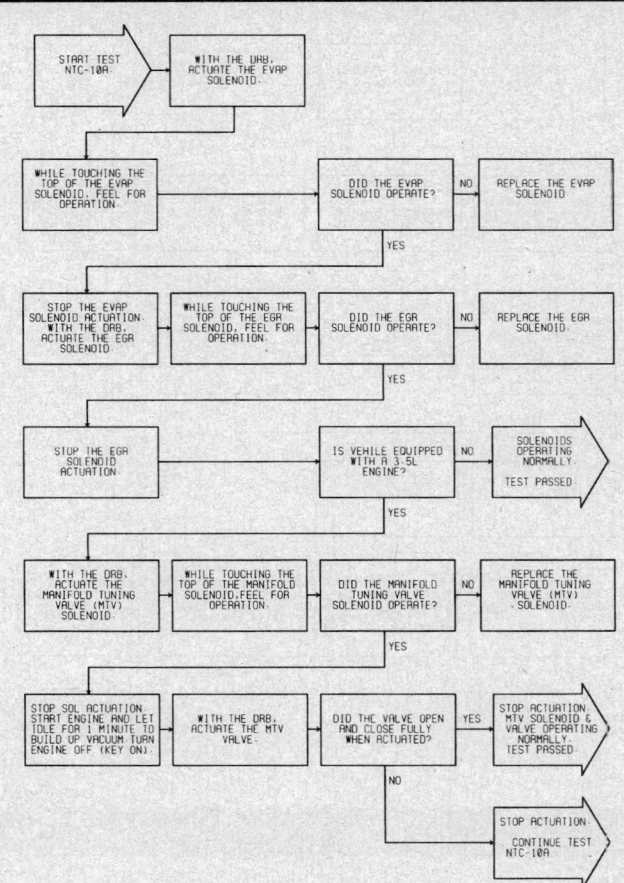

Fig. 175   Test NTC-10A: Checking Park/Neutral Position Switch (Part 1 of 2)

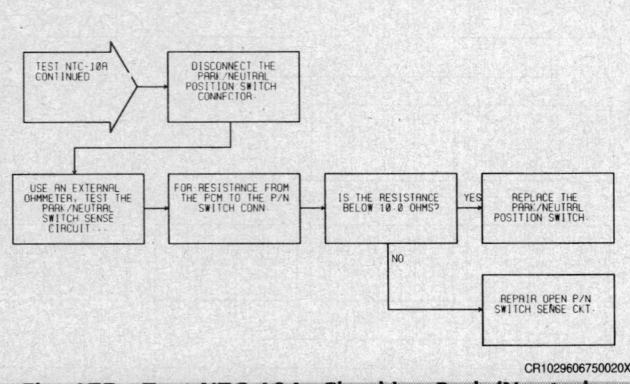

Fig. 175   Test NTC-10A: Checking Park/Neutral Position Switch (Part 2 of 2)

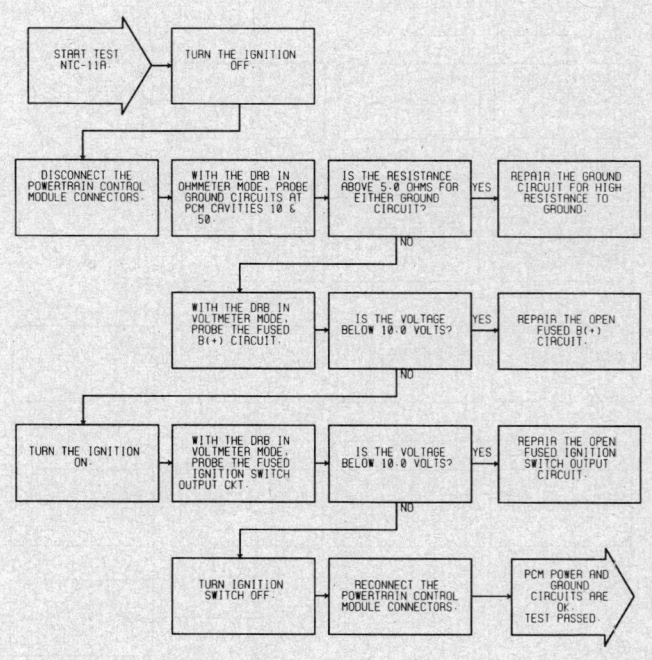

Fig. 176   Test NTC-11A: Checking The PCM Power & Grounds

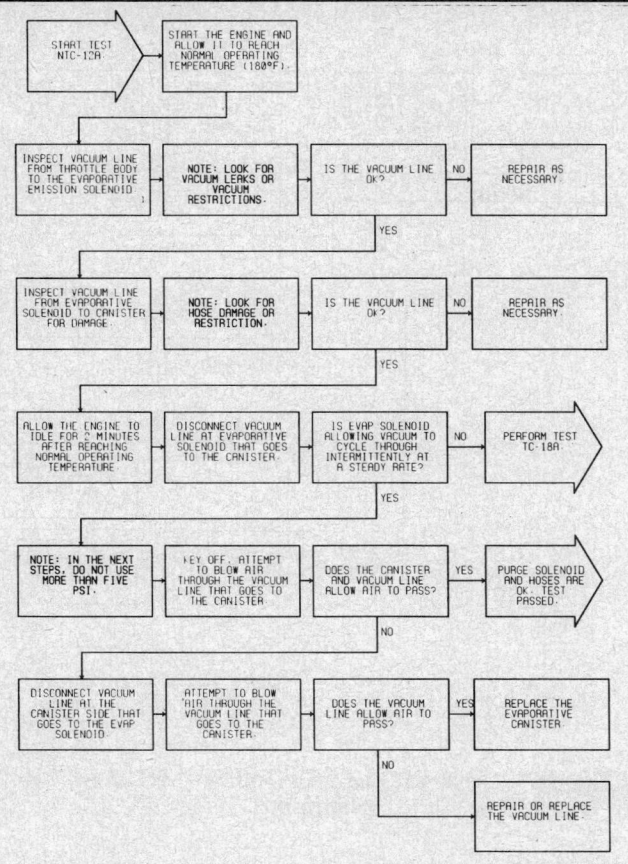

Fig. 177   Test NTC-12A: Checking The Evaporative Emissions Systems

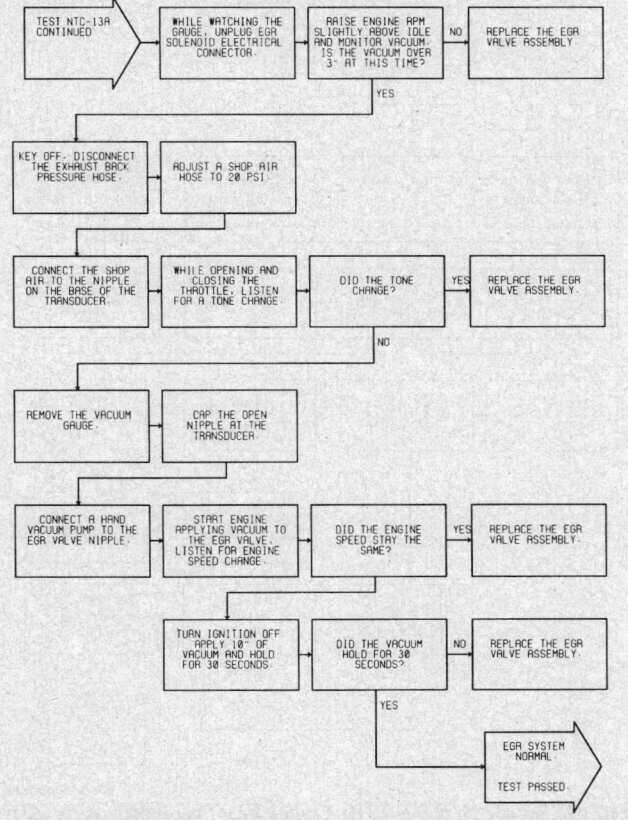

Fig. 178   Test NTC-13A: Checking EGR Systems (Part 2 of 2)

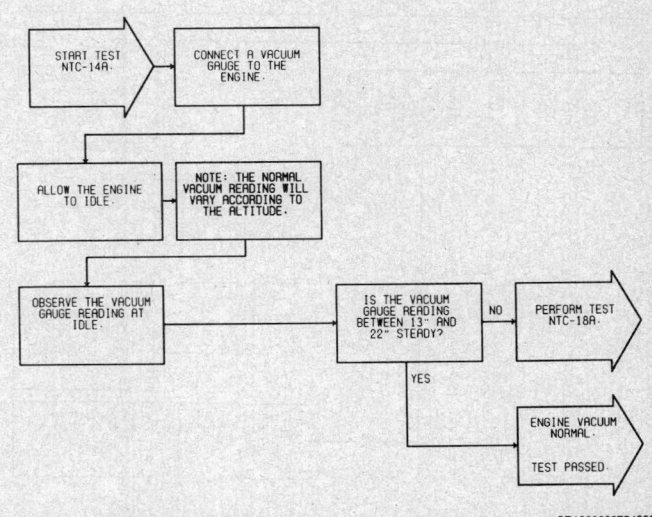

Fig. 178   Test NTC-13A: Checking EGR Systems (Part 1 of 2)

Fig. 179   Test NTC-14A: Checking The Engine Vacuum

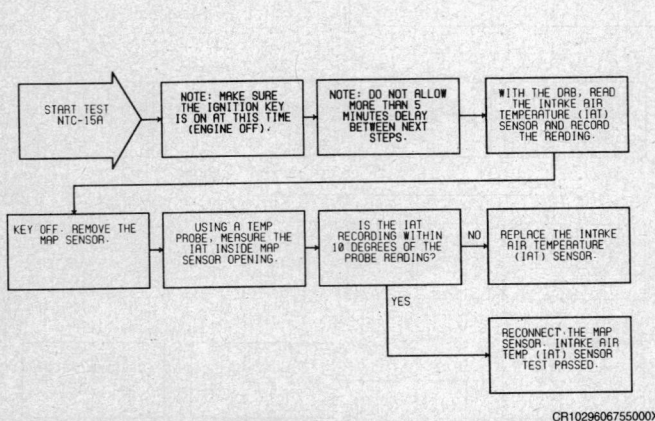

Fig. 180   Test NTC-15A: Checking The Intake Air Temperature Sensor

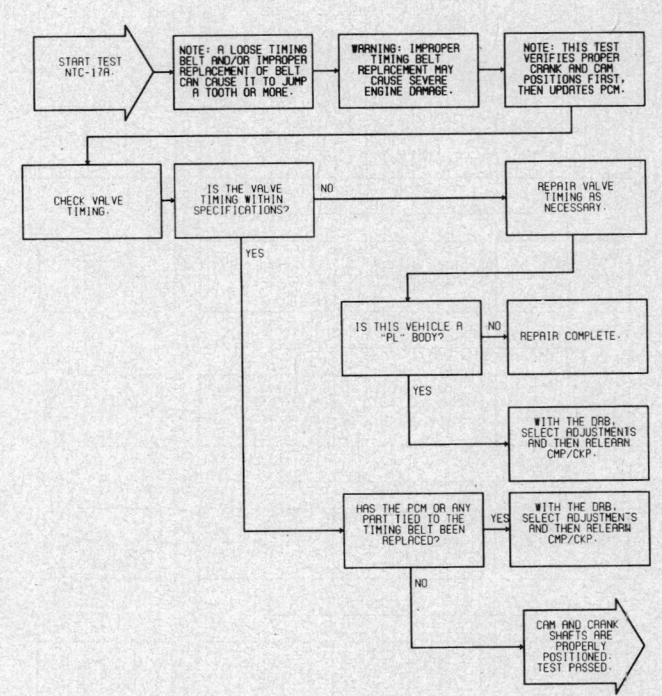

Fig. 181   Test NTC-16A: Checking The Timing Belt Alignment

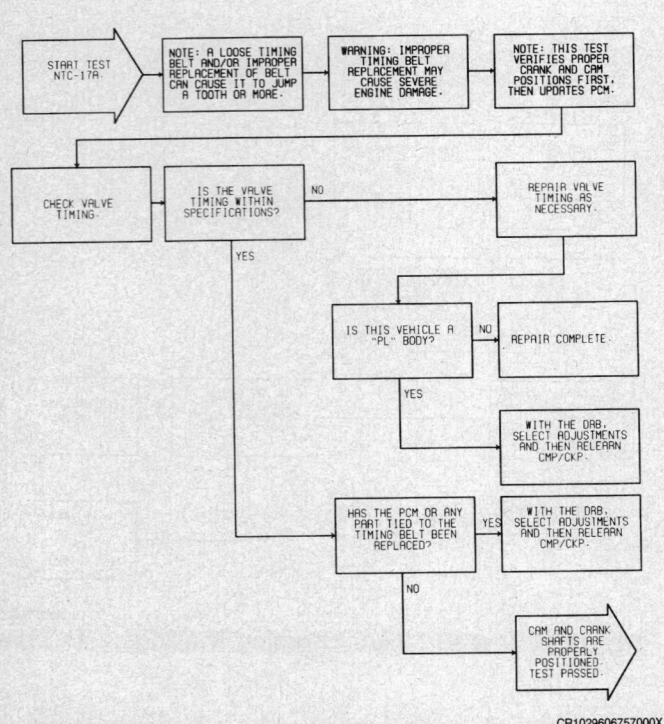

Fig. 182   Test NTC-17A: Checking The Minimum Idle Air Flow

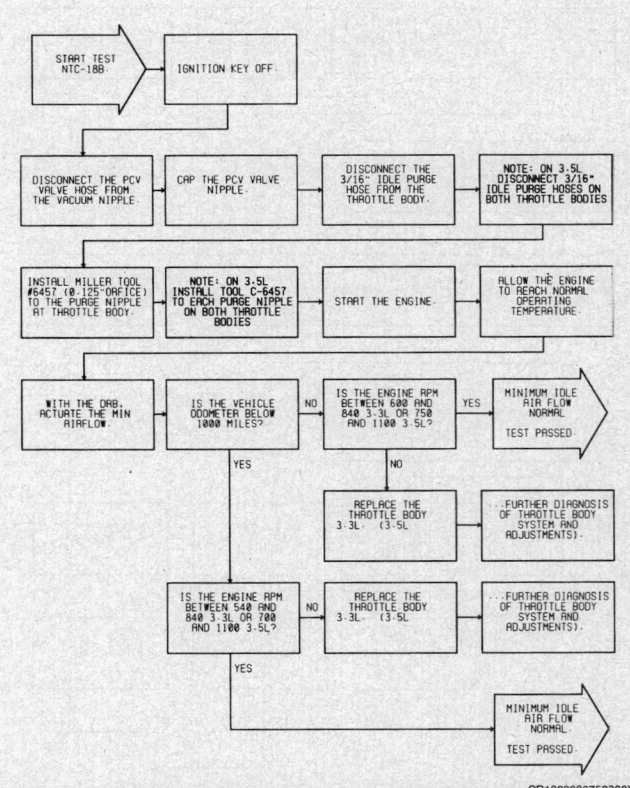

Fig. 183   Test NTC-17B: Checking The Minimum Idle Air Flow

At this point in the diagnostic test procedure, you have determined that all of the **engine electrical systems** are operating as designed; therefore, they **are not the cause of the driveability problem.** The following additional items should be checked as possible mechanical causes of the problem:

1. **ENGINE VACUUM** - must be at least 13 inches in neutral *(see below)* †

2. **ENGINE VALVE TIMING** - must be within specifications

3. **ENGINE COMPRESSION** - must be within specifications

4. **CAMSHAFT LOBES** - check for abnormal wear

5. **CRANK SENSOR PICK-UP** - check crankshaft slots for debris/deterioration

6. **ENGINE EXHAUST SYSTEM** - must be free of any restrictions

7. **ENGINE PCV SYSTEM** - must flow freely

8. **ENGINE DRIVE SPROCKET** - must be properly positioned

9. **TORQUE CONVERTER STALL SPEED** - must be within specifications

10. **POWER BRAKE BOOSTER** - no internal vacuum leaks

11. **FUEL** - must be free of contamination

12. **FUEL INJECTOR** - plugged or restricted injector; control wire not connected to correct injector

NOTE: If you came to this test from the oxygen sensor, and the rich or lean condition is not caused by one of the first items above, replace the powertrain control module and perform TEST VER-2A (Road Test Verification).

Always look for any Technical Service Bulletins that may relate to the problem.

† The readings   are only indicators of possible mechanical engine problems.

CR1029606759010X

Fig. 184   Test NTC-18A: Checking The Engine Mechanical Systems (Part 1 of 2)

| NORMAL READING RANGE AT IDLE | BLOWN HEAD GASKET AT IDLE | NORMAL READING RAPID ACCELERATION/ DECELERATION | WORN RINGS OR DILUTED OIL RAPID ACCELERATION/ DECELERATION | LATE VALVE TIMING, VACUUM LEAK AT IDLE |

| RESTRICTED EXHAUST (DROPS TOWARD ZERO AS ENGINE RPM INCREASES) | POOR VALVE SEATING AT IDLE | STICKING VALVE AT IDLE | WORN VALVE GUIDES (STEADIES AS ENGINE SPEED INCREASES) | WORN VALVE SPRINGS (MORE PRONOUNCED AS ENGINE SPEED INCREASES) |

CR1029606759020X

Fig. 184   Test NTC-18A: Checking The Engine Mechanical Systems (Part 2 of 2)

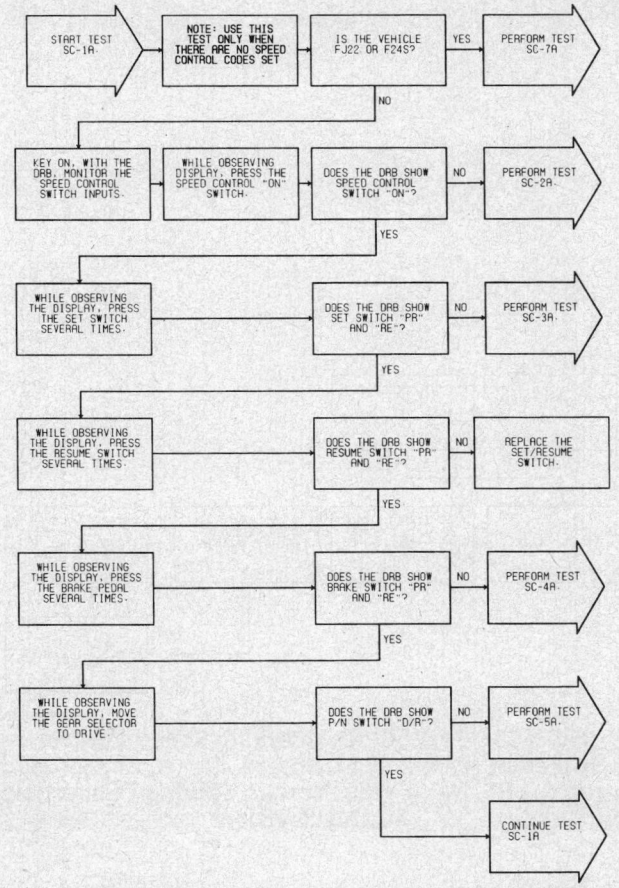

CR1029606760010X

Fig. 185   Test SC-1A: Checking Speed Control Operation (Part 1 of 2). Breeze, Cirrus, Concorde, Intrepid, LHS, Neon, New Yorker, Sebring Convertible, Stratus & Vision

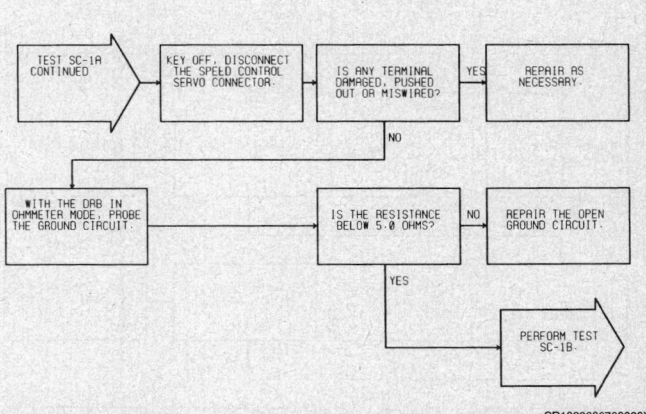

CR1029606760020X

Fig. 185   Test SC-1A: Checking Speed Control Operation (Part 2 of 2). Breeze, Cirrus, Concorde, Intrepid, LHS, Neon, New Yorker, Sebring Convertible, Stratus & Vision

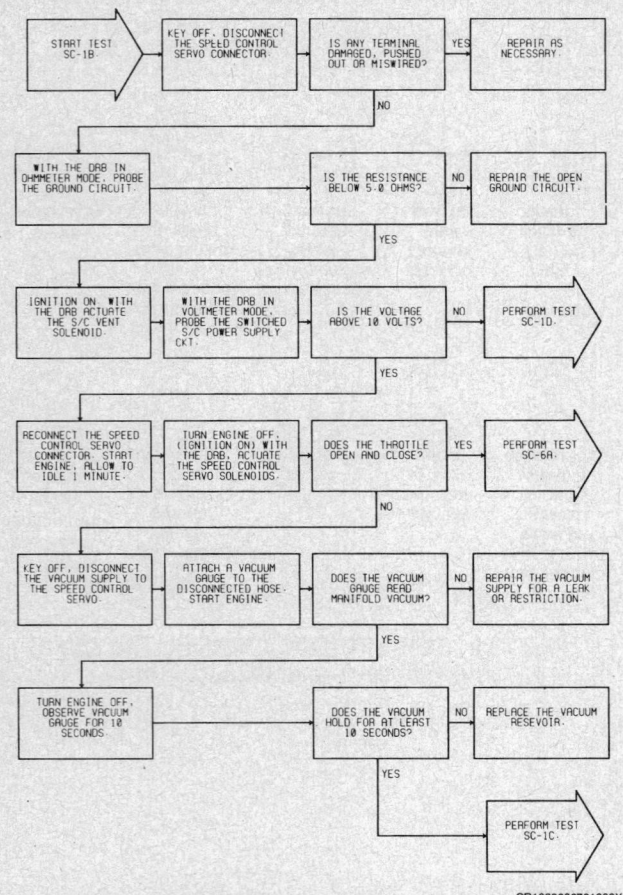

Fig. 186 Test SC-1B: Checking Speed Control Operation. Breeze, Cirrus, Concorde, Intrepid, LHS, Neon, New Yorker, Sebring Convertible, Stratus & Vision

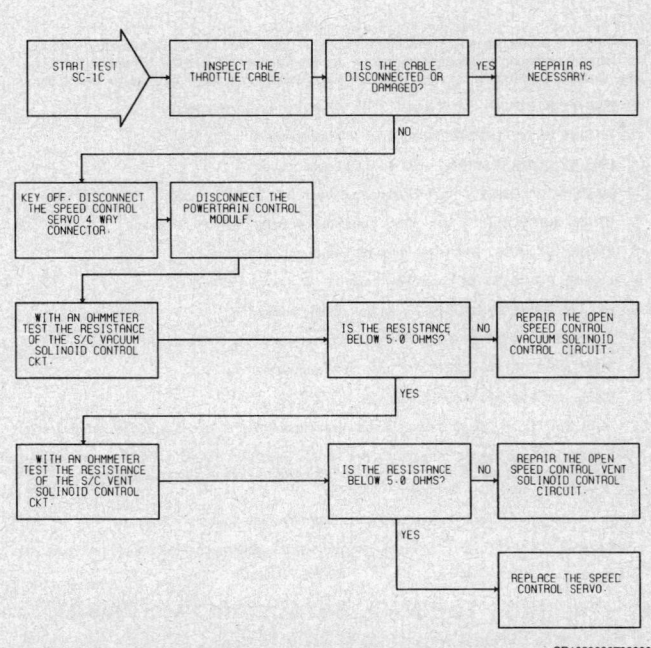

Fig. 187 Test SC-1C: Checking Speed Control Operation. Breeze, Cirrus, Concorde, Intrepid, LHS, Neon, New Yorker, Sebring Convertible, Stratus & Vision

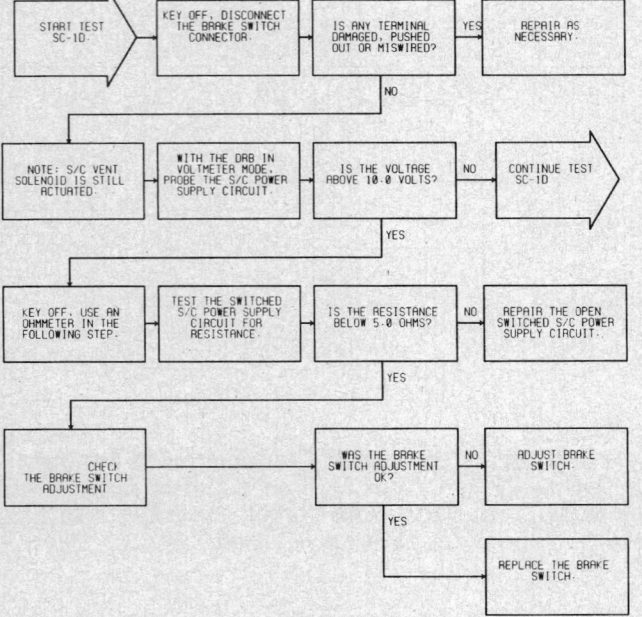

Fig. 188 Test SC-1D: Checking Speed Control Operation (Part 1 of 2). Breeze, Cirrus, Concorde, Intrepid, LHS, Neon, New Yorker, Sebring Convertible, Stratus & Vision

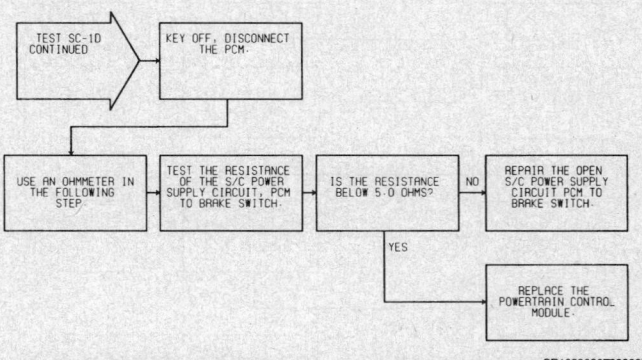

Fig. 188 Test SC-1D: Checking Speed Control Operation (Part 2 of 2). Breeze, Cirrus, Concorde, Intrepid, LHS, Neon, New Yorker, Sebring Convertible, Stratus & Vision

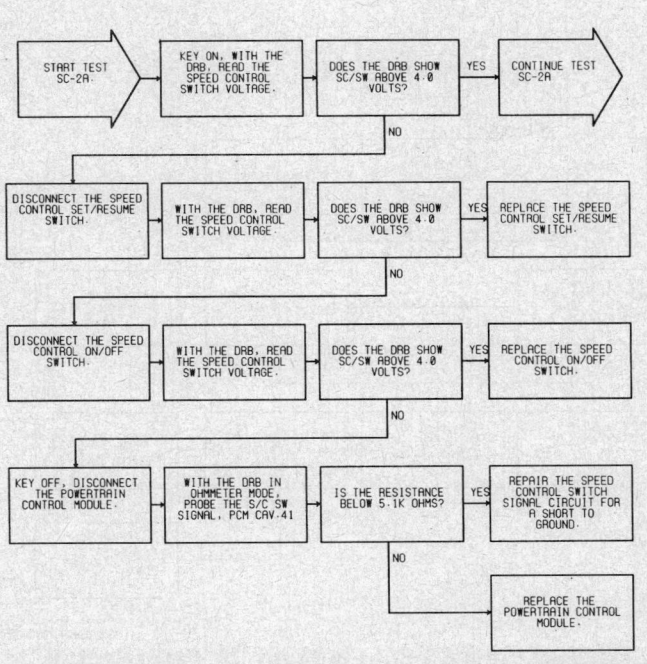

Fig. 189   Test SC-2A: Checking Speed Control On/Off Switch (Part 1 of 2). Breeze, Cirrus, Concorde, Intrepid, LHS, Neon, New Yorker, Sebring Convertible, Stratus & Vision

CR1029606764010X

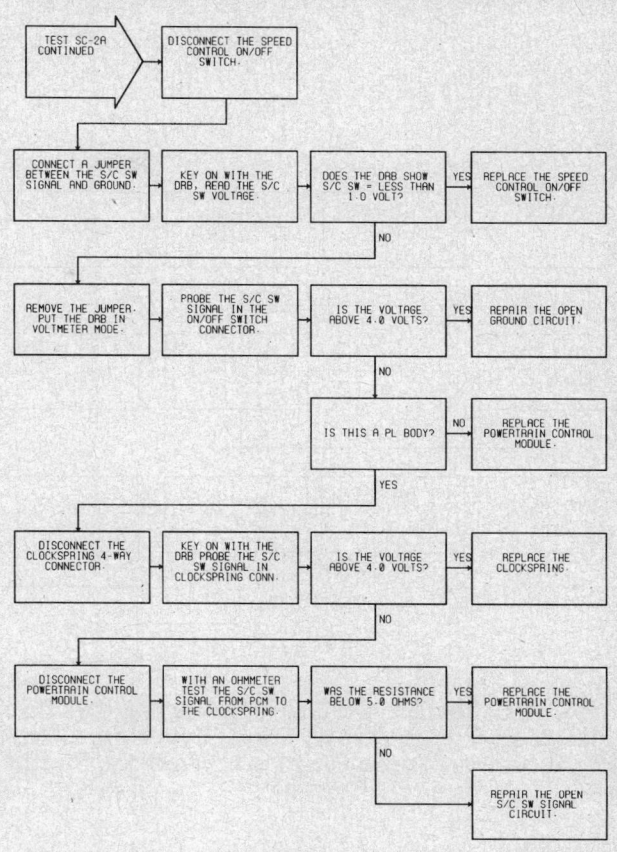

CR1029606764020X

Fig. 189   Test SC-2A: Checking Speed Control On/Off Switch (Part 2 of 2). Breeze, Cirrus, Concorde, Intrepid, LHS, Neon, New Yorker, Sebring Convertible, Stratus & Vision

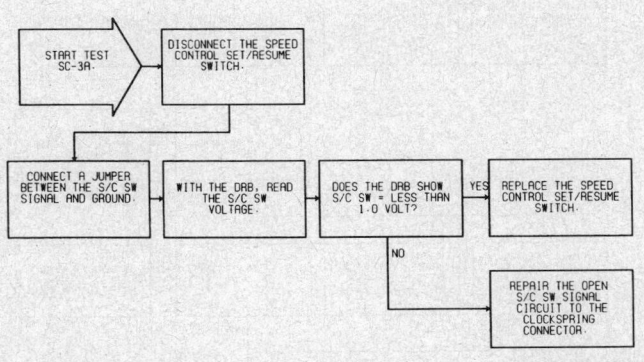

CR1029606765000X

Fig. 190   Test SC-3A: Checking Speed Control Set/Resume Switch. Breeze, Cirrus, Concorde, Intrepid, LHS, Neon, New Yorker, Sebring Convertible, Stratus & Vision

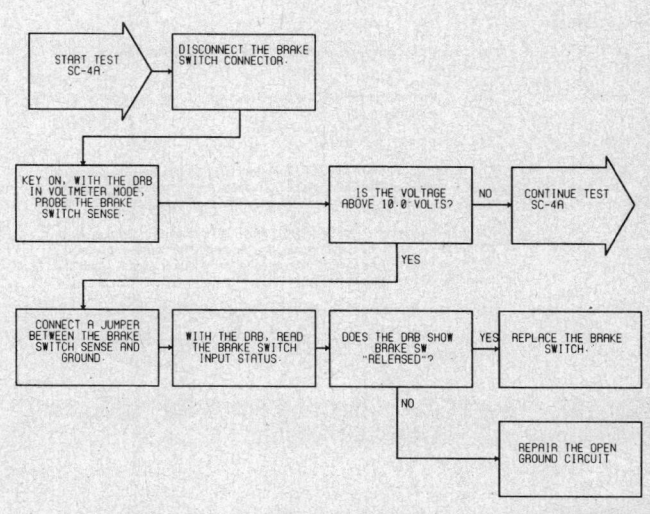

CR1029606766010X

Fig. 191   Test SC-4A: Checking The Brake Switch Sense (Part 1 of 2). Breeze, Cirrus, Concorde, Intrepid, LHS, Neon, New Yorker, Sebring Convertible, Stratus & Vision

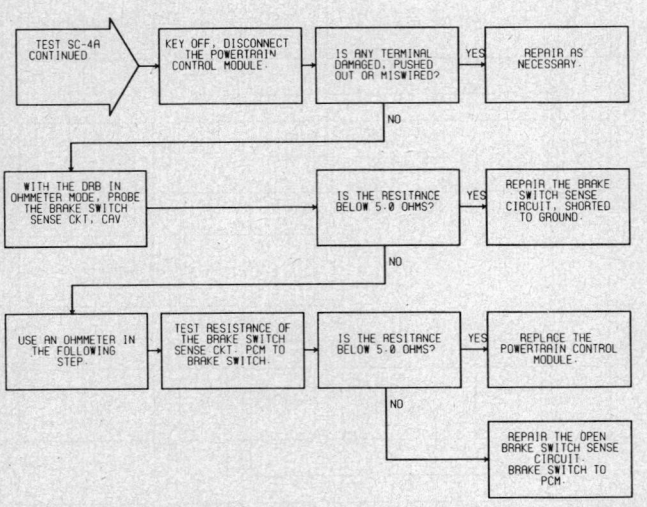

Fig. 191   Test SC-4A: Checking The Brake Switch Sense (Part 2 of 2). Breeze, Cirrus, Concorde, Intrepid, LHS, Neon, New Yorker, Sebring Convertible, Stratus & Vision

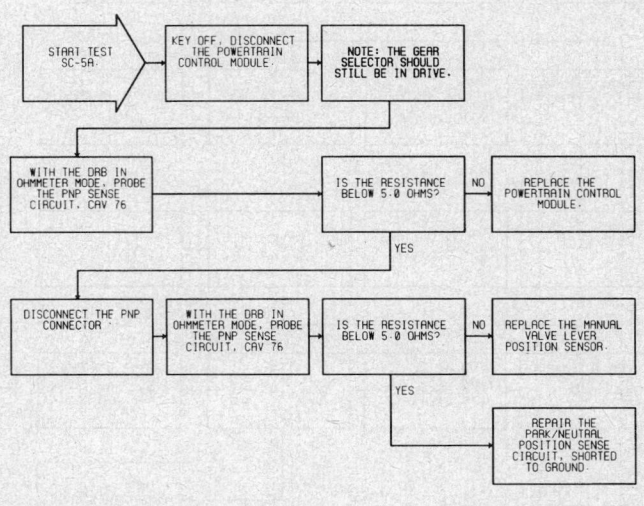

Fig. 192   Test SC-5A: Checking The Park/Neutral Position Switch. Breeze, Cirrus, Concorde, Intrepid, LHS, Neon, New Yorker, Sebring Convertible, Stratus & Vision

At this time the speed control switch and servo functions appear to operate properly. Using the DRB, monitor the speed control "output" status. Road test the vehicle at speeds over 35 mph and attempt to set the speed control. The following items will not allow the speed control to set. The last or most recent cause for speed control not to set is indicated by the "Denied" status.

Denied Message

ON/OFF	The powertrain control module does not see an "ON" signal from the switch at cavity 41.
SPEED	The vehicle speed as seen by the powertrain control module at cavity 66 is not greater than 36 mph.
RPM	The engine rpm is excessively high.
BRAKE	The brake switch sense circuit is open indicating to the powertrain control module that the brakes are applied. The sense circuit, cavity 62 of the PCM, is grounded through the brake pedal switch when the brakes are released.
P/N	The park/neutral switch sense circuit is grounded indicating to the powertrain control module that the transmission is not in gear. The sense circuit, cavity 76 of the PCM, is grounded through the park/neutral switch when the transmission is in park or neutral.
RPM/SPD	The PCM senses excessive engine rpm for a given vehicle speed.
SOL FLT	The powertrain control module senses a servo solenoid circuit trouble code that is maturing or set in memory.

Fig. 193   Test SC-6A: Checking For A Speed Control Denied Message

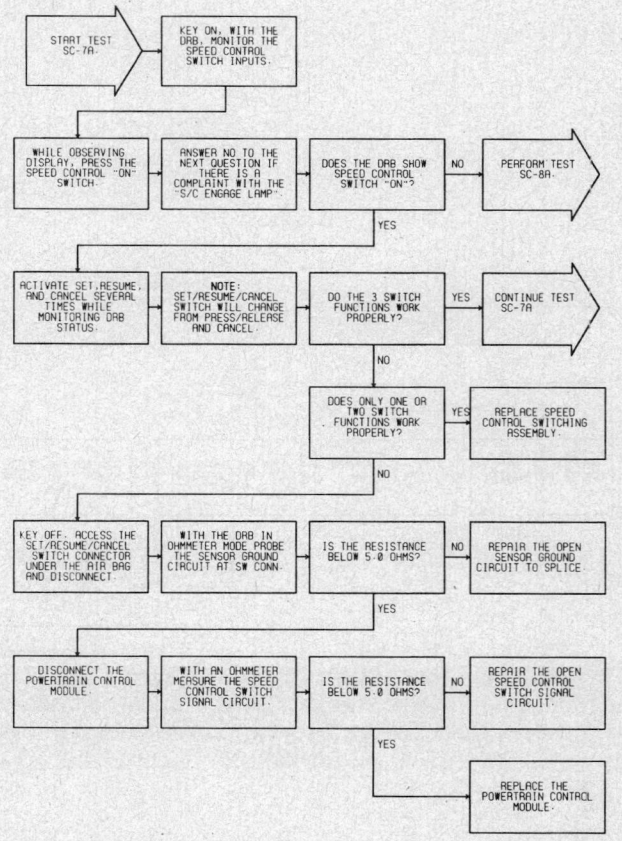

Fig. 194   Test SC-7A: Checking Speed Control Operation (Part 1 of 2). Avenger, Sebring Coupe & Talon

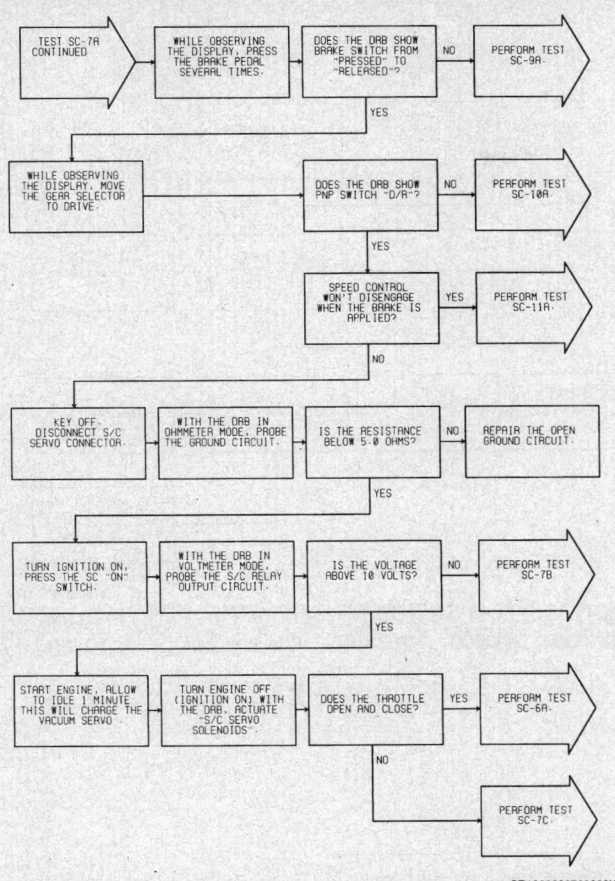

Fig. 194   Test SC-7A: Checking Speed Control Operation (Part 2 of 2). Avenger, Sebring Coupe & Talon

CR1029606769020X

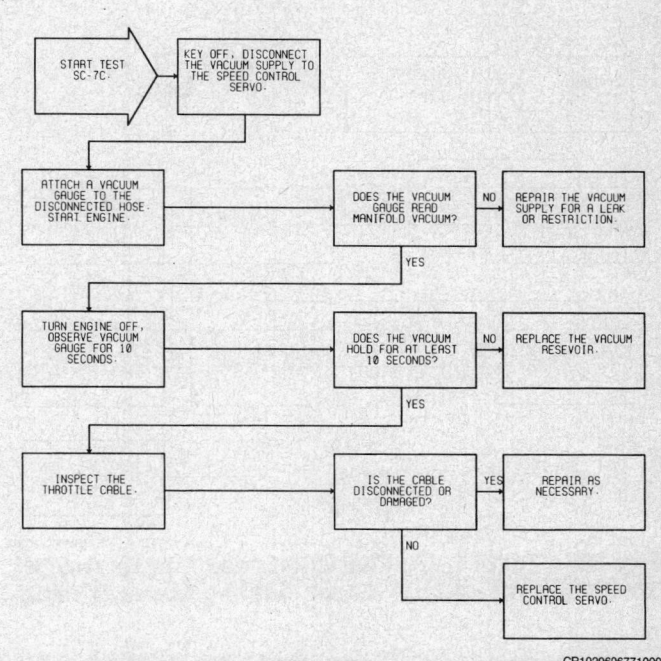

Fig. 196   Test SC-7C: Checking Speed Control Operation. Avenger, Sebring Coupe & Talon

CR1029606771000X

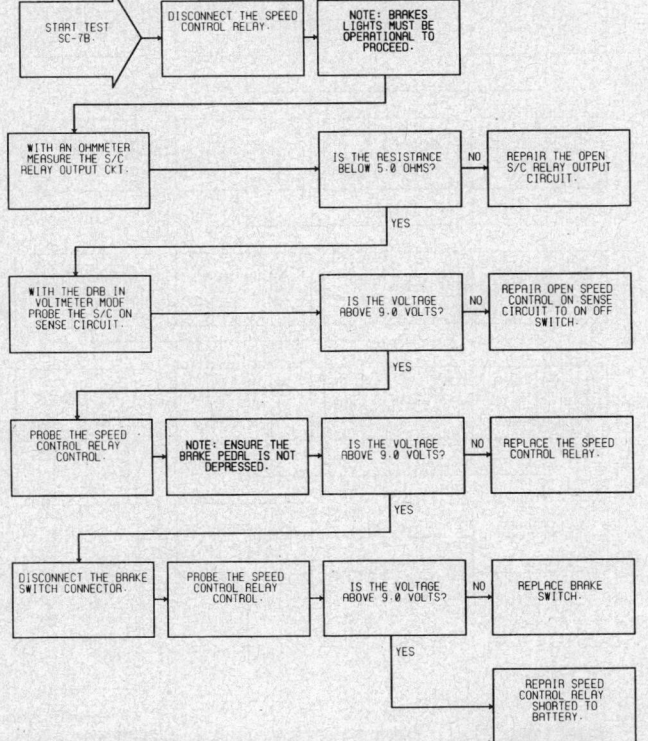

Fig. 195   Test SC-7B: Checking Speed Control Operation. Avenger, Sebring Coupe & Talon

CR1029606770000X

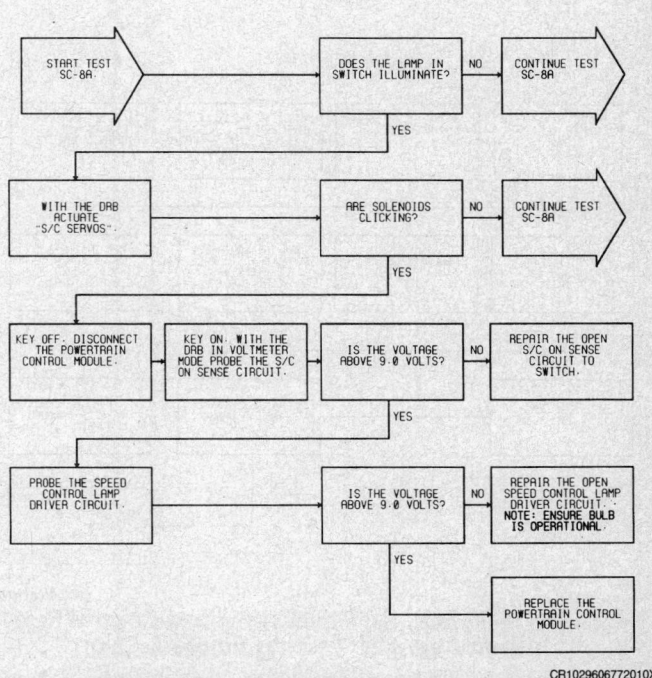

Fig. 197   Test SC-8A: Checking Speed Control On/Off Switch (Part 1 of 2). Avenger, Sebring Coupe & Talon

CR1029606772010X

CHRYSLER–Fuel Injection

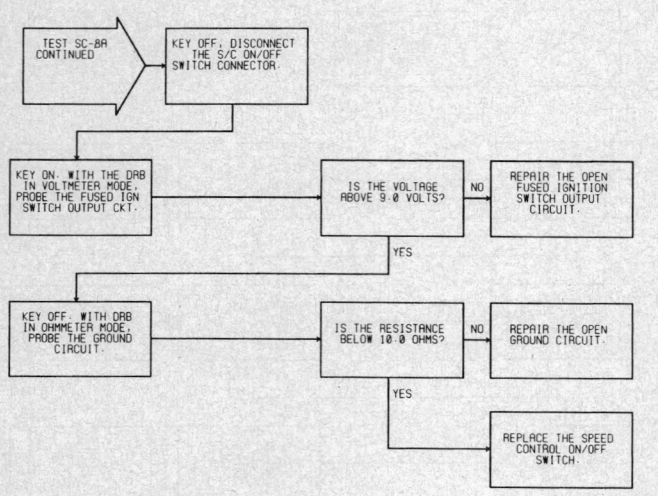

Fig. 197   Test SC-8A: Checking Speed Control On/Off Switch (Part 2 of 2). Avenger, Sebring Coupe & Talon

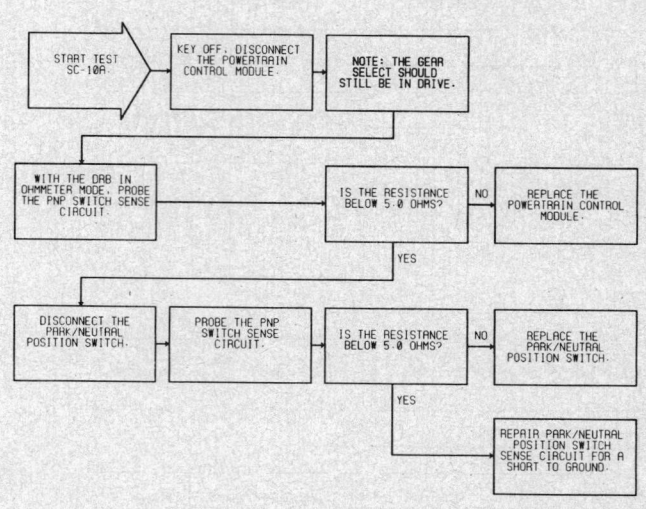

Fig. 198   Test SC-10A: Checking The Park/Neutral Position Switch. Avenger, Sebring Coupe & Talon

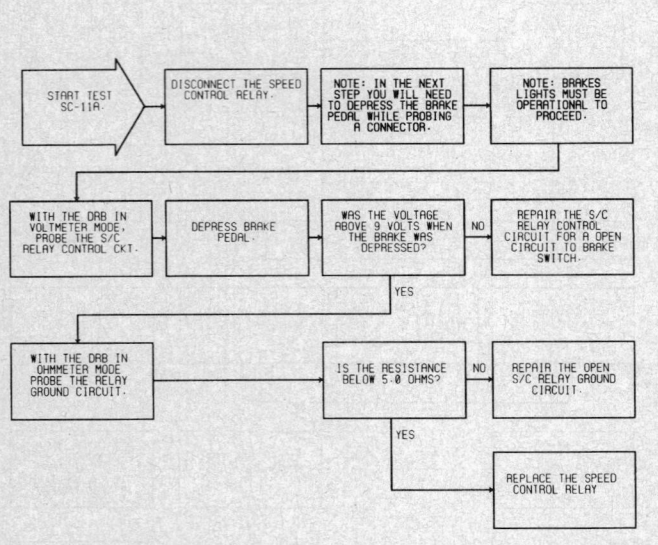

Fig. 199   Test SC-11A: Checking Speed Control Relay Output. Avenger, Sebring Coupe & Talon

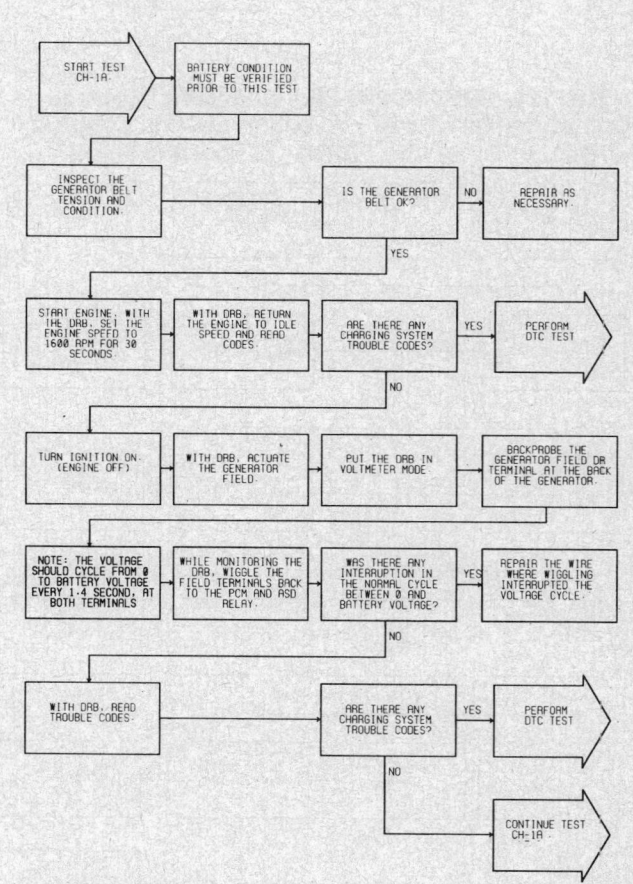

Fig. 200   Test CH-1A: Charging System No Code Test (Part 1 of 3)

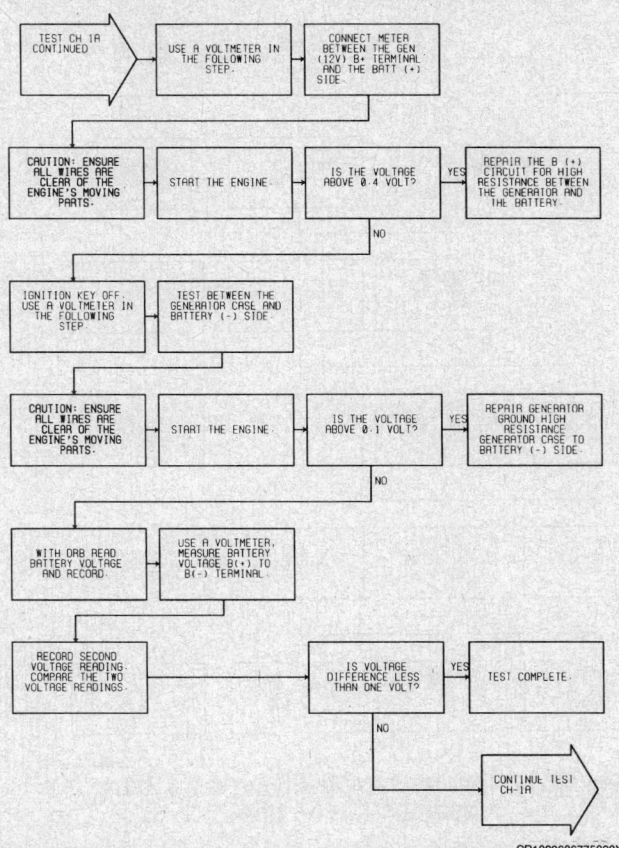

Fig. 200   Test CH-1A: Charging System No Code Test (Part 2 of 3)

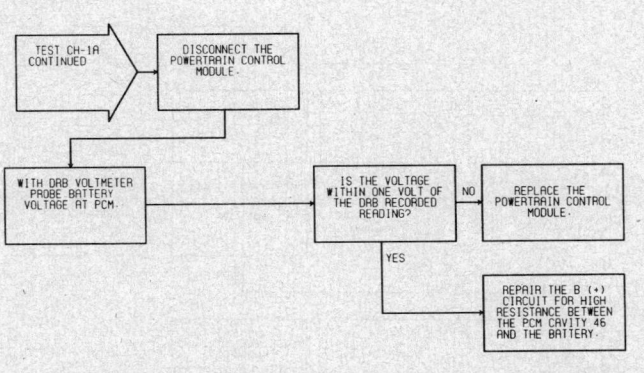

Fig. 200   Test CH-1A: Charging System No Code Test (Part 3 of 3)

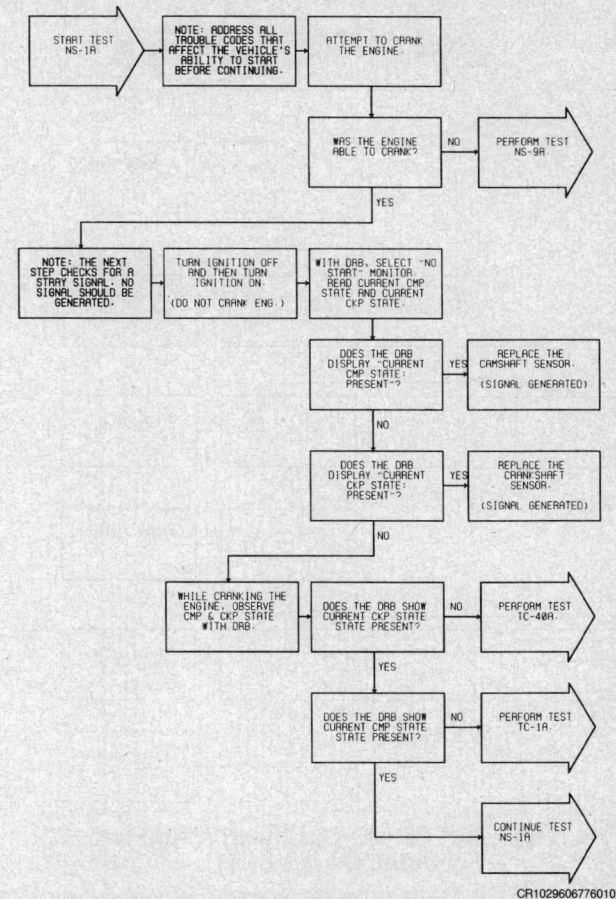

Fig. 201   Test NS-1A: Qualifying A No Start Condition (Part 1 of 4)

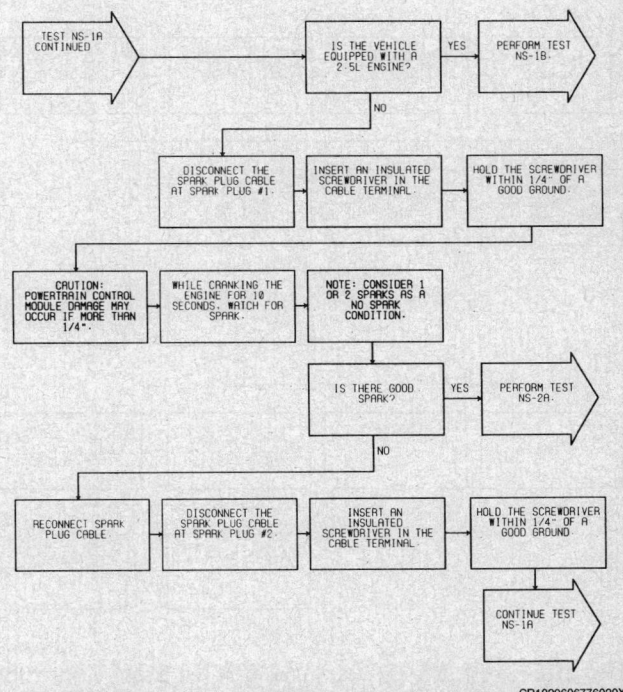

Fig. 201   Test NS-1A: Qualifying A No Start Condition (Part 2 of 4)

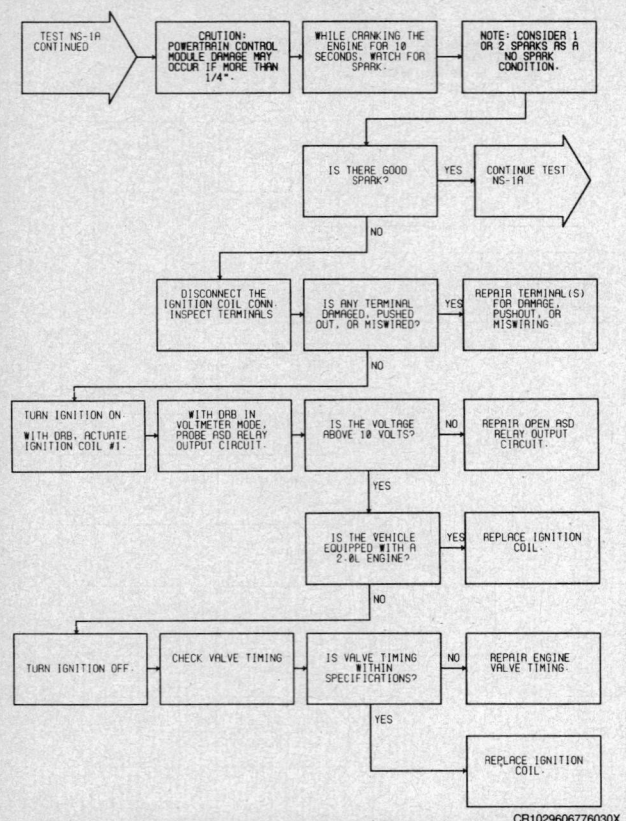

Fig. 201   Test NS-1A: Qualifying A No Start
Condition (Part 3 of 4)

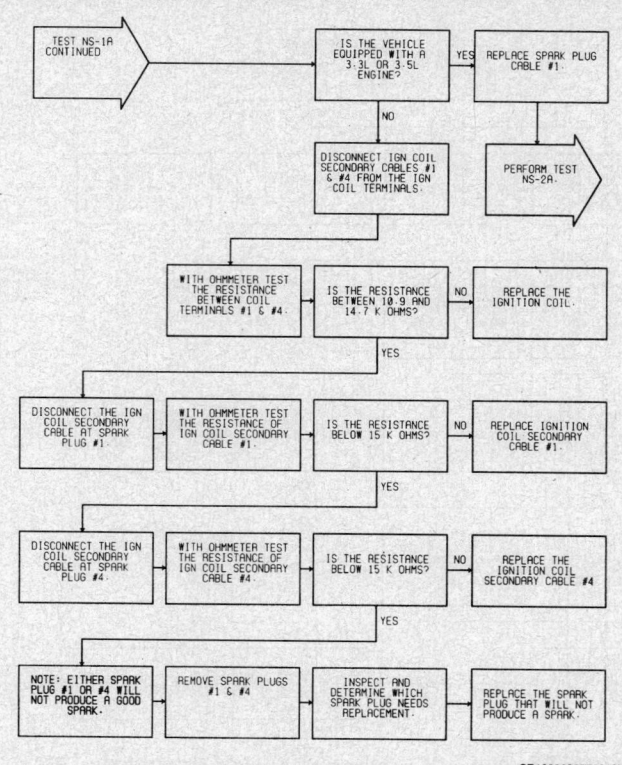

Fig. 201   Test NS-1A: Qualifying A No Start
Condition (Part 4 of 4)

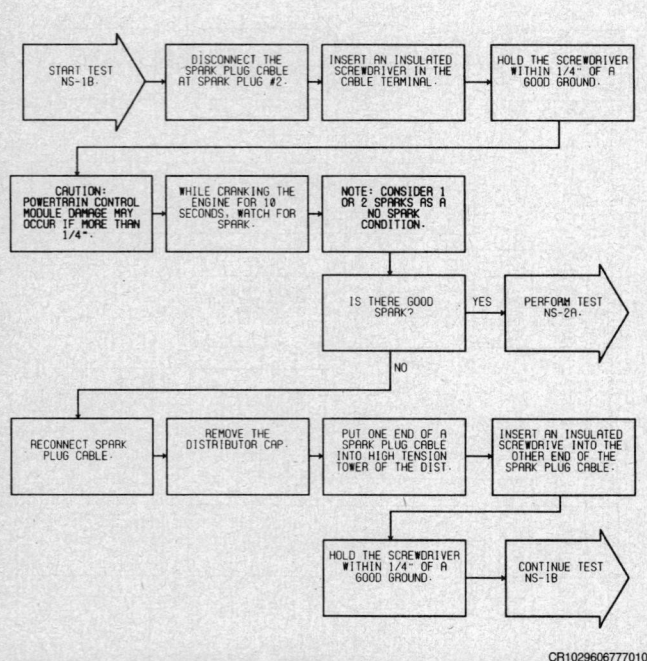

Fig. 202   Test NS-1B: Qualifying A No Start Condition
(Part 1 of 4)

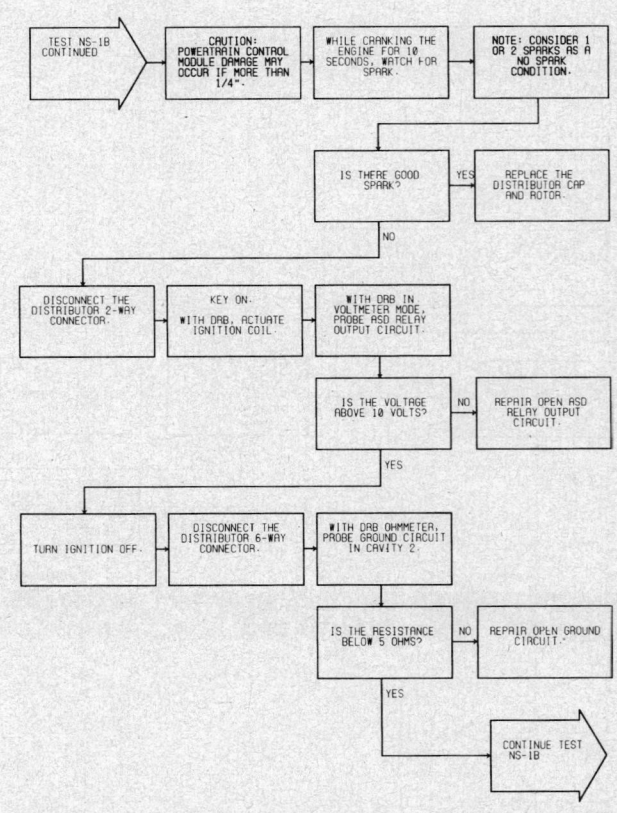

Fig. 202   Test NS-1B: Qualifying A No Start
Condition (Part 2 of 4)

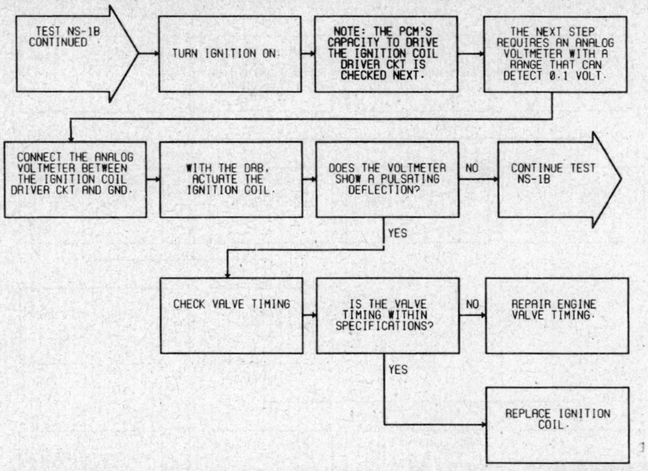

TEST NS-1B CONTINUED
TURN IGNITION ON.
NOTE: THE PCM'S CAPACITY TO DRIVE THE IGNITION COIL DRIVER CKT IS CHECKED NEXT.
THE NEXT STEP REQUIRES AN ANALOG VOLTMETER WITH A RANGE THAT CAN DETECT 0.1 VOLT.
CONNECT THE ANALOG VOLTMETER BETWEEN THE IGNITION COIL DRIVER CKT AND GND.
WITH THE DRB, ACTUATE THE IGNITION COIL.
DOES THE VOLTMETER SHOW A PULSATING DEFLECTION?
NO
CONTINUE TEST NS-1B
YES
CHECK VALVE TIMING
IS THE VALVE TIMING WITHIN SPECIFICATIONS?
NO
REPAIR ENGINE VALVE TIMING.
YES
REPLACE IGNITION COIL.

CR1029606777030X

Fig. 202 Test NS-1B: Qualifying A No Start Condition (Part 3 of 4)

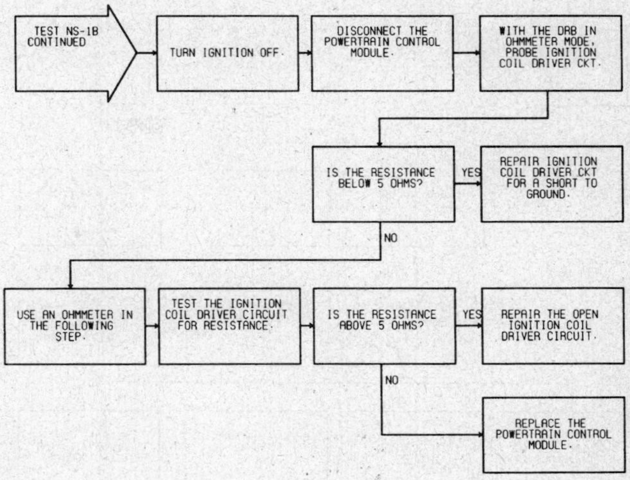

TEST NS-1B CONTINUED
TURN IGNITION OFF.
DISCONNECT THE POWERTRAIN CONTROL MODULE.
WITH THE DRB IN OHMMETER MODE, PROBE IGNITION COIL DRIVER CKT.
IS THE RESISTANCE BELOW 5 OHMS?
YES
REPAIR IGNITION COIL DRIVER CKT FOR A SHORT TO GROUND.
NO
USE AN OHMMETER IN THE FOLLOWING STEP.
TEST THE IGNITION COIL DRIVER CIRCUIT FOR RESISTANCE.
IS THE RESISTANCE ABOVE 5 OHMS?
YES
REPAIR THE OPEN IGNITION COIL DRIVER CIRCUIT.
NO
REPLACE THE POWERTRAIN CONTROL MODULE.

CR1029606777040X

Fig. 202 Test NS-1B: Qualifying A No Start Condition (Part 4 of 4)

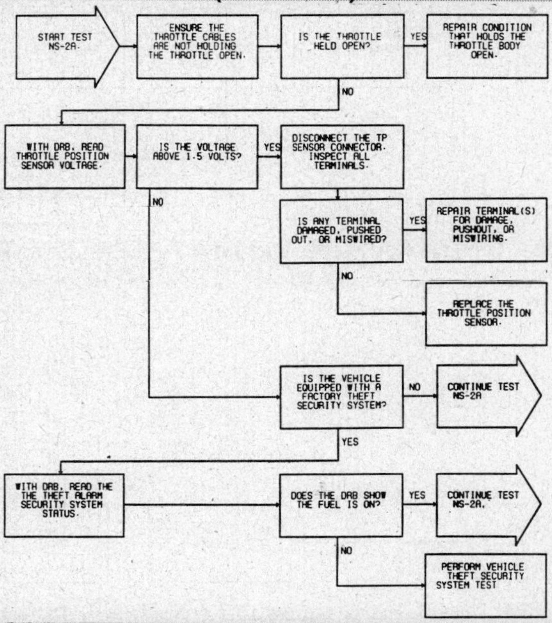

START TEST NS-2A.
ENSURE THE THROTTLE CABLES ARE NOT HOLDING THE THROTTLE OPEN.
IS THE THROTTLE HELD OPEN?
YES
REPAIR CONDITION THAT HOLDS THE THROTTLE BODY OPEN.
NO
WITH DRB, READ THROTTLE POSITION SENSOR VOLTAGE.
IS THE VOLTAGE ABOVE 1.5 VOLTS?
YES
DISCONNECT THE TP SENSOR CONNECTOR. INSPECT ALL TERMINALS.
IS ANY TERMINAL DAMAGED, PUSHED OUT, OR MISWIRED?
YES
REPAIR TERMINAL(S) FOR DAMAGE, PUSHOUT, OR MISWIRING.
NO
REPLACE THE THROTTLE POSITION SENSOR.
NO
IS THE VEHICLE EQUIPPED WITH A FACTORY THEFT SECURITY SYSTEM?
NO
CONTINUE TEST NS-2A
YES
WITH DRB, READ THE THE THEFT ALARM SECURITY SYSTEM STATUS.
DOES THE DRB SHOW THE FUEL IS ON?
YES
CONTINUE TEST NS-2A.
NO
PERFORM VEHICLE THEFT SECURITY SYSTEM TEST

Fig. 203 Test NS-2A: Checking Fuel System (Part 1 of 2)

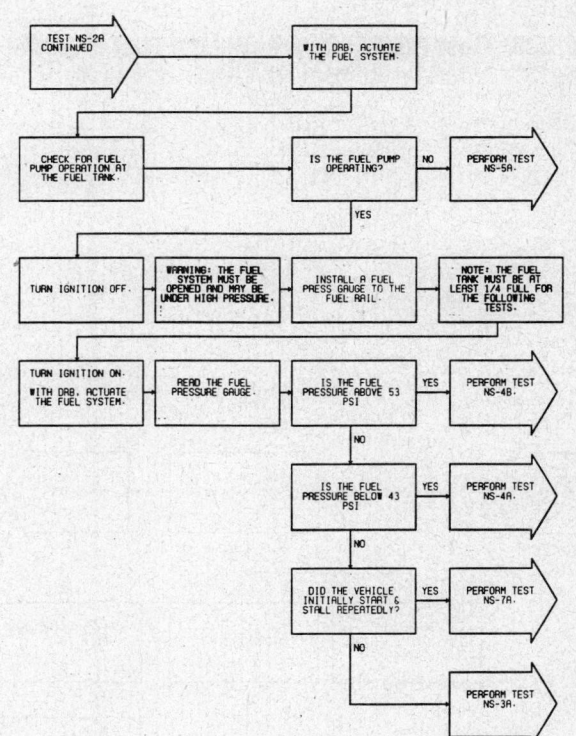

TEST NS-2A CONTINUED
WITH DRB, ACTUATE THE FUEL SYSTEM.
CHECK FOR FUEL PUMP OPERATION AT THE FUEL TANK.
IS THE FUEL PUMP OPERATING?
NO
PERFORM TEST NS-5A.
YES
TURN IGNITION OFF.
WARNING: THE FUEL SYSTEM MUST BE OPENED AND MAY BE UNDER HIGH PRESSURE.
INSTALL A FUEL PRESS GAUGE TO THE FUEL RAIL.
NOTE: THE FUEL TANK MUST BE AT LEAST 1/4 FULL FOR THE FOLLOWING TESTS.
TURN IGNITION ON.
WITH DRB, ACTUATE THE FUEL SYSTEM.
READ THE FUEL PRESSURE GAUGE.
IS THE FUEL PRESSURE ABOVE 53 PSI
YES
PERFORM TEST NS-4B.
NO
IS THE FUEL PRESSURE BELOW 43 PSI
YES
PERFORM TEST NS-4A.
NO
DID THE VEHICLE INITIALLY START & STALL REPEATEDLY?
YES
PERFORM TEST NS-7A.
NO
PERFORM TEST NS-3A.

Fig. 203 Test NS-2A: Checking Fuel System (Part 2 of 2)

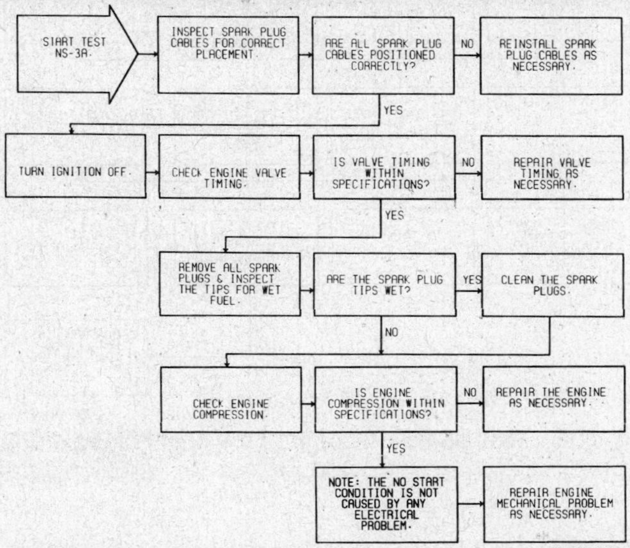

START TEST NS-3A.
INSPECT SPARK PLUG CABLES FOR CORRECT PLACEMENT.
ARE ALL SPARK PLUG CABLES POSITIONED CORRECTLY?
NO
REINSTALL SPARK PLUG CABLES AS NECESSARY.
YES
TURN IGNITION OFF.
CHECK ENGINE VALVE TIMING.
IS VALVE TIMING WITHIN SPECIFICATIONS?
NO
REPAIR VALVE TIMING AS NECESSARY.
YES
REMOVE ALL SPARK PLUGS & INSPECT THE TIPS FOR WET FUEL.
ARE THE SPARK PLUG TIPS WET?
YES
CLEAN THE SPARK PLUGS.
NO
CHECK ENGINE COMPRESSION.
IS ENGINE COMPRESSION WITHIN SPECIFICATIONS?
NO
REPAIR THE ENGINE AS NECESSARY.
YES
NOTE: THE NO START CONDITION IS NOT CAUSED BY ANY ELECTRICAL PROBLEM.
REPAIR ENGINE MECHANICAL PROBLEM AS NECESSARY.

CR1029606779000X

Fig. 204 Test NS-3A: Checking The Engine Mechanical Systems

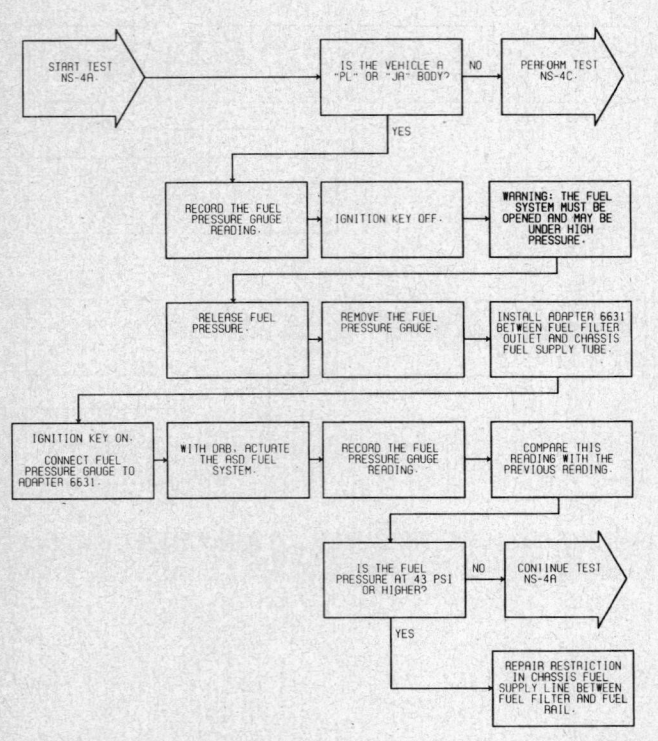

Fig. 205   Test NS-4A: Repairing Low Fuel Pressure (Part 1 of 2)

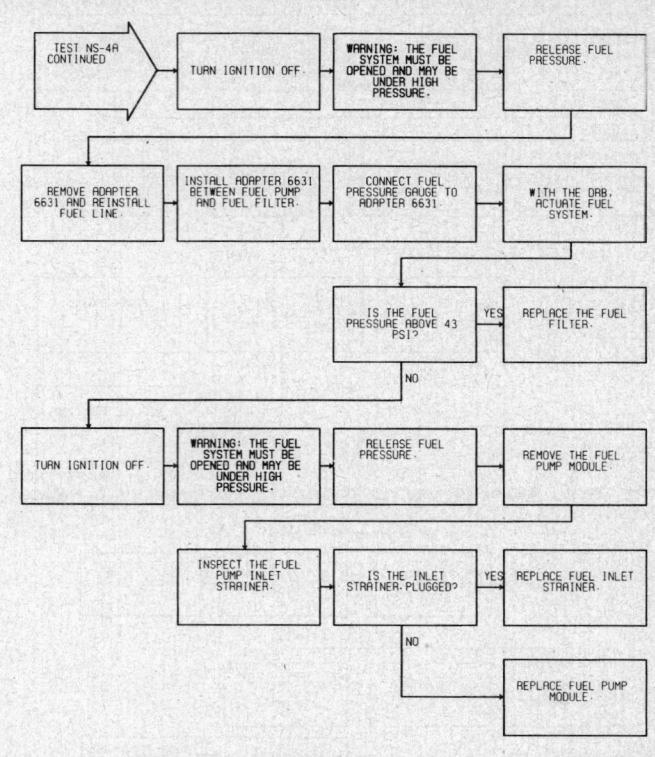

Fig. 205   Test NS-4A: Repairing Low Fuel Pressure (Part 2 of 2)

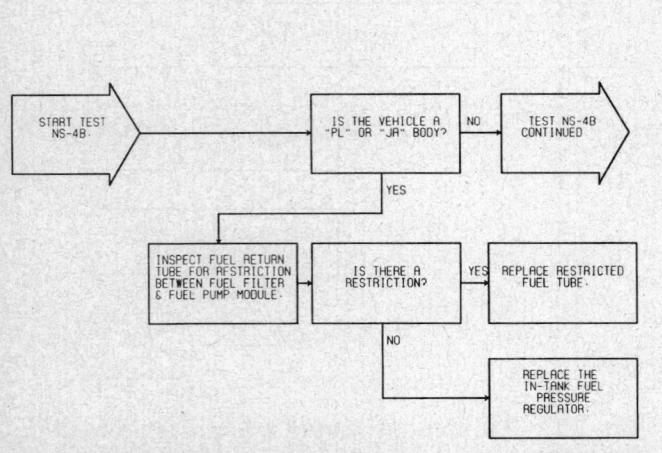

Fig. 206   Test NS-4B: Repairing Low Fuel Pressure (Part 1 of 2)

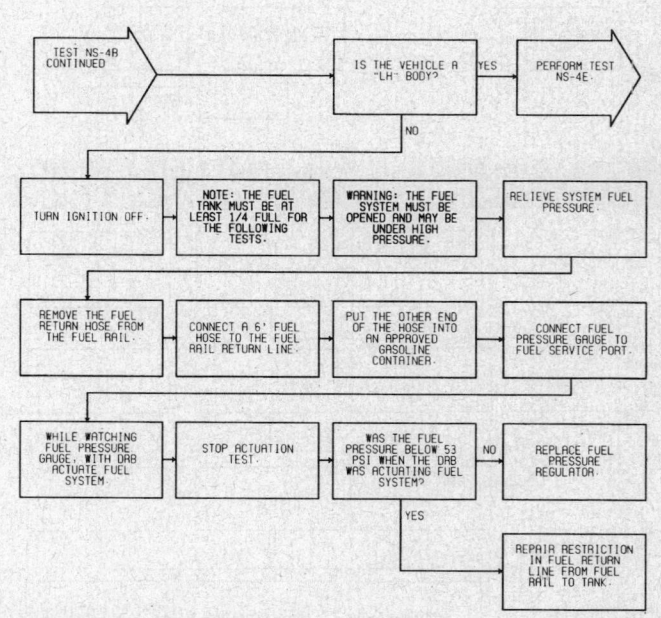

Fig. 206   Test NS-4B: Repairing Low Fuel Pressure (Part 2 of 2)

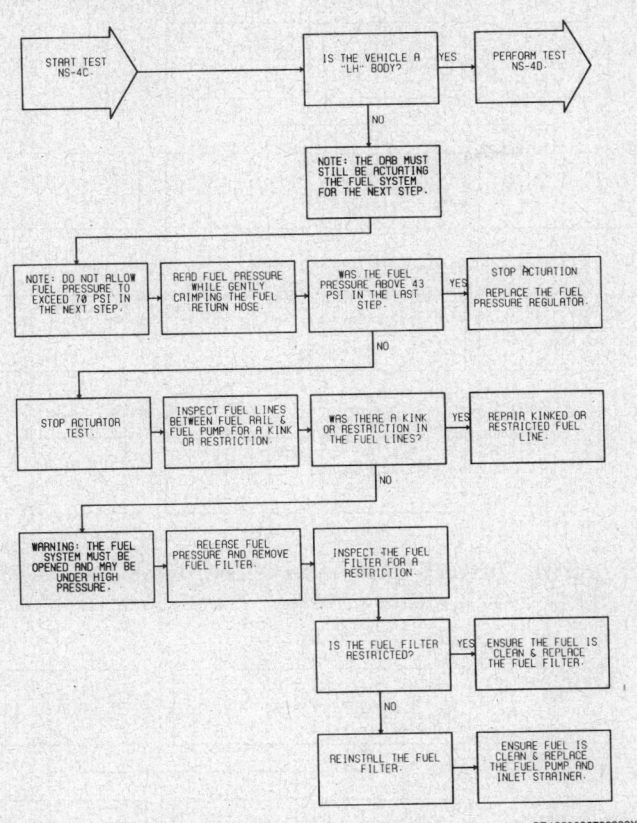

Fig. 207 Test NS-4C: Repairing Low Fuel Pressure

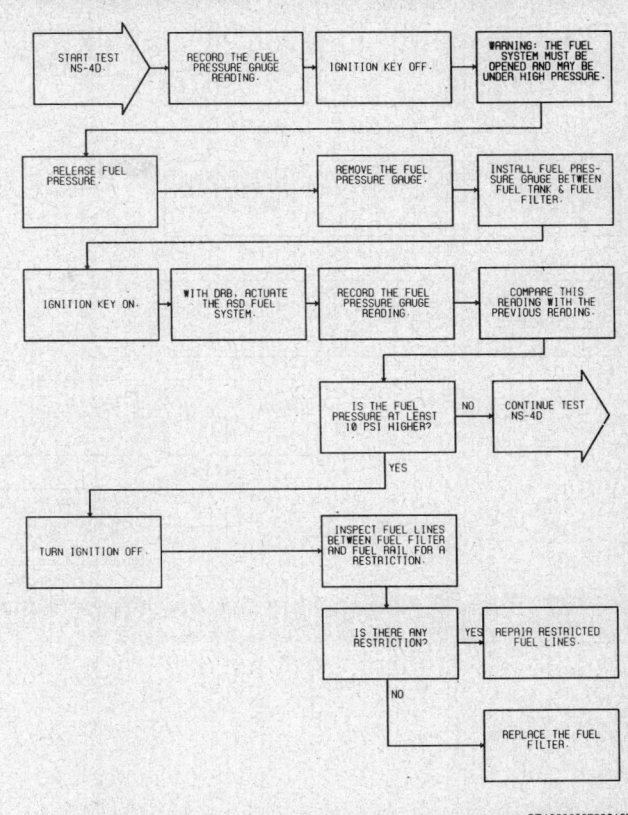

Fig. 208 Test NS-4D: Repairing Low Fuel Pressure (Part 1 of 2)

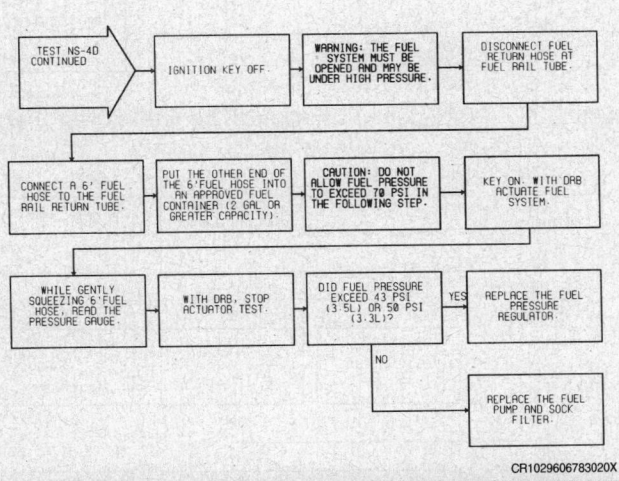

Fig. 208 Test NS-4D: Repairing Low Fuel Pressure (Part 2 of 2)

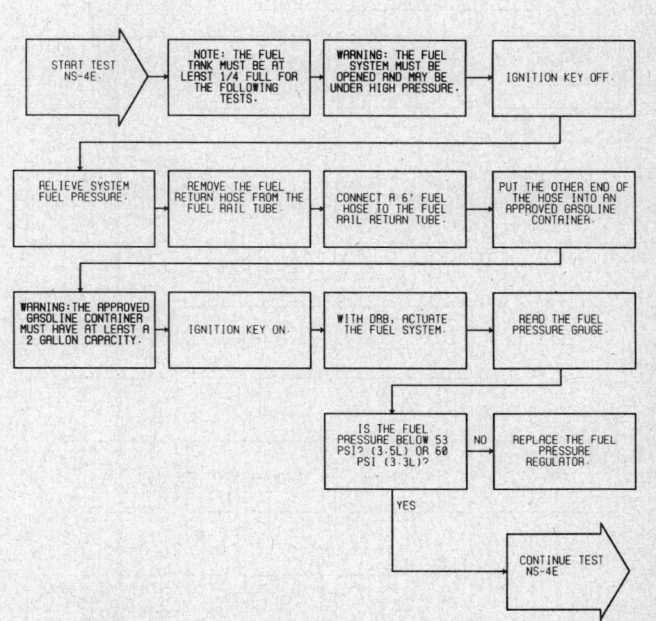

Fig. 209 Test NS-4E: Repairing Low Fuel Pressure (Part 1 of 2)

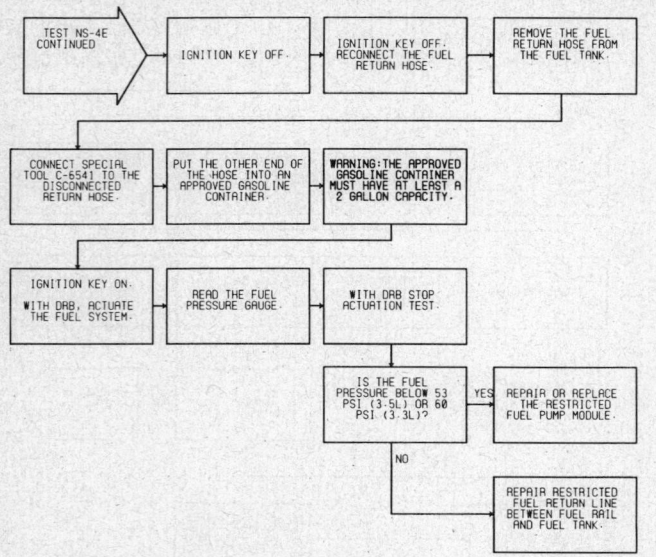

Fig. 209 Test NS-4E: Repairing Low Fuel Pressure (Part 2 of 2)

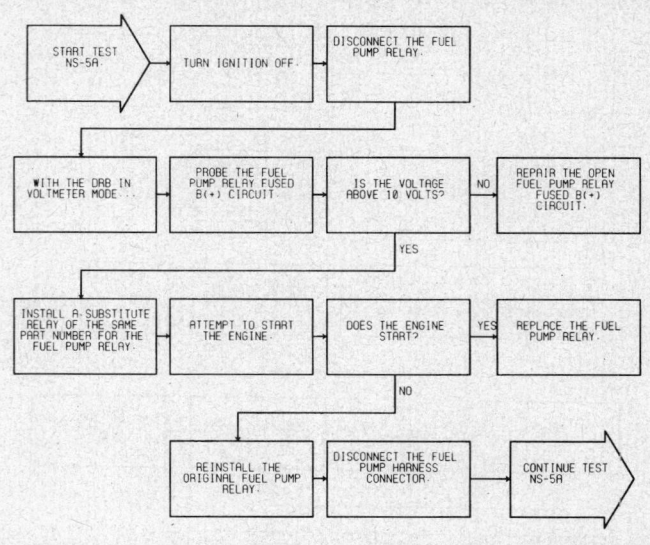

Fig. 210 Test NS-5A: Checking The Fuel Pump (Part 1 of 2)

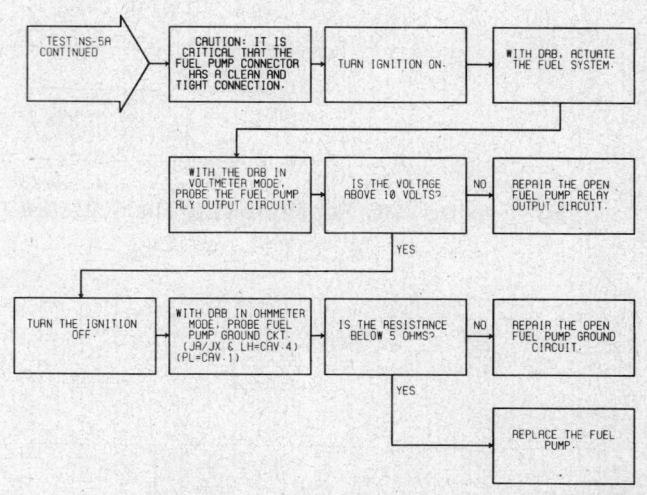

Fig. 210 Test NS-5A: Checking The Fuel Pump (Part 2 of 2)

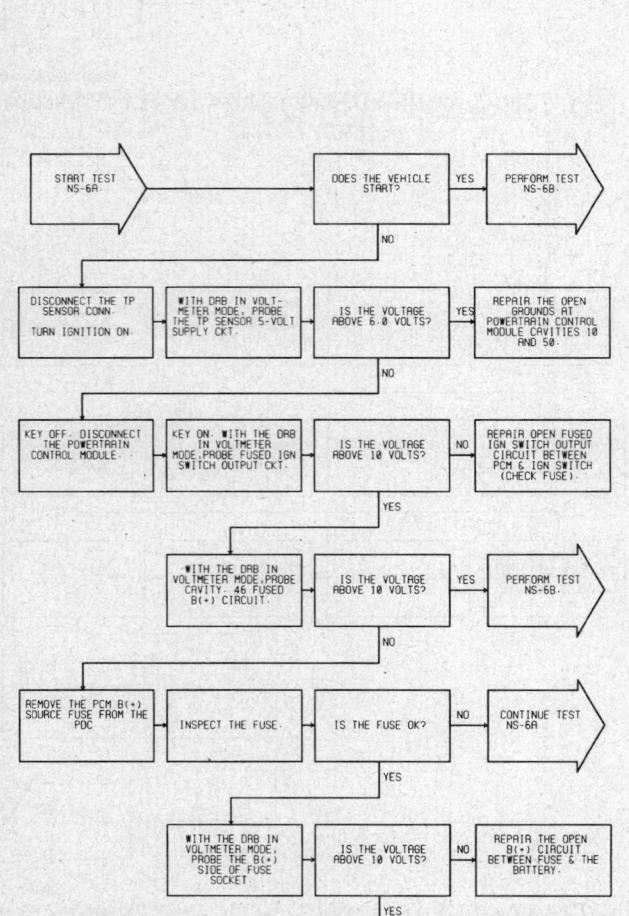

Fig. 211 Test NS-6A: Repairing A No Response Condition (Part 1 of 5)

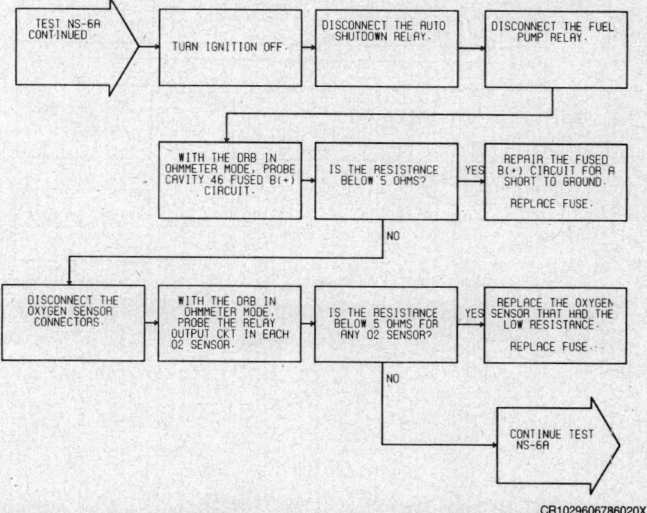

Fig. 211 Test NS-6A: Repairing A "No Response" Condition (Part 2 of 5)

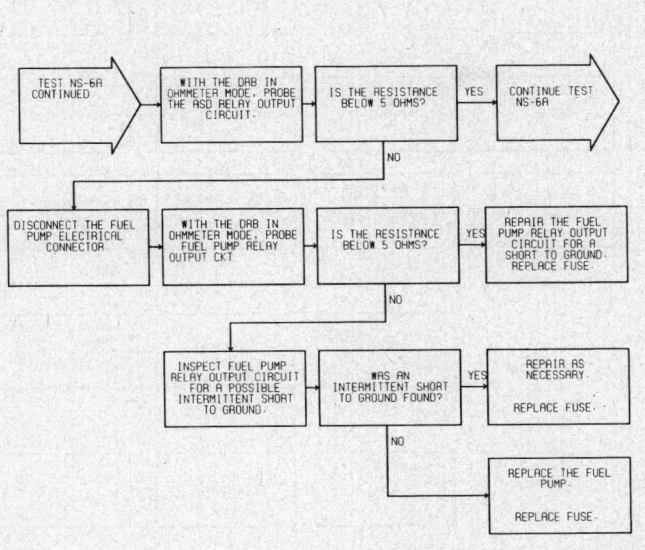

Fig. 211   Test NS-6A: Repairing A "No Response" Condition (Part 3 of 5)

CR1029606786030X

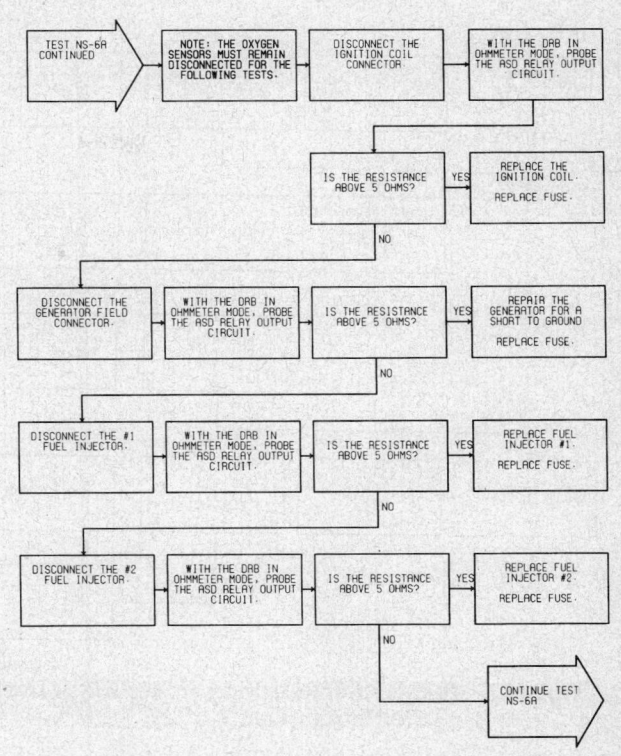

Fig. 211   Test NS-6A: Repairing "A No Response" Condition (Part 4 of 5)

CR1029606786040X

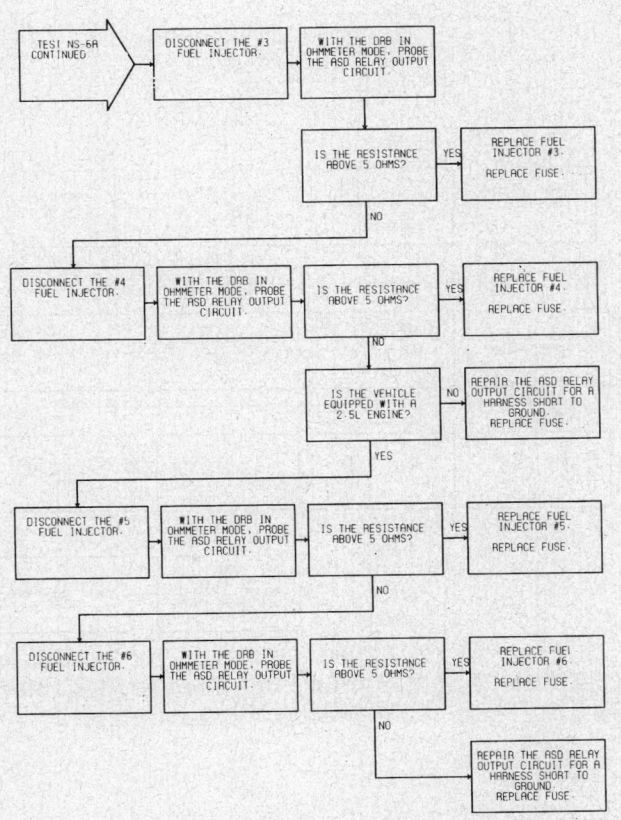

Fig. 211   Test NS-6A: Repairing "A No Response" Condition (Part 5 of 5)

CR1029606786050X

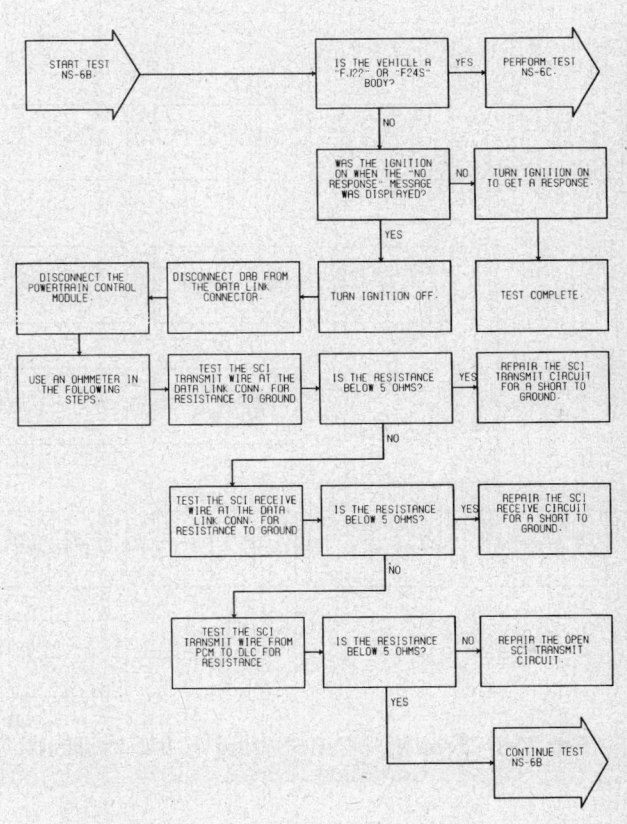

Fig. 212   Test NS-6B: Repairing A "No Response" Condition (Part 1 of 2)

CR1029606787010X

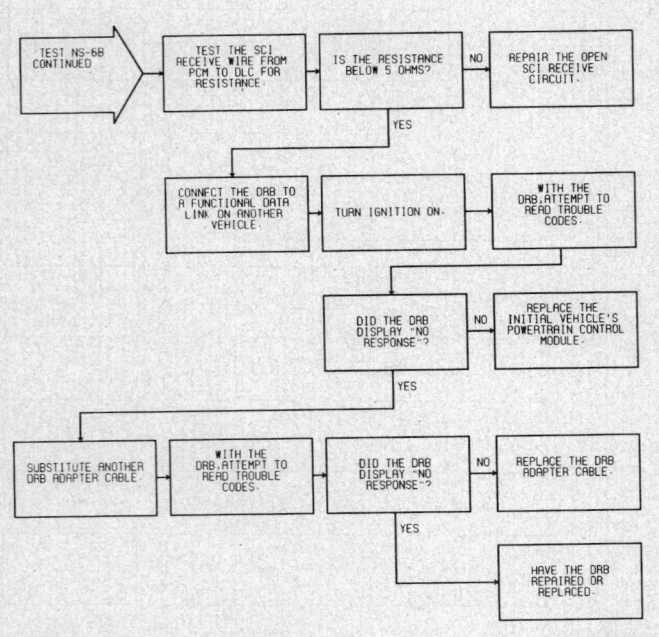

Fig. 212   Test NS-6B: Repairing A "No Response" Condition (Part 2 of 2)

CR1029606787020X

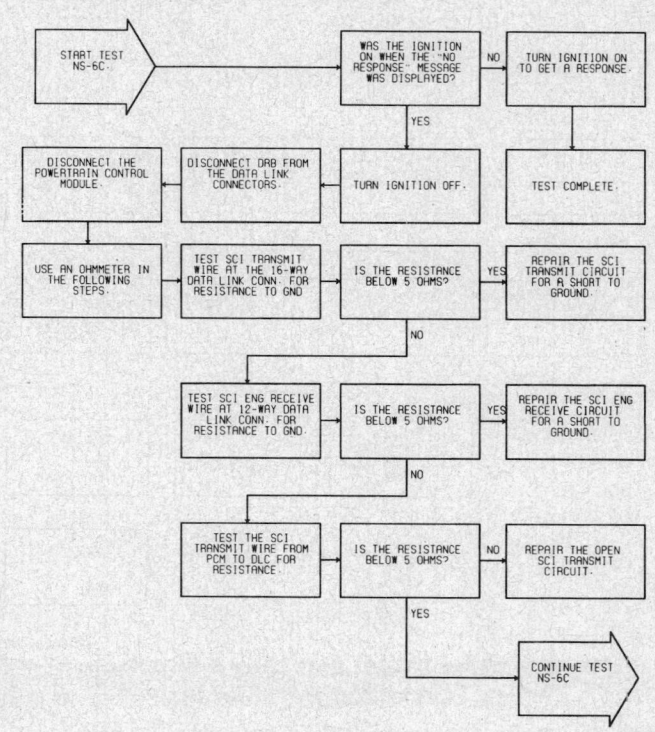

Fig. 213   Test NS-6C: Repairing A "No Response" Condition (Part 1 of 2)

CR1029606788010X

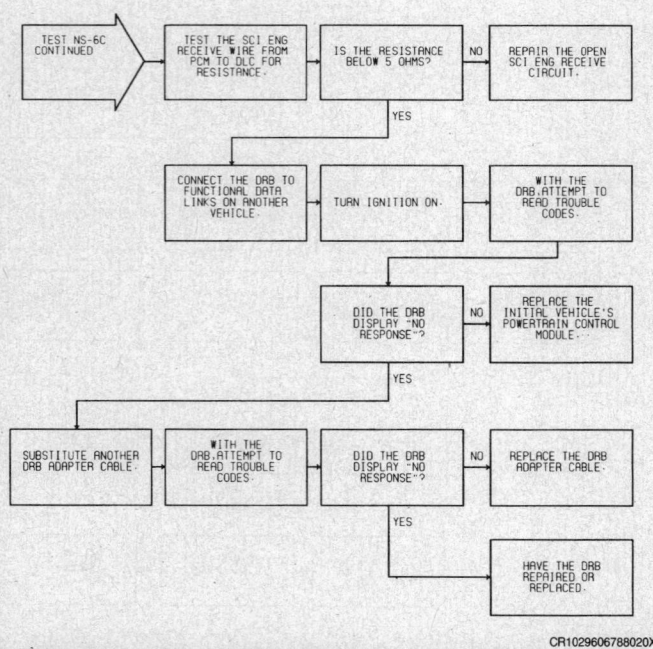

Fig. 213   Test NS-6C: Repairing A "No Response" Condition (Part 2 of 2)

CR1029606788020X

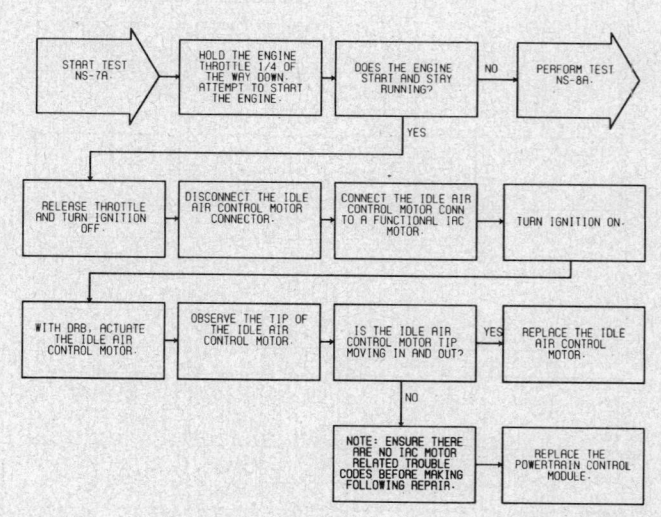

Fig. 214   Test NS-7A: Checking The Idle Air Control Motor Operation

CR1029606789000X

At this point in the diagnostic test procedure, you have determined that all of the **engine electrical systems** are operating as designed; therefore, they are **not the cause of the start and stall problem.** The following additional items should be checked as possible mechanical causes of the no start condition. Any one or more of these items can produce a no start condition, none can be overlooked as a possible cause.

1. **ENGINE VALVE TIMING** – must be within specifications

2. **ENGINE COMPRESSION** – must be within specifications

3. **ENGINE EXHAUST SYSTEM** – must be free of any restrictions

4. **ENGINE PCV SYSTEM** – must flow freely

5. **ENGINE DRIVE SPROCKETS OR TIMING BELT** – must be properly positioned

6. **FUEL** – must be free of contamination

7. **ENGINE SECONDARY IGNITION CHECK** – must exhibit a normal scope pattern

Always look for any Technical Service Bulletins that may relate to this condition.

CR1029606790000X

Fig. 215   Test NS-8A: Repairing A Start & Stall Condition

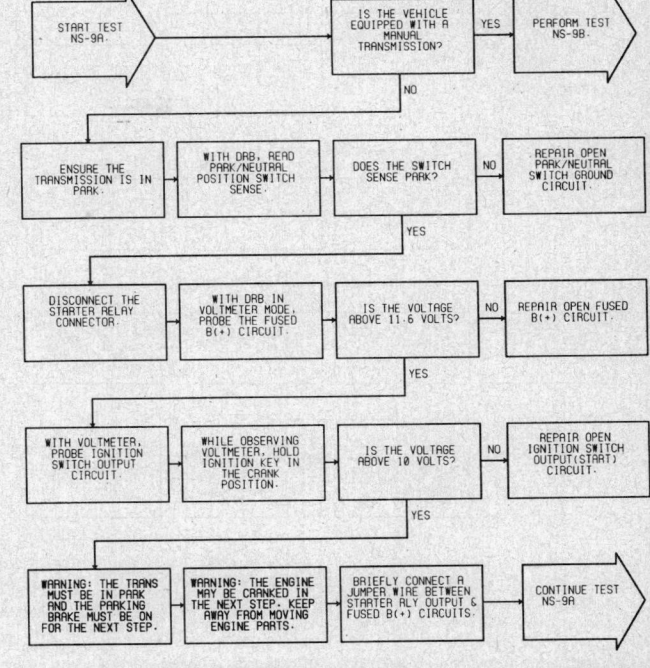

CR1029606791010X

Fig. 216   Test NS-9A: Repairing A No Crank Condition (Part 1 of 3)

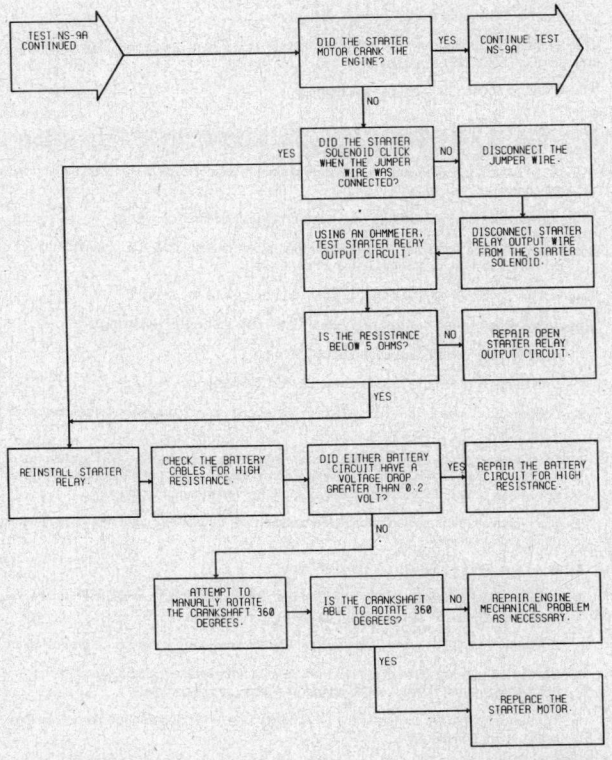

CR1029606791020X

Fig. 216   Test NS-9A: Repairing A No Crank Condition (Part 2 of 3)

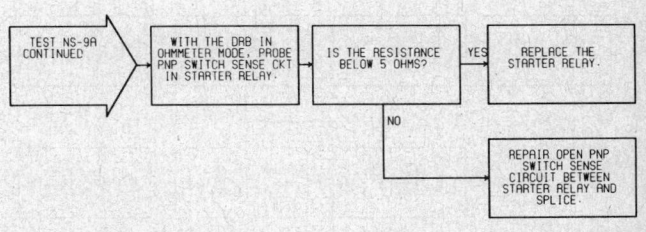

CR1029606791030X

Fig. 216   Test NS-9A: Repairing A No Crank Condition (Part 3 of 3)

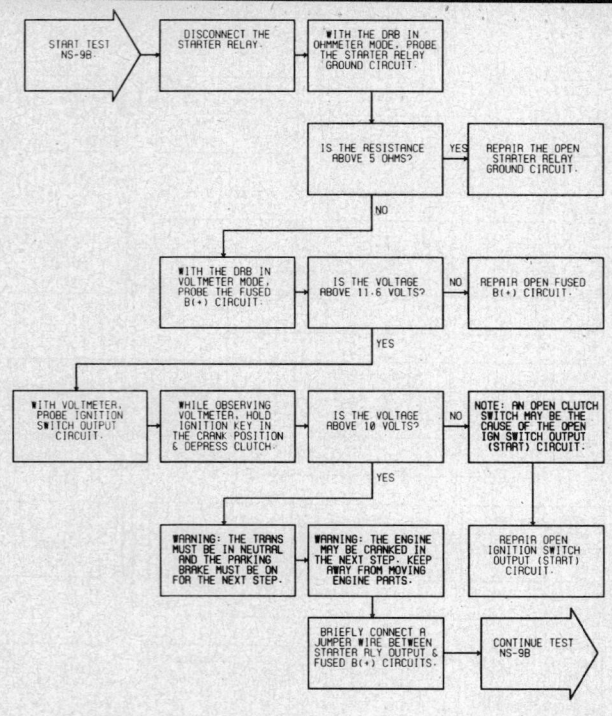

CR1029606792010X

Fig. 217   Test NS-9B: Repairing A No Crank Condition (Part 1 of 2)

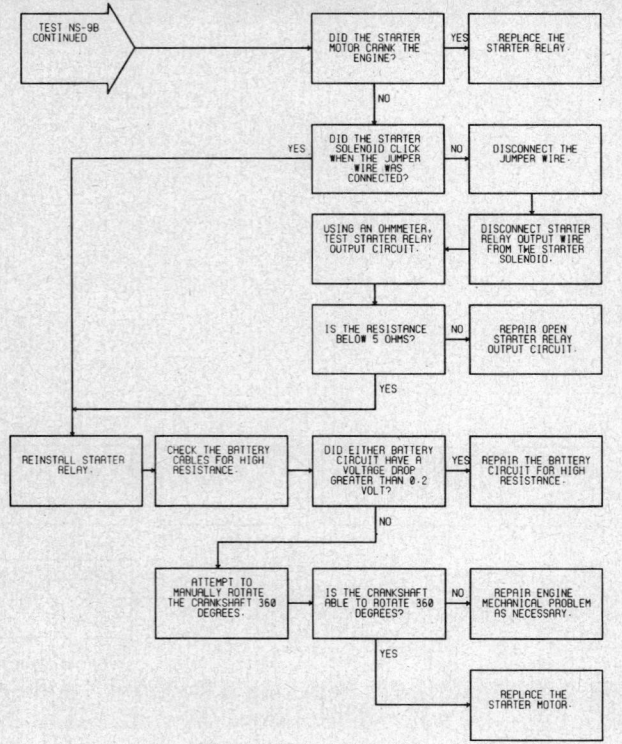

CR1029606792020X

Fig. 217   Test NS-9B: Repairing A No Crank Condition (Part 2 of 2)

Inspect the vehicle to ensure that all engine components are connected. Reassemble and reconnect components as necessary.

Inspect the engine for contamination. If it is contaminated, change the oil and filter.

Attempt to start the engine.

If the engine is **unable** to start, look for any Technical Service Bulletins that may relate to this condition. Return to **DTC TEST** if necessary.

The repair is now complete.

CR1029606793000X

Fig. 218   Test VER-1A: No Start Verification

Inspect the vehicle to ensure that all engine components are connected. Reassemble and reconnect all components as necessary.

If this verification procedure is being performed after a NO TROUBLE CODE test, do the following:

1. Check to see if the initial symptom still exists.

2. If the initial or another symptom exists, the repair is not complete. Check all pertinent Technical Service Bulletins and return to **TEST NTC-1A** if necessary.

If this verification procedure is being performed after an OBDII trouble code test, perform VER-5. For all other trouble codes, continue with this verification.

For previously read trouble codes that have not been dealt with, return to **DTC TEST** and follow the path specified; otherwise, continue.

If the powertrain control module has not been changed:

1. Connect the DRB to the PCM data link connector and erase trouble codes.

2. With the DRB, reset all values in the adaptive memory.

3. Disconnect the DRB.

Ensure no trouble code remains by doing the following:

1. If this test is for an **A/C Relay Control Circuit Code,** drive the vehicle for at least five minutes with the A/C on. For some of the drive, go at least 40 mph; at some point stop the car and turn the engine off for 10 seconds or more; then restart and continue. Ensure the transmission shifts through all gears. Upon completion of the road test, turn the engine off, and read trouble codes with the DRB.

2. If the repaired code has reset, the repair is not complete. Check all related Technical Service Bulletins and return to **DTC TEST** if necessary. If another trouble code has set, return to **DTC TEST** and follow the path specified for that trouble code. If there are no trouble codes, the repair was successful and is now complete.

CR1029606794000X

Fig. 219   Test VER-2A: Road Test Verification

Inspect the vehicle to ensure that all engine components are connected. Reassemble and reconnect components as necessary.

If the powertrain control module has been changed, do the following:

1. If the vehicle is equipped with a factory theft alarm, start the vehicle at least 20 times so that the alarm system may be activated when desired.

Connect the DRB to the PCM data link connector and erase the codes.

Ensure no other charging system problems remain by doing the following:

1. Start the engine.

2. Raise the engine speed to 2000 rpm for at least 30 seconds.

3. Allow the engine to idle.

4. Turn the engine off.

5. Turn the ignition key on.

6. With the DRB, read trouble code messages.

If the repaired code has reset, or another one has set, check all pertinent Technical Service Bulletins and return to **DTC TEST** if necessary.

If there are no codes, the repair is now complete.

CR1029606795000X

Fig. 220   Test VER-3A: Charging Verification

Inspect the vehicle to ensure that all engine components are connected. Reassemble and reconnect all components as necessary.

If the powertrain control module has been changed, do the following:

1. If the vehicle is equipped with a factory theft alarm, start the vehicle at least 20 times so that the alarm system may be activated when desired.

Connect the DRB to the PCM data link connector and erase the codes.

Ensure no other speed control problems remain by doing the following:

1. Road test the vehicle at a speed above 35 mph.

2. Turn the speed control ON/OFF switch to the ON position.

3. Depress and release the SET switch. If the speed control did not engage, the repair is not complete.*

4. For stalk switch equipped vehicles, quickly depress and release the SET switch. For steering wheel switch equipped vehicles, quickly depress and release the RESUME/ACCEL switch. If the vehicle speed did not increase by 2 mph, the repair is not complete.*

5. Using caution, depress and release the brake pedal. If the speed control did not disengage, the repair is not complete.*

6. Bring the vehicle speed back up to 35 mph.

7. Depress the RESUME/ACCEL switch. If the speed control did not resume the previously set speed, the repair is not complete.*

8. Hold down the SET switch. If the vehicle did not decelerate, the repair is not complete.*

9. Ensure the vehicle speed is greater than 35 mph and release the SET switch. If the vehicle did not adjust and set a new vehicle speed, the repair is not complete.*

10. Turn on the ON/OFF switch to the OFF position. If the speed control did not disengage, the repair is not complete.*

If the vehicle successfully passed all of the previous tests, the speed control system is now functioning as designed. The repair is now complete.

* Check for Technical Service Bulletins that pertain to this speed control problem and then, if necessary, return to **DTC TEST.**

CR1029606796000X

Fig. 221   Test VER-4A: Speed Control Verification

Inspect the vehicle to ensure that all engine components are connected. Reassemble and reconnect components as necessary.

If there are any existing diagnostic trouble codes that have not been repaired, perform **DTC TEST** and follow the path specified. After all diagnostic trouble codes have been repaired, return to **TEST VER-5A** and run the monitor for the previously repaired OBDII trouble code.

1. Connect the DRB to the data link connector.

2. Ensure the fuel tank has at least a quarter tank of fuel.

3. Turn the air conditioning off.

4. The proper way to verify that the trouble code has been repaired is to allow the powertrain control module to run the monitor. The technician can see the monitor run using the DRBIII.

Read the enabling conditions for the trouble code that was repaired. The enabling conditions are different for each OBDII code.

5. With the DRBIII, monitor the pre-test enabling conditions until all conditions have been met. Once the enabling conditions have been met, monitor the appropriate OBDII monitor with the DRBIII.

6. If the repaired OBDII trouble code has reset or was seen in the OBDII monitor while on the road test, the repair is not complete. Check for any related Technical Service Bulletins and return to **DTC TEST.**

   – If another trouble code has set, return to **DTC TEST** and follow the path specified for that trouble code.

   – If there are no trouble codes, the repair was successful and is now complete.

CR1029606797000X

Fig. 222   Test VER-5A: Road Test For OBD II Trouble Codes

SYSTEM SERVICE
Fuel System Pressure Relief
AVENGER & SEBRING COUPE

1. Remove rear seat cushion.
2. Remove protector to disconnect fuel pump connector.
3. Start engine and run until it stops naturally, then turn ignition switch off.
4. Connect fuel pump connector and install protector.
5. Install rear cushion.

BREEZE, CIRRUS, SEBRING CONVERTIBLE & STRATUS w/2.0L/4-122 & 2.4L/4-148 ENGINES, CONCORDE, INTREPID, LHS, NEON, NEW YORKER & VISION

1. Disconnect ground cable from auxiliary jumper terminal or battery.
2. Remove fuel filler cap.
3. Remove protective cap from fuel pressure test port on fuel rail.
4. Place open end of fuel pressure release hose tool No. C-4799-1, or equivalent, into a suitable gasoline container, then connect other hose end to fuel pressure test port. Fuel pressure should bleed off through hose into container.

BREEZE, CIRRUS, SEBRING CONVERTIBLE & STRATUS w/2.5L/V6-152 ENGINE

1. Disconnect fuel rail electrical harness from engine harness.
2. Connect suitable jumper wire between fuel rail harness connector terminal A142 and 12 volt power source.
3. Connect another suitable jumper wire to ground source, then momentarily ground one injector harness connector terminal, to release fuel system pressure.
4. Repeat procedure for 2 to 3 injectors.

TALON

1. Disconnect fuel pump harness connector at fuel tank.
2. Start engine and let it run until it stalls, then turn ignition switch to Off position.
3. Reconnect fuel pump harness connector.

Component Replacement
THROTTLE BODY
2.0L/4-122 ENGINE
Neon

1. Relieve fuel system pressure as described under "Precautions."
2. **On models equipped with manual transaxle,** proceed as follows:
   a. Remove throttle cable from throttle body lever, then compress retaining tabs on cable and slide cable out of bracket.
   b. Slide clasp out from throttle cable hole to remove speed control cable from throttle lever.
3. **On models equipped with automatic transaxle,** proceed as follows:
   a. Remove throttle cable from throttle body cam, then compress retaining tabs on cable and slide cable out of bracket.
   b. While holding throttle lever in wide open position, use finger pressure to push kickdown cable connector off pivot. **Do not attempt to pull connector away from lever.**
   c. Compress kickdown cable retaining tabs and slide cable out of bracket; then, while holding throttle lever in wide open position, use finger pressure to push speed control cable connector off pivot. **Do not attempt to pull connector away from lever.**
   d. Compress speed control cable retaining tabs and slide cable out of bracket.
4. **On all models,** remove cable mounting bracket screws and throttle body mounting bolts, then remove throttle body.
5. Reverse procedure to install.

Breeze, Cirrus, Sebring Convertible & Stratus

1. Relieve fuel system pressure as described under "Precautions."
2. Remove air inlet resonator and disconnect throttle cable at throttle body lever, then compress cable retaining tabs and slide cable out of bracket.
3. Slide speed control cable clasp out through throttle cable hole to remove cable, then disconnect evaporative purge hose at throttle body nipple.
4. Remove cable mounting bracket screws and throttle body mounting bolts, then lift throttle body until Throttle Position Sensor (TPS) and idle air control motor connectors can be removed.
5. Remove throttle body assembly.
6. Reverse procedure to install. Intake manifold O-ring gasket is reusable, but should be wiped clean prior to throttle body installation.

Avenger, Sebring Coupe & Talon

1. Release fuel system pressure as described under "Precautions."
2. Disconnect cables, vacuum hoses and electrical connectors.
3. Remove throttle body from intake manifold plenum.
4. Reverse procedure to install.

2.4L/4-148 ENGINE
Breeze, Cirrus, Sebring Convertible & Stratus

Refer to "2.0L/4-122 Engine" in this section for throttle body replacement procedure.

2.5L/V6-152 ENGINE

1. Remove air tube from throttle body, then the throttle cable from throttle body lever.
2. Pry retainer tab back on throttle cable and slide cable out of bracket.
3. **On models equipped with speed control,** slide speed control cable out of bracket.
4. **On all models,** remove EVAP purge hose from nipple on throttle body, then the connectors from throttle position sensor and idle air control motor.
5. Remove throttle body to intake manifold bolts, then the throttle body.
6. Reverse procedure to install. **Torque** throttle body to intake manifold bolts to 250 inch lbs., then the clamps to 20-30 inch lbs.

3.3L/V6-201 ENGINE

1. Disconnect PCV air hose from cylinder head cover.
2. Remove air cleaner tube from throttle disconnect purge hose from throttle body.

3. disconnect purge hose from throttle body.
4. Rotate throttle lever to wide open throttle position and remove throttle and speed control cables.
5. Remove throttle body mounting bolts then the throttle body.
6. Clean gasket surface on throttle body and intake manifold plenum.
7. Reverse procedure to install. **Torque** throttle body bolts to 19 ft. lbs.

3.5L/V6-215 ENGINE

Removal

1. Disconnect battery ground cable.
2. For left throttle body replacement, hold throttle lever in wide open position and remove throttle and speed control cables from throttle arm.
3. Remove tube connecting air cleaner to air plenum.
4. Disconnect air plenum from throttle bodies, PCV air tube and IAC motor.
5. Remove plenum from right side of vehicle.
6. Disconnect purge hose from throttle body.
7. For right throttle body replacement, disconnect electrical connector to the TPS sensor.
8. Remove throttle body mounting nuts. The end throttle body shaft has a ball stud that fits into a socket in the synchronization shaft. Also, the tang on the end of the throttle body lever fits into an opening in the bracket on the synchronization shaft.
9. Slide throttle body back off of mounting studs. Seperate throttle body from the synchronization shaft. Remove throttle body.
10. Clean gasket mating surfaces.

Installation

Prior to installing either throttle body, remove and clean opposite throttle body.
1. Position new gasket over throttle body mounting studs.
2. Connect left throttle body synchronization shaft. ensure ball stud enters socket in the end of synchronization shaft. Ensure spring attaches to shaft and throttle body arm. Ensure spring does not bind when opening and closing the throttle blade.
3. Connect right throttle body synchronization shaft. Ensure ball stud on throttle shaft enters socket in end of synchronization shaft. At the same time, the tang on the throttle lever locks into the bracket on the synchronization shaft.
4. Install left and/or throttle body over mounting studs and **torque** nuts to 19 ft. lbs.
5. Connect purge tube to nipple on throttle body.
6. Hold left throttle lever in wide open throttle position and install throttle and speed control cables.
7. Connect TPS sensor electrical connector to right throttle body.
8. Check throttle body synchronization as outlined under "Adjustments."
9. Install air plenum and air cleaner to plenum tube.
10. Connect battery ground cable.

AIR INLET RESONATOR

2.0L/4-122 & 2.4L/4-148 ENGINES

1. **On models equipped with 2.0L/4-122 engine,** remove two bolts securing air inlet resonator to intake manifold.
2. **On all models,** loosen resonator to throttle body screw.
3. Loosen air inlet tube clamp, then remove resonator from vehicle.
4. Reverse procedure to install. **Torque** clamps to 20-30 inch lbs.

2.5L/V6-152 ENGINE

1. Remove resonator to intake manifold bolt.
2. Loosen resonator to air inlet tube clamp, then remove resonator.
3. Reverse procedure to install. **Torque** resonator to intake manifold bolt to 40-50 inch lbs.

FUEL RAIL

2.0L/4-122 & 2.4L/4-148 ENGINES

1. Disconnect battery ground cable, then relieve fuel system pressure as described under "Fuel System Pressure Relief" in this section.
2. Disconnect fuel supply line at fuel rail, then disconnect injector electrical connectors.
3. Remove fuel rail mounting screws, then lift rail off intake manifold. **Cover fuel injector bores to prevent entry of foreign matter.**
4. Reverse procedure to install, noting the following:
   a. Apply a light coat of clean engine oil to O-rings on injector nozzle ends.
   b. **Torque** fuel rail mounting screws to 14-19 ft. lbs.

2.5L/V6-152 ENGINE

1. Disconnect battery ground cable from auxiliary jumper terminal.
2. Relieve fuel system pressure as described under "Fuel System Pressure Relief" in this section.
3. Disconnect fuel supply tube from rail, then disconnect connectors from MAP and intake air temperature sensors.
4. Remove air inlet resonator to intake plenum bolt, then loosen throttle body air inlet hose clamp.
5. Release air cleaner housing cover to housing snaps.
6. Remove air cleaner cover and inlet hoses from engine.
7. Disconnect TPS and idle air control motor connectors.
8. Pry retainer tab back on throttle cable and slide cable out of bracket.
9. **On models equipped with speed control,** slide speed control cable out of bracket.
10. **On all models,** remove EGR tube from intake plenum, then the plenum support bracket bolt located rearward of EGR tube.
11. Remove upper intake plenum bolts, then the plenum.
12. Disconnect electrical connectors from

fuel injectors.
13. Remove fuel rail bolts, then the fuel rail off engine. There are spacers under each fuel rail bolt.
14. Reverse procedure to install, noting the following:
   a. Apply light coating of clean engine oil to O-ring on nozzle end of each injector.
   b. **Torque** fuel rail bolts to 8 ft. lbs.
   c. Install new intake plenum gasket. **Torque** plenum bolts to 13 ft. lbs.
   d. **Torque** plenum support bracket bolts to 13 ft. lbs.
   e. **Torque** air inlet tube clamps to 20-30 inch lbs.

3.3L/V6-201 ENGINE

1. Release fuel system pressure as outlined under "Fuel System Pressure Relief" in this section.
2. Disconnect battery ground cable.
3. Disconnect air plenum from air cleaner and throttle body.
4. Hold throttle lever in wide open position and remove throttle and speed control cables.
5. Compress locking tabs on throttle and speed control cable housings and remove from bracket.
6. Disconnect EET solenoid, IAC motor, TPS and MAP sensor connectors.
7. Disconnect PCV and brake booster hoses.
8. Disconnect vacuum line from pressure regulator.
9. Disconnect purge hose from throttle body.
10. Remove EGR tube mounting screws at intake manifold plenum.
11. Remove intake manifold plenum and cover intake manifold opening to prevent entry of foreign objects.
12. Disconnect fuel supply and return hoses at rear of manifold.
13. Remove screw from fuel tube clamp then separate fuel tubes from bracket.
14. Rotate injectors toward center of engine. Tag injector connectors with their cylinder number.
15. Remove fuel rail mounting bolts, lift fuel rail straight off engine.
16. Reverse procedure to install, noting the following:
   a. Apply a light coat of clean engine oil to O-rings of injectors.
   b. **Torque** fuel rail mounting screws to 16 ft. lbs.
   c. **Torque** intake manifold plenum bolts to 21 ft. lbs. in sequence shown in **Fig. 223.**

3.5L/V6-215 ENGINE

Refer to "Intake Manifold Plenum" and "Fuel Injector" for fuel rail replacement procedure.

FUEL INJECTORS

2.0L/4-122, 2.4L/4-148, 2.5L/V6-152 & 3.3L/V6-201 ENGINES

1. Remove fuel rail as described in this section.
2. **On Avenger, Sebring Coupe and Talon models equipped with 2.0L/4-122 engine,** remove battery and air intake hose, then remove in-

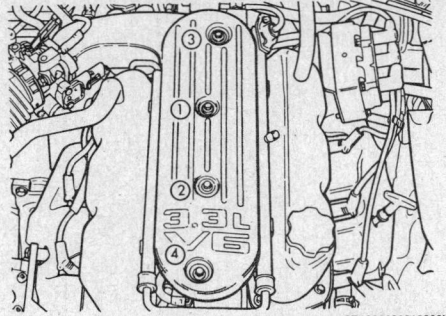

Fig. 223 Intake manifold plenum bolt tightening sequence. 3.3L/V6-201 engine

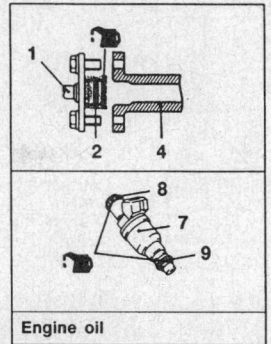

Engine oil

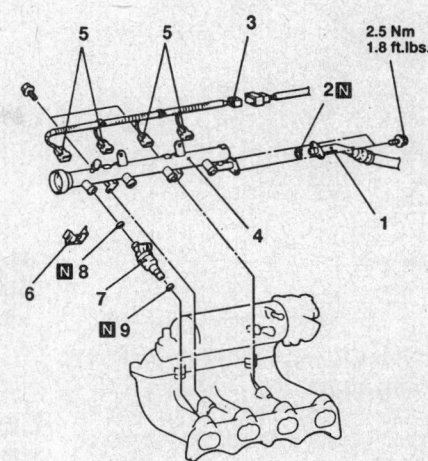

2.5 Nm
1.8 ft.lbs.

Removal steps

1. High-pressure fuel hose connection
2. O-ring
3. Injector harness connector
4. Fuel rail
5. Injector connectors

6. Retainers
7. Injectors
8. O-rings
9. O-rings

Fig. 224 Fuel injector replacement. Avenger, Sebring Coupe & Talon w/2.0L/4-122 engine

jectors in numbered sequence shown, **Fig. 224.** Fuel rail may be removed with injectors attached.
3. **On all models except Avenger, Sebring and Talon with 2.0L/4-122 engine,** remove fuel injector clip, then pull injector out of fuel rail.
4. **On all models,** reverse procedure to install. Install new fuel injector O-rings coated lightly in clean engine oil.

3.5L/V6-215 ENGINE

1. Release fuel system pressure as outlined under "Fuel System Pressure Relief" in this section.
2. Remove intake manifold plenum as outlined under "Intake Manifold Plenum" in this section.
3. Disconnect fuel supply and return tubes from fuel rail.
4. Connect fuel gauge adapter tool No. 6631, or equivalent, to the fuel supply tube end of the fuel rail.
5. Connect fuel hose tool No. 6668, or equivalent, to the return tube end of the fuel rail.
6. Place other end of fuel hose tool into a suitable container.
7. Purge fuel from fuel rail by spraying a maximum of 55 psi of compressed air into the fuel gauge adapter tool.
8. Tag injector connectors with their cylinder number.
9. Disconnect fuel injector electrical connector.
10. Remove vacuum tube from fuel pressure regulator.
11. Remove fuel rail mounting bolts.
12. Remove injector clamp screw.
13. Slide injector clamp toward rear of engine, then lift clamp off the rail.
14. Install fuel rail mounting bolts finger tight.
15. Using a thin flat screwdriver, pry fuel injector out of fuel rail.
16. Ensure upper and lower O-rings were removed with injector.
17. Reverse procedure to install, noting the following:
    a. Lightly lubricate O-rings with clean engine oil.
    b. Index injector with tab in fuel rail.
    c. **Torque** fuel rail bolts to 8–9 ft. lbs.

INTAKE MANIFOLD PLENUM
3.5L/V6-215 ENGINE

1. Release fuel system pressure as outlined under "Fuel System Pressure

Relief" in this section.
2. Disconnect battery ground cable.
3. Remove engine cover from top of intake manifold plenum.
4. Remove throttle and speed control cables from throttle arm.
5. Disconnect IAC motor, charge air temperature, MAP and TP sensors.
6. Disconnect purge hose from throttle bodies.
7. Disconnect PCV air and IAC motor hoses.
8. Remove air inlet tube from behind manifold.
9. Disconnect EGR tube from intake manifold plenum.
10. Disconnect support bracket from plenum.
11. Remove intake manifold plenum bolts. **Plenum uses two different length bolts. Mark locations when removing.**
12. Remove intake manifold plenum and cover intake opening to prevent entry of foreign objects.
13. Reverse procedure to install, **torquing** intake manifold plenum bolts to 250 inch lbs. in sequence shown in **Fig. 225.**

IDLE AIR CONTROL MOTOR
2.0L/4-122, 2.4L/4-148 & 2.5L/V6-152 ENGINES

1. Disconnect evaporative purge hose from throttle body, then disconnect throttle position sensor and idle air control motor electrical connectors.
2. Remove throttle body as described under "Throttle Body" in this section, then remove idle air control motor mounting screws and motor. **Ensure O-ring is removed with motor.**
3. Reverse procedure to install, noting the following:

a. If installing a new idle air control motor, replacement unit will already have an O-ring in place.
b. If pintle on new idle air control motor measures more than one inch, it must be retracted prior to installation using a DRB III to perform an AIS Motor Open/Close Test. Battery must be connected for this procedure.

3.3L/V6-201 & 3.5L/V6-215 ENGINES

1. Remove PCV air hose.
2. Disconnect IAC motor electrical connector.
3. Remove IAC motor mounting screws then the IAC motor. Ensure O-ring is removed with engine.
4. Reverse procedure to install, noting the following:
   a. When installing, if the pintle is extended more than 1 inch in must be retracted using the DRB II scan tool in the AIS Motor Open/Close Test screen.
   b. **Torque** IAC motor screws to 25 inch lbs.

CAMSHAFT POSITION (CMP) SENSOR
2.0L/4-122, 2.4L/4-148 & 2.5L/V6-152 ENGINES

1. Disconnect filtered air tube from throttle body, air cleaner housing and oil separator hose, then remove tube.
2. Remove air cleaner inlet tube, then disconnect engine coolant sensor and camshaft position sensor electrical connectors.
3. Remove brake booster hose and electrical connector from retainers at end of cylinder head cover, then remove camshaft position sensor mounting screws and sensor.

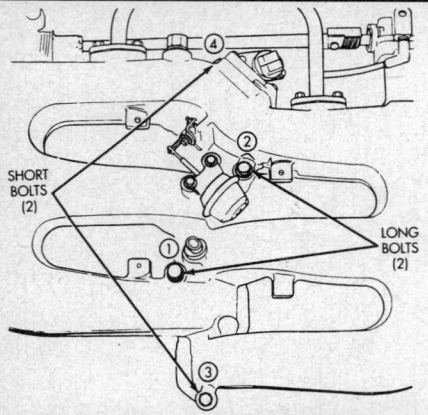

Fig. 225 Intake manifold plenum bolt tightening sequence. 3.5L/V6-215 engine

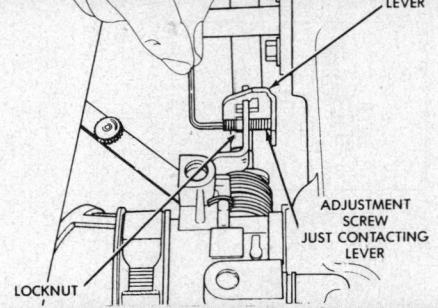

Fig. 226 Throttle body adjustment screw & linkage lever. 3.5L/V6-215 engine

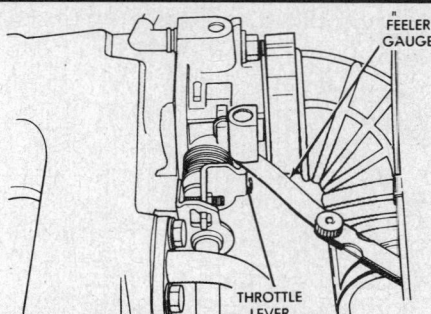

Fig. 227 Idle speed screw throttle lever gap. 3.5L/V6-215 engine

4. Remove target magnet from rear of camshaft.
5. Reverse procedure to install.

3.3L/V6-201 & 3.5L/V6-215 ENGINES

1. Disconnect CMP sensor connector.
2. Remove CMP sensor screw.
3. Pull sensor out of timing chain case cover.
4. Reverse procedure to install, noting the following:
   a. When reusing sensor, old paper spacer must be replaced. When a new sensor is being used, verify paper spacer is installed on sensor.
   b. **Torque** sensor screw to 9 ft. lbs.

CRANKSHAFT POSITION (CKP) SENSOR

2.0L/4-122 & 2.4L/4-148 ENGINES

1. Disconnect electrical connector from crankshaft position sensor.
2. Remove sensor mounting screw, then the sensor.
3. Reverse procedure to install.

2.5L/V6-152 ENGINE

1. Remove speed control servo from driver side strut tower, then remove CKP sensor retaining bolt.
2. Pull CKP sensor upward out of transaxle housing, then disconnect sensor electrical connector.
3. Reverse procedure to install, noting the following:
   a. After sensor is positioned in transaxle, push down until contact is made with driveplate, then **torque** bolt to 9 ft. lbs.
   b. **Torque** speed control servo nuts to 80 inch lbs.

3.3L/V6-201 & 3.5L/V6-215 ENGINES

1. Disconnect CKP sensor connector.
2. Remove sensor mounting screw.
3. Remove sensor.
4. Reverse procedure to install.

INTAKE AIR TEMPERATURE SENSOR

2.0L/4-122, 2.4L/4-148 & 2.5L/V6-152 ENGINES

1. Disconnect electrical connector from

sensor, then remove sensor from intake manifold plenum.
2. Reverse procedure to install.

ENGINE COOLANT TEMPERATURE SENSOR

2.0L/4-122, 2.4L/4-148 & 2.5L/V6-152 ENGINES

1. With engine cold and with a suitable container positioned below draincock, drain coolant until level drops below cylinder head.
2. Disconnect coolant temperature sensor electrical sensor, then remove sensor from cylinder head.
3. Reverse procedure to install. Refill cooling system.

3.3L/V6-201 & 3.5L/V6-215 ENGINES

1. Ensure engine temperature is cold.
2. Remove radiator pressure cap.
3. Disconnect ECT sensor connector.
4. Remove sensor from thermostat housing.
5. Reverse procedure to install, **torquing** sensor to 20 ft. lbs.

MANIFOLD ABSOLUTE PRESSURE (MAP) SENSOR

1. Disconnect MAP sensor electrical connector and remove sensor mounting screws, then remove sensor.
2. Reverse procedure to install. Ensure O-ring seal is not damaged during installation.

THROTTLE POSITION SENSOR

2.0L/4-122 & 2.4L/4-148 ENGINES

1. Disconnect evaporative purge hose from throttle body, then disconnect idle air control motor and throttle position sensor electrical connectors.
2. Remove throttle body as described under "Throttle Body" in this section, then remove throttle position sensor screws and sensor.
3. Reverse procedure to install.

2.5L/V6-152 ENGINE

1. Disconnect EVAP purge hose from throttle body, then the idle air control motor and TPS electrical connector.
2. Remove throttle body as described in this section.
3. Remove TPS screws, then the sensor.
4. Reverse procedure to install, noting the following:
   a. Throttle shaft end of throttle body

slides into socket in TPS. Socket has two tabs inside and throttle shaft rests against tabs. When indexed correctly, TPS can rotate clockwise few degrees to line up screw holes with screw holes in throttle body.
   b. TPS has slight tension when rotated into position. If it is difficult to rotate TPS into position, install sensor with throttle shaft on other side of tabs in socket.
   c. **Torque** screws to 17 inch lbs.
   d. After installing TPS, throttle plate should be closed. If plate is open, install sensor on other side of tabs in socket.

3.3L/V6-201 & 3.5L/V6-215 ENGINES

1. Disconnect sensor electrical connector.
2. Remove sensor mounting screws, then the sensor.
3. Reverse procedure to install, noting the following:
   a. Align throttle shaft and tabs in TPS sensor so that shaft rests against the tabs. When indexed correctly, the TPS can be rotated clockwise a few degrees to line up the mounting screw holes. If it is difficult to rotate the sensor, install sensor with shaft on other side of tabs in the TPS.
   b. **Torque** sensor screws to 25 inch lbs.

Adjustments

THROTTLE BODY SYNCHRONIZATION
3.5L/V6-215 ENGINE

Synchronize the throttle bodies if there is a gap between the adjustment screw and the linkage lever, **Fig. 226**, as follows:
1. Install a .004 inch feeler gauge between idle speed screw and the throttle lever on the right throttle body, **Fig. 227**.
2. Loosen adjustment screw locknut on synchronization shaft.
3. Turn adjustment screw until it just contacts the lever on the synchronization shaft. **Torque** locknut to 36 inch lbs.
4. Check clearance between throttle lever and idle speed screw. The .004 inch feeler gauge should drag when removed and a .006 inch feeler gauge should not fit between throttle lever and idle speed screw.

NOTE: If Uncertain About The Proper Use Of Information Contained In This Section, Please Refer To "How To Use This Manual" Located In The Front Of This Manual.

INDEX

Page No.

Description: 15-1
   Multi-Point Fuel Injection......... 15-1
   Single Point Fuel Injection 15-1
Diagnosis & Testing: 15-3
   Fuel System Pressure Test 15-3
   Multi-Point Fuel Injection......... 15-4
   Single Point Fuel Injection 15-3
Fuel Pump Relay Location: 15-1
   Acclaim, Daytona, Dynasty,
     Imperial, LeBaron, Shadow,
     Spirit, Sundance & 1993 New
     Yorker..................... 15-1
   Avenger, Sebring Coupe &
     1995-96 Talon
     w/Non-Turbocharged Engine .. 15-2
   Breeze, Cirrus, Concorde, Intrepid,
     LHS, Neon, Sebring Convertible,

Page No.

     Stratus, Vision & 1994-96 New
     Yorker..................... 15-2
   Colt & Summit................. 15-2
   Colt Vista & Summit Wagon...... 15-2
   Laser & 1993-94 Talon.......... 15-2
   Stealth....................... 15-2
   1995-96 Talon w/Turbocharged
     Engine..................... 15-2
Fuel Pump Replacement: 15-8
   Acclaim, Daytona, Dynasty,
     Imperial, LeBaron, Shadow,
     Spirit, Sundance & 1993 New
     Yorker..................... 15-8
   Avenger, Sebring Coupe, Laser &
     Talon....................... 15-9
   Breeze, Cirrus, Sebring
     Convertible & Stratus 15-8

Page No.

   Colt & Summit.................. 15-9
   Colt Vista & Summit Wagon...... 15-9
   Concorde, Intrepid, LHS, Vision &
     1994-96 New Yorker.......... 15-9
   Neon.......................... 15-9
   Stealth........................ 15-9
Fuel System Pressure Relief: 15-2
   Multi-Point Fuel Injection......... 15-3
   Single Point Fuel Injection 15-2
Precautions: 15-1
   Fuel System Pressure Relief 15-1
Technical Service Bulletins: 15-11
   Fuel Filter Replacement 15-11
   Fuel Pressure Regulator
     Installation.................. 15-11

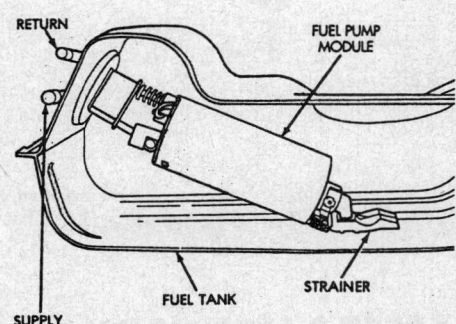

Fig. 1 Fuel pump & tank assembly

PRECAUTIONS

FUEL SYSTEM PRESSURE RELIEF

The electronic fuel injection system is under constant fuel pressure. Fuel system pressure should be released prior to servicing fuel tank, fuel pump, fuel lines, fuel filter or fuel components of the throttle body.

To relieve fuel system pressure, refer to "Fuel System Pressure Relief ."

DESCRIPTION

SINGLE POINT FUEL INJECTION

The fuel pump used in the EFI system, **Fig. 1**, is a positive displacement, roller vane, immersible pump with a permanent magnet type electric motor. The fuel is drawn in through the filter sock and pushed through the electric motor to the outlet. The pump contains check valves that restrict fuel movement in either direction when the pump is not operational. Operating voltage is supplied to the pump through the Auto Shutdown (ASD) relay.

MULTI-POINT FUEL INJECTION

Except Colt, Colt Vista, Laser, Stealth, Summit, Summit Wagon & Talon

The fuel pump used in the MPFI system, **Figs. 1 and 2**, is a positive displacement, roller vane, immersible pump with a permanent magnet type electric motor. The fuel is drawn in through the filter sock and pushed through the electric motor to the outlet. The pump contains two check valves. One valve is used to relieve internal fuel pump pressure and regulate maximum pump output. The other check valve, located near the pump outlet, restricts fuel movement in either direction when the pump is not operational. Operating voltage is supplied to the pump through the Auto Shutdown (ASD) relay.

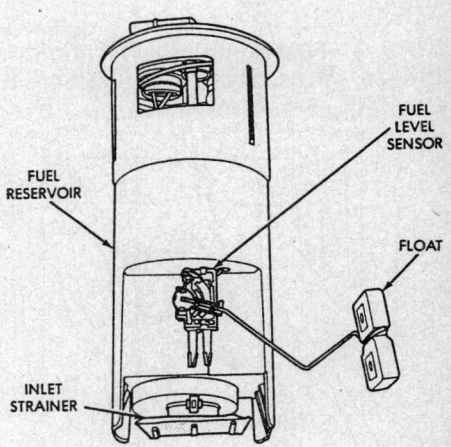

Fig. 2 Fuel pump. Multi-point fuel injection

FUEL PUMP RELAY LOCATION

ACCLAIM, DAYTONA, DYNASTY, IMPERIAL, LEBARON, SHADOW, SPIRIT, SUNDANCE & 1993 NEW YORKER

The fuel pump relay is mounted on the relay block in the lefthand side of the engine compartment.

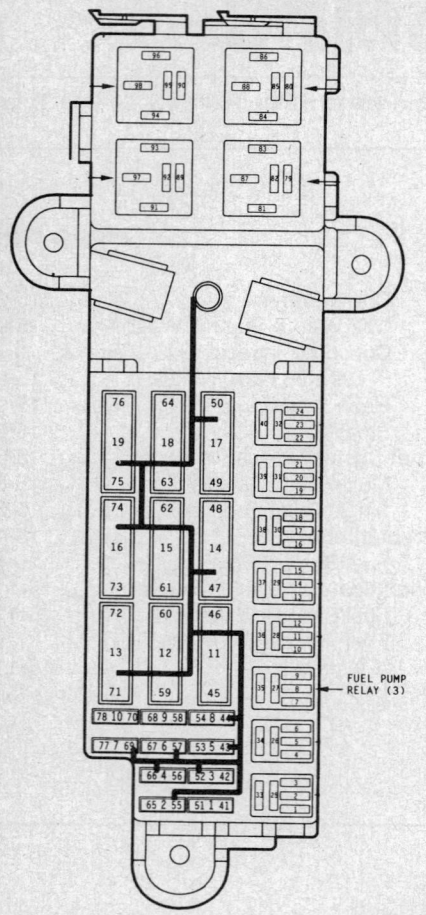

Fig. 3 Fuel pump relay location. Breeze, Cirrus, Sebring Convertible & Stratus

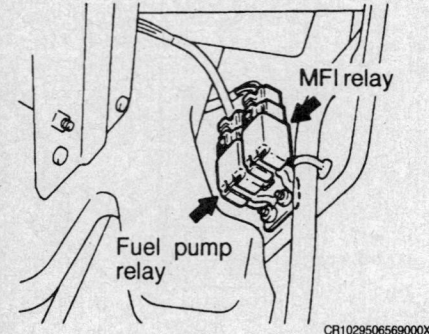

Fig. 7 Fuel pump relay location. 1995-96 Talon w/turbocharged engine

BREEZE, CIRRUS, CONCORDE, INTREPID, LHS, NEON, SEBRING CONVERTIBLE, STRATUS, VISION & 1994—96 NEW YORKER

The fuel pump relay is located in the Power Distribution Center (PDC), **Figs. 3 through 5**, which is positioned beside the vehicle battery.

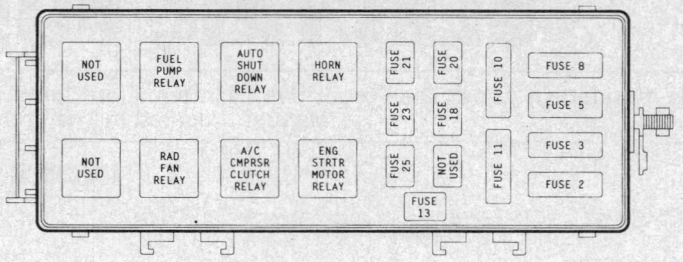

Fig. 4 Fuel pump relay location. Neon

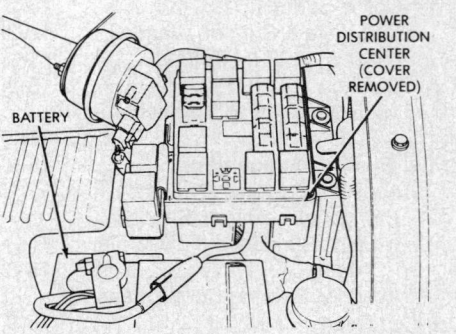

Fig. 5 Power distribution center. Concorde, Intrepid, LHS, Vision & 1994—96 New Yorker

AVENGER, SEBRING COUPE & 1995—96 TALON w/NON-TURBOCHARGED ENGINE

The fuel pump relay, **Fig. 6**, is located in the rear lefthand corner of the engine compartment at the firewall.

1995—96 TALON w/TURBOCHARGED ENGINE

The fuel pump relay, **Fig. 7**, is located inside the front righthand side of the center console.

COLT & SUMMIT

The fuel pump is controlled by the multi point fuel injection (MPI) relay, which is located behind the righthand side of the center console of the dash panel.

COLT VISTA & SUMMIT WAGON

AWD & 1993—94 FWD & 1995—96 Federal FWD Models

The fuel pump is controlled by the multi point fuel injection (MPI) relay, which is located behind the righthand side of the glove compartment.

1995—96 California FWD Models

The fuel pump relay is located behind the righthand side of the center console of the dash panel.

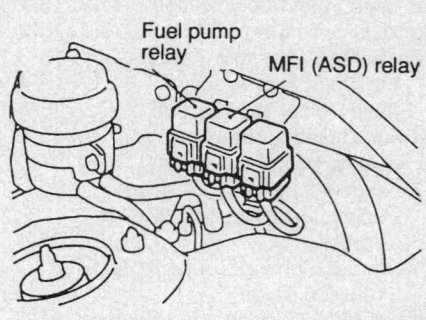

Fig. 6 Fuel pump relay location. Avenger, Sebring Coupe & 1995—96 Talon w/non-turbocharged engine

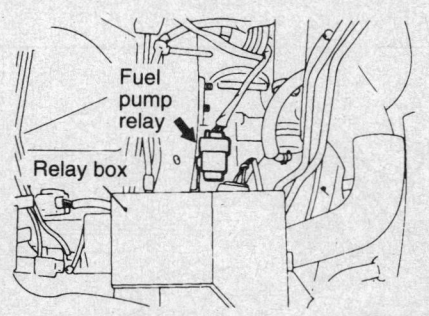

Fig. 8 Fuel pump relay location. Stealth

LASER & 1993—94 TALON

The fuel pump relay is located behind the center dash panel.

STEALTH

The fuel pump relay, **Fig. 8**, is located on the righthand side of the engine compartment.

FUEL SYSTEM PRESSURE RELIEF

The EFI system is under constant fuel pressure. Fuel system pressure must be released prior to servicing fuel tank, fuel pump, fuel lines, fuel filter or fuel components of the throttle body.

SINGLE POINT FUEL INJECTION

1. Loosen gas cap to relieve any pressure in fuel tank.
2. Disconnect injector wiring harness at edge of throttle body.

3. Connect jumper wire between terminal No. 1 of injector harness, **Fig. 9**, and engine ground.
4. Connect jumper wire to terminal No. 2 of injector harness, **Fig. 9**, and touch battery positive post for no longer than 5 seconds.

MULTI-POINT FUEL INJECTION

ACCLAIM, DAYTONA, DYNASTY, IMPERIAL, LEBARON, SHADOW, SPIRIT, SUNDANCE & 1993 NEW YORKER

3.0L/V6-181 Engine

1. Loosen gas cap to release any residual pressure in fuel tank.
2. **On 1993-94 models,** proceed as follows:
   a. Disconnect electrical connector from fuel injector.
   b. Using a suitable jumper wire, ground one injector terminal, then connect another jumper wire to other injector terminal and touch battery positive post for no more than 10 seconds.
   c. Remove jumper wires from injector terminals.
3. **On 1995 models,** proceed as follows:
   a. Loosen gas cap to release any residual pressure in fuel tank.
   b. Disconnect fuel injector wiring harness from engine harness.
   c. Connect one jumper wire between A142 circuit terminal of fuel rail harness connector and 12 volt power source.
   d. Connect another jumper wire to a good ground, then ground fuel injector momentarily by touching wire to injector terminal in harness connector.
   e. Repeat procedure for remaining injectors, then disconnect and remove jumper wires.

Except 3.0L/V6-181 Engine

1. Disconnect battery ground cable.
2. Remove fuel filler cap.
3. Remove protective cap from fuel pressure test port on fuel rail.
4. Place open end of hose tool No. C-4799-1, or equivalent, into a suitable container.
5. Connect other end of hose tool to test port on fuel rail to release fuel pressure.
6. Allow fuel to bleed off, then remove hose tool.
7. Continue fuel system service.

CONCORDE, INTREPID, LHS, NEON, VISION & 1994-96 NEW YORKER & BREEZE, CIRRUS, SEBRING CONVERTIBLE & STRATUS w/2.0L/4-122 & 2.4L/4-148 ENGINES

1. Disconnect battery ground cable.
2. Remove fuel filler cap.

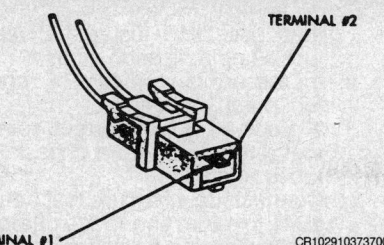

Fig. 9 Fuel injector harness connector terminals. Single point fuel injection

3. Remove protective cap from fuel pressure test port on fuel rail.
4. Place open end of hose tool No. C-4799-1, or equivalent, into a suitable container.
5. Connect other end of hose tool to test port on fuel rail to release fuel pressure.
6. Allow fuel to bleed off, then remove hose tool.
7. Continue fuel system service.

BREEZE, CIRRUS, SEBRING CONVERTIBLE & STRATUS w/2.5L/V6-152 ENGINE

1. Disconnect the fuel rail electrical harness from engine harness.
2. Connect one end of a jumper wire to the A142 circuit terminal of the fuel rail harness and connect the other end to a 12V power source.
3. Connect one end of a jumper wire to a good ground source.
4. Momentarily ground one of the fuel injectors by connecting the other end of the grounded wire to an injector terminal in the harness connector.
5. Repeat procedure for remaining injectors.

AVENGER, SEBRING COUPE & 1995-96 TALON

1. Remove rear seat cushion, then remove protective cover and disconnect fuel pump connector.
2. Start engine and wait until it stalls, then place ignition switch in Off position.
3. Connect fuel pump connector, then install protective cover and rear seat cushion.

STEALTH

1. Disconnect battery ground cable.
2. Remove fuel gauge cover in luggage compartment.
3. Disconnect fuel pump electrical connector.
4. Start and run engine until it runs out of fuel, then turn ignition off.
5. Connect fuel pump electrical connector after fuel system service is complete.
6. Apply Mopar rope caulk sealer part No. 4026044, or equivalent, to rear floor pan prior to installing fuel gauge cover.

LASER & 1993-94 TALON

1. Loosen gas cap to release any pressure in fuel tank.
2. Disconnect fuel pump harness connector at fuel tank.

3. Start and run engine until it runs out of fuel, then turn ignition off.
4. Disconnect battery ground cable, then connect fuel pump harness connector.

COLT & SUMMIT

1. Remove rear seat cushion and pull back carpet.
2. Disconnect fuel pump electrical connector.
3. Start and run engine until it runs out of fuel, then turn ignition off.
4. Connect fuel pump electrical connector, then install carpet and seat cushion.

COLT VISTA & SUMMIT WAGON

1. Remove grommet below floor, then disconnect fuel pump electrical connector.
2. Start engine, when engine stalls due to lack of fuel, turn ignition Off and connect fuel pump connector.

DIAGNOSIS & TESTING

Fuel System Pressure Test

SINGLE POINT FUEL INJECTION

Fuel system pressure should be released any time a fuel line is to be disconnected.

1. Relieve fuel system pressure as described under "Fuel System Pressure Relief."
2. Remove fuel supply hose quick connector from chassis lines at engine.
3. Connect fuel pressure gauge tool No. C-4799, or equivalent, to fuel pressure adapter tool No. 6539, or equivalent, then install adapter between fuel supply hose and chassis fuel line assembly.
4. Place ignition switch in On position, engine Off. Using DRB II tester, access ASD fuel system test. This test will activate fuel pump and pressurize system. **When using ASD fuel system test, Auto Shutdown (ASD) relay remains energized either for seven minutes, until test is stopped, or until ignition switch is turned to Off position.**
5. Observe gauge. If reading is 39 psi, further testing is not required. If pressure is at least 5 psi higher than specified, replace fuel filter.
6. If pressure is still above specifications, remove fuel return hose from chassis fuel lines at engine.
7. Attach Fuel Pressure Test Connector Adapter 6541 to fuel return hose, then place other end into an approved two gallon gasoline container. If pressure is now correct, check for restricted fuel return line. If no change is observed, replace fuel pressure regulator.
8. If fuel pressure is lower than specified, gently squeeze fuel return hose. If

pressure increases, replace pressure regulator.

9. If there is no change in pressure by squeezing fuel return hose, check for a plugged inlet strainer or defective fuel pump.
10. Remove test equipment, then connect fuel lines.
11. Check system for leaks.

MULTI-POINT FUEL INJECTION

ACCLAIM, CONCORDE, DAYTONA, DYNASTY, IMPERIAL, INTREPID, LEBARON, LHS, NEW YORKER, SHADOW, SPIRIT, SUNDANCE & VISION

2.2L/4-135 & 2.5L/4-153 Engines

1. Release fuel system pressure as outlined under "Fuel System Pressure Relief."
2. Remove vacuum hose from pressure regulator before checking fuel pressure.
3. Connect fuel pressure gauge tool No. C-4799, or equivalent, to service port on fuel rail.
4. Place ignition switch in On position.
5. Using DRB, access ASD fuel system test to activate fuel pump and pressurize system.
6. Observe gauge. If pressure is 55 psi, system is operating normally.
7. If pressure is lower than 55 psi, record pressure and remove gauge tool. Ensure system is not leaking, then proceed as follows:
   a. Release fuel system pressure as outlined under "Fuel System Pressure Relief."
   b. Install fuel pressure gauge tool and pressure test adapter tool Nos. C-4799 and 6539, or equivalents, in fuel supply line between fuel tank and fuel filter.
   c. Turn ignition switch On, then use DRB tester and repeat fuel pump activation steps.
   d. If pressure is at least 5 psi higher than first reading, replace fuel filter.
   e. If pressure is same as first reading, squeeze return hose.
   f. If, after squeezing return hose, fuel pressure increases, replace regulator. If pressure does not change, problem is either a plugged inlet strainer or defective fuel pump.
8. If pressure is higher than 55 psi, record pressure and remove gauge tool. Ensure system is not leaking, then proceed as follows:
   a. Release fuel system pressure as outlined under "Fuel System Pressure Relief."
   b. Remove fuel return line hose at fuel tank.
   c. Connect fuel pressure test adapter tool No. 6541, or equivalent, to return line. Place other end of adapter into an approved gasoline container.
   d. Turn ignition switch to On position,

then use DRB tester and repeat fuel pump activation steps.
   e. If pressure is now correct, replace fuel pump assembly.
   f. If pressure is not correct, remove fuel return hose from chassis fuel tubes at engine.
   g. Connect fuel pressure test adapter 6541 to return line. Place other end of adapter into an approved gasoline container.
   h. Turn ignition switch to On position, then use DRB tester and repeat fuel pump activation steps.
   i. If pressure is now correct, check for restricted fuel return line. If no change in pressure is observed, replace fuel pressure regulator.

3.0L/V6-181, 3.3L/V6-201, 3.5L/V6-215 & 3.8L/V6-231 Engines

1. Release fuel system pressure as outlined under "Fuel System Pressure Relief."
2. **On models equipped with 3.3L/V6-201, 3.5L/V6-215 and 3.8L/V6-231 engines,** remove protective cover from service valve on fuel rail.
3. **On models equipped with 3.0L/V6-181 engine,** remove fuel hose quick connector from chassis lines.
4. **On all models,** connect fuel pressure gauge tool No. C-4799, or equivalent, to fuel rail service valve or to fuel pressure test adapter tool No. C-6539, or equivalent, between fuel supply hose and chassis fuel line assembly.
5. Using diagnostic tester and key in run position, use ASD fuel system test. This will activate fuel pump and pressurize system.
6. **On all models except Concorde, Intrepid, LHS, Vision & 1994-95 New Yorker with 3.3L/V6-201 engine,** if gauge reads 48 psi, further testing in not required.
7. **On Concorde, Intrepid, LHS, Vision & 1994-95 New Yorker with 3.3L/V6-201 engine,** if gauge reads 55 psi, further testing in not required.
8. **On all models,** if pressure is not correct, record pressure and remove gauge tool.
9. Use ASD fuel system test to activate fuel pump. Ensure fuel does not leak from fuel rail service valve or fuel connection point.
10. If fuel pressure is below specification, proceed as follows:
    a. Install fuel pressure gauge tool and adapter in fuel supply line between fuel tank and fuel filter at rear of vehicle.
    b. Repeat fuel pressure measurement steps. If pressure is at least 5 psi higher than previously recorded, gently squeeze return hose.
    c. If pressure increases, replace pressure regulator.
    d. If pressure does not change, problem is either a plugged pump filter or defective fuel pump.
11. If pressure is above specification, proceed as follows:

    a. Remove fuel return line hose from fuel tank.
    b. Connect fuel pressure test adapter to return line, then place other end into a suitable two gallon container.
    c. Repeat fuel pressure measurement steps. If pressure is now correct, replace fuel pump assembly as described under "Fuel Pump, Replace."
    d. If pressure is still high, remove fuel return hose from chassis fuel tubes. Connect adapter tool to return hose and place other end into a suitable container.
    e. Repeat fuel pressure measurement steps. If pressure is now correct, check for restricted fuel return line.
    f. If no change in pressure is observed, replace fuel pressure regulator.

BREEZE, CIRRUS, SEBRING CONVERTIBLE & STRATUS

2.0L/4-122 & 2.4L/4-148 Engines

1. Relieve fuel pressure as described under "Fuel System Pressure Relief."
2. Install fuel pressure gauge tool No. C-4799B, or equivalent, to test port located on fuel rail.
3. Place ignition switch in On position.
4. Using a suitable DRB scan tool, access the ASD Fuel System Test. The ASD Fuel Test will active the fuel pump and pressurize the system.
5. If the pressure gauge reads approximately 48 psi, no further testing is needed.
6. If the pressure is above specifications, check for a kinked or restricted fuel return tube from fuel filter to pump module.
7. If the pressure is below specifications, refer to **Fig. 10.**

2.5L/V6-152 Engine

1. Relieve fuel pressure as described under "Fuel System Pressure Relief."
2. Remove fuel supply hose quick connector from the chassis line at engine.
3. Connect fuel pressure gauge tool No. C-4799 and fuel pressure test adapter tool No. 6539, or equivalents, between fuel supply hose and chassis line.
4. Place ignition switch in On position.
5. Using a suitable DRB scan tool, access the ASD Fuel System Test. The ASD Fuel Test will active the fuel pump and pressurize the system.
6. If the pressure gauge reads 48 psi, no further testing is needed.
7. If the pressure is above specifications, check for a kinked or restricted fuel return tube from fuel filter to pump module.
8. If the pressure is below specifications, refer to **Fig. 10.**

AVENGER, SEBRING COUPE & 1995–96 TALON

2.0L/4-122 Non-Turbocharged Engine

1. Release fuel system pressure as described under "Fuel System Pressure

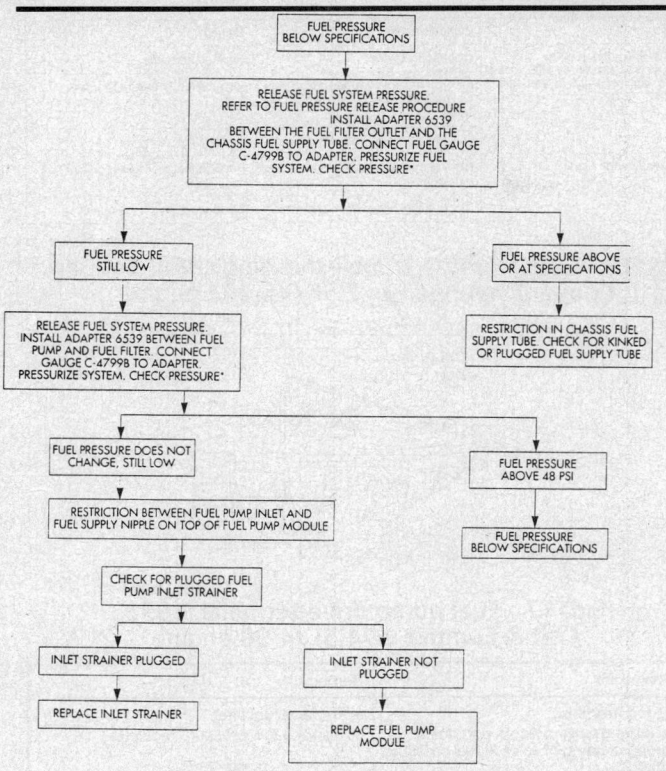

Fig. 10   Low fuel pressure test chart. Breeze, Cirrus, Sebring Convertible & Stratus

*Pressure gauge should rise rapidly. If pressure rises slowly, inlet strainer is plugged enough to cause drive ability problems.

Symptom	Probable cause	Remedy
• Fuel pressure too low • No fuel pressure in fuel return hose	Clogged fuel filter	Replace fuel filter
	Fuel leaking to return side due to poor fuel regulator valve seating or settled spring	Replace fuel pressure regulator
	Low fuel pump delivery pressure	Replace fuel pump
Fuel pressure too high	Binding valve in fuel pressure regulator	Replace fuel pressure regulator
	Clogged fuel return hose or pipe	Clean or replace hose or pipe

Fig. 11   Fuel pressure troubleshooting chart. Avenger, Sebring Coupe & 1995–96 Talon w/2.0L/4-122 non-turbocharged engine

Symptom	Probable cause	Remedy
Fuel pressure drops gradually after engine is stopped	Leaky injector	Replace injector
	Leaky fuel regulator valve seat	Replace fuel pressure regulator
Fuel pressure drops sharply immediately after engine is stopped	Check valve in fuel pump is held open	Replace fuel pump

Fig. 12   Fuel pressure drop diagnosis chart. Avenger, Sebring Coupe & 1995–96 Talon w/2.0L/4-122 non-turbocharged engine

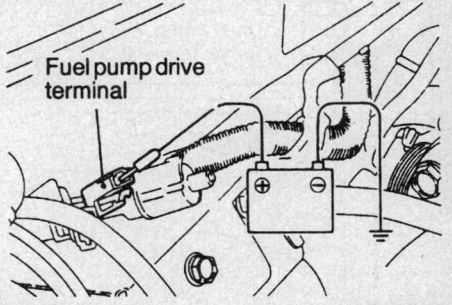

Fig. 13   Fuel pump drive terminal. 1995–96 Talon w/2.0L/4-122 turbocharged engine

Relief," then remove protective cover from fuel rail service valve.

2. Connect fuel pressure gauge tool No. C-4799, or equivalent, to service valve, then place ignition switch in On position.

3. Using a suitable diagnostic scan tool, access "Fuel System Test" following tool prompts. **This test will activate fuel pump and pressurize system. Fuel pump relay will remain energized for seven minutes unless test is stopped or ignition switch is placed in Off position. Ensure no leaks exist at test port connections.**

4. Observe fuel pressure gauge; indicated pressure should be 47–50 psi. If it is not, refer to **Fig. 11** for fuel pressure troubleshooting; repair system as indicated.

5. With ignition switch in On position, use scan tool to repeat fuel system test, then place ignition switch in Off position.

6. Observe fuel pressure gauge. If indicated pressure does not drop within two minutes, system is functioning normally; if pressure drops, proceed to **Fig. 12** for fuel system troubleshooting; repair system as indicated.

7. Relieve fuel system pressure as described under "Fuel System Pressure Relief," then remove pressure gauge and install fuel rail service valve cover.

2.0L/4-122 Turbocharged Engine

1. Relieve fuel system pressure as described under "Fuel System Pressure Relief," then disconnect high pressure

fuel hose at fuel rail. **Cover hose with shop towel to prevent fuel spray or spillage.**

2. Remove union joint and nut from adapter hose tool No. MD998709, or equivalent, and connect hose adapter tool No. MD998742, or equivalent, in its place.

3. Install a suitable fuel pressure gauge on adapter hose with an O-ring or gasket to prevent leakage between gauge and hose.

4. Install tool assembly between fuel rail and high pressure hose.

5. Using a suitable jumper wire, connect fuel pump drive terminal to battery positive terminal, **Fig. 13**, then inspect pressure gauge and adapter hoses for leaks.

6. Disconnect jumper wire, then start engine and run at idle. Fuel pressure should be 33 psi.

7. Disconnect and plug fuel pressure regulator vacuum hose, then measure fuel pressure while plugging hose end with finger. Pressure should be 42–45 psi with engine at idle.

8. Race engine repeatedly. While doing so, ensure fuel pressure does not drop and fuel return hose pressure can be felt by squeezing lightly between fingers.

9. If results of preceding steps are not as specified, proceed to **Fig. 14** and repair system as indicated.

2.5L/V6-152 Engine

1. Relieve fuel system pressure as described under "Fuel System Pressure Relief," then remove fuel plate from fuel rail. **Cover plate with shop tow-**

el to prevent fuel spray or spillage.

2. Remove union joint and bolt from adapter hose tool No. MD998709, or equivalent, and connect hose adapter tool No. MD998742, or equivalent, in its place.

3. Connect a suitable fuel pressure gauge to adapter hose with an O-ring or gasket to prevent leakage between gauge and hose.

4. Install tool assembly between fuel rail and high pressure hose.

5. Using a suitable diagnostic scan tool, run "Fuel System Test" to activate fuel pump. Ensure no leaks exist at pressure gauge and adapter hose connections.

6. Start engine and run at idle, then measure fuel pressure. Pressure should be 47–50 psi.

7. Race engine repeatedly, then return to idle and ensure fuel pressure does not drop.

8. If results of preceding steps are not as specified, proceed to **Fig. 15** for fuel pressure troubleshooting procedures. Repair system as indicated.

9. Stop engine and note fuel pressure. If pressure does not drop within two minutes, system is operating satisfactorily; if it does drop, note rate at which pressure drop occurs and proceed to **Fig. 16**. Repair system as indicated.

10. Relieve fuel system pressure as described under "Fuel System Pressure

Symptom	Probable cause	Remedy
• Fuel pressure too low • Fuel pressure drops after racing • No fuel pressure in fuel return hose	Clogged fuel filter	Replace fuel filter
	Fuel leaking to return side due to poor fuel regulator valve seating or settled spring	Replace fuel pressure regulator
	Low fuel pump delivery pressure	Replace fuel pump
Fuel pressure too high	Binding valve in fuel pressure regulator	Replace fuel pressure regulator
	Clogged fuel return hose or pipe	Clean or replace hose or pipe
Same fuel pressure when vacuum hose is connected and when disconnected	Damaged vacuum hose or clogged nipple	Replace vacuum hose or clean nipple
	Malfunction of the fuel pressure control system	Checking the fuel pressure control system

CR1029506574000X

Fig. 14 Fuel pressure troubleshooting chart. 1995–96 Talon w/2.0L/4-122 turbocharged engine

Symptom	Probable cause	Remedy
Fuel pressure drops gradually after engine is stopped	Leaky injector	Replace injector
	Leaky fuel regulator valve seat	Replace fuel pressure regulator
Fuel pressure drops sharply immediately after engine is stopped	Check valve in fuel pump is held open	Replace fuel pump

CR1029506576000X

Fig. 16 Fuel pressure drop diagnosis chart. Sebring Coupe & Avenger w/2.5L/V6-152 engine

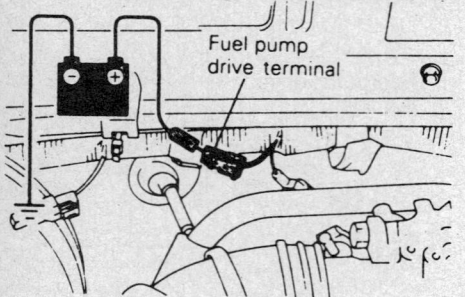

CR1029403743000X

Fig. 18 Fuel pump drive terminal. 1994 Colt & 1994–96 Summit

Symptom	Probable cause	Remedy
• Fuel pressure too low • Fuel pressure drops after racing • No fuel pressure in fuel return hose	Clogged fuel filter	Replace fuel filter
	Fuel leaking to return side due to poor fuel regulator valve seating or settled spring	Replace fuel pressure regulator
	Low fuel pump delivery pressure	Replace fuel pump
Fuel pressure too high	Binding valve in fuel pressure regulator	Replace fuel pressure regulator
	Clogged fuel return hose or pipe	Clean or replace hose or pipe

CR1029506575000X

Fig. 15 Fuel pressure troubleshooting chart. Sebring Coupe & Avenger w/2.5L/V6-152 engine

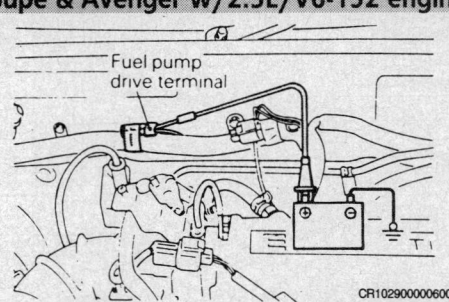

CR1029000006000X

Fig. 17 Fuel pump drive terminal. 1993 Colt & Summit w/1.5L/4-90 engine

Condition	Probable cause	Remedy
Fuel pressure too low	a. Clogged fuel filter b. Fuel leaking toward return port due to improper seating of valve in fuel pressure regulator c. Low delivery pressure of fuel pump	a. Replace fuel filter. b. Replace fuel pressure regulator. c. Replace fuel pump
Fuel pressure too high	a. Stuck valve in fuel pressure regulator b. Clogged or bent fuel return hose or pipe	a. Replace fuel pressure regulator. b. Repair or replace hose or pipe
Fuel pressure with vacuum hose connected not different from fuel pressure with vacuum hose not connected	a. Clogged or broken vacuum hose or nipple b. Stuck valve in fuel pressure regulator or defective valve seating	a. Repair or replace the vacuum hose or nipple b. Replace fuel pressure regulator.

CR1029103740000X

Fig. 19 Fuel pressure troubleshooting chart. Colt, Colt Vista, Laser, Summit, Summit Wagon & 1993–94 Talon

Relief," then remove gauge and adapter tools from fuel rail.
11. Replace fuel plate O-ring, then install plate on fuel rail and **torque** bolts to 43 inch lbs.
12. Inspect fuel system for leaks.

COLT & SUMMIT

1. Release fuel system pressure as outlined under "Fuel System Pressure Relief."
2. Disconnect high pressure hose from delivery pipe. **Cover hose end with shop towel to prevent splash of fuel.**
3. Connect fuel pressure gauge to hose adapter, then install gauge between delivery pipe and high pressure hose.
4. Connect battery negative terminal, if disconnected.
5. Apply 12 volts to fuel pump drive terminal, **Figs. 17 and 18,** to activate fuel pump. Ensure there is no fuel leakage from gauge or hose adapter, then disconnect 12 volts from fuel pump drive terminal.
6. Start engine and run at idle speed, then disconnect and cap vacuum hose from pressure regulator. Observe gauge; pressure should be 47-50 psi.
7. Connect vacuum hose. Observe gauge; pressure should be 38 psi.
8. Race engine repeatedly, and ensure fuel pressure does not fall when engine returns to idle.
9. While racing engine, ensure there is

pressure in fuel return line by squeezing line.
10. If measurements are not within specifications, refer to **Fig. 19** to determine probable cause and necessary repairs.
11. Stop engine and check for change in gauge pressure reading, pressure should not drop. If pressure drops, refer to **Figs. 20 and 21** to determine probable cause and necessary repairs.
12. Release fuel pressure, then disconnect high pressure hose and remove gauge from delivery pipe. Reconnect high pressure hose to delivery pipe.
13. Apply 12 volts to fuel pump drive terminal, **Figs. 17 and 18** to activate fuel pump. Ensure there is no fuel leakage.

COLT VISTA & SUMMIT WAGON

1. Release fuel pressure in fuel line, then disconnect high pressure hose from delivery pipe. **Cover hose end with shop towel to prevent splash of fuel.**
2. Remove union joint and bolt from fuel pressure gauge adapter hose, then install hose adapter tool No. MD998742, or equivalent, on fuel

gauge. **Ensure gaskets or O-rings are installed between fuel pressure gauge and hose adapter to prevent fuel leakage.**
3. Install gauge assembly between height pressure hose and delivery pipe.
4. Connect battery negative terminal, if disconnected.
5. Apply 12 volts to fuel pump drive terminal, located near top center of engine cowl, to activate fuel pump. Ensure there is no fuel leakage from gauge or hose adapter, then disconnect power source from fuel pump drive terminal.
6. Start engine and run at idle speed, Observe gauge; pressure should be 38 psi at curb idle.
7. Disconnect vacuum hose from fuel pressure regulator, then cover hose end with finger. Observe gauge; pressure should be 47-50 psi at curb idle.
8. Race engine repeatedly, then ensure fuel pressure does not fall when engine returns to idle.
9. While racing engine, ensure there is pressure in fuel return line by squeezing line.
10. If measurements are not within specifications, refer to **Fig. 19** to determine probable cause and necessary repairs.

Condition	Probable cause	Remedy
Fuel pressure drops slowly after engine is stopped.	Leakage from injector	Replace injector.
Fuel pressure drops immediately after engine is stopped.	Check valve in fuel pump does not close	Replace fuel pump.

CR1029103741000X

Fig. 20 Fuel system troubleshooting chart. Laser, 1993–94 Talon & 1993 Colt, Colt Vista, Summit & Summit Wagon

Symptom	Probable cause	Remedy
Fuel pressure drops gradually after engine is stopped	Leaky injector	Replace injector
	Leaky fuel regulator valve seat	Replace fuel pressure regulator
Fuel pressure drops sharply immediately after engine is stopped	Check valve in fuel pump is held open	Replace fuel pump

CR1029403742000X

Fig. 21 Troubleshooting. 1994 Colt & Colt Vista & 1994–96 Summit & Summit Wagon

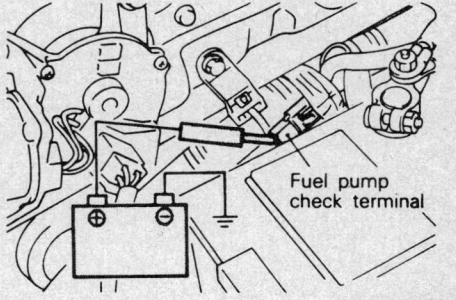

CR1029001313000X

Fig. 22 Fuel pump check terminal. Laser & 1993–94 Talon

11. Stop engine and check for change in gauge pressure reading, pressure should not drop. If pressure drops, refer to **Figs. 20 and 21** to determine probable cause and necessary repairs.
12. Release fuel pressure, then disconnect high pressure hose and remove gauge from delivery pipe. Reconnect high pressure hose to delivery pipe.
13. **Torque** delivery pipe to fuel pressure hose retaining bolts to 43 inch lbs.
14. Check system for leaks.

LASER & 1993–94 TALON

1. Relieve fuel pressure in fuel line, then disconnect high pressure hose from delivery pipe. **Cover hose end with shop towel to prevent splash of fuel.**
2. **On models equipped with 2.0L/4-122 engine,** remove throttle body stay.
3. **On all models,** connect fuel pressure gauge to hose adapter, then install gauge between delivery pipe and high pressure hose.
4. Connect battery ground cable, if disconnected.
5. Apply 12 volts to fuel pump check terminal, **Fig. 22,** to activate fuel pump. Ensure there is no fuel leakage from gauge or hose adapter.
6. Start engine and run at idle speed, then disconnect and cap vacuum hose from pressure regulator. Observe gauge and note the following:
   a. **On models equipped with 1.8L/4-107 engine or 2.0L/4-122 non-turbocharged engine,** pressure should be 47–50 psi.
   b. **On models equipped with 2.0L/4-122 turbocharged engine and manual transaxle,** pressure should be 36–38 psi.
   c. **On models equipped with 2.0L/4-122 turbocharged engine and automatic transaxle,** pressure should be 41–46 psi.
7. Connect vacuum hose to pressure regulator. Again observe gauge and note the following:

a. **On models equipped with 1.8L/4-107 engine or 2.0L/4-122 non-turbocharged engine,** pressure should be 38 psi.
b. **On models equipped with 2.0L/4-122 turbocharged engine and manual transaxle,** pressure should be 27 psi.
c. **On models equipped with 2.0L/4-122 turbocharged engine and automatic transaxle,** pressure should be 33 psi.
8. Increase engine RPM repeatedly in three series. Ensure fuel pressure does not fall when engine returns to idle.
9. While increasing engine RPM, ensure there is pressure in fuel return line by squeezing line.
10. If measurements are not within specifications, refer to **Fig. 19** to determine probable cause and necessary repairs.
11. Stop engine and check for change in gauge pressure reading. Pressure should not drop. If pressure does drop, refer to **Fig. 20** to determine probable cause and necessary repairs.
12. Release fuel pressure, then disconnect high pressure hose and remove gauge from delivery pipe. Reconnect high pressure hose to delivery pipe.
13. Apply 12 volts to fuel pump check terminal, **Fig. 22,** to activate fuel pump. Ensure there is no fuel leakage.

NEON

1. Relieve fuel pressure as described under "Fuel System Pressure Relief."
2. Install fuel pressure gauge tool No. C-4799B, or equivalent, to test port located on fuel rail.
3. Place ignition in the ON position.
4. Using a suitable DRB scan tool, access the ASD Fuel System Test. The ASD Fuel Test will active the fuel pump and pressurize the system.
5. If the pressure gauge reads 48 psi, no further testing is needed.
6. If the pressure is above specifications,

check for a kinked or restricted fuel return tube from fuel filter to pump module.
7. If the pressure is below specifications, refer to **Fig. 23.**

STEALTH

1. Relieve fuel system pressure as described under "Fuel System Pressure Relief."
2. Disconnect battery ground cable.
3. Disconnect fuel high pressure hose at delivery pipe side.
4. Install a suitable fuel pressure gauge and O-ring on adapter tool Nos. MD998709 and MB998742, or equivalents.
5. Connect adapter tool and gauge between delivery pipe and high pressure hose.
6. Connect battery ground cable and fuel pump connector.
7. Connect a jumper wire from fuel pump test terminal, located at right hand fire wall in engine compartment near wiper motor assembly, to positive battery post.
8. With pressure applied, ensure no leaks exist at adapter tool connection.
9. Disconnect jumper wire, then start and idle engine.
10. **On models equipped with non-turbocharged engine,** ensure fuel pressure is 38 psi at curb idle.
11. **On models equipped with turbocharged engine,** ensure fuel pressure is 34 psi at curb idle.
12. **On all models,** disconnect vacuum hose from fuel pressure regulator, then measure fuel pressure while plugging end of vacuum hose, noting the following:
   a. **On models equipped with non-turbocharged engine,** fuel system pressure should be 47-50 psi at curb idle.
   b. **On models equipped with turbocharged engine,** fuel system pressure should be 43-45 psi at curb idle.
13. If fuel pressure is not as specified, refer to **Fig. 24** for probable cause and remedy.
14. Stop engine end ensure no decrease fuel system pressure.
15. If fuel pressure decreases, note rate of decrease and refer to **Fig. 25** for probable cause and remedy.
16. Release fuel system pressure and disconnect adapter tool.

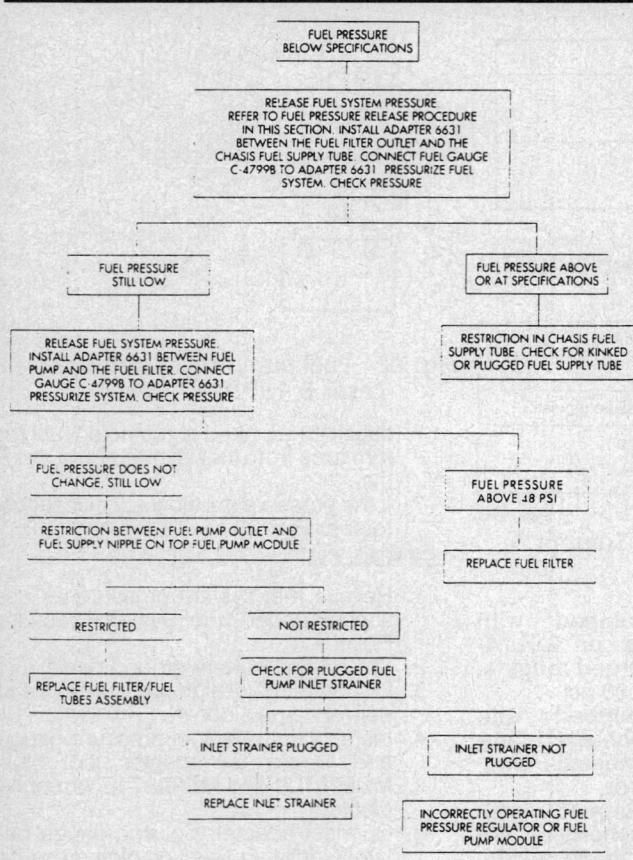

Fig. 23   Low fuel pressure test chart. Neon

Condition	Probable cause	Remedy
• Fuel pressure is too low. • Fuel pressure drops during racing. • No fuel pressure in fuel return hose.	Fuel filter is clogged.	Replace the fuel filter.
	Malfunction of the valve seat within the fuel pressure regulator, or fuel leakage to return side caused by spring deterioration.	Replace the fuel pressure regulator.
	Fuel pump low discharge pressure.	Replace the fuel pump.
Fuel pressure is too high.	The valve within the fuel pressure regulator is sticking.	Replace the fuel pressure regulator.
	Clogging of the fuel return hose and/ or the pipe.	Clean or replace the hose and/or pipe.
No change of the fuel pressure when the vacuum hose is connected and when not connected.	Damaged vacuum hose or nipple clogging.	Replace the vacuum hose, or clean the nipple.
	Malfunction of the fuel pressure control system <Turbo>	Checking the fuel pressure control system <Turbo>

CR1029103738000X

Fig. 24   Fuel pressure troubleshooting chart. Stealth

Condition	Probable cause	Remedy
After the engine is stopped, the fuel pressure drops gradually.	Injector leakage.	Replace the injector.
	Leakage at the fuel pressure regulator valve seat.	Replace the fuel pressure regulator.
There is a sudden sharp drop of the fuel pressure immediately after the engine is stopped.	The check valve (within the fuel pump) is not closed.	Replace the fuel pump.

CR1029103739000X

Fig. 25   Fuel system troubleshooting chart. Stealth

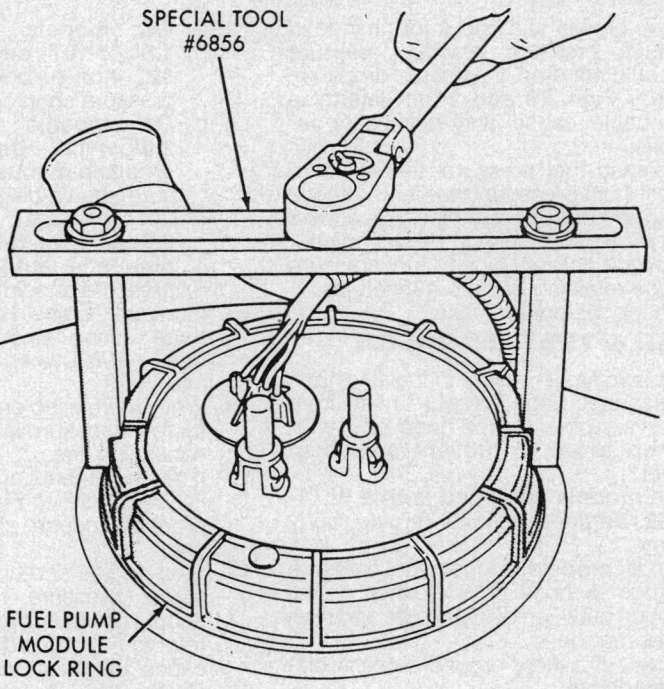

Fig. 26   Fuel pump replacement. Breeze, Cirrus, Sebring Convertible & Stratus

17. Replace O-ring at fuel high pressure hose.
18. Connect high pressure hose and **torque** to 43 inch lbs.
19. Check for leaks.

FUEL PUMP REPLACEMENT

ACCLAIM, DAYTONA, DYNASTY, IMPERIAL, LEBARON, SHADOW, SPIRIT, SUNDANCE & 1993 NEW YORKER

1. Relieve fuel system pressure as described under "Fuel System Pressure Relief."
2. Disconnect battery ground cable, then remove filler cap.
3. Raise and support vehicle, then drain fuel into approved gasoline container.
4. Remove fuel filler tube to quarter panel screws. **The right rear tire may have to be removed for easier access to filler tube.**
5. Remove draft tube cap on sending unit and siphon fuel from tank.
6. Disconnect all fuel lines and electrical connections to fuel tank.
7. Place transmission jack under fuel tank, then loosen retaining strap attaching bolts and lower tank from vehicle.
8. Using a brass drift punch and hammer, carefully tap lock ring counter

clockwise to release pump, then remove fuel pump and discard O-ring.
9. Wipe tank area clean, then place a new O-ring seal on pump assembly.
10. Position fuel pump in tank with locking ring.
11. Using a brass drift punch and hammer, drive locking ring clockwise to lock pump in place. **Do not overtighten lock ring or leakage could occur.**

BREEZE, CIRRUS, SEBRING CONVERTIBLE & STRATUS

1. Release fuel system pressure as outlined under "Fuel System Pressure Relief."
2. Disconnect battery ground cable.

3. Raise and properly support vehicle.
4. Disconnect electrical connector and fuel supply lines from fuel pump module.
5. Properly drain and remove fuel tank.
6. Disconnect fuel filter lines from pump module.
7. Clean top of tank to remove loose dirt and debris.
8. Using fuel pump module ring spanner tool No. 6856, or equivalent, remove lock ring to release pump module, **Fig. 26.**
9. Remove pump module and O-ring. Discard O-ring.
10. Reverse procedure to install, noting the following:
   a. Install new O-ring.
   b. Using tool No. 6856, or equivalent, **torque** lock ring to 40 ft. lbs.

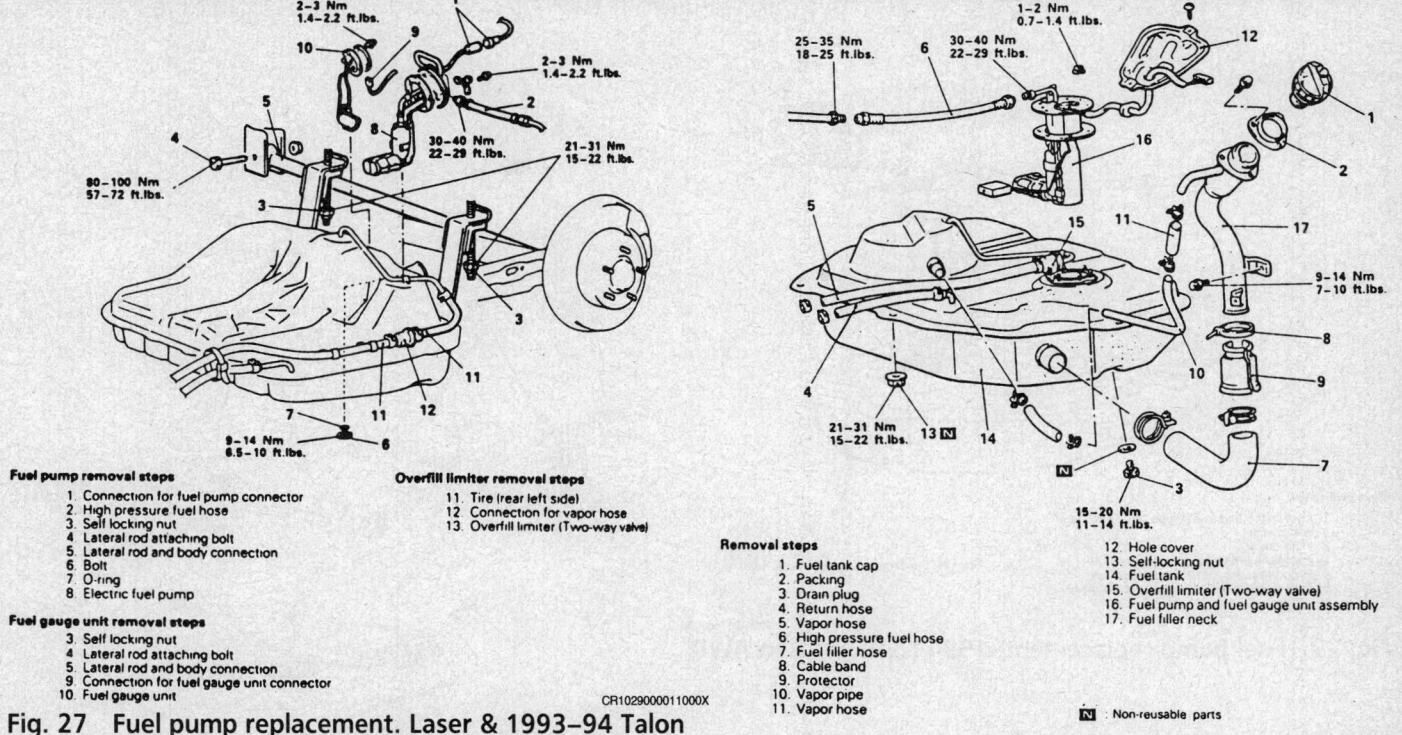

Fuel pump removal steps
1. Connection for fuel pump connector
2. High pressure fuel hose
3. Self locking nut
4. Lateral rod attaching bolt
5. Lateral rod and body connection
6. Bolt
7. O-ring
8. Electric fuel pump

Fuel gauge unit removal steps
3. Self locking nut
4. Lateral rod attaching bolt
5. Lateral rod and body connection
9. Connection for fuel gauge unit connector
10. Fuel gauge unit

Overfill limiter removal steps
11. Tire (rear left side)
12. Connection for vapor hose
13. Overfill limiter (Two-way valve)

Fig. 27 Fuel pump replacement. Laser & 1993–94 Talon FWD

Removal steps
1. Fuel tank cap
2. Packing
3. Drain plug
4. Return hose
5. Vapor hose
6. High pressure fuel hose
7. Fuel filler hose
8. Cable band
9. Protector
10. Vapor pipe
11. Vapor hose
12. Hole cover
13. Self-locking nut
14. Fuel tank
15. Overfill limiter (Two-way valve)
16. Fuel pump and fuel gauge unit assembly
17. Fuel filler neck

N : Non-reusable parts

Fig. 28 Fuel pump replacement. 1993 Laser & Talon AWD

AVENGER, SEBRING COUPE, LASER & TALON

1. Remove fuel pump in numbered sequence, **Figs. 27 through 31,** noting the following:
   a. Release fuel system pressure as outlined under "Fuel System Pressure Relief."
   b. Cover all fuel connections with rags prior to disconnecting.
2. Reverse numbered sequence for installation, noting the following:
   a. Align three positioning projections of packing with holes in fuel pump and fuel gauge unit assembly.
   b. Apply Mopar rope caulk sealer part No. 4026044, or equivalent, to rear floor pan prior to installing fuel gauge cover.

COLT & SUMMIT

1. Release fuel system pressure as outlined under "Fuel System Pressure Relief."
2. Remove fuel tank cap, raise and support rear of vehicle and drain fuel into suitable container.
3. Disconnect filler hose from tank, support tank with suitable jack and remove nuts securing tank straps.
4. Lower fuel tank, then mark and disconnect fuel hoses, vapor hoses and electrical connectors.
5. Remove nuts securing fuel pump assembly, then the fuel pump and gasket.
6. Reverse procedure to install.

COLT VISTA & SUMMIT WAGON

1. Release fuel system pressure as outlined under "Fuel System Pressure Relief."

2. Remove fuel tank cap, raise and support rear of vehicle and drain fuel into suitable container.
3. Disconnect filler hose from tank, then support tank with suitable jack and remove nuts securing tank straps.
4. Lower fuel tank, then mark and disconnect fuel hoses, vapor hoses and electrical connectors.
5. Remove nuts securing fuel pump assembly, then the fuel pump and gasket.
6. Reverse procedure to install.

CONCORDE, INTREPID, LHS, VISION & 1994–96 NEW YORKER

1. Relieve fuel system pressure as described under "Fuel System Pressure Relief," then disconnect battery ground cable.
2. Remove trunk liner, then the fuel pump access panel and gasket from floor of trunk.
3. Disconnect all fuel lines and electrical connections from fuel pump.
4. Loosen band clamp until fuel pump rises from tank.
5. To absorb possible fuel spillage, place shop towel around access opening. Without removing fuel pump, tip pump backwards to allow fuel in reservoir to drain back into fuel tank.
6. Float arm of level sensor catches on inside of tank while removing fuel pump. Tilt fuel pump to one side when removing pump from fuel tank.
7. Remove fuel pump and gasket from tank.

8. Reverse procedure to install, noting the following:
   a. Install a new fuel pump gasket.
   b. Align marks on fuel tank and pump as shown in **Fig. 32.**
   c. **Torque** fuel pump band clamp to 31 inch lbs.

NEON

1. Release fuel system pressure as outlined under "Fuel System Pressure Relief."
2. Properly drain fuel tank.
3. Raise and properly support vehicle.
4. Disconnect electrical connector.
5. Disconnect fuel lines from fuel pump module by depressing quick connect retainers with thumb and forefinger.
6. Using a suitable hammer and a brass drift punch, carefully tap pump lock ring counterclockwise to release pump.
7. Remove fuel pump and O-ring from tank. Discard old O-ring. **Use suitable shop towel to absorb fuel that may spill out of pump module.**
8. Reverse procedure to install, ensuring to use new O-ring. **Do not over tighten lock ring.**

STEALTH

1. Drain fuel from fuel tank using a suitable siphon/storage tank.
2. Relieve fuel system pressure as outlined under "Fuel System Pressure Relief."
3. Remove fuel pump in numbered sequence shown in **Fig. 33,** noting the following:
   a. Cover all fuel connections with rags prior to disconnecting.

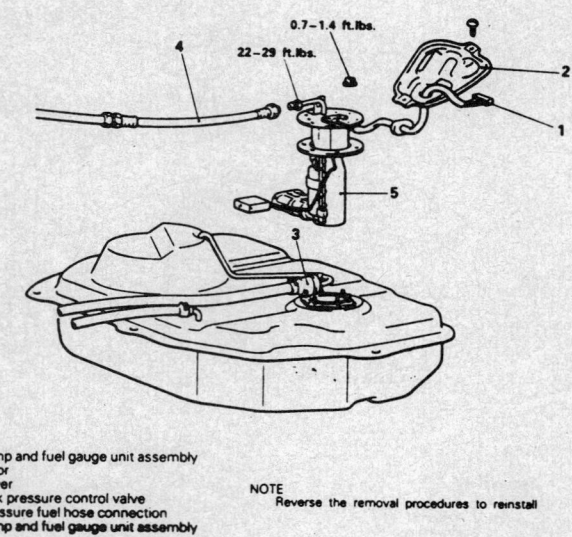

Removal steps
1. Fuel pump and fuel gauge unit assembly connector
2. Hole cover
3. Fuel tank pressure control valve
4. High pressure fuel hose connection
5. Fuel pump and fuel gauge unit assembly

NOTE
Reverse the removal procedures to reinstall

CR1029403744000X

Fig. 29   Fuel pump replacement. 1994 Laser & Talon AWD

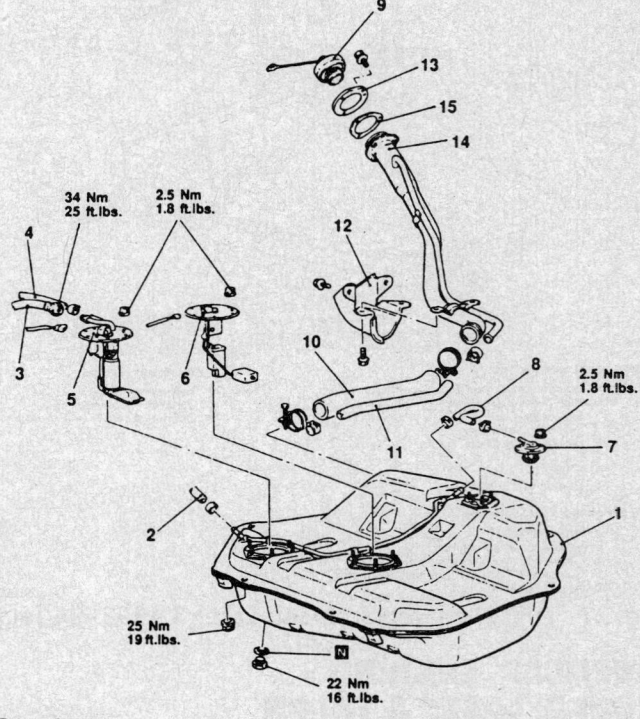

Removal steps
1. Fuel tank
2. Vapor hose
3. High-pressure fuel hose
4. Return hose
5. Fuel pump assembly
6. Fuel gauge unit
7. Fuel cut-off valve assembly
8. Vapor hose
9. Fuel tank filler tube cap
10. Filler hose
11. Vapor hose
12. Fuel tank filler tube protector
13. Reinforcement
14. Fuel tank filler tube assembly
15. Packing

CR1029505390000X

Fig. 30   Fuel pump replacement. Avenger, Sebring Coupe & 1995–96 Talon FWD

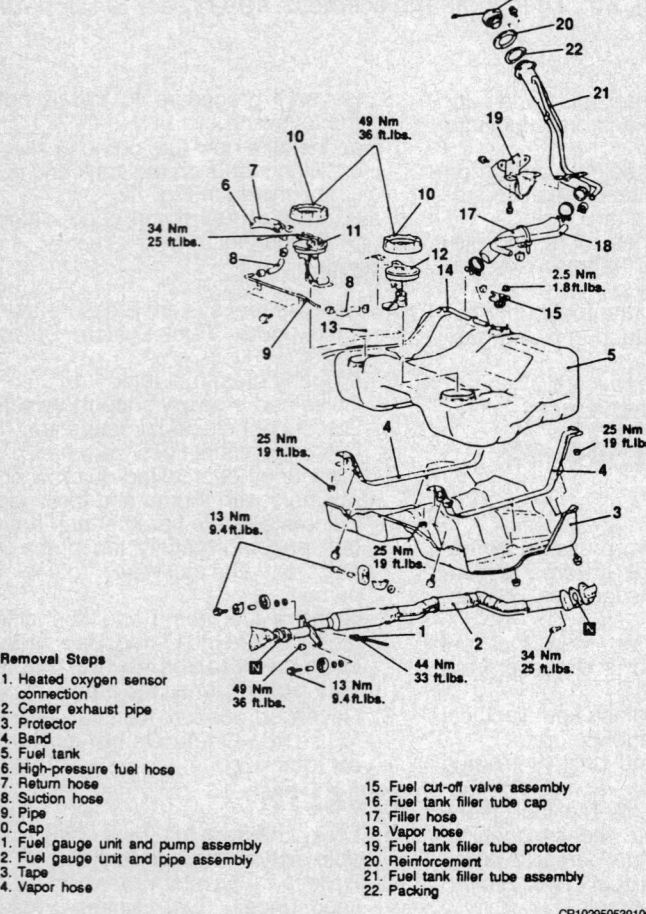

Removal Steps
1. Heated oxygen sensor connection
2. Center exhaust pipe
3. Protector
4. Band
5. Fuel tank
6. High-pressure fuel hose
7. Return hose
8. Suction hose
9. Pipe
10. Cap
11. Fuel gauge unit and pump assembly
12. Fuel gauge unit and pipe assembly
13. Tape
14. Vapor hose
15. Fuel cut-off valve assembly
16. Fuel tank filler tube cap
17. Filler hose
18. Vapor hose
19. Fuel tank filler tube protector
20. Reinforcement
21. Fuel tank filler tube assembly
22. Packing

CR1029505391000X

Fig. 31   Fuel pump replacement. 1995–96 Talon AWD

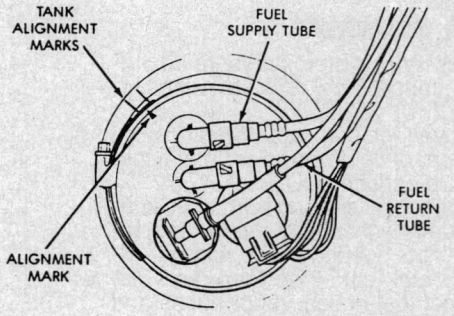

CR1029300008000X

Fig. 32   Fuel pump alignment. Concorde, Intrepid, LHS, Vision, & 1994–96 New Yorker

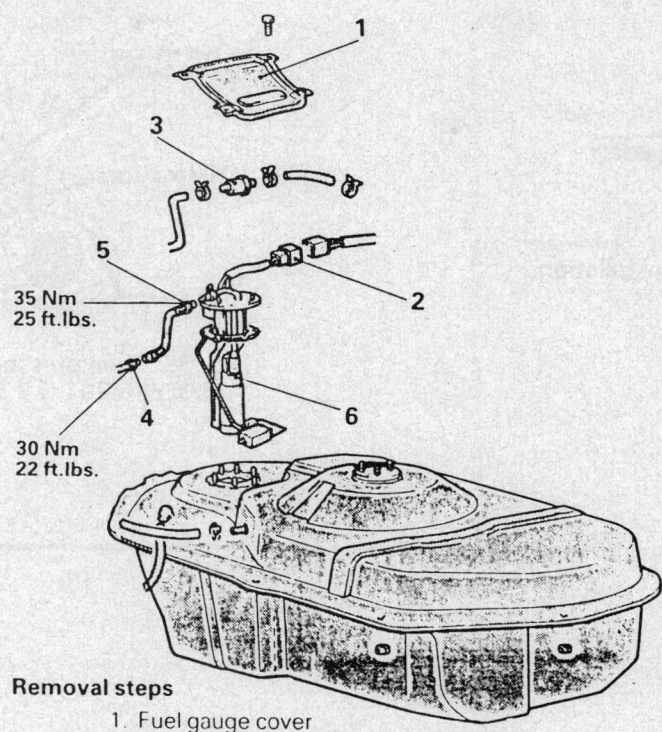

Removal steps

1. Fuel gauge cover
2. Fuel pump and fuel gauge unit assembly connector
3. Overfill limiter (Two-way valve)
4. High pressure fuel hose connection (body side)
5. High pressure fuel hose connection (fuel pump side)
6. Fuel pump and fuel gauge unit assembly

CR1029000009000X

Fig. 33   Fuel pump replacement. Stealth

b. Hold high pressure fuel hose nut on pump side with a suitable wrench while turning nut on hose side.
4. Inspect overfill limiter valve by blowing through valve as follows:
   a. Lightly blow from inlet side. Air should pass through after a slight resistance.
   b. Lightly blow from outlet side. Air should pass through with no resistance.
5. Install fuel pump in reverse numbered sequence shown in **Fig. 33**, noting the following:
   a. Align three positioning projections of packing with holes in fuel pump and fuel gauge unit assembly.
   b. Tighten flare nut temporarily by hand, then tighten fully. **Avoid twisting fuel hose.**
   c. Install overfill valve as shown in **Fig. 34.**
   d. Apply Mopar rope caulk sealer part No. 4026044, or equivalent, to rear

floor pan prior to installing fuel gauge cover.

TECHNICAL SERVICE BULLETINS

FUEL FILTER REPLACEMENT

Acclaim, Concorde, Dynasty, Imperial, Intrepid, LeBaron, LHS, New Yorker, Shadow, Spirit, Sundance & Vision

After replacing fuel pump it is necessary to check and or replace the fuel filter. Fuel pressure must not exceed a drop of 5 psi. across the fuel filter, if so replace the filter. Failure to replace a defective fuel filter, after fuel pump replacement, may cause malfunction or premature replacement pump failure. On flex fuel vehicles, always

replace the fuel filter whenever fuel pump is replaced.

FUEL PRESSURE REGULATOR INSTALLATION

1993 Dynasty, Imperial & New Yorker & 1993–94 Concorde, Intrepid & Vision, 1994 LHS & New Yorker w/3.3L/V6-202 & 3.5L/V6-215 Engines

When replacing the fuel pressure regulator, the O-rings may remain attached to the regulator. Removal of the O-rings from the regulator is required as they must be separately installed in the fuel rail cavity. Apply a light coat of clean engine oil to the O-rings, then seat them in the cavity prior to inserting regulator, **Fig. 35.** Failure to perform this procedure as described could result in the regulator being misdiagnosed as defective.

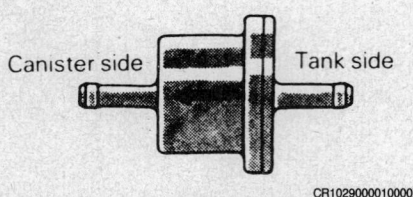

Canister side   Tank side

CR1029000010000X

Fig. 34   Overfill limiter installation.
Stealth

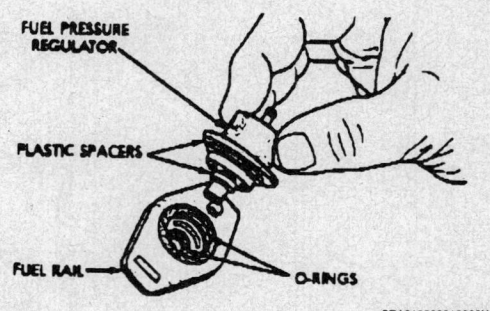

FUEL PRESSURE
REGULATOR

PLASTIC SPACERS

FUEL RAIL

O-RINGS

CRA019200012000X

Fig. 35   Fuel pressure O-ring installation.
3.3L/V6-201 & 3.5L/V6-215 engines

TU~~RBOC~~ ~~HARG~~ ~~ERS~~

If Unsure Of The System Used On The Vehicle Being Serviced, Refer To The "Engine Systems Identification Chart." Further Assistance For The Proper Use Of Information Contained In This Section Can Also Be Found In The Front Of This Tabbed Section Under "How To Use This Manual."

Prior To Performing Any Service Operations Listed In This Section, Consult The Technical Service Bulletin Section For Related Information.

INDEX

	Page No.		Page No.		Page No.
Description	16-1	Turbo Bypass Valve	16-2	System Service:	16-7
Diagnosis & Testing:	16-1	Turbocharger Supercharging		Except Laser, Stealth & Talon	16-7
Intake Charge Pressure Control		Pressure	16-1	Laser & Talon	16-8
System	16-1	Wastegate Solenoid	16-2	Stealth	16-7

DESCRIPTION

The turbocharger, **Figs. 1 through 5,** is an exhaust driven device which compresses the air being delivered to the engine through the intake system. The turbocharger is used to increase engine power on a demand basis, allowing a smaller and more economical engine to be used.

Exhaust gases flow through a turbine which is connected through a shaft to the impeller (compressor). During normal, steady operation, the turbine does not rotate fast enough to boost pressure. As speed increases, the air is compressed, allowing a denser mixture to enter the combustion chambers and develop more engine power during the combustion process.

The intake manifold pressure (boost pressure) is controlled by a wastegate valve which is used to bypass a portion of the exhaust gases around the turbine at a predetermined point in the cycle, limiting boost pressure.

DIAGNOSIS & TESTING

TURBOCHARGER SUPERCHARGING PRESSURE

1995–96 Stealth & Talon

1. Disconnect black hose at turbocharger wastegate solenoid and connect pressure gauge to hose, **Fig. 6,** then plug nipple from which hose was removed.
2. Drive vehicle at full throttle and accelerate engine to 3500 RPM in second gear. **Drive vehicle in an area in which a full throttle acceleration can be performed safely and in accordance with traffic laws. Have a front seat passenger read pressure gauge during test drive.**
3. Record supercharging pressure when pointer stabilizes:

   a. **On Stealth models,** pressure should be 2.9–8.7 psi.
   b. **On Talon Models,** pressure should be 6.4–14.7 psi.
4. If pressure is higher than specified, inspect the following items and repair as necessary:
   a. Inspect turbocharger wastegate actuator or valve for signs of malfunction.
   b. Inspect wastegate actuator hose for cracking or improper connections.
5. If pressure is lower than specified, inspect the following items and repair as necessary:
   a. Inspect turbocharger wastegate actuator for signs of malfunction.
   b. Check for supercharging pressure leaks.
   c. Inspect turbocharger assembly for signs of malfunction.

INTAKE CHARGE PRESSURE CONTROL SYSTEM

Laser & 1993–94 Talon

1. Disconnect white striped vacuum hose from turbocharger wastegate actuator, then connect a hand vacuum pump to hose.
2. Disconnect black vacuum hose from intake port A, **Fig. 7,** then plug open port.
3. Disconnect battery ground cable for at least 10 seconds, then reconnect cable.
4. Apply vacuum. Check for air tightness both when black hose end is plugged or open and with engine idling or stopped, noting the following:
   a. With engine not running and black hose open, vacuum should leak down.
   b. With engine not running and black hose plugged, vacuum level should remain steady.
   c. With engine idling and black hose plugged, vacuum should leak down.
   d. If vacuum is not as specified, check wastegate solenoid or vacuum hose.
5. With black vacuum hose closed and engine idling, apply vacuum. Check for air tightness both when knock sensor connector is connected or disconnected.
   a. With engine idling and knock sensor connector connected, vacuum level should leak down.
   b. With engine idling and knock sensor connector disconnected, vacuum level should remain steady.
   c. If vacuum is not as specified, check knock sensor circuit.
6. Turn ignition switch to Off position.
7. Disconnect battery ground cable for at least 10 seconds, then reconnect cable.

1995–96 Talon

1. Ensure ignition switch is in Off position, then disconnect and plug black hose at turbocharger wastegate solenoid, **Fig. 8.**
2. Connect a hand vacuum pump to solenoid nipple at which black hose was disconnected, **Fig. 8.**
3. Apply vacuum while engine is stopped and ignition switch is in On position. Vacuum pressure should be maintained.
4. Apply vacuum while engine is idling at operating temperature. Vacuum pressure should leak down.
5. If results are not as specified, wastegate solenoid is broken. Repair as necessary.

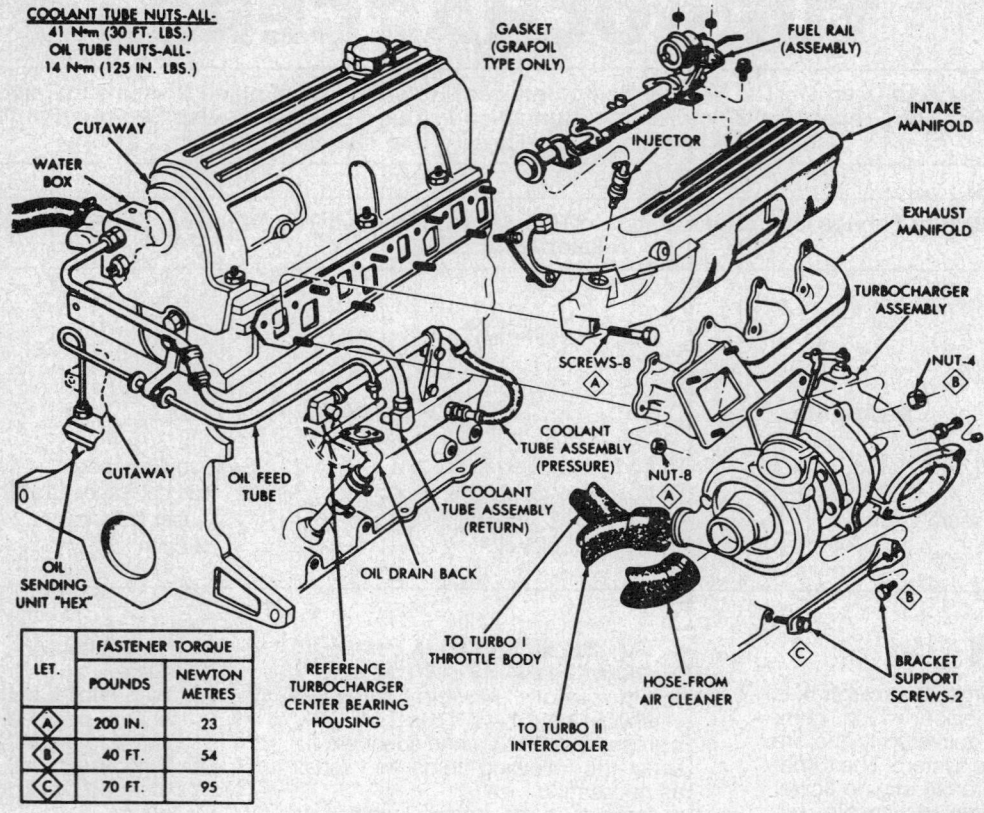

COOLANT TUBE NUTS-ALL-
41 N·m (30 FT. LBS.)
OIL TUBE NUTS-ALL-
14 N·m (125 IN. LBS.)

GASKET
(GRAFOIL
TYPE ONLY)

FUEL RAIL
(ASSEMBLY)

CUTAWAY

WATER
BOX

INJECTOR

INTAKE
MANIFOLD

EXHAUST
MANIFOLD

TURBOCHARGER
ASSEMBLY

SCREWS-8

NUT-4

CUTAWAY

OIL FEED
TUBE

COOLANT
TUBE ASSEMBLY
(PRESSURE)

NUT-8

OIL
SENDING
UNIT "HEX"

COOLANT
TUBE ASSEMBLY
(RETURN)

OIL DRAIN BACK

REFERENCE
TURBOCHARGER
CENTER BEARING
HOUSING

TO TURBO I
THROTTLE BODY

HOSE-FROM
AIR CLEANER

BRACKET
SUPPORT
SCREWS-2

TO TURBO II
INTERCOOLER

LET.	FASTENER TORQUE	
	POUNDS	NEWTON METRES
A	200 IN.	23
B	40 FT.	54
C	70 FT.	95

CR1059000001000X

Fig. 1   2.2L/4-135 & 2.5L/4-153 turbocharged engine components

Stealth

1. Disconnect black hose from turbocharger wastegate solenoid and connect a three-way joint between hose and solenoid.
2. Connect hand vacuum pump to three-way joint.
3. Disconnect hose (with end painted red) from wastegate actuator, then plug open port.
4. Apply vacuum. Check for vacuum leaks both when hose end (with end painted red) is closed and open.
   a. With ignition switch On and hose end open, vacuum level should leak down.
   b. With ignition switch On and hose end plugged, vacuum level should remain steady.
   c. With engine idling, warmed up to normal operating temperature and with hose end plugged, vacuum level should leak down.
   d. If vacuum is not as specified, wastegate actuator, wastegate solenoid or hose is broken.

WASTEGATE SOLENOID

Laser & Talon

1. Using a hand vacuum pump, apply vacuum to solenoid valve nipple on which white vacuum hose is connect-

ed. Check air tightness when voltage is applied and disconnected from solenoid valve terminal, **Fig. 9.**
   a. With battery voltage applied and other nipple of solenoid valve open, vacuum level should leak down.
   b. With battery voltage applied and other nipple of solenoid valve plugged, vacuum level should remain steady.
   c. With battery voltage disconnected and other nipple of solenoid valve open, vacuum level should remain steady.
2. Connect ohmmeter across solenoid terminals. Resistance should be 36-44 ohms at 68°F.

Stealth

1. Using a hand vacuum pump, apply vacuum to solenoid valve nipple A, **Fig. 10.**
2. Connect solenoid valve to battery as shown in **Fig. 10.**
3. Check air tightness when negative jumper lead is applied and disconnected from solenoid valve terminal, noting the following:
   a. With negative lead connected and B nipple open, vacuum level should leak down.
   b. With negative lead connected and B nipple plugged, vacuum level should remain steady.

   c. With negative lead disconnected and B nipple open, vacuum level should remain steady.
4. Connect ohmmeter across solenoid terminals. Resistance should be 36-44 ohms at 68°F.

TURBO BYPASS VALVE

Except Laser, Stealth & Talon

1. Remove vacuum hose from turbo bypass valve vacuum converter, located on air cleaner assembly.
2. Apply 15 inches of vacuum to valve. If vacuum holds, bypass valve is good. If vacuum leaks, replace air cleaner assembly.

Laser & Talon

1. Remove turbocharger bypass valve, then connect hand vacuum pump to nipple on valve.
2. Apply vacuum of approximately 7.7 psi. Valve should start to open.
3. Ensure vacuum level remains steady.

Stealth

1. Remove turbocharger bypass valve, then connect hand vacuum pump to nipple on valve.
2. Apply vacuum of approximately 16 inches of mercury. Valve should start to open.
3. Ensure vacuum level remains steady.

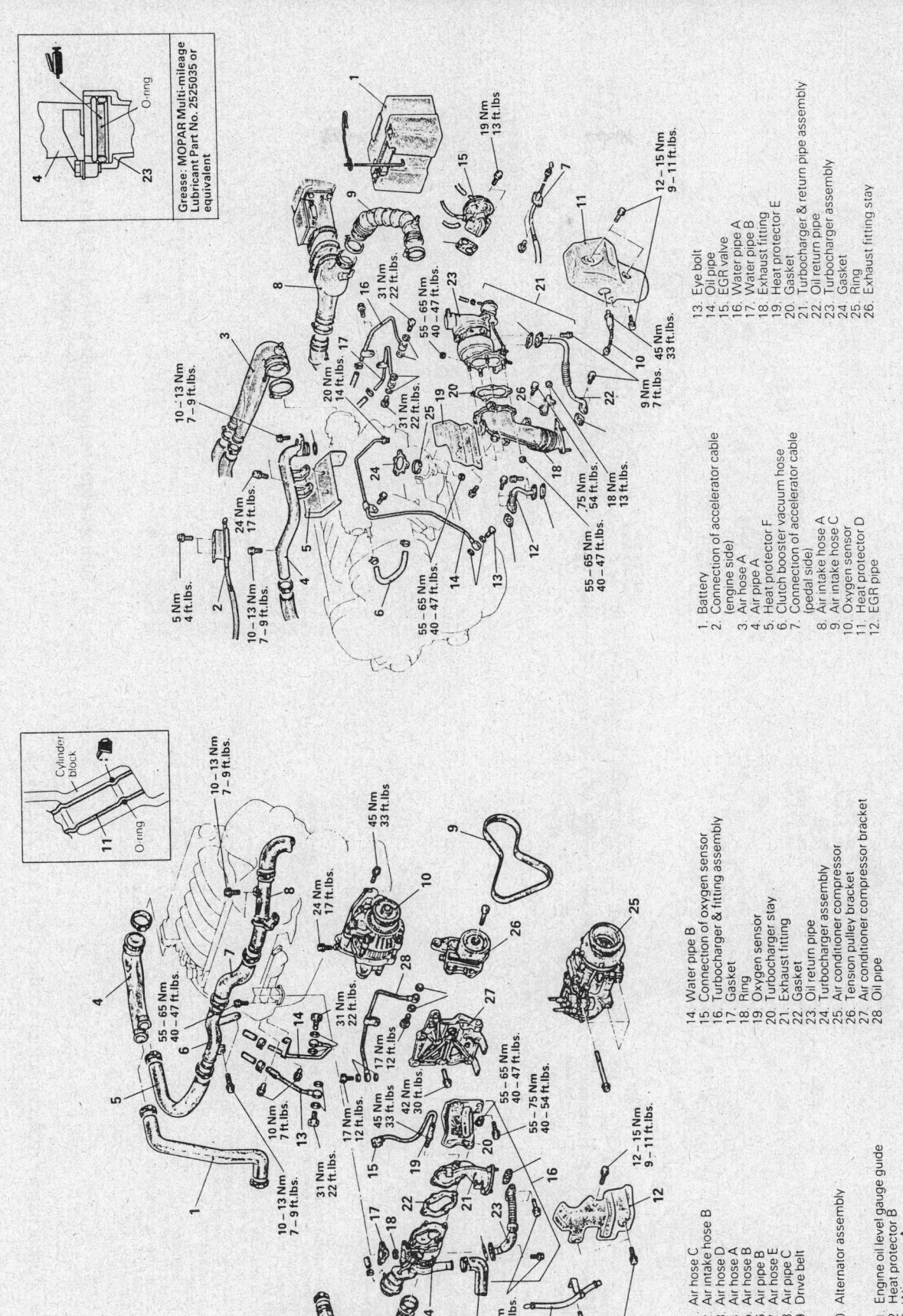

Grease: MOPAR Multi-mileage Lubricant Part No. 2525035 or equivalent

O-ring

Cylinder block

O-ring

Fig. 2   Front turbocharger replacement procedure. Stealth

1. Air hose C
2. Air intake hose B
3. Air hose D
4. Air hose A
5. Air pipe B
6. Air hose B
7. Air pipe E
8. Air pipe C
9. Drive belt
10. Alternator assembly
11. Engine oil level gauge guide
12. Heat protector B
13. Water pipe A
14. Water pipe B
15. Connection of oxygen sensor
16. Turbocharger & fitting assembly
17. Gasket
18. Ring
19. Oxygen sensor
20. Turbocharger stay
21. Exhaust fitting
22. Gasket
23. Oil return pipe
24. Turbocharger assembly
25. Air conditioner compressor
26. Tension pulley bracket
27. Air conditioner compressor bracket
28. Oil pipe

Fig. 3   Rear turbocharger replacement procedure. Stealth

1. Battery
2. Connection of accelerator cable (engine side)
3. Air hose A
4. Air pipe A
5. Heat protector F
6. Clutch booster vacuum hose
7. Connection of accelerator cable (pedal side)
8. Air intake hose A
9. Air intake hose C
10. Oxygen sensor
11. Heat protector D
12. EGR pipe
13. Eye bolt
14. Oil pipe
15. EGR valve
16. Water pipe A
17. Water pipe B
18. Exhaust fitting
19. Heat protector E
20. Gasket
21. Turbocharger & return pipe assembly
22. Oil return pipe
23. Turbocharger assembly
24. Gasket
25. Ring
26. Exhaust fitting stay

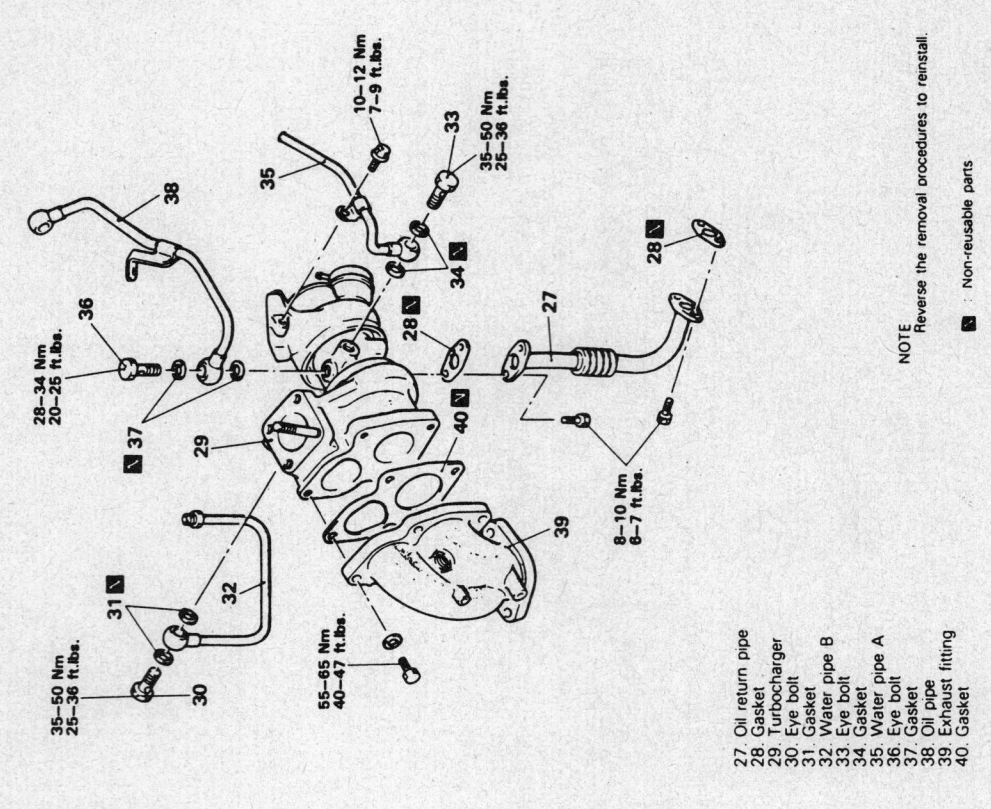

10–12 Nm
7–9 ft.lbs.

35–50 Nm
25–36 ft.lbs.

28–34 Nm
20–25 ft.lbs.

8–10 Nm
6–7 ft.lbs.

35–50 Nm
25–36 ft.lbs.

55–85 Nm
40–47 ft.lbs.

27. Oil return pipe
28. Gasket
29. Turbocharger
30. Eye bolt
31. Gasket
32. Water pipe B
33. Eye bolt
34. Eye bolt
35. Water pipe A
36. Eye bolt
37. Gasket
38. Oil pipe
39. Exhaust fitting
40. Gasket

NOTE
Reverse the removal procedures to reinstall.

☑ = Non-reusable parts

CR10590000004020X

Fig. 4 Turbocharger replacement procedure (Part 2 of 2). Laser & 1993–94 Talon

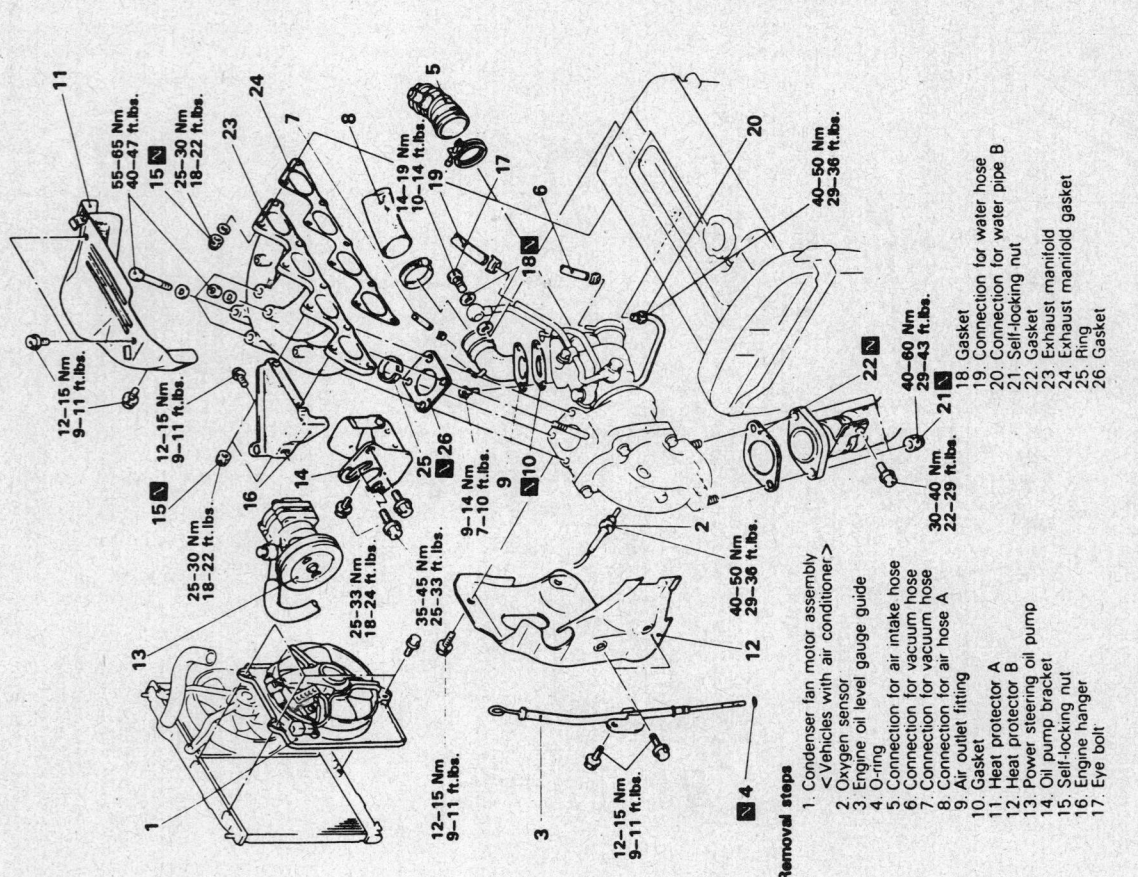

CR10590000004010X

55–85 Nm
40–47 ft.lbs.

25–30 Nm
18–22 ft.lbs.

14–19 Nm
10–14 ft.lbs.

40–50 Nm
29–36 ft.lbs.

40–60 Nm
29–43 ft.lbs.

30–40 Nm
22–29 ft.lbs.

40–50 Nm
29–36 ft.lbs.

12–15 Nm
9–11 ft.lbs.

12–15 Nm
9–11 ft.lbs.

25–30 Nm
18–22 ft.lbs.

25–33 Nm
18–24 ft.lbs.

35–45 Nm
25–33 ft.lbs.

9–14 Nm
7–10 ft.lbs.

12–15 Nm
9–11 ft.lbs.

Removal steps

1. Condenser fan motor assembly
   <Vehicles with air conditioner>
2. Oxygen sensor
3. Engine oil level gauge guide
4. O-ring
5. Connection for air intake hose
6. Connection for vacuum hose
7. Connection for vacuum hose
8. Connection for air hose A
9. Air outlet fitting
10. Gasket
11. Heat protector A
12. Heat protector B
13. Power steering oil pump
14. Oil pump bracket
15. Self-locking nut
16. Engine hanger
17. Eye bolt
18. Gasket
19. Connection for water hose
20. Connection for water pipe B
21. Self-locking nut
22. Gasket
23. Exhaust manifold
24. Exhaust manifold gasket
25. Ring
26. Gasket

Fig. 4 Turbocharger replacement procedure (Part 1 of 2). Laser & 1993–94 Talon

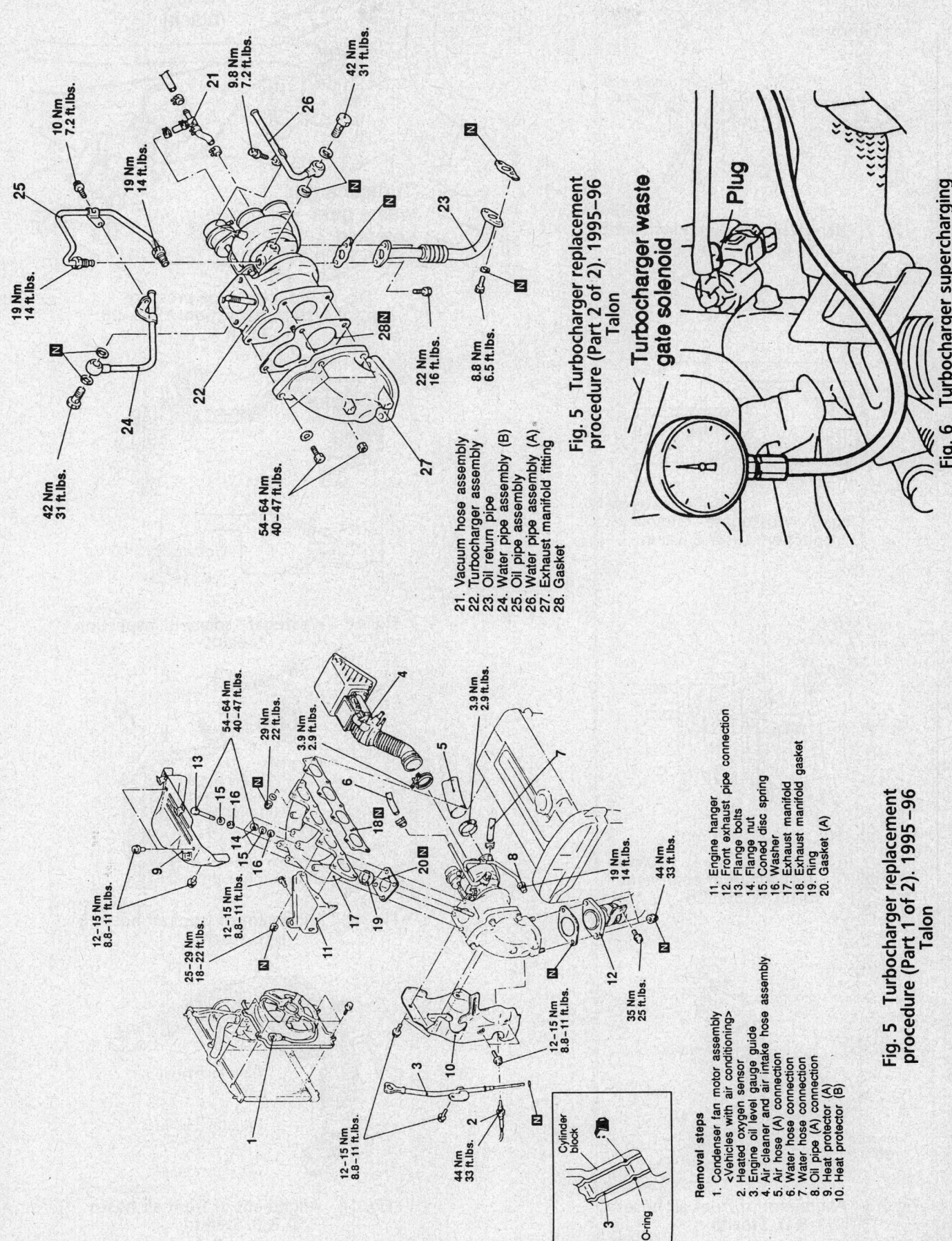

10 Nm
7.2 ft.lbs.

9.8 Nm
7.2 ft.lbs.

42 Nm
31 ft.lbs.

19 Nm
14 ft.lbs.

25

19 Nm
14 ft.lbs.

21

26

23

24

22

28

27

22 Nm
16 ft.lbs.

8.8 Nm
6.5 ft.lbs.

42 Nm
31 ft.lbs.

54–64 Nm
40–47 ft.lbs.

21. Vacuum hose assembly
22. Turbocharger assembly
23. Oil return pipe
24. Water pipe assembly (B)
25. Oil pipe assembly
26. Water pipe assembly (A)
27. Exhaust manifold fitting
28. Gasket

Fig. 5 Turbocharger replacement
procedure (Part 2 of 2). 1995–96
Talon

Plug

Turbocharger waste
gate solenoid

Fig. 6 Turbocharger supercharging
pressure inspection. 1995–96 Talon

54–64 Nm
40–47 ft.lbs.

29 Nm
22 ft.lbs.

3.9 Nm
2.9 ft.lbs.

3.9 Nm
2.9 ft.lbs.

4

5

6

13

15

16

14

15

14

16

18

20

17

19

8

19 Nm
14 ft.lbs.

44 Nm
33 ft.lbs.

12–15 Nm
8.8–11 ft.lbs.

12–15 Nm
8.8–11 ft.lbs.

25–29 Nm
18–22 ft.lbs.

9

11

12

12

35 Nm
25 ft.lbs.

12–15 Nm
8.8–11 ft.lbs.

3

10

1

2

12–15 Nm
8.8–11 ft.lbs.

44 Nm
33 ft.lbs.

Cylinder
block

O-ring

Removal steps
1. Condenser fan motor assembly
   <Vehicles with air conditioning>
2. Heated oxygen sensor
3. Engine oil level gauge guide
4. Air cleaner and air intake hose assembly
5. Air hose (A) connection
6. Water hose connection
7. Water pipe connection
8. Oil pipe (A) connection
9. Heat protector (A)
10. Heat protector (B)

11. Engine hanger
12. Front exhaust pipe connection
13. Flange bolts
14. Flange nut
15. Coned disc spring
16. Washer
17. Exhaust manifold
18. Exhaust manifold gasket
19. Ring
20. Gasket (A)

Fig. 5 Turbocharger replacement
procedure (Part 1 of 2). 1995–96
Talon

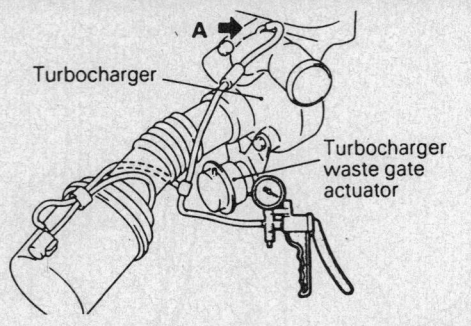

Fig. 7   Hand vacuum pump installation. Laser & 1993–94 Talon

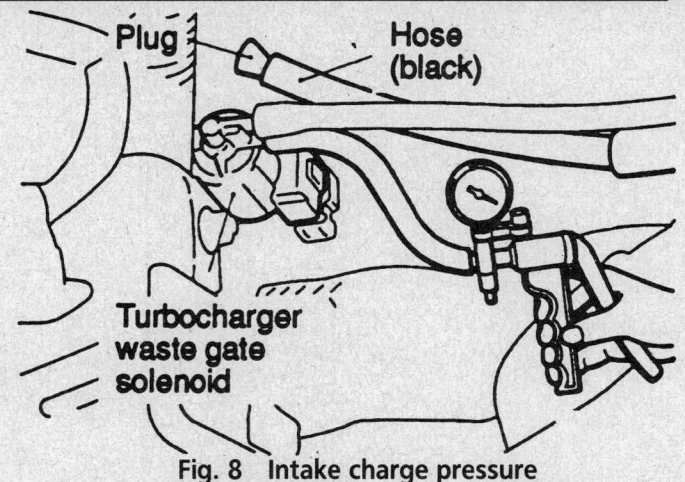

Fig. 8   Intake charge pressure control system inspection. 1995–96 Talon

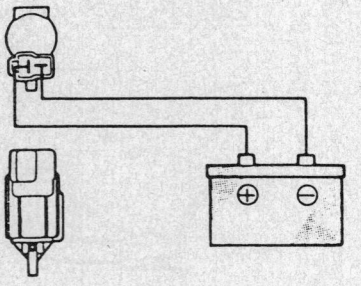

Fig. 9   Wastegate solenoid inspection. Laser & Talon

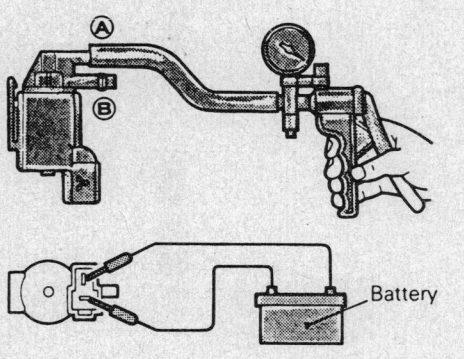

Fig. 10   Wastegate solenoid inspection. Stealth

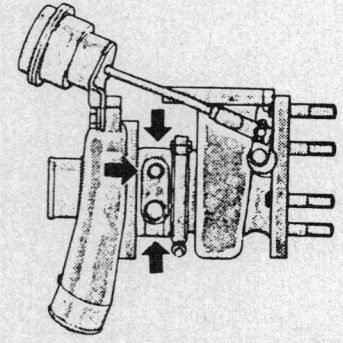

Fig. 11   Turbocharger alignment surfaces. Stealth

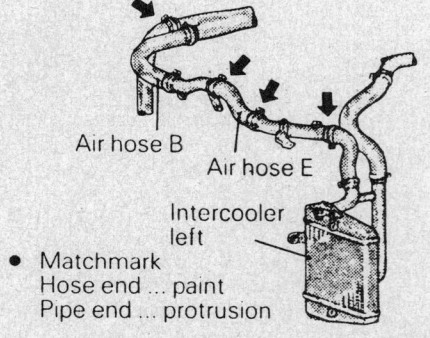

Fig. 12   Alignment of front air hoses E & B. Stealth

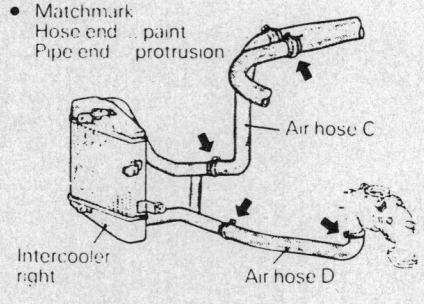

Fig. 13   Alignment of front air hoses C & D. Stealth

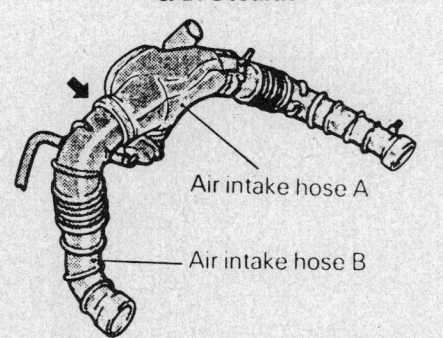

Fig. 14   Alignment of front air hoses A & B. Stealth

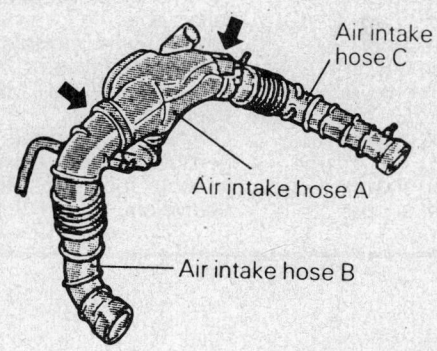

Fig. 15 Alignment of rear air hoses A, B & C. Stealth

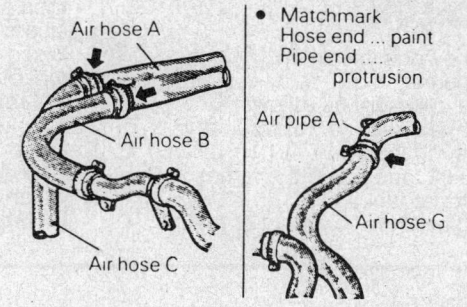

Fig. 16 Alignment of rear air hoses A & G. Stealth

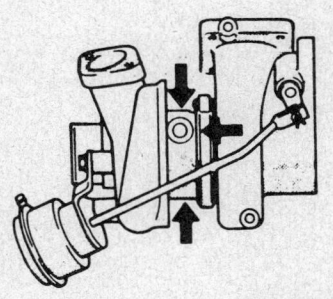

Fig. 17 Turbocharger alignment surfaces. Laser & 1993–94 Talon

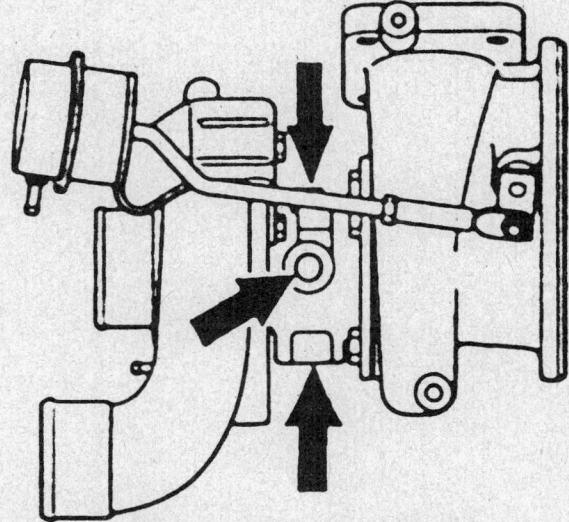

Fig. 18 Turbocharger alignment points. 1995–96 Talon

SYSTEM SERVICE

EXCEPT LASER, STEALTH & TALON

1. Raise and support vehicle, then remove right front wheel.
2. Remove air deflector, if necessary.
3. Remove right driveshaft assembly.
4. Remove turbocharger to block support bracket.
5. Separate oil drain back tube fitting from turbocharger housing, then remove fitting and hose.
6. Remove remaining turbocharger to manifold retaining nut.
7. Disconnect exhaust pipe joint from turbocharger housing.
8. Remove lower coolant line and turbocharger inlet fitting.
9. Lift turbocharger off manifold studs and lower assembly down out of vehicle.
10. Reverse procedure to install, noting the following:
    a. Position turbocharger assembly on exhaust manifold and apply suitable anti-seize compound to threads of exhaust manifold studs, then install lower passenger side retaining nut. **Torque** to 40 ft. lbs.
    b. Apply thread sealant compound to lower (inlet) coolant line fitting.
    c. Install turbocharger to block support bracket, installing screws finger tight. **Torque** block screw to 40 ft. lbs. first, then **torque** screw to turbocharger housing to 20 ft. lbs.

STEALTH

Front

1. Remove radiator assembly and transmission stay bracket.
2. Remove front exhaust pipe assembly.
3. Remove front turbocharger in sequence shown in **Fig. 2**, noting the following:
    a. Disconnect oxygen sensor connector and remove using oxygen sensor remover tool No. MD998770 or equivalent.
    b. Disconnect A/C compressor with hoses attached. Position aside using suitable support wire.
4. Reverse procedure to install, noting the following:
    a. Clean alignment surfaces shown in **Fig. 11** and supply clean engine oil into oil pipe installation hole.
    b. Install oxygen sensor using oxygen sensor wrench tool No. MD998770, or equivalent.
    c. Align marks on air hose E and B indicated by arrows in **Fig. 12** and seat completely into stepper portion of pipe or until seated.

    d. Align marks on air hose D and C indicated by arrows in **Fig. 13** and seat completely into stepper portion of pipe or until seated.
    e. Align and engage air intake hose notches mark with an arrow in **Fig. 14** until fully seated.

Rear

1. Drain engine cooling system.
2. Remove front exhaust pipe.
3. Remove rear turbocharger in sequence shown in **Fig. 3**. Disconnect oxygen sensor connector and remove using oxygen sensor remover tool No. MD998770 or equivalent.
4. Reverse procedure to install, noting the following:
    a. Clean alignment surfaces shown in **Fig. 11** and supply clean engine oil into oil pipe installation hole.
    b. Install oxygen sensor using oxygen sensor wrench tool No. MD998770 or equivalent.
    c. Align and engage air intake hose notches mark with an arrow in **Fig. 15** until fully seated.
    d. Align marks on air pipe A indicated by arrows in **Fig. 16** and seat completely into stepper portion of pipe or until seated.

LASER & TALON

1. Drain engine cooling system.
2. Drain engine oil.
3. Relieve fuel pressure as follows:
   a. Loosen gas cap to release any pressure in fuel tank.
   b. Disconnect fuel pump harness connector at fuel tank.
   c. Run engine until it runs out of fuel, then turn ignition switch to Off position.
   d. Disconnect battery ground cable.
4. Remove turbocharger assembly in numbered sequence shown in **Figs. 4 and 5.**
5. Reverse procedure to install, noting the following:
   a. Clean alignment surfaces shown in **Figs. 17 and 18** and supply clean engine oil into oil pipe installation hole.
   b. **On 1993-94 models,** install oxygen sensor using oxygen sensor wrench tool No. MD998748 or equivalent.
   c. **On 1995-96 models,** install oxygen sensor using oxygen sensor wrench tool No. MD998770 or equivalent.

EMISSION CONTROL SYSTEM
APPLICATION CHARTS

TABLE OF CONTENTS

	Page No.		Page No.
1993	17-1	**1995**	17-4
1994	17-2	**1996**	17-5

1993

NOTE: Refer To Page 17-6 For Description Of Abbreviations Used In This Chart.

Engine Liters/ CID/ Type	Certification Type C A	Certification Type F E D	Trans. Type A T	Trans. Type M T	Computerized Engine Management	Fuel Induction System Type	Ignition Timing, Deg. BTDC @RPM	PCV	ACL	AIS	EGR	EVAP	CAT	SPK	FR	O2S
1.5L/89.6/L4	—	X	X	X	YES[22]	MFI	5@750[1]	X	—	—	—	X	X[2]	X[3]	X	X[4]
1.5L/89.6/L4	X	—	X	X	YES[22]	MFI	5@750[1]	X	—	—	X[20]	X	X[2]	X[3]	X	X[15]
1.8L/107/L4[26]	—	X	X	X	YES[22]	MFI	5@700[1]	X	—	—	—	X	X[2]	X[3]	X	X[4]
1.8L/107/L4[26]	X	—	X	X	YES[22]	MFI	5@700[1]	X	—	—	X[20]	X	X[2]	X[3]	X	X[25]
1.8L/111.9/L4[27]	X	—	X	X	YES[23]	MFI	5@700[1]	X	—	—	X[20]	X	X[2]	X[3]	X	X[15]
1.8L/111.9/L4[27]	—	X	X	X	YES[23]	MFI	5@700[1]	X	—	—	—	X	X[2]	X[3]	X	X[4]
2.0L/122/L4	X	X	X	X	YES[22]	MFI	5@750[1]	X	—	—	X[20]	X	X[2]	X[18]	X	X[4]
2.0L/122/L4 Turbo	X	X	X	X	YES[22]	MFI	5@750[1]	X	—	—	X[20]	X	X[2]	X[18]	X	X[4]
2.2L/135/L4	—	X	—	X	YES[23]	TBI	[5]	X	X	X[6]	X[19]	X	X[2]	X[21]	X	X[25]
2.2L/135/L4	—	X	—	—	YES[23]	TBI	[5]	X	X	—	X[19]	X	X[2]	X[21]	X	X[25]
2.2L/135/L4	X	—	X	X	YES[23]	TBI	[5]	X	X	—	X[19]	X	X[2]	X[21]	X	X[25]
2.2L/135/L4 Turbo III	X	—	X	X	YES[22]	MFI	[7]	X	—	—	—	X	X[2]	X[18]	X	X[25]
2.4L/143.4/L4	—	X	X	X	YES[22]	MFI	5@750[1]	X	—	—	X[20]	X	X[2]	X[3]	X	X[4]
2.4L/143.4/L4	X	—	X	X	YES[22]	MFI	5@750[1]	X	—	—	X[20]	X	X[2]	X[3]	X	X[15]
2.5L/153/L4	—	X	—	X	YES[23]	TBI	[5]	X	X	X[6]	X[19]	X	X[2]	X[21]	X	X[25]
2.5L/153/L4	—	X	X	—	YES[23]	TBI	[5]	X	X	—	X[19]	X	X[2]	X[21]	X	X[25]
2.5L/153/L4	X	—	X	X	YES[23]	TBI	[5]	X	X	—	X[19]	X	X[2]	X[21]	X	X[25]
2.5L/153/L4[8]	—	X	—	X	YES[22]	MFI[8]	[9]	X	X	—	—	X	X[2]	X[18]	X	X[25]
3.0L/181/V6 SOHC[10]	X	X	—	X	YES[22]	MFI	—	X	—	—	—	X	X[2]	X[21]	X	X[25]
3.0L/181/V6 SOHC[10]	X	X	X	—	YES[22]	MFI	[11]	X	—	—	X[19]	X	X[2]	X[21]	X	X[25]
3.0L/181/V6 SOHC[12]	—	X	X	X	YES[22]	MFI	5@700[13]	X	—	—	—	X	X[2]	X[3]	X	X[25]
3.0L/181/V6 SOHC[12]	X	—	X	X	YES[22]	MFI	5@700[13]	X	—	—	X[19]	X	X[2]	X[3]	X	X[25]
3.0L/181/V6 DOHC[12]	—	X	X	X	YES[22]	MFI	5@700[13]	X	—	—	—	X	X[2]	X[18]	X	X[25]
3.0L/181/V6 DOHC[12]	X	—	X	X	YES[22]	MFI	5@700[13]	X	—	—	X[19]	X	X[2]	X[18]	X	X[25]
3.0L/181/V6 DOHC Turbo[12]	—	X	X	X	YES[22]	MFI	5@700[13]	X	—	—	—	X	X[14]	X[18]	X	X[15]

Continued

CHRYSLER—Emission Control System Application Charts

1993-Continued

Engine Liters/ CID/ Type	C	A	F E D	AT	MT	Computerized Engine Management	Fuel Induction System Type	Ignition Timing, Deg. BTDC @RPM	P C V	A C L	A I S	E G R	E V A P	C A T	S P K	F R	O 2 S
3.0L/181/V6 DOHC Turbo[12]	X	—		X	X	YES[22]	MFI	5@700[13]	X	—	—	X[19]	X	X[14]	X[18]	X	X[15]
3.3L/201/V6[16]	X	X		X	—	YES[22]	MFI	[7]	X	—	—	X[19]	X	X[2]	X[18]	X	X[25]
3.3L/201/V6[17]	X	X		X	—	YES[24]	SFI	[7]	X	—	—	X[19]	X	X[2]	X[21]	X	X[15]
3.5L/215/V6	X	X		X	—	YES[24]	SFI	[7]	X	—	—	X[19]	X	X[2]	X[18]	X	X[15]
3.8L/238/V6	X	X		X	—	YES[22]	MFI	[7]	X	—	—	X[19]	X	X[2]	X[18]	X	X[25]
8.0L/488/V10	X	X		—	X	YES[24]	SFI	[7]	X	—	—	—		X[26]	X[18]	X	X[27]

X—Equipped
—Not Equipped
[1]—Timed at No. 1 cylinder w/engine at normal operating temperature, all accessories & cooling fan off & transaxle in Neutral or Park. The basic ignition timing is checked w/jumper wire connected between ignition timing adjustment connector & ground.
[2]—Type, TWC; number of catalytic converters, 1.
[3]—DI/ECM controlled.
[4]—One O2S.
[5]—12°BTDC. On models less than 1000 miles, at 600—1200 RPM. On models more than 1000 miles, at 800—1200 RPM. Timed at No. 1 cylinder w/engine at normal operating temperature & coolant temperature sensor wire disconnected.
[6]—PAIR.
[7]—Ignition timing is controlled by PCM, no adjustment. Specification not available.
[8]—Flexible Fuel.
[9]—12° BTDC. On models w/less than 1000 miles, at 650-1400 RPM. On models w/more than 1000 miles, at 700-1400 RPM. Timed at No. 1 cylinder w/engine at normal operating temperature & coolant temperature sensor wire disconnected.
[10]—Except Stealth.
[11]—12°BTDC. On models less than 1000 miles, at 560—910 RPM. On models more than 1000 miles, at 610—910 RPM. Timed at No. 1 cylinder w/engine at normal operating temperature & coolant temperature sensor wire disconnected.
[12]—Stealth.
[13]—Basis ignition timing.
[14]—Type, TWC & WU-TWC; number of catalytic converters, 3.
[15]—Two HO2S.
[16]—Except Concorde, Intrepid & Vision.
[17]—Concorde, Intrepid & Vision.
[18]—EI/Direct Ignition System.
[19]—Electronic EGR Transducer.
[20]—Controlled flow EGR.
[21]—DI/PCM controlled.
[22]—MFI System.
[23]—TBI System.
[24]—SFI System.
[25]—One HO2S.
[26]—Type, TWC; number of catalytic converters, 2.
[27]—Two O2S.

1994

NOTE: Refer To Page 17-6 For Description Of Abbreviations Used In This Chart.

Engine Liters/ CID/ Type	C	A	F E D	AT	MT	Computerized Engine Management	Fuel Induction System Type	Ignition Timing, Deg. BTDC @RPM	P C V	A C L	A I S	E G R	E V A P	C A T	S P K	F R	O 2 S
1.5L/89.6/L4	X	X		X	X	YES[23]	MFI	5@750[1]	X	—	—	X[20]	X	X[2]	X[3]	X	X[15]
1.8L/107/L4[16]	X	X	X	X	X	YES[23]	MFI	5@700[1]	X	—	—	X[20]	X	X[2]	X[3]	X	X[15]
1.8L/111.9/L4[17]	X	X	X	X	X	YES[23]	MFI	5@700[1]	X	—	—	X[20]	X	X[2]	X[3]	X	X[15]
2.0L/122/L4	X	X	X	X	X	YES[23]	MFI	5@750[1]	X	—	—	X[20]	X	X[2]	X[18]	X	X[4]
2.0L/122/L4 Turbo	X	X	X	X	X	YES[23]	MFI	5@750[1]	X	—	—	—	X	X[2]	X[18]	X	X[4]
2.2L/135/L4	—	X	—	—	X	YES[24]	TBI	[5]	X	X	X[6]	X[19]	X	X[2]	X[22]	X	X[4]
2.2L/135/L4	—	X	—	X	—	YES[24]	TBI	[5]	X	X	—	X[19]	X	X[2]	X[22]	X	X[4]
2.2L/135/L4	X	—		X	X	YES[24]	TBI	[5]	X	X	—	X[19]	X	X[2]	X[22]	X	X[4]
2.4L/143.4/L4	X	X	X	X	X	YES[23]	MFI	5@750[1]	X	—	—	X[20]	X	X[2]	X[3]	X	X[15]
2.5L/153/L4	—	X	—	—	X	YES[24]	TBI	[5]	X	X	X[6]	X[19]	X	X[2]	X[22]	X	X[4]
2.5L/153/L4	—	X	—	X	—	YES[24]	TBI	[5]	X	X	—	X[19]	X	X[2]	X[22]	X	X[4]
2.5L/153/L4	X	—		X	X	YES[24]	TBI	[5]	X	X	—	X[19]	X	X[2]	X[22]	X	X[4]
2.5L/153/L4[8]	—	X	—	X	—	YES[23]	MFI[8]	[9]	X	—	—	X[19]	X	X[2]	X[22]	X	X[4]
3.0L/181/V6 SOHC[10]	X	—		X	X	YES[23]	MFI	[11]	X	—	—	—	X	X[2]	X[22]	X	X[4]
3.0L/181/V6 SOHC[10]	X	X	X	X	—	YES[23]	MFI	[11]	X	—	—	X[19]	X	X[2]	X[22]	X	X[4]

Continued

1994-Continued

Engine Liters/ CID/ Type	Certification Type			Trans. Type		Computerized Engine Management	Fuel Induction System Type	Ignition Timing, Deg. BTDC @RPM	Emission Control Systems								
	C	A	F E D	A T	M T				P C V	A C L	A I S	E G R	E V P	C A T	S P K	F R	O2 S
3.0L/181/V6 SOHC ⑫	—		X	X	X	YES㉓	MFI	5@700⑬	X	—	—	—	X	X②	X㉒	X	X④
3.0L/181/V6 SOHC ⑫	X		—	X	X	YES㉓	MFI	5@700⑬	X	—	—	X⑲	X	X⑭	X㉒	X	X㉑
3.0L/181/V6 DOHC ⑫	—		X	X	X	YES㉓	MFI	5@700⑬	X	—	—	—	X	X②	X⑱	X	X④
3.0L/181/V6 DOHC ⑫	X		—	X	X	YES㉓	MFI	5@700⑬	X	—	—	X⑲	X	X⑭	X⑱	X	X㉑
3.0L/181/V6 DOHC Turbo ⑫	—		X	X	X	YES㉓	MFI	5@700⑬	X	—	—	X⑲	X	X⑭	X⑱	X	X⑮
3.0L/181/V6 DOHC Turbo ⑫	X		—	X	X	YES㉓	MFI	5@700⑬	X	—	—	X⑲	X	X⑭	X⑱	X	X㉑
3.3L/201/V6	X	X	X	X	—	YES㉔	SFI	⑦	X	—	—	X⑲	X	X②	X㉒	X	X⑮
3.5L/215/V6	X	X	X	X	—	YES㉔	SFI	⑦	X	—	—	X⑲	X	X②	X⑱	X	X⑮
3.8L/238/V6	X	X	X	X	—	YES㉓	MFI	⑦	X	—	—	X⑲	X	X②	X⑱	X	X④
8.0L/488/V10	X	X	—	—	X	YES㉔	SFI	⑦	X	—	—	—	X	X㉖	X⑱	X	X㉕

X—Equipped
—Not Equipped

①—Timed at No. 1 cylinder w/engine at normal operating temperature, all accessories & cooling fan off & transaxle in Neutral or Park. The basic ignition timing is checked w/jumper wire connected between ignition timing adjustment connector & ground.
②—Type, TWC; number of catalytic converters, 1.
③—DI/ECM controlled.
④—One HO2S.
⑤—12°BTDC. On models less than 1000 miles, at 600—1200 RPM. On models more than 1000 miles, at 800—1200 RPM. Timed at No. 1 cylinder w/engine at normal operating temperature & coolant temperature

sensor wire disconnected.
⑥—PAIR.
⑦—Ignition timing is controlled by PCM, no adjustment.
⑧—Flexible Fuel.
⑨—12°BTDC. On models w/less than 1000 miles, at 650—1400 RPM. On models w/more than 1000 miles, at 700 — 1400 RPM. Timed at No. 1 cylinder w/engine at normal operating temperature & coolant temperature sensor wire disconnected.
⑩—Except Stealth.
⑪—12°BTDC. On models less than 1000 miles, at 560—910 RPM. On models more than 1000 miles, at 610—910 RPM. Timed at No. 1 cylinder w/engine at normal operating temperature & coolant temperature

sensor wire disconnected.
⑫—Stealth.
⑬—Basis ignition timing.
⑭—Type, TWC & WU-TWC; number of catalytic converters, 3.
⑮—Two HO2S.
⑯—Laser & Talon.
⑰—Colt, Colt Vista, Summit & Summit Wagon.
⑱—EI/Direct Ignition System.
⑲—Electronic EGR Transducer.
⑳—Controlled flow EGR.
㉑—Four HO2S.
㉒—DI/PCM controlled.
㉓—MFI System.
㉔—TBI System.
㉕—Two O2S.
㉖—Type, TWC; number of catalytic converters, 2.

1995

NOTE: Refer To Page 17-6 For Description Of Abbreviations Used In This Chart.

Engine Liters/ CID/ Type	Certification Type — C	A	FED	Trans. Type — AT	MT	Computerized Engine Management	Fuel Induction System Type	Ignition Timing, Deg. BTDC @RPM	PCV	ACL	AIS	EGR	EVAP	CAT	SPK	FR	O2S
1.5L/89.6/L4	X	—		X	X	YES[27]	MFI	5@750[1]	X	—	—	X[20]	X	X[30]	X[3]	X	X[15]
1.5L/89.6/L4	—	X		X	X	YES[27]	MFI	5@750[1]	X	—	—	X[20]	X	X[2]	X[3]	X	X[15]
1.8L/111.9/L4	X	—		X	X	YES[27]	MFI	5@700[1]	X	—	—	X[20]	X	X[30]	X[3]	X	X[15]
1.8L/111.9/L4	—	X		X	X	YES[27]	MFI	5@700[1]	X	—	—	X[20]	X	X[2]	X[3]	X	X[15]
2.0L/122/L4 SOHC [24]	X	X		X	X	YES[27]	MFI	[7]	X	—	—	—	X	X[2]	X[18]	X	X[15]
2.0L/122/L4 SOHC [26]	X	X		X	X	YES[27]	MFI	[7]	X	—	—	X[19]	X	X[2]	X[18]	X	X[15]
2.0L/122/L4 DOHC [22]	X	X		X	—	YES[27]	MFI	12@700[7]	X	—	—	X[19]	X	X[2]	X[18]	X	X[15]
2.0L/122/L4 DOHC [22]	X	X		—	X	YES[27]	MFI	12@700[7]	X	—	X[6]	X[19]	X	X[2]	X[18]	X	X[15]
2.0L/122/L4 DOHC [26]	X	X		X	X	YES[27]	MFI	[7]	X	—	—	X[19]	X	X[2]	X[18]	X	X[15]
2.0L/122/L4 Turbo	X	X		X	X	YES[27]	MFI	5@750[7]	X	—	—	X[20]	X	X[2]	X[18]	X	X[15]
2.4L/143.4/L4 [17]	X	X		X	X	YES[27]	MFI	[7]	X	—	—	X[20]	X	X[2]	X[3]	X	X[4]
2.4L/148/L4 [24]	X	X		X	X	YES[27]	MFI	[7]	X	—	—	X[19]	X	X[2]	X[18]	X	X[4]
2.5L/152/V6 [24]	X	X		X	X	YES[27]	MFI	[7]	X	—	—	X[19]	X	X[2]	X[25]	X	X[15]
2.5L/152/V6 [16]	X	X		X	—	YES[27]	MFI	10@750[7]	X	—	—	X[19]	X	X[14]	X[25]	X	X[15]
2.5L/153/L4	—	—		—	X	YES[28]	TBI	[5]	X	X	X[6]	X[19]	X	X[2]	X[3]	X	X[4]
2.5L/153/L4	—	X		X	—	YES[28]	TBI	[5]	X	X	—	X[19]	X	X[2]	X[3]	X	X[4]
2.5L/153/L4	X	—		X	X	YES[28]	TBI	[5]	X	X	—	X[19]	X	X[2]	X[3]	X	X[4]
2.5L/153/L4 [8]	—	X		—	X	YES[27]	MFI[8]	[9]	X	X	—	—	X	X[2]	X[3]	X	X[4]
3.0L/181/V6 SOHC [10]	X	—		—	X	YES[27]	MFI	[11]	X	—	—	—	X	X[2]	X[3]	X	X[4]
3.0L/181/V6 SOHC [10]	X	X		X	—	YES[27]	MFI	[11]	X	—	—	X[19]	X	X[2]	X[3]	X	X[4]
3.0L/181/V6 SOHC [12]	—	X		X	X	YES[27]	MFI	5@700[13]	X	—	—	—	X	X[2]	X[3]	X	X[4]
3.0L/181/V6 SOHC [12]	X	—		X	X	YES[27]	MFI	5@700[13]	X	—	—	X[19]	X	X[14]	X[3]	X	X[21]
3.0L/181/V6 DOHC [12]	—	X		X	X	YES[27]	MFI	5@700[13]	X	—	—	—	X	X[2]	X[18]	X	X[4]
3.0L/181/V6 DOHC [12]	X	—		X	X	YES[27]	MFI	5@700[13]	X	—	—	X[19]	X	X[14]	X[18]	X	X[21]
3.0L/181/V6 DOHC Turbo [12]	—	X		X	X	YES[27]	MFI	5@700[13]	X	—	—	X[19]	X	X[14]	X[18]	X	X[15]
3.0L/181/V6 DOHC Turbo [12]	X	—		X	X	YES[27]	MFI	5@700[13]	X	—	—	X[19]	X	X[14]	X[18]	X	X[21]
3.3L/201/V6	X	X		X	—	YES[29]	SFI	[7]	X	—	—	X[19]	X	X[23]	X[18]	X	X[15]
3.5L/215/V6	X	X		X	—	YES[29]	SFI	[7]	X	—	—	X[19]	X	X[23]	X[18]	X	X[15]
8.0L/488/V10	X	X		—	X	YES[29]	SFI	[7]	X	—	—	—	X	X[30]	X[18]	X	X[15]

Continued

1995-Continued

X—Equipped
—Not Equipped
① —Timed at No. 1 cylinder w/engine at normal operating temperature, all accessories & cooling fan off & transaxle in Neutral or Park. The basic ignition timing is checked w/jumper wire connected between ignition timing adjustment connector & ground.
② —Type, TWC; number of catalytic converters, 1.
③ —DI/ECM controlled.
④ —One HO2S.
⑤ —12°BTDC. On models less than 1000 miles, at 600—1200 RPM. On models more than 1000 miles, at 800—1200 RPM. Timed at No. 1 cylinder w/engine at normal operating temperature & coolant temperature sensor wire disconnected.
⑥ —PAIR.

⑦ —Ignition timing is controlled by PCM, no adjustment.
⑧ —Flexible Fuel.
⑨ —12°BTDC. On models w/less than 1000 miles, at 650—1400 RPM. On models w/more than 1000 miles, at 700 — 1400 RPM. Timed at No. 1 cylinder w/engine at normal operating temperature & coolant temperature sensor wire disconnected.
⑩ —Except Stealth.
⑪ —12°BTDC. On models less than 1000 miles, at 560—910 RPM. On models more than 1000 miles, at 610—910 RPM. Timed at No. 1 cylinder w/engine at normal operating temperature & coolant temperature sensor wire disconnected.
⑫ —Stealth.
⑬ —Basic ignition timing.
⑭ —Type, TWC & WU-TWC; number of

catalytic converters, 3.
⑮ —Two HO2S.
⑯ —Avenger & Sebring.
⑰ —Summit & Summit Wagon.
⑱ —EI/Direct Ignition System.
⑲ —Electronic EGR Transducer.
⑳ —Controlled flow EGR.
㉑ —Four HO2S.
㉒ —Avenger, Sebring & Talon.
㉓ —Type, Close Coupled; number of catalytic converters, 2; type, TWC under floor; number of catalytic converters, 1
㉔ —Cirrus & Stratus.
㉕ —DI/PCM controlled.
㉖ —Neon.
㉗ —MFI System.
㉘ —TBI System.
㉙ —SFI System.
㉚ —Type, TWC; number of catalytic converters, 2.

1996

NOTE: Refer To Page 17-6 For Description Of Abbreviations Used In This Chart.

Engine Liters/ CID/ Type	Certification Type C A	D F E	Trans. Type A T	M T	Computerized Engine Management	Fuel Induction System Type	Ignition Timing, Deg. BTDC @RPM	P C V	A C	L A	I S	E G R	E V A P	C A T	S P K	F R	O 2 S
1.5L/89.6/L4	X	—	X	X	YES⑪	MFI	5@750①	X	—	—	X⑳	X	X⑩	X③	X	X⑮
1.5L/89.6/L4	—	X	X	X	YES⑪	MFI	5@750①	X	—	—	X⑳	X	X②	X③	X	X⑮
1.8L/111.9/L4	X	—	X	X	YES⑪	MFI	5@700①	X	—	—	X⑳	X	X⑩	X③	X	X⑮
1.8L/111.9/L4	—	X	X	X	YES⑪	MFI	5@700①	X	—	—	X⑳	X	X②	X③	X	X⑮
2.0L/122/L4 SOHC⑧	X	X	X	X	YES⑪	MFI	⑦	X	—	—	—	X	X②	X⑱	X	X⑮
2.0L/122/L4 SOHC⑤	X	X	X	X	YES⑪	MFI	⑦	X	—	—	X⑲	X	X②	X⑱	X	X⑮
2.0L/122/L4 DOHC㉒	X	X	X	X	YES⑪	MFI	12@800⑦	X	—	—	X⑲	X	X②	X⑱	X	X⑮
2.0L/122/L4 DOHC⑤	X	X	X	X	YES⑪	MFI	⑦	X	—	—	X⑲	X	X②	X⑱	X	X⑮
2.0L/122/L4 Turbo	X	X	X	X	YES⑪	MFI	5@750⑦	X	—	—	X⑳	X	X②	X⑱	X	X⑮
2.4L/143.4/L4⑰	X	X	X	X	YES⑪	MFI	⑦	X	—	—	X⑳	X	X②	X③	X	X④
2.4L/148/L4⑯	X	X	X	X	YES⑪	MFI	⑦	X	—	—	X⑲	X	X②	X⑱	X	X④
2.5L/152/V6⑧	X	X	X	X	YES⑪	MFI	⑦	X	—	—	X⑲	X	X②	X⑧	X	X⑮
2.5L/152/V6⑯	X	X	X	—	YES⑪	MFI	10@750⑦	X	—	—	X⑲	X	X⑭	X⑧	X	X㉑
3.0L/181/V6 SOHC	X	X	X	X	YES⑪	MFI	5@700⑬	X	—	—	X⑲	X	X⑭	X③	X	X㉑
3.0L/181/V6 DOHC	X	X	X	X	YES⑪	MFI	5@700⑬	X	—	—	X⑲	X	X⑭	X⑱	X	X㉑
3.0L/181/V6 DOHC Turbo	X	X	X	X	YES⑪	MFI	5@700⑬	X	—	—	X⑲	X	X⑭	X⑱	X	X㉑
3.3L/201/V6	X	X	X	—	YES⑫	SFI	⑦	X	—	—	X⑲	X	X⑨	X⑱	X	X㉑
3.5L/215/V6	X	X	X	—	YES⑫	SFI	⑦	X	—	—	X⑲	X	X⑨	X⑱	X	X㉑

Continued

1996-Continued

X—Equipped
—Not Equipped
① —Timed at No. 1 cylinder w/engine at normal operating temperature, all accessories & cooling fan off & transaxle in Neutral or Park. The basic ignition timing is checked w/jumper wire connected between ignition timing adjustment connector & ground.
② —Type, TWC; number of catalytic converters, 1.
③ —DI/ECM controlled.
④ —One HO2S.
⑤ —Neon.
⑥ —DI/PCM controlled.
⑦ —Ignition timing is controlled by PCM, no adjustment.
⑧ —Cirrus & Stratus.
⑨ —Type, Close Coupled; number of catalytic converters, 2; type, TWC under floor; number of catalytic converters, 1.
⑩ —Type, TWC; number of catalytic converters, 2.
⑪ —MFI System.
⑫ —SFI System.
⑬ —Basic ignition timing.
⑭ —Type, TWC & WU-TWC; number of catalytic converters, 3.
⑮ —Two HO2S.
⑯ —Avenger & Sebring.
⑰ —Summit & Summit Wagon.
⑱ —EI/Direct Ignition System.

⑲ —Electronic EGR Transducer.
⑳ —Controlled flow EGR.
㉑ —Four HO2S.
㉒ —Avenger, Sebring & Talon.
ACL—Air Cleaner (Thermostatic Air Cleaner)
AIS—Secondary Air Injection
AT—Automatic Transmission
BID—Breakerless Inductive Discharge
BTDC—Before Top Dead Center
C4—Computer Controlled Catalytic Converter System
CA—California
CAT—Catalytic Converter
CEC—Computerized Emission Control System
CID—Cubic Inch Displacement
DI—Distributor Ignition
DIS—Direct Ignition System
DLC—Data Link Connector
DOHC—Dual Overhead Cam
DSAS—Deceleration Spark Advance System
ECM—Engine Control Module
ECU—Engine Control Unit
EFC—Electronic Feedback Carburetor
EGR—Exhaust Gas Recirculation
EI—Electronic Ignition
EICU—Electronic Ignition Control Unit
ELB—Electronic Lean Burn
ESA—Electronic Spark Advance
ESC—Electronic Spark Control
EVAP—Evaporative Emission Control System

FED—Federal
FR—Fillpipe Restrictor
HO2S—Heated Oxygen Sensor
HE—Hall Effect Ignition System
HEI—High Energy Ignition
ICM—Ignition Control Module
ICTO—Ignition Coolant Temperature Override
MFI—Multiport Fuel Injection
MT—Manual Transmission
O2S—Oxygen Sensor
OC—Oxidation Catalytic Converter
OSAC—Orifice Spark Advance Control
PCM—Powertrain Control Module
PCV—Positive Crankcase Ventilation
RPM—Revolutions Per Minute
SBEC—Single Board Engine Controller
SCTO—Spark Coolant Temperature Override
SFI—Sequential Multiport Fuel Injection
SMEC—Single Module Engine Controller
SOHC—Single Overhead Cam
SPK—Spark Control
SRI—Service Reminder Indicator
SSI—Solid State Ignition System
TBI—Throttle Body Fuel Injection
TCS—Transmission Control Spark
TSB—Technical Service Bulletin
TWC—Three Way Catalytic Converter
WU-TWC—Warm Up Three Way Catalytic Converter

VACUUM HOSE ROUTINGS

TABLE OF CONTENTS

	Page No.		Page No.
1993	18-1	1995	18-25
1994	18-15	1996	18-38

1993
INDEX

	Page No. 18-	Fig. No.
Colt:		
1.5L/4-90 Engine:		
California Emissions	2	2
Federal Emissions	2	1
1.8L/4-110 Engine:		
California Emissions	3	4
Federal Emissions	3	3
Colt Vista:		
California Emissions	8	14
Federal Emissions:		
1.8L/4-110 Engine	5	7
2.4L/4-143 Engine	8	13
Concorde:		
3.3L/V6-201 Engine	14	24
3.5L/V6-215 Engine	15	25
Dynasty:		
3.0L/V6-181 Engine:		
Less ABS	10	17
With ABS	10	18
3.3L/V6-201 & 3.8L/V6-231		
Engines	14	23
Fifth Ave.:		
3.0L/V6-181 Engine:		
Less ABS	10	17
With ABS	10	18
3.3L/V6-201 & 3.8L/V6-231		
Engines	14	23
Imperial:		
3.0L/V6-181 Engine:		
Less ABS	10	17
With ABS	10	18
3.3L/V6-201 & 3.8L/V6-231		
Engines	14	23
Intrepid:		
3.3L/V6-201 Engine	14	24
3.5L/V6-215 Engine	15	25
Laser:		
1.8L/4-107 Engine:		
California Emissions	4	6
Federal Emissions	4	5
2.0L/4-122 Non-Turbocharged Engine:		
California Emissions	6	9
Federal Emissions	5	8
2.0L/4-122 Turbocharged Engine:		
California Emissions	7	11
Federal Emissions	6	10
New Yorker:		
3.0L/V6-181 Engine:		
Less ABS	10	17

	Page No. 18-	Fig. No.
With ABS	10	18
3.3L/V6-201 & 3.8L/V6-231		
Engines	14	23
Stealth:		
Non-Turbocharged Engine:		
California Emissions	12	21
Federal Emissions	11	20
Turbocharged Engine	13	22
Summit:		
1.5L/4-90 Engine:		
California Emissions	2	2
Federal Emissions	2	1
1.8L/4-110 Engine:		
California Emissions	3	4
Federal Emissions	3	3
Summit Wagon:		
California Emissions	8	14
Federal Emissions:		
1.8L/4-110 Engine	5	7
2.4L/4-143 Engine	8	13
Talon:		
1.8L/4-107 Engine:		
California Emissions	4	6
Federal Emissions	4	5
2.0L/4-122 Non-Turbocharged Engine:		
California Emissions	6	9
Federal Emissions	5	8
2.0L/4-122 Turbocharged Engine:		
California Emissions	7	11
Federal Emissions	6	10
Vision:		
3.3L/V6-201 Engine	14	24
3.5L/V6-215 Engine	15	25
2.2L/4-135 Engine:		
TBI	9	15
Turbo III	7	12
2.5L/4-153 Engine:		
MPI	9	16
TBI	9	15
3.0L/V6-181 Engine:		
Dynasty, Fifth Ave., Imperial & New Yorker w/ABS	10	18
Except Dynasty, Fifth Ave., Imperial & New Yorker w/ABS, Stealth & Models w/Manual Transaxle	10	17
Manual Transaxle	11	19

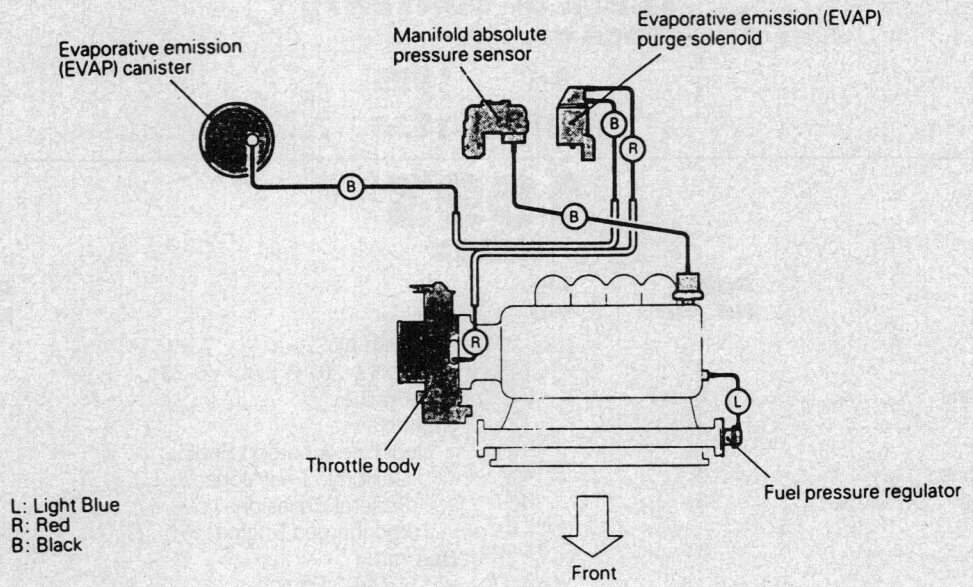

L: Light Blue
R: Red
B: Black

Fig. 1   Vacuum hose routing. 1.5L/4-90 engine w/Federal emissions

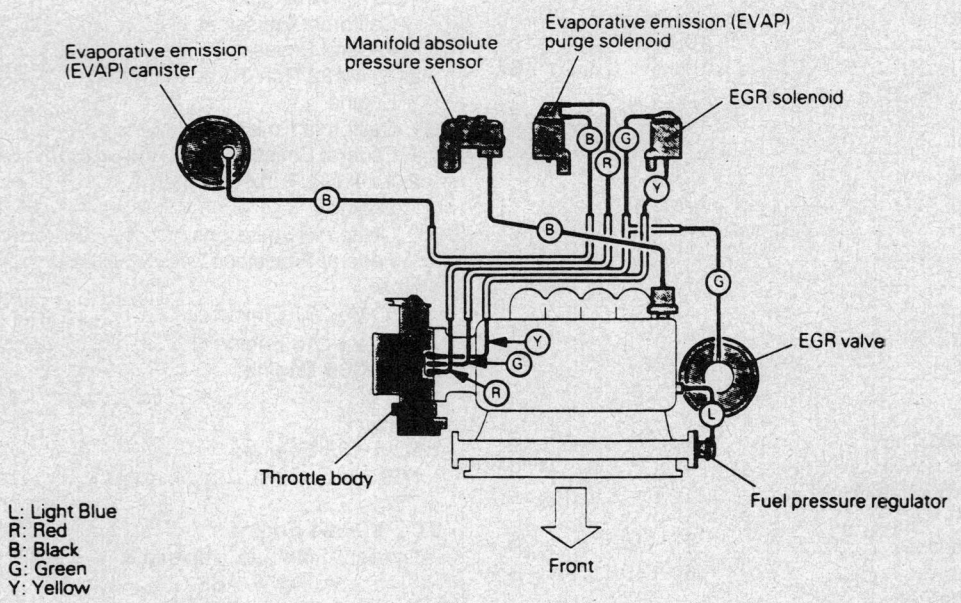

L: Light Blue
R: Red
B: Black
G: Green
Y: Yellow

Fig. 2   Vacuum hose routing. 1.5L/4-90 engine w/California emissions

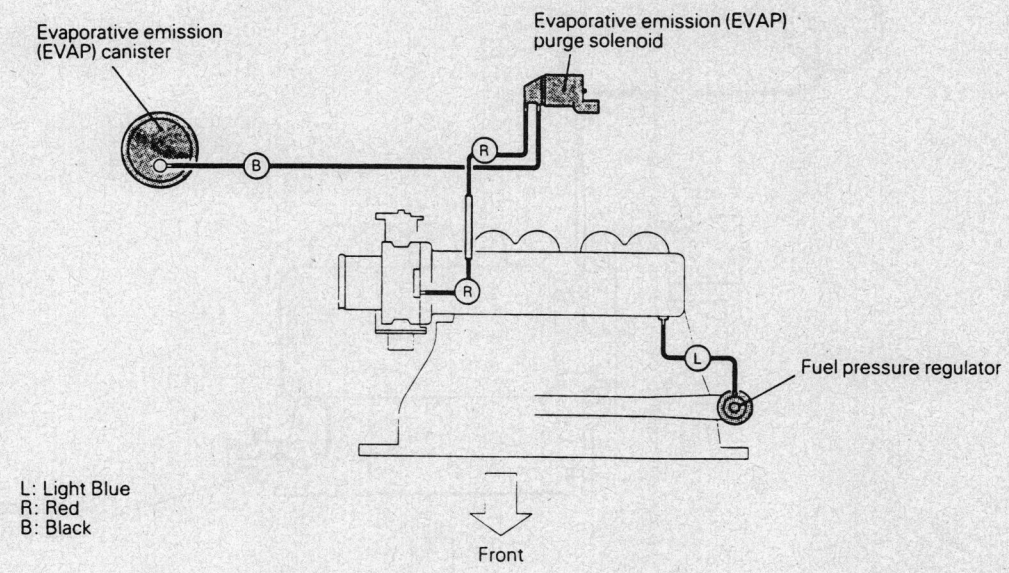

Fig. 3   Vacuum hose routing. Colt & Summit w/1.8L/4-110 engine & Federal emissions

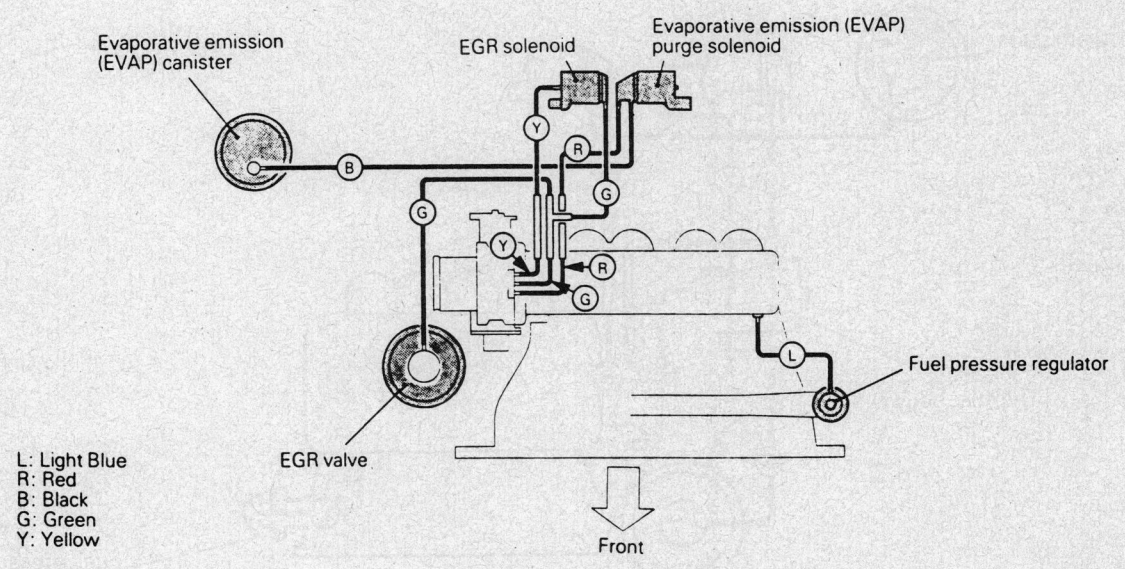

Fig. 4   Vacuum hose routing. Colt & Summit w/1.8L/4-110 engine & California emissions

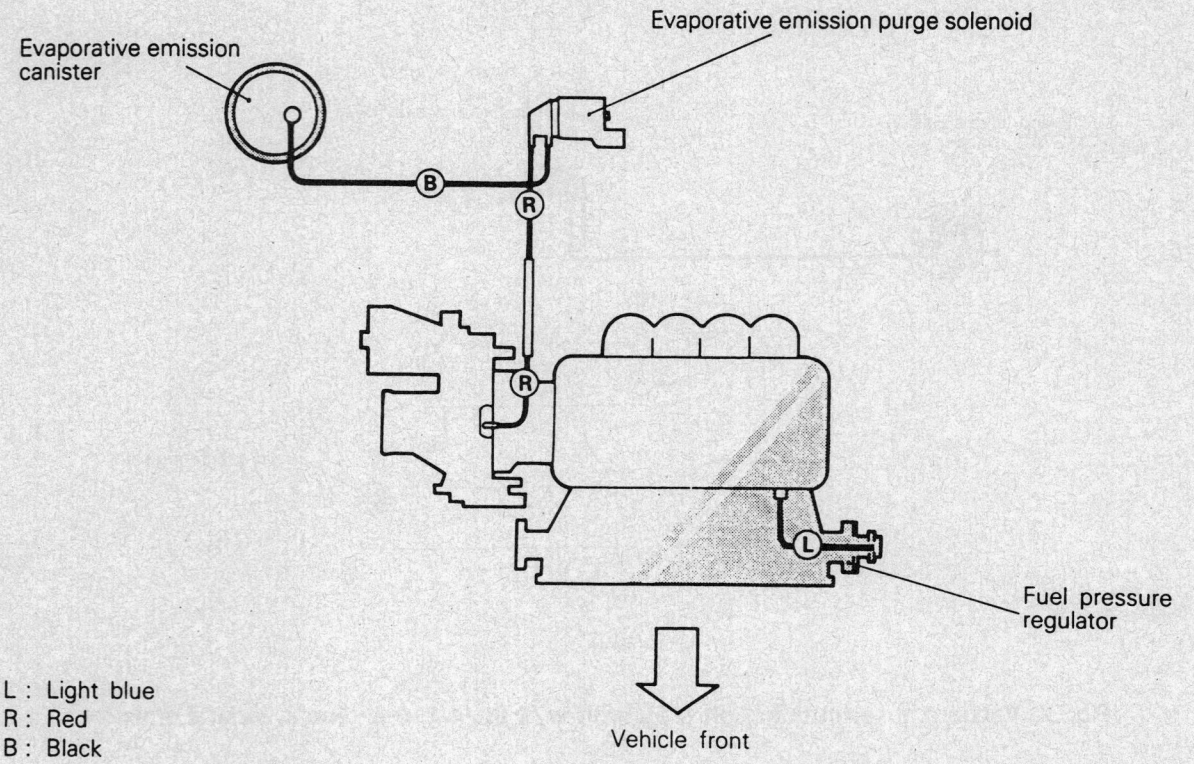

L : Light blue
R : Red
B : Black

Fig. 5 Vacuum hose routing. Laser & Talon w/1.8L/4-107 engine & Federal emissions

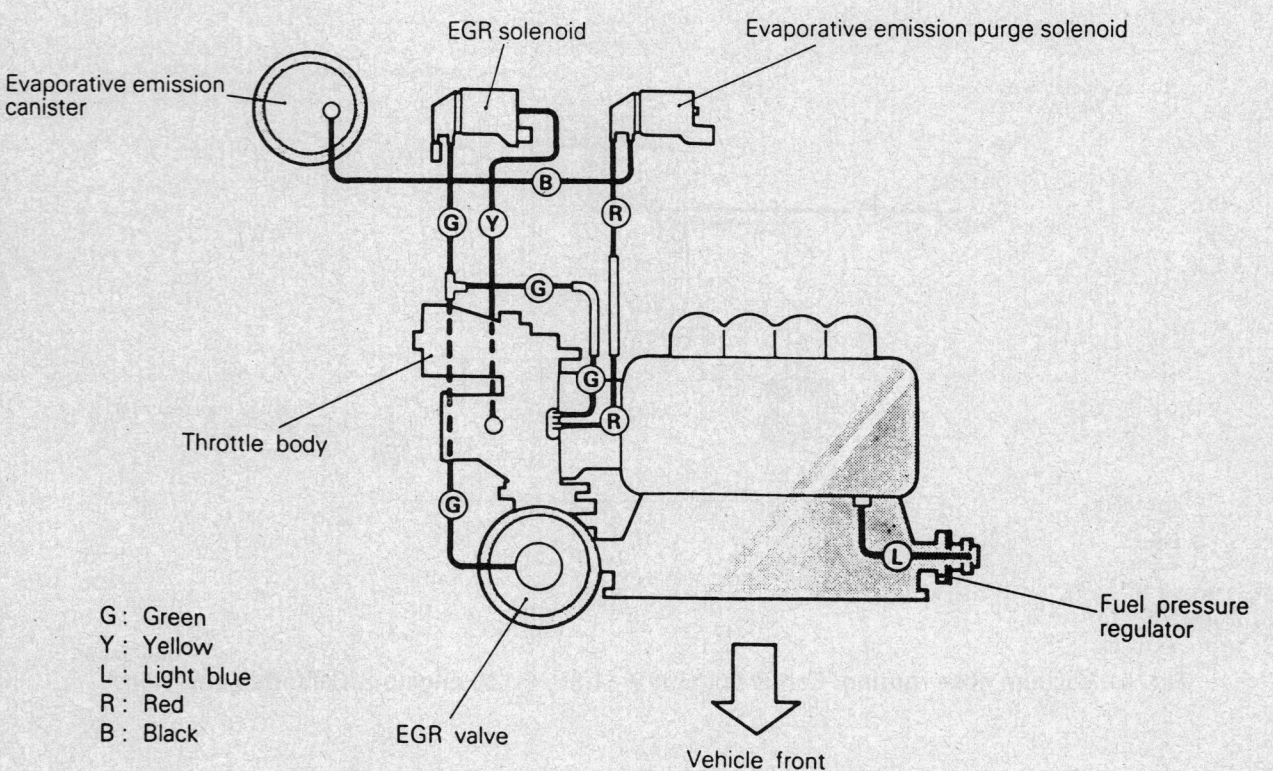

G : Green
Y : Yellow
L : Light blue
R : Red
B : Black

Fig. 6 Vacuum hose routing. Laser & Talon w/1.8L/4-107 engine & California emissions

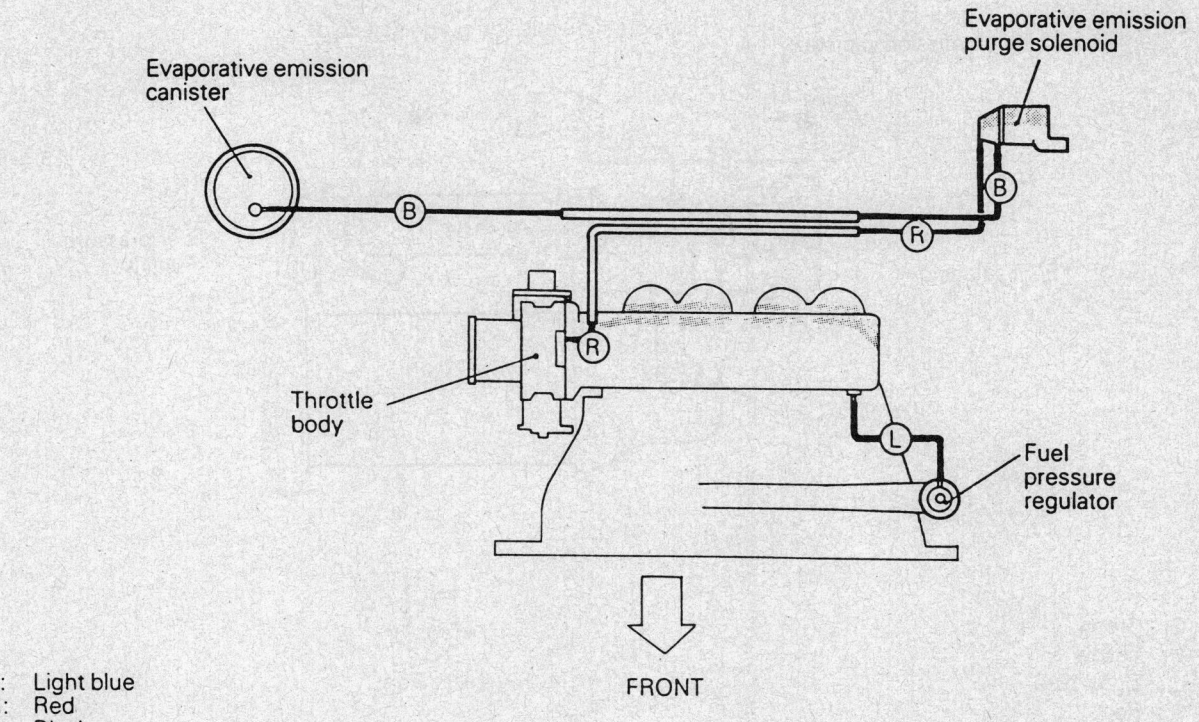

L: Light blue
R: Red
B: Black

FRONT

Fig. 7 Vacuum hose routing. Colt Vista & Summit Wagon w/1.8L/4-110 engine & Federal emissions

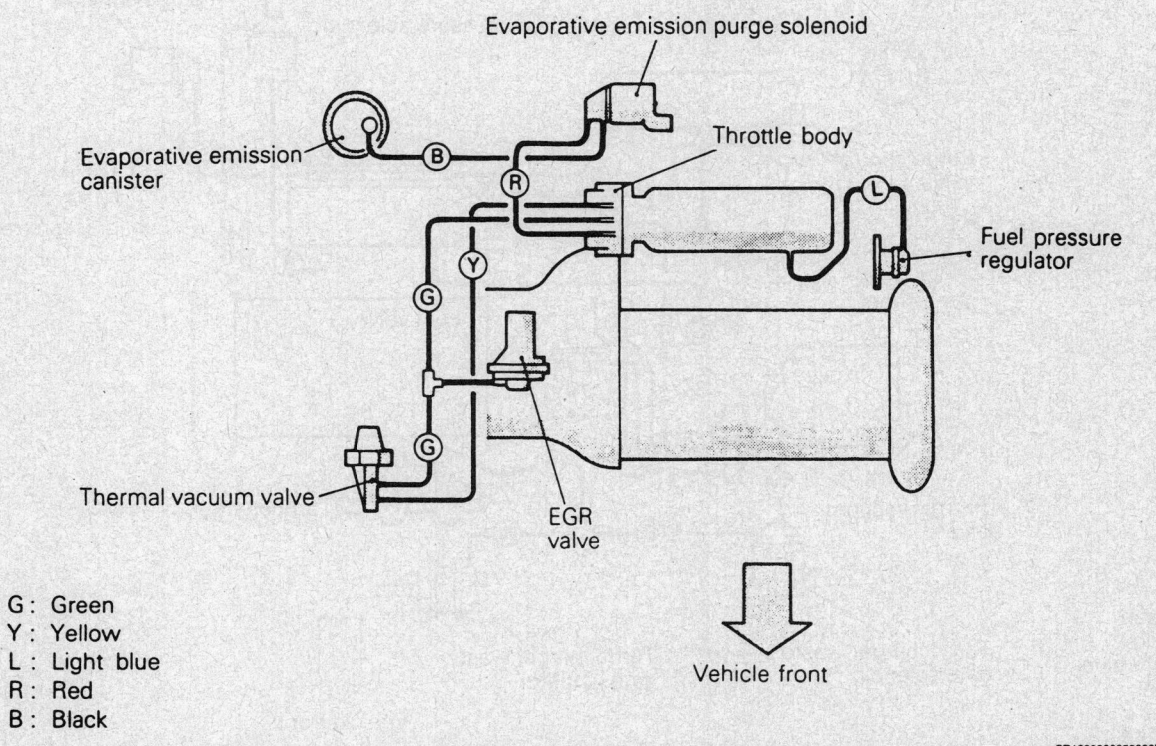

G: Green
Y: Yellow
L: Light blue
R: Red
B: Black

Vehicle front

Fig. 8 Vacuum hose routing. 2.0L/4-122 non-turbocharged engine & Federal emissions

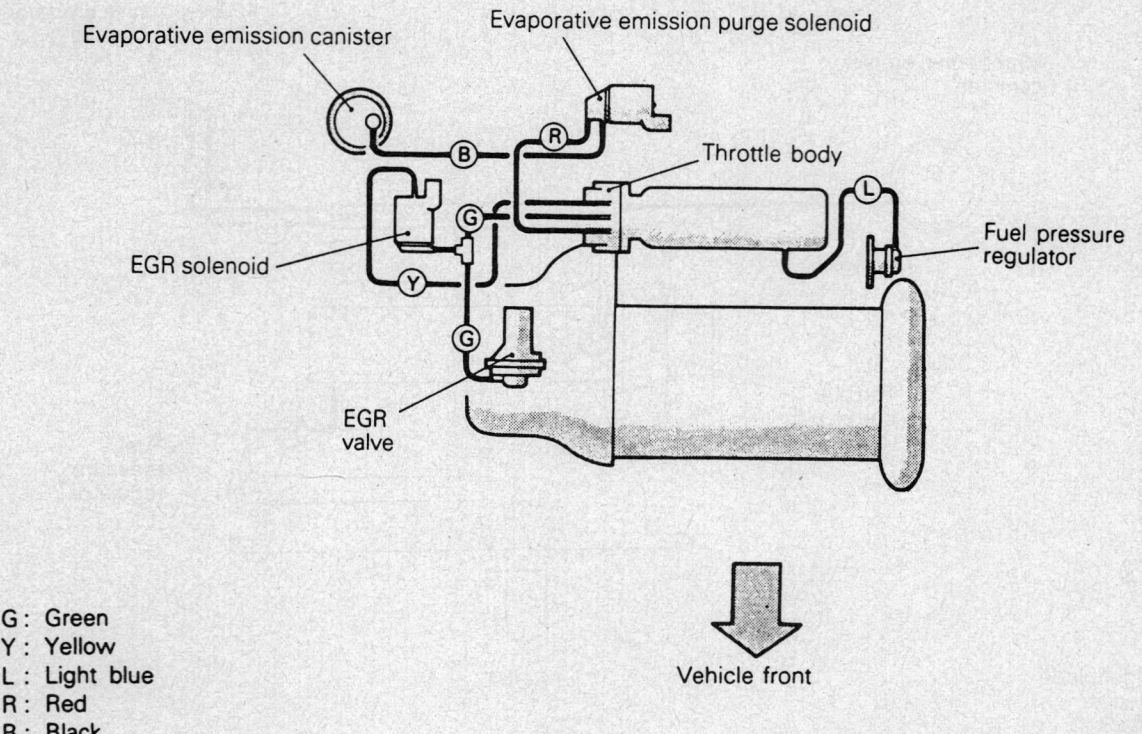

G : Green
Y : Yellow
L : Light blue
R : Red
B : Black

CR1039300059000X

Fig. 9   Vacuum hose routing. 2.0L/4-122 non-turbocharged engine & California emissions

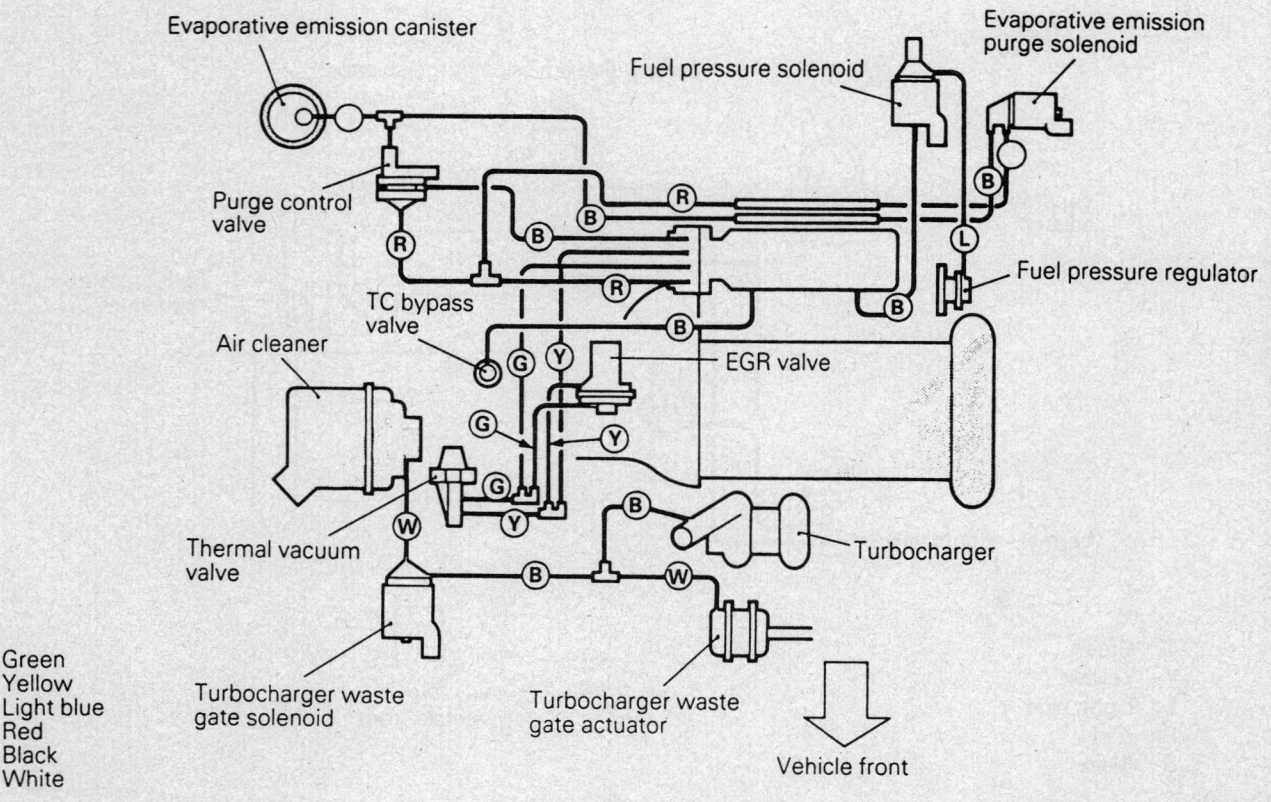

G : Green
Y : Yellow
L : Light blue
R : Red
B : Black
W : White

CR1039300060000X

Fig. 10   Vacuum hose routing. 2.0L/4-122 turbocharged engine & Federal emissions

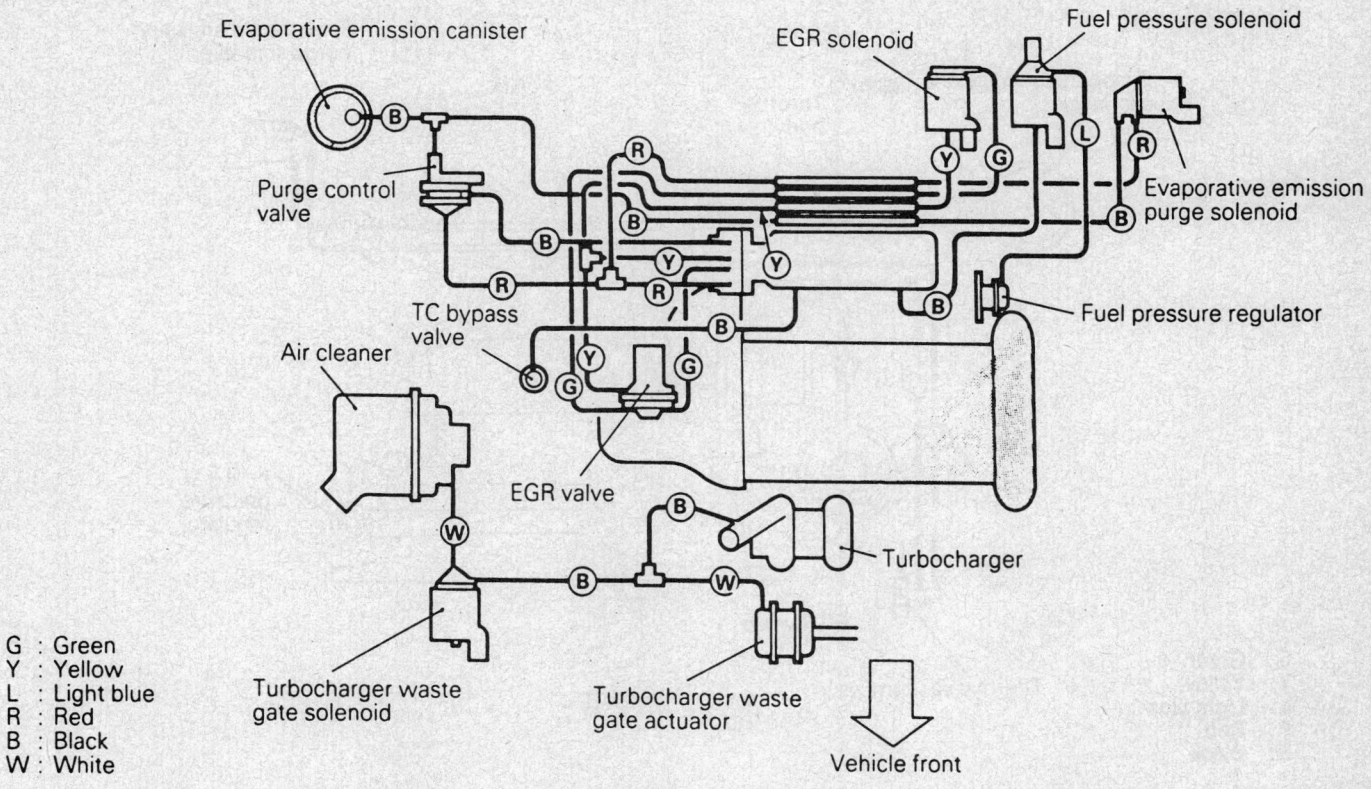

Fig. 11   Vacuum hose routing. 2.0L/4-122 turbocharged engine & California emissions

G : Green
Y : Yellow
L : Light blue
R : Red
B : Black
W : White

CR1039300061000X

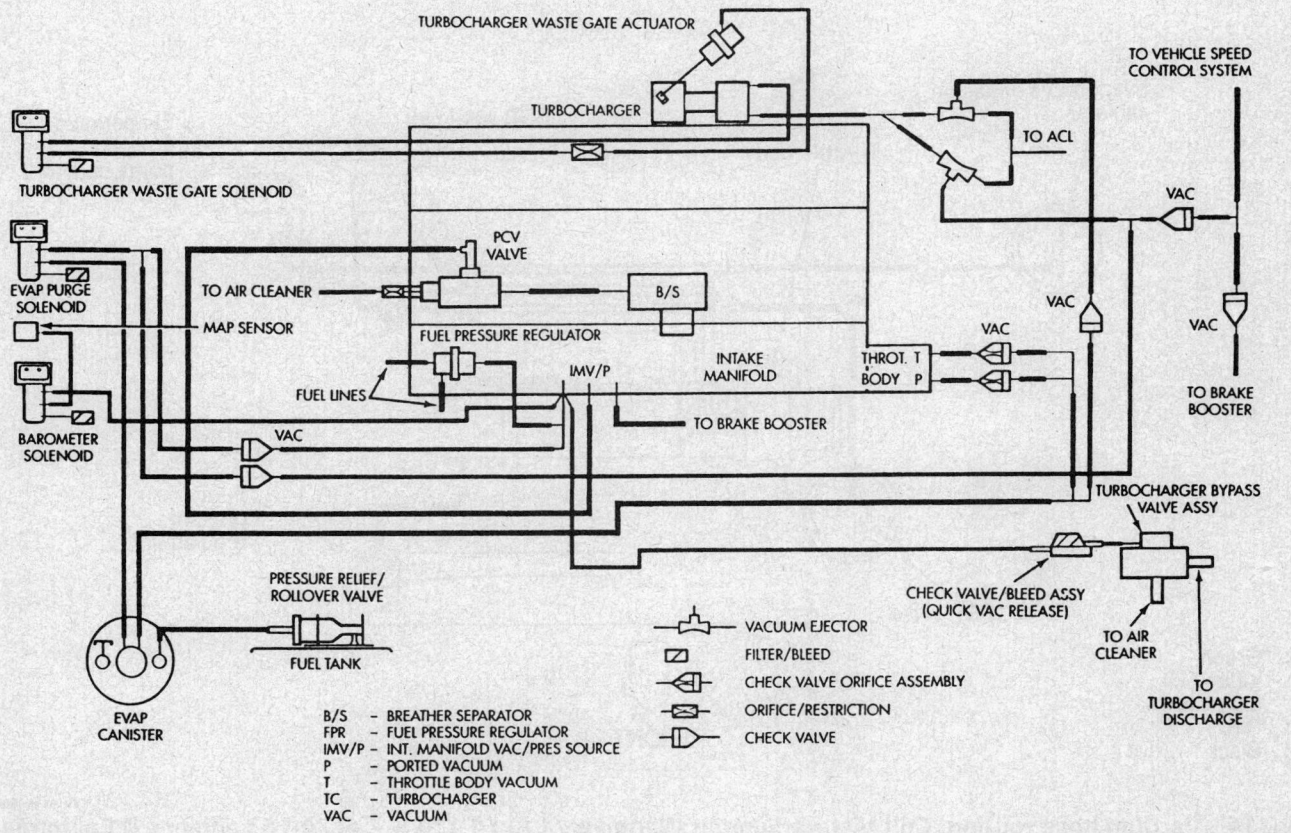

B/S — BREATHER SEPARATOR
FPR — FUEL PRESSURE REGULATOR
IMV/P — INT. MANIFOLD VAC/PRES SOURCE
P — PORTED VACUUM
T — THROTTLE BODY VACUUM
TC — TURBOCHARGER
VAC — VACUUM

Fig. 12   Vacuum hose routing. 2.2L/4-135 Turbo III engine

CR1039300062000X

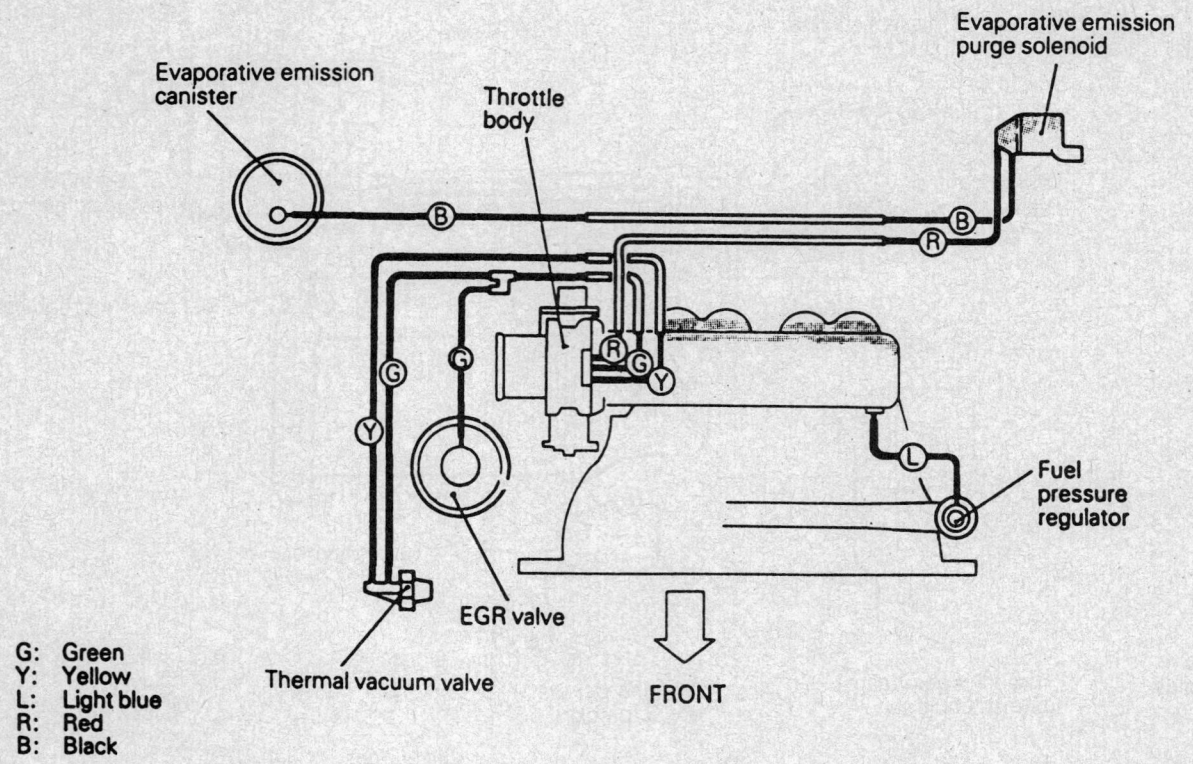

G: Green
Y: Yellow
L: Light blue
R: Red
B: Black

Fig. 13 Vacuum hose routing. Colt Vista & Summit Wagon w/2.4L/4-143 engine & Federal emissions

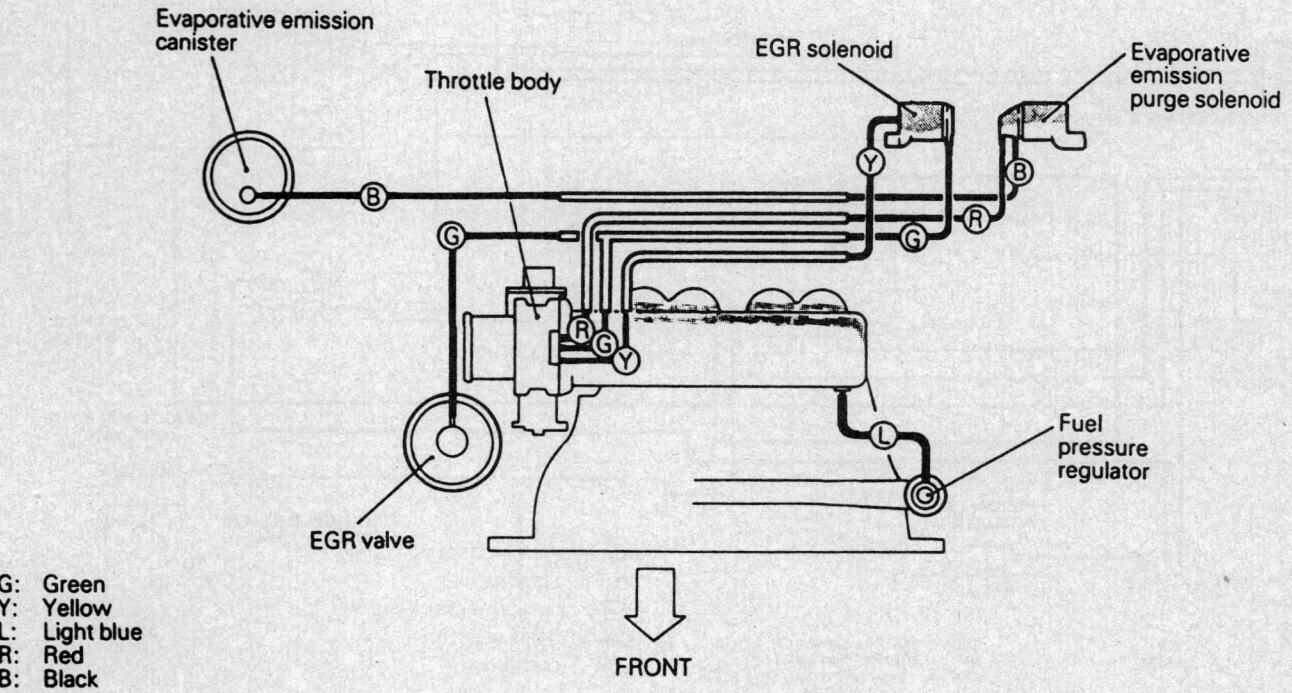

G: Green
Y: Yellow
L: Light blue
R: Red
B: Black

Fig. 14 Vacuum hose routing. Colt Vista & Summit Wagon w/1.8L/4-110 & 2.4L/4-143 engines & California emissions

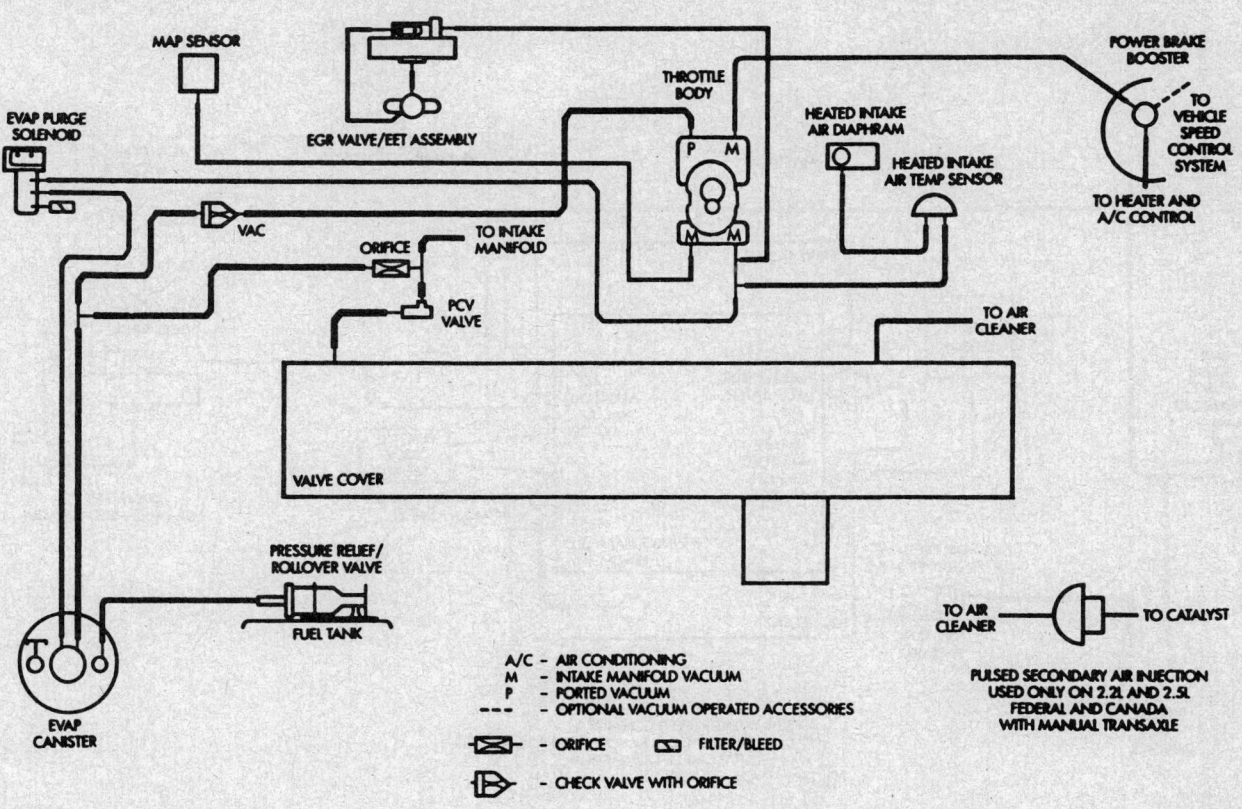

Fig. 15   Vacuum hose routing. 2.2L/4-135 & 2.5L/4-153 TBI engines

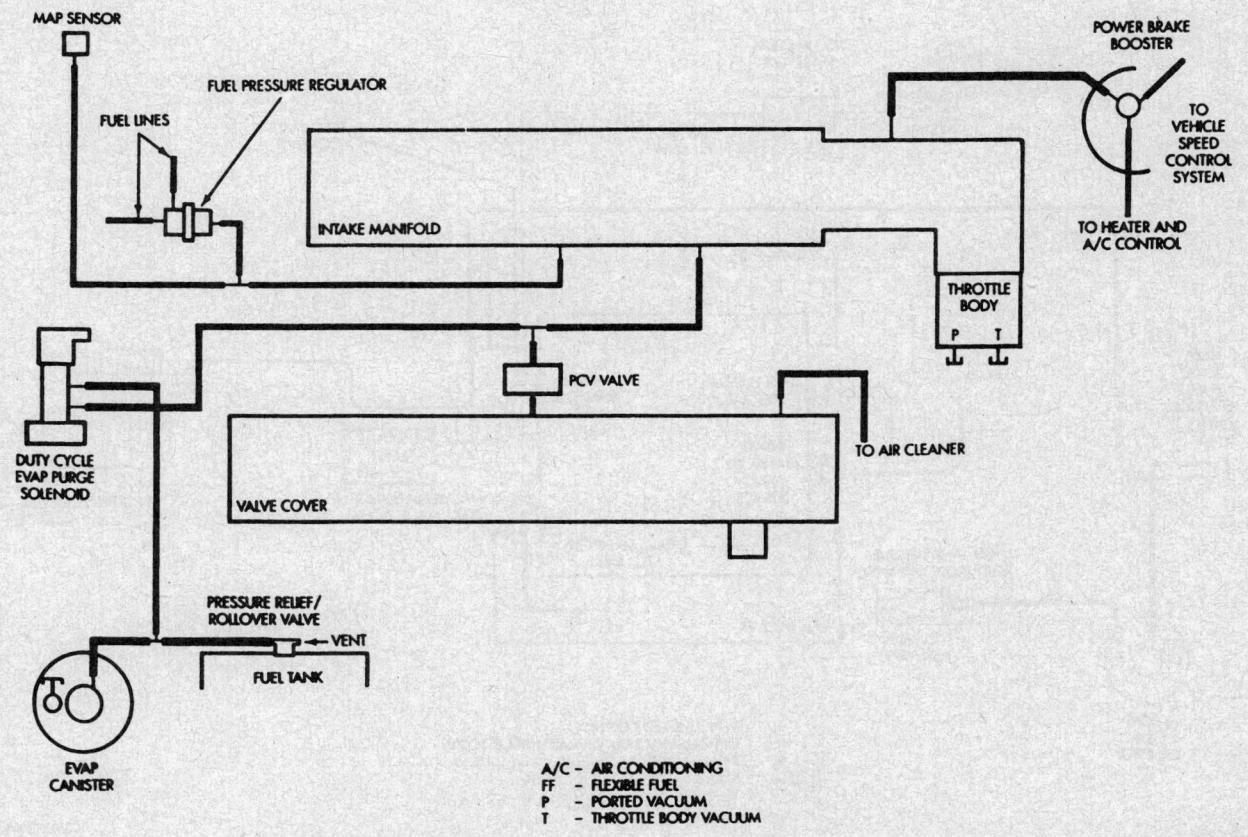

Fig. 16   Vacuum hose routing. 2.5L/4-153 MPI engine

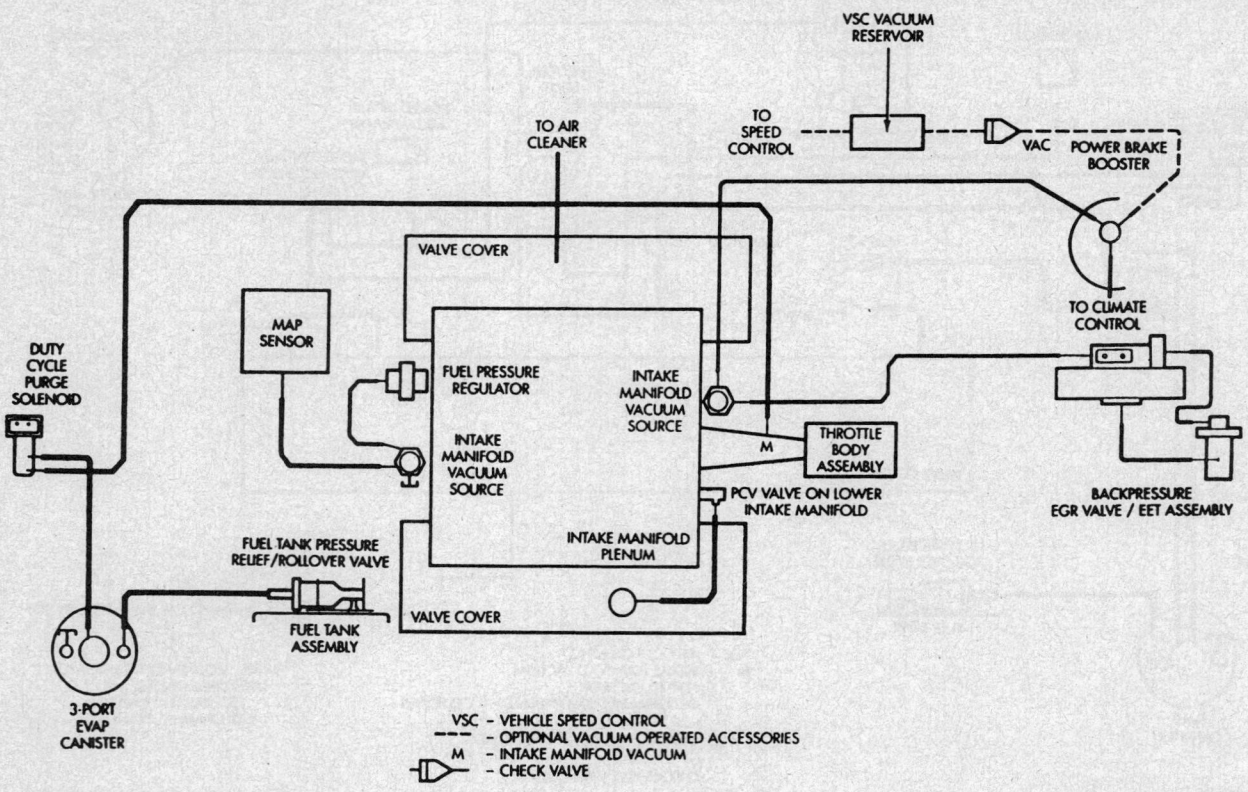

Fig. 17 Vacuum hose routing. 3.0L/V6-181 engine w/automatic transaxle & ABS, except Stealth & Dynasty Fifth Avenue Imperial New Yorker

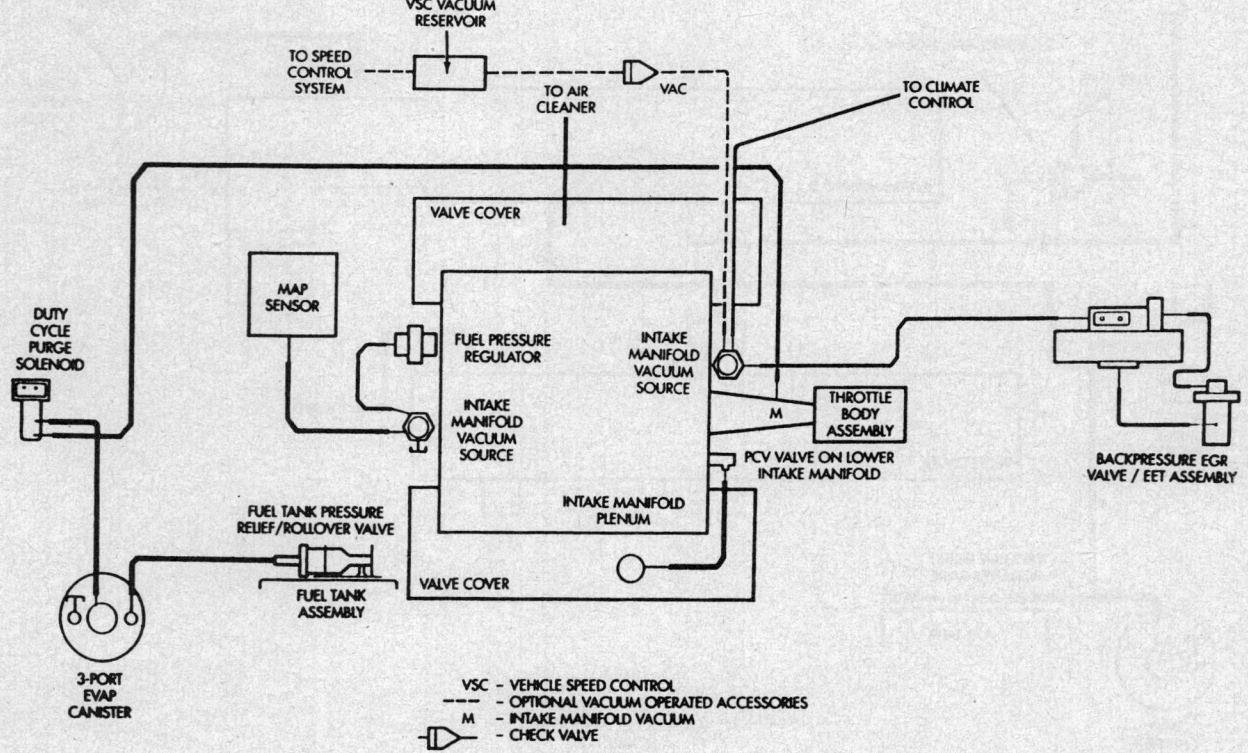

Fig. 18 Vacuum hose routing. Dynasty, Fifth Ave., Imperial & New Yorker w/3.0L/V6-181 engine, automatic transaxle & ABS

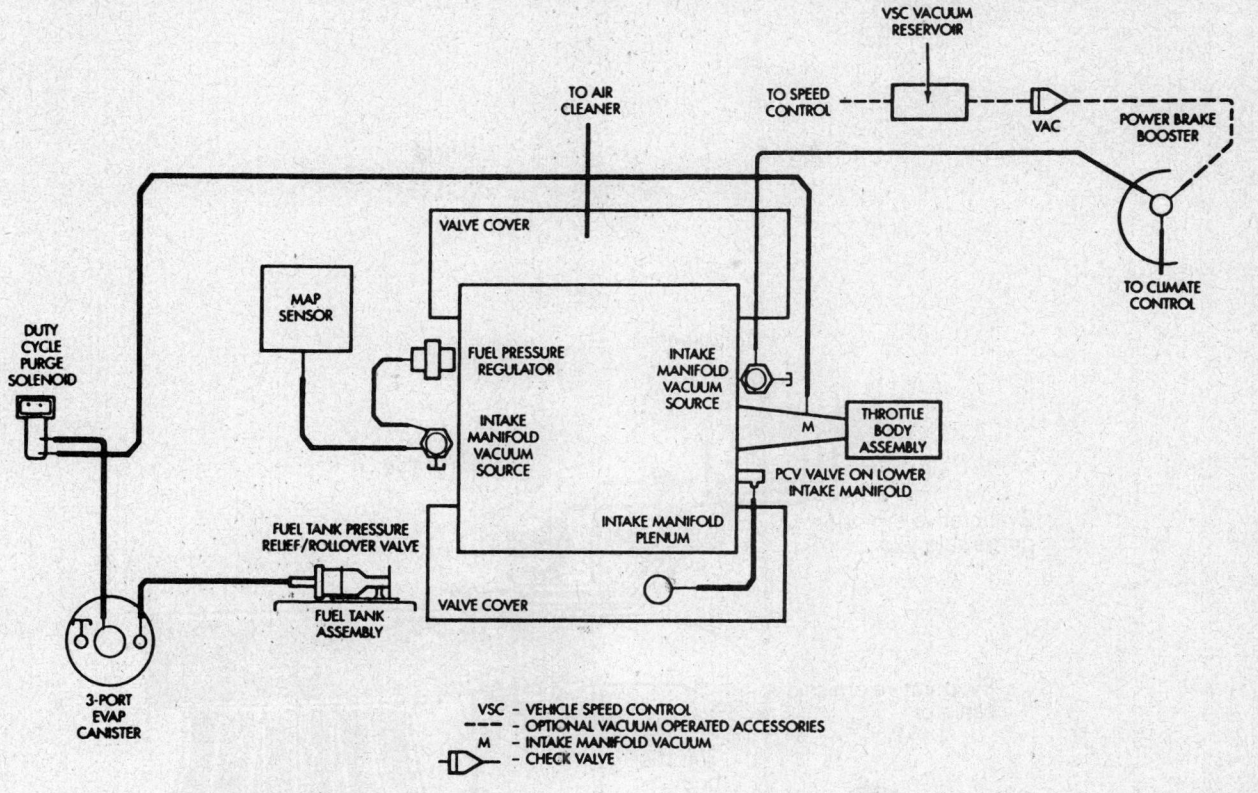

Fig. 19   Vacuum hose routing. 3.0L/V6-181 engine w/manual transaxle

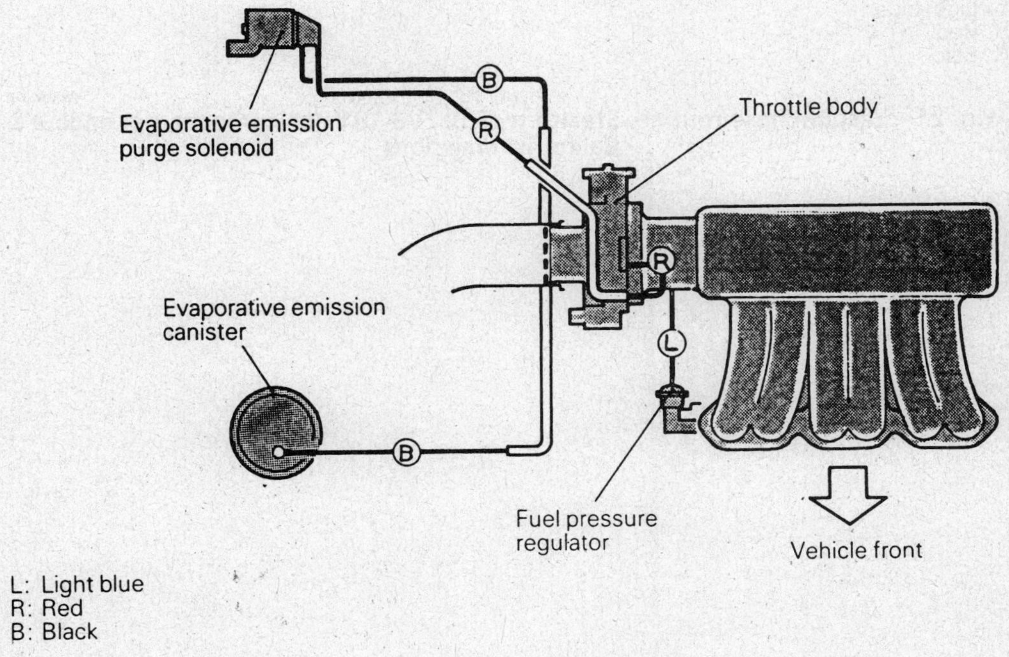

Evaporative emission
purge solenoid

Throttle body

Evaporative emission
canister

Fuel pressure
regulator

Vehicle front

L: Light blue
R: Red
B: Black

CR10393000070000X

**Fig. 20   Vacuum hose routing. Stealth w/3.0L/V6-181 non-turbocharged engine &
Federal emissions**

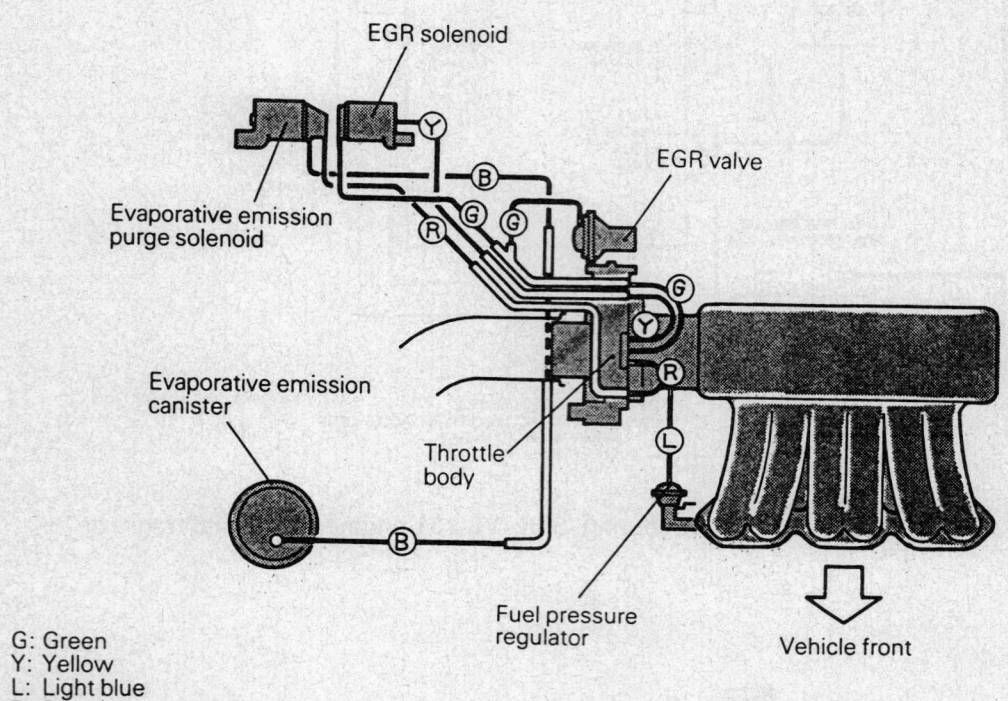

G: Green
Y: Yellow
L: Light blue
R: Red
B: Black

CR1039300071000X

Fig. 21   Vacuum hose routing. Stealth w/3.0L/V6-181 non-turbocharger engine & California emissions

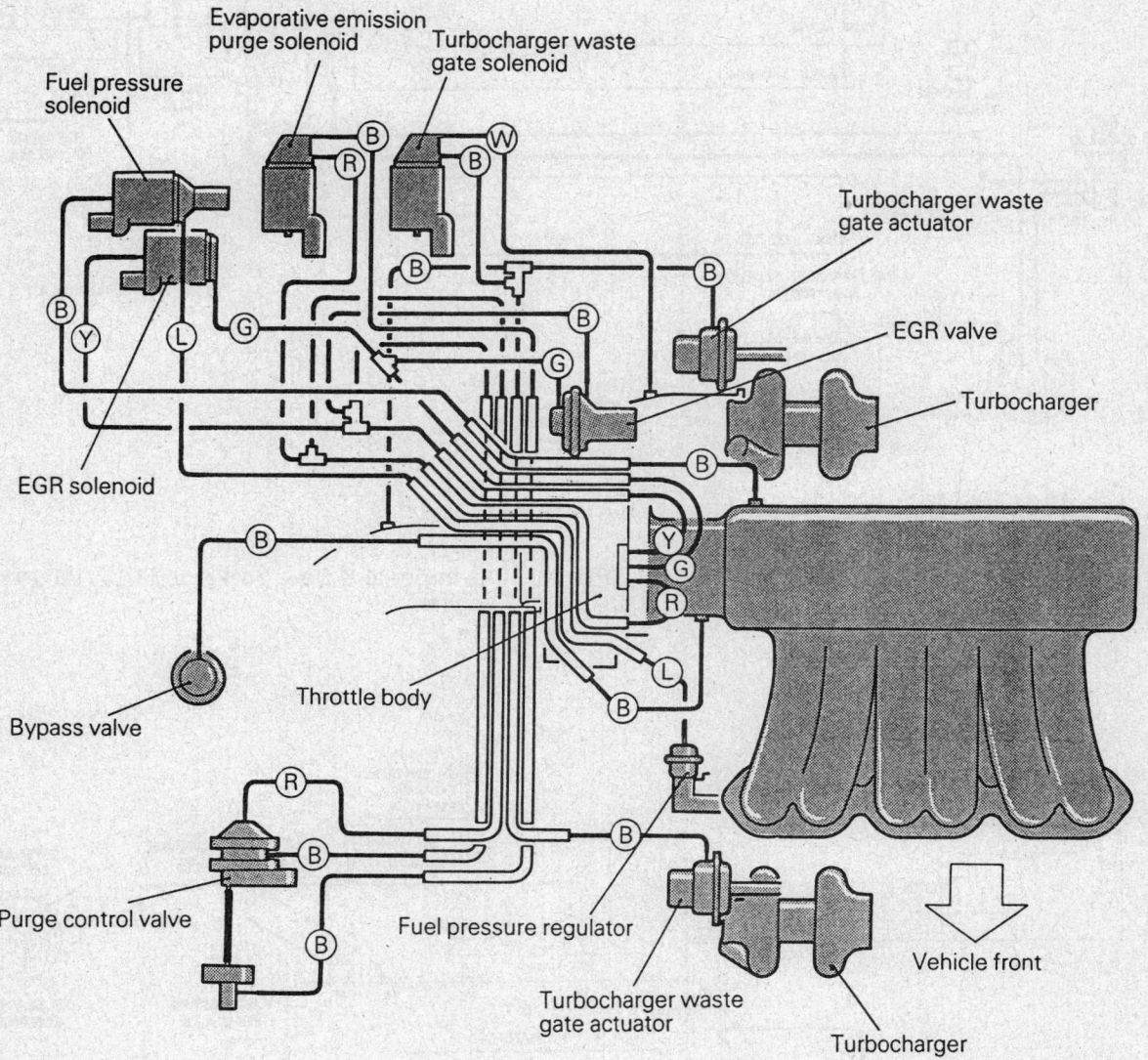

Fuel pressure solenoid

Evaporative emission purge solenoid

Turbocharger waste gate solenoid

Turbocharger waste gate actuator

EGR valve

Turbocharger

EGR solenoid

Bypass valve

Throttle body

Purge control valve

Fuel pressure regulator

Turbocharger waste gate actuator

Vehicle front

Turbocharger

G: Green
Y: Yellow
L: Light blue
R: Red
B: Black
W: White

**Fig. 22   Vacuum hose routing.
Stealth w/3.0L/V6-181
turbocharged engine**

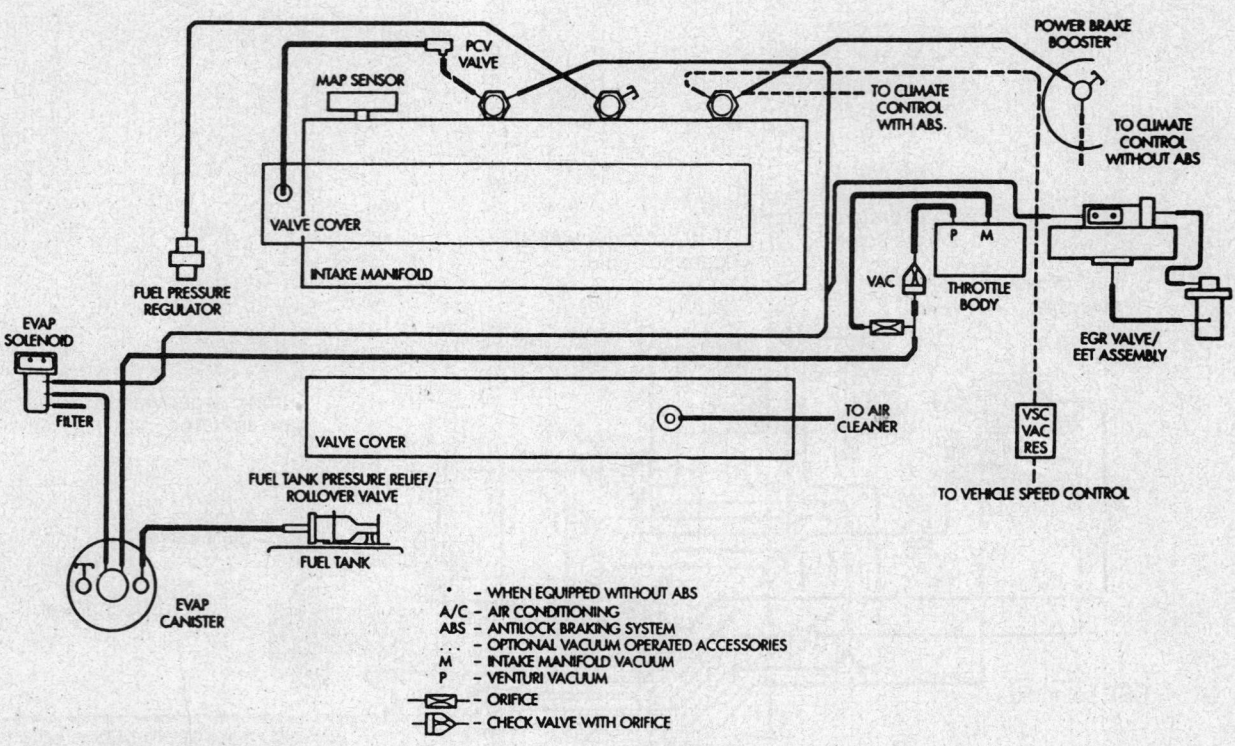

Fig. 23 Vacuum hose routing. Dynasty, Fifth Avenue, Imperial & New Yorker w/3.3L/V6-201 & 3.8L/V6-231 engine

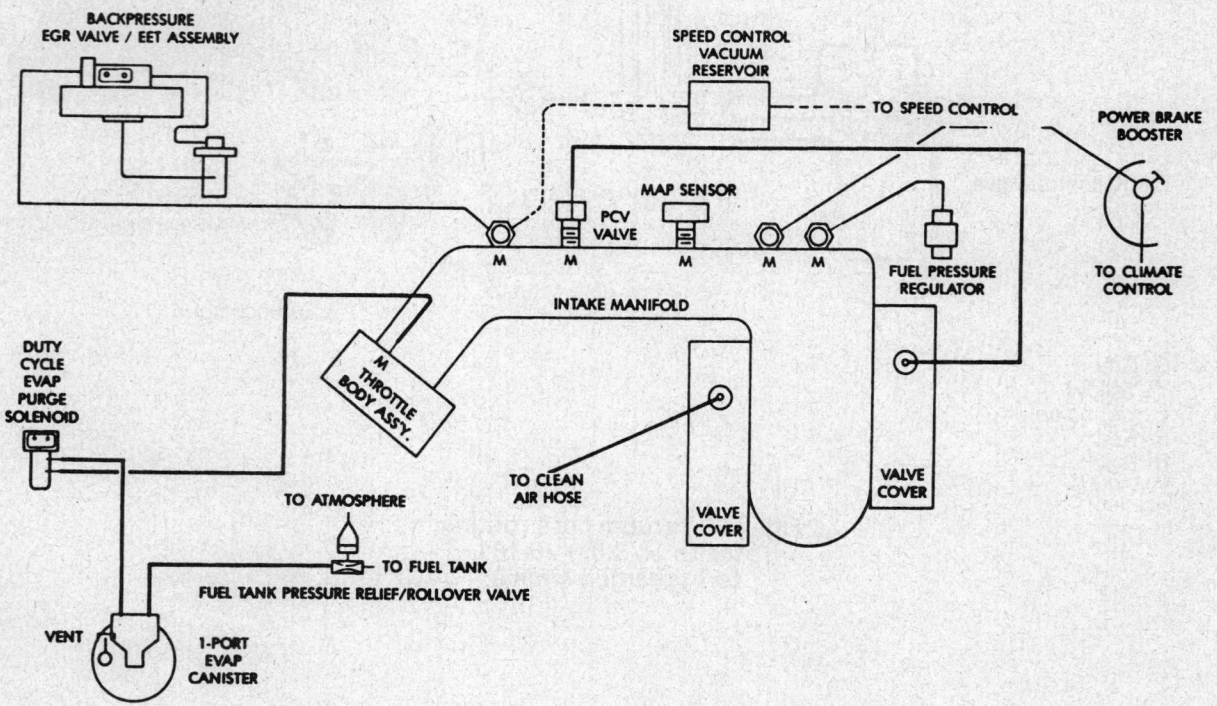

Fig. 24 Vacuum hose routing. Concorde, Intrepid & Vision w/3.3L/V6-201 engine

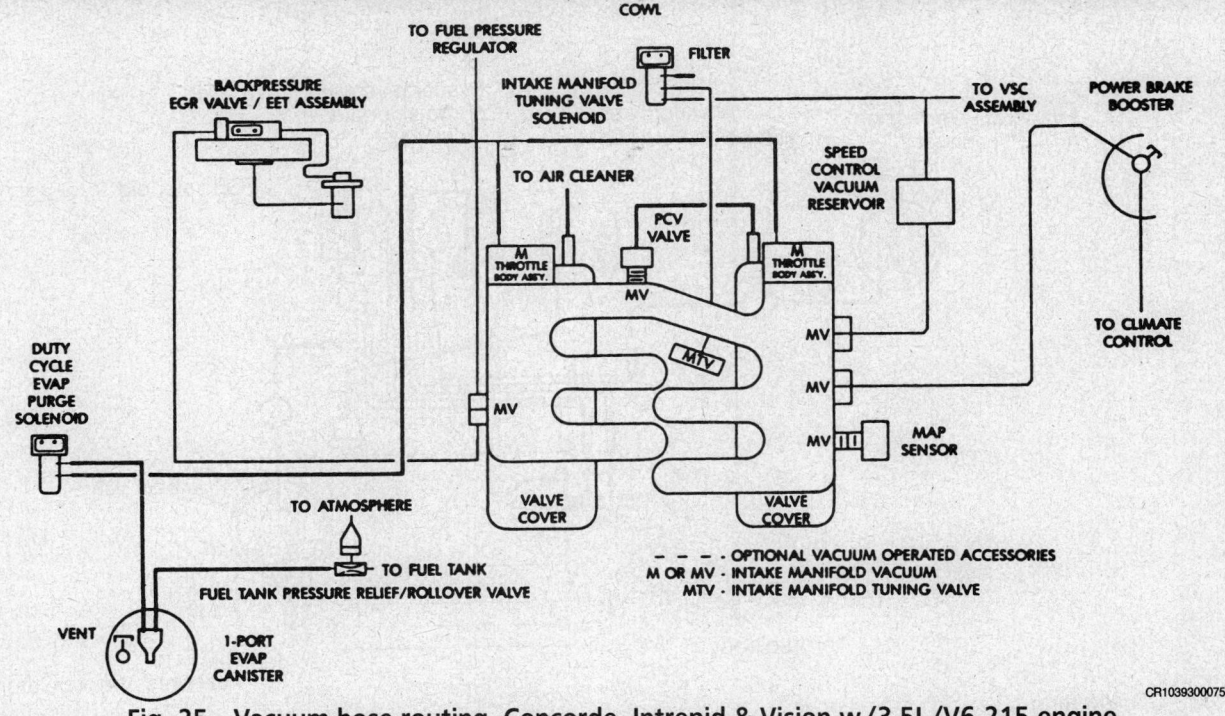

Fig. 25 Vacuum hose routing. Concorde, Intrepid & Vision w/3.5L/V6-215 engine

1994
INDEX

	Page No. 18-	Fig. No.
Colt:		
1.5L/4-90 Engine	16	1
1.8L/4-110 Engine	18	5
Colt Vista	17	4
Concorde:		
3.3L/V6-201 Engine	24	16
3.5L/V6-215 Engine	24	17
Intrepid:		
3.3L/V6-201 Engine	24	16
3.5L/V6-215 Engine	24	17
Laser:		
1.8L/4-107 Engine:		
California Emissions	17	3
Federal Emissions	16	2
2.0L/4-122 Non-Turbocharged Engine:		
California Emissions	19	7
Federal Emissions	18	6
2.0L/4-122 Turbocharged Engine:		
California Emissions	20	9
Federal Emissions	19	8
LHS:		
3.3L/V6-201 Engine	24	16
3.5L/V6-215 Engine	24	17
New Yorker:		
3.3L/V6-201 Engine	24	16
3.5L/V6-215 Engine	24	17
Stealth:		
Non-Turbocharged Engine:		
California Emissions	22	14
Federal Emissions	22	13
Turbocharged Engine	23	15

	Page No. 18-	Fig. No.
Summit:		
1.5L/4-90 Engine	16	1
1.8L/4-110 Engine	18	5
Summit Wagon	17	4
Talon:		
1.8L/4-107 Engine:		
California Emissions	17	3
Federal Emissions	16	2
2.0L/4-122 Non-Turbocharged Engine:		
California Emissions	19	7
Federal Emissions	18	6
2.0L/4-122 Turbocharged Engine:		
California Emissions	20	9
Federal Emissions	19	8
Vision:		
3.3L/V6-201 Engine	24	16
3.5L/V6-215 Engine	24	17
2.2L/4-135 Engine	20	10
2.5L/4-153 Engine	20	10
3.0L/V6-181 Engine:		
Except Stealth:		
Automatic Transaxle	21	11
Manual Transaxle	21	12
Stealth:		
Non-Turbocharged w/California Emissions	22	14
Non-Turbocharged w/Federal Emissions	22	13
Turbocharged	23	15

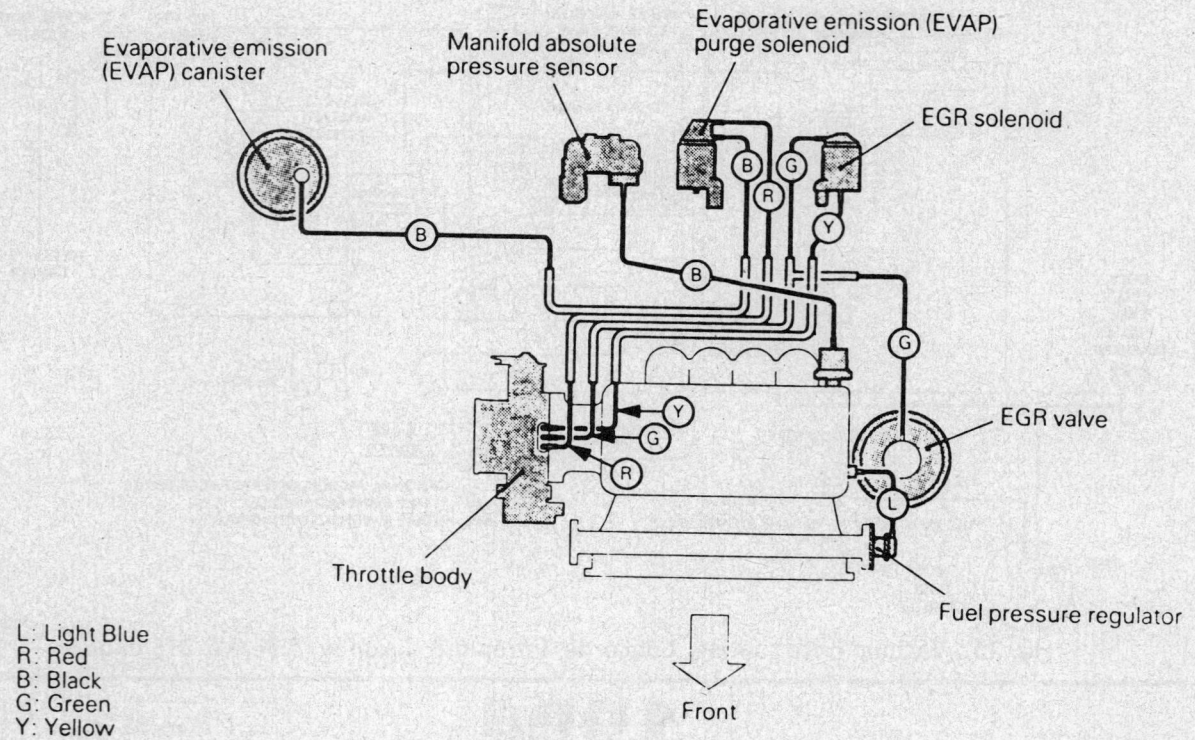

Evaporative emission
(EVAP) canister

Manifold absolute
pressure sensor

Evaporative emission (EVAP)
purge solenoid

EGR solenoid

EGR valve

Throttle body

Fuel pressure regulator

Front

L: Light Blue
R: Red
B: Black
G: Green
Y: Yellow

CR1039400163000X

Fig. 1   Vacuum hose routing. 1.5L/4-90 engine

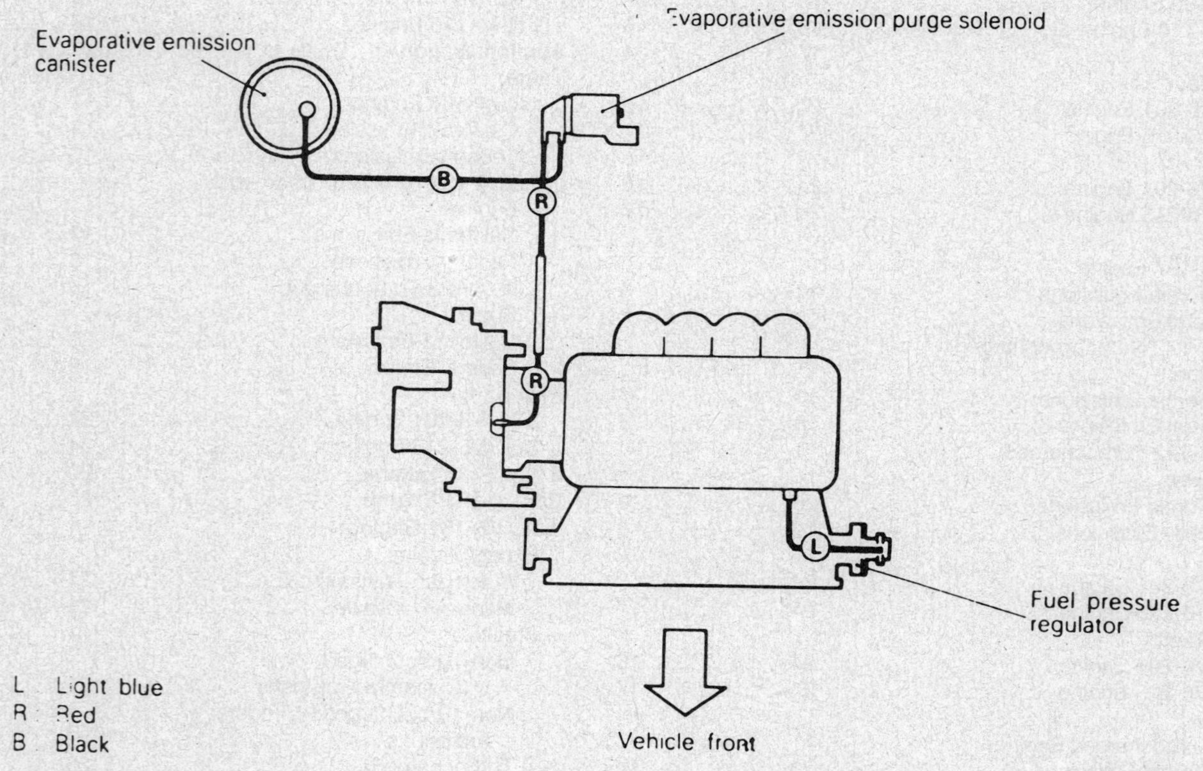

Evaporative emission
canister

Evaporative emission purge solenoid

Fuel pressure
regulator

Vehicle front

L   Light blue
R   Red
B   Black

CR1039400164000X

Fig. 2   Vacuum hose routing. Laser & Talon w/1.8L/4-107 engine & Federal emissions

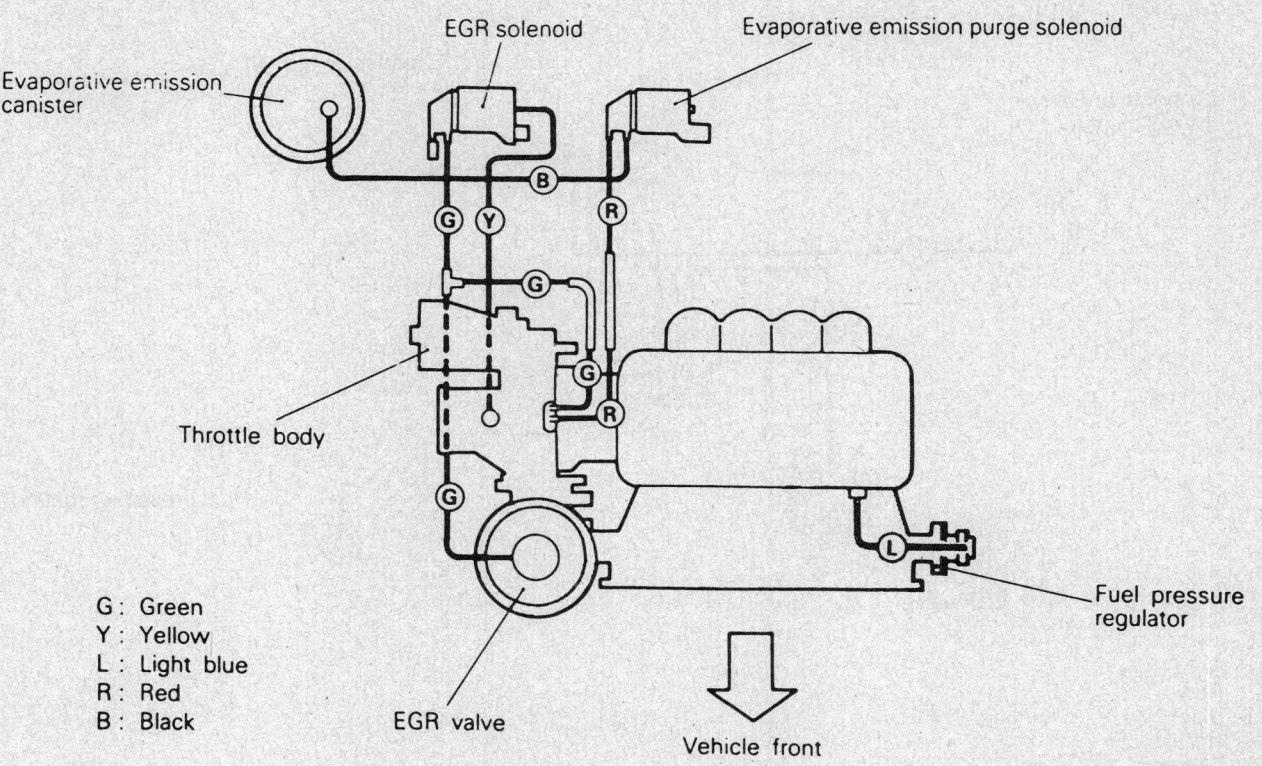

G : Green
Y : Yellow
L : Light blue
R : Red
B : Black

Vehicle front

CR1039400165000X

Fig. 3   Vacuum hose routing. Laser & Talon w/1.8L/4-107 engine & California emissions

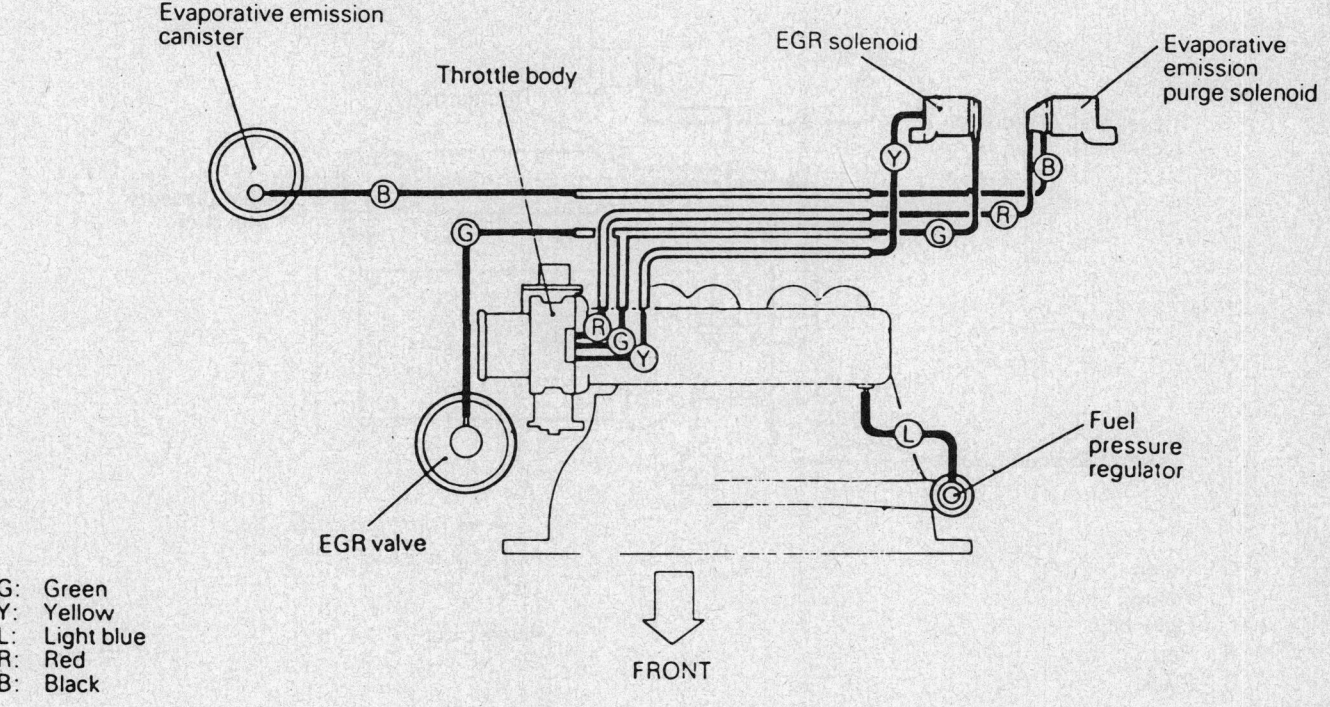

G : Green
Y : Yellow
L : Light blue
R : Red
B : Black

FRONT

CR1039400166000X

Fig. 4   Vacuum hose routing. Colt Vista & Summit Wagon w/1.8L/4-110 & 2.4L/4-146 engines

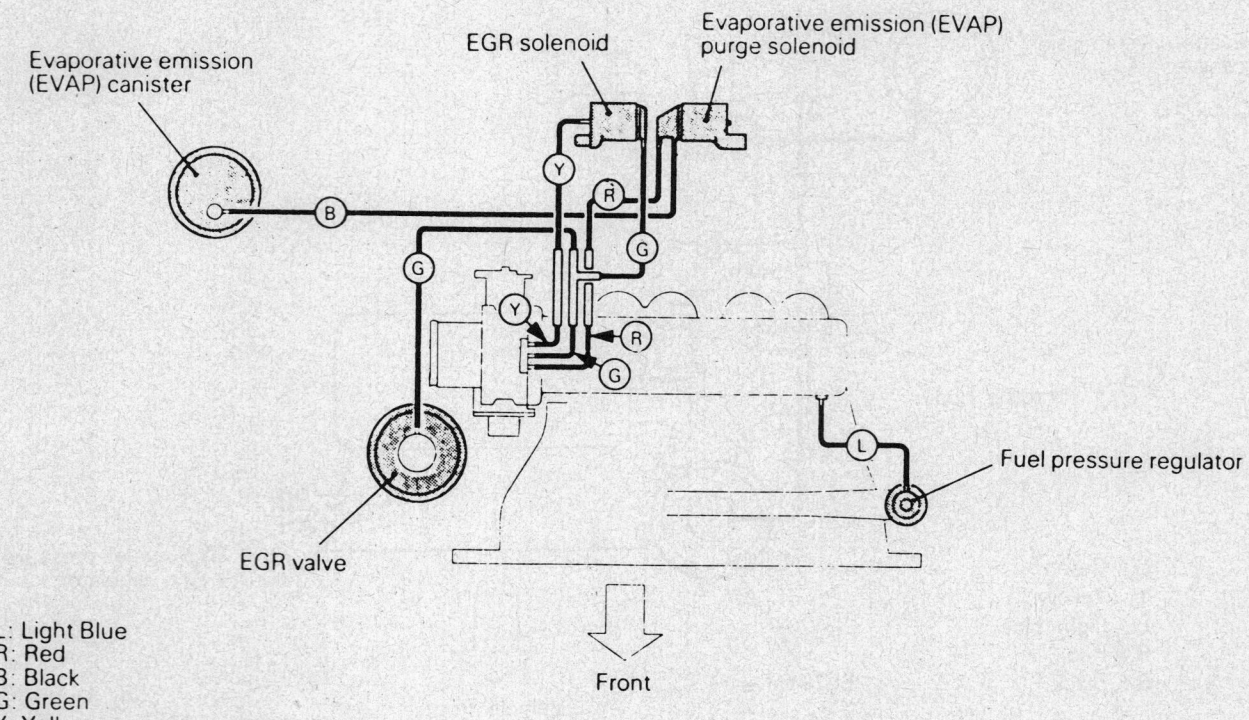

Evaporative emission
(EVAP) canister

EGR solenoid

Evaporative emission (EVAP)
purge solenoid

Fuel pressure regulator

EGR valve

L: Light Blue
R: Red
B: Black
G: Green
Y: Yellow

Front

CR1039400167000X

Fig. 5   Vacuum hose routing. Colt & Summit w/1.8L/4-110 engine

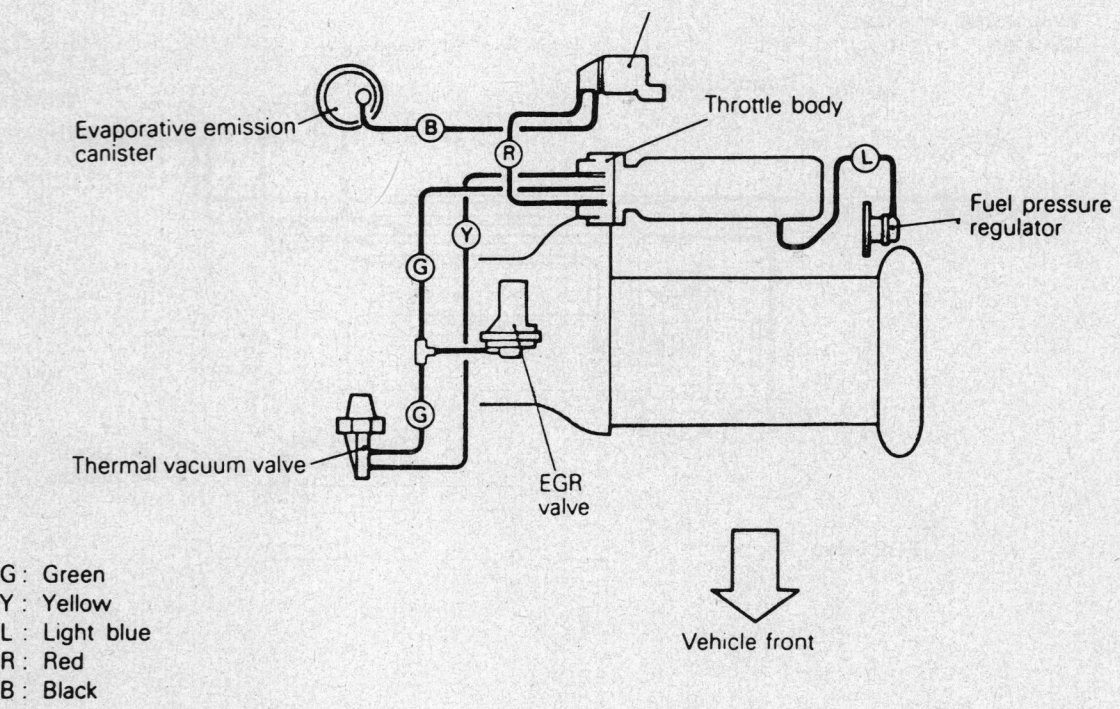

Evaporative emission
canister

Throttle body

Fuel pressure
regulator

Thermal vacuum valve

EGR
valve

G : Green
Y : Yellow
L : Light blue
R : Red
B : Black

Vehicle front

CR1039400168000X

Fig. 6   Vacuum hose routing. 2.0L/4-122 non-turbocharged engine w/Federal emissions

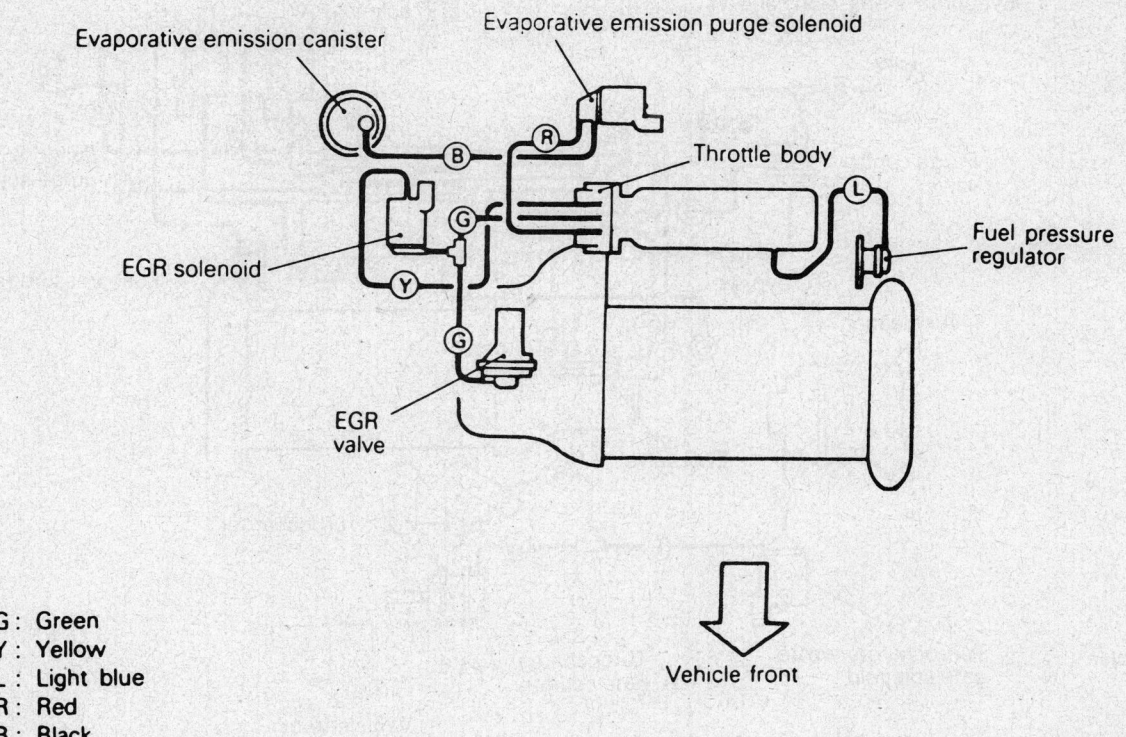

G : Green
Y : Yellow
L : Light blue
R : Red
B : Black

CR1039400169000X

Fig. 7   Vacuum hose routing. 2.0L/4-122 non-turbocharged engine w/California emissions

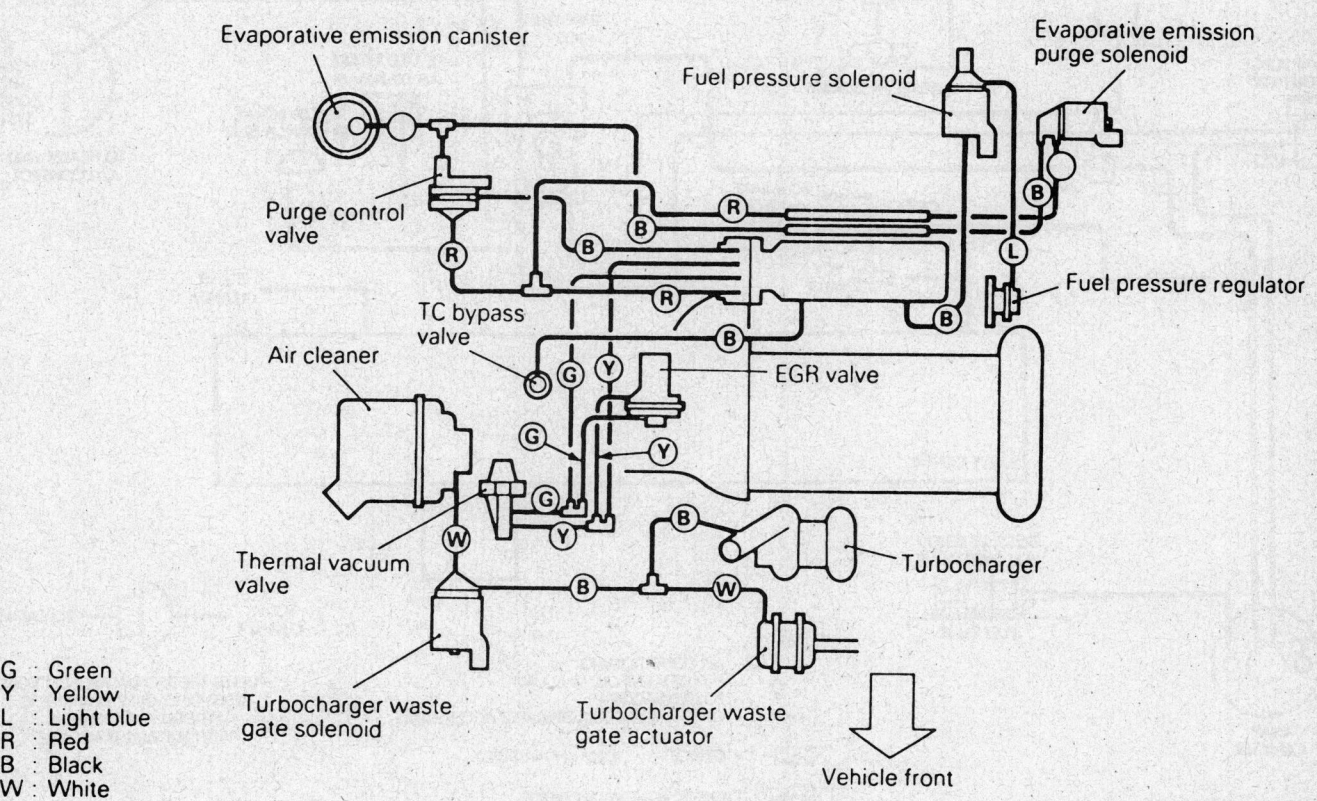

G : Green
Y : Yellow
L : Light blue
R : Red
B : Black
W : White

CR1039400170000X

Fig. 8   Vacuum hose routing. 2.0L/4-122 turbocharged engine w/Federal emissions

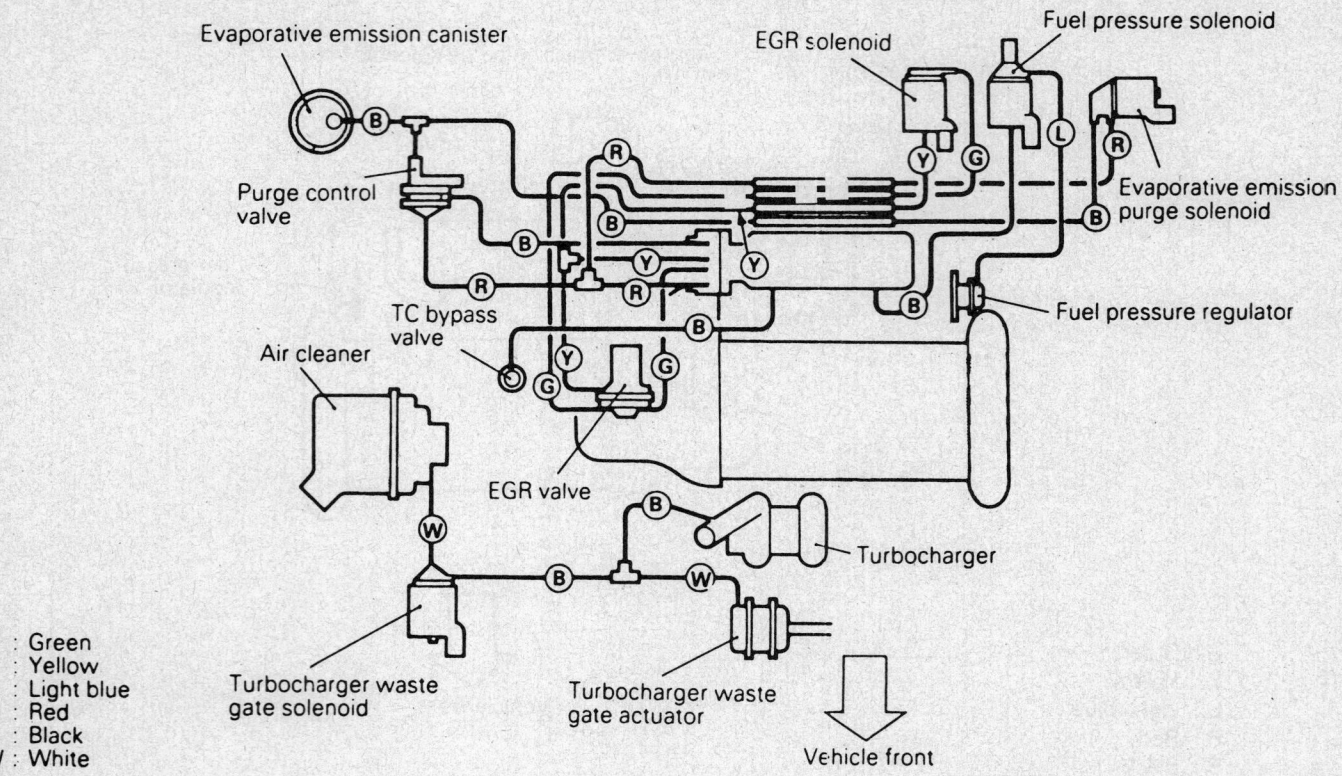

Evaporative emission canister

Purge control valve

Air cleaner

TC bypass valve

EGR valve

EGR solenoid

Fuel pressure solenoid

Evaporative emission purge solenoid

Fuel pressure regulator

Turbocharger

Turbocharger waste gate solenoid

Turbocharger waste gate actuator

Vehicle front

G : Green
Y : Yellow
L : Light blue
R : Red
B : Black
W : White

CR1039400171000X

Fig. 9 Vacuum hose routing. 2.0L/4-122 turbocharged engine w/California emissions

MAP SENSOR

EVAP PURGE SOLENOID

EGR VALVE/EET ASSEMBLY

VAC

ORIFICE

TO INTAKE MANIFOLD

PCV VALVE

THROTTLE BODY

P   M

M   M

HEATED INTAKE AIR DIAPHRAM

HEATED INTAKE AIR TEMP SENSOR

POWER BRAKE BOOSTER

TO VEHICLE SPEED CONTROL SYSTEM

TO HEATER AND A/C CONTROL

TO AIR CLEANER

VALVE COVER

PRESSURE RELIEF/ ROLLOVER VALVE

FUEL TANK

EVAP CANISTER

A/C – AIR CONDITIONING
M   – INTAKE MANIFOLD VACUUM
P   – PORTED VACUUM
--- – OPTIONAL VACUUM OPERATED ACCESSORIES

⊲⊳ – ORIFICE   ▭ FILTER/BLEED

⊳ – CHECK VALVE WITH ORIFICE

TO AIR CLEANER   TO CATALYST

PULSED SECONDARY AIR INJECTION USED ONLY ON 2.2L AND 2.5L FEDERAL AND CANADA WITH MANUAL TRANSAXLE

CR1039400172000X

Fig. 10 Vacuum hose routing. 2.2L/4-135 & 2.5L/4-153 engines

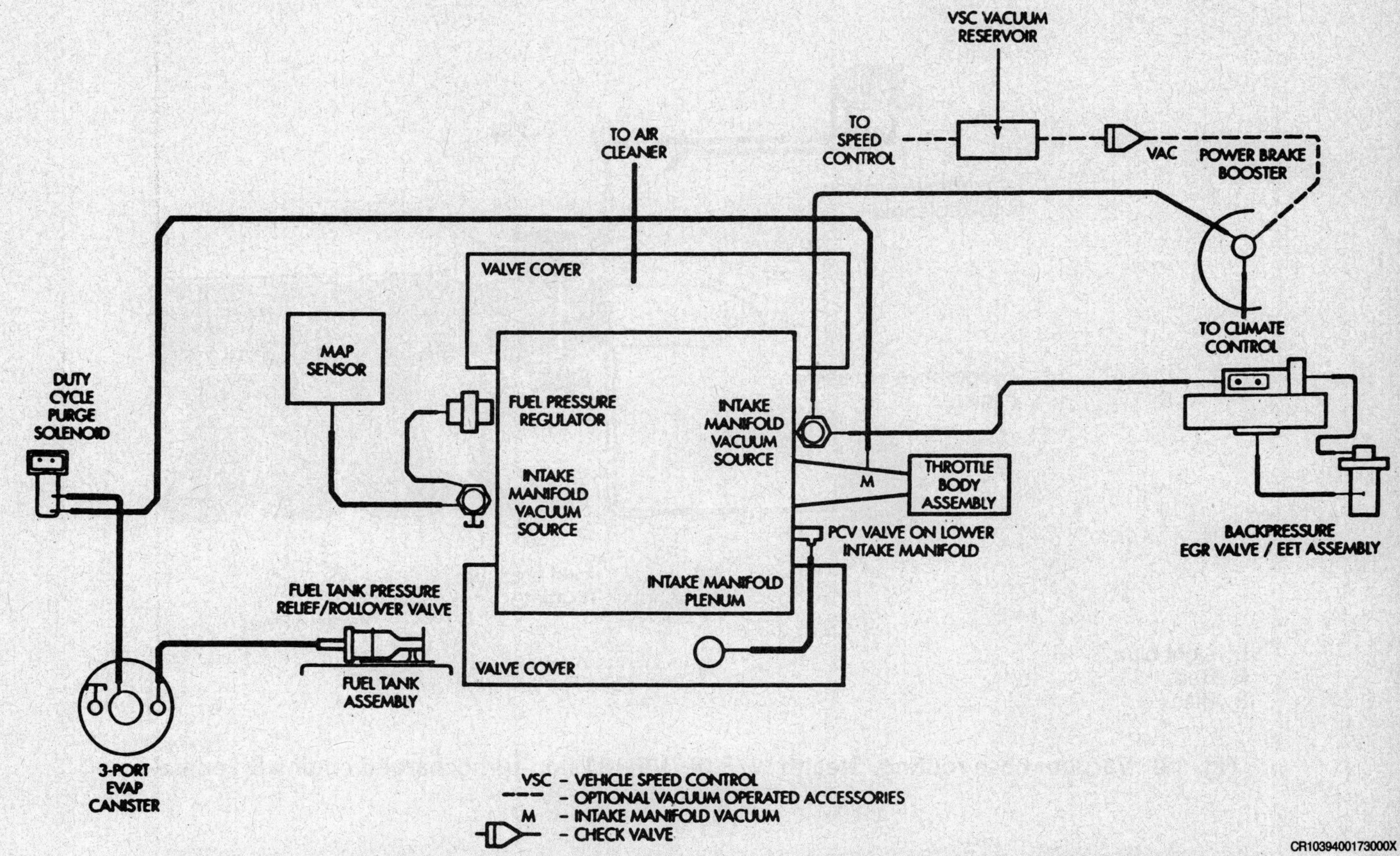

Fig. 11 Vacuum hose routing. 3.0L/V6-181 engine w/automatic transaxle except Stealth

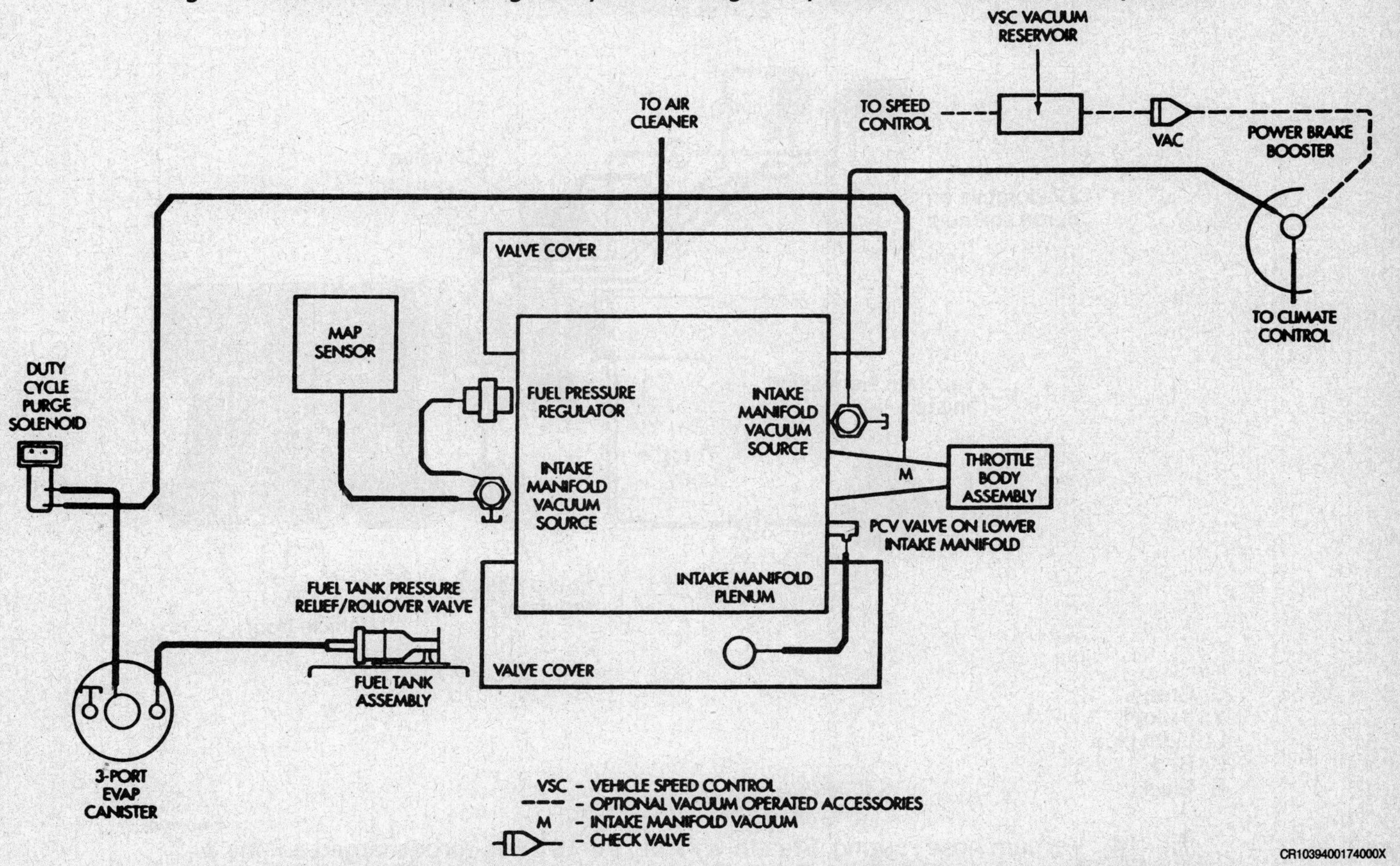

Fig. 12 Vacuum hose routing. 3.0L/V6-181 engine w/manual transaxle except Stealth

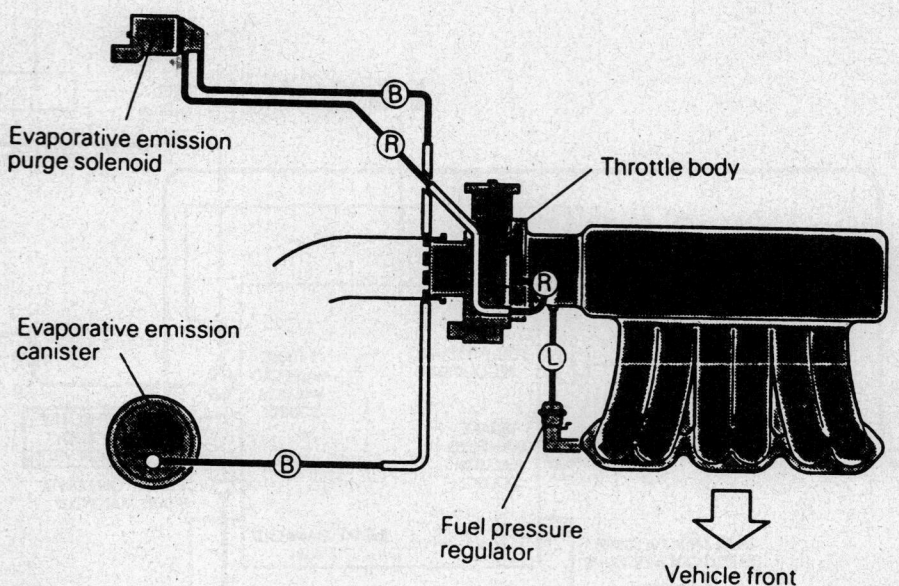

L: Light blue
R: Red
B: Black

CR1039400175000X

Fig. 13   Vacuum hose routing. Stealth w/3.0L/V6-181 non-turbocharged engine & Federal emissions

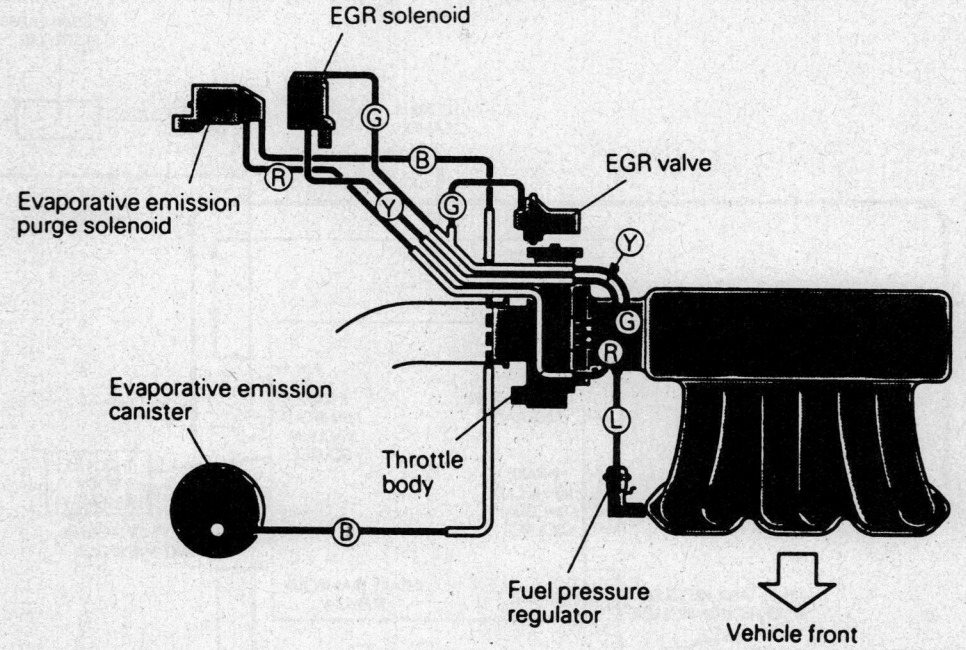

G: Green
Y: Yellow
L: Light blue
R: Red
B: Black

CR1039400176000X

Fig. 14   Vacuum hose routing. Stealth w/3.0L/V6-181 non-turbocharged engine & California emissions

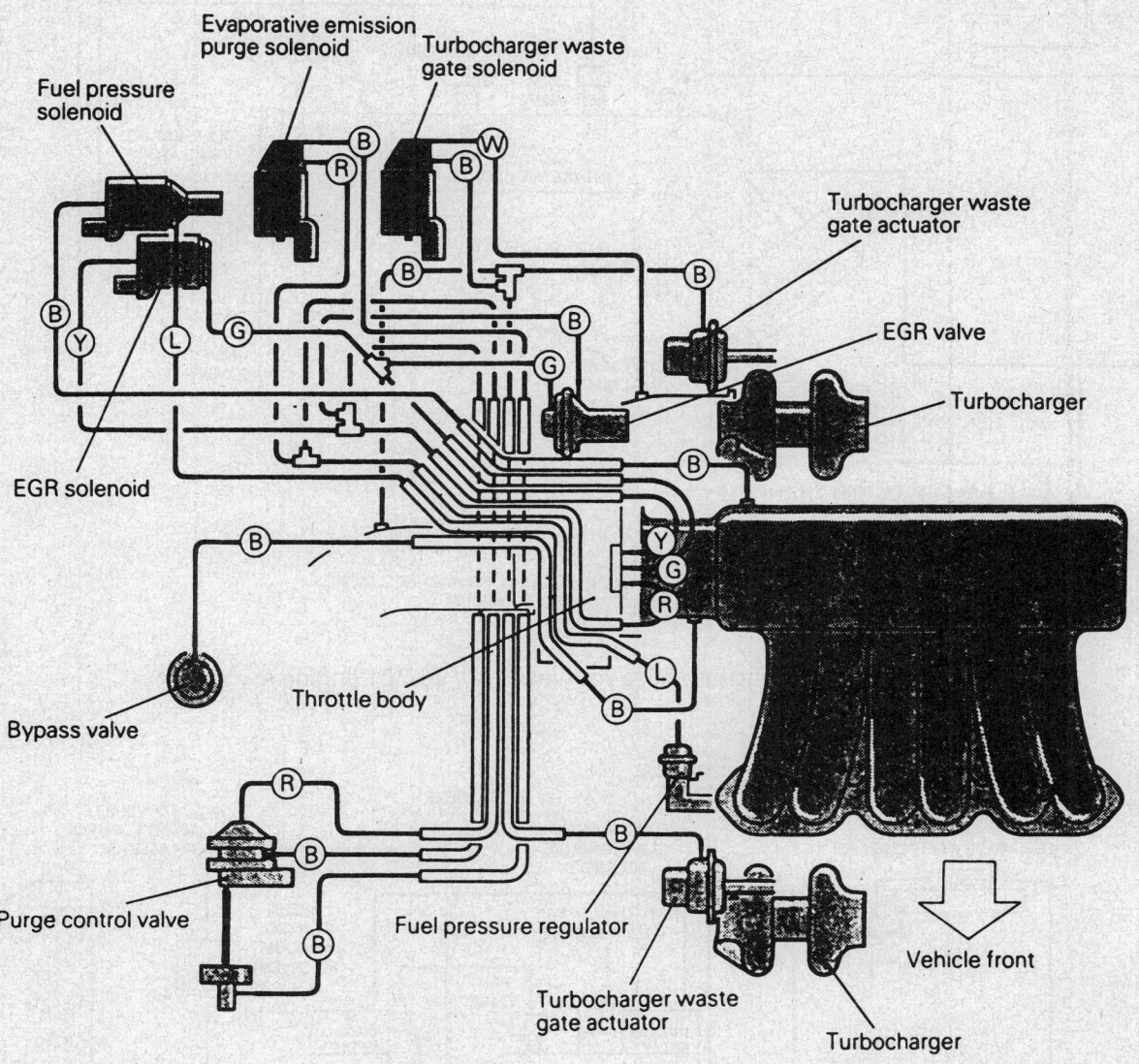

Fuel pressure
solenoid

Evaporative emission
purge solenoid

Turbocharger waste
gate solenoid

Turbocharger waste
gate actuator

EGR valve

Turbocharger

EGR solenoid

Bypass valve

Throttle body

Purge control valve

Fuel pressure regulator

Turbocharger waste
gate actuator

Vehicle front

Turbocharger

G: Green
Y: Yellow
L: Light blue
R: Red
B: Black
W: White

CR1039400177000X

Fig. 15 Vacuum hose routing. Stealth w/3.0L/V6-181 turbocharged engine

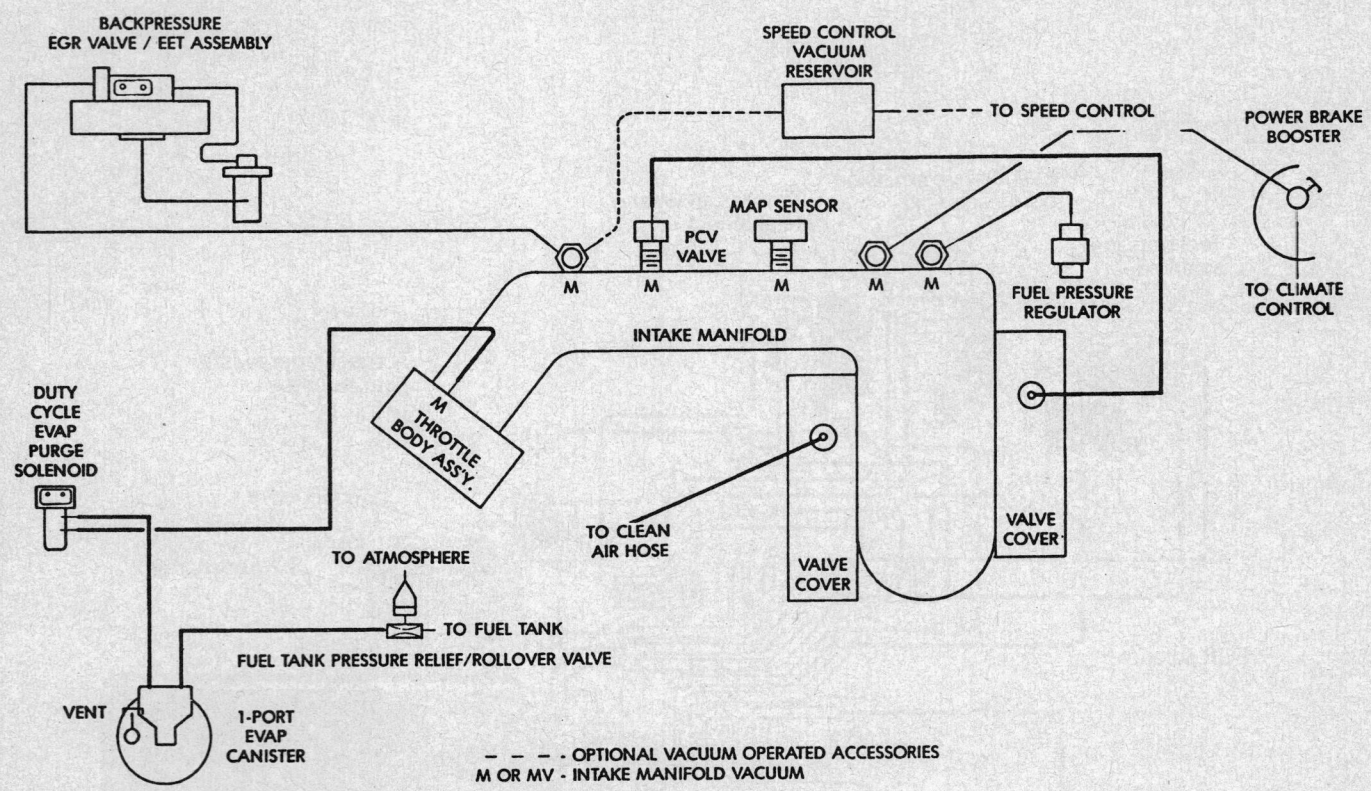

Fig. 16   Vacuum hose routing. 3.3L/V6-201 engine

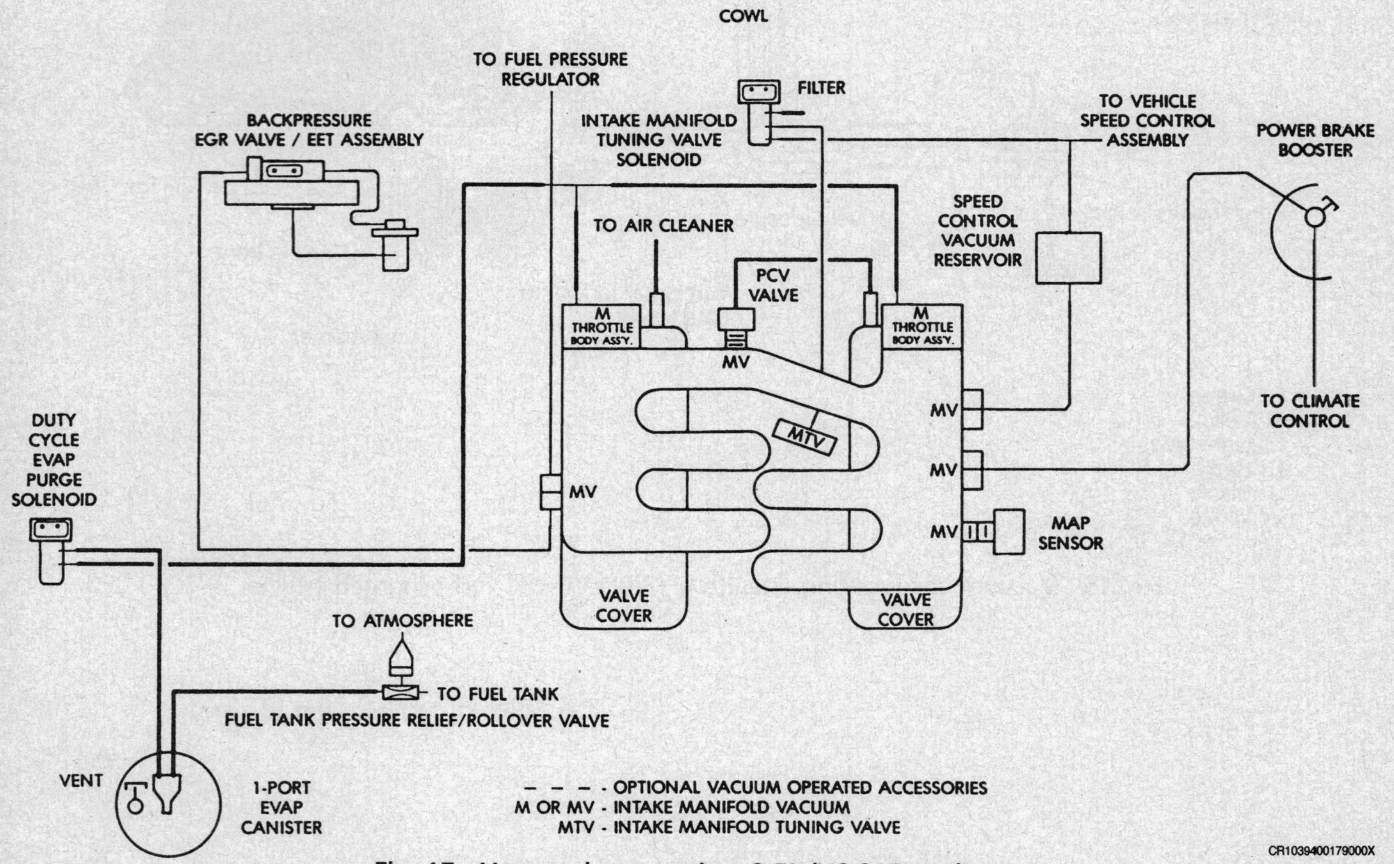

Fig. 17   Vacuum hose routing. 3.5L/V6-215 engine

INDEX

Acclaim:
- 2.5L/4-153 Engine:
  - Flex Fuel 32 14
  - TBI 33 15
- 3.0L/V6-181 Engine:
  - Automatic Transaxle 33 16

Cirrus:
- 2.0L/4-122 Engine 28 6
- 2.4L/4-148 Engine 30 10
- 2.5L/V6-152 Engine 31 13

Concorde:
- 3.3L/V6-201 Engine 37 21
- 3.5L/V6-215 Engine 37 22

Intrepid:
- 3.3L/V6-201 Engine 37 21
- 3.5L/V6-215 Engine 37 22

LeBaron:
- 3.0L/V6-181 Engine:
  - Automatic Transaxle 33 16
  - Manual Transaxle 34 17

LHS:
- 3.5L/V6-215 Engine 37 22

Neon:
- 2.0L/4-122 Engine 28 7

New Yorker:
- 3.5L/V6-215 Engine 37 22

Spirit:
- 2.5L/4-153 Engine:
  - Flex Fuel 32 14
  - TBI 33 15

3.0L/V6-181 Engine:
- Automatic Transaxle 33 16

Stealth:
- Non-Turbocharged Engine:
  - Federal Emissions 34 18
  - California Emissions 35 19
- Turbocharged Engine 36 20

Summit:
- 1.5L/4-90 Engine:
  - California Emissions 26 2
  - Federal Emissions 25 1
- 1.8L/4-110 Engine:
  - California Emissions 27 4
  - Federal Emissions 26 3

Summit Wagon:
- 1.8L/4-110 Engine 27 5
- 2.4L/4-143 Engine:
  - AWD 31 12
  - FWD 30 11

Stratus:
- 2.0L/4-122 Engine 28 6
- 2.4L/4-148 Engine 30 10
- 2.5L/V6-152 Engine 31 13

Talon:
- Non-Turbocharged Engine 29 8
- Turbocharged Engine 29 9

Vision:
- 3.3L/V6-201 Engine 37 21
- 3.5L/V6-215 Engine 37 22

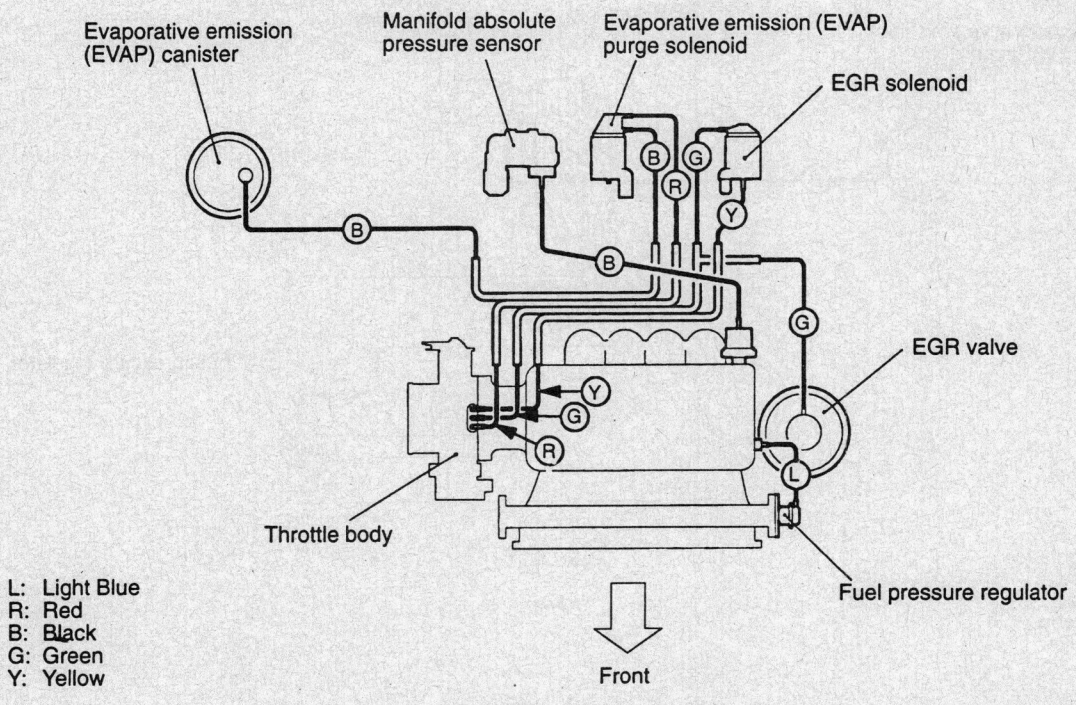

L: Light Blue
R: Red
B: Black
G: Green
Y: Yellow

Fig. 1   Vacuum hose routing.
Summit w/1.5L/4-90 engine &
Federal emissions

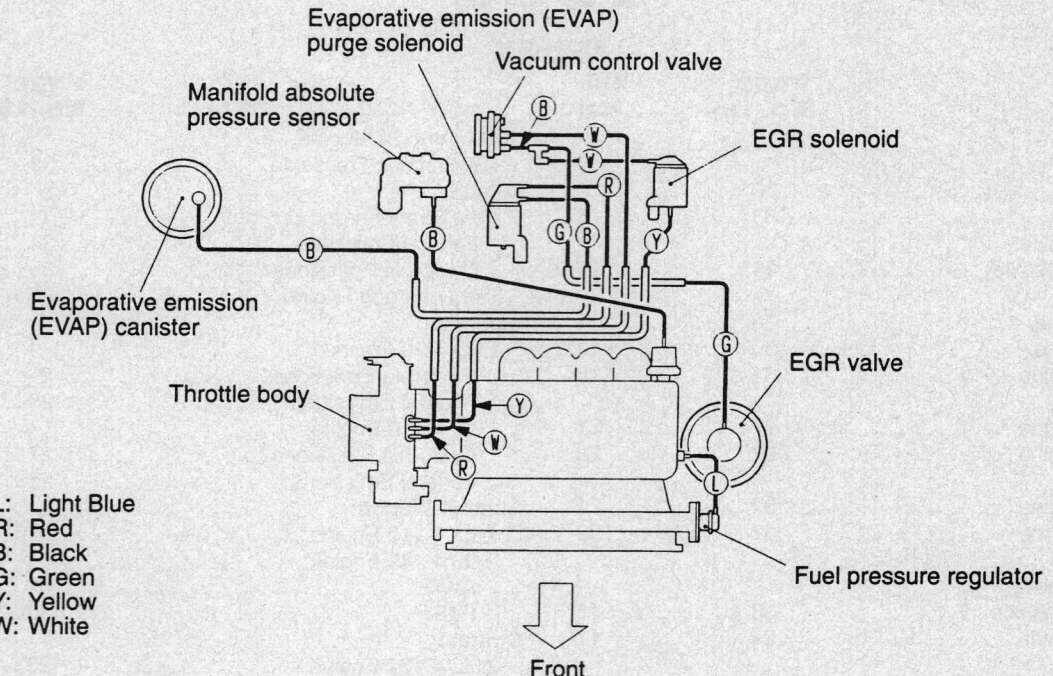

**Fig. 2   Vacuum hose routing.
Summit w/1.5L/4-90 engine &
California emissions**

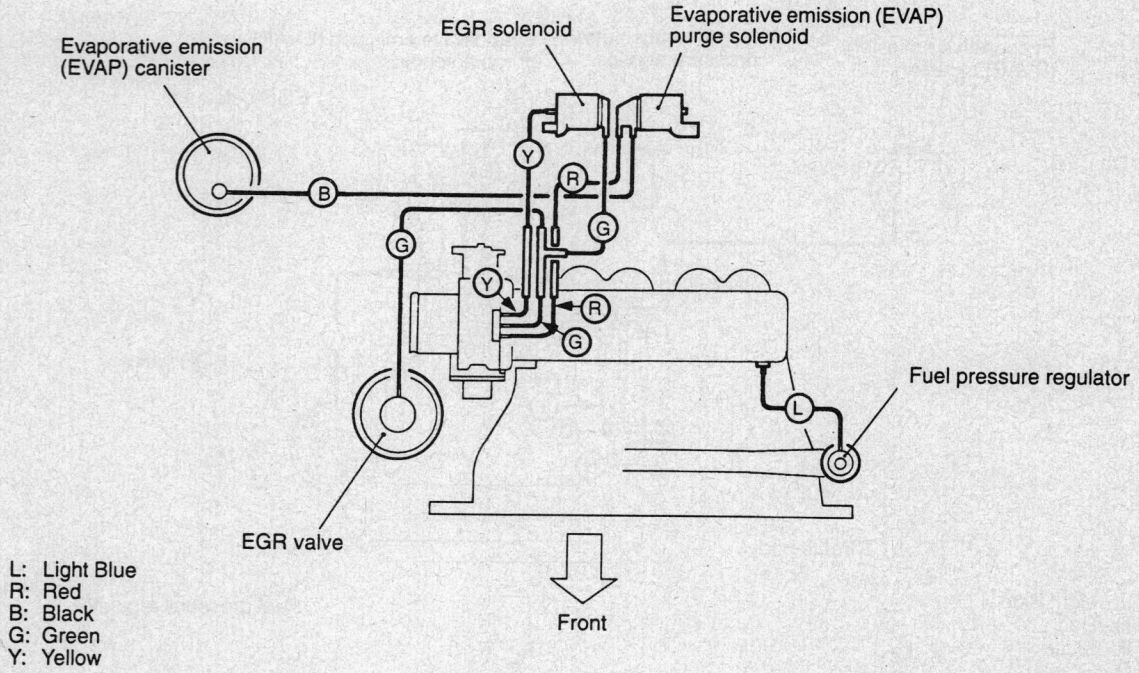

**Fig. 3   Vacuum hose routing.
Summit w/1.8L/4-110 engine &
Federal emissions**

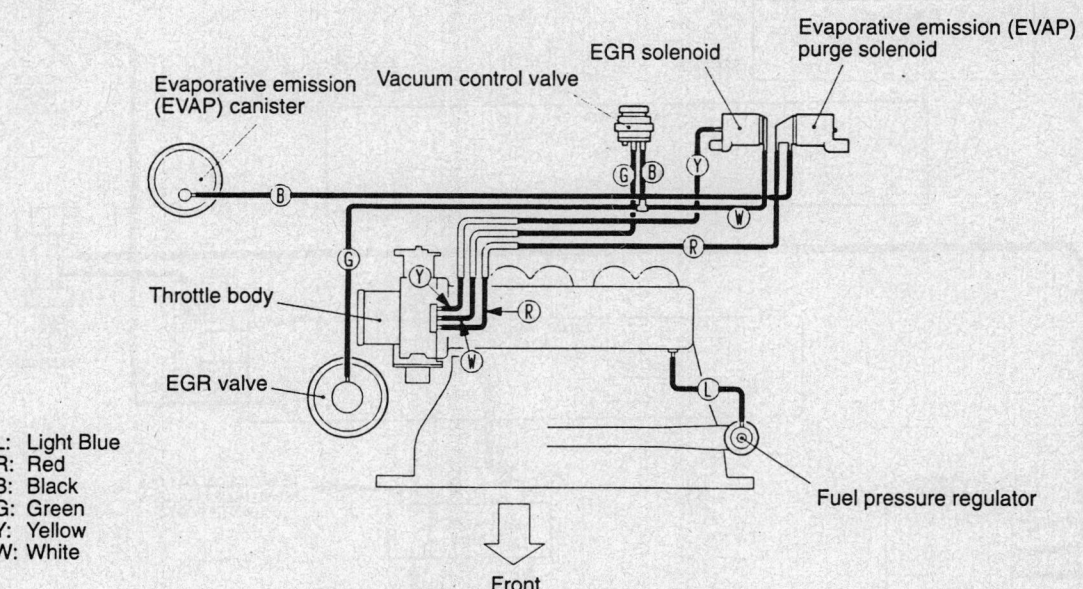

L: Light Blue
R: Red
B: Black
G: Green
Y: Yellow
W: White

Front

**Fig. 4   Vacuum hose routing.
Summit w/1.8L/4-110 engine &
California emissions**

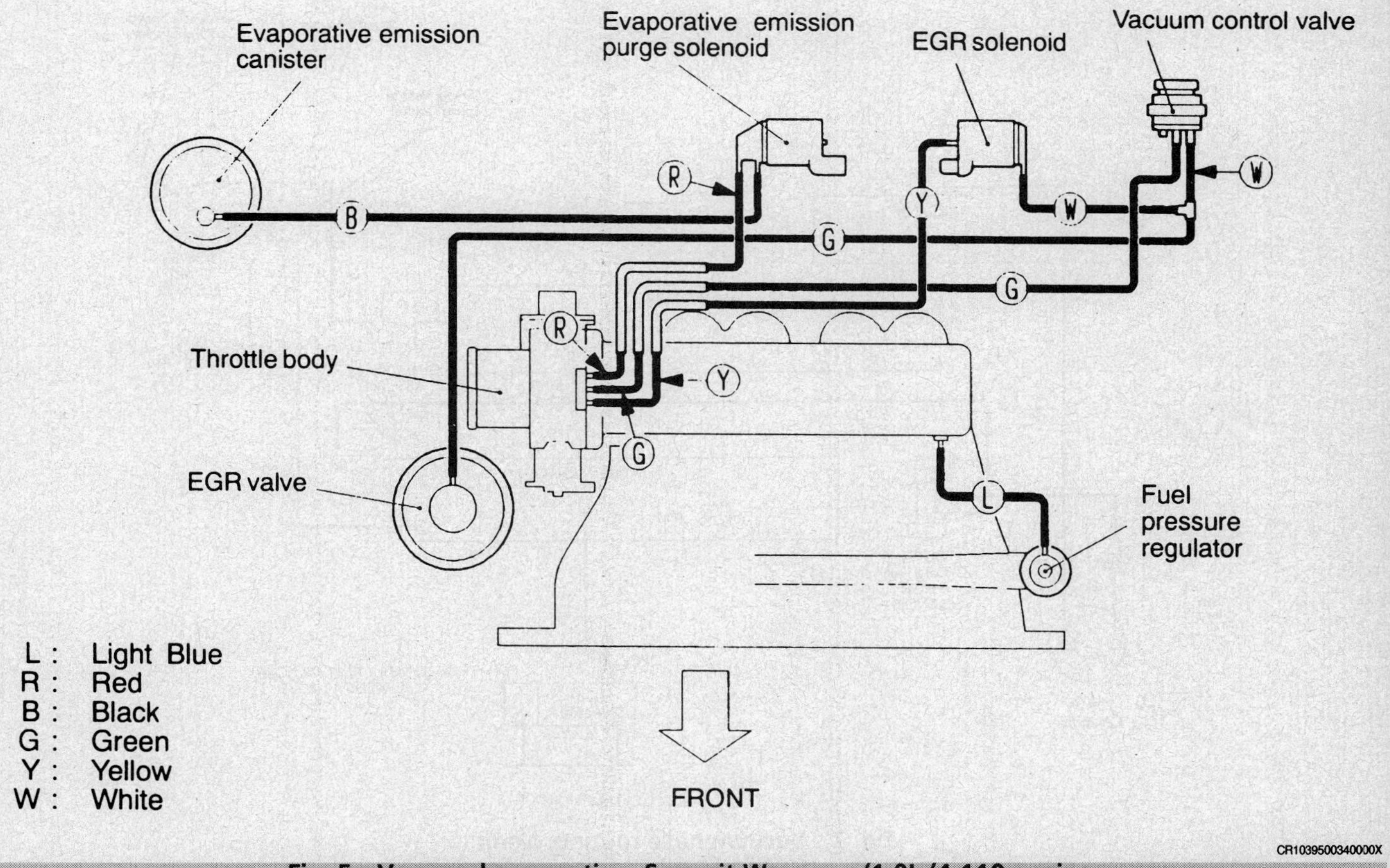

L : Light Blue
R : Red
B : Black
G : Green
Y : Yellow
W : White

FRONT

CR1039500340000X

Fig. 5   Vacuum hose routing. Summit Wagon w/1.8L/4-110 engine

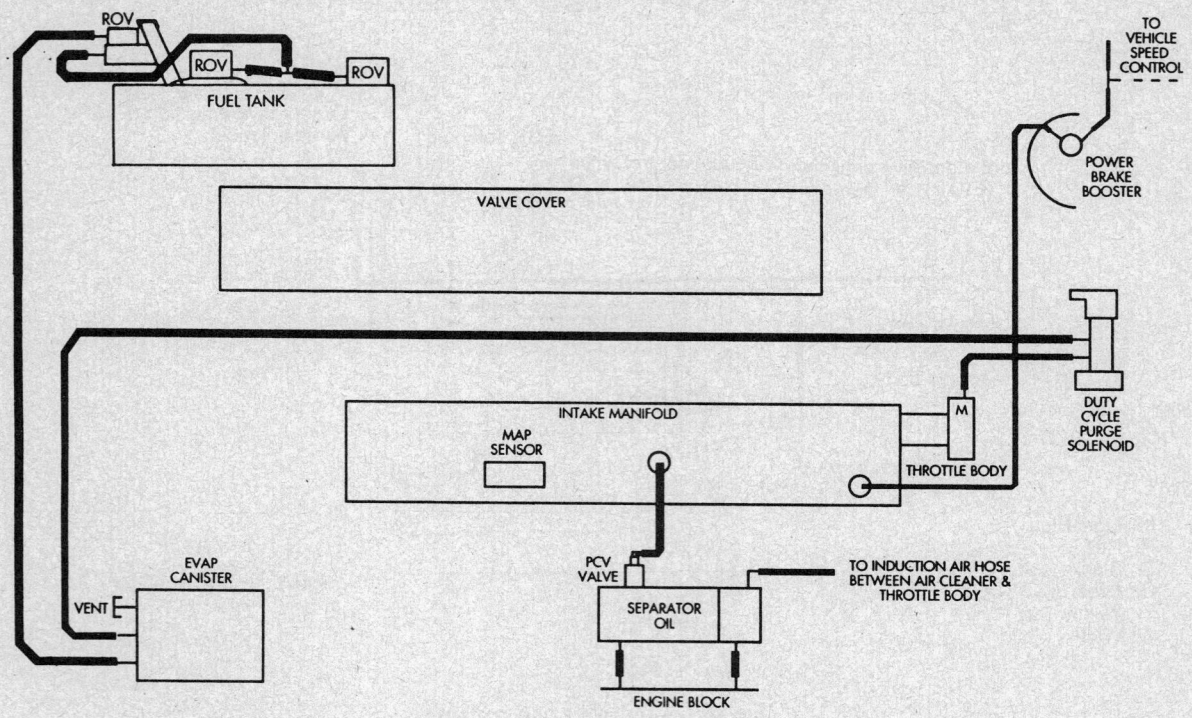

Fig. 6   Vacuum hose routing. Cirrus & Stratus w/2.0L/4-122 engine

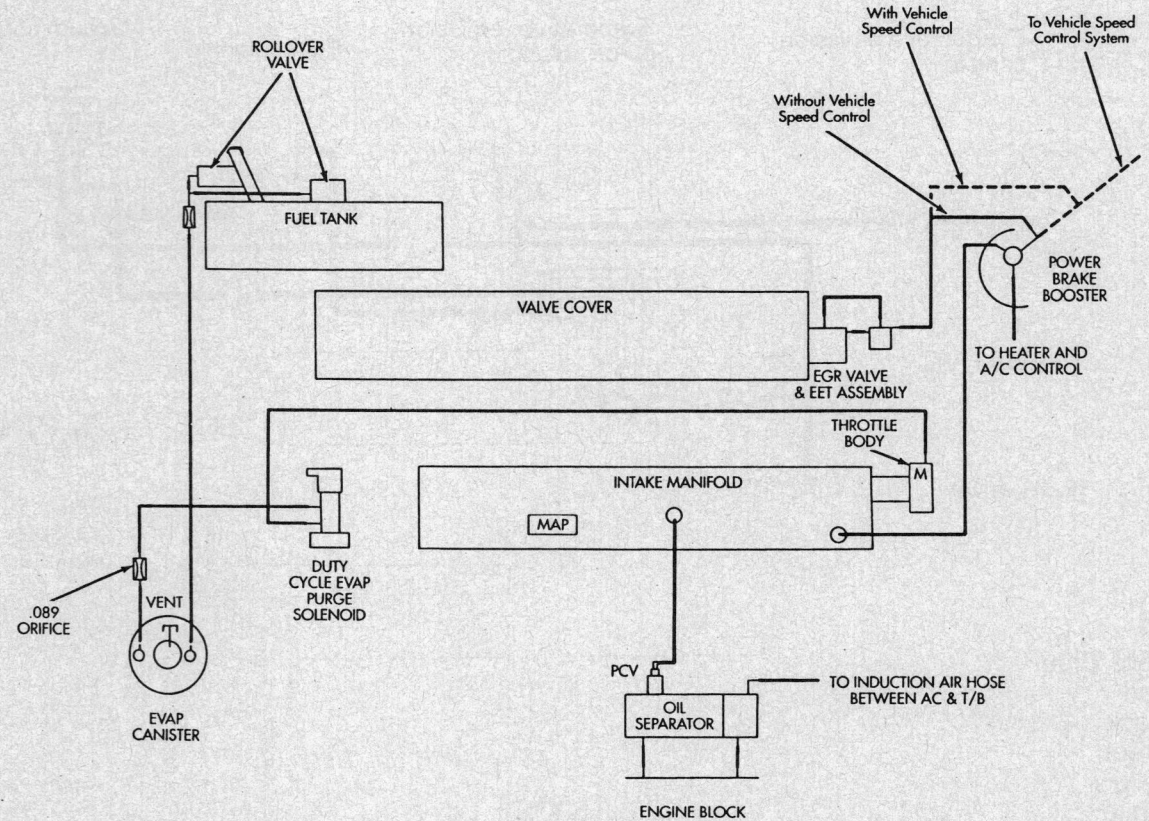

Fig. 7   Vacuum hose routing. Neon w/2.0L/4-122 engine

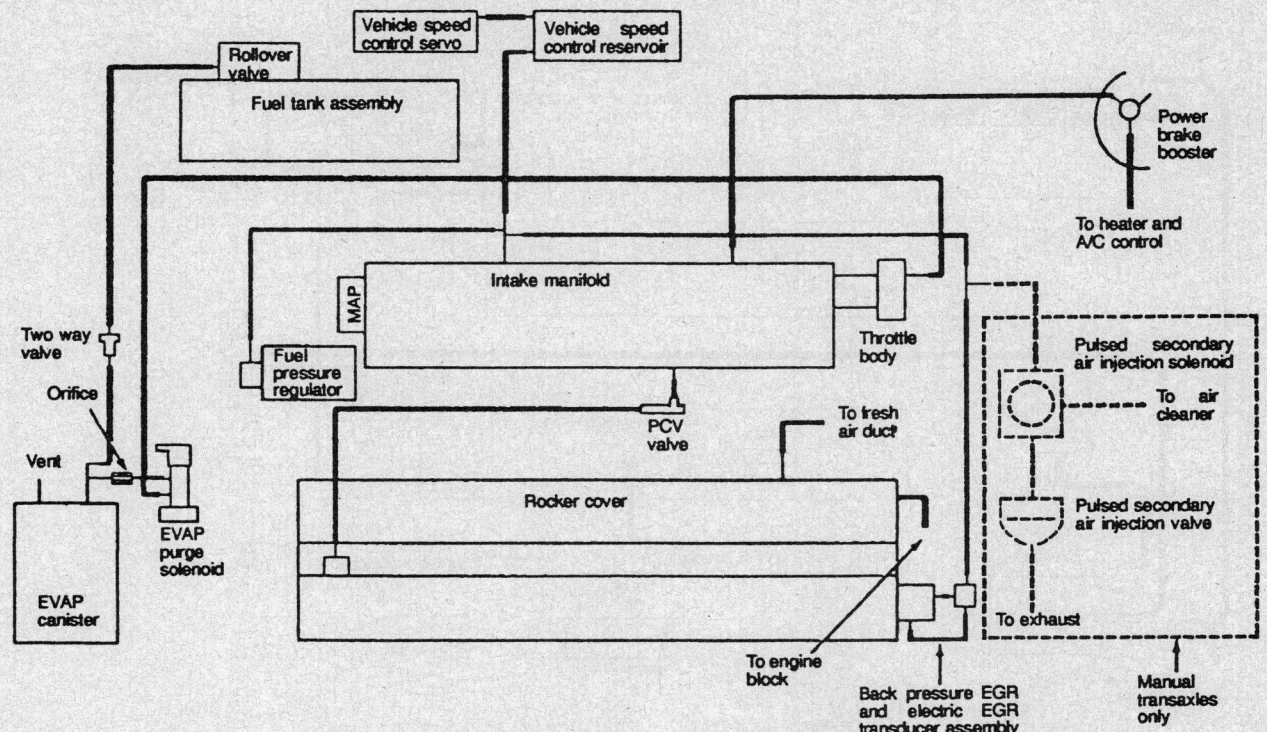

Fig. 8 Vacuum hose routing. Talon w/2.0L/4-122 non-turbocharged engine

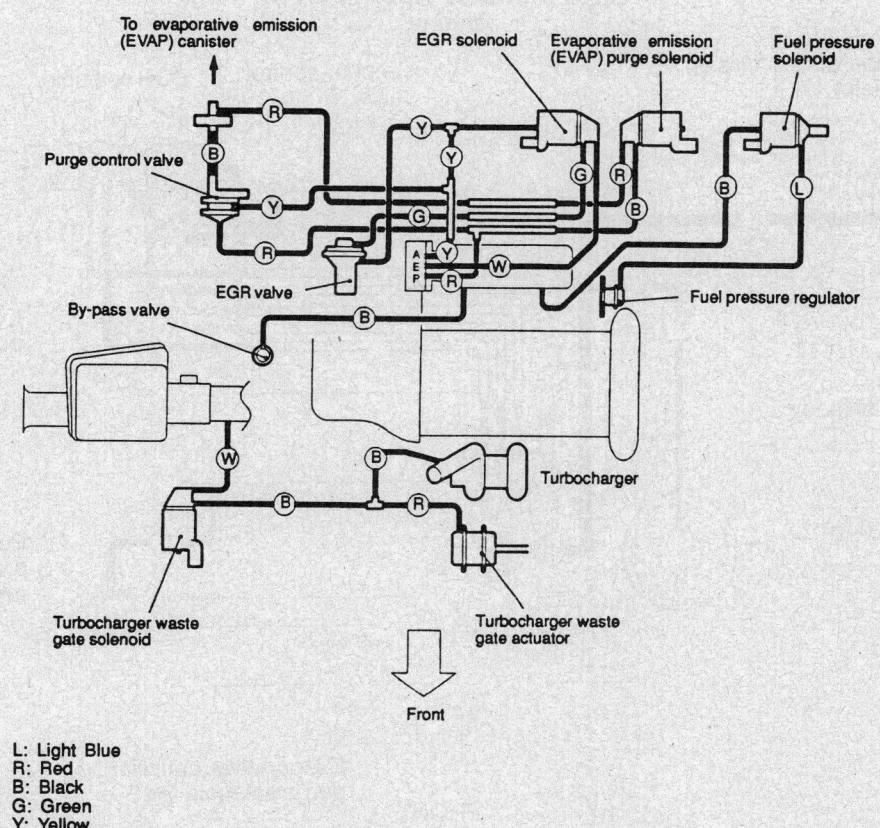

L: Light Blue
R: Red
B: Black
G: Green
Y: Yellow
W: White

Fig. 9 Vacuum hose routing. Talon w/2.0L/4-122 turbocharged engine

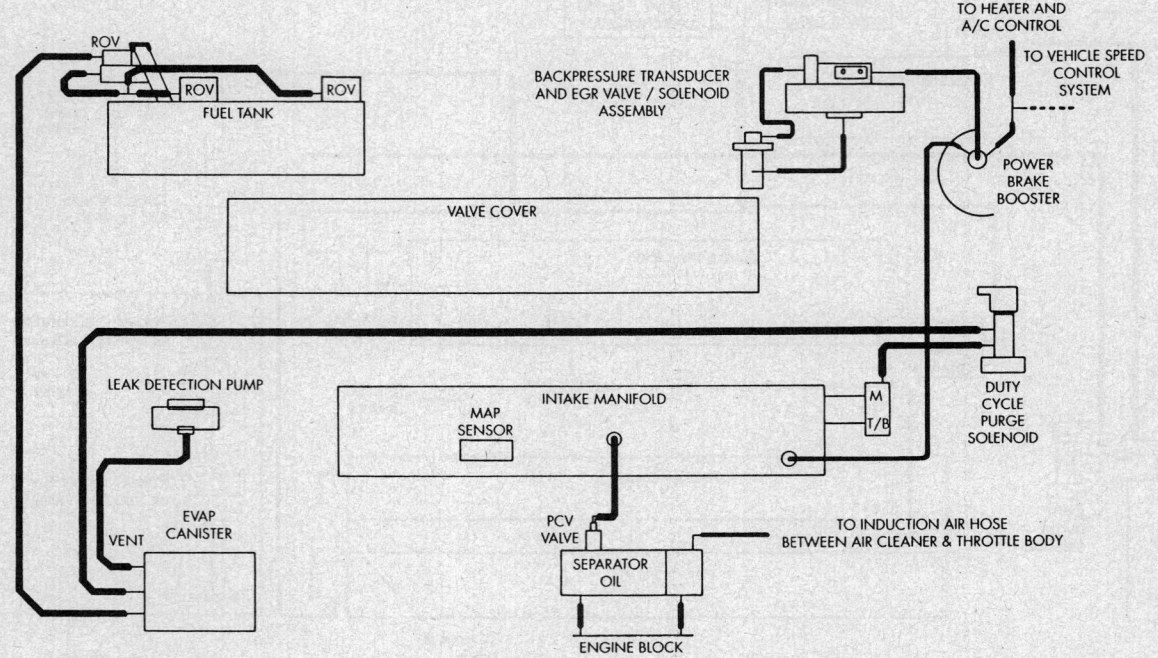

**Fig. 10   Vacuum hose routing.
Cirrus & Stratus w/2.4L/4-148
engine**

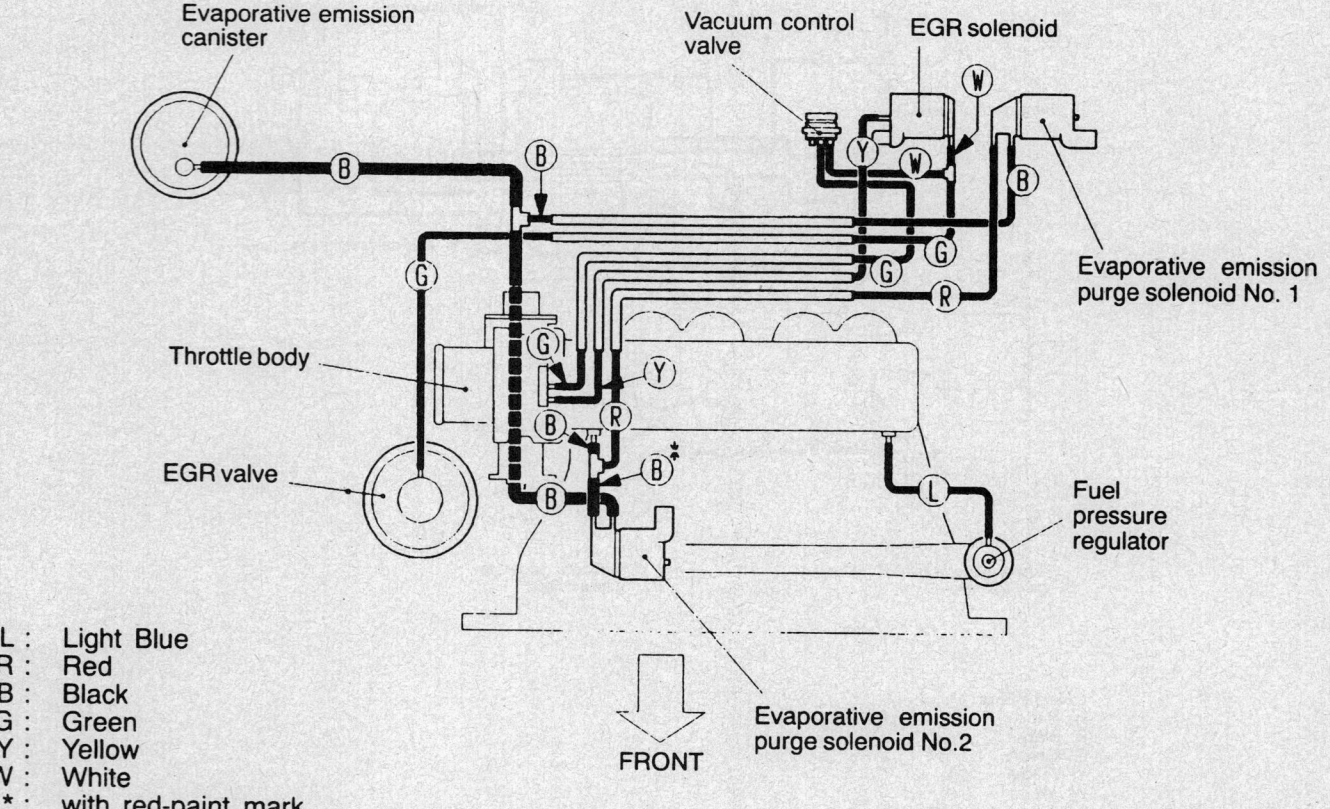

L : Light Blue
R : Red
B : Black
G : Green
Y : Yellow
W : White
* : with red-paint mark

FRONT

Fig. 11   Vacuum hose routing. FWD Summit Wagon w/2.4L/4-143 engine

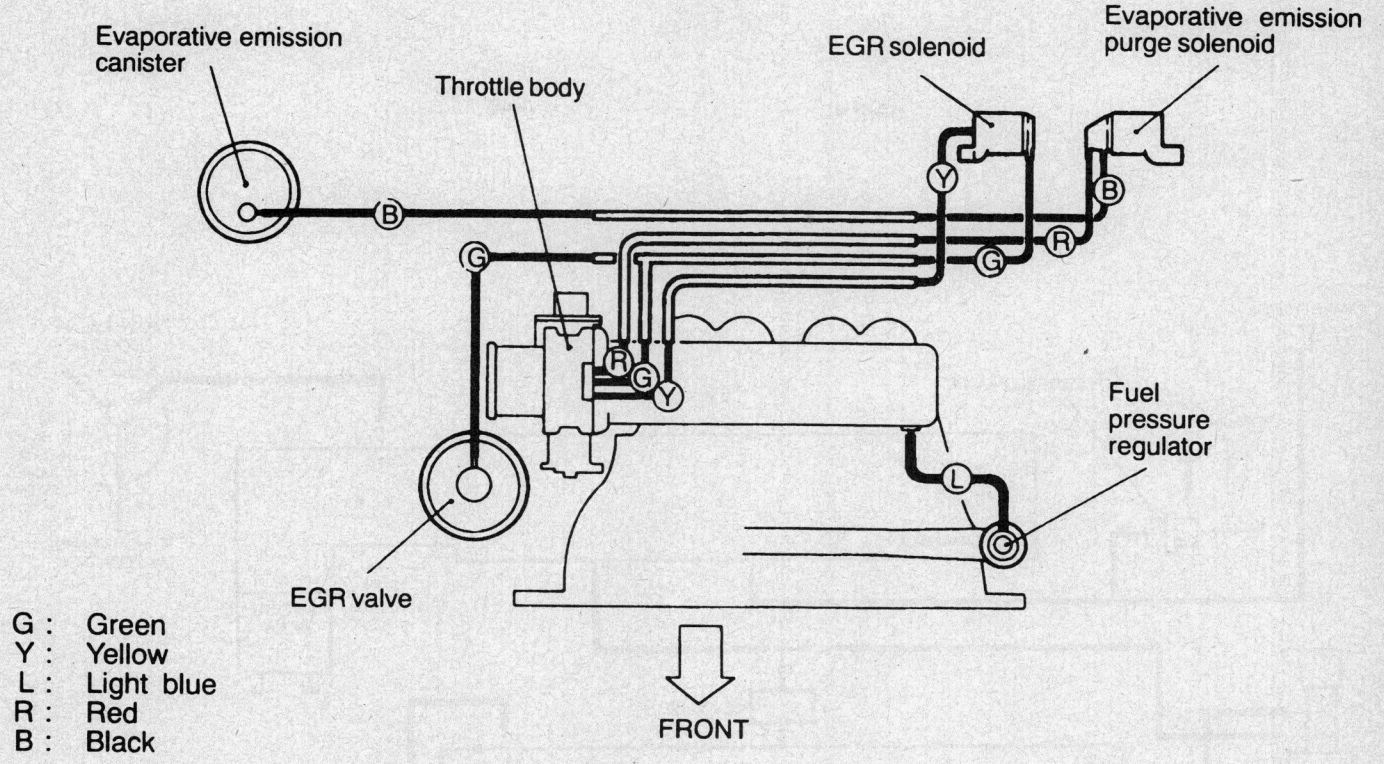

Evaporative emission canister
Throttle body
EGR solenoid
Evaporative emission purge solenoid
B
G
Y
R
L
Fuel pressure regulator
EGR valve
FRONT
G : Green
Y : Yellow
L : Light blue
R : Red
B : Black

CR1039500342000X

Fig. 12 Vacuum hose routing. AWD Summit Wagon w/2.4L/4-143 engine

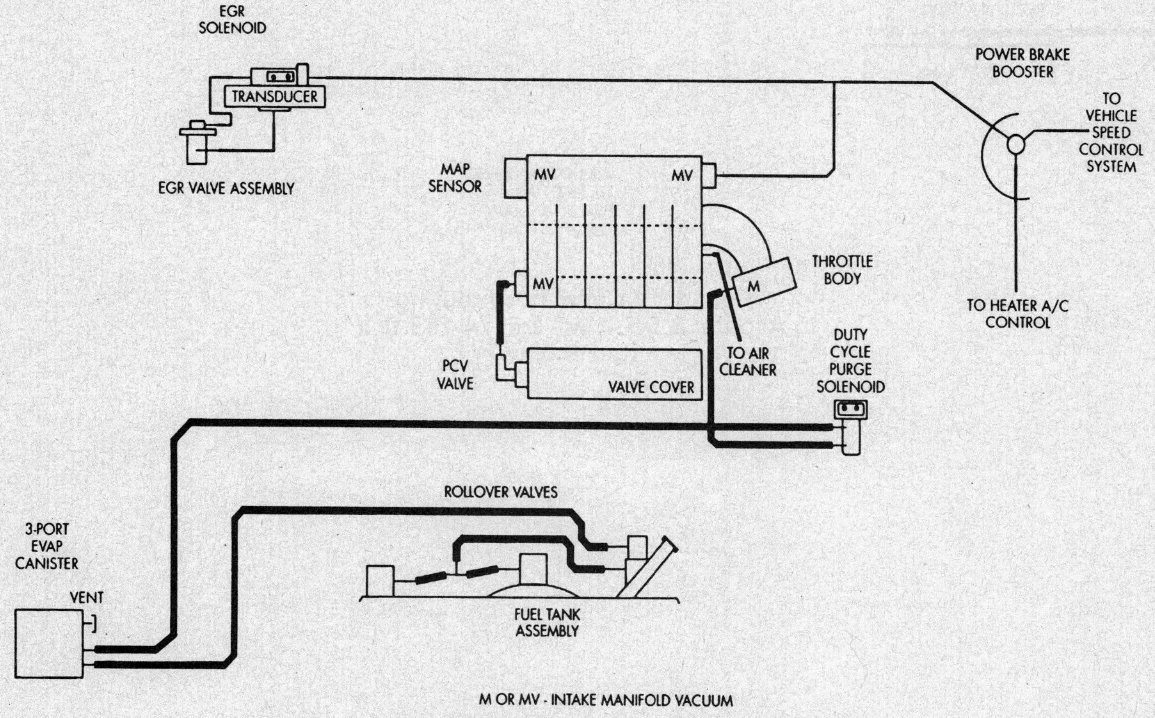

EGR SOLENOID
TRANSDUCER
EGR VALVE ASSEMBLY
POWER BRAKE BOOSTER
TO VEHICLE SPEED CONTROL SYSTEM
MAP SENSOR
MV
MV
MV
M
THROTTLE BODY
TO HEATER A/C CONTROL
PCV VALVE
VALVE COVER
TO AIR CLEANER
DUTY CYCLE PURGE SOLENOID
ROLLOVER VALVES
3-PORT EVAP CANISTER
VENT
FUEL TANK ASSEMBLY
M OR MV - INTAKE MANIFOLD VACUUM

Fig. 13 Vacuum hose routing. Cirrus & Stratus w/2.5L/V6-152 engine

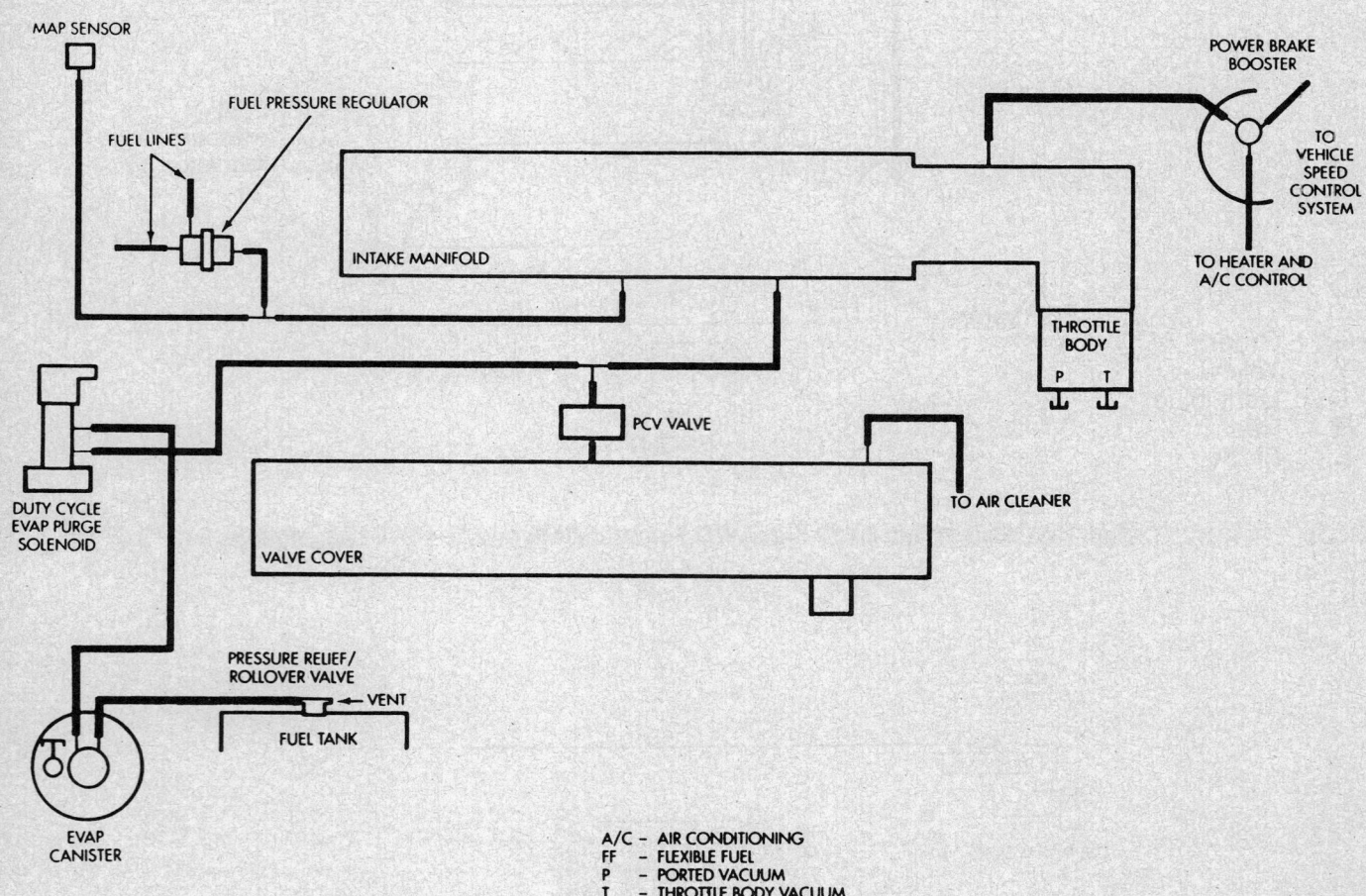

Fig. 14   Vacuum hose routing.
Acclaim & Spirit w/ 2.5L/4-153 flex
fuel engine

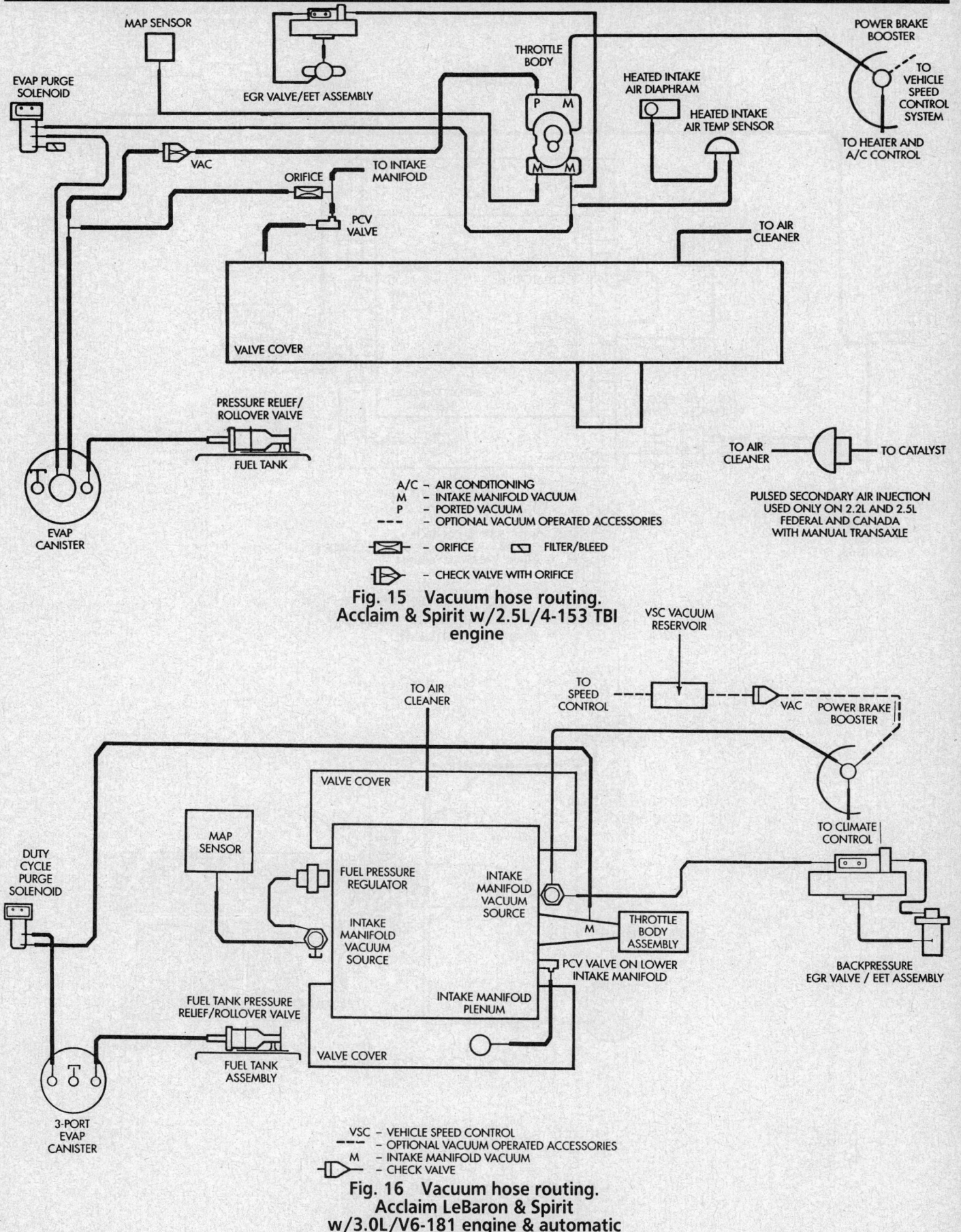

Fig. 15 Vacuum hose routing.
Acclaim & Spirit w/2.5L/4-153 TBI
engine

Fig. 16 Vacuum hose routing.
Acclaim LeBaron & Spirit
w/3.0L/V6-181 engine & automatic
transaxle

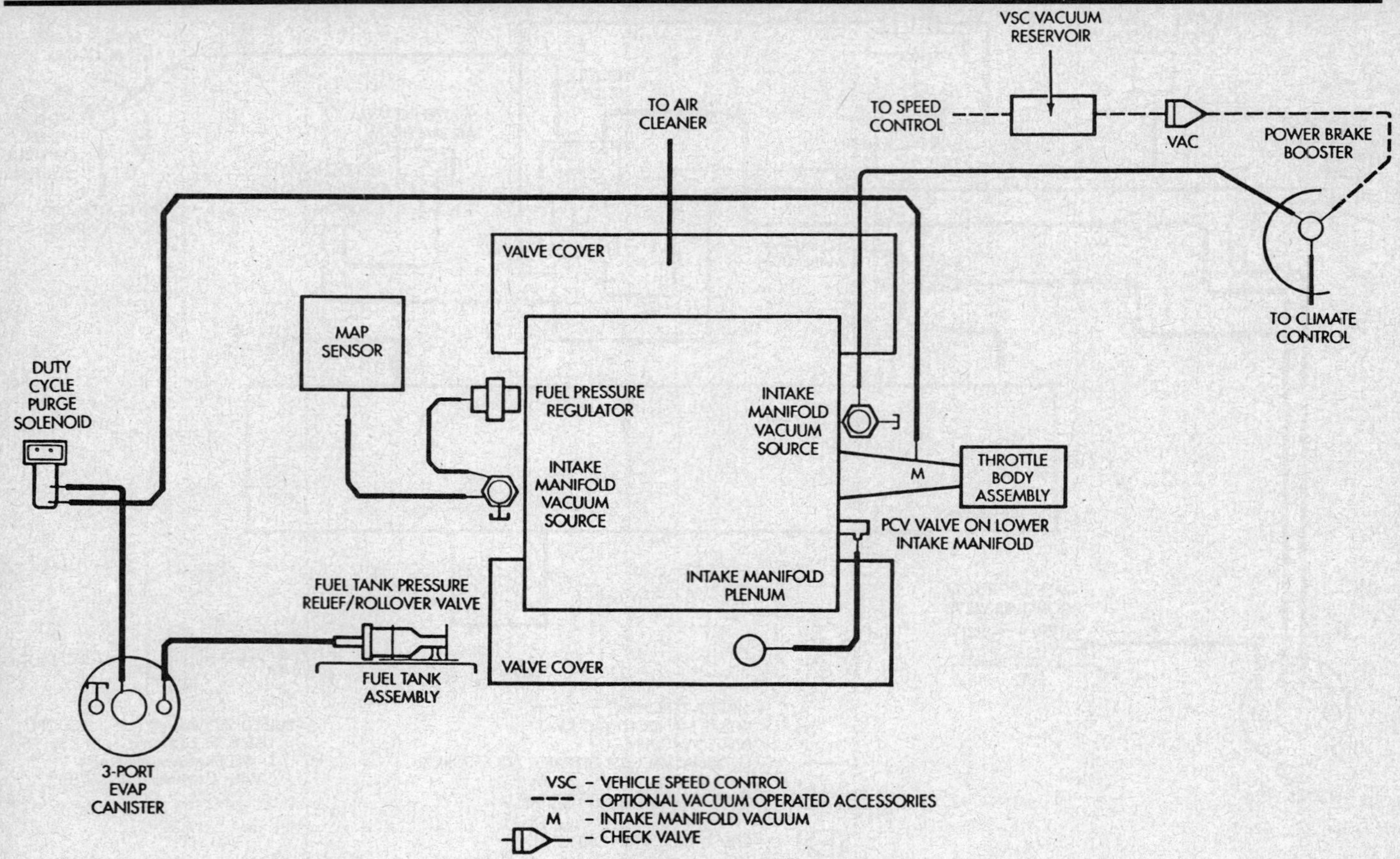

VSC VACUUM RESERVOIR

TO AIR CLEANER

TO SPEED CONTROL

VAC

POWER BRAKE BOOSTER

VALVE COVER

TO CLIMATE CONTROL

MAP SENSOR

DUTY CYCLE PURGE SOLENOID

FUEL PRESSURE REGULATOR

INTAKE MANIFOLD VACUUM SOURCE

INTAKE MANIFOLD VACUUM SOURCE

M

THROTTLE BODY ASSEMBLY

INTAKE MANIFOLD VACUUM SOURCE

PCV VALVE ON LOWER INTAKE MANIFOLD

FUEL TANK PRESSURE RELIEF/ROLLOVER VALVE

INTAKE MANIFOLD PLENUM

FUEL TANK ASSEMBLY

VALVE COVER

3-PORT EVAP CANISTER

VSC – VEHICLE SPEED CONTROL
- - - – OPTIONAL VACUUM OPERATED ACCESSORIES
M – INTAKE MANIFOLD VACUUM
– CHECK VALVE

**Fig. 17   Vacuum hose routing.
LeBaron w/3.0L/V6-181 engine &
manual transaxle**

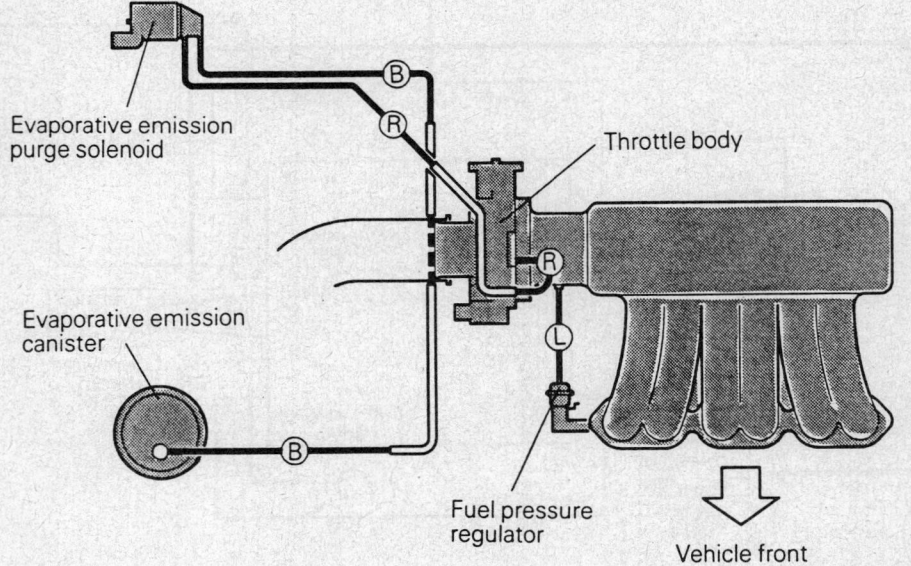

Evaporative emission purge solenoid

Throttle body

Evaporative emission canister

Fuel pressure regulator

Vehicle front

L: Light blue
R: Red
B: Black

**Fig. 18   Vacuum hose routing.
Stealth w/3.0L/V6-181
non-turbocharged engine & Federal
emissions**

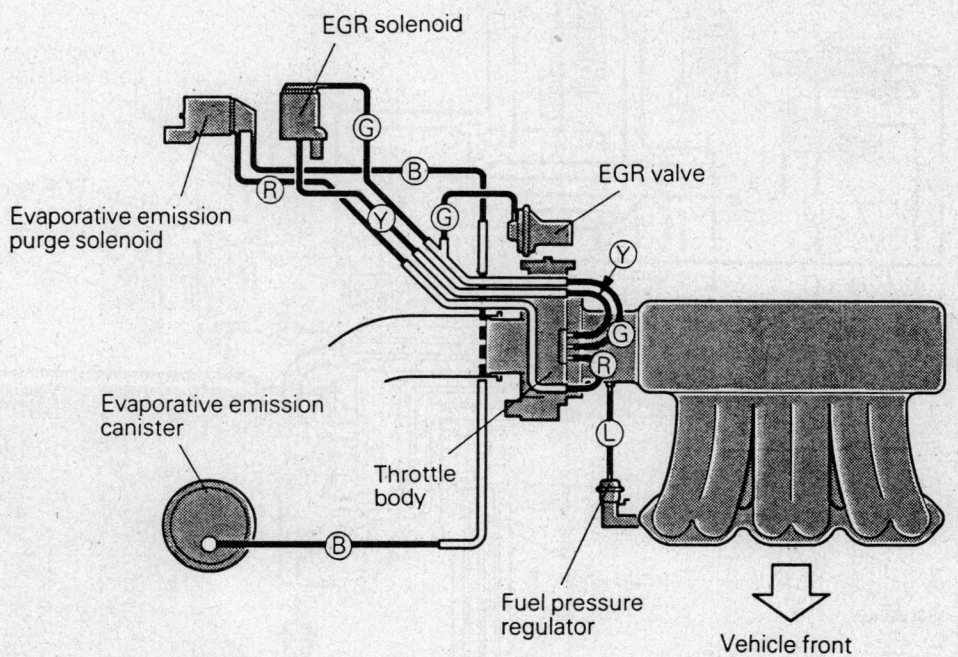

EGR solenoid

EGR valve

Evaporative emission purge solenoid

Evaporative emission canister

Throttle body

Fuel pressure regulator

Vehicle front

G: Green
Y: Yellow
L: Light blue
R: Red
B: Black

**Fig. 19   Vacuum hose routing.
Stealth w/3.0L/V6-181
non-turbocharged engine &
California emissions**

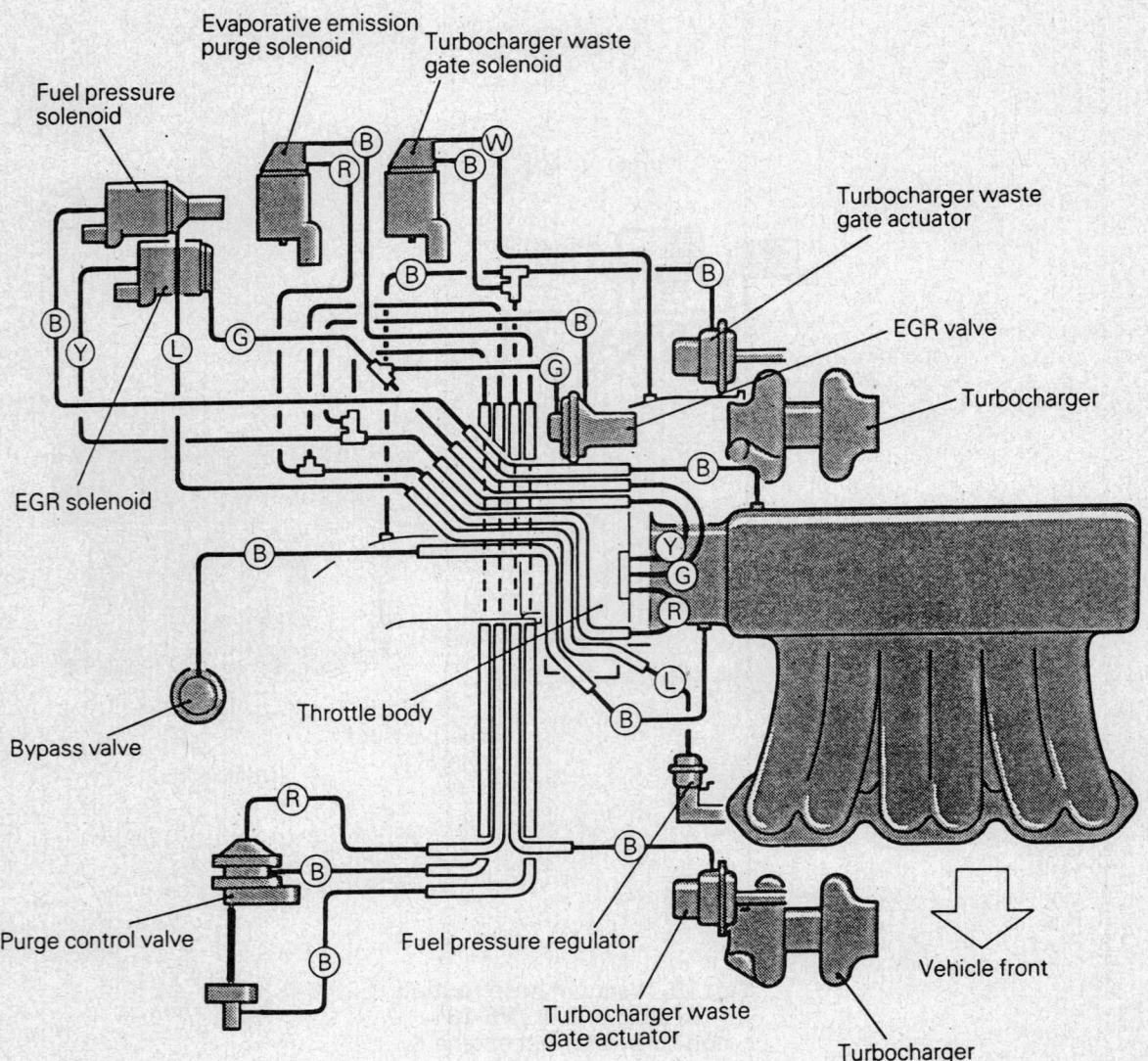

Fuel pressure solenoid

Evaporative emission purge solenoid

Turbocharger waste gate solenoid

Turbocharger waste gate actuator

EGR valve

Turbocharger

EGR solenoid

Bypass valve

Throttle body

Purge control valve

Fuel pressure regulator

Turbocharger waste gate actuator

Vehicle front

Turbocharger

G: Green
Y: Yellow
L: Light blue
R: Red
B: Black
W:White

**Fig. 20   Vacuum hose routing.
Stealth w/3.0L/V6-181
turbocharged engine**

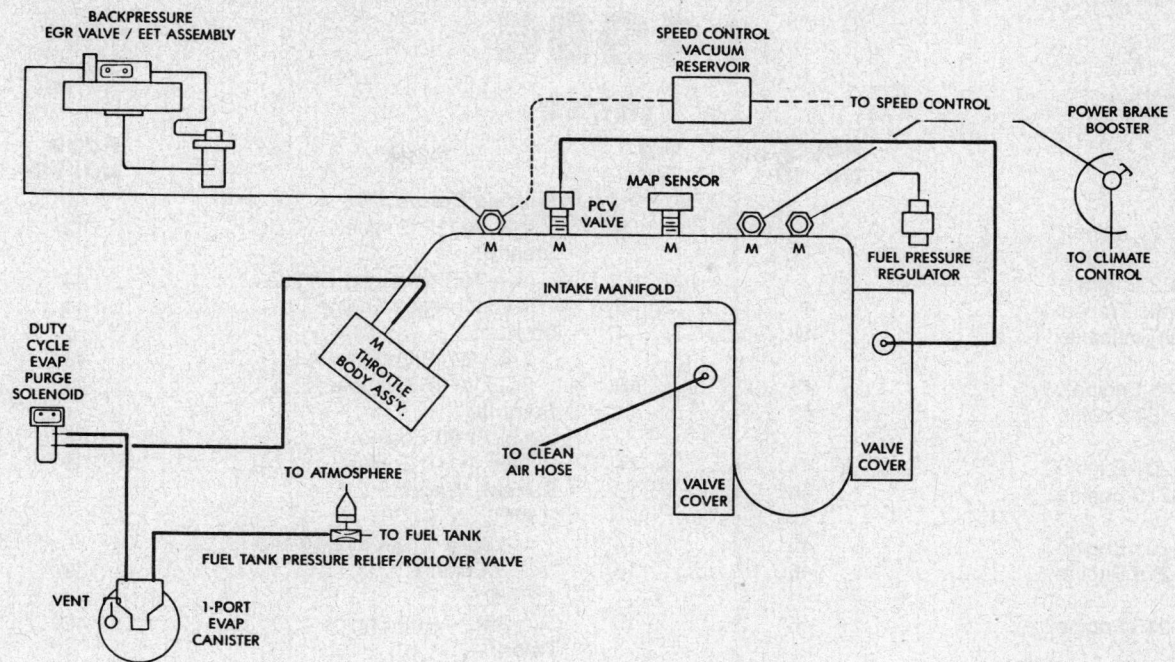

Fig. 21   Vacuum hose routing.
Concorde Intrepid & Vision
w/3.3L/V6-201 engine

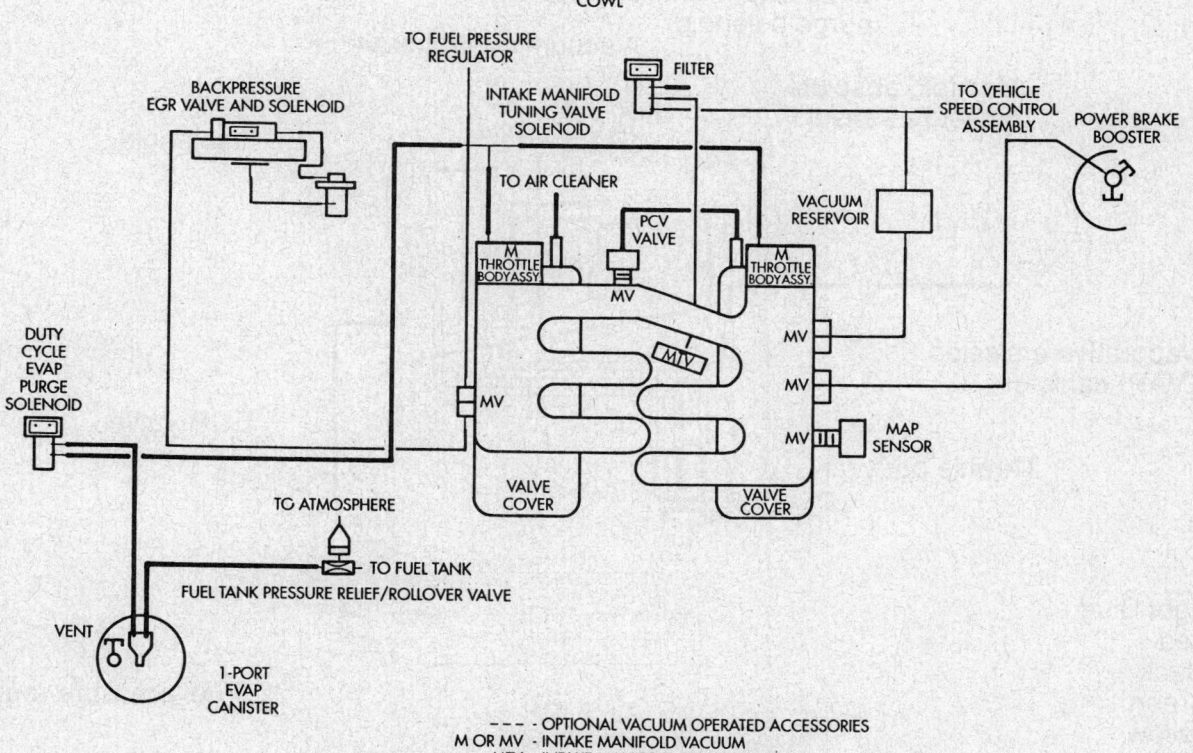

Fig. 22   Vacuum hose routing.
Concorde Intrepid LHS New Yorker &
Vision w/3.5L/V6-215 engine

1996

INDEX

	Page No. 18-	Fig. No.
Avenger:		
2.0L/4-122 Engine	42	8
Breeze:		
2.0L/4-122 Engine:		
Automatic Transaxle	40	5
Manual Transaxle	40	4
Cirrus:		
2.4L/4-148 Engine	43	10
2.5L/V6-152 Engine	43	11
Concorde:		
3.3L/V6-201 Engine	45	14
3.5L/V6-215 Engine	46	15
Intrepid:		
3.3L/V6-201 Engine	45	14
3.5L/V6-215 Engine	46	15
LHS:		
3.5L/V6-215 Engine	46	15
Neon:		
DOHC Engine	41	7
SOHC Engine	41	6
New Yorker:		
3.5L/V6-215 Engine	46	15
Sebring Convertible:		
2.5L/V6-152 Engine	43	11

	Page No. 18-	Fig. No.
Sebring Coupe:		
2.0L/4-122 Engine	42	8
Stealth:		
Non-Turbocharged Engine	44	12
Turbocharged Engine	44	13
Stratus:		
2.4L/4-148 Engine	43	10
2.5L/V6-152 Engine	43	11
Summit:		
1.5L/4-90 Engine	38	1
1.8L/4-110 Engine	39	2
Summit Wagon:		
AWD:		
1.8L/4-110 & 2.4L/4-143		
Engines	39	3
FWD:		
2.4L/4-143 Engine	42	9
Talon:		
2.0L/4-122 Engine	42	8
Vision:		
3.3L/V6-201 Engine	45	14
3.5L/V6-215 Engine	46	15

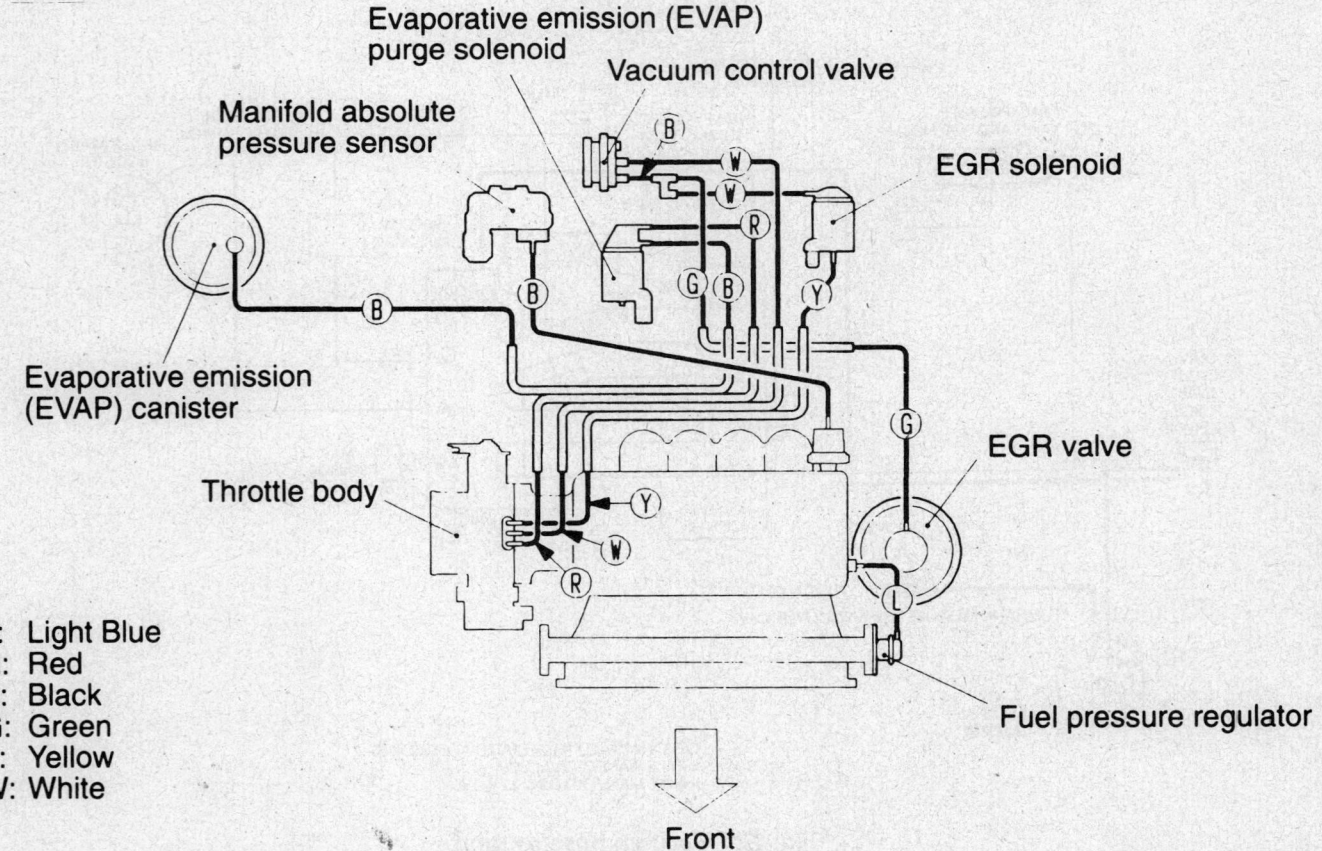

L: Light Blue
R: Red
B: Black
G: Green
Y: Yellow
W: White

CF1039600344000X

Fig. 1 Vacuum hose routing. Summit w/1.5L/4-90 engine

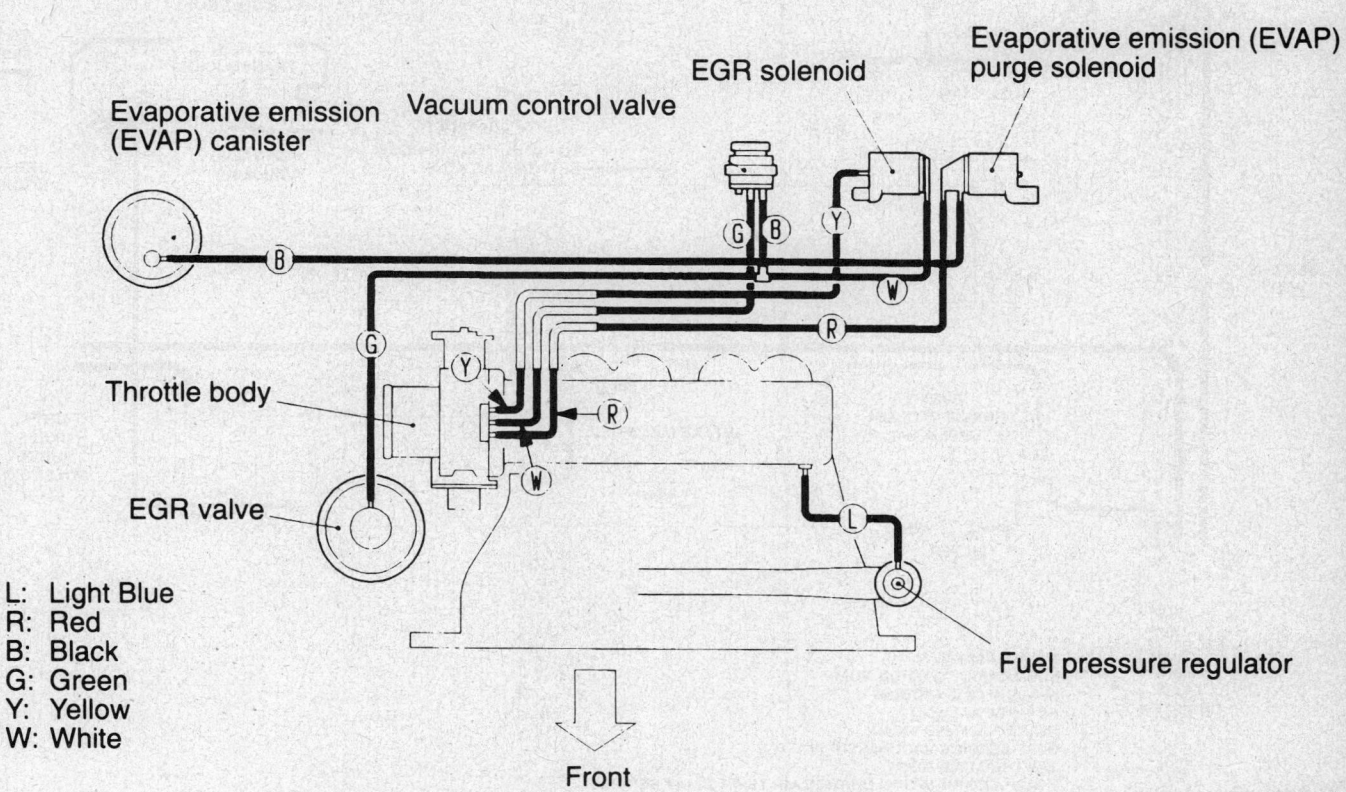

L: Light Blue
R: Red
B: Black
G: Green
Y: Yellow
W: White

CR1039600345000X

Fig. 2   Vacuum hose routing. Summit w/ 1.8L/4-110 engine

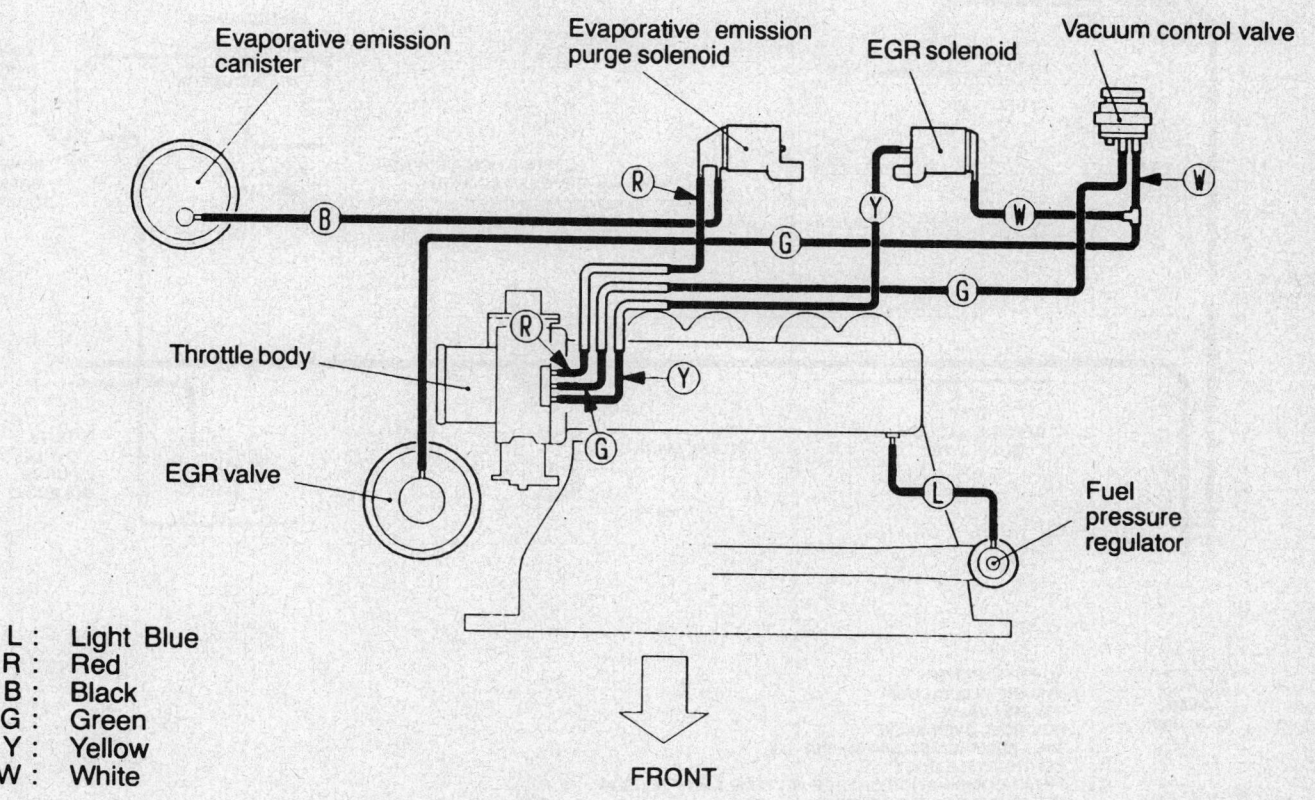

L : Light Blue
R : Red
B : Black
G : Green
Y : Yellow
W : White

CR1039600346000X

Fig. 3   Vacuum hose routing. AWD Summit Wagon w/1.8L/4-110 & 2.4L/4-143 engines

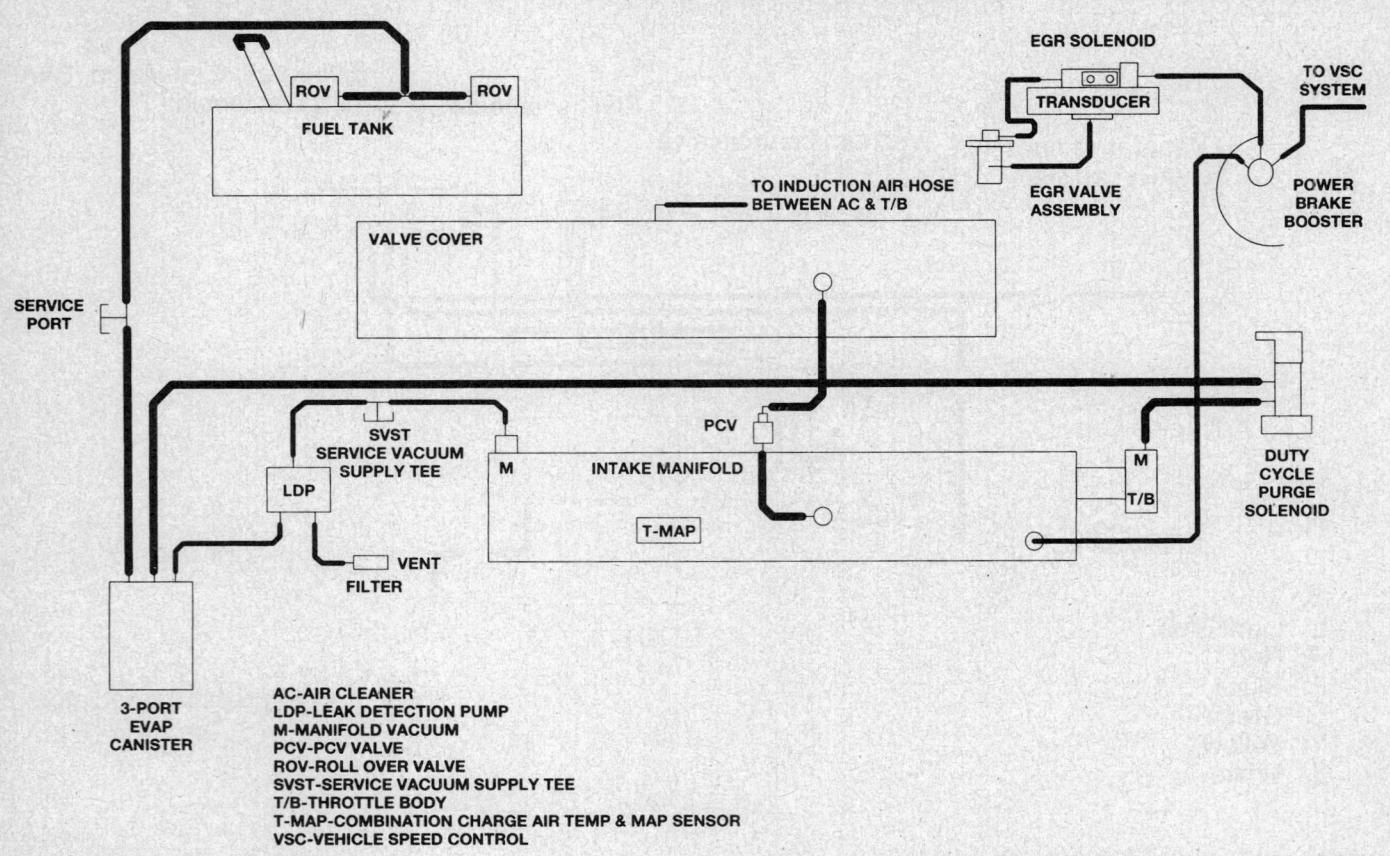

EGR SOLENOID

TRANSDUCER

TO VSC SYSTEM

EGR VALVE ASSEMBLY

POWER BRAKE BOOSTER

TO INDUCTION AIR HOSE BETWEEN AC & T/B

ROV   ROV

FUEL TANK

VALVE COVER

SERVICE PORT

PCV

DUTY CYCLE PURGE SOLENOID

SVST SERVICE VACUUM SUPPLY TEE

LDP

M

INTAKE MANIFOLD

T-MAP

M
T/B

VENT FILTER

3-PORT EVAP CANISTER

AC-AIR CLEANER
LDP-LEAK DETECTION PUMP
M-MANIFOLD VACUUM
PCV-PCV VALVE
ROV-ROLL OVER VALVE
SVST-SERVICE VACUUM SUPPLY TEE
T/B-THROTTLE BODY
T-MAP-COMBINATION CHARGE AIR TEMP & MAP SENSOR
VSC-VEHICLE SPEED CONTROL

CR103960C347000X

Fig. 4   Vacuum hose routing. Breeze w/2.0L/4-122 engine & manual transaxle

EGR SOLENOID

TRANSDUCER

TO VSC SYSTEM

EGR VALVE ASSEMBLY

POWER BRAKE BOOSTER

TO INDUCTION AIR HOSE BETWEEN AC & T/B

ROV   ROV

FUEL TANK

VALVE COVER

SERVICE PORT

PCV

DUTY CYCLE PURGE SOLENOID

SVST SERVICE VACUUM SUPPLY TEE

M

INTAKE MANIFOLD

T-MAP

M.
T/B

VENT

3-PORT EVAP CANISTER

AC-AIR CLEANER
M-MANIFOLD VACUUM
PCV-PCV VALVE
ROV-ROLL OVER VALVE
SVST-SERVICE VACUUM SUPPLY TEE
T/B-THROTTLE BODY
T-MAP-COMBINATION CHARGE AIR TEMP & MAP SENSOR
VSC-VEHICLE SPEED CONTROL

CR10396000348000X

Fig. 5   Vacuum hose routing. Breeze w/2.0L/4-122 engine & automatic transaxle

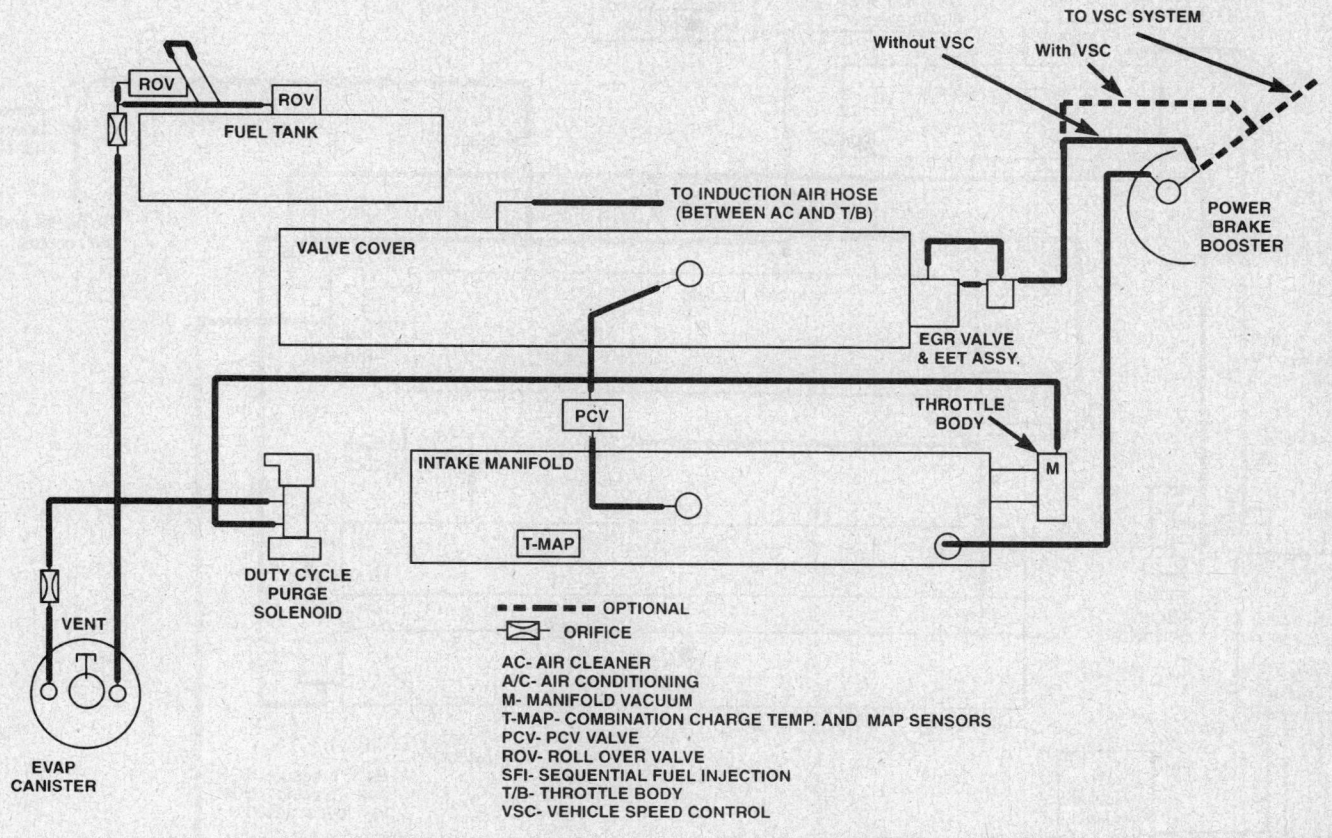

Fig. 6   Vacuum hose routing. Neon w/2.0L/4-122 SOHC engine

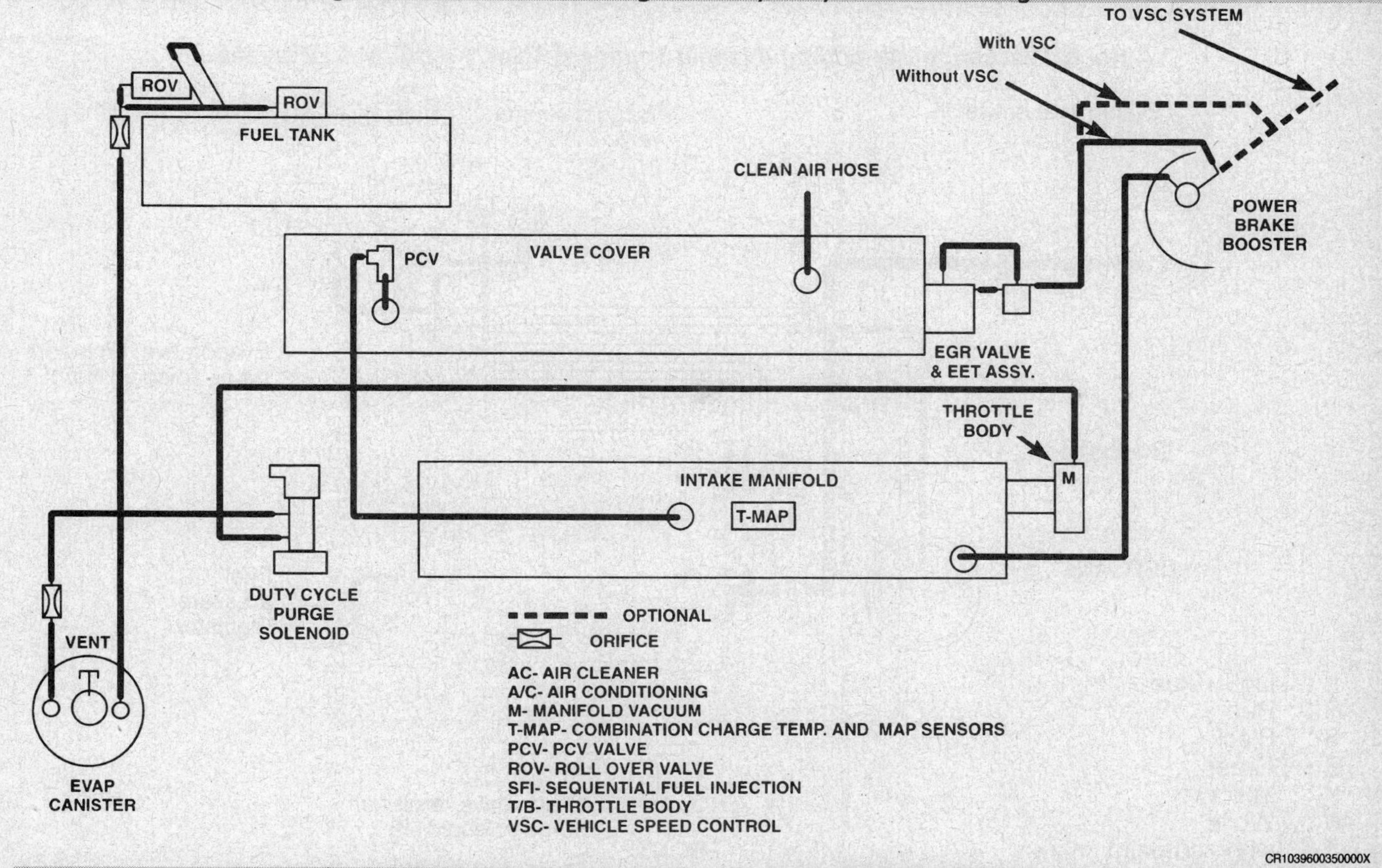

Fig. 7   Vacuum hose routing. Neon w/2.0L/4-122 DOHC engine

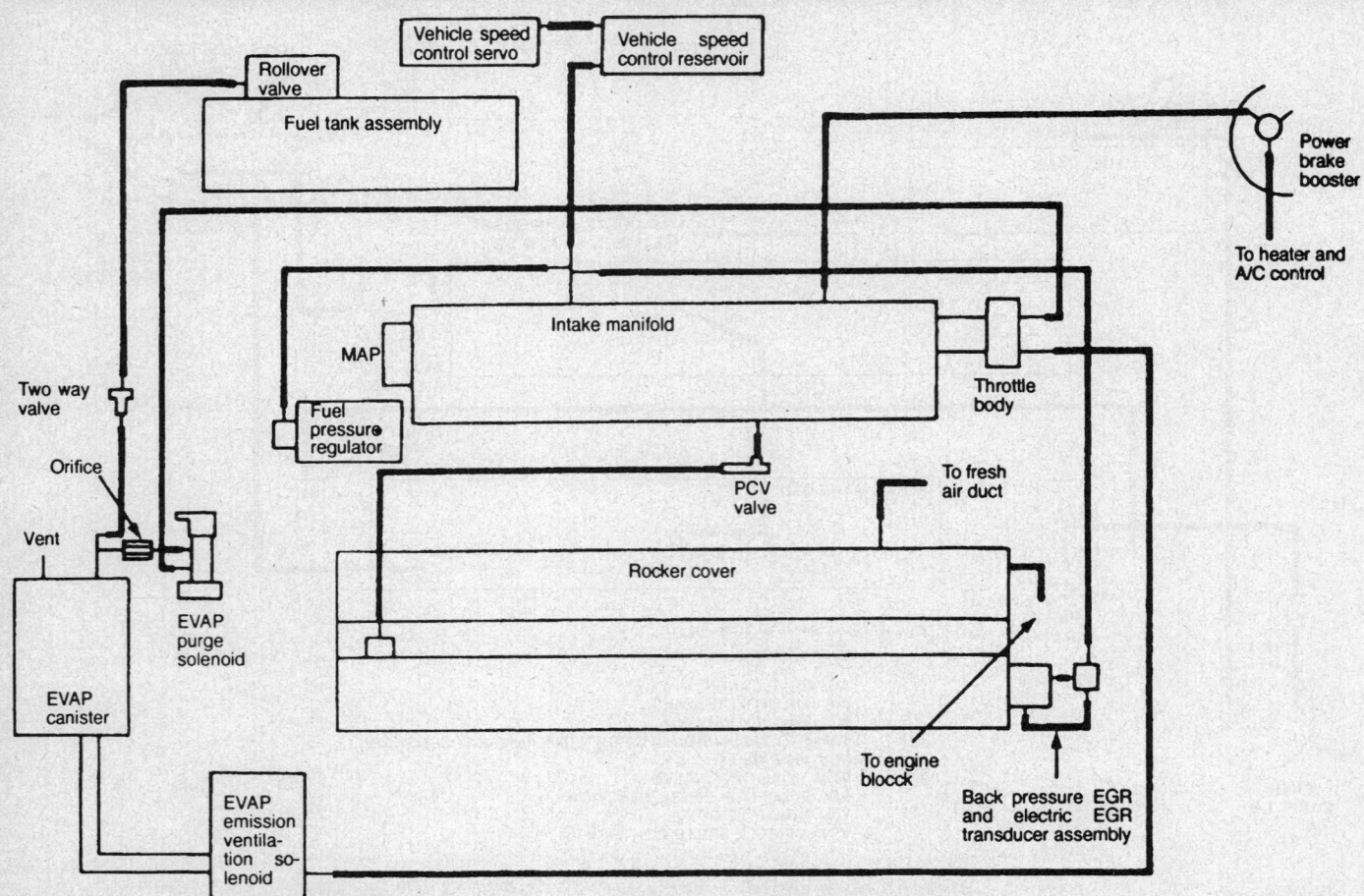

Fig. 8   Vacuum hose routing. Avenger Sebring & Talon w/2.0L/4-122 engine

CR1039600351000X

Evaporative emission canister

Vacuum control valve

EGR solenoid

Throttle body

EGR valve

Evaporative emission purge solenoid No. 1

Evaporative emission purge solenoid No.2

Fuel pressure regulator

FRONT

L : Light Blue
R : Red
B : Black
G : Green
Y : Yellow
W : White
* : with red-paint mark

Fig. 9   Vacuum hose routing. FWD Summit Wagon w/ 2.4L/4-143 engine

CR1039600352000X

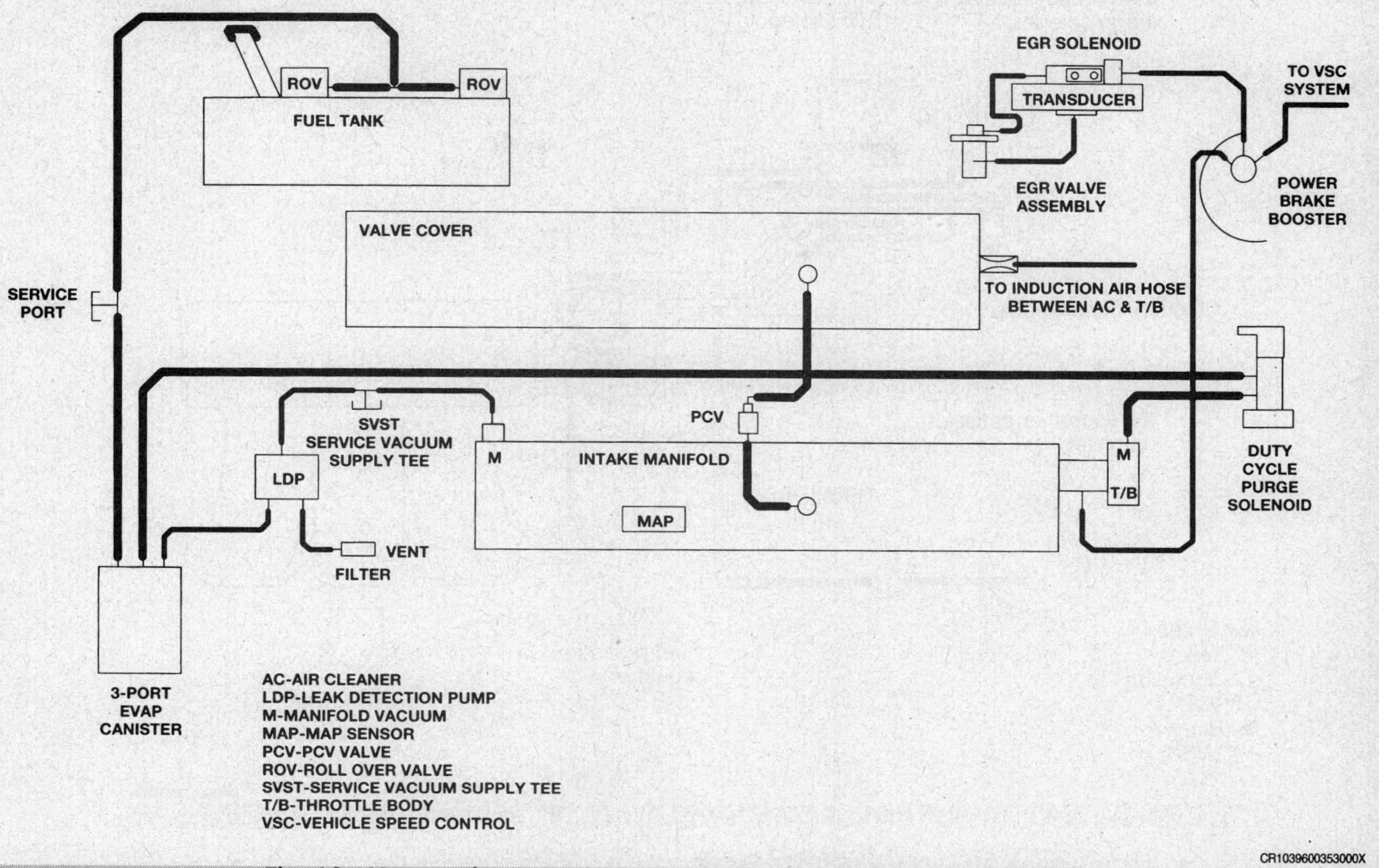

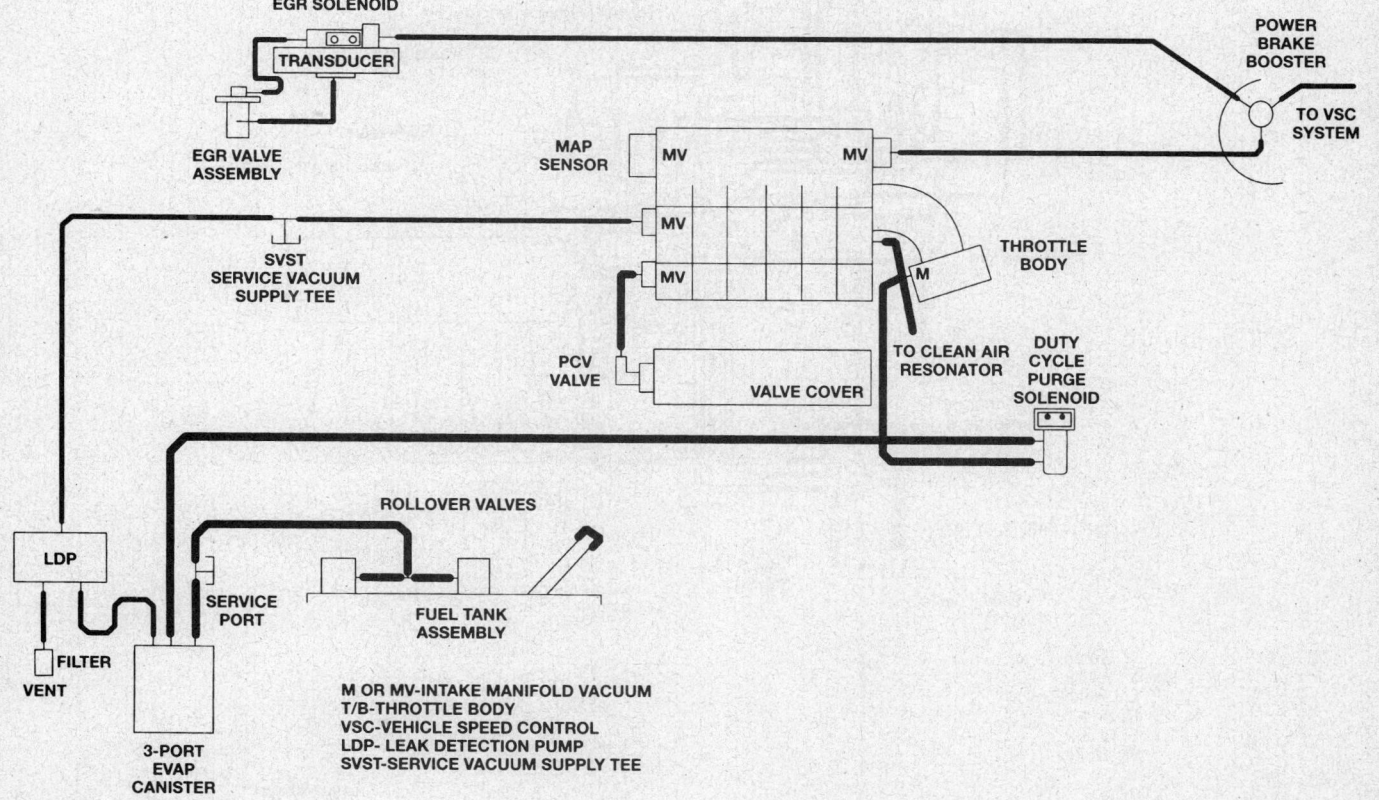

ROV **ROV**
FUEL TANK

EGR SOLENOID
TRANSDUCER
TO VSC SYSTEM
EGR VALVE ASSEMBLY
POWER BRAKE BOOSTER

VALVE COVER

TO INDUCTION AIR HOSE BETWEEN AC & T/B

SERVICE PORT

PCV

SVST SERVICE VACUUM SUPPLY TEE

LDP

M

INTAKE MANIFOLD

MAP

M
T/B

DUTY CYCLE PURGE SOLENOID

VENT FILTER

3-PORT EVAP CANISTER

AC-AIR CLEANER
LDP-LEAK DETECTION PUMP
M-MANIFOLD VACUUM
MAP-MAP SENSOR
PCV-PCV VALVE
ROV-ROLL OVER VALVE
SVST-SERVICE VACUUM SUPPLY TEE
T/B-THROTTLE BODY
VSC-VEHICLE SPEED CONTROL

CR1039600353000X

Fig. 10   Vacuum hose routing. Cirrus & Stratus w/2.4L/4-148 engine

EGR SOLENOID
TRANSDUCER
POWER BRAKE BOOSTER
TO VSC SYSTEM
EGR VALVE ASSEMBLY

MAP SENSOR
MV   MV
MV
MV
M
THROTTLE BODY

SVST SERVICE VACUUM SUPPLY TEE

PCV VALVE
VALVE COVER

TO CLEAN AIR RESONATOR
DUTY CYCLE PURGE SOLENOID

LDP

FILTER
VENT

SERVICE PORT

ROLLOVER VALVES

FUEL TANK ASSEMBLY

3-PORT EVAP CANISTER

M OR MV-INTAKE MANIFOLD VACUUM
T/B-THROTTLE BODY
VSC-VEHICLE SPEED CONTROL
LDP- LEAK DETECTION PUMP
SVST-SERVICE VACUUM SUPPLY TEE

CR1039600354000X

Fig. 11   Vacuum hose routing. Cirrus Sebring Convertible & Stratus w/ 2.5L/4-152 engine

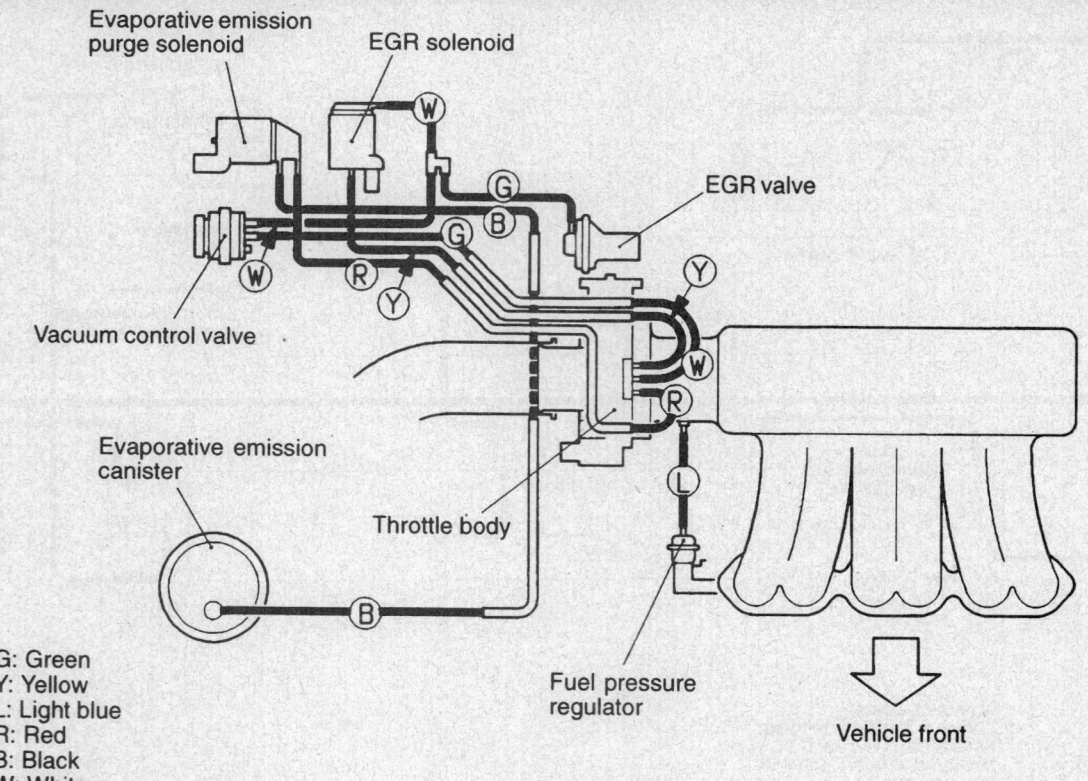

G: Green
Y: Yellow
L: Light blue
R: Red
B: Black
W: White

CR1039600355000X

Fig. 12   Vacuum hose routing. Stealth w/3.0L/V6-181 non-turbocharged engine

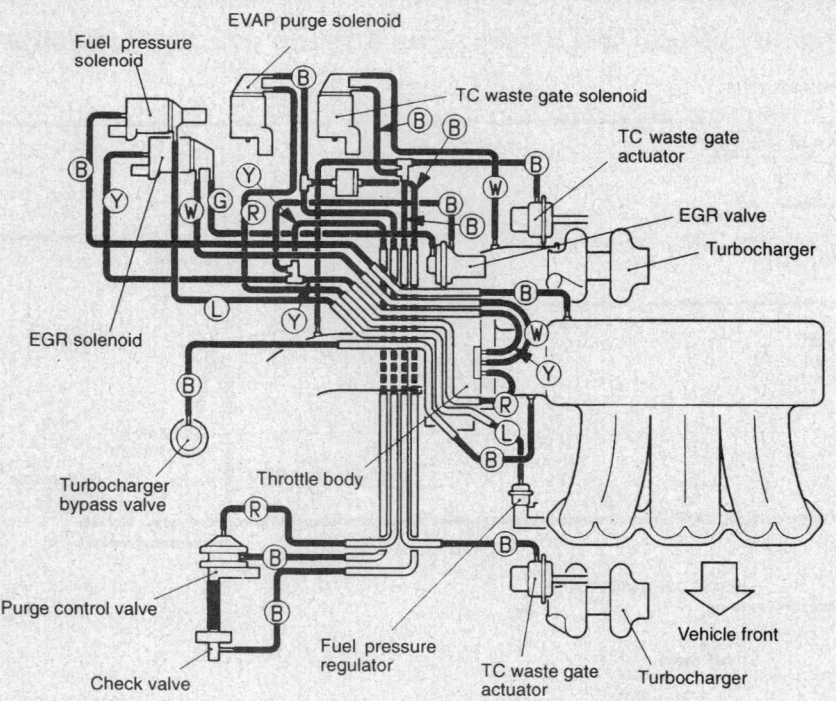

G: Green
Y: Yellow
L: Light blue
R: Red
B: Black
W: White

CR1039600356000X

Fig. 13   Vacuum hose routing. Stealth w/3.0L/V6-181 turbocharged engine

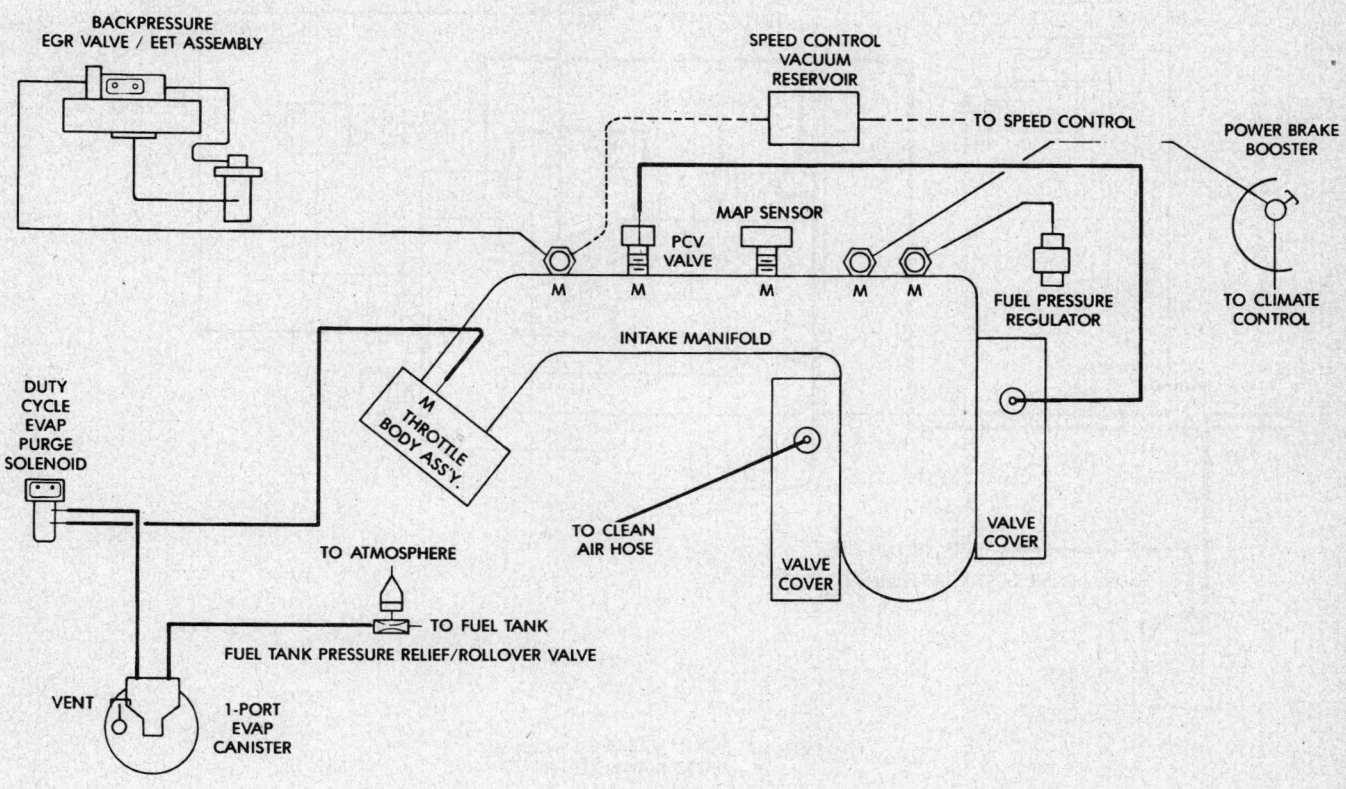

Fig. 14   Vacuum hose routing. Concorde Intrepid & Vision w/3.3L/V6-201 engine

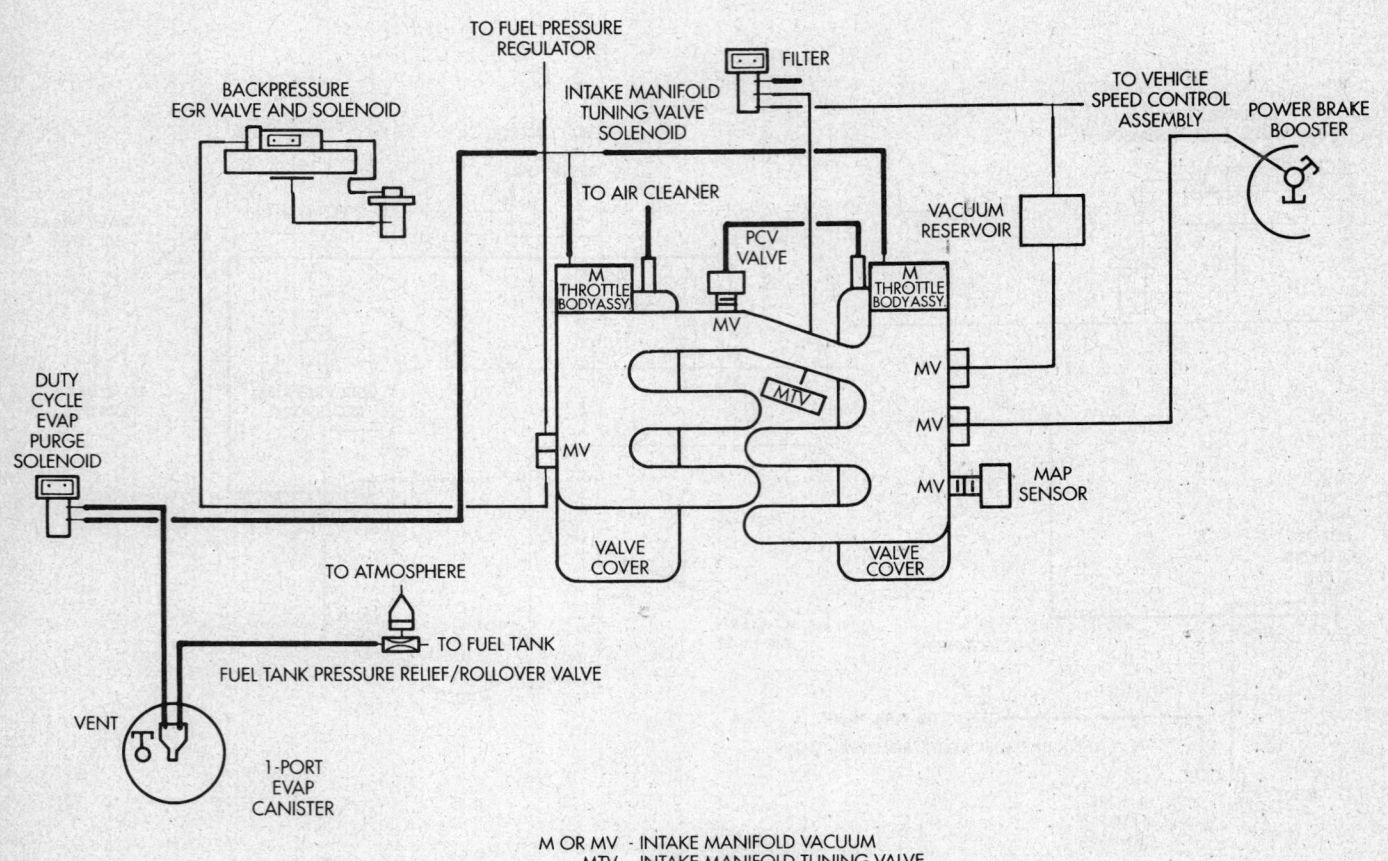

M OR MV - INTAKE MANIFOLD VACUUM
MTV - INTAKE MANIFOLD TUNING VALVE

CR1039600358000X

Fig. 15 Vacuum hose routing. Concorde Intrepid LHS New Yorker & Vision w/3.5L/V6-215 engine

ENGINE COMPARTMENT REFERENCE DIAGRAMS

INDEX

	Page No. 19-	Fig. No.		Page No. 19-	Fig. No.
Engine Compartment Diagrams:			Summit:		
Acclaim:			1993 w/1.5L/4-89.5	13	15
1993	9	12	1993 w/1.8L/4-110	16	16
1994-95	10	13	1994-95 w/1.5L/4-89.5	18	17
Breeze	12	14	1994-95 w/1.8L/4-110	20	18
Cirrus	12	14	1996 w/1.5L/4-89.5	22	19
Colt:			1996 w/1.8L/4-110	24	20
1993 w/1.5L/4-89.5	13	15	Summit Wagon:		
1993 w/1.8L/4-110	16	16	1993 w/1.8L/4-110	26	21
1994 w/1.5L/4-89.5	18	17	1993 w/2.4L/4-146	28	22
1994 w/1.8L/4-110	20	18	1994-95 w/1.8L/4-110	30	23
Colt Vista:			1994-95 w/2.4L/4-146	32	24
1993 w/1.8L/4-110	26	21	1996 w/1.8L/4-110	34	25
1993 w/2.4L/4-146	28	22	1996 w/2.4L/4-146	36	26
1994 w/1.8L/4-110	30	23	Sundance	49	34
1994 w/2.4L/4-146	32	24	Talon:		
Daytona	38	27	1993-94 w/1.8L/4-107	61	40
Dynasty:			1993-94 w/2.0L/4-122		
2.5L/4-153	41	29	Non-Turbocharged	62	41
3.0L/V6-182	43	30	1993-94 w/2.0L/4-122		
3.3L/V6-202 & 3.8L/V6-231	44	31	Turbocharged	63	42
Imperial	46	32	1995-96	64	43
Laser:			**Engine Diagrams:**		
1.8L/4-107	61	40	Breeze, Cirrus, Stratus &		
2.0L/4-122			Sebring Convertible:		
Non-Turbocharged	62	41	2.0L/4-122	2	1
2.0L/4-122 Turbocharged	63	42	2.4L/4-148	4	4
LeBaron:			2.5L/V6-152	5	7
1993 Convertible & Coupe	38	27	Concorde, Intrepid, LHS, Vision		
1993 Sedan	9	12	& 1994-96 New Yorker:		
1994-95 Convertible & Coupe	40	28	3.3L/V6-202	7	9
1994-95 Sedan	10	13	3.5L/V6-215	8	11
Neon	48	33	Neon	2	1
Shadow	49	34	2.2L/4-135:		
Spirit:			Non-Turbocharged	3	2
1993	9	12	Turbocharged	3	3
1994-95	10	13	2.5L/4-153:		
Stealth:			Non-Turbocharged	3	2
1993-95 w/DOHC &			Turbocharged, Left View	4	5
California Emissions	51	35	Turbocharged, Right View	5	6
1993-95 w/DOHC & Federal			3.0L/V6-182	6	8
Emissions	53	36	3.3L/V6-202 & 3.8L/V6-231		
1993-95 w/SOHC	55	37	Except Concorde, Intrepid,		
1996 w/DOHC	57	38	LHS, Vision & 1994-96 New		
1996 w/SOHC	59	39	Yorker	7	10
Stratus	12	14			

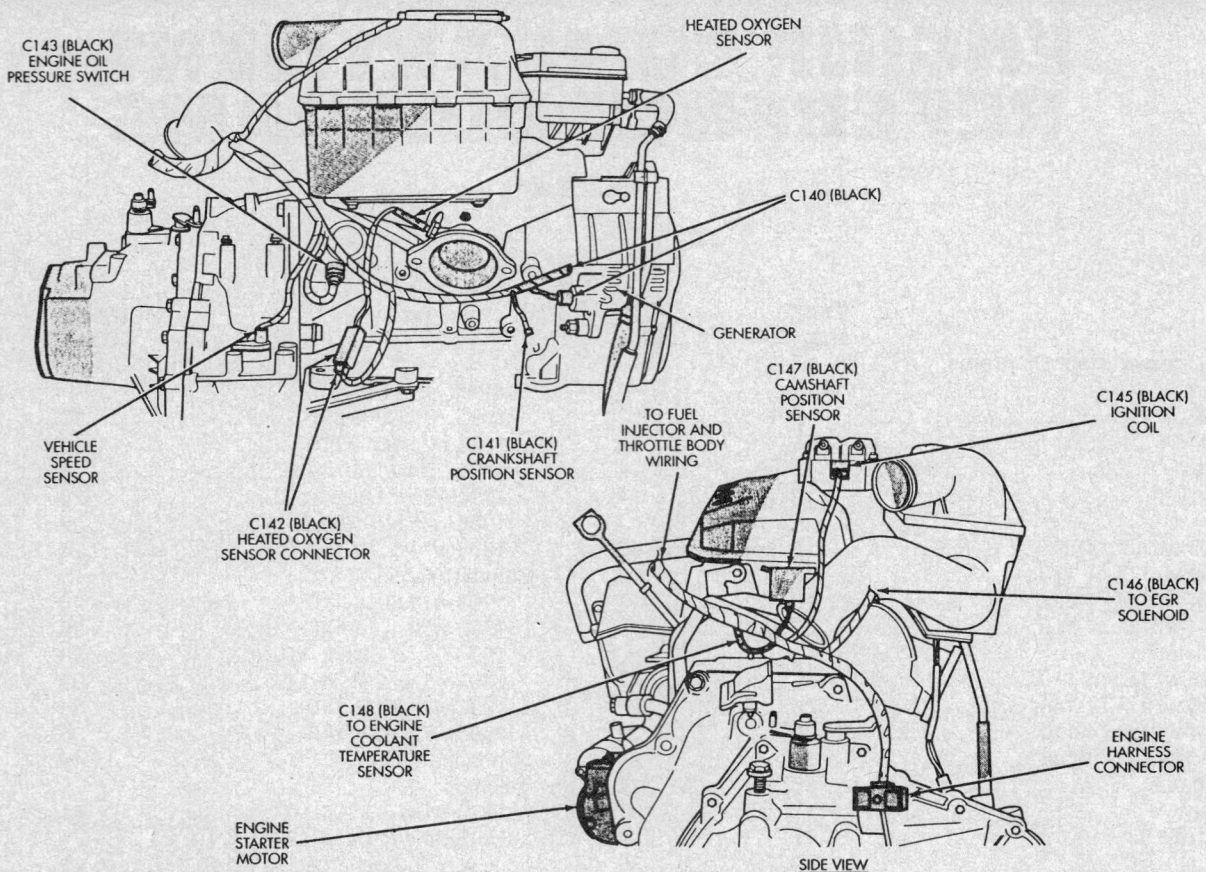

Fig. 1   Engine diagram (Part 1 of 2). Cirrus, Neon & Stratus w/2.0L/4-122 engine

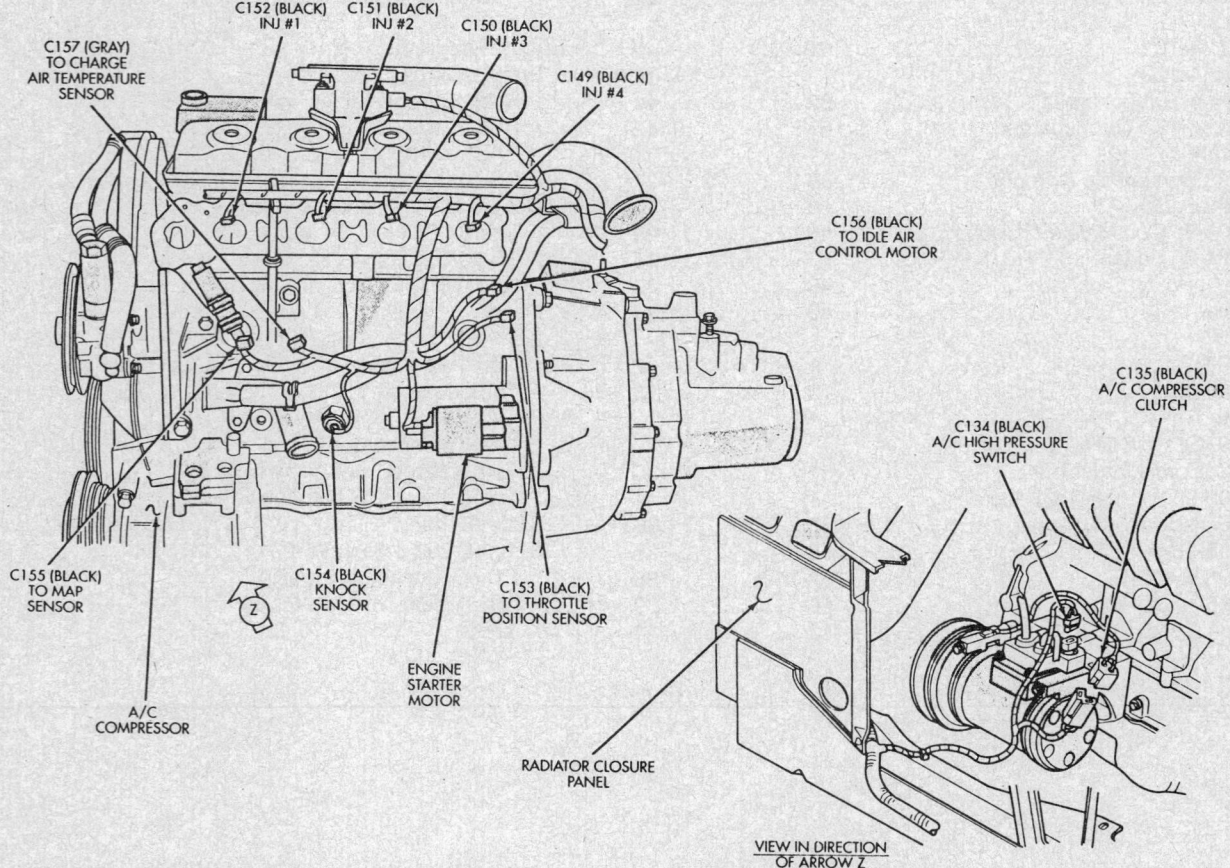

Fig. 1   Engine diagram (Part 2 of 2). Cirrus, Neon & Stratus w/2.0L/4-122 engine

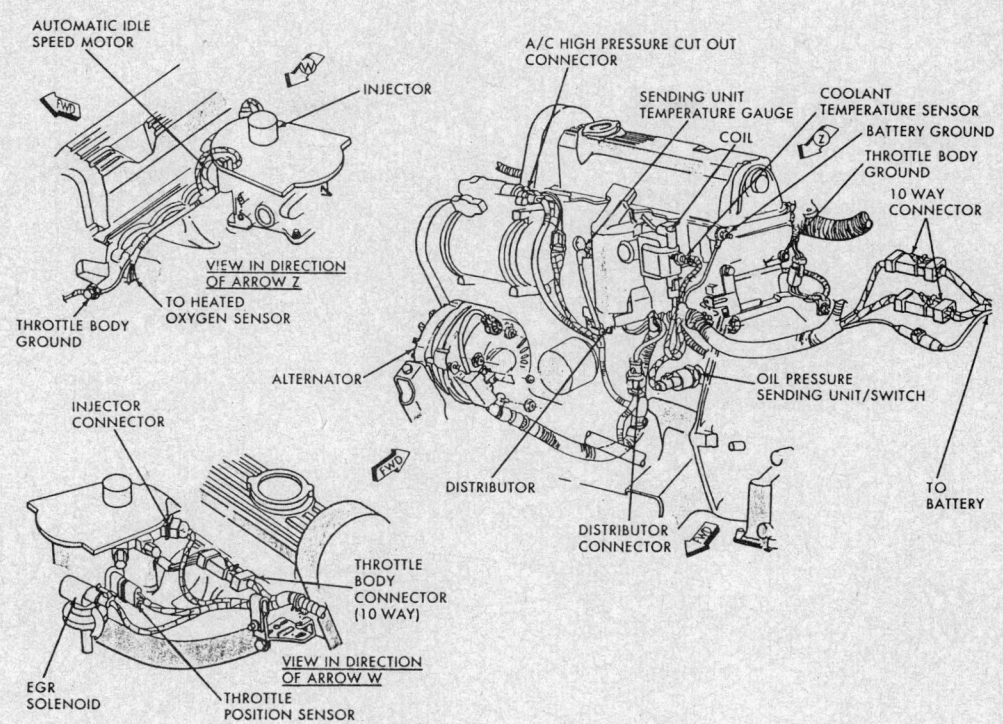

Fig. 2   Engine diagram. 2.2L/4-135
& 2.5L/4-153, non-turbocharged

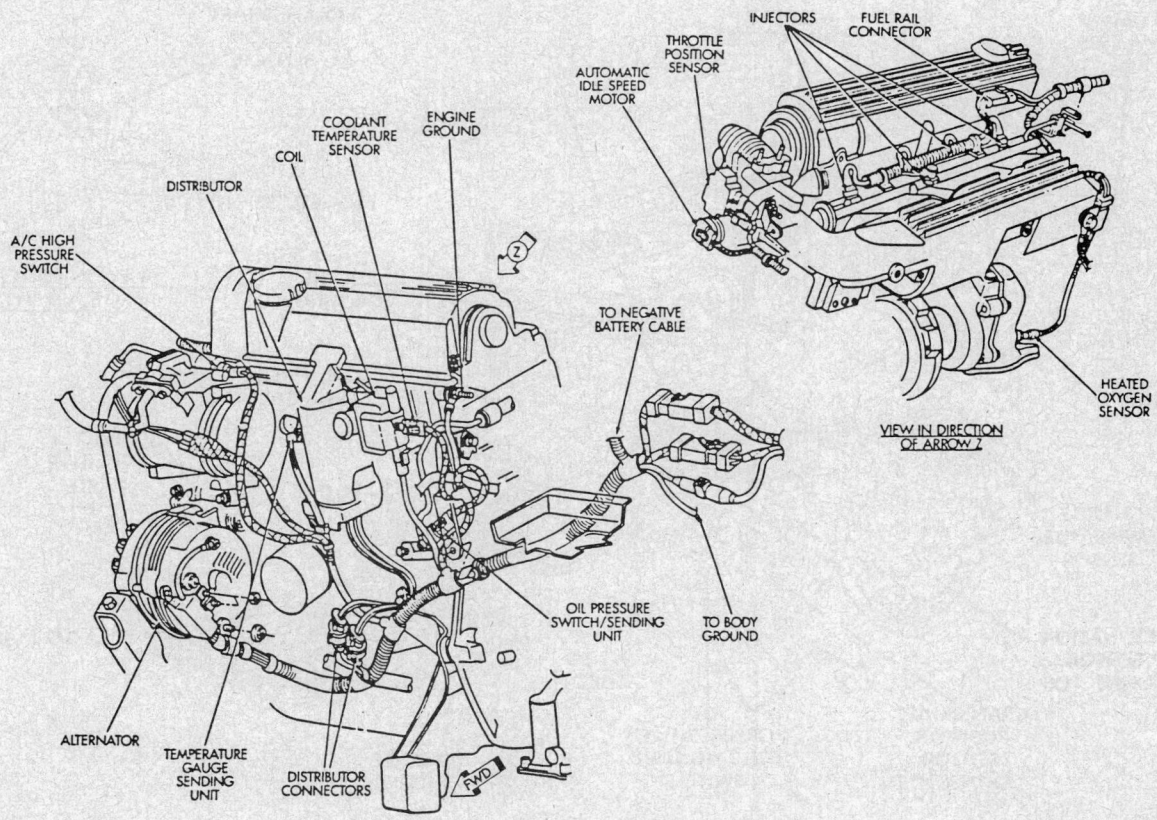

Fig. 3   Engine diagram. 1993
w/2.2L/4-135 turbocharged

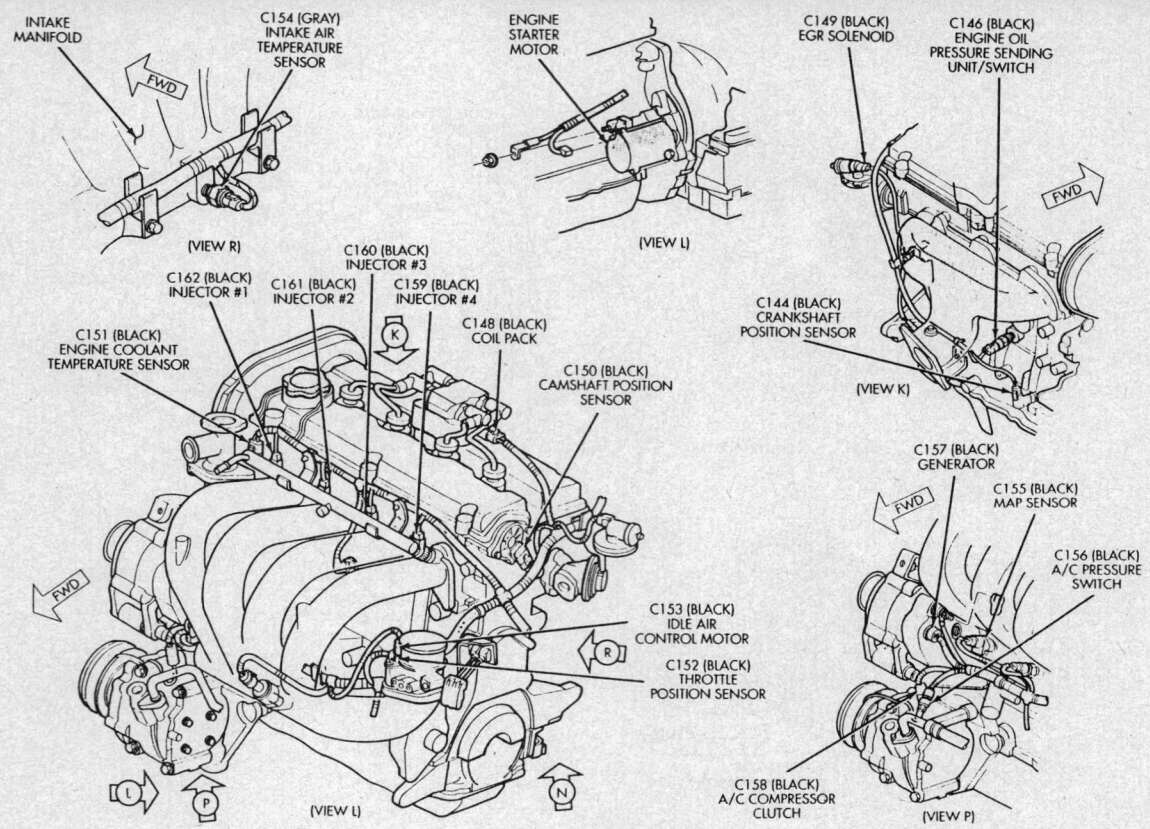

Fig. 4   Engine diagram. Cirrus,
Stratus & Sebring Convertible
w/2.4L/4-148

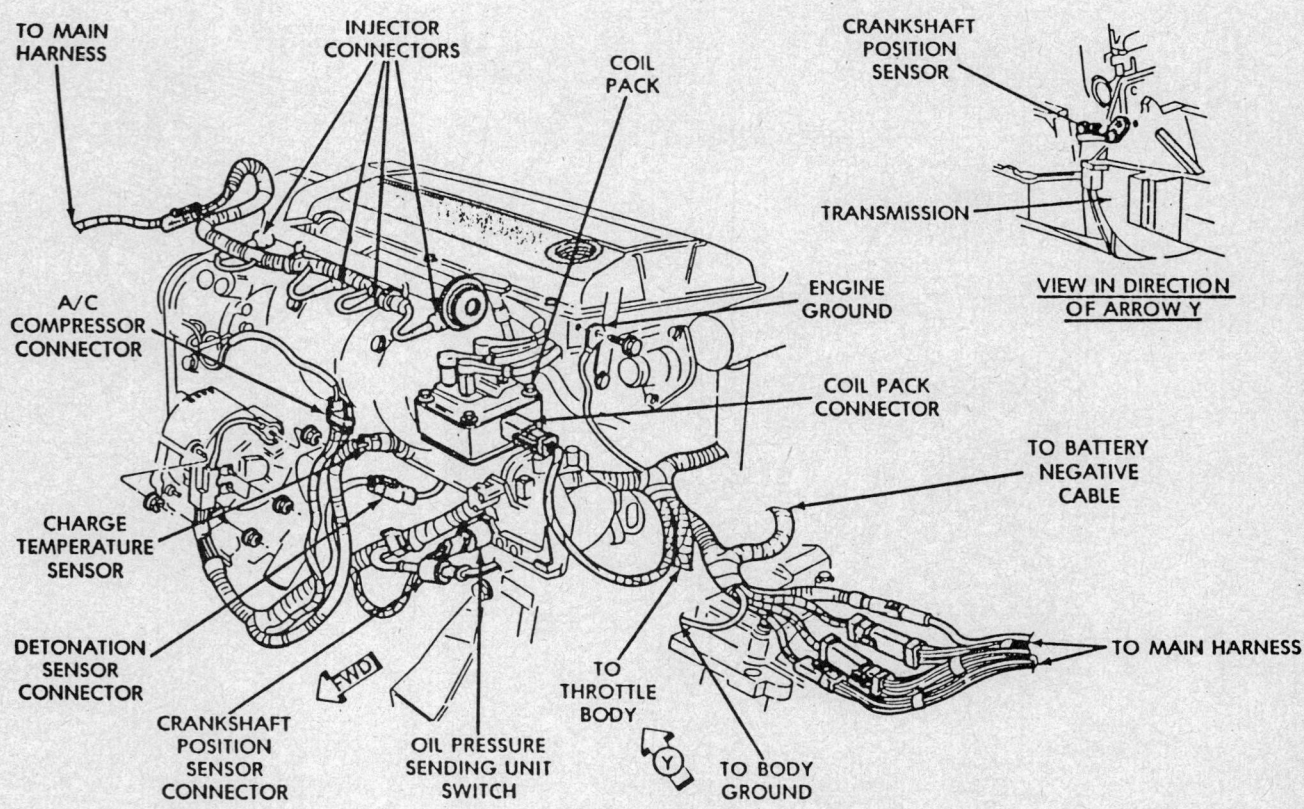

Fig. 5   Engine diagram. 2.5L/4-153
turbocharged, left view

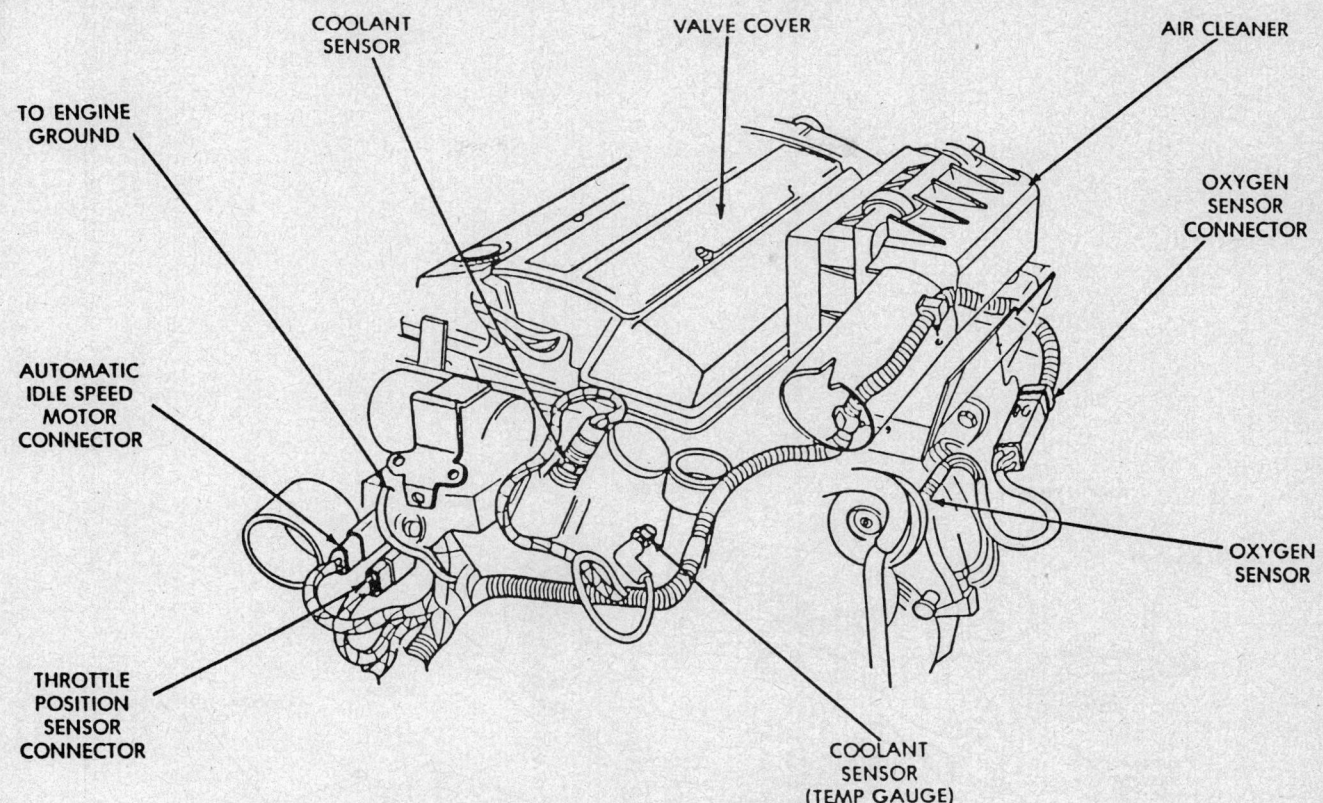

COOLANT SENSOR

VALVE COVER

AIR CLEANER

TO ENGINE GROUND

OXYGEN SENSOR CONNECTOR

AUTOMATIC IDLE SPEED MOTOR CONNECTOR

OXYGEN SENSOR

THROTTLE POSITION SENSOR CONNECTOR

COOLANT SENSOR (TEMP GAUGE)

Fig. 6   Engine diagram. 2.5L/4-153
turbocharged, right view

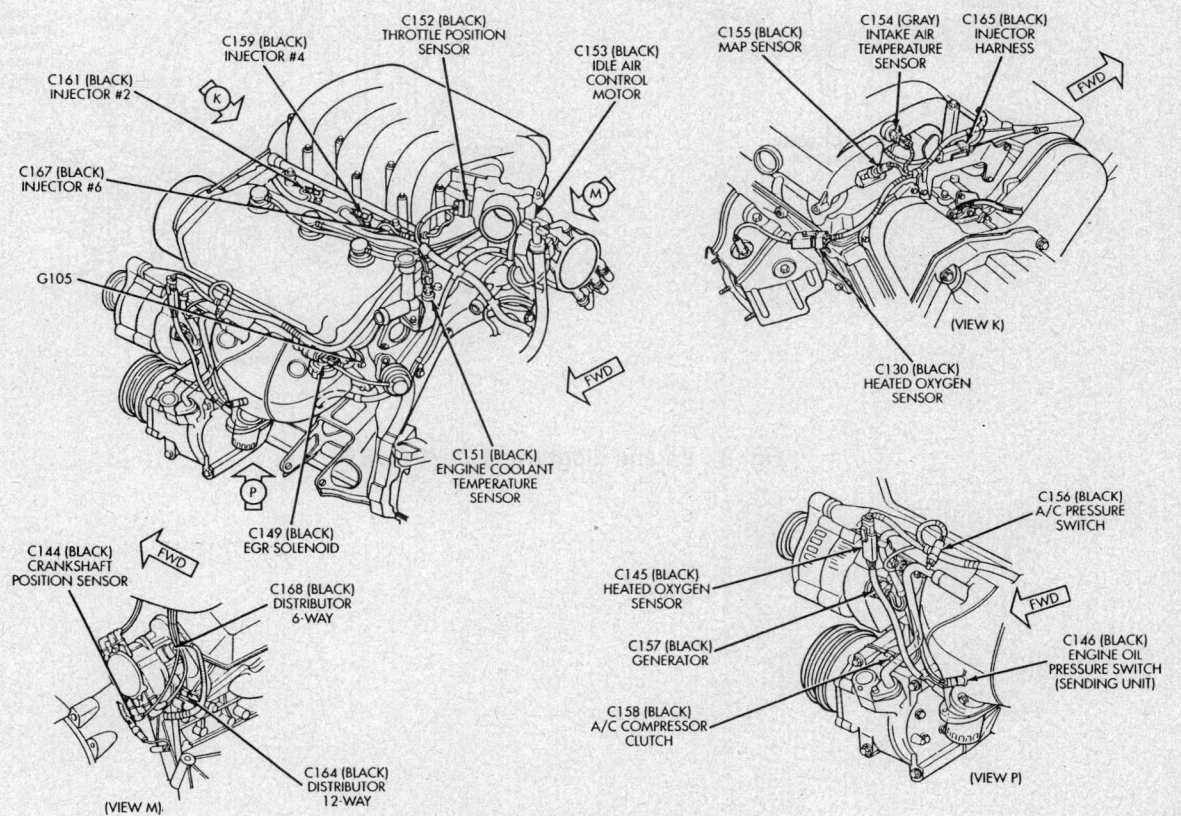

C159 (BLACK) INJECTOR #4

C152 (BLACK) THROTTLE POSITION SENSOR

C153 (BLACK) IDLE AIR CONTROL MOTOR

C155 (BLACK) MAP SENSOR

C154 (GRAY) INTAKE AIR TEMPERATURE SENSOR

C165 (BLACK) INJECTOR HARNESS

C161 (BLACK) INJECTOR #2

C167 (BLACK) INJECTOR #6

G105

C151 (BLACK) ENGINE COOLANT TEMPERATURE SENSOR

C149 (BLACK) EGR SOLENOID

C130 (BLACK) HEATED OXYGEN SENSOR

(VIEW K)

C144 (BLACK) CRANKSHAFT POSITION SENSOR

C168 (BLACK) DISTRIBUTOR 6-WAY

C164 (BLACK) DISTRIBUTOR 12-WAY

(VIEW M)

C145 (BLACK) HEATED OXYGEN SENSOR

C157 (BLACK) GENERATOR

C158 (BLACK) A/C COMPRESSOR CLUTCH

C156 (BLACK) A/C PRESSURE SWITCH

C146 (BLACK) ENGINE OIL PRESSURE SWITCH (SENDING UNIT)

(VIEW P)

Fig. 7   Engine diagram. Cirrus,
Stratus & Sebring Convertible
w/2.5L/V6-152

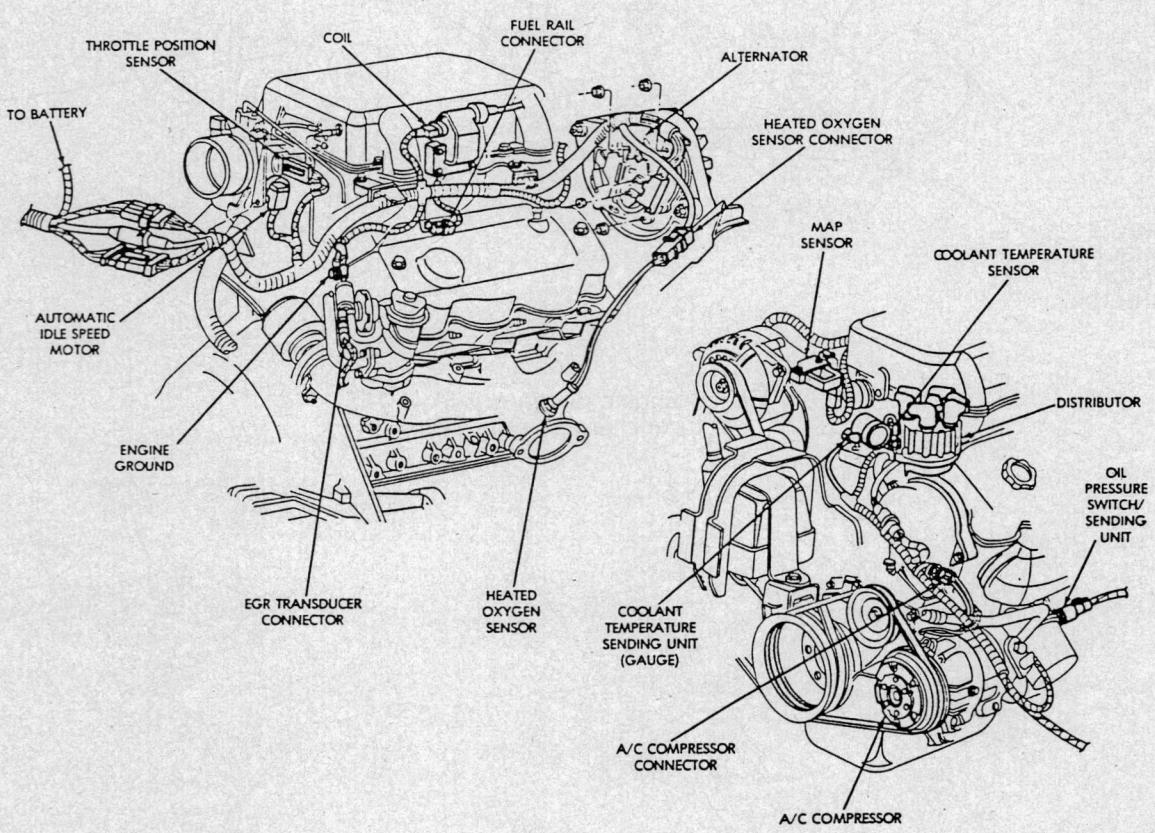

Fig. 8   Engine diagram. 3.0L/V6-182

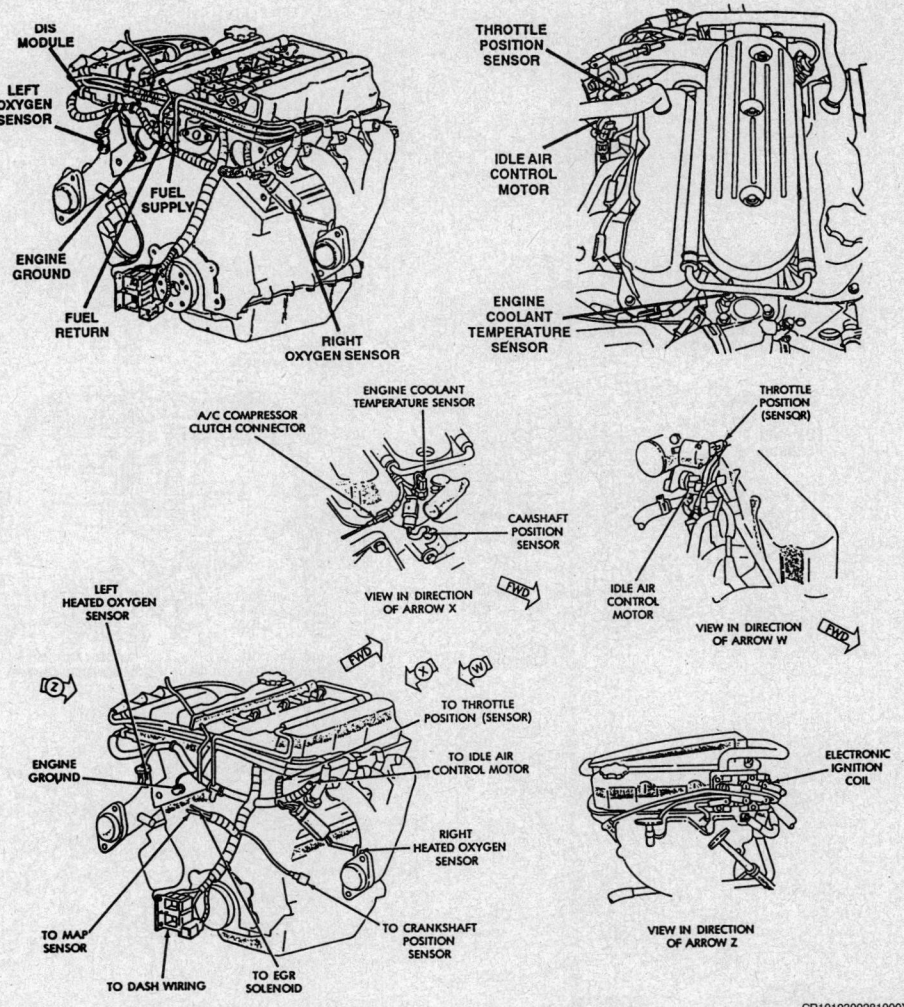

Fig. 9   Engine diagram. Concorde, Intrepid, LHS, Vision & 1994–96 New Yorker w/3.3L/V6-202

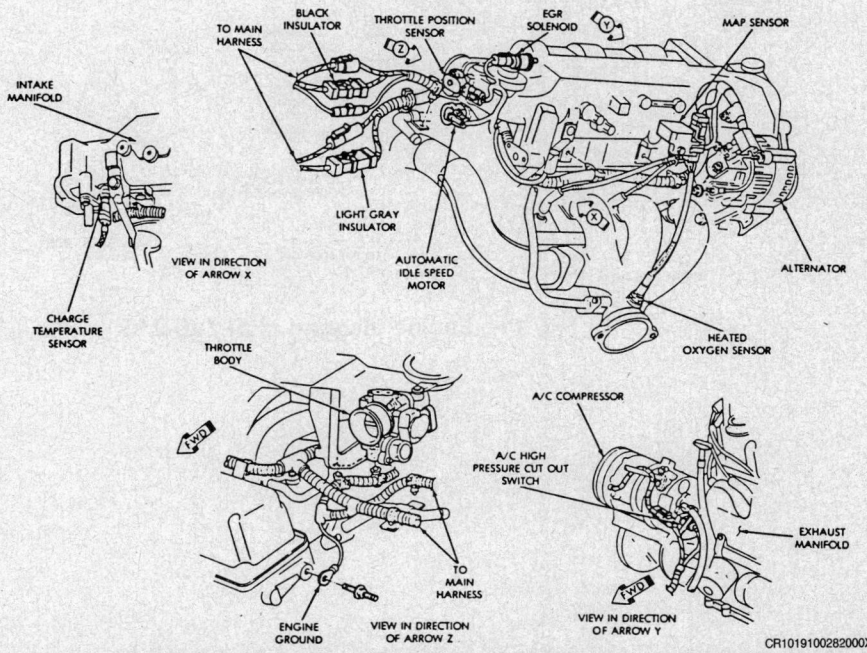

Fig. 10   Engine diagram. 3.3L/V6-202 & 3.8L/V6-231, except Concorde, Intrepid, LHS, Vision & 1994–96 New Yorker

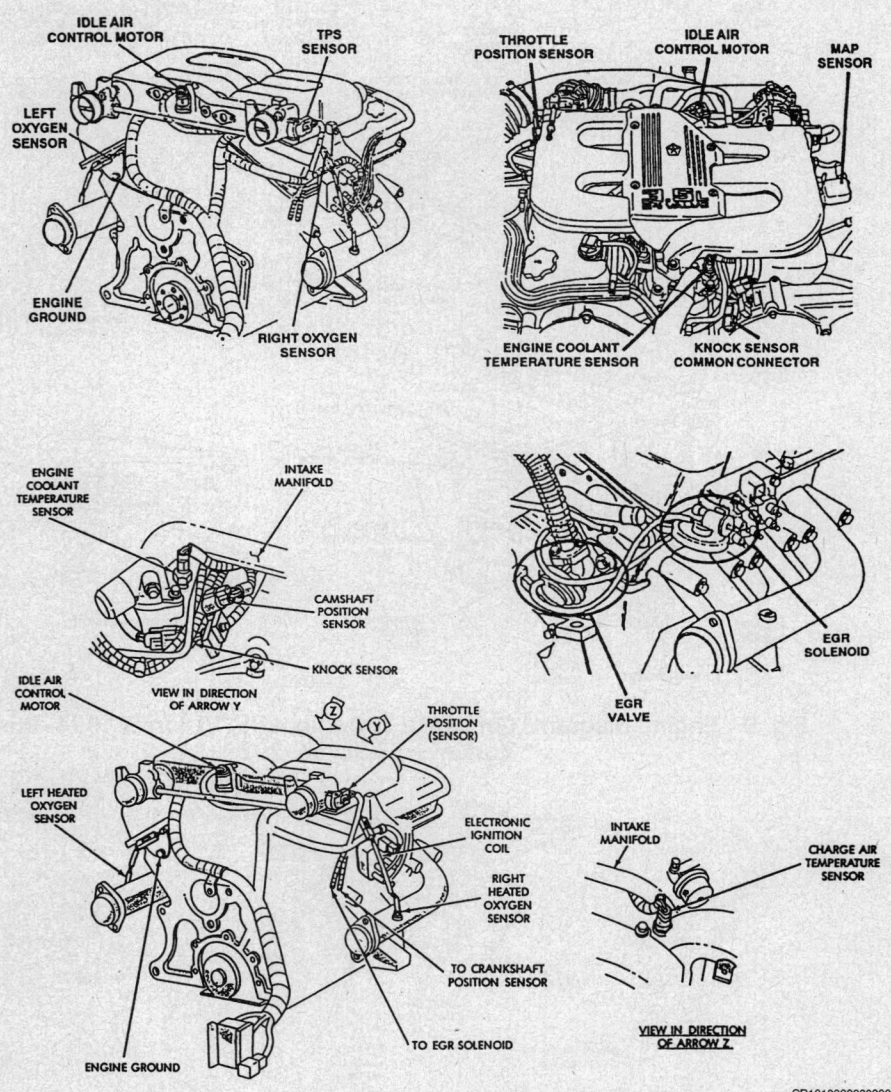

Fig. 11   Engine diagram. 3.5L/V6-215

CR1019300283000X

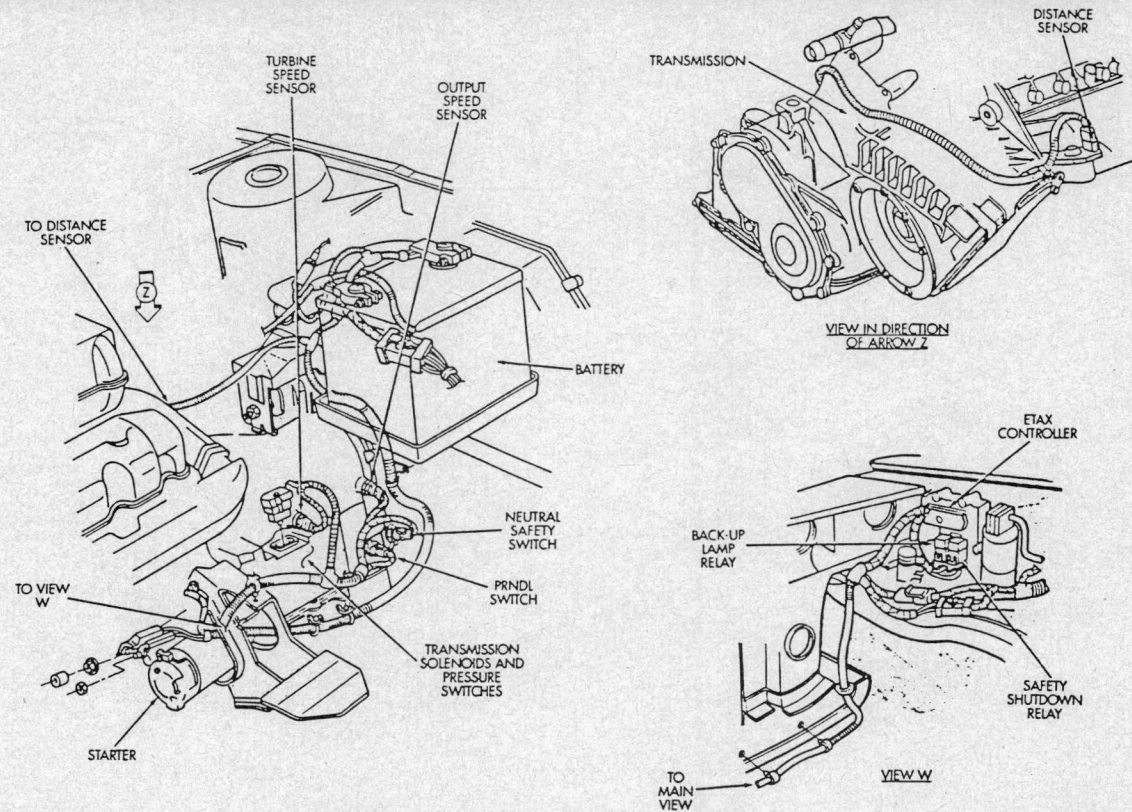

Fig. 12 Engine compartment diagram (Part 1 of 3). 1993 Acclaim, LeBaron Sedan & Spirit

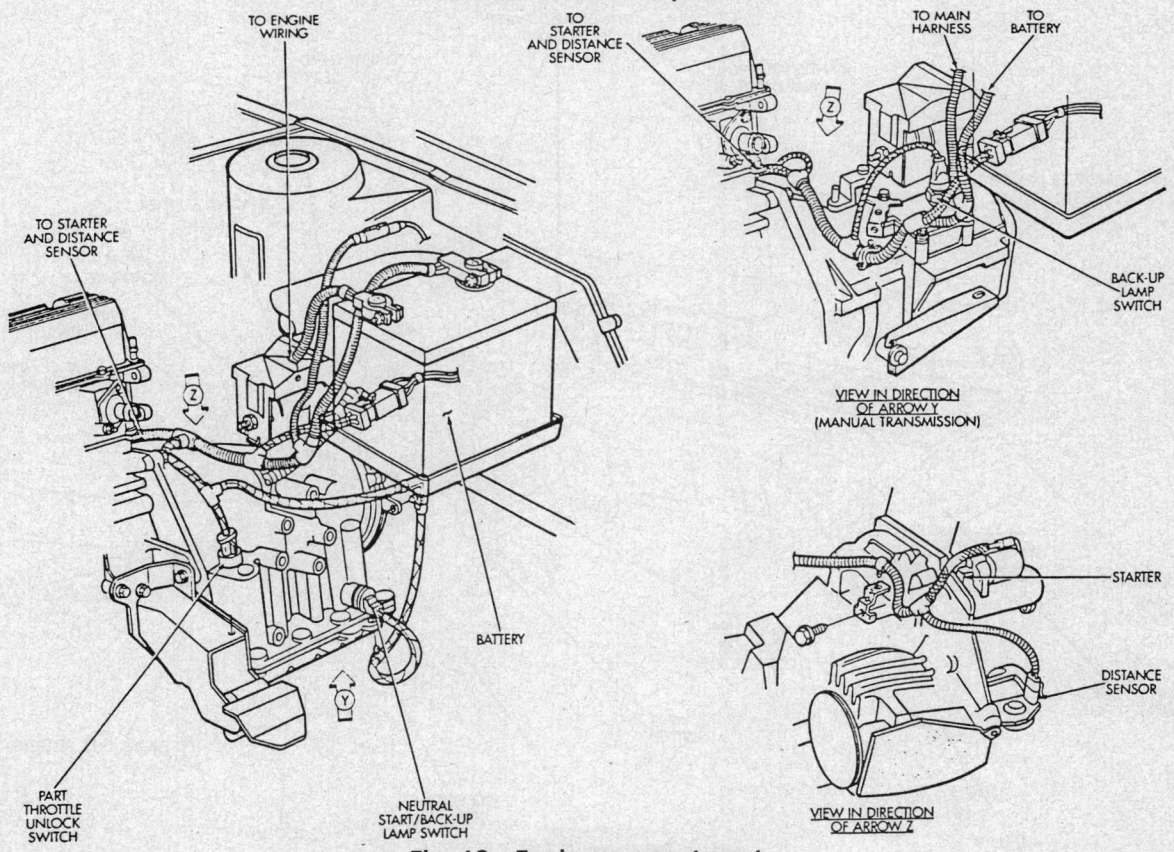

Fig. 12 Engine compartment diagram (Part 2 of 3). 1993 Acclaim, LeBaron Sedan & Spirit

A/C HEATER RESISTOR BLOCK
WINDSHIELD WIPER MOTOR
TO THROTTLE BODY WIRING
SPEED CONTROL SERVO
LOW WASHER FLUID SENSOR
FUEL SHUT-DOWN RELAY
TO UNDERHOOD LAMP
STARTER RELAY
ANTI-LOCK PUMP MOTOR RELAY
RADIATOR FAN RELAY
IGNITION OFF DRAW CONNECTOR
A/C CLUTCH RELAY
RIGHT FRONT WHEEL SENSOR CONNECTOR (ABS)
LEFT FRONT WHEEL SENSOR CONNECTOR (ABS)
BRAKE WARNING SWITCH
TO BATTERY
RELAY FUEL PUMP
WASTEGATE SOLENOID (TURBO)
TO ENGINE WIRING
TO ENGINE CONTROLLER
MAP SENSOR
GROUND
DIAGNOSTIC CONNECTOR
BARO READ SOLENOID (2.5 EFI/TURBO)
BEYOND THIS POINT SEE VIEW X
A/C LOW PRESSURE SWITCH
ENGINE CONTROLLER
TO LEFT SIDE MARKER LAMP
TO LEFT HEADLAMP
PURGE SOLENOID (EFI/TURBO)
MAP SENSOR (TURBO III ONLY)
RADIATOR FAN MOTOR
FWD
TO RIGHT HEADLAMP
WIRING THROUGH
TO ENGINE WIRING
BARO/READ SOLENOID (TURBO III ONLY)
GROUND
BEYOND THIS POINT SEE VIEW W
AIRBAG SENSOR
PURGE SOLENOID (3.0L ONLY)
AIRBAG SENSOR
VIEW IN DIRECTION OF ARROW Z
ABS SYSTEM RELAY
ABS WARNING LAMP SWITCH
TO FRONT END LIGHTING
ABS HYDRAULIC ASSEMBLY
ABS CONTROL MODULE
ABS WARNING LAMP RELAY
VIEW W RIGHT SIDE ROUTING
VIEW X (LEFT SIDE ROUTING)

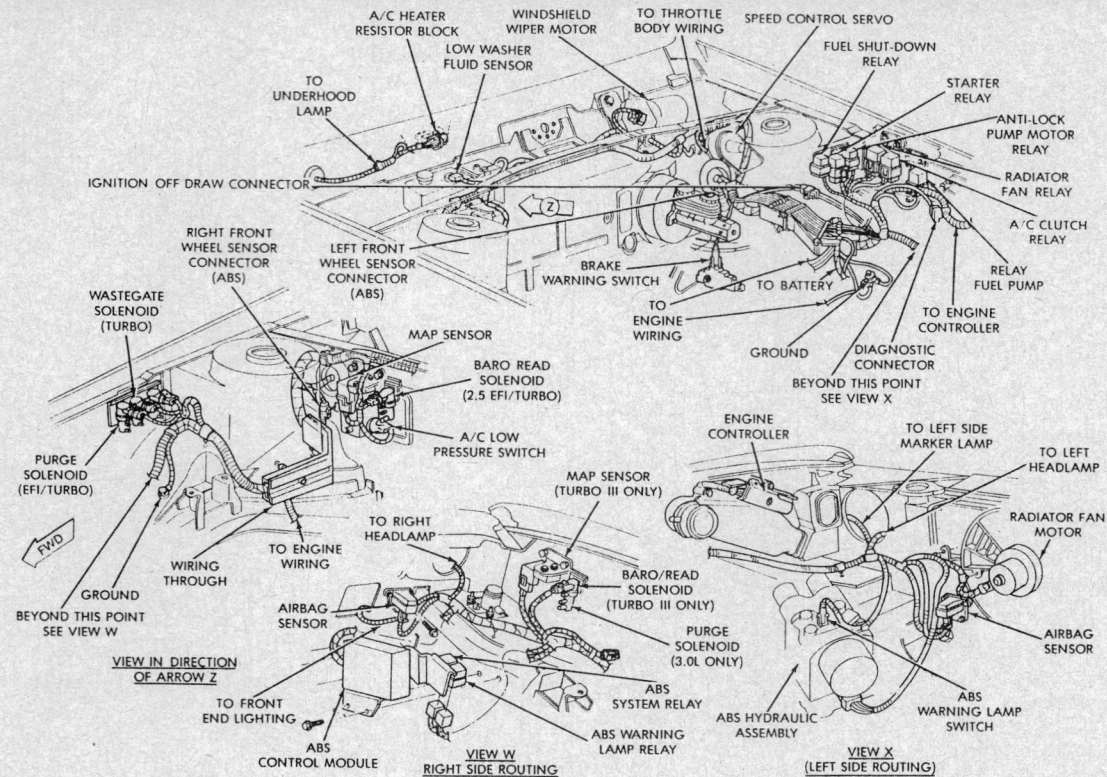

Fig. 12 Engine compartment diagram (Part 3 of 3). 1993 Acclaim, LeBaron Sedan & Spirit

WINDSHIELD WIPER MOTOR
WINDSHIELD WASHER PUMP MOTOR
VEHICLE SPEED CONTROL SERVO
FUEL SHUTDOWN RELAY
BLOWER MOTOR RESISTOR BLOCK
ENGINE STARTER RELAY
ABS PUMP MOTOR RELAY
FAN CONTROL RELAY
A/C COMPRESSOR CLUTCH RELAY
FUEL PUMP RELAY
TO P.C.M.
UNDERHOOD LAMP CONNECTOR
DATA LINK CONNECTOR
ABS WHEEL SENSOR CONNECTOR
TO BATTERY
LOW WASHER FLUID SWITCH
BRAKE WARNING SWITCH
TO FRONT END LIGHTING
TO ENGINE WIRING
A/C LOW PRESSURE SWITCH
IGNITION-OFF DRAW CONNECTOR
GROUND
CR1019400105010X

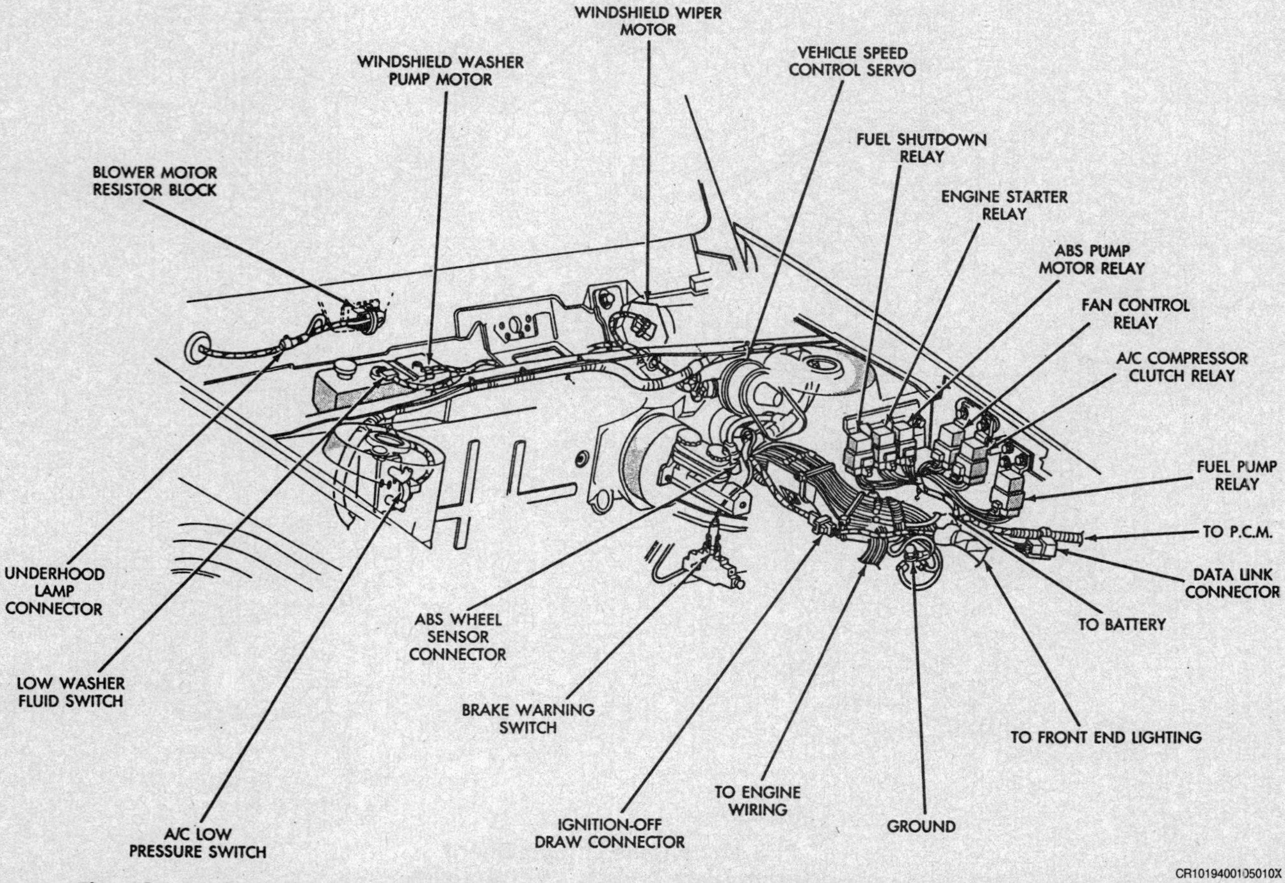

Fig. 13 Engine compartment diagram (Part 1 of 4). 1994–95 Acclaim, LeBaron Sedan & Spirit

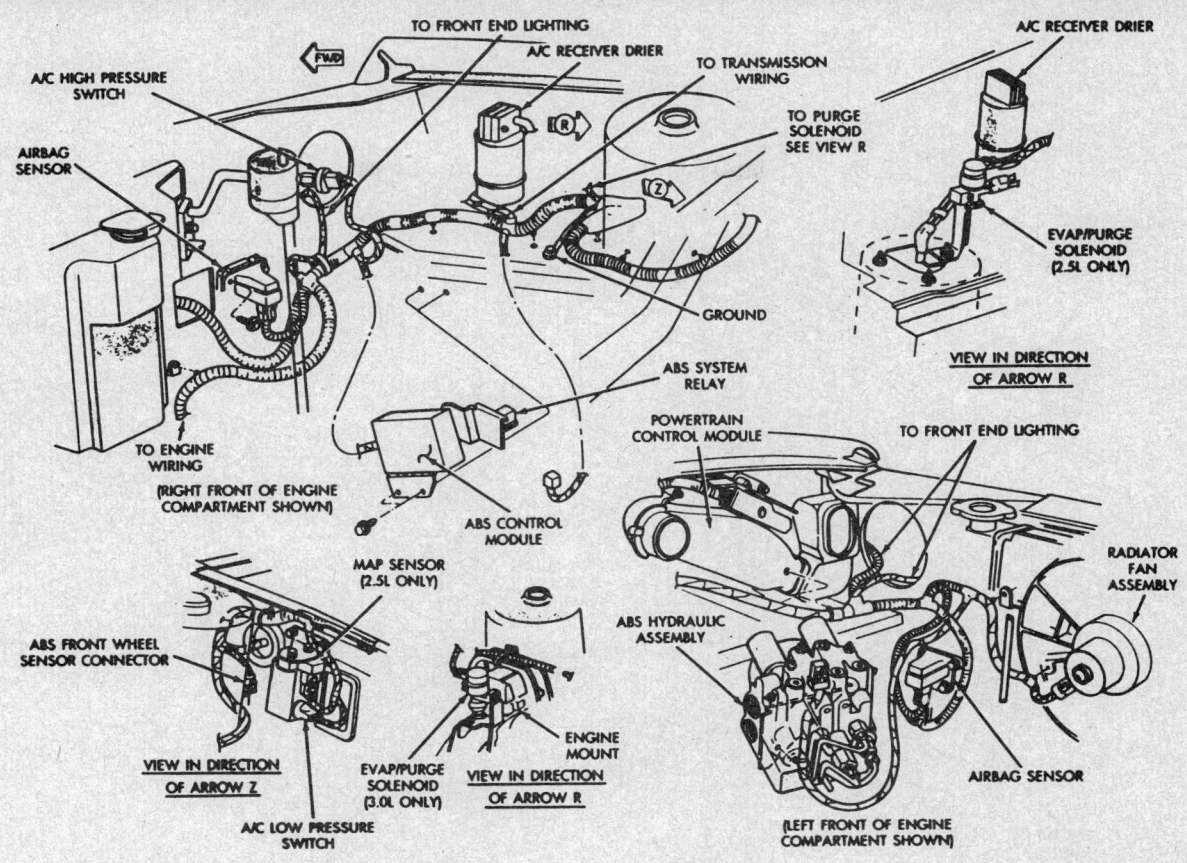

Fig. 13   Engine compartment diagram (Part 2 of 4). 1994–95 Acclaim, LeBaron Sedan & Spirit

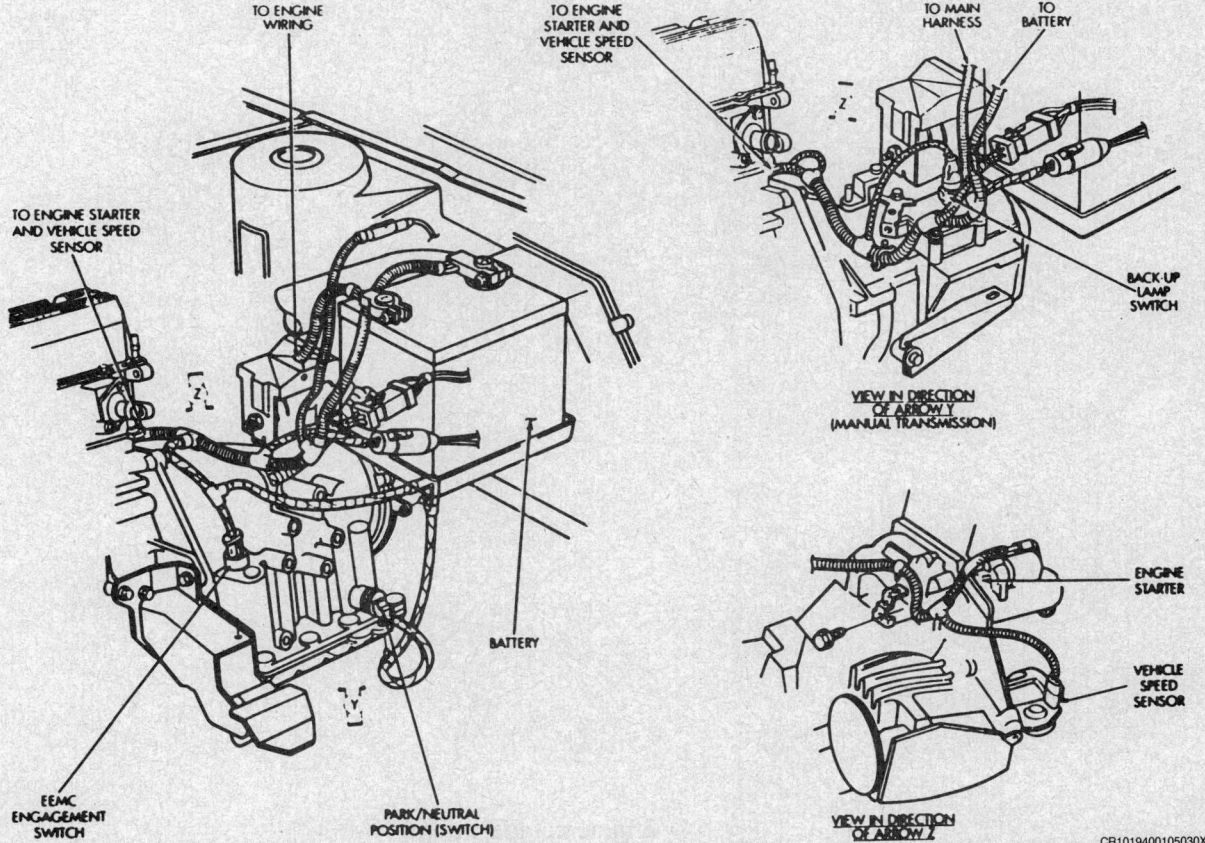

Fig. 13   Engine compartment diagram (Part 3 of 4). 1994–95 Acclaim, LeBaron Sedan & Spirit

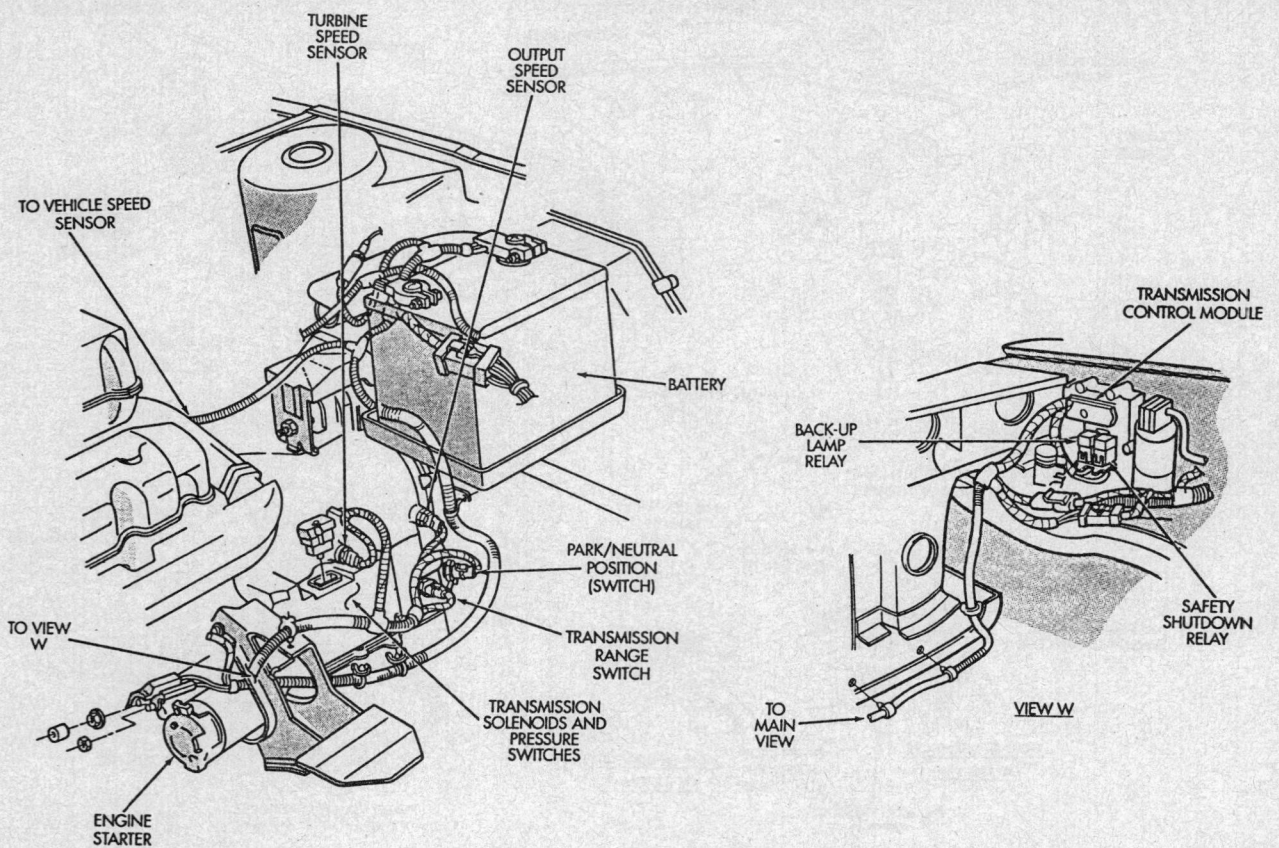

Fig. 13 Engine compartment diagram (Part 4 of 4). 1994–95 Acclaim, LeBaron Sedan & Spirit

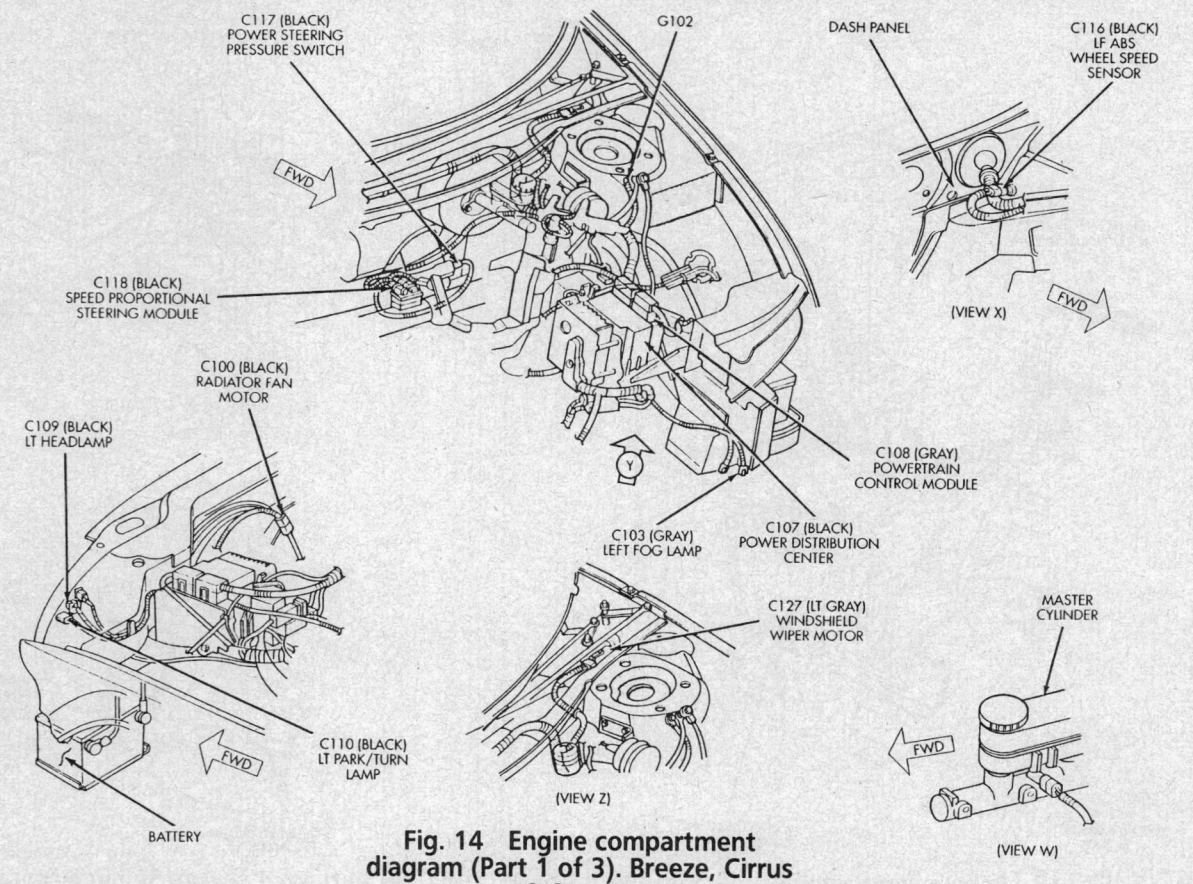

Fig. 14 Engine compartment diagram (Part 1 of 3). Breeze, Cirrus & Stratus

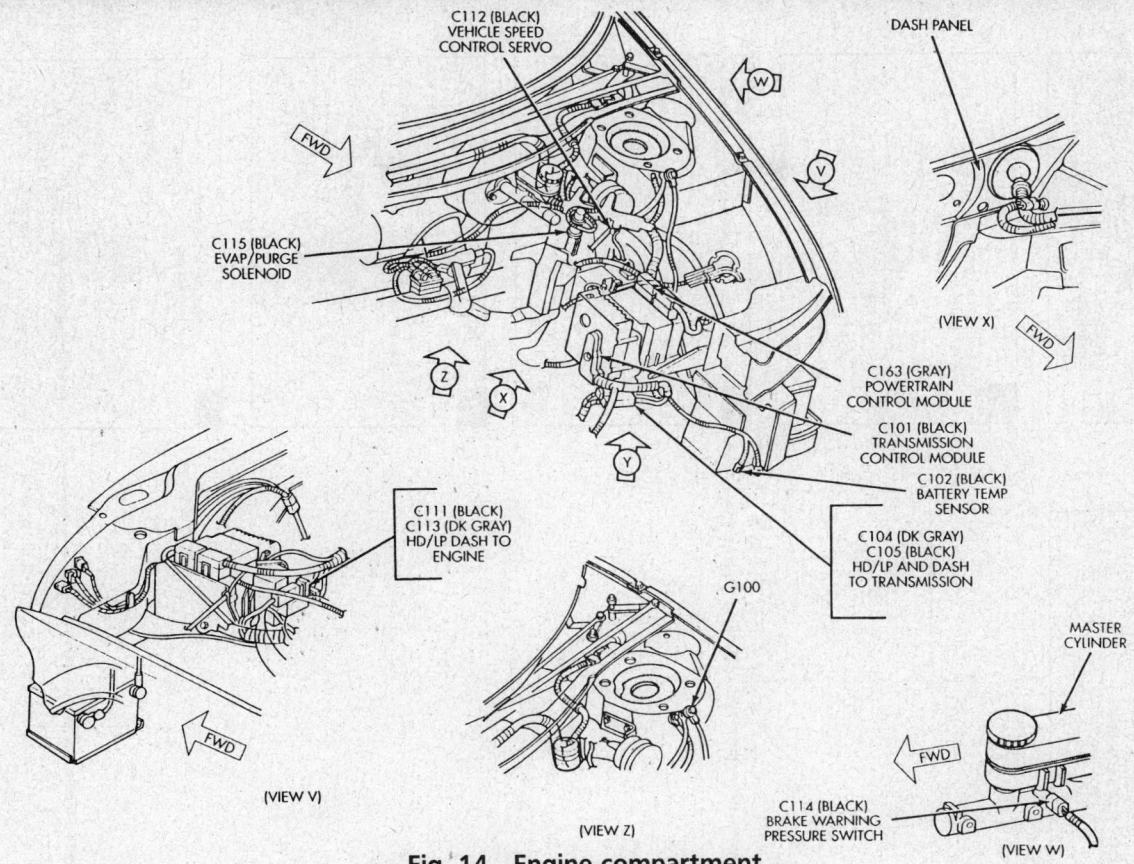

Fig. 14 Engine compartment
diagram (Part 2 of 3). Breeze, Cirrus
& Stratus

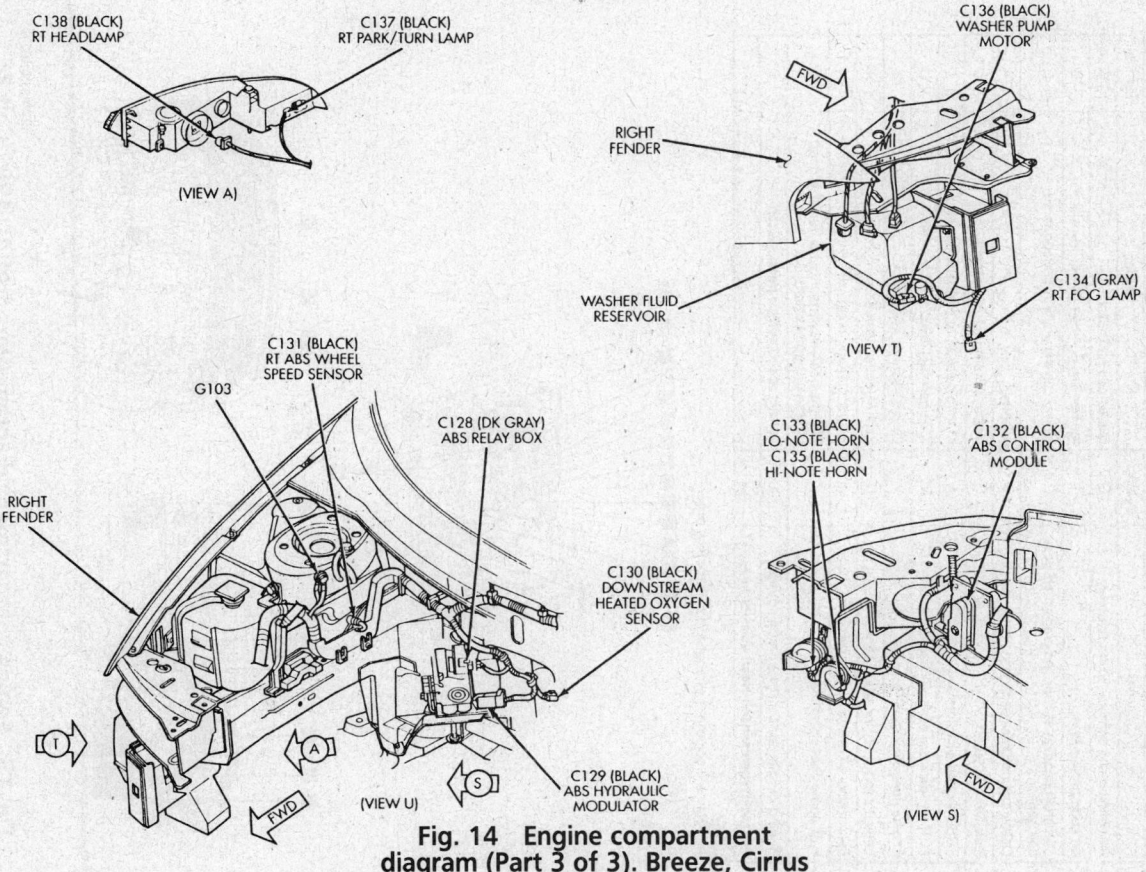

Fig. 14 Engine compartment
diagram (Part 3 of 3). Breeze, Cirrus
& Stratus

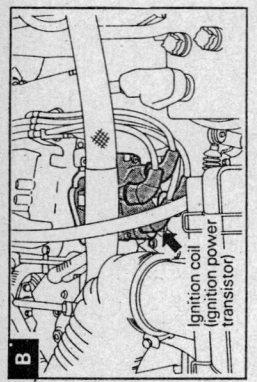

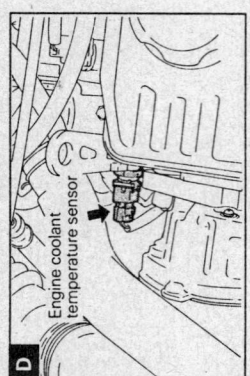

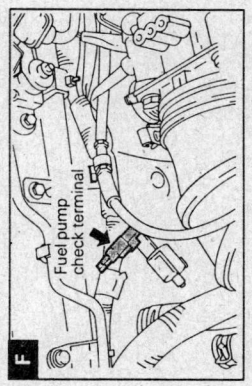

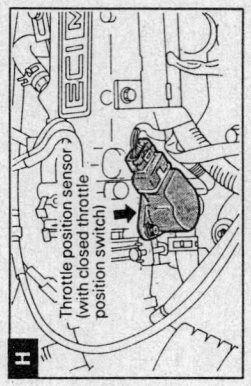

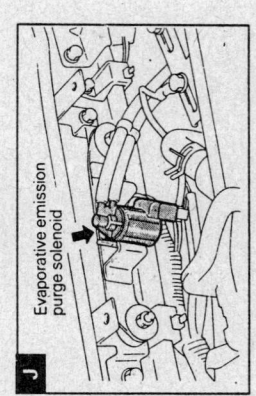

B — Ignition coil (ignition power transistor)

D — Engine coolant temperature sensor

F — Fuel pump check terminal

H — Throttle position sensor (with closed throttle position switch)

J — Evaporative emission purge solenoid

CR1019300109020X

Fig. 15 Engine compartment diagram (Part 2 of 4). 1993 Colt & Summit w/1.5L/4-89.5

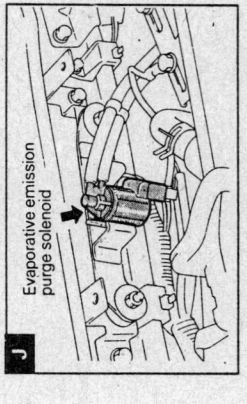

A — Park/Neutral position switch

Name	Symbol
Air conditioning compressor clutch relay	O
Air conditioning switch	T
Camshaft position sensor and crankshaft position sensor	C
Check engine / Malfunction indicator lamp	R
Data link connector	Q
EGR solenoid <California>	K
EGR temperature sensor <California>	M
Engine control module	V
Engine coolant temperature sensor	D
Evaporative emission purge solenoid	J
Fuel pump check terminal	F
Heated oxygen sensor (Front) <California>	X
Heated oxygen sensor (Rear) <California>	W
Idle air control motor	G
Ignition coil (ignition power transistor)	B
Ignition timing adjustment connector	E
Injector	P
Intake air temperature sensor	L
Manifold absolute pressure sensor	I
Multiport fuel injection (MFI) relay	U
Oxygen sensor <Federal>	Y
Park / Neutral position switch	A
Power steering pressure switch	N
Throttle position sensor (with built-in closed throttle position switch)	H
Vehicle speed sensor (reed switch)	S
	—

NOTE
The " Name " column is arranged in alphabetical order.

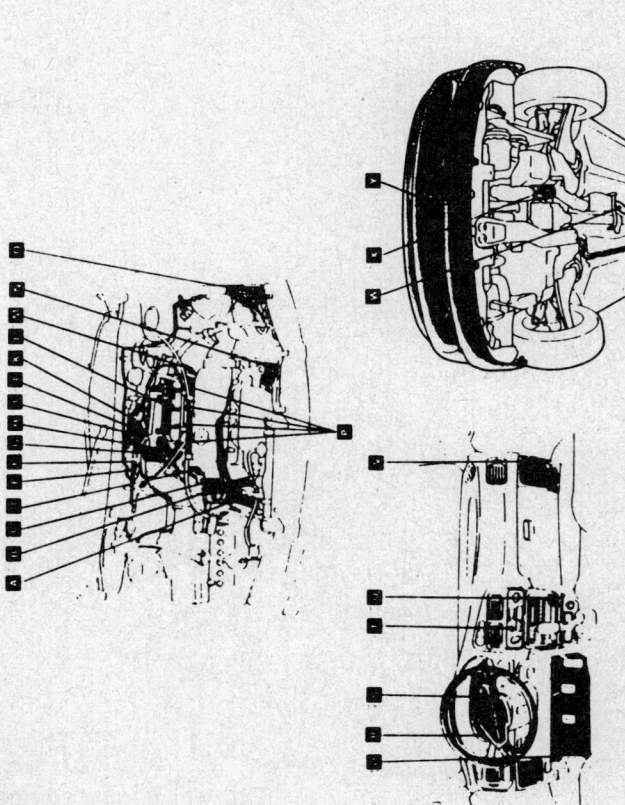

CR1019300109010X

Fig. 15 Engine compartment diagram (Part 1 of 4). 1993 Colt & Summit w/1.5L/4-89.5

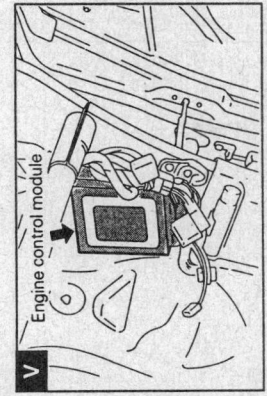

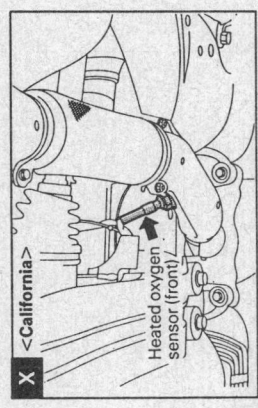

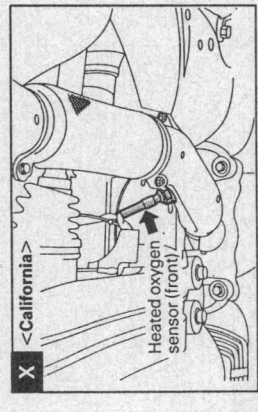

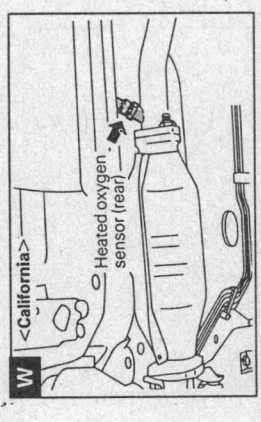

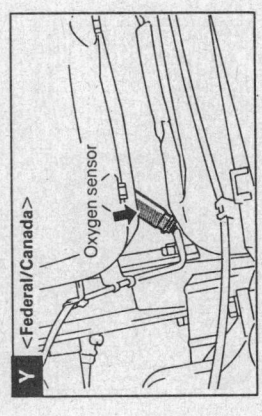

Fig. 15 Engine compartment diagram (Part 4 of 4). 1993 Colt & Summit w/1.5L/4-89.5

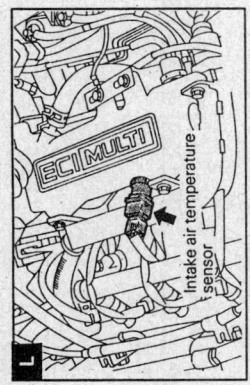

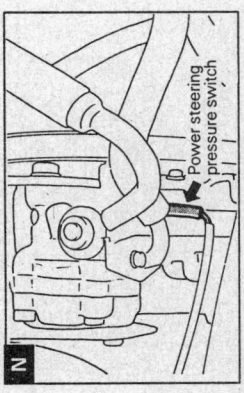

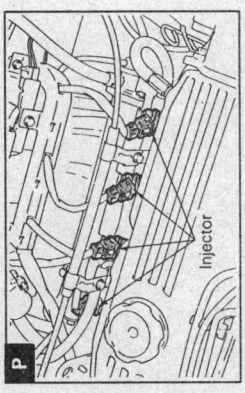

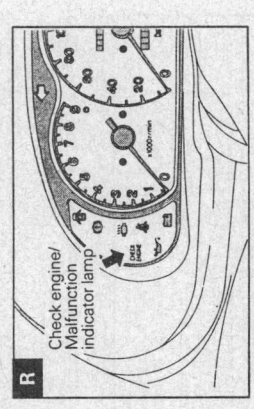

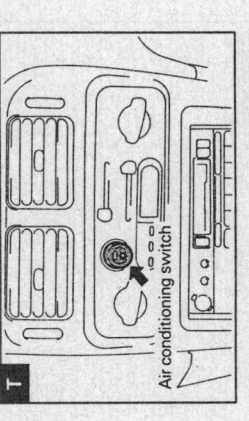

Fig. 15 Engine compartment diagram (Part 3 of 4). 1993 Colt & Summit w/1.5L/4-89.5

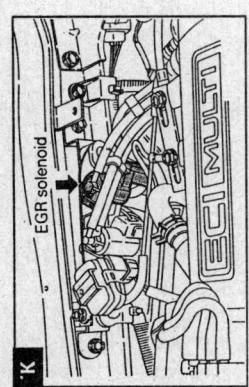

CR101930011002OX

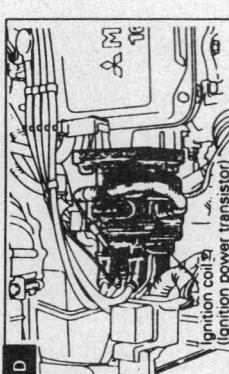

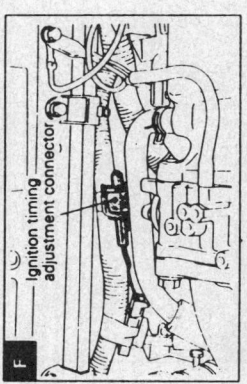

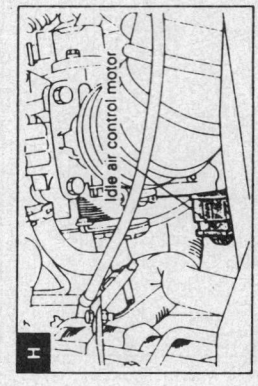

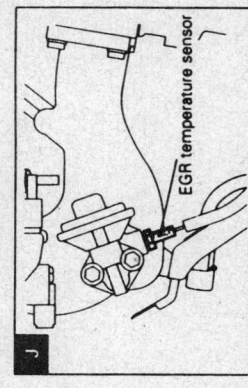

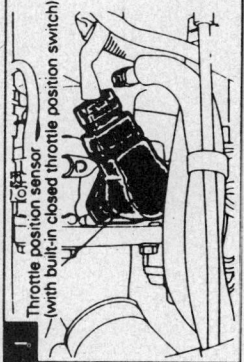

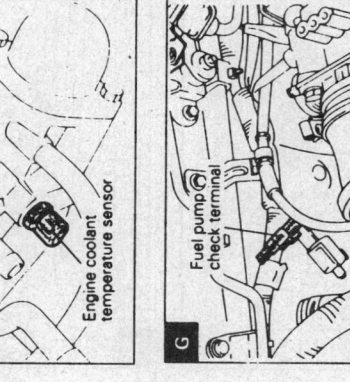

Fig. 16   Engine compartment diagram (Part 2 of 4). 1993 Colt & Summit w/1.8L/4-110

Name	Symbol
Air conditioning compressor clutch relay	V
Air conditioning switch	H
Camshaft position sensor and crankshaft position sensor	D
Check engine / Malfunction indicator lamp	F
Data link connector	M
EGR solenoid <California>	T
EGR temperature sensor <California>	X
Engine control module	A
Engine coolant temperature sensor	N
Evaporative emission purge solenoid	I
Fuel pump check terminal	R
Heated oxygen sensor (Front) <California>	B
Heated oxygen sensor (Rear) <California>	O
Idle air control motor	S
Ignition coil (ignition power transistor)	C
Ignition timing adjustment connector	Q
Injector	P
Multiport fuel injection (MFI) relay	K
Oxygen sensor <Federal>	J
Park / Neutral position switch	U
Power steering pressure switch	E
Throttle position sensor (with built-in closed throttle position switch)	L
Vehicle speed sensor (reed switch)	G
Volume air flow sensor (with built-in intake air temperature sensor and barometric pressure sensor)	W

NOTE:
The "Name" column is arranged in alphabetical order.

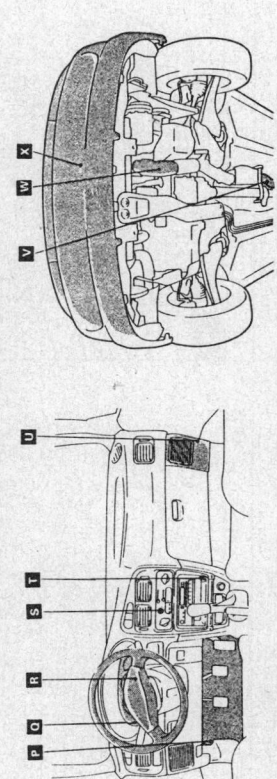

CR101930011001OX

Fig. 16   Engine compartment diagram (Part 1 of 4). 1993 Colt & Summit w/1.8L/4-110

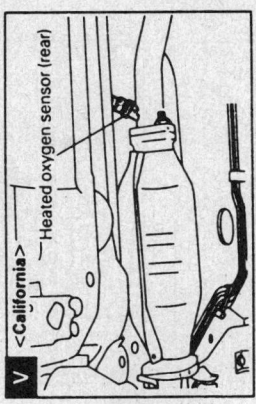

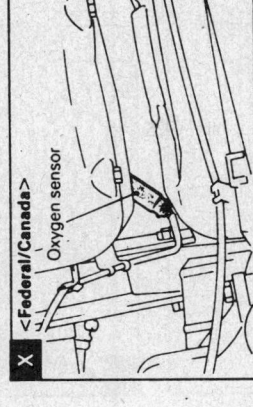

CR101930011004OX

Fig. 16 Engine compartment diagram (Part 4 of 4). 1993 Colt & Summit w/1.8L/4-110

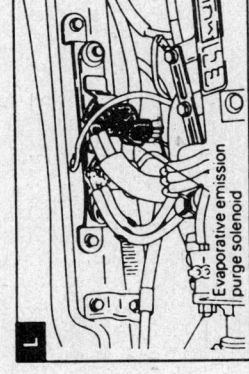

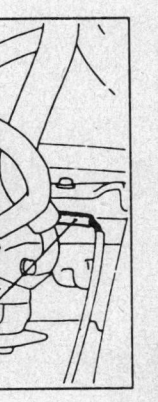

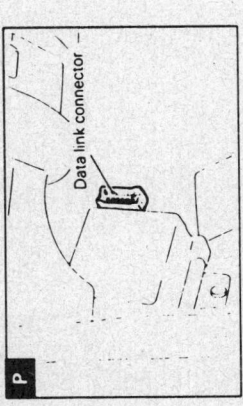

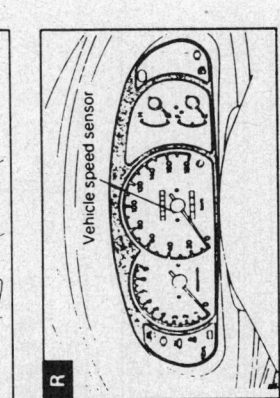

CR101930011003OX

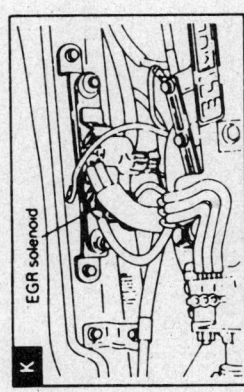

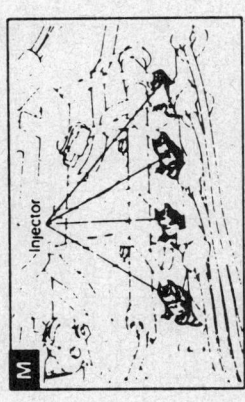

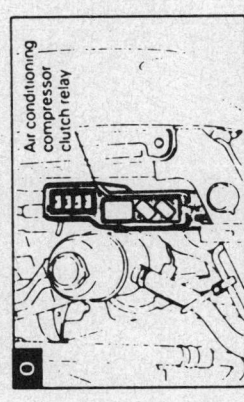

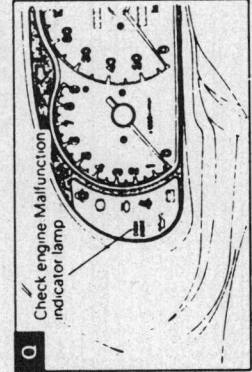

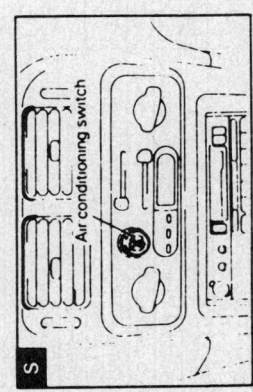

Fig. 16 Engine compartment diagram (Part 3 of 4). 1993 Colt & Summit w/1.8L/4-110

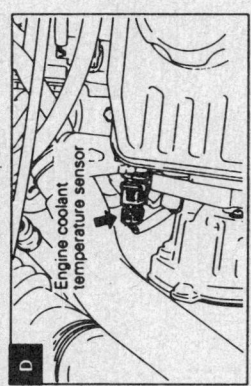
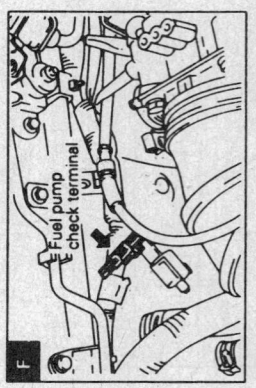
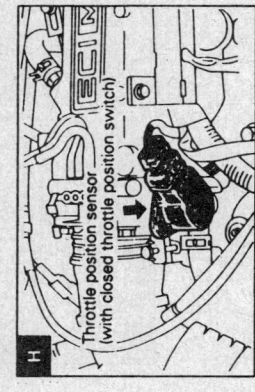
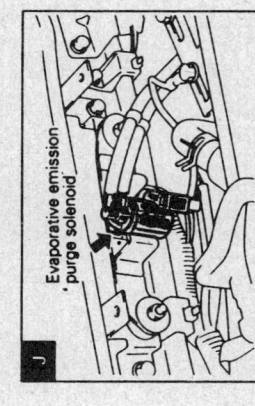

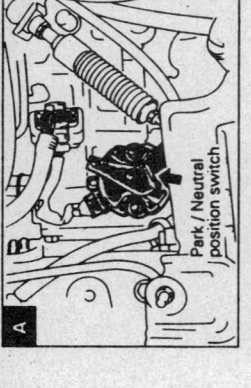
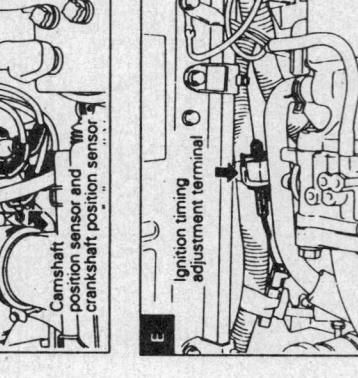
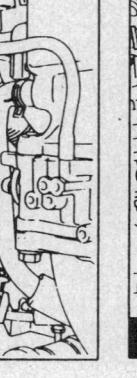
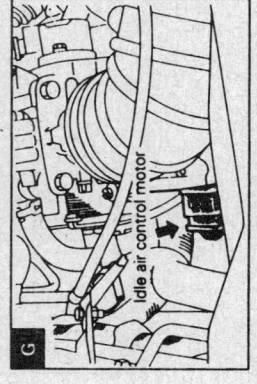
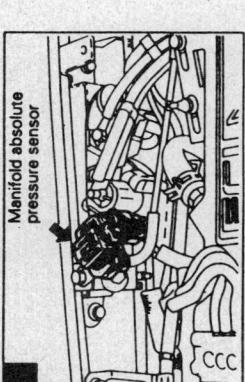

Fig. 17 Engine compartment diagram (Part 2 of 4). 1994–95 Colt & Summit w/1.5L/4-89.5

Name	Symbol
Air conditioning compressor clutch relay	W
Air conditioning switch	G
Camshaft position sensor and crankshaft position sensor	B
Check engine / Malfunction indicator lamp	E
Data link connector	P
EGR solenoid	L
EGR temperature sensor <Federal/California>	I
Engine coolant temperature sensor	U
Evaporative emission purge solenoid	A
Fuel pump check terminal	N
Heated oxygen sensor (Front)	S
Heated oxygen sensor (Rear)	O
Idle air control motor	T
Ignition coil (ignition power transistor)	C
Ignition timing adjustment connector	R
Injector	Q
Intake air temperature sensor	K
Manifold absolute pressure sensor	M
Multiport fuel injection (MFI) relay	V
Park / Neutral position switch	D
Power steering pressure switch	J
Throttle position sensor (with built-in closed throttle position switch)	F
Vehicle speed sensor (reed switch)	X

NOTE
The "Name" column is arranged in alphabetical order.

Fig. 17 Engine compartment diagram (Part 1 of 4). 1994–95 Colt & Summit w/1.5L/4-89.5

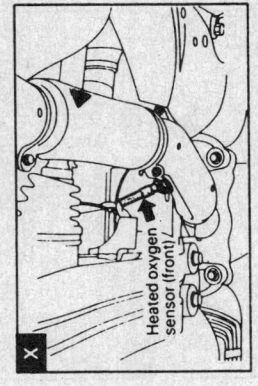

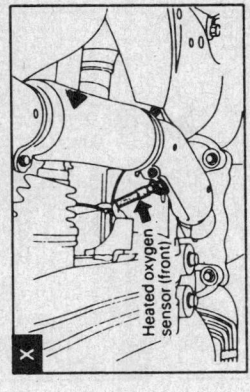

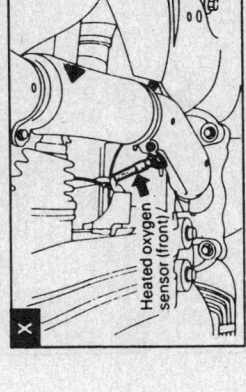

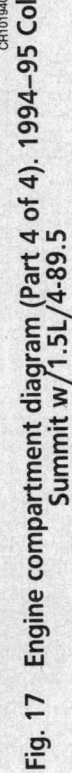

Fig. 17 Engine compartment diagram (Part 4 of 4). 1994-95 Colt & Summit w/1.5L/4-89.5

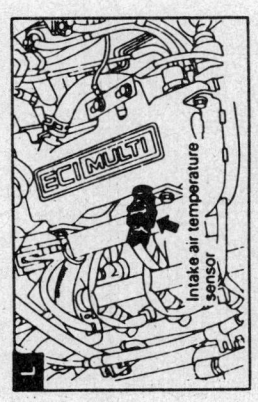

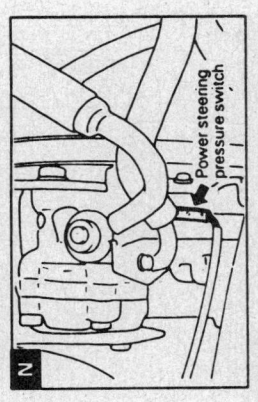

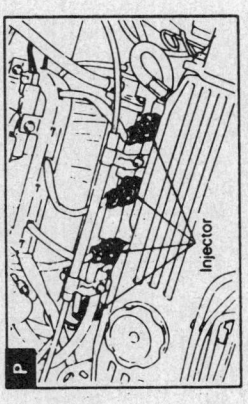

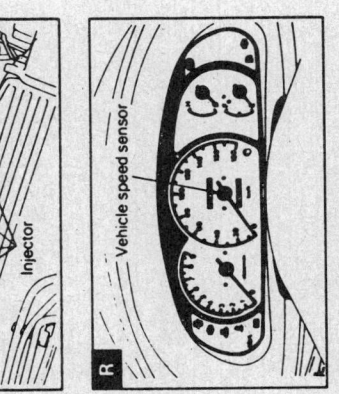

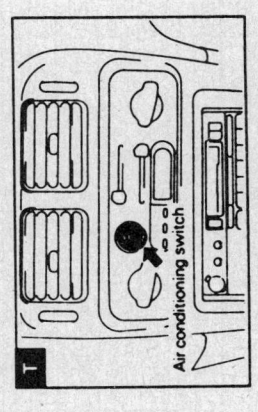

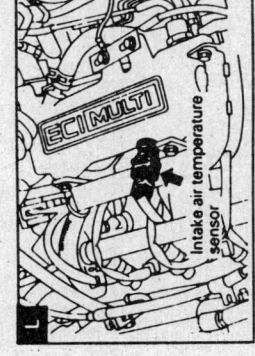

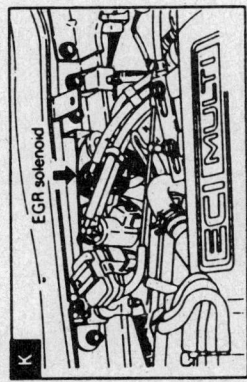

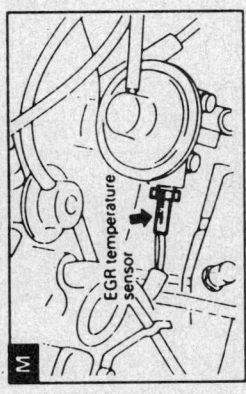

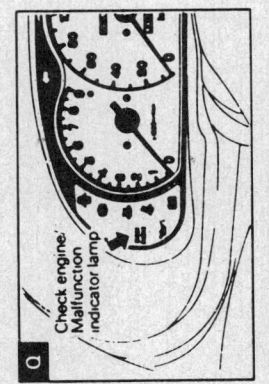

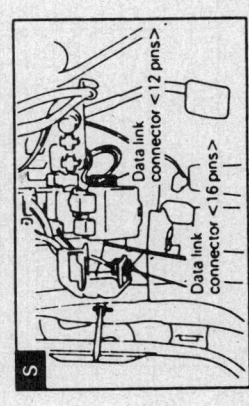

Fig. 17 Engine compartment diagram (Part 3 of 4). 1994-95 Colt & Summit w/1.5L/4-89.5

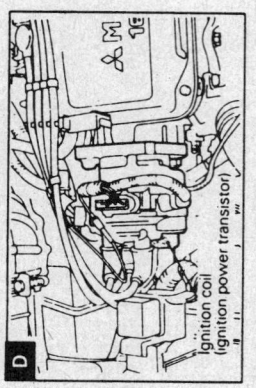

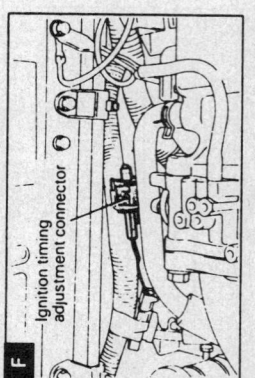

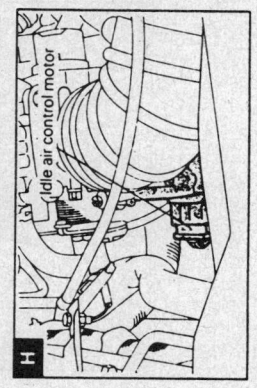

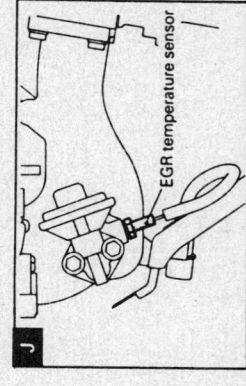

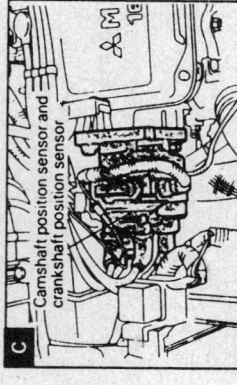

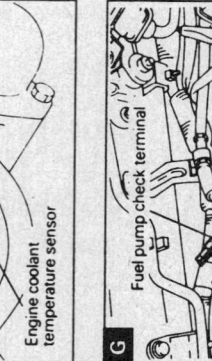

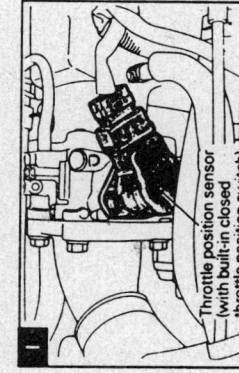

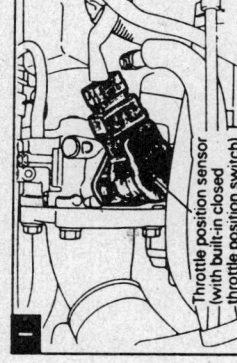

CR101940011202OX

Fig. 18 Engine compartment diagram (Part 2 of 4). 1994–95 Colt & Summit w/1.8L/4-110

Name	Symbol
Air conditioning compressor clutch relay	X
Air conditioning refrigerant intermediate pressure switch	W
Air conditioning switch	H
Camshaft position sensor and crankshaft position sensor	D
Check engine / Malfunction indicator lamp	F
Data link connector	M
EGR solenoid	U
EGR temperature sensor	A
Engine control module	N
Engine coolant temperature sensor	I
Evaporative emission purge solenoid	S
Fuel pump check terminal	B

Name	Symbol
Heated oxygen sensor (Front)	P
Heated oxygen sensor (Rear)	O
Idle air control motor	T
Ignition coil (ignition power transistor)	C
Ignition timing adjustment connector	R
Injector	Q
Multiport fuel injection (MFI) relay	K
Park / Neutral position switch	J
Power steering pressure switch	V
Throttle position sensor (with built-in closed throttle position switch)	E
Vehicle speed sensor (reed switch)	L
Volume air flow sensor (with built-in intake air temperature sensor and barometric pressure sensor)	G

NOTE
The " Name " column is arranged in alphabetical order.

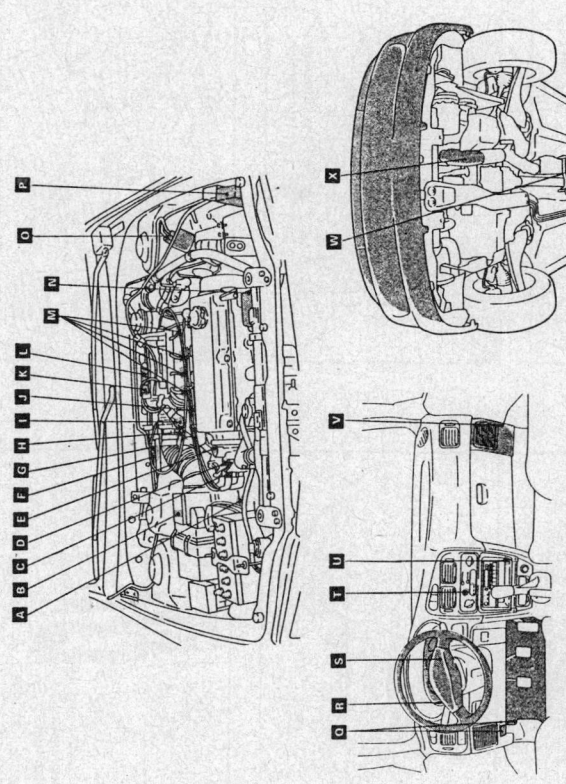

CR101940011201OX

Fig. 18 Engine compartment diagram (Part 1 of 4). 1994–95 Colt & Summit w/1.8L/4-110

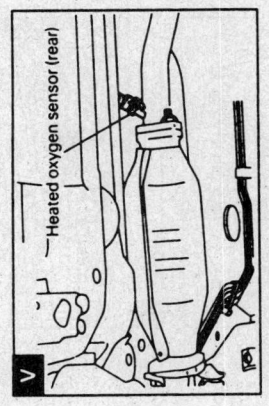

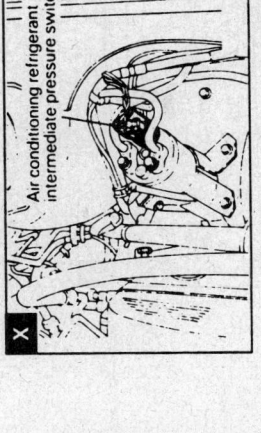

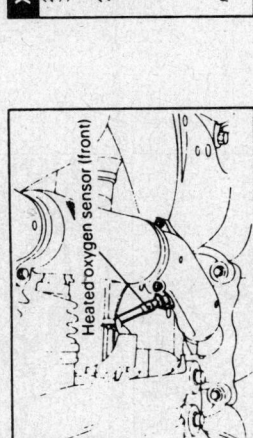

Fig. 18 Engine compartment diagram (Part 4 of 4). 1994-95 Colt & Summit w/1.8L/4-110

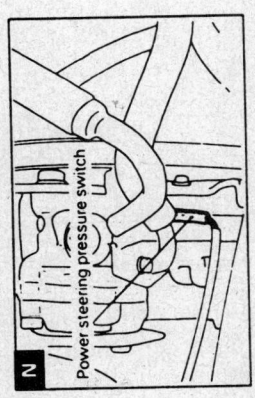

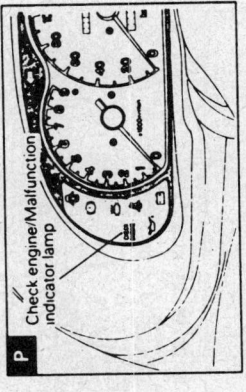

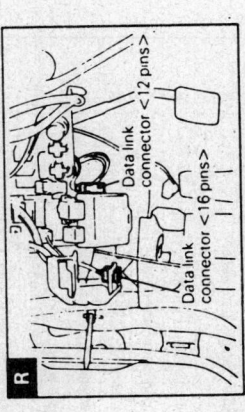

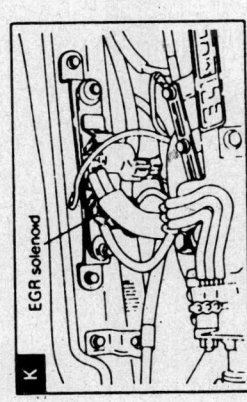

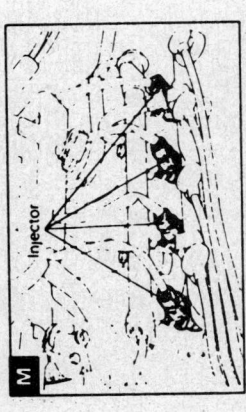

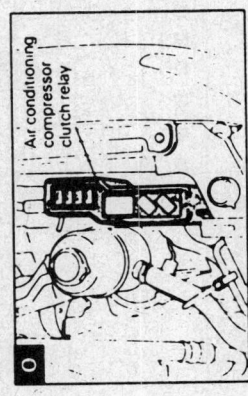

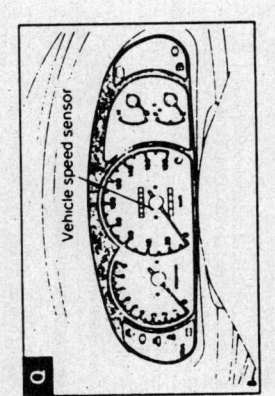

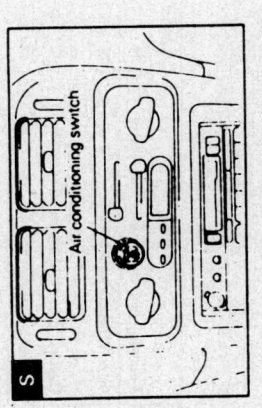

Fig. 18 Engine compartment diagram (Part 3 of 4). 1994-95 Colt & Summit w/1.8L/4-110

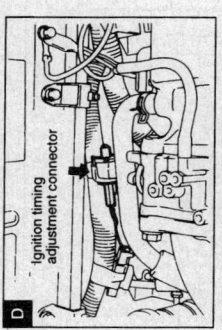

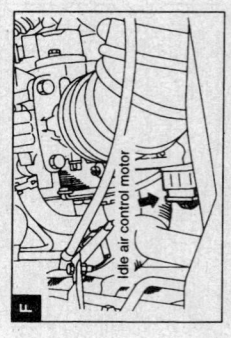

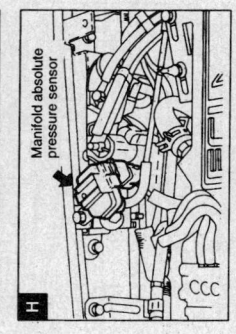

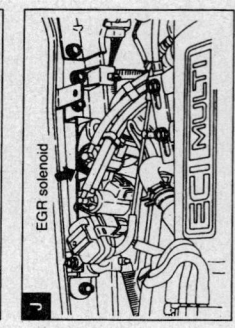

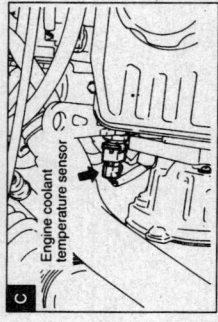

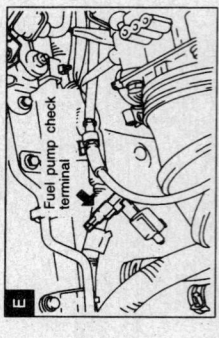

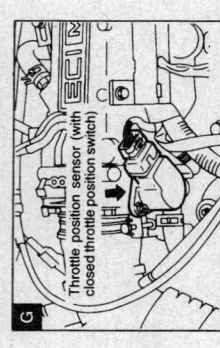

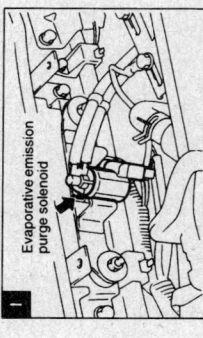

Fig. 19 Engine compartment diagram (Part 2 of 4). 1996 Summit w/1.5L/4-89.5

Name	Symbol
Air conditioning compressor clutch relay	W
Air conditioning switch	V
Check engine / Malfunction indicator lamp	F
Crankshaft position sensor	D
Data link connector	O
Distributor (with built-in camshaft position sensor, ignition coil and ignition power transistor)	K
EGR solenoid	H
Engine control module	T
Engine coolant temperature sensor	A
Evaporative emission purge solenoid	L
Fuel pump check terminal	G
Heated oxygen sensor (Front) <California>	X
Heated oxygen sensor (Front) <Except for California>	W
Heated oxygen sensor (Rear) <California>	N
Heated oxygen sensor (Rear) <Except for California>	S
Idle air control motor	Q
Ignition timing adjustment connector	M
Injector	P
Intake air temperature sensor	B
Manifold absolute pressure sensor	J
Multiport fuel injection (MFI) relay	U
Park / Neutral position switch	C
Power steering pressure switch	I
Throttle position sensor (with built-in closed throttle position switch)	E
Vehicle speed sensor (reed switch)	R

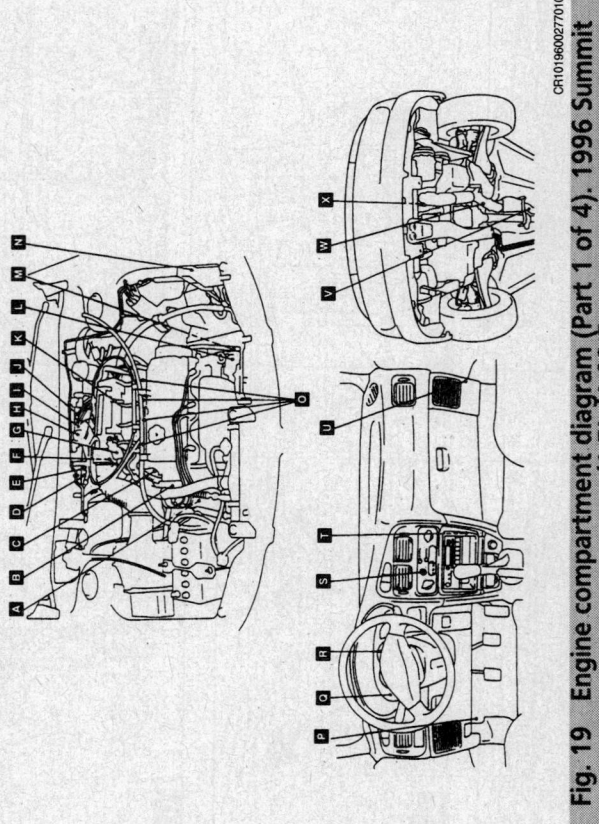

Fig. 19 Engine compartment diagram (Part 1 of 4). 1996 Summit w/1.5L/4-89.5

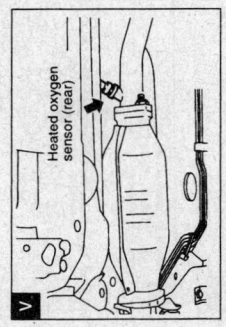

Fig. 19 Engine compartment diagram (Part 4 of 4). 1996 Summit w/1.5L/4-89.5

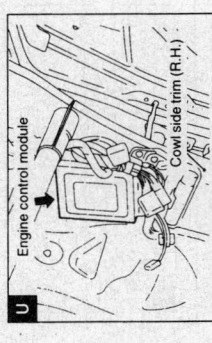

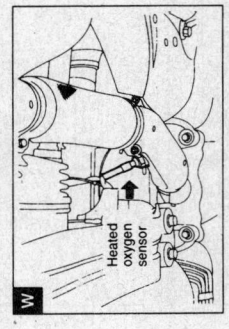

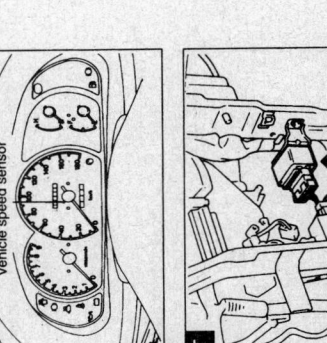

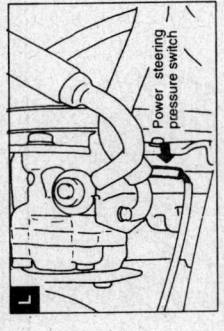

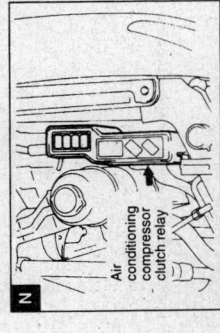

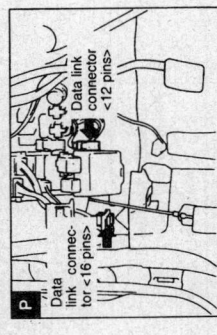

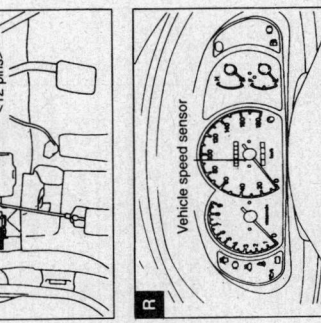

Fig. 19 Engine compartment diagram (Part 3 of 4). 1996 Summit w/1.5L/4-89.5

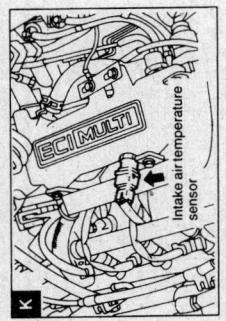

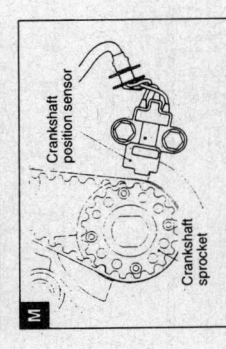

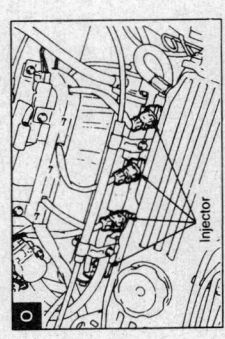

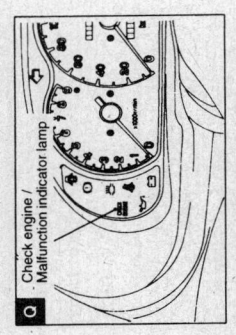

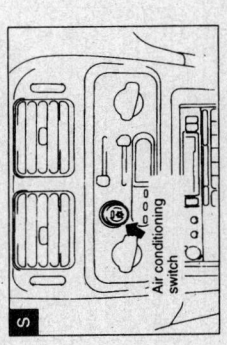

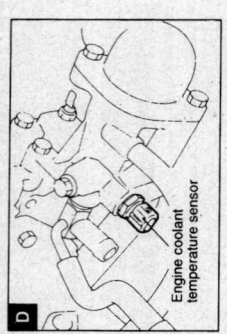
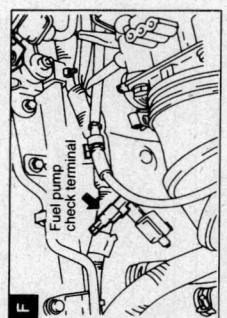
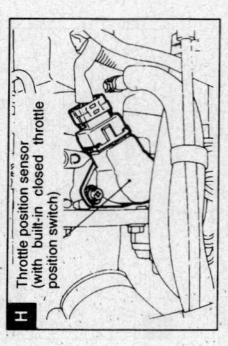
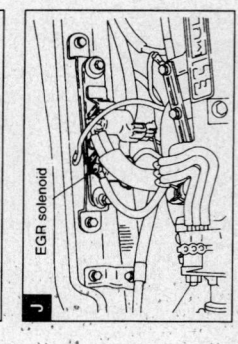

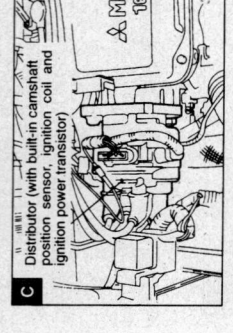
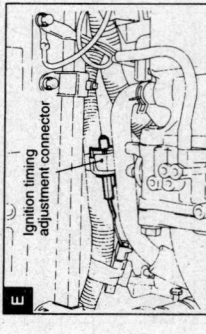
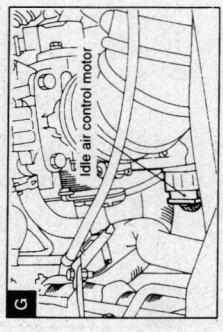
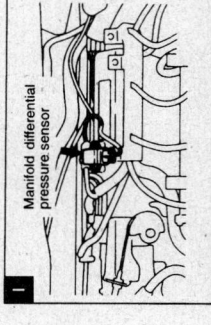
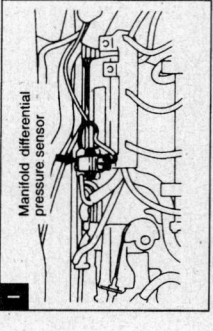

Fig. 20 Engine compartment diagram (Part 2 of 4). 1996 Summit w/1.8L/4-110

Name	Symbol
Air conditioning compressor clutch relay	X
Air conditioning refrigerant intermediate pressure switch	X
Air conditioning switch	W
Check engine / Malfunction indicator lamp	G
Crankshaft position sensor	E
Data link connector	L
Distributor (with built-in camshaft position sensor, ignition coil and ignition power transistor)	I
EGR solenoid	U
Engine control module	A
Engine coolant temperature sensor	M
Evaporative emission purge solenoid	H
Fuel pump check terminal	S
Heated oxygen sensor (Front) <California>	B

Name	Symbol
Heated oxygen sensor (Front) <Except for California>	P
Heated oxygen sensor (Rear) <California>	O
Heated oxygen sensor (Rear) <Except for California>	T
Idle air control motor	R
Ignition timing adjustment connector	N
Injector	Q
Manifold differential pressure sensor	C
Multiport fuel injection (MFI) relay	J
Park / Neutral position switch	V
Power steering pressure switch	D
Throttle position sensor (with built-in closed throttle position switch)	K
Vehicle speed sensor (reed switch)	F
Volume air flow sensor (with built-in intake air temperature sensor and barometric pressure sensor)	Y

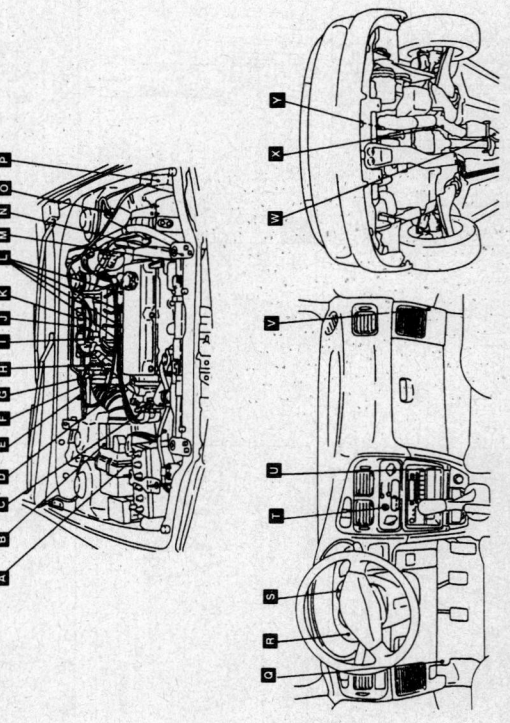

Fig. 20 Engine compartment diagram (Part 1 of 4). 1996 Summit w/1.8L/4-110

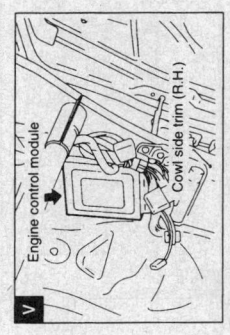

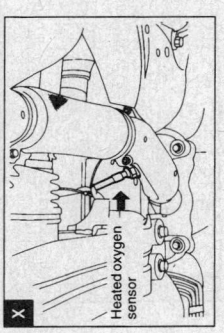

CR101960027804OX

Fig. 20 Engine compartment diagram (Part 4 of 4). 1996 Summit w/1.8L/4-110

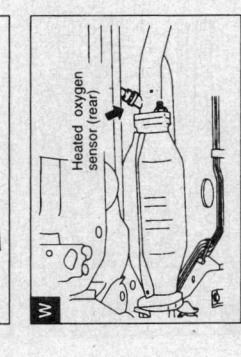

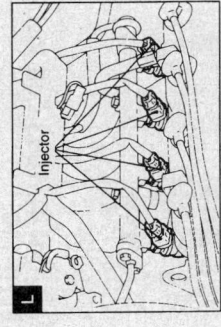

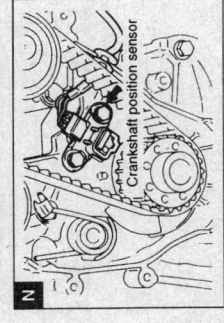

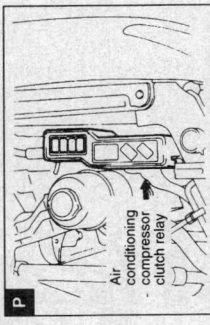

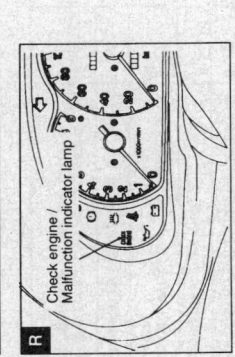

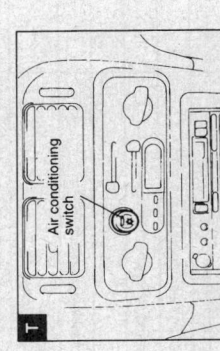

CR101960027803OX

Fig. 20 Engine compartment diagram (Part 3 of 4). 1996 Summit w/1.8L/4-110

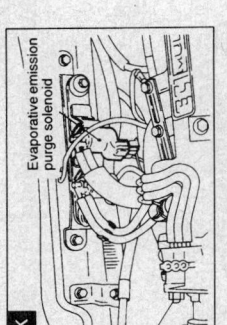

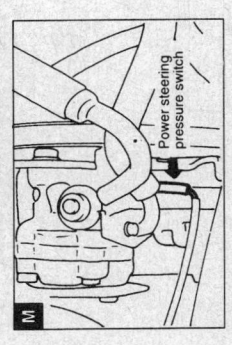

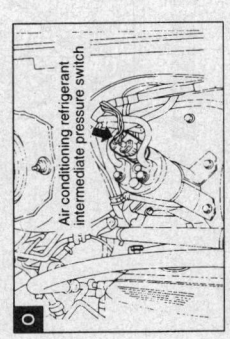

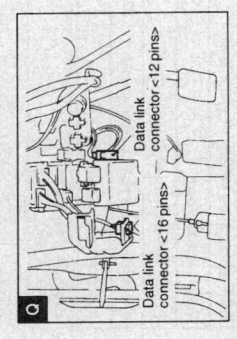

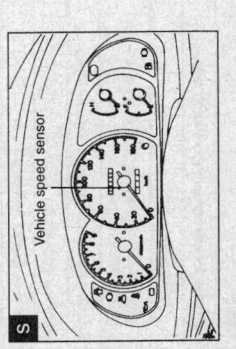

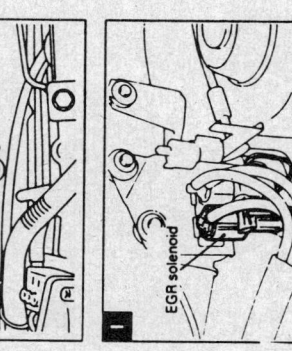

Fig. 21 Engine compartment diagram (Part 2 of 4). 1993 Colt Vista & Summit Wagon w/1.8L/4-110

Name	Symbol
Air conditioning compressor clutch relay	D
Air conditioning switch	L
Camshaft position sensor and crankshaft position sensor	K
Check engine/malfunction indicator lamp	H
Data link connector	W
EGR solenoid <California>	N
EGR temperature sensor <California>	B
Engine control module	P
Engine coolant temperature sensor	E
Evaporative emission purge solenoid	S
Fuel pump check terminal	C
Heated oxygen sensor <California>	C

Symbol	Name
A	Idle air control motor
U	Ignition coil (ignition power transistor)
M	Ignition timing adjustment terminal
T	Injector
R	Multiport fuel injection relay
I	Oxygen sensor <Federal and Canada>
O	Park/Neutral position switch (A/T)
V	Power steering pressure switch
F	Throttle position sensor (with closed throttle position switch)
J	Vehicle speed sensor (reed switch)
G	Volume air flow sensor (with incorporated intake air temperature sensor and barometric pressure sensor)

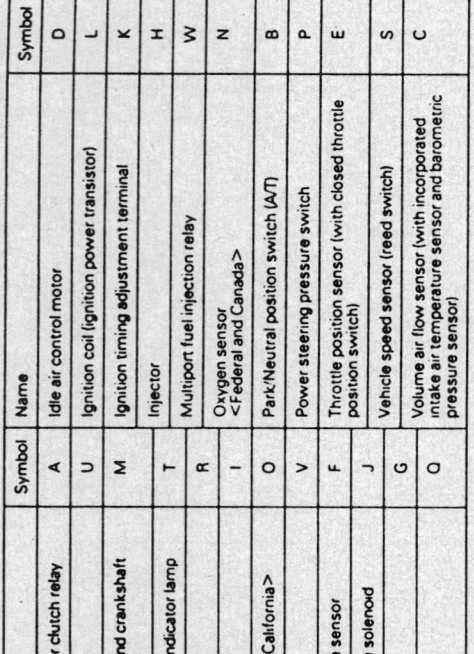

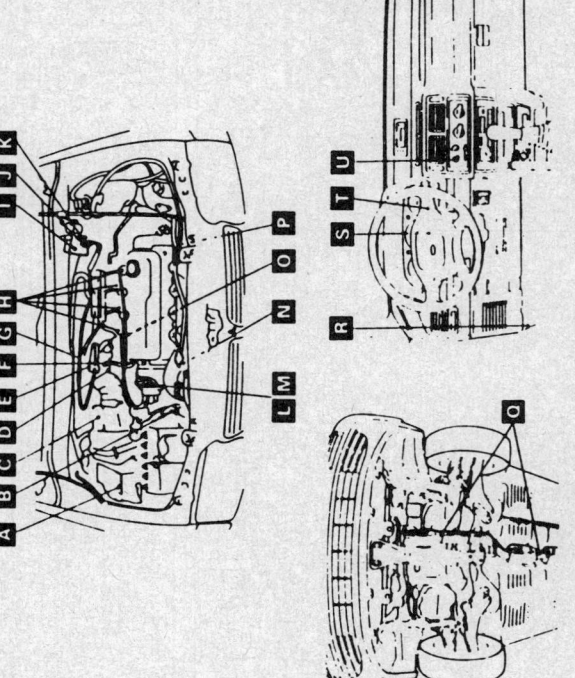

Fig. 21 Engine compartment diagram (Part 1 of 4). 1993 Colt Vista & Summit Wagon w/1.8L/4-110

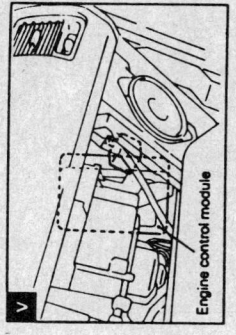
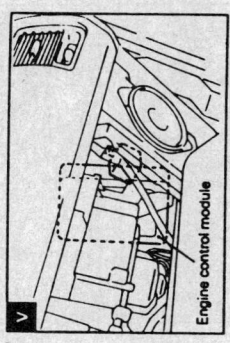

V — Engine control module

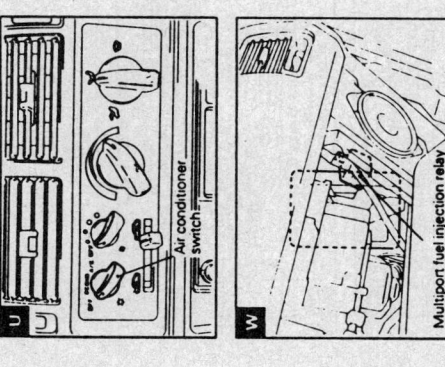

U — Air conditioner switch
W — Multiport fuel injection relay

Fig. 21 Engine compartment diagram (Part 4 of 4). 1993 Colt Vista & Summit Wagon w/1.8L/4-110

CR101930011304OX

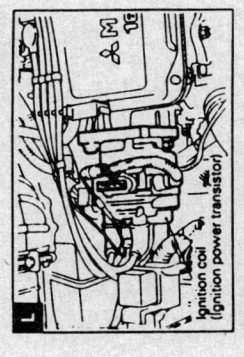
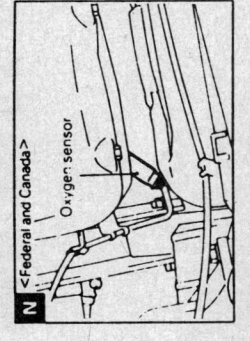
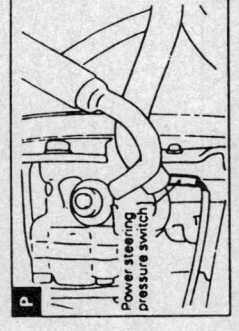
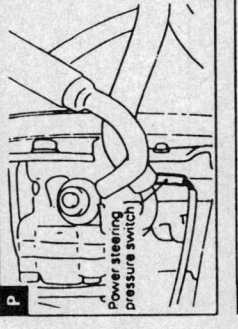

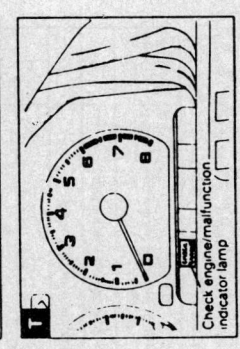
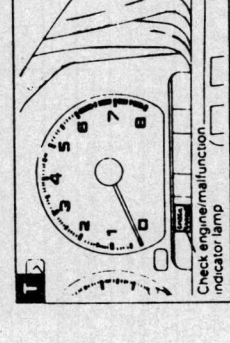

L — Ignition coil (ignition power transistor)
N — <Federal and Canada> Oxygen sensor
P — Power steering pressure switch
R — Data link connector
T — Check engine/malfunction indicator lamp

Fig. 21 Engine compartment diagram (Part 3 of 4). 1993 Colt Vista & Summit Wagon w/1.8L/4-110

CR101930011303OX

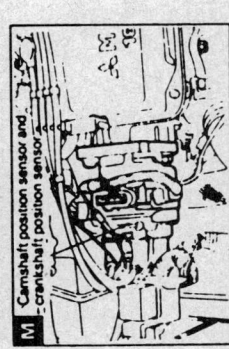
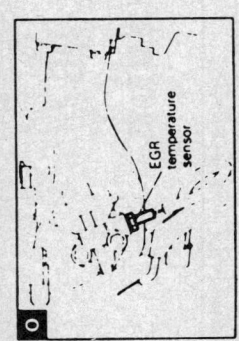
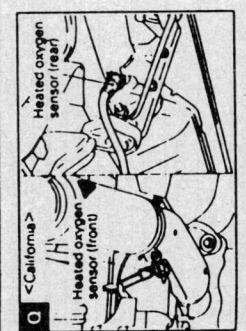
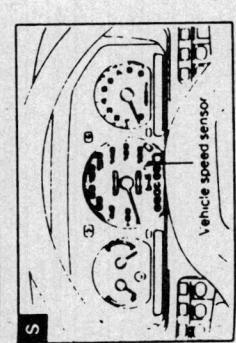

K — Ignition timing adjustment terminal
M — Camshaft position sensor and crankshaft position sensor
O — EGR temperature sensor
Q — <California> Heated oxygen sensor (rear) Heated oxygen sensor (front)
S — Vehicle speed sensor

Fig. 21 Engine compartment diagram (Part 3 of 4). 1993 Colt Vista & Summit Wagon w/1.8L/4-110

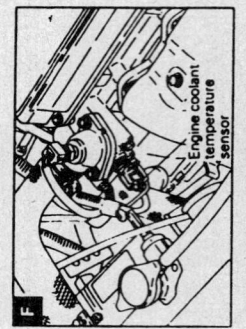
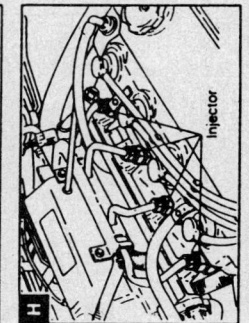

CR101930011402OX

Fig. 22 Engine compartment diagram (Part 2 of 4). 1993 Colt Vista & Summit Wagon w/2.4L/4-146

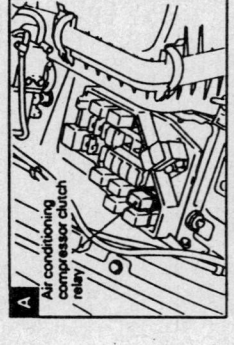

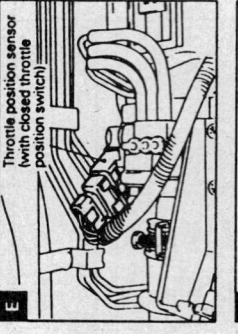
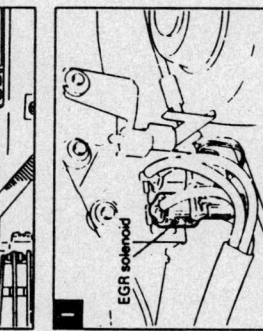
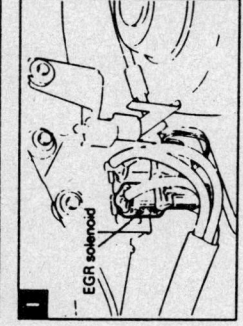

Name	Symbol
Air conditioning compressor clutch relay	D
Air conditioning switch	L
Camshaft position sensor and crankshaft position sensor	K
Check engine/malfunction indicator lamp	H
Data link connector	W
EGR solenoid <California>	N
EGR temperature sensor <California>	B
Engine control module	P
Engine coolant temperature sensor	E
Evaporative emission purge solenoid	S
Fuel pump check terminal	G
Heated oxygen sensor <California>	C

Name	Symbol
Idle air control motor	A
Ignition coil (ignition power transistor)	U
Ignition timing adjustment terminal	M
Injector	T
Multiport fuel injection relay	R
Oxygen sensor <Federal and Canada>	I
Park/Neutral position switch (A/T)	O
Power steering pressure switch	V
Throttle position sensor (with closed throttle position switch)	F
Vehicle speed sensor (reed switch)	J
Volume air flow sensor (with incorporated intake air temperature sensor and barometric pressure sensor)	Q

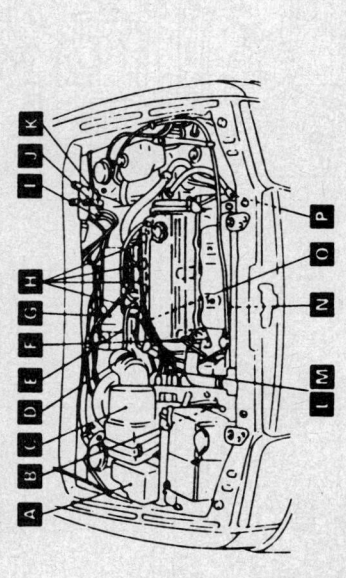
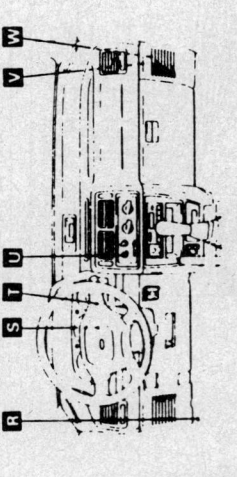
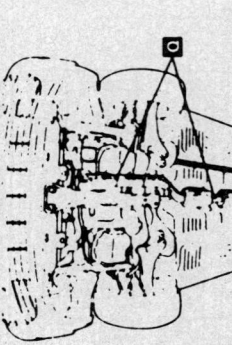

CR101930011401OX

Fig. 22 Engine compartment diagram (Part 1 of 4). 1993 Colt Vista & Summit Wagon w/2.4L/4-146

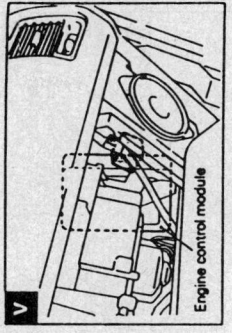

V

Engine control module

CR10193001140340X

Fig. 22   Engine compartment diagram (Part 4 of 4). 1993 Colt Vista & Summit Wagon w/2.4L/4-146

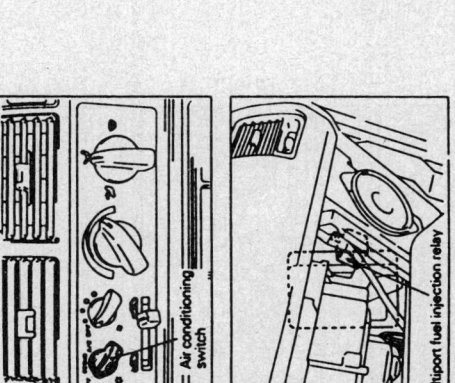

U

Air conditioning switch

W

Multiport fuel injection relay

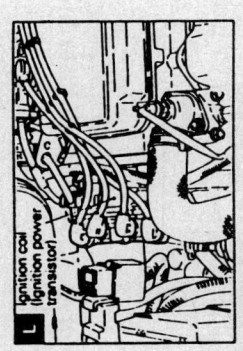

L

Ignition coil (Ignition power transistor)

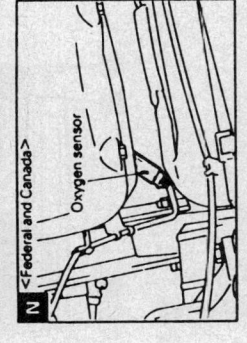

N

<Federal and Canada>

Oxygen sensor

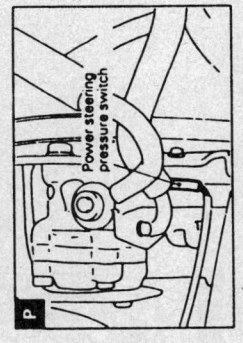

P

Power steering pressure switch

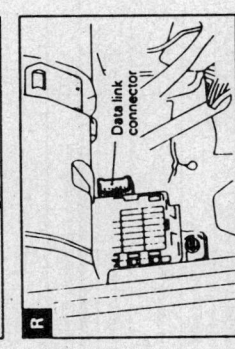

R

Data link connector

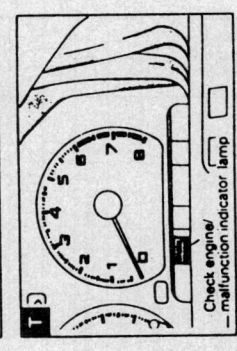

T

Check engine/ malfunction indicator lamp

CR101930011403OX

Fig. 22   Engine compartment diagram (Part 3 of 4). 1993 Colt Vista & Summit Wagon w/2.4L/4-146

K

Ignition timing adjustment terminal

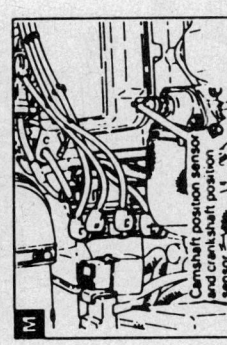

M

Camshaft position sensor and crankshaft position sensor

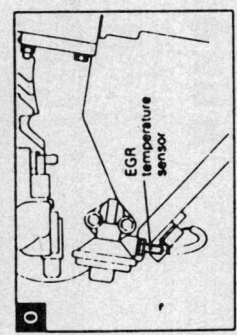

O

EGR temperature sensor

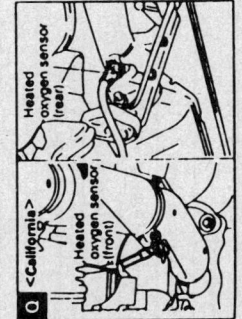

Q

<California>

Heated oxygen sensor (rear)

Heated oxygen sensor (front)

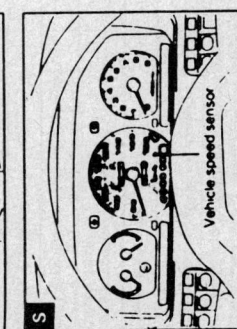

S

Vehicle speed sensor

Fig. 22   Engine compartment diagram (Part 3 of 4). 1993 Colt Vista & Summit Wagon w/2.4L/4-146

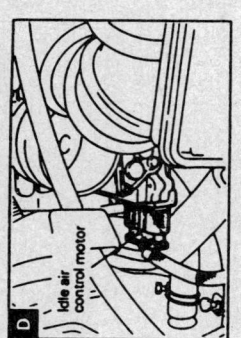

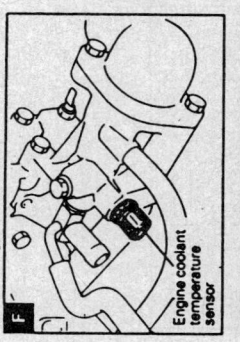

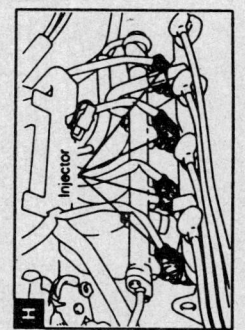

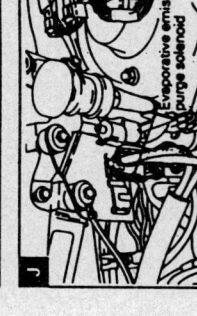

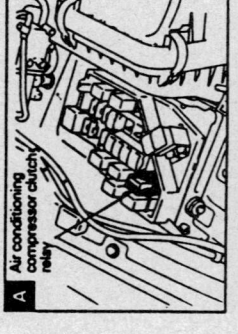

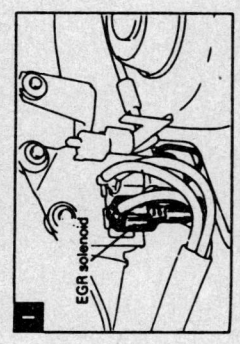

Fig. 23   Engine compartment diagram (Part 2 of 4). 1994–95 Colt Vista & Summit Wagon w/1.8L/4-110

Name	Symbol
Air conditioning compressor clutch relay	A
Air conditioning refrigerant medium pressure switch	P
Air conditioning switch	T
Camshaft position sensor and crankshaft position sensor	M
Check engine/malfunction indicator lamp	S
Data link connector	W
EGR solenoid	I
EGR temperature sensor	N
Engine control module	U
Engine coolant temperature sensor	F
Evaporative emission purge solenoid	J
Fuel pump check terminal	G
Heated oxygen sensor	Q
Idle air control motor	D
Ignition coil (ignition power transistor)	L
Ignition timing adjustment terminal	K
Injector	H
Multiport fuel injection relay	V
Park/Neutral position switch (A/T)	B
Power steering pressure switch	O
Throttle position sensor (with closed throttle position switch)	E
Vehicle speed sensor (reed switch)	R
Volume air flow sensor (with incorporated intake air temperature sensor and barometric pressure sensor)	C

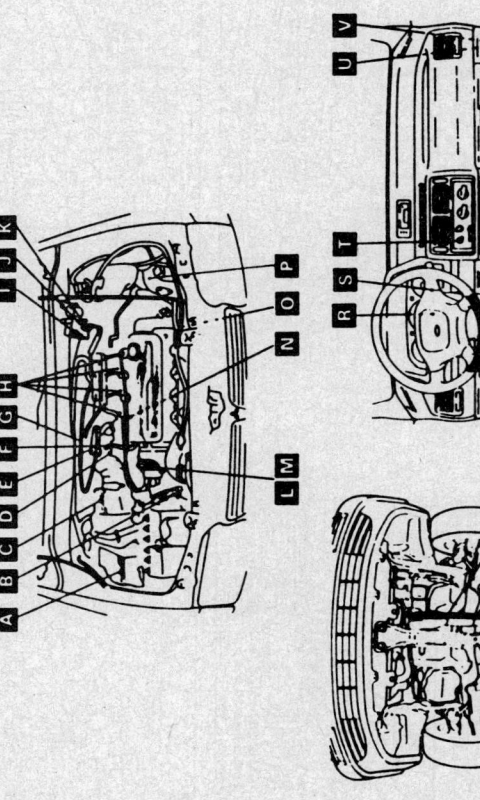

Fig. 23   Engine compartment diagram (Part 1 of 4). 1994–95 Colt Vista & Summit Wagon w/1.8L/4-110

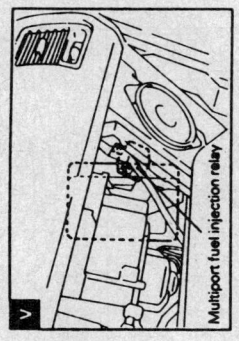

V — Multiport fuel injection relay

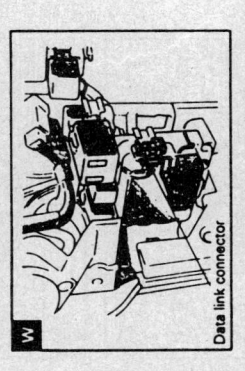

U — Engine control module

W — Data link connector

Fig. 23 Engine compartment diagram (Part 4 of 4). 1994–95 Colt Vista & Summit Wagon w/1.8L/4-110

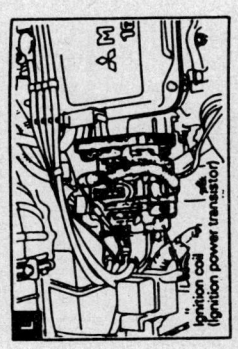

L — Ignition coil (ignition power transistor)

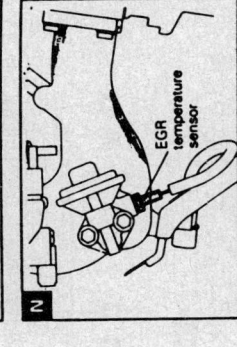

N — EGR temperature sensor

P — Air conditioning refrigerant medium pressure switch

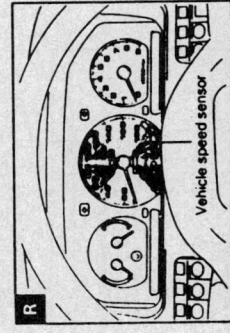

R — Vehicle speed sensor

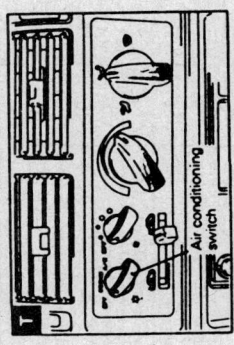

T — Air conditioning switch

K — Ignition timing adjustment terminal

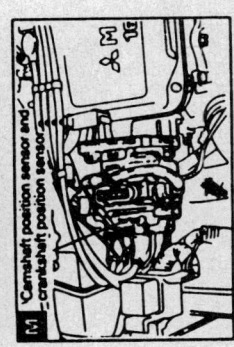

M — Camshaft position sensor and crankshaft position sensor

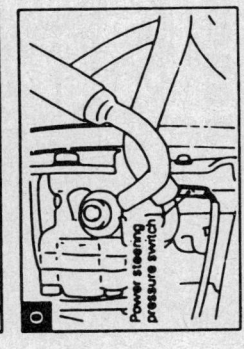

O — Power steering pressure switch

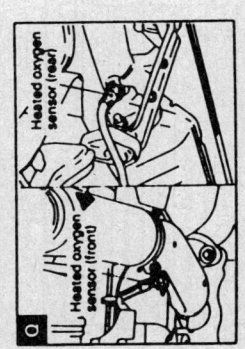

Q — Heated oxygen sensor (rear); Heated oxygen sensor (front)

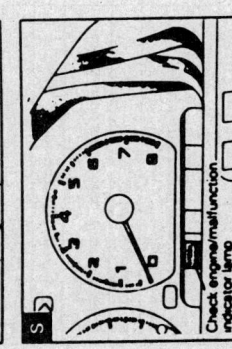

S — Check engine/malfunction indicator lamp

Fig. 23 Engine compartment diagram (Part 3 of 4). 1994–95 Colt Vista & Summit Wagon w/1.8L/4-110

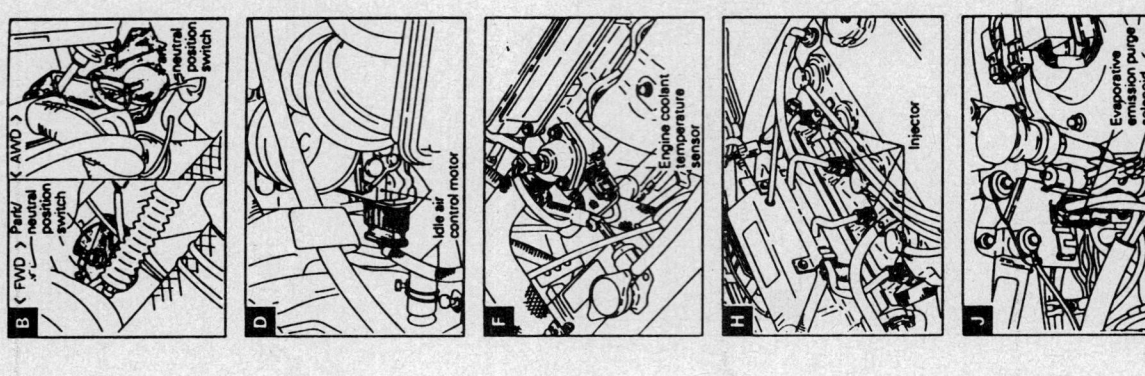

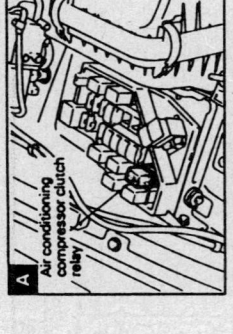

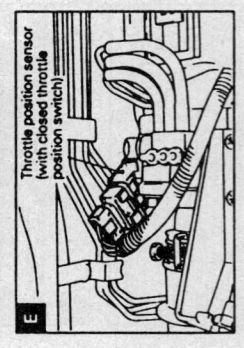
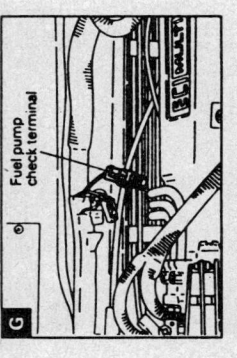

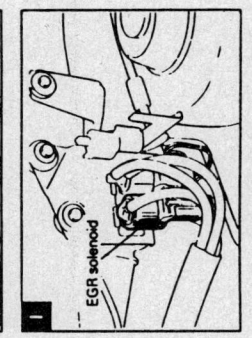

CR1019400116020X

Fig. 24   Engine compartment diagram (Part 2 of 4). 1994–95 Colt Vista & Summit Wagon w/2.4L/4-146

Name	Symbol
Air conditioning compressor clutch ready	A
Air conditioning refrigerant intermediate pressure switch	P
Air conditioning switch	T
Camshaft position sensor and crankshaft position sensor	M
Check engine/malfunction indicator lamp	S
Data link connector	W
EGR solenoid	I
EGR temperature sensor	N
Engine control module	U
Engine coolant temperature sensor	F
Evaporative emission purge solenoid	J
Fuel pump check terminal	G

Name	Symbol
Heated oxygen sensor	Q
Idle air control motor	D
Ignition coil (ignition power transistor)	L
Ignition timing adjustetment terminal	K
Injector	H
Multiport fuel injection relay	V
Park/Neutral position switch (A/T)	B
Power steering pressure switch	O
Throttle position sensor (with closed throttle position switch)	E
Vehicle speed sensor (reed switch)	R
Volume air flow sensor (with incorporated intake air temperature sensor and barometric pressure sensor)	C

CR1019400116010X

Fig. 24   Engine compartment diagram (Part 1 of 4). 1994–95 Colt Vista & Summit Wagon w/2.4L/4-146

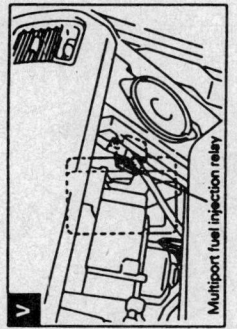

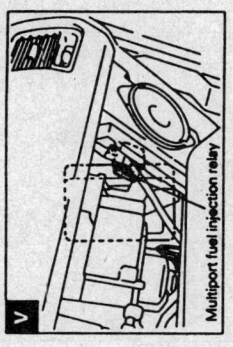

Fig. 24 Engine compartment diagram (Part 4 of 4). 1994–95 Colt Vista & Summit Wagon w/2.4L/4-146

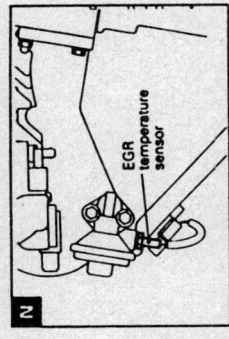

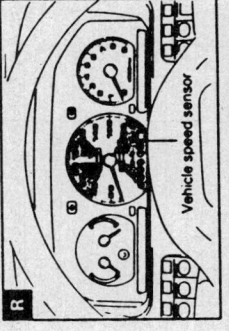

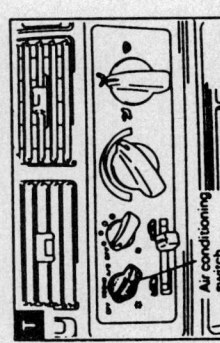

Fig. 24 Engine compartment diagram (Part 3 of 4). 1994–95 Colt Vista & Summit Wagon w/2.4L/4-146

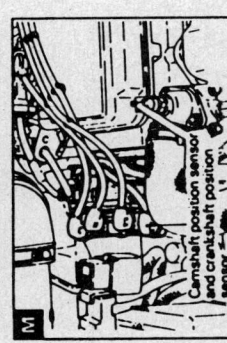

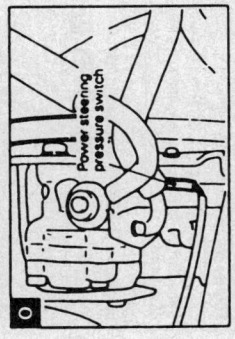

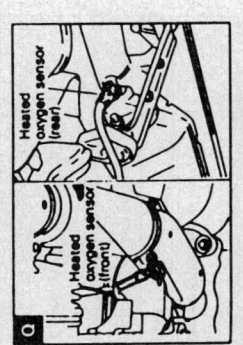

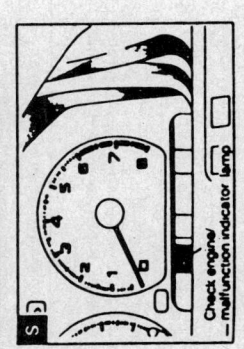

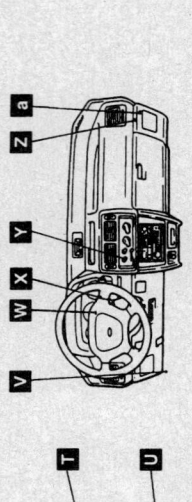

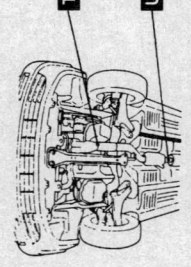

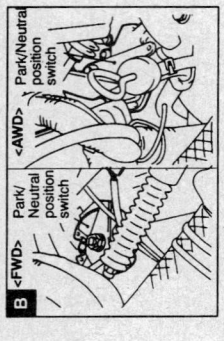

B <FWD> Park/Neutral position switch
<AWD> Park/Neutral position switch

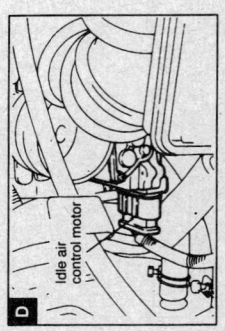

D Idle air control motor

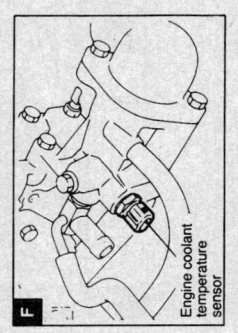

F Engine coolant temperature sensor

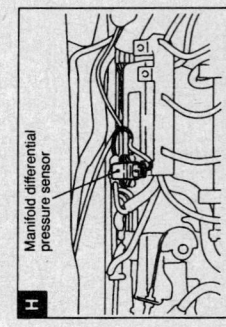

H Manifold differential pressure sensor

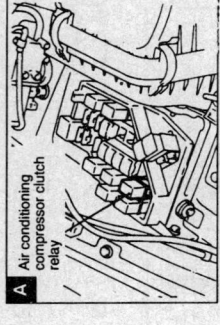

A Air conditioning compressor clutch relay

C Volume air flow sensor (with incorporated intake air temperature sensor and barometric pressure sensor)

E Throttle position sensor (with closed throttle position switch)

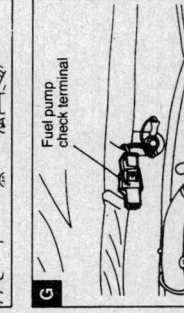

G Fuel pump check terminal

Fig. 25 Engine compartment diagram (Part 2 of 4). 1996 Summit Wagon w/1.8L/4-110

Name	Symbol
Air conditioning compressor clutch relay	Q
Air conditioning switch	U
Camshaft position sensor and crankshaft position sensor	D
	R
Check engine/malfunction indicator lamp	L
Crankshaft position sensor <California>	I
Data link connector	H
EGR solenoid	a
EGR temperature sensor	B
Engine control module	N
Engine coolant temperature sensor	E
Evaporative emission purge solenoid	M
Fuel pump check terminal	W
Heated oxygen sensor (front) <Federal and Canada> or heated oxygen sensor (rear) <California>	C
Heated oxygen sensor (front) <California>	A
Heated oxygen sensor (rear) <Federal and Canada>	Y
Idle air control motor	S
Ignition coil (ignition power transistor)	X
Ignition timing adjustment terminal	O
Injector	V
Manifold differential pressure sensor <California>	J
MFI relay	P
Park/Neutral position switch (A/T)	Z
Power steering pressure switch	F
Throttle position sensor (with closed throttle position switch)	K
Triple pressure switch	G
Vehicle speed sensor (reed switch)	T
Volume air flow sensor (with incorporated intake air temperature sensor and barometric pressure sensor)	

NOTE
The "Name" column is arranged in alphabetical order.

Fig. 25 Engine compartment diagram (Part 1 of 4). 1996 Summit Wagon w/1.8L/4-110

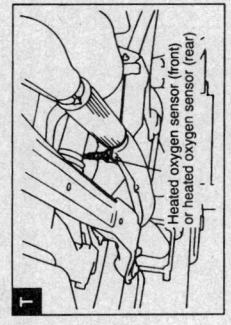

T — Heated oxygen sensor (front) or heated oxygen sensor (rear)

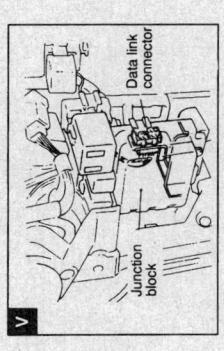

V — Data link connector / Junction block

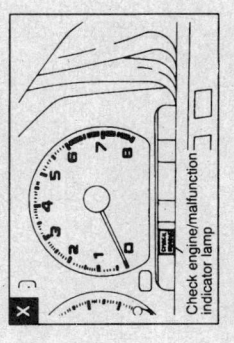

X — Check engine/malfunction indicator lamp

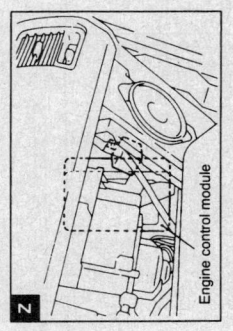

Z — Engine control module

CR101960027504OX

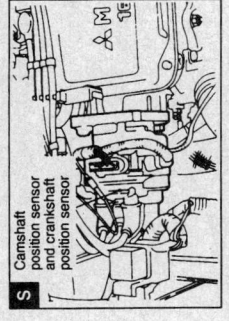

S — Camshaft position sensor and crankshaft position sensor

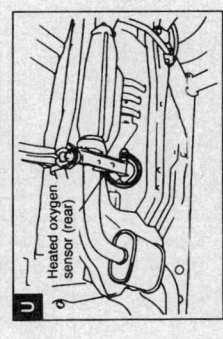

U — Heated oxygen sensor (rear)

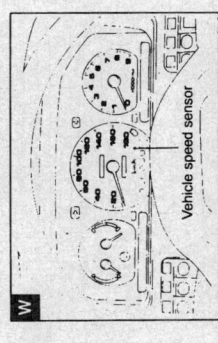

W — Vehicle speed sensor

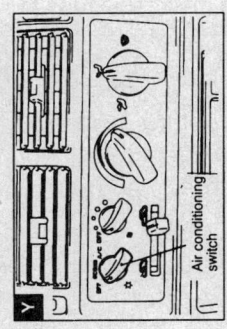

Y — Air conditioning switch

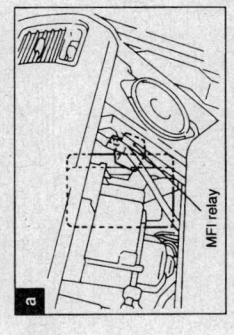

a — MFI relay

Fig. 25 Engine compartment diagram (Part 4 of 4). 1996 Summit Wagon w/1.8L/4-110

CR101960027503OX

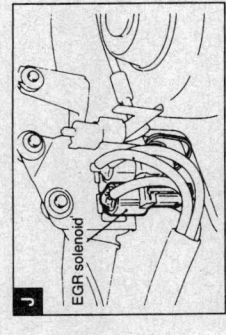

J — EGR solenoid

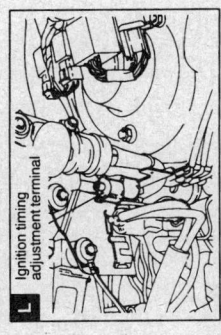

L — Ignition timing adjustment terminal

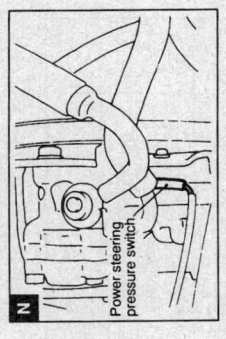

N — Power steering pressure switch

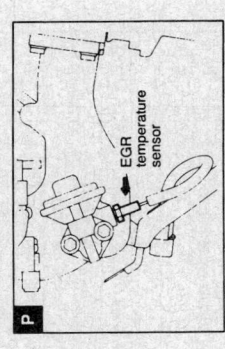

P — EGR temperature sensor

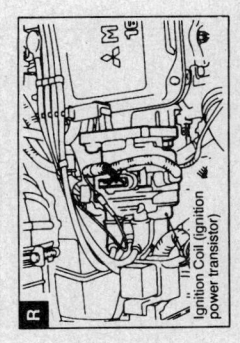

R — Ignition Coil (ignition power transistor)

Fig. 25 Engine compartment diagram (Part 3 of 4). 1996 Summit Wagon w/1.8L/4-110

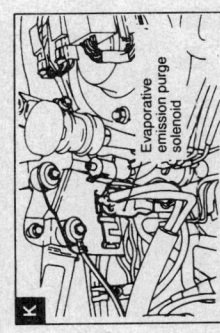

I — Injector

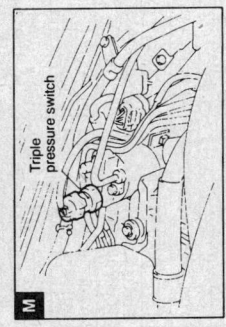

K — Evaporative emission purge solenoid

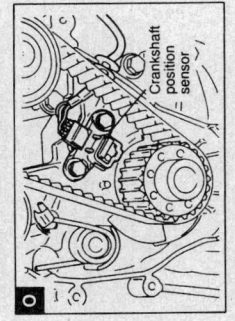

M — Triple pressure switch

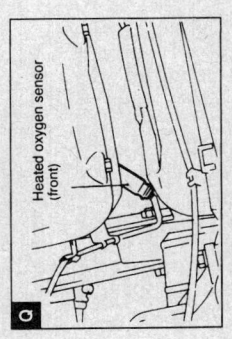

O — Crankshaft position sensor

Q — Heated oxygen sensor (front)

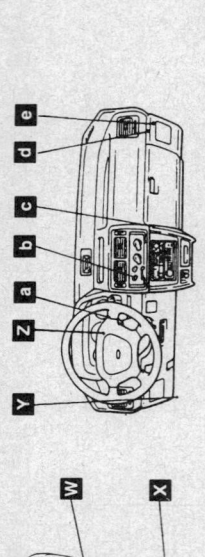

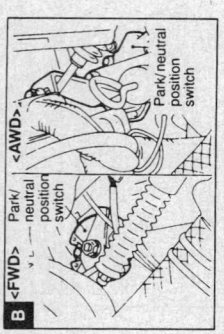

B `<FWD>` Park/neutral position switch `<AWD>` Park/neutral position switch

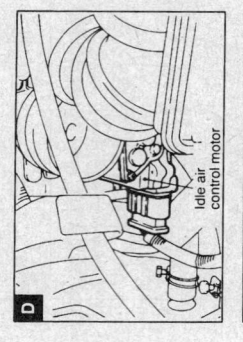

D Idle air control motor

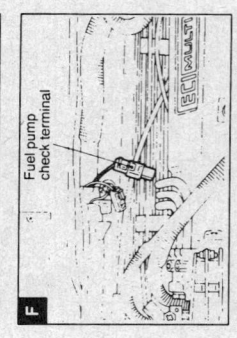

F Fuel pump check terminal

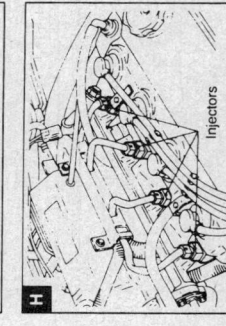

H Injectors

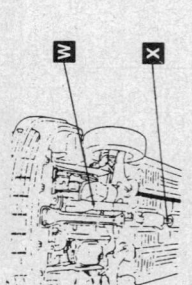

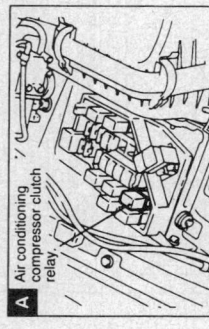

A Air conditioning compressor clutch relay

C Volume air flow sensor (with incorporated intake air temperature sensor and barometric pressure sensor)

E Throttle position sensor (with closed throttle position switch)

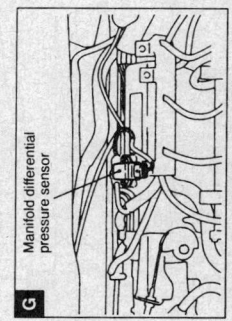

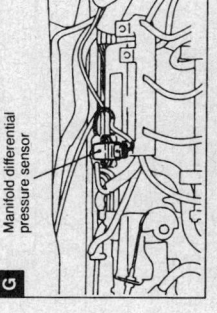

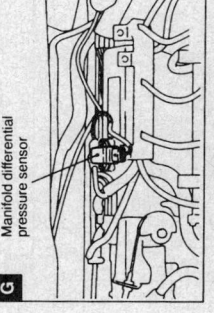

G Manifold differential pressure sensor

Fig. 26 Engine compartment diagram (Part 2 of 5). 1996 Summit Wagon w/2.4L/4-146

Name	Symbol	Name	Symbol
Air conditioning compressor clutch relay	A	Heated oxygen sensor (front) <Federal, Canada and California-AWD> or heated oxygen sensor (rear) <California-FWD>	W
Air conditioning switch	b	Heated oxygen sensor (rear) <Federal, Canada and California-AWD>	X
Camshaft position sensor and crankshaft position sensor	M	Idle air control motor	D
Check engine/malfunction indicator lamp	a	Ignition coil (ignition power transistor)	N
Crankshaft position sensor	S	Ignition timing adjustment terminal	K
Data link connector	Y	Injectors	H
EGR solenoid	I	MFI relay	P
EGR temperature sensor	e	Manifold differential pressure sensor	G
Engine control module	T	Park/Neutral position switch (A/T)	B
Engine coolant temperature sensor	O	Power steering pressure switch	J
Evaporative emission purge solenoid	U	Throttle position sensor (with closed throttle position switch)	E
Evaporative emission purge solenoid 1	R	Triple pressure switch	F
Evaporative emission ventilation solenoid <California-FWD>	V	Vehicle speed sensor (reed switch)	Z
Fuel pump check terminal	F	Volume air flow sensor (with incorporated intake air temperature sensor and barometric pressure sensor)	C
Fuel pump relay module	c		
Fuel tank differential pressure sensor <California-FWD>	L		
Heated oxygen sensor (front) <California-FWD>	Q		

NOTE
The "Name" column is arranged in alphabetical order.

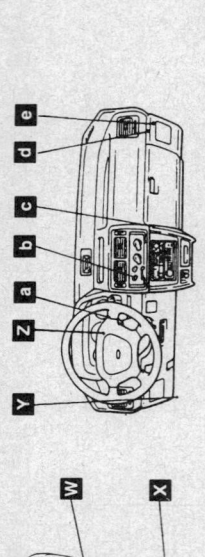

Fig. 26 Engine compartment diagram (Part 1 of 5). 1996 Summit Wagon w/2.4L/4-146

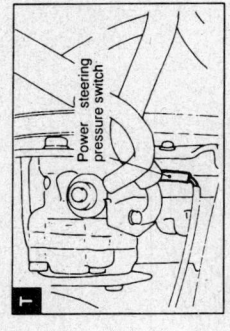

T — Power steering pressure switch

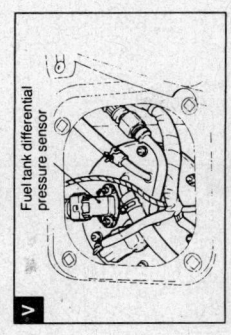

V — Fuel tank differential pressure sensor

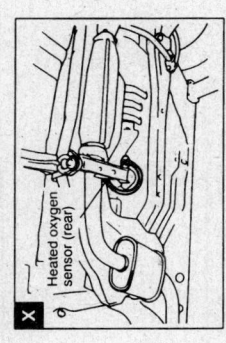

X — Heated oxygen sensor (rear)

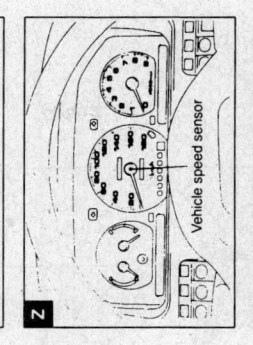

Z — Vehicle speed sensor

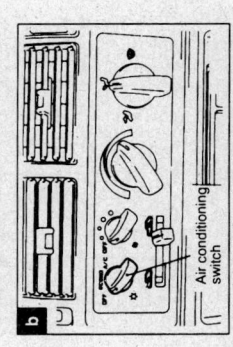

b — Air conditioning switch

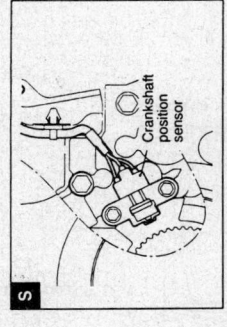

S — Crankshaft position sensor

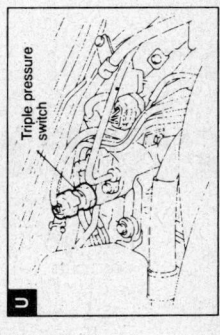

U — Triple pressure switch

W — Heated oxygen sensor (front) or heated oxygen sensor (rear)

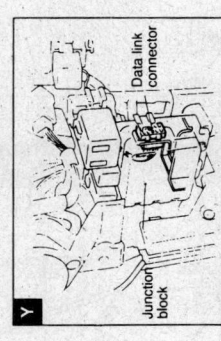

Y — Data link connector / Junction block

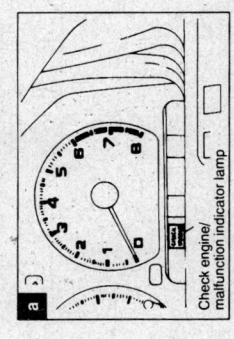

a — Check engine/ malfunction indicator lamp

Fig. 26 Engine compartment diagram (Part 4 of 5). 1996 Summit Wagon w/2.4L/4-146

CR101960027604OX

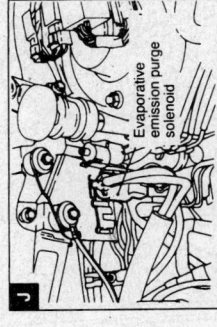

J — Evaporative emission purge solenoid

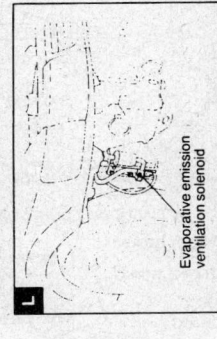

L — Evaporative emission ventilation solenoid

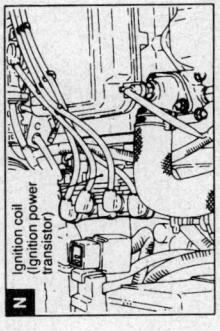

N — Ignition coil (ignition power transistor)

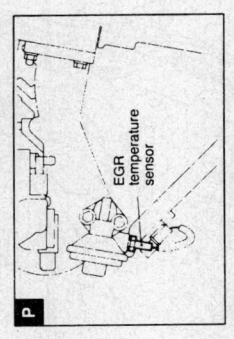

P — EGR temperature sensor

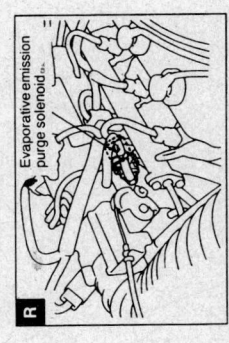

R — Evaporative emission purge solenoid

Fig. 26 Engine compartment diagram (Part 3 of 5). 1996 Summit Wagon w/2.4L/4-146

CR101960027603OX

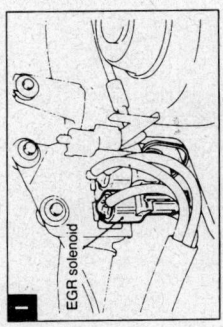

I — EGR solenoid

K — Ignition timing adjustment terminal

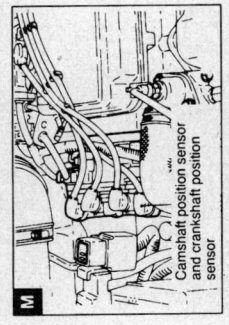

M — Camshaft position sensor and crankshaft position sensor

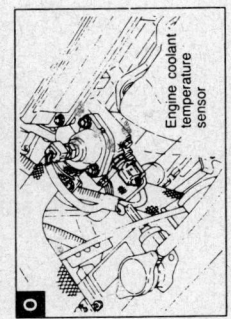

O — Engine coolant temperature sensor

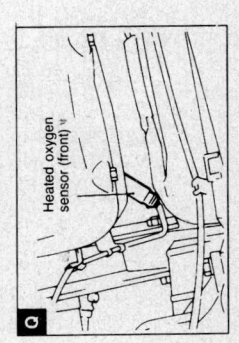

Q — Heated oxygen sensor (front)

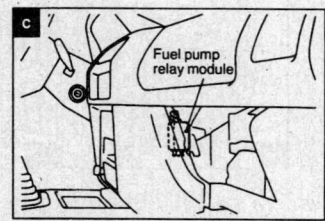

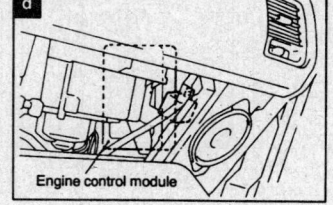

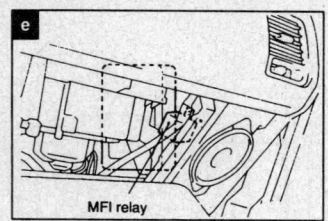

CR1019600276050X

Fig. 26   Engine compartment diagram (Part 5 of 5). 1996 Summit Wagon w/2.4L/4-146

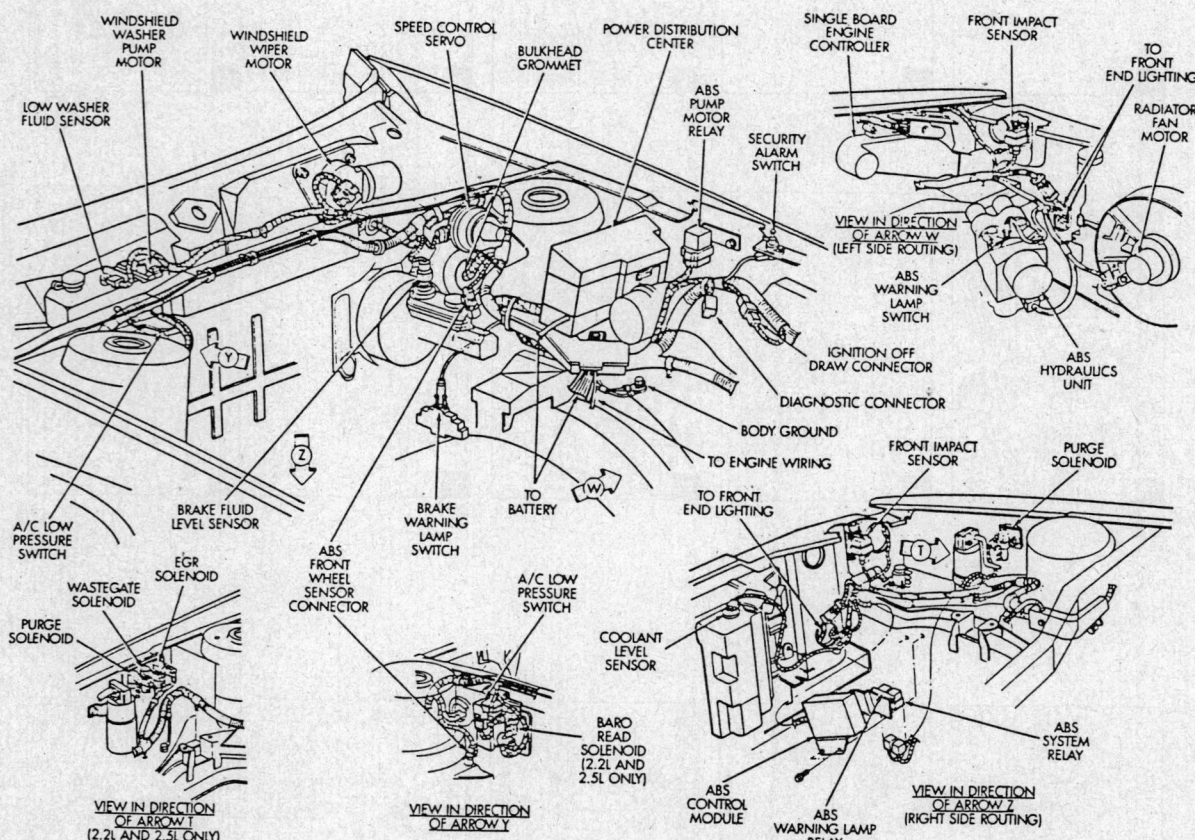

Fig. 27   Engine compartment diagram (Part 1 of 3). 1993 Daytona & LeBaron

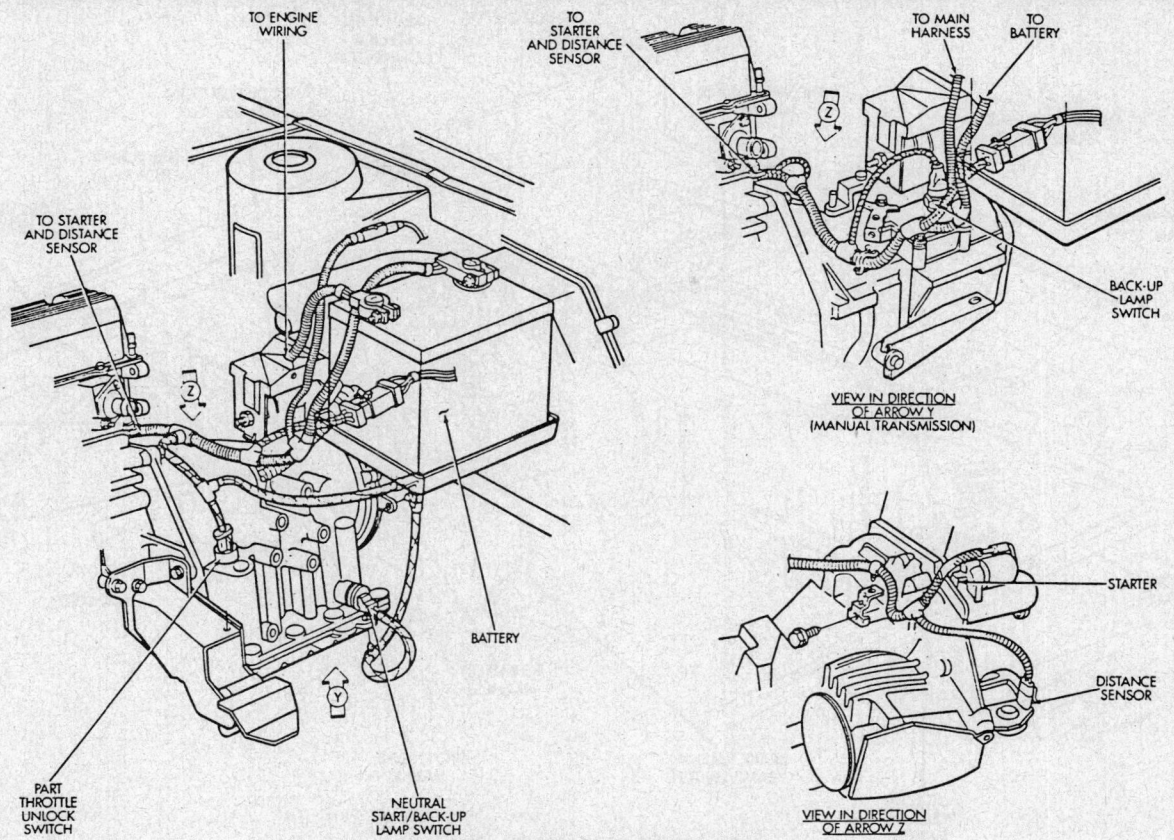

Fig. 27   Engine compartment diagram (Part 2 of 3). 1993 Daytona & LeBaron

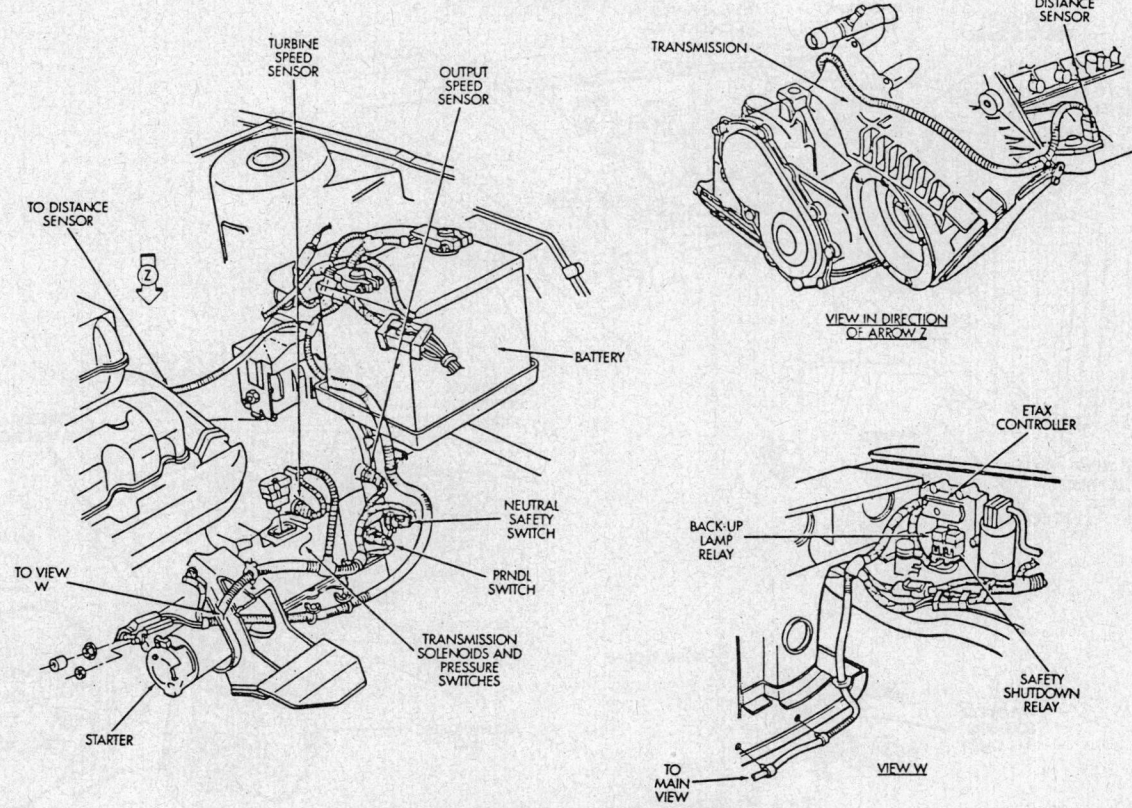

Fig. 27   Engine compartment diagram (Part 3 of 3). 1993 Daytona & LeBaron

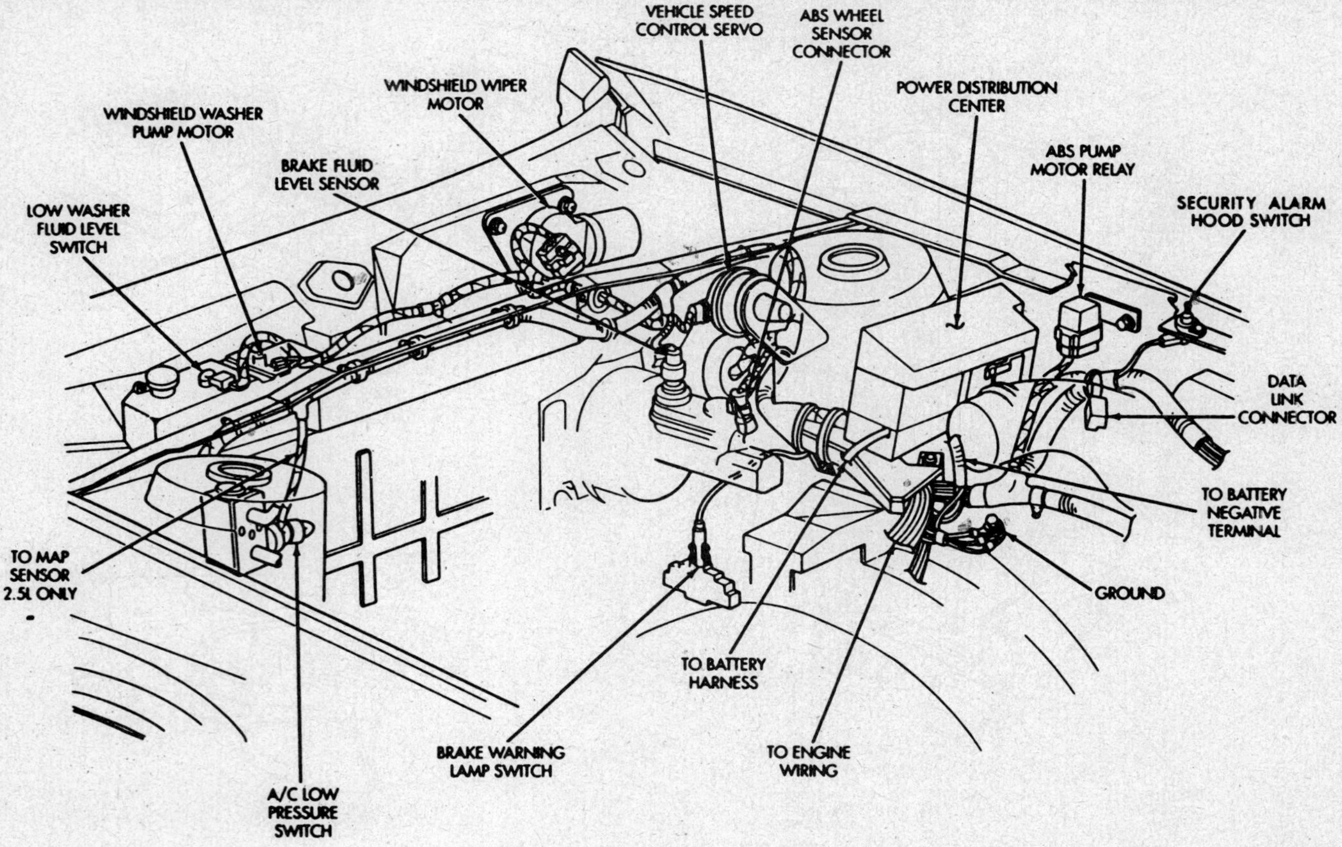

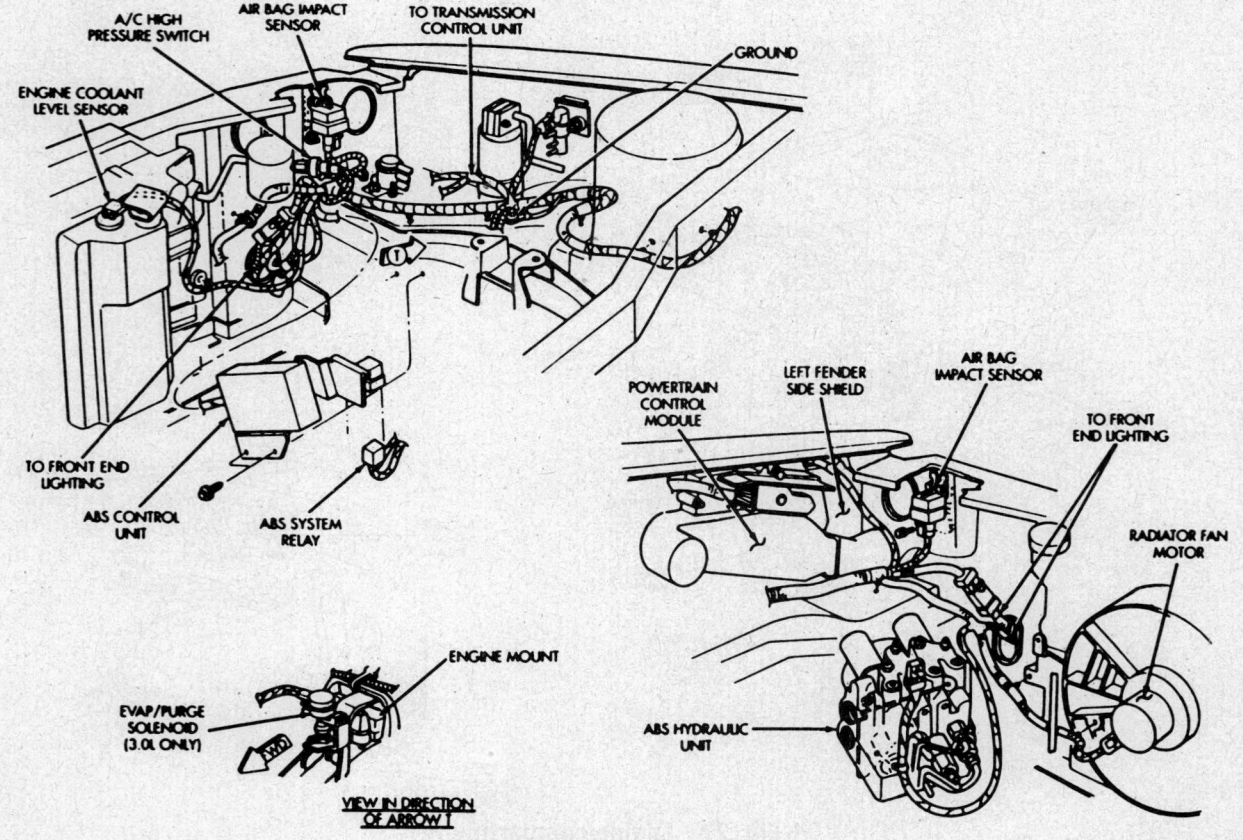

WINDSHIELD WASHER
PUMP MOTOR

VEHICLE SPEED
CONTROL SERVO

ABS WHEEL
SENSOR
CONNECTOR

BRAKE FLUID
LEVEL SENSOR

WINDSHIELD WIPER
MOTOR

POWER DISTRIBUTION
CENTER

LOW WASHER
FLUID LEVEL
SWITCH

ABS PUMP
MOTOR RELAY

SECURITY ALARM
HOOD SWITCH

DATA
LINK
CONNECTOR

TO BATTERY
NEGATIVE
TERMINAL

TO MAP
SENSOR
2.5L ONLY

GROUND

TO BATTERY
HARNESS

TO ENGINE
WIRING

BRAKE WARNING
LAMP SWITCH

A/C LOW
PRESSURE
SWITCH

CF1019400104010X

Fig. 28   Engine compartment diagram (Part 1 of 3). 1994–95 LeBaron

A/C HIGH
PRESSURE SWITCH

AIR BAG IMPACT
SENSOR

TO TRANSMISSION
CONTROL UNIT

GROUND

ENGINE COOLANT
LEVEL SENSOR

LEFT FENDER
SIDE SHIELD

AIR BAG
IMPACT SENSOR

POWERTRAIN
CONTROL
MODULE

TO FRONT
END LIGHTING

TO FRONT END
LIGHTING

RADIATOR FAN
MOTOR

ABS CONTROL
UNIT

ABS SYSTEM
RELAY

EVAP/PURGE
SOLENOID
(3.0L ONLY)

ENGINE MOUNT

ABS HYDRAULIC
UNIT

VIEW IN DIRECTION
OF ARROW T

CR1019400104020X

Fig. 28   Engine compartment diagram (Part 2 of 3). 1994–95 LeBaron

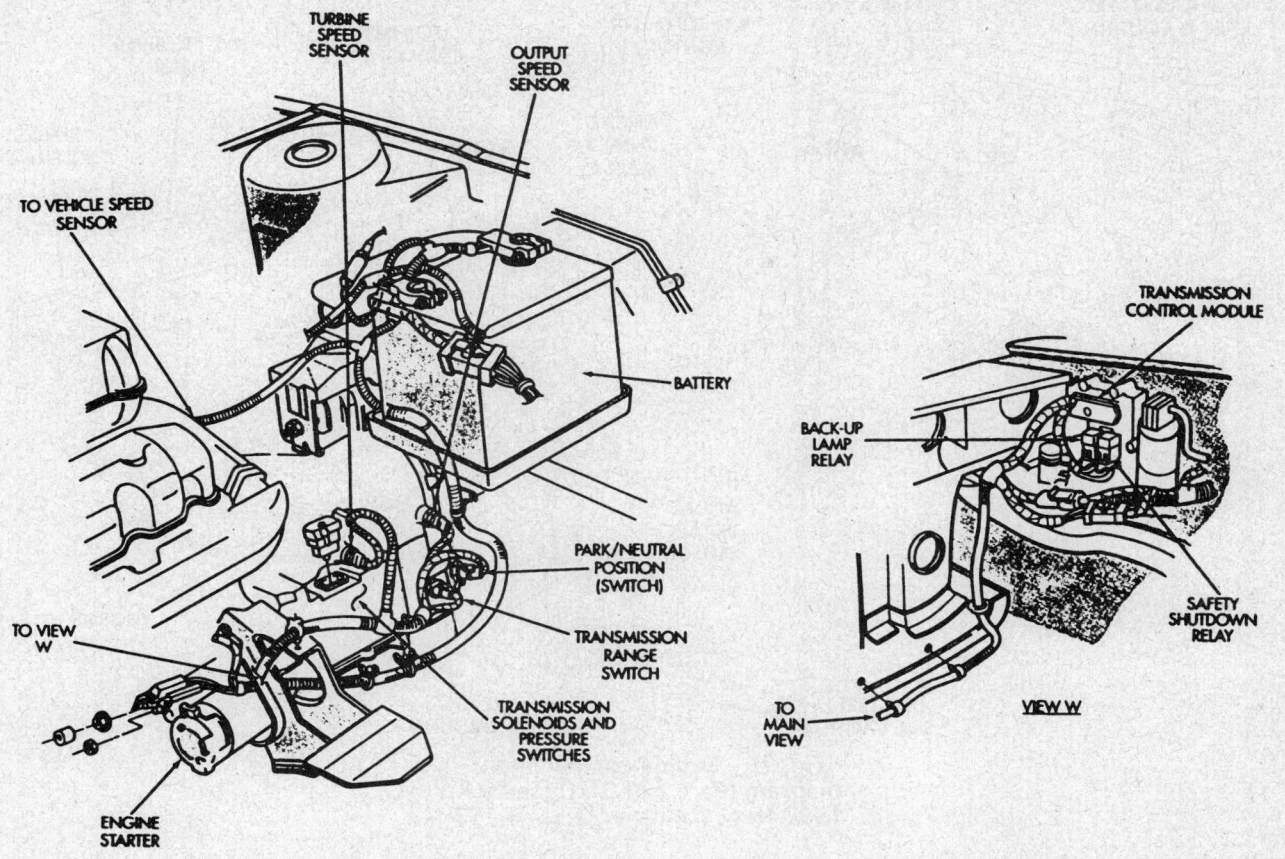

Fig. 28 Engine compartment diagram (Part 3 of 3). 1994–95 LeBaron

CR1019400104030X

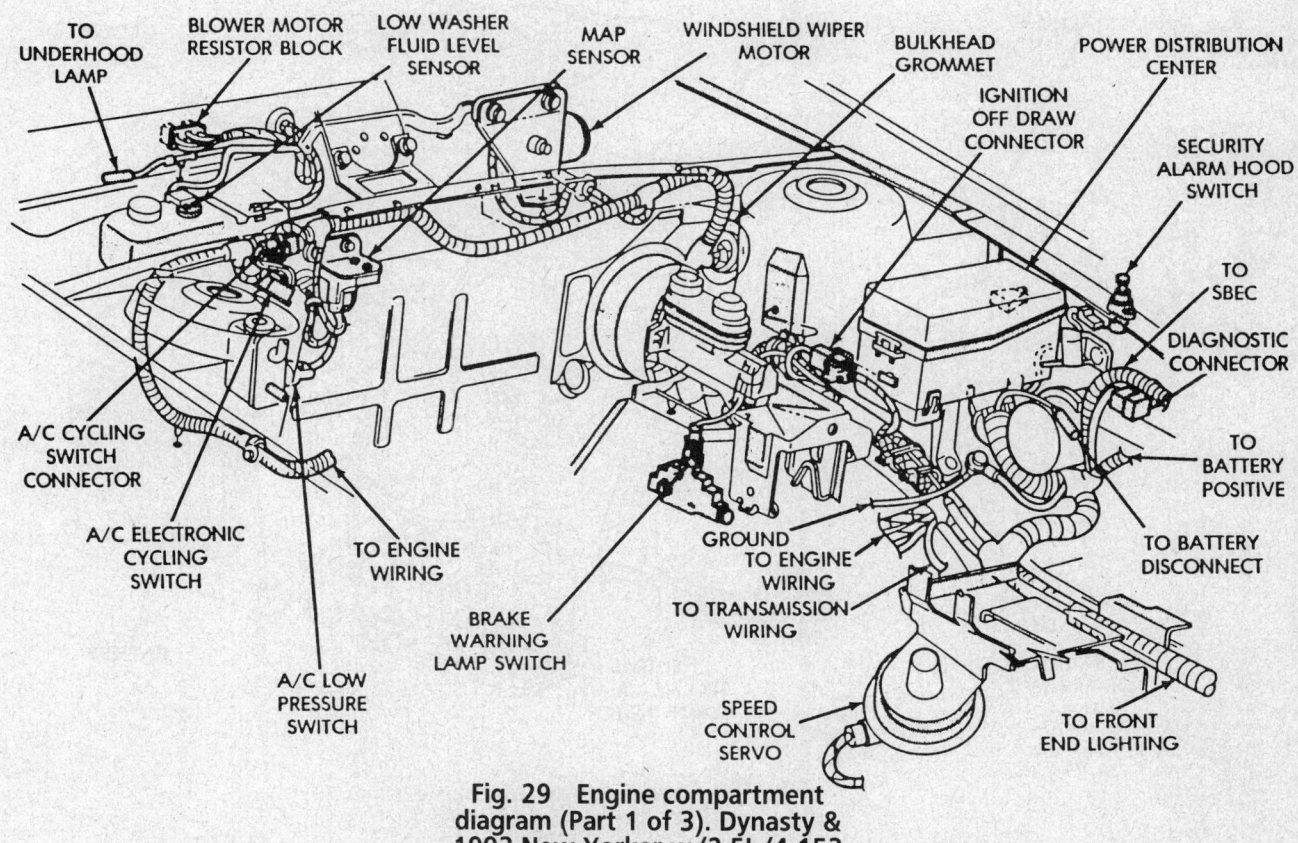

Fig. 29 Engine compartment diagram (Part 1 of 3). Dynasty & 1993 New Yorker w/2.5L/4-153

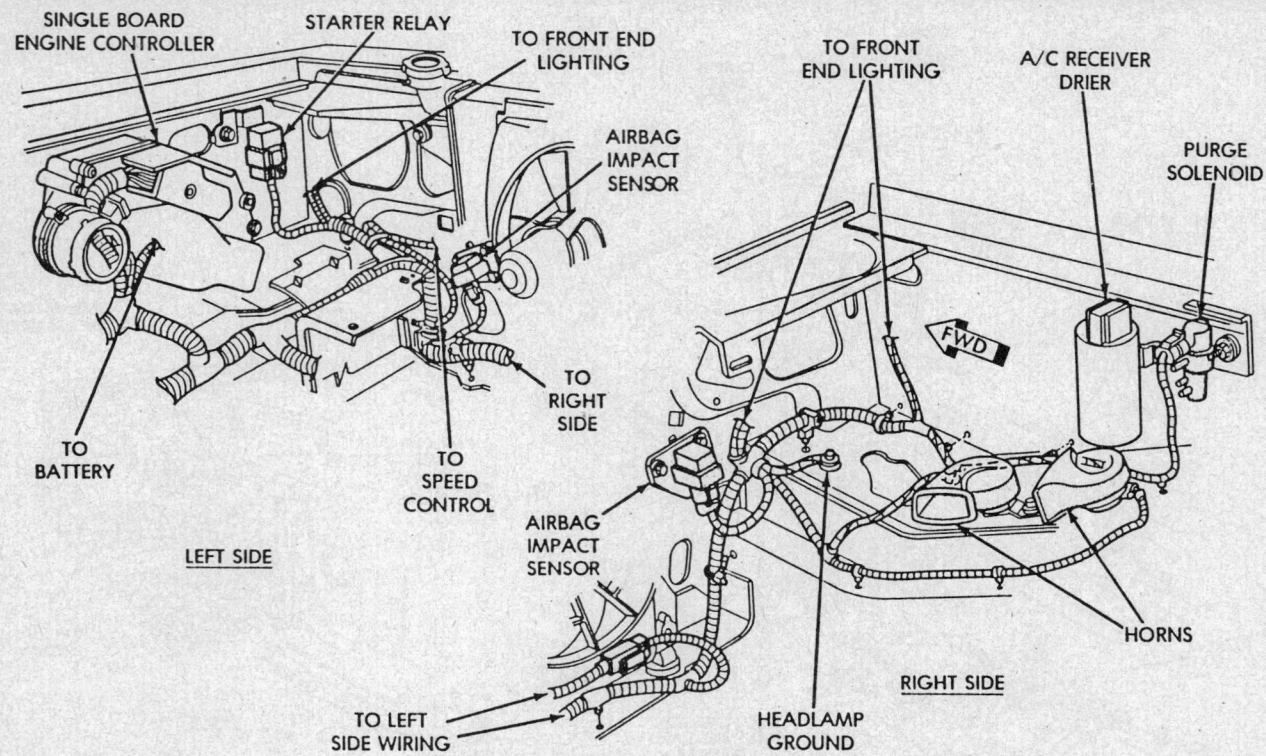

SINGLE BOARD
ENGINE CONTROLLER

STARTER RELAY

TO FRONT END
LIGHTING

AIRBAG
IMPACT
SENSOR

TO FRONT
END LIGHTING

A/C RECEIVER
DRIER

PURGE
SOLENOID

TO
BATTERY

TO
SPEED
CONTROL

LEFT SIDE

TO
RIGHT
SIDE

AIRBAG
IMPACT
SENSOR

FWD

TO LEFT
SIDE WIRING

HEADLAMP
GROUND

HORNS

RIGHT SIDE

Fig. 29 Engine compartment
diagram (Part 2 of 3). Dynasty &
1993 New Yorker w/2.5L/4-153

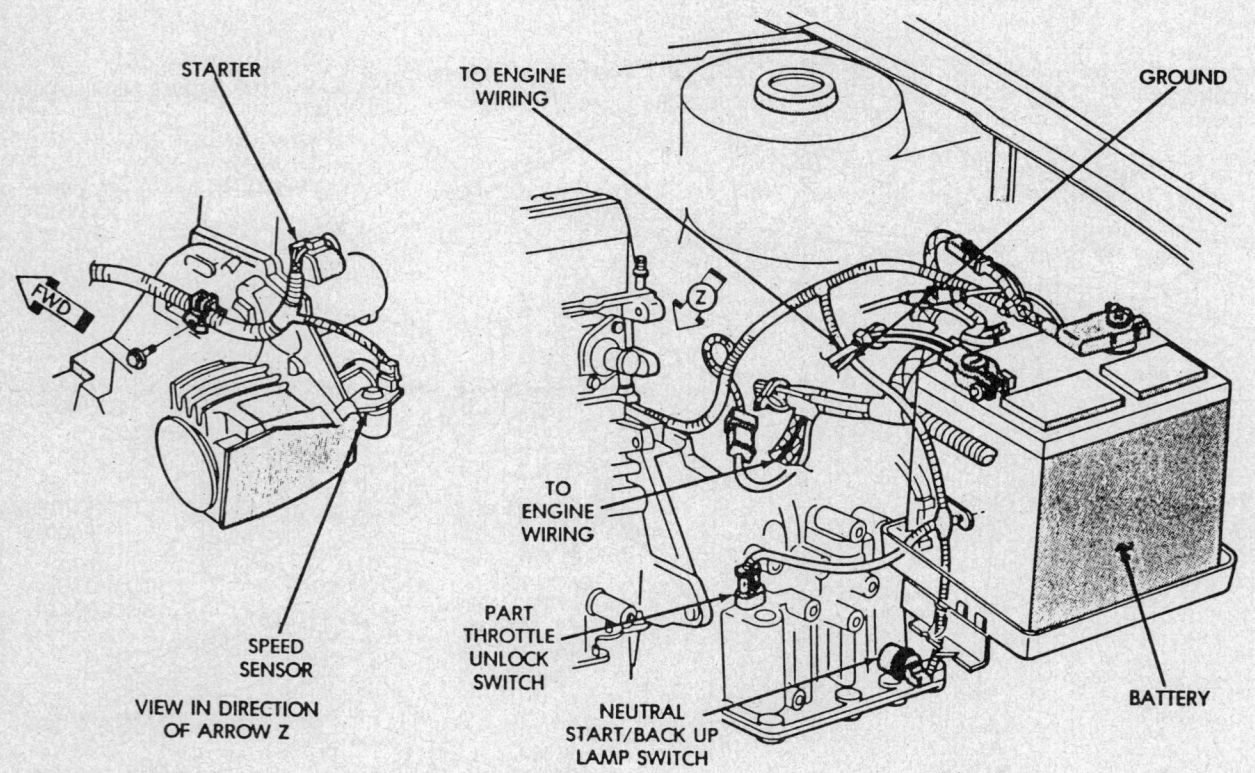

STARTER

TO ENGINE
WIRING

GROUND

FWD

TO
ENGINE
WIRING

PART
THROTTLE
UNLOCK
SWITCH

NEUTRAL
START/BACK UP
LAMP SWITCH

BATTERY

SPEED
SENSOR

VIEW IN DIRECTION
OF ARROW Z

Fig. 29 Engine compartment
diagram (Part 3 of 3). Dynasty &
1993 New Yorker w/2.5L/4-153

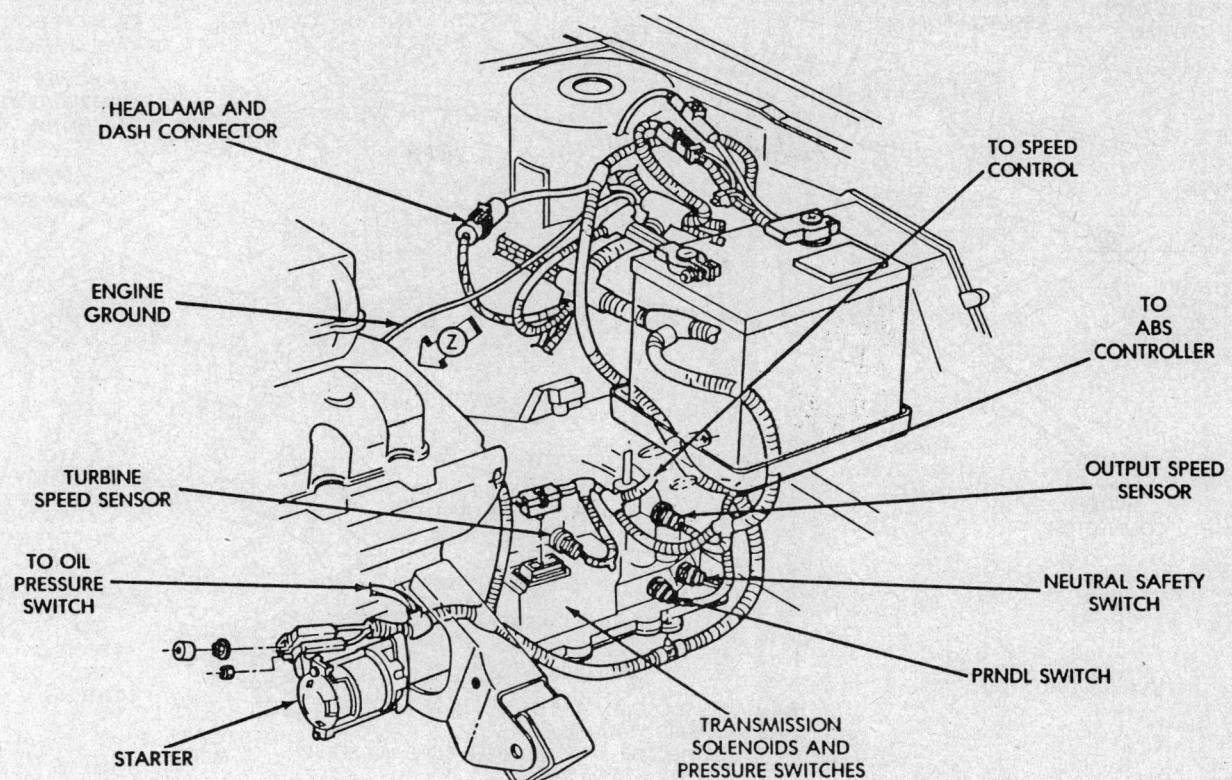

Fig. 30 Engine compartment diagram (Part 1 of 2). Dynasty & 1993 New Yorker w/3.0L/V6-182

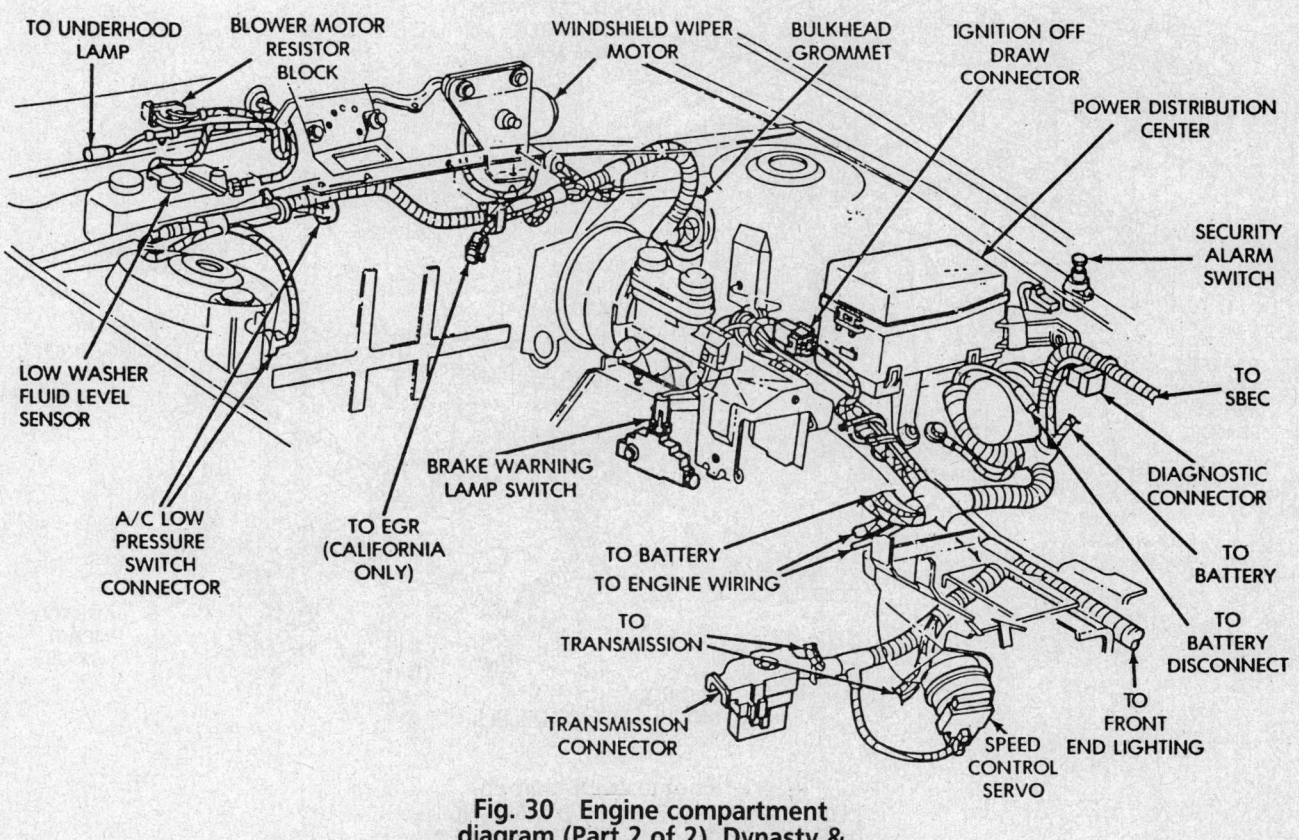

Fig. 30 Engine compartment diagram (Part 2 of 2). Dynasty & 1993 New Yorker w/3.0L/V6-182

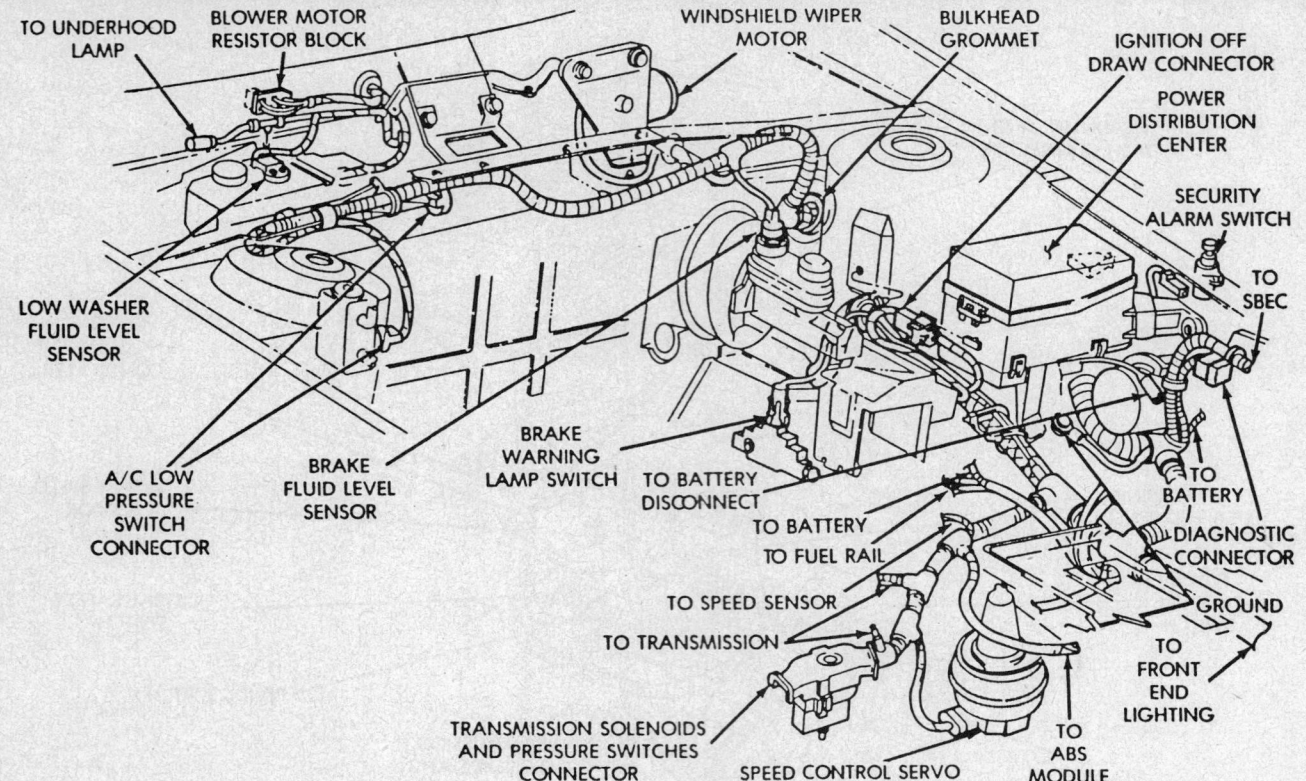

Fig. 31 Engine compartment diagram (Part 1 of 4). Dynasty & 1993 New Yorker w/3.3L/V6-202 & 3.8L/V6-231

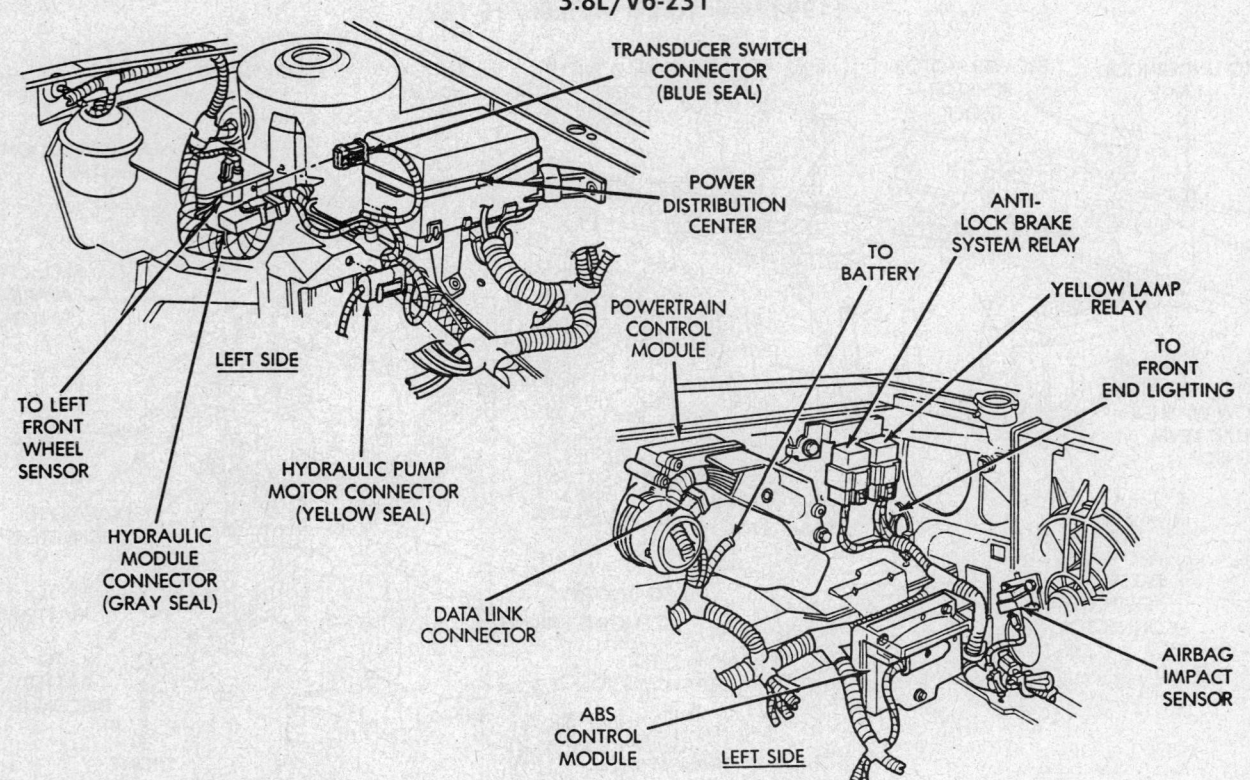

Fig. 31 Engine compartment diagram (Part 2 of 4). Dynasty & 1993 New Yorker w/3.3L/V6-202 & 3.8L/V6-231

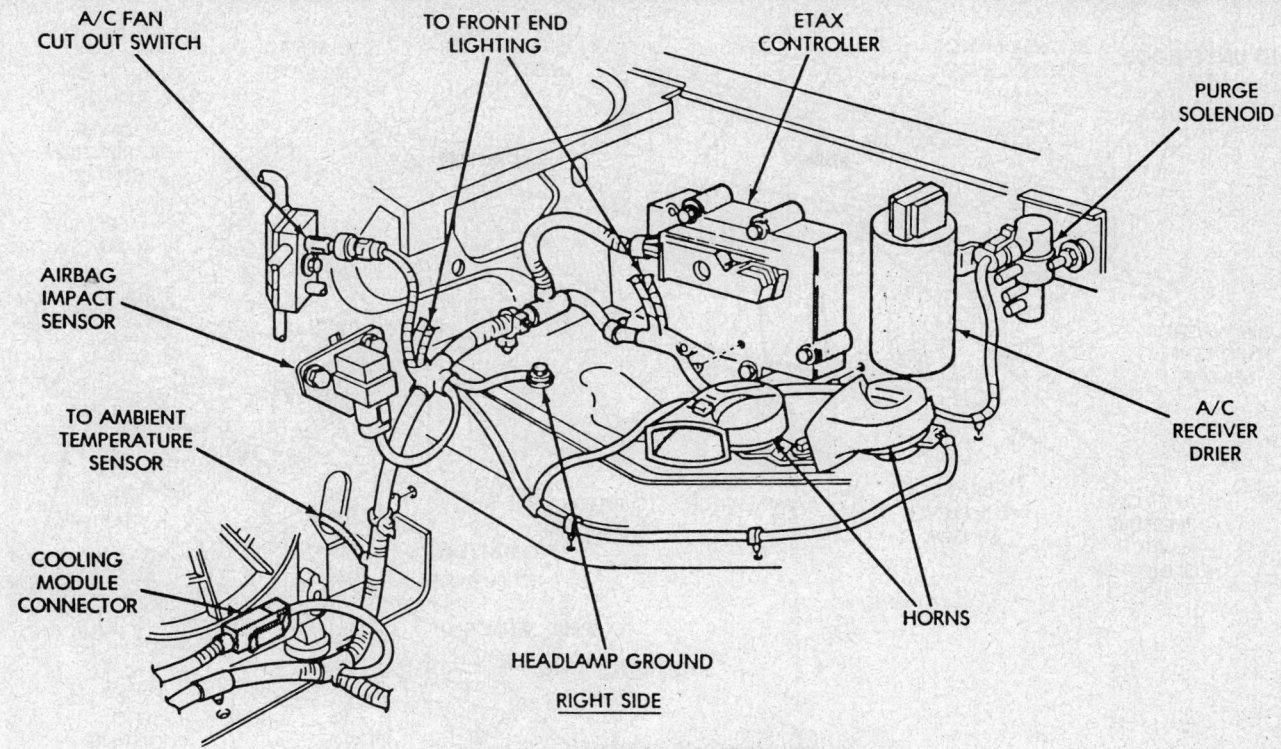

Fig. 31   Engine compartment
diagram (Part 3 of 4). Dynasty &
1993 New Yorker w/3.3L/V6-202 &
3.8L/V6-231

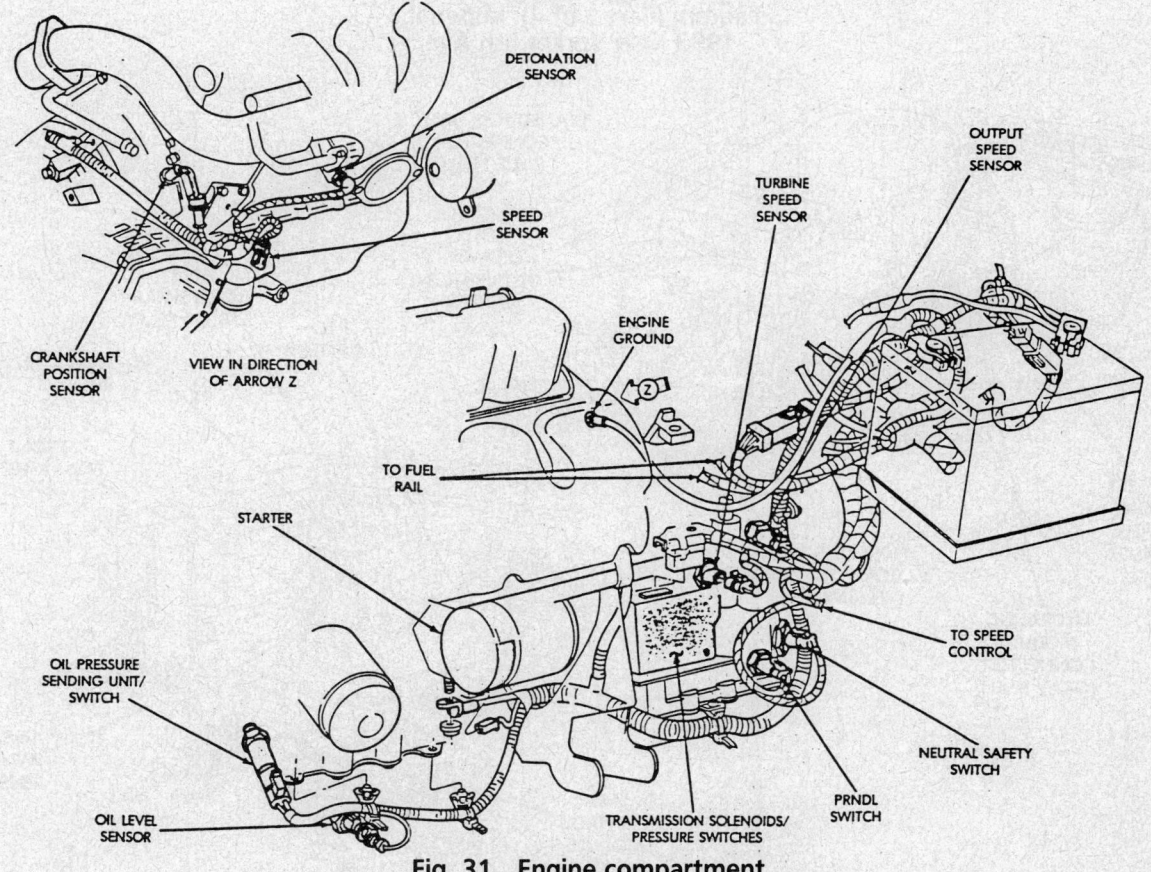

Fig. 31   Engine compartment
diagram (Part 4 of 4). Dynasty &
1993 New Yorker w/3.3L/V6-202 &
3.8L/V6-231

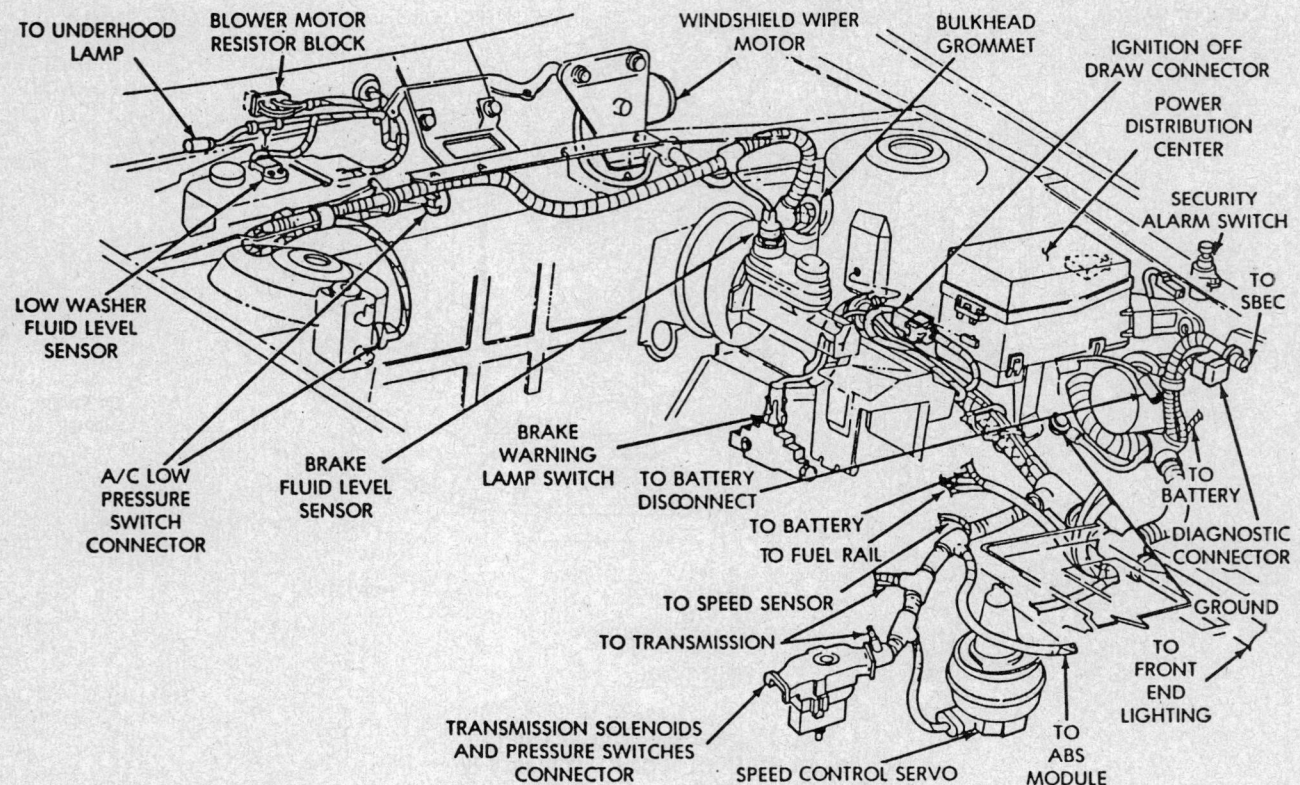

Fig. 32 Engine compartment diagram (Part 1 of 4). Imperial & 1993 New Yorker 5th Ave.

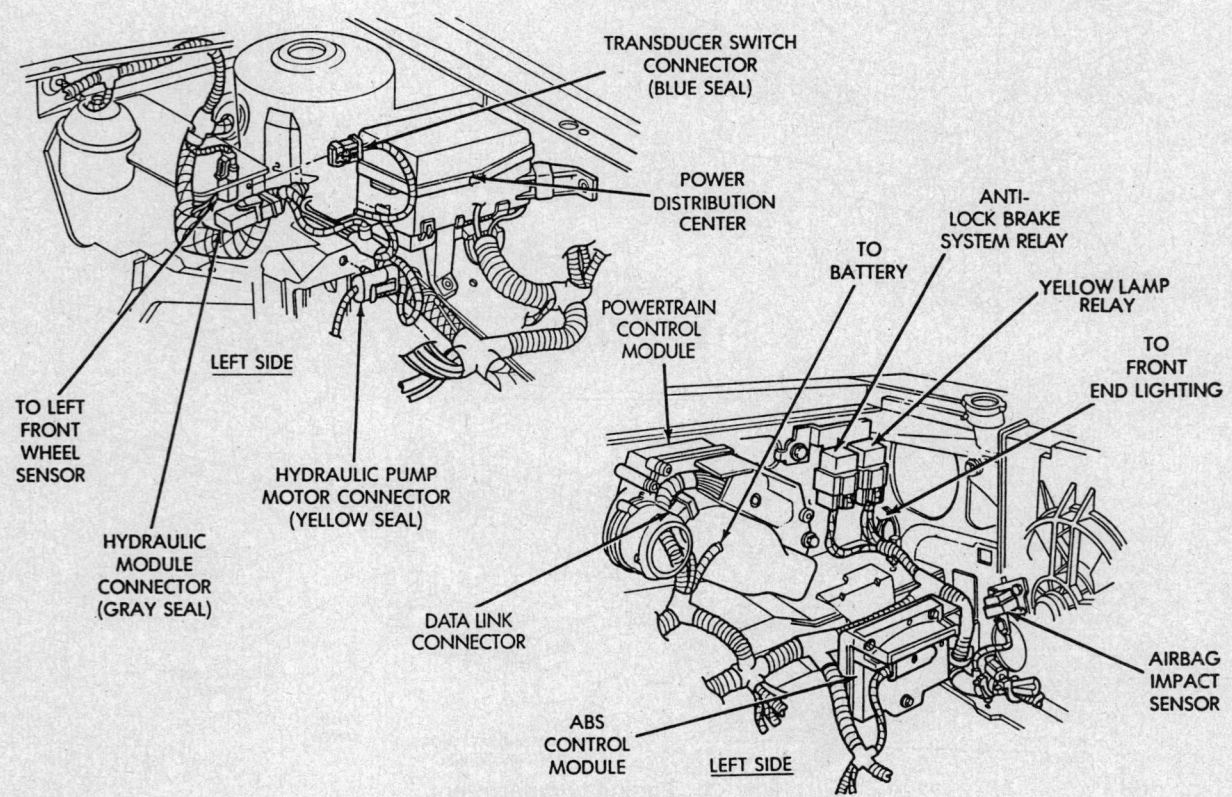

Fig. 32 Engine compartment diagram (Part 2 of 4). Imperial & 1993 New Yorker 5th Ave.

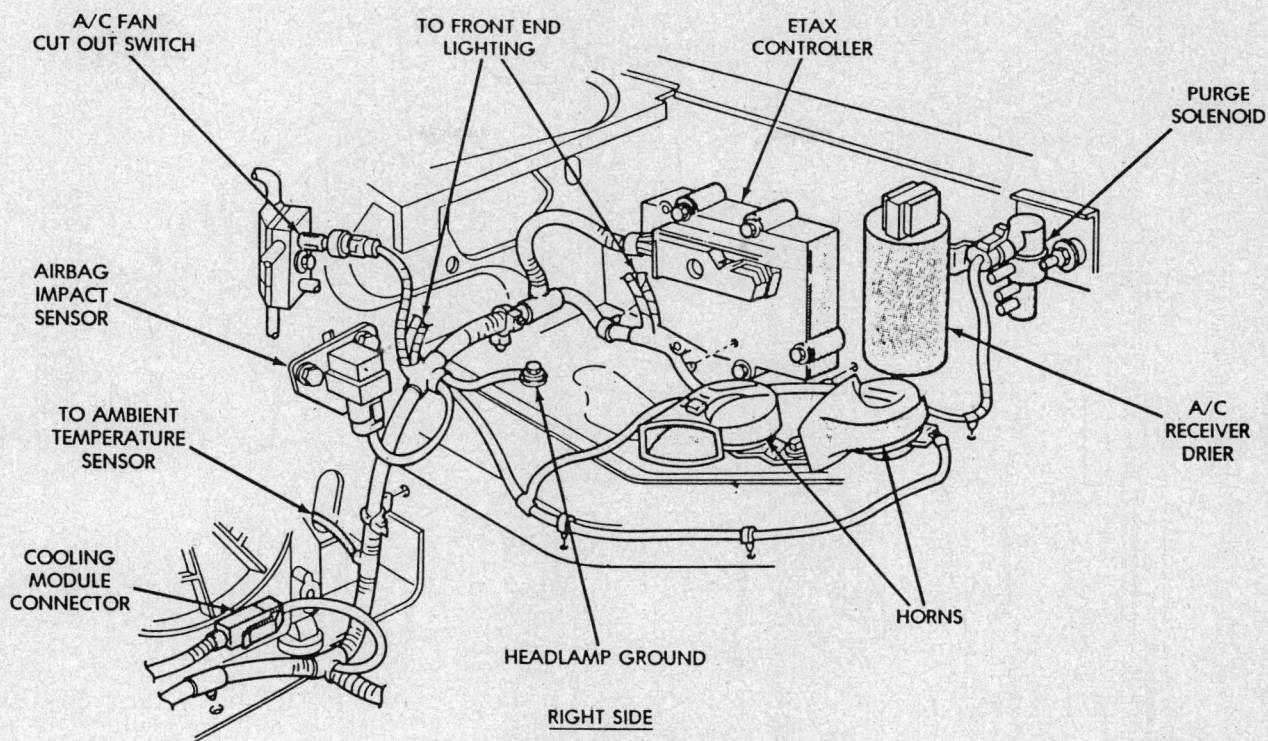

A/C FAN
CUT OUT SWITCH

TO FRONT END
LIGHTING

ETAX
CONTROLLER

PURGE
SOLENOID

AIRBAG
IMPACT
SENSOR

TO AMBIENT
TEMPERATURE
SENSOR

COOLING
MODULE
CONNECTOR

A/C
RECEIVER
DRIER

HEADLAMP GROUND

HORNS

RIGHT SIDE

Fig. 32 Engine compartment diagram (Part 3 of 4). Imperial & 1993 New Yorker 5th Ave.

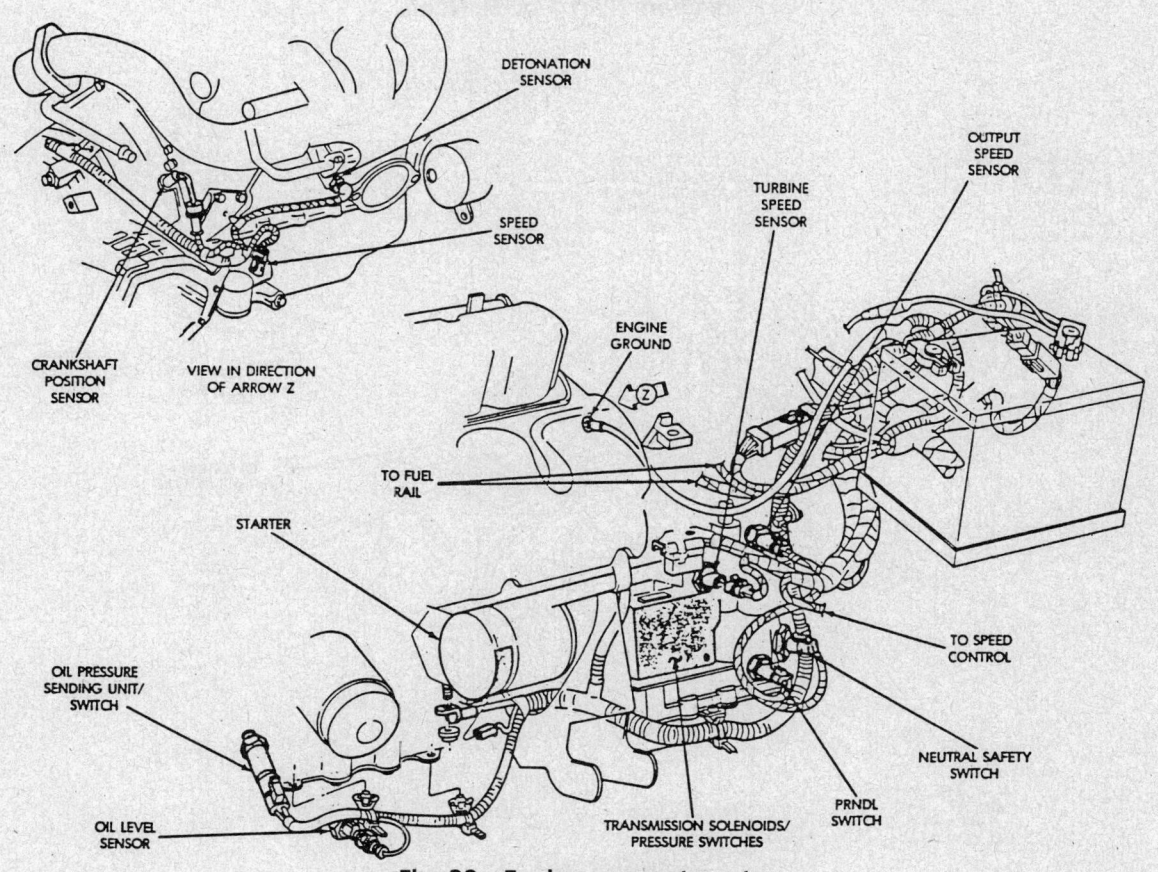

DETONATION
SENSOR

OUTPUT
SPEED
SENSOR

TURBINE
SPEED
SENSOR

SPEED
SENSOR

CRANKSHAFT
POSITION
SENSOR

VIEW IN DIRECTION
OF ARROW Z

ENGINE
GROUND

TO FUEL
RAIL

TO SPEED
CONTROL

STARTER

OIL PRESSURE
SENDING UNIT/
SWITCH

NEUTRAL SAFETY
SWITCH

OIL LEVEL
SENSOR

TRANSMISSION SOLENOIDS/
PRESSURE SWITCHES

PRNDL
SWITCH

Fig. 32 Engine compartment diagram (Part 4 of 4). Imperial & 1993 New Yorker 5th Ave.

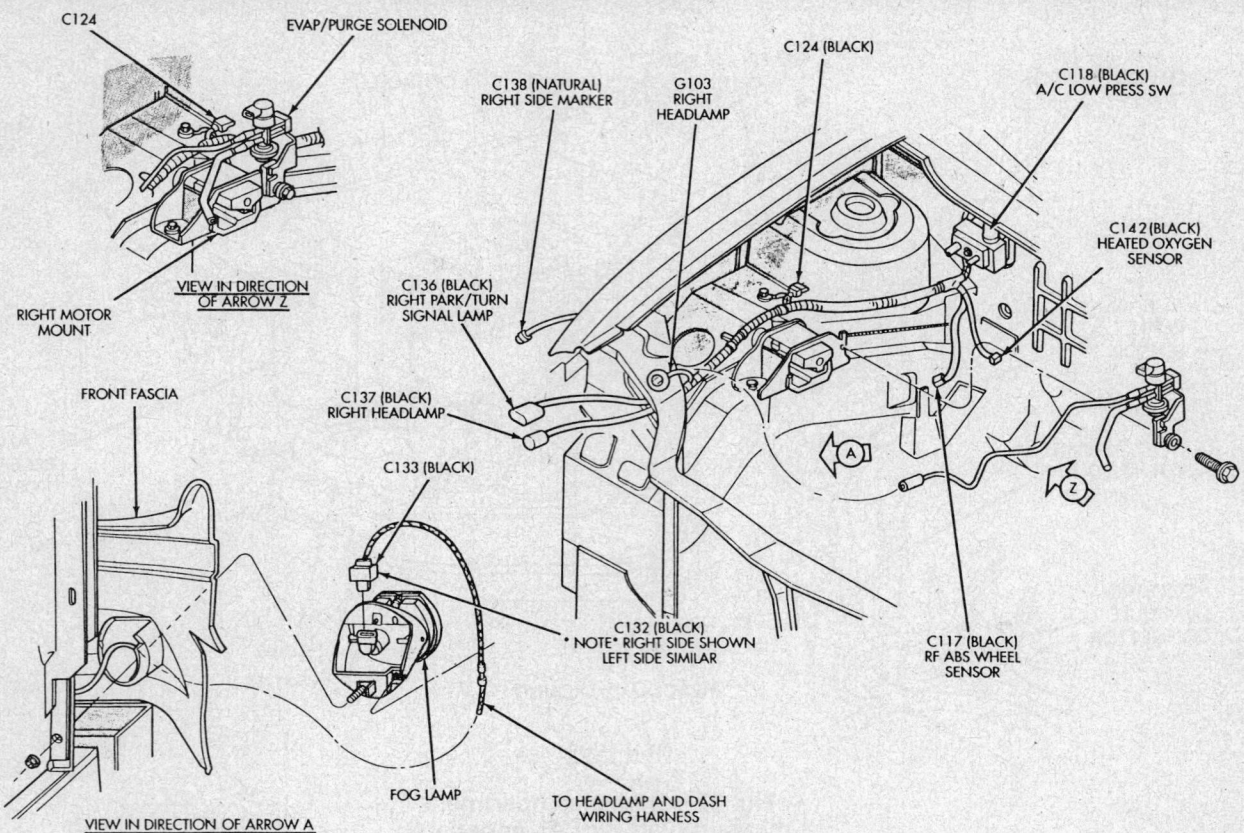

C124
EVAP/PURGE SOLENOID
VIEW IN DIRECTION OF ARROW Z
RIGHT MOTOR MOUNT

C138 (NATURAL) RIGHT SIDE MARKER
G103 RIGHT HEADLAMP
C124 (BLACK)
C118 (BLACK) A/C LOW PRESS SW
C142 (BLACK) HEATED OXYGEN SENSOR

C136 (BLACK) RIGHT PARK/TURN SIGNAL LAMP

FRONT FASCIA

C137 (BLACK) RIGHT HEADLAMP

C133 (BLACK)

C132 (BLACK) *NOTE* RIGHT SIDE SHOWN LEFT SIDE SIMILAR

C117 (BLACK) RF ABS WHEEL SENSOR

FOG LAMP
TO HEADLAMP AND DASH WIRING HARNESS

VIEW IN DIRECTION OF ARROW A

Fig. 33   Engine compartment diagram (Part 1 of 3). Neon

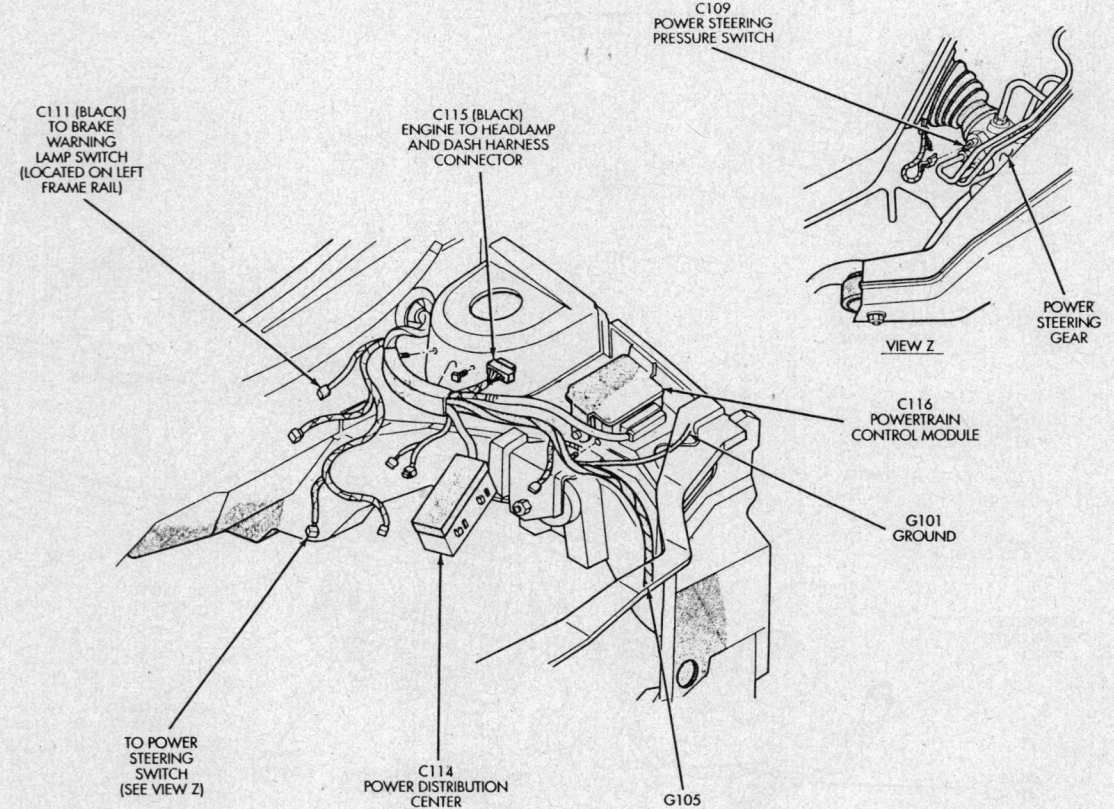

C109 POWER STEERING PRESSURE SWITCH

C111 (BLACK) TO BRAKE WARNING LAMP SWITCH (LOCATED ON LEFT FRAME RAIL)

C115 (BLACK) ENGINE TO HEADLAMP AND DASH HARNESS CONNECTOR

VIEW Z
POWER STEERING GEAR

C116 POWERTRAIN CONTROL MODULE

G101 GROUND

TO POWER STEERING SWITCH (SEE VIEW Z)

C114 POWER DISTRIBUTION CENTER

G105

Fig. 33   Engine compartment diagram (Part 2 of 3). Neon

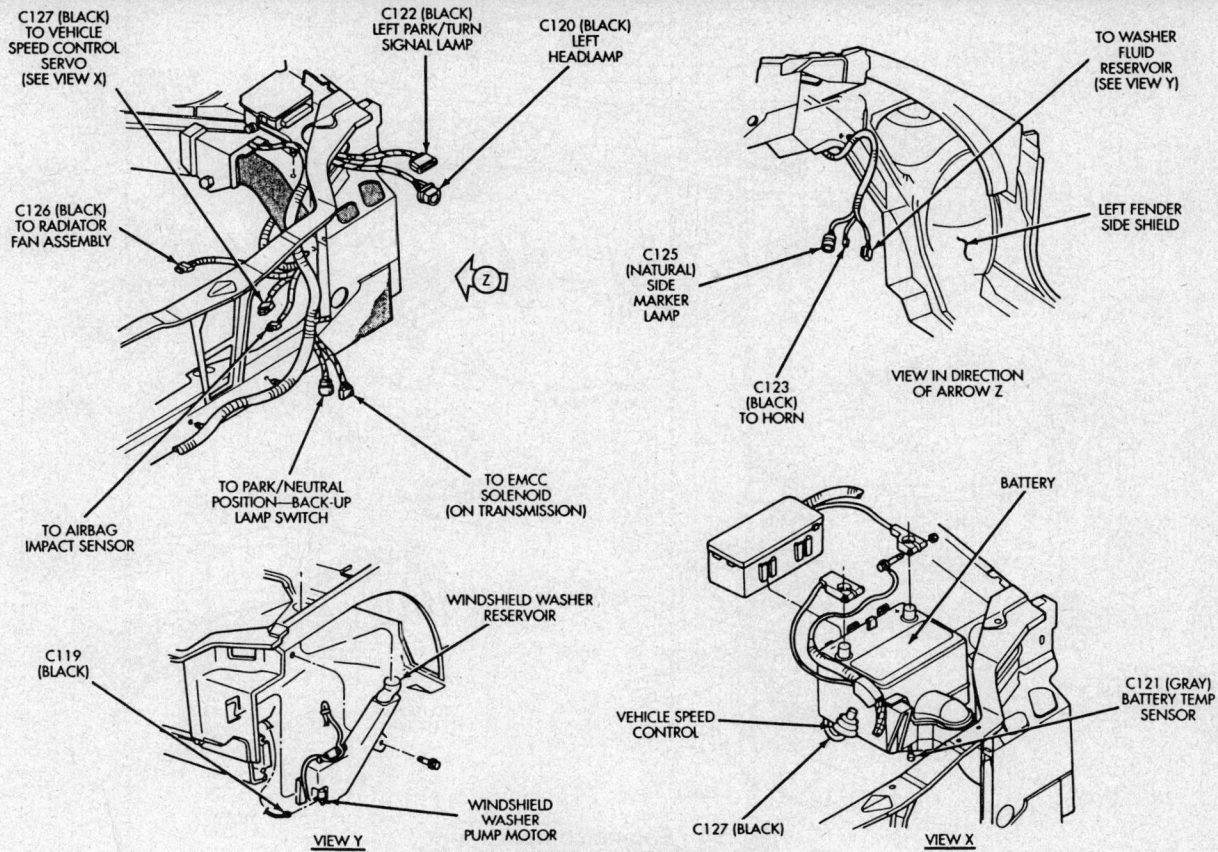

Fig. 33 Engine compartment
diagram (Part 3 of 3). Neon

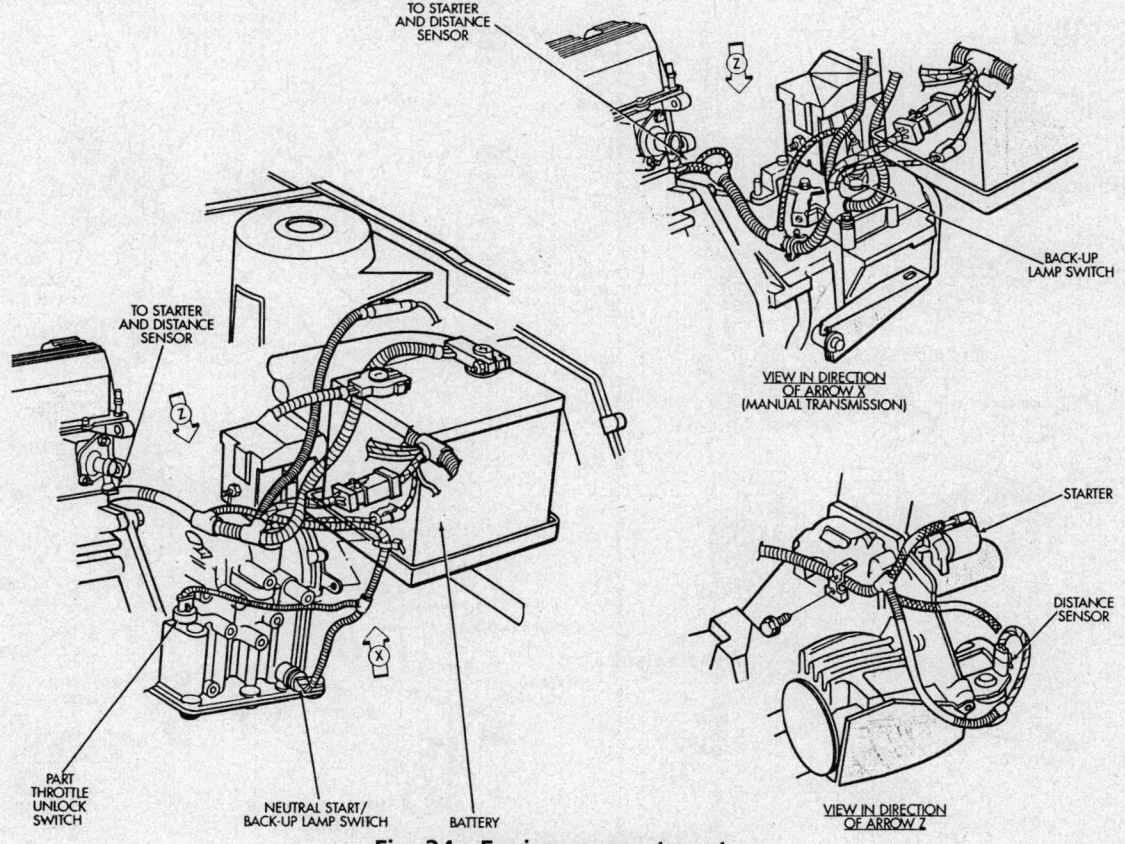

Fig. 34 Engine compartment
diagram (Part 1 of 2). 1993–94
Shadow & Sundance

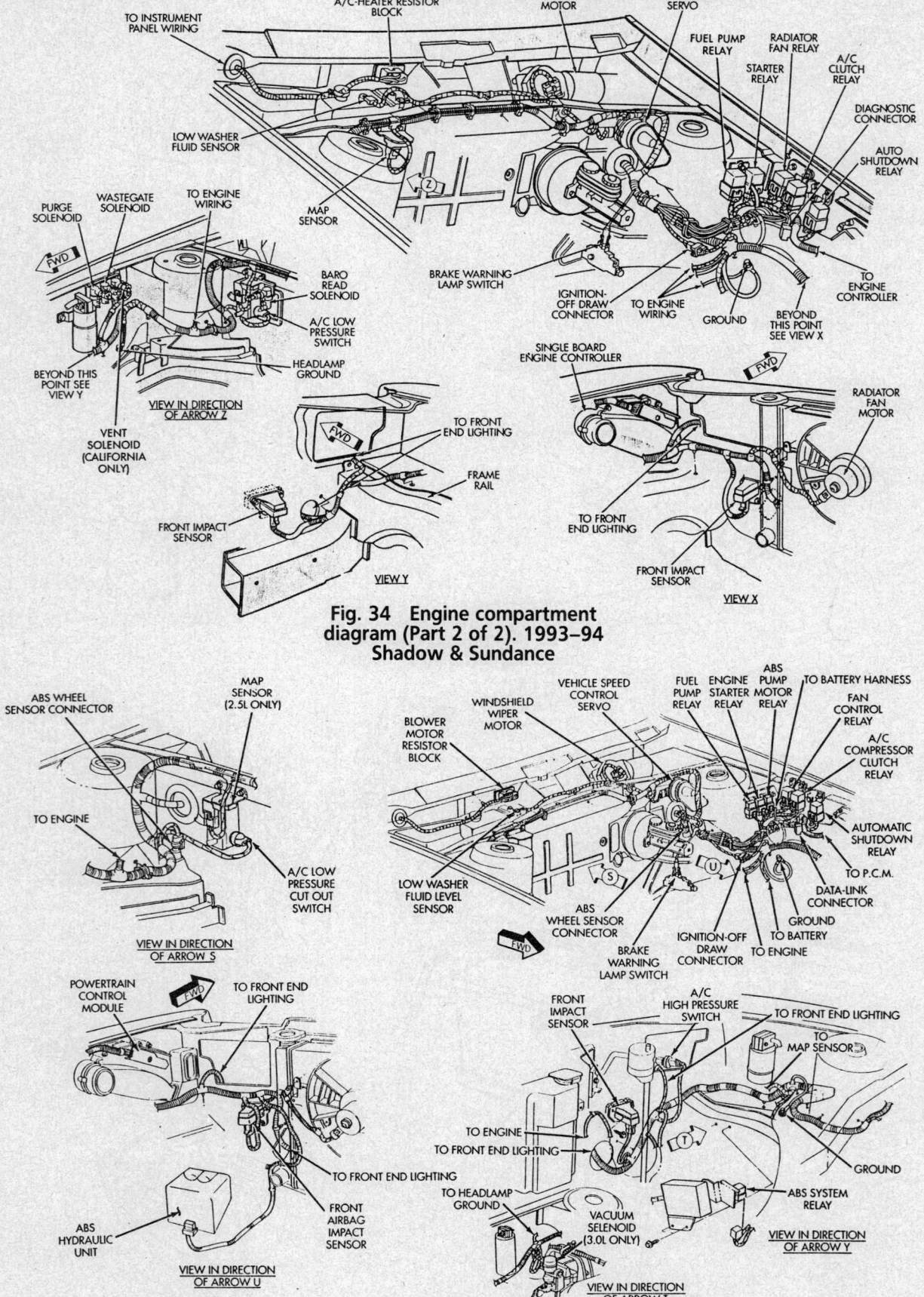

Fig. 34 Engine compartment diagram (Part 2 of 2). 1993–94 Shadow & Sundance

Fig. 34 Engine compartment diagram (Part 2 of 2). 1993–94 Shadow & Sundance

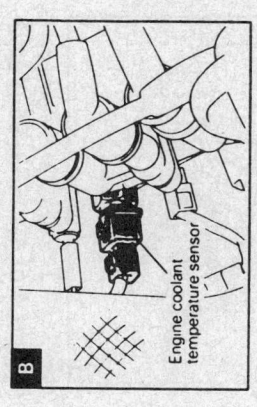
B
Engine coolant temperature sensor

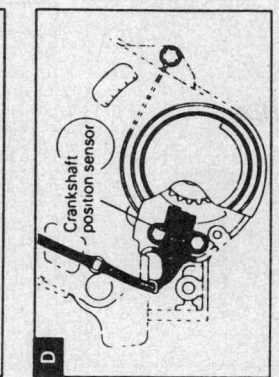
D
Crankshaft position sensor

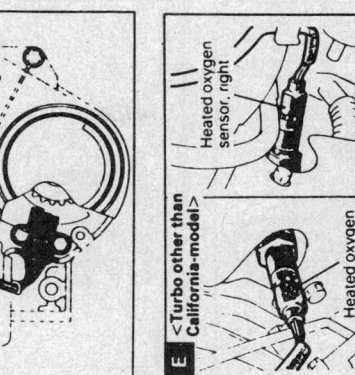
E <Turbo other than California-model>
Heated oxygen sensor, right
Heated oxygen sensor, left

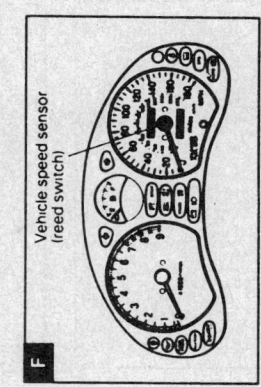
F
Vehicle speed sensor (reed switch)

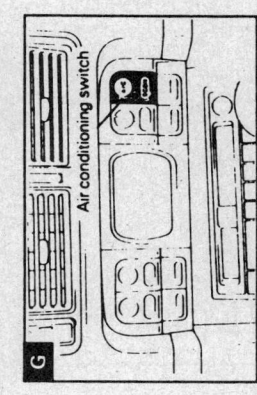
G
Air conditioning switch

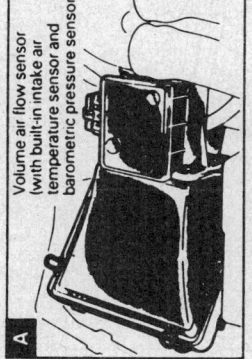
A
Volume air flow sensor (with built-in intake air temperature sensor and barometric pressure sensor)

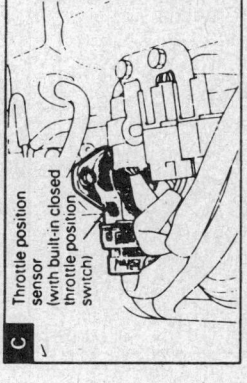
C
Throttle position sensor (with built-in closed throttle position switch)

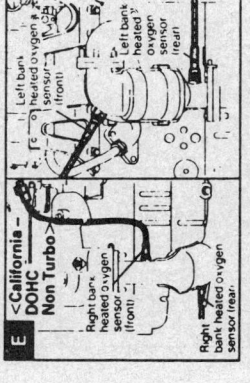
E <California — DOHC Non Turbo>
Left bank heated oxygen sensor (front)
Left bank heated oxygen sensor (rear)
Right bank heated oxygen sensor (front)
Right bank heated oxygen sensor (rear)

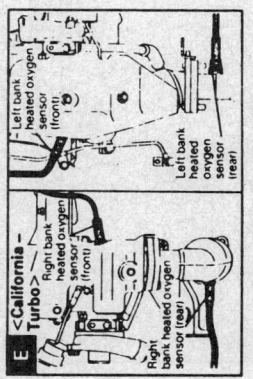
E <California — Turbo>
Left bank heated oxygen sensor (front)
Left bank heated oxygen sensor (rear)
Right bank heated oxygen sensor (front)
Right bank heated oxygen sensor (rear)

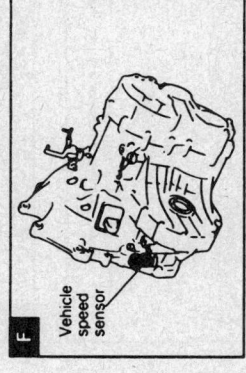
F
Vehicle speed sensor

CR1019300108020X

Fig. 35 Engine compartment diagram (Part 2 of 4). 1993–95 Stealth w/DOHC & California emissions

Name	Symbol
Air-conditioning relay	O
Air-conditioning switch	G
Camshaft position sensor	AA
Check engine malfunction indicator lamp	P
Crankshaft position sensor	D
Diagnostic output terminal and diagnostic test mode control terminal	R
EGR solenoid	Z
EGR temperature sensor	Y
Engine control module	S
Engine coolant temperature sensor	B
Evaporative emission purge solenoid	X
Fuel pressure solenoid <Turbo>	V
Heated oxygen sensor	E
Idle air control motor (stepper motor)	L
Ignition coil ignition power transistor)	M
Ignition timing adjusting terminal	Q
Injector	K
Knock sensor	T
Multiport fuel injection (MFI) relay	N
Park Neutral position switch <AT>	I
Power steering pressure switch	H
Resistor <Turbo>	W
Throttle position sensor (with built-in closed throttle position switch)	C
Turbocharger waste gate solenoid <Turbo>	U
Variable induction control motor (DC motor) (with built-in induction control valve position sensor) <Non Turbo>	J
Vehicle speed sensor (reed switch)	F
Volume air flow sensor (with built-in intake air temperature sensor and barometric pressure sensor)	A

NOTE
The "Name" column is in alphabetical order.

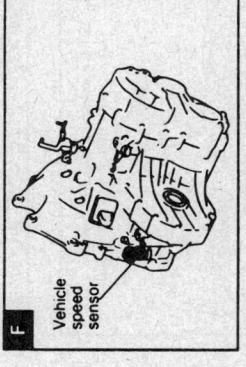

CR1019300108010X

Fig. 35 Engine compartment diagram (Part 1 of 4). 1993–95 Stealth w/DOHC & California emissions

S — Engine control module

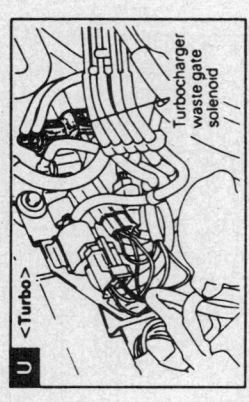

U <Turbo> — Turbocharger waste gate solenoid

W <Turbo> — Resistor

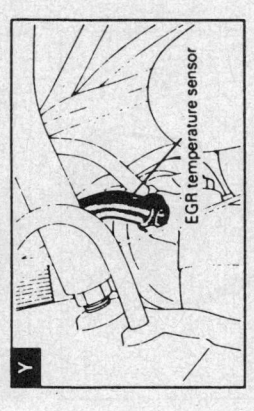

Y — EGR temperature sensor

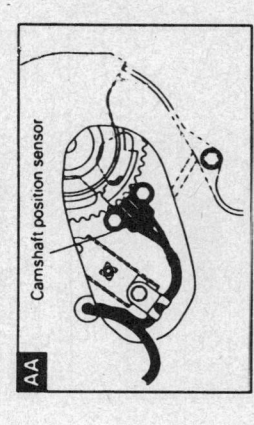

AA — Camshaft position sensor

CR101930010804D

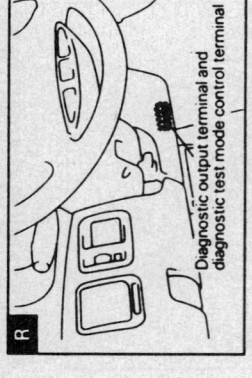

R — Diagnostic output terminal and diagnostic test mode control terminal

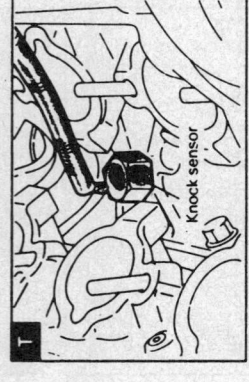

T — Knock sensor

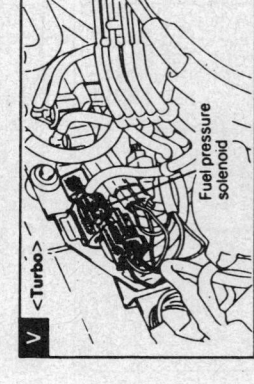

V <Turbo> — Fuel pressure solenoid

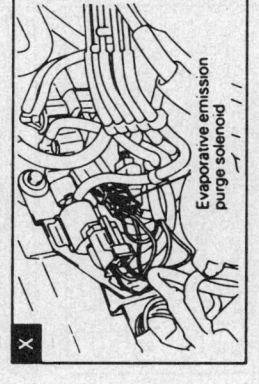

X — Evaporative emission purge solenoid

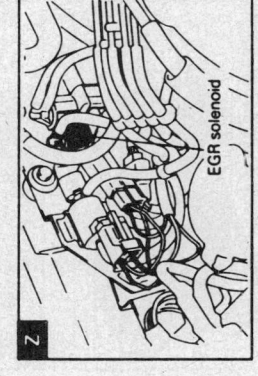

Z — EGR solenoid

Fig. 35   Engine compartment diagram (Part 4 of 4). 1993–95 Stealth w/DOHC & California emissions

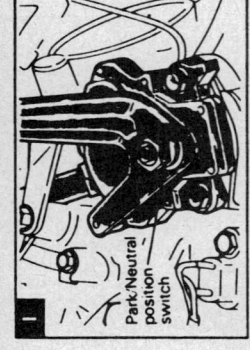

I — Park/Neutral position switch

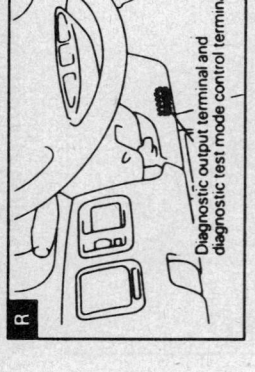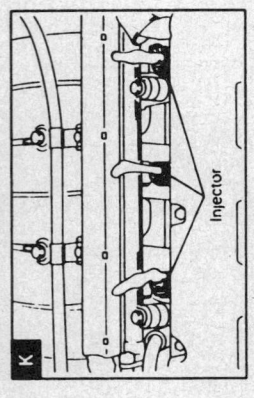

K — Injector

M — Ignition coil (ignition power transistor)

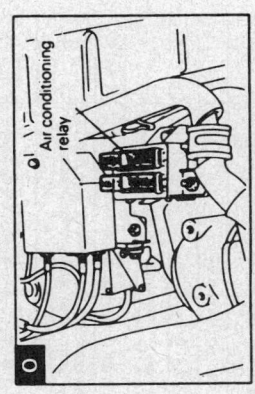

O — Air conditioning relay

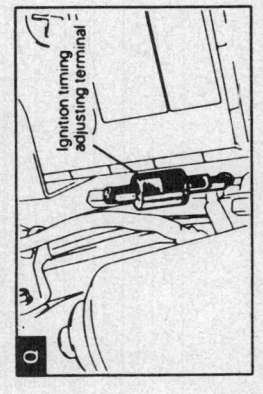

Q — Ignition timing adjusting terminal

CR101930010803DX

Fig. 35   Engine compartment diagram (Part 3 of 4). 1993–95 Stealth w/DOHC & California emissions

H — Power steering pressure switch

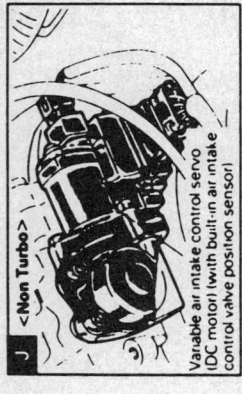

J <Non Turbo> — Variable air intake control servo (IAC motor) (with built-in air intake control valve position sensor)

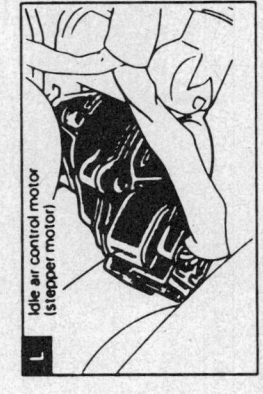

L — Idle air control motor (stepper motor)

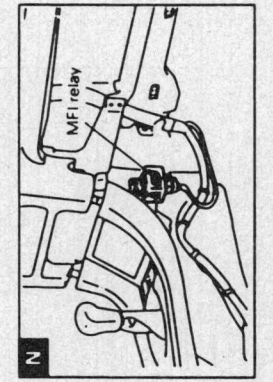

N — MFI relay

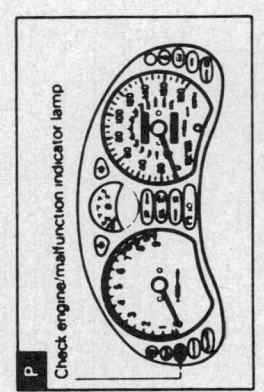

P — Check engine/malfunction indicator lamp

B — Engine coolant temperature sensor

D — Crankshaft position sensor

F — Vehicle speed sensor (reed switch)

H — Power steering pressure switch

J — Variable air intake control servo (DC motor) (with built-in intake control valve position sensor)

A — Volume air flow sensor (with built-in intake air temperature sensor and barometric pressure sensor)

C — Throttle position sensor (with built-in closed throttle position switch)

E — Heated oxygen sensor

G — Air conditioning switch

I — Park/neutral position switch

CR1019300107020X

Fig. 36 Engine compartment diagram (Part 2 of 4). 1993–95 Stealth w/DOHC & Federal emissions

Name	Symbol
Air-conditioning relay	O
Air-conditioning switch	G
Camshaft position sensor	V
Check engine/malfunction indicator lamp	P
Crankshaft position sensor	D
Diagnostic output terminal and diagnostic test mode control terminal	R
Engine control module	S
Engine coolant temperature sensor	B
Evaporative emission purge solenoid	U
Heated oxygen sensor	E
Idle air control motor (stepper motor)	L
Ignition coil (ignition power transistor)	M
Ignition timing adjusting terminal	Q
Injector	K
Knock sensor	T
Multiport fuel injection (MFI) relay	N
Park/Neutral position switch <AT>	I
Power steering pressure switch	H
Throttle position sensor (with built-in closed throttle position switch)	C
Variable induction control motor (DC motor) (with built-in induction control valve position sensor)	J
Vehicle speed sensor	F
Volume air flow sensor (with built-in intake air temperature sensor and barometric pressure sensor)	A

NOTE
The "Name" column is in alphabetical order.

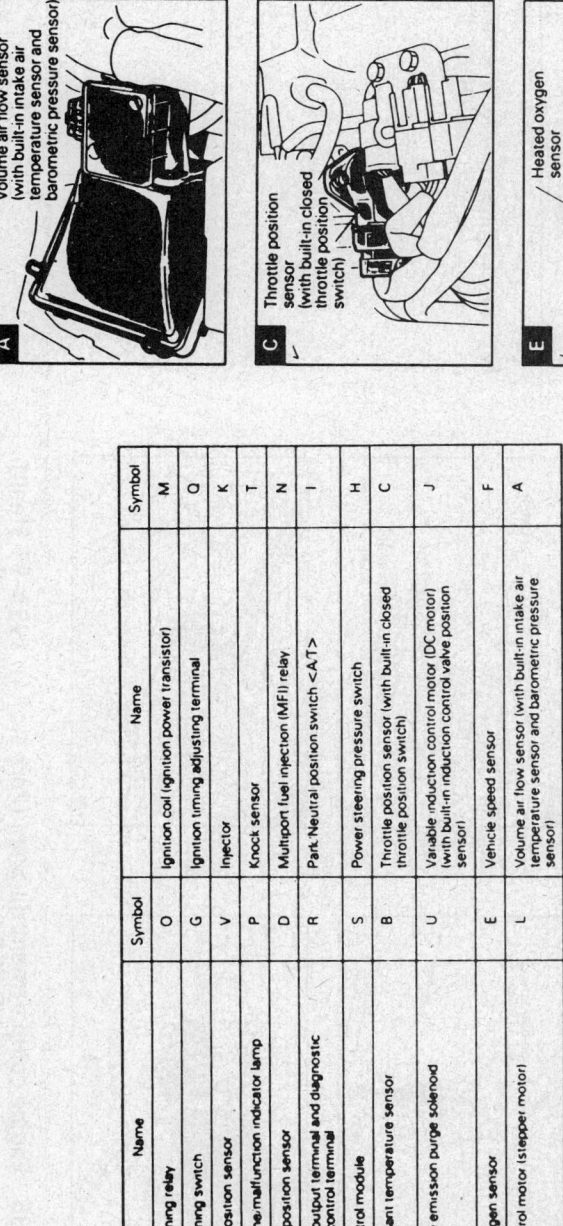

CR1019300107010X

Fig. 36 Engine compartment diagram (Part 1 of 4). 1993–95 Stealth w/DOHC & Federal emissions

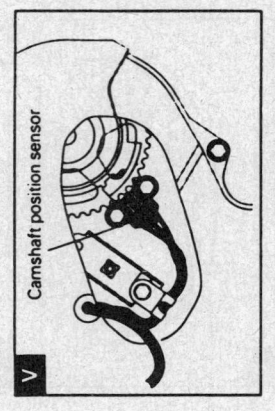

CR101930010704DX

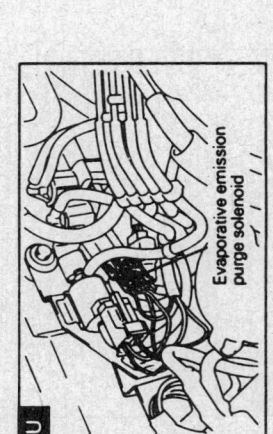

Fig. 36 Engine compartment diagram (Part 4 of 4). 1993–95 Stealth w/DOHC & Federal emissions

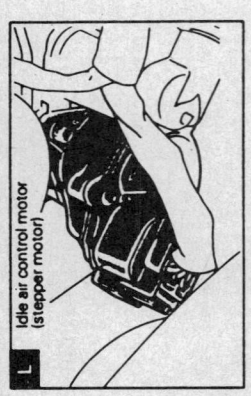

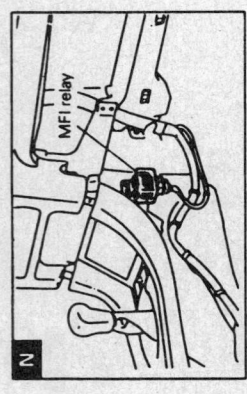

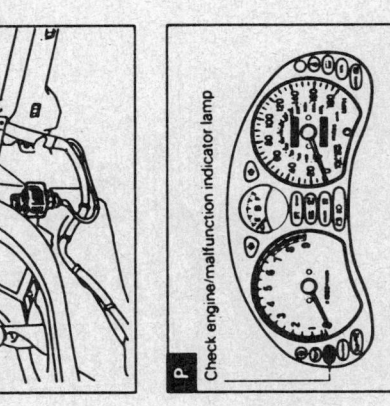

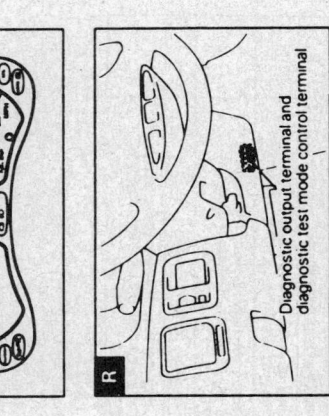

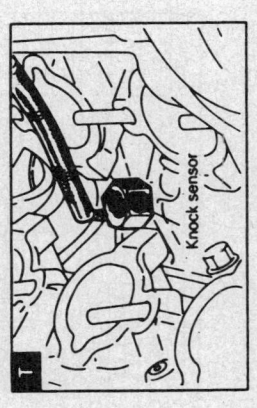

CR101930010703DX

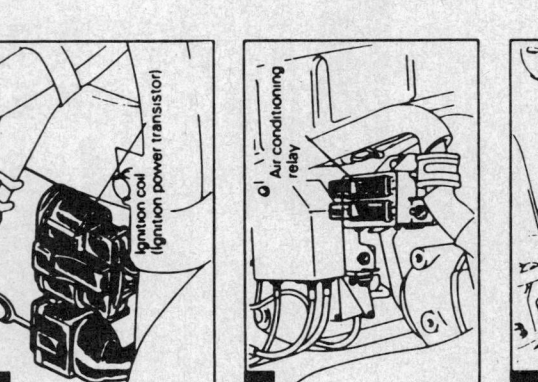

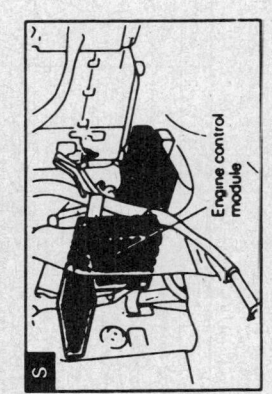

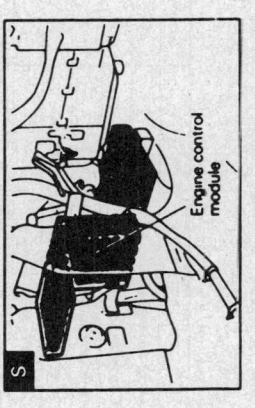

Fig. 36 Engine compartment diagram (Part 3 of 4). 1993–95 Stealth w/DOHC & Federal emissions

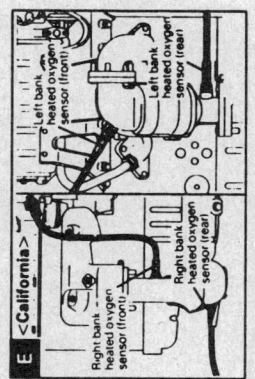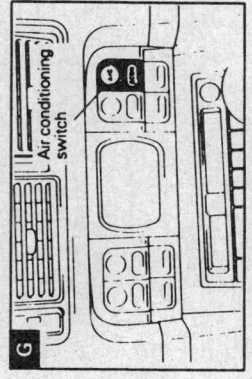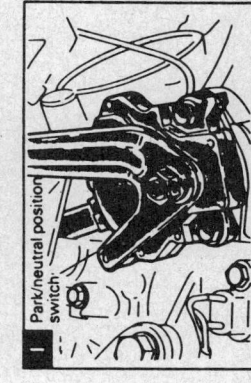

B — Engine coolant temperature sensor

D — Camshaft position sensor and crankshaft position sensor

E — <California> Left bank heated oxygen sensor (front), Left bank heated oxygen sensor (rear), Right bank heated oxygen sensor (front), Right bank heated oxygen sensor (rear)

G — Air conditioning switch

I — Park/neutral position switch

CR101930010602OX

Fig. 37   Engine compartment diagram (Part 2 of 4). 1993–95 Stealth w/SOHC

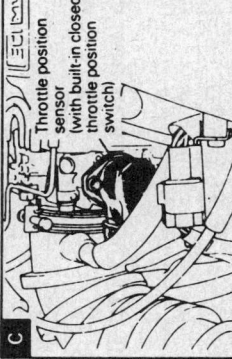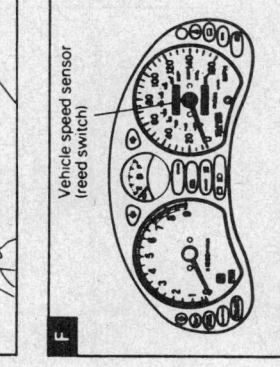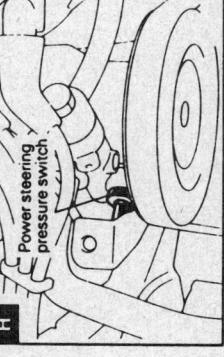

A — Volume air flow sensor (with built-in intake air temperature sensor and barometric pressure sensor)

C — Throttle position sensor (with built-in closed throttle position switch)

E — <Federal, Canada> Heated oxygen sensor

F — Vehicle speed sensor (reed switch)

H — Power steering pressure switch

CR101930010601OX

Name	Symbol
Air conditioning relay	O
Air conditioning switch	G
Camshaft position sensor and crankshaft position sensor	D
Check engine/malfunction indicator lamp	P
EGR solenoid <California>	V
EGR temperature sensor <California>	T
Engine control module	S
Engine coolant temperature sensor	B
Evaporative emission purge solenoid	U
Heated oxygen sensor	E
Idle air control motor (stepper motor)	L
Ignition coil (ignition power transistor)	M
Ignition timing adjusting terminal	Q
Injector	K
Multiport fuel injection (MFI) relay	N
Diagnostic output terminal and diagnostic test mode control terminal	R
Park/Neutral position switch <AT>	I
Power steering pressure switch	H
Throttle position sensor (with built-in closed throttle position switch)	C
Variable air intake control servo (DC motor) (with built-in air intake control valve position sensor)	J
Vehicle speed sensor (reed switch)	F
Volume air flow sensor (with built-in intake air temperature sensor and barometric pressure sensor)	A

NOTE
The "Name" column is in alphabetical order.

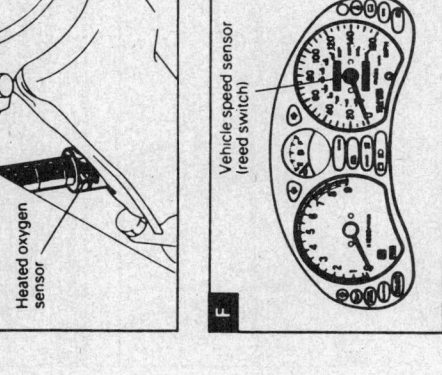

Fig. 37   Engine compartment diagram (Part 1 of 4). 1993–95 Stealth w/SOHC

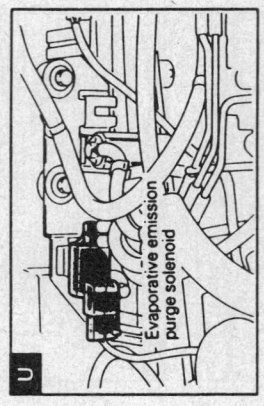

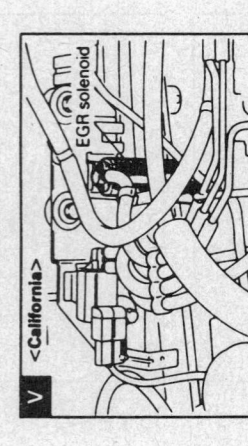

Fig. 37 Engine compartment diagram (Part 4 of 4). 1993-95 Stealth w/SOHC

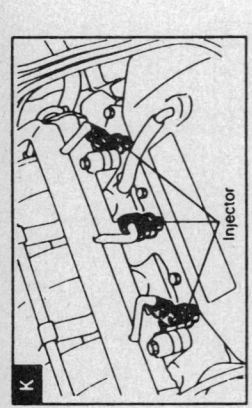

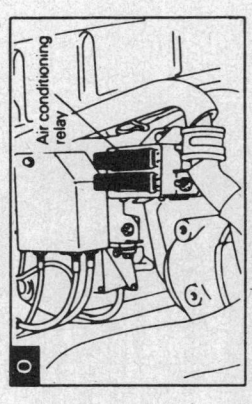

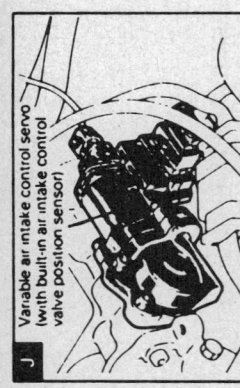

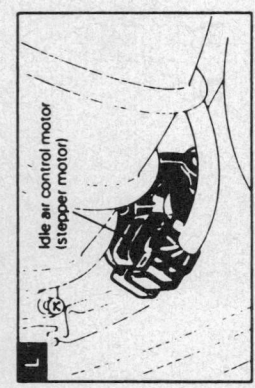

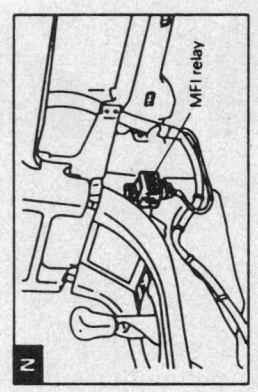

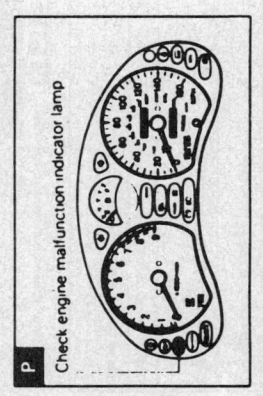

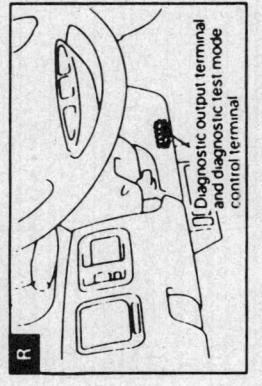

Fig. 37 Engine compartment diagram (Part 3 of 4). 1993-95 Stealth w/SOHC

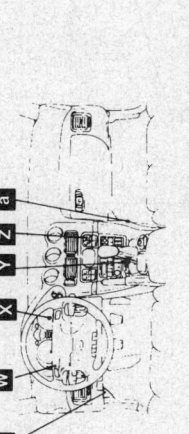

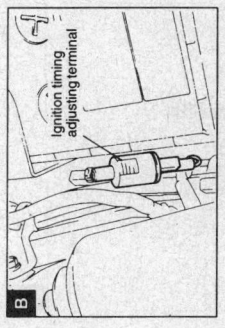

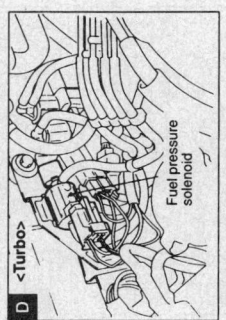

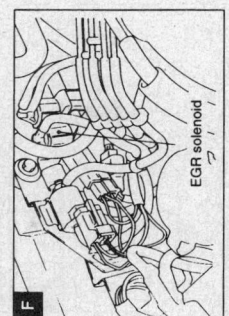

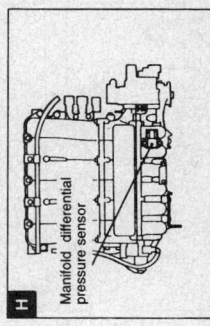

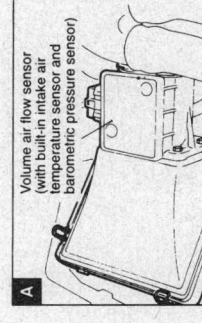

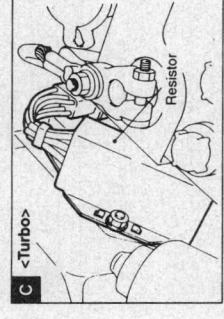

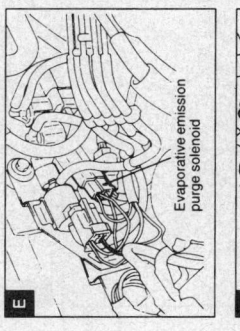

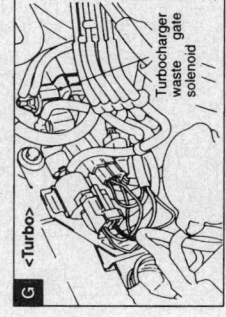

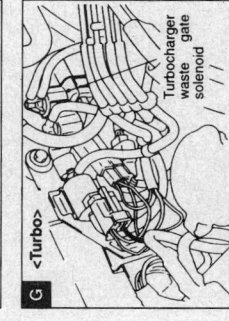

CR10196002800020X

Fig. 38 Engine compartment diagram (Part 2 of 4). 1996 Stealth w/DOHC

Name	Symbol
Air-conditioning relay	M
Air-conditioning switch	Q
Camshaft position sensor	K
Check engine/malfunction indicator lamp	T
Crankshaft position sensor	N
Diagnostic output terminal and diagnostic test mode control terminal	I
Engine control module	H
Engine coolant temperature sensor	C
Evaporative emission purge solenoid	J
Heated oxygen sensor	F
Idle air control motor (stepper motor)	A
Ignition coil (ignition power transistor)	O
Ignition timing adjusting terminal	G
Injector	V
Knock sensor	P
Multiport fuel injection (MFI) relay	D
Park/Neutral position switch <A/T>	R
Power steering pressure switch	S
Throttle position sensor (with built-in closed throttle position switch)	B
Variable induction control motor (DC motor) (with built-in induction control valve position sensor)	U
Vehicle speed sensor	E
Volume air flow sensor (with built-in intake air temperature sensor and barometric pressure sensor)	L

NOTE
The "Name" column is in alphabetical order.

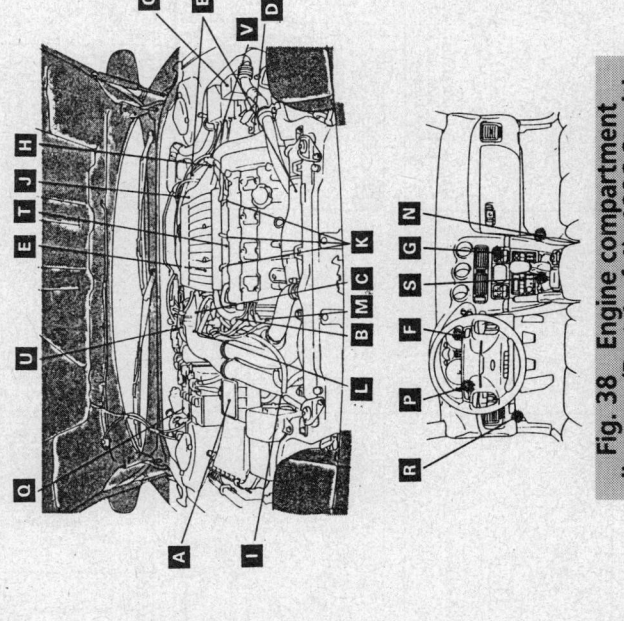

Fig. 38 Engine compartment diagram (Part 1 of 4). 1996 Stealth w/DOHC

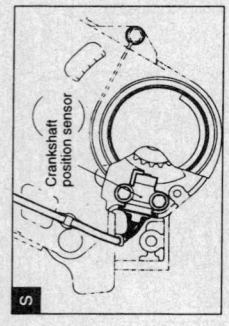

Crankshaft position sensor

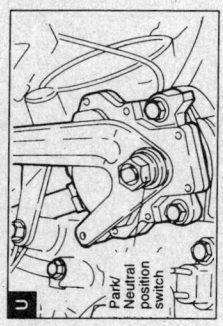

Park/Neutral position switch

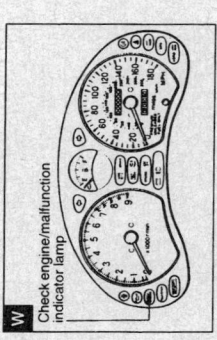

Check engine/malfunction indicator lamp

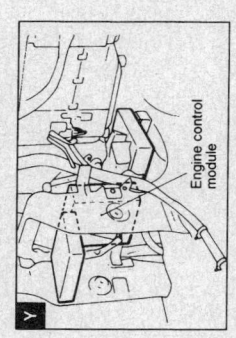

Engine control module

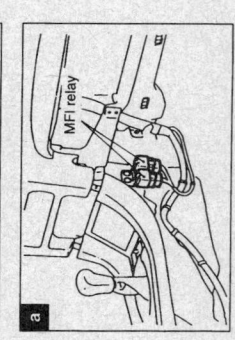

MFI relay

Engine coolant temperature sensor

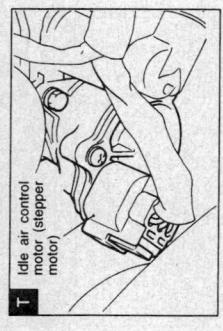

Idle air control motor (stepper motor)

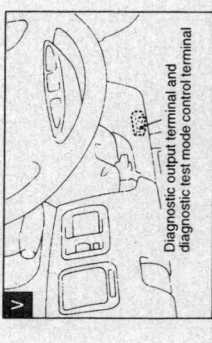

Diagnostic output terminal and diagnostic test mode control terminal

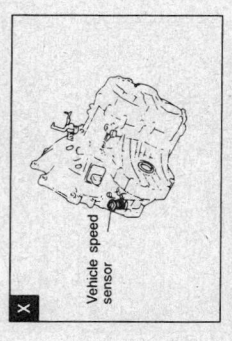

Vehicle speed sensor

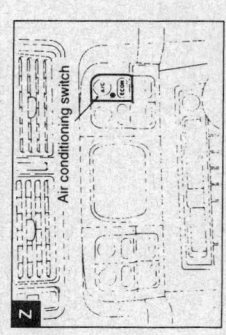

Air conditioning switch

CR1019600280040X

Fig. 38 Engine compartment diagram (Part 4 of 4). 1996 Stealth w/DOHC

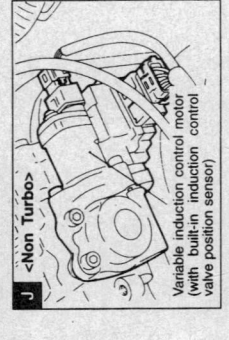

Variable induction control motor (with built-in induction control valve position sensor) <Non Turbo>

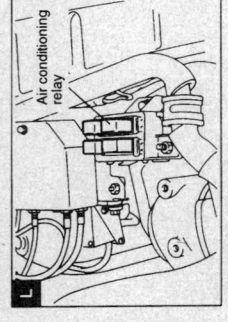

Air conditioning relay

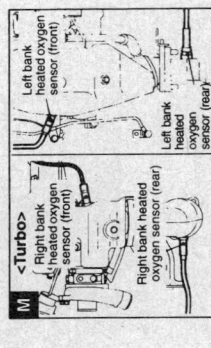

Left bank heated oxygen sensor (front)
Left bank heated oxygen sensor (rear) <Turbo>
Right bank heated oxygen sensor (front)
Right bank heated oxygen sensor (rear)

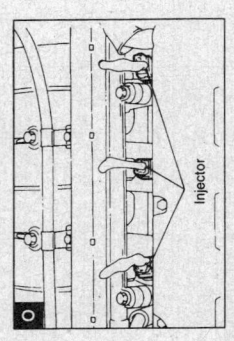

Injector

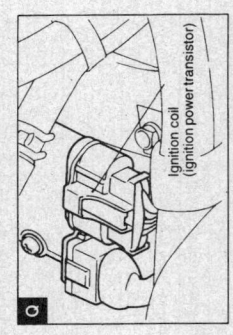

Ignition coil (ignition power transistor)

CR1019600280030X

Fig. 38 Engine compartment diagram (Part 3 of 4). 1996 Stealth w/DOHC

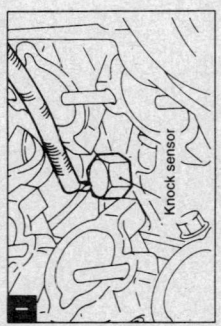

Knock sensor

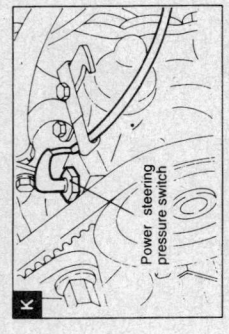

Power steering pressure switch

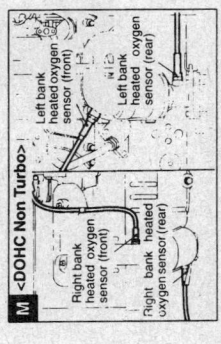

Left bank heated oxygen sensor (front)
Left bank heated oxygen sensor (rear) <DOHC Non Turbo>
Right bank heated oxygen sensor (front)
Right bank heated oxygen sensor (rear)

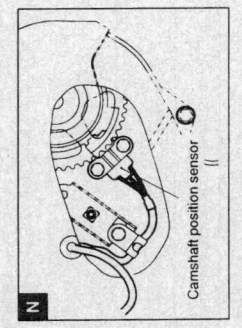

Camshaft position sensor

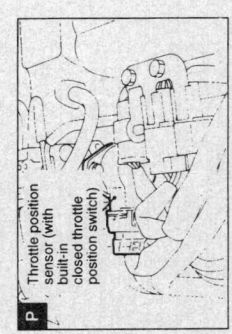

Throttle position sensor (with built-in closed throttle position switch)

CR1019600279020X

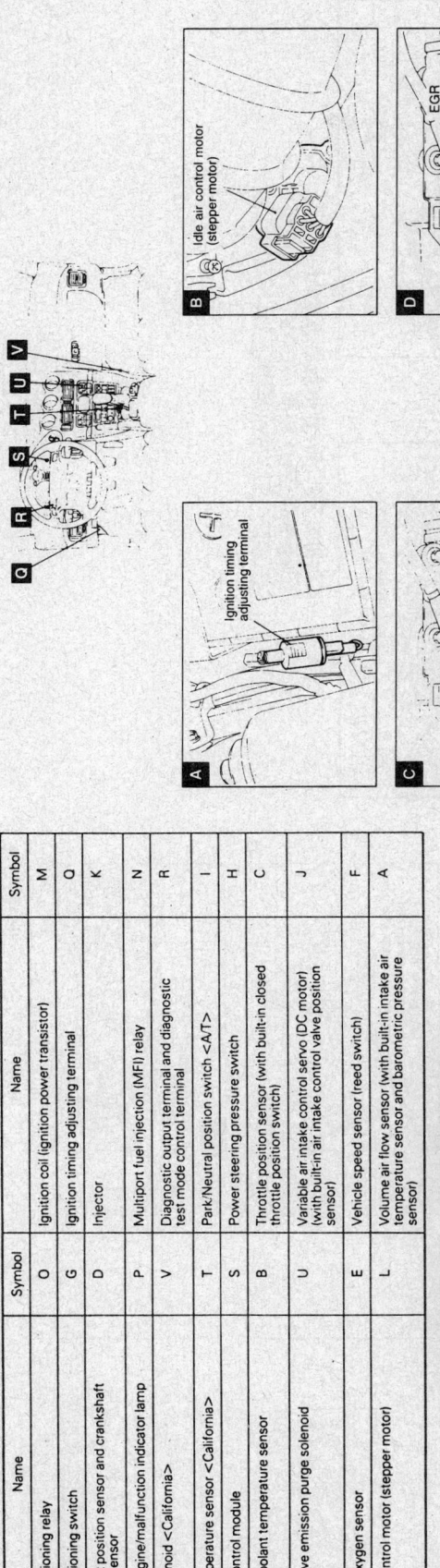

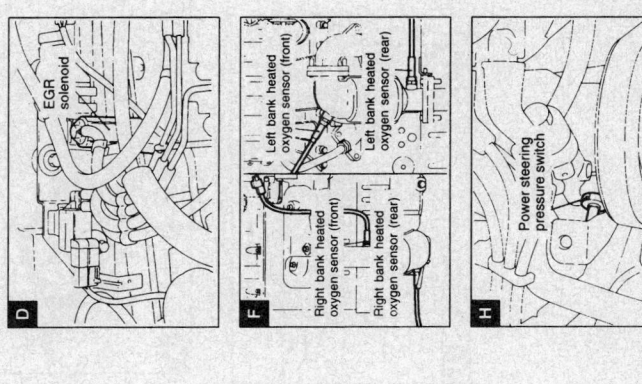

B	Idle air control motor (stepper motor)
D	EGR solenoid
F	Left bank heated oxygen sensor (front) / Left bank heated oxygen sensor (rear) / Right bank heated oxygen sensor (front) / Right bank heated oxygen sensor (rear)
H	Power steering pressure switch

A	Ignition timing adjusting terminal
C	Evaporative emission purge solenoid
E	Manifold differential pressure sensor
G	Camshaft position sensor

Fig. 39 Engine compartment diagram (Part 2 of 4). 1996 Stealth w/SOHC

Name	Symbol
Air conditioning relay	M
Air conditioning switch	Q
Camshaft position sensor and crankshaft position sensor	K
Check engine/malfunction indicator lamp	N
EGR solenoid <California>	R
EGR temperature sensor <California>	I
Engine control module	H
Engine coolant temperature sensor	C
Evaporative emission purge solenoid	J
Heated oxygen sensor	F
Idle air control motor (stepper motor)	A

Name	Symbol
Ignition coil (ignition power transistor)	O
Ignition timing adjusting terminal	G
Injector	D
Multiport fuel injection (MFI) relay	P
Diagnostic output terminal and diagnostic test mode control terminal	V
Park/Neutral position switch <A/T>	T
Power steering pressure switch	S
Throttle position sensor (with built-in closed throttle position switch)	B
Variable air intake control servo (DC motor) (with built-in air intake control valve position sensor)	U
Vehicle speed sensor (reed switch)	E
Volume air flow sensor (with built-in intake air temperature sensor and barometric pressure sensor)	L

NOTE
The "Name" column is in alphabetical order.

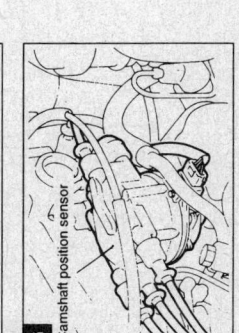
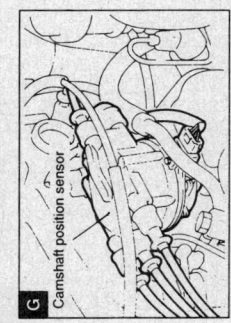

Fig. 39 Engine compartment diagram (Part 1 of 4). 1996 Stealth w/SOHC

Knock sensor

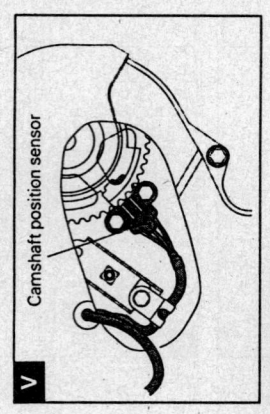

Camshaft position sensor

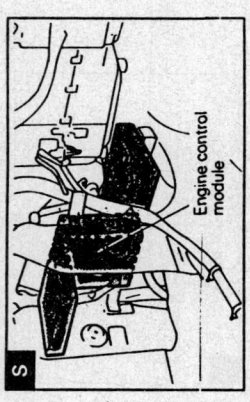

Engine control module

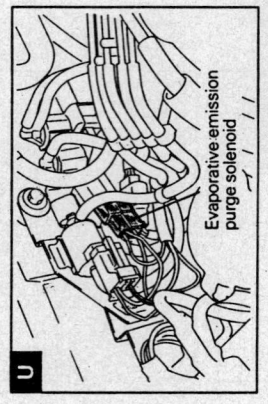

Evaporative emission purge solenoid

Fig. 39   Engine compartment diagram (Part 4 of 4). 1996 Stealth w/SOHC

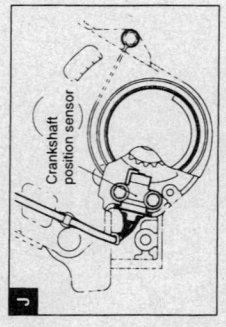

J — Crankshaft position sensor

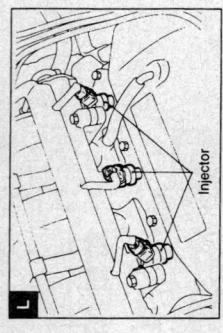

L — Injector

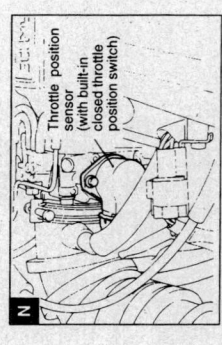

N — Throttle position sensor (with built-in closed throttle position switch)

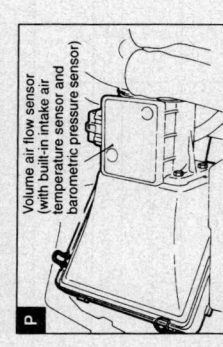

P — Volume air flow sensor (with built-in intake air temperature sensor and barometric pressure sensor)

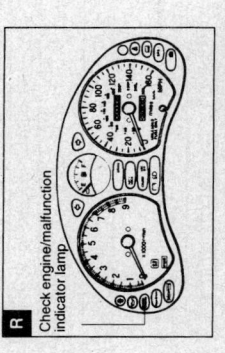

R — Check engine/malfunction indicator lamp

CR10196002790301X

Fig. 39   Engine compartment diagram (Part 3 of 4). 1996 Stealth w/SOHC

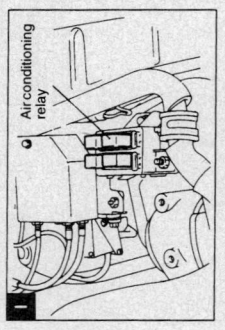

I — Air conditioning relay

K — Ignition coil (ignition power transistor)

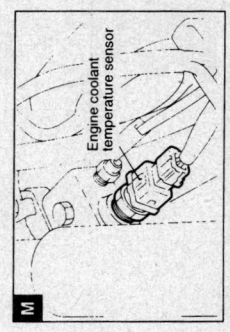

M — Engine coolant temperature sensor

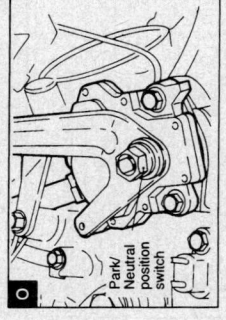

O — Park/Neutral position switch

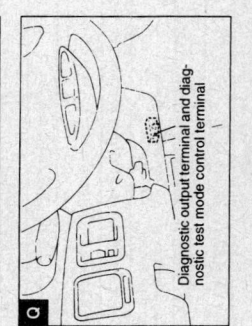

Q — Diagnostic output terminal and diagnostic test mode control terminal

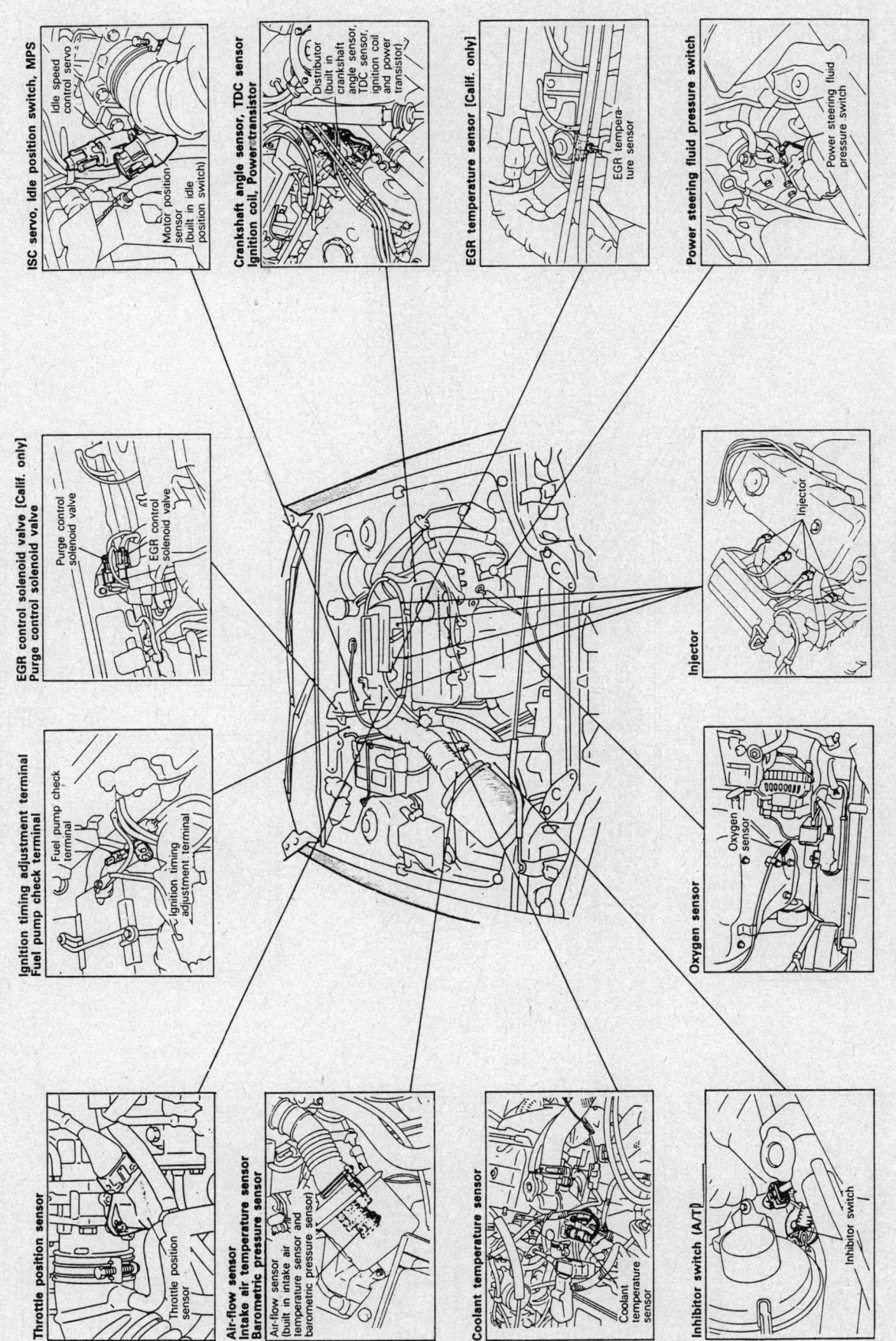

ISC servo, Idle position switch, MPS

Idle speed control control servo

Motor position sensor (built in idle position switch)

Crankshaft angle sensor, TDC sensor
Ignition coil, Power-transistor

Distributor (built in crankshaft angle sensor, TDC sensor, ignition coil and power transistor)

EGR temperature sensor [Calif. only]

EGR temperature sensor

Power steering fluid pressure switch

Power steering fluid pressure switch

EGR control solenoid valve [Calif. only]
Purge control solenoid valve

Purge control solenoid valve

EGR control solenoid valve

Injector

Injector

Ignition timing adjustment terminal
Fuel pump check terminal

Fuel pump check terminal

Ignition timing adjustment terminal

Oxygen sensor

Oxygen sensor

Throttle position sensor

Throttle position sensor

Air-flow sensor
Intake air temperature sensor
Barometric pressure sensor

Air-flow sensor (built in intake air temperature sensor and barometric pressure sensor)

Coolant temperature sensor

Coolant temperature sensor

Inhibitor switch [A/T]

Inhibitor switch

Fig. 40 Engine compartment diagram. 1993–94 Laser & Talon w/1.8L/4-107

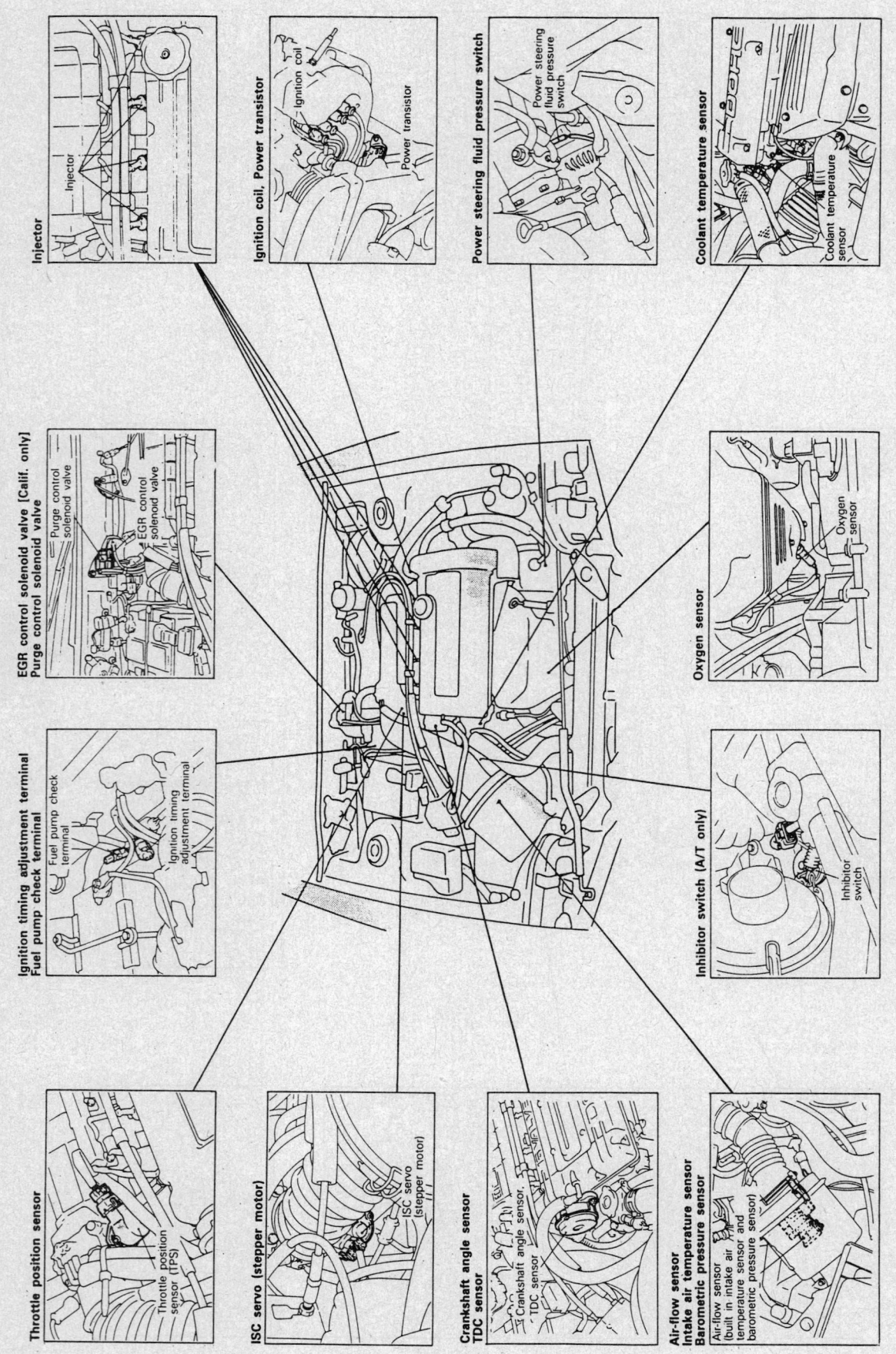

Injector

Ignition coil, Power transistor

Power steering fluid pressure switch

Coolant temperature sensor

EGR control solenoid valve [Calif. only]
Purge control solenoid valve

Ignition timing adjustment terminal
Fuel pump check terminal

Oxygen sensor

Inhibitor switch (A/T only)

Throttle position sensor

ISC servo (stepper motor)

Crankshaft angle sensor
TDC sensor

Air-flow sensor
Intake air temperature sensor
Barometric pressure sensor

Fig. 41 Engine compartment diagram. 1993–94 Laser & Talon w/2.0L/4-122 non-turbocharged

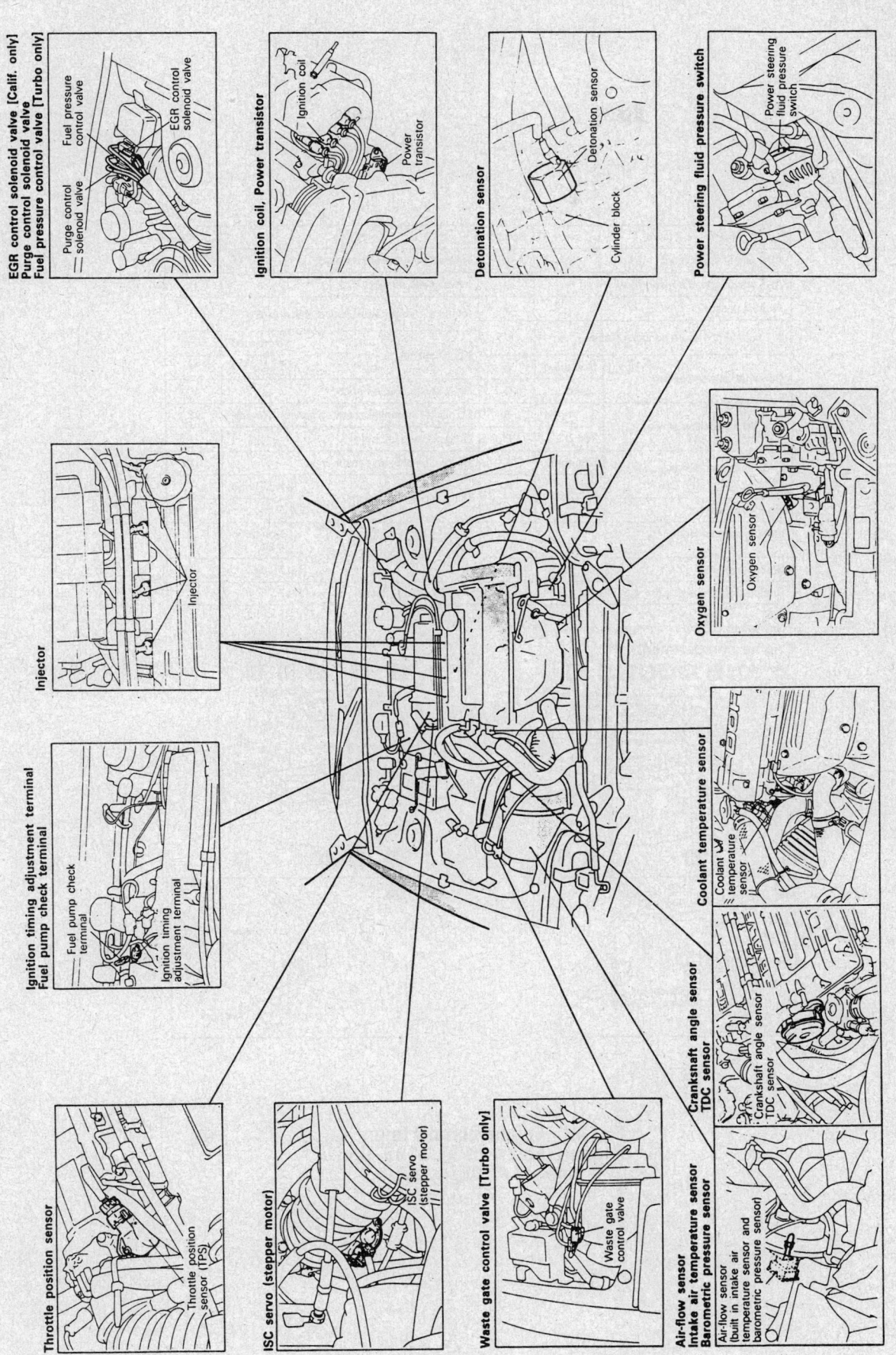

EGR control solenoid valve [Calif. only]
Purge control solenoid valve
Fuel pressure control valve [Turbo only]

Purge control solenoid valve

Fuel pressure control valve

EGR control solenoid valve

Ignition coil, Power transistor

Ignition coil

Power transistor

Detonation sensor

Detonation sensor

Cylinder block

Power steering fluid pressure switch

Power steering fluid pressure switch

Injector

Injector

Oxygen sensor

Oxygen sensor

Ignition timing adjustment terminal
Fuel pump check terminal

Fuel pump check terminal

Ignition timing adjustment terminal

Coolant temperature sensor

Coolant temperature sensor

Crankshaft angle sensor
TDC sensor

Crankshaft angle sensor
TDC sensor

Throttle position sensor

Throttle position sensor (TPS)

ISC servo (stepper motor)

ISC servo (stepper motor)

Waste gate control valve [Turbo only]

Waste gate control valve

Air-flow sensor
Intake air temperature sensor
Barometric pressure sensor

Air-flow sensor (built in intake air temperature sensor and barometric pressure sensor)

Fig. 42 Engine compartment diagram. 1993–94 Laser & Talon w/2.0L/4-122 turbocharged

Name		Symbol	Name		Symbol
ABS wheel-speed sensor (front)		X	Heated oxygen sensor (rear)		Z
ABS wheel-speed sensor (rear)		a	Input speed sensor		H
Air inlet sensor		V	Intake air temperature sensor <Non-turbo>		D
A/T fluid temperature sensor <Turbo>		R	Knock sensor	Non-turbo	E
Camshaft position sensor	Non-turbo	G		Turbo	N
	Turbo	O	MAP sensor <Non-turbo>		B
Crankshaft position sensor	Non-turbo	C	Manifold differential pressure sensor <Turbo>		M
	Turbo	P	Output speed sensor		H
Engine coolant temperature sensor	Non-turbo	A	Revolution pick-up sensor		J
	Turbo	K	Throttle position sensor	Non-turbo	F
Fin thermo sensor		U		Turbo	L
Front impact sensor		W	Vehicle speed sensor	Non-turbo -M/T	I
G sensor (ABS)		T		Turbo	Q
Heated oxygen sensor (front)		Y	Volume air flow sensor		S

NOTE
The "Name" column is arranged in alphabetical order.

Engine compartment

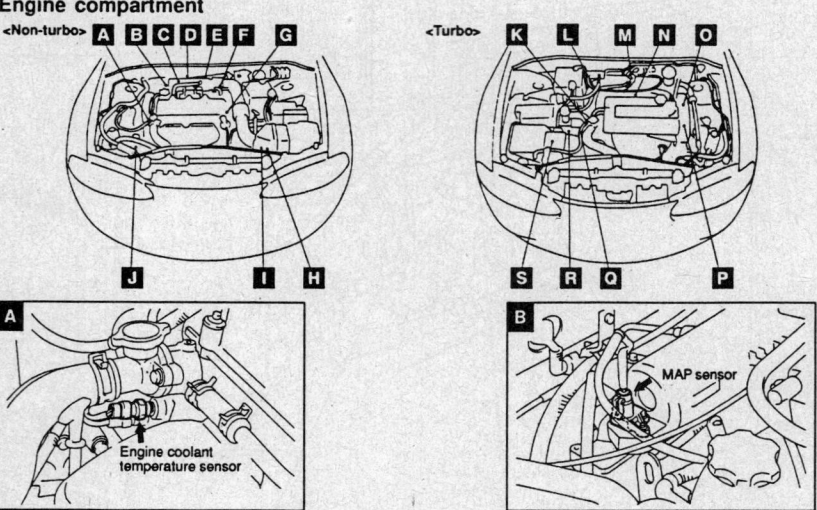

Fig. 43   Engine compartment
diagram (Part 1 of 3). 1995–96
Talon w/2.0L/4-122

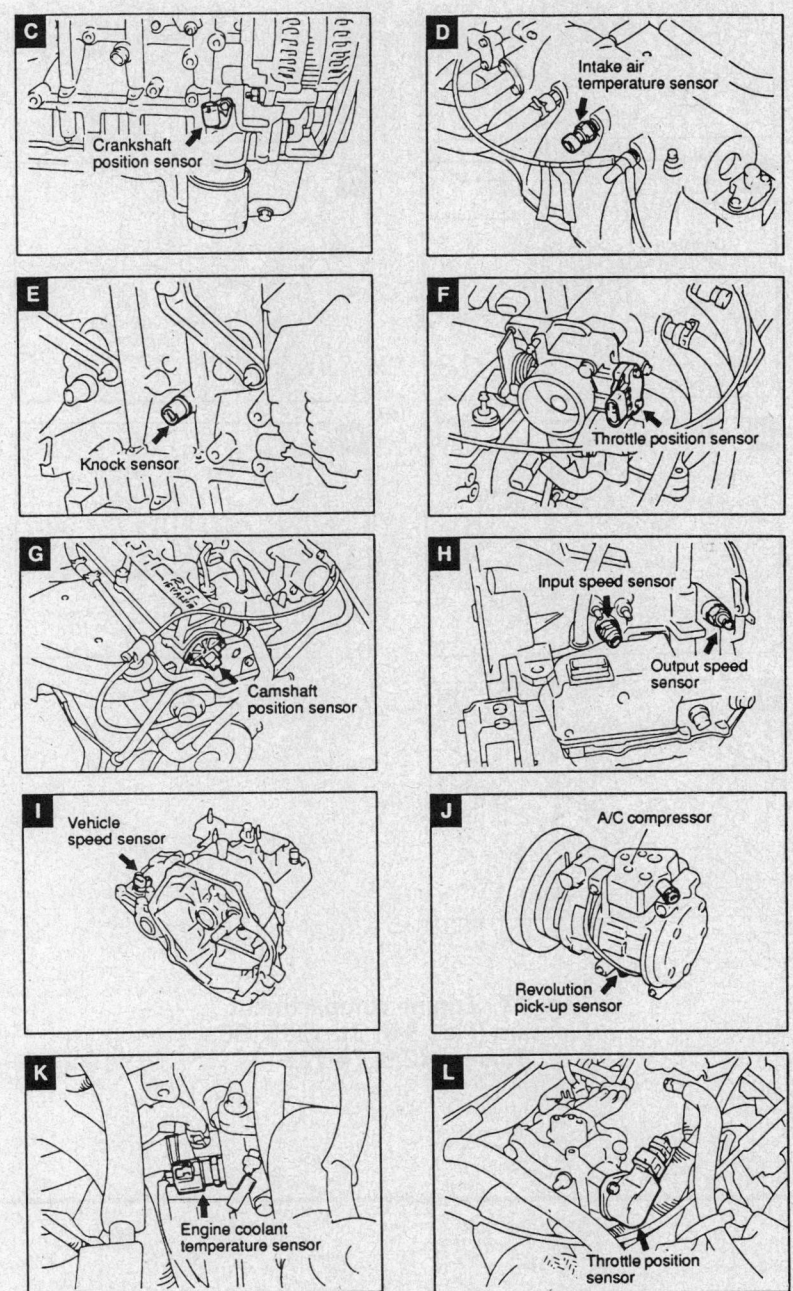

Fig. 43 Engine compartment
diagram (Part 2 of 3). 1995–96
Talon w/2.0L/4-122

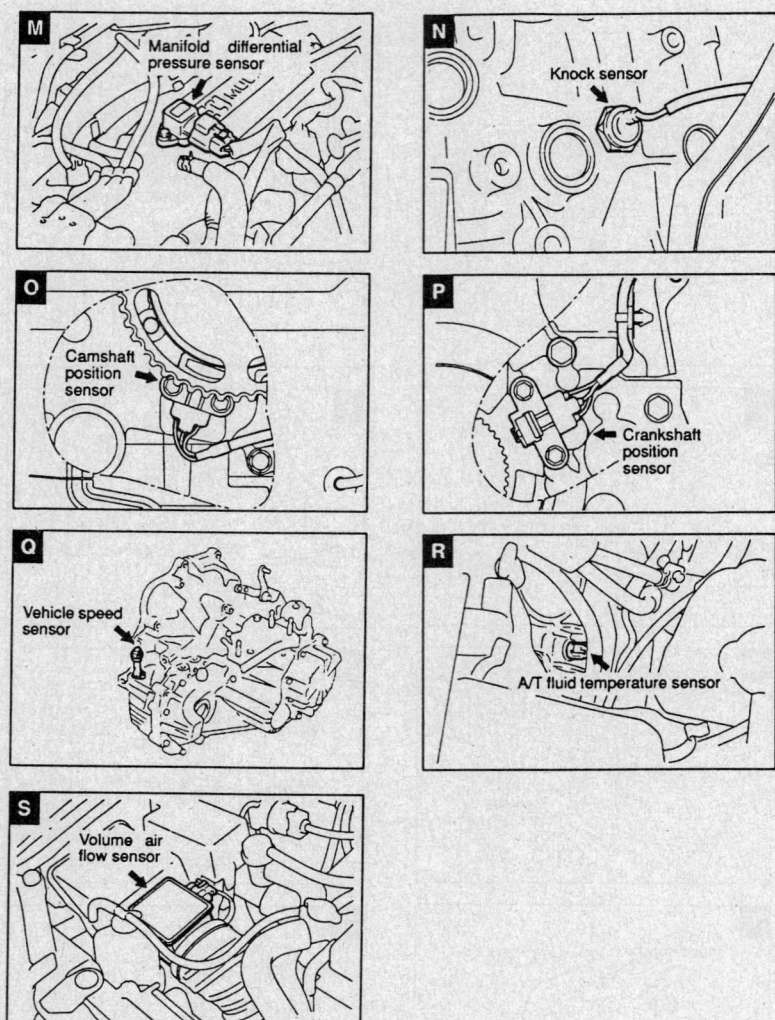

Fig. 43 Engine compartment diagram (Part 3 of 3). 1995–96 Talon w/2.0L/4-122

EMISSION CONTROLS

INDEX

Page No.	Page No.	Page No.
Aspirator Air System: 20-1	Purge Control Solenoid Valve 20-4	System Service 20-6
Description 20-1	Purge Control System 20-3	EGR Control Valve 20-6
Diagnosis & Testing 20-1	Purge Control Valve 20-4	EGR Tube, Replace 20-6
System Service 20-1	System Service 20-4	EGR Valve & Electric EGR
Aspirator Tube Assembly, Replace 20-1	**Exhaust Gas Recirculation (EGR):** .. 20-4	Transducer, Replace 20-6
Aspirator Valve, Replace 20-1	Description 20-4	**Heated Inlet Air System:** 20-1
Catalytic Converters: 20-1	System Description 20-4	Description 20-1
Description 20-1	System Operation 20-4	Diagnosis & Testing 20-2
System Service 20-1	Diagnosis & Testing 20-5	System Service 20-2
Evaporative Emission Control	Charge Temperature Switch (Cts) 20-6	Sensor, Replace 20-2
System: 20-2	EGR Solenoid 20-6	**Positive Crankcase Ventilation**
Description 20-2	EGR System 20-5	**(PCV) System:** 20-7
Component Description 20-2	EGR Temperature Sensor 20-6	Description 20-7
System Description 20-2	EGR Valve 20-5	Diagnosis & Testing 20-7
Diagnosis & Testing 20-3	Thermo Valve 20-6	System Service 20-7

ASPIRATOR AIR SYSTEM

Description

The aspirator valve, **Fig. 1,** uses exhaust pressure pulsations to draw air into the exhaust system to reduce CO and HC emissions. It draws fresh air from the "clean" side of the air cleaner past a one-way spring loaded diaphragm. The diaphragm opens to permit fresh air to mix with the exhaust gases during negative pressure (vacuum) pulses. When the pressure is positive, the diaphragm closes and no exhaust gases are allowed to flow past the valve.

The aspirator valve works most efficiently at and slightly above idle, when the negative pulses are greatest. At higher engine speeds, the aspirator valve remains closed.

Diagnosis & Testing

The aspirator valve is not repairable and, as a result, must be replaced if operation is not satisfactory. Aspirator valve failure results in excessive exhaust system noise under the hood at idle and hardening of the rubber hose from the valve to the air cleaner.

If there is excessive exhaust noise from under the hood, first check the aspirator tube exhaust manifold assembly joint and hose connections at the aspirator valve and air cleaner for leakage. If the aspirator tube exhaust manifold assembly joint is leaking, remove aspirator tube assembly, then replace the gasket. If either hose connection is leaking and the rubber hose has not hardened, install hose clamps.

To determine if the aspirator valve is inoperative, disconnect hose from aspirator valve inlet. With the engine idling and the transaxle in Neutral position, the vacuum exhaust pulses can be felt at the aspirator valve inlet. If hot exhaust gas is escaping from the aspirator inlet, the aspirator valve is inoperative and must be replaced.

System Service

ASPIRATOR VALVE, REPLACE

1. Disconnect air hose from aspirator valve inlet.
2. Remove aspirator valve from aspirator tube assembly.
3. Reverse procedure to install. **Torque** valve to 25 ft. lbs.

ASPIRATOR TUBE ASSEMBLY, REPLACE

1. Disconnect air hose from aspirator valve inlet.
2. Remove bolts securing aspirator tube assembly to exhaust manifold and engine.
3. Remove aspirator tube assembly from engine.
4. Remove any remaining gasket material from exhaust manifold and aspirator tube flange.
5. Reverse procedure to install, noting the following:
   a. Install new gasket.
   b. **On models equipped with four cylinder engine, torque** aspirator tube nut to 40 ft. lbs. and bracket bolt to 95 ft. lbs.

CATALYTIC CONVERTERS

Description

The catalytic converter, **Fig. 2,** is an emission control device added to the exhaust system to reduce levels of carbon monoxide (CO), hydrocarbons (HC), and oxides of nitrogen (NOx) in the exhaust gases. This occurs through a chemical reaction between the exhaust gases and the catalyst in the converter.

Some vehicles incorporate two "mini-oxidation" catalytic converters, **Fig. 3,** in conjunction with the main converter. The mini-ox converters initiate the chemical reaction to further reduce harmful exhaust gases.

The "hybrid" converter, **Fig. 3,** utilizes large and small biscuit type elements. A power heat control valve is incorporated to increase exhaust gas flow through the left-hand exhaust manifold to rapidly bring the mini-catalyst up to operating temperature.

System Service

The catalytic converters are not serviceable. After determining that catalyst has lost its effectiveness, the catalytic converter assembly must be replaced.

Inspect for damage, cracking or deterioration. Replace if faulty.

Operation of any type, including idling, should be avoided if engine misfiring occurs. Under this condition the exhaust system will operate at abnormally high temperature, which may cause damage to the catalyst or underbody parts of the vehicle.

Alteration or deterioration of ignition or fuel system, or any type of operating condition which results in engine misfiring, must be corrected to avoid overheating the catalytic converter.

Proper maintenance and tune up according to manufacturer's specifications should be made to correct the conditions as soon as possible.

HEATED INLET AIR SYSTEM

Description

The heated air inlet air system is only on engines with throttle body injection.

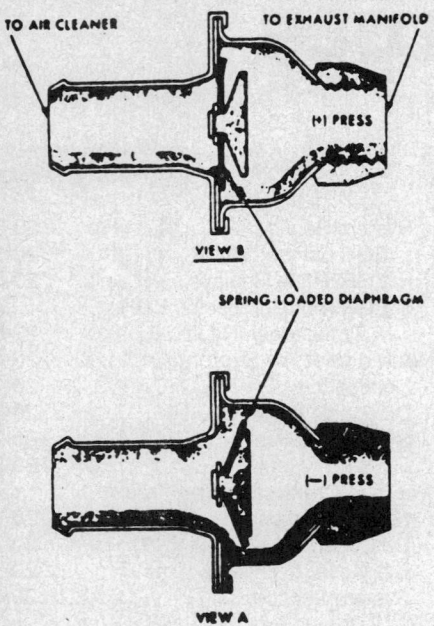

Fig. 1 Aspirator valve

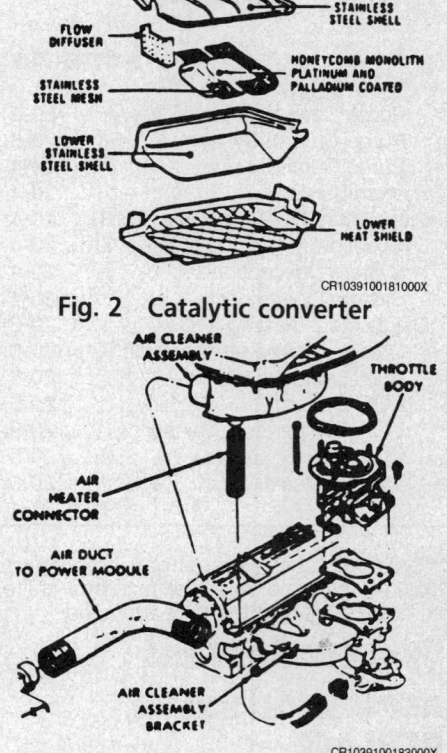

Fig. 2 Catalytic converter

Fig. 4 Heated inlet air system.
2.2L/4-135 & 2.5L/4-153 engines

Fig. 3 Mini catalytic converters

When ambient temperatures are low, this assembly, **Fig. 4**, warms the air before it enters the throttle body. The heated air assembly reduces emissions, improves engine warm-up characteristics and minimizes icing.

The heated air assembly contains a vacuum operated blend door. The blend door opens to either heated air from a stove on the exhaust manifold or outside air. A vacuum diaphragm operates the door. A spring opposes the vacuum diaphragm. A temperature sensor controls the vacuum diaphragm.

Air flows through the outside air inlet when ambient air temperature is at least 15°F above the air temperature sensor control temperature.

When ambient air temperature falls below the control temperature, air flows through both the ambient and heated circuits. This occurs after the engine has been started and the exhaust manifold starts to give off heat. Colder ambient air cause greater air flow through the heat stove on the exhaust manifold. Warmer ambient air results in greater ambient air flow through the air cleaner snorkel.

Diagnosis & Testing

1. Ensure all vacuum hoses and stove to air cleaner flexible connector are properly installed and in good condition.
2. With engine cold and ambient temperature in engine compartment below 115°F, heat control door (valve plate) should be in up (heat on) position.
3. With engine warmed to operating temperature and running, check air temperature entering snorkel, or passing sensor. When temperature is 140°F or higher, door should be in down (heat off) position.
4. Remove air cleaner from engine and allow it to cool down to a temperature

of 115°F. Using vacuum pump, apply 20 inches of vacuum to sensor. Control door should be in up (heat on) position. If not, check vacuum diaphragm.

5. To test vacuum diaphragm, proceed as follows:
   a. Apply 20 inches of vacuum directly to diaphragm.
   b. Diaphragm should not bleed down more than 10 inches of vacuum in five minutes.
   c. Control door should not lift off bottom of snorkel at less than two inches of vacuum.
   d. Door should be in full up position with no more than 4 inches of vacuum.
   e. If diaphragm does not operate as described, replace heated air assembly.
6. If diaphragm performs properly but proper temperature is not maintained, replace sensor and repeat procedure.

System Service

SENSOR, REPLACE

1. Remove air cleaner housing from vehicle.
2. Disconnect vacuum hose from sensor, then remove sensor retaining clips.
3. Remove sensor and gasket assembly from air cleaner.
4. Reverse procedure to install.

EVAPORATIVE EMISSION CONTROL SYSTEM

Description

SYSTEM DESCRIPTION

The evaporation control system prevents the emission of fuel tank vapors into the atmosphere. When fuel evaporates in the fuel tank, the vapors pass through vent hoses or tubes to a charcoal canister. The canister temporarily holds the vapors. The engine controller allows intake manifold vacuum to draw vapors into the combustion chambers under certain operating conditions. The controller uses the canister purge solenoid to regulate vapor flow.

COMPONENT DESCRIPTION

Pressure-Vacuum Filler Cap

The fuel tank is sealed with a pressure vacuum relief filler cap. The relief valves in the filler cap are a safety feature and operate only to prevent excessive pressure or vacuum in the tank caused by malfunction in the system or damage to the vent lines.

Charcoal Canister

The service free canister is constructed of polypropylene and is located in the wheelwell area of the engine compartment. Fuel tank pressure vents into the canister. The canister holds the fuel vapors until intake manifold vacuum draws them into the combustion chamber. The purge solenoid purges vapors from the canister at predetermined intervals and engine conditions.

Rollover & Pressure Relief Valve

This valve enables fuel vapors to travel from the fuel tank to the canister. The valve prevents fuel leakage when a vehicle rollover occurs. This valve also incor-

Engine operating condition	Applying vacuum	Result
Idling	50 kPa (14.8 in.Hg.)	Vacuum is maintained
3.000 rpm		

CR1039100184000X

Fig. 5 Purge control system inspection w/cold engine. Laser, Stealth & 1993–94 Talon

Engine operating condition	Applying vacuum	Result
Idling	400 mmHg (15.7 in.Hg)	Vacuum is maintained
Within 3 minutes after engine start 3.000 rpm	Try applying vacuum	Vacuum leaks
After 3 minutes have passed after engine start 3.000 rpm	400 mmHg (15.7 in.Hg)	Vacuum will be maintained momentarily, after which it will leak. NOTE The vacuum will leak continuously if the altitude is 2.200 m (7.200 ft.) or higher, or the intake air temperature is 50°C (122°F) or higher.

Fig. 7 Purge control system inspection w/hot engine. 1993 Colt, Colt Vista, Summit & Summit Wagon

Engine operating condition	Applying vacuum	Result
Idling	400 mmHg (15.7 in.Hg)	Vacuum is maintained
3.000 rpm		

CR1039100185000X

Fig. 6 Purge control system inspection w/cold engine. Colt, Colt Vista, Summit & Summit Wagon

Vacuum	Engine status	Normal condition
400 mmHg (15.7 in.Hg)	Idling	Vacuum is maintained
	3,000 rpm	Vacuum will leak for approximately 3 minutes was after the engine is started. After 3 minutes have elapsed, the vacuum will be maintained momentarily, after which it will again leak.*

NOTE
* The vacuum will leak continuously if the atmospheric pressure is approximately 580 mmHg (22.8 in.Hg) or less, or the temperature of the intake air is approximately 50°C (122°F) or higher.

CR1039400188000X

Fig. 8 Purge control system inspection w/hot engine. 1994 Colt & Colt Vista & 1994–96 Summit & Summit Wagon

porates a pressure relief mechanism which releases pressure to the atmosphere when fuel tank pressure exceeds that of the calibrated sealing valve.

Canister Purge Solenoid

The canister purge solenoid, used on some vehicles, is controlled by the engine controller. During warm-up and for a specified period after hot starts, the engine controller grounds the purge solenoid valve to energize it. This prevents vacuum from reaching the charcoal canister valve. When engine temperature reaches a specified operating temperature and the time delay interval has occurred, the engine controller de-energizes the solenoid. Once this occurs, vacuum flows to the canister purge valve and purges fuel vapors through the throttle body.

Duty Cycle Purge Solenoid

The duty cycle purge solenoid is used on some vehicles. It is controlled by the engine controller. During cold start warm-up and hot start time delay, the engine controller does not energize the solenoid. When de-energized, no vapors are purged. The engine controller de-energizes the solenoid during open loop operation.

The engine enters closed loop operation after it reaches a specified temperature and the time delay ends. During closed loop operation, the engine controller energizes and de-energizes the solenoid approximately 5-10 times per second, depending upon operating conditions. The engine controller varies the flow rate by changing the amount of time the solenoid energizes (pulse width). The engine controller adjusts pulse width based on engine air flow.

Diagnosis & Testing
PURGE CONTROL SYSTEM
Colt, Colt Vista, Laser, Stealth, Summit, Summit Wagon & 1993–94 Talon

1. **On non-turbocharged models,** disconnect vacuum hose (red striped) from throttle body, then connect hand pump.
2. Plug nipple from which vacuum hose was removed.
3. **On turbocharged models,** disconnect purge air hose from air intake hose, then plug air intake hose.
4. Connect hand vacuum pump to purge air hose.
5. **On Laser, Stealth, 1993-94 Talon and 1993 Colt, Colt Vista, Summit and Summit Wagon models,** ensure engine coolant temperature is below 140°F and refer to **Figs. 5 and 6** for specifications.
6. **On 1994 Colt and Colt Vista and 1994-96 Summit and Summit Wagon models,** ensure engine coolant temperature is below 104°F and refer to **Fig. 5** for specifications.
7. **On Laser, Stealth, 1993-94 Talon and 1993 Colt, Colt Vista, Summit and Summit Wagon models,** ensure engine coolant temperature is at least 158°F, then refer to **Figs. 7 through 9** for specifications.

8. **On 1994 Colt and Colt Vista and 1994-96 Summit and Summit Wagon models,** ensure engine coolant temperature is at least 176°F and refer to **Fig. 10** for specifications.

1995–96 Talon w/Non-Turbocharged Engine & Avenger & Sebring Coupe

1. Disconnect vacuum hose at throttle body and connect to a hand vacuum pump, then plug nipple from which hose was removed.
2. Start engine and allow coolant to warm to at least 176°F, then apply a vacuum with engine at idle.
3. If results are not as specified in **Fig. 11,** purge control system is not operating satisfactorily. Service or replace components as necessary.

1995–96 Talon w/Turbocharged Engine

1. Disconnect red striped vacuum hose at throttle body and connect to a hand vacuum pump, then plug nipple from which vacuum hose was removed.
2. Apply 16 inches Hg of vacuum to ensure performance is as follows:
   a. With engine coolant at or below 104°F and engine speed at 3000 RPM, vacuum should be maintained.
   b. With engine coolant at or above 176°F and engine speed at 3000 RPM, vacuum should leak down.

Engine operating condition	Applying vacuum	Result
3,000 rpm within three minutes after starting engine	Try applying vacuum	Vacuum leaks
3,000 rpm after three minutes have elapsed after starting engine	375 mmHg (14.8 in.Hg)	Vacuum will be maintained momentarily, after which it will leak. NOTE The vacuum will leak continuously if the altitude is 2,200 m (7,200 ft.) or higher, or the intake air temperature is 50°C (122°F) or higher.

CR103940018900X

Fig. 9 Purge control system inspection w/hot engine. 1994–96 Stealth w/turbocharged engine

Vacuum	Engine status	Normal condition
400 mmHg (15.7 in.Hg)	right after starting engine	Vacuum is maintained
	10 or more minutes later	Vacuum leaks

Fig. 11 Purge control system inspection. 1995–96 Talon w/non-turbocharged engine & Avenger & Sebring Coupe

3. Disconnect hand vacuum pump and connect red striped hose to throttle body, then disconnect purge air hose from air intake hose and connect to hand pump.
4. Plug air intake hose nipple, then apply 16 inches Hg to ensure performance is as follows:
   a. With engine coolant below 176°F and engine at idle, vacuum should be maintained.
   b. When engine is raced suddenly, vacuum should leak down.
5. If results are not as specified, purge control system is not operating satisfactorily. Service or replace components as necessary.

PURGE CONTROL VALVE
Laser, Stealth & Talon w/Turbocharged Engine

1. Remove purge control valve, then connect vacuum pump to nipple of purge control valve.
2. Apply 15.7 inches Hg of vacuum, then check system for leaks.
3. Blow air in lightly from canister side nipple, then check conditions as found in **Fig. 12**.
4. Connect hand vacuum pump to positive pressure nipple of purge control valve.
5. Apply 15.7 inches Hg of vacuum, then check system for leaks.

PURGE CONTROL SOLENOID VALVE
Colt, Colt Vista, Laser, Stealth, Summit, Summit Wagon, Talon & Avenger & Sebring Coupe

1. Disconnect vacuum hoses from solenoid valve.
2. Disconnect harness connector from solenoid valve.

3. Connect hand vacuum pump to nipple from which red striped hose was removed.
4. Apply vacuum, then check system for leaks when voltage is both applied and discontinued from purge control solenoid valve.
5. **On all models except Avenger, Sebring Coupe and 1995-96 Talon,** refer to **Fig. 13** for valve performance specifications.
6. **On Avenger, Sebring Coupe and 1995-96 Talon models,** vacuum pressure should leak down when battery voltage is applied and should remain constant when battery voltage is not applied.
7. **On all models,** measure resistance between terminals of solenoid valve. Resistance should measure 36-44 ohms at 68°F.

System Service

Ensure all vacuum hoses and electrical wires are routed clear of the exhaust manifold to prevent heat deterioration. Vacuum hoses should always be a minimum of three inches from the exhaust manifold. When servicing the charcoal canister, mark, then disconnect vacuum hoses from charcoal canister to ensure proper installation.

EXHAUST GAS RECIRCULATION (EGR)
Description

SYSTEM DESCRIPTION

The EGR system reduces nitrogen emissions in the exhaust system and

Engine operating condition	Applying vacuum	Result
Idling	50 kPa (14.8 in.Hg.)	Vacuum is maintained
3,000 rpm within three minutes after starting engine	Try applying vacuum	Vacuum leaks
3,000 rpm after three minutes have elapsed after starting engine	50 kPa (14.8 in.Hg.)	Vacuum will be maintained momentarily, after which it will leak. NOTE The vacuum will leak continuously if the altitude is 2,200 m (7,200 ft.) or higher, or the intake air temperature is 50°C (122°F) or lower.

CF103910018600X

Fig. 10 Purge control system inspection w/hot engine. Laser, 1993 Stealth, 1994–96 Stealth w/non-turbocharged engine & 1993–94 Talon

Hand vacuum pump vacuum	Normal condition
0 kPa (0 in.Hg.) (No vacuum is applied)	Air does not blow through
27 kPa (8.0 in.Hg.) or more	Air blow through

CR103910019000X

Fig. 12 Purge control valve inspection. Laser, Stealth & Talon w/turbocharged engine

helps prevent spark knock. The system allows a predetermined amount of hot exhaust gas to recirculate and dilute the incoming air/fuel mixture. The diluted air/fuel mixture reduces peak flame temperature during combustion.

SYSTEM OPERATION
Except Colt, Colt Vista, Laser, Stealth, Summit, Summit Wagon & Talon

Models without the electronic EGR system utilize a backpressure transducer. This unit measures the amount of exhaust backpressure on the exhaust side of the EGR valve and varies the strength of the vacuum signal applied to the EGR valve. The backpressure transducer adjusts the EGR signal to provide programmed amounts of exhaust gas recirculation under all conditions.

Models with the electronic EGR system utilize an electronic EGR transducer. The electronic EGR transducer contains an electrically operated solenoid and a backpressure transducer. The engine controller operates the solenoid. Exhaust system backpressure controls the transducer.

When the engine controller de-energizes the solenoid and backpressure closes the transducer bleed valve, vacuum flows through the transducer to operate the EGR valve.

De-energizing the solenoid, but not fully closing the transducer bleed hole (because of low backpressure), varies the strength of vacuum applied to the EGR valve. Varying the strength of vacuum changes the amount of EGR supplied to the engine. This provides the correct amount of exhaust gas recirculation for different operating conditions.

Battery voltage		Result
Non-Turbo	When applied	Vacuum leaks
	When discontinued	Vacuum is maintained
Turbo	When applied	Vacuum is maintained
	When discontinued	Vacuum leaks

CR1039100191000X

Fig. 13 Purge control solenoid valve inspection. Colt, Colt Vista, Laser, Stealth, Summit, Summit Wagon & Talon

Applying vacuum	Result
6 kPa (1.8 in.Hg.) or less	Air does not blow through
29 kPa (8.5 in.Hg.) or more	Air blows through

CR1039100192000X

Fig. 14 EGR valve inspection. Avenger & Sebring Coupe w/2.0L/4-122 engine, Colt, Colt Vista, Laser, Stealth, Summit, Summit Wagon & Talon

Diagnosis & Testing

EGR SYSTEM

EXCEPT COLT, COLT VISTA, LASER, STEALTH, SUMMIT, SUMMIT WAGON, 1993–94 TALON & 1995–96 TALON W/TURBOCHARGED ENGINE

The complete EGR system should be inspected and tested at the recommended intervals. To assure proper operation of this system, all passages and moving parts must operate properly and be free of deposits. Also, hoses and connections must be free from leaks.

Warm engine, then allow engine to idle in neutral, with the throttle closed. Abruptly accelerate the engine to approximately 2000 RPM, but not over 3000 RPM. Visible movement of the EGR valve stem should occur during this operation. This can be determined by change in the relative position of the groove on the EGR valve stem. This operation should be repeated several times to confirm movement. Stem movement indicates the control system is functioning correctly.

Connect a hand vacuum pump to the EGR valve vacuum motor. With the engine running at idle speed, slowly apply vacuum. Engine speed should begin to drop when vacuum reaches 2.0-3.5 inches Hg. Engine speed may drop quickly or engine may even stall. This indicates that EGR gas is flowing through the system. If engine speed change does not occur, exhaust deposits in the EGR valve, EGR tube or intake manifold EGR passages are indicated.

EGR On-Board Diagnostics

The engine controller performs an on-board diagnostic check of the EGR system on all California vehicles with EGR systems. The diagnostic system uses the electric EGR transducer (EET) for the system tests.

The diagnostic check activates only during selected engine/driving conditions. When the conditions are met, the engine controller energizes the transducer solenoid to disable the EGR. The controller checks for a change in the oxygen sensor signal. If the air/fuel mixture goes lean, the engine controller will attempt to enrich the mixture. The engine controller registers a fault if the EGR system has failed or degraded. After registering a fault, the engine controller turns the Check Engine light on. If a malfunction is indicated by the Check Engine light and a diagnostic trouble code for the EGR system, check for proper operation of the EGR system.

1993 COLT VISTA, LASER, SUMMIT WAGON & TALON W/FEDERAL EMISSIONS

1. Disconnect green striped vacuum hose from throttle body, then connect hand vacuum pump to vacuum hose.
2. Plug nipple from which vacuum hose is disconnected.
3. With engine cold and idling, apply vacuum. Vacuum should leak down.
4. With engine hot, apply 1.7 inches Hg of vacuum (1.8 inches for Laser and Talon). Vacuum should remain steady and engine should idle normally.
5. With engine hot, apply 7.5 inches Hg of vacuum (8.5 inches for Laser and Talon). Vacuum should remain steady and engine idle should become unstable.

1993 COLT VISTA, LASER, SUMMIT WAGON & TALON W/CALIFORNIA EMISSIONS, 1994 COLT VISTA, LASER & TALON, 1994–96 SUMMIT WAGON & 1995–96 TALON W/TURBOCHARGED ENGINE

1. Disconnect green striped vacuum hose from EGR valve, then install three-way adapter on end of hose.
2. Connect hand vacuum pump to adapter, then connect adapter to EGR valve.
3. With engine cold, start and race engine. There should be no vacuum (atmospheric pressure).
4. With engine hot, start and race engine. Vacuum should temporarily rise to 3.9 inches Hg or more.
5. Stop engine, then disconnect three-way adapter and connect hand vacuum pump directly to EGR valve.
6. Start engine and check if engine stalls or idling is unstable when 6.8 inches or more of vacuum is applied to EGR valve.

1993 COLT & SUMMIT W/1.8L/4-110 ENGINE & STEALTH W/CALIFORNIA EMISSIONS, 1994 COLT & 1994–96 SUMMIT & STEALTH

1. Disconnect green striped vacuum hose from EGR valve, then install three-way adapter on end of hose.
2. Connect hand vacuum pump to adapter, then connect adapter to EGR valve.
3. With engine cold, start and race engine. There should be no vacuum (atmospheric pressure).

4. With engine hot, start and race engine. Vacuum should temporarily rise to 3.9 inches Hg or more.
5. Stop engine, then disconnect three-way adapter and connect hand vacuum pump directly to EGR valve.
6. Start engine and check if engine stalls or idling is unstable when 6.8 inches Hg or more of vacuum is applied to EGR valve.

1993 COLT & SUMMIT (CALIFORNIA), 1994 COLT & 1994–96 SUMMIT W/1.5L/4-90 ENGINE

1. Disconnect green striped vacuum hose from throttle body and connect a hand vacuum pump to vacuum hose, then plug nipple from which hose was removed.
2. With engine cold and at idle, apply a vacuum to system. Idling should remain stable and vacuum pressure should leak down.
3. With engine hot and at idle, apply a vacuum of 1.6 inches Hg to system. Idling should remain stable and vacuum pressure should be maintained.
4. With engine hot and at idle, apply a vacuum of 7.9 inches Hg to system. Idling should become slightly unstable and vacuum pressure should be maintained.
5. If results are not as specified, EGR system is not performing satisfactorily. Service or replace components as necessary.

EGR VALVE

COLT, COLT VISTA, LASER, STEALTH, SUMMIT, SUMMIT WAGON, TALON & AVENGER & SEBRING COUPE

1. Remove EGR valve. Check for sticking, carbon, or other deposits. If deposits are present, clean EGR valve in specified solvent.
2. Connect hand vacuum pump, then apply 19.8 inches Hg vacuum. Check for leaks.
3. Blow air in from one passage of EGR, then check conditions with Figs. 14 and 15.
4. Install new gasket, then EGR valve.

BREEZE, CIRRUS, STRATUS & AVENGER & SEBRING CONVERTIBLE

1. With engine off, disconnect rubber hose from vacuum motor fitting at top of EGR valve.
2. Connect a hand vacuum pump to fitting and apply 15 inches of vacuum, then observe reading on pump.
3. If vacuum leaks down, EGR valve diaphragm is ruptured; replace valve.

Vacuum	Passage of air
8.5 kPa (2.5 in.Hg) or less	Air blows out of opposite passage.
20 kPa (6 in.Hg) or more	Air does not blow out of opposite passage.

CR1039500339000X

Fig. 15 EGR valve inspection. Avenger & Sebring Coupe w/2.5L/V6-152 engine

Engine coolant temperature	Result
50°C (122°F) or less	Vacuum leaks.
80°C (176°F) or more	Vacuum is maintained.

CR1039100193C00X

Fig. 16 Thermo valve inspection. Colt, Colt Vista, Laser, Stealth, Summit, Summit Wagon & Talon

4. If vacuum does not leak down, disconnect backpressure hose at EGR valve fitting, then remove air inlet tube from throttle body.
5. Using compressed air and a rubber-tipped air nozzle, apply approximately 50 psi of regulated air to metal backpressure fitting on EGR valve, then open throttle to wide open position by hand.
6. If air cannot be heard coming from intake manifold, system is operating satisfactorily; if air is heard, poppet valve at bottom of EGR valve is leaking and EGR valve replacement is necessary.

THERMO VALVE

COLT, COLT VISTA, LASER, SUMMIT, SUMMIT WAGON & TALON

1. Disconnect vacuum hoses from thermo valve, then connect hand vacuum pump to nipple of the thermo valve.
2. Apply vacuum, then check air passage through thermo valve, **Fig. 16.**

EGR TEMPERATURE SENSOR

COLT, COLT VISTA, LASER, STEALTH, SUMMIT, SUMMIT WAGON & TALON

1. Remove EGR temperature sensor.
2. Place temperature sensor in water. Connect ohmmeter between terminals 1 and 2.
3. Measure resistance while gradually increasing water temperature. Replace EGR temperature sensor if significant change from original reading is noticed, **Fig. 17.**
4. Install EGR temperature sensor. **Torque** to 7.3-8.6 ft. lbs.

EGR SOLENOID

COLT, COLT VISTA, LASER, STEALTH, SUMMIT, SUMMIT WAGON & TALON

1. Mark, then disconnect yellow/green stripe vacuum hose from control solenoid valve.
2. Disconnect harness connector.
3. Connect hand vacuum pump to nipple which yellow/green hose was connected.
4. Apply vacuum, then check for leaks with battery voltage applied directly to and discontinued from EGR control solenoid, **Fig. 18.**
5. Measure resistance between terminals of solenoid valve. Resistance should measure 36-44 ohms at 68°F.

CHARGE TEMPERATURE SWITCH (CTS)

1. No EGR operation with engine warm:
   a. Check hose routing and EGR solenoid operation.
   b. Remove center connector from CTS and wait 90 seconds.
   c. If EGR operation now resumes, replace CTS.
2. EGR operation with engine cold:
   a. Check hose routing and EGR solenoid operation.
   b. Remove center connector from CTS and check for 10 ohms resistance between center terminal of CTS and ground.
   c. If ohmmeter indicates an open circuit, replace CTS.
   d. If ohmmeter does not indicate an open CTS circuit, check for open circuit in CTS to engine ground wire. **Torque** switch to 60 inch lbs. Over-torquing will break off nylon threads in intake manifold.

System Service

EGR CONTROL VALVE

The EGR control valve should be checked for deposits with particular attention to the poppet and seat area. If deposits exceed a thin film condition, the EGR valve should be cleaned. If wear of the stem or other moving components is noted, the EGR valve should be replaced.

Extreme care should be exercised during the cleaning operation to prevent spilling of solvent on the valve diaphragm, as this will cause diaphragm failure. Do not push on diaphragm to operate valve, use the vacuum source only.

EGR TUBE, REPLACE

AVENGER, BREEZE, CIRRUS, NEON, STRATUS & SEBRING CONVERTIBLE

1. Remove screws attaching EGR tube to intake manifold and EGR valve, then remove tube.
2. Clean EGR valve gasket surface and intake manifold grommet.
3. Reverse procedure to install. **Torque** all screws to 95 inch lbs.

CONCORDE, INTREPID, LHS, VISION & 1994-96 NEW YORKER

1. **On models with 3.5L/V6-215 engine,** remove air cleaner plenum from rear of engine, then remove EGR tube to EGR valve screws.
2. **On all models,** remove EGR tube to intake manifold plenum screws.
3. **On models with 3.3L/V6-201 engine,** remove EGR tube mounting screws at exhaust manifold.
4. **On all models,** remove EGR tube, then clean gasket mating surfaces and discard gaskets.
5. Reverse procedure to install, noting the following:
   a. Install new gaskets.
   b. **Torque** EGR tube to intake manifold plenum screws to 16 ft. lbs.
   c. **On models with 3.3L/V6-201 engine, torque** EGR tube to exhaust manifold screws to 16 ft. lbs.
   d. **On models with 3.5L/V6-215 engine, torque** EGR tube to EGR valve screws to 95 inch lbs. and ensure insulation on EGR tube is aligned and in contact with insulation on rear engine vacuum harness.

EGR VALVE & ELECTRIC EGR TRANSDUCER, REPLACE

AVENGER, BREEZE, CIRRUS, CONCORDE, INTREPID, LHS, NEON, STRATUS, VISION, & SEBRING CONVERTIBLE & 1994-96 NEW YORKER

1. Disconnect vacuum supply tube and electrical connector from solenoid.
2. **On Concorde, Intrepid, LHS, Vision and 1994-96 New Yorker models with 3.5L/V6-215 engine,** slide transducer up and out of mounting bracket and loosen (but do not remove) EGR tube to intake manifold screws, then remove EGR tube lower screws at EGR valve.
3. **On Avenger, Breeze, Cirrus, Stratus and Sebring Convertible models with 2.4L/4-148 engine and Neon models,** remove EGR tube to EGR valve mounting screws.
4. **On Avenger, Breeze, Cirrus, Stratus and Sebring Convertible models with 2.5L/V6-152 engine,** proceed as follows:
   a. Remove backpressure hose from transducer, then pull transducer/solenoid off bracket.
   b. Remove Transaxle Control Module (TCM) screws from bracket and position TCM aside to gain access to EGR screws, then remove EGR tube to EGR valve mounting screws.
5. **On all models,** remove EGR valve mounting screws, then the EGR valve and transducer.
6. Clean gasket surfaces and, if necessary, EGR passages. Discard old gaskets.

Temperature °C (°F)	Resistance kΩ
50 (122)	60–83
100 (212)	11–14

CR1039100194000X

Fig. 17 EGR temperature sensor inspection. Colt, Colt Vista, Laser, Stealth, Summit, Summit Wagon & Talon

Battery voltage	Result
When applied	Vacuum is maintained.
When discontinued	Vacuum leaks.

CR1039100276000X

Fig. 18 EGR control solenoid valve inspection. Colt, Colt Vista, Laser, Stealth, Summit, Summit Wagon & Talon

7. Reverse procedure to install, noting the following:
   a. Install new gaskets.
   b. **Torque** EGR tube screws to 95 inch lbs.
   c. **Torque** EGR valve mounting screws to 16 ft. lbs.

POSITIVE CRANKCASE VENTILATION (PCV) SYSTEM

Description

This system, **Fig. 19,** is used on all engines to prevent the emission of blow-by gases from the engine's crankcase. These blow-by gases are the result of high pressures which are developed within the combustion chamber during the combustion process and contain undesirable pollutants.

When the engine is running, air is drawn by manifold vacuum from the air cleaner through a hose, to the crankcase inlet air cleaner. From the crankcase inlet air cleaner, the air mixes with the vapors in the rocker arm chamber and crankcase and are then drawn up through the PCV valve in the cylinder head cover to a hose connected to either the intake manifold or carburetor base. These gases become part of the calibrated air/fuel mixture and are then drawn into the combustion chamber, burned and expelled with the exhaust gases.

Diagnosis & Testing

1. With engine idling, remove PCV valve from rocker cover. If valve is not plugged, a hissing sound will be heard as air passes through the valve, and a strong vacuum should be felt when a finger is placed over valve inlet.
2. **On models equipped with screw-in type valves,** insert thin stick into threaded end of valve. Check for plunger movement. If plunger does not move, PCV valve is plugged. Replace valve and **torque** to 6-8.5 ft. lbs.
3. **On all models,** if the system passes above tests, no further service is required. If not, replace PCV valve and recheck system. **Do not attempt to clean PCV valve.**

System Service

Every 30,000 miles, replace PCV valve and clean crankcase inlet air cleaner. If vehicle is used extensively for short trips with frequent idling, this service may have to be performed sooner.

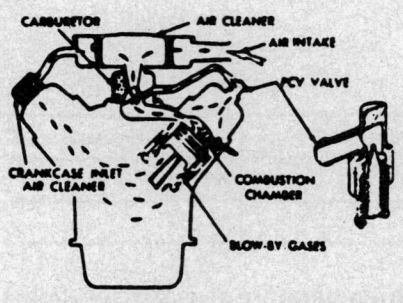

CR1039100277000X

Fig. 19   PCV system (typical)

ELECTRO IC INSTRUME TATION & BODY CONTROLS

NOTE: If Uncertain About The Proper Use Of Information Contained In This Section, Please Refer To "How To Use This Manual" Located In The Front Of This Manual.

On Air Bag Equipped Models, Refer To "Air Bag System Precautions" Located In The Front Of This Manual For System Disarming & Arming Procedures.

Prior To Performing Any Service Operations Listed In This Section, Consult The "Technical Service Bulletins" Section For Related Information.

Electrical Symbol & Wire Color Code Identification Located In The Front Of This Manual May Be Used As An Aid When Using Wiring Circuits Found In This Section.

INDEX

Page No.

Body Code Identification........... 21-1
Description........................ 21-1
Diagnosis & Testing:............... 21-1
  Body System Test (CCD BUS) ... 21-2
  Connector & Terminal
    Identification 21-2

Page No.

Electronic Instrumentation Test... 21-2
Using The Diagnostic Readout
  Box (DRB) Scan Tool 21-2
Visual Inspection................. 21-1
Diagnostic Chart Index:........... 21-6

Page No.

Body System (BUS)............. 21-7
Electronic Instrumentation 21-6

BODY CODE IDENTIFICATION

Body Code	Vehicle Line
1993	
AA	Acclaim, LeBaron Landau & Spirit
AC	Dynasty & New Yorker
AG	Daytona
AJ	LeBaron Coupe/Convertible
AP	Shadow & Sundance
AY	Fifth Avenue & Imperial
LH	Concorde, Intrepid & Vision
1994	
AA	Acclaim, LeBaron Landau & Spirit
AJ	LeBaron Convertible

Body Code	Vehicle Line
1993 -Continued	
AP	Shadow & Sundance
LH	Concorde, Intrepid, LHS, New Yorker & Vision
1995	
AA	Acclaim & Spirit
AJ	LeBaron Convertible
JA	Cirrus & Stratus
LH	Concorde, Intrepid, LHS, New Yorker & Vision
1996	
JA	Cirrus & Stratus
LH	Concorde, Intrepid, LHS, New Yorker & Vision

DESCRIPTION

Chassis electronic components on these models are equipped with an on-board diagnostic system. This system utilizes test procedures which enable the technician to quickly locate and correct malfunctions using a Diagnostic Readout Box (DRB).

DRB II system is used for 1993-95 models and DRB III system for 1996 models.

The Chrysler Collision Detection Multiplex System (CCD Bus) is a chassis electronic system designed to maintain system integrity. This system also has on-board diagnostic capabilities, including a separate set of test procedures.

DIAGNOSIS & TESTING

VISUAL INSPECTION

All diagnostic procedures must starts with a thorough visual inspection of the vehicle.

1. Verify all fuel system electrical connections and harness condition.
   a. Connectors must lock together.
   b. Look for terminals that are pushed out, loose or corroded.
   c. Ensure wiring between connectors is not pinched behind other components or screws.
2. Look for any added accessories that may affect normal operation of the body system.
3. All hoses and vacuum lines connections must be secure and hoses must not be pinched.
4. All air intake hoses and air cleaner housings must be in placed and secure.
5. Battery must be fully charged.

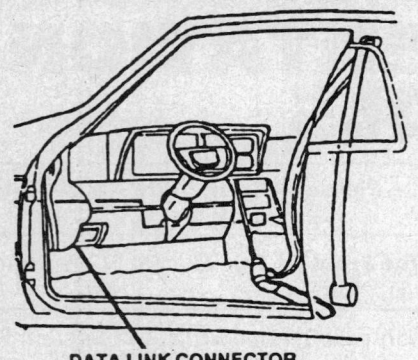
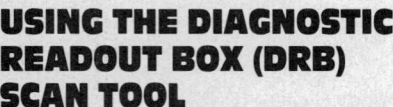

Fig. 1 Diagnostic data link connector. Acclaim, Spirit & LeBaron

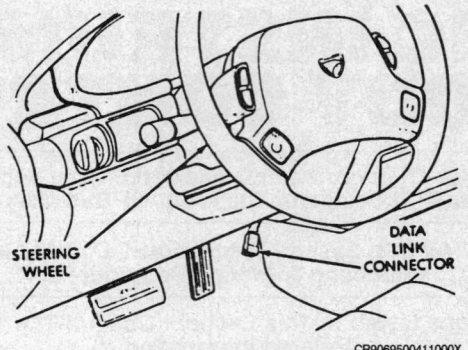

Fig. 2 Diagnostic data link connector. Concorde, Intrepid, LHS, 1994–95 New Yorker & Vision

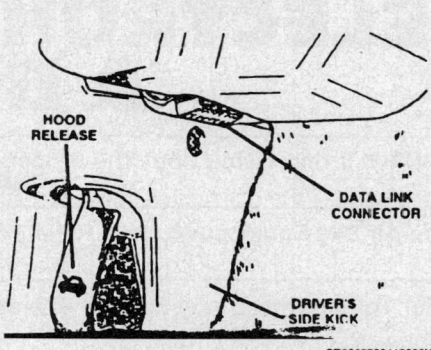

Fig. 3 Diagnostic data link connector. Cirrus & Stratus

USING THE DIAGNOSTIC READOUT BOX (DRB) SCAN TOOL

1. Connect DRB to the data link (diagnostic bus) connector located under the center of the instrument panel or along side of the fuse panel, **Figs. 1 through 3.**
2. Once connected, the DRB will perform a self-test. **Do not touch the keypad during the self-test.** If the message "Hardware Failure" is displayed, the DRB is defective and must be repaired.
3. After the self-test an identification logo will be displayed, then after a few more seconds the display will read "Select Model Year."
4. Press the F1 or F2 key until the display indicates the desired model year, then press the Yes key.
5. Press the F1 or F2 again key until the desired chassis systems is displayed, then press the Yes key.
6. After a few seconds the display will read "Select Module." Press the F1 or F2 key until the module to be tested is displayed, then press the Yes key.
7. From this point, follow the instructions given in the test procedure charts in order for each system.

CONNECTOR & TERMINAL IDENTIFICATION

Refer to **Figs. 4 through 19**, for connector and terminal identification.

ELECTRONIC INSTRUMENTATION TEST

1993 Dynasty, Fifth Avenue, Imperial & New Yorker

For electronic instrumentation diagnosis refer to **Figs. 20 through 38.**

1993 Daytona & LeBaron Coupe/Convertible

For electronic instrumentation diagnosis refer to **Figs. 39 through 59.**

Acclaim & Spirit

For electronic instrumentation diagnosis refer to **Figs. 60 through 71.**

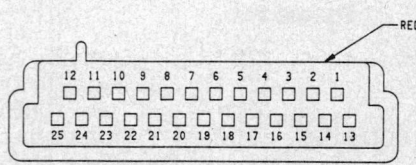

CONNECTOR VIEWED FROM TERMINAL END

CAV	CIRCUIT	FUNCTION
1	G74 22TN/RD ✶	RIGHT FRONT DOOR AJAR LIGHT
2	G78 22TN/BK ✶	DECK LID AJAR SWITCH
3	L70 22BR/YL ✶	LEFT AND RIGHT TAIL LAMP OUTAGE
4	———	
5	G5 20DB/WT ✶	WARNING LAMP FEED
6	G5 20DB/WT ✶	WARNING LAMP FEED
7	———	
8	———	
9	L4 16VT/WT ✶	HEADLAMP (LOW-BEAM)
10	E2 22OR	HEADLAMP SWITCHED DIMMABLE LAMP
11	G60 22GY/YL ✶	OIL PRESSURE GAUGE SENDING UNIT
12	L52 20GY/RD ✶	B+ TO CONCEALED HEADLAMP
13	G77 22TN/OR ✶	LEFT REAR DOOR AJAR LIGHT
14	G76 22TN/YL ✶	RIGHT REAR DOOR AJAR LIGHT
15	G46 22LB/BK ✶	BRAKE LAMP OUTAGE SIGNAL
16	G45 22OR/LG ✶	LOW-BEAM OUTAGE INDICATOR
17	G11 22WT/BK ✶	PARK BRAKE SWITCH
18	G5 20DB/WT ✶	WARNING LAMP FEED
19	G29 20BK/TN ✶	LOW WASHER FLUID INDICATOR
20	———	
21	L3 16RD/OR ✶	HEADLAMP (HIGH-BEAM)
22	———	
23	G6 22GY	LOW OIL PRESSURE WARNING LAMP
24	G20 22VT/YL ✶	WATER TEMPERATURE SENDING UNIT
25	L51 20GY/PK ✶	B+ TO CONCEALED HEADLAMP

Fig. 4 Body computer module connector, red (electronic cluster). 1993 Dynasty, Fifth Avenue, Imperial & New Yorker

BODY SYSTEM TEST (CCD BUS)

1993
Concorde, Daytona, Dynasty, Imperial, Intrepid, LeBaron, New Yorker, Shadow & Sundance

Refer to **Figs. 72 through 111** for procedures on the body system.

1994–95
Except Cirrus & Stratus

Refer to **Figs. 112 through 154** for procedures on the body system.

Cirrus & Stratus

Refer to **Figs. 155 through 180** for procedures on the body system.

1996

Breeze, Cirrus & Stratus

Refer to **Figs. 181 through 196** for procedures on the body system.

Concorde, Intrepid, LHS, New Yorker & Vision

Refer to **Figs. 197 through 211** for procedures on the body system.

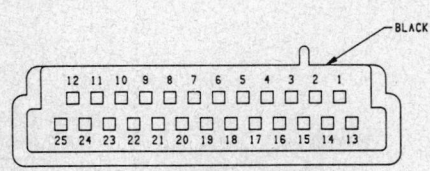

CAV	CIRCUIT	FUNCTION
1	G75 22TN	DOOR AJAR LIGHTS
2	G26 20LB	KEY-IN BUZZER/CHIME
3	E17 20YL/BK*	ELECTRONIC DISPLAY INTENSITY
4	P35 18OR/VT*	POWER DOOR LOCK B+
5	V10 18BR	WINDSHIELD WASHER
6	G5 20DB/WT*	WARNING LAMP FEED
7	D1 20VT/BR*	SERIAL BUSS B+
8	M11 18PK/LB*	COURTESY LAMP FEED
9	——	
10	V5 18DG	WINDSHIELD WIPER MOTOR FEED
11	F13 18DB	FRONT WIPER PARK
12	V9 18BK	ANALOG IN SWITCH
13	G16 22BK/LB*	BUZZER/CHIME PASSIVE RESTRAINT
14	G10 22LG/RD*	SEAT BELT WARNING SWITCH
15	L6 18RD/WT*	FEED FROM TURN SIGNAL FLASHER
16	M22 22WT	ILLUMINATED ENTRY RELAY GROUND
17	V7 18WT/BK*	PULSE WIPE PARK (B−)
18	G4 22DB/YL*	FUEL TANK SENDING UNIT
19	Z2 20BK/LG*	SENSOR GROUND
19	Z2 20BK/LG*	SENSOR GROUND
20	D2 20WT/BK*	SERIAL BUSS B−
21	P38 20OR/WT*	AUTO DOOR LOCK RELAY COIL (B+)
22	J25 18YL/RD*	IGNITION SWITCH LAMP
23	——	
24	——	
25	M2 20YL	DOOR AND LIFT GROUND SWITCHES

● TWISTED PAIR

Fig. 5 Body computer module connector, black (electronic cluster). 1993 Dynasty, Fifth Avenue, Imperial & New Yorker

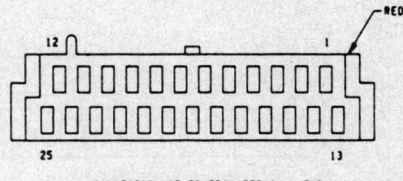

CAV	CIRCUIT	FUNCTION
1	M31 22TN/WT*	DOOR AJAR LIGHTS
2	G78 22TN/BK*	DECK LID AJAR SWITCH
3	——	
3	——	
4	——	
5	——	
6	——	
7	——	
9	L4 16VT/WT*	HEADLAMP (LOW-BEAM)
10	——	
11	——	
12	L52 20GY/RD*	B+ TO CONCEALED HEADLAMP
13	——	
14	——	
15	——	
16	——	
17	——	
18	——	
19	——	
20	——	
21	L3 16RD/OR*	HEADLAMP (HIGH-BEAM)
22	——	
23	——	
24	——	
25	L51 20GY/PK*	B+ TO CONCEALED HEADLAMP

CR9069300218000X

Fig. 6 Body computer module connector, red (mechanical cluster w/visual message center). 1993 Dynasty, Fifth Avenue, Imperial & New Yorker

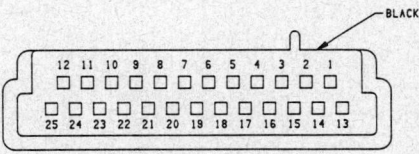

CAV	CIRCUIT	FUNCTION
1	M31 22TN/WT*	DOOR AJAR LIGHTS
2	G26 20LB	KEY-IN BUZZER/CHIME
3	L7 18BK/YL*	TAIL, LICENSE, SIDE MARKER LAMP
3	E17 20YL/BK*	ELECTRONIC DISPLAY INTENSITY
4	P35 18OR/VT*	POWER DOOR LOCK B+
5	V10 18BR	WINDSHIELD WASHER
6	G5 20DB/WT*	WARNING LAMP FEED
7	D1 20WT/BR*	SERIAL BUSS B+
8	M11 18PK/LB*	COURTESY LAMP FEED
9	G41 22LB/RD*	LOW FUEL OUTPUT
10	V5 18DG	WINDSHIELD WIPER MOTOR FEED
11	F13 18DB	FRONT WIPER PARK
12	V9 18BK	ANALOG IN SWITCH
13	G16 22BK/LB*	BUZZER/CHIME PASSIVE RESTRAINT
14	G10 22LG/RD*	SEAT BELT WARNING SWITCH
15	L6 18RD/WT*	FEED FROM TURN SIGNAL FLASHER
16	M22 22WT	ILLUMINATED ENTRY RELAY GROUND
17	V7 18WT/BK*	PULSE WIPE PARK (B−)
18	G4 22DB/YL*	FUEL TANK SENDING UNIT
19	Z2 20BK/LG*	SENSOR GROUND
19	Z2 20BK/LG*	SENSOR GROUND
20	D2 20WT/BK*	SERIAL BUSS B−
21	P38 20OR/WT*	AUTO DOOR LOCK RELAY COIL (B+)
22	J25 18YL/RD*	IGNITION SWITCH LAMP
23	G13 22DB/RD*	SEAT BELT LAMP
24	G1 22WT/RD*	BRAKE PAD WEAR SENSOR
25	M2 20YL	DOOR AND LIFT GROUND SWITCHES

● TWISTED PAIR

Fig. 7 Body computer module connector, black (mechanical cluster w/visual message center). 1993 Dynasty, Fifth Avenue, Imperial & New Yorker

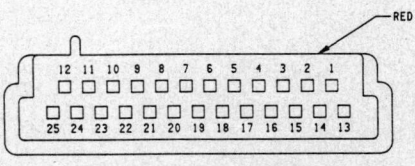

CAV	CIRCUIT	FUNCTION
1	——	
2	G78 22TN/BK*	DECK LID AJAR SWITCH
3	——	
4	——	
5	——	
6	——	
7	——	
8	——	
9	L4 16VT/WT*	HEADLAMP (LOW-BEAM)
10	——	
11	——	
12	L52 20GY/RD*	B+ TO CONCEALED HEADLAMP
13	——	
14	——	
15	——	
16	——	
17	——	
18	——	
19	——	
20	L3 16RD/OR*	HEADLAMP (HIGH-BEAM)
22	——	
23	——	
24	——	
25	L51 20GY/PK*	B+ TO CONCEALED HEADLAMP

Fig. 8 Body computer module connector, red (mechanical cluster less visual message center). 1993 Dynasty, Fifth Avenue, Imperial & New Yorker

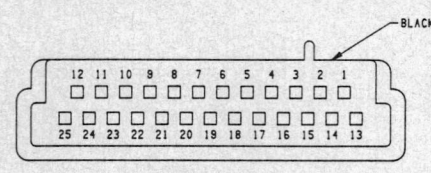

CAV	CIRCUIT	FUNCTION
1	M31 22TN/RD*	DOOR AJAR LIGHTS
2	G26 20LB	KEY-IN BUZZER/CHIME
3	L7 18BK/YL*	TAIL, LICENSE, SIDE MARKER LAMP
E17 20YL/BK*		ELECTRONIC DISPLAY INTENSITY
4	P35 18OR/VT*	POWER DOOR LOCK B+
5	V10 18BR	WINDSHIELD WASHER
6	G5 20DB/WT*	WARNING LAMP FEED
7	D1 20VT/BR*	SERIAL BUSS B+
8	M11 18PK/LB*	COURTESY LAMP FEED
9	G41 22LB/RD*	LOW FUEL OUTPUT
10	V5 18DG	WINDSHIELD WIPER MOTOR FEED
11	F13 18DB	FRONT WIPER PARK
12	V9 18BK	ANALOG IN SWITCH
13	G16 22BK/LB*	BUZZER/CHIME PASSIVE RESTRAINT
14	G10 22LG/RD*	SEAT BELT WARNING SWITCH
15	L6 18RD/WT*	FEED FROM TURN SIGNAL FLASHER
16	M22 22WT	ILLUMINATED ENTRY RELAY GROUND
17	V7 18WT/BK*	PULSE WIPE PARK (B-)
18	G4 22DB/YL*	FUEL TANK SENDING UNIT
19	Z2 20BK/LG*	SENSOR GROUND
19	Z2 20BK/LG*	SENSOR GROUND
20	D2 20VT/BK*	SERIAL BUSS B-
21	P38 20OR/WT*	AUTO DOOR LOCK RELAY COIL (B+)
22	J25 18YL/RD*	IGNITION SWITCH LAMP
23	G13 22DB/RD*	SEAT BELT LAMP
24	G1 22WT/RD*	BRAKE PAD WEAR SENSOR
25	M2 20YL	DOOR AND LIFT GROUND SWITCHES

● TWISTED PAIR

Fig. 9 Body computer module connector, black (mechanical cluster less visual message center). 1993 Dynasty, Fifth Avenue, Imperial & New Yorker

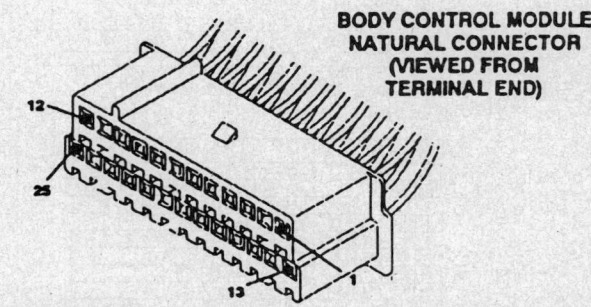

CAV	COLOR	FUNCTION
1	TN/RD	RIGHT FRONT DOOR AJAR SWITCH SENSE
7	TN	RIGHT TURN SIGNAL
8	BR	FUSED PARK LAMP RELAY OUTPUT
9	RD/YL	HIGH BEAM RELAY CONTROL
10	OR/BK	DIMMER SWITCH SIGNAL
20	OR/WT	LOW BEAM RELAY CONTROL
21	OR/WT	LOW BEAM RELAY CONTROL
22	OR	PANEL LAMPS DRIVER

CR9069500413000X

Fig. 10 Body computer module connector (black). 1993 Daytona & 1993–95 LeBaron

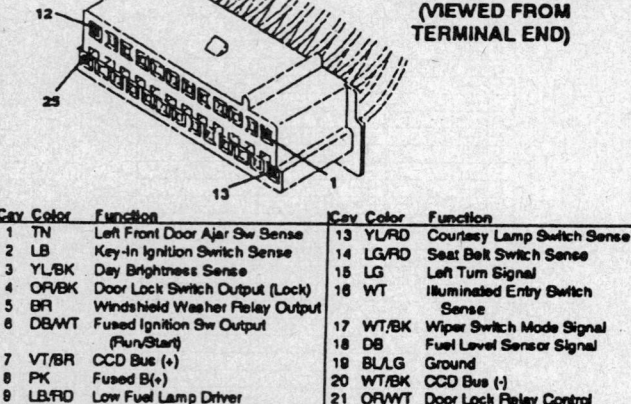

Cav	Color	Function	Cav	Color	Function
1	TN	Left Front Door Ajar Sw Sense	13	YL/RD	Courtesy Lamp Switch Sense
2	LB	Key-In Ignition Switch Sense	14	LG/RD	Seat Belt Switch Sense
3	YL/BK	Day Brightness Sense	15	LG	Left Turn Signal
4	OR/BK	Door Lock Switch Output (Lock)	16	WT	Illuminated Entry Switch Sense
5	BR	Windshield Washer Relay Output			
6	DB/WT	Fused Ignition Sw Output (Run/Start)	17	WT/BK	Wiper Switch Mode Signal
			18	DB	Fuel Level Sensor Signal
7	VT/BR	CCD Bus (+)	19	BL/LG	Ground
8	PK	Fused B(+)	20	WT/BK	CCD Bus (-)
9	LB/RD	Low Fuel Lamp Driver	21	OR/WT	Door Lock Relay Control
10	DG	Wiper Park Switch Sense	22	YL/RD	Key-In Lamp Driver
11	DB	Fused Ignition Sw Output (Run/Acc)	23	DB/RD	Seat Belt Lamp Driver
			24	DG/YL	Check Gauges Lamp Driver
12	DG/WT	Wiper Switch Mode Sense	25	YL	Courtesy Lamps Driver

CR9069500414000X

Fig. 11 Body computer module connector (natural). 1993 Daytona & 1993–95 LeBaron

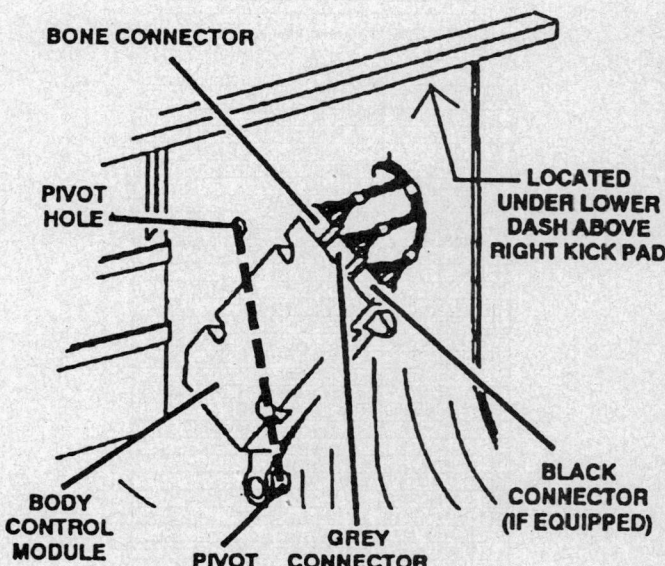

CR90E9500415000X

Fig. 12 Body computer module location. Concorde, Intrepid, LHS, Vision & 1994–96 New Yorker

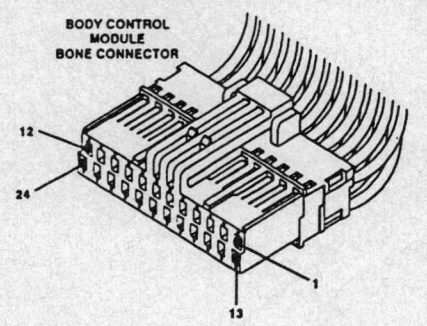

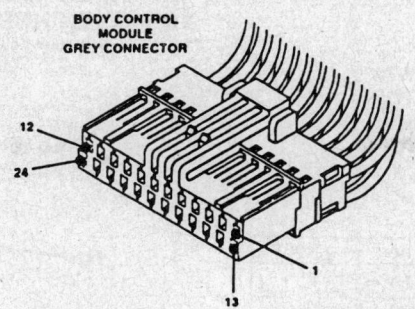

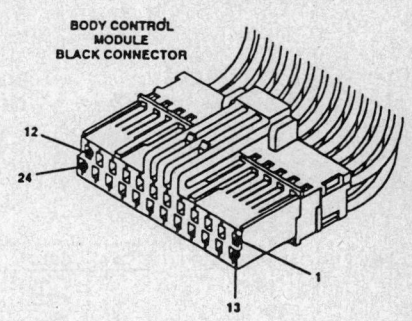

CAV	CIRCUIT	FUNCTION
1	V14 DG/YL	Wiper On/Off Relay Control
2	V55 TN/RD	Wiper Park Switch Sense
3	F37 RD/LG	Fused Headlamp Switch Output
4	E19 OR/DB	Dimmer Switch Signal
5	M50 YL/RD	Key-In Lamp Driver
6	G129 RD	Washer Fluid Lamp Driver
7	D2 WT/BK	CCD Bus (-)
8	D1 VT/BR	CCD Bus (+)
9	P35 OR/VT	Door Lock Switch Output
10	V10 BR	Washer Pump Control Switch Output
12	M2 YL	Courtesy Lamps Driver
13	G5 DB/WT	Fused Ignition Switch Output (Run/Start)
14	Z2 BK/LG	Ground
15	C57 GY/TN	Sensor Ground
16	V52 DG/RD	Windshield Wiper Switch Signal
18	V16 VT	Wiper Hi/Lo Relay Control
19	M1 PK	Fused B(+)
20	G26 LB	Key-In Ignition Switch Sense
21	Z1 BK	Ground
22	F11 RD/WT	Fused Ignition Switch Output (Off/Run/Start)
23	L7 BK/YL	Park Lamp Switch Output

CR9069500416000X

Fig. 13 Body computer module connector (bone). Concorde, Intrepid, LHS, Vision & 1994–96 New Yorker

CAV	CIRCUIT	FUNCTION
2	G50 RD/DB	Headlamp Delay Relay Control
3	G74 TN/RD	Door Ajar Switch Sense
4*	C37 RD	Mode Door Feedback Signal
5	G10 LG/RD	Seat Belt Switch Sense
6	G75 TN	Left Front Door Ajar Switch Sense
7	D14 LB	Cluster Mode Sense
8	E2 OR	Panel Lamps Driver
9	G0 PK/BK	Door Ajar Lamp Driver
10*	G31 VT/LG	Ambient Temperature Sensor Signal
11	M32 YL/RD	Courtesy Lamp Switch Sense
12	D13 OR/DB	Cluster ID Sense
13	C12 LG/BK	Evaporator Temperature Sensor Signal
15	M22 WT	Illuminated Entry Switch Sense
17	G29 BR/TN	Washer Fluid Switch Sense
18	P38 OR/WT	Door Lock Relay Control
20*	C38 DB/RD	Sun Sensor Signal
21	P36 PK/VT	Door Unlock Relay Control
22	C21 DB/OR	A/C Switch Sense (manual A/C only)
23	G4 DB	Fuel Level Sensor Signal
24*	G51 LB	Park Lamp Relay Control

* If equipped

CR9069500417000X

Fig. 14 Body computer module connector (gray). Concorde, Intrepid, LHS, Vision & 1994–96 New Yorker

CAV	CIRCUIT	FUNCTION
1*	C10 RD/TN	In-Car Temperature Sensor Input/Sense
3*	G73 LG/OR	VTSS Disarm Sense
4*	C56 RD/LG	Blower Motor Driver
5*	C36 RD/WT	Blend Door Feedback Signal
6*	C26 PK/DB	5-Volt Supply
8*	X03 BK/RD	Horn Relay Control
10*	G69 BK/OR	VTSS Indicator Lamp Driver
11*	G52 YL	Auto Headlamp Switch Output
12*	C9 YL/DG	Aspirator Motor Driver
16*	C35 DG/YL	Mode Door Driver
18*	C32 GY/DB	Recirculation Door Driver
20*	C33 DB/RD	Blend Air Door Driver
22*	C34 DB/WT	Common Door Driver
24*	G71 VT/YL	Trunk Key Cylinder Sense

* If equipped.

CR9069500418000X

Fig. 15 Body computer module connector (black). Concorde, Intrepid, LHS, Vision & 1994-96 New Yorker

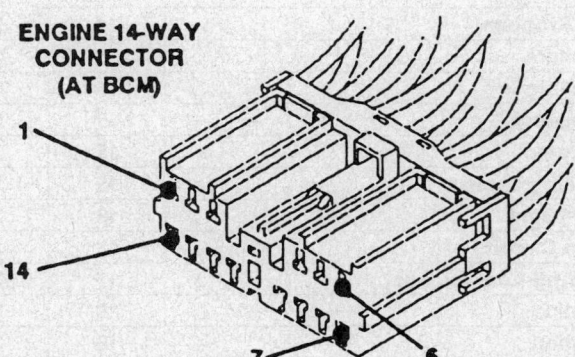

CAV	COLOR	FUNCTION
1	VT/DG	CCD BUS (+)
2	VT/BR	CCD BUS (+)
3	BK/LG	GROUND
5	WT/GY	WIPER PARK SWITCH SENSE
7	PK/VT	INTERMITTENT WIPER RELAY CONTROL
8	VT/PK	HI/LO WIPER RELAY CONTROL
10	BR/DB	WASHER PUMP CONTROL SWITCH OUTPUT
12	BK/LG	GROUND
13	WT/BK	CCD BUS(-)
14	WT/DG	CCD BUS (-)

CR9069500419000X

Fig. 16 Body computer module connector (14-way). Cirrus & Stratus

INSTRUMENT PANEL
22-WAY CONNECTOR
(AT BCM)

CAV	COLOR	FUNCTION
1	DG/YL	Windshield Wiper Switch Signal
4	LG/BK	Evaporator Temp Sensor Signal
5	YL	Mode Door Feedback Signal
6	RD	HVAC Mode Sense
7	BK/VT	Ground
8	VT/GY	CCD Bus (+)
9	VT	CCD Bus (+)
10	VT/BR	CCD Bus (+)
11	WT/DB	CCD Bus (-)
12	WT/BK	CCD Bus (-)
13	WT/DG	CCD Bus (-)
14	BK/LG	Ground
15	BR/DB	Washer Pump Control Switch Output
16	DB/OR	A/C Switch Sense
17	LB	Key-In Ignition Switch Sense
18	RD	Dimmer Switch Signal
19	BK/PK	Ground
20	GY/TN	Sensor Ground
21	GY	Sensor Ground
22	BK/TN	Ground

CR9069500420000X

Fig. 17 Body computer module connector (22-way). Cirrus & Stratus

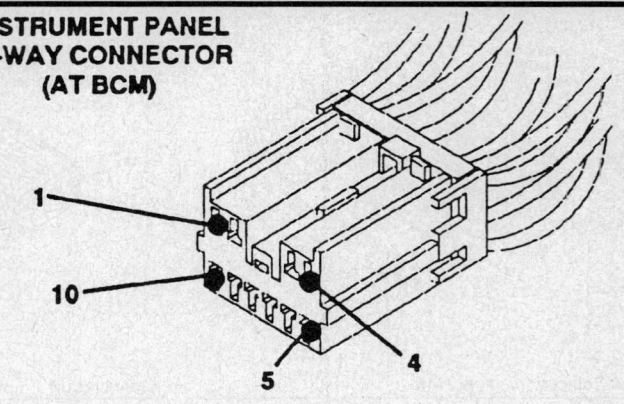

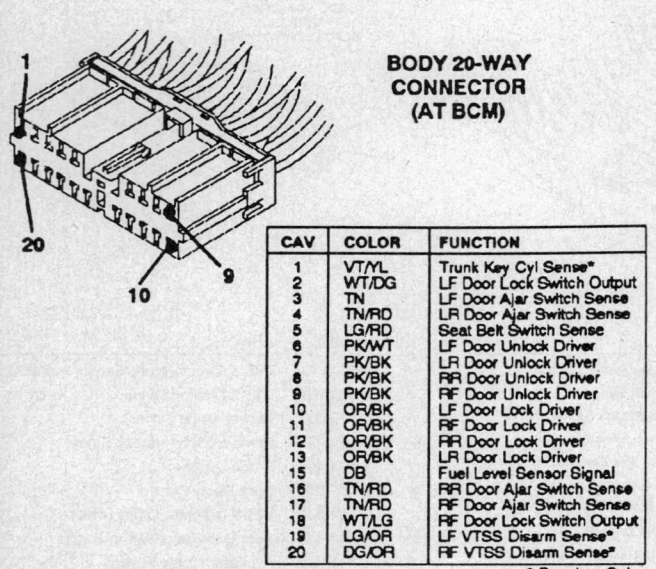

BODY 20-WAY CONNECTOR (AT BCM)

CAV	COLOR	FUNCTION
1	VT/YL	Trunk Key Cyl Sense*
2	WT/DG	LF Door Lock Switch Output
3	TN	LF Door Ajar Switch Sense
4	TN/RD	LR Door Ajar Switch Sense
5	LG/RD	Seat Belt Switch Sense
6	PK/WT	LF Door Unlock Driver
7	PK/BK	LR Door Unlock Driver
8	PK/BK	RR Door Unlock Driver
9	PK/BK	RF Door Unlock Driver
10	OR/BK	LF Door Lock Driver
11	OR/BK	RF Door Lock Driver
12	OR/BK	RR Door Lock Driver
13	OR/BK	LR Door Lock Driver
15	DB	Fuel Level Sensor Signal
16	TN/RD	RR Door Ajar Switch Sense
17	TN/RD	RF Door Ajar Switch Sense
18	WT/LG	RF Door Lock Switch Output
19	LG/OR	LF VTSS Disarm Sense*
20	DG/OR	RF VTSS Disarm Sense*

* Premium Only

Fig. 18 Body computer module connector (20-way). Cirrus & Stratus

INSTRUMENT PANEL 10-WAY CONNECTOR (AT BCM)

CAV	COLOR	FUNCTION
1	OR/BR	PANEL LAMPS DRIVER
2	OR/YL	PANEL LAMPS DRIVER
3	DG/YL	MODE DOOR DRIVER (+)
4	BK/OR	VTSS INDICATOR LAMP DRIVER
5	PK/DB	5-VOLT SUPPLY
6	DB/YL	MODE DOOR DRIVER (-)
7	YL/RD	KEY-IN LAMP DRIVER
9	OR	PANEL LAMPS DRIVER
10	OR/GY	PANEL LAMPS DRIVER

Fig. 19 Body computer module connector (10-way). Cirrus & Stratus

DIAGNOSTIC CHART INDEX
ELECTRONIC INSTRUMENTATION

Test	Symptom	Page No. 21-	Fig. No.
DYNASTY, FIFTH AVENUE, IMPERIAL & 1993 NEW YORKER			
Test 15A	Electronic Instrument Cluster	14	20
Test 15B	Blank Electronic Cluster Display	14	21
Test 16A	Identifying Faulty Gauge	14	22
Test 17A	Temperature Gauge Problem	14	23
Test 18A	Speedometer Failure	15	24
Test 18B	Speedometer Failure	15	25
Test 19A	Warning Lamp Diagnosis	15	26
Test 19B	Faulty Warning Lamp	15	27
Test 19C	Faulty Door/Deck Warning Lamp	16	28
Test 20A	Seat Belt Warning Lamp	16	29
Test 21A	Brake Warning Lamp Circuit	17	30
Test 21B	Brake Pressure Switch (Less Anti-Lock Brakes)	17	31
Test 22A	Cluster Illumination	18	32
Test 22B	Cluster Illumination	18	33
Test 22C	Cluster Illumination	18	34
Test 22D	Cluster Illumination	19	35
Test 22E	Cluster Illumination	19	36
Test 23A	Cluster Illuminated Upon Entry	20	37
Test 24A	Cluster Switch	20	38
DAYTONA & 1993 LEBARON			
Test 32A	Electronic Instrument Cluster	20	39
Test 33A	Identifying Electronic Instrument Cluster DTC	21	40
Test 34A	Electronic Cluster " No Fault" Path	21	41
Test 34B	Repairing Electronic Cluster Speedometer/Odometer Problem	22	42
Test 34C	Repairing Electronic Cluster Switches Operation	22	43
Test 35A	Identifying Faulty Gauge	22	44
Test 36A	Repairing Temperature Gauge Problems	22	45

Continued

ELECTRONIC INSTRUMENTATION-Continued

Test	Symptom	Page No. 21-	Fig. No.
DAYTONA & 1993 LEBARON-CONTINUED			
Test 37A	Identifying Faulty Warning Lamp Or Indicator	23	46
Test 37B	Repairing Faulty Warning Lamp Condition	23	47
Test 38A	Repairing Seat Belt Warning Lamp Problem	24	48
Test 39A	Repairing Brake Warning Lamp & Parking Brake Switch Problems	24	49
Test 39B	Repairing Brake Warning Lamp & Brake Pressure Switch Problems	25	50
Test 39C	Repairing Brake Warning Lamp & Brake Pressure Switch Problems	25	51
Test 40A	Dimming Interior Displays	26	52
Test 40B	Dimming Interior Displays	26	53
Test 40C	Dimming Interior Displays	26	54
Test 40D	Dimming Interior Displays	27	55
Test 40E	Dimming Interior Displays	27	56
Test 40F	Dimming Interior Displays	27	57
Test 40G	Dimming Interior Displays	27	58
Test 40H	Dimming Interior Displays	28	59
ACCLAIM & SPIRIT			
Test 31A	"No Response" Condition	28	60
Test 31B	Open Fused Ignition Switch Output	29	61
Test 31C	Instrument Cluster Battery Power Supply (1993)	29	62
Test 31D	Instrument Cluster Battery Power Supply (1994-95)	30	63
Test 33A	Instrument Cluster ID Circuits	31	64
Test 34A	Switch Operation	31	65
Test 36A	Speedometer & Odometer	31	66
Test 38A	Instrument Cluster Or Compass/Mini-Trip Illumination	32	67
Test 38B	Open Pod Switch Control	32	68
Test 39A	Park Lamp	33	69
Test 40A	Shorted Panel Lamps Power Supply	33	70
Test 41A	Cluster Illumination Supply	34	71

BODY SYSTEM (BUS)

Test	Symptom	Page No. 21-	Fig. No.
1993 ACCLAIM & SPIRIT			
Test 1A	Bus Failure Messages	34	72
Test 1C	Blank Screen On DRB	34	73
Test 1D	RAM Test Failure	35	74
Test 1E	Cartridge Failure	35	75
Test 1F	Key Pad Test Failure	35	76
Test 1G	Low Or High Battery	35	77
Test 7A	Short To Battery Failure	35	78
Test 7B	Short To Battery Failure	36	79
Test 7C	Short To Battery Failure	36	80
Test 7D	Short To Battery Failure	37	81
Test 7E	Short To Battery Failure	37	82
Test 7F	Short To Battery Failure	37	83
Test 8A	Short To 5 Volts Failure	38	84
Test 8B	Short To 5 Volts Failure	39	85
Test 8D	Short To 5 Volts Failure	39	86
Test 8E	Short To 5 Volts Failure	39	87
Test 8F	Short To 5 Volts Failure	39	88
Test 8G	Short To 5 Volts Failure	39	89
Test 9A	Short To Ground Failure	40	90
Test 9B	Short To Ground Failure	41	91
Test 10A	Bus (+) & Bus (-) Shorted Together Failure	41	92
Test 11A	No Termination Failure	42	93

CHRYSLER–Electronic Instrumentation & Body Controls

BODY SYSTEM (BUS)-Continued

Test	Symptom	Page No. 21-	Fig. No.
1993 ACCLAIM & SPIRIT -CONTINUED			
Test 11B	No Termination Failure	42	94
Test 12A	Bus Bias Level Or Bus (+/-) Open Failure	44	98
Test 12B	Bus Bias Level Or Bus (+/-) Open Failure	44	99
Test 13A	No Bus Bias Failure	48	104
Test 13B	No Bus Bias Failure	49	105
Test 13K	No Bus Bias Failure	52	109
Test 14A	Not Receiving Bus Messages Correctly Failure	52	110
Test VER-1	Verification Test	53	111
1994-95 ACCLAIM & SPIRIT			
Test 1A	Bus Failure Messages	53	112
Test 2A	Blank Screen On DRB	53	113
Test 3A	RAM Test Error	54	114
Test 4A	Cartridge Failure Error	54	115
Test 5A	Key Pad Test Failure	54	116
Test 6A	Testing For Low Or High Battery	54	117
Test 7A	Short To Battery Failure	55	118
Test 7B	Short To Battery Failure	55	119
Test 7C	Short To Battery Failure	56	120
Test 7D	Short To Battery Failure	56	121
Test 7E	Short To Battery Failure	56	122
Test 7H	Short To Battery Failure	57	125
Test 8A	Short To 5 Volts Failure	58	126
Test 8B	Short To 5 Volts Failure	59	127
Test 8D	Short To 5 Volts Failure	59	128
Test 8E	Short To 5 Volts Failure	59	129
Test 8F	Short To 5 Volts Failure	59	130
Test 8G	Short To 5 Volts Failure	59	131
Test 8H	Short To 5 volts Failure	60	132
Test 9A	Short To Ground Failure	61	133
Test 9B	Short To Ground Failure	61	134
Test 10A	Bus (+) & Bus (-) Shorted Together Failure	62	135
Test 11A	No Termination Failure	62	136
Test 11B	No Termination Failure	65	142
Test 12B	Bus Bias Level Or Bus (+/-) Open Failure	65	141
Test 12G	Bus Bias Level Or Bus (+/-) Open Failure	68	145
Test 13A	No Bus Bias Failure	69	146
Test 13B	No Bus Bias Failure	69	147
Test 13K	No Bus Bias Failure	72	151
Test 14A	Not Receiving Bus Messages Correctly Failure	73	153
Test VER-1A	Verification Test	74	154
1993 DAYTONA & LEBARON			
Test 1A	Bus Failure Messages	34	72
Test 1C	Blank Screen On DRB	34	73
Test 1D	RAM Test Failure	35	74
Test 1E	Cartridge Failure	35	75
Test 1F	Key Pad Test Failure	35	76
Test 1G	Low Or High Battery	35	77
Test 7A	Short To Battery Failure	35	78
Test 7B	Short To Battery Failure	36	79
Test 7C	Short To Battery Failure	36	80
Test 7D	Short To Battery Failure	37	81
Test 7E	Short To Battery Failure	37	82
Test 7F	Short To Battery Failure	37	83
Test 8A	Short To 5 Volts Failure	38	84

Test	Symptom	Page No. 21-	Fig. No.
1993 DAYTONA & LEBARON-CONTINUED			
Test 8B	Short To 5 Volts Failure	39	85
Test 8D	Short To 5 Volts Failure	39	86
Test 8E	Short To 5 Volts Failure	39	87
Test 8F	Short To 5 Volts Failure	39	88
Test 8G	Short To 5 Volts Failure	39	89
Test 9A	Short To Ground Failure	40	90
Test 9B	Short To Ground Failure	41	91
Test 10A	Bus (+) & Bus (-) Shorted Together Failure	41	92
Test 11A	No Termination Failure	42	93
Test 11D	No Termination Failure	43	96
Test 12A	Bus Bias Level Or Bus (+/-) Open Failure	44	98
Test 12D	Bus Bias Level Or Bus (+/-) Open Failure	46	101
Test 12G	Bus Bias Level Or Bus (+/-) Open Failure	47	102
Test 13A	No Bus Bias Failure	48	104
Test 13D	No Bus Bias Failure	50	107
Test 13K	No Bus Bias Failure	52	109
Test 14A	Not Receiving Bus Messages Correctly Failure	52	110
Test VER-1	Verification Test	53	111
1994-95 LEBARON			
Test 1A	Bus Failure Messages	53	112
Test 2A	Blank Screen On DRB	53	113
Test 3A	RAM Test Error	54	114
Test 4A	Cartridge Failure Error	54	115
Test 5A	Key Pad Test Failure	54	116
Test 6A	Testing For Low Or High Battery	54	117
Test 7A	Short To Battery Failure	55	118
Test 7B	Short To Battery Failure	55	119
Test 7C	Short To Battery Failure	56	120
Test 7D	Short To Battery Failure	56	121
Test 7E	Short To Battery Failure	56	122
Test 7F	Short To Battery Failure	56	123
Test 7H	Short To Battery Failure	57	125
Test 8A	Short To 5 Volts Failure	58	126
Test 8B	Short To 5 Volts Failure	59	127
Test 8D	Short To 5 Volts Failure	59	128
Test 8E	Short To 5 Volts Failure	59	129
Test 8F	Short To 5 Volts Failure	59	130
Test 8G	Short To 5 Volts Failure	59	131
Test 8H	Short To 5 volts Failure	60	132
Test 9A	Short To Ground Failure	61	133
Test 9B	Short To Ground Failure	61	134
Test 10A	Bus (+) & bus (-) Shorted Together Failure	62	135
Test 11A	No Termination Failure	62	136
Test 11D	No Termination Failure	64	139
Test 11H	No Termination Failure	65	142
Test 12A	Bus Bias Level Or Bus (+/-) Open Failure	65	141
Test 12B	Bus Bias Level Or Bus (+/-) Open Failure	67	144
Test 12D	Bus Bias Level Or Bus (+/-) Open Failure	68	145
Test 12H	Bus Bias Level Or Bus (+/-) Open Failure	69	146
Test 13A	No Bus Bias Failure	69	147
Test 13D	No Bus Bias Failure	71	150
Test 13H	No Bus Bias Failure	72	151
Test 14A	Not Receiving Bus Messages Correctly Failure	73	153
Test VER-1A	Verification Test	74	154

Test	Symptom	Page No. 21-	Fig. No.
DYNASTY, FIFTH AVENUE, IMPERIAL & 1993 NEW YORKER			
Test 1A	Bus Failure Messages	34	72
Test 1C	Blank Screen On DRB	34	73
Test 1D	RAM Test Failure	35	74
Test 1E	Cartridge Failure	35	75
Test 1F	Key Pad Test Failure	35	76
Test 1G	Low Or High Battery	35	77
Test 7A	Short To Battery Failure	35	78
Test 7B	Short To Battery Failure	36	79
Test 7C	Short To Battery Failure	36	80
Test 7D	Short To Battery Failure	37	81
Test 7E	Short To Battery Failure	37	82
Test 7F	Short To Battery Failure	37	83
Test 8A	Short To 5 Volts Failure	38	84
Test 8B	Short To 5 Volts Failure	39	85
Test 8D	Short To 5 Volts Failure	39	86
Test 8E	Short To 5 Volts Failure	39	87
Test 8F	Short To 5 Volts Failure	39	88
Test 8G	Short To 5 Volts Failure	39	89
Test 9A	Short To Ground Failure	40	90
Test 9B	Short To Ground Failure	41	91
Test 10A	Bus (+) & Bus (-) Shorted Together Failure	41	92
Test 11A	No Termination Failure	42	93
Test 11C	No Termination Failure	43	95
Test 12A	Bus Bias Level Or Bus (+/-) Open Failure	44	98
Test 12C	Bus Bias Level Or Bus (+/-) Open Failure	45	100
Test 12G	Bus Bias Level Or Bus (+/-) Open Failure	47	102
Test 13A	No Bus Bias Failure	48	104
Test 13C	No Bus Bias Failure	49	106
Test 13K	No Bus Bias Failure	52	109
Test 14A	Not Receiving Bus Messages Correctly Failure	52	110
Test VER-1	Verification Test	53	111
1993 SHADOW & SUNDANCE			
Test 1A	Bus Failure Messages	34	72
Test 1C	Blank Screen On DRB	34	73
Test 1D	RAM Test Failure	35	74
Test 1E	Cartridge Failure	35	75
Test 1F	Key Pad Test Failure	35	76
Test 1G	Low Or High Battery	35	77
Test 7A	Short To Battery Failure	35	78
Test 7B	Short To Battery Failure	36	79
Test 7C	Short To Battery Failure	36	80
Test 7D	Short To Battery Failure	37	81
Test 7E	Short To Battery Failure	37	82
Test 7F	Short To Battery Failure	37	83
Test 8A	Short To 5 Volts Failure	38	84
Test 8B	Short To 5 Volts Failure	39	85
Test 8D	Short To 5 Volts Failure	39	86
Test 8E	Short To 5 Volts Failure	39	87
Test 8F	Short To 5 Volts Failure	39	88
Test 8G	Short To 5 Volts Failure	39	89
Test 9A	Short To Ground Failure	40	90
Test 9B	Short To Ground Failure	41	91
Test 10A	Bus (+) & Bus (-) Shorted Together Failure	41	92
Test 11A	No Termination Failure	42	93

Test	Symptom	Page No. 21-	Fig. No.
1993 SHADOW & SUNDANCE-CONTINUED			
Test 11C	No Termination Failure	43	96
Test 12A	Bus Bias Level Or Bus (+/-) Open Failure	46	101
Test 12G	Bus Bias Level Or Bus (+/-) Open Failure	47	102
Test 12H	Bus Bias Level Or Bus (+/-) Open Failure	48	103
Test 13A	No Bus Bias Failure	48	104
Test 13H	No Bus Bias Failure	51	108
Test 13K	No Bus Bias Failure	52	109
Test 14A	Not Receiving Bus Messages Correctly Failure	52	110
Test VER-1	Verification Test	52	111
1994 SHADOW & SUNDANCE			
Test 1A	Bus Failure Messages	53	112
Test 2A	Blank Screen On DRB	53	113
Test 3A	RAM Test Error	54	114
Test 4A	Cartridge Failure Error	54	115
Test 5A	Key Pad Test Failure	54	116
Test 6A	Testing For Low Or High Battery	54	117
Test 7A	Short To Battery Failure	55	118
Test 7B	Short To Battery Failure	55	119
Test 7C	Short To Battery Failure	56	120
Test 7D	Short To Battery Failure	56	121
Test 7E	Short To Battery Failure	56	122
Test 7H	Short To Battery Failure	57	125
Test 8A	Short To 5 Volts Failure	58	126
Test 8B	Short To 5 Volts Failure	59	127
Test 8D	Short To 5 Volts Failure	59	128
Test 8E	Short To 5 Volts Failure	59	129
Test 8F	Short To 5 Volts Failure	59	130
Test 8G	Short To 5 Volts Failure	59	131
Test 8H	Short To 5 volts Failure	60	132
Test 9A	Short To Ground Failure	61	133
Test 9B	Short To Ground Failure	61	134
Test 10A	Bus (+) & bus (-) Shorted Together Failure	62	135
Test 11A	No Termination Failure	62	136
Test 11H	No Termination Failure	65	142
Test 12A	Bus Bias Level Or Bus (+/-) Open Failure	65	141
Test 12G	Bus Bias Level Or Bus (+/-) Open Failure	68	145
Test 12H	Bus Bias Level Or Bus (+/-) Open Failure	69	146
Test 13A	No Bus Bias Failure	69	147
Test 13H	No Bus Bias Failure	72	151
Test 14A	Not Receiving Bus Messages Correctly Failure	73	153
Test VER-1A	Verification Test	74	154
1993 CONCORDE, INTREPID & VISION			
Test 1A	Bus Failure Messages	34	72
Test 1C	Blank Screen On DRB	34	73
Test 1D	RAM Test Failure	35	74
Test 1E	Cartridge Failure	35	75
Test 1F	Key Pad Test Failure	35	76
Test 1G	Low Or High Battery	35	77
Test 7A	Short To Battery Failure	35	78
Test 7B	Short To Battery Failure	36	79
Test 7C	Short To Battery Failure	36	80
Test 7D	Short To Battery Failure	37	81
Test 7E	Short To Battery Failure	37	82
Test 7F	Short To Battery Failure	37	83

Test	Symptom	Page No. 21-	Fig. No.
1993 CONCORDE, INTREPID & VISION -CONTINUED			
Test 8A	Short To 5 Volts Failure	38	84
Test 8B	Short To 5 Volts Failure	39	85
Test 8D	Short To 5 Volts Failure	39	86
Test 8E	Short To 5 Volts Failure	39	87
Test 8F	Short To 5 Volts Failure	39	88
Test 8G	Short To 5 Volts Failure	39	89
Test 9A	Short To Ground Failure	40	90
Test 9B	Short To Ground Failure	41	91
Test 10A	Bus (+) & Bus (-) Shorted Together Failure	41	92
Test 11A	No Termination Failure	42	93
Test 11D	No Termination Failure	43	96
Test 12A	Bus Bias Level Or Bus (+/-) Open Failure	44	98
Test 12D	Bus Bias Level Or Bus (+/-) Open Failure	46	101
Test 12G	Bus Bias Level Or Bus (+/-) Open Failure	47	102
Test 13A	No Bus Bias Failure	48	104
Test 13D	No Bus Bias Failure	50	107
Test 13K	No Bus Bias Failure	52	109
Test 14A	Not Receiving Bus Messages Correctly Failure	52	110
Test VER-1	Verification Test	53	111
1994-95 CONCORDE, INTREPID, LHS, NEW YORKER & VISION			
Test 1A	Bus Failure Messages	53	112
Test 2A	Blank Screen On DRB	53	113
Test 3A	RAM Test Error	54	114
Test 4A	Cartridge Failure Error	54	115
Test 5A	Key Pad Test Failure	54	116
Test 6A	Testing For Low Or High Battery	54	117
Test 7A	Short To Battery Failure	55	118
Test 7B	Short To Battery Failure	55	119
Test 7C	Short To Battery Failure	56	120
Test 7D	Short To Battery Failure	56	121
Test 7E	Short To Battery Failure	56	122
Test 7G	Short To Battery Failure	57	124
Test 7H	Short To Battery Failure	57	125
Test 8A	Short To 5 Volts Failure	58	126
Test 8B	Short To 5 Volts Failure	59	127
Test 8D	Short To 5 Volts Failure	59	128
Test 8E	Short To 5 Volts Failure	59	129
Test 8F	Short To 5 Volts Failure	59	130
Test 8G	Short To 5 Volts Failure	59	131
Test 8H	Short To 5 volts Failure	60	132
Test 9A	Short To Ground Failure	61	133
Test 9B	Short To Ground Failure	61	134
Test 10A	Bus (+) & Bus (-) Shorted Together Failure	62	135
Test 11A	No Termination Failure	62	136
Test 11C	No Termination Failure	64	138
Test 12C	Bus Bias Level Or Bus (+/-) Open Failure	66	143
Test 12G	Bus Bias Level Or Bus (+/-) Open Failure	68	145
Test 13A	No Bus Bias Failure	69	147
Test 13C	No Bus Bias Failure	70	149
Test 14A	Not Receiving Bus Messages Correctly Failure	73	153
Test VER-1A	Verification Test	74	154
1996 CONCORDE, INTREPID, LHS, NEW YORKER & VISION			
Test 132A	Bus Failure Message	90	197
Test 133A	Short To Battery Failure	91	198

Electronic Instrumentation & Body Controls—CHRYSLER

1996 CONCORDE, INTREPID, LHS, NEW YORKER & VISION -CONTINUED

Test 133B	Short To Battery Failure	91	199
Test 133C	Short To Battery Failure	91	200
Test 133D	Short To Battery Failure	92	201
Test 133E	Short To Battery Failure	92	202
Test 134A	Short To 5 Volts Failure	92	203
Test 134B	Short To 5 Volts Failure	93	204
Test 134C	Short To 5 Volts Failure	93	205
Test 135A	Short To Ground Failure	94	206
Test 136A	Bus (+) & Bus (+) Shorted Together Failure	95	207
Test 137A	No Termination Failure	97	208
Test 138A	Bus Bias Level Or Bus (+/-) Open Failure	98	209
Test 139A	No Bus Bias Failure	100	210
Test 140A	Not Receiving Bus Messages Correctly Failure	102	211

1995 BREEZE, CIRRUS & STRATUS

Test 1A	Bus Failure Message	74	155
Test 3A	RAM Test Error	74	156
Test 4A	Cartridge Failure Error	74	157
Test 5A	Key Pad Test Failure	75	158
Test 6A	Low Or High Battery	75	159
Test 7A	Short To Battery Failure	75	160
Test 7B	Short To Battery Failure	76	161
Test 7C	Short To Battery Failure	76	162
Test 7D	Short To Battery Failure	76	163
Test 7E	Short To Battery Failure	76	164
Test 7H	Short To Battery Failure	76	165
Test 7J	Short To Battery Failure	76	166
Test 8A	Short To 5 Volts Failure	77	167
Test 8B	Short To 5 Volts Failure	78	168
Test 8D	Short To 5 Volts Failure	78	169
Test 8E	Short To 5 Volts Failure	78	170
Test 8F	Short To 5 Volts Failure	78	171
Test 8J	Short To 5 Volts Failure	78	172
Test 9A	Short To Ground Failure	78	173
Test 9B	Short To Ground Failure	79	174
Test 10A	Bus (+) & Bus (+) Shorted Together Failure	80	175
Test 11L	No Termination Failure	81	176
Test 12L	Bus Bias Level Or Bus (+/-) Open Failure	81	177
Test 13M	No Bus Bias Failure	82	178
Test 14A	Not Receiving Bus Messages Correctly Failure	83	179
Test VER-1A	Verification Test	83	180

1996 BREEZE, CIRRUS & STRATUS

Test 1A	Bus Failure Message	84	181
Test 2A	Short To Battery Failure	84	182
Test 2B	Short To Battery Failure	84	183
Test 2C	Short To Battery Failure	85	184
Test 2D	Short To Battery Failure	85	185
Test 3A	Short To 5 Volts Failure	85	186
Test 3B	Short To 5 Volts Failure	85	187
Test 3C	Short To 5 Volts Failure	86	188
Test 3D	Short To 5 Volts Failure	86	189
Test 4A	Short To Ground Failure	86	190
Test 5A	Bus (+) & Bus (+) Shorted Together Failure	87	191
Test 6A	No Termination Failure	88	192
Test 7A	No Bus Bias To High/Low Failure	88	193
Test 8A	No Bus Bias Or Bus (+/-) Open Failure	89	194
Test 9A	Not Receiving Bus Messages Correctly Failure	90	195
Test VER 1A	Verification Test	90	196

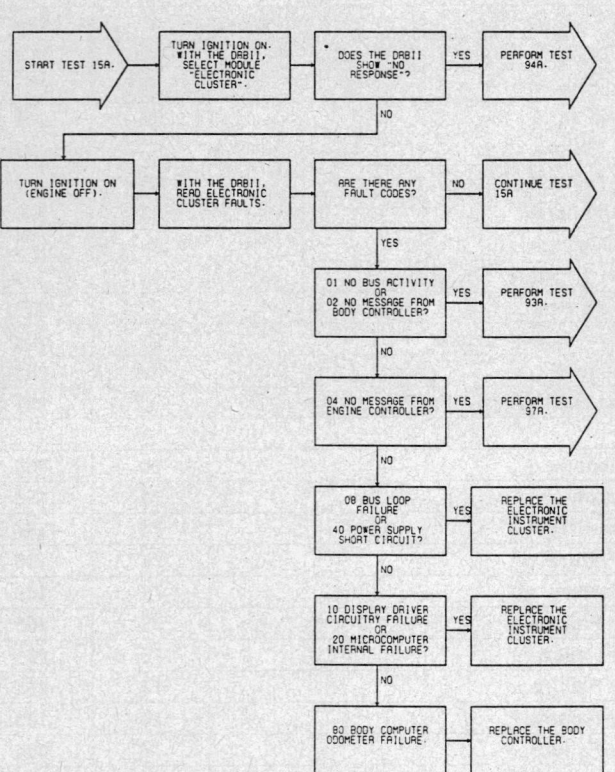

Fig. 20   Test 15A: Electronic Instrument Cluster.
1993 Dynasty, Fifth Avenue, Imperial & New Yorker

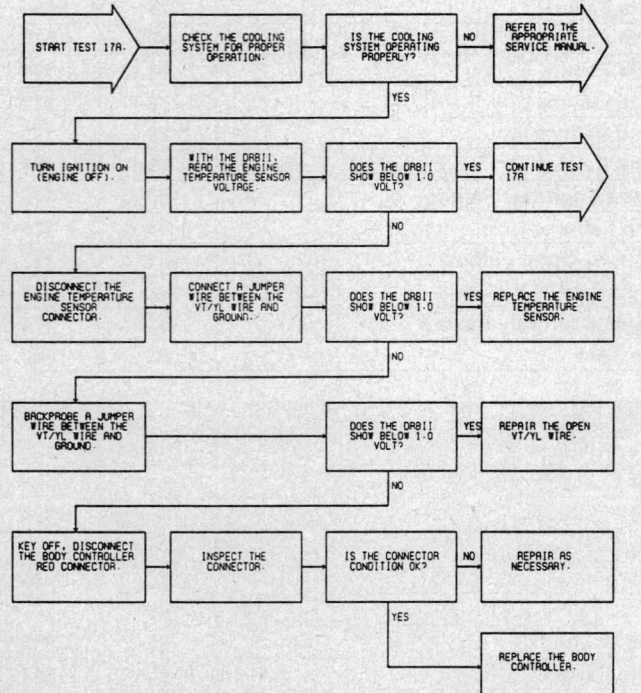

Fig. 23   Test 17A: Temperature Gauge Problem (Part 1 of 2). 1993 Dynasty, Fifth Avenue, Imperial & New Yorker

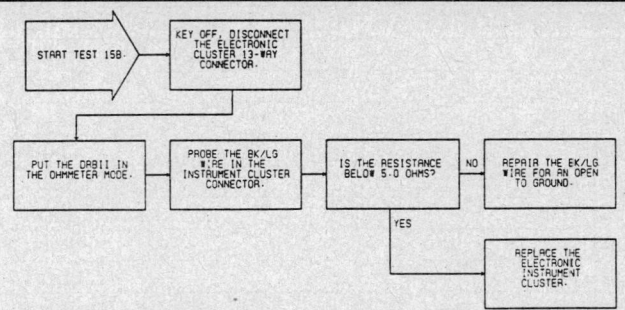

Fig. 21   Test 15B: Blank Electronic Cluster Display.
1993 Dynasty, Fifth Avenue, Imperial & New Yorker

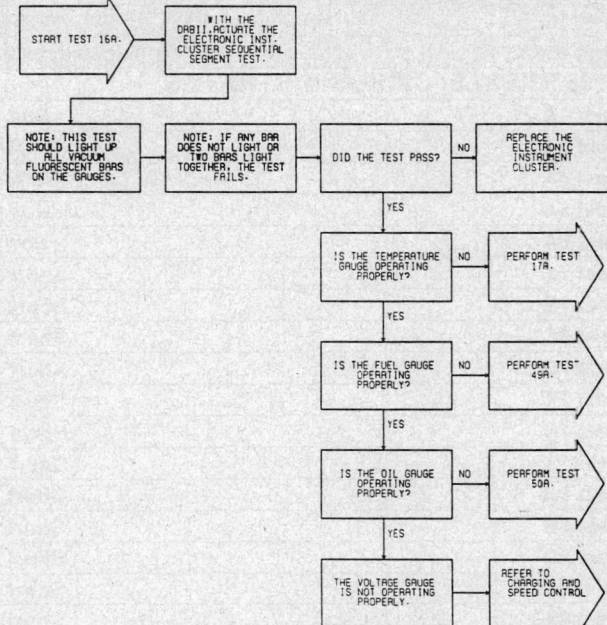

Fig. 22   Test 16A: Identifying Faulty Gauge. 1993 Dynasty, Fifth Avenue, Imperial & New Yorker

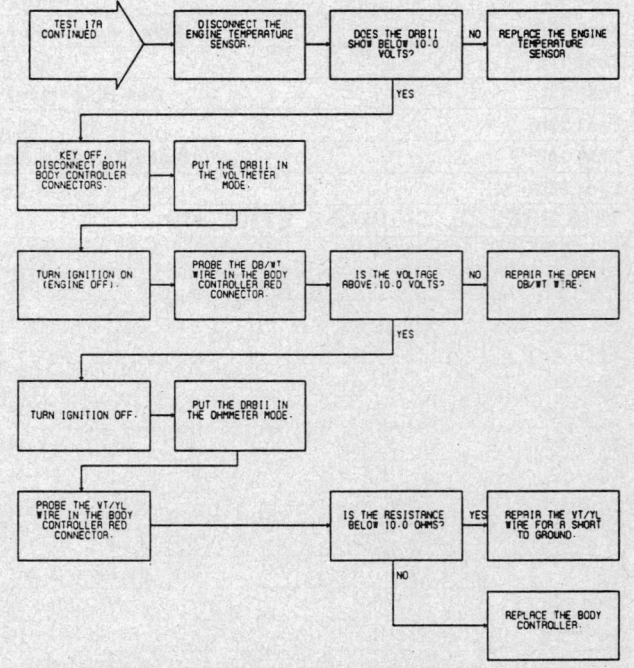

Fig. 23   Test 17A: Temperature Gauge Problem (Part 2 of 2). 1993 Dynasty, Fifth Avenue, Imperial & New Yorker

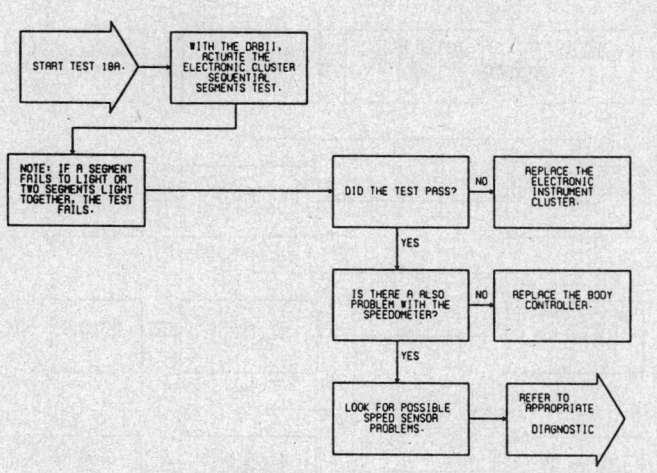

Fig. 24   Test 18A: Speedometer Failure. 1993 Dynasty, Fifth Avenue, Imperial & New Yorker

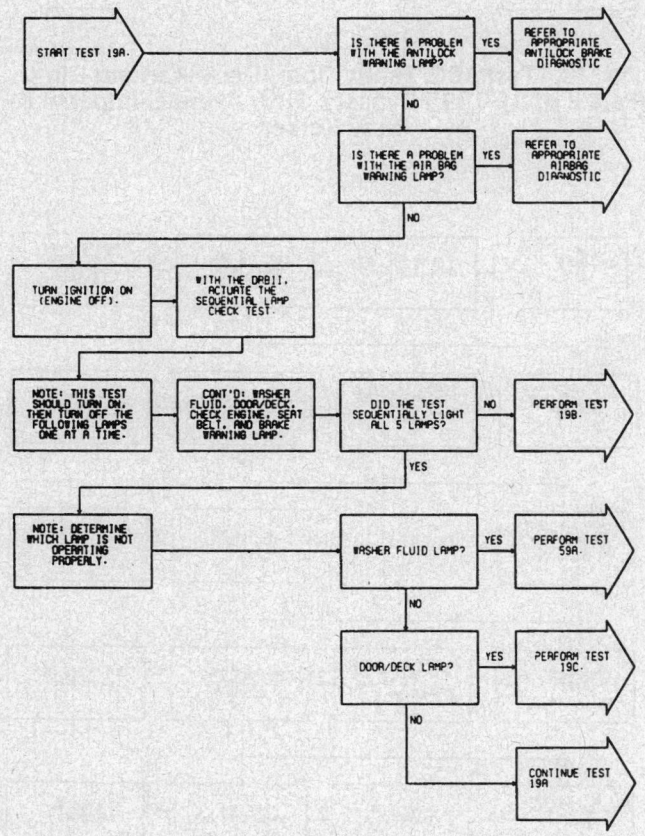

Fig. 26   Test 19A: Warning Lamp Diagnosis (Part 1 of 2). 1993 Dynasty, Fifth Avenue, Imperial & New Yorker

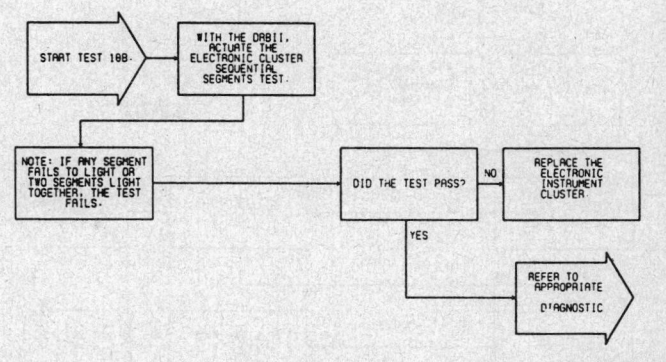

Fig. 25   Test 18B: Speedometer Failure. 1993 Dynasty, Fifth Avenue, Imperial & New Yorker

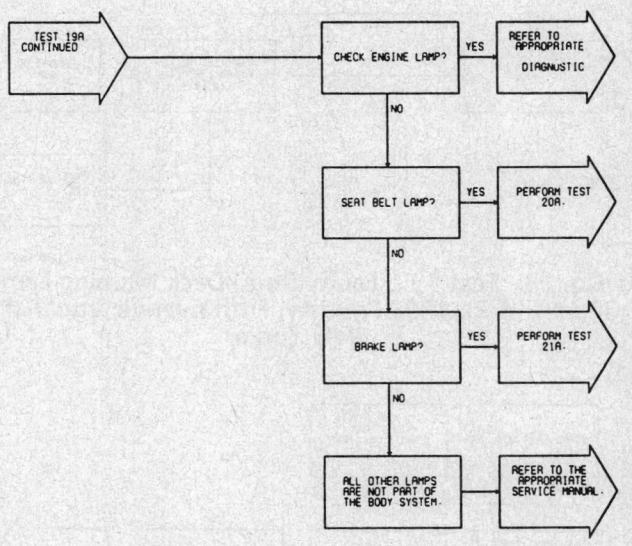

Fig. 26   Test 19A: Warning Lamp Diagnosis (Part 2 of 2). 1993 Dynasty, Fifth Avenue, Imperial & New Yorker

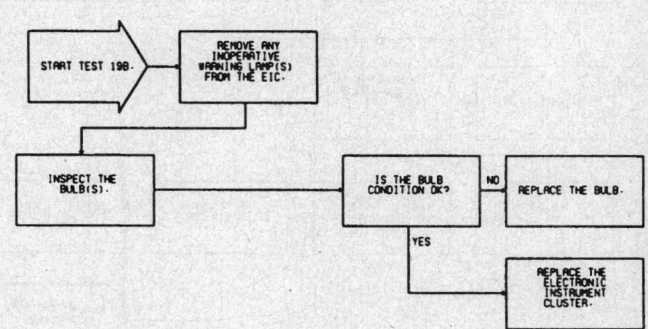

Fig. 27   Test 19B: Faulty Warning Lamp. 1993 Dynasty, Fifth Avenue, Imperial & New Yorker

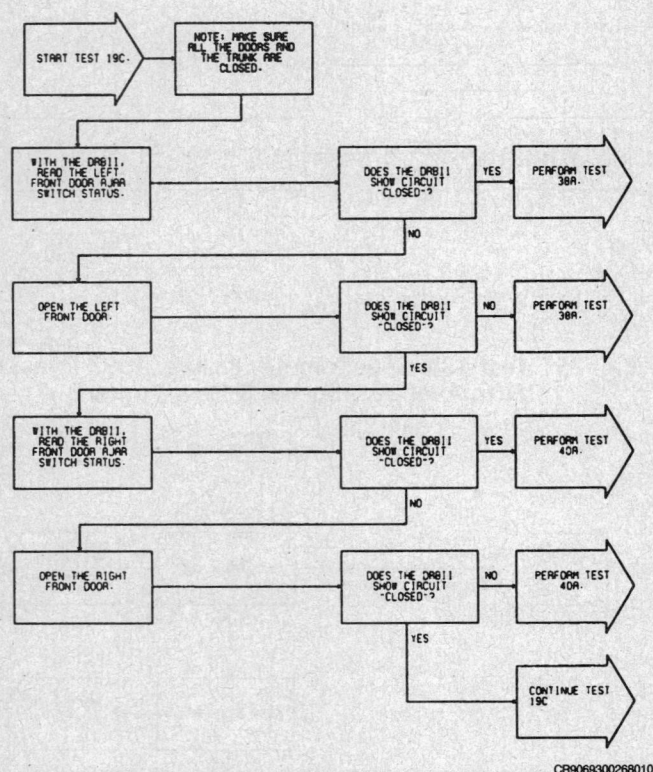

Fig. 28 Test 19C: Faulty Door/Deck Warning Lamp (Part 1 of 2). 1993 Dynasty, Fifth Avenue, Imperial & New Yorker

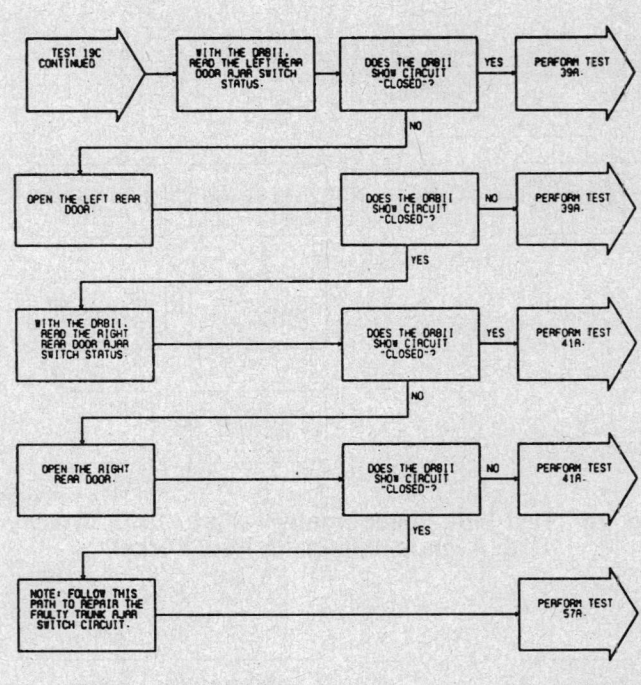

Fig. 28 Test 19C: Faulty Door/Deck Warning Lamp (Part 2 of 2). 1993 Dynasty, Fifth Avenue, Imperial & New Yorker

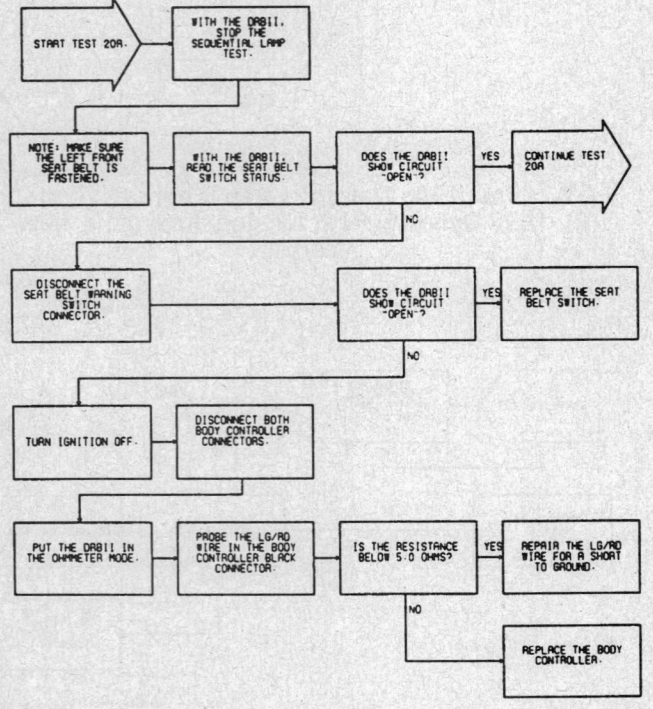

Fig. 29 Test 20A: Seat Belt Warning Lamp (Part 1 of 2). 1993 Dynasty, Fifth Avenue, Imperial & New Yorker

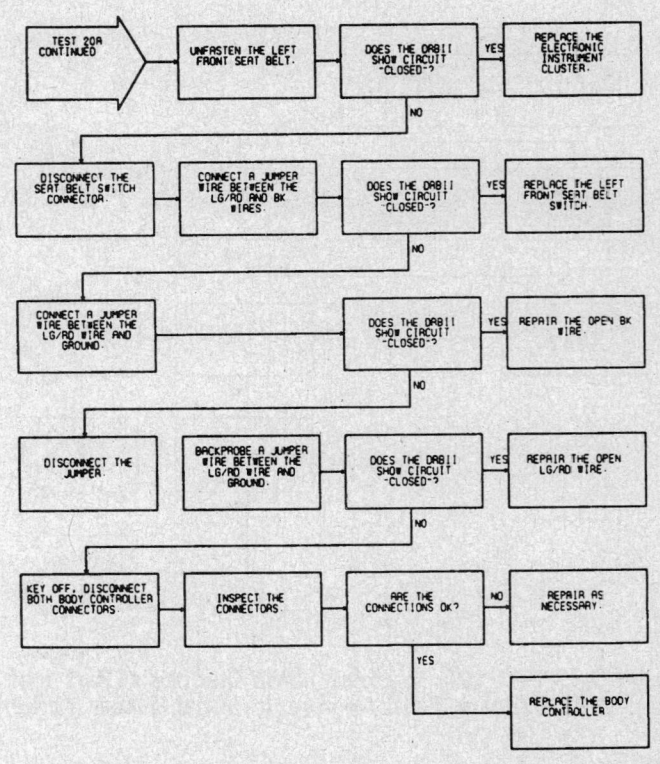

Fig. 29 Test 20A: Seat Belt Warning Lamp (Part 2 of 2). 1993 Dynasty, Fifth Avenue, Imperial & New Yorker

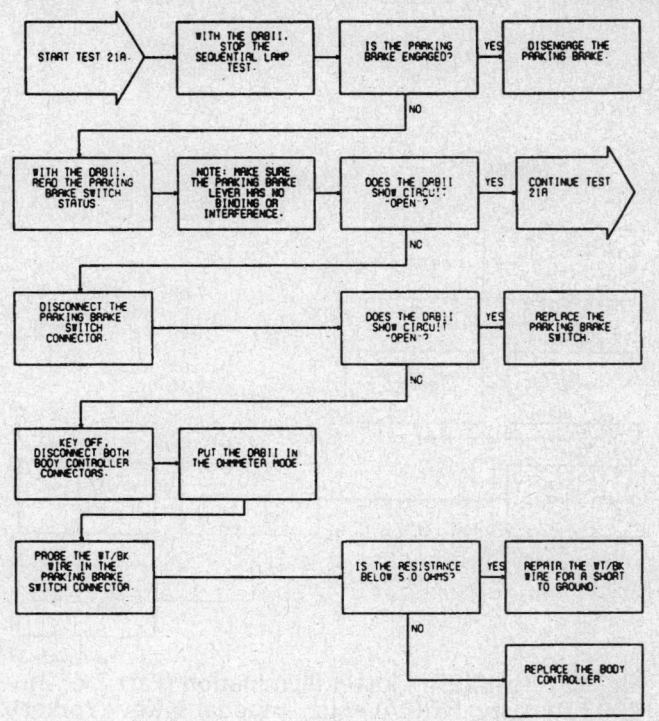

Fig. 30   Test 21A: Brake Warning Lamp Circuit (Part 1 of 2). 1993 Dynasty, Fifth Avenue, Imperial & New Yorker

Fig. 30   Test 21A: Brake Warning Lamp Circuit (Part 2 of 2). 1993 Dynasty, Fifth Avenue, Imperial & New Yorker

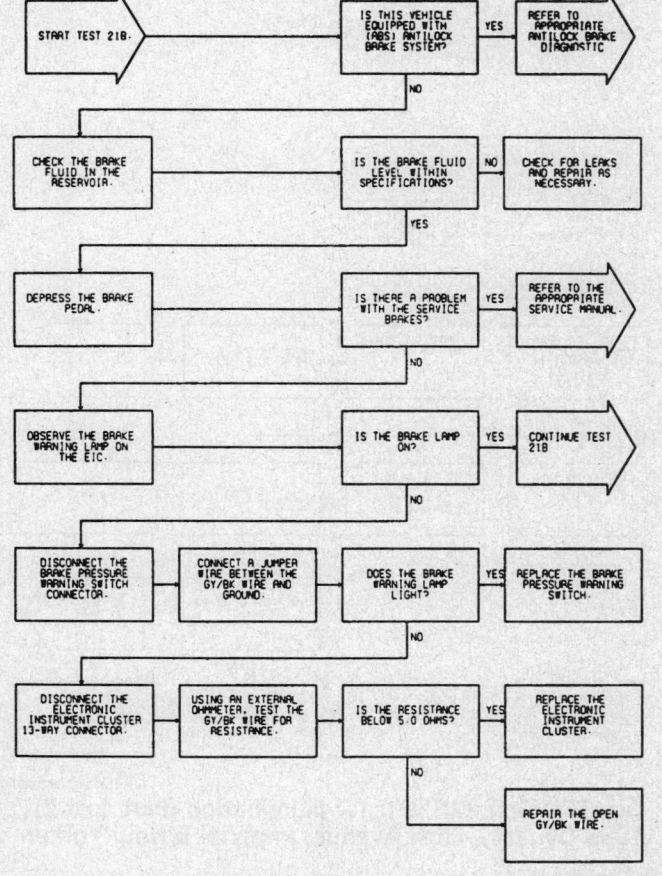

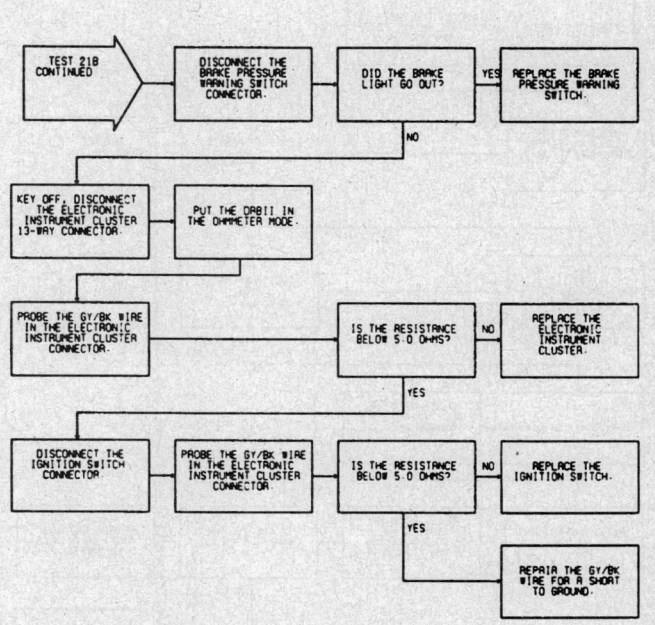

Fig. 31   Test 21B: Brake Pressure Switch (Part 2 of 2). 1993 Dynasty, Fifth Avenue, Imperial & New Yorker Less Anti-Lock Brakes

Fig. 31   Test 21B: Brake Pressure Switch (Part 1 of 2). 1993 Dynasty, Fifth Avenue, Imperial & New Yorker Less Anti-Lock Brakes

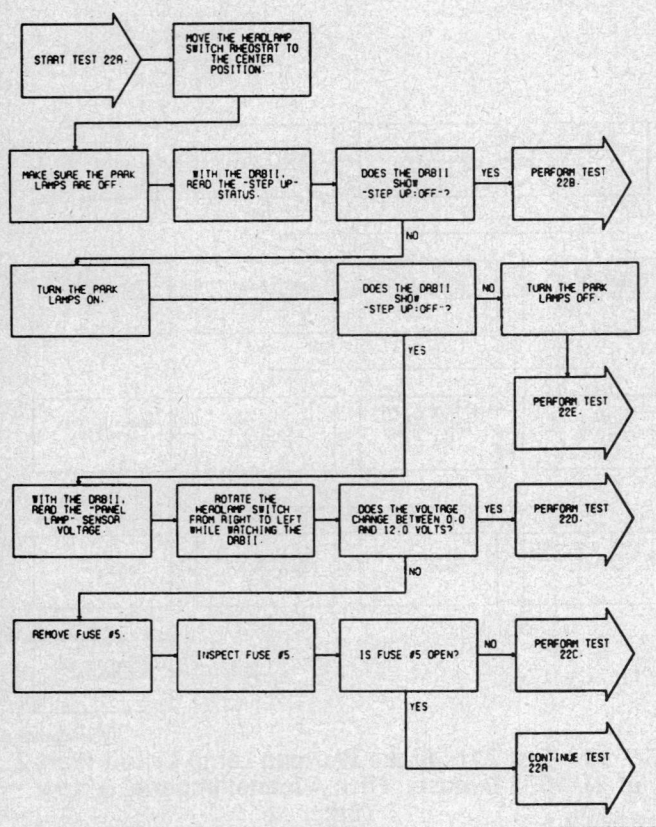

Fig. 32   Test 22A: Cluster Illumination (Part 1 of 2).
1993 Dynasty, Fifth Avenue, Imperial & New Yorker

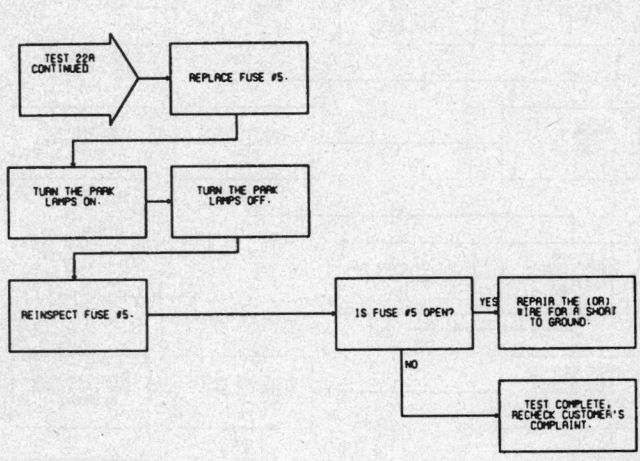

Fig. 32   Test 22A: Cluster Illumination (Part 2 of 2).
1993 Dynasty, Fifth Avenue, Imperial & New Yorker

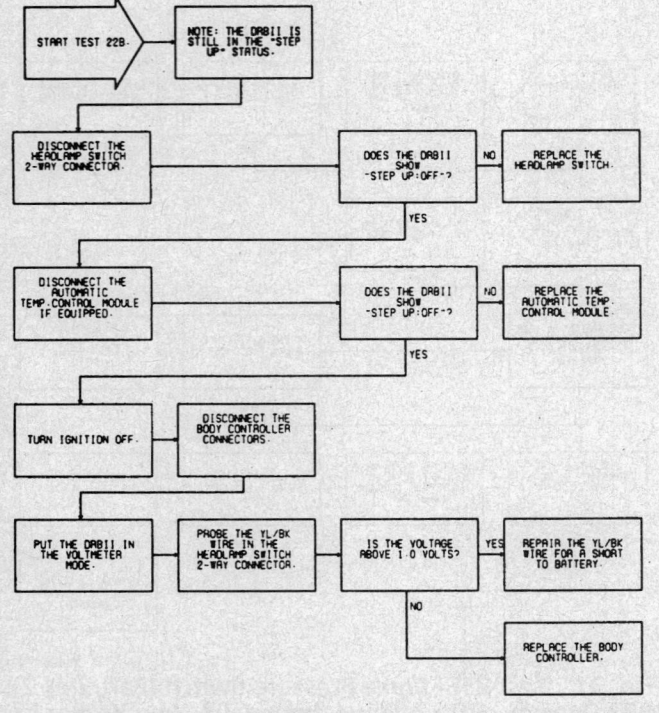

Fig. 33   Test 22B: Cluster Illumination. 1993 Dynasty,
Fifth Avenue, Imperial & New Yorker

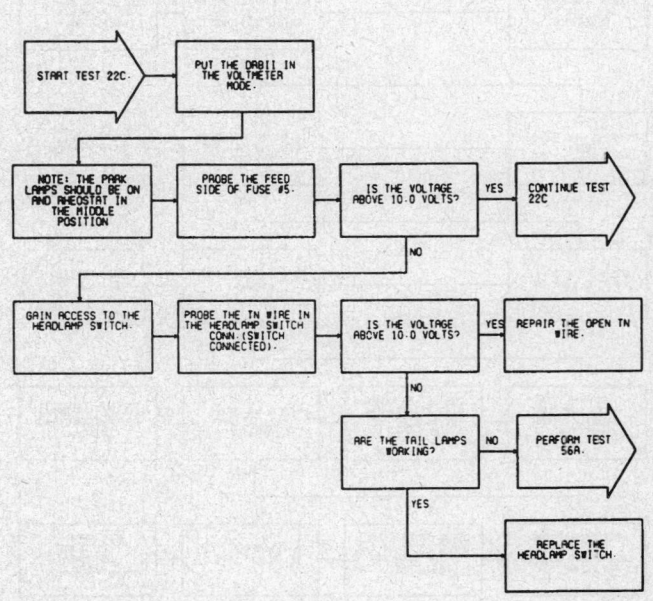

Fig. 34   Test 22C: Cluster Illumination (Part 1 of 2).
1993 Dynasty, Fifth Avenue, Imperial & New Yorker

CR9069300274020X

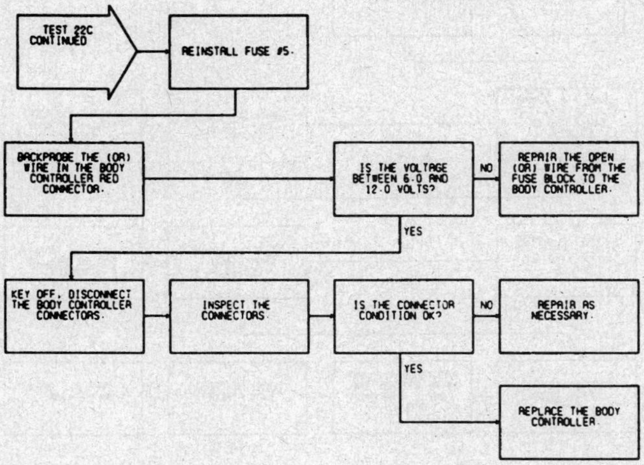

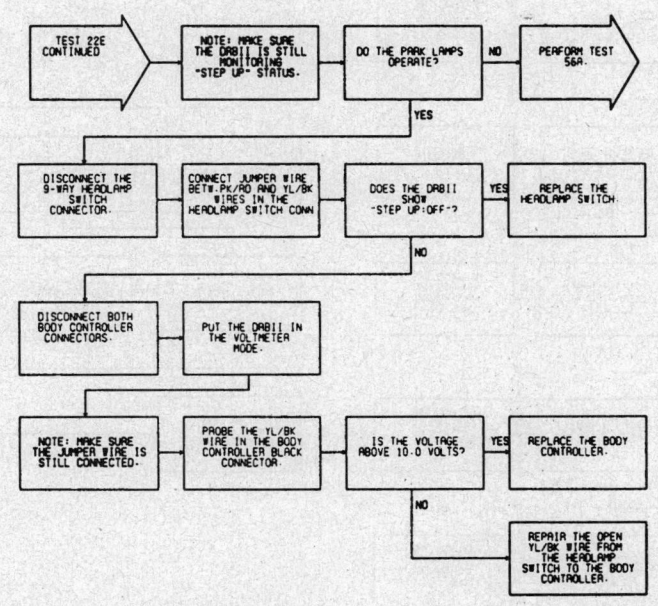

Fig. 34 Test 22C: Cluster Illumination (Part 2 of 2). 1993 Dynasty, Fifth Avenue, Imperial & New Yorker

CR9069300275000X

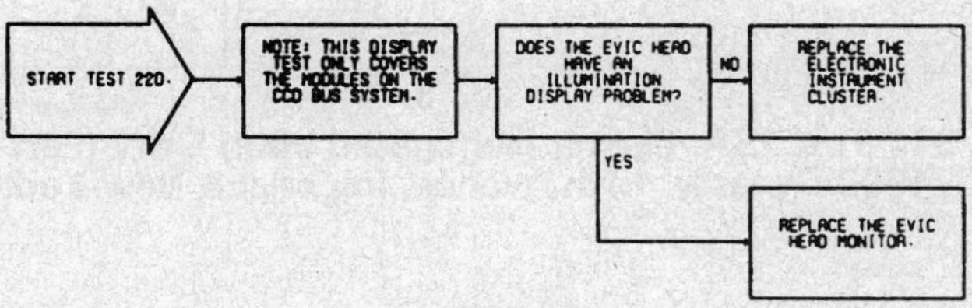

Fig. 35 Test 22D: Cluster Illumination. 1993 Dynasty, Fifth Avenue, Imperial & New Yorker

CR9069300276010X

Fig. 36 Test 22E: Cluster Illumination (Part 1 of 2). 1993 Dynasty, Fifth Avenue, Imperial & New Yorker

CR9069300276020X

Fig. 36 Test 22E: Cluster Illumination (Part 2 of 2). 1993 Dynasty, Fifth Avenue, Imperial & New Yorker

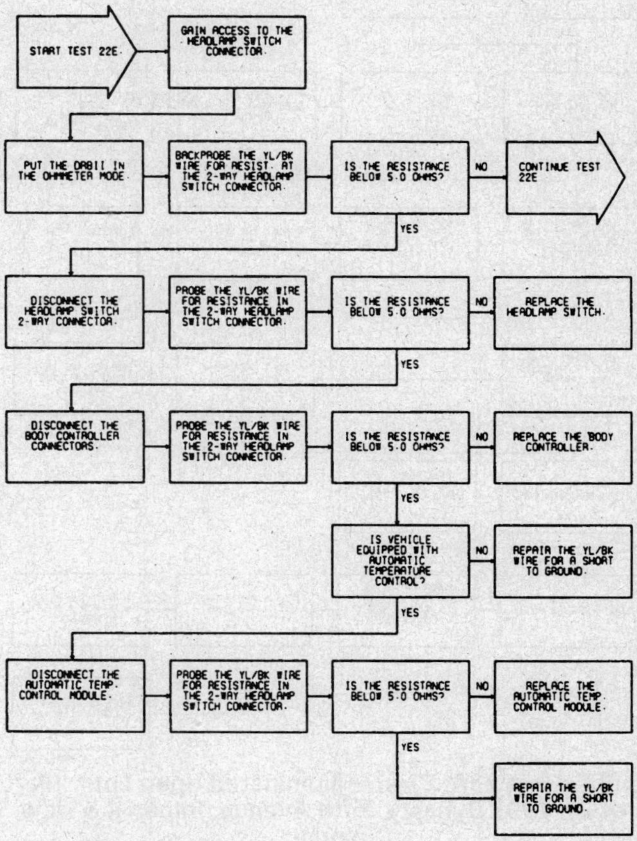

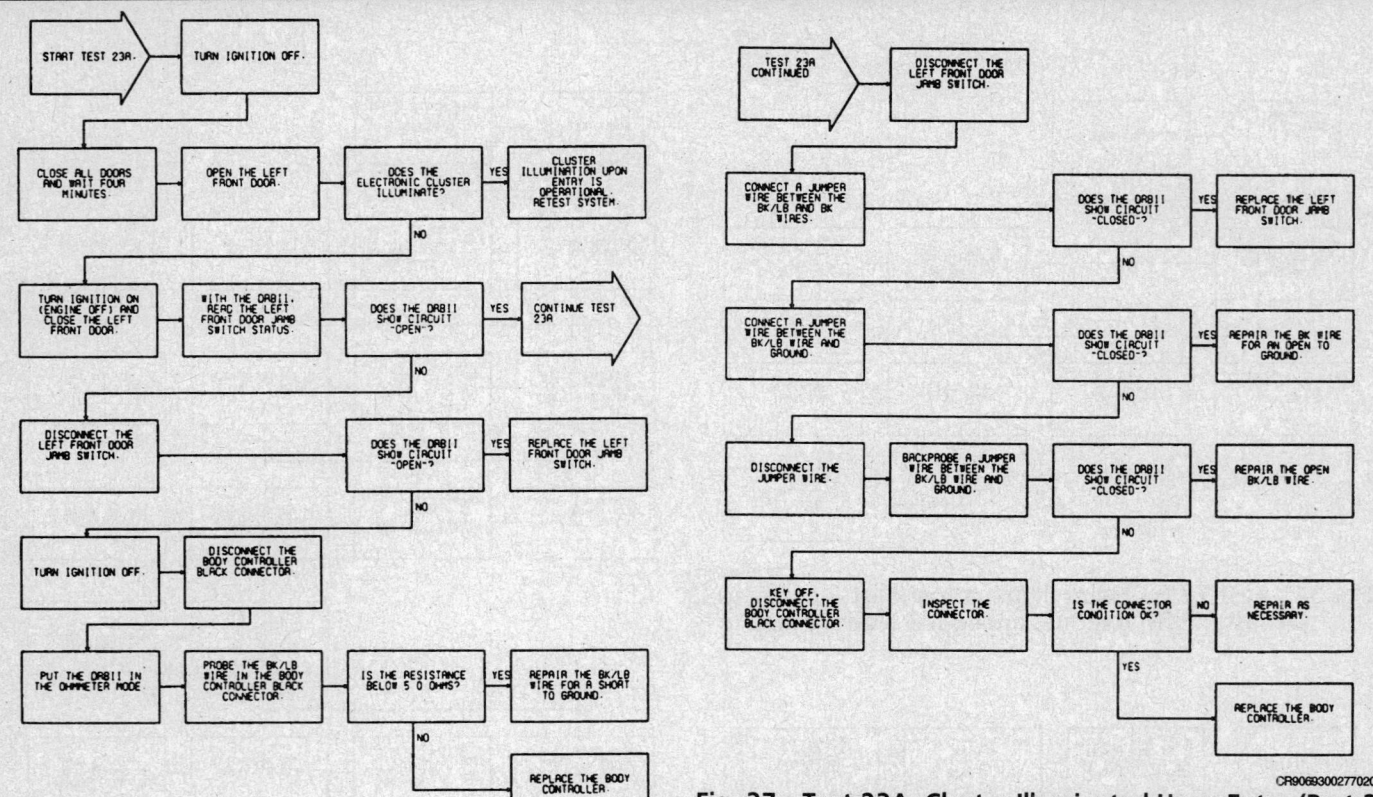

Fig. 37   Test 23A: Cluster Illuminated Upon Entry (Part 1 of 2). 1993 Dynasty, Fifth Avenue, Imperial & New Yorker

Fig. 37   Test 23A: Cluster Illuminated Upon Entry (Part 2 of 2). 1993 Dynasty, Fifth Avenue, Imperial & New Yorker

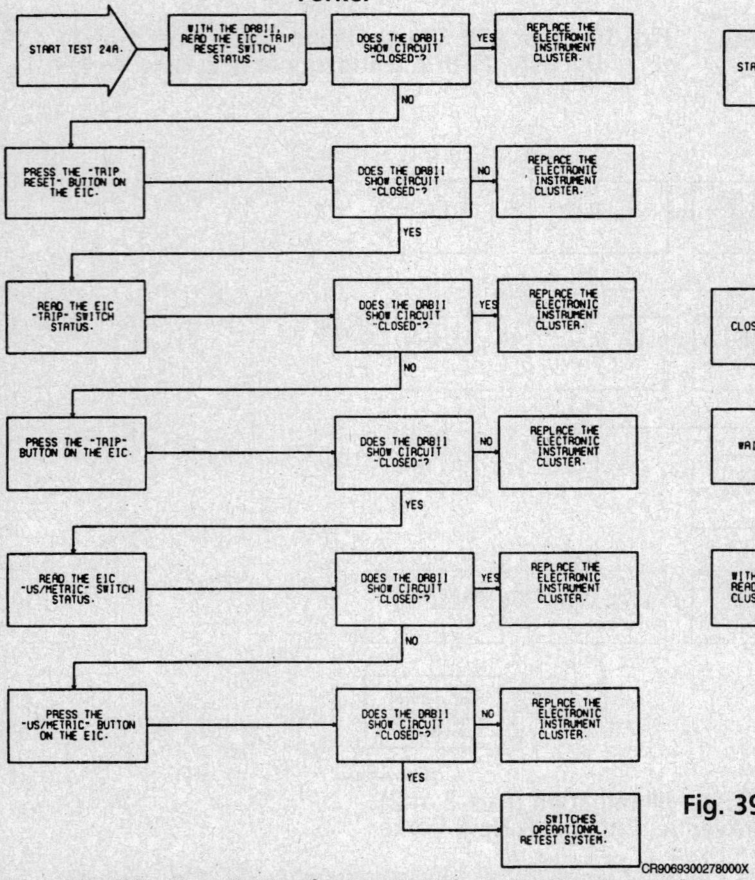

Fig. 38   Test 24A: Cluster Switch. 1993 Dynasty, Fifth Avenue, Imperial & New Yorker

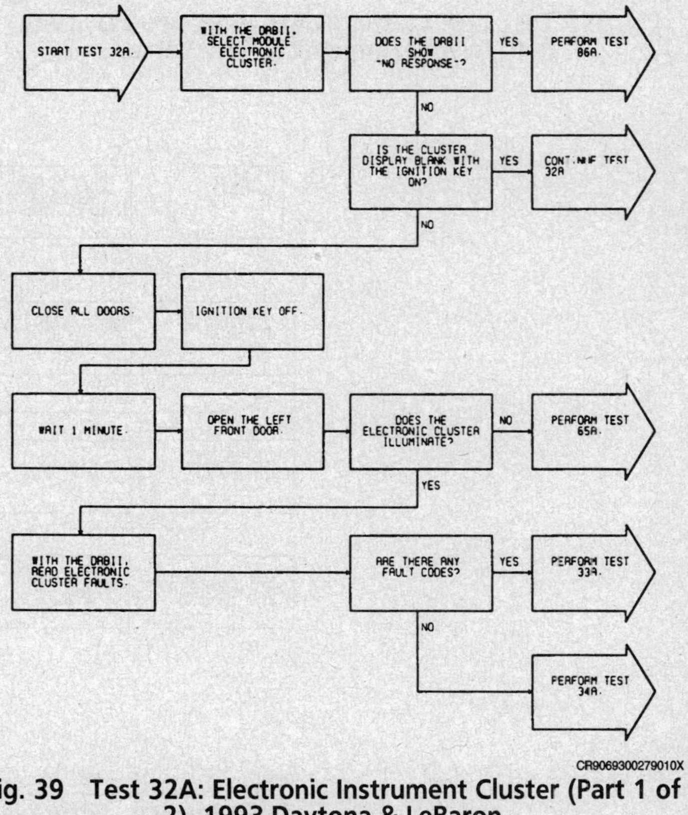

Fig. 39   Test 32A: Electronic Instrument Cluster (Part 1 of 2). 1993 Daytona & LeBaron

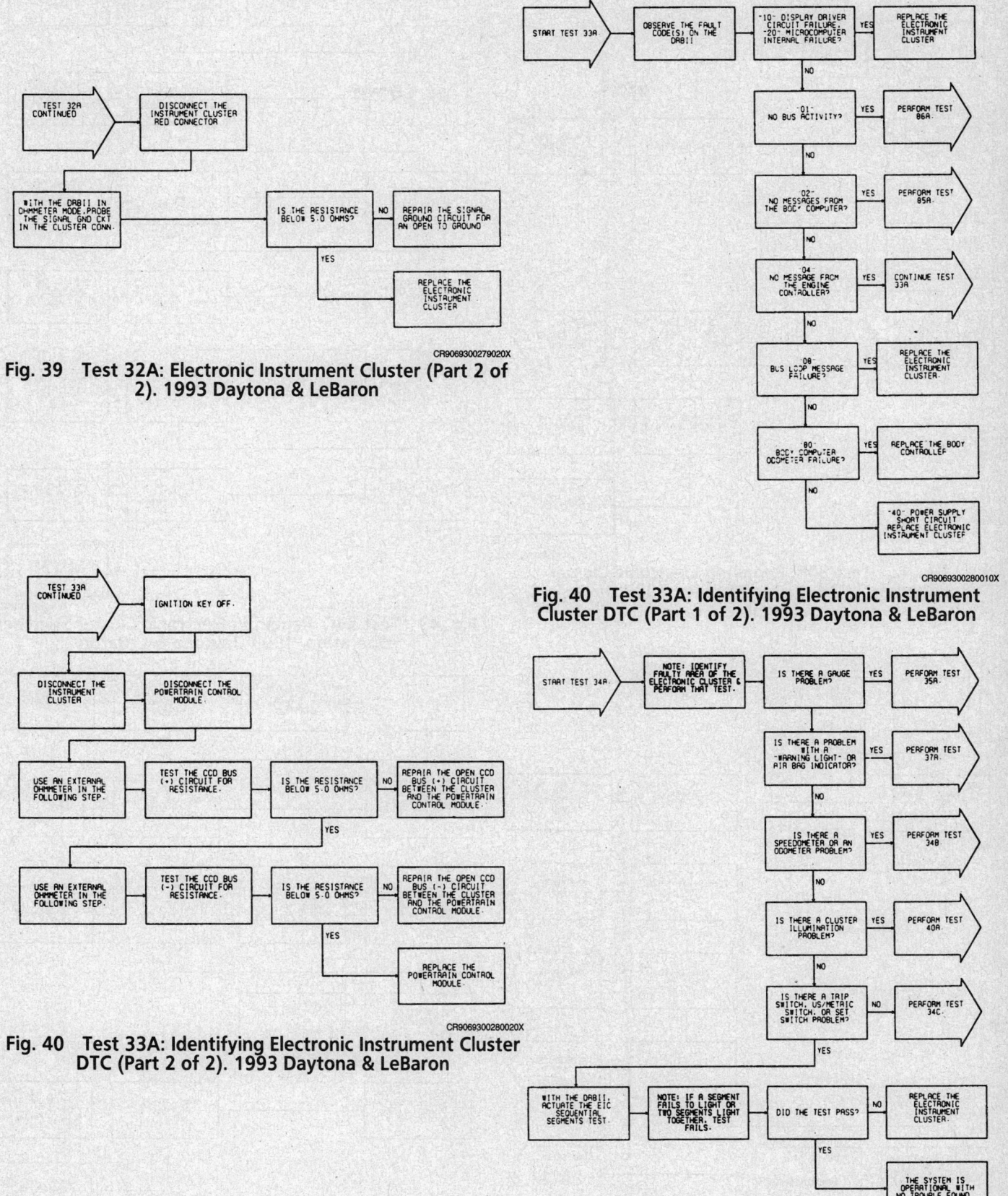

Fig. 39   Test 32A: Electronic Instrument Cluster (Part 2 of 2). 1993 Daytona & LeBaron

Fig. 40   Test 33A: Identifying Electronic Instrument Cluster DTC (Part 2 of 2). 1993 Daytona & LeBaron

Fig. 40   Test 33A: Identifying Electronic Instrument Cluster DTC (Part 1 of 2). 1993 Daytona & LeBaron

Fig. 41   Test 34A: Electronic Cluster "No Fault" Path. 1993 Daytona & LeBaron

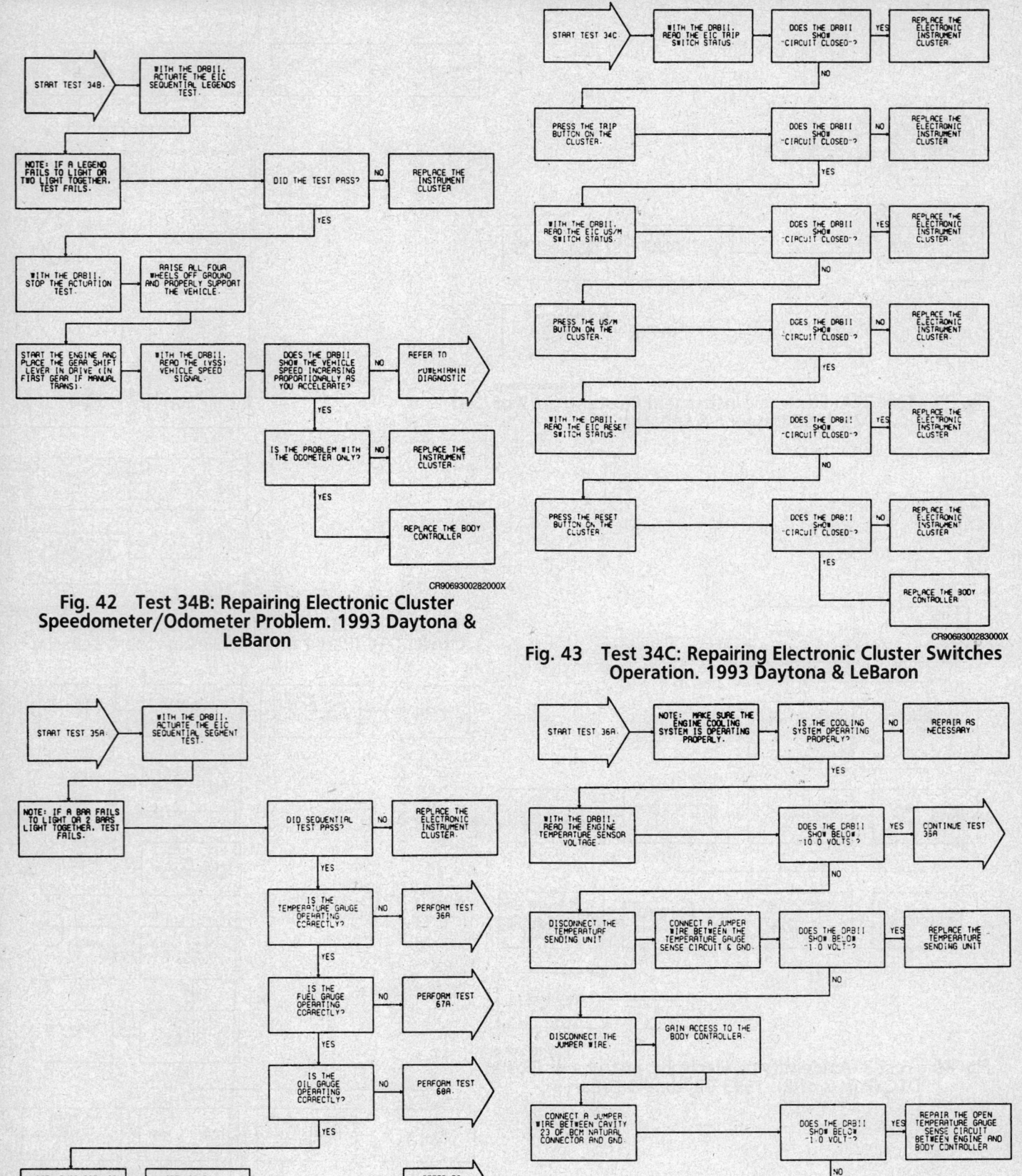

Fig. 42 Test 34B: Repairing Electronic Cluster Speedometer/Odometer Problem. 1993 Daytona & LeBaron

Fig. 43 Test 34C: Repairing Electronic Cluster Switches Operation. 1993 Daytona & LeBaron

Fig. 44 Test 35A: Identifying Faulty Gauge. 1993 Daytona & LeBaron

Fig. 45 Test 36A: Repairing Temperature Gauge Problems (Part 1 of 2). 1993 Daytona & LeBaron

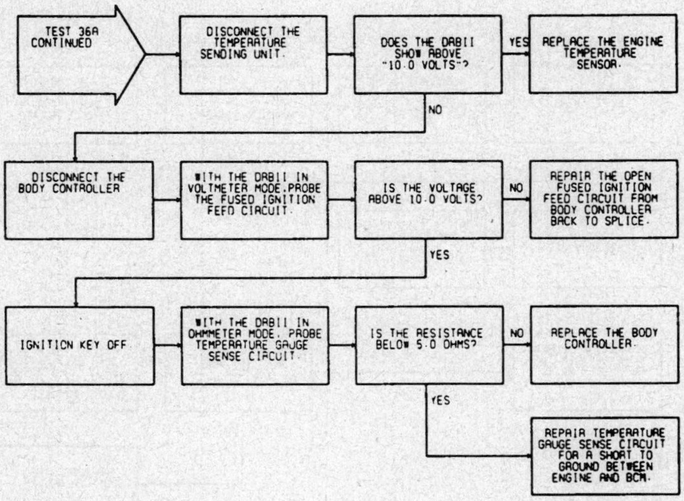

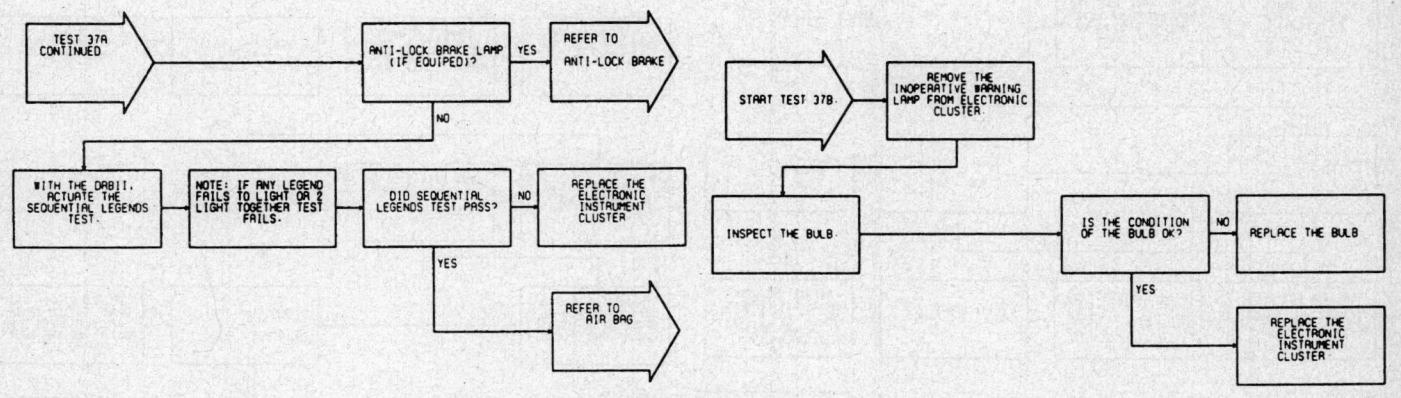

Fig. 45   Test 36A: Repairing Temperature Gauge
Problems (Part 2 of 2). 1993 Daytona & LeBaron

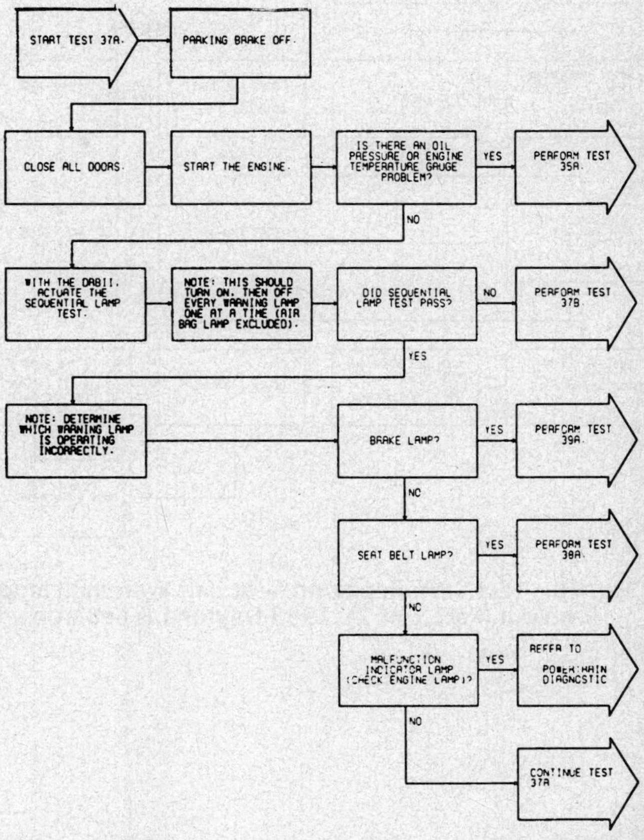

Fig. 46   Test 37A: Identifying Faulty Warning Lamp Or
Indicator (Part 1 of 2). 1993 Daytona & LeBaron

Fig. 46   Test 37A: Identifying Faulty Warning Lamp Or
Indicator (Part 2 of 2). 1993 Daytona & LeBaron

Fig. 47   Test 37B: Repairing Faulty Warning Lamp
Condition. 1993 Daytona & LeBaron

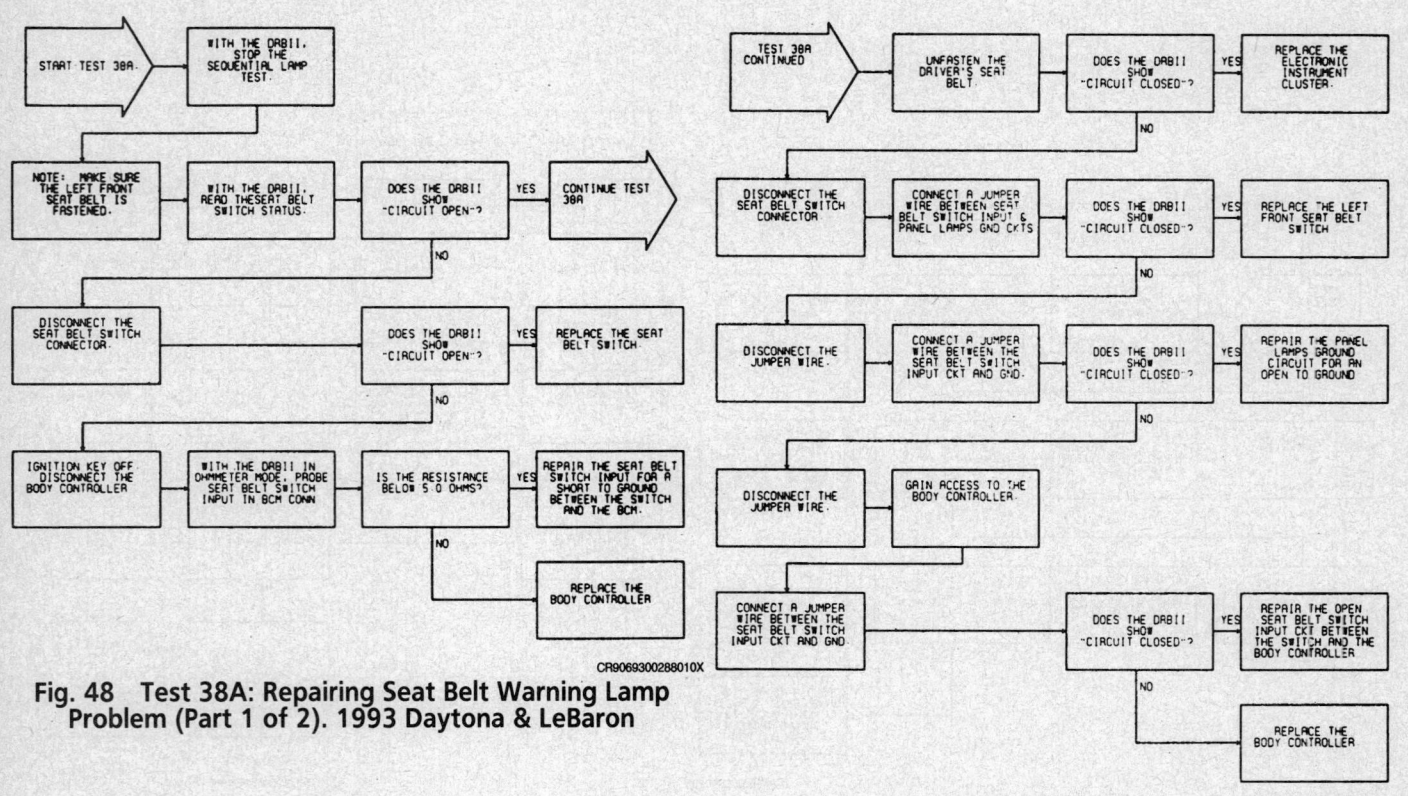

Fig. 48   Test 38A: Repairing Seat Belt Warning Lamp Problem (Part 1 of 2). 1993 Daytona & LeBaron

Fig. 48   Test 38A: Repairing Seat Belt Warning Lamp Problem (Part 2 of 2). 1993 Daytona & LeBaron

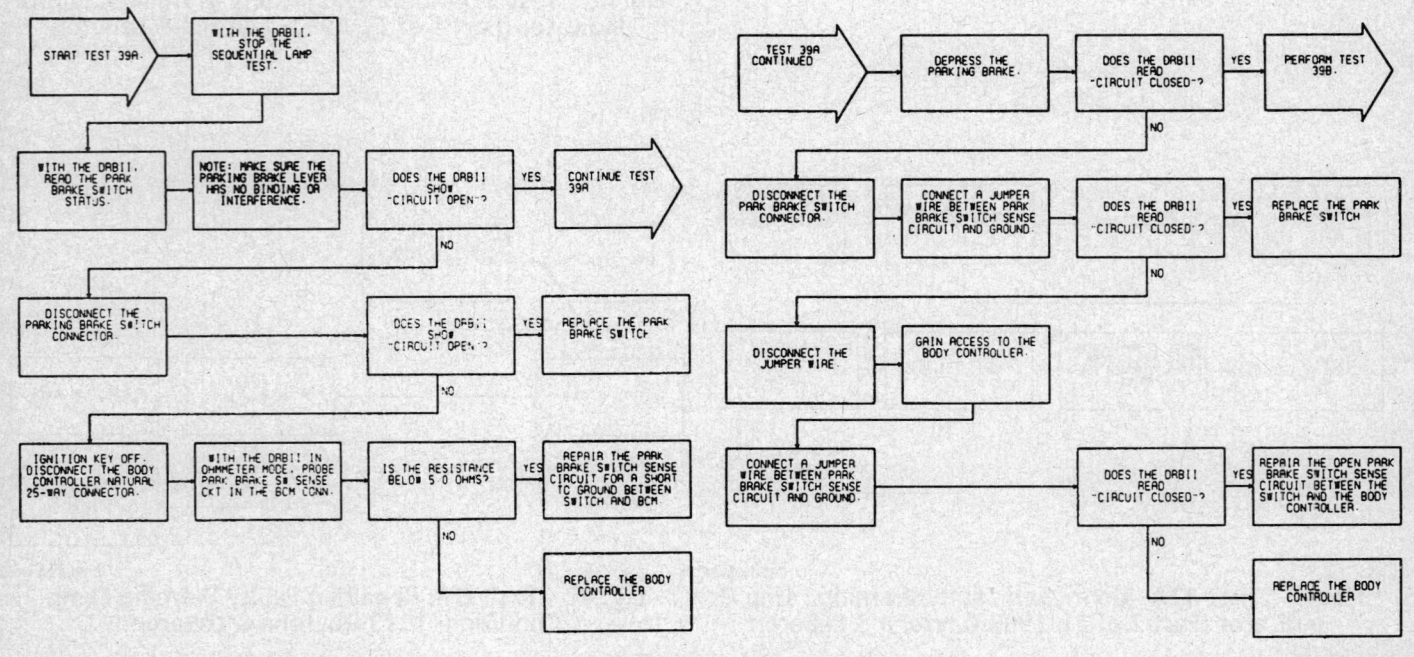

Fig. 49   Test 39A: Repairing Brake Warning Lamp & Parking Brake Switch Problems (Part 1 of 2). 1993 Daytona & LeBaron

Fig. 49   Test 39A: Repairing Brake Warning Lamp & Parking Brake Switch Problems (Part 2 of 2). 1993 Daytona & LeBaron

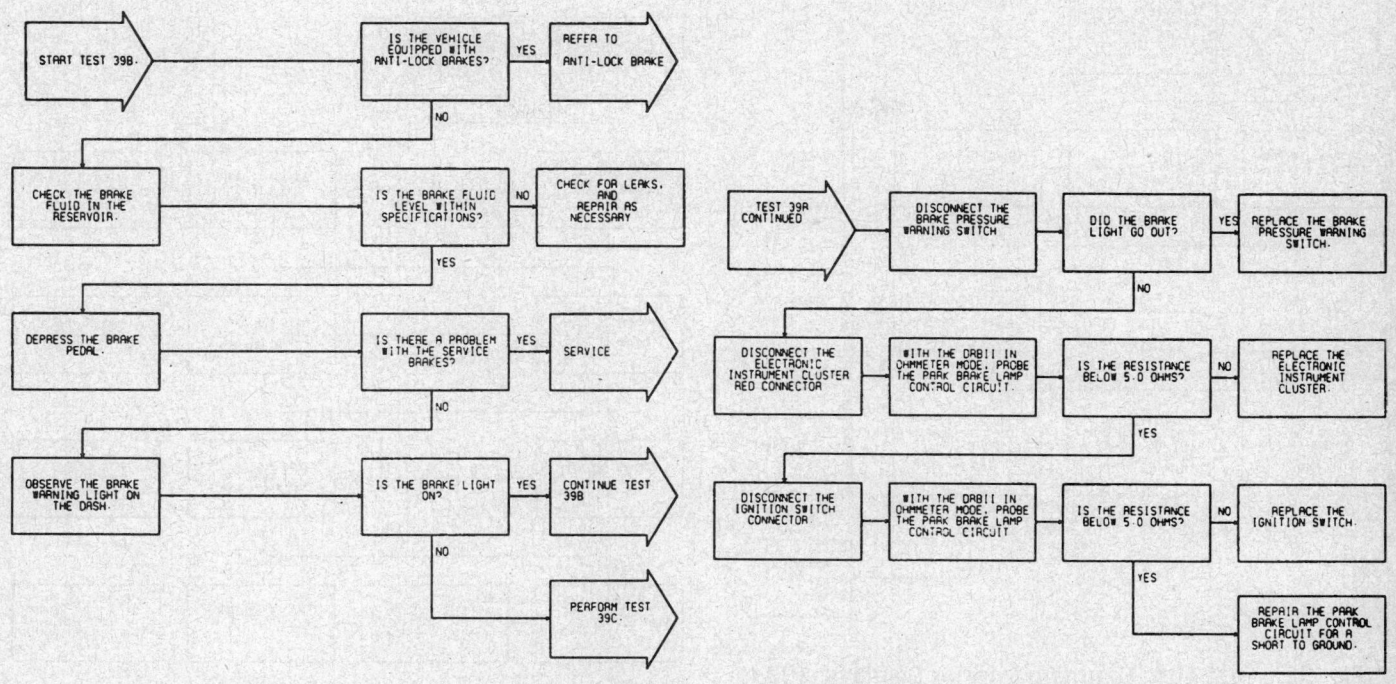

Fig. 50   Test 39B: Repairing Brake Warning Lamp & Brake Pressure Switch Problems (Part 1 of 2). 1993 Daytona & LeBaron

Fig. 50   Test 39B: Repairing Brake Warning Lamp & Brake Pressure Switch Problems (Part 2 of 2). 1993 Daytona & LeBaron

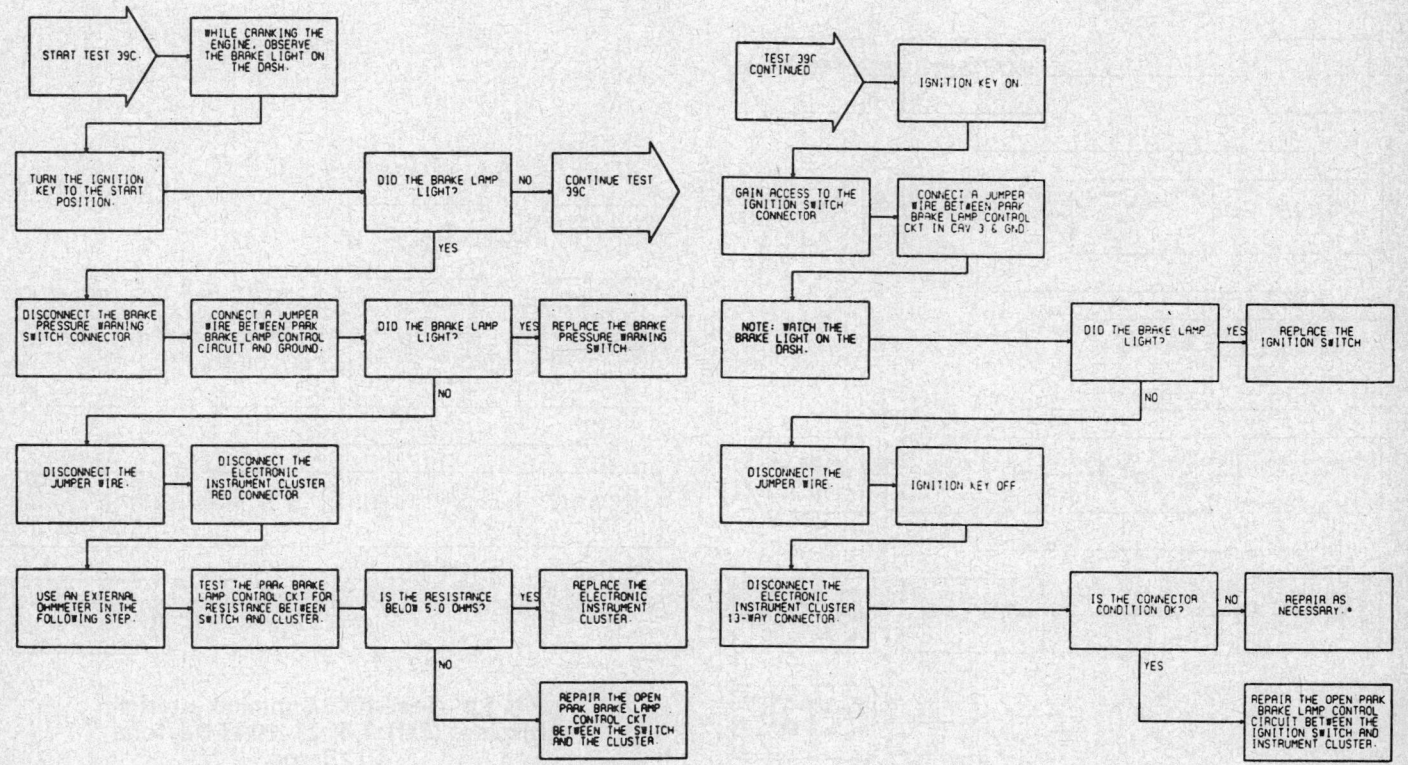

Fig. 51   Test 39C: Repairing Brake Warning Lamp & Brake Pressure Switch Problems (Part 1 of 2). 1993 Daytona & LeBaron

Fig. 51   Test 39C: Repairing Brake Warning Lamp & Brake Pressure Switch Problems (Part 2 of 2). 1993 Daytona & LeBaron

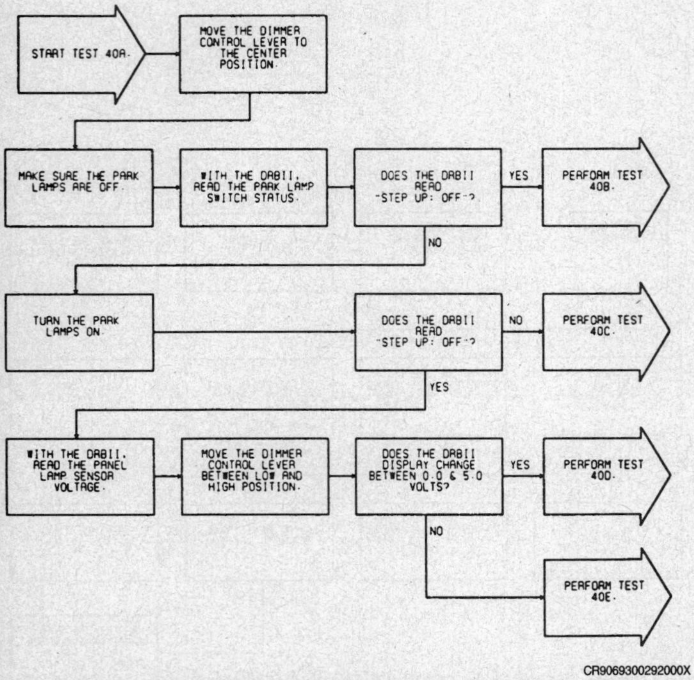

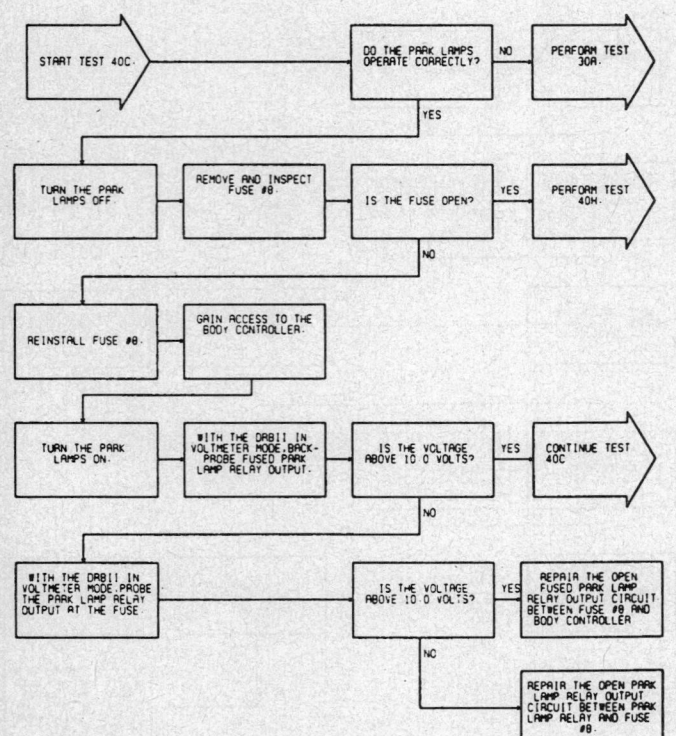

Fig. 52   Test 40A: Dimming Interior Displays. 1993 Daytona & LeBaron

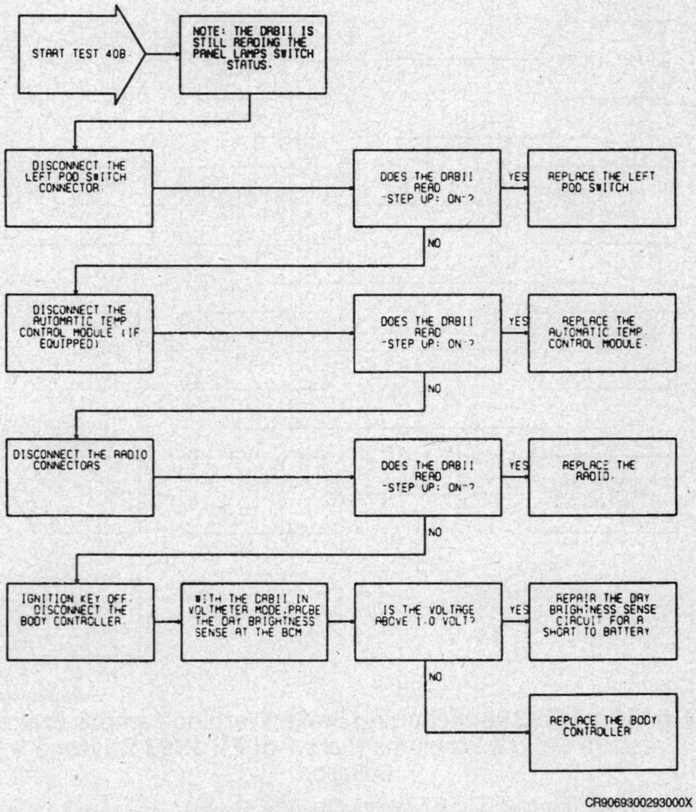

Fig. 53   Test 40B: Dimming Interior Displays. 1993 Daytona & LeBaron

Fig. 54   Test 40C: Dimming Interior Displays (Part 2 of 2). 1993 Daytona & LeBaron

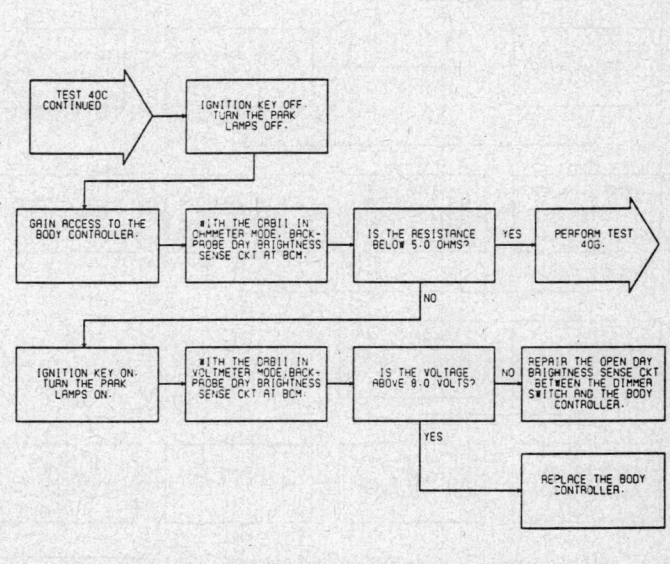

Fig. 54   Test 40C: Dimming Interior Displays (Part 1 of 2). 1993 Daytona & LeBaron

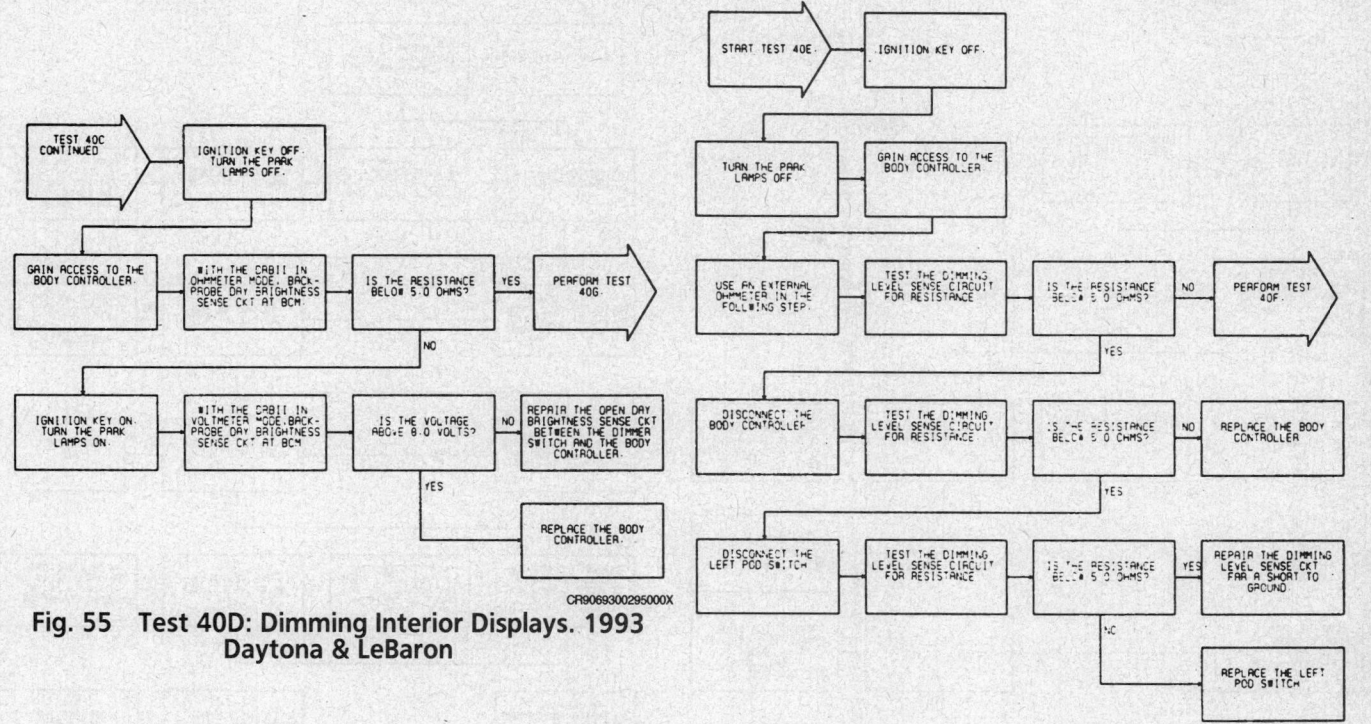

Fig. 55   Test 40D: Dimming Interior Displays. 1993 Daytona & LeBaron

Fig. 56   Test 40E: Dimming Interior Displays. 1993 Daytona & LeBaron

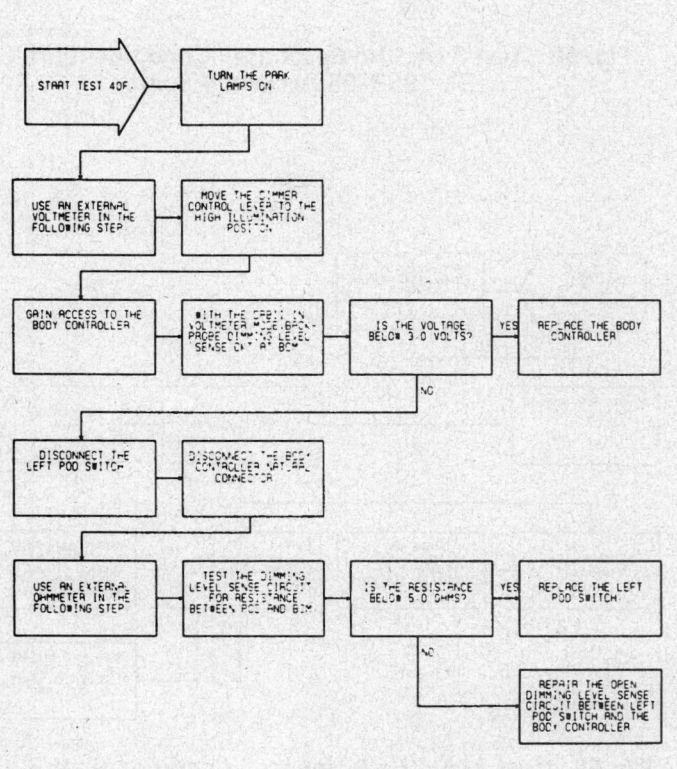

Fig. 57   Test 40F: Dimming Interior Displays. 1993 Daytona & LeBaron

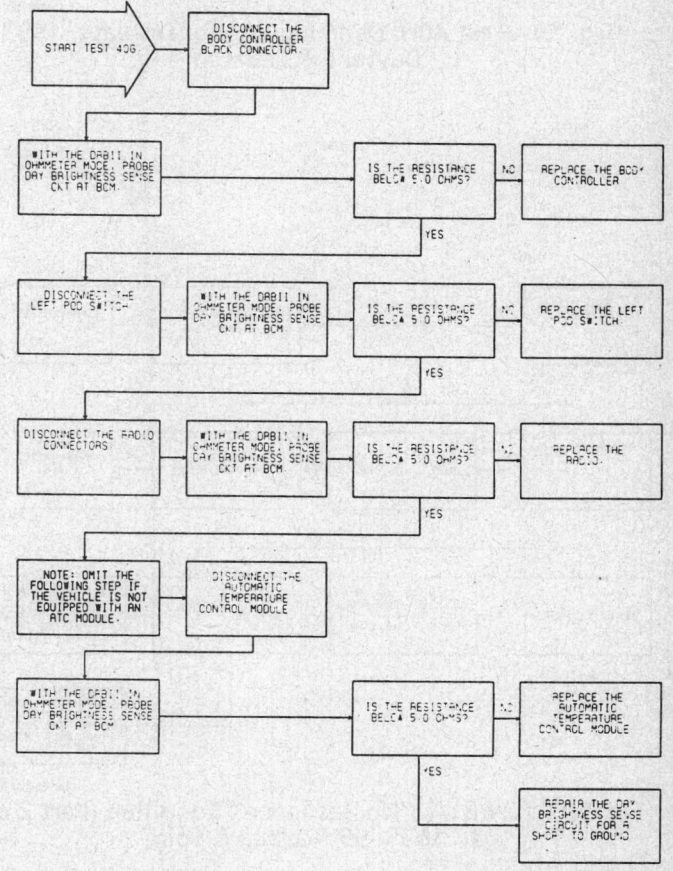

Fig. 58   Test 40G: Dimming Interior Displays. 1993 Daytona & LeBaron

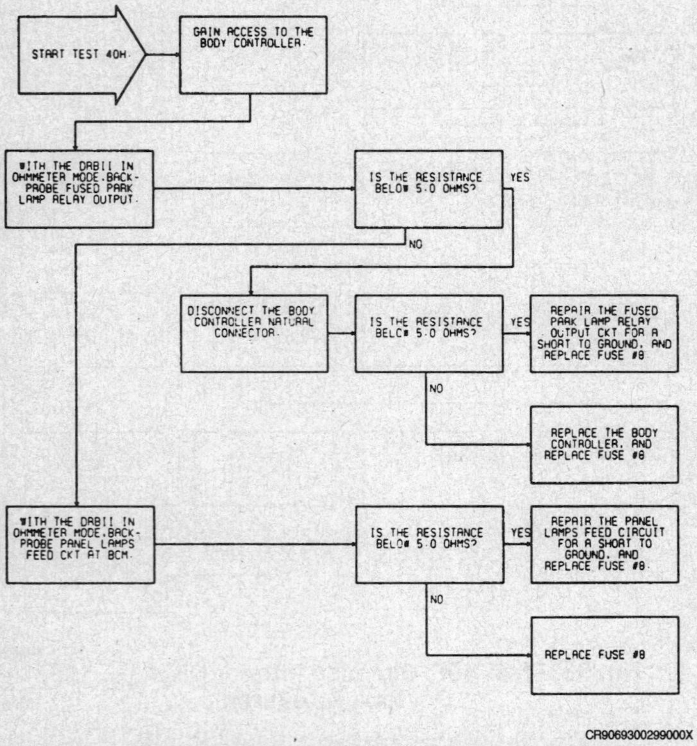

Fig. 59 — Test 40H: Dimming Interior Displays flowchart:

- START TEST 40H
- GAIN ACCESS TO THE BODY CONTROLLER.
- WITH THE DRBII IN OHMMETER MODE, BACK-PROBE FUSED PARK LAMP RELAY OUTPUT.
- IS THE RESISTANCE BELOW 5.0 OHMS? — YES
- NO
- DISCONNECT THE BODY CONTROLLER NATURAL CONNECTOR.
- IS THE RESISTANCE BELOW 5.0 OHMS? — YES → REPAIR THE FUSED PARK LAMP RELAY OUTPUT CKT FOR A SHORT TO GROUND, AND REPLACE FUSE #8
- NO → REPLACE THE BODY CONTROLLER, AND REPLACE FUSE #8
- WITH THE DRBII IN OHMMETER MODE, BACK-PROBE PANEL LAMPS FEED CKT AT BCM.
- IS THE RESISTANCE BELOW 5.0 OHMS? — YES → REPAIR THE PANEL LAMPS FEED CIRCUIT FOR A SHORT TO GROUND, AND REPLACE FUSE #8
- NO → REPLACE FUSE #8

CR9069300299000X

Fig. 59   Test 40H: Dimming Interior Displays. 1993 Daytona & LeBaron

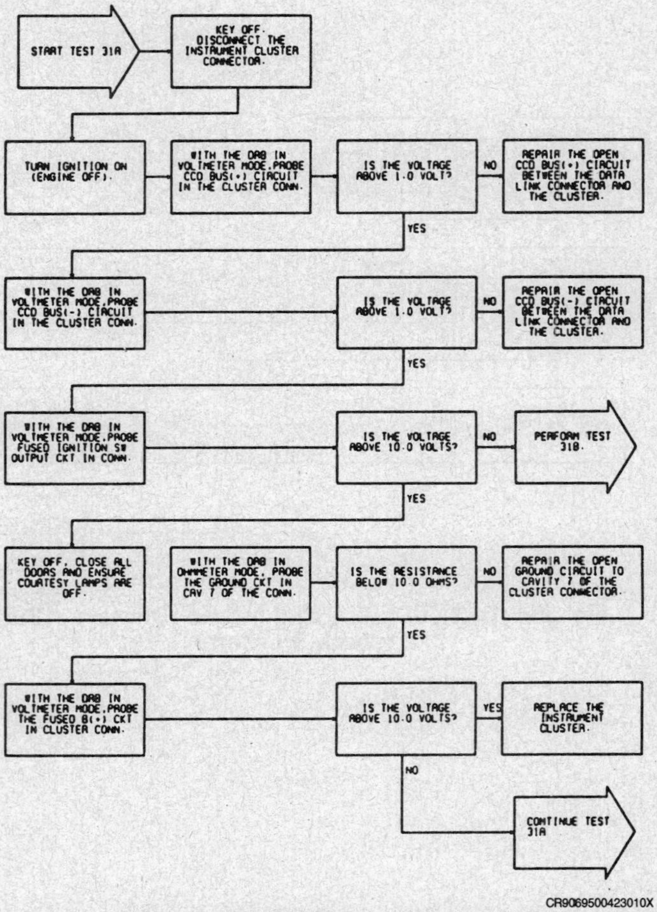

Fig. 60 — Test 31A: "No Response" Condition (Part 1 of 3) flowchart:

- START TEST 31A
- KEY OFF. DISCONNECT THE INSTRUMENT CLUSTER CONNECTOR.
- TURN IGNITION ON (ENGINE OFF).
- WITH THE DRB IN VOLTMETER MODE, PROBE CCD BUS(+) CIRCUIT IN THE CLUSTER CONN.
- IS THE VOLTAGE ABOVE 1.0 VOLTS? — NO → REPAIR THE OPEN CCD BUS(+) CIRCUIT BETWEEN THE DATA LINK CONNECTOR AND THE CLUSTER.
- YES
- WITH THE DRB IN VOLTMETER MODE, PROBE CCD BUS(-) CIRCUIT IN THE CLUSTER CONN.
- IS THE VOLTAGE ABOVE 1.0 VOLTS? — NO → REPAIR THE OPEN CCD BUS(-) CIRCUIT BETWEEN THE DATA LINK CONNECTOR AND THE CLUSTER.
- YES
- WITH THE DRB IN VOLTMETER MODE, PROBE FUSED IGNITION SW OUTPUT CKT IN CONN.
- IS THE VOLTAGE ABOVE 10.0 VOLTS? — NO → PERFORM TEST 31B.
- YES
- KEY OFF. CLOSE ALL DOORS AND ENSURE COURTESY LAMPS ARE OFF.
- WITH THE DRB IN OHMMETER MODE, PROBE THE GROUND CKT IN CAV 7 OF THE CONN.
- IS THE RESISTANCE BELOW 10.0 OHMS? — NO → REPAIR THE OPEN GROUND CIRCUIT TO CAVITY 7 OF THE CLUSTER CONNECTOR.
- YES
- WITH THE DRB IN VOLTMETER MODE, PROBE THE FUSED B(+) CKT IN CLUSTER CONN.
- IS THE VOLTAGE ABOVE 10.0 VOLTS? — YES → REPLACE THE INSTRUMENT CLUSTER.
- NO → CONTINUE TEST 31A

CR9069500423010X

Fig. 60   Test 31A: "No Response" Condition (Part 1 of 3). 1993–95 Acclaim & Spirit

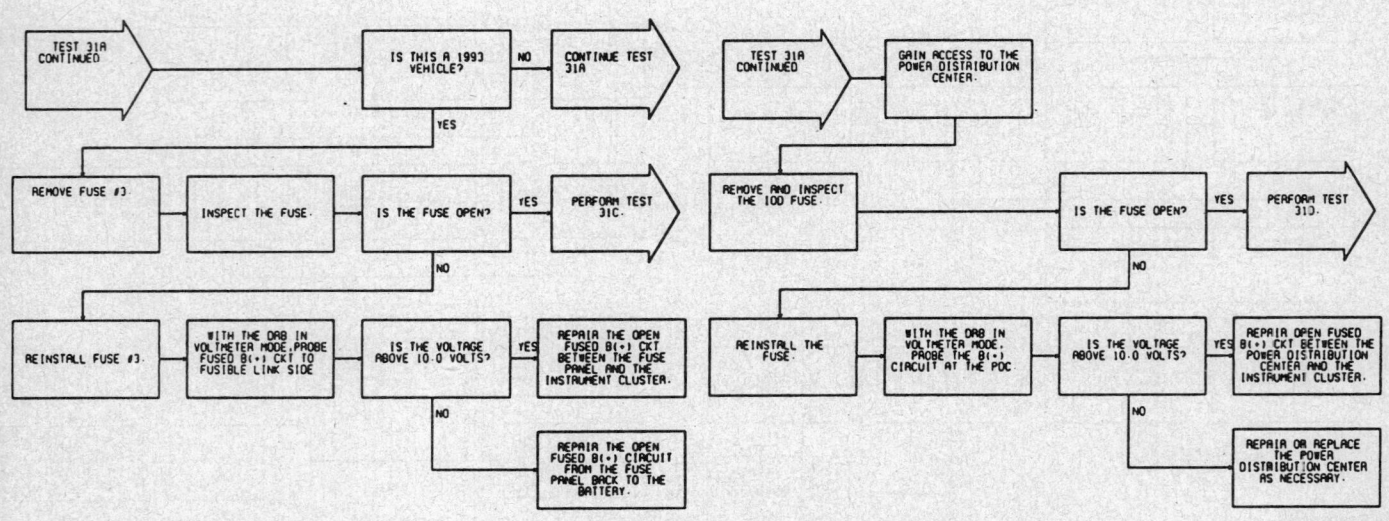

Fig. 60 — Test 31A (Part 2 of 3) flowchart:

- TEST 31A CONTINUED
- IS THIS A 1993 VEHICLE? — NO → CONTINUE TEST 31A
- YES
- REMOVE FUSE #3.
- INSPECT THE FUSE.
- IS THE FUSE OPEN? — YES → PERFORM TEST 31C.
- NO
- REINSTALL FUSE #3.
- WITH THE DRB IN VOLTMETER MODE, PROBE FUSED B(+) CKT TO FUSIBLE LINK SIDE.
- IS THE VOLTAGE ABOVE 10.0 VOLTS? — YES → REPAIR THE OPEN FUSED B(+) CKT BETWEEN THE FUSE PANEL AND THE INSTRUMENT CLUSTER.
- NO → REPAIR THE OPEN FUSED B(+) CIRCUIT FROM THE FUSE PANEL BACK TO THE BATTERY.

CR9069500423020X

Fig. 60   Test 31A: "No Response" Condition (Part 2 of 3). 1993–95 Acclaim & Spirit

Fig. 60 — Test 31A (Part 3 of 3) flowchart:

- TEST 31A CONTINUED
- GAIN ACCESS TO THE POWER DISTRIBUTION CENTER.
- REMOVE AND INSPECT THE 10D FUSE.
- IS THE FUSE OPEN? — YES → PERFORM TEST 31D.
- NO
- REINSTALL THE FUSE.
- WITH THE DRB IN VOLTMETER MODE, PROBE THE B(+) CIRCUIT AT THE PDC.
- IS THE VOLTAGE ABOVE 10.0 VOLTS? — YES → REPAIR OPEN FUSED B(+) CKT BETWEEN THE POWER DISTRIBUTION CENTER AND THE INSTRUMENT CLUSTER.
- NO → REPAIR OR REPLACE THE POWER DISTRIBUTION CENTER AS NECESSARY.

CR9069500423030X

Fig. 60   Test 31A: "No Response" Condition (Part 3 of 3). 1993–95 Acclaim & Spirit

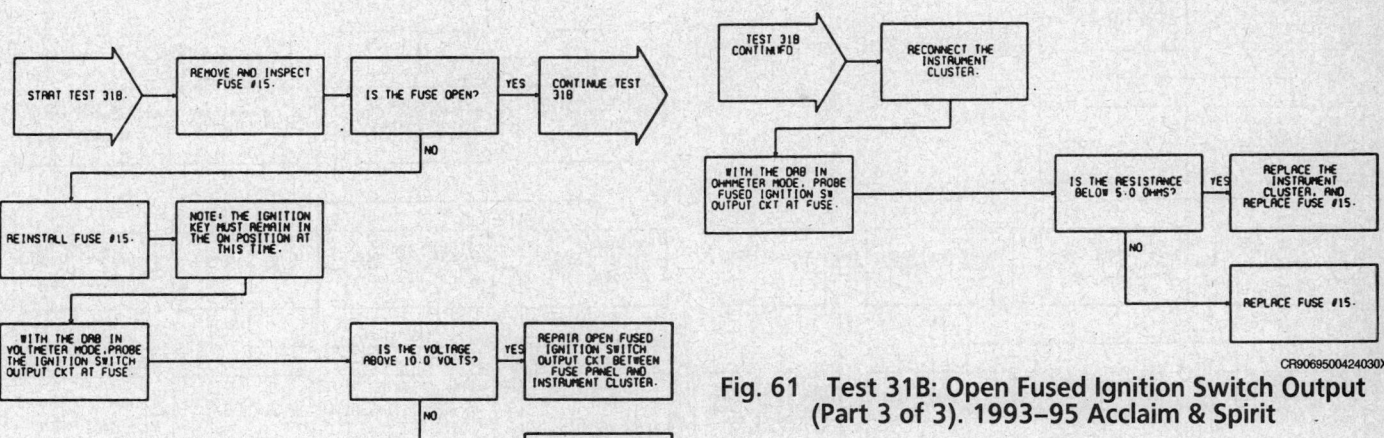

Fig. 61   Test 31B: Open Fused Ignition Switch Output
(Part 1 of 3). 1993–95 Acclaim & Spirit

Fig. 61   Test 31B: Open Fused Ignition Switch Output
(Part 3 of 3). 1993–95 Acclaim & Spirit

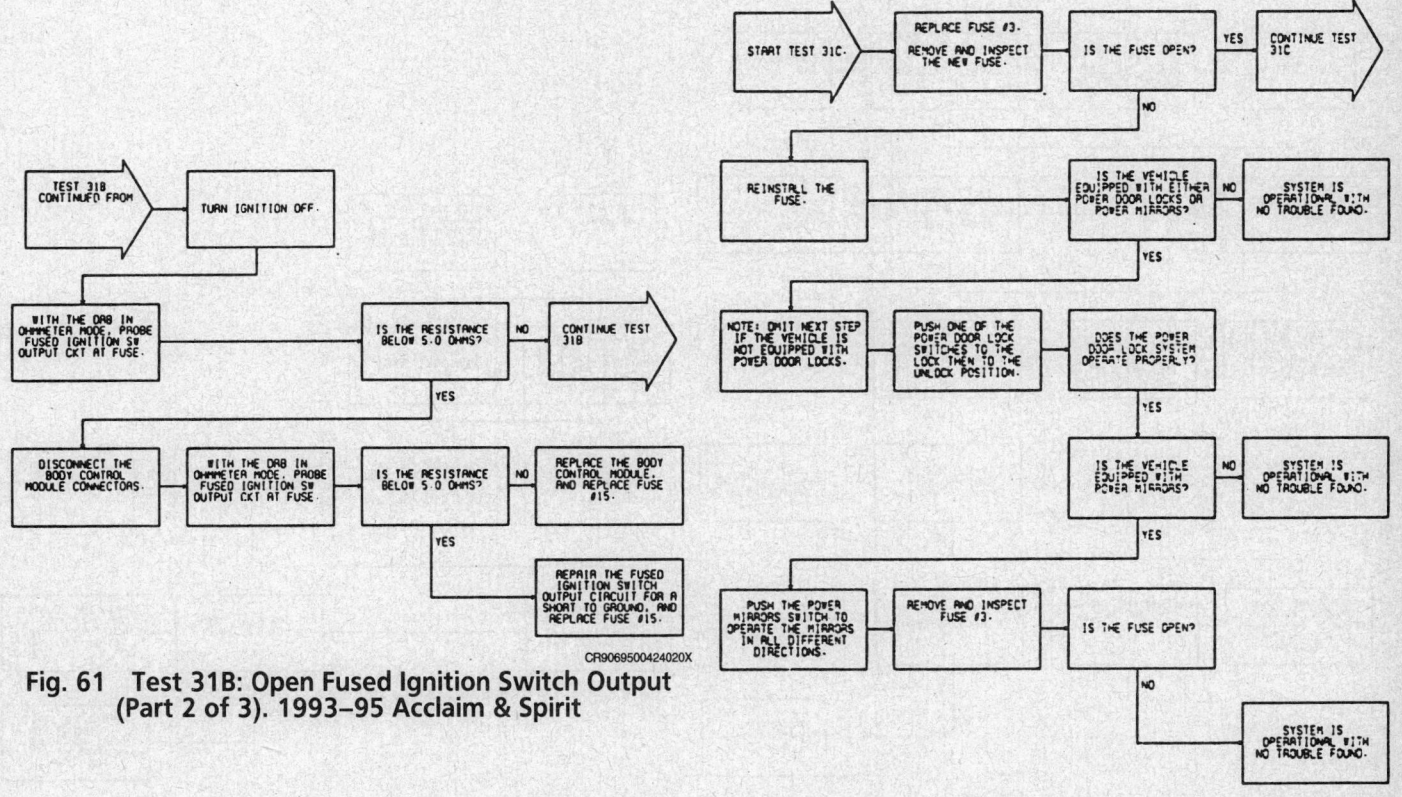

Fig. 61   Test 31B: Open Fused Ignition Switch Output
(Part 2 of 3). 1993–95 Acclaim & Spirit

Fig. 62   Test 31C: Instrument Cluster Battery Power
Supply (Part 1 of 3). 1993 Acclaim & Spirit

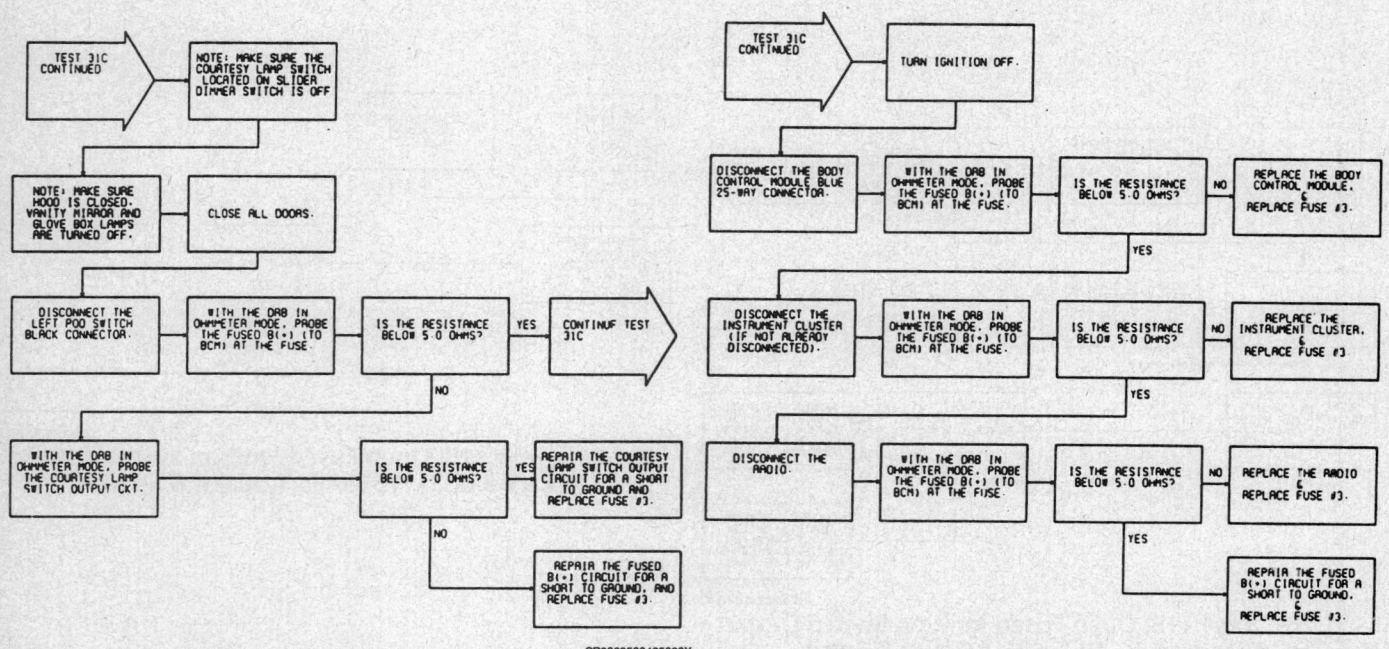

Fig. 62   Test 31C: Instrument Cluster Battery Power Supply (Part 2 of 3). 1993 Acclaim & Spirit

Fig. 62   Test 31C: Instrument Cluster Battery Power Supply (Part 3 of 3). 1993 Acclaim & Spirit

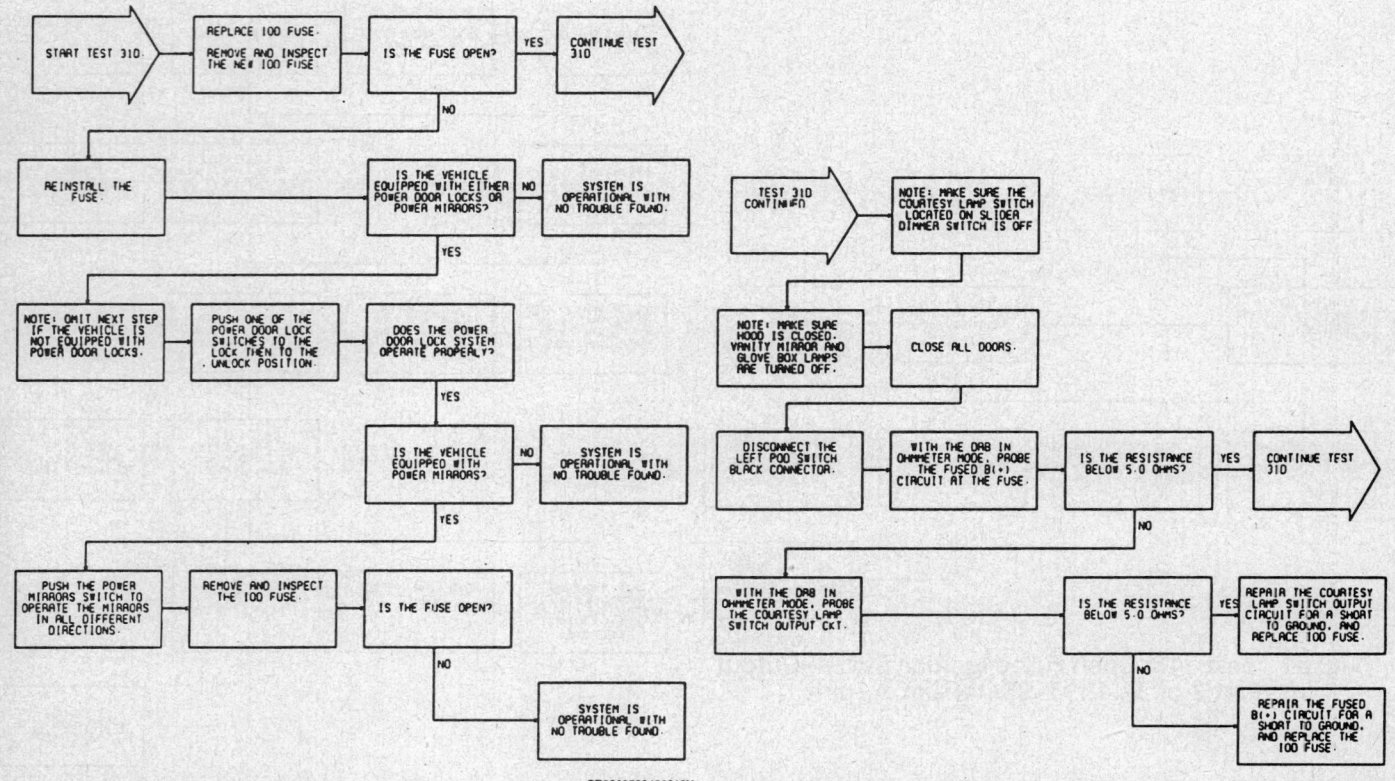

Fig. 63   Test 31D: Instrument Cluster Battery Power Supply (Part 1 of 3). 1994–95 Acclaim & Spirit

Fig. 63   Test 31D: Instrument Cluster Battery Power Supply (Part 2 of 3). 1994–95 Acclaim & Spirit

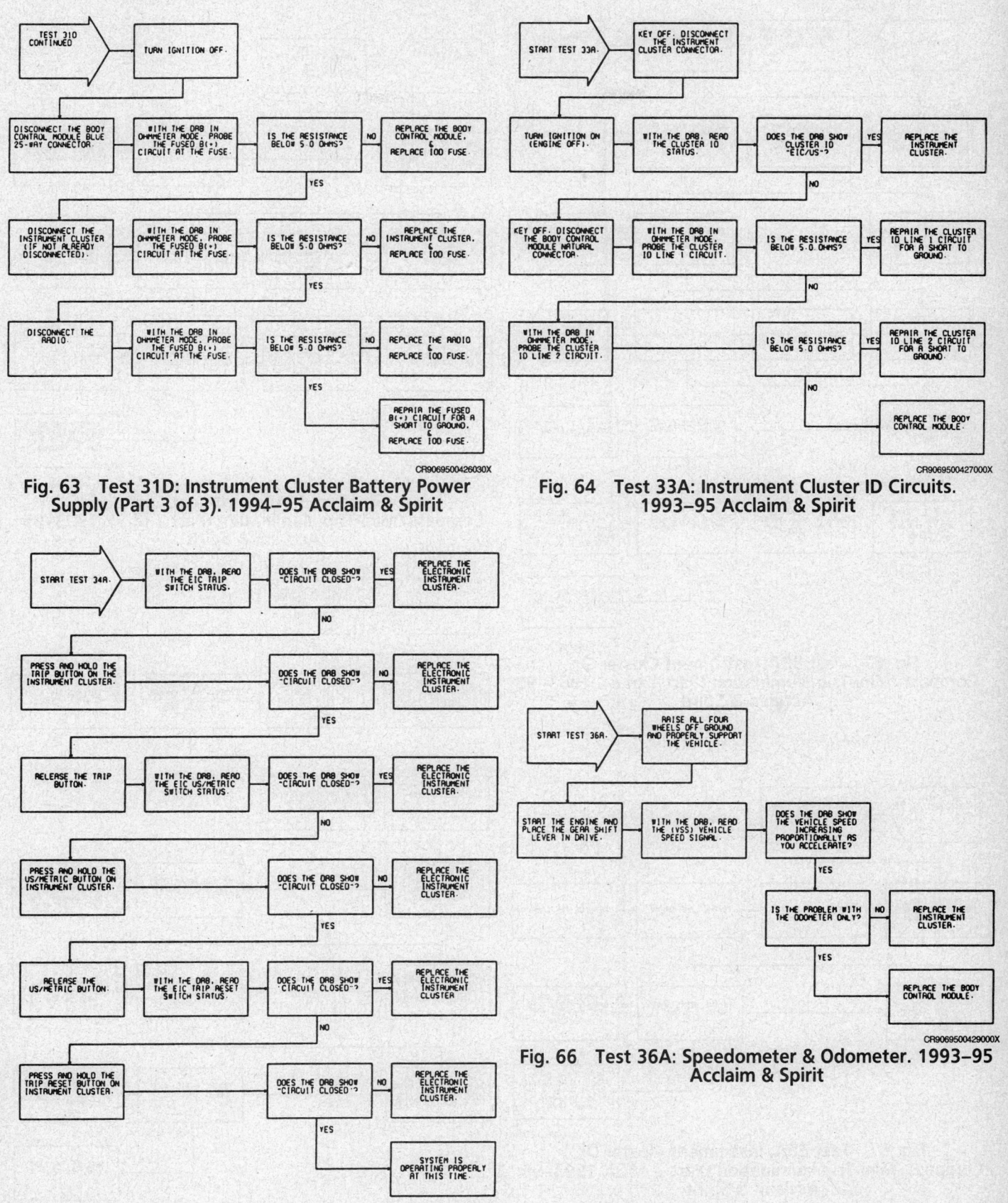

Fig. 63 Test 31D: Instrument Cluster Battery Power Supply (Part 3 of 3). 1994–95 Acclaim & Spirit

Fig. 64 Test 33A: Instrument Cluster ID Circuits. 1993–95 Acclaim & Spirit

Fig. 65 Test 34A: Switch Operation. 1993–95 Acclaim & Spirit

Fig. 66 Test 36A: Speedometer & Odometer. 1993–95 Acclaim & Spirit

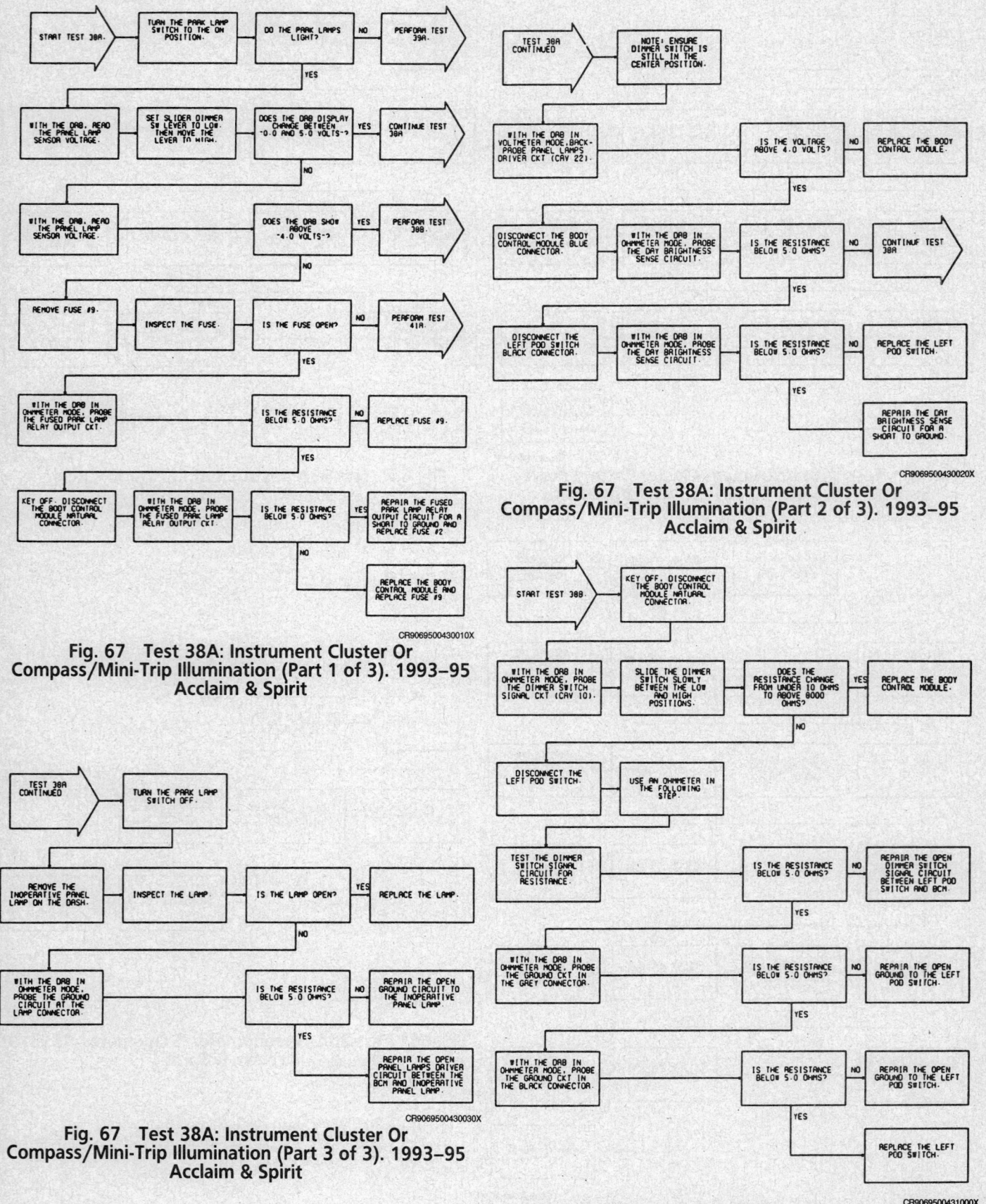

Fig. 67   Test 38A: Instrument Cluster Or Compass/Mini-Trip Illumination (Part 1 of 3). 1993–95 Acclaim & Spirit

CR9069500430010X

Fig. 67   Test 38A: Instrument Cluster Or Compass/Mini-Trip Illumination (Part 2 of 3). 1993–95 Acclaim & Spirit

CR9069500430020X

Fig. 67   Test 38A: Instrument Cluster Or Compass/Mini-Trip Illumination (Part 3 of 3). 1993–95 Acclaim & Spirit

CR9069500430030X

Fig. 68   Test 38B: Open Pod Switch Control. 1993–95 Acclaim & Spirit

CR9069500431000X

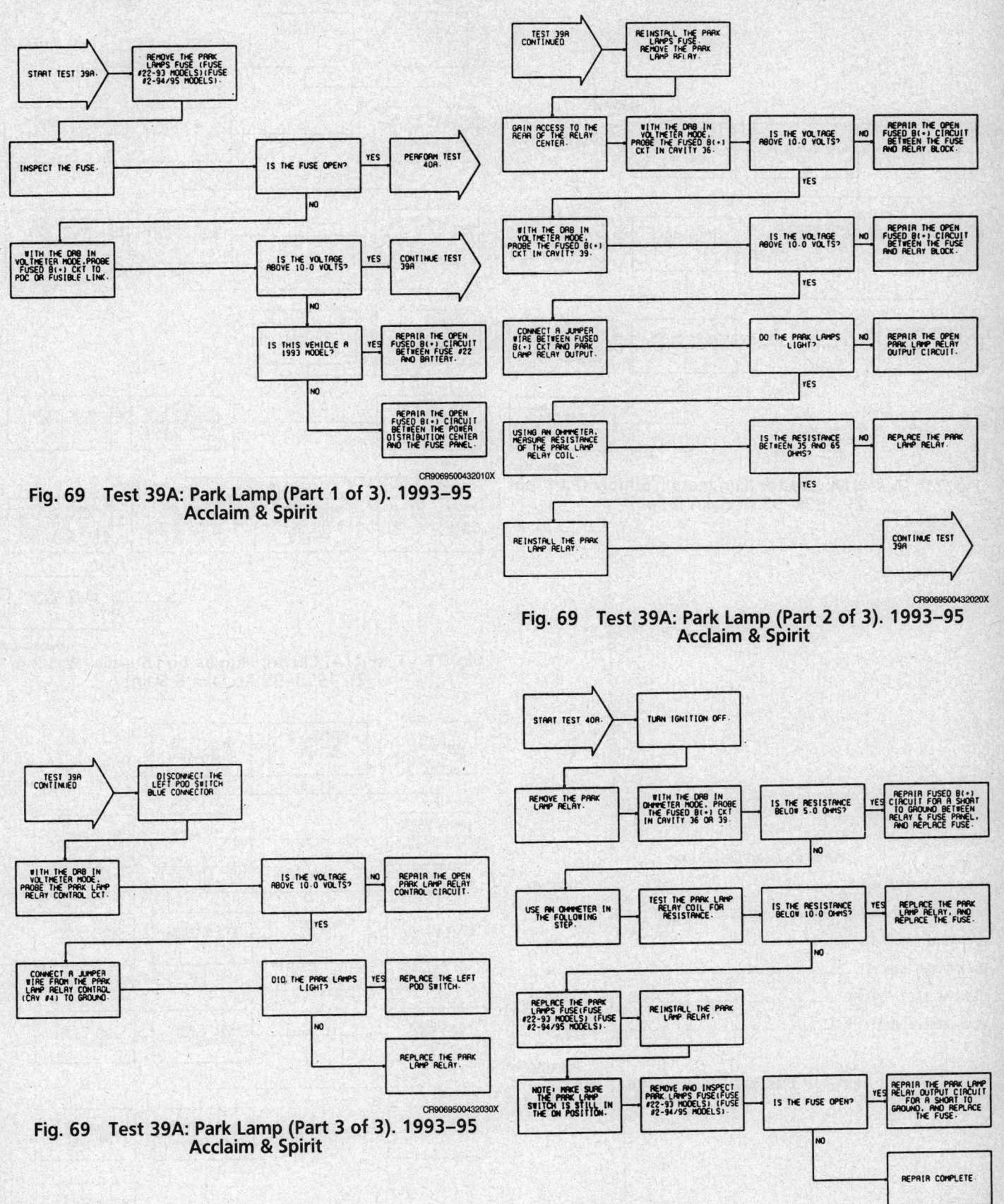

Fig. 69   Test 39A: Park Lamp (Part 1 of 3). 1993–95 Acclaim & Spirit

Fig. 69   Test 39A: Park Lamp (Part 2 of 3). 1993–95 Acclaim & Spirit

Fig. 69   Test 39A: Park Lamp (Part 3 of 3). 1993–95 Acclaim & Spirit

Fig. 70   Test 40A: Shorted Panel Lamps Power Supply. 1993–95 Acclaim & Spirit

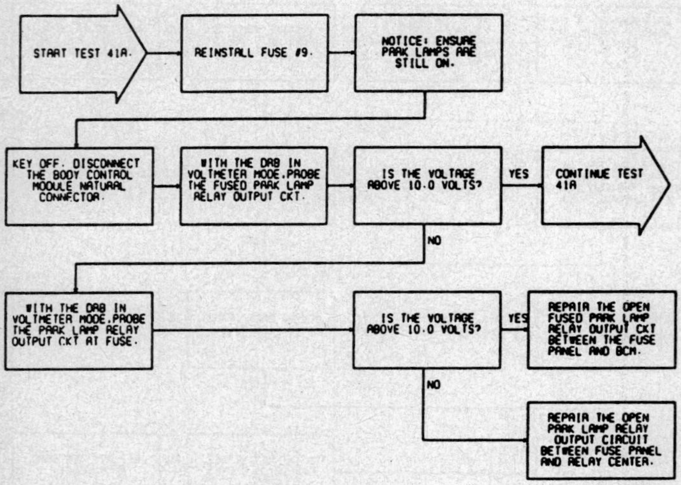

Fig. 71 Test 41A: Cluster Illumination Supply (Part 1 of 2). 1993–95 Acclaim & Spirit

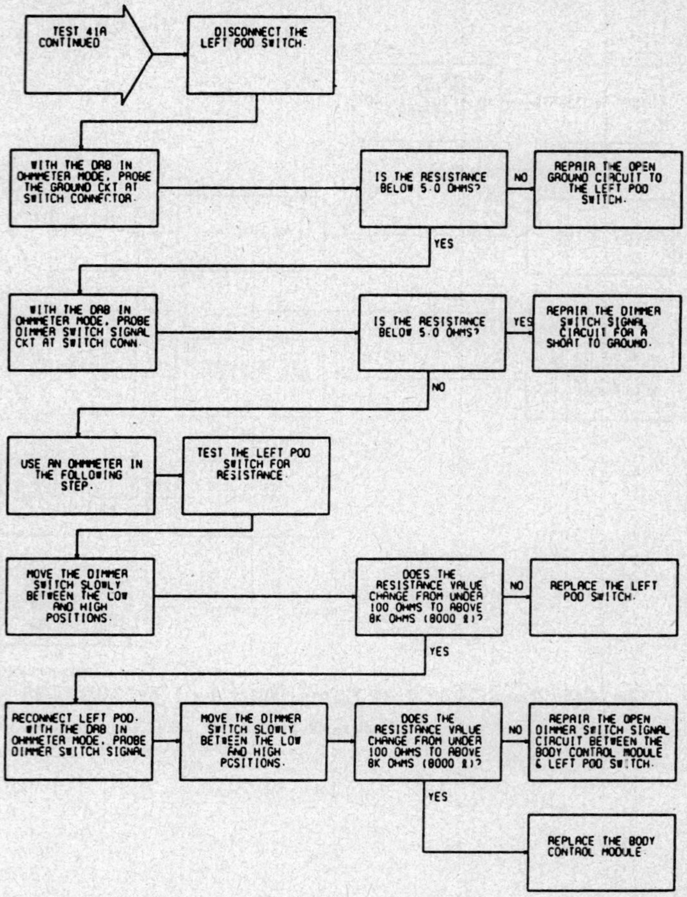

CR9069500434010X

Fig. 71 Test 41A: Cluster Illumination Supply (Part 2 of 2). 1993–95 Acclaim & Spirit

CR9069500434020X

DRBII FAILURE MESSAGES

FAILURE MESSAGES	TEST NO.
BLANK SCREEN ON THE DRBII	1C
RAM TEST FAILURE	1D
CARTRIDGE ERROR	1E
KEY PAD TEST FAILURE	1F
LOW OR HIGH BATTERY	1G

CR9069300326000X

Fig. 72 Test 1A: Bus Failure Messages. 1993

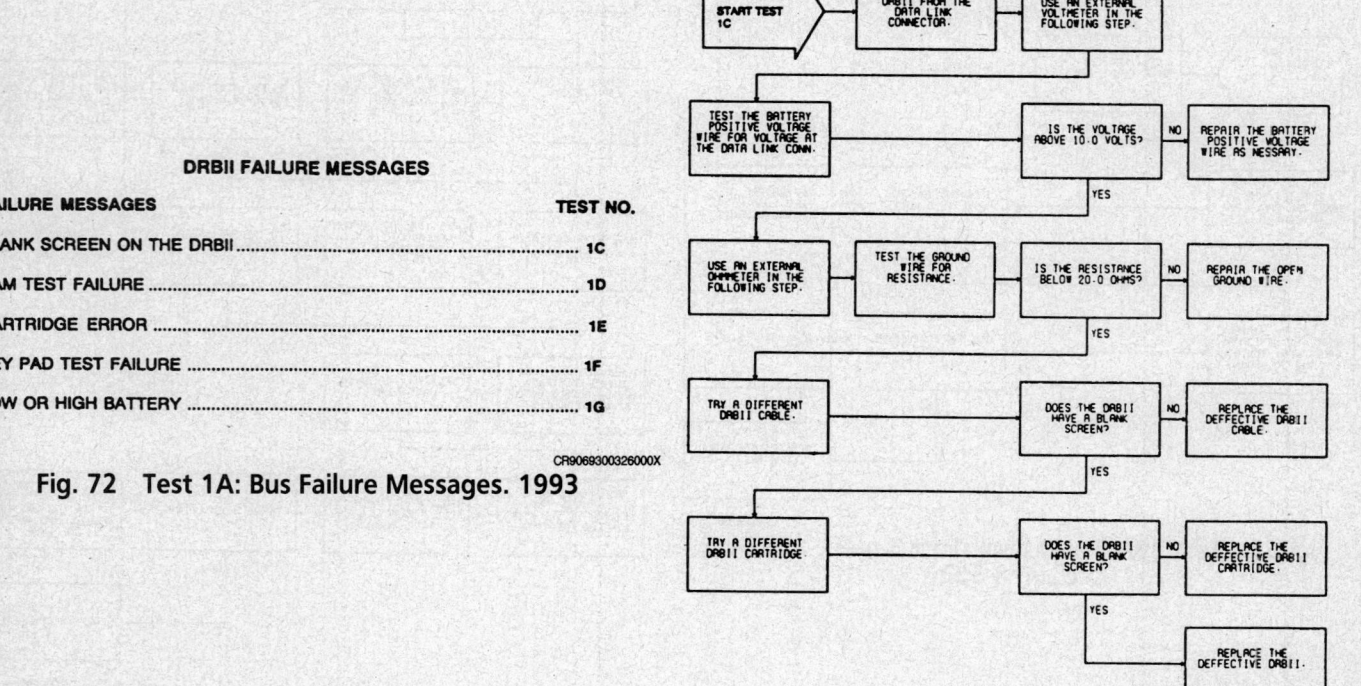

CR9069300327000X

Fig. 73 Test 1C: Blank Screen On DRB. 1993

CR9069300328000X

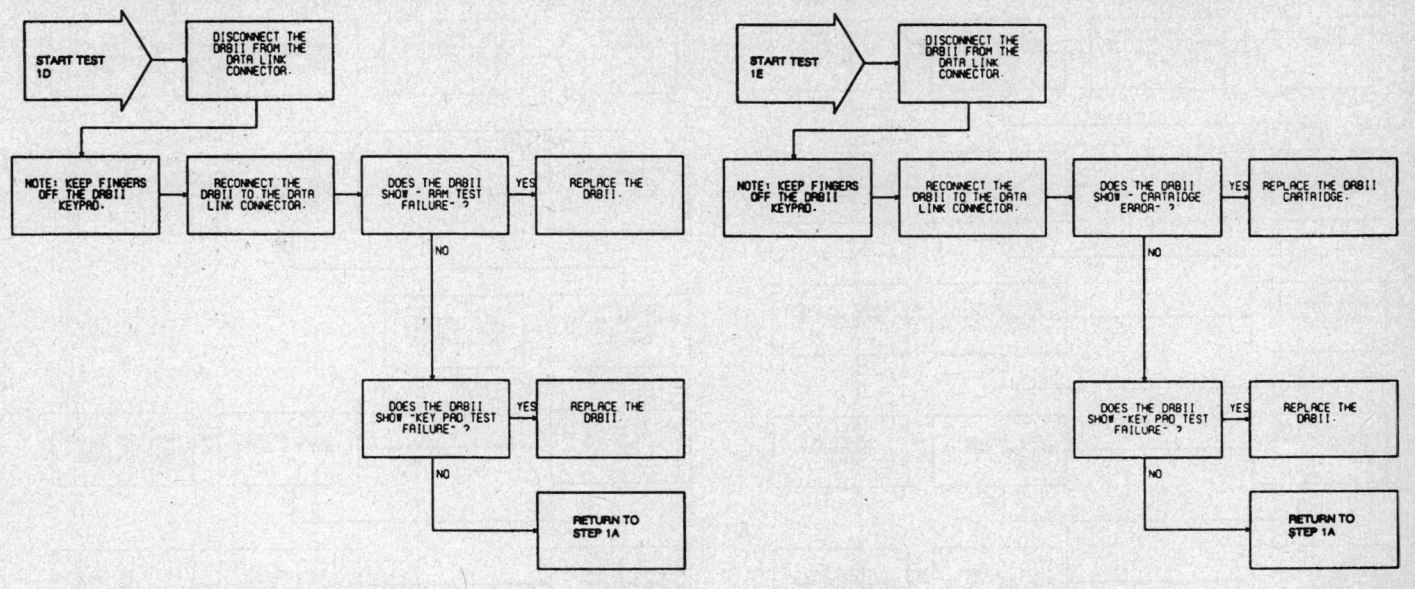

Fig. 74 Test 1D: RAM Test Failure. 1993

CR9069300329000X

Fig. 75 Test 1E: Cartridge Failure. 1993

CR9069300330000X

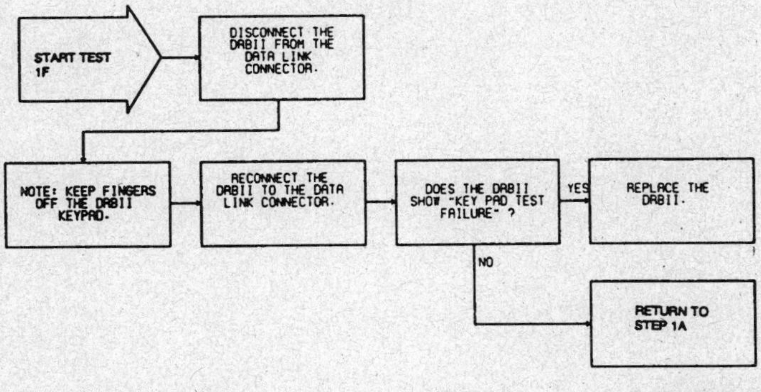

Fig. 76 Test 1F: Key Pad Test Failure. 1993

CR9069300331000X

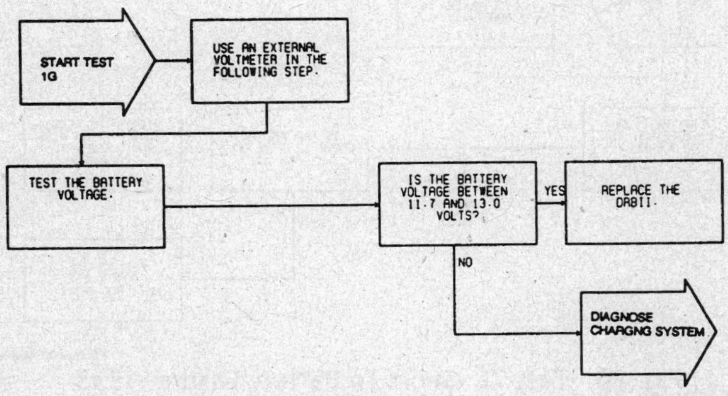

Fig. 77 Test 1G: Low Or High Battery. 1993

CR9069300332010X

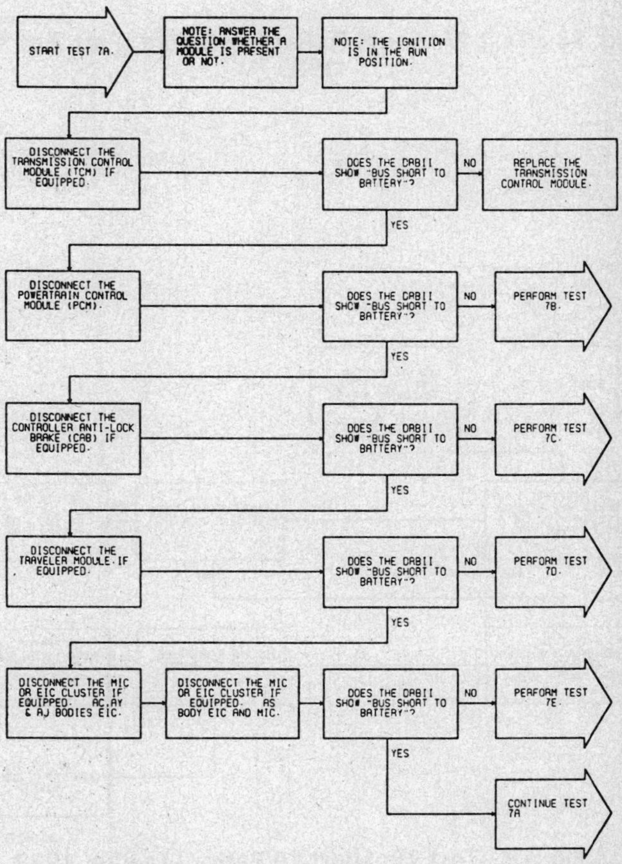

Fig. 78 Test 7A: Short To Battery Failure (Part 1 of 3). 1993

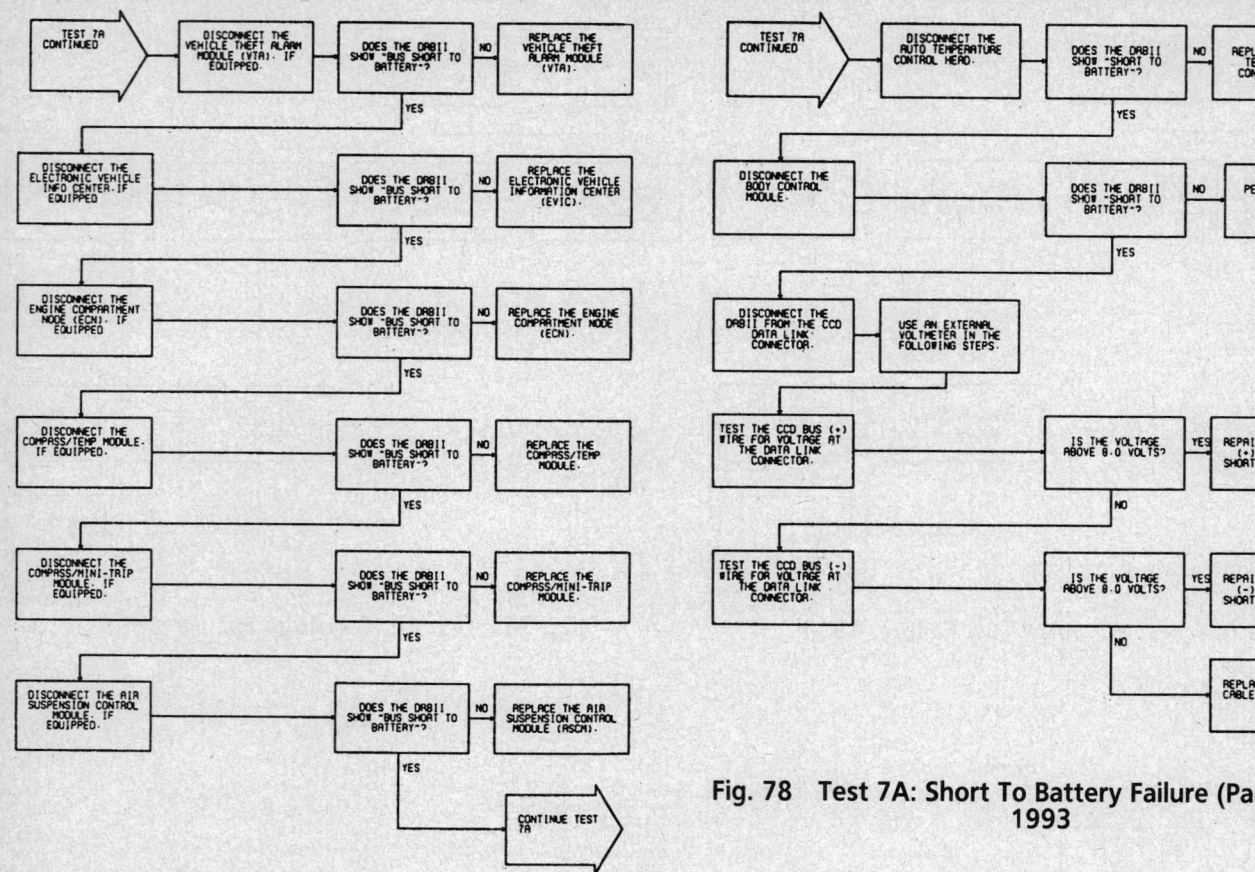

Fig. 78   Test 7A: Short To Battery Failure (Part 2 of 3).
1993

Fig. 78   Test 7A: Short To Battery Failure (Part 3 of 3).
1993

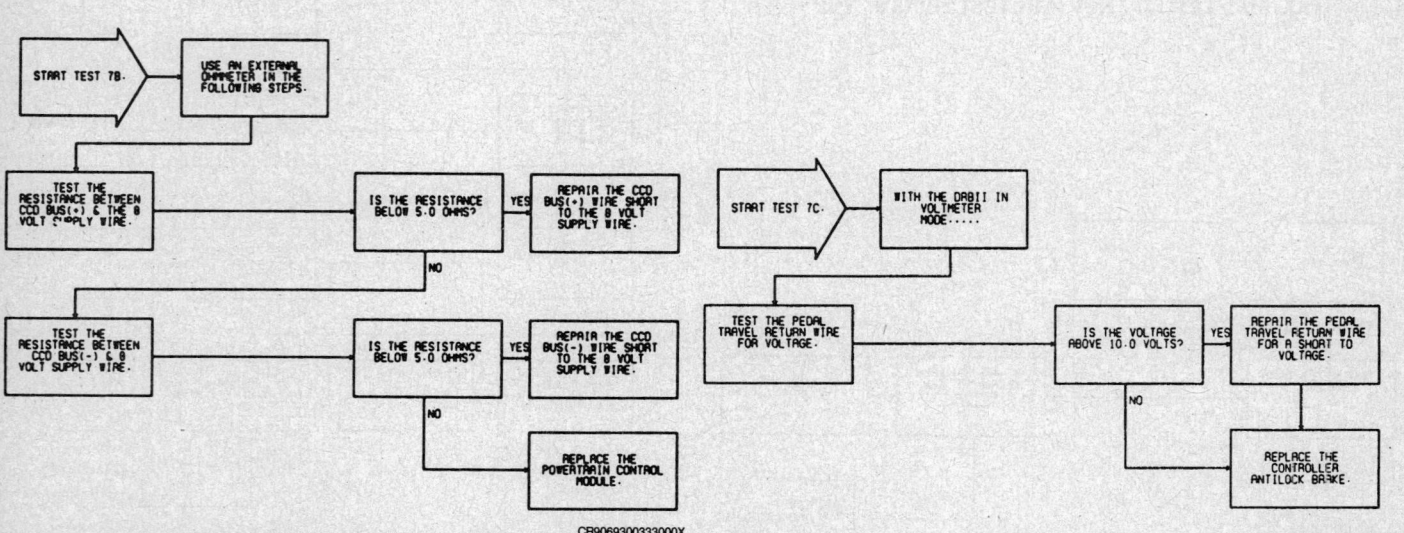

Fig. 79   Test 7B: Short To Battery Failure. 1993

Fig. 80   Test 7C: Short To Battery Failure. 1993

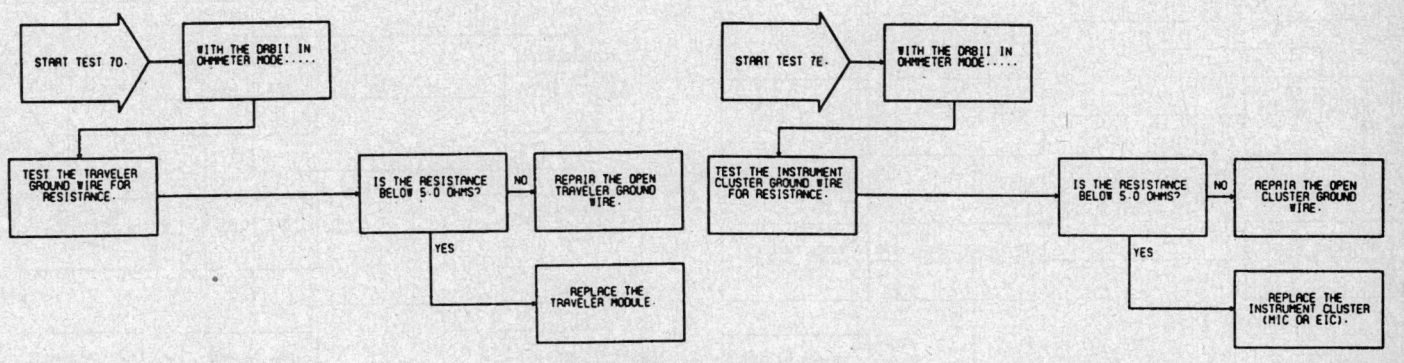

Fig. 81   Test 7D: Short To Battery Failure. 1993

Fig. 82   Test 7E: Short To Battery Failure. 1993

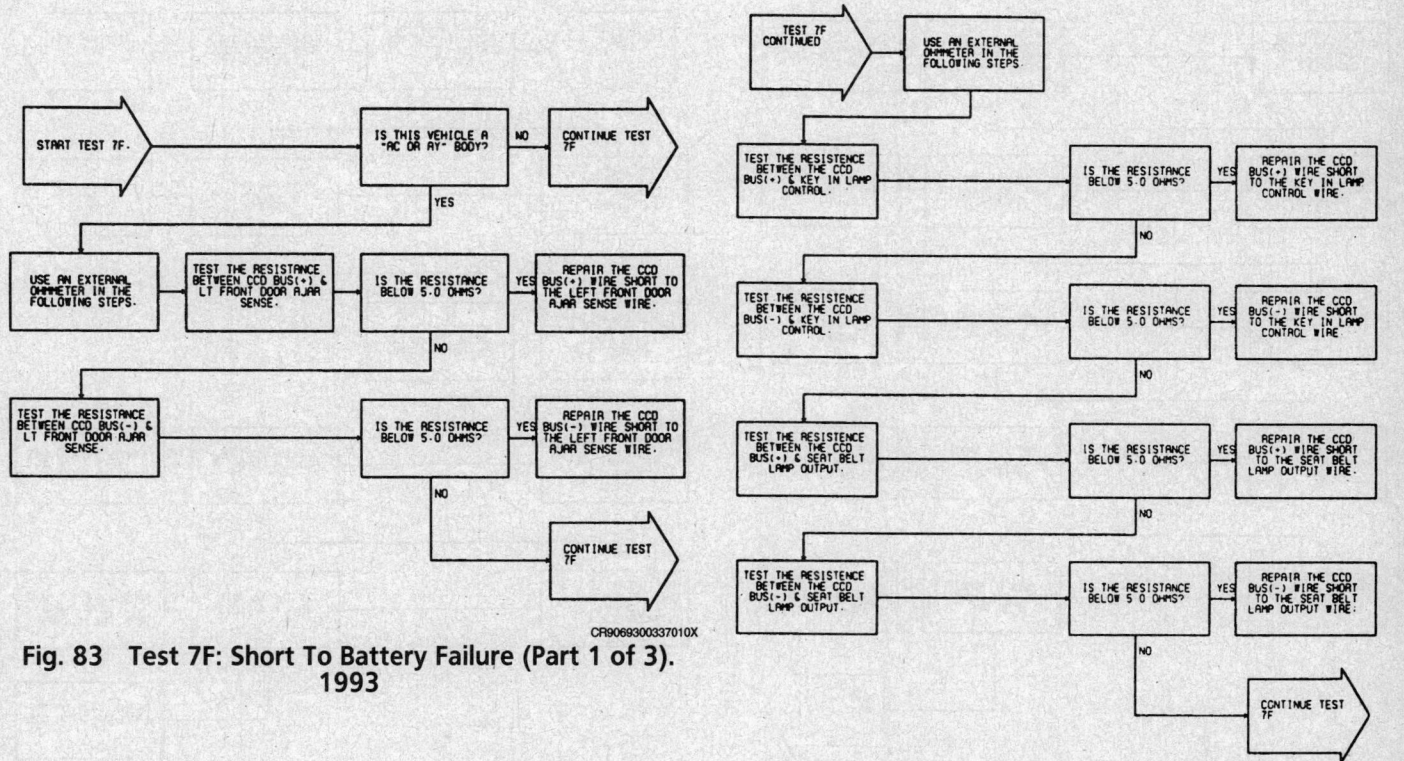

Fig. 83   Test 7F: Short To Battery Failure (Part 1 of 3).
1993

Fig. 83   Test 7F: Short To Battery Failure (Part 2 of 3).
1993

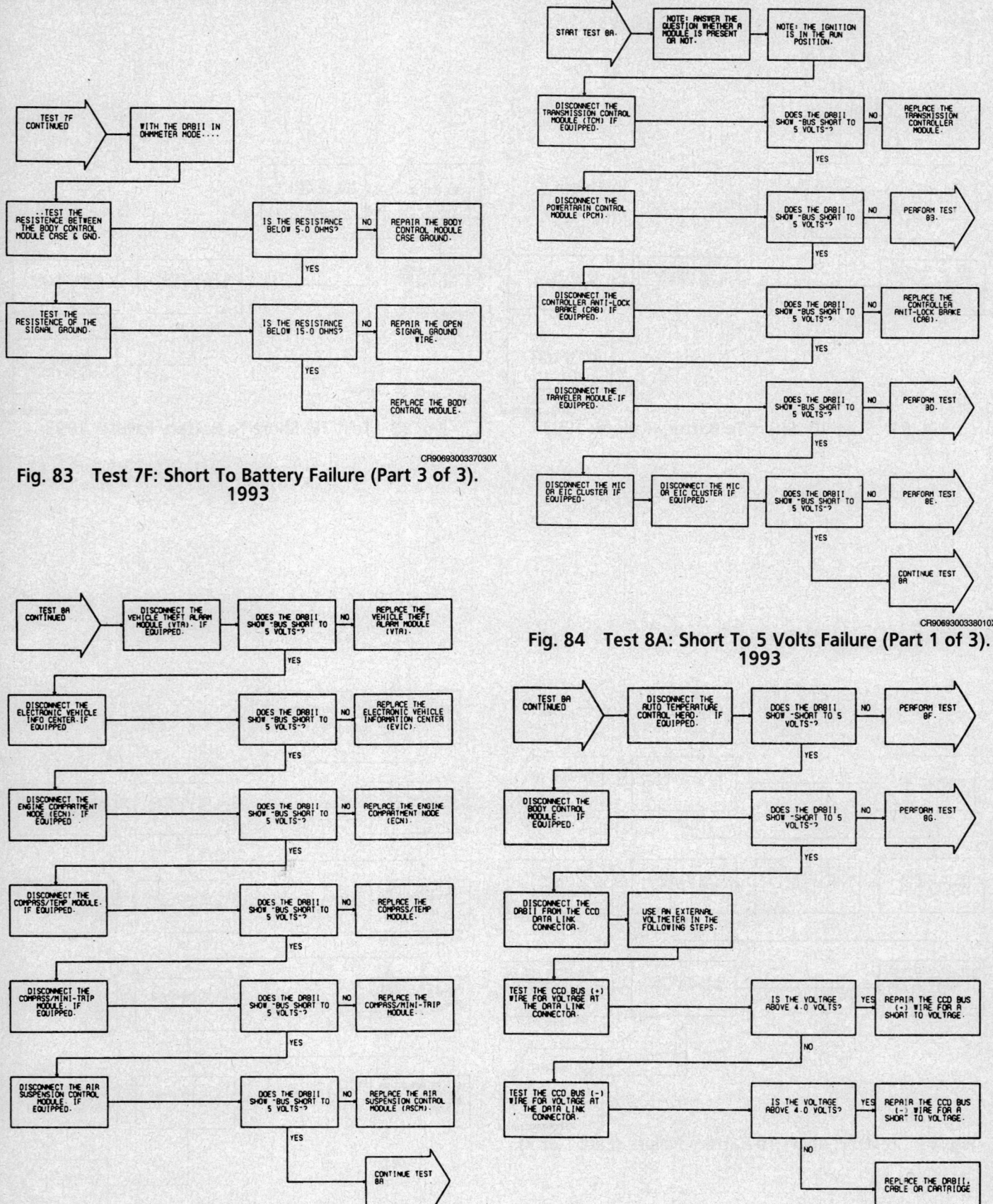

Fig. 83   Test 7F: Short To Battery Failure (Part 3 of 3). 1993

Fig. 84   Test 8A: Short To 5 Volts Failure (Part 1 of 3). 1993

Fig. 84   Test 8A: Short To 5 Volts Failure (Part 2 of 3). 1993

Fig. 84   Test 8A: Short To 5 Volts Failure (Part 3 of 3). 1993

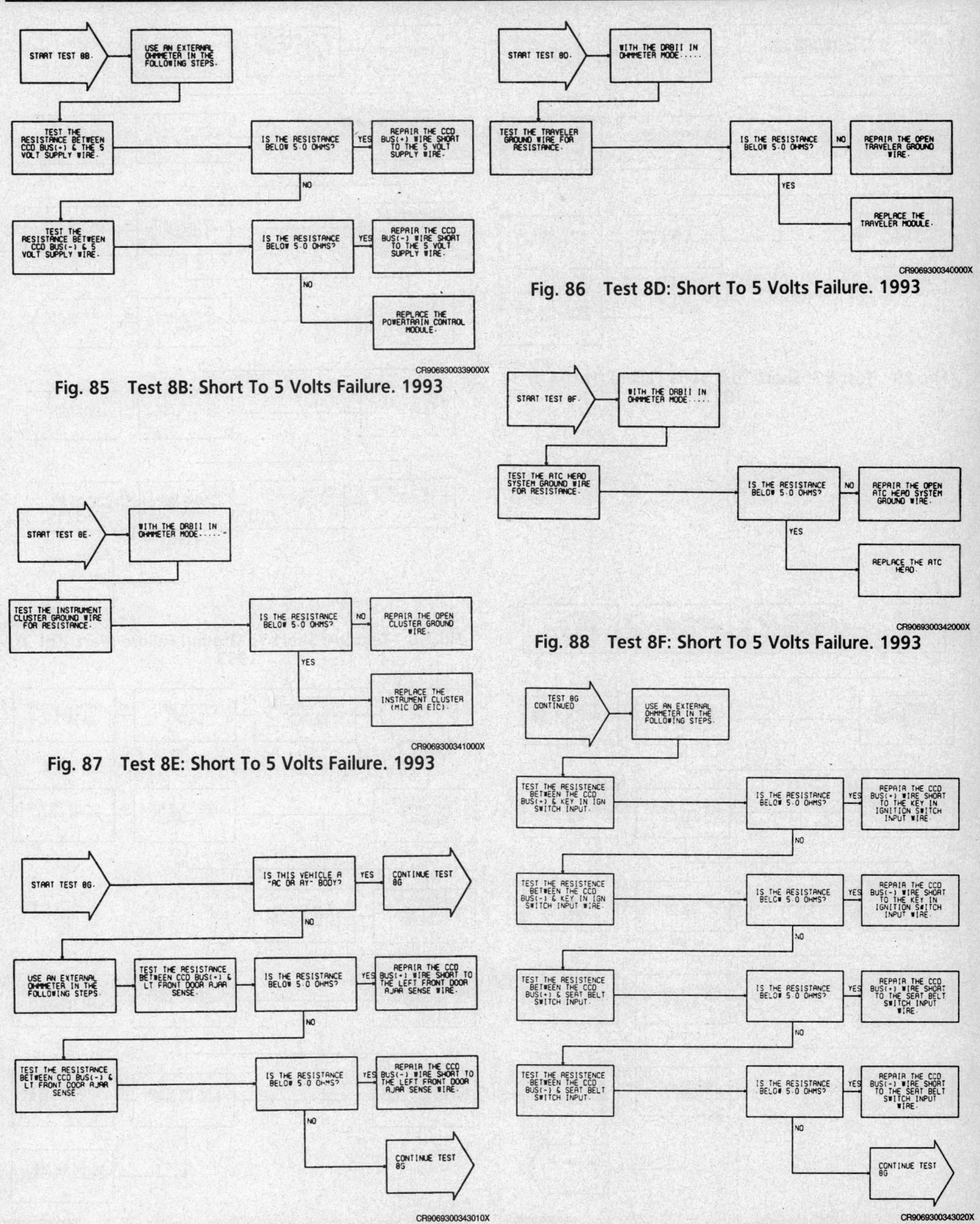

Fig. 85   Test 8B: Short To 5 Volts Failure. 1993

Fig. 86   Test 8D: Short To 5 Volts Failure. 1993

Fig. 87   Test 8E: Short To 5 Volts Failure. 1993

Fig. 88   Test 8F: Short To 5 Volts Failure. 1993

Fig. 89   Test 8G: Short To 5 Volts Failure (Part 1 of 3).
1993

Fig. 89   Test 8G: Short To 5 Volts Failure (Part 2 of 3).
1993

CHRYSLER–Electronic Instrumentation & Body Controls

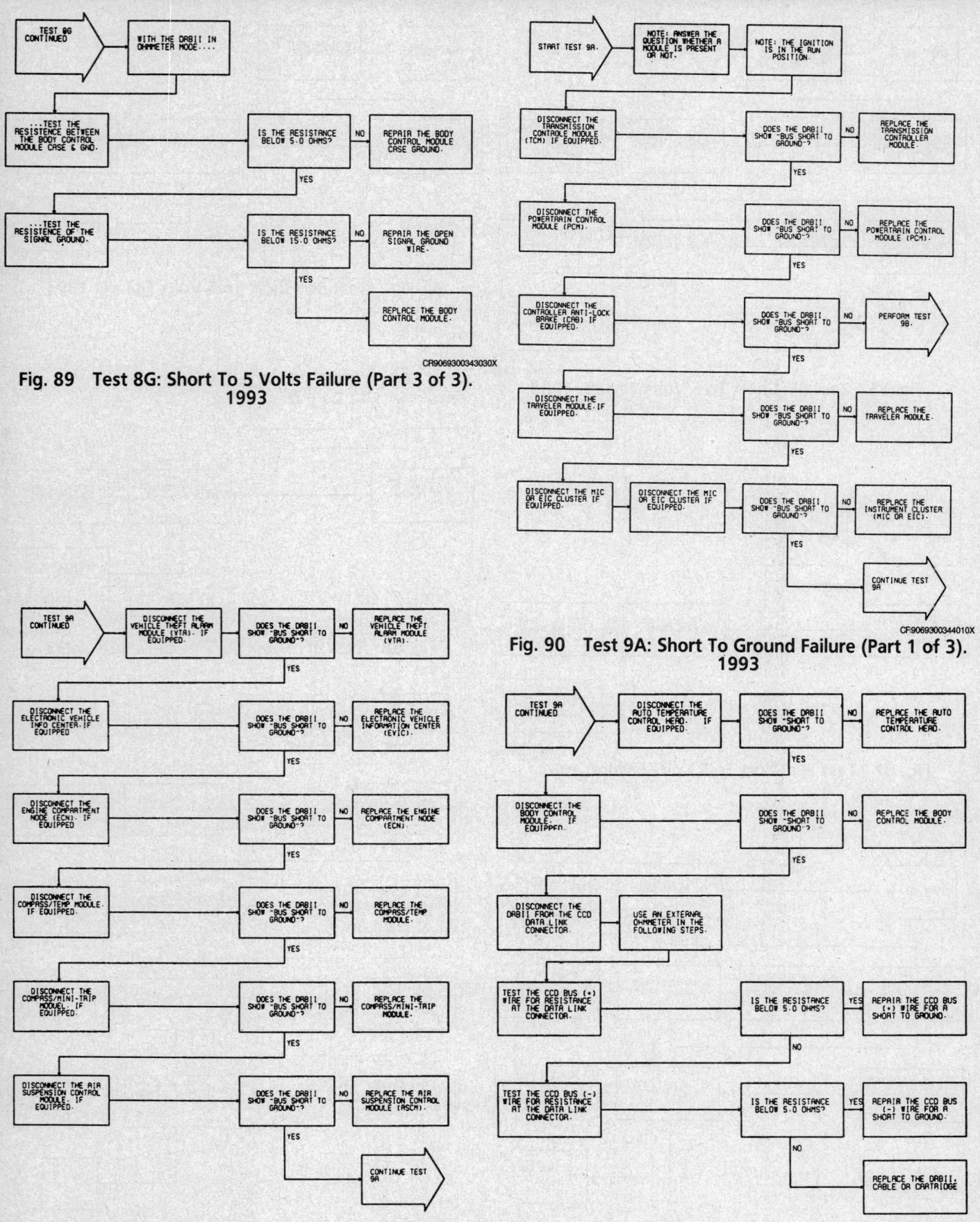

Fig. 89   Test 8G: Short To 5 Volts Failure (Part 3 of 3). 1993

CR9069300343030X

Fig. 90   Test 9A: Short To Ground Failure (Part 1 of 3). 1993

CF9069300344010X

Fig. 90   Test 9A: Short To Ground Failure (Part 2 of 3). 1993

CR9069300344020X

Fig. 90   Test 9A: Short To Ground Failure (Part 3 of 3). 1993

CR9069300344030X

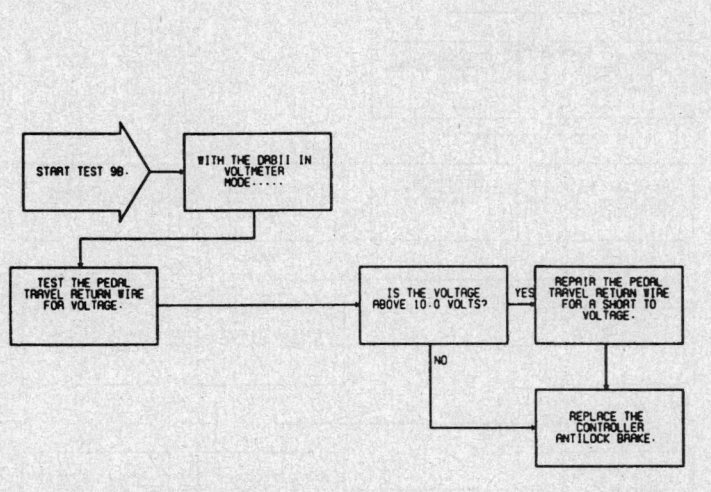

Fig. 91   Test 9B: Short To Ground Failure. 1993

CR9069300345000X

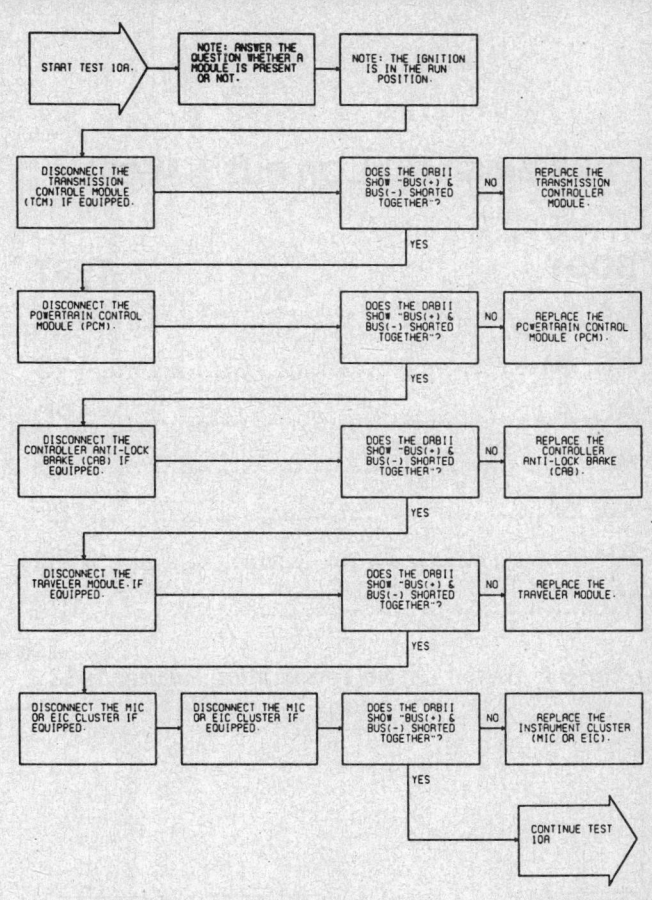

Fig. 92   Test 10A: Bus (+) & Bus (-) Shorted Together Failure (Part 1 of 3). 1993

CR9069300346010X

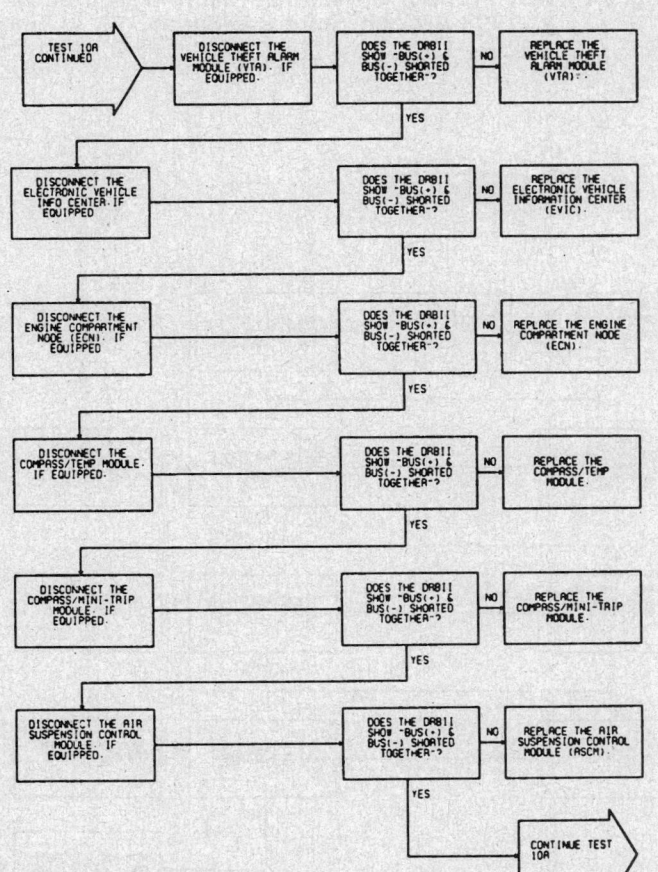

Fig. 92   Test 10A: Bus (+) & Bus (-) Shorted Together Failure (Part 2 of 3). 1993

CR9069300346020X

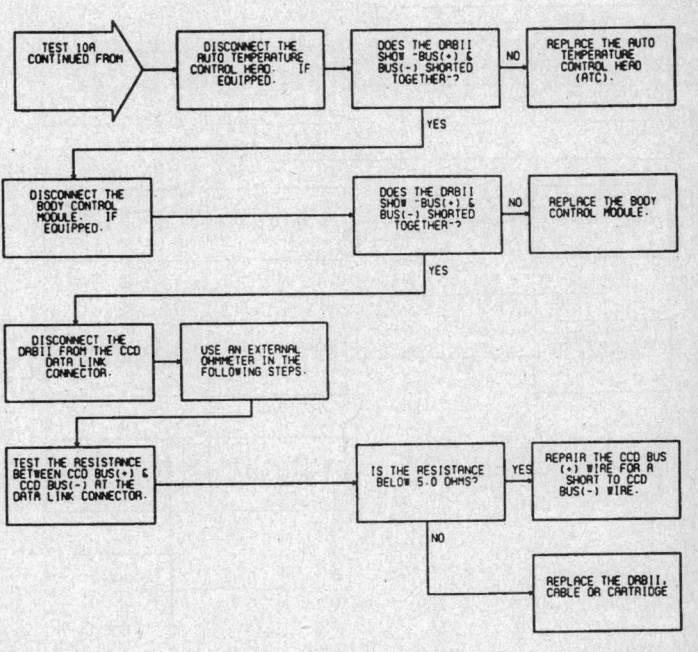

Fig. 92   Test 10A: Bus (+) & Bus (-) Shorted Together Failure (Part 3 of 3). 1993

CR9069300346030X

BUS BIAS LEVEL OR BUS (+/-) OPEN

BODY	TEST
AA	12B
AC, AY	12C
AG, AJ	12D
AS	12E
XJ, ZJ	12F
AP	12H
YJ	12J

CR9069300347000X

Fig. 93 Test 11A: No Termination Failure. 1993

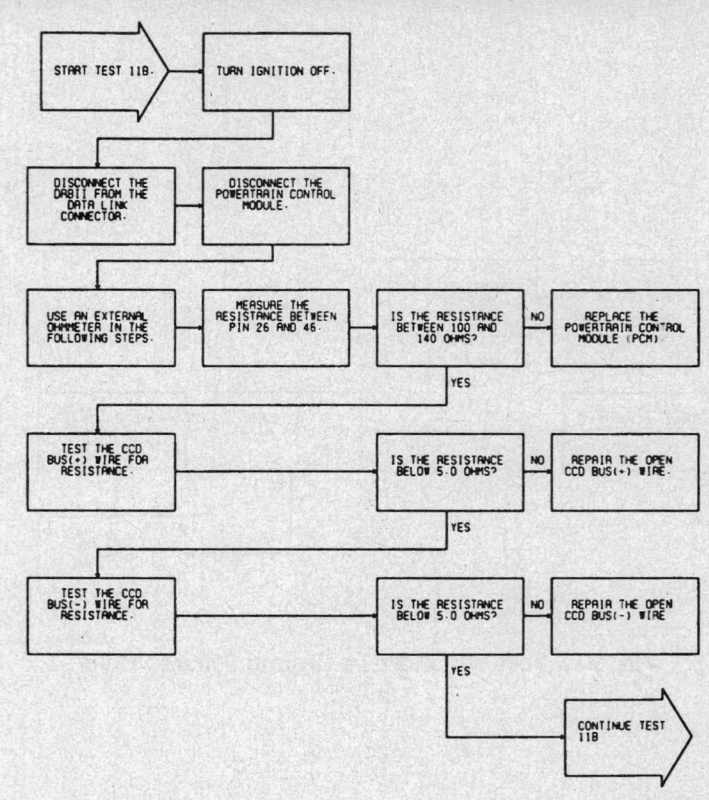

CR9069300348010X

Fig. 94 Test 11B: No Termination Failure (Part 1 of 3). 1993 Acclaim, Spirit & LeBaron

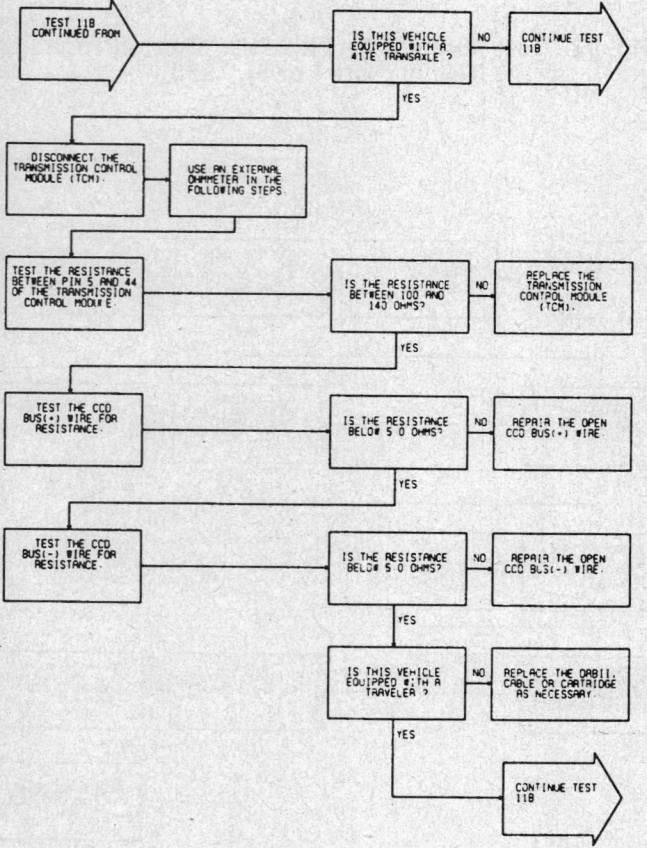

CR9069300348020X

Fig. 94 Test 11B: No Termination Failure (Part 2 of 3). 1993 Acclaim, Spirit & LeBaron

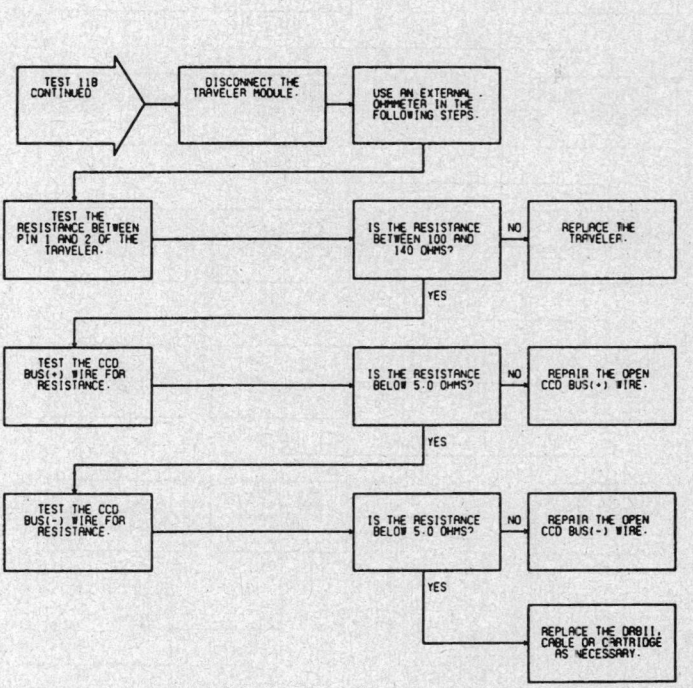

CR9069300348030X

Fig. 94 Test 11B: No Termination Failure (Part 3 of 3). 1993 Acclaim, Spirit & LeBaron

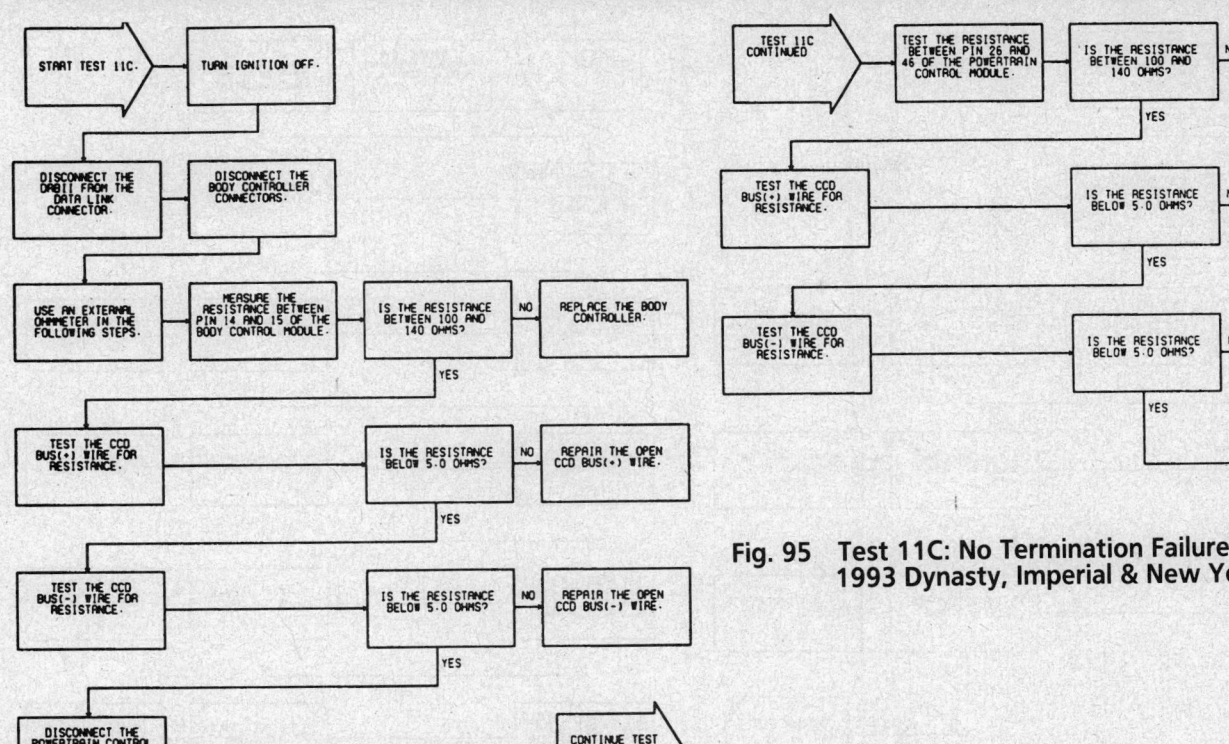

Fig. 95   Test 11C: No Termination Failure (Part 1 of 2).
1993 Dynasty, Imperial & New Yorker

Fig. 95   Test 11C: No Termination Failure (Part 2 of 2).
1993 Dynasty, Imperial & New Yorker

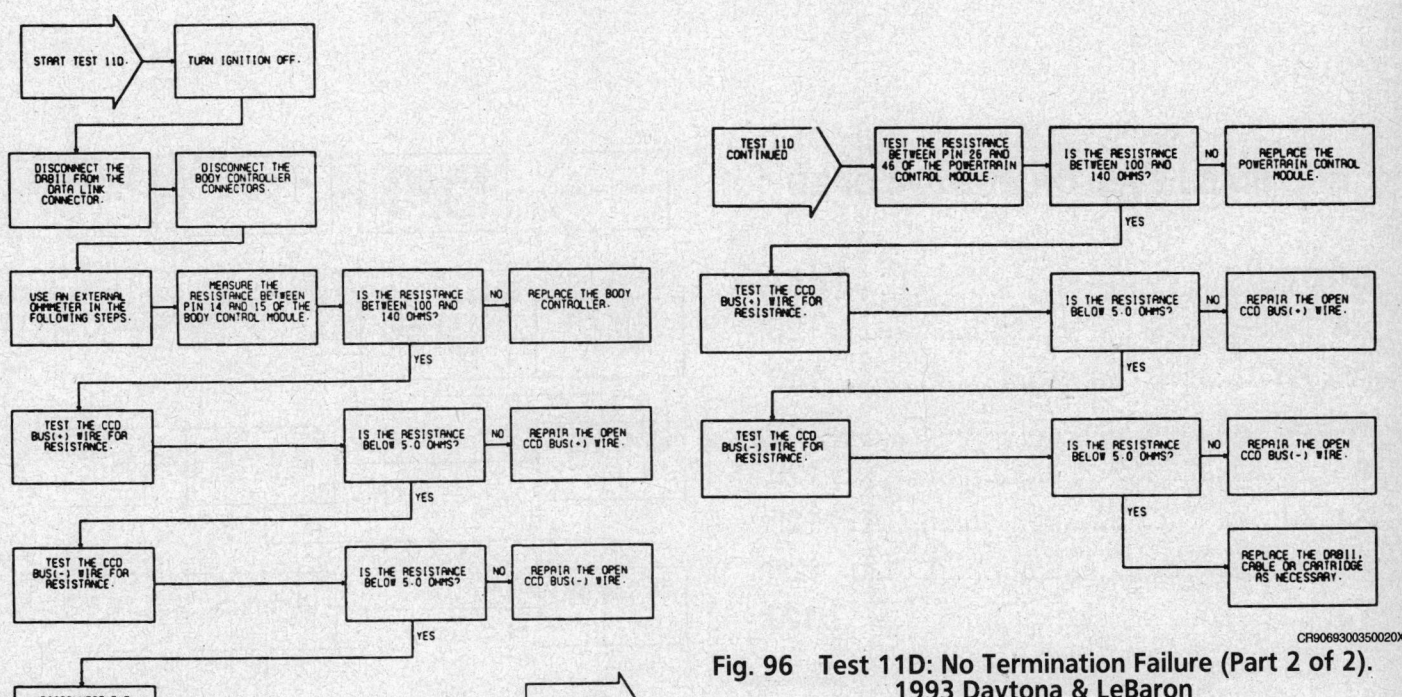

Fig. 96   Test 11D: No Termination Failure (Part 1 of 2).
1993 Daytona & LeBaron

Fig. 96   Test 11D: No Termination Failure (Part 2 of 2).
1993 Daytona & LeBaron

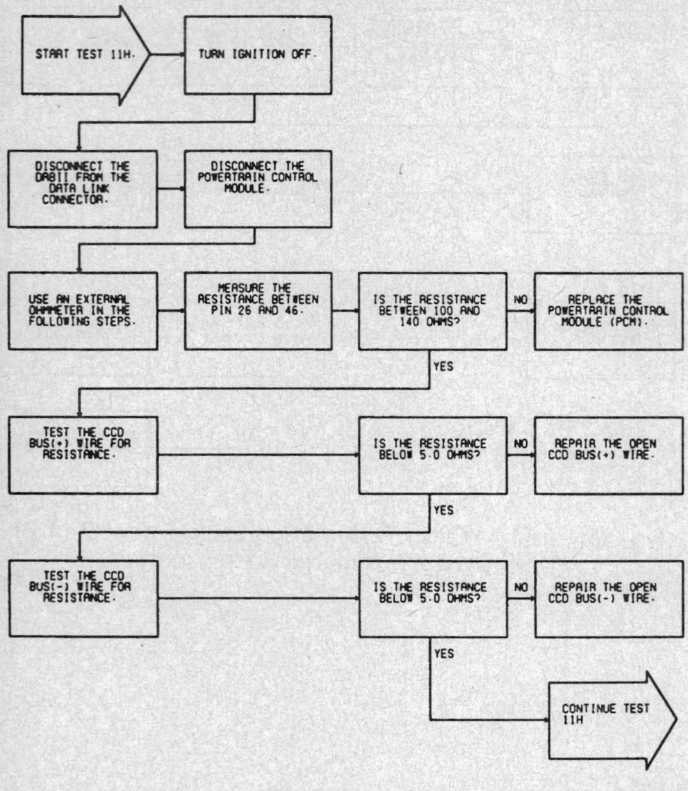

Fig. 97 Test 11H: No Termination Failure (Part 1 of 2). 1993 Shadow & Sundance

START TEST 11H. → TURN IGNITION OFF.

DISCONNECT THE DRB II FROM THE DATA LINK CONNECTOR. → DISCONNECT THE POWERTRAIN CONTROL MODULE.

USE AN EXTERNAL OHMMETER IN THE FOLLOWING STEPS. → MEASURE THE RESISTANCE BETWEEN PIN 26 AND 46. → IS THE RESISTANCE BETWEEN 100 AND 140 OHMS? —NO→ REPLACE THE POWERTRAIN CONTROL MODULE (PCM).

YES

TEST THE CCD BUS(+) WIRE FOR RESISTANCE. → IS THE RESISTANCE BELOW 5.0 OHMS? —NO→ REPAIR THE OPEN CCD BUS(+) WIRE.

YES

TEST THE CCD BUS(-) WIRE FOR RESISTANCE. → IS THE RESISTANCE BELOW 5.0 OHMS? —NO→ REPAIR THE OPEN CCD BUS(-) WIRE.

YES

CONTINUE TEST 11H

CR9069300351010X

Fig. 97 Test 11H: No Termination Failure (Part 2 of 2). 1993 Shadow & Sundance

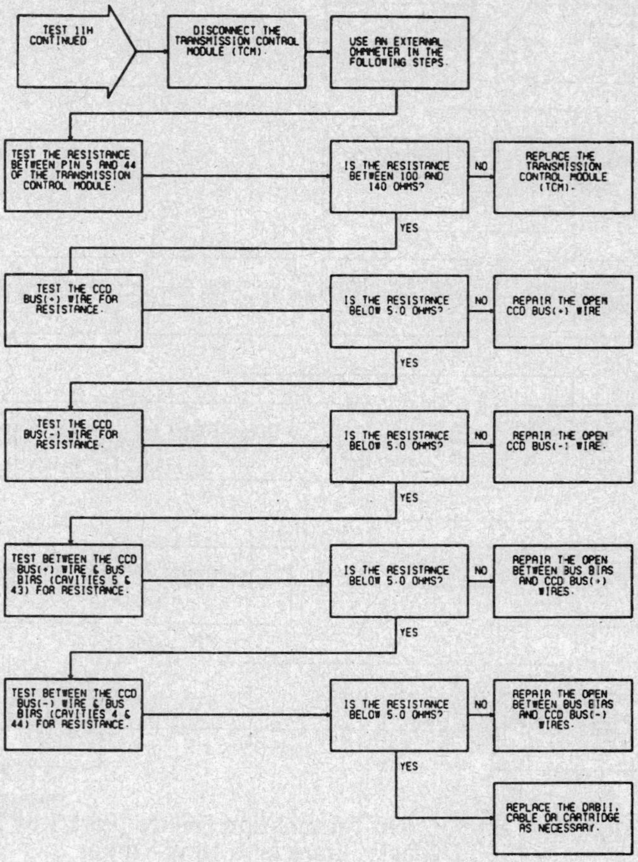

TEST 11H CONTINUED → DISCONNECT THE TRANSMISSION CONTROL MODULE (TCM). → USE AN EXTERNAL OHMMETER IN THE FOLLOWING STEPS.

TEST THE RESISTANCE BETWEEN PIN 5 AND 44 OF THE TRANSMISSION CONTROL MODULE. → IS THE RESISTANCE BETWEEN 100 AND 140 OHMS? —NO→ REPLACE THE TRANSMISSION CONTROL MODULE (TCM).

YES

TEST THE CCD BUS(+) WIRE FOR RESISTANCE. → IS THE RESISTANCE BELOW 5.0 OHMS? —NO→ REPAIR THE OPEN CCD BUS(+) WIRE

YES

TEST THE CCD BUS(-) WIRE FOR RESISTANCE. → IS THE RESISTANCE BELOW 5.0 OHMS? —NO→ REPAIR THE OPEN CCD BUS(-) WIRE.

YES

TEST BETWEEN THE CCD BUS(+) WIRE & BUS BIAS (CAVITIES 5 & 43) FOR RESISTANCE. → IS THE RESISTANCE BELOW 5.0 OHMS? —NO→ REPAIR THE OPEN BETWEEN BUS BIAS AND CCD BUS(+) WIRES.

YES

TEST BETWEEN THE CCD BUS(-) WIRE & BUS BIAS (CAVITIES 4 & 44) FOR RESISTANCE. → IS THE RESISTANCE BELOW 5.0 OHMS? —NO→ REPAIR THE OPEN BETWEEN BUS BIAS AND CCD BUS(-) WIRES.

YES

REPLACE THE DRB II, CABLE OR CARTRIDGE AS NECESSARY.

CR9069300351020X

BUS BIAS LEVEL OR BUS (+/-) OPEN

BODY	TEST
AA	12B
AC, AY	12C
AG, AJ	12D
AS	12E
XJ, ZJ	12F
AP	12H
YJ	12J

CR9069300352000X

Fig. 98 Test 12A: Bus Bias Level Or Bus (+/-) Open Failure. 1993

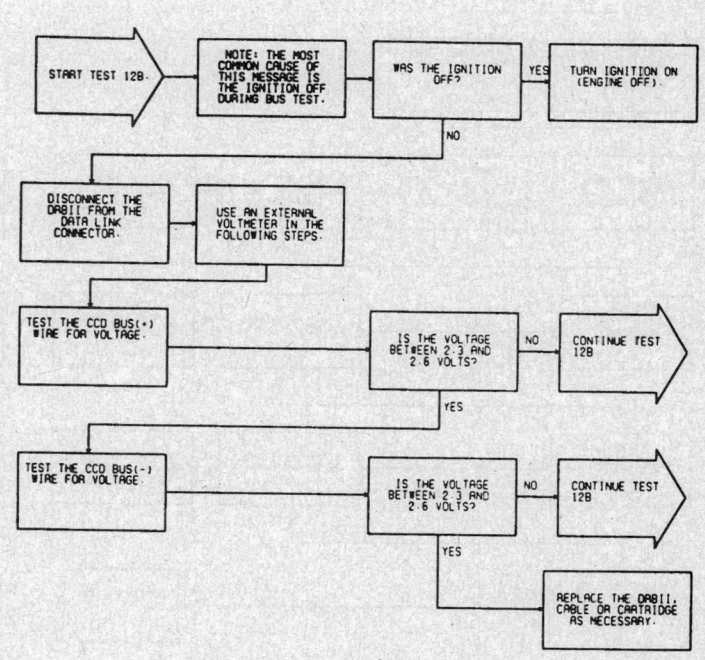

START TEST 12B → NOTE: THE MOST COMMON CAUSE OF THIS MESSAGE IS THE IGNITION OFF DURING BUS TEST. → WAS THE IGNITION OFF? —YES→ TURN IGNITION ON (ENGINE OFF).

NO

DISCONNECT THE DRB II FROM THE DATA LINK CONNECTOR. → USE AN EXTERNAL VOLTMETER IN THE FOLLOWING STEPS.

TEST THE CCD BUS(+) WIRE FOR VOLTAGE. → IS THE VOLTAGE BETWEEN 2.3 AND 2.6 VOLTS? —NO→ CONTINUE TEST 12B

YES

TEST THE CCD BUS(-) WIRE FOR VOLTAGE. → IS THE VOLTAGE BETWEEN 2.3 AND 2.6 VOLTS? —NO→ CONTINUE TEST 12B

YES

REPLACE THE DRB II, CABLE OR CARTRIDGE AS NECESSARY.

CR9069300353010X

Fig. 99 Test 12B: Bus Bias Level Or Bus (+/-) Open Failure (Part 1 of 4). 1993 Acclaim, Spirit & LeBaron

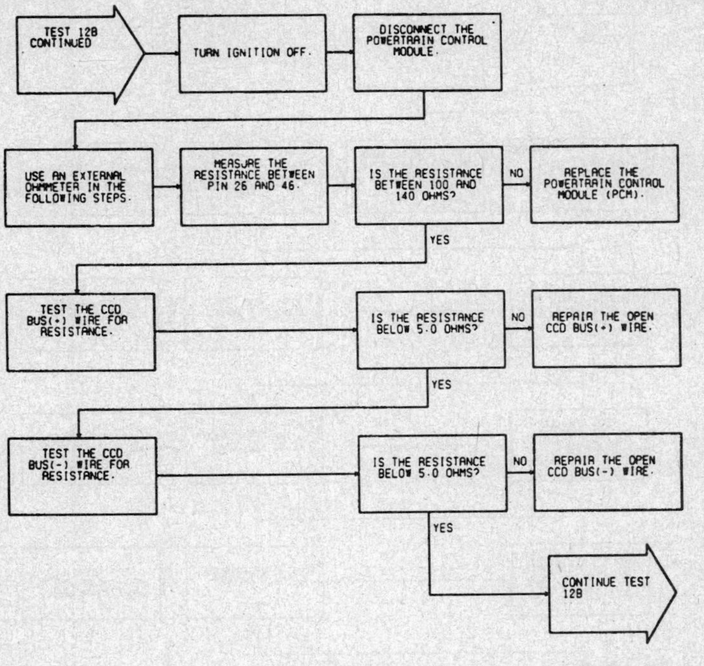

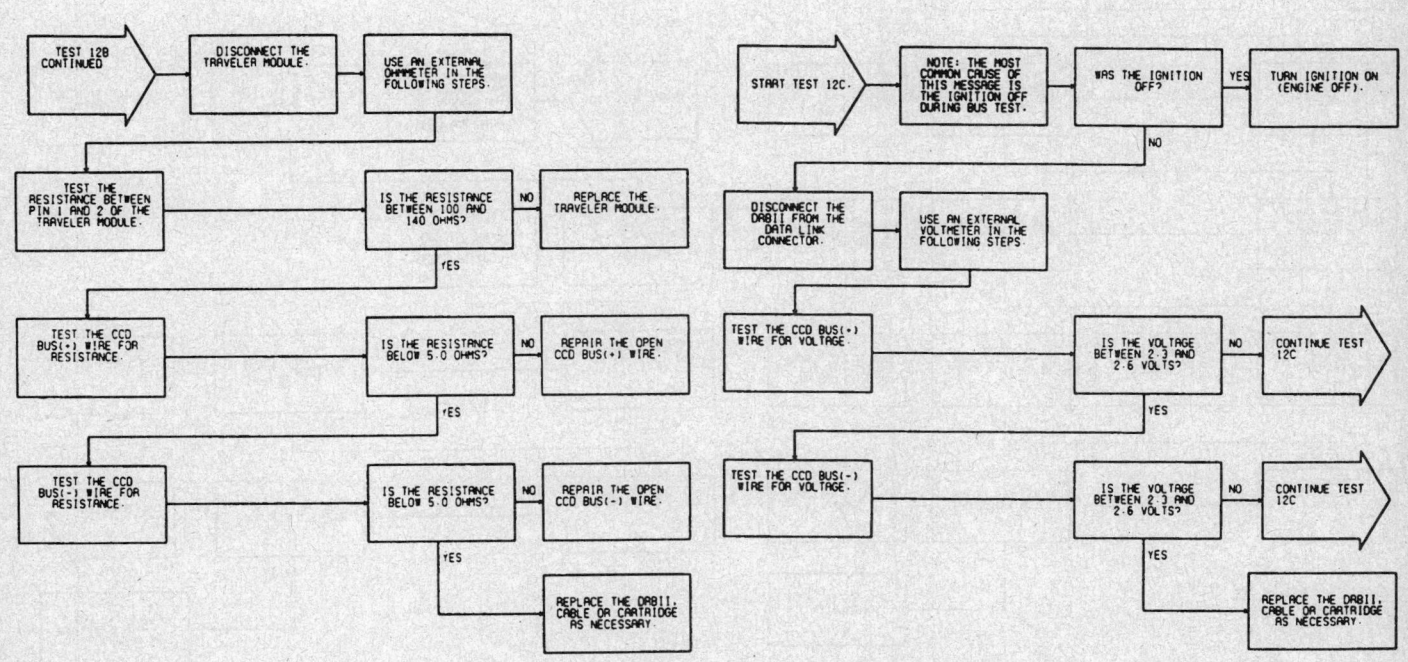

Fig. 99   Test 12B: Bus Bias Level Or Bus (+ /-) Open Failure (Part 2 of 4). 1993 Acclaim, Spirit & LeBaron

CR9069300353020X

Fig. 99   Test 12B: Bus Bias Level Or Bus (+ /-) Open Failure (Part 3 of 4). 1993 Acclaim, Spirit & LeBaron

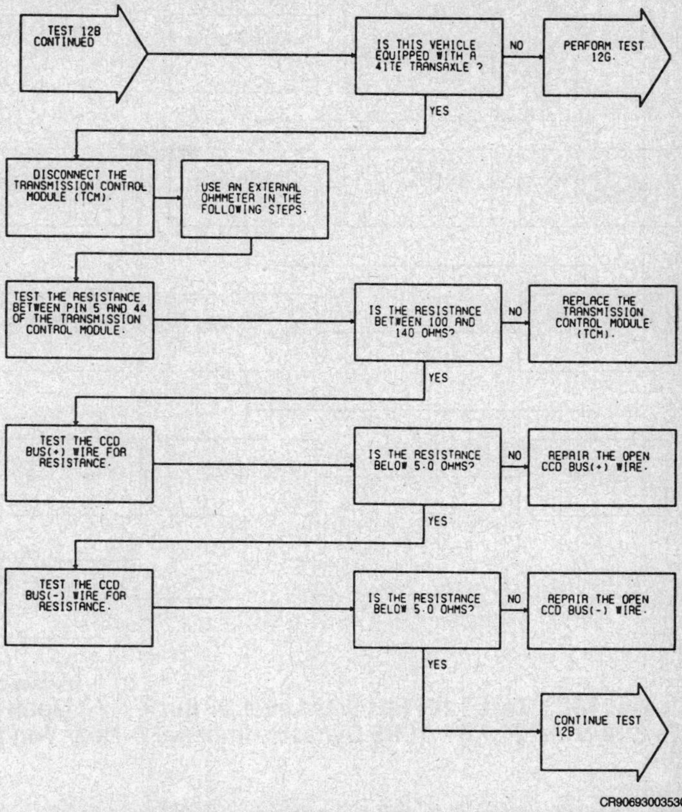

CR9069300353030X

Fig. 99   Test 12B: Bus Bias Level Or Bus (+ /-) Open Failure (Part 4 of 4). 1993 Acclaim, Spirit & LeBaron

CR9069300353040X

Fig. 100   Test 12C: Bus Bias Level Or Bus (+ /-) Open Failure (Part 1 of 4). 1993 Dynasty, Imperial & New Yorker

CR9069300354010X

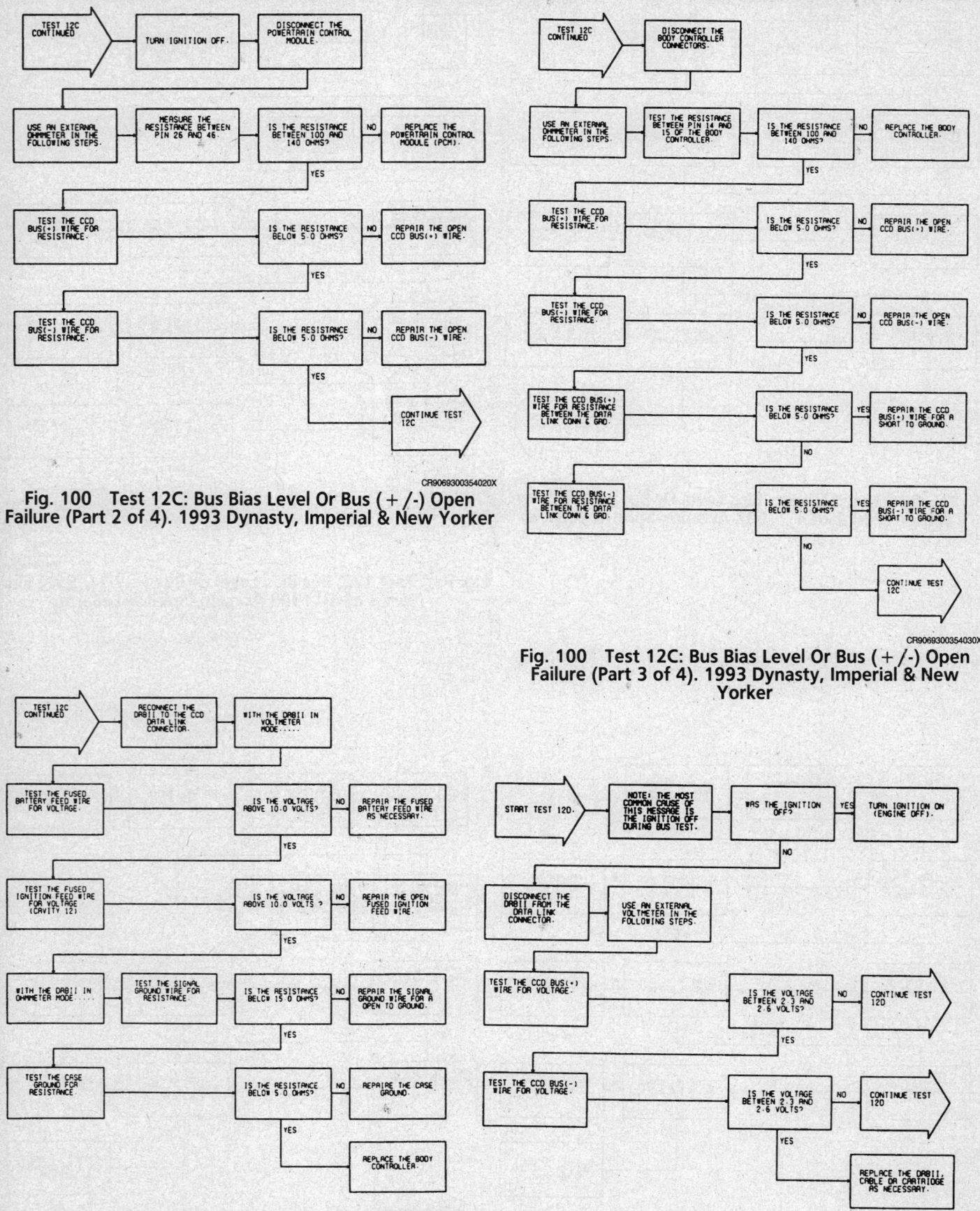

Fig. 100 Test 12C: Bus Bias Level Or Bus (+ /-) Open Failure (Part 2 of 4). 1993 Dynasty, Imperial & New Yorker

Fig. 100   Test 12C: Bus Bias Level Or Bus (+ /-) Open Failure (Part 3 of 4). 1993 Dynasty, Imperial & New Yorker

Fig. 100   Test 12C: Bus Bias Level Or Bus (+ /-) Open Failure (Part 4 of 4). 1993 Dynasty, Imperial & New Yorker

Fig. 101   Test 12D: Bus Bias Level Or Bus (+ /-) Open Failure (Part 1 of 4). 1993 Daytona & LeBaron

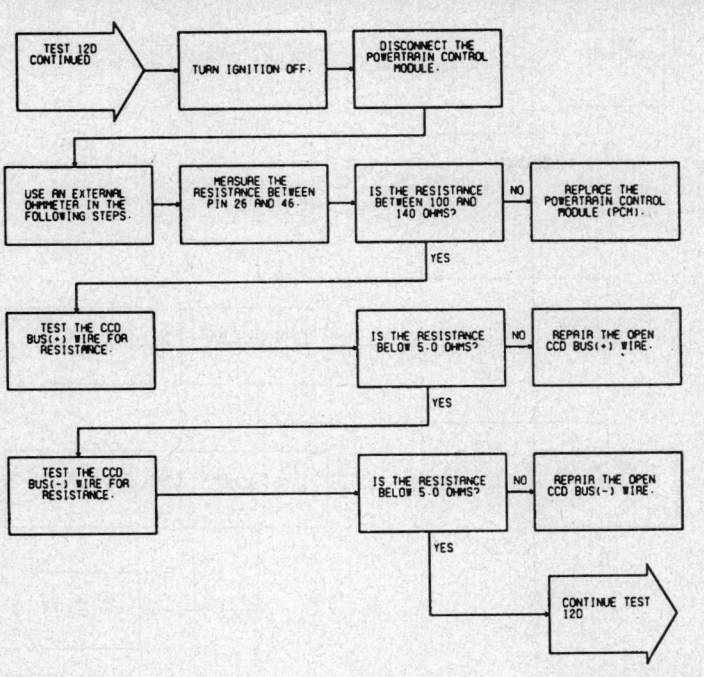

Fig. 101 Test 12D: Bus Bias Level Or Bus (+/-) Open Failure (Part 2 of 4). 1993 Daytona & LeBaron

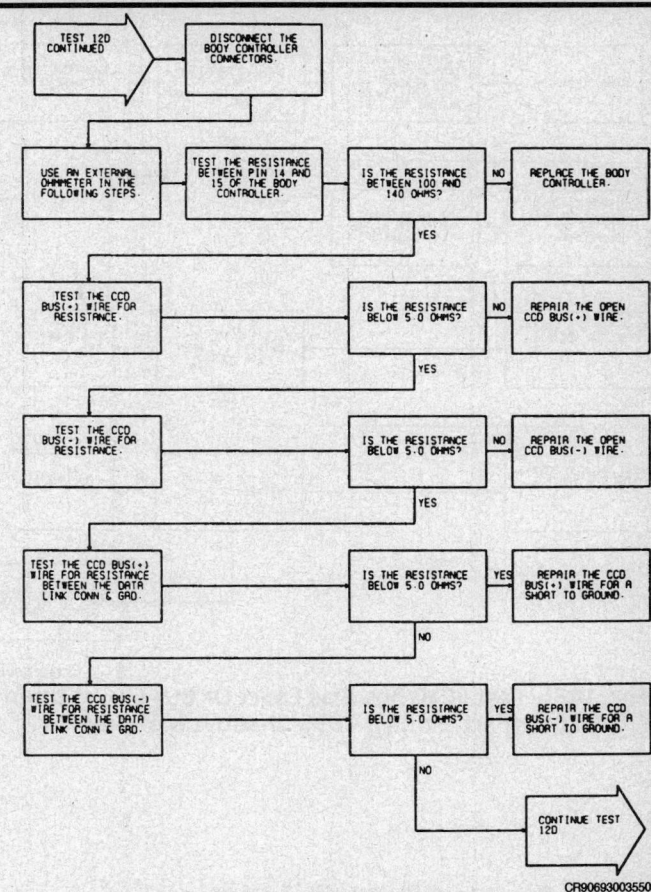

Fig. 101 Test 12D: Bus Bias Level Or Bus (+/-) Open Failure (Part 3 of 4). 1993 Daytona & LeBaron

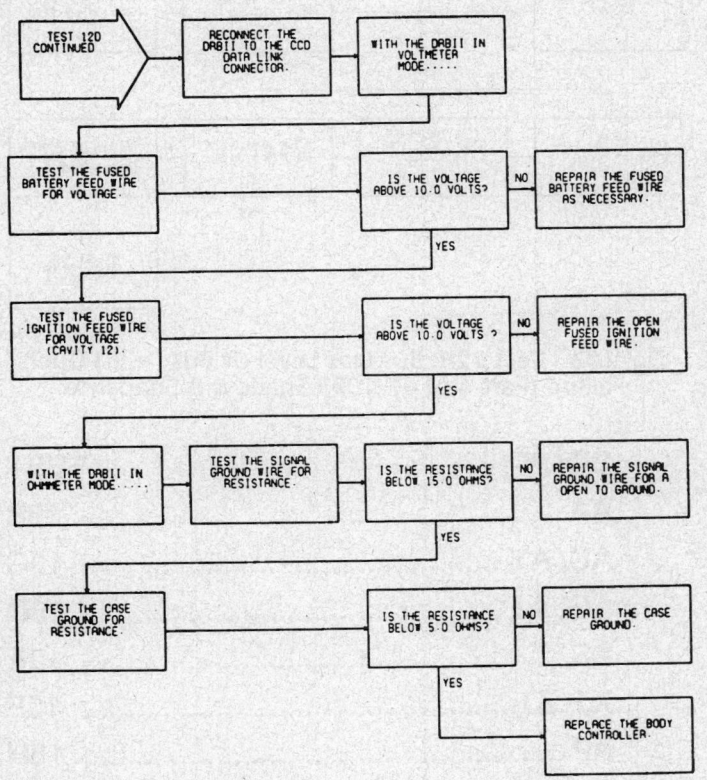

Fig. 101 Test 12D: Bus Bias Level Or Bus (+/-) Open Failure (Part 4 of 4). 1993 Daytona & LeBaron

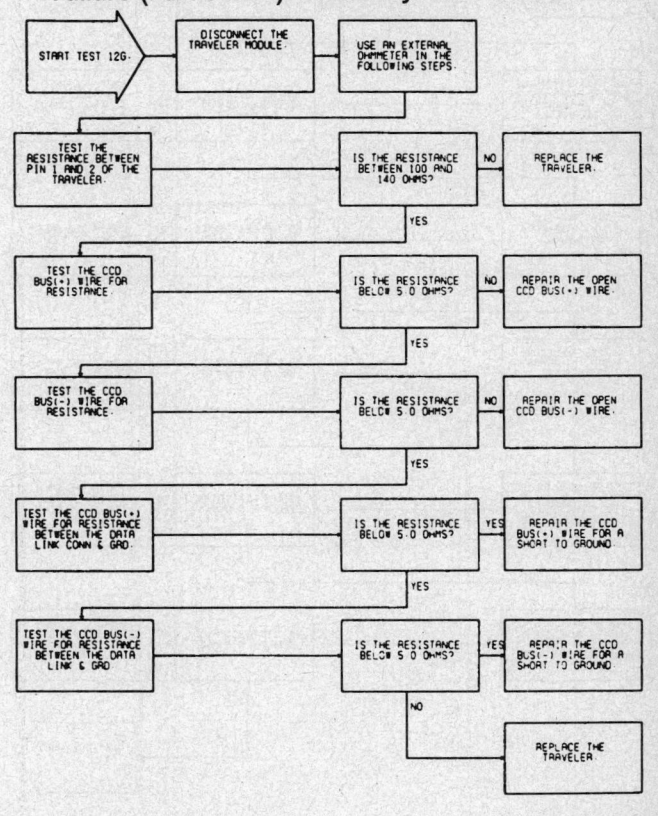

Fig. 102 Test 12G: Bus Bias Level Or Bus (+/-) Open Failure. 1993

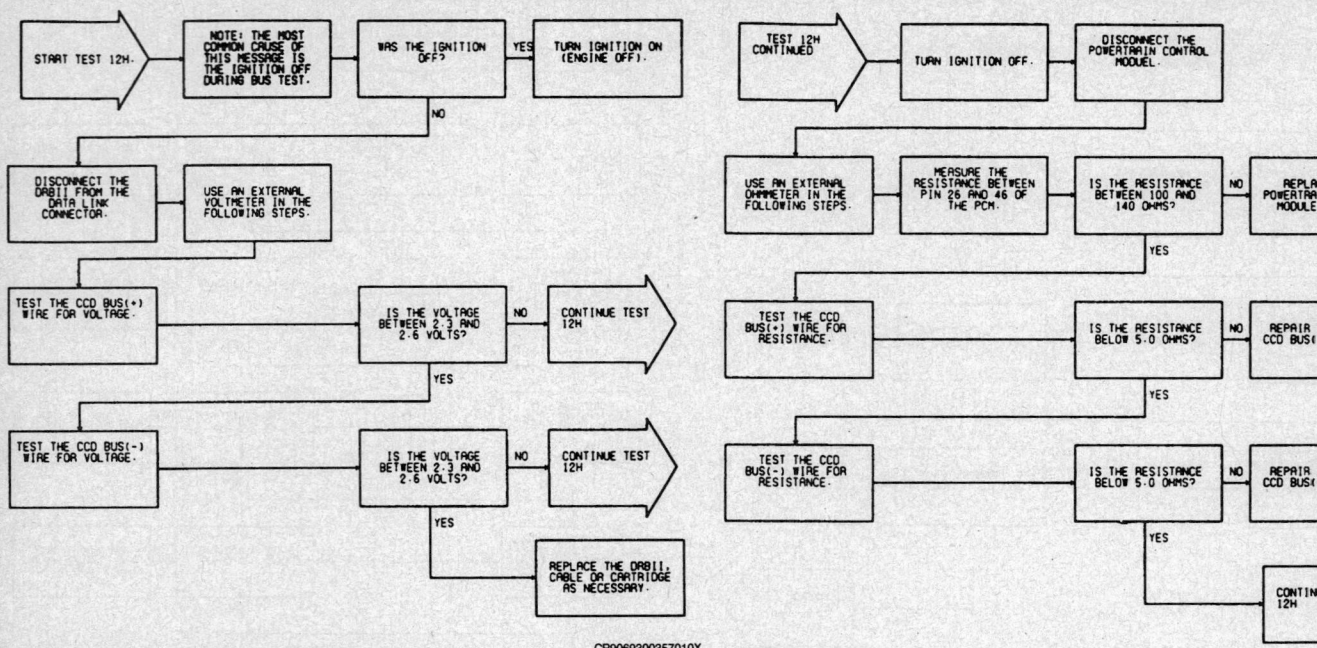

Fig. 103   Test 12H: Bus Bias Level Or Bus (+ /-) Open
Failure (Part 1 of 4). 1993 Shadow & Sundance

CR9069300357010X

Fig. 103   Test 12H: Bus Bias Level Or Bus (+ /-) Open
Failure (Part 2 of 4). 1993 Shadow & Sundance

CR9069300357020X

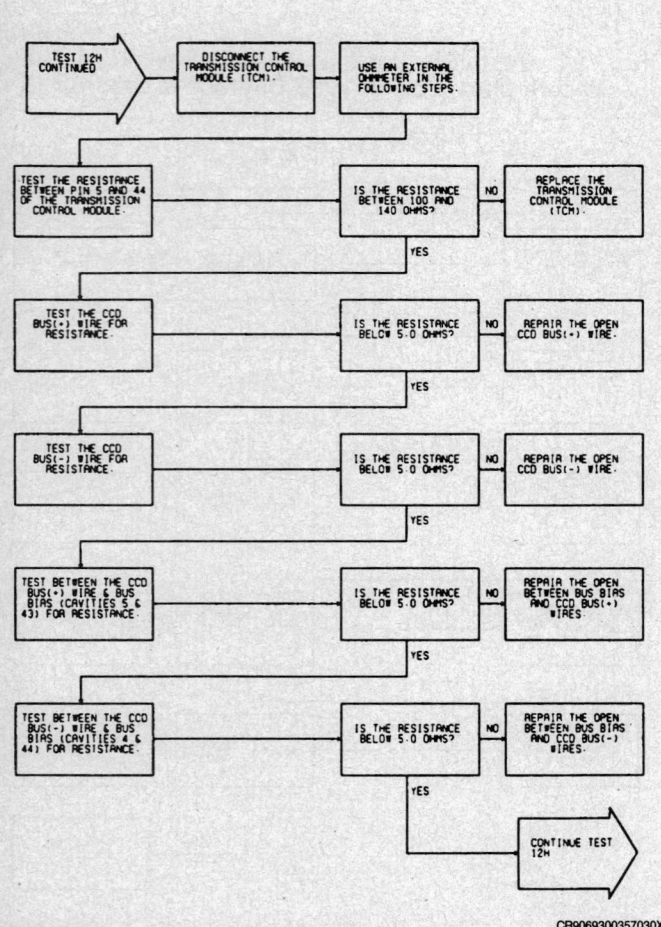

Fig. 103   Test 12H: Bus Bias Level Or Bus (+ /-) Open
Failure (Part 3 of 4). 1993 Shadow & Sundance

CR9069300357030X

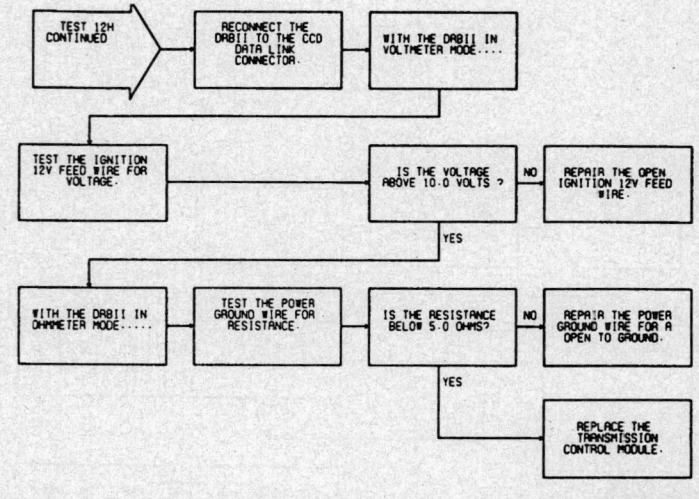

Fig. 103   Test 12H: Bus Bias Level Or Bus (+ /-) Open
Failure (Part 4 of 4). 1993 Shadow & Sundance

CR9069300357040X

BODY	TEST
AA	13B
AC, AY	13C
AG, AJ	13D
AS	13E
XJ, ZJ	13F
AP	13H
YJ	13J

Fig. 104   Test 13A: No Bus Bias Failure. 1993

CR9069300358000X

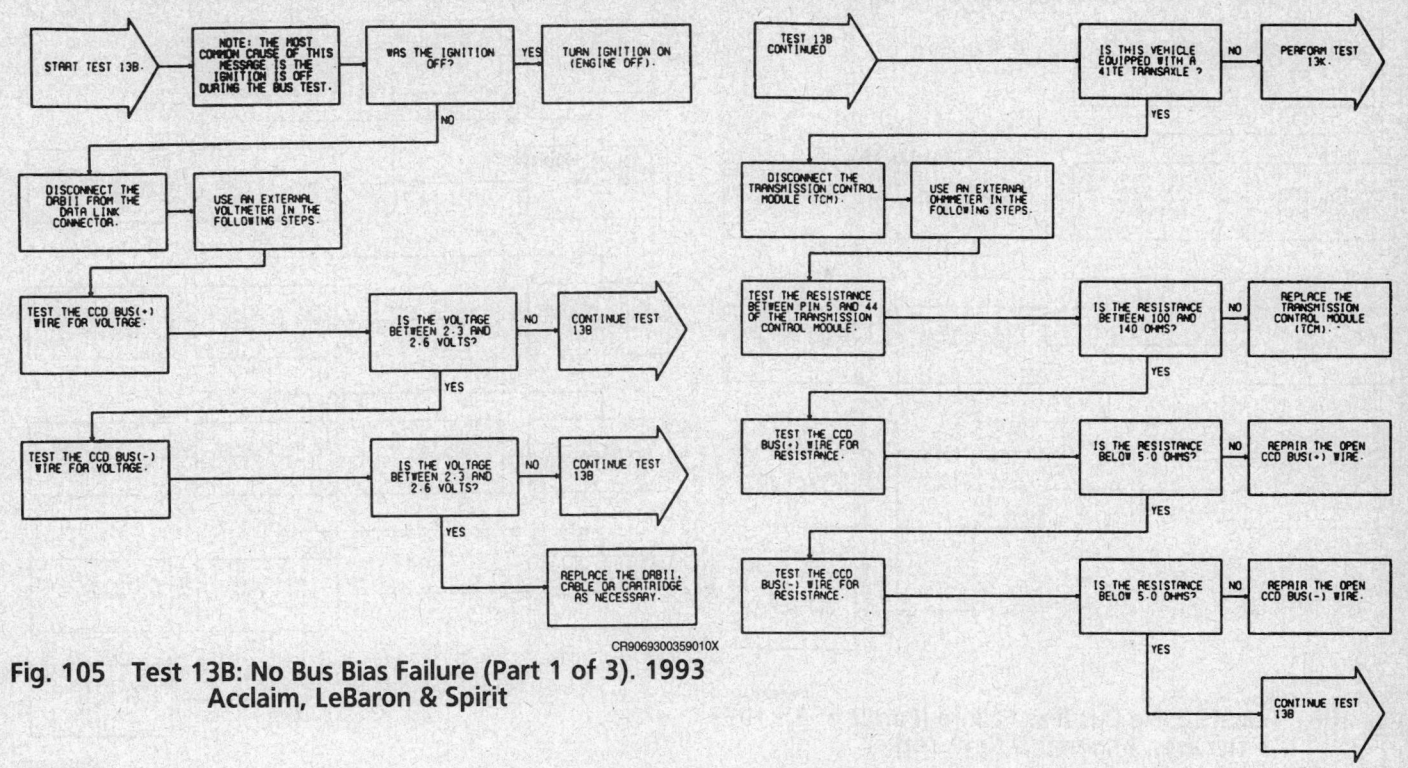

Fig. 105   Test 13B: No Bus Bias Failure (Part 1 of 3). 1993 Acclaim, LeBaron & Spirit

Fig. 105   Test 13B: No Bus Bias Failure (Part 2 of 3). 1993 Acclaim, LeBaron & Spirit

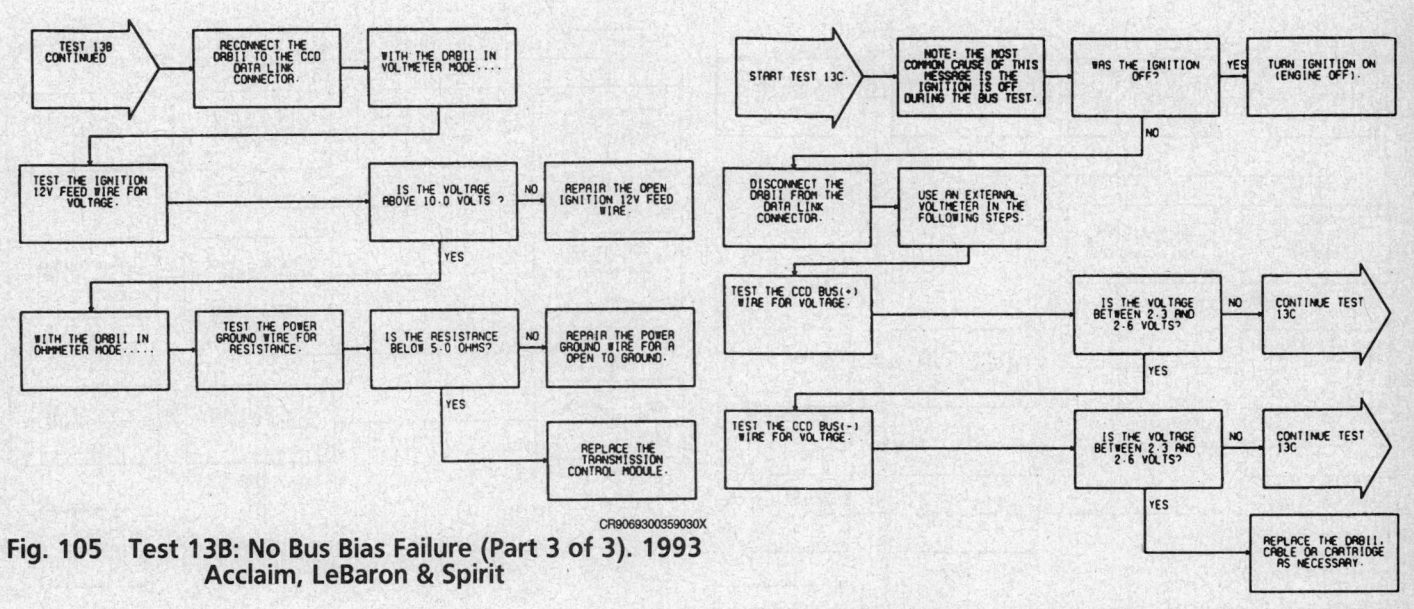

Fig. 105   Test 13B: No Bus Bias Failure (Part 3 of 3). 1993 Acclaim, LeBaron & Spirit

Fig. 106   Test 13C: No Bus Bias Failure (Part 1 of 3). 1993 Dynasty, Imperial & New Yorker

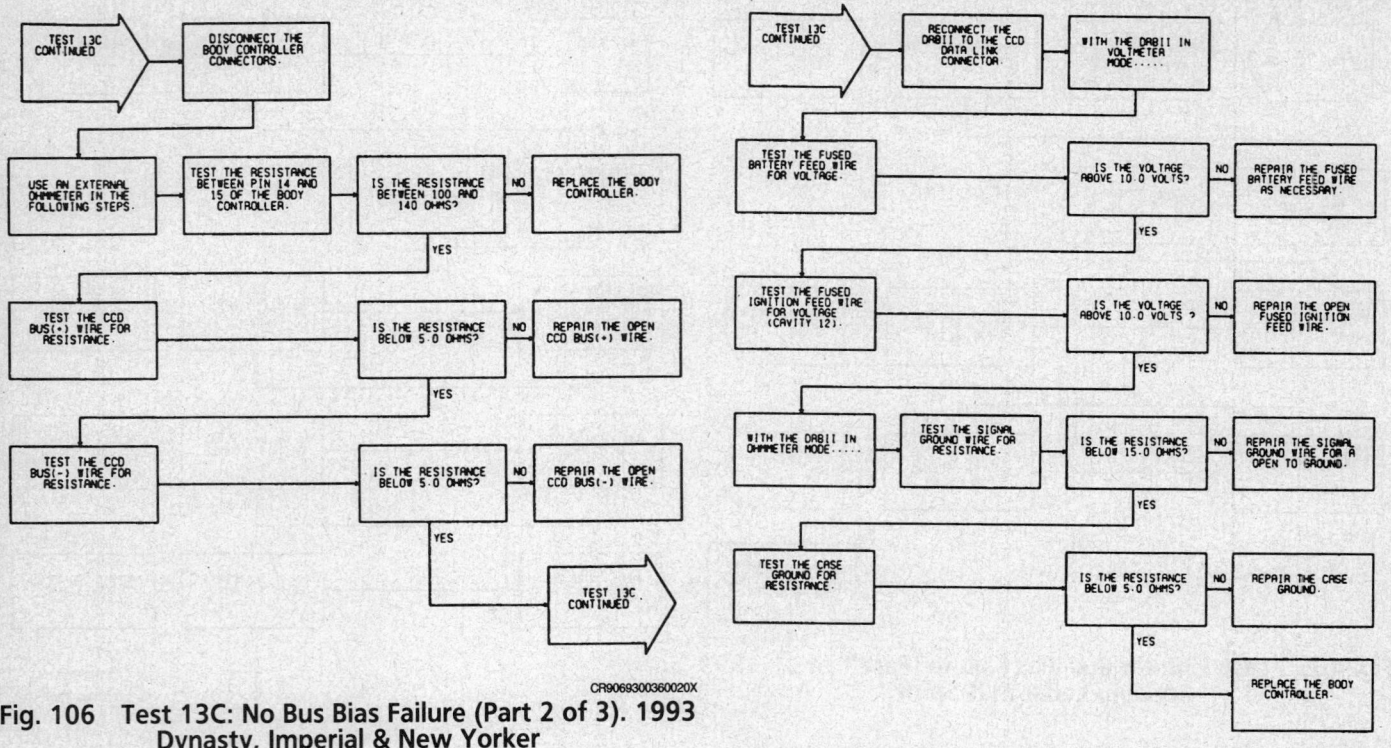

Fig. 106   Test 13C: No Bus Bias Failure (Part 2 of 3). 1993 Dynasty, Imperial & New Yorker

Fig. 106   Test 13C: No Bus Bias Failure (Part 3 of 3). 1993 Dynasty, Imperial & New Yorker

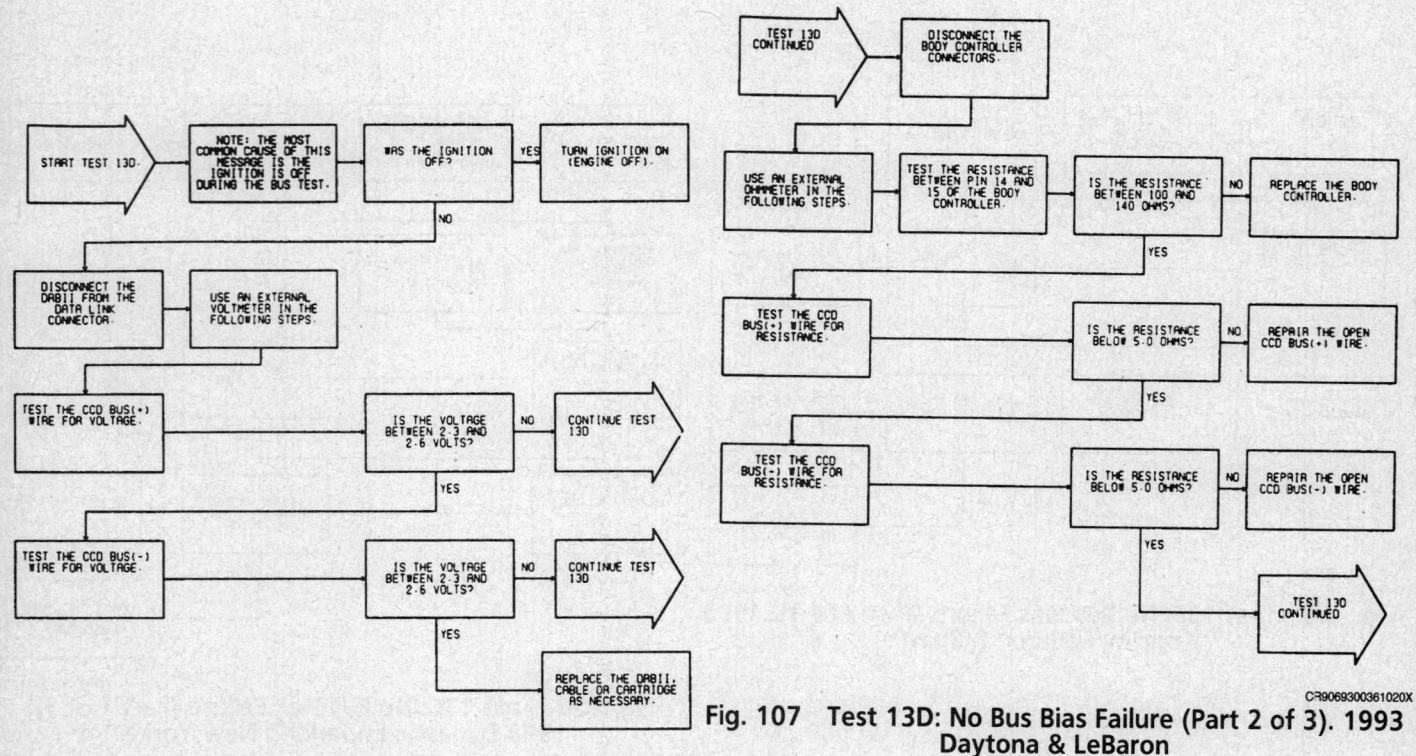

Fig. 107   Test 13D: No Bus Bias Failure (Part 2 of 3). 1993 Daytona & LeBaron

Fig. 107   Test 13D: No Bus Bias Failure (Part 1 of 3). 1993 Daytona & LeBaron

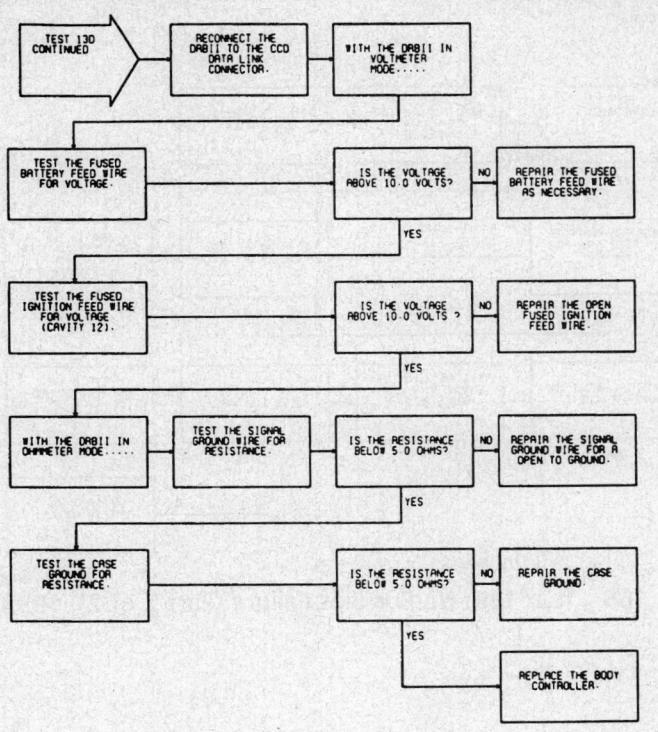

Fig. 107   Test 13D: No Bus Bias Failure (Part 3 of 3).
1993 Daytona & LeBaron

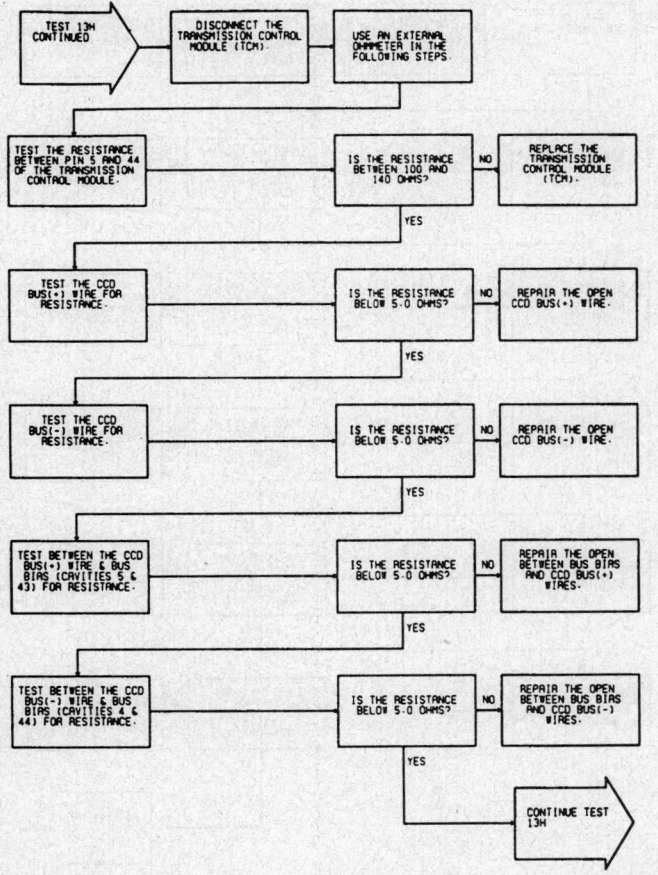

Fig. 108   Test 13H: No Bus Bias Failure (Part 2 of 3).
1993 Shadow & Sundance

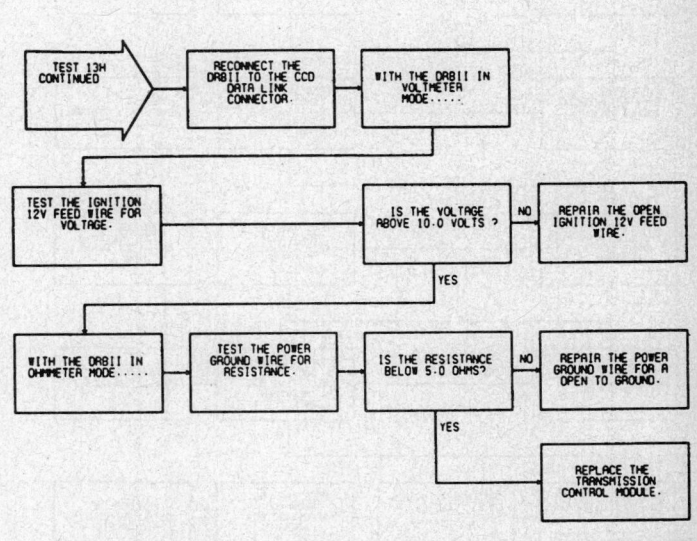

Fig. 108   Test 13H: No Bus Bias Failure (Part 1 of 3). 1993
Shadow & Sundance

Fig. 108   Test 13H: No Bus Bias Failure (Part 3 of 3). 1993
Shadow & Sundance

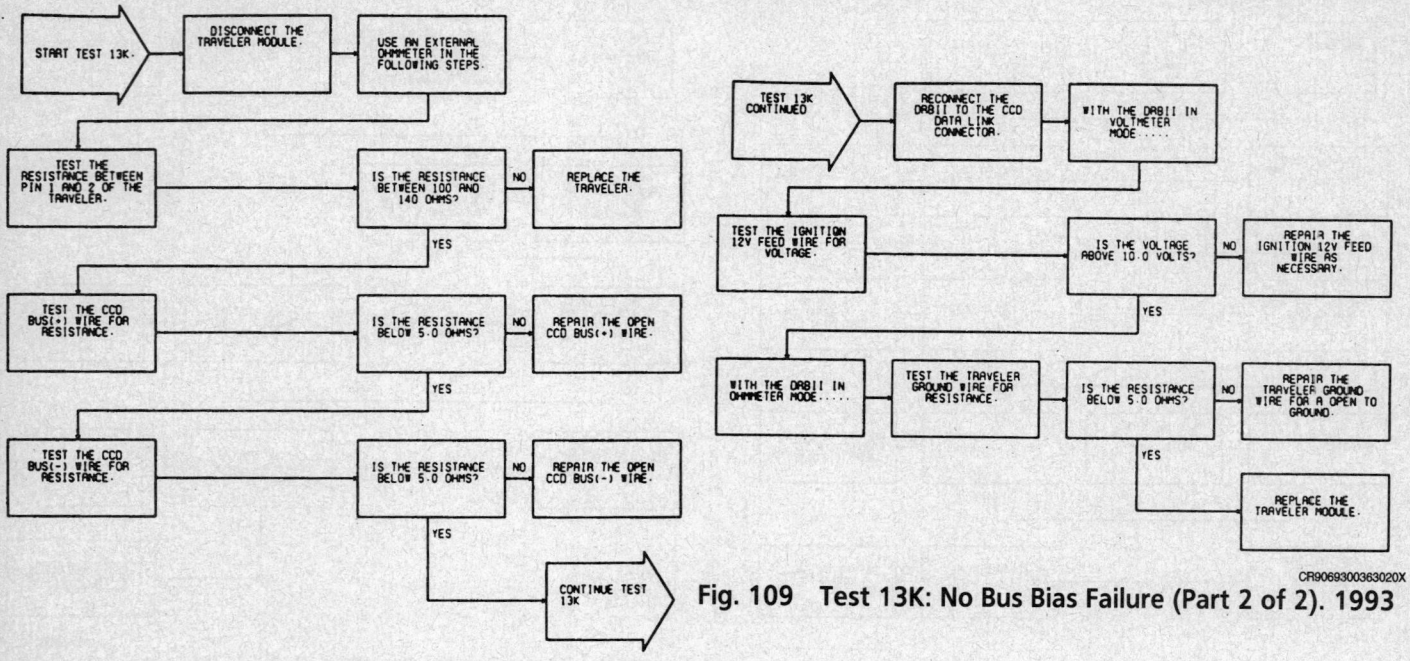

CR9069300363010X

Fig. 109   Test 13K: No Bus Bias Failure (Part 1 of 2). 1993

CR9069300363020X

Fig. 109   Test 13K: No Bus Bias Failure (Part 2 of 2). 1993

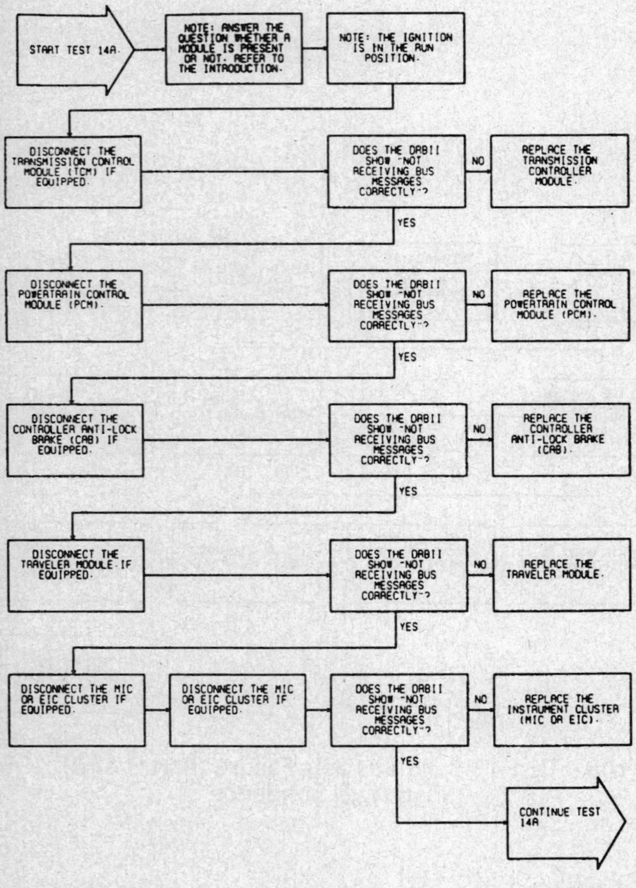

CR9069300364010X

Fig. 110   Test 14A: Not Receiving Bus Messages Correctly Failure (Part 1 of 3). 1993

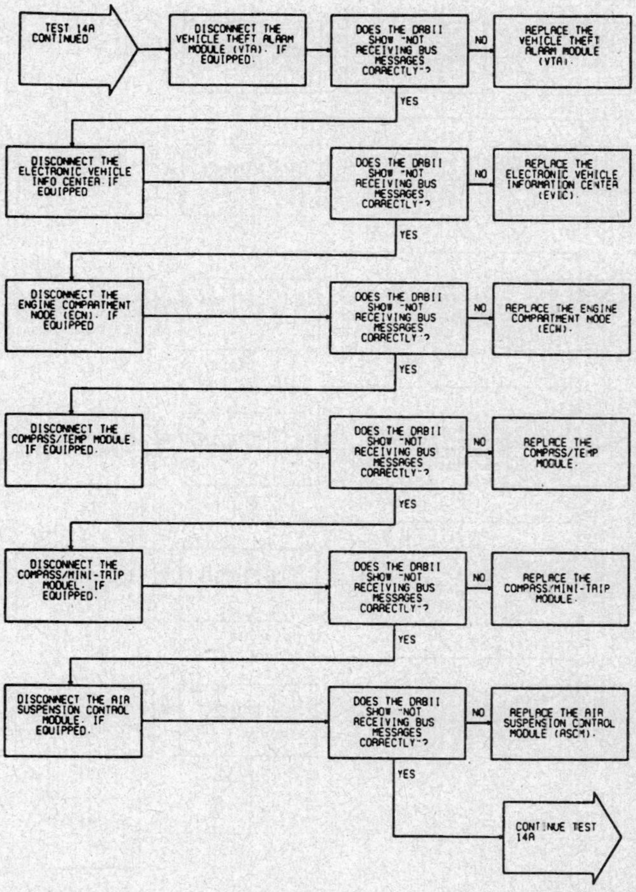

CR9069300364020X

Fig. 110   Test 14A: Not Receiving Bus Messages Correctly Failure (Part 2 of 3). 1993

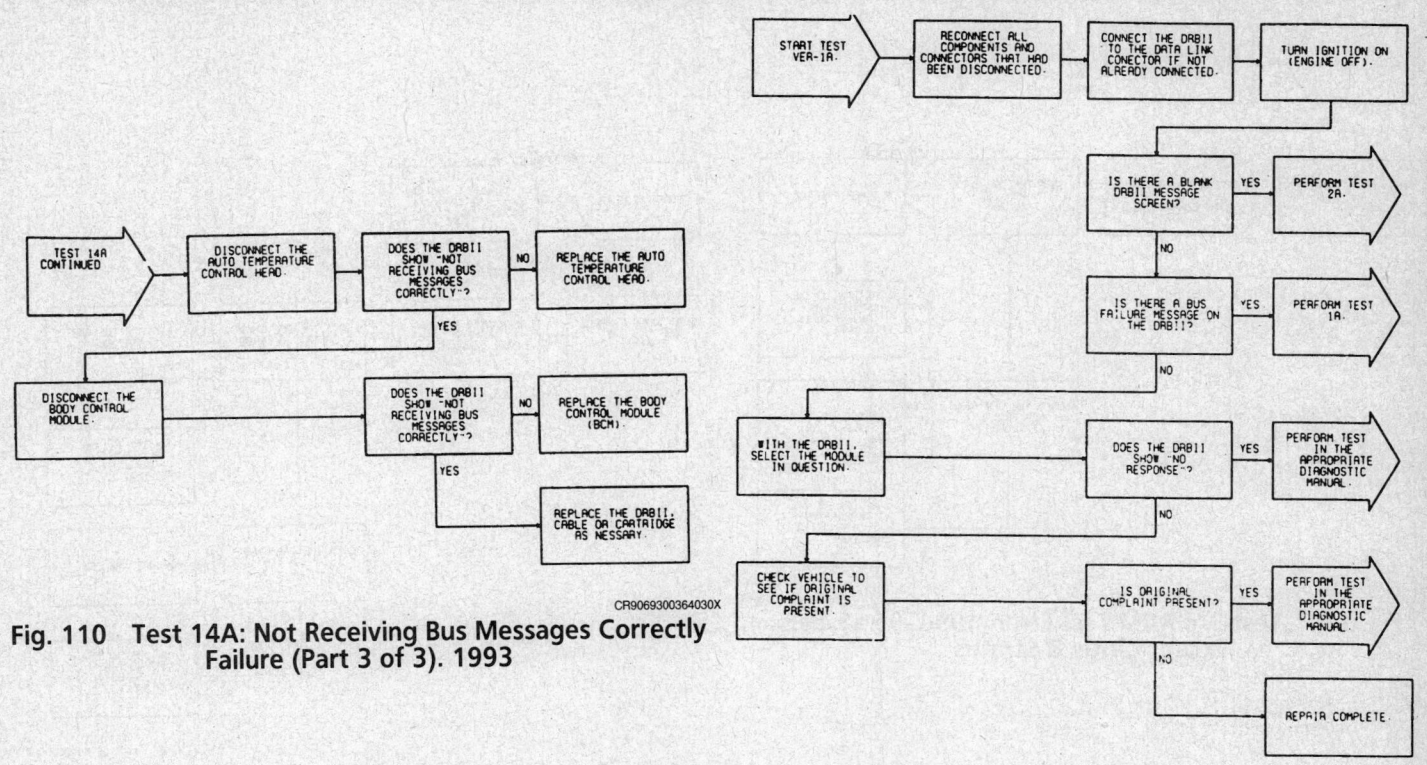

Fig. 110   Test 14A: Not Receiving Bus Messages Correctly Failure (Part 3 of 3). 1993

CR9069300364030X

Fig. 111   Test VER-1: Verification Test. 1993

CR9069300365000X

DRB FAILURE MESSAGES

FAILURE MESSAGES	TEST NO.
BLANK SCREEN ON THE DRB	2A
RAM TEST FAILURE	3A
CARTRIDGE ERROR	4A
KEY PAD TEST FAILURE	5A
LOW OR HIGH BATTERY	6A

BUS FAILURE MESSAGES

BUS FAILURE MESSAGES	TEST NO.
SHORT TO BATTERY	7A
SHORT TO 5 VOLTS	8A
SHORT TO GROUND	9A
BUS (+) & BUS (-) SHORTED TOGETHER	10A
NO TERMINATION	11A
BUS BIAS LEVEL TOO LOW	12A
BUS BIAS LEVEL TOO HIGH	12A
NO BUS BIAS	13A
BUS (+) OPEN	12A
BUS (-) OPEN	12A
BUS (+) & (-) OPEN	12A
NOT RECEIVING BUS MESSAGES CORRECTLY	14A

CR9069400366000X

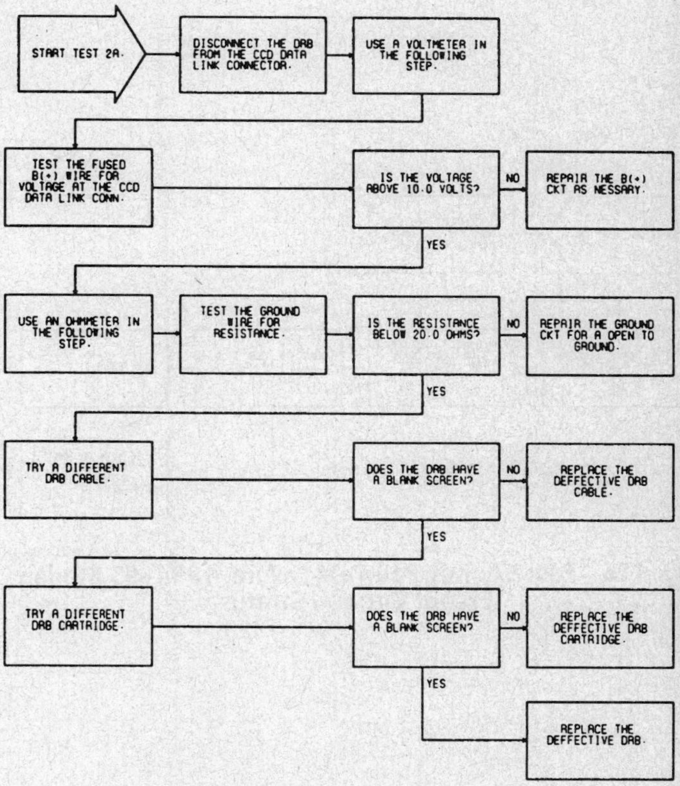

CR9069400367000X

Fig. 112   Test 1A: Bus Failure Messages. 1994–95 Models Except Cirrus & Stratus

Fig. 113   Test 2A: Blank Screen On DRB. 1994–95 Models Except Cirrus & Stratus

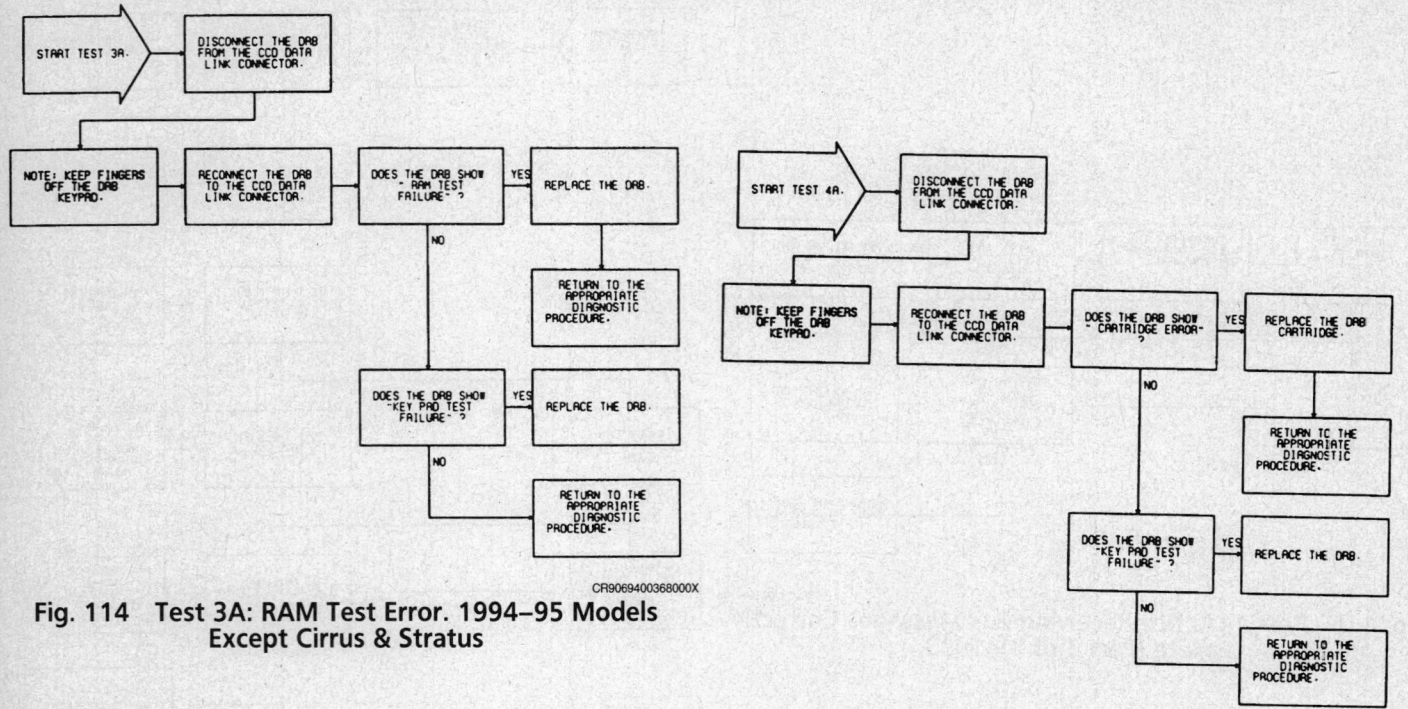

Fig. 114   Test 3A: RAM Test Error. 1994–95 Models Except Cirrus & Stratus

Fig. 115   Test 4A: Cartridge Failure Error. 1994–95 Models Except Cirrus & Stratus

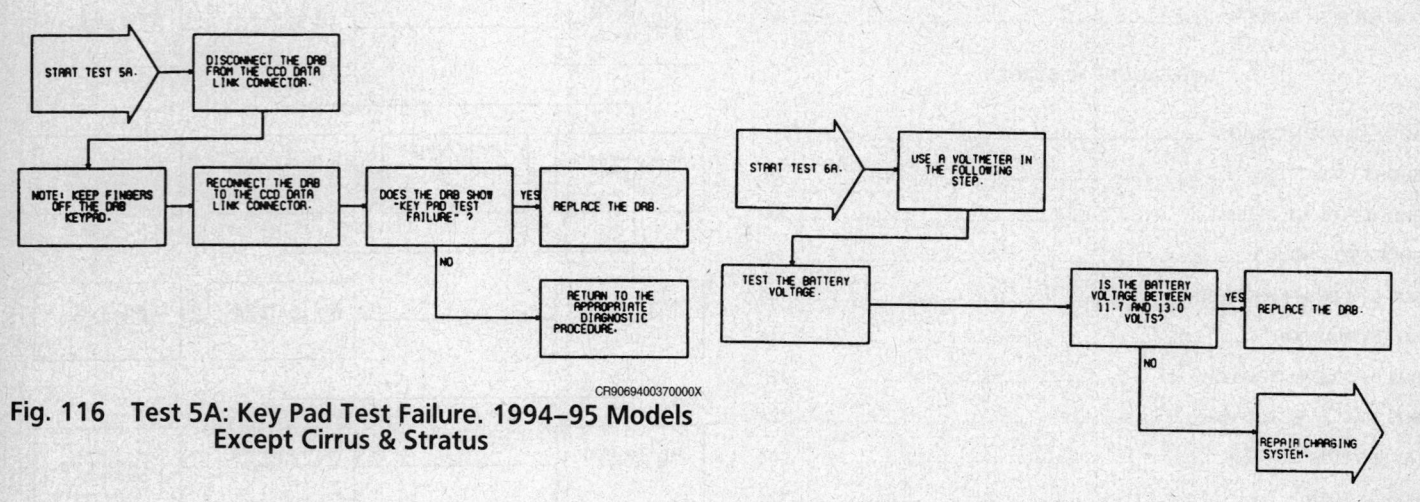

Fig. 116   Test 5A: Key Pad Test Failure. 1994–95 Models Except Cirrus & Stratus

Fig. 117   Test 6A: Testing For Low Or High Battery. 1994–95 Models Except Cirrus & Stratus

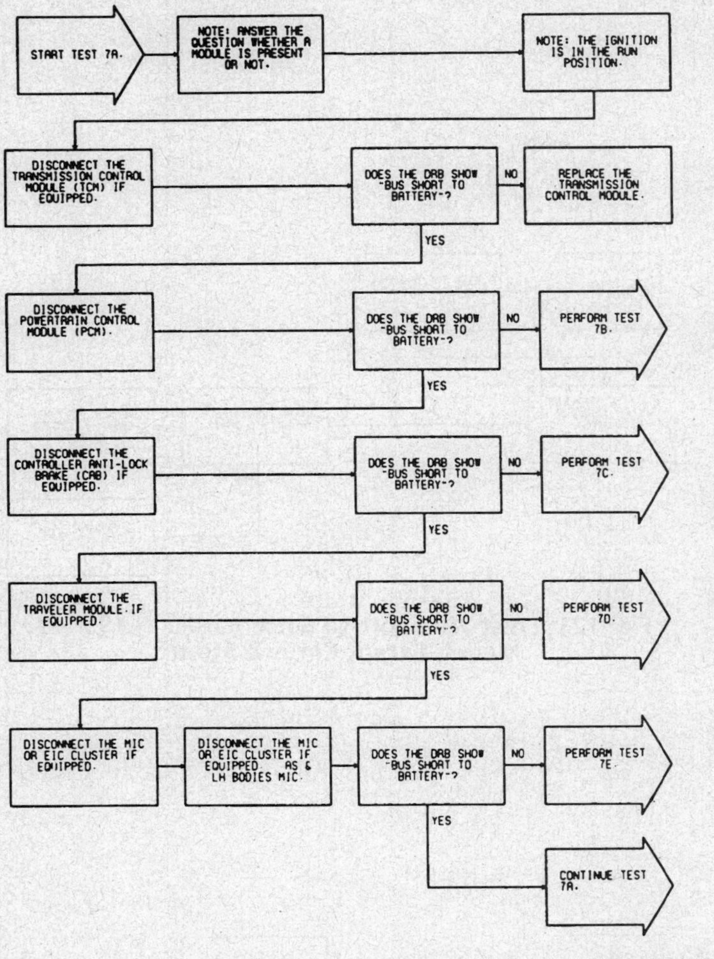

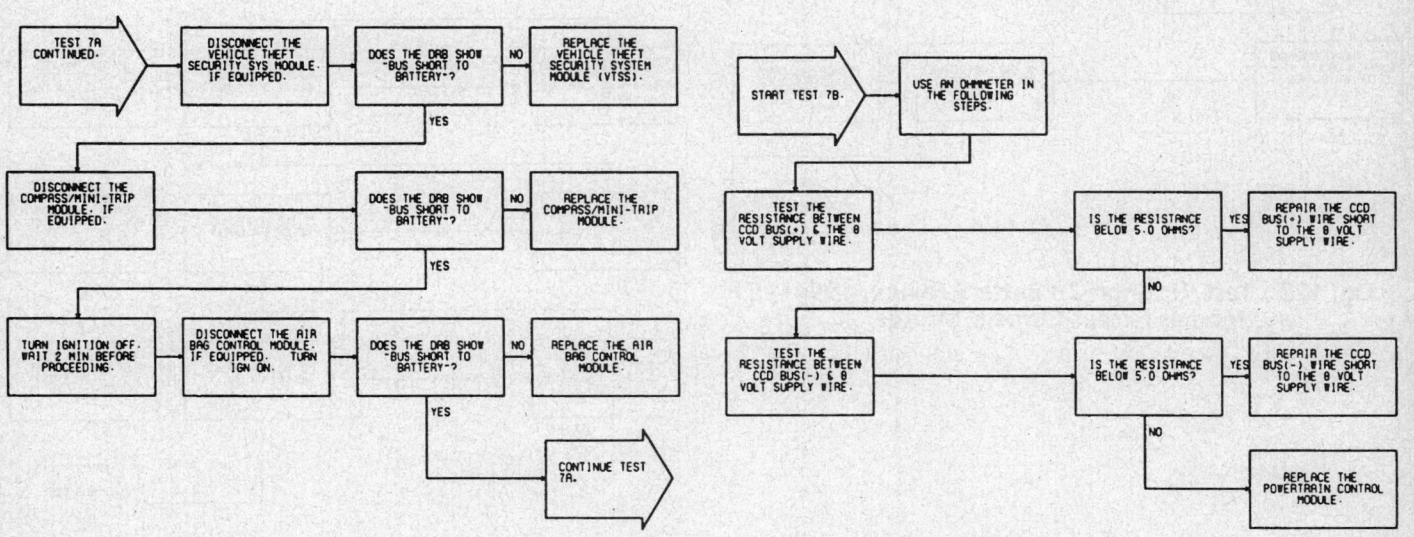

CR9069400372010X

Fig. 118 Test 7A: Short To Battery Failure (Part 1 of 3). 1994–95 Models Except Cirrus & Stratus

CR9069400372030X

Fig. 118 Test 7A: Short To Battery Failure (Part 3 of 3). 1994–95 Models Except Cirrus & Stratus

CR9069400372020X

Fig. 118 Test 7A: Short To Battery Failure (Part 2 of 3). 1994–95 Models Except Cirrus & Stratus

CR9069400373000X

Fig. 119 Test 7B: Short To Battery Failure. 1994–95 Models Except Cirrus & Stratus

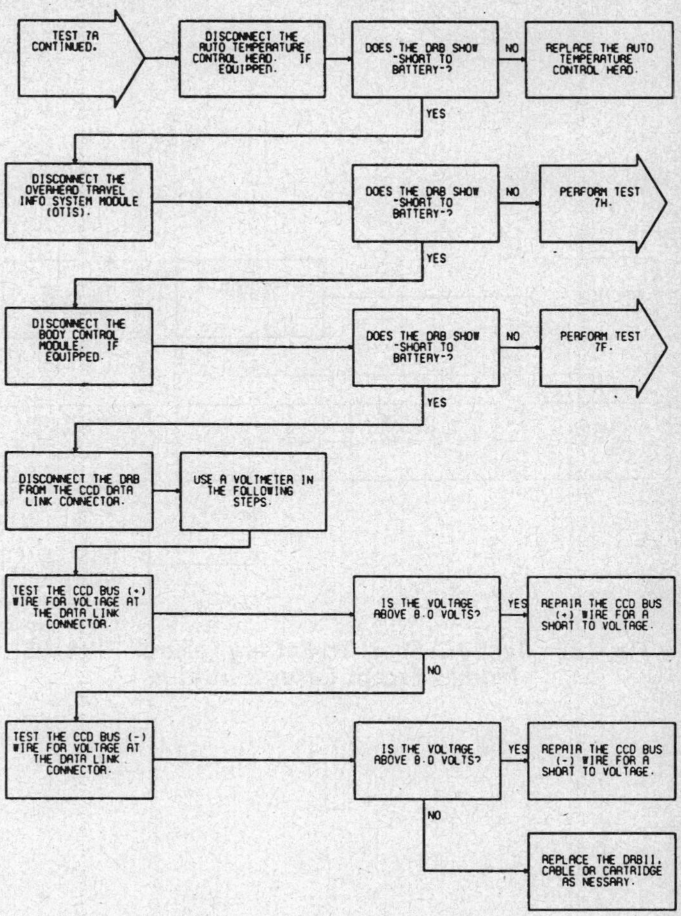

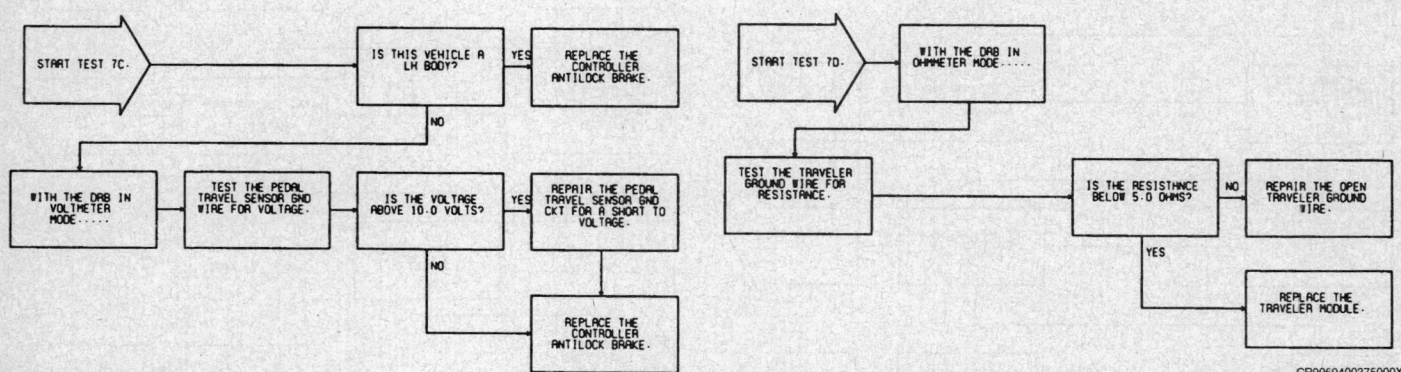

Fig. 120 Test 7C: Short To Battery Failure. 1994–95 Models Except Cirrus & Stratus

Fig. 121 Test 7D: Short To Battery Failure. 1994–95 Models Except Cirrus & Stratus

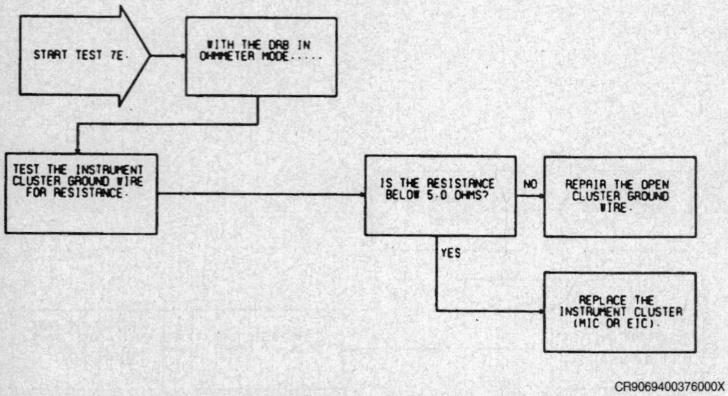

Fig. 122 Test 7E: Short To Battery Failure. 1994–95 Models Except Cirrus & Stratus

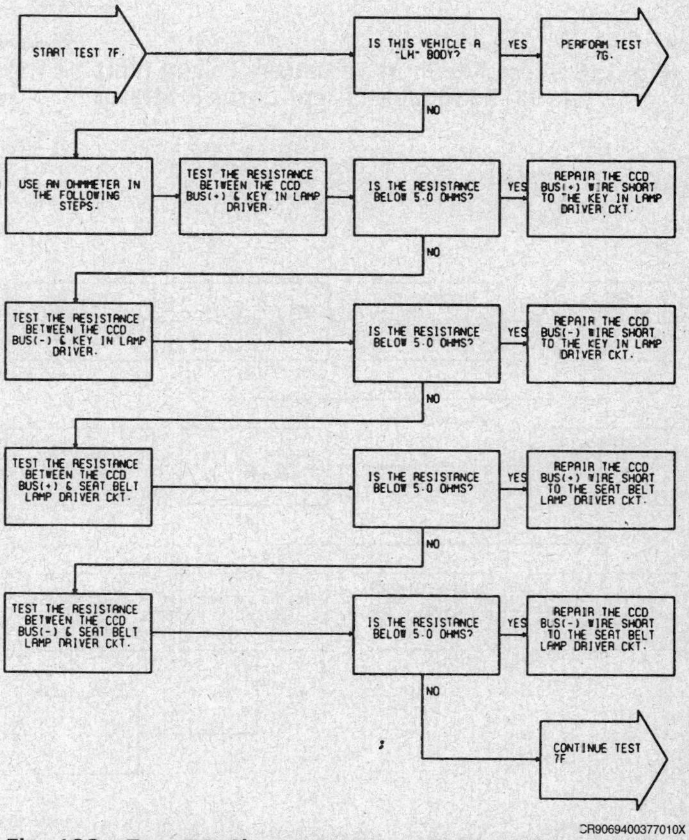

Fig. 123 Test 7F: Short To Battery Failure (Part 1 of 2). 1994–95 LeBaron

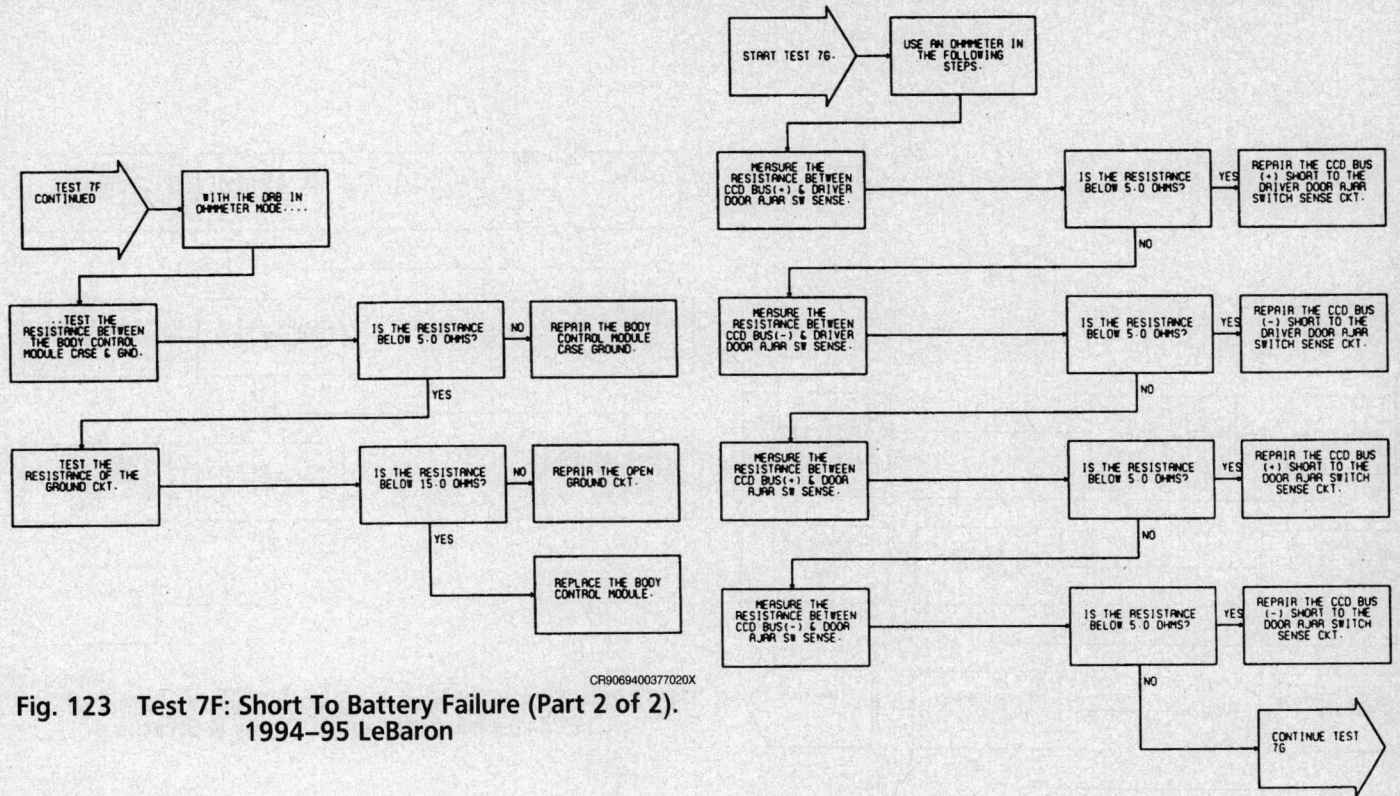

Fig. 123   Test 7F: Short To Battery Failure (Part 2 of 2).
1994–95 LeBaron

Fig. 124   Test 7G: Short To Battery Failure (Part 1 of 2).
1993–95 Concorde, Intrepid, LHS, Vision & 1994–95 New
Yorker

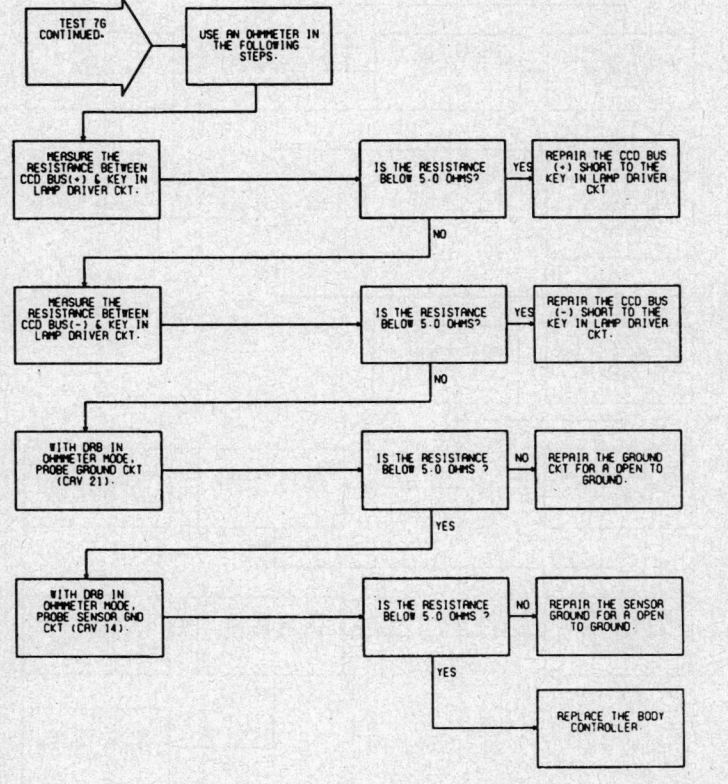

Fig. 124   Test 7G: Short To Battery Failure (Part 2 of 2).
1993–95 Concorde, Intrepid, LHS, Vision & 1994–95 New
Yorker

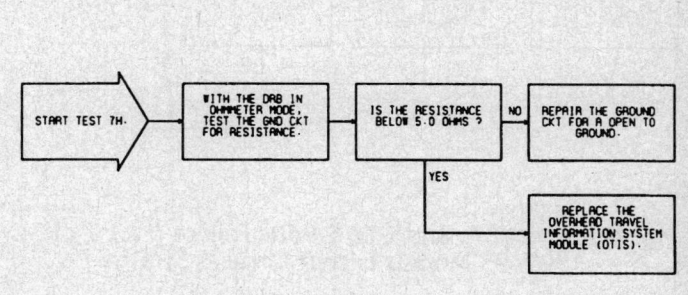

Fig. 125   Test 7H: Short To Battery Failure. 1994–95
Models Except Cirrus & Stratus

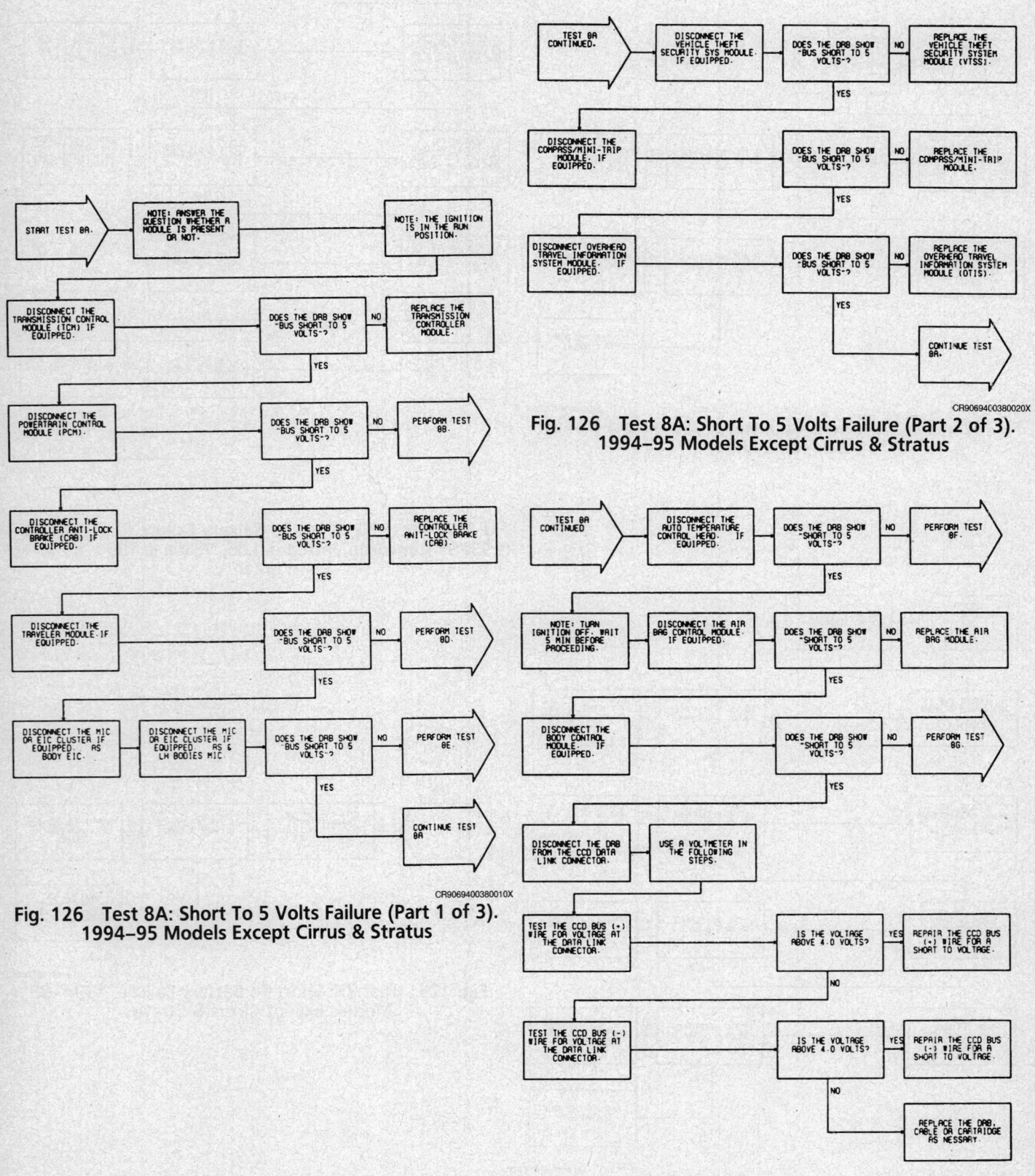

Fig. 126   Test 8A: Short To 5 Volts Failure (Part 1 of 3).
1994–95 Models Except Cirrus & Stratus

Fig. 126   Test 8A: Short To 5 Volts Failure (Part 2 of 3).
1994–95 Models Except Cirrus & Stratus

Fig. 126   Test 8A: Short to 5 Volts Failure (Part 3 of 3).
1994–95 Models Except Cirrus & Stratus

CR9069400381000X

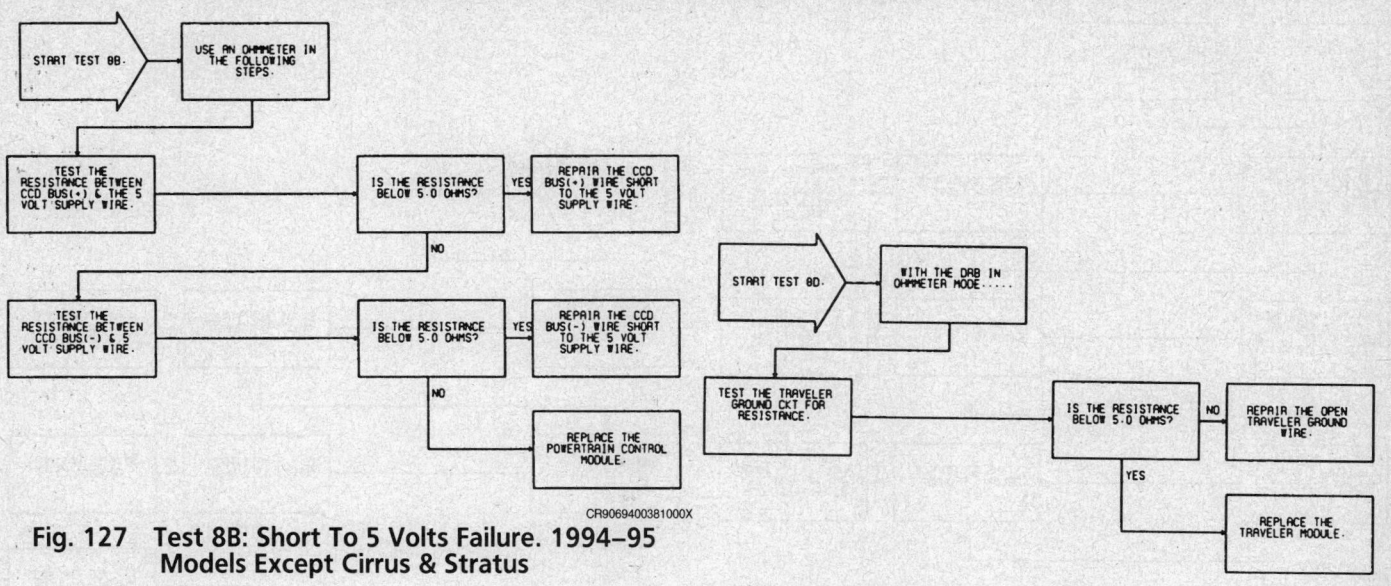

Fig. 127 Test 8B: Short To 5 Volts Failure. 1994–95 Models Except Cirrus & Stratus

CR9069400382000X

Fig. 128 Test 8D: Short To 5 Volts Failure. 1994–95 Models Except Cirrus & Stratus

CR9069400383000X

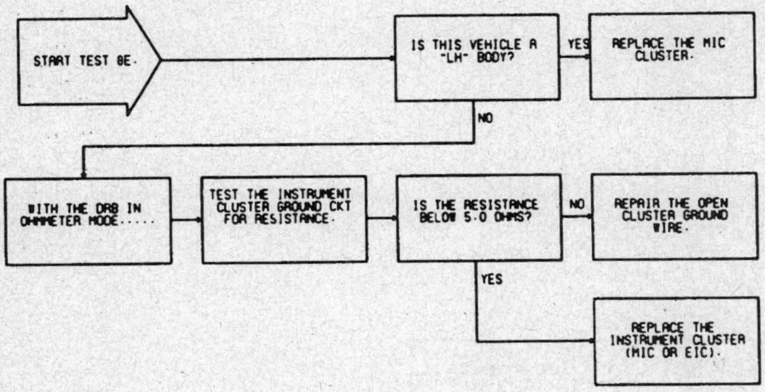

Fig. 129 Test 8E: Short To 5 Volts Failure. 1994–95 Models Except Cirrus & Stratus

CR9069400385010X

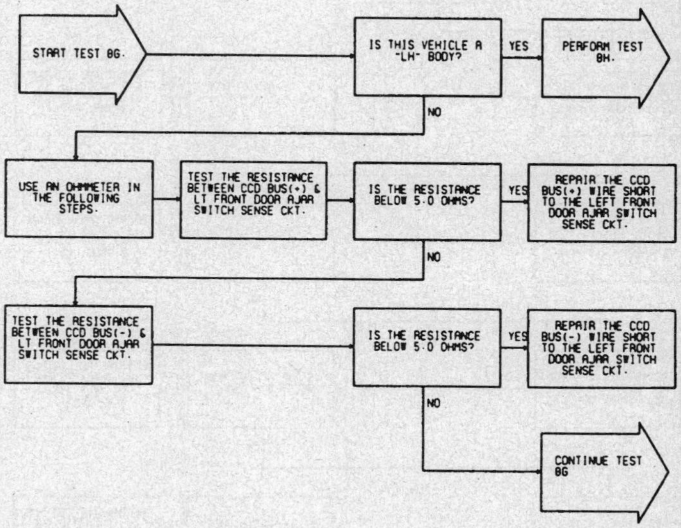

Fig. 131 Test 8G: Short To 5 Volts Failure (Part 1 of 3). 1994–95 Models Except Cirrus & Stratus

CR9069400384000X

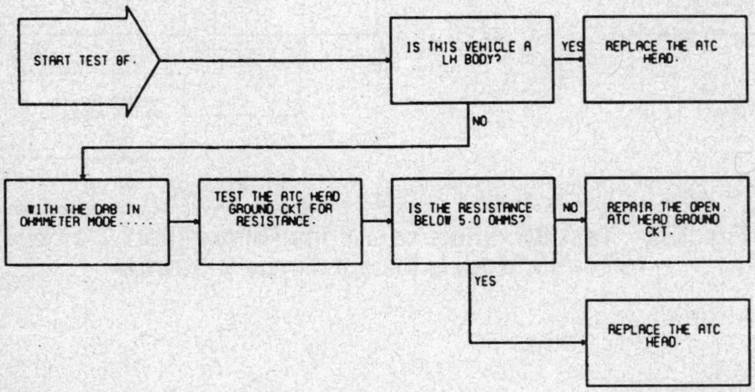

Fig. 130 Test 8F: Short To 5 Volts Failure. 1994–95 Models Except Cirrus & Stratus

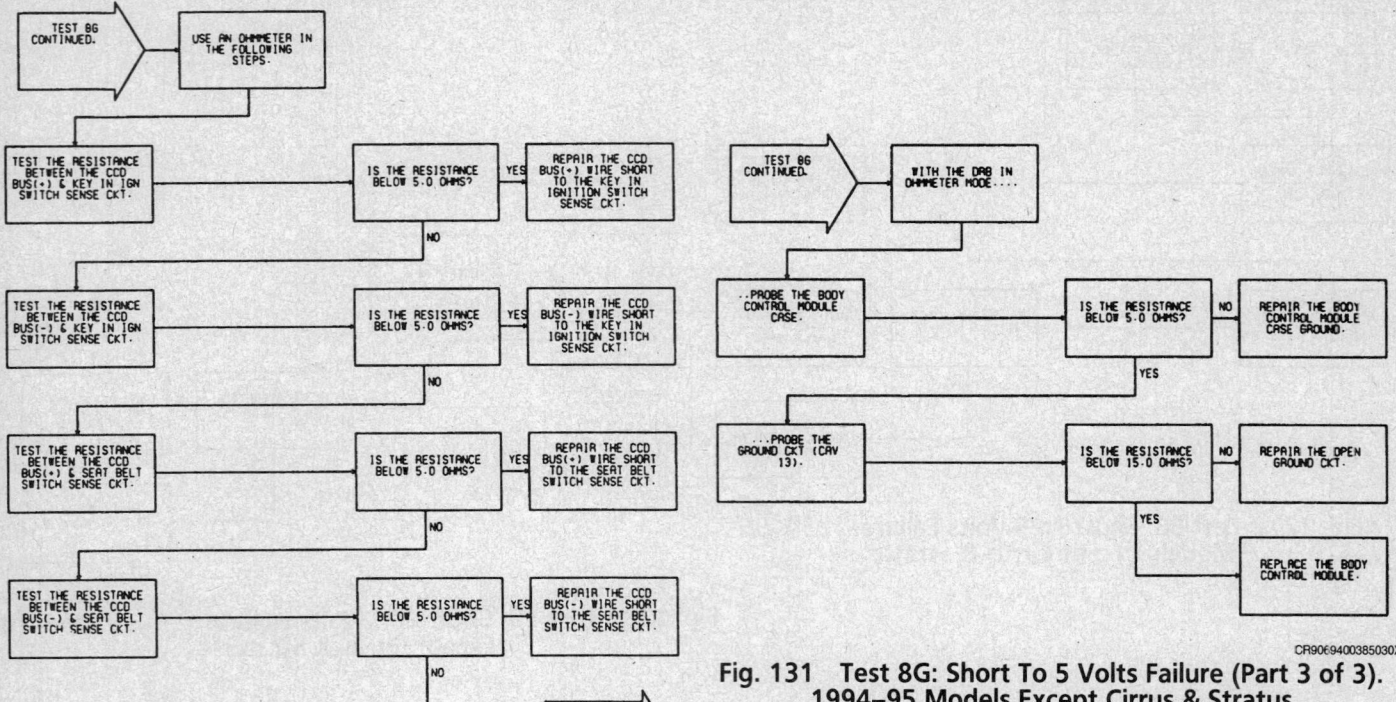

Fig. 131   Test 8G: Short To 5 Volts Failure (Part 2 of 3).
1994–95 Models Except Cirrus & Stratus

Fig. 131   Test 8G: Short To 5 Volts Failure (Part 3 of 3).
1994–95 Models Except Cirrus & Stratus

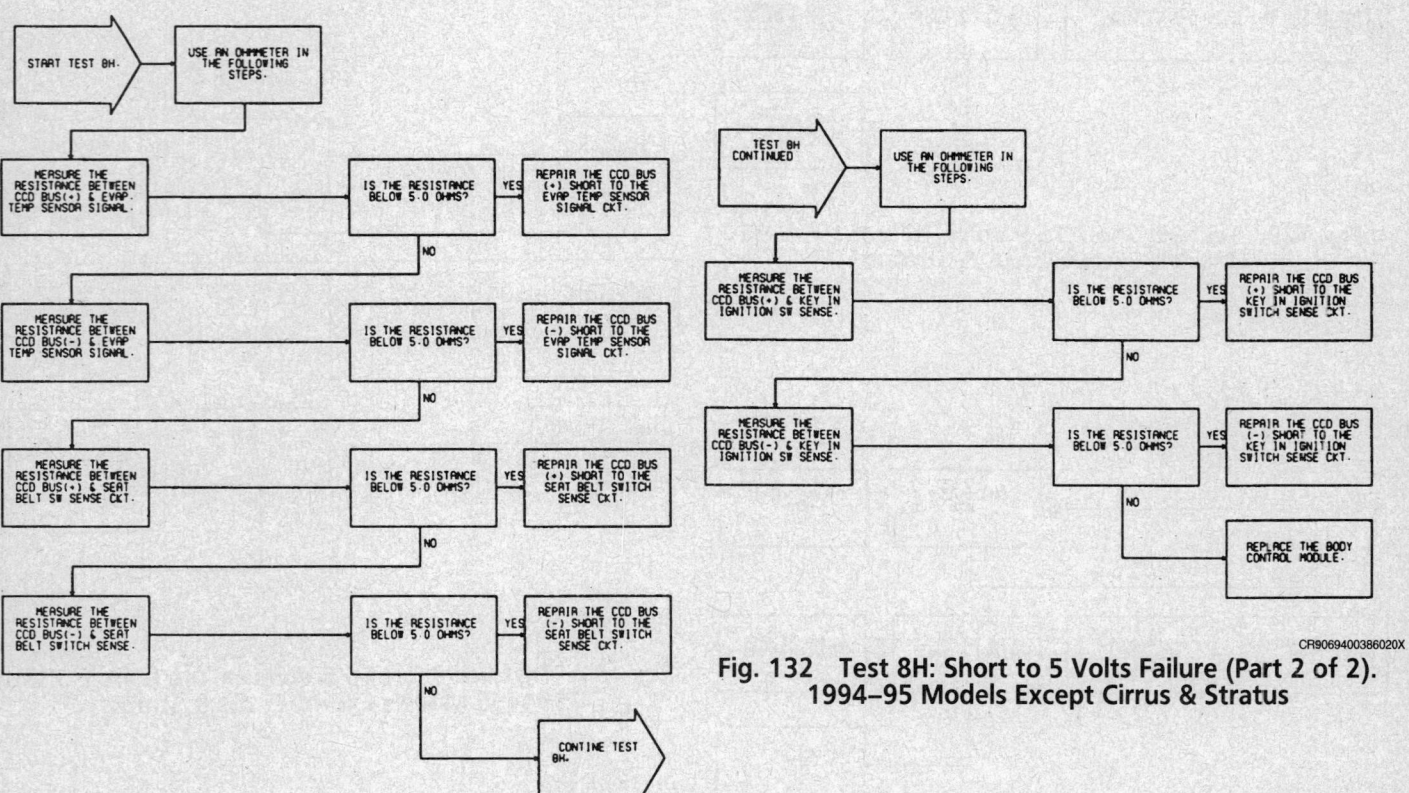

Fig. 132   Test 8H: Short To 5 volts Failure (Part 1 of 2).
1994–95 Models Except Cirrus & Stratus

Fig. 132   Test 8H: Short to 5 Volts Failure (Part 2 of 2).
1994–95 Models Except Cirrus & Stratus

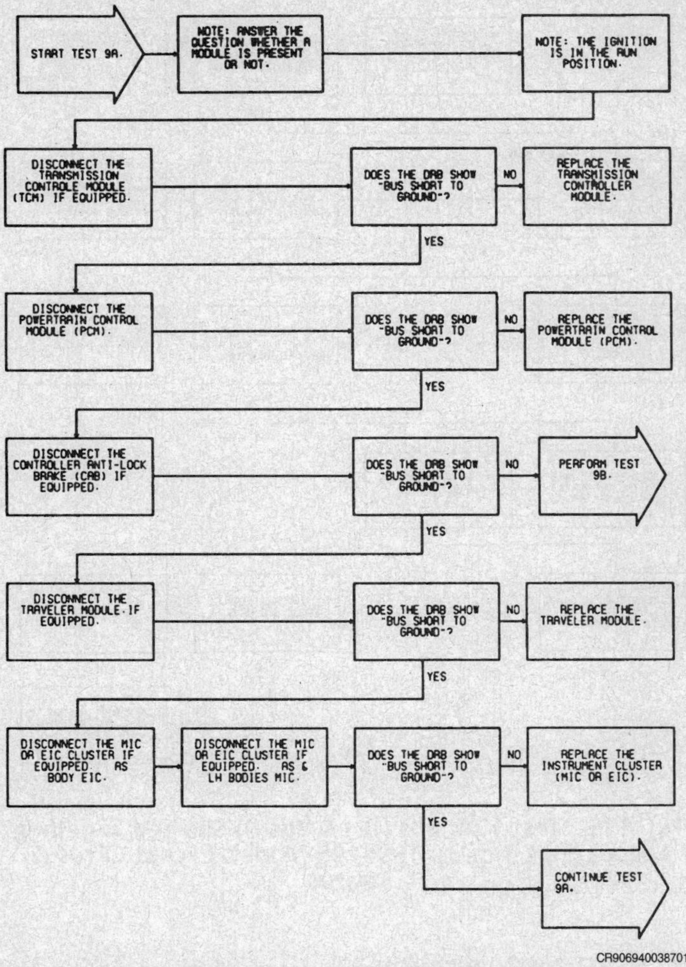

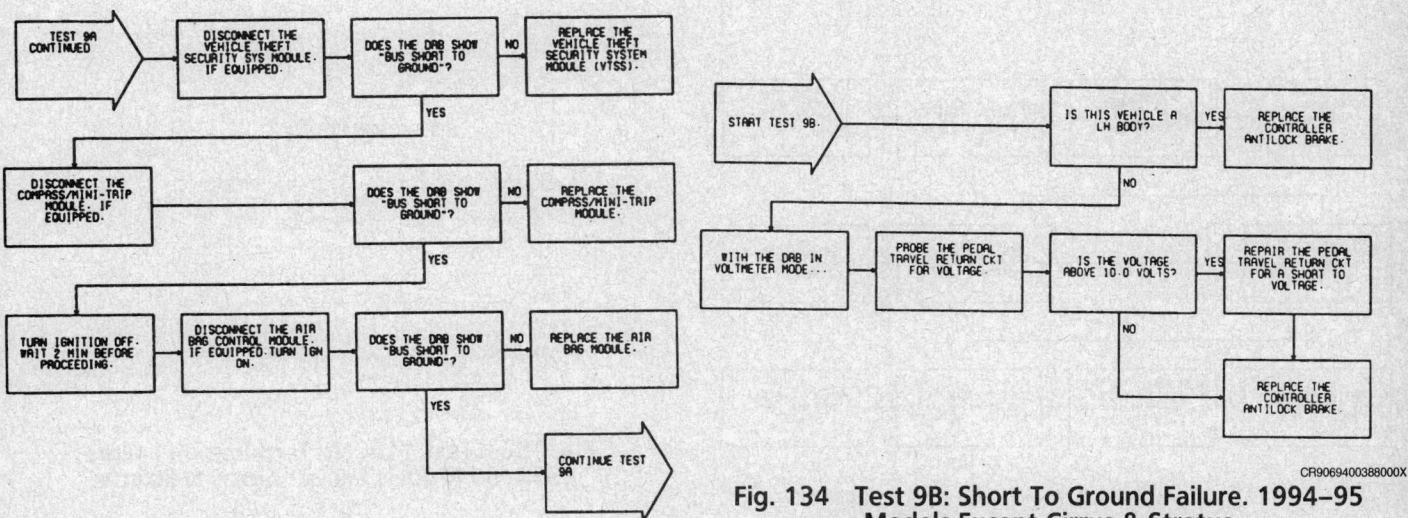

CR9069400387010X

Fig. 133 Test 9A: Short To Ground Failure (Part 1 of 3). 1994–95 Models Except Cirrus & Stratus

CR9069400387020X

Fig. 133 Test 9A: Short To Ground Failure (Part 2 of 3). 1994–95 Models Except Cirrus & Stratus

CR9069400387030X

Fig. 133 Test 9A: Short To Ground Failure (Part 3 of 3). 1994–95 Models Except Cirrus & Stratus

CR9069400388000X

Fig. 134 Test 9B: Short To Ground Failure. 1994–95 Models Except Cirrus & Stratus

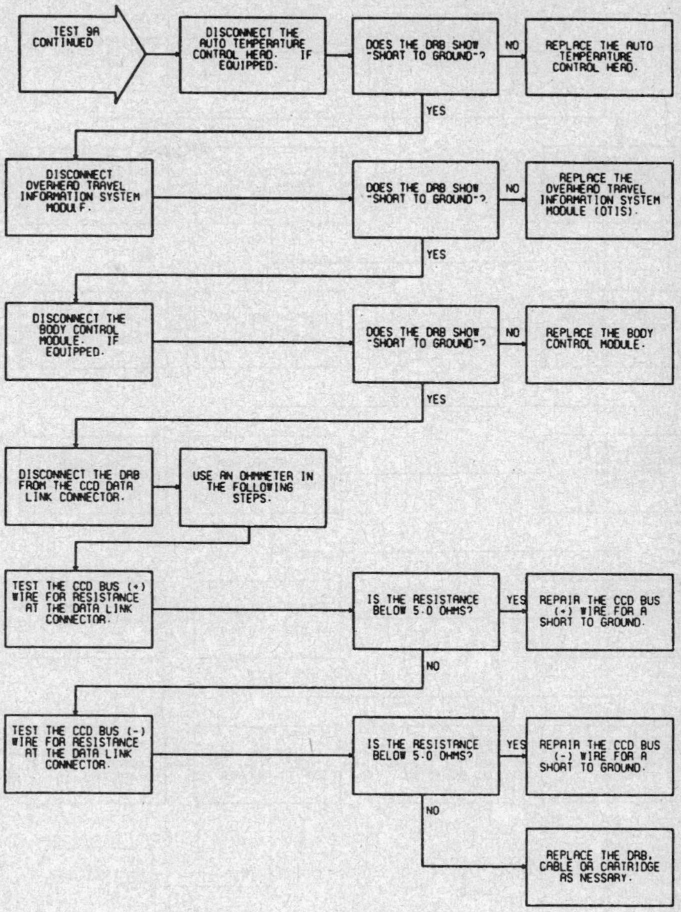

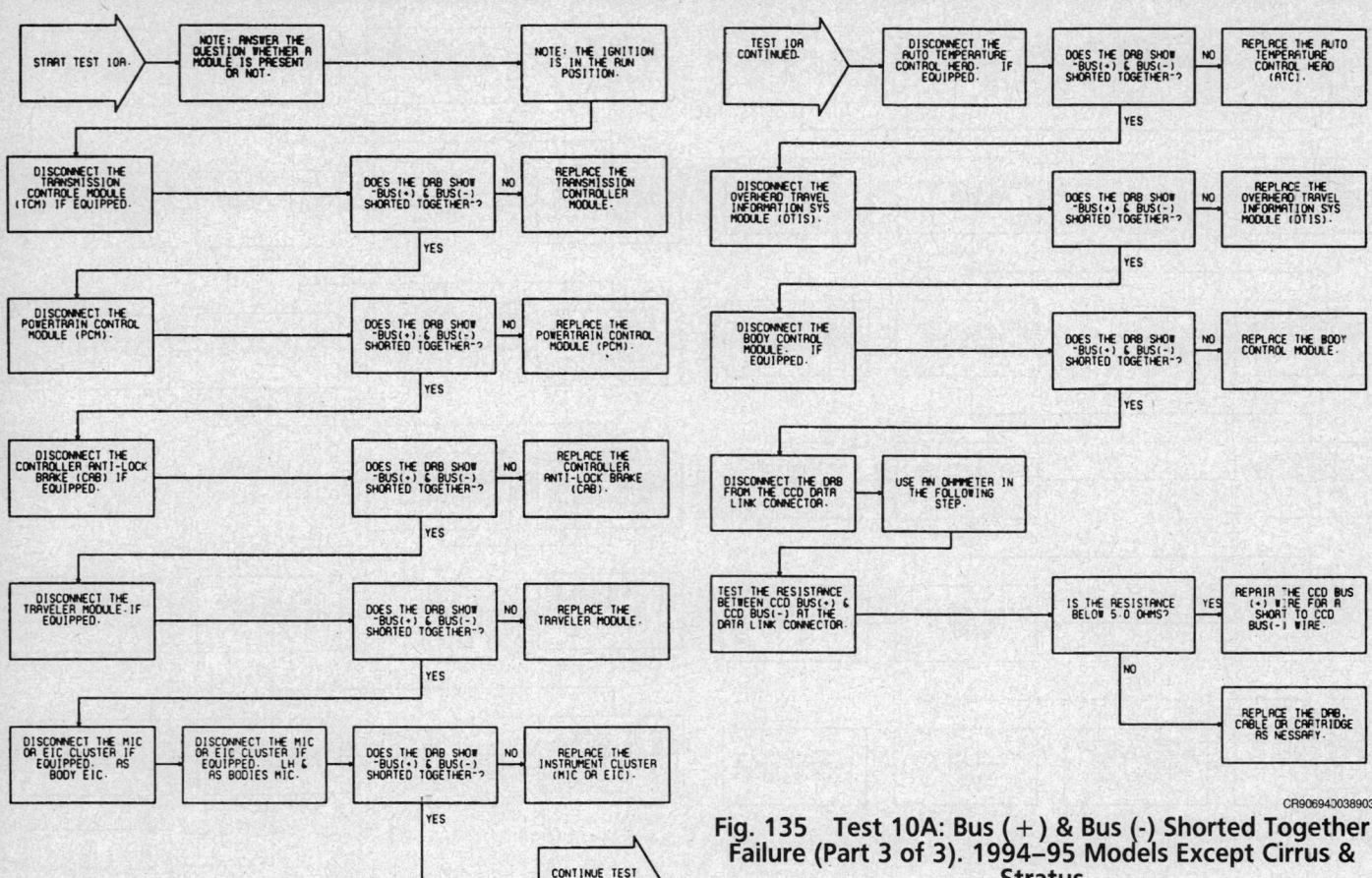

Fig. 135   Test 10A: Bus (+) & bus (-) Shorted Together Failure (Part 1 of 3). 1994–95 Models Except Cirrus & Stratus

Fig. 135   Test 10A: Bus (+) & Bus (-) Shorted Together Failure (Part 3 of 3). 1994–95 Models Except Cirrus & Stratus

Fig. 135   Test 10A: Bus (+) & Bus (-) Shorted Together Failure (Part 2 of 3). 1994–95 Models Except Cirrus & Stratus

NO TERMINATION

BODY	TEST
AA	11B
LH	11C
AJ	11D
AS	11E
AP	11H

Fig. 136   Test 11A: No Termination Failure. 1994–95 Models Except Cirrus & Stratus

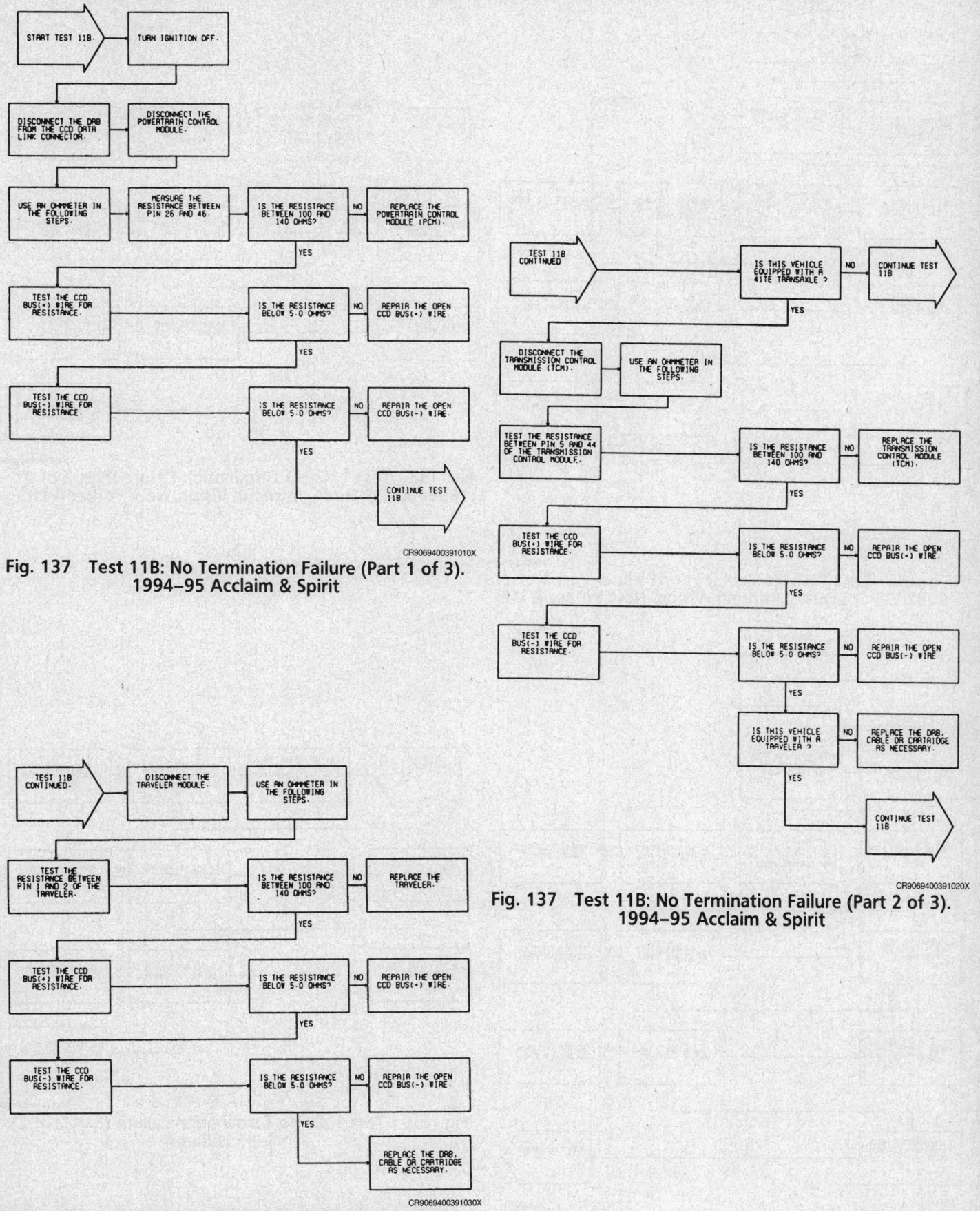

Fig. 137   Test 11B: No Termination Failure (Part 1 of 3).
1994–95 Acclaim & Spirit

Fig. 137   Test 11B: No Termination Failure (Part 2 of 3).
1994–95 Acclaim & Spirit

Fig. 137   Test 11B: No Termination Failure (Part 3 of 3).
1994–95 Acclaim & Spirit

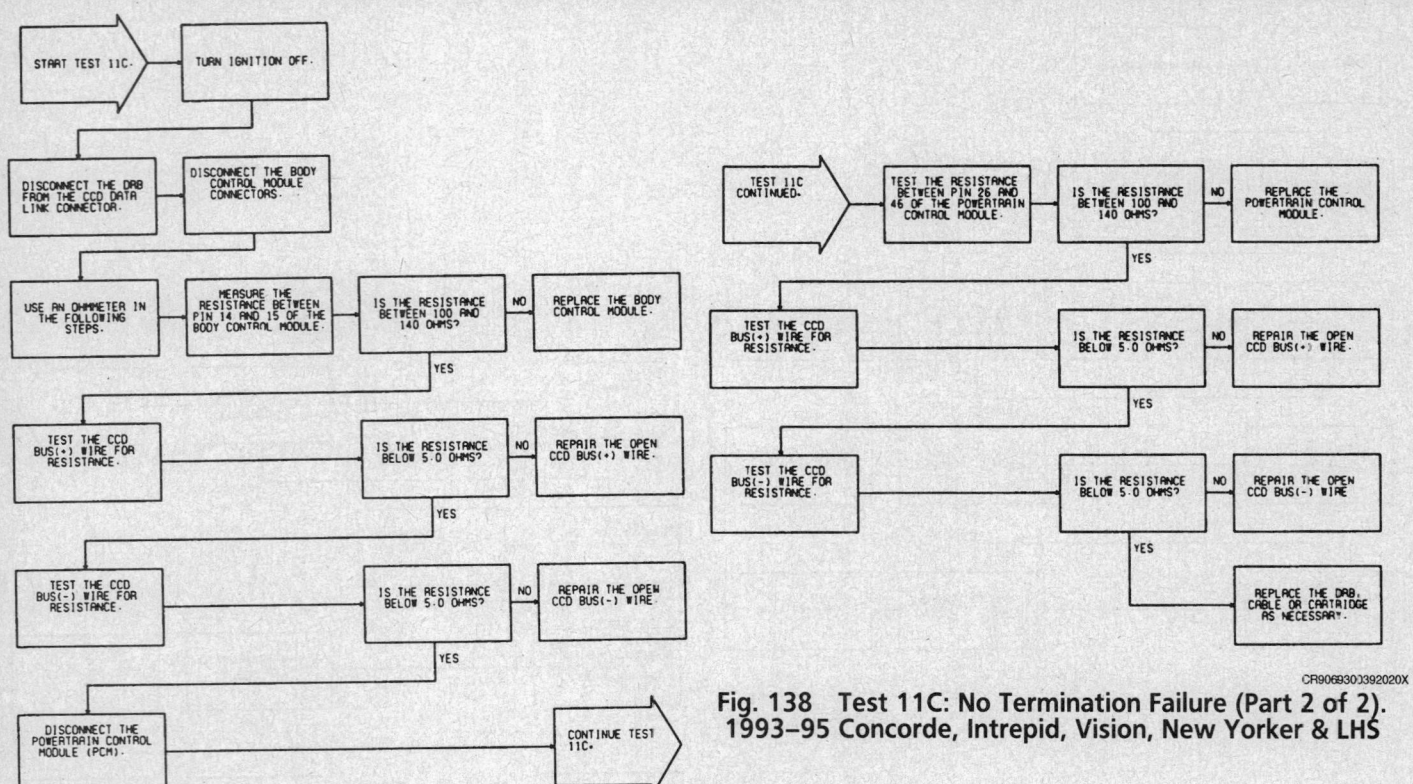

Fig. 138   Test 11C: No Termination Failure (Part 1 of 2).
1993–95 Concorde, Intrepid, Vision, New Yorker & LHS

Fig. 138   Test 11C: No Termination Failure (Part 2 of 2).
1993–95 Concorde, Intrepid, Vision, New Yorker & LHS

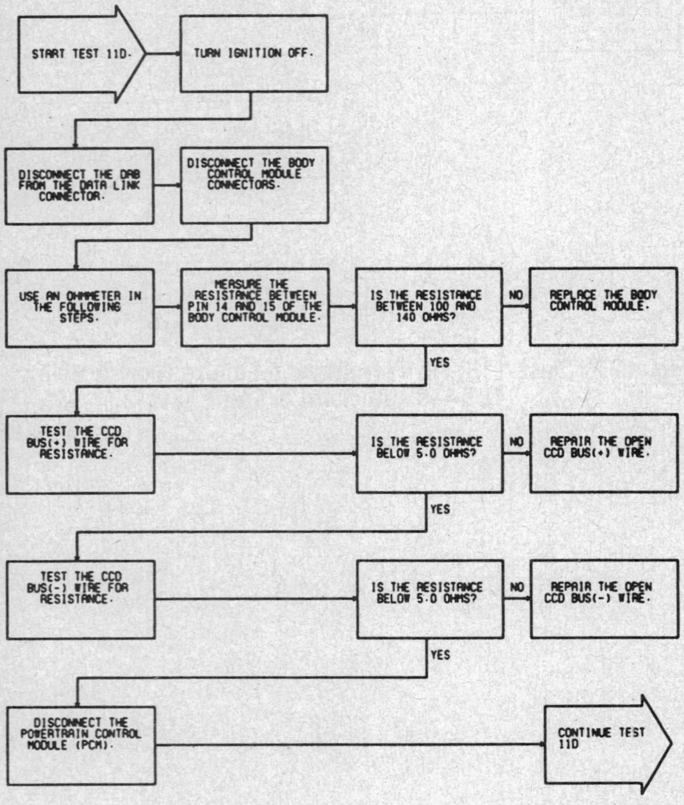

Fig. 139   Test 11D: No Termination Failure (Part 2 of 2).
1994–95 LeBaron

Fig. 139   Test 11D: No Termination Failure (Part 1 of 2).
1994–95 LeBaron

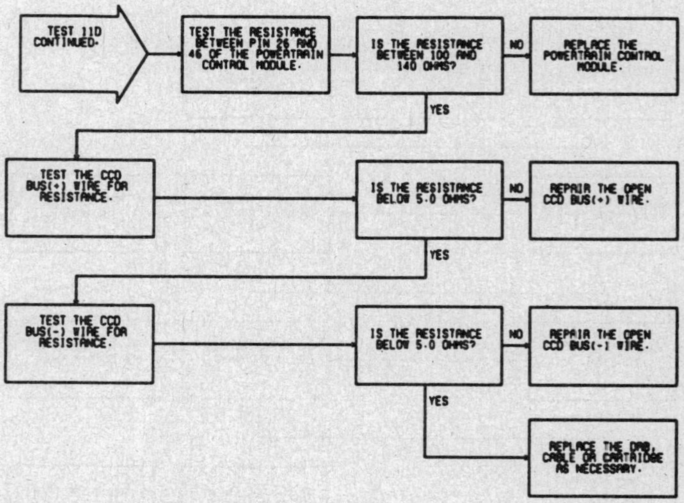

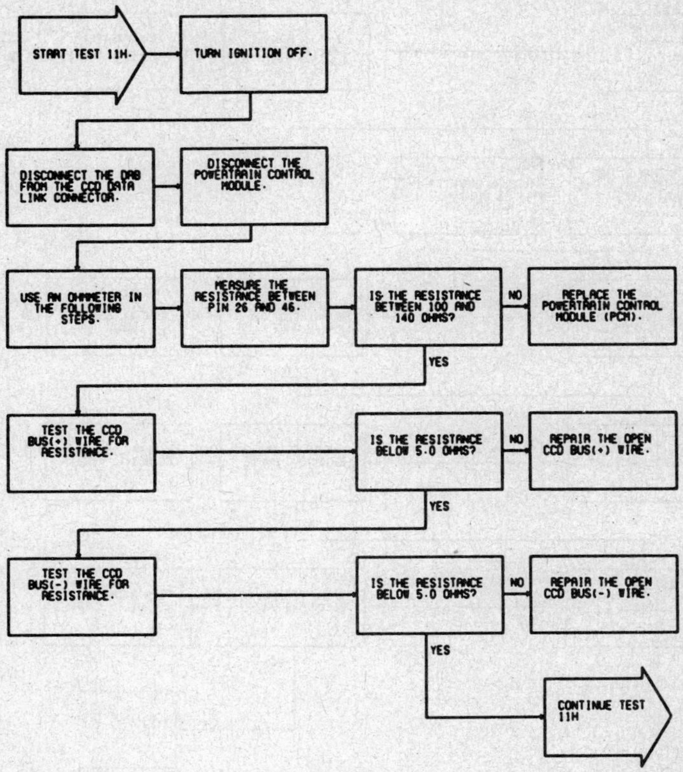

Top-left flowchart (Fig. 140 Part 1):

START TEST 11H → TURN IGNITION OFF.

DISCONNECT THE DRB FROM THE CCD DATA LINK CONNECTOR. → DISCONNECT THE POWERTRAIN CONTROL MODULE.

USE AN OHMMETER IN THE FOLLOWING STEPS. → MEASURE THE RESISTANCE BETWEEN PIN 26 AND 46. → IS THE RESISTANCE BETWEEN 100 AND 140 OHMS? — NO → REPLACE THE POWERTRAIN CONTROL MODULE (PCM).

YES

TEST THE CCD BUS(+) WIRE FOR RESISTANCE. → IS THE RESISTANCE BELOW 5.0 OHMS? — NO → REPAIR THE OPEN CCD BUS(+) WIRE.

YES

TEST THE CCD BUS(-) WIRE FOR RESISTANCE. → IS THE RESISTANCE BELOW 5.0 OHMS? — NO → REPAIR THE OPEN CCD BUS(-) WIRE.

YES → CONTINUE TEST 11H

CR9069400394010X

Fig. 140 Test 11H: No Termination Failure (Part 1 of 2). 1994 Shadow & Sundance

Top-right flowchart (Fig. 140 Part 2):

TEST 11H CONTINUED → DISCONNECT THE TRANSMISSION CONTROL MODULE (TCM). → USE AN OHMMETER IN THE FOLLOWING STEPS.

TEST THE RESISTANCE BETWEEN PIN 5 AND 44 OF THE TRANSMISSION CONTROL MODULE. → IS THE RESISTANCE BETWEEN 100 AND 140 OHMS? — NO → REPLACE THE TRANSMISSION CONTROL MODULE (TCM).

YES

TEST THE CCD BUS(+) WIRE FOR RESISTANCE. → IS THE RESISTANCE BELOW 5.0 OHMS? — NO → REPAIR THE OPEN CCD BUS(+) WIRE.

YES

TEST THE CCD BUS(-) WIRE FOR RESISTANCE. → IS THE RESISTANCE BELOW 5.0 OHMS? — NO → REPAIR THE OPEN CCD BUS(-) WIRE.

YES

TEST BETWEEN THE CCD BUS(+) WIRE & BUS BIAS (CAVITIES 5 & 43) FOR RESISTANCE. → IS THE RESISTANCE BELOW 5.0 OHMS? — NO → REPAIR THE OPEN BETWEEN BUS BIAS AND CCD BUS(+) WIRES.

YES

TEST BETWEEN THE CCD BUS(-) WIRE & BUS BIAS (CAVITIES 4 & 44) FOR RESISTANCE. → IS THE RESISTANCE BELOW 5.0 OHMS? — NO → REPAIR THE OPEN BETWEEN BUS BIAS AND CCD BUS(-) WIRES.

YES → REPLACE THE DRB, CABLE OR CARTRIDGE AS NECESSARY.

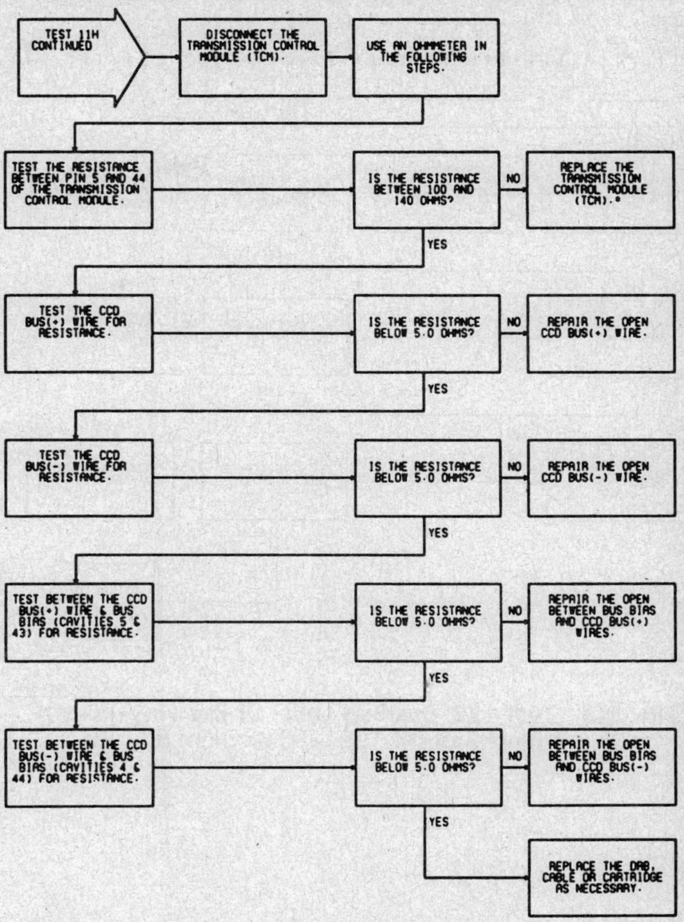

CR9069400394020X

Fig. 140 Test 11H: No Termination Failure (Part 2 of 2). 1994 Shadow & Sundance

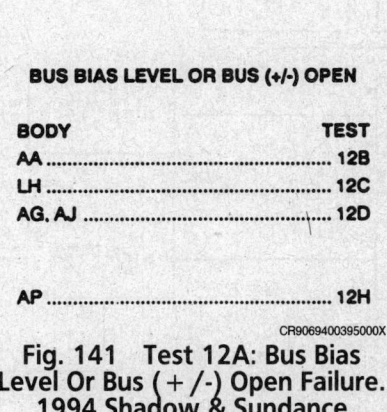

BUS BIAS LEVEL OR BUS (+/-) OPEN

BODY	TEST
AA	12B
LH	12C
AG, AJ	12D
AP	12H

CR9069400395000X

Fig. 141 Test 12A: Bus Bias Level Or Bus (+/-) Open Failure. 1994 Shadow & Sundance

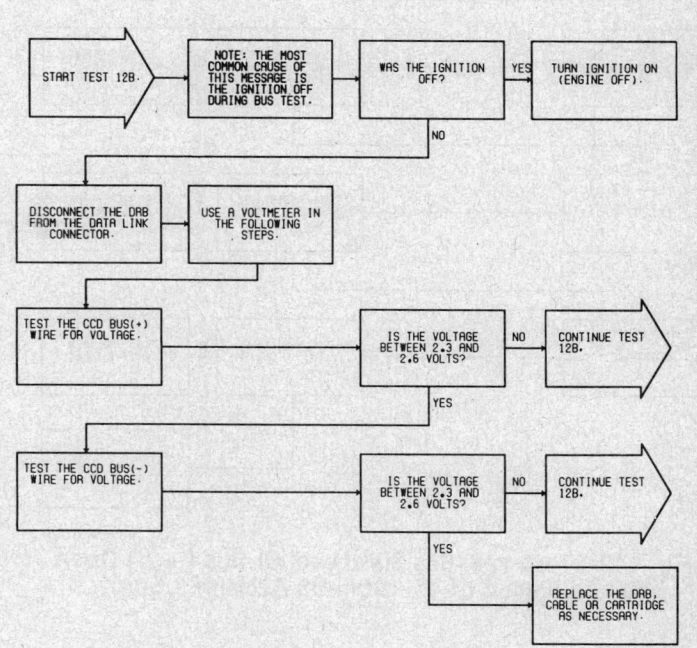

START TEST 12B → NOTE: THE MOST COMMON CAUSE OF THIS MESSAGE IS THE IGNITION OFF DURING BUS TEST. → WAS THE IGNITION OFF? — YES → TURN IGNITION ON (ENGINE OFF).

NO

DISCONNECT THE DRB FROM THE DATA LINK CONNECTOR. → USE A VOLTMETER IN THE FOLLOWING STEPS.

TEST THE CCD BUS(+) WIRE FOR VOLTAGE. → IS THE VOLTAGE BETWEEN 2.3 AND 2.6 VOLTS? — NO → CONTINUE TEST 12B.

YES

TEST THE CCD BUS(-) WIRE FOR VOLTAGE. → IS THE VOLTAGE BETWEEN 2.3 AND 2.6 VOLTS? — NO → CONTINUE TEST 12B.

YES → REPLACE THE DRB, CABLE OR CARTRIDGE AS NECESSARY.

CR9069400396010X

Fig. 142 Test 12B: Bus Bias Level Or Bus (+/-) Open Failure (Part 1 of 4). 1994–95 Acclaim & Spirit

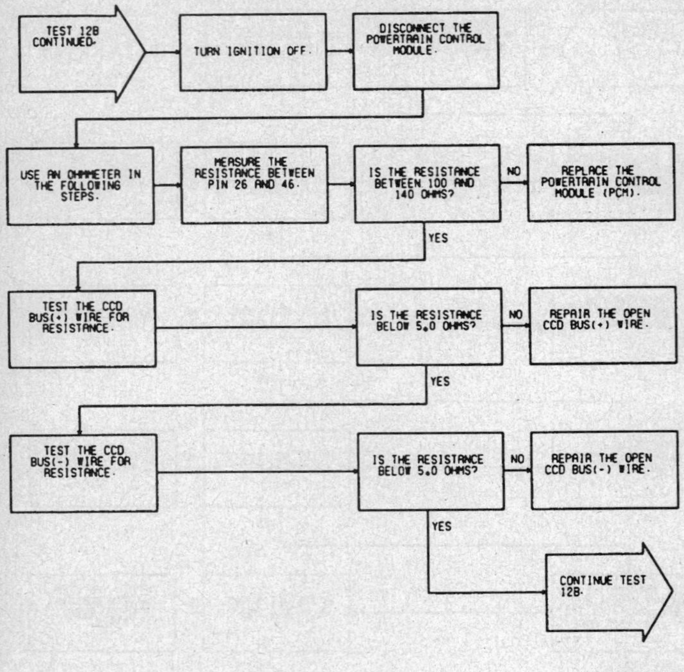

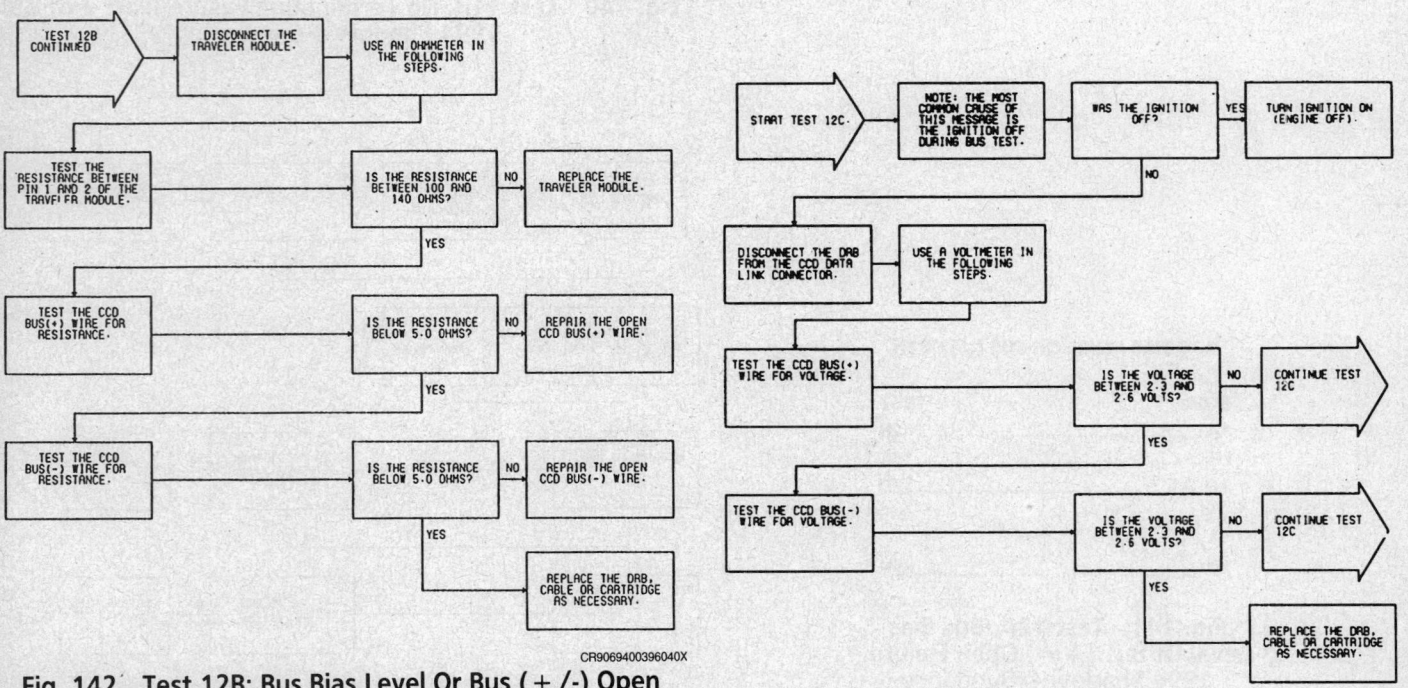

CR9069400396020X

Fig. 142 Test 12B: Bus Bias Level Or Bus (+/-) Open Failure (Part 2 of 4). 1994–95 Acclaim & Spirit

CR9069400396030X

Fig. 142 Test 12B: Bus Bias Level Or Bus (+/-) Open Failure (Part 3 of 4). 1994–95 Acclaim & Spirit

CR9069400396040X

Fig. 142 Test 12B: Bus Bias Level Or Bus (+/-) Open Failure (Part 4 of 4). 1994–95 Acclaim & Spirit

CR9069300397010X

Fig. 143 Test 12C: Bus Bias Level Or Bus (+/-) Open Failure (Part 1 of 4). 1993–95 Concorde, Intrepid, LHS, Vision & 1994–95 New Yorker

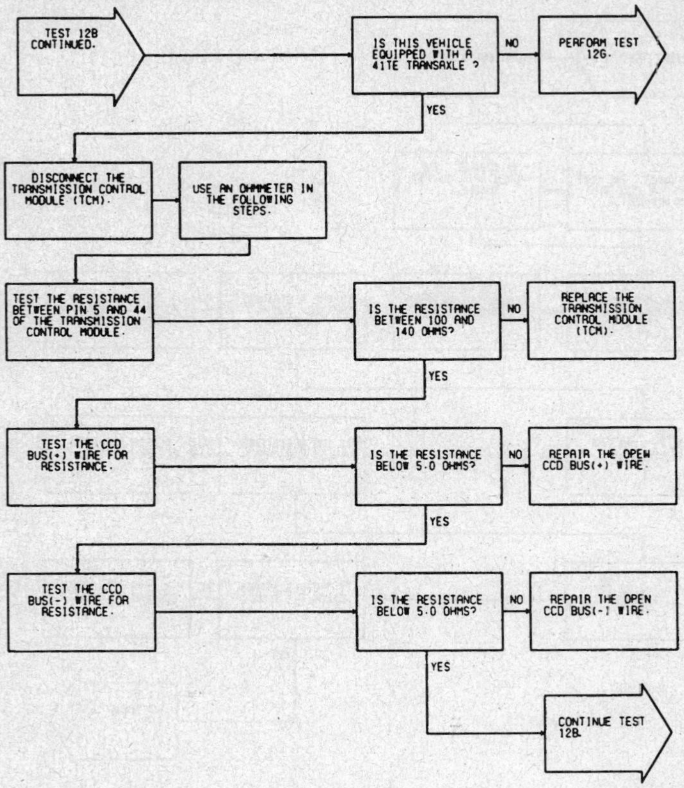

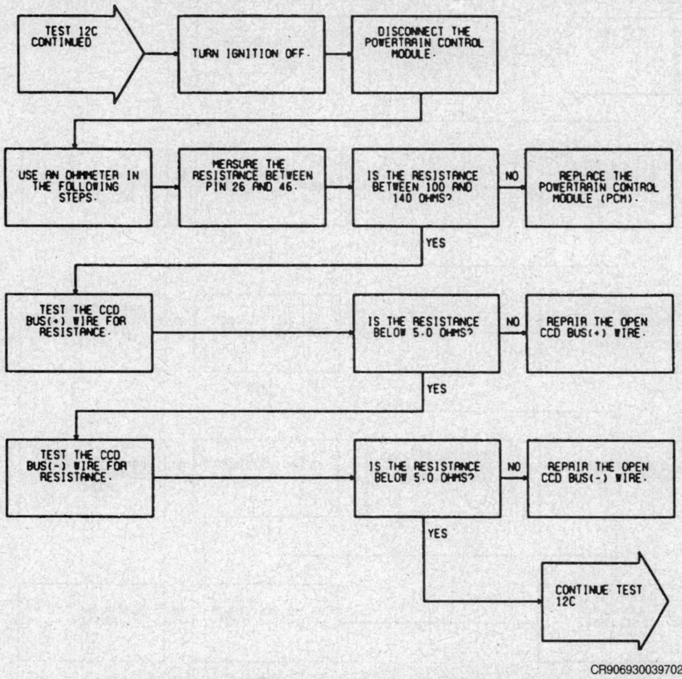

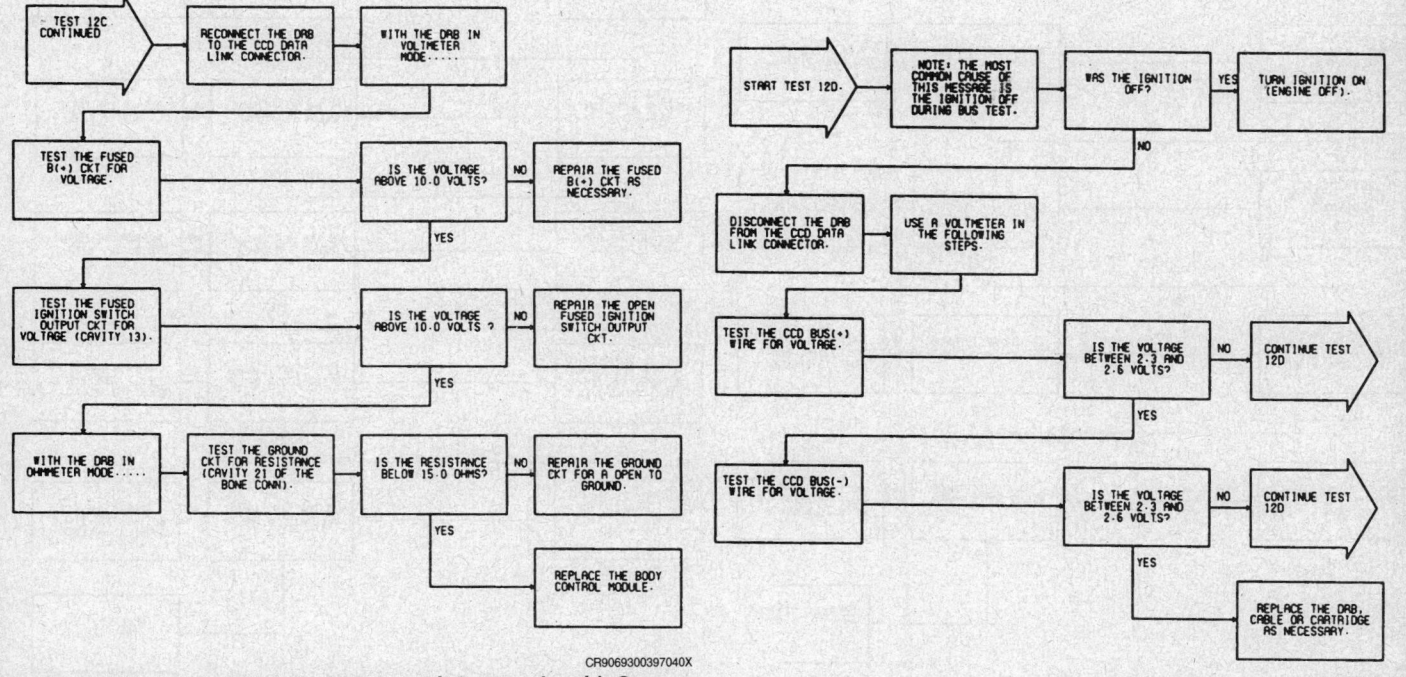

Fig. 143   Test 12C: Bus Bias Level Or Bus (+ /-) Open
Failure (Part 2 of 4). 1993–95 Concorde, Intrepid, LHS,
Vision & 1994–95 New Yorker

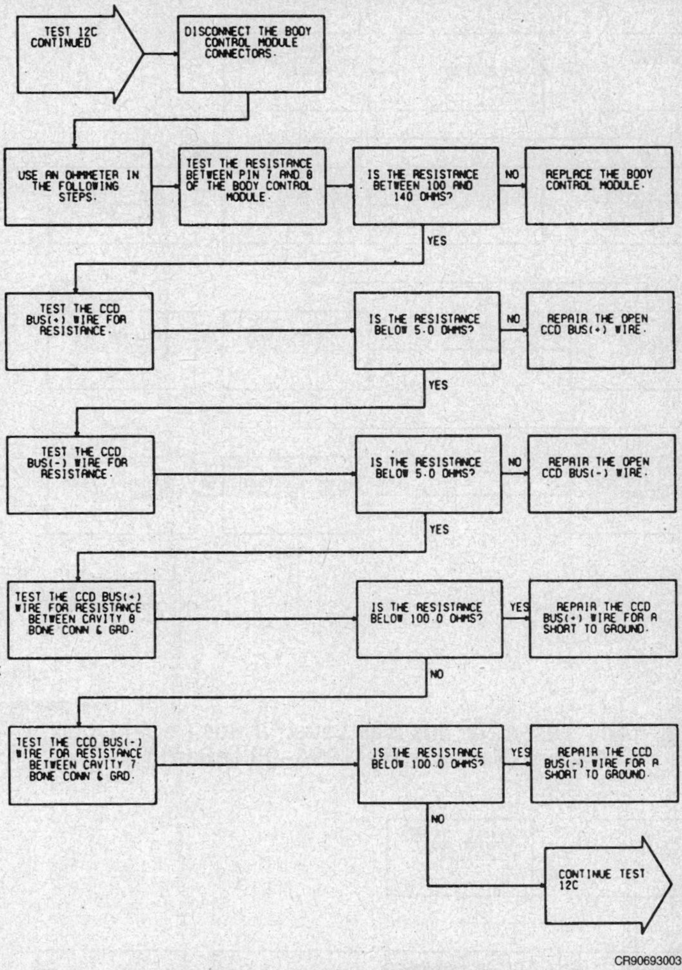

Fig. 143   Test 12C: Bus Bias Level Or Bus (+ /-) Open Failure
(Part 3 of 4). 1993–95 Concorde, Intrepid, LHS, Vision &
1994–95 New Yorker

Fig. 143   Test 12C: Bus Bias Level Or Bus (+ /-) Open
Failure (Part 4 of 4). 1993–95 Concorde, Intrepid, LHS,
Vision & 1994–95 New Yorker

Fig. 144   Test 12D: Bus Bias Level Or Bus (+ /-) Open
Failure (Part 1 of 4). 1994–95 LeBaron

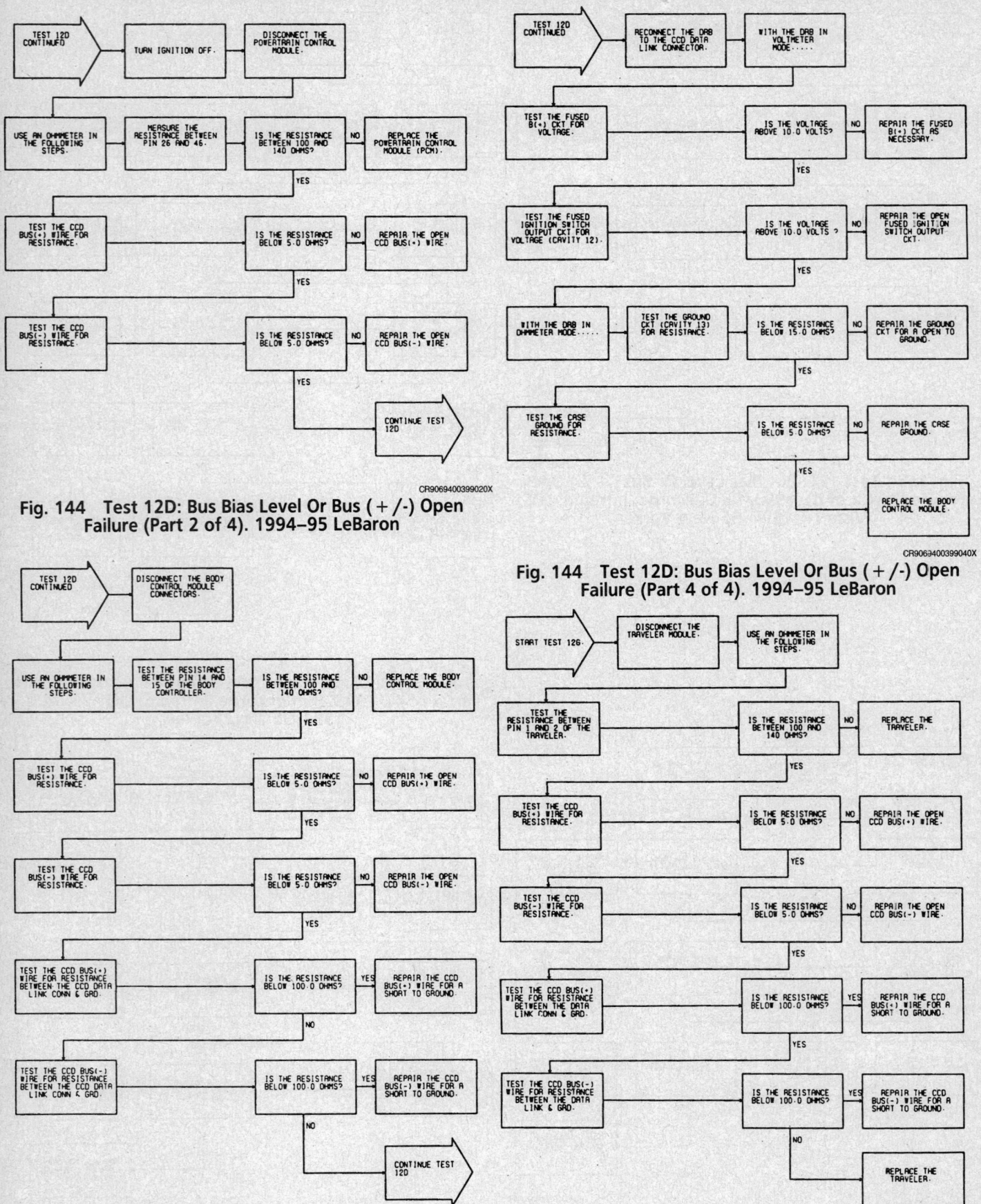

Fig. 144   Test 12D: Bus Bias Level Or Bus (+/-) Open Failure (Part 2 of 4). 1994–95 LeBaron

Fig. 144   Test 12D: Bus Bias Level Or Bus (+/-) Open Failure (Part 4 of 4). 1994–95 LeBaron

Fig. 144   Test 12D: Bus Bias Level Or Bus (+/-) Open Failure (Part 3 of 4). 1994–95 LeBaron

Fig. 145   Test 12G: Bus Bias Level Or Bus (+/-) Open Failure. 1994–95 Models Except Cirrus & Stratus

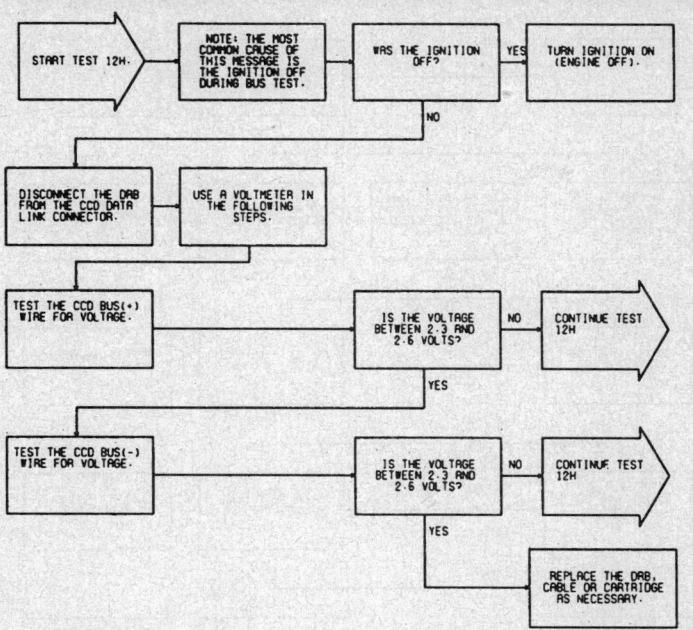

Fig. 146 Test 12H: Bus Bias Level Or Bus (+/-) Open Failure (Part 1 of 4). 1994 Shadow & Sundance

CR9069400401010X

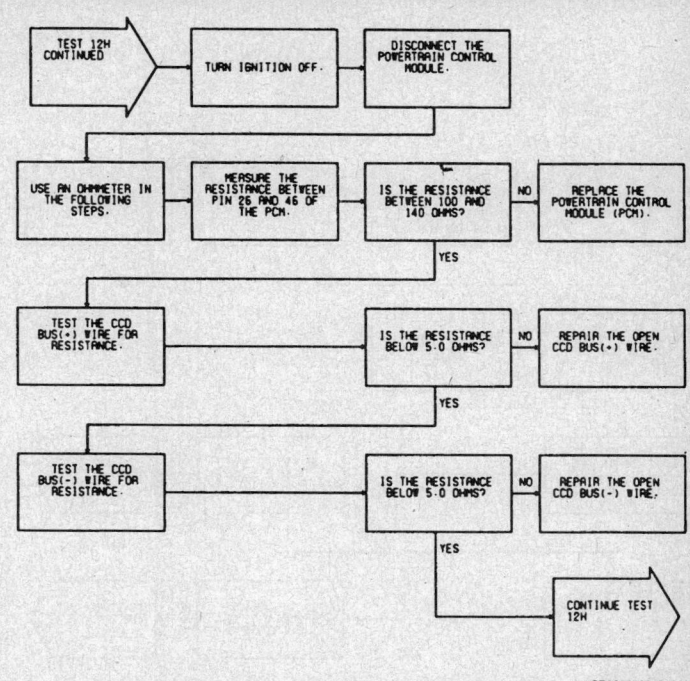

Fig. 146 Test 12H: Bus Bias Level Or Bus (+/-) Open Failure (Part 2 of 4). 1994 Shadow & Sundance

CR9069400401020X

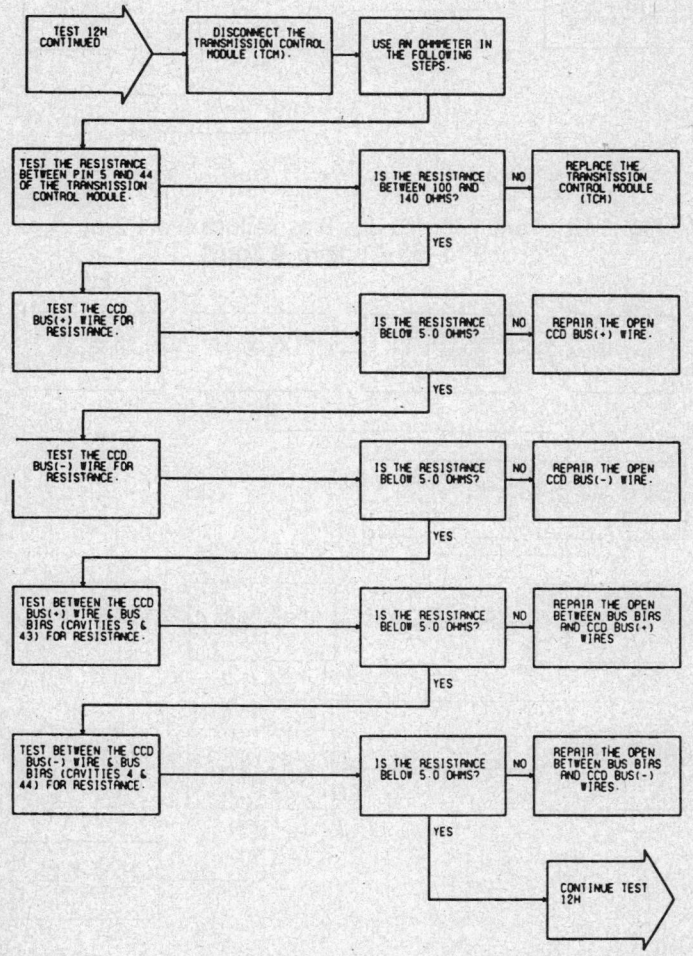

Fig. 146 Test 12H: Bus Bias Level Or Bus (+/-) Open Failure (Part 3 of 4). 1994 Shadow & Sundance

CR9069400401030X

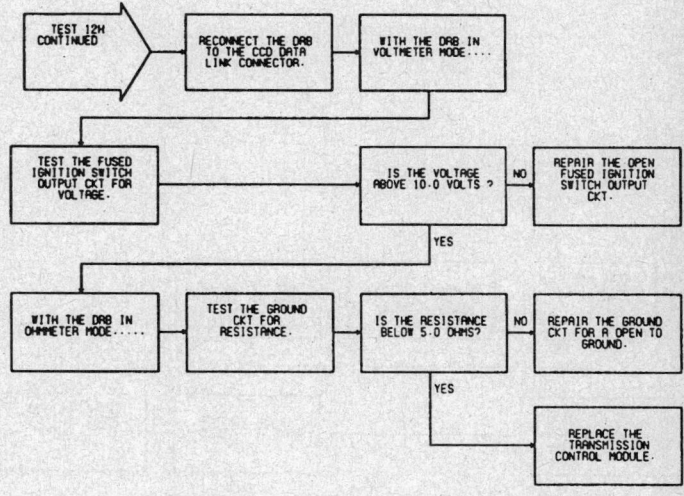

Fig. 146 Test 12H: Bus Bias Level Or Bus (+/-) Open Failure (Part 4 of 4). 1994 Shadow & Sundance

CR9069400402000X

NO BUS BIAS

BODY	TEST
AA	13B
LH	13C
AJ	13D
AS	13E
AP	13H

Fig. 147 Test 13A: No Bus Bias Failure. 1994–95 Models Except Cirrus & Stratus

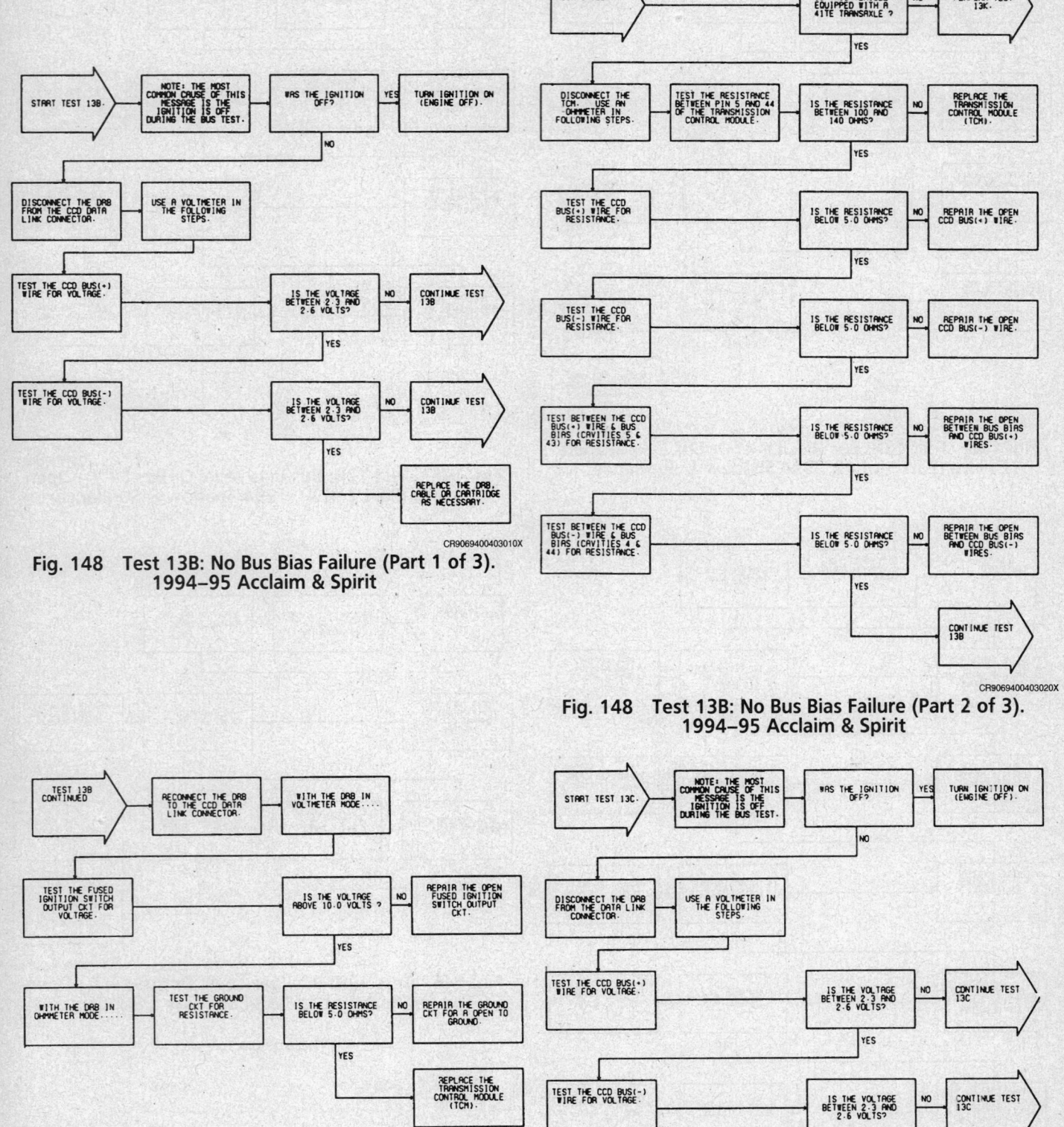

Fig. 148   Test 13B: No Bus Bias Failure (Part 1 of 3).
1994–95 Acclaim & Spirit

Fig. 148   Test 13B: No Bus Bias Failure (Part 2 of 3).
1994–95 Acclaim & Spirit

Fig. 148   Test 13B: No Bus Bias Failure (Part 3 of 3).
1994–95 Acclaim & Spirit

Fig. 149   Test 13C: No Bus Bias Failure (Part 1 of 3).
1993–95 Concorde, Intrepid, LHS, Vision & 1994–95 New
Yorker

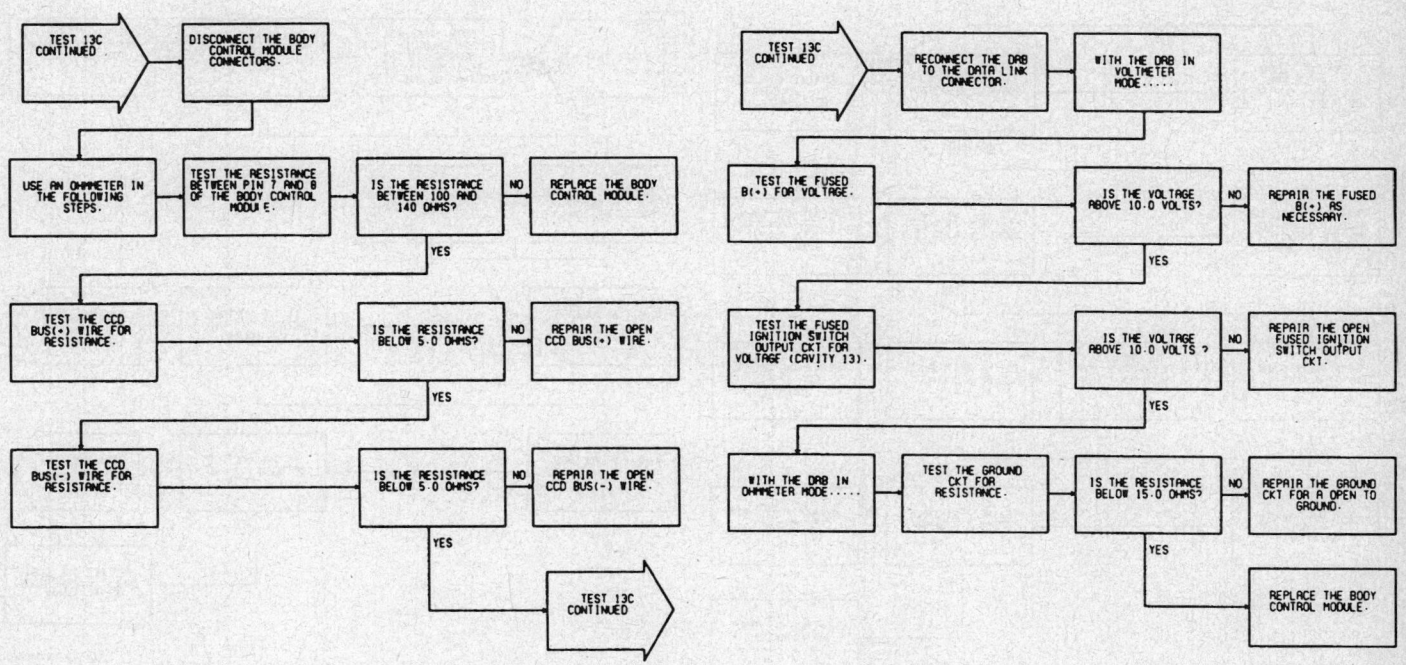

CR9069300404020X

Fig. 149   Test 13C: No Bus Bias Failure (Part 2 of 3). 1993–95 Concorde, Intrepid, LHS, Vision & 1994–95 New Yorker

CR9069300404030X

Fig. 149   Test 13C: No Bus Bias Failure (Part 3 of 3). 1993–95 Concorde, Intrepid, LHS, Vision & 1994–95 New Yorker

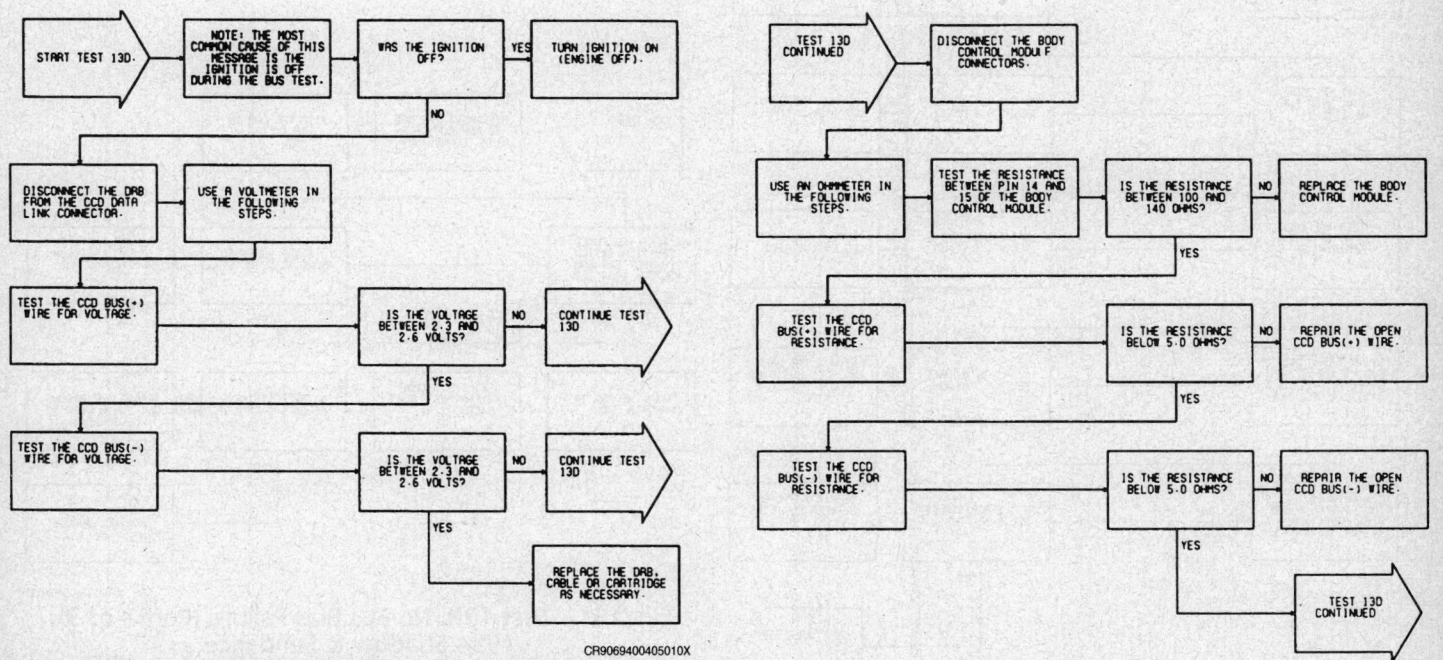

CR9069400405010X

Fig. 150   Test 13D: No Bus Bias Failure (Part 1 of 3). 1994–95 LeBaron

CR9069400405020X

Fig. 150   Test 13D: No Bus Bias Failure (Part 2 of 3). 1994–95 LeBaron

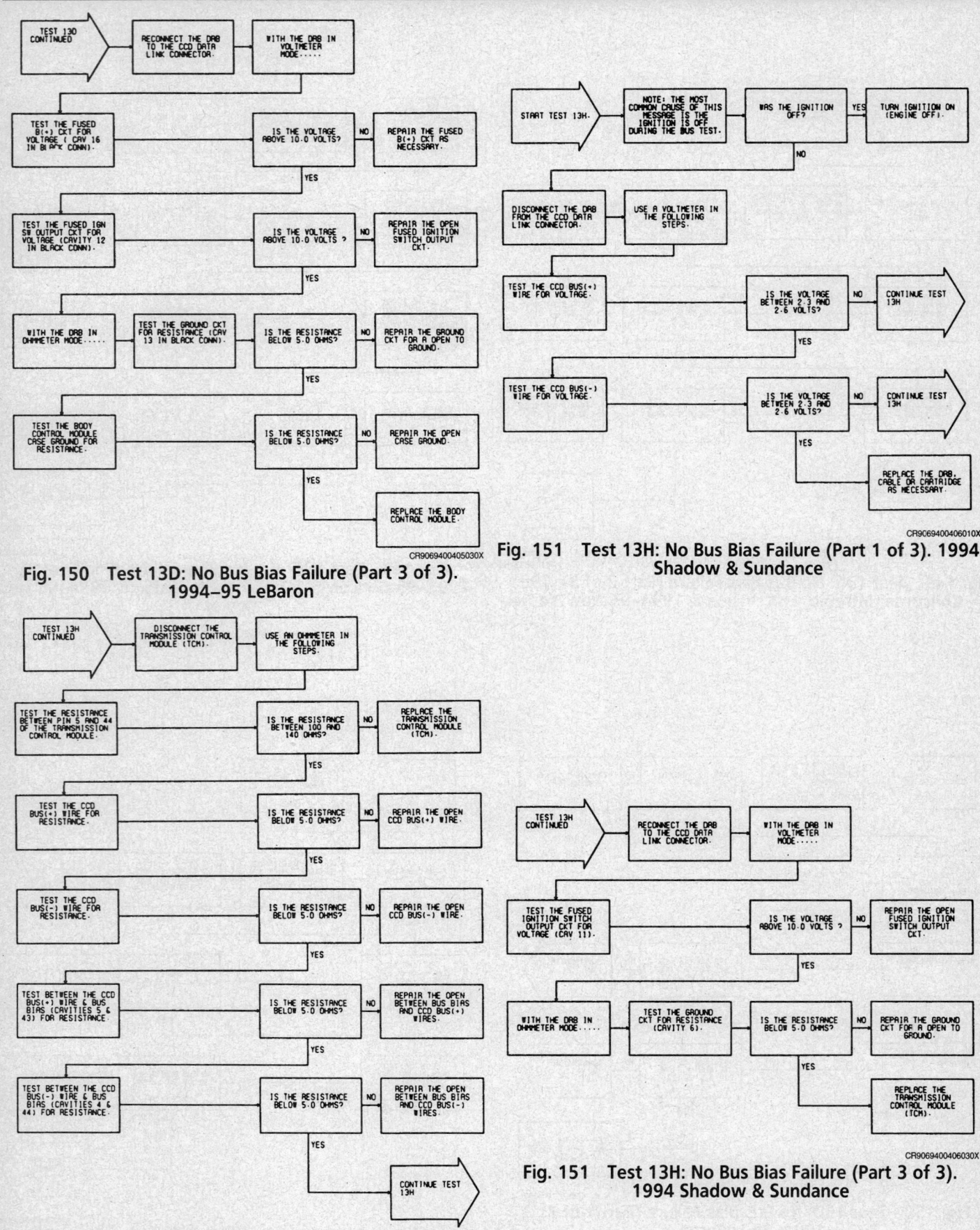

Fig. 150   Test 13D: No Bus Bias Failure (Part 3 of 3). 1994–95 LeBaron

Fig. 151   Test 13H: No Bus Bias Failure (Part 1 of 3). 1994 Shadow & Sundance

Fig. 151   Test 13H: No Bus Bias Failure (Part 2 of 3). 1994 Shadow & Sundance

Fig. 151   Test 13H: No Bus Bias Failure (Part 3 of 3). 1994 Shadow & Sundance

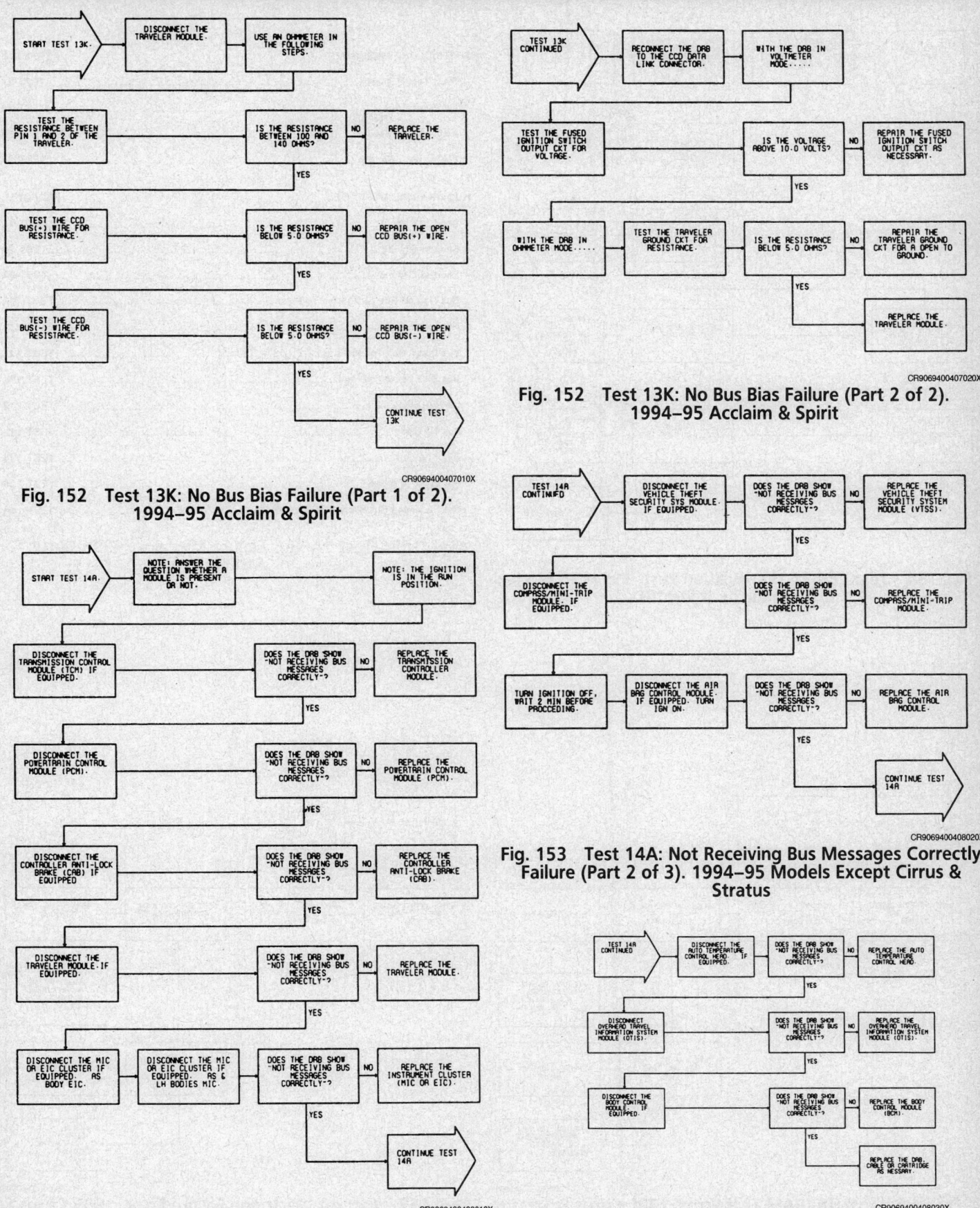

Fig. 152   Test 13K: No Bus Bias Failure (Part 1 of 2).
1994–95 Acclaim & Spirit

CR9069400407010X

Fig. 152   Test 13K: No Bus Bias Failure (Part 2 of 2).
1994–95 Acclaim & Spirit

CR9069400407020X

Fig. 153   Test 14A: Not Receiving Bus Messages Correctly
Failure (Part 1 of 3). 1994–95 Models Except Cirrus &
Stratus

CR9069400408010X

Fig. 153   Test 14A: Not Receiving Bus Messages Correctly
Failure (Part 2 of 3). 1994–95 Models Except Cirrus &
Stratus

CR9069400408020)

Fig. 153   Test 14A: Not Receiving Bus
Messages Correctly Failure (Part 3 of 3).
1994–95 Models Except Cirrus & Stratus

CR9069400408030X

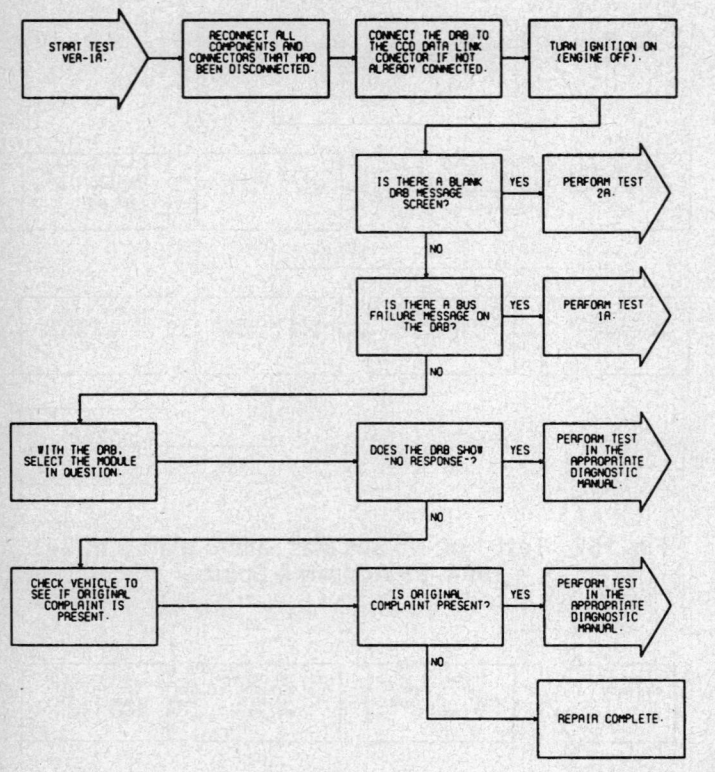

Fig. 154 Test VER-1A: Verification Test. 1994–95 Models Except Cirrus & Stratus

DRB FAILURE MESSAGE:	PERFORM:
RAM Test Failure	TEST 3A
Cartridge Error	TEST 4A
Keypad Test Failure	TEST 5A
Low or High Battery	TEST 6A

BUS FAILURE MESSAGE:	PERFORM:
Short to Battery	TEST 7A
Short to 5 Volts	TEST 8A
Short to Ground	TEST 9A
Bus (+) and Bus (-) Shorted Together	TEST 10A
No Termination	TEST 11L
Bus Bias Level Too low	TEST 12L
Bus Bias Level Too High	TEST 12L
No Bus Bias	TEST 13M
Bus (+) Open	TEST 12L
Bus (-) Open	TEST 12L
Bus (+) & (-) Open	TEST 12L
Not Receiving Bus Messages Correctly	TEST 14A

Fig. 155 Test 1A: Bus Failure Message. 1995 Cirrus & Stratus

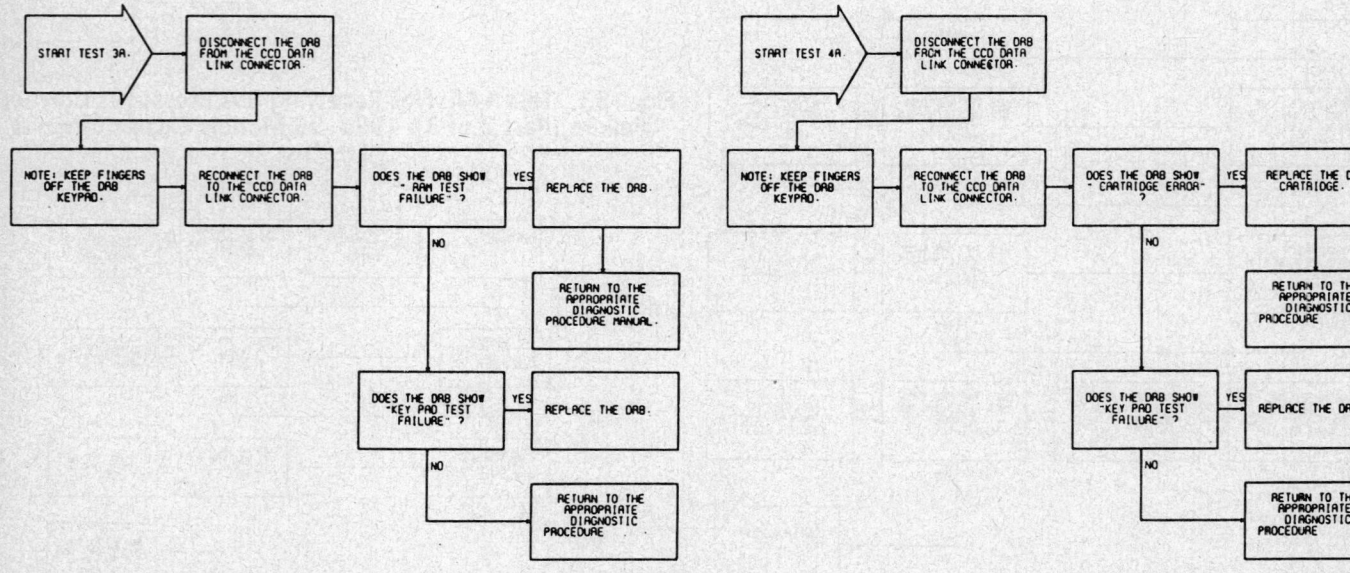

Fig. 156 Test 3A: RAM Test Error. 1995 Cirrus & Stratus

Fig. 157 Test 4A: Cartridge Failure Error. 1995 Cirrus & Stratus

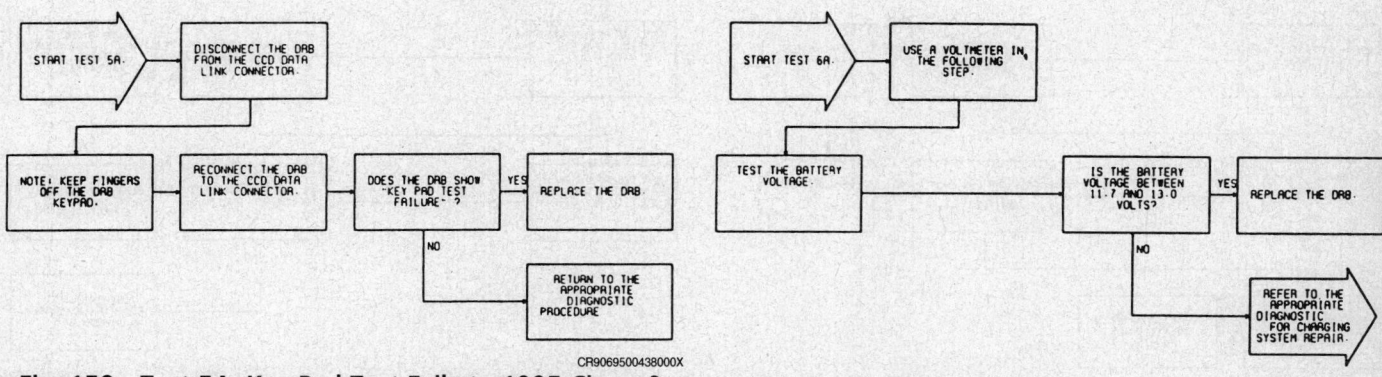

Fig. 158   Test 5A: Key Pad Test Failure. 1995 Cirrus & Stratus

CR9069500438000X

Fig. 159   Test 6A: Low Or High Battery. 1995 Cirrus & Stratus

CR9069500439000X

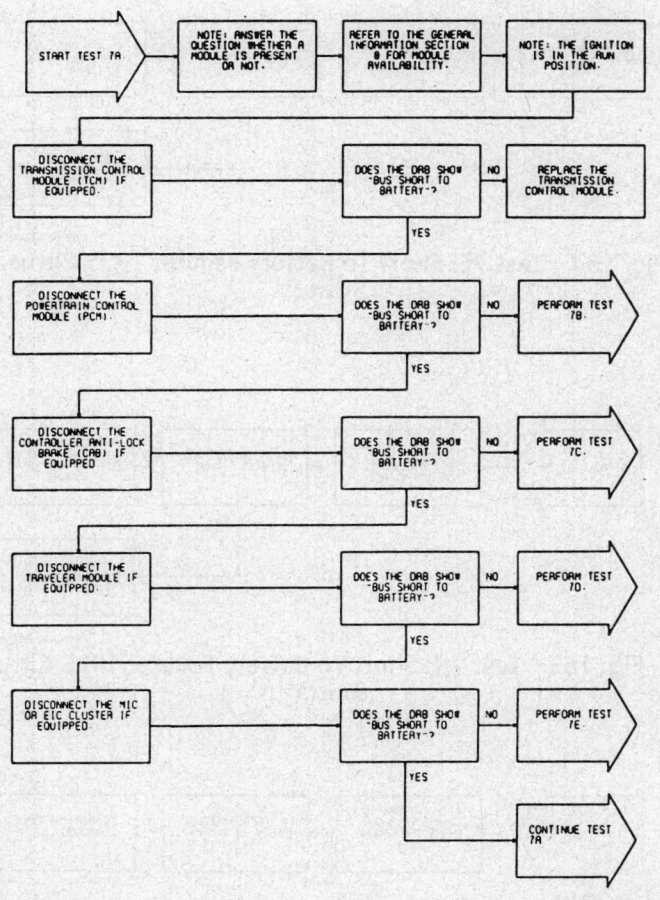

Fig. 160   Test 7A: Short To Battery Failure (Part 1 of 3). 1995 Cirrus & Stratus

CR9069500440010X

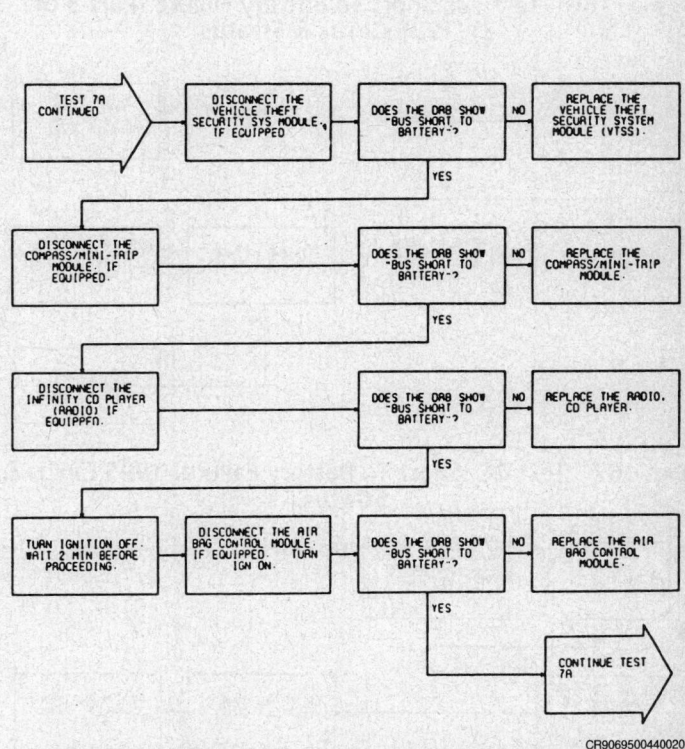

Fig. 160   Test 7A: Short To Battery Failure (Part 2 of 3). 1995 Cirrus & Stratus

CR9069500440020X

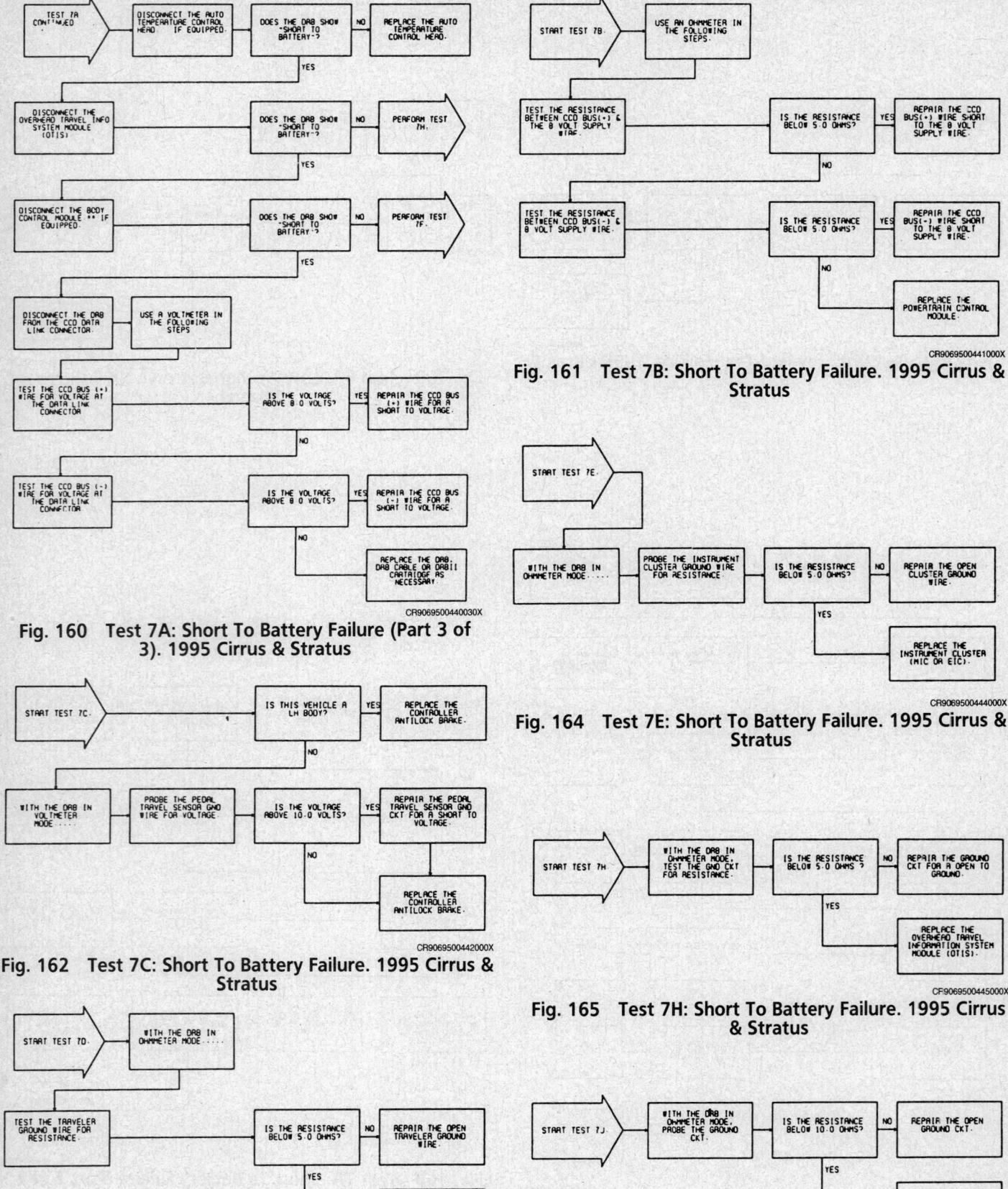

Fig. 160 Test 7A: Short To Battery Failure (Part 3 of 3). 1995 Cirrus & Stratus

Fig. 161 Test 7B: Short To Battery Failure. 1995 Cirrus & Stratus

Fig. 162 Test 7C: Short To Battery Failure. 1995 Cirrus & Stratus

Fig. 163 Test 7D: Short To Battery Failure. 1995 Cirrus & Stratus

Fig. 164 Test 7E: Short To Battery Failure. 1995 Cirrus & Stratus

Fig. 165 Test 7H: Short To Battery Failure. 1995 Cirrus & Stratus

Fig. 166 Test 7J: Short To Battery Failure. 1995 Cirrus & Stratus

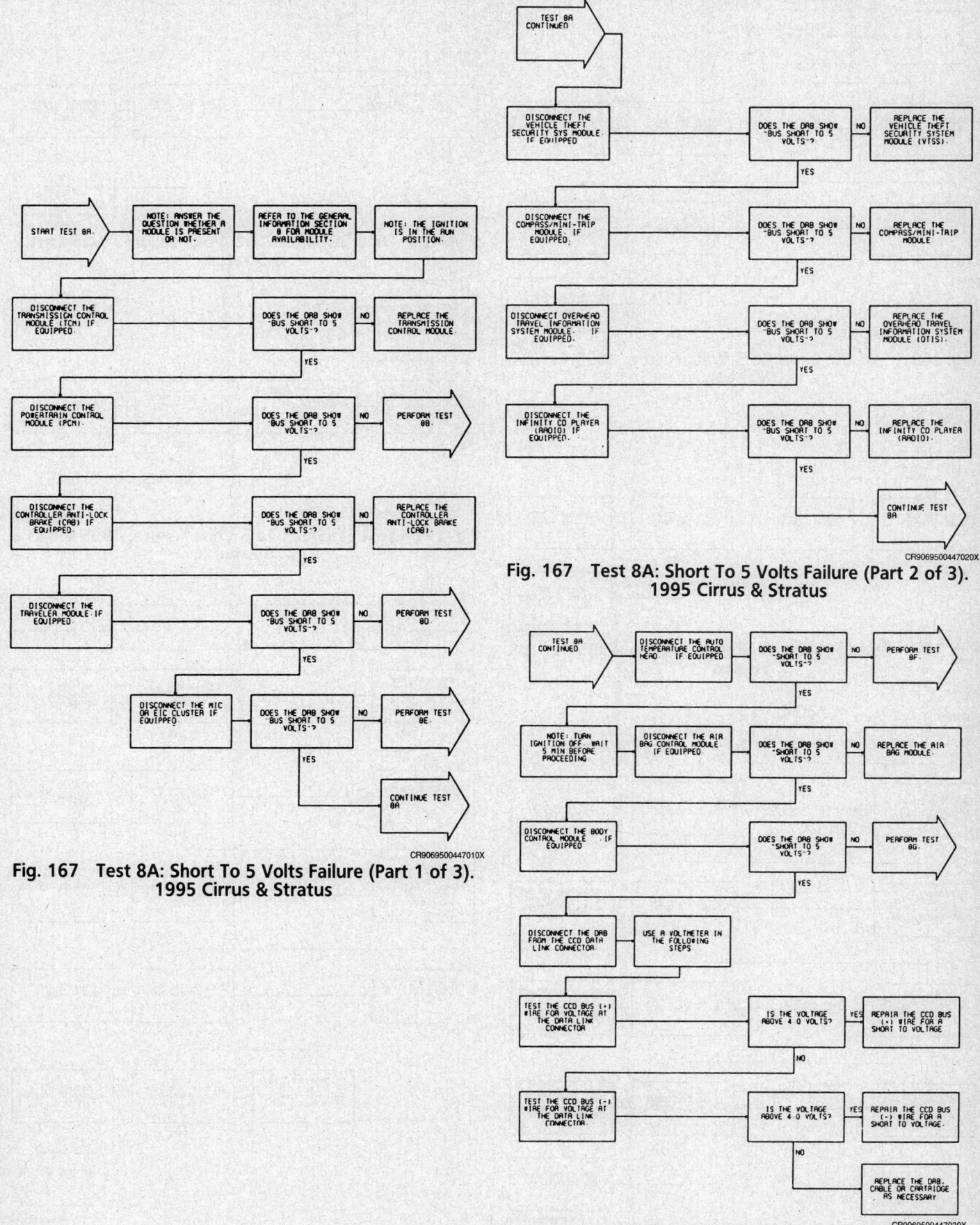

Fig. 167   Test 8A: Short To 5 Volts Failure (Part 1 of 3).
            1995 Cirrus & Stratus

CR9069500447010X

Fig. 167   Test 8A: Short To 5 Volts Failure (Part 2 of 3).
            1995 Cirrus & Stratus

CR9069500447020X

Fig. 167   Test 8A: Short To 5 Volts Failure (Part 3 of
            3). 1995 Cirrus & Stratus

CR9069500447030X

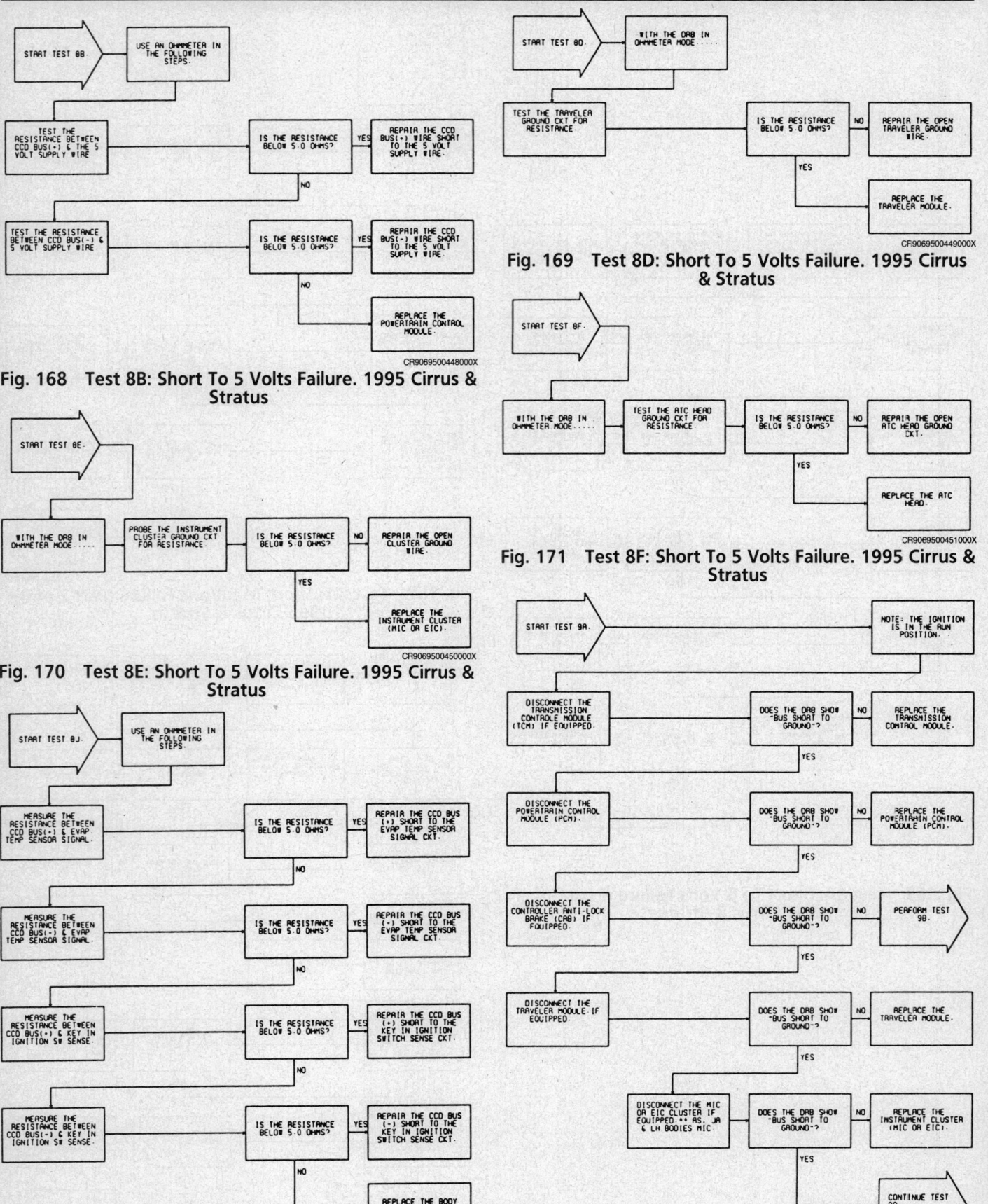

Fig. 168   Test 8B: Short To 5 Volts Failure. 1995 Cirrus & Stratus

Fig. 169   Test 8D: Short To 5 Volts Failure. 1995 Cirrus & Stratus

Fig. 170   Test 8E: Short To 5 Volts Failure. 1995 Cirrus & Stratus

Fig. 171   Test 8F: Short To 5 Volts Failure. 1995 Cirrus & Stratus

Fig. 172   Test 8J: Short To 5 Volts Failure. 1995 Cirrus & Stratus

Fig. 173   Test 9A: Short To Ground Failure (Part 1 of 4). 1995 Cirrus & Stratus

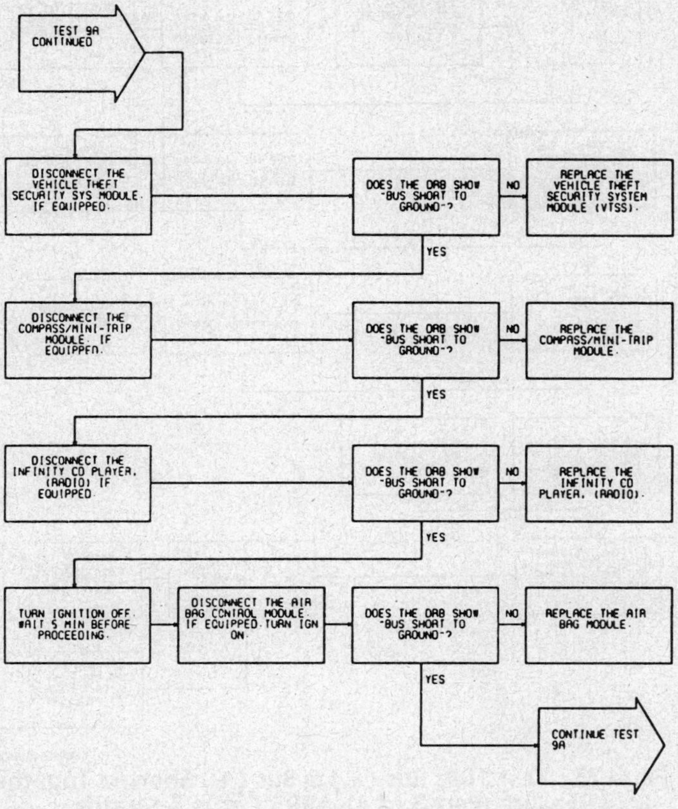

Part 2 of 4 (top left flowchart)

TEST 9A CONTINUED

DISCONNECT THE VEHICLE THEFT SECURITY SYS MODULE. IF EQUIPPED. → DOES THE DRB SHOW "BUS SHORT TO GROUND"? → NO → REPLACE THE VEHICLE THEFT SECURITY SYSTEM MODULE (VTSS). / YES ↓

DISCONNECT THE COMPASS/MINI-TRIP MODULE. IF EQUIPPED. → DOES THE DRB SHOW "BUS SHORT TO GROUND"? → NO → REPLACE THE COMPASS/MINI-TRIP MODULE. / YES ↓

DISCONNECT THE INFINITY CD PLAYER. (RADIO) IF EQUIPPED. → DOES THE DRB SHOW "BUS SHORT TO GROUND"? → NO → REPLACE THE INFINITY CD PLAYER. (RADIO). / YES ↓

TURN IGNITION OFF. WAIT 5 MIN BEFORE PROCEEDING. → DISCONNECT THE AIR BAG CONTROL MODULE. IF EQUIPPED. TURN IGN ON. → DOES THE DRB SHOW "BUS SHORT TO GROUND"? → NO → REPLACE THE AIR BAG MODULE. / YES ↓

CONTINUE TEST 9A

CR9069500453020X

Fig. 173   Test 9A: Short To Ground Failure (Part 2 of 4). 1995 Cirrus & Stratus

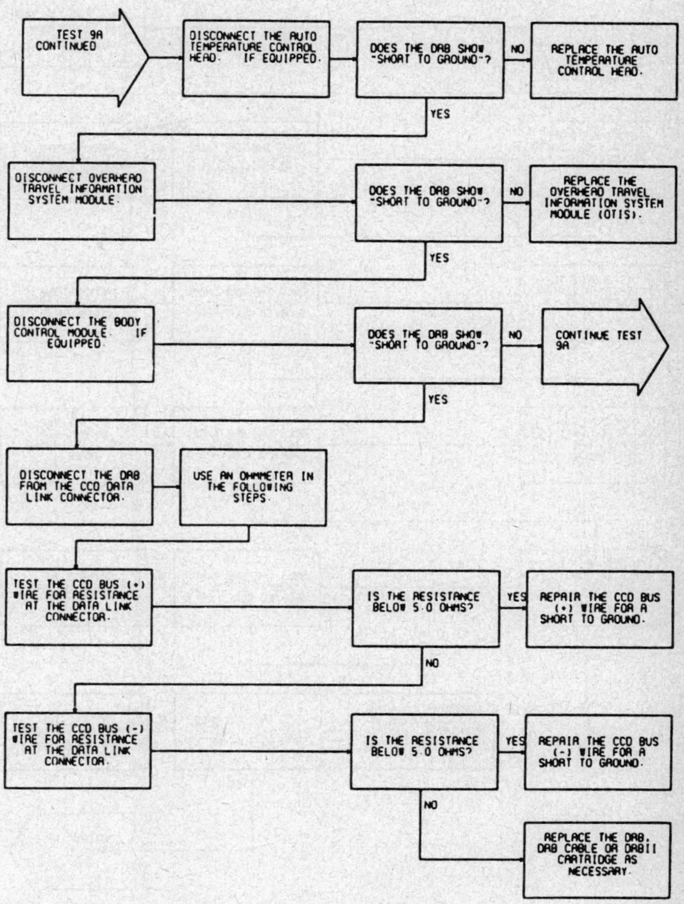

Part 3 of 4 (top right flowchart)

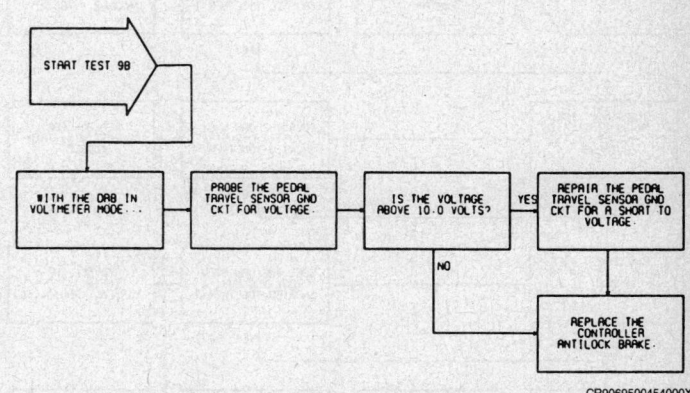

TEST 9A CONTINUED → DISCONNECT THE AUTO TEMPERATURE CONTROL HEAD. IF EQUIPPED. → DOES THE DRB SHOW "SHORT TO GROUND"? → REPLACE THE AUTO TEMPERATURE CONTROL HEAD. / YES ↓

DISCONNECT OVERHEAD TRAVEL INFORMATION SYSTEM MODULE. → DOES THE DRB SHOW "SHORT TO GROUND"? → NO → REPLACE THE OVERHEAD TRAVEL INFORMATION SYSTEM MODULE (OTIS). / YES ↓

DISCONNECT THE BODY CONTROL MODULE. IF EQUIPPED. → DOES THE DRB SHOW "SHORT TO GROUND"? → NO → CONTINUE TEST 9A / YES ↓

DISCONNECT THE DRB FROM THE CCD DATA LINK CONNECTOR. → USE AN OHMMETER IN THE FOLLOWING STEPS. ↓

TEST THE CCD BUS (+) WIRE FOR RESISTANCE AT THE DATA LINK CONNECTOR. → IS THE RESISTANCE BELOW 5.0 OHMS? → YES → REPAIR THE CCD BUS (+) WIRE FOR A SHORT TO GROUND. / NO ↓

TEST THE CCD BUS (–) WIRE FOR RESISTANCE AT THE DATA LINK CONNECTOR. → IS THE RESISTANCE BELOW 5.0 OHMS? → YES → REPAIR THE CCD BUS (–) WIRE FOR A SHORT TO GROUND. / NO ↓

REPLACE THE DRB, DRB CABLE OR DRBII CARTRIDGE AS NECESSARY.

CR9069500453030X

Fig. 173   Test 9A: Short To Ground Failure (Part 3 of 4). 1995 Cirrus & Stratus

Part 4 of 4 (bottom left flowchart)

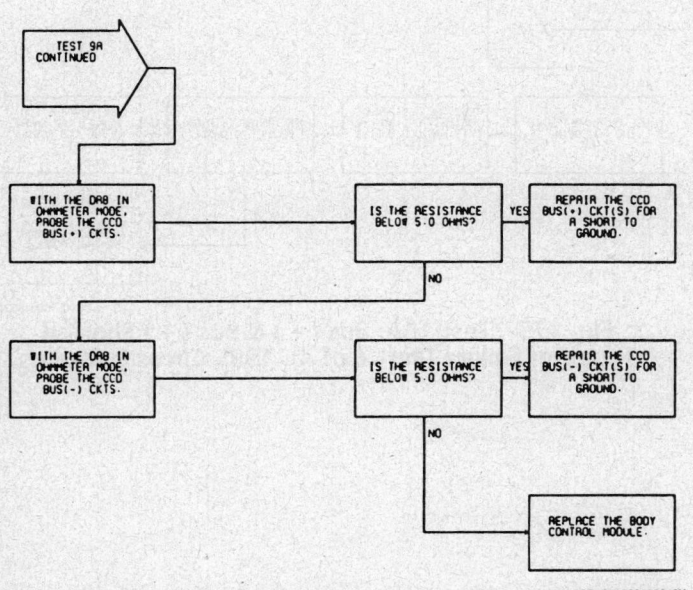

TEST 9A CONTINUED

WITH THE DRB IN OHMMETER MODE, PROBE THE CCD BUS(+) CKTS. → IS THE RESISTANCE BELOW 5.0 OHMS? → YES → REPAIR THE CCD BUS(+) CKT(S) FOR A SHORT TO GROUND. / NO ↓

WITH THE DRB IN OHMMETER MODE, PROBE THE CCD BUS(–) CKTS. → IS THE RESISTANCE BELOW 5.0 OHMS? → YES → REPAIR THE CCD BUS(–) CKT(S) FOR A SHORT TO GROUND. / NO ↓

REPLACE THE BODY CONTROL MODULE.

CR9069500453040X

Fig. 173   Test 9A: Short To Ground Failure (Part 4 of 4). 1995 Cirrus & Stratus

Bottom right flowchart (Test 9B)

START TEST 9B

WITH THE DRB IN VOLTMETER MODE... → PROBE THE PEDAL TRAVEL SENSOR GND CKT FOR VOLTAGE. → IS THE VOLTAGE ABOVE 10.0 VOLTS? → YES → REPAIR THE PEDAL TRAVEL SENSOR GND CKT FOR A SHORT TO VOLTAGE. / NO ↓

REPLACE THE CONTROLLER ANTILOCK BRAKE.

CR9069500454000X

Fig. 174   Test 9B: Short To Ground Failure. 1995 Cirrus & Stratus

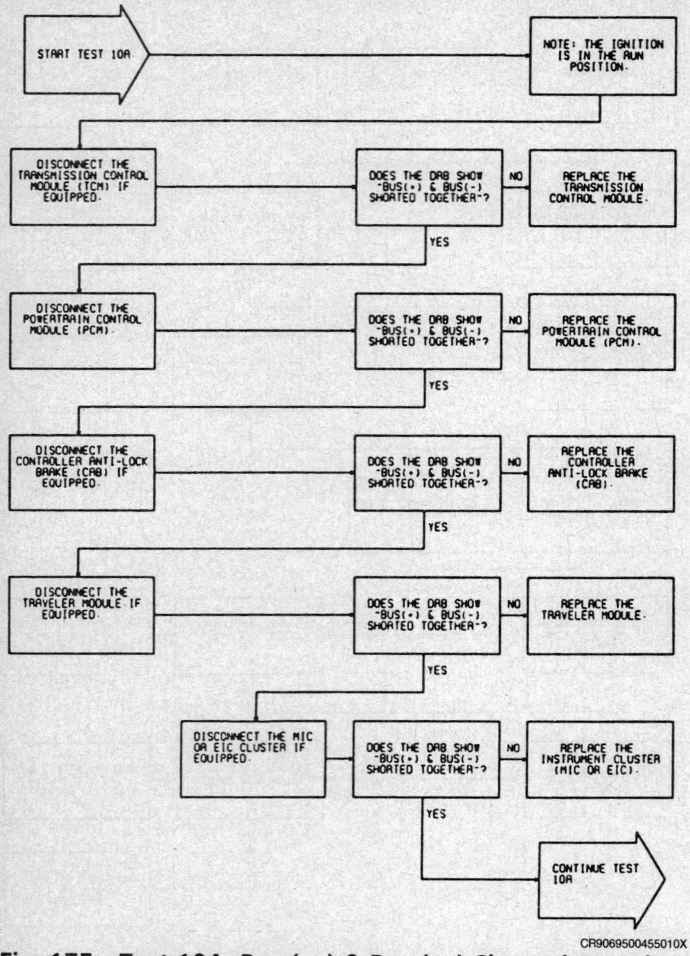

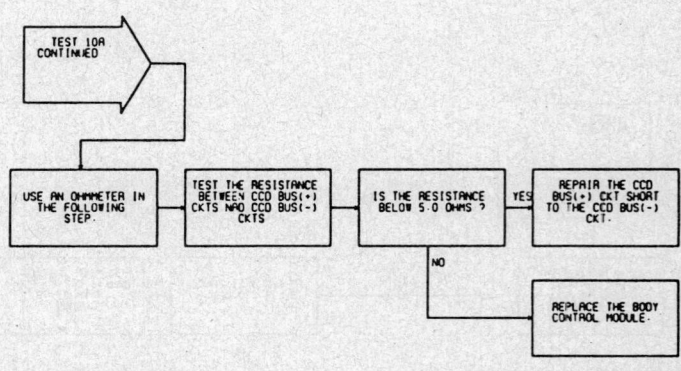

Fig. 175   Test 10A: Bus (+) & Bus (+) Shorted Together Failure (Part 3 of 4). 1995 Cirrus & Stratus

Fig. 175   Test 10A: Bus (+) & Bus (+) Shorted Together Failure (Part 1 of 4). 1995 Cirrus & Stratus

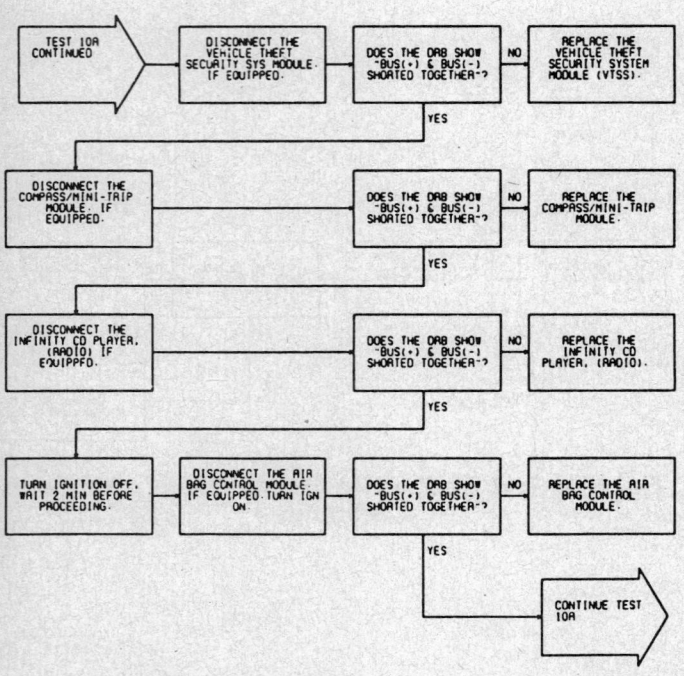

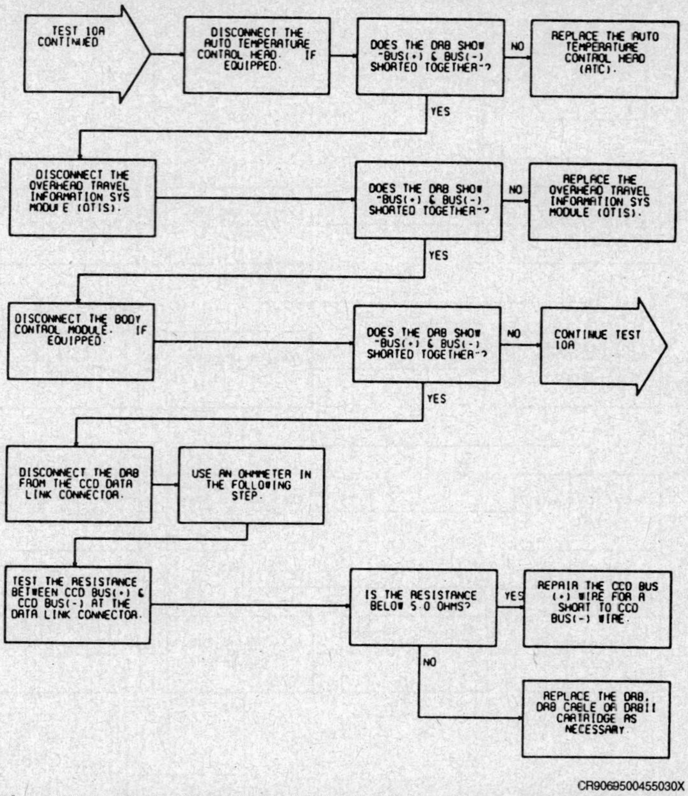

Fig. 175   Test 10A: Bus (+) & Bus (+) Shorted Together Failure (Part 4 of 4). 1995 Cirrus & Stratus

Fig. 175   Test 10A: Bus (+) & Bus (+) Shorted Together Failure (Part 2 of 4). 1995 Cirrus & Stratus

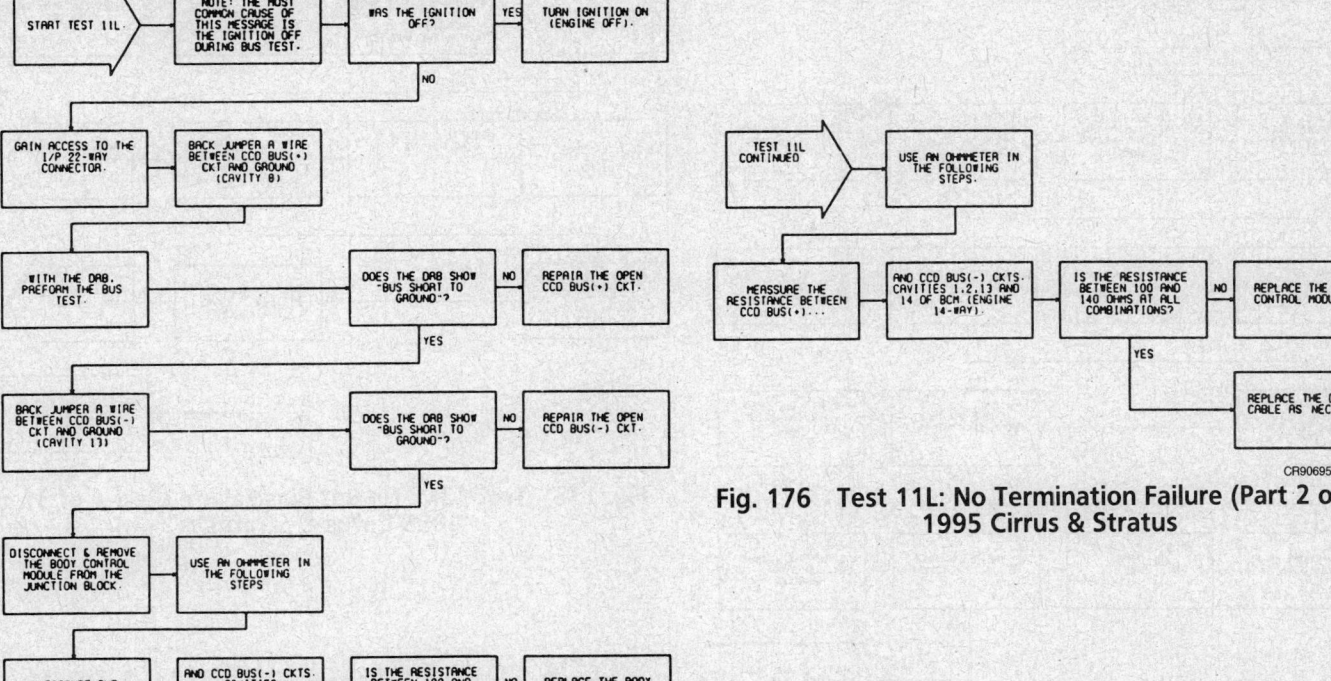

Fig. 176   Test 11L: No Termination Failure (Part 1 of 2).
1995 Cirrus & Stratus

CR9069500456010X

Fig. 176   Test 11L: No Termination Failure (Part 2 of 2).
1995 Cirrus & Stratus

CR9069500456020X

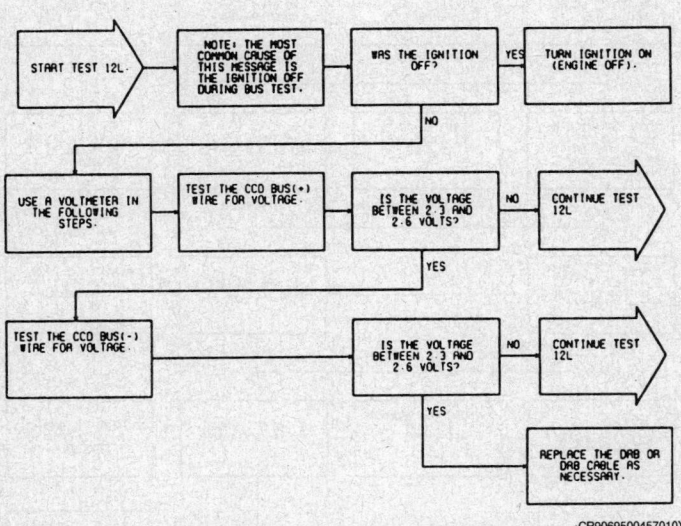

Fig. 177   Test 12L: Bus Bias Level Or Bus (+/-) Open
Failure (Part 1 of 3). 1995 Cirrus & Stratus

CR9069500457010X

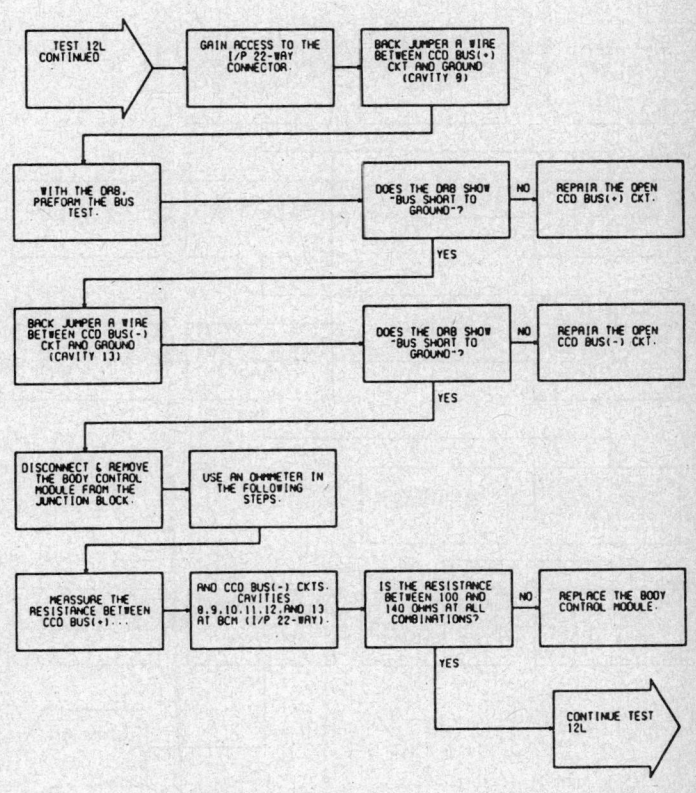

Fig. 177   Test 12L: Bus Bias Level Or Bus (+/-) Open
Failure (Part 2 of 3). 1995 Cirrus & Stratus

CR9069500457020X

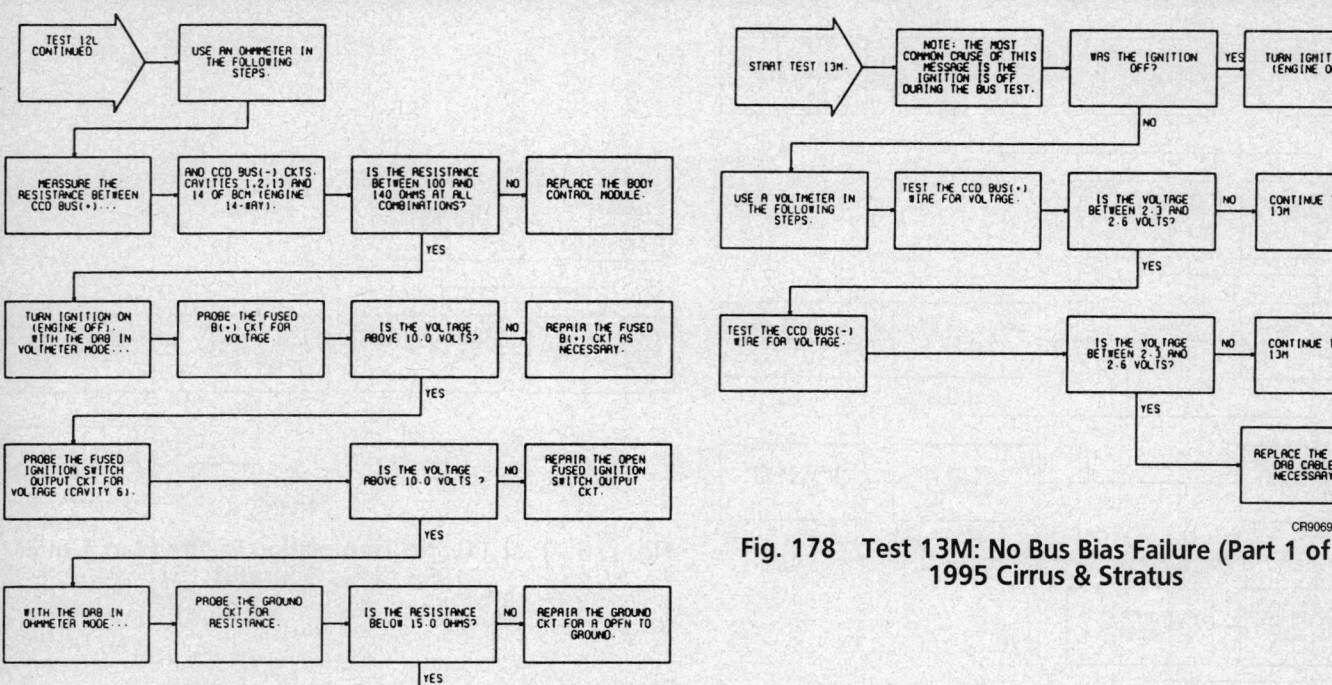

Fig. 177   Test 12L: Bus Bias Level Or Bus (+/-) Open
Failure (Part 3 of 3). 1995 Cirrus & Stratus

Fig. 178   Test 13M: No Bus Bias Failure (Part 1 of 3).
1995 Cirrus & Stratus

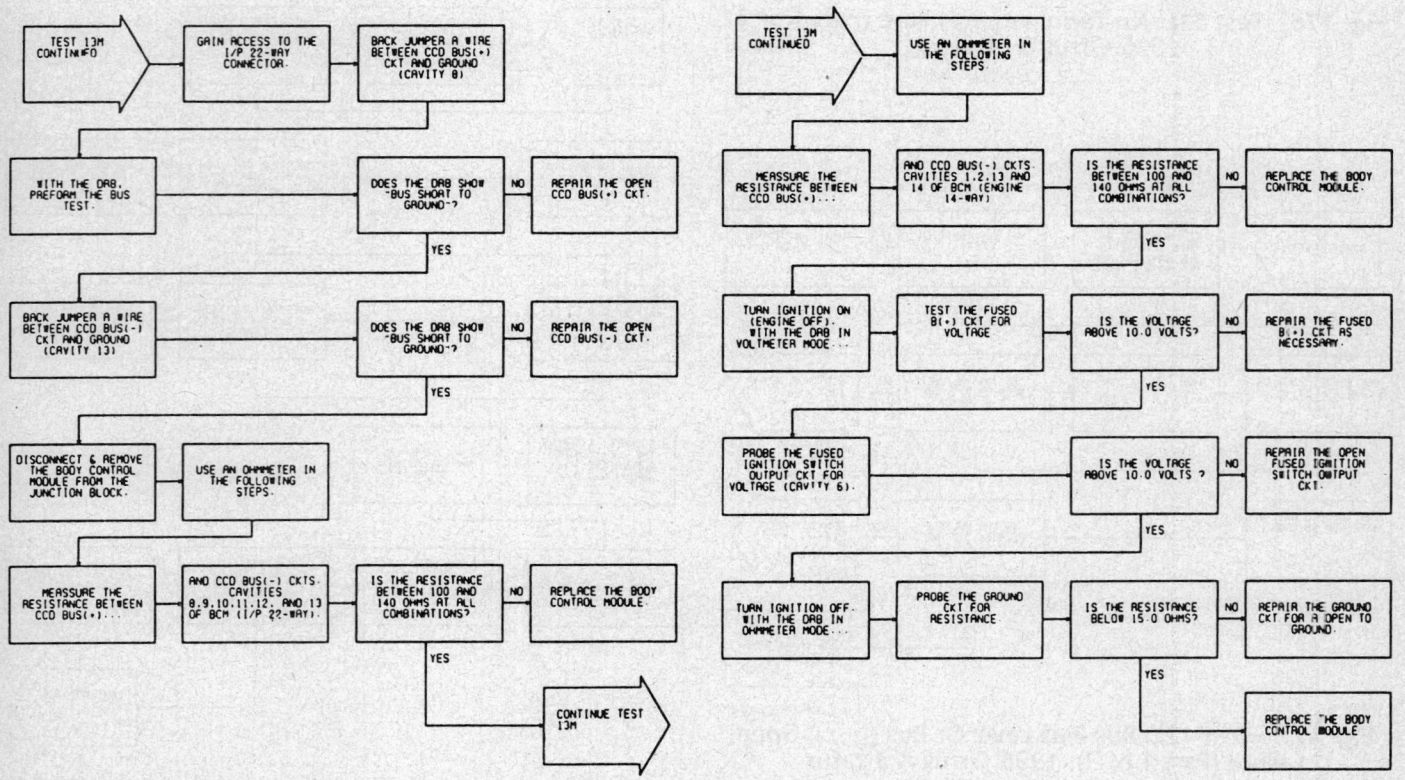

Fig. 178   Test 13M: No Bus Bias Failure (Part 2 of 3).
1995 Cirrus & Stratus

Fig. 178   Test 13M: No Bus Bias Failure (Part 3 of 3).
1995 Cirrus & Stratus

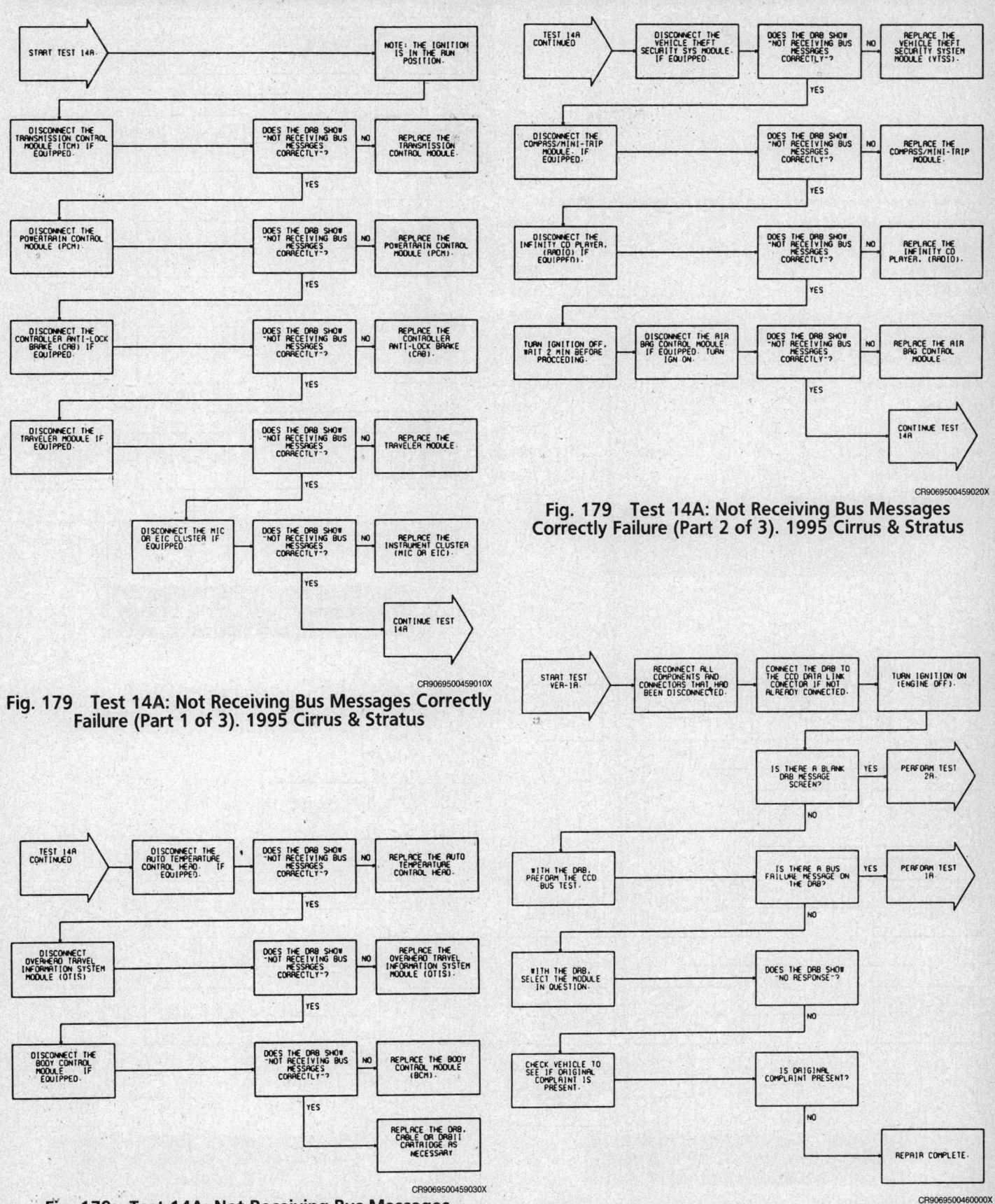

Fig. 179   Test 14A: Not Receiving Bus Messages Correctly Failure (Part 1 of 3). 1995 Cirrus & Stratus

Fig. 179   Test 14A: Not Receiving Bus Messages Correctly Failure (Part 2 of 3). 1995 Cirrus & Stratus

Fig. 179   Test 14A: Not Receiving Bus Messages Correctly Failure (Part 3 of 3). 1995 Cirrus & Stratus

Fig. 180   Test VER 1A: Verification Test. 1995 Cirrus & Stratus

Choose the applicable failure message from the list below and perform the indicated test.

BUS FAILURE MESSAGE: **PERFORM:**

Short to Battery . . . . .TEST 2A

Short to 5 Volts . . . . .TEST 3A

Short to Ground . . . . .TEST 4A

Bus (+) and Bus (-) Shorted Together . . . . .TEST 5A

No Termination . . . . .TEST 6A

Bus Bias Level Too Low . . . . .TEST 7A

Bus Bias Level Too High . . . . .TEST 7A

No Bus Bias . . . . .TEST 8A

Bus (+) Open . . . . .TEST 8A

Bus (–) Open . . . . .TEST 8A

Bus (+) and (–) Open . . . . .TEST 8A

Not Receiving Bus Messages Correctly . . . . .TEST 9A

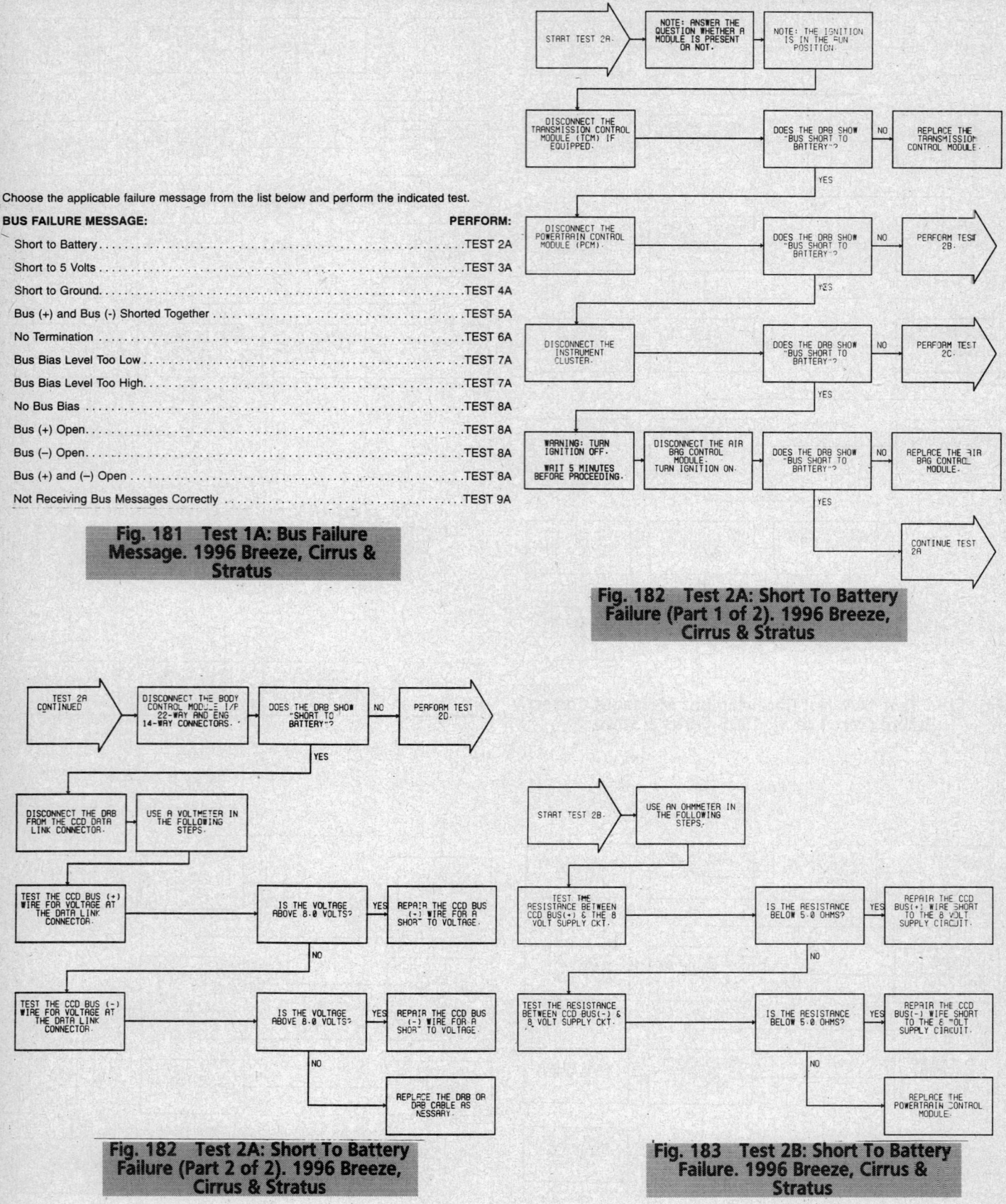

Fig. 181   Test 1A: Bus Failure Message. 1996 Breeze, Cirrus & Stratus

Fig. 182   Test 2A: Short To Battery Failure (Part 1 of 2). 1996 Breeze, Cirrus & Stratus

Fig. 182   Test 2A: Short To Battery Failure (Part 2 of 2). 1996 Breeze, Cirrus & Stratus

Fig. 183   Test 2B: Short To Battery Failure. 1996 Breeze, Cirrus & Stratus

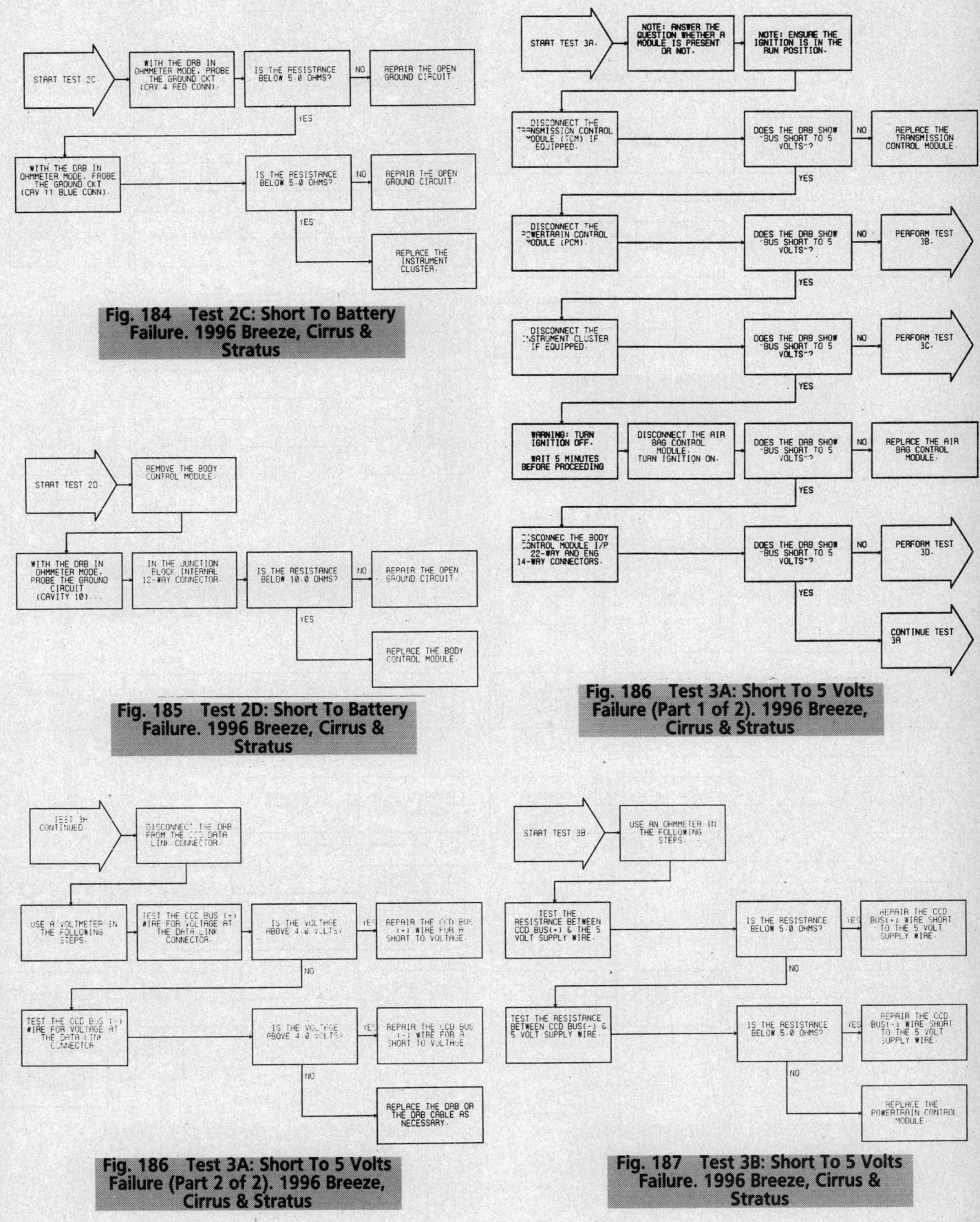

Fig. 184   Test 2C: Short To Battery Failure. 1996 Breeze, Cirrus & Stratus

Fig. 185   Test 2D: Short To Battery Failure. 1996 Breeze, Cirrus & Stratus

Fig. 186   Test 3A: Short To 5 Volts Failure (Part 1 of 2). 1996 Breeze, Cirrus & Stratus

Fig. 186   Test 3A: Short To 5 Volts Failure (Part 2 of 2). 1996 Breeze, Cirrus & Stratus

Fig. 187   Test 3B: Short To 5 Volts Failure. 1996 Breeze, Cirrus & Stratus

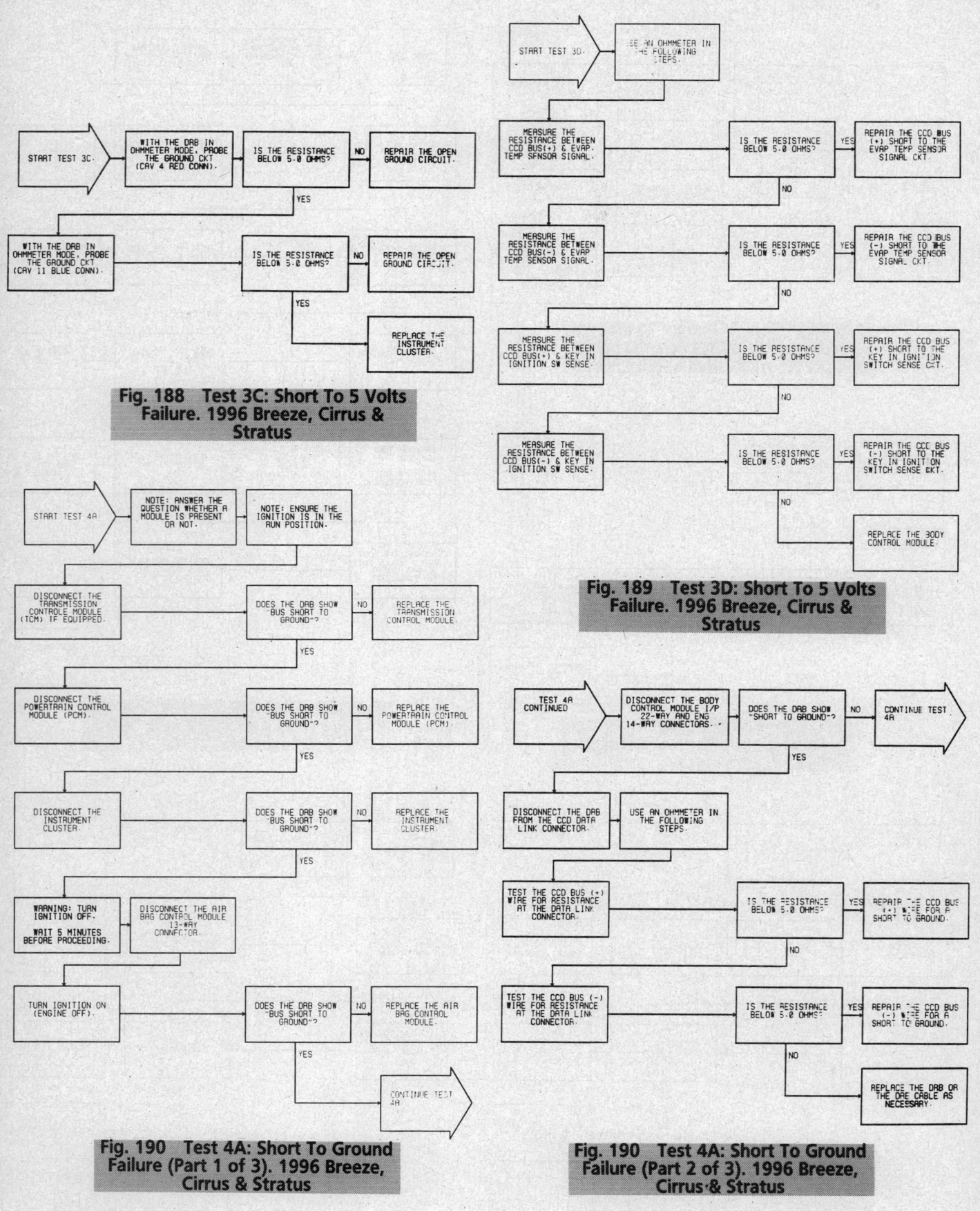

Fig. 188 Test 3C: Short To 5 Volts Failure. 1996 Breeze, Cirrus & Stratus

Fig. 189 Test 3D: Short To 5 Volts Failure. 1996 Breeze, Cirrus & Stratus

Fig. 190 Test 4A: Short To Ground Failure (Part 1 of 3). 1996 Breeze, Cirrus & Stratus

Fig. 190 Test 4A: Short To Ground Failure (Part 2 of 3). 1996 Breeze, Cirrus & Stratus

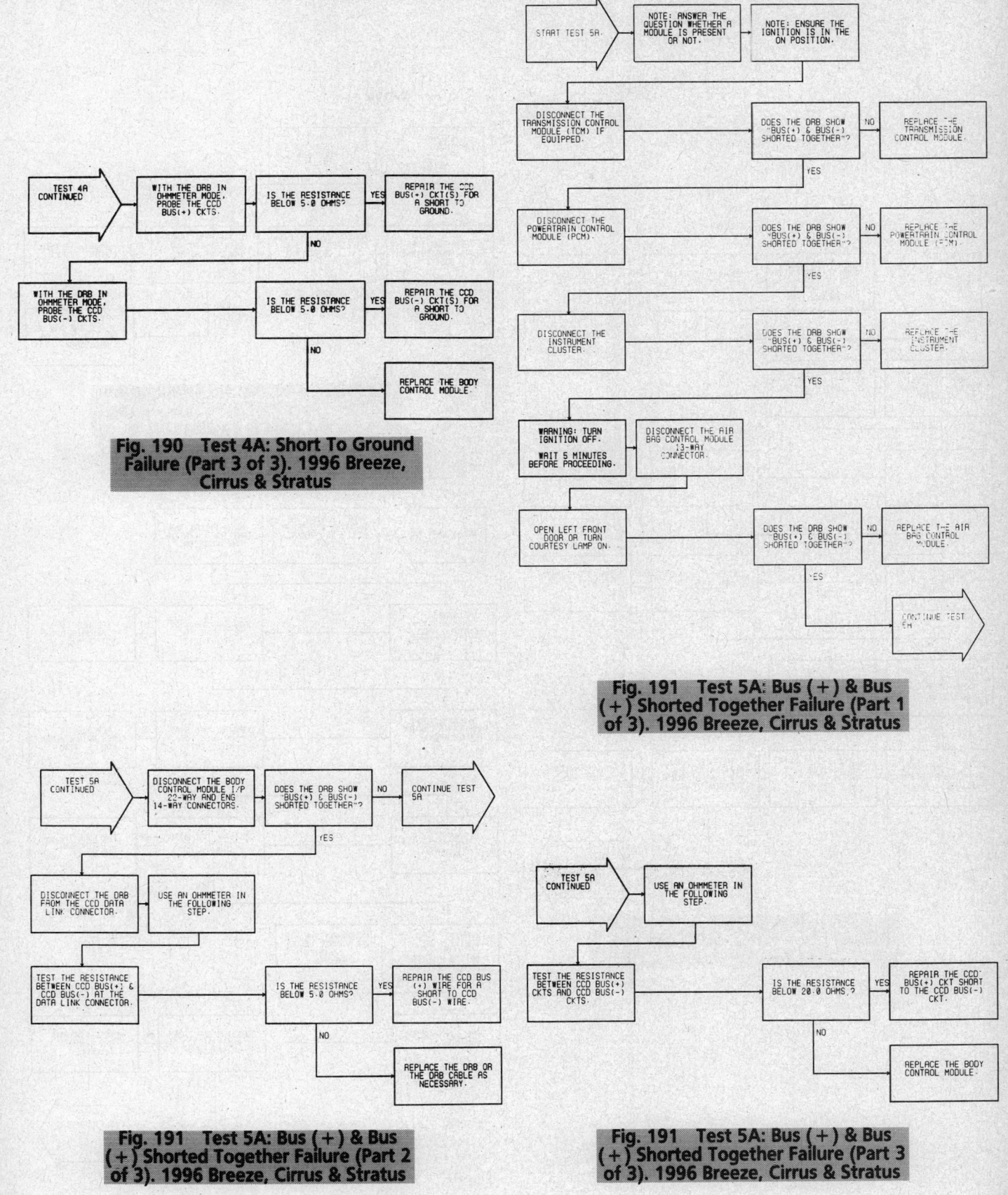

Fig. 190 Test 4A: Short To Ground Failure (Part 3 of 3). 1996 Breeze, Cirrus & Stratus

Fig. 191 Test 5A: Bus (+) & Bus (+) Shorted Together Failure (Part 1 of 3). 1996 Breeze, Cirrus & Stratus

Fig. 191 Test 5A: Bus (+) & Bus (+) Shorted Together Failure (Part 2 of 3). 1996 Breeze, Cirrus & Stratus

Fig. 191 Test 5A: Bus (+) & Bus (+) Shorted Together Failure (Part 3 of 3). 1996 Breeze, Cirrus & Stratus

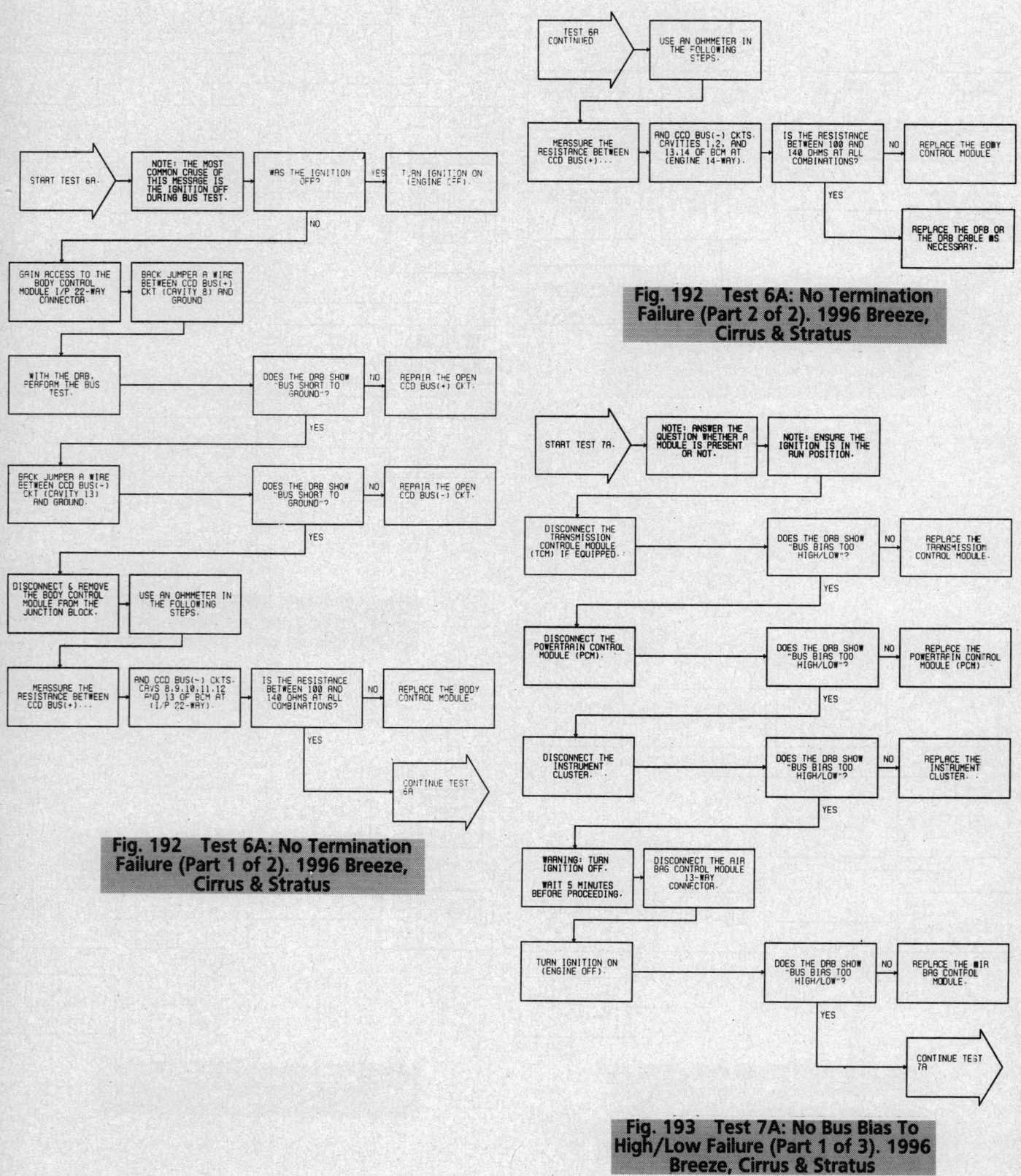

Fig. 192   Test 6A: No Termination Failure (Part 2 of 2). 1996 Breeze, Cirrus & Stratus

Fig. 192   Test 6A: No Termination Failure (Part 1 of 2). 1996 Breeze, Cirrus & Stratus

Fig. 193   Test 7A: No Bus Bias To High/Low Failure (Part 1 of 3). 1996 Breeze, Cirrus & Stratus

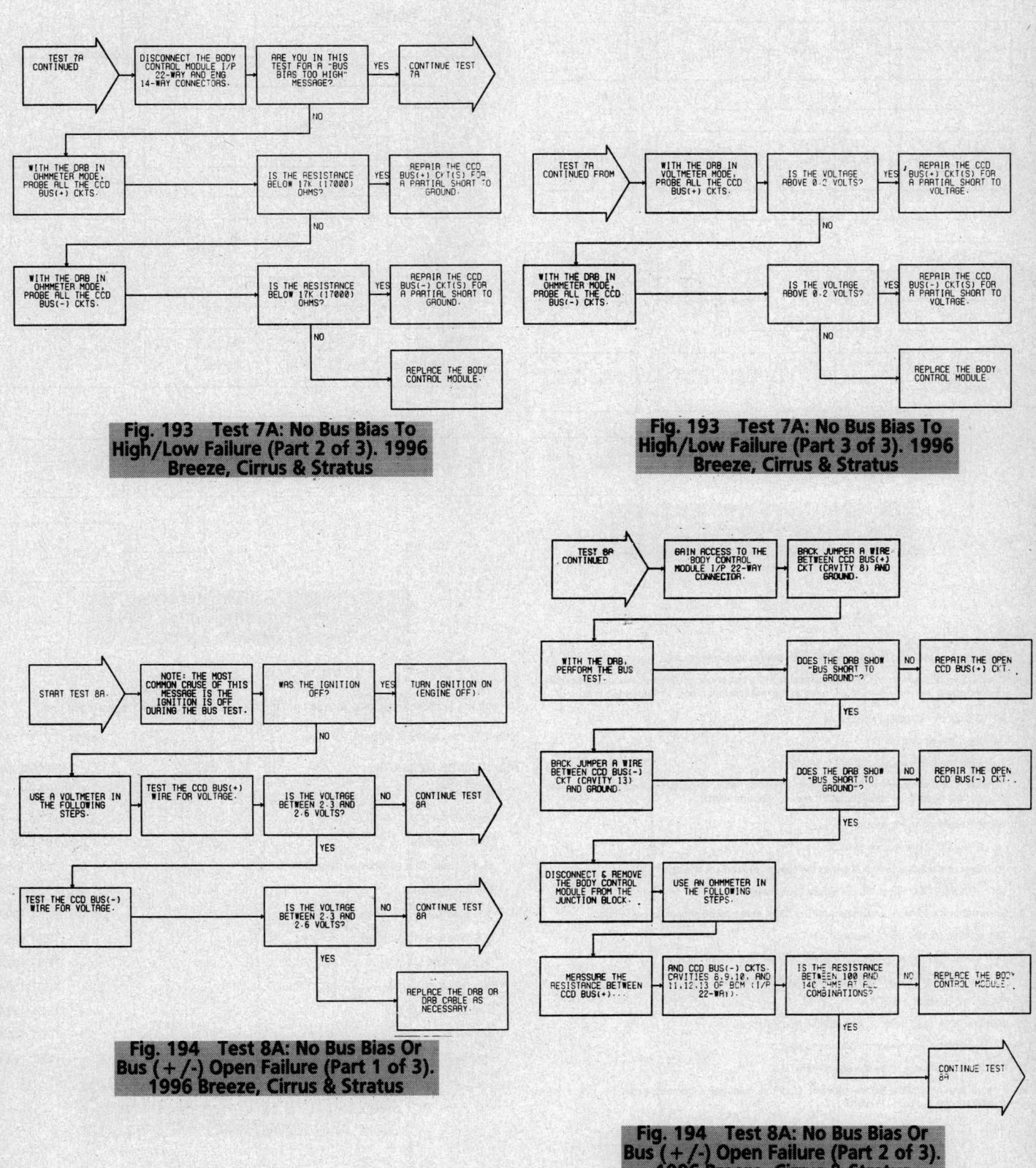

Fig. 193 Test 7A: No Bus Bias To High/Low Failure (Part 2 of 3). 1996 Breeze, Cirrus & Stratus

Fig. 193 Test 7A: No Bus Bias To High/Low Failure (Part 3 of 3). 1996 Breeze, Cirrus & Stratus

Fig. 194 Test 8A: No Bus Bias Or Bus (+ / -) Open Failure (Part 1 of 3). 1996 Breeze, Cirrus & Stratus

Fig. 194 Test 8A: No Bus Bias Or Bus (+ / -) Open Failure (Part 2 of 3). 1996 Breeze, Cirrus & Stratus

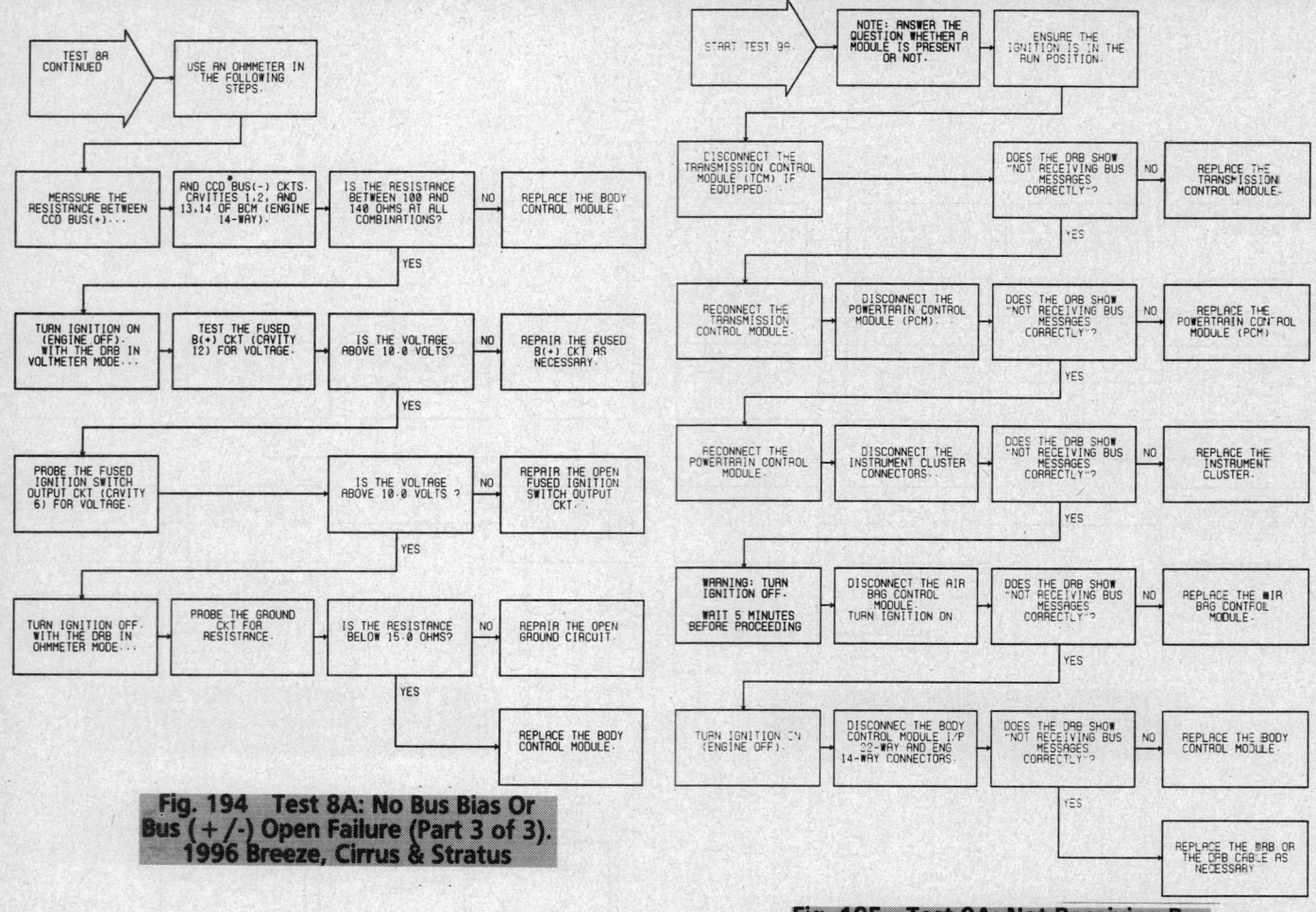

Fig. 194   Test 8A: No Bus Bias Or Bus (+/-) Open Failure (Part 3 of 3). 1996 Breeze, Cirrus & Stratus

Fig. 195   Test 9A: Not Receiving Bus Messages Correctly Failure. 1996 Breeze, Cirrus & Stratus

1. Reconnect all previously disconnected components and connectors.

2. If repairs were made to the HVAC system, or if the battery or body control module has been disconnected, the HVAC doors will need to be recalibrated. If not, continue to step 3.

   HVAC Door Recalibration Procedure:

   a. Start the engine.

   b. With the DRB, recalibrate the HVAC doors.

3. If the body control module or the multi-function switch has been replaced, the intermittent wiper function will need to be recalibrated. If not, continue to step 4.

   Wiper Recalibration Procedure:

   a. Ensure that the ignition is on.

   b. Ensure the wiper switch is set to the lowest intermittent position.

   c. With the DRB, select "Reset Wiper Switch Minimum."

4. Ensure that the ignition is on, and with the DRB, erase all diagnostic trouble codes.

5. Turn ignition off and wait 5 seconds.

6. Turn ignition on and fully operate the system that was malfunctioning.

   – If the system is operating properly, continue to step 8.

   – If not, perform TEST 1A.

7. With the DRB, read body control module trouble codes.

   – If no codes are present, continue to step 9.

   – If any codes are present, repeat TEST 1A.

8. If there are no trouble codes present, and the customer's complaint can no longer be duplicated, the repair is complete.

Fig. 196   Test VER 1A: Verification Test. 1996 Breeze, Cirrus & Stratus

Choose the applicable failure message from the list below and perform the indicated test.

If the DRB has a blank screen . . . . .perform TEST 115A

BUS FAILURE MESSAGE: **PERFORM:**

Short to Battery . . . . .TEST 133A

Short to 5 Volts . . . . .TEST 134A

Short to Ground . . . . .TEST 135A

Bus (+) and Bus (-) Shorted Together . . . . .TEST 136A

No Termination . . . . .TEST 137A

Bus Bias Level Too Low . . . . TEST 138A

Bus Bias Level Too High . . . . TEST 138A

No Bus Bias . . . . .TEST 139A

Bus (+) Open . . . . TEST 138A

Bus (-) Open . . . . .TEST 138A

Bus (+) & (-) Open . . . . .TEST 138A

Not Receiving Bus Messages Correctly . . . . .TEST 140A

Fig. 197   Test 132A: Bus Failure Message. 1996 Concorde, Intrepid, LHS, New Yorker & Vision

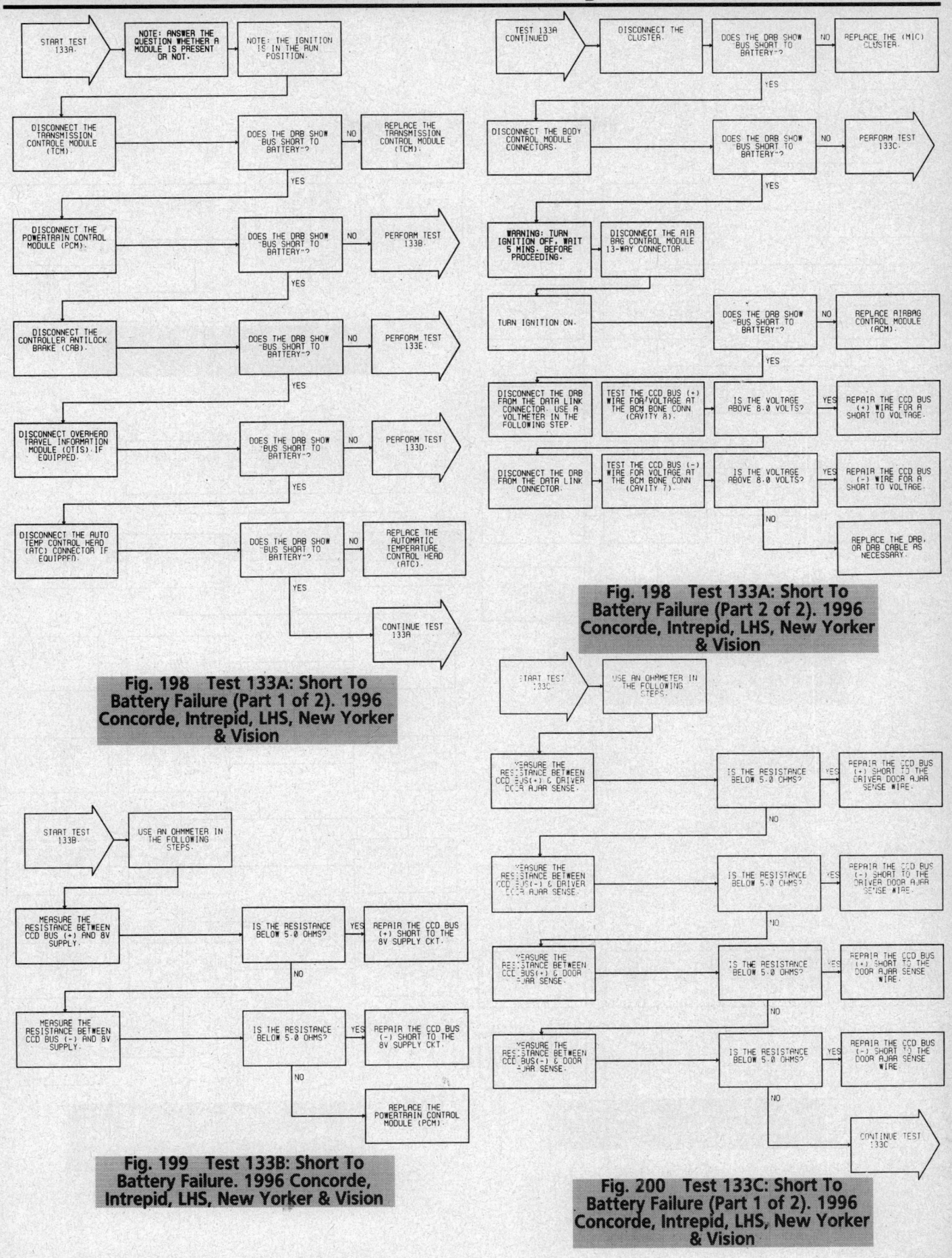

Fig. 198 Test 133A: Short To Battery Failure (Part 1 of 2). 1996 Concorde, Intrepid, LHS, New Yorker & Vision

Fig. 198 Test 133A: Short To Battery Failure (Part 2 of 2). 1996 Concorde, Intrepid, LHS, New Yorker & Vision

Fig. 199 Test 133B: Short To Battery Failure. 1996 Concorde, Intrepid, LHS, New Yorker & Vision

Fig. 200 Test 133C: Short To Battery Failure (Part 1 of 2). 1996 Concorde, Intrepid, LHS, New Yorker & Vision

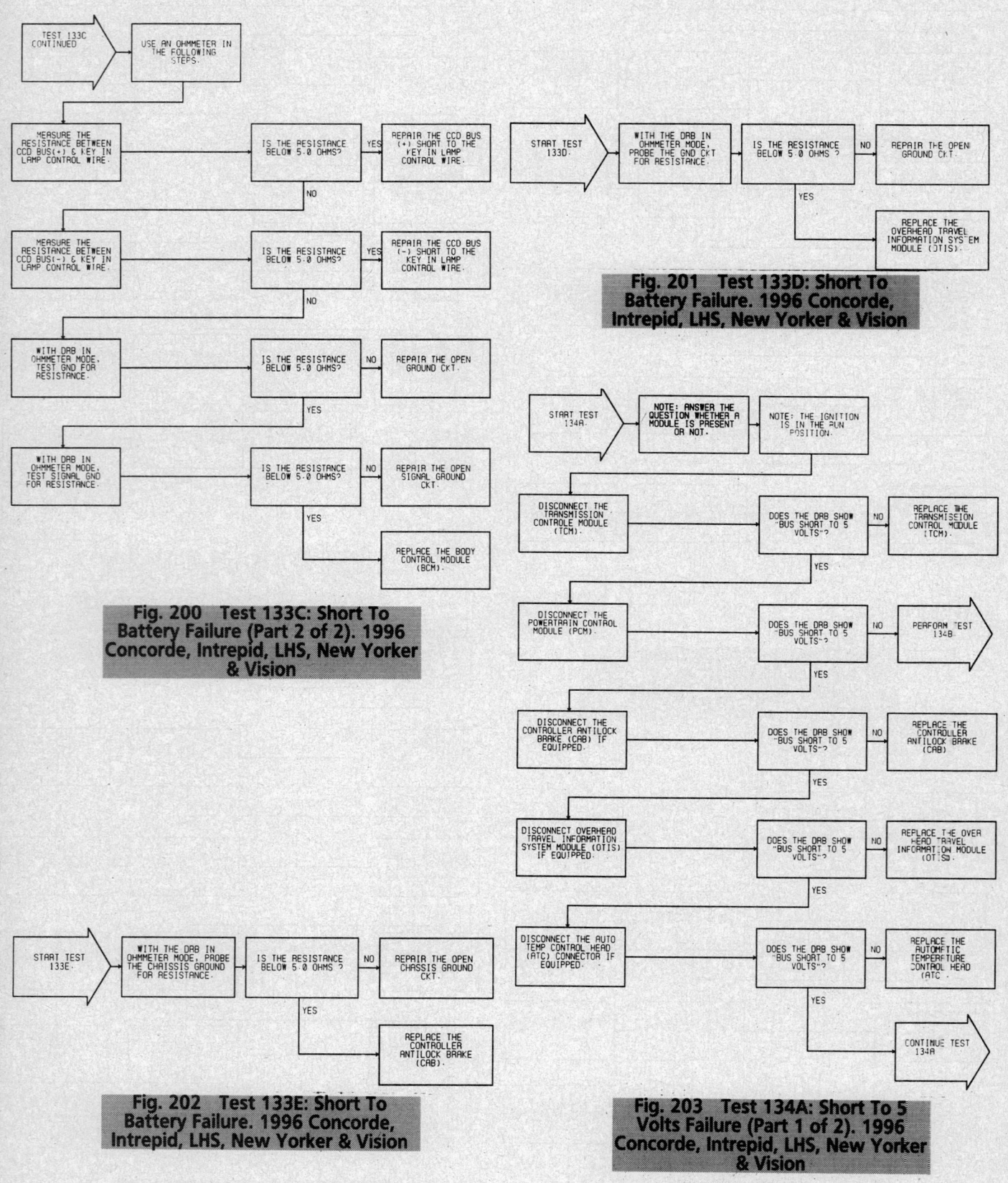

Fig. 200 Test 133C: Short To Battery Failure (Part 2 of 2). 1996 Concorde, Intrepid, LHS, New Yorker & Vision

Fig. 201 Test 133D: Short To Battery Failure. 1996 Concorde, Intrepid, LHS, New Yorker & Vision

Fig. 202 Test 133E: Short To Battery Failure. 1996 Concorde, Intrepid, LHS, New Yorker & Vision

Fig. 203 Test 134A: Short To 5 Volts Failure (Part 1 of 2). 1996 Concorde, Intrepid, LHS, New Yorker & Vision

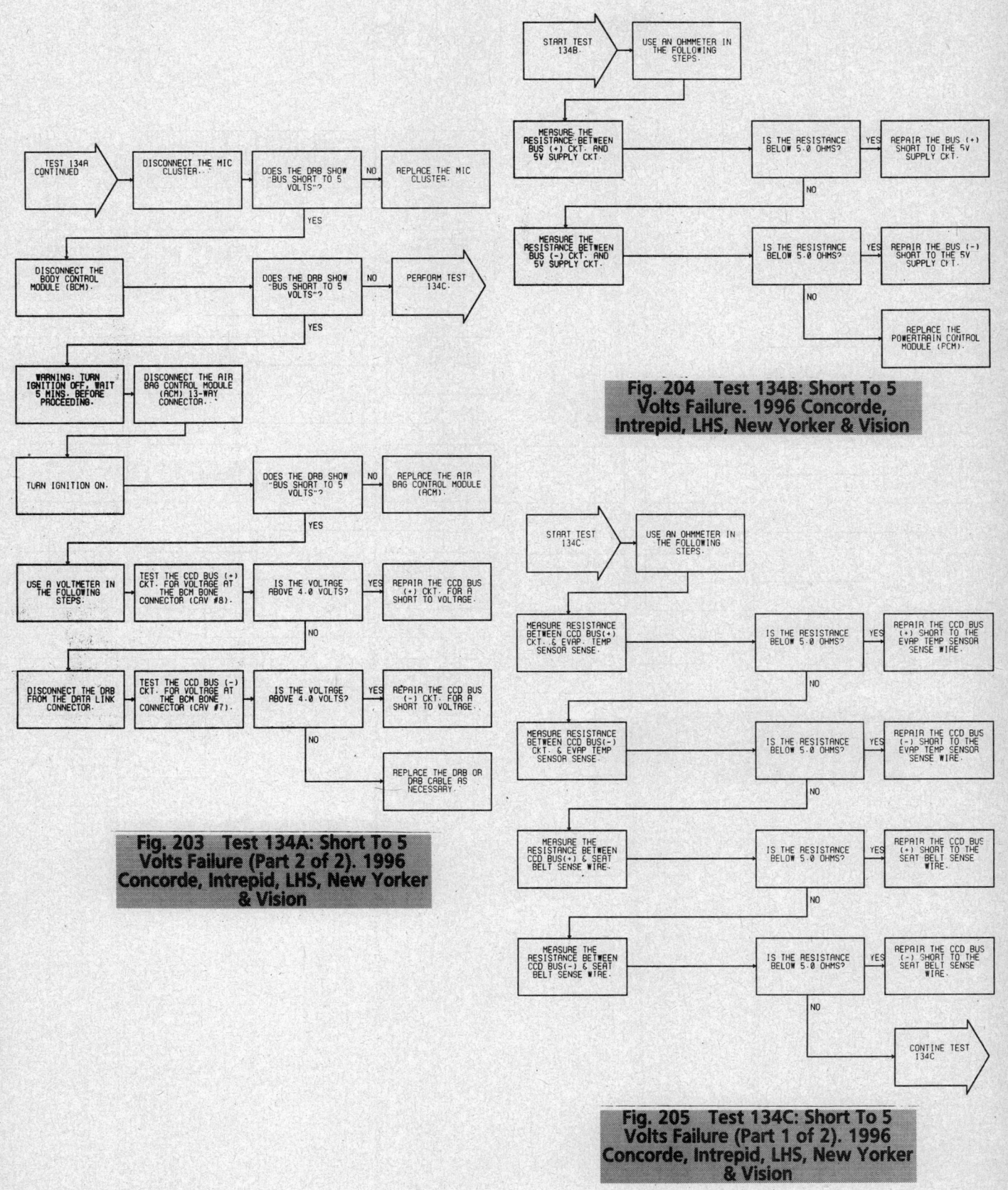

Fig. 203   Test 134A: Short To 5 Volts Failure (Part 2 of 2). 1996 Concorde, Intrepid, LHS, New Yorker & Vision

Fig. 204   Test 134B: Short To 5 Volts Failure. 1996 Concorde, Intrepid, LHS, New Yorker & Vision

Fig. 205   Test 134C: Short To 5 Volts Failure (Part 1 of 2). 1996 Concorde, Intrepid, LHS, New Yorker & Vision

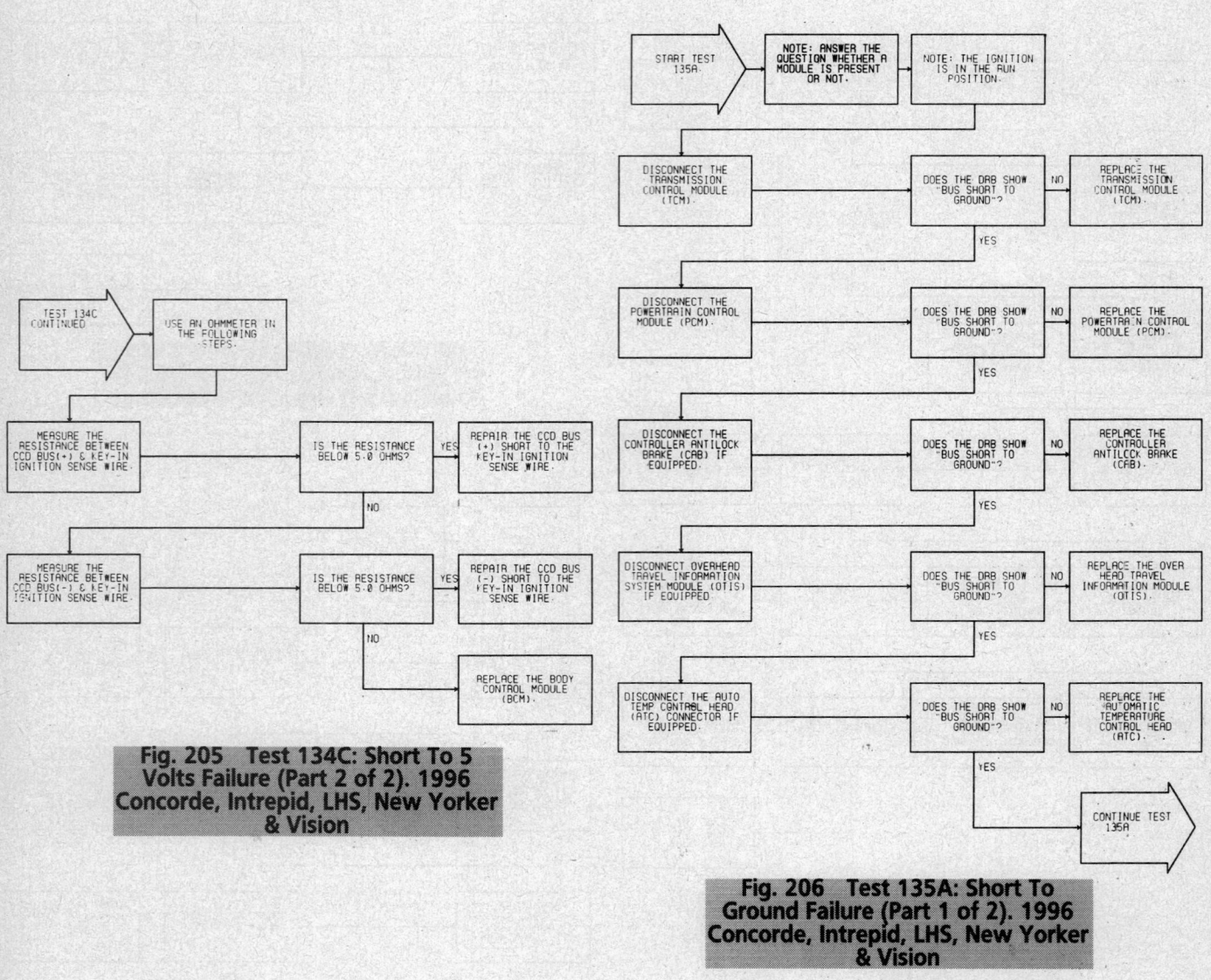

Fig. 205   Test 134C: Short To 5 Volts Failure (Part 2 of 2). 1996 Concorde, Intrepid, LHS, New Yorker & Vision

Fig. 206   Test 135A: Short To Ground Failure (Part 1 of 2). 1996 Concorde, Intrepid, LHS, New Yorker & Vision

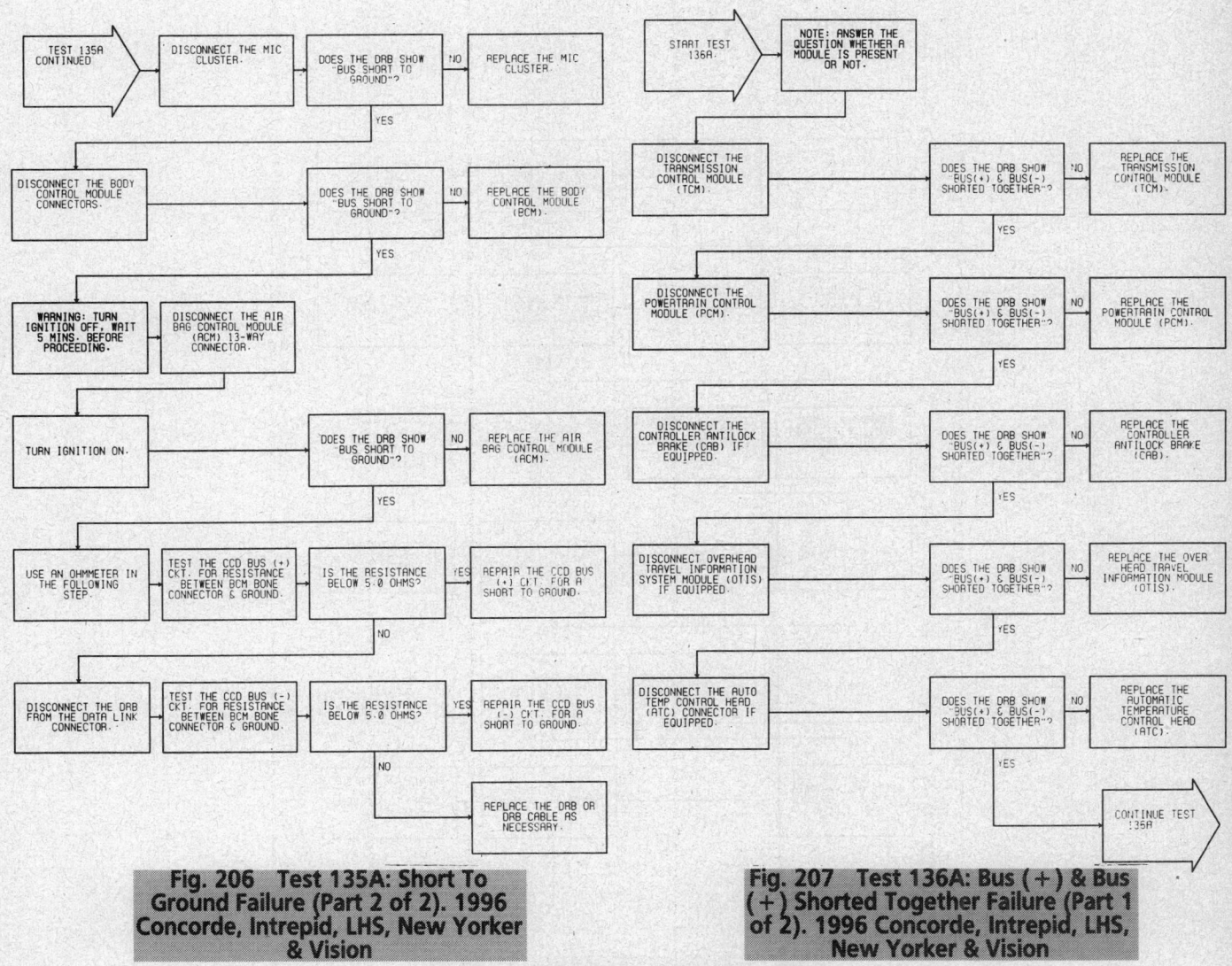

Fig. 206   Test 135A: Short To Ground Failure (Part 2 of 2). 1996 Concorde, Intrepid, LHS, New Yorker & Vision

Fig. 207   Test 136A: Bus (+) & Bus (+) Shorted Together Failure (Part 1 of 2). 1996 Concorde, Intrepid, LHS, New Yorker & Vision

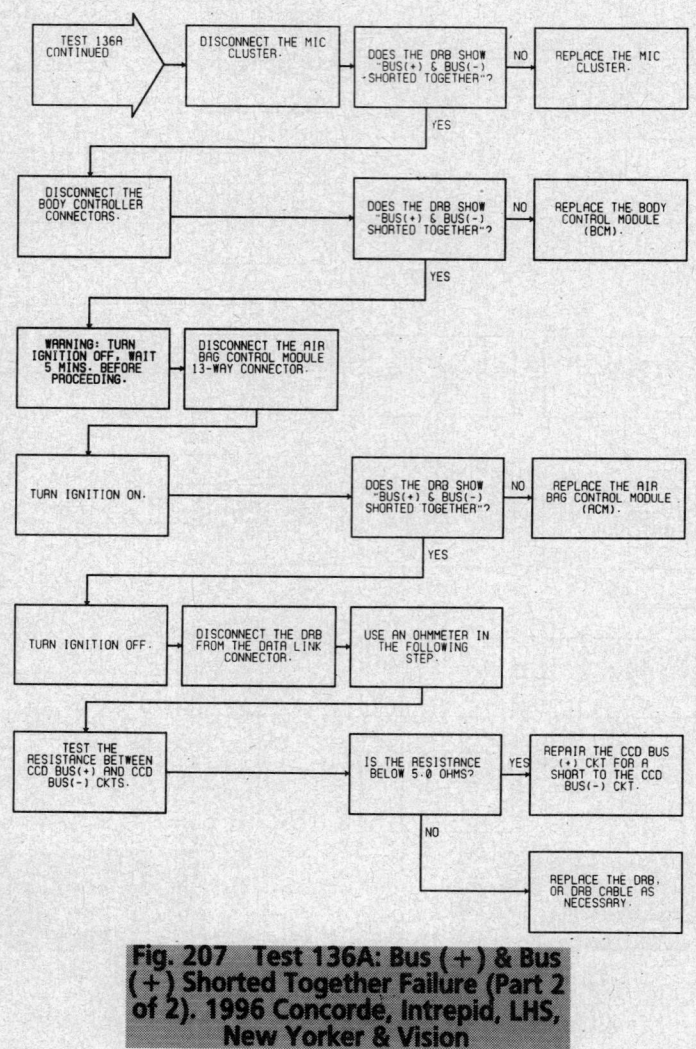

Fig. 207   Test 136A: Bus (+) & Bus (+) Shorted Together Failure (Part 2 of 2). 1996 Concorde, Intrepid, LHS, New Yorker & Vision

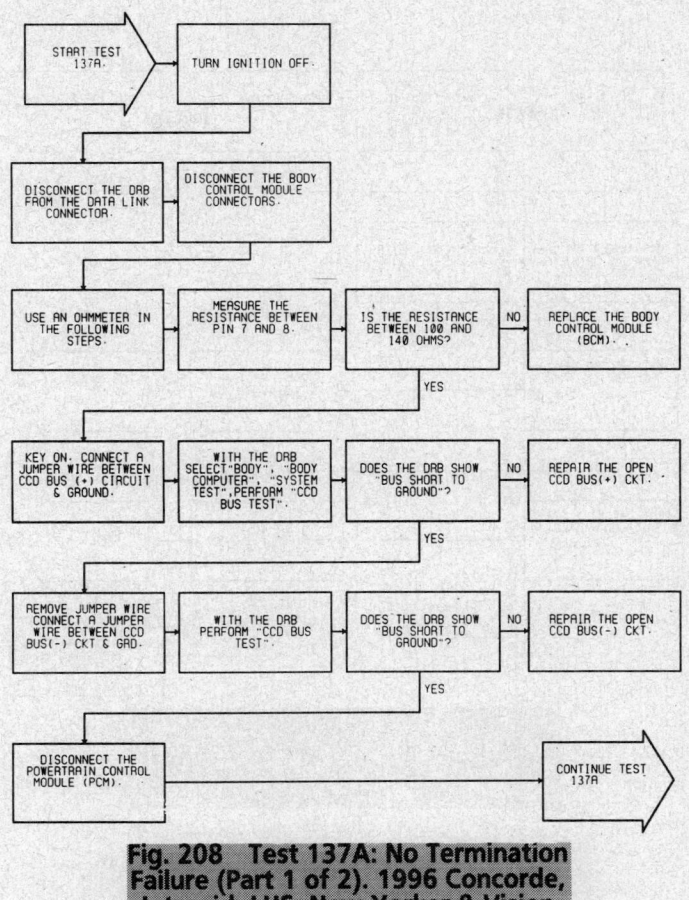

Fig. 208   Test 137A: No Termination Failure (Part 1 of 2). 1996 Concorde, Intrepid, LHS, New Yorker & Vision

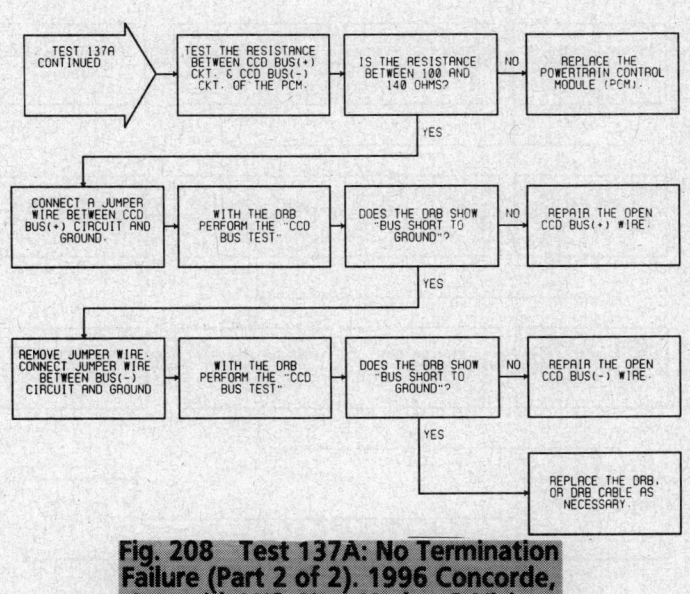

Fig. 208   Test 137A: No Termination Failure (Part 2 of 2). 1996 Concorde, Intrepid, LHS, New Yorker & Vision

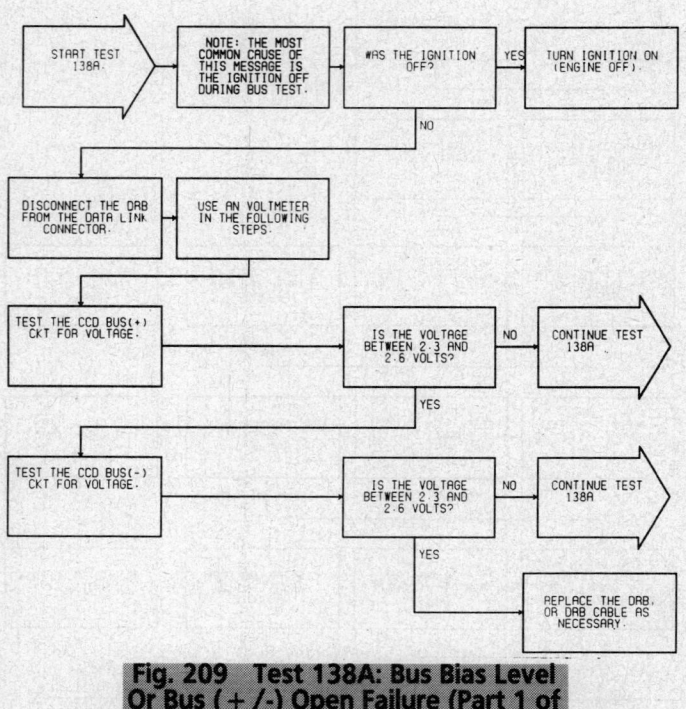

Fig. 209   Test 138A: Bus Bias Level Or Bus (+ /-) Open Failure (Part 1 of 3). 1996 Concorde, Intrepid, LHS, New Yorker & Vision

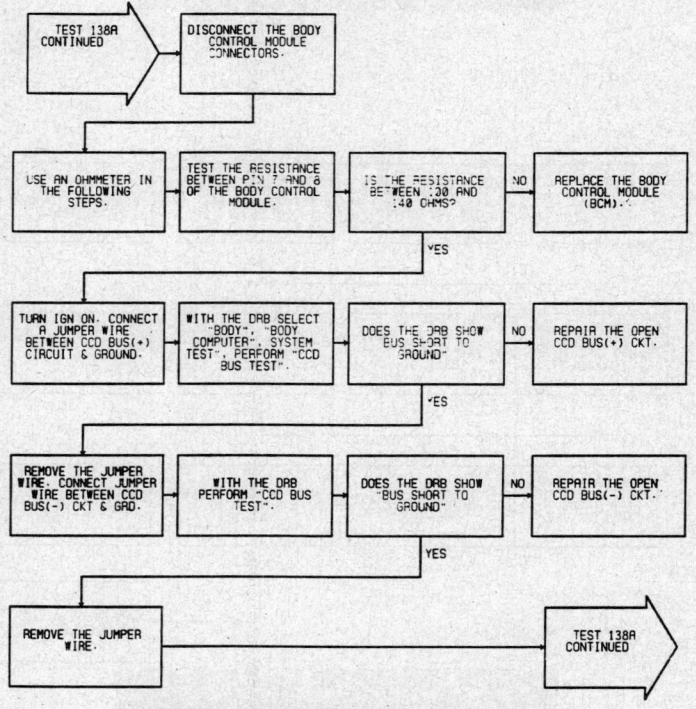

Fig. 209   Test 138A: Bus Bias Level Or Bus (+ /-) Open Failure (Part 2 of 3). 1996 Concorde, Intrepid, LHS, New Yorker & Vision

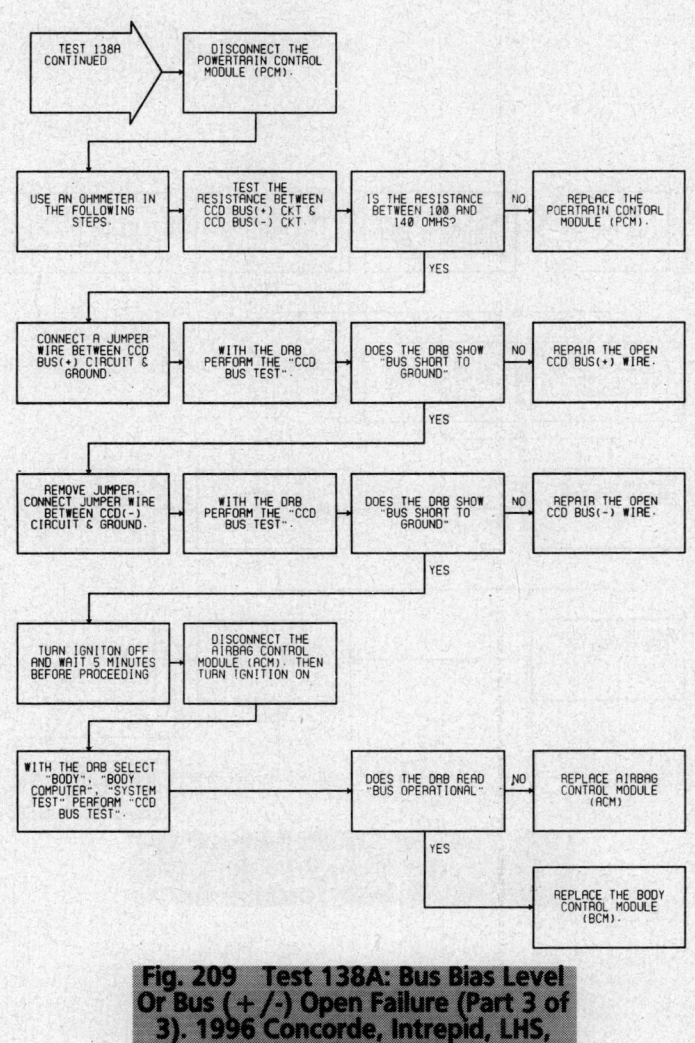

Fig. 209 Test 138A: Bus Bias Level Or Bus (+/-) Open Failure (Part 3 of 3). 1996 Concorde, Intrepid, LHS, New Yorker & Vision

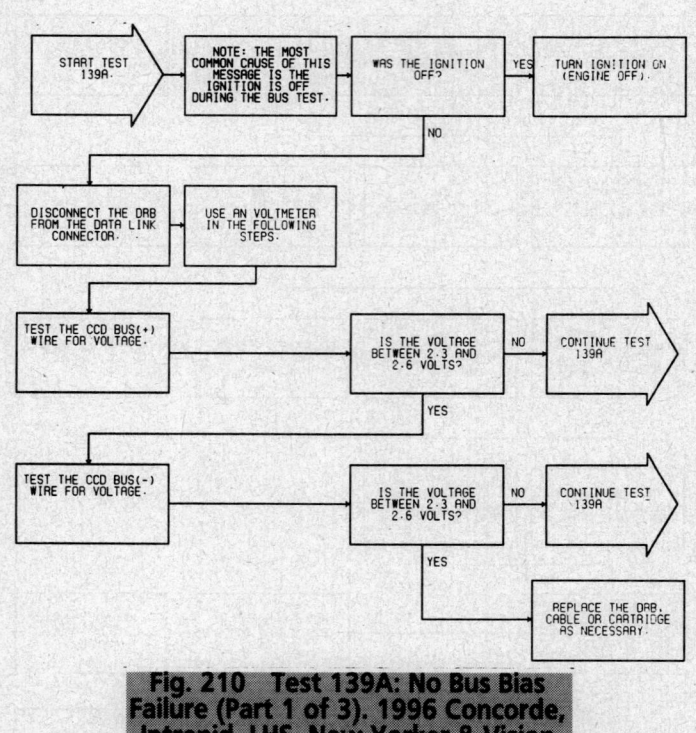

Fig. 210 Test 139A: No Bus Bias Failure (Part 1 of 3). 1996 Concorde, Intrepid, LHS, New Yorker & Vision

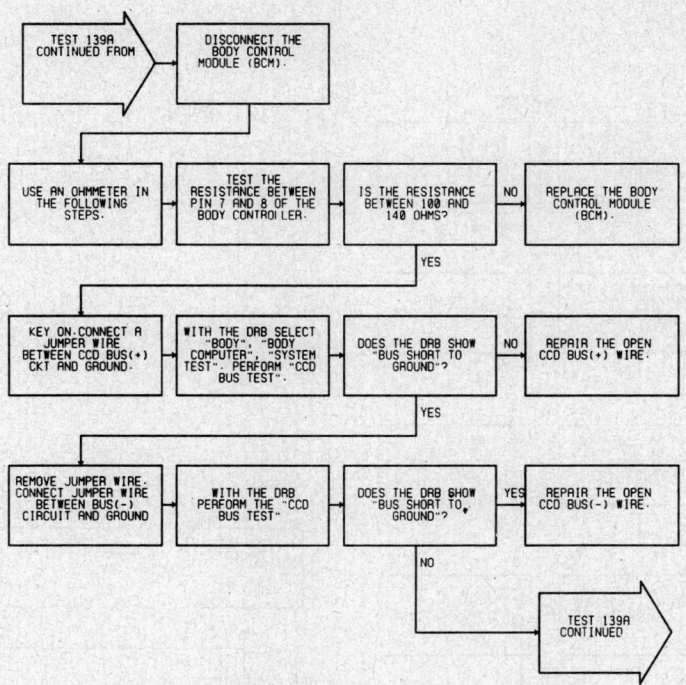

Fig. 210   Test 139A: No Bus Bias Failure (Part 2 of 3). 1996 Concorde, Intrepid, LHS, New Yorker & Vision

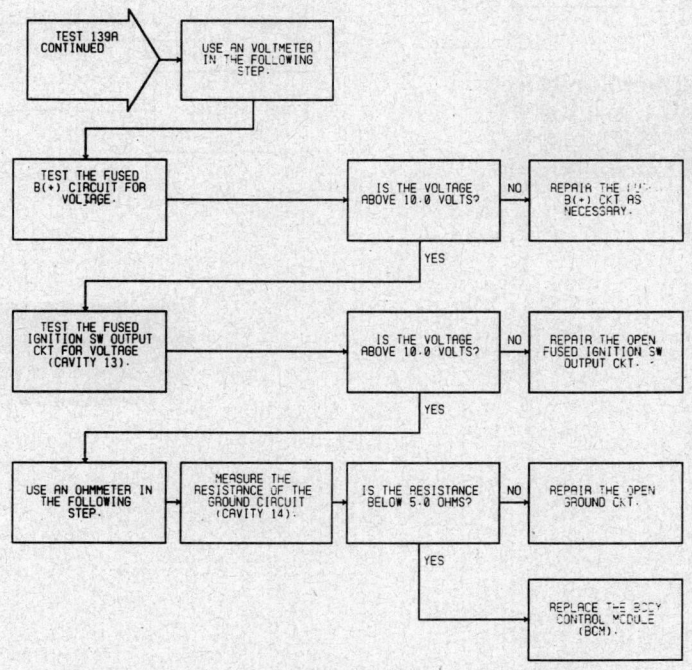

Fig. 210   Test 139A: No Bus Bias Failure (Part 3 of 3). 1996 Concorde, Intrepid, LHS, New Yorker & Vision

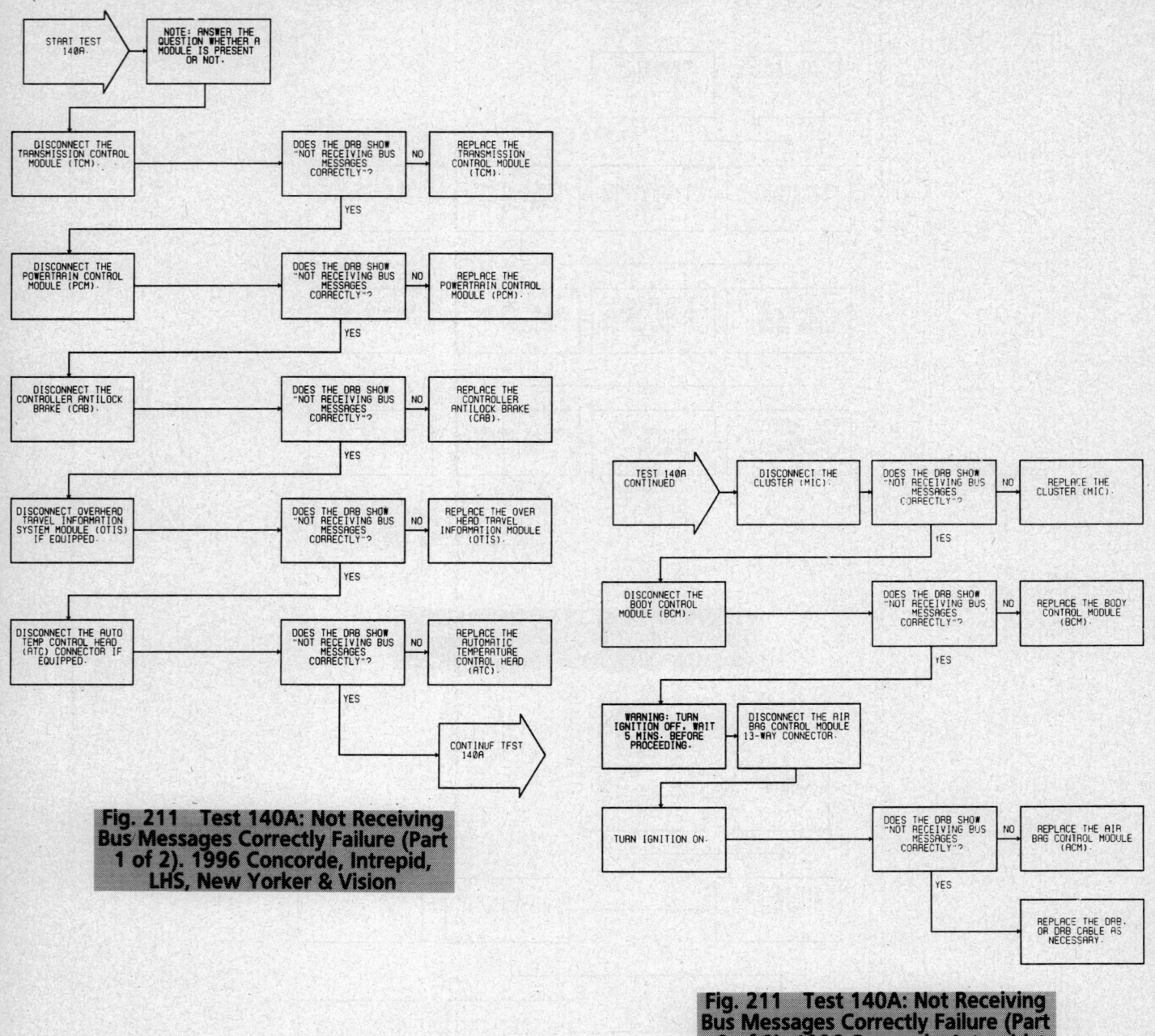

Fig. 211   Test 140A: Not Receiving Bus Messages Correctly Failure (Part 1 of 2). 1996 Concorde, Intrepid, LHS, New Yorker & Vision

Fig. 211   Test 140A: Not Receiving Bus Messages Correctly Failure (Part 2 of 2). 1996 Concorde, Intrepid, LHS, New Yorker & Vision

NOTE: If Uncertain About The Proper Use Of Information Contained In This Section, Please Refer To "How To Use This Manual" Located In The Front Of This Tabbed Section.

Buck & Miss: 22-7
   1993 Concorde, Intrepid & Vision
     w/3.5L/V6-215 Engine 2-7
Check Engine Lamp On, DTC 15,
  Rough Idle: 22-6
   1993-94 Laser & Talon
     w/1.8L/4-110 SOHC Engine... 22-6
Deceleration Shudder At Low
  Speed: 22-1
   1993 Acclaim, Daytona, Dynasty,
     LeBaron, Shadow, Sundance
     w/California Emissions &
     3.0L/V6-181 Engine 22-1
   1993 Dynasty, Imperial & New
     Yorker w/Federal Emissions &
     3.0L/V6-181 Engine 22-2
Delayed, Erratic & Harsh Shifts: 22-6
   1994 Concorde, Intrepid, LHS,
     New Yorker & Vision
     w/3.3L/V6-201 & 3.5L/V6-215
     Engines 22-6
Duty Cycle Purge Solenoid (DCPS)
  Noise: 22-4
   Concorde, Intrepid & Vision 22-4
Engine Knock & Poor Driveablity
  When Cold: 22-2
   1993 Acclaim, Daytona, Dynasty,
     LeBaron, Shadow & Sundance
     w/2.5L/4-153 Engine 22-2
Engine Knock When Cold: 22-2
   1993 Dynasty, Imperial & New
     Yorker w/3.3L/V6-201 &
     3.8L/V6-238 Engines 22-2
Engine Miss: 22-5
   1995 Avenger, Neon, Sebring &
     Talon w/2.0L/4-122 DOHC
     Non-Turbo Engine 22-5

Engine Stall On Start-Up, Low
  Power, & Erratic Shifting: 22-3
   1993 Acclaim, Dynasty, Imperial,
     LeBaron, Shadow, Spirit &
     Sundance & 1993-94 Concorde,
     Intrepid, LHS, New Yorker &
     Vision 22-3
Fuel Gauge Does Not Read Full: 22-3
   1993 Daytona, LeBaron, Shadow
     & Sundance 22-3
Hard Crank, Long Crank Time &
  Engine Miss 22-7
   1993-94 Concorde, Intrepid, LHS
     & Vision & 1994 New Yorker
     w/3.5L/V6-215 Engine 22-7
Hard Or No Start In Low Ambient
  Temperatures: 22-3
   1993 Shadow & Sundance
     w/3.0L/V6-181 Engine 22-3
Hard Start Or Long Cranking Times: 22-4
   1993 Concorde, Intrepid & Vision . 22-4
Hard Start Or Long Cranking Times
  & Rough Engine Idle: 22-4
   1993-94 Concorde, Intrepid, LHS
     & Vision & 1994 New Yorker
     w/3.5L/V6-215 Engine 22-4
Hesitation, Sagging & Surging: 22-6
   1995 Neon 22-6
Intermittent No Start, Poor
  Performance, & Loud Engine
  Noise: 22-4
   1993-94 Concorde, Intrepid, LHS
     & Vision & 1994 New Yorker... 22-4

No Crank, Slow Crank: 22-6
   1995 Cirrus & Stratus 22-6
No Start After PCM/BCM Swapping: 22-4
   1993-94 Concorde, Intrepid, LHS
     & Vision & 1994 New Yorker... 22-4
No Start In Cold Weather: 22-5
   1993-94 Concorde, Intrepid, LHS,
     New Yorker & Vision
     w/3.5L/V6-215 Engine 22-6
   1995 Concorde, Intrepid, LHS,
     New Yorker & Vision
     w/3.5L/V6-215 Engine 22-5
Revised Diagnostic Trouble Code
  (DTC) Descriptions: 22-5
   1995 Neon 22-5
Revised Powertrain Control Module
  (PCM) 60 Way Connector: 22-5
   1995 Neon 22-5
Rough Idle In Reverse: 22-7
   1993-94 Shadow & Sundance
     w/2.2L/4-135 & 2.5L/4-153
     Engines w/Automatic Transaxle 22-7
Rough Idle, Lack Of Power &
  Hesitation; Intake Valve Carbon
  Deposits: 22-3
   1993 Acclaim, Daytona, Dynasty,
     LeBaron, New Yorker, Shadow,
     & Sundance 22-3
Rough Idle & Steering Wheel Shake: 22-7
   1995 Neon 22-7
Start-Up Die Outs, No DTCs: 22-6
   1995 Acclaim, LeBaron & Spirit... 22-6

DECELERATION SHUDDER AT LOW SPEED

1993 ACCLAIM, DAYTONA, DYNASTY, LEBARON, SHADOW & SUNDANCE w/CALIFORNIA EMISSIONS & 3.0L/V6-181 ENGINE

Some vehicles may experience a closed throttle deceleration vibration or shudder while in gear at speeds between 25 and 40 mph. The actual speed of this condition will depend on vehicle final drive gear ratio. This condition can be corrected by reprogramming the powertrain control module (PCM) with new software calibrations. This repair involves selectively erasing and programming the PCM. The under hood temperature must be between -40°F and +185°F during programming.

It is important to first, verify all vehicle systems are functioning properly using tool No. CH1000 Scan Tool DRB II or equivalent. If any diagnostic trouble codes are present record them for future reference and correct the cause of all DTC's prior to proceeding as follows:

1. Insert tool No. CH3501 Flash Programming Cartridge or equivalent into tool No. CH1000 Scan Tool DRBII or equivalent.
2. Connect DRB II to tool No. CH1500 Flash Programming adapter or equivalent.
3. Connect Flash Programming adapter to engine six way cable.
4. Connect the engine six way cable to tool No. CC2000 Engine Diagnostic connector or equivalent.
5. Connect engine six way cable red battery clip to battery positive terminal.
6. Place ignition switch in the On position.

7. DRB II will power up and prompt through the sequence of windows as shown in **Fig. 1.**
8. When update is complete, place ignition switch in the Off position.
9. If an error occurs, write error message on paper, then press Mode and ATM keys together on the Scan tool to retry (reboot).
10. Attach completed "Authorized Software Update Label" to PCM as required by law.
11. Attach completed "Authorized Modification Label" near the Vehicle Emission Control Label as required by law.

1993 DYNASTY, IMPERIAL & NEW YORKER W/FEDERAL EMISSIONS & 3.0L/V6-181 ENGINE

Some vehicles may experience a closed throttle deceleration vibration or shudder while in gear at speeds between 25 and 40 mph. The actual speed of this condition will depend on vehicle final drive gear ratio. This condition can be corrected by reprogramming the powertrain control module (PCM) with new software calibrations. This repair involves selectively erasing and programming the PCM.

It is important to first, verify all vehicle systems are functioning properly using tool No. CH1000 Scan Tool DRB II or equivalent. If any diagnostic trouble codes are present record them for future reference and correct the cause of all DTC's prior to proceeding as follows:
1. Insert tool No. A115 Flash Programming Cartridge or equivalent into tool No. CH1000 Scan Tool DRBII or equivalent.
2. Connect DRB II to tool No. CH1500 Flash Programming adapter or equivalent.
3. Connect Flash Programming adapter to engine six way cable.
4. Connect the engine six way cable to tool No. CC2000 Engine Diagnostic connector or equivalent.
5. Connect engine six way cable red battery clip to battery positive terminal.
6. Place ignition switch in the On position.
7. DRB II will power up and prompt through the sequence of windows as shown in **Fig. 1.**
8. When update is complete, place ignition switch in the Off position.
9. If an error occurs, write error message on paper, then press Mode and ATM keys together on the Scan tool to retry (reboot).
10. Attach completed "Authorized Software Update Label" to PCM as required by law.
11. Attach completed "Authorized Modification Label" near the Vehicle Emission Control Label as required by law.

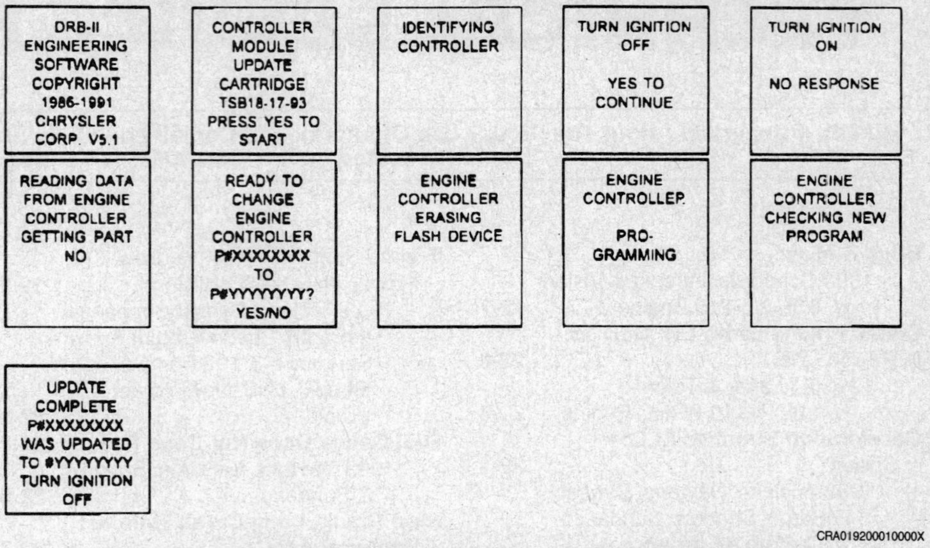

Fig. 1   DRB II sequence of windows. 3.0L/V6-181 engine

Model	Emission	Trans.	PCM Std.	PCM RFI.
AA,AG,AJ,AP	FED	Auto	4727026	4727027
AA,AG,AJ,AP	CAL	Auto	4727028	4727097
AA,AG,AP	FED/CAL	Man	4727106	4727107
AC	FED	Auto	4727100	4727101

Fig. 2   Revised powertrain control module (PCM) chart. 1993 2.5L/4-153 engine

ENGINE KNOCK & POOR DRIVEABLITY WHEN COLD
1993 ACCLAIM, DAYTONA, DYNASTY, LEBARON, SHADOW & SUNDANCE W/2.5L/4-153 ENGINE

Some vehicles may experience a cold engine knock for a few seconds after start-up that last for three to five minutes. The knock is most prevalent in the 2000 to 2500 RPM range making a sound similar to a valve lifter noise. The colder the ambient temperature, generally the worse the perceived noise. The noise is usually gone upon reaching normal operating engine coolant temperature.

This piston noise is not an indication of impending failure. This condition may also be accompanied by a cold idle roughness and a poor driveability concern when ambient temperature is zero to plus 30°F lasting until engine coolant temperature reaches 50-60°F. To correct these conditions proceed as follows:
1. Normalize engine to ambient temperature, then run engine at 2000-2500 RPM.
2. Disconnect manifold absolute pressure sensor (MAP) electrical connector.

3. Maintain 2000-2500 RPM, throttle movement may be required due to the disconnected MAP sensor.
4. If knock is eliminated when MAP is disconnected, replace the powertrain control module (PCM) with revised PCM, refer to **Fig. 2,** then correct driveability concern as follows:
   a. Verify heated air system is functioning properly.
   b. Normalize engine to an ambient temperature of 40°F or less, then within the first 90 seconds of engine operation tip in the throttle to 1/4 throttle position and release, quickly repeat and let idle.
   c. If any rough running condition is noticed, replace PCM, refer to **Fig. 2.**

ENGINE KNOCK WHEN COLD
1993 DYNASTY, IMPERIAL & NEW YORKER W/3.3L/V6-201 & 3.8L/V6-238 ENGINES

Some vehicle may experience light engine knock during light acceleration or neutral rev-up following cold start-up. This condition is usually more prevalent in lower ambient temperatures after a five or six hour soak. This condition can be corrected

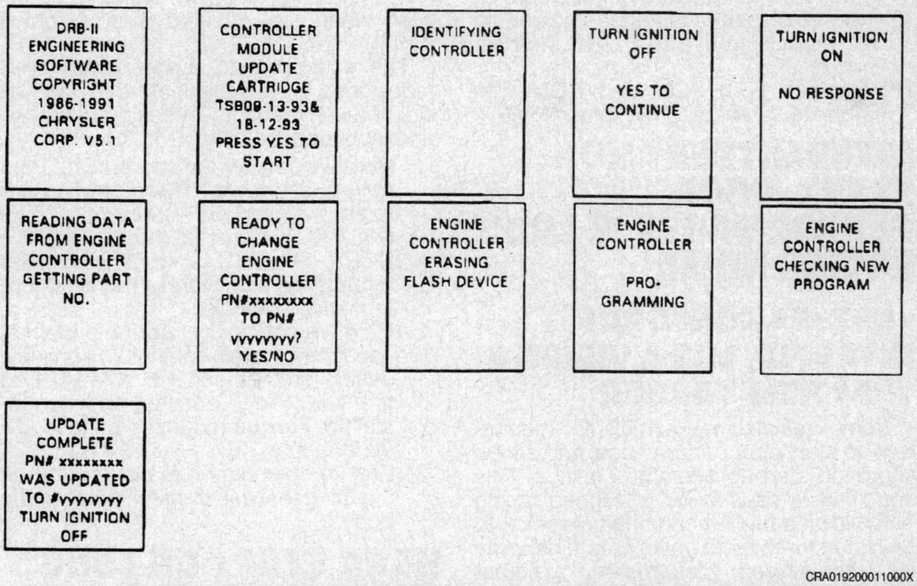

```
┌─────────────┐  ┌─────────────┐  ┌─────────────┐  ┌─────────────┐  ┌─────────────┐
│ DRB-II      │  │ CONTROLLER  │  │ IDENTIFYING │  │ TURN IGNITION│ │ TURN IGNITION│
│ ENGINEERING │  │ MODULE      │  │ CONTROLLER  │  │ OFF         │  │ ON          │
│ SOFTWARE    │  │ UPDATE      │  │             │  │             │  │             │
│ COPYRIGHT   │  │ CARTRIDGE   │  │             │  │ YES TO      │  │ NO RESPONSE │
│ 1986-1991   │  │ TSB09-13-93&│  │             │  │ CONTINUE    │  │             │
│ CHRYSLER    │  │ 18-12-93    │  │             │  │             │  │             │
│ CORP. V5.1  │  │ PRESS YES TO│  │             │  │             │  │             │
│             │  │ START       │  │             │  │             │  │             │
└─────────────┘  └─────────────┘  └─────────────┘  └─────────────┘  └─────────────┘
┌─────────────┐  ┌─────────────┐  ┌─────────────┐  ┌─────────────┐  ┌─────────────┐
│ READING DATA│  │ READY TO    │  │ ENGINE      │  │ ENGINE      │  │ ENGINE      │
│ FROM ENGINE │  │ CHANGE      │  │ CONTROLLER  │  │ CONTROLLER  │  │ CONTROLLER  │
│ CONTROLLER  │  │ ENGINE      │  │ ERASING     │  │             │  │ CHECKING NEW│
│ GETTING PART│  │ CONTROLLER  │  │ FLASH DEVICE│  │ PRO-        │  │ PROGRAM     │
│ NO.         │  │ PN#xxxxxxxx │  │             │  │ GRAMMING    │  │             │
│             │  │ TO PN#      │  │             │  │             │  │             │
│             │  │ vvvvvvvv?   │  │             │  │             │  │             │
│             │  │ YES/NO      │  │             │  │             │  │             │
└─────────────┘  └─────────────┘  └─────────────┘  └─────────────┘  └─────────────┘
┌─────────────┐
│ UPDATE      │
│ COMPLETE    │
│ PN# xxxxxxxx│
│ WAS UPDATED │
│ TO #vvvvvvvv│
│ TURN IGNITION│
│ OFF         │
└─────────────┘
```

CRA019200011000X

Fig. 3 DRB II sequence of windows. 3.3L/V6-201 & 3.8L/V6-238 engines

by reprogramming the powertrain control module (PCM) with new software calibrations. This repair involves selectively erasing and programming the PCM. **The under hood temperature must be between −40°F and +185°F during reprogramming.**

It is important to first verify all vehicle systems are functioning properly using DRB II scan tool. If any diagnostic trouble codes are present, record for future reference. Correct cause of all DTC's prior to proceeding as follows:

1. Insert tool No. A115 Flash Programming Cartridge or equivalent, into tool No. CH1000 DRBII scan tool.
2. Connect DRB II to tool No. CH1500 Flash Programming adapter or equivalent.
3. Connect Flash Programming adapter to engine six way cable
4. Connect the engine six way cable to tool No. CC2000 engine diagnostic connector or equivalent.
5. Connect engine six way cable red battery clip to battery positive terminal.
6. Place ignition switch in the On position.
7. DRB II will power up and prompt through the sequence of windows as shown in **Fig. 3**.
8. When update is complete, place ignition switch in the Off position.
9. If an error occurs, write error message on paper, then press Mode and ATM keys together on the Scan tool to retry (reboot).
10. Attach completed "Authorized Software Update Label" to PCM as required by law.
11. Attach completed "Authorized Modification Label" near the Vehicle Emission Control Label as required by law.

ENGINE STALL ON START-UP, LOW POWER, & ERRATIC SHIFTING
1993 ACCLAIM, DYNASTY, IMPERIAL, LEBARON, SHADOW, SPIRIT & SUNDANCE & 1993–94 CONCORDE, INTREPID, LHS, NEW YORKER & VISION

Some vehicles may experience a stall on start-up, reduced power, or erratic shifting. This may be the result of low fuel pressure caused by the check valve in the fuel pump not seating properly. To correct this condition fuel pump replacement is necessary.

On 1993 Acclaim, Dynasty, Fifth Avenue, Imperial, LeBaron, Shadow, Spirit and Sundance models, replace with fuel pump part No. 4682087.

On 1993 Concorde, Intrepid, Vision and 1994 LHS and New Yorker models, replace with fuel pump No. 4741717.

FUEL GAUGE DOES NOT READ FULL
1993 DAYTONA, LEBARON, SHADOW & SUNDANCE

After fill up, some vehicle instrument panel fuel gauges may read between ⅞ of a tank and "F" tank (full). To correct this condition proceed as follows.
1. Disconnect battery ground cable, then remove fuel tank level unit.
2. Install revised fuel level unit, part No. 4746819.
3. Reverse procedure to install.

ROUGH IDLE, LACK OF POWER & HESITATION; INTAKE VALVE CARBON DEPOSITS
1993 ACCLAIM, DAYTONA, DYNASTY, LEBARON, NEW YORKER, SHADOW, & SUNDANCE

Driveway die-out, rough idle, lack of power, sags, and hesitation may be caused by carbon deposits forming on the back of the intake valves. This condition can cause blockage of fuel delivery to the combustion chamber resulting in fuel starvation. The deposits are a result of fuel blending methods that have insufficient or ineffective fuel detergent additives. Using fuel with a higher minimum posted octane number does not guarantee that fuel is of high quality or that the fuel is blended with adequate or effective detergent, corrosion and stability additives. It is recommended that fuels available from companies that offer products "warranted" to contain the necessary additives for efficient and clean operation are preferred. To correct vehicles exhibiting any of the above mentioned conditions, proceed as follows:

1. Verify all vehicle systems are functioning as designed.
2. Using tool No. CH1000 Scan Tool DRB II or equivalent, verify engine systems are functioning as designed.
3. If any Diagnostic Trouble Codes (DTC) are present, record for future reference, then repair existing set DTC problems.
4. If all systems are functioning as designed, inquire as to the fuel being used in the vehicle. If there is a question in regards to the quality of fuel, suggest that only fuels "warranted" against build up of deposits be used.
5. Remove existing deposits as follows:
   a. **For light deposits,** add one bottle of fuel injector cleaner part No. 4318007 or equivalent to a full tank of gas. **This method not intended for continuous use.**
   b. **For medium to heavy deposits,** remove cylinder head from vehicle, disassemble head, then remove carbon deposits from valves with a wire brush.
   c. **For both light and heavy deposits,** recommend other brands of gasoline.

HARD OR NO START IN LOW AMBIENT TEMPERATURES
1993 SHADOW & SUNDANCE w/3.0L/V6-181 ENGINE

Some vehicles may be hard to start or will not start in cool to cold ambient temperatures. This condition may be caused by the Engine Coolant Temperature (ECT) sensor wiring connector, resulting in the illumination of the Check Engine lamp.

To diagnose this condition, check for DTC 22. If fault is present, perform engine coolant temperature sensor test as outlined in the appropriate fuel injection section. If sensor is not defective, proceed as follows:

1. Disconnect battery ground cable, then cut off old ECT sensor wiring harness connector within 1 inch of connector.
2. Strip 1 inch of insulation from remaining wire and slide a piece of heat shrink tubing onto each wire.
3. Strip 1 inch of insulation from wires on repair pigtail, part No. 4419901.
4. Matching wire colors, connect wires from wiring harness and repair pigtail.
5. Solder connections, then heat joint until tubing is tightly sealed and sealant come out of both ends of tubing.
6. Wrap electrical tape around wire harness including area of splice.
7. Connect ECT sensor wiring and battery ground cable.
8. Using tool CH1000 Scan Tool DRB II or equivalent, clear fault message from memory. Start engine and verify fault message does not reoccur.

NO START AFTER PCM/BCM SWAPPING

1993–94 CONCORDE, INTREPID, LHS & VISION & 1994 NEW YORKER

Some vehicles may experience a no start condition after swapping the Powertrain Control Module (PCM) or the Body Control Module (BCM) between a non-Vehicle Theft Security System (VTSS) and VTSS equipped vehicle. The VTSS function on LH vehicles resides in the PCM and BCM. Either module becomes programmed to support VTSS when they are installed in an enabled vehicle. The module will carry this information with them if they are transported from one vehicle to another, and will teach the new vehicle that it has VTSS. This will occur as soon as the ignition is turned on. Installing a VTSS enabled module in a non-VTSS equipped vehicle will cause a no start condition.

To prevent no start conditions due to the VTSS being enabled on a non-VTSS, PCM and BCM on LH vehicles must not be exchanged between vehicles or installed in a vehicle and then returned to the parts department. Once a module is VTSS enabled it can only be used on a VTSS equipped vehicle. To correct this condition proceed as follows.

1. Disconnect battery ground cable, then remove PCM, refer to "Fuel Injection" section.
2. Remove right instrument panel end cover.
3. Remove righthand cowl side trim panel and pull carpeting back, exposing dash liner.
4. Remove righthand heat distribution duct.
5. Cut dash liner along perforated lines and pull back dash liner.

6. Remove screw through oblong access hole at right end of knee bolster.
7. Remove push-in fastener at lower leg of module from below I/P, then remove BCM.
8. Replace both PCM and BCM with non-VTSS enabled modules.

INTERMITTENT NO START, POOR PERFORMANCE, & LOUD ENGINE NOISE

1993–94 CONCORDE, INTREPID, LHS & VISION & 1994 NEW YORKER

Some vehicle may exhibit an intermittent no start, poor performance, and a loud knock on start-up attempt condition. This condition is caused by a skipped timing belt allowing the left camshaft sprocket to be two to three teeth out of time. If difficulty is encountered determining whether sprocket is out of time, install camshaft alignment tool No. 6642-A to the rear of the cylinder and align the crankshaft sprocket with TDC mark on the oil pump housing. If the plates do not align properly, the camshaft is out of time. To correct this condition replacement of the timing belt tensioner pivot snubber is required.

Replace timing belt tensioner pivot snubber as follows:

1. Disconnect battery ground cable.
2. Remove timing belt cover, timing belt tensioner, then compress tensioner and install pin to lock tensioner in the compressed position for installation.
3. Apply Bond All Gel part No. 4467709 or equivalent to bottom outside edge of the new timing belt tensioner pivot snubber, part No. 46635080.
4. Install new timing belt tensioner pivot snubber part No. 4663580 with the word "TOP" facing up, on top of the tensioner body with snubber centered over the plunger.
5. Install the timing belt tensioner to the engine.
6. Align the camshafts, noting the following:
   a. Inspect the tensioner pulley bracket pivot bolt for binding or tight spots.
   b. Pivot bolt should rotate freely, if not then remove and clean with steel wool or emery cloth.

DUTY CYCLE PURGE SOLENOID (DCPS) NOISE

CONCORDE, INTREPID & VISION

The DCPS operation creates a solenoid vibration which can transmit through the body to the passenger compartment. The vibration creates a low frequency clicking noise that can easily be mistaken for an engine knock or a failed valve lifter. The noise is most noticeable with the engine warmed up, and at idle. If can be heard best in the front passenger seat coming

from the floor under the glove compartment. The noise problem can also be noticed when the solenoid is cold (below 25°F).

The solenoid bracket and isolator were redesigned to help eliminate this noise inside the vehicle. Install redesigned bracket and isolator assembly, as follows:

1. Remove solenoid(s) and bracket from right shock tower. There are two different styles of brackets. The 3.3L/V6-201 bracket mounts only the DCPS. The 3.5L/V6-215 bracket mounts the DCPS and a manifold tuning valve solenoid.
2. Remove solenoid(s) from old bracket assembly. Install solenoid(s) on new design bracket part No. 4740419 so the word "Top" is facing up when installed. **Torque** mounting bolts to 60-90 inch lbs.
3. Ensure solenoid does not ground on anything that can transmit noise to the body.

HARD START OR LONG CRANKING TIMES

1993 CONCORDE, INTREPID & VISION

Some vehicles may experience hard starting or long cranking times (over 5 seconds) when the engine is at normal operating temperature. This condition may be caused by the loss of fuel pressure after the engine has been turned off.

To diagnose this condition, connect a fuel pressure gauge to fuel rail service valve and confirm the immediate loss of fuel system pressure after the engine has been turned off. If fuel pressure does not drop off, proceed with normal diagnostic procedures.

If fuel pressure does drop off after engine is shutoff, disconnect fuel return line from fuel rail. Attach a fuel approved temporary rubber hose to rail and position other end of hose into an approved fuel container. Start vehicle to obtain system operating pressure. At the same time the engine is turned off, completely pinch off temporary return line hose. Check fuel pressure gauge reading. If system pressure does not hold, fuel pump check valve is leaking. If system pressure is holding with temporary return hose pinch in place, but drops off as pinch is released, the regulator and/or O-rings are leaking.

To correct either condition, install new fuel pump part No. 4723358.

HARD START OR LONG CRANKING TIMES & ROUGH ENGINE IDLE

1993–94 CONCORDE, INTREPID, LHS & VISION & 1994 NEW YORKER w/3.5L/V6-215 ENGINE

Some vehicles may experience hard starting, long cranking times (over 5 seconds) and rough engine or miss at idle

11**	P1390	Timing belt skipped 1 tooth or more	Timing belt skipped 1 tooth or more from initial learned value
	or		
	P1391	Intermittent Loss of CMP or CKP	Intermittent loss of either camshaft or crankshaft position sensor
	or		
		No Crank Reference Signal at PCM	No crank reference signal detected during engine cranking.
12*		Battery Disconnect	Direct battery input to PCM was disconnected within the last 50 Key-on cycles.
13**	P1297	No Change in MAP From Start to Run	No difference recognized between the engine MAP reading and the barometric (atmospheric) pressure reading from start-up.
14**	P0107	MAP Sensor Voltage Too Low	MAP sensor input below minimum acceptable voltage.
	or		
	P0108	MAP Sensor Voltage Too High	MAP sensor input above maximum acceptable voltage.
15**	P0500	No Vehicle Speed Sensor Signal	No vehicle speed sensor signal detected during road load conditions.
17**	P0125	Closed Loop Temp Not Reached	Closed loop operation temperature not reached.
	or	Engine Cold Too Long	Does not reach operating temperature within 20 minutes with vehicle speed signal.
21**	P0132	Upstream O2S Shorted to Voltage	Upstream oxygen sensor input voltage maintained above the normal operating range.
** or	P0133	Upstream O2S Response	Upstream oxygen sensor response slower than minimum required switching frequency or value does not go above .745 volts. **
	or		
	P0134	Upstream O2S Stays at Center	Neither rich or lean condition detected from the upstream oxygen sensor input.
	or		
	P0135	Upstream O2S Heater Failure	Upstream oxygen sensor heating element circuit malfunction
	or		

* Check Engine Lamp will not illuminate at all times if this Diagnostic Trouble Code was recorded. Cycle Ignition key as described in manual and observe code flashed by Check Engine lamp.
** Check Engine Lamp will illuminate during engine operation if this Diagnostic Trouble Code was recorded.

CRA019500013000X

Fig. 4   Revised Diagnostic Trouble Code (DTC) descriptions. 1995 Neon

with no Diagnostic Trouble Codes (DTCs) set. These conditions may require replacement of the fuel rail assembly. On 1993-94 models, built before 7-26-93, use Fuel Rail Assembly part No. 4762923. On 1994 models, built after 7-26-93, use Fuel Rail Assembly part No. 4762924.

If fuel pressure regulator and O-rings are not properly transferred to the new fuel rail a loss of fuel pressure will result. When removing the fuel pressure regulator, the O-rings may remain attached to the regulator. These O-rings must be removed from the regulator and installed in the fuel rail cavity. Apply a light coat of clean engine oil and seat O-rings into the cavity before inserting the regulator.

Diagnose and correct these conditions as follows:
1. With engine warm and at idle in the Park position, using tool No. CH1000 Scan Tool DRB II or equivalent in the "Select System" menu, monitor left and right cylinder bank adaptive memory.
2. Read Adaptive Memory Monitor Screen left and right oxygen sensor adaptive values. Normal readings are between plus five and minus five.
3. If left bank value reads between minus six and minus twenty, then replace the fuel rail assembly.
4. Inspect No. 2 spark plug for fouling.
5. Perform fuel system pressure test using fuel rail pressure test port, refer to "Electric Fuel Pump" section, then check for slow loss of pressure after engine is turned off.
6. If one or more of these diagnostic procedures indicate a problem, then replace the fuel rail assembly.

REVISED DIAGNOSTIC TROUBLE CODE (DTC) DESCRIPTIONS
1995 NEON

Diagnostic Trouble Code (DTC) descriptions for the 1995 Neon models have been revised. Refer to **Fig. 4** for revised DTC description. Other description revisions read as follows.
1. DTC 21 Oxygen Sensor Monitor P0133/P0139 test conditions was revised, information should read, oxygen sensor voltage (revision) "above .745 volts."
2. DTC 32 EGR Monitor P0401 TPS voltage should read between ".6 and 1.2 volts."
3. DTC 32 EGR Monitor P0401 under Test Conditions revision should read, "Short term fuel control less than a positive 4.4 percent. This monitor is performed three times each trip. If the measured change in the A/F ratio during the test is less than 7.4 percent or greater than 18.0 percent, the monitor fails. If the monitor is outside this range for two trips the PCM registers a DTC at the end of the second trip and turns on the Malfunction Indicator Lamp (MIL)(Check Engine)."
4. DTC 43 Misfire Monitor P0300/P0301/P0302/P0303/P0304 under Monitor Description, revision should read, "The fuel system monitor continuously checks the short term fuel correction and the long term memory fuel trim adjustments. Each has the authority to enrich or lean out

from a base fuel pulse by plus or minus 25 percent. If the sum of the two values goes beyond: 25 percent rich or 37 percent lean, a fault will be set."
5. DTC 64 Catalyst Monitor P0422 under Test Condition revision should read, "The catalyst monitor test is run two time per trip. Once the system is out of limits for two trips (4 tests), the MIL will illuminate and a permanent DTC will be stored. The MIL will remain on for more than one trip, but will go out if the conditions that set the DTC are not found on subsequent trips."

REVISED POWERTRAIN CONTROL MODULE (PCM) 60 WAY CONNECTOR
1995 NEON

The Powertrain Control Module (PCM) 60 way connector for the 1995 Neon models have been revised. Refer to **Fig. 5** for the new PCM 60 way connector diagram.

ENGINE MISS
1995 AVENGER, NEON, SEBRING & TALON W/2.0L/4-122 DOHC NON-TURBO ENGINE

This condition may occur at idle or under load, and the check engine lamp may illuminate. Diagnostic trouble codes of "Cylinder 1, 2, 3, or 4 Misfire" or "Multiple Cylinder Misfire" may be present. This may be caused by the spark plugs and spark plug cables.

To correct these conditions, inspect the spark plugs and cable boots for carbon tracking. If tracking is present, replace all four plugs (part No. 4671057 Champion RC-9-YC for Neon; part No. 5269556 Champion RC-9-YC5 for all other models), and install a replacement cable set (part No. 4773841).

NO START IN COLD WEATHER
1995 CONCORDE, INTREPID, LHS, NEW YORKER & VISION W/3.5L/V6-215 ENGINE

This condition may occur in temperatures below 0°F. Jump starting may also have no effect. This may be caused by fouled spark plugs and the use of motor oil with the incorrect grade.

To correct this condition, proceed as follows:
1. Drain crankcase, discard oil filter, then install Mopar 5W30 oil (part No. 4761838) and filter (part No. 5281090). **5W30 oil should not be used above 32°F.**
2. Gap replacement spark plugs (part No. 56027275 Champion RC-12-LYC) to .035 inch and install. **Torque to 20 ft. lbs.**

NO CRANK, SLOW CRANK

1995 CIRRUS & STRATUS

This may be caused by a blown fuse or poor battery connections.

To correct, first inspect for a blown A1 fuse in cavity number 8 of the power distribution center (PDC) and replace if needed, then proceed as follows:

1. Inspect nut at "Positive Jump Start Attachment" on PDC. **Torque** to 140-160 inch. lbs.
2. Inspect for paint and corrosion build-up on the "Negative Attachment" stud on lefthand shock tower. **Torque** lower nut to 200-300 inch lbs. and upper nut to 140-160 inch lbs.
3. Inspect negative ground cable at lefthand engine mount and **torque** to 35-55 ft. lbs.
4. Inspect starter motor battery nut positive and **torque** to 70-110 inch lbs.
5. Inspect for cross-threading at battery cables and posts and repair or replace as needed. **Torque** to 145-175 inch lbs.

START-UP DIE OUTS, NO DTCs

1995 ACCLAIM, LEBARON & SPIRIT

On these models, equipped with 41TE automatic transaxles and a transmission control module (TCM) with the last four digits of the serial number/bar code between 2104 through 2174, these conditions and the following may occur: die outs at engine speeds above idle; transaxle goes into Second gear default with DTCs 26 and 42. This may be caused by the TCM.

To correct these conditions on models that die out with no DTCs, disconnect the TCM and start the engine. If condition ceases, install a replacement TCM (part No. 4686606). On models with DTCs 26 and 42, install the module (part No. 4686606) and use the DRB III to program this bulletin number (18-04-95) into the TCM currently on the vehicle.

NO START IN COLD WEATHER

1993-94 CONCORDE, INTREPID, LHS, NEW YORKER & VISION w/3.5L/V6-215 ENGINE

This condition may occur in temperatures of 0°F and below. The engine may crank and fire intermittently but fail to keep running. This may be caused by the PCM.

To correct this condition, proceed as follows:

1. Install replacement PCM (part No. 4606150 for 1993 Federal emissions, 4606160 for 1994 Federal; 4606151 for 1993 California, 4606161 for 1994 California).

CAV	WIRE COLOR	DESCRIPTION	CAV	WIRE COLOR	DESCRIPTION
1	BK/GY*	IGNITION COIL DRIVER #2	37	TN/BK*	CHARGING SYSTEM INDICATOR LAMP
2	BK/TN*	POWER GROUND	38	BR	FUEL PUMP RELAY
3	YL/WT*	FUEL INJECTOR #3	39	GY/YL*	EGR SOLENOID
4	WT/DB*	FUEL INJECTOR #1	40	TN/RD*	SPEED CONTROL VACUUM SOLENOID
5	WT/OR*	VEHICLE SPEED SENSOR	41	DG	GENERATOR FIELD
6	BK/RD*	INTAKE AIR TEMPERATURE SENSOR	42	DG/OR*	IGNITION SENSE
7	DG/BK*	DOWNSTREAM HEATED OXYGEN SENSOR	43	VT/WT*	5 VOLT SUPPLY (FOR MAP AND TPS)
8	BK/DG*	UPSTREAM HEATED OXYGEN SENSOR	44	OR	9 VOLT SUPPLY
9	LG	DATA LINK	45		
10	OR/DB*	THROTTLE POSITION SENSOR	46		
11	RD/WT*	DIRECT BATTERY VOLTAGE	47	YL/RD*	SPEED CONTROL SERVO
12			48	GY/LB*	TACHOMETER
13			49	VT/LG	BATTERY TEMPERATURE SENSOR SIGNAL
14	YL/BK*	IDLE AIR CONTROL MOTOR DRIVER #2	50	BR/YL*	PARK/NEUTRAL SWITCH
15	GY/RD*	IDLE AIR CONTROL MOTOR DRIVER #3	51	BK/LB*	SENSOR GROUND
16	PK/BK*	DUTY CYCLE EVAP PURGE SOLENOID	52	BK/WT*	SIGNAL GROUND
17	OR/BK*	TORQUE CONVERTOR CLUTCH SOLENOID (AUTO. TRANS.)	53		
18	DB/YL*	AUTOMATIC SHUTDOWN RELAY	54	LG/BK*	IGNITION SWITCH
19	DB/PK*	RADIATOR FAN RELAY	55		
20			56	WT	POWER STEERING PRESSURE SWITCH
21	DB/YL*	IGNITION COIL DRIVER #1	57		
22	BK/TN*	POWER GROUND	58		
23	TN	FUEL INJECTOR #2	59	DB/OR*	A/C COMPRESSOR CLUTCH RELAY
24	LB/BR*	FUEL INJECTOR #4	60	LG/RD*	SPEED CONTROL VENT SOLENOID
25	GY/BK*	CRANKSHAFT POSITION SENSOR			
26	TN/YL*	CAMSHAFT POSITION SENSOR			
27	BK/LG*	KNOCK SENSOR			
28	TN/BK*	ENGINE COOLANT TEMPERATURE SENSOR			
29	DG/RD*	MAP SENSOR			
30	PK	DATA LINK			
31	RD/LG*	SPEED CONTROL SELECT SIGNAL			
32	WT/PK*	BRAKE SWITCH			
33	BR/OR*	A/C PRESSURE SWITCH			
34	VT/BK*	IDLE AIR CONTROL MOTOR DRIVER #4			
35	BR/WT*	IDLE AIR CONTROL MOTOR DRIVER #1			
36	BK/PK*	MALFUNCTION INDICATOR LAMP			

WIRE COLOR CODES							
BK	BLACK	LG	LIGHT GREEN	LB	LIGHT BLUE	VT	VIOLET
BR	BROWN	OR	ORANGE			WT	WHITE
DB	DARK BLUE	PK	PINK			YL	YELLOW
DG	DARK GREEN	RD	RED			*	WITH TRACER
GY	GRAY	TN	TAN				

CONNECTOR TERMINAL SIDE SHOWN

CRA019500014000X

Fig. 5   Revised Powertrain Control Module (PCM) 60 way connector. 1995 Neon

Transmission Type	Emission Type	Altitude	Part No.
Manual	Federal	Low	5269646
	Federal & California	High	5269643
Automatic	Federal	Low	5269647
	Federal & California	High	5269664

Fig. 6   PCM replacement parts. 1995 Neon

2. Change engine oil and filter. **5W30 oil should not be used above 32°F.**
3. Replace all spark plugs with Champion RC-12-LYC and gap to .035 inch.
4. Install replacement 685 CCA battery.

CHECK ENGINE LAMP ON, DTC 15, ROUGH IDLE

1993-94 LASER & TALON W/1.8L/4-110 SOHC ENGINE

Intermittent rough idle or driveway die out may be caused by poor ground connections in the engine compartment.

To correct these conditions, ensure all engine controls and the idle speed control position sensor are functioning correctly and repair or replace as needed. If conditions persist, proceed as follows:

1. Disconnect battery ground cable and isolate end, then remove battery.
2. Remove tape covering plastic corrugated wiring harness protector along top of engine side of dash panel.
3. Isolate green/black wire, follow its length and locate two taped splice connections. Remove tape from this point.
4. Fabricate a ten inch 18 gauge jumper wire that fits battery ground connector/stud on dash. Solder this wire to

inboard splice located in previous step.
5. Clean and solder outboard splice.
6. Perform continuity inspection of green/black wire from outboard splice to stud on dash, then tape splices and reinstall battery.

HESITATION, SAGGING & SURGING
1995 NEON

These conditions may occur at varying road speeds, throttle positions or accessory usage. This may be caused by the PCM.

To correct these conditions, first ensure no DTCs are present and repair as needed. If conditions persist, proceed as follows:

1. **On models equipped with manual transaxle,** install replacement PCM from chart and crankshaft position sensor (part No. 5235377), **Fig. 6.**
2. **On all models,** install replacement PCM.

DELAYED, ERRATIC & HARSH SHIFTS
1994 CONCORDE, INTREPID, LHS, NEW YORKER & VISION W/3.3L/V6-201 & 3.5L/V6-215 ENGINES

These conditions may be noticed more

6	4573938	Tube - Spark Plug
6	4573943	Nut - Spark Plug Tube
6	4536538	Seal - Spark Plug Tube
6	4609076	Spark Plug
1	4728944	Cable Set
2	4556593	Gasket - Cylinder Head Cover
2	4556557	Gasket - Intake Manifold To Head
1	4556556	Gasket - Plenum to Intake Manifold

Fig. 7   Spark plug & cable replacement parts. 1993 Concorde, Intrepid & Vision w/3.5L/V6-215 engine

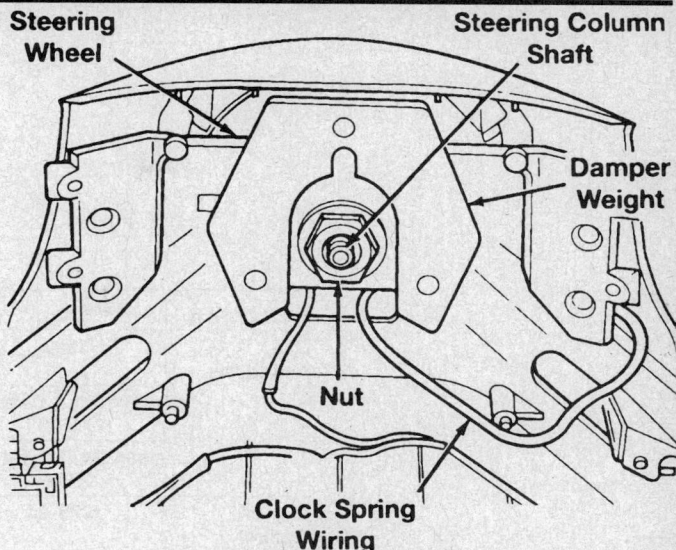

Fig. 8   Steering wheel & damper replacement. 1995 Neon

when the engine is cold and during warm-ups. This may be caused by the throttle position sensor (TPS).

To correct these conditions, first ensure no DTCs are present and repair as needed.

Connect DRB III, then operate throttle lever and read TPS voltage, which should read 1.2 or less fully closed and reach 3.7 volts or higher wide open. If any sticking, erratic or missing readings are noted, install a replacement TPS (part No. 4759001).

BUCK & MISS

1993 CONCORDE, INTREPID & VISION w/ 3.5L/V6-215 ENGINE

These conditions may be noticed at speeds of 40-55 mph, especially during full converter clutch (EMCC) operation. This may be caused by the spark plugs and cables.

To correct these conditions, first ensure no DTCs are present and repair as needed. If conditions persist, install replacement parts, Fig. 7.

ROUGH IDLE & STEERING WHEEL SHAKE

1995 NEON

These conditions may be caused by the PCM's calibrations and lack of damping in the steering wheel.

To correct these conditions, proceed as follows:

1. Remove steering wheel and ignition lock cylinder.
2. Separate column shrouds and disconnect clockspring connectors, then remove and discard clockspring.
3. **Ensure front wheels are not moved,** then install replacement clockspring (part No. 4793004 with speed control, part No. 4793003 without). Remove "T" pin from clockspring

and turn rotor 180° clockwise. Connect wiring.

4. Install steering wheel and new damper weight (part No. 5274431), **Fig. 8. Torque** wheel nut to 40 ft. lbs.
5. Ensure air bag connector is securely latched and wire is pointing toward bottom of air bag.
6. Reinstall components removed previously and inspect air bag for correct operation.
7. **On models with air conditioning,** remove two upper radiator isolator bracket mounting screws, and loosen radiator to battery strut screw.
8. **On all models,** raise cooling module high enough to free two lower isolator bushings from crossmember and support module in this position.
9. Install replacement lower bushings (part No. 4546657).
10. Install module into lower brackets, then **torque** upper screws to 65 inch lbs.
11. Use Mopar Diagnostic System and DRB III to reprogram PCM.

HARD CRANK, LONG CRANK TIME & ENGINE MISS

1993-94 CONCORDE, INTREPID, LHS & VISION & 1994 NEW YORKER w/3.5L/V6-215 ENGINE

These conditions may occur without a Diagnostic Trouble Code having been set. This may be caused by the fuel rail assembly.

To correct these conditions, bring engine to operating temperature in Park. Use the DRB II scan tool and select Engine, Fuel/Ignition, Monitors and Adaptive Memory from the menu to monitor left and righthand oxygen (O2) sensor adaptive memory. Normal adaptive values will read between +5 and -5. If the lefthand bank

reads between -6 and -20, install a replacement fuel rail assembly **Fig. 9.**

ROUGH IDLE IN REVERSE

1993-94 SAHDOW & SUNDANCE w/2.2L/4-135 & 2.5L/4-153 ENGINES & AUTOMATIC TRANSAXLE

This condition may be caused by contact between the front bumper (which is part of a tuned anti-vibration system) and adjacent components.

To correct these conditions, first ensure no diagnostic trouble codes are present and repair as needed. If conditions persist, proceed as follows:

1. Bring engine to operating temperature.
2. Apply parking brake, then place selector lever in Reverse.
3. While engine idles, observe vibration level in driver's seat. This may be increased by operating air conditioning.
4. Inspect for loose body components, bumper damage and/or collision damage. If no faults are noted, perform following steps:
   a. Insert a 3x5 inch card or business card as a gauge between top of front bumper fascia and grille and fenders. Move gauge from side to side to determine if there is contact between these components.
   b. If fascia contacts these areas, lower bumper by its mounting bolts at energy absorbers. Adjust to maintain an even, uniform gap at upper body.
   c. Inspect driver's seat vibration again, and if it is still objectionable, insert gauge card between top of fascia and fenders near wheel well openings. If fascia contacts fenders, adjust fender mounted slider brackets to maintain an even, uniform gap.

Description	Year	Part No.	Quantity
Rail Assembly	1993	4762923	1
	1994 Built Before 7/26/93	4762923	1
	1994 Built After 7/26/93	4762924	1
Plenum Gasket	1993-94	4556556	1
EGR Tube Gasket	1993-94	4612184	2
Rail To Manifold Gasket	1993-94	4573378	2

Fig. 9 Fuel rail replacement parts. 1993-94 Concorde, Intrepid, LHS & Vision & 1994 New Yorker w/3.5L/V6-215 engine

ABBREVIATIONS & ACRONYMS

A/C ATS: A/C Ambient Temperature Switch
A/C: Air Conditioning
A/F: Air/Fuel
ACL: Air Cleaner
AIR: Secondary Air Injection
AP: Accelerator Pedal
ASD: Automatic Speed Device
ATDC: After Top Dead Center
AWD: All Wheel Drive
B +: Battery Positive Voltage
BARO: Barometric Pressure
BTDC: Before Top Dead Center
CAC: Charge Air Cooler
CAT: Charge Air Temperature
CCD +: Chrysler Collision Detection Bus (+)
CCD-: Chrysler Collision Detection Bus (-)
CFI: Continuous Fuel Injection
CID: Cubic Inch Displacement
CKP: Crankshaft Position Sensor
CL: Closed Loop
CMP: Camshaft Position Sensor
CO2: Carbon Dioxide
CO: Carbon Monoxide
CPP: Clutch Pedal Position
CTOX: Continuous Trap Oxidizer
CTP: Closed Throttle Position
DFI: Direct Fuel Injection
DI: Distributor Ignition
DLC: Data Link Connector
DOHC: Dual Overhead Camshaft
DTC: Diagnostic Trouble Code
DTM: Diagnostic Test Mode
ECM: Engine Control Module
ECT: Engine Coolant Temperature Sensor
EEPROM: Electronic Erasable Programmable Read Only Memory
EET: Electronic EGR Transducer
EETS: Electric EGR Transducer Solenoid
EFE: Early Fuel Evaporation
EGR: Exhaust Gas Recirculation
EI: Electronic Ignition
EM: Engine Modification
EVAP: Evaporative Emission
FC: Fan Control
FED: Federal (49 State)
FF: Flexible Fuel
FWD: Front Wheel Drive
GEN: Generator

HC: Hydrocarbon
HD: Heavy Duty
HO2S: Heated Oxygen Sensor
HO: High Output
HPTBI: High Pressure TBI
IAC: Idle Air Control
ICM: Ignition Control Module
IFI: Indirect Fuel Injection
IFS: Inertial Fuel Shutoff
ISC: Idle Speed Control
KS: Knock Sensor
L: Liter
LPTBI: Low Pressure TBI
MAF: Mass Air Flow
MAP: Manifold Absolute Pressure
MC: Mixture Control
MDP: Manifold Differential Pressure
MIL: Malfunction Indicator Lamp
MST: Intake Manifold Surface Temperature
MTV: Intake Manifold Tuning Valve
MVLPS: Manual Valve Lever Position Switch (See Also PNP Switch)
MVZ: Manifold Vacuum Zone
NVRAM: Non-Volatile Random Access Memory
O2S: Oxygen Sensor (Left Sensor When Two Sensors Are Used)
OS2R: Right Oxygen Sensor
OBD: On-Board Diagnostic
OC: Oxidation Catalytic Converter
OL: Open Loop
PAIR: Pulse Secondary Air Injection
PCM: Powertrain Control Module
PNP: Park/Neutral Position
PROM: Programmable Read Only Memory
PSP: Power Steering Pressure
PTOX: Periodic Trap Oxidizer
RAM: Random Access Memory
RM: Relay Module
ROM: Read Only Memory
RWD: Rear Wheel Drive
SAS: Speed Adjusting Screw
SC: Supercharger
SCB: Supercharger Bypass
SFI: Sequential Multiport Fuel Injection
SIL: Shift Indicator Lamp
SOHC: Single Overhead Camshaft
SPL: Smoke Puff Limiter
SRI: Service Reminder Indicator
SRT: System Readiness Test
ST: Scan Tool
TBI: Throttle Body Injection
TC: Turbocharged

TCC: Torque Converter Clutch
TCM: Transmission Control Module
TDC: Top Dead Center
TP: Throttle Position
TR: Transmission Range
TSB: Technical Service Bulletin
TVV: Thermal Vacuum Valve
TWC + OC: Three-Way + Oxidation Catalytic Converter
TWC: Three-Way Catalytic Converter

V: Volt
VAF: Volume Air Flow
VOM: Volt-Ohm Meter
VR: Voltage Regulator
VSC: Vehicle Speed Control
VSS: Vehicle Speed Sensor
WOT: Wide Open Throttle
WU-OC: Warm Up Oxidation Catalytic Converter
WU-TWC: Warm Up Three-Way Catalytic Converter

FORD MOTOR COMPANY

Page No.

ABBREVIATIONS & ACRONYMS.........................17-1
APPLICATION CHARTS 11-1
COMPUTERIZED ENGINE CONTROLS
   EEC-IV...8-1
   EEC-V 9-1
   EEC 10-1
ELECTRIC FUEL PUMPS...............................6-1
ELECTRONIC INSTRUMENTATION.....................15-1
EMISSION CONTROLS 14-1
EMISSION CONTROL SYSTEM APPLICATION CHARTS..11-1
ENGINE COMPARTMENT REFERENCE DIAGRAMS......13-1
ENGINE SYSTEMS IDENTIFICATION 1-1
ENGINE TUNE UP & PERFORMANCE
  4 Cylinder Engine:
   Compression Pressure.............................3-1
   Engine Identification 3-1
   Fuel Injection Cleaning............................3-5
   Idle Speed & Mixture Adjustments..................3-3
   Ignition Timing....................................3-2
   Ignition Wire Resistance..........................3-1
   Sensor Adjustments...............................3-6
   Spark Plugs.......................................3-1
   Valves..3-4
  V6 Engine:
   Compression Pressure.............................3-8
   Engine Identification 3-8
   Fuel Injection Cleaning...........................3-10
   Idle Speed & Mixture Adjustments..................3-9
   Ignition Timing....................................3-8
   Ignition Wire Resistance..........................3-8

Page No.

   Sensor Adjustments 3-11
   Spark Plugs.......................................3-8
   Valves..3-9
  V8 Engine:
   Compression Pressure............................3-12
   Engine Identification 3-12
   Fuel Injection Cleaning...........................3-13
   Idle Speed & Mixture Adjustments.................3-12
   Ignition Timing...................................3-12
   Ignition Wire Resistance..........................3-12
   Sensor Adjustments 3-13
   Spark Plugs......................................3-12
   Valves...3-12
FUEL INJECTION....................................5-1
FUEL PUMPS.......................................6-1
HOW TO USE THIS MANUAL 0-1
IGNITION SYSTEMS 4-1
QUICK REFERENCE.................................0-1
SERVICE BULLETINS 16-1
SPECIFICATIONS
  Tune Up 2-1
SUPERCHARGERS..................................7-1
TECHNICAL SERVICE BULLETINS 16-1
TUNE UP PROCEDURES:
  4 Cylinder Engine 3-1
  V6 Engine..3-8
  V8 Engine 3-12
TUNE UP SPECIFICATIONS...........................2-1
TURBOCHARGERS...................................7-1
VACUUM HOSE ROUTINGS..........................12-1

FORD MOTOR COMPANY

Page No.

ABBREVIATIONS & ACRONYMS. 17-1
APPLICATION CHARTS 11-1
COMPUTERIZED ENGINE CONTROLS
   EEC-IV. 8-1
   EEC-V 9-1
   EEC 10-1
ELECTRIC FUEL PUMPS. 6-1
ELECTRONIC INSTRUMENTATION. 15-1
EMISSION CONTROLS 14-1
EMISSION CONTROL SYSTEM APPLICATION CHARTS . . 11-1
ENGINE COMPARTMENT REFERENCE DIAGRAMS 13-1
ENGINE SYSTEMS IDENTIFICATION 1-1
ENGINE TUNE UP & PERFORMANCE
   4 Cylinder Engine:
      Compression Pressure 3-1
      Engine Identification 3-1
      Fuel Injection Cleaning 3-5
      Idle Speed & Mixture Adjustments 3-3
      Ignition Timing 3-2
      Ignition Wire Resistance 3-1
      Sensor Adjustments 3-6
      Spark Plugs 3-1
      Valves 3-4
   V6 Engine:
      Compression Pressure 3-8
      Engine Identification 3-8
      Fuel Injection Cleaning 3-10
      Idle Speed & Mixture Adjustments 3-9
      Ignition Timing 3-8
      Ignition Wire Resistance 3-8

Page No.

      Sensor Adjustments 3-11
      Spark Plugs. 3-8
      Valves. 3-9
   V8 Engine:
      Compression Pressure 3-12
      Engine Identification 3-12
      Fuel Injection Cleaning. 3-13
      Idle Speed & Mixture Adjustments. 3-12
      Ignition Timing. 3-12
      Ignition Wire Resistance. 3-12
      Sensor Adjustments 3-13
      Spark Plugs 3-12
      Valves. 3-12
FUEL INJECTION. 5-1
FUEL PUMPS. 6-1
HOW TO USE THIS MANUAL 0-1
IGNITION SYSTEMS 4-1
QUICK REFERENCE. 0-1
SERVICE BULLETINS 16-1
SPECIFICATIONS
   Tune Up 2-1
SUPERCHARGERS. 7-1
TECHNICAL SERVICE BULLETINS 16-1
TUNE UP PROCEDURES:
   4 Cylinder Engine 3-1
   V6 Engine. 3-8
   V8 Engine 3-12
TUNE UP SPECIFICATIONS. 2-1
TURBOCHARGERS. 7-1
VACUUM HOSE ROUTINGS. 12-1

2-FORD MOTOR COMPANY

QUICK REFERENCE

Application	Page No.
ACCESSING DIAGNOSTIC TROUBLE CODES	
EEC	10-9
EEC-IV	8-8
EEC-V	9-5
CLEARING DIAGNOSTIC TROUBLE CODES	
EEC	10-11
EEC-IV	8-11
EEC-V	9-7
COMPRESSION PRESSURE SPECIFICATIONS	
4 Cylinder Gasoline Engine	3-1
V6 Gasoline Engine	3-8
V8 Gasoline Engine	3-12
DIAGNOSTIC CHART INDEX	
EEC	10-35
EEC-IV	8-106
EEC-V	9-105
FUEL PRESSURE SPECIFICATIONS	
All	6-39
IGNITION COIL SPECIFICATIONS	
Type 1	4-2
Type 2	4-15
Type 3	4-45
Type 4	4-62
Type 5	4-105
Type 6	4-127
SENSOR SPECIFICATIONS	
EEC	10-2
EEC-IV	8-2
EEC-V	9-1

HOW TO USE THIS MANUAL

Be aware of the possibility that replacement underhood labels may be incorrect for the application. Replacement labels may also be more current than this publication. Check for existing Technical Service Bulletins (TSBs) and emission recall notices. Some states may fasten an official "Engine Identification" label to the vehicle if it has had an engine change, if it is a kit-car, or gray-market car, or for other reasons. If so, observe the ECS information on the state-installed label.

It is the technician's responsibility to cross-check available information sources. If a discrepancy exists between label information on the vehicle and this publication, the vehicle appears to be as originally equipped, and you are unable to make a positive determination or are unfamiliar with the vehicle to be tested, refer the motorist to a dealership or other inspection facility specializing in that make of vehicle. If a conflict still exists in determining the required ECS, refer the motorist to the state's referee facility for verification.

You may contact MOTOR at 1-800-4A MOTOR to report errors or missing information.

WHAT IS & IS NOT CONTAINED IN THIS MANUAL

This manual contains specifications, diagnostic and service procedures related to fuel, ignition, emissions, engine control and other electronic automotive systems. Information on mechanical systems and components such as engines and brakes can be found in **MOTOR's Auto Repair Manual.** A detailed breakdown of individual systems and procedures can be found inside the back cover of this manual.

AIR QUALITY STANDARDS

This section, located in the front of this manual, includes Federal, State and District Of Columbia mandated emissions specifications.

GETTING STARTED

All testing should begin with verification of the customer complaint and a basic visual inspection. Successful isolation of a specific problem in a suspected system must follow a thorough and logical approach.

Before performing any detailed system diagnostics, review the various manufacturer's Technical Service Bulletin (TSB) information found in that chapter. The TSBs are listed according to symptom and vehicle application. Many times, you will find that driveability complaints can be readily identified and easily repaired using the information contained in this section.

If a basic vehicle inspection and a check of the TSBs leave the problem unresolved, further testing will be necessary.

The following outline divides this manual into three categories; Engine Control Systems, Related Information and Additional Features. The time you invest in familiarizing yourself with the books contents before attempting to use it will be time well spent.

For immediate access to frequently used information each manufacturer chapter includes a Quick Reference chart. These charts, located on the first page of each chapter allow easy access to information, such as accessing diagnostic trouble codes, diagnostic chart index, fuel pressure and compression pressure, ignition coil and sensor specifications.

ENGINE CONTROL SYSTEMS

ENGINE SYSTEMS IDENTIFICATION

Before beginning any diagnostic work on a vehicle, the vehicle as well as its engine and related systems must be properly identified. This often-overlooked step is **the key to successful diagnosis and repair.**

Presented in chart form, the Engine Systems Identification will identify the Fuel, Ignition and Computer systems used on the vehicle and direct you to the specific page that information on each system can be found.

To verify the engine used in the vehicle, check the Engine Code in the Vehicle Identification Number (VIN). If you are unfamiliar with the VIN system, consult the Vehicle Identification section found in the front of this manual as well as the Engine Identification portion of the Engine Tune Up & Performance section.

IGNITION SYSTEMS

Information found in this section will include basic testing and servicing of the ignition system and its components. Use the information in this section if the ignition system is suspect and you have been directed here from the Engine Systems Identification Chart.

FUEL INJECTION

Although this section does provide some diagnosis and testing information, it is primarily intended to assist in component service. Because of the interrelation between various engine control systems on Ford vehicles, most diagnostic information will be found in the Computerized Engine Control portion of this manual.

COMPUTERIZED ENGINE CONTROLS

If an engine control problem is suspected (check engine light, etc.), or a reference from another section has been made, the application chart found at the front of this chapter will identify the vehicle's control system and where it may be found.

After identifying the system, familiarize yourself with its operation by reviewing the descriptive information found at the beginning of the section. Next, proceed to the Quick Tests, Diagnostic Routines or Diagnostic Sub-Routine/Quick Tests, which will give testing and trouble code retrieval procedures. **If trouble codes are present,** there are several methods to read codes, which are described in the System Description & Operation section.

After reading trouble codes, refer to the index for the location of the quick test codes and code definition to determine what each code means. The Quick Test or Diagnostic Sub-Routine/Quick Test will also refer to a Pinpoint Test that will test that specific component or code. Once referred to a Pinpoint Test, proceed to that test. Pinpoint Tests may also be identified and located using the Pinpoint Test Index, located near the front of each section.

When using either the Quick, Diagnostic Sub-Routine/Quick or Pinpoint Tests, connector pin usage and wiring diagrams are provided near the front of each section. When a test gives a sensor specification, refer to Sensor Specifications listed in the front of each section. At some point in a Pinpoint Test, you may be instructed to clear the memory of codes. This information may be found in the System Description & Operation section.

RELATED INFORMATION

TUNE UP SPECIFICATIONS

These charts provide basic tune up specifications including spark plug gap, ignition timing, idle speeds and fuel pump pressure. Illustrations of firing orders and timing marks are also included.

ENGINE TUNE UP & PERFORMANCE

These sections are grouped by engine configuration and offer procedures for such maintenance routines as measuring compression pressures, spark plug replacement and fuel injector cleaning. Also included in these sections are valve, throttle position sensor, idle speed and mixture adjustments.

ELECTRIC FUEL PUMPS

Diagnosis, testing and servicing procedures of the electric fuel pump system can be found in this section. Also included are specifications and fuel system pressure relief procedures.

TURBOCHARGERS & SUPERCHARGERS

Descriptions, troubleshooting and service procedures for turbochargers and superchargers can be found in this section.

EMISSION CONTROL SYSTEM APPLICATION CHARTS

Application charts provide a quick reference for identifying the emission control systems and devices used on a vehicle.

VACUUM HOSE ROUTINGS

Vacuum hose routings provide a visual reference to these devices and systems and their installation on the vehicle. This information may be used for inspection, hose rerouting or tracing components that may not be readily visible.

ENGINE COMPARTMENT REFERENCE DIAGRAMS

This section will help to readily identify various fuel, ignition and emission-related components on the vehicle. These illustrations are intended to avoid wasted time when searching for components that require servicing.

EMISSION CONTROLS

After consulting the Emission Control Systems Application Chart, detailed emission system information can be found in this section. Information will include descriptions, testing and servicing procedures.

TECHNICAL SERVICE BULLETINS

The Technical Service Bulletins are listed according to symptom and vehicle application. Many common driveability complaints can be readily identified and easily repaired using the information contained in this section.

ADDITIONAL FEATURES

VEHICLE IDENTIFICATION

This section, located in the front of this manual, provides a explanation and breakdown of the Vehicle Identification Number (VIN) system.

VEHICLE MAINTENANCE SCHEDULES

Located in the front of this manual, Vehicle Maintenance Schedules provide a handy reference for identifying factory-recommended maintenance operations and service intervals.

ELECTRICAL SYMBOL & WIRE COLOR CODE IDENTIFICATION

Throughout this manual, many wiring diagrams and schematics will be found. The Wire Color Code & Electrical Symbol Identification information, found in the front of this book provides explanations of the various symbols and wire color abbreviations used in the diagrams.

SERVICE REMINDER & WARNING LAMP RESET PROCEDURES

This section, located in the front of the manual, includes illustrated procedures for resetting the various service reminder lights found on Ford vehicles.

ELECTRONIC INSTRUMENTATION

This section provides diagnosis and testing for electronic instrumentation. To use this section, from the Table of Contents, go to the specific model section. Then, beginning with the Diagnostic Chart Index, proceed to recommended Pinpoint Test.

NGI E SYST M I TI ICATIUN

The eighth digit of the VIN denotes engine code.

Identification							
Engine Code	Engine	Fuel Control System	Page No.	Ignition System	Page No.	Computer System	Page No.
1993							
H	1.3L/4-81	Multi-Point Fuel Injection	5-1	Type 5	4-105	Electronic Engine Control (EEC)	10-1
Z	1.6L/4-98	Multi-Point Fuel Injection	5-1	Type 5	4-105	Electronic Engine Control (EEC)	10-1
6	1.6L/4-98 Turbo	Multi-Point Fuel Injection	5-1	Type 5	4-105	Electronic Engine Control (EEC)	10-1
8	1.8L/4-112	Multi-Point Fuel Injection	5-1	Type 5	4-105	Electronic Engine Control (EEC)	10-1
J	1.9L/4-116	Sequential Multi-Point Fuel Injection	5-1	Type 4	4-62	Electronic Engine Control IV (EEC-IV)	8-1
A	2.0L/4-122	Multi-Point Fuel Injection	5-1	Type 5	4-105	Electronic Engine Control IV (EEC-IV)	8-1
M	2.3L/4-140 OHC	Multi-Point Fuel Injection	5-1	Type 2	4-14	Electronic Engine Control IV (EEC-IV)	8-1
X	2.3L/4-140 HSC	Sequential Multi-Point Fuel Injection	5-1	Type 1	4-1	Electronic Engine Control IV (EEC-IV)	8-1
B	2.5L/V6-153	Multi-Point Fuel Injection	5-1	Type 5	4-105	Electronic Engine Control (EEC)	10-1
U	3.0L/V6-182 ①	Sequential Multi-Point Fuel Injection	5-1	Type 1	4-1	Electronic Engine Control IV (EEC-IV)	8-1
U	3.0L/V6-182 ②	Sequential Multi-Point Fuel Injection	5-1	Type 3	4-45	Electronic Engine Control IV (EEC-IV)	8-1
Y	3.0L/V6-182 SHO	Sequential Multi-Point Fuel Injection	5-1	Type 2	4-14	Electronic Engine Control IV (EEC-IV)	8-1
P	3.2L/V6-195 SHO	Sequential Multi-Point Fuel Injection	5-1	Type 2	4-14	Electronic Engine Control IV (EEC-IV)	8-1
4	3.8L/V6-232	Sequential Multi-Point Fuel Injection	5-1	Type 1	4-1	Electronic Engine Control IV (EEC-IV)	8-1
C,R	3.8L/V6-232 SC	Sequential Multi-Point Fuel Injection	5-1	Type 2	4-14	Electronic Engine Control IV (EEC-IV)	8-1
W	4.6L/V8-281	Sequential Multi-Point Fuel Injection	5-1	Type 4	4-62	Electronic Engine Control IV (EEC-IV)	8-1
E,T	5.0L/V8-302	Sequential Multi-Point Fuel Injection	5-1	Type 1	4-1	Electronic Engine Control IV (EEC-IV)	8-1

① —Except flexible fuel engine.
② —Flexible fuel engine.

ENGINE SYSTEMS IDENTIFICATION—Continued

The eighth digit of the VIN denotes engine code.

Identification							
Engine Code	Engine	Fuel Control System	Page No.	Ignition System	Page No.	Computer System	Page No.
1994							
H	1.3L/4-81	Multi-Point Fuel Injection	5-1	Type 5	4-105	Electronic Engine Control (EEC)	10-1
Z	1.6L/4-98	Multi-Point Fuel Injection	5-1	Type 5	4-105	Electronic Engine Control (EEC)	10-1
6	1.6L/4-98 Turbo	Multi-Point Fuel Injection	5-1	Type 5	4-105	Electronic Engine Control (EEC)	10-1
8	1.8L/4-112 ⑤	Multi-Point Fuel Injection	5-1	Type 5	4-105	Electronic Engine Control (EEC)	10-1
J	1.9L/4-116	Sequential Multi-Point Fuel Injection	5-1	Type 4	4-62	Electronic Engine Control IV (EEC-IV)	8-1
A	2.0L/4-122 ⑤	Multi-Point Fuel Injection	5-1	Type 5	4-105	Electronic Engine Control IV (EEC-IV)	8-1
X	2.3L/4-140 HSC	Sequential Multi-Point Fuel Injection	5-1	Type 1	4-1	Electronic Engine Control IV (EEC-IV)	8-1
B	2.5L/V6-153	Multi-Point Fuel Injection	5-1	Type 5	4-105	Electronic Engine Control (EEC)	10-1
U	3.0L/V6-182 ①	Sequential Multi-Point Fuel Injection	5-1	Type 1	4-1	Electronic Engine Control IV (EEC-IV)	8-1
U	3.0L/V6-182 ②	Sequential Multi-Point Fuel Injection	5-1	Type 3	4-45	Electronic Engine Control IV (EEC-IV)	8-1
Y	3.0L/V6-182 SHO	Sequential Multi-Point Fuel Injection	5-1	Type 2	4-14	Electronic Engine Control IV (EEC-IV)	8-1
P	3.2L/V6-195 SHO	Sequential Multi-Point Fuel Injection	5-1	Type 2	4-14	Electronic Engine Control IV (EEC-IV)	8-1
4	3.8L/V6-232 ③	SFI/Sequential Multi-Point Fuel Injection	5-1	Type 1	4-1	Electronic Engine Control IV (EEC-IV)	8-1
4	3.8L/V6-232 ④	Sequential Multi-Point Fuel Injection	5-1	Type 6	4-127	Electronic Engine Control V (EEC-V)	9-1
R	3.8L/V6-232 SC	Sequential Multi-Point Fuel Injection	5-1	Type 3	4-45	Electronic Engine Control IV (EEC-IV)	8-1
V,W	4.6L/V8-281 ⑤	Sequential Multi-Point Fuel Injection	5-1	Type 4	4-62	Electronic Engine Control IV (EEC-IV)	8-1
W	4.6L/V8-281 ⑥	Sequential Multi-Point Fuel Injection	5-1	Type 6	4-127	Electronic Engine Control V (EEC-V)	9-1
D,T	5.0L/V8-302 ①	Sequential Multi-Point Fuel Injection	5-1	Type 1	4-1	Electronic Engine Control IV (EEC-IV)	8-1

①—Except flexible fuel engine.
②—Flexible fuel engine.
③—Except Mustang.
④—Mustang.
⑤—Except Cougar & Thunderbird.
⑥—Cougar & Thunderbird.

ENGINE SYSTEMS IDENTIFICATION—Continued

The eighth digit of the VIN denotes engine code.

	Identification							
Engine Code	Engine	Fuel Control System	Page No.	Ignition Type	Page No.	Computer System	Page No.
1995							
H	1.3L/4-81	Sequential Multi-Point Fuel Injection	5-1	Type 5	4-105	Electronic Engine Control (EEC)	10-1
8	1.8L/4-112⑤	**Multi-Point Fuel Injection**	5-1	Type 5	4-105	Electronic Engine Control (EEC)	10-1
J	1.9L/4-116	Sequential Multi-Point Fuel Injection	5-1	Type 4	4-62	Electronic Engine Control IV (EEC-IV)	8-1
A	2.0L/4-122①	Sequential Multi-Point Fuel Injection	5-1	Type 5	4-105	Electronic Engine Control IV (EEC-IV)	8-1
A	2.0L/4-122②	Sequential Multi-Point Fuel Injection	5-1	Type 4	4-62	Electronic Engine Control IV (EEC-IV)	8-1
B	2.5L/V6-152①	Sequential Multi-Point Fuel Injection	5-1	Type 5	4-105	Electronic Engine Control (EEC)	10-1
B	2.5L/V6-153②	Sequential Multi-Point Fuel Injection	5-1	Type 3	4-45	Electronic Engine Control IV (EEC-IV)	8-1
U	3.0L/V6-182③	Sequential Multi-Point Fuel Injection	5-1	Type 1	4-1	Electronic Engine Control IV (EEC-IV)	8-1
U	3.0L/V6-182④	Sequential Multi-Point Fuel Injection	5-1	Type 3	4-45	Electronic Engine Control IV (EEC-IV)	8-1
Y	3.0L/V6-182 SHO	Sequential Multi-Point Fuel Injection	5-1	Type 2	4-14	Electronic Engine Control IV (EEC-IV)	8-1
P	3.2L/V6-195 SHO	Sequential Multi-Point Fuel Injection	5-1	Type 2	4-14	Electronic Engine Control IV (EEC-IV)	8-1
4	3.8L/V6-232⑤	Sequential Multi-Point Fuel Injection	5-1	Type 1	4-1	Electronic Engine Control IV (EEC-IV)	8-1
4	3.8L/V6-232⑥	Sequential Multi-Point Fuel Injection	5-1	Type 3	4-45	Electronic Engine Control IV (EEC-IV)	8-1
4	3.8L/V6-232⑦	Sequential Multi-Point Fuel Injection	5-1	Type 6	4-127	Electronic Engine Control IV (EEC-V)	9-1
R	3.8L/V6-232 SC	Sequential Multi-Point Fuel Injection	5-1	Type 3	4-45	Electronic Engine Control IV (EEC-IV)	8-1
W	4.6L/V8-281⑧	Sequential Multi-Point Fuel Injection	5-1	Type 6	4-127	Electronic Engine Control V (EEC-V)	9-1
V	4.6L/V8-281⑨	Sequential Multi-Point Fuel Injection	5-1	Type 4	4-62	Electronic Engine Control IV (EEC-IV)	8-1
D,T	5.0L/V8-302	Sequential Multi-Point Fuel Injection	5-1	Type 1	4-1	Electronic Engine Control IV (EEC-IV)	8-1

①—Probe.
②—Contour & Mystique.
③—Except Flexible Fuel.
④—Flexible Fuel.
⑤—Cougar, Sable, Taurus &
Thunderbird Federal Models.
⑥—Cougar, Sable, Taurus &
Thunderbird California Models.
⑦—Mustang.
⑧—Except Mark VIII.
⑨—Mark VIII.

ENGINE SYSTEMS IDENTIFICATION—Continued

The eighth digit of the VIN denotes engine code.

Engine Code	Identification	Fuel Control System	Page No.	Ignition Type	Page No.	Computer System	Page No.
	Engine						
1996							
H	1.3L/4-81	Sequential Multi-Point Fuel Injection	5-1	Type 5	4-105	Electronic Engine Control (EEC)	-
8	1.8L/4-112	Multi-Point Fuel Injection	5-1	Type 5	4-105	Electronic Engine Control (EEC)	-
J	1.9L/4-116	Sequential Multi-Point Fuel Injection	5-1	Type 6	4-127	Electronic Engine Control V (EEC-V)	9-1
A	2.0L/4-121①	Sequential Multi-Point Fuel Injection	5-1	Type 6	4-127	Electronic Engine Control V (EEC-V)	9-1
3	2.0L/4-122②	Sequential Multi-Point Fuel Injection	5-1	Type 6	4-127	Electronic Engine Control V (EEC-V)	9-1
B	2.5L/V6-152①	Sequential Multi-Point Fuel Injection	5-1	Type 5	4-105	Electronic Engine Control (EEC)	-
L	2.5L/V6-153②	Sequential Multi-Point Fuel Injection	5-1	Type 6	4-127	Electronic Engine Control V (EEC-V)	9-1
U	3.0L/V6-182③	Sequential Multi-Point Fuel Injection	5-1	Type 6	4-127	Electronic Engine Control V (EEC-V)	9-1
I	3.0L/V6-182④	Sequential Multi-Point Fuel Injection	5-1	Type 6	4-127	Electronic Engine Control V (EEC-V)	9-1
S	3.0L/V6-181⑤	Sequential Multi-Point Fuel Injection	5-1	Type 6	4-127	Electronic Engine Control System V (EEC-V)	9-1
4	3.8L/V6-232	Sequential Multi-Point Fuel Injection	5-1	Type 6	4-127	Electronic Engine Control V (EEC-V)	9-1
W	4.6L/V8-281⑤	Sequential Multi-Point Fuel Injection	5-1	Type 6	4-127	Electronic Engine Control V (EEC-V)	-
V	4.6L/V8-281⑥	Sequential Multi-Point Fuel Injection	5-1	Type 6	4-127	Electronic Engine Control V (EEC-V)	9-1

①—Probe.
②—Contour & Mystique.
③—Except Flexible Fuel.
④—Flexible Fuel.
⑤—SOHC.
⑥—DOHC.

TU E UP SPECIFICATIONS

INDEX

	Page No. 2-	Fig. No.		Page No. 2-	Fig. No.
Ford Aspire & Festiva	2-10		Ford Escort & Mercury Tracer	2-9	Ford Tempo & Mercury Topaz	2-2
Ford Contour & Mercury Mystique	2-3		Ford Mustang	2-5	Lincoln	2-4
Ford Crown Victoria & Thunderbird, Mercury Cougar & Grand Marquis	2-1		Ford Probe	2-8	Mercury Capri	2-8
			Ford Taurus & Mercury Sable	2-7		

FORD CROWN VICTORIA & THUNDERBIRD, MERCURY COUGAR & GRAND MARQUIS

Engine Liter/CID (VIN Code) ①	Spark Plug Gap	Ignition Timing BTDC				Curb Idle Speed RPM		Fast Idle Speed RPM		Fuel Pump Pressure, psi.	Valve Clearance, Inch
		Firing Order Fig. ③	Man. Trans.	Auto. Trans. ④	Mark Fig.	Man. Trans.	Auto. Trans.	Man. Trans.	Auto. Trans.		
1993											
3.8L/V6-232 (4)	.054	A	—	10 ⑨	E	—	600D ⑥	—	⑥	35—40 ⑦	.089—.189 ⑫
3.8L/V6-232 SC (R)	.054	B	10 ⑤	10 ⑤	②	750 ⑥	⑥	⑥	⑥	35-40 ⑦	.089—.189 ⑫
4.6L/V8-281 (W)	.054	C ⑩	—	10 ⑤	②	—	560D ⑥	—	⑥	35-40 ⑦	⑧
5.0L/V8-302 HO (T)	.054	D	—	10 ⑨	F	—	⑥	—	⑥	30-40 ⑦	.098—.198 ⑫
1994											
3.8L/V6-232 (4)	.054	A	—	10 ⑨	E	—	600D ⑥	—	⑥	35-40 ⑦	.089—.189 ⑫
3.8L/V6-232 SC (R)	.054	B	10 ⑤	10 ⑤	②	700 ⑥	510 ⑥	⑥	⑥	35-40 ⑦	.089—.189 ⑫
4.6L/V8-281 (W)	.054	⑩ ⑪	—	10 ⑤	②	—	565D ⑥	—	⑥	35-40 ⑦	⑧
1995											
3.8L/V6-232 (4)	.054	A	—	10 ⑨	E	—	⑥	—	⑥	35-40 ⑦	.089—.189 ⑫
3.8L/V6-232 SC (R)	.054	B	10 ⑤	10 ⑤	②	⑥	⑥	⑥	⑥	35-40 ⑦	.089—.189 ⑫
4.6L/V8-281 (W)	.054	⑩ ⑪	—	10 ⑤	②	—	790-815 ⑥	—	⑥	35-40 ⑦	⑧
1996											
3.8L/V6-232 (4)	.054	H ⑬	—	⑤	—	—	⑥	—	⑥	35-40 ⑦	.089—.189 ⑫
4.6L/V8-281 (W)	.054	⑩ ⑪	—	⑤	②	—	640N ⑥	—	⑥	35-40 ⑦	⑧

BTDC— Before Top Dead Center.

① —The eighth digit of Vehicle Identification Number (VIN) denotes engine code.

② —Equipped w/crankshaft sensor.

③ —D:Drive. When checking idle speed, set parking brake & block drive wheels.

④ —Before disconnecting wires from distributor cap, determine location of No. 1 wire in cap, as distributor position may have been altered from that shown at the end of this chart.

⑤ —Non-adjustable.

⑥ —Idle speed is controlled by an automatic idle speed control, no adjustment.

⑦ —Wrap shop towel around fuel diagnostic valve to prevent fuel spillage. Connect suitable fuel pressure gauge to fuel diagnostic valve. Place ignition switch in On position to energize fuel pump & check pressure gauge reading.

⑧ —Collapsed tappet gap: intake .020-.069 inch, exhaust, .046-.095 inch.

⑨ —Disconnect inline spout connector, then start engine & adjust ignition timing as necessary. After completing adjustment, reconnect spout connector.

⑩ —Cylinder numbering front to rear, right bank, 1, 2, 3, 4; left bank, 5, 6, 7, 8. Firing order 1-3-7-2-6-5-4-8.

⑪ —Cougar & Thunderbird, refer to Fig. G. Crown Victoria & Grand Marquis, Fig. C.

⑫ —Collapsed tappet gap.

⑬ —Cylinder numbering front to rear, right bank, 1, 2, 3; left bank, 4, 5, 6. Firing order, 1-4-2-5-3-6.

TUNE UP SPECIFICATIONS

Continued

FORD CROWN VICTORIA & THUNDERBIRD, MERCURY COUGAR & GRAND MARQUIS —Continued

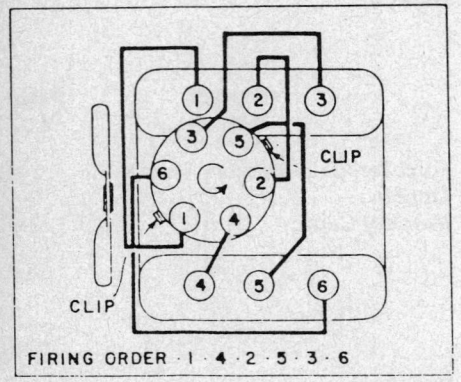

FIRING ORDER · 1 · 4 · 2 · 5 · 3 · 6

FM1139100104000X

Fig. A

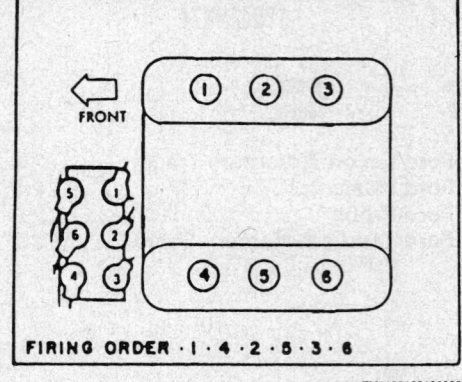

FIRING ORDER · 1 · 4 · 2 · 5 · 3 · 6

FM1139100106000X

Fig. B

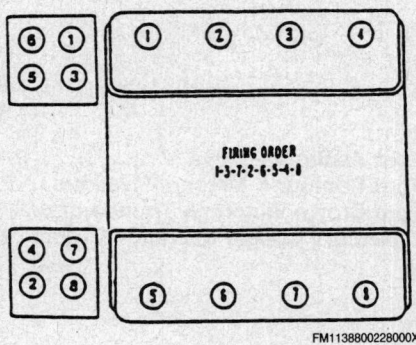

FIRING ORDER 1-3-7-2-6-5-4-8

FM1138800228000X

Fig. C

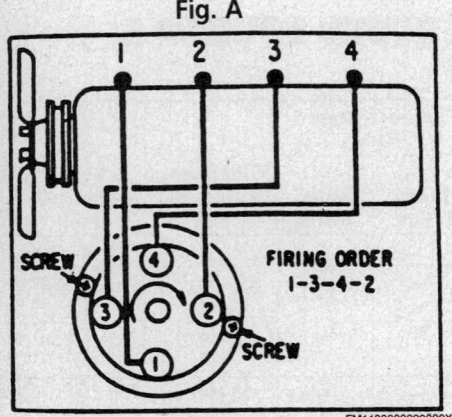

FIRING ORDER 1-3-4-2

FM1138800229000X

Fig. D

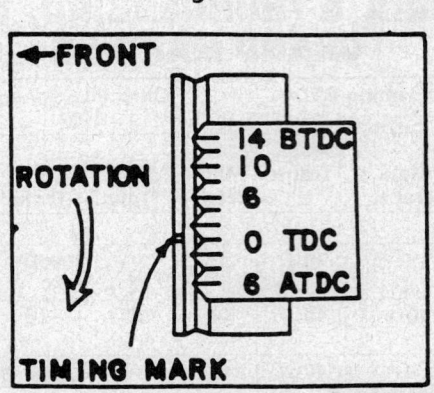

FM1138800232000X

Fig. E

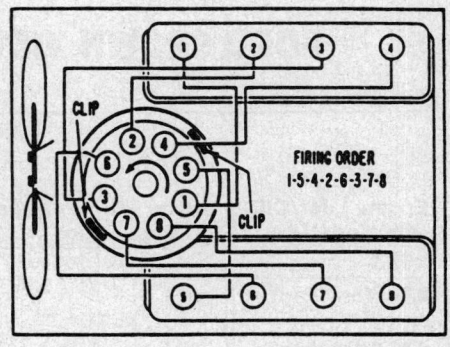

FIRING ORDER 1-5-4-2-6-3-7-8

FM1138800233000X

Fig. F

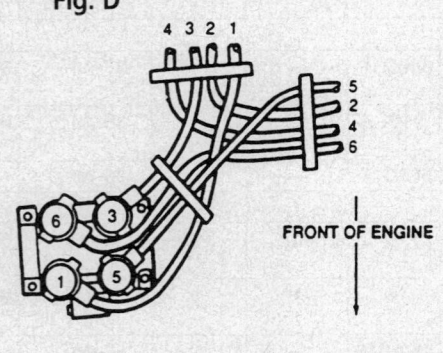

FM1139400436000X

Fig. G

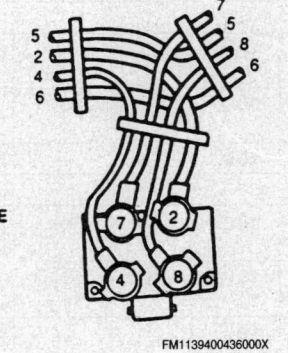

Fig. G

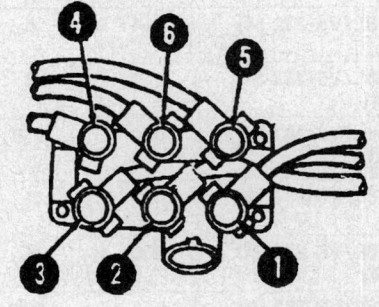

NOTE: ALL IGNITION WIRES MUST BE FULLY SEATED ON IGNITION COIL BY HAND

FM1138800242000X

Fig. H

FORD TEMPO & MERCURY TOPAZ

| Year & Engine/ VIN Code ① | Spark Plug Gap | Ignition Timing BTDC | | | | Curb Idle Speed ② | | Fast Idle Speed | | Fuel Pump Pressure, psi ⑥ | Valve Clearance, Inch |
		Firing Order Fig. ③	Man. Trans.	Auto. Trans.	Timing Mark Fig.	Man. Trans.	Auto. Trans.	Man. Trans.	Auto. Trans.		
1993											
2.3L/4-140/X	.054	A	15⑦	15⑦	⑧	⑤	⑤	⑤	⑤	50-60	④
3.0L/V6-182/U	.044	C	10⑦	10⑦	B	800⑤	740D⑤	⑤	⑤	35-40	④
1994											
2.3L/4-140/X	.054	A	10⑦	10⑦	⑧	⑤	⑤	⑤	⑤	50-60	④
3.0L/V6-182/U	.044	C	10⑦	10⑦	B	800⑤	740D⑤	⑤	⑤	35-40	④

BTDC—Before Top Dead Center.
①—The eighth digit of the Vehicle Identification Number (VIN) denotes engine code.

②—D: Drive.
③—Before disconnecting wires from distributor cap, determine location of No. 1 wire in cap, as distributor

position may have been altered from that shown at the end of this chart.
④—Equipped with hydraulic valve

Continued

FORD TEMPO & MERCURY TOPAZ—Continued

lifters, no adjustment required.
⑤—Idle speed controlled by an automatic idle speed control.
⑥—Wrap shop towel around fuel diagnostic valve fitting to prevent

, fuel spillage. Connect a suitable fuel pressure gauge to fuel diagnostic valve. Energize fuel pump & check fuel pressure gauge reading.
⑦—Disconnect inline spout connector,

then start engine & adjust ignition timing as necessary. After completing adjustment, reconnect spout connector.
⑧—Mark located on crankshaft pulley.

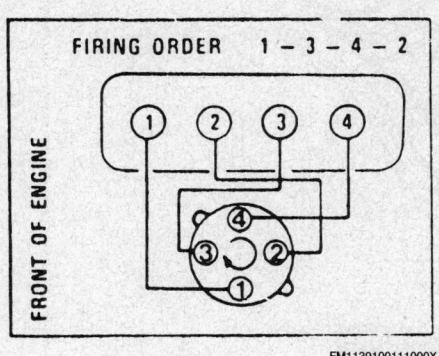

Fig. A

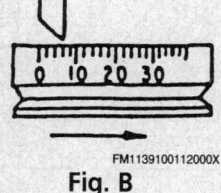

Fig. B

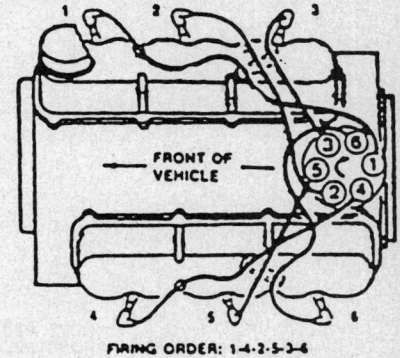

Fig. C

FORD CONTOUR & MERCURY MYSTIQUE

Year & Engine (VIN Code) ①	Spark Plug Gap	Ignition Timing BTDC				Curb Idle Speed		Fast Idle Speed		Fuel Pump Pressure, psi. ③	Valve Clearance, Inch
		Firing Order Fig.	Man. Trans.	Auto Trans.	Mark Fig.	Man. Trans.	Auto Trans.	Man. Trans.	Auto Trans.		
1995-96											
2.0L/4-122 (3)	.048-.052	A	8-12④	8-12④	C	②	②	②	②	39	⑤
2.5/V6-153 (L)	.052-.056	B	8-12④	8-12④	D	②	②	②	②	40	⑤

BTDC—Before Top Dead Center.
①—Eighth digit of Vehicle Identification Number (VIN) denotes engine code.
②—Idle speed is controlled by Idle Air Control (IAC) valve.
③—Wrap shop towel around diagnostic valve to prevent fuel spillage. Connect suitable fuel pressure gauge to fuel diagnostic valve. Place ignition switch in On position to energize fuel pump & check pressure gauge reading.
④—Non-adjustable.
⑤—Valve clearance is hydraulically controlled, no adjustment is necessary.

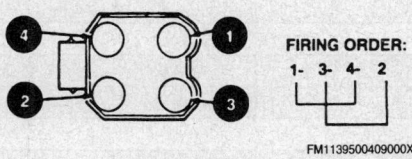

Fig. A

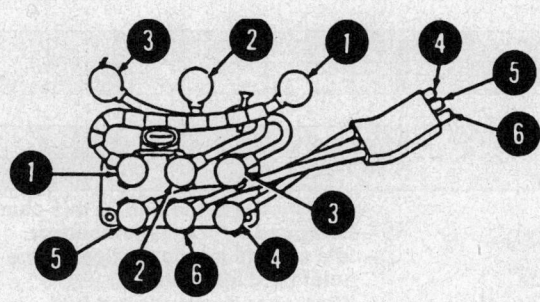

Fig. B

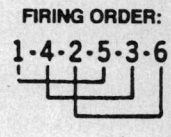

FIRING ORDER: 1-4-2-5-3-6

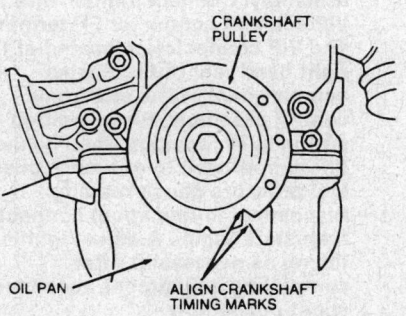

Fig. C

Continued

FORD CONTOUR & MERCURY MYSTIQUE—Continued

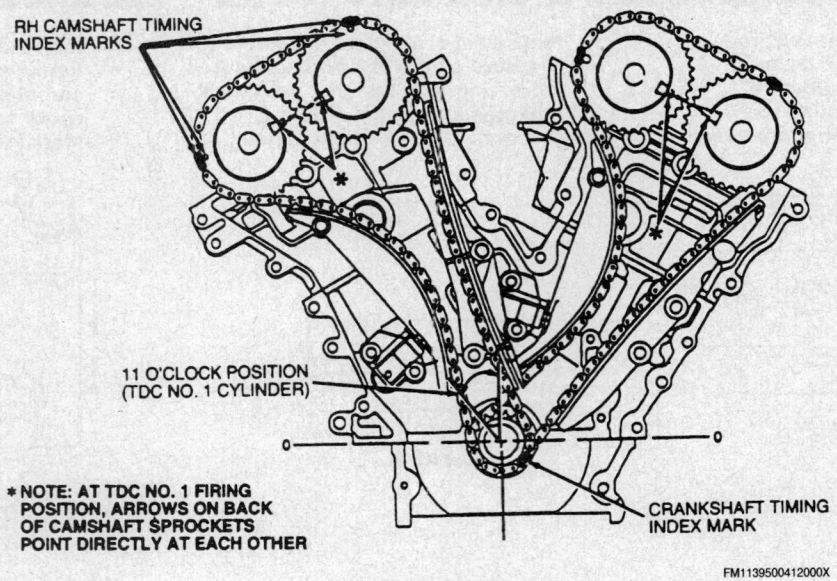

RH CAMSHAFT TIMING INDEX MARKS

11 O'CLOCK POSITION (TDC NO. 1 CYLINDER)

CRANKSHAFT TIMING INDEX MARK

*NOTE: AT TDC NO. 1 FIRING POSITION, ARROWS ON BACK OF CAMSHAFT SPROCKETS POINT DIRECTLY AT EACH OTHER

FM1139500412000X

Fig. D

LINCOLN

| Year & Engine Liter/ CID/VIN Code ① | Spark Plug Gap, inch | Ignition Timing, °BTDC | | | Curb Idle Speed RPM | Fast Idle Speed RPM | Fuel Pump Pressure, psi | Valve Clearance ③ |
		Firing Order, Fig. ④	Degrees	Timing Mark Fig.				
1993								
3.8L/V6-232 (4)	.054	C	10⑨	B	⑥	⑥	35—40⑧	.089—.189
4.6L/V8-281 SOHC (W)	.054	A	10②	⑤	⑥	⑥	35—40⑦	.080—.120
4.6L/V8-281 DOHC (V)	.054	D	10②	⑤	⑥	⑥	35—40⑦	.080—.120
1994								
3.8L/V6-232 (4)	.054	C	10⑨	B	⑥	⑥	35—40⑧	.089—.189
4.6L/V8-281 SOHC (W)	.054	A	10②	⑤	⑥	⑥	35—40⑦	.080—.120
4.6L/V8-281 DOHC (V)	.054	D	10②	⑤	⑥	⑥	35—40⑦	.080—.120
1995								
4.6L/V8-281 SOHC (W)	.054	A	10②	⑤	⑥	⑥	35—40⑦	.80—.120
4.6L/V8-281 DOHC (V)	.054	D	10②	⑤	⑥	⑥	35—40⑦	.80—.120
1996								
4.6L/V8-281 SOHC (W)	.054	A	10②	⑤	⑥	⑥	35—40⑦	.80—.120
4.6L/V8-281 DOHC (V)	.054	D	10②	⑤	⑥	⑥	35—40⑦	.80—.120

BTDC—Before Top Dead Center.
DOHC—Dual Overhead Cam.
SOHC—Single Overhead Cam.
①—The eighth digit of the Vehicle Identification Number (VIN) denotes engine code.
②—Non-adjustable.
③—With cylinder at top dead center, hold steady pressure on lifter until fully collapsed to check clearance.
④—Before disconnecting wires from distributor cap, determine location of No. 1 wire in cap, as distributor position may have been altered from that shown at the end of this chart.
⑤—Equipped w/crankshaft sensor.
⑥—Idle speeds are controlled by the automatic idle control.
⑦—Wrap shop towel around fuel diagnostic valve to prevent fuel spillage. Connect a suitable fuel pressure gauge to fuel diagnostic valve. Energize fuel pump & note fuel pressure gauge reading.
⑧—Wrap shop towel around fitting to prevent fuel spillage, then connect a suitable fuel pressure gauge to fuel diagnostic valve on fuel rail assembly. Connect jumper wire to VIP self test connector FP terminal. The VIP connector is located at the right hand rear of the engine compartment at the electronic control assembly. Place ignition switch in On position, then connect VIP jumper wire to ground & check fuel pressure gauge reading.
⑨—Disconnect in-line spout connector, then start engine & adjust ignition timing as necessary. After completing adjustment, reconnect spout connector.

Continued

LINCOLN—Continued

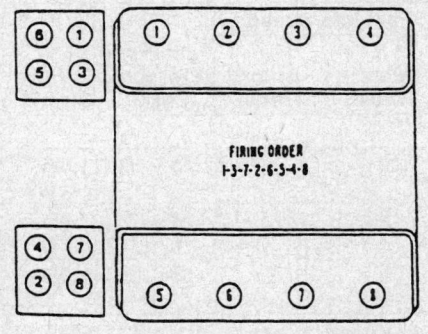

Fig. A

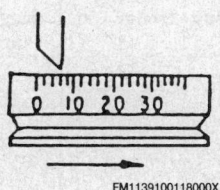

Fig. B

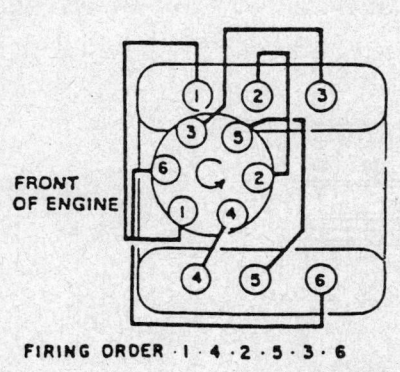

Fig. C

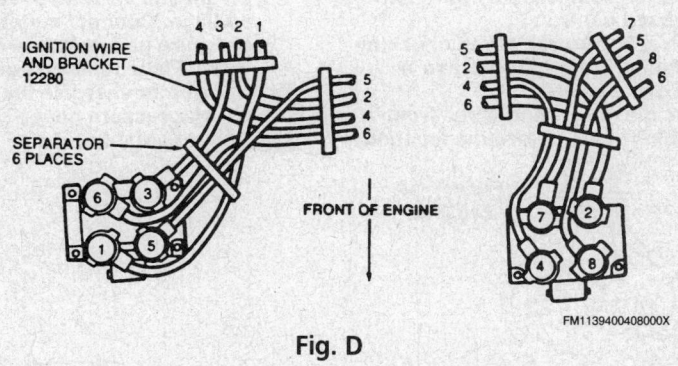

Fig. D

FORD MUSTANG

| Year & Engine/ VIN Code ① | Spark Plug Gap | Ignition Timing BTDC | | | | Curb Idle Speed ③ | | Fast Idle Speed | | Fuel Pump Pressure, psi. ⑥ | Valve Clearance |
		Firing Order Fig. ④	Man. Trans.	Auto. Trans.	Mark Fig.	Man. Trans.	Auto Trans.	Man. Trans.	Auto. Trans.		
1993											
2.3L/4-140/M	.044	D	10⑦	10⑦	⑧	②	②	②	②	35—40	.040—.050
5.0L/V8-302/E HO	.054	B	10⑤	10⑤	C	675②	625N②	②	②	35—40	.123—.146
1994											
3.8L/V6-232	.054	E⑩	14⑦	14⑦	F	720②	650D②	②	②	35—40	.089—.189
5.0L/V8-302 HO	.054	B	10⑤	10⑤	C	675②	625N②	②	②	35—40	.123—.146
5.0L/V8-302 SHP	.054	B	10⑤	10⑤	C	675②	625N②	②	②	35—40	.123—.146
1995											
3.8L/V6-232	.054	E⑩	14⑦	14⑦	F	680—710②	680—710N②	②	②	35—40	.089—.189
5.0L/V8-302 HO	.054	B	10⑤	10⑤	C	640②	704N②	②	②	35—40	.123—.146
5.0L/V8-302 SHP	.054	B	10⑤	10⑤	C	②	②	②	②	35—40	.123—.146

Continued

FORD MUSTANG—Continued

Year & Engine/ VIN Code ①	Spark Plug Gap	Ignition Timing BTDC				Curb Idle Speed ③		Fast Idle Speed		Fuel Pump Pressure, psi. ⑥	Valve Clearance
		Firing Order Fig. ④	Man. Trans.	Auto. Trans.	Mark Fig.	Man. Trans.	Auto Trans.	Man. Trans.	Auto. Trans.		
1996											
3.8L/V6-232	.054	E ⑩	10 ⑦	10 ⑦	F	②	②	②	②	35—40	.089— .189
4.6L/V8-281 SOHC	.054	A ⑪	⑦	⑦	⑧	②	②	②	②	35—40	.080— .120
4.6L/V8-281 DOHC	.054	A ⑪	⑦	⑦	⑧	②	②	②	②	35—40	.080— .120

BTDC—Before Top Dead Center.
DOHC—Double Overhead Cam; four valves per cylinder.
HO—High Output.
SHP—Special High Perfromance.
SOHC—Single Overhead Cam; two valves per cylinder.

① —Eighth digit of Vehicle Identification Number (VIN) denotes engine code.
② —Idle speed controlled by automatic idle speed control.
③ —D: Drive. N: Neutral. When checking idle speed, set parking brake & block drive wheels.
④ —Before disconnecting wires from distributor cap, determine location of No. 1 wire in cap, as distributor position may have been altered from that shown at end of this chart.
⑤ —Disconnect in-line spout connector, then start engine & adjust ignition timing as necessary. After completing adjustment, reconnect spout connector.
⑥ —Wrap shop towel around fuel diagnostic valve to prevent fuel spillage. Connect suitable fuel pressure gauge to fuel diagnostic valve. Place ignition switch in On position to energize fuel pump & check pressure gauge reading.
⑦ —Non-adjustable.
⑧ —Vehicle has crankshaft position sensor.
⑨ —Collapsed Tappet gap. Intake & exhaust with cylinder at top dead center. Hold steady pressure on lifter until fully collapsed to check clearance.
⑩ —Cylinder numbering front to rear, right bank, 1, 2, 3 ; left bank, 4, 5, 6. Firing order 1-4-2-5-3-6.
⑪ —Cylinder numbering front to rear, right bank, 1, 2, 3, 4; left bank, 5, 6, 7, 8. Firing order 1-3-7-2-6-5-4-8.

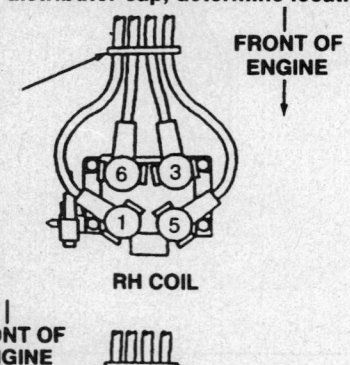

RH COIL

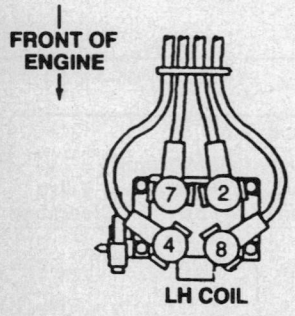

LH COIL

Fig. A

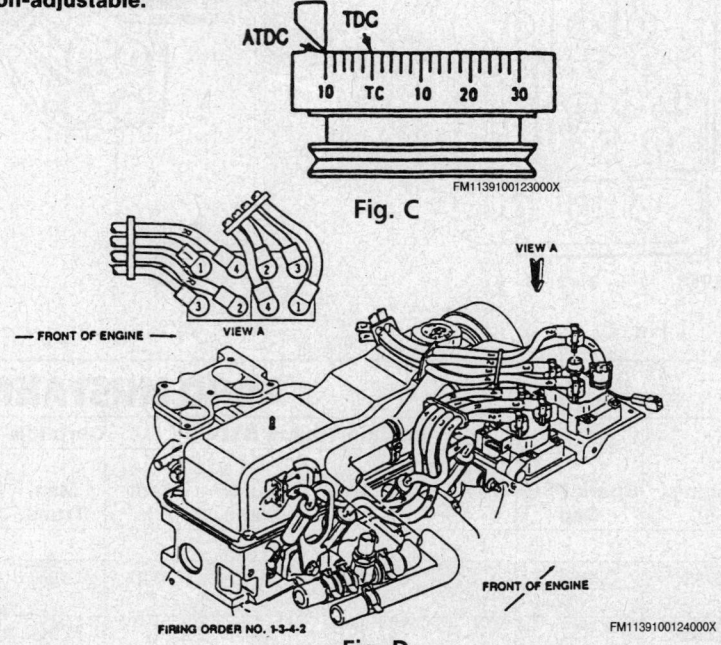

FIRING ORDER NO. 1-3-4-2

Fig. C

Fig. D

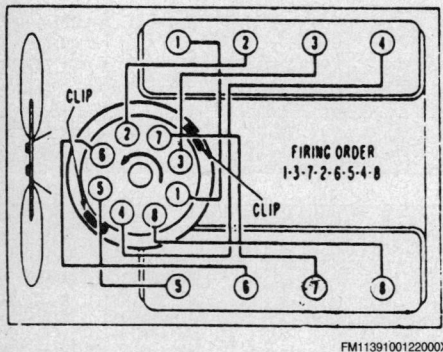

FIRING ORDER 1-3-7-2-6-5-4-8

Fig. B

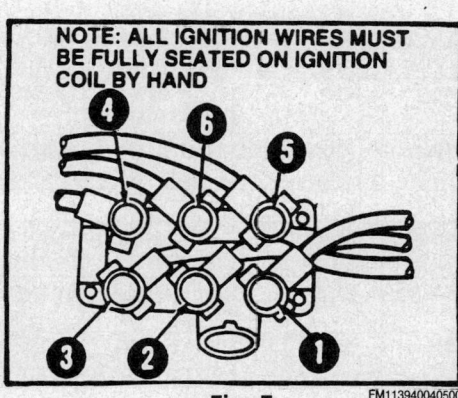

NOTE: ALL IGNITION WIRES MUST BE FULLY SEATED ON IGNITION COIL BY HAND

Fig. E

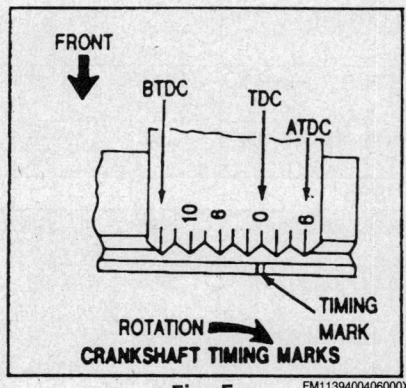

FRONT

BTDC   TDC   ATDC

ROTATION   TIMING MARK

CRANKSHAFT TIMING MARKS

Fig. F

FORD TAURUS & MERCURY SABLE

Liter/CID (VIN Code) ①	Spark Plug Gap	Firing Order Fig. ②	Ignition Timing,°BTDC			Curb Idle Speed ③		Fast Idle Speed		Fuel Pump Pressure, psi	Valve Clearance
			Man. Trans.	Auto. Trans.	Mark Fig.	Man. Trans.	Auto. Trans.	Man. Trans.	Auto. Trans.		
1993—95											
3.0L/V6-182 (U)	.044	D	—	10⑤	C	—	④	—	④	35—45⑥	⑩
3.0L/V6-182 (U) ⑨	.044	D	—	10⑦	C	—	④	—	④	35—45⑥	⑩
3.0L/V6-182 (Y)	.044	A	10⑦	—	⑧	800④	—	④	—	30—45⑥	⑩
3.2L/V6-195 (P)	.044	A	—	10⑦	⑧	—	700D④	—	④	30—45⑥	⑩
3.8L/V6-238 (4)	.054	B	—	10⑤	C	—	④	—	④	35—45⑥	⑩
1996											
3.0L/V6-182 (U)	.044	A	—	⑦	⑧	—	④	—	④	35—40⑥	⑩
3.0L/V6-182 (1) ⑨	.044	A	—	⑦	⑧	—	④	—	④	35—40⑧	⑩
3.0L/V6-181 (S)	.054	E	—	10⑦	⑧	—	④	—	④	35—40⑧	⑩
3.4L/V8-207	—	—	—	⑦	⑧	—	④	—	④	35—40⑧	⑩

BTDC–Before Top Dead Center.

①—The eighth digit of the VIN denotes engine code.

②—Before disconnecting wires from distributor cap or coil , determine location of wire, as position may have been altered from that shown at the end of this chart.

③—Drive.

④—Idle speed is controlled by an automatic idle control system.

⑤—Disconnect in-line spout connector, then start engine & adjust ignition timing as necessary. After completing adjustment, reconnect spout connector.

⑥—Wrap shop towel around fitting to prevent fuel spillage, then connect a suitable fuel pressure gauge to fuel diagnostic valve on fuel rail assembly. Connect jumper wire to VIP self test connector FP terminal. The VIP connector is located at the right hand rear of the engine compartment at the electronic control assembly. Place ignition switch in On position, then connect VIP jumper wire to ground and check fuel pressure gauge reading.

⑦—Non-adjustable.

⑧—Equipped w/crankshaft position sensor.

⑨—Flexible fuel vehicle (FFV).

⑩—Equipped with hydraulic valve lifters, there is no provision for adjustment.

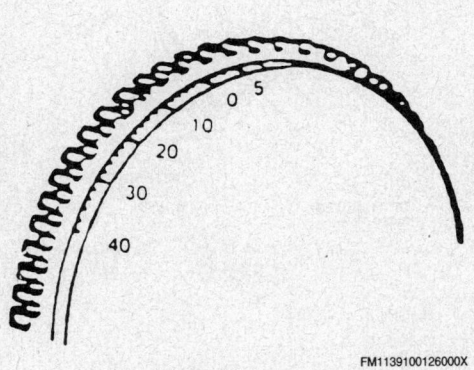

Fig. A

FM1139100126000X

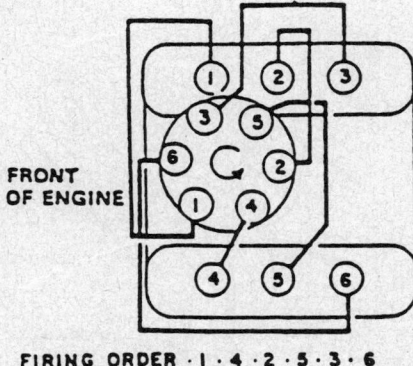

FRONT OF ENGINE

FIRING ORDER · 1 · 4 · 2 · 5 · 3 · 6

Fig. B

FM1139100127000X

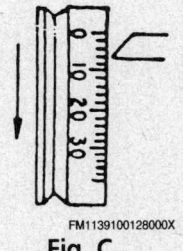

Fig. C

FM1139100128000X

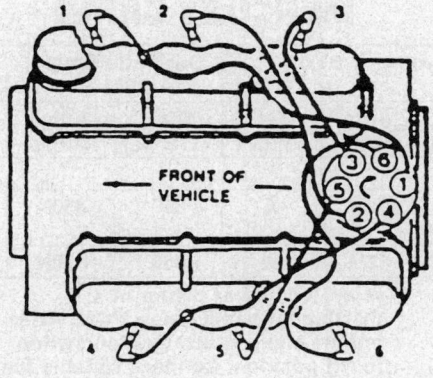

FRONT OF VEHICLE

FIRING ORDER: 1-4-2-5-3-6

Fig. D

FM1139100129000X

FORD PROBE

Year & Engine/ VIN Code ①	Spark Plug Gap	Ignition Timing BTDC				Curb Idle Speed		Fast Idle Speed		Fuel Pump Pressure, psi.	Valve Clearance, Inch
		Firing Order Fig. ②	Man. Trans.	Auto. Trans.	Mark Fig.	Man. Trans.	Auto. Trans.	Man. Trans.	Auto. Trans.		
2.0L/4-121/A	.040-.043	A	9-11	11-13	B	700	700	—	—	30—38	③
2.5L/V6-152	.040-.043	C	9-11	9-11	D	650	650	—	—	37—46	③

BTDC—Before Top Dead Center
N—Neutral
①—The eighth digit of the Vehicle Identification Number (VIN) denotes engine code.
②—Before disconnecting wires from distributor cap, determine location of No. 1 wire in cap, as distributor position may have been altered from that shown at the end of this chart.
③—Equipped with hydraulic valve lifters, no adjustment necessary.

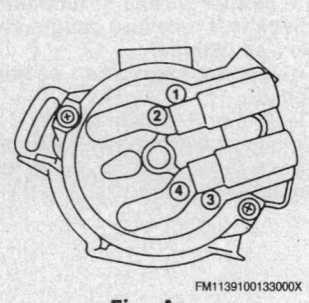

Fig. A

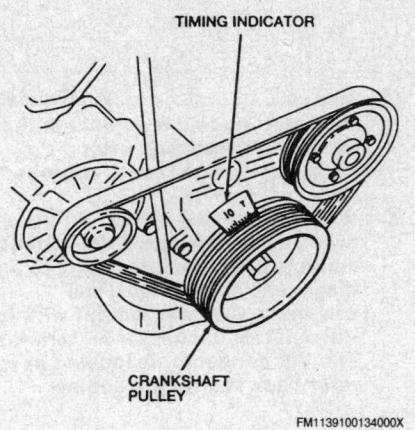

TIMING INDICATOR

CRANKSHAFT PULLEY

FM1139100134000X

Fig. B

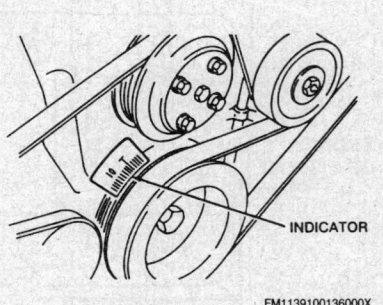

INDICATOR

FM1139100136000X

Fig. D

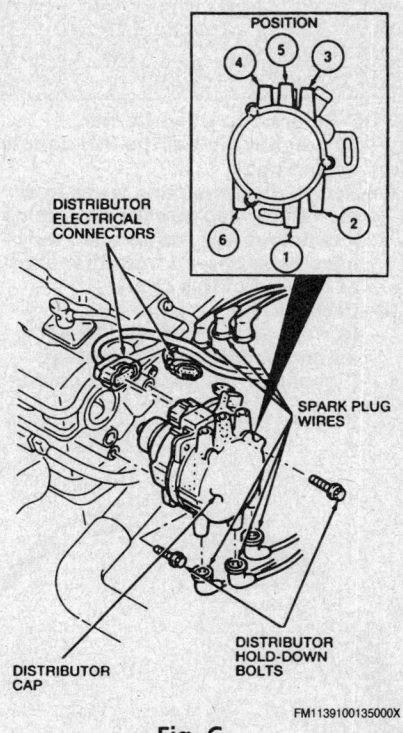

POSITION

DISTRIBUTOR ELECTRICAL CONNECTORS

SPARK PLUG WIRES

DISTRIBUTOR CAP

DISTRIBUTOR HOLD-DOWN BOLTS

FM1139100135000X

Fig. C

MERCURY CAPRI

Year & Engine (VIN Code) ①	Spark Plug Gap	Ignition Timing @ BTDC				Curb Idle Speed, RPM ③		Fast Idle Speed, RPM		Fuel Pump Pressure, psi	Valve Clearance, Inch
		Firing Order	Man. Trans.	Auto. Trans.	Mark Fig.	Man. Trans.	Auto. Trans.	Man. Trans.	Auto. Trans.		
1993—94											
1.6L/4-98(Z) DOHC	.041	1-3-4-2	2⑤	2⑤	A	850	850N	②	②	64—85④	⑥
1.6L/4-98(6) Turbo	.041	1-3-4-2	12⑤	12⑤	A	850	850N	②	②	64—85④	⑥

BTDC—Before Top Dead Center.
①—The eighth digit of the Vehicle Identification Number (VIN) denotes engine code.
②—Controlled by ECA (Electronic Control Assembly).
③—N: Neutral.
④—Start engine. Remove fuel pump relay, located at center of instrument panel below PCM. After engine stalls, place ignition switch in Off position. Connect suitable fuel pressure test gauge between fuel filter & fuel rail. Install fuel pump relay. On all models, connect a jumper wire between fuel pump test connector terminals. Place ignition switch in On position & note fuel pressure.
⑤—With distributor vacuum advance hose disconnected & plugged.
⑥—Equipped with hydraulic valve lash adjusters, no adjustment is necessary.

Continued

MERCURY CAPRI—Continued

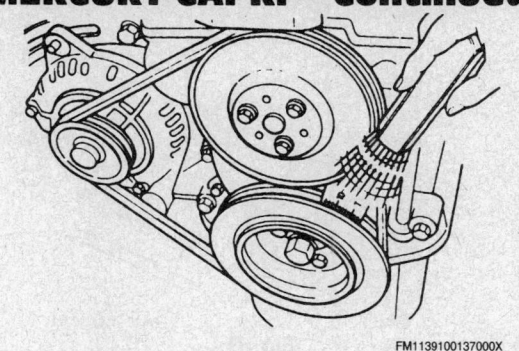

Fig. A

FM1139100137000X

FORD ESCORT & MERCURY TRACER

Engine (VIN Code) ①	Spark Plug Gap	Ignition Timing, °BTDC				Curb Idle Speed ③		Fast Idle Speed		Fuel Pump Pressure, psi ⑧	Valve Clearance, Inch
		Firing Order Fig. ④	Man. Trans.	Auto. Trans.	Timing Mark Fig.	Man. Trans.	Auto. Trans.	Man. Trans.	Auto Trans.		
1993—94											
1.8L/4-112	.041	⑦	10⑤	10⑤	B	750	750N	⑥	⑥	38—46	⑪
1.9L/4-116	.054	②	10②	10②	⑨	730—830	730—830N	⑩	⑩	35—40	⑪
1995-96											
1.8L/4-112	.041	⑦	10⑤	10⑤	B	700-800	700-800N	⑥	⑥	38—46	⑪
1.9L/4-116	.054	②	10②	10②	⑨	450-750	450-750	⑩	⑩	35—40	⑪

BTDC—Before Top Dead Center.
①—The eighth digit of the Vehicle Identification Number (VIN) denotes engine code.
②—Firing order, 1-3-4-2. Refer to Fig. C for spark plug wire connections at coil unit.
③—Neutral.
④—Before disconnecting wires from distributor cap, determine location of No. 1 wire in cap, as distributor position may have been altered from that shown at the end of this chart.
⑤—With STI connector grounded, refer to Fig. D.
⑥—Computer controlled, non-adjustable.
⑦—Firing order, 1-3-4-2. Refer to Fig. A for spark plug wire connections at distributor cap.
⑧—Wrap shop towel around fitting to prevent fuel spillage, then connect a suitable fuel pressure gauge to fuel diagnostic valve on fuel rail assembly. Place ignition switch in On position & check fuel pressure gauge reading.
⑨—Equipped with a crankshaft position sensor.
⑩—Idle speed controlled by an automatic idle speed control.
⑪—Equipped with hydraulic valve lash adjusters.

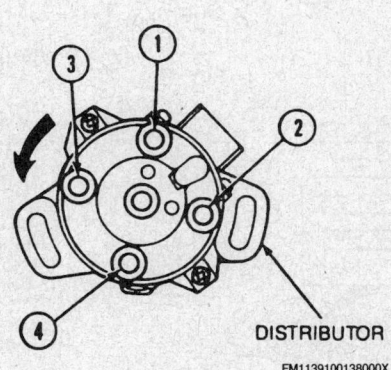

DISTRIBUTOR
FM1139100138000X
Fig. A

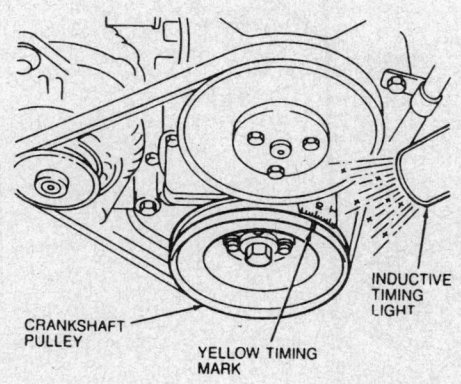

CRANKSHAFT PULLEY
YELLOW TIMING MARK
INDUCTIVE TIMING LIGHT
FM1139100139000X
Fig. B

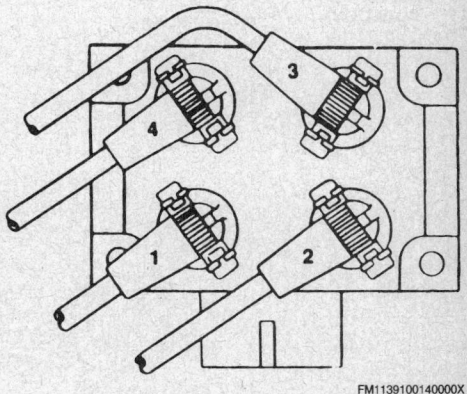

FM1139100140000X
Fig. C

Continued

FORD ESCORT & MERCURY TRACER—Continued

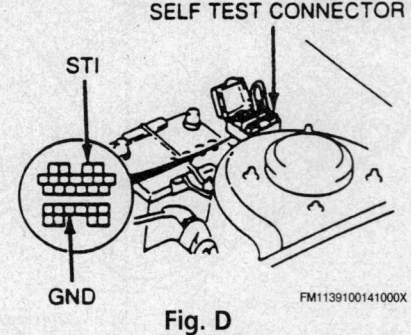

Fig. D

FORD ASPIRE & FESTIVA

| Year & Engine | Spark Plug Gap | Ignition Timing BTDC | | | | Curb Idle Speed | | Fast Idle Speed | | Fuel Pump Pressure, psi | Valve Clearance, Inch |
		Firing Order Fig.	Man. Trans.	Auto. Trans.	Mark Fig.	Man. Trans.	Auto. Trans.	Man. Trans.	Auto. Trans.		
1993											
1.3L/4-81	.041	A	10①	10①	B	700	850N	②	②	30-38③	⑦
1994-96											
1.3L/4-81	.041	A	10④	10④	D⑤	650-750	700-800	②	②	38-46⑥	⑦

BTDC— Before Top Dead Center.
N— Neutral
P—Park
①—With STI connector grounded, refer to Fig. C.
②— Controlled by ECA (Electronic Control Assembly).
③—Removing rear seat cushion, then release fuel system by starting engine & disconnecting fuel pump electrical connector. After engine has stalled, place ignition switch in the Off position. Connect a suitable fuel pressure gauge to fuel pump outlet connection. Connect a jumper wire between fuel pump test connector terminals, then place ignition switch in On position & check fuel pressure.
④—With jumper wire connected between DCL TEN & GND terminals. Refer to Fig. E.
⑤—On 1994 models, align pointer with white mark on pulley. On 1995—96 models, align pointer with yellow mark.
⑥—Remove fuel tank filler cap & allow fuel tank pressure to release. Start engine, then disconnect fuel pump relay connector. After engine has stalled, place ignition switch in Off position & connect fuel pump relay connector. Connect fuel pressure test gauge to fuel hose between fuel filter & fuel rail. Connect jumper wire between DCL F/P terminal & GND terminal, Fig. E.
⑦—Equipped with hydraulic valve lash adjusters, no adjustment required.

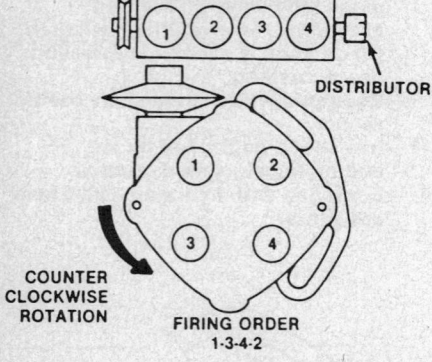

Fig. A

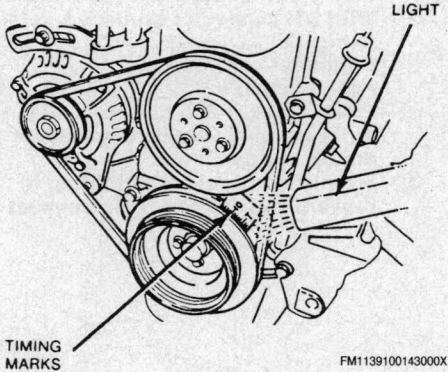

Fig. B

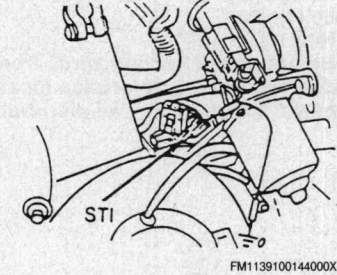

Fig. C

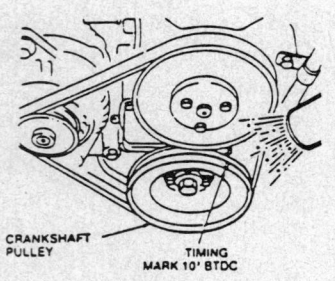

Fig. D

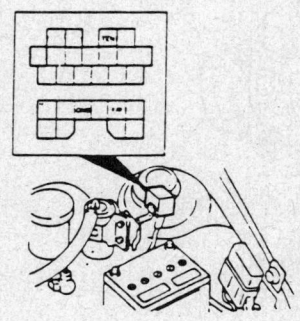

Fig. E

ENGINE TUNE UP & PERFORMANCE

TABLE OF CONTENTS

	Page No.		Page No.
V6 GASOLINE ENGINE	3-8	4-CYLINDER GASOLINE ENGINE	3-1
V8 GASOLINE ENGINE	3-12		

4-Cylinder Gasoline Engine

If Uncertain About The Proper Use Of Information Contained In This Section, Please Refer To "How To Use This Manual" Located In The Front Of This Tabbed Section.

Prior To Performing Any Service Operations Listed In This Section, Consult The Technical Service Bulletin Section For Related Information.

INDEX

Page No.		Page No.		Page No.
Compression Pressure:	3-1	Aspire	3-2	1.8L/4-112 DOHC Engine	3-6
Except Festiva	3-1	Capri	3-2	1994-96 2.0L/4-121 Engine	3-7
Festiva	3-2	Contour & Mystique	3-2	Spark Plugs	3-1
Engine Identification	3-1	Escort & Tracer:	3-2	Valves:	3-4
Fuel Injection Cleaning	3-5	1.8L/4-112 DOHC Engine	3-2	Valve Adjustment:	3-5
Idle Speed & Mixture Adjustments:	3-3	1.9L/4-116 Engine	3-2	1.3L/4-81, 1.6L/4-98, 1.8L/4-112,	
Curb Idle Speed:	3-3	Festiva	3-2	2.0L/4-121 & 2.0L/4-122 Zetec	
1.3L/4-81 Engine	3-3	Mustang	3-3	Engines	3-5
1.6L/4-98 DOHC Engine	3-3	Probe	3-3	1.9L/4-116 Engine	3-5
1.8L/4-112 DOHC Engine	3-3	Tempo & Topaz	3-3	2.3L/4-140 OHC Engine	3-5
1.9L/4-116 Engine	3-4	Ignition Wire Resistance	3-1	2.3L/4-140 OHV High Swirl	
2.0L/4-121 Engine	3-4	Sensor Adjustments:	3-6	Combustion (HSC) Engine	3-5
2.0L/4-122 Zetec Engine	3-4	Throttle Position Sensor:	3-6	Valve Arrangement:	3-4
2.3L/4-140 Engine	3-4	1.3L/4-81 Engine	3-6	Front To Rear	3-4
Fast Idle Speed	3-4	1.6L/4-97, 1.9L/4-116, 2.0L/4-122			
Ignition Timing:	3-2	Zetec, 2.3L/4-140 (OHV & OHC)			
		& 1993 2.0L/4-121 Engines	3-6		

ENGINE IDENTIFICATION

The engine code is the eighth digit of the Vehicle Identification Number (VIN). The VIN is stamped on a metal tag located on top left side of dash and visible through the windshield.

SPARK PLUGS

Spark plugs should be replaced and properly tightened at recommended intervals. Refer to **Fig. 1,** for replacement interval and tightening specifications.

IGNITION WIRE RESISTANCE

Without removing the high tension wires from the spark plugs, distributor cap or coil, wipe the wires with a clean, damp cloth and inspect them for visible cracks, cuts, pinching or torn boots. Replace only the wires that are damaged.

Spark plug wire resistance specifications are not available from the manufacturer.

COMPRESSION PRESSURE

Except Festiva

When checking cylinder compression, the lowest cylinder must be within 75% of the highest cylinder. Perform compression test with engine at normal operating temperature, with spark plugs and air cleaner removed, throttle wide open and distributor end of coil secondary wire grounded.

Festiva

Cylinder compression pressure should range between 134 psi (being the lowest maximum pressure) and 250 psi (being the highest maximum pressure) at an engine cranking speed of 180 RPM minimum. The compression in each cylinder should fall within the specified compression pressure range with no more than a 75% variance in compression.

IGNITION TIMING

Refer to Tune Up Specifications chart for correct ignition timing and firing order.

Aspire

1. Start engine and allow it to warm up to normal operating temperature, then shut off all accessories.
2. Connect Rotunda Timing Analyzer tool No. 059-00014, or equivalent, then, using jumper, ground Self-Test Input (STI) terminal at Data Link Connector (DLC).
3. Check base ignition timing. Ignition timing mark on crankshaft pulley (white on 1994 models, yellow on 1995-96 models) should line up with pointer on timing belt cover.
4. If timing marks line up, proceed to next step. If timing marks do not line up, continue as follows:
   a. Loosen distributor bolts, then rotate distributor until timing marks are properly aligned.
   b. **Torque** distributor bolts to 14-19 ft. lbs.
   c. Check timing marks to ensure they did not move when bolts were tightened.
5. Remove jumper from STI terminal at DLC, then the timing analyzer tool.

Capri

1. Connect timing light following manufacturer's instructions.
2. Apply parking brake, then start engine and warm to normal operating temperature.
3. Turn off electrical loads and accessories.
4. Disconnect and plug vacuum hoses from vacuum diaphragm.
5. Ensure engine idle speed is 800-900 RPM.
6. Check ignition timing, if adjustment is necessary, loosen distributor retaining bolts and rotate distributor until timing is within specification. Base timing for non-turbo engine is 0-4° BTDC, for turbo engines 11-13° BTDC.
7. Tighten distributor retaining bolts while ensuring distributor does not move.
8. Connect vacuum diaphragm hose.

Contour & Mystique

The ignition timing is not adjustable on these vehicles.

Escort & Tracer
1.8L/4-112 DOHC ENGINE

1. Apply parking brake, then start engine

Engine	Replacement Interval In Miles	Torque/Ft. Lbs.
1993		
1.3L/4-81	30,000	10—17
1.6L/4-98	30,000	11—16
1.8L/4-112	30,000	11—17
1.9L/4-116	60,000	7—15
2.0L/4-121 ③	30,000	11—17
2.3L/4-140 ①	30,000	6—11
2.3L/4-140 ②	30,000	5—10
1994		
1.3L/4-81	30,000	15—22
1.6L/4-98	30,000	11—16
1.8L/4-112	30,000	11—17
1.9L/4-116	60,000	7—15
2.0L/4-121 ③	30,000	11—17
2.3L/4-140 ①	30,000	6—11
1995		
1.3L/4-81	30,000	15—22
1.8L/4-112	30,000	11—17
1.9L/4-116	60,000	7—15
2.0L/4-121 ③	30,000	11—17
2.0L/4-122 Zetec ④	60,000	9—13
1996		
1.3L/4-81	30,000	15—22
1.8L/4-112	30,000	11—17
1.9L/4-116	60,000	7—15
2.0L/4-121 ③	30,000	11—17
2.0L/4-122 Zetec ④	60,000	9—13

①—Tempo & Topaz.
②—Mustang.
③—Probe.
④—Contour & Mystique.

Fig. 1   Spark plug tightening specification & replacement interval chart

and warm to normal operating temperature.
2. Turn off electrical loads and accessories.
3. Using jumper wire, connect ground terminal to ten terminal on diagnosis connector.
4. Using Rotunda Tachometer tool No. 059-00010, or equivalent, connect tachometer positive lead to IG terminal on diagnosis connector and tachometer negative lead to battery ground terminal.
5. Using timing light, inspect ignition timing. Ignition timing should be 9-11° BTDC at 700-800 RPM. Yellow mark on crankshaft should be aligned with corresponding mark on timing belt cover.
6. If marks are not aligned, loosen distributor mounting bolts and turn distributor until ignition timing is within specification.
7. **Torque** distributor mounting bolts to 14-19 ft. lbs.
8. Remove jumper wire from diagnosis connector.
9. Remove timing light, then the tachometer.

1.9L/4-116 ENGINE

Initial timing is 8-12° BTDC and is not adjustable.

Festiva

Refer to "Tune Up Specifications" for correct ignition timing and firing order.
1. Place transaxle in Park or Neutral, then turn all accessories off.
2. Connect inductive timing light tool No. 059-00006, or equivalent, to No. 1 spark plug wire.
3. Connect inductive tachometer tool No. 059-00010, or equivalent, to single pin white test connector.
4. Start engine and allow to reach normal operating temperature.
5. Ground single pin black Self-Test Input (STI) test connector (Y/BL wire) located near brake master cylinder.
6. Check idle speed and adjust as necessary.
7. Check base ignition timing. White ignition timing mark on crankshaft pulley should align with white pointer on timing belt cover.
8. Loosen distributor mounting bolt, then

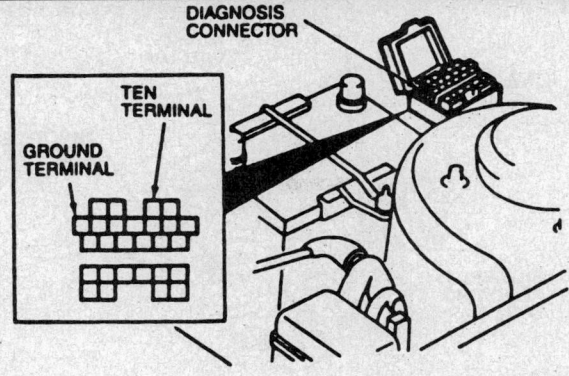

Fig. 2 Diagnosis connector terminal identification. 1.8L/4-112 DOHC & 1993 2.0L/4-121 w/automatic transaxle

rotate distributor until marks are aligned.
9. **Torque** distributor mounting bolt to 14–18 ft. lbs., then recheck timing marks.
10. Remove jumper wire from STI connector and ground.
11. Increase engine RPM, then check timing marks to ensure ignition timing changes.
12. Turn ignition off and remove test equipment.

Mustang

Ignition timing is preset to 8–12° and is not adjustable.

Probe

1. Start engine and allow to reach normal operating temperature.
2. Stop engine and turn off all electrical accessories.
3. Connect Rotunda Digital Tachometer tool No. 059-00007, or equivalent, following manufacturer's instructions.
4. Connect timing light to engine.
5. **On 1993 models equipped with automatic transaxle,** connect jumper wire between STI (10) terminal and GRD terminal on Data Link Connector (DLC).
6. **On 1994–96 models,** remove shorting bar from double wire SPOUT connector.
7. **On all models,** check idle speed, then adjust to specifications.
8. Check ignition timing.
9. If timing is within specifications, loosen distributor hold-down bolt and turn distributor housing until correct reading is obtained.
10. **Torque** hold-down bolt to 14–18 ft. lbs.
11. Recheck ignition timing, then disconnect jumper wire from DLC or reconnect shorting bar.
12. Remove test equipment from engine.

Tempo & Topaz

Adjust ignition timing with engine at normal operating temperature and all accessories OFF.

To properly set ignition timing, a remote starter switch should not be used. Use the ignition switch only to start the vehicle. A remote starter switch will cause the TFI module to revert to start mode timing.

1. Place transaxle in Park or Neutral, then turn accessories Off.
2. Disconnect and plug vacuum hose to distributor.
3. Connect inductive timing light tool No. 059-00006, or equivalent, following manufacturer's instructions.
4. Connect inductive tachometer tool No. 059-00010, or equivalent, following manufacturer's instructions.
5. Disconnect single wire inline (SPOUT) electrical connector or remove shorting bar from double wire spout connector.
6. **On models equipped with barometric pressure switch,** disconnect barometric pressure switch electrical connector (yellow and black wires) from ignition module. Install suitable jumper wire across pressure switch pins of ignition module.
7. **On all models,** with engine at normal operating temperature, adjust ignition timing as necessary.
8. Disconnect test equipment, then connect vacuum line and spout connector.

IDLE SPEED & MIXTURE ADJUSTMENTS

Refer to Tune Up Specifications chart for curb and fast idle speeds.

Curb Idle Speed
1.3L/4-81 ENGINE

1993

Prior to adjusting idle speed, ensure ignition timing is correct. If idle speed and ignition timing are not within specifications, it will be necessary to readjust the ignition timing and idle speed progressively.

This adjustment must be done while the cooling fan motor is not running.

1. Ensure engine is at normal operating temperature and all electrical accessories are turned Off.
2. Connect tachometer tool No. 059-00010, or equivalent, to one-pin check connector.
3. Connect jumper wire between black STI connector (one pin, Y/BL wire) and ground.
4. Place transaxle in Park position (automatic transaxles) or Neutral position

(manual transaxles), then set parking brake.
5. Check idle speed. Idle speed should be 680–720 RPM on models equipped with manual transaxle, or 830–870 RPM on models equipped with automatic transaxle.
6. If idle speed is not within specification, turn air adjustment screw, located on top of throttle body, next to air intake tube.
7. Check ignition timing. Readjust if necessary, then check idle speed.
8. Remove jumper wire, then test equipment.

1994–96

Before adjusting idle speed, ensure ignition timing is adjusted to specification.

Turn off all lamps and other electrical loads. This adjustment must be done when the cooling fan motor is not operating.

1. Connect Rotunda 88 Digital Multimeter tool No. 105-00053, or equivalent, with inductive pickup attached to number one spark plug wire.
2. Ground PCM STI (10) pin at Data Link Connector (DLC), then start engine.
3. Run engine until it reaches operating temperature, then note idle speed.
4. Adjust idle speed adjustment screw for correct idle speed. Idle speed specifications are as follows:
   a. **On models equipped with manual transaxle,** 650–750 RPM, with transaxle in Neutral position.
   b. **On models equipped with automatic transaxle,** 700–800 RPM, with transaxle in Park (P) position.
5. **On all models,** turn engine off and allow engine to cool, then remove ground from PCM STI (10) pin at DLC.
6. After engine has cooled, start and run engine until it reaches operating temperature and ensure idle speed is to specifications.

1.6L/4-98 DOHC ENGINE

Before adjusting idle speed, ensure ignition timing is adjusted to specification.

1. Turn off electrical loads and accessories.
2. Start engine and bring engine up to normal operating temperature.
3. Attach Rotunda Tachometer tool No. 059-00010, or equivalent, to test connector (white, Pin 1), located near battery in engine compartment.
4. Check idle speed on tachometer.
5. Connect jumper wire between test connector (Green: Pin 1) and ground, then turn adjustment screw to obtain correct idle speed of 800–900 RPM.
6. Remove jumper wire and tachometer.

1.8L/4-112 DOHC ENGINE

1. Apply parking brake, then start engine and warm it up to normal operating temperature.
2. Turn off electrical loads and accessories.
3. Using jumper wire, connect ground terminal on diagnosis connector, **Fig. 2.**
4. Using Rotunda Tachometer tool No. 059-00010, or equivalent, connect tachometer positive lead to IG terminal on diagnosis connector and tachome-

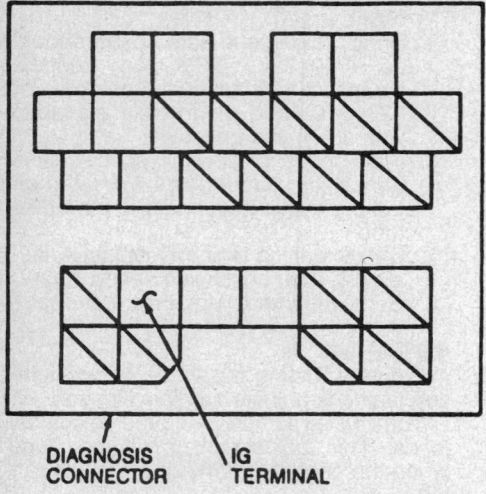

Fig. 3   IG terminal location

ter negative lead to negative battery post, **Fig. 3.**
5. Using tachometer, check idle speed. Idle speed should be 700-800 RPM. **Do not check idle speed when engine cooling fan is in operation.**
6. If idle speed is not within specification, adjust idle speed by turning idle speed adjusting screw until idle speed is within specification, **Fig. 4.**
7. Remove jumper wire from diagnosis connector, then the tachometer.

1.9L/4-116 ENGINE

The curb idle speed is controlled by the EEC-IV processor and is not adjustable.

2.0L/4-121 ENGINE

1993 Models w/Automatic Transaxle

1. Apply parking brake, then position gearshift lever in Park or Neutral.
2. Start engine and allow to reach normal operating temperature.
3. Turn off all electrical loads and accessories.
4. Using jumper wire, connect ground terminal to STI (10) terminal on Data Link Connector (DLC), **Fig. 2.**
5. Connect tachometer positive lead of Rotunda Digital Tachometer/Multimeter tool No. 055-00101, or equivalent, to No. 1 spark plug wire.
6. Check idle speed. Idle speed should be 650-750 RPM. **Do not check idle speed while electric cooling fan is operating.**
7. If idle speed is not as specified, adjust idle speed by turning idle speed adjusting screw, **Fig. 5,** until idle speed is within specification.
8. Remove jumper wire from DLC, then the tachometer.

1993 Models w/Manual Transaxle & 1994—96 Models Except 2.0L/4-122 Zetec Engine

1. Apply parking brake, then position gearshift lever in Park or Neutral.
2. Start engine and run until operating temperature is reached.

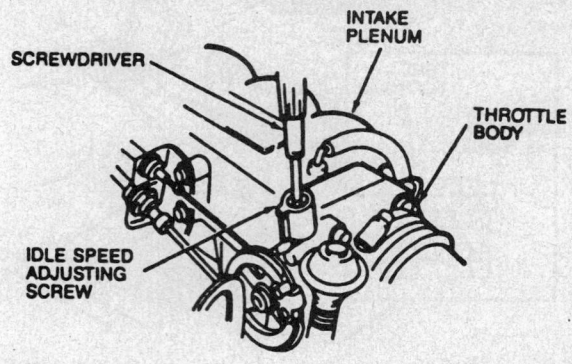

Fig. 4   Idle speed adjusting screw location

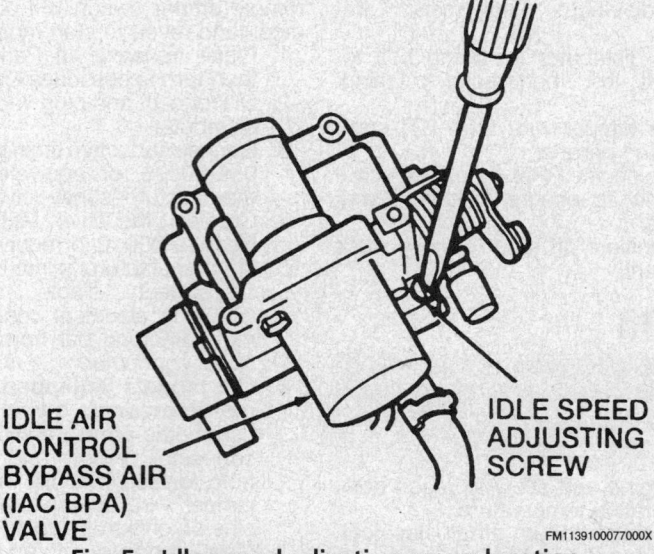

IDLE AIR CONTROL BYPASS AIR (IAC BPA) VALVE

IDLE SPEED ADJUSTING SCREW

Fig. 5   Idle speed adjusting screw location

3. Turn off all electrical loads and accessories.
4. Connect tachometer positive lead of Rotunda Digital Tachometer/Multimeter tool No. 055-00101, or equivalent, to No. 1 spark plug wire.
5. Disconnect Idle Air Control Bypass (IAC BPA) connector.
6. Start and run engine at 2500 RPM for 30 seconds, then allow engine to return to idle.
7. Check idle speed, idle speed should be 650-750 RPM. **Do not check idle speed while electric cooling fan is operating.**
8. If idle speed is not as specified, turn idle speed adjusting screw to set idle speed to specification, **Fig. 5.**
9. Turn engine Off, then re-run test to ensure idle speed is correct.
10. Connect the IAC BPA connector, then remove test equipment.

2.0L/4-122 ZETEC ENGINE

The idle speed is electronically controlled and is not adjustable.

2.3L/4-140 ENGINE

If curb idle speed is not within specification, it will be necessary to perform **appropriate EEC-IV diagnostic procedure.**

Fast Idle Speed

If fast idle speed is not within specification, it will be necessary to perform the appropriate EEC-IV diagnostic procedure.

VALVES

Valve Arrangement

FRONT TO REAR

1.3L/4-81 .... I-E-E-I-I-E-E-I
1.6L/4-97 DOHC:
Rear Side .... I-I-I-I-I-I-I-I
Front Side .... E-E-E-E-E-E-E-E
1.8L/4-112:
Rear Side .... I-I-I-I
Front Side .... E-E-E-E
1.9L/4-116:
Rear Side .... I-I-I-I
Front Side .... E-E-E-E
2.0L/4-121 DOHC:
Rear Side .... I-I-I-I-I-I-I-I
Front Side .... E-E-E-E-E-E-E-E
2.0L/4-122 DOHC ZETEC:
Rear Side .... I-I-I-I-I-I-I-I
Front Side .... E-E-E-E-E-E-E-E
2.3L/4-140 OHV .... E-I-E-I-E-I-E-I
2.3L/4-140 OHC:
Rear Side .... I-I-I-I
Front Side .... E-E-E-E

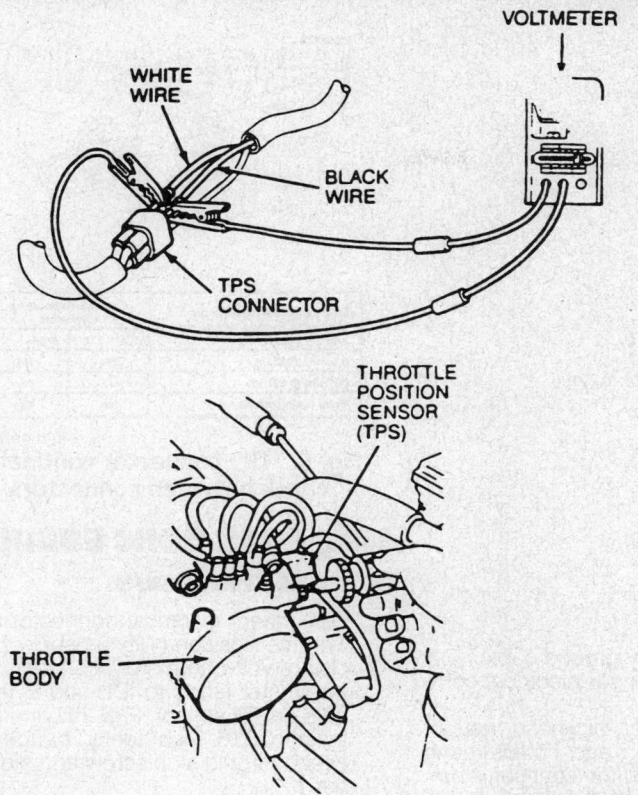

Fig. 6   Collapsed tappet clearance check.
2.3L/4-140 engine

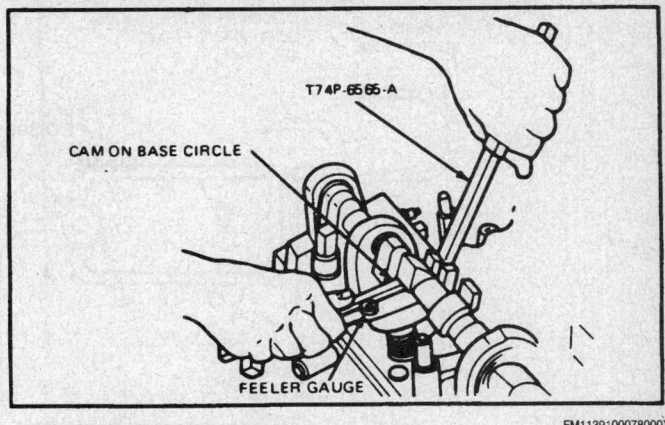

Fig. 7   Collapsed cam follower clearance check.
2.3L/4-140 overhead cam engine

6. If the valve spring installed height is correct, check camshaft dimensions.
7. If camshaft dimensions are correct, remove, clean and test lash adjuster.
8. Install lash adjuster, then recheck clearance.
9. Replace damaged or worn parts as necessary.

FUEL INJECTION CLEANING

Some models are equipped with Deposit Resistant Injectors (DRI), these type of injectors should not be cleaned.

Fuel injectors with the following part numbers are deposit resistant injectors; FIZE-9F593-BC, FOSE-9F593-AA, FOTE-9F593-CA, FIZE-9F593-B4C and FO3E-9F593-A2B.

To properly clean fuel injectors, follow the procedure below using cleaner tool No. 113-00001, or equivalent.

1. Place shutoff valve on test stand in on position.
2. Using paint filter, pour clean gasoline into fuel tank up to fill line, then add injector cleaner solvent from lower fill line to upper fill line. Mixture should be approximately 1 ounce of cleaner to 7 ounces of gasoline.
3. Connect cleaner tool power supply lines to battery. Red light on cleaner will flash, indicating power connection is made and cleaner unit is off.
4. Activate 10 minute timer switch and check pressure gauge to ensure pressure reading is 38-40 psi. If necessary, adjust pressure by placing shutoff valve in on position and removing black cap, then loosening locknut and turning screw until achieving proper reading.
5. Connect fuel supply hose to outlet and place other end of hose back in tank. Actuate 10 minute timer switch and turn flow meter switch from No. 1 position to No. 2 position. Repeatedly turn switch between positions to purge system of air. Flow meter should be in No. 2 position for cleaning of injectors.
6. Disconnect engine fuel line inlet line at supply manifold, then connect supply hose from cleaner.

Valve Adjustment

1.3L/4-81, 1.6L/4-98, 1.8L/4-112, 2.0L/4-121 & 2.0L/4-122 ZETEC ENGINES

These engines use hydraulic lash adjusters and do not require adjustment.

1.9L/4-116 ENGINE

1. Rotate engine until No. 1 piston is on TDC of compression stroke.
2. Position suitable hydraulic lifter compressor tool onto rocker arm and slowly apply pressure to bleed tappet. Continue applying pressure until lifter plunger bottoms. Hold tappet in this position and check clearance between rocker arm and valve stem tip with feeler gauge. Collapsed tappet gap should be .007-.177 inch. If clearance is less than specified, check for worn or damaged fulcrums, tappets or camshaft lobes.
3. With the No. 1 piston on TDC of compression stroke, check the following valves: No. 1 intake, No. 1 exhaust and No. 2 intake.
4. Rotate crankshaft 180° from above position and check the following valves: No. 3 intake & No. 3 exhaust.
5. Rotate crankshaft another 180° from above position and check the following valves: No. 4 intake, No. 4 exhaust and No. 2 exhaust.

2.3L/4-140 OHV HIGH SWIRL COMBUSTION (HSC) ENGINE

1. Rotate camshaft to position A, Fig. 6, and check intake and exhaust valve clearances indicated in chart with tappet fully collapsed. Collapsed tappet clearance should be .072-.174 inch.
2. Rotate camshaft to position B, Fig. 6, and check intake and exhaust valve clearances indicated in chart with tappet fully collapsed.
3. If clearance is not as specified, check for worn or damaged components. Replace as necessary.

2.3L/4-140 OHC ENGINE

1. Position camshaft so base circle of cam lobe is facing cam follower of valve to be checked.
2. Using valve spring compressor tool No. T88P-6565-BH, or equivalent, slowly apply pressure onto cam follower until lash adjuster is completely collapsed.
3. Hold follower in this position and insert proper size feeler gauge between base circle of cam and cam follower, Fig. 7. Collapsed lifter gap should be between 0.040-0.050 inch.
4. If clearance is excessive, remove cam follower and inspect for damage.
5. If cam follower appears to be intact and not excessively worn, measure valve spring installed height to ensure valve is not sticking.

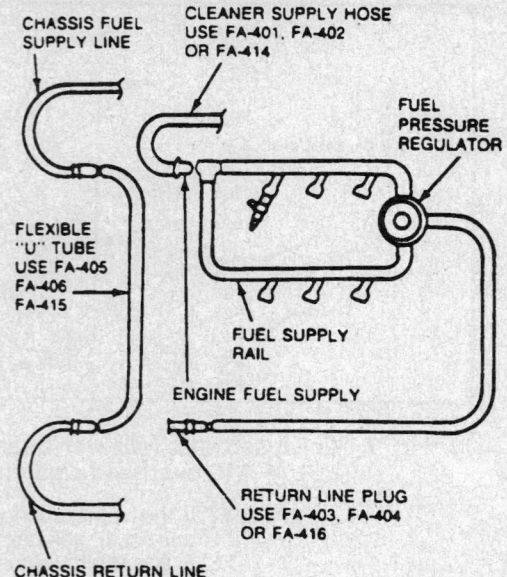

Fig. 8 U-tube installation

Insert thickness gauge between the throttle adjust screw and stop lever	Continuity between terminals	
	IDL – TL	PSW – TL
0.5 mm (0.02 in)	Yes	No
0.7 mm (0.027 in)	No	No
Fully open throttle lever	No	Yes

FM1139100211000X

Fig. 9 TPS connector continuity check between connectors

7. Disconnect fuel return line and plug, then install U-tube between chassis return line and chassis supply line, **Fig. 8.**
8. Install turn buckle loosely between throttle control rod and suitable hook up point on fenderwell.
9. Activate 10 minute timer switch, start engine and check for leaks. **Ensure vehicle is in park or neutral position and parking brake is applied or wheels are blocked.**
10. When engine speed has stabilized, set idle speed to 2000 RPM using turnbuckle.
11. Reset remaining 10 minute cycle. Place ignition switch in off position, then remove turnbuckle.
12. Disconnect cleaner supply hose from fuel supply manifold.
13. Place power switch in off position and disconnect power lines, then connect vehicle fuel lines.
14. Start engine and check for leaks. **Lubricate O-rings prior to installation and ensure fuel lines are securely connected.**

SENSOR ADJUSTMENTS
Throttle Position Sensor

1.6L/4-97, 1.9L/4-116, 2.0L/4-122 ZETEC, 2.3L/4-140 (OHV & OHC) & 1993 2.0L/4-121 ENGINES

The Throttle Position (TP) sensor is preset at the factory and cannot be adjusted.

1.3L/4-81 ENGINE
1993

Before adjusting the Throttle Position (TP) sensor, ensure the idle speed and ignition timing are set to specification.

1. Disconnect battery ground cable.
2. Disconnect TP sensor electrical connector.
3. Insert appropriate thickness gauge between throttle and adjustment screw, then check for continuity between terminals, **Fig. 9.**
4. Use chart to determine need for adjustment. If necessary, adjust TP sensor by loosening hold-down screw and rotating TP sensor in necessary direction.
5. Tighten hold-down screws when correct readings are obtained.

1994–96
1. Disconnect Throttle Position (TP) sensor electrical connector, then connect Rotunda 73 digital multimeter tool No. 105-00051, or equivalent, between terminals A and B.
2. Turn throttle lever to Wide Open Throttle (WOT) position and check resistance reading on multimeter. Resistance should be approximately 5 Kohms.
3. Turn throttle lever to fully closed position and check reading on multimeter. Reading should be below 1 ohm.
4. If resistance is within specifications, continue to next step. If resistance is not within specifications, proceed as follows:
   a. Loosen, but do not remove, TP sensor screw, then, with throttle lever in closed position, adjust TP sensor until multimeter reads below 1 ohm.
   b. Turn throttle lever to WOT position and check resistance. Resistance should be approximately 5 Kohms. If sensor cannot be adjusted to specification, throttle body must be replaced.
   c. After TP sensor resistance readings are within specification, **torque** sensor screws to 14-20 inch lbs.
5. Connect TP sensor electrical connector.

1.8L/4-112 DOHC ENGINE
Manual Transaxle

1. Disconnect electrical connector from Throttle Position (TP) sensor.
2. Using volt-ohmmeter, connect volt-ohmmeter leads to IDL and E terminals on TP sensor, **Fig. 10.**
3. Insert 0.016 inch feeler gauge between throttle stop screw and stop lever.
4. Loosen TP sensor mounting screws.
5. Rotate throttle position sensor clockwise approximately 30°, then rotate counterclockwise until continuity exists.
6. Replace 0.016 inch feeler gauge with 0.027 inch gauge, then ensure continuity no longer exists.
7. If continuity still exists, repeat Steps 3 through 6.
8. Tighten throttle position sensor mounting screws while making sure sensor does not move.
9. Open throttle plate to its wide open position several times, then recheck adjustment on throttle position sensor.

Automatic Transaxle

1. Disconnect electrical connector from Throttle Position (TP) sensor.
2. Using volt-ohmmeter, connect meter leads to IDL and E terminals on TP sensor, **Fig. 11.**
3. Loosen TP sensor mounting screws.
4. Insert 0.01 inch feeler gauge between throttle stop screw and stop lever.
5. Rotate TP sensor clockwise approximately 30°, then rotate counterclockwise until continuity exists.
6. Replace 0.01 inch feeler gauge with 0.016 inch gauge, then ensure continuity no longer exists.
7. If continuity still exists, repeat Steps 3 through 6.
8. Tighten TP sensor mounting screws while making sure TP sensor does not move.
9. Open throttle plate to its wide open position several times and ensure resistance between E and Vt terminals on TP sensor is approximately 5K ohms.

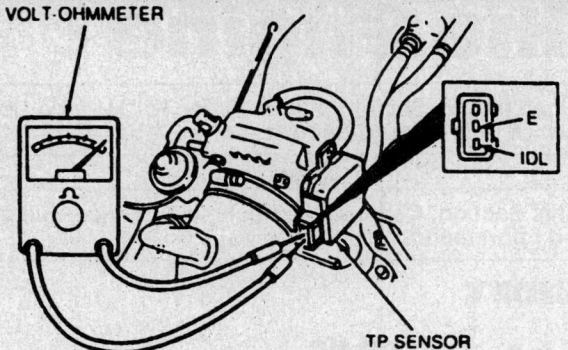

Fig. 10   Throttle position sensor
Volt-ohmmeter connections

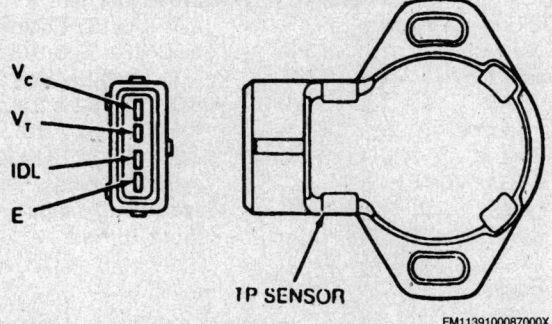

Fig. 11   Throttle position sensor terminal
locations

1994–96 2.0L/4-121 ENGINE

1. Connect Rotunda Breakout Box tool No. 014-00322 and Rotunda Breakout Box Adapter tool No. T92C-6000-AH, or equivalents, to Powertrain Control Module (PCM).
2. Place ignition switch in on position, then measure voltage between breakout box pin 47 and ground while rotating throttle linkage by hand.
3. Voltage must measure .5 volts with throttle valve fully closed and 4.1 volts with throttle valve fully open. If voltage is satisfactory, Throttle Position (TP) sensor does not require adjustment. If voltage is not within specifications, proceed to next step for adjustment.
4. Loosen TP sensor setscrews, then, with throttle valve fully closed, rotate sensor until voltage is .1 - 1.1 volts.
5. With throttle valve fully open, verify voltage is 3.1 - 4.4 volts.
6. **Torque** TP sensor setscrews to 18 inch lbs.

If Uncertain About The Proper Use Of Information Contained In This Section, Please Refer To "How To Use This Manual" Located In The Front Of This Tabbed Section.

Prior To Performing Any Service Operations Listed In This Section, Consult The Technical Service Bulletin Section For Related Information.

INDEX

	Page No.
Compression Pressure	3-8
Engine Identification	3-8
Fuel Injection Cleaning	3-10
Idle Speed & Mixture Adjustments:	3-9
Curb Idle Speed:	3-9
2.5L/V6-152 Engine	3-9
2.5L/V6-153 & 3.0L/V6-181 Duratec Engines	3-9
3.0L/V6-182, 3.2L/V6-192 & 3.8L/V6-232 Engines	3-9
Fast Idle Speed	3-9
Ignition Timing:	3-8
2.5L/V6-152 Engine	3-8
2.5L/V6-153 & 3.0L/V6-181 Duratec Engines	3-8

	Page No.
3.0L/V6-182 & 3.8L/V6-232 Non-Supercharged Engines	3-8
3.0L/V6-182 SHO, 3.2L/V6-195 SHO & 3.8L/V6-232 Supercharged Engines	3-8
Ignition Wire Resistance	3-8
Sensor Adjustments:	3-11
Throttle Position Sensor:	3-11
2.5L/V6-152 Engine	3-11
2.5L/V6-153 & 3.0L/V6-181 Duratec Engines	3-11
3.0L/V6-182 & 3.2L/V6-195 Engines	3-11
3.8L/V6-232 Engine	3-11

	Page No.
Spark Plugs	3-8
Valves:	3-9
Valve Adjustment:	3-9
2.5L/V6-152 Engine	3-9
2.5L/V6-153 & 3.0L/V6-181 Duratec Engines	3-9
3.0L/V6-182 & 3.8L/V6-232 Engines	3-10
3.0L/V6-182 SHO & 3.2L/V6-195 SHO Engines	3-10
Valve Arrangement:	3-9
Front To Rear	3-9

ENGINE IDENTIFICATION

The engine code is the eighth digit of the Vehicle Identification Number (VIN). The VIN is stamped on a metal tag located on top left side of dash and visible through the windshield.

SPARK PLUGS

Spark plugs should be replaced and properly tightened at recommended intervals. Refer to **Fig. 1**, for replacement interval and tightening specifications.

IGNITION WIRE RESISTANCE

Without removing the high tension wires from the spark plugs, distributor cap or coil, wipe the wires with a clean, damp cloth and inspect them for visible cracks, cuts, pinching or torn boots. Replace only the wires that are damaged.

Spark plug wire resistance specifications are not available from the manufacturer.

COMPRESSION PRESSURE

When checking cylinder compression, the lowest cylinder must be within 75% of the highest cylinder. Perform compression test with engine at normal operating temperature, spark plugs removed and throttle wide open.

IGNITION TIMING

Refer to Tune Up Specifications chart for correct ignition timing and firing order.

2.5L/V6-152 Engine

1. Connect Rotunda Digital Tachometer/Multimeter tool No. 055-00101, or equivalent, to No. 1 spark plug wire, then the timing light.
2. Run engine at idle until normal operating temperature is reached.
3. Connect terminals STI (10) and GRD of Data Link Connector (DLC), **Fig. 2**, with jumper wire.
4. Ensure idle speed is 600-700 RPM, then check ignition timing. Ignition timing should be 9-11° BTDC.
5. If timing is not within specification, loosen distributor hold-down bolts.
6. Turn distributor until correct timing is obtained.
7. **Torque** distributor hold-down bolts to 14-18 ft. lbs.
8. Remove tachometer, timing light and jumper wire.

2.5L/V6-153 & 3.0L/V6-181 Duratec Engines

The ignition timing on the Duratec engine is not adjustable.

3.0L/V6-182 & 3.8L/V6-232 Non-Supercharged Engines

To set ignition timing correctly, a remote starter switch should not be used. Use ignition switch only to start the vehicle. Disconnecting the start wire at the starter solenoid will cause the Ignition Control Module (ICM) to revert to start mode timing after the vehicle is started. Reconnecting to start wire after the vehicle is running will not correct the ignition timing.

1. Place transaxle in Park or Neutral position, then turn A/C and heater off.
2. Connect Rotunda Timing Analyzer tool No. 059-00014, or equivalent, to No. 1 cylinder ignition wire, following manufacturer's instructions.
3. Disconnect single wire in in-line SPOUT connector, then start engine and allow to warm to operating temperature.
4. With engine at specified RPM, check/adjust ignition timing to specifications. Refer to Tune Up Specifications Chart for timing specifications.
5. Reconnect single wire in-line SPOUT connector and check ignition timing advance while varying engine RPM to verify distributor is advancing beyond initial ignition timing setting.
6. Remove timing analyzer tool.

3.0L/V6-182 SHO, 3.2L/V6-195 SHO & 3.8L/V6-232 Supercharged Engines

On these engines, the ignition timing cannot be adjusted. The ignition timing can be checked using the following procedure:

1. Start engine and allow to reach operating temperature.
2. Place ignition switch in Off position, then disconnect the in-line spout connector.
3. Connect inductive timing light 059-00014, or equivalent, according to timing light manufacturer's instructions.
4. Set parking brake and block drive

Engine	Replacement Interval In Miles	Torque/Ft. Lbs.
1993		
2.5L/V6-152	30,000	11—17
3.0L/V6-182	②	6—10
3.0L/V6-182 SHO	30,000	12—19
3.2L/V6-195 SHO	30,000	16—20
3.8L/V6-232	①	6—10
1994		
2.5L/V6-152	30,000	11—17
3.0L/V6-182	②	7—15
3.0L/V6-182 SHO	30,000	12—19
3.2L/V6-195 SHO	30,000	15—22
3.8L/V6-232	①	6—10
1995		
2.5L/V6-152 ③	30,000	11—17
2.5L/V6-153 Duratec ④	100,000	7—15
3.0L/V6-182	30,000	7—15
3.0L/V6-182 SHO	30,000	15—22
3.2L/V6-195 SHO	30,000	15—22
3.8L/V6-232	①	6—10
1996		
2.5L/V6-152	30,000	11—17
2.5L/V6-153 Duratec	100,000	7—15
3.0L/V6-181 Duratec	100,000	7—15
3.0L/V6-182	⑤	7—15
3.8L/V6-232 Essex	60,000	7—15

①—Federal & normally aspirated engines, 30,000 miles; California & supercharged engines w/Essex block, 60,000 miles.

②—Sable & Taurus 30,000 miles; Tempo & Topaz 60,000 miles.

③—Probe.

④—Contour & Mystique.

⑤—With flexible fuel, 30,000 miles; less flexible fuel 60,000 miles.

Fig. 1 Spark plug tightening specification & replacement interval chart

wheels, then start engine and place transmission in Neutral.
5. With all accessories turned off, check ignition timing. If timing is not as listed in the Tune Up Specifications, refer to the "Ignition Systems" section for further diagnosis.

IDLE SPEED & MIXTURE ADJUSTMENTS

Refer to Tune Up Specifications chart for curb and fast idle speeds.

Curb Idle Speed

2.5L/V6-152 ENGINE

All accessories must be Off during this procedure.
1. Apply parking brake, then place gearshift in Park (automatic transaxle) or Neutral (manual transaxle).
2. Run engine until normal operating temperature is reached.
3. Connect positive lead of Rotunda Digital Inductive Tach/Dwell Multimeter tool No. 055-00101, or equivalent, to No. 1 spark plug wire.
4. Connect jumper wire between terminals STI (10) and GRD of Data Link Connector (DLC), **Fig. 2**.
5. Check idle speed. Idle speed should be 600-700 RPM.
6. If idle speed is not as specified, connect Rotunda Advance Timing Analyzer tool No. 059-00006, or equivalent. Ensure ignition timing is 9-11° BTDC.
7. If ignition timing is not as specified, loosen distributor hold-down bolt and adjust timing to specification.
8. Remove jumper wire from STI and GRD. Ensure ignition timing is 6-18° BTDC.
9. Reconnect jumper wire, then adjust idle speed screw, **Fig. 3**, until specified RPM is obtained.
10. Turn engine off, then remove jumper wire and test equipment from vehicle.

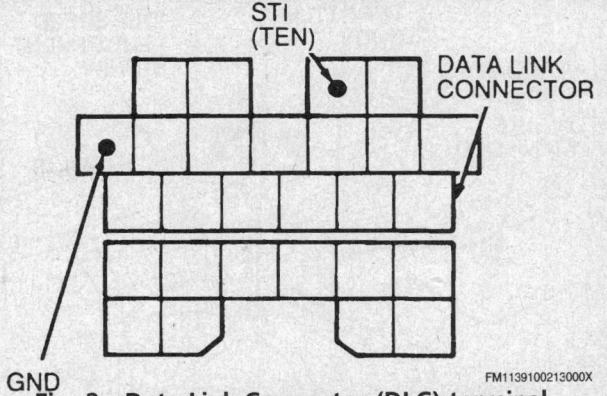

Fig. 2 Data Link Connector (DLC) terminal identification

2.5L/V6-153 & 3.0L/V6-181 DURATEC ENGINES

The idle speed is not adjustable on the Duratec engine.

3.0L/V6-182, 3.2L/V6-192 & 3.8L/V6-232 ENGINES

Refer to "Computerized Engine Controls" chapter to diagnose Throttle Position (TP) sensor and/or possible adjustment, if applicable.

Fast Idle Speed

Fast idle speed is computer controlled and is not adjustable. If idle speed is not within specification and/or not operating correctly, refer to "Computerized Engine Controls" chapter for diagnostic procedures.

VALVES
Valve Arrangement
FRONT TO REAR

2.5L/V6-152 DOHC:
Inner Camshafts .... Intake
Outer Camshafts .... Exhaust
2.5L/V6-153 & 3.0L/V6-181 DURATEC:
Inner Camshafts .... Intake
Outer Camshafts .... Exhaust
3.0L/V6-182 & 3.2L/V6-195 SHO:
Inner Camshafts .... Intake
Outer Camshafts .... Exhaust
3.0L/V6-182 OHV:
Left .... I-E-I-E-I-E
Right .... E-I-E-I-E-I
3.8L/V6-232 OHV:
Left .... E-I-E-I-E-I
Right .... I-E-I-E-I-E

Valve Adjustment
2.5L/V6-152 ENGINE

Hydraulic Lash Adjusters provide automatic lash adjustment. They are designed to maintain zero clearance between the camshaft lobes and valve stems. No adjustment is provided.

2.5L/V6-153 & 3.0L/V6-181 DURATEC ENGINES

These engines use Hydraulic Lash Adjusters to provide automatic lash adjustment. No adjustment is provided.

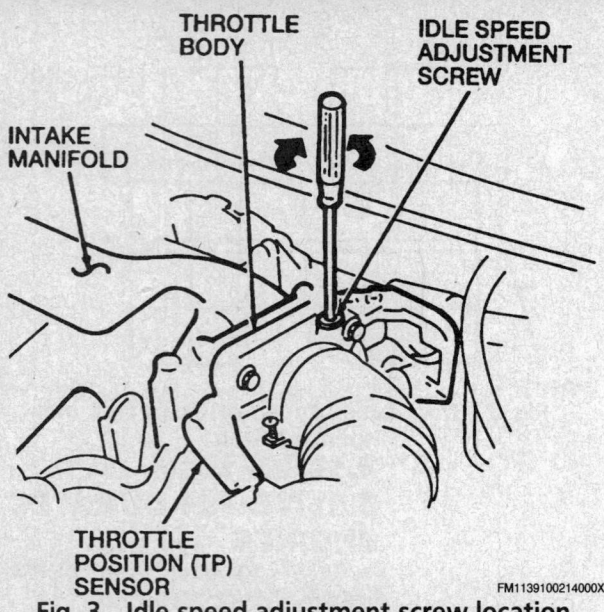

Fig. 3 Idle speed adjustment screw location

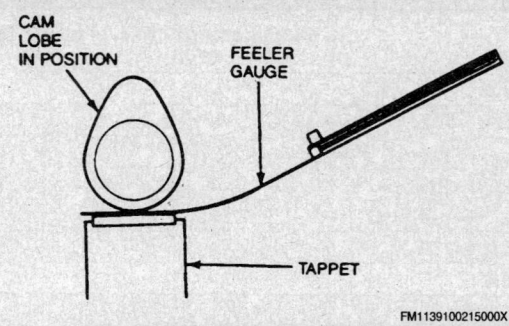

Fig. 4 Cam lobe position & feeler gauge installation

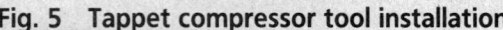

Fig. 5 Tappet compressor tool installation

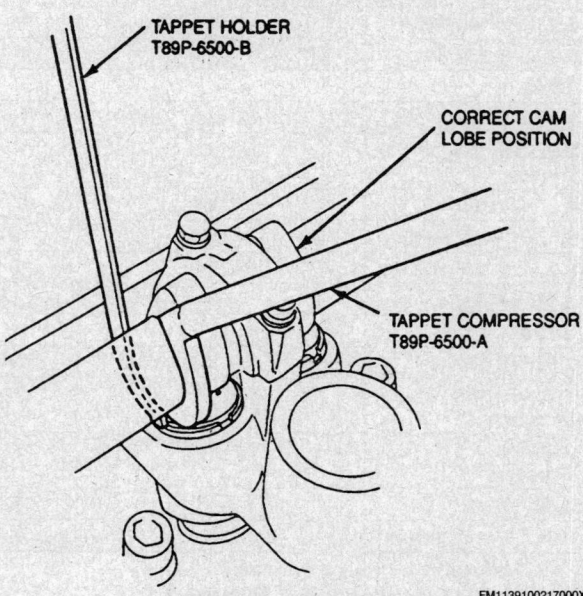

Fig. 6 Tappet holder tool installation

3.0L/V6-182 SHO & 3.2L/V6-195 SHO ENGINES

1. Disconnect battery ground cable, then isolate cable end with suitable electrical tape.
2. Remove intake manifold assembly, then the valve covers.
3. **On models equipped with 3.2L/V6-195 engine**, remove EGR tube sub-assembly from righthand exhaust manifold to gain clearance for right-hand valve cover removal.
4. **On all models,** insert feeler gauge, **Fig. 4. Cam lobes must be directed 90° or more away from tappet.**
5. Intake valve clearance should be 0.006–0.010 inch (cold). Exhaust valve clearance should be 0.010–0.014 inch (cold).
6. To adjust clearance, insert tappet compressor tool No. T89P-6500-A, or equivalent, under camshaft next to lobe and rotate down to depress bucket tappet, **Fig. 5.**
7. Insert tappet holder tool No. T89P-6500-B, or equivalent, then remove compressor tool, **Fig. 6.**
8. Using pick tool No. T71P-19703-C, or equivalent, lift adjusting shim, then remove with magnet, **Fig. 7.**
9. Determine shim size by numbers on bottom face of shim or by measuring

with micrometer. Install replacement shim to provide specified clearance.
10. Install shim with numbers down. Ensure shim is properly seated.
11. Release tappet holder by installing tappet compressor tool.
12. Repeat procedure for each valve, rotating engine crankshaft as necessary.
13. After all valve clearances have been checked and/or adjusted, inspect all valve shims to ensure they are fully seated in their buckets.
14. Inspect valve cover gaskets. Replace as necessary.
15. Install intake manifold, then the valve covers.

3.0L/V6-182 & 3.8L/V6-232 ENGINES

These engines have hydraulic lash adjusters. No adjustment is provided or necessary.

FUEL INJECTION CLEANING

Some models are equipped with Deposit Resistant Injectors (DRI), these type of injectors should not be cleaned.

Fuel injectors with the following part numbers are deposit resistant injectors: E59E-9F593-AB, FO5E-9F593-AA, FI5E-9F593-DA, FO3E-9F593-A2B, FO3E-9F593-AB, FO5E-9F593-B1A, FI5E-9F593-E1A, FO5E-9F593-B5A, F3DE-9F593-B4C, F1SE-9F593-E1A, F3DE-9F593-A2B, F3DE-99F593-B2A.

To properly clean fuel injectors follow this procedure, using cleaner tool No. 113-00001, or equivalent.

1. Turn shutoff valve on test stand to On position.
2. Using paint filter, pour clean gasoline into fuel tank up to fill line, then add injector cleaner solvent from lower fill line to upper fill line. **Mixture should be approximately 1 ounce of cleaner to 7 ounces of gasoline.**
3. Connect cleaner tool power supply lines to battery, red light on cleaner will flash indicating power connection is made and cleaner unit is off.
4. Activate 10 minute timer switch and check pressure gauge to ensure pressure reading is 38–40 psi. If necessary, adjust pressure as follows:
   a. Place shutoff valve in On position, then remove black cap.
   b. Loosen locknut and turning screw until proper reading is achieved.
5. Connect fuel supply hose to outlet and place other end of hose back in tank.
6. Actuate 10 minute timer switch and turn flow meter switch from No. 1 position to No. 2 position. Turn switch repeatedly between positions to purge

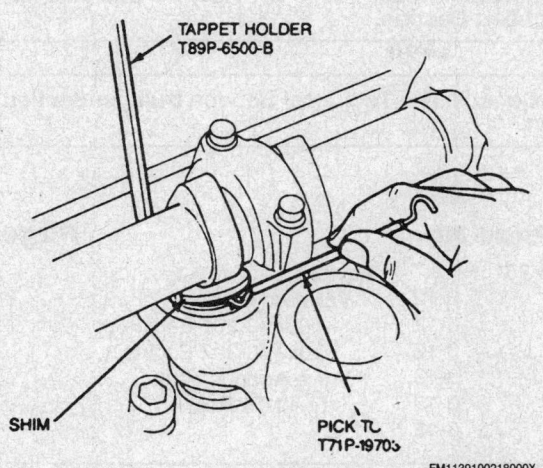

Fig. 7   Tappet shim removal

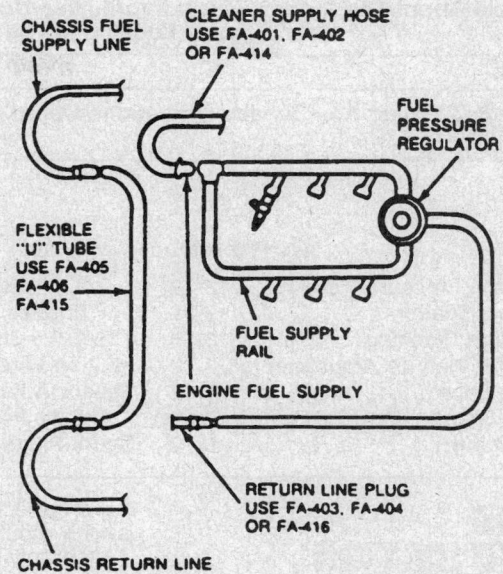

Fig. 8   U-tube installation

system of air. **Flow meter should be in No. 2 position for cleaning of injectors.**

7. Disconnect engine fuel line inlet line at supply manifold, then connect supply hose from cleaner.
8. Disconnect fuel return line and plug, **Fig. 8,** then install U-tube between chassis return line and chassis supply line, **Fig. 8.**
9. Install turn buckle loosely between throttle control rod and suitable hook up point on fenderwell.
10. Activate 10 minute timer switch, then start engine and check for leaks. **Ensure vehicle is in park or neutral position, parking brake is applied or wheels are blocked.**
11. When engine speed has stabilized, set idle speed to 2000 RPM using turnbuckle.
12. Reset remaining 10 minute cycle, then place ignition switch in Off position and remove turnbuckle.
13. Disconnect cleaner supply hose from fuel supply manifold.
14. Place power switch in Off position and disconnect power lines.
15. Connect vehicle fuel lines, then start engine and check for leaks. **Lubricate O-rings prior to installation and ensure fuel lines are securely connected.**

SENSOR ADJUSTMENTS
Throttle Position Sensor
2.5L/V6-152 ENGINE

1. Connect Rotunda Breakout Box tool

No. 014-00322 and Breakout Box Adapter tool No. T92C-6000-AH, or equivalents, to Powertrain Control Module (PCM).
2. Place ignition switch in On position, then measure voltage between Breakout Box pin 47 and ground.
3. Rotate throttle linkage by hand and observe voltage readings.
4. With throttle valve fully closed, voltage reading should measure 0.1-1.1 volts.
5. With throttle valve fully open, voltage reading should measure 3.1-4.4 volts.
6. If voltage readings are not as specified, adjust throttle position sensor as follows:
   a. Loosen TPS bolts.
   b. With throttle valve fully closed, rotate TPS until voltage reading is 0.1-1.1 volts.
   c. With throttle valve fully open, ensure voltage reading is 3.1-4.4 volts.
   d. **Torque** TPS bolts to 14-20 inch lbs.

2.5L/V6-153 & 3.0L/V6-181 DURATEC ENGINES

The Throttle Position (TP) sensor on the Duratec engine is not adjustable.

3.0L/V6-182 & 3.2L/V6-195 ENGINES

The Throttle Position (TP) sensor is not adjustable.

3.8L/V6-232 ENGINE

There are two types of Throttle Position (TP) sensors employed on these engines: a level C adjustable TP sensor and a level D/RD non-adjustable TP sensor. The following procedure is for a level C throttle position sensor only. Level C throttle position sensors can be identified by large retaining holes which provide adjustment. Level D/RD sensors must be replaced if diagnosed as defective.

1. Install Rotunda EEC-IV Breakout Box tool No. T83L-50-EEC-IV, or equivalent.
2. Attach Rotunda Digital Volt Ohm Meter (DVOM) tool No. 014-00407, or equivalent, on 20 volt scale. Connect positive lead to test Pin 47 and negative lead to test Pin 46.
3. Place ignition key in Run position. Do not start engine.
4. Rotate throttle position until DVOM reads between 0.9-1.1 volt.
5. While observing DVOM, move throttle to wide-open and back to idle position. For proper operation, the DVOM should move from 1.0 to at least 4.0 and back to 1.0 volt.
6. Place ignition key in Off position, then disconnect breakout box.

V8 Gasolin ngin

If Uncertain About The Proper Use Of Information Contained In This Section, Please Refer To "How To Use This Manual" Located In The Front Of This Tabbed Section.

Prior To Performing Any Service Operations Listed In This Section, Consult The Technical Service Bulletin Section For Related Information.

INDEX

	Page No.		Page No.		Page No.
Compression Pressure	3-12	3.4L/V8-207 SHO & 4.6L/V8-281		Valves:	3-12
Engine Identification	3-12	Engines	3-12	Valve Adjustment:	3-12
Fuel Injection Cleaning	3-13	5.0L/V8-302 Engine	3-12	4.6L/V8-281 Engine	3-12
Idle Speed & Mixture Adjustments:	3-12	Ignition Wire Resistance	3-12	5.0L/V8-302 Engine	3-12
Curb Idle Speed	3-12	Sensor Adjustments:	3-13	Valve Arrangement:	3-12
Fast Idle Speed	3-12	Throttle Position Sensor	3-13	Front To Rear	3-12
Ignition Timing:	3-12	Spark Plugs	3-12		

ENGINE IDENTIFICATION

The engine code is the eighth digit of the Vehicle Identification Number (VIN). The VIN is stamped on a metal tag located on top left side of dash and visible through the windshield.

SPARK PLUGS

Spark plugs should be replaced and properly tightened at recommended intervals. Refer to **Fig. 1** for replacement interval and tightening specifications.

IGNITION WIRE RESISTANCE

Without removing the high tension wires from the spark plugs, distributor cap or coil, wipe the wires with a clean, damp cloth and inspect them for visible cracks, cuts, pinching or torn boots. Replace only the wires that are damaged.

Spark plug wire resistance specifications are not available from the manufacturer.

COMPRESSION PRESSURE

Cylinder compression pressure should range between 134 psi (being the lowest maximum pressure), and 250 psi (being the highest maximum pressure), at an engine cranking speed of 180 RPM minimum. The compression in each cylinder should fall within the specified compression pressure range with no more than a 75% variance in compression.

IGNITION TIMING

Refer to Tune Up Specifications chart for correct ignition and firing order. Base ignition timing should only be adjusted if the distributor has been removed from the engine assembly.

Adjust ignition timing with engine at normal operating temperature and all accessories Off.

To correctly set timing, a remote starter switch should not be used. Use the ignition switch only to start the vehicle, a remote starter switch will cause the TFI module to revert to start mode timing.

3.4L/V8-207 SHO & 4.6L/V8-281 Engines

The ignition timing on these engines is not adjustable.

5.0L/V8-302 Engine

1. Place transmission in Park or Neutral position, then turn A/C and heater off.
2. **On 1993-94 models,** connect Rotunda Inductive Timing Light tool No. 059-00006, or equivalent, according to manufacturer's instructions.
3. **On 1995 models,** connect Rotunda Timing Analyzer tool No. 059-00014, or equivalent, to No. 1 cylinder ignition wire, according to manufacturer's instructions.
4. **On all models,** disconnect single wire in-line (SPOUT) connector, then start engine and allow to warm to operating temperature.
5. With engine at specified RPM, check/adjust initial timing to specification. Refer to Vehicle Emission Control Information (VECI) label in engine compartment for specifications.
6. Connect single wire in-line SPOUT connector and check ignition timing advance while varying engine RPM to verify distributor is advancing beyond initial ignition timing setting.
7. Remove timing analyzer tool.

IDLE SPEED & MIXTURE ADJUSTMENTS

Refer to Tune Up Specifications chart for curb and fast idle specifications.

Curb Idle Speed

The curb idle speed on the V8 engines is not adjustable. Curb idle is electronically controlled.

Fast Idle Speed

The fast idle speed on the V8 engines is not adjustable. Fast idle is electronically controlled.

VALVES

Valve Arrangement

FRONT TO REAR

4.6L/V8-281 SOHC:
Inner Valves .... Intake
Outer Valves .... Exhaust
4.6L/V8-281 DOHC:
Inner Camshafts .... Intake
Outer Camshafts .... Exhaust
5.0L/V8-302:
Left .... E-I-E-I-E-I-E-I
Right .... I-E-I-E-I-E-I-E

Valve Adjustment

4.6L/V8-281 ENGINE

These engines uses roller finger followers with hydraulic lash adjusters. No adjustment is required or necessary.

5.0L/V8-302 ENGINE

For these engines, a .060 inch longer or a .060 inch shorter pushrod is available to provide a means of compensating for dimensional changes in the valve train and rocker arm. If the clearance is less than the minimum, the .060 inch shorter pushrod should be used. If clearance is more than the maximum the .060 inch longer pushrod should be used.

To check valve clearance, proceed as follows:

1. Install auxiliary starter switch between battery and "S" terminal of starter solenoid, then crank engine with ignition switch in Off position until No. 1 piston is on TDC on compression stroke.

Engine	Replacement Interval In Miles	Torque/Ft. Lbs.
1993		
4.6L/V8-281 ③	30,000	6.6—7.3
4.6L/V8-281 ④	30,000	7
5.0L/V8-302	30,000	7—15
1994		
4.6L/V8-281 ③ ④	30,000	7—15
4.6L/V8-281 ②	①	7—15
5.0L/V8-302	30,000	7—15
1995		
4.6L/V8-281 ③ ④ ⑤	30,000	7—15
4.6L/V8-281 ②	100,000	7—15
5.0L/V8-302	30,000	7—15
1996		
4.6L/V8-281	100,000	7—15
3.4L/V8-207 SHO	100,000	—

① —Federal, 30,000 miles; California, 60,000 miles.
② —Continental
③ —Crown Victoria, Grand Marquis & Town Car.
④ —Mark VIII.
⑤ —Cougar & Thunderbird.

Fig. 1 Spark plug tightening specification & replacement interval chart

2. With crankshaft in position designated in the following steps, position tappet bleed down wrench tool No. T71P-6513-B, or equivalent, on rocker arm, then slowly apply pressure to bleed down valve tappet until plunger is completely bottomed. Hold tappet in this position and check clearance between rocker arm and valve stem tip with feeler gauge.
   a. With No. 1 piston on TDC at end of compression stroke, check No. 1 intake and No. 1 exhaust, No. 4 intake and No. 3 exhaust, then the No. 8 intake and No. 7 exhaust.
   b. Rotate crankshaft 360 degrees (one revolution) and check No. 3 intake and No. 2 exhaust and No. 7 intake and No. 6 exhaust.
   c. Rotate crankshaft 90 degrees (1/4 revolution) and check No. 2 intake and No. 4 exhaust, No. 5 intake and No. 5 exhaust, and No. 6 intake and No. 8 exhaust.
3. If clearance is less than specification, install shorter pushrod. If clearance is greater than specification, install longer pushrod.

FUEL INJECTION CLEANING

Some models are equipped with Deposit Resistant Injectors (DRI), this type of injectors should not be cleaned.

Fuel injectors with the following part numbers are deposit resistant injectors: FOTE-9F593-DA, FOTE-9F593-D1A, FIZE-9F593-C2A, F2LE-9F593-B2A, F1ZE-9F593-C2A and F1ZE-9F593-A2B.

To properly clean fuel injectors follow this procedure, using cleaner tool No. 113-700001, or equivalent.
1. Place shutoff valve on test stand to On position.
2. Using paint filter, pour clean gasoline into fuel tank up to fill line, then add injector cleaner solvent from lower fill line to upper fill line. **Mixture should be approximately 1 ounce of cleaner to 7 ounces of gasoline.**
3. Connect cleaner tool power supply lines to battery. Red light on cleaner will flash, indicating power connection is made and cleaner unit is off.
4. Activate 10 minute timer switch and check pressure gauge to ensure pressure reading is 38-40 psi. If necessary, adjust pressure as follows:
   a. Place shutoff valve in On position, then remove black cap.
   b. Loosen locknut and turning screw until proper reading is achieved.
5. Connect fuel supply hose to outlet and place other end of hose back in tank, then actuate 10 minute timer switch and turn flow meter switch from No. 1 position to No. 2 position. Repeatedly turn switch between positions to purge air from system. **Flow meter should be in No. 2 position for cleaning injectors.**
6. Disconnect engine fuel line inlet line at supply manifold, then connect supply hose from cleaner.
7. Disconnect fuel return line and plug, **Fig. 2,** then install U-tube between chassis return line and chassis supply line, **Fig. 2.**
8. Install turn buckle loosely between throttle control rod and suitable hook up point on fenderwell.
9. Activate 10 minute timer switch, then start engine and check for leaks. **Ensure transmission is in park or neutral position, parking brake is applied or wheels are blocked.**
10. When engine speed has stabilized, set idle speed to 2000 RPM using turnbuckle.
11. Reset remaining 10 minute cycle, then place ignition switch in Off position and remove turnbuckle.
12. Disconnect cleaner supply hose from fuel supply manifold.
13. Place power switch in Off position and disconnect power lines.
14. Connect vehicle fuel lines, then start engine and check for leaks. **Lubricate O-rings prior to installation and ensure fuel lines are securely connected.**

SENSOR ADJUSTMENTS

Throttle Position Sensor

The Throttle Position (TP) sensor on the V8 engines is not adjustable.

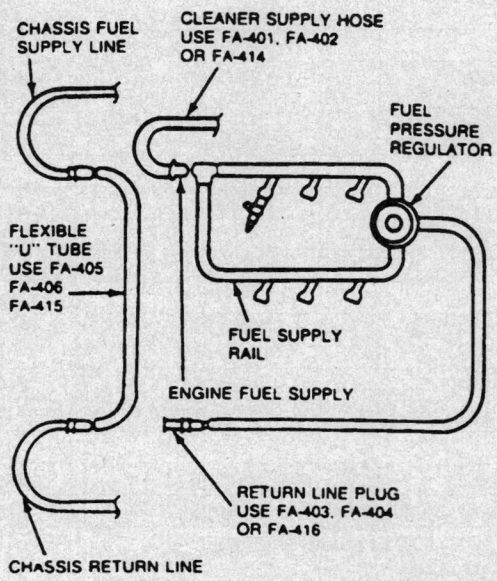

CHASSIS FUEL
SUPPLY LINE

CLEANER SUPPLY HOSE
USE FA-401, FA-402
OR FA-414

FUEL
PRESSURE
REGULATOR

FLEXIBLE
"U" TUBE
USE FA-405
FA-406
FA-415

FUEL SUPPLY
RAIL

ENGINE FUEL SUPPLY

RETURN LINE PLUG
USE FA-403, FA-404
OR FA-416

CHASSIS RETURN LINE

FM1139100224000X

Fig. 2 U-tube installation

IGNITION SYSTEMS

NOTE: If Unsure Of The System Used On The Vehicle Being Serviced, Refer To The "Engine Systems Identification Chart." Further Assistance For The Proper Use Of Information Contained In This Section Can Also Be Found In The Front Of This Tabbed Section Under "How To Use This Manual."

TABLE OF CONTENTS

	Page No.		Page No.
TYPE 1	4-1	TYPE 4	4-62
TYPE 2	4-14	TYPE 5	4-105
TYPE 3	4-45	TYPE 6	4-127

Type 1

INDEX

	Page No.		Page No.		Page No.
Description	4-1	Secondary Circuit Tests	4-10	Ignition Module	4-12
Diagnosis & Testing:	4-2	Wiring Diagrams	4-2	Octane Rod	4-13
Intermittent Diagnosis	4-2	System Service:	4-10	Stator	4-13
Primary Circuit Tests	4-2	Component Replacement	4-10		
Quick Test	4-2	Distributor Assembly	4-10		

DESCRIPTION

The Distributor Ignition (DI) (TFI-IV) system has two distinct types. On the first type, **Figs. 1 and 2**, the Ignition Control Module (ICM) (ignition module) is mounted on the distributor and has three pins which plug into the hall effect Camshaft Position (CMP) (Profile Ignition Pickup (PIP)) sensor inside the distributor (Systems A and E). This type of system is called a distributor mounted Ignition Control Module (ICM) ((push start) TFI-IV). On the second type, **Fig. 3**, the ICM is remotely mounted within the engine compartment (System F). This type of system is called a remote mounted ICM ((Closed Bowl Distributor) TFI-IV).

Both systems consist of the ICM (ignition control (TFI-IV) module), distributor, hall effect CMP (PIP) sensor and the E-core ignition coil. The distributor mounted ICM (TFI-IV) system uses a universal distributor and has an opening through which the ICM (ignition module) pins plug into the CMP (PIP) sensor. The remote mounted ICM (TFI-IV) system uses a sealed distributor. The hall effect CMP (PIP) sensor is located inside the distributor on both types.

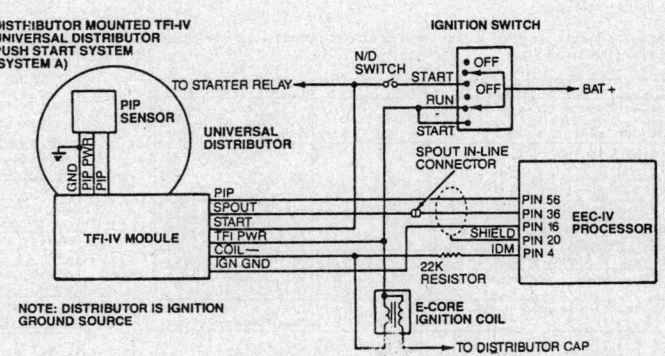

Fig. 1   DI (TFI-IV) ignition system (System A)

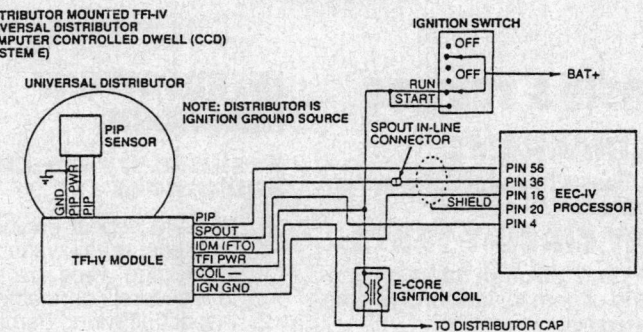

Fig. 2   DI/CCD (TFI-IV/CCD) ignition system (System E)

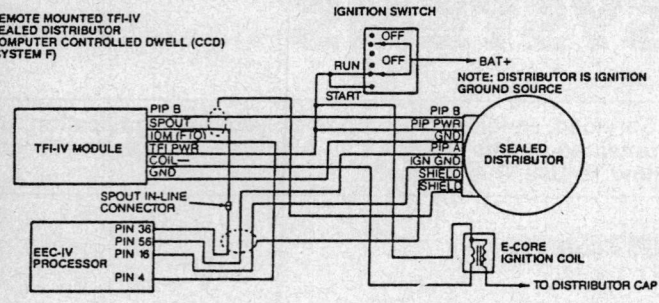

Fig. 3 DI/CCD (TFI-IV/CBD/CCD) ignition system (System F)

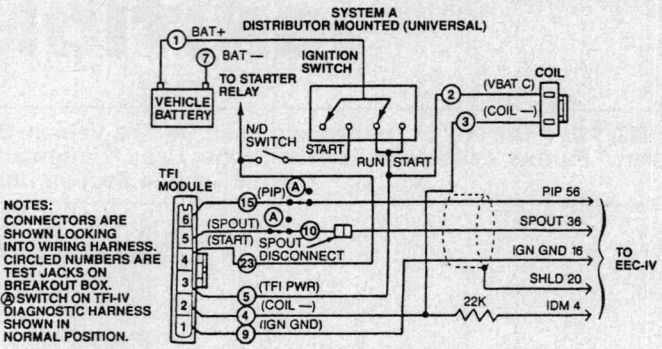

Fig. 4 DI (TFI-IV) (System A) wiring diagram. Diagnostic harness installed

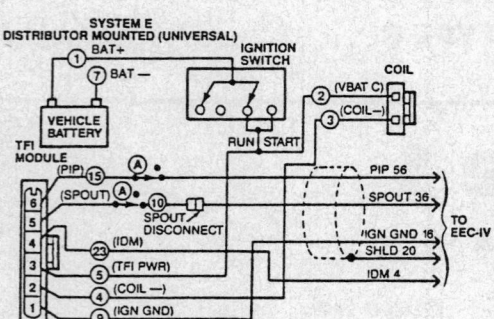

Fig. 5 DI/CCD (TFI-IV/CCD) (System E) wiring diagram. Diagnostic harness installed

Fig. 6 DI/CCD (TFI-IV/CBD/CCD) (System F) wiring diagram. Diagnostic harness installed

Refer to TFI-IV Ignition System Application.

Pinpoint Test Sections A, AA, B, and C are written to catch "Hard Faults"; intermittent failures will be difficult or impossible to diagnose using these procedures.

TEST STEP	ACTION TO TAKE
•Engine No Start and Clear Codes —Distributor Mounted TFI-IV (Systems A, E) —Remote Mounted TFI-IV (Systems B, C, D, F, G)	GO to A1 GO to AA1
•Engine No Start and Code 211 or 14c (PIP at EEC processor fault) —Distributor Mounted TFI-IV (Systems A, E) —Remote Mounted TFI-IV (Systems B, C, D, F, G)	GO to A1 GO to AA1
•Code 212 or 18c — IDM missing	GO to B1
•Timing off, Code 213 or 18r—SPOUT open, Lack of Power, Poor Fuel Economy	GO to C1
•Clear Codes, Code 14c or 211, intermittent miss or stall	GO to D1
•Clear Codes and Misfire under load — secondary short to ground	GO to Secondary System Diagnostic Procedures
•Car continues to run after key is turned off.	CHECK TFI PWR for short to battery power.

NOTE: If a remote starter is used, the ignition key must be in the ON position during cranking when using the pinpoint diagnostics.

Fig. 7 Pinpoint Test Index (Part 1 of 2)

Refer to Distributor Ignition System Application.

Pinpoint Test Sections A, AA, AAA, B, and C are written to catch "Hard Faults"; intermittent failures will be difficult or impossible to diagnose using these procedures.

TEST STEP	ACTION TO TAKE
•Engine No Start and Pass DTCs Distributor Mounted ICM (Systems A, E) Remote Mounted ICM (Systems B, C, D, F, G, H)	GO to A1 GO to AA1
•Engine No Start and/or DTC 211 or 14c, 212 or 18c (PIP at PCM fault) Distributor Mounted ICM (Systems A, E) Remote Mounted ICM (Systems B, C, D, F, G, H)	GO to A1 GO to AA1
•Vehicle runs normally until SPOUT in-line connector is disconnected	Leave SPOUT in-line connector disconnected and GO to AAA1
•Code 212 or 18c — IDM missing, engine runs	GO to B1
•Timing off, Code 213 or 18r—SPOUT open, Lack of Power, Poor Fuel Economy	GO to C1
•Pass DTCs, DTC 14c or 211, 212 or 18c intermittent miss or stall	GO to D1
•Pass DTC and Misfire under load — secondary short to ground	GO to Secondary System Diagnostic Procedures
•Car continues to run after key is turned off	CHECK ICM PWR for short to battery power
•No Crank (Systems A, B, C, D)	CHECK start line to ICM for short to GND

NOTE: If a remote starter is used, the ignition key must be in the ON position during cranking when using the pinpoint diagnostics.

Fig. 7 Pinpoint Test Index (Part 2 of 2)

DIAGNOSIS & TESTING

WIRING DIAGRAMS

Refer To **Figs. 4 through 6**, for system wiring diagrams.

PRIMARY CIRCUIT TESTS

Refer to **Figs. 7 through 14** for diagnosis and testing of primary ignition systems.

QUICK TEST

Refer to "Computerized Engine Controls section for Quick Test.

INTERMITTENT DIAGNOSIS

Preliminary Check & Equipment

1. Visually inspect engine compartment and ensure all vacuum hoses and spark plug wires are properly routed and securely connected.
2. Inspect all wiring harnesses and connectors for damaged insulation and burned, overheated, loose or broken conditions.

3. Obtain one of the following pieces of test equipment or a suitable equivalent:
   a. Rotunda TFI-IV Intermittent Analyzer tool No. 007-00035, or equivalent, which provides a quick connection to DI (TFI-IV ignition) system, but cannot be used on modules with Computer Controlled Dwell (CCD) unless a CCD update is added to analyzer.
   b. Rotunda Ignition System Tester tool No. 007-00008, or equivalent, which provides a quick means of separating ignition system problems from other system problems.

TEST STEP		RESULT	▶	ACTION TO TAKE
A1	WERE TESTS IN EEC-IV QUICK TEST COMPLETED			
	• Were all tests accomplished according to EEC-IV Quick Test procedures?	Yes	▶	GO to A2.
		No	▶	Go to EEC-IV Quick Test
A2	CHECK FOR GOOD BATTERY			
	• Is battery voltage greater than 12 volts DC with the key on?	Yes	▶	GO to A3.
		No	▶	SERVICE battery.
A3	CHECK FOR SPARK AT COIL DURING CRANK			
	• Using an Air Gap Spark Tester (D81P-6666-A) or a Neon Bulb Spark Tester (D89P-6666-A) or equivalent, check for spark during crank at coil wire.	Yes	▶	GO to A9.
		No	▶	GO to A4.
	• Was spark present during crank?			
A4	CHECK FOR TFI POWER			
	• Key off.	Yes	▶	GO to A5.
	• Connect TFI diagnostic harness to EEC breakout box, connect BAT— lead to negative post of battery, and connect TFI module TEE to TFI module and vehicle harness.	No	▶	SERVICE power open to TFI module in harness or connector. REMOVE all test equipment. RECONNECT all components. CLEAR Continuous Memory. RERUN Quick Test.
	• Do not connect BAT+ lead of TFI diagnostic harness to battery.			
	CAUTION: Do not connect EEC processor to EEC Breakout Box when it is used with TFI diagnostic harness.			
	• Make sure PIP OPEN/NORMAL/SPOUT OPEN switch on TFI diagnostic harness is in the NORMAL position.			
	• Use TFI overlay on breakout box.			
	• DVOM on 20 volt DC scale.			
	• Key on.			
	• Measure voltage between J5 (TFI PWR) and J7 (BAT—) at breakout box.			
	• Is voltage greater than 10 volts DC?			
A5	CHECK FOR PIP SIGNAL			
	• DVOM on 20 volt AC scale.	Yes	▶	GO to A6.
	• Crank engine and measure voltage between J15 (PIP) and J7 (BAT—).	No	▶	GO to A11.
	• Is voltage between 3.0 and 8.5 volts AC?			

Fig. 8   Test A: No Start (Part 1 of 7).
DI (TFI-IV) & DI/CCD (TFI-IV/CCD)

TEST STEP		RESULT	▶	ACTION TO TAKE
A6	CHECK FOR SPOUT SIGNAL			
	• Crank engine and measure voltage between J10 (SPOUT) and J7 (BAT—).	Yes	▶	GO to A7.
		No	▶	GO to A15.
	• Is voltage between 3.0 and 8.5 volts AC?			
A7	CHECK VBAT AT COIL			
	• Key off.	Yes	▶	GO to A8.
	• Connect diagnostic harness coil TEE to vehicle harness; do not connect diagnostic harness to coil.	No	▶	SERVICE power open to coil in harness or connector. REMOVE all test equipment. RECONNECT all components. CLEAR Continuous Memory. RERUN Quick Test.
	• Key on.			
	• DVOM on 20 volt DC scale.			
	• Measure voltage between J2 (VBAT C) and J7 (BAT—).			
	• Is voltage greater than 10 volts DC?			
A8	CHECK FOR COIL— SIGNAL			
	• Key off.	Yes	▶	REPLACE coil. REMOVE all test equipment. RECONNECT all components. CLEAR Continuous Memory. RERUN Quick Test.
	• Connect BAT+ lead of TFI diagnostic harness to positive post of battery.			
	• Connect 12 volt incandescent test lamp between J1 (BAT+) and J3 (COIL—).			
	• Crank engine.	No	▶	GO to A23.
	• Did test lamp flash brightly?			
A9	CHECK FOR SPARK AT ALL WIRES			
	• Using an Air Gap Spark Tester (D81P-6666-A) or Neon Bulb Spark Tester (D89P-6666-A) or equivalent, check for spark at all wires.	Yes	▶	GO to A10.
		No	▶	SERVICE distributor cap, rotor, plugs or plug wires. REMOVE all test equipment. RECONNECT all components. CLEAR Continuous Memory. RERUN Quick Test.
	• Was spark present at all plugs during crank?			
A10	CHECK PLUGS			
	• Remove and check plugs for damage, wear, carbon deposits and proper plug gap.	Yes	▶	Not an Ignition problem.
	• Are plugs OK?			
		No	▶	SERVICE plugs. REMOVE all test equipment. RECONNECT all components. CLEAR Continuous Memory. RERUN Quick Test.

Fig. 8   Test A: No Start (Part 2 of 7).
DI (TFI-IV) & DI/CCD (TFI-IV/CCD)

TEST STEP		RESULT	▶	ACTION TO TAKE
A11	CHECK FOR PIP FROM TFI			
	• Turn switch on diagnostic cable to PIP OPEN.	Yes	▶	GO to A12.
	• DVOM on 20 volt AC scale.	No	▶	GO to A14.
	• Crank engine and measure the voltage between J15 (PIP) and J7 (BAT—).			
	• Is voltage between 3.0 and 8.5 volts AC?			
A12	CHECK FOR PIP SHORT HIGH IN HARNESS			
	• Key off.	Yes	▶	GO to A13.
	• Turn switch on diagnostic cable to NORMAL.	No	▶	SERVICE PIP between EEC processor and TFI module in harness for short high. REMOVE all test equipment. RECONNECT all components. CLEAR Continuous Memory. RERUN Quick Test.
	• Disconnect EEC processor.			
	• DVOM on 20 volt DC scale.			
	• Disconnect diagnostic harness TFI module TEE from TFI module only; leave TFI module TEE connected to vehicle harness.			
	• Key on.			
	• Measure voltage between J15 (PIP) and J7 (BAT—).			
	• Is voltage less than 0.5 volts DC?			
A13	CHECK FOR PIP SHORT LOW IN HARNESS			
	• Key off.	Yes	▶	REPLACE EEC processor. REMOVE all test equipment. RECONNECT all components. CLEAR Continuous Memory. RERUN Quick Test.
	• DVOM on 20K ohm scale.			
	• Measure resistance between J15 (PIP) and J7 (BAT—).			
	• Is resistance greater than 10K ohms?			
		No	▶	SERVICE PIP between EEC processor and TFI module in harness for short low. REMOVE all test equipment. RECONNECT all components. CLEAR Continuous Memory. RERUN Quick Test.

Fig. 8   Test A: No Start (Part 3 of 7).
DI (TFI-IV) & DI/CCD (TFI-IV/CCD)

TEST STEP		RESULT	▶	ACTION TO TAKE
A14	RESISTANCE CHECK OF TFI MODULE			
	• Key off.	Yes	▶	CHECK stator and wiring inside distributor, if OK REPLACE PIP sensor. REMOVE all test equipment. RECONNECT all components. CLEAR Continuous Memory. RERUN Quick Test.
	• Disconnect diagnostic harness from TFI module.			
	• Remove TFI module from distributor.			

Measure the resistance between:	Is the reading:
PIP IN and PIP OUT	less than 150
PIP PWR and TFI PWR	less than 150
GND and PIP IN	greater than 500
GND and IGN GND	less than 5
PIP PWR and PIP IN	between 900 and 1.5K

	• Are readings OK?	No	▶	REPLACE TFI module. REMOVE all test equipment. RECONNECT all components. CLEAR Continuous Memory. RERUN Quick Test.

GND
PIP POWER
PIP IN

PIP OUT
SPOUT
START ON PUSH START TFI-IV MODULE
IDM ON CCD TFI-IV MODULE
TFI POWER
TACH
IGN GND

TEST STEP		RESULT	▶	ACTION TO TAKE
A15	CHECK FOR SPOUT IN HARNESS			
	• Turn switch on diagnostic cable to SPOUT OPEN.	Yes	▶	REPLACE TFI module. REMOVE all test equipment. RECONNECT all components. CLEAR Continuous Memory. RERUN Quick Test.
	• Crank engine and measure voltage between J10 (SPOUT) and J7 (BAT—).			
	• Is voltage between 3.0 and 8.5 volts AC?			
	NOTE: Engine may start, continue diagnostics.	No	▶	GO to A16.

Fig. 8   Test A: No Start (Part 4 of 7).
DI (TFI-IV) & DI/CCD (TFI-IV/CCD)

TEST STEP		RESULT	▶	ACTION TO TAKE
A16	CHECK FOR SPOUT HIGH			
	• Key off. • Disconnect diagnostic harness TFI module TEE from TFI module only; leave TFI module TEE connected to vehicle harness. • Turn switch to NORMAL on diagnostic harness. • DVOM on 20 volt DC scale. • Key on. • Measure voltage between J10 (SPOUT) and J7 (BAT—). • **Is voltage less than 0.5 volt DC?**	Yes No	▶ ▶	GO to A18. GO to A17.
A17	CHECK FOR SPOUT SHORT HIGH IN HARNESS			
	• Key off. • Disconnect EEC processor. • Key on. • Measure voltage between J10 (SPOUT) and J7 (BAT—). • **Is voltage less than 0.5 volt DC?**	Yes No	▶ ▶	GO to A20. SERVICE SPOUT between EEC processor and TFI module in harness for short high. REMOVE all test equipment. RECONNECT all components. CLEAR Continuous Memory. RERUN Quick Test.
A18	CHECK FOR SPOUT SHORT LOW			
	• Key off. • DVOM on 20K ohm scale. • Measure resistance between J10 (SPOUT) and J7 (BAT—). • **Is resistance greater than 10K ohms?**	Yes No	▶ ▶	GO to A20. GO to A19.
A19	CHECK FOR SPOUT SHORT LOW IN HARNESS			
	• Disconnect EEC processor. • Measure resistance between J10 (SPOUT) and J7 (BAT—). • **Is resistance greater than 10K ohms?**	Yes No	▶ ▶	GO to A20. SERVICE SPOUT between EEC processor and TFI module in harness for short low. REMOVE all test equipment. RECONNECT all components. CLEAR Continuous Memory. RERUN Quick Test.

Fig. 8 Test A: No Start (Part 5 of 7). DI (TFI-IV) & DI/CCD (TFI-IV/CCD)

TEST STEP		RESULT	▶	ACTION TO TAKE
A20	CHECK FOR PIP OPEN IN HARNESS			
	• Key off. • DVOM on 200 ohm scale. • Disconnect EEC processor. • Measure resistance between Pin 56 (PIP) of the EEC processor harness connector and J15 (PIP) at the breakout box. • **Is resistance less than 5 ohms?**	Yes No	▶ ▶	GO to A21. SERVICE PIP open between EEC processor connector and TFI module in harness. REMOVE all test equipment. RECONNECT all components. CLEAR Continuous Memory. RERUN Quick Test.
A21	CHECK IGN GND AT EEC PROCESSOR			
	• Reconnect diagnostic harness TFI module TEE to TFI module. • Measure resistance between Pin 16 (IGN GND) of EEC processor harness connector and J7 (BAT—) at the breakout box. • **Is resistance less than 5 ohms?**	Yes No	▶ ▶	REPLACE EEC processor. REMOVE all test equipment. RECONNECT all components. CLEAR Continuous Memory. RERUN Quick Test. GO to A22.
A22	CHECK FOR IGN GND OPEN IN HARNESS			
	• Disconnect diagnostic harness TFI module TEE from TFI module only; leave TFI module TEE connected to vehicle harness. • Measure resistance between Pin 16 (IGN GND) of EEC processor harness connector and J9 (IGN GND) at the breakout box. • **Is resistance less than 5 ohms?**	Yes No	▶ ▶	REPLACE TFI module. REMOVE all test equipment. RECONNECT all components. CLEAR Continuous Memory. RERUN Quick Test. SERVICE IGN GND open between EEC processor and TFI module in harness. REMOVE all test equipment. RECONNECT all components. CLEAR Continuous Memory. RERUN Quick Test.

Fig. 8 Test A: No Start (Part 6 of 7). DI (TFI-IV) & DI/CCD (TFI-IV/CCD)

TEST STEP		RESULT	▶	ACTION TO TAKE
A23	CHECK FOR COIL— OPEN IN HARNESS			
	• Key off. • Disconnect diagnostic harness TFI module TEE from TFI module only; leave TFI module TEE connected to vehicle harness. • Disconnect BAT+ lead of TFI diagnostic harness from battery. • DVOM on 200 ohm scale. • Measure resistance between J3 (COIL—) and J4 (TFI COIL—)? • **Is resistance less than 5 ohms?**	Yes No	▶ ▶	GO to A24. SERVICE open COIL— between TFI module and coil in harness. REMOVE all test equipment. RECONNECT all components. CLEAR Continuous Memory. RERUN Quick Test.
A24	CHECK FOR COIL— SHORT LOW IN HARNESS			
	• Key off. • DVOM on 20K ohm scale. • Measure resistance between J3 (COIL—) and J7 (BAT—). • **Is resistance greater than 10K ohms?**	Yes No	▶ ▶	GO to A25. SERVICE COIL— short low in harness between TFI module and coil. Coil may be damaged. REMOVE all test equipment. RECONNECT all components. CLEAR Continuous Memory. RERUN Quick Test.
A25	CHECK FOR COIL— SHORT HIGH IN HARNESS			
	• DVOM on 20 volt DC scale. • Key on. • Measure voltage between J3 (COIL—) and J7 (BAT—). • **Is voltage less than 5.5 volts DC?**	Yes No	▶ ▶	REPLACE TFI module. REMOVE all test equipment. RECONNECT all components. CLEAR Continuous Memory. RERUN Quick Test. SERVICE COIL— short high in harness between TFI module and coil. REMOVE all test equipment. RECONNECT all components. CLEAR Continuous Memory. RERUN Quick Test.

Fig. 8 Test A: No Start (Part 7 of 7). 1992 TFI-IV & TFI-IV/CCD

TEST STEP		RESULT	▶	ACTION TO TAKE
A24	CHECK FOR COIL- SHORT HIGH IN HARNESS			
	• DVOM on 20 volt DC scale. • Key on. • Measure voltage between J3 (COIL-) and J7 (B-). • **Is voltage less than 5.5 volts DC?**	Yes No	▶ ▶	GO to A25. SERVICE coil- short high in harness between ICM and coil. Coil may be damaged. REMOVE all test equipment. RECONNECT all components. CLEAR Continuous Memory. RERUN Quick Test.
A25	CHECK FOR COIL- SHORT LOW IN HARNESS			
	• Key off. • DVOM on 20K ohm scale. • Measure resistance between J3 (COIL-) and J7 (B-). • **Is resistance greater than 10K ohms?**	Yes No	▶ ▶	REPLACE ICM. REMOVE all test equipment. RECONNECT all components. CLEAR Continuous Memory. RERUN Quick Test. SERVICE coil- short low in harness between ICM and coil. REMOVE all test equipment. RECONNECT all components. CLEAR Continuous Memory. RERUN Quick Test.

Fig. 8 Test A: No Start (Part 7 of 7). 1993–95 Distributor Mounted DI & DI/CCD

TEST STEP		RESULT	▶	ACTION TO TAKE
AA1	WERE TESTS IN EEC-IV QUICK TEST COMPLETED			
	• Were all tests accomplished according to EEC-IV Quick Test procedures?	Yes No	▶ ▶	GO to AA2. Go to EEC-IV Quick Test
AA2	CHECK FOR GOOD BATTERY			
	• Is battery voltage greater than 12 volts DC with the key on?	Yes No	▶ ▶	GO to AA3. SERVICE battery.
AA3	CHECK FOR SPARK AT COIL DURING CRANK			
	• Using an Air Gap Spark Tester (D81P-6666-A) or a Neon Bulb Spark Tester (D89P-6666-A) or equivalent, check for spark during crank at coil wire. • Was spark present during crank?	Yes No	▶ ▶	GO to AA9. GO to AA4.
AA4	CHECK FOR TFI POWER			
	• Key off. • Connect TFI diagnostic harness to EEC breakout box, connect BAT— lead to negative post of battery, and connect TFI module TEE to TFI module and vehicle harness. • Do not connect BAT+ lead of TFI diagnostic harness to battery. **CAUTION: Do not connect EEC processor to EEC Breakout Box when it is used with TFI diagnostic harness.** • Make sure PIP OPEN/NORMAL/SPOUT OPEN switch on TFI diagnostic harness is in the NORMAL position. • Use TFI overlay on breakout box. • DVOM on 20 volt DC scale. • Key on. • Measure voltage between J5 (TFI PWR) and J7 (BAT—) at breakout box. • Is voltage greater than 10 volts DC?	Yes No	▶ ▶	GO to AA5. SERVICE power open to TFI module in harness or connector. REMOVE all test equipment. RECONNECT all components. CLEAR Continuous Memory. RERUN Quick Test.
AA5	CHECK FOR PIP SIGNAL			
	• DVOM on 20 volt AC scale. • Crank engine and measure voltage between J15 (PIP) and J7 (BAT—). • Is voltage between 3.0 and 8.5 volts AC?	Yes No	▶ ▶	GO to AA6. GO to AA11.

Fig. 9 Test AA: No Start (Part 1 of 10). TFI-IV/CBD & TFI-IV/CBD/CCD

TEST STEP		RESULT	▶	ACTION TO TAKE
AA6	CHECK FOR SPOUT SIGNAL			
	• Crank engine and measure voltage between J10 (SPOUT) and J7 (BAT—). • Is voltage between 3.0 and 8.5 volts AC?	Yes No	▶ ▶	GO to AA7. GO to AA18.
AA7	CHECK VBAT AT COIL			
	• Key off. • Connect diagnostic harness coil TEE to vehicle harness; do not connect diagnostic harness to coil. • Key on. • DVOM on 20 volt DC scale. • Measure voltage between J2 (VBAT C) and J7 (BAT—). • Is voltage greater than 10 volts DC?	Yes No	▶ ▶	GO to AA8. SERVICE power open to coil in harness or connector. REMOVE all test equipment. RECONNECT all components. CLEAR Continuous Memory. RERUN Quick Test.
AA8	CHECK FOR COIL— SIGNAL			
	• Key off. • Connect BAT+ lead of TFI diagnostic harness to positive post of battery. • Connect 12 volt incandescent test lamp between J1 (BAT+) and J3 (COIL—). • Key on. • Crank engine. • Did test lamp flash brightly?	Yes No	▶ ▶	REPLACE coil. REMOVE all test equipment. RECONNECT all components. CLEAR Continuous Memory. RERUN Quick Test. GO to AA27.
AA9	CHECK FOR SPARK AT ALL WIRES			
	• Using an Air Gap Spark Tester (D81P-6666-A) or Neon Bulb Spark Tester (D89P-6666-A) or equivalent, check for spark at all wires. • Was spark present at all plugs during crank?	Yes No	▶ ▶	GO to AA10. SERVICE distributor cap, rotor, plugs or plug wires. REMOVE all test equipment. RECONNECT all components. CLEAR Continuous Memory. RERUN Quick Test.

Fig. 9 Test AA: No Start (Part 2 of 10). TFI-IV/CBD & TFI-IV/CBD/CCD

TEST STEP		RESULT	▶	ACTION TO TAKE
AA10	CHECK PLUGS			
	• Remove and check plugs for damage, wear, carbon deposits and proper plug gap. • Are plugs OK?	Yes No	▶ ▶	Not an Ignition problem. SERVICE plugs. REMOVE all test equipment. RECONNECT all components. CLEAR Continuous Memory. RERUN Quick Test.
AA11	CHECK FOR PIP POWER AT PIP SENSOR			
	• Connect diagnostic harness PIP sensor TEE to the PIP sensor and vehicle harness. • DVOM on 20 volt DC scale. • Key on. • Measure voltage between: —J22 (PIP PWR) and J7 (BAT—) if 8 pin PIP sensor connector or —J27 (PIP PWR) and J7 (BAT—) if 4 pin PIP sensor connector • Is voltage greater than 10 volts DC?	Yes No	▶ ▶	GO to AA12. SERVICE power to PIP sensor in harness or connector. REMOVE all test equipment. RECONNECT all components. CLEAR Continuous Memory. RERUN Quick Test.
AA12	CHECK FOR PIP FROM PIP SENSOR			
	• Turn switch on diagnostic cable to PIP OPEN. • DVOM on 20 volt AC scale. • Crank engine and measure voltage between: —J34 (PIP A) and J7 (BAT—) if 8 pin PIP sensor connector or —J13 (PIP) and J7 (BAT—) if 4 pin PIP sensor connector • Is voltage between 3.0 and 8.5 volts AC?	Yes No	▶ ▶	GO to AA13. CHECK PIP sensor wiring, if OK REPLACE PIP sensor. REMOVE all test equipment. RECONNECT all components. CLEAR Continuous Memory. RERUN Quick Test.

Fig. 9 Test AA: No Start (Part 3 of 10). TFI-IV/CBD & TFI-IV/CBD/CCD

TEST STEP		RESULT	▶	ACTION TO TAKE
AA13	CHECK PIP WITH TFI DISCONNECTED			
	• Key off. • Turn switch on diagnostic cable to NORMAL. • Disconnect diagnostic harness TFI module TEE from TFI module only; leave TFI module TEE connected to vehicle harness. • Crank engine and measure voltage between: —J34 (PIP A) and J7 (BAT—) if 8 pin PIP sensor connector or —J13 (PIP) and J7 (BAT—) if 4 pin PIP sensor connector • Is voltage between 3.0 and 8.5 volts AC?	Yes No	▶ ▶	REPLACE TFI module. REMOVE all test equipment. RECONNECT all components. CLEAR Continuous Memory. RERUN Quick Test. GO to AA14.
AA14	CHECK PIP WITH EEC PROCESSOR DISCONNECTED			
	• Disconnect EEC processor. • Crank engine and measure voltage between: —J34 (PIP A) and J7 (BAT—) if 8 pin PIP sensor connector or —J13 (PIP) and J7 (BAT—) if 4 pin PIP sensor connector • Is voltage between 3.0 and 8.5 volts AC?	Yes No	▶ ▶	REPLACE EEC processor. REMOVE all test equipment. RECONNECT all components. CLEAR Continuous Memory. RERUN Quick Test. GO to AA15.

Fig. 9 Test AA: No Start (Part 4 of 10). TFI-IV/CBD & TFI-IV/CBD/CCD

TEST STEP	RESULT	▶	ACTION TO TAKE
AA15 CHECK PIP A TO EEC PROCESSOR FOR SHORT HIGH • Key off. • Disconnect diagnostic harness PIP sensor TEE from PIP sensor only; leave PIP sensor TEE connected to vehicle harness. • DVOM on 20 volt DC scale. • Key on. • Measure voltage between: —J34 (PIP A) and J7 (BAT—) if 8 pin PIP sensor connector or —J13 (PIP) and J7 (BAT—) if 4 pin PIP sensor connector • **Is voltage less than 0.5 volt DC?**	Yes No	▶ ▶	For Systems B and F: GO TO **AA16**. For all other systems, SERVICE PIP between PIP sensor and EEC processor or TFI module in harness for short low. REMOVE all test equipment. RECONNECT all components. CLEAR Continuous Memory. RERUN Quick Test. For Systems B and F: SERVICE PIP A between PIP sensor and EEC processor in harness for short high. REMOVE all test equipment. RECONNECT all components. CLEAR Continuous Memory. RERUN Quick Test. For all other systems, SERVICE PIP between PIP sensor and EEC processor or TFI module in harness for short high. REMOVE all test equipment. RECONNECT all components. CLEAR Continuous Memory. RERUN Quick Test.
AA16 CHECK PIP B TO TFI FOR SHORT HIGH • Key on. • Measure the voltage between J41 (PIP B) and J7 (BAT—). • **Is the voltage less than 0.5 volt DC?**	Yes No	▶ ▶	GO TO **AA17**. SERVICE PIP B between PIP sensor and TFI module in harness for short high. REMOVE all test equipment. RECONNECT all components. CLEAR Continuous Memory. RERUN Quick Test.

Fig. 9 Test AA: No Start (Part 5 of 10). TFI-IV/CBD & TFI-IV/CBD/CCD

TEST STEP	RESULT	▶	ACTION TO TAKE
AA17 CHECK PIP IN HARNESS FOR SHORT LOW • Key off. • DVOM on 20K ohm scale. • Measure the resistance between J41 (PIP B) and J7 (BAT—). • **Is the resistance greater than 10K ohms?**	Yes No	▶ ▶	SERVICE PIP A between PIP sensor and EEC processor in harness for short low. REMOVE all test equipment. RECONNECT all components. CLEAR Continuous Memory. RERUN Quick Test. SERVICE PIP B between PIP sensor and TFI module in harness for short low. REMOVE all test equipment. RECONNECT all components. CLEAR Continuous Memory. RERUN Quick Test.
AA18 CHECK FOR SPOUT IN HARNESS • Turn switch to SPOUT OPEN position on diagnostic harness. • Crank engine and measure voltage between J10 (SPOUT) and J7 (BAT—). • **Is voltage between 3.0 and 8.5 volts AC?** NOTE: Engine may start, continue diagnostics.	Yes No	▶ ▶	REPLACE TFI module. REMOVE all test equipment. RECONNECT all components. CLEAR Continuous Memory. RERUN Quick Test. GO to **AA19**.
AA19 CHECK FOR SPOUT HIGH • Key off. • Disconnect diagnostic harness TFI module TEE from TFI module only; leave TFI module TEE connected to vehicle harness. • Turn switch to NORMAL on diagnostic harness. • DVOM on 20 volt DC scale. • Measure voltage between J10 (SPOUT) and J7 (BAT—), with key on. • **Is voltage less than 0.5 volt DC?**	Yes No	▶ ▶	GO to **AA21**. GO to **AA20**.

Fig. 9 Test AA: No Start (Part 6 of 10). TFI-IV/CBD & TFI-IV/CBD/CCD

TEST STEP	RESULT	▶	ACTION TO TAKE
AA20 CHECK FOR SPOUT SHORT HIGH IN HARNESS • Key off. • Disconnect EEC processor. • Measure voltage between J10 (SPOUT) and J7 (BAT—) with key on. • **Is voltage less than 0.5 volt DC?**	Yes No	▶ ▶	GO to **AA23**. SERVICE SPOUT between EEC processor and TFI module in harness for short high. REMOVE all test equipment. RECONNECT all components. CLEAR Continuous Memory. RERUN Quick Test.
AA21 CHECK FOR SPOUT SHORT LOW • Key off. • DVOM on 20K ohm scale. • Measure resistance between J10 (SPOUT) and J7 (BAT—). • **Is resistance greater than 10K ohms?**	Yes No	▶ ▶	GO to **AA23**. GO to **AA22**.
AA22 CHECK FOR SPOUT SHORT LOW IN HARNESS • Disconnect EEC processor. • Measure resistance between J10 (SPOUT) and J7 (BAT—). • **Is resistance greater than 10K ohms?**	Yes No	▶ ▶	GO to **AA23**. SERVICE SPOUT between EEC processor and TFI module in harness for short low. REMOVE all test equipment. RECONNECT all components. CLEAR Continuous Memory. RERUN Quick Test.
AA23 CHECK FOR PIP OPEN IN HARNESS • Key off. • DVOM on 20 volt AC scale. • Disconnect EEC processor. • Crank engine and measure voltage between Pin 56 (PIP) of EEC processor harness connector and J7 (BAT—). • **Is voltage between 3.0 and 8.5 volts AC?**	Yes No	▶ ▶	GO to **AA24**. GO to **AA26**.

Fig. 9 Test AA: No Start (Part 7 of 10). TFI-IV/CBD & TFI-IV/CBD/CCD

TEST STEP	RESULT	▶	ACTION TO TAKE
AA24 CHECK IGN GND AT EEC PROCESSOR • Key off. • Reconnect diagnostic harness TFI module TEE to TFI module. • DVOM on 200 ohm scale. • Measure resistance between Pin 16 (IGN GND) of EEC processor harness connector and J7 (BAT—) at the breakout box. • **Is resistance less than 5 ohms?**	Yes No	▶ ▶	REPLACE EEC processor. REMOVE all test equipment. RECONNECT all components. CLEAR Continuous Memory. RERUN Quick Test. GO to **AA25**.
AA25 CHECK FOR IGN GND AT PIP SENSOR • Connect diagnostic harness PIP sensor TEE to PIP sensor and vehicle harness. • Measure resistance between: —J35 (IGN GND) and J7 (BAT—) if 8 pin PIP sensor connector or —J19 (IGN GND) and J7 (BAT—) if 4 pin PIP sensor connector • **Is resistance less than 5 ohms?**	Yes No	▶ ▶	SERVICE IGN GND between EEC processor and PIP sensor in harness for open. REMOVE all test equipment. RECONNECT all components. CLEAR Continuous Memory. RERUN Quick Test. SERVICE IGN GND open in PIP sensor. SERVICE IGN GND wire or REPLACE PIP sensor. REMOVE all test equipment. RECONNECT all components. CLEAR Continuous Memory. RERUN Quick Test.

Fig. 9 Test AA: No Start (Part 8 of 10). TFI-IV/CBD & TFI-IV/CBD/CCD

TEST STEP		RESULT	▶	ACTION TO TAKE
AA26	CHECK PIP A AT PIP SENSOR			
	• Turn switch from NORMAL to PIP OPEN position. • Connect diagnostic harness PIP sensor TEE to PIP sensor and vehicle harness. • Crank engine and measure voltage between: —J34 (PIP A) and J7 (BAT—) if 8 pin PIP sensor connector or —J13 (PIP) and J7 (BAT—) if 4 pin PIP sensor connector • **Is voltage between 3.0 and 8.5 volts AC?**	Yes No	▶ ▶	SERVICE PIP open in harness between EEC module and PIP sensor. REMOVE all test equipment. RECONNECT all components. CLEAR Continuous Memory. RERUN Quick Test. SERVICE PIP open in PIP sensor. SERVICE PIP wire or REPLACE PIP sensor. REMOVE all test equipment. RECONNECT all components. CLEAR Continuous Memory. RERUN Quick Test.
AA27	CHECK FOR COIL—OPEN IN HARNESS			
	• Key off. • Disconnect diagnostic harness TFI module TEE from TFI module only; leave TFI module TEE connected to vehicle harness. • Disconnect BAT+ lead of TFI diagnostic harness from battery. • DVOM on 200 ohm scale. • Measure the resistance between J3 (COIL—) and J4 (TFI COIL—). • **Is resistance less than 5 ohms?**	Yes No	▶ ▶	GO to AA28. SERVICE open COIL—between TFI module and coil in harness. REMOVE all test equipment. RECONNECT all components. CLEAR Continuous Memory. RERUN Quick Test.
AA28	CHECK FOR COIL—SHORT LOW IN HARNESS			
	• Key off. • DVOM on 20K ohm scale. • Measure resistance between J3 (COIL—) and J7 (BAT—). • **Is resistance greater than 10K ohms?**	Yes No	▶ ▶	GO to AA29. SERVICE COIL—short low in harness between coil and TFI module. Coil may be damaged. REMOVE all test equipment. RECONNECT all components. CLEAR Continuous Memory. RERUN Quick Test.

Fig. 9 Test AA: No Start (Part 9 of 10). TFI-IV/CBD & TFI-IV/CBD/CCD

TEST STEP		RESULT	▶	ACTION TO TAKE
AA28	CHECK FOR COIL - SHORT HIGH IN HARNESS			
	• DVOM on 20 volt DC scale. • Key on. • Measure voltage between J3 (COIL-) and J7 (B-). • **Is voltage less than 5.5 volts DC?**	Yes No	▶ ▶	GO to AA29. SERVICE coil - short high in harness between coil and ICM. Coil may be damaged. REMOVE all test equipment. RECONNECT all components. CLEAR Continuous Memory. RERUN Quick Test.
AA29	CHECK FOR COIL- SHORT LOW IN HARNESS			
	• Key off. • DVOM on 20K ohm scale. • Measure resistance between J3 (COIL-) and J7 (B-). • **Is resistance greater than 10K ohms?**	Yes No	▶ ▶	GO to AA30. SERVICE coil - short low in harness between coil and ICM. REMOVE all test equipment. RECONNECT all components. CLEAR Continuous Memory. RERUN Quick Test.
AA30	CHECK GND AT ICM			
	• Key off. • DVOM on 200 ohm scale. • Measure resistance between J9 (GND) and J7 (B-). • **Is resistance less than 5.0 ohms?**	Yes No	▶ ▶	REPLACE ICM. REMOVE all test equipment. RECONNECT all components. CLEAR Continuous Memory. RERUN Quick Test. GO to AA31.

Fig. 9 Test AA: No Start (Part 10 of 10). Remote Mounted DI/CCD

TEST STEP		RESULT	▶	ACTION TO TAKE
AAA1	WERE TESTS IN EEC QUICK TEST COMPLETED			
	• Were all tests accomplished according to EEC Quick Test procedures?	Yes No	▶ ▶	GO to AAA2. REFER to Diagnostic Routines.
AAA2	CHECK FOR GOOD BATTERY			
	• Is battery voltage greater than 12 volts DC with the key on?	Yes No	▶ ▶	GO to AAA3. SERVICE battery.
AAA3	CHECK FOR PIP SIGNAL			
	• Key off. • Connect DI diagnostic harness to EEC breakout box, connect B- lead to negative post of battery, and connect ICM tee to ICM and vehicle harness. • Do not connect B+ lead of DI diagnostic harness to battery. **CAUTION: Do not connect PCM to EEC breakout box when it is used with DI diagnostic harness.** • Make sure PIP OPEN/NORMAL/SPOUT OPEN switch on DI diagnostic harness is in the NORMAL position. • Use DI overlay on breakout box. • Make sure SPOUT in-line connector is disconnected. • DVOM on 20 volt AC scale. • Crank engine and measure voltage between J15 (PIP) and J7 (B-). • **Is voltage between 3.0 and 8.5 volts AC?**	Yes No	▶ ▶	REPLACE ICM. REMOVE all test equipment. RECONNECT all components. CLEAR Continuous Memory. RERUN Quick Test. GO to AAA4.

Fig. 10 Test AAA: No Start With SPOUT In-Line Connector Disconnected (Part 1 of 2). 1993–95 Remote Mounted DI/CCD

TEST STEP		RESULT	▶	ACTION TO TAKE
AAA4	CHECK FOR PIP FROM PIP SENSOR			
• Connect diagnostic harness CMP sensor tee to CMP sensor and vehicle harness. • Turn switch on diagnostic cable to PIP OPEN. • DVOM on 20 volt AC scale. • Crank engine and measure voltage between: -J41 (PIP B) and J7 (B-) if 8 pin CMP sensor connector for systems B and F or -J34 (PIP) and J7 (B-) if 8 pin CMP sensor connector for systems D and H or -J13 (PIP) and J7 (B-) if 4 pin CMP sensor connector for systems C and G. • Is voltage between 3.0 and 8.5 volts AC?		Yes	▶	For 8 pin CMP sensor connector (systems B and F), SERVICE PIP open in harness between ICM and CMP sensor. For 4 pin CMP sensor, connector (systems C and G) and 8 pin CMP sensor connector (systems D and H). SERVICE PIP between ICM and PIP splice in harness for open.
		No	▶	CHECK CMP sensor wiring and connector, if OK REPLACE CMP sensor. REMOVE all test equipment. RECONNECT all components. CLEAR Continuous Memory. RERUN Quick Test.

Fig. 10 Test AAA: No Start With SPOUT In-Line Connector Disconnected (Part 2 of 2). 1993–95 Remote Mounted DI/CCD

TEST STEP		RESULT	▶	ACTION TO TAKE
B4	CHECK FOR OPEN IDM IN HARNESS			
• DVOM on 200K ohm scale. • Measure resistance between Pin 4 (IDM) of the EEC processor connector and J4 (COIL—) at the breakout box. • Is resistance between 20K and 24K ohms?		Yes	▶	REPLACE EEC processor. REMOVE all test equipment. RECONNECT all components. CLEAR Continuous Memory. RERUN Quick Test.
		No	▶	IDM shorted or open in harness between EEC processor connector and COIL— line (REFER to schematics). SERVICE or REPLACE IDM line or IDM resistor in harness. REMOVE all test equipment. RECONNECT all components. CLEAR Continuous Memory. RERUN Quick Test.
B5	CHECK IDM SIGNAL AT PROCESSOR CONNECTOR			
• Key off. • DVOM on 20 volt AC scale. • Crank engine and measure voltage between Pin 4 (IDM) of the EEC processor connector and J7 (BAT—). • Is voltage greater than 1.0 volt AC?		Yes	▶	REPLACE EEC processor. REMOVE all test equipment. RECONNECT all components. CLEAR Continuous Memory. RERUN Quick Test.
		No	▶	GO to B6.
B6	CHECK FOR IDM SHORT HIGH IN HARNESS			
• Key off. • Disconnect diagnostic harness TFI module TEE from TFI module only; leave TFI module TEE connected to vehicle harness. • DVOM on 20 volt DC scale. • Key on. • Measure voltage between J23 (IDM) and J7 (BAT—). • Is voltage less than 0.5 volt DC?		Yes	▶	GO to B7.
		No	▶	SERVICE IDM short high in harness between EEC processor connector and TFI module connector. REMOVE all test equipment. RECONNECT all components. CLEAR Continuous Memory. RERUN Quick Test.

Fig. 11 Test B: IDM Missing Code 18C Or 212C (Part 1 of 3). 1993–94

TEST STEP		RESULT	▶	ACTION TO TAKE
B1	CHECK FOR PUSH START ICM OR CCD ICM			
• Key off. • Connect DI diagnostic harness to EEC breakout box, connect B- lead to negative post of battery, and connect ICM tee to ICM and vehicle harness. • Make sure PIP OPEN / NORMAL / SPOUT OPEN switch on DI diagnostic harness is in NORMAL position. • Use DI diagnostic overlay on breakout box. • Disconnect PCM. • Is ICM CCD or push start? NOTE: Gray module-push start ICM Black module-CCD ICM.		Push start	▶	GO to B2.
		CCD	▶	GO to B5.
B2	CHECK FOR IDM SHORT HIGH			
• Key on. • DVOM on 40 volt DC scale. • Disconnect coil from vehicle harness. • Measure voltage between Pin 4 (IDM) of PCM connector and J7 (B-) at breakout box. • Is voltage less than 5.5 volts DC?		Yes	▶	GO to B3.
		No	▶	SERVICE IDM short high in harness between PCM connector and the 22K ohm IDM resistor. REMOVE all test equipment. RECONNECT all components. CLEAR Continuous Memory. RERUN Quick Test.
B3	CHECK FOR IDM SHORT LOW			
• Key off. • DVOM on 20K ohm scale. • Measure resistance between Pin 4 (IDM) of the PCM connector and J7 (B-) at breakout box. • Is resistance greater than 10K ohms?		Yes	▶	GO to B4.
		No	▶	SERVICE IDM short low in harness between PCM connector and 22K ohm IDM resistor. REMOVE all test equipment. RECONNECT all components. CLEAR Continuous Memory. RERUN Quick Test.

Fig. 12 Test B: IDM Missing Code 18C Or 212C (Part 1 of 3). 1995

TEST STEP		RESULT	▶	ACTION TO TAKE
B4	CHECK FOR OPEN IDM IN HARNESS			
• DVOM on 200K ohm scale. • Measure resistance between Pin 4 (IDM) of the PCM connector and J4 (COIL-) at the breakout box. • Is resistance between 20K and 24K ohms?		Yes	▶	REPLACE PCM. REMOVE all test equipment. RECONNECT all components. CLEAR Continuous Memory. RERUN Quick Test.
		No	▶	IDM shorted or open in harness between PCM connector and coil-in-line (REFER to schematics). SERVICE or REPLACE IDM line or IDM resistor in harness. REMOVE all test equipment. RECONNECT all components. CLEAR Continuous Memory. RERUN Quick Test.
B5	CHECK IDM SIGNAL AT PCM CONNECTOR			
• Key off. • DVOM on 40 volt AC scale. • Crank engine and measure voltage between Pin 4 (IDM) of the PCM connector and J7 (B-). • Is voltage greater than 1.0 volt AC?		Yes	▶	REPLACE PCM. REMOVE all test equipment. RECONNECT all components. CLEAR Continuous Memory. RERUN Quick Test.
		No	▶	GO to B6.
B6	CHECK FOR IDM SHORT HIGH IN HARNESS			
• Key off. • Disconnect diagnostic harness ICM tee from ICM only; leave ICM tee connected to vehicle harness. • DVOM on 40 volt DC scale. • Key on. • Measure voltage between J23 (IDM) and J7 (B-). • Is voltage less than 0.5 volt DC?		Yes	▶	GO to B7.
		No	▶	SERVICE IDM short high in harness between PCM connector and ICM connector. REMOVE all test equipment. RECONNECT all components. CLEAR Continuous Memory. RERUN Quick Test.

FM111940022102BX

Fig. 12 Test B: IDM Missing Code 18C Or 212C (Part 2 of 3). 1994–95

TEST STEP		RESULT	▶	ACTION TO TAKE
B4	CHECK FOR OPEN IDM IN HARNESS			
	• DVOM on 200K ohm scale. • Measure resistance between Pin 4 (IDM) of the PCM connector and J4 (COIL-) at the breakout box. • **Is resistance between 20K and 24K ohms?**	Yes	▶	REPLACE PCM. REMOVE all test equipment. RECONNECT all components. CLEAR Continuous Memory. RERUN Quick Test.
		No		IDM shorted or open in harness between PCM connector and coil-in-line (REFER to schematics). SERVICE or REPLACE IDM line or IDM resistor in harness. REMOVE all test equipment. RECONNECT all components. CLEAR Continuous Memory. RERUN Quick Test.
B5	CHECK IDM SIGNAL AT PCM CONNECTOR			
	• Key off. • DVOM on 40 volt AC scale. • Crank engine and measure voltage between Pin 4 (IDM) of the PCM connector and J7 (B-). • **Is voltage greater than 1.0 volt AC?**	Yes	▶	REPLACE PCM. REMOVE all test equipment. RECONNECT all components. CLEAR Continuous Memory. RERUN Quick Test.
		No	▶	GO to B6.
B6	CHECK FOR IDM SHORT HIGH IN HARNESS			
	• Key off. • Disconnect diagnostic harness ICM tee from ICM only; leave ICM tee connected to vehicle harness. • DVOM on 40 volt DC scale. • Key on. • Measure voltage between J23 (IDM) and J7 (B-). • **Is voltage less than 0.5 volt DC?**	Yes	▶	GO to B7.
		No		SERVICE IDM short high in harness between PCM connector and ICM connector. REMOVE all test equipment. RECONNECT all components. CLEAR Continuous Memory. RERUN Quick Test.

Fig. 12 Test B: IDM Missing Code 18C Or 212C (Part 2 of 3). 1993

TEST STEP		RESULT	▶	ACTION TO TAKE
B7	CHECK FOR IDM SHORT LOW IN HARNESS			
	• Key off. • DVOM on 20K ohm scale. • Measure resistance between J23 (IDM) and J7 (BAT—). • **Is resistance greater than 10K ohms?**	Yes	▶	GO to B8.
		No	▶	SERVICE IDM short low in harness between EEC processor connector and TFI module connector. REMOVE all test equipment. RECONNECT all components. CLEAR Continuous Memory. RERUN Quick Test.
B8	CHECK FOR IDM OPEN IN HARNESS			
	• Measure resistance between J23 (IDM) and Pin 4 of the EEC processor connector. • **Is resistance less than 5 ohms?**	Yes	▶	REPLACE TFI module. REMOVE all test equipment. RECONNECT all components. CLEAR Continuous Memory. RERUN Quick Test.
		No	▶	SERVICE IDM open in harness between TFI module and EEC processor connector. REMOVE all test equipment. RECONNECT all components. CLEAR Continuous Memory. RERUN Quick Test.

Fig. 12 Test B: IDM Missing Code 18C Or 212C (Part 3 of 3)

TEST STEP		RESULT	▶	ACTION TO TAKE
C1	CHECK BASE TIMING			
	CAUTION: Do not use a remote starter while doing timing check.	Yes	▶	GO to C2.
		No	▶	REFER to Initial Timing Set Procedure.
	• Key off. • Install timing light. • Remove SPOUT in line connector. • Run engine at normal operating condition. • **Is base timing within ± 3 degrees of specified base timing?**			
C2	CHECK FOR SPARK ADVANCE			
	• Key off. • Reconnect SPOUT in line connector. • Idle engine at normal operating condition. • **Is timing greater than 18 degrees, does spark advance?**	Yes	▶	Not an ignition problem.
		No	▶	GO to C3.
C3	CHECK FOR GOOD SPOUT TO TFI MODULE			
	• Connect TFI diagnostic harness to EEC breakout box, connect BAT— lead to negative post of battery, and connect TFI module and vehicle harness. • Turn switch on diagnostic cable to SPOUT OPEN. • Use TFI overlay on breakout box. • DVOM on 20 volt AC scale. • Run engine and measure voltage between J10 (SPOUT) and J7 (BAT—). • **Is voltage between 3.0 and 8.5 volts AC?**	Yes	▶	REPLACE TFI module. REMOVE all test equipment. RECONNECT all components. CLEAR Continuous Memory. RERUN Quick Test.
		No	▶	GO to C4.

Fig. 13 Test C: Timing Off, Code 18R Or 213–SPOUT Open Poor Fuel Economy Poor Driveability (Part 1 of 2). 1993-94

TEST STEP		RESULT	▶	ACTION TO TAKE
C4	CHECK FOR SPOUT OPEN IN HARNESS			
	• Key off. • Disconnect EEC processor. • Disconnect diagnostic harness TFI module TEE from TFI module only; leave TFI module TEE connected to vehicle harness. • DVOM on 200 ohm scale. • Measure resistance between Pin 36 (SPOUT) of the EEC vehicle harness connector and J10 (SPOUT) at the breakout box. • **Is resistance less than 5 ohms?**	Yes	▶	REPLACE EEC processor. REMOVE all test equipment. RECONNECT all components. CLEAR Continuous Memory. RERUN Quick Test.
		No		SERVICE SPOUT open in harness between EEC processor and TFI module. REMOVE all test equipment. RECONNECT all components. CLEAR Continuous Memory. RERUN Quick Test.

Fig. 13 Test C: Timing Off, Code 18R Or 213–SPOUT Open Poor Fuel Economy Poor Driveability (Part 2 of 2). 1993–94

TEST STEP		RESULT	▶	ACTION TO TAKE
C1	CHECK BASE TIMING			
	CAUTION: Do not use a remote starter while doing timing check.	Yes	▶	GO to C2.
		No	▶	REFER to Initial Timing Set Procedure.
	• Key off. • Install timing light. • Remove SPOUT in line connector. • Run engine at normal operating condition. • **Is base timing within ±3 degrees of specified base timing?**			
C2	CHECK FOR SPARK ADVANCE			
	• Key off. • Reconnect SPOUT in line connector. • Idle engine at normal operating condition. • **Is timing greater than 18 degrees, does spark advance?**	Yes	▶	Not an ignition problem, REFER to Section 2A, Diagnostic Routines.
		No	▶	GO to C3.
C3	CHECK FOR GOOD SPOUT TO ICM			
	• Connect DI diagnostic harness to EEC breakout box, connect B- lead to negative post of battery, and connect ICM and vehicle harness. • Turn switch on diagnostic cable to SPOUT OPEN. • Use DI overlay on breakout box. • DVOM on 40 volt AC scale. • Run engine and measure voltage between J10 (SPOUT) and J7 (B-). • **Is voltage between 3.0 and 8.5 volts AC?**	Yes	▶	REPLACE ICM. REMOVE all test equipment. RECONNECT all components. CLEAR Continuous Memory. RERUN Quick Test.
		No	▶	GO to C4.
C4	CHECK FOR SPOUT OPEN IN HARNESS			
	• Key off. • Disconnect PCM. • Disconnect diagnostic harness ICM tee from ICM only; leave ICM tee connected to vehicle harness. • DVOM on 200 ohm scale. • Measure resistance between Pin 36 (SPOUT) of the EEC vehicle harness connector and J10 (SPOUT) at the breakout box. • **Is resistance less than 5.0 ohms?**	Yes	▶	REPLACE PCM. REMOVE all test equipment. RECONNECT all components. CLEAR Continuous Memory. RERUN Quick Test.
		No	▶	SERVICE SPOUT open in harness between PCM and ICM. REMOVE all test equipment. RECONNECT all components. CLEAR Continuous Memory. RERUN Quick Test.

Fig. 14 Test C: Timing Off, Code 18R Or 213–SPOUT Open Poor Fuel Economy Poor Driveability. 1995

FM1119500223000X

TEST STEP		RESULT	▶	ACTION TO TAKE
D1	FIND SYMPTOMS			
	• Talk to customer.		▶	Symptoms
D2	REVIEW VEHICLE HISTORY			
	• Review vehicle service history.		▶	Number of previous repairs and components replaced.
D3	TEST EQUIPMENT			
	• Is a Rotunda TFI/EEC-IV Intermittent Ignition Analyzer 007-00035 or equivalent available?	Yes	▶	FOLLOW test procedure instructions supplied with tester.
	NOTE: The TFI-IV Intermittent analyzer can not be used with TFI-IV modules with Computer Controlled Dwell (CCD) unless a CCD update is added to the analyzer.	No	▶	GO to D4.
D4	BEGIN DIAGNOSIS			
	• Will engine start?	Yes	▶	GO to D5.
		No	▶	GO to the appropriate TFI-IV ignition system diagnostics no start section.
D5	COLD WIGGLE TEST			
	• Engine at idle, raise hood, shake wiring harness and pull wires at connectors for ignition components.	Yes	▶	SERVICE wiring harness or connector.
	• Does engine quit?	No	▶	GO to D6.
D6	ENGINE WARM-UP			
	• Engine at idle, close hood, A/C On, blower on medium speed; allow engine to run for 15 minutes.	Yes	▶	GO to D10.
	• Does engine quit?	No	▶	GO to D7.
D7	HOT RESTART TEST			
	• Engine off, hood closed, hot soak for 10 minutes.	Yes	▶	GO to D8.
	• Will engine restart?	No	▶	GO to the appropriate TFI-IV ignition system diagnostics no start section.
D8	HOT WIGGLE TEST			
	• Engine at idle, raise hood, shake wiring harness and pull wires at connectors for ignition components.	Yes	▶	SERVICE wiring harness or connector.
	• Does engine quit?	No	▶	GO to D9.

Fig. 15   Test D: Intermittent Diagnosis (Part 1 of 2)

NOTE: To provide accurate results, it is essential that the calibration of your engine analyzer be maintained. Refer to your equipment manual. If this is not available, an estimate of the calibration can be made by connecting the spark tester (D81P-6666-A or equivalent) to a properly operating ignition system and measuring the firing voltage of the spark tester only. Do not include the firing voltage of the rotor-to-cap gap. The spark tester firing voltage should be approximately 28 KV.

TEST STEP	RESULT	▶	ACTION TO TAKE
1			
• Connect engine analyzer to view **parade** display of ignition system secondary.			
• While **slowly** increasing engine rpm from idle to 2,000 rpm, compare engine analyzer display to the following illustrations. The illustrations shown are four cylinder but are typical for all engines.			
• Disconnect engine analyzer.			
2	The average value of spark plug firing voltage: 15 KV or less with evenness of spark plug firing voltage: 5 KV or less	▶	These are normal values for a properly operating ignition system.

Fig. 17   Test 2: Secondary Display (Part 1 of 4)

TEST STEP		RESULT	▶	ACTION TO TAKE
D9	ROAD TEST			
	• Road test.	Yes	▶	GO to D10.
	• Does engine quit?	No	▶	Test complete (Problem not duplicated).
D10	FINAL TEST			
	• Raise hood, shake wiring harness, pull wires at connectors, separate and reconnect connectors for ignition components.	Yes	▶	SERVICE wiring harness or connector.
	• Does engine start?	No	▶	GO to the appropriate TFI-IV ignition system diagnostics no start section.

Fig. 15   Test D: Intermittent Diagnosis (Part 2 of 2)

	TEST STEP	RESULT	▶	ACTION TO TAKE
1				
	• Will engine start and run?	Yes	▶	Test Result OK. GO to Test 2.
		No	▶	INSPECT ignition coil for damage or carbon tracking. MEASURE resistance of ignition coil wire. REPLACE if greater than 7,000 ohms per foot. GO to Symptom Index.

Fig. 16   Test 1: Ignition Coil Secondary Voltage

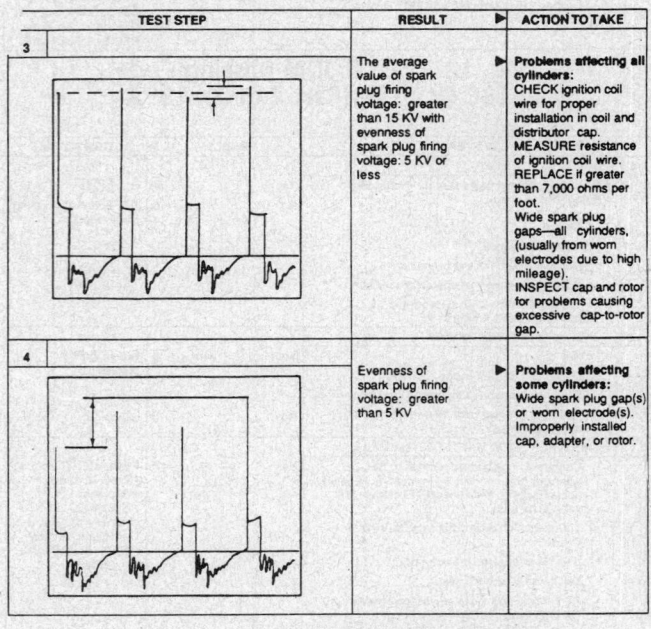

	TEST STEP	RESULT	▶	ACTION TO TAKE
3		The average value of spark plug firing voltage: greater than 15 KV with evenness of spark plug firing voltage: 5 KV or less	▶	**Problems affecting all cylinders:** CHECK ignition coil wire for proper installation in coil and distributor cap. MEASURE resistance of ignition coil wire. REPLACE if greater than 7,000 ohms per foot. Wide spark plug gaps—all cylinders, (usually from worn electrodes due to high mileage). INSPECT cap and rotor for problems causing excessive cap-to-rotor gap.
4		Evenness of spark plug firing voltage: greater than 5 KV	▶	**Problems affecting some cylinders:** Wide spark plug gap(s) or worn electrode(s). Improperly installed cap, adapter, or rotor.

Fig. 17   Test 2: Secondary Display (Part 2 of 4)

b. Rotunda Engine Analyzer tool No. 002-00373.
c. Rotunda Volt/Ohm Meter tool No. 014-00407 or 007-00001.

Testing

Refer to **Figs. 16 through 18** for diagnosis and testing of secondary ignition systems.

SYSTEM SERVICE
Component Replacement
DISTRIBUTOR ASSEMBLY
1.8L ENGINE
Removal

1. Disconnect battery ground cable, then

Testing

Refer to **Fig. 15** to aid in diagnosing intermittent problems.

SECONDARY CIRCUIT TESTS

Preliminary Check & Equipment

1. Visually inspect engine compartment and ensure all vacuum hoses and spark plug wires are properly routed and securely connected.
2. Inspect all wiring harnesses and connectors for damaged insulation and burned, overheated, loose or broken conditions.
3. Ensure battery is fully charged and all accessories are off during testing.
4. Spark plug with broken side electrode is not sufficient to check for spark.
5. Obtain the following test equipment or a suitable equivalent:
   a. Spark Tester tool No. D81P-6666-A.

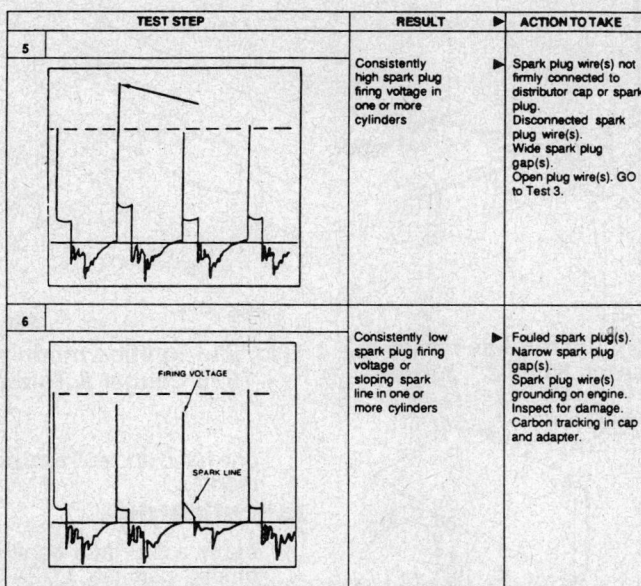

TEST STEP		RESULT	►	ACTION TO TAKE
5		Consistently high spark plug firing voltage in one or more cylinders	►	Spark plug wire(s) not firmly connected to distributor cap or spark plug. Disconnected spark plug wire(s). Wide spark plug gap(s). Open plug wire(s). GO to Test 3.
6		Consistently low spark plug firing voltage or sloping spark line in one or more cylinders	►	Fouled spark plug(s). Narrow spark plug gap(s). Spark plug wire(s) grounding on engine. Inspect for damage. Carbon tracking in cap and adapter.

Fig. 17 Test 2: Secondary Display (Part 3 of 4)

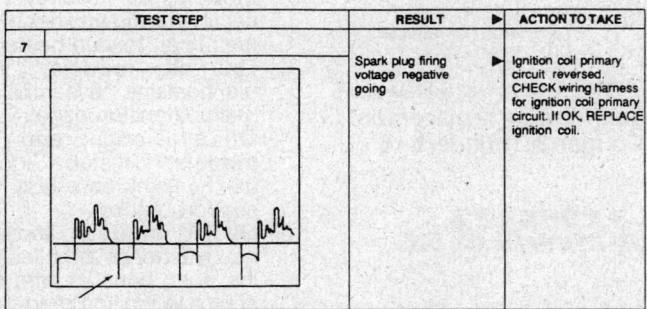

TEST STEP		RESULT	►	ACTION TO TAKE
7		Spark plug firing voltage negative going	►	Ignition coil primary circuit reversed. CHECK wiring harness for ignition coil primary circuit. If OK, REPLACE ignition coil.

Fig. 17 Test 2: Secondary Display (Part 4 of 4)

TEST STEP	RESULT	►	ACTION TO TAKE
1 • Remove distributor cap from distributor. • Check for spark plug wires firmly seated on cap. • Disconnect spark plug end of suspect wire(s). • Measure resistance from terminal in cap to spark plug terminal. • Reinstall distributor cap and connect spark plug wire to spark plug. CAUTION: Do not, under any circumstances, puncture a spark plug wire when measuring resistance. Measure only as instructed. • Was resistance less than 7,000 ohms per foot?	Yes No	► ►	Spark plug wire resistance OK. REPLACE spark plug wire(s).

Fig. 18 Test 3: Spark Plug Wire Resistance

the ignition wire to distributor high tension wiring.

2. Disconnect electrical connector from distributor, then mark position of No. 1 cylinder on distributor base for reference when installing.
3. Remove distributor cap screws, then the cap and position cap aside with wires still attached.
4. Remove distributor hold-down bolts, then the distributor.
5. Replace distributor base gasket, if necessary.

Installation

1. Install distributor in cylinder head, seating offset tang of drive coupling into groove on end of camshaft. **Distributor can only be installed in one direction. Be careful not to force it into position.**
2. Install hold-down bolts. **Torque** hold-down bolts to 14-19 ft. lbs.
3. Connect electrical connector to distributor, then install cap and cap screws. **Torque** cap screws to 14-26 inch lbs.
4. Check ignition timing and adjust if necessary.

2.3L HSC, 2.3L OHC, 3.0L, 3.8L, 5.0L & 5.0L HO ENGINES
Removal

1. Disconnect distributor wiring harness connector, then mark position of No. 1 wire tower on distributor base for future reference.
2. Loosen distributor cap hold-down screws and lift cap straight off distributor to prevent damage to rotor blade and spring. Position cap aside with wires attached.
3. Remove rotor, then the distributor hold-down bolt, clamp and distributor assembly.

Installation

1. Align No. 1 piston at TDC of compression stroke.
2. Align locating boss on rotor with hole on armature, then fully seat rotor on distributor shaft.
3. Rotate distributor shaft so blade on rotor is pointing toward mark on distributor base.
4. While installing distributor assembly, rotate rotor slightly so leading edge of vane is centered in vane switch stator assembly.
5. Rotate distributor in block to align leading edge and vane switch stator assembly. Verify rotor is pointing at No. 1 mark on distributor base.
6. If vane and vane switch stator cannot be aligned by rotating distributor in block, pull distributor out of block enough to disengage distributor gear and rotate shaft to engage different gear tooth. Repeat steps 2 through 5 as necessary to achieve correct alignment.
7. Install hold-down bolt and clamp, do not tighten at this time.
8. Install distributor cap and **torque** hold-down screws to 18-23 inch lbs., then connect distributor wiring harness.

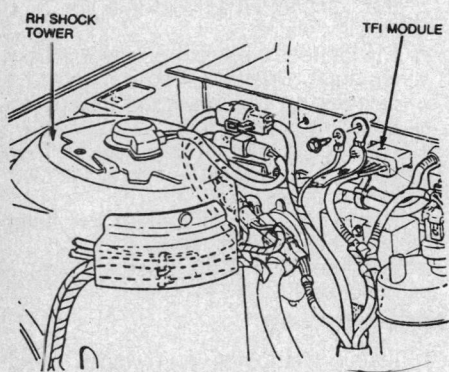

Fig. 19 Ignition module location.
Continental, Sable & Taurus

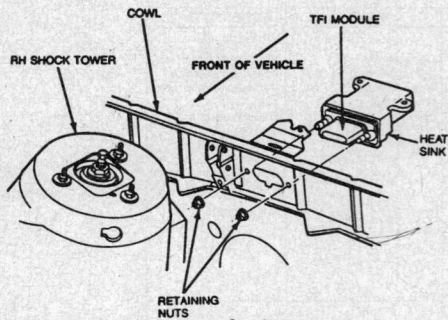

Fig. 20 Ignition module removal.
Continental, Sable & Taurus

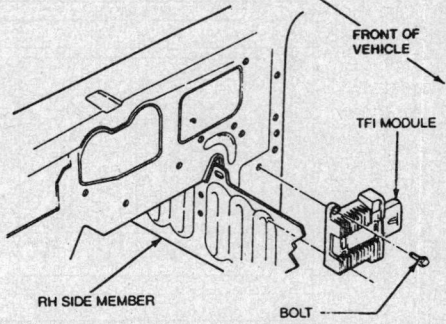

Fig. 21 Ignition module removal.
1993 Cougar & Thunderbird

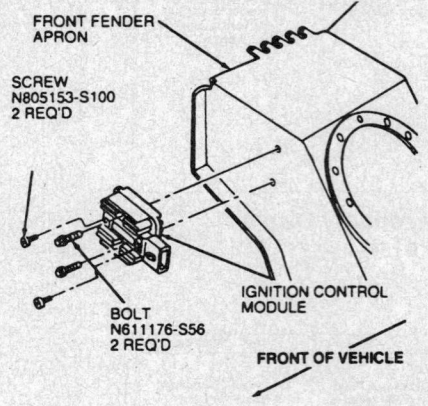

FM1119400231000X

Fig. 22 Ignition module replacement.
1994–95 Cougar & Thunderbird

9. Check ignition timing and adjust if necessary, then **torque** distributor hold-down bolts to 17-25 ft. lbs. on 2.3L HSC and HSC Plus and 5.0L and 5.0L HO engines, 14-21 ft. lbs. on 2.3L OHC and 3.0L engines and 20-29 ft. lbs. on 3.8L engine.

IGNITION MODULE

1.8L ENGINE

1. Disconnect battery ground cable, then the ICM electrical connector.
2. Remove ICM nuts and screws, then the ICM.
3. Reverse procedure to install.

2.3L HSC, 2.3L OHC, 3.0L, & 1993 5.0L & 5.0L HO ENGINES EXCEPT COUGAR & THUNDERBIRD

Removal

1. Remove distributor as previously described.
2. Remove module screws.
3. Pull righthand side of module down distributor mounting flange, then back-up to disengage terminals from connector in distributor base.
4. Pull toward flange and away from distributor to remove. Do not attempt to lift from mounting surface before moving entire ignition module toward distributor flange, as connector pins will be damaged.

Installation

1. Apply a ¹⁄₃₂ inch coating of silicone grease part No. D7ZA-19A331-A or equivalent to metal base of module.
2. Position module on distributor mounting flange.
3. Carefully position module toward distributor bowl and securely engage three distributor connector pins.
4. Install module screws. **Torque** module screws to 15-35 inch lbs.
5. Install distributor as previously described.

1993 3.8L & COUGAR & THUNDERBIRD w/5.0L HO ENGINE

Removal

1. **On Continental, Sable and Taurus models,** use Phillips tip screwdriver to remove screws attaching leaf screen to top of cowl assembly.
2. Separate engine compartment/cowl seal strip from leaf screen and cowl dash extension panel in area of ignition module assembly, **Fig. 19,** then remove leaf screen to allow access to ignition module assembly.
3. Disconnect harness connector from module assembly. Connector latch is underneath ignition module shroud and must be pressed upward to unlatch.
4. Remove module/heatsink assembly to cowl dash extension panel nut/washer assemblies, **Fig. 20.**
5. Remove module/heatsink assembly. Assembly is mounted with heatsink fins pointing downward.
6. **On all Cougar and Thunderbird models,** remove module/heatsink assembly to radiator support bracket screws, **Fig. 21,** then disconnect harness connector from ignition module.
7. **On all models,** remove ignition module screws, then the ignition module from heatsink.
8. **On Continental, Sable and Taurus models,** hold module connector in

one hand and pull seal off other end of module.

Installation

1. Apply a ¹⁄₃₂ inch coating of silicone grease part No. D7ZA-19A331-A or equivalent to metal base of module.
2. Place module onto heatsink, then install screws. **Torque** module to heatsink screws to 15-35 inch lbs.
3. **On Continental, Sable and Taurus models,** push seal over module connector shroud and heatsink studs with metal part toward heatsink.
4. **On all models,** install module/heatsink assembly onto cowl dash extension panel.
5. **On all Cougar and Thunderbird models,** install ignition module/heatsink assembly onto radiator support bracket.
6. **On all models, torque** mounting nut/washer assemblies to 44-70 inch lbs., then connect wire harness connector to ignition module assembly.
7. **On Continental, Sable and Taurus models,** install leaf screen, then the engine compartment/cowl panel and seal strip.

1994–95 3.8L, 5.0L & 5.0L HO ENGINES

1. Disconnect ICM at wiring harness connectors.
2. Remove ICM bolts and heatsink from front fender apron.
3. Remove ICM to heatsink screws, **Figs. 22 and 23,** then the heatsink.
4. Reverse procedure to install, noting the following:
   a. Coat ICM metal base plate evenly with suitable silicone dielectric compound.
   b. **On 1994 Cougar and Thunderbird models, torque** ICM to heatsink screws to 15-35 inch lbs., then the ICM bolts to 44-70 inch lbs.
   c. **On 1995 Cougar and Thunderbird models, torque** ICM to heatsink screws to 11-16 inch lbs., then the ICM bolts to 35-40 inch lbs.
   d. **On 1994-95 Mustang models, torque** ICM to heatsink screws to 15-35 inch lbs., then the ICM bolts to 90-120 inch lbs.

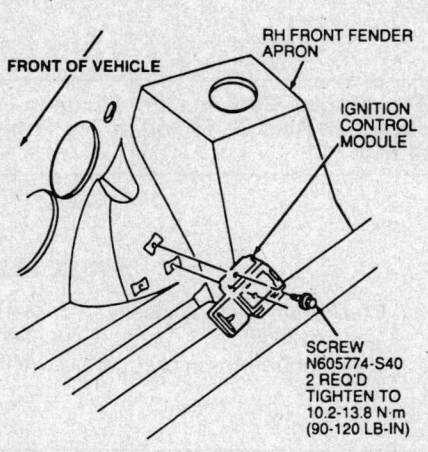

Fig. 23 Ignition module replacement. 1994–95 Mustang

OCTANE ROD

1. Remove distributor cap and rotor.
2. Remove octane rod screw from octane adjustment boss.
3. Slide octane rod and grommet out and disengage from stator retaining post, **Fig. 24.**
4. Reverse procedure to install. **Torque** octane rod screw to 15–35 inch lbs.

STATOR

2.3L HSC, 2.3L OHC, 3.0L, 3.8L, 5.0L & 5.0L HO ENGINES

Removal

Do not attempt to replace stator without an arbor press.

1. Remove distributor from engine as previously described.
2. Remove ignition module assembly as previously described. Wipe grease from base and module, keeping surfaces free of dirt.
3. Mark armature and gear with a felt tip pen, to note location for reassembly.
4. Remove armature screws, then the armature. Hold gear to loosen armature screws. Do not hold armature. Discard pin in gear.

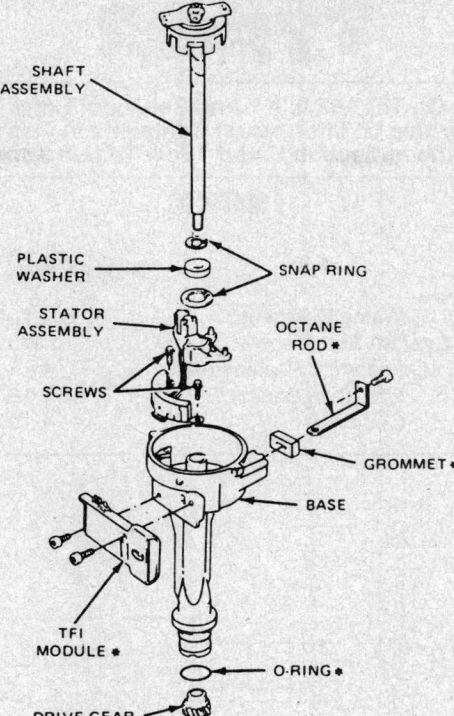

Fig. 24 Exploded view of universal distributor (Systems A & E)

5. Invert distributor and install in axle bearing/seal plate tool No. T75L-1165-B, or equivalent, and press off gear using bearing remover tool No. D84L-950-A, or equivalent, **Fig. 25.**
6. Deburr and polish shaft with emery paper and wipe clean so shaft slides out freely from distributor base.
7. Remove shaft assembly, then the stator assembly screws and stator assembly from top of bowl.
8. Inspect bushing for wear or signs of excess heat concentration, base O-ring for tears or cuts and base for cracks and wear. Replace complete distributor assembly if any of aforementioned are discovered.

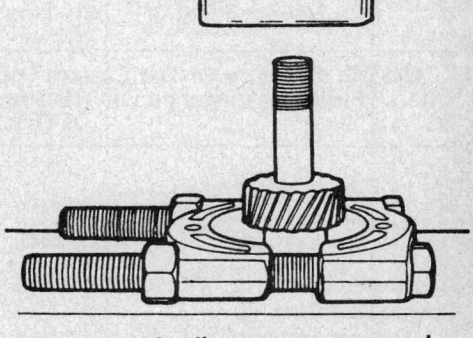

Fig. 25 Distributor gear removal

Installation

1. Install stator over bushing and press down to seat.
2. Install stator connector in position. Tab should fit in notch on base and fastening eyelets should be aligned with their screw holes. Position wires away from moving parts.
3. Install stator screws. **Torque** to 15–35 inch lbs.
4. Apply light coat of motor oil to distributor shaft below armature. Do not over lubricate.
5. Install shaft assembly through base bushing, then place a 1/2 inch deep well socket over shaft. Invert and place on arbor plate.
6. Place distributor gear on shaft end and line up mark on armature and gear. Hole in shaft and gear must be lined up as close as possible to ensure ease of roll pin installation.
7. Place a 5/8 inch deep well socket over shaft and gear and press gear to align with drill hole. If gear holes do not align, gear must be removed and pressed on again.
8. Install new roll pin through gear and shaft.
9. Install armature and **torque** screws to 25–35 inch lbs. Check distributor for free movement over full rotation of shaft. If armature contacts stator, distributor assembly must be replaced.
10. Install ignition module as previously described.
11. Install distributor as previously described.

Type 2

NOTE: If Unsure Of The System Used On The Vehicle Being Serviced, Refer To The "Engine Systems Identification Chart." Further Assistance For The Proper Use Of Information Contained In This Section Can Also Be Found In The Front Of This Tabbed Section Under "How To Use This Manual."

INDEX

	Page No.		Page No.		Page No.
Description	4-15	Wiring Diagrams	4-15	Crankshaft Timing Sensor	4-15
Diagnosis & Testing:	4-15	System Service:	4-15	Ignition Module	4-17
Component Location	4-15	Component Replacement	4-15	Synchronizer Assembly	4-16
Quick Test	4-15	Camshaft Sensor	4-16		
Testing	4-15	Coil Pack	4-19		

DESCRIPTION

The Electronic Ignition (EI) (Distributorless Ignition System (DIS)) (EI, Low Data Rate), **Figs. 1 and 2,** eliminates the use of a distributor by using multiple coils. Each coil fires two spark plugs at the same time. The plugs are paired so one fires on the compression stroke, while the other fires on the exhaust stroke. Timing is controlled by signal inputs to the Powertrain Control Module (PCM) (Electronic Engine Control IV (EEC-IV) processor) from a Crankshaft Position (CKP) sensor (Crankshaft Sensor (CS)), which then sends a signal to the Ignition Control Module (ICM) (DIS module) indicating when to fire the spark plugs and for what length of time.

DIAGNOSIS & TESTING
COMPONENT LOCATION

Refer to **Figs. 3 through 5,** for system component locations.

WIRING DIAGRAMS

Refer To **Figs. 6 through 8,** for ignition system wiring diagrams.

TESTING

When performing secondary circuit tests, check the following prior to testing:
1. Visually inspect engine compartment and ensure all vacuum hoses and spark plug wires are properly routed and securely connected.
2. Inspect all wiring harnesses and connectors for damaged insulation and burned, overheated, loose or broken conditions.
3. Ensure battery is fully charged and all accessories are off during testing.
4. Obtain the following test equipment or suitable equivalents:
   a. Rotunda EI (Low Data Rate) Diagnostic Harness (DIS Adapter) tool No. 007-00044.
   b. Rotunda Engine Analyzer tool No. 002-00373.
   Refer to **Figs. 9 through 15** for 2.3L Dual Plug engine and **Figs. 16 through 28** for 3.0L & 3.2L SHO and 3.8L SC engines.

QUICK TEST

Refer to "Computerized Engine Controls section for Quick Test.

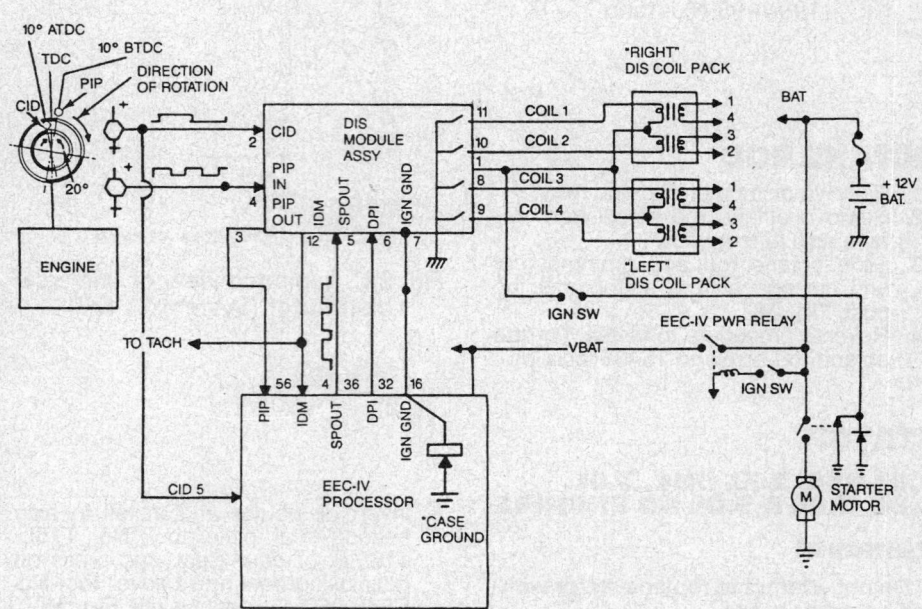

*IGN GND CIRCUIT USED IN SOME EEC PROCESSORS

Fig. 1 Ignition system. 2.3L dual plug engine

SYSTEM SERVICE
Component Replacement
CRANKSHAFT TIMING SENSOR
2.3L Dual Plug Engine

1. Disconnect battery ground cable, then the crankshaft timing sensor electrical connector.
2. Remove large electrical connector end from crankshaft timing sensor assembly by prying out red retaining clip and removing four wires. **Note location of wires for reassembly.**
3. Remove outer timing belt cover as follows:

   a. Remove water pump pulley and rotate tensioner(s) away from accessory drive belt(s), then remove drive belt(s) and tensioner(s).
   b. Drain cooling system, then remove upper radiator hose, crankshaft pulley bolt and pulley.
   c. Remove thermostat housing and gasket and outer timing belt cover bolt, then release cover interlocking tabs and remove cover.
4. Rotate crankshaft so keyway is at 10 o'clock position. This will place vane window of both inner and outer vane cups over crankshaft timing sensor assembly.
5. Remove two sensor assembly bolts and plastic wire retainer, then the crankshaft timing sensor assembly, sliding electrical wires out from be-

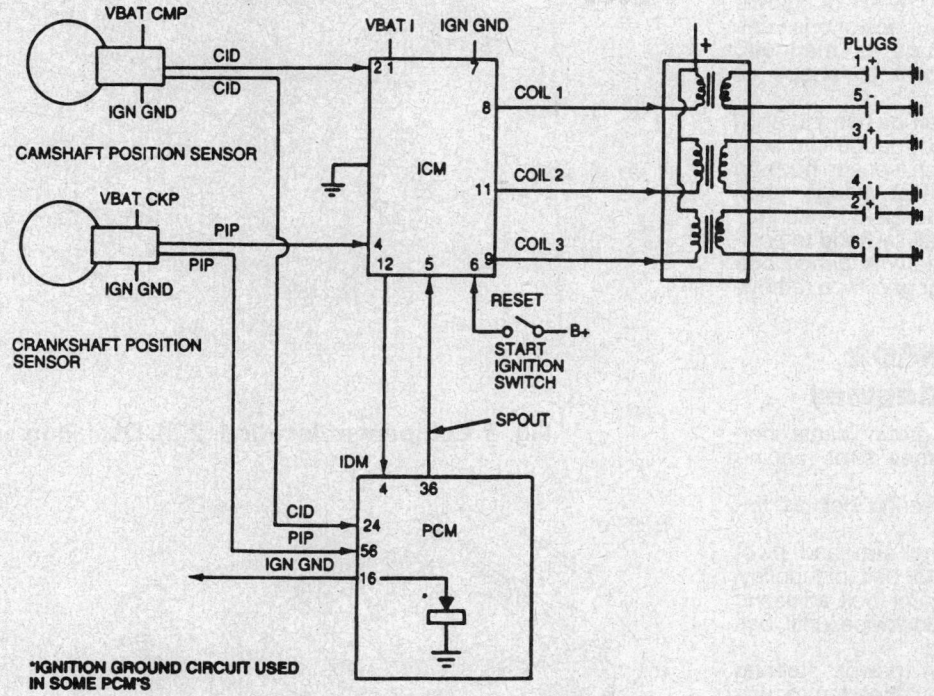

Fig. 2   Ignition system. 1993–95 3.0L & 3.2L SHO & 1993 3.8L SC engines

hind inner timing belt cover.
6. Reverse procedure to install, **Fig. 29,** noting the following:
   a. If installing new sensor, remove large electrical connector end from crankshaft timing sensor assembly as described previously.
   b. Route electrical wires behind inner timing belt cover, then position crankshaft timing sensor assembly and loosely install bolts. Do not tighten at this time.
   c. Install large electrical connector end, ensuring wires are installed in their proper locations, then connect electrical connector to engine harness.
   d. Install crankshaft hall effect sensor positioner tool No. T89P-6316-A, or equivalent, **Fig. 29,** then rotate crankshaft so outer vane on crankshaft pulley hub engages both sides of positioner tool. **Torque** crankshaft timing sensor bolts to 22-31 inch lbs.
   e. Rotate crankshaft so vane on crankshaft pulley hub no longer engages positioning tool, then remove tool.
   f. **Torque** crankshaft pulley assembly bolts to 114-151 ft. lbs.

3.0L & 3.2L SHO Engines

1. Disconnect battery ground cable.
2. Loosen tensioner pulleys for A/C compressor and power steering pump belts, then remove belts from crankshaft pulley.
3. Disconnect DIS module electrical connector, then remove intake manifold crossover tube.
4. Remove upper timing belt cover, then disconnect crankshaft timing sensor electrical harness at connector and route through belt cover.
5. Raise and support vehicle, then remove righthand front wheel and tire assembly.
6. Remove crankshaft pulley using universal puller tool No. T67L-3600-A, or equivalent.
7. Remove center and lower timing belt covers, then rotate crankshaft by hand to position metal vane of shutter outside of sensor air gap.
8. Remove crankshaft timing sensor screws, then the sensor.
9. Reverse procedure to install, noting the following:
   a. Route sensor electrical harness through belt cover, then install sen-

sor assembly on mounting pad and loosely install screws. Do not tighten screws at this time.
   b. Set clearance between crankshaft sensor and one vane on crankshaft timing pulley using .03 inch feeler gauge. **Torque** screws to 22-31 inch lbs.
   c. **Torque** crankshaft pulley to 112-127 ft. lbs.
   d. **Torque** intake manifold crossover tube nuts to 11-66 ft. lbs.
   e. **Torque** wheel lug nuts to 85-104 ft. lbs.

3.8L SC Engine

1. Disconnect battery ground cable, then the crankshaft timing sensor electrical connectors from engine wiring harness.
2. Raise and support vehicle, then remove upper and lower damper shield assemblies.
3. Rotate crankshaft by hand to position metal vane of shutter attached to rear of damper outside of sensor air gap.
4. Remove crankshaft timing sensor screw, then the sensor.

5. Reverse procedure to install, noting the following:
   a. Install sensor assembly on mounting pad and loosely install screws. Do not tighten screws at this time.
   b. Install crankshaft sensor gauge tool No. T89P-6316-AH, or equivalent, to outside surface of one vane of shutter. **Gauge is magnetic and will conform to shape of vane.**
   c. Rotate crankshaft by hand to align shutter vane with gauge into sensor air gap, push sensor housing inward to contact gauge, then **torque** screws to 22-31 inch lbs.
   d. Rotate crankshaft by hand to position shutter vane with gauge outside of sensor air gap, then remove gauge.

CAMSHAFT SENSOR

3.0L & 3.2L SHO Engines

1. Disconnect battery ground cable, then remove engine torque strut (engine support damper).
2. Remove power steering belt as follows:
   a. Loosen adjusting arm and pivot bolts for alternator belt idler pulley, then turn alternator belt adjusting screw counterclockwise until belt can be removed.
   b. Loosen nut on power steering pump idler pulley, then turn power steering pump belt adjusting screw counterclockwise until belt can be removed.
3. Remove power steering pump pulley as follows:
   a. Remove radiator overflow bottle to gain access to pump pulley to hub bolts.
   b. Mark pulley to hub positions with grease pencil or paint for reassembly to maintain balance.
   c. Remove bolts, then the pulleys from hub.
4. Disconnect camshaft sensor electrical connector, then remove sensor bolts and sensor.
5. Reverse procedure to install, noting the following:
   a. **Torque** camshaft sensor bolts to 22-31 inch lbs.
   b. **Torque** power steering pump pulley bolts to 16-23 ft. lbs.

3.8L SC Engine

1. Disconnect battery ground cable, then the camshaft sensor electrical connector.
2. Remove camshaft sensor screws, then the camshaft sensor.
3. Reverse procedure to install. **Torque** camshaft sensor screws to 22-31 inch lbs.

SYNCHRONIZER ASSEMBLY

3.8L SC ENGINE

Prior to beginning this procedure, set cylinder No. 1 to 26° After Top Dead Center (ATDC) of compression stroke,

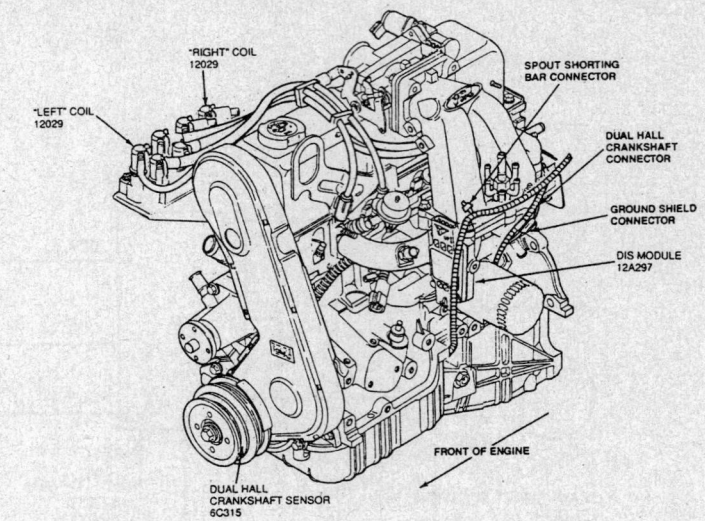

Fig. 3 Component location. 2.3L Dual Plug engine

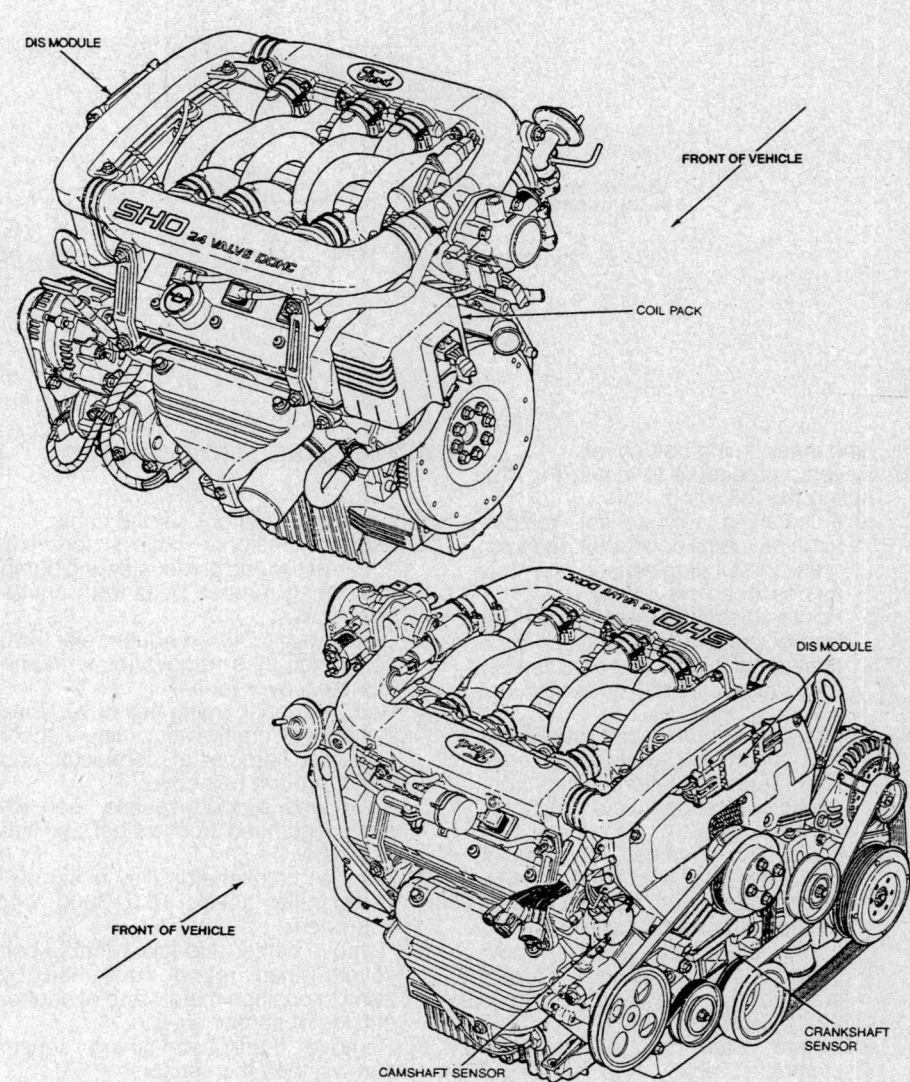

Fig. 4 Component location. 3.0L & 3.2L SHO engines

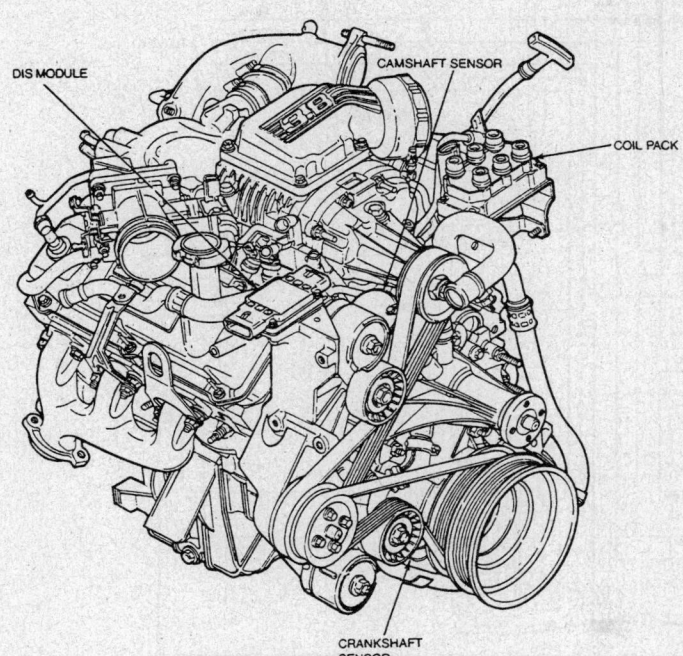

Fig. 5 Component location. 1993 3.8L SC engine

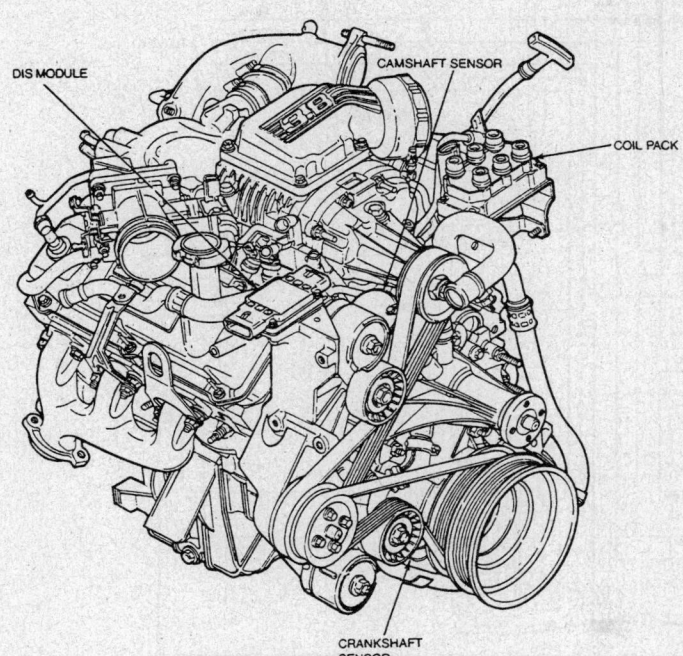

NOTE: CONNECTORS ARE SHOWN LOOKING INTO THE WIRING HARNESS. IGN GND IS A LOW CURRENT REFERENCE FOR THE EEC-IV PROCESSOR AND DIS MODULE. IT IS CONNECTED TO BATTERY NEGATIVE (GROUND) VIA THE DIS MODULE METAL BASE PLATE. PROPER SYSTEM OPERATION DEPENDS ON A LOW RESISTANCE PATH TO GROUND. FIRING ORDER: 1, 3, 4, 2

Fig. 6 Ignition system wiring diagram. 2.3L Dual Plug engine

then note position of camshaft sensor electrical connector. Installation procedure requires connector to be located in same position.

Removal

1. Disconnect battery ground cable, then remove camshaft sensor as described under "Camshaft Sensor, Replace."
2. Remove synchronizer clamp (bolt and washer), **Fig. 30,** then the synchronizer assembly along with intermediate oil pump driveshaft from front engine cover assembly.

Installation

If replacement synchronizer does not contain a plastic locator cover tool, a synchro positioner tool No. T89P-12200-A, or equivalent, must be obtained before installing the replacement synchronizer. Failure to follow this procedure will result in improper synchronizer alignment, causing ignition system and fuel system to be out of time with engine, possibly causing engine damage.

1. If plastic locator cover tool is not attached to synchronizer assembly, attach synchro positioner as follows:
   a. Engage synchronizer vane in radial slot of positioner.
   b. Rotate positioner on synchronizer base until positioner boss engages base notch. **Positioner should be square and in contact with entire top surface of synchronizer base.**
2. Transfer intermediate oil pump driveshaft from old synchronizer to replacement synchronizer, then install synchronizer assembly so gear engagement occurs when arrow on locator tool is pointed approximately 30° counterclockwise from front face of engine block. **This will locate camshaft sensor electrical connector in pre-removal position.**
3. Install synchronizer base clamp and **torque** to 15-22 ft. lbs.
4. Remove locator tool, then install camshaft sensor as previously described.
5. **If camshaft sensor electrical connector is not positioned properly as previously described, do not reposition connector by rotating synchronizer assembly base. This will result in ignition and fuel systems being out of time with engine, possibly causing engine damage. Repeat entire "Installation" procedure, starting with Step 1.**

IGNITION MODULE

Ignition module is located on the lower intake manifold on 2.3L Dual Plug engines, the upper intake manifold on 3.0L & 3.2L SHO engines and on the tensioner bracket assembly on 3.8L SC engine.

1. Disconnect battery ground cable, then the electrical connectors from ignition module.
2. Remove module bolts, then the module.
3. Reverse procedure to install, noting the following:

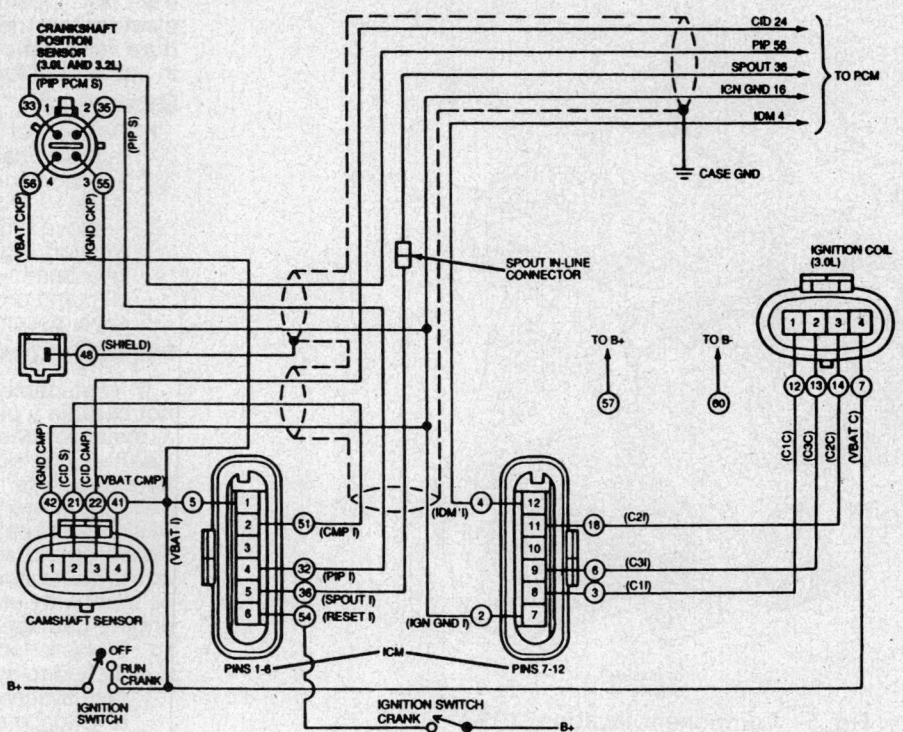

Fig. 7   Ignition system wiring diagram. 3.0L & 3.2L SHO engines

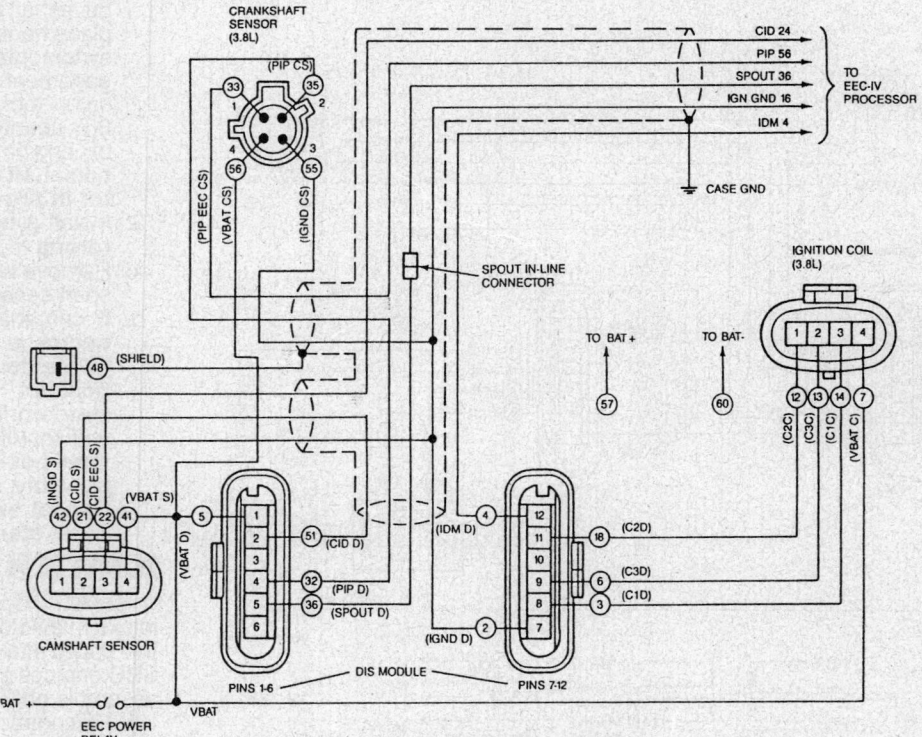

Fig. 8   Ignition system wiring
diagram. 1993 3.8L SC engine

The following voltage readings are typical for a normal vehicle with DIS cable attached. Do not use a "true RMS" type A/C voltmeter such as the Fluke 8060a or 87.

Measure Between Pins		Key On Engine Off (volts)	Key On Engine Cranking (volts)	Key On Engine Running (volts)
First Pin	Second Pin			
RC1C J23	IGNGND D J2	14.5 DC	1.2 AC	1.6 AC
RC2C J24	IGNGND D J2	14.5 DC	1.2 AC	1.6 AC
LC3C J30	IGNGND D J2	14.5 DC	1.2 AC	1.6 AC
LC4C J6	IGNGND D J2	14.5 DC	1.2 AC	1.6 AC
RC1D J18	IGNGND D J2	14.4 DC	1.2 AC	1.6 AC
RC2D J10	IGNGND D J2	14.4 DC	1.2 AC	1.6 AC
LC3D J3	IGNGND D J2	14.4 DC	1.2 AC	1.6 AC
LC4D J6	IGNGND D J2	14.6 DC	1.2 AC	1.6 AC
VBATR J26	IGNGND D J2	14.6 DC	13.0 DC	14.8 DC
VBATL J15	IGNGND D J2	14.6 DC	13.0 DC	14.8 DC
IDMD J4	IGNGND D J2	0.2 DC	4.9 AC	5.2 AC
IGN GND D J2	IGNGND D J2	0.1 DC	0.1 DC	0.1 DC
DPI J54	IGNGND D J2	0.1 DC	0.1 DC	0.1 DC
SPOUTD J36	IGNGND D J2	11.8 DC	0.1 AC	3.0 DC
PIPD J31	IGNGND D J2	11.8/0.2 DC	5.0 AC	6.8 AC
CIDD J51	IGNGND D J2	11.8/0.2 DC	4.0 AC	7.0 AC
VBATD J5	IGNGND D J2	14.7 DC	13.0 DC	14.8 DC
PIPS J33	IGNGND D J2	11.8/0.2 DC	5.0 AC	6.8 AC
CIDS J35	IGNGND D J2	11.8/0.2 DC	4.0 AC	7.0 AC
IGNDS J55	IGNGND D J2	0.2 DC	0.2 DC	0.2 DC
VBATS J56	IGNGND D J2	14.7 DC	13.0 DC	14.8 DC
SHIELD J48	IGNGND D J2	0.1 DC	0.1 DC	0.1 DC

NOTE: The battery voltage was 14.6 volts DC when these readings were taken.

● CID and PIP may be high or low Key On Engine Off (KOEO) depending on whether or not a tooth is in the air gap of the sensor.
● If the SPOUT jumper is removed the PIP signal will be fed through the DIS module and appear on SPOUT at J36 of the DIS module.

Fig. 9 Diagnostics By Service Code & Symptom (Part 2 of 3). 2.3L Dual Plug Engine

These diagnostics (Pinpoint Tests A through G) are written to catch "Hard Faults"; intermittent failures will be difficult or impossible to diagnose unless they are present the entire time these procedures are used.

TEST STEP	ACTION TO TAKE
●No Start and No Diagnostic Trouble Codes.	GO to A1.
●No Start and 211 —PIP circuit fault.	GO to A3.
●No Start with Diagnostic Trouble Code not listed elsewhere in this index.	GO to A1.
●222 and Erratic Start (Engine will start normally at least once out of five attempts). When it fails to start, the cranking rpm is erratic (Ignition is firing out of time) but when it starts it starts normally — CID circuit fault.	GO to B1.
●214 CID open at PCM	GO to B20.
●222 and Normal Start. — IDM low circuit fault or right coil fault.	GO to B12.
●218 — IDM circuit fault high or open or left coil pack open.	GO to C1.
●224 — C1, C2, C3 or C4 circuit fault or 215, 216, 217.	GO to D1.
●223 — DPI circuit fault open or high. SPOUT circuit fault high.	GO to E1.
●213 — SPOUT circuit failure open or low.	GO to F1.

Fig. 9 Diagnostics By Service Code & Symptom (Part 1 of 3). 2.3L Dual Plug Engine

CAUTION

A 12 volt incandescent test lamp should not be used to test CID, IDM, Spout or PIP circuit signals. It will load the circuit and may cause erroneous measurements or improper DIS/EEC-IV operations (i.e. Engine stall). An incandescent test lamp is required to verify proper coil circuit operation in Section D.

Note

● When a DVOM on the DC range, correct Test Lead Polarity must be followed. The red lead is positive (+) and the black lead is negative (-).
● To check PIP or CID, the engine is "bumped" with the starter while watching the voltmeter. Both the CID and PIP signals are digital and should switch between VBAT and ground as the engine turns. To see the signal change using the DVOM, the engine must be turned in very short bursts.
● Refer to the appropriate EVTM for wire colors.

● The 2.3L engine used in the Mustang has a bank-to-bank sequential fuel injection system. The CID signal is connected to the EEC processor as well as the DIS Module to allow the EEC to "fire" one or the other bank at the proper time.
● Both coils are activated during cranking and running except when the temperature is less than -7°C (20°F). Below -7°C (20°F) the engine cranks on the right coil then runs on both coils. However, the Ranger truck engine starts on right coil only and runs on both coils. Three digit service codes are used on some DIS and EDIS engines in 1991.
● The A/C voltage reading from a "true RMS" type DVOM (Fluke 87) may be significantly different taken from a "standard" or averaging DVOM (Rotunda Digital Volt Ohmmeter 007-0001, Fluke 88, 75, etc) leading to incorrect answer of Pinpoint Test Steps.

Fig. 9 Diagnostics By Service Code & Symptom (Part 3 of 3). 2.3L Dual Plug Engine

a. Apply even coat of silicone dielectric compound part No. D7AZ-19A331-A or equivalent, approximately 1/32 inch thick to mounting surface of ignition module before installing.
b. **Torque** ignition module bolts to 22-31 inch lbs.

COIL PACK

2.3L Dual Plug Engine

1. Disconnect battery ground cable, then remove spark plug wires by squeezing locking tabs to release coil boot retainers.

TEST STEP		RESULT	▶	ACTION TO TAKE
A1	PERFORM EEC-IV QUICK TEST			
	● perform EEC-IV Quick Test.	Yes	▶	GO to A2.
	● Are pass codes or no service codes present (KOEO, KOER or Continuous Memory)?	No	▶	SERVICE any EEC-IV codes first. If still no start, GO to A2.
A2	CHECK FOR SPARK DURING CRANK			
	● Using a Neon Bulb Spark Tester (D89P6666-A) or Air Gap Spark Tester (D81P-6666-A), check for spark at each right side spark plug wire while cranking.	Yes	▶	GO to A12.
		No	▶	GO to A3.
	● Was park present on all right side park plug wires and consistent (one spark per crank revolution)?			
A3	DETERMINE MISSING SPARK COMBINATION—SPARK FAULT			
	● Was spark missing from both number 1 and number 4 plug wires but present at other plug wires?	Yes	▶	GO to A5.
	or	No	▶	GO to A4.
	● Was spark missing from both number 2 and number 3 plug wires but present at other plug wires?			
A4	CHECK PLUGS AND WIRES—SPARK FAULT—KEY OFF			
	● Check spark plug wires for insulation damage, looseness, shorting or other damge.	Yes	▶	REINSTALL plugs and wires. GO to A5.
	● Remove and check spark plugs for damage, wear, carbon deposits and proper plug gap.	No		SERVICE or REPLACE damaged or worn spark plugs or plug wires.
	● Are plugs and wires OK?			
A5	CHECK DIS MODULE VBAT—KOEO—SPARK FAULT			
	● Connect DIS diagnostic cable to breakout box.	Yes	▶	GO to A6.
	● Use 2.3L overlay.	No	▶	CHECK connectors, SERVICE or REPLACE harness. VBAT to DIS module open.
	● Connect DIS diagnostic negative lead.			
	● Install 1-6 DIS module Tee.			
	● DVOM on 20 volt DC scale.			
	● Key on.			
	● Measure voltage between (+)J5 (VBAT D) and (-)J60 (BAT-).			
	● Is voltage greater than 10 volts DC?			

Fig. 10 Test A: No Start (Part 1 of 8). 2.3L Dual Plug Engine

2. Disconnect electrical connector from coil pack, then remove coil pack retaining screws and coil pack.
3. Reverse procedure to install. **Torque** coil pack screws to 30-41 ft. lbs.

3.0L & 3.2L SHO & 1993 3.8L SC Engines

1. Disconnect battery ground cable, then remove cover from coil pack.
2. Disconnect electrical connector from coil pack, then remove spark plug wires by squeezing locking tabs to release coil boot retainers.
3. Remove coil pack screws, then the coil pack.
4. Reverse procedure to install. **Torque** coil pack screws to 40-62 inch lbs.

TEST STEP		RESULT	▶	ACTION TO TAKE
A6	CHECK IGN GND AT DIS MODULE—KEY OFF—SPARK FAULT			
	• Key off.	Yes	▶	GO to A7.
	• Install 7-12 DIS mocule Tee.	No	▶	GO to A17. IGN GND D open fault.
	• DVOM on 200 ohm scale.			
	• **Is resistance between J2 (IGND D) and J60 (BAT-) less than 5.0 ohms?**			
	NOTE: If a negative resistance value is obtained, switch leads of DVOM and repeat measurements.			
A7	CHECK FOR C1/C2 HIGH AT DIS MODULE—KOEO			
	• DVOM on 20 volt DC scale.	Yes	▶	GO to A8.
	• Key on.	No	▶	GO to A18. C1/C2 low fault.
	• Measure voltage between (+)J18 (RC1D) and (-)J60 (BAT-).			
	• Measure voltage between (+)J10 (RC2D) and (-)J60 (BAT-).			
	• **Is voltage greater than 10 volts DC in both tests?**			
A8	CHECK PIP AT DIS MODULE—KOEC—SPARK FAULT			
	• DVOM to 20 volt DC scale.	Yes	▶	GO to A9.
	• Connect leads of DVOM between (+)J32 (PIP D) and (-)J60 (BAT-).	No	▶	GO to A21. PIP fault.
	• Bump engine in short bursts with starter without starting engine for at least five engine revolutions and watch for change in DVOM reading.			
	• **Does DVOM reading switch between low (less than 2.0 volts DC) and higher (more than 8.0 volts DC)?**			

Fig. 10   Test A: No Start (Part 2 of 8). 2.3L Dual Plug Engine

TEST STEP		RESULT	▶	ACTION TO TAKE
A9	CHECK DIS MODULE—COIL DISCONNECTED—KOEC—SPARK FAULT			
	• Key off.	Yes	▶	GO to A10.
	• Connect positive lead of diagnostic cable to battery.	No	▶	REPLACE DIS odule. No C1/C2 output.
	• Disconnect vehicle wiring harness from right coil.			
	• Connect incandescent test lamp between each if the two pairs of test points given below. Crank the engine each time. See if lamp blinks continuously during crank.			
	• Check between J18 (RC1D) and J57 (BAT+).			
	• Check between J10 (RC2D) and J57 (BAT+).			
	• **Does test lamp blink each time?**			
A10	CHECK RIGHT COIL PACK VBAT—KOEO—SPARK FAULT			
	• DVOM on 20 volt DC scale.	Yes	▶	GO to A11.
	• Key on.	No	▶	CHECK connector, SERVICE or REPLACE harness. VBAT open.
	• Reconnect coil.			
	• Measure voltage between (+)26 (VBAT R) and (-)J60 (BAT-).			
	• **Is voltage greater than 10 volts DC?**			
A11	CHECK C1/C2 AT RIGHT COIL—KOEO—SPARK FAULT			
	• Connect incandescent test lamp between each of the two pairs of test points given below. Crank engine each time. See if lamp blinks continuously during crank.	Yes	▶	REPLACE right coil pack. No ouput, input OK.
	• Check between J23 (RC1C) and J57 (BAT+).	No	▶	CHECK connectors, SERVICE or REPLACE harness. One or both coil wires may be open. Coil pack may be damaged.
	• Check between J24 (RC2C) and J57 (BAT+).			
	• **Does test lamp blink each time?**			

Fig. 10   Test A: No Start (Part 3 of 8). 2.3L Dual Plug Engine

TEST STEP		RESULT	▶	ACTION TO TAKE
A12	CHECK PIP EEC AT DIS MODULE—KOEC			
	• Connect diagnstic cable to breakout box.	Yes	▶	GO to A13.
	• Use 2.3L overlay.	No	▶	REPLACE DIS module. PIP open in DIS.
	• Install 1-6 DIS module Tee.			
	• DVOM to 20 volt DC scale.			
	• Connect leads of DVOM between (+)J31 (PIP EEC) and (-)J60 (BAT-).			
	• Bump engine in short bursts with starter without starting engine for at least five engine revolutions and watch for change in DVOM reading.			
	• **Does DVOM reading switch between low (less than 2.0 volts DC) and high (more than 8.0 volts DC)?**			
A13	CHECK PIP TO PROCESSOR CONTINUITY—KEY OFF			
	• Key off.	Yes	▶	GO to A14.
	• DVOM on 200 ohm scale.	No	▶	SERVICE harness and connectors. PIP open in harness.
	• Disconnect processor.			
	• Connect second breakout box to EEC vehicle harness connector.			
	• Measure resistance between Pin 56 of second breakout box and J31 (PIP EEC).			
	• **Is resistance less than 5.0 ohms?**			
A14	CHECK IGN GND AT DIS MODULE—GND FAULT			
	• Key off.	Yes	▶	GO to A16.
	• Install 7-12 DIS module tee.	No	▶	GO to A15.
	• Measure resistance between J2 (IGN D D) and J60 (BAT-).			
	• **Is resistance less than 5.0 ohms?**			
A15	CHECK DIS MODULE MOUNTING SCREWS FOR CORROSION OR LOOSENESS.			
	• Check DIS module mounting screws for corrosion or looseness.	Yes	▶	REPLACE DIS module.
	• **Are mounting screws clean and tight?**	No	▶	TIGHTEN, CLEAN or REPLACE mounting screws. CLEAN mounting area on DIS module. Be sure to REPLACE any heat sink grease that is removed.

Fig. 10   Test A: No Start (Part 4 of 8). 2.3L Dual Plug Engine

TEST STEP		RESULT	▶	ACTION TO TAKE
A16	CHECK IGN GND TO PROCESSOR CONTINUITY—KEY OFF			
	• Key off.	Yes	▶	Ignition System OK.
	• Set DVOM to 200 ohm scale.	No	▶	CHECK connectors, SERVICE or REPLACE harness IGN GND open between EEC processor and DIS module.
	• Disconnect processor and install the second EEC breakout box to the EEC vehicle harness connector.			
	• Measure resistance between Pin 16 of second breakout box and J2 (IGND D).			
	• **Is resistance less than 5.0 ohms?**			
A17	CHECK DIS MODULE MOUNTING SCREWS—KEY OFF—GND FAULT			
	• Check DIS module mounting screws for corrosion or looseness.	Yes	▶	REPLACE DIS module. IGN GND open.
	• **Are mounting screws clean and tight?**	No	▶	TIGHTEN, CLEAN or REPLACE mounting screws. CLEAN mounting area on DIS module.
A18	CHECK FOR C1/C2 HIGH AT DIS CONNECTOR—DIS MODULE DISCONNECTED KOEO—C1/C2 LOW FAULT			
	• Key off.	Yes	▶	REPLACE DIS module. C1 or C2 short to GND. Coil pack may be damaged.
	• Set DVOM to 20 volt DC scale.	No	▶	GO to A19. C1/C2 low fault.
	• Disconnect diagnostic cable connector from DIS module (Pins 7-12). Do not disconnect vehicle harness from other side of 7-12 DIS module tee.			
	• Key on.			
	• Measure voltage between (+)J18 (RC1D) and (-) J60 (BAT-).			
	• Measure voltage between (+)J10 (RC2D) and (-) J60 (BAT-).			
	• **Is voltage greater than 10 volts DC in both tests?**			
A19	CHECK RIGHT COIL PACK VBAT—KEY OFF C1/C2 LOW FAULT			
	• Key off.	Yes	▶	GO to A20.
	• DVOM on 20 volt DC scale.	No	▶	CHECK connectors, SERVICE or REPLACE harness. VBAT open.
	• Install DIS cable right coil tee.			
	• Key on.			
	• Measure voltage between (+)J26 (VBAT R) and (-)J60 (BAT-).			
	• **Is voltage greater than 10 volts DC?**			

Fig. 10   Test A: No Start (Part 5 of 8). 2.3L Dual Plug Engine

TEST STEP		RESULT	▶	ACTION TO TAKE
A20	CHECK FOR C1/C2 HIGH AT RIGHT COIL—KOEO C1/C2 LOW FAULT			
	• DVOM on 20 volt DC scale.	Yes	▶	SERVICE connectors and harness. One or both coil wires are open.
	• Key on.			
	• Measure voltage between (+)J23 (RC1C) and (-)J60 (BAT-).	No	▶	REPLACE coil C1/C2 open.
	• Measure voltage between (+)J24 (R2C2) and (-)J60 (BAT-).			
	• **Is voltage greater than 10 volts DC in both tests?**			
A21	CHECK PIP AT DIS MODULE—KOEC DIS MODULE DISCONNECTED—PIP FAILURE			
	• Key off.	Yes	▶	GO to A22.
	• Disconnect diagnostic cable connector from DIS module (Pins 1-6). Do not disconnect vehicle harness from DIS module 1-6 tee.	No	▶	GO to A25. PIP circuit failure.
	• DVOM to 20 volt DC scale.			
	• Connect leads of DVOM between (+)J32 (PIP D) and (-)J60 (BAT-).			
	• Bump enging in short bursts with starter without starting engine for at least five engine revolutions and watch for change in DVOM reading.			
	• **Does DVOM reading switch between low (less than 2.0 volts DC) and high (more than 8.0 volts DC)?**			
A22	CHECK FOR PROCESSOR SHORTING PIP—PROCESSOR DISCONNECT—KOEC—PIP FAULT			
	• Key off.	Yes	▶	REPLACE processor. PIP shorted.
	• Reconnect diagnostic cable connector to DIS module (Pins 1-6).	No	▶	GO to A23.
	• Disconnect EEC-IV processor.			
	• DVOM on 20 volt DC scale.			
	• Connect leads of DVOM between (+)J32 (PIP D) and (-)J60 (BAT-).			
	• Bump engine in short bursts with starter without starting engine for at least five engine revolutions and watch for change in DVOM reading.			
	• **Does DVOM reading switch between low (less than 2.0 volts DC) and high (more than 8.0 volts DC)?**			

Fig. 10 Test A: No Start (Part 6 of 8). 2.3L Dual Plug Engine

TEST STEP		RESULT	▶	ACTION TO TAKE
A23	CHECK PIP EEC FOR SHORT HIGH—DIS MODULE AND PROCESSOR DISCONNECTED—KOEC—PIP FAULT			
	• Key off.	Yes	▶	GO to A24.
	• DVOM on 20 volt DC scale.	No	▶	CHECK connectors, SERVICE or REPLACE harness. PIP EEC is shorted high.
	• Disconnect diagnostic cable connector from DIS module (Pins 1-6).			
	• Key on.			
	• Measure voltage between (+)J31 (PIP EEC) and (-)J60 (BAT-).			
	• **Is voltage less than 0.5 volts?**			
A24	CHECK PIP EEC FOR SHORT LOW—DIS MODULE AND PROCESSOR DISCONNECTED—KOEC—PIP FAULT			
	• Key off.	Yes	▶	REPLACE DIS module. No PIP EEC output.
	• DVOM on 20K ohm scale.	No	▶	CHECK connectors, SERVICE or REPLACE harness. PIP EEC is shorted to ground.
	• Do not reconnect DIS module or EEC processor.			
	• Measure resistance between J31 (PIP EEC) and J60 (BAT-).			
	• **Is resistance more than 10K ohms?**			
A25	CHECK VBAT AT CRANKSHAFT SENSOR—KOEO—PIP FAULT			
	• Key off.	Yes	▶	GO to A26.
	• Reconnect the 1-6 DIS module tee.	No	▶	CHECK connectors, SERVICE or REPLACE harness. VBAT to sensor open.
	• Install crankshaft sensor tee.			
	• DVOM on 20 volt DC scale.			
	• Key on.			
	• Measure the voltage between (+)J56 (VBAT S) and (-)J2 (IGND D).			
	• **Is voltage greater than 10 volts?**			
A26	CHECK IGN GND AT CRANKSHAFT SENSOR—KEY OFF—PIP FAULT			
	• Key off.	Yes	▶	GO to A27.
	• DVOM on 200 ohm scale.	No	▶	CHECK connectors, SERVICE or REPLACE harness. IGN GND to sensor open.
	• **Is resistance between J55 (IGND S) and J60 (BAT-) less than 5.0 ohms?**			

Fig. 10 Test A: No Start (Part 7 of 8). 2.3L Dual Plug Engine

TEST STEP		RESULT	▶	ACTION TO TAKE
A27	CHECK PIP S AT CRANKSHAFT SENSOR—KOEC—PIP FAULT			
	• DVOM on 20 volt DC scale.	Yes	▶	CHECK connectors, SERVICE or REPLACE harness. PIP is open between sensor and DIS module.
	• Connect leads of DVOM between (+)J33 (PIP S) and (-)J60 (BAT-).			
	• Bump engine in short bursts with starter without starting engine for at least five engine revolutions and watch for change in DVOM reading.	No	▶	GO to A28. PIP fault.
	• **Does DVOM reading switch between low (less than 2.0 volts DC) and high (more than 8.0 volts DC)?**			
A28	CHECK PIP CIRCUIT FOR SHORT HIGH—CRANKSHAFT SENSOR AND DIS MODULE DISCONNECTED—KEY ON—PIP FAULT			
	• Key off.	Yes	▶	GO to A29.
	• Disconnect diagnostic cable connector from crankshaft sensor. Do not disconnect vehicle harness from crankshaft sensor tee.	No	▶	CHECK connectors, SERVICE or REPLACE harness. PIP is shorted high between the sensor and DIS module.
	• DVOM on 20 volt DC scale.			
	• Disconnect diagnostic cable connector from DIS module Pins 1-6.			
	• Key on.			
	• Measure voltage between (+)J33 (PIP S) and (-)J60 (BAT-).			
	• **Is voltage less than 0.5 volts?**			
A29	CHECK PIP CIRCUIT FOR SHORT TO GROUND—CRANKSAHFT SENSOR AND DIS MODULE DISCONNECTED KEY OFF—PIP FAULT			
	• Key off.	Yes	▶	GO to A30.
	• DVOM on 20K ohm scale.	No	▶	CHECK connectors, SERVICE or REPLACE harness. PIP is shorted to ground between the sensor and the DIS module.
	• Measure resistance between J33 (PIP S) and J60 (BAT-).			
	• **Is resistance greater than 10K ohms?**			
A30	CHECK CRANKSHAFT VANE—KEY OFF—PIP FAULT			
	• Does crankshaft vane move through sensor air gap when the engine is cranked?	Yes	▶	REPLACE crankshaft sensor. No output.
		No	▶	service vane damage.

Fig. 10 Test A: No Start (Part 8 of 8). 2.3L Dual Plug Engine

TEST STEP		RESULT	▶	ACTION TO TAKE
B1	CHECK FOR SPARK FROM RIGHT COIL—KOER			
	• Using a Neon Spark Tester Special Service Tool (D89P-6666-A), check for spark at each of the right side spark plug wires while cranking engine, or if engine will start, engine running.	Yes	▶	GO to B2.
		No	▶	GO to D1. Right coil pack failure.
	• **Is spark consistent on one or more plug wires (one spark per crank revolution)?**			
B2	VERIFY ERRATIC START—KOEC			
	• Attempt to start vehicle five times.	Yes	▶	GO to B3.
	NOTE: Engine will start normally at least once out of five attempts. When it fails to start, cranking rpm is erratic (ignition is firing out of time—CID circuit fault).	No	▶	GO to B12. IDM low fault or DPI high fault.
	• **Does engine fail to start at least once?**			
B3	CID FAULT—CHECK CID AT DIS MODULE—KOER			
	• Key off.	Yes	▶	REPLACE DIS module. Does not respond to CID input. REMOVE all test equipment. RECONNECT all components. CLEAR Continuous Memory. RERUN Quick Test.
	• Install DIS diagnostic cable tee to Pins 1-6 side of DIS module.			
	• Connect diagnostic cable negative lead to battery.			
	• Connect diagnostic cable to EEC breakout box.			
	• Use 2.3L DP DIS overlay.	No	▶	GO to B4.
	• Set DVOM to 20 volt DC scale.			
	• Start engine.			
	• Measure voltage between (+)J51 (CIDD) and (-)J60 (BAT-).			
	• Bump engine in short bursts with starter without starting engine for at least ten engine revolutions.			
	• **Does DVOM reading switch between low (less than 2.0 volts DC) and high (greater than 8.0 volts DC)?**			

Fig. 11 Test B: Code 222, CID Failure, IDM Low Fault, DPI High Fault Or Right Coil Pack Failure, Code 222 (Part 1 of 8). 2.3L Dual Plug Engine

TEST STEP	RESULT	▶	ACTION TO TAKE
B4 CID FAULT—CHECK CID AT CRANKSHAFT SENSOR—KOER • Key off. • Connect crankshaft sensor tee. • Set DVOM to 20 volt DC scale. • Measure voltage between (+)J35 (CIDS) and (-)J60 (BAT-). • Bump engine in short bursts with starter without starting engine for at least ten engine revolutions. • **Does DVOM reading switch between low (less than 2.0 volts DC) and high (greater than 8.0 volts DC)?**	Yes No	▶ ▶	CHECK connectors, SERVICE or REPLACE the harness. CID circuit is open. REMOVE all test equipment. RECONNECT all components. CLEAR Continuous Memory. RERUN Quick Test. GO to **B5**.
B5 CID FAULT—CHECK VBAT AT CRANKSHAFT SENSOR—KOEO • Set DVOM to 20 volt DC range. • Key on. • Measure voltage between (+)J56 (VBATS) and (-)J60 (BAT-). • **Is voltage greater than 10 volts?**	Yes No	▶ ▶	GO to **B6**. CHECK connectors, SERVICE or REPLACE harness. VBATS is open. REMOVE all test equipment. RECONNECT all components. CLEAR Continuous Memory. RERUN Quick Test.
B6 CID FAULT—CHECK IGN GND AT CRANKSHAFT SENSOR—KEY OFF • Key off. • Set DVOM to 200 ohm range. • Measure resistance between J55 (IGNDS) and J60 (BAT-). • **Is resistance less than 5.0 ohms?** NOTE: If a negative resistance valve is obtained, switch leads of the DVOM and repeat measurement.	Yes No	▶ ▶	GO to **B7**. CHECK connectors, SERVICE or REPLACE the harness. IGNDS is open. REMOVE all test equipment. RECONNECT all components. CLEAR Continuous Memory. RERUN Quick Test.

Fig. 11   Test B: Code 222, CID Failure, IDM Low Fault, DPI High Fault Or Right Coil Pack (Part 2 of 8). 2.3L Dual Plug Engine

TEST STEP	RESULT	▶	ACTION TO TAKE
B7 CHECK CID AT CRANKSHAFT SENSOR—DIS MODULE DISCONNECTED—KOEC • Key off. • Disconnect DIS module tee 1-6 from DIS module. Do not disconnect vehicle harness from other side of tee. • Set DVOM to 20 volt DC scale. • Measure voltage between (+)J35 (CIDS) and (-)J60 (BAT-). • Bump engine in short bursts with starter without starting engine for at least ten engine revolutions. • **Does DVOM reading switch between low (less than 2.0 volts DC) and high (greater than 8.0 volts DC)?**	Yes No	▶ ▶	REPLACE DIS module. CID shorted low. REMOVE all test equipment. RECONNECT all components. CLEAR Continuous Memory. RERUN Quick Test. GO to **B8**.
B8 CHECK CID AT CRANKSHAFT SENSOR—DIS MODULE AND PROCESSOR DISCONNECTED—KOEC—CID FAULT • Key off. • Disconnect EEC processor from vehicle harness. • Set DVOM to 20 volts DC scale. • Measure voltage between (+)J35 (CIDS) and (-)J60 (BAT-). • Bump engine in short bursts with starter without starting engine for at least ten engine revolutions. • **Does DVOM reading switch between low (less than 2.0 volts DC) and high (greater than 8.0 volts DC)?**	Yes No	▶ ▶	REPLACE EEC processor. CID shorted. REMOVE all test equipment. RECONNECT all components. CLEAR Continuous Memory. RERUN Quick Test. GO to **B9**.
B9 CHECK FOR CID SHORT HIGH—DIS MODULE, PROCESSOR AND CRANKSHAFT SENSOR DISCONNECTED—KEY OFF—CID FAULT • Key off. • Disconnect diagnostic cable CID sensor tee from sensor. Do not disconnect vehicle harness from other side of tee. • Key on. • Set DVOM to 20 volt DC scale. • Measure voltage between (+)J51 (CIDD) and (-)J60 (BAT-). • **Is DVOM reading less than 0.5 volts DC?**	Yes No	▶ ▶	GO to **B10**. SERVICE connectors and harness. CID shorted high. REMOVE test equipment. RECONNECT all components. CLEAR Continuous Memory. RERUN Quick Test.

Fig. 11   Test B: Code 222, CID Failure, IDM Low Fault, DPI High Fault Or Right Coil Pack Failure (Part 3 of 8). 2.3L Dual Plug Engine

TEST STEP	RESULT	▶	ACTION TO TAKE
B10 CHECK FOR CID SHORT LOW—DIS MODULE, PROCESSOR AND CRANKSHAFT SENSOR DISCONNECTED—KOEO—CID FAULT • Key off. • Set DVOM to 20K ohm scale. • Measure resistance between (+)J51 (CIDD) and (-) J60 (BAT-). • **Is DVOM reading greater than 10K ohms?**	Yes No	▶ ▶	GO to **B11**. CHECK connectors, SERVICE or REPLACE harness. CID shorted low. REMOVE test equipment. RECONNECT all components. CLEAR Continuous Memory. RERUN Quick Test.
B11 CHECK VANE—KOEC—CID FAULT • Does CID vane move through sensor air gap when engine is cranked or running?	Yes No	▶ ▶	REPLACE crank sensor. No CID output. REMOVE test equipment. RECONNECT all components. CLEAR Continuous Memory. RERUN Quick Test. **Repair as necessary**
B12 CHECK DPI AT DIS MODULE—KOEO—DPI HIGH FAULT OR IDM LOW FAULT • Key off. • Install DIS module tee to Pins 1-6 side of DIS module. • Connect DIS diagnostic cable to EEC breakout box. • Use 2.3L DP DIS overlay. • Connect diagnostic cable negative lead to battery. • Set DVOM to 20 volt DC range. • Start engine. • Measure voltage between (+)J54 (DPID) and (-)J60 (BAT-). • **Is voltage less than 1.0 volt DC?**	Yes No	▶ ▶	GO to **B15**. IDM low fault. GO to **B13**. DPI high fault.

Fig. 11   Test B: Code 222, CID Failure, IDM Low Fault, DPI High Fault Or Right Coil Pack Failure (Part 4 of 8). 2.3L Dual Plug Engine

TEST STEP	RESULT	▶	ACTION TO TAKE
B13 CHECK DPI—DIS MODULE DISCONNECTED—KOEO—DPI HIGH FAULT • Key off. • Set DVOM to 20 volt DC scale. • Disconnect 1-6 DIS module tee from DIS module only. Do not disconnect vehicle harness from other side of tee. • Key on. • Measure voltage between (+)J54 (DPID) and (-)J60 (BAT-). • **Is voltage greater than 1.0 volt DC?**	Yes No	▶ ▶	GO to **B14**. REPLACE DIS module. DPI short high. REMOVE test equipment. RECONNECT all components. CLEAR Continuous Memory. RERUN Quick Test.
B14 CHECK FOR DPI SHORT HIGH—DIS MODULE AND PROCESSOR DISCONNECTED—KOEO—DPI HIGH FAULT • Key off. • Disconnect EEC processor. • Set DVOM to 20 volt DC range. • Key on. • Measure voltage between (+)J54 (DPID) and (-)J60 (BAT-). • **Is voltage less than 0.5 volts DC?**	Yes No	▶ ▶	REPLACE EEC processor. DPI shorted high. REMOVE test equipment. RECONNECT all components. CLEAR Continuous Memory. RERUN Quick Test. CHECK connectors, SERVICE or REPLACE harness. DPI shorted high. REMOVE test equipment. RECONNECT all components. CLEAR Continuous Memory. RERUN Quick Test.
B15 CHECK IDM AT DIS MODULE—KOER—IDM LOW FAULT • Set DVOM to 20 volt AC range. • Start engine. • Measure voltage between J4 (IDMD) and J60 (BAT-). • **Is voltage greater than 2.0 volts AC?**	Yes No	▶ ▶	GO to **B19**. GO to **B16**.

Fig. 11   Test B: Code 222, CID Failure, IDM Low Fault, DPI High Fault Or Right Coil Pack Failure (Part 5 of 8). 2.3L Dual Plug Engine

TEST STEP		RESULT	►	ACTION TO TAKE
B16	CHECK IDM AT DIS MODULE—PROCESSOR DISCONNECTED—KOEC—IDM LOW FAULT			
	• Key off.	Yes	►	REPLACE processor. IDM short low. REMOVE test equipment. RECONNECT all components. CLEAR Continuous Memory. RERUN Quick Test.
	• Disconnect EEC processor.			
	• Set DVOM to 20 volt AC range.			
	• Measure voltage between J4 (IDMD) and J60 (BAT-) while cranking engine.			
	• Is settled voltage greater than 3.0 volts AC?	No	►	GO to B17.
B17	CHECK FOR IDM SHORT LOW—DIS MODULE DISCONNECTED—KEY OFF—IDM SHORT FAULT			
	• Key off.	Yes	►	GO to B18.
	• Disconnect DIS diagnostic cable tee from Pins 7-12 side of DIS module. Do not disconnect vehicle harness from other side of tee.	No	►	CHECK connectors, SERVICE or REPLACE harness. IDM shorted low. REMOVE all test equipment. RECONNECT all components. CLEAR Continuous Memory. RERUN Quick Test.
	• Set DVOM to 200 ohm range.			
	• Measure resistance between J4 (IDMD) J60 (BAT-).			
	• Is resistance greater than 10K ohms?			
B18	CHECK FOR IDM SHORT HIGH—DIS MODULE DISCONNECTED—KOEO—IDM SHORT LOW			
	• Set DVOM to 20 volt DC range.	Yes	►	REPLACE DIS module. No IDM output. REMOVE test equipment. RECONNECT all components. CLEAR Continuous Memory. RERUN Quick Test.
	• Key on.			
	• Measure voltage between (+)J4 (IDMD) and (-)J60 (BAT-).			
	• Is voltage less than 0.5 volt?	No	►	CHECK connectors, SERVICE or REPLACE harness. IDM shorted high. REMOVE test equipment. RECONNECT all components. CLEAR Continuous Memory. RERUN Quick Test.

Fig. 11   Test B: Code 222, CID Failure, IDM Low Fault, DPI High Fault Or Right Coil Pack Failure (Part 6 of 8). 2.3L Dual Plug Engine

TEST STEP		RESULT	►	ACTION TO TAKE
B19	CHECK FOR IDM OPEN—KEY OFF—IDM LOW FAULT			
	• Key off.	Yes	►	REPLACE EEC processor. Does not respond to IDM input. REMOVE test equipment. RECONNECT all components. CLEAR Continuous Memory. RERUN Quick Test.
	• Disconnect EEC processor.			
	• Connect the second EEC breakout box to EEC vehicle harness connector.			
	• Measure resistance between J4 (IDMD) and J4 (IDME) of second EEC breakout box.			
	• Is resistance less than 5.0 ohms?	No	►	CHECK connectors, SERVICE or REPLACE harness. IDM open. REMOVE test equipment. RECONNECT all components. CLEAR Continuous Memory. RERUN Quick Test.

Fig. 11   Test B: Code 222, CID Failure, IDM Low Fault, DPI High Fault Or Right Coil Pack Failure (Part 7 of 8). 2.3L Dual Plug Engine

TEST STEP		RESULT	►	ACTION TO TAKE
B20	CHECK CID AT PCM CONNECTOR—PCM DISCONNECTED—KOEC			
	• Key off.	Yes	►	REPLACE PCM. Does not respond to CID input. REMOVE all test equipment. RECONNECT all components. CLEAR Continuous Memory. RERUN Quick Test.
	• Disconnect PCM.			
	• Connect EEC breakout box to PCM vehicle harness connector.			
	• DVOM on 20 volt DC scale.			
	• Connect DVOM lead between Pin 5 (CID) and -J60 ground.			
	• Bump engine in short bursts with starter without starting the engine for at least five engine revolutions and watch for a change in DVOM reading.	No	►	CHECK connectors. SERVICE or REPLACE harness. CID open. REMOVE test equipment. RECONNECT all components. CLEAR Continuous Memory. RERUN Quick Test.
	• Does the DVOM reading switch between low (less than 2.0 volts DC) and high (greater than 8.0 volts DC)?			

Fig. 11   Test B: Code 222, CID Failure, IDM Low Fault, DPI High Fault Or Right Coil Pack Failure (Part 8 of 8). 2.3L Dual Plug Engine

TEST STEP		RESULT	►	ACTION TO TAKE
C1	CHECK FOR ANY LEFT SIDE SPARK—KOER—IDM OPEN, IDM HIGH OR LEFT COIL PACK FAILURE			
	• Start engine.	Yes	►	GO to C2.
	• Using a Neon Bulb Spark Tester (D89P-6666-A) or air gap spark tester, check for spark at each left spark plug wire.	No	►	GO to D1.
	• Is spark present at any left spark plug wire?			
C2	CHECK IDM—KOER—IDM OPEN OR IDM HIGH FAULT			
	• Key off.	Yes	►	GO to C3.
	• Install DIS module tee to Pins 7-12 side of DIS module.	No	►	GO to C4.
	• Connect negative lead of DIS diagnostic cable to battery.			
	• Connect DIS diagnostic cable to EEC breakout box.			
	• Use 2.3L DP DIS overlay.			
	• Set DVOM to 20 volt AC range.			
	• Start engine.			
	• Measure voltage between J4 (IDMD) and J60 (BAT-).			
	• Is voltage greater than 1.0 volt AC?			
C3	CHECK IDM TO PROCESSOR CONTINUITY—KEY OFF—IDM OPEN FAULT			
	• Key off.	Yes	►	REPLACE EEC processor. Does not respond to IDM input. REMOVE test equipment. RECONNECT all components. CLEAR Continuous Memory. RERUN Quick Test.
	• Set DVOM to 200 ohm range.			
	• Disconnect EEC processor.			
	• Connect second EEC breakout box to EEC vehicle harness connector.			
	• Measure resistance between J4 (IDMD) and J4 (IDME) of second breakout box.	No	►	CHECK connectors, SERVICE or REPLACE harness. IDM open. REMOVE test equipment. RECONNECT all components. CLEAR Continuous Memory. RERUN Quick Test.
	• Is resistance less than 5.0 ohms?			

Fig. 12   Test C: Code 218, IDM Open, IDM High Or Left Coil Pack Failure (Part 1 of 2). 2.3L Dual Plug Engine

TEST STEP		RESULT	►	ACTION TO TAKE
C4	CHECK IDM—PROCESSOR DISCONNECTED—KOEC—IDM OPEN FAULT			
	• Key off.	Yes	►	REPLACE EEC processor. IDM short high. REMOVE test equipment. RECONNECT all components. CLEAR Continuous Memory. RERUN Quick Test.
	• Disconnect EEC processor.			
	• Set DVOM to 20 volt AC range.			
	• Measure voltage between J4 (IDMD) and J60 (BAT-) while cranking engine.			
	• Is voltage greater than 1.0 volt AC?	No	►	GO to C5.
C5	CHECK IDM FOR SHORT HIGH—DIS MODULE AND PROCESSOR DISCONNECTED—KOEO—IDM HIGH FAULT			
	• Key off.	Yes	►	GO to C6.
	• Disconnect 7-12 DIS module tee from DIS module only. Do not disconnect other side of tee from vehicle harness.	No	►	CHECK connectors, SERVICE or REPLACE harness. IDM shorted high. REMOVE test equipment. RECONNECT all components. CLEAR Continuous Memory. RERUN Quick Test.
	• Set DVOM to 20 volt DC range.			
	• Key on.			
	• Measure voltage between (+)J4 (IDMD) and (-)J60 (BAT-).			
	• Is voltage less than 6.0 volt AC?			
C6	CHECK IDMD FOR SHORT LOW—DIS MODULE AND PROCESSOR DISCONNECTED—KEY OFF—IDM HIGH FAULT			
	• Key off.	Yes	►	REPLACE DIS module. IDM shorted high. REMOVE all test equipment. RECONNECT all components. CLEAR Continuous Memory. RERUN Quick Test.
	• Set DVOM to 20K ohm range.			
	• Measure resistance between J4 (IDMD) and J60 (BAT-).			
	• Is resistance greater than 10K ohms?	No	►	CHECK connectors, SERVICE or REPLACE harness. No IDM input. REMOVE test equipment. RECONNECT all components. CLEAR Continuous Memory. RERUN Quick Test.

Fig. 12   Test C: Code 218, IDM Open, IDM High Or Left Coil Pack Failure (Part 2 of 2). 2.3L Dual Plug Engine

TEST STEP	RESULT	▶	ACTION TO TAKE
D1 CHECK FOR SPARK DURING CRANK			
• Using a Neon Bulb Spark Tester (OTC D89P-6666-A) or Air Gap Spark Tester (D81P-6666-A), check for spark at all spark plug wires while cranking. • **Was spark consistent on ALL spark plug wires?**	Yes No	▶ ▶	Ignition system is OK. GO to **D2**.
D2 CHECK FOR SPARK AT RIGHT SPARK PLUG WIRES DURING CRANK—SPARK FAULT			
• **Was spark consistent on all right spark plug wires (one spark per crankshaft revolution)?** NOTE: Check spark at all spark plugs.	Yes No	▶ ▶	GO to **D3**. GO to **D19**.
D3 CHECK LEFT SPARK PLUGS AND WIRES—LEFT SPARK FAULT			
• Check left spark plug wires for insulation damage, looseness, shorting or other damage. • Remove and check left spark plugs for damage, wear, carbon deposits and proper plug gap. NOTE: Left coil plugs and wires are attached to the left coil. • **Are spark plugs and wires OK?**	Yes No	▶ ▶	REINSTALL plugs and wires. GO to **D4**. SERVICE or REPLACE damaged component. REMOVE all test equipment. RECONNECT all components. CLEAR Continuous Memory. RERUN Quick Test.
D4 CHECK VBAT AT LEFT COIL—LEFT SPARK FAULT			
WARNING: NEVER CONNECT EEC-IV PROCESSOR TO THE EEC-IV BREAKOUT BOX WHEN PERFORMING EDIS DIAGNOSTICS. • Key off. • Install left coil tee only at this time. • Connect DIS diagnostic cable BAT(+) and BAT(-) leads to battery. • Use 2.3L DP DIS overlay. • DVOM on 20 volt DC scale. • Key on, engine off. • Measure voltage between (+)J15 (VBAT L) and (-)J60 (BAT-) at breakout box. • **Is DC voltage greater than 10 volts?**	Yes No	▶ ▶	GO to **D5**. SERVICE open circuit in harness. VBAT L is open. REMOVE all test equipment. RECONNECT all components. CLEAR Continuous Memory. RERUN Quick Test.

Fig. 13   Test D: No Start And/Or Code 224: Coil Failure (Part 1 of 11). 2.3L Dual Plug Engine

TEST STEP	RESULT	▶	ACTION TO TAKE
D5 CHECK FOR C3 HIGH AT COIL PACK—KOEO—COIL FAULT			
• DVOM on 20 volt DC scale. • Key on, engine off. • Measure voltage between (+)J30 (LC3C) and (-)J60 (BAT-) at breakout box. • **Is DC voltage reading greater than 10 volts DC?**	Yes No	▶ ▶	GO to **D6**. GO to **D13**.
D6 CHECK FOR C4 HIGH AT COIL PACK—KOEO—COIL FAILURE			
• DVOM on 20 volt DC scale. • Key on, engine off. • Measure voltage between (+)J28 (LC4C) and (-)J60 (BAT-) at breakout box. • **Is DC voltage reading greater than 10 volts DC?**	Yes No	▶ ▶	GO to **D7**. GO to **D11**.
D7 CHECK FOR C3 HIGH AT DIS MODULE—KOEO—COIL FAULT			
• Key off. • Connect DIS module 7-12 tee to the DIS module and vehicle harness connector. • DVOM on 20 volt DC scale. • Key on, engine off. • Measure voltage between (+)J3 (LC3D) and (-)J60 (BAT-) at breakout box. • **Is DC voltage reading greater than 10 volts DC?**	Yes No	▶ ▶	GO to **D8**. SERVICE open circuit. C3 open in harness. REMOVE all test equipment. RECONNECT all components. CLEAR Continuous Memory. RERUN Quick Test.
D8 CHECK FOR C4 HIGH AT DIS MODULE—KOEO—COIL FAULT			
• DVOM on 20 volt DC scale. • Key on, engine off. • Measure voltage between (+)J6 (LC4D) and (-)J60 (BAT-) at breakout box. • **Is DC voltage reading greater than 10 volts DC?**	Yes No	▶ ▶	GO to **D9**. SERVICE open circuit. C4 open in harness. REMOVE all test equipment. RECONNECT all components. CLEAR Continuous Memory. RERUN Quick Test.

Fig. 13   Test D: No Start And/Or Code 224: Coil Failure (Part 2 of 11). 2.3L Dual Plug Engine

TEST STEP	RESULT	▶	ACTION TO TAKE
D9 CHECK FOR C3 LOW AT COIL PACK—KOEO—COIL DISCONNECTED			
• Key off. • Disconnect left coil pack from coil tee, leave vehicle harness connected to coil tee. • DVOM on 20 volt DC scale. • Key on, engine off. • Measure voltage between (+)J30 (LC3C) and (-)J60 (BAT-) at breakout box. • **Is DC voltage reading less than 0.5 volts DC?**	Yes No	▶ ▶	GO to **D15**. GO to **D10**.
D10 CHECK FOR C3 LOW—DIS MODULE AND LEFT COIL DISCONNECTED—COIL FAULT—KOEO			
• Key off. • Disconnect DIS module from the DIS module tee, leave vehicle harness connected to coil tee. • DVOM on 20 volt DC scale. • Key on, engine off. • Measure voltage between (+)J30 (LC3C) and (-)J60 (BAT-) at breakout box. • **Is DC voltage reading less than 1.0 volts DC?**	Yes No	▶ ▶	REPLACE DIS module. C3 shorted high. REMOVE all test equipment. RECONNECT all components. CLEAR Continuous Memory. RERUN Quick Test. SERVICE short circuit. C3 shorted high in harness. REMOVE all test equipment. RECONNECT all components. CLEAR Continuous Memory. RERUN Quick Test.
D11 CHECK FOR C4 CIRCUIT SHORT TO GROUND COIL FAULT—KEY OFF			
• Key off. • DVOM on 20K ohm scale. • Measure resistance between J60 (BAT-) and J28 (LC4C) at breakout box. • **Is resistance reading greater than 10K ohms?** NOTE: If a negative resistance value is obtained, switch the leads of the DVOM and repeat measurement.	Yes No	▶ ▶	REPLACE left coil pack. C4 open in coil. REMOVE all test equipment. RECONNECT all components. CLEAR Continuous Memory. RERUN Quick Test. GO to **D12**.

Fig. 13   Test D: No Start And/Or Code 224: Coil Failure (Part 3 of 11). 2.3L Dual Plug Engine

TEST STEP	RESULT	▶	ACTION TO TAKE
D12 CHECK FOR C4 SHORT TO GROUND IN HARNESS—ICM DISCONNECTED—COIL FAULT LOW • Key off. • Disconnect ICM from ICM 7-12 tee, leave vehicle harness connected to module tee. • DVOM on 20K ohm scale. • Measure resistance between J60 (B-) and J28 (LC4C) at breakout box. • **Is resistance reading greater than 10K ohms?**	Yes	▶	REPLACE ICM. C4 is shorted to ground. REMOVE all test equipment. RECONNECT all components. CLEAR Continuous Memory. RERUN Quick Test.
	No	▶	SERVICE short circuit. C4 is shorted to ground in harness. REMOVE all test equipment. RECONNECT all components. CLEAR Continuous Memory. RERUN Quick Test.
D13 CHECK FOR C3 SHORT TO GROUND—COIL FAULT LOW • Key off. • DVOM on 20K ohm scale. • Measure resistance between J60 (B-) and J30 (LC3C) at breakout box. • **Is resistance reading greater than 10K ohms?**	Yes	▶	REPLACE left coil pack. C3 open in coil. REMOVE all test equipment. RECONNECT all components. CLEAR Continuous Memory. RERUN Quick Test.
	No	▶	GO to D14.
D14 CHECK FOR C3 SHORT LOW—ICM DISCONNECTED—COIL FAULT • Key off. • Disconnect ICM from the ICM 7-12 tee, leave vehicle harness connected to module tee. • DVOM on 20K ohm scale. • Measure resistance between J60 (B-) and J30 (LC3C) at breakout box. • **Is resistance greater than 10K ohms?**	Yes	▶	REPLACE ICM. C3 shorted low. REMOVE all test equipment. RECONNECT all components. CLEAR Continuous Memory. RERUN Quick Test.
	No	▶	SERVICE short circuit. C4 shorted low in harness. REMOVE all test equipment. RECONNECT all components. CLEAR Continuous Memory. RERUN Quick Test.

Fig. 13   Test D: No Start And/Or Code 224: Coil Failure (Part 4 of 11). 2.3L Dual Plug Engine

TEST STEP	RESULT	▶	ACTION TO TAKE
D15 CHECK FOR C4 LOW—KOEO—COIL DISCONNECTED • DVOM on 20 volt DC scale. • Key on, engine off. • Measure voltage between (+)J28 (LC4C) and (-)J60 (BAT-) at breakout box. • **Is DC voltage reading less than 0.5 volts DC?**	Yes	▶	GO to D17.
	No	▶	GO to D16.
D16 CHECK FOR C4 SHORT HIGH—KOEO—DIS MODULE AND COIL DISCONNECTED—COIL FAULT • Key off. • Disconnect DIS module from the DIS module 7-12 tee, leave vehicle harness connected to module tee. • DVOM on 20 volt DC scale. • Key on, engine off. • Measure voltage between (+)J28 (LC4C) and (-)J60 (BAT-) at breakout box. • **Is DC voltage reading less than 1.0 volts DC?**	Yes	▶	REPLACE DIS module. C4 is shorted high in DIS module. REMOVE all test equipment. RECONNECT all components. CLEAR Continuous Memory. RERUN Quick Test.
	No	▶	SERVICE short circuit. C4 is shorted high in harness. REMOVE all test equipment. RECONNECT all components. CLEAR Continuous Memory. RERUN Quick Test.
D17 CHECK C3 AT COIL PACK—KOEC—COILS DISCONNECTED • Key off. • Disconnect left and right coils. • Connect positive lead of diagnostic cable to battery. • Connect left coil tee to vehicle harness. Do not connect left coil to tee. • Connect incandescent test lamp between J57 (BAT+) and J30 (LC3C). • Crank engine. • **Does test lamp blink during crank?**	Yes	▶	GO to D18.
	No	▶	REPLACE DIS module. C3 open in DIS. REMOVE all test equipment. RECONNECT all components. CLEAR Continuous Memory. RERUN Quick Test.

Fig. 13   Test D: No Start And/Or Code 224: Coil Failure (Part 5 of 11). 2.3L Dual Plug Engine

TEST STEP	RESULT	▶	ACTION TO TAKE
D18 CHECK C4 AT COIL PACK—KOEC—COILS DISCONNECTED • Key off. • Connect incandescent test lamp between J57 (BAT+) and J28 (LC4C). • Crank engine. • **Does test lamp blink during crank?**	Yes	▶	REPLACE left coil pack. Input to coil pack is OK, but no high voltage output. REMOVE all test equipment. RECONNECT all components. CLEAR Continuous Memory. RERUN Quick Test.
	No	▶	REPLACE DIS module. No C4 output. REMOVE all test equipment. RECONNECT all components. CLEAR Continuous Memory. RERUN Quick Test.
D19 CHECK RIGHT PLUGS AND WIRES—RIGHT SPARK FAULT • Check right spark plug wires for insulation damage, looseness, shorting or other damage. • Remove and check right spark plugs for damage, wear, carbon deposits and proper plug gap. **NOTE: Right coil plugs and wires are attached to right coil.** • **Are spark plugs and wires OK?**	Yes	▶	REINSTALL plugs and wires. GO to D20.
	No	▶	SERVICE or REPLACE damaged component. REMOVE all test equipment. RECONNECT all components. CLEAR Continuous Memory. RERUN Quick Test.
D20 CHECK FOR VBAT OPEN AT RIGHT COIL—RIGHT SPARK FAULT—KOEO **WARNING: NEVER CONNECT EEC-IV PROCESSOR TO THE EEC-IV BREAKOUT BOX WHEN PERFORMING DIS DIAGNOSTICS.** • Key off. • Connect negative lead to battery. • Install right coil tee. • DVOM on 20 volt DC scale. • Key on, engine off. • Measure voltage between (+)J26 (VBAT R) and (-)J60 (VBAT) at breakout box. • **Is DC voltage greater than 10 volts DC?**	Yes	▶	GO to D21.
	No	▶	SERVICE open circuit in harness. VBAT is open. REMOVE all test equipment. RECONNECT all components. CLEAR Continuous Memory. RERUN Quick Test.

Fig. 13   Test D: No Start And/Or Code 224: Coil Failure (Part 6 of 11). 2.3L Dual Plug Engine

TEST STEP	RESULT	▶	ACTION TO TAKE
D21 CHECK FOR C1 HIGH AT COIL PACK—KOEO—COIL FAULT • DVOM on 20 volt DC scale. • Key on, engine off. • Measure voltage between (+)J23 (RC1C) and (-)J60 (BAT-) at breakout box. • **Is DC voltage reading greater than 10 volts DC?**	Yes	▶	GO to D22.
	No	▶	GO to D27.
D22 CHECK FOR C2 HIGH—KOEO—COIL FAULT • DVOM on 20 volt DC scale. • Key on, engine off. • Measure voltage between (+)J24 (RC2C) and (-)J60 (BAT-) at breakout box. • **Is DC voltage reading greater than 10 volts DC?**	Yes	▶	GO to D23.
	No	▶	GO to D29.
D23 CHECK FOR C1 HIGH AT DIS MODULE—KOEO—COIL FAULT • Key off. • Install DIS 7-12 tee. • DVOM on 20 volt DC scale. • Key on, engine off. • Measure voltage between (+)J18 (RC1D) and (-)J60 (BAT-) at breakout box. • **Is DC voltage reading greater than 10 volts DC?**	Yes	▶	GO to D24.
	No	▶	SERVICE open circuit. C1 open in harness. REMOVE all test equipment. RECONNECT all components. CLEAR Continuous Memory. RERUN Quick Test.
D24 CHECK FOR C2 HIGH AT DIS MODULE—KOEO—COIL FAULT • DVOM on 20 volt DC scale. • Key on, engine off. • Measure voltage between (+)J10 (RC2D) and (-)J60 (BAT-) at breakout box. • **Is DC voltage reading greater than 10 volts DC?**	Yes	▶	GO to D25.
	No	▶	SERVICE open circuit. C2 open in harness. REMOVE all test equipment. RECONNECT all components. CLEAR Continuous Memory. RERUN Quick Test.

Fig. 13   Test D: No Start And/Or Code 224: Coil Failure (Part 7 of 11). 2.3L Dual Plug Engine

TEST STEP	RESULT	▶	ACTION TO TAKE
D25 CHECK FOR C1 LOW AT COIL PACK—KOEO—COIL FAILURE—DISCONNECT COIL • Key off. • Disconnect right coil from coil tee. Leave vehicle harness connected to coil tee. • DVOM on 20 volt DC scale. • Key on, engine off. • Measure voltage between (+)J23 (RC1C) and (-)J60 (BAT-) at breakout box. • **Is DC voltage reading less than 0.5 volts DC?**	Yes No	▶ ▶	GO to **D31**. GO to **D26**.
D26 CHECK FOR C1 SHORT LOW AT COIL PACK—DISCONNECT DIS MODULE AND COIL—COIL FAULT • Key off. • Disconnected DIS module from the DIS module 7-12 tee, leave vehicle harness connected to module tee. • DVOM on 20 volt DC scale. • Key on, engine off. • Measure voltage between (+)J23 (RC1C) and (-)J60 (BAT-) at breakout box. • **Is DC voltage reading less than 1.0 volts DC?**	Yes No	▶ ▶	REPLACE DIS module. C1 shorted high. REMOVE all test equipment. RECONNECT all components. CLEAR Continuous Memory. RERUN Quick Test. SERVICE short circuit. C1 shorted high in harness. REMOVE all test equipment. RECONNECT all components. CLEAR Continuous Memory. RERUN Quick Test.
D27 CHECK FOR C1 SHORT LOW—COIL FAULT LOW • Key off. • DVOM on 2K ohm scale. • Measure resistance between J60 (BAT-) and J23 (RC1C) at breakout box. • **Is resistance reading greater than 10K ohms?**	Yes No	▶ ▶	REPLACE Right Coil Pack. C1 open in coil. REMOVE all test equipment. RECONNECT all components. CLEAR Continuous Memory. RERUN Quick Test. GO to **D28**.

Fig. 13   Test D: No Start And/Or Code 224: Coil Failure (Part 8 of 11). 2.3L Dual Plug Engine

TEST STEP	RESULT	▶	ACTION TO TAKE
D28 CHECK FOR C1 SHORT TO GROUND IN DIS MODULE DIS MODULE DISCONNECTED—COIL FAULT LOW • Key off. • Disconnect DIS module from DIS module 7-12 tee, leave vehicle harness connected to module tee. • DVOM on 2K ohm scale. • Measure resistance between J60 (BAT-) and J23 (RC1C) at breakout box. • **Is resistance reading greater than 10K ohms?**	Yes No	▶ ▶	REPLACE DIS module. C1 is shorted to ground in DIS module. REMOVE all test equipment. RECONNECT all components. CLEAR Continuous Memory. RERUN Quick Test. SERVICE short circuit. C1 is shorted to ground in harness. REMOVE all test equipment. RECONNECT all components. CLEAR Continuous Memory. RERUN Quick Test.
D29 CHECK FOR C2 SHORT LOW—COIL FAULT LOW—KEY OFF • Key off. • DVOM on 2K ohm scale. • Measure resistance between J60 (BAT-) and J24 (RC2C) at breakout box. • **Is resistance reading greater than 100 ohms?**	Yes No	▶ ▶	REPLACE Right Coil Pack. C2 open in coil. REMOVE all test equipment. RECONNECT all components. CLEAR Continuous Memory. RERUN Quick Test. GO to **D30**.

Fig. 13   Test D: No Start And/Or Code 224: Coil Failure (Part 9 of 11). 2.3L Dual Plug Engine

TEST STEP	RESULT	▶	ACTION TO TAKE
D30 CHECK FOR C2 SHORT LOW AT COIL PACK—DISCONNECT DIS MODULE—COIL FAULT—KEY OFF • Key off. • Disconnect DIS module from DIS module 7-12 tee, leave vehicle harness connected to module tee. • DVOM on 2K ohm scale. • Measure resistance between J24 (RC2C) and J60 (BAT-) at breakout box. • **Is resistance reading greater than 10K ohms?**	Yes No	▶ ▶	SERVICE short circuit. C2 shorted low in harness. REMOVE all test equipment. RECONNECT all components. CLEAR Continuous Memory. RERUN Quick Test. REPLACE DIS module. C2 shorted low. REMOVE all test equipment. RECONNECT all components. CLEAR Continuous Memory. RERUN Quick Test.
D31 CHECK FOR C2 LOW AT COIL PACK—DISCONNECT RIGHT COIL—KOEO • DVOM on 20 volt DC scale. • Key on, engine off. • Measure voltage between (+)J24 (RC2C) and (-)J60 (BAT-) at breakout box. • **Is DC voltage reading less than 0.5 volts DC?**	Yes No	▶ ▶	GO to **D33**. GO to **D32**.
D32 CHECK FOR SHORT HIGH IN DIS MODULE C2—KOEO—DIS MODULE DISCONNECTED—COIL FAULT • Key off. • Disconnect DIS module from DIS module 7-12 tee, leave DIS diagnostic cable connected to vehicle harness connector. • DVOM on 20 volt DC scale. • Key on, engine off. • Measure voltage between (+)J24 (RC2C) and (-)J60 (BAT-) at breakout box. • **Is DC voltage reading less than 0.5 volts DC?**	Yes No	▶ ▶	REPLACE DIS module. C2 shorted high in DIS module. REMOVE all test equipment. RECONNECT all components. CLEAR Continuous Memory. RERUN Quick Test. SERVICE short circuit. C2 shorted high in harness. REMOVE all test equipment. RECONNECT all components. CLEAR Continuous Memory. RERUN Quick Test.

Fig. 13   Test D: No Start And/Or Code 224: Coil Failure (Part 10 of 11). 2.3L Dual Plug Engine

TEST STEP	RESULT	▶	ACTION TO TAKE
D33 CHECK C1 AT COIL PACK—KOEC—COILS DISCONNECTED • Connect diagnostic cable positive lead to battery. • Connect incandescent test lamp between J57 (BAT+) and J23 (RC1C). • Disconnect left coil from vehicle harness. Do not install left coil tee. • Crank engine. • **Does test lamp blink during crank?**	Yes No	▶ ▶	GO to **D34**. REPLACE DIS module. C1 driver damaged. REMOVE all test equipment. RECONNECT all components. CLEAR Continuous Memory. RERUN Quick Test.
D34 CHECK C2 AT COIL PACK—KOEC—COILS DISCONNECTED—COIL FAULT • Key off. • Connect incandescent test lamp between J57 (BAT+) and J24 (RC2C). • Crank engine. • **Does test lamp blink during crank?**	Yes No	▶ ▶	REPLACE right coil pack. Input to coil pack is OK, but no high voltage output. REMOVE all test equipment. RECONNECT all components. CLEAR Continuous Memory. RERUN Quick Test. SERVICE harness. C2 open in harness. REMOVE all test equipment. RECONNECT all components. CLEAR Continuous Memory. RERUN Quick Test.

Fig. 13   Test D: No Start And/Or Code 224: Coil Failure (Part 11 of 11). 2.3L Dual Plug Engine

	TEST STEP	RESULT	▶	ACTION TO TAKE
E1	CHECK SPOUT AT DIS MODULE			
	• Key off.	Yes	▶	GO to E2.
	• Connect DIS diagnostic cable negative and positive lead to battery.	No	▶	GO to E6. SPOUT high fault.
	• Install DIS diagnostic cable to breakout box and the DIS module (Pin 1-6).			
	• Use 2.3L DP DIS overlay.			
	• Connect DVOM between (+)36 (SPOUT) and (-)J60 (BAT-).			
	• Set DVOM to 2.0 volt AC range.			
	• Start engine.			
	• **Is voltage greater than 2.0 volts AC?**			
E2	DP FAULT—VERIFY DUAL PLUG OPERATION			
	• Using a Neon Spark Tester (D89P-6666-A), check for spark at each left side plug wire with the engine running.	Yes	▶	REPLACE DIS module. Module not indicating dual plug operation. REMOVE all test equipment. RECONNECT all components. CLEAR Continuous Memory. RERUN Quick Test.
	• **Is spark present at one or more wires during dual plug operation?**			
		No	▶	GO to E3.
E3	DP FAULT—CHECK DPI CONTINUITY—PROCESSOR AND DIS MODULE DISCONNECTED			
	• Key off.	Yes	▶	GO to E4.
	• Set DVOM to 200 ohm scale.	No	▶	CHECK connectors, SERVICE or REPLACE the harness. DPI is open between the DIS module and the processor. REMOVE all test equipment. RECONNECT all components. CLEAR Continuous Memory. RERUN Quick Test.
	• Disconnect EEC-IV processor.			
	• Disconnect DIS module from DIS 1-6 tee. Leave vehicle harness connected to module tee.			
	• Measure resistance between Test Pin 32 (DPI) at the EEC vehicle harness connector and J54 (DPI).			
	• **Is resistance less than 5.0 ohms?**			

Fig. 14 Test E: DPI Open, DPI High Or Spout High (Part 1 of 3). 2.3L Dual Plug Engine

	TEST STEP	RESULT	▶	ACTION TO TAKE
E4	DPI FAULT—CHECK FOR DPI SHORT HIGH—PROCESSOR AND DIS MODULE DISCONNECTED			
	• Key on.	Yes	▶	GO to E5.
	• Set DVOM to 20 volt DC range.	No	▶	SERVICE harness. DPI short high. REMOVE all test equipment. RECONNECT all components. CLEAR Continuous Memory. RERUN Quick Test.
	• Measure voltage between (+)J54 (DPI) and (-)J60 (BAT-).			
	• **Is the voltage less than 0.5 volt DC?**			
E5	FORCE DUAL PLUG COMMAND AT DIS MODULE (DPI LOW)—DPI FAULT—KOER			
	• Connect a jumper between J54 (DPI) and J60 (BAT-).	Yes	▶	REPLACE EEC processor. Processor not sending DPI signal. REMOVE all test equipment. RECONNECT all components. CLEAR Continuous Memory. RERUN Quick Test.
	• Reconnect EEC processor.			
	• Reconnect DIS tee (1-6) to DIS module.			
	CAUTION: Do not jumper J54 to VBAT+ or BAT+; the DPI circuit in the EEC-IV processor may be damaged.			
	• Start engine.	No	▶	REPLACE DIS module. Module not responding to DPI signal. REMOVE all test equipment. RECONNECT all components. CLEAR Continuous Memory. RERUN Quick Test.
	• **Is there spark at any left plug wire?**			
E6	CHECK EEC SIDE OF SPOUT CONNECTOR—SPOUT HIGH FAULT—OPEN SPOUT CIRCUIT—KOER			
	• Remove SPOUT jumper.	Yes	▶	GO to E7.
	• Set DVOM to 20 volt AC range.	No	▶	GO to E8.
	• Start engine.			
	• Measure voltage between EEC side of SPOUT jumper and J60 (BAT-).			
	• **Is voltage greater than 3.0 volts AC?**			

DIS SIDE —[◻◻]— EEC SIDE

SPOUT IN-LINE VEHICLE HARNESS CONNECTOR

Fig. 14 Test E: Code 213, DPI Open, DPI High Or Spout High (Part 2 of 3). 2.3L Dual Plug Engine

	TEST STEP	RESULT	▶	ACTION TO TAKE
E7	CHECK DIS SIDE OF SPOUT CONNECTOR FOR SPOUT HIGH—OPEN SPOUT CIRCUIT—SPOUT HIGH FAULT—KOEO			
	• Key off.	Yes	▶	REPLACE DIS module. SPOUT is shorted high. REMOVE all test equipment. RECONNECT all components. CLEAR Continuous Memory. RERUN Quick Test.
	• Disconnect DIS module (Pin 1-6) diagnostic cable tee. Do not disconnect vehicle wiring connector from other end of tee.			
	• Set DVOM to 20 volt DC range.			
	• Key on.	No	▶	SERVICE harness and connectors. SPOUT is shorted high between SPOUT jumper and DIS module. REMOVE all test equipment. RECONNECT all components. CLEAR Continuous Memory. RERUN Quick Test.
	• Measure voltage between +DIS side of SPOUT connector and -J60.			
	• **Is voltage less than 0.5 volt DC?**			

DIS SIDE —[◻◻]— EEC SIDE

SPOUT IN-LINE VEHICLE HARNESS CONNECTOR

	TEST STEP	RESULT	▶	ACTION TO TAKE
E8	CHECK EEC SIDE OF SPOUT CONNECTOR FOR SPOUT HIGH—SPOUT HIGH FAULT—KOEO			
	• Key off.	Yes	▶	REPLACE EEC processor. SPOUT is shorted high. REMOVE all test equipment. RECONNECT all components. CLEAR Continuous Memory. RERUN Quick Test.
	• Disconnect EEC processor.			
	• Set DVOM to 20 volt DC range.			
	• Key on.			
	• Measure voltage between +EEC side of SPOUT connector and -J60.	No	▶	SERVICE harness and connectors. SPOUT is shorted high between SPOUT jumper and EEC harness connector. REMOVE all test equipment. RECONNECT all components. CLEAR Continous Memory. RERUN Quick Test.
	• **Is voltage less than 0.5 volt DC?**			

DIS SIDE —[◻◻]— EEC SIDE

SPOUT IN-LINE VEHICLE HARNESS CONNECTOR

Fig. 14 Test E: Code 213, DPI Open, DPI High Or Spout High (Part 3 of 3). 2.3L Dual Plug Engine

TEST STEP		RESULT	▶	ACTION TO TAKE
F1	**CHECK FOR GREATER THAN 16 DEGREES BTDC TIMING AT IDLE**			
	● Key off.	Yes	▶	
	● Install timing light.			Ignition system is OK.
	● Engine running at normal operating temperature.	No	▶	GO to F2.
	● Transmission out of gear.			
	● Engine at idle.			
	● Check timing.			
	● **Is timing greater than 16 degrees BTDC?**			
F2	**CHECK FOR BASE TIMING (10 DEGREES BTDC)**			
	● Key off.	Yes	▶	GO to F3.
	● Remove SPOUT harness jumper plug from spout vehicle harness connector.	No	▶	GO to F4.
	● **Is engine timing 10 ± 2 degrees BDTC or ATDC?**			
F3	**SPOUT FAULT—CHECK SPOUT AT DIS MODULE**			
	● Key off.	Yes	▶	GO to F5.
	● Replace SPOUT harness jumper plug to SPOUT vehicle harness connector.	No	▶	GO to F8.
	● Install 1-6 DIS module tee.			
	● Use 2.3L DP DIS overlay.			
	● Connect DIS diagnostic cable negative and positive leads to the battery.			
	● Set DVOM on 20 volt AC range.			
	● Start engine and measure voltage between J36 (SPOUT) and J60 (BAT-) at the breakout box.			
	● **Is voltage greater than 2.0 volts AC?**			

Fig. 15   Test F: Code 213/412 Or No Codes & Lack Of Power, Spout Open Or Low (Part 1 of 5). 1993 2.3L Dual Plug Engine

TEST STEP		RESULT	▶	ACTION TO TAKE
F4	**SPOUT FAULT—INSPECT SENSOR / TRIGGER WHEEL—KEY OFF**			
	● **Is sensor or trigger wheel damaged?**	Yes	▶	REPLACE or SERVICE as required. REMOVE all test equipment. RECONNECT all components. CLEAR Continuous Memory. RERUN Quick Test.
		No	▶	REPLACE ICM. ICM not responding to input signals. REMOVE all test equipment. RECONNECT all components. CLEAR Continuous Memory. RERUN Quick Test.
F5	**CHECK FOR SPOUT SHORT LOW—SPOUT FAULT—KEY OFF—PCM DISCONNECTED**			
	● Key off.	Yes	▶	REPLACE PCM. SPOUT shorted to ground. REMOVE all test equipment. RECONNECT all components. CLEAR Continuous Memory. RERUN Quick Test.
	● Disconnect the PCM.			
	● Set DVOM to 200 ohm range.			
	● Measure resistance between J36 (SPOUT) and J60 (B-).			
	● **Is resistance greater than 10 ohms?**	No	▶	SERVICE harness and connectors. SPOUT shorted to ground between PCM and ICM. REMOVE all test equipment. RCONNECT all components. CLEAR Continuous Memory. RERUN Quick Test.

Fig. 15   Test F: Code 213/412 Or No Codes & Lack Of Power, Spout Open Or Low (Part 2 of 5). 1993 2.3L Dual Plug Engine

TEST STEP		RESULT	▶	ACTION TO TAKE
F6	**CHECK SPOUT CIRCUIT CONTINUITY—PCM DISCONNECTED—ICM DISCONNECTED**			
	● Key off.	Yes	▶	GO to F7.
	● Disconnect PCM and install a second EEC breakout box at PCM vehicle harness connector.	No	▶	SERVICE open circuit in harness between PCM and ICM. REMOVE all test equipment. RECONNECT all components. CLEAR Continuous Memory. RERUN Quick Test.
	● Set DVOM to 200 ohm range.			
	● Measure resistance between J36 (SPOUT) at the second breakout box and J36 (SPOUT) at the first breakout box.			
	● **Is resistance less than 5.0 ohms?**			
F7	**CHECK SPOUT TRANSMISSION FROM PCM TO ICM—SPOUT JUMPER DISCONNECTED**			
	● Key off.	Yes	▶	REPLACE ICM. ICM is short to ground or open. REMOVE all test equipment. RECONNECT all components. CLEAR Continuous Memory. RERUN Quick Test.
	● Reconnect PCM and ICM.			
	● Remove SPOUT harness jumper plug from SPOUT vehicle harness connector.			
	● Set DVOM to 20 volt AC range.			
	● Start engine and measure voltage between J36 (SPOUT) at the second breakout box and J60 (B-).	No	▶	REPLACE PCM. SPOUT not being transmitted. REMOVE all test equipment. RECONNECT all components. CLEAR Continuous Memory. RERUN Quick Test.
	● **Is voltage greater than 2.0 volts AC?**			

Fig. 15   Test F: Code 213/412 Or No Codes & Lack Of Power, Spout Open Or Low (Part 3 of 5). 1993 2.3L Dual Plug Engine

TEST STEP		RESULT	▶	ACTION TO TAKE
F8	CHECK FOR SPOUT LOW—SPOUT FAULT—DIS MODULE DISCONNECTED—KEY OFF			
	• Key off.	Yes	▶	REPLACE DIS module. SPOUT shorted to ground in DIS module. REMOVE all test equipment. RECONNECT all components. CLEAR Continuous Memory. RERUN Quick Test.
	• Disconnect 1-6 DIS module tee from DIS module only. Do not disconnect other side of tee from vehicle harness. DIS diagnostic cable connected to the vehicle harness connector.			
	• Set DVOM to 200 ohm range.			
	• Measure resistance between J36 (SPOUT) and J60 (BAT-).			
	• Is resistance greater than 10 ohms?	No	▶	GO TO F9.
F9	CHECK FOR SPOUT SHORT LOW—SPOUT FAULT—PROCESSOR DISCONNECTED—KEY OFF			
	• Key off.	Yes	▶	REPLACE processor. SPOUT shorted to ground in the processor. REMOVE all test equipment. RECONNECT all components. CLEAR Continuous Memory. RERUN Quick Test.
	• Disconnect EEC processor.			
	• Set DVOM to 200 ohm range.			
	• Measure resistance between J36 (SPOUT) and J60 (BAT-).			
	• Is resistance greater than 10 ohms?	No	▶	GO to F10.

Fig. 15 Test F: Code 213/412 Or No Codes & Lack Of Power, Spout Open Or Low (Part 4 of 5). 2.3L Dual Plug Engine

TEST STEP		RESULT	▶	ACTION TO TAKE
F10	CHECK FOR SPOUT LOW—REMOVE SPOUT JUMPER—SPOUT FAULT—CHECK CONTINUITY			
	• Key off.	Yes	▶	SERVICE harness and connectors. SPOUT shorted to ground between the processor and the SPOUT connector. REMOVE all test equipment. RECONNECT all components. CLEAR Continuous Memory. RERUN Quick Test.
	• Remove SPOUT harness jumper plug from vehicle harness connector.			
	• Set DVOM to 200 ohm scale.			
	• Measure resistance between J60 (BAT-) and the DIS side of the SPOUT connector.			
	• Is resistance greater than 5.0 ohms?			
	DIS SIDE — [🔲] — EEC SIDE	No	▶	SERVICE harness. SPOUT shorted to ground in harness between the DIS module and the SPOUT connector. REMOVE all test equipment. RECONNECT all components. CLEAR Continuous Memory. RERUN Quick Test.
	SPOUT IN-LINE VEHICLE HARNESS CONNECTOR			

Fig. 15 Test F: Code 213/412 Or No Codes & Lack Of Power, Spout Open Or Low (Part 5 of 5). 2.3L Dual Plug Engine

These diagnostics (Pinpoint Tests A through G) are written to catch "Hard Faults"; intermittent failures will be difficult or impossible to diagnose using these procedures.

TEST STEP	ACTION TO TAKE
3.0L and 3.2L SFI SHO/3.8L SFI SC	
●No Start-With or Without Diagnostic Trouble Codes:	GO to A1.
—Diagnostic Trouble Code 211 (PIP failure)	GO to A1.
●Engine Runs With:	
—Diagnostic Trouble Code 212 (loss of IDM) or CID Failure	GO to B1.
—Diagnostic Trouble Code 212 and 214 or 214 and 212	GO to C1.
—Diagnostic Trouble Code 214 (CID failure at PCM)	GO to C1.
—Diagnostic Trouble Code 215-Coil 1, 216-Coil 2 or 217-Coil 3 (failure)	GO to D1.
—Erratic Start (Engine will start normally at least once out of five attempts) but when it starts, it starts normally. When it fails to start, the cranking rpm is erratic (ignition is firing out of time).	GO to B1.
—Diagnostic Trouble Code 213 (SPOUT failure)	GO to E1.
—Misses—Acceleration	GO to F1.
—Miss/Stall—Intermittent	GO to G1.
—Stalls/quits at idle	CHECK CID synchronizer.

Fig. 16 Diagnostics By Service Code & Symptom (Part 1 of 3). 1993 3.0L & 3.2L SHO & 3.8L SC Engines

These diagnostics (Pinpoint Tests A through G) are written to catch "Hard Faults"; intermittent failures will be difficult or impossible to diagnose using these procedures.

TEST STEP	ACTION TO TAKE
3.0L and 3.2L SFI SHO	
●No Start-With or Without Diagnostic Trouble Codes:	GO to A1.
—Diagnostic Trouble Code 211 (PIP failure)	GO to A1.
●No Start While SPOUT Connector Disconnected. Disconnect spout connector.	GO to A3.
●Engine Runs With:	
—Diagnostic Trouble Code 212 (loss of IDM) or CID Failure	GO to B1.
—Diagnostic Trouble Code 212 and 214 or 214 and 212	GO to C1.
—Diagnostic Trouble Code 214 (CID failure at PCM)	GO to C1.
—Diagnostic Trouble Code 215-Coil 1, 216-Coil 2 or 217-Coil 3 (failure)	GO to D1.
—Erratic Start (Engine will start normally at least once out of five attempts) but when it starts, it starts normally. When it fails to start, the cranking rpm is erratic (ignition is firing out of time).	GO to B1.
—Diagnostic Trouble Code 213 (SPOUT failure)	GO to E1.
—Misses—Acceleration	GO to F1.
—Stall—Miss—Stumble—Surge—Loss of Power—Intermittent	GO to Ignition System Intermittent Diagnostic Procedures
—Stalls/quits at idle	CHECK CID synchronizer.

Fig. 16 Diagnostics By Service Code & Symptom (Part 1 of 3). 1994–95 3.0L & 3.2L SHO Engines

The following voltage readings are typical for a normal vehicle with EI (Low Data Rate) Diagnostic harness attached. Do not use a "true RMS" type A/C voltmeter such as the Fluke 8060a or 87.

Measure Between Pins		Key On Engine Off (volts)	Engine Cranking (volts)	Engine Idling (volts)
First Pin	Second Pin			
C1C J4 (3.8L SC)	IGN GND J2	14.5 DC	1.2 AC	1.6 AC
C1C J12 (3.0 SHO)	IGN GND J2	14.5 DC	1.2 AC	1.6 AC
C2C J12 (3.8L SC)	IGN GND J2	14.5 DC	1.2 AC	1.6 AC
C2C J14 (3.0L SHO)	IGN GND J2	14.5 DC	1.2 AC	1.6 AC
C3C J13	IGN GND J2	14.5 DC	1.2 AC	1.6 AC
C1D J3	IGN GND J2	14.5 DC	1.2 AC	1.6 AC
C2D J18	IGN GND J2	14.5 DC	1.2 AC	1.6 AC
C3D J6	IGN GND J2	14.5 DC	1.2 AC	1.6 AC
ICM PWR J5	IGN GND J2	14.6 DC	13.0 DC	14.8 DC
CID I J51	IGN GND J2	11.8/0.2 DC	4.0 AC	7.0 AC
CMP CKP J21	IGN GND J2	11.8/0.2 DC	4.0 AC	7.0 AC
PIP ICM J32	IGN GND J2	11.8/0.2 DC	5.0 AC	6.8 AC
PIP CKP J35	IGN GND J2	11.8/0.2 DC	5.0 AC	6.8 AC
PIP PCM J33	IGN GND J2	11.8/0.2 DC	5.0 AC	6.8 AC
SPOUT I J36	IGN GND J2	11.8/ DC	0.1 AC	3.0 AC
IDM I J4	IGN GND J2	0.2 DC	4.0 AC	4.6 AC
COIL PWR J7	IGN GND J2	14.7 DC	13.0 DC	14.8 DC
CMP PWR J41	IGN GND J2	14.7 DC	13.0 DC	14.8 DC
CKP PWR J56	IGN GND J2	14.7 DC	13.0 DC	14.8 DC
RESET J54	IGN GND J2	0.2 DC	13.0 DC	0.2 DC

NOTE: The battery voltage was 14.8 volts DC when these readings were taken.

• The CID and PIP signals may be "high" (greater than 8 volts DC) or "low" KOEO depending on whether or not a tooth is in the air gap of the sensor.

• If the SPOUT jumper is removed, PIP will be fed through the ICM and appear on the SPOUT Test Jack J36 of the ICM.

• If a "true RMS" DVOM (Fluke 87) is used instead of the required "averaging" type DVOM (Rotunda 007-0001 or Fluke 88, 75 etc.) the value obtained will be significantly different in some cases than the values used in these Pinpoint Tests, resulting in incorrect answers to the pinpoint questions.

• Reset should be high only when the ignition switch is in the start (crank) position.

Fig. 16 Diagnostics By Service Code & Symptom (Part 2 of 3). 3.0L & 3.2L SHO & 1993 3.8L SC Engines

<table>
<tr><th colspan="2">TEST STEP</th><th>RESULT</th><th>▶</th><th>ACTION TO TAKE</th></tr>
</table>

	TEST STEP	RESULT	▶	ACTION TO TAKE
A1	PERFORM EEC QUICK TEST			
	• perform EEC Quick Test. • **Are any error service codes (KOEO, KOER or Continuous Memory) present?**	Yes No	▶ ▶	SERVICE any PCM code first. If still no start, GO TO A2. GO to A2.
A2	CHECK FOR SPARK DURING CRANK			
	• Using a Neon Bulb Spark Tester (Special Service Tool D89P-6666-A) or Air Gap Spark Tester (Special Service Tool D81P-6666-A), check for spark at all spark plug wires while cranking. • **Was spark present on all spark plug wires and consistent (one spark per crankshaft revolution)?**	Yes No	▶ ▶	GO to A8. GO to A3. Spark fault.
A3	CHECK PLUGS AND WIRES—SPARK FAULT			
	• Check spark plug wires for insulation damage, looseness, shorting or other damage. • Remove and check spark plugs for damage, wear, carbon deposits and proper plug gap. • **Are spark plugs and wires OK?**	Yes No	▶ ▶	REINSTALL plugs and wires. GO to A4. SERVICE or REPLACE damaged component. REMOVE all test equipment. RECONNECT all components. CLEAR Continuous Memory. RERUN Quick Test.
A4	CHECK IGN GND AT ICM			
	• Key off. • Install ICM 7-12 output tee. • Connect EI diagnostic harness to breakout box. • Use 3.0L / 3.2L / 3.8L overlay. • Connect EI diagnostic harness positive and negative leads to battery. • Set DVOM to 200 ohm scale. • Measure resistance between J60 (B-) and J2 (IGN GND I). • **Is resistance less than 5.0 ohms?**	Yes No	▶ ▶	GO to A5. GO to A13. IGN GND fault.
A5	CHECK ICM PWR			
	• Install the ICM (1-6) input tee. • Set DVOM to 20 volt DC scale. • Connect DVOM between (-) J2 (IGN GND I) and (+) J5 (ICM PWR). • Key on. • **Is DVOM reading greater than 10 volts DC?**	Yes No	▶ ▶	GO to A6. CHECK connectors, SERVICE or REPLACE harness. ICM PWR open. REMOVE all test equipment. RECONNECT all components. CLEAR Continuous Memory. RERUN Quick Test.

FM1119200252010X

Fig. 16 Diagnostics By Service Code & Symptom (Part 3 of 3). 3.0L & 3.2L SHO & 1993 3.8L SC Engines

Fig. 17 Test A: No Start (Part 1 of 6). 1993 3.0L & 3.2L SHO & 3.8L SC Engines

Note

• When using a DVOM, correct test lead polarity must be followed. The red lead is positive (+) and the black lead is negative (-).

• To check PIP or CID the engine is "bumped" one revolution of the crankshaft with the starter while watching the voltmeter (do not start engine). Both the CID and PIP signals are digital and should switch between "High" (greater than 8 volts DC) and "Low" (less than 2 volts DC) as the engine turns. To see the signal change using the VOM the engine must be turned in very short bursts.

IMPORTANT NOTE:

Most DVOM's used by auto technicians belong to a class or type known as "averaging." Examples are the Rotunda Digital Volt-Ohmmeter 007-0001, Fluke 70, 20 series and Fluke 88. Recently technicians have started to use DVOM'S of a different class (True RMS, DVOM's, Fluke 87, 8060A, 8062A, etc.). True RMS DVOM's should not be used with the Pinpoint Tests because they may display different voltage readings depending upon if the DVOM is turned on first and then the test leads are connected, or if the leads are connected first and then the DVOM is turned on. Also they may not auto range to the same range every time and some display significantly different values depending on the range selected. It would be impossible to list all of the meters and how to use each, so we are requesting that you perform the following test to verify your DVOM is compatible with the Pinpoint Tests.

Using a known good EI vehicle, install the EI (Low Data Rate) EI (High Data Rate) diagnostic harness, connect the EEC Breakout Box to the EI diagnostic harness, start the vehicle and measure the AC voltage between J18 (RC1I) and ground. The battery should be charged and the engine must be idling between 700 and 900 rpm. On any EI vehicle (except 1992 Escort / Tracer) the value should be between 1.0 and 2.0 volts AC (1.5 volts AC is typical). If you have the EI (Low Data Rate) hand held testers they may be used instead of the EI Diagnostic Harness / EEC Breakout Box to gain access to J18 (RC1D) and J31 (PIP PCM). Next, with the engine idling, measure between PIP and ground. This reading should be between 6 and 8 volts AC.

Because the Escort / Tracer EI (High Data Rate) ignition system fires the coil differently (repetitive spark) at idle, the coil to ground voltage reading should be between 2 to 7 volts AC (4.5 volts AC is typical). The PIP to ground reading on the Escort / Tracer is the same as the other EI systems.

If the readings you get agree with our test, your DVOM is OK to use with the Ignition Pinpoint Tests. If not, do not use it, it will lead to false parts replacement and the root cause will be difficult or impossible to find.

	TEST STEP	RESULT	▶	ACTION TO TAKE
A6	CHECK PIP AT ICM			
	• Set DVOM to 20 volt DC scale. • Connect DVOM between (+) J32 (PIP I) and (-) J60 (B-). • Bump engine in short bursts with starter without starting engine for at least five engine revolutions. • **Does DVOM reading switch between a low (less than 2.0 volts DC) and high (more than 8.0 volts DC)?**	Yes No	▶ ▶	GO to D1. GO to A7. PIP fault.
A7	CHECK PIP CIRCUIT—ICM INPUT DISCONNECTED—PIP CIRCUIT FAILURE			
	• Key off. • Set DVOM to 20 volts DC scale. • Disconnect ICM input tee (1-6) from ICM. Leave vehicle harness connected to module tee. • Connect DVOM between (+) J32 (PIP I) and (-) J60 (B-) • Bump engine in short bursts with starter without starting engine for at least five engine revolutions. • **Does DVOM reading switch between a low and high?**	Yes No	▶ ▶	REPLACE ICM. PIP shorted. REMOVE all test equipment. RECONNECT all components. CLEAR Continuous Memory. RERUN Quick Test. GO to A14. PIP fault.

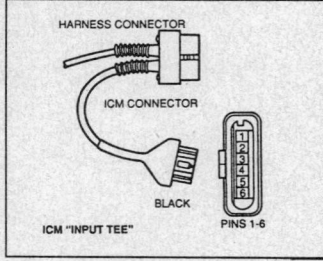 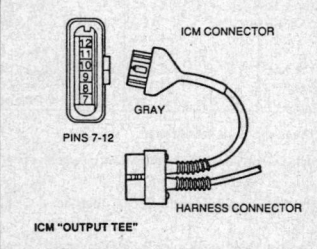

Fig. 17 Test A: No Start (Part 2 of 6). 1993 3.0L & 3.2L SHO & 3.8L SC Engines

---

	TEST STEP	RESULT	▶	ACTION TO TAKE
A8	CHECK PIP P AT CRANKSHAFT SENSOR			
	• Key off. • Install EI diagnostic harness crankshaft sensor tee. • Connect EI diagnostic harness negative lead to battery negative terminal. • Connect EI diagnostic harness to breakout box. • Set DVOM to 20 volts DC scale. • Use 3.0L / 3.8L overlay. • Connect DVOM between (+) J33 (PIP PCM S) and (-) J60 (B-). • Bump engine in short bursts with starter without starting engine for at least five engine revolutions. • **Does DVOM reading switch between a low (less than 2.0 volts DC) and high (more than 8.0 volts DC)?**	Yes No	▶ ▶	GO to A9. REPLACE crankshaft sensor. No output. REMOVE all test equipment. RECONNECT all components. CLEAR Continuous Memory. RERUN Quick Test.
A9	CHECK PIP P TO PCM CONTINUITY—PCM DISCONNECTED			
	• Key off. • Set DVOM to 200 ohm scale. • Disconnect PCM from vehicle harness connector. • Install second PCM breakout box at PCM vehicle harness connector. • Measure resistance between Test Pin 56 (PIP) of the second PCM breakout box and J33 (PIP PCM S). • **Is DVOM reading less than 5.0 ohms?**	Yes No	▶ ▶	GO to A10. SERVICE open PIP PCM S circuit. CHECK connectors, SERVICE or REPLACE harness. REMOVE all test equipment RECONNECT all components. CLEAR Continuous Memory. RERUN Quick Test.
A10	CHECK IGN GND AT ICM			
	• Key off. • Install ICM output tee (7-12). • Set DVOM to 200 ohm scale. • Measure the resistance between J2 (IGN GND I) and J60 (B-). • **Is DVOM reading less than 5.0 ohms?**	Yes No	▶ ▶	GO to A12. GO to A11. IGN GND fault.
A11	CHECK ICM MOUNTING SCREWS			
	• Check ICM mounting screws for corrosion or looseness. • **Are mounting screws clean and tight?**	Yes No	▶ ▶	REPLACE ICM. IGN GND open. CLEAN, REPLACE or TIGHTEN mounting screws.

Fig. 17   Test A: No Start (Part 3 of 6). 1993 3.0L 3.2L SHO & 3.8L SC Engines

TEST STEP	RESULT	▶	ACTION TO TAKE
A12 CHECK IGN GND TO PCM CONTINUITY—PCM DISCONNECTED • Key off. • Set DVOM to 200 ohm scale. • Disconnect PCM from vehicle harness. • Install second EEC breakout box at EEC vehicle harness. • Measure resistance between Test Pin 56 (PIP) of second EEC breakout box and J33 (PIP PCM S). • **Is DVOM reading less than 5.0 ohms?**	Yes No	▶ ▶	Ignition System checks out OK. CHECK connectors. SERVICE or REPLACE harness, IGN GND is open.
A13 CHECK ICM MOUNTING SCREWS • Check ICM mounting screws for corrosion or looseness. • **Are mounting screws clean and tight?**	Yes No	▶ ▶	REPLACE ICM. RERUN Quick Test. Ignition ground open. CLEAN, REPLACE or TIGHTEN mounting screws. RERUN Quick Test.
A14 CHECK PIP CIRCUIT—PCM DISCONNECTED • Key off. • Reconnect EI diagnostic harness input tee connector (1-6) to ICM. • Disconnect PCM. • Set DVOM to 20 volts DC scale. • Connect DVOM between (+) J32 (PIP I) anc (-) J60 (B-). • Bump engine in short bursts with starter without starting for at least five engine revolutions. • **Does DVOM reading switch between low and high?**	Yes No	▶ ▶	REPLACE PCM. PIP shorted. GO to [A15]. PIP fault.
A15 CHECK PIP AT CRANKSHAFT SENSOR • Set DVOM to 20 volt DC scale. • Install crankshaft sensor tee (the word "SENSOR" is printed on the tee in green letters.) • Connect DVOM between (+) J35 (PIP S) and (-) J2 (IGN GND I). • Bump engine in short bursts with starter without starting engine for at least five engine revolutions. • **Does DVOM reading switch between low and high?**	Yes No	▶ ▶	CHECK connectors. SERVICE or REPLACE harness. REMOVE all test equipment. RECONNECT all components. CLEAR Continuous Memory. RERUN Quick Test. PIP open. GO to [A16].

Fig. 17   Test A: No Start (Part 4 of 6). 1993 3.0L & 3.2L SHO & 3.8L SC Engines

TEST STEP	RESULT	▶	ACTION TO TAKE
A16 CHECK CKP SENSOR IGNITION GROUND • Key off. • Measure resistance between J55 (IGND CKP) and J2 (IGN GND I). • **Is resistance less than 5.0 ohms?**	Yes No	▶ ▶	GO to [A17]. CHECK connectors. IGN GND open. REMOVE all test equipment. RECONNECT all components. CLEAR Continuous Memory. RERUN Quick Test.
A17 CHECK CKP SENSOR CKP PWR • Set DVOM to 20 volt DC scale. • Connect DVOM between (+) J56 (CKP PWR) and (-) J2 (IGN GND I). • Key on. • **Is DVOM reading greater tha 10 volts DC?**	Yes No	▶ ▶	GO to [A19]. CHECK connectors. SERVICE or REPLACE harness. CKP PWR is open. REMOVE all test equipment. RECONNECT all components. CLEAR Continuous Memory. RERUN Quick Test.
A18 CHECK PIP FOR SHORT TO GROUND—CRANKSHAFT SENSOR AND ICM INPUT DISCONNECTED • Key off. • Set DVOM to 20K ohm scale. • Disconnect EI diagnostic harness connector from crankshaft sensor. Leave vehicle harness connected to sensor tee. • Disconnect EI diagnostic harness connector from ICM (Pins 1-6). Leave vehicle harness connected to module tee. • Connect DVOM between J35 (PIP S) and J60 (B-). • **Is DVOM reading greater than 10K ohms?**	Yes No	▶ ▶	GO to [A19]. CHECK connectors. SERVICE or REPLACE harness. PIP is shorted to ground between sensor and ICM. REMOVE all test equipment. CLEAR Continuous Memory. RERUN Quick Test.
A19 CHECK PIP S FOR SHORT HIGH—CRANKSHAFT SENSOR AND ICM INPUT TEE DISCONNECTED • Key off. • Set DVOM to 20 DC scale. • Connect DVOM between (+) J35 (PIP S) and (-) J60 (B-). • Key on. • **Is DVOM reading less than 0.5 volts?**	Yes No	▶ ▶	GO to [A20]. CHECK connectors, SERVICE or REPLACE harness. PIP is shorted high between sensor and ICM. REMOVE all test equipment. RECONNECT all components. CLEAR Continuous Memory. RERUN Quick Test.

Fig. 17   Test A: No Start (Part 5 of 6). 1993 3.0L & 3.2L SHO & 3.8L SC Engines

TEST STEP	RESULT	▶	ACTION TO TAKE
A20 CHECK PIP PCM FOR SHORT HIGH—CRANKSHAFT SENSOR, ICM INPUT AND PCM DISCONNECTED • Key off. • Set DVOM to 20 volt DC scale. • Disconnect PCM from vehicle harness. • Connect DVOM between (+) J33 (PIP PCM S) and (-) J60 (B-). • Key on. • **Is DVOM reading less than 0.5 volts DC?**	Yes No	▶ ▶	GO to [A21]. CHECK connectors, SERVICE or REPLACE harness. PIP is shorted high. REMOVE all test equipment. RECONNECT all components. CLEAR Continuous Memory. RERUN Quick Test.
A21 CHECK PIP P FOR SHORT TO GROUND—CRANKSHAFT SENSOR, ICM INPUT AND PCM DISCONNECTED • Key off. • Set DVOM to 20K ohms scale. • Connect DVOM between J33 (PIP PCM S) and J60 (B-). • **Is resistance greater than 10K ohms?**	Yes No	▶ ▶	Go to [A22]. CHECK connectors. SERVICE or REPLACE harnss. PIP is shorted to ground. REMOVE all test equipment. RECONNECT all components. CLEAR Continuous Memory. RERUN Quick Test.
A22 CHECK CRANKSHAFT VANE • **Does crankshaft vane move through sensor air gap when engine is cranked?**	Yes No	▶	REPLACE crankshaft sensor. REMOVE all test equipment. RECONNECT all components. CLEAR Continuous Memory. RERUN Quick Test. service vane damage.
A23 CHECK CRANKSHAFT VANE • **Does crankshaft vane move through sensor air gap when engine is cranked?**	Yes No	▶	REPLACE crankshaft sensor. REMOVE all test equipment. RECONNECT all components. CLEAR Continuous Memory. RERUN Quick Test. service vane damage.

Fig. 17   Test A: No Start (Part 6 of 6). 1993 3.0L & 3.2L SHO & 3.8L SC Engines

TEST STEP		RESULT	▶	ACTION TO TAKE
A1	PERFORM EEC QUICK TEST			
	• perform EEC Quick Test. • Are any error service codes (KOEO, KOER or Continuous Memory) present?	Yes	▶	SERVICE any PCM code first. If still no start, GO TO A2.
		No	▶	GO to A2.
A2	CHECK FOR SPARK DURING CRANK			
	• Using a Neon Bulb Spark Tester (Special Service Tool D89P-6666-A) or Air Gap Spark Tester (Special Service Tool D81P-6666-A), check for spark at all spark plug wires while cranking. • Was spark present on all spark plug wires and consistent (one spark per crankshaft revolution)?	Yes	▶	GO to A8.
		No	▶	GO to A3. Spark fault.
A3	CHECK PLUGS AND WIRES — SPARK FAULT			
	• Check spark plug wires for insulation damage, looseness, shorting or other damage. • Remove and check spark plugs for damage, wear, carbon deposits and proper plug gap. • Are spark plugs and wires OK?	Yes	▶	REINSTALL plugs and wires. GO to A4.
		No	▶	SERVICE or REPLACE damaged component. REMOVE all test equipment. RECONNECT all components. CLEAR Continuous Memory. RERUN Quick Test.
A4	CHECK IGN GND AT ICM			
	• Key off. • Install ICM 7-12 output tee. • Connect EI diagnostic harness to breakout box. • Use 3.0L / 3.2L overlay. • Connect EI diagnostic harness positive and negative leads to battery. • Set DVOM to 200 ohm scale. • Measure resistance between J60 (B-) and J2 (IGN GND I). • Is resistance less than 5.0 ohms?	Yes	▶	GO to A5.
		No	▶	GO to A13. IGN GND fault.
A5	CHECK ICM PWR			
	• Install the ICM (1-6) input tee. • Set DVOM to 40 volt DC scale. • Connect DVOM between (-) J2 (IGN GND I) and (+) J5 (ICM PWR). • Key on. • Is DVOM reading greater than 10 volts DC?	Yes	▶	GO to A6.
		No	▶	CHECK connectors, SERVICE or REPLACE harness. ICM PWR open. REMOVE all test equipment. RECONNECT all components. CLEAR Continuous Memory. RERUN Quick Test.

FM1119400253010X

Fig. 18   Test A: No Start (Part 1 of 6). 1994–95 3.0L & 3.2L SHO Engines

TEST STEP		RESULT	▶	ACTION TO TAKE
A6	CHECK PIP AT ICM			
	• Set DVOM to 40 volt DC scale. • Connect DVOM between (+) J32 (PIP I) and (-) J60 (B-). • Bump engine in short bursts with starter without starting engine for at least five engine revolutions. • Does DVOM reading switch between a low (less than 2.0 volts DC) and high (more than 8.0 volts DC)?	Yes	▶	GO to D1.
		No	▶	GO to A7. PIP fault.
A7	CHECK PIP CIRCUIT — ICM INPUT DISCONNECTED — PIP CIRCUIT FAILURE			
	• Key off. • Set DVOM to 40 volts DC scale. • Disconnect ICM input tee (1-6) from ICM. Leave vehicle harness connected to module tee. • Connect DVOM between (+) J32 (PIP I) and (-) J60 (B-). • Bump engine in short bursts with starter for at least five engine revolutions. • Does DVOM reading switch between a low and high?	Yes	▶	REPLACE ICM. PIP shorted. REMOVE all test equipment. RECONNECT all components. CLEAR Continuous Memory. RERUN Quick Test.
		No	▶	GO to A14. PIP fault.

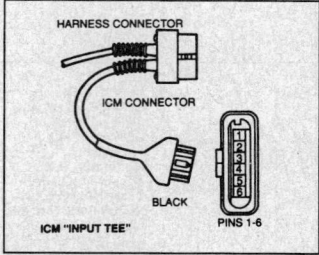 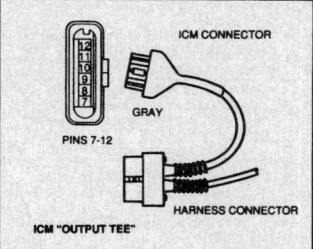

FM1119400253020X

Fig. 18   Test A: No Start (Part 2 of 6). 1994–95 3.0L & 3.2L SHO Engines

TEST STEP		RESULT	▶	ACTION TO TAKE
A8	CHECK PIP P AT CRANKSHAFT SENSOR			
	• Key off. • Install EI diagnostic harness crankshaft sensor tee. • Connect EI diagnostic harness negative lead to battery negative terminal. • Connect EI diagnostic harness to breakout box. • Set DVOM to 40 volts DC scale. • Use 3.0L overlay. • Connect DVOM between (+) J33 (PIP PCM S) and (-) J60 (B-). • Bump engine in short bursts with starter without starting engine for at least five engine revolutions. • Does DVOM reading switch between a low (less than 2.0 volts DC) and high (more than 8.0 volts DC)?	Yes	▶	GO to A9.
		No	▶	REPLACE crankshaft sensor. No output. REMOVE all test equipment. RECONNECT all components. CLEAR Continuous Memory. RERUN Quick Test.
A9	CHECK PIP P TO PCM CONTINUITY — PCM DISCONNECTED			
	• Key off. • Set DVOM to 200 ohm scale. • Disconnect PCM from vehicle harness connector. • Install second PCM breakout box at PCM vehicle harness connector. • Measure resistance between Test Pin 56 (PIP) of the second PCM breakout box and J33 (PIP PCM S). • Is DVOM reading less than 5.0 ohms?	Yes	▶	GO to A10.
		No	▶	SERVICE open PIP PCM S circuit. CHECK connectors, SERVICE or REPLACE harness. REMOVE all test equipment RECONNECT all components. CLEAR Continuous Memory. RERUN Quick Test.
A10	CHECK IGN GND AT ICM			
	• Key off. • Install ICM output tee (7-12). • Set DVOM to 200 ohm scale. • Measure the resistance between J2 (IGN GND I) and J60 (B-). • Is DVOM reading less than 5.0 ohms?	Yes	▶	GO to A12.
		No	▶	GO to A11. IGN GND fault.
A11	CHECK ICM MOUNTING SCREWS			
	• Check ICM mounting screws for corrosion or looseness. • Are mounting screws clean and tight?	Yes	▶	REPLACE ICM. IGN GND open.
		No	▶	CLEAN, REPLACE or TIGHTEN mounting screws.

FM1119400253030X

Fig. 18   Test A: No Start (Part 3 of 6). 1994–95 3.0L & 3.2L SHO Engines

TEST STEP	RESULT	▶	ACTION TO TAKE
A12 CHECK IGN GND TO PCM CONTINUITY — PCM DISCONNECTED • Key off. • Set DVOM to 200 ohm scale. • Disconnect PCM from vehicle harness. • Install second EEC breakout box at EEC vehicle harness. • Measure resistance between Test Pin 56 (PIP) of second EEC breakout box and J33 (PIP PCM S). • **Is DVOM reading less than 5.0 ohms?**	Yes No	▶ ▶	REFER to Section 2A. Ignition System checks out OK. CHECK connectors. SERVICE or REPLACE harness. IGN GND is open.
A13 CHECK ICM MOUNTING SCREWS • Check ICM mounting screws for corrosion or looseness. • **Are mounting screws clean and tight?**	Yes No	▶ ▶	REPLACE ICM. RERUN Quick Test. Ignition ground open. CLEAN, REPLACE or TIGHTEN mounting screws. RERUN Quick Test.
A14 CHECK PIP CIRCUIT — PCM DISCONNECTED • Key off. • Reconnect EI diagnostic harness input tee connector (1-6) to ICM. • Disconnect PCM. • Set DVOM to 40 volts DC scale. • Connect DVOM between (+) J32 (PIP I) and (-) J60 (B-). • Bump engine in short bursts with starter for at least five engine revolutions. • **Does DVOM reading switch between low and high?**	Yes No	▶ ▶	REPLACE PCM. PIP shorted. GO to **A15**. PIP fault.
A15 CHECK PIP AT CRANKSHAFT SENSOR • Set DVOM to 40 volt DC scale. • Install crankshaft sensor tee (the word "SENSOR" is printed on the tee in green letters). • Reconnect SPOUT in line connector. • Reconnect PCM. • Connect DVOM between (+) J35 (PIP S) and (-) J2 (IGN GND I). • Bump engine in short bursts with starter engine for at least five engine revolutions. • **Does DVOM reading switch between low and high?**	Yes No	▶ ▶	CHECK connectors. SERVICE or REPLACE harness. PIP open. REMOVE all test equipment. RECONNECT all components. CLEAR Continuous Memory. RERUN Quick Test. PIP open. GO to **A16**.

FM1119400253040X

Fig. 18   Test A: No Start (Part 4 of 6). 1994–95 3.0L & 3.2L SHO Engines

TEST STEP	RESULT	▶	ACTION TO TAKE
A16 CHECK CKP SENSOR IGNITION GROUND • Key off. • Disconnect PCM. • Measure resistance between J55 (IGND CKP) and J2 (IGN GND I). • **Is resistance less than 5.0 ohms?**	Yes No	▶ ▶	GO to **A17**. CHECK connectors. IGN GND is open. REMOVE all test equipment. RECONNECT all components. CLEAR Continuous Memory. RERUN Quick Test.
A17 CHECK CKP SENSOR CKP PWR • Set DVOM to 40 volt DC scale. • Connect DVOM between (+) J56 (CKP PWR) and (-) J2 (IGN GND I). • Key on. • **Is DVOM reading greater than 10 volts DC?**	Yes No	▶ ▶	GO to **A18**. CHECK connectors. SERVICE or REPLACE harness. CKP PWR is open. REMOVE all test equipment. RECONNECT all components. CLEAR Continuous Memory. RERUN Quick Test.
A18 CHECK PIP FOR SHORT TO GROUND — CRANKSHAFT SENSOR AND ICM INPUT DISCONNECTED • Key off. • Set DVOM to 20K ohm scale. • Disconnect EI diagnostic harness connector from crankshaft sensor. Leave vehicle harness connected to sensor tee. • Disconnect EI diagnostic harness connector from ICM (Pins 1-6). Leave vehicle harness connected to module tee. • Connect DVOM between J35 (PIP S) and J60 (B-). • **Is DVOM reading greater than 10K ohms?**	Yes No	▶ ▶	GO to **A19**. CHECK connectors. SERVICE or REPLACE harness. PIP is shorted to ground between sensor and ICM. REMOVE all test equipment. CLEAR Continuous Memory. RERUN Quick Test.
A19 CHECK PIP S FOR SHORT HIGH — CRANKSHAFT SENSOR AND ICM INPUT TEE DISCONNECTED • Key off. • Set DVOM to 40 DC scale. • Connect DVOM between (+)J35 (PIP S) and (-) J60 (B-). • Key on. • **Is DVOM reading less than 0.5 volts?**	Yes No	▶ ▶	GO to **A20**. CHECK connectors, SERVICE or REPLACE harness. PIP is shorted high between sensor and ICM. REMOVE all test equipment. RECONNECT all components. CLEAR Continuous Memory. RERUN Quick Test.

FM1119400253050X

Fig. 18   Test A: No Start (Part 5 of 6). 1994–95 3.0L & 3.2L SHO Engines

TEST STEP	RESULT	▶	ACTION TO TAKE
A20 CHECK PIP PCM FOR SHORT HIGH — CRANKSHAFT SENSOR, ICM INPUT AND PCM DISCONNECTED • Key off. • Set DVOM to 40 volt DC scale. • Disconnect PCM from vehicle harness. • Connect DVOM between (+) J33 (PIP PCM S) and (-) J60 (B-). • Key on. • **Is DVOM reading less than 0.5 volts DC?**	Yes No	▶ ▶	GO to **A21**. CHECK connectors, SERVICE or REPLACE harness. PIP is shorted high. REMOVE all test equipment. RECONNECT all components. CLEAR Continuous Memory. RERUN Quick Test.
A21 CHECK PIP P FOR SHORT TO GROUND — CRANKSHAFT SENSOR, ICM INPUT AND PCM DISCONNECTED • Key off. • Set DVOM to 20K ohms scale. • Connect DVOM between J33 (PIP PCM S) and J60 (B-). • **Is resistance greater than 10K ohms?**	Yes No	▶ ▶	Go to **A22**. CHECK connectors. SERVICE or REPLACE harnss. PIP is shorted to ground. REMOVE all test equipment. RECONNECT all components. CLEAR Continuous Memory. RERUN Quick Test.
A22 CHECK CRANKSHAFT VANE • **Does crankshaft vane move through sensor air gap when engine is cranked?**	Yes No	▶ ▶	REPLACE crankshaft sensor. REMOVE all test equipment. RECONNECT all components. CLEAR Continuous Memory. RERUN Quick Test. SERVICE vane.

FM1119400253060X

Fig. 18   Test A: No Start (Part 6 of 6). 1994–95 3.0L & 3.2L SHO Engines

TEST STEP	RESULT	▶	ACTION TO TAKE
B1 VERIFY ERRATIC STARTING • Is starting erratic? (i.e., engine will start normally at lease once out of five attempts but when it does not start the cranking rpm is erratic (ignition system firing coils out of sequence)	Yes No	▶ ▶	GO to **B2**. GO to **B4**.
B2 CHECK CID AT ICM • Key off. • Install ICM input (1-6) tee. • Connect EI diagnostic harness positive and negative leads. • Connect EI diagnostic harness to breakout box. • Set DVOM to 20 volt DC scale. • Use 3.0L / 3.2L / 3.8L overlay. • Connect the DVOM between (+) J51 (CID I) and (-)J60 (B-). • Bump engine is short bursts with starter without starting engine for at least ten engine revolutions. • **Does DVOM reading switch between low (less than 2.0 volts DC) and high (more than 8.0 volts DC)?**	Yes No	▶ ▶	REPLACE ICM. Does not respond to CID input. REMOVE all test equipment. RECONNECT all components. CLEAR Continuous Memory. RERUN Quick Test. GO to **B3**. CID fault.
B3 CHECK CMP AT SENSOR — CMP FAULT • Key off. • Install CMP sensor tee (the word "SENSOR" is printed in yellow letters). • Set DVOM to 20 volt DC scale. • Connect the DVOM between (+)J21 (CID S) and (-)J60 (B-). • Bump engine in short bursts with starter without starting engine for at least ten engine revolutions. • **Does DVOM reading switch between low and high?**	Yes No	▶ ▶	CHECK connectors or SERVICE harness. CID circuit is open between the camshaft sensor and ICM. REMOVE all test equipment. RECONNECT all components. CLEAR Continuous Memory. RERUN Quick Test. REPLACE CMP sensor, CID S is open.
B4 CHECK ICM IDM OUTPUT — IDM FAULT • Key off. • Set DVOM to 20 volt AC scale. • Install ICM (7-12) output tee. • Connect EI diagnostic harness positive and negative leads to battery. • Connect EI diagnostic harness to breakout box. • Use 3.0L / 3.2L / 3.8L overlay. • Connect DVOM between J4 (IDM I) and J60 (B-). • Start engine. • **Is DVOM reading greater than 1.0 volt AC?**	Yes No	▶ ▶	GO to **B5**. GO to **B6**.

Fig. 19   Test B: Code 212, IDM Low Or CMP Circuit To ICM Open Or Erratic Starting (Part 1 of 3). 1993 3.0L SHO & 3.8L SC & 1993 3.2L SHO Engines

TEST STEP	RESULT	▶	ACTION TO TAKE
B6 CHECK PROCESSOR—IDM FAULT—PROCESSOR DISCONNECTED • Key off. • Set DVOM to 20 volt scale. • Disconnect processor. • Connect the DVOM between (+)J21 (CID CS) and (-)J60 (BAT-). • Bump the engine in short bursts with the starter without starting engine for at least ten engine revolutions. • **Does DVOM reading switch between low and high?**	Yes No	▶ ▶ ▶	REPLACE processor. Does not respond to CID input. REMOVE all test equipment. RECONNECT all components. CLEAR Continuous Memory. RERUN Quick Test. GO to **B7**. SERVICE harness and connectors. IDM is shorted to ground between DIS module and processor. REMOVE all test equipment. RECONNECT all components. CLEAR Continuous Memory. RERUN Quick Test.
B7 CHECK FOR SHORT HIGH—IDM FAULT—DIS MODULE AND PROCESSOR DISCONNECTED • Key off. • Disconnect DIS module output tee (7-12) from DIS module. Leave vehicle harness connected to output tee. • Set DVOM to 20 VDC scale. • Connect DVOM between (+)J4 (IDMD) and (-)J60 (BAT-). • Key on. • **Is DVOM reading greater than 5.0 volts DC?**	Yes No	▶ ▶	SERVICE harness and connectors. IDM is shorted high between DIS module and processor. REMOVE all test equipment. RECONNECT all components. CLEAR Continuous Memory. RERUN Quick Test. GO to **B8**.

Fig. 19   Test B: Code 212, IDM Low Or CMP Circuit To ICM Open Or Erratic Starting (Part 2 of 3). 1993 3.0L & 3.8L SC & 1993 & 3.2L SHO Engines

TEST STEP	RESULT	▶	ACTION TO TAKE
B8 CHECK FOR IDM SHORT LOW—IDM FAULT—ICM AND PCM DISCONNECTED • Key off. • Set DVOM to 20K ohm scale. • Measure resistance between J4 (IDM I) and J60 (B-). • **Is DVOM reading greater than 10K ohms?**	Yes No	▶ ▶	REPLACE ICM. No IDM output. REMOVE all test equipment. RECONNECT all components. CLEAR Continuous Memory. RERUN Quick Test. SERVICE harness and connectors. IDM is shorted high between ICM and PCM. REMOVE all test equipment. RECONNECT all components. CLEAR Continuous Memory. RERUN Quick Test.

Fig. 19   Test B: Code 212, IDM Low Or CMP Circuit To ICM Open Or Erratic Starting (Part 3 of 3). 1993 3.0L & 3.8L SC & 3.2L SHO Engines

TEST STEP	RESULT	▶	ACTION TO TAKE
B1 VERIFY ERRATIC STARTING • Is starting erratic? (i.e., engine will start normally at lease once out of five attempts but when it does not start the cranking rpm is erratic) (ignition system firing coils out of sequence)	Yes No	▶ ▶	GO to **B2**. GO to **B4**.
B2 CHECK CID AT ICM • Key off. • Install ICM input (1-6) tee. • Connect EI diagnostic harness positive and negative leads. • Connect EI diagnostic harness to breakout box. • Set DVOM to 40 volt DC scale. • Use 3.0L / 3.2L overlay. • Connect the DVOM between (+) J51 (CID I) and (-)J60 (B-). • Bump engine in short bursts with starter for at least ten engine revolutions. • **Does DVOM reading switch between low (less than 2.0 volts DC) and high (more than 8.0 volts DC)?**	Yes No	▶ ▶	REPLACE ICM. Does not respond to CID input. REMOVE all test equipment. RECONNECT all components. CLEAR Continuous Memory. RERUN Quick Test. GO to **B3**. CID fault.
B3 CHECK CMP AT SENSOR—CMP FAULT • Key off. • Install CMP sensor tee (the word "SENSOR" is printed in yellow letters). • Set DVOM to 40 volt DC scale. • Connect the DVOM between (+)J21 (CID S) and (-)J60 (B-). • Bump engine in short bursts with starter without starting engine for at least ten engine revolutions. • **Does DVOM reading switch between low and high?**	Yes No	▶ ▶	CHECK connectors or SERVICE harness. CID circuit is open between the camshaft sensor and ICM. REMOVE all test equipment. RECONNECT all components. CLEAR Continuous Memory. RERUN Quick Test. REPLACE CMP sensor. CID S is open.
B4 CHECK ICM IDM OUTPUT—IDM FAULT • Key off. • Set DVOM to 40 volt AC scale. • Install ICM (7-12) output tee. • Connect EI diagnostic harness positive and negative leads to battery. • Connect EI diagnostic harness to breakout box. • Use 3.0L/3.2L overlay. • Connect DVOM between J4 (IDM I) and J60 (B-). • Start engine. • Is DVOM reading greater than 1.0 volt AC?	Yes No	▶ ▶	GO to **B5**. GO to **B6**.

FM1119400255010X

Fig. 20   Test B: Code 212, IDM Low Or CID Circuit To EI Open Or Erratic Starting (Part 1 of 3). 1994–95 3.0L & 3.2L SHO Engines

TEST STEP	RESULT	▶	ACTION TO TAKE
B5 CHECK IDM CONTINUITY—IDM FAULT—PCM DISCONNECTED • Key off. • Set DVOM to 200 ohm scale. • Disconnect PCM. • Install the second EEC breakout box to the EEC vehicle connector. • Connect the DVOM between Test Pin 4 (IDM I) of the second EEC breakout box and J4 (IDM I). • **Is DVOM reading less than 5.0 ohms?**	Yes No	▶ ▶	REPLACE PCM. Does not respond to IDM input. REMOVE all test equipment. RECONNECT all components. CLEAR Continuous Memory. RERUN Quick Test. SERVICE harness and connectors. IDM is open between ICM and PCM. REMOVE all test equipment. RECONNECT all components. CLEAR Continuous Memory. RERUN Quick Test.
B6 CHECK PCM—IDM FAULT—PCM DISCONNECTED • Key off. • Set DVOM to 40 volt scale. • Disconnect PCM. • Connect the DVOM between (+)J4 (IDM I) and (-)J60 (B-). • Bump the engine in short bursts with the starter for at least ten engine revolutions. • **Does DVOM reading switch between low and high?**	Yes No	▶ ▶	REPLACE PCM. Does not respond to IDM input. REMOVE all test equipment. RECONNECT all components. CLEAR Continuous Memory. RERUN Quick Test. GO to **B7**.
B7 CHECK FOR IDM SHORT HIGH—IDM FAULT—ICM AND PCM DISCONNECTED • Key off. • PCM disconnected. • Disconnect ICM output tee (7-12) from ICM. Leave vehicle harness connected to output tee. • Set DVOM to 40 VDC scale. • Connect DVOM between (+)J4 (IDM I) and (-)J60 (B-). • Key on. • **Is DVOM reading less than 6.0 volts DC?**	Yes No	▶ ▶	GO to **B8**. SERVICE harness and connectors. IDM is shorted high between ICM and PCM. REMOVE all test equipment. RECONNECT all components. CLEAR Continuous Memory. RERUN Quick Test.

FM1119400255020X

Fig. 20   Test B: Code 212, IDM Low Or CID Circuit To EI Open Or Erratic Starting (Part 2 of 3). 1994–95 3.0L & 3.2L SHO Engines

TEST STEP	RESULT	▶	ACTION TO TAKE
B8 CHECK FOR IDM SHORT LOW—IDM FAULT—ICM AND PCM DISCONNECTED • Key off. • Set DVOM to 20K ohm scale. • Measure resistance between J4 (IDM I) and J60 (B-). • **Is DVOM reading greater than 10K ohms?**	Yes	▶	REPLACE ICM. No IDM output. REMOVE all test equipment. RECONNECT all components. CLEAR Continuous Memory. RERUN Quick Test.
	No	▶	SERVICE harness and connectors. IDM is shorted high between ICM and PCM. REMOVE all test equipment. RECONNECT all components. CLEAR Continuous Memory. RERUN Quick Test.

FM1119400255030X

Fig. 20   Test B: Code 212, IDM Low Or CID Circuit To EI Open Or Erratic Starting (Part 3 of 3). 1994–95 3.0L & 3.2L SHO Engines

TEST STEP	RESULT	▶	ACTION TO TAKE
C3 CHECK CID S AT CAMSHAFT SENSOR—CID FAULT—KOEC • Key off. • Set DVOM to 40 volt DC scale. • Connect DVOM between (+)J21 (CID S) and (-)J60 (B-). • Bump engine in short bursts with starter without starting engine for at least 10 engine revolutions. • **Does DVOM reading switch between low and high?**	Yes	▶	REPLACE CMP sensor. CID is open between J21 (CID S) and J22 (CID PCM S). REMOVE all test equipment. RECONNECT all components. CLEAR Continuous Memory. RERUN Quick Test.
	No	▶	GO to C4.
C4 CHECK CAMSHAFT SENSOR CMP PWR—CID FAULT—KOEO • Key off. • Set DVOM to 40 volt DC scale. • Connect DVOM between (+)J41 (CMP PWR) and (-)J60 (B-). • Key on. • **Is DVOM reading greater than 10 volts DC?**	Yes	▶	GO to C5.
	No	▶	SERVICE connectors and harness. CMP PWR open, fault at sensor. REMOVE all test equipment. RECONNECT all components. CLEAR Continuous Memory. RERUN Quick Test.
C5 CHECK CAMSHAFT SENSOR IGNITION GROUND—CMP FAULT—KEY OFF • Key off. • Set DVOM to 40 ohm scale. • Connect DVOM between J42 (IGND CMP) and J60 (B-). • **Is DVOM reading less than 5.0 ohms?**	Yes	▶	GO to C6.
	No	▶	SERVICE connectors and harness. IGN GND open at sensor. REMOVE all test equipment. RECONNECT all components. CLEAR Continuous Memory. RERUN Quick Test.
C6 CHECK ICM—ICM INPUT DISCONNECTED—CID FAULT—KOEC • Key off. • Set DVOM to 40 volt DC scale. • Disconnect ICM (1-6) vehicle harness input connector from ICM. • Connect the DVOM between (+)J21 (CID S) and (-)J60 (B-). • Bump the engine in short bursts without starting engine for at least 10 engine revolutions. • **Does DVOM reading switch between low and high?**	Yes	▶	REPLACE ICM. RERUN Quick Test.
	No	▶	GO to C7.

Fig. 21   Test C: Code 214, CID To PCM Failure (Part 2 of 4). 1993 3.0L, 3.2L SHO & 3.8L SC

TEST STEP	RESULT	▶	ACTION TO TAKE
C11 CHECK CID S FOR SHORT TO GND—ICM, PCM AND CMP SENSOR DISCONNECTED—FAULT—KEY OFF • Key off. • Set DVOM to 20K ohm scale. • Connect DVOM between J21 (CID S) and J60 (B-). • **Is DVOM reading greater than 10K ohms?**	Yes	▶	GO to C12.
	No	▶	SERVICE connectors and harness. CID S is shorted to GND. REMOVE all test equipment. RECONNECT all components. CLEAR Continuous Memory. RERUN Quick Test.
C12 CHECK CMP SENSOR VANE—CMP FAULT—KOEC • Does vane move through air gap when engine is cranked?	Yes	▶	REPLACE CMP sensor. No CID output.
	No	▶	SERVICE vane.

Fig. 21   Test C: Code 214, CID To PCM Failure (Part 4 of 4). 1993 3.0L, 3.2L SHO & 3.8L SC

TEST STEP	RESULT	▶	ACTION TO TAKE
C1 CHECK CID CMP S AT CAMSHAFT SENSOR—KOEC NOTE: For proper results of this test, and all other Pinpoint Test Steps C, the Star Tester must be disconnected. • Key off. • Set DVOM to 40 volt DC scale. • Install CMP sensor tee (the word "SENSOR" is printed in yellow letters on the tee). • Connect EI diagnostic harness to breakout box. • Disconnect PCM. • Connect diagnostic harness positive and negative leads to battery. • Use 3.0L/3.2L overlay. • Connect DVOM between (+)J22 (CID PCM S) and (-)J60 (B-). • Bump engine in short bursts with the starter without starting engine for at least 10 engine revolutions. • **Does DVOM reading switch between "low" (less than 2.0 volts DC) and "high" (more than 8.0 volts DC)?**	Yes	▶	GO to C2.
	No	▶	GO to C3. CMP fault.
C2 CHECK CID TO PCM CONTINUITY—PCM DISCONNECTED—KEY OFF • Key off. • Set DVOM to 200 ohm scale. • PCM disconnected. • Connect second EEC breakout box to the PCM vehicle connector. • Connect DVOM between J22 (CID PCM S) and Test Pin 24 (CID) of second EEC breakout box. • **Is DVOM reading less than 5.0 ohms?**	Yes	▶	REPLACE PCM. Does not respond to CMP inputs. REMOVE all test equipment. RECONNECT all components. CLEAR Continuous Memory. RERUN Quick Test.
	No	▶	SERVICE harness and connectors. CID P is open between CMP sensor and PCM. REMOVE all test equipment. RECONNECT all components. CLEAR Continuous Memory. RERUN Quick Test.

Fig. 21   Test C: Code 214, CID To PCM Failure (Part 1 of 4). 1993 3.0L & 3.8L SC & 1993 3.2L SHO Engines

TEST STEP	RESULT	▶	ACTION TO TAKE
C7 CHECK PCM—ICM INPUT AND PCM DISCONNECTED—CMP FAULT—KOEC • Key off. • Set DVOM to 40 volt DC scale. • Connect DVOM between (+)J22 (CID PCM S) and (-)J60 (B-). • Disconnect PCM. • Bump engine in short bursts without starting engine for at least 10 engine revolutions. • **Does DVOM reading switch between low and high?**	Yes	▶	REPLACE PCM. CID PCM S shorted. REMOVE all test equipment. RECONNECT all components. CLEAR Continuous Memory. RERUN Quick Test.
	No	▶	GO to C8.
C8 CHECK CID CMP S FOR SHORT HIGH—ICM, PCM AND CMP SENSOR DISCONNECTED—CID FAULT—KOEO • Key off. • Set DVOM to 40 volt DC scale. • Disconnect EI diagnostic harness connector from camshaft sensor. Do not disconnect vehicle harness from camshaft sensor tee. • Connect DVOM between (+)J21 (CID S) and (-)J60 (B-). • Key on. • **Is DVOM reading less than 0.5 volts DC?**	Yes	▶	GO to C9.
	No	▶	SERVICE connectors and harness. CID is shorted high between sensor and ICM. RERUN Quick Test.
C9 CHECK CID CMP S FOR SHORT LOW, ICM, CMP SENSOR AND PCM DISCONNECTED—FAULT—KEY OFF • Key off. • Set DVOM to 20K ohm scale. • Connect DVOM between J22 (CID PCM S) and J60 (B-). • **Is DVOM reading greater than 10K ohms?**	Yes	▶	GO to C10.
	No	▶	SERVICE connectors and harness. CID PCM S is shorted to ground between sensor and PCM. REMOVE all test equipment. RECONNECT all components. CLEAR Continuous Memory. RERUN Quick Test.
C10 CHECK CID S FOR SHORT HIGH—ICM, PCM AND CMP SENSOR DISCONNECTED—CID FAULT—KOEO • Key off. • Set DVOM to 40 volt DC scale. • Connect DVOM between (+)J21 (CID S) and (-)J60 (B-). • Key on. • Is DVOM reading less than 0.5 volts DC?	Yes	▶	GO to C11.
	No	▶	SERVICE connectors and harness. CID S is shorted high. REMOVE all test equipment. RECONNECT all components. CLEAR Continuous Memory. RERUN Quick Test.

Fig. 21   Test C: Code 214, CID To PCM Failure (Part 3 of 4). 1993 3.0L, 3.2L SHO & 3.8L SC

TEST STEP	RESULT	▶	ACTION TO TAKE
C1 CHECK CID CMP S AT CAMSHAFT SENSOR—KOEC NOTE: For proper results of this test, and all other Pinpoint Test Steps C, the Star Tester must be disconnected. • Key off. • Set DVOM to 40 volt DC scale. • Install CMP sensor tee (the word "SENSOR" is printed in yellow letters on the tee.) • Connect EI diagnostic harness to breakout box. • Disconnect PCM. • Connect diagnostic harness positive and negative leads to battery. • Use 3.0L / 3.2L overlay. • Connect DVOM between (+)J22 (CID PCM S) and (-)J60 (B-). • Bump engine in short bursts with the starter without starting engine for at least 10 engine revolutions. • **Does DVOM reading switch between "low" (less than 2.0 volts DC) and "high" (more than 8.0 volts DC)?**	Yes No	▶ ▶	GO to **C2**. GO to **C3**. CMP fault.
C2 CHECK CID TO PCM CONTINUITY—PCM DISCONNECTED—KEY OFF • Key off. • Set DVOM to 200 ohm scale. • PCM disconnected. • Connect second EEC breakout box to the PCM vehicle connector. • Connect DVOM between J22 (CID PCM S) and Test Pin 24 (CID) of second EEC breakout box. • **Is DVOM reading less than 5.0 ohms?**	Yes No	▶ ▶	REPLACE PCM. Does not respond to CMP inputs. REMOVE all test equipment. RECONNECT all components. CLEAR Continuous Memory. RERUN Quick Test. SERVICE harness and connectors. CID P is open between CMP sensor and PCM. REMOVE all test equipment. RECONNECT all components. CLEAR Continuous Memory. RERUN Quick Test.

FM1119400257010X

Fig. 22 Test C: Code 214, CID To PCM Failure (Part 1 of 4). 1994–95 3.0L & 3.2L SHO Engines

TEST STEP	RESULT	▶	ACTION TO TAKE
C3 CHECK CID S AT CAMSHAFT SENSOR—CID FAULT—KOEC • Key off. • Set DVOM to 40 volt DC scale. • Connect DVOM between (+)J21 (CID S) and (-)J60 (B-). • Bump engine in short bursts with starter without starting engine for at least 10 engine revolutions. • **Does DVOM reading switch between low and high?**	Yes No	▶ ▶	REPLACE CMP sensor. CID is open between J21 (CID S) and J22 (CID PCM S). REMOVE all test equipment. RECONNECT all components. CLEAR Continuous Memory. RERUN Quick Test. GO to **C4**.
C4 CHECK CAMSHAFT SENSOR CMP PWR—CID FAULT—KOEO • Key off. • Set DVOM to 40 volt DC scale. • Connect DVOM between (+)J41 (CMP PWR) and (-)J60 (B-). • Key on. • **Is DVOM reading greater than 10 volts DC?**	Yes No	▶ ▶	GO to **C5**. SERVICE connectors and harness. CMP PWR open, fault at sensor. REMOVE all test equipment. RECONNECT all components. CLEAR Continuous Memory. RERUN Quick Test.
C5 CHECK CAMSHAFT SENSOR IGNITION GROUND—CMP FAULT—KEY OFF • Key off. • Set DVOM to 40 ohm scale. • Connect DVOM between J42 (IGND CMP) and J60 (B-). • **Is DVOM reading less than 5.0 ohms?**	Yes No	▶ ▶	GO to **C6**. SERVICE connectors and harness. IGN GND open at sensor. REMOVE all test equipment. RECONNECT all components. CLEAR Continuous Memory. RERUN Quick Test.
C6 CHECK ICM—ICM INPUT DISCONNECTED—CID FAULT—KOEC • Key off. • Set DVOM to 40 volt DC scale. • Disconnect ICM (1-6) vehicle harness input connector from ICM. • Connect the DVOM between (+)J21 (CID S) and (-)J60 (B-). • Bump the engine in short bursts without starting engine for at least 10 engine revolutions. • **Does DVOM reading switch between low and high?**	Yes No	▶ ▶	REPLACE ICM. RERUN Quick Test. GO to **C7**.

FM1119400257020X

Fig. 22 Test C: Code 214, CID To PCM Failure (Part 2 of 4). 1994–95 3.0L & 3.2L SHO Engines

TEST STEP	RESULT	▶	ACTION TO TAKE
C7 CHECK PCM — ICM INPUT AND PCM DISCONNECTED—CMP FAULT—KOEC • Key off. • Set DVOM to 40 volt DC scale. • Connect DVOM between (+)J22 (CID PCM S) and (-)J60 (B-). • Disconnect PCM. • Bump engine in short bursts without starting engine for at least 10 engine revolutions. • **Does DVOM reading switch between low and high?**	Yes No	▶ ▶	REPLACE PCM. CID PCM S shorted. REMOVE all test equipment. RECONNECT all components. CLEAR Continuous Memory. RERUN Quick Test. GO to **C8**.
C8 CHECK CID CMP S FOR SHORT HIGH—ICM, PCM AND CMP SENSOR DISCONNECTED—CID FAULT—KOEO • Key off. • Set DVOM to 40 volt DC scale. • Disconnect EI diagnostic harness connector from camshaft sensor. Do not disconnect vehicle harness from camshaft sensor tee. • Connect DVOM between (+)J21 (CID S) and (-)J60 (B-). • Key on. • **Is DVOM reading less than 0.5 volts DC?**	Yes No	▶ ▶	GO to **C9**. SERVICE connectors and harness. CID is shorted high between sensor and ICM. RERUN Quick Test.
C9 CHECK CID CMP S FOR SHORT LOW, ICM, CMP SENSOR AND PCM DISCONNECTED—FAULT—KEY OFF • Key off. • Set DVOM to 20K ohm scale. • Connect DVOM between (+)J22 (CID PCM S) and J60 (B-). • **Is DVOM reading greater than 10K ohms?**	Yes No	▶ ▶	GO to **C10**. SERVICE connectors and harness. CID PCM S is shorted to ground between sensor and PCM. REMOVE all test equipment. RECONNECT all components. CLEAR Continuous Memory. RERUN Quick Test.
C10 CHECK CID S FOR SHORT HIGH—ICM, PCM AND CMP SENSOR DISCONNECTED—CID FAULT—KOEO • Key off. • Set DVOM to 40 volt DC scale. • Connect DVOM between (+)J21 (CID S) and (-)J60 (B-). • Key on. • **Is DVOM reading less than 0.5 volts DC?**	Yes No	▶ ▶	GO to **C11**. SERVICE connectors and harness. CID S is shorted high. REMOVE all test equipment. RECONNECT all components. CLEAR Continuous Memory. RERUN Quick Test.

FM1119400257030X

Fig. 22 Test C: Code 214, CID To PCM Failure (Part 3 of 4). 1994–95 3.0L & 3.2L SHO Engines

TEST STEP	RESULT	▶	ACTION TO TAKE
C11 CHECK CID S FOR SHORT TO GND—ICM, PCM AND CMP SENSOR DISCONNECTED—FAULT—KEY OFF • Key off. • Set DVOM to 20K ohm scale. • Connect DVOM between J21 (CID S) and J60 (B-). • **Is DVOM reading greater than 10K ohms?**	Yes No	▶ ▶	GO to **C12**. SERVICE connectors and harness. CID S is shorted to GND. REMOVE all test equipment. RECONNECT all components. CLEAR Continuous Memory. RERUN Quick Test.
C12 CHECK CMP SENSOR VANE—CMP FAULT—KOEC • **Does vane move through air gap when engine is cranked?**	Yes No	▶ ▶	REPLACE CMP sensor. No CID output. SERVICE vane.

FM1119400257040X

Fig. 22 Test C: Code 214, CID To PCM Failure (Part 4 of 4). 1994–95 3.0L & 3.2L SHO Engines

TEST STEP		RESULT	▶	ACTION TO TAKE
D1	CHECK FOR SPARK DURING CRANK—KOER OR KOEC			
	• Using a Neon Bulb Spark Tester (Special Service Tool D89P-6666-A) or Air Gap Spark Tester (D81P-6666-A), check for spark during crank. • Was spark consistent on all spark plug wires?	Yes No	▶ ▶	Ignition System checks OK. GO to **D2**. Spark fault.
D2	CHECK FOR COIL PWR AT COIL—KOEO			
	WARNING: NEVER CONNECT THE PCM TO EEC BREAKOUT BOX WHEN PERFORMING IGNITION DIAGNOSTICS. • Key off. • Install EI (Low Data Rate) diagnostic harness to EEC breakout box and coil pack. • Install coil tee (the word ''COIL'' is printed in blue letters on the tee and the tee connectors have 4 pins). • Use DIS-6 overlay. • Connect EI diagnostic harness negative and positive lead to battery. • Set DVOM to 40 volts DC scale. • Key on, engine off. • Measure the voltage between (+) J7 (COIL PWR) and (-) J60 (B-). • Is voltage greater than 10 volts DC?	Yes No	▶ ▶	GO to **D3**. CHECK connector, SERVICE or REPLACE harness. COIL PWR is open. REMOVE diagnostic harness. REMOVE all test equipment. RECONNECT all components. CLEAR Continuous Memory. RERUN Quick Test.
D3	CHECK FOR C1 HIGH AT COIL PACK—KOEO			
	• Set DVOM to 40 volt DC scale. • Key on. • Measure voltage between (+) J12 (C1C) and (-) J60 (B-). • Is voltage greater than 10 volts DC?	Yes No	▶ ▶	GO to **D4**. GO to **D15**. C1 low fault.
D4	CHECK FOR C2 HIGH AT COIL PACK—KOEO			
	• Set DVOM to 40 volt DC scale. • Key on. • Measure voltage between (+) J14 (C2C) and (-) J60 (B-). • Is voltage greater than 10 volts DC?	Yes No	▶ ▶	GO to **D5**. GO to **D17**. C2 low fault.
D5	CHECK FOR C3 HIGH AT COIL PACK—KOEO			
	• Set DVOM to 40 volt DC scale. • Key on. • Measure voltage between (+) J13 (C3C) and (-) J60 (B-). • Is voltage greater than 10 volts DC?	Yes No	▶ ▶	GO to **D6**. GO to **D19**. C3 low fault.

Fig. 23   Test D: Codes 215, 216 Or 217, Coil 1, 2 Or 3 Failure (Part 1 of 8). 1993 3.0L, 3.2L SHO & 3.8L SC

TEST STEP		RESULT	▶	ACTION TO TAKE
D6	CHECK FOR C1 HIGH AT ICM—KOEO			
	• Key off. • Set DVOM to 40 volt DC scale. • Install ICM output tee (7-12). • Key on. • Measure voltage between (+) J3 (C1I) and J60 (B-). • Is voltge greater than 10 volts DC?	Yes No	▶ ▶	GO to **D7**. CHECK connectors, SERVICE or REPLACE harness. C1 open in harness. REMOVE diagnostic harness. REMOVE all test equipment. RECONNECT all components. CLEAR Continuous Memory. RERUN Quick.
D7	CHECK FOR C2 HIGH AT ICM—KOEO			
	• Key on. • Set DVOM to 40 volt DC scale. • Measure volts between (+) J18 (C2I) and J60 (B-). • Key on. • Is voltage greater than 10 volts DC?	Yes No	▶ ▶	GO to **D8**. CHECK connectors, SERVICE or REPLACE harness. C2 open in harness. REMOVE diagnostic harness. REMOVE all test equipment. RECONNECT all components. CLEAR Continuous Memory. RERUN Quick Test.
D8	CHECK FOR C3 HIGH AT ICM—KOEO			
	• Key on. • Set DVOM to 40 volt DC scale. • Measure voltage between (+) J6 (C3I) and J60 (B-). • Is voltage greater than 10 volts DC?	Yes No	▶ ▶	GO to **D9**. CHECK connectors, SERVICE or REPLACE harness. C3 open in harness. REMOVE diagnostic harness. REMOVE all test equipment. RECONNECT all components. CLEAR Continuous Memory. RERUN Quick Test.
D9	CHECK C1 AT COIL PACK FOR SHORT HIGH—COIL DISCONNECTED—KOEO			
	• Key off. • Set DVOM to 40 volt DC scale. • Disconnect coil from coil tee. Leave vehicle harness connected to the coil tee. • Key on. • Measure voltage between (+) J12 (C1C) and (-) J60 (B-). • Is voltage less than 0.5 volts DC?	Yes No	▶ ▶	GO to **D10**. GO to **D21**. C1 short high fault.

Fig. 23   Test D: Codes 215, 216 Or 217, Coil 1, 2 Or 3 Failure (Part 2 of 8). 1993 3.0L, 3.2L SHO & 3.8L

TEST STEP		RESULT	▶	ACTION TO TAKE
D10	CHECK C2 AT COIL PACK FOR SHORT HIGH—COIL DISCONNECTED			
	• Key on. • DVOM to 40 volts DC scale. • Measure voltage between (+) J14 (C2C) and (-) J60 (B-). • Is voltage less than 0.5 volts DC?	Yes No	▶ ▶	GO to **D11**. GO to **D22**. C2 short high fault.
D11	CHECK C3 AT COIL PACK FOR SHORT HIGH—COIL DISCONNECTED			
	• Key on. • Set DVOM to 40 volts DC scale. • Measure voltage between (+) J13 (C3C) and (-) J60 (B-). • Is voltage less than 0.5 volts DC?	Yes No	▶ ▶	GO to **D12**. GO to **D23**. C3 short high fault.
D12	CHECK C1 DRIVER AT ICM—COIL DISCONNECTED—KOEC			
	• Connect incandescent test lamp between J3 (C1I) and J57 (B+) and crank engine. • Does test lamp blink brightly once per crankshaft revolution?	Yes No	▶ ▶	GO to **D13**. REPLACE ICM. No C1 output. REMOVE diagnostic harness. REMOVE all test equipment. RECONNECT all components. CLEAR Continuous Memory. RERUN Quick Test.
D13	CHECK C2 DRIVER AT ICM—COIL DISCONNECTED—KOEC			
	• Connect incandescent test lamp between J18 (C2D) and J57 (B+) and crank engine. • Does test lamp blink brightly once per crankshaft revolution?	Yes No	▶ ▶	GO to **D14**. REPLACE ICM. C2 open. No C2 output. REMOVE diagnostic harness. REMOVE all test equipment. RECONNECT all components. CLEAR Continuous Memory. RERUN Quick Test.

Fig. 23   Test D: Codes 215, 216 Or 17, Coil 1, 2 Or 3 Failure (Part 3 of 8). 1993 3.0L, 3.2L SHO & 3.8L SC

TEST STEP		RESULT	▶	ACTION TO TAKE
D14	CHECK C3 DRIVER AT ICM—COIL DISCONNECTED—KOEC			
	• Connect incandescent test lamp between J6 (C3I) and J57 (B+) and crank engine. • Does test lamp blink brightly once per crankshaft revolution?	Yes No	▶ ▶	REPLACE coil pack. Inputs to coil OK but no high voltage output. REMOVE EI diagnostic harness. REMOVE all test equipment. RECONNECT all components. CLEAR Continuous Memory. RERUN Quick Test. REPLACE ICM. No C3 output. REMOVE diagnostic harness. REMOVE all test equipment. RECONNECT all components. CLEAR Continuous Memory. RERUN Quick Test.
D15	CHECK FOR C1 SHORT LOW—COIL DISCONNECTED—KEY OFF			
	• Key off. • Disconnect coil from EI diagnostic harness. Do not disconnect vehicle harness from tee. • Set DVOM to 20K ohm scale. • Measure resistance between J12 (C1C) and J60 (B-). • Is resistance greater than 2K ohms?	Yes No	▶ ▶	REPLACE coil pack. C1 open or shorted low in coil. REMOVE diagnostic harness. REMOVE all test equipment. RECONNECT all components. CLEAR Continuous Memory. RERUN Quick Test. GO to **D16**.

Fig. 23   Test D: Codes 215, 216 Or 217, Coil 1, 2 Or 3 Failure (Part 4 of 8). 1993 3.0L, 3.2L SHO & 3.8L SC

TEST STEP	RESULT	▶	ACTION TO TAKE
D16 CHECK FOR C1 SHORT LOW IN HARNESS—ICM AND COIL DISCONNECTED—KEY OFF			
• Key off. • Set DVOM to 20K ohm scale. • Disconnect coil tee from coil. Leave vehicle harness connected to coil tee. • Disconnect ICM output tee (7-12) from ICM. Leave vehicle harness connected to output tee. • Measure resistance between J3 (C1I) and J60 (B-). • **Is resistance greater than 10K ohms?**	Yes	▶	REPLACE ICM. C1 is shorted low. REMOVE EI diagnostic harness. REMOVE all test equipment. RECONNECT all components. CLEAR Continuous Memory. RERUN Quick Test.
	No	▶	CHECK connectors, SERVICE or REPLACE harness. C1 is shorted low. Coil may be damaged. REMOVE EI diagnostic harness. REMOVE all test equipment. RECONNECT all components. CLEAR Continuous Memory. RERUN Quick Test.
D17 CHECK FOR C2 OPEN IN COIL—COIL DISCONNECTED—C2 LOW FAULT—KEY OFF			
• Key off. • Disconnect coil from coil tee. Leave vehicle harness connected to coil tee. • Set DVOM to 20K ohm scale. • Measure resistance between J14 (C2C) and J60 (B-). • **Is resistance less than 2K ohms?**	Yes	▶	GO to D18.
	No	▶	REPLACE coil pack. C2 open or shorted low. REMOVE diagnostic harness. REMOVE all test equipment. RECONNECT all components. CLEAR Continuous Memory. RERUN Quick Test.

Fig. 23   Test D: Codes 215, 216 Or 217, Coil 1, 2 Or 3 Failure (Part 5 of 8). 1993 3.0L, 3.2L SHO & 3.8L SC Engines

TEST STEP	RESULT	▶	ACTION TO TAKE
D18 CHECK FOR C2 SHORT LOW IN HARNESS—ICM AND COIL DISCONNECTED			
• Key off. • Set DVOM to 20K ohm scale. • Disconnect ICM output tee (7-12) from ICM. Leave vehicle harness connect to output tee. • Measure resistance between J14 (C2C) and J60 (B-). • **Is resistance greater than 10K ohms?**	Yes	▶	REPLACE ICM. C2 is shorted low. REMOVE diagnostic harness. REMOVE all test equipment. RECONNECT all components. CLEAR Continuous Memory. RERUN Quick Test.
	No	▶	CHECK connectors, SERVICE or REPLACE harness. C2 is shorted low. Coil may be damaged. REMOVE diagnostic harness. REMOVE all test equipment. RECONNECT all components. CLEAR Continuous Memory. RERUN Quick Test.
D19 CHECK FOR C3 OPEN IN COIL—COIL DISCONNECTED—KEY OFF			
• Key off. • Disconnect coil from coil tee. Leave vehicle harness connected to coil tee. • Set DVOM to 20K ohms scale. • Measure resistance between J13 (C3C) and J60 (B-). • **Is resistance less than 2K ohms?**	Yes	▶	GO to D20.
	No	▶	REPLACE coil pack. C3 open or shorted low in coil. REMOVE diagnostic harness. REMOVE all test equipment. RECONNECT all components. CLEAR Continuous Memory. RERUN Quick Test.

Fig. 23   Test D: Codes 215, 216 Or 217, Coil 1, 2 Or 3 Failure (Part 6 of 8). 1993 3.0L, 3.2L SHO & 3.8L SC Engines

TEST STEP	RESULT	▶	ACTION TO TAKE
D20 CHECK FOR C3 SHORT LOW IN HARNESS—ICM AND COIL DISCONNECTED—KEY OFF			
• Key off. • Set DVOM to 20K ohm scale. • Disconnect ICM output tee (7-12) from ICM. Leave vehicle harness connected to output tee. • Measure resistance between J13 (C3C) and J60 (B-). • **Is resistance greater than 10K ohms?**	Yes	▶	REPLACE ICM. C3 is shorted low in the harness. REMOVE diagnostic harness. REMOVE all test equipment. RECONNECT all components. CLEAR Continuous Memory. RERUN Quick Test.
	No	▶	CHECK connectors, SERVICE or REPLACE harness. C3 is shorted low. Coil may be damaged. REMOVE diagnostic harness. REMOVE all test equipment. RECONNECT all components. CLEAR Continuous Memory. RERUN Quick Test.
D21 CHECK FOR C1 HIGH AT COIL PACK—ICM AND COIL DISCONNECTED—KOEO			
• Key off. • Set DVOM to 40 volts DC scale. • Disconnect ICM output tee (7-12) from ICM. Leave vehicle harness connected to output tee. • Key on. • Measure the voltage between (+)J12 (C1C) and (-)J60 (B-). • **Is voltage less than 0.5 volts DC?**	Yes	▶	REPLACE ICM. C1 is shorted high. REMOVE diagnostic harness. REMOVE all test equipment. RECONNECT all components. CLEAR Continuous Memory. RERUN Quick Test.
	No	▶	CHECK connectors, SERVICE or REPLACE harness. C1 is shorted high in the harness. REMOVE diagnostic harness. REMOVE all test equipment. RECONNECT all components. CLEAR Continuous Memory. RERUN Quick Test.

Fig. 23   Test D: Codes 215, 216 Or 217, Coil 1, 2 Or 3 Failure (Part 7 of 8). 1993 3.0L, 3.2L SHO & 3.8L SC

TEST STEP	RESULT	▶	ACTION TO TAKE
D22 CHECK FOR C2 HIGH AT COIL PACK—ICM AND COIL DISCONNECTED—KOEO			
• Key off. • Set DVOM to 40 volt DC scale. • Disconnect ICM output tee (7-12) from ICM. Leave vehicle harness connected to output tee. • Key on. • Measure the voltage between (+)J14 (C2C) and (-)J60 (B-). • **Is voltage less than 0.5 volt DC?**	Yes	▶	REPLACE ICM. C2 is shorted high. REMOVE diagnostic harness. REMOVE all test equipment. RECONNECT all components. CLEAR Continuous Memory. RERUN Quick Test.
	No	▶	CHECK connectors, SERVICE or REPLACE harness, C2 is shorted high in the harness. REMOVE diagnostic harness. REMOVE all test equipment. RECONNECT all components. CLEAR Continuous Memory. RERUN Quick Test.
D23 CHECK FOR C3 HIGH AT COIL PACK—ICM AND COIL DISCONNECTED—KOEO			
• Key off. • DVOM to 40 volt DC scale. • Disconnect ICM output tee (7-12) from ICM. Leave vehicle harness connected to output tee. • Key on. • Measure voltage between (+)J13 (C3C) and (-)J60 (B-). • **Is voltage less than 0.5 volt DC?**	Yes	▶	REPLACE ICM. C3 is shorted high. REMOVE diagnostic harness. REMOVE all test equipment. RECONNECT all components. CLEAR Continuous Memory. RERUN Quick Test.
	No	▶	CHECK connector, SERVICE or REPLACE harness. C3 is shorted high in the harness. REMOVE diagnostic harness. REMOVE all test equipment. RECONNECT all components. CLEAR Continuous Memory. RERUN Quick Test.

Fig. 23   Test D: Codes 215, 216 Or 217, Coil 1, 2 Or 3 Failure (Part 8 of 8). 1993 3.0L, 3.2L SHO & 3.8L SC

TEST STEP		RESULT	▶	ACTION TO TAKE
D1	CHECK FOR SPARK DURING CRANK—KOER OR KCEC			
	• Using a Neon Bulb Spark Tester (Special Service Tool D89P-6666-A) or Air Gap Spark Tester (D81P-6666-A), check for spark during crank. • **Was spark consistent on all spark plug wires?**	Yes No	▶ ▶	Ignition System checks OK. GO to **D2**. Spark fault.
D2	CHECK FOR COIL PWR AT COIL—KOEO			
	WARNING: NEVER CONNECT THE PCM TO EEC BREAKOUT BOX WHEN PERFORMING IGNITION DIAGNOSTICS. • Key off. • Install EI (Low Data Rate) diagnostic harness to EEC breakout box and coil pack. • Install coil tee (the word "COIL" is printed in blue letters on the tee and the tee connectors have 4 pins). • Use DIS-6 overlay. • Connect EI diagnostic harness negative and positive lead to battery. • Set DVOM to 40 volts DC scale. • Key on, engine off. • Measure the voltage between (+) J7 (COIL PWR) and (-) J60 (B-). • **Is voltage greater than 10 volts DC?**	Yes No	▶ ▶	GO to **D3**. CHECK connector, SERVICE or REPLACE harness. COIL PWR is open. REMOVE diagnostic harness. REMOVE all test equipment. RECONNECT all components. CLEAR Continuous Memory. RERUN Quick Test.
D3	CHECK FOR C1 HIGH AT COIL PACK—KOEC			
	• Set DVOM to 40 volt DC scale. • Key on. • Measure voltage between (+) J12 (C1C) and (-) J60 (B-). • **Is voltage greater than 10 volts DC?**	Yes No	▶ ▶	GO to **D4**. GO to **D15**. C1 low fault.
D4	CHECK FOR C2 HIGH AT COIL PACK—KOEC			
	• Set DVOM to 40 volt DC scale. • Key on. • Measure voltage between (+) J14 (C2C) and (-) J60 (B-). • **Is voltage greater than 10 volts DC?**	Yes No	▶ ▶	GO to **D5**. GO to **D17**. C2 low fault.
D5	CHECK FOR C3 HIGH AT COIL PACK—KOEO			
	• Set DVOM to 40 volt DC scale. • Key on. • Measure voltage between (+) J13 (C3C) and J60 (B-). • **Is voltage greater than 10 volts DC?**	Yes No	▶ ▶	GO to **D6**. GO to **D19**. C3 low fault.

FM1119400259010X

Fig. 24   Test D: Codes 215, 216 Or 217, Coil 1, 2 Or 3 Failure (Part 1 of 8). 1994–95 3.0L & 3.2L SHO Engines

TEST STEP		RESULT	▶	ACTION TO TAKE
D6	CHECK FOR C1 HIGH AT ICM—KOEO			
	• Key off. • Set DVOM to 40 volt DC scale. • Install ICM output tee (7-12). • Key on. • Measure voltage between (+) J3 (C1I) and J60 (B-). • **Is voltge greater than 10 volts DC?**	Yes No	▶ ▶	GO to **D7**. CHECK connectors, SERVICE or REPLACE harness. C1 open in harness. REMOVE diagnostic harness. REMOVE all test equipment. RECONNECT all components. CLEAR Continuous Memory. RERUN Quick.
D7	CHECK FOR C2 HIGH AT ICM—KOEO			
	• Key on. • Set DVOM to 40 volt DC scale. • Measure volts between (+) J18 (C2I) and J60 (B-). • Key on. • **Is voltage greater than 10 volts DC?**	Yes No	▶ ▶	GO to **D8**. CHECK connectors, SERVICE or REPLACE harness. C2 open in harness. REMOVE diagnostic harness. REMOVE all test equipment. RECONNECT all components. CLEAR Continuous Memory. RERUN Quick Test.
D8	CHECK FOR C3 HIGH AT ICM—KOEO			
	• Key on. • Set DVOM to 40 volt DC scale. • Measure voltage between (+) J6 (C3I) and J60 (B-). • **Is voltage greater than 10 volts DC?**	Yes No	▶ ▶	GO to **D9**. CHECK connectors, SERVICE or REPLACE harness. C3 open in harness. REMOVE diagnostic harness. REMOVE all test equipment. RECONNECT all components. CLEAR Continuous Memory. RERUN Quick Test.
D9	CHECK C1 AT COIL PACK FOR SHORT HIGH—COIL DISCONNECTED—KOEO			
	• Key off. • Set DVOM to 40 volt DC scale. • Disconnect coil from coil tee. Leave vehicle harness connected to the coil tee. • Key on. • Measure voltage between (+) J12 (C1C) and (-) J60 (B-). • **Is voltage less than 0.5 volts DC?**	Yes No	▶ ▶	GO to **D10**. GO to **D21**. C1 short high fault.

FM1119400259020X

Fig. 24   Test D: Codes 215, 216 Or 217, Coil 1, 2 Or 3 Failure (Part 2 of 8). 1994–95 3.0L & 3.2L SHO Engines

TEST STEP		RESULT	▶	ACTION TO TAKE
D10	CHECK C2 AT COIL PACK FOR SHORT HIGH—COIL DISCONNECTED			
	• Key on. • DVOM to 40 volts DC scale. • Measure voltage between (+) J14 (C2C) and (-) J60 (B-). • **Is voltage less than 0.5 volts DC?**	Yes No	▶ ▶	GO to **D11**. GO to **D22**. C2 short high fault.
D11	CHECK C3 AT COIL PACK FOR SHORT HIGH—COIL DISCONNECTED			
	• Key on. • Set DVOM to 40 volts DC scale. • Measure voltage between (+) J13 (C3C) and (-) J60 (B-). • **Is voltage less than 0.5 volts DC?**	Yes No	▶ ▶	GO to **D12**. GO to **D23**. C3 short high fault.
D12	CHECK C1 DRIVER AT ICM—COIL DISCONNECTED—KOEC			
	• Connect incandescent test lamp between J3 (C1I) and J57 (B+) and crank engine. • **Does test lamp blink brightly once per crankshaft revolution?**	Yes No	▶ ▶	GO to **D13**. REPLACE ICM. No C1 output. REMOVE diagnostic harness. REMOVE all test equipment. RECONNECT all components. CLEAR Continuous Memory. RERUN Quick Test.
D13	CHECK C2 DRIVER AT ICM—COIL DISCONNECTED—KOEC			
	• Connect incandescent test lamp between J18 (C2D) and J57 (B+) and crank engine. • **Does test lamp blink brightly once per crankshaft revolution?**	Yes No	▶ ▶	GO to **D14**. REPLACE ICM. C2 open. No C2 output. REMOVE diagnostic harness. REMOVE all test equipment. RECONNECT all components. CLEAR Continuous Memory. RERUN Quick Test.

FM1119400259030X

Fig. 24   Test D: Codes 215, 216 Or 217, Coil 1, 2 Or 3 Failure (Part 3 of 8). 1994–95 3.0L & 3.2L SHO Engines

TEST STEP		RESULT	▶	ACTION TO TAKE
D14	CHECK C3 DRIVER AT ICM—COIL DISCONNECTED—KOEC			
	• Connect incandescent test lamp between J6 (C3I) and J57 (B+) and crank engine. • **Does test lamp blink brightly once per crankshaft revolution?**	Yes No	▶ ▶	REPLACE coil pack. Inputs to coil OK but no high voltage output. REMOVE EI diagnostic harness. REMOVE all test equipment. RECONNECT all components. CLEAR Continuous Memory. RERUN Quick Test. REPLACE ICM. No C3 output. REMOVE diagnostic harness. REMOVE all test equipment. RECONNECT all components. CLEAR Continuous Memory. RERUN Quick Test.
D15	CHECK FOR C1 SHORT LOW—COIL DISCONNECTED—KEY OFF			
	• Key off. • Disconnect coil from EI diagnostic harness. Do not disconnect vehicle harness from tee. • Set DVOM to 20K ohm scale. • Measure resistance between J12 (C1C) and J60 (B-). • **Is resistance greater than 2K ohms?**	Yes No	▶ ▶	REPLACE coil pack. C1 open or shorted low in coil. REMOVE diagnostic harness. REMOVE all test equipment. RECONNECT all components. CLEAR Continuous Memory. RERUN Quick Test. GO to **D16**.

FM1119400259040X

Fig. 24   Test D: Codes 215, 216 Or 217, Coil 1, 2 Or 3 Failure (Part 4 of 8). 1994–95 3.0L & 3.2L SHO Engines

TEST STEP	RESULT	▶	ACTION TO TAKE
D16 CHECK FOR C1 SHORT LOW IN HARNESS—ICM AND COIL DISCONNECTED—KEY OFF ● Key off. ● Set DVOM to 20K ohm scale. ● Disconnect coil tee from coil. Leave vehicle harness connected to coil tee. ● Disconnect ICM output tee (7-12) from ICM. Leave vehicle harness connected to output tee. ● Measure resistance between J3 (C1I) and J60 (B-). ● **Is resistance greater than 10K ohms?**	Yes	▶	REPLACE ICM. C1 is shorted low. REMOVE EI diagnostic harness. REMOVE all test equipment. RECONNECT all components. CLEAR Continuous Memory. RERUN Quick Test.
	No	▶	CHECK connectors, SERVICE or REPLACE harness. C1 is shorted low. Coil may be damaged. REMOVE EI diagnostic harness. REMOVE all test equipment. RECONNECT all components. CLEAR Continuous Memory. RERUN Quick Test.
D17 CHECK FOR C2 OPEN IN COIL—COIL DISCONNECTED—C2 LOW FAULT—KEY OFF ● Key off. ● Disconnect coil from coil tee. Leave vehicle harness connected to coil tee. ● Set DVOM to 20K ohm scale. ● Measure resistance between J14 (C2C) and J60 (B-). ● **Is resistance less than 2K ohms?**	Yes	▶	GO to **D18**.
	No	▶	REPLACE coil pack. C2 open or shorted low. REMOVE diagnostic harness. REMOVE all test equipment. RECONNECT all components. CLEAR Continuous Memory. RERUN Quick Test.

FM1119400259050X

Fig. 24   Test D: Codes 215, 216 Or 217, Coil 1, 2 Or 3 Failure (Part 5 of 8). 1994–95 3.0L & 3.2L SHO Engines

TEST STEP	RESULT	▶	ACTION TO TAKE
D18 CHECK FOR C2 SHORT LOW IN HARNESS—ICM AND COIL DISCONNECTED ● Key off. ● Set DVOM to 20K ohm scale. ● Disconnect ICM output tee (7-12) from ICM. Leave vehicle harness connect to output tee. ● Measure resistance between J14 (C2C) and J60 (B-). ● **Is resistance greater than 10K ohms?**	Yes	▶	REPLACE ICM. C2 is shorted low. REMOVE diagnostic harness. REMOVE all test equipment. RECONNECT all components. CLEAR Continuous Memory. RERUN Quick Test.
	No	▶	CHECK connectors, SERVICE or REPLACE harness. C2 is shorted low. Coil may be damaged. REMOVE diagnostic harness. REMOVE all test equipment. RECONNECT all components. CLEAR Continuous Memory. RERUN Quick Test.
D19 CHECK FOR C3 OPEN IN COIL—COIL DISCONNECTED—KEY OFF ● Key off. ● Disconnect coil from coil tee. Leave vehicle harness connected to coil tee. ● Set DVOM to 20K ohms scale. ● Measure resistance between J13 (C3C) and J60 (B-). ● **Is resistance less than 2K ohms?**	Yes	▶	GO to **D20**.
	No	▶	REPLACE coil pack. C3 open or shorted low in coil. REMOVE diagnostic harness. REMOVE all test equipment. RECONNECT all components. CLEAR Continuous Memory. RERUN Quick Test.

FM1119400259060X

Fig. 24   Test D: Codes 215, 216 Or 217, Coil 1, 2 Or 3 Failure (Part 6 of 8). 1994–95 3.0L & 3.2L SHO Engines

TEST STEP	RESULT	▶	ACTION TO TAKE
D20 CHECK FOR C3 SHORT LOW IN HARNESS—ICM AND COIL DISCONNECTED—KEY OFF ● Key off. ● Set DVOM to 20K ohm scale. ● Disconnect ICM output tee (7-12) from ICM. Leave vehicle harness connected to output tee. ● Measure resistance between J13 (C3C) and J60 (B-). ● **Is resistance greater than 10K ohms?**	Yes	▶	REPLACE ICM. C3 is shorted low in the harness. REMOVE diagnostic harness. REMOVE all test equipment. RECONNECT all components. CLEAR Continuous Memory. RERUN Quick Test.
	No	▶	CHECK connectors, SERVICE or REPLACE harness. C3 is shorted low. Coil may be damaged. REMOVE diagnostic harness. REMOVE all test equipment. RECONNECT all components. CLEAR Continuous Memory. RERUN Quick Test.
D21 CHECK FOR C1 HIGH AT COIL PACK—ICM AND COIL DISCONNECTED—KOEO ● Key off. ● Set DVOM to 40 volts DC scale. ● Disconnect ICM output tee (7-12) from ICM. Leave vehicle harness connected to output tee. ● Key on. ● Measure the voltage between (+)J12 (C1C) and (-)J60 (B-). ● **Is voltage less than 0.5 volts DC?**	Yes	▶	REPLACE ICM. C1 is shorted high. REMOVE diagnostic harness. REMOVE all test equipment. RECONNECT all components. CLEAR Continuous Memory. RERUN Quick Test.
	No	▶	CHECK connectors, SERVICE or REPLACE harness. C1 is shorted high in the harness. REMOVE diagnostic harness. REMOVE all test equipment. RECONNECT all components. CLEAR Continuous Memory. RERUN Quick Test.

FM1119400259070X

Fig. 24   Test D: Codes 215, 216 Or 217, Coil 1, 2 Or 3 Failure (Part 7 of 8). 1994–95 3.0L & 3.2L SHO Engines

TEST STEP	RESULT	▶	ACTION TO TAKE
D22 CHECK FOR C2 HIGH AT COIL PACK—ICM AND COIL DISCONNECTED—KOEO • Key off. • Set DVOM to 40 volt DC scale. • Disconnect ICM output tee (7-12) from ICM. Leave vehicle harness connected to output tee. • Key on. • Measure the voltage between (+)J14 (C2C) and (-)J60 (B-). • **Is voltage less than 0.5 volt DC?**	Yes	▶	REPLACE ICM. C2 is shorted high. REMOVE diagnostic harness. REMOVE all test equipment. RECONNECT all components. CLEAR Continuous Memory. RERUN Quick Test.
	No	▶	CHECK connectors, SERVICE or REPLACE harness. C2 is shorted high in the harness. REMOVE diagnostic harness. REMOVE all test equipment. RECONNECT all components. CLEAR Continuous Memory. RERUN Quick Test.
D23 CHECK FOR C3 HIGH AT COIL PACK—ICM AND COIL DISCONNECTED—KOEO • Key off. • DVOM to 40 volt DC scale. • Disconnect ICM output tee (7-12) from ICM. Leave vehicle harness connected to output tee. • Key on. • Measure voltage between (+)J13 (C3C) and (-)J60 (B-). • **Is voltage less than 0.5 volt DC?**	Yes	▶	REPLACE ICM. C3 is shorted high. REMOVE diagnostic harness. REMOVE all test equipment. RECONNECT all components. CLEAR Continuous Memory. RERUN Quick Test.
	No	▶	CHECK connector, SERVICE or REPLACE harness. C3 is shorted high in the harness. REMOVE diagnostic harness. REMOVE all test equipment. RECONNECT all components. CLEAR Continuous Memory. RERUN Quick Test.

FM1119400259080X

Fig. 24 Test D: Codes 215, 216 Or 217, Coil 1, 2 Or 3 Failure (Part 8 of 8). 1994–95 3.0L & 3.2L SHO Engines

TEST STEP	RESULT	▶	ACTION TO TAKE
E1 CHECK FOR SPOUT SIGNAL AT ICM—KOEP • Key off. • Set DVOM to 20 volts AC scale. • Install input tee (1-6). • Connect EI diagnostic harness to breakout box. • Use 3.0L / 3.2L / 3.8L overlay. • Connect DVOM between (+)J36 (SPOUT I) and (-)J60 (B-). • Start engine. • **Is DVOM reading greater than 1.0 volts AC?**	Yes	▶	REPLACE ICM. Does not respond to spout input. REMOVE all test equipment. RECONNECT all components. CLEAR Continuous Memory. RERUN Quick Test.
	No	▶	GO to E2.
E2 CHECK SPOUT CIRCUIT FOR SHORT HIGH—ICM AND PCM DISCONNECTED—KOEO • Key off. • Disconnect ICM (Pins 1-6) from ICM diagnostic harness tee. Do not disconnect vehicle wiring connector from the other end of the tee. • Disconnect the PCM from the vehicle wiring harness. • Set DVOM to 20 volt DC scale. • Key on. • Measure the voltage between J36 (SPOUT) and J60 (B-). • **Is voltage greater than 0.5 volts DC?**	Yes	▶	SERVICE connectors. SERVICE or REPLACE harness. SPOUT circuit is shorted high in harness between ICM and PCM. REMOVE all test equipment. RECONNECT all components. CLEAR Continuous Memory. RERUN Quick Test.
	No	▶	GO to E3.
E3 CHECK SPOUT CIRCUIT FOR SHORT LOW—ICM AND PCM DISCONNECTED—KEY OFF • Key off. • Set DVOM to 20K ohm scale. • Measure the resistance between J36 (SPOUT) and J60 (B-). • **Is the resistance greater than 10K ohms?**	Yes	▶	GO to E4.
	No	▶	SERVICE connector. SERVICE or REPLACE harness. SPOUT circuit is shorted to ground between ICM and PCM. REMOVE all test equipment. RECONNECT all components. CLEAR Continuous Memory. RERUN Quick Test.

Fig. 25 Test F: Code 49/213, Spout Open, Short High Or Short To Ground (Part 1 of 2). 1993 3.0L & 3.2L SHO & 3.8L SC engines

TEST STEP	RESULT	▶	ACTION TO TAKE
E4 CHECK SPOUT HARNESS CONTINUITY—ICM AND PCM DISCONNECTED—KEY OFF • Key off. • Set DVOM to 200 ohm scale. • Install a second PCM breakout box at the PCM vehicle harness connector. • Measure the resistance between J36 (SPOUT) on the first breakout box and test Pin 36 on the second breakout box. • **Is the resistance less than 5.0 ohms?**	Yes	▶	REPLACE PCM. PCM is open, short to VBAT or short to ground in SPOUT circuit. REMOVE all test equipment. RECONNECT all components. CLEAR Continuous Memory. RERUN Quick Test.
	No	▶	SERVICE connectors. SERVICE or REPLACE harness. SPOUT circuit is open between ICM and PCM. CHECK SPOUT jumper. REMOVE all test equipment. RECONNECT all components. CLEAR Continuous Memory. RERUN Quick Test.

Fig. 25 Test E: Code 49/213, Spout Open, Short High Or Short To Ground (Part 2 of 2). 1993 3.0L & 3.2L SHO & 3.8L SC Engines

TEST STEP	RESULT	▶	ACTION TO TAKE
E1 CHECK FOR SPOUT SIGNAL AT ICM—KOER			
• Key off. • Set DVOM to 40 volts AC scale. • Install ICM input tee (1-6). • Connect EI diagnostic harness to breakout box. • Use 3.0L / 3.2L overlay. • Connect DVOM between (+)J36 (SPOUT I) and (-)J60 (B-). • Start engine. • **Is DVOM reading greater than 1.0 volts AC?**	Yes	▶	REPLACE ICM. Does not respond to SPOUT input. REMOVE all test equipment. RECONNECT all components. CLEAR Continuous Memory. RERUN Quick Test.
	No	▶	GO to **E2**.
E2 CHECK SPOUT CIRCUIT FOR SHORT HIGH—ICM AND PCM DISCONNECTED—KOEO			
• Key off. • Disconnect ICM (Pins 1-6) from ICM diagnostic harness tee. Do not disconnect vehicle wiring connector from the other end of the tee. • Disconnect the PCM from the vehicle wiring harness. • Set DVOM to 40 volt DC scale. • Key on. • Measure the voltage between J36 (SPOUT) and J60 (B-). • **Is voltage greater than 0.5 volts DC?**	Yes	▶	SERVICE connectors. SERVICE or REPLACE harness. SPOUT circuit is shorted high in harness between ICM and PCM. REMOVE all test equipment. RECONNECT all components. CLEAR Continuous Memory. RERUN Quick Test.
	No	▶	GO to **E3**.
E3 CHECK SPOUT CIRCUIT FOR SHORT LOW—ICM AND PCM DISCONNECTED—KEY OFF			
• Key off. • Set DVOM to 20K ohm scale. • Measure the resistance between J36 (SPOUT) and J60 (B-). • **Is the resistance greater than 10K ohms?**	Yes	▶	GO to **E4**.
	No	▶	SERVICE connector. SERVICE or REPLACE harness. SPOUT circuit is shorted to ground between ICM and PCM. REMOVE all test equipment. RECONNECT all components. CLEAR Continuous Memory. RERUN Quick Test.

FM1119400262010X

Fig. 26   Test E: Code 49/213, SPOUT Open, Short High Or Short To Ground (Part 1 of 2). 1994–95 3.0L & 3.2L SHO Engines

TEST STEP	RESULT	▶	ACTION TO TAKE
E4 CHECK SPOUT HARNESS CONTINUITY—ICM AND PCM DISCONNECTED—KEY OFF			
• Key off. • Set DVOM to 200 ohm scale. • Install a second PCM breakout box at the PCM vehicle harness connector. • Measure the resistance between J36 (SPOUT) on the first breakout box and test Pin 36 on the second breakout box. • **Is the resistance less than 5.0 ohms?**	Yes	▶	REPLACE PCM. PCM is open, short to VBAT or short to ground in SPOUT circuit. REMOVE all test equipment. RECONNECT all components. CLEAR Continuous Memory. RERUN Quick Test.
	No	▶	SERVICE connectors. SERVICE or REPLACE harness. SPOUT circuit is open between ICM and PCM. CHECK SPOUT jumper. REMOVE all test equipment. RECONNECT all components. CLEAR Continuous Memory. RERUN Quick Test.

FM1119400262020X

Fig. 26   Test E: Code 49/213, SPOUT Open, Short High Or Short To Ground (Part 2 of 2). 1994–95 3.0L & 3.2L SHO Engines

Preliminary Notes

The engine analyzer is used to diagnose problems in the secondary side of the ignition system.

Checkout

- Visually inspect the engine compartment to ensure all vacuum hoses and spark plug wires are properly routed and securely connected.
- Examine all wiring harnesses and connectors for insulation damage, burned, overheated, loose or broken conditions.
- Be certain the battery is fully charged.
- All accessories should be off during diagnosis.

Equipment

Obtain the following test equipment or an equivalent:

- EI (Low Data Rate) Adapter (Rotunda 007-00044).
- Engine Analyzer (Rotunda 002-00373).

NOTE: If this portion of the diagnostic procedure is to provide accurate results, it is essential that the calibration of your engine analyzer be maintained. Refer to your equipment manual. If this is not available, an estimate of the calibration can be made by connecting the spark tester (Special Service Tool D81P-6666-A or equivalent) to a properly operating ignition system and measuring the firing voltage of the spark tester only. Do not include the firing voltage of the rotor-to-cap gap. The spark tester firing voltage should be approximately 28 KV.

TEST STEP	RESULT	▶	ACTION TO TAKE
F1 • Connect engine analyzer to view parade display of ignition system secondary. • While slowly increasing engine rpm from idle to 2000 rpm, compare engine analyzer display to the following illustrations. The illustrations shown are four cylinder but are typical for all engines. • Disconnect engine analyzer.			

Fig. 27 Test F: Misfire Under Load (Bad Plugs, Wires Or Short To Ground) (Part 1 of 3). 3.0L & 3.2L SHO & 1993 3.8L SC Engines

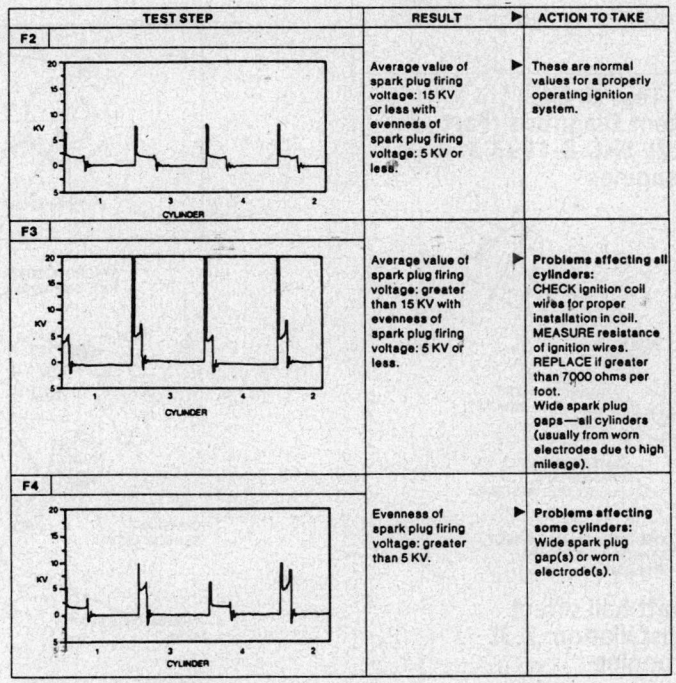

TEST STEP	RESULT	▶	ACTION TO TAKE
F2	Average value of spark plug firing voltage: 15 KV or less with evenness of spark plug firing voltage: 5 KV or less.	▶	These are normal values for a properly operating ignition system.
F3	Average value of spark plug firing voltage: greater than 15 KV with evenness of spark plug firing voltage: 5 KV or less.	▶	Problems affecting all cylinders: CHECK ignition coil wires for proper installation in coil. MEASURE resistance of ignition wires. REPLACE if greater than 7000 ohms per foot. Wide spark plug gaps—all cylinders (usually from worn electrodes due to high mileage).
F4	Evenness of spark plug firing voltage: greater than 5 KV.	▶	Problems affecting some cylinders: Wide spark plug gap(s) or worn electrode(s).

Fig. 27 Test F: Misfire Under Load (Bad Plugs, Wires Or Short To Ground) (Part 2 of 3). 3.0L & 3.2L SHO & 1993 3.8L SC Engines

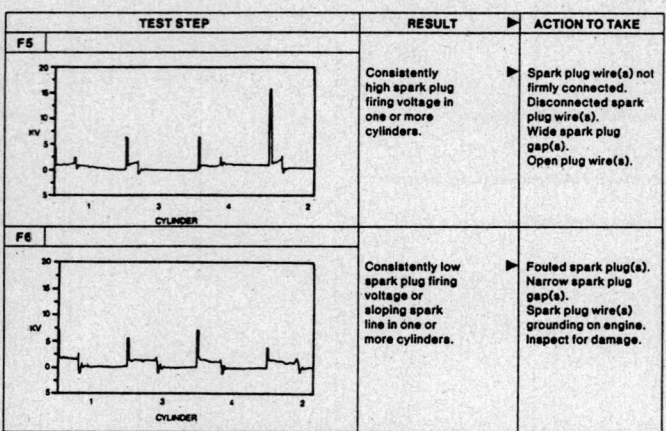

TEST STEP	RESULT	▶	ACTION TO TAKE
F5			
	Consistently high spark plug firing voltage in one or more cylinders.	▶	Spark plug wire(s) not firmly connected. Disconnected spark plug wire(s). Wide spark plug gap(s). Open plug wire(s).
F6			
	Consistently low spark plug firing voltage or sloping spark line in one or more cylinders.	▶	Fouled spark plug(s). Narrow spark plug gap(s). Spark plug wire(s) grounding on engine. Inspect for damage.

Fig. 27   Test F: Misfire Under Load
(Bad Plugs, Wires Or Short To
Ground) (Part 3 of 3). 3.0L & 3.2L
SHO & 1993 3.8L SC Engines

TEST STEP	RESULT	▶	ACTION TO TAKE
G9 ROAD TEST			
• Road test	Yes	▶	GO to G10.
• Does engine quit?	No	▶	Problem not Duplicated.
G10 FINAL TEST			
• Raise hood, shake wiring harness, pull wires at connectors, separate and reconnect connectors for ignition components.	Yes	▶	SERVICE wiring harness or connector. REMOVE all test equipment. RECONNECT all components. CLEAR Continuous Memory. RERUN Quick Test.
• Does engine start?	No	▶	GO to G11.
G11 CHECK SENSOR SHIELD			
• Key off.	Yes	▶	GO to A1.
• Measure resistance between sensor shield (find exposed shield in sensor cable) and negative terminal of the battery.	No	▶	SERVICE shield ground path.
• Is ohm meter reading less than 5.0 ohms?			
NOTE: "Misting" the plug wires and coil with water may aid in the detection of arcing.			

Fig. 28   Test G: No
Codes—Intermittent Diagnosis (Part
2 of 2). 3.0L & 3.2L SHO & 1993 3.8L
SC engines

TEST STEP	RESULT	▶	ACTION TO TAKE
G1 FIND SYMPTOMS			
• Talk to owner.		▶	Symptoms.
G2 REVIEW VEHICLE HISTORY			
• Review vehicle service history.		▶	Number of previous repairs and components replaced.
G3 TEST EQUIPMENT			
• Is Rotunda DIS Intermittent System Tester (DIST) or equivalent available?	Yes	▶	Follow test procedure instructions supplied with tester.
	No	▶	GO to G4.
G4 BEGIN DIAGNOSTICS			
• Will engine start?	Yes	▶	GO to G5.
	No	▶	GO to A1.
G5 COLD WIGGLE TEST			
• Engine at idle, Raise hood, Shake wiring harness and pull wires at connectors for ignition components.	Yes	▶	SERVICE wiring harness or connector. CHECK ICM mounting bolts. REMOVE all test equipment. RECONNECT all components. CLEAR Continuous Memory. RERUN Quick Test.
• Does engine quit?	No	▶	GO to G6.
G6 ENGINE WARM-UP			
• Engine at idle, close hood, A/C ON, blower on medium speed. Allow engine to run for 15 minutes.	Yes	▶	GO to G10.
	No	▶	GO to G7.
• Does engine quit?			
G7 HOT RESTART TEST			
• Engine off, hood closed, hot soak for 10 minutes.	Yes	▶	GO to G8.
	No	▶	GO to A1.
• Will engine restart?			
G8 HOT WIGGLE TEST			
• Engine at idle, raise hood, shake wiring harness and pull wires at connectors for ignition components.	Yes	▶	SERVICE wiring harness or connector. REMOVE all test equipment. RECONNECT all components. CLEAR Continuous Memory. RERUN Quick Test.
• Does engine quit?	No	▶	GO to G9.

Fig. 28   Test G: No
Codes—Intermittent Diagnosis (Part
1 of 2). 3.0L & 3.2L SHO & 1993 3.8L
SC Engines

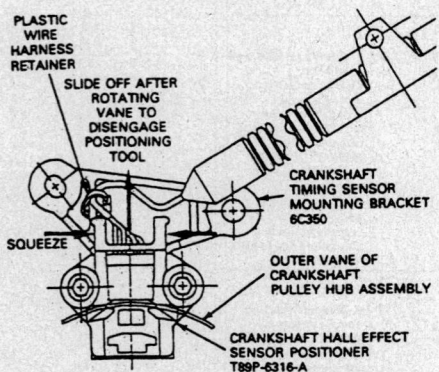

Fig. 29   Crankshaft hall effect
sensor positioner installation. 2.3L
Dual Plug engine

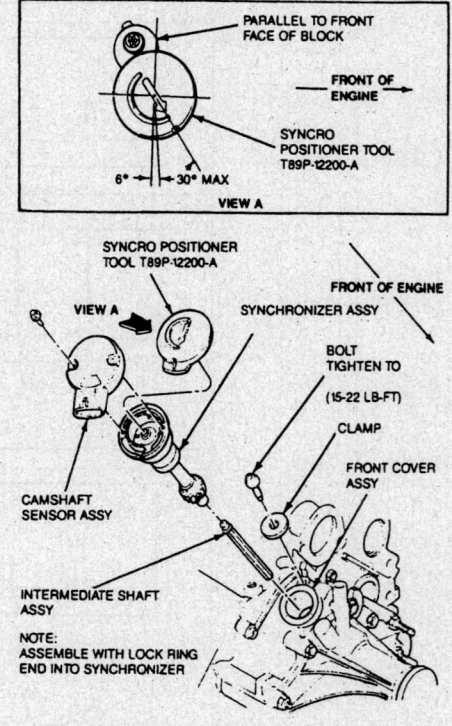

Fig. 30   Synchronizer assembly.
1993 3.8L SC engine

Type 3

NOTE: If Unsure Of The System Used On The Vehicle Being Serviced, Refer To The "Engine Systems Identification Chart." Further Assistance For The Proper Use Of Information Contained In This Section Can Also Be Found In The Front Of This Tabbed Section Under "How To Use This Manual."

INDEX

	Page No.		Page No.		Page No.
Description	4-45	Preliminary Notes	4-45	Wiring Diagrams	4-45
Diagnosis & Testing:	4-45	Quick Test	4-46	System Service:	4-46
Component Location	4-45	Required Equipment	4-45	Component Replacement	4-46
Preliminary Check	4-45	Testing	4-46		

DESCRIPTION

The 3.0L Flexible Fuel, 2.5L, and 1994-95 3.8L SFI SC and 3.8L SFI California Electronic Ignition (EI) (High Data Rate, 6) system, **Fig. 1**, consists of a Crankshaft Position (CKP) sensor, an Ignition Control Module (ICM), Powertrain Control Module (PCM) and one six-tower coil pack. This system operates by sending crankshaft position information from the CKP sensor to the ICM. The module generates a PIP signal and sends it to the PCM. The PCM responds with a SPOUT signal containing advance or retard timing information which is sent back to the ICM. The ICM processes the CKP and SPOUT signals and decides which coils to fire. Also, the module generates an Ignition Diagnostic Monitor (IDM) signal to the PCM which is used to indicate a failure mode and also provide a tach output signal.

DIAGNOSIS & TESTING

PRELIMINARY CHECK

1. Visually inspect engine compartment to ensure all vacuum hoses and spark plug wires are properly and securely connected.
2. Inspect wiring harnesses and connectors for damaged insulation, burns, overheating, damaged pins and loose or broken connectors.
3. Inspect sensor shield connector, and ensure ICM mounting screws are tight.
4. Ensure battery is fully charged, and all accessories are off during tests.

REQUIRED EQUIPMENT

Obtain the following test equipment or a suitable equivalent:
1. EI Rotunda Diagnostic Harness (High Data Rate) tool No. 007-00059.
2. Neon bulb type spark tester tool No. D89P-6666-A.
3. Rotunda Volt/Ohmmeter tool No. 007-00001, 105-00050, 105-00051, 105-00052, 105-00053 or scan tool.
4. Remote starter switch.
5. Rotunda EEC Breakout Box tool No. T83L-50-EEC-IV.
6. Gap type spark tester tool No. D81P-6666-A.

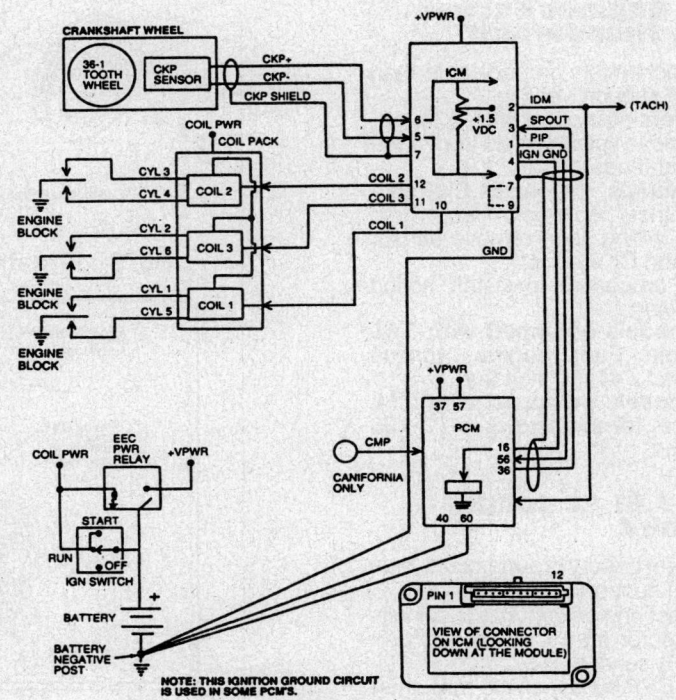

Fig. 1   Electronic Ignition (EI) (High Data Rate, 6) system

7. Rotunda Inductive Timing Light tool No. 059-00014, EI compatible.
8. Rotunda Tachometer Adapter tool No. 007-00061, EI compatible.

PRELIMINARY NOTES

1. When taking measurements on wiring harnesses, both visual inspection and continuity test should be performed. Inspect connector pins for damage when directed to remove a connector.
2. Spark timing adjustments cannot be performed.
3. When taking voltage measurements, a GROUND reading indicates any value within a range of 0 to 1 volt. Also VPWR or COIL PWR readings indicate any value that falls within a range of B + to 2 volts less than B + .
4. When taking voltage measurements and a reference to ground is made, use either negative battery lead or cast iron on engine. B + indicates positive battery cable at battery.
5. When using spark plug firing indicator, place grooved end as close as possible to plug boot. Very weak or no flashing may be caused by fouled plug.
6. Do not use incandescent test lamp to check CKPS-, CKPS +, PIP, IDM or SPOUT circuits. Lamp will prevent circuit from operating.

COMPONENT LOCATION

Refer to **Figs. 2 through 5** for system component locations.

WIRING DIAGRAMS

Refer to **Fig. 6** for system wiring diagrams.

TESTING

Refer to **Figs. 7 through 15,** for diagnosis and testing of system.

QUICK TEST

Refer to "Computerized Engine Controls section for Quick Test.

SYSTEM SERVICE

Component Replacement

CRANKSHAFT POSITION SENSOR (CKP) ASSEMBLY

2.5L, 3.0L Flexible Fuel and 1994–95 3.8L SFI California & 3.8L SC Engines Except Cougar & Thunderbird

1. Disconnect battery ground cable, then raise and support vehicle.
2. **On models equipped with 2.5L engine,** remove splash shield from right-hand front fender apron.
3. **On all models,** disconnect CKP sensor electrical connector from fuel charging wiring, then remove sensor screws and CKP sensor.
4. Reverse procedure to install, noting the following:
   a. **On models equipped with 3.0L Flexible Fuel engine,** torque screws to 44-61 inch lbs.
   b. **On models equipped with 2.5L engine, torque** screws to 71-106 inch lbs.

1994–95 3.8L SC Cougar & Thunderbird

1. Disconnect battery ground cable, then raise and support vehicle.
2. Disconnect engine control sensor wiring connector from Crankshaft Position (CKP) sensor.
3. Remove CKP sensor shield nuts, then the shield.
4. remove sensor stud bolts, then the sensor.
5. Reverse procedure to install. **Torque** CKP sensor stud bolts to 40-61 inch lbs., then the sensor shield nuts to 18-35 inch lbs.

COIL PACK

3.0L Flexible Fuel Engine

1. Disconnect electrical connectors from coil pack and capacitor, then the spark plug wires by squeezing locking tabs and twisting while pulling upward.
2. Remove coil pack bolts, then the coil pack and capacitor. Save capacitor for installation with new coil pack.
3. Reverse procedure to install, noting the following:
   a. **Torque** coil pack bolts to 44-61 inch lbs.
   b. Apply silicone dielectric compound D7AZ-19A331-A, ESE-M1C171-A or their equivalents to all spark plug boots.

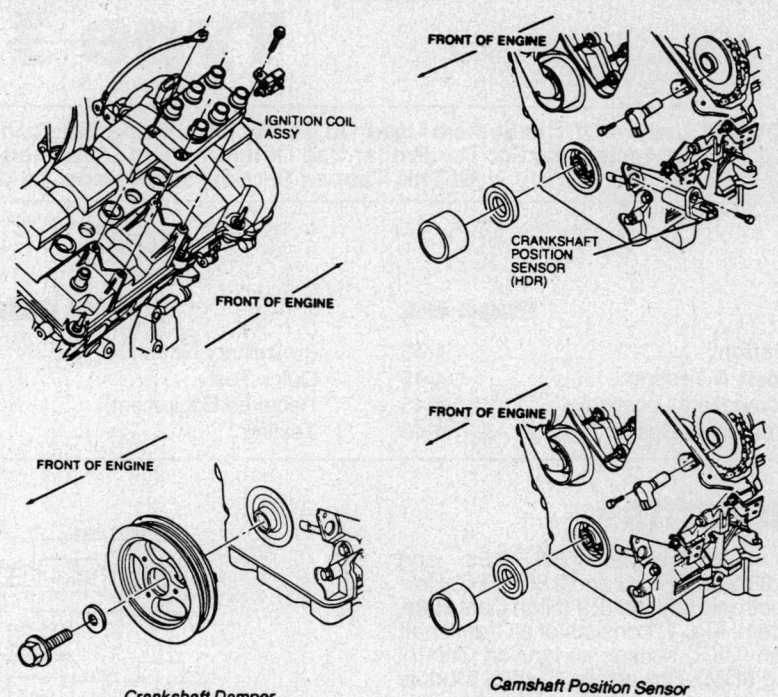

Crankshaft Damper   Camshaft Position Sensor

FM1119200268000X

Fig. 2 EI system component locations. 2.5L engine

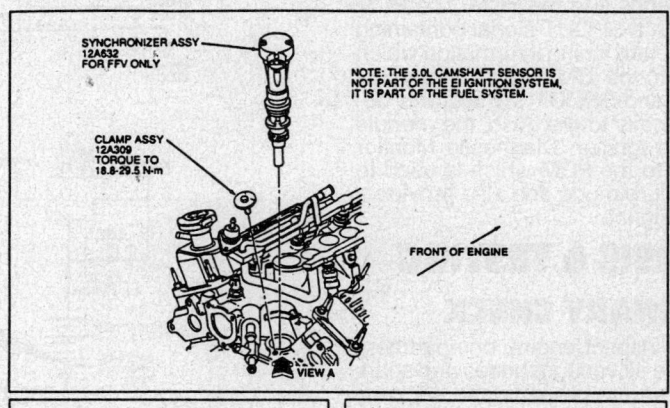

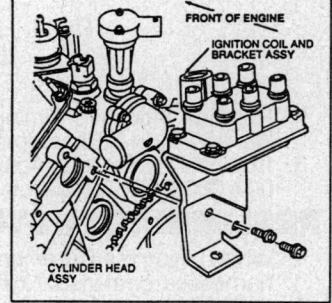

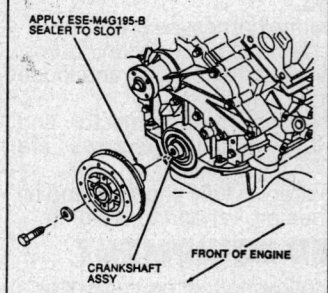

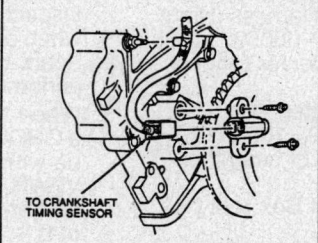

Fig. 3 EI system component locations. 3.0L flexible fuel engine

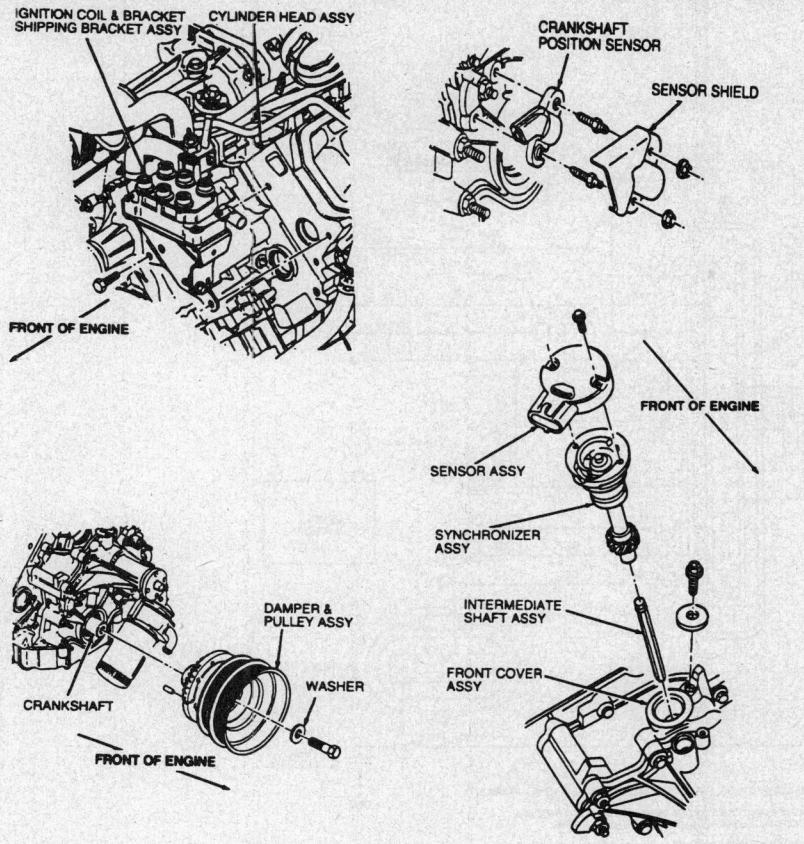

Fig. 4   EI system component locations. 1994–95 3.8L SC engine

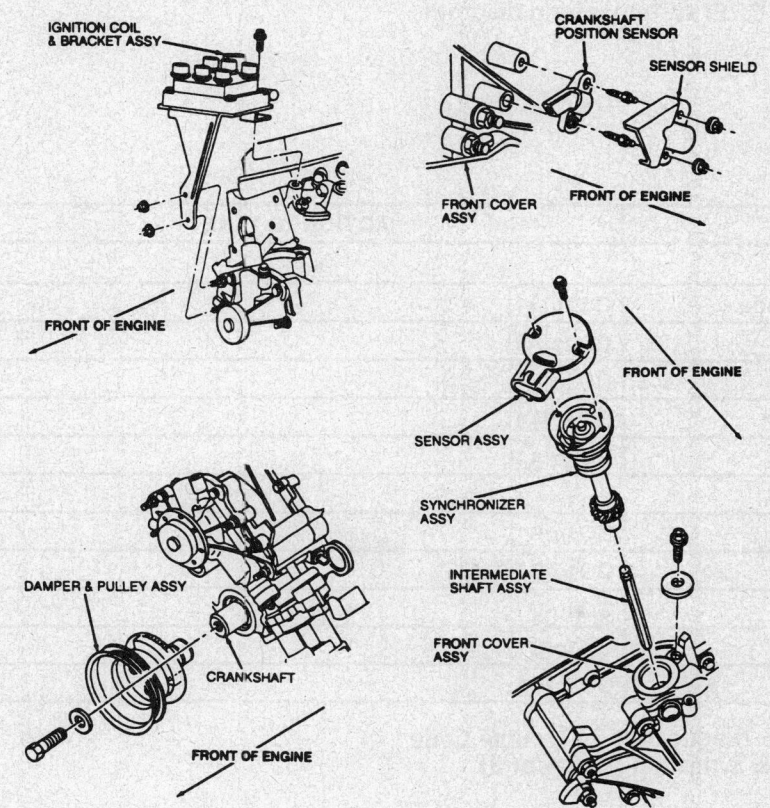

Fig. 5   EI system component locations. 1994–95 3.8L SFI California engine

2.5L Engine

1. Disconnect battery ground cable, then the fuel charging from ignition coil.
2. Disconnect fuel charging wiring from radio ignition interference capacitor.
3. Remove EGR vacuum regulator control from upper vacuum intake manifold.
4. Disconnect ignition wires by squeezing locking tabs and twisting while pulling upward.
5. Reverse procedure to install, noting the following:
   a. **Torque** ignition coil bolts to 40-61 inch lbs.
   b. Apply silicone dielectric compound D7AZ-19A331-A, ESE-M1C171-A or their equivalents to all spark plug boots.

1994–95 3.8L SC & 3.8L SFI California Engines

1. Disconnect battery ground cable, then raise and support vehicle.
2. Disconnect engine control sensor wiring connectors from ignition coil and radio ignition interference capacitor.
3. Remove ignition wires by squeezing locking tabs to release ignition coil boot retainers.
4. Remove ignition coil screws, then the ignition coil and radio ignition interference capacitor.
5. Reverse procedure to install. **Torque** ignition coil and radio ignition interference capacitor screws to 40-61 inch lbs.

IGNITION CONTROL MODULE (ICM)

3.0L Flexible Fuel Engine

1. Disconnect ICM electrical connector by pushing down on connector finger ends while grasping connector body and pulling away from ICM.
2. Remove ICM screws, then the ICM.
3. Reverse procedure to install. **Torque** ICM screws to 24-32 inch lbs.

2.5L Engine

1. Disconnect battery ground cable, then the Ignition Control Module (ICM) electrical connector by carefully lifting up on connector finger ends while grasping connector body and pulling away from ICM.
2. Remove ICM screws, then the module from ICM bracket.
3. Reverse procedure to install. **Torque** ICM screws to 24-35 inch lbs.

1994–95 3.8L SC & 3.8L SFI California Engines

1. Disconnect battery ground cable, then the engine control sensor wiring connector at Ignition Control Module (ICM) by lifting on locking tab, then removing connector.
2. Remove ICM and ICM bracket from front fender apron.
3. Remove ICM screws, then the ICM from ICM bracket.
4. Reverse procedure to install. **Torque** ICM to ICM bracket screws to 24-33 inch lbs., then the ICM bracket to front fender apron bolts to 35-50 inch lbs.

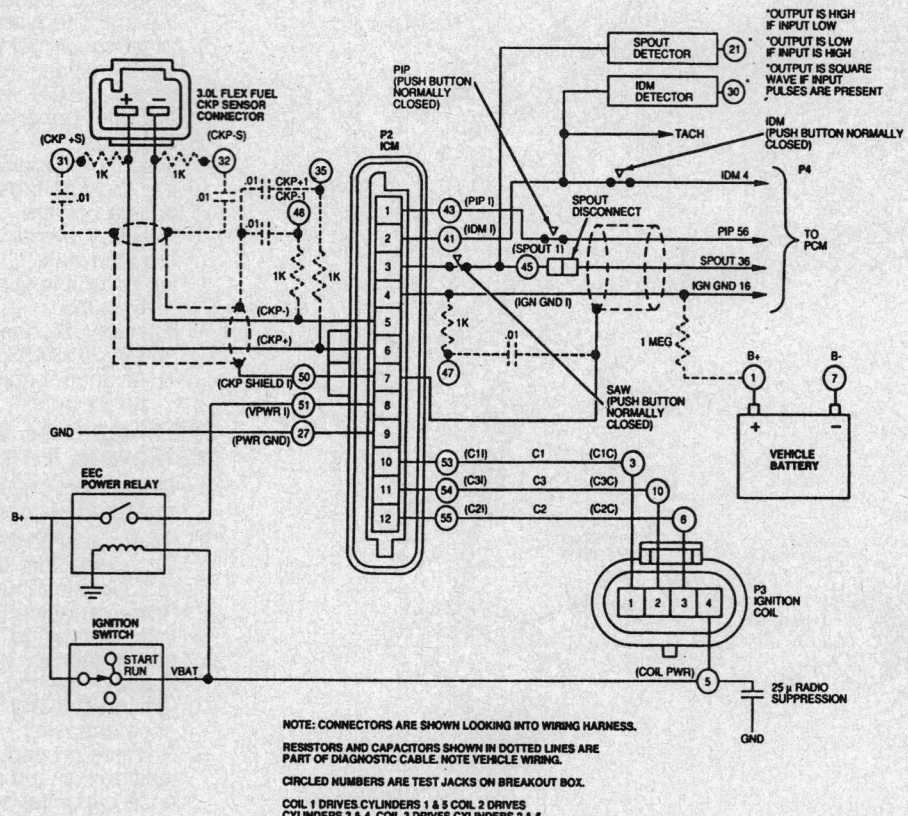

Fig. 6   EI system wiring diagram

CONDITION		ACTION TO TAKE
No Start with:		
●PASS service code or no Diagnostic Trouble Code	GO to A1.	
●Code 212 (IDM at PCM Fault)	GO to A1.	
●Code 226 (IDM at PCM Fault)	GO to A1.	
●Code 211 (PIP at PCM Fault)	GO to A1.	
●MIL stays on during engine cranking	GO to A1.	
Vehicle Runs (engine is running) with:		
●Code 226	GO to B1.	
●Code 212 (IDM at PCM Fault)	GO to B1.	
●Code 232 or 215, 216, 217 (Coil 1, 2, 3)	GO to D1.	
●Code 213 (SPOUT Circuit Fault)	GO to C1.	
●Lack of power or poor fuel economy	GO to C1.	

Fig. 7   Diagnostics By Trouble Code
& Symptom (Part 1 of 3)

The Following Voltage Readings are Typical for a Normal Vehicle with Diagnostic Harness Attached (Except for Positive Battery Cable Lead).

Measure Between Pins		Key On Engine Off (Volts)	Engine Cranking (Volts)	Engine Idling (Volts)
First Pin	Second Pin			
CKP-S (J31)	CKP-S (J32)	0.0 AC	0.3 - 1.2 AC	2.0 - 6.0 AC
CKP-I (J35)	CKP-I (J48)	0.0 AC	0.3 - 1.2 AC	2.0 - 6.0 AC
PIP I (J43)	PWR GND (J7)	0.0 AC	4.0 - 6.0 AC	6.0 - 8.0 AC
C1I (J53)	PWR GND (J7)	B+ DC	0 - 1.0 AC	1.0 - 2.0 AC
C2I (J55)	PWR GND (J7)	B+ DC	0 - 1.0 AC	1.0 - 2.0 AC
C3I (J54)	PWR GND (J7)	B+ DC	0 - 1.0 AC	1.0 - 2.0 AC
C1C (J3)	PWR GND (J7)	B+ DC	0 - 1.0 AC	1.0 - 2.0 AC
C2C (J6)	PWR GND (J7)	B+ DC	0 - 1.0 AC	1.0 - 2.0 AC
C3C (J10)	PWR GND (J7)	B+ DC	0 - 1.0 AC	1.0 - 2.0 AC
SPOUT I (J45)	PWR GND (J7)	0.0 AC	0 - 0.6 AC	0.4 - 2.0 AC
IDM I (J41)	PWR GND (J7)	0.0 AC	0 - 0.6 AC	0.1 - 1.0 AC
CKP+ (J35)	PWR GND (J7)	0.5 - 1.5 DC	0 - 0.6 AC	1.0 - 2.0 AC
CKP-I (J48)	PWR GND (J7)	0.5 - 1.5 DC	0 - 0.6 AC	1.0 - 2.0 AC

NOTE:
- Do not connect the positive lead of the EI diagnostic harness or CKP sensor tee until directed to do so.
- The SPOUT and IDM detectors in the diagnostic harness will not work unless the positive and negative leads of the EI diagnostic harness are connected.
- The vehicle battery voltage must be at least 12 volts DC.
- Be careful not to bring a fluorescent trouble lamp close to the vehicle wiring. If the key is ON and the CKP sensor is disconnected, the ICM may fire the coil.
- When using a DVOM to measure DC voltage readings, connect the positive lead to the jack identified with a (+) sign and the negative lead to the jack with a (-) sign.

Fig. 7   Diagnostics By Trouble Code & Symptom (Part 2 of 3)

IMPORTANT NOTE:

Most DVOM's used by auto technicians belong to a class or type known as "averaging." Examples are the Rotunda Digital Volt-Ohmmeter 007-0001, Fluke 70, 20 series and Fluke 88. Recently technicians have started to use DVOM'S of a different class (True RMS, DVOM's, Fluke 87, 8060A, 8062A, etc.). True RMS DVOM's should not be used with the Pinpoint Tests because they may display different voltage readings depending upon if the DVOM is turned on first and then the test leads are connected, or if the leads are connected first and the DVOM is turned on. Also they may not auto range to the same range every time and some display significantly different values depending on the range selected. It would be impossible to list all of the meters and how to use each, so we are requesting that you perform the following test to verify your DVOM is compatible with the Pinpoint Tests.

Using a known good EI vehicle, install the EI (High Data Rate) diagnostic harness, connect the EEC Breakout Box to the diagnostic cable, start the vehicle and measure the AC between J53 (C1I) and ground. The battery should be charged and the engine must be idling between 700 and 900 rpm. On any EI vehicle (except 1992 Escort/Tracer) the value should be between 1.0 and 2.0 volts AC (1.5 volts AC is typical). Next, with the engine idling, measure between PIP and ground. This reading should be between 6 and 8 volts AC.

Because the Escort/Tracer EI (High Data Rate) ignition system fires the coil differently (repetitive spark) at idle, the coil to ground voltage reading should be between 2 to 7 volts AC (4.5 volts AC is typical). The PIP to ground reading on the Escort/Tracer is the same as the other EI systems.

If the readings you get agree with our test, your DVOM is OK to use with the Ignition Pinpoint Tests. If not, do not use it, it will lead to false parts replacement and the root cause will be difficult or impossible to find.

Fig. 7   Diagnostics By Trouble Code & Symptom (Part 3 of 3)

	TEST STEP	RESULT	▶	ACTION TO TAKE
A1	PERFORM EEC QUICK TEST			
	• Was Quick Test performed according to the procedures?	Yes	▶	GO to A2.
		No	▶	PERFORM Quick Test.
	NOTE: These diagnostic procedures are designed to correct one ignition failure at a time. When a component is replaced or a service is completed, reconnect all components and rerun Quick Test.			
A2	CHECK FOR SPARK DURING CRANK—KOEC			
	• Using a Neon Bulb Spark Tester (Special Service Tool D89P-6666-A) or Air Gap Spark Tester (Special Service Tool D81P-6666-A), check for spark at all spark plug wires while cranking.	Yes	▶	GO to A13.
	• Was spark consistent on all spark plug wires (one spark per crankshaft revolution)?	No	▶	GO to A3.
A3	CHECK PLUGS AND WIRES—KEY OFF			
	• Check spark plug wires for insulation damage, looseness, shorting or other damage.	Yes	▶	REINSTALL plugs and wires. GO to A4.
	• Remove and check spark plugs for damage, wear, carbon deposits and proper plug gap. • Are spark plugs and wires OK?	No	▶	SERVICE or REPLACE damaged component. REMOVE all test equipment. RECONNECT all components. CLEAR Continuous Memory. RERUN Quick Test.
A4	CHECK FOR VEHICLE START WITH DIAGNOSTIC HARNESS INSTALLED			
	WARNING: NEVER CONNECT THE PCM TO THE EEC BREAKOUT BOX WHEN PERFORMING EI DIAGNOSTICS.	Yes	▶	GO to A32.
		No	▶	GO to A5.
	• Key off. • Install EI diagnostic harness to breakout box and ICM. **Do not connect CKP sensor tee or coil tee.** • Use EI (High Data Rate) 6 overlay. • Connect EI diagnostic harness negative lead to battery, leave positive lead disconnected. • Set EI diagnostic harness box type switch to 4/6 position. • Will vehicle start and run?			

FM1119200274010X

Fig. 8   Test A: No Start (Part 1 of 10). 3.0L Flexible Fuel Engine

	TEST STEP	RESULT	▶	ACTION TO TAKE
A5	CHECK PWR GND TO ICM—KEY OFF			
	• Key off. • DVOM on 200 ohm scale. • Measure resistance between J27 (PWR GND) and J7 (B-) at breakout box. • Is resistance less than 5.0 ohms?	Yes	▶	GO to A6.
		No	▶	CHECK connectors, SERVICE or REPLACE harness. PWR GND to ICM is open. REMOVE all test equipment. RECONNECT all components. CLEAR Continuous Memory. RERUN Quick Test.
A6	CHECK FOR VPWR TO ICM—KEY OFF			
	• Key off. • DVOM on 20 volt DC scale. • Key on, engine off. • Measure voltage between (+)J51 (VPWR I) and (-)J7 (B-) at breakout box. • Is DC voltage greater than 10.5 volts?	Yes	▶	GO to A7.
		No	▶	CHECK connectors, SERVICE or REPLACE harness. VPWR to ICM is open. REMOVE all test equipment. RECONNECT all components. CLEAR Continuous Memory. RERUN Quick Test.
A7	CHECK CKP+ BIAS AT ICM—KOEO			
	• Key off. • DVOM on 20 volt DC scale. • Key on, engine off. • Measure voltage between (+)J35 (CKP+ I) and (-)J7 (B-) at breakout box. • Is DC voltage between 1.0 and 2.0 volts?	Yes	▶	GO to A21.
		No	▶	GO to A8. Bias fault.
A8	CHECK CKP+ — BIAS FAULT—CKP SENSOR DISCONNECTED—KOEO			
	• Key off. • Disconnect CKP sensor from vehicle harness connector. • DVOM on 20 volt DC scale. • Key on, engine off. • Measure voltage between (+)J35 (CKP+ I) and (-)J7 (B-) at breakout box. • Is DC voltage greater than 1.0 volt but less than 2.0 volts?	Yes	▶	GO to A9.
		No	▶	GO to A29. Bias fault.

Fig. 8   Test A: No Start (Part 2 of 10). 3.0L Flexible Fuel Engine

	TEST STEP	RESULT	▶	ACTION TO TAKE
A9	CHECK CKP S—BIAS—CKP SENSOR DISCONNECTED—KOEO			
	• Key off. • DVOM on 20 volt DC scale. • Key on, engine off. • Measure voltage between (+)J48 (CKP- I) and (-)J7 (B-) at breakout box. • Is DC voltage between 1.0 and 2.0 volts?	Yes	▶	REPLACE CKP sensor. Short to ground. REMOVE all test equipment. RECONNECT all components. CLEAR Continuous Memory. RERUN Quick Test.
		No	▶	GO to A10.
A10	CHECK FOR BIAS HIGH OR BIAS LOW FAULT—BIAS FAULT			
	• Was bias voltage reading in Step A9 less than 1.0 volt?	Yes	▶	GO to A11. Bias fault.
		No	▶	GO to A12. Bias fault.
A11	CHECK CKP- CIRCUIT—FOR SHORT TO GROUND—BIAS LOW FAULT—CKP SENSOR AND ICM DISCONNECTED			
	• Key off. • Disconnect ICM from ICM tee, leave EI diagnostic harness connected to vehicle harness connector. • DVOM on 20K ohm scale. • Measure resistance between J48 (CKP- I) and J7 (B-) at breakout box. • Is resistance greater than 10K ohms?	Yes	▶	REPLACE ICM. CKP-shorted low. REMOVE all test equipment. RECONNECT all components. CLEAR Continuous Memory. RERUN Quick Test.
		No	▶	CHECK connectors, SERVICE or REPLACE harness. CKP- is shorted low. REMOVE all test equipment. RECONNECT all components. CLEAR Continuous Memory. RERUN Quick Test.

Fig. 8   Test A: No Start (Part 3 of 10). 3.0L Flexible Fuel Engine

TEST STEP	RESULT	▶	ACTION TO TAKE
A12 CHECK CKP- —FOR SHORT HIGH—BIAS HIGH FAULT —CKP SENSOR AND ICM DISCONNECTED—KOEO • Key off. • Disconnect ICM from ICM tee; leave EI diagnostic harness connected to vehicle harness connector. • DVOM 20 volt DC scale. • Key on, engine off. • Measure voltage between (+)J48 (CKP-I) and (-)J7 (B-) at breakout box. • Is DC voltage less than 0.5 volts?	Yes No	▶ ▶	REPLACE ICM. CKP- shorted high. REMOVE all test equipment. RECONNECT all components. CLEAR Continuous Memory. RERUN Quick Test. CHECK connectors, SERVICE or REPLACE harness. CKP- is shorted high. REMOVE all test equipment. RECONNECT all components. CLEAR Continuous Memory. RERUN Quick Test.
A13 CHECK PIP AT ICM—KOEC WARNING: NEVER CONNECT THE PCM TO THE EEC BREAKOUT BOX WHEN PERFORMING EI DIAGNOSTICS. • Key off. • Install EI diagnostic harness to breakout box and ICM. Do not connect CKP sensor tee or coil pack. • Use EI 6 overlay. • Connect EI diagnostic harness negative lead to battery, leave positive lead disconnected. • Set EI diagnostic harness type switch to 4/6 position. • DVOM on 20 volt AC scale. • Crank engine and measure voltage between J43 (PIP I) and J7 (B-) at breakout box. • Is settled AC voltage reading greater than 3.5 volts?	Yes No	▶ ▶	GO to A14. GO to A18. PIP fault.
A14 CHECK FOR PIP OPEN TO PCM—PCM DISCONNECTED—KEY OFF • Key off. • DVOM on 200 ohm scale. • Install a second EEC breakout box to PCM vehicle harness connector. • Measure resistance between J43 (PIP I) at breakout box and Pin 56 (PIP) at second EEC breakout box. • Is resistance less than 5.0 ohms?	Yes No	▶ ▶	GO to A15. CHECK connectors, SERVICE or REPLACE harness. PIP is open. REMOVE all test equipment. RECONNECT all components. CLEAR Continuous Memory. RERUN Quick Test.

Fig. 8   Test A: No Start (Part 4 of 10). 3.0L Flexible Fuel Engine

TEST STEP	RESULT	▶	ACTION TO TAKE
A15 CHECK IGN GND AT ICM—PCM DISCONNECTED—KEY OFF • Key off. • DVOM on 2K ohm scale. • Measure resistance between J47 (IGN GND I) and J7 (B-) at breakout box. • Is resistance less than 1050 ohms?	Yes No	▶ ▶	GO to A16. GO to A17. Ground fault.
A16 CHECK FOR IGN GND OPEN TO PCM—PCM DISCONNECTED • Key off. • DVOM on 2K ohm scale. • Measure resistance between J47 (IGN GND I) at breakout box and Pin 16 (IGN GND) at second EEC breakout box. • Is resistance less than 1050 ohms?	Yes No	▶ ▶	Ignition system is OK. REMOVE all test equipment. RECONNECT all components. CLEAR Continuous Memory. RERUN Quick Test. CHECK connectors, SERVICE or REPLACE harness. IGN GND is open. REMOVE all test equipment. RECONNECT all components. CLEAR Continuous Memory. RERUN Quick Test.
A17 CHECK PWR GND TO ICM—PWR GND FAULT • Key off. • DVOM on 200 ohm scale. • Measure resistance between J27 (PWR GND) and J7 (B-) at breakout box. • Is resistance less than 5.0 ohms?	Yes No	▶ ▶	REPLACE ICM. IGN GND open. REMOVE all test equipment. RECONNECT all components. CLEAR Continuous Memory. RERUN Quick Test. CHECK connectors, SERVICE or REPLACE harness. Power ground to ICM is open. REMOVE all test equipment. RECONNECT all components. CLEAR Continuous Memory. RERUN Quick Test.

Fig. 8   Test A: No Start (Part 5 of 10). 3.0L Flexible Fuel Engine

TEST STEP	RESULT	▶	ACTION TO TAKE
A18 CHECK PIP AT ICM—PIP FAULT—PIP CIRCUIT OPEN—KOEC • Key off. • DVOM 20 volt AC scale. • Push and hold EI diagnostic harness PIP push button down (opens PIP circuit to PCM). • Crank engine and measure voltage between J43 (PIP I) and J7 (B-) at breakout box. • Is settled AC voltage reading greater than 3.5 volts?	Yes No	▶ ▶	GO to A19. REPLACE ICM. No PIP output. REMOVE all test equipment. RECONNECT all components. CLEAR Continuous Memory. RERUN Quick Test.
A19 CHECK FOR PIP SHORT HIGH—ICM AND PCM DISCONNECTED—KOEO • Key off. • DVOM on 20 volt DC scale. • Key on, engine off. • Measure voltage between J43 (PIP I) and J7 (B-) at breakout box. • Is DC voltage less than 0.5 volts?	Yes No	▶ ▶	GO to A20. CHECK connectors, SERVICE or REPLACE harness. PIP is shorted high. REMOVE all test equipment. RECONNECT all components. CLEAR Continuous Memory. RERUN Quick Test.
A20 CHECK FOR PIP SHORT TO GROUND—ICM AND PCM DISCONNECTED—KEY OFF • Key off. • Disconnect PCM. • Disconnect ICM from ICM tee. Leave EI diagnostic harness cable connected to vehicle harness connector. • DVOM on 20K ohm scale. • Measure resistance between J43 (PIP I) and J7 (B-) at breakout box. • Is resistance greater than 10K ohms?	Yes No	▶ ▶	REPLACE PCM. PIP shorted. REMOVE all test equipment. RECONNECT all components. CLEAR Continuous Memory. RERUN Quick Test. CHECK connectors, SERVICE or REPLACE harness. PIP is shorted low. REMOVE all test equipment. RECONNECT all components. CLEAR Continuous Memory. RERUN Quick Test.
A21 CHECK CKP AMPLITUDE AT ICM • Key off. • DVOM on 20 volt AC scale. • Crank engine and measure voltage between J35 (CKP+ I) and J48 (CKP- I) at breakout box. • Is settled AC voltage reading greater than 0.4 volts?	Yes No	▶ ▶	GO to Pinpoint Test Step D1. GO to A22. Amplitude fault.

Fig. 8   Test A: No Start (Part 6 of 10). 3.0L Flexible Fuel Engine

TEST STEP	RESULT	▶	ACTION TO TAKE
A22 CHECK CKP AMPLITUDE AT ICM—AMPLITUDE FAULT—ICM DISCONNECTED—KOEC • Key off. • Disconnect ICM from ICM tee, leave EI diagnostic harness connected to vehicle harness connector. • DVOM 20 volt AC scale. • Crank engine and measure voltage between J35 (CKP+ I) and J48 (CKP- I) at breakout box. • Is settled AC voltage reading greater than 0.4 volts?	Yes No	▶ ▶	REPLACE ICM. CKP is shorted in ICM. REMOVE all test equipment. RECONNECT all components. CLEAR Continuous Memory. RERUN Quick Test. GO to A23.
A23 CHECK CKP CIRCUIT RESISTANCE—ICM DISCONNECTED—AMPLITUDE FAULT—KEY OFF • Key off. • DVOM on 20K ohm scale. • Measure resistance between J48 (CKP- I) and J35 (CKP+ I) at breakout box. • Is resistance between 2580 and 2700 ohms?	Yes No	▶ ▶	GO to A27. GO to A24. Resistance fault.
A24 CHECK FOR RESISTANCE HIGH OR RESISTANCE LOW FAULT • Was the resistance from Step A23 or A32 less than 2580 ohms?	Yes No	▶ ▶	GO to A28. Resistance low fault. GO to A25. Resistance high fault.
A25 CHECK CKP+ OPEN—RESISTANCE HIGH FAULT—KEY OFF • Key off. • Connect CKP sensor tee to CKP sensor and vehicle harness connector. • DVOM on 20K ohm scale. • Measure resistance between J31 (CKP+ S) and J35 (CKP+ I) at breakout box. • Is resistance less than 2050 ohms?	Yes No	▶ ▶	GO to A26. CHECK connectors, SERVICE or REPLACE harness. CKP+ open. REMOVE all test equipment. RECONNECT all components. CLEAR Continuous Memory. RERUN Quick Test.

Fig. 8   Test A: No Start (Part 7 of 10). 3.0L Flexible Fuel Engine

TEST STEP	RESULT	►	ACTION TO TAKE
A26 CHECK CKP CIRCUIT FOR OPEN—RESISTANCE HIGH FAULT—KEY OFF			
• Key off. • DVOM on 20K ohm scale. • Measure resistance between J32 (CKP- S) and J48 (CKP- I) at breakout box. • Is resistance less than 2050 ohms?	Yes	►	REPLACE CKP sensor. High resistance. REMOVE all test equipment. RECONNECT all components. CLEAR Continuous Memory. RERUN Quick Test.
	No	►	CHECK connectors, SERVICE or REPLACE harness. CKP- open. REMOVE all test equipment. RECONNECT all components. CLEAR Continuous Memory. RERUN Quick Test.
A27 CHECK CKPS AIR GAP AND TRIGGER WHEEL			
• Key off. • Check trigger wheel and CKP sensor for damage. • Is CKP sensor and trigger data wheel OK?	Yes	►	REPLACE CKP sensor. No output from sensor. REMOVE all test equipment. RECONNECT all components. CLEAR Continuous Memory. RERUN Quick Test.
	No	►	SERVICE or REPLACE bad parts. REMOVE all test equipment. RECONNECT all components. CLEAR Continuous Memory. RERUN Quick Test.

Fig. 8   Test A: No Start (Part 8 of 10). 3.0L Flexible Fuel Engine

TEST STEP	RESULT	►	ACTION TO TAKE
A28 CHECK FOR CKP+ SHORTED TO CKP- —RESISTANCE LOW FAULT—CKP SENSOR AND ICM DISCONNECTED—KEY OFF			
• Key off. • Disconnect CKP sensor from vehicle harness connector. • DVOM on 20K ohm scale. • Measure resistance between J35 (CKP+ I) and J48 (CKP- I) at breakout box. • Is resistance greater than 3K ohms?	Yes	►	REPLACE CKP sensor. Shorted sensor windings. REMOVE all test equipment. RECONNECT all components. CLEAR Continuous Memory. RERUN Quick Test.
	No	►	CHECK connectors, SERVICE or REPLACE harness. CKP+ shorted to CKP- in harness. REMOVE all test equipment. RECONNECT all components. CLEAR Continuous Memory. RERUN Quick Test.
A29 CHECK FOR BIAS VOLTAGE HIGH OR BIAS VOLTAGE LOW FAULT			
• Was bias voltage reading in Step A8 less than 1.0 volts?	Yes	►	GO to A30. Bias voltage low fault.
	No	►	GO to A31. Bias voltage high fault.
A30 CHECK CKPS+ CIRCUIT FOR SHORT TO GROUND—CKP SENSOR AND ICM DISCONNECTED—KEY OFF—BIAS LOW FAULT			
• Key off. • Disconnect ICM from ICM tee, leave EI diagnostic harness connected to vehicle harness connector. • DVOM on 20K ohm scale. • Measure resistance between J35 (CKP+ I) and J7 (B-) at breakout box. • Is resistance greater than 10K ohms?	Yes	►	REPLACE ICM. REMOVE all test equipment. RECONNECT all components. CLEAR Continuous Memory. RERUN Quick Test.
	No	►	CHECK connectors, SERVICE or REPLACE harness. CKP+ is shorted low. REMOVE all test equipment. RECONNECT all components. CLEAR Continuous Memory. RERUN Quick Test.

Fig. 8   Test A: No Start (Part 9 of 10). 3.0L Flexible Fuel Engine

TEST STEP	RESULT	►	ACTION TO TAKE
A31 CHECK CKPS+ CIRCUIT FOR SHORT HIGH—BIAS HIGH FAULT—CKP SENSOR AND ICM DISCONNECTED—KOEO			
• Key off. • Disconnect ICM from ICM tee, leave EI diagnostic harness connected to vehicle harness connector. • DVOM on 20 volt DC scale. • Key on, engine off. • Measure voltage between +J35 (CKP+ I) and -J7 (B-) at breakout box. • Is DC voltage less than 0.5 volts?	Yes	►	REPLACE ICM. REMOVE all test equipment. RECONNECT all components. CLEAR Continuous Memory. RERUN Quick Test.
	No	►	CHECK connectors, SERVICE or REPLACE harness. CKP+ is shorted high. REMOVE all test equipment. RECONNECT all components. CLEAR Continuous Memory. RERUN Quick Test.
A32 CHECK CKP CIRCUIT RESISTANCE—ICM DISCONNECTED—KEY OFF			
• Key off. • Disconnect ICM from ICM tee, leave EI diagnostic harness connected to vehicle harness connector. • DVOM on 20K ohm scale. • Measure resistance between J48 (CKP- I) and J35 (CKP+ I) at breakout box. • Is resistance between 2300 and 2500 ohms?	Yes	►	REPLACE ICM. REMOVE all test equipment. RECONNECT all components. CLEAR Continuous Memory. RERUN Quick Test.
	No	►	GO to A24. Resistance fault.

Fig. 8   Test A: No Start (Part 10 of 10). 3.0L Flexible Fuel Engine

TEST STEP	RESULT	►	ACTION TO TAKE
B1 CHECK FOR IDM AT ICM—KOER			
WARNING: NEVER CONNECT THE PCM TO EEC BREAKOUT BOX WHEN PERFORMING EI DIAGNOSTICS.	Yes No	► ►	GO to B2. GO to B3. IDM fault.

• Key off.
• Install EI diagnostic harness to breakout box and ICM.
  Do not connect CKP sensor tee or coil tee.
• Use EI 6 overlay.
• Connect EI diagnostic harness negative and positive leads to battery.
• Set EI diagnostic harness type switch to 4/6 position.
• DVOM on 20 volt AC scale.
• Start engine and measure voltage between (+)J30 (EI diagnostic harness IDM detector) and (-)J7 (B-) at breakout box.
  NOTE: If pulses are present, the IDM detector output will be between 5.0 and 7.0 volts AC.
• Is AC voltage between 5.0 and 7.0 volts?			

B2 CHECK FOR IDM CONTINUITY TO PCM—IDM FAULT—ICM AND PCM DISCONNECTED—KEY OFF			
• Key off. • Disconnect PCM. • Disconnect ICM from ICM tee, leave EI diagnostic harness connected to vehicle harness connector. • DVOM on 200 ohm scale. • Install a second EEC breakout box to the PCM vehicle harness connector. • Measure resistance between J41 (IDM I) at breakout box and Pin 4 at the second EEC breakout box. • Is resistance less than 5.0 ohms?	Yes	►	REPLACE PCM. PCM does not respond to IDM input. REMOVE all test equipment. RECONNECT all components. CLEAR Continuous Memory. RERUN Quick Test.
	No	►	CHECK connectors, SERVICE or REPLACE harness. IDM is open. REMOVE all test equipment. RECONNECT all components. CLEAR Continuous Memory. RERUN Quick Test.

Fig. 9   Test B: Code 212, IDM Failure (Part 1 of 3). 3.0L Flexible Fuel Engine

	TEST STEP	RESULT	►	ACTION TO TAKE
B3	CHECK IDM OUTPUT FROM ICM—IDM FAULT—IDM CIRCUIT OPEN—KOER • Key off. • DVOM on 20 volt AC scale. • Push and hold IDM button at EI diagnostic harness connector to breakout box (opens IDM circuit to PCM). • Start engine and measure voltage between J30 (EI diagnostic harness IDM detector) and J7 (B-) at breakout box. • Is AC voltage greater than 5.0 volts?	Yes No	► ►	GO to **B4**. REPLACE ICM. No IDM output from module. REMOVE all test equipment. RECONNECT all components. CLEAR Continuous Memory. RERUN Quick Test.
B4	CHECK FOR IDM SHORT IN PCM—PCM DISCONNECTED—KOEC • Key off. • Disconnect PCM. • DVOM on 20 volt AC scale. • Crank engine and measure voltage between J30 (EI diagnostic harness IDM detector) and J7 (B-) at breakout box. • Is AC voltage greater than 5.0 volts?	Yes No	► ►	REPLACE PCM. PCM is loading IDM signal. REMOVE all test equipment. RECONNECT all components. CLEAR Continuous Memory. RERUN Quick Test. GO to **B5**.
B5	CHECK FOR IDM SHORT HIGH IN HARNESS—ICM AND PCM DISCONNECTED—KOEO • Key off. • DVOM on 20 volt DC scale. • Key on, engine off. • Measure voltage between (+)J41 (IDM I) and (-)J7 (B-) at breakout box. • Is DC voltage less than 0.5 volts?	Yes No	► ►	GO to **B6**. CHECK connectors, SERVICE or REPLACE harness. IDM is shorted high. REMOVE all test equipment. RECONNECT all components. CLEAR Continuous Memory. RERUN Quick Test.

Fig. 9 Test B: Code 212, IDM Failure (Part 2 of 3). 3.0L Flexible Fuel Engine

	TEST STEP	RESULT	►	ACTION TO TAKE
B6	CHECK FOR IDM SHORT TO GROUND IN HARNESS—ICM AND PCM DISCONNECTED • Key off. • Disconnect ICM from ICM tee, leave EI diagnostic harness connected to vehicle harness connector. • DVOM on 20K ohm scale. • Measure resistance between J41 (IDM I) and (-) J7 (B-) at breakout box. • Is resistance greater than 10K ohms?	Yes No	► ►	CHECK connectors, SERVICE or REPLACE harness. IDM is shorted to another wire between ICM and PCM. REMOVE all test equipment. RECONNECT all components. CLEAR Continuous Memory. RERUN Quick Test. CHECK connectors, SERVICE or REPLACE harness. IDM is shorted low. REMOVE all test equipment. RECONNECT all components. CLEAR Continuous Memory. RERUN Quick Test.

Fig. 9 Test B: Code 212, IDM Failure (Part 3 of 3). 3.0L Flexible Fuel Engine

	TEST STEP	RESULT	►	ACTION TO TAKE
C1	CHECK BASE TIMING WARNING: NEVER CONNECT PCM TO EEC BREAKOUT BOX WHEN PERFORMING EI DIAGNOSTICS. • Key off. • Install EI diagnostic harness to breakout box and ICM. Do not connect the CKP sensor tee or coil tee. • Use EI 6 overlay. • Connect EI diagnostic harness negative and positive leads to battery. • Set EI diagnostic harness type switch to 4/6 position. • Connect timing light (must be EI compatible). • Start engine and allow it to warm up. • Is timing 10 ± 2 degrees BTDC when the EI diagnostic harness SPOUT detector button is pushed and held down (opens SPOUT circuit)?	Yes No	► ►	GO to **C2**. GO to **C6**. Base timing fault.
C2	CHECK FOR SPARK ANGLE ADVANCE • Is engine timing greater than 15 degrees BTDC when the EI diagnostic harness SPOUT detector button is released?	Yes No	► ►	ICM is OK. GO to **C3**. No advance timing fault.
C3	CHECK SPOUT AT ICM—NO ADVANCE TIMING FAULT—KOER • Key off. • DVOM on 20 volt AC scale. • Start engine and measure voltage between J21 (EI diagnostic harness SPOUT detector) and (-)J7 (B-) at breakout box. • Is AC voltage reading greater than 5.0 volts?	Yes No	► ►	REPLACE ICM. SPOUT input to ICM is OK, but no spark advance is present. REMOVE all test equipment. RECONNECT all components. CLEAR Continuous Memory. RERUN Quick Test. GO to **C4**. SPOUT circuit fault.

Fig. 10 Test C: Code 213 Or Lack Of Power Or Poor Fuel Economy (Part 1 of 3). 3.0L Flexible Fuel Engine

	TEST STEP	RESULT	►	ACTION TO TAKE
C4	CHECK FOR SPOUT SHORT IN ICM—SPOUT FAULT—SPOUT CIRCUIT OPEN—KOER • Key off. • DVOM on 20 volt AC scale. • Push and hold diagnostic cable SPOUT button (open SPOUT circuit to ICM). • Start engine and measure voltage between (+)J21 (EI diagnostic harness SPOUT detector) and (-)J7 (B-) at breakout box. • Is AC voltage reading greater than 5.0 volts?	Yes No	► ►	REPLACE ICM. SPOUT is shorted in ICM. REMOVE all test equipment. RECONNECT all components. CLEAR Continuous Memory. RERUN Quick Test. GO to **C5**.
C5	CHECK FOR SPOUT SHORT HIGH IN HARNESS—ICM AND PCM DISCONNECTED • Key off. • DVOM on 20 volt DC scale. • Disconnect PCM. • Disconnect the ICM from ICM tee. Do not disconnect the vehicle harness from the tee. • Disconnect EI diagnostic harness positive lead to battery. • Key on, engine off. • Measure voltage between J45 (SPOUT I) and J7 (B-) at breakout box. • Is DC voltage reading less than 0.5 volts?	Yes No	► ►	GO to **C6**. CHECK connectors, SERVICE or REPLACE harness. SPOUT is shorted high. REMOVE all test equipment. RECONNECT all components. CLEAR Continuous Memory. RERUN Quick Test.
C6	CHECK FOR SPOUT SHORT TO GROUND IN HARNESS—ICM AND PCM DISCONNECTED • Key off. • DVOM on 20K ohm scale. • Measure resistance between J45 (SPOUT I) and J7 (B-) at breakout box. • Is the resistance greater than 10K ohms?	Yes No	► ►	GO to **C7**. CHECK connectors, SERVICE or REPLACE harness. SPOUT is shorted low. SERVICE short circuit. REMOVE all test equipment. RECONNECT all components. CLEAR Continuous Memory. RERUN Quick Test.

Fig. 10 Test C: Code 213 Or Lack Of Power Or Poor Fuel Economy (Part 2 of 3). 3.0L Flexible Fuel Engine

TEST STEP	RESULT	▶	ACTION TO TAKE
C7 CHECK FOR SPOUT CONTINUITY TO ICM—ICM AND PCM DISCONNECTED—KEY OFF • Key off. • DVOM on 200 ohm scale. • Install a second EEC breakout box to vehicle harness connector. • Measure resistance between J45 (SPOUT I) at breakout box and Pin 36 at the second EEC breakout box. • Is resistance less than 5.0 ohms?	Yes No	▶ ▶	CHECK connectors, SERVICE or REPLACE harness. SPOUT is open. REMOVE all test equipment. RECONNECT all components. CLEAR Continuous Memory. RERUN Quick Test. REPLACE PCM. SPOUT is not being transmitted by the PCM. REMOVE all test equipment. RECONNECT all components. CLEAR Continuous Memory. RERUN Quick Test.
C8 INSPECT CKP/TRIGGER WHEEL—BASE TIMING FAULT • Is CKP sensor or trigger wheel damaged, i.e., loose or misaligned?	Yes No	▶ ▶	SERVICE or REPLACE as required. REMOVE all test equipment. RECONNECT all components. CLEAR Continuous Memory. RERUN Quick Test. REPLACE ICM. Incorrect output from ICM. REMOVE all test equipment. RECONNECT all components. CLEAR Continuous Memory. RERUN Quick Test.

Fig. 10 Test C: Code 213 Or Lack Of Power Or Poor Fuel Economy (Part 3 of 3). 3.0L Flexible Fuel Engine

TEST STEP	RESULT	▶	ACTION TO TAKE
D1 CHECK FOR SPARK DURING CRANK • Using a Neon Bulb Spark Tester (OTC D89P-6666-A) or Air Gap Spark Tester (D81P-6666-A), check for spark at all spark plug wires while cranking. • Was spark consistent on all spark plug wires (one spark per crankshaft revolution)?	Yes No	▶ ▶	Ignition System OK. GO to D2. Spark fault.
D2 CHECK PLUGS AND WIRES • Check spark plug wires for insulation damage, looseness, shorting or other damage. • Remove and check spark plugs for damage, wear, carbon deposits and proper plug gap. • Are spark plugs and wires OK?	Yes No	▶ ▶	REINSTALL plugs and wires. GO to D3. SERVICE or REPLACE damaged component. REMOVE all test equipment. RECONNECT all components. CLEAR Continuous Memory. RERUN Quick Test.
D3 CHECK FOR COIL PWR AT COIL **WARNING: NEVER CONNECT PCM TO THE EEC BREAKOUT BOX WHEN PERFORMING EI DIAGNOSTICS.** • Key off. • Install EI diagnostic harness to breakout box. • Connect negative lead to battery. • Set EI diagnostic harness type switch to 4/6 position. • Install the coil tee (the tee is blue with 4 pins). • Use EI (High Data Rate) 6 overlay. • DVOM on 20 volt DC scale. • Key on, engine off. • Measure voltage between (+)J5 (COIL PWR) and (-)J7 (B-) at breakout box. • Is DC voltage greater than 10.0 volts?	Yes No	▶ ▶	GO to D4. CHECK connectors, SERVICE or REPLACE harness. COIL PWR is open. REMOVE all test equipment. RECONNECT all components. CLEAR Continuous Memory. RERUN Quick Test.
D4 CHECK FOR C1 HIGH AT COIL PACK—KOEO • Key on, engine off. • Measure voltage between (+)J3 (C1C) and (-)J7 (B-) at breakout box. • Is DC voltage reading greater than 10.0 volts?	Yes No	▶ ▶	GO to D5. GO to D16. C1 low fault.
D5 CHECK FOR C2 HIGH AT COIL PACK—KOEO • Key on, engine off. • Measure voltage between (+)J6 (C2C) and (-)J7 (B-) at breakout box. • Is DC voltage reading greater than 10.0 volts?	Yes No	▶ ▶	GO to D6. GO to D18. C2 low fault.

Fig. 11 Test D: No Start Or Code 232, 215, 216, 217 Or Coil 1, 2, 3 Failure Test D (Part 1 of 8). 3.0L Flexible Fuel Engine

TEST STEP	RESULT	▶	ACTION TO TAKE
D6 CHECK FOR C3 HIGH AT COIL PACK—KOEO • Key on, engine off. • Measure voltage between (+)J10 (C3C) and (-)J7 (B-) at breakout box. • Is DC voltage reading greater than 10.0 volts?	Yes No	▶ ▶	GO to D7. GO to D20. C3 low fault.
D7 CHECK FOR C1 HIGH AT ICM—KOEO • Key off. • Connect ICM tee to ICM and vehicle harness connector. • DVOM on 20 volt DC scale. • Key on, engine off. • Measure voltage between (+)J53 (C1I) and (-)J7 (B-) at breakout box. • Is DC voltage reading greater than 10.0 volts?	Yes No	▶ ▶	GO to D8. CHECK connectors, SERVICE or REPLACE harness. C1 is open. REMOVE all test equipment. RECONNECT all components. CLEAR Continuous Memory. RERUN Quick Test.
D8 CHECK FOR C2 HIGH AT ICM—KOEO • Key on, engine off. • Measure voltage between (+)J55 (C2I) and (-)J7 (B-) at breakout box. • Is DC voltage reading greater than 10.0 volts?	Yes No	▶ ▶	GO to D9. CHECK connectors, SERVICE or REPLACE harness. C2 is open. REMOVE all test equipment. RECONNECT all components. CLEAR Continuous Memory. RERUN Quick Test.
D9 CHECK FOR C3 HIGH AT ICM—KOEO • Key on, engine off. • Measure voltage between (+)J54 (C3I) and -J7 (B-) at breakout box. • Is DC voltage reading greater than 10.0 volts?	Yes No	▶ ▶	GO to D10. CHECK connectors, SERVICE or REPLACE harness. C3 is open. REMOVE all test equipment. RECONNECT all components. CLEAR Continuous Memory. RERUN Quick Test.

Fig. 11 Test D: No Start Or Code 232, 215, 216, 217 Or Coil 1, 2, 3 Failure Test D (Part 2 of 8). 3.0L Flexible Fuel Engine

TEST STEP	RESULT	▶	ACTION TO TAKE
D10 CHECK FOR C1 LOW AT COIL CONNECTOR—COIL DISCONNECTED—KOEO • Key off. • Disconnect the coil from the coil tee. Leave EI diagnostic harness coil tee connected to vehicle harness coil connector. • DVOM on 20 volt DC scale. • Key on, engine off. • Measure voltage between (+)J6 (C1C) and (-)J7 (B-) at breakout box. • Is DC voltage reading less than 0.5 volts?	Yes No	▶ ▶	GO to D11. GO to D22. C1 high fault.
D11 CHECK FOR C2 LOW AT COIL CONNECTOR—COIL DISCONNECTED—KOEO • Key on, engine off. • Measure voltage between (+)J3 (C2C) and (-)J7 (B-) at breakout box. • Is DC voltage reading less than 0.5 volts?	Yes No	▶ ▶	GO to D12. GO to D23. C2 high fault.
D12 CHECK FOR C3 LOW AT COIL CONNECTOR—COIL DISCONNECTED • Key on, engine off. • Measure voltage between (+)J10 (C3C) and (-)J7 (B-) at breakout box. • Is DC voltage reading less than 0.5 volts?	Yes No	▶ ▶	GO to D13. GO to D24. C3 high fault.
D13 CHECK C1 AT COIL CONNECTOR WHILE CRANKING ENGINE—COIL DISCONNECTED—KOEC • Connect EI diagnostic harness positive lead to battery. • Connect incandescent test lamp between J1 (B+) and J6 (C1C). • Crank engine. • Does lamp blink consistently and brightly (one blink per engine revolution)?	Yes No	▶ ▶	GO to D14. REPLACE ICM. C1 open in ICM. REMOVE all test equipment. RECONNECT all components. CLEAR Continuous Memory. RERUN Quick Test.
D14 CHECK C2 AT COIL CONNECTOR WHILE CRANKING ENGINE—COIL DISCONNECTED—KOEC • Connect incandescent test lamp between J1 (B+) and J6 (C2C). • Crank engine. • Does lamp blink consistently and brightly (one blink per engine revolution)?	Yes No	▶ ▶	GO to D15. REPLACE ICM. C3 open in ICM. REMOVE all test equipment. RECONNECT all components. CLEAR Continuous Memory. RERUN Quick Test.

FM1119200277030X

Fig. 11 Test D: No Start Or Code 232, 215, 216, 217 Or Coil 1, 2, 3 Failure Test D (Part 3 of 8). 3.0L Flexible Fuel Engine

TEST STEP		RESULT	▶	ACTION TO TAKE
D15	**CHECK C3 AT COIL CONNECTOR WHILE CRANKING ENGINE—COIL DISCONNECTED—KOEC**			
	• Connect test lamp between J1 (B+) and J10 (C3C). • Crank engine. • **Does lamp blink consistently and brightly (one blink per engine revolution)?**	Yes	▶	REPLACE right coil pack. Input to coil pack is OK, but no high voltage output. REMOVE all test equipment. RECONNECT all components. CLEAR Continuous Memory. RERUN Quick Test.
		No	▶	REPLACE ICM. C3 open in ICM. REMOVE all test equipment. RECONNECT all components. CLEAR Continuous Memory. RERUN Quick Test.
D16	**CHECK FOR C1 SHORT LOW—COIL DISCONNECTED—KEY OFF**			
	• Key off. • DVOM on 20K ohm scale. • Disconnect coil from coil tee, leave EI diagnostic harness connected to vehicle harness coil connector. • Measure resistance between J7 (B-) and J3 (C1C) at breakout box. • **Is resistance reading greater than 2K ohms?**	Yes	▶	REPLACE coil pack. C1 open in coil. REMOVE all test equipment. RECONNECT all components. CLEAR Continuous Memory. RERUN Quick Test.
		No	▶	GO to D17.

Fig. 11 Test D: No Start Or Code 232, 215, 216, 217 Or Coil 1, 2, 3 Failure Test D (Part 4 of 8). 3.0L Flexible Fuel Engine

TEST STEP		RESULT	▶	ACTION TO TAKE
D17	**CHECK FOR C1 SHORT LOW—ICM AND COIL DISCONNECTED—KEY OFF**			
	• Key off. • Disconnect ICM from vehicle harness connector. • DVOM on 20K ohm scale. • Measure resistance between J7 (B-) and J3 (C1C) at breakout box. • **Is resistance reading greater than 10K ohms?**	Yes	▶	REPLACE ICM. C1 is shorted low. REMOVE all test equipment. RECONNECT all components. CLEAR Continuous Memory. RERUN Quick Test.
		No	▶	CHECK connectors, SERVICE or REPLACE harness. C1 is shorted low. REMOVE all test equipment. RECONNECT all components. CLEAR Continuous Memory. RERUN Quick Test. NOTE: A C1 short to ground may have damaged the coil.
D18	**CHECK FOR C2 SHORT LOW—COIL DISCONNECTED—KEY OFF**			
	• Key off. • DVOM on 20K ohm scale. • Disconnect coil from coil tee, leave EI diagnostic harness connected to vehicle harness coil connector. • Measure resistance between J7 (B-) and J6 (C2C) at breakout box. • **Is resistance reading greater than 2K ohms?**	Yes	▶	REPLACE coil pack. C2 open in coil. REMOVE all test equipment. RECONNECT all components. CLEAR Continuous Memory. RERUN Quick Test.
		No	▶	GO to D19.

Fig. 11 Test D: No Start Or Code 232, 215, 216, 217 Or Coil 1, 2, 3 Failure Test D (Part 5 of 8). 3.0L Flexible Fuel Engine

TEST STEP		RESULT	▶	ACTION TO TAKE
D19	**CHECK FOR C2 LOW—ICM AND COIL DISCONNECTED—KEY OFF**			
	• Key off. • Disconnect ICM from vehicle harness connector. • DVOM on 20K ohm scale. • Measure resistance between J6 (C2C) and J7 (B-) at breakout box. • **Is resistance reading greater than 10K ohms?**	Yes	▶	REPLACE ICM. C2 shorted low. REMOVE all test equipment. RECONNECT all components. CLEAR Continuous Memory. RERUN Quick Test.
		No	▶	CHECK connectors, SERVICE or REPLACE harness. C2 is shorted low. REMOVE all test equipment. RECONNECT all components. CLEAR Continuous Memory. RERUN Quick Test. NOTE: A C2 short to ground may have damaged the coil.
D20	**CHECK FOR C3 SHORT LOW—COIL DISCONNECTED—KEY OFF**			
	• Key off. • DVOM on 20K ohm scale. • Disconnect coil from coil tee, leave EI diagnostic harness connected to vehicle harness coil connector. • Measure resistance between J7 (B-) and J10 (C3C) at breakout box. • **Is resistance reading greater than 2K ohms?**	Yes	▶	REPLACE coil pack. C3 open in coil. REMOVE all test equipment. RECONNECT all components. CLEAR Continuous Memory. RERUN Quick Test.
		No	▶	GO to D21.

Fig. 11 Test D: No Start Or Code 232, 215, 216, 217 Or Coil 1, 2, 3 Failure Test D (Part 6 of 8). 3.0L Flexible Fuel Engine

TEST STEP		RESULT	▶	ACTION TO TAKE
D21	**CHECK FOR C3 SHORT LOW—ICM AND COIL DISCONNECTED—KEY OFF**			
	• Key off. • Disconnect ICM from vehicle harness connector. • DVOM on 20K ohm scale. • Measure resistance between J7 (B-) and J10 (C3C) at breakout box. • **Is resistance greater than 10K ohms?**	Yes	▶	REPLACE ICM. C3 is shorted low. REMOVE all test equipment. RECONNECT all components. CLEAR Continuous Memory. RERUN Quick Test.
		No	▶	CHECK connectors, SERVICE or REPLACE harness. C3 is shorted low. REMOVE all test equipment. RECONNECT all components. CLEAR Continuous Memory. RERUN Quick Test. NOTE: A C3 short to ground may have damaged the coil.
D22	**CHECK FOR C1 LOW—ICM AND COIL DISCONNECTED—KOEO**			
	• Key off. • Disconnect ICM from the ICM tee, leave EI diagnostic harness connected to vehicle harness connector. • DVOM on 20 volt DC scale. • Key on, engine off. • Measure voltage between (+)J3 (C1C) and (-)J7 (B-) at breakout box. • **Is DC voltage reading less than 0.5 volts?**	Yes	▶	REPLACE ICM. C1 is shorted high. REMOVE all test equipment. RECONNECT all components. CLEAR Continuous Memory. RERUN Quick Test.
		No	▶	CHECK connectors, SERVICE or REPLACE harness. C1 is shorted high. REMOVE all test equipment. RECONNECT all components. CLEAR Continuous Memory. RERUN Quick Test.

Fig. 11 Test D: No Start Or Code 232, 215, 216, 217 Or Coil 1, 2, 3 Failure Test D (Part 7 of 8). 3.0L Flexible Fuel Engine

TEST STEP	RESULT	▶	ACTION TO TAKE
D23 CHECK FOR C2 LOW—ICM AND COIL DISCONNECTED • Key off. • Disconnect ICM from the ICM tee, leave EI diagnostic harness connected to vehicle harness connector. • DVOM on 20 volt DC scale. • Key on, engine off. • Measure voltage between (+)J6 (C2C) and (-)J7 (B-) at breakout box. • **Is DC voltage reading less than 0.5 volts?**	Yes	▶	REPLACE ICM. C2 is shorted high. REMOVE all test equipment. RECONNECT all components. CLEAR Continuous Memory. RERUN Quick Test. CHECK connectors, SERVICE or REPLACE harness. C2 is shorted high. REMOVE all test equipment. RECONNECT all components. CLEAR Continuous Memory. RERUN Quick Test.
D24 CHECK FOR C3 LOW—ICM AND COIL DISCONNECTED • Key off. • Disconnect ICM from the ICM tee, leave EI diagnostic harness connected to vehicle harness connector. • DVOM on 20 volt DC scale. • Key on, engine off. • Measure voltage between (+)J10 (C3C) and (-)J7 (B-) at breakout box. • **Is DC voltage reading less than 0.5 volts?**	Yes No	▶	REPLACE ICM. C3 is shorted high. REMOVE all test equipment. RECONNECT all components. CLEAR Continuous Memory. RERUN Quick Test. CHECK connectors, SERVICE or REPLACE harness. C3 is shorted high. REMOVE all test equipment. RECONNECT all components. CLEAR Continuous Memory. RERUN Quick Test.

Fig. 11   Test D: No Start Or Code 232, 215, 216, 217 Or Coil 1, 2, 3 Failure Test D (Part 8 of 8). 3.0L Flexible Fuel Engine

TEST STEP	RESULT	▶	ACTION TO TAKE
A1 PERFORM EEC QUICK TEST • **Was Quick Test performed according to the procedures ?** NOTE: These diagnostic procedures are designed to correct one ignition failure at a time. When a component is replaced or a service is completed, remove all test equipment, reconnect all components and rerun Quick Test.	Yes No	▶	GO to **A2**. PERFORM Quick Test.
A2 CHECK FOR SPARK DURING CRANK—KOEC • Using a Neon Bulb Spark Tester (Special Service Tool D89P-6666-A) or Air Gap Spark Tester (Special Service Tool D81P-6666-A), check for spark at all spark plug wires while cranking. • **Was spark consistent on all spark plug wires (one spark per crankshaft revolution)?**	Yes No	▶	GO to **A13**. GO to **A3**.
A3 CHECK PLUGS AND WIRES—KEY OFF • Check spark plug wires for insulation damage, looseness, shorting or other damage. • Remove and check spark plugs for damage, wear, carbon deposits and proper plug gap. • **Are spark plugs and wires OK?**	Yes No	▶	REINSTALL plugs and wires. GO to **A4**. SERVICE or REPLACE damaged component. REMOVE all test equipment. RECONNECT all components. CLEAR Continuous Memory. RERUN Quick Test.
A4 CHECK FOR VEHICLE START WITH DIAGNOSTIC HARNESS INSTALLED **WARNING: NEVER CONNECT THE PCM TO THE EEC BREAKOUT BOX WHEN PERFORMING EI DIAGNOSTICS.** • Key off. • Install EI diagnostic harness to breakout box and ICM. **Do not connect CKP sensor tee or coil tee.** • Use EI (High Data Rate) 6 overlay. • Connect EI diagnostic harness negative lead to battery, leave positive lead disconnected. • Set EI diagnostic harness box type switch to 4/6 position. • **Will vehicle start and run?**	Yes No	▶	GO to **A32**. GO to **A5**.

FM1119200278010X

Fig. 12   Test A: No Start (Part 1 of 10). 2.5L & 1994–95 3.8L SC & 3.8L SFI California Engines

TEST STEP	RESULT	▶	ACTION TO TAKE
A5 CHECK PWR GND TO ICM—KEY OFF • Key off. • DVOM on 200 ohm scale. • Measure resistance between J27 (PWR GND) and J7 (B-) at breakout box. • **Is resistance less than 5.0 ohms?**	Yes No	▶	GO to **A6**. CHECK connectors, SERVICE or REPLACE harness. PWR GND to ICM is open. REMOVE all test equipment. RECONNECT all components. CLEAR Continuous Memory. RERUN Quick Test.
A6 CHECK FOR VPWR TO ICM—KEY OFF • Key off. • DVOM on 40 volt DC scale. • Key on, engine off. • Measure voltage between (+)J51 (VPWR I) and (-)J7 (B-) at breakout box. • **Is DC voltage greater than 10.5 volts?**	Yes No	▶	GO to **A7**. CHECK connectors, SERVICE or REPLACE harness. VPWR to ICM is open. REMOVE all test equipment. RECONNECT all components. CLEAR Continuous Memory. RERUN Quick Test.
A7 CHECK CKP+ BIAS AT ICM—KOEO • Key off. • DVOM on 40 volt DC scale. • Key on, engine off. • Measure voltage between (+)J35 (CKP+ I) and (-)J7 (B-) at breakout box. • **Is DC voltage between 1.0 and 2.0 volts?**	Yes No	▶	GO to **A21**. GO to **A8**. Bias fault.
A8 CHECK CKP+ —BIAS FAULT—CKP SENSOR DISCONNECTED—KOEO • Key off. • Disconnect CKP sensor from vehicle harness connector. • DVOM on 40 volt DC scale. • Key on, engine off. • Measure voltage between (+)J35 (CKP+ I) and (-)J7 (B-) at breakout box. • **Is DC voltage greater than 1.0 volt but less than 2.0 volts?**	Yes No	▶	GO to **A9**. GO to **A29**. Bias fault.

FM1119200278020X

Fig. 12   Test A: No Start (Part 2 of 10). 2.5L & 1994–95 3.8L SC & 3.8L SFI California Engines

TEST STEP	RESULT	▶	ACTION TO TAKE
A9 CHECK CKPS—BIAS—CKP SENSOR DISCONNECTED—KOEO • Key off. • DVOM on 40 volt DC scale. • Key on, engine off. • Measure voltage between (+)J48 (CKP- I) and (-)J7 (B-) at breakout box. • **Is DC voltage between 1.0 and 2.0 volts?**	Yes No	▶	REPLACE CKP sensor. Short to ground. REMOVE all test equipment. RECONNECT all components. CLEAR Continuous Memory. RERUN Quick Test. GO to **A10**.
A10 CHECK FOR BIAS HIGH OR BIAS LOW FAULT—BIAS FAULT • **Was bias voltage reading in Step A9 less than 1.0 volt?**	Yes No	▶	GO to **A11**. Bias fault. GO to **A12**. Bias fault.
A11 CHECK CKP- CIRCUIT— FOR SHORT TO GROUND—BIAS LOW FAULT—CKP SENSOR AND ICM DISCONNECTED • Key off. • Disconnect ICM from ICM tee, leave EI diagnostic harness connected to vehicle harness connector. • DVOM on 20K ohm scale. • Measure resistance between J48 (CKP- I) and J7 (B-) at breakout box. • **Is resistance greater than 10K ohms?**	Yes No	▶	REPLACE ICM. CKP- shorted low. REMOVE all test equipment. RECONNECT all components. CLEAR Continuous Memory. RERUN Quick Test. CHECK connectors, SERVICE or REPLACE harness. CKP- is shorted low. REMOVE all test equipment. RECONNECT all components. CLEAR Continuous Memory. RERUN Quick Test.

FM1119200278030X

Fig. 12   Test A: No Start (Part 3 of 10). 2.5L & 1994–95 3.8L SC & 3.8L SFI California Engines

TEST STEP	RESULT	▶	ACTION TO TAKE
A12 CHECK CKP- —FOR SHORT HIGH—BIAS HIGH FAULT—CKP SENSOR AND ICM DISCONNECTED—KOEC • Key off. • Disconnect ICM from ICM tee; leave EI diagnostic harness connected to vehicle harness connector. • DVOM 40 volt DC scale. • Key on, engine off. • Measure voltage between (+)J48 (CKP- I) and (-)J7 (B-) at breakout box. • **Is DC voltage less than 0.5 volts?**	Yes No	▶ ▶	REPLACE ICM. CKP- shorted high. REMOVE all test equipment. RECONNECT all components. CLEAR Continuous Memory. RERUN Quick Test. CHECK connectors, SERVICE or REPLACE harness. CKP- is shorted high. REMOVE all test equipment. RECONNECT all components. CLEAR Continuous Memory. RERUN Quick Test.
A13 CHECK PIP AT ICM—KOEC **WARNING: NEVER CONNECT THE PCM TO THE EEC BREAKOUT BOX WHEN PERFORMING EI DIAGNOSTICS.** • Key off. • Install EI diagnostic harness to breakout box and ICM. **Do not connect CKP sensor tee or coil tee.** • Use EI 6 overlay. • Connect EI diagnostic harness negative lead to battery, leave positive lead disconnected. • Set EI diagnostic harness type switch to 4/6 position. • DVOM on 40 volt AC scale. • Crank engine and measure voltage between J43 (PIP I) and J7 (B-) at breakout box. • **Is settled AC voltage reading greater than 3.5 volts?**	Yes No	▶ ▶	GO to A14. GO to A18. PIP fault.
A14 CHECK FOR PIP OPEN TO PCM—PCM DISCONNECTED—KEY OFF • Key off. • DVOM on 200 ohm scale. • Install a second EEC breakout box to PCM vehicle harness connector. • Measure resistance between J43 (PIP I) at breakout box and Pin 56 (PIP) at second EEC breakout box. • **Is resistance less than 5.0 ohms?**	Yes No	▶ ▶	GO to A15. CHECK connectors, SERVICE or REPLACE harness. PIP is open. REMOVE all test equipment. RECONNECT all components. CLEAR Continuous Memory. RERUN Quick Test.

FM1119200278040X

Fig. 12   Test A: No Start (Part 4 of 10). 2.5L & 1994–95 3.8L SC & 3.8L SFI California Engines

TEST STEP	RESULT	▶	ACTION TO TAKE
A15 CHECK IGN GND AT ICM—PCM DISCONNECTED—KEY OFF • Key off. • DVOM on 2K ohm scale. • Measure resistance between J47 (IGN GND I) and J7 (B-) at breakout box. • **Is resistance less than 1050 ohms?**	Yes No	▶ ▶	GO to A16. GO to A17. Ground fault.
A16 CHECK FOR IGN GND OPEN TO PCM—PCM DISCONNECTED • Key off. • DVOM on 2K ohm scale. • Measure resistance between J47 (IGN GND I) at breakout box and Pin 16 (IGN GND) at second EEC breakout box. • **Is resistance less than 1050 ohms?**	Yes No	▶ ▶	Ignition system is OK. REMOVE all test equipment. RECONNECT all components. CLEAR Continuous Memory. RERUN Quick Test. CHECK connectors, SERVICE or REPLACE harness. IGN GND is open. REMOVE all test equipment. RECONNECT all components. CLEAR Continuous Memory. RERUN Quick Test.
A17 CHECK PWR GND TO ICM—PWR GND FAULT • Key off. • DVOM on 200 ohm scale. • Measure resistance between J27 (PWR GND) and J7 (B-) at breakout box. • **Is resistance less than 5.0 ohms?**	Yes No	▶ ▶	REPLACE ICM. IGN GND open. REMOVE all test equipment. RECONNECT all components. CLEAR Continuous Memory. RERUN Quick Test. CHECK connectors, SERVICE or REPLACE harness. Power ground to ICM is open. REMOVE all test equipment. RECONNECT all components. CLEAR Continuous Memory. RERUN Quick Test.

FM1119200278050X

Fig. 12   Test A: No Start (Part 5 of 10). 2.5L & 1994–95 3.8L SC & 3.8L SFI California Engines

TEST STEP	RESULT	▶	ACTION TO TAKE
A18 CHECK PIP AT ICM—PIP FAULT—PIP CIRCUIT OPEN—KOEC • Key off. • DVOM 40 volt AC scale. • Push and hold EI diagnostic harness PIP push button down (opens PIP circuit to PCM). • Crank engine and measure voltage between J43 (PIP I) and J7 (B-) at breakout box. • **Is settled AC voltage reading greater than 3.5 volts?**	Yes No	▶ ▶	GO to A19. REPLACE ICM. No PIP output. REMOVE all test equipment. RECONNECT all components. CLEAR Continuous Memory. RERUN Quick Test.
A19 CHECK FOR PIP SHORT HIGH—ICM AND PCM DISCONNECTED—KOEO • Key off. • DVOM on 40 volt DC scale. • Key on, engine off. • Measure voltage between J43 (PIP I) and J7 (B-) at breakout box. • **Is DC voltage less than 0.5 volts?**	Yes No	▶ ▶	GO to A20. CHECK connectors, SERVICE or REPLACE harness. PIP is shorted high. REMOVE all test equipment. RECONNECT all components. CLEAR Continuous Memory. RERUN Quick Test.
A20 CHECK FOR PIP SHORT TO GROUND—ICM AND PCM DISCONNECTED—KEY OFF • Key off. • Disconnect PCM. • Disconnect ICM from ICM tee. Leave EI diagnostic harness cable connected to vehicle harness connector. • DVOM on 20K ohm scale. • Measure resistance between J43 (PIP I) and J7 (B-) at breakout box. • **Is resistance greater than 10K ohms?**	Yes No	▶ ▶	REPLACE PCM. PIP shorted. REMOVE all test equipment. RECONNECT all components. CLEAR Continuous Memory. RERUN Quick Test. CHECK connectors, SERVICE or REPLACE harness. PIP is shorted low. REMOVE all test equipment. RECONNECT all components. CLEAR Continuous Memory. RERUN Quick Test.
A21 CHECK CKP AMPLITUDE AT ICM • Key off. • DVOM on 40 volt AC scale. • Crank engine and measure voltage between J35 (CKP+ I) and J48 (CKP- I) at breakout box. • **Is settled AC voltage reading greater than 0.4 volts?**	Yes No	▶ ▶	GO to Pinpoint Test Step D1. GO to A22. Amplitude fault.

FM1119200278060X

Fig. 12   Test A: No Start (Part 6 of 10). 2.5L & 1994–95 3.8L SC & 3.8L SFI California Engines

TEST STEP	RESULT	▶	ACTION TO TAKE
A22 CHECK CKP AMPLITUDE AT ICM—AMPLITUDE FAULT—ICM DISCONNECTED—KOEC • Key off. • Disconnect ICM from ICM tee, leave EI diagnostic harness connected to vehicle harness connector. • DVOM 40 volt AC scale. • Crank engine and measure voltage between J35 (CKP+ I) and J48 (CKP- I) at breakout box. • **Is settled AC voltage reading greater than 0.4 volts?**	Yes No	▶ ▶	REPLACE ICM. CKP is shorted in ICM. REMOVE all test equipment. RECONNECT all components. CLEAR Continuous Memory. RERUN Quick Test. GO to A23.
A23 CHECK CKP CIRCUIT RESISTANCE—ICM DISCONNECTED—AMPLITUDE FAULT—KEY OFF • Key off. • DVOM on 20K ohm scale. • Measure resistance between J48 (CKP- I) and J35 (CKP+ I) at breakout box. • **Is resistance between 2580 and 2700 ohms?**	Yes No	▶ ▶	GO to A27. GO to A24. Resistance fault.
A24 CHECK FOR RESISTANCE HIGH OR RESISTANCE LOW FAULT • **Was the resistance from Step A23 or A32 less than 2580 ohms?**	Yes No	▶ ▶	GO to A28. Resistance low fault. GO to A25. Resistance high fault.
A25 CHECK CKP+ OPEN—RESISTANCE HIGH FAULT—KEY OFF • Key off. • Connect CKP sensor tee to CKP sensor and vehicle harness connector. • DVOM on 20K ohm scale. • Measure resistance between J31 (CKP+ S) and J35 (CKP+ I) at breakout box. • **Is resistance less than 2050 ohms?**	Yes No	▶ ▶	GO to A26. CHECK connectors, SERVICE or REPLACE harness. CKP+ open. REMOVE all test equipment. RECONNECT all components. CLEAR Continuous Memory. RERUN Quick Test.

FM1119200278070X

Fig. 12   Test A: No Start (Part 7 of 10). 2.5L & 1994–95 3.8L SC & 3.8L SFI California Engines

TEST STEP		RESULT	▶	ACTION TO TAKE
A26	CHECK CKP CIRCUIT FOR OPEN—RESISTANCE HIGH FAULT—KEY OFF			
	• Key off. • DVOM on 20K ohm scale. • Measure resistance between J32 (CKP-S) and J48 (CKP-I) at breakout box. • **Is resistance less than 2050 ohms?**	Yes	▶	REPLACE CKP sensor. High resistance. REMOVE all test equipment. RECONNECT all components. CLEAR Continuous Memory. RERUN Quick Test.
		No	▶	CHECK connectors, SERVICE or REPLACE harness. CKP- open. REMOVE all test equipment. RECONNECT all components. CLEAR Continuous Memory. RERUN Quick Test.
A27	CHECK CKPS AIR GAP AND TRIGGER WHEEL.			
	• Key off. • Check trigger wheel and CKP sensor for damage. • **Is CKP sensor and trigger data wheel OK?**	Yes	▶	REPLACE CKP sensor. No output from sensor. REMOVE all test equipment. RECONNECT all components. CLEAR Continuous Memory. RERUN Quick Test.
		No	▶	SERVICE or REPLACE bad parts. REMOVE all test equipment. RECONNECT all components. CLEAR Continuous Memory. RERUN Quick Test.

FM1119200278080X

Fig. 12   Test A: No Start (Part 8 of 10). 2.5L & 1994–95 3.8L SC & 3.8L SFI California Engines

TEST STEP		RESULT	▶	ACTION TO TAKE
A28	CHECK FOR CKP+ SHORTED TO CKP- —RESISTANCE LOW FAULT—CKP SENSOR AND ICM DISCONNECTED—KEY OFF			
	• Key off. • Disconnect CKP sensor from vehicle harness connector. • DVOM on 20K ohm scale. • Measure resistance between J35 (CKP+ I) and J48 (CKP- I) at breakout box. • **Is resistance greater than 3K ohms?**	Yes	▶	REPLACE CKP sensor. Shorted sensor windings. REMOVE all test equipment. RECONNECT all components. CLEAR Continuous Memory. RERUN Quick Test.
		No	▶	CHECK connectors, SERVICE or REPLACE harness. CKP+ shorted to CKP- in harness. REMOVE all test equipment. RECONNECT all components. CLEAR Continuous Memory. RERUN Quick Test.
A29	CHECK FOR BIAS VOLTAGE HIGH OR BIAS VOLTAGE LOW FAULT			
	• Was bias voltage reading in Step A8 less than 1.0 volts?	Yes	▶	GO to A30. Bias voltage low fault.
		No	▶	GO to A31. Bias voltage high fault.
A30	CHECK CKPS+ CIRCUIT FOR SHORT TO GROUND—CKP SENSOR AND ICM DISCONNECTED—BIAS LOW FAULT—KEY OFF			
	• Key off. • Disconnect ICM from ICM tee, leave EI diagnostic harness connected to vehicle harness connector. • DVOM on 20K ohm scale. • Measure resistance between J35 (CKP+ I) and J7 (B-) at breakout box. • **Is resistance greater than 10K ohms?**	Yes	▶	REPLACE ICM. REMOVE all test equipment. RECONNECT all components. CLEAR Continuous Memory. RERUN Quick Test.
		No	▶	CHECK connectors, SERVICE or REPLACE harness. CKP+ is shorted low. REMOVE all test equipment. RECONNECT all components. CLEAR Continuous Memory. RERUN Quick Test.

FM1119200278090X

Fig. 12   Test A: No Start (Part 9 of 10). 2.5L & 1994–95 3.8L SC & 3.8L SFI California Engines

TEST STEP		RESULT	▶	ACTION TO TAKE
A31	CHECK CKPS+ CIRCUIT FOR SHORT HIGH—BIAS HIGH FAULT—CKP SENSOR AND ICM DISCONNECTED—KOEO			
	• Key off. • Disconnect ICM from ICM tee, leave EI diagnostic harness connected to vehicle harness connector. • DVOM on 40 volt DC scale. • Key on, engine off. • Measure voltage between +J35 (CKP I) and -7 (B-) at breakout box. • **Is DC voltage less than 0.5 volts?**	Yes	▶	REPLACE ICM. REMOVE all test equipment. RECONNECT all components. CLEAR Continuous Memory. RERUN Quick Test.
		No	▶	CHECK connectors, SERVICE or REPLACE harness. CKP+ is shorted high. REMOVE all test equipment. RECONNECT all components. CLEAR Continuous Memory. RERUN Quick Test.
A32	CHECK CKP CIRCUIT RESISTANCE—ICM DISCONNECTED—KEY OFF			
	• Key off. • Disconnect ICM from ICM tee, leave EI diagnostic harness connected to vehicle harness connector. • DVOM on 20K ohm scale. • Measure resistance between J48 (CKP- I) and J35 (CKP+ I) at breakout box. • **Is resistance between 2300 and 2500 ohms?**	Yes	▶	REPLACE ICM. REMOVE all test equipment. RECONNECT all components. CLEAR Continuous Memory. RERUN Quick Test.
		No	▶	GO to A24. Resistance fault.

FM111920027810AX

Fig. 12   Test A: No Start (Part 10 of 10). 2.5L Engine

TEST STEP		RESULT	▶	ACTION TO TAKE
A31	CHECK CKPS+ CIRCUIT FOR SHORT HIGH—BIAS HIGH FAULT—CKP SENSOR AND ICM DISCONNECTED—KOEO			
	• Key off. • Disconnect ICM from ICM tee, leave EI diagnostic harness connected to vehicle harness connector. • DVOM on 40 volt DC scale. • Key on, engine off. • Measure voltage between +J35 (CKP I) and -J7 (B-) at breakout box. • **Is DC voltage less than 0.5 volts?**	Yes	▶	REPLACE ICM. REMOVE all test equipment. RECONNECT all components. CLEAR Continuous Memory. RERUN Quick Test.
		No	▶	CHECK connectors, SERVICE or REPLACE harness. CKP+ is shorted high. REMOVE all test equipment. RECONNECT all components. CLEAR Continuous Memory. RERUN Quick Test.
A32	CHECK CKP CIRCUIT RESISTANCE—ICM DISCONNECTED—KEY OFF			
	• Key off. • Disconnect ICM from ICM tee, leave EI diagnostic harness connected to vehicle harness connector. • DVOM on 20K ohm scale. • Measure resistance between J48 (CKP- I) and J35 (CKP+ I) at breakout box. • **Is resistance between 2300 and 2700 ohms?**	Yes	▶	REPLACE ICM. REMOVE all test equipment. RECONNECT all components. CLEAR Continuous Memory. RERUN Quick Test.
		No	▶	GO to A24. Resistance fault.

FM111940027810BX

Fig. 12   Test A: No Start (Part 10 of 10). 1994–95 3.8L SC & 3.8L SFI California Engines

TEST STEP		RESULT	▶	ACTION TO TAKE
B1	CHECK FOR IDM AT ICM—KOER			
	WARNING: NEVER CONNECT THE PCM TO EEC BREAKOUT BOX WHEN PERFORMING EI DIAGNOSTICS. • Key off. • Install EI diagnostic harness to breakout box and ICM. **Do not connect CKP sensor tee or coil tee.** • Use EI 6 overlay. • Connect EI diagnostic harness negative and positive leads to battery. • Set EI diagnostic harness type switch to 4/6 position. • DVOM on 40 volt AC scale. • Start engine and measure voltage between (+)J30 (EI diagnostic harness IDM detector) and (-)J7 (B-) at breakout box. NOTE: If pulses are present, the IDM detector output will be between 5.0 and 7.0 volts AC. • **Is AC voltage between 5.0 and 7.0 volts?**	Yes No	▶ ▶	GO to **B2**. GO to **B3**. IDM fault.
B2	CHECK FOR IDM CONTINUITY TO PCM—IDM FAULT—ICM AND PCM DISCONNECTED—KEY OFF			
	• Key off. • Disconnect PCM. • Disconnect ICM from ICM tee, leave EI diagnostic harness connected to vehicle harness connector. • DVOM on 200 ohm scale. • Install a second EEC breakout box to the PCM vehicle harness connector. • Measure resistance between J41 (IDM I) at breakout box and Pin 4 at the second EEC breakout box. • **Is resistance less than 5.0 ohms?**	Yes No	▶ ▶	REPLACE PCM. PCM does not respond to IDM input. REMOVE all test equipment. RECONNECT all components. CLEAR Continuous Memory. RERUN Quick Test. CHECK connectors, SERVICE or REPLACE harness. IDM is open. REMOVE all test equipment. RECONNECT all components. CLEAR Continuous Memory. RERUN Quick Test.

FM1119200279010X

Fig. 13   Test B: Code 212, IDM Failure (Part 1 of 3). 2.5L & 1994–95 3.8L SC & 3.8L SFI California Engines

TEST STEP		RESULT	▶	ACTION TO TAKE
B3	CHECK IDM OUTPUT FROM ICM—IDM FAULT—IDM CIRCUIT OPEN—KOER			
	• Key off. • DVOM on 40 volt AC scale. • Push and hold IDM button at EI diagnostic harness connector to breakout box (opens IDM circuit to PCM). • Start engine and measure voltage between J30 (EI diagnostic harness IDM detector) and J7 (B-) at breakout box. • **Is AC voltage greater than 5.0 volts?**	Yes No	▶ ▶	GO to **B4**. REPLACE ICM. No IDM output from module. REMOVE all test equipment. RECONNECT all components. CLEAR Continuous Memory. RERUN Quick Test.
B4	CHECK FOR IDM SHORT IN PCM—PCM DISCONNECTED—KOEC			
	• Key off. • Disconnect PCM. • DVOM on 40 volt AC scale. • Crank engine and measure voltage between J30 (EI diagnostic harness IDM detector) and -J7 (B-) at breakout box. • **Is AC voltage greater than 5.0 volts?**	Yes No	▶ ▶	REPLACE PCM. PCM is loading IDM signal. REMOVE all test equipment. RECONNECT all components. CLEAR Continuous Memory. RERUN Quick Test. GO to **B5**.
B5	CHECK FOR IDM SHORT HIGH IN HARNESS—ICM AND PCM DISCONNECTED—KOEO			
	• Key off. • DVOM on 40 volt DC scale. • Key on, engine off. • Measure voltage between (+)J41 (IDM I) and (-)J7 (B-) at breakout box. • **Is DC voltage less than 0.5 volts?**	Yes No	▶ ▶	GO to **B6**. CHECK connectors, SERVICE or REPLACE harness. IDM is shorted high. REMOVE all test equipment. RECONNECT all components. CLEAR Continuous Memory. RERUN Quick Test.

FM1119200279020X

Fig. 13   Test B: Code 212, IDM Failure (Part 2 of 3). 2.5L & 1994–95 3.8L SC & 3.8L SFI California Engines

TEST STEP		RESULT	▶	ACTION TO TAKE
B6	CHECK FOR IDM SHORT TO GROUND IN HARNESS—ICM AND PCM DISCONNECTED			
	• Key off. • Disconnect ICM from ICM tee, leave EI diagnostic harness connected to vehicle harness connector. • DVOM on 20K ohm scale. • Measure resistance between J41 (IDM I) and (-) J7 (B-) at breakout box. • **Is resistance greater than 10K ohms?**	Yes No	▶ ▶	CHECK connectors, SERVICE or REPLACE harness. IDM is shorted to another wire between ICM and PCM. REMOVE all test equipment. RECONNECT all components. CLEAR Continuous Memory. RERUN Quick Test. CHECK connectors, SERVICE or REPLACE harness. IDM is shorted low. REMOVE all test equipment. RECONNECT all components. CLEAR Continuous Memory. RERUN Quick Test.

FM1119200279030X

Fig. 13   Test B: Code 212, IDM Failure (Part 3 of 3). 2.5L & 1994–95 3.8L SC & 3.8L SFI California Engines

TEST STEP		RESULT	▶	ACTION TO TAKE
C1	CHECK BASE TIMING			
	WARNING: NEVER CONNECT PCM TO EEC BREAKOUT BOX WHEN PERFORMING EI DIAGNOSTICS. • Key off. • Install EI diagnostic harness to breakout box and ICM. **Do not connect the CKP sensor tee or coil tee.** • Use EI 6 overlay. • Connect EI diagnostic harness negative and positive leads to battery. • Set EI diagnostic harness type switch to 4/6 position. • Connect timing light (must be EI compatible). • Start engine and allow it to warm up. • **Is timing 10 ± 2 degrees BTDC when the EI diagnostic harness SPOUT detector button is pushed and held down (opens SPOUT circuit)?**	Yes No	▶ ▶	GO to **C2**. GO to **C8**. Base timing fault.
C2	CHECK FOR SPARK ANGLE ADVANCE			
	• **Is engine timing greater than 15 degrees BTDC when the EI diagnostic harness SPOUT detector button is released?**	Yes No	▶ ▶	ICM is OK. GO to **C3**. No advance timing fault.
C3	CHECK SPOUT AT ICM—NO ADVANCE TIMING FAULT—KOER			
	• Key off. • DVOM on 40 volt AC scale. • Start engine and measure voltage between J21 (EI diagnostic harness SPOUT detector) and (-)J7 (B-) at breakout box. • **Is AC voltage reading greater than 5.0 volts?**	Yes No	▶ ▶	REPLACE ICM. SPOUT input to ICM is OK, but no spark advance is present. REMOVE all test equipment. RECONNECT all components. CLEAR Continuous Memory. RERUN Quick Test. GO to **C4**. SPOUT circuit fault.

FM1119200280010X

Fig. 14   Test C: Code 213 Or Lack Of Power Or Poor Fuel Economy (Part 1 of 3). 2.5L & 1994–95 3.8L SC & 3.8L SFI California Engines

TEST STEP	RESULT	►	ACTION TO TAKE
C4 CHECK FOR SPOUT SHORT IN ICM—SPOUT FAULT—SPOUT CIRCUIT OPEN—KOER • Key off. • DVOM on 40 volt AC scale. • Push and hold diagnostic cable SPOUT button (open SPOUT circuit to ICM). • Start engine and measure voltage between (+)J21 (EI diagnostic harness SPOUT detector) and (-)J7 (B-) at breakout box. • **Is AC voltage reading greater than 5.0 volts?**	Yes No	► ►	REPLACE ICM. SPOUT is shorted in ICM. GO to C5.
C5 CHECK FOR SPOUT SHORT HIGH IN HARNESS—ICM AND PCM DISCONNECTED • Key off. • DVOM on 40 volt DC scale. • Disconnect PCM. • Disconnect the ICM from ICM tee. Do not disconnect the vehicle harness from the tee. • Disconnect EI diagnostic harness positive lead to battery. • Key on, engine off. • Measure voltage between J45 (SPOUT I) and J7 (B-) at breakout box. • **Is DC voltage reading less than 0.5 volts?**	Yes No	► ►	GO to C6. CHECK connectors, SERVICE or REPLACE harness. SPOUT is shorted high. REMOVE all test equipment. RECONNECT all components. CLEAR Continuous Memory. RERUN Quick Test.
C6 CHECK FOR SPOUT SHORT TO GROUND IN HARNESS—ICM AND PCM DISCONNECTED • Key off. • DVOM on 20K ohm scale. • Measure resistance between J45 (SPOUT I) and J7 (B-) at breakout box. • **Is the resistance greater than 10K ohms?**	Yes No	► ►	GO to C7. CHECK connectors, SERVICE or REPLACE harness. SPOUT is shorted low. SERVICE short circuit. REMOVE all test equipment. RECONNECT all components. CLEAR Continuous Memory. RERUN Quick Test.

FM1119200280020X

Fig. 14 Test C: Code 213 Or Lack Of Power Or Poor Fuel Economy (Part 2 of 3). 2.5L & 1994–95 3.8L SC & 3.8L SFI California Engines

TEST STEP	RESULT	►	ACTION TO TAKE
C7 CHECK FOR SPOUT CONTINUITY TO ICM—ICM AND PCM DISCONNECTED—KEY OFF • Key off. • DVOM on 200 ohm scale. • Install a second EEC breakout box to vehicle harness connector. • Measure resistance between J45 (SPOUT I) at breakout box and Pin 36 at the second EEC breakout box. • **Is resistance less than 5.0 ohms?**	Yes No	► ►	REPLACE PCM. SPOUT is not being transmitted by the PCM. REMOVE all test equipment. RECONNECT all components. CLEAR Continuous Memory. RERUN Quick Test. CHECK connectors, SERVICE or REPLACE harness. SPOUT is open. REMOVE all test equipment. RECONNECT all components. CLEAR Continuous Memory. RERUN Quick Test.
C8 INSPECT CKP / TRIGGER WHEEL—BASE TIMING FAULT • **Is CKP sensor or trigger wheel damaged, i.e., loose or misaligned?**	Yes No	► ►	SERVICE or REPLACE as required. REMOVE all test equipment. RECONNECT all components. CLEAR Continuous Memory. RERUN Quick Test. REPLACE ICM. Incorrect output from ICM. REMOVE all test equipment. RECONNECT all components. CLEAR Continuous Memory. RERUN Quick Test.

FM1119200280030X

Fig. 14 Test C: Code 213 Or Lack Of Power Or Poor Fuel Economy (Part 3 of 3). 2.5L & 1994–95 3.8L SC & 3.8L SFI California Engines

TEST STEP	RESULT	►	ACTION TO TAKE
D1 CHECK FOR SPARK DURING CRANK • Using a Neon Bulb Spark Tester (OTC D89P-6666-A) or Air Gap Spark Tester (D81P-6666-A), check for spark at all spark plug wires while cranking. • **Was spark consistent on all spark plug wires (one spark per crankshaft revolution)?**	Yes No	► ►	Ignition System OK. GO to D2. Spark fault.
D2 CHECK PLUGS AND WIRES • Check spark plug wires for insulation damage, looseness, shorting or other damage. • Remove and check spark plugs for damage, wear, carbon deposits and proper plug gap. • **Are spark plugs and wires OK?**	Yes No	► ►	REINSTALL plugs and wires. GO to D3. SERVICE or REPLACE damaged component. REMOVE all test equipment. RECONNECT all components. CLEAR Continuous Memory. RERUN Quick Test.
D3 CHECK FOR COIL PWR AT COIL **WARNING: NEVER CONNECT PCM TO THE EEC BREAKOUT BOX WHEN PERFORMING EI DIAGNOSTICS.** • Key off. • Install EI diagnostic harness to breakout box. • Connect negative lead to battery. • Set EI diagnostic harness type switch to 4/6 position. • Install the coil tee (the tee is blue with 4 pins). • Use EI (High Data Rate) 6 overlay. • DVOM on 40 volt DC scale. • Key on, engine off. • Measure voltage between (+)J5 (COIL PWR) and (-)J7 (B-) at breakout box. • **Is DC voltage greater than 10.0 volts?**	Yes No	► ►	GO to D4. CHECK connectors, SERVICE or REPLACE harness. COIL PWR is open. REMOVE all test equipment. RECONNECT all components. CLEAR Continuous Memory. RERUN Quick Test.
D4 CHECK FOR C1 HIGH AT COIL PACK—KOEO • Key on, engine off. • Measure voltage between (+)J6 (C1C) and (-)J7 (B-) at breakout box. • **Is DC voltage reading greater than 10.0 volts?**	Yes No	► ►	GO to D5. GO to D16. C1 low fault.
D5 CHECK FOR C2 HIGH AT COIL PACK—KOEO • Key on, engine off. • Measure voltage between (+)J3 (C2C) and (-)J7 (B-) at breakout box. • **Is DC voltage reading greater than 10.0 volts?**	Yes No	► ►	GO to D6. GO to D18. C2 low fault.

FM1119200281010X

Fig. 15 Test D: No Start Or Code 2323, 215, 216, 217 Or Coil 1, 2, 3 Failure (Part 1 of 8). 2.5L & 1994–95 3.8L SC & 3.8L SFI California Engines

TEST STEP	RESULT	►	ACTION TO TAKE
D6 CHECK FOR C3 HIGH AT COIL PACK—KOEO • Key on, engine off. • Measure voltage between (+)J10 (C3C) and (-)J7 (B-) at breakout box. • **Is DC voltage reading greater than 10.0 volts?**	Yes No	► ►	GO to D7. GO to D20. C3 low fault.
D7 CHECK FOR C1 HIGH AT ICM—KOEO • Key off. • Connect ICM tee to ICM and vehicle harness connector. • DVOM on 40 volt DC scale. • Key on, engine off. • Measure voltage between (+)J53 (C1I) and (-)J7 (B-) at breakout box. • **Is DC voltage reading greater than 10.0 volts?**	Yes No	► ►	GO to D8. CHECK connectors, SERVICE or REPLACE harness. C1 is open. REMOVE all test equipment. RECONNECT all components. CLEAR Continuous Memory. RERUN Quick Test.
D8 CHECK FOR C2 HIGH AT ICM—KOEO • Key on, engine off. • Measure voltage between (+)J55 (C2I) and (-)J7 (B-) at breakout box. • **Is DC voltage reading greater than 10.0 volts?**	Yes No	► ►	GO to D9. CHECK connectors, SERVICE or REPLACE harness. C2 is open. REMOVE all test equipment. RECONNECT all components. CLEAR Continuous Memory. RERUN Quick Test.
D9 CHECK FOR C3 HIGH AT ICM—KOEO • Key on, engine off. • Measure voltage between (+)J54 (C3I) and -J7 (B-) at breakout box. • **Is DC voltage reading greater than 10.0 volts?**	Yes No	► ►	GO to D10. CHECK connectors, SERVICE or REPLACE harness. C3 is open. REMOVE all test equipment. RECONNECT all components. CLEAR Continuous Memory. RERUN Quick Test.

FM1119200281020X

Fig. 15 Test D: No Start Or Code 2323, 215, 216, 217 Or Coil 1, 2, 3 Failure (Part 2 of 8). 2.5L & 1994–95 3.8L SC & 3.8L SFI California Engines

TEST STEP	RESULT	▶	ACTION TO TAKE
D10 CHECK FOR C1 LOW AT COIL CONNECTOR—COIL DISCONNECTED—KOEO • Key off. • Disconnect the coil from the coil tee. Leave EI diagnostic harness coil tee connected to vehicle harness coil connector. • DVOM on 40 volt DC scale. • Key on, engine off. • Measure voltage between (+)J6 (C1C) and (-)J7 (B-) at breakout box. • **Is DC voltage reading less than 0.5 volts?**	Yes No	▶ ▶	GO to D11. GO to D22. C1 high fault.
D11 CHECK FOR C2 LOW AT COIL CONNECTOR—COIL DISCONNECTED—KOEO • Key on, engine off. • Measure voltage between (+)J3 (C2C) and (-)J7 (B-) at breakout box. • **Is DC voltage reading less than 0.5 volts?**	Yes No	▶ ▶	GO to D12. GO to D23. C2 high fault.
D12 CHECK FOR C3 LOW AT COIL CONNECTOR—COIL DISCONNECTED • Key on, engine off. • Measure voltage between (+)J10 (C3C) and (-)J7 (B-) at breakout box. • **Is DC voltage reading less than 0.5 volts?**	Yes No	▶ ▶	GO to D13. GO to D24. C3 high fault.
D13 CHECK C1 AT COIL CONNECTOR WHILE CRANKING ENGINE—COIL DISCONNECTED—KOEC • Connect EI diagnostic harness positive lead to battery. • Connect incandescent test lamp between J1 (B+) and J6 (C1C). • Crank engine. • **Does lamp blink consistently and brightly (one blink per engine revolution)?**	Yes No	▶ ▶	GO to D14. REPLACE ICM. C1 open in ICM. REMOVE all test equipment. RECONNECT all components. CLEAR Continuous Memory. RERUN Quick Test.
D14 CHECK C2 AT COIL CONNECTOR WHILE CRANKING ENGINE—COIL DISCONNECTED—KOEC • Connect incandescent test lamp between J1 (B+) and J3 (C2C). • Crank engine. • **Does lamp blink consistently and brightly (one blink per engine revolution)?**	Yes No	▶ ▶	GO to D15. REPLACE ICM. C2 open in ICM. REMOVE all test equipment. RECONNECT all components. CLEAR Continuous Memory. RERUN Quick Test.

FM1119200281030X

Fig. 15 Test D: No Start Or Code 2323, 215, 216, 217 Or Coil 1, 2, 3 Failure (Part 3 of 8). 2.5L & 1994–95 3.8L SC & 3.8L SFI California Engines

TEST STEP	RESULT	▶	ACTION TO TAKE
D15 CHECK C3 AT COIL CONNECTOR WHILE CRANKING ENGINE—COIL DISCONNECTED—KOEC • Connect test lamp between J1 (B+) and J10 (C3C). • Crank engine. • **Does lamp blink consistently and brightly (one blink per engine revolution)?**	Yes No	▶ ▶	REPLACE right coil pack. Input to coil pack is OK, but no high voltage output. REMOVE all test equipment. RECONNECT all components. CLEAR Continuous Memory. RERUN Quick Test. REPLACE ICM. C3 open in ICM. REMOVE all test equipment. RECONNECT all components. CLEAR Continuous Memory. RERUN Quick Test.
D16 CHECK FOR C1 SHORT LOW—COIL DISCONNECTED—KEY OFF • Key off. • DVOM on 20K ohm scale. • Disconnect coil from coil tee, leave EI diagnostic harness connected to vehicle harness coil connector. • Measure resistance between J7 (B-) and J6 (C1C) at breakout box. • **Is resistance reading greater than 2K ohms?**	Yes No	▶ ▶	REPLACE coil pack. C1 open in coil. REMOVE all test equipment. RECONNECT all components. CLEAR Continuous Memory. RERUN Quick Test. GO to D17.

FM1119200281040X

Fig. 15 Test D: No Start Or Code 2323, 215, 216, 217 Or Coil 1, 2, 3 Failure (Part 4 of 8). 2.5L & 1994–95 3.8L SC & 3.8L SFI California Engines

TEST STEP	RESULT	▶	ACTION TO TAKE
D17 CHECK FOR C1 SHORT LOW—ICM AND COIL DISCONNECTED—KEY OFF • Key off. • Disconnect ICM from vehicle harness connector. • DVOM on 20K ohm scale. • Measure resistance between J7 (B-) and J6 (C1C) at breakout box. • **Is resistance reading greater than 10K ohms?**	Yes No	▶ ▶	REPLACE ICM. C1 is shorted low. REMOVE all test equipment. RECONNECT all components. CLEAR Continuous Memory. RERUN Quick Test. CHECK connectors, SERVICE or REPLACE harness. C1 is shorted low. REMOVE all test equipment. RECONNECT all components. CLEAR Continuous Memory. RERUN Quick Test. NOTE: A C1 short to ground may have damaged the coil.
D18 CHECK FOR C2 SHORT LOW—COIL DISCONNECTED—KEY OFF • Key off. • DVOM on 20K ohm scale. • Disconnect coil from coil tee, leave EI diagnostic harness connected to vehicle harness coil connector. • Measure resistance between J7 (B-) and J3 (C2C) at breakout box. • **Is resistance reading greater than 2K ohms?**	Yes No	▶ ▶	REPLACE coil pack. C2 open in coil. REMOVE all test equipment. RECONNECT all components. CLEAR Continuous Memory. RERUN Quick Test. GO to D19.

FM1119200281050X

Fig. 15 Test D: No Start Or Code 2323, 215, 216, 217 Or Coil 1, 2, 3 Failure (Part 5 of 8). 2.5L & 1994–95 3.8L SC & 3.8L SFI California Engines

TEST STEP	RESULT	▶	ACTION TO TAKE
D19 CHECK FOR C2 LOW—ICM AND COIL DISCONNECTED—KEY OFF • Key off. • Disconnect ICM from vehicle harness connector. • DVOM on 20K ohm scale. • Measure resistance between J3 (C2C) and J7 (B-) at breakout box. • **Is resistance reading greater than 10K ohms?**	Yes No	▶ ▶	REPLACE ICM. C2 shorted low. REMOVE all test equipment. RECONNECT all components. CLEAR Continuous Memory. RERUN Quick Test. CHECK connectors, SERVICE or REPLACE harness. C2 is shorted low. REMOVE all test equipment. RECONNECT all components. CLEAR Continuous Memory. RERUN Quick Test. NOTE: A C2 short to ground may have damaged the coil.
D20 CHECK FOR C3 SHORT LOW—COIL DISCONNECTED—KEY OFF • Key off. • DVOM on 20K ohm scale. • Disconnect coil from coil tee, leave EI diagnostic harness connected to vehicle harness coil connector. • Measure resistance between J7 (B-) and J10 (C3C) at breakout box. • **Is resistance reading greater than 2K ohms?**	Yes No	▶ ▶	REPLACE coil pack. C3 open in coil. REMOVE all test equipment. RECONNECT all components. CLEAR Continuous Memory. RERUN Quick Test. GO to D21.

FM1119200281060X

Fig. 15 Test D: No Start Or Code 2323, 215, 216, 217 Or Coil 1, 2, 3 Failure (Part 6 of 8). 2.5L & 1994–95 3.8L SC & 3.8L SFI California Engines

	TEST STEP	RESULT	▶	ACTION TO TAKE
D21	CHECK FOR C3 SHORT LOW—ICM AND COIL DISCONNECTED—KEY OFF • Key off. • Disconnect ICM from vehicle harness connector. • DVOM on 20K ohm scale. • Measure resistance between J7 (B-) and J10 (C3C) at breakout box. • Is resistance greater than 10K ohms?	Yes	▶	REPLACE ICM. C3 is shorted low. REMOVE all test equipment. RECONNECT all components. CLEAR Continuous Memory. RERUN Quick Test.
		No	▶	CHECK connectors, SERVICE or REPLACE harness. C3 is shorted low. REMOVE all test equipment. RECONNECT all components. CLEAR Continuous Memory. RERUN Quick Test. NOTE: A C3 short to ground may have damaged the coil.
D22	CHECK FOR C1 LOW—ICM AND COIL DISCONNECTED—KOEO • Key off. • Disconnect ICM from the ICM tee, leave EI diagnostic harness connected to vehicle harness connector. • DVOM on 40 volt DC scale. • Key on, engine off. • Measure voltage between (+)J6 (C1C) and (-)J7 (B-) at breakout box. • Is DC voltage reading less than 0.5 volts?	Yes	▶	REPLACE ICM. C1 is shorted high. REMOVE all test equipment. RECONNECT all components. CLEAR Continuous Memory. RERUN Quick Test.
		No	▶	CHECK connectors, SERVICE or REPLACE harness. C1 is shorted high. REMOVE all test equipment. RECONNECT all components. CLEAR Continuous Memory. RERUN Quick Test.

FM1119200281070X

Fig. 15   Test D: No Start Or Code 2323, 215, 216, 217 Or Coil 1, 2, 3 Failure (Part 7 of 8). 2.5L & 1994–95 3.8L SC & 3.8L SFI California Engines

	TEST STEP	RESULT	▶	ACTION TO TAKE
D23	CHECK FOR C2 LOW—ICM AND COIL DISCONNECTED • Key off. • Disconnect ICM from the ICM tee, leave EI diagnostic harness connected to vehicle harness connector. • DVOM on 40 volt DC scale. • Key on, engine off. • Measure voltage between (+)J3 (C2C) and (-)J7 (B-) at breakout box. • Is DC voltage reading less than 0.5 volts?	Yes	▶	REPLACE ICM. C2 is shorted high. REMOVE all test equipment. RECONNECT all components. CLEAR Continuous Memory. RERUN Quick Test.
		No	▶	CHECK connectors, SERVICE or REPLACE harness. C2 is shorted high. REMOVE all test equipment. RECONNECT all components. CLEAR Continuous Memory. RERUN Quick Test.
D24	CHECK FOR C3 LOW—ICM AND COIL DISCONNECTED • Key off. • Disconnect ICM from the ICM tee, leave EI diagnostic harness connected to vehicle harness connector. • DVOM on 40 volt DC scale. • Key on, engine off. • Measure voltage between (+)J10 (C3C) and (-)J7 (B-) at breakout box. • Is DC voltage reading less than 0.5 volts?	Yes	▶	REPLACE ICM. C3 is shorted high. REMOVE all test equipment. RECONNECT all components. CLEAR Continuous Memory. RERUN Quick Test.
		No	▶	CHECK connectors, SERVICE or REPLACE harness. C3 is shorted high. REMOVE all test equipment. RECONNECT all components. CLEAR Continuous Memory. RERUN Quick Test.

FM1119200281080X

Fig. 15   Test D: No Start Or Code 2323, 215, 216, 217 Or Coil 1, 2, 3 Failure (Part 8 of 8). 2.5L & 1994–95 3.8L SC & 3.8L SFI California Engines

Type 4

NOTE: If Unsure Of The System Used On The Vehicle Being Serviced, Refer To The "Engine Systems Identification Chart." Further Assistance For The Proper Use Of Information Contained In This Section Can Also Be Found In The Front Of This Tabbed Section Under "How To Use This Manual."

INDEX

	Page No.		Page No.		Page No.
Description	4-62	Preliminary Notes	4-63	Wiring Diagrams	4-63
Diagnosis & Testing:	4-62	Quick Test	4-63	System Service:	4-63
Component Location	4-63	Required Equipment	4-62	Component Replacement	4-63
Preliminary Check	4-62	Testing	4-63		

DESCRIPTION

The Electronic Ignition (EI) (Electronic Distributorless Ignition System (EDIS)) (High Data Rate System), **Figs. 1 through 3,** eliminates the use of a distributor by using a Crankshaft Position (CKP) (variable reluctance) sensor (Variable Reluctance Sensor (VRS)), an Ignition Control Module (ICM) (EDIS module), A Powertrain Control Module (PCM) (Electronic Engine Control-IV (EEC-IV) processor) and one 4-tower coil pack on 1.9L and 2.0L Zetec engines or two 4-tower coil packs on 4.6L engines. This system operates by sending crankshaft position information from the CKP (VRS) to the ICM (EDIS module). The module generates a Profile Ignition Pickup (PIP) signal and sends it to the PCM (EEC-IV processor). The PCM responds with a SPOUT (Spark Angle Word (SAW)) signal containing advance or retard timing information back to the ICM. The module processes the CKP and SPOUT signals and decides which coils to fire. In addition, the module generates an Ignition Diagnostic Monitor (IDM) signal to the module which is used to indicate a failure mode and also provide a tach output signal.

DIAGNOSIS & TESTING
PRELIMINARY CHECK

1. Visually inspect engine compartment to ensure all vacuum hoses and spark plug wires are properly and securely connected.
2. Inspect wiring harnesses and connectors for damaged insulation, burns, overheating, damaged pins and loose or broken connectors.
3. Inspect sensor shield connector, and ensure ICM mounting screws are tight.
4. Ensure battery is fully charged, and all accessories are OFF during tests.

REQUIRED EQUIPMENT

Obtain the following test equipment or a suitable equivalent:
1. EI (High Data Rate) (EDIS) diagnostic harness (Rotunda 007-00059).
2. Neon bulb type spark tester (OTC D89P-6666-A).
3. Volt/ohmmeter (Rotunda 007-00001, 105-00050, 105-00051, 105-00052, 105-00053, or scan tool).

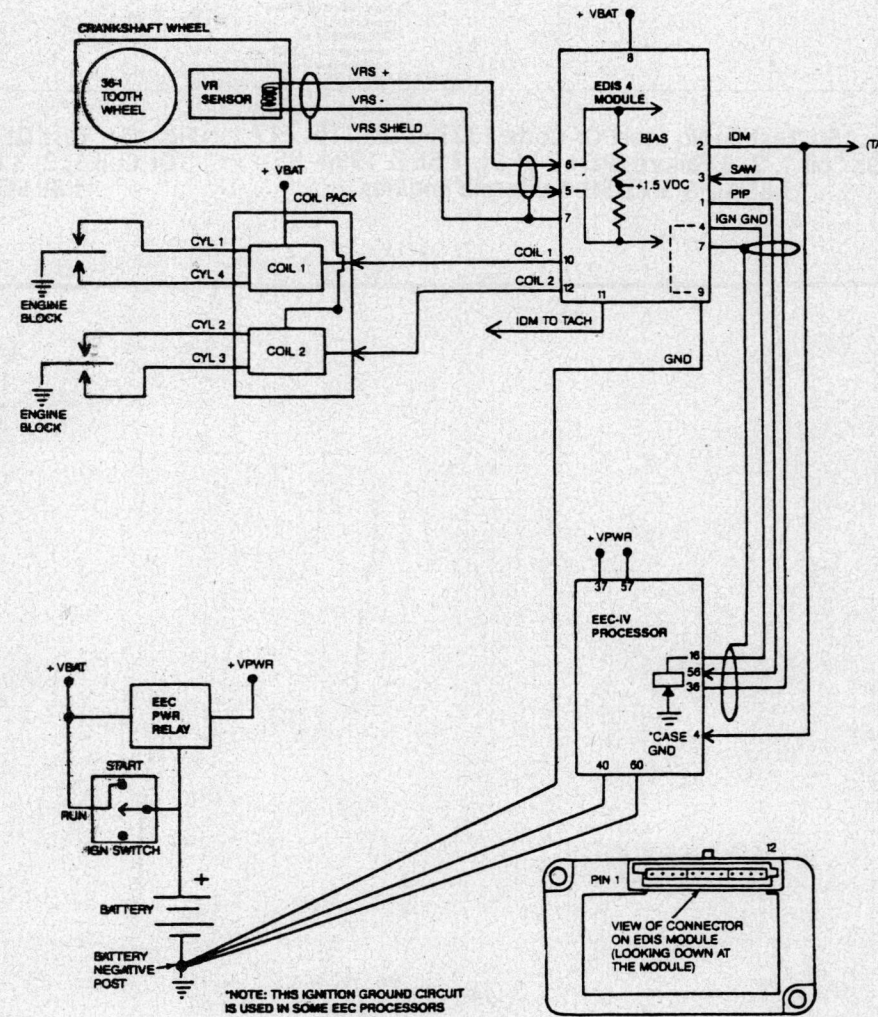

Fig. 1   EI (EDIS) (High Data Rate)
ignition system. 1.9L engine

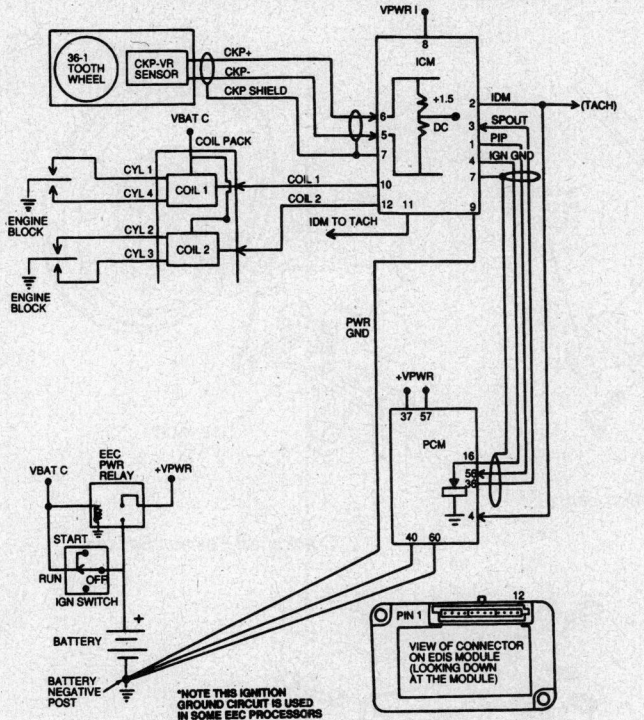

Fig. 2   DI (EDIS) (High Data Rate) ignition system. 2.0L Zetec engine

Fig. 3   EI (EDIS) (High Date Rate) ignition system. 4.6L engine

4. 12 volt incandescent test lamp.
5. Remote starter switch.
6. Two EEC Breakout Boxes (Rotunda T83L-50-EEC-IV).
7. Gap type spark tester (D81P-6666-A).
8. Inductive timing light (Rotunda 059-00006).
9. Tachometer adapter (Rotunda 007-00061) EI (DIS/EDIS) compatible.

PRELIMINARY NOTES

1. When taking measurements on wiring harnesses, both a visual inspection and a continuity test should be performed. Inspect connector pins for damage when directed to remove a connector.
2. Spark timing adjustments cannot be performed.
3. When taking voltage measurements, a GROUND or LOW reading indicates any value within a range of 0 to 1 volt. Also VPWR or COIL PWR (VBAT or HIGH) readings indicate any value that falls within a range of B+ (VBAT) to 2 volts less than B+.
4. When taking voltage measurements and a reference to ground is made, use either negative battery lead or cast iron on engine. B+ (BAT+) indicates positive battery cable at battery.
5. When using spark plug firing indicator, place grooved end as close as possible to plug boot. Very weak or no flashing may be caused by a fouled plug.
6. A 12 volt test lamp should not be used to test circuit signals. It will load circuit and may cause incorrect measurements or improper EI (EDIS/EEC-IV)

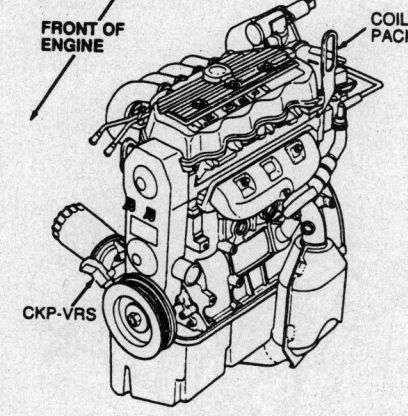

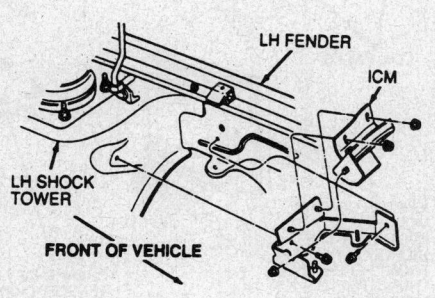

Fig. 4   EI (EDIS) (High Data Rate) component locations. 1.9L engine

operation (engine stall).
7. Spark timing will vary at idle due to feedback spark strategy used to control idle speed.
8. Do not use an incandescent test lamp to check CKP- (VRS-), CKP+ (VRS+), PIP, IDM or SPOUT (SAW) circuits. Lamp will prevent circuit from operating.

COMPONENT LOCATION

Refer to **Figs. 4 through 7** for system component locations.

WIRING DIAGRAMS

Refer To **Figs. 8 through 10**, for system wiring diagrams.

TESTING

Refer to **Figs. 11 through 15** diagnosis and testing of the EDIS ignition system on the 1993 1.9L engine, **Figs. 16 through 20** for the 1994-95 1.9L engine, **Figs. 21 through 25** for the 2.0L Zetec engine, **Figs. 26 through 30** for the 1993 4.6L engine and **Figs. 31 through 35** for the 1994-95 4.6L engine.

QUICK TEST

Refer to "Computerized Engine Controls for Quick Test.

SYSTEM SERVICE
Component Replacement

CRANKSHAFT POSITION SENSOR

1.9L Engine

1. **On 1993 models**, place ignition switch in Off position.

2. **On 1994-95 models,** disconnect battery ground cable.
3. **On all models,** raise and support vehicle.
4. Remove righthand splash shield, then disconnect Crankshaft Position (CKP) sensor electrical connector from wiring harness.
5. Remove CKP sensor screws, then the sensor.
6. Reverse procedure to install. **Torque** CKP sensor screws to 40-61 inch lbs.

2.0L Zetec Engine

1. Disconnect battery ground cable, then raise and support vehicle.
2. Disconnect fuel charging wiring or engine control sensor wiring from Crankshaft Position (CKP) sensor.
3. Remove sensor bolt, then the sensor.
4. Reverse procedure to install, noting the following:
   a. Ensure CKP sensor mounting surface is clean and O-ring is in proper location.
   b. **Do not overtighten CKP sensor bolt or damage to CKP sensor may occur.**
   c. **Torque** CKP sensor bolt to 71-106 inch lbs.

4.6L Engine

1. Disconnect battery ground cable, then remove serpentine drive belt as follows:
   a. Rotate tensioner away from belt using a 1/2 inch breaker bar installed in hole in tensioner arm.
   b. Lift belt over alternator pulley flange and remove.
2. Raise and support vehicle, then disconnect Crankshaft Position (CKP) sensor and A/C compressor electrical connectors from wiring harness.
3. Discharge/recover A/C system, then remove A/C compressor as follows:
   a. Drain and save radiator coolant, then disconnect and remove fan and shroud assembly.
   b. Disconnect upper and lower radiator hoses, then loosen transmission oil cooler lines while holding radiator connector with back-up wrench.
   c. Remove radiator upper support bolts, then the supports.
   d. Lift radiator from vehicle.
   e. Disconnect A/C clutch wire, then loosen compressor bolts.
   f. Raise and support vehicle, then loosen and remove compressor drive belt from underneath vehicle.
   g. disconnect heated oxygen sensor wire connector, then remove A/C muffler supporting bracket screw from sub-frame.
   h. Disconnect A/C system hose from A/C condenser core and suction accumulator/drier using suitable spring lock coupling disconnect tool, then immediately cap lines.
   i. Support compressor, then remove bolts.

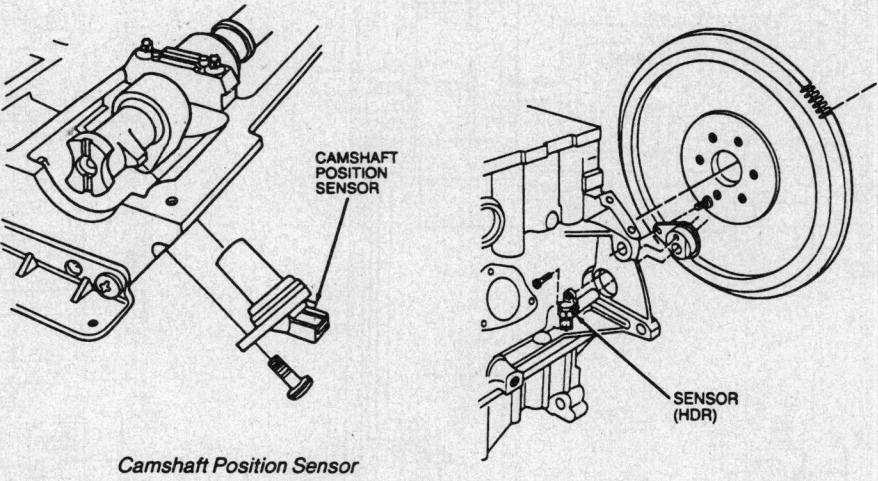

Camshaft Position Sensor

Crankshaft Position Sensor

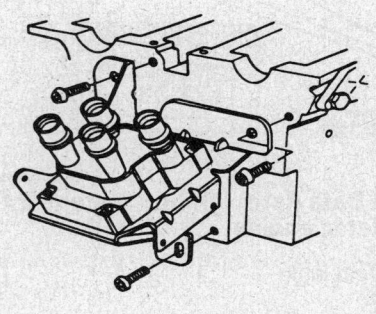

4 Tower Coil Pack

FM1119200286000X

Fig. 5 EI (EDIS) (High Data Rate) component locations. 2.0L Zetec engine

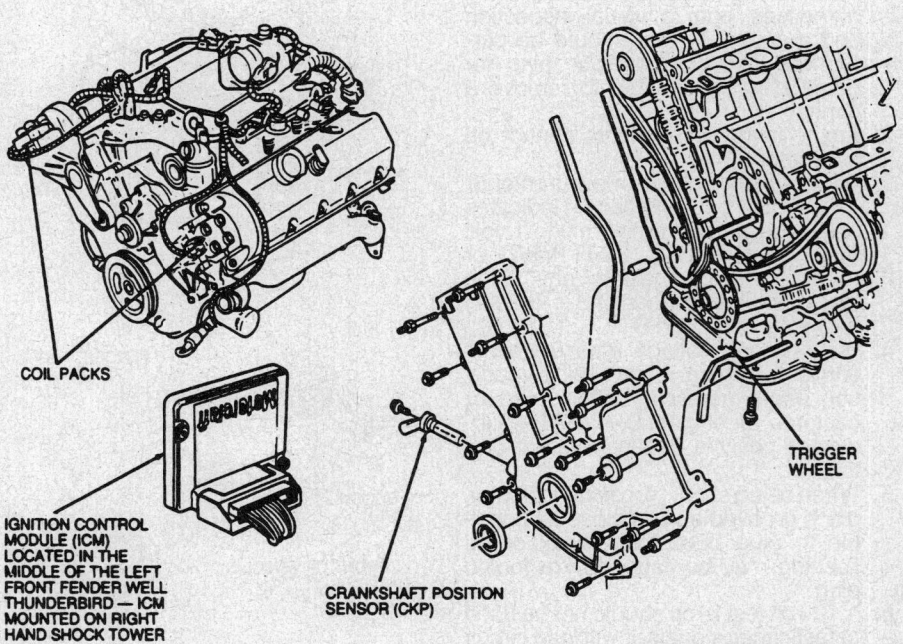

FM1119200287000X

Fig. 6 EI (EDIS) (High Date Rate) component locations. 1993 4.6L engine

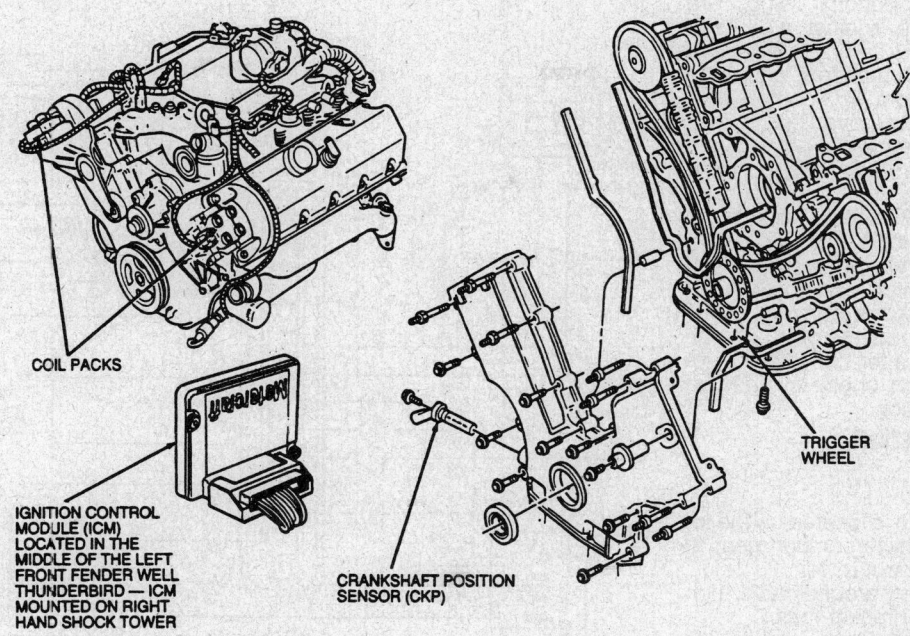

COIL PACKS

IGNITION CONTROL MODULE (ICM) LOCATED IN THE MIDDLE OF THE LEFT FRONT FENDER WELL THUNDERBIRD — ICM MOUNTED ON RIGHT HAND SHOCK TOWER

CRANKSHAFT POSITION SENSOR (CKP)

TRIGGER WHEEL

Fig. 7   EI (EDIS) (High Data Rate) component locations. 1994–95 4.6L engine

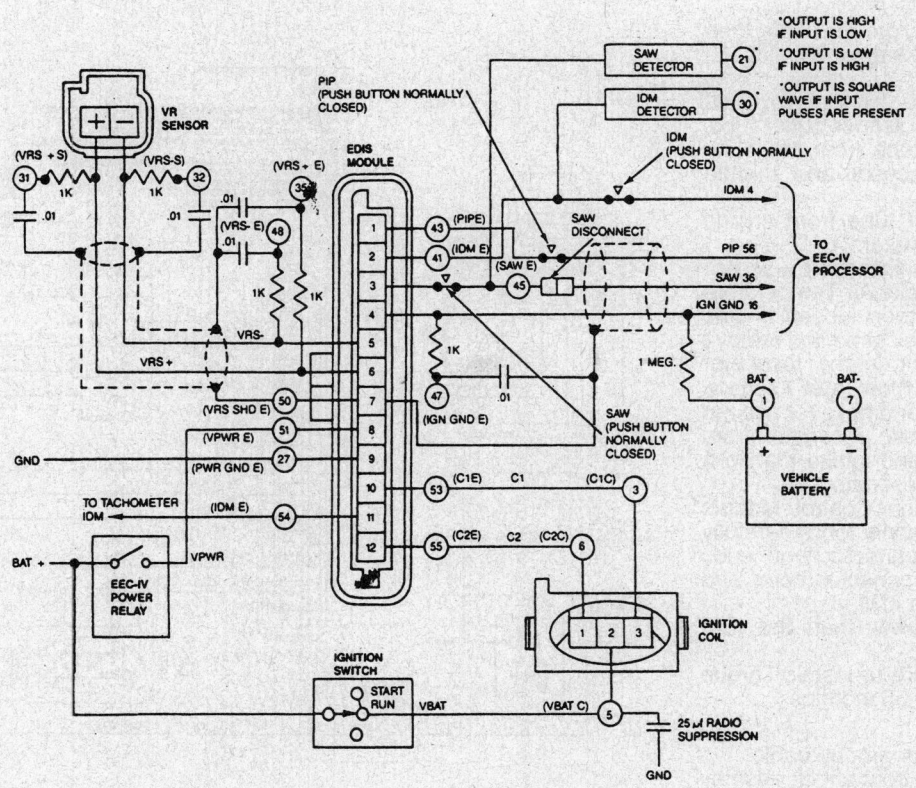

Fig. 8   EI (EDIS) (High Data Rate) wiring diagram. 1.9L engine

FORD–Ignition Systems

j. Remove A/C compressor and A/C manifold and tube assemblies from vehicle as a unit. Remove assembly from bottom, using care not to scrape against A/C condenser core.

k. Remove A/C manifold and tube assemblies from A/C compressor.

4. **On all models,** remove CKP sensor screw, then the sensor.

5. Reverse procedure to install, noting the following:

   a. **Torque** CKP sensor screw to 71-106 inch lbs.

   b. Bolt and lock washer may be used in place of stud and locknut for A/C compressor mounting.

   c. Leak test, evacuate and charge A/C system after compressor installation, then check system for proper operation.

IGNITION MODULE

1.9L Engine

The ignition module is located on the lefthand side of the engine compartment, in front of the lefthand strut tower.

1. Disconnect battery ground cable, then remove module bracket nuts.

2. Gently pull bracket and module assembly straight up, then disconnect module electrical connector.

3. Remove module from bracket.

4. Reverse procedure to install. **Torque** module to bracket screws to 24-35 inch lbs. and sub-bracket to inner fender screws to 62-88 inch lbs.

2.0L Zetec Engine

1. Disconnect battery ground cable, then the engine air intake resonators as follows:

   a. Loosen engine air cleaner tube clamps on air cleaner outlet tube, then remove tube from Mass Air Flow (MAF) sensor and throttle body.

   b. Remove outlet tube from engine air intake resonators.

   c. Disconnect engine control sensor wiring from Intake Air Temperature (IAT) sensor, then loosen engine air cleaner tube clamp and remove one engine air intake resonator from Mass Air Flow (MAF) sensor.

   d. Remove nuts and bolts for second engine air intake resonator from throttle body and intake manifold, then remove resonator.

2. Disconnect Ignition Control Module (ICM) electrical connector by carefully lifting up on the connector finger ends while grasping connector body and pulling away from ICM.

3. Remove ICM screw, then the ICM from ICM bracket.

4. Reverse procedure to install. Torque ICM screw to 24-35 inch lbs.

4.6L Engine

1. Disconnect battery ground cable.

2. Remove lefthand front shock absorber strut cover cup screws, then the cup.

3. Disconnect module electrical connector.

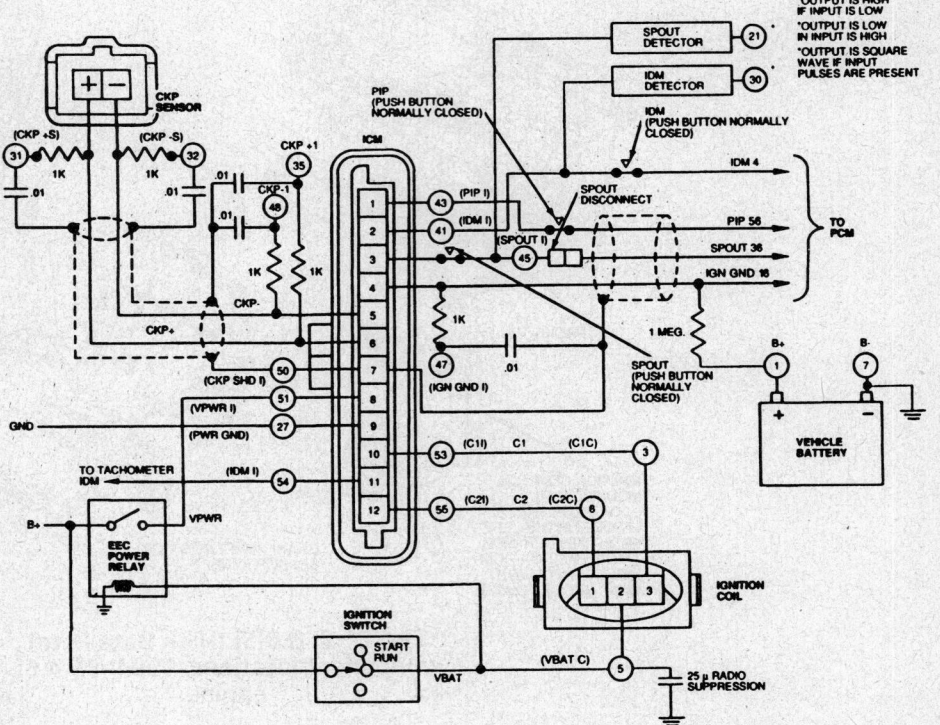

Fig. 9   EI (EDIS) (High Date Rate) wiring diagram. 2.0L Zetec engine

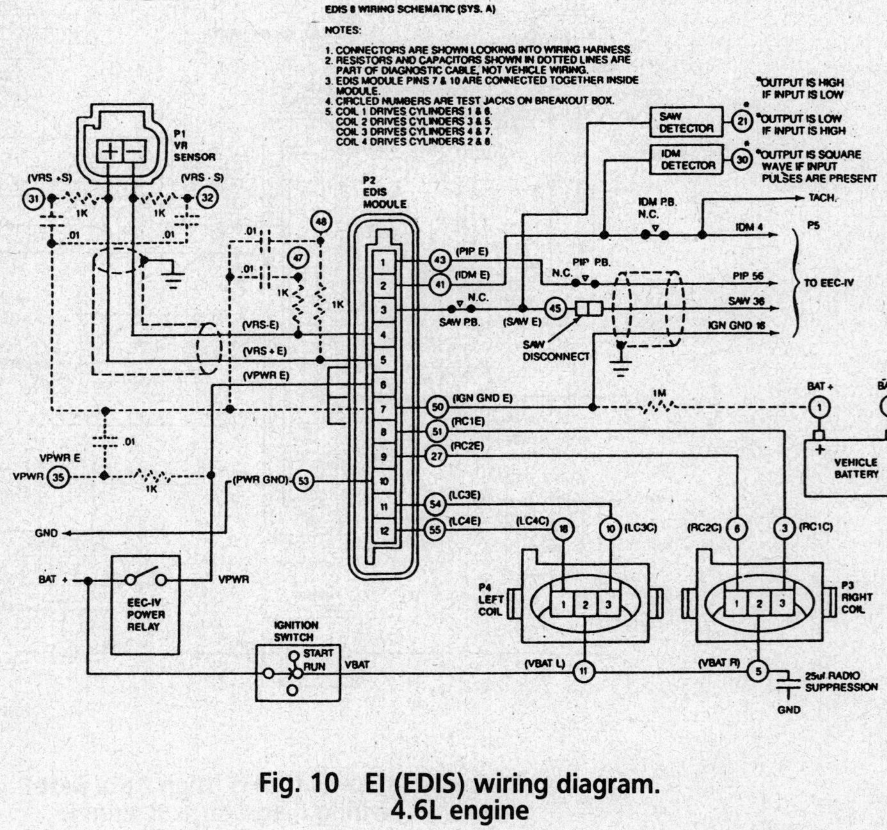

Fig. 10   EI (EDIS) wiring diagram. 4.6L engine

CONDITION	ACTION TO TAKE
No start with error Diagnostic Trouble Code not listed elsewhere in this index.	GO to A1 .
• No start and no error service code.	GO to A1 .
• No start with Code 211 (PIP at PCM fault).	GO to A3 .
• No start and MIL stays on during engine crank (PIP FAULT).	GO to A1 .
• Engine starts with Code 212 (IDM to PCM failure).	GO to B1 .
• Engine starts with 213 (SPOUT CIRCUIT FAULT).	GO to C1 .
• Engine starts with Code 215 or 216 (Coil Fault).	GO to D1 .

FM1119200292010X

Fig. 11 Diagnostics By Service Code & Symptom (Part 1 of 3). 1993 1.9L Engine

The AC voltage reading from a "true RMS" type DVOM (Fluke 87) may be significantly different from a reading taken when using a "standard" or averaging type DVOM (Rotunda 007-0001, Fluke 88, 75 etc.) leading to incorrect answers to Pinpoint Test questions.

TYPICAL VOLTAGE READINGS

Measure Between Pins		KOEO (Volts)	Engine Cranking (Volts AC)	Engine Running (Volts AC)
First Pin	Second Pin			
VRS+S (J31)	VRS-S(J32)	0.0 AC	0.5 - 2.0	4.0 - 6.0
VRS+E (J35)	VRS-E(J48)	0.0 AC	0.5 - 2.0	4.0 - 6.0
PIP E (J43)	PWR GND (J7)	0.0 AC	6.0 - 8.0	6.0 - 8.0
C1E (J53)	PWR GND (J7)	VBAT DC	1.0 - 4.0	2.0 - 7.0
C2E (J55)	PWR GND (J7)	VBAT DC	1.0 - 4.0	2.0 - 7.0
C1C (J3)	PWR GND (J7)	VBAT DC	1.0 - 4.0	2.0 - 7.0
C2C (J6)	PWR GND (J7)	VBAT DC	1.0 - 4.0	2.0 - 7.0
SAW E (J45)	PWR GND (J7)	0.0 AC	0.1 - 2.0	3.0 - 4.0
IDM E (J41)	PWR GND (J7)	0.0 AC	0.5 - 2.0	0.3 - 2.0
VRS+S (J31)	PWR GND (J7)	1.0-2.0 DC		
VRS-S (J32)	PWR GND (J7)	1.0-2.0 DC		

NOTE: Do not connect the positive lead of the EDIS diagnostic cable or the VR sensor tee until directed to do so.
The SAW and IDM detectors in the EDIS diagnostic cable will not work unless the positive and negative leads of the EDIS diagnostic cable are connected.
KOEO = Key On, Engine Off.
KOEC = Key On, Engine Cranking.
The vehicle battery voltage must be at least 12 volts DC.
Be careful not to bring a fluorescent trouble lamp close to the vehicle wiring. If the key is ON and the VRS sensor is disconnected, the EDIS module may fire the coil.
When using a DVOM to measure DC voltage readings, connect the positive lead to the jack identified with a (+) sign and the negative lead to the jack with a (-) sign.

• Repetitive Spark Mode will cause coil circuits to read higher than other non-repetitive EDIS/DIS coil circuits.

• These diagnostics (Pinpoint Tests A through G) are written to catch "Hard Faults" (Due to limitations of test equipment) only; intermittent failures will be difficult or impossible to diagnose using these procedures unless the failure is constantly present when these Pinpoint Tests are run.

Fig. 11 Diagnostics By Service Code & Symptom (Part 2 of 3). 1993 1.9L Engine

Most DVOM's used by auto technicians belong to a class or type known as "averaging". Examples are the Rotunda Digital Volt-Ohmmeter 0C7-0001, Fluke 70, 20 series and Fluke 88. Recently technicians have started to use DVOM'S of a different class (True RMS, DVOM's, Fluke 87, 8060A, 8062A, etc.). True RMS DVOM's should not be used with the Pinpoint Tests because they may display different voltage readings depending upon if the DVOM is turned on first and then the test leads are connected, or if the leads are connected first and then DVOM is turned on. Also they may not auto range to the same range every time and some display significantly different values depending on the range selected. It would be impossible to list all of the meters and how to use each, so we are requesting that you perform the following test to verify your DVOM is compatible with the Pinpoint Tests.

Using a known good EI vehicle, install the EI (Low Data Rate) DIS or EI (High Data Rate) EDIS diagnostic cable, connect the EEC Breakout Box to the diagnostic cable, start the vehicle and measure the AC voltage between J53 (C1I) and ground. The battery should be charged and the engine must be idling between 700 and 900 rpm. On any EI vehicle (except 1992 Escort / Tracer) the value should be between 1.0 and 2.0 volts AC (1.5 volts AC is typical). If you use the EI (Low Data Rate) hand held testers they may be used instead of the Diagnostic Cable / EEC Breakout Box to gain access to J53 (C1I) and J43 (PIP I). Next, with the engine idling, measure between PIP and ground. This reading should be between 6 and 8 volts AC.

Because the Escort / Tracer EI (High Data Rate) ignition system fires the coil differently (repetitive spark) at idle, the coil to ground voltage reading should be between 2 to 7 volts AC (4.5 volts AC is typical). The PIP to ground reading on the Escort / Tracer is the same as the other EI systems.

If the readings you get agree with our test, your DVOM is OK to use with the Ignition Pinpoint Tests. If not, do not use it, it will lead to false parts replacement and the root cause will be difficult or impossible to find.

FM1119200292030X

Fig. 11 Diagnostics By Service Code & Symptom (Part 3 of 3). 1993 1.9L Engine

4. Remove module screws, then the module.
5. Reverse procedure to install, noting the following:
   a. **Torque** module to inner fender screws to 24-35 inch lbs.
   b. When connecting electrical connector, ensure connector is properly sealed to ignition control module interface. Push until connector fingers are locked over locking wedge feature on ICM.

COIL PACK
1.9L Engine
1. **On 1993 models,** place ignition switch in Off position.
2. **On 1994-95 models,** disconnect battery ground cable.
3. **On all models,** disconnect electrical connector from coil pack and capacitor assembly.
4. Remove spark plug wires by squeezing locking tabs to release coil boot retainers.
5. Remove coil pack bolts and capacitor assembly, saving capacitor for installation with new coil pack.
6. Remove coil pack.
7. Reverse procedure to install. **Torque** coil pack bolts to 40-61 inch lbs.

2.0L Zetec Engine
1. Disconnect battery ground cable, then remove engine air intake resonators as follows:
   a. Loosen engine air cleaner tube clamps on air cleaner outlet tube, then remove tube from Mass Air Flow (MAF) sensor and throttle body.
   b. Remove outlet tube from engine air intake resonators.
   c. Disconnect engine control sensor wiring from Intake Air Temperature (IAT) sensor, then loosen engine air cleaner tube clamp and remove one engine air intake resonator from Mass Air Flow (MAF) sensor.
   d. Remove nuts and bolts for second engine air intake resonator from throttle body and intake manifold, then remove resonator.
2. Disconnect fuel charging wiring or engine control sensor wiring from ignition coil.
3. Remove ignition coil bolts or screws, then the ignition coil.
4. Reverse procedure to install.

4.6L Engine
1. Disconnect battery ground cable, then the electrical connectors from coil pack and capacitor.
2. Remove spark plug wires by squeezing locking tabs to release coil boot retainers.
3. Remove coil pack bolts, then the coil pack and capacitor, saving capacitor for installation with new coil pack.
4. Reverse procedure to install, noting the following:
   a. Apply silicone dielectric compound D7AZ-19A331-A or equivalent to all spark plug wire boots.
   b. **Torque** coil pack mounting bolts to 40-61 inch lbs.

TEST STEP	RESULT	▶	ACTION TO TAKE
A1 PERFORM EEC-IV QUICK TEST • Was Quick Test performed NOTE: These diagnostic procedures are designed to correct one ignition failure at a time. When a component is replaced or a service is completed, remove all test equipment, reconnect all components and rerun Quick Test.	Yes No	▶ ▶	GO to A2. PERFORM Quick Test.
A2 CHECK FOR SPARK DURING CRANK • Using a Neon Bulb Spark Tester (Special Service Tool D89P-6666-A) or Air Gap Spark Tester (Special Service Tool D81P-6666-A), check for spark at all spark plug wires while cranking. • Was spark consistent on ALL spark plug wires (one spark per crankshaft revolution)?	Yes No	▶ ▶	GO to A13. GO to A3.
A3 CHECK PLUGS AND WIRES • Check spark plug wires for insulation damage, looseness, shorting or other damage. • Remove and check spark plugs for damage, wear, carbon deposits and proper plug gap. • Are spark plugs and wires OK?	Yes No	▶ ▶	REINSTALL plugs and wires. GO to A4. SERVICE or REPLACE damaged component. REMOVE all test equipment. RECONNECT all components. CLEAR Continuous Memory. RERUN Quick Test.
A4 CHECK VEHICLE PERFORMANCE WITH EDIS DIAGNOSTIC CABLE INSTALLED WARNING: NEVER CONNECT THE EEC-IV PROCESSOR TO THE EEC-IV BREAKOUT BOX WHEN PERFORMING EDIS DIAGNOSTICS. • Key off. • Install EDIS diagnostic cable to breakout box and EDIS module. Do not connect VRS tee or coil tee. • Use EDIS 4 overlay. • Connect EDIS diagnostic cable negative lead to battery, leave positive lead disconnected. • Set EDIS diagnostic cable box switch to "4/6 cylinder" position. • Will vehicle start and run?	Yes No	▶ ▶	GO to A32. GO to A5.

Fig. 12 Test A: No Start (Part 1 of 11). 1993 1.9L Engine

TEST STEP	RESULT	▶	ACTION TO TAKE
A5 CHECK PWR GND TO EDIS MODULE • Key off. • DVOM on 200K ohm scale. • Measure resistance between J27 (PWR GND) and J7 (BAT) at the breakout box. • Is the resistance less than 5.0 ohms?	Yes No	▶ ▶	GO to A6. CHECK connectors, SERVICE or REPLACE harness. PWR GND to EDIS module is open. REMOVE all test equipment. RECONNECT all components. CLEAR Continuous Memory. RERUN Quick Test.
A6 CHECK FOR VBAT TO EDIS MODULE • Key off. • DVOM on 20 volt DC scale. • Key on, engine off. • Measure voltage between (+)J51 (VPWR E) and (-)J7 (BAT-) at breakout box. • Is DC voltage greater than 10.5 volts?	Yes No	▶ ▶	GO to A7. CHECK connectors, SERVICE or REPLACE harness. VBAT to EDIS module is open. REMOVE all test equipment. RECONNECT all components. CLEAR Continuous Memory. RERUN Quick Test.
A7 CHECK VRS + BIAS AT EDIS MODULE • Key off. • DVOM on 20 volt DC scale. • Key on, engine off. • Measure voltage between (+)J35 (VRS+ E) and (-)J7 (BAT-) at breakout box. • Is DC voltage between 1.0 and 2.0 volts?	Yes No	▶ ▶	GO to A21. GO to A8.
A8 CHECK VRS + BIAS —BIAS FAULT—VR SENSOR DISCONNECTED • Key off. • Disconnect VRS from vehicle harness connector. • DVOM on 20 volt DC scale. • Key on, engine off. • Measure voltage between (+)J35 (VRS+ E) and (-)J7 (BAT-) at breakout box. • Is DC voltage greater than 1.0 volt but less than 2.0 volts?	Yes No	▶ ▶	GO to A9. GO to A29.

Fig. 12 Test A: No Start (Part 2 of 11). 1993 1.9L Engine

TEST STEP	RESULT	▶	ACTION TO TAKE
A9 CHECK VRS — BIAS—VRS DISCONNECTED • Key off. • DVOM on 20 volt DC scale. • Key on, engine off. • Measure voltage between (+)J48 (VRS- E) and (-)J7 (BAT-) at breakout box. • Is DC voltage between 1.0 and 2.0 volts?	Yes No	▶	REPLACE VR sensor. Short to ground in VR sensor. REMOVE all test equipment. RECONNECT all components. CLEAR Continuous Memory. RERUN Quick Test. GO to A10.
A10 CHECK VRS — HIGH or LOW BIAS—BIAS FAULT • Was bias voltage reading in Step A9 less than 1.0 volt DC?	Yes No	▶ ▶	GO to A11. GO to A12.
A11 CHECK VRS — FOR SHORT TO GROUND—BIAS LOW FAULT—VRS AND EDIS MODULE DISCONNECTED • Key off. • Disconnect EDIS module from EDIS module tee, leave EDIS diagnostic cable connected to vehicle harness connector. • DVOM on 20K ohm scale. • Measure resistance between J48 (VRS-E) and J7 (BAT-) at breakout box. • Is resistance greater than 10K ohms?	Yes No	▶	REPLACE EDIS module. VRS shorted low. REMOVE all test equipment. RECONNECT all components. CLEAR Continuous Memory. RERUN Quick Test. CHECK connectors, SERVICE or REPLACE harness. VRS is shorted low. REMOVE all test equipment. RECONNECT all components. CLEAR Continuous Memory. RERUN Quick Test.

Fig. 12 Test A: No Start (Part 3 of 11). 1993 1.9L Engine

TEST STEP	RESULT	▶	ACTION TO TAKE
A12 CHECK VRS -- FOR SHORT HIGH—BIAS HIGH FAULT —VRS AND EDIS MODULE DISCONNECTED • Key off. • Disconnect EDIS module from EDIS module tee; leave EDIS diagnostic cable connected to vehicle harness connector. • DVOM 20 volt DC scale. • Key on, engine off. • Measure voltage between (+)J48 (VRS- E) and (-)J7 (BAT-) at breakout box. • Is DC voltage less than 0.5 volts?	Yes No	▶	REPLACE EDIS module. VRS(-) shorted high. REMOVE all test equipment. RECONNECT all components. CLEAR Continuous Memory. RERUN Quick Test. CHECK connectors, SERVICE or REPLACE harness. VRS is shorted high. REMOVE all test equipment. RECONNECT all components. CLEAR Continuous Memory. RERUN Quick Test.
A13 CHECK PIP AT EDIS MODULE WARNING: NEVER CONNECT THE EEC-IV PROCESSOR TO THE EEC-IV BREAKOUT BOX WHEN PERFORMING EDIS DIAGNOSTICS. • Key off. • Install EDIS diagnostic cable to the breakout box and EDIS module. Do not connect VR sensor tee or coil tee. • Use EDIS 4 overlay. • Connect EDIS diagnostic cable negative lead to battery, leave positive lead disconnected. • Set EDIS diagnostic cable box switch to "4/6 cylinder" position. • DVOM on 20 volt AC scale. • Crank engine and measure voltage between J43 (PIP E) and J7 (BAT-) at breakout box. • Is the settled AC voltage reading greater than 3.5 volts?	Yes No	▶ ▶	GO to A14. GO to A18.

Fig. 12 Test A: No Start (Part 4 of 11). 1993 1.9L Engine

TEST STEP	RESULT	▶	ACTION TO TAKE
A14 CHECK FOR PIP CONTINUITY TO PROCESSOR—PROCESSOR DISCONNECTED • Key off. • DVOM on 200 ohm scale. • Install a second breakout box to processor vehicle harness connector. • Measure resistance between J43 (PIP E) at the breakout box and Pin 56 (PIP) at the second breakout box. • Is resistance less than 5.0 ohms?	Yes No	▶ ▶	GO to **A15**. CHECK connectors, SERVICE or REPLACE harness. PIP is open. REMOVE all test equipment. RECONNECT all components. CLEAR Continuous Memory. RERUN Quick Test.
A15 CHECK IGN GND AT EDIS MODULE—PROCESSOR DISCONNECTED • Key off. • DVOM on 2K ohm scale. • Measure resistance between J47 (IGN GND E) and J7 (BAT-) at breakout box. • Is resistance less than 1025 ohms?	Yes No	▶ ▶	GO to **A16**. GO to **A17**.
A16 CHECK FOR IGN GND CONTINUITY TO PROCESSOR—PROCESSOR DISCONNECTED • Key off. • DVOM on 2K ohm scale. • Measure resistance between J47 (IGN GND E) at the breakout box and Pin 16 (IGN GND) at the second breakout box. • Is resistance less than 1025 ohms?	Yes No	▶ ▶	Ignition system is OK. REMOVE all test equipment. RECONNECT all components. CLEAR Continuous Memory. RERUN Quick Test. CHECK connectors, SERVICE or REPLACE harness. IGN GND is open. REMOVE all test equipment. RECONNECT all components. CLEAR Continuous Memory. RERUN Quick Test.

Fig. 12 Test A: No Start (Part 5 of 11). 1993 1.9L Engine

TEST STEP	RESULT	▶	ACTION TO TAKE
A17 CHECK PWR GND AT EDIS MODULE—PWP GND FAULT • Key off. • DVOM on 200 ohm scale. • Measure resistance between J27 (PWR GND) and J7 (BAT-) at breakout box. • Is resistance less than 5.0 ohms?	Yes No	▶ ▶	REPLACE EDIS module. IGN GND open. REMOVE all test equipment. RECONNECT all components. CLEAR Continuous Memory. RERUN Quick Test. CHECK connectors, SERVICE or REPLACE harness. SERVICE open circuit. Power ground to EDIS module is open. REMOVE all test equipment. RECONNECT all components. CLEAR Continuous Memory. RERUN Quick Test.
A18 CHECK PIP AT EDIS MODULE—PIP FAULT—PIP CIRCUIT DISCONNECTED • Key off. • DVOM 20 volt AC scale. • Push and hold EDIS diagnostic cable PIP push button down (opens PIP circuit to processor). • Crank engine and measure voltage between J43 (PIP E) and J7 (BAT-) at breakout box. • Is settled AC voltage reading greater than 3.5 volts?	Yes No	▶ ▶	GO to **A19**. REPLACE EDIS module. No PIP output from EDIS. REMOVE all test equipment. RECONNECT all components. CLEAR Continuous Memory. RERUN Quick Test.
A19 CHECK FOR PIP SHORT TO GROUND IN HARNESS—EDIS MODULE AND PROCESSOR DISCONNECTED • Key off. • Disconnect EEC processor. • Disconnect EDIS module from EDIS module tee. Leave EDIS diagnostic cable connected to EDIS vehicle harness connector. • DVOM on 20K ohm scale. • Measure resistance between J43 (PIP E) and J7 (BAT-) at breakout box. • Is resistance greater than 10K ohms?	Yes No	▶ ▶	GO to **A20**. CHECK connectors, SERVICE or REPLACE harness. PIP is shorted low. REMOVE all test equipment. RECONNECT all components. CLEAR Continuous Memory. RERUN Quick Test.

Fig. 12 Test A: No Start (Part 6 of 11). 1993 1.9L Engine

TEST STEP	RESULT	▶	ACTION TO TAKE
A20 CHECK FOR PIP SHORT HIGH—EDIS MODULE AND PROCESSOR DISCONNECTED • Key off. • DVOM on 20 volt DC scale. • Key on, engine off. • Measure voltage between (+)J43 (PIP E) and (-)J7 (BAT-) at breakout box. • Is DC voltage less than 0.5 volts?	Yes No	▶ ▶	REPLACE processor. PIP is shorted in processor. REMOVE all test equipment. RECONNECT all components. CLEAR Continuous Memory. RERUN Quick Test. CHECK connectors, SERVICE or REPLACE harness. PIP is shorted high. REMOVE all test equipment. RECONNECT all components. CLEAR Continuous Memory. RERUN Quick Test.
A21 CHECK VRS AMPLITUDE AT EDIS MODULE • Key off. • DVOM on 20 volt AC scale. • Crank engine and measure voltage between J35 (VRS+ E) and J48 (VRS- E) at breakout box. • Is settled AC voltage reading greater than 0.4 volts?	Yes No	▶ ▶	GO to Pinpoint Test Step **D1**. GO to **A22**.
A22 CHECK VRS AMPLITUDE AT EDIS MODULE—AMPLITUDE FAULT—EDIS MODULE DISCONNECTED • Key off. • Disconnect EDIS module from EDIS module tee, leave EDIS diagnostic cable connected to vehicle harness connector. • DVOM 20 volt AC scale. • Crank engine and measure voltage between J35 (VRS+ E) and J48 (VRS- E) at breakout box. • Is settled AC voltage reading greater than 0.4 volts?	Yes No	▶ ▶	REPLACE EDIS module. VRS is shorted in EDIS module. REMOVE all test equipment. RECONNECT all components. CLEAR Continuous Memory. RERUN Quick Test. GO to **A23**.

Fig. 12 Test A: No Start (Part 7 of 11). 1993 1.9L Engine

TEST STEP	RESULT	▶	ACTION TO TAKE
A23 CHECK VRS RESISTANCE • Key off. • DVOM on 20K ohm scale. • Measure resistance between J48 (VRS-E) and J35 (VRS+ E) at the breakout box. • Is resistance between 2300 and 2500 ohms?	Yes No	▶ ▶	GO to A27. GO to A24.
A24 CHECK VRS HIGH OR LOW RESISTANCE—RESISTANCE FAULT • Key off. • DVOM on 20K ohm scale. • Measure resistance between J48 (VRS-E) and J35 (VRS+ E) at breakout box. • Is resistance less than 2550 ohms?	Yes No	▶ ▶	GO to A28. GO to A25.
A25 CHECK VRS + CONTINUITY—RESISTANCE HIGH FAULT • Key off. • Connect VR sensor tee to VR sensor and vehicle harness connector. • DVOM on 20K ohm scale. • Measure resistance between J31 (VRS+S) and J35 (VRS+ E) at the breakout box. • Is resistance less than 2025 ohms?	Yes No	▶ ▶	GO to A26. CHECK connectors, SERVICE or REPLACE harness. VRS + open. REMOVE all test equipment. RECONNECT all components. CLEAR Continuous Memory. RERUN Quick Test.
A26 CHECK VRS- CONTINUITY—RESISTANCE HIGH FAULT • Key off. • DVOM on 20K ohm scale. • Measure resistance between J32 (VRS-S) and J48 (VRS- E) at the breakout box. • Is resistance less than 2025 ohms?	Yes No	▶ ▶	REPLACE VR sensor. High resistance. REMOVE all test equipment. RECONNECT all components. CLEAR Continuous Memory. RERUN Quick Test. CHECK connectors, SERVICE or REPLACE harness. VRS— open. REMOVE all test equipment. RECONNECT all components. CLEAR Continuous Memory. RERUN Quick Test.

Fig. 12   Test A: No Start (Part 8 of 11). 1993 1.9L Engine

TEST STEP	RESULT	▶	ACTION TO TAKE
A27 CHECK VRS AIR GAP AND TRIGGER WHEEL • Key off. • Check trigger wheel for damage. • Check VRS air gap. • Are air gap and trigger data wheel OK?	Yes No	▶ ▶	REPLACE VR sensor. No output from sensor. REMOVE all test equipment. RECONNECT all components. CLEAR Continuous Memory. RERUN Quick Test. SERVICE or REPLACE bad parts. REMOVE all test equipment. RECONNECT all components. CLEAR Continuous Memory. RERUN Quick Test.
A28 CHECK VRS + SHORTED TO VRS— RESISTANCE LOW FAULT—VRS DISCONNECTED • Key off. • Disconnect VR sensor from vehicle harness connector. • DVOM on 20K ohm scale. • Measure resistance between J35 (VRS+E) and J48 (VRS- E) at breakout box. • Is resistance greater than 3K ohms?	Yes No	▶ ▶	REPLACE VR sensor. Shorted sensor windings. REMOVE all test equipment. RECONNECT all components. CLEAR Continuous Memory. RERUN Quick Test. CHECK connectors, SERVICE or REPLACE harness. VRS+ shorted to VRS- in harness. REMOVE all test equipment. RECONNECT all components. CLEAR Continuous Memory. RERUN Quick Test.
A29 CHECK VRS + HIGH or LOW—VR SENSOR DISCONNECTED • Was bias voltage reading in Step A8 less than 1.0 volts?	Yes No	▶ ▶	GO to A30. GO to A31.

Fig. 12   Test A: No Start (Part 9 of 11). 1993 1992–93 1.9L Engine

TEST STEP		RESULT	▶	ACTION TO TAKE
A30	CHECK VRS + FOR SHORT TO GROUND—VRS AND EDIS MODULE DISCONNECTED			
	• Key off. • Disconnect the EDIS module from EDIS module tee, leave EDIS diagnostic cable connected to vehicle harness connector. • DVOM on 20K ohm scale. • Measure resistance between J35 (VRS+E) and J7 (BAT-) at breakout box. • Is resistance greater than 10K ohms?	Yes	▶	REPLACE EDIS module. VRS+ is shorted low. REMOVE all test equipment. RECONNECT all components. CLEAR Continuous Memory. RERUN Quick Test.
		No	▶	CHECK connectors, SERVICE or REPLACE harness. VRS+ is shorted low. REMOVE all test equipment. RECONNECT all components. CLEAR Continuous Memory. RERUN Quick Test.
A31	CHECK VRS + FOR SHORT HIGH—BIAS HIGH FAULT—VRS AND EDIS MODULE DISCONNECTED			
	• Key off. • Disconnect EDIS module from EDIS module tee, leave EDIS diagnostic cable connected to vehicle harness connector. • DVOM on 20 volt DC scale. • Key on, engine off. • Measure voltage between (+)J35 (VRS+ E) and (-)J7 (BAT-) at breakout box. • Is DC voltage less than 0.5 volts?	Yes	▶	REPLACE EDIS module. VRS+ is shorted high. REMOVE all test equipment. RECONNECT all components. CLEAR Continuous Memory. RERUN Quick Test.
		No	▶	CHECK connectors, SERVICE or REPLACE harness. VRS+ is shorted high. REMOVE all test equipment. RECONNECT all components. CLEAR Continuous Memory. RERUN Quick Test.

Fig. 12   Test A: No Start (Part 10 of 11). 1993 1.9L Engine

TEST STEP		RESULT	▶	ACTION TO TAKE
A32	CHECK VRS RESISTANCE			
	• Key off. • Disconnect EDIS module from EDIS module tee. Leave EDIS diagnostic cable connected to vehicle harness connector. • DVOM on 20K ohm scale. • Measure resistance between J48 (VRS- E) and J35 (VRS+ E) at breakout box. • Is resistance between 2300 and 2500 ohms?	Yes	▶	REPLACE EDIS module. REMOVE all test equipment. RECONNECT all components. CLEAR Continuous Memory. RERUN Quick Test.
		No	▶	GO to A24.

Fig. 12   Test A: No Start (Part 11 of 11). 1993 1.9L Engine

TEST STEP		RESULT	▶	ACTION TO TAKE
B3	CHECK IDM OUTPUT FROM EDIS MODULE—IDM FAULT—IDM CIRCUIT DISCONNECTED			
	• Key off. • DVOM on 20 volt AC scale. • Push and hold down EDIS IDM button at EDIS diagnostic cable connector to breakout box (opens IDM circuit to processor). • Start engine and measure voltage between J30 (EDIS diagnostic cable IDM detector) and J7 (BAT-) at breakout box. • Is AC voltage greater than 5.0 volts?	Yes	▶	GO to B4.
		No	▶	REPLACE EDIS module. No IDM output from module. REMOVE all test equipment. RECONNECT all components. CLEAR Continuous Memory. RERUN Quick Test.
B4	CHECK FOR IDM SHORT IN PROCESSOR—PROCESSOR DISCONNECTED			
	• Key off. • Disconnect processor. • DVOM on 20 volt AC scale. • Crank engine and measure voltage between J30 (EDIS diagnostic cable IDM detector) and (-)J7 (BAT-) at breakout box. • Is AC voltage greater than 5.0 volts?	Yes	▶	REPLACE processor. Processor is loading IDM signal. REMOVE all test equipment. RECONNECT all components. CLEAR Continuous Memory. RERUN Quick Test.
		No	▶	GO to B5.
B5	CHECK FOR IDM SHORT TO GROUND IN HARNESS—EDIS MODULE AND PROCESSOR DISCONNECTED			
	• Key off. • Disconnect EDIS module from EDIS module tee, leave EDIS diagnostic cable connected to vehicle harness connector. • DVOM on 20K ohm scale. • Measure resistance between J41 (IDM E) and (-)J7 (BAT-) at breakout box. • Is resistance greater than 10 ohms?	Yes	▶	GO to B6.
		No	▶	CHECK connectors, SERVICE or REPLACE harness. IDM is shorted to low. REMOVE all test equipment. RECONNECT all components. CLEAR Continuous Memory. RERUN Quick Test.

Fig. 13   Test B: Code 222 or 212, IDM Failure (Part 2 of 3). 1993 1.9L Engine

TEST STEP		RESULT	▶	ACTION TO TAKE
B1	CHECK FOR IDM AT EDIS MODULE			
	WARNING: NEVER CONNECT THE EEC-IV PROCESSOR TO EEC-IV BREAKOUT BOX WHEN PERFORMING EDIS DIAGNOSTICS. • Key off. • Install EDIS diagnostic cable to breakout box, and EDIS module. Do not connect VR sensor tee or coil tee. • Use EDIS 4 overlay. • Connect EDIS diagnostic cable negative and positive leads to battery. • Set EDIS diagnostic cable box switch to "4/6 cylinder" position. • DVOM on 20 volt AC scale. • Start engine and measure voltage between (+)J30 (EDIS diagnostic cable IDM detector) and (-)J7 (BAT-) at breakout box. NOTE: If pulses are present, the IDM detector output will be between 5.0 and 7.0 volts AC. • Is AC voltage between 5.0 and 7.0 volts?	Yes	▶	GO to B2.
		No	▶	GO to B3.
B2	CHECK FOR IDM CONTINUITY TO PROCESSOR—IDM FAULT—EDIS MODULE AND PROCESSOR DISCONNECTED			
	• Key off. • Disconnect processor. • Disconnect EDIS module from EDIS module tee, leave EDIS diagnostic cable connected to vehicle harness connector. • DVOM on 200 ohm scale. • Install a second breakout box to the processor vehicle harness connector. • Measure resistance between J41 (IDM E) at breakout box and Pin 4 at the second breakout box. • Is resistance less than 5.0 ohms?	Yes	▶	REPLACE processor. Processor does not respond to IDM input. REMOVE all test equipment. RECONNECT all components. CLEAR Continuous Memory. RERUN Quick Test.
		No	▶	CHECK connectors, SERVICE or REPLACE harness. IDM is open. REMOVE all test equipment. RECONNECT all components. CLEAR Continuous Memory. RERUN Quick Test.

Fig. 13   Test B: Code 222 or 212, IDM Failure (Part 1 of 3). 1993 1.9L Engine

TEST STEP		RESULT	▶	ACTION TO TAKE
B6	CHECK FOR IDM SHORT TO GROUND IN HARNESS—ICM AND PCM DISCONNECTED—KEY OFF			
	• Key off. • Disconnect ICM from ICM tee, leave EI diagnostic harness connected to vehicle harness connector. • DVOM on 20K ohm scale. • Measure resistance between J41 (IDM I) and (-)J7 (B-) at breakout box. • Is resistance greater than 10 ohms?	Yes	▶	CHECK connectors, SERVICE or REPLACE harness. IDM is shorted to another wire between ICM and PCM. REMOVE all test equipment. RECONNECT all components. CLEAR Continuous Memory. RERUN Quick Test.
		No	▶	CHECK connectors, SERVICE or REPLACE harness. IDM is shorted to low. REMOVE all test equipment. RECONNECT all components. CLEAR Continuous Memory. RERUN Quick Test.

Fig. 13   Test B: Code 222 or 212, IDM Failure (Part 3 of 3). 1993 1.9L Engine

TEST STEP		RESULT	▶	ACTION TO TAKE
C1	**CHECK BASE TIMING**			
	WARNING: NEVER CONNECT EEC-IV PROCESSOR TO EEC-IV BREAKOUT BOX WHEN PERFORMING EDIS DIAGNOSTICS.	Yes	▶	GO to **C2**
		No	▶	GO to **C3**
	• Key off.			
	• Install EDIS diagnostic cable to breakout box and EDIS module.			
	Do not connect the VR sensor tee or coil tee.			
	• Use EDIS 4 overlay.			
	• Connect EDIS diagnostic cable negative and positive leads to battery.			
	• Set EDIS diagnostic cable switch to "4/6 cylinder" position.			
	• Connect timing light (must be EDIS/DIS compatible).			
	• Start engine and allow it to warm up.			
	• Is timing 10 ± 2 degrees BTDC when the EDIS diagnostic cable SAW detector button is pushed and held down (opens SPOUT circuit)?			
C2	**CHECK FOR SPARK ANGLE ADVANCE**			
	• Is engine timing greater than 15 degrees BTDC when the EDIS diagnostic cable SAW detector button is released?	Yes	▶	EDIS Ignition System is OK.
		No	▶	GO to **C3**
C3	**CHECK SAW AT EDIS MODULE**			
	• Key off.	Yes	▶	REPLACE EDIS module. SAW input to EDIS module is OK, but no spark advance is present. REMOVE all test equipment. RECONNECT all components. CLEAR Continuous Memory. RERUN Quick Test.
	• DVOM on 20 volt AC scale.			
	• Start engine and measure voltage between J21 (EDIS diagnostic cable SAW detector) and (-)J7 (BAT-) at breakout box.			
	• Is AC voltage reading greater than 5.0 volts?	No	▶	GO to **C4**

Fig. 14   Test C: Code 213 Or Lack Of Power Or Poor Fuel Economy (Part 1 of 3). 1993 1.9L Engine

TEST STEP		RESULT	▶	ACTION TO TAKE
C4	**CHECK FOR SAW SHORT IN EDIS MODULE—SAW FAULT—SAW CIRCUIT DISCONNECTED**			
	• Key off.	Yes	▶	REPLACE EDIS module. SAW is shorted in EDIS module. REMOVE all test equipment. RECONNECT all components. CLEAR Continuous Memory. RERUN Quick Test.
	• DVOM on 20 volt AC scale.			
	• Push and hold down EDIS SAW button at EDIS diagnostic cable connector to breakout box (open SAW circuit to EDIS module).			
	• Start engine and measure voltage between J21 (EDIS diagnostic cable SAW detector) and J7 (BAT-) at breakout box.			
	• Is AC voltage reading greater than 5.0 volts?	No	▶	GO to **C5**
C5	**CHECK FOR SAW SHORT TO GROUND IN HARNESS—EDIS MODULE AND PROCESSOR DISCONNECTED**			
	• Key off.	Yes	▶	GO to **C6**
	• Disconnect processor.	No	▶	CHECK connectors, SERVICE or REPLACE harness. SAW is shorted low. SERVICE short circuit. REMOVE all test equipment. RECONNECT all components. CLEAR Continuous Memory. RERUN Quick Test.
	• Disconnect the EDIS module from EDIS module tee, leave EDIS diagnostic cable connected to vehicle harness connector.			
	• DVOM on 20K ohm scale.			
	• Disconnect EDIS diagnostic cable positive lead to battery.			
	• Measure resistance between J45 (SAW E) and J7 (BAT-) at breakout box.			
	• Is the resistance greater than 10K ohms?			
C6	**CHECK FOR SAW SHORT HIGH IN HARNESS—EDIS MODULE AND PROCESSOR DISCONNECTED**			
	• Key off.	Yes	▶	GO to **C7**. SAW is shorted high.
	• DVOM on 20 volt DC scale.	No	▶	CHECK connectors, SERVICE or REPLACE harness. SAW shorted high. REMOVE all test equipment. RECONNECT all components. CLEAR Continuous Memory. RERUN Quick Test.
	• Key on, engine off.			
	• Measure voltage between J45 (SAW E) and J7 (BAT-) at the breakout box.			
	• Is DC voltage reading less than 0.5 volts?			

Fig. 14   Test C: Code 213 Or Lack Of Power Or Poor Fuel Economy (Part 2 of 3). 1993 1.9L Engine

	TEST STEP	RESULT	▶	ACTION TO TAKE
C7	CHECK FOR SAW CONTINUITY TO EDIS MODULE—EDIS MODULE AND PROCESSOR DISCONNECTED • Key off. • DVOM on 200 ohm scale. • Install a second breakout box to the vehicle harness connector. • Measure resistance between J45 (SAW E) at breakout box and Pin 36 at the second breakout box. • Is resistance less than 5.0 ohms?	Yes No	▶ ▶	REPLACE processor. SAW is not being transmitted by processor. REMOVE all test equipment. RECONNECT all components. CLEAR Continuous Memory. RERUN Quick Test. CHECK connectors, SERVICE or REPLACE harness. SAW is open. REMOVE all test equipment. RECONNECT all components. CLEAR Continuous Memory. RERUN Quick Test.
C8	INSPECT VR SENSOR / TRIGGER WHEEL—TIMING FAULT • Is VR sensor or trigger wheel damaged i.e., loose or misaligned?	Yes No	▶ ▶	REPLACE or SERVICE as required. REMOVE all test equipment. RECONNECT all components. CLEAR Continuous Memory. RERUN Quick Test. REPLACE EDIS module. Incorrect output from EDIS module. REMOVE all test equipment. RECONNECT all components. CLEAR Continuous Memory. RERUN Quick Test.

NORMAL WHEEL NOTE RELATIONSHIP BETWEEN NOTCH (A) AND MISSING TOOTH (B)

Fig. 14   Test C: Code 213 Or Lack Of Power Or Poor Fuel Economy (Part 3 of 3). 1993 1.9L Engine

	TEST STEP	RESULT	▶	ACTION TO TAKE
D1	CHECK FOR SPARK DURING CRANK • Using a Neon Bulb Spark Tester (OTC D89P-666-A) or Air Gap Spark Tester (D81P-666-A), check for spark at all spark plug wires while cranking. • Was spark consistent on ALL spark plug wires (one spark per crankshaft revolution)?	Yes No	▶ ▶	Ignition system is OK. GO to D2.
D2	CHECK SPARK PLUGS AND WIRES • Check spark plug wires for insulation damage, looseness, shorting or other damage. • Remove and check right spark plugs for damage, wear, carbon deposits and proper plug gap. • Are spark plugs and wires OK?	Yes No	▶ ▶	REINSTALL plugs and wires. GO to D3. SERVICE or REPLACE damaged component. REMOVE all test equipment. RECONNECT all components. CLEAR Continuous Memory. RERUN Quick Test.
D3	CHECK FOR VBAT AT COIL WARNING: NEVER CONNECT EEC-IV PROCESSOR TO EEC-IV BREAKOUT BOX WHEN PERFORMING EDIS DIAGNOSTICS. • Key off. • Install EDIS diagnostic cable to breakout box. • Connect negative lead to battery. • Set EDIS diagnostic cable box switch to "4/6 cylinder" position. • Install right (blue) coil tee. • Use EDIS 4 overlay. • DVOM on 20 volt DC scale. • Key on, engine off. • Measure voltage between (+)J5 (VBAT) and (-)J7 (VBAT-) at breakout box. • Is DC voltage greater than 10.0 volts?	Yes No	▶ ▶	GO to D4. CHECK connectors, SERVICE or REPLACE harness. VBAT is open. REMOVE all test equipment. RECONNECT all components. CLEAR Continuous Memory. RERUN Quick Test.
D4	CHECK FOR C1 HIGH AT COIL PACK • Key on, engine off. • Measure voltage between (+)J3 (C1C) and (-)J7 (BAT-) at breakout box. • Is DC voltage reading greater than 10.0 volts?	Yes No	▶ ▶	GO to D5. GO to D12.

Fig. 15   Test D: No Code 215 Or 216 Coil Failure (Part 1 of 6). 1993 1.9L Engine

	TEST STEP	RESULT	▶	ACTION TO TAKE
D5	CHECK FOR C2 HIGH AT COIL PACK • DVOM on 20 volt DC scale. • Key on, engine off. • Measure voltage between (+)J6 (C2C) and (-)J7 (BAT-) at breakout box. • Is DC voltage reading greater than 10.0 volts?	Yes No	▶ ▶	GO to D6. GO to D14.
D6	CHECK FOR C1 HIGH AT EDIS MODULE • Key off. • Connect EDIS module tee to EDIS module and vehicle harness connector. • DVOM on 20 volt DC scale. • Key on, engine off. • Measure voltage between (+)J53 (RC1E) and (-)J7 (BAT-) at breakout box. • Is DC voltage reading greater than 10.0 volts?	Yes No	▶ ▶	GO to D7. CHECK connectors, SERVICE or REPLACE harness. C1 is open. REMOVE all test equipment. RECONNECT all components. CLEAR Continuous Memory. RERUN Quick Test.
D7	CHECK FOR C2 HIGH AT EDIS MODULE • Key on, engine off. • Measure voltage between (+)J55 (RC2E) and (-)J7 (BAT-) at breakout box. • Is DC voltage reading greater than 10.0 volts?	Yes No	▶ ▶	GO to D8. CHECK connectors, SERVICE or REPLACE harness. C2 is open. REMOVE all test equipment. RECONNECT all components. CLEAR Continuous Memory. RERUN Quick Test.
D8	CHECK FOR C1 HIGH AT COIL CONNECTOR—COIL DISCONNECTED • Key off. • Disconnect the coil from the coil tee, leave EDIS diagnostic cable coil tee connected to the vehicle harness coil connector. • DVOM on 20 volt DC scale. • Key on, engine off. • Measure voltage between (+)J3 (C1C) and (-)J7 (BAT-) at breakout box. • Is DC voltage reading less than 0.5 volts?	Yes No	▶ ▶	GO to D9. GO to D16.

Fig. 15   Test D: No Code 215 Or 216 Coil Failure (Part 2 of 6). 1993 1.9L Engine

TEST STEP		RESULT	▶	ACTION TO TAKE
D9	CHECK FOR C2 HIGH AT COIL CONNECTOR—COIL DISCONNECTED			
	• Key on, engine off.	Yes	▶	GO to **D10**.
	• DVOM on 20 volt DC scale.	No	▶	GO to **D17**.
	• Measure voltage between (+)J6 (C2C) and (–)J7 (BAT–) at breakout box.			
	• Is DC voltage reading less than 0.5 volts?			
D10	CHECK C1 AT COIL CONNECTOR WHILE CRANKING ENGINE—COIL DISCONNECTED			
	• Connect an incandescent test lamp between J1 (BAT+) and J3 (C1C).	Yes	▶	GO to **D11**.
	• Connect positive lead of diagnostic cable to battery.	No	▶	REPLACE EDIS module. C1 open in EDIS module. REMOVE all test equipment. RECONNECT all components. CLEAR Continuous Memory. RERUN Quick Test.
	• Crank engine.			
	• Does lamp blink consistently and brightly (one blink per engine revolution)?			
D11	CHECK C2 AT COIL CONNECTOR WHILE CRANKING ENGINE—COIL DISCONNECTED			
	• Connect an incandescent test lamp between J1 (BAT+) and J6 (C2C).	Yes	▶	REPLACE coil pack. Input to coil pack is OK, but no high voltage output. REMOVE all test equipment. RECONNECT all components. CLEAR Continuous Memory. RERUN Quick Test.
	• Crank engine.			
	• Does lamp blink consistently and brightly (one blink per engine revolution)?	No	▶	REPLACE EDIS module. C2 open in EDIS module. REMOVE all test equipment. RECONNECT all components. CLEAR Continuous Memory. RERUN Quick Test.
D12	CHECK FOR C1 SHORT LOW—COIL DISCONNECTED			
	• Key off.	Yes	▶	REPLACE right coil pack. C1 open in coil. REMOVE all test equipment. RECONNECT all components. CLEAR Continuous Memory. RERUN Quick Test.
	• DVOM on 20K ohm scale.			
	• Disconnect coil from coil tee, leave EDIS diagnostic cable connected to vehicle harness coil connector.			
	• Measure resistance between J7 (BAT–) and J3 (RC1C) at breakout box.	No	▶	GO to **D13**.
	• Is resistance reading less than 2K ohms?			

Fig. 15   Test D: No Code 215 Or 216 Coil Failure (Part 3 of 6). 1993 1.9L Engine

TEST STEP		RESULT	▶	ACTION TO TAKE
D13	CHECK FOR C1 SHORT LOW—EDIS MODULE AND COIL DISCONNECTED			
	• Key off.	Yes	▶	REPLACE EDIS module. C1 is shorted low in EDIS module. REMOVE all test equipment. RECONNECT all components. CLEAR Continuous Memory. RERUN Quick Test. NOTE: A C1 short to ground may have damaged the coil.
	• Disconnect EDIS module from EDIS module tee, leave EDIS diagnostic cable connected to vehicle harness connector.			
	• DVOM on 20K ohm scale.			
	• Measure resistance between J7 (BAT–) and J3 (RC1C) at breakout box.	No	▶	CHECK connectors, SERVICE or REPLACE harness. C1 is shorted low. REMOVE all test equipment. RECONNECT all components. CLEAR Continuous Memory. RERUN Quick Test.
	• Is resistance reading greater than 10 ohms?			
D14	CHECK FOR C2 SHORT LOW—COIL DISCONNECTED			
	• Key off.	Yes	▶	REPLACE coil pack. C2 open in coil. REMOVE all test equipment. RECONNECT all components. CLEAR Continuous Memory. RERUN Quick Test.
	• DVOM on 20K ohm scale.			
	• Disconnect coil from coil tee, leave EDIS diagnostic cable connected to vehicle harness coil connector.			
	• Measure resistance between J7 (BAT–) and J6 (RC2C) at breakout box.	No	▶	GO to **D15**.
	• Is resistance reading greater than 2K ohms?			

Fig. 15   Test D: No Code 215 Or 216 Coil Failure (Part 4 of 6). 1993 1.9L Engine

TEST STEP		RESULT	▶	ACTION TO TAKE
D17	CHECK FOR C2 HIGH—EDIS MODULE AND COIL DISCONNECTED			
	• Key off.	Yes	▶	REPLACE EDIS module. C2 is shorted high. REMOVE all test equipment. RECONNECT all components. CLEAR Continuous Memory. RERUN Quick Test.
	• Disconnect EDIS module from vehicle harness.			
	• DVOM on 20 volt DC scale.			
	• Key on, engine off.			
	• Measure voltage between (+)J6 (C2C) and (–)J7 (BAT–) at breakout box.	No	▶	CHECK connectors, SERVICE or REPLACE harness. C2 is shorted high. REMOVE all test equipment. RECONNECT all components. CLEAR Continuous Memory. RERUN Quick Test.
	• Is DC voltage reading less than 0.5 volts?			

Fig. 15   Test D: No Code 215 Or 216 Coil Failure (Part 6 of 6). 1993 1.9L Engine

TEST STEP		RESULT	▶	ACTION TO TAKE
D15	CHECK FOR C2 LOW—EDIS MODULE AND COIL DISCONNECTED			
	• Key off.	Yes	▶	REPLACE EDIS module. C2 shorted low. REMOVE all test equipment. RECONNECT all components. CLEAR Continuous Memory. RERUN Quick Test.
	• Disconnect EDIS module from vehicle harness.			
	• DVOM on 20K ohm scale.			
	• Measure resistance between J6 (C2C) and J7 (BAT–) at breakout box.	No	▶	CHECK connector, SERVICE or REPLACE harness. C2 is shorted low. REMOVE all test equipment. RECONNECT all components. CLEAR Continuous Memory. RERUN Quick Test. NOTE: A C2 short to ground may have damaged the coil.
	• Is resistance reading greater than 10K ohms?			
D16	CHECK FOR C1 HIGH—EDIS MODULE AND COIL DISCONNECTED			
	• Key off.	Yes	▶	REPLACE EDIS module. C1 is shorted high. REMOVE all test equipment. RECONNECT all components. CLEAR Continuous Memory. RERUN Quick Test.
	• Disconnect EDIS module from the EDIS module tee, leave EDIS diagnostic cable connected to vehicle harness connector.			
	• DVOM on 20 volt DC scale.			
	• Key on, engine off.			
	• Measure voltage between (+)J3 (C1C) and (–)J7 (BAT–) at breakout box.	No	▶	CHECK connector, SERVICE or REPLACE harness. C1 is shorted high. REMOVE all test equipment. RECONNECT all components. CLEAR Continuous Memory. RERUN Quick Test.
	• Is DC voltage reading less than 0.5 volts?			

Fig. 15   Test D: No Code 215 Or 216 Coil Failure (Part 5 of 6). 1993 1.9L Engine

TYPICAL VOLTAGE READINGS

Measure Between Pins		KOEO (Volts)	Engine Cranking (Volts AC)	Engine Idling (Volts AC)
First Pin	Second Pin			
CKP+S (J31)	CKP–S (J32)	0.0 AC	0.5 – 2.0	4.0 – 6.0
CKP+I (J35)	CKP–I (J48)	0.0 AC	0.5 – 2.0	4.0 – 6.0
PIP I (J43)	PWR GND (J7)	0.0 AC	6.0 – 8.0	6.0 – 8.0
C1I (J53)	PWR GND (J7)	B+ DC	1.0 – 4.0	2.0 – 7.0
C2I (J55)	PWR GND (J7)	B+ DC	1.0 – 4.0	2.0 – 7.0
C1C (J3)	PWR GND (J7)	B+ DC	1.0 – 4.0	2.0 – 7.0
C2C (J6)	PWR GND (J7)	B+ DC	1.0 – 4.0	2.0 – 7.0
SPOUT I (J45)	PWR GND (J7)	0.0 AC	0.1 – 2.0	3.0 – 4.0
IDM I (J41)	PWR GND (J7)	0.0 AC	0.5 – 2.0	0.3 – 2.0
CKP+S (J31)	PWR GND (J7)	1.0 – 2.0 DC		
CKP–S (J32)	PWR GND (J7)	1.0 – 2.0 DC		

NOTE: Do not connect the positive lead of the EI (High Data Rate) diagnostic harness or the CKP-VR sensor tee until directed to do so.
The SPOUT and IDM detectors in the diagnostic harness will not work unless the positive and negative leads of the diagnostic harness are connected.
KOEO = Key On, Engine Off.
KOEC = Key On, Engine Cranking.
The vehicle battery voltage must be at least 12 volts DC.
Be careful not to bring a fluorescent trouble lamp close to the vehicle wiring. If the key is ON and the CKP sensor is disconnected, the ICM may fire the coil.
When using a DVOM to measure DC voltage readings, connect the positive lead to the jack identified with a (+) sign and the negative lead to the jack with a (–) sign.

• Repetitive Spark Mode will cause coil circuits to read higher than other non-repetitive EI coil circuits.

• These diagnostics (Pinpoint Tests A through G) are written to catch "Hard Faults" (Due to limitations of test equipment) only; intermittent failures will be difficult or impossible to diagnose using these procedures unless the failure is constantly present when these Pinpoint Tests are run.

FM1119400297010X

Fig. 16   Diagnostics By Diagnostic Trouble Code & Symptom (Part 1 of 3). 1994–95 1.9L Engine

CONDITION	ACTION TO TAKE
No start with error Diagnostic Trouble Code not listed elsewhere in this index.	GO to A1.
• No start and no error service code.	GO to A1.
• No start with Code 211 (PIP at PCM fault).	GO to A3.
• No start and MIL stays on during engine crank (PIP FAULT).	GO to A1.
• Engine starts with Code 212 (IDM to PCM failure).	GO to B1.
• Engine starts with 213 (SPOUT CIRCUIT FAULT) or lacks power or has poor fuel economy.	GO to C1.
• Engine starts with Code 215 or 216 (Coil Fault).	GO to D1.

FM1119400297020X

Fig. 16   Diagnostics By Diagnostic Trouble Code & Symptom (Part 2 of 3). 1994–95 1.9L Engine

Most DVOM's used by auto technicians belong to a class or type known as "averaging". Examples are the Rotunda Digital Volt-Ohmmeter 007-00001, Fluke 70, 20 series and Fluke 88. Recently technicians have started to use DVOM'S of a different class (True RMS, DVOM's, Fluke 87, 8060A, 8062A, etc.). True RMS DVOM's should not be used with the Pinpoint Tests because they may display different voltage readings depending upon if the DVOM is turned on first and then the test leads are connected, or if the leads are connected first and then DVOM is turned on. Also they may not auto range to the same range every time and some display significantly different values depending on the range selected. It would be impossible to list all of the meters and how to use each, so we are requesting that you perform the following test to verify your DVOM is compatible with the Pinpoint Tests.

Using a known good EI vehicle, install the EI (Low Data Rate) DIS or EI (High Data Rate) EDIS diagnostic cable, connect the EEC Breakout Box to the diagnostic cable, start the vehicle and measure the AC voltage between J53 (C1I) and ground. The battery should be charged and the engine must be idling between 700 and 900 rpm. On any EI vehicle (except Escort) the value should be between 1.0 and 2.0 volts AC (1.5 volts AC is typical). If you have the EI (Low Data Rate) hand held testers they may be used instead of the Diagnostic Cable / EEC Breakout Box to gain access to J53 (C1I) and J43 (PIP I). Next, with the engine idling, measure between PIP and ground. This reading should be between 6 and 8 volts AC.

Because the Escort EI (High Data Rate) ignition system fires the coil differently (repetitive spark) at idle, the coil to ground voltage reading should be between 2 to 7 volts AC (4.5 volts AC is typical). The PIP to ground reading on the Escort is the same as the other EI systems.

If the readings you get agree with our test, your DVOM is OK to use with the Ignition Pinpoint Tests. If not, do not use it, it will lead to false parts replacement and the root cause will be difficult or impossible to find.

FM1119400297030X

Fig. 16   Diagnostics By Diagnostic Trouble Code & Symptom (Part 3 of 3). 1994–95 1.9L Engine

	TEST STEP	RESULT	▶	ACTION TO TAKE
A1	PERFORM EEC QUICK TEST			
	• Was Quick Test performed according to the procedures? NOTE: These diagnostic procedures are designed to correct one ignition failure at a time. When a component is replaced or a service is completed, remove all test equipment, reconnect all components and rerun Quick Test.	Yes No	▶ ▶	GO to A2. PERFORM Quick Test.
A2	CHECK FOR SPARK DURING CRANK			
	• Using a Neon Bulb Spark Tester (Special Service Tool D89P-6666-A) or Air Gap Spark Tester (Special Service Tool D81P-6666-A), check for spark at all spark plug wires while cranking. • Was spark consistent on ALL spark plug wires (one spark per crankshaft revolution)?	Yes No	▶ ▶	GO to A13. GO to A3.
A3	CHECK PLUGS AND WIRES			
	• Check spark plug wires for insulation damage, looseness, shorting or other damage. • Remove and check spark plugs for damage, wear, carbon deposits and proper plug gap. • Are spark plugs and wires OK?	Yes No	▶ ▶	REINSTALL plugs and wires. GO to A4. SERVICE or REPLACE damaged component. REMOVE all test equipment. RECONNECT all components. CLEAR Continuous Memory. RERUN Quick Test.
A4	CHECK FOR VEHICLE START WITH EI (HIGH DATA RATE) DIAGNOSTIC CABLE INSTALLED			
	WARNING: NEVER CONNECT THE PCM TO THE EEC BREAKOUT BOX WHEN PERFORMING EI DIAGNOSTICS. • Key off. • Install EI (High Data Rate) diagnostic harness to breakout box to both the ICM and vehicle harness. Do not connect CKP- VRS tee or coil tee. • Use EI (High Data Rate) 4 overlay. • Connect diagnostic harness negative lead to battery, leave positive lead disconnected. • Set diagnostic harness box type switch to "4/6 cylinder" position. • Will vehicle start and run?	Yes No	▶ ▶	GO to A32. GO to A5.

FM1119400298010X

Fig. 17   Test A: No Start (Part 1 of 11). 1994–95 1.9L Engine

	TEST STEP	RESULT	▶	ACTION TO TAKE
A5	CHECK PWR GND TO ICM—KEY OFF			
	• Key off. • DVOM on 200K ohm scale. • Measure resistance between J27 (PWR GND) and J7 (B-) at the breakout box. • Is the resistance less than 5.0 ohms?	Yes No	▶ ▶	GO to A6. CHECK connectors, SERVICE or REPLACE harness. PWR GND to ICM is open. REMOVE all test equipment. RECONNECT all components. CLEAR Continuous Memory. RERUN Quick Test.
A6	CHECK FOR VPWR TO ICM—KOEO			
	• Key off. • DVOM on 40 volt DC scale. • Key on, engine off. • Measure voltage between (+)J51 (VPWR I) and (-)J7 (B-) at breakout box. • Is DC voltage greater than 10.5 volts?	Yes No	▶ ▶	GO to A7. CHECK connectors, SERVICE or REPLACE harness. VPWR to ICM is open. REMOVE all test equipment. RECONNECT all components. CLEAR Continuous Memory. RERUN Quick Test.
A7	CHECK CKP + BIAS AT ICM—KOEO			
	• Key off. • DVOM on 40 volt DC scale. • Key on, engine off. • Measure voltage between (+)J35 (CKP+ I) and (-)J7 (B-) at breakout box. • Is DC voltage between 1.0 and 2.0 volts? NOTE: The ICM supplies +1.5 volts DC to both the CKP+ and CKP- wires. This is called the bias voltage.	Yes No	▶ ▶	GO to A21. GO to A8. Bias fault.
A8	CHECK CKP + BIAS — BIAS FAULT—CKP SENSOR DISCONNECTED—KOEO			
	• Key off. • Disconnect CKP sensor from vehicle harness connector. • DVOM on 40 volt DC scale. • Key on, engine off. • Measure voltage between (+)J35 (CKP+ I) and (-)J7 (B-) at breakout box. • Is DC voltage greater than 1.0 volt but less than 2.0 volts?	Yes No	▶ ▶	GO to A9. GO to A29.

FM1119400298020X

Fig. 17   Test A: No Start (Part 2 of 11). 1994–95 1.9L Engine

TEST STEP	RESULT	▶	ACTION TO TAKE
A9 CHECK CKP — BIAS FAULT—CKP SENSOR DISCONNECTED—KOEO • Key off. • DVOM on 40 volt DC scale. • Key on, engine off. • Measure voltage between (+)J48 (CKP- I) and (-)J7 (B-) at breakout box. • **Is DC voltage between 1.0 and 2.0 volts?**	Yes No	▶ ▶	REPLACE CKP sensor. Short to ground. REMOVE all test equipment. RECONNECT all components. CLEAR Continuous Memory. RERUN Quick Test. GO to **A10**. Bias fault.
A10 CHECK CKP CIRCUIT— HIGH or LOW BIAS—BIAS FAULT • **Was bias voltage reading in Step A9 less than 1.0 volt DC?**	Yes No	▶ ▶	GO to **A11**. Bias low fault. GO to **A12**. Bias high fault.
A11 CHECK CKP — FOR SHORT TO GROUND—BIAS LOW FAULT —CKP SENSOR AND ICM DISCONNECTED—KEY OFF • Key off. • Disconnect ICM from ICM tee, leave EI diagnostic harness connected to vehicle harness connector. • DVOM on 20K ohm scale. • Measure resistance between J48 (CKP- I) and J7 (B-) at breakout box. • **Is resistance greater than 10K ohms?**	Yes No	▶ ▶	REPLACE ICM. CKP shorted low. REMOVE all test equipment. RECONNECT all components. CLEAR Continuous Memory. RERUN Quick Test. CHECK connectors, SERVICE or REPLACE harness. CKP is shorted low. REMOVE all test equipment. RECONNECT all components. CLEAR Continuous Memory. RERUN Quick Test.

FM1119400298030X

Fig. 17   Test A: No Start (Part 3 of 11). 1994–95 1.9L Engine

TEST STEP	RESULT	▶	ACTION TO TAKE
A12 CHECK CKP CIRCUIT— HIGH—BIAS HIGH FAULT—CKP AND ICM DISCONNECTED—KOEO • Key off. • Disconnect ICM from ICM tee; leave EI diagnostic harness connected to vehicle harness connector. • DVOM 40 volt DC scale. • Key on, engine off. • Measure voltage between (+)J48 (CKP- I) and (-)J7 (B-) at breakout box. • **Is DC voltage less than 0.5 volts?**	Yes No	▶ ▶	REPLACE ICM. CKP-shorted high. REMOVE all test equipment. RECONNECT all components. CLEAR Continuous Memory. RERUN Quick Test. CHECK connectors, SERVICE or REPLACE harness. CKP is shorted high. REMOVE all test equipment. RECONNECT all components. CLEAR Continuous Memory. RERUN Quick Test.
A13 CHECK PIP AT ICM—KOEC **WARNING: NEVER CONNECT THE PCM TO THE EEC BREAKOUT BOX WHEN PERFORMING DIAGNOSTICS.** • Key off. • Install EI (high data rate) diagnostic harness to the breakout box and to both the ICM and vehicle harness. **Do not connect CKP- sensor tee or coil tee.** • Use EI (High Data Rate) 4 overlay. • Connect EI diagnostic harness negative lead to battery, leave positive lead disconnected. • Set EI diagnostic harness box type switch to ''4/6 cylinder'' position. • DVOM on 40 volt AC scale. • Crank engine and measure voltage between J43 (PIP I) and J7 (B-) at breakout box. • **Is the settled AC voltage reading greater than 3.5 volts?**	Yes No	▶ ▶	GO to **A14**. GO to **A18**. PIP fault.

FM1119400298040X

Fig. 17   Test A: No Start (Part 4 of 11). 1994–95 1.9L Engine

TEST STEP	RESULT	▶	ACTION TO TAKE
A14 CHECK FOR PIP CONTINUITY TO PCM—PCM DISCONNECTED—KEY OFF • Key off. • DVOM on 200 ohm scale. • Install a second breakout box to PCM vehicle harness connector. • Measure resistance between J43 (PIP I) at the breakout box and Pin 56 (PIP) at the second breakout box. • **Is resistance less than 5.0 ohms?**	Yes No	▶ ▶	GO to **A15**. CHECK connectors, SERVICE or REPLACE harness. PIP is open. REMOVE all test equipment. RECONNECT all components. CLEAR Continuous Memory. RERUN Quick Test.
A15 CHECK IGN GND AT ICM—PCM DISCONNECTED—KEY OFF • Key off. • DVOM on 2K ohm scale. • Measure resistance between J47 (IGN GND I) and J7 (B-) at breakout box. • **Is resistance less than 1050 ohms?***	Yes No	▶ ▶	GO to **A16**. GO to **A17**.
A16 CHECK FOR IGN GND CONTINUITY TO PCM—PCM DISCONNECTED—KEY OFF • Key off. • DVOM on 2K ohm scale. • Measure resistance between J47 (IGN GND I) at the breakout box and J16 (IGN GND) at the second breakout box. • **Is resistance less than 1050 ohms?** NOTE: * There is a 1000 ohm resistance inside the EI diagnostic harness that is between J47 and the ignition ground circuit.	Yes No	▶ ▶	Ignition system is OK. REMOVE all test equipment. RECONNECT all components. CLEAR Continuous Memory. RERUN Quick Test. CHECK connectors, SERVICE or REPLACE harness. IGN GND is open. REMOVE all test equipment. RECONNECT all components. CLEAR Continuous Memory. RERUN Quick Test.

FM1119400298050X

Fig. 17   Test A: No Start (Part 5 of 11). 1994–95 1.9L Engine

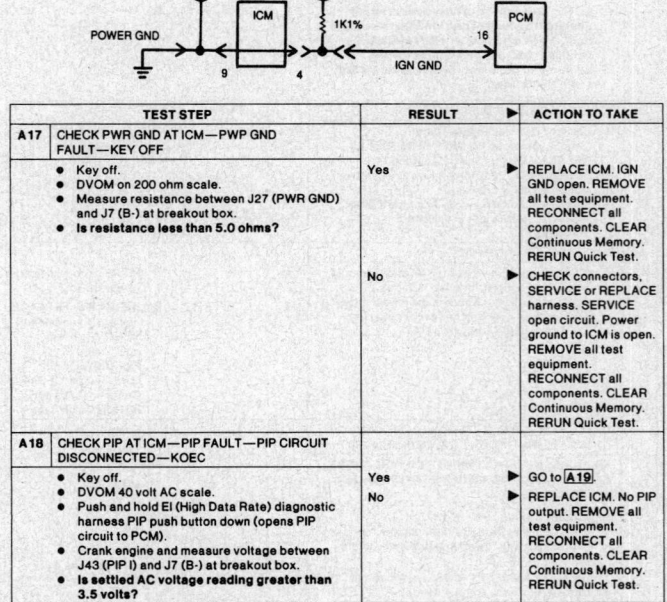

TEST STEP	RESULT	▶	ACTION TO TAKE
A17 CHECK PWR GND AT ICM—PWP GND FAULT—KEY OFF • Key off. • DVOM on 200 ohm scale. • Measure resistance between J27 (PWR GND) and J7 (B-) at breakout box. • **Is resistance less than 5.0 ohms?**	Yes No	▶ ▶	REPLACE ICM. IGN GND open. REMOVE all test equipment. RECONNECT all components. CLEAR Continuous Memory. RERUN Quick Test. CHECK connectors, SERVICE or REPLACE harness. SERVICE open circuit. Power ground to ICM is open. REMOVE all test equipment. RECONNECT all components. CLEAR Continuous Memory. RERUN Quick Test.
A18 CHECK PIP AT ICM—PIP FAULT—PIP CIRCUIT DISCONNECTED—KOEC • Key off. • DVOM 40 volt AC scale. • Push and hold EI (High Data Rate) diagnostic harness PIP push button down (opens PIP circuit to PCM). • Crank engine and measure voltage between J43 (PIP I) and J7 (B-) at breakout box. • **Is settled AC voltage reading greater than 3.5 volts?**	Yes No	▶ ▶	GO to **A19**. REPLACE ICM. No PIP output. REMOVE all test equipment. RECONNECT all components. CLEAR Continuous Memory. RERUN Quick Test.

FM1119400298060X

Fig. 17   Test A: No Start (Part 6 of 11). 1994–95 1.9L Engine

TEST STEP	RESULT	▶	ACTION TO TAKE
A19 CHECK FOR PIP SHORT TO GROUND IN HARNESS—ICM AND PCM DISCONNECTED—KEY OFF • Key off. • Disconnect PCM. • Disconnect ICM from ICM tee. Leave EI diagnostic harness connected to vehicle harness connector. • DVOM on 20K ohm scale. • Measure resistance between J43 (PIP I) and J7 (B-) at breakout box. • **Is resistance greater than 10K ohms?**	Yes No	▶ ▶	GO to **A20**. CHECK connectors, SERVICE or REPLACE harness. PIP is shorted low. REMOVE all test equipment. RECONNECT all components. CLEAR Continuous Memory. RERUN Quick Test.
A20 CHECK FOR PIP SHORT HIGH—ICM AND PCM DISCONNECTED—KOEO • Key off. • DVOM on 40 volt DC scale. • Key on, engine off. • Measure voltage between (+)J43 (PIP I) and (-)J7 (B-) at breakout box. • **Is DC voltage less than 0.5 volts?**	Yes No	▶ ▶	REPLACE PCM. PIP is shorted. REMOVE all test equipment. RECONNECT all components. CLEAR Continuous Memory. RERUN Quick Test. CHECK connectors, SERVICE or REPLACE harness. PIP is shorted high. REMOVE all test equipment. RECONNECT all components. CLEAR Continuous Memory. RERUN Quick Test.
A21 CHECK CKP AMPLITUDE AT ICM—KOEC • Key off. • DVOM on 40 volt AC scale. • Crank engine and measure voltage between J35 (CKP+ I) and J48 (CKP- I) at breakout box. • **Is settled AC voltage reading greater than 0.4 volts?**	Yes No	▶ ▶	GO to Pinpoint Test Step **D1**. GO to **A22**. Amplitude fault.

FM1119400298070X

Fig. 17   Test A: No Start (Part 7 of 11). 1994–95 1.9L Engine

TEST STEP	RESULT	▶	ACTION TO TAKE
A22 CHECK ICM—AMPLITUDE FAULT—ICM DISCONNECTED—KOEC • Key off. • Disconnect ICM from ICM tee, leave EI diagnostic harness connected to vehicle harness connector. • DVOM 40 volt AC scale. • Crank engine and measure voltage between J35 (CKP+ I) and J48 (CKP- I) at breakout box. • **Is settled AC voltage reading greater than 0.4 volts?**	Yes No	▶ ▶	REPLACE ICM. CKP is shorted. REMOVE all test equipment. RECONNECT all components. CLEAR Continuous Memory. RERUN Quick Test. GO to **A23**.
A23 CHECK CKP CIRCUIT RESISTANCE—KEY OFF • Key off. • DVOM on 20K ohm scale. • Measure resistance between J48 (CKP-I) and J35 (CKP+ I) at the breakout box. • **Is resistance between 2300 and 2500 ohms?**	Yes No	▶ ▶	GO to **A27**. GO to **A24**. CKP resistance fault.
A24 DETERMINE IF RESISTANCE HIGH OR RESISTANCE LOW FAULT • Key off. • **Was the resistance reading from A23 less than 2300 ohms?**	Yes No	▶ ▶	GO to **A28**. Resistance low fault. GO to **A25**. Resistance high fault.
A25 CHECK CKP + CONTINUITY—RESISTANCE HIGH FAULT—KEY OFF • Key off. • Connect CKP sensor tee to CKP sensor and vehicle harness connector. • DVOM on 20K ohm scale. • Measure resistance between J31 (CKP+S) and J35 (CKP+ I) at the breakout box. • **Is resistance less than 2050 ohms?**	Yes No	▶ ▶	GO to **A26**. CHECK connectors, SERVICE or REPLACE harness. CKP + open. REMOVE all test equipment. RECONNECT all components. CLEAR Continuous Memory. RERUN Quick Test.

FM1119400298080X

Fig. 17   Test A: No Start (Part 8 of 11). 1994–95 1.9L Engine

TEST STEP	RESULT	▶	ACTION TO TAKE
A26 CHECK CKP- CONTINUITY—RESISTANCE HIGH FAULT—KEY OFF • Key off. • DVOM on 20K ohm scale. • Measure resistance between J32 (CKP-S) and J48 (CKP- I) at the breakout box. • **Is resistance less than 2050 ohms?**	Yes No	▶ ▶	REPLACE CKP. High resistance. REMOVE all test equipment. RECONNECT all components. CLEAR Continuous Memory. RERUN Quick Test. CHECK connectors, SERVICE or REPLACE harness. CKP- open. REMOVE all test equipment. RECONNECT all components. CLEAR Continuous Memory. RERUN Quick Test.
A27 CHECK CKP SENSOR AND TRIGGER WHEEL—KEY OFF • Key off. • Check trigger wheel for damage. • **Is the sensor and trigger data wheel OK?**	Yes No	▶ ▶	REPLACE CKP sensor. No output. REMOVE all test equipment. RECONNECT all components. CLEAR Continuous Memory. RERUN Quick Test. SERVICE or REPLACE bad parts. REMOVE all test equipment. RECONNECT all components. CLEAR Continuous Memory. RERUN Quick Test.

FM1119400298090X

Fig. 17   Test A: No Start (Part 9 of 11). 1994–95 1.9L Engine

TEST STEP	RESULT	▶	ACTION TO TAKE
A28 CHECK CKP+ CIRCUIT SHORTED TO CKP- CIRCUIT—RESISTANCE LOW FAULT—CKP SENSOR DISCONNECTED—KEY OFF • Key off. • Disconnect CKP sensor from vehicle harness connector. • DVOM on 20K ohm scale. • Measure resistance between J35 (CKP+I) and J48 (CKP- I) at breakout box. • **Is resistance greater than 3K ohms?**	Yes No	▶ ▶	REPLACE CKP sensor. Shorted sensor windings. REMOVE all test equipment. RECONNECT all components. CLEAR Continuous Memory. RERUN Quick Test. CHECK connectors, SERVICE or REPLACE harness. CKP+ shorted to CKP- in harness. REMOVE all test equipment. RECONNECT all components. CLEAR Continuous Memory. RERUN Quick Test.
A29 CHECK FOR CKP+ BIAS HIGH OR LOW FAULT—CKP SENSOR DISCONNECTED • Was bias voltage reading in Step **A8** less than 1.0 volts?	Yes No	▶ ▶	GO to **A30**. Bias low fault. GO to **A31**. Bias high fault.
A30 CHECK CKP + FOR SHORT TO GROUND—CKP SENSOR AND ICM DISCONNECTED—KEY OFF • Key off. • Disconnect the ICM from ICM tee, leave EI diagnostic harness connected to vehicle harness connector. • DVOM on 20K ohm scale. • Measure resistance between J35 (CKP+I) and J7 (B-) at breakout box. • **Is resistance greater than 10K ohms?**	Yes No	▶ ▶	REPLACE ICM. CKP+ is shorted low. REMOVE all test equipment. RECONNECT all components. CLEAR Continuous Memory. RERUN Quick Test. CHECK connectors, SERVICE or REPLACE harness. CKP+ is shorted low. REMOVE all test equipment. RECONNECT all components. CLEAR Continuous Memory. RERUN Quick Test.

FM1119400298100X

Fig. 17   Test A: No Start (Part 10 of 11). 1994–95 1.9L Engine

TEST STEP		RESULT	►	ACTION TO TAKE
A31	CHECK CKP+ FOR SHORT HIGH—BIAS HIGH FAULT—CKP SENSOR AND ICM DISCONNECTED—KOEO • Key off. • Disconnect ICM from ICM tee, leave EI diagnostic harness connected to vehicle harness connector. • DVOM on 40 volt DC scale. • Key on, engine off. • Measure voltage between (+)J35 (CKP+ I) and (-)J7 (B-) at breakout box. • Is DC voltage less than 0.5 volts?	Yes No	►	REPLACE ICM. CKP+ is shorted high. REMOVE all test equipment. RECONNECT all components. CLEAR Continuous Memory. RERUN Quick Test. CHECK connectors, SERVICE or REPLACE harness. CKP+ is shorted high. REMOVE all test equipment. RECONNECT all components. CLEAR Continuous Memory. RERUN Quick Test.
A32	CHECK CKP CIRCUIT RESISTANCE—KEY OFF • Key off. • Disconnect ICM from ICM tee. Leave EI diagnostic harness connected to vehicle harness connector. • DVOM on 20K ohm scale. • Measure resistance between J48 (CKP- I) and J35 (CKP+ I) at breakout box. • Is resistance between 2300 and 2500 ohms?	Yes No	►	REPLACE ICM. REMOVE all test equipment. RECONNECT all components. CLEAR Continuous Memory. RERUN Quick Test. GO to A24. Circuit resistance fault.

Fig. 17   Test A: No Start (Part 11 of 11). 1994–95 1.9L Engine

TEST STEP		RESULT	►	ACTION TO TAKE
B3	CHECK IDM OUTPUT FROM ICM—IDM FAULT—IDM CIRCUIT DISCONNECTED—KOER • Key off. • DVOM on 40 volt AC scale. • Push and hold down diagnostic harness IDM button (opens IDM circuit to PCM). • Start engine and measure voltage between J30 (EI diagnostic harness IDM detector) and J7 (B-) at breakout box. • Is AC voltage greater than 5.0 volts?	Yes No	►	GO to B4. REPLACE ICM. No IDM output from module. REMOVE all test equipment. RECONNECT all components. CLEAR Continuous Memory. RERUN Quick Test.
B4	CHECK FOR IDM SHORT IN PCM—PCM DISCONNECTED—KOEC • Key off. • Disconnect PCM. • DVOM on 40 volt AC scale. • Crank engine and measure voltage between J30 (EI diagnostic harness IDM detector) and (-)J7 (B-) at breakout box. • Is AC voltage greater than 5.0 volts?	Yes No	►	REPLACE PCM. PCM is loading IDM signal. REMOVE all test equipment. RECONNECT all components. CLEAR Continuous Memory. RERUN Quick Test. GO to B5.
B5	CHECK FOR IDM SHORT HIGH IN HARNESS—ICM AND PCM DISCONNECTED • Key off. • DVOM on 40 volt DC scale. • Key on, engine off. • Measure voltage between (+)J41 (IDM I) and (-)J7 (B-) at breakout box. • Is DC voltage less than 0.5 volts?	Yes No	►	GO to B6. SERVICE short circuit or REPLACE harness. IDM is shorted high. REMOVE all test equipment. RECONNECT all components. CLEAR Continuous Memory. RERUN Quick Test.

FM1119400299020X

Fig. 18   Test B: Code 212, IDM Failure (Part 2 of 3). 1994–95 1.9L Engine

TEST STEP		RESULT	►	ACTION TO TAKE
B6	CHECK FOR IDM SHORT TO GROUND IN HARNESS—ICM AND PCM DISCONNECTED—KEY OFF • Key off. • Disconnect ICM from ICM tee, leave EI diagnostic harness connected to vehicle harness connector. • DVOM on 20K ohm scale. • Measure resistance between J41 (IDM I) and (-)J7 (B-) at breakout box. • Is resistance greater than 10 ohms?	Yes No	►	CHECK connectors, SERVICE or REPLACE harness. IDM is shorted to another wire between ICM and PCM. REMOVE all test equipment. RECONNECT all components. CLEAR Continuous Memory. RERUN Quick Test. CHECK connectors, SERVICE or REPLACE harness. IDM is shorted to low. REMOVE all test equipment. RECONNECT all components. CLEAR Continuous Memory. RERUN Quick Test.

FM1119400299030X

Fig. 18   Test B: Code 212, IDM Failure (Part 3 of 3). 1994–95 1.9L Engine

TEST STEP		RESULT	►	ACTION TO TAKE

B1	CHECK FOR IDM AT ICM—KOER
	WARNING: NEVER CONNECT THE PCM TO EEC BREAKOUT BOX WHEN PERFORMING DIAGNOSTICS.
	• Key off.
	• Install EI (High Data Rate) diagnostic harness to breakout box, and to both the ICM and vehicle harness.
	  Do not connect CKP sensor tee or coil tee.
	• Use EI (High Data Rate) 4 overlay.
	• Connect EI diagnostic harness negative and positive leads to battery.
	• Set EI diagnostic harness box type switch to "4/6 cylinder" position.
	• DVOM on 40 volt AC scale.
	• Start engine and measure voltage between (+)J30 (diagnostic harness IDM detector) and (-)J7 (B-) at breakout box.
	  NOTE: If pulses are present, the IDM detector output will be between 5.0 and 7.0 volts AC.
	• Is AC voltage between 5.0 and 7.0 volts?
		Yes
		No
			►	GO to B2.
				GO to B3. IDM fault.

B2	CHECK FOR IDM CONTINUITY TO PCM—IDM FAULT—ICM AND PCM DISCONNECTED—KEY OFF • Key off. • Disconnect PCM. • Disconnect ICM from ICM tee, leave EI diagnostic harness connected to vehicle harness connector. • DVOM on 200 ohm scale. • Install a second breakout box to the PCM vehicle harness connector. • Measure resistance between J41 (IDM I) at breakout box and Pin 4 at the second breakout box. • Is resistance less than 5.0 ohms?	Yes No	►	REPLACE PCM. PCM does not respond to IDM input. REMOVE all test equipment. RECONNECT all components. CLEAR Continuous Memory. RERUN Quick Test. CHECK connectors, SERVICE or REPLACE harness. IDM is open. REMOVE all test equipment. RECONNECT all components. CLEAR Continuous Memory. RERUN Quick Test.

Fig. 18   Test B: Code 212, IDM Failure (Part 1 of 3). 1994–95 1.9L Engine

TEST STEP		RESULT	►	ACTION TO TAKE
C1	CHECK BASE TIMING—KOER WARNING: NEVER CONNECT PCM TO EEC BREAKOUT BOX WHEN PERFORMING EI DIAGNOSTICS. • Key off. • Install EI (High Data Rate) diagnostic harness to breakout box and to both the ICM and vehicle harness. Do not connect the CKP sensor tee or coil tee. • Use EI (High Data Rate) 4 overlay. • Connect EI diagnostic harness negative and positive leads to battery. • Set EI diagnostic harness type switch to "4/6 cylinder" position. • Connect timing light (must be EI compatible). • Start engine and allow it to warm up. • Is timing 10 ± 2 degrees BTDC when the EI diagnostic harness SPOUT button is pushed and held down (opens SPOUT circuit)?	Yes No	►	GO to C2. GO to C8. Base timing fault.
C2	CHECK FOR SPARK ANGLE ADVANCE—KOER • Is engine timing greater than 15 degrees BTDC when the EI diagnostic harness SPOUT button is released?	Yes No	►	Ignition System is OK. for further driveability symptom diagnosis. GO to C3. Advance timing fault.
C3	CHECK SPOUT AT ICM—KOER • Key off. • DVOM on 40 volt AC scale. • Start engine and measure voltage between J21 (EI diagnostic harness SPOUT detector) and (-)J7 (B-) at breakout box. • Is AC voltage reading greater than 5.0 volts?	Yes No	►	REPLACE ICM. SPOUT input to ICM is OK, but no spark advance is present. REMOVE all test equipment. RECONNECT all components. CLEAR Continuous Memory. RERUN Quick Test. GO to C4.

FM1119400300010X

Fig. 19   Test C: Code 213 Or Lack Of Power Or Poor Fuel Economy (Part 1 of 3). 1994–95 1.9L Engine

Top Left Table (C4-C6)

	TEST STEP	RESULT	▶	ACTION TO TAKE
C4	CHECK FOR SPOUT SHORT IN ICM—OPEN SPOUT FAULT—SPOUT CIRCUIT—KOER			
	• Key off. • DVOM on 40 volt AC scale. • Push and hold down EI diagnostic harness SPOUT button (open SPOUT circuit to ICM). • Start engine and measure voltage between J21 (EI diagnostic harness SPOUT detector) and J7 (B-) at breakout box. • Is AC voltage reading greater than 5.0 volts?	Yes No	▶ ▶	REPLACE ICM. SPOUT is shorted. REMOVE all test equipment. RECONNECT all components. CLEAR Continuous Memory. RERUN Quick Test. GO to C5. SPOUT fault.
C5	CHECK FOR SPOUT SHORT HIGH IN HARNESS—ICM AND PCM DISCONNECTED—KOEO			
	• Key off. • Disconnect PCM. • Disconnect the ICM from ICM tee, leave EI diagnostic harness connected to vehicle harness connector. • DVOM on 40 volt DC scale. • Key on, engine off. • Measure voltage between J45 (SPOUT I) and J7 (B-) at breakout box. • Is DC voltage reading less than 0.5 volts?	Yes No	▶ ▶	GO to C6. CHECK connectors, SERVICE or REPLACE harness. SPOUT shorted high. REMOVE all test equipment. RECONNECT all components. CLEAR Continuous Memory. RERUN Quick Test.
C6	CHECK FOR SPOUT SHORT TO GROUND IN HARNESS—ICM AND PCM DISCONNECTED—KEY OFF			
	• Key off. • DVOM on 20K ohm scale. • Disconnect EI diagnostic harness positive lead to battery. • Measure resistance between J45 (SPOUT I) and J7 (B-) at breakout box. • Is the resistance greater than 10K ohms?	Yes No	▶ ▶	GO to C7. CHECK connectors, SERVICE or REPLACE harness. SPOUT is shorted low. SERVICE short circuit. REMOVE all test equipment. RECONNECT all components. CLEAR Continuous Memory. RERUN Quick Test.

FM1119400300020X

Fig. 19   Test C: Code 213 Or Lack Of Power Or Poor Fuel Economy (Part 2 of 3). 1994–95 1.9L Engine

Top Right Table (C7-C8)

	TEST STEP	RESULT	▶	ACTION TO TAKE
C7	CHECK FOR SPOUT CONTINUITY TO ICM—ICM AND PCM DISCONNECTED—KEY OFF			
	• Key off. • DVOM on 200 ohm scale. • Install a second breakout box to the vehicle harness connector. • Measure resistance between J45 (SPOUT I) at breakout box and Pin 36 at the second breakout box. • Is resistance less than 5.0 ohms?	Yes No	▶ ▶	REPLACE PCM. SPOUT is not being transmitted by PCM. REMOVE all test equipment. RECONNECT all components. CLEAR Continuous Memory. RERUN Quick Test. CHECK connectors, SERVICE or REPLACE harness. SPOUT is open. REMOVE all test equipment. RECONNECT all components. CLEAR Continuous Memory. RERUN Quick Test.
C8	INSPECT CKP SENSOR AND TRIGGER WHEEL—TIMING FAULT			
	• Is CKP sensor or trigger wheel damaged, i.e., loose or misaligned? NORMAL WHEEL NOTE RELATIONSHIP BETWEEN NOTCH AND MISSING TOOTH	Yes No	▶ ▶	REPLACE or SERVICE as required. REMOVE all test equipment. RECONNECT all components. CLEAR Continuous Memory. RERUN Quick Test. REPLACE ICM. Incorrect spark output from ICM. REMOVE all test equipment. RECONNECT all components. CLEAR Continuous Memory. RERUN Quick Test.

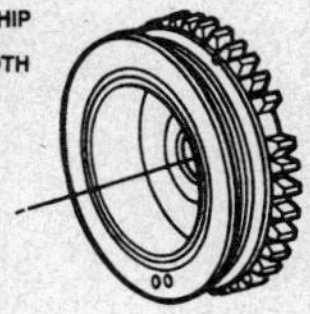

FM1119400300030X

Fig. 19   Test C: Code 213 Or Lack Of Power Or Poor Fuel Economy (Part 3 of 3). 1994–95 1.9L Engine

Bottom Left Table (D1-D4)

	TEST STEP	RESULT	▶	ACTION TO TAKE
D1	CHECK FOR SPARK DURING CRANK—KOEC			
	• Using a Neon Bulb Spark Tester (Special Service Tool D89P-6666-A) or Air Gap Spark Tester (D81P-6666-A), check for spark at all spark plug wires while cranking. • Was spark consistent on ALL spark plug wires (one spark per crankshaft revolution)?	Yes No	▶ ▶	Ignition system is OK. GO to D2. Spark fault.
D2	CHECK SPARK PLUGS AND WIRES—KEY OFF			
	• Check spark plug wires for insulation damage, looseness, shorting or other damage. • Remove and check right spark plugs for damage, wear, carbon deposits and proper plug gap. • Are spark plugs and wires OK?	Yes No	▶ ▶	REINSTALL plugs and wires. GO to D3. SERVICE or REPLACE damaged component. REMOVE all test equipment. RECONNECT all components. CLEAR Continuous Memory. RERUN Quick Test.
D3	CHECK FOR COIL PWR AT COIL—KOEO			
	WARNING: NEVER CONNECT PCM TO EEC BREAKOUT BOX WHEN PERFORMING EI DIAGNOSTICS. • Key off. • Install EI (High Data Rate) diagnostic harness to breakout box. • Connect negative lead to battery. • Set EI diagnostic harness box type switch to "4/6 cylinder" position. • Install right (blue) coil tee. • Use EI (High Data Rate) 4 overlay. • DVOM on 40 volt DC scale. • Key on, engine off. • Measure voltage between (+)J5 (COIL PWR) and (-)J7 (B-) at breakout box. • Is DC voltage greater than 10.0 volts?	Yes No	▶ ▶	GO to D4. CHECK connectors, SERVICE or REPLACE harness. COIL PWR is open. REMOVE all test equipment. RECONNECT all components. CLEAR Continuous Memory. RERUN Quick Test.
D4	CHECK FOR C1 HIGH AT COIL PACK—KOEO			
	• Key on, engine off. • Measure voltage between (+)J3 (C1C) and (-)J7 (B-) at breakout box. • Is DC voltage reading greater than 10.0 volts?	Yes No	▶ ▶	GO to D5. GO to D12. C1 low fault.

FM1119400301010X

Fig. 20   Test D: No Start Code 215 Or 216 (Coil 1 Or Coil 2) Failure (Part 1 of 6). 1994–95 1.9L Engine

Bottom Right Table (D5-D9)

	TEST STEP	RESULT	▶	ACTION TO TAKE
D5	CHECK FOR C2 HIGH AT COIL PACK—KOEO			
	• DVOM on 40 volt DC scale. • Key on, engine off. • Measure voltage between (+)J6 (C2C) and (-)J7 (B-) at breakout box. • Is DC voltage reading greater than 10.0 volts?	Yes No	▶ ▶	GO to D6. GO to D14. C2 low fault.
D6	CHECK FOR C1 HIGH AT ICM—KOEO			
	• Key off. • Connect ICM tee to ICM and vehicle harness connector. • DVOM on 40 volt DC scale. • Key on, engine off. • Measure voltage between (+)J53 (C1I) and (-)J7 (B-) at breakout box. • Is DC voltage reading greater than 10.0 volts?	Yes No	▶ ▶	GO to D7. CHECK connectors, SERVICE or REPLACE harness. C1 is open. REMOVE all test equipment. RECONNECT all components. CLEAR Continuous Memory. RERUN Quick Test.
D7	CHECK FOR C2 HIGH AT ICM—KOEO			
	• Key on, engine off. • Measure voltage between (+)J55 (C2I) and (-)J7 (B-) at breakout box. • Is DC voltage reading greater than 10.0 volts?	Yes No	▶ ▶	GO to D8. CHECK connectors, SERVICE or REPLACE harness. C2 is open. REMOVE all test equipment. RECONNECT all components. CLEAR Continuous Memory. RERUN Quick Test.
D8	CHECK FOR C1 LOW AT COIL CONNECTOR—COIL DISCONNECTED—KOEO			
	• Key off. • Disconnect the coil from the coil tee, leave EI diagnostic harness coil tee connected to the vehicle harness coil connector. • DVOM on 40 volt DC scale. • Key on, engine off. • Measure voltage between (+)J3 (C1C) and (-)J7 (B-) at breakout box. • Is DC voltage reading less than 0.5 volts?	Yes No	▶ ▶	GO to D9. GO to D16. C1 high fault.
D9	CHECK FOR C2 LOW AT COIL CONNECTOR—COIL DISCONNECTED—KOEO			
	• Key off. • DVOM on 40 volt DC scale. • Key on, engine off. • Measure voltage between (+)J6 (C2C) and (-)J7 (B-) at breakout box. • Is DC voltage reading less than 0.5 volts?	Yes No	▶ ▶	GO to D10. GO to D17. C2 high fault.

FM1119400301020X

Fig. 20   Test D: No Start Code 215 Or 216 (Coil 1 Or Coil 2) Failure (Part 2 of 6). 1994–95 1.9L Engine

TEST STEP	RESULT	▶	ACTION TO TAKE
D10 CHECK C1 AT COIL CONNECTOR WHILE CRANKING ENGINE—COIL DISCONNECTED—KOEC • Connect an incandescent test lamp between J1 (B+) and J3 (C1C). • Connect positive lead of EI diagnostic harness to battery. • Crank engine. • **Does lamp blink consistently and brightly (one blink per engine revolution)?**	Yes No	▶ ▶	GO to D11. REPLACE ICM. C1 open. REMOVE all test equipment. RECONNECT all components. CLEAR Continuous Memory. RERUN Quick Test.
D11 CHECK C2 AT COIL CONNECTOR WHILE CRANKING ENGINE—COIL DISCONNECTED—KOEC • Connect an incandescent test lamp between J1 (B+) and J6 (C2C). • Crank engine. • **Does lamp blink consistently and brightly (one blink per engine revolution)?**	Yes No	▶ ▶	REPLACE coil pack. Input to coil pack is OK, but no high voltage output. REMOVE all test equipment. RECONNECT all components. CLEAR Continuous Memory. RERUN Quick Test. REPLACE ICM. C2 open in ICM. REMOVE all test equipment. RECONNECT all components. CLEAR Continuous Memory. RERUN Quick Test.
D12 CHECK FOR C1 SHORT LOW—COIL DISCONNECTED—KEY OFF • Key off. • DVOM on 20K ohm scale. • Disconnect coil from coil tee, leave EI diagnostic harness connected to vehicle harness coil connector. • Measure resistance between J7 (B-) and J3 (RC1C) at breakout box. • **Is resistance reading greater than 2K ohms?**	Yes No	▶ ▶	REPLACE right coil pack. C1 open in coil. REMOVE all test equipment. RECONNECT all components. CLEAR Continuous Memory. RERUN Quick Test. GO to D13.

FM1119400301030X

Fig. 20   Test D: No Start Code 215 Or 216 (Coil 1 Or Coil 2) Failure (Part 3 of 6). 1994–95 1.9L Engine

TEST STEP	RESULT	▶	ACTION TO TAKE
D13 CHECK FOR C1 SHORT LOW—ICM AND COIL DISCONNECTED—KEY OFF • Key off. • Disconnect ICM from ICM tee, leave EI diagnostic harness connected to vehicle harness connector. • DVOM on 20K ohm scale. • Measure resistance between J7 (B-) and J3 (C1C) at breakout box. • **Is resistance reading greater than 10 ohms?**	Yes No	▶ ▶	REPLACE ICM. C1 is shorted low in ICM. REMOVE all test equipment. RECONNECT all components. CLEAR Continuous Memory. RERUN Quick Test. NOTE: A C1 short to ground may have damaged the coil. CHECK connectors, SERVICE or REPLACE harness. C1 is shorted low. REMOVE all test equipment. RECONNECT all components. CLEAR Continuous Memory. RERUN Quick Test.
D14 CHECK FOR C2 SHORT LOW—COIL DISCONNECTED—KEY OFF • Key off. • DVOM on 20K ohm scale. • Disconnect coil from coil tee, leave EI diagnostic harness connected to vehicle harness coil connector. • Measure resistance between J7 (B-) and J6 (C2C) at breakout box. • **Is resistance reading greater than 2K ohms?**	Yes No	▶ ▶	REPLACE coil pack. C2 open in coil. REMOVE all test equipment. RECONNECT all components. CLEAR Continuous Memory. RERUN Quick Test. GO to D15.

FM1119400301040X

Fig. 20   Test D: No Start Code 215 Or 216 (Coil 1 Or Coil 2) Failure (Part 4 of 6). 1994–95 1.9L Engine

TEST STEP	RESULT	▶	ACTION TO TAKE
D17 CHECK FOR C2 HIGH—ICM AND COIL DISCONNECTED—KOEO • Key off. • Disconnect ICM from vehicle harness. • DVOM on 40 volt DC scale. • Key on, engine off. • Measure voltage between (+)J6 (C2C) and (-)J7 (B-) at breakout box. • **Is DC voltage reading less than 0.5 volts?**	Yes No	▶ ▶	REPLACE ICM. C2 is shorted high. REMOVE all test equipment. RECONNECT all components. CLEAR Continuous Memory. RERUN Quick Test. CHECK connectors, SERVICE or REPLACE harness. C2 is shorted high. REMOVE all test equipment. RECONNECT all components. CLEAR Continuous Memory. RERUN Quick Test.

FM1119400301060X

Fig. 20   Test D: No Start Code 215 Or 216 (Coil 1 Or Coil 2) Failure (Part 6 of 6). 1994–95 1.9L Engine

TEST STEP	RESULT	▶	ACTION TO TAKE
D15 CHECK FOR C2 LOW—ICM AND COIL DISCONNECTED—KEY OFF • Key off. • Disconnect ICM from vehicle harness. • DVOM on 20K ohm scale. • Measure resistance between J6 (C2C) and J7 (B-) at breakout box. • **Is resistance reading greater than 10K ohms?**	Yes No	▶ ▶	REPLACE ICM. C2 shorted low. REMOVE all test equipment. RECONNECT all components. CLEAR Continuous Memory. RERUN Quick Test. CHECK connector, SERVICE or REPLACE harness. C2 is shorted low. REMOVE all test equipment. RECONNECT all components. CLEAR Continuous Memory. RERUN Quick Test. NOTE: A C2 short to ground may have damaged the coil.
D16 CHECK FOR C1 HIGH—ICM AND COIL DISCONNECTED—KOEO • Key off. • Disconnect ICM from the ICM tee, leave EI diagnostic harness connected to vehicle harness connector. • DVOM on 40 volt DC scale. • Key on, engine off. • Measure voltage between (+)J3 (C1C) and (-)J7 (B-) at breakout box. • **Is DC voltage reading less than 0.5 volts?**	Yes No	▶ ▶	REPLACE ICM. C1 is shorted high. REMOVE all test equipment. RECONNECT all components. CLEAR Continuous Memory. RERUN Quick Test. CHECK connector, SERVICE or REPLACE harness. C1 shorted high. REMOVE all test equipment. RECONNECT all components. CLEAR Continuous Memory. RERUN Quick Test.

FM1119400301050X

Fig. 20   Test D: No Start Code 215 Or 216 (Coil 1 Or Coil 2) Failure (Part 5 of 6). 1994–95 1.9L Engine

Measure Between Pins		KOEO (Volts)	Engine Cranking (Volts AC)	Engine Idling (Volts AC)
First Pin	Second Pin			
CKP+S (J31)	CKP-S(J32)	0.0 AC	0.5 - 2.0	4.0 - 6.0
CKP+I (J35)	CKP-I(J48)	0.0 AC	0.5 - 2.0	4.0 - 6.0
PIP I (J43)	PWR GND (J7)	0.0 AC	6.0 - 8.0	6.0 - 8.0
C1I (J53)	PWR GND (J7)	B+ DC	1.0 - 4.0	2.0 - 7.0
C2I (J55)	PWR GND (J7)	B+ DC	1.0 - 4.0	2.0 - 7.0
C1C (J3)	PWR GND (J7)	B+ DC	1.0 - 4.0	2.0 - 7.0
C2C (J6)	PWR GND (J7)	B+ DC	1.0 - 4.0	2.0 - 7.0
SPOUT I (J45)	PWR GND (J7)	0.0 AC	0.1 - 2.0	3.0 - 4.0
IDM I (J41)	PWR GND (J7)	0.0 AC	0.5 - 2.0	0.3 - 2.0
CKP+S (J31)	PWR GND (J7)	1.0-2.0 DC		
CKP-S (J32)	PWR GND (J7)	1.0-2.0 DC		

NOTE: Do not connect the positive lead of the EI (High Data Rate) diagnostic harness or the CKP-VR sensor tee until directed to do so.

The SPOUT and IDM detectors in the diagnostic harness will not work unless the positive and negative leads of the diagnostic harness are connected.

KOEO = Key On, Engine Off.

KOEC = Key On, Engine Cranking.

The vehicle battery voltage must be at least 12 volts DC.

Be careful not to bring a fluorescent trouble lamp close to the vehicle wiring. If the key is ON and the CKP sensor is disconnected, the ICM may fire the coil.

When using a DVOM to measure DC voltage readings, connect the positive lead to the jack identified with a (+) sign and the negative lead to the jack with a (-) sign.

● Repetitive Spark Mode will cause coil circuits to read higher than other non-repetitive EI coil circuits.

● These diagnostics (Pinpoint Tests A through G) are written to catch "Hard Faults" (Due to limitations of test equipment) only; intermittent failures will be difficult or impossible to diagnose using these procedures unless the failure is constantly present when these Pinpoint Tests are run.

FM1119200302010X

Fig. 21   Diagnostics By Service Code & Symptom (Part 1 of 3). 2.0L Zetec Engine

CONDITION	ACTION TO TAKE
No start with error Diagnostic Trouble Code not listed elsewhere in this index.	GO to **A1**.
• No start and no error service code.	GO to **A1**.
• No start with Code 211 (PIP at PCM fault).	GO to **A3**.
• No start and MIL stays on during engine crank (PIP FAULT).	GO to **A1**.
• Engine starts with Code 212 or Code 226 (IDM to PCM failure).	GO to **B1**.
• Engine starts with 213 (SPOUT CIRCUIT FAULT) or lack of power or poor fuel economy.	GO to **C1**.
• Engine starts with Code 215 or 216 (Coil Fault).	GO to **D1**.
• Stall / Miss / Stumble / Surge / Loss of Power—Intermittent	GO to Intermittent Diagnostic Procedures.
•Engine Miss	GO to 3.0L / 3.2L Pinpoint Test **F**.

FM1119200302020X

Fig. 21   Diagnostics By Service Code & Symptom (Part 2 of 3). 2.0L Zetec Engine

Most DVOM's used by auto technicians belong to a class or type known as "averaging". Examples are the Rotunda Digital Volt-Ohmmeter 007-0001, Fluke 70, 20 series and Fluke 88. Recently technicians have started to use DVOM'S of a different class (True RMS, DVOM's, Fluke 87, 8060A, 8062A, etc.). True RMS DVOM's should not be used with the Pinpoint Tests because they may display different voltage readings depending upon if the DVOM is turned on first and then the test leads are connected, or if the leads are connected first then the DVOM is turned on. Also they may not auto range to the same range every time and some display significantly different values depending on the range selected. It would be impossible to list all of the meters and how to use each, so we are requesting that you perform the following test to verify your DVOM is compatible with the Pinpoint Tests.

Using a known good EI vehicle, install the EI (Low Data Rate) DIS or EI (High Data Rate) EDIS diagnostic cable, connect the EEC Breakout Box to the diagnostic cable, start the vehicle and measure the AC voltage between J53 (C1I) and ground. The battery should be charged and the engine must be idling between 700 and 900 rpm. On any EI vehicle the value should be between 1.0 and 2.0 volts AC (1.5 volts AC is typical). If you have the EI (Low Data Rate) hand held testers they may be used instead of the Diagnostic Cable / EEC Breakout Box to gain access to J53 (C1I) and J43 (PIP I). Next, with the engine idling, measure between PIP and ground. This reading should be between 6 and 8 volts AC.

If the readings you get agree with our test, your DVOM is OK to use with the Ignition Pinpoint Tests. If not, do not use it, it will lead to false parts replacement and the root cause will be difficult or impossible to find.

FM1119200302030X

Fig. 21   Diagnostics By Service Code & Symptom (Part 3 of 3). 2.0L Zetec Engine

	TEST STEP	RESULT	▶	ACTION TO TAKE
A1	PERFORM EEC QUICK TEST			
	• Was Quick Test performed according to the procedures?	Yes	▶	GO to **A2**.
		No	▶	PERFORM Quick Test.
	NOTE: These diagnostic procedures are designed to correct one ignition failure at a time. When a component is replaced or a service is completed, remove all test equipment, reconnect all components and rerun Quick Test.			
A2	CHECK FOR SPARK DURING CRANK			
	• Using a Neon Bulb Spark Tester (Special Service Tool D89P-6666-A) or Air Gap Spark Tester (Special Service Tool D81P-6666-A), check for spark at all spark plug wires while cranking.	Yes	▶	GO to **A13**.
		No	▶	GO to **A3**.
	• Was spark consistent on ALL spark plug wires (one spark per crankshaft revolution)?			
A3	CHECK PLUGS AND WIRES			
	• Check spark plug wires for insulation damage, looseness, shorting or other damage.	Yes	▶	REINSTALL plugs and wires. GO to **A4**.
	• Remove and check spark plugs for damage, wear, carbon deposits and proper plug gap.	No	▶	SERVICE or REPLACE damaged component. REMOVE all test equipment. RECONNECT all components. CLEAR Continuous Memory. RERUN Quick Test.
	• Are spark plugs and wires OK?			
A4	CHECK FOR VEHICLE START WITH EI (HIGH DATA RATE) DIAGNOSTIC CABLE INSTALLED			
	WARNING: NEVER CONNECT THE PCM TO THE EEC BREAKOUT BOX WHEN PERFORMING EI DIAGNOSTICS.	Yes	▶	GO to **A32**.
		No	▶	GO to **A5**.
	• Key off.			
	• Install EI (High Data Rate) diagnostic harness to breakout box to both the ICM and vehicle harness.			
	Do not connect CKP- VRS tee or coil tee.			
	• Use EI (High Data Rate) 4 overlay.			
	• Connect diagnostic harness negative lead to battery, leave positive lead disconnected.			
	• Set diagnostic harness box type switch to "4 / 6 cylinder" position.			
	• Will vehicle start and run?			

FM1119200303010X

Fig. 22   Test A: No Start (Part 1 of 10). 2.0L Zetec Engine

	TEST STEP	RESULT	▶	ACTION TO TAKE
A5	CHECK PWR GND TO ICM—KEY OFF			
	• Key off.	Yes	▶	GO to **A6**.
	• DVOM on 200K ohm scale.	No	▶	CHECK connectors, SERVICE or REPLACE harness. PWR GND to ICM is open. REMOVE all test equipment. RECONNECT all components. CLEAR Continuous Memory. RERUN Quick Test.
	• Measure resistance between J27 (PWR GND) and J7 (B-) at the breakout box.			
	• Is the resistance less than 5.0 ohms?			
A6	CHECK FOR VPWR TO ICM—KOEO			
	• Key off.	Yes	▶	GO to **A7**.
	• DVOM on 40 volt DC scale.	No	▶	CHECK connectors, SERVICE or REPLACE harness. VPWR to ICM is open. REMOVE all test equipment. RECONNECT all components. CLEAR Continuous Memory. RERUN Quick Test.
	• Key on, engine off.			
	• Measure voltage between (+)J51 (VPWR I) and (-)J7 (B-) at breakout box.			
	• Is DC voltage greater than 10.5 volts?			
A7	CHECK CKP + BIAS AT ICM—KOEO			
	• Key off.	Yes	▶	GO to **A21**.
	• DVOM on 40 volt DC scale.	No	▶	GO to **A8**. Bias fault.
	• Key on, engine off.			
	• Measure voltage between (+)J35 (CKP+ I) and (-)J7 (B-) at breakout box.			
	• Is DC voltage between 1.0 and 2.0 volts?			
	NOTE: The ICM supplies +1.5 volts DC to both the CKP+ and CKP- wires. This is called the bias voltage.			
A8	CHECK CKP + BIAS —BIAS FAULT—CKP SENSOR DISCONNECTED—KOEO			
	• Key off.	Yes	▶	GO to **A9**.
	• Disconnect CKP sensor from vehicle harness connector.	No	▶	GO to **A29**.
	• DVOM on 40 volt DC scale.			
	• Key on, engine off.			
	• Measure voltage between (+)J35 (CKP+ I) and (-)J7 (B-) at breakout box.			
	• Is DC voltage greater than 1.0 volt but less than 2.0 volts?			

FM1119200303020X

Fig. 22   Test A: No Start (Part 2 of 10). 2.0L Zetec Engine

TEST STEP	RESULT	▶	ACTION TO TAKE
A9 CHECK CKP — BIAS FAULT—CKP SENSOR DISCONNECTED—KOEO • Key off. • DVOM on 40 volt DC scale. • Key on, engine off. • Measure voltage between (+)J48 (CKP- I) and (-)J7 (B-) at breakout box. • Is DC voltage between 1.0 and 2.0 volts?	Yes No	▶ ▶	REPLACE CKP sensor. Short to ground. REMOVE all test equipment. RECONNECT all components. CLEAR Continuous Memory. RERUN Quick Test. GO to A10. Bias fault.
A10 CHECK CKP CIRCUIT — HIGH or LOW BIAS—BIAS FAULT • Was bias voltage reading in Step A9 less than 1.0 volt DC?	Yes No	▶ ▶	GO to A11. Bias low fault. GO to A12. Bias high fault.
A11 CHECK CKP — FOR SHORT TO GROUND—BIAS LOW FAULT—CKP SENSOR AND ICM DISCONNECTED—KEY OFF • Key off. • Disconnect ICM from ICM tee, leave EI diagnostic harness connected to vehicle harness connector. • DVOM on 20K ohm scale. • Measure resistance between J48 (CKP- I) and J7 (B-) at breakout box. • Is resistance greater than 10K ohms?	Yes No	▶ ▶	REPLACE ICM. CKP shorted low. REMOVE all test equipment. RECONNECT all components. CLEAR Continuous Memory. RERUN Quick Test. CHECK connectors, SERVICE or REPLACE harness. CKP is shorted low. REMOVE all test equipment. RECONNECT all components. CLEAR Continuous Memory. RERUN Quick Test.

FM1119200303030X

Fig. 22 Test A: No Start (Part 3 of 10). 2.0L Zetec Engine

TEST STEP	RESULT	▶	ACTION TO TAKE
A12 CHECK CKP CIRCUIT — FOR SHORT HIGH—BIAS HIGH FAULT—CKP AND ICM DISCONNECTED—KOEO • Key off. • Disconnect ICM from ICM tee; leave EI diagnostic harness connected to vehicle harness connector. • DVOM 40 volt DC scale. • Key on, engine off. • Measure voltage between (+)J48 (CKP- I) and (-)J7 (B-) at breakout box. • Is DC voltage less than 0.5 volts?	Yes No	▶ ▶	REPLACE ICM. CKP- shorted high. REMOVE all test equipment. RECONNECT all components. CLEAR Continuous Memory. RERUN Quick Test. CHECK connectors, SERVICE or REPLACE harness. CKP is shorted high. REMOVE all test equipment. RECONNECT all components. CLEAR Continuous Memory. RERUN Quick Test.
A13 CHECK PIP AT ICM—KOEC **WARNING: NEVER CONNECT THE PCM TO THE EEC BREAKOUT BOX WHEN PERFORMING DIAGNOSTICS.** • Key off. • Install EI (high data rate) diagnostic harness to the breakout box and to both the ICM and vehicle harness. **Do not connect CKP- sensor tee or coil tee.** • Use EI (High Data Rate) 4 overlay. • Connect EI diagnostic harness negative lead to battery, leave positive lead disconnected. • Set EI diagnostic harness box type switch to "4/6 cylinder" position. • DVOM on 40 volt AC scale. • Crank engine and measure voltage between J43 (PIP I) and J7 (B-) at breakout box. • Is the settled AC voltage reading greater than 3.5 volts?	Yes No	▶ ▶	GO to A14. GO to A18. PIP fault.

FM1119200303040X

Fig. 22 Test A: No Start (Part 4 of 10). 2.0L Zetec Engine

TEST STEP	RESULT	▶	ACTION TO TAKE
A14 CHECK FOR PIP CONTINUITY TO PCM—PCM DISCONNECTED—KEY OFF • Key off. • DVOM on 200 ohm scale. • Install a second breakout box to PCM vehicle harness connector. • Measure resistance between J43 (PIP I) at the breakout box and Pin 56 (PIP) at the second breakout box. • Is resistance less than 5.0 ohms?	Yes No	▶ ▶	GO to A15. CHECK connectors, SERVICE or REPLACE harness. PIP is open. REMOVE all test equipment. RECONNECT all components. CLEAR Continuous Memory. RERUN Quick Test.
A15 CHECK IGN GND AT ICM—PCM DISCONNECTED—KEY OFF • Key off. • DVOM on 2K ohm scale. • Measure resistance between J47 (IGN GND I) and J7 (B-) at breakout box. • Is resistance less than 1050 ohms?*	Yes No	▶ ▶	GO to A16. GO to A17.
A16 CHECK FOR IGN GND CONTINUITY TO PCM—PCM DISCONNECTED—KEY OFF • Key off. • DVOM on 2K ohm scale. • Measure resistance between J47 (IGN GND I) at the breakout box and J16 (IGN GND) at the second breakout box. • Is resistance less than 1050 ohms? NOTE: * There is a 1000 ohm resistance inside the EI diagnostic harness that is between J47 and the ignition ground circuit.	Yes No	▶ ▶	Ignition system is OK. REMOVE all test equipment. RECONNECT all components. CLEAR Continuous Memory. RERUN Quick Test. CHECK connectors, SERVICE or REPLACE harness. IGN GND is open. REMOVE all test equipment. RECONNECT all components. CLEAR Continuous Memory. RERUN Quick Test.

POWER GND — J27 — ICM — 9 — 4 — J47 — 1K1% — IGN GND — 16 — PCM

FM1119200303050X

Fig. 22 Test A: No Start (Part 5 of 10). 2.0L Zetec Engine

TEST STEP	RESULT	▶	ACTION TO TAKE
A17 CHECK PWR GND AT ICM—PWP GND FAULT—KEY OFF • Key off. • DVOM on 200 ohm scale. • Measure resistance between J27 (PWR GND) and J7 (B-) at breakout box. • Is resistance less than 5.0 ohms?	Yes No	▶ ▶	REPLACE ICM. IGN GND open. REMOVE all test equipment. RECONNECT all components. CLEAR Continuous Memory. RERUN Quick Test. CHECK connectors, SERVICE or REPLACE harness. SERVICE open circuit. Power ground to ICM is open. REMOVE all test equipment. RECONNECT all components. CLEAR Continuous Memory. RERUN Quick Test.
A18 CHECK PIP AT ICM—PIP FAULT—PIP CIRCUIT DISCONNECTED—KOEC • Key off. • DVOM 40 volt AC scale. • Push and hold EI (High Data Rate) diagnostic harness PIP push button down (opens PIP circuit to PCM). • Crank engine and measure voltage between J43 (PIP I) and J7 (B-) at breakout box. • Is settled AC voltage reading greater than 3.5 volts?	Yes No	▶ ▶	GO to A19. REPLACE ICM. No PIP output. REMOVE all test equipment. RECONNECT all components. CLEAR Continuous Memory. RERUN Quick Test.
A19 CHECK FOR PIP SHORT TO GROUND IN HARNESS—ICM AND PCM DISCONNECTED—KEY OFF • Key off. • Disconnect PCM. • Disconnect ICM from ICM tee. Leave EI diagnostic harness connected to vehicle harness connector. • DVOM on 20K ohm scale. • Measure resistance between J43 (PIP I) and J7 (B-) at breakout box. • Is resistance greater than 10K ohms?	Yes No	▶ ▶	GO to A20. CHECK connectors, SERVICE or REPLACE harness. PIP is shorted low. REMOVE all test equipment. RECONNECT all components. CLEAR Continuous Memory. RERUN Quick Test.

FM1119200303060X

Fig. 22 Test A: No Start (Part 6 of 10). 2.0L Zetec Engine

TEST STEP		RESULT	▶	ACTION TO TAKE
A20	CHECK FOR PIP SHORT HIGH—ICM AND PCM DISCONNECTED—KOEO			
	• Key off. • DVOM on 40 volt DC scale. • Key on, engine off. • Measure voltage between (+)J43 (PIP I) and (-)J7 (B-) at breakout box. • **Is DC voltage less than 0.5 volts?**	Yes	▶	REPLACE PCM. PIP is shorted. REMOVE all test equipment. RECONNECT all components. CLEAR Continuous Memory. RERUN Quick Test.
		No	▶	CHECK connectors, SERVICE or REPLACE harness. PIP is shorted high. REMOVE all test equipment. RECONNECT all components. CLEAR Continuous Memory. RERUN Quick Test.
A21	CHECK CKP AMPLITUDE AT ICM—KOEC			
	• Key off. • DVOM on 40 volt AC scale. • Crank engine and measure voltage between J35 (CKP+ I) and J48 (CKP- I) at breakout box. • **Is settled AC voltage reading greater than 0.4 volts?**	Yes	▶	GO to Pinpoint Test Step **D1**.
		No	▶	GO to **A22**. Amplitude fault.
A22	CHECK ICM—AMPLITUDE FAULT—ICM DISCONNECTED—KOEC			
	• Key off. • Disconnect ICM from ICM tee, leave EI diagnostic harness connected to vehicle harness connector. • DVOM 40 volt AC scale. • Crank engine and measure voltage between J35 (CKP+ I) and J48 (CKP- I) at breakout box. • **Is settled AC voltage reading greater than 0.4 volts?**	Yes	▶	REPLACE ICM. CKP is shorted. REMOVE all test equipment. RECONNECT all components. CLEAR Continuous Memory. RERUN Quick Test.
		No	▶	GO to **A23**.
A23	CHECK CKP CIRCUIT RESISTANCE—KEY OFF			
	• Key off. • DVOM on 20K ohm scale. • Measure resistance between J48 (CKP-I) and J35 (CKP+ I) at the breakout box. • **Is resistance between 2300 and 2500 ohms?**	Yes	▶	GO to **A27**.
		No	▶	GO to **A24**. CKP resistance fault.

FM1119200303070X

Fig. 22   Test A: No Start (Part 7 of 10). 2.0L Zetec Engine

TEST STEP		RESULT	▶	ACTION TO TAKE
A24	DETERMINE IF RESISTANCE HIGH OR RESISTANCE LOW FAULT			
	• Key off. • **Was the resistance reading from A23 less than 2300 ohms?**	Yes	▶	GO to **A28**. Resistance low fault.
		No	▶	GO to **A25**. Resistance high fault.
A25	CHECK CKP + CONTINUITY—RESISTANCE HIGH FAULT—KEY OFF			
	• Key off. • Connect CKP sensor tee to CKP sensor and vehicle harness connector. • DVOM on 20K ohm scale. • Measure resistance between J31 (CKP+S) and J35 (CKP+ I) at the breakout box. • **Is resistance less than 2050 ohms?**	Yes	▶	GO to **A26**.
		No	▶	CHECK connectors, SERVICE or REPLACE harness. CKP + open. REMOVE all test equipment. RECONNECT all components. CLEAR Continuous Memory. RERUN Quick Test.
A26	CHECK CKP- CONTINUITY—RESISTANCE HIGH FAULT—KEY OFF			
	• Key off. • DVOM on 20K ohm scale. • Measure resistance between J32 (CKP-S) and J48 (CKP- I) at the breakout box. • **Is resistance less than 2050 ohms?**	Yes	▶	REPLACE CKP. High resistance. REMOVE all test equipment. RECONNECT all components. CLEAR Continuous Memory. RERUN Quick Test.
		No	▶	CHECK connectors, SERVICE or REPLACE harness. CKP- open. REMOVE all test equipment. RECONNECT all components. CLEAR Continuous Memory. RERUN Quick Test.

FM1119200303080X

Fig. 22   Test A: No Start (Part 8 of 10). 2.0L Zetec Engine

TEST STEP		RESULT	▶	ACTION TO TAKE
A27	CHECK CKP SENSOR AND TRIGGER WHEEL—KEY OFF			
	• Key off. • Check trigger wheel for damage. • **Is the sensor and trigger data wheel OK?**	Yes	▶	REPLACE CKP sensor. No output. REMOVE all test equipment. RECONNECT all components. CLEAR Continuous Memory. RERUN Quick Test.
		No	▶	SERVICE or REPLACE bad parts. REMOVE all test equipment. RECONNECT all components. CLEAR Continuous Memory. RERUN Quick Test.
A28	CHECK CKP+ CIRCUIT SHORTED TO CKP- CIRCUIT—RESISTANCE LOW FAULT—CKP SENSOR DISCONNECTED—KEY OFF			
	• Key off. • Disconnect CKP sensor from vehicle harness connector. • DVOM on 20K ohm scale. • Measure resistance between J35 (CKP+I) and J48 (CKP- I) at breakout box. • **Is resistance greater than 3K ohms?**	Yes	▶	REPLACE CKP sensor. Shorted sensor windings. REMOVE all test equipment. RECONNECT all components. CLEAR Continuous Memory. RERUN Quick Test.
		No	▶	CHECK connectors, SERVICE or REPLACE harness. CKP+ shorted to CKP- in harness. REMOVE all test equipment. RECONNECT all components. CLEAR Continuous Memory. RERUN Quick Test.
A29	CHECK FOR CKP+ BIAS HIGH OR LOW FAULT—CKP SENSOR DISCONNECTED			
	• **Was bias voltage reading in Step A8 less than 1.0 volts?**	Yes	▶	GO to **A30**. Bias low fault.
		No	▶	GO to **A31**. Bias high fault.

FM1119200303090X

Fig. 22   Test A: No Start (Part 9 of 10). 2.0L Zetec Engine

TEST STEP		RESULT	▶	ACTION TO TAKE
A30	CHECK CKP + FOR SHORT TO GROUND—CKP SENSOR AND ICM DISCONNECTED—KEY OFF			
	• Key off. • Disconnect the ICM from ICM tee, leave EI diagnostic harness connected to vehicle harness connector. • DVOM on 20K ohm scale. • Measure resistance between J35 (CKP+I) and J7 (B-) at breakout box. • **Is resistance greater than 10K ohms?**	Yes	▶	REPLACE ICM. CKP+ is shorted low. REMOVE all test equipment. RECONNECT all components. CLEAR Continuous Memory. RERUN Quick Test.
		No	▶	CHECK connectors, SERVICE or REPLACE harness. CKP+ is shorted low. REMOVE all test equipment. RECONNECT all components. CLEAR Continuous Memory. RERUN Quick Test.
A31	CHECK CKP+ FOR SHORT HIGH—BIAS HIGH FAULT—CKP SENSOR AND ICM DISCONNECTED—KOEO			
	• Key off. • Disconnect ICM from ICM tee, leave EI diagnostic harness connected to vehicle harness connector. • DVOM on 40 volt DC scale. • Key on, engine off. • Measure voltage between (+)J35 (CKP+ I) and (-)J7 (B-) at breakout box. • **Is DC voltage less than 0.5 volts?**	Yes	▶	REPLACE ICM. CKP+ is shorted high. REMOVE all test equipment. RECONNECT all components. CLEAR Continuous Memory. RERUN Quick Test.
		No	▶	CHECK connectors, SERVICE or REPLACE harness. CKP+ is shorted high. REMOVE all test equipment. RECONNECT all components. CLEAR Continuous Memory. RERUN Quick Test.
A32	CHECK CKP CIRCUIT RESISTANCE—KEY OFF			
	• Key off. • Disconnect ICM from ICM tee. Leave EI diagnostic harness connected to vehicle harness connector. • DVOM on 20K ohm scale. • Measure resistance between J48 (CKP- I) and J35 (CKP+ I) at breakout box. • **Is resistance between 2300 and 2500 ohms?**	Yes	▶	REPLACE ICM. REMOVE all test equipment. RECONNECT all components. CLEAR Continuous Memory. RERUN Quick Test.
		No	▶	GO to **A24**. Circuit resistance fault.

FM1119200303100X

Fig. 22   Test A: No Start (Part 10 of 10). 2.0L Zetec Engine

TEST STEP	RESULT	▶	ACTION TO TAKE
B1 CHECK FOR IDM AT ICM—KOER **WARNING: NEVER CONNECT THE PCM TO EEC BREAKOUT BOX WHEN PERFORMING DIAGNOSTICS.** • Key off. • Install EI (High Data Rate) diagnostic harness to breakout box, and to both the ICM and vehicle harness. **Do not connect CKP sensor tee or coil tee.** • Use EI (High Data Rate) 4 overlay. • Connect EI diagnostic harness negative and positive leads to battery. • Set EI diagnostic harness box type switch to "4/6 cylinder" position. • DVOM on 40 volt AC scale. • Start engine and measure voltage between (+)J30 (diagnostic harness IDM detector) and (-)J7 (B-) at breakout box. NOTE: If pulses are present, the IDM detector output will be between 5.0 and 7.0 volts AC. • Is AC voltage between 5.0 and 7.0 volts?	Yes No	▶ ▶	GO to **B2**. GO to **B3**. IDM fault.
B2 CHECK FOR IDM CONTINUITY TO PCM—IDM FAULT—ICM AND PCM DISCONNECTED—KEY OFF • Key off. • Disconnect PCM. • Disconnect ICM from ICM tee, leave EI diagnostic harness connected to vehicle harness connector. • DVOM on 200 ohm scale. • Install a second breakout box to the PCM vehicle harness connector. • Measure resistance between J41 (IDM I) at breakout box and Pin 4 at the second breakout box. • Is resistance less than 5.0 ohms?	Yes No	▶ ▶	REPLACE PCM. PCM does not respond to IDM input. REMOVE all test equipment. RECONNECT all components. CLEAR Continuous Memory. RERUN Quick Test. CHECK connectors, SERVICE or REPLACE harness. IDM is open. REMOVE all test equipment. RECONNECT all components. CLEAR Continuous Memory. RERUN Quick Test.

FM1119200304010X

Fig. 23   Test B: Code 212, IDM Failure (Part 1 of 3). 2.0L Zetec Engine

TEST STEP	RESULT	▶	ACTION TO TAKE
B3 CHECK IDM OUTPUT FROM ICM—IDM FAULT—IDM CIRCUIT DISCONNECTED—KOER • Key off. • DVOM on 40 volt AC scale. • Push and hold down diagnostic harness IDM button (opens IDM circuit to PCM). NOTE: If the vehicle has an electronic dash, you must pull the fuse that controls the tachometer, (see owners manual). Replace after finishing test step. • Start engine and measure voltage between J30 (EI diagnostic harness IDM detector) and J7 (B-) at breakout box. • Is AC voltage greater than 5.0 volts?	Yes No	▶ ▶	GO to **B4**. REPLACE ICM. No IDM output from module. REMOVE all test equipment. RECONNECT all components. CLEAR Continuous Memory. RERUN Quick Test.
B4 CHECK FOR IDM SHORT IN PCM—PCM DISCONNECTED—KOEC • Key off. • Disconnect PCM. • DVOM on 40 volt AC scale. • Crank engine and measure voltage between J30 (EI diagnostic harness IDM detector) and (-)J7 (B-) at breakout box. • Is AC voltage greater than 5.0 volts?	Yes No	▶ ▶	REPLACE PCM. PCM is loading IDM signal. REMOVE all test equipment. RECONNECT all components. CLEAR Continuous Memory. RERUN Quick Test. GO to **B5**.
B5 CHECK FOR IDM SHORT HIGH IN HARNESS—ICM AND PCM DISCONNECTED • Key off. • DVOM on 40 volt DC scale. • Key on, engine off. • Measure voltage between (+)J41 (IDM I) and (-)J7 (B-) at breakout box. • Is DC voltage less than 0.5 volts?	Yes No	▶ ▶	GO to **B6**. SERVICE short circuit or REPLACE harness. IDM is shorted high. REMOVE all test equipment. RECONNECT all components. CLEAR Continuous Memory. RERUN Quick Test.

FM1119200304020X

Fig. 23   Test B: Code 212, IDM Failure (Part 2 of 3). 2.0L Zetec Engine

TEST STEP	RESULT	▶	ACTION TO TAKE
B6 CHECK FOR IDM SHORT TO GROUND IN HARNESS—ICM AND PCM DISCONNECTED—KEY OFF • Key off. • Disconnect ICM from ICM tee, leave EI diagnostic harness connected to vehicle harness connector. • DVOM on 20K ohm scale. • Measure resistance between J41 (IDM I) and (-)J7 (B-) at breakout box. • Is resistance greater than 10 ohms?	Yes No	▶ ▶	CHECK connectors, SERVICE or REPLACE harness. IDM is shorted to another wire between ICM and PCM. REMOVE all test equipment. RECONNECT all components. CLEAR Continuous Memory. RERUN Quick Test. CHECK connectors, SERVICE or REPLACE harness. IDM is shorted to low. REMOVE all test equipment. RECONNECT all components. CLEAR Continuous Memory. RERUN Quick Test.

FM1119200304030X

Fig. 23   Test B: Code 212, IDM Failure (Part 3 of 3). 2.0L Zetec Engine

TEST STEP	RESULT	▶	ACTION TO TAKE
C1 CHECK BASE TIMING—KOER **WARNING: NEVER CONNECT PCM TO EEC BREAKOUT BOX WHEN PERFORMING EI DIAGNOSTICS.** • Key off. • Install EI (High Data Rate) diagnostic harness to breakout box and to both the ICM and vehicle harness. **Do not connect the CKP sensor tee or coil tee.** • Use EI (High Data Rate) 4 overlay. • Connect EI diagnostic harness negative and positive leads to battery. • Set EI diagnostic harness type switch to "4/6 cylinder" position. • Connect timing light (must be EI compatible). • Start engine and allow it to warm up. • Is timing 10 ± 2 degrees BTDC when the EI diagnostic harness SPOUT button is pushed and held down (opens SPOUT circuit)?	Yes No	▶ ▶	GO to **C2**. GO to **C8**. Base timing fault.
C2 CHECK FOR SPARK ANGLE ADVANCE—KOER • Is engine timing greater than 15 degrees BTDC when the EI diagnostic harness SPOUT button is released?	Yes No	▶ ▶	Ignition System is OK. GO to **C3**. Advance timing fault.
C3 CHECK SPOUT AT ICM—KOER • Key off. • DVOM on 40 volt AC scale. • Start engine and measure voltage between J21 (EI diagnostic harness SPOUT detector) and (-)J7 (B-) at breakout box. • Is AC voltage reading greater than 5.0 volts?	Yes No	▶ ▶	REPLACE ICM. SPOUT input to ICM is OK, but no spark advance is present. REMOVE all test equipment. RECONNECT all components. CLEAR Continuous Memory. RERUN Quick Test. GO to **C4**.

FM1119200305010X

Fig. 24   Test C: Code 213 Or Lack Of Power Or Lack Of Poor Fuel Economy (Part 1 of 3). 2.0L Zetec Engine

Fig. 24 Test C (Part 2 of 3)

TEST STEP	RESULT	▶	ACTION TO TAKE
C7 CHECK FOR SPOUT CONTINUITY TO ICM—ICM AND PCM DISCONNECTED—KEY OFF • Key off. • DVOM on 200 ohm scale. • Install a second breakout box to the vehicle harness connector. • Measure resistance between J45 (SPOUT I) at breakout box and Pin 36 at the second breakout box. • Is resistance less than 5.0 ohms?	Yes	▶	REPLACE PCM. SPOUT is not being transmitted by PCM. REMOVE all test equipment. RECONNECT all components. CLEAR Continuous Memory. RERUN Quick Test.
	No	▶	CHECK connectors, SERVICE or REPLACE harness. SPOUT is open. REMOVE all test equipment. RECONNECT all components. CLEAR Continuous Memory. RERUN Quick Test.
C8 INSPECT CKP SENSOR AND TRIGGER WHEEL—TIMING FAULT • Is CKP sensor or trigger wheel damaged, i.e., loose or misaligned? NORMAL WHEEL NOTE RELATIONSHIP BETWEEN NOTCH AND MISSING TOOTH — A14335-C	Yes	▶	REPLACE or SERVICE as required. REMOVE all test equipment. RECONNECT all components. CLEAR Continuous Memory. RERUN Quick Test.
	No	▶	REPLACE ICM. Incorrect spark output from ICM. REMOVE all test equipment. RECONNECT all components. CLEAR Continuous Memory. RERUN Quick Test.

FM1119200305030X

Fig. 24 Test C: Code 213 Or Lack Of Power Or Lack Of Poor Fuel Economy (Part 2 of 3). 2.0L Zetec Engine

Fig. 24 Test C (Part 3 of 3)

TEST STEP	RESULT	▶	ACTION TO TAKE
C4 CHECK FOR SPOUT SHORT IN ICM—OPEN SPOUT FAULT—SPOUT CIRCUIT—KOER • Key off. • DVOM on 40 volt AC scale. • Push and hold down EI diagnostic harness SPOUT button (open SPOUT circuit to ICM). • Start engine and measure voltage between J21 (EI diagnostic harness SPOUT detector) and J7 (B-) at breakout box. • Is AC voltage reading greater than 5.0 volts?	Yes	▶	REPLACE ICM. SPOUT is shorted. REMOVE all test equipment. RECONNECT all components. CLEAR Continuous Memory. RERUN Quick Test.
	No	▶	GO to C5. SPOUT fault.
C5 CHECK FOR SPOUT SHORT HIGH IN HARNESS—ICM AND PCM DISCONNECTED—KOEO • Key off. • Disconnect PCM. • Disconnect the ICM from ICM tee, leave EI diagnostic harness connected to vehicle harness connector. • DVOM on 40 volt DC scale. • Key on, engine off. • Measure voltage between J45 (SPOUT I) and J7 (B-) at the breakout box. • Is DC voltage reading less than 0.5 volts?	Yes	▶	GO to C6.
	No	▶	CHECK connectors, SERVICE or REPLACE harness. SPOUT shorted high. REMOVE all test equipment. RECONNECT all components. CLEAR Continuous Memory. RERUN Quick Test.
C6 CHECK FOR SPOUT SHORT TO GROUND IN HARNESS—ICM AND PCM DISCONNECTED—KEY OFF • Key off. • DVOM on 20K ohm scale. • Disconnect EI diagnostic harness positive lead to battery. • Measure resistance between J45 (SPOUT I) and J7 (B-) at breakout box. • Is the resistance greater than 10K ohms?	Yes	▶	GO to C7.
	No	▶	CHECK connectors, SERVICE or REPLACE harness. SPOUT is shorted low. SERVICE short circuit. REMOVE all test equipment. RECONNECT all components. CLEAR Continuous Memory. RERUN Quick Test.

FM1119200305020X

Fig. 24 Test C: Code 213 Or Lack Of Power Or Lack Of Poor Fuel Economy (Part 3 of 3). 2.0L Zetec Engine

Fig. 25 Test D (Part 1 of 6)

TEST STEP	RESULT	▶	ACTION TO TAKE
D1 CHECK FOR SPARK DURING CRANK—KOEC • Using a Neon Bulb Spark Tester (OTC D89P-666-A) or Air Gap Spark Tester (D81P-666-A), check for spark at all spark plug wires while cranking. • Was spark consistent on ALL spark plug wires (one spark per crankshaft revolution)?	Yes	▶	Ignition system is OK.
	No	▶	GO to D2. Spark fault.
D2 CHECK SPARK PLUGS AND WIRES—KEY OFF • Check spark plug wires for insulation damage, looseness, shorting or other damage. • Remove and check right spark plugs for damage, wear, carbon deposits and proper plug gap. • Are spark plugs and wires OK?	Yes	▶	REINSTALL plugs and wires. GO to D3.
	No	▶	SERVICE or REPLACE damaged component. REMOVE all test equipment. RECONNECT all components. CLEAR Continuous Memory. RERUN Quick Test.
D3 CHECK FOR COIL PWR AT COIL—KOEO WARNING: NEVER CONNECT PCM TO EEC BREAKOUT BOX WHEN PERFORMING EI DIAGNOSTICS. • Key off. • Install EI (High Data Rate) diagnostic harness to breakout box. • Connect negative lead to battery. • Set EI diagnostic harness box type switch to "4/6 cylinder" position. • Install right (blue) coil tee. NOTE: Remove blue insert and red rubber gasket from the coil harness connector before installing right (blue) coil tee. After completing diagnostics replace blue insert and red rubber gasket. • Use EI (High Data Rate) 4 overlay. • DVOM on 40 volt DC scale. • Key on, engine off. • Measure voltage between (+)J5 (COIL PWR) and (-)J7 (B-) at breakout box. • Is DC voltage greater than 10.0 volts?	Yes	▶	GO to D4.
	No	▶	CHECK connectors, SERVICE or REPLACE harness. COIL PWR is open. REMOVE all test equipment. RECONNECT all components. CLEAR Continuous Memory. RERUN Quick Test.
D4 CHECK FOR C1 HIGH AT COIL PACK—KOEO • Key on, engine off. • Measure voltage between (+)J3 (C1C) and (-)J7 (B-) at breakout box. • Is DC voltage reading greater than 10.0 volts?	Yes	▶	GO to D5.
	No	▶	GO to D12. C1 low fault.

FM1119200306010X

Fig. 25 Test D: No Start Code 215 Or 216, Coil 1 Or Coil 2 Failure (Part 1 of 6). 2.0L Zetec Engine

Fig. 25 Test D (Part 2 of 6)

TEST STEP	RESULT	▶	ACTION TO TAKE
D5 CHECK FOR C2 HIGH AT COIL PACK—KOEO NOTE: Remove blue insert and red rubber gasket from the coil harness connector before installing right (blue) coil tee. After completing diagnostics, replace the blue insert and red rubber gasket. • DVOM on 40 volt DC scale. • Key on, engine off. • Measure voltage between (+)J6 (C2C) and (-)J7 (B-) at breakout box. • Is DC voltage reading greater than 10.0 volts?	Yes	▶	GO to D6.
	No	▶	GO to D14. C2 low fault.
D6 CHECK FOR C1 HIGH AT ICM—KOEO • Key off. • Connect ICM tee to ICM and vehicle harness connector. • DVOM on 40 volt DC scale. • Key on, engine off. • Measure voltage between (+)J53 (C1I) and (-)J7 (B-) at breakout box. • Is DC voltage reading greater than 10.0 volts?	Yes	▶	GO to D7.
	No	▶	CHECK connectors, SERVICE or REPLACE harness. C1 is open. REMOVE all test equipment. RECONNECT all components. CLEAR Continuous Memory. RERUN Quick Test.
D7 CHECK FOR C2 HIGH AT ICM—KOEO • Key on, engine off. • Measure voltage between (+)J55 (C2I) and (-)J7 (B-) at breakout box. • Is DC voltage reading greater than 10.0 volts?	Yes	▶	GO to D8.
	No	▶	CHECK connectors, SERVICE or REPLACE harness. C2 is open. REMOVE all test equipment. RECONNECT all components. CLEAR Continuous Memory. RERUN Quick Test.
D8 CHECK FOR C1 LOW AT COIL CONNECTOR—COIL DISCONNECTED—KOEO • Key off. • Disconnect the coil from the coil tee, leave EI diagnostic harness coil tee connected to the vehicle harness coil connector. • DVOM on 40 volt DC scale. • Key on, engine off. • Measure voltage between (+)J3 (C1C) and (-)J7 (B-) at breakout box. • Is DC voltage reading less than 0.5 volts?	Yes	▶	GO to D9.
	No	▶	GO to D16. C1 high fault.

FM1119200306020X

Fig. 25 Test D: No Start Code 215 Or 216, Coil 1 Or Coil 2 Failure (Part 2 of 6). 2.0L Zetec Engine

TEST STEP	RESULT	▶	ACTION TO TAKE
D9 CHECK FOR C2 LOW AT COIL CONNECTOR—COIL DISCONNECTED—KOEO • Key on, engine off. • DVOM on 40 volt DC scale. • Measure voltage between (+)J6 (C2C) and (-)J7 (B-) at breakout box. • **Is DC voltage reading less than 0.5 volts?**	Yes No	▶ ▶	GO to D10. GO to D17. C2 high fault.
D10 CHECK C1 AT COIL CONNECTOR WHILE CRANKING ENGINE—COIL DISCONNECTED—KOEC • Connect an incandescent test lamp between J1 (B+) and J3 (C1C). • Connect positive lead of EI diagnostic harness to battery. • Crank engine. • **Does lamp blink consistently and brightly (one blink per engine revolution)?**	Yes No	▶ ▶	GO to D11. REPLACE ICM. C1 open. REMOVE all test equipment. RECONNECT all components. CLEAR Continuous Memory. RERUN Quick Test.
D11 CHECK C2 AT COIL CONNECTOR WHILE CRANKING ENGINE—COIL DISCONNECTED—KOEC • Connect an incandescent test lamp between J1 (B+) and J6 (C2C). • Crank engine. • **Does lamp blink consistently and brightly (one blink per engine revolution)?**	Yes No	▶ ▶	REPLACE coil pack. Input to coil pack is OK, but no high voltage output. REMOVE all test equipment. RECONNECT all components. CLEAR Continuous Memory. RERUN Quick Test. REPLACE ICM. C2 open in ICM. REMOVE all test equipment. RECONNECT all components. CLEAR Continuous Memory. RERUN Quick Test.
D12 CHECK FOR C1 SHORT LOW—COIL DISCONNECTED—KEY OFF • Key off. • DVOM on 20K ohm scale. • Disconnect coil from coil tee, leave EI diagnostic harness connected to vehicle harness coil connector. • Measure resistance between J7 (B-) and J3 (RC1C) at breakout box. • **Is resistance reading greater than 2K ohms?**	Yes No	▶ ▶	REPLACE right coil pack. C1 open in coil. REMOVE all test equipment. RECONNECT all components. CLEAR Continuous Memory. RERUN Quick Test. GO to D13.

FM1119200306030X

Fig. 25   Test D: No Start Code 215 Or 216, Coil 1 Or Coil 2 Failure (Part 3 of 6). 2.0L Zetec Engine

TEST STEP	RESULT	▶	ACTION TO TAKE
D13 CHECK FOR C1 SHORT LOW—ICM AND COIL DISCONNECTED—KEY OFF • Key off. • Disconnect ICM from ICM tee, leave EI diagnostic harness connected to vehicle harness connector. • DVOM on 20K ohm scale. • Measure resistance between J7 (B-) and J3 (C1C) at breakout box. • **Is resistance reading greater than 10 ohms?**	Yes No	▶ ▶	REPLACE ICM. C1 is shorted low in ICM. REMOVE all test equipment. RECONNECT all components. CLEAR Continuous Memory. RERUN Quick Test. **NOTE: A C1 short to ground may have damaged the coil.** CHECK connectors, SERVICE or REPLACE harness. C1 is shorted low. REMOVE all test equipment. RECONNECT all components. CLEAR Continuous Memory. RERUN Quick Test.
D14 CHECK FOR C2 SHORT LOW—COIL DISCONNECTED—KEY OFF • Key off. • DVOM on 20K ohm scale. • Disconnect coil from coil tee, leave EI diagnostic harness connected to vehicle harness coil connector. • Measure resistance between J7 (B-) and J6 (C2C) at breakout box. • **Is resistance reading greater than 2K ohms?**	Yes No	▶ ▶	REPLACE coil pack. C2 open in coil. REMOVE all test equipment. RECONNECT all components. CLEAR Continuous Memory. RERUN Quick Test. GO to D15.

FM1119200306040X

Fig. 25   Test D: No Start Code 215 Or 216, Coil 1 Or Coil 2 Failure (Part 4 of 6). 2.0L Zetec Engine

TEST STEP	RESULT	▶	ACTION TO TAKE
D15 CHECK FOR C2 LOW—ICM AND COIL DISCONNECTED—KEY OFF • Key off. • Disconnect ICM from vehicle harness. • DVOM on 20K ohm scale. • Measure resistance between J6 (C2C) and J7 (B-) at breakout box. • **Is resistance reading greater than 10K ohms?**	Yes No	▶ ▶	REPLACE ICM. C2 shorted low. REMOVE all test equipment. RECONNECT all components. CLEAR Continuous Memory. RERUN Quick Test. CHECK connector, SERVICE or REPLACE harness. C2 is shorted low. REMOVE all test equipment. RECONNECT all components. CLEAR Continuous Memory. RERUN Quick Test. **NOTE: A C2 short to ground may have damaged the coil.**
D16 CHECK FOR C1 HIGH—ICM AND COIL DISCONNECTED—KOEO • Key off. • Disconnect ICM from the ICM tee, leave EI diagnostic harness connected to vehicle harness connector. • DVOM on 40 volt DC scale. • Key on, engine off. • Measure voltage between (+)J3 (C1C) and (-)J7 (B-) at breakout box. • **Is DC voltage reading less than 0.5 volts?**	Yes No	▶ ▶	REPLACE ICM. C1 is shorted high. REMOVE all test equipment. RECONNECT all components. CLEAR Continuous Memory. RERUN Quick Test. CHECK connector, SERVICE or REPLACE harness. C1 shorted high. REMOVE all test equipment. RECONNECT all components. CLEAR Continuous Memory. RERUN Quick Test.

FM1119200306050X

Fig. 25   Test D: No Start Code 215 Or 216, Coil 1 Or Coil 2 Failure (Part 5 of 6). 2.0L Zetec Engine

TEST STEP	RESULT	▶	ACTION TO TAKE
D17 CHECK FOR C2 HIGH—ICM AND COIL DISCONNECTED—KOEO • Key off. • Disconnect ICM from vehicle harness. • DVOM on 40 volt DC scale. • Key on, engine off. • Measure voltage between (+)J6 (C2C) and (-)J7 (B-) at breakout box. • **Is DC voltage reading less than 0.5 volts?**	Yes No	▶ ▶	REPLACE ICM. C2 is shorted high. REMOVE all test equipment. RECONNECT all components. CLEAR Continuous Memory. RERUN Quick Test. CHECK connectors, SERVICE or REPLACE harness. C2 is shorted high. REMOVE all test equipment. RECONNECT all components. CLEAR Continuous Memory. RERUN Quick Test.

FM1119200306060X

Fig. 25   Test D: No Start Code 215 Or 216, Coil 1 Or Coil 2 Failure (Part 6 of 6). 2.0L Zetec Engine

You must perform Quick Test and follow instructions in the EEC Pinpoint Test Steps before starting this section.

CONDITION	ACTION TO TAKE
• No start without service codes	GO to A1.
• PASS service Code 111.	GO to A1.
• Code 226.	GO to A1.
• Code 211 (PIP at EEC processor fault).	GO to A1.
• Service Engine Light stays on during engine cranking.	GO to A1.
• Vehicle Runs (engine is running) with:	
• Code 213 (EEC/EDIS system did not respond to spark angle commands during Self-Test).	GO to C1.
• Code 212 or 226 (IDM at EEC processor fault).	GO to B1.
• Code 215 and/or 216 (Coil 1 or Coil 2 fault).	GO to D19.
• Code 217 and/or 238 (Coil 3 or Coil 4 fault).	GO to D3.
• Lack of power or poor fuel economy.	GO to C1.

Using a DVOM

When using a DVOM to check the PIP signal, the engine must be turned very slowly ("Bumped") with the starter. This is a digital signal and should switch from ground (0 VDC to .5 VDC) to BAT+ (8 VDC to 14 VDC) or BAT+ to ground. When using the DVOM correct test lead polarity must be used. The red lead is positive (+) and black lead is negative (-).

Fig. 26 Diagnostic Pinpoint Test Index (Part 1 of 2). 1993 4.6L Engine

The Following Voltage Readings are Typical for a Normal Vehicle:

Measure Between Pins		Key On Engine Off (Volts)	Engine Cranking (Volts AC)	Engine Running (Volts AC)
First Pin	Second Pin			
VRS+S (J31)	VRS-S(J32)	0	0.5-1.5	2-5
VRS+E (J48)	VRS-E(J47)	0	0.5-1.5	2-5
PIPE (J43)	PWR GND (J53)	0	—	5-7
C1E (J51)	PWR GND (J53)	VBAT VDC	1-1.5	1.2-1.6
C2E (J27)	PWR GND (J53)	VBAT VDC	1-1.5	1.2-1.6
C3E (J54)	PWR GND (J53)	VBAT VDC	1-1.5	1.2-1.6
C4E (J55)	PWR GND (J53)	VBAT VDC	1-1.5	1.2-1.6
C1C (J3)	PWR GND (J53)	0	0.1-0.8	0.2-0.4
C2C (J6)	PWR GND (J53)	0	0.1-0.8	0.2-0.4
C3C (J10)	PWR GND (J53)	0	0.1-0.8	0.2-0.4
C4C (J18)	PWR GND (J53)	0	0.1-0.8	0.2-0.4
SAW (J45)	PWR GND (J53)	0	0.01-0.3	0.5-3
IDME (J41)	PWR GND (J53)	0	0.1-0.5	0.2-2.0
VRS+E (J48)	PWR GND (J53)	0	0.1-0.9	1.5-1.9
VRS-E (J47)	PWR GND (J53)	0	0.1-0.9	1.5-1.9

NOTE:

- Do not connect the positive lead of the EDIS diagnostic cable or VRS tee until directed to do so.
- The SAW and IDM detectors in the EDIS diagnostic will not work unless the positive and negative leads of the cable are connected.
- The vehicle battery voltage must be at least 12 volts DC.
- Be careful not to bring a fluorescent trouble lamp close to the vehicle wiring. If the key is on and the VRS is disconnected, the EDIS module may fire the coil.
- When using a DVOM to measure DC voltage readings, connect the positive lead to the jack identified with A (+) sign and the negative lead to the jack with A (-) sign.

Fig. 26 Diagnostic Pinpoint Test Index (Part 2 of 2). 1993 4.6L Engine

TEST STEP		RESULT	▶	ACTION TO TAKE
A1	PERFORM EEC-IV QUICK TEST			
	• Was Quick Test performed	Yes	▶	GO to A2.
		No	▶	PERFORM Quick Test.
	NOTE: These diagnostic procedures are designed to correct one ignition failure at a time. When a component is replaced or a service is completed, remove all test equipment, reconnect all components and rerun Quick Test.			
A2	CHECK FOR SPARK DURING CRANK			
	• Using a Neon Bulb Spark Tester (Special Service Tool D89P-6666-A) or Air Gap Spark Tester (Special Service Tool D81P-6666-A), check for spark at all spark plug wires while cranking.	Yes	▶	GO to A13.
		No	▶	GO to A3.
	• Was spark consistent on ALL spark plug wires (one spark per crankshaft revolution)?			
A3	CHECK PLUGS AND WIRES			
	• Check spark plug wires for insulation damage, looseness, shorting or other damage.	Yes	▶	REINSTALL plugs and wires. GO to A4.
	• Remove and check spark plugs for damage, wear, carbon deposits and proper plug gap.	No	▶	SERVICE or REPLACE damaged component. REMOVE all test equipment. RECONNECT all components. CLEAR Continuous Memory. RERUN Quick Test.
	• Are spark plugs and wires OK?			
A4	CHECK VEHICLE PERFORMANCE WITH EDIS DIAGNOSTIC CABLE INSTALLED			
	WARNING: NEVER CONNECT THE EEC-IV PROCESSOR TO THE EEC-IV BREAKOUT BOX WHEN PERFORMING EDIS DIAGNOSTICS.	Yes	▶	GO to A32.
		No	▶	GO to A5.
	• Key off.			
	• Install EDIS diagnostic cable to breakout box and EDIS module.			
	Do not connect VRS tee or coil tee.			
	• Use EDIS 8 overlay.			
	• Connect EDIS diagnostic cable negative lead to battery, leave positive lead disconnected.			
	• Set EDIS diagnostic cable box switch to "8 cylinder" position.			
	• Will vehicle start and run?			

Fig. 27 Test A: No Start (Part 1 of 10). 1993 4.6L Engine

TEST STEP	RESULT	▶	ACTION TO TAKE
A5 CHECK PWR GND TO ICM—KEY OFF			
• Key off. • Install EI diagnostic harness breakout box and ICM. • Do not connect CKP sensor or coil tees at this time. • Use EI (High Data Rate) 8 overlay. • Connect only the EI diagnostic harness negative lead. Do not connect positive lead. • Set diagnostic harness switch to the 8 position. • DVOM on 200 ohm scale. • Measure resistance between J53 (PWR GND) and J7 (B-) at breakout box. • **Is the resistance less than 5.0 ohms?**	Yes No	▶ ▶	GO to **A6**. CHECK connectors, SERVICE or REPLACE harness. Power ground is open. REMOVE all test equipment. RECONNECT all components. CLEAR Continuous Memory. RERUN Quick Test.
A6 CHECK FOR VPWR TO ICM—KOEO			
• Key off. • DVOM on 20 volt DC scale. • Key on, engine off. • Measure voltage between (+)J35 (VPWR I) and (-)J7 (B-) at breakout box. • **Is DC voltage greater than 10.5 volts?**	Yes No	▶ ▶	GO to **A7**. CHECK connectors, SERVICE or REPLACE harness. VPWR to ICM is open. REMOVE all test equipment. RECONNECT all components. CLEAR Continuous Memory. RERUN Quick Test.
A7 CHECK CKP+ BIAS AT ICM—KOEO			
• Key off. • DVOM on 20 volt DC scale. • Key on, engine off. • Measure voltage between (+)J48 (CKP+ I) and (-)J7 (B-) at breakout box. • **Is DC voltage between 1.0 and 2.0 volts?**	Yes No	▶ ▶	GO to **A21**. GO to **A8**. Bias fault.
A8 CHECK CKP+ BIAS SENSOR DISCONNECTED—BIAS FAULT—KOEO			
• Key off. • Disconnect CKP sensor from vehicle harness connector. • DVOM on 20 volt DC scale. • Key on, engine off. • Measure voltage between (+)J48 (CKP+ I) and (-)J7 (B-) at breakout box. • **Is DC voltage greater than 1.0 volt but less than 2.0 volts?**	Yes No	▶ ▶	GO to **A9**. GO to **A29**. Bias fault.

FM11930030902BX

Fig. 27 Test A: No Start (Part 2 of 10). 1993 4.6L Engine

TEST STEP	RESULT	▶	ACTION TO TAKE
A9 CHECK VRS — BIAS—VRS DISCONNECTED			
• Key off. • DVOM on 20 volt DC scale. • Key on, engine off. • Measure voltage between (+)J47 (VRS-E) and (-)J7 (BAT-) at breakout box. • **Is DC voltage between 1.0 and 2.0 volts?**	Yes No	▶ ▶	REPLACE VR sensor. Short to ground in VR sensor. REMOVE all test equipment. RECONNECT all components. CLEAR Continuous Memory. RERUN Quick Test. GO to **A10**.
A10 CHECK VRS — HIGH or LOW BIAS—BIAS FAULT			
• Was bias voltage reading in Step **A9** less than 1.0 volt?	Yes No	▶ ▶	GO to **A11**. GO to **A12**.
A11 CHECK VRS — FOR SHORT TO GROUND—BIAS LOW FAULT — VR SENSOR AND EDIS MODULE DISCONNECTED			
• Key off. • Disconnect EDIS module from EDIS module tee, leave EDIS diagnostic cable connected to vehicle harness connector. • DVOM on 20K ohm scale. • Measure resistance between J47 (VRS-E) and J7 (BAT-) at breakout box. • **Is the resistance greater than 10K ohms?**	Yes No	▶ ▶	REPLACE EDIS module. VRS is shorted low. REMOVE all test equipment. RECONNECT all components. CLEAR Continuous Memory. RERUN Quick Test. CHECK connectors, SERVICE or REPLACE harness. VRS is shorted low. REMOVE all test equipment. RECONNECT all components. CLEAR Continuous Memory. RERUN Quick Test.

Fig. 27 Test A: No Start (Part 3 of 10). 1993 4.6L Engine

TEST STEP	RESULT	▶	ACTION TO TAKE
A12 CHECK VRS FOR SHORT HIGH—BIAS HIGH FAULT—VRS AND EDIS MODULE DISCONNECTED			
• Key off. • Disconnect EDIS module from EDIS module tee; leave EDIS diagnostic cable connected to vehicle harness connector. • DVOM 20 volt DC scale. • Key on, engine off. • Measure voltage between (+)J47 (VRS- E) and (-)J7 (BAT-) at the breakout box. • **Is DC voltage less than 0.5 volts?**	Yes No	▶ ▶	REPLACE EDIS module. VRS- shorted high. REMOVE all test equipment. RECONNECT all components. CLEAR Continuous Memory. RERUN Quick Test. CHECK connectors, SERVICE or REPLACE harness. VRS- is shorted high. REMOVE all test equipment. RECONNECT all components. CLEAR Continuous Memory. RERUN Quick Test.
A13 CHECK PIP AT EDIS MODULE			
WARNING: NEVER CONNECT THE EEC-IV PROCESSOR TO THE EEC-IV BREAKOUT BOX WHEN PERFORMING EDIS DIAGNOSTICS. • Key off. • Install EDIS diagnostic cable to the breakout box and EDIS module. Do not connect VR sensor tee or coil tee. • Use EDIS 8 overlay. • Connect EDIS diagnostic cable negative lead to battery, leave positive lead disconnected. • Set EDIS diagnostic cable box switch to ''8 cylinder'' position. • DVOM on 20 volt AC scale. • Crank engine and measure voltage between J43 (PIP E) and J7 (BAT-) at the breakout box. • **Is the settled AC voltage reading greater than 3.5 volts?**	Yes No	▶ ▶	GO to **A14**. GO to **A18**.

Fig. 27 Test A: No Start (Part 4 of 10). 1993 4.6L Engine

TEST STEP	RESULT	▶	ACTION TO TAKE
A14 CHECK FOR PIP OPEN TO PROCESSOR—PROCESSOR DISCONNECTED			
• Key off. • DVOM on 200 ohm scale. • Install a second breakout box to processor vehicle harness connector. • Measure resistance between J43 (PIP E) at the breakout box and Pin 56 (PIP) at the second breakout box. • **Is resistance less than 5.0 ohms?**	Yes No	▶ ▶	GO to **A15**. CHECK connectors, SERVICE or REPLACE harness. PIP is open. REMOVE all test equipment. RECONNECT all components. CLEAR Continuous Memory. RERUN Quick Test.
A15 CHECK IGN GND AT EDIS MODULE—PROCESSOR DISCONNECTED			
• Key off. • DVOM on 2K ohm scale. • Measure resistance between J50 (IGN GND E) and J7 (BAT-) at breakout box. • **Is resistance less than 1025 ohms?**	Yes No	▶ ▶	GO to **A16**. GO to **A17**.
A16 CHECK FOR IGN GND OPEN TO PROCESSOR—PROCESSOR DISCONNECTED			
• Key off. • DVOM on 2K ohm scale. • Measure resistance between J50 (IGN GND E) at the breakout box and Pin 16 (IGN GND) at the second breakout box. • **Is resistance less than 1025 ohms?**	Yes No	▶ ▶	Ignition system is OK. REMOVE all test equipment. RECONNECT all components. CLEAR Continuous Memory. RERUN Quick Test. CHECK connectors, SERVICE or REPLACE harness. IGN GND is open. REMOVE all test equipment. RECONNECT all components. CLEAR Continuous Memory. RERUN Quick Test.

Fig. 27 Test A: No Start (Part 5 of 10). 1993 4.6L Engine

	TEST STEP	RESULT	▶	ACTION TO TAKE
A17	CHECK PWR GND TO EDIS MODULE—PWR GND FAULT			
	• Key off.	Yes	▶	REPLACE EDIS module. REMOVE all test equipment. RECONNECT all components. CLEAR Continuous Memory. RERUN Quick Test.
	• DVOM on 200 ohm scale.			
	• Measure resistance between J53 (PWR GND) and J7 (BAT-) at breakout box.			
	• **Is resistance less than 5.0 ohms?**	No	▶	CHECK connectors, SERVICE or REPLACE harness. Power ground to EDIS module is open. REMOVE all test equipment. RECONNECT all components. CLEAR Continuous Memory. RERUN Quick Test.
A18	CHECK PIP AT EDIS MODULE—PIP FAULT—PIP CIRCUIT DISCONNECTED			
	• Key off.	Yes	▶	GO to A19.
	• DVOM 20 volt AC scale.	No	▶	REPLACE EDIS module. No PIP output from EDIS. REMOVE all test equipment. RECONNECT all components. CLEAR Continuous Memory. RERUN Quick Test.
	• Push and hold EDIS diagnostic cable PIP push button down (opens PIP circuit to processor).			
	• Crank engine and measure voltage between J43 (PIP E) and J7 (BAT-) at breakout box.			
	• **Is settled AC voltage reading greater than 3.5 volts?**			
A19	CHECK FOR PIP SHORT TO GROUND IN HARNESS—EDIS MODULE AND PROCESSOR DISCONNECTED			
	• Key off.	Yes	▶	GO to A20.
	• Disconnect EEC processor.	No	▶	CHECK connectors, SERVICE or REPLACE harness. PIP is shorted low. REMOVE all test equipment. RECONNECT all components. CLEAR Continuous Memory. RERUN Quick Test.
	• Disconnect EDIS module from EDIS module tee. Leave EDIS diagnostic cable connected to EDIS vehicle harness connector.			
	• Disconnect EDIS diagnostic cable positive lead to battery.			
	• DVOM on 20K ohm scale.			
	• Measure resistance between J43 (PIP E) and J7 (BAT-) at breakout box.			
	• **Is resistance greater than 10K ohms?**			

Fig. 27   Test A: No Start (Part 6 of 10). 1993 4.6L Engine

	TEST STEP	RESULT	▶	ACTION TO TAKE
A20	CHECK FOR PIP SHORT HIGH—EDIS MODULE AND PROCESSOR DISCONNECTED			
	• Key off.	Yes	▶	REPLACE processor. PIP is shorted in processor. REMOVE all test equipment. RECONNECT all components. CLEAR Continuous Memory. RERUN Quick Test.
	• DVOM on 20 volt DC scale.			
	• Key on, engine off.			
	• Measure voltage between J43 (PIP E) and J7 (BAT-) at breakout box.			
	• **Is DC voltage less than 0.5 volts?**	No	▶	CHECK connectors, SERVICE or REPLACE harness. PIP is shorted high. REMOVE all test equipment. RECONNECT all components. CLEAR Continuous Memory. RERUN Quick Test.
A21	CHECK VRS AMPLITUDE AT EDIS MODULE			
	• Key off.	Yes	▶	GO to Pinpoint Test Step D1.
	• DVOM on 20 volt AC scale.	No	▶	GO to A22.
	• Crank engine and measure voltage between J48 (VRS+ E) and J47 (VRS- E) at breakout box.			
	• **Is settled AC voltage reading greater than 0.4 volts?**			
A22	CHECK VRS AMPLITUDE AT EDIS MODULE—AMPLITUDE FAULT—EDIS MODULE DISCONNECTED			
	• Key off.	Yes	▶	REPLACE EDIS module. VRS is shorted in EDIS module. REMOVE all test equipment. RECONNECT all components. CLEAR Continuous Memory.
	• Disconnect EDIS module from EDIS module tee, leave EDIS diagnostic cable connected to vehicle harness connector.			
	• DVOM 20 volt AC scale.			
	• Crank engine and measure voltage between J48 (VRS+ E) and J47 (VRS- E) at breakout box.			
	• **Is settled AC voltage reading greater than 0.4 volts?**	No	▶	GO to A23.

Fig. 27   Test A: No Start (Part 7 of 10). 1993 4.6L Engine

TEST STEP	RESULT	▶	ACTION TO TAKE
A23 CHECK VRS RESISTANCE			
• Key off.	Yes	▶	GO to **A27**.
• DVOM on 20K ohm scale.	No	▶	GO to **A24**.
• Measure resistance between J47 (VRS-E) and J48 (VRS+ E) at the breakout box.			
• **Is resistance between 2300 and 2500 ohms?**			
A24 CHECK VRS HIGH OR LOW RESISTANCE—RESISTANCE FAULT			
• Key off.	Yes	▶	GO to **A28**.
• DVOM on 20K ohm scale.	No	▶	GO to **A25**.
• Measure resistance between J47 (VRS-E) and J48 (VRS+ E) at breakout box.			
• **Is resistance less than 2550 ohms?**			
A25 CHECK VRS + OPEN—RESISTANCE HIGH FAULT			
• Key off.	Yes	▶	GO to **A26**.
• Connect VR sensor tee to VR sensor and vehicle harness connector.	No	▶	CHECK connectors, SERVICE or REPLACE harness. VRS+ open. REMOVE all test equipment. RECONNECT all components. CLEAR Continuous Memory. RERUN Quick Test.
• DVOM on 20K ohm scale.			
• Measure resistance between J31 (VRS+S) and J48 (VRS+ E) at the breakout box.			
• **Is resistance less than 2025 ohms?**			
A26 CHECK VRS — OPEN FAULT			
• Key off.	Yes	▶	REPLACE VR sensor. High resistance. REMOVE all test equipment. RECONNECT all components. CLEAR Continuous Memory. RERUN Quick Test.
• DVOM on 20K ohm scale.			
• Measure resistance between J32 (VRS-S) and J47 (VRS- E) at the breakout box.			
• **Is resistance less than 2025 ohms?**	No	▶	CHECK connectors, SERVICE or REPLACE harness. VRS— open. REMOVE all test equipment. RECONNECT all components. CLEAR Continuous Memory. RERUN Quick Test.

Fig. 27   Test A: No Start (Part 8 of 10). 1993 4.6L Engine

TEST STEP	RESULT	▶	ACTION TO TAKE
A27 CHECK VRS AIR GAP AND TRIGGER WHEEL			
• Key off.	Yes	▶	REPLACE VR sensor. No output from sensor. REMOVE all test equipment. RECONNECT all components. CLEAR Continuous Memory. RERUN Quick Test.
• Check trigger wheel for damage.			
• Check VRS air gap.			
• **Are air gap and trigger data wheel OK?**	No	▶	SERVICE or REPLACE bad parts. REMOVE all test equipment. RECONNECT all components. CLEAR Continuous Memory. RERUN Quick Test.
A28 CHECK VRS + SHORTED TO VRS—RESISTANCE LOW FAULT—VRS DISCONNECTED			
• Key off.	Yes	▶	REPLACE VR sensor. Shorted sensor windings. REMOVE all test equipment. RECONNECT all components. CLEAR Continuous Memory. RERUN Quick Test.
• Disconnect VR sensor from the vehicle harness connector.			
• DVOM on 20K ohm scale.			
• Measure resistance between J48 (VRS+E) and J47 (VRS- E) at the breakout box.	No	▶	CHECK connectors, SERVICE or REPLACE harness. VRS+ shorted to VRS- in harness. REMOVE all test equipment. RECONNECT all components. CLEAR Continuous Memory. RERUN Quick Test.
• **Is resistance greater than 3K ohms?**			
A29 CHECK VRS + HIGH or LOW—VR SENSOR DISCONNECTED			
• **Was bias voltage reading in Step A8 less than 1.0 volts?**	Yes	▶	GO to **A30**.
	No	▶	GO to **A31**.

Fig. 27   Test A: No Start (Part 9 of 10). 1993 4.6L Engine

TEST STEP	RESULT	▶	ACTION TO TAKE
A30 CHECK VRS + FOR SHORT TO GROUND—VRS AND EDIS MODULE DISCONNECTED • Key off. • Disconnect the EDIS module from EDIS module tee, leave EDIS diagnostic cable connected to vehicle harness connector. • DVOM on 20K ohm scale. • Measure resistance between J48 (VRS+E) and J7 (BAT-) at breakout box. • **Is resistance greater than 10K ohms?**	Yes No	▶ ▶	REPLACE EDIS module. REMOVE all test equipment. RECONNECT all components. CLEAR Continuous Memory. RERUN Quick Test. CHECK connectors, SERVICE or REPLACE harness. VRS+ is shorted low. REMOVE all test equipment. RECONNECT all components. CLEAR Continuous Memory. RERUN Quick Test.
A31 CHECK VRS + FOR SHORT HIGH—BIAS HIGH FAULT—VRS AND EDIS MODULE DISCONNECTED • Key off. • Disconnect EDIS module from EDIS module tee, leave EDIS diagnostic cable connected to vehicle harness connector. • DVOM on 20 volt DC scale. • Key on, engine off. • Measure voltage between +J48 (VRS+ E) and -J7 (BAT-) at breakout box. • **Is DC voltage less than 0.5 volts?**	Yes No	▶ ▶	REPLACE EDIS module. REMOVE all test equipment. RECONNECT all components. CLEAR Continuous Memory. RERUN Quick Test. CHECK connectors, SERVICE or REPLACE harness. VRS+ is shorted high. REMOVE all test equipment. RECONNECT all components. CLEAR Continuous Memory. RERUN Quick Test.
A32 CHECK VRS RESISTANCE • Key off. • Disconnect EDIS module from EDIS module tee. Leave EDIS diagnostic cable connected to vehicle harness connector. • DVOM on 20K ohm scale. • Measure resistance between J47 (VRS- E) and J48 (VRS+ E) at breakout box. • **Is resistance between 2300 and 2500 ohms?**	Yes No	▶ ▶	REPLACE EDIS module. REMOVE all test equipment. RECONNECT all components. CLEAR Continuous Memory. RERUN Quick Test. GO to A24.

Fig. 27   Test A: No Start (Part 10 of 10). 1993 4.6L Engine

TEST STEP	RESULT	▶	ACTION TO TAKE
B1 CHECK FOR IDM AT EDIS MODULE **WARNING: NEVER CONNECT THE EEC-IV PROCESSOR TO EEC-IV BREAKOUT BOX WHEN PERFORMING EDIS DIAGNOSTICS.** • Key off. • Install EDIS diagnostic cable to breakout box, and EDIS module. **Do not connect VR sensor tee or coil tees.** • Use EDIS 8 overlay. • Connect EDIS diagnostic cable negative and positive leads to battery. • Set EDIS diagnostic cable box switch to "8 cylinder" position. • DVOM on 20 volt AC scale. • Start engine and measure voltage between (+)J30 (EDIS diagnostic cable IDM detector) and (-)J7 (BAT-) at breakout box. NOTE: If pulses are present, the IDM detector output will be between 5.0 and 7.0 volts AC. • **Is AC voltage between 5.0 and 7.0 volts?**	Yes No	▶ ▶	GO to B2. GO to B3.
B2 CHECK FOR IDM OPEN TO PROCESSOR—IDM FAULT—EDIS MODULE AND PROCESSOR DISCONNECTED • Key off. • Disconnect processor. • Disconnect EDIS module from EDIS module tee, leave EDIS diagnostic cable connected to vehicle harness connector. • DVOM on 200 ohm scale. • Install a second breakout box to processor vehicle harness connector. • Measure resistance between J41 (IDM E) at breakout box and Pin 4 at second breakout box. • **Is resistance less than 5.0 ohms?**	Yes No	▶ ▶	REPLACE processor. Processor does not respond to IDM input. REMOVE all test equipment. RECONNECT all components. CLEAR Continuous Memory. RERUN Quick Test. CHECK connectors, SERVICE or REPLACE harness. IDM is open. REMOVE all test equipment. RECONNECT all components. CLEAR Continuous Memory. RERUN Quick Test.

Fig. 28   Test B: Code 212, IDM Failure (Part 1 of 3). 1993 4.6L Engine

TEST STEP	RESULT	▶	ACTION TO TAKE
B3 CHECK IDM OUTPUT FROM ICM—IDM FAULT—IDM CIRCUIT OPEN—KOER • Key off. • DVOM on 20 volt AC scale. • Push and hold EI diagnostic harness IDM button down (opens IDM circuit to PCM). • Start engine and measure voltage between J30 (EI diagnostic harness IDM detector) and J7 (B-) at breakout box. • **Is AC voltage greater than 5.0 volts?**	Yes No	▶ ▶	GO to B4. REPLACE ICM. No IDM output from module. REMOVE all test equipment. RECONNECT all components. CLEAR Continuous Memory. RERUN Quick Test.
B4 CHECK FOR IDM SHORT IN PCM—PCM DISCONNECTED—KOEC • Key off. • Disconnect PCM. • DVOM on 20 volt AC scale. • Crank engine and measure voltage between J30 (EI diagnostic harness IDM detector) and (-)J7 (B-) at breakout box. • **Is AC voltage less than 5.0 volts?**	Yes No	▶ ▶	GO to B5. REPLACE PCM. PCM is loading IDM signal. REMOVE all test equipment. RECONNECT all components. CLEAR Continuous Memory. RERUN Quick Test.
B5 CHECK FOR IDM SHORT HIGH IN HARNESS—ICM AND PCM DISCONNECTED—KOEO • Key off. • DVOM on 20 volt DC scale. • Key on, engine off. • Measure voltage between (+)J41 (IDM I) and (-)J7 (B-) at breakout box. • **Is DC voltage less than 0.5 volts?**	Yes No	▶ ▶	GO to B6. CHECK connectors, SERVICE or REPLACE harness. IDM is shorted high. REMOVE all test equipment. RECONNECT all components. CLEAR Continuous Memory. RERUN Quick Test.

Fig. 28   Test B: Code 212, IDM Failure (Part 2 of 3). 1993 4.6L Engine

	TEST STEP	RESULT	▶	ACTION TO TAKE
B6	CHECK FOR IDM SHORT TO GROUND IN HARNESS—ICM AND PCM DISCONNECTED—KEY OFF • Key off. • Disconnect ICM from ICM tee, leave EI diagnostic harness connected to vehicle harness connector. • DVOM on 20K ohm scale. • Measure resistance between J41 (IDM I) and (-) J7 (B-) at breakout box. • Is resistance greater than 10K ohms?	Yes	▶	CHECK connectors, SERVICE or REPLACE harness. IDM is shorted to another wire between the ICM and PCM. REMOVE all test equipment. RECONNECT all components. CLEAR Continuous Memory. RERUN Quick Test.
		No	▶	CHECK connectors, SERVICE or REPLACE harness. IDM is shorted low. REMOVE all test equipment. RECONNECT all components. CLEAR Continuous Memory. RERUN Quick Test.

Fig. 28   Test B: Code 212, IDM Failure (Part 3 of 3). 1993 4.6L Engine

	TEST STEP	RESULT	▶	ACTION TO TAKE
C1	CHECK BASE TIMING WARNING: NEVER CONNECT EEC-IV PROCESSOR TO EEC-IV BREAKOUT BOX WHEN PERFORMING EDIS DIAGNOSTICS. • Key off. • Install EDIS diagnostic cable to breakout box and EDIS module. Do not connect the VR sensor tee or coil tees. • Use EDIS 8 overlay. • Connect EDIS diagnostic cable negative and positive leads to battery. • Set EDIS diagnostic cable switch to "8 cylinder" position. • Connect timing light (must be EDIS/DIS compatible). • Start engine and allow it to warm up. • Is timing 10 ± 2 degrees BTDC when the EDIS diagnostic cable SAW detector button is pushed?	Yes	▶	GO to C2.
		No	▶	GO to C8.
C2	CHECK FOR SPARK ANGLE ADVANCE • Is engine timing greater than 15 degrees BTDC when the EDIS diagnostic cable SAW detector button is released?	Yes	▶	EDIS Ignition System is OK.
		No	▶	GO to C3.
C3	CHECK SAW AT EDIS MODULE • Key off. • DVOM on 20 volt AC scale. • Start engine and measure voltage between J21 (EDIS diagnostic cable SAW detector) and (-)J7 (BAT-) at breakout box. • Is AC voltage reading greater than 5.0 volts?	Yes	▶	REPLACE EDIS module. SAW input to EDIS module is OK, but no spark advance is present. REMOVE all test equipment. RECONNECT all components. CLEAR Continuous Memory. RERUN Quick Test.
		No	▶	GO to C4.

Fig. 29   Test C: Code 213 Or Lack Of Power Or Poor Fuel Economy (Part 1 of 3). 1993 4.6L Engine

	TEST STEP	RESULT	▶	ACTION TO TAKE
C4	CHECK FOR SAW SHORT IN EDIS MODULE—SAW FAULT—SAW CIRCUIT DISCONNECTED • Key off. • DVOM on 20 volt AC scale. • Push and hold EDIS diagnostic cable SAW button down (open SAW circuit to EDIS module). • Start engine and measure voltage between (+)J21 (EDIS diagnostic cable SAW detector) and (-)J7 (BAT-) at breakout box. • Is AC voltage reading greater than 5.0 volts?	Yes	▶	REPLACE EDIS module. SAW is shorted in EDIS module. REMOVE all test equipment. RECONNECT all components. CLEAR Continuous Memory. RERUN Quick Test.
		No	▶	GO to C5.
C5	CHECK FOR SAW SHORT TO GROUND IN HARNESS—EDIS MODULE AND PROCESSOR DISCONNECTED • Key off. • Disconnect processor. • Disconnect the EDIS module from EDIS module tee, leave EDIS diagnostic cable connected to vehicle harness connector. • DVOM on 20K ohm scale. • Disconnect EDIS diagnostic cable positive lead to battery. • Measure resistance between J45 (SAW E) and J7 (BAT-) at breakout box. • Is the resistance greater than 10K ohms?	Yes	▶	GO to C6.
		No	▶	CHECK connectors, SERVICE or REPLACE harness. SAW is shorted low. REMOVE all test equipment. RECONNECT all components. CLEAR Continuous Memory. RERUN Quick Test.
C6	CHECK FOR SAW SHORT HIGH IN HARNESS—EDIS MODULE AND PROCESSOR DISCONNECTED • Key off. • DVOM on 20 volt DC scale. • Key on, engine off. • Measure voltage between J45 (SAW E) and J7 (BAT-) at the breakout box. • Is DC voltage reading less than 0.5 volts?	Yes	▶	GO to C7.
		No	▶	CHECK connectors, SERVICE or REPLACE harness. SAW is shorted high. REMOVE all test equipment. RECONNECT all components. CLEAR Continuous Memory. RERUN Quick Test.

Fig. 29   Test C: Code 213 Or Lack Of Power Or Poor Fuel Economy (Part 2 of 3). 1993 4.6L Engine

TEST STEP		RESULT	▶	ACTION TO TAKE
C7	CHECK FOR SAW OPEN TO EDIS MODULE—EDIS MODULE AND PROCESSOR DISCONNECTED. ● Key off. ● DVOM on 200 ohm scale. ● Install a second breakout box to the vehicle harness connector. ● Measure resistance between J45 (SAW E) at breakout box and Pin 36 at the second breakout box. ● **Is resistance less than 5.0 ohms?**	Yes	▶	REPLACE processor. SAW is not being transmitted by the processor. REMOVE all test equipment. RECONNECT all components. CLEAR Continuous Memory. RERUN Quick Test.
		No	▶	CHECK connectors, SERVICE or REPLACE harness. SAW is open. REMOVE all test equipment. RECONNECT all components. CLEAR Continuous Memory. RERUN Quick Test.
C8	INSPECT VRS / TRIGGER WHEEL—TIMING FAULT ● Is the VR sensor or Trigger Wheel damaged, i.e., loose or misaligned?	Yes	▶	REPLACE or SERVICE as required. REMOVE all test equipment. RECONNECT all components. CLEAR Continuous Memory. RERUN Quick Test.
		No	▶	REPLACE EDIS module. Incorrect output from EDIS module. REMOVE all test equipment. RECONNECT all components. CLEAR Continuous Memory. RERUN Quick Test.

Fig. 29 Test C: Code 213 Or Lack Of Power Or Poor Fuel Economy (Part 3 of 3). 1993 4.6L Engine

TEST STEP		RESULT	▶	ACTION TO TAKE
D1	CHECK FOR SPARK DURING CRANK ● Using a Neon Bulb Spark Tester (Special Service Tool D89P-6666-A) or Air Gap Spark Tester (D81P-6666-A), check for spark at all spark plug wires while cranking. ● Was spark consistent on ALL spark plug wires (one spark per crankshaft revolution?)	Yes	▶	Ignition system is OK.
		No	▶	GO to D2.
D2	CHECK FOR SPARK AT RIGHT SPARK PLUG WIRES DURING CRANK ● Was spark consistent on all right spark plug wires (one spark per crankshaft revolution)? NOTE: Check spark at spark plugs.	Yes	▶	GO to D3.
		No	▶	GO to D19.
D3	CHECK LEFT SPARK PLUGS AND WIRES ● Check left side coil pack spark plug wires for insulation damage, looseness, shorting or other damage. ● Remove and check left side spark plugs for damage, wear, carbon deposits and proper plug gap. ● Left coil plugs and wires are attached to the left coil pack. ● Are spark plugs and wires OK?	Yes	▶	REINSTALL plugs and wires. GO to D4.
		No	▶	SERVICE or REPLACE damaged component. REMOVE all test equipment. RECONNECT all components. CLEAR Continuous Memory. RERUN Quick Test.
D4	CHECK FOR VBAT TO LEFT COIL FAULT **WARNING: NEVER CONNECT EEC-IV PROCESSOR TO THE EEC-IV BREAKOUT BOX WHEN PERFORMING EDIS DIAGNOSTICS.** ● Key off. ● Install EDIS diagnostic cable to breakout box. ● Install the left coil tee. ● Connect EDIS diagnostic cable negative lead to battery. ● Use 4.6L EDIS 8 overlay. ● Set EDIS cable box switch to 8 cylinder position. ● DVOM on 20 volt DC scale. ● Key on, engine off. ● Measure voltage between (+)J11 (VBAT L) and (-)J7 (BAT-) at breakout box. ● **Is DC voltage greater than 10.0 volts?**	Yes	▶	GO to D5.
		No	▶	CHECK connectors, SERVICE or REPLACE harness. VBAT is open to left coil. REMOVE all test equipment. RECONNECT all components. CLEAR Continuous Memory. RERUN Quick Test.

Fig. 30 Test D: No Start Or Code 217 Or 238 and/or Coil Failure (Part 1 of 12). 1993 4.6L Engine

TEST STEP		RESULT	▶	ACTION TO TAKE
D5	CHECK FOR C3 HIGH AT COIL PACK ● Key on, engine off. ● Measure voltage between (+)J10 (LC3C) and (-)J7 (BAT-) at breakout box. ● **Is DC voltage reading greater than 10.0 volts?**	Yes	▶	GO to D6.
		No	▶	GO to D13.
D6	CHECK FOR C4 HIGH AT COIL PACK ● Key on, engine off. ● Measure voltage between (+)J18 (LC4C) and (-)J7 (BAT-) at the breakout box. ● **Is DC voltage reading greater than 10.0 volts?**	Yes	▶	GO to D7.
		No	▶	GO to D15.
D7	CHECK FOR C3 HIGH AT EDIS MODULE ● Key off. ● Connect EDIS module tee to the EDIS module and vehicle harness connector. ● DVOM on 20 volt DC scale. ● Key on, engine off. ● Measure voltage between (+)J54 (LC3E) and (-)J7 (BAT-) at the breakout box. ● **Is DC voltage reading greater than 10.0 volts?**	Yes	▶	GO to D8.
		No	▶	CHECK connectors, SERVICE or REPLACE harness. C3 is open. REMOVE all test equipment. RECONNECT all components. CLEAR Continuous Memory. RERUN Quick Test.
D8	CHECK FOR C4 HIGH AT EDIS MODULE ● Key on, engine off. ● Measure voltage between (+)J55 (LC4E) and (-)J7 (BAT-) at breakout box. ● **Is DC voltage reading greater than 10.0 volts?**	Yes	▶	GO to D9.
		No	▶	CHECK connectors, SERVICE or REPLACE harness. C4 is open. REMOVE all test equipment. RECONNECT all components. CLEAR Continuous Memory. RERUN Quick Test.
D9	CHECK FOR C3 HIGH AT COIL CONNECTOR—COIL DISCONNECTED ● Key off. ● Disconnect left coil pack from coil tee, leave EDIS diagnostic cable connected to vehicle harness left coil connector. ● DVOM on 20 volt DC scale. ● Key on, engine off. ● Measure voltage between (+)J10 (LC3C) and (-)J7 (BAT-) at breakout box. ● **Is DC voltage reading less than 0.5 volts?**	Yes	▶	GO to D10.
		No	▶	GO to D17.

Fig. 30 Test D: No Start Or Code 217 Or 238 and/or Coil Failure (Part 2 of 12). 1993 4.6L Engine

TEST STEP	RESULT	▶	ACTION TO TAKE
D 10 CHECK FOR C4 LOW AT COIL CONNECTOR—COIL DISCONNECTED—KOEO • Key on, engine off. • Measure voltage between (+)J18 (LC4C) and (-)J7 (B-) at breakout box. • Is DC voltage reading less than 0.5 volts?	Yes No	▶ ▶	GO to D11. GO to D18. C4 high fault.
D 11 CHECK C3 AT COIL CONNECTOR WHILE CRANKING—COIL DISCONNECTED—KOEC • Connect EI diagnostic harness positive lead to battery. • Connect an incandescent test lamp between J1 (B+) and J10 (LC3C). • Crank engine. • Does lamp blink consistently and brightly (one blink per engine revolution)?	Yes No	▶ ▶	GO to D12. REPLACE ICM. C3 open. REMOVE all test equipment. RECONNECT all components. CLEAR Continuous Memory. RERUN Quick Test.
D 12 CHECK C4 AT COIL CONNECTOR WHILE CRANKING—COIL DISCONNECTED—KOEC • Connect an incandescent test lamp between J1 (B+) and J18 (LC4C). • Crank engine. • Does lamp blink consistently and brightly (one blink per engine revolution)?	Yes No	▶ ▶	REPLACE left coil pack. Input to coil pack is OK, but no high voltage output. REMOVE all test equipment. RECONNECT all components. CLEAR Continuous Memory. RERUN Quick Test. REPLACE ICM. C4 open in ICM. REMOVE all test equipment. RECONNECT all components. CLEAR Continuous Memory. RERUN Quick Test.
D 13 CHECK FOR C3 SHORT LOW—COIL DISCONNECTED—KEY OFF • Key off. • DVOM on 20K ohm scale. • Disconnect coil from coil tee, leave EI diagnostic harness connected to vehicle harness coil connector. • Measure resistance between J7 (B-) and J10 (C3C) at breakout box. • Is resistance reading less than 2K ohms?	Yes No	▶ ▶	GO to D14. REPLACE Left Coil Pack. C3 open in coil. REMOVE all test equipment. RECONNECT all components. CLEAR Continuous Memory. RERUN Quick Test.

Fig. 30   Test D: No Start Or Code 217 Or 238 and/or Coil Failure (Part 3 of 12). 1993 4.6L Engine

TEST STEP	RESULT	▶	ACTION TO TAKE
D 14 CHECK FOR C3 SHORT LOW—ICM AND COIL DISCONNECTED—KEY OFF • Key off. • Disconnect ICM from vehicle harness. • DVOM on 20K ohm scale. • Measure resistance between J7 (B-) and J10 (C3C) at breakout box. • Is resistance greater than 10K ohms?	Yes No	▶ ▶	REPLACE ICM. C3 is shorted low. REMOVE all test equipment. RECONNECT all components. CLEAR Continuous Memory. RERUN Quick Test. CHECK connectors, SERVICE or REPLACE harness. C3 is shorted low. REMOVE all test equipment. RECONNECT all components. CLEAR Continuous Memory. RERUN Quick Test.
D 15 CHECK FOR C4 SHORT LOW—COIL DISCONNECTED—KEY OFF • Key off. • DVOM on 20K ohm scale. • Disconnect coil from coil tee, leave EI diagnostic harness connected to vehicle harness coil connector. • Measure resistance between J7 (B-) and J18 (LC4C) at breakout box. • Is resistance reading less than 2K ohms?	Yes No	▶ ▶	GO to D16. REPLACE left coil pack. C4 open in coil. REMOVE all test equipment. RECONNECT all components. CLEAR Continuous Memory. RERUN Quick Test.
D 16 CHECK FOR C4 SHORT LOW—ICM AND COIL DISCONNECTED—KEY OFF • Key off. • Disconnect ICM from vehicle harness connector. • DVOM on 20K ohm scale. • Measure resistance between J7 (B-) and J18 (LC4C) at breakout box. • Is resistance reading greater than 10K ohms?	Yes No	▶ ▶	REPLACE ICM. C4 is shorted low. REMOVE all test equipment. RECONNECT all components. CLEAR Continuous Memory. RERUN Quick Test. CHECK connectors, SERVICE or REPLACE harness. C4 is shorted low. REMOVE all test equipment. RECONNECT all components. CLEAR Continuous Memory. RERUN Quick Test.

Fig. 30   Test D: No Start Or Code 217 Or 238 and/or Coil Failure (Part 4 of 12). 1993 4.6L Engine

TEST STEP	RESULT	▶	ACTION TO TAKE
D16 CHECK FOR C4 SHORT LOW—EDIS MODULE AND COIL DISCONNECTED			
• Key off. • Disconnect EDIS module from vehicle harness connector. • DVOM on 20K ohm scale. • Measure resistance between J7 (BAT-) and J18 (LC4C) at breakout box. • **Is resistance reading greater than 10K ohms?**	Yes	▶	REPLACE EDIS module. C4 is shorted low in EDIS module. REMOVE all test equipment. RECONNECT all components. CLEAR Continuous Memory. RERUN Quick Test.
	No	▶	CHECK connectors, SERVICE or REPLACE harness. C4 is shorted low. REMOVE all test equipment. RECONNECT all components. CLEAR Continuous Memory. RERUN Quick Test.
D17 CHECK FOR C3 HIGH—EDIS MODULE AND COIL DISCONNECTED			
• Key off. • Disconnect EDIS module from the EDIS module tee, leave EDIS diagnostic cable connected to vehicle harness connector. • DVOM on 20 volt DC scale. • Key on, engine off. • Measure voltage between (+)J10 (LC3C) and (-)J7 (BAT-) at breakout box. • **Is DC voltage reading less than 0.5 volts?**	Yes	▶	REPLACE EDIS module. C3 is shorted high. REMOVE all test equipment. RECONNECT all components. CLEAR Continuous Memory. RERUN Quick Test.
	No	▶	CHECK connectors, SERVICE or REPLACE harness. C3 is shorted high. REMOVE all test equipment. RECONNECT all components. CLEAR Continuous Memory. RERUN Quick Test.

Fig. 30   Test D: No Start Or Code 217 Or 238 and/or Coil Failure (Part 5 of 12). 1993 4.6L

TEST STEP	RESULT	▶	ACTION TO TAKE
D18 CHECK FOR C4 HIGH—EDIS MODULE AND COIL DISCONNECTED			
• Key off. • Disconnect EDIS module from EDIS module tee, leave EDIS diagnostic cable connected to vehicle harness connector. • DVOM on 20 volt DC scale. • Key on, engine off. • Measure voltage between (+)J18 (LC4C) and (-)J7 (BAT-) at breakout box. • **Is DC voltage reading less than 0.5 volts?**	Yes	▶	REPLACE EDIS module. C4 is shorted high in EDIS module. REMOVE all test equipment. RECONNECT all components. CLEAR Continuous Memory. RERUN Quick Test.
	No	▶	CHECK connectors, SERVICE or REPLACE harness. C4 is shorted high. REMOVE all test equipment. RECONNECT all components. CLEAR Continuous Memory. RERUN Quick Test.

Fig. 30   Test D: No Start Or Code 217 Or 238 and/or Coil Failure (Part 6 of 12). 1993 4.6L Engine

TEST STEP	RESULT	▶	ACTION TO TAKE
D19 CHECK RIGHT PLUGS AND WIRES			
• Check right side coil pack spark plug wires for insulation damage, looseness, shorting or other damage. • Remove and check right spark plugs for damage, wear, carbon deposits and proper plug gap. NOTE: **Right coil plugs and wires are attached to the right coil.** • **Are spark plugs and wires OK?**	Yes	▶	REINSTALL plugs and wires. GO to D20.
	No	▶	SERVICE or REPLACE damaged component. REMOVE all test equipment. RECONNECT all components. CLEAR Continuous Memory. RERUN Quick Test.
D20 CHECK FOR VBAT OPEN TO RIGHT COIL			
WARNING: NEVER CONNECT EEC-IV PROCESSOR TO THE EEC-IV BREAKOUT BOX WHEN PERFORMING EDIS DIAGNOSTICS. • Key off. • Install EDIS diagnostic cable to the breakout box. • Connect EDIS diagnostic cable negative lead to battery. • Install the right coil tee. • Use 4.6L EDIS 8 overlay. • DVOM on 20 volt DC scale. • Set EDIS cable box switch to 8 cylinder position. • Key on, engine off. • Measure voltage between (+)J5 (VBAT R) and (-)J7 (BAT-) at breakout box. • **Is DC voltage greater than 10.0 volts?**	Yes	▶	GO to D21.
	No	▶	CHECK connectors, SERVICE or REPLACE harness. VBAT is open to right coil. REMOVE all test equipment. RECONNECT all components. CLEAR Continuous Memory. RERUN Quick Test.
D21 CHECK FOR C1 HIGH AT COIL PACK			
• DVOM on 20 volt DC scale. • Key on, engine off. • Measure voltage between (+)J3 (RC1C) and (-)J7 (BAT-) at breakout box. • **Is DC voltage reading greater than 10.0 volts?**	Yes	▶	GO to D22.
	No	▶	GO to D29.
D22 CHECK FOR C2 HIGH AT COIL PACK			
• Key on, engine off. • Measure voltage between (+)J6 (RC2C) and (-)J7 (BAT-) at breakout box. • **Is DC voltage reading greater than 10.0 volts?**	Yes	▶	GO to D23.
	No	▶	GO to D31.

Fig. 30   Test D: No Start Or Code 217 Or 238 and/or Coil Failure (Part 7 of 12). 1993 4.6L Engine

TEST STEP	RESULT	▶	ACTION TO TAKE
D23 CHECK FOR C1 HIGH AT EDIS MODULE			
• Key off. • Connect EDIS module tee to the EDIS module and vehicle harness connector. • DVOM on 20 volt DC scale. • Key on, engine off. • Measure voltage between (+)J51 (RC1E) and (-)J7 (BAT-) at breakout box. • **Is DC voltage reading greater than 10.0 volts?**	Yes	▶	GO to D24.
	No	▶	CHECK connectors, SERVICE or REPLACE harness. C1 is open. REMOVE all test equipment. RECONNECT all components. CLEAR Continuous Memory. RERUN Quick Test.
D24 CHECK FOR C2 HIGH AT EDIS MODULE			
• Key on, engine off. • Measure voltage between (+)J27 (RC2E) and (-)J7 (BAT-) at breakout box. • **Is DC voltage reading greater than 10.0 volts?**	Yes	▶	GO to D25.
	No	▶	CHECK connectors, SERVICE or REPLACE harness. C2 is open. REMOVE all test equipment. RECONNECT all components. CLEAR Continuous Memory. RERUN Quick Test.
D25 CHECK C1 HIGH AT COIL CONNECTOR—COIL DISCONNECTED			
• Key off. • Disconnect right coil from coil tee, leave EDIS diagnostic cable connected to vehicle harness right coil connector. • DVOM on 20 volt DC scale. • Key on, engine off. • Measure voltage between (+)J3 (RC1C) and (-)J7 (BAT-) at breakout box. • **Is DC voltage reading less than 0.5 volts?**	Yes	▶	GO to D26.
	No	▶	GO to D33.
D26 CHECK FOR C2 HIGH AT COIL CONNECTOR—COIL DISCONNECTED			
• Key on, engine off. • Measure voltage between (+)J6 (RC2C) and (-)J7 (BAT-) at breakout box. • **Is DC voltage reading less than 0.5 volts?**	Yes	▶	GO to D27.
	No	▶	GO to D34.

Fig. 30   Test D: No Start Or Code 217 Or 238 and/or Coil Failure (Part 8 of 12). 1993 4.6L Engine

TEST STEP		RESULT	▶	ACTION TO TAKE
D27	CHECK C1 AT COIL CONNECTOR WHILE CRANKING ENGINE—COIL DISCONNECTED			
	• Connect EI diagnostic harness positive lead to battery. • Connect an incandescent test lamp between J1 (B+) and J3 (RC1C). • Crank engine. • **Does lamp blink consistently and brightly (one blink per engine revolution)?**	Yes	▶	GO to D28.
		No	▶	REPLACE ICM. C1 is open. REMOVE all test equipment. RECONNECT all components. CLEAR Continuous Memory. RERUN Quick Test.
D28	CHECK C2 AT COIL CONNECTOR WHILE CRANKING ENGINE—COIL DISCONNECTED			
	• Connect an incandescent test lamp between J1 (B+) and J6 (RC2C). • Crank engine. • **Does lamp blink consistently and brightly (one blink per engine revolution)?**	Yes	▶	REPLACE Right Coil Pack. Input to coil pack is OK, but no high voltage output. REMOVE all test equipment. RECONNECT all components. CLEAR Continuous Memory. RERUN Quick Test.
		No	▶	REPLACE ICM. C2 is open in ICM. REMOVE all test equipment. RECONNECT all components. CLEAR Continuous Memory. RERUN Quick Test.
D29	CHECK FOR C1 SHORT LOW—COIL DISCONNECTED			
	• Key off. • DVOM on 20K ohm scale. • Disconnect coil from coil tee, leave EI diagnostic harness connected to vehicle harness coil connector. • Measure resistance between J7 (B-) and J3 (RC1C) at breakout box. • **Is resistance reading less than 2K ohms?**	Yes	▶	GO to D30.
		No	▶	REPLACE Right Coil Pack. C1 is open in coil. REMOVE all test equipment. RECONNECT all components. CLEAR Continuous Memory. RERUN Quick Test.

Fig. 30   Test D: No Start Or Code 217 Or 238 and/or Coil Failure (Part 9 of 12). 1993 4.6L Engine

TEST STEP		RESULT	▶	ACTION TO TAKE
D30	CHECK FOR C1 SHORT LOW—ICM AND COIL DISCONNECTED			
	• Key off. • Disconnect ICM from vehicle harness. • DVOM on 20K ohm scale. • Measure resistance between J7 (B-) and J3 (RC1C) at breakout box. • **Is resistance reading greater than 10K ohms?**	Yes	▶	REPLACE ICM. C1 is shorted low. REMOVE all test equipment. RECONNECT all components. CLEAR Continuous Memory. RERUN Quick Test.
		No	▶	CHECK connectors, SERVICE or REPLACE harness. C1 is shorted to low. REMOVE all test equipment. RECONNECT all components. CLEAR Continuous Memory. RERUN Quick Test.
D31	CHECK FOR C2 SHORT LOW—COIL DISCONNECTED			
	• Key off. • DVOM on 20K ohm scale. • Disconnect coil from coil tee, leave EI diagnostic harness connected to vehicle harness coil connector. • Measure resistance between J7 (B-) and J6 (RC2C) at breakout box. • **Is resistance reading less than 2K ohms?**	Yes	▶	GO to D32.
		No	▶	REPLACE Right Coil Pack. C2 open in coil. REMOVE all test equipment. RECONNECT all components. CLEAR Continuous Memory. RERUN Quick Test.
D32	CHECK FOR C2 SHORT LOW—ICM AND COIL DISCONNECTED			
	• Key off. • Disconnect ICM from vehicle harness. • DVOM on 20K ohm scale. • Measure resistance between J6 (RC2C) and J7 (B-) at breakout box. • **Is resistance reading greater than 10K ohms?**	Yes	▶	REPLACE ICM. C2 is shorted low. REMOVE all test equipment. RECONNECT all components. CLEAR Continuous Memory. RERUN Quick Test.
		No	▶	CHECK connectors, SERVICE or REPLACE harness. C2 is shorted low. REMOVE all test equipment. RECONNECT all components. CLEAR Continuous Memory. RERUN Quick Test.

Fig. 30   Test D: No Start Or Code 217 Or 238 and/or Coil Failure (Part 10 of 12). 1993 4.6L Engine

TEST STEP	RESULT	▶	ACTION TO TAKE
D32 CHECK FOR C2 SHORT LOW—EDIS MODULE AND COIL DISCONNECTED • Key off. • Disconnect EDIS module from vehicle harness. • DVOM on 20K ohm scale. • Measure resistance between J6 (RC2C) and J7 (BAT-) at breakout box. • **Is resistance reading greater than 10K ohms?**	Yes	▶	REPLACE EDIS module. C2 is shorted low. REMOVE all test equipment. RECONNECT all components. CLEAR Continuous Memory. RERUN Quick Test.
	No	▶	CHECK connectors, SERVICE or REPLACE harness. C2 is shorted low. REMOVE all test equipment. RECONNECT all components. CLEAR Continuous Memory. RERUN Quick Test.
D33 CHECK FOR C1 HIGH—EDIS MODULE AND COIL DISCONNECTED • Key off. • Disconnect EDIS module from EDIS module tee, leave EDIS diagnostic cable connected to vehicle harness connector. • DVOM on 20 volt DC scale. • Key on, engine off. • Measure voltage between (+)J3 (RC1C) and (-)J7 (BAT-) at breakout box. • **Is DC voltage reading less than 0.5 volts?**	Yes	▶	REPLACE EDIS module. REMOVE all test equipment. RECONNECT all components. CLEAR Continuous Memory. RERUN Quick Test.
	No	▶	CHECK connectors, SERVICE or REPLACE harness. C1 is shorted high. REMOVE all test equipment. RECONNECT all components. CLEAR Continuous Memory. RERUN Quick Test.

Fig. 30 Test D: No Start Or Code 217 Or 238 and/or Coil Failure (Part 11 of 12). 1993 4.6L Engine

TEST STEP	RESULT	▶	ACTION TO TAKE
D34 CHECK FOR C2 HIGH—EDIS MODULE AND COIL DISCONNECTED • Key off. • Disconnect EDIS module from EDIS module tee, leave EDIS diagnostic cable connected to vehicle harness connector. • DVOM on 20 volt DC scale. • Key on, engine off. • Measure voltage between (+)J6 (RC2C) and (-)J7 (BAT-) at breakout box. • **Is DC voltage reading less than 0.5 volts?**	Yes	▶	REPLACE EDIS module. REMOVE all test equipment. RECONNECT all components. CLEAR Continuous Memory. RERUN Quick Test.
	No	▶	CHECK connectors, SERVICE or REPLACE harness. C2 is shorted high. REMOVE all test equipment. RECONNECT all components. CLEAR Continuous Memory. RERUN Quick Test.

Fig. 30 Test D: No Start Or Code 217 Or 238 and/or Coil Failure (Part 12 of 12). 1993 4.6L Engine

You must perform Quick Test and follow instructions in the EEC Pinpoint Test Steps before starting this section.

CONDITION	ACTION TO TAKE
•No start without Diagnostic Trouble Codes	GO to A1.
•PASS Code 111.	GO to A1.
•No Start with Diagnostic Trouble Code 226.	GO to A1.
•Code 211 (PIP at PCM fault).	GO to A1.
•MIL stays on during engine cranking.	GO to A1.
•Vehicle Runs (engine is running) with:	
•Code 212 or 226 (IDM at PCM fault).	GO to B1.
•Code 213 (SPOUT Circuit Fault)	GO to C1.
•Code 215 and/or 216 (Coil 1 or Coil 2 fault).	GO to D19.
•Code 217 and/or 238 (Coil 3 or Coil 4 fault).	GO to D3.
•Lack of power or poor fuel economy.	GO to C1.
•Engine Miss.	GO to 3.0L/3.2L F.

Using a DVOM

When using a DVOM to check the PIP signal, the engine must be turned very slowly ("Bumped") with the starter without starting the engine. This is a digital signal and should switch from ground (0 VDC to 0.5 VDC) to B+ (8 volts DC to 14 volts DC) or B+ to ground. When using the DVOM correct test lead polarity must be used. The red lead is positive (+) and black lead is negative (-).

FM1119400313010X

Fig. 31 Diagnostics By Diagnostic Trouble Code & Symptom (Part 1 of 3). 1994–95 4.6L Engine

The Following Voltage Readings are Typical for a Normal Vehicle:

Measure Between Pins		Key On Engine Off (Volts)	Engine Cranking (Volts AC)	4.6L 2V Engine Idling (Volts AC)	4.6L 4V Engine Idling (Volts AC)
First Pin	Second Pin				
CKPS+S (J31)	CKPS-S(J32)	0	0.5-1.5	2-5	2-5
CKPS+I (J48)	CKPS-I(J47)	0	0.5-1.5	2-5	2-5
PIPI (J43)	PWR GND (J53)	0	—	5-7	3-7
C1I (J51)	PWR GND (J53)	B+ DC	1-1.5	1.2-2	.5-1.2
C2I (J27)	PWR GND (J53)	B+ DC	1-1.5	1.2-2	.5-1.2
C3I (J54)	PWR GND (J53)	B+ DC	1-1.5	1.2-2	.5-1.2
C4I (J55)	PWR GND (J53)	B+ DC	1-1.5	1.2-2	.5-1.2
C1C (J3)	PWR GND (J53)	B+ DC	0.1-0.8	1.2-2	.5-1.2
C2C (J6)	PWR GND (J53)	B+ DC	0.1-0.8	1.2-2	.5-1.2
C3C (J10)	PWR GND (J53)	B+ DC	0.1-0.8	1.2-2	.5-1.2
C4C (J18)	PWR GND (J53)	B+ DC	0.1-0.8	1.2-2	.5-1.2
SPOUT (J45)	PWR GND (J53)	0	0.01-0.3	0.5-3	.5-3.0
IDMI (J41)	PWR GND (J53)	0	0.1-0.5	0.2-2.0	2-2.0
CKPS+I (J48)	PWR GND (J53)	1-20 DC	0.1-0.9	1.5-1.9	1.2-1.9
CKPS-I (J47)	PWR GND (J53)	1-20 DC	0.1-0.9	1.5-1.9	1.2-1.9

NOTE:
- Do not connect the positive lead of the EI (High Data Rate) diagnostic harness or CKP sensor tee until directed to do so.
- The SPOUT and IDM detectors in the EI (High Data Rate) diagnostic harness will not work unless the positive and negative leads of the harness are connected.
- The vehicle battery voltage must be at least 12 volts DC.
- Be careful not to bring a fluorescent trouble lamp close to the vehicle wiring. If the key is on and the CKP sensor is disconnected, the ICM may fire the coil.
- When using a DVOM to measure DC voltage readings, connect the positive lead to the jack identified with a (+) sign and the negative lead to the jack with a (-) sign.

FM1119400313020X

Fig. 31 Diagnostics By Diagnostic Trouble Code & Symptom (Part 2 of 3). 1994–95 4.6L Engine

IMPORTANT NOTE:

Most DVOM's used by auto technicians belong to a class or type known as ''averaging.'' Examples are the Rotunda Digital Volt-Ohmmeter 007-00001, Fluke 70, 20 series and Fluke 88. Recently technicians have started to use DVOM's of a different class (True RMS, DVOM's, Fluke 87, 8060A, 8062A, etc.). True RMS DVOM's should not be used with the Pinpoint Tests because they may display different voltage readings depending upon if the DVOM is turned on first and then the test leads are connected, or if the leads are connected first and the DVOM is turned on. Also they may not auto range to the same range every time and some display significantly different values depending on the range selected. It would be impossible to list all of the meters and how to use each, so we are requesting that you perform the following test to verify your DVOM is compatible with the Pinpoint Tests.

Using a known good EI vehicle, install the EI diagnostic harness, connect the PCM Breakout Box to the diagnostic harness, start the vehicle and measure the AC voltage between J51 (RC1I) and ground. The battery should be charged and the engine must be idling between 700 and 900 rpm. On any EI vehicle (except 1992 Escort) the value should be between 1.0 and 2.0 volts AC (1.5 volts AC is typical). If you have the EI (Low Data Rate) hand held testers they may be used instead of the Diagnostic Harness/EEC Breakout Box to gain access to J51 (RC1I) and J43 (PIP I). Next, with the engine idling, measure between PIP and ground. This reading should be between 6 and 8 volts AC.

If the readings you get agree with our test, your DVOM is OK to use with the Ignition Pinpoint Tests. If not, do not use it, it will lead to false parts replacement and the root cause will be difficult or impossible to find.

FM1119400313030X

Fig. 31 Diagnostics By Diagnostic Trouble Code & Symptom (Part 3 of 3). 1994–95 4.6L Engine

TEST STEP	RESULT	▶	ACTION TO TAKE
A1 PERFORM EEC QUICK TEST			
• Was Quick Test performed according to the procedures in Section 5A? NOTE: These diagnostic procedures are designed to correct one ignition failure at a time. When a component is replaced or a service is completed, remove all test equipment, reconnect all components and rerun Quick Test.	Yes No	▶ ▶	GO to **A2**. PERFORM Quick Test.
A2 CHECK FOR SPARK DURING CRANK—KOEC			
• Using a Neon Bulb Spark Tester (Special Service Tool D89P-6666-A) or Air Gap Spark Tester (Special Service Tool D81P-6666-A), check for spark at all spark plug wires while cranking. • Was spark consistent on ALL spark plug wires (one spark per crankshaft revolution)?	Yes No	▶ ▶	GO to **A13**. GO to **A3**. Spark fault.
A3 CHECK PLUGS AND WIRES—KEY OFF			
• Check spark plug wires for insulation damage, looseness, shorting or other damage. • Remove and check spark plugs for damage, wear, carbon deposits and proper plug gap. • Are spark plugs and wires OK?	Yes No	▶ ▶	REINSTALL plugs and wires. GO to **A4**. SERVICE or REPLACE damaged component. REMOVE all test equipment. RECONNECT all components. CLEAR Continuous Memory. RERUN Quick Test.
A4 CHECK FOR VEHICLE START WITH DIAGNOSTIC HARNESS INSTALLED			
WARNING: NEVER CONNECT THE PCM TO THE EEC BREAKOUT BOX WHEN PERFORMING EI DIAGNOSTICS. • Key off. • Install EI diagnostic harness to breakout box and to both the ICM and vehicle harness. **Do not connect CKP sensor tee or coil tee.** • Use EI (High Data Rate) 8 overlay. • Connect EI diagnostic harness negative lead to battery, leave positive lead disconnected. • Set EI diagnostic harness box type switch to ''8 cylinder'' position. • Will vehicle start and run?	Yes No	▶ ▶	GO to **A32**. GO to **A5**.

FM1119400314010X

Fig. 32 Test A: No Start (Part 1 of 10). 1994–95 4.6L Engine

TEST STEP	RESULT	▶	ACTION TO TAKE
A5 CHECK PWR GND TO ICM—KEY OFF			
• Key off. • Install EI diagnostic harness breakout box and ICM. • Do not connect CKP sensor or coil tees at this time. • Use EI (High Data Rate) 8 overlay. • Connect only the EI diagnostic harness negative lead. Do not connect positive lead. • Set diagnostic harness switch to the 8 position. • DVOM on 200 ohm scale. • Measure resistance between J53 (PWR GND) and J7 (B-) at breakout box. • Is the resistance less than 5.0 ohms?	Yes No	▶ ▶	GO to **A6**. CHECK connectors, SERVICE or REPLACE harness. Power ground is open. REMOVE all test equipment. RECONNECT all components. CLEAR Continuous Memory. RERUN Quick Test.
A6 CHECK FOR VPWR TO ICM—KOEO			
• Key off. • DVOM on 40 volt DC scale. • Key on, engine off. • Measure voltage between (+)J35 (VPWR I) and (-)J7 (B-) at breakout box. • Is DC voltage greater than 10.5 volts?	Yes No	▶ ▶	GO to **A7**. CHECK connectors, SERVICE or REPLACE harness. VPWR to ICM is open. REMOVE all test equipment. RECONNECT all components. CLEAR Continuous Memory. RERUN Quick Test.
A7 CHECK CKP+ BIAS AT ICM—KOEO			
• Key off. • DVOM on 40 volt DC scale. • Key on, engine off. • Measure voltage between (+)J48 (CKP I) and (-)J7 (B-) at breakout box. • Is DC voltage between 1.0 and 2.0 volts?	Yes No	▶ ▶	GO to **A21**. GO to **A8**. Bias fault.
A8 CHECK CKP+ BIAS SENSOR DISCONNECTED—BIAS FAULT—KOEO			
• Key off. • Disconnect CKP sensor from vehicle harness connector. • DVOM on 40 volt DC scale. • Key on, engine off. • Measure voltage between (+)J48 (CKP I) and (-)J7 (B-) at breakout box. • Is DC voltage greater than 1.0 volt but less than 2.0 volts?	Yes No	▶ ▶	GO to **A9**. GO to **A29**. Bias fault.

FM1119400314020X

Fig. 32 Test A: No Start (Part 2 of 10). 1994–95 4.6L Engine

TEST STEP	RESULT	▶	ACTION TO TAKE
A9 CHECK CKP- SENSOR — BIAS FAULT—CKP SENSOR DISCONNECTED—KOEO			
• Key off. • DVOM on 40 volt DC scale. • Key on, engine off. • Measure voltage between (+)J47 (CKP-I) and (-)J7 (B-) at breakout box. • Is DC voltage between 1.0 and 2.0 volts?	Yes No	▶ ▶	REPLACE CKP sensor. Short to ground. REMOVE all test equipment. RECONNECT all components. CLEAR Continuous Memory. RERUN Quick Test. GO to **A10**. Bias fault.
A10 DETERMINE IF BIAS HIGH OR BIAS LOW FAULT—KEY OFF			
• Was bias voltage reading in Step **A9** less than 1.0 volt?	Yes No	▶ ▶	GO to **A11**. Bias low fault. GO to **A12**. Bias high fault.
A11 CHECK CKP SENSOR — FOR SHORT TO GROUND—BIAS LOW FAULT—CKP SENSOR AND ICM DISCONNECTED—KEY OFF			
• Key off. • Disconnect ICM from ICM tee, leave EI diagnostic harness connected to vehicle harness connector. • DVOM on 20K ohm scale. • Measure resistance between J47 (CKP-I) and J7 (B-) at breakout box. • Is the resistance greater than 10K ohms?	Yes No	▶ ▶	REPLACE ICM. CKP- is shorted low. REMOVE all test equipment. RECONNECT all components. CLEAR Continuous Memory. RERUN Quick Test. CHECK connectors, SERVICE or REPLACE harness. CKP- is shorted low. REMOVE all test equipment. RECONNECT all components. CLEAR Continuous Memory. RERUN Quick Test.

FM1119400314030X

Fig. 32 Test A: No Start (Part 3 of 10). 1994–95 4.6L Engine

TEST STEP	RESULT	▶	ACTION TO TAKE
A12 CHECK CKP- SENSOR FOR SHORT HIGH—BIAS HIGH FAULT—CKP SENSOR AND ICM DISCONNECTED—KOEO • Key off. • Disconnect ICM from ICM tee; leave EI diagnostic harness connected to vehicle harness connector. • DVOM 40 volt DC scale. • Key on, engine off. • Measure voltage between (+)J47 (CKP- I) and (-)J7 (B-) at the breakout box. • **Is DC voltage less than 0.5 volts?**	Yes	▶	REPLACE ICM. CKP- shorted high. REMOVE all test equipment. RECONNECT all components. CLEAR Continuous Memory. RERUN Quick Test.
	No	▶	CHECK connectors, SERVICE or REPLACE harness. CKP- is shorted high. REMOVE all test equipment. RECONNECT all components. CLEAR Continuous Memory. RERUN Quick Test.
A13 CHECK PIP AT ICM—KOEO **WARNING: NEVER CONNECT THE PCM TO THE EEC BREAKOUT BOX WHEN PERFORMING EI DIAGNOSTICS.** • Key off. • Install EI diagnostic harness to the breakout box and to both the ICM and vehicle harness. **Do not connect CKP sensor tee or coil tee.** • Use EI (High Data Rate) 8 overlay. • Connect EI diagnostic harness negative lead to battery, leave positive lead disconnected. • Set EI diagnostic harness type switch to 8 position. • Crank engine and measure voltage between J43 (PIP I) and J7 (B-) at the breakout box. • **Is the settled AC voltage reading greater than 3.5 volts?**	Yes	▶	GO to A14.
	No	▶	GO to A18.
A14 CHECK FOR PIP OPEN TO PCM—PCM DISCONNECTED—KEY OFF • Key off. • DVOM on 200 ohm scale. • Install a second breakout box to PCM vehicle harness connector. • Measure resistance between J43 (PIP I) at the breakout box and Pin 56 (PIP) at the second breakout box. • **Is resistance less than 5.0 ohms?**	Yes	▶	GO to A15.
	No	▶	CHECK connectors, SERVICE or REPLACE harness. PIP is open. REMOVE all test equipment. RECONNECT all components. CLEAR Continuous Memory. RERUN Quick Test.

FM1119400314040X

Fig. 32   Test A: No Start (Part 4 of 10). 1994–95 4.6L Engine

TEST STEP	RESULT	▶	ACTION TO TAKE
A15 CHECK IGN GND AT ICM—PCM DISCONNECTED • Key off. • DVOM on 2K ohm scale. • Measure resistance between J50 (IGN GND I) and J7 (B-) at breakout box. • **Is resistance less than 1050 ohms?**	Yes	▶	GO to A16.
	No	▶	GO to A17. Ground fault.
A16 CHECK FOR IGN GND OPEN TO PCM—PCM DISCONNECTED —KEY OFF • Key off. • DVOM on 2K ohm scale. • Measure resistance between J50 (IGN GND I) at the breakout box and Pin 16 (IGN GND) at the second breakout box. • **Is resistance less than 1050 ohms?**	Yes	▶	Ignition system is OK. REMOVE all test equipment. RECONNECT all components. CLEAR Continuous Memory. RERUN Quick Test.
	No	▶	CHECK connectors, SERVICE or REPLACE harness. IGN GND is open. REMOVE all test equipment. RECONNECT all components. CLEAR Continuous Memory. RERUN Quick Test.
A17 CHECK PWR GND TO ICM—PWR GND FAULT—KEY OFF • Key off. • DVOM on 200 ohm scale. • Measure resistance between J53 (PWR GND) and J7 (B-) at breakout box. • **Is resistance less than 5.0 ohms?**	Yes	▶	REPLACE ICM. Ground open. REMOVE all test equipment. RECONNECT all components. CLEAR Continuous Memory. RERUN Quick Test.
	No	▶	CHECK connectors, SERVICE or REPLACE harness. Power ground to ICM is open. REMOVE all test equipment. RECONNECT all components. CLEAR Continuous Memory. RERUN Quick Test.

FM1119400314050X

Fig. 32   Test A: No Start (Part 5 of 10). 1994–95 4.6L Engine

TEST STEP	RESULT	▶	ACTION TO TAKE
A18 CHECK PIP AT ICM—PIP FAULT—PIP CIRCUIT OPEN—KOEC • Key off. • DVOM 40 volt AC scale. • Push and hold EI diagnostic harness PIP push button down (opens PIP circuit to PCM). • Crank engine and measure voltage between J43 (PIP I) and J7 (B-) at breakout box. • **Is settled AC voltage reading greater than 3.5 volts?**	Yes	▶	GO to A19.
	No	▶	REPLACE ICM. No PIP output. REMOVE all test equipment. RECONNECT all components. CLEAR Continuous Memory. RERUN Quick Test.
A19 CHECK FOR PIP SHORT HIGH—ICM AND PCM DISCONNECTED—KOEO • Key off. • DVOM on 40 volt DC scale. • Key on, engine off. • Measure voltage between J43 (PIP I) and J7 (B-) at breakout box. • **Is DC voltage less than 0.5 volts?**	Yes	▶	GO to A20.
	No	▶	CHECK connectors, SERVICE or REPLACE harness. PIP is shorted high. REMOVE all test equipment. RECONNECT all components. CLEAR Continuous Memory. RERUN Quick Test.
A20 CHECK FOR PIP SHORT TO GROUND—ICM AND PCM DISCONNECTED—KEY OFF • Key off. • Disconnect PCM. • Disconnect ICM from ICM tee, leave EI diagnostic harness connected to vehicle harness connector. • Disconnect EI diagnostic harness positive lead to battery. • DVOM on 20K ohm scale. • Measure resistance between J43 (PIP I) and J7 (B-) at breakout box. • **Is resistance greater than 10K ohms?**	Yes	▶	REPLACE PCM. PIP is shorted. REMOVE all test equipment. RECONNECT all components. CLEAR Continuous Memory. RERUN Quick Test.
	No	▶	CHECK connectors, SERVICE or REPLACE harness. PIP is shorted low. REMOVE all test equipment. RECONNECT all components. CLEAR Continuous Memory. RERUN Quick Test.
A21 CHECK CKP SENSOR AMPLITUDE AT ICM—KOEC • Key off. • DVOM on 40 volt AC scale. • Crank engine and measure voltage between J48 (CKP+ I) and J47 (CKP- I) at breakout box. • **Is settled AC voltage reading greater than 0.4 volts?**	Yes	▶	GO to Pinpoint Test Step D1.
	No	▶	GO to A22. Amplitude fault.

FM1119400314060X

Fig. 32   Test A: No Start (Part 6 of 10). 1994–95 4.6L Engine

TEST STEP	RESULT	▶	ACTION TO TAKE
A22 CHECK CKP AMPLITUDE AT ICM—AMPLITUDE FAULT—ICM DISCONNECTED—KOEC • Key off. • Disconnect ICM from ICM tee, leave EI diagnostic harness connected to vehicle harness connector. • DVOM 40 volt AC scale. • Crank engine and measure voltage between J48 (CKP+ I) and J47 (CKP- I) at breakout box. • **Is settled AC voltage reading greater than 0.4 volts?**	Yes	▶	REPLACE ICM. CKP is shorted in ICM. REMOVE all test equipment. RECONNECT all components. CLEAR Continuous Memory. RERUN Quick Test.
	No	▶	GO to A23.
A23 CHECK CIRCUIT RESISTANCE—AMPLITUDE FAULT—KEY OFF • Key off. • DVOM on 20K ohm scale. • Measure resistance between J47 (CKP- I) and J48 (CKP+ I) at the breakout box. • **Is resistance between 2300 and 2500 ohms?**	Yes	▶	GO to A27.
	No	▶	GO to A24. CKP- circuit resistance fault.
A24 DETERMINE IF RESISTANCE HIGH OR RESISTANCE LOW FAULT • **Was the resistance reading from Step A23 less than 2300 ohms?**	Yes	▶	GO to A28. Low resistance fault.
	No	▶	GO to A25. High resistance fault.
A25 CHECK CKP+ SENSOR OPEN—RESISTANCE HIGH FAULT—KEY OFF • Key off. • Connect CKP sensor tee to CKP sensor and vehicle harness connector. • DVOM on 20K ohm scale. • Measure resistance between J31 (CKP+ S) and J48 (CKP+ I) at the breakout box. • **Is resistance less than 2050 ohms?**	Yes	▶	GO to A26.
	No	▶	CHECK connectors, SERVICE or REPLACE harness. CKP+ open. REMOVE all test equipment. RECONNECT all components. CLEAR Continuous Memory. RERUN Quick Test.

FM1119400314070X

Fig. 32   Test A: No Start (Part 7 of 10). 1994–95 4.6L Engine

TEST STEP	RESULT	▶	ACTION TO TAKE
A26 CHECK FOR CKP OPEN—RESISTANCE HIGH FAULT—KEY OFF • Key off. • DVOM on 20K ohm scale. • Measure resistance between J32 (CKP-S) and J47 (CKP-I) at the breakout box. • **Is resistance less than 2050 ohms?**	Yes	▶	REPLACE CKP sensor. High resistance. REMOVE all test equipment. RECONNECT all components. CLEAR Continuous Memory. RERUN Quick Test.
	No	▶	CHECK connectors, SERVICE or REPLACE harness. CKP- open. REMOVE all test equipment. RECONNECT all components. CLEAR Continuous Memory. RERUN Quick Test.
A27 CHECK CKP SENSOR AND TRIGGER WHEEL • Key off. • Check trigger wheel and CKP sensor for damage. • **Is CKP sensor and trigger data wheel OK?**	Yes	▶	REPLACE CKP sensor. No output from sensor. REMOVE all test equipment. RECONNECT all components. CLEAR Continuous Memory. RERUN Quick Test.
	No	▶	SERVICE or REPLACE bad parts. REMOVE all test equipment. RECONNECT all components. CLEAR Continuous Memory. RERUN Quick Test.

FM1119400314080X

Fig. 32 Test A: No Start (Part 8 of 10). 1994–95 4.6L Engine

TEST STEP	RESULT	▶	ACTION TO TAKE
A28 CHECK FOR CKP+ SHORTED TO CKP-—RESISTANCE LOW FAULT—CKP SENSOR DISCONNECTED—KEY OFF • Key off. • Disconnect CKP sensor from the vehicle harness connector. • DVOM on 20K ohm scale. • Measure resistance between J48 (CKP+I) and J47 (CKP-I) at the breakout box. • **Is resistance greater than 3K ohms?**	Yes	▶	REPLACE CKP sensor. Shorted sensor windings. REMOVE all test equipment. RECONNECT all components. CLEAR Continuous Memory. RERUN Quick Test.
	No	▶	CHECK connectors, SERVICE or REPLACE harness. CKP+ shorted to CKP- in harness. REMOVE all test equipment. RECONNECT all components. CLEAR Continuous Memory. RERUN Quick Test.
A29 DETERMINE IF BIAS VOLTAGE HIGH OR BIAS VOLTAGE LOW FAULT • **Was bias voltage reading in Step A8 less than 1.0 volts?**	Yes	▶	GO to A30. Low bias voltage fault.
	No	▶	GO to A31. High bias voltage fault.
A30 CHECK CKP+ SENSOR FOR SHORT TO GROUND—CKP SENSOR AND ICM DISCONNECTED—LOW BIAS VOLTAGE FAULT—KEY OFF • Key off. • Disconnect the ICM from ICM tee, leave EI diagnostic harness connected to vehicle harness connector. • DVOM on 20K ohm scale. • Measure resistance between J48 (CKP+I) and J7 (B-) at breakout box. • **Is resistance greater than 10K ohms?**	Yes	▶	REPLACE ICM. CKP+ shorted low. REMOVE all test equipment. RECONNECT all components. CLEAR Continuous Memory. RERUN Quick Test.
	No	▶	CHECK connectors, SERVICE or REPLACE harness. CKP+ is shorted low. REMOVE all test equipment. RECONNECT all components. CLEAR Continuous Memory. RERUN Quick Test.

FM1119400314090X

Fig. 32 Test A: No Start (Part 9 of 10). 1994–95 4.6L Engine

TEST STEP	RESULT	▶	ACTION TO TAKE
A31 CHECK CKP+ SENSOR FOR SHORT HIGH—BIAS VOLTAGE HIGH FAULT—CKP SENSOR AND ICM DISCONNECTED—KOEO • Key off. • Disconnect ICM from ICM tee, leave EI diagnostic harness connected to vehicle harness connector. • DVOM on 40 volt DC scale. • Key on, engine off. • Measure voltage between +J48 (CKP+I) and -J7 (B-) at breakout box. • **Is DC voltage less than 0.5 volts?**	Yes	▶	REPLACE ICM. CKPS+ shorted high. REMOVE all test equipment. RECONNECT all components. CLEAR Continuous Memory. RERUN Quick Test.
	No	▶	CHECK connectors, SERVICE or REPLACE harness. CKP+ is shorted high. REMOVE all test equipment. RECONNECT all components. CLEAR Continuous Memory. RERUN Quick Test.
A32 CHECK CKP SENSOR RESISTANCE—CKP CIRCUIT FAULT—KEY OFF • Key off. • Disconnect ICM from ICM tee, leave EI diagnostic harness connected to vehicle harness connector. • DVOM on 20K ohm scale. • Measure resistance between J47 (CKP-I) and J48 (CKP+I) at breakout box. • **Is resistance between 2300 and 2500 ohms?**	Yes	▶	REPLACE ICM. REMOVE all test equipment. RECONNECT all components. CLEAR Continuous Memory. RERUN Quick Test.
	No	▶	GO to A24. Resistance fault.

FM1119400314100X

Fig. 32 Test A: No Start (Part 10 of 10). 1994–95 4.6L Engine

TEST STEP	RESULT	▶	ACTION TO TAKE
B1 CHECK FOR IDM AT ICM—KOER **WARNING: NEVER CONNECT THE PCM TO EEC BREAKOUT BOX WHEN PERFORMING EI DIAGNOSTICS.** • Key off. • Install EI diagnostic harness to breakout box, and to both the ICM and vehicle harness. **Do not connect CKP sensor tee or coil tees.** • Use EI (High Data Rate) 8 overlay. • Connect EI diagnostic harness negative and positive leads to battery. • Set EI diagnostic harness type switch to "8" position. • DVOM on 40 volt AC scale. • Start engine and measure voltage between (+)J30 (EI diagnostic harness IDM detector) and (-)J7 (B-) at breakout box. NOTE: If pulses are present, the IDM detector output will be between 5.0 and 7.0 volts AC. • **Is AC voltage between 5.0 and 7.0 volts?**	Yes No	▶ ▶	GO to B2. GO to B3. IDM fault.
B2 CHECK FOR IDM OPEN TO PCM—IDM FAULT—ICM AND PCM DISCONNECTED—KEY OFF • Key off. • Disconnect PCM. • Disconnect ICM from ICM tee, leave EI diagnostic harness connected to vehicle harness connector. • DVOM on 200 ohm scale. • Install a second breakout box to PCM vehicle harness connector. • Measure resistance between J41 (IDM I) at breakout box and Pin 4 at second breakout box. • **Is resistance less than 5.0 ohms?**	Yes	▶	REPLACE PCM. PCM does not respond to IDM input. REMOVE all test equipment. RECONNECT all components. CLEAR Continuous Memory. RERUN Quick Test.
	No	▶	CHECK connectors, SERVICE or REPLACE harness. IDM is open. REMOVE all test equipment. RECONNECT all components. CLEAR Continuous Memory. RERUN Quick Test.

FM1119400315010X

Fig. 33 Test B: Code 212, IDM Failure (Part 1 of 3). 1994–95 4.6L Engine

TEST STEP	RESULT	▶	ACTION TO TAKE
B3 CHECK IDM OUTPUT FROM ICM—IDM FAULT—IDM CIRCUIT OPEN—KOER • Key off. • DVOM on 40 volt AC scale. • Push and hold EI diagnostic harness IDM button down (opens IDM circuit to PCM). • Start engine and measure voltage between J30 (EI diagnostic harness IDM detector) and J7 (B-) at breakout box. • **Is AC voltage greater than 5.0 volts?**	Yes No	▶ ▶	GO to **B4**. REPLACE ICM. No IDM output from module. REMOVE all test equipment. RECONNECT all components. CLEAR Continuous Memory. RERUN Quick Test.
B4 CHECK FOR IDM SHORT IN PCM—PCM DISCONNECTED—KOEC • Key off. • Disconnect PCM. • DVOM on 40 volt AC scale. • Crank engine and measure voltage between J30 (EI diagnostic harness IDM detector) and (-)J7 (B-) at breakout box. • **Is AC voltage less than 5.0 volts?**	Yes No	▶ ▶	GO to **B5**. REPLACE PCM. PCM is loading IDM signal. REMOVE all test equipment. RECONNECT all components. CLEAR Continuous Memory. RERUN Quick Test.
B5 CHECK FOR IDM SHORT HIGH IN HARNESS—ICM AND PCM DISCONNECTED—KOEO • Key off. • DVOM on 40 volt DC scale. • Key on, engine off. • Measure voltage between (+)J41 (IDM I) and (-)J7 (B-) at breakout box. • **Is DC voltage less than 0.5 volts?**	Yes No	▶ ▶	GO to **B6**. CHECK connectors, SERVICE or REPLACE harness. IDM is shorted high. REMOVE all test equipment. RECONNECT all components. CLEAR Continuous Memory. RERUN Quick Test.

FM1119400315020X

Fig. 33 Test B: Code 212, IDM Failure (Part 2 of 3). 1994–95 4.6L Engine

TEST STEP	RESULT	▶	ACTION TO TAKE
B6 CHECK FOR IDM SHORT TO GROUND IN HARNESS—ICM AND PCM DISCONNECTED—KEY OFF • Key off. • Disconnect ICM from ICM tee, leave EI diagnostic harness connected to vehicle harness connector. • DVOM on 20K ohm scale. • Measure resistance between J41 (IDM I) and (-) J7 (B-) at breakout box. • **Is resistance greater than 10K ohms?**	Yes No	▶ ▶	CHECK connectors, SERVICE or REPLACE harness. IDM is shorted to another wire between the ICM and PCM. REMOVE all test equipment. RECONNECT all components. CLEAR Continuous Memory. RERUN Quick Test. CHECK connectors, SERVICE or REPLACE harness. IDM is shorted low. REMOVE all test equipment. RECONNECT all components. CLEAR Continuous Memory. RERUN Quick Test.

FM1119400315030X

Fig. 33 Test B: Code 212, IDM Failure (Part 3 of 3). 1994–95 4.6L Engine

TEST STEP	RESULT	▶	ACTION TO TAKE
C1 CHECK BASE TIMING—KOER **WARNING: NEVER CONNECT PCM TO EEC BREAKOUT BOX WHEN PERFORMING EI DIAGNOSTICS.** • Key off. • Install EI diagnostic harness to breakout box and to both the ICM and vehicle harness. **Do not connect the CKP sensor tee or coil tees.** • Use EI (High Data Rate) 8 overlay. • Connect EI diagnostic harness negative and positive leads to battery. • Set EI diagnostic harness type switch to "8" position. • Connect timing light (must be EI compatible). • Start engine and allow it to warm up. • **Is timing 10 ± 2 degrees BTDC when the diagnostic harness SPOUT button is pushed?**	Yes No	▶ ▶	GO to **C2**. GO to **C8**. Base timing fault.
C2 CHECK FOR SPARK ANGLE ADVANCE—KOER • **Is engine timing greater than 15 degrees BTDC when the diagnostic harness SPOUT button is released?**	Yes No	▶ ▶	Ignition System is OK. GO to **C3**. Advance spark fault.
C3 CHECK SPOUT AT ICM—KOER • Key off. • DVOM on 40 volt AC scale. • Start engine and measure voltage between J21 (EI diagnostic harness SPOUT detector) and (-)J7 (B-) at breakout box. • **Is AC voltage reading greater than 5.0 volts?**	Yes No	▶ ▶	REPLACE ICM. SPOUT input to ICM is OK, but no spark advance is present. REMOVE all test equipment. RECONNECT all components. CLEAR Continuous Memory. RERUN Quick Test. GO to **C4**. SPOUT fault.

FM1119400316010X

Fig. 34 Test C: Code 213 Or Lack Of Power Or Poor Fuel Economy (Part 1 of 3). 1994–95 4.6L Engine

TEST STEP	RESULT	▶	ACTION TO TAKE
C4 CHECK FOR SPOUT SHORT IN ICM—SPOUT FAULT—SPOUT CIRCUIT OPEN—KOER • Key off. • DVOM on 40 volt AC scale. • Push and hold EI diagnostic harness SPOUT button down (opens SPOUT circuit to ICM). • Start engine and measure voltage between (+)J21 (EI diagnostic harness SPOUT detector) and (-)J7 (B-) at breakout box. • **Is AC voltage reading greater than 5.0 volts?**	Yes No	▶ ▶	REPLACE ICM. SPOUT is shorted in ICM. REMOVE all test equipment. RECONNECT all components. CLEAR Continuous Memory. RERUN Quick Test. GO to **C5**.
C5 CHECK FOR SPOUT SHORT HIGH IN HARNESS—ICM AND PCM DISCONNECTED—KOEO • Key off. • Disconnect PCM. • Disconnect the ICM tee from the ICM, but leave the vehicle harness connected to module tee. • DVOM on 40 volt DC scale. • Key on, engine off. • Measure voltage between J45 (SPOUT I) and J7 (B-) at the breakout box. • **Is DC voltage reading less than 0.5 volts?**	Yes No	▶ ▶	GO to **C6**. CHECK connectors, SERVICE or REPLACE harness. SPOUT is shorted high. REMOVE all test equipment. RECONNECT all components. CLEAR Continuous Memory. RERUN Quick Test.
C6 CHECK FOR SPOUT SHORT TO GROUND IN HARNESS—ICM AND PCM DISCONNECTED—KEY OFF • Key off. • DVOM on 20K ohm scale. • Disconnect EI diagnostic harness positive lead to battery. • Measure resistance between J45 (SPOUT I) and J7 (B-) at breakout box. • **Is the resistance greater than 10K ohms?**	Yes No	▶ ▶	GO to **C7**. CHECK connectors, SERVICE or REPLACE harness. SPOUT is shorted low. REMOVE all test equipment. RECONNECT all components. CLEAR Continuous Memory. RERUN Quick Test.

FM1119400316020X

Fig. 34 Test C: Code 213 Or Lack Of Power Or Poor Fuel Economy (Part 2 of 3). 1994–95 4.6L Engine

TEST STEP		RESULT	▶	ACTION TO TAKE
C7	CHECK FOR SPOUT OPEN TO ICM—ICM AND PCM DISCONNECTED—KEY OFF			
	• Key off. • DVOM on 200 ohm scale. • Install a second breakout box to the vehicle harness connector. • Measure resistance between J45 (SPOUT I) at breakout box and Pin 36 at the second breakout box. • **Is resistance less than 5.0 ohms?**	Yes	▶	REPLACE PCM. SPOUT is not being transmitted by the PCM. REMOVE all test equipment. RECONNECT all components. CLEAR Continuous Memory. RERUN Quick Test.
		No	▶	CHECK connectors, SERVICE or REPLACE harness. SPOUT is open. REMOVE all test equipment. RECONNECT all components. CLEAR Continuous Memory. RERUN Quick Test.
C8	INSPECT CKP SENSOR AND TRIGGER WHEEL — TIMING FAULT			
	• Is the CKP sensor or Trigger Wheel damaged, i.e., loose or misaligned?	Yes	▶	REPLACE or SERVICE as required. REMOVE all test equipment. RECONNECT all components. CLEAR Continuous Memory. RERUN Quick Test.
		No	▶	REPLACE ICM. Incorrect output. REMOVE all test equipment. RECONNECT all components. CLEAR Continuous Memory. RERUN Quick Test.

FM1119400316030X

Fig. 34 Test C: Code 213 Or Lack Of Power Or Poor Fuel Economy (Part 3 of 3). 1994–95 4.6L Engine

TEST STEP		RESULT	▶	ACTION TO TAKE
D1	CHECK FOR SPARK DURING CRANK—KOEC			
	• Using a Neon Bulb Spark Tester (Special Service Tool D89P-6666-A) or Air Gap Spark Tester (D81P-6666-A), check for spark at all spark plug wires while cranking. • **Was spark consistent on all spark plug wires (one spark per crankshaft revolution)?**	Yes	▶	ignition system is OK.
		No	▶	GO to D2. Spark fault.
D2	CHECK FOR SPARK AT ALL RIGHT SPARK PLUG WIRES DURING CRANK—KOEC			
	• **Was spark consistent on all right spark plug wires (one spark per crankshaft revolution)?** NOTE: Check spark at spark plugs.	Yes	▶	GO to D3.
		No	▶	GO to D19.
D3	CHECK LEFT SPARK PLUGS AND WIRES—KEY OFF			
	• Check left side coil pack spark plug wires for insulation damage, looseness, shorting or other damage. • Remove and check left side spark plugs for damage, wear, carbon deposits and proper plug gap. • Left coil plugs and wires are attached to the left coil pack. • **Are spark plugs and wires OK?**	Yes	▶	REINSTALL plugs and wires. GO to D4.
		No	▶	SERVICE or REPLACE damaged component. REMOVE all test equipment. RECONNECT all components. CLEAR Continuous Memory. RERUN Quick Test.
D4	CHECK FOR COIL PWR TO LEFT COIL FAULT—KOEO			
	WARNING: NEVER CONNECT PCM TO THE EEC BREAKOUT BOX WHEN PERFORMING EI DIAGNOSTICS. • Key off. • Install EI (High Data Rate) diagnostic harness to breakout box. • Install the left coil tee. The tee is yellow (left coil). • Connect EI diagnostic harness negative lead to battery. • Use 4.6L EI (High Data Rate) 8 overlay. • Set EI harness type switch to "8" position. • DVOM on 40 volt DC scale. • Key on, engine off. • Measure voltage between (+)J11 (COIL PWR L) and (-)J7 (B-) at breakout box. • **Is DC voltage greater than 10.0 volts?**	Yes	▶	GO to D5.
		No	▶	CHECK connectors, SERVICE or REPLACE harness. COIL PWR is open to left coil. REMOVE all test equipment. RECONNECT all components. CLEAR Continuous Memory. RERUN Quick Test.

FM1119400317010X

Fig. 35 Test D: No Start Or Code 215 Or 216 And/Or coil Failure (Part 1 of 10). 1994–95 4.6L Engine

TEST STEP		RESULT	▶	ACTION TO TAKE
D5	CHECK FOR C3 HIGH AT COIL PACK—KOEO			
	• Key on, engine off. • Measure voltage between (+)J10 (LC3C) and (-)J7 (B-) at breakout box. • **Is DC voltage reading greater than 10.0 volts?**	Yes	▶	GO to D6.
		No	▶	GO to D13. C3 low fault.
D6	CHECK FOR C4 HIGH AT COIL PACK—KOEO			
	• Key on, engine off. • Measure voltage between (+)J18 (LC4C) and (-)J7 (B-) at the breakout box. • **Is DC voltage reading greater than 10.0 volts?**	Yes	▶	GO to D7.
		No	▶	GO to D15. C4 low fault.
D7	CHECK FOR C3 HIGH AT ICM—KOEO			
	• Key off. • Connect ICM tee to the ICM and vehicle harness connector. • DVOM on 40 volt DC scale. • Key on, engine off. • Measure voltage between (+)J54 (LC3I) and (-)J7 (B-) at breakout box. • **Is DC voltage reading greater than 10.0 volts?**	Yes	▶	GO to D8.
		No	▶	CHECK connectors, SERVICE or REPLACE harness. C3 is open. REMOVE all test equipment. RECONNECT all components. CLEAR Continuous Memory. RERUN Quick Test.
D8	CHECK FOR C4 HIGH AT ICM—KOEO			
	• Key on, engine off. • Measure voltage between (+)J55 (LC4I) and (-)J7 (B-) at breakout box. • **Is DC voltage reading greater than 10.0 volts?**	Yes	▶	GO to D9.
		No	▶	CHECK connectors, SERVICE or REPLACE harness. C4 is open. REMOVE all test equipment. RECONNECT all components. CLEAR Continuous Memory. RERUN Quick Test.
D9	CHECK FOR C3 LOW AT COIL CONNECTOR—COIL DISCONNECTED—KOEO			
	• Key off. • Disconnect left coil pack from coil tee, leave EI diagnostic harness connected to vehicle harness left coil connector. • DVOM on 40 volt DC scale. • Key on, engine off. • Measure voltage between (+)J10 (LC3C) and (-)J7 (B-) at breakout box. • **Is DC voltage reading less than 0.5 volts?**	Yes	▶	GO to D10.
		No	▶	GO to D17. C3 high fault.

FM1119400317020X

Fig. 35 Test D: No Start Or Code 215 Or 216 And/Or coil Failure (Part 2 of 10). 1994–95 4.6L Engine

TEST STEP		RESULT	▶	ACTION TO TAKE
D10	CHECK FOR C4 LOW AT COIL CONNECTOR—COIL DISCONNECTED—KOEO			
	• Key on, engine off. • Measure voltage between (+)J18 (LC4C) and (-)J7 (B-) at breakout box. • **Is DC voltage reading less than 0.5 volts?**	Yes	▶	GO to D11.
		No	▶	GO to D18. C4 high fault.
D11	CHECK FOR C3 AT COIL CONNECTOR WHILE CRANKING—COIL DISCONNECTED—KOEC			
	• Connect EI diagnostic harness positive lead to battery. • Connect an incandescent test lamp between J1 (B+) and J10 (LC3C). • Crank engine. • **Does lamp blink consistently and brightly (one blink per engine revolution)?**	Yes	▶	GO to D12.
		No	▶	REPLACE ICM. C3 open. REMOVE all test equipment. RECONNECT all components. CLEAR Continuous Memory. RERUN Quick Test.
D12	CHECK FOR C4 AT COIL CONNECTOR WHILE CRANKING—COIL DISCONNECTED—KOEC			
	• Connect an incandescent test lamp between J1 (B+) and J18 (LC4C). • Crank engine. • **Does lamp blink consistently and brightly (one blink per engine revolution)?**	Yes	▶	REPLACE left coil pack. Input to coil pack is OK, but no high voltage output. REMOVE all test equipment. RECONNECT all components. CLEAR Continuous Memory. RERUN Quick Test.
		No	▶	REPLACE ICM. C4 open in ICM. REMOVE all test equipment. RECONNECT all components. CLEAR Continuous Memory. RERUN Quick Test.
D13	CHECK FOR C3 SHORT LOW—COIL DISCONNECTED—KEY OFF			
	• Key off. • DVOM on 20K ohm scale. • Disconnect coil from coil tee, leave EI diagnostic harness connected to vehicle harness coil connector. • Measure resistance between J7 (B-) and J10 (C3C) at breakout box. • **Is resistance reading less than 2K ohms?**	Yes	▶	GO to D14.
		No	▶	REPLACE Left Coil Pack. C3 short in coil. REMOVE all test equipment. RECONNECT all components. CLEAR Continuous Memory. RERUN Quick Test.

FM1119400317030X

Fig. 35 Test D: No Start Or Code 215 Or 216 And/Or coil Failure (Part 3 of 10). 1994–95 4.6L Engine

TEST STEP	RESULT	▶	ACTION TO TAKE
D14 CHECK FOR C3 SHORT LOW—ICM AND COIL DISCONNECTED—KEY OFF • Key off. • Disconnect ICM from vehicle harness. • DVOM on 20K ohm scale. • Measure resistance between J7 (B-) and J10 (C3C) at breakout box. • **Is resistance greater than 10K ohms?**	Yes	▶	REPLACE ICM. C3 is shorted low. REMOVE all test equipment. RECONNECT all components. CLEAR Continuous Memory. RERUN Quick Test.
	No	▶	CHECK connectors, SERVICE or REPLACE harness. C3 is shorted low. REMOVE all test equipment. RECONNECT all components. CLEAR Continuous Memory. RERUN Quick Test.
D15 CHECK FOR C4 SHORT LOW—COIL DISCONNECTED—KEY OFF • Key off. • DVOM on 20K ohm scale. • Disconnect coil from coil tee, leave EI diagnostic harness connected to vehicle harness coil connector. • Measure resistance between J7 (B-) and J18 (LC4C) at breakout box. • **Is resistance reading less than 2K ohms?**	Yes	▶	GO to D16.
	No	▶	REPLACE left coil pack. C4 open in coil. REMOVE all test equipment. RECONNECT all components. CLEAR Continuous Memory. RERUN Quick Test.
D16 CHECK FOR C4 SHORT LOW—ICM AND COIL DISCONNECTED—KEY OFF • Key off. • Disconnect ICM from vehicle harness connector. • DVOM on 20K ohm scale. • Measure resistance between J7 (B-) and J18 (LC4C) at breakout box. • **Is resistance reading greater than 10K ohms?**	Yes	▶	REPLACE ICM. C4 is shorted low. REMOVE all test equipment. RECONNECT all components. CLEAR Continuous Memory. RERUN Quick Test.
	No	▶	CHECK connectors, SERVICE or REPLACE harness. C4 is shorted low. REMOVE all test equipment. RECONNECT all components. CLEAR Continuous Memory. RERUN Quick Test.

FM1119400317040X

Fig. 35   Test D: No Start Or Code 215 Or 216 And/Or coil Failure (Part 4 of 10). 1994–95 4.6L Engine

TEST STEP	RESULT	▶	ACTION TO TAKE
D17 CHECK FOR C3 LOW—ICM AND COIL DISCONNECTED—KOEO • Key off. • Disconnect ICM from the ICM tee, leave EI diagnostic harness connected to vehicle harness connector. • DVOM on 40 volt DC scale. • Key on, engine off. • Measure voltage between (+)J10 (LC3C) and (-)J7 (B-) at breakout box. • **Is DC voltage reading less than 0.5 volts?**	Yes	▶	REPLACE ICM. C3 is shorted high. REMOVE all test equipment. RECONNECT all components. CLEAR Continuous Memory. RERUN Quick Test.
	No	▶	CHECK connectors, SERVICE or REPLACE harness. C3 is shorted high. REMOVE all test equipment. RECONNECT all components. CLEAR Continuous Memory. RERUN Quick Test.
D18 CHECK FOR C4 LOW—ICM AND COIL DISCONNECTED—KOEO • Key off. • Disconnect ICM from ICM tee, leave EI diagnostic harness connected to vehicle harness connector. • DVOM on 40 volt DC scale. • Key on, engine off. • Measure voltage between (+)J18 (LC4C) and (-)J7 (B-) at breakout box. • **Is DC voltage reading less than 0.5 volts?**	Yes	▶	REPLACE ICM. C4 is shorted high. REMOVE all test equipment. RECONNECT all components. CLEAR Continuous Memory. RERUN Quick Test.
	No	▶	CHECK connectors, SERVICE or REPLACE harness. C4 is shorted high. REMOVE all test equipment. RECONNECT all components. CLEAR Continuous Memory. RERUN Quick Test.

FM1119400317050X

Fig. 35   Test D: No Start Or Code 215 Or 216 And/Or coil Failure (Part 5 of 10). 1994–95 4.6L Engine

TEST STEP	RESULT	▶	ACTION TO TAKE
D19 CHECK RIGHT PLUGS AND WIRES—KEY OFF • Check right side coil pack spark plug wires for insulation damage, looseness, shorting or other damage. • Remove and check right spark plugs for damage, wear, carbon deposits and proper plug gap. NOTE: Right coil plugs and wires are attached to the right coil. • **Are spark plugs and wires OK?**	Yes	▶	REINSTALL plugs and wires. GO to D20.
	No	▶	SERVICE or REPLACE damaged component. REMOVE all test equipment. RECONNECT all components. CLEAR Continuous Memory. RERUN Quick Test.
D20 CHECK FOR RIGHT COIL PWR—KOEO WARNING: NEVER CONNECT PCM TO THE EEC BREAKOUT BOX WHEN PERFORMING EI DIAGNOSTICS. • Key off. • Install EI diagnostic harness to the breakout box. • Connect EI diagnostic harness negative lead to battery. • Install the right coil tee. • Use 4.6L EI (High Data Rate) 8 overlay. • DVOM on 40 volt DC scale. • Set EI harness box type switch to 8 cylinder position. • Key on, engine off. • Measure voltage between (+)J5 (COIL PWR R) and (-)J7 (B-) at breakout box. • **Is DC voltage greater than 10.0 volts?**	Yes	▶	GO to D21.
	No	▶	CHECK connectors, SERVICE or REPLACE harness. COIL PWR is open to right coil. REMOVE all test equipment. RECONNECT all components. CLEAR Continuous Memory. RERUN Quick Test.
D21 CHECK FOR C1 HIGH AT RIGHT COIL PACK—KOEO • DVOM on 40 volt DC scale. • Key on, engine off. • Measure voltage between (+)J3 (RC1C) and (-)J7 (B-) at breakout box. • **Is DC voltage reading greater than 10.0 volts?**	Yes	▶	GO to D22.
	No	▶	GO to D29. C1 low fault.
D22 CHECK FOR C2 HIGH AT RIGHT COIL PACK • Key on, engine off. • Measure voltage between (+)J6 (RC2C) and (-)J7 (B-) at breakout box. • **Is DC voltage reading greater than 10.0 volts?**	Yes	▶	GO to D23.
	No	▶	GO to D31. C2 low fault.

FM1119400317060X

Fig. 35   Test D: No Start Or Code 215 Or 216 And/Or coil Failure (Part 6 of 10). 1994–95 4.6L Engine

TEST STEP	RESULT	▶	ACTION TO TAKE
D23 CHECK FOR C1 HIGH AT ICM—KOEO • Key off. • Connect ICM tee to the ICM and vehicle harness connector. • DVOM on 40 volt DC scale. • Key on, engine off. • Measure voltage between (+)J51 (RC1I) and (-)J7 (B-) at breakout box. • **Is DC voltage reading greater than 10.0 volts?**	Yes	▶	GO to D24.
	No	▶	CHECK connectors, SERVICE or REPLACE harness. C1 is open. REMOVE all test equipment. RECONNECT all components. CLEAR Continuous Memory. RERUN Quick Test.
D24 CHECK FOR C2 HIGH AT ICM • Key on, engine off. • Measure voltage between (+)J27 (RC2I) and (-)J7 (B-) at breakout box. • **Is DC voltage reading greater than 10.0 volts?**	Yes	▶	GO to D25.
	No	▶	CHECK connectors, SERVICE or REPLACE harness. C2 is open. REMOVE all test equipment. RECONNECT all components. CLEAR Continuous Memory. RERUN Quick Test.
D25 CHECK C1 LOW AT COIL CONNECTOR—COIL DISCONNECTED • Key off. • Disconnect right coil from coil tee, leave EI diagnostic harness connected to vehicle harness right coil connector. • DVOM on 40 volt DC scale. • Key on, engine off. • Measure voltage between (+)J3 (RC1C) and (-)J7 (B-) at breakout box. • **Is DC voltage reading less than 0.5 volts?**	Yes	▶	GO to D26.
	No	▶	GO to D33. C1 high fault.
D26 CHECK FOR C2 LOW AT COIL CONNECTOR—COIL DISCONNECTED • Key on, engine off. • Measure voltage between (+)J6 (RC2C) and (-)J7 (B-) at breakout box. • **Is DC voltage reading less than 0.5 volts?**	Yes	▶	GO to D27.
	No	▶	GO to D34. C2 high fault.

FM1119400317070X

Fig. 35   Test D: No Start Or Code 215 Or 216 And/Or coil Failure (Part 7 of 10). 1994–95 4.6L Engine

TEST STEP	RESULT	▶	ACTION TO TAKE
D27 CHECK C1 AT COIL CONNECTOR WHILE CRANKING ENGINE—COIL DISCONNECTED • Connect EI diagnostic harness positive lead to battery. • Connect an incandescent test lamp between J1 (B+) and J3 (RC1C). • Crank engine. • **Does lamp blink consistently and brightly (one blink per engine revolution)?**	Yes No	▶ ▶	GO TO **D28**. REPLACE ICM. C1 is open. REMOVE all test equipment. RECONNECT all components. CLEAR Continuous Memory. RERUN Quick Test.
D28 CHECK C2 AT COIL CONNECTOR WHILE CRANKING ENGINE—COIL DISCONNECTED • Connect an incandescent test lamp between J1 (B+) and J6 (RC2C). • Crank engine. • **Does lamp blink consistently and brightly (one blink per engine revolution)?**	Yes No	▶ ▶	REPLACE Right Coil Pack. Input to coil pack is OK, but no high voltage output. REMOVE all test equipment. RECONNECT all components. CLEAR Continuous Memory. RERUN Quick Test. REPLACE ICM. C2 is open in ICM. REMOVE all test equipment. RECONNECT all components. CLEAR Continuous Memory. RERUN Quick Test.
D29 CHECK FOR C1 SHORT LOW—COIL DISCONNECTED • Key off. • DVOM on 20K ohm scale. • Disconnect coil from coil tee, leave EI diagnostic harness connected to vehicle harness coil connector. • Measure resistance between J7 (B-) and J3 (RC1C) at breakout box. • **Is resistance reading less than 2K ohms?**	Yes No	▶ ▶	GO to **D30**. REPLACE Right Coil Pack. C1 is open in coil. REMOVE all test equipment. RECONNECT all components. CLEAR Continuous Memory. RERUN Quick Test.

FM1119400317080X

Fig. 35   Test D: No Start Or Code 215 Or 216 And/Or coil Failure (Part 8 of 10). 1994–95 4.6L Engine

TEST STEP	RESULT	▶	ACTION TO TAKE
D30 CHECK FOR C1 SHORT LOW—ICM AND COIL DISCONNECTED • Key off. • Disconnect ICM from vehicle harness. • DVOM on 20K ohm scale. • Measure resistance between J7 (B-) and J3 (RC1C) at breakout box. • **Is resistance reading greater than 10K ohms?**	Yes No	▶ ▶	REPLACE ICM. C1 is shorted low. REMOVE all test equipment. RECONNECT all components. CLEAR Continuous Memory. RERUN Quick Test. CHECK connectors, SERVICE or REPLACE harness. C1 is shorted to low. REMOVE all test equipment. RECONNECT all components. CLEAR Continuous Memory. RERUN Quick Test.
D31 CHECK FOR C2 SHORT LOW—COIL DISCONNECTED • Key off. • DVOM on 20K ohm scale. • Disconnect coil from coil tee, leave EI diagnostic harness connected to vehicle harness coil connector. • Measure resistance between J7 (B-) and J6 (RC2C) at breakout box. • **Is resistance reading less than 2K ohms?**	Yes No	▶ ▶	GO to **D32**. REPLACE Right Coil Pack. C2 open in coil. REMOVE all test equipment. RECONNECT all components. CLEAR Continuous Memory. RERUN Quick Test.
D32 CHECK FOR C2 SHORT LOW—ICM AND COIL DISCONNECTED • Key off. • Disconnect ICM from vehicle harness. • DVOM on 20K ohm scale. • Measure resistance between J6 (RC2C) and J7 (B-) at breakout box. • **Is resistance reading greater than 10K ohms?**	Yes No	▶ ▶	REPLACE ICM. C2 is shorted low. REMOVE all test equipment. RECONNECT all components. CLEAR Continuous Memory. RERUN Quick Test. CHECK connectors, SERVICE or REPLACE harness. C2 is shorted low. REMOVE all test equipment. RECONNECT all components. CLEAR Continuous Memory. RERUN Quick Test.

FM1119400317090X

Fig. 35   Test D: No Start Or Code 215 Or 216 And/Or coil Failure (Part 9 of 10). 1994–95 4.6L Engine

TEST STEP	RESULT	▶	ACTION TO TAKE
D33 CHECK FOR C1 HIGH—ICM AND COIL DISCONNECTED • Key off. • Disconnect ICM from ICM tee, leave EI diagnostic harness connected to vehicle harness connector. • DVOM on 40 volt DC scale. • Key on, engine off. • Measure voltage between (+)J3 (RC1C) and (-)J7 (B-) at breakout box. • **Is DC voltage reading less than 0.5 volts?**	Yes No	▶ ▶	REPLACE ICM. REMOVE all test equipment. RECONNECT all components. CLEAR Continuous Memory. RERUN Quick Test. CHECK connectors, SERVICE or REPLACE harness. C1 is shorted high. REMOVE all test equipment. RECONNECT all components. CLEAR Continuous Memory. RERUN Quick Test.
D34 CHECK FOR C2 LOW—ICM AND COIL DISCONNECTED—KOEO • Key off. • Disconnect ICM from ICM tee, leave EI diagnostic harness connected to vehicle harness connector. • DVOM on 40 volt DC scale. • Key on, engine off. • Measure voltage between (+)J6 (RC2C) and (-)J7 (B-) at breakout box. • **Is DC voltage reading less than 0.5 volts?**	Yes No	▶ ▶	REPLACE ICM. REMOVE all test equipment. RECONNECT all components. CLEAR Continuous Memory. RERUN Quick Test. CHECK connectors, SERVICE or REPLACE harness. C2 is shorted high. REMOVE all test equipment. RECONNECT all components. CLEAR Continuous Memory. RERUN Quick Test.

FM1119400317100X

Fig. 35   Test D: No Start Or Code 215 Or 216 And/Or coil Failure (Part 10 of 10). 1994–95 4.6L Engine

Type 5

NOTE: If Unsure Of The System Used On The Vehicle Being Serviced, Refer To The "Engine Systems Identification Chart." Further Assistance For The Proper Use Of Information Contained In This Section Can Also Be Found In The Front Of This Tabbed Section Under "How To Use This Manual."

INDEX

Page No.		Page No.		Page No.
Description...................... 4-105		Component Replacement......... 4-109		Ignition Module............... 4-115
Diagnosis & Testing:............. 4-105		Condenser................... 4-116		Suppression Capacitor 4-116
Quick Test................... 4-106		Distributor Assembly........... 4-109		Component Service.............. 4-106
Specifications 4-126		Ignition Coil 4-114		Distributor Assembly........... 4-106
System Service:................. 4-106				

DESCRIPTION

These ignition systems provide spark control to the engine during all modes of operation, and consist of three sub systems: primary ignition, secondary ignition and timing advance.

The primary ignition system consists of the coil primary circuit, power relay, ignition module and ignition switch. When the ignition switch is placed in On position, the power relay closes and charges the primary coil windings. When the engine is running, the ignition module grounds the negative side of the coil primary circuit which actuates spark.

The secondary ignition system consists of the spark plugs, spark plug wires, distributor cap, rotor, coil wire and coil secondary circuit. When the ignition module grounds the primary circuit, the inductive charge built up in the secondary circuit sends a spark from the coil to the distributor.

The timing advance system on 1.6L engines consists of governor weights and a dual diaphragm vacuum advance to control timing advance. On 1.6L Turbo engines, governor weights, a knock controller and a vacuum advance/boost retard diaphragm are used to control timing advance. On 2.2L engines, a vacuum advance/retard diaphragm, a vacuum delay valve and governor weights are used to control timing advance. All other engines use the ECA or PCM to determine spark advance and retard functions.

The 1.8L engine uses a TI3 module which relays spark control signals from the ECA to the coil. The 2.2L Turbo uses the TI5 module which receives signals from the ECA to spark control, grounds the coil negative side and sends a feedback signal to the ECA. TI3 and TI5 modules are mounted on the coil bracket. 1.6L, 1.6L Turbo and 2.2L engines use a DMIVA module which operates independantly from the ECA. DMIVA modules are located inside the distributor.

DIAGNOSIS & TESTING

Refer to **Figs. 1 through 17,** for diagnosis and testing of TI3, TI5, DMIVA, Aspire and Probe DI systems.

System Inspection

1. Visually inspect the components of the ignition system.

   Look for:

ELECTRICAL	MECHANICAL
● Discharged Battery	● Damaged Vacuum Hoses to Distributor
● Damaged, Loose Connections	● Damaged or Worn Distributor Cap and Rotor
● Damaged Insulation	● Damaged Spark Plugs
● Poor Coil, Distributor and Spark Plug Connections	● Distributor Cap, Rotor and Spark Plug Wires are Properly Seated
● Ignition Module Connection Loose or Corroded	
● Blown Fuses	

2. Check the vehicle's maintenance schedule to ensure the spark plugs and the wires have been properly maintained.

3. Check the spark plug wires and boots for signs of poor insulation that could cause cross firing.

4. A damaged or worn timing belt can cause symptoms that appear to be ignition timing related. Refer to the shop manual basic engine section if necessary.

5. Make sure the engine idle speed is within specification.

Fig. 1   System Inspection. 1993

System Inspection

1. Visually inspect the components of the ignition system.

VISUAL INSPECTION CHART

Mechanical	Electrical
● Damaged or worn distributor cap and rotor	● Discharged battery
● Damaged spark plugs	● Damaged or loose connectors
● Improperly seated spark plug, distributor cap or rotor	● Damaged insulation
● Corroded, contaminated, or carbon fouled distributor cap	● Poor coil, distributor and spark plug connections
	● Blown fuses

2. Check the vehicle's maintenance schedule to ensure that the spark plugs and the wires have been properly maintained.

3. Check the spark plug wires and boots for signs of poor insulation that could cause cross firing.

4. A damaged or worn timing belt can cause symptoms that appear to be timing related.

5. Make sure the engine idle speed and base timing is within specification.

   NOTE: For ignition system diagnostics on all engines except the 2.0L MTX go to IGN1. For 2.0L MTX, see symptom chart below.

2.0L MTX SYMPTOM CHART

Symptom	Action To Take
Engine no start and clear codes	GO to IGNA1.
Engine no start and code 211 - PIP circuit failure	GO to IGNA1.
Code 212 - IDM missing	GO to IGNB1.
Timing off, code 213 - Spark Output (SPOUT) open, lack of power, poor fuel economy	GO to IGNC1.
Clear codes or code 211 - intermittent miss or stall	GO to IGND1.
Clear codes and misfire under load - secondary short to ground	GO to IGN3.
Car continues to run after key is turned to OFF	CHECK ICM PWR for short to battery power.

Fig. 2   System Inspection. 1994

System Inspection

1. Visually inspect the components of the ignition system.

VISUAL INSPECTION CHART

Mechanical	Electrical
● Damaged or worn distributor cap and rotor	● Discharged battery
● Damaged spark plugs	● Damaged or loose connectors
● Improperly seated spark plug, distributor cap, or rotor	● Damaged insulation
● Corroded, contaminated, or carbon fouled distributor cap	● Poor coil, distributor and spark plug connections
	● Blown fuses

2. Check the vehicle's maintenance schedule to ensure that the spark plugs and the wires have been properly maintained.

3. Check the spark plug wires and boots for signs of poor insulation that could cause cross firing.

4. A damaged or worn timing belt can cause symptoms that appear to be timing related. Refer to the service manual basic engine section if necessary.

5. Make sure the engine idle speed and base timing are within specification.

6. Refer to the appropriate Symptom Chart.

SYMPTOM CHART — 1.3L, 1.8L, 2.5L

Symptom	Action To Take
Engine No Start	GO to Pinpoint Test IGN1
Engine Runs Rough	GO to Pinpoint Test IGN1
Engine Stalls	GO to Pinpoint Test IGN1
Lack of Power / Poor Fuel Economy	GO to Pinpoint Test IGN1

SYMPTOM CHART — 2.0L

Symptom	Action To Take
Engine No Start and No Codes	GO to Pinpoint Test IGNA1
Engine No Start and Code 211 - PIP Circuit Failure	GO to Pinpoint Test IGNA1
Code 212 - IDM Missing	GO to Pinpoint Test IGNB1
Timing Off, Code 213 - Spark Output (SPOUT) Open, Lack of Power, Poor Fuel Economy	GO to Pinpoint Test IGNC1
Clear Codes or Code 211 - Intermittent Miss or Stall	GO to Pinpoint Test IGND1
Clear Codes and Misfire Under Load - Secondary Short to Ground	GO to Pinpoint Test IGN3
Engine Continues to Run After Key is Turned to OFF	CHECK ICM PWR for short to battery power.

Fig. 3 System Inspection. 1995

QUICK TEST

Refer to "Computerized Engine Controls for Quick Test.

SYSTEM SERVICE

Component Service

DISTRIBUTOR ASSEMBLY

ASPIRE, ESCORT, FESTIVA, PROBE w/2.0L, 2.2L TURBOCHARGED & 2.5L ENGINES & TRACER

The distributor cannot be disassembled. If the distributor is malfunctioning or defective, it must be replaced.

CAPRI w/1.6L NON-TURBOCHARGED ENGINE

Refer to **Fig. 18** when servicing this distributor.

Disassembly

1. Remove rotor, pick-up unit and radio noise suppressor, then disconnect electrical connectors from igniter. Note location for reassembly.
2. Remove igniter screws, then, using suitable puller, pull armature and pin from upper shaft.
3. Remove igniter assembly, then the screws and mounting plate.
4. Remove clip and screws from vacuum control unit, then the vacuum control unit.
5. Remove breaker plate screws, then the breaker plate assembly.
6. Remove advance plate snap ring, then the advance plate and spacer.
7. Mark upper shaft and advance weight pin with paint, then remove upper shaft screw and shaft.
8. Mark position of lower shaft to drive collar with paint, then drive out roll pin with suitable punch.
9. Remove bearing plate screws, then the lower shaft.
10. Remove clips and springs from advance weight, then the advance weights.
11. If necessary, press off bearing from lower shaft, and/or remove oil seal from housing.

Inspection

Wipe all distributor components clean using a clean cloth. Carefully inspect O-rings and replace if required. Check distributor base for excessive wear and/or damage. Inspect lower shaft for looseness or binding. Lubricate all pivoting and sliding surfaces with grease ESF-M2C70-A or equivalent. Apply a thin, even film of silicone dielectric compound D7AZ-19A331-A or equivalent to the igniter mounting surface.

Assembly

1. If necessary, press bearing onto lower shaft, and/or install oil seal in housing.
2. Install advance weights, clips and springs, then the lower shaft into housing.
3. Install bearing plate screws, then install drive collar onto lower shaft.
4. Align paint marks, then drive in roll pin flush with collar outer surface.
5. Install upper shaft and align paint marks, then install screw in upper shaft.
6. Install spacer, advance plate and snap ring, then the breaker plate and screws.
7. Position vacuum control unit on housing, ensuring actuating arm is installed on stud of breaker plate, then install vacuum control unit screws and actuating arm clip.
8. Position mounting plate and secure with screws.
9. Position igniter assembly and secure with screws.
10. Using suitable socket and palm of your hand, press armature and pin onto upper shaft until it bottoms against shoulder of upper shaft.
11. Connect electrical connectors to igniter, then install radio noise suppressor, pick-up unit and rotor.

CAPRI w/1.6L TURBOCHARGED ENGINE

Refer to **Fig. 19** when servicing distributor.

Disassembly

1. Remove distributor rotor, then the dust cover and signal rotor.
2. Disconnect electrical connector from pick-up assembly, then remove pick-up assembly screws and pick-up assembly.

TEST STEP		RESULT	▶	ACTION TO TAKE
IGN1	CHECK FIRING ORDER			
	• Inspect the routing of the spark plug wires. • Make sure the wires follow the firing order 1-3-4-2 on all engines except 2.5L (1-2-3-4-5-6 on 2.5L). • **Is firing order OK?**	Yes No	▶ ▶	GO to IGN2. SERVICE as required.
IGN2	TEST SPARK AT PLUG(S)			
	• Connect a Rotunda Air Gap Spark Tester D81P-6666-A, or equivalent between the spark plug wire (plug end) and ground. Crank the engine, repeat on all spark plug wires. • **Does spark jump at each wire?**	Yes (Engine Runs) Yes (Engine Does Not Run) No (1.3L, 1.6L and 1.8L) No (2.0L 4EAT and 2.5L)	▶ ▶ ▶ ▶	INSPECT the spark plugs, GO to IGN3. GO to ELECTRIC FUEL PUMPS GO to IGN10. GO to IGN11.

Fig. 4   Test IGN: System Check (Part 1 of 11). 1993

TEST STEP		RESULT	▶	ACTION TO TAKE
IGN3	CHECK SECONDARY DISPLAY		▶	GO to IGN4.
	NOTE: If this portion of the diagnostic procedure is to provide accurate results, it is essential that the calibration of your engine analyzer be maintained. Refer to your equipment manual. If this is not available, an estimate of the calibration can be made by connecting the spark tester to a properly operating ignition system and measuring the firing voltage of the spark tester only. Do not include the firing voltage to the rotor-to-cap gap. The spark tester firing voltage should be approximately 28KV.			
	• Connect a Rotunda Engine Analyzer 002-00373, or equivalent to view parade display of ignition secondary system. • Slowly increase the engine rpm from idle to 2000 rpm, and compare the engine analyzer display to the following illustrations.			

Fig. 4   Test IGN: System Check (Part 2 of 11). 1993

3. Remove mounting plate screws and mounting plate, then the snap armature and pin snap ring.
4. Using suitable puller, pull armature and pin from upper shaft.
5. Disconnect electrical connectors from igniter, noting location for reassembly, then remove igniter screws and igniter.
6. Remove spacer plate screws, then the spacer plate.
7. If necessary, remove electrical harness screw and harness.
8. Remove clip and screws from vacuum control unit, then the vacuum control unit.

9. Remove breaker plate, then the snap ring and advance plate.
10. Remove upper shaft, advance springs and advance weights.
11. Drive out drive assembly roll pin through lower shaft and remove drive assembly.
12. Remove lower shaft and, if necessary, oil seal.

Inspection

Refer to "Capri w/1.6L Non-Turbocharged Engine."

Assembly

1. If necessary, install oil seal.

2. Install lower shaft into housing, then position drive assembly onto lower shaft. Align holes and install roll pin.
3. Install advance weights and springs, upper shaft, advance plate and snap ring and breaker plate.
4. Position vacuum control unit, ensuring actuating arm is installed on stud of breaker plate, then install vacuum control unit retaining screws and clip.
5. If necessary, install electrical harness screw and harness.
6. Position igniter, then install igniter screws and connect electrical connectors.
7. Using suitable socket and palm of

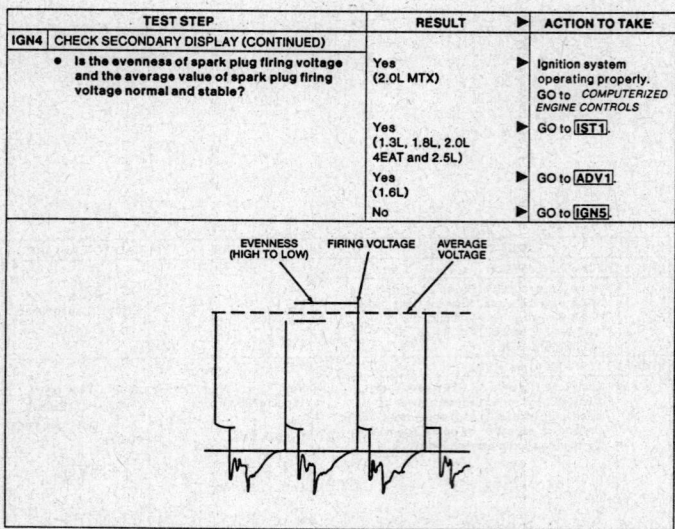

TEST STEP	RESULT	▶	ACTION TO TAKE
IGN4 CHECK SECONDARY DISPLAY (CONTINUED)			
• Is the evenness of spark plug firing voltage and the average value of spark plug firing voltage normal and stable?	Yes (2.0L MTX)	▶	Ignition system operating properly. GO to *COMPUTERIZED ENGINE CONTROLS*
	Yes (1.3L, 1.8L, 2.0L 4EAT and 2.5L)	▶	GO to IST1.
	Yes (1.6L)	▶	GO to ADV1.
	No	▶	GO to IGN5.

Fig. 4   Test IGN: System Check (Part 3 of 11). 1993

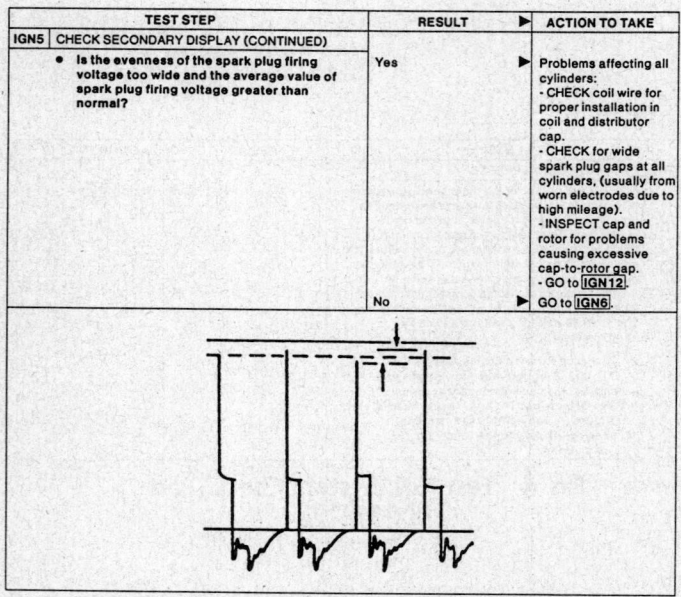

TEST STEP	RESULT	▶	ACTION TO TAKE
IGN5 CHECK SECONDARY DISPLAY (CONTINUED)			
• Is the evenness of the spark plug firing voltage too wide and the average value of spark plug firing voltage greater than normal?	Yes	▶	Problems affecting all cylinders: - CHECK coil wire for proper installation in coil and distributor cap. - CHECK for wide spark plug gaps at all cylinders, (usually from worn electrodes due to high mileage). - INSPECT cap and rotor for problems causing excessive cap-to-rotor gap. - GO to IGN12.
	No	▶	GO to IGN6.

Fig. 4   Test IGN: System Check (Part 4 of 11). 1993

your hand, press armature and pin onto upper shaft until it bottoms against shoulder of upper shaft.

8. Install armature and pin snap ring, then the mounting plate with screws.
9. Install pick-up assembly and screws, then connect electrical connector on pick-up assembly.
10. Position signal rotor onto upper shaft and secure with screw, then install dust cover and distributor rotor.

PROBE w/2.2L NON-TURBOCHARGED ENGINE

Disassembly

1. Remove rotor, cover and gasket.
2. Mark position of lower shaft to drive cog, then remove drive cog pin and drive cog.
3. Remove signal rotor screw, then, us-

ing puller tool No. D80L-1002-L, or equivalent, remove signal rotor and pin from upper shaft. Note direction of arrow stamped into rotor.

4. Disconnect pick-up coil wires, noting wire location for proper installation.
5. Remove electrical harness from distributor housing.
6. Remove pickup coil screws, then the pickup coil.
7. Remove pickup coil mounting plate

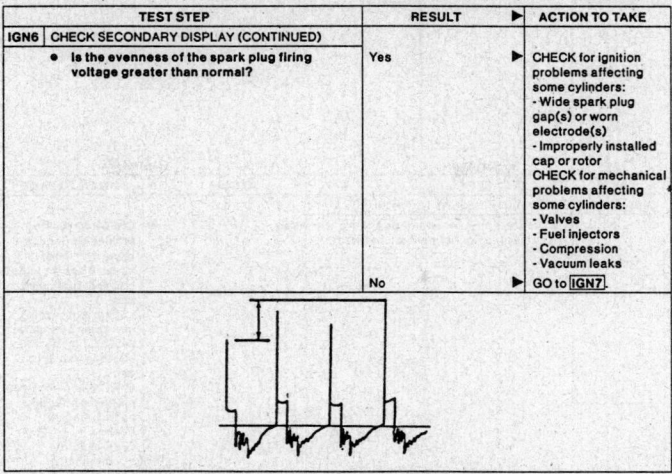

TEST STEP	RESULT	▶	ACTION TO TAKE
IGN6 CHECK SECONDARY DISPLAY (CONTINUED)			
• Is the evenness of the spark plug firing voltage greater than normal?	Yes	▶	CHECK for ignition problems affecting some cylinders: - Wide spark plug gap(s) or worn electrode(s) - Improperly installed cap or rotor CHECK for mechanical problems affecting some cylinders: - Valves - Fuel injectors - Compression - Vacuum leaks
	No	▶	GO to IGN7.

Fig. 4   Test IGN: System Check (Part 5 of 11). 1993

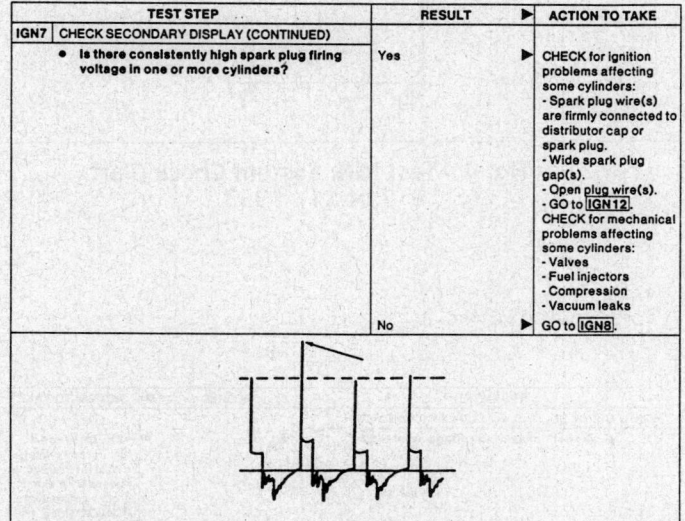

TEST STEP	RESULT	▶	ACTION TO TAKE
IGN7 CHECK SECONDARY DISPLAY (CONTINUED)			
• Is there consistently high spark plug firing voltage in one or more cylinders?	Yes	▶	CHECK for ignition problems affecting some cylinders: - Spark plug wire(s) are firmly connected to distributor cap or spark plug. - Wide spark plug gap(s). - Open plug wire(s). - GO to IGN12. CHECK for mechanical problems affecting some cylinders: - Valves - Fuel injectors - Compression - Vacuum leaks
	No	▶	GO to IGN8.

Fig. 4   Test IGN: System Check (Part 6 of 11). 1993

screws, then the mounting plate.
8. Remove stator plate E-clips, then the vacuum diaphragm screws and vacuum diaphragm.
9. Remove stator plate screws, stator plate and upper shaft, then the stator from upper shaft.
10. Remove lower shaft screws, then the lower shaft from distributor housing.
11. Remove two E-clips, springs, weights, bearing and retainer from lower shaft.
12. Remove seal from distributor housing.

Assembly

1. Install new seal into distributor housing.
2. Install bearing, retainer, weights, springs and E-clips onto lower shaft. Ensure weight pivot pins engage advance mechanism.
3. Install upper shaft onto lower shaft, then seat shaft assembly to distributor housing and install shaft screws. Ensure bearing retainer aligns with housing recess.
4. Install stator plate, vacuum diaphragm, E-clips, pickup coil mounting plate and electrical harness.
5. Install pickup coil and connect electrical harness.
6. Using socket, press signal rotor and pin onto upper shaft until seated against shoulder of upper shaft. Note direction of arrow stamped in rotor.
7. Align marks on drive cog and lower shaft made during disassembly, then install drive cog and pin.
8. Install gasket and cover, then the rotor.

Component Replacement

DISTRIBUTOR ASSEMBLY

ASPIRE

1. Disconnect battery ground cable, then remove distributor cap screws.
2. Remove distributor cap and position aside, then disconnect distributor electrical connectors.
3. Scribe reference mark across distributor base flange and cylinder head for installation, then note position of rotor.
4. Remove distributor bolts, then the distributor.
5. Remove and discard distributor O-ring from distributor.
6. Reverse procedure to install, noting the following:
   a. **Torque** distributor bolts to 14-19 ft. lbs.
   b. If new distributor is installed, check and adjust ignition timing as necessary.

CAPRI

1. Disconnect battery ground cable.
2. Disconnect vacuum hose from vacuum control unit, then the electrical connectors.
3. Disconnect coil wire from distributor cap, then remove distributor cap screws and position cap and spark plug wires aside.

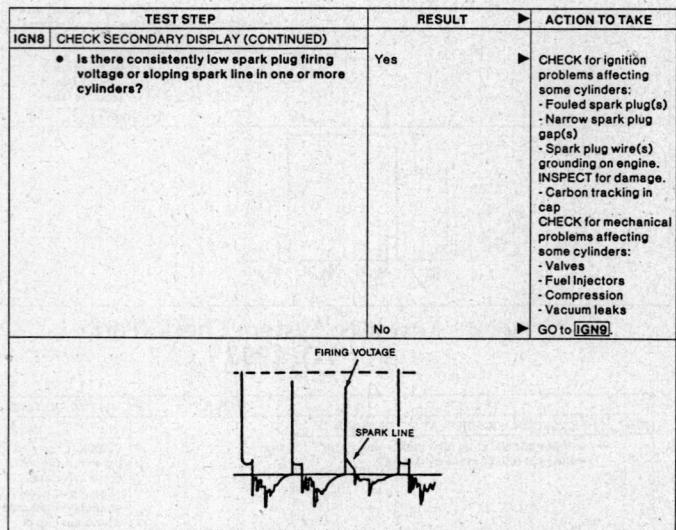

TEST STEP	RESULT	▶	ACTION TO TAKE
IGN8 CHECK SECONDARY DISPLAY (CONTINUED)			
• Is there consistently low spark plug firing voltage or sloping spark line in one or more cylinders?	Yes	▶	CHECK for ignition problems affecting some cylinders: - Fouled spark plug(s) - Narrow spark plug gap(s) - Spark plug wire(s) grounding on engine. INSPECT for damage. - Carbon tracking in cap CHECK for mechanical problems affecting some cylinders: - Valves - Fuel Injectors - Compression - Vacuum leaks
	No	▶	GO to IGN9.

Fig. 4   Test IGN: System Check (Part 7 of 11). 1993

TEST STEP	RESULT	▶	ACTION TO TAKE
IGN9 CHECK SECONDARY DISPLAY (CONTINUED)			
• Is spark plug firing voltage reversed?	Yes	▶	- CHECK to see if ignition coil primary circuit is reversed. If necessary make proper connections. - CHECK wiring harness for ignition coil primary circuit. If OK, REPLACE ignition coil (1.3L, 1.6L, 1.8L and 2.0L MTX) or distributor (2.0L 4EAT and 2.5L).
	No (all except 2.0L MTX)	▶	GO to IGN12.
	No (2.0L MTX)	▶	REEVALUATE symptom and RETURN to symptom chart
IGN10 CHECK SPARK FROM COIL			
• Connect a spark tester between coil secondary output terminal and ground. • Crank the engine. • Does spark jump?	Yes	▶	GO to IGN11.
	No	▶	GO to IGN13.
IGN11 CHECK DISTRIBUTOR ASSEMBLY			
• Check rotor, distributor cap, armature and module for wear, breakage, cracks and carbon buildup (black buildup) and oxidation (white buildup). • Crank the engine and verify the rotor turns steadily. • Is the distributor assembly OK and does the rotor turn freely?	Yes	▶	GO to IGN12.
	No	▶	SERVICE as required.

Fig. 4   Test IGN: System Check (Part 8 of 11). 1993

TEST STEP	RESULT	▶	ACTION TO TAKE
IGN12 CHECK SPARK PLUG WIRE RESISTANCE			
• Remove spark plug wire. CAUTION: Do not under any circumstances puncture a spark plug wire when measuring resistance. Measure only as instructed. • Measure the resistance of each spark plug wire. • Is the resistance between 4,000-7,000 ohms per foot?	Yes (1.3L and 1.8L)	▶	GO to IST1
	Yes (1.6L)	▶	GO to ADV1
	Yes (2.0L MTX)	▶	REEVALUATE symptom and RETURN to symptom chart
	Yes (2.0L 4EAT and 2.5L)	▶	GO to IGN13
	No	▶	REPLACE the spark plug wire(s).

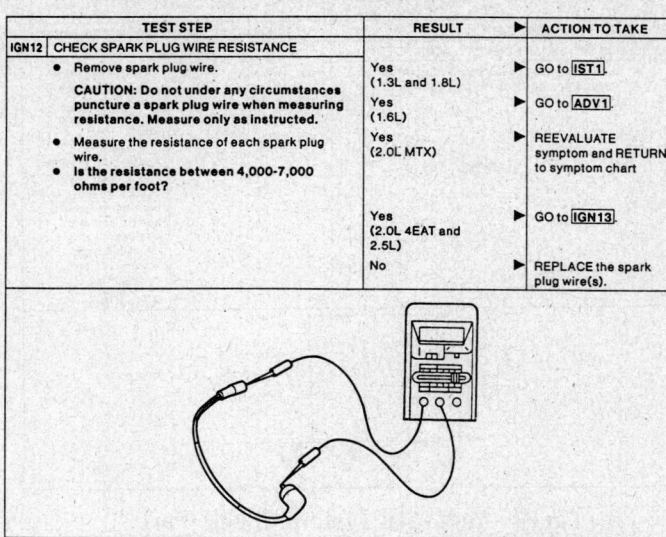

Fig. 4 Test IGN: System Check (Part 9 of 11). 1993

TEST STEP	RESULT	▶	ACTION TO TAKE
IGN14 CHECK IGNITION COIL RESISTANCE			

Engine	Coil	Terminals	Resistance
1.3L, 1.6L, 1.8L	Primary	Positive to negative	0.8 to 1.6 ohms
	Secondary	Positive to high voltage	6 to 30 kohms
2.0L 4EAT	Primary	Positive to negative	0.58 to 1.10 ohms
	Secondary	Positive to high voltage	1.15 to 18.5 kohma
2.5L	Primary	Positive to negative	0.58 to 0.86 ohms
	Secondary	Positive to high voltage	1.15 to 18.5 kohma

• Disconnect the wire(s) from the ignition coil.
• Measure:
• Are the resistance readings within specifications?

RESULT / ACTION:
Yes (1.3L, 1.6L and 1.8L) ▶ GO to EEC Pinpoint Test IDM
Yes (2.0L 4EAT and 2.5L) ▶ GO to EEC Pinpoint Test ICM
No ▶ REPLACE the ignition coil (1.3L, 1.6L and 1.8L) or distributor (2.0L 4EAT and 2.5L).

1.3L, 1.6L and 1.8L

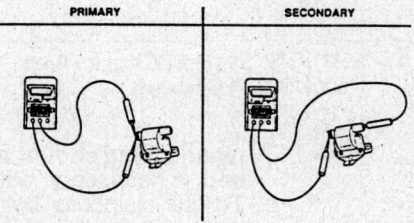

2.0L 4EAT and 2.5L

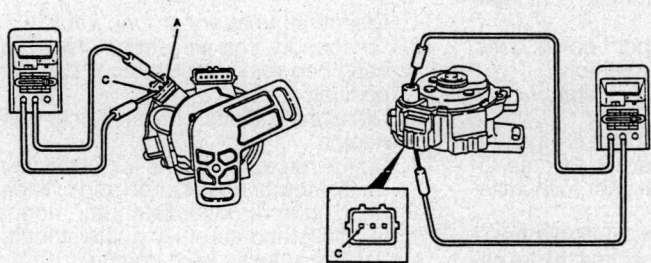

Fig. 4 Test IGN: System Check (Part 11 of 11). 1993

TEST STEP	RESULT	▶	ACTION TO TAKE
IGN13 CHECK VOLTAGE AT IGNITION COIL			
• Disconnect the ignition coil connector (on distributor). • Key ON. • Measure the voltage on the follow wire at the ignition coil connector (on distributor for 2.0L 4EAT and 2.5L).	Yes	▶	GO to IGN14
	No	▶	SERVICE the wire between the ignition switch and the ignition coil connector.

Engine	Wire Color
1.3L	BK/W
1.6L	BK/W
1.8L	BL
2.0L 4EAT	BK/PK
2.5L	BK/PK

• Is the voltage greater than 10 volts?

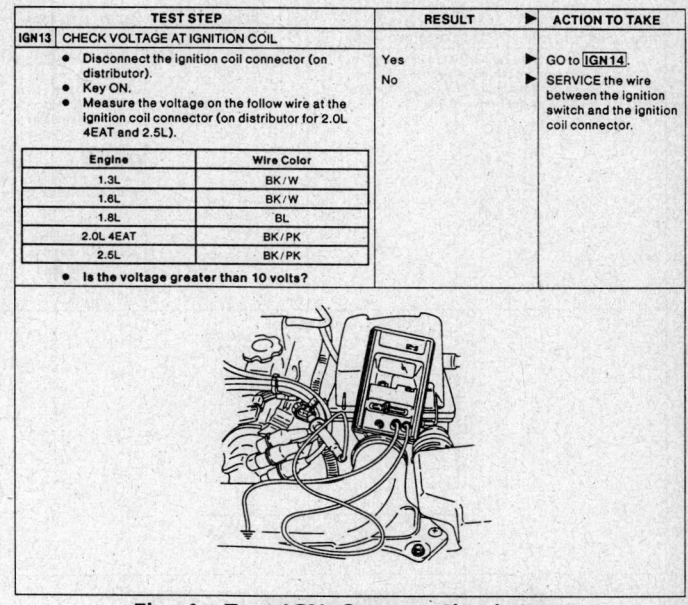

Fig. 4 Test IGN: System Check (Part 10 of 11). 1993

TEST STEP	RESULT	▶	ACTION TO TAKE
IGN1 CHECK FIRING ORDER			
• Inspect the routing of the spark plug wires. • Make sure the wires follow the firing order 1-3-4-2 on all engines except 2.5L (1-2-3-4-5-6 on 2.5L). • Is firing order OK?	Yes	▶	GO to IGN2
	No	▶	SERVICE as required.
IGN2 TEST SPARK AT PLUG(S)			
• Connect an Air Gap Spark Tester D81P-6666-A, or equivalent between the spark plug wire (plug end) and ground. Crank the engine, repeat on all spark plug wires. • Does spark jump at each wire?	Yes (Engine Runs)	▶	INSPECT the spark plugs, GO to IGN3
	Yes (Engine Does Not Run)	▶	GO to TURBOCHARGERS & SUPERCHARGERS
	No (1.6L and 1.8L)	▶	GO to IGN9
	No (1.3L and 2.5L)	▶	GO to IGN10

Fig. 5 Test IGN: System Check (Part 1 of 10). 1994 1.6L & 1994–95 1.3L, 1.8L & 2.5L Engines

TEST STEP	RESULT	▶	ACTION TO TAKE
IGN3 CHECK SECONDARY DISPLAY			
NOTE: If this portion of the diagnostic procedure is to provide accurate results, it is essential that the calibration of your engine analyzer be maintained. Refer to your equipment manual. If this is not available, an estimate of the calibration can be made by connecting the spark tester to a properly operating ignition system and measuring the firing voltage of the spark tester only. Do not include the firing voltage to the cap-to-rotor gap. The spark tester firing voltage should be approximately 28KV (±10%). • Connect a Rotunda Engine Analyzer 010-00575, or equivalent to view parade display of ignition secondary system. • Slowly increase the engine rpm from idle to 2000 rpm, and compare the engine analyzer display to the illustrations in the next six test steps. • Is the evenness of spark plug firing voltage and the average value of spark plug firing voltage normal and stable?	Yes (2.0L)	▶	Ignition system operating properly. RETURN to COMPUTERIZED ENGINE CONTROLS
	Yes (1.3L, 1.8L, and 2.5L)	▶	GO to IST1
	Yes (1.6L)	▶	GO to ADV1
	No	▶	GO to IGN4

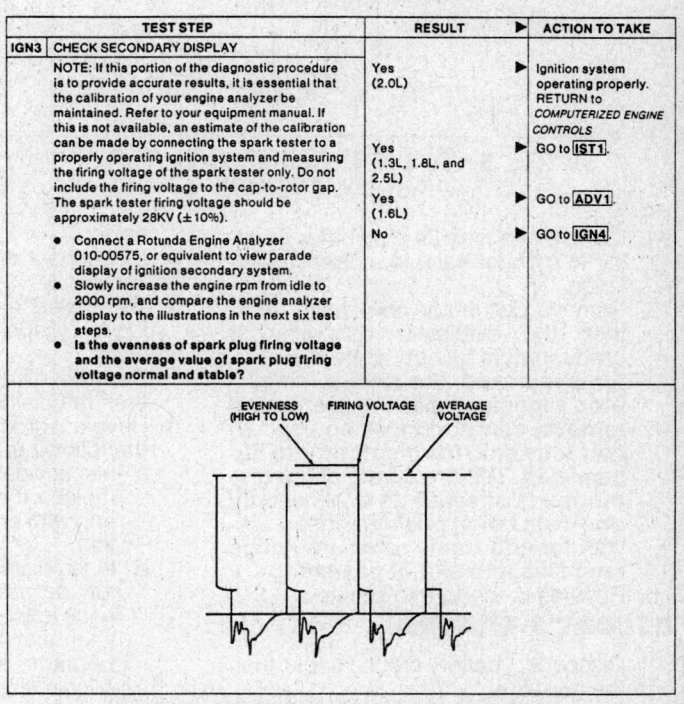

Fig. 5 Test IGN: System Check (Part 2 of 10). 1994–95

TEST STEP		RESULT	▶	ACTION TO TAKE
IGN4	CHECK SECONDARY DISPLAY (CONTINUED)			
• Are both the evenness of the spark plug firing voltage too wide and the average value of spark plug firing voltage greater than the normal value of 28KV?		Yes	▶	Problems affecting all cylinders: - CHECK coil wire for proper installation in coil and distributor cap. - CHECK for wide spark plug gaps at all cylinders, (usually from worn electrodes due to high mileage). - INSPECT cap and rotor for problems causing excessive cap-to-rotor gap. - GO to IGN11.
		No	▶	GO to IGN5.

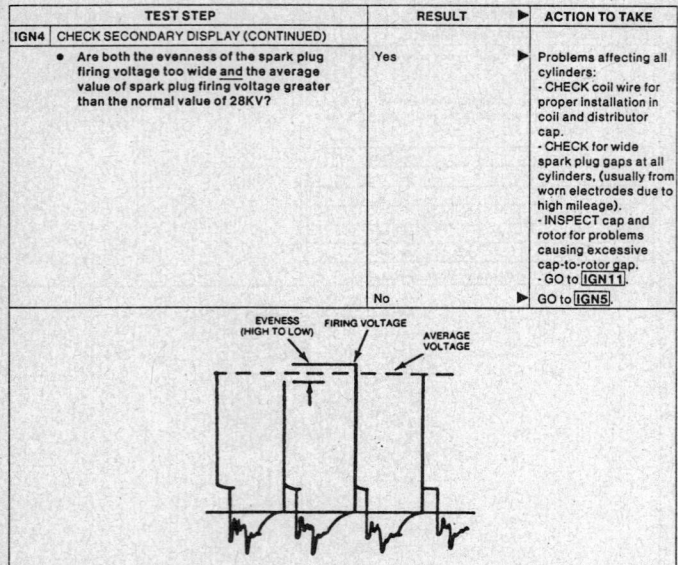

Fig. 5 Test IGN: System Check (Part 3 of 10). 1994–95

TEST STEP		RESULT	▶	ACTION TO TAKE
IGN5	CHECK SECONDARY DISPLAY (CONTINUED)			
• Is the evenness of the spark plug firing voltage greater than normal voltage of 28KV?		Yes	▶	CHECK for ignition problems affecting some cylinders: - Wide spark plug gap(s) or worn electrode(s) - Improperly installed cap or rotor CHECK for mechanical problems affecting some cylinders: - Valves - Fuel injectors - Compression - Vacuum leaks
		No	▶	GO to IGN6.

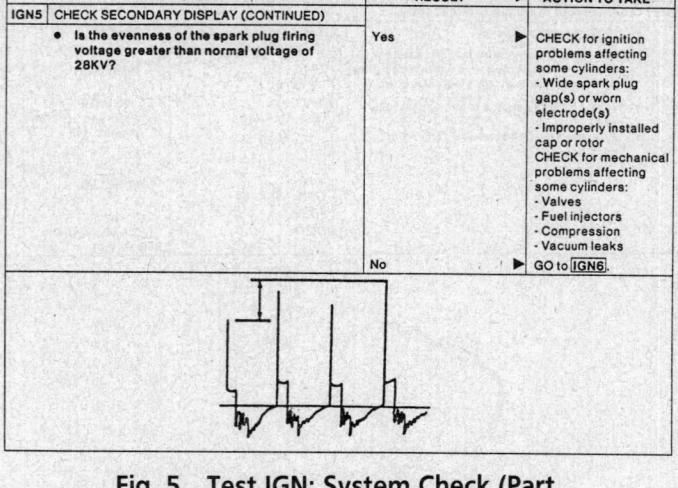

Fig. 5 Test IGN: System Check (Part 4 of 10). 1994–95

TEST STEP		RESULT	▶	ACTION TO TAKE
IGN6	CHECK SECONDARY DISPLAY (CONTINUED)			
• Is there consistently high spark plug firing voltage in one or more cylinders?		Yes	▶	CHECK for ignition problems affecting some cylinders: - Spark plug wire(s) are firmly connected to distributor cap or spark plug. - Wide spark plug gap(s). - Open plug wire(s). - CHECK for mechanical problems affecting some cylinders: - Valves - Fuel injectors - Compression - Vacuum leaks - GO to IGN11.
		No	▶	GO to IGN7.

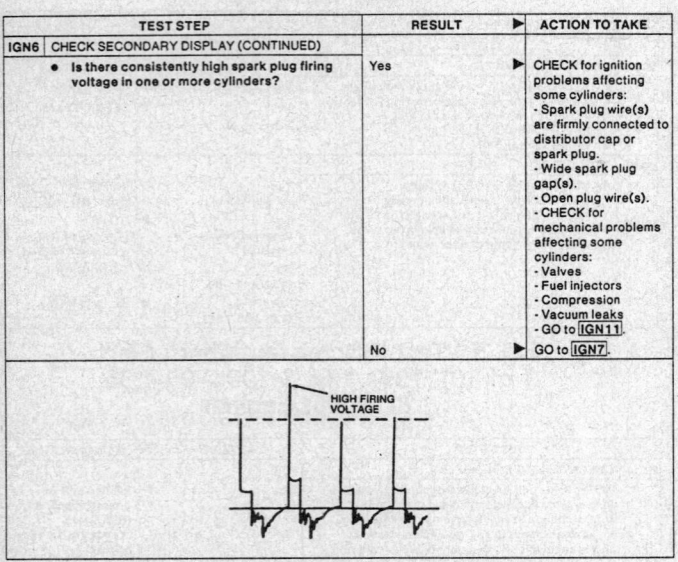

Fig. 5 Test IGN: System Check (Part 5 of 10). 1994–95

TEST STEP		RESULT	▶	ACTION TO TAKE
IGN7	CHECK SECONDARY DISPLAY (CONTINUED)			
• Is there consistently low spark plug firing voltage or sloping spark line in one or more cylinders?		Yes	▶	CHECK for ignition problems affecting some cylinders: - Fouled spark plug(s) - Narrow spark plug gap(s) - Spark plug wire(s) grounding on engine. INSPECT for damage. - Carbon tracking in cap CHECK for mechanical problems affecting some cylinders: - Valves - Fuel injectors - Compression - Vacuum leaks
		No	▶	GO to IGN8.

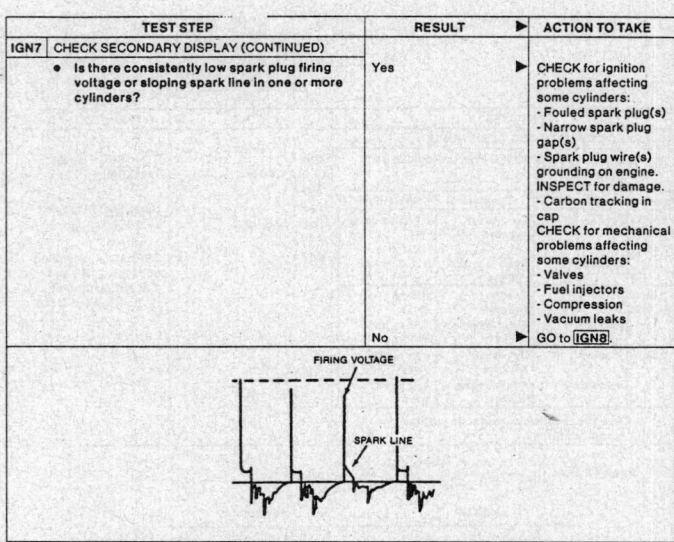

Fig. 5 Test IGN: System Check (Part 6 of 10). 1994–95

4. Mark relationship of distributor housing to cylinder head for correct installation.
5. Remove distributor hold-down bolts, then the distributor assembly. **If crankshaft is turned while distributor is removed, the rotor to distributor alignment mark made during removal can no longer be used to correctly time the distributor to the camshaft. The drive tang of the distributor is offset so as to allow only one installation position. Insert distributor and rotate rotor until drive tang falls into slot of camshaft.**
6. Reverse procedure to install.

ESCORT & TRACER

1. Disconnect battery ground cable, then the coil wire.
2. Remove distributor cap screws, then position cap and spark plug wires aside.
3. Disconnect distributor electrical connector.
4. Mark relationship of distributor housing to cylinder head for correct installation.
5. Remove distributor hold-down bolts, then the distributor assembly.
6. Reverse procedure to install, noting the following:
   a. Inspect distributor base O-ring and replace if necessary. Lubricate O-ring with engine oil prior to installation.
   b. Insert distributor into cylinder head, turning rotor as necessary to engage offset drive tang with camshaft slot. **Rotor position should be same as when removed.**
   c. Align reference marks made during removal.
   d. **If new distributor is installed, ignition timing should be checked and, if necessary, adjusted.**
   e. **Torque** distributor bolts to 14-19 ft. lbs., then the distributor cap screws to 14-26 inch lbs.

FESTIVA

1. Disconnect battery ground cable.
2. Disconnect coil wire from distributor cap, then remove distributor cap and position aside.
3. Disconnect distributor electrical connector.
4. Scribe reference marks for installation on distributor base flange and cylinder head, then remove distributor mounting bolts and carefully pull distributor assembly away from engine.
5. Reverse procedure to install, noting the following:
   a. Inspect distributor base O-ring and replace if necessary. Lubricate O-ring with engine oil before installing.

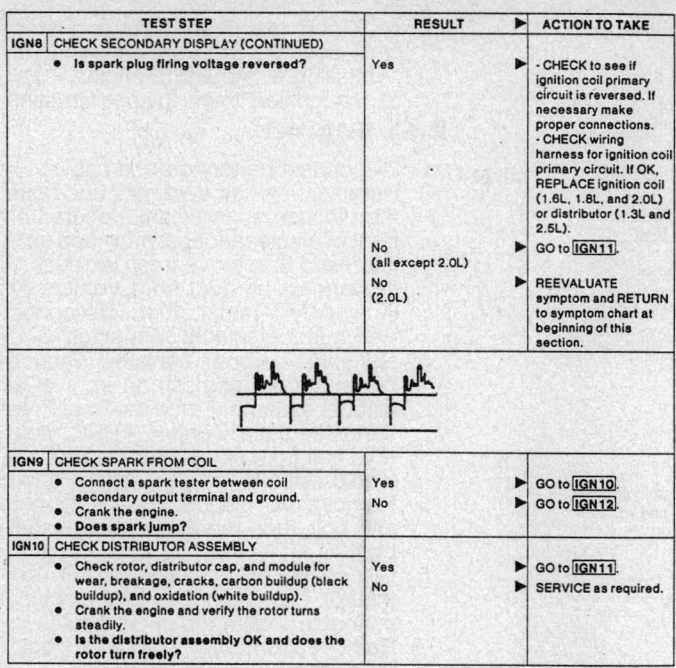

TEST STEP	RESULT	▶	ACTION TO TAKE
IGN8 CHECK SECONDARY DISPLAY (CONTINUED)			
• Is spark plug firing voltage reversed?	Yes	▶	- CHECK to see if ignition coil primary circuit is reversed. If necessary make proper connections. - CHECK wiring harness for ignition coil primary circuit. If OK, REPLACE ignition coil (1.6L, 1.8L, and 2.0L) or distributor (1.3L and 2.5L).
	No (all except 2.0L)	▶	GO to **IGN11**.
	No (2.0L)	▶	REEVALUATE symptom and RETURN to symptom chart at beginning of this section.
IGN9 CHECK SPARK FROM COIL			
• Connect a spark tester between coil secondary output terminal and ground. • Crank the engine. • **Does spark jump?**	Yes	▶	GO to **IGN10**.
	No	▶	GO to **IGN12**.
IGN10 CHECK DISTRIBUTOR ASSEMBLY			
• Check rotor, distributor cap, and module for wear, breakage, cracks, carbon buildup (black buildup), and oxidation (white buildup). • Crank the engine and verify the rotor turns steadily. • Is the distributor assembly OK and does the rotor turn freely?	Yes	▶	GO to **IGN11**.
	No	▶	SERVICE as required.

Fig. 5 Test IGN: System Check (Part 7 of 10). 1994–95

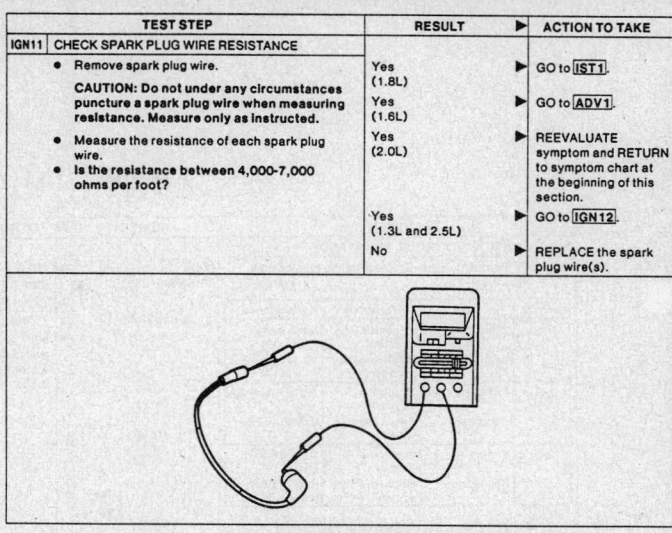

TEST STEP	RESULT	▶	ACTION TO TAKE
IGN11 CHECK SPARK PLUG WIRE RESISTANCE			
• Remove spark plug wire. **CAUTION: Do not under any circumstances puncture a spark plug wire when measuring resistance. Measure only as instructed.** • Measure the resistance of each spark plug wire. • Is the resistance between 4,000–7,000 ohms per foot?	Yes (1.8L)	▶	GO to **IST1**.
	Yes (1.6L)	▶	GO to **ADV1**.
	Yes (2.0L)	▶	REEVALUATE symptom and RETURN to symptom chart at the beginning of this section.
	Yes (1.3L and 2.5L)	▶	GO to **IGN12**.
	No	▶	REPLACE the spark plug wire(s).

Fig. 5 Test IGN: System Check (Part 8 of 10). 1994–95

TEST STEP	RESULT	▶	ACTION TO TAKE
IGN12 CHECK VOLTAGE AT IGNITION COIL			
• Disconnect the ignition coil connector (on distributor). • Key ON. • Measure the voltage on the following wire at the ignition coil connector (on distributor for 1.3L and 2.5L).	Yes	▶	GO to **IGN13**.
	No	▶	SERVICE the wire between the ignition switch and the ignition coil connector.

Engine	Wire Color
1.3L	BL
1.6L	BK/W
1.8L	BL
2.5L	BK/PK

• Is the voltage greater than 10 volts?

Fig. 5 Test IGN: System Check (Part 9 of 10). 1994 1.6L & 1994–95 1.3L, 1.8L & 2.5L Engines

b. Insert distributor into cylinder head, turning rotor as necessary to engage offset drive tang with camshaft slot. **Rotor position should be same as when removed.**

c. Align reference marks made during removal.

d. **If new distributor has been installed, ignition timing should be checked and, if necessary, adjusted.**

PROBE

2.0L Engine

1. Disconnect battery ground cable, then disconnect distributor electrical connector.

2. **On 1993 models equipped with automatic transaxle,** disconnect coil electrical connector.

3. **On all models,** remove distributor cap and position aside, then rotate engine until No. 1 piston is at TDC on compression stroke.

4. Remove distributor hold-down bolt(s), then the distributor.

5. Reverse procedure to install, noting the following:

a. Match up alignment marks on distributor shaft and housing and apply oil to O-ring before installation.

b. Ensure distributor drive gear is engaged into camshaft distributor drive gear.

c. Ensure rotor points to No. 1 wire tower after installation. If not, pull distributor out and rotate shaft to next tooth and install. Repeat this step until rotor is aligned with No. 1 wire tower.

d. Temporarily tighten hold-down bolt(s), then adjust ignition timing, if necessary.

e. **Torque** distributor hold-down bolt(s) to 14-18 ft. lbs.

2.2L Engine

1. Disconnect battery ground cable.

2. **On models less turbocharger,** proceed as follows:

a. Disconnect distributor vacuum hoses, noting location of each hose for proper installation.

b. Disconnect distributor electrical connector from coil, noting wire location for proper installation.

3. **On models equipped with turbocharger,** disconnect distributor electrical connector near distributor.

4. **On all models,** remove distributor cap and position aside.

5. Position No. 1 piston at TDC on compression stroke.

6. Mark position of distributor in engine and position of rotor on distributor housing for installation reference.

7. Remove distributor hold-down bolts, then lift distributor out of engine. **Do not crank engine after distributor has been removed.**

8. Reverse procedure to install, noting the following:

a. Ensure No. 1 piston is at TDC on compression stroke.

b. Install new O-ring onto distributor shaft and lubricate O-ring with engine oil.

TEST STEP				RESULT	▶	ACTION TO TAKE
IGN13	**CHECK IGNITION COIL RESISTANCE**					
• Disconnect the wire(s) from the ignition coil. • Measure:				Yes (1.6L and 1.8L)	▶	GO to EEC Pinpoint Test **IDM**.
Engine	Coil	Terminals	Resistance	Yes (1.3L and 2.5L)	▶	GO to EEC Pinpoint Test **ICM**.
1.3L	Primary	Positive to negative	0.5-0.7 ohms	No	▶	REPLACE the ignition coil (1.6L and 1.8L) or distributor (1.3L and 2.5L).
	Secondary	Positive to high voltage	20-31 k-ohms			
1.6L, 1.8L	Primary	Positive to negative	0.8 to 1.6 ohms			
	Secondary	Positive to high voltage	6 to 30 k-ohms			
2.5L	Primary	Positive to negative	0.58 to 0.86 ohms			
	Secondary	Positive to high voltage	1.15 to 18.5 k-ohms			

NOTE: Refer to illustrations after Test Steps.

• **Are the resistance readings within specifications?**

1.3L

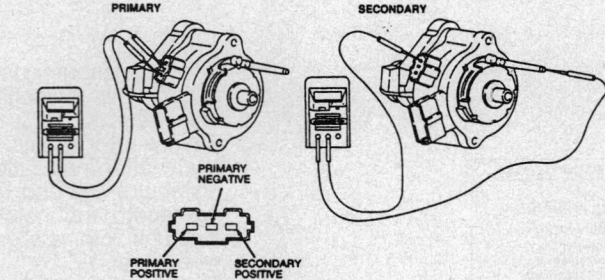

1.6L and 1.8L

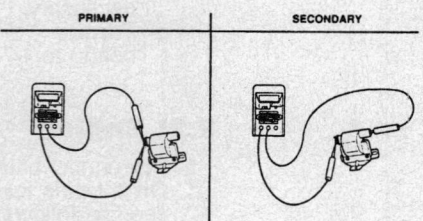

2.5L

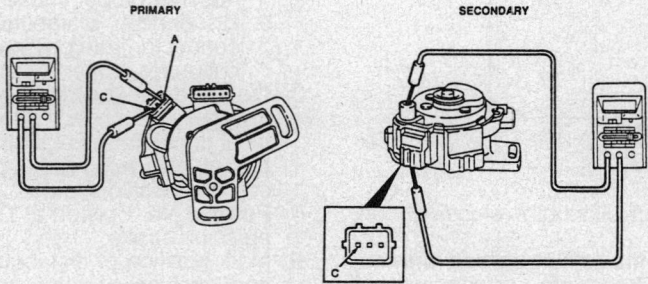

Fig. 5   Test IGN: System Check (Part 10 Of 10). 1994 1.6L & 1994-95 1.3L, 1.8L & 2.5L Engines

c. Ensure distributor drive cog is engaged into camshaft slot when installing distributor to engine.
d. Set ignition timing to specifications.

2.5L Engine

1. Disconnect battery ground cable.
2. Remove fresh air duct nuts and bolts, then loosen spring clamp located on front of air cleaner assembly and slide it forward to remove fresh air duct.
3. Disconnect air duct from Volume Air Flow (VAF) meter, then disconnect VAF meter electrical connector.
4. Remove carbon canister vacuum hose from routing clip on front of air cleaner assembly, then the Fuel Pressure Regulator Control (FPRC) solenoid bolt from air cleaner. Position solenoid aside.
5. Remove air cleaner assembly nuts and bolt, then the air cleaner assembly.
6. Disconnect spark plug wires from distributor cap, then the two electrical connectors from top of distributor.
7. Remove distributor hold-down bolts, then the distributor.
8. Reverse procedure to install, noting the following:
   a. Align distributor shaft with camshaft end and install. **One tang of distributor shaft is larger than other to allow installation of distributor in one direction only.**
   b. **Torque** air cleaner nuts and bolt to 14-18 ft. lbs., then the fresh air duct nuts and bolts to 71-88 inch lbs.
   c. Check and adjust ignition timing if necessary, then **torque** distributor hold-down bolts to 14-18 ft. lbs.

IGNITION COIL

ASPIRE

The ignition coil is part of the distributor and cannot be serviced. If the ignition coil requires service, the distributor must be replaced.

CAPRI

1. Disconnect battery ground cable.
2. Disconnect coil secondary lead off coil tower.
3. Disconnect electrical connectors from coil, remove attaching bolts, then the coil from air cleaner housing.
4. Reverse procedure to install.

ESCORT & TRACER

1. Disconnect battery ground cable.
2. Disconnect coil secondary lead off coil tower.
3. Disconnect electrical connectors from coil, remove nuts, then the coil and bracket assembly.
4. Remove bracket from coil.
5. Reverse procedure to install.

FESTIVA

1. Disconnect battery ground cable.
2. Disconnect coil secondary lead off coil tower.

Idle Speed and Timing Adjustments (IST) (1.3L, 1.8L, 2.0L 4EAT, 2.5L)

TEST STEP		RESULT	▶	ACTION TO TAKE
IST1	CHECK IDLE SPEED			
• Start the engine and run until at normal operating temperature. • Engine at idle. • All electrical loads off. • Connect Rotunda Digital Photoelectric Tachometer 055-00108, or equivalent. • Ground STI connector. • Compare idle speed with chart:		Yes No	▶ ▶	GO to IST2. ADJUST idle speed.

Engine	Idle Speed
1.3L MTX	700 ± 20 rpm
1.3L ATX	850 ± 20 rpm
1.8L	750 ± 50 rpm
2.0L 4EAT	700 ± 50 rpm
2.5L	650 ± 50 rpm

• Is idle speed within specifications?

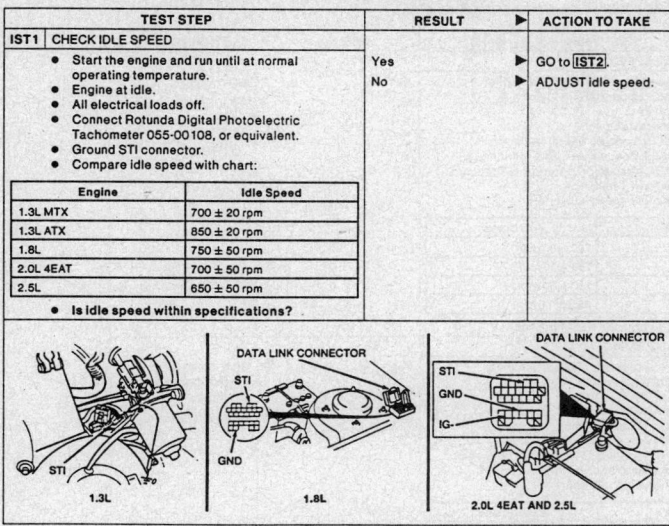

Fig. 6 Test IST: Idle Speed & Timing Adjustments (Part 1 of 2). 1993

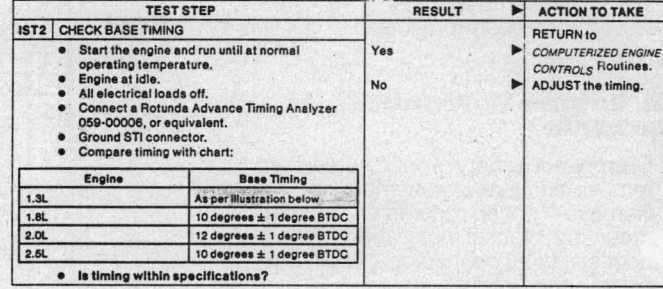

TEST STEP		RESULT	▶	ACTION TO TAKE
IST2	CHECK BASE TIMING			
• Start the engine and run until at normal operating temperature. • Engine at idle. • All electrical loads off. • Connect a Rotunda Advance Timing Analyzer 059-00006, or equivalent. • Ground STI connector. • Compare timing with chart:		Yes No	▶ ▶	RETURN to COMPUTERIZED ENGINE CONTROLS Routines. ADJUST the timing.

Engine	Base Timing
1.3L	As per illustration below
1.8L	10 degrees ± 1 degree BTDC
2.0L	12 degrees ± 1 degree BTDC
2.5L	10 degrees ± 1 degree BTDC

• Is timing within specifications?

1.3L
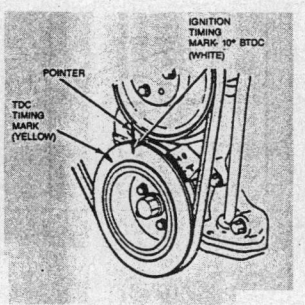

1.8L
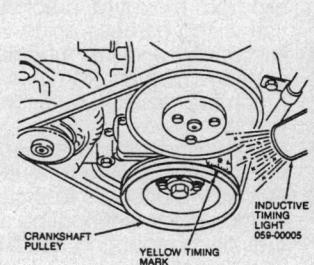

2.0L
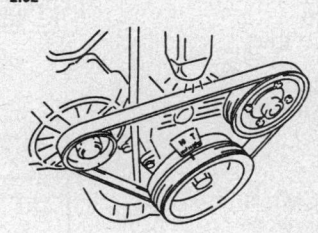

2.5L

Fig. 6 Test IST: Idle Speed & Timing Adjustments (Part 2 of 2). 1993

3. Disconnect electrical connector from coil, remove nuts, screws and bracket from coil, then the coil.
4. Reverse procedure to install.

PROBE

1993 2.0L Engine w/Manual Transaxle

1. Disconnect battery ground cable, then the coil secondary lead off coil tower.
2. Remove ignition coil connector cover, then disconnect electrical connector from ignition coil.
3. Remove ignition coil attaching nut, then the ignition coil.
4. Reverse procedure to install. **Torque** attaching nut to 71-88 inch lbs.

1993 2.0L Engine w/Automatic Transaxle

The ignition coil is integral with the distributor. If the ignition coil requires replacement, the distributor assembly must be replaced.

1994–95 2.0L Engine

1. Disconnect battery ground cable, then remove ignition coil to distributor high tension wiring from ignition coil by first twisting, then pulling from ignition coil terminal.
2. Pull ignition coil connector cover off the connector, then disconnect ignition coil connector from ignition coil.
3. Remove ignition coil nut, then the ignition coil.
4. Reverse procedure to install. **Torque** ignition coil nut to 71-88 inch lbs.

2.2L Non-Turbocharged Engine

1. Disconnect battery ground cable.
2. Disconnect coil secondary lead off coil tower.

3. Disconnect electrical connectors from coil, remove nuts, then the coil and bracket assembly.
4. Loosen clamp screw at coil bracket, then remove coil.
5. Reverse procedure to install.

2.2L Turbocharged Engine

1. Disconnect battery ground cable.
2. Disconnect coil secondary lead off coil tower.
3. Disconnect igniter electrical harness, remove nuts, then lift coil and igniter assembly to gain access to coil and noise suppressor electrical harness.
4. Disconnect coil and noise suppressor electrical harnesses, then remove noise suppressor.
5. Remove screws and igniter assembly, then the igniter module mounting bracket and coil.
6. Reverse procedure to install.

2.5L Engine

The ignition coil is part of the distributor and cannot be serviced. If the ignition coil requires service, the distributor must be replaced.

IGNITION MODULE

ASPIRE

The ignition module is part of the distributor and cannot be serviced. If the ignition module requires service, the distributor must be replaced.

ESCORT, FESTIVA & TRACER

Electronic modules are sensitive to static electrical charges. If exposed to these charges, damage may result. Static charge generation may be created by walking across carpeting or over a vinyl floor, working at a bench or sliding across a vehicle seat.

Leave electronic modules in their original packaging until ready to install, avoid touching module connector pins or laying module on nonconductive surfaces. As an added safeguard, use a 3M Static Protection Kit 18293 or equivalent, when replacing electronic module.

1. Disconnect battery ground cable, then the electrical connector from ignition module.

2. Remove ignition module nuts and screws, then the module.
3. Reverse procedure to install.

PROBE

2.0L Engine w/Manual Transaxle

1. Disconnect battery ground cable, then remove air cleaner assembly.
2. Remove speed control actuator mounting bracket nuts, then disconnect electrical connector and position aside.
3. Disconnect wiring harness mounting clip from mounting bracket and position wiring harness aside.
4. Disconnect ignition module electrical connector, then remove fuel filter mounting bracket nuts and position fuel filter aside.
5. Remove ignition module screws, then the ignition module from strut tower.
6. Reverse procedure to install. **Torque** ignition module mounting screws and fuel filter mounting bracket nuts to 71–88 inch lbs.

2.0L Engine w/Automatic Transaxle

The Ignition Control Module (ICM) is located below the upper radiator hose.
1. Disconnect battery ground cable, then the ICM electrical connector.
2. Remove ICM bolts, then the ICM.
3. Reverse procedure to install. **Torque** ICM bolts to 71–88 inch lbs.

2.5L Engine

The Ignition Control Module (ICM) is part of the distributor and is not serviceable. If the ICM requires service, the distributor must be replaced.

SUPPRESSION CAPACITOR

Escort, Festiva & Tracer

1. Disconnect battery ground cable, then the electrical connector from capacitor.
2. Remove mounting nut, then the capacitor.
3. Reverse procedure to install.

CONDENSER

PROBE

2.0L Engine

Models equipped with automatic transaxle do not have a condenser.
1. Disconnect battery ground cable, then remove condenser mounting nut from side of ignition coil.
2. Lift condenser, then disconnect electrical connector.
3. Remove condenser.
4. Reverse procedure to install. **Torque** condenser mounting nut to 61–86 inch lbs.

2.5L Engine

The condenser is part of the distributor and is not serviceable. If the condenser requires service, the distributor must be replaced.

Idle Speed and Timing Adjustments (IST) (1.3L, 1.8L, 2.5L)

TEST STEP		RESULT	►	ACTION TO TAKE
IST1 CHECK IDLE SPEED				
• Start the engine and run until at normal operating temperature. • Engine at idle. • All electrical loads off. • Connect Rotunda 88 Digital Multimeter 105-00053, or equivalent as a tachometer. • Ground STI connector. Refer to illustrations after Pinpoint Test Steps. • Compare idle speed with chart:		Yes No	► ►	GO to IST2. ADJUST idle speed.
Engine	Idle Speed			
1.3L MTX	700 ± 50 rpm			
1.3L ATX	750 ± 50 rpm			
1.8L	750 ± 50 rpm			
2.5L	650 ± 100 rpm			
• Is idle speed within specifications?				
IST2 CHECK BASE TIMING				
• Start the engine and run until at normal operating temperature. • Engine at idle. • All electrical loads off. • Connect a Rotunda Timing Analyzer 059-00014, or equivalent. • Ground STI connector (refer to STI Connector Locations illustration on the next page). • Compare timing with chart:		Yes No	► ►	RETURN to *COMPUTERIZED ENGINE CONTROLS* ADJUST the timing.
Engine	Base Timing			
1.3L, 1.8L, 2.5L	10 degrees ± 1 degree BTDC			
• Is timing within specifications?				

STI Connector Locations

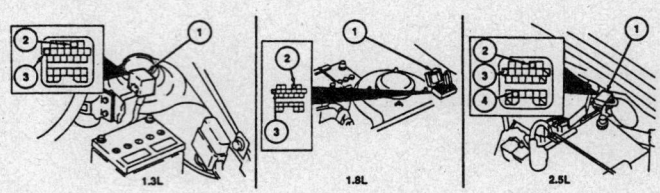

Item	Description
1	Data Link Connector
2	STI
3	GND
4	IGN (-)

Base Timing Check

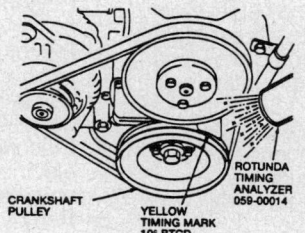

Fig. 7   Test IST: Idle Speed & Timing Adjustments. 1994–95 1.3L, 1.8L & 2.5L Engines

Vacuum Advance (ADV) (1.6L)

TEST STEP	RESULT	▶	ACTION TO TAKE
ADV1 CHECK VACUUM SUPPLY			
• Check the vacuum hoses to the distributor diaphragm for cracks or poor connections. • Remove the vacuum delay valve. • Apply 635 mm-Hg (25 in-Hg) of vacuum to the green side of the valve. • **Does the vacuum delay valve hold vacuum for 10-20 seconds?**	Yes No	▶ ▶	GO to **ADV2**. SERVICE hose as required or REPLACE the vacuum delay valve.
ADV2 INSPECT TIMING			
• Disconnect and plug the vacuum hoses from the vacuum diaphragm. • Ground the Self Test Input (STI) connector. • Engine at operating temperature. • All electrical loads off. • At idle: — 1.6L Non-Turbo: 850 ± 50 rpm — 1.6L Turbo: 850 ±50 rpm • Connect a Rotunda Timing Analyzer 059-00014 or equivalent. • Check timing: — 1.6L Non-Turbo: 2° ±1° BTDC — 1.6L Turbo: 12° ±1° BTDC • **Is the ignition base timing correct?**	Yes No	▶ ▶	GO to **ADV3**. ADJUST the timing.

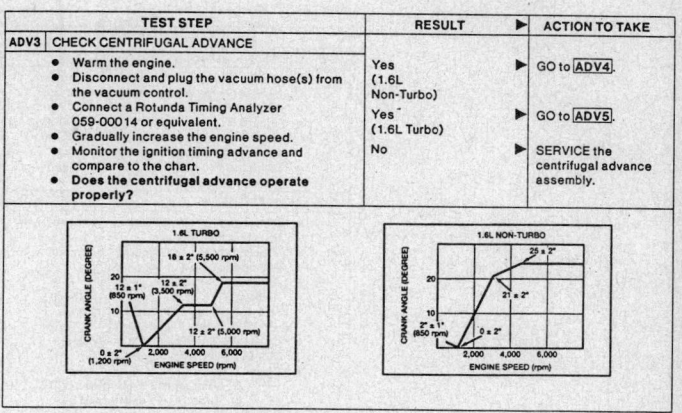

Fig. 8   Test ADV: Vacuum Advance
(Part 1 of 4). 1993 1.6L & 1.6L Turbo
Engines

TEST STEP	RESULT	▶	ACTION TO TAKE
ADV3 CHECK CENTRIFUGAL ADVANCE			
• Warm the engine. • Disconnect and plug the vacuum hose(s) from the vacuum control. • Connect a Rotunda Timing Analyzer 059-00014 or equivalent. • Gradually increase the engine speed. • Monitor the ignition timing advance and compare to the chart. • **Does the centrifugal advance operate properly?**	Yes (1.6L Non-Turbo) Yes (1.6L Turbo) No	▶ ▶ ▶	GO to **ADV4**. GO to **ADV5**. SERVICE the centrifugal advance assembly.

Fig. 8   Test ADV: Vacuum Advance
(Part 2 of 4). 1993 1.6L & 1.6L Turbo
Engines

TEST STEP	RESULT	▶	ACTION TO TAKE
ADV4 CHECK VACUUM DIAPHRAGM			
• Disconnect and plug the vacuum hose(s) from the vacuum diaphragm. • Connect a Rotunda Vacuum Tester 021-00014 or equivalent to the vacuum diaphragm. • Connect a Rotunda Timing Analyzer 059-00014 or equivalent. • Engine at idle. • Apply vacuum to chamber A and then to chamber B. • Monitor the ignition timing and compare to the chart. • **Is the vacuum advance operating properly?**	Yes No	▶ ▶	CHECK the vacuum hoses for leaks, cracks, and breakage. REPAIR as required. RETURN to the *COMPUTERIZED ENGINE CONTROLS* REPLACE the vacuum diaphragm.

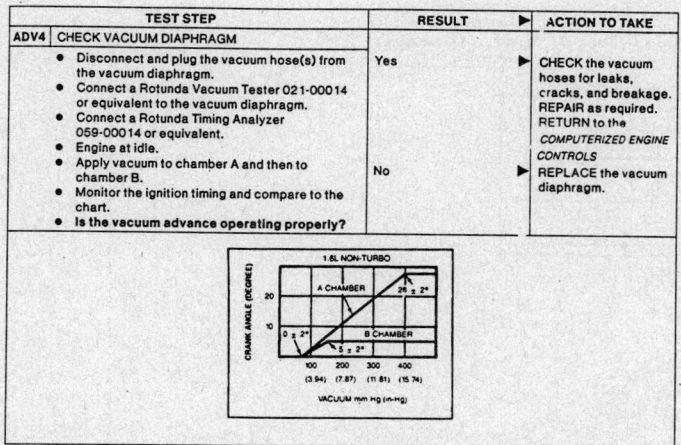

Fig. 8   Test ADV: Vacuum Advance
(Part 3 of 4). 1993 1.6L Engine

TEST STEP	RESULT	▶	ACTION TO TAKE
ADV5 CHECK VACUUM ADVANCE			
• Disconnect and plug the vacuum hose. • Apply vacuum to the advance diaphragm and monitor the ignition timing. See chart below. • Remove vacuum and apply air pressure to the advance diaphragm 68.9 kPa (10 psi MAX). Monitor the ignition timing. • Compare the readings to the chart below. • **Does the vacuum advance operate properly?**	Yes No	▶ ▶	CHECK the vacuum hoses for leaks, cracks, breakage and proper routing SERVICE as required. RETURN to *COMPUTERIZED ENGINE CONTROLS* REPLACE the advance diaphragm.

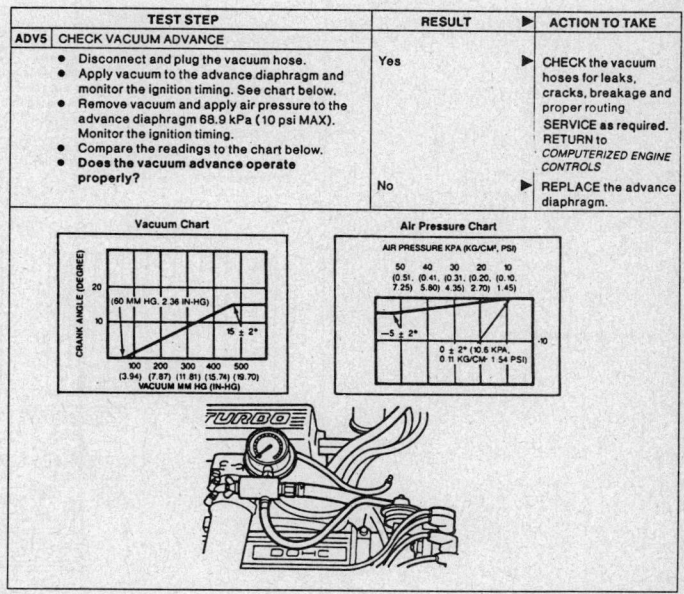

Fig. 8   Test ADV: Vacuum Advance
(Part 4 of 4). 1993 1.6L Turbo
Engine

Vacuum Advance (ADV) (1.6L)

TEST STEP	RESULT	▶	ACTION TO TAKE
ADV1 CHECK VACUUM SUPPLY • Check the vacuum hoses to the distributor diaphragm for cracks or poor connections. • Remove the vacuum delay valve. • Using a Rotunda Vacuum Tester 021-00014, or equivalent apply 635 mm-Hg (25 in-Hg) of vacuum to the green side of the valve. • Does the vacuum delay valve hold vacuum for 10-20 seconds?	Yes No	▶ ▶	GO to ADV2. SERVICE hose as required or REPLACE the vacuum delay valve.
ADV2 INSPECT TIMING • Disconnect and plug the vacuum hoses from the vacuum diaphragm. • Ground the Self Test Input (STI) connector. • Engine at operating temperature. • All electrical loads off. • At idle: — 1.6L Non-Turbo: 850 ± 50 rpm — 1.6L Turbo: 850 ±50 rpm • Connect a Rotunda Timing Analyzer 059-00014 or equivalent. • Check timing: — 1.6L Non-Turbo: 2 ±1 degrees BTDC — 1.6L Turbo: 12 ±1 degrees BTDC • Is the ignition base timing correct?	Yes No	▶ ▶	GO to ADV3. ADJUST the timing.

Fig. 9   Test ADV: Vacuum Advance (Part 1 of 4). 1994 1.6L & 1.6L Turbo Engines

TEST STEP	RESULT	▶	ACTION TO TAKE
ADV5 CHECK VACUUM ADVANCE • Disconnect and plug the vacuum hose. • Apply vacuum to the advance diaphragm and monitor the ignition timing. See chart below. • Remove vacuum and apply air pressure to the advance diaphragm 68.9 kPa (10 psi MAX). Monitor the ignition timing. • Compare the readings to the chart below. • Does the vacuum advance operate properly?	Yes No	▶ ▶	CHECK the vacuum hoses for leaks, cracks, breakage, and proper routing. SERVICE as required. RETURN to *COMPUTERIZED ENGINE CONTROLS* REPLACE the advance diaphragm.

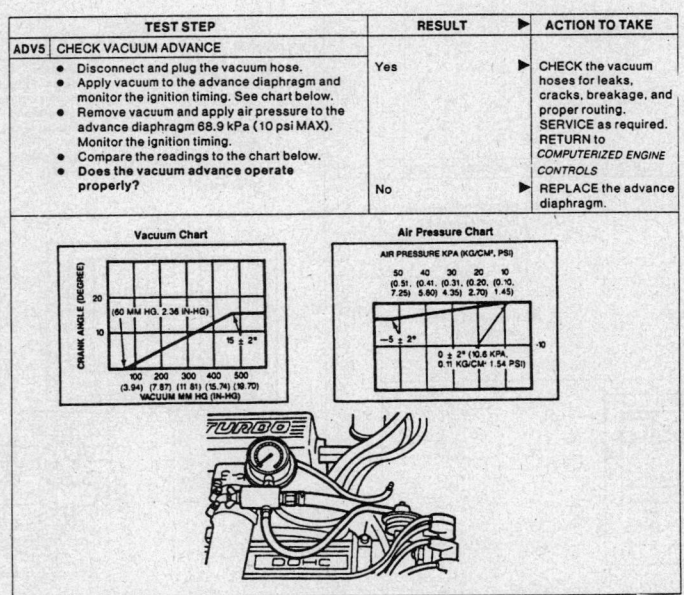

Fig. 9   Test ADV: Vacuum Advance (Part 2 of 4). 1994 1.6L & 1.6L Turbo Engines

TEST STEP		RESULT	▶	ACTION TO TAKE
ADV3	CHECK CENTRIFUGAL ADVANCE			
	• Warm the engine. • Disconnect and plug the vacuum hose(s) from the vacuum control. • Connect a Rotunda Timing Analyzer 059-00014 or equivalent. • Gradually increase the engine speed. • Monitor the ignition timing advance and compare to the chart. • **Does the centrifugal advance operate properly?**	Yes (1.6L Non-Turbo) Yes (1.6L Turbo) No	▶ ▶ ▶	GO to ADV4. GO to ADV5. SERVICE the centrifugal advance assembly.

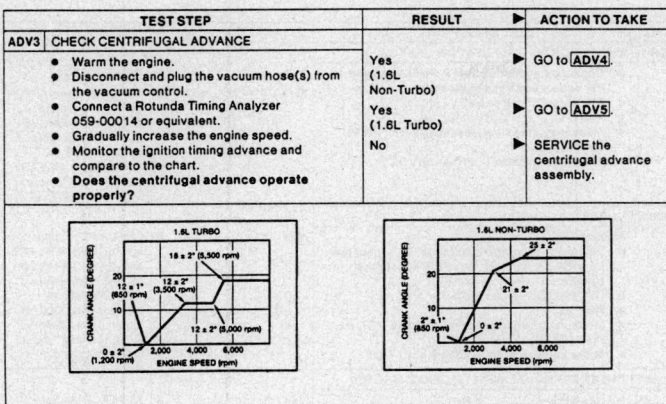

Fig. 9 Test ADV: Vacuum Advance (Part 3 of 4). 1994 1.6L & 1.6L Turbo Engines

TEST STEP		RESULT	▶	ACTION TO TAKE
ADV4	CHECK VACUUM DIAPHRAGM			
	• Disconnect and plug the vacuum hose(s) from the vacuum diaphragm. • Connect a Rotunda Vacuum Tester 021-00014 or equivalent to the vacuum diaphragm. • Connect a Rotunda Timing Analyzer 059-00014 or equivalent. • Engine at idle. • Apply vacuum to chamber A (outer chamber) and then to chamber B (inner chamber). • Monitor the ignition timing and compare to the chart. Increased vacuum should advance (increase) the crank angle. • **Is the vacuum advance operating properly?**	Yes No	▶ ▶	CHECK the vacuum hoses for leaks, cracks, and breakage. REPAIR as required. RETURN to *COMPUTERIZED ENGINE CONTROLS*. REPLACE the vacuum diaphragm.

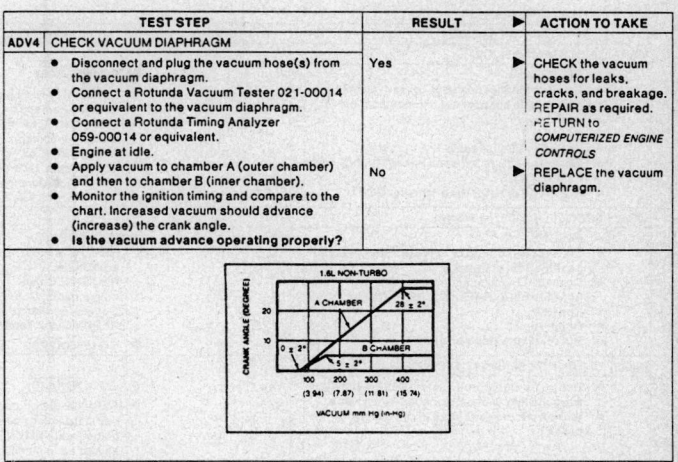

Fig. 9 Test ADV: Vacuum Advance (Part 4 of 4). 1994 1.6L Turbo Engine

TEST STEP		RESULT	▶	ACTION TO TAKE
IGNA1	CHECK FOR EEC IV QUICK TEST COMPLETION			
	• Were all tests accomplished according to EEC IV Quick Test procedures?	Yes No	▶ ▶	GO to IGNA2. REFER to Diagnostic Routines.
IGNA2	CHECK FOR GOOD BATTERY			
	• **Is battery voltage greater than 10 volts DC with the key ON?**	Yes No	▶ ▶	GO to IGNA3. SERVICE battery.
IGNA3	CHECK FOR SPARK AT COIL DURING CRANK			
	• Use an Air Gap Spark Tester (D81P-6666-A) or equivalent to check for spark during crank at coil wire. • **Was spark present during crank?**	Yes No	▶ ▶	GO to IGNA9. GO to IGNA4.
IGNA4	CHECK FOR TFI POWER			
	• Key OFF. • Connect Rotunda TFI Diagnostic Cable 007-00097, or equivalent to Rotunda Breakout Box 007-00033, or equivalent connect BAT- lead to negative post of battery, and connect TFI module tee to Ignition Control Module and vehicle harness. • Do not connect BAT+ lead of TFI Diagnostic Cable to battery. **CAUTION: Do not connect PCM to Breakout Box when it is used with TFI Diagnostic Cable.** • Make sure PIP OPEN / NORMAL / SPOUT OPEN switch on TFI Diagnostic Cable is in the NORMAL position. • Use TFI overlay on Breakout Box. • DVOM on DC volt scale. • Key ON. • Measure voltage between Pin 5 (ICM PWR) and Pin 7 (BAT-) at Breakout Box. • **Is voltage greater than 10 volts DC?**	Yes No	▶ ▶	GO to IGNA5. SERVICE power open to Ignition Control Module in harness or connector. REMOVE all test equipment. RECONNECT all components. CLEAR Continuous Memory. RERUN Quick Test.
IGNA5	CHECK FOR PIP SIGNAL			
	• DVOM on AC volt scale. • Crank engine and measure voltage between Pin 15 (PIP) and Pin 7 (BAT-). • **Is voltage between 3.0 and 8.5 volts AC?**	Yes No	▶ ▶	GO to IGNA6. GO to IGNA11.
IGNA6	CHECK FOR SPOUT SIGNAL			
	• Crank engine and measure voltage between Pin 10 (SPOUT) and Pin 7 (BAT-). • **Is voltage between 3.0 and 8.5 volts AC?**	Yes No	▶ ▶	GO to IGNA7. GO to IGNA15.

Fig. 10 Test IGNA: Engine No Start (Part 1 of 7). 1993 2.0L Engine w/Manual Transaxle

TEST STEP	RESULT	▶	ACTION TO TAKE
IGNA7 CHECK VBAT AT COIL			
• Key OFF. • Connect diagnostic cable coil tee to vehicle harness; do not connect diagnostic cable to coil. • Key ON. • DVOM on DC volt scale. • Measure voltage between Pin 2 (VBAT C) and Pin 7 (BAT-). • Is voltage greater than 10 volts DC?	Yes No	▶ ▶	GO to **IGNA8**. SERVICE power open to coil in harness or connector. REMOVE all test equipment. RECONNECT all components. CLEAR Continuous Memory. RERUN Quick Test.
IGNA8 CHECK FOR COIL (-) SIGNAL			
• Key OFF. • Connect BAT+ lead of TFI diagnostic cable to positive post of battery. • Connect 12 volt incandescent test lamp between Pin 1 (BAT+) and Pin 3 (COIL-). • Key ON. • Crank engine. • Did test lamp flash brightly?	Yes No	▶ ▶	REPLACE coil. REMOVE all test equipment. RECONNECT all components. CLEAR Continuous Memory. RERUN Quick Test. GO to **IGNA23**.
IGNA9 CHECK FOR SPARK AT ALL WIRES			
• Use an Air Gap Spark Tester (D81P-6666-A) or equivalent to check for spark at all wires. • Was spark present at all plugs during crank?	Yes No	▶ ▶	GO to **IGNA10**. SERVICE distributor cap, rotor, plugs or plug wires. REMOVE all test equipment. RECONNECT all components. CLEAR Continuous Memory. RERUN Quick Test.
IGNA10 CHECK PLUGS			
• Remove and check plugs for damage, wear, carbon deposits and proper plug gap. • Are plugs OK?	Yes No	▶ ▶	Not an Ignition problem, REFER to *COMPUTERIZED ENGINE CONTROLS* SERVICE plugs. REMOVE all test equipment. RECONNECT all components. CLEAR Continuous Memory. RERUN Quick Test.

Fig. 10   Test IGNA: Engine No Start (Part 2 of 7). 1993 2.0L Engine w/Manual Transaxle

TEST STEP	RESULT	▶	ACTION TO TAKE
IGNA11 CHECK FOR PIP POWER AT PIP SENSOR			
• Connect diagnostic cable PIP sensor tee to PIP sensor and vehicle harness. • DVOM on DC volt scale. • Key ON. • Measure voltage between Pin 22 (PIP PWR) and Pin 7 (BAT-). • Is voltage greater than 10 volts DC?	Yes No	▶ ▶	GO to **IGNA12**. SERVICE power to PIP sensor in harness or connector. REMOVE all test equipment. RECONNECT all components. CLEAR Continuous Memory. RERUN Quick Test.
IGNA12 CHECK PIP SENSOR			
• Key OFF. • Disconnect diagnostic harness PIP sensor tee from PIP sensor only; leave PIP sensor tee connected to vehicle harness. • DVOM on DC volt scale. • Key ON. • Measure the voltage between Pin 34 (PIP) and Pin 7 (BAT). • Is the voltage greater than 9 volts DC?	Yes No	▶ ▶	CHECK PIP sensor wiring, if OK REPLACE distributor. REMOVE all test equipment. RECONNECT all components. CLEAR Continuous Memory. RERUN Quick Test. GO to **IGNA13**.
IGNA13 CHECK PIP SIGNAL WITH TFI DISCONNECTED			
• Key OFF. • Reconnect diagnostic harness PIP sensor tee to PIP sensor. • Turn switch on diagnostic cable to NORMAL. • Disconnect diagnostic harness TFI module tee from Ignition Control Module only; leave TFI module tee connected to vehicle harness. • Crank engine and measure voltage between Pin 34 (PIP) and Pin 7 (BAT-). • Is voltage between 3.0 and 8.5 volts AC?	Yes No	▶ ▶	REPLACE Ignition Control Module. REMOVE all test equipment. RECONNECT all components. CLEAR Continuous Memory. RERUN Quick Test. GO to **IGNA14**.
IGNA14 CHECK PCM PIP SIGNAL			
• Key OFF. • Disconnect diagnostic cable PIP sensor tee from PIP sensor only; leave PIP sensor tee connected to vehicle harness. • Disconnect PCM. • Measure the resistance between Pin 34 (PIP) and ground. • Is the resistance greater than 10,000 ohms?	Yes No	▶ ▶	REPLACE the PCM. REMOVE all test equipment. RECONNECT all components. CLEAR Continuous Memory. RERUN Quick Test. SERVICE PIP between PIP sensor and PCM or Ignition Control Module in harness for short. REMOVE all test equipment. RECONNECT all components. CLEAR Continuous Memory. RERUN Quick Test.

Fig. 10   Test IGNA: Engine No Start (Part 3 of 7). 1993 2.0L Engine w/Manual Transaxle

TEST STEP	RESULT	▶	ACTION TO TAKE
IGNA15 CHECK FOR SPOUT SIGNAL IN HARNESS			
• Turn switch to SPOUT OPEN position on diagnostic cable. • Crank engine and measure voltage between Pin 10 (SPOUT) and Pin 7 (BAT-). • Is voltage between 3.0 and 8.5 volts AC? NOTE: Engine may start, continue diagnostics.	Yes No	▶ ▶	REPLACE Ignition Control Module. REMOVE all test equipment. RECONNECT all components. CLEAR Continuous Memory. RERUN Quick Test. GO to **IGNA16**.
IGNA16 CHECK SPOUT SIGNAL VOLTAGE			
• Key OFF. • Disconnect diagnostic cable TFI module tee from Ignition Control Module only; leave TFI module tee connected to vehicle harness. • Turn switch to NORMAL on diagnostic cable. • DVOM on DC volt scale. • Measure voltage between Pin 10 (SPOUT) and Pin 7 (BAT-), with key ON. • Is voltage less than 0.5 volt DC?	Yes No	▶ ▶	GO to **IGNA18**. GO to **IGNA17**.
IGNA17 CHECK FOR SPOUT CIRCUIT SHORT TO POWER			
• Key OFF. • Disconnect PCM. • Measure voltage between Pin 10 (SPOUT) and Pin 7 (BAT-) with key ON. • Is voltage less than 0.5 volt DC?	Yes No	▶ ▶	GO to **IGNA19**. SERVICE SPOUT between PCM and Ignition Control Module in harness for short to power. REMOVE all test equipment. RECONNECT all components. CLEAR Continuous Memory. RERUN Quick Test.
IGNA18 CHECK FOR SPOUT CIRCUIT SHORT TO GROUND			
• Disconnect PCM. • Measure resistance between Pin 10 (SPOUT) and Pin 7 (BAT-). • Is resistance greater than 10K ohms?	Yes No	▶ ▶	GO to **IGNA19**. SERVICE SPOUT between PCM and Ignition Control Module in harness for short to ground. REMOVE all test equipment. RECONNECT all components. CLEAR Continuous Memory. RERUN Quick Test.

Fig. 10   Test IGNA: Engine No Start (Part 4 of 7). 1993 2.0L Engine w/Manual Transaxle

TEST STEP	RESULT	▶	ACTION TO TAKE
IGNA19 CHECK FOR PIP CIRCUIT OPEN			
• Key OFF. • DVOM on AC volt scale. • Install Breakout Box. • Crank engine and measure voltage between BOB Pin 56 (PIP) and BOB Pin 60 (GND). • Is voltage between 3.0 and 8.5 volts AC?	Yes No	▶ ▶	GO to **IGNA20**. GO to **IGNA22**.
IGNA20 CHECK IGN GND AT PCM			
• Key OFF. • Reconnect diagnostic cable TFI module tee to Ignition Control Module. • DVOM on ohm scale. • Disconnect PCM. • Measure resistance between Pin 16 (IGN GND) of PCM harness connector and Pin 7 (BAT-) at the breakout box. • Is resistance less than 5.0 ohms?	Yes No	▶ ▶	REPLACE PCM. REMOVE all test equipment. RECONNECT all components. CLEAR Continuous Memory. RERUN Quick Test. GO to **IGNA21**.
IGNA21 CHECK FOR IGN GND AT PIP SENSOR			
• Connect diagnostic cable PIP sensor tee to PIP sensor and vehicle harness. • Measure resistance between Pin 35 (IGN GND) and Pin 7 (BAT-). • Is resistance less than 5.0 ohms?	Yes No	▶ ▶	SERVICE IGN GND between PCM and PIP sensor in harness for open. REMOVE all test equipment. RECONNECT all components. CLEAR Continuous Memory. RERUN Quick Test. SERVICE IGN GND wire or REPLACE distributor. IGN GND open in PIP sensor. REMOVE all test equipment. RECONNECT all components. CLEAR Continuous Memory. RERUN Quick Test.

Fig. 10   Test IGNA: Engine No Start (Part 5 of 7). 1993 2.0L Engine w/Manual Transaxle

TEST STEP	RESULT	▶	ACTION TO TAKE
IGNA22 CHECK PIP SIGNAL AT PIP SENSOR			
• Key OFF. • Connect diagnostic cable PIP sensor tee to vehicle harness. • DVOM on DC volt scale. • Key ON. • Measure the voltage between Pin 34 (PIP) and Pin 7 (BAT-). • Is the voltage greater than 9 volts DC?	Yes	▶	REPLACE distributor. PIP open in PIP sensor. REMOVE all test equipment. RECONNECT all components. CLEAR Continuous Memory. RERUN Quick Test.
	No	▶	SERVICE PIP open in harness between PCM and PIP sensor. REMOVE all test equipment. RECONNECT all components. CLEAR Continuous Memory. RERUN Quick Test.
IGNA23 CHECK FOR COIL (-) OPEN IN HARNESS			
• Key OFF. • Disconnect the PCM. • Disconnect diagnostic cable TFI module tee from Ignition Control Module only; leave TFI module tee connected to vehicle harness. • Disconnect BAT+ lead of TFI diagnostic cable from battery. • DVOM on ohm scale. • Measure the resistance between Pin 3 (COIL-) and Pin 4 (TFI2 COIL-). • Is resistance less than 5.0 ohms?	Yes	▶	GO to IGNA24.
	No	▶	SERVICE open coil- between Ignition Control Module and coil in harness. REMOVE all test equipment. RECONNECT all components. CLEAR Continuous Memory. RERUN Quick Test.
IGNA24 CHECK FOR COIL (-) CIRCUIT SHORT TO GROUND			
• Key OFF. • Disconnect the PCM. • DVOM on ohm scale. • Measure resistance between Pin 3 (COIL-) and Pin 7 (BAT-). • Is resistance greater than 10K ohms?	Yes	▶	GO to IGNA25.
	No	▶	SERVICE coil - short to ground in harness between coil and Ignition Control Module. Coil may be damaged. REMOVE all test equipment. RECONNECT all components. CLEAR Continuous Memory. RERUN Quick Test.

Fig. 10   Test IGNA: Engine No Start (Part 6 of 7). 1993 2.0L Engine w/Manual Transaxle

TEST STEP	RESULT	▶	ACTION TO TAKE
IGNA25 CHECK FOR COIL (-) SHORT TO POWER			
• DVOM on DC volt scale. • Key ON. • Measure voltage between Pin 3 (COIL-) and Pin 7 (BAT-). • Is voltage less than 5.5 volts DC?	Yes	▶	GO to IGNA26.
	No	▶	SERVICE coil - short to power in harness between coil and Ignition Control Module. REMOVE all test equipment. RECONNECT all components. CLEAR Continuous Memory. RERUN Quick Test.
IGNA26 CHECK GND AT IGNITION CONTROL MODULE			
• Key OFF. • DVOM on ohm scale. • Measure resistance between Pin 9 (IGN GND) and Pin 7 (BAT-). • Is resistance less than 5.0 ohms?	Yes	▶	REPLACE Ignition Control Module. REMOVE all test equipment. RECONNECT all components. CLEAR Continuous Memory. RERUN Quick Test.
	No	▶	GO to IGNA27.
IGNA27 CHECK GND AT PIP SENSOR			
• Connect diagnostic cable PIP sensor tee to the PIP sensor and vehicle harness. • Measure resistance between Pin 35 (GND) and Pin 7 (BAT-). • Is resistance less than 5.0 ohms?	Yes	▶	SERVICE open GND in harness between PIP sensor and Ignition Control Module. REMOVE all test equipment. RECONNECT all components. CLEAR Continuous Memory. RERUN Quick Test.
	No	▶	SERVICE GND wire or REPLACE distributor. GND open in PIP sensor or connector. REMOVE all test equipment. RECONNECT all components. CLEAR Continuous Memory. RERUN Quick Test.

Fig. 10   Test IGNA: Engine No Start (Part 7 of 7). 1993 2.0L Engine w/Manual Transaxle

TEST STEP	RESULT	▶	ACTION TO TAKE
IGNA1 CHECK FOR EEC IV QUICK TEST COMPLETION			
• Were all tests accomplished according to EEC IV Quick Test procedures?	Yes	▶	GO to IGNA2.
	No	▶	REFER to *COMPUTERIZED ENGINE CONTROLS*
IGNA2 CHECK FOR GOOD BATTERY			
• Is battery voltage greater than 10 volts DC with the key ON?	Yes	▶	GO to IGNA3.
	No	▶	SERVICE battery.
IGNA3 CHECK FOR SPARK AT COIL DURING CRANK			
• Use an Air Gap Spark Tester (D81P-6666-A) or equivalent to check for spark during crank at coil wire. • Was spark present during crank?	Yes	▶	GO to IGNA9.
	No	▶	GO to IGNA4.
IGNA4 CHECK FOR TFI POWER			
• Key OFF. • Connect Rotunda TFI Diagnostic Cable 007-00097, or equivalent and PIP Adapter 007-00083 to Rotunda Breakout Box 007-00033, or equivalent connect BAT- lead to negative post of battery, and connect TFI module tee to Ignition Control Module and vehicle harness. • Do not connect BAT+ lead of TFI Diagnostic Cable to battery. CAUTION: Do not connect PCM to Breakout Box when it is used with TFI Diagnostic Cable. • Make sure PIP OPEN/NORMAL/SPOUT OPEN switch on TFI Diagnostic Cable is in the NORMAL position. • Use TFI overlay on Breakout Box. • DVOM on DC volt scale. • Key ON. • Measure voltage between Pin 5 (TFI PWR) and Pin 7 (VEHICLE BAT-) at Breakout Box. • Is voltage greater than 10 volts DC?	Yes	▶	GO to IGNA5.
	No	▶	SERVICE power open to Ignition Control Module in harness or connector. REMOVE all test equipment. RECONNECT all components. CLEAR Continuous Memory. RERUN Quick Test.
IGNA5 CHECK FOR PIP SIGNAL			
• DVOM on AC volt scale. • Crank engine and measure voltage between Pin 15 (PIP) and Pin 7 (VEHICLE BAT-). • Is voltage between 3.0 and 8.5 volts AC?	Yes	▶	GO to IGNA6.
	No	▶	GO to IGNA11.

Fig. 11   Test IGNA: Engine No Start (Part 1 of 8). 1994-95 2.0L Engine

TEST STEP	RESULT	▶	ACTION TO TAKE
IGNA6 CHECK FOR SPOUT SIGNAL			
• DVOM on AC volt scale. • Crank engine and measure voltage between Pin 10 (SPOUT) and Pin 7 (VEHICLE BAT-). • Is voltage between 3.0 and 8.5 volts AC?	Yes	▶	GO to IGNA7.
	No	▶	GO to IGNA15.
IGNA7 CHECK VBAT AT COIL			
• Key OFF. • Connect diagnostic cable coil tee to vehicle harness; do not connect diagnostic cable to coil. • Key ON. • DVOM on DC volt scale. • Measure voltage between Pin 2 (VBAT C) and Pin 7 (VEHICLE BAT-). • Is voltage greater than 10 volts DC?	Yes	▶	GO to IGNA8.
	No	▶	SERVICE power open to coil in harness or connector. REMOVE all test equipment. RECONNECT all components. CLEAR Continuous Memory. RERUN Quick Test.
IGNA8 CHECK FOR COIL (-) SIGNAL			
• Key OFF. • Connect BAT+ lead of TFI diagnostic cable to positive post of battery. • Connect 12 volt incandescent test lamp between Pin 1 (VEHICLE BAT+) and Pin 3 (COIL-). • Key ON. • Crank engine. • Did test lamp flash brightly?	Yes	▶	REPLACE coil. REMOVE all test equipment. RECONNECT all components. CLEAR Continuous Memory. RERUN Quick Test.
	No	▶	GO to IGNA23.
IGNA9 CHECK FOR SPARK AT ALL WIRES			
• Use an Air Gap Spark Tester (D81P-6666-A) or equivalent to check for spark at all wires. • Was spark present at all plugs during crank?	Yes	▶	GO to IGNA10.
	No	▶	SERVICE distributor cap, rotor, plugs, or plug wires. REMOVE all test equipment. RECONNECT all components. CLEAR Continuous Memory. RERUN Quick Test.
IGNA10 CHECK PLUGS			
• Remove and check plugs for damage, wear, carbon deposits, and proper plug gap. • Are plugs OK?	Yes	▶	Not an ignition problem, REFER to *COMPUTERIZED ENGINE CONTROLS*
	No	▶	SERVICE plugs. REMOVE all test equipment. RECONNECT all components. CLEAR Continuous Memory. RERUN Quick Test.

Fig. 11   Test IGNA: Engine No Start (Part 2 of 8). 1994-95 2.0L Engine

TEST STEP	RESULT	▶	ACTION TO TAKE
IGNA11 CHECK FOR PIP POWER AT PIP SENSOR (DISTRIBUTOR) • Connect diagnostic cable PIP sensor tee to PIP sensor (distributor) and vehicle harness. • DVOM on DC volt scale. • Key ON. • Measure voltage between Pin 22 (PIP PWR) and Pin 7 (VEHICLE BAT-). • Is voltage greater than 10 volts DC?	Yes No	▶ ▶	GO to IGNA12. SERVICE power to PIP sensor (distributor) in harness or connector. REMOVE all test equipment. RECONNECT all components. CLEAR Continuous Memory. RERUN Quick Test.
IGNA12 CHECK PIP SENSOR • Key OFF. • Disconnect diagnostic harness PIP sensor tee from PIP sensor (distributor) only; leave PIP sensor tee connected to vehicle harness. • DVOM on DC volt scale. • Key ON. • Measure the voltage between Pin 34 (PIP) and Pin 7 (VEHICLE BAT-). • Is the voltage greater than 9 volts DC?	Yes No	▶ ▶	CHECK PIP sensor (distributor) wiring, if OK REPLACE distributor. REMOVE all test equipment. RECONNECT all components. CLEAR Continuous Memory. RERUN Quick Test. GO to IGNA13.
IGNA13 CHECK PIP SIGNAL WITH TFI DISCONNECTED • Key OFF. • Reconnect diagnostic harness PIP sensor tee to PIP sensor (distributor). • Turn switch on diagnostic cable to NORMAL. • Disconnect diagnostic harness TFI module tee from Ignition Control Module only; leave TFI module tee connected to vehicle harness. • DVOM on AC range. • Crank engine and measure voltage between Pin 34 (PIP) and Pin 7 (VEHICLE BAT-). • Is voltage between 3.0 and 8.5 volts AC?	Yes No	▶ ▶	REPLACE Ignition Control Module. REMOVE all test equipment. RECONNECT all components. CLEAR Continuous Memory. RERUN Quick Test. GO to IGNA14.

Fig. 11   Test IGNA: Engine No Start (Part 3 of 8). 1994–95 2.0L Engine

TEST STEP	RESULT	▶	ACTION TO TAKE
IGNA14 CHECK PCM PIP SIGNAL • Key OFF. • Disconnect diagnostic cable PIP sensor tee from PIP sensor (distributor) only; leave PIP sensor tee connected to vehicle harness. • Disconnect PCM. • Measure the resistance between Pin 34 (PIP) and ground. • Is the resistance greater than 10,000 ohms?	Yes No	▶ ▶	REPLACE the PCM. REMOVE all test equipment. RECONNECT all components. CLEAR Continuous Memory. RERUN Quick Test. SERVICE PIP between PIP sensor (distributor) and PCM or Ignition Control Module in harness for short. REMOVE all test equipment. RECONNECT all components. CLEAR Continuous Memory. RERUN Quick Test.
IGNA15 CHECK FOR SPOUT SIGNAL IN HARNESS • Turn switch to SPOUT OPEN position on diagnostic cable. • DVOM on AC range. • Crank engine and measure voltage between Pin 10 (SPOUT) and Pin 7 (VEHICLE BAT-). • Is voltage between 3.0 and 8.5 volts AC? NOTE: Engine may start, continue diagnostics.	Yes No	▶ ▶	REPLACE Ignition Control Module. REMOVE all test equipment. RECONNECT all components. CLEAR Continuous Memory. RERUN Quick Test. GO to IGNA16.
IGNA16 CHECK SPOUT SIGNAL VOLTAGE • Key OFF. • Disconnect diagnostic cable TFI module tee from Ignition Control Module only; leave TFI module tee connected to vehicle harness. • Turn switch to NORMAL on diagnostic cable. • DVOM on DC volt scale. • Measure voltage between Pin 10 (SPOUT) and Pin 7 (VEHICLE BAT-), with key ON. • Is voltage less than 0.5 volt DC?	Yes No	▶ ▶	GO to IGNA18. GO to IGNA17.

Fig. 11   Test IGNA: Engine No Start (Part 4 of 8). 1994–95 2.0L Engine

TEST STEP	RESULT	▶	ACTION TO TAKE
IGNA17 CHECK FOR SPOUT CIRCUIT SHORT TO POWER • Key OFF. • Disconnect PCM. • DVOM on DC volt scale. • Measure voltage between Pin 10 (SPOUT) and Pin 7 (VEHICLE BAT-) with key ON. • Is voltage less than 0.5 volt DC?	Yes No	▶ ▶	GO to IGNA19. SERVICE SPOUT between PCM and Ignition Control Module in harness for short to power. REMOVE all test equipment. RECONNECT all components. CLEAR Continuous Memory. RERUN Quick Test.
IGNA18 CHECK FOR SPOUT CIRCUIT SHORT TO GROUND • Disconnect PCM. • Measure resistance between Pin 10 (SPOUT) and Pin 7 (VEHICLE BAT-). • Is resistance greater than 10K ohms?	Yes No	▶ ▶	GO to IGNA19. SERVICE SPOUT circuit between PCM and Ignition Control Module in harness for short to ground. REMOVE all test equipment. RECONNECT all components. CLEAR Continuous Memory. RERUN Quick Test.
IGNA19 CHECK FOR PIP CIRCUIT OPEN • Key OFF. • DVOM on AC volt scale. • Install Breakout Box. • Crank engine and measure voltage between BOB Pin 56 (PIP) and BOB Pin 60 (GND). • Is voltage between 3.0 and 8.5 volts AC?	Yes No	▶ ▶	GO to IGNA20. GO to IGNA22.
IGNA20 CHECK IGN GND AT PCM • Key OFF. • Reconnect diagnostic cable TFI module tee to Ignition Control Module. • DVOM on ohm scale. • Disconnect PCM. • Measure resistance between Pin 16 (IGN GND) of PCM harness connector and Pin 7 (VEHICLE BAT-) at the breakout box. • Is resistance less than 5.0 ohms?	Yes No	▶ ▶	REPLACE PCM. REMOVE all test equipment. RECONNECT all components. CLEAR Continuous Memory. RERUN Quick Test. GO to IGNA21.

Fig. 11   Test IGNA: Engine No Start (Part 5 of 8). 1994–95 2.0L Engine

TEST STEP	RESULT	▶	ACTION TO TAKE
IGNA21 CHECK FOR IGN GND AT PIP SENSOR • Connect diagnostic cable PIP sensor tee to PIP sensor (distributor) and vehicle harness. • Measure resistance between Pin 35 (IGN GND) and Pin 7 (VEHICLE BAT-). • Is resistance less than 5.0 ohms?	Yes No	▶ ▶	SERVICE IGN GND between PCM and PIP sensor (distributor) in harness for open. REMOVE all test equipment. RECONNECT all components. CLEAR Continuous Memory. RERUN Quick Test. SERVICE IGN GND wire or REPLACE distributor. IGN GND open in PIP sensor. REMOVE all test equipment. RECONNECT all components. CLEAR Continuous Memory. RERUN Quick Test.
IGNA22 CHECK PIP SIGNAL AT PIP SENSOR • Key OFF. • Connect diagnostic cable PIP sensor tee to vehicle harness. • DVOM on DC volt scale. • Key ON. • Measure the voltage between Pin 34 (PIP) and Pin 7 (VEHICLE BAT-). • Is the voltage greater than 9 volts DC?	Yes No	▶ ▶	REPLACE distributor. PIP open in PIP sensor (distributor). REMOVE all test equipment. RECONNECT all components. CLEAR Continuous Memory. RERUN Quick Test. SERVICE PIP open in harness between PCM and PIP sensor (distributor). REMOVE all test equipment. RECONNECT all components. CLEAR Continuous Memory. RERUN Quick Test.

Fig. 11   Test IGNA: Engine No Start (Part 6 of 8). 1994–95 2.0L Engine

TEST STEP		RESULT	▶	ACTION TO TAKE
IGNA23	CHECK FOR COIL (-) OPEN IN HARNESS			
• Key OFF. • Disconnect the PCM. • Disconnect diagnostic cable TFI module tee from Ignition Control Module only; leave TFI module tee connected to vehicle harness. • Disconnect BAT+ lead of TFI diagnostic cable from battery. • DVOM on ohm scale. • Measure the resistance between Pin 3 (COIL-) and Pin 4 (TFI2 COIL-). • **Is resistance less than 5.0 ohms?**		Yes No	▶ ▶	GO to IGNA24. SERVICE open coil between Ignition Control Module and coil in harness. REMOVE all test equipment. RECONNECT all components. CLEAR Continuous Memory. RERUN Quick Test.
IGNA24	CHECK FOR COIL (-) CIRCUIT SHORT TO GROUND			
• Key OFF. • Disconnect the PCM. • DVOM on ohm scale. • Measure resistance between Pin 3 (COIL-) and Pin 7 (VEHICLE BAT-). • **Is resistance greater than 10K ohms?**		Yes No	▶ ▶	GO to IGNA25. SERVICE coil - short to ground in harness between coil and Ignition Control Module. Coil may be damaged. REMOVE all test equipment. RECONNECT all components. CLEAR Continuous Memory. RERUN Quick Test.
IGNA25	CHECK FOR COIL (-) SHORT TO POWER			
• DVOM on DC volt scale. • Key ON. • Measure voltage between Pin 3 (COIL-) and Pin 7 (VEHICLE BAT-). • **Is voltage less than 5.5 volts DC?**		Yes No	▶ ▶	GO to IGNA26. SERVICE coil - short to power in harness between coil and Ignition Control Module. REMOVE all test equipment. RECONNECT all components. CLEAR Continuous Memory. RERUN Quick Test.
IGNA26	CHECK GND AT IGNITION CONTROL MODULE			
• Key OFF. • DVOM on ohm scale. • Measure resistance between Pin 9 (IGN GND) and Pin 7 (VEHICLE BAT-). • **Is resistance less than 5.0 ohms?**		Yes No	▶ ▶	REPLACE Ignition Control Module. REMOVE all test equipment. RECONNECT all components. CLEAR Continuous Memory. RERUN Quick Test. GO to IGNA27.

Fig. 11   Test IGNA: Engine No Start
(Part 7 of 8). 1994–95 2.0L Engine

TEST STEP		RESULT	▶	ACTION TO TAKE
IGNA27	CHECK GND AT PIP SENSOR			
• Connect diagnostic cable PIP sensor tee to the PIP sensor (distributor) and vehicle harness. • Measure resistance between Pin 35 (GND) and Pin 7 (VEHICLE BAT-). • **Is resistance less than 5.0 ohms?**		Yes No	▶ ▶	SERVICE open GND in harness between PIP sensor (distributor) and Ignition Control Module. REMOVE all test equipment. RECONNECT all components. CLEAR Continuous Memory. RERUN Quick Test. SERVICE GND wire or REPLACE distributor. GND open in PIP sensor (distributor) or connector. REMOVE all test equipment. RECONNECT all components. CLEAR Continuous Memory. RERUN Quick Test.

Fig. 11   Test IGNA: Engine No Start
(Part 8 of 8). 1994–95 2.0L Engine

TEST STEP		RESULT	▶	ACTION TO TAKE
IGNB4	CHECK FOR IDM OPEN IN HARNESS			
• Disconnect PCM. • Measure resistance between Pin 23 (IDM) diagnostic cable and Pin 4 of the PCM connector. • **Is resistance less than 5.0 ohms?**		Yes No	▶ ▶	REPLACE Ignition Control Module. REMOVE all test equipment. RECONNECT all components. CLEAR Continuous Memory. RERUN Quick Test. SERVICE IDM open in harness between Ignition Control Module and PCM connector. REMOVE all test equipment. RECONNECT all components. CLEAR Continuous Memory. RERUN Quick Test.

Fig. 12   Test IGNB: Code 212, IDM
Missing (Part 2 of 2). 1993 2.0L
Engine w/Manual Transaxle

TEST STEP		RESULT	▶	ACTION TO TAKE
IGNB1	CHECK IDM SIGNAL AT PCM CONNECTOR			
• Key OFF. • Install Rotunda Breakout Box 007-00033, or equivalent. • DVOM on AC volt scale. • Crank engine and measure voltage between BOB Pin 4 (IDM) and ground. • **Is voltage greater than 1.0 volt AC?**		Yes No	▶ ▶	REPLACE PCM. REMOVE all test equipment. RECONNECT all components. CLEAR Continuous Memory. RERUN Quick Test. GO to IGNB2.
IGNB2	CHECK FOR IDM SHORT TO POWER			
• Key OFF. • Connect TFI Diagnostic Cable 007-00097, or equivalent to PCM breakout box, connect BAT- lead to negative post of battery, and connect TFI module tee to vehicle harness. • DVOM on DC volt scale. • Key ON. • Measure voltage between Pin 23 (IDM) and Pin 7 (BAT-). • **Is voltage less than 0.5 volt DC?**		Yes No	▶ ▶	GO to IGNB3. SERVICE IDM short to power in harness between PCM connector and Ignition Control Module. REMOVE all test equipment. RECONNECT all components. CLEAR Continuous Memory. RERUN Quick Test.
IGNB3	CHECK FOR IDM SHORT TO GROUND			
• Key OFF. • Disconnect PCM. • DVOM on ohm scale. • Measure resistance between Pin 23 (IDM) and Pin 7 (BAT-). • **Is resistance greater than 10K ohms?**		Yes No	▶ ▶	GO to IGNB4. SERVICE IDM short to ground in harness between PCM connector and Ignition Control Module. REMOVE all test equipment. RECONNECT all components. CLEAR Continuous Memory. RERUN Quick Test.

Fig. 12   Test IGNB: Code 212, IDM
Missing (Part 1 of 2). 1993 2.0L
Engine w/Manual Transaxle

TEST STEP		RESULT	▶	ACTION TO TAKE
IGNB1	CHECK IDM SIGNAL AT PCM CONNECTOR			
• Key OFF. • Install Rotunda Breakout Box 007-00033, or equivalent. • DVOM on AC volt scale. • Crank engine and measure voltage between BOB Pin 4 (IDM) and ground. • **Is voltage greater than 1.0 volt AC?**		Yes No	▶ ▶	REPLACE PCM. REMOVE all test equipment. RECONNECT all components. CLEAR Continuous Memory. RERUN Quick Test. GO to IGNB2.
IGNB2	CHECK FOR IDM SHORT TO POWER			
• Key OFF. • Connect TFI Diagnostic Cable 007-00097, or equivalent to PCM breakout box, connect BAT- lead to negative post of battery, and connect TFI module tee to vehicle harness. • DVOM on DC volt scale. • Key ON. • Measure voltage between Pin 23 (IDM) and Pin 7 (VEHICLE BAT-). • **Is voltage less than 0.5 volt DC?**		Yes No	▶ ▶	GO to IGNB3. SERVICE IDM short to power in harness between PCM connector and Ignition Control Module. REMOVE all test equipment. RECONNECT all components. CLEAR Continuous Memory. RERUN Quick Test.
IGNB3	CHECK FOR IDM SHORT TO GROUND			
• Key OFF. • Disconnect PCM. • DVOM on ohm scale. • Measure resistance between Pin 23 (IDM) and Pin 7 (VEHICLE BAT-). • **Is resistance greater than 10K ohms?**		Yes No	▶ ▶	GO to IGNB4. SERVICE IDM short to ground in harness between PCM connector and Ignition Control Module. REMOVE all test equipment. RECONNECT all components. CLEAR Continuous Memory. RERUN Quick Test.

Fig. 13   Test IGNB: Code 212, IDM
Missing (Part 1 of 2). 1994–95 2.0L
Engine

TEST STEP	RESULT	▶	ACTION TO TAKE
IGNB4 CHECK FOR IDM OPEN IN HARNESS			
• Disconnect PCM. • Measure resistance between Pin 23 (IDM) diagnostic cable and Pin 4 of the PCM connector. • **Is resistance less than 5.0 ohms?**	Yes	▶	REPLACE Ignition Control Module. REMOVE all test equipment. RECONNECT all components. CLEAR Continuous Memory. RERUN Quick Test.
	No	▶	SERVICE IDM open in harness between Ignition Control Module and PCM connector. REMOVE all test equipment. RECONNECT all components. CLEAR Continuous Memory. RERUN Quick Test.

Fig. 13 Test IGNB: Code 212, IDM Missing (Part 2 of 2). 1994–95 2.0L Engine

TEST STEP	RESULT	▶	ACTION TO TAKE
IGNC1 CHECK BASE TIMING			
CAUTION: Do not use a remote starter while doing timing check. • Key OFF. • Install timing light. • Remove SPOUT in line connector. • Run engine at normal operating condition. • **Is base timing within ±3 degrees of specified base timing (see Specifications Chart)?**	Yes	▶	GO to IGNC2.
	No	▶	REFER to Initial Timing Set Procedure.
IGNC2 CHECK FOR SPARK ADVANCE			
• Key OFF. • Reconnect SPOUT in line connector. • Idle engine at normal operating condition. • **Is timing greater than 18 degrees and does spark advance from base timing position?**	Yes	▶	Not an ignition problem, REFER to *COMPUTERIZED ENGINE CONTROLS*
	No	▶	GO to IGNC3.
IGNC3 CHECK FOR GOOD SPOUT TO IGNITION CONTROL MODULE			
• Connect Rotunda TFI Diagnostic Cable 007-00097, or equivalent, to Rotunda Breakout Box 007-00033, or equivalent, connect BAT- lead to negative post of battery, and connect Ignition Control Module and vehicle harness. • Turn switch on diagnostic cable to SPOUT OPEN. • Use TFI overlay on Breakout Box. • DVOM on AC volt scale. • Run engine and measure voltage between Pin 10 (SPOUT) and Pin 7 (BAT-). • **Is voltage between 3.0 and 8.5 volts AC?**	Yes	▶	REPLACE Ignition Control Module. REMOVE all test equipment. RECONNECT all components. CLEAR Continuous Memory. RERUN Quick Test.
	No	▶	GO to IGNC4.

Fig. 14 Test IGNC: Timing Off (Part 1 of 2). 1993 2.0L Engine w/Manual transaxle

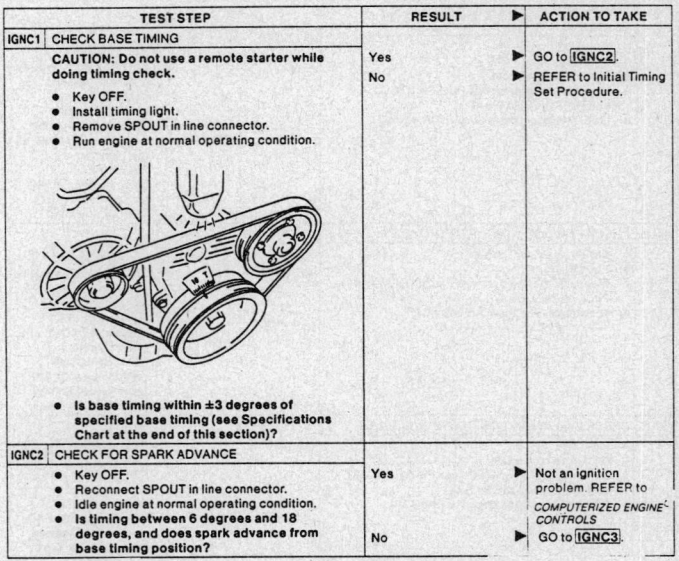

TEST STEP	RESULT	▶	ACTION TO TAKE
IGNC1 CHECK BASE TIMING			
CAUTION: Do not use a remote starter while doing timing check. • Key OFF. • Install timing light. • Remove SPOUT in line connector. • Run engine at normal operating condition.	Yes	▶	GO to IGNC2.
	No	▶	REFER to Initial Timing Set Procedure.
• **Is base timing within ±3 degrees of specified base timing (see Specifications Chart at the end of this section)?**			
IGNC2 CHECK FOR SPARK ADVANCE			
• Key OFF. • Reconnect SPOUT in line connector. • Idle engine at normal operating condition. • **Is timing between 6 degrees and 18 degrees, and does spark advance from base timing position?**	Yes	▶	Not an ignition problem. REFER to *COMPUTERIZED ENGINE CONTROLS*
	No	▶	GO to IGNC3.

Fig. 15 Test IGNC: Timing Off (Part 1 of 2). 1994–95 2.0L Engine

TEST STEP	RESULT	▶	ACTION TO TAKE
IGNC4 CHECK FOR SPOUT OPEN IN HARNESS			
• Key OFF. • Disconnect PCM. • Disconnect diagnostic cable TFI module tee from Ignition Control Module only; leave TFI module tee connected to vehicle harness. • DVOM on ohm scale. • Measure resistance between Pin 36 (SPOUT) of the PCM vehicle harness connector and Pin 10 (SPOUT) at the breakout box. • **Is resistance less than 5.0 ohms?**	Yes	▶	REPLACE PCM. REMOVE all test equipment. RECONNECT all components. CLEAR Continuous Memory. RERUN Quick Test.
	No	▶	SERVICE SPOUT open in harness between PCM and Ignition Control Module. REMOVE all test equipment. RECONNECT all components. CLEAR Continuous Memory. RERUN Quick Test.

Fig. 14 Test IGNC: Timing Off (Part 2 of 2). 1993 2.0L Engine w/Manual transaxle

TEST STEP	RESULT	▶	ACTION TO TAKE
IGNC3 CHECK FOR GOOD SPOUT TO IGNITION CONTROL MODULE			
• Connect Rotunda TFI Diagnostic Cable 007-00097, or equivalent, to Rotunda Breakout Box 007-00033, or equivalent, connect BAT- lead to negative post of battery, and connect Ignition Control Module and vehicle harness. • Turn switch on diagnostic cable to SPOUT OPEN. • Use TFI overlay on Breakout Box. • DVOM on AC volt scale. • Run engine and measure voltage between Pin 10 (SPOUT) and Pin 7 (VEHICLE BAT-). • **Is voltage between 3.0 and 8.5 volts AC?**	Yes	▶	REPLACE Ignition Control Module. REMOVE all test equipment. RECONNECT all components. CLEAR Continuous Memory. RERUN Quick Test.
	No	▶	GO to IGNC4.
IGNC4 CHECK FOR SPOUT OPEN IN HARNESS			
• Key OFF. • Disconnect PCM. • Disconnect diagnostic cable TFI module tee from Ignition Control Module only; leave TFI module tee connected to vehicle harness. • DVOM on ohm scale. • Measure resistance between Pin 36 (SPOUT) of the PCM vehicle harness connector and Pin 10 (SPOUT) at the breakout box. • **Is resistance less than 5.0 ohms?**	Yes	▶	REPLACE PCM. REMOVE all test equipment. RECONNECT all components. CLEAR Continuous Memory. RERUN Quick Test.
	No	▶	SERVICE SPOUT open in harness between PCM and Ignition Control Module. REMOVE all test equipment. RECONNECT all components. CLEAR Continuous Memory. RERUN Quick Test.

Fig. 15 Test IGNC: Timing Off (Part 2 of 2). 1994–95 2.0L Engine

TEST STEP		RESULT	▶	ACTION TO TAKE
IGND1	FIND SYMPTOMS			
	● Talk to customer.		▶	Symptoms.
IGND2	REVIEW VEHICLE HISTORY			
	● Review vehicle service history.		▶	Number of previous repairs and components replaced.
IGND3	TEST EQUIPMENT			
	● Is a Rotunda TFI/EEC-IV Intermittent Ignition Analyzer 007-00035 or equivalent available?	Yes	▶	FOLLOW test procedure instructions supplied with tester.
	NOTE: The TFI-IV intermittent analyzer cannot be used with TFI-IV modules with Computer Controlled Dwell (CCD) unless a CCD update is added to the analyzer.	No	▶	GO to IGND4.
IGND4	BEGIN DIAGNOSIS			
	● Will engine start?	Yes	▶	GO to IGND5.
		No	▶	GO to IGNA1.
IGND5	COLD WIGGLE TEST			
	● Engine at idle, raise hood, shake wiring harness and pull wires at connectors for ignition components.	Yes	▶	SERVICE wiring harness or connector.
	● Does engine quit?	No	▶	GO to IGND6.
IGND6	ENGINE WARM-UP			
	● Engine at idle, close hood, A/C ON, blower on medium speed; allow engine to run for 15 minutes.	Yes	▶	GO to IGND10.
	● Does engine quit?	No	▶	GO to IGND7.
IGND7	HOT RESTART TEST			
	● Engine off, hood closed, hot soak for 10 minutes.	Yes	▶	GO to IGND8.
	● Will engine restart?	No	▶	GO to IGNA1.
IGND8	HOT WIGGLE TEST			
	● Engine at idle, raise hood, shake wiring harness and pull wires at connectors for ignition components.	Yes	▶	SERVICE wiring harness or connector.
	● Does engine quit?	No	▶	GO to IGND9.
IGND9	ROAD TEST			
	● Road test.	Yes	▶	GO to IGND10.
	● Does engine quit?	No	▶	Test complete (Problem not duplicated).

**Fig. 16   Test IGND: Intermittent
Miss Or Stall (Part 1 of 2). 1993 2.0L
Engine w/Manual Transaxle**

TEST STEP		RESULT	▶	ACTION TO TAKE
IGND10	FINAL TEST			
	● Raise hood, shake wiring harness, pull wires at connectors, separate and reconnect connectors for ignition components.	Yes	▶	SERVICE wiring harness or connector.
	● Does engine start?	No	▶	GO to IGNA1.

**Fig. 16   Test IGND: Intermittent
Miss Or Stall (Part 2 of 2). 1993 2.0L
Engine w/Manual Transaxle**

Intermittent Miss or Stall (IGND) (2.0L)

Before conducting this test, talk to the customer to get the symptoms. Then review the vehicle history to get the number of previous repairs and what components have been replaced.

TEST STEP		RESULT	▶	ACTION TO TAKE
IGND1	TEST EQUIPMENT			
	● Is a Rotunda TFI/EEC-IV Intermittent Ignition Analyzer 007-00078 or equivalent available?	Yes	▶	FOLLOW test procedure instructions supplied with tester.
	NOTE: The TFI-IV intermittent analyzer cannot be used with TFI-IV modules with Computer Controlled Dwell (CCD) unless a CCD update is added to the analyzer.	No	▶	GO to IGND2.
IGND2	BEGIN DIAGNOSIS			
	● Will engine start?	Yes	▶	GO to IGND3.
		No	▶	GO to IGNA1.
IGND3	COLD WIGGLE TEST			
	● Engine at idle, raise hood, shake wiring harness and pull wires at connectors for ignition components.	Yes	▶	SERVICE wiring harness or connector.
	● Does engine quit?	No	▶	GO to IGND4.
IGND4	ENGINE WARM-UP			
	● Engine at idle, close hood, A/C ON, blower on medium speed; allow engine to run for 15 minutes.	Yes	▶	GO to IGND8.
	● Does engine quit?	No	▶	GO to IGND5.
IGND5	HOT RESTART TEST			
	● Engine off, hood closed, hot soak for 10 minutes.	Yes	▶	GO to IGND6.
	● Will engine restart?	No	▶	GO to IGNA1.
IGND6	HOT WIGGLE TEST			
	● Engine at idle, raise hood, shake wiring harness and pull wires at connectors for ignition components.	Yes	▶	SERVICE wiring harness or connector.
	● Does engine quit?	No	▶	GO to IGND7.
IGND7	ROAD TEST			
	● Road test.	Yes	▶	GO to IGND8.
	● Does engine quit?	No	▶	Test complete (Problem not duplicated).
IGND8	FINAL TEST			
	● Raise hood, shake wiring harness, pull wires at connectors, separate and reconnect connectors for ignition components.	Yes	▶	SERVICE wiring harness or connector.
	● Does engine start?	No	▶	GO to IGNA1.

**Fig. 17   Test IGND: Intermittent
Miss Or Stall. 1994–95 2.0L Engine**

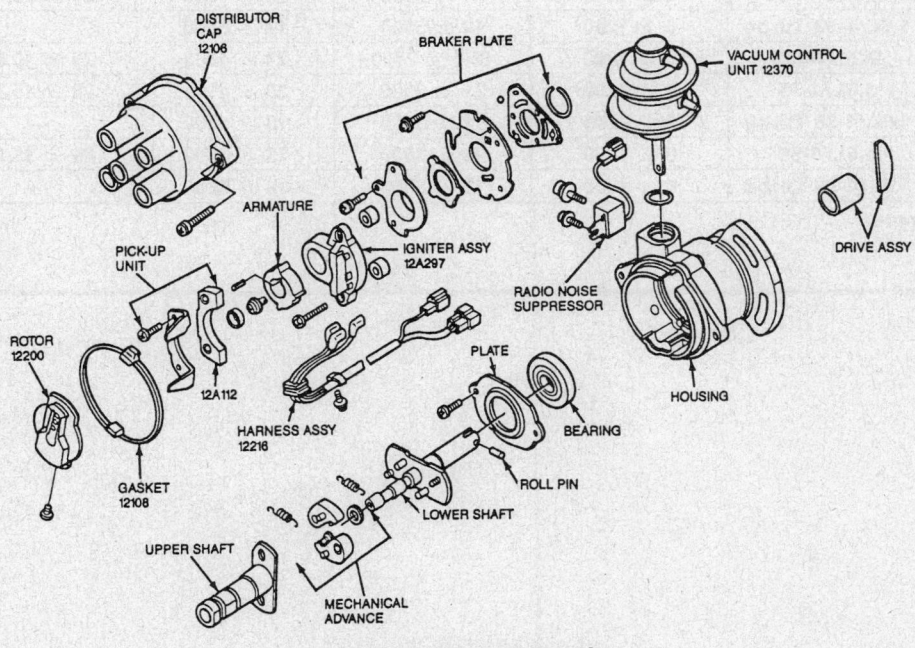

**Fig. 18   Exploded view of
distributor assembly. Capri w/1.6L
engine**

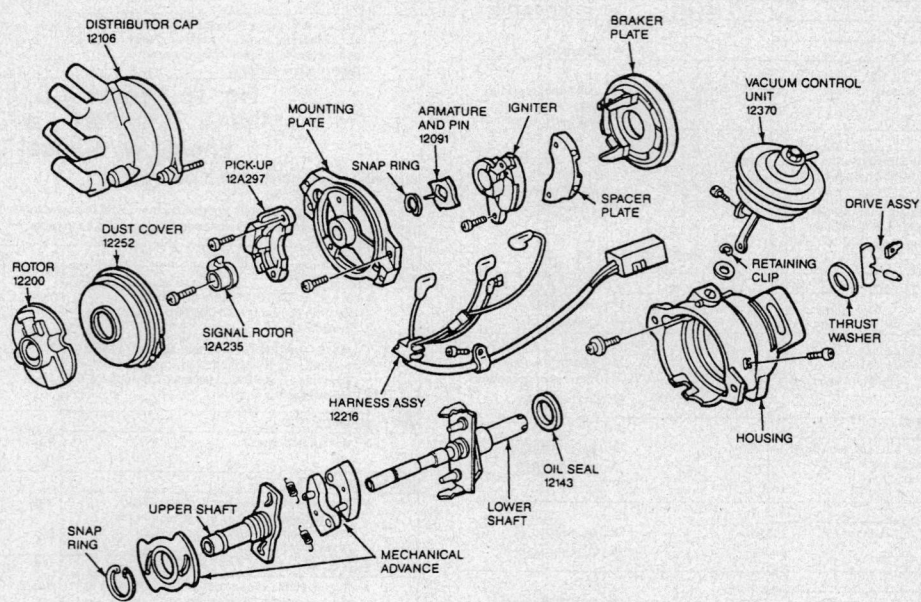

Fig. 19   Exploded view of distributor assembly. Capri w/1.6L Turbocharged engine

SPECIFICATIONS

| Year | Engine | Centrifugal Advance Degrees @ RPM of Distributor | | | Vacuum Advance Degrees @ In. Hg ① | |
		Advance Starts	Intermediate Advance	Full Advance	A Diaphragm	B Diaphragm
1992	1.6L/4-98	0 @ 1200	21 @ 3000	25 @ 4500	28 @ 15.75	5 @ 5.91
	1.6L/4-98 Turbo	0 @ 1200	12 @ 5500	18 @ 5500	—	—
	2.2L/4-133	0 @ 1200	12.4 @ 2400	22 @ 4500	20 @ 10.83	6 @ 7.87
1993	1.6L/4-98	0 @ 1200	21 @ 3000	25 @ 4500	28 @ 15.75	5 @ 5.91
	1.6L/4-98 Turbo	0 @ 1200	12 @ 3500	18 @ 5500	—	—
1994	1.6L/4-98	0 @ 1200	21 @ 3000	25 @ 4500	28 @ 15.75	5 @ 5.91
	1.6L/4-98 Turbo	0 @ 1200	12 @ 3500	18 @ 5500	—	—

①—Maximum advance.

Type 6

INDEX

Page No.

Description. 4-127
Diagnosis & Testing. 4-127
System Service: 4-127
   Component Replacement. 4-127

NOTE: On 1996 Models Equipped w/EEC-V Engine Control System, Refer To "Computerized Engine Controls" For Ignition System Service.

DESCRIPTION

The Electronic Ignition (EI) (High Data Rate) systems, **Figs. 1 through 6,** consist of an Ignition Control Module (ICM), a Crankshaft Position Sensor (CKP), a Powertrain Control Module (PCM) and connecting wiring harnesses. Six cylinder applications use a six-tower coil pack and eight cylinder applications use two four-tower coil packs.

The following vehicles use an EI system with a stand-alone ICM: 3.8L Mustang and 4.6L Cougar, Crown Victoria, Grand Marquis, Thunderbird & Town Car.

The EI High Data Rate system eliminates the need for a distributor by using multiple coil packs. Each coil within the pack fires two spark plugs at the same time. The plugs are paired so as one fires during the compression stroke, the other fires during the exhaust stroke. The next time the coil is fired, the plug on exhaust will be on compression and the plug on compression will be on exhaust.

The CKP is used to indicate crankshaft position and speed information to the ICM. By sensing a missing tooth on a trigger wheel mounted on the crankshaft damper, the CKP is also able to identify a specific point in the travel of No. 1 piston. The ICM uses this information from the CKP to generate a Profile Ignition Pickup (PIP) signal which is sent to the PCM.

Once the PCM recognizes the PIP signal, fuel and spark functions are enabled. The calculated spark target is sent from the PCM to the ICM as a pulse width modulated digital signal called the Spark Output (SPOUT). The ICM decodes the SPOUT signal and fires the next spark at the commanded spark target.

Coil firing is initiated by energizing the ICM coils in sequence, using the missing tooth as a reference and firing at the commanded spark target.

By energizing the primary side of the coils on proper sequence and connecting the secondary wires in accordance with the engine firing order, a power stroke is achieved on each cylinder. In addition, an Ignition Diagnostic Monitor (IDM) signal is transmitted on each spark firing. This signal communicates information by pulse width modulation and provides a clean, buffered signal with a frequency proportional to engine speed for tachometer operation.

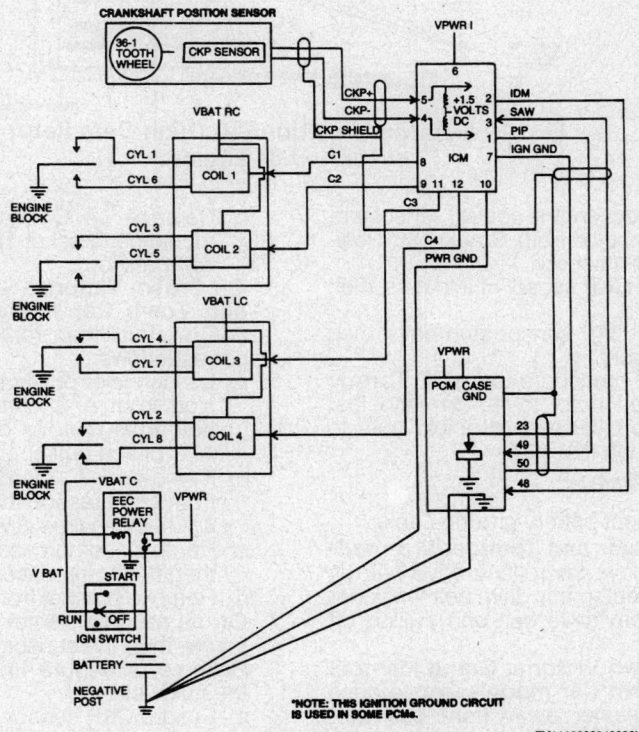

Fig. 1 Electronic Ignition (EI) (High Data Rate) system. 4.6L Engine

The ICM also serves as an electric switch for a coil primary circuit. When the switch closes, current flows and a magnetic field expands around the primary coil. When the switch opens, the field collapses and causes the secondary coil to fire the spark plugs at high voltage.

DIAGNOSIS & TESTING

Refer to "Computerized Engine Controls section for diagnosis and testing of this EEC-V ignition system.

SYSTEM SERVICE

Component Replacement

CRANKSHAFT POSITION SENSOR

3.8L Engine

1. Disconnect battery ground cable, then raise and support vehicle.

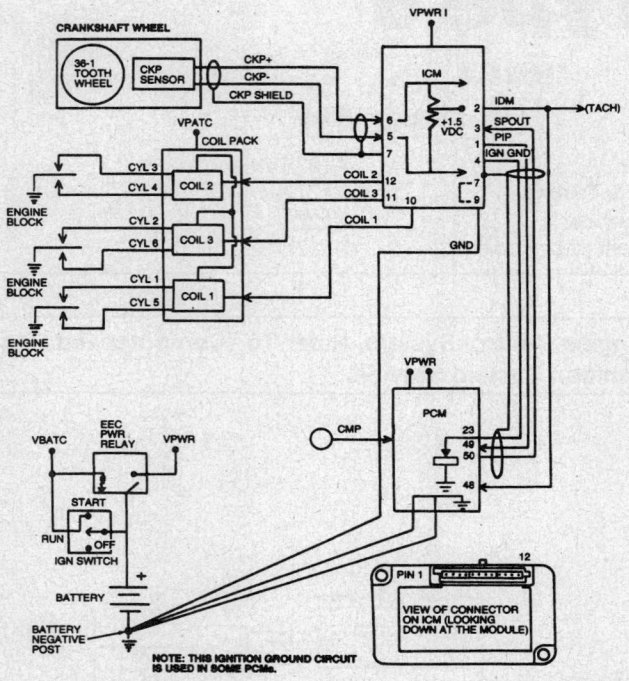

Fig. 2 Electronic Ignition (EI) (High Data Rate) system. 3.8L Engine

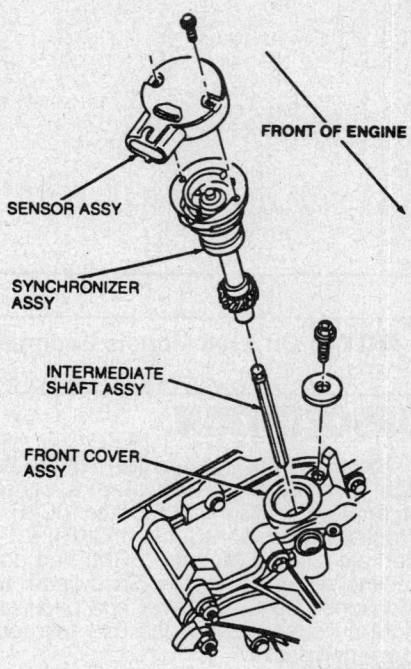

Fig. 3 Component Locations (Part 1 of 2). 3.8L Engine

2. Disconnect engine control sensor wiring connector from Crankshaft Position (CKP) sensor.
3. Remove CKP sensor shield nuts, then the shield.
4. Remove CKP sensor stud bolts, then the sensor.
5. Reverse procedure to install. **Torque** CKP stud bolts to 40-61 lbs., then the CKP sensor shield nuts to 18-35 inch lbs.

4.6L Engine

1. Disconnect battery ground cable.
2. **On Cougar and Thunderbird models,** remove serpentine drive belt by rotating automatic drive belt tensioner away from drive belt and pulling off belt.
3. **On Crown Victoria, Grand Marquis and Town Car models,** rotate drive belt tensioner away from belt with breaker bar installed in 1/2 inch square hole in drive belt tensioner arm, then lift belt over generator pulley flange.
4. **On all models,** raise and support vehicle, then disconnect engine control sensor wiring from Crankshaft Position (CKP) sensor and A/C compressor.
5. **On Cougar and Thunderbird models,** discharge A/C system, then remove compressor as follows:
   a. Remove A/C compressor drive belt.
   b. Remove suction and discharge manifold and tube assembly from A/C compressor, then cap suction and discharge ports in manifold and tube assembly and compressor to prevent entry of dirt or moisture.

c. Remove A/C compressor to mounting bracket bolts, then the compressor.
6. **On Crown Victoria, Grand Marquis and Town Car models,** discharge A/C system, then remove compressor as follows:
   a. Loosen idler pulley to remove tension from A/C compressor drive belt, then remove drive belt from A/C clutch pulley.
   b. Remove A/C manifold and tube from compressor, then disconnect A/C clutch wires at wire connector.
   c. Remove compressor lower bolts, then the compressor.
   d. Remove bracket from compressor.
7. **On all models,** remove CKP sensor screw, then the sensor.
8. Reverse procedure to install, noting the following:
   a. Ensure CKP sensor mounting surface is clean and sensor O-ring is in proper location on sensor.
   b. **Do not overtighten CKP sensor screw or damage to sensor may occur. Torque** sensor screw to 71-106 inch lbs.
   c. **On Cougar and Thunderbird models,** torque A/C compressor to mounting bracket bolts to 31-44 ft. lbs.
   d. **On all models,** torque suction and discharge manifold and tube assembly bolt to 13-17 ft. lbs.

IGNITION COIL

3.8L Engine

1. Disconnect battery ground cable, then the engine control sensor wiring connector from ignition coil and radio igni-

tion interference capacitor.
2. Remove ignition wires by squeezing locking tabs to release ignition coil boot retainers.
3. Remove ignition coil screws, then the coil and radio ignition interference capacitor.
4. Reverse procedure to install **Torque** ignition coil screws to 40-61 inch lbs.

4.6L Engine

1. Disconnect engine control sensor wiring from ignition coils and radio ignition interference capacitors.
2. Disconnect ignition wires by squeezing lock tabs and twisting by pulling upward.
3. Remove ignition coil screws, then the coils and radio ignition interference capacitors. Save capacitors for installation with ignition coils.
4. Reverse procedure to install, noting the following:
   a. **Torque** ignition coil screws to 40-61 inch lbs.
   b. Apply silicone dielectric compound D7AZ-19A331-A or equivalent to all ignition wire spark plugs.

IGNITION CONTROL MODULE

3.8L Engine & 4.6L Cougar & Thunderbird

1. Disconnect battery ground cable.
2. Disconnect engine control sensor wiring connector at Ignition Control Module (ICM) by pressing down on locking tab where it is stamped PUSH, then remove connector.
3. Remove ICM screws, then the ICM from ICM bracket mounted on front fender apron.

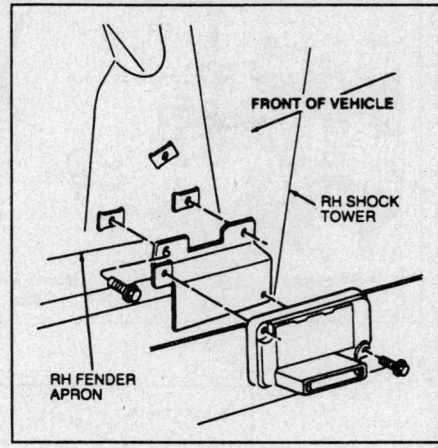

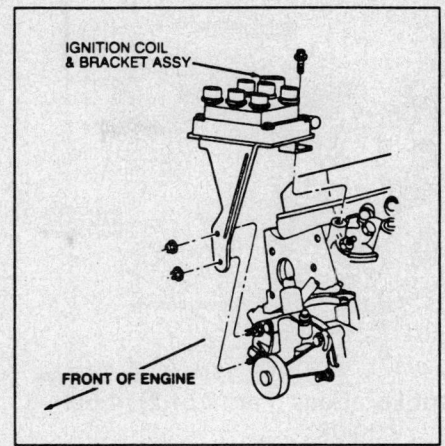

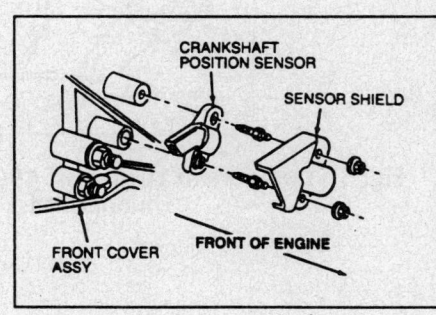

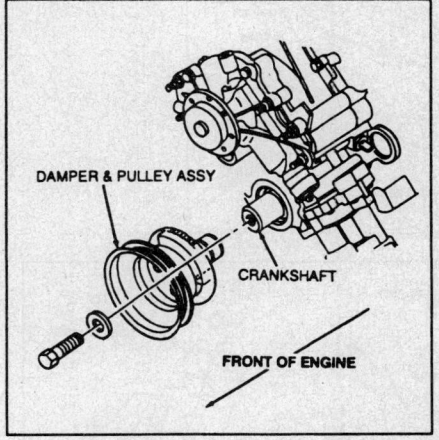

FM1119200342020X

Fig. 3 Component Locations (Part 2 of 2). 3.8L Engine

4. Reverse procedure to install, noting the following:
   a. **On Mustang models, torque** ICM screws to 29-47 inch lbs.
   b. **On Cougar & Thunderbird models, torque** ICM screws to 24-33 inch lbs., then the ICM bracket bolts to 35-50 inch lbs.

4.6L Crown Victoria, Grand Marquis & Town Car

1. Disconnect Ignition Control Module (ICM) electrical connector by pushing down on connector finger ends while grasping connector body and pulling away from ICM.
2. Remove ICM screws, then the module
3. Reverse procedure to install. **Torque** ICM screws to 24-35 inch lbs.

RADIO IGNITION INTERFERENCE CAPACITOR

1. Disconnect engine control sensor wiring from radio ignition interference capacitor(s).
2. Remove capacitor screw(s), then the capacitor(s) from ignition coil(s) and mounting bracket.
3. Reverse procedure to install. **Torque** capacitor screw to 40-61 inch lbs.

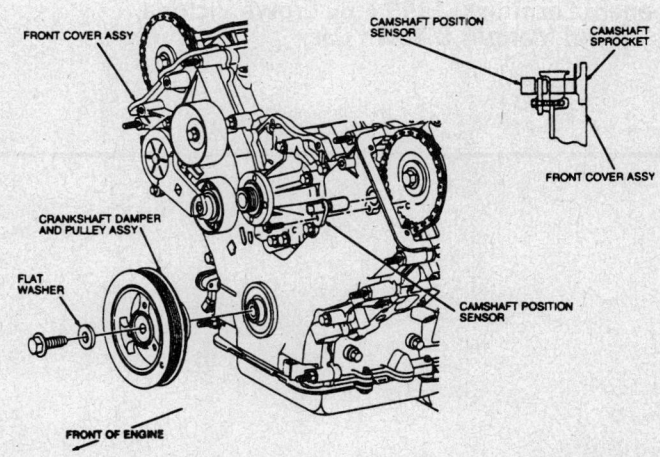

FM1119200343010X

Fig. 4 Component Locations (Part 1 of 2). 4.6L Engine

TYPE 6

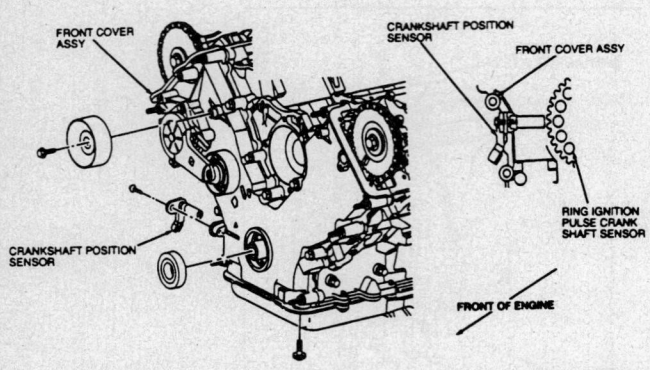

FM1119200343020X

Fig. 4   Component Locations (Part 2 of 2). 4.6L Engine

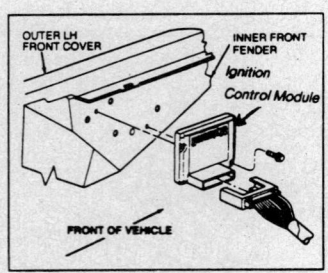

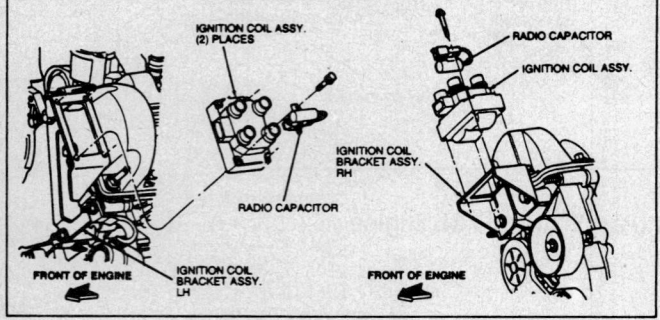

FM1119500345000X

Fig. 6   Component Locations. 1995 4.6L Crown Victoria, Grand Marquis & Town Car

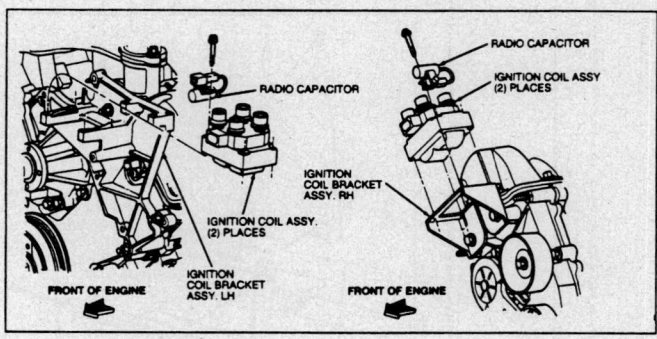

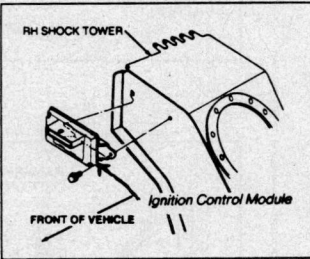

FM1119500344000X

Fig. 5   Component Locations. 1995 4.6L Cougar & Thunderbird

FUEL INJECTION

If Unsure Of The System Used On The Vehicle Being Serviced, Refer To The "Engine Systems Identification Chart." Further Assistance For The Proper Use Of Information Contained In This Section Can Also Be Found In The Front Of This Tabbed Section Under "How To Use This Manual."

Prior To Performing Any Service Operations Listed In This Section, Consult The Technical Service Bulletin Section For Related Information.

Electrical Symbol & Wire Color Code Identification Located In The Front Of This Manual May Be Used As An Aid When Using Wiring Circuits Found In This Section.

Refer To "Electric Fuel Pumps" Section For Fuel Pump Relay Locations.

INDEX

	Page No.		Page No.		Page No.
Description:	5-2	Component Replacement:	5-4	Oxygen Sensor	5-18
System Components & Operation	5-2	Air Bypass Valve	5-17	Pressure Relief Valve	5-18
System Overview	5-2	Clutch Switch	5-18	Supercharger & Throttle Body	5-8
Diagnosis & Testing	5-4	Coolant Temperature Sensor	5-18	Throttle Body	5-16
Precautions:	5-1	Engine Coolant Temperature		Throttle Lever	5-17
Fuel System Pressure Relief	5-1	Sensor	5-18	Throttle Position Sensor	5-17
System Service:	5-4	Fuel Charging Assembly	5-4	Upper Intake Manifold	5-9
Adjustments:	5-19	Fuel Injector	5-18	Upper Intake Manifold & Throttle	
Idle Speed	5-20	Fuel Pressure Regulator	5-18	Body	5-15
Idle Switch	5-20	Neutral Switch	5-18	Volume Air Meter	5-18
Throttle Position Sensor	5-19				

PRECAUTIONS
FUEL SYSTEM PRESSURE RELIEF

1.3L/4-81 ENGINE

1. Remove fuel filler cap and release tank pressure.
2. Locate fuel pump relay electrical connector behind left side of instrument cluster.
3. Start engine, then disconnect fuel pump relay electrical connector and wait for engine to stall.
4. Disconnect battery ground cable.

1.6L/4-98, 1.8L/4-112 & 1.9L/4-116 ENGINES

1. Remove gas cap to release residual fuel pressure in the tank.
2. Start engine, then disconnect fuel pump connector.
3. When engine stalls turn ignition switch off.
4. Disconnect battery ground cable.

PROBE w/2.0L/4-121 & 2.5L/V6-152 ENGINES
1993—94

1. Start engine, then disconnect fuel pump relay.
2. When engine stalls turn ignition switch off.
3. Reconnect fuel pump relay.
4. Disconnect battery ground cable.

1995—96

1. Remove gas cap to release residual fuel pressure in the tank.
2. Disconnect battery ground cable and position aside.
3. Using fuel pressure gauge tool No. T80L-9974-B, or equivalent, relieve pressure from system at pressure relief valve cap on fuel injection supply manifold.

CONTOUR & MYSTIQUE w/2.0L/4-122 & 2.5L/V6-153 ENGINES

1. Remove gas cap to release residual fuel pressure in the tank.
2. Disconnect battery ground cable and position aside.
3. Using fuel pressure gauge tool No. T80L-9974-B, or equivalent, relieve pressure from system at pressure relief valve cap on fuel injection supply manifold.

2.3L/4-140, 3.0L/V6-182, 3.2L/V6-195, 3.8L/V6-232, 4.6L/V8-281 & 5.0L/V8-302 ENGINES

Fuel system pressure may be relieved by the fuel pressure relief valve, located on the fuel injection supply manifold.

1. Remove air cleaner assembly.
2. Connect EFI and CFI fuel pressure gauge tool No. T80L-9974-B or equivalent, to fuel pressure relief valve cap.
3. Open manual valve on pressure gauge to relieve fuel system pressure.

4.6L/V8-281 NATURAL GAS ENGINE

The fuel system is always pressurized to 120 psi downstream of the fuel pressure regulator. When servicing any component of the fuel charging system, fuel pressure should be released using the following procedure.

1. Thump inertia fuel shutoff switch and verify switch has been tripped or close the quarter-turn ball valve.
2. Disconnect battery ground cable.
3. Connect natural gas fuel rail pressure tester from Rotunda NG Tool Kit No. 134-0048 or equivalent, to schrader valve on fuel injection supply manifold.
4. Position testing kit vent hose end outside or into natural gas vent stack.
5. Gradually open testing kit valve to relieve fuel pressure. A small amount (5 psi) will remain in the injection supply manifold. High pressure still exists in the fuel tanks and upstream of the quarter-turn manual shutoff valve, if closed.
6. Cycle ignition switch from Run to Off several times without starting engine.
7. Using combustible gas detector tool No. 005-00107 or equivalent, check for fuel system leaks.
8. To pressurize system after service, slowly open manual shutoff valve or set inertia fuel shutoff valve, if tripped.

DESCRIPTION

SYSTEM OVERVIEW

Gasoline Engines

On Capri, Escort, Festiva and Tracer, the electronic fuel injection (EFI) system is a multi-point, pulse fuel injection system. This system supplies the engine with air/fuel mixture necessary for combustion. An air induction system and a fuel injection system work in conjunction with an engine control system which consists of various sensors, switches and an powertrain control module (PCM). All sensors and switches are connected to the PCM which interprets the data it receives and computes when and for how long the electrically operated injectors are energized.

The system used on all other models is a sequential, multi-point, pulse timed, speed density control fuel injection system. Fuel is metered into each intake port through injectors mounted on a tuned intake manifold. The EEC-IV or EEC-V engine control system receives signals from various engine sensors and computes the required rate of fuel flow to maintain an optimum air/fuel ratio throughout the entire range of engine operation.

The fuel charging manifold assembly, **Figs. 1 through 18**, houses the injectors which are mounted directly above each of the engine's intake ports. When energized, the injectors spray a metered quantity of fuel into the intake air stream.

Natural Gas Engine

The fuel system, **Figs. 19 and 20**, consists of a fuel tank, fuel shutoff valve assemblies, fuel supply lines, fuel filter, schrader service valve, fuel rail and fuel pressure regulator. When the ignition switch is turned to the Run or Start position, the PCM energizes the fuel shutoff relay which opens the fuel shutoff valves. The fuel shutoff valves will remain open as long as the PCM receives a signal that the engine is turning. When the ignition switch is turned from Off to Run, the shutoff valves are energized for one second to pressurize the fuel rail prior to starting the engine. The fuel pressure regulator keeps fuel pressure constant at 120 psi. The fuel injectors are controlled by the PCM and are cycled on or off to deliver a calculated amount of fuel at the intake valve.

SYSTEM COMPONENTS & OPERATION

AIR INDUCTION SYSTEM

MFI System

The air induction system supplies filtered air to the engine to mix with fuel for combustion purposes. It consists of an air cleaner assembly, volume air flow meter, throttle body and a bypass air (BPA) valve. The volume air flow meter mounted to the air filter housing measures the amount of airflow and air temperature and provides this information to the power control module (PCM).

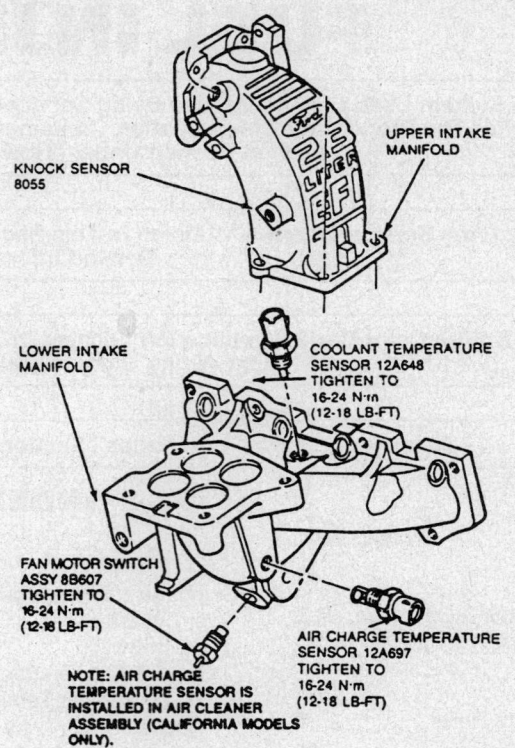

Fig. 1 Exploded view of fuel charging assembly. 2.3L/4-140 OHC engine

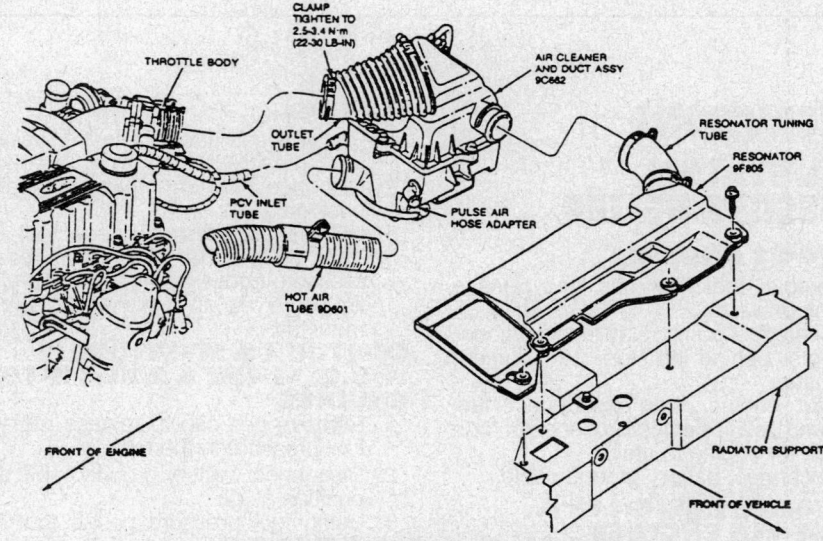

Fig. 2 Exploded view of fuel charging assembly. 2.3L/4-140 HSC engine

SFI System

The air induction system supplies filtered air to the engine to mix with fuel for combustion purposes. It consists of an air cleaner assembly, mass air flow (MAF) sensor, throttle body and an idle air control bypass air (BPA) valve. The MAF sensor mounted to the air filter housing measures the amount of airflow and air temperature and provides this information to the power control module (PCM). For natural gas engines, the SFI system is fuel pressure and temperature compensated.

AIR INTAKE MANIFOLD

The air intake manifold is a one or two-piece aluminum casting which provides mounting flanges for the throttle body assembly, fuel supply manifold, accelerator control brackets and the EGR valve and supply tube. Runner lengths are precisely tuned to optimize engine torque and power output. Vacuum taps in the manifold are provided to support various engine accessories. Cutouts for the fuel injectors are specially machined to prevent both air and fuel leakage.

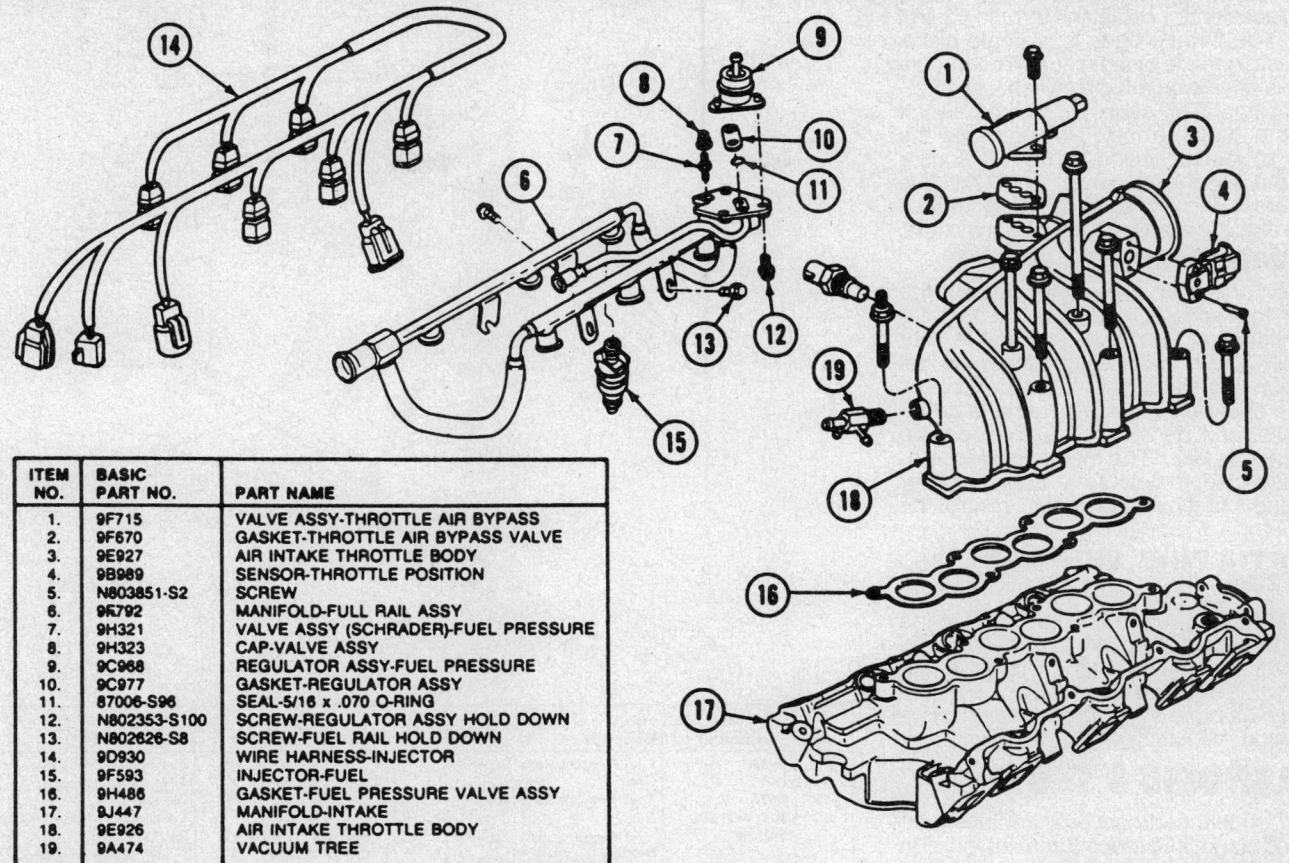

ITEM NO.	BASIC PART NO.	PART NAME
1.	9F715	VALVE ASSY-THROTTLE AIR BYPASS
2.	9F670	GASKET-THROTTLE AIR BYPASS VALVE
3.	9E927	AIR INTAKE THROTTLE BODY
4.	9B989	SENSOR-THROTTLE POSITION
5.	N803851-S2	SCREW
6.	9F792	MANIFOLD-FULL RAIL ASSY
7.	9H321	VALVE ASSY (SCHRADER)-FUEL PRESSURE
8.	9H323	CAP-VALVE ASSY
9.	9C968	REGULATOR ASSY-FUEL PRESSURE
10.	9C977	GASKET-REGULATOR ASSY
11.	87006-S96	SEAL-5/16 x .070 O-RING
12.	N802353-S100	SCREW-REGULATOR ASSY HOLD DOWN
13.	N802626-S8	SCREW-FUEL RAIL HOLD DOWN
14.	9D930	WIRE HARNESS-INJECTOR
15.	9F593	INJECTOR-FUEL
16.	9H486	GASKET-FUEL PRESSURE VALVE ASSY
17.	9J447	MANIFOLD-INTAKE
18.	9E926	AIR INTAKE THROTTLE BODY
19.	9A474	VACUUM TREE

FM1029100044000X

Fig. 3   Exploded view of fuel charging assembly. 1993–95 3.0L/V6-182 engine except SHO

BYPASS AIR CONTROL VALVE (BPA)

The BPA valve consists of the air bypass valve which functions only during cold engine conditions and the idle air control (IAC) valve which works throughout the entire engine temperature range.

FUEL INJECTORS

The fuel injectors, **Fig. 21,** are electromechanical devices which meter and atomize fuel for combustion. The injectors, located in the lower intake manifold, are installed so fuel is directed just ahead of the intake valves. The injector solenoid receives an electrical control signal from the ECU/PCM which causes the pintle to move off its seat, allowing fuel to flow. Because the fuel pressure drop across the injector tip is constant and the injector orifice is fixed, fuel flow is regulated by the length of time the solenoid is energized.

Fuel injectors used in a natural gas engine are similar to those used in gasoline engines, however the flow capacity is 6 to 12 times greater compared to a gasoline engine fuel injector. Electrical resistance is also much lower in this type of injector. To accommodate this lower resistance, an injector driver module is used to convert the EEC-V injector driver signal to the signal required by the driver.

FUEL PRESSURE PULSE DAMPER

The fuel injection systems supply fuel to each cylinder by opening and closing all injectors simultaneously once every engine revolution. At idle, when fuel demand is low, this opening and closing of injectors is very abrupt and causes a hydraulic pressure plate pulse to feed back through the fuel system. This noise is more pronounced when ambient temperatures are low. Due to tolerance reasons, the fuel rail is mounted solid to the engine. At this point there is an unavoidable transmission of hydraulic pulsations to the engine block. These pulses feed into the passenger compartment wherever fuel lines are attached and create an unacceptable ticking or hydraulic hammering noise.

FUEL PRESSURE REGULATOR
Gasoline Engines

The fuel pressure regulator, **Fig. 22,** is located on the fuel supply manifold and regulates fuel pressure supplied to the injectors. One side of the diaphragm in the regulator senses fuel pressure, while intake manifold pressure is applied to the other side. Nominal fuel pressure is established by spring tension applied to the diaphragm. A constant fuel pressure drop across the injectors is maintained by balancing one side of the diaphragm with manifold pressure. Excess fuel is bypassed through the regulator and returned to the fuel tank.

Natural Gas Engine

The fuel pressure regulator, **Fig. 23,** used on the NG engine is a single-stage pressure reducing regulator which expands natural gas from storage pressures of 200-3000 psi to injector pressures of 105-125 psi. The regulator contains a pressure relief valve (275 psi check valve) which protects the low pressure fuel system.

When gas expands, the fuel temperature drops causing extreme cold temperatures that may damage synthetic fuel system components as well as cause water vapor in the fuel to condense, freeze and plug lines and injectors. To prevent this, engine coolant is routed through the regulator to warm the fuel before it expands. The regulator has an internal thermostat to control the flow of engine coolant.

FUEL SUPPLY MANIFOLD

The fuel supply manifold delivers high pressure fuel from the fuel supply line to the injectors. The manifold assembly consists of a single pre-formed tube with either four, six or eight injector connectors, a fuel pressure regulator mounting flange, a pressure relief valve and mounting attachments. The pressure relief valve is used for diagnostic testing and bleeding of fuel system pressure.

THROTTLE BODY

Air flow to the engine is controlled by the throttle body through a single butterfly-type valve. Throttle position is controlled by an accelerator cable and throttle control lever. The throttle body is a single piece, die casting made of aluminum. The throttle body is fitted with an idle switch and throttle position (TP) sensor. The idle switch sends a signal to the PCM informing the PCM of idle conditions. The TP sensor sends a varying signal to the PCM. The PCM uses the signal to measure throttle valve angle and adjust the air/fuel mixture.

VOLUME AIR FLOW METER

The volume air flow meter detects the intake to a voltage reading by means of a potentiometer. The voltage signal is sent to the PCM which helps it to determine fuel injection quantities. The voltage increases as the opening in the measuring plate increases, and decreases as the opening becomes smaller. The meter also incorporates a sensor to detect intake air temperature and a fuel pump switch to control the fuel pump.

INERTIA FUEL SHUTOFF SWITCH

The inertia fuel shutoff (IFS) switch is used in conjunction with the electric fuel shutoff valves to stop fuel flow in the event of an accident. One the switch is open, the IFS switch must be manually reset before restarting the vehicle.

DIAGNOSIS & TESTING

For trouble code access, troubleshooting and diagnostic procedures not found in this section, refer to the "Computerized Engine Controls" section.

SYSTEM SERVICE

Component Replacement

FUEL CHARGING ASSEMBLY

Refer to **Figs. 1 through 18** when servicing fuel charging assembly.

1.3L/4-81 Engine

1. Disconnect battery ground cable, then drain cooling system.
2. Disconnect accelerator cable from throttle linkage.
3. Remove air duct from throttle body.
4. Mark vacuum hoses for reference during assembly, then disconnect hoses from throttle body.
5. Disconnect throttle position sensor electrical connector.
6. Remove intake plenum retaining bolts and nuts.
7. Remove intake plenum and gasket.
8. Reverse procedure to install.

1.8L/4-112 & 1.9L/4-116 Engines

1. Relieve fuel pressure as outlined under "Precautions," and disconnect battery ground cable.
2. Remove fuel tube clip and twist the spring lock coupling fitting to free it from any adhesion at O-ring.

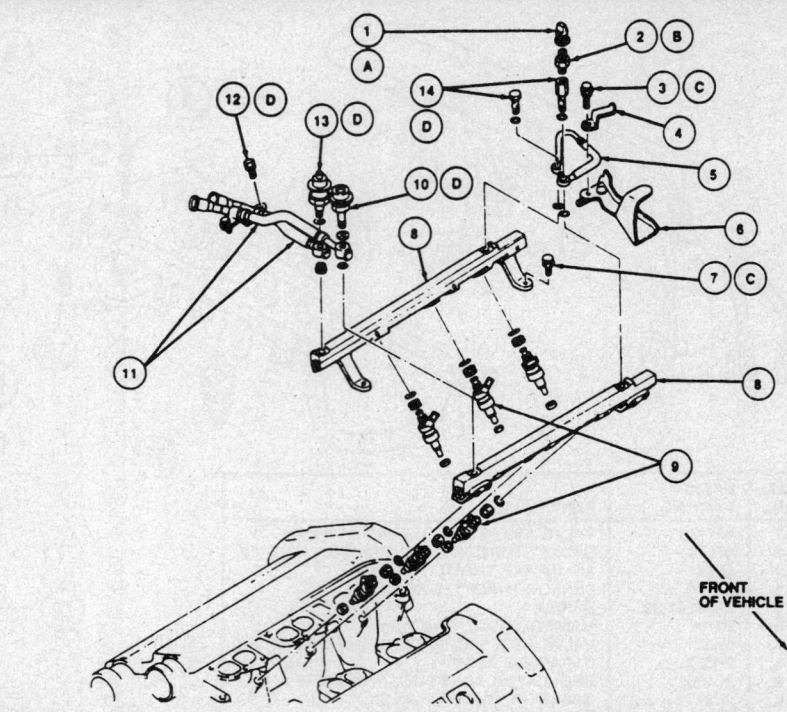

FRONT OF VEHICLE

Item	Part Number	Description
1A	9H323	Fuel Pressure Relief Valve Cap
2B	9H321	Fuel Pressure Relief Valve
3C	90119-06171	Bolt
4	9W276	Fuel Injector Supply Manifold Bracket
5	9F754	Fuel Injection Supply Manifold Connector
6	9J444	Intake Manifold Support
7C	—	Bolt (4 Req'd)
8	9D280	Fuel Injection Supply Manifold (2 Req'd)

Item	Part Number	Description
9	9F593	Fuel Injector (6 Req'd)
10D	9F775	Fuel Injection Pulse Dampener
11	9A321	Fuel Supply and Return Lines
12D	9119-06171	Bolt (2 Req'd)
13D	9C968	Fuel Pressure Regulator
14D	9J446	Bolt Union (2 Req'd)
A		Tighten to 0.6 N·m (5.5 Lb-In)
B		Tighten to 7.75 N·m (66 Lb-In)
C		Tighten to 15-23 N·m (11-17 Lb-Ft)
D		Tighten to 25-34 N·m (18-25 Lb-Ft)

FM1029100045000X

Fig. 4 Exploded view of fuel charging assembly. 1993–95 3.0L/V6-182 & 3.2L/V6-195 SHO engines

3. Fit spring lock coupling disconnect tool No. D87L-9280-A (3/8 inch) or D87L-9280-B (1/2 inch), or equivalents, to the locking spring coupling.
4. Close the tool and push it into the opening side of cage to expand the garter spring and release female fitting.
5. Close tool and push it into open side of cage to expand garter spring and release female fitting.
6. After garter spring is expanded, separate fittings, then remove tool.
7. Disconnect fuel supply line and crankcase ventilation hose from upper intake manifold and valve cover.
8. Disconnect fuel pressure regulator vacuum hose and fuel charging wiring harness electrical connectors.
9. Remove three fuel injection supply manifold bolts, then the fuel injection supply manifold.
10. Reverse procedure to install, replacing all O-rings.

2.3L/4-140 Except HSC & Turbocharged Engines

1. Disconnect the following electrical connectors:

a. Air bypass valve
b. Throttle position sensor.
c. Injector wiring harness.
d. Knock sensor.
e. Fan switch and coolant temperature sensor.
f. Air charge temperature sensor and EGR valve.

2. Disconnect upper manifold vacuum connections.
3. Disconnect throttle linkage and position aside.
4. Disconnect air intake hose from throttle body and PCV hose from manifold.
5. Disconnect water bypass hose at lower intake manifold.
6. Disconnect EGR tube from EGR valve.
7. Remove oil dipstick bracket to manifold attaching bolt.
8. Remove upper intake manifold attaching nuts, then the upper intake manifold assembly.
9. Disconnect fuel return line from fuel supply manifold using spring lock coupling removal tool No. D87L9280-A/B, or equivalent.
10. Disconnect all four fuel injector electrical connectors and position harness to one side.

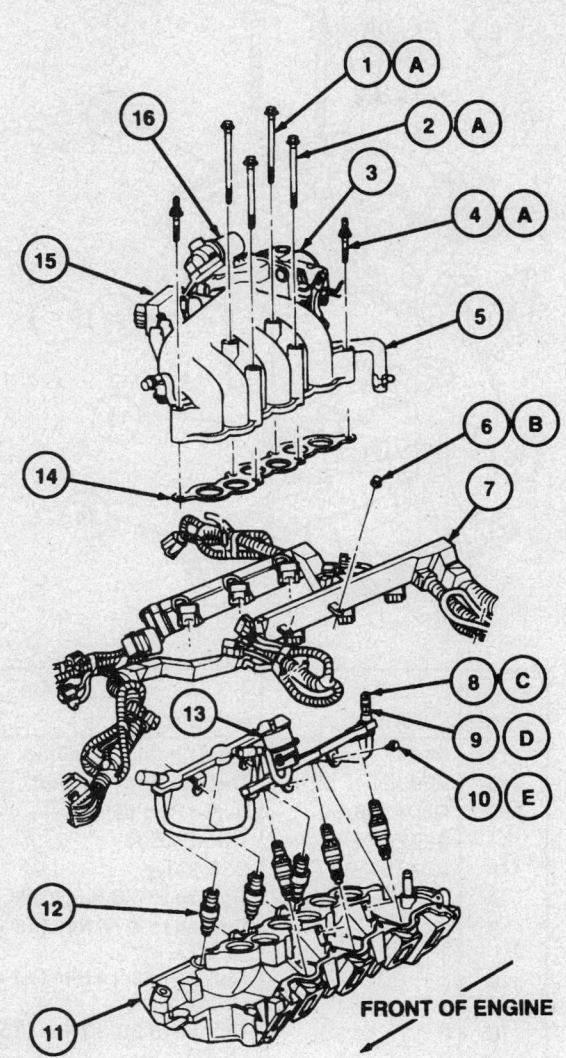

Item	Description
13	Fuel Pressure Regulator
14	Intake Manifold Upper Gasket
15	EGR Backpressure Transducer
16	Idle Air Control Valve
A	Tighten to 20-30 N·m (15-22 Lb-Ft)
B	Tighten to 2.5-3.5 N·m (22-30 Lb-In)
C	Tighten to 0.6 N·m (5 Lb-In)
D	Tighten to 7.75 N·m (68 Lb-In)
E	Tighten to 8-12 N·m (71-106 Lb-In)

FM1029600235020X

Fig. 5 Exploded view of fuel charging assembly (Part 2 of 2). 1996 3.0L/V6-182 engine

11. Remove fuel supply manifold attaching bolts, then the fuel supply manifold.
12. Remove lower intake manifold attaching bolts, then the lower intake manifold assembly.
13. Reverse procedure to install, noting the following:
   a. Ensure mating surfaces of fuel charging assembly and cylinder head are clean and not damaged.
   b. Clean and lubricate manifold stud threads before installation.
   c. Install new gasket on lower intake manifold assembly.
   d. **Torque** lower manifold bolts to 12-15 ft. lbs. in sequence shown in **Fig. 24.**
   e. **Torque** fuel manifold attaching bolts to 12-15 ft. lbs.
   f. **Torque** EGR tube flange nuts to 6-8.5 ft. lbs.
   g. Install new gasket on fuel charging assembly air throttle body mounting flange.
   h. **Torque** upper intake manifold attaching bolts to 15-22 ft. lbs.
   i. **Torque** four air throttle body to fuel charging assembly attaching bolts to 15-22 ft. lbs.

2.3L/4-140 HSC Engine

1. Remove air cleaner outlet tube between air cleaner and throttle body.
2. Disconnect accelerator and speed control cables, as equipped and position aside.
3. Disconnect top manifold vacuum connections.
4. Disconnect PCV hose from intake manifold.
5. Disconnect EGR vacuum line from EGR valve.
6. Disconnect EGR tube from upper intake manifold.
7. Disconnect upper intake manifold support bracket by removing top bolt.
8. Disconnect electrical connectors from main engine harness.
9. Remove fuel supply and return lines.

Item	Description
1	Bolt (2 Req'd)
2	Bolt (2 Req'd)
3	Throttle Body
4	Stud Bolt (2 Req'd)
5	Water Hose
6	Nut (4 Req'd)
7	Engine Control Sensor Wiring
8	Fuel Pressure Relief Valve Cap
9	Fuel Pressure Relief Valve
10	Bolt (4 Req'd)
11	Lower Intake Manifold
12	Fuel Injector (6 Req'd)

FM1029600235010X

Fig. 5 Exploded view of fuel charging assembly (Part 1 of 2). 1996 3.0L/V6-182 engine

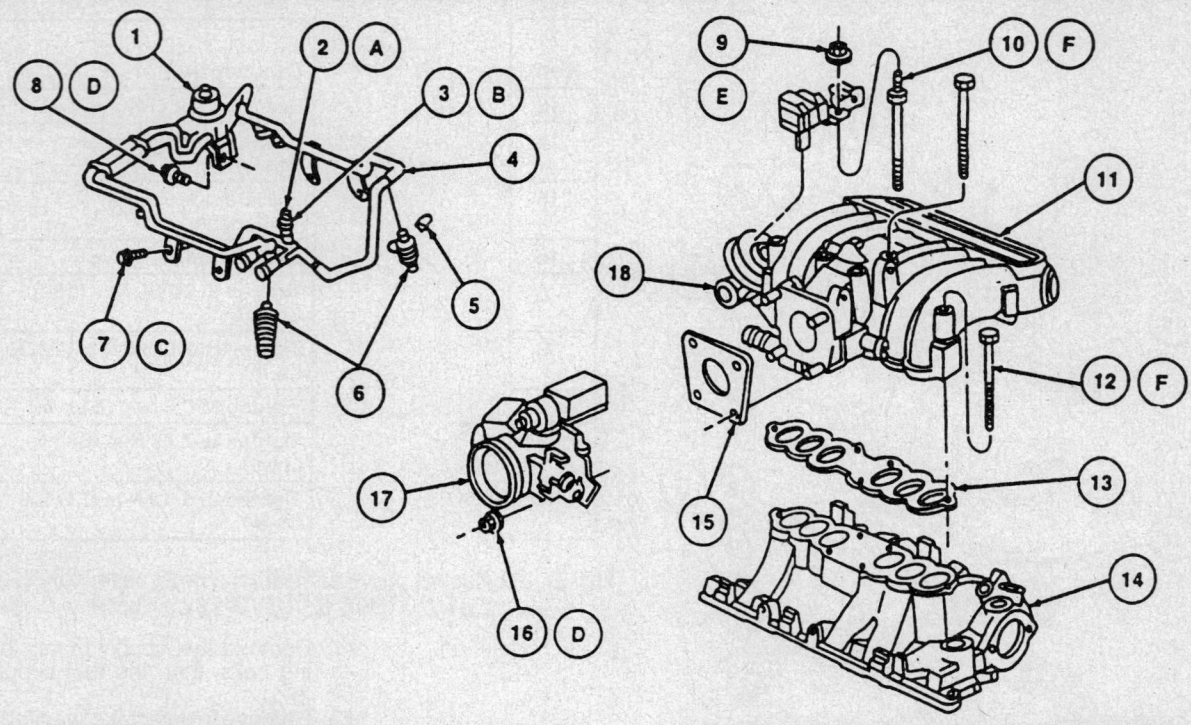

Item	Part Number	Description
1	9C968	Fuel Pressure Regulator
2A	9H323	Fuel Pressure Relief Valve Cap
3B	9H321	Fuel Pressure Relief Valve
4	9F792	Fuel Injection Supply Manifold
5	N804836-S53	Retaining Clip
6	9F593	Fuel Injector
7C	N80517-S8M	Bolt (4 Req'd)
8D	N606691-S2	Bolt
9E	N804758-S2	Nut
10F	N804835-S2	Stud Bolt (2 Req'd)
11	9424	Upper Intake Manifold
12F	N804839-S2	Bolt (4 Req'd)
13	9H486	Intake Manifold Upper Gasket

Item	Part Number	Description
14	9424	Lower Intake Manifold
15	9E936	Throttle Body Gasket
16D	N804758-S2	Nut (4 Req'd)
17	9E926	Throttle Body
18	9D475	EGR Valve
A		Tighten to 0.6 N·m (5.5 Lb-In)
B		Tighten to 7.75 N·m (66 Lb-In)
C		Tighten to 8-11 N·m (71-97 Lb-In)
D		Tighten to 20-30 N·m (15-22 Lb-Ft)
E		Tighten to 11-15 N·m (8-11 Lb-Ft)
F		Tighten in three steps: •10 N·m (8 Lb-Ft) •20 N·m (15 Lb-Ft) •32 N·m (24 Lb-Ft)

FM1029100046000X

Fig. 6 Exploded view of fuel charging assembly. 3.8L/V6-232 non-supercharged engine

10. Remove eight intake manifold attaching bolts.
11. Disconnect lower manifold support bracket by removing top bolt.
12. Remove manifold.
13. Reverse procedure to install, noting the following:
   a. **Torque** manifold attaching bolts to 15-22 ft. lbs.
   b. **Torque** manifold support bracket bolts to 15-22 ft. lbs.
   c. **Torque** EGR tube to 29-40 ft. lbs.

2.3L/4-140 Turbocharged Engine

1. Disconnect the following electrical connectors:
   a. Air bypass valve
   b. Throttle position sensor.
   c. Injector wiring harness.
   d. Knock sensor.
   e. Coolant temperature sensor.
   f. Air charge temperature sensor.
2. Disconnect upper manifold vacuum connections.
3. Disconnect throttle linkage and position aside.
4. Remove two cast tube assembly to turbocharger assembly attaching bolts.
5. Remove four air throttle body to fuel charging assembly attaching nuts or two nuts and two bolts.
6. Separate cast tube from turbocharger assembly and remove gasket.

7. Remove throttle body, cast tube if equipped, then disconnect PCV hose from fitting on underside of upper intake manifold.
8. Disconnect water bypass hose at lower intake manifold.
9. Disconnect EGR tube from EGR valve.
10. Remove upper intake manifold attaching nuts, then the upper intake manifold assembly.
11. Disconnect fuel return line from fuel supply manifold using push connect disassembly tool No. T82L-9500-AH, or equivalent.
12. Disconnect all four fuel injector electrical connectors and position harness to one side.

threads before installation.

c. Install new gasket on lower intake manifold assembly.
d. **Torque** EGR tube flange nuts to 6–8 ft. lbs.
e. Install new gasket on fuel charging assembly air throttle body mounting flange.
f. **Torque** two cast tube attaching bolts to 14–21 ft. lbs.
g. **Torque** four air throttle body/cast tube assembly to fuel charging assembly attaching nuts and/or bolts to 12–15 ft. lbs.

1.9L/4-116 Engine

1. Disconnect battery ground cable.
2. Relieve fuel system pressure as outlined under "Precautions."
3. Remove spring lock coupling retaining clips from fuel supply and return fittings.
4. Disconnect fuel supply and fuel return lines.
5. Disconnect wiring harness from four injectors.
6. Remove two fuel supply manifold retaining bolts, then the supply manifold from fuel injectors.
7. Disconnect vacuum line from fuel pressure regulator valve and remove manifold.
8. Reverse procedure to install noting the following:
   a. Lubricate O-rings with light engine oil ESE-M2C39-F or equivalent.
   b. **Torque** supply manifold bolts to 20–30 ft. lbs.
   c. Start engine and let idle for two minutes, then turn off engine and inspect for leaks.

3.0L/V6-182 Engine

1. Disconnect battery ground cable.
2. Release fuel system pressure as described under "Precautions."
3. Remove upper intake manifold.
4. Disconnect fuel supply and return hoses from fuel injection supply manifold using spring lock coupling disconnect tool No. D87L-9280-A or equivalent.
5. Disconnect sensor wiring connectors from fuel injectors.
6. Remove four fuel injection supply manifold retaining bolts.
7. Disengage fuel injection supply manifold from fuel injectors by lifting and gently rocking manifold.
8. Remove fuel injectors by lifting while gently rocking side to side.
9. Reverse procedure to install. **Torque** fuel injection supply manifold to intake manifold bolts to 71–106 inch lbs.

4.6L/V8-281 Engine

1. Relieve fuel system pressure as outlined under "Precautions."
2. Disconnect vacuum line at pressure regulator.
3. Remove spring lock coupling retainer clip from fuel inlet and return fittings.
4. Using spring lock coupling removal tool No. D87L-9280-A, or equivalent, disconnect crossover fuel hose from fuel rail assembly.

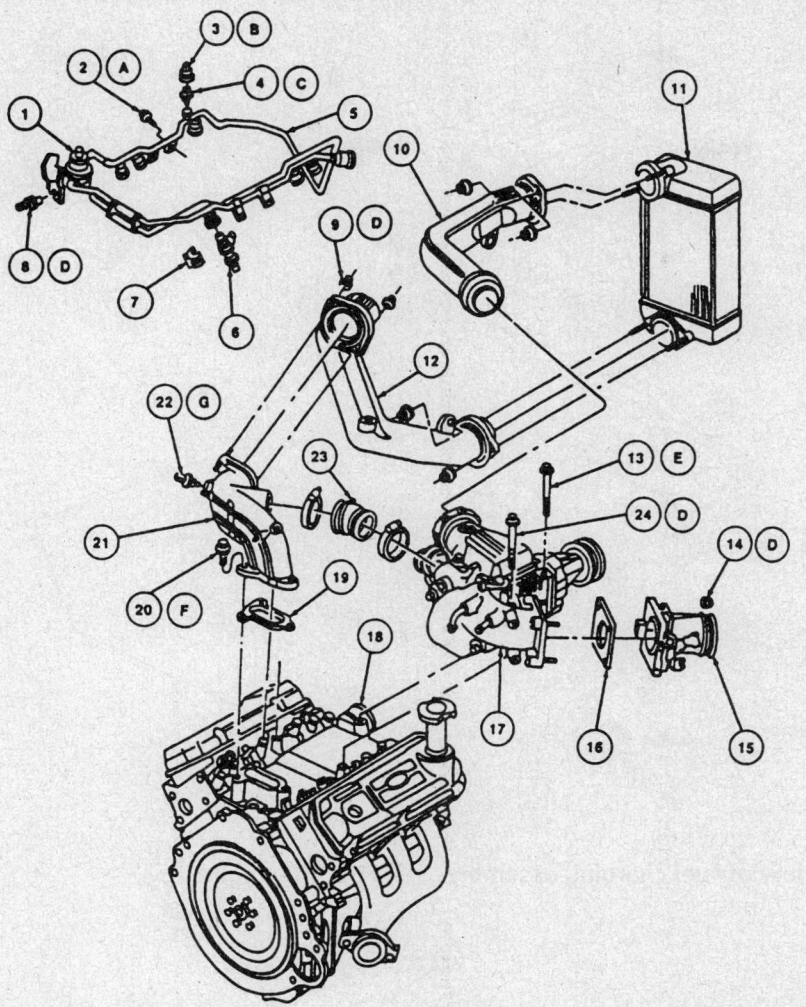

Item	Part Number	Description
1	9C968	Fuel Pressure Regulator
2A	N805117-S8M	Bolt (4 Req'd)
3B	9H323	Fuel Pressure Relief Valve Cap
4C	9H321	Fuel Pressure Relief Valve
5	9F792	Fuel Injection Supply Manifold
6	9F593	Fuel Injector
7	N804838-S53	Retainer Clip
8D	N802353-S100	Stud Bolt
9D	N801248-S100	Nut (6 Req'd)
10	6F072	Charge Air Cooler Inlet Tube
11	6K775	Charge Air Cooler
12	6F073	Charge Air Cooler Outlet Tube
13E	N606590-S40	Bolt
14D	N804758-S2	Nut (4 Req'd)
15	9E926	Throttle Body
16	9F627	Supercharger Inlet Plenum Gasket
17	6F066	Supercharger
18	9424	Lower Intake Manifold
19	9E936	Throttle Body Gasket
20F	N605909-S2	Bolt (3 Req'd)

Item	Part Number	Description
21	6C643	Charge Air Cooler to Intake Manifold Adapter
22G	12A697	Intake Air Temperature Sensor
23	9F287	Supercharger Bypass Valve Hose
24D	N805964-S36B	Bolt (2 Req'd)
A		Tighten to 8-11 N·m (71-97 Lb-In)
B		Tighten to 0.6 N·m (5.5 Lb-In)
C		Tighten to 7.75 N·m (66 Lb-In)
D		Tighten to 20-30 N·m (15-22 Lb-Ft)
E		Tighten to 70-95 N·m (52-70 Lb-Ft)
F		Tighten to 26-38 N·m (20-28 Lb-Ft)
G		Tighten to 8-13 N·m (6-9 Lb-Ft)

FM1029100047000X

Fig. 7 Exploded view of fuel charging assembly. 3.8L/V6-232 supercharged engine

13. Remove fuel supply manifold attaching bolts, then the fuel supply manifold.
14. Remove lower intake manifold attaching bolts, then the lower intake manifold assembly.

15. Reverse procedure to install, noting the following:
   a. Ensure mating surfaces of fuel charging assembly and cylinder head are clean and not damaged.
   b. Clean and lubricate manifold stud

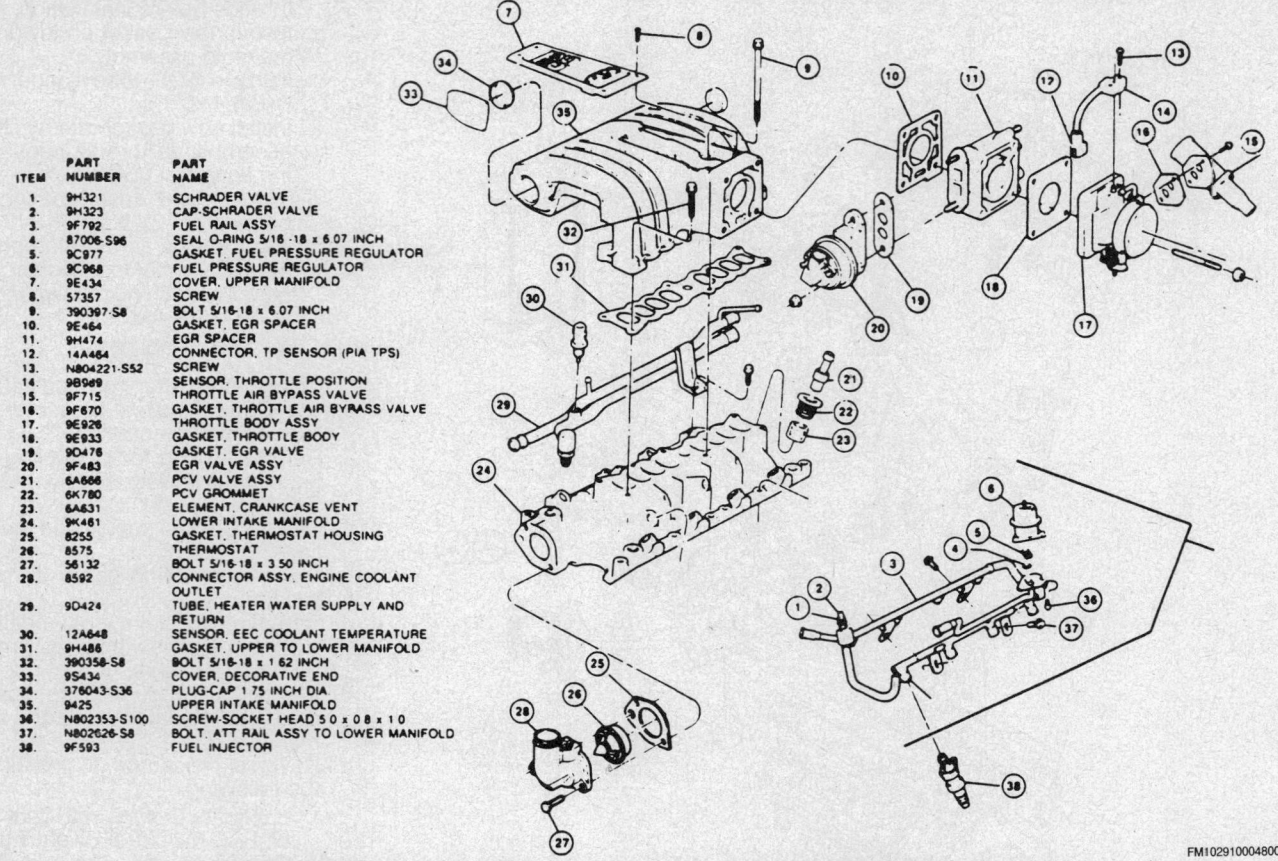

ITEM	PART NUMBER	PART NAME
1.	9H321	SCHRADER VALVE
2.	9H323	CAP-SCHRADER VALVE
3.	9F792	FUEL RAIL ASSY
4.	87006-S96	SEAL O-RING 5/16 -18 x 6 07 INCH
5.	9C977	GASKET, FUEL PRESSURE REGULATOR
6.	9C968	FUEL PRESSURE REGULATOR
7.	9E434	COVER, UPPER MANIFOLD
8.	57357	SCREW
9.	390397-S8	BOLT 5/16-18 x 6 07 INCH
10.	9E464	GASKET, EGR SPACER
11.	9H474	EGR SPACER
12.	14A464	CONNECTOR, TP SENSOR (PIA TPS)
13.	N804221-S52	SCREW
14.	9B989	SENSOR, THROTTLE POSITION
15.	9F715	THROTTLE AIR BYPASS VALVE
16.	9F670	GASKET, THROTTLE AIR BYPASS VALVE
17.	9E926	THROTTLE BODY ASSY
18.	9E933	GASKET, THROTTLE BODY
19.	9D476	GASKET, EGR VALVE
20.	9F483	EGR VALVE ASSY
21.	6A666	PCV VALVE ASSY
22.	6K780	PCV GROMMET
23.	6A631	ELEMENT, CRANKCASE VENT
24.	9K461	LOWER INTAKE MANIFOLD
25.	8255	GASKET, THERMOSTAT HOUSING
26.	8575	THERMOSTAT
27.	56132	BOLT 5/16-18 x 3 50 INCH
28.	8592	CONNECTOR ASSY, ENGINE COOLANT OUTLET
29.	9D424	TUBE, HEATER WATER SUPPLY AND RETURN
30.	12A648	SENSOR, EEC COOLANT TEMPERATURE
31.	9H486	GASKET, UPPER TO LOWER MANIFOLD
32.	390356-S8	BOLT 5/16-18 x 1 62 INCH
33.	9S434	COVER, DECORATIVE END
34.	376043-S36	PLUG-CAP 1 75 INCH DIA
35.	9425	UPPER INTAKE MANIFOLD
36.	N802353-S100	SCREW-SOCKET HEAD 5 0 x 0 8 x 1 0
37.	N802026-S8	BOLT, ATT RAIL ASSY TO LOWER MANIFOLD
38.	9F593	FUEL INJECTOR

Fig. 8 Exploded view of fuel charging assembly. 5.0L/V8-302 engine

5. Remove four fuel rail assembly retaining bolts.
6. Remove fuel rail from fuel injectors.
7. Reverse procedure to install noting the following:
   a. **Torque** retaining bolts to 70-105 inch lbs.
   b. With injector wiring disconnected, turn ignition to run position to allow fuel pump to pressurize system.
   c. Connect fuel injector wiring harness and run vehicle at idle for two minutes.
   d. Turn engine off and inspect for leaks.

5.0L/V8-302 Engine

1. Disconnect battery ground cable.
2. Release fuel system pressure as described under "Fuel System Pressure Relief."
3. Remove upper intake manifold.
4. Disconnect vacuum line at pressure regulator.
5. Remove spring lock coupling retainer clip from fuel inlet and return fittings.
6. Disconnect fuel supply and return hoses from fuel injection supply manifold using spring lock coupling disconnect tool No. D87L-9280-A or equivalent.
7. Remove four fuel injector supply manifold retaining bolts.
8. Disconnect fuel charging wiring connectors from fuel injectors.
9. Remove fuel injectors by pulling while rocking side to side.

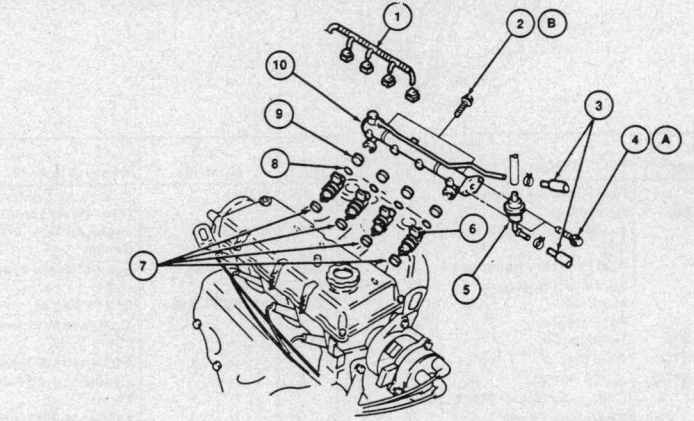

Item	Description
1	Fuel Charging Wiring
2	Fuel Injection Supply Manifold Bolts (2 Req'd)
3	Fuel Tube Hoses
4	Fuel Pressure Regulator Bolts (2 Req'd)
5	Fuel Pressure Regulator
6	Fuel Injectors
7	Fuel Injector O-Rings

Item	Description
8	O-Rings
9	Fuel Injector Insulators
10	Fuel Injection Supply Manifold
A	Tighten to 8-11 N·m (71-97 lb-in)
B	Tighten to 19-23 N·m (14-17 lb-ft)

Fig. 9 Exploded view of fuel charging assembly. 1.3L/4-81 engine

10. Reverse procedure to install, noting the following:
   a. **Torque** fuel supply manifold bolts to 71-106 inch lbs.
   b. With fuel charging wiring disconnected, turn ignition switch to Run position several times to allow fuel pump to pressurize. Using clean towel, check for leaks.

SUPERCHARGER & THROTTLE BODY

3.8L/V6-232 Engine

Refer to **Fig. 7**, when performing the following procedure.

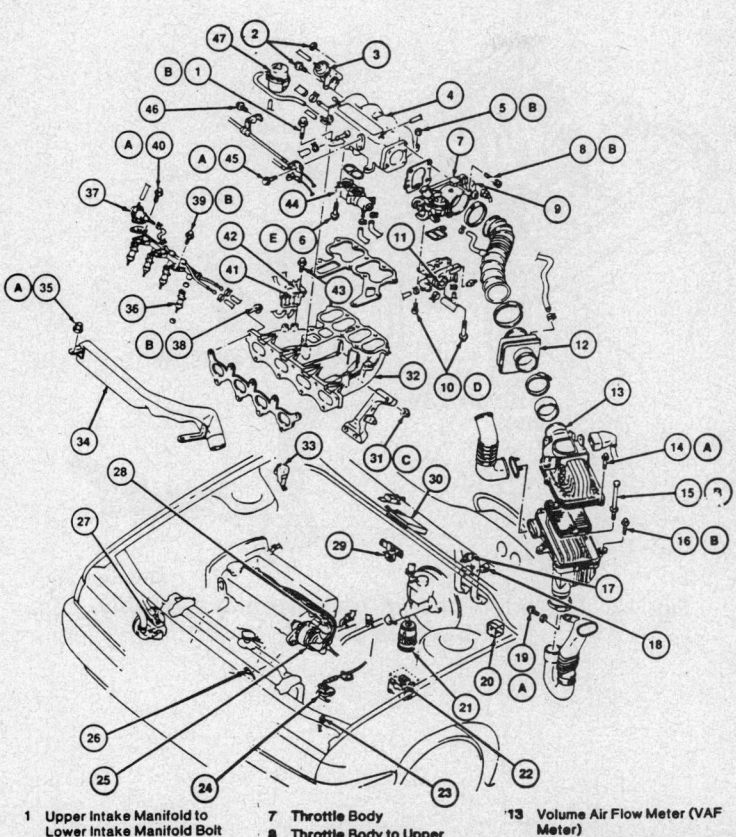

29 Evaporative Emission Canister Purge Valve
30 Powertrain Control Module (PCM)
31 Intake Manifold to Cylinder Block Bracket Bolt (3 Req'd)
32 Intake Manifold, Lower
33 A/C Relay
34 Engine Air Intake Resonator (Duct)
35 Engine Air Intake Resonator Duct Bolt (2 Req'd)
36 Fuel Injector
37 Fuel Pressure Regulator
38 Intake Manifold Nut (9 Req'd)
39 Fuel Injection Supply Manifold Bolt (3 Req'd)
40 Fuel Pressure Regulator Bolt (2 Req'd)
41 Fuel Pressure Regulator Control (FPRC) Solenoid
42 High Speed Inlet Air (HSIA) Solenoid
43 Fuel Pressure Regulator and HSIA Solenoid Bolt
44 Secondary Air Injection Control Valve
45 Accelerator Cable Bracket Bolt (2 Req'd)
46 Accelerator Cable Support Bracket Bolt
47 Vacuum Chamber Canister
A Tighten to 7.8-11 N·m (69-95 Lb-In)
B Tighten to 19-25 N·m (14-19 Lb-Ft)
C Tighten to 37-52 N·m (27-38 Lb-Ft)
D Tighten to 2.8-4.0 N·m (25-36 Lb-In)
E Tighten to 4.5-5.5 N·m (40-58 Lb-In)

Fig. 10 Exploded view of fuel charging assembly. 1.8L/4-112 & 1.9L/4-116 engines

1 Upper Intake Manifold to Lower Intake Manifold Bolt (5 Req'd)
2 HSIA Actuator Valve Bolt and Nut
3 High Speed Inlet Air (HSIA) Shutter Valve Actuator (Part of 9424)
4 Intake Manifold, Upper
5 Upper Intake Manifold Nut (2 Req'd)
6 Secondary Air Injection Control Valve Bolt (4 Req'd)
7 Throttle Body
8 Throttle Body to Upper Intake Manifold Bolt (4 Req'd)
9 Throttle Position Sensor (TP sensor)
10 Idle Air Control Valve to Throttle Body Bolt
11 Idle Air Control Valve (IAC Valve)
12 Engine Air Intake Resonator
13 Volume Air Flow Meter (VAF Meter)
14 Engine Air Cleaner Case Bolt (4 Req'd)
15 Engine Air Cleaner to Body, Extension Bolt
16 Engine Air Cleaner to Body Bolt (2 Req'd)
17 Brake On/Off (BOO) Switch
18 Clutch Pedal Position (CPP) Switch
19 Engine Air Intake Tube Bolt
20 Data Link Connector (DLC)
21 Fuel Filter
22 Fuel Injector Main Relay
23 Park/Neutral Position (PNP) Switch (MTX)
24 Transmission Range (TR) Switch (4EAT)
25 Distributor
26 Heated Oxygen Sensor (HO2S)
27 Power Steering Pressure Switch (PSP Switch)
28 Engine Coolant Temperature (ECT) Sensor

1. Disconnect battery ground cable.
2. Remove throttle body air inlet tube, then the cowl vent screens.
3. Drain cooling system.
4. Disconnect righthand side plug wires from coil assembly and position aside.
5. Disconnect the following electrical connectors:
   a. Idle air control valve.
   b. Throttle position sensor.
   c. Intake air temperature sensor.
6. Disconnect vacuum lines from inlet plenum assembly, then disconnect PCV tube.
7. Disconnect vacuum line from EGR transducer, then remove EGR transducer from bracket.
8. Disconnect throttle linkage at throttle housing, then remove bracket attaching bolts and position brackets aside.
9. Remove supercharger drive belt.
10. Disconnect coolant hoses from throttle body, then remove supercharger drive belt.
11. Remove intercooler inlet and outlet hoses.
12. Remove three intake elbow retaining bolts, then the three supercharger retaining bolts.
13. Remove supercharger and charge air cooler to intake manifold adapter as an assembly.

14. Reverse procedure to install, noting the following:
   a. Clean and inspect all gasket surfaces.
   b. **Torque** 12mm supercharger retaining bolt to 52-70 ft. lbs.
   c. **Torque** 8mm supercharger retaining bolts to 15-22 ft. lbs.
   d. **Torque** intake elbow retaining bolts to 20-28 ft. lbs.
   e. Seal intercooler tube threads using teflon tape.
   f. **Torque** outlet tube to intake manifold adapter nuts to 14-22 ft. lbs.
   g. **Torque** inlet and outlet tube to bracket bolt and nut to 30-40 ft. lbs.
   h. **Torque** outlet tube adapter collar to 48 ft. lbs.
   i. **Torque** inlet and outlet tubes to intercooler to 14-22 ft. lbs.

UPPER INTAKE MANIFOLD

1.3L/4-81 Engine

1. Release fuel pressure as outlined under "Precautions."
2. Disconnect battery ground cable, then drain cooling system.
3. Remove intake manifold support bolts, and the upper manifold.
4. Disconnect accelerator cable from throttle control lever.
5. Remove air cleaner tube, coolant hoses from upper intake manifold.
6. Tag and disconnect necessary vacuum lines and electrical connectors.
7. Remove upper intake manifold to lower manifold bolts, then the upper manifold.
8. Reverse procedure to install, noting the following:
   a. Replace gasket between cylinder head and upper intake manifold, ensuring sealing surfaces are properly cleaned of old gasket material.
   b. **Torque** intake manifold nuts to 14-20 ft. lbs.

1.8L/4-112 Engine

1. Disconnect battery ground cable, then partially drain cooling system.
2. Remove air cleaner outlet tube that connects to throttle body, then engine air intake resonator.
3. Disconnect throttle cable and throttle valve control actuating cable.
4. Remove accelerator and throttle valve control actuating cable bracket bolt and accelerator and throttle valve control actuating cable bracket from upper intake manifold.
5. Disconnect throttle body electrical connectors.
6. Disconnect all vacuum hose from upper intake manifold, then air bypass and idle control coolant hoses.
7. Remove idle air control hose, then upper intake manifold attaching nuts.
8. Raise and support vehicle, then remove lower upper intake manifold bolts.
9. Lower vehicle, then remove upper intake manifold from lower intake manifold.

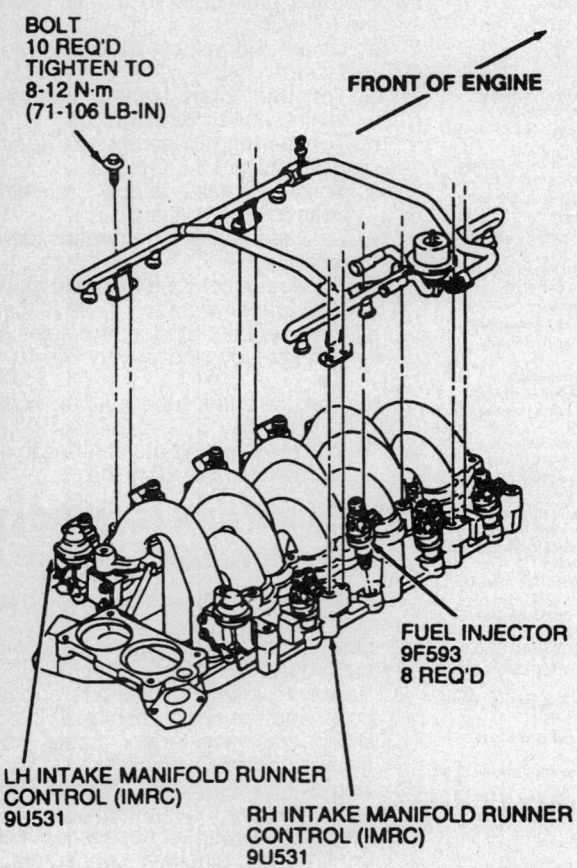

BOLT
10 REQ'D
TIGHTEN TO
8-12 N·m
(71-106 LB-IN)

FRONT OF ENGINE

FUEL INJECTOR
9F593
8 REQ'D

LH INTAKE MANIFOLD RUNNER
CONTROL (IMRC)
9U531

RH INTAKE MANIFOLD RUNNER
CONTROL (IMRC)
9U531

FM1029100051000X

Fig. 11   Exploded view of fuel charging
assembly. 4.6L/V8-281 engine

FUEL RAIL
9308 (TURBOCHARGED VEHICLES)
9A318 (NATURALLY ASPIRATED VEHICLES)

PRESSURE
REGULATOR
9C968

FUEL
FILTER

TO CANISTER

INJECTOR ASSY
9F593

FM1029100052000X

Fig. 12   Exploded view of fuel charging assembly.
1.6L/4-98 engine

10. Reverse procedure to install noting
the following:
   a. Replace upper intake manifold
      gasket.
   b. **Torque** upper intake manifold
      bolts 14-19 ft. lbs.
   c. **Torque** lower bolts to 14-19 ft. lbs.
   d. **Torque** accelerator and throttle
      valve control actuating cable
      bracket to 69-95 inch lbs.

2.2L/4-133 Engine

1. Disconnect accelerator cable from
   throttle body and position aside.
2. Remove air duct from throttle body.
3. Remove vacuum hoses from throttle
   body.
4. Disconnect throttle position sensor,
   idle switch and air control valve electrical connectors.
5. Remove engine lifting bracket bolts
   from engine block and throttle body.
6. Remove coolant line and throttle cable retaining brackets.
7. **On non-turbocharged models,** remove wire loom bracket and EGR
   transducer bracket from right side of
   intake manifold.
8. **On turbocharged models,** remove
   wire loom bracket and vacuum pipe
   mounting bolts from right side of intake manifold.
9. **On all models,** remove PCV hose
   from intake manifold.

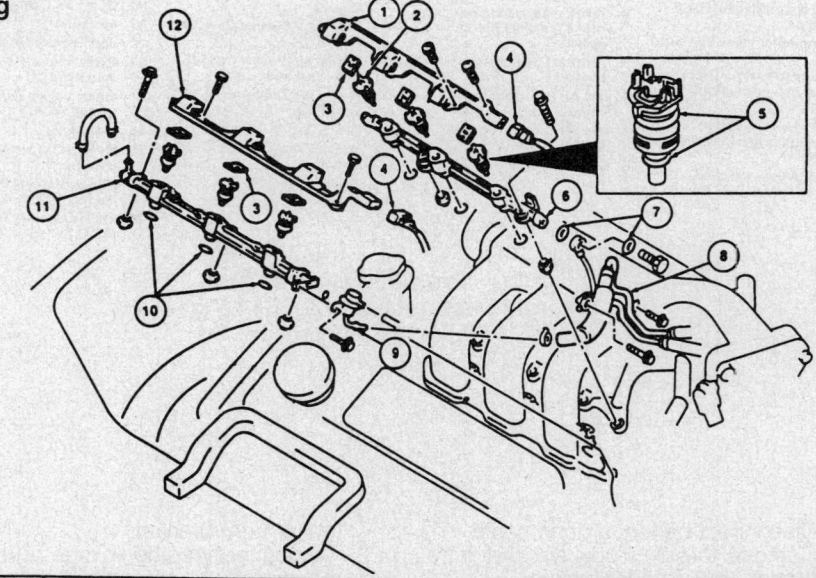

Item	Part Number	Description
1	9D930	Fuel Charging Wiring
2	9F593	Fuel Injector
3	9229	Spacer
4	—	Fuel Charging Wiring Electrical Connector O-Ring
5	9229	Fuel Injection Supply Manifold
6	9F792	Fuel Injection Supply Manifold
7	6734	*Crush Washer

Item	Part Number	Description
8	—	Fuel Return Tube (Part of 9369)
9	9C968	Fuel Pressure Regulator
10	9C991	Fuel Injector O-Ring
11	9F792	Fuel Injection Supply Manifold
12	9D930	Fuel Charging Wiring

FM1029100053000X

Fig. 13   Exploded view of fuel charging assembly. Probe 2.5L/V6-153
engine

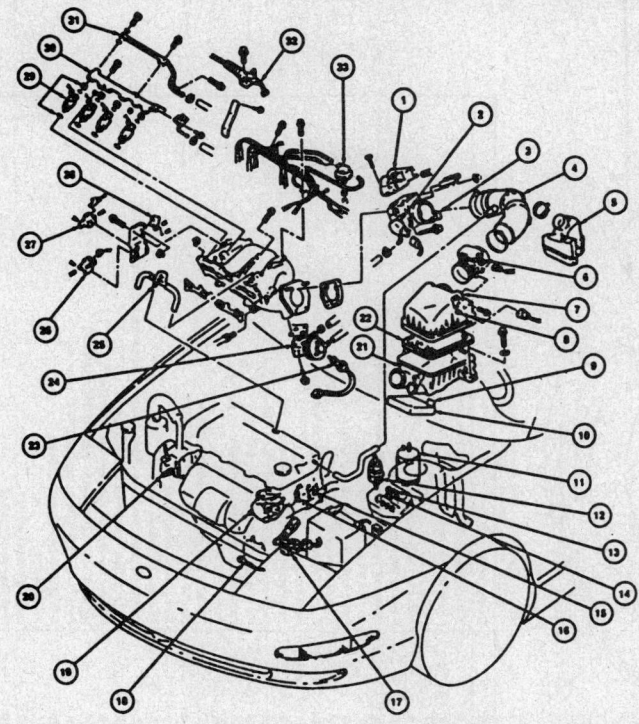

Item	Description
1	Idle Air Control Bypass Air (IAC BPA) Valve
2	Throttle Position (TP) Sensor
3	Idle Switch
4	Air Duct
5	Resonance Chamber No. 2
6	Mass Air Flow (MAF) Sensor
7	Air Cleaner Upper Cover
8	Intake Air Temperature (IAT) Sensor
9	Barometric (BARO) Pressure Sensor
10	Powertrain Control Module (PCM)
11	Carbon Canister
12	Fuel Filter
13	Main Relay
14	Fuel Pump (Circuit Opening) Relay
15	Cooling Fan Engine Coolant Temperature (ECTF) Sensor
16	Engine Coolant Temperature (ECT) Sensor
17	Manual Lever Position (MLP) Switch
18	Heated Oxygen Sensor (HO2S)
19	Distributor
20	Power Steering Pressure (PSP) Switch
21	Air Cleaner Lower Cover
22	Air Cleaner Element
23	Exhaust Gas Recirculation (EGR) Temperature Sensor (California Only)
24	Exhaust Gas Recirculation (EGR) Valve
25	Positive Crankshaft Ventilation (PCV) Valve
26	Exhaust Gas Recirculation Control (EGRC) Solenoid
27	Fuel Pressure Regulator Control (FPRC) Solenoid
28	Canister Purge Regulator Valve
29	Fuel Injector
30	Low-Pressure Fuel Rail
31	High-Pressure Fuel Rail
32	Accelerator Cable
33	EGR Back-Pressure Variable Transducer (BVT)

FM1029300054000X

Fig. 14 Exploded view of fuel charging assembly. Probe 2.0L/4-122 engine & automatic transmission

10. Remove vacuum line assembly bracket from rear of intake manifold.
11. Remove intake manifold attaching bolts, then the manifold and gasket. **Cover lower intake manifold with a clean cloth to prevent dust and dirt from entering.**
12. Reverse procedure to install. **Torque** manifold attaching bolts to 14-19 ft. lbs.

2.3L/4-140 Except HSC & Turbocharged Engines

1. Disconnect the following electrical connectors:
   a. Air bypass valve
   b. Throttle position sensor.
   c. Knock sensor.
   d. EGR valve
2. Disconnect upper intake manifold vacuum connections.
3. Disconnect throttle linkage and position aside.
4. Disconnect air intake hose and crankcase vent hose.
5. Disconnect PCV hose from manifold.
6. Disconnect EGR tube from EGR valve.
7. Remove upper manifold attaching bolts, then the upper manifold.
8. Remove and discard gasket from lower manifold assembly.
9. Reverse procedure to install, noting the following:
   a. **Torque** upper manifold attaching bolts to 15-22 ft. lbs. in sequence shown in **Fig. 24.**

b. **Torque** EGR tube to 6-8.5 ft. lbs.

2.3L/4-140 HSC Engine

1. Remove air cleaner outlet tube between air cleaner and throttle body.
2. Disconnect accelerator and speed control cables, as equipped and position aside.
3. Disconnect upper manifold vacuum connections.
4. Disconnect throttle position sensor electrical connector.
5. Disconnect EGR tube from upper manifold.
6. Disconnect air bypass vale electrical connector.
7. Disconnect upper manifold support bracket by removing top bolt.
8. Remove fuel supply manifold shield.
9. Remove four upper manifold attaching bolts and one stud.
10. Remove upper manifold assembly.
11. Remove and discard the manifold gasket.
12. Reverse procedure to install, noting the following:
    a. **Torque** manifold attaching bolts to 15-22 ft. lbs.
    b. **Torque** manifold support bracket bolts to 15-22 ft. lbs.
    c. **Torque** EGR tube to 29-40 ft. lbs.

2.3L/4-140 Turbocharged Engine

1. Perform steps 1 through 8 under "Fuel Charging Assembly, Replace" procedure.
2. Disconnect EGR hose from EGR valve.
3. Remove upper intake manifold attaching bolts, then the manifold assembly.
4. Reverse procedure to install. **Torque** manifold attaching bolts to 15-22 ft. lbs.

2.5L/V6-153 Engine

1. Disconnect battery ground cable, then remove four bolt attaching water pump shield to left side valve cover, then the shield.
2. Depress block retainer with screwdriver on upper intake manifold and disconnect main emission vacuum control connector from upper intake manifold.
3. Remove air cleaner outlet tube and disconnect accelerator cable and speed control actuator from throttle body.
4. Remove accelerator cable bracket from intake manifold, then fresh air supply hose from fitting on manifold.
5. Disconnect throttle position sensor, idle air control valve and EGR vacuum regulator control.
6. Remove vacuum supply hose from upper intake manifold to PCV and vacuum supply hoses to EGR and position aside.
7. Remove intake manifold bolts as outlined in, **Fig. 25.**
8. Remove upper intake manifold and gaskets.
9. Reverse procedure to install. **Torque** retaining bolts to 6-9 ft. lbs. in sequence shown in **Fig. 25.**

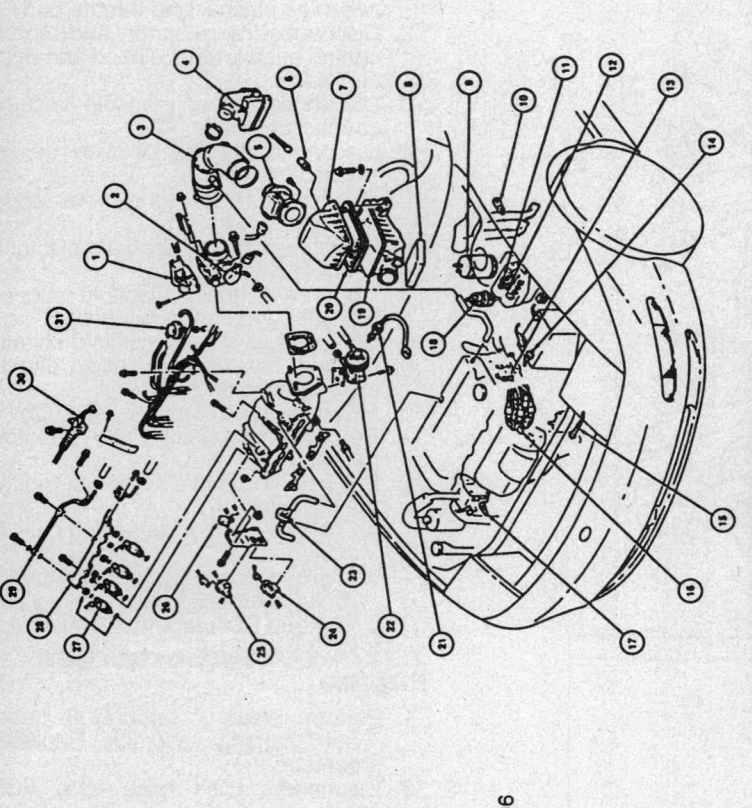

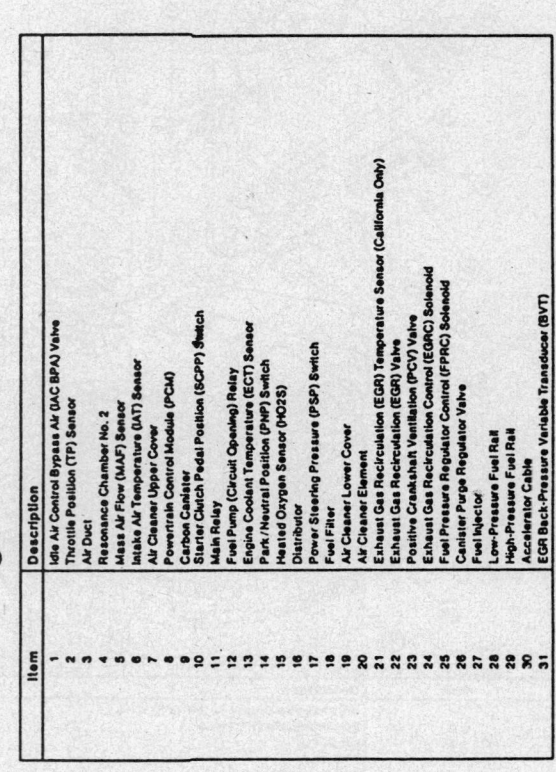

Item	Description
1	Idle Air Control Bypass Air (IAC BPA) Valve
2	Throttle Position (TP) Sensor
3	Air Duct
4	Resonance Chamber No. 2
5	Mass Air Flow (MAF) Sensor
6	Intake Air Temperature (IAT) Sensor
7	Air Cleaner Upper Cover
8	Powertrain Control Module (PCM)
9	Carbon Canister
10	Starter Clutch Pedal Position (SCPP) Switch
11	Main Relay
12	Fuel Pump (Circuit Opening) Relay
13	Engine Coolant Temperature (ECT) Sensor
14	Park/Neutral Position (PNP) Switch
15	Heated Oxygen Sensor (HO2S)
16	Distributor
17	Power Steering Pressure (PSP) Switch
18	Fuel Filter
19	Air Cleaner Lower Cover
20	Air Cleaner Element
21	Exhaust Gas Recirculation (EGR) Temperature Sensor (California Only)
22	Exhaust Gas Recirculation (EGR) Valve
23	Positive Crankshaft Ventilation (PCV) Valve
24	Exhaust Gas Recirculation Control (EGRC) Solenoid
25	Fuel Pressure Regulator Control (FPRC) Solenoid
26	Canister Purge Regulator Valve
27	Fuel Injector
28	Low-Pressure Fuel Rail
29	High-Pressure Fuel Rail
30	Accelerator Cable
31	EGR Back-Pressure Variable Transducer (BVT)

FM10293000550000X

Fig. 16 Exploded view of fuel charging assembly. Probe w/2.0L/4-121 engine & manual transaxle

1 Bolt (3 Req'd)
2 Fuel Pressure Regulator
3 Fuel Injector (4 Req'd)
4 Intake Manifold
5 Retainer Clip
6 Fuel Injection Supply Manifold
A Tighten to 8-12 N·m (71-106 Lb-In)

FRONT OF ENGINE

Fig. 15 Exploded view of fuel charging assembly. Contour & Mystique 2.0L/4-122 engine

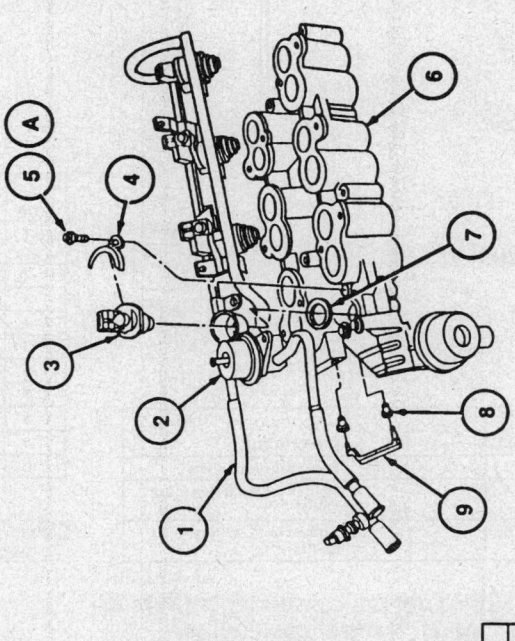

1 Fuel Injection Supply Manifold
2 Fuel Pressure Regulator
3 Fuel Injector (6 Req'd)
4 Fuel Injector Retainer (6 Req'd)
5 Bolt (7 Req'd)
6 Lower Intake Manifold (IMRC)
7 Fuel Injector Seal (6 Req'd)
8 IMRC Linkage Rod Bushings (2 Req'd)
9 IMRC Linkage Rod
A Tighten to 8-12 N·m (71-106 Lb-In)

Fig. 18 Fuel rail & fuel injectors. Contour & Mystique 2.5L/V6-153 engine

Item	Description
1	Air Intake Pipe
2	Accelerator Cable
3	Throttle Body
4	Idle Air Control Bypass Air (IAC BPA) Valve
5	Air Duct
6	Volume Air Flow (VAF) Meter
7	Accelerator Pedal
8	Air Cleaner Element
9	Fresh Air Duct
10	Fuel Supply and Return Line Assembly
11	Fuel Pressure Regulator
12	Fuel Rails
13	Intake Manifold
14	Vacuum Chamber
15	Check Valve
16	Shutter Valve Actuator
17	VRIS Shutter Valve (1)
18	VRIS Shutter Valve (2)

FM1029300056000X

Fig. 17 Exploded view of fuel charging assembly. Probe w/2.5L/V6-152 engine

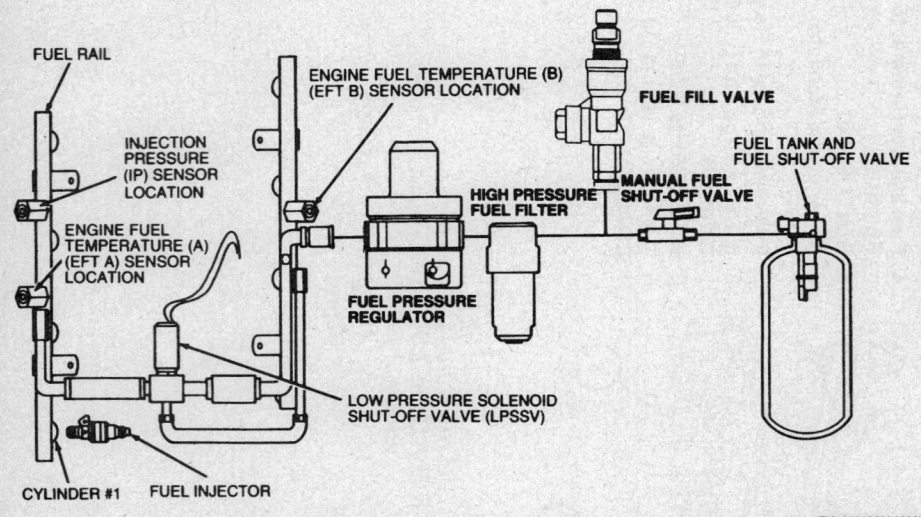

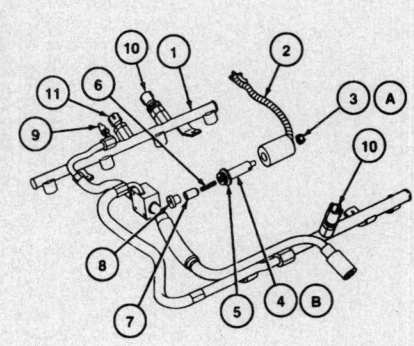

Fig. 19   Natural gas fuel system

FM1029600236000X

Item		Description
1		Fuel Injection Supply Manifold
2	—	Fuel Isolation Valve Coil
3	—	Nut
4	—	Brass Core
5	—	O-Ring
6	—	Spring
7	—	Plunger
8	—	Plunger
9	—	Pressure Relief Valve
10	—	Fuel Temperature Sensor

FM1029600238010X

Fig. 20   Fuel rail components (Part 1 of 2). Natural gas engine

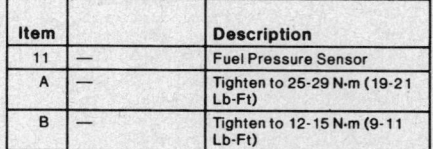

Item		Description
11	—	Fuel Pressure Sensor
A	—	Tighten to 25-29 N·m (19-21 Lb-Ft)
B	—	Tighten to 12-15 N·m (9-11 Lb-Ft)

FM1029600238020X

Fig. 20   Fuel rail components (Part 2 of 2). Natural gas engine

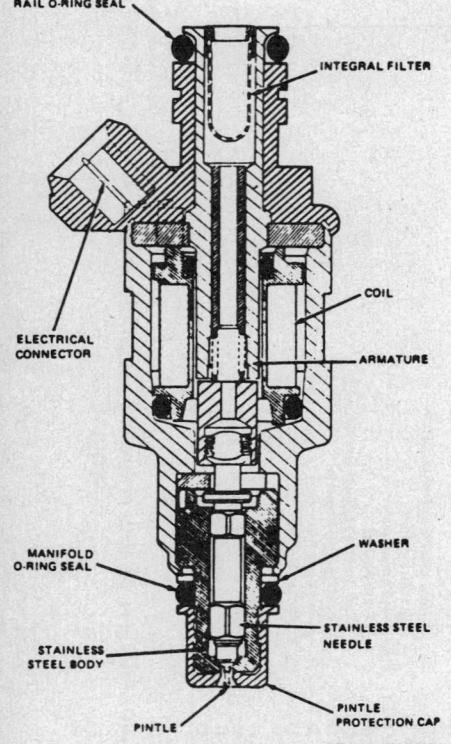

FM1029100057000X

Fig. 21   Fuel injector

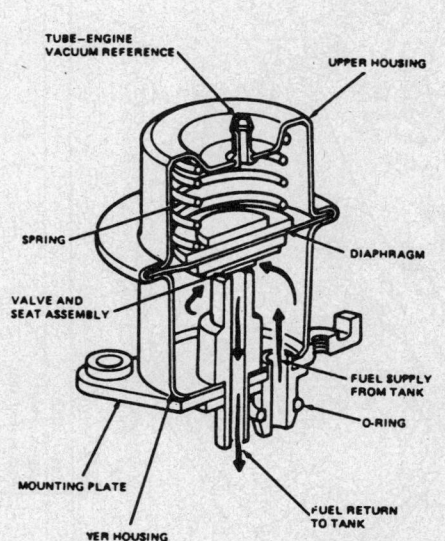

FM1029100058000X

Fig. 22   Fuel pressure regulator. Gasoline engines

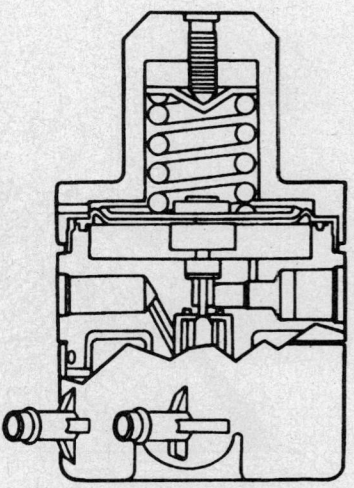

FM1029600237000X

Fig. 23   Fuel pressure regulator. Natural gas engine

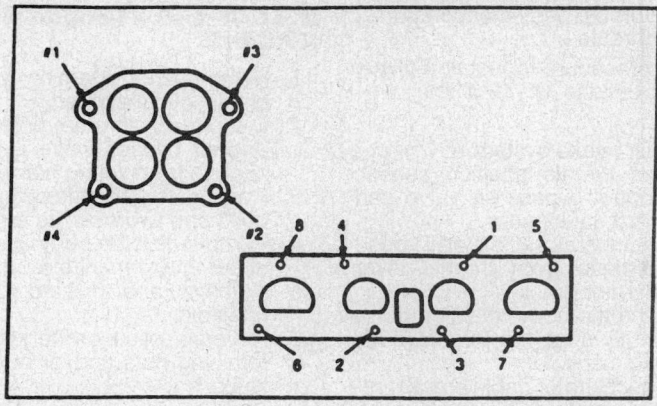

Fig. 24 Manifold bolt tightening sequence

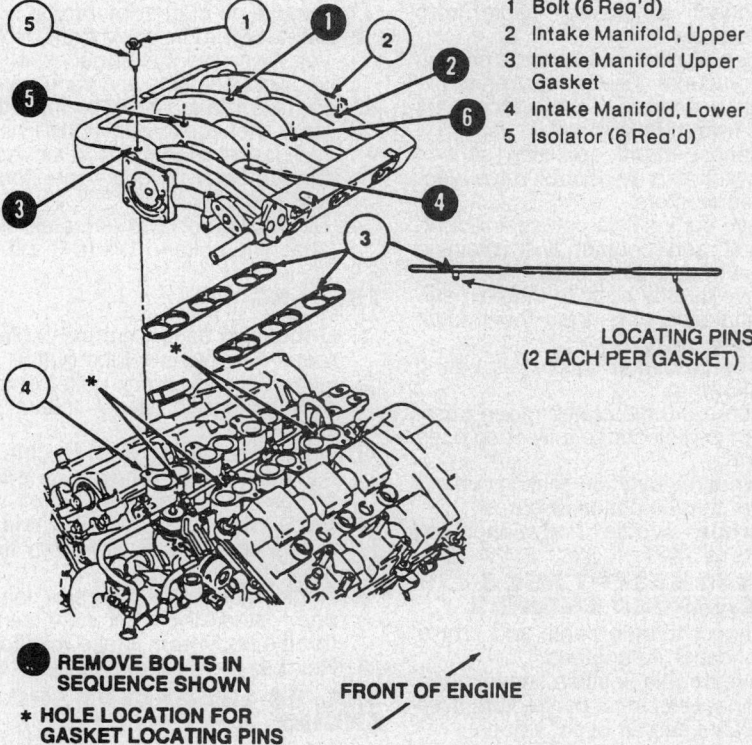

1 Bolt (6 Req'd)
2 Intake Manifold, Upper
3 Intake Manifold Upper Gasket
4 Intake Manifold, Lower
5 Isolator (6 Req'd)

LOCATING PINS
(2 EACH PER GASKET)

● REMOVE BOLTS IN SEQUENCE SHOWN
* HOLE LOCATION FOR GASKET LOCATING PINS

FRONT OF ENGINE

Fig. 25 Manifold bolt tightening sequence. 2.5L/V6-153 engine. Contour & Mystique

UPPER INTAKE MANIFOLD & THROTTLE BODY

1.9L/4-116 Engine

1. Disconnect battery ground cable.
2. Remove air intake tube from throttle body.
3. Disconnect throttle position sensor and air bypass valve connectors.
4. Remove vacuum hose from bottom side of throttle body.
5. Remove accelerator cable, then the kickdown cable from throttle lever.
6. Remove four throttle body mounting bolts, then the throttle body from intake manifold assembly.
7. Reverse procedure to install, making sure gasket surfaces are clean.

3.8L/V6-232 & 5.0L/V8-302 Engines

1. Disconnect electrical connectors from throttle position sensor, air bypass valve and EGR position sensor.
2. Disconnect throttle linkage from ball and transmission linkage from throttle body. Remove two throttle cable bracket-to-intake manifold attaching bolts and position bracket and cables aside.
3. Disconnect upper intake manifold vacuum connections. Disconnect all lines to vacuum tree, EGR valve and fuel pressure regulator.

4. Disconnect PCV hose from rear of upper manifold.
5. **On V8 models,** disconnect two canister purge lines from throttle body.
6. Remove flange nut and disconnect EGR tube from EGR valve.
7. Remove upper intake support bracket-to-upper manifold attaching bolt.
8. Remove upper intake manifold attaching bolts, then the upper intake manifold and throttle body as an assembly from lower intake manifold.
9. Reverse procedure to install, noting the following:
   a. Install new gasket on lower intake manifold mating surface.
   b. **Torque** upper intake manifold attaching bolts on all V8 engines to 15-22 ft. lbs., and on 3.8L/V6-232 engines to 20-28 ft. lbs.
   c. **Torque** throttle cable bracket attaching bolts to 8-10 ft. lbs.

3.0L/V6-182 Engine Except SHO

1. Remove air cleaner outlet tube between air cleaner and throttle body.
2. Remove snow shield attaching nut and bolt, then the shield.
3. Disconnect vacuum hoses from air intake throttle body.
4. Disconnect accelerator and speed control cables, as equipped and position aside.
5. **On models with automatic transmission,** disconnect throttle valve linkage from throttle lever.
6. Remove manifold attaching bolts, then the manifold.
7. Remove and discard gasket between manifolds.
8. Reverse procedure to install. **Torque** manifold attaching bolts to 15-22 ft. lbs. in sequence shown in **Fig. 24.**

3.0L/V6-182 SHO Engine

1. Remove intake air boot from throttle body and airflow sensor, then disconnect throttle cable.
2. Disconnect the following electrical connectors:
   a. Throttle position sensor.
   b. Air bypass valve.
   c. Vacuum switching valve.
   d. DIS module.
3. Disconnect coolant bypass hoses and vacuum lines.
4. Disconnect EGR pipe from EGR valve.
5. Remove eight intake manifold support bracket attaching bolts, then the brackets.
6. Remove coolant hose bracket retaining bolt.
7. Disconnect PCV hoses, then remove 12 manifold retaining nuts.
8. Remove intake manifold and throttle body as an assembly.
9. Reverse procedure to install noting the following:
   a. **Torque** intake manifold bolts to 11-17 ft. lbs.
   b. **Torque** manifold support bracket bolts to 11-17 ft. lbs.

THROTTLE BODY

1.3L/4-81 ENGINE

1. Disconnect battery ground cable, then drain cooling system.
2. Remove resonance chamber.
3. Disconnect accelerator cable from throttle linkage.
4. Remove air duct.
5. Mark vacuum and coolant hoses for reference during assembly, then remove hoses.
6. Disconnect throttle position sensor.
7. Remove throttle body attaching bolts and nuts, then the throttle body.
8. Reverse procedure to install.

1.6L/4-98 ENGINE

1. Disconnect battery ground cable.
2. Remove accelerator cable from throttle body.
3. Remove air duct.
4. Partially drain cooling system.
5. Mark all vacuum and coolant hoses for ease of reassembly, then disconnect from throttle body.
6. Remove three attaching bolts, then the attaching nut.
7. Remove throttle body and gaskets.
8. Reverse procedure to install noting the following:
   a. Clean throttle body gasket surface.
   b. Refill cooling system.

1.8L/4-112 ENGINE

1. Disconnect battery ground cable.
2. Remove air inlet duct that connects throttle body to resonance chamber.
3. Disconnect throttle body electrical connectors.
4. Disconnect idle speed control and bypass air hoses from ISC valve.
5. Disconnect accelerator and kickdown cables from throttle cam.
6. Remove throttle body mounting bolts, then the throttle body.
7. Reverse procedure to install.

1.9L/4-116 ENGINE

1. Disconnect battery ground cable, then remove air cleaner outlet tube from throttle body.
2. Disconnect throttle position sensor and idle air control valve electrical connectors.
3. Remove vacuum hose from bottom of throttle body.
4. Remove accelerator cable and throttle control actuating cable front throttle lever.
5. Remove four throttle body bolts, then carefully separate throttle body from intake manifold.
6. Reverse procedure to install. **Torque** throttle body bolts to 15-22 ft. lbs.

2.0L/4-122 ENGINE

1993–94

1. Remove air intake system.
2. Disconnect throttle position sensor, idle air control bypass air valve and idle switch, if equipped.
3. Disconnect throttle cable, throttle body coolant line and idle air control bypass coolant line.
4. Disconnect vacuum lines from throttle body.

5. Remove throttle body mounting bolts, then the throttle body.
6. Reverse procedure to install. **Torque** attaching bolts to 14-19 ft. lbs.

1995–96

1. Remove air intake system.
2. Disconnect throttle position sensor, idle air control bypass air valve and idle switch, if equipped.
3. Remove accelerator cable and speed control actuator from throttle lever and accelerator bracket.
4. Remove throttle body retaining bolts, then carefully separate throttle body from intake manifold.
5. Remove accelerator cable bracket retainers and accelerator cable bracket.
6. Reverse procedure to install. **Torque** throttle body retaining bolts to 6-9 ft. lbs.

2.2L/4-133 ENGINE

1. Disconnect accelerator cable from throttle body.
2. Remove air duct from throttle body.
3. Mark vacuum hoses for reference during assembly, then disconnect hoses from throttle body.
4. Disconnect throttle position sensor, idle switch and air control valve electrical connectors.
5. Remove engine lifting bracket mounting bolt and coolant line retaining bracket from throttle body.
6. Remove throttle body-to-intake manifold attaching nuts, then the throttle body and gasket.
7. Reverse procedure to install, noting the following:
   a. Ensure throttle plates move freely from fully closed to fully open position.
   b. Do not remove thin sealing coating from throttle plates or bores.
   c. **Torque** throttle body attaching nuts to 14-19 ft. lbs.

2.3L/4-140 EXCEPT HSC & TURBOCHARGED ENGINES

1. Disconnect throttle cable and cruise control cable, if equipped.
2. Remove throttle position sensor, then disconnect electrical connectors from EGR valve and air bypass hose.
3. Remove two nuts and two bolts attaching throttle body to manifold.
4. Remove throttle body from manifold.
5. Remove and discard gasket between throttle body and upper manifold.
6. Reverse procedure to install. **Torque** throttle body attaching bolts to 12-15 ft. lbs.

2.3L/4-140 HSC ENGINE

1. Remove throttle body attaching bolts, then disconnect throttle position sensor.
2. Disconnect air bypass hose.
3. Disconnect throttle control cable and speed control cable, as equipped.
4. Remove throttle bracket.
5. Remove throttle body from upper intake manifold.
6. Remove and discard gasket between throttle body and manifold.
7. Reverse procedure to install. **Torque** manifold attaching bolts to 12-15 ft. lbs.

2.3L/4-140 TURBOCHARGED ENGINE

1. Remove fuel charging assembly as previously described.
2. Disconnect throttle position sensor and air bypass valve electrical connectors from wiring harness.
3. Remove four throttle body nuts or two bolts and two nuts, as equipped.
4. Remove throttle body assembly from upper intake manifold.
5. Remove and discard gasket from manifold.
6. Reverse procedure to install. **Torque** retaining nuts and/or bolts to 12-15 ft. lbs.

2.5L/V6-153 ENGINE

1993–94

1. Disconnect battery ground cable, then remove air duct from throttle body.
2. Remove throttle cable from throttle lever, then disconnect necessary electrical connections and vacuum hoses.
3. Remove attaching bolts from throttle body, then the throttle body. Ensure all old gasket material is removed from throttle body to intake manifold contact surfaces.
4. Reverse procedure to install. **Torque** attaching bolts to 14-19 ft. lbs.

1995–96

1. Disconnect battery ground cable, then remove air cleaner tube outlet.
2. Remove water pump pulley shield as outlined under "Upper Intake Manifold, Replace."
3. Disconnect wiring from throttle position sensor and remove wiring retainer from throttle body.
4. Disconnect accelerator cable and speed control actuator from throttle lever.
5. Remove three throttle body bolts and one stud, then carefully separate throttle body from intake manifold.
6. Reverse procedure to install.

3.0L/V6-182 EXCEPT SHO ENGINE

1993–95

1. Remove air cleaner outlet tube between air cleaner and throttle body.
2. Remove snow shield retaining nut and bolts and the shield, if necessary.
3. Disconnect vacuum hoses from intake manifold.
4. Disconnect accelerator cable and speed control cable, if equipped, from accelerator mounting bracket and throttle lever.
5. **On models equipped with automatic transmission,** disconnect transmission valve linkage from throttle lever.
6. Remove throttle body attaching bolts and the throttle body.
7. Remove and discard gasket from lower intake manifold.
8. Reverse procedure to install. **Torque** attaching bolts to 15-22 ft. lbs. in sequence shown, **Fig. 26.**

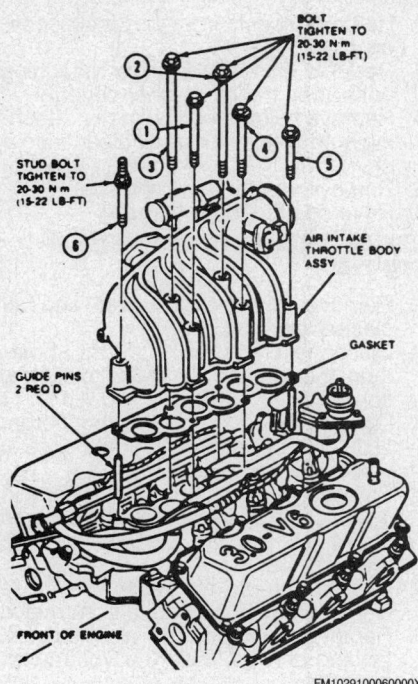

Fig. 26 Throttle body bolt tightening sequence. 3.0L/V6-182 engine except SHO

1996

1. Disconnect battery ground cable.
2. Release fuel system pressure as described under "Precautions."
3. Disconnect spring lock couplings from fuel hose fittings.
4. Loosen air cleaner tube clamp.
5. Disconnect crankcase ventilation tube, IAT sensor and aspirator hoses from air cleaner outlet tube, then remove air cleaner outlet tube.
6. Remove accelerator cable shield from throttle body.
7. Disconnect accelerator cable, then speed control actuator from throttle body lever.
8. Remove two accelerator cable bracket bolts from sides of throttle body.
9. Position accelerator cable bracket, accelerator cable and speed control actuator aside.
10. Disconnect throttle position sensor wiring harness.
11. Remove ignition wire separator and position ignition wires aside.
12. Remove throttle body retaining bolts and stud bolts.
13. Remove throttle body from intake manifold and discard throttle body gasket.
14. Reverse procedure to install.

3.0L/V6-182 & 3.2L/V6-195 SHO ENGINES

1. Remove intake air boot and throttle cable.
2. Disconnect electrical connectors from throttle position sensor and air bypass valve.
3. Remove coolant bypass hoses, then disconnect PCV hoses.
4. Remove four throttle body retaining bolts, then the throttle body.

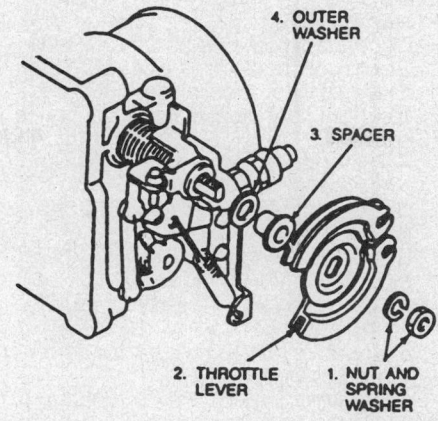

Fig. 27 Throttle lever removal. 2.2L/4-133 engine

5. Reverse procedure to install. **Torque** throttle body attaching bolts to 11-17 ft. lbs.

3.8L/V6-232 ENGINE

1. Disconnect throttle position sensor and throttle air bypass valve electrical connectors.
2. Disconnect heater hoses from throttle body.
3. Remove four throttle body attaching nuts, then separate throttle body from intake manifold.
4. Remove and discard gasket between throttle body and manifold.
5. Reverse procedure to install, using a new gasket. **Torque** throttle body attaching nuts on V8 models to 12-18 ft. lbs. and on V6 models to 15-22 ft. lbs.

4.6L/V8-281 ENGINE

1. Disconnect throttle position sensor and throttle linkage at throttle lever.
2. Remove four throttle body retaining bolts.
3. Separate air throttle body from intake manifold adapter.
4. Reverse procedure to install, **Torque** retaining bolts to 6-8 ft. lbs.

5.0L/V8-302 ENGINE

1. Remove air cleaner outlet tube from throttle body.
2. Disconnect accelerator at throttle lever.
3. Disconnect fuel charging wiring connectors from throttle position sensor and idle air control valve.
4. Remove four throttle body retaining nuts, then carefully separate throttle body from upper intake manifold.
5. Remove and discard throttle body gasket.
6. Reverse procedure to install. **Torque** throttle body nuts to 12-18 ft. lbs.

AIR BYPASS VALVE

1. Disconnect air bypass valve electrical connector from wiring harness.
2. Remove air bypass valve attaching screws and valve.
3. Remove and discard gasket.
4. Reverse procedure to install, using new gasket. **Torque** valve attaching screws to 71-102 inch lbs.

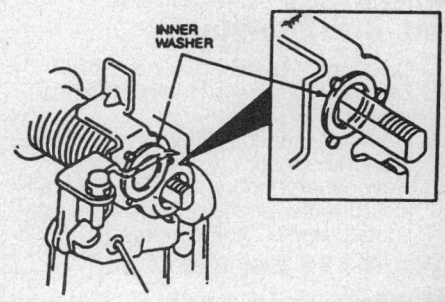

Fig. 28 Throttle lever washer installation

THROTTLE LEVER

2.2L/4-133 Engine

1. Remove throttle lever as shown if **Fig. 27.** Hold throttle valves in full open position when removing throttle lever nut to prevent damaging idle switch.
2. Reverse procedure to install, noting the following:
   a. Ensure inner washer is properly positioned, **Fig. 28.**
   b. Hold throttle plates fully closed when installing nut to prevent damaging stopper lever.
   c. **Torque** throttle lever attaching nut to 12-17 ft. lbs.
   d. Ensure throttle operates smoothly.

THROTTLE POSITION SENSOR

Except 1.3L/4-81, 1.6L/4-98, 1.8L/4-112, 1.9L/4-116, 3.0L/V6-182 & 3.2L/V6-195 SHO & 3.8L/V6-232 SC Engines

1. Disconnect sensor electrical connector from wiring harness.
2. Scribe alignment marks on throttle body and throttle position sensor for installation reference.
3. Remove two sensor attaching screws and the sensor.
4. Reverse procedure to install. Ensure rotary tangs on sensor are properly aligned, then **torque** sensor attaching screws to 11-16 inch lbs. **When installing sensor, slide rotary tangs over throttle shaft blade, then rotate sensor clockwise to installed position. Failure to perform this operation may result in incorrect idle speeds.**

1.3L/4-81 Engine

1. Disconnect battery ground cable.
2. Disconnect sensor electrical connector.
3. Remove sensor attaching screws, then the sensor.
4. Reverse procedure to install, then adjust throttle position sensor as described under "Adjustments."

1.6L/4-98 Engine

1. Disconnect battery ground cable.
2. Disconnect electrical connector at sensor.
3. Remove two hold-down bolts, then the sensor.

4. Reverse procedure to install.

1.8L/4-112 Engine

1. Disconnect battery ground cable.
2. Disconnect sensor electrical connector.
3. Remove sensor attaching screws, then the sensor.
4. Reverse procedure to install, then adjust throttle position sensor as described under "Adjustments."

1.9L/4-116 Engine

1. Remove air intake tube.
2. Disconnect sensor connector.
3. Remove two sensor retaining screws, then the sensor.
4. Reverse procedure to install.

3.0L/V6-182 SHO Engine

1. Disconnect throttle position electrical connector.
2. Remove sensor attaching screws, then the sensor.
3. Reverse procedure to install, noting the following:
   a. Align tab on throttle shaft with slot in sensor, then rotate sensor into position.
   b. **Torque** sensor attaching screws to 14-16 ft. lbs.

3.8L/V6-232 SC Engine

1. Disconnect throttle position sensor electrical connector.
2. Remove throttle position sensor attaching screws, then the sensor.
3. Reverse procedure to install. **Torque** attaching screws to 24-27 inch lbs.

PRESSURE RELIEF VALVE

If pressure relief valve is to be removed with fuel charging assembly installed on engine, release fuel system pressure as previously described.

1. Remove pressure relief valve from fuel injection manifold using suitable tool.
2. Install valve and cap into manifold. **Torque** valve to 48-84 inch lbs. and cap to 4-6 inch lbs.

FUEL PRESSURE REGULATOR
Gasoline Engines

If pressure relief valve is to be removed with fuel charging assembly installed on engine, release fuel system pressure as described under "Precautions."

1. Disconnect vacuum line from regulator.
2. Remove three pressure regulator attaching screws and regulator.
3. Remove and discard gasket and inspect O-ring for wear or damage.
4. Reverse procedure to install, using new gasket. **Torque** regulator attaching screws to 27-40 inch lbs.

Natural Gas Engine

1. Relieve fuel system pressure as described under "Precautions."
2. Raise and support vehicle.
3. Remove fuel pressure regulator shield.

4. Remove four fuel pressure regulator bracket bolts.
5. Disconnect fuel inlet and outlet lines.
6. Clamp off fuel pressure regulator heater hoses, then disconnect pressure regulator heater inlet and outlet hoses.
7. Remove fuel pressure regulator and coalescer/filter assembly.
8. Disconnect filter from pressure regulator.
9. Reverse procedure to install, noting the following:
   a. **Torque** fuel pressure regulator mounting bolts to 14-20 ft. lbs.
   b. Remove fuel pump relay from power distribution box.
   c. Connect jumper wire to fuel pump circuit from sockets 87 to 30 to pressurize system.
   d. Remove jumper wire and install fuel pump relay.

FUEL INJECTOR

1. Remove fuel manifold as previously described.
2. Remove electrical connectors from injectors as required.
3. Pull injector(s) out of manifold.
4. Remove O-rings and pintle protective cap and inspect for wear or damage. Replace as necessary.
5. Reverse procedure to install. Lubricate O-rings with suitable light oil.

VOLUME AIR METER
1.3L/4-81 Engine

1. Disconnect battery ground cable.
2. Disconnect volume air flow meter electrical connector.
3. Remove air duct.
4. Remove meter attaching bolt and four attaching nuts, then the meter.
5. Reverse procedure to install. **Torque** attaching nuts to 110-152 inch lbs.

1.6L/4-98 Engine

1. Disconnect battery ground cable.
2. Disconnect primary and secondary wires from coil.
3. Remove air duct from volume air flow meter.
4. Remove retaining bolt and ground wire from air cleaner cover.
5. Remove air cleaner retaining bolts, then the air cleaner cover.
6. Remove volume air flow meter retaining nuts from inside air cleaner cover, then the air flow meter.
7. Reverse procedure to install.

1.8L/4-112 Engine

1. Disconnect battery ground cable.
2. Disconnect resonance chamber from volume air flow meter and position aside.
3. Disconnect volume air flow meter electrical connector.
4. Remove ignition coil wire routing bracket nut, then the bracket.
5. Remove volume air flow meter mounting nuts, then the air flow meter.
6. Reverse procedure to install.

2.2L/4-133 Engine

1. Disconnect volume airflow meter electrical connector.

2. Remove air duct from the air filter cover.
3. Remove air cleaner cover attaching bolts, then the air cleaner cover.
4. Remove volume airflow meter attaching nuts from inside of air cleaner cover.
5. Remove volume airflow meter.
6. Reverse procedure to install.

2.3L/4-140 Turbocharged Engine

1. Remove air cleaner cover and air cleaner element.
2. Disconnect carbon canister hose, then the volume air meter electrical connector.
3. Loosen hose clamp on turbocharger air inlet hose, then disconnect hose at volume air meter.
4. Remove four volume air meter bracket attaching screws, then the volume air meter and air cleaner housing bracket.
5. Loosen volume air meter inlet hose clamp, then remove hose from meter.
6. Remove three volume air meter attaching screws, then the volume air meter.
7. Reverse procedure to install. **Torque** volume air meter attaching screws to 15-22 ft. lbs.

ENGINE COOLANT TEMPERATURE SENSOR

1. Disconnect battery ground cable.
2. Drain coolant from engine.
3. Disconnect electrical connector from temperature switch.
4. Remove temperature sensor from intake manifold.
5. Reverse procedure to install.

COOLANT TEMPERATURE SENSOR

1. Disconnect battery ground cable.
2. Drain coolant from engine.
3. Disconnect electrical connector from coolant switch.
4. Remove temperature sensor from radiator.
5. Reverse procedure to install.

OXYGEN SENSOR

1. Disconnect battery ground cable.
2. Disconnect sensor electrical connector.
3. Remove oxygen sensor.
4. Reverse procedure to install.

CLUTCH SWITCH

1. Disconnect battery ground cable.
2. Disconnect electrical connector from clutch switch.
3. Remove locknut, then the clutch switch.
4. Reverse procedure to install.

NEUTRAL SWITCH

1. Disconnect battery ground cable.
2. Disconnect electrical connector from switch.
3. Drain transaxle fluid, if necessary.
4. Remove switch from transaxle.
5. Reverse procedure to install.

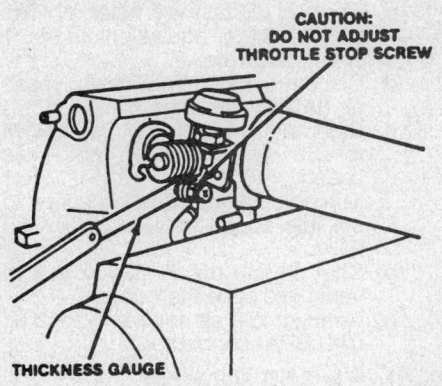

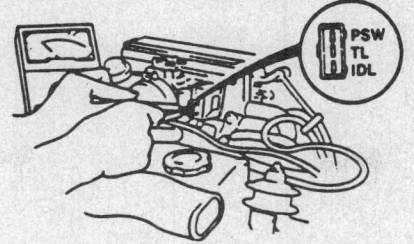

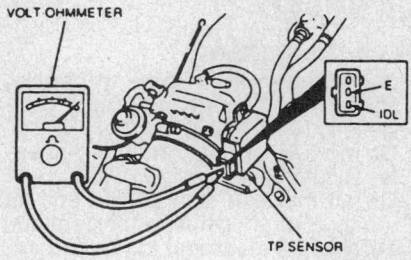

Fig. 30 Throttle position sensor test connections. 1.8L/4-112 engine w/manual transaxle

Insert thickness gauge between the throttle adjust screw and stop lever.	Continuity between terminals	
	IDL – TL	PSW – TL
0.5 mm (0.02 in)	Yes	No
0.7 mm (0.027 in)	No	No
Fully open throttle lever	No	Yes

Fig. 29 Throttle position sensor test

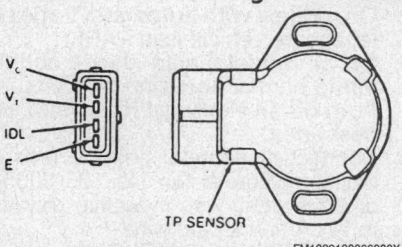

Fig. 31 Throttle position sensor test connections. 1.8L/4-112 engine w/ automatic transaxle

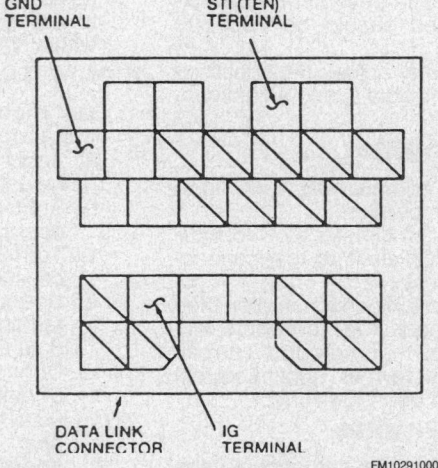

Fig. 32 Idle speed test connections

Adjustments
THROTTLE POSITION SENSOR

1.3L/4-81 ENGINE

1. Disconnect battery ground cable.
2. Disconnect sensor electrical connector.
3. Insert appropriate thickness gauge between throttle and adjustment screw, then check for continuity between terminals shown, **Fig. 29.**
4. If necessary, adjust throttle position sensor by loosening attaching screws, then rotating sensor until desired readings are obtained and tighten attaching bolts.
5. Connect throttle position sensor electrical connector.
6. Connect battery ground cable.

1.8L/4-112 ENGINE

1. **On manual transaxle equipped vehicles,** adjust as follows:
   a. Disconnect electrical connector from sensor.
   b. Using a suitable ohmmeter, connect leads to IDL and E terminals **Fig. 30.**
   c. Insert a .016 inch feeler gauge between throttle stop screw and stop lever.
   d. Loosen sensor mounting screws.
   e. Rotate sensor clockwise approximately 30°, then rotate it counterclockwise until continuity exists.
   f. Replace .016 inch feeler gauge with a .027 inch feeler gauge and insert it between throttle stop screw and stop lever.

g. Verify continuity no longer exists.
h. Tighten sensor mounting screws, then open throttle plate to wide open position several times and recheck adjustment.

2. **On automatic transaxle equipped vehicles,** adjust as follows:
   a. Disconnect electrical connector from sensor.
   b. Using a suitable ohmmeter connect leads to IDL and E terminals **Fig. 31.**
   c. Loosen sensor mounting screws.
   d. Insert a .01 inch feeler gauge between throttle stop screw and stop lever.
   e. Rotate sensor clockwise approximately 30°, then rotate counterclockwise until continuity exists.
   f. Replace .01 inch feeler gauge with .016 inch feeler gauge and insert between throttle stop screw and stop lever.
   g. Verify continuity no longer exists.
   h. Tighten sensor mounting screws, then open throttle plate to wide open position several times and verify resistance between terminals E an Vt is approximately 5000 ohms.

2.0L/4-122 ENGINE

The throttle position sensor is not adjustable. The throttle body must be replaced if the throttle position sensor requires adjustment.

2.5L/V6-153 ENGINE

1. Using breakout box adapter tool T92C-6000-AH, or equivalent, connect breakout box tool No. 014-00322, or equivalent, to powertrain control module (PCM).
2. Turn ignition switch to On position and measure voltage between Breakout Box pin 47 and ground.
3. Rotate throttle linkage by hand and observe voltage readings.
4. With throttle valve fully closed, voltage should be 0.1-1.1 volts.
5. With throttle valve fully open, voltage should be 3.1-4.4 volts.
6. If voltage is not within specifications, adjust throttle position sensor as follows:
   a. Loosen throttle position sensor bolts.
   b. With throttle valve fully closed, rotate throttle position sensor until voltage is 0.1-1.1 volts.
   c. With throttle valve fully open, verify voltage is 3.1-4.4 volts.
   d. **Torque** throttle position sensor bolts to 14-20 inch lbs.

FORD—Fuel Injection

IDLE SPEED

1.3L/4-81 Engine

1. On models with manual transaxle, apply parking brake and ensure vehicle is in NEUTRAL.
2. On models with automatic transaxle, ensure vehicle is in PARK.
3. On all models, start engine and let run to normal operating temperature. Turn off all electrical loads and accessories.
4. Connect tachometer positive lead of digital multimeter 105-00053, or equivalent with inductive pick-up, to number one spark plug wire.
5. Ground TEN pin at DLC, Fig. 32, then make a note of idle speed.
6. On models with manual transaxle, idle speed should be 650-750 RPM.
7. On models with automatic transaxle, idle speed should be 700-800 RPM.
8. On all models, adjust idle speed as necessary with idle speed adjustment screw.

1.6L/4-98 Engine

1. Start engine and allow to warm up to operating temperature.
2. Attach digital Multimeter tool No. 059-00010, or equivalent, to test connector, white pin No. 1.
3. Check idle speed on tachometer, then connect jumper wire between STI, green pin No. 1, and ground. Turn air adjustment screw to obtain correct idle speed of 800-900 RPM.

1.8L/4-112 Engine

1. Apply parking brake and ensure vehicle is in NEUTRAL.
2. Start engine and let run to normal operating temperature. Turn off all electrical loads and accessories.
3. Using a jumper wire, connect ground terminal to TEN terminal on DLC, Fig. 32.
4. Connect tachometer positive lead of digital multimeter tool No. 105-00051, or equivalent, to IG terminal on DLC and tachometer ground lead to battery ground post.
5. Check idle speed with tachometer. Speed should be 700-800 RPM.
6. If idle speed is not within specification,

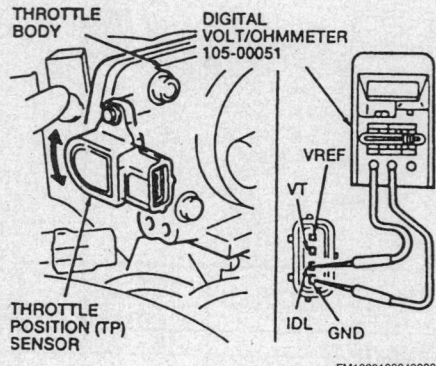

Fig. 33   Idle switch test connections

adjust idle speed by turning idle speed adjusting screw until idle speed is within specifications.

2.0L/4-122 Engine

1. On models equipped with automatic transaxle, proceed as follows:
   a. Apply parking brake and place gearshift in Neutral or Park.
   b. Start engine and warm to normal operating temperature.
   c. Turn Off all electrical loads and accessories.
   d. Use jumper wire, connect ground terminal to STI (TEN) terminal on data link connector (DLC), Fig. 32.
   e. Connect tachometer positive lead of digital multimeter tool No. 055-00101, or equivalent, to No. 1 spark plug wire. Do not check idle speed while electric cooling fan is operating.
   f. Check vehicle idle speed. Idle speed should be 650-750 RPM.
   g. If idle speed is not within specifications, adjust idle speed by turning idle speed adjusting screw until idle speed is within specification.
   h. Remove jumper wire from DLC.
   i. Remove tachometer.
2. On models equipped with manual transaxle, adjust as follows:
   a. Start engine and allow to run to normal operating temperature, then turn engine Off.
   b. Turn all accessories to Off position.

c. Connect digital multimeter tool No. 055-00101, or equivalent, to No. 1 spark plug wire.
d. Disconnect idle air control bypass air (IAC BPA) connector.
e. Start and run engine at 2500 RPM for 30 seconds, then note idle speed.
f. Turn idle speed adjusting screw to set idle speed between 650-750 RPM.
g. Shut engine off and rerun test to verify idle speed is correct.
h. Connect idle air control bypass air (IAC BPA) connector.

2.5L/V6-153 Engine

1. On models with manual transaxle, apply parking brake and ensure vehicle is in NEUTRAL.
2. On models with automatic transaxle, ensure vehicle is in PARK.
3. On all models, start engine and let run to normal operating temperature. Turn off all electrical loads and accessories.
4. Connect tachometer positive lead of digital multimeter tool No. 105-00053, or equivalent, with inductive pick-up, to No. 1 spark plug wire.
5. Ground TEN pin at DLC, located in front left corner of engine compartment near battery, then make a note of idle speed.
6. Idle speed should be 600-700 RPM. If not, adjust idle speed as necessary with idle speed adjustment screw.

IDLE SWITCH

2.5L/V6-153 Engine

1. Disconnect throttle position sensor connector.
2. Connect digital multimeter tool No. 105-0051, or equivalent, to Data Link Connector (DLC) terminals IDL and GND, Fig. 33.
3. Insert a .006 inch feeler gauge between stopper and throttle lever. Continuity should exist.
4. Insert a .020 inch feeler gauge between stopper and throttle lever. Continuity should not exist.
5. If continuity is not within specifications, adjust throttle position sensor as described under "Adjustments."

ELECTRIC FUEL PUMPS

On Air Bag Equipped Models, Refer To "Air Bag System Precautions" Located In The Front Of This Manual For System Disarming & Arming Procedures.

Electrical Symbol & Wire Color Code Identification Located In The Front Of This Manual May Be Used As An Aid When Using Wiring Circuits Found In This Section.

If Uncertain About The Proper Use Of Information Contained In This Section, Please Refer To "How To Use This Manual" Located In The Front Of This Manual.

Prior To Performing Any Service Operations Listed In This Section, Consult The "Technical Service Bulletins" Section For Related Information.

INDEX

Page No.

Description 6-1
Diagnosis & Testing: 6-2
 Aspire, Capri & Festiva 6-2
 Continental 6-2
 Contour & Mystique 6-2
 Cougar, Mustang & Thunderbird . . . 6-2
 Crown Victoria, Grand Marquis &
  Town Car 6-2
 Escort & Tracer 6-2
 Mark VIII 6-31
 Probe 6-31
 Sable & Taurus 6-31
 Tempo & Topaz 6-31
Fuel Pump Relay Location: 6-1
 Aspire & Festiva 6-1
 Capri 6-1
 Continental 6-1
 Contour & Mystique 6-1
 Cougar & Thunderbird 6-2
 Crown Victoria & Grand Marquis . . . 6-2

Page No.

 Escort & Tracer 6-2
 Mark VIII 6-2
 Mustang 6-2
 Probe 6-2
 Taurus & Sable 6-2
 Tempo & Topaz 6-2
 Town Car 6-2
Fuel Pump Replacement: 6-31
 Aspire & Festiva 6-31
 Capri 6-31
 Continental, Crown Victoria, Grand
  Marquis, Mustang, Sable,
  Taurus Except Flexible Fuel,
  Town Car & Tempo & Topaz . . . 6-36
 Contour & Mystique 6-36
 Cougar, Mark VIII & Thunderbird . . 6-36
 Escort & Tracer 6-37
 Probe 6-37
 Taurus w/Flexible Fuel 6-37

Page No.

Fuel Pump Specifications 6-39
Fuel System Pressure Relief: 6-2
 Contour & Mystique w/2.0L/4-122
  & 2.5L/V6-153 Engines 6-2
 Probe w/2.0L/4-121 &
  2.5L/V6-152 Engines 6-2
 1.3L/4-81 Engine 6-2
 1.6L/4-98, 1.8L/4-112 &
  1.9L/4-116 Engines 6-2
 2.3L/4-140, 3.0L/V6-182,
  3.2L/V6-195, 3.8L/V6-232,
  4.6L/V8-281 & 5.0L/V8-302
  Engines 6-2
Inertia Switch: 6-38
 Switch Location 6-38
 Precautions: 6-1
 Air Bag Systems 6-1
 Flexible Fuel Vehicles 6-1

PRECAUTIONS

AIR BAG SYSTEMS

Refer to "Air Bag System Precautions" in the front of this manual for system disarming and arming procedures.

FLEXIBLE FUEL VEHICLES

1. Handle methanol-gasoline fuel blends with extreme caution. Wear chemical goggles and nitrile gloves.
2. Do not eat, smoke or drink when fuel is being handled.
3. Flames from methanol or methanol-gasoline blends may be invisible.
4. Inhaling vapors from methanol-gasoline blends may be harmful. Handle only in well ventilated areas. If overcome by vapors, move to fresh air, if not breathing, give artificial respiration or CPR.
5. If gasoline is swallowed, do not induce vomiting, seek medical attention.
6. If methanol or a methanol/gasoline blend is swallowed, induce vomiting, under the direction of a physician or Poison Control Center, seek medical attention.

7. If methanol or a methanol/gasoline blend is splashed in eyes, flush with large amounts of water for 15 minutes, remove contact lenses, if worn and seek medical attention.
8. If methanol or a methanol/gasoline blend is swallowed, blindness may occur.
9. If methanol or a methanol/gasoline blend is swallowed, onset of serious health effects may be delayed 12 to 24 hours.

DESCRIPTION

The fuel pump is mounted on the fuel sending unit assembly inside the fuel tank. The pump assembly includes a check valve located at the fuel pump outlet. This valve maintains pressure in the system after the vehicle is shutoff. This pressure retention helps to prevent starting difficulties when the engine is hot. A pressure relief valve is provided to regulate the maximum fuel pump outlet pressure. The fuel pump is protected at its inlet by a filter element. This element filters dirt and contaminants which could plug or damage the internal pump components.

The fuel pump only operates when the engine is cranking or running. It does not operate when the engine is not running, even with the ignition switch turned On.

FUEL PUMP RELAY LOCATION

ASPIRE & FESTIVA

The fuel pump relay is located behind the instrument panel, at the lefthand cowl.

CAPRI

The fuel pump relay is located behind the lower center of the instrument panel, below the PCM.

CONTINENTAL

The fuel pump relay, is part of the Constant Control Relay Module (CCRM). The fuel pump control module is located at the front right side of the luggage compartment.

CONTOUR & MYSTIQUE

The fuel pump relay is located in the front lefthand corner of the engine compartment, in the engine compartment fuse box.

FORD—Electric Fuel Pumps

COUGAR & THUNDERBIRD

The fuel pump relay is located in the relay center on the front lefthand side of the engine compartment.

CROWN VICTORIA & GRAND MARQUIS

The fuel pump relay is located in the power distribution box on the righthand side of the engine compartment.

ESCORT & TRACER

The fuel pump relay is located below the center of the instrument panel.

MARK VIII

The low speed fuel pump relay is part of the Variable Control Relay Module (VCRM). The high speed fuel pump relay is located in the engine compartment fuse box, found on left side of the engine compartment, next to the coolant bottle.

MUSTANG

1993

2.3L/4-140 Engine

The fuel pump relay is part of the constant control relay module (CCRM), located on the side of the righthand front strut tower.

5.0L/V8-302 Engine

The fuel pump relay is located on the righthand side of the engine compartment, on the lower front of the wheelwell.

1994—96

The fuel pump relay is part of the constant control relay module (CCRM), located on the bracket behind the engine coolant reservoir.

PROBE

The fuel pump relay is located at the engine compartment fuse box, in the lefthand side of the engine compartment.

TAURUS & SABLE

The fuel pump relay is located at the front center of the engine compartment, in the power distribution center.

TEMPO & TOPAZ

The fuel pump relay is integrated into the constant control relay module (CCRM). The CCRM is located in the rear lefthand side of the engine compartment, next to the left shock tower.

TOWN CAR

The fuel pump relay is located in the relay center, located on top of the left wheelwell in engine compartment.

FUEL SYSTEM PRESSURE RELIEF

Fuel supply lines will remain pressurized for long periods of time after engine shutdown. This pressure must be relieved before attempting to service the fuel system.

1.3L/4-81 ENGINE

1. Remove fuel filler cap and release tank pressure.
2. Locate fuel pump relay electrical connector behind left side of instrument cluster.
3. Start engine, then disconnect fuel pump relay electrical connector and wait for engine to stall.
4. Disconnect battery ground cable.

1.6L/4-98, 1.8L/4-112 & 1.9L/4-116 ENGINES

1. Remove gas cap to release residual fuel pressure in the tank.
2. Start engine, then disconnect fuel pump connector.
3. When engine stalls turn ignition switch off.
4. Disconnect battery ground cable.

PROBE w/2.0L/4-121 & 2.5L/V6-152 ENGINES

1993—94

1. Start engine, then disconnect fuel pump relay.
2. When engine stalls turn ignition switch off.
3. Reconnect fuel pump relay.
4. Disconnect battery ground cable.

1995—96

1. Remove gas cap to release residual fuel pressure in the tank.
2. Disconnect battery ground cable and position aside.
3. Using fuel pressure gauge tool No. T80L-9974-B, or equivalent, relieve pressure from system at pressure relief valve cap on fuel injection supply manifold.

CONTOUR & MYSTIQUE w/2.0L/4-122 & 2.5L/V6-153 ENGINES

1. Remove gas cap to release residual fuel pressure in the tank.
2. Disconnect battery ground cable and position aside.
3. Using fuel pressure gauge tool No. T80L-9974-B, or equivalent, relieve pressure from system at pressure relief valve cap on fuel injection supply manifold.

2.3L/4-140, 3.0L/V6-182, 3.2L/V6-195, 3.8L/V6-232, 4.6L/V8-281 & 5.0L/V8-302 ENGINES

Fuel system pressure may be relieved by the fuel pressure relief valve, located on the fuel injection supply manifold.

1. Remove air cleaner assembly.
2. Connect EFI and CFI fuel pressure gauge tool No. T80L-9974-B or equivalent, to fuel pressure relief valve cap.
3. Open manual valve on pressure gauge to relieve fuel system pressure.

DIAGNOSIS & TESTING

Refer to individual model wiring diagrams, **Figs. 1** through **21**, as aids while using charts during diagnosis and testing procedures.

ASPIRE, CAPRI & FESTIVA

1993

Refer to **Fig. 22** for fuel pump diagnostic procedures.

1994

Refer to **Fig. 23** for fuel pump diagnostic procedures.

1995

Refer to **Fig. 24** for fuel pump diagnostic procedures.

CONTINENTAL

1993—94

Refer to **Fig. 25** for fuel pump diagnostic procedures.

1995

Refer to **Fig. 26** for fuel pump diagnostic procedures.

1996

Refer to EEC-V section under "Computerized Engine Controls" for fuel pump system diagnostic and testing procedures.

CONTOUR & MYSTIQUE

1995

Refer to **Fig. 26** for fuel pump diagnostic procedures.

1996

Refer to EEC-V section of "Computerized Engine Controls" for fuel pump system diagnostic and testing procedures.

COUGAR, MUSTANG & THUNDERBIRD

1993

Refer to **Fig. 27** for fuel pump diagnostic procedures.

1994—95

Refer to **Fig. 26** for fuel pump diagnostic procedures.

1996

Refer to EEC-V section under "Computerized Engine Controls" for fuel pump system diagnostic and testing procedures.

CROWN VICTORIA, GRAND MARQUIS & TOWN CAR

1993

Refer to **Fig. 28** for fuel pump diagnostic procedures.

1994—95

Refer to **Fig. 26** for fuel pump diagnostic procedures.

1996

Refer to EEC-V section under "Computerized Engine Controls" for fuel pump system diagnostic and testing procedures.

ESCORT & TRACER

1993 1.8L/4-112 Engine

Refer to **Fig. 22** for fuel pump diagnostic procedures.

Continued on page 6-31

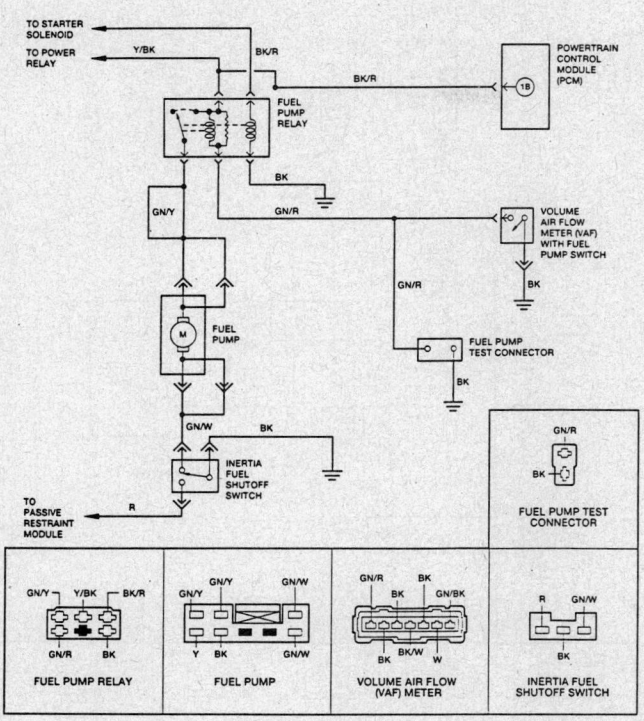

Fig. 1   Fuel system wiring circuit.
1993 1.3L/4-81 engine

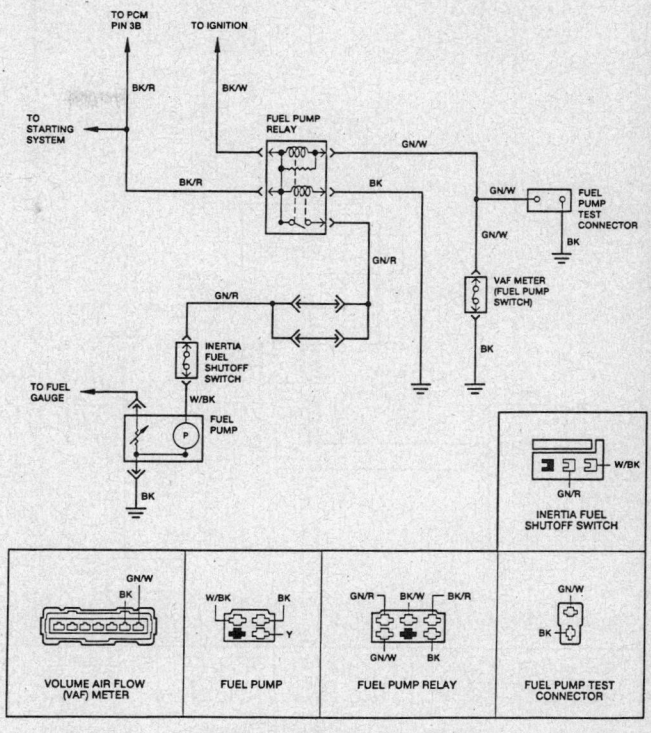

Fig. 2   Fuel system wiring circuit.
1993 1.6L/4-98 engine

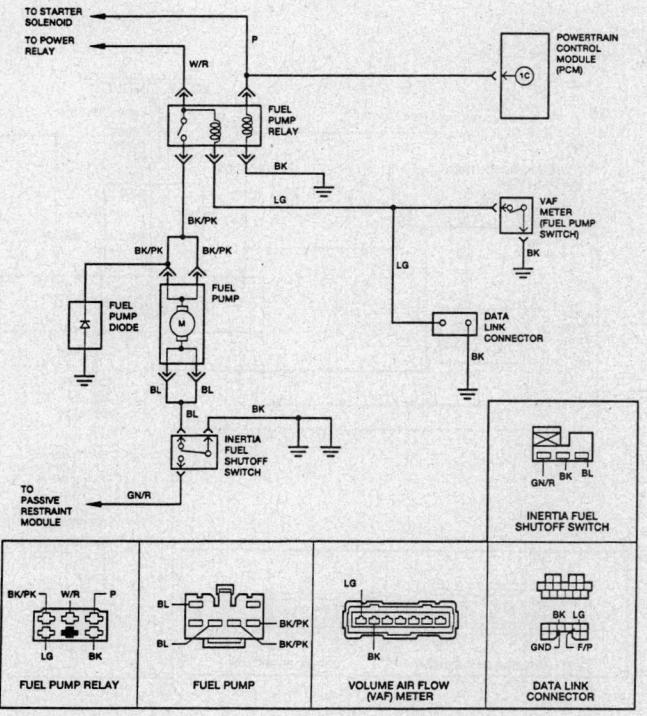

Fig. 3   Fuel system wiring circuit.
1993 1.8L/4-112 engine

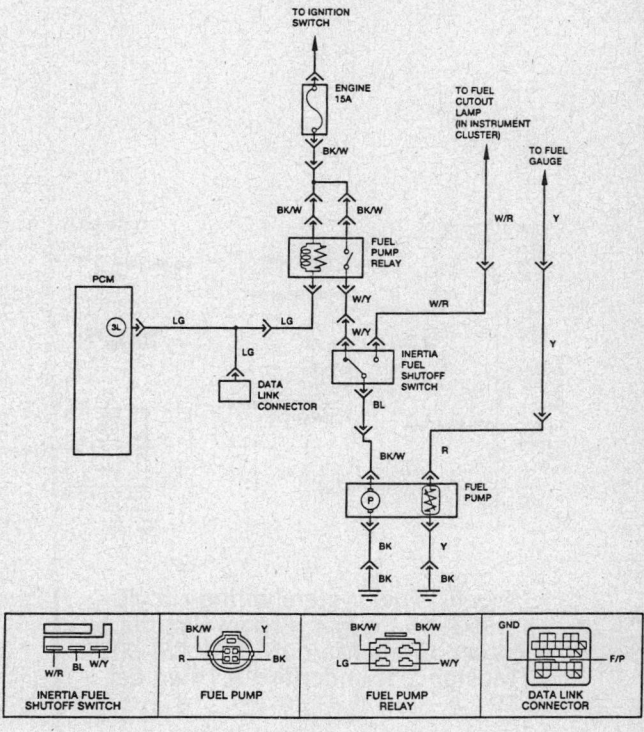

Fig. 4   Fuel system wiring circuit.
1993 2.0L/4-122 engine

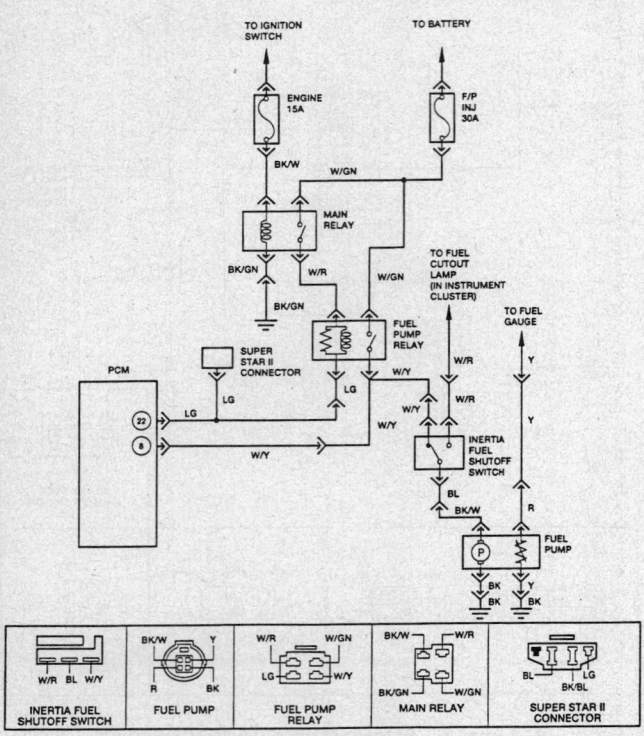

Fig. 5 Fuel system wiring circuit.
1993 2.0L/4-122 MTX engine

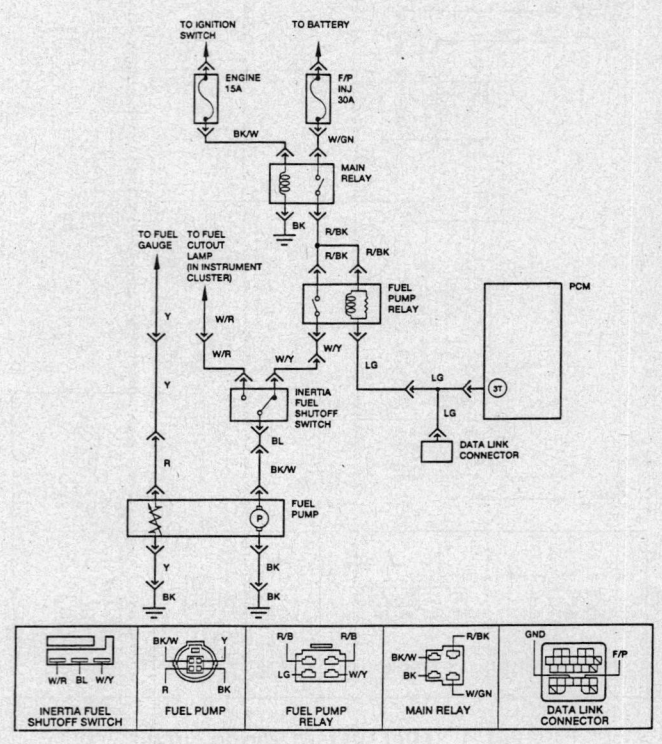

Fig. 6 Fuel system wiring circuit.
1993 2.5L/V6-153 MTX engine

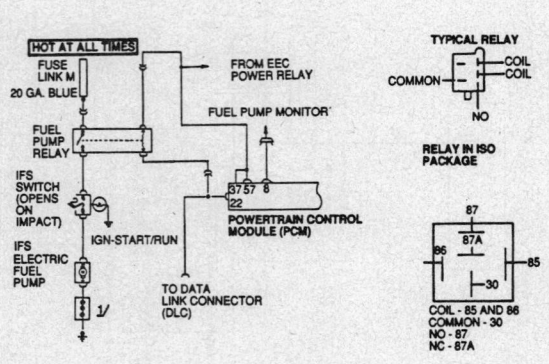

Fig. 7 Fuel system wiring circuit.
1993–95 Cougar, Crown Victoria,
Escort, Grand Marquis, 5.0L/V8-302
Mustang, Thunderbird & Town Car

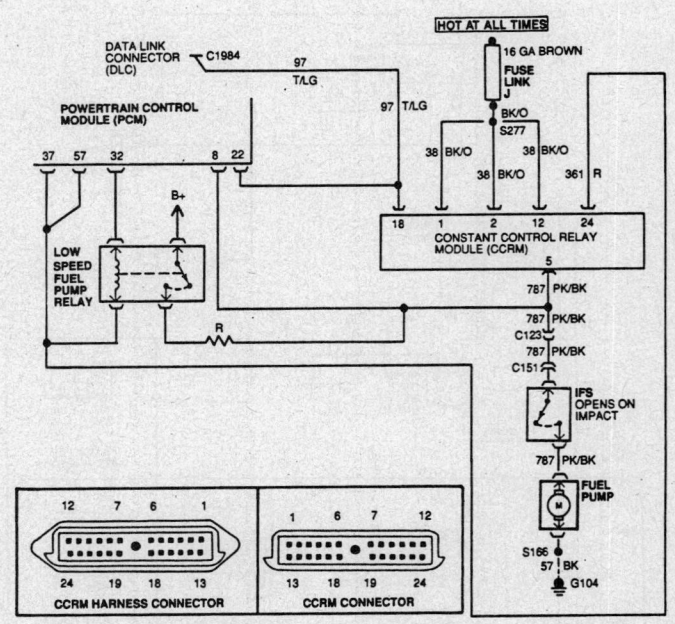

Fig. 8 Fuel system wiring circuit.
1993–95 Taurus FF w/3.0L/V6-182
engine

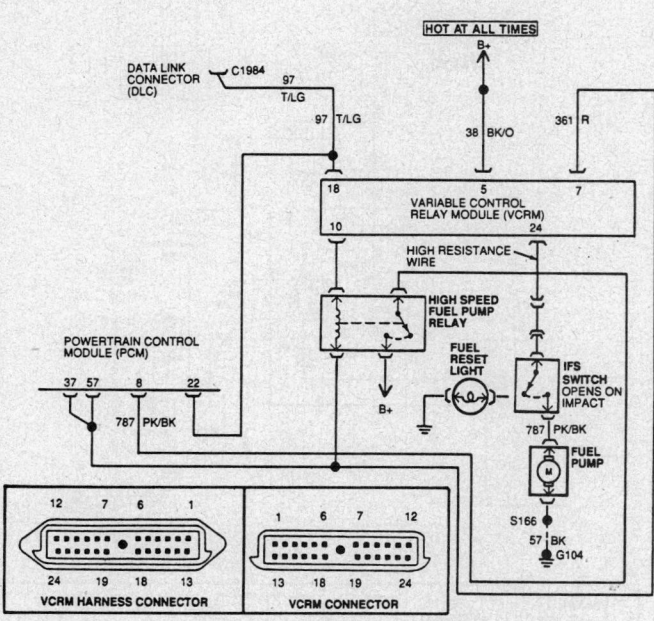

Fig. 9 Fuel system wiring circuit. 1993–95 Mark VIII

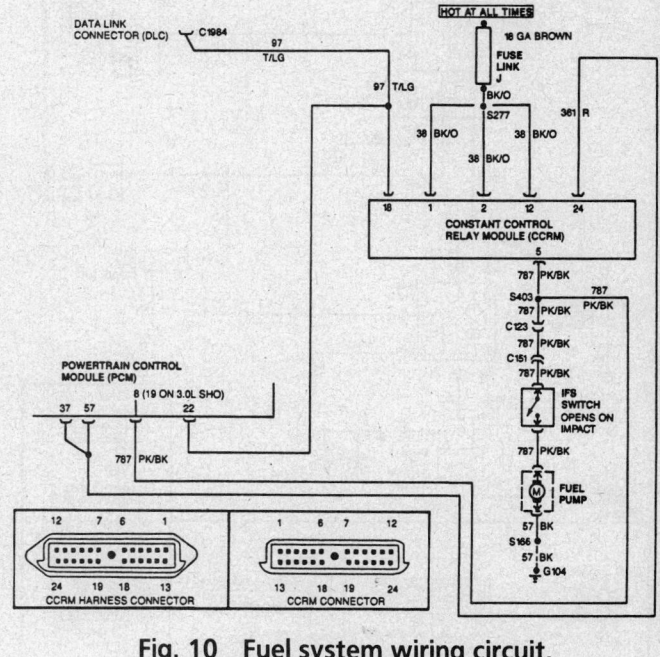

Fig. 10 Fuel system wiring circuit. 1993–95 Continental, Taurus, Tempo, Topaz, Taurus w/3.0L/V6-182 SHO engine, Sable & 1993–94 Mustang w/2.3L/4-140 engine

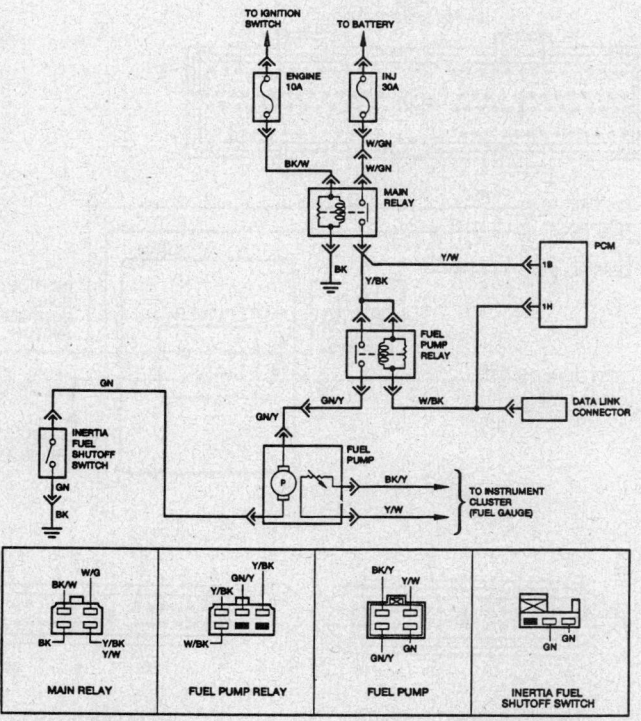

Fig. 11 Fuel system wiring circuit. 1994–95 1.3L/4-81 engine

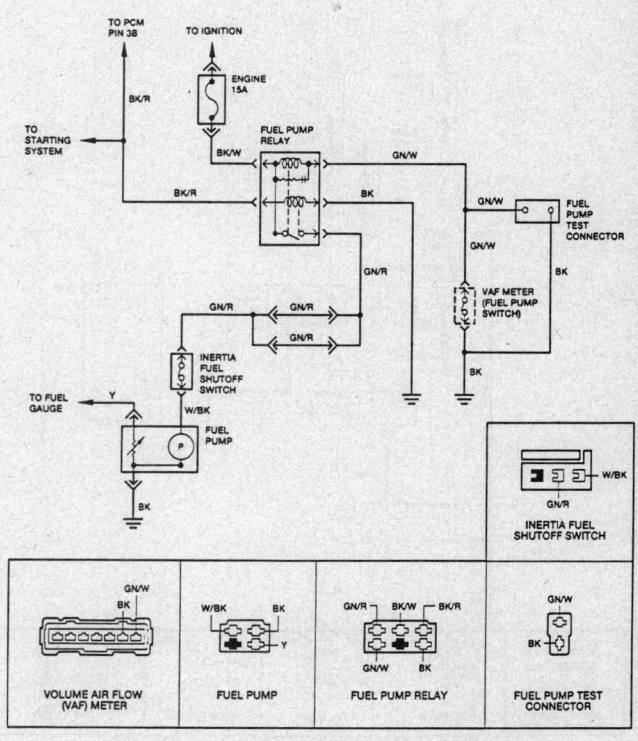

Fig. 12 Fuel system wiring circuit. 1994 1.6L/4-98 engine

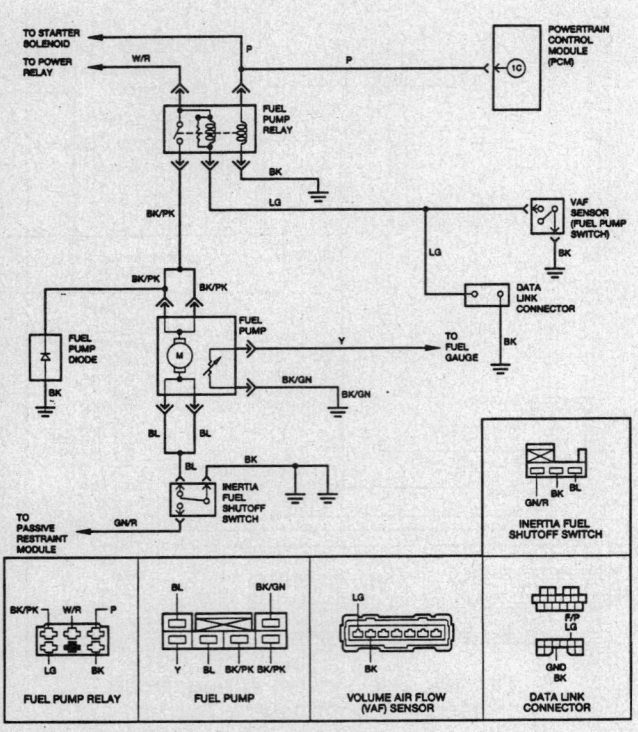

Fig. 13   Fuel system wiring circuit.
1994–95 1.8L/4-112 engine

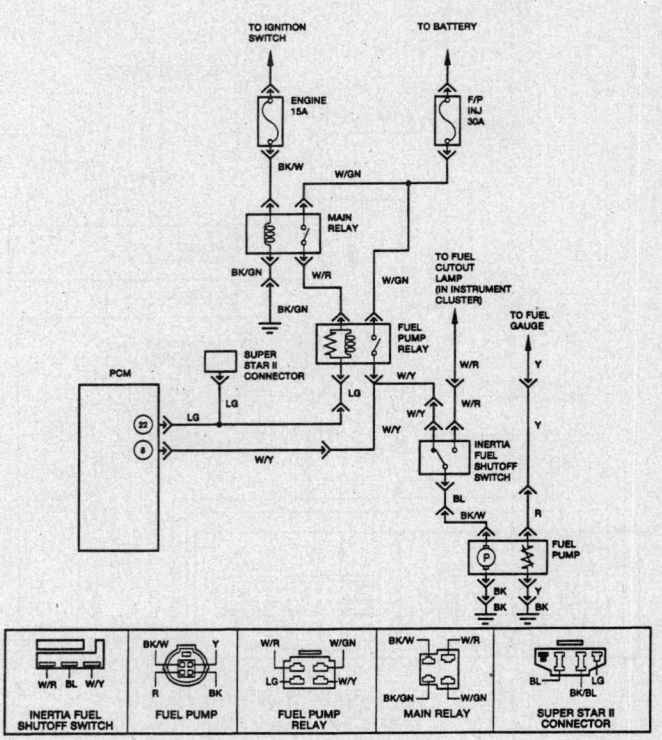

Fig. 14   Fuel system wiring circuit.
1994–95 2.0L/4-122 engine

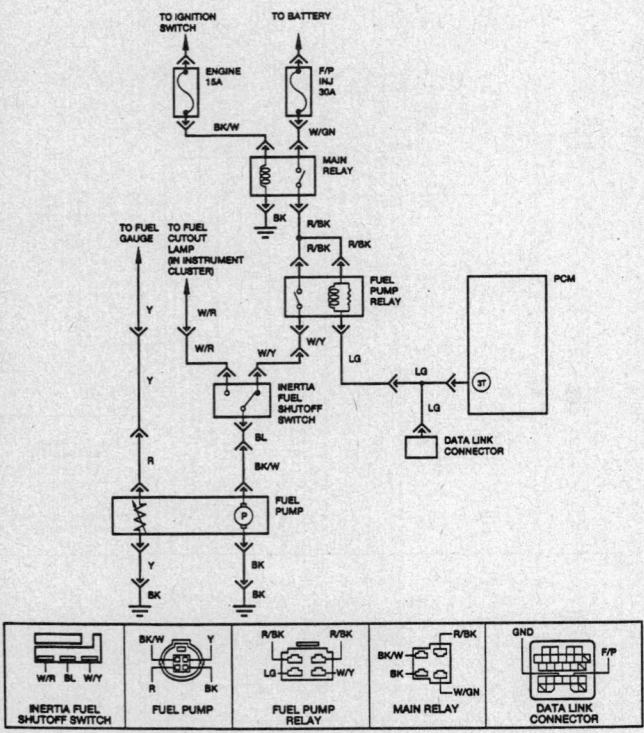

Fig. 15   Fuel system wiring circuit.
1994–95 2.5L/V6-153 MTX engine

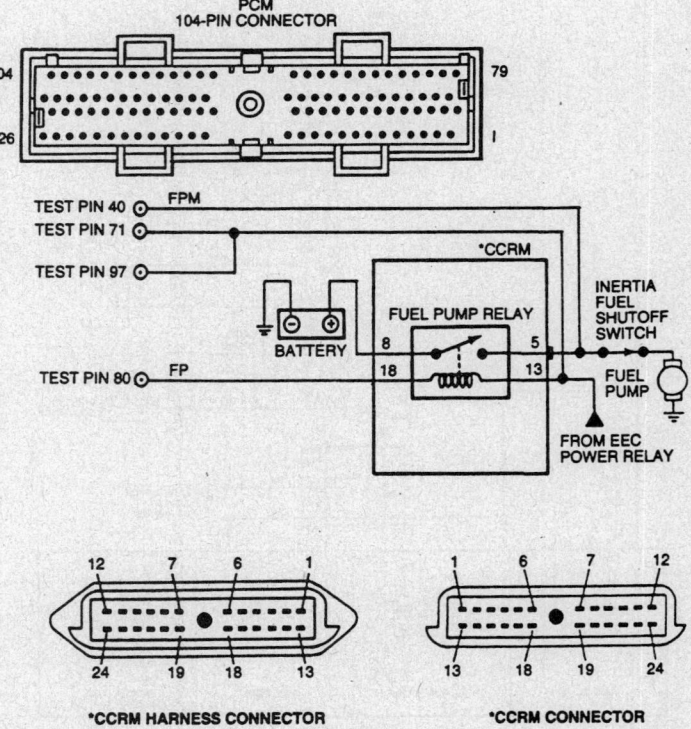

Fig. 16   Fuel system wiring circuit.
1995 3.8L/V6-232 & 4.6L/V8-281
engines

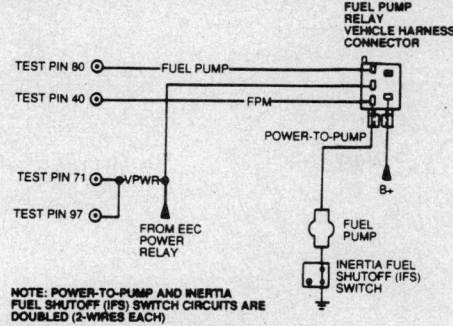

Fig. 17   Fuel system wiring circuit. 1996 Escort & Tracer

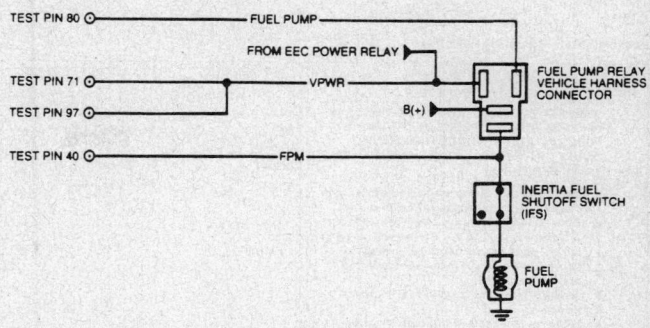

Fig. 18   Fuel system wiring circuit. 1996 Contour & Mystique

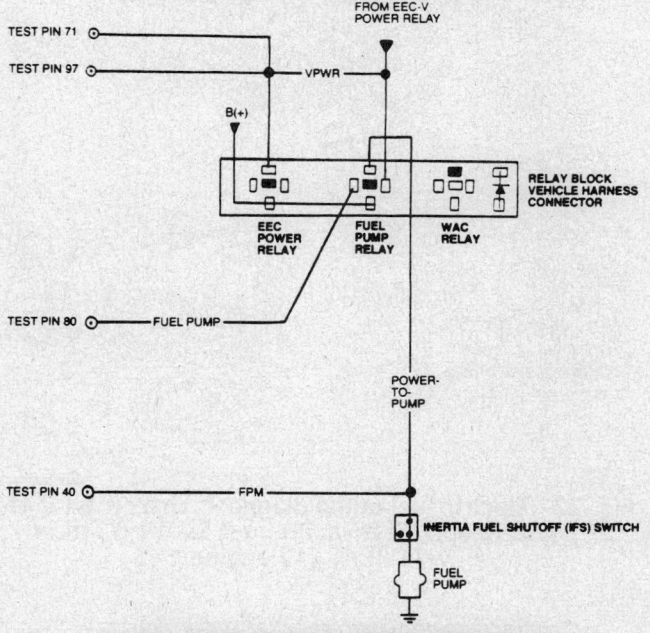

Fig. 19   Fuel system wiring circuit. 1996 Crown Victoria, Grand Marquis & Town Car

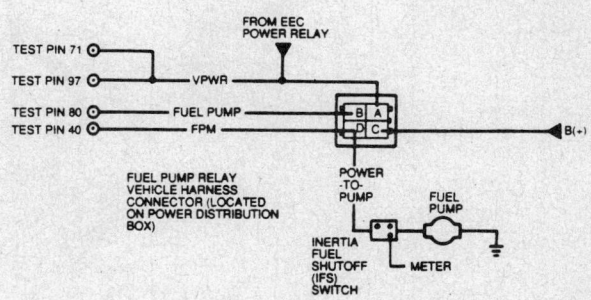

Fig. 20   Fuel system wiring circuit. 1996 Probe

System Inspection

1. Visually inspect the components of the fuel delivery system.

VISUAL INSPECTION CHART

Mechanical	Electrical
• Loose, leaking, or damaged fuel or vacuum lines	• Discharged battery
• Leaking fuel injectors	• Damaged connectors
• Adverse driveability symptoms, such as rough idle, hard to start, misses, surges, hesitates, backfires	• Damaged insulation
• Insufficient fuel in fuel tank	• Damaged components in the fuel system
	• Fuse integrity
	• Tripped inertia fuel shutoff switch

2. Exercise the wiring and connectors for the solenoids and other electrical components for obvious problems due to looseness, corrosion, or other damage.

3. If a component is suspected as the obvious cause of a malfunction, correct the cause before proceeding to the next step.

4. If all system inspection checks are OK, proceed to the Pinpoint Tests.

WARNING

— INSTRUCTIONS
FUEL IN THE FUEL SYSTEM REMAINS UNDER HIGH PRESSURE EVEN WHEN THE ENGINE IS NOT RUNNING. TO AVOID INJURY OR FIRE, RELEASE THE FUEL PRESSURE FROM THE FUEL SYSTEM BEFORE DISCONNECTING ANY FUEL LINE. TO RELEASE THE PRESSURE FROM THE SYSTEM PERFORM THE FOLLOWING:

a. Start the engine.

b. To stop the fuel pump, remove the fuel pump relay.

Engine	Location
1.3L	LH front engine compartment behind LH headlamp.
1.6L	Center of instrument panel below the PCM.
1.8L	Center of instrument panel in front of selector lever.
2.0L and 2.5L	Main fuse panel in the engine compartment.

c. After the engine stalls, turn off the ignition.

d. Install the fuel pump relay.

e. Use a rag as protection from the fuel spray when disconnecting the hoses. Plug the hoses after disconnection.

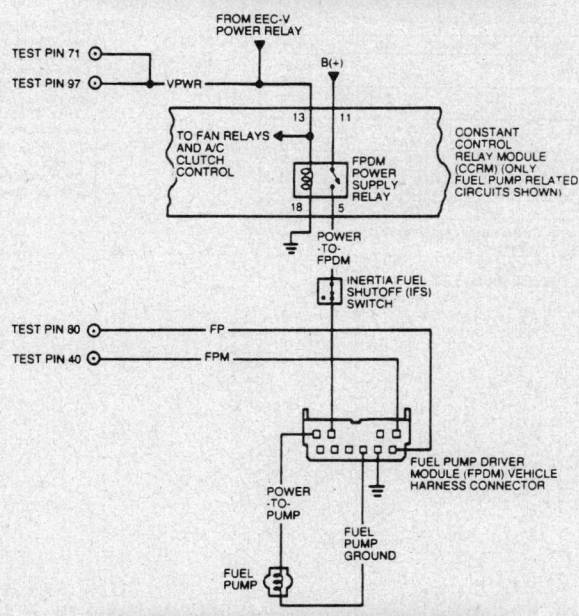

Fig. 21   Fuel system wiring circuit. 1996 Continental, Mark VIII & Mustang

FM1029300078010X

Fig. 22   Electric fuel pump diagnosis chart (Part 1 of 20). 1993 Capri, Festiva, Probe & Escort & Tracer w/1.8L/4-112 engine

Pinpoint Test F — Fuel Pressure Test

TEST STEP	RESULT	▶	ACTION TO TAKE
F1	PERFORM FUEL PRESSURE TEST	Yes	▶	GO to FD1.
WARNING: BEFORE STARTING THESE TESTS, RELEASE THE FUEL PRESSURE FROM THE FUEL SYSTEM TO REDUCE THE RISK OF INJURY OR FIRE, AS OUTLINED IN "WARNING — INSTRUCTIONS".	No, (If zero)	▶	GO to FA1.
	(If low)	▶	GO to FB1.
	(If high)	▶	GO to FC1.

* After releasing the fuel pressure as outlined in this section, install Rotunda Fuel Pressure Tester 014-00748 or equivalent with EFI Test Adapter D87C-9974-A in the fuel line between the fuel filter and the fuel rail (between fuel rails on 2.5L), with its main valve open and its drain valve closed.
* Jump the fuel pump test terminal to ground.
* Key ON.
* Is the fuel pressure within specification (refer to specifications in this section)?

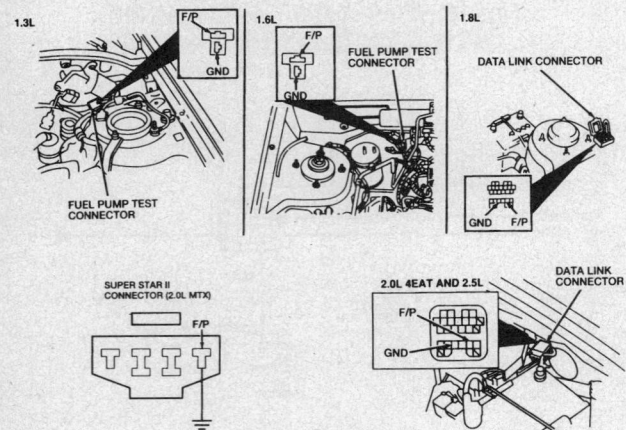

FM1029300078020X

Fig. 22 Electric fuel pump diagnosis chart (Part 2 of 20). 1993 Capri, Festiva, Probe & Escort & Tracer w/1.8L/4-112 engine

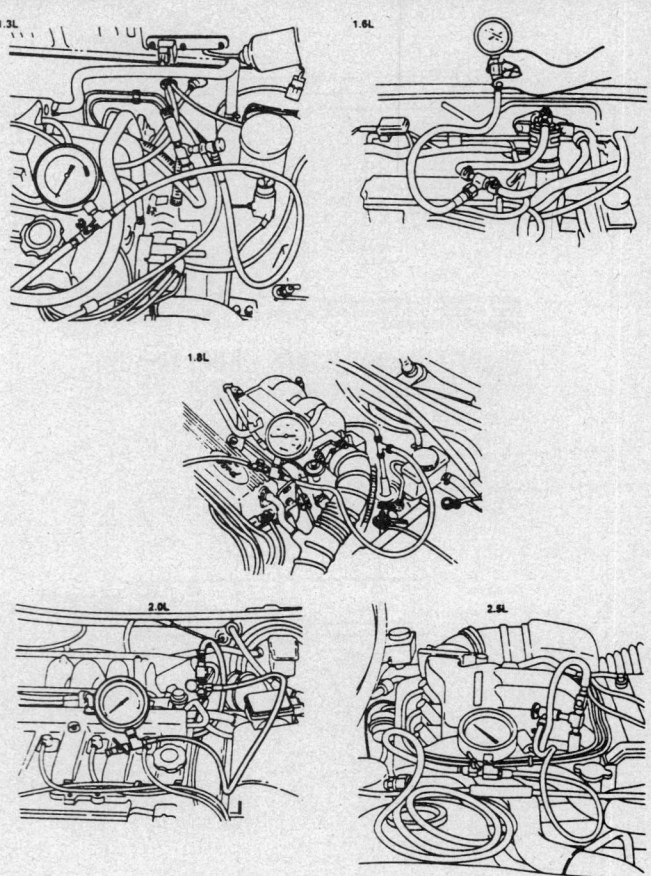

FM1029300078030X

Fig. 22 Electric fuel pump diagnosis chart (Part 3 of 20). 1993 Capri, Festiva, Probe & Escort & Tracer w/1.8L/4-112 engine

Pinpoint Test FA — No Fuel Pressure Test

TEST STEP	RESULT	▶	ACTION TO TAKE
FA1	CHECK VOLTAGE TO FUEL PUMP	Yes	▶	GO to FA11.
	No	▶	GO to FA2.

* Key OFF.
* Jump the fuel pump test terminal to ground. Refer to illustration in Test Step F1.
* Disconnect the fuel pump connector at the fuel pump assembly.
* Key ON.
* Measure the voltage on the following wire at the fuel pump connector.

Engine	Wire Color
1.3L	GN/Y
1.6L	W/BK
1.8L	BK/PK
2.0L	BK/W
2.5L	BK/W

* Is the voltage between 10-14 volts?

FA2	CHECK FOR SHORT(S)	Yes	▶	SERVICE the wire(s) in question for short.
	No	▶	GO to FA3.

* Key OFF.
* Remove the fuel pump relay.
* Disconnect the PCM on 2.0L and 2.5L.
* Disconnect the fuel pump connector at the fuel pump assembly.
* Measure the resistance between the following wire and ground at the fuel pump relay connector.

Engine	Wire Color
1.3L	GN/Y
1.6L	GN/R
1.8L	BK/PK
2.0L	LG W/Y
2.5L	LG W/Y

* Are the resistances less than 10,000 ohms?

NOTE: Check inertia fuel shutoff switch for "tripped" condition. Reset if tripped.

FM1029300078040X

Fig. 22 Electric fuel pump diagnosis chart (Part 4 of 20). 1993 Capri, Festiva, Probe & Escort & Tracer w/1.8L/4-112 engine

TEST STEP	RESULT	▶	ACTION TO TAKE
FA3	CHECK POWER SUPPLY TO FUEL PUMP RELAY	Yes	▶	GO to FA4.
	No (1.3L, 1.6L, 1.8L)	▶	SERVICE the wire in question.
	No (2.0L 4EAT)	▶	CHECK 15A ENGINE fuse. If blown, REPLACE fuse. If fuse blows again after replacement, SERVICE short. If fuse is OK, SERVICE "BK/W" wire for open.
	No (2.0L MTX, 2.5L)	▶	GO to Pinpoint Test VPWR. If VPWR is OK, SERVICE wire(s) for open(s).

* Key OFF.
* Remove the fuel pump relay.
* Key ON.
* Measure the voltage on the following wires at the fuel pump relay connector.

Engine	Wire Color	Key	Voltage
1.3L	Y/BK	ON	10-14 volts
	BK/R	START	10-14 volts
1.6L	BK/W	ON	10-14 volts
	BK/R	START	10-14 volts
1.8L	W/R	ON	10-14 volts
	P	START	10-14 volts
2.0L MTX	W/R	ON	10-14 volts
	W/GN	ON	10-14 volts
2.0L 4EAT	BK/W	ON	10-14 volts
2.5L	R/BK	ON	10-14 volts

* Is the voltage approximately battery voltage?

2.0L And 2.5L Shown

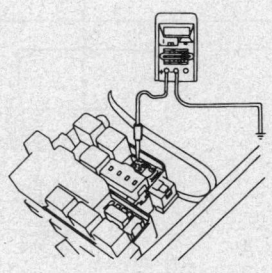

FM1029300078050X

Fig. 22 Electric fuel pump diagnosis chart (Part 5 of 20). 1993 Capri, Festiva, Probe, Escort & Tracer w/1.8L/4-112 engine

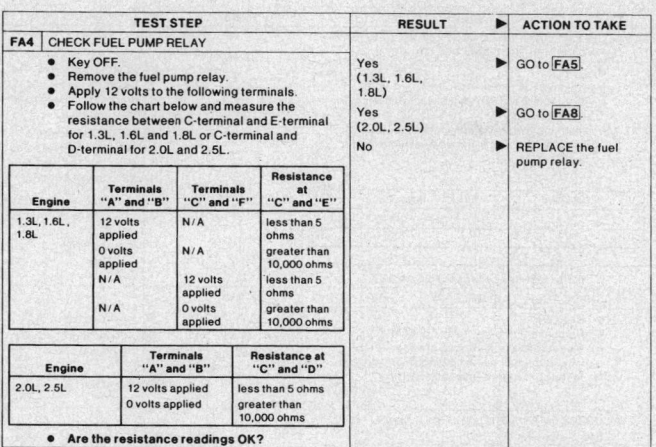

TEST STEP				RESULT	▶	ACTION TO TAKE
FA4 CHECK FUEL PUMP RELAY						
• Key OFF. • Remove the fuel pump relay. • Apply 12 volts to the following terminals. • Follow the chart below and measure the resistance between C-terminal and E-terminal for 1.3L, 1.6L and 1.8L or C-terminal and D-terminal for 2.0L and 2.5L.				Yes (1.3L, 1.6L, 1.8L)	▶	GO to FA5.
				Yes (2.0L, 2.5L)	▶	GO to FA8.
				No	▶	REPLACE the fuel pump relay.

Engine	Terminals "A" and "B"	Terminals "C" and "F"	Resistance at "C" and "E"
1.3L, 1.6L, 1.8L	12 volts applied	N/A	less than 5 ohms
	0 volts applied	N/A	greater than 10,000 ohms
	N/A	12 volts applied	less than 5 ohms
	N/A	0 volts applied	greater than 10,000 ohms

Engine	Terminals "A" and "B"	Resistance at "C" and "D"
2.0L, 2.5L	12 volts applied	less than 5 ohms
	0 volts applied	greater than 10,000 ohms

• Are the resistance readings OK?

1.3L, 1.6L and 1.8L

FUEL PUMP RELAY TERMINALS*

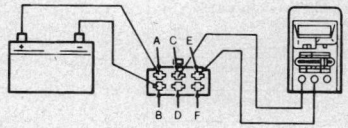

*NOTE: This is not the harness connector.

FM1029300078060X

Fig. 22   Electric fuel pump diagnosis chart (Part 6 of 20). 1993 Capri, Festiva, Probe & Escort & Tracer w/1.8L/4-112 engine

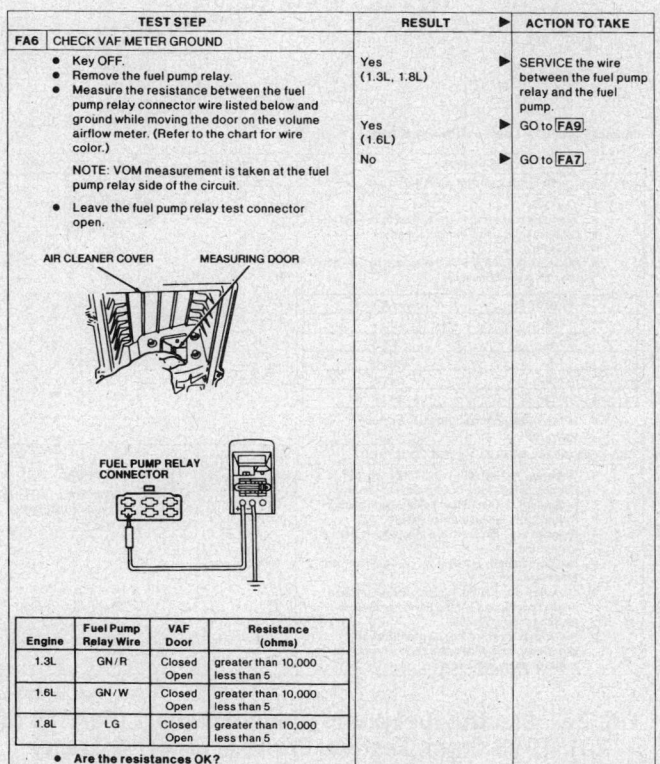

TEST STEP				RESULT	▶	ACTION TO TAKE
FA6 CHECK VAF METER GROUND						
• Key OFF. • Remove the fuel pump relay. • Measure the resistance between the fuel pump relay connector wire listed below and ground while moving the door on the volume airflow meter. (Refer to the chart for wire color.) NOTE: VOM measurement is taken at the fuel pump relay side of the circuit. • Leave the fuel pump relay test connector open.				Yes (1.3L, 1.8L)	▶	SERVICE the wire between the fuel pump relay and the fuel pump.
				Yes (1.6L)	▶	GO to FA9.
				No	▶	GO to FA7.

AIR CLEANER COVER   MEASURING DOOR

FUEL PUMP RELAY CONNECTOR

Engine	Fuel Pump Relay Wire	VAF Door	Resistance (ohms)
1.3L	GN/R	Closed Open	greater than 10,000 less than 5
1.6L	GN/W	Closed Open	greater than 10,000 less than 5
1.8L	LG	Closed Open	greater than 10,000 less than 5

• Are the resistances OK?

FM1029300078080X

Fig. 22   Electric fuel pump diagnosis chart (Part 8 of 20). 1993 Capri, Festiva, Probe & Escort & Tracer w/1.8L/4-112 engine

2.0L and 2.5L

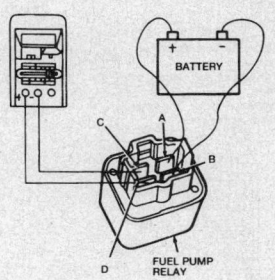

TEST STEP	RESULT	▶	ACTION TO TAKE
FA5 CHECK FUEL PUMP RELAY GROUND			
• Key OFF. • Remove the fuel pump relay from the harness. • Measure the resistance between the fuel pump relay connector "BK" wire and ground. • Is the resistance less than 5 ohms?	Yes	▶	GO to FA6.
	No	▶	SERVICE the "BK" wire for opens.

FM1029300078070X

Fig. 22   Electric fuel pump diagnosis chart (Part 7 of 20). 1993 Capri, Festiva, Probe & Escort & Tracer w/1.8L/4-112 engine

TEST STEP				RESULT	▶	ACTION TO TAKE
FA7 CHECK VAF FUEL PUMP SWITCH						
• Key OFF. • Disconnect the VAF meter wire harness connector. • Measure the resistance between the following terminals on the volume airflow meter. (Match the wire colors shown with the corresponding VAF terminals.)				Yes	▶	SERVICE the VAF "BK" wire, or the wire from the fuel pump relay to the VAF.
				No	▶	REPLACE the VAF meter.

Engine	VAF Terminals	Door	Resistance (ohms)
1.3L	GN R-BK	Closed Open	greater than 10,000 less than 5
1.6L	GN W-BK	Closed Open	greater than 10,000 less than 5
1.8L	LG-BR	Closed Open	greater than 10,000 less than 5

• Are resistances OK?

TEST STEP				RESULT	▶	ACTION TO TAKE
FA8 CHECK FUEL PUMP RELAY TO PCM CONTINUITY (2.0L and 2.5L ONLY)						
• Key OFF. • Remove the fuel pump relay. • Disconnect the PCM. • Install the Rotunda Breakout Box 007-00033 or equivalent. • Measure the resistance of the following wires between the fuel pump relay and the PCM.				Yes	▶	GO to FA9.
				No	▶	SERVICE wire(s) in question for open.

Engine	PCM Pin	BOB Pin	PCM Wire Color	Fuel Pump Relay Wire Color
2.0L MTX	22 8	22 8	LG W Y	LG W Y
2.0L 4EAT	3L 8	8	LG	LG
2.5L	3T	52B	LG	LG

• Is the resistance less than 5 ohms?

FM1029300078090X

Fig. 22   Electric fuel pump diagnosis chart (Part 9 of 20). 1993 Capri, Festiva, Probe & Escort & Tracer w/1.8L/4-112 engine

TEST STEP	RESULT	▶	ACTION TO TAKE
FA9 CHECK INERTIA FUEL SHUTOFF SWITCH (1.6L, 2.0L AND 2.5L ONLY) • Key OFF. • Disconnect and remove the inertia fuel shutoff switch from the vehicle. • Sharply shake the inertia fuel shutoff switch to verify that the switch trips. • Measure the resistance between the terminals shown on the inertia fuel shutoff switch.	Yes No	▶ ▶	GO to **FA10**. REPLACE the inertia fuel shutoff switch.

Switch Position	Resistance
Open (Tripped)	Greater than 10,000 ohms
Closed (Set)	Less than 5 ohms

• Are the resistances OK and does the switch trip when shaken sharply?

FM1029300078100X

Fig. 22 Electric fuel pump diagnosis chart (Part 10 of 20). 1993 Capri, Festiva, Probe & Escort & Tracer w/1.8L/4-112 engine

TEST STEP	RESULT	▶	ACTION TO TAKE
FA10 CHECK FOR OPEN TO INERTIA FUEL SHUTOFF SWITCH (1.6L, 2.0L AND 2.5L ONLY) • Key OFF. • Remove the fuel pump relay. • Disconnect the inertia fuel shutoff switch connector. • Measure the resistance of the following wire between the fuel pump relay and the inertia fuel shutoff switch.	Yes No	▶ ▶	SERVICE the wire between the inertia fuel shutoff switch and the fuel pump. SERVICE the wire between the fuel pump relay and the inertia fuel shutoff switch.

Engine	Wire Color
1.6L	GN/R
2.0L	W/Y
2.5L	W/Y

• Is the resistance less than 5 ohms?

TEST STEP	RESULT	▶	ACTION TO TAKE
FA11 CHECK FUEL PUMP GROUND • Key OFF. • Disconnect the fuel pump connector. • Measure the resistance between the "BK" wire at the fuel pump connector and ground. • Is the resistance less than 5 ohms?	Yes No (1.6L, 2.0L, 2.5L) No (1.3L, 1.8L)	▶ ▶ ▶	GO to **FA14**. SERVICE ground wire of the fuel pump. GO to **FA12**.
FA12 CHECK INERTIA FUEL SHUTOFF SWITCH (1.3L AND 1.8L) • Key OFF. • Disconnect and remove the inertia fuel shutoff switch from the vehicle. • Shake the inertia fuel shutoff switch sharply to verify that the switch trips. • Measure the resistance between the indicated terminals of the inertia fuel shutoff switch under the following conditions:	Yes No	▶ ▶	GO to **FA13**. REPLACE the inertia fuel shutoff switch.

Engine	Resistance Check Points
1.3L	Between the switch terminals that connect to the GN/W and BK wires
1.8L	Between the switch terminals that connect to the BL and BK wires

Switch Position	Resistance
Open (tripped)	Greater than 10,000 ohms
Closed (set)	Less than 5 ohms

• Are the resistances OK and does the inertia fuel shutoff switch trip when shaken sharply?

FM1029300078110X

Fig. 22 Electric fuel pump diagnosis chart (Part 11 of 20). 1993 Capri, Festiva, Probe & Escort & Tracer w/1.8L/4-112 engine

TEST STEP	RESULT	▶	ACTION TO TAKE
FA13 CHECK INERTIA FUEL SHUTOFF SWITCH GROUND • Key OFF. • Disconnect the inertia fuel shutoff switch connector. • Measure the resistance between the inertia fuel shutoff switch wire (at the harness side connector of the fuel pump) and ground.	Yes No	▶ ▶	SERVICE the wire between the inertia fuel shutoff switch and the fuel pump. SERVICE the "BK" wire.

Engine	Wire	Resistance (ohms)
1.3L	BK	less than 5
1.8L	BK	less than 5

• Is the resistance OK?

TEST STEP	RESULT	▶	ACTION TO TAKE
FA14 CHECK FUEL PUMP MOTOR • Relieve the fuel pressure; follow the procedures as outlined in this section. • Connect Rotunda Fuel Pressure Tester 014-00748 or equivalent to the fuel filter with main valve closed and drain valve closed as shown in test step F.1. • Jump the fuel pump test terminal to ground as shown in test step F.1. • Key ON. • Is the maximum fuel pressure within specification (refer to specifications in this section)?	Yes No	▶ ▶	GO to **FB2**. REPLACE the fuel pump.

FM1029300078120X

Fig. 22 Electric fuel pump diagnosis chart (Part 12 of 20). 1993 Capri, Festiva, Probe & Escort & Tracer w/1.8L/4-112 engine

Pinpoint Test FB — Low Fuel Pressure Test

TEST STEP	RESULT	▶	ACTION TO TAKE
FB1 CHECK POWER SUPPLY TO FUEL PUMP • Key OFF. • Jump the fuel pump test terminal to ground. • Disconnect the fuel pump connector. • Key ON. • Measure the voltage on the following wire at the fuel pump connector.	Yes No	▶ ▶	GO to **FB2**. GO to **FA1**.

Engine	Wire Color
1.3L	GN/Y
1.6L	W/BK
1.8L	BK/PK
2.0L	BK/W
2.5L	BK/W

• Is the voltage approximately battery voltage?

TEST STEP	RESULT	▶	ACTION TO TAKE
FB2 CHECK IN-LINE FUEL FILTER CONDITION • Observe "WARNING — INSTRUCTIONS" at the beginning of the Diagnosis and Testing procedures to avoid fuel spillage and injury. • Release the fuel system pressure. • Remove the high pressure in-line fuel filter for inspection. • Inspect the filter element for contamination or blockage. • Compare the customer's service record and driving conditions versus the recommended maintenance schedule. • Is the fuel filter free of contamination, blockage, and within the recommended maintenance schedule?	Yes No	▶ ▶	GO to **FB3**. SERVICE the fuel filter as required. RERUN Test **F1**.

FM1029300078130X

Fig. 22 Electric fuel pump diagnosis chart (Part 13 of 20). 1993 Capri, Festiva, Probe & Escort & Tracer w/1.8L/4-112 engine

Electric Fuel Pumps—FORD

TEST STEP		RESULT	▶	ACTION TO TAKE
FB3	CHECK FUEL PRESSURE REGULATOR DIAPHRAGM CONDITION			
	• Observe "WARNING — INSTRUCTIONS" at the beginning of the Diagnosis and Testing procedures to avoid fuel spillage and injury. • Install Rotunda Fuel Pressure Tester 014-00748 or equivalent with EFI Test Adapter D87C-9974-A in the fuel line between the fuel filter and fuel rail (between fuel rails on 2.5L), with its main valve open and its drain valve closed. • Start the engine and run for 10 seconds. • Stop the engine and wait 10 seconds. • Start the engine again and run for 10 seconds. • Stop the engine and remove the vacuum hose from the pressure regulator. • Examine the vacuum port in the pressure regulator for evidence of the fuel leakage through the diaphragm. • **Is the vacuum port OK?**	Yes No	▶ ▶	GO to FB4. REPLACE the fuel pressure regulator and RERUN Test F1.
FB4	CHECK FUEL PRESSURE REGULATOR PRESSURE LEAKDOWN			
	• Reconnect the vacuum hose. • With the Rotunda Fuel Pressure Tester 014-00748 still installed from previous test, run the engine for a minimum of 30 seconds. • Stop the engine and observe the fuel pressure after 5 minutes. • **Is the fuel pressure greater than 147 kPa (21 psi) after 5 minutes?**	Yes No	▶ ▶	GO to FB5. REPEAT this test step. If the fuel pressure still drops more than specified, REPLACE the fuel pressure regulator. RERUN Test F1.

FM1029300078140X

Fig. 22 Electric fuel pump diagnosis chart (Part 14 of 20). 1993 Capri, Festiva, Probe & Escort & Tracer w/1.8L/4-112 engine

TEST STEP		RESULT	▶	ACTION TO TAKE
FB5	CHECK FUEL PRESSURE REGULATOR VALVE SEAT LEAKAGE			
	• Connect Rotunda Vacuum Tester 021-00037 or equivalent to the fuel return tube and apply a 508 mm-Hg (20 in-Hg) vacuum. • Observe the vacuum gauge for at least 10 seconds. • **Does the vacuum drop lower than 254 mm-Hg (10 in-Hg) in 10 seconds?**	Yes No	▶ ▶	REPLACE the fuel pressure regulator. RERUN Test F1. GO to FB6.

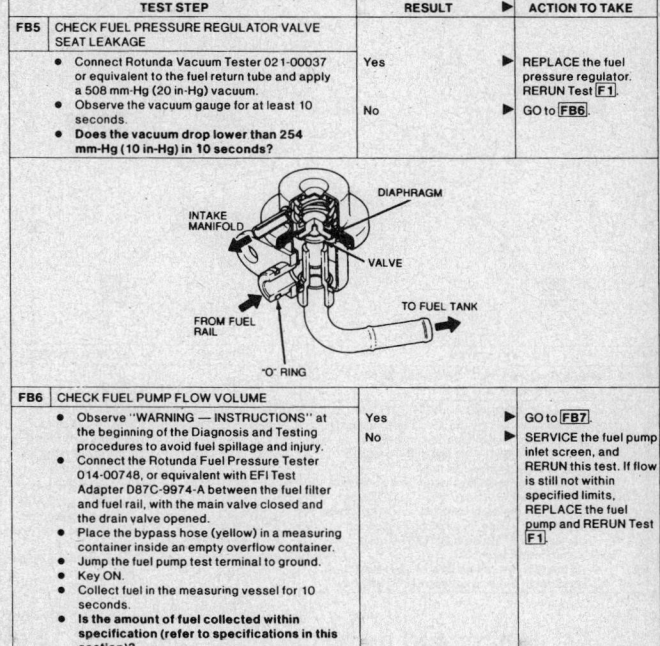

FB6	CHECK FUEL PUMP FLOW VOLUME			
	• Observe "WARNING — INSTRUCTIONS" at the beginning of the Diagnosis and Testing procedures to avoid fuel spillage and injury. • Connect the Rotunda Fuel Pressure Tester 014-00748, or equivalent with EFI Test Adapter D87C-9974-A between the fuel filter and fuel rail, with the main valve closed and the drain valve opened. • Place the bypass hose (yellow) in a measuring container inside an empty overflow container. • Jump the fuel pump test terminal to ground. • Key ON. • Collect fuel in the measuring vessel for 10 seconds. • **Is the amount of fuel collected within specification (refer to specifications in this section)?**	Yes No	▶ ▶	GO to FB7. SERVICE the fuel pump inlet screen, and RERUN this test. If flow is still not within specified limits, REPLACE the fuel pump and RERUN Test F1.

FM1029300078150X

Fig. 22 Electric fuel pump diagnosis chart (Part 15 of 20). 1993 Capri, Festiva, Probe & Escort & Tracer w/1.8L/4-112 engine

2.0L Shown

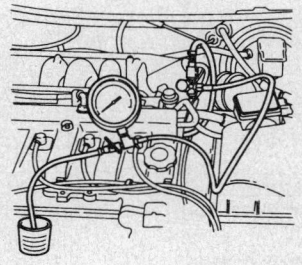

TEST STEP		RESULT	▶	ACTION TO TAKE
FB7	CHECK FUEL PUMP VALVE LEAKDOWN			
	• Observe "WARNING — INSTRUCTIONS" at the beginning of the Diagnosis and Testing procedures to avoid fuel spillage and injury. • Connect the Rotunda Fuel Pressure Tester 014-00748 or equivalent with EFI Test Adapter D87C-9974-A between the fuel filter and fuel rail with both the main and drain valves closed. • Jump the fuel pump test terminal to ground. • Key ON. • Run the fuel pump for 30 seconds minimum. • Remove the jumper and note fuel pressure on the gauge for 3 minutes. • **Does the output fuel pressure decrease more than 13.78 kPa (2 psi) in 3 minutes?**	Yes No	▶ ▶	GO to FD1. REPLACE the fuel pump. RERUN Test F1.

FM1029300078160X

Fig. 22 Electric fuel pump diagnosis chart (Part 16 of 20). 1993 Capri, Festiva, Probe & Escort & Tracer w/1.8L/4-112 engine

Pinpoint Test FC — High Fuel Pressure Test

TEST STEP		RESULT	▶	ACTION TO TAKE
FC1	CHECK FUEL PRESSURE REGULATOR FOR CAUSE OF HIGH PRESSURE			
	• Observe "WARNING — INSTRUCTIONS" at the beginning of the Diagnosis and Testing procedures to avoid fuel spillage and injury. • Check leaks in the engine vacuum system due to loose or misthreaded fittings, cracks, or blockage that could cause insufficient vacuum to properly control the fuel pressure regulator. • Check the fuel pressure regulator housing for damage or dents that could cause a higher spring load on the fuel pressure regulator. • Check the integrity of the fuel pressure regulator diaphragm in the procedure described in Test Step FB3. • **Is the fuel system free of defects that could cause the fuel pressure regulator to produce excessive fuel system pressure? (Refer to fuel pressure specification in the specifications chart.)**	Yes No	▶ ▶	GO to FC2. REPAIR or REPLACE damaged components as required. RERUN Test Step F1. If the pressure is still high, GO to FC2.

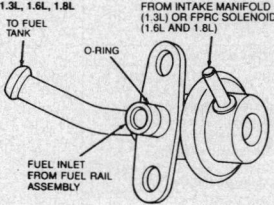

FM1029300078170X

Fig. 22 Electric fuel pump diagnosis chart (Part 17 of 20). 1993 Capri, Festiva, Probe & Escort & Tracer w/1.8L/4-112 engine

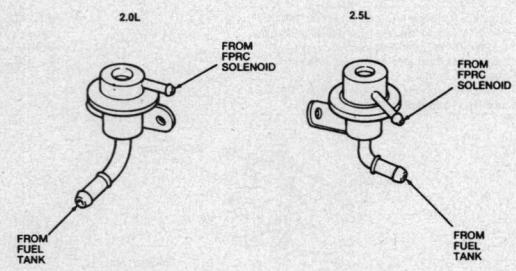

2.0L 2.5L

FROM
FPRC
SOLENOID

FROM
FPRC
SOLENOID

FROM
FUEL
TANK

FROM
FUEL
TANK

TEST STEP	RESULT	▶	ACTION TO TAKE
FC2 CHECK FUEL RETURN FOR CAUSE OF HIGH FUEL PRESSURE			
• Observe "WARNING — INSTRUCTIONS" at the beginning of the Diagnosis and Testing procedures to avoid fuel spillage and injury. • Remove the fuel return line at the pressure regulator and at the fuel tank. • Provide a suitable fuel receptacle at the tank end of the return line to avoid fuel spillage. • Check the fuel return line for restriction due to blockage, kinking, or pinching by blowing through it with 34.5-68.9 kPa (5-10 psi) regulated shop air. • Is the fuel return line free of any restriction that could cause excessive fuel pressure?	Yes No	▶ ▶	REPLACE the fuel pressure regulator. RERUN Test Step F1. If the pressure is still high, GO to FD1. REPAIR the defects. CLEAN or REPLACE the faulty components as required to remove the cause of high pressure. RERUN Test F1.

FM1029300078180X

Fig. 22 Electric fuel pump diagnosis chart (Part 18 of 20). 1993 Capri, Festiva, Probe & Escort & Tracer w/1.8L/4-112 engine

Pinpoint Test FD — Fuel Injector Test

TEST STEP	RESULT	▶	ACTION TO TAKE
FD1 CHECK FUEL INJECTION FUNCTION			
• With the engine warmed and idling (or cranking if it does not start) and using a mechanic's stethoscope or equivalent, listen for regularly operating sounds at each fuel injector. • Is operating sound present?	Yes No	▶ ▶	GO to FD4. GO to FD2.
FD2 CHECK FUEL INJECTOR ELECTRICAL SIGNAL			
CAUTION: Do not connect a test lamp to the injector harness. Damage may result to the PCM. • Check the electrical continuity of the injector between each injector and the PCM as follows: — Disconnect the fuel injector lead and insert the continuity checker from Rotunda Fuel Injector Tester / Cleaner 113-0001A or equivalent into the injector lead plug. — Start or crank engine. — Observe whether the continuity checker blinks (showing a completed circuit for the injector being tested). • Repeat the check for each injector. • Do all injector circuit leads show continuity?	Yes No	▶ ▶	GO to FD3. CHECK for 12 volts at each injector wire with key ON. SERVICE wire as required. REFER to Pinpoint Test SCG.
FD3 CHECK FUEL INJECTOR RESISTANCE			
• Observe "WARNING — INSTRUCTIONS" at the beginning of the Diagnosis and Testing procedures to avoid fuel spillage and injury. • Remove the electrical connectors from the injectors. If necessary, remove the fuel injectors to gain access to the injector terminals. • Measure the electrical resistance of each injector. • Is the resistance of all injectors approximately 12-16 ohms (20°C [68°F])?	Yes No	▶ ▶	GO to FD4. REPLACE the faulty injectors. RERUN Test Step FD1 and if OK, GO to Test Step FD4.

FM1029300078190X

Fig. 22 Electric fuel pump diagnosis chart (Part 19 of 20). 1993 Capri, Festiva, Probe & Escort & Tracer w/1.8L/4-112 engine

TEST STEP	RESULT	▶	ACTION TO TAKE
FD4 CHECK FUEL INJECTORS (CLEANING AND LEAKAGE)	Yes No	▶ ▶	RETURN to **System Inspection**. REPLACE faulty fuel injectors as required.
NOTE: This procedure does not require the matching of injector color with flow gauge band color on the Fuel Injector Tester / Cleaner. • Observe "WARNING — INSTRUCTIONS" at the beginning of the Diagnosis and Testing procedures to avoid fuel spillage and injury. • Use the Rotunda Fuel Injector Tester / Cleaner 113-0001A, or equivalent and accompanying instructions to clean the fuel injectors. • With the fuel injector tester / cleaner still installed on the fuel system, note any significant pressure loss due to injector leakage when the tester pump is turned to OFF. • Check each fuel injector individually for leakage as required, using the injector bench tester and the fuel injector bench testing procedure associated with the fuel injector tester / cleaner. Verify that each injector leakage rate is within specification (1 drop / 2 minutes maximum). NOTE: The 2.5L fuel injector has side inject fuel injectors. Therefore they cannot be bench tested. See procedure below. • For 2.5L disconnect the fuel rail from the intake manifold. Leave fuel hoses connected. Jumper the F / P terminal of Data Link Connector to ground. Key ON. Verify that each injector leakage rate is within specification (1 drop / 2 minutes maximum). • Is the leakage rate for individual injectors within specifications?			

INJECTOR BENCH TEST FIXTURE

INJECTOR SHOWN IN BENCH TEST FIXTURE

Item	Description
1	Flow Gauge
2	Reservoir
3	Battery
4	Cleaner / Tester
5	Test Harness
6	Cleaner Supply Hose
7	Fuel Supply Line
8	Injectors
9	Fuel Rail
10	Fuel Pressure Regulator
11	Plug Line Fuel Return
12	"U" Tube
13	Filter
14	Fuel Return
15	Fuel Supply

FM1029300078200X

Fig. 22 Electric fuel pump diagnosis chart (Part 20 of 20). 1993 Capri, Festiva, Probe & Escort & Tracer w/1.8L/4-112 engine

1. Visually inspect the components of the fuel delivery system.

VISUAL INSPECTION CHART

Mechanical	Electrical
• Loose, leaking, or damaged fuel or vacuum lines • Leaking fuel injectors • Adverse driveability symptoms, such as rough idle, hard to start, misses, surges, hesitates, backfires • Insufficient fuel in fuel tank	• Discharged battery • Damaged connectors • Damaged insulation • Damaged components in the fuel system • Fuse integrity • Tripped inertia fuel shutoff switch

2. Exercise the wiring and connectors for the solenoids and other electrical components for obvious problems due to looseness, corrosion, or other damage.

3. If a component is suspected as the obvious cause of a malfunction, correct the cause before proceeding to the next step.

4. If all system inspection checks are OK, proceed to the Pinpoint Tests.

WARNING

— INSTRUCTIONS
FUEL IN THE FUEL SYSTEM REMAINS UNDER HIGH PRESSURE EVEN WHEN THE ENGINE IS NOT RUNNING. TO AVOID INJURY OR FIRE, RELEASE THE FUEL PRESSURE FROM THE FUEL SYSTEM BEFORE DISCONNECTING ANY FUEL LINE. TO RELEASE THE PRESSURE FROM THE SYSTEM PERFORM THE FOLLOWING:

a. Start the engine.

b. To stop the fuel pump, disconnect the fuel pump relay.

Engine	Location
1.3L	Under LH side of instrument panel.
1.6L	Center of instrument panel next to the PCM.
1.8L	Center of instrument panel in front of selector lever.
2.0L and 2.5L	Main fuse panel in the engine compartment.

c. After the engine stalls, turn off the ignition.

d. Install the fuel pump relay.

e. Use a rag as protection from the fuel spray and disconnect the fuel hoses. Plug the hoses after disconnection.

f. Before testing or starting the vehicle, prime the system by grounding the fuel pump test pin and turning the key ON for 10 seconds.

g. Check for fuel leaks.

h. Turn the key OFF and remove ground.

FM1029400080010X

Fig. 23 Electric fuel pump diagnosis chart (Part 1 of 21). 1994 Aspire, Capri, Probe & Escort & Tracer w/1.8L/4-112 engine

Fuel Pressure Test Setup

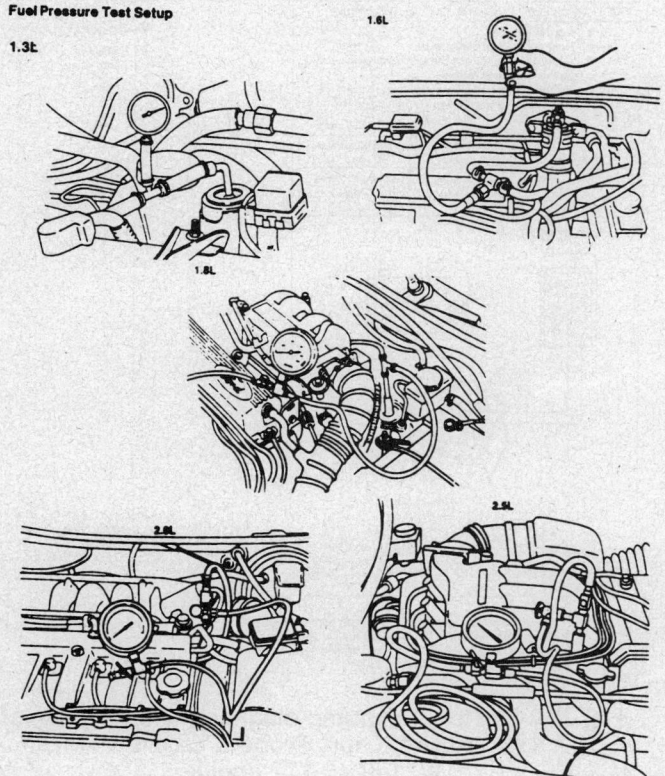

FM1029400080030X

Fig. 23 Electric fuel pump diagnosis chart (Part 3 of 21). 1994 Aspire, Capri, Probe & Escort & Tracer w/1.8L/4-112 engine

Pinpoint Tests F — Fuel Pressure Test

	TEST STEP	RESULT	▶	ACTION TO TAKE
F1	PERFORM FUEL PRESSURE TEST			
	WARNING: BEFORE STARTING THESE TESTS, RELEASE THE FUEL PRESSURE FROM THE FUEL SYSTEM TO REDUCE THE RISK OF INJURY OR FIRE, AS OUTLINED IN "WARNING — INSTRUCTIONS". • After releasing the fuel pressure as outlined in System Inspection, install Rotunda Fuel Pressure Tester 014-00748 or equivalent with EFI Test Adapter D87C-9974-A in the fuel line between the fuel filter and the fuel rail (between fuel rails on 2.5L), with its main valve open and its drain valve closed. Refer to illustration on following page. • Jump the fuel pump test terminal to ground. Refer to illustration below. • Key ON. • Is the fuel pressure within specification (refer to specifications in this section)?	Yes No, (If zero) (If low) (If high)	▶ ▶ ▶ ▶	GO to FD1 GO to FA1 GO to FB1 GO to FC1

Fuel Pump Test Connector

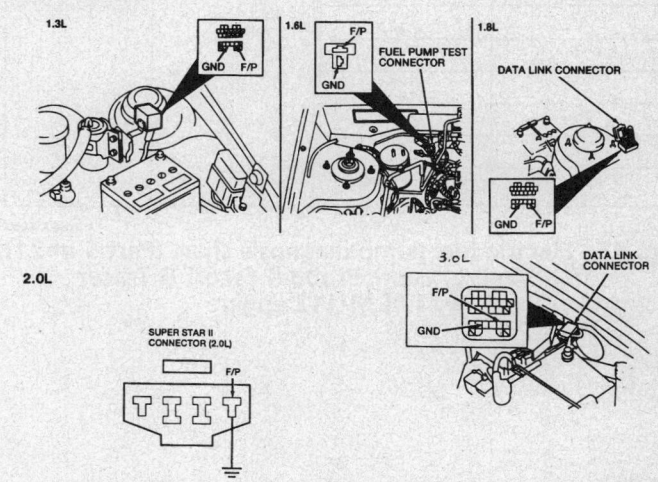

FM1029400080020X

Fig. 23 Electric fuel pump diagnosis chart (Part 2 of 21). 1994 Aspire, Capri, Probe & Escort & Tracer w/1.8L/4-112 engine

Pinpoint Tests FA — No Fuel Pressure Test

	TEST STEP	RESULT	▶	ACTION TO TAKE
FA1	CHECK FUEL PUMP MOTOR			
	• Relieve the fuel pressure; follow the procedures as outlined in "WARNING—INSTRUCTIONS" in System Inspection at the beginning of the Diagnosis and Testing procedures. • Connect Rotunda Fuel Pressure Tester 014-00748 or equivalent to the fuel filter with main valve closed and drain valve closed. Refer to illustrations in Test Step F1. • Jump the fuel pump test terminal to ground. Refer to illustrations in Test Step F1 for terminal locations. • Key ON. • Is the maximum fuel pressure within specification (refer to specifications)?	Yes No	▶ ▶	GO to FA2 REPLACE the fuel pump.
FA2	CHECK VOLTAGE TO FUEL PUMP			
	• Key OFF. • Jump the fuel pump test terminal to ground. Refer to illustration in Test Step F1 for terminal locations. • Disconnect the fuel pump connector at the fuel pump assembly. • Key ON. • Measure the voltage on the following wires at the fuel pump connector.	Yes (1.3L, 1.8L) Yes (1.6L, 2.0L, 2.5L) No	▶ ▶ ▶	GO to FA14 GO to FA13 GO to FA3

Engine	Wire Color
1.3L	GN·Y
1.6L	W/BK
1.8L	BK/PK
2.0L	BK·W
2.5L	BK/W

• Is the voltage between 10-14 volts?

NOTE: Check inertia fuel shutoff switch for "tripped" condition. Reset if tripped.

FM1029400080040X

Fig. 23 Electric fuel pump diagnosis chart (Part 4 of 21). 1994 Aspire, Capri, Probe & Escort & Tracer w/1.8L/4-112 engine

TEST STEP		RESULT	▶	ACTION TO TAKE
FA3	CHECK FOR SHORT(S) TO GROUND	Yes	▶	GO to FA4.
• Key OFF. • Disconnect the fuel pump relay. • Disconnect the Powertrain Control Module (PCM) on 1.3L, 2.0L, and 2.5L. • Disconnect the fuel pump connector at the fuel pump assembly. • Measure the resistance between the following wires at the fuel pump relay connector and ground.		No	▶	SERVICE the wire(s) in question for short.

Engine	Wire Color
1.3L	GN/Y W/BK
1.6L	GN/R GN/W
1.8L	BK/PK LG
2.0L	LG W/Y
2.5L	LG W/Y

• Are the resistances greater than 10,000 ohms?

FM1029400080050X

Fig. 23   Electric fuel pump diagnosis chart (Part 5 of 21). 1994 Aspire, Capri, Probe & Escort & Tracer w/1.8L/4-112 engine

TEST STEP				RESULT	▶	ACTION TO TAKE
FA4	CHECK POWER SUPPLY TO FUEL PUMP RELAY			Yes (2.0L, 2.5L)	▶	GO to FA6.
• Key OFF. • Disconnect the fuel pump relay. • Key ON. • Measure the voltage on the following wires at the fuel pump relay connector.				Yes(1.3L, 1.6L, 1.8L)	▶	GO to FA5.
				No (1.6L, 1.8L)	▶	SERVICE the wire(s) in question.

Engine	Wire Color	Key	Voltage
1.3L	Y/BK Y/BK	ON ON	10-14 volts 10-14 volts
1.6L	BK/W BK/R	ON START	10-14 volts 10-14 volts
1.8L	W/R P	ON START	10-14 volts 10-14 volts
2.0L	W/R W/GN	ON ON	10-14 volts 10-14 volts
2.5L	R/BK R/BK	ON ON	10-14 volts 10-14 volts

No
(1.3L, 2.0L, 2.5L) ▶ GO to Pinpoint Test **VPWR** in EEC Pinpoint Tests   If VPWR is OK, SERVICE wire(s) for open(s).

2.0L and 2.5L Shown

• Is the voltage approximately battery voltage?

FM1029400080060X

Fig. 23   Electric fuel pump diagnosis chart (Part 6 of 21). 1994 Aspire, Capri, Probe & Escort & Tracer w/1.8L/4-112 engine

TEST STEP					RESULT	▶	ACTION TO TAKE
FA5	CHECK FUEL PUMP RELAY (1.3L, 1.6L, AND 1.8L ONLY)				Yes (1.6L, 1.8L)	▶	GO to FA7.
• Key OFF. • Remove the fuel pump relay. • Apply 12 volts across the following terminals on the fuel pump relay. • Follow the chart below and measure the resistance between the C-terminal and the A-terminal.					Yes (1.3L)	▶	GO to FA10.
					No	▶	REPLACE the fuel pump relay.

Engine	Terminals "E" and "F"	Terminals "C" and "B"	Resistance at "C" and "A"
1.3L, 1.6L, 1.8L	12 volts applied	N/A	Less than 5 ohms
	0 volts applied	N/A	Greater than 10,000 ohms
1.6L, 1.8L	N/A	12 volts applied	Less than 5 ohms
	N/A	0 volts applied	Greater than 10,000 ohms

Fuel Pump Relay Terminals 1.3L, 1.6L, and 1.8L

• Are the resistance readings OK?

NOTE: This is not the harness connector.

FM1029400080070X

Fig. 23   Electric fuel pump diagnosis chart (Part 7 of 21). 1994 Aspire, Capri, Probe & Escort & Tracer w/1.8L/4-112 engine

TEST STEP				RESULT	▶	ACTION TO TAKE
FA6	CHECK FUEL PUMP RELAY (2.0L, 2.5L ONLY)			Yes	▶	GO to FA10.
• Key OFF. • Remove the fuel pump relay. • Apply 12 volts across the following terminals on the fuel pump relay. • Follow the chart below and measure the resistance between the C-terminal and the D-terminal.				No	▶	REPLACE the fuel pump relay.

Engine	Terminals "A" and "B"	Resistance at "C" and "D"
2.0L, 2.5L	12 volts applied	Less than 5 ohms
	0 volts applied	Greater than 10,000 ohms

2.0L and 2.5L

• Are the resistance readings OK?

FA7	CHECK FUEL PUMP RELAY GROUND (1.6L, 1.8L ONLY)			Yes	▶	GO to FA8.
• Key OFF. • Remove the fuel pump relay from the harness. • Measure the resistance between the fuel pump relay connector "BK" wire and ground. • Is the resistance less than 5 ohms?				No	▶	SERVICE the "BK" wire for opens.

FM1029400080080X

Fig. 23   Electric fuel pump diagnosis chart (Part 8 of 21). 1994 Aspire, Capri, Probe & Escort & Tracer w/1.8L/4-112 engine

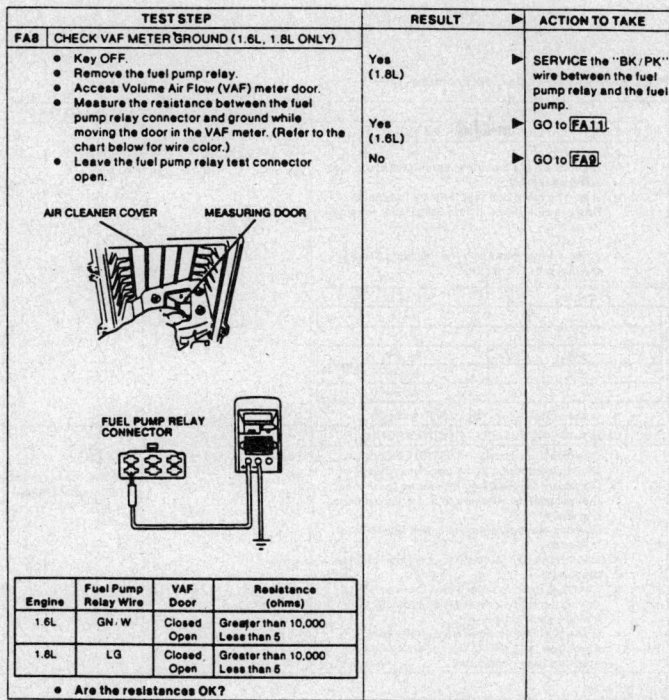

TEST STEP			RESULT	▶	ACTION TO TAKE
FA8	CHECK VAF METER GROUND (1.6L, 1.8L ONLY)				
• Key OFF. • Remove the fuel pump relay. • Access Volume Air Flow (VAF) meter door. • Measure the resistance between the fuel pump relay connector and ground while moving the door in the VAF meter. (Refer to the chart below for wire color.) • Leave the fuel pump relay test connector open.			Yes (1.8L)	▶	SERVICE the "BK/PK" wire between the fuel pump relay and the fuel pump.
			Yes (1.6L)	▶	GO to FA11.
			No	▶	GO to FA9.

Engine	Fuel Pump Relay Wire	VAF Door	Resistance (ohms)
1.6L	GN/W	Closed Open	Greater than 10,000 Less than 5
1.8L	LG	Closed Open	Greater than 10,000 Less than 5

• Are the resistances OK?

FM1029400080090X

Fig. 23 Electric fuel pump diagnosis chart (Part 9 of 21). 1994 Aspire, Capri, Probe & Escort & Tracer w/1.8L/4-112 engine

TEST STEP			RESULT	▶	ACTION TO TAKE
FA9	CHECK VAF FUEL PUMP SWITCH (1.6L, 1.8L ONLY)				
• Key OFF. • Disconnect the Volume Air Flow (VAF) meter wire harness connector. • Measure the resistance between the following terminals on the VAF meter while moving the VAF meter door. (Match the wire colors shown with the corresponding VAF terminals.)			Yes	▶	SERVICE the VAF "BK" wire, or the wire from the fuel pump relay to the VAF.
			No	▶	REPLACE the VAF meter.

Engine	VAF Terminals	Door	Resistance (ohms)
1.6L	GN/W, BK	Closed Open	Greater than 10,000 Less than 5
1.8L	LG, BK	Closed Open	Greater than 10,000 Less than 5

• Are the resistances OK?

TEST STEP			RESULT	▶	ACTION TO TAKE
FA10	CHECK FUEL PUMP RELAY TO PCM CONTINUITY (1.3L, 2.0L and 2.5L ONLY)				
• Key OFF. • Remove the fuel pump relay. • Disconnect the Powertrain Control Module (PCM). • Install the Rotunda Breakout Box 007-00033 or equivalent. • Measure the resistance of the following wires between the fuel pump relay and the PCM.			Yes (1.3L)	▶	SERVICE the "GN Y" wire between the fuel pump relay and the fuel pump.
			Yes (2.0L, 2.5L)	▶	GO to FA11.
			No	▶	SERVICE wire(s) in question for open.

Engine	PCM Pin	BOB Pin	PCM Wire Color	Fuel Pump Relay Wire Color
1.3L	1H	55	W BK	W BK
2.0L	22 8	22 8	LG W Y	LG W Y
2.5L	3T	52B	LG	LG

• Is the resistance less than 5 ohms?

FM1029400080100X

Fig. 23 Electric fuel pump diagnosis chart (Part 10 of 21). 1994 Aspire, Capri, Probe & Escort & Tracer w/1.8L/4-112 engine

TEST STEP		RESULT	▶	ACTION TO TAKE
FA11	CHECK INERTIA FUEL SHUTOFF SWITCH (1.6L, 2.0L AND 2.5L ONLY)			
• Key OFF. • Disconnect and remove the inertia fuel shutoff switch from the vehicle. • Measure the resistance between the terminals shown on the inertia fuel shutoff switch. • Sharply shake the inertia fuel shutoff switch to verify that the switch trips. • Measure the resistance between the terminals shown on the inertia fuel shutoff switch.		Yes	▶	GO to FA12.
		No	▶	REPLACE the inertia fuel shutoff switch.

Switch Position	Resistance
Open (Tripped)	Greater than 10,000 ohms
Closed (Set)	Less than 5 ohms

• Are the resistances OK and does the switch trip when shaken sharply?

FM1029400080110X

Fig. 23 Electric fuel pump diagnosis chart (Part 11 of 21). 1994 Aspire, Capri, Probe & Escort & Tracer w/1.8L/4-112 engine

TEST STEP		RESULT	▶	ACTION TO TAKE
FA12	CHECK FOR OPEN TO INERTIA FUEL SHUTOFF SWITCH (1.6L, 2.0L AND 2.5L ONLY)			
• Key OFF. • Remove the fuel pump relay. • Disconnect the inertia fuel shutoff switch connector. • Measure the resistance of the following wires between the fuel pump relay and the inertia fuel shutoff switch. Refer to electrical schematic in this section.		Yes	▶	SERVICE the wire between the inertia fuel shutoff switch and the fuel pump.
		No	▶	SERVICE the wire between the fuel pump relay and the inertia fuel shutoff switch.

Engine	Wire Color
1.6L	GN/R
2.0L	W/Y
2.5L	W/Y

• Is the resistance less than 5 ohms?

TEST STEP		RESULT	▶	ACTION TO TAKE
FA13	CHECK FUEL PUMP GROUND (1.6L, 2.0L, 2.5L ONLY)			
• Key OFF. • Disconnect the fuel pump connector. • Measure the resistance between the "BK" wire at the fuel pump connector and ground. • Is the resistance less than 5 ohms?		Yes	▶	GO to FB2.
		No (1.6L, 2.0L, 2.5L)	▶	SERVICE ground wire of the fuel pump.
FA14	CHECK WIRE TO INERTIA FUEL SHUTOFF SWITCH (1.3L, 1.8L ONLY)			
• Key OFF. • Disconnect the fuel pump connector. • Disconnect the inertia fuel shutoff switch connector. • Measure the resistance of the "GN" wire (1.3L) or the "BL" wire (1.8L) between the fuel pump connector and the inertia fuel shutoff switch connector. • Is the resistance less than 5 ohms?		Yes	▶	GO to FA15.
		No	▶	SERVICE wire to inertia fuel shutoff switch for open.

FM1029400080120X

Fig. 23 Electric fuel pump diagnosis chart (Part 12 of 21). 1994 Aspire, Probe & Escort & Tracer, and 1994 Capri w/1.8L/4-112 engine

TEST STEP		RESULT	▶	ACTION TO TAKE
FA15	CHECK INERTIA FUEL SHUTOFF SWITCH (1.3L AND 1.8L) • Key OFF. • Disconnect and remove the inertia fuel shutoff switch from the vehicle. • Shake the inertia fuel shutoff switch sharply to verify that the switch trips. • Measure the resistance between the indicated terminals of the inertia fuel shutoff switch under the following conditions:	Yes No	▶ ▶	GO to **FA16**. REPLACE the inertia fuel shutoff switch.

Engine	Resistance Check Points
1.3L	Between the switch terminals that connect to the GN and BK wires
1.8L	Between the switch terminals that connect to the BL and BK wires

Switch Position	Resistance
Open (tripped)	Greater than 10,000 ohms
Closed (set)	Less than 5 ohms

• Are the resistances OK and does the inertia fuel shutoff switch trip when shaken sharply?

TEST STEP		RESULT	▶	ACTION TO TAKE
FA16	CHECK INERTIA FUEL SHUTOFF SWITCH GROUND (1.3L AND 1.8L ONLY) • Key OFF. • Disconnect the inertia fuel shutoff switch connector. • Measure the resistance between the inertia fuel shutoff switch connector and ground.	Yes No	▶ ▶	GO to **FB2**. SERVICE the "BK" wire.

Engine	Wire	Resistance (ohms)
1.3L	BK	Less than 5
1.8L	BK	Less than 5

• Is the resistance less than 5 ohms?

FM1029400080130X

Fig. 23 Electric fuel pump diagnosis chart (Part 13 of 21). 1994 Aspire, Capri, Probe & Escort & Tracer w/1.8L/4-112 engine

Pinpoint Tests FB — Low Fuel Pressure Test

TEST STEP		RESULT	▶	ACTION TO TAKE
FB1	CHECK POWER SUPPLY TO FUEL PUMP • Key OFF. • Disconnect the fuel pump connector at the fuel pump assembly. • Jump the fuel pump test terminal to ground. Refer to illustration in Test Step F1 for terminal locations. • Key ON. • Measure the voltage on the following wires at the fuel pump connector.	Yes No	▶ ▶	GO to **FB2**. GO to **FA1**.

Engine	Wire Color
1.3L	GN/Y
1.6L	W/BK
1.8L	BK/PK
2.0L	BK/W
2.5L	BK/W

• Is the voltage between 10-14 volts?

TEST STEP		RESULT	▶	ACTION TO TAKE
FB2	CHECK IN-LINE FUEL FILTER CONDITION • Observe "WARNING — INSTRUCTIONS" in System Inspection at the beginning of the Diagnosis and Testing procedures to release the fuel system pressure to avoid fuel spillage and injury. • Remove the high pressure in-line fuel filter for inspection. • Inspect the filter element for contamination or blockage. • Compare the customer's service record and driving conditions versus the recommended maintenance schedule. • Is the fuel filter free of contamination, blockage, and within the recommended maintenance schedule?	Yes No	▶ ▶	GO to **FB3**. SERVICE the fuel filter as required RERUN Test **F1**.

FM1029400080140X

Fig. 23 Electric fuel pump diagnosis chart (Part 14 of 21). 1994 Aspire, Capri, Probe & Escort & Tracer w/1.8L/4-112 engine

TEST STEP		RESULT	▶	ACTION TO TAKE
FB3	CHECK FUEL PRESSURE REGULATOR DIAPHRAGM CONDITION • Observe "WARNING — INSTRUCTIONS" in System Inspection at the beginning of the Diagnosis and Testing procedures to avoid fuel spillage and injury. • Install Rotunda Fuel Pressure Tester 014-00748 or equivalent with EFI Test Adapter D87C-9974-A in the fuel line between the fuel filter and fuel rail (between fuel rails on 2.5L), with its main valve open and its drain valve closed. Refer to illustrations in Test Step F1. • Start the engine and run for 10 seconds. • Stop the engine and wait 10 seconds. • Start the engine again and run for 10 seconds. • Stop the engine and remove the vacuum hose from the pressure regulator. • Examine the vacuum port in the pressure regulator for evidence of fuel leakage through the diaphragm. • Is the vacuum port OK?	Yes No	▶ ▶	GO to **FB4**. REPLACE the fuel pressure regulator and RERUN Test **F1**.
FB4	CHECK FUEL PRESSURE REGULATOR PRESSURE LEAKDOWN • Reconnect the vacuum hose. • With the Rotunda Fuel Pressure Tester 014-00748 or equivalent still installed from previous test, run the engine for a minimum of 30 seconds. • Stop the engine and observe the fuel pressure after 5 minutes. • Is the fuel pressure greater than 147 kPa (21 psi) after 5 minutes?	Yes No	▶ ▶	GO to **FB5**. REPEAT this test step. If the fuel pressure still drops more than specified, test the injector for leakage (refer to Test Step FD4). If injectors are OK, REPLACE the fuel pressure regulator. RERUN Test **F1**.

FM1029400080150X

Fig. 23 Electric fuel pump diagnosis chart (Part 15 of 21). 1994 Aspire, Capri, Probe & Escort & Tracer w/1.8L/4-112 engine

TEST STEP		RESULT	▶	ACTION TO TAKE
FB5	CHECK FUEL PRESSURE REGULATOR VALVE SEAT LEAKAGE • Connect Rotunda Vacuum Tester 021-00037 or equivalent to the fuel return tube on the fuel pressure regulator and apply a 508 mm-Hg (20 in-Hg) vacuum. • Observe the vacuum gauge for at least 10 seconds.	Yes No	▶ ▶	REPLACE the fuel pressure regulator. RERUN Test **F1**. GO to **FB6**.

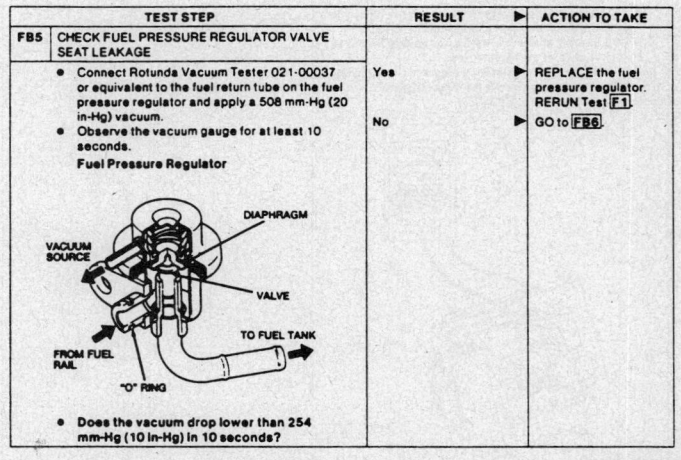

• Does the vacuum drop lower than 254 mm-Hg (10 in-Hg) in 10 seconds?

FM1029400080160X

Fig. 23 Electric fuel pump diagnosis chart (Part 16 of 21). 1994 Aspire, Capri, Probe & Escort & Tracer w/1.8L/4-112 engine

TEST STEP		RESULT	▶	ACTION TO TAKE
FB6	**CHECK FUEL PUMP FLOW VOLUME**			
	• Observe "WARNING — INSTRUCTIONS" in System Inspection at the beginning of the Diagnosis and Testing procedures to avoid fuel spillage and injury.	Yes	▶	GO to **FB7**.
		No	▶	SERVICE the fuel pump inlet screen, and RERUN this test. If flow is still not within specified limits, REPLACE the fuel pump and RERUN Test **F1**.
	• Connect the Rotunda Fuel Pressure Tester 014-00748, or equivalent with EFI Test Adapter D87C-9974-A between the fuel filter and fuel rail (between fuel rails on 2.5L), with the main valve closed and the drain valve opened. Refer to illustrations in Test Step F1.			
	• Place the bypass hose (yellow) in a measuring container inside an empty overflow container.			
	• Jump the fuel pump test terminal to ground. Refer to the illustrations in Test Step F 1 for terminal locations.			
	• Key ON.			
	• Collect fuel in the measuring vessel for 10 seconds.			
	2.0L Shown			

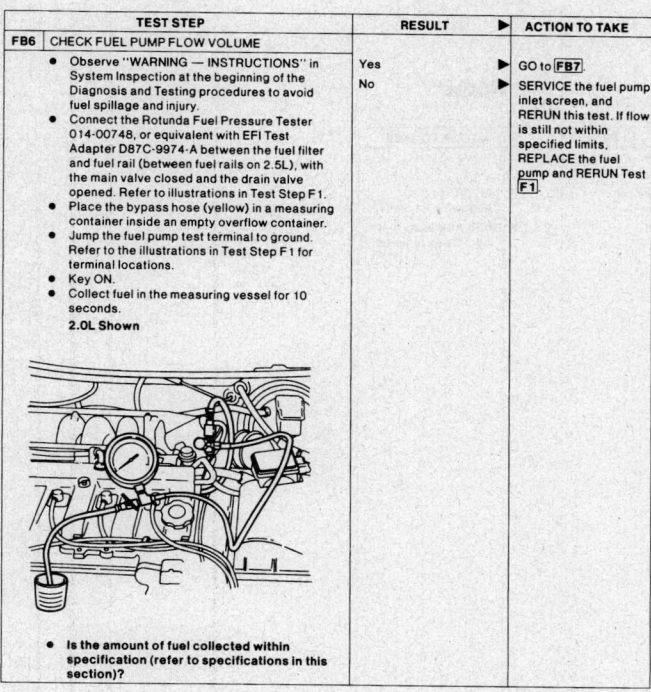

	• Is the amount of fuel collected within specification (refer to specifications in this section)?			

FM1029400080170X

Fig. 23   Electric fuel pump diagnosis chart (Part 17 of 21). 1994 Aspire, Capri, Probe & Escort & Tracer w/1.8L/4-112 engine

TEST STEP		RESULT	▶	ACTION TO TAKE
FB7	**CHECK FUEL PUMP VALVE LEAKDOWN**			
	• Observe "WARNING — INSTRUCTIONS" in System Inspection at the beginning of the Diagnosis and Testing procedures to avoid fuel spillage and injury.	Yes	▶	REPLACE the fuel pump. RERUN Test **F1**.
		No	▶	GO to **FD1**.
	• Connect the Rotunda Fuel Pressure Tester 014-00748, or equivalent with EFI Test Adapter D87C-9974-A between the fuel filter and fuel rail with both the main and drain valves closed. Refer to illustration in Test Step F1.			
	• Jump the fuel pump test terminal to ground. Refer to illustration in Test Step F1 for terminal locations.			
	• Key ON.			
	• Run the fuel pump for 30 seconds minimum.			
	• Remove the jumper and note fuel pressure on the gauge for 3 minutes.			
	• Does the output fuel pressure decrease more than 13.78 kPa (2 psi) in 3 minutes?			

FM1029400080180X

Fig. 23   Electric fuel pump diagnosis chart (Part 18 of 21). 1994 Aspire, Capri, Probe & Escort & Tracer w/1.8L/4-112 engine

Pinpoint Tests FC — High Fuel Pressure Test

TEST STEP		RESULT	▶	ACTION TO TAKE
FC1	**CHECK FUEL PRESSURE REGULATOR FOR CAUSE OF HIGH PRESSURE**			
	• Observe "WARNING — INSTRUCTIONS" in System Inspection at the beginning of the Diagnosis and Testing procedures to avoid fuel spillage and injury.	Yes	▶	GO to **FC2**.
		No	▶	REPAIR or REPLACE damaged components as required. RERUN Test Step **F1**. If the pressure is still high, GO to **FC2**.
	• Check the fuel pressure regulator housing for damage or dents that could cause a higher spring load on the fuel pressure regulator.			
	• Check the integrity of the fuel pressure regulator diaphragm (refer to the procedure described in Test Step FB3).			
	• Is the fuel system free of defects that could cause the fuel pressure regulator to produce excessive fuel system pressure? (Refer to fuel pressure specification in the specifications chart.)			
FC2	**CHECK FUEL RETURN FOR CAUSE OF HIGH FUEL PRESSURE**			
	• Observe "WARNING — INSTRUCTIONS" in System Inspection at the beginning of the Diagnosis and Testing procedures to avoid fuel spillage and injury.	Yes	▶	REPLACE the fuel pressure regulator. RERUN Test Step **F1**.
		No	▶	REPAIR the defects. CLEAN or REPLACE the faulty components as required to remove the cause of high pressure. RERUN Test **F1**.
	• Remove the fuel return line at the pressure regulator and at the fuel tank.			
	• Provide a suitable fuel receptacle at the tank end of the return line to avoid fuel spillage.			
	• Check the fuel return line for restriction due to blockage, kinking, or pinching by blowing through it with 34.5-68.9 kPa (5-10 psi) regulated shop air.			
	• Is the fuel return line free of any restriction that could cause excessive fuel pressure?			

FM1029400080190X

Fig. 23   Electric fuel pump diagnosis chart (Part 19 of 21). 1994 Aspire, Capri, Probe & Escort & Tracer w/1.8L/4-112 engine

Pinpoint Tests FD — Fuel Injector Test

TEST STEP		RESULT	▶	ACTION TO TAKE
FD1	**CHECK FUEL INJECTION FUNCTION**			
	• With the engine warmed and idling (or cranking if it does not start) and using a mechanic's stethoscope or equivalent, listen for regularly operating sounds at each fuel injector.	Yes	▶	GO to **FD4**.
		No	▶	GO to **FD2**.
	• Is normal operating sound present?			
FD2	**CHECK FUEL INJECTOR ELECTRICAL SIGNAL**			
	CAUTION: Do not connect a test lamp to the injector harness. Damage may result to the Powertrain Control Module (PCM).	Yes	▶	GO to **FD3**.
		No	▶	CHECK for 12 volts at each injector wire with key ON. SERVICE wire as required. REFER to Pinpoint Test **SCG**.
	• Check the electrical continuity of the injector between each injector and the PCM as follows:			
	— Disconnect the fuel injector lead and insert the continuity checker from Rotunda Fuel Injector Tester / Cleaner 113-00015 or equivalent into the injector lead plug.			
	— Start or crank engine.			
	— Observe whether the continuity checker blinks (showing a completed circuit for the injector being tested).			
	• Repeat the check for each injector.			
	• Do all injector circuit leads show continuity?			
FD3	**CHECK FUEL INJECTOR RESISTANCE**			
	• Observe "WARNING — INSTRUCTIONS" in System Inspection at the beginning of the Diagnosis and Testing procedures to avoid fuel spillage and injury.	Yes	▶	GO to **FD4**.
		No	▶	REPLACE the faulty injectors. RERUN Test Step **FD1** and if OK, GO to Test Step **FD4**.
	• Disconnect the electrical connectors from the injectors. If necessary, remove the fuel injectors to gain access to the injector terminals.			
	• Measure the electrical resistance across the terminals of each injector.			
	• Is the resistance of each injector approximately 12-16 ohms (20°C [68°F])?			

FM1029400080200X

Fig. 23   Electric fuel pump diagnosis chart (Part 20 of 21). 1994 Aspire, Capri, Probe & Escort & Tracer w/1.8L/4-112 engine

	TEST STEP	RESULT	▶	ACTION TO TAKE
FD4	**CHECK FUEL INJECTORS (CLEANING AND LEAKAGE)**			
	NOTE: This procedure does not require the matching of injector color with flow gauge band color on the Fuel Injector Tester/Cleaner.	Yes No	▶ ▶	RETURN to the Diagnostic Routines. REPLACE faulty fuel injectors as required.
	● Observe "WARNING — INSTRUCTIONS" in System Inspection at the beginning of the Diagnosis and Testing procedures to avoid fuel spillage and injury.			
	● Use the Rotunda Fuel Injector Tester/Cleaner 113-00015, or equivalent and accompanying instructions to clean the fuel injectors.			
	● With the Fuel Injector Tester/Cleaner still installed on the fuel system, note any significant pressure loss due to injector leakage when the tester pump is turned to OFF.			
	● Check each fuel injector individually for leakage as required, using the fuel injector bench tester and the fuel injector bench testing procedure associated with the Fuel Injector Tester/Cleaner. Verify that each injector leakage rate is within specification (1 drop/2 minutes maximum).			
	NOTE: The 2.5L fuel injector has side inject fuel injectors. Therefore they can not be bench tested. See procedure below.			
	● For 2.5L injector testing: — Disconnect the fuel rail from the intake manifold. Leave fuel hoses connected. — Jumper the F/P terminal of Data Link Connector to ground. — Key ON. — Verify that each injector leakage rate is within specification (1 drop/2 minutes maximum).			
	● Is the leakage rate for individual injectors within specifications?			

Fuel Injector Tester/Cleaner

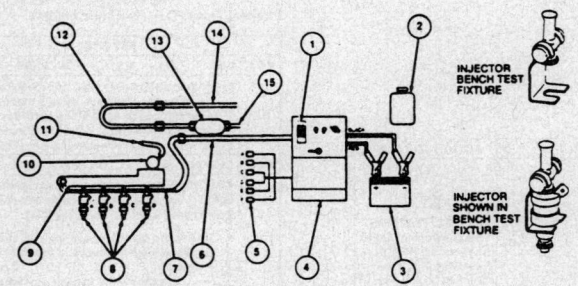

Item	Description
1	Flow Gauge
2	Reservoir
3	Battery
4	Cleaner/Tester
5	Test Harness
6	Cleaner Supply Hose
7	Fuel Supply Line
8	Injectors
9	Fuel Rail
10	Fuel Pressure Regulator
11	Plug Line Fuel Return
12	"U" Tube
13	Filter
14	Fuel Return
15	Fuel Supply

FM1029400080210X

Fig. 23   Electric fuel pump diagnosis chart (Part 21 of 21). 1994 Aspire, Capri, Probe & Escort & Tracer w/1.8L/4-112 engine

TEST STEP			RESULT	►	ACTION TO TAKE
F1	**PERFORM FUEL PRESSURE TEST**		Yes	►	GO to FD1.
	WARNING: BEFORE STARTING THESE TESTS, RELEASE THE FUEL PRESSURE FROM THE FUEL SYSTEM TO REDUCE THE RISK OF INJURY OR FIRE, AS OUTLINED IN FUEL SYSTEM DEPRESSURIZATION.		No, (If zero)	►	GO to FA1.
			(If low)	►	GO to FB1.
	• After releasing the fuel pressure, install Rotunda Fuel Pressure Testing Kit 134-00087 or equivalent with Multiport Fuel Injection (MFI) Test Adapter D87C-9974-A or equivalent in the fuel line between the fuel filter and the fuel rail (between fuel rails on 2.5L), with its main valve open and its drain valve closed. Refer to the following illustration.		(If high)	►	GO to FC1.
	• Jump the fuel pump test terminal to ground. Refer to the following illustration.				
	• Key ON.				
	• Is the fuel pressure within specification (refer to specifications in this section)?				

Fuel Pump Test Connector

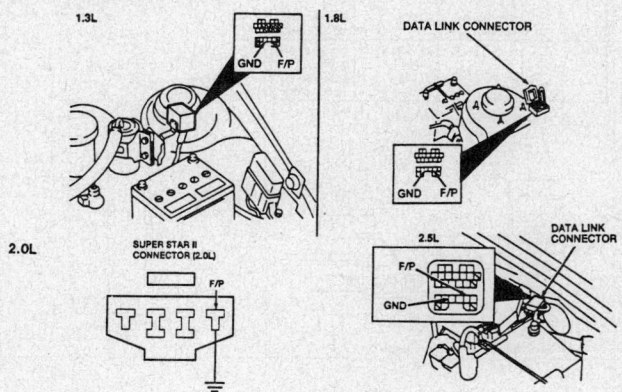

Fuel Pressure Test Setup

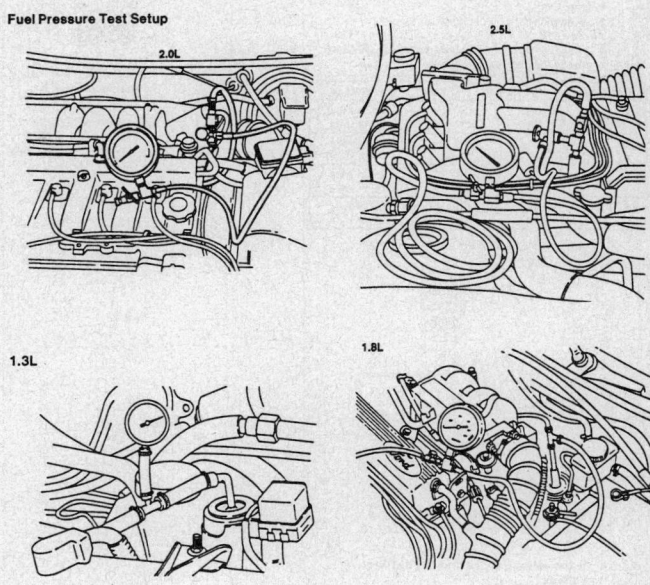

Fig. 24 Electric fuel pump diagnosis chart (Part 1 of 21). 1995 Aspire, Capri, Probe & Escort & Tracer w/1.8L/4-112 engine

Fig. 24 Electric fuel pump diagnosis chart (Part 2 of 21). 1995 Aspire, Capri, Probe & Escort & Tracer w/1.8L/4-112 engine

TEST STEP			RESULT	►	ACTION TO TAKE
FA1	**CHECK FUEL PUMP TEST WIRE CONTINUITY**		Yes	►	GO to FA2.
	• Disconnect the fuel pump relay connector.		No	►	SERVICE the fuel pump test wire. GO to F1.
	• NOTE: Refer to the illustration in test step F1 for Fuel Pump Test Connectors.				
	Measure the resistance of the fuel pump test wire between the fuel pump relay connector and fuel pump test terminal as listed below:				

Engine	Wire Color	Fuel Pump Test Connector
1.3L	W/BK	Data Link Connector
1.8L	LG	Data Link Connector
2.0L	W/Y	Super STAR II Connector
2.5L	LG	Data Link Connector

• Is the resistance less than 5 ohms?

TEST STEP			RESULT	►	ACTION TO TAKE
FA2	**CHECK VOLTAGE TO FUEL PUMP**		Yes (1.3L, 1.8L)	►	GO to FA14.
	• Key OFF.		Yes (2.0L, 2.5L)	►	GO to FA13.
	• Jump the fuel pump test terminal to ground. Refer to illustration in test step F1 for terminal locations.		No	►	GO to FA3.
	• Disconnect the fuel pump connector at the fuel pump assembly.				
	• Key ON.				
	• Measure the voltage on the following wires at the fuel pump connector:				

Engine	Wire Color
1.3L	GN/Y
1.8L	BK/PK
2.0L	BK/W
2.5L	BK/W

• Is the voltage between 10-14 volts?

NOTE: Check inertia fuel shutoff switch for "tripped" condition. Reset if tripped.

Fig. 24 Electric fuel pump diagnosis chart (Part 3 of 21). 1995 Aspire, Capri, Probe & Escort & Tracer w/1.8L/4-112 engine

TEST STEP			RESULT	►	ACTION TO TAKE
FA3	**CHECK FOR SHORT(S) TO GROUND**		Yes	►	GO to FA4.
	• Key OFF.		No	►	SERVICE the wire(s) in question for short.
	• Disconnect the fuel pump relay.				
	• Disconnect the Powertrain Control Module (PCM) on 1.3L, 2.0L, and 2.5L.				
	• Disconnect the fuel pump connector at the fuel pump assembly.				
	• Measure the resistance between the following wires at the fuel pump relay connector and ground.				

Engine	Wire Color
1.3L	GN/Y W/BK
1.8L	BK/PK LG
2.0L	LG W/Y
2.5L	LG W/Y

• Are the resistances greater than 10,000 ohms?

Fig. 24 Electric fuel pump diagnosis chart (Part 4 of 21). 1995 Aspire, Capri, Probe & Escort & Tracer w/1.8L/4-112 engine

TEST STEP				RESULT	▶	ACTION TO TAKE
FA4	CHECK POWER SUPPLY TO FUEL PUMP RELAY			Yes (2.0L, 2.5L)	▶	GO to FA6.
• Key OFF. • Disconnect the fuel pump relay. • Key ON. • Measure the voltage on the following wires at the fuel pump relay connector.				Yes (1.3L, 1.8L)	▶	GO to FA5.
				No (1.8L)	▶	SERVICE the wire(s) in question.
Engine	Wire Color	Key	Voltage	No (1.3L, 2.0L, 2.5L)	▶	GO to Pinpoint Test VPWR in EEC Pinpoint Tests, Section 6B. If VPWR is OK, SERVICE wire(s) for open(s).
1.3L	Y/BK Y/BK	ON ON	10-14 volts 10-14 volts			
1.8L	W/R P	ON START	10-14 volts 10-14 volts			
2.0L	W/R W/GN	ON ON	10-14 volts 10-14 volts			
2.5L	R/BK R/BK	ON ON	10-14 volts 10-14 volts			

2.0L and 2.5L Shown

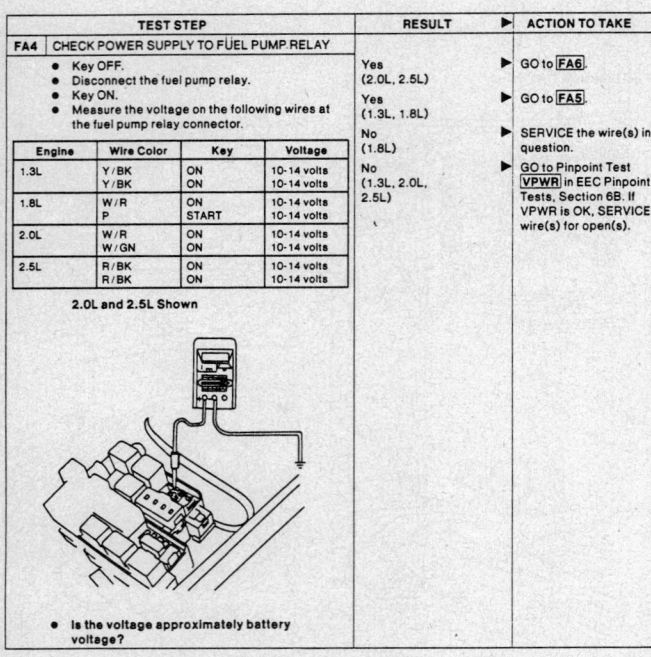

• Is the voltage approximately battery voltage?

Fig. 24   Electric fuel pump diagnosis chart (Part 5 of 21). 1995 Aspire, Capri, Probe & Escort & Tracer w/1.8L/4-112 engine

TEST STEP				RESULT	▶	ACTION TO TAKE
FA5	CHECK FUEL PUMP RELAY (1.3L AND 1.8L ONLY)			Yes (1.8L)	▶	GO to FA7.
• Key OFF. • Remove the fuel pump relay. • Apply 12 volts across the following terminals on the fuel pump relay. • Follow the chart below and measure the resistance between the C-terminal and the A-terminal.				Yes (1.3L)	▶	GO to FA10.
				No	▶	REPLACE the fuel pump relay.
Engine	Terminals "E" and "F"	Terminals "C" and "B"	Resistance at "C" and "A"			
1.3L, 1.8L	12 volts applied	N/A	Less than 5 ohms			
	0 volts applied	N/A	Greater than 10,000 ohms			
1.8L	N/A	12 volts applied	Less than 5 ohms			
	N/A	0 volts applied	Greater than 10,000 ohms			

Fuel Pump Relay Terminals
1.3L and 1.8L

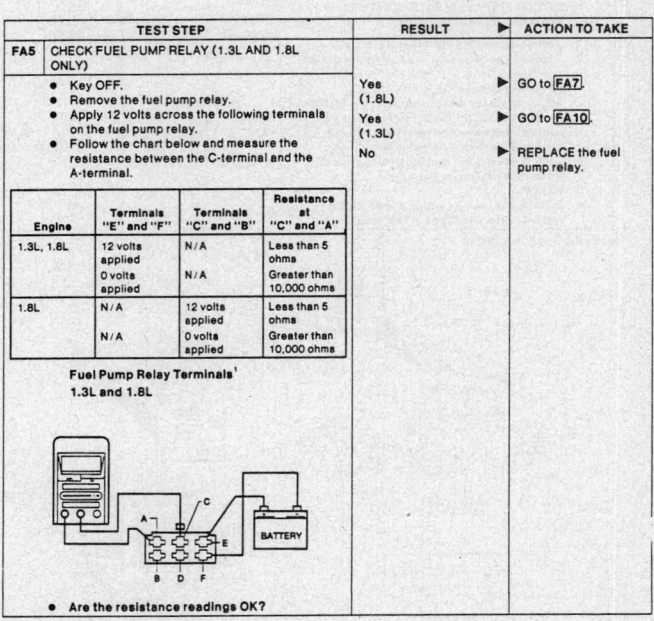

• Are the resistance readings OK?

Fig. 24   Electric fuel pump diagnosis chart (Part 6 of 21). 1995 Aspire, Capri, Probe & Escort & Tracer w/1.8L/4-112 engine

TEST STEP			RESULT	▶	ACTION TO TAKE
FA6	CHECK FUEL PUMP RELAY (2.0L, 2.5L ONLY)		Yes	▶	GO to FA10.
• Key OFF. • Remove the fuel pump relay. • Apply 12 volts across the following terminals on the fuel pump relay. • Follow the chart below and measure the resistance between the C-terminal and the D-terminal.			No	▶	REPLACE the fuel pump relay.
Engine	Terminals "A" and "B"	Resistance at "C" and "D"			
2.0L, 2.5L	12 volts applied	Less than 5 ohms			
	0 volts applied	Greater than 10,000 ohms			

2.0L and 2.5L

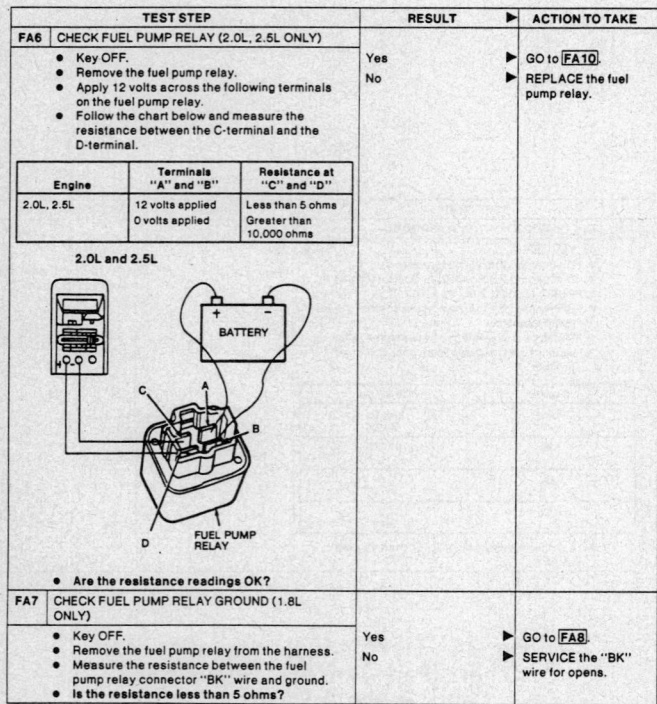

• Are the resistance readings OK?

FA7	CHECK FUEL PUMP RELAY GROUND (1.8L ONLY)		Yes	▶	GO to FA8.
• Key OFF. • Remove the fuel pump relay from the harness. • Measure the resistance between the fuel pump relay connector "BK" wire and ground. • Is the resistance less than 5 ohms?			No	▶	SERVICE the "BK" wire for opens.

Fig. 24   Electric fuel pump diagnosis chart (Part 7 of 21). 1995 Aspire, Capri, Probe & Escort & Tracer w/1.8L/4-112 engine

TEST STEP			RESULT	▶	ACTION TO TAKE
FA8	CHECK VAF SENSOR GROUND (1.8L ONLY)		Yes	▶	SERVICE the "BK/PK" wire between the fuel pump relay and the fuel pump.
• Key OFF. • Remove the fuel pump relay. • Access Volume Air Flow (VAF) sensor door. • Measure the resistance between the fuel pump relay connector and ground while moving the door in the VAF sensor. (Refer to the chart below for wire color.) • Leave the fuel pump relay test connector open.			No	▶	GO to FA9.

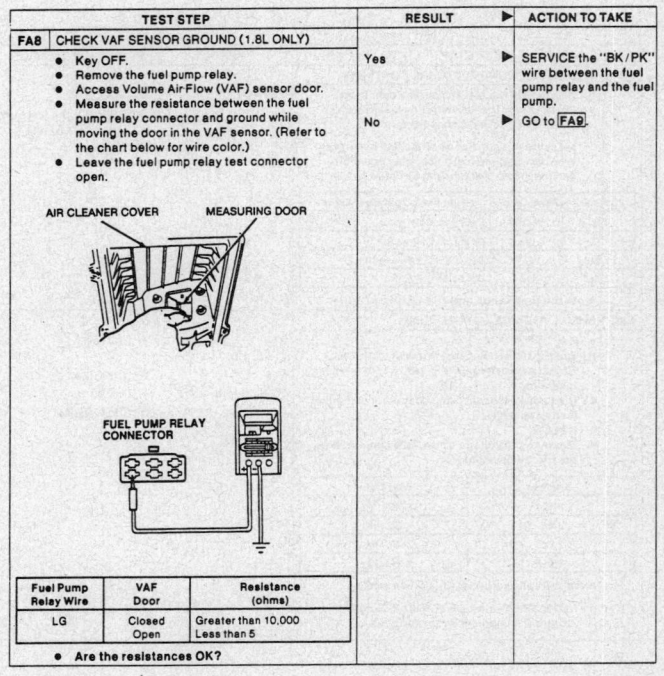

Fuel Pump Relay Wire	VAF Door	Resistance (ohms)
LG	Closed Open	Greater than 10,000 Less than 5

• Are the resistances OK?

Fig. 24   Electric fuel pump diagnosis chart (Part 8 of 21). 1995 Aspire, Capri, Probe & Escort & Tracer w/1.8L/4-112 engine

TEST STEP			RESULT	▶	ACTION TO TAKE
FA9	CHECK VAF FUEL PUMP SWITCH (1.8L ONLY)				
• Key OFF. • Disconnect the VAF sensor wire harness connector. • Measure the resistance between the following terminals on the VAF sensor while moving the VAF sensor door. (Match the wire colors shown with the corresponding VAF terminals.)			Yes No	▶ ▶	SERVICE the VAF "BK" wire, or the wire from the fuel pump relay to the VAF. REPLACE the VAF sensor.

VAF Terminals	Door	Resistance (ohms)
LG, BK	Closed	Greater than 10,000
	Open	Less than 5

• Are the resistances OK?

TEST STEP			RESULT	▶	ACTION TO TAKE
FA10	CHECK FUEL PUMP RELAY TO PCM CONTINUITY (1.3L, 2.0L and 2.5L ONLY)				
• Key OFF. • Remove the fuel pump relay. • Disconnect the Powertrain Control Module (PCM). • Install the Rotunda 60-Pin Breakout Box 007-00033 or equivalent. • Measure the resistance of the following wires between the fuel pump relay and the PCM.			Yes (1.3L) Yes (2.0L, 2.5L) No	▶ ▶ ▶	SERVICE the "GN/Y" wire between the fuel pump relay and the fuel pump. GO to FA11. SERVICE wire(s) in question for open.

Engine	PCM Pin	BOB Pin	PCM Wire Color	Fuel Pump Relay Wire Color
1.3L	1H	55	W/BK	W/BK
2.0L	22 8	22 8	LG W/Y	LG W/Y
2.5L	3T	52B	LG	LG

• Is the resistance less than 5 ohms?

Fig. 24   Electric fuel pump diagnosis chart (Part 9 of 21). 1995 Aspire, Capri, Probe & Escort & Tracer w/1.8L/4-112 engine

TEST STEP			RESULT	▶	ACTION TO TAKE
FA11	CHECK INERTIA FUEL SHUTOFF SWITCH (2.0L AND 2.5L ONLY)				
• Key OFF. • Disconnect and remove the inertia fuel shutoff switch from the vehicle. • Measure the resistance between the terminals shown on the inertia fuel shutoff switch. • Sharply shake the inertia fuel shutoff switch to verify that the switch trips. • Measure the resistance between the terminals shown on the inertia fuel shutoff switch.			Yes No	▶ ▶	GO to FA12. REPLACE the inertia fuel shutoff switch.

Switch Position	Resistance
Open (Tripped)	Greater than 10,000 ohms
Closed (Set)	Less than 5 ohms

• Are the resistances OK and does the switch trip when shaken sharply?

Fig. 24   Electric fuel pump diagnosis chart (Part 10 of 21). 1995 Aspire, Capri, Probe & Escort & Tracer w/1.8L/4-112 engine

TEST STEP			RESULT	▶	ACTION TO TAKE
FA12	CHECK FOR OPEN TO INERTIA FUEL SHUTOFF SWITCH (2.0L AND 2.5L ONLY)				
• Key OFF. • Remove the fuel pump relay. • Disconnect the inertia fuel shutoff switch connector. • Measure the resistance of the following wires between the fuel pump relay and the inertia fuel shutoff switch. Refer to electrical schematic in this section.			Yes No	▶ ▶	SERVICE the wire between the inertia fuel shutoff switch and the fuel pump. SERVICE the wire between the fuel pump relay and the inertia fuel shutoff switch.

Engine	Wire Color
2.0L	W/Y
2.5L	W/Y

• Is the resistance less than 5 ohms?

TEST STEP			RESULT	▶	ACTION TO TAKE
FA13	CHECK FUEL PUMP GROUND (2.0L AND 2.5L ONLY)				
• Key OFF. • Disconnect the fuel pump connector. • Measure the resistance between the "BK" wire at the fuel pump connector and ground. • Is the resistance less than 5 ohms?			Yes No	▶ ▶	GO to FB2. SERVICE ground wire of the fuel pump.
FA14	CHECK WIRE TO INERTIA FUEL SHUTOFF SWITCH (1.3L AND 1.8L ONLY)				
• Key OFF. • Disconnect the fuel pump connector. • Disconnect the inertia fuel shutoff switch connector. • Measure the resistance of the "GN" wire (1.3L) or the "BL" wire (1.8L) between the fuel pump connector and the inertia fuel shutoff switch connector. • Is the resistance less than 5 ohms?			Yes No	▶ ▶	GO to FA15. SERVICE wire to inertia fuel shutoff switch for open.

Fig. 24   Electric fuel pump diagnosis chart (Part 11 of 21). 1995 Aspire, Capri, Probe & Escort & Tracer w/1.8L/4-112 engine

TEST STEP			RESULT	▶	ACTION TO TAKE
FA15	CHECK INERTIA FUEL SHUTOFF SWITCH (1.3L AND 1.8L)				
• Key OFF. • Disconnect and remove the inertia fuel shutoff switch from the vehicle. • Shake the inertia fuel shutoff switch sharply to verify that the switch trips. • Measure the resistance between the indicated terminals of the inertia fuel shutoff switch under the following conditions:			Yes No	▶ ▶	GO to FA16. REPLACE the inertia fuel shutoff switch.

Engine	Resistance Check Points
1.3L	Between the switch terminals that connect to the GN and BK wires
1.8L	Between the switch terminals that connect to the BL and BK wires

Switch Position	Resistance
Open (tripped)	Greater than 10,000 ohms
Closed (set)	Less than 5 ohms

• Are the resistances OK and does the inertia fuel shutoff switch trip when shaken sharply?

TEST STEP			RESULT	▶	ACTION TO TAKE
FA16	CHECK INERTIA FUEL SHUTOFF SWITCH GROUND (1.3L AND 1.8L ONLY)				
• Key OFF. • Disconnect the inertia fuel shutoff switch connector. • Measure the resistance between the inertia fuel shutoff switch connector and ground.			Yes No	▶ ▶	GO to FB2. SERVICE the "BK" wire.

Engine	Wire	Resistance (ohms)
1.3L	BK	Less than 5
1.8L	BK	Less than 5

• Is the resistance less than 5 ohms?

Fig. 24   Electric fuel pump diagnosis chart (Part 12 of 21). 1995 Aspire, Probe & Escort & Tracer, and 1995 Capri w/1.8L/4-112

TEST STEP		RESULT	▶	ACTION TO TAKE
FB1	CHECK POWER SUPPLY TO FUEL PUMP			
	• Key OFF. • Disconnect the fuel pump connector at the fuel pump assembly. • Jump the fuel pump test terminal to ground. Refer to illustration in test step F1 for terminal locations. • Key ON. • Measure the voltage on the following wires at the fuel pump connector.	Yes No	▶ ▶	GO to **FB2**. GO to **FA1**.

Engine	Wire Color
1.3L	GN/Y
1.8L	BK/PK
2.0L	BK/W
2.5L	BK/W

TEST STEP		RESULT	▶	ACTION TO TAKE
	• Is the voltage between 10-14 volts?			
FB2	CHECK IN-LINE FUEL FILTER CONDITION			
	• Observe "WARNING — INSTRUCTIONS" in Fuel System Depressurization at the beginning of the diagnosis and testing procedures to release the fuel system pressure to avoid fuel spillage and injury. • Remove the high pressure in-line fuel filter for inspection. • Inspect the filter element for contamination or blockage. • Compare the customer's service record and driving conditions versus the recommended maintenance schedule. • Is the fuel filter free of contamination, blockage, and within the recommended maintenance schedule?	Yes No	▶ ▶	GO to **FB3**. SERVICE the fuel filter as required. RERUN test **F1**.

Fig. 24 Electric fuel pump diagnosis chart (Part 13 of 21). 1995 Aspire, Capri, Probe & Escort & Tracer w/1.8L/4-112 engine

TEST STEP		RESULT	▶	ACTION TO TAKE
FB3	CHECK FUEL PRESSURE REGULATOR DIAPHRAGM CONDITION			
	• Observe "WARNING — INSTRUCTIONS" in Fuel System Depressurization at the beginning of the diagnosis and testing procedures to avoid fuel spillage and injury. • Install Rotunda Fuel Pressure Testing Kit 134-00087 or equivalent with Multiport Fuel Injection (MFI) Test Adapter D87C-9974-A or equivalent in the fuel line between the fuel filter and fuel rail (between fuel rails on 2.5L), with its main valve open and its drain valve closed. Refer to illustrations in test step F1. • Start the engine and run for 10 seconds. • Stop the engine and wait 10 seconds. • Start the engine again and run for 10 seconds. • Stop the engine and remove the vacuum hose from the pressure regulator. • Examine the vacuum port in the pressure regulator for evidence of fuel leakage through the diaphragm. • Is the vacuum port OK?	Yes No	▶ ▶	GO to **FB4**. REPLACE the fuel pressure regulator and RERUN test **F1**.
FB4	CHECK FUEL PRESSURE REGULATOR PRESSURE LEAKDOWN			
	• Reconnect the vacuum hose. • With the Rotunda Fuel Pressure Tester 014-00748 or equivalent still installed from previous test, run the engine for a minimum of 30 seconds. • Stop the engine and observe the fuel pressure after 5 minutes. • Is the fuel pressure greater than 147 kPa (21 psi) after 5 minutes?	Yes No	▶ ▶	GO to **FB5**. REPEAT this test step. If the fuel pressure still drops more than specified, test the injector for leakage (refer to test step FD4). If injectors are OK, REPLACE the fuel pressure regulator. RERUN test **F1**.

Fig. 24 Electric fuel pump diagnosis chart (Part 14 of 21). 1995 Aspire, Capri, Probe & Escort & Tracer w/1.8L/4-112 engine

TEST STEP		RESULT	▶	ACTION TO TAKE
FB5	CHECK FUEL PRESSURE REGULATOR VALVE SEAT LEAKAGE			
	• Connect Rotunda Vacuum Tester 021-00037 or equivalent to the fuel return tube on the fuel pressure regulator and apply a 508 mm-Hg (20 in-Hg) vacuum. • Observe the vacuum gauge for at least 10 seconds. **Fuel Pressure Regulator**	Yes No	▶ ▶	REPLACE the fuel pressure regulator. RERUN test **F1**. GO to **FB6**.

• Does the vacuum drop lower than 254 mm-Hg (10 in-Hg) in 10 seconds?				

Fig. 24 Electric fuel pump diagnosis chart (Part 15 of 21). 1995 Aspire, Capri, Probe & Escort & Tracer w/1.8L/4-112 engine

TEST STEP		RESULT	▶	ACTION TO TAKE
FB6	CHECK FUEL PUMP FLOW VOLUME			
	• Observe "WARNING — INSTRUCTIONS" in Fuel System Depressurization at the beginning of the diagnosis and testing procedures to avoid fuel spillage and injury. • Connect the Rotunda Fuel Pressure Testing Kit 134-00087, or equivalent with Multiport Fuel Injection (MFI) Test Adapter D87C-9974-A or equivalent between the fuel filter and fuel rail (between fuel rails on 2.5L), with the main valve closed and the drain valve opened. Refer to illustrations in test step F1. • Place the bypass hose (yellow) in a measuring container inside an empty overflow container. • Jump the fuel pump test terminal to ground. Refer to the illustrations in test step F1 for terminal locations. • Key ON. • Collect fuel in the measuring vessel for 10 seconds. **2.0L Shown**	Yes No	▶ ▶	GO to **FB7**. SERVICE the fuel pump inlet screen, and RERUN this test. If flow is still not within specified limits, REPLACE the fuel pump and RERUN test **F1**.

• Is the amount of fuel collected within specification (refer to specifications in this section)?				

Fig. 24 Electric fuel pump diagnosis chart (Part 16 of 21). 1995 Aspire, Capri, Probe & Escort & Tracer w/1.8L/4-112 engine

TEST STEP		RESULT	▶	ACTION TO TAKE
FB7	CHECK FUEL PUMP VALVE LEAKDOWN			
	• Observe "WARNING — INSTRUCTIONS" in Fuel System Depressurization at the beginning of the diagnosis and testing procedures to avoid fuel spillage and injury. • Connect the Rotunda Fuel Pressure Testing Kit 134-00087, or equivalent with Multiport Fuel Injection (MFI) Test Adapter D87C-9974-A or equivalent between the fuel filter and fuel rail with both the main and drain valves closed. Refer to illustration in test step F1. • Jump the fuel pump test terminal to ground. Refer to illustration in test step F1 for terminal locations. • Key ON. • Run the fuel pump for 30 seconds minimum. • Remove the jumper and note fuel pressure on the gauge for 3 minutes. • Does the output fuel pressure decrease more than 13.78 kPa (2 psi) in 3 minutes?	Yes No	▶ ▶	REPLACE the fuel pump. RERUN test F1. GO to FD1.

Fig. 24   Electric fuel pump diagnosis chart (Part 17 of 21). 1995 Aspire, Capri, Probe & Escort & Tracer w/1.8L/4-112 engine

TEST STEP		RESULT	▶	ACTION TO TAKE
FC1	CHECK FUEL PRESSURE REGULATOR FOR CAUSE OF HIGH PRESSURE			
	• Observe "WARNING — INSTRUCTIONS" in Fuel System Depressurization at the beginning of the diagnosis and testing procedures to avoid fuel spillage and injury. • Check the fuel pressure regulator housing for damage or dents that could cause a higher spring load on the fuel pressure regulator. • Check the integrity of the fuel pressure regulator diaphragm (refer to the procedure described in test step FB3). • Is the fuel system free of defects that could cause the fuel pressure regulator to produce excessive fuel system pressure? (Refer to fuel pressure specification in the specifications chart.)	Yes No	▶ ▶	GO to FC2. REPAIR or REPLACE damaged components as required. RERUN test step F1. If the pressure is still high, GO to FC2.
FC2	CHECK FUEL RETURN FOR CAUSE OF HIGH FUEL PRESSURE			
	• Observe "WARNING — INSTRUCTIONS" in Fuel System Depressurization at the beginning of the diagnosis and testing procedures to avoid fuel spillage and injury. • Remove the fuel return line at the pressure regulator and at the fuel tank. • Provide a suitable fuel receptacle at the tank end of the return line to avoid fuel spillage. • Check the fuel return line for restriction due to blockage, kinking, or pinching by blowing through it with 34.5-68.9 kPa (5-10 psi) regulated shop air. • Is the fuel return line free of any restriction that could cause excessive fuel pressure?	Yes No	▶ ▶	REPLACE the fuel pressure regulator. RERUN test step F1. REPAIR the defects. CLEAN or REPLACE the faulty components as required to remove the cause of high pressure. RERUN test F1.

Fig. 24   Electric fuel pump diagnosis chart (Part 18 of 21). 1995 Aspire, Capri, Probe & Escort & Tracer w/1.8L/4-112 engine

TEST STEP		RESULT	▶	ACTION TO TAKE
FD1	CHECK FUEL INJECTION FUNCTION			
	• With the engine warmed and idling (or cranking if it does not start) and using a mechanic's stethoscope or equivalent, listen for regularly operating sounds at each fuel injector. • Is normal operating sound present?	Yes No	▶ ▶	GO to FD4. GO to FD2.
FD2	CHECK FUEL INJECTOR ELECTRICAL SIGNAL			
	CAUTION: Do not connect a test lamp to the injector harness. Damage may result to the Powertrain Control Module (PCM). • Check the electrical continuity of the injector between each injector and the PCM as follows: — Disconnect the fuel injector lead and insert the continuity checker from Rotunda Fuel Injector Tester/Cleaner 113-00015 or equivalent into the injector lead plug. — Start or crank engine. — Observe whether the continuity checker blinks (showing a completed circuit for the injector being tested). • Repeat the check for each injector. • Do all injector circuit leads show continuity?	Yes No	▶ ▶	GO to FD3. CHECK for 12 volts at each injector wire with key ON. SERVICE wire as required.
FD3	CHECK FUEL INJECTOR RESISTANCE			
	• Observe "WARNING — INSTRUCTIONS" in Fuel System Depressurization at the beginning of the diagnosis and testing procedures to avoid fuel spillage and injury. • Disconnect the electrical connectors from the injectors. If necessary, remove the fuel injectors to gain access to the injector terminals. • Measure the electrical resistance across the terminals of each injector. • Is the resistance of each injector approximately 12-16 ohms (20°C [68°F])?	Yes No	▶ ▶	GO to FD4. REPLACE the faulty injectors. RERUN test step FD1 and if OK, GO to test step FD4.

Fig. 24   Electric fuel pump diagnosis chart (Part 19 of 21). 1995 Aspire, Capri, Probe & Escort & Tracer w/1.8L/4-112 engine

TEST STEP		RESULT	▶	ACTION TO TAKE
FD4	CHECK FUEL INJECTORS (CLEANING AND LEAKAGE)			
	NOTE: This procedure does not require the matching of injector color with flow gauge band color on the Fuel Injector Tester/Cleaner. • Observe "WARNING — INSTRUCTIONS" in Fuel System Depressurization at the beginning of the diagnosis and testing procedures to avoid fuel spillage and injury. • Use the Rotunda Fuel Injector Tester/Cleaner 113-00015, or equivalent and accompanying instructions to clean the fuel injectors. Refer to the following illustration. • With the Fuel Injector Tester/Cleaner still installed on the fuel system, note any significant pressure loss due to injector leakage when the tester pump is turned to OFF. • Check each fuel injector individually for leakage as required, using the fuel injector bench tester and the fuel injector bench testing procedure associated with the Fuel Injector Tester/Cleaner. Verify that each injector leakage rate is within specification (1 drop/2 minutes maximum). NOTE: The 2.5L fuel injector has side inject fuel injectors. Therefore they can not be bench tested. See procedure below. • For 2.5L injector testing: — Disconnect the fuel rail from the intake manifold. Leave fuel hoses connected. — Jumper the F/P terminal of Data Link Connector to ground. — Key ON. — Verify that each injector leakage rate is within specification (1 drop/2 minutes maximum). • Is the leakage rate for individual injectors within specifications?	Yes No	▶ ▶	RETURN to the Diagnostic Routines. REPLACE faulty fuel injectors as required.

Fig. 24   Electric fuel pump diagnosis chart (Part 20 of 21). 1995 Aspire, Capri, Probe & Escort & Tracer w/1.8L/4-112 engine

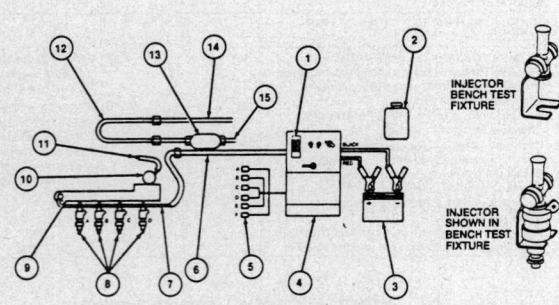

Fuel Injector Tester/Cleaner

Item	Part Number	Description
1	—	Flow Gauge
2	—	Reservoir
3	—	Battery
4	—	Cleaner/Tester
5	—	Test Harness
6	—	Cleaner Supply Hose
7	—	Fuel Supply Line
8	—	Injectors
9	—	Fuel Rail
10	—	Fuel Pressure Regulator
11	—	Plug Line Fuel Return
12	—	"U" Tube
13	—	Filter
14	—	Fuel Return
15	—	Fuel Supply

Fig. 24   Electric fuel pump diagnosis chart (Part 21 of 21). 1995 Aspire, Capri, Probe & Escort & Tracer w/1.8L/4-112 engine

	TEST STEP	RESULT	▶	ACTION TO TAKE
A1	**INITIAL SYSTEM INSPECTION** • Check fuel system for adequate fuel supply. • Visually inspect the fuel delivery system including fuel tank lines, filter, injectors, pressure regulator, battery, electrical lines and connectors for leakage, looseness, cracks, pinching, kinking, corrosion, grounding, abrasion, or other damage caused by accident, collision, assembly or usage. • Verify that the battery is fully charged. • Check fuse integrity. • Is the system free of any evidence of leakage, damage, or any evident cause for concern?	Yes No	▶ ▶	GO to **A2**. SERVICE or REPLACE. GO to **A2**.

FM1029200075010X

Fig. 25   Electric fuel pump diagnosis chart (Part 1 of 6). 1993–94 Continental

	TEST STEP	RESULT	▶	ACTION TO TAKE
A2	**STATIC FUEL PRESSURE CHECK** • Ground the fuel pump lead of the self-test connector through a jumper at the FP lead. • Install the fuel pressure tester. • Turn the ignition key to the RUN position to operate the fuel pump. • Verify that the observed fuel pressure is within specified limits for the engine being tested (refer to chart). • Is the fuel pressure within specification?	Yes No	▶ ▶	GO to **A3**. If pressure High, GO to **A5**. If pressure is low, GO to **A6**.
A3	**STATIC LEAKDOWN TEST** • Run fuel pump for 10 seconds and note pressure (ground FP lead of self test connector and turn ignition switch to the RUN position). • Turn off pump and monitor pressure for 60 seconds. (Remove ground or turn ignition switch to the OFF position). • Does fuel line pressure remain within 34 kPa (5 psi) of shut off pressure for 60 seconds?	Yes No	▶ ▶	GO to **A4**. GO to **A10**.
A4	**VEHICLE LOAD TEST** • Remove and block vacuum line to pressure regulator. • Run vehicle at idle and then increase engine speed to 2000 rpm or more in short bursts. • Does fuel system pressure remain within chart limits? NOTE: Running vehicle under load (road test) should give same results.	Yes No	▶ ▶	If a SHO vehicle, GO to **A13**, if not, fuel system is OK. DISCONNECT all test connections. CONNECT vacuum line to pressure regulator. GO to **A12**.
A5	**FUEL PRESSURE REGULATOR CHECK** • Disconnect return line at fuel pressure regulator. Connect outlet of regulator to appropriate receptacle to catch return fuel. • Turn on fuel pump (ground FP lead and turn ignition to the RUN position) and monitor pressure. • Is fuel pressure within chart limits?	Yes No	▶ ▶	CHECK and SERVICE return fuel line for restrictions. RECHECK pressure as in A2. GO to **A3**. ADJUST or REPLACE fuel regulator as required. RECHECK pressure as in A2. GO to **A3**.

FM1029200075020X

Fig. 25   Electric fuel pump diagnosis chart (Part 2 of 6). 1993–94 Continental

TEST STEP	RESULT	▶	ACTION TO TAKE
A6 CHECK FUEL PUMP			
• Turn on Fuel Pump (ground FP lead and turn ignition to the RUN position).	Yes	▶	GO to A9.
• Raise vehicle on hoist and use stethoscope to listen at fuel tank to monitor fuel pump sound.	No	▶	GO to A7.
• Is Fuel Pump running?			
A7 INERTIA SWITCH AND GROUND CHECK			
• Check inertia switch to see if it is tripped.	Yes	▶	GO to A8.
• Check fuel pump ground connection in vehicle.	No	▶	RESET switch or SERVICE ground connection as required. RECHECK pressure as in A2 and GO to A3.
• Are inertia switch and ground connections OK?			
A8 VOLTAGE CHECK			
• Check for: continuity through fuel pump to ground by connecting to pump power wire lead as close to pump as possible.	Yes	▶	REPLACE fuel pump and RECHECK pressure as in A2. If pressure is OK, GO to A3. If pressure is not OK RECHECK fuel pump connector for oversize connectors or other sources of open electrical circuit. SERVICE as required. GO to A3.
• Check voltage as close to fuel pump as possible (Turn on pump as indicated in A6).			
• Is voltage within 0.5 Volts of battery voltage and is there continuity through pump?	No	▶	If voltage not present, CHECK fuel pump relay, EEC relay, and wiring for problem. If no ground, CHECK connection at fuel tank, etc. After repair, RECHECK pressure as in A2 and GO to A3 when correct.
A9 PRESSURE REGULATOR CHECK			
• Replace fuel filter (if not replaced previously) and recheck pressure as in A2. If pressure is not OK, continue. If pressure is OK, go to A3.	Yes	▶	ADJUST or REPLACE regulator as required. RECHECK pressure as in A2 and GO to A3 if OK. If not OK, REPEAT step A2 until trouble found. If trouble not located, REPLACE pump and REPEAT A2.
• Open return line at pressure regulator. Attach return fitting from regulator to suitable container to catch gasoline.			
• Turn on fuel pump as in A2.			
• Is fuel being returned from regulator with low pressure in system?	No	▶	RECHECK system for pressure restrictions and if none found REPLACE pump. RECHECK pressure as in A2 and continue to A3.

FM1029200075030X

Fig. 25   Electric fuel pump diagnosis chart (Part 3 of 6). 1993–94 Continental

TEST STEP	RESULT	▶	ACTION TO TAKE
A10 PRESSURE REGULATOR LEAK TEST			
• Open return line at pressure regulator and attach suitable container to catch return fuel. Line should be clear to observe fuel flow.	Yes	▶	REPLACE regulator and RECHECK pressure and leakage as in A2 and A3. If OK, GO to A4. If not OK, REPEAT step A2 and follow procedure.
• Run fuel pump as in A2.			
• Turn off fuel pump by removing ground from self test connector or turning ignition to OFF.			
• Observe fuel return flow from regulator and system pressure when pump is off.	No	▶	GO to A12.
• Is there return flow when pump is turned off and system pressure is dropping?			
A11 PUMP CHECK VALVE TEST			
• Open pressure line from fuel pump and attach pressure gauge to line and block line to allow pressure build up.	Yes	▶	CHECK injectors for leakage or regulator for internal leakage. Fuel pump check valve is OK. When serviced GO to A4.
• Operate pump momentarily as in A2 and bring pressure to about system pressure.			
• Observe fuel pressure for one minute.			
• Does pressure remain within 34 kPa (5 psi) of starting pressure over one minute period?	No	▶	CHECK lines and fittings from pump to rail for leakage, if none found REPLACE pump assembly. RECHECK pressure as in A2 and when OK go to A4.
A12 FUEL SYSTEM RESTRICTION OR USAGE TEST			
• Replace fuel line filter (if not previously replaced during this procedure) and repeat test A5.	Yes	▶	System is OK, DISCONNECT all test connections and RECONNECT all loosened or removed parts and lines.
• Does system pressure remain within chart limits?	No	▶	CHECK pressure lines for kinks or restrictions. CHECK at fuel pump for low voltage. CHECK for wrong size injectors (too large). If no problem found, REPLACE pump and REPEAT A4. If problem found, SERVICE and REPEAT A4.

FM1029200075040X

Fig. 25   Electric fuel pump diagnosis chart (Part 4 of 6). 1993–94 Continental

TEST STEP	RESULT	▶	ACTION TO TAKE
A13 CONSTANT CONTROL RELAY MODULE (CCRM) (12B577) FUNCTION TEST			
• Ground fuel pump lead of data link connector.	Yes	▶	SERVICE wire between Pin 5 and inertia fuel shutoff switch.
• Connect DVOM to Pin 5 of constant control relay module connector with connector in place on module. Set DVOM to 20 VDC scale.	No	▶	GO to A14.
• Key ON, Engine OFF.			

• Is voltage greater than 10.5 volts present at Pin 5?

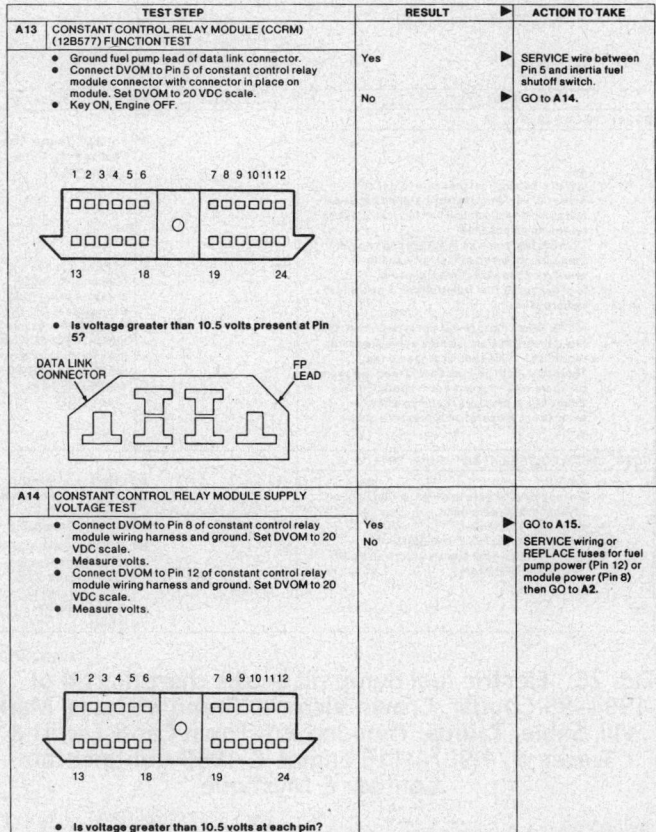

A14 CONSTANT CONTROL RELAY MODULE SUPPLY VOLTAGE TEST			
• Connect DVOM to Pin 8 of constant control relay module wiring harness and ground. Set DVOM to 20 VDC scale.	Yes	▶	GO to A15.
• Measure volts.	No	▶	SERVICE wiring or REPLACE fuses for fuel pump power (Pin 12) or module power (Pin 8) then GO to A2.
• Connect DVOM to Pin 12 of constant control relay module wiring harness and ground. Set DVOM to 20 VDC scale.			
• Measure volts.			

• Is voltage greater than 10.5 volts at each pin?

FM1029200075050X

Fig. 25   Electric fuel pump diagnosis chart (Part 5 of 6). 1993–94 Continental

TEST STEP	RESULT	▶	ACTION TO TAKE
A15 CHECK VOLTAGE AT PIN 22 (PROCESSOR)			
• Key OFF.	Yes	▶	CHECK processor for malfunction. After condition is corrected, GO to A2.
• Battery fully charged.			
• Remove EEC-IV processor.	No	▶	SERVICE wire between EEC-IV and FP relay/IRCM. CHECK at Vlp connector for lead presence. GO to A2 when condition has been corrected.
• Install Rotunda breakout Box, T83L-50-EEC-IV, or Rotunda EEC-IV Monitor 007-00018 or equivalent.			
• Key ON, Engine OFF.			
• DVOM on 20 volt scale.			
• Measure the voltage on Pin 22 of the breakout box, or			
• With EEC-IV Monitor, install the appropriate overlay according to engine size and year. Place selector switch "A" on Pin 22. "FP", turn EEC-IV Monitor power on and read voltage on Pin 22 from LCD readout.			
• Is voltage greater than 10.5 volts?			

FM1029200075060X

Fig. 25   Electric fuel pump diagnosis chart (Part 6 of 6). 1993–94 Continental

NOTE: Grounding the FP lead at the DLC will allow the pump to run continuously with the ignition switch on.

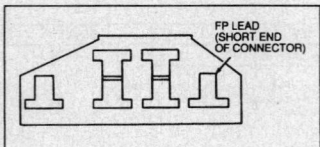

TEST STEP	RESULT	▶	ACTION TO TAKE
FDS1 SYSTEM INTEGRITY CHECK			
Flex Fuel, DTC 141 indicates the engine ran lean an excessive period of time. Follow this procedure. For 3.0L Taurus • Visually inspect the complete fuel delivery system, including fuel tank lines, reservoir, filter, pumps, injectors, pressure regulator, battery, electrical lines and connectors for leakage, looseness, cracks, pinching, kinking, corrosion, grounding, abrasion, or other damage caused by accident, collision, assembly or usage. • Verify vehicle has followed maintenance scheduling. • Run self-test to verify pass code. If fuel related DTCs are present, repair them first. For DTC 141, continue with this procedure. • Verify IFS switch set. • Verify that the battery is fully charged. • Check for sufficient fuel in the fuel tank. • Is system free of any evidence of leakage, damage, or any other cause for concern?	Yes No	▶ ▶	GO to FDS2. SERVICE or REPLACE as required. VERIFY service.

FM1029400081010X

Fig. 26   Electric fuel pump diagnosis chart (Part 1 of 7). 1994–95 Cougar, Crown Victoria, Grand Marquis, Mark VIII, Sable, Taurus, Thunderbird, Town Car & Escort & Tracer w/1.9L/4-116 engine & 1995 Continental, Contour & Mystique

TEST STEP	RESULT	▶	ACTION TO TAKE
FDS2 FUEL PRESSURE TEST			
WARNING: BEFORE SERVICING OR REPLACING ANY COMPONENTS IN THE FUEL SYSTEM, REDUCE THE POSSIBILITY OF INJURY OR FIRE • Key off. • Install the fuel pressure tester. • Ground the fuel pump lead of the Data Link Connector (DLC) with a jumper at the FP lead. • Key On, Engine Off, to operate the fuel pump(s). • Verify that the observed fuel pressure is within specified limits for the engine being checked. Specification: Fuel System Pressure (Key On, Engine Off) Refer to "Fuel Pressure Specification Table." • Is fuel pressure within specification?	Yes No	▶ ▶	GO to FDS3. If low: GO to FDS10 If high: GO to FDS11
FDS3 CHECK FUEL PRESSURE LEAKDOWN			
• Observe the "Notes, Cautions and Warnings" to avoid fuel spillage and injury. • Connect the Fuel Pressure Test Kit at the fuel pressure test point. • Connect a jumper to the FP lead of the DLC. • Key on, engine off. • Ground the test lead using the jumper wire to run the fuel pump. • Run the fuel pump for 30 seconds minimum. • Remove the test lead ground and note fuel pressure on the gauge. • Verify whether the fuel pressure remains within the specified 5 psi for 1 minute after the test lead is ungrounded. • On dual tank system, perform test for both tanks. • Does fuel pressure remain within 5 psi for 1 minute after the test lead is ungrounded?	Yes No	▶ ▶	GO to FDS5. GO to FDS4.

FM1029400081020X

Fig. 26   Electric fuel pump diagnosis chart (Part 2 of 7). 1994–95 Cougar, Crown Victoria, Grand Marquis, Mark VIII, Sable, Taurus, Thunderbird, Town Car & Escort & Tracer w/1.9L/4-116 engine & 1995 Continental, Contour & Mystique

TEST STEP	RESULT	▶	ACTION TO TAKE
FDS4 CHECK PRESSURE REGULATOR DIAPHRAGM CONDITION			
• Key off. • Connect Fuel Pressure Test Kit at Schrader fitting on rail. • Start engine and run for 10 seconds. • Stop engine and wait 10 seconds. • Start engine and run for 10 seconds. • Stop engine and remove vacuum hose from pressure regulator. • Examine vacuum port in the pressure regulator for evidence of fuel leakage through the diaphragm. • Is vacuum port free of any fuel?	Yes No	▶ ▶	leak test. REPLACE pressure regulator and RERUN test FDS2.
FDS5 CHECK FUEL PRESSURE WITH ENGINE LOAD			
• Fuel pressure test kit installed. • Disconnect vacuum hose at the fuel pressure regulator and plug it. • Observe fuel pressure while driving vehicle with heavy accelerations. • Does fuel pressure reading remain within ± 3 psi during the test?	Yes No	▶ ▶	UNPLUG vacuum hose and connect it to fuel pressure regulator. GO to FDS6. GO to FDS8.
FDS6 CHECK FUEL PRESSURE REGULATOR			
• Fuel pressure test kit installed. • Install vacuum gauge at intake manifold. • Start engine and observe both gauge readings. • Accelerate the engine speed to lower the vacuum gauge reading. • Does fuel pressure gauge reading increase as the vacuum gauge reading decreases, and/or does fuel pressure gauge reading decrease as vacuum gauge reading increases?	Yes No	▶ ▶	REMOVE vacuum gauge and fuel pressure test kit. GO to FDS7.
FDS7 CHECK VACUUM SUPPLY			
• Key off. • Vacuum hose removed from the fuel pressure regulator and plugged. • Install a hand operated vacuum pump to the fuel pressure regulator. • Start engine. • Observe fuel pressure while applying vacuum. • Does fuel pressure reading change as the vacuum changes?	Yes No	▶ ▶	SERVICE vacuum system. REMOVE plug from vacuum hose and RECONNECT to fuel pressure regulator. REPLACE fuel pressure regulator.

FM1029400081030X

Fig. 26   Electric fuel pump diagnosis chart (Part 3 of 7). 1994–95 Cougar, Crown Victoria, Grand Marquis, Mark VIII, Sable, Taurus, Thunderbird, Town Car & Escort & Tracer w/1.9L/4-116 engine & 1995 Continental, Contour & Mystique

TEST STEP	RESULT	▶	ACTION TO TAKE
FDS8 CHECK FUEL FILTER			
• Key Off. • Install a second fuel pressure tester on Schrader valve equivalent installed between fuel pump and the in-line fuel filter, as close to fuel pump as possible. • Operate fuel pump as in FDS2 and compare pressure observed at fuel rail with the pressure observed at the fuel pump. • Is pressure at fuel pump within 5 psi of fuel rail pressure? NOTE: When fuel pump is not in operation, the fuel delivery system is at the same pressure, regardless of location of pressure tap. Therefore, both gauges should read the same pressure when pump is not in operation. Any difference in pressure readings when fuel pump is not in operation is pressure gauge error.	Yes No	▶ ▶	For 3.0L Taurus Flex Fuel and Mark VIII: GO to FDS9. REPLACE in-line fuel filter and RECHECK pressure as in FDS2. If pressure is OK, GO to FDS3. If pressure is not OK, RECHECK fuel lines for kinks or other restrictions. SERVICE and RECHECK as in Step FDS2.
FDS9 CHECK VOLTAGE AT BOTH PUMP SPEEDS			
• Key off. • Connect DVOM between Inertia Fuel Shut-off (IFS) and chassis ground. • Start and run engine. • Read voltage at idle and at 3500 rpm. • Is the voltage near 9 volts at idle and near 13 volts at 3500 rpm?	Yes No	▶ ▶	CHECK fuel pump ground connection and service. If OK, REPLACE fuel pump. CHECK CCRM/VCRM for proper operation. CHECK fuses of the fuel pump circuits high and low. RERUN FDS2.

FM1029400081040X

Fig. 26   Electric fuel pump diagnosis chart (Part 4 of 7). 1994–95 Cougar, Crown Victoria, Grand Marquis, Mark VIII, Sable, Taurus, Thunderbird, Town Car & Escort & Tracer w/1.9L/4-116 engine & 1995 Continental, Contour & Mystique

TEST STEP		RESULT	▶	ACTION TO TAKE
FDS10	CHECK REGULATOR FOR LOW PRESSURE CAUSES			
	• Key off. • Remove return fuel line at fuel rail and connect short hose from rail to measured container of at least one quart capacity. • Ground FP lead as in step FDS2. • Key on, Engine off. • Record fuel pressure and note whether fuel is being returned to measured container. Unground FP lead after 10 seconds or if container is more than half full. • Is fuel being returned while pressure is still low?	Yes No	▶ ▶	REPLACE fuel pressure regulator and GO to FDS2. REPLACE fuel pump assembly. GO to FDS2. NOTE: When replacing fuel pump, clean out tank and replace fuel filter.
FDS11	CHECK REGULATOR FOR HIGH PRESSURE CAUSES			
	• Key off. • Remove return fuel line at fuel rail and connect short hose from rail to measured container of at least one quart capacity. • Ground FP lead as in step FDS2. • Key on, Engine off. • Record fuel pressure and note whether fuel is being returned to measured container. Unground FP lead after 10 seconds or if container is more than half full. • Is fuel pressure within specification?	Yes No	▶ ▶	REPLACE fuel pressure regulator and GO to FDS2. GO to FDS13.
FDS12	CHECK FUEL RETURN SYSTEM			
	• Check the fuel return system(s) for restriction due to blockage, kinking, or pinching. • Remove the fuel return line at the fuel pressure regulator. • Apply 3-5 psi regulated shop air to the fuel return line. • Do you hear air entering either tank?	Yes No	▶ ▶	REPLACE in-tank unit where air is entering. RECONNECT fuel return line. GO to FDS2. GO to FDS13.

FM1029400081050X

Fig. 26   Electric fuel pump diagnosis chart (Part 5 of 7). 1994–95 Cougar, Crown Victoria, Grand Marquis, Mark VIII, Sable, Taurus, Thunderbird, Town Car & Escort & Tracer w/1.9L/4-116 engine & 1995 Continental, Contour & Mystique

TEST STEP		RESULT	▶	ACTION TO TAKE
FDS13	CHECK FUEL RETURN SYSTEM			
	• Key off. • Fuel return line disconnected at the fuel pressure regulator. • Check the fuel return system(s) for restriction due to blockage, kinking, or pinching. • Disconnect the fuel return line near the fuel tank. • Apply 3-5 psi regulated shop air to the return line at the pressure regulator side. • Does air flow freely through the line?	Yes No	▶ ▶	 REPLACE fuel pump assembly. GO to FDS2. SERVICE the fuel return line. RECONNECT fuel line. GO to FDS2.
FDS14	CHECK FUEL INJECTOR FLOW AND LEAKAGE			
	• Verify that the fuel injectors flow within specification, using Rotunda Injector Tester 113-00001, SBDS Injector Flow Tester or equivalent. • Is flow rate for individual injectors within specification?	Yes No	▶ ▶	CHECK fuel lines for leaks. then REPEAT Pinpoint Test Step FDS2. REPLACE the defective injectors as required. RERUN test FDS14. REPEAT FDS3.

Fuel Pump Noise on 3.0L Taurus Flex Fuel

Conditions that can produce noise are low Methanol fuel blends (less than 30%), high fuel volatility, low fuel level (quarter fill or less), and temperature greater than 75°F. Fuel system noise may become objectionable at start-up or at high engine speed if any of the conditions are present and are considered normal. The noise level can be reduced by taking corrective action.

TEST STEP		RESULT	▶	ACTION TO TAKE
FDS15	CHECK PUMP NOISE			
	• Key off. • Drain fuel tank to less than a quarter tank, then fill tank to at least half with M85 fuel (15% gasoline, 85% methanol). • Start engine and check for excessive fuel pump noise. • Was pump noise reduced by adding M85 fuel?	Yes No	▶ ▶	ADVISE customer accordingly. GO to FDS16.

FM1029400081060X

Fig. 26   Electric fuel pump diagnosis chart (Part 6 of 7). 1994–95 Cougar, Crown Victoria, Grand Marquis, Mark VIII, Sable, Taurus, Thunderbird, Town Car & Escort & Tracer w/1.9L/4-116 engine & 1995 Continental, Contour & Mystique

TEST STEP		RESULT	▶	ACTION TO TAKE
FDS16	CHECK PUMP SPEEDS			
	• Key off. • Connect DVOM into Inertia Fuel Shutoff (IFS) switch connector. • Start engine and monitor voltage at the IFS. • Is voltage between 12 and 14 volts during crank and initial idle speed, then drops between 7 and 10 volts after a short time?	Yes No	▶ ▶	GO to FDS17. Dual voltage system may be damaged. PERFORM Quick Test and repair DTC codes.
FDS17	CHECK PRESSURE DIFFERENCE			
	• Key off. • Install fuel pressure test kit. • Install a second fuel pressure tester on Schrader valve equivalent between fuel pump and the in-line fuel filter, as close to the pump as possible. • Disconnect and plug vacuum hose from fuel pressure regulator. • Start engine and observe fuel pressure difference between gauges. • Key off, compare gauge readings within 10 seconds. Both should read the same, or else one gauge is in error. • Is fuel pressure difference between gauges less than 10 psi?	Yes No	▶ ▶	REPLACE fuel pump assembly. INSPECT inside of tank for interference, contamination of fuel. SERVICE as necessary. REPLACE fuel filter. FILL tank with fresh fuel. REPLACE fuel filter and CHECK system

FM1029400081070X

Fig. 26   Electric fuel pump diagnosis chart (Part 7 of 7). 1994–95 Cougar, Crown Victoria, Grand Marquis, Mark VIII, Sable, Taurus, Thunderbird, Town Car & Escort & Tracer w/1.9L/4-116 engine & 1995 Continental, Contour & Mystique

TEST STEP		RESULT	▶	ACTION TO TAKE
A1	INITIAL SYSTEM INSPECTION			
	• Check fuel system for adequate fuel supply. • Visually inspect the fuel delivery system including fuel tank lines, filter, injectors, pressure regulator, battery, electrical lines and connectors for leakage, looseness, cracks, pinching, kinking, corrosion, grounding, abrasion, or other damage caused by accident, collision, assembly or usage. • Verify that the battery is fully charged. • Check fuse integrity. • Is the system free of any evidence of leakage, damage, or any evident cause for concern?	Yes No	▶ ▶	GO to A2. SERVICE or REPLACE. GO to A2.

FM1029200076010X

Fig. 27   Electric fuel pump diagnosis chart (Part 1 of 8). 1993 Cougar, Mustang & Thunderbird

TEST STEP		RESULT	▶	ACTION TO TAKE
A2	STATIC FUEL PRESSURE CHECK			
	• Install Rotunda Fuel Pressure Tester 014-00748 or equivalent. • Check for a connection at the FP lead. Ground FP lead if present. If no connection exists, check for separate connector located in the area. The test connector is a two pin connector. Use the "SPOUT" or similar connector to jumper this connection to run fuel pump. • Turn the ignition key to the RUN position to operate the fuel pump. • Verify that the observed fuel pressure is within specified limits for the engine being tested (refer to chart). • **Is the fuel pressure within specifications?**	Yes No	▶ ▶ ▶	GO to A3. If pressure is high, GO to A5. If pressure is low, GO to A6.
A3	STATIC LEAKDOWN TEST			
	• Run fuel pump for 10 seconds and note pressure (ground FP lead of data link connector and turn ignition switch to the RUN position). • Turn off pump and monitor pressure for 60 seconds. (Remove ground or turn ignition switch to the OFF position.) • **Does fuel line pressure remain within 34 kPa (5 psi) of shut off pressure for 60 seconds?**	Yes No	▶ ▶	GO to A4. GO to A10.
A4	VEHICLE LOAD TEST			
	• Remove and block vacuum hose to pressure regulator. NOTE: Running vehicle under load with vacuum hose removed from fuel pressure regulator (road test) may give better results. • Run vehicle at idle and then increase engine speed to 2000 rpm or more in short bursts. • **Does fuel system pressure remain within chart limits?**	Yes No	▶ ▶	Fuel system is OK. DISCONNECT all test connections. CONNECT vacuum hose to pressure regulator. GO to A12.
A5	FUEL PRESSURE REGULATOR CHECK			
	• Disconnect return line at fuel pressure regulator. Connect outlet of regulator to appropriate receptacle to catch return fuel. • Turn on fuel pump (ground FP lead and turn ignition to the RUN position) and monitor pressure. • **Is fuel pressure within chart limits?**	Yes No	▶ ▶	CHECK and SERVICE return fuel line for restrictions. RECHECK fuel pressure as in A2. GO to A3. REPLACE fuel regulator. RECHECK pressure as in A2. GO to A3.

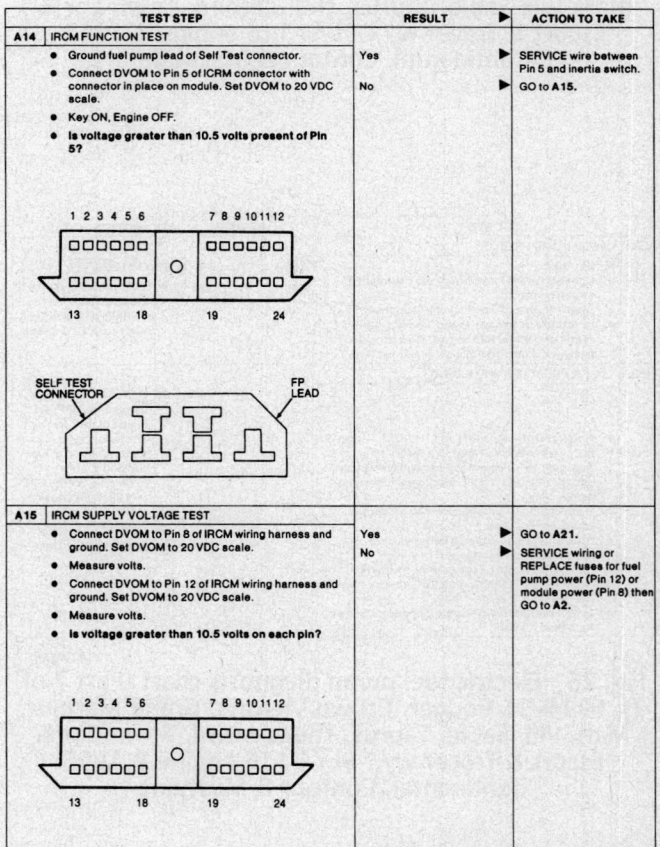

Fig. 27 Electric fuel pump diagnosis chart (Part 2 of 8). 1993 Cougar, Mustang & Thunderbird

FM1029200076020X

TEST STEP		RESULT	▶	ACTION TO TAKE
A6	CHECK FUEL PUMP			
	• Turn on fuel pump (ground FP lead and turn ignition to the RUN position). • Raise vehicle on hoist and use stethoscope to listen to fuel tank to monitor fuel pump sound. • **Is fuel pump running?**	Yes No	▶ ▶	GO to A9. GO to A7.
A7	INERTIA FUEL SHUTOFF (IFS) (9341) SWITCH AND GROUND CHECK			
	• Check inertia fuel shutoff switch to see if it is open. • Check fuel pump ground connection in vehicle. • **Are inertia fuel shutoff switch and ground connections OK?**	Yes No	▶ ▶	GO to A8. RESET or REPLACE switch or SERVICE ground connection as required. RECHECK pressure as in A2. GO to A3.
A8	VOLTAGE CHECK			
	• Check for continuity through fuel pump to ground by connecting to pump power wire lead as close to pump as possible. • Check voltage as close to fuel pump as possible (Turn on pump as indicated in A6). • **Is voltage within 0.5 volt of battery voltage and is there continuity through pump?**	Yes No	▶ ▶	REPLACE fuel pump and RECHECK pressure as in A2. If pressure is OK, GO to A3. If pressure is not OK, RECHECK fuel pump connector for oversize connectors or other sources of open electrical circuit. SERVICE as required. GO to A3. GO to A12.
A9	PRESSURE REGULATOR CHECK			
	• Replace fuel filter (if not replaced previously) and recheck pressure as in A2. If pressure is not OK, continue. If pressure is OK, go to A3. • Open return line at pressure regulator. Attach return fitting from regulator to suitable container to catch gasoline. • Turn on fuel pump as in A2. • **Is fuel being returned from regulator with low pressure in system?**	Yes No	▶ ▶	ADJUST or REPLACE regulator as required. RECHECK pressure as in A2 until trouble found. If not OK, REPEAT Step A2 until trouble found. If trouble not located, REPLACE pump and REPEAT A2. RECHECK system for pressure restrictions and if none found, REPLACE pump. RECHECK pressure as in A2 and continue to A3.

FM1029200076030X

Fig. 27 Electric fuel pump diagnosis chart (Part 3 of 8). 1993 Cougar, Mustang & Thunderbird

TEST STEP		RESULT	▶	ACTION TO TAKE
A10	PRESSURE REGULATOR LEAK TEST			
	• Open return line at pressure regulator and attach suitable container to catch return fuel. Line should be clear to observe fuel flow. • Run fuel pump as in A2. • Turn off fuel pump by removing ground from self test connector or turning ignition to OFF. • Observe fuel return flow from regulator and system pressure when pump is off. • Remove vacuum hose from fuel pressure regulator and check for presence of fuel in fitting (diaphragm leak). • **Is there return flow when pump is turned off and system pressure is dropping or fuel in regulator fitting?**	Yes No	▶ ▶	REPLACE regulator and RECHECK pressure and leakage as in A2 and A3. If OK, GO to A4. If not OK, REPEAT Step A2 and follow procedure GO to A11.
A11	PUMP CHECK VALVE TEST			
	• Open pressure line from fuel pump and attach pressure gauge to line and block line to allow pressure build up. • Operate pump momentarily as in A2 and bring pressure to about system pressure. • Observe fuel pressure for one minute. • **Does pressure remain within 34 kPa (5 psi) of starting pressure over one minute period?**	Yes No	▶ ▶	CHECK injectors for leakage or regulator for internal leakage. Fuel pump check valve is OK. When serviced GO to A4. CHECK lines and fittings from pump to rail for leakage, if none found, REPLACE pump assembly. RECHECK pressure as in A2 and when OK, GO to A4.
A12	FUEL SYSTEM RESTRICTION OR USAGE TEST			
	• Replace fuel line filter (if not previously replaced during this procedure) and repeat test A5. • **Does system pressure remain within chart limits?**	Yes No	▶ ▶	System is OK. DISCONNECT all test connections and RECONNECT all loosened or removed parts and lines. CHECK pressure lines for kinks or restrictions. CHECK at fuel pump for low voltage. GO to A13. CHECK for wrong size injectors (too large). If no concern found, REPLACE pump and REPEAT A4. If concern found, SERVICE and REPEAT A4.
A13	RELAY TYPE CHECK			
	• Does vehicle use IRCM (Integrated Relay Control Module) for fuel pump control? Control module is located on upper radiator support bracket.	Yes No	▶ ▶	Use IRCM tester to check module function. SERVICE or REPLACE if needed then GO to A2. If function OK, GO to A14. GO to A16.

FM1029200076040X

Fig. 27 Electric fuel pump diagnosis chart (Part 4 of 8). 1993 Cougar, Mustang & Thunderbird

TEST STEP		RESULT	▶	ACTION TO TAKE
A14	IRCM FUNCTION TEST			
	• Ground fuel pump lead of Self Test connector. • Connect DVOM to Pin 5 of ICRM connector with connector in place on module. Set DVOM to 20 VDC scale. • Key ON, Engine OFF. • **Is voltage greater than 10.5 volts present of Pin 5?**	Yes No	▶ ▶	SERVICE wire between Pin 5 and inertia switch. GO to A15.

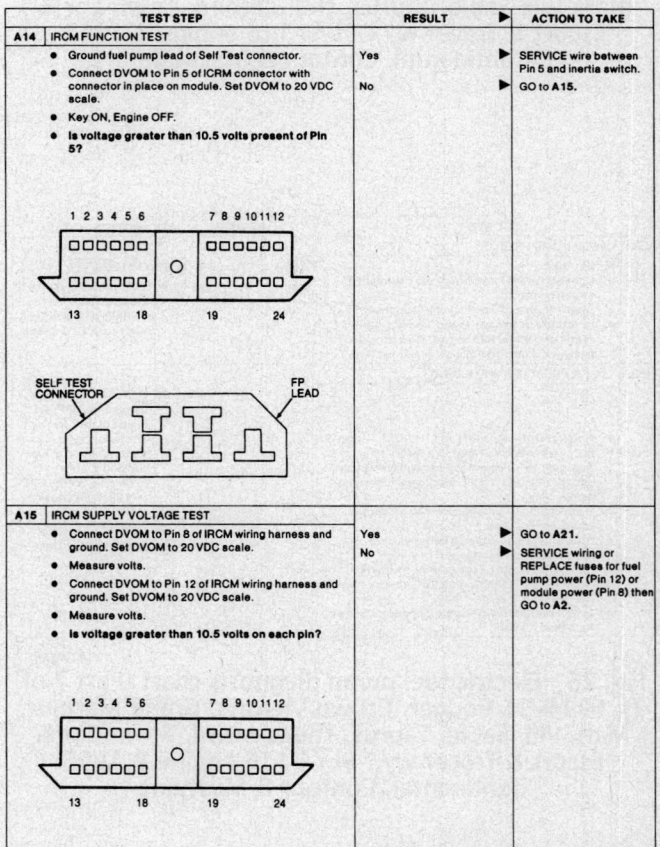

TEST STEP		RESULT	▶	ACTION TO TAKE
A15	IRCM SUPPLY VOLTAGE TEST			
	• Connect DVOM to Pin 8 of IRCM wiring harness and ground. Set DVOM to 20 VDC scale. • Measure volts. • Connect DVOM to Pin 12 of IRCM wiring harness and ground. Set DVOM to 20 VDC scale. • Measure volts. • **Is voltage greater than 10.5 volts on each pin?**	Yes No	▶ ▶	GO to A21. SERVICE wiring or REPLACE fuses for fuel pump power (Pin 12) or module power (Pin 8) then GO to A2.

FM1029200076050X

Fig. 27 Electric fuel pump diagnosis chart (Part 5 of 8). 1993 Cougar, Mustang & Thunderbird

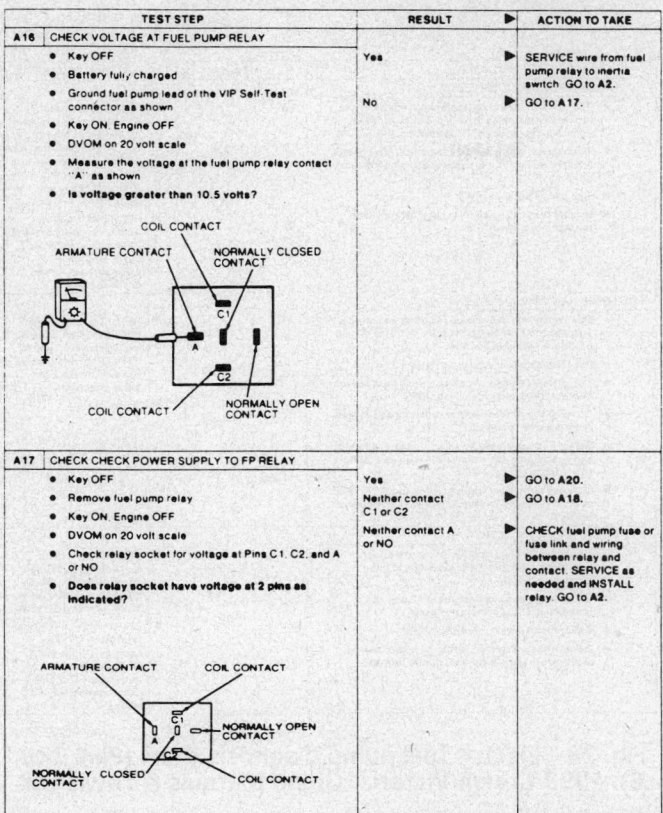

TEST STEP	RESULT	▶	ACTION TO TAKE
A16 CHECK VOLTAGE AT FUEL PUMP RELAY • Key OFF • Battery fully charged • Ground fuel pump lead of the VIP Self-Test connector as shown • Key ON, Engine OFF • DVOM on 20 volt scale • Measure the voltage at the fuel pump relay contact "A" as shown • Is voltage greater than 10.5 volts?	Yes No	▶ ▶	SERVICE wire from fuel pump relay to inertia switch. GO to A2. GO to A17.
A17 CHECK CHECK POWER SUPPLY TO FP RELAY • Key OFF • Remove fuel pump relay • Key ON, Engine OFF • DVOM on 20 volt scale • Check relay socket for voltage at Pins C1, C2, and A or NO • Does relay socket have voltage at 2 pins as indicated?	Yes Neither contact C1 or C2 Neither contact A or NO	▶ ▶ ▶	GO to A20. GO to A18. CHECK fuel pump fuse or fuse link and wiring between relay and contact. SERVICE as needed and INSTALL relay. GO to A2.

FM1029200076060X

Fig. 27 Electric fuel pump diagnosis chart (Part 6 of 8). 1993 Cougar, Mustang & Thunderbird

TEST STEP	RESULT	▶	ACTION TO TAKE
A20 CHECK FUEL PUMP OR EEC RELAY OPERATION • Remove relay from vehicle. • Connect a +12 volt supply to terminal C1 as shown. • Ground terminal C2 as shown. • DVOM on 200 ohm scale. • Measure the resistance between terminals A and NO as shown. • Is resistance lower than 1 ohm with power on and greater than 10K ohms with power off?	Yes No	▶ ▶	GO to A21. REPLACE and REINSERT fuel pump and/or EEC relay as required. GO to A2.
A21 CHECK VOLTAGE AT PIN 22 (PROCESSOR) • Key OFF. • Battery fully charged. • Remove EEC-IV processor. • Install Rotunda Breakout Box, T83L-50-EEC-IV, or Rotunda EEC-IV Monitor 007-00018 or equivalent. • Key ON, engine OFF. • DVOM on 20 volt scale. • Measure the voltage on Pin 22 of the breakout box, or with EEC-IV Monitor, install the appropriate overlay according to engine size and year. Place selector switch "A" on Pin 22, "FP", turn EEC-IV Monitor power on and read voltage on Pin 22 from LCD readout. • Is voltage greater than 10.5 volts?	Yes No.	▶ ▶	CHECK processor for malfunction. After condition is corrected, GO to A2. SERVICE wire between EEC-IV and FP relay/IRCM. CHECK at VIP connector for lead presence. GO to A2 when condition has been corrected.

FM1029200076080X

Fig. 27 Electric fuel pump diagnosis chart (Part 8 of 8). 1993 Cougar, Mustang & Thunderbird

TEST STEP	RESULT	▶	ACTION TO TAKE
A18 CHECK EEC RELAY AND WIRING • Key OFF. • Remove EEC Relay. • Key ON, Engine OFF. • DVOM on 20 volts. • Check relay socket for voltage at Pins C1, or C2 and A or NO. • Note which pins have voltage present (there should only be voltage on one pin of each pair, if voltage present on both pins of one pair, look for shorted wiring). • Are voltages greater than 10.5 volts on relay socket?	Yes Neither contact C1 or C2 Neither contact A or NO	▶ ▶ ▶	GO to A19. CHECK and SERVICE wiring between ignition switch and relay coil then INSTALL relay. GO to A2. SERVICE wiring or REPLACE fuse or fuse link between EEC relay and contact then INSTALL relay. GO to A2.
A19 CHECK EEC RELAY GROUND • Key OFF. • EEC relay removed. • DVOM on low OHMS scale. • Check EEC relay coil pin which did not have voltage in Step A18 (either C1 or C2) for ground. • Is ground on coil pin of EEC relay less than 1 ohm?	Yes No	▶ ▶	GO to A20. SERVICE ground wire at EEC relay, REINSERT EEC and fuel pump relays and GO to A2.

FM1029200076070X

Fig. 27 Electric fuel pump diagnosis chart (Part 7 of 8). 1993 Cougar, Mustang & Thunderbird

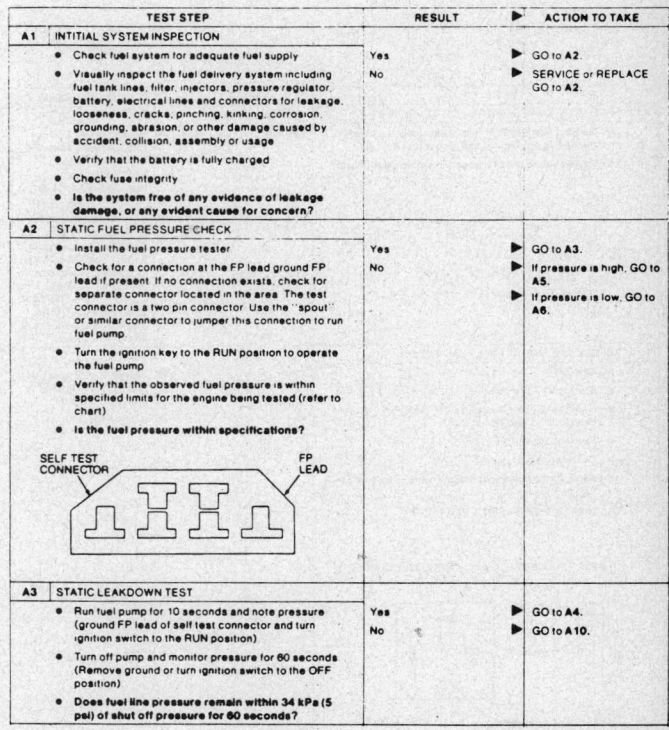

TEST STEP	RESULT	▶	ACTION TO TAKE
A1 INITIAL SYSTEM INSPECTION • Check fuel system for adequate fuel supply • Visually inspect the fuel delivery system including fuel tank lines, filter, injectors, pressure regulator, battery, electrical lines and connectors for leakage, looseness, cracks, pinching, kinking, corrosion, grounding, abrasion, or other damage caused by accident, collision, assembly or usage • Verify that the battery is fully charged • Check fuse integrity • Is the system free of any evidence of leakage damage, or any evident cause for concern?	Yes No	▶ ▶	GO to A2. SERVICE or REPLACE GO to A2.
A2 STATIC FUEL PRESSURE CHECK • Install the fuel pressure tester • Check for a connection at the FP lead ground FP lead if present. If no connection exists, check for separate connector located in the area. The test connector is a two pin connector. Use the "spout" or similar connector to jumper this connection to run fuel pump. • Turn the ignition key to the RUN position to operate the fuel pump • Verify that the observed fuel pressure is within specified limits for the engine being tested (refer to chart) • Is the fuel pressure within specifications?	Yes No	▶ ▶ ▶	GO to A3. If pressure is high, GO to A5. If pressure is low, GO to A6.
A3 STATIC LEAKDOWN TEST • Run fuel pump for 10 seconds and note pressure (ground FP lead of self test connector and turn ignition switch to the RUN position) • Turn off pump and monitor pressure for 60 seconds (Remove ground or turn ignition switch to the OFF position) • Does fuel line pressure remain within 34 kPa (5 psi) of shut off pressure for 60 seconds?	Yes No	▶ ▶	GO to A4. GO to A10.

FM1029200074010X

Fig. 28 Electric fuel pump diagnosis chart (Part 1 of 6). 1993 Crown Victoria, Grand Marquis & Town Car

TEST STEP		RESULT	▶	ACTION TO TAKE
A4	VEHICLE LOAD TEST			
	• Remove and block vacuum hose to pressure regulator. • Run vehicle at idle and then increase engine speed to 2000 rpm or more in short bursts. • Does fuel system pressure remain within chart limits? NOTE: Running vehicle under load with vacuum hose removed from fuel pressure regulator (road test) may give better results.	Yes	▶	Fuel system is OK. DISCONNECT all test connections. CONNECT vacuum hose to pressure regulator.
		No	▶	GO to A12.
A5	FUEL PRESSURE REGULATOR CHECK			
	• Disconnect return line at fuel pressure regulator. Connect outlet of regulator to appropriate receptacle to catch return fuel. • Turn on fuel pump (ground FP lead and turn ignition to the RUN position) and monitor pressure. • Is fuel pressure within chart limits?	Yes	▶	CHECK and SERVICE return fuel line for restrictions. RECHECK pressure as in A2. GO to A3.
		No	▶	REPLACE fuel regulator. RECHECK pressure as in A2. GO to A3.
A6	CHECK FUEL PUMP			
	• Turn on fuel pump (ground FP lead and turn ignition to the RUN position). • Raise vehicle on hoist and use stethoscope to listen to fuel tank to monitor fuel pump sound. • Is fuel pump running?	Yes	▶	GO to A9.
		No	▶	GO to A7.
A7	INERTIA SWITCH AND GROUND CHECK			
	• Check inertia switch to see if it is open. • Check fuel pump ground connection in vehicle. • Are inertia switch and ground connections OK?	Yes	▶	GO to A8.
		No	▶	RESET or REPLACE switch or SERVICE ground connection as required. RECHECK pressure as in A2. GO to A3.
A8	VOLTAGE CHECK			
	• Check for continuity through fuel pump to ground by connecting to pump power wire lead as close to pump as possible. • Check voltage as close to fuel pump as possible (Turn on pump as indicated in A6). • Is voltage within 0.5 volts of battery voltage and is there continuity through pump?	Yes	▶	REPLACE fuel pump and RECHECK pressure as in A2. If pressure is OK, GO to A3. If pressure is not OK, RECHECK fuel pump connector for oversize connectors or other sources of open electrical circuit. SERVICE as required. GO to A3.
		No	▶	GO to A12.

FM1029200074020X

Fig. 28   Electric fuel pump diagnosis chart (Part 2 of 6). 1993 Crown Victoria, Grand Marquis & Town Car

TEST STEP		RESULT	▶	ACTION TO TAKE
A9	PRESSURE REGULATOR CHECK			
	• Replace fuel filter (if not replaced previously) and recheck pressure as in A2. If pressure is not OK, continue. If pressure is OK, go to A3. • Open return line at pressure regulator. Attach return fitting from regulator to suitable container to catch gasoline. • Turn on fuel pump as in A2. • Is fuel being returned from regulator with low pressure in system?	Yes	▶	REPLACE regulator. RECHECK pressure as in A2 and GO to A3 if OK. If not OK, REPEAT Step A2 until trouble found. If trouble not located, REPLACE pump and REPEAT A2.
		No	▶	RECHECK system for pressure restrictions and if none found, REPLACE pump. RECHECK pressure as in A2 and continue to A3.
A10	PRESSURE REGULATOR LEAK TEST			
	• Open return line at pressure regulator and attach suitable container to catch return fuel. Line should be clear to observe fuel flow. • Run fuel pump as in A2. • Turn off fuel pump by removing ground from self test connector or turning ignition to OFF. • Observe fuel return flow from regulator and system pressure when pump is off. • Remove vacuum hose from fuel pressure regulator and check for presence of fuel in regulator fitting (diaphragm leak). • Is there return flow when pump is turned off and system pressure is dropping or fuel in regulator fitting?	Yes	▶	REPLACE regulator and RECHECK pressure and leakage as in A2 and A3. If OK, GO to A4. If not OK, REPEAT Step A2 and follow procedure.
		No	▶	GO to A11.
A11	PUMP CHECK VALVE TEST			
	• Open pressure line from fuel pump and attach pressure gauge to line and block line to allow pressure build up. • Operate pump momentarily as in A2 and bring pressure to about system pressure. • Observe fuel pressure for one minute. • Does pressure remain within 34 kPa (5 psi) of starting pressure over one minute period?	Yes	▶	CHECK injectors for leakage or regulator for internal leakage. Fuel pump check valve is OK. When serviced GO to A4.
		No	▶	CHECK lines and fittings from pump to rail for leakage, if none found, REPLACE pump assembly. RECHECK pressure as in A2 and when OK, GO to A4.

FM1029200074030X

Fig. 28   Electric fuel pump diagnosis chart (Part 3 of 6). 1993 Crown Victoria, Grand Marquis & Town Car

TEST STEP		RESULT	▶	ACTION TO TAKE
A12	FUEL SYSTEM RESTRICTION OR USAGE TEST			
	• Replace fuel line filter (if not previously replaced during this procedure) and repeat test A5. • Does system pressure remain within chart limits?	Yes	▶	System is OK. DISCONNECT all test connections and RECONNECT all loosened or removed parts and lines.
		No	▶	CHECK pressure lines for kinks or restrictions. CHECK at fuel pump for low voltage. GO to A13. CHECK for wrong size injectors (too large). If no concern found, REPLACE pump and REPEAT A4. If concern found, SERVICE and REPEAT A4.
A13	CHECK VOLTAGE AT FUEL PUMP RELAY			
	• Key OFF. • Battery fully charged. • Ground fuel pump lead of the VIP Self-Test connector as shown. • Key ON, engine OFF. • DVOM on 20 volt scale. • Measure the voltage at the fuel pump relay contact "A" as shown. • Is voltage greater than 10.5 volts?	Yes	▶	SERVICE wire from fuel pump relay to inertia switch. GO to A2.
		No	▶	GO to A14.

FM1029200074040X

Fig. 28   Electric fuel pump diagnosis chart (Part 4 of 6). 1993 Crown Victoria, Grand Marquis & Town Car

TEST STEP		RESULT	▶	ACTION TO TAKE
A14	CHECK CHECK POWER SUPPLY TO FP RELAY			
	• Key OFF. • Remove fuel pump relay. • Key ON, engine OFF. • DVOM on 20 volt scale. • Check relay socket for voltage at Pins C1, C2, and A or NO. • Does relay socket have voltage at 2 pins as indicated?	Yes	▶	GO to A17.
		Neither contact C1 nor C2	▶	GO to A15.
		Neither contact A nor NO	▶	CHECK fuel pump fuse or fuse link and wiring between relay and contact. SERVICE as needed and INSTALL relay. GO to A2.
A15	CHECK EEC RELAY AND WIRING			
	• Key OFF. • Remove EEC Relay. • Key ON, engine OFF. • DVOM on 20 volts. • Check relay socket for voltage at Pins C1, or C2 and A or NO. • Note which pins have voltage present (there should only be voltage on one pin if each pair, if voltage present on both pins of one pair, look for shorted wiring). • Are voltages greater than 10.5 volts on relay socket?	Yes	▶	GO to A16.
		Neither contact C1 nor C2	▶	CHECK and SERVICE wiring between ignition switch and relay coil then INSTALL relay. GO to A2.
		Neither contact A nor NO	▶	SERVICE wiring or REPLACE fuse or fuse link between EEC relay and contact then INSTALL relay. GO to A2.

FM1029200074050X

Fig. 28   Electric fuel pump diagnosis chart (Part 5 of 6). 1993 Crown Victoria, Grand Marquis & Town Car

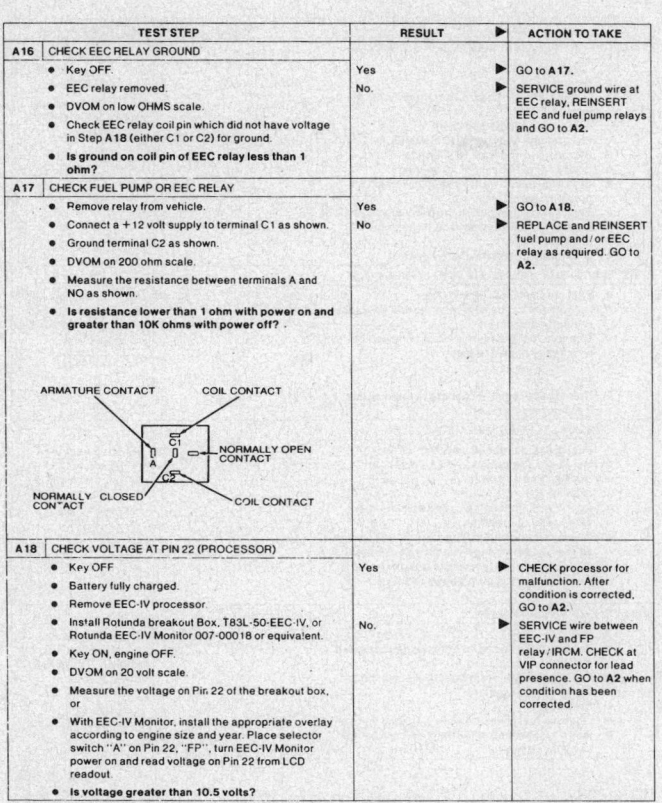

TEST STEP	RESULT	▶	ACTION TO TAKE
A16 CHECK EEC RELAY GROUND			
• Key OFF.	Yes	▶	GO to A17.
• EEC relay removed.	No.	▶	SERVICE ground wire at EEC relay, REINSERT EEC and fuel pump relays and GO to A2.
• DVOM on low OHMS scale.			
• Check EEC relay coil pin which did not have voltage in Step A18 (either C1 or C2) for ground.			
• **Is ground on coil pin of EEC relay less than 1 ohm?**			
A17 CHECK FUEL PUMP OR EEC RELAY			
• Remove relay from vehicle.	Yes	▶	GO to A18.
• Connect a +12 volt supply to terminal C1 as shown.	No	▶	REPLACE and REINSERT fuel pump and/or EEC relay as required. GO to A2.
• Ground terminal C2 as shown.			
• DVOM on 200 ohm scale.			
• Measure the resistance between terminals A and NO as shown.			
• Is resistance lower than 1 ohm with power on and greater than 10K ohms with power off? .			
A18 CHECK VOLTAGE AT PIN 22 (PROCESSOR)			
• Key OFF.	Yes	▶	CHECK processor for malfunction. After condition is corrected, GO to A2.
• Battery fully charged.			
• Remove EEC-IV processor.	No.	▶	SERVICE wire between EEC-IV and FP relay/IRCM. CHECK at VIP connector for lead presence. GO to A2 when condition has been corrected.
• Install Rotunda breakout Box, T83L-50-EEC-IV, or Rotunda EEC-IV Monitor 007-00018 or equivalent.			
• Key ON, engine OFF.			
• DVOM on 20 volt scale.			
• Measure the voltage on Pin 22 of the breakout box, or			
• With EEC-IV Monitor, install the appropriate overlay according to engine size and year. Place selector switch "A" on Pin 22, "FP", turn EEC-IV Monitor power on and read voltage on Pin 22 from LCD readout.			
• **Is voltage greater than 10.5 volts?**			

FM1029200074060X

Fig. 28   Electric fuel pump diagnosis chart (Part 6 of 6). 1993 Crown Victoria, Grand Marquis & Town Car

NOTE: Grounding the FP lead at the DLC will allow the pump to run continuously with the ignition switch on.

FP LEAD
(SHORT END
OF CONNECTOR)

Figure A : Data Link Connector (DLC)

TEST STEP	RESULT	▶	ACTION TO TAKE
EFD1 SYSTEM INTEGRITY CHECK			
• Visually inspect the complete fuel delivery system, including fuel tank lines, reservoir, filter, pumps, injectors, pressure regulator, battery, electrical lines and connectors for leakage, looseness, cracks, pinching, kinking, corrosion, grounding, abrasion, or other damage caused by accident, collision, assembly or usage.	Yes	▶	GO to EFD2.
	No	▶	SERVICE or REPLACE as required. VERIFY service.
• Verify vehicle has followed maintenance scheduling.			
• Run self test to verify "no electrical system" DTC.			
• Verify IFS switch set.			
• Verify that the battery is fully charged.			
• Check electrical/fuse integrity.			
• Check for sufficient fuel in the fuel tank.			
• **Is system free of any evidence of leakage, damage, or any other cause for concern?**			

FM1029100072010X

Fig. 29   Electric fuel pump diagnosis chart (Part 1 of 12). 1993 Escort & Tracer w/1.9L/4-116 engine

1994 1.8L/4-112 Engine

Refer to **Fig. 23** for fuel pump diagnostic procedures.

1995 1.8L/4-112 Engine

Refer to **Fig. 24** for fuel pump diagnostic procedures.

1993 1.9L/4-116 Engine

Refer to **Fig. 29** for fuel pump diagnostic procedures.

1994—95 1.9L/4-116 Engine

Refer to **Fig. 26** for fuel pump diagnostic procedures.

MARK VIII

1993

Refer to **Fig. 30** for fuel pump diagnostic procedures.

1994—95

Refer to **Fig. 26** for fuel pump diagnostic procedures.

1996

Refer to EEC-V section under "Computerized Engine Controls" for fuel pump system diagnostic and testing procedures.

PROBE

1993

Refer to **Fig. 22** for fuel pump diagnostic procedures.

1994

Refer to **Fig. 23** for fuel pump diagnostic procedures.

1995

Refer to **Fig. 24** for fuel pump diagnostic procedures.

1996

Refer to EEC-V section under "Computerized Engine Controls" for fuel pump system diagnostic and testing procedures.

SABLE & TAURUS

1993

Refer to **Fig. 30** for fuel pump diagnostic procedures.

1994—95

Refer to **Fig. 26** for fuel pump diagnostic procedures.

1996

Refer to EEC-V section under "Computerized Engine Controls" for fuel pump system diagnostic and testing procedures.

TEMPO & TOPAZ

1993—94

Refer to **Fig. 31** for fuel pump diagnostic procedures.

FUEL PUMP REPLACEMENT

Some models are equipped with Poly-

ethylene fuel tanks. These fuel tanks are not repairable including all portions of the tank body and the plastic fittings attached to it. There is no acceptable repair procedure that meets new tank standards. If tank is damaged it must be replaced. Extreme care must be taken to avoid damaging the assembly.

ASPIRE & FESTIVA

1. Relieve fuel system pressure as outlined under "Precautions."
2. Remove rear carpet retainers, then fold carpet forward until pump/sending unit access plate is uncovered.
3. Remove access plate screws, then lift access plate and disconnect pump/sending unit electrical connector.
4. Disconnect fuel line at pump/sending unit, then remove pump/sending.
5. Remove fuel pump filter from pump, then disconnect two fuel pump wires from sending unit.
6. Remove retaining clamp screw, then the pump outlet hose clamp.
7. Remove fuel pump from sending unit.
8. Reverse procedure to install.

CAPRI

1. Relieve fuel system pressure as outlined under "Precautions."
2. Disconnect fuel pump ground wire from access cover, then remove access cover.

Continued on page 6-36

TEST STEP		RESULT	▶	ACTION TO TAKE
EFD2	**FUEL PRESSURE TEST**	Yes	▶	GO to **EFD3**.
	WARNING: BEFORE SERVICING OR REPLACING ANY COMPONENTS IN THE FUEL SYSTEM, REDUCE THE POSSIBILITY OF INJURY OR FIRE.	No	▶	If zero or low: GO to **EFD8**. If high: GO to **EFD26**.
	• Key off.			
	• Before releasing fuel system pressure at the Schrader fitting, observe the Warning Instructions to avoid fuel spillage and injury.			
	• Install the fuel pressure tester.			
	• Ground the fuel pump lead of the Data Link Connector (DLC) (Figure **A**) with a jumper at the FP lead.			
	• Key On, Engine Off, to operate the fuel pump(s).			
	• Verify that the observed fuel pressure is within specified limits for the engine being checked. Specification: Fuel System Pressure (Key On, Engine Off) Refer to "Fuel Pressure Specification Table."			
	• **Is fuel pressure within specification?**			
EFD3	**CHECK FUEL PRESSURE LEAKDOWN**	Yes	▶	GO to **EFD5**.
	Caution avoid fuel spillage and injury.	No	▶	GO to **EFD4**.
	• Connect the Fuel Pressure Test Kit at the fuel pressure test point.			
	• Connect a jumper to the FP lead of the DLC.			
	• Key on, engine off.			
	• Ground the test lead using the jumper wire to run the fuel pump.			
	• Run the fuel pump for 30 seconds minimum.			
	• Remove the test lead ground and note fuel pressure on the gauge.			
	• Verify whether the fuel pressure remains within the specified 5 psi for 1 minute after the test lead is ungrounded.			
	• On dual tank system, perform test for both tanks.			
	• **Does fuel pressure remain within 5 psi for 1 minute after the test lead is ungrounded?**			

FM1029100072020X

Fig. 29   Electric fuel pump diagnosis chart (Part 2 of 12). 1993 Escort & Tracer w/1.9L/4-116 engine

TEST STEP		RESULT	▶	ACTION TO TAKE
EFD4	**CHECK PRESSURE REGULATOR DIAPHRAGM CONDITION**	Yes	▶	GO to **EFD29**.
	• Key off.	No	▶	REPLACE pressure regulator and RERUN test **EFD2**.
	• Connect Fuel Pressure Test Kit at Schrader fitting on rail. Warning avoid fuel spillage and injury.			
	• Start engine and run for 10 seconds.			
	• Stop engine and wait 10 seconds.			
	• Start engine and run for 10 seconds.			
	• Stop engine and remove vacuum hose from pressure regulator.			
	• Examine vacuum port in the pressure regulator for evidence of fuel leakage through the diaphragm.			
	• **Is vacuum port free of any fuel?**			
EFD5	**CHECK FUEL PRESSURE WITH ENGINE LOAD**	Yes	▶	UNPLUG vacuum hose and connect it to fuel pressure regulator. GO to **EFD6**.
	• Fuel pressure test kit installed.	No	▶	GO to **EFD21**.
	• Disconnect vacuum hose at the fuel pressure regulator and plug it.			
	• Observe fuel pressure while driving vehicle with heavy accelerations.			
	• **Does fuel pressure reading remain within ± 3 psi during the test?**			
EFD6	**CHECK FUEL PRESSURE REGULATOR**	Yes	▶	REMOVE vacuum gauge and fuel pressure test kit.
	• Fuel pressure test kit installed.			possible causes.
	• Install vacuum gauge to intake manifold.	No	▶	GO to **EFD7**.
	• Start engine and observe gauge reading.			
	• Accelerate the engine speed to lower the vacuum gauge reading.			
	• **Does fuel pressure gauge reading increase as the vacuum gauge reading decreases, and/or does fuel pressure gauge reading decrease as vacuum gauge reading increases?**			
EFD7	**CHECK VACUUM SUPPLY**	Yes	▶	SERVICE vacuum system. REMOVE plug hose and RECONNECT to fuel pressure regulator.
	• Key off.			
	• Vacuum hose removed from the fuel pressure regulator and plugged.	No	▶	REPLACE fuel pressure regulator.
	• Install a hand operated vacuum pump to the fuel pressure regulator.			
	• Start engine.			
	• Observe fuel pressure while applying vacuum.			
	• **Does fuel pressure reading change as the vacuum changes?**			

FM1029100072030X

Fig. 29   Electric fuel pump diagnosis chart (Part 3 of 12). 1993 Escort & Tracer w/1.9L/4-116 engine

TEST STEP		RESULT	▶	ACTION TO TAKE
EFD8	**CHECK VOLTAGE AT INERTIA FUEL SHUTOFF (IFS) SWITCH**	Yes	▶	GO to **EFD15**.
	• Key off.	No	▶	For voltage at one pin only REPLACE IFS switch as required. For voltage at neither pin.
	• IFS switch set.			
	• Battery fully charged.			Vehicle with CCRM: GO to **EFD9**. All others: GO to **EFD12**.
	• Ground fuel pump lead of the DLC as shown.			
	• Key On, Engine Off.			
	• IFS switch connected.			
	• Measure the voltage at the IFS switch as shown (one pin at the time).			
	• **Is voltage greater than 10.5 volts at both pins?**			
EFD9	**CHECK VOLTAGE AT CONSTANT CONTROL RELAY MODULE (CCRM)**	Yes	▶	GO to **EFD11**.
	• Key off.	No	▶	GO to **EFD10**.
	• Verify IFS switch is set.			
	• Verify vehicle has CCRM.			
	• CCRM connected to the vehicle harness.			
	• Ground FP lead at the DLC.			
	• Key On, Engine Off.			
	• Measure voltage between Pin 5 of the CCRM vehicle harness connector and chassis ground.			
	• **Is voltage greater than 10.5 volts?**			
EFD10	**CHECK FOR VOLTAGE TO THE CCRM**	Yes	▶	VERIFY CCRM function, use CCRM tester. If OK, GO to Quick Test, VERIFY voltage at Pin 22. GO to **EFD2**.
	• Key off.			
	• Disconnect the CCRM vehicle harness connector. Inspect for damage or pushed out pins, corrosion, loose wire, etc. Service as necessary.	No	▶	SERVICE open. GO to **EFD12**.
	• Key On, Engine Off.			
	• Measure voltage between Pin 8 and 12 at the CCRM connector and chassis ground.			
	• **Are both voltages greater than 10.5 volts?**			

FM1029100072040X

Fig. 29   Electric fuel pump diagnosis chart (Part 4 of 12). 1993 Escort & Tracer w/1.9L/4-116 engine

TEST STEP		RESULT	▶	ACTION TO TAKE
EFD11	**CHECK FUEL PUMP RESISTANCE**	Yes	▶	REPLACE the fuel pump assembly. GO to **EFD2**.
	• Key off.	No	▶	GO to **EFD16**.
	• CCRM disconnected.			
	• Measure resistance between Pin 5 of the CCRM vehicle harness connector and chassis ground.			
	• **Is resistance less than 5 ohms?**			
EFD12	**CHECK FOR VOLTAGE AT FP RELAY**	Yes	▶	SERVICE open circuit between fuel pump relay and IFS switch.
	• Key off.	No	▶	GO to **EFD13**.
	• Battery fully charged.			
	• Ground fuel pump lead of the DLC as shown.			
	• Key On, Engine Off.			
	• Measure the voltage at the fuel pump relay. Contacts NO (Normally Open) and Common. Refer to the Electrical Schematics.			
	• **Is voltage greater than 10.5 volts?**			
EFD13	**CHECK POWER SUPPLY TO FP RELAY**	Yes	▶	GO to **EFD14**.
	• Key off.	No	▶	SERVICE open circuit between fuel pump relay and EEC power relay or B+.
	• Battery fully charged.			
	• Disconnect/remove fuel pump relay.			
	• Key On, Engine Off.			
	• Measure the voltage between chassis ground of the fuel pump relay connector and all pins. Refer to Electrical Schematics.			
	• **Is voltage on one coil and Common or NO (Normally Open) contact wires greater than 10.5 volts on at least 2 pins?**			
EFD14	**CHECK FUEL PUMP RELAY OPERATION**	Yes	▶	GO to EEC-IV Quick Test Section
	• Remove the fuel pump relay from vehicle.	No	▶	REPLACE fuel pump relay. VERIFY service.
	• Refer to the electrical schematic.			
	• Connect a +12v supply to the coil terminal.			
	• Measure the resistance between terminals Common and NO (Normally Open).			
	• **Is resistance lower than 1 ohm with the power applied and greater than 10,000 ohms with power off?**			
EFD15	**CHECK PUMP OPERATION AUDIBLE**	Yes	▶	GO to **EFD21**.
	• Key off.	No	▶	GO to **EFD16**.
	• Battery fully charged.			
	• Verify that a good electrical connection is made to the pump/sender unit.			
	• Ground the fuel pump lead of the DLC.			
	• Key On, Engine Off.			
	• Listen to fuel pump.			
	• On Type 2 system perform test for both tanks.			
	• **Is fuel pump running?**			

FM1029100072050X

Fig. 29   Electric fuel pump diagnosis chart (Part 5 of 12). 1993 Escort & Tracer w/1.9L/4-116 engine

TEST STEP		RESULT	▶	ACTION TO TAKE
EFD16	CHECK VOLTAGE SUPPLY TO SELECTOR SWITCH (TYPE 2)			
	• Key off. • Battery fully charged. • Ground fuel pump lead of the DLC as shown. • Disconnect selector switch. • Key On, Engine Off. • Measure voltage at Pin 2 of selector switch as shown. • **Is voltage greater than 10.5 volts?**	Yes No	▶ ▶	GO to EFD17. SERVICE wire from selector switch to IFS switch.
EFD17	CHECK VOLTAGE AT SELECTOR SWITCH (TYPE 2)			
	• Key off. • Battery fully charged. • Ground fuel pump lead of the DLC as shown. • Key On, Engine Off. • Place selector switch in "F" position. • DVOM on 20 volt scale. • Measure voltage at pin 1 of the selector switch as shown. • Repeat with selector switch in "R" position for AFT axle tank and measure voltage on Pin 3 as shown. • **Is voltage greater than 10.5 volts?**	Yes No	▶ ▶	GO to EFD18. REPLACE Selector Switch, GO to EFD2.

FM1029100072060X

Fig. 29 Electric fuel pump diagnosis chart (Part 6 of 12). 1993 Escort & Tracer w/1.9L/4-116 engine

TEST STEP		RESULT	▶	ACTION TO TAKE
EFD18	CHECK VOLTAGE TO PUMP			
	• Battery fully charged. • Ground the fuel pump lead of the DLC as shown. • Place selector switch in "F" position if equipped with dual tank. • Disconnect the front fuel tank electrical connector. • Key On, Engine Off. • Measure the voltage on the power supply lead to fuel pump as shown. • Repeat procedure with selector switch in "R" position and measure voltage at rear tank sender / pump unit connector. • **Is voltage greater than 10.5 volts?**	Yes No	▶ ▶	GO to EFD19. SERVICE circuit between Inertia Switch and the fuel pump connector. GO to EFD2.
EFD19	CHECK FUEL PUMP GROUND			
	• Key off. • Disconnect electrical connector at the tank. • Measure the resistance of the wire to chassis ground as shown. • On Type 2 system perform test for both tanks. • **Is resistance less than 1 ohm?**	Yes No	▶ ▶	REPLACE Fuel Pump. GO to EFD2. SERVICE open wire to ground. GO to EFD2.

FM1029100072070X

Fig. 29 Electric fuel pump diagnosis chart (Part 7 of 12). 1993 Escort & Tracer w/1.9L/4-116 engine

TEST STEP		RESULT	▶	ACTION TO TAKE
EFD20	CHECK FUEL PUMP RESISTANCE			
	• Key off. • Measure resistance between IFS switch and ground. • **Is resistance less than 5 ohms?**	Yes No	▶ ▶	REPLACE fuel pump assembly. GO to EFD2. GO to EFD18.
EFD21	CHECK FUEL FILTER			
	• Observe Warning Instructions to avoid fuel spillage and injury. • Key Off. • Install a second fuel pressure tester on Schrader valve equivalent installed between fuel pump and the in-line fuel filter, as close to fuel pump as possible. • Operate fuel pump as in EFD2 and compare pressure observed at fuel rail with the pressure observed at the fuel pump. • **Is pressure at fuel pump within 5 psi of fuel rail pressure?** NOTE: When fuel pump is not in operation, the fuel delivery system is at the same pressure, regardless of location of pressure tap. Therefore, both gauges should read the same pressure when pump is not in operation. Any difference in pressure readings when fuel pump is not in operation is pressure gauge error.	Yes No	▶ ▶	GO to EFD22. REPLACE in-line fuel filter and RECHECK pressure as in EFD2. If pressure is OK, GO to EFD3. If pressure is not OK, RECHECK fuel lines for kinks or other restrictions. SERVICE and RECHECK as in Step EFD2.
EFD22	FUEL PUMP CHECK VALVE TEST			
	• Install fuel pressure tester on Schrader valve equivalent installed between fuel pump and in-line fuel filter, as close to fuel pump as possible. • Operate fuel pump momentarily as in EFD2 and bring pressure to about system pressure. • Observe fuel pressure for 1 minute. • **Does pressure remain within 34 kPa (5 psi) of starting pressure over 1 minute period?**	Yes No	▶ ▶	GO to EFD7. REPLACE fuel pump assembly. RECHECK pressure as in EFD2.

FM1029100072080X

Fig. 29 Electric fuel pump diagnosis chart (Part 8 of 12). 1993 Escort & Tracer w/1.9L/4-116 engine

TEST STEP		RESULT	▶	ACTION TO TAKE
EFD23	CHECK REAR TANK FUEL DELIVERY ASSEMBLY			
	• Fuel return line connected. • Remove the fuel supply line from the sender port of the front tank and install fuel pressure gauge to the fuel line. • Move the tank selector to REAR position. • Key On, Engine Off. • Wait until fuel pump stops (approximately 1 second). • Key off, observe fuel pressure. • **Does fuel pressure drop?**	Yes No	▶ ▶	REPLACE rear tank Fuel Delivery Assembly. REMOVE fuel pressure gauge. RERUN EFD2. REMOVE fuel pressure gauge. RECONNECT fuel supply line to front tank. GO to EFD24.
EFD24	CHECK FRONT TANK FUEL DELIVERY ASSEMBLY			
	• Remove the fuel supply line from the sender port of the rear tank and install fuel pressure gauge to the fuel line. • Move the tank selector to FRONT position. • Key On, Engine Off. • Wait until fuel pump stops (approximately 1 second). • Key off, observe fuel pressure. • **Does fuel pressure drop?**	Yes No	▶ ▶	REPLACE front tank Fuel Delivery Assembly. REMOVE fuel pressure gauge. RERUN EFD2. REMOVE fuel pressure gauge. RECONNECT fuel supply line to rear tank. GO to EFD25. VERIFY no leaks.

FM1029100072090X

Fig. 29 Electric fuel pump diagnosis chart (Part 9 of 12). 1993 Escort & Tracer w/1.9L/4-116 engine

TEST STEP	RESULT	▶	ACTION TO TAKE
EFD25 CHECK PRESSURE REGULATOR VALVE SEAT LEAKAGE **Warning** — avoid fuel spillage and injury. • Remove the fuel pressure regulator. • Inspect the O-ring and the gasket and mounting surfaces for cracks, cuts or other defects that may affect sealing. • Connect the vacuum tester to the fuel return tube (shown below) and apply a 20 in-Hg vacuum. • Verify whether the vacuum retention meets specification of 10 in-Hg maximum loss of vacuum within 10 seconds. • **Does vacuum drop below 10 in-Hg within 10 seconds?**	Yes No	▶ ▶	REPLACE the regulator. RERUN test **EFD2**. GO to **EFD29**.

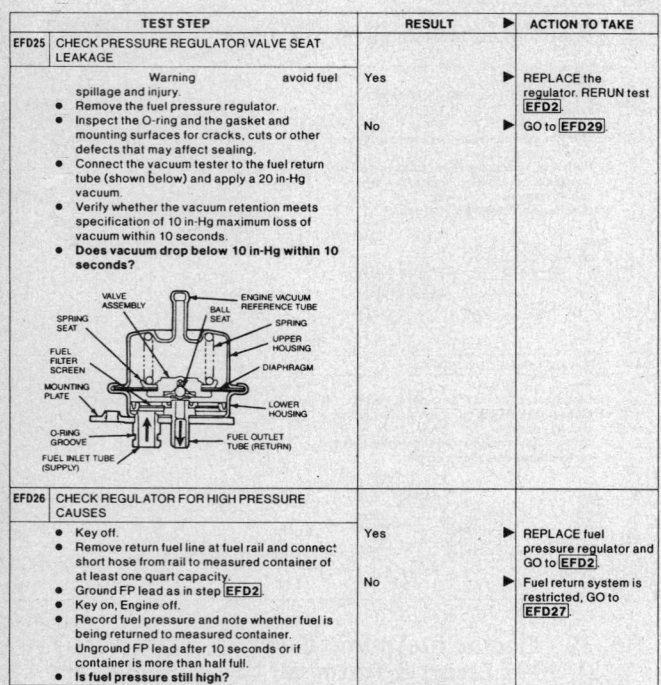

TEST STEP	RESULT	▶	ACTION TO TAKE
EFD26 CHECK REGULATOR FOR HIGH PRESSURE CAUSES • Key off. • Remove return fuel line at fuel rail and connect short hose from rail to measured container of at least one quart capacity. • Ground FP lead as in step **EFD2**. • Key on, Engine off. • Record fuel pressure and note whether fuel is being returned to measured container. Unground FP lead after 10 seconds or if container is more than half full. • **Is fuel pressure still high?**	Yes No	▶ ▶	REPLACE fuel pressure regulator and GO to **EFD2**. Fuel return system is restricted, GO to **EFD27**.

FM1029100072100X

Fig. 29   Electric fuel pump diagnosis chart (Part 10 of 12). 1993 Escort & Tracer w/1.9L/4-116 engine

TEST STEP	RESULT	▶	ACTION TO TAKE
EFD31 CHECK FUEL INJECTOR ELECTRICAL CONTINUITY SIGNAL • Key off. • Disconnect the injector lead and insert the continuity checker FA-407 (from the Rotunda Fuel Injector Tester) into the injector lead plug. • Start the engine. • Observe whether the continuity checker blinks (showing a completed circuit for the injector being tested). • Repeat the check for each injector. • **Do all injector circuits show continuity?**	Yes No	▶ ▶	GO to **EFD32**. CHECK for 12 volts at each injector lead. SERVICE or REPLACE leads as required. REFER to EEC-IV Quick Test Section
EFD32 CHECK FUEL INJECTOR FLOW AND LEAKAGE **Warning** — avoid fuel spillage and injury. • Verify that the fuel injectors flow within specification, using Rotunda Injector Tester 113-00001, SBDS Injector Flow Tester or equivalent. • **Is flow rate for individual injectors within specification?**	Yes No	▶ ▶	CHECK fuel lines for leaks. If none found REPLACE fuel pump assembly. GO to **EFD2**. REPLACE the defective injectors as required. RERUN test **EFD32**. REPEAT **EFD3**.

FM1029100072120X

Fig. 29   Electric fuel pump diagnosis chart (Part 12 of 12). 1993 Escort & Tracer w/1.9L/4-116 engine

	TEST STEP	RESULT	▶	ACTION TO TAKE
EFD27	CHECK FUEL RETURN SYSTEM FOR HIGH PRESSURE CAUSES (TYPE 2) **Warning** — avoid fuel spillage and injury. • Check the fuel return system(s) for restriction due to blockage, kinking, or pinching. • Remove the fuel return line at the fuel pressure regulator. • Apply 3-5 psi regulated shop air to the fuel return line. • **Do you hear air entering either tank?**	Yes No	▶ ▶	RECONNECT fuel return line. SERVICE Fuel system GO to **EFD28**.
EFD28	CHECK FUEL RETURN SYSTEM • Key off. **Warning** — avoid fuel spillage and injury. • Fuel return line disconnected at the fuel pressure regulator. • Disconnect the fuel return line near the fuel tank. • Apply 3-5 psi regulated shop air to the return line at the pressure regulator side. • On Type 2 system perform test for both tanks. • **Does air flow freely through the line?**	Yes No	▶ ▶	REPLACE fuel pump assembly. GO to **EFD2**. SERVICE the fuel return line. RECONNECT fuel line. GO to **EFD2**.
EFD29	CHECK FUEL INJECTOR FUNCTION • With the engine warmed and idling (or cranking if it does not start) and using a mechanics' stethoscope or equivalent, listen for regularly spaced operating sounds at each fuel injector. • **Is operating sound present?**	Yes No	▶ ▶	GO to **EFD32**. GO to **EFD30**.
EFD30	CHECK FUEL INJECTOR RESISTANCE • Key off. • Disconnect the electrical connector of the injector (one at a time). • Measure the resistance of each injector, using the DVOM. • Refer to the fuel injector application chart. • **Are all resistances between 13.0 and 16.0 ohms?**	Yes No	▶ ▶	GO to **EFD31**. REPLACE the faulty injectors. RECONNECT injectors.

FM1029100072110X

Fig. 29   Electric fuel pump diagnosis chart (Part 11 of 12). 1993 Escort & Tracer w/1.9L/4-116 engine

FF Vehicles

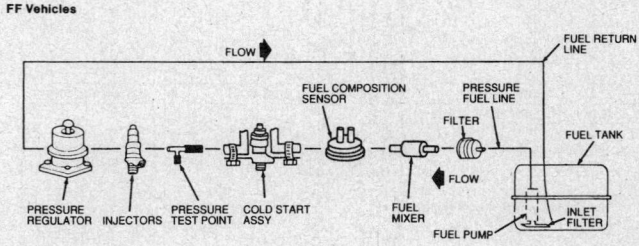

PINPOINT TEST A: FUEL SYSTEM DIAGNOSTICS

	TEST STEP	RESULT	▶	ACTION TO TAKE
A1	INSPECT SYSTEM • Run Self-Test to verify no electrical codes. • Check fuel system for adequate fuel supply. • Check inertia fuel shutoff (IFS) switch. • Verify that the battery is fully charged. • Check fuse for open condition. • Visually inspect the fuel delivery system including fuel tank, lines, filter, injectors, pressure regulator, battery, electrical lines, and connectors for leakage, looseness, cracks, pinching, kinking, corrosion, grounding, abrasion, or other damage caused by accident, collision, assembly or usage. • **Is the system free of any evidence of leakage, damage, or any evident cause for concern?**	Yes No	▶ ▶	GO to **A2**. SERVICE or REPLACE components as necessary. GO to **A2**.
A2	CHECK FUEL PUMP FUNCTION • Install the fuel pressure tester on the schrader valve on the fuel injection supply manifold. • Locate the data link connector (DLC) in the engine compartment. Ground fuel pump (FP) lead. • Turn the ignition key to the RUN position to operate the fuel pump. • Raise vehicle on hoist and use stethoscope to listen to fuel tank to monitor fuel pump sound. CAUTION: Unless otherwise specified, at the completion of each step, shut off the fuel pump by removing ground from jumper to FP lead or by turning ignition switch to the OFF position. Grounding the FP lead allows the fuel pump to run continuously when the ignition switch is in the RUN position. • **Is fuel pump running?**	Yes No	▶ ▶	GO to **A3**. GO to **A6**.

FM1029300079010X

Fig. 30   Electric fuel pump diagnosis chart (Part 1 of 5). 1993 Mark VIII, Sable & Taurus

PINPOINT TEST A: FUEL SYSTEM DIAGNOSTICS (Continued)

TEST STEP	RESULT	▶	ACTION TO TAKE
A3 CHECK FUEL INJECTION SUPPLY MANIFOLD STATIC PRESSURE • Run fuel pump as in A2. • Verify that the observed fuel pressure is within 255-297 kPa (37-43 psi). • Observe the time it takes to reach the specified fuel pressure limits. • **Is the fuel pressure with 255-297 kPa (37-43 psi) within 3 seconds of turning key to RUN?** NOTE: If fuel has been evacuated from the lines which occurs when a line is disconnected or schrader valve is depressed for an extended time (no fuel in lines), it may take up to 12 seconds to obtain pressure.	Yes No	▶ ▶	GO to A4. If pressure is high, GO to A11. Otherwise, GO to A12.
A4 CHECK FUEL INJECTION SUPPLY MANIFOLD STATIC LEAKDOWN • Run fuel pump as in A2 for 10 seconds and note pressure. • Turn off fuel pump and monitor pressure for 1 minute. (Remove ground or turn ignition switch to the OFF position.) • **Does the fuel rail pressure remain within 34 kPa (5 psi) of shut off pressure for one-minute?**	Yes No	▶ ▶	GO to A5. GO to A13.
A5 TEST VEHICLE UNDER LOAD • Remove and block vacuum hose to pressure regulator. • Run vehicle at idle and then increase engine speed to 2000 rpm or more in short bursts. • **Does fuel injection supply pressure remain 210-310 kPa (30-45 psi) with engine running?** NOTE: Running vehicle under load with vacuum hose removed from fuel pressure regulator (road test) may give better results. NOTE: The Taurus FF vehicle has a voltage control system for the fuel pump. When starting and when the engine speed is greater than 3300 rpm, the fuel pump electrical supply will be at system voltage. At other times, voltage to the fuel pump will be reduced. If this system fails to operate properly, a diagnostic test code will be produced.	Yes No	▶ ▶	Fuel system is OK. DISCONNECT all test connections. CONNECT vacuum hose to pressure regulator. GO to A14 to check injectors. CONNECT vacuum hose to pressure regulator, GO to A6.
A6 CHECK FUEL PUMP VOLTAGE SUPPLY • Check for voltage to fuel pump through the wiring harness by connecting pump power to ground wire leads through a voltmeter. Test point should be in the body wiring harness as close to the fuel pump as is possible. • Attempt to run pump as in A2. • Check battery voltage with voltmeter. • **Is voltage greater than 10.5 volts and within 0.5 volt of battery voltage?** NOTE: The Taurus FF vehicle has a voltage control system for the fuel pump. When operating the fuel as in Step A2, the fuel pump is powered by system voltage.	Yes No	▶ ▶	GO to A7. RUN Self-Test to check electrical system diagnostics. SERVICE as needed, then GO to A3 to verify.

FM1029300079020X

Fig. 30   Electric fuel pump diagnosis chart (Part 2 of 5). 1993 Mark VIII, Sable & Taurus

PINPOINT TEST A: FUEL SYSTEM DIAGNOSTICS (Continued)

TEST STEP	RESULT	▶	ACTION TO TAKE
A7 CHECK ELECTRICAL RESISTANCE OF FUEL PUMP • Check for continuity through fuel pump by connecting ohmmeter to pump power and ground wire leads as close to fuel pump as possible. • **Is there continuity through the fuel pump?**	Yes No	▶ ▶	If fuel pump runs, GO to A8. If fuel pump does not run, GO to A10. REPLACE fuel pump and RECHECK as in A2. If fuel pump runs, GO to A3. If fuel pump does not run, RECHECK fuel pump connectors for oversize connectors or other source of non-continuous electrical circuit. SERVICE as required, GO to A3.
A8 CHECK FUEL PUMP STATIC PRESSURE (IN-LINE FUEL FILTER CHECK) • Install a second fuel pressure tester on schrader valve equivalent installed between fuel pump and the in-line fuel filter, as close to fuel pump as possible. • Operate fuel pump as in A3 and compare pressure observed at the fuel injection supply manifold with the pressure observed at the fuel pump. • **Is pressure at fuel pump within 68 kPa (10 psi) of fuel injection supply manifold pressure?** NOTE: When fuel pump is not in operation, the fuel delivery system is at the same pressure, regardless of location of pressure tap. Therefore, both gauges should read the same pressure when fuel pump is not in operation. Any difference in pressure readings when fuel pump is not in operation is due to pressure gauge error.	Yes No	▶ ▶	GO to A10. REPLACE in-line fuel filter and GO to A3. If pressure is OK, GO to A4. If pressure is not OK, RECHECK fuel lines for kinks or other restrictions. SERVICE and RECHECK as in Step A3.
A9 TEST FUEL PUMP CHECK VALVE • Install fuel pressure tester on schrader valve equivalent installed between fuel pump and in-line fuel filter, as close to fuel pump as possible. • Operate fuel pump momentarily as in A2 and bring pressure to about system pressure. • Observe fuel pressure for one minute. • **Does pressure remain within 34 kPa (5 psi) of starting pressure over one minute period?**	Yes No	▶ ▶	GO to A5. REPLACE fuel pump assembly. RECHECK pressure in Step A3.
A10 CHECK STATIC FUEL PUMP CURRENT DRAW • Install an ammeter in series with the fuel pump electrical circuit. • Operate fuel pump as in A2. • **Is current draw within 2-9 amps?**	Yes No	▶ ▶	Static test of fuel pump is OK. GO to A14 to check injectors. Dynamic testing may be required to detect root cause. REPLACE fuel pump assembly. If current is high, contamination may be a concern. INSPECT fuel tank for debris and CLEAN tank as needed. GO to A2.
A11 CHECK FUEL PRESSURE REGULATOR • Disconnect return line at fuel pressure regulator. Connect outlet of regulator to appropriate receptacle to catch return fuel. • Run fuel pump as in Step A2. • **Is fuel pressure within 255-297 kPa (37-43 psi)?**	Yes No	▶ ▶	GO to A18. REPLACE fuel pressure regulator. RECHECK pressure as in Step A3.

FM1029300079030X

Fig. 30   Electric fuel pump diagnosis chart (Part 3 of 5). 1993 Mark VIII, Sable & Taurus

PINPOINT TEST A: FUEL SYSTEM DIAGNOSTICS (Continued)

TEST STEP	RESULT	▶	ACTION TO TAKE
A12 CHECK FUEL PRESSURE REGULATOR • Disconnect return line at fuel pressure regulator. Connect outlet of regulator to appropriate receptacle to catch return fuel. • Run fuel pump as in Step A2. • **Is fuel being returned from regulator with low pressure in system?**	Yes No	▶ ▶	REPLACE regulator. RECHECK pressure as in Step A3. GO to A4.
A13 CHECK FUEL PRESSURE REGULATOR FOR LEAKS • Disconnect return line at fuel pressure regulator. Connect outlet of regulator to appropriate receptacle to catch return fuel. • Run fuel pump as in A2. • Turn off fuel pump by removing ground or turning ignition to OFF position. • Observe fuel return flow from regulator and system when pump is off. • Remove vacuum hose from fuel pressure regulator and check for presence of fuel in regulator fitting (diaphragm leak). • **Is there return flow when pump is turned off and system pressure is dropping or is there fuel in regulator fitting?**	Yes No	▶ ▶	REPLACE regulator and RECHECK pressure and leakage as in Steps A3 and A4. If OK, GO to A5. If not OK, REPEAT Step A3. If leakdown concern exists, GO to A8. Otherwise, GO to A7.
A14 CHECK FUEL INJECTOR FUNCTION • With the engine warmed and idling (or cranking it if it does not start) and using a mechanics stethoscope or equivalent, listen for regularly spaced operating sounds at each fuel injector. • **Is operating sound present?**	Yes No	▶ ▶	GO to A17. GO to A15.
A15 CHECK FUEL INJECTOR RESISTANCE • Key off. • Disconnect the electrical connector of the injector (one at the time). • Measure the resistance of each injector, using the DVOM. • **Are all resistances between 13.0 and 18.0 ohms?**	Yes No	▶ ▶	GO to A16. REPLACE the worn or damaged injectors. RECONNECT injectors.
A16 CHECK FUEL INJECTOR ELECTRICAL CONTINUITY SIGNAL • Key off. • Disconnect the injector lead and insert the continuity checker FA-407 (from the Rotunda Fuel Injector Tester 113-00001) into the injector lead plug. • Start the engine. • Observe whether the continuity checker blinks (showing a completed circuit for the injector being tested). • Repeat the check for each injector. • **Do all injector circuits show continuity?**	Yes No	▶ ▶	GO to A17. CHECK for 12 volts at each injector lead. SERVICE or REPLACE leads as required. REFER to EEC-IV Quick Test.

FM1029300079040X

Fig. 30   Electric fuel pump diagnosis chart (Part 4 of 5). 1993 Mark VIII, Sable & Taurus

PINPOINT TEST A: FUEL SYSTEM DIAGNOSTICS (Continued)

TEST STEP	RESULT	▶	ACTION TO TAKE
A17 CHECK FUEL INJECTOR FLOW AND LEAKAGE • Observe "Note, Caution and Warning" to avoid fuel spillage and injury. • Using the Fuel Injector Tester as described in the accompanying instruction test the fuel injectors and verify that the flow rate for injector group is within specification. • With the tester still installed on the fuel system, note any significant pressure loss due to injector leakage when the tester pump is turned off. • Check the fuel injectors individually for leakage as required using the Injector Bench Fixture and the Fuel Injector Bench Testing Procedure associated with the Rotunda Tester as required and verify that each injector leakage rate is within specification (1 drop per minute maximum). • **Is flow rate for the injector group and the leakage rate for individual injectors within specification?**	Yes No	▶ ▶	Fuel injectors are OK. If pressure leakdown concern exists in system, CHECK lines and connections between fuel pump and pressure regulator for leaks. SERVICE as necessary. REPLACE the worn or damaged injectors as necessary. REPEAT test Step A17. When OK, GO to A3 to verify system.
A18 CHECK FUEL RETURN SYSTEM FOR HIGH PRESSURE CAUSES • Observe the "Note, Caution and Warning" to avoid fuel spillage and injury. • Check the fuel return system for restriction due to blockage, kinking, or pinching. • Remove the fuel return line at the fuel pressure regulator. • Apply 21-34 kPa (3-5 psi) regulated, filtered, shop air to the fuel return line. • **Do you hear air entering the tank?**	Yes No	▶ ▶	GO to A19. GO to A19.
A19 CHECK FUEL RETURN SYSTEM PRESSURE • Key off. • Reconnect fuel return line at the fuel pressure regulator. • Install a second fuel pressure tester on schrader valve equivalent installed in the return line at the fuel tank. • Operate fuel pump as in Step A3 and compare pressure observed at fuel injection supply manifold with the pressure observed at the fuel tank. • **Is pressure at the fuel tank within 34 kPa (5 psi) of fuel injection supply manifold pressure?**	Yes No	▶ ▶	VERIFY that fuel injection supply manifold pressure is higher than specification limits. REPLACE pressure regulator and RECHECK as in Step A3. SERVICE the return fuel line to remove excessive restriction. REPEAT Step A3 to verify.

FM1029300079050X

Fig. 30   Electric fuel pump diagnosis chart (Part 5 of 5). 1993 Mark VIII, Sable & Taurus

TEST STEP		RESULT	▶	ACTION TO TAKE
A1	**INITIAL SYSTEM INSPECTION**			
	• Check fuel system for adequate fuel supply.	Yes	▶	GO to A2.
	• Visually inspect the fuel delivery system including fuel tank lines, filter, injectors, pressure regulator, battery, electrical lines and connectors for leakage, looseness, cracks, pinching, kinking, corrosion, grounding, abrasion, or other damage caused by accident, collision, assembly or usage.	No	▶	SERVICE or REPLACE. GO to A2.
	• Verify that the battery is fully charged.			
	• Check fuse integrity.			
	• **Is the system free of any evidence of leakage damage, or any evident cause for concern?**			

FM1029200077010X

Fig. 31 Electric fuel pump diagnosis chart (Part 1 of 6). 1993–94 Tempo & Topaz

3. Disconnect pump/sending unit electrical connector, then remove pump/sending unit retaining screws.
4. Disconnect and plug fuel supply and return lines, then remove pump/sending unit from fuel tank.
5. Disconnect two fuel pump wires from sending unit, then remove retaining clamp screw and clamp.
6. Remove rubber retaining band, then the pump from sending unit.
7. Reverse procedure to install. **Torque** pump/sending unit retaining screws to 9-15 inch lbs.

CONTINENTAL, CROWN VICTORIA, GRAND MARQUIS, MUSTANG, SABLE, TAURUS EXCEPT FLEXIBLE FUEL, TOWN CAR & TEMPO & TOPAZ

Removal

1. Relieve fuel system pressure as outlined under "Precautions."
2. Disconnect battery ground cable, then drain fuel from tank using fuel storage tanker tool No. 034-00002, or equivalent.
3. Raise and support vehicle, then disconnect and remove fuel filler tube.
4. Support fuel tank, then remove fuel tank support straps.
5. Disconnect fuel lines, vent hose and electrical connector(s), then place tank aside.
6. Clean area surrounding fuel pump retaining flange.
7. Turn the fuel pump locking ring counterclockwise and remove, using fuel tank sender wrench tool No. D84P-9275-A, or equivalent.
8. Remove fuel pump and bracket assembly, then remove and discard gasket.

Installation

1. Clean fuel pump mounting flange, fuel tank mounting surface and the seal ring groove.
2. Apply a light coat of premium long-life grease to new seal ring, then install in ring groove.
3. Install fuel pump and bracket/sender assembly. **Use care not to damage filter. Ensure locating keys are in keyways and seal ring remains in groove.**

4. While holding assembly, install locking ring finger tight. **Ensure all locking tabs are under tank lock ring tabs.**
5. Secure fuel pump assembly by rotating locking ring clockwise until ring stops against stop tabs.
6. Connect fuel hoses and tubes, secure tank straps, then lower vehicle.
7. Install filler tube and retaining screws.
8. Fill tank with a minimum of 10 gallons of gasoline. Check for leaks.
9. With the fuel pressure gauge tool No. T80L-9974-B, or equivalent, connected to the fuel diagnostic valve, turn ignition switch to the On position for three seconds. Repeat this procedure from five to ten times, until pressure reads at least 35 psi. Check for leaks.
10. Remove pressure gauge, start engine, then check for leaks.

CONTOUR & MYSTIQUE

1. Relieve fuel system pressure as outlined under "Precautions."
2. Disconnect battery ground cable.
3. Remove rear seat cushion, then plastic grommet from floor pan.
4. Disconnect fuel pump module electrical connectors.
5. Disconnect fuel and vapor return lines.
6. Using fuel tank sender wrench D84P-9275-A, or equivalent, turn fuel pump module locking ring counterclockwise, then remove ring.
7. Remove fuel pump module.
8. Reverse procedure to install.

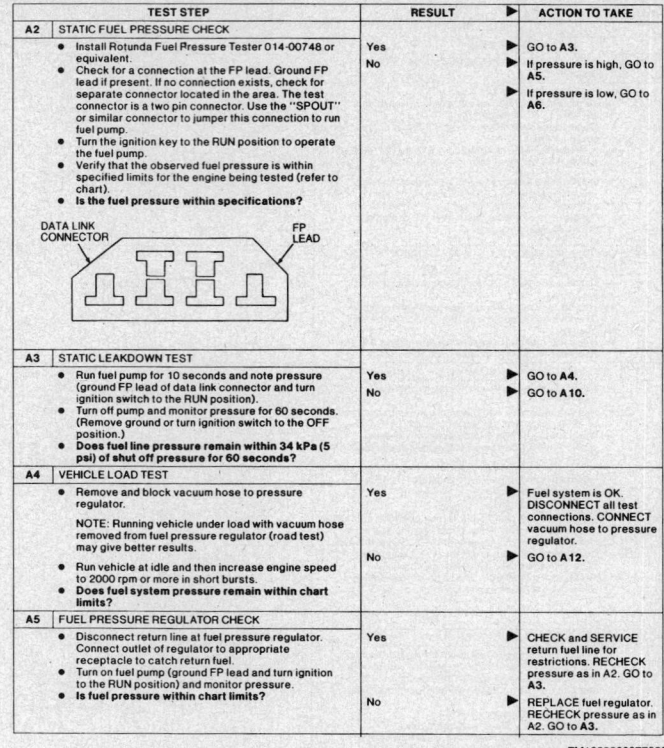

TEST STEP		RESULT	▶	ACTION TO TAKE
A2	**STATIC FUEL PRESSURE CHECK**			
	• Install Rotunda Fuel Pressure Tester 014-00748 or equivalent.	Yes	▶	GO to A3.
	• Check for a connection at the FP lead. Ground FP lead if present. If no connection exists, check for separate connector located in the area. The test connector is a two pin connector. Use the "SPOUT" or similar connector to jumper this connection to run fuel pump.	No	▶	If pressure is high, GO to A5.
	• Turn the ignition key to the RUN position to operate the fuel pump.		▶	If pressure is low, GO to A6.
	• Verify that the observed fuel pressure is within specified limits for the engine being tested (refer to chart).			
	• **Is the fuel pressure within specifications?**			
A3	**STATIC LEAKDOWN TEST**			
	• Run fuel pump for 10 seconds and note pressure (ground FP lead of data link connector and turn ignition switch to the RUN position).	Yes	▶	GO to A4.
	• Turn off pump and monitor pressure for 60 seconds. (Remove ground or turn ignition switch to the OFF position.)	No	▶	GO to A10.
	• **Does fuel line pressure remain within 34 kPa (5 psi) of shut off pressure for 60 seconds?**			
A4	**VEHICLE LOAD TEST**			
	• Remove and block vacuum hose to pressure regulator.	Yes	▶	Fuel system is OK. DISCONNECT all test connections. CONNECT vacuum hose to pressure regulator.
	NOTE: Running vehicle under load with vacuum hose removed from fuel pressure regulator (road test) may give better results.			
	• Run vehicle at idle and then increase engine speed to 2000 rpm or more in short bursts.	No	▶	GO to A12.
	• **Does fuel system pressure remain within chart limits?**			
A5	**FUEL PRESSURE REGULATOR CHECK**			
	• Disconnect return line at fuel pressure regulator. Connect outlet of regulator to appropriate receptacle to catch return fuel.	Yes	▶	CHECK and SERVICE return fuel line for restrictions. RECHECK pressure as in A2. GO to A3.
	• Turn on fuel pump (ground FP lead and turn ignition to the RUN position) and monitor pressure.			
	• **Is fuel pressure within chart limits?**	No	▶	REPLACE fuel regulator. RECHECK pressure as in A2. GO to A3.

FM1029200077020X

Fig. 31 Electric fuel pump diagnosis chart (Part 2 of 6). 1993–94 Tempo & Topaz

COUGAR, MARK VIII & THUNDERBIRD
Removal

1. Relieve fuel system pressure as outlined under "Precautions."
2. Disconnect battery ground cable, then drain fuel from tank using fuel storage tanker 034-00002, or equivalent.
3. Raise and support vehicle.
4. **On Cougar and Thunderbird,** remove exhaust pipe and shield.
5. **On all vehicles,** disconnect fuel hoses and tubes.
6. Disconnect the end of the vapor crossover over rear of driveshaft, then the filler hose. **The plastic fuel tube connections are on the top of the fuel tank. The tank must be lowered to gain access.**
7. Support fuel tank, then remove the bolts from fuel tank straps.
8. Lower the fuel tank, then disconnect the fuel lines and electrical connectors from sender.
9. Clean area surrounding fuel pump retaining flange.
10. Turn the fuel pump locking ring counterclockwise and remove, using fuel tank sender wrench tool No. D84P-9275-A, or equivalent.
11. Remove pump and sender assembly, then the seal ring. Discard seal ring.

Installation

1. Clean the fuel pump mounting flange, tank mounting surface and the seal ring groove.

TEST STEP		RESULT	▶	ACTION TO TAKE
A6	CHECK FUEL PUMP			
	• Turn on fuel pump (ground FP lead and turn ignition to the RUN position). • Raise vehicle on hoist and use stethoscope to listen to fuel tank to monitor fuel pump sound. • Is fuel pump running?	Yes	▶	GO to A9.
		No	▶	GO to A7.
A7	INERTIA FUEL SHUTOFF (IFS) SWITCH (9341) AND GROUND CHECK			
	• Check inertia fuel shutoff switch to see if it is open. • Check fuel pump ground connection in vehicle. • Are inertia fuel shutoff switch and ground connections OK?	Yes	▶	GO to A8.
		No	▶	RESET or REPLACE switch or SERVICE ground connection as required. RECHECK pressure as in A2. GO to A3.
A8	VOLTAGE CHECK			
	• Check for continuity through fuel pump to ground by connecting to pump power wire lead as close to pump as possible. • Check voltage as close to fuel pump as possible (Turn on pump as indicated in A6). • Is voltage within 0.5 Volt of battery voltage and is there continuity through pump?	Yes	▶	REPLACE fuel pump and RECHECK pressure as in A2. If pressure is OK, GO to A3. If pressure is not OK, RECHECK fuel pump connector for oversize connectors or other sources of open electrical circuit. SERVICE as required. GO to A3.
		No	▶	GO to A12.
A9	PRESSURE REGULATOR CHECK			
	• Replace fuel filter (if not replaced previously) and recheck pressure as in A2. If pressure is not OK, continue. If pressure is OK, go to A3. • Open return line at pressure regulator. Attach return fitting from regulator to suitable container to catch gasoline. • Turn on fuel pump as in A2. • Is fuel being returned from regulator with low pressure in system?	Yes	▶	REPLACE regulator as required. RECHECK pressure as in A2 and GO to A3 if OK. If not OK, REPEAT Step A2 until trouble found. If trouble not located, REPLACE pump and REPEAT A2.
		No	▶	RECHECK system for pressure restrictions and if none found, REPLACE pump. RECHECK pressure as in A2 and continue to A3.

FM1029200077030X

Fig. 31 Electric fuel pump diagnosis chart (Part 3 of 6). 1993–94 Tempo & Topaz

TEST STEP		RESULT	▶	ACTION TO TAKE
A10	PRESSURE REGULATOR LEAK TEST			
	• Open return line at pressure regulator and attach suitable container to catch return fuel. Line should be clear to observe fuel flow. • Run fuel pump as in A2. • Turn off fuel pump by removing ground from self test connector or turning ignition to OFF. • Observe fuel return flow from regulator and system pressure when pump is off. • Remove vacuum hose from fuel pressure regulator and check for presence of fuel in regulator fitting (diaphragm leak). • Is there return flow when pump is turned off and system pressure is dropping or fuel in regulator fitting?	Yes	▶	REPLACE regulator and RECHECK pressure and leakage as in A2 and A3. If OK, GO to A4. If not OK, REPEAT Step A2 and follow procedure.
		No	▶	GO to A11.
A11	PUMP CHECK VALVE TEST			
	• Open pressure line from fuel pump and attach pressure gauge to line and block line to allow pressure build up. • Operate pump momentarily as in A2 and bring pressure to about system pressure. • Observe fuel pressure for one minute. • Does pressure remain within 34 kPa (5 psi) of starting pressure over one minute period?	Yes	▶	CHECK injectors for leakage or regulator for internal leakage. Fuel pump check valve is OK. When serviced GO to A4.
		No	▶	CHECK lines and fittings from pump to rail for leakage, if none found, REPLACE pump assembly. RECHECK pressure as in A2 and when OK, GO to A4.
A12	FUEL SYSTEM RESTRICTION OR USAGE TEST			
	• Replace fuel line filter (if not previously replaced during this procedure) and repeat test A5. • Does system pressure remain within chart limits?	Yes	▶	System is OK, DISCONNECT all test connections and RECONNECT all loosened or removed parts and lines.
		No	▶	CHECK pressure lines for kinks or restrictions. CHECK at fuel pump for low voltage. GO to A13. CHECK for wrong size injectors (too large). If no concern found, REPLACE pump and REPEAT A4. If concern found, SERVICE and REPEAT A4.
A13	RELAY TYPE CHECK			
	• Does vehicle use IRCM (integrated Relay Control Module) for fuel pump control? Control module is located on upper radiator support bracket.	Yes	▶	Use IRCM tester to check module function, SERVICE or REPLACE if needed then GO to A2. If function OK, GO to A14.
		No	▶	GO to A16.

FM1029200077040X

Fig. 31 Electric fuel pump diagnosis chart (Part 4 of 6). 1993–94 Tempo & Topaz

2. Apply a light coating of premium long-life grease onto a new seal ring, then install into ring groove.
3. Install fuel pump sender assembly. **Ensure locating keys are in keyways and seal ring remains in ring groove.**
4. While holding pump assembly in place, install locking ring finger tight. **Ensure all locking tabs are under tang lock ring tabs.**
5. Turn locking ring clockwise until ring stops against stops.
6. Connect fuel hoses and tubes to tank, then secure tank with retaining straps.
7. Connect the filler hose and the exhaust pipe, then lower the vehicle.
8. Fill tank with a minimum of 10 gallons of gasoline, then check for leaks.
9. Install fuel pressure gauge tool No. T80L-9974-B, or equivalent, to fuel diagnostic valve. Turn ignition switch from the Off to the On position for three seconds. Repeat this procedure five to ten times, until pressure reads at least 35 psi. Check for leaks.
10. Remove pressure gauge, start the engine, then check for leaks.

ESCORT & TRACER

1. Relieve fuel system pressure as outlined under "Precautions."
2. Disconnect battery ground cable, then the fuel pump electrical connector.
3. Disconnect ground strap, then remove fuel pump assembly cover screws.
4. Remove fuel pump assembly cover, then the clips from fuel hoses.
5. Disconnect hoses from fuel pump, then remove spanner nut retaining pump assembly.
6. Remove fuel pump assembly and discard gasket.
7. Reverse procedure to install.

PROBE

1. Relieve fuel system pressure as outlined under "Precautions."
2. Disconnect battery ground cable.
3. Raise and support vehicle, then drain fuel from fuel tank.
4. Loosen filler neck hose clamp, then remove filler hose.
5. Loosen overflow, fuel supply and fuel return hose clamps, then remove hoses from fuel tank.
6. Remove two fuel tank vapor lines from fuel tank.
7. Disconnect fuel pump sender electrical connector from body harness.
8. Remove five nuts retaining exhaust heat shield to fuel tank.
9. Support fuel tank, then remove center fuel tank strap.
10. Remove righthand tank strap, then fuel tank heat shield from vehicle.
11. Remove lefthand tank strap, then lower fuel tank from vehicle.
12. Clean fuel tank thoroughly with steam or other approved method to sufficiently remove all explosive fuel vapor.
13. Remove fuel pump locking ring, then fuel pump/sending unit assembly.
14. Reverse procedure to install. **Do not apply excessive force to the bottom of fuel tank with floor jack. Possible damage to the fuel pump bracket inside the fuel tank could result.**

TAURUS w/FLEXIBLE FUEL

1. Relieve fuel system pressure as outlined under "Precautions."
2. Drain fuel tank as follows:
   a. Remove foam cover and protective rubber cover from drain tube, **Fig. 32.**
   b. Connect drain tube quick disconnect fitting to fuel storage tanker and adapter hose tool No. 034-00020, or equivalent, then drain fuel from fuel tank.
3. Raise and support vehicle, then remove fuel filler pipe.
4. Support fuel tank and remove tank support straps, then lower tank and disconnect fuel supply, vapor and vent lines and electrical connectors.
5. Remove fuel tank, then clean area surrounding fuel pump flange.
6. Remove fuel pump locking retainer ring using fuel tank sender wrench tool No. D90P-9275-A, or equivalent.
7. Lift pump/sending unit upward rotating left, while aligning float wiper arm retainer and return line into fuel tank location slots. Apply slight pressure to remove pump/sending unit.
8. Lift float wiper arm through lefthand fuel tank slot and pass pump motor retaining bracket through righthand fuel tank slot.
9. Remove pump/sending unit, keeping

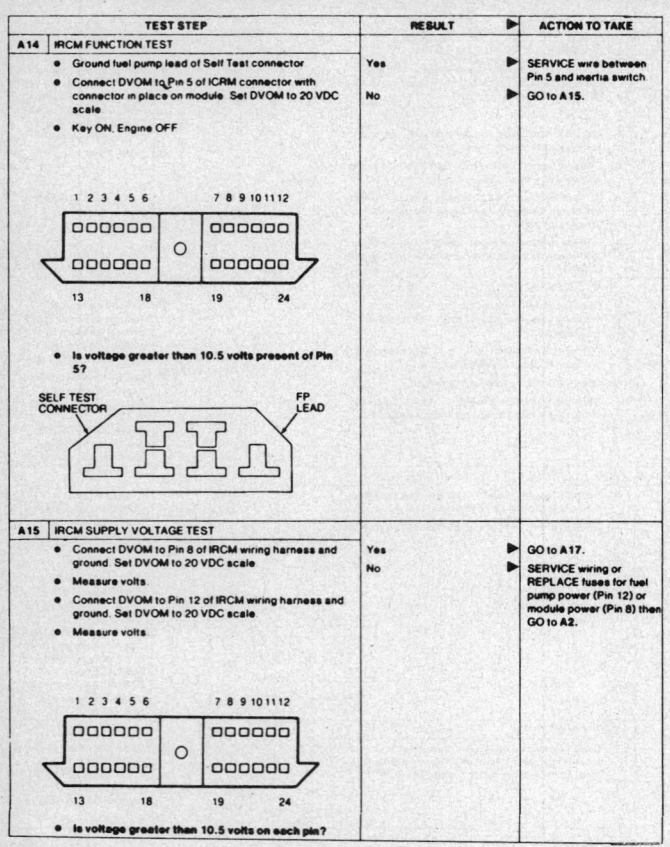

A14	IRCM FUNCTION TEST	RESULT	▶	ACTION TO TAKE
	• Ground fuel pump lead of Self Test connector	Yes	▶	SERVICE wire between Pin 5 and inertia switch.
	• Connect DVOM to Pin 5 of ICRM connector with connector in place on module. Set DVOM to 20 VDC scale	No	▶	GO to A15.
	• Key ON, Engine OFF			

• Is voltage greater than 10.5 volts present of Pin 5?

SELF TEST CONNECTOR   FP LEAD

A15	IRCM SUPPLY VOLTAGE TEST		▶	
	• Connect DVOM to Pin 8 of IRCM wiring harness and ground. Set DVOM to 20 VDC scale	Yes	▶	GO to A17.
	• Measure volts.	No	▶	SERVICE wiring or REPLACE fuses for fuel pump power (Pin 12) or module power (Pin 8) then GO to A2.
	• Connect DVOM to Pin 12 of IRCM wiring harness and ground. Set DVOM to 20 VDC scale			
	• Measure volts.			

• Is voltage greater than 10.5 volts on each pin?

FM1029200077050X

Fig. 31   Electric fuel pump diagnosis chart (Part 5 of 6). 1993–94 Tempo & Topaz

A16	CHECK VOLTAGE AT FUEL PUMP RELAY	RESULT	▶	ACTION TO TAKE
	• Key OFF.	Yes	▶	SERVICE wire from fuel pump relay to inertia fuel shutoff switch. GO to A2.
	• Battery fully charged.	No	▶	GO to A17.
	• Ground fuel pump lead of the data link connector as shown.			
	• Key ON, Engine OFF.			
	• DVOM on 20 volt scale.			
	• Measure the voltage at the fuel pump relay contact "A" as shown.			
	• Is voltage greater than 10.5 volts?			

COIL CONTACT
ARMATURE CONTACT   NORMALLY CLOSED CONTACT
COIL CONTACT   NORMALLY OPEN CONTACT

A17	CHECK VOLTAGE AT PIN 22 (PCM)		▶	
	• Key OFF.	Yes	▶	CHECK PCM for malfunction. After condition is corrected, GO to A2.
	• Battery fully charged.	No.	▶	SERVICE wire between powertrain control module and FP relay / CCRM. CHECK at VIP connector for lead presence. GO to A2 when condition corrected.
	• Remove powertrain control module (PCM) (12A650).			
	• Install Rotunda 60-Pin Breakout Box 007-00033 or Rotunda EEC-IV Monitor 007-0047C or equivalent.			
	• Key ON, Engine OFF.			
	• DVOM on 20 volt scale.			
	• Measure the voltage at Pin 22 of the breakout box, or			
	• With EEC-IV Monitor, install the appropriate overlay according to engine size and year. Place selector switch "A" on Pin 22, "FP", turn EEC-IV Monitor power on and read voltage at Pin 22 from LCD readout.			
	• Is voltage greater than 10.5 volts?			

FM1029200077060X

Fig. 31   Electric fuel pump diagnosis chart (Part 6 of 6). 1993–94 Tempo & Topaz

return line in fuel tank slot. Lift fuel pump inlet filter, then sender arm float through fuel tank opening.
10. Reverse procedure to install.

INERTIA SWITCH

In the event of a collision, the electrical contacts within the inertia switch open and the fuel pump automatically shuts off. The fuel pump will shutoff even if the engine does not stop running. The engine, however, will stop a few seconds after the fuel pump stops operating. It is not possible to start the engine until the inertia switch is manually reset.

To reset the switch, depress the button on the switch assembly. **Do not reset the switch until the fuel system has been checked for leaks.**

SWITCH LOCATION

ASPIRE
The switch is located on the lower lefthand side of rear compartment, behind wheelwell.

CAPRI
The switch is located on lefthand rear corner of luggage compartment.

CONTINENTAL
The switch is located on lefthand side of luggage compartment, below air suspension control module.

CONTOUR & MYSTIQUE
The switch is located under lefthand side of instrument panel, behind kick panel.

COUGAR & THUNDERBIRD
The switch is located on lefthand side of luggage compartment, behind trim panel.

CROWN VICTORIA & GRAND MARQUIS
The switch is located on lefthand side of luggage compartment, on support.

ESCORT & TRACER
On hatchback and wagon models, the switch is located on righthand side of rear compartment, under trim panel and above rear wheelwell.
On sedan models, the switch is located on righthand side of trunk, behind strut tower.

FESTIVA
The switch is located on lefthand side of rear compartment, above wheelwell.

MARK VIII
The switch is located on lefthand side of luggage compartment, behind wheelwell.

MUSTANG
1993
The switch is located in center rear of luggage compartment.

1994–96
The switch is located in lefthand rear lower of luggage compartment.

PROBE
The switch is located on lower righthand side of luggage compartment, behind wheelwell.

SABLE & TAURUS
1993–95
On wagon models the switch is located on righthand side of rear compartment, under trim panel and behind rear wheelwell.
On sedan models the switch is located on lefthand side of luggage compartment, above wheelwell.

1996
On wagon models the switch is located on righthand side of rear compartment, under trim panel and behind rear wheelwell.
On sedan models the switch is located on righthand side of luggage compartment, in front of wheelwell.

TOWN CAR
The switch is located in lefthand front of luggage compartment, mounted on package tray support.

TEMPO & TOPAZ
The switch is located in luggage compartment, on lefthand hinge support.

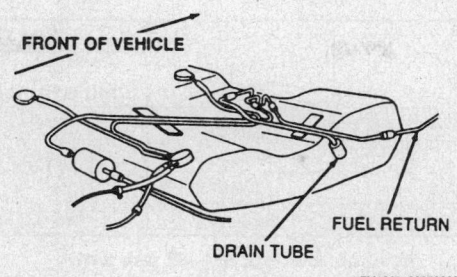

Fig. 32 Drain tube location. Taurus
w/Flexible Fuel

FUEL PUMP SPECIFICATIONS

Engine	Year	Fuel Pressure, psi	
		Engine Running	Key On/Engine Off ①
1.3L/4-81	1993	25—31	64—85
	1994—95	②	③
1.6L/4-98	1993	28—31	64—85
	1994	④	64—85
1.8L/4-112	1993	30—37	64—85
	1994—95	⑤	64—85
1.9L/4-116	1993-95	30—45	30—45
2.0L/4-121	1993	37—46	—
	1994—95	⑥	64—92
	1996	30—38	37—46
2.0L/4-122 DOHC Zetec	1995-96	37—41	39—43
2.3L/4-140 HSC	1993—94	45—60	50—60
2.3L/4-140 OHC	1993—94	30—45	35—40
2.5L/V6-152	1993	39—45	—
	1994—95	⑦	72—92
	1996	30—36	39—45
2.5L/V6-153 DOHC Duratec	1995-96	37—41	39—43
3.0L/V6-182 OHV	1993—95	30—45	35—40
	1996	30—45	37—43
3.0L/V6-182 DOHC Duratec	1996	30—45	37—43
3.0L/V6-182 SHO	1993—95	28—33	30—45
3.2L/V6-195 SHO	1993—95	28—33	30—45
3.8L/V6-232	1993—95	30—45	35—40
	1996	⑧	35—45
3.8L/V6-232 SC	1993—95	30—40	35—40

Continued

FUEL PUMP SPECIFICATIONS –Continued

Engine	Year	Fuel Pressure, psi	
		Engine Running	Key On/Engine Off ①
3.4L/V8-207 SHO	1996	—	—
4.6L/V8-281	1993—95	30—45	35—40
	1996	⑨	⑩
5.0L/V8-302	1993—95	30—45	35—40

①—Maximum output.
②—With pressure regulator vacuum hose connected, 30—38 psi; with pressure regulator vacuum hose disconnected, 38—46 psi.
③—Greater than 50 psi.
④—With pressure regulator vacuum hose connected, 27—34 psi; with pressure regulator vacuum hose disconnected, 36—43 psi.
⑤—With pressure regulator vacuum

hose connected, 31—38 psi; with pressure regulator vacuum hose disconnected, 40—49 psi.
⑥—With pressure regulator vacuum hose connected, 30—38 psi; with pressure regulator vacuum hose disconnected, 39—45 psi.
⑦—With pressure regulator vacuum hose connected, 30—36 psi; with pressure regulator vacuum hose

disconnected, 39—45 psi.
⑧—Mustang, 35—45 psi; Cougar & Thunderbird, 28—54 psi.
⑨—Continental, Crown Victoria, Grand Marquis, Mark VIII & Town Car, 30-45 psi, Mustang, 35-45 psi.
⑩—Continental, Crown Victoria, Grand Marquis & Town Car, 35-40 psi, Mark VIII, 37-43 psi, Mustang, 35-45 psi.

TURBOCHARGERS & SUPERCHARGERS

NOTE: On Air Bag Equipped Models, Refer To "Air Bag System Precautions" Located In The Front Of This Manual For System Disarming & Arming Procedures.

NOTE: If Unsure Of The System Used On The Vehicle Being Serviced, Refer To The "Engine Systems Identification Chart." Further Assistance For The Proper Use Of Information Contained In This Section Can Also Be Found In The Front Of This Tabbed Section Under "How To Use This Manual."

INDEX

	Page No.		Page No.		Page No.
Description:	7-1	Capri	7-2	Troubleshooting:	7-1
Capri	7-1	System Service:	7-3	Capri	7-1
Thunderbird	7-1	Capri	7-3	Thunderbird	7-2
Diagnosis & Testing:	7-2	Thunderbird	7-5		

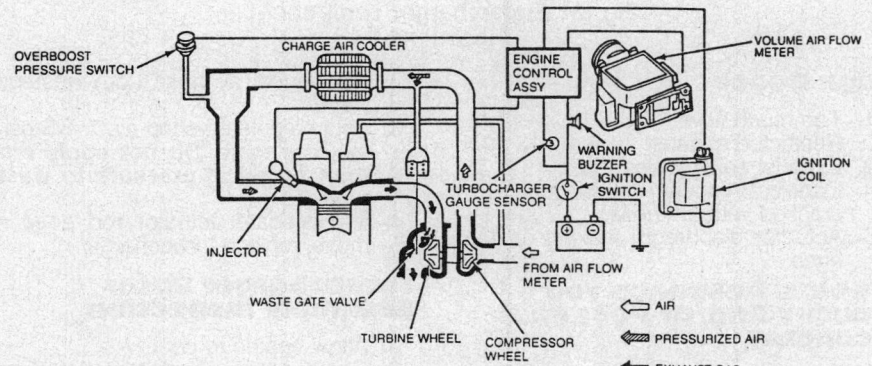

Fig. 1   Air-fuel & exhaust gas flow.
Capri w/DOHC & turbocharger

DESCRIPTION

CAPRI

TURBOCHARGER

The turbocharger is an on demand system that boosts engine output at high load/high speed conditions. The intercooler located next to the radiator cools intake air from the turbocharger before it enters the engine, providing for a denser air charge and increased engine performance, **Fig. 1.**

The turbocharger is part of a highly integrated engine turbocharging system. Turbocharged parts and equipment are not interchangeable with similar parts on non-turbocharged engines.

Lubrication

Turbochargers are lubricated by engine oil. This turbocharger operates at speeds up to 150,000 RPM which makes the lubrication of the bearings which support the shaft important for cooling as well as friction reduction. To check oil pressure proceed as follows:

1. Turbocharger oil pressure is obtained through an adapter fitting on rear of engine.

2. Oil pressure is supplied to turbocharger through an oil supply tube. Oil enters turbocharger through a controlled orifice in center housing, which controls flow of oil into turbocharger.
3. Center housing bearings are lubricated through oil passages which direct oil to bearings. A piston ring seal is used at each end of the turbocharger shaft to prevent engine oil leakage into compressor and turbine housing. **Exhaust system suction can caused oil to leak past these seal during diagnosis.**
4. Oil drains from turbocharger through a return port in bottom of center housing.
5. Oil returns to engine through an oil return line.

THUNDERBIRD

SUPERCHARGER

The supercharger is a positive displacement pump. Its purpose is to supply an excess volume of intake air to the engine by increasing air pressure and density in the intake manifold. The supercharger is matched to the engine by its displacement and belt ratio, and can provide excess airflow to the engine at any speed.

The supercharger is serviced only as a assembly.

Lubrication

The supercharger has a self contained oiling system that does not require a fluid change for the life of the vehicle. However, the oil level should be checked every 30,000 miles. To check oil level proceed as follows:

1. Park vehicle on level ground, then allow engine to cool.
2. Remove Allen head plug located at the front of the supercharger.
3. The oil level should be at the bottom of the fill plug threads when cold. If level is low, add synthetic supercharger fluid part No. E9SZ-19577-A or equivalent.
4. Install Allen plug.

TROUBLESHOOTING

CAPRI

No Boost

1. Compressor inlet hose collapsed.
2. Compressor outlet to throttle body hose leaking.
3. Turbocharger turbine or compressor wheel damage.
4. Turbocharger bearings seized.
5. Wastegate stuck open.
6. Clogged air cleaner element or restriction upstream of compressor.

Lack Of Power

1. Low engine compression.
2. Incorrect valve timing and/or clearance.
3. Incorrect ignition timing.
4. Clogged air cleaner element or restriction upstream of compressor.
5. Insufficient fuel supply.
6. Restriction.
7. Low fuel pressure.
8. Oxygen sensor malfunctioning.

9. Electronic control assembly malfunctioning.
10. Volume air flow meter malfunctioning.

Detonation w/No Boost

1. Low grade fuel.
2. Ignition timing advanced too far.

Detonation w/Normal Boost

1. Low grade fuel.
2. Ignition timing advanced too far.
3. Insufficient fuel supply.
4. Restriction.
5. Low fuel pressure.
6. Oxygen sensor malfunctioning.
7. Powertrain control module malfunctioning.
8. Engine overheating.
9. Oil leaking into compressor from turbocharger.
10. Valve seals leaking oil.

Excessive Fuel Consumption (Black Exhaust Smoke)

1. Engine out of tune.
2. Volume air flow meter malfunctioning.
3. High fuel pressure.
4. Pressure regulator.
5. Fuel return line plugged or kinked.
6. Injectors leaking.
7. Oxygen sensor malfunctioning.
8. Powertrain control module malfunctioning.

Excessive Oil Consumption (Blue, Gray, or White Exhaust Smoke)

1. Incorrect type or grade of oil.
2. Extended oil change intervals.
3. Clogged air cleaner element or restriction upstream of compressor.
4. Engine wear (piston rings, valve guides).
5. PCV system malfunctioning.
6. Turbocharger oil seals leaking.

Noise Or Vibration

1. Leaks at turbocharger inlet and outlet connections.
2. Foreign object damage to turbine or compressor blades.
3. Turbine bearing failure.

High Boost

1. Wastegate not operating.
2. Leak in exhaust system before muffler.
3. Leak in wastegate activator to compressor.
4. Discharge hose.

THUNDERBIRD

Low Boost

1. Air leak at intercooler, flanges, ducts, supercharger housing.
2. Contamination in system, blockage.
3. Supercharger not turning.
4. Bypass not closing.
5. Insufficient flow from supercharger.
6. Incorrect rotor clearances.
7. Supercharger pulley slipping on shaft.
8. Incorrect vacuum hose routing or cracked vacuum hose.
9. Incorrect drive belt tension.

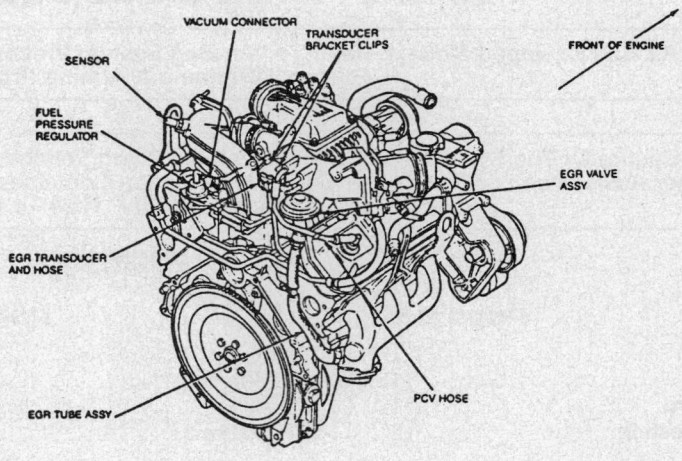

Fig. 2 Supercharger component locations

High Boost

1. Too much flow.
2. Restricted exhaust system.
3. Exhaust catalyst damaged.
4. Incorrect vacuum hose routing or cracked vacuum hose.
5. Actuator diaphragm leaking or damaged.

Vehicle Response Too Touchy And/Or Poor Fuel Economy

1. Bypass actuator not functioning properly.
2. Bypass not opening.
3. Incorrect vacuum hose routing or cracked vacuum hose.
4. Actuator diaphragm leaking or damaged.

Supercharger Noisy

1. Gear rattle or mechanical damage to supercharger.
2. Rough engine idle.
3. Supercharger bypass valve not opening.
4. Low supercharger oil level.
5. Foreign object ingestion.

Noise In Air Handling System

1. Air leaks in air tube flanges.
2. Supercharger components not properly isolated.

Oil Outside Of Supercharger

1. Leaking seals.
2. Loose fill plug.
3. Input shaft damaged at seal.

DIAGNOSIS & TESTING

CAPRI

Wastegate Functioning Check

1. Allow engine to cool.

2. Disconnect air hose from wastegate valve.
3. Apply regulated shop air, 7-8.5 psi to the wastegate. **Do not apply more than 14 psi of pressure to wastegate.**
4. If wastegate actuator rod does not move, replace turbocharger.

Turbocharger Rotor Assembly Inspection

1. Allow engine to cool.
2. Remove turbocharger inlet air duct.
3. Spin rotor by hand and check for rough or noisy operation, if rotation is not smooth and quiet, replace turbocharger.

Turbocharger Rotor Vane Inspection

1. With air duct removed, check rotor blades for wear, damage or contamination.
2. If these conditions are found, replace turbocharger.

Turbocharger Lube System Inspection

1. Allow engine to cool.
2. Remove oil line from turbocharger and inspect for blockage or carbonized oil.
3. If blockage is found in turbocharger, replace turbocharger.
4. If blockage is found in oil line, replace as necessary.

Turbocharger Seal Leakage Check

1. Allow engine to cool.
2. Disconnect turbocharger pipes and hoses.
3. Examine hoses, pipes and turbocharger passages for signs of oil and/or coolant leaks.
4. If these conditions are found, replace turbocharger.

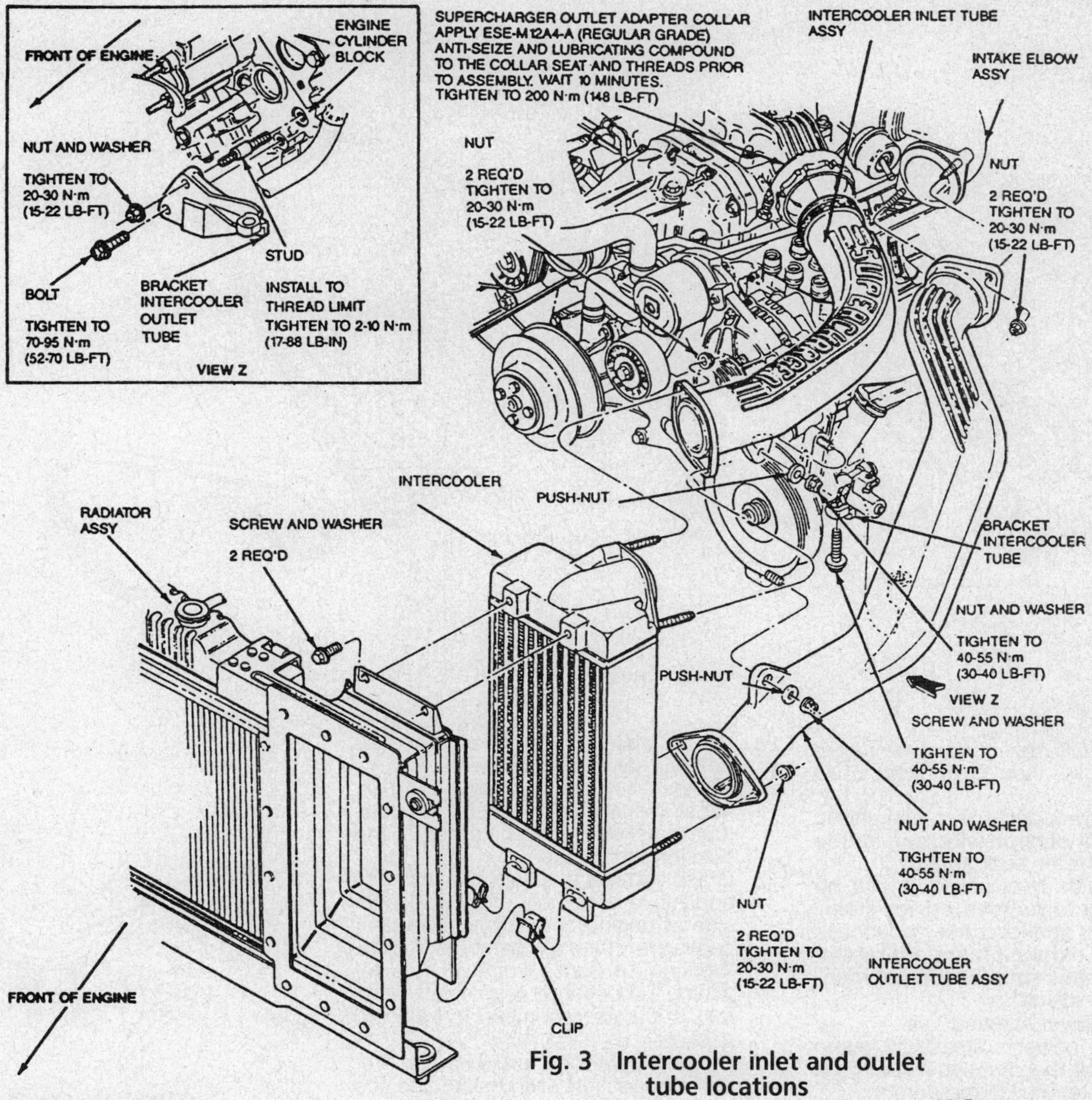

ENGINE
CYLINDER
BLOCK

FRONT OF ENGINE

NUT AND WASHER

TIGHTEN TO
20-30 N·m
(15-22 LB-FT)

BOLT
TIGHTEN TO
70-95 N·m
(52-70 LB-FT)

BRACKET
INTERCOOLER
OUTLET
TUBE

STUD

INSTALL TO
THREAD LIMIT
TIGHTEN TO 2-10 N·m
(17-88 LB-IN)

VIEW Z

SUPERCHARGER OUTLET ADAPTER COLLAR
APPLY ESE-M12A4-A (REGULAR GRADE)
ANTI-SEIZE AND LUBRICATING COMPOUND
TO THE COLLAR SEAT AND THREADS PRIOR
TO ASSEMBLY. WAIT 10 MINUTES.
TIGHTEN TO 200 N·m (148 LB-FT)

INTERCOOLER INLET TUBE
ASSY

INTAKE ELBOW
ASSY

NUT
2 REQ'D
TIGHTEN TO
20-30 N·m
(15-22 LB-FT)

NUT
2 REQ'D
TIGHTEN TO
20-30 N·m
(15-22 LB-FT)

INTERCOOLER

PUSH-NUT

RADIATOR
ASSY

SCREW AND WASHER
2 REQ'D

FRONT OF ENGINE

PUSH-NUT

CLIP

BRACKET
INTERCOOLER
TUBE

NUT AND WASHER
TIGHTEN TO
40-55 N·m
(30-40 LB-FT)

VIEW Z
SCREW AND WASHER
TIGHTEN TO
40-55 N·m
(30-40 LB-FT)

NUT AND WASHER
TIGHTEN TO
40-55 N·m
(30-40 LB-FT)

NUT
2 REQ'D
TIGHTEN TO
20-30 N·m
(15-22 LB-FT)

INTERCOOLER
OUTLET TUBE ASSY

Fig. 3 Intercooler inlet and outlet tube locations

SYSTEM SERVICE
CAPRI
TURBOCHARGER, REPLACE
Removal

Turbocharger is serviced by replacement only.

Before starting any turbocharger service or removal procedure, clean area around turbocharger assembly with suitable non-caustic solution. Cover opening of engine assembly and turbocharger connections to prevent entry of foreign matter while turbocharger is off engine. When removing turbocharger assembly, be careful not to bend, nick or in any way damage the compressor wheel blades. Any damage may result in rotating assembly imbalance, and failure of bearings and oil seals.

1. Disconnect battery ground cable, then drain cooling system.
2. Remove throttle body air intake tube.
3. Disconnect intercooler hose from turbocharger assembly, then position aside.

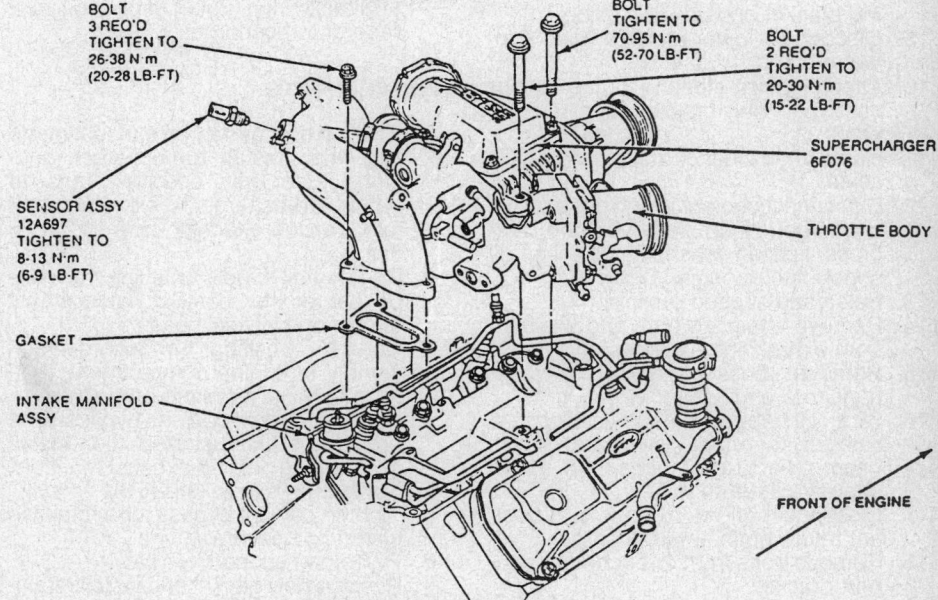

BOLT
3 REQ'D
TIGHTEN TO
26-38 N·m
(20-28 LB-FT)

BOLT
TIGHTEN TO
70-95 N·m
(52-70 LB-FT)

BOLT
2 REQ'D
TIGHTEN TO
20-30 N·m
(15-22 LB-FT)

SUPERCHARGER
6F076

THROTTLE BODY

SENSOR ASSY
12A697
TIGHTEN TO
8-13 N·m
(6-9 LB-FT)

GASKET

INTAKE MANIFOLD
ASSY

FRONT OF ENGINE

Fig. 4 Supercharger retaining bolt locations

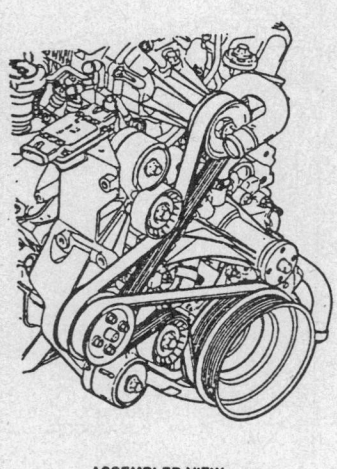

ASSEMBLED VIEW

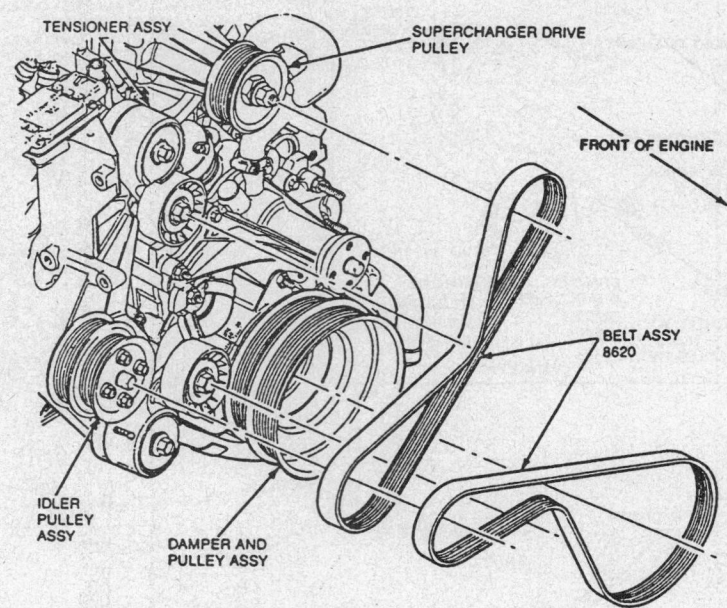

Fig. 5 Supercharger drive belt routing

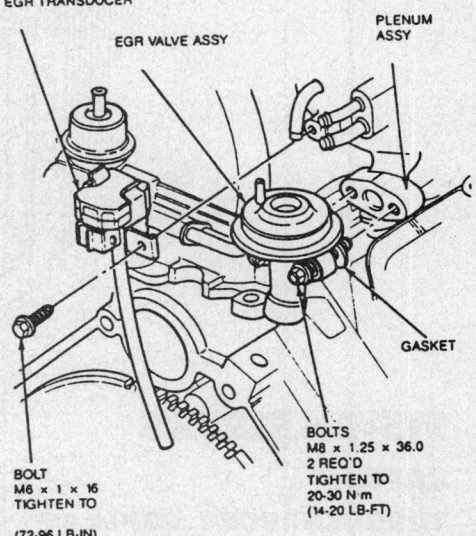

Fig. 6 EGR component locations. Thunderbird

4. Remove EGO sensor connector from retaining clip, then disconnect EGO sensor.
5. Remove lower and upper heat shield. **Feed EGO sensor wire and guide through upper heat shield.**
6. Remove side heat shield. **It will be necessary to remove power steering pump and bracket to access lower left exhaust manifold retaining nut, then remove exhaust manifold from studs.**
7. Remove power steering belt.
8. Remove power steering pump through bolt, then remove nut and bolt from adjuster. Pull pump from mounting bracket and position aside.
9. Disconnect lower radiator hose from water pump.
10. Attach power steering pump to access mounting bracket, then remove bracket.
11. Remove air cleaner duct and position aside.
12. Disconnect coolant return hose at turbocharger, then remove bolt and brass sealing washers retaining oil supply line at engine block.
13. Raise and support vehicle.
14. Remove attaching nuts and washers from exhaust pipe flange.
15. Remove bolts retaining exhaust hanger to engine block.
16. Slide off rubber exhaust hangers at catalyst, then pull downward on exhaust pipe to gain access to turbocharger oil return hose.
17. Disconnect oil return hose and coolant return hose at turbocharger.
18. Remove bolts from turbocharger support bracket.
19. Remove bolts retaining coolant bypass tube outlet to water pump.
20. Lower vehicle.

21. Loosen clamp bolt on coolant bypass tube at rear of cylinder head.
22. Remove 11 retaining nuts from exhaust manifold. Pull coolant bypass tube bracket from exhaust stud and position tube aside.
23. Grasp exhaust manifold, pull off studs and move assembly slightly to right side of engine compartment to clear cooling fan, then remove from vehicle.
24. Working on bench, remove nuts retaining turbocharger to exhaust manifold, separate assembly and discard gasket.
25. Before installing turbocharger, remove all gaskets and sealant and add 1.53 cubic inch (25cc) of oil in oil passage of turbocharger.

Installation

1. Position new gasket on exhaust manifold, then install turbocharger onto studs. Use only specified nuts to mount turbocharger to exhaust manifold. **Torque** attaching nuts to 20-25 ft. lbs.
2. Remove oil supply tube line from turbocharger, then position new exhaust gasket on cylinder head.
3. Carefully position turbocharger assembly in engine compartment, then slide exhaust manifold onto studs.
4. Position heater coolant bypass tube bracket on exhaust stud, then install 11 retaining nuts on exhaust manifold. **Torque** nuts to 29-42 ft. lbs.
5. Tighten coolant bypass tube retaining clamp bolt securely.
6. Raise and support vehicle.
7. Position new gasket and install retaining bolts on coolant bypass tube outlet. **Torque** bolts to 14-19 ft. lbs.
8. Install retaining bolts into turbochar-

er support bracket. **Torque** bolts to 32-45 ft. lbs.
9. Connect coolant return hose and oil return hose.
10. Position exhaust pipe onto turbocharger, then install bolts on exhaust hanger at engine.
11. Slide on rubber exhaust hangers at catalyst. **Torque** exhaust pipe retaining nuts to 17-24 ft. lbs.
12. Lower vehicle.
13. Install retaining bolt and brass washers on oil supply line, then carefully position oil line into vehicle and hand start bolt into engine block. Connect oil line to turbocharger and finger tighten. Ensure one brass washer is

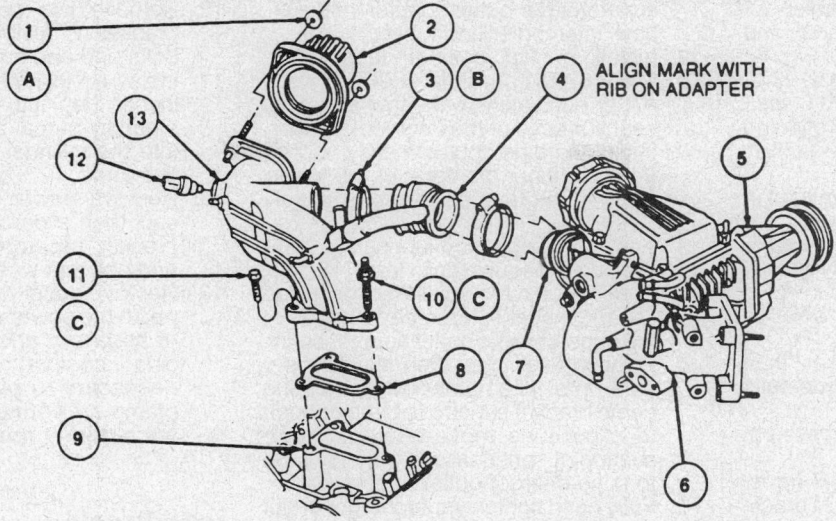

ALIGN MARK WITH RIB ON ADAPTER

Item	Description
1	Nut (2 Req'd)
2	Charge Air Cooler Outlet Tube
3	Hose Clamp (2 Req'd)
4	Supercharger Bypass Valve Hose
5	Supercharger
6	Supercharger Inlet Plenum
7	Supercharger Bypass Valve Actuator
8	Gasket
9	Lower Intake Manifold

Item	Description
10	Stub Bolt
11	Bolt (2 Req'd)
12	Intake Air Temperature Sensor
13	Charge Air Cooler to Intake Manifold Adapter
A	Tighten to 20-30 N·m (15-22 Lb-Ft)
B	Tighten to 2.3-3.4 N·m (20-30 Lb-In)
C	Tighten to 26-38 N·m (20-28 Lb-Ft)

FM1059500085000X

Fig. 7 Supercharger air cooler to intake manifold adapter. Thunderbird

on each side of oil line fitting. **Torque** oil supply line on turbocharger to 12-17 ft. lbs.

14. Connect coolant supply hose, then position air cleaner duct tube on turbocharger and tighten clamp.
15. Install screws retaining air cleaner duct tube.
16. Position power steering pump bracket on engine, then install retaining bolts and nut. **Torque** retaining nut to 35-48 ft. lbs.
17. Position power steering pump on mounting bracket, then install through bolts and adjuster.
18. Connect lower radiator hose and install power steering belt.
19. Install side heat shield and upper heat shield. Feed EGO sensor wire through upper heat shield. Install wire retainer under left bolt. **Torque** heat shields retaining bolts to 14-19 ft. lbs.
20. Connect EGO sensor and install into retaining clip.
21. Position intercooler hose on turbocharger and secure with clamp.
22. Install throttle body air intake tube.
23. Connect battery ground cable, then fill cooling system.
24. After installing turbocharger, disconnect electrical connector from ignition coil and crank engine for approximately 20 seconds then reconnect electrical connector to ignition coil.

25. Start engine and run at idle for approximately 30 seconds, then check for leaks.

OIL SUPPLY LINE, REPLACE

1. Disconnect battery ground cable.
2. Remove screws retaining air cleaner duct tube, loosen clamp at turbocharger and position aside.
3. Remove oil line fitting at turbocharger.
4. Remove bolt and brass sealing washer from oil line at engine block.
5. Remove oil supply line.
6. Reverse procedure to install.

INTERCOOLER, REPLACE

1. Raise and support vehicle, remove bumper assembly.
2. Loosen retaining clamps, then disconnect intercooler hose from intercooler.
3. Remove nuts retaining intercooler to core support.
4. Remove intercooler.
5. Reverse procedure to install.

THUNDERBIRD
SUPERCHARGER, REPLACE
Removal

Before starting any supercharger service, clean areas around supercharger assembly. Cover openings of the engine and supercharger while supercharger is removed to prevent damage by foreign materials.

1. Disconnect battery ground cable.
2. Remove throttle body air inlet tube.
3. Remove cowl vent screens.
4. Disconnect righthand side plug wires at coil assembly, and position out of way.
5. Disconnect electrical connections at air bypass valve.
6. Disconnect vacuum lines from the inlet/plenum assembly, then remove EGR transducer from bracket and disconnect vacuum line, **Fig. 2**.
7. Disconnect PCV tube, then throttle linkage at throttle housing.
8. Remove linkage bracket attaching bolts, then position bracket out of way.
9. Disconnect speed control, if equipped.
10. Remove two EGR attaching bolts, then position EGR valve away from intake assembly, if equipped.
11. Remove supercharger drive belt.
12. Remove intercooler inlet and outlet tubes as outlined in this section, **Fig. 3**.
13. Remove three intake elbow retaining bolts.
14. Remove three supercharger retaining bolts.
15. Lift supercharger and intake elbow assembly from vehicle as a unit.

Installation

1. Clean and inspect all gasket surfaces.
2. Position new gasket on intake mani-

FORD–Turbocharger & Supercharger

fold using guide pins, if available.

3. Install supercharger, throttle body and intake elbow as an assembly, **Fig. 4.**
4. **Torque** two 8mm bolts to 15-22 ft. lbs., then 12mm bolt to 52-70 ft. lbs.
5. Install three intake elbow retaining bolts, then **torque** bolts to 20-28 ft. lbs.
6. Install intercooler tubes as outlined in this section.
7. Install supercharger drive belt, **Fig. 5.**
8. Connect EGR valve with new gasket to supercharger inlet elbow, if equipped. **Torque** retaining bolts to 15-22 ft. lbs.
9. Install throttle linkage bracket, then connect throttle linkage. **Torque** bolts to 10-15 ft. lbs.
10. Connect vacuum lines to inlet assembly.
11. Connect vacuum line to EGR transducer, then install transducer in bracket, **Fig. 6.**
12. Connect PCV tube, then install spark plug wires. Connect electrical connectors at air bypass valve, throttle position sensor and air charge temperature sensor.
13. Install cowl covers, then throttle body air inlet tube.
14. Connect battery ground cable.
15. Start engine and check for leaks and proper operation.

INLET TUBE, REPLACE
Removal

When reinstalling the inlet tube and related components the system must be torqued in sequence and to the specification for that step. This is required for proper alignment of the system to ensure proper sealing of the intercooler tubes.

1. Disconnect inlet tube from supercharger outlet adapter using spanner nut wrench tool No. T89P-6634-A or equivalent.
2. Remove four nuts retaining inlet and outlet tubes to intercooler. **The outlet tube must be disconnected from the intercooler so the sealing surfaces and retaining studs are not damaged while removing the inlet tube.**
3. Remove nut and push-on nut retaining inlet tube to alternator-power steering pump bracket. **To remove the inlet tube in the vehicle, the stud must also be removed from the alternator-power steering pump bracket.**
4. Remove inlet tube. **Use extreme care during removal and installation of the intercooler tubes as not to scratch, nick or contaminate the sealing surfaces.**

Installation

Whenever the outlet tube is disconnected from the intercooler, the outlet tube to intercooler sealing surface must be resealed. This is necessary because the existing seal may be disturbed or broken from unintentional bending while removing the inlet tube.

1. Clean and inspect sealing surfaces of supercharger outlet adapter intake elbow, intercooler and tubes.
2. Install gasket sealant tape, ESE-M4G167-B, from kit No. E9PE-6F091-AA, or equivalent to the four spherical seat surfaces of the intercooler tubes. Install the tape approximately 1/8 inch from the inner diameter of the tubes. Overlap the tape ends approximately 1/4 inch.
3. Apply anti-seize and lubricating compound or equivalent, from kit No. E9PE-6F091-AA to inner backside spherical seat surface and threads of the supercharger outlet adapter collar.
4. Position inlet tube, then install upper stud into alternator-power steering pump bracket surface but free enough to allow tube movement to ensure seating of spherical seat on inlet tube to supercharger outlet adapter.
5. Fully hand tighten supercharger outlet adapter collar onto threaded tube end of inlet tube assembly, **Fig. 3.**
6. Install intercooler assembly to inlet and outlet tubes. install nuts to studs tight enough to retain intercooler and tubes together but free enough to allow movement on spherical seats. **Do not tighten at this time.**
7. **Torque** supercharger outlet adapter collar to inlet tube to 148 ft. lbs. Wait ten minutes minimum, then **torque** supercharger outlet adapter collar to 148 ft. lbs. a second time.
8. The clamping connectors should be installed so they are visually parallel to the stud mounting face of the intercooler assembly. **Torque** inlet and outlet tube to intercooler retaining nuts to 15-22 ft. lbs.
9. Install inlet tube to alternator-power steering pump support bracket retaining nut and **torque** to 30-40 ft. lbs.
10. Start engine and check for leaks.

OUTLET TUBE, REPLACE
Removal

1. Remove two nuts retaining outlet tube to intake elbow assembly.
2. Raise and support vehicle.
3. Remove bolt retaining outlet tube to cylinder block front upper support bracket.
4. Loosen but do not remove support bracket at front of cylinder block. **The bracket must be close to the front face of the cylinder block to allow the bracket to pivot during outlet tube installation.**
5. Remove nut and push-on nut retaining outlet tube to alternator-power steering pump bracket.
6. Remove upper intercooler tube stud from the alternator-power steering pump bracket.
7. Remove power steering drive belt.
8. Disconnect spark plug wires from coil. Note location of spark plug wires for proper installation.
9. Remove power steering pump bracket brace to water pump retaining stud nuts.
10. Remove two power steering pump bracket to cylinder head retaining bolts and one nut.
11. Install a 10x1.5mmx170mm bolt (6.5 inches long) into top hole in the power steering pump bracket. Thread bolt into the cylinder head approximately five turns.
12. Remove power steering pump filler cap, then slide power steering pump bracket assembly forward on stud and bolt that was installed in Step 11.
13. Remove outlet tube by pulling underneath the power steering pump bracket assembly and up through the engine compartment. **It may be necessary to pivot the outlet tube clamping connector to gain clearance during removal.**

Installation

1. Clean and inspect the sealing surfaces of the supercharger outlet adapter, intake elbow, intercooler and tubes.
2. Install gasket sealant tape, ESE-M4G167-B, from kit No. E9PE-6F091-AA, or equivalent to the four spherical seat surfaces of the intercooler tubes. Install the tape approximately 1/8 inch from the inner diameter of the tubes. Overlap the tape ends approximately 1/4 inch.
3. Guide the outlet tube down through the engine compartment and underneath the power steering pump bracket assembly. **It may be necessary to rotate the lower outlet tube clamping connector to gain clearance while installing the outlet tube.**
4. Slide power steering pump bracket into position, then install retaining stud nut. **Torque** stud nut to 30-40 ft. lbs.
5. Remove bolt installed in Step 11, then install power steering pump bracket to cylinder head bolts. **Torque** bolts to 30-40 ft. lbs.
6. Install power steering pump bracket brace to water pump retaining stud nuts. **Torque** nuts to 15-22 ft. lbs.
7. Install outlet tube over lower stud on alternator-power steering pump bracket.
8. Install push-on nut onto stud, tight enough to retain tube against the alternator-power steering pump bracket surface but free enough to allow tube movement to ensure seating of spherical seat on outlet tube to inlet elbow assembly.
9. Install outlet tube clamping connector over studs on intake elbow assembly and secure with two nuts. **Torque** both nuts to 15-22 ft. lbs.
10. Install nut to the stud on alternator-power steering pump bracket and **torque** to 30-40 ft. lbs.
11. Install bolt to secure outlet tube to cylinder block support bracket and **torque** to 30-40 ft. lbs.
12. **Torque** support bracket to front of cylinder block retaining nut to 15-22 ft. lbs. and bolt to 52-70 ft. lbs.

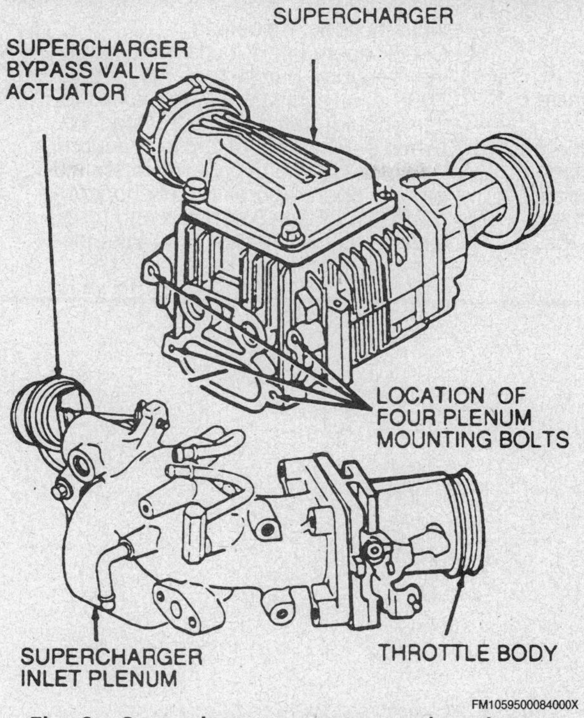

SUPERCHARGER

SUPERCHARGER
BYPASS VALVE
ACTUATOR

LOCATION OF
FOUR PLENUM
MOUNTING BOLTS

SUPERCHARGER
INLET PLENUM

THROTTLE BODY

FM1059500084000X

**Fig. 8 Supercharger component locations.
Thunderbird**

AIR COOLER TO INTAKE MANIFOLD ADAPTER, REPLACE

Removal

1. Remove cowl vent screens.
2. Disconnect fuel charging wiring connection at air intake temperature sensor.
3. Disconnect vacuum lines at air cooler to intake manifold adapter, then remove two nuts attaching air cooler outlet tube to air cooler to intake manifold adapter.
4. Remove EGR transducer.
5. Loosen air cooler outlet tube at alternator/power steering pump bracket.
6. Slightly loosen air cooler tube bracket at front of cylinder block, **Fig. 7.** Allow air cooler tube bracket to pivot during air cooler outlet tube installation.
7. Loosen clamp at supercharger bypass valve.
8. Remove three air cooler to intake manifold adapter retaining bolts and slide air cooler to intake manifold adapter from supercharger bypass hose.

Installation

1. Clean and inspect gasket surfaces and install new gasket on lower intake manifold.
2. Slide air cooler to intake manifold adapter into supercharger bypass valve hose. Align mark on hose with rib on air cooler to intake manifold adapter, then **torque** clamps to 20-30 inch lbs.
3. Position air cooler to intake manifold adapter and gasket, then install three

retaining bolt and **torque** bolt to 20-28 ft. lbs.
4. Install air cooler inlet and outlet tubes as outlined previously.
5. Install EGR transducer.
6. Connect vacuum lines, fuel charging wiring connection to air temperature sensor and EGR transducer.
7. Install cowl vent screens, then start engine and check for proper operation and leaks.

INLET PLENUM

Removal

1. Remove cowl screens.
2. Remove air cooler to intake manifold adapter.
3. Remove air cleaner outlet tube from throttle body.
4. Remove accelerator cable bracket retaining bolts and move bracket out of the way.
5. Disconnect crankcase ventilation tube, then vacuum line from inlet plenum.
6. Disconnect fuel charging wiring connections at throttle position sensor and idle air control valve.
7. Remove four inlet plenum retaining bolts, then loosen bypass valve hose clamp.
8. Remove EGR to exhaust manifold tube from EGR valve.
9. Remove EGR transducer.
10. Remove inlet plenum and throttle body as an assembly.
11. Remove four throttle body retaining nuts and separate inlet plenum from throttle body, **Fig. 8.**

Installation

1. Clean and inspect gasket surfaces.

2. Install throttle body to inlet plenum with new gasket. **Torque** nuts 15-22 ft. lbs.
3. Apply threadlock compound 262EZFZ-19554-B, or equivalent and WSK-M2G351-A6, or equivalent, to inlet plenum mating surface. Slide inlet plenum into bypass valve hose and install inlet plenum and four retaining bolts. **Torque** bolts to 16-24 ft. lbs. and hose clamps to 20-30 inch lbs.
4. Install EGR transducer and **torque** retainers to 6-9 ft. lbs., then install EGR valve to exhaust manifold tube.
5. Connect fuel charging wiring to throttle position sensor, idle air control valve and EGR transducer.
6. Connect vacuum line at inlet plenum, then the crankcase ventilation tube.
7. Install accelerator bracket and cable. **Torque** bolts to 15-22 ft. lbs.
8. Install air cleaner outlet tube, then the air cooler to intake manifold adapter.
9. Install vent cowl screens, then start engine and check for proper operation and leaks.

BYPASS VALVE ACTUATOR, REPLACE

Removal

1. Disconnect vacuum hose from bypass valve actuator, then remove inlet plenum.
2. Remove bypass valve actuator to supercharger retaining bolts.
3. Remove two self-tapping screws.
4. Rotate bypass valve actuator to allow actuator rod to pass through keyed slot in bypass valve lever.

FORD–Turbocharger & Supercharger

Installation

1. Install actuator rod in bypass valve actuator into position.
2. Install 8 mm bolt and hand tighten.
3. Rotate bypass valve actuator to bring bypass valve lever against its stop, then rotate an additional .050 inches. **Torque** 8 mm bolt to 15-20 ft. lbs.,

while holding in position.

4. Check operation of bypass valve using vacuum pump tool No. D83L-7059-A, or equivalent. The bypass lever should stay against its stop between 0-3 inch Hg of applied vacuum. At 8 inch Hg, the bypass valve should be fully open (approximately horizontal). If not, loosen 8 mm bolt and reset.
5. Drill a 1/8 hole .40 inches in inlet plenum using the bottom pre-punched hole in bypass valve actuator bracket as guide. **Do not drill through inlet plenum.** Install new self-tapping screw and repeat procedure for top hole in bypass valve actuator bracket.
6. Connect vacuum hose, then install inlet plenum.
7. Start engine and check for proper operation and leaks.

COMPUTERIZED ENGINE CONTROLS

If Uncertain About The Proper Use Of Information Contained In This Section, Please Refer To "How To Use This Manual" Located In The Front Of This Manual.

Electrical Symbol & Wire Color Code Identification Located In The Front Of This Manual May Be Used As An Aid When Using Wiring Circuits Found In This Section.

Prior To Performing Any Service Operations Listed In This Section, Consult The "Technical Service Bulletins" Section For Related Information.

TABLE OF CONTENTS

Page No.

APPLICATION CHART 8-1

Page No.

ELECTRONIC ENGINE CONTROL SYSTEM IV (EEC-IV) 8-2

Application Chart

Year	Model	System	Page	Year	Model	System	Page
1993	Capri	EEC	10-1	1994—Cont'd	Mark VIII	EEC-IV	8-2
	Continental	EEC-IV	8-2		Mustang (3.8L)	EEC-V	9-1
	Cougar/Thunderbird	EEC-IV	8-2		Mustang (5.0L)	EEC-IV	8-2
	Crown Victoria/Grand Marquis	EEC-IV	8-2		Probe GT	EEC	10-1
					Probe LX	EEC-IV	8-2
	Escort/Tracer (1.8L)	EEC	10-1		Sable/Taurus	EEC-IV	8-2
	Escort/Tracer (1.9L)	EEC-IV	8-2		Tempo/Topaz	EEC-IV	8-2
					Town Car	EEC-IV	8-2
	Festiva	EEC	10-1	1995	Aspire	EEC	10-1
	Mark VIII	EEC-IV	8-2		Continental	EEC-V	9-1
	Mustang	EEC-IV	8-2		Contour	EEC-IV	8-2
	Probe GT	EEC	10-1		Cougar/Thunderbird (3.8L)	EEC-IV	8-2
	Probe LX	EEC-IV	8-2				
	Sable/Taurus	EEC-IV	8-2		Cougar/Thunderbird (4.6L)	EEC-V	9-1
	Tempo/Topaz	EEC-IV	8-2				
	Town Car	EEC-IV	8-2		Crown Victoria/Grand Marquis	EEC-V	9-1
1994	Aspire	EEC	10-1				
	Capri	EEC	10-1				
	Continental	EEC-IV	8-2		Escort/Tracer (1.8L)	EEC	10-1
	Cougar/Thunderbird (3.8L)	EEC-IV	8-2		Escort/Tracer (1.9L)	EEC-IV	8-2
					Mark VIII	EEC-IV	8-2
	Cougar/Thunderbird (4.6L)	EEC-V	9-1		Mustang (3.8L)	EEC-V	9-1
					Mustang (5.0L)	EEC-IV	8-2
	Crown Victoria/Grand Marquis	EEC-IV	8-2		Mystique	EEC-IV	8-2
					Probe GT	EEC	10-1
	Escort/Tracer (1.8L)	EEC	10-1		Probe LX	EEC-IV	8-2
					Sable/Taurus	EEC-IV	8-2
	Escort/Tracer (1.9L)	EEC-IV	8-2		Tempo/Topaz	EEC-IV	8-2
					Town Car	EEC-V	9-1

Continued

APPLICATION CHART–Continued

Year	Model	System	Page	Year	Model	System	Page
1996	Aspire	EEC	10-1		Escort/Tracer (1.9L)	EEC-V	9-1
	Continental	EEC-V	9-1		Mark VIII	EEC-V	9-1
	Contour	EEC-V	9-1		Mustang (3.8L)	EEC-V	9-1
	Cougar/Thunderbird (3.8L)	EEC-V	9-1		Mustang (5.0L)	EEC-V	9-1
					Mystique	EEC-V	9-1
	Cougar/Thunderbird (4.6L)	EEC-V	9-1		Probe GT	EEC	10-1
					Probe LX	EEC-V	9-1
	Crown Victoria/Grand Marquis	EEC-V	9-1		Sable/Taurus	EEC-V	9-1
					Town Car	EEC-V	9-1
	Escort/Tracer (1.8L)	EEC	10-1				

Electronic Engine Control System IV (EEC-IV)

INDEX

Page No.

Description: 8-4
  Inputs & Outputs.................. 8-8
  System Components 8-4
  System Operation................. 8-4
Diagnosis & Testing: 8-8
  Accessing Diagnostic Trouble Codes. 8-8
  Analog Voltmeter 8-8
  Check Engine Light/Malfunction
    Indicator Lamp (MIL) 8-10
  Message Center 8-11
  New Generation Star (NGS)
    Tester....................... 8-10
  Self-Test Automatic Readout
    (STAR) Or Equivalent 8-8
  Super Self-Test Automatic
    Readout (Super STAR II) Or
    Equivalent 8-10
  Clearing Diagnostic Trouble Codes . 8-11
  Continuous Memory............. 8-11
  Diagnostic Routines & Diagnostic
    Sub-Routines/Quick Tests..... 8-12

Page No.

Diagnostic Sub-Routines/Quick
  Test Diagnostic Trouble Codes
  & Diagnostic Trouble Code
  Definitions 8-11
Keep Alive Memory (KAM)....... 8-11
Pinpoint Test................... 8-12
Wiring Diagrams & Connector
  Terminal Identification........ 8-11
Component Locations 8-12
Description 8-8
Brake On/Off Switch Test 8-8
Continuous Memory Diagnostic
  Trouble Codes 8-8
Engine Identification Codes 8-8
Engine Running Test............ 8-8
Key-On, Engine Off.............. 8-8
Power Steering Pressure Switch
  Test......................... 8-8
Diagnostic Aids.................. 8-12
Adaptive Strategy............... 8-12

Page No.

Continuous Monitor Test (Wiggle
  Test)........................ 8-12
Cylinder Balance Test........... 8-12
Failure Mode Effects Management
  (FMEM) 8-12
Output State Check............. 8-12
Diagnostic Trouble Code
  Interpretation 8-11
Fast/Slow Diagnostic Trouble
  Codes....................... 8-11
Standard Diagnostic Trouble
  Codes....................... 8-11
Pinpoint Test 8-13
Quick Test 8-12
Diagnostic Chart Index........... 8-106
Precautions:.................... 8-4
  Flexible Fuel Models 8-4
Sensor Specifications 8-2

SENSOR SPECIFICATIONS

Sensor	Shift Position	Temperature, °F	Altitude	Voltage	Resistance	MPH	Valve Open %	Throttle Angle°	Vacuum, psi
Barometric Pressure ①	—	—	0	1.59	—	—	—	—	—
	—	—	1000	1.56	—	—	—	—	—
	—	—	2000	1.53	—	—	—	—	—
	—	—	3000	1.50	—	—	—	—	—
	—	—	4000	1.47	—	—	—	—	—
	—	—	5000	1.44	—	—	—	—	—
	—	—	6000	1.41	—	—	—	—	—
	—	—	7000	1.39	—	—	—	—	—
Delta Pressure Feedback EGR —Cont'd	—	—	—	.45	—	—	—	—	0

SENSOR SPECIFICATIONS –Continued

Sensor	Shift Position	Temperature, °F	Altitude	Voltage	Resistance	MPH	Valve Open %	Throttle Angle°	Vacuum, psi
Delta Pressure Feedback EGR —Cont'd	—	—	—	1.48	—	—	—	—	1.08
	—	—	—	2.51	—	—	—	—	2.17
	—	—	—	3.54	—	—	—	—	3.25
	—	—	—	4.56	—	—	—	—	4.34
EGR Valve Position	—	—	—	.40	—	—	0	—	—
	—	—	—	.75	—	—	10	—	—
	—	—	—	1.10	—	—	20	—	—
	—	—	—	1.45	—	—	30	—	—
	—	—	—	1.80	—	—	40	—	—
	—	—	—	2.15	—	—	50	—	—
	—	—	—	2.50	—	—	60	—	—
	—	—	—	2.85	—	—	70	—	—
	—	—	—	3.20	—	—	80	—	—
	—	—	—	3.55	—	—	90	—	—
	—	—	—	3.90	—	—	100	—	—
Engine Coolant Temperature	—	50	—	3.52	58,750	—	—	—	—
	—	68	—	3.06	27,300	—	—	—	—
	—	86	—	2.62	24,270	—	—	—	—
	—	104	—	2.16	16,150	—	—	—	—
	—	122	—	1.72	10,970	—	—	—	—
	—	140	—	1.35	7700	—	—	—	—
	—	158	—	1.04	5370	—	—	—	—
	—	176	—	.80	3840	—	—	—	—
	—	194	—	.61	2800	—	—	—	—
	—	212	—	.47	2070	—	—	—	—
	—	230	—	.36	1550	—	—	—	—
	—	248	—	.28	1180	—	—	—	—
Intake Air Temperature	—	50	—	3.52	58,750	—	—	—	—
	—	68	—	3.06	27,300	—	—	—	—
	—	86	—	2.62	24,270	—	—	—	—
	—	104	—	2.16	16,150	—	—	—	—
	—	122	—	1.72	10,970	—	—	—	—
	—	140	—	1.35	7700	—	—	—	—
	—	158	—	1.04	5370	—	—	—	—
	—	176	—	.80	3840	—	—	—	—
	—	194	—	.61	2800	—	—	—	—
	—	212	—	.47	2070	—	—	—	—
	—	230	—	.36	1550	—	—	—	—
	—	248	—	.28	1180	—	—	—	—
Mass Airflow	—	—	—	.80	—	0	—	—	—
	—	—	—	1.0	—	20	—	—	—
	—	—	—	1.7	—	40	—	—	—
	—	—	—	2.1	—	60	—	—	—
Manifold Absolute Pressure ①	—	—	0	1.59	—	—	—	—	—
	—	—	1000	1.56	—	—	—	—	—
	—	—	2000	1.53	—	—	—	—	—
	—	—	3000	1.50	—	—	—	—	—
	—	—	4000	1.47	—	—	—	—	—
	—	—	5000	1.44	—	—	—	—	—
	—	—	6000	1.41	—	—	—	—	—
	—	—	7000	1.39	—	—	—	—	—

Continued

FORD—Computerized Engine Controls

SENSOR SPECIFICATIONS –Continued

Sensor	Shift Position	Temperature, °F	Altitude	Voltage	Resistance	MPH	Valve Open %	Throttle Angle°	Vacuum, psi
Manual Lever Position Sensor	1	—	—	.68	81	—	—	—	—
	2	—	—	1.37	211	—	—	—	—
	D	—	—	2.09	401	—	—	—	—
	N	—	—	2.83	733	—	—	—	—
	R	—	—	3.60	1440	—	—	—	—
	P	—	—	4.41	4160	—	—	—	—

① — ±.04 volt.

PRECAUTIONS
FLEXIBLE FUEL MODELS

1. Handle methanol-gasoline fuel blends with extreme caution, wear chemical goggles and gloves.
2. Do not eat, smoke or drink when fuel is being handled.
3. Flames from methanol or methanol-gasoline blends may be invisible.
4. Inhaling vapors from methanol-gasoline blends may be harmful; handle only in well ventilated areas. If overcome by vapors, move to fresh air, if not breathing, give artificial respiration or CPR.
5. If gasoline is swallowed, do not induce vomiting; seek medical attention.
6. If methanol or a methanol/gasoline blend is swallowed, induce vomiting, under the direction of a physician or Poison Control Center, seek medical attention.
7. If methanol or a methanol/gasoline blend is splashed in eyes, flush with large amounts of water for 15 minutes, remove contact lenses, if worn and seek medical attention.
8. If methanol or a methanol/gasoline blend is swallowed, blindness may occur.
9. If methanol or a methanol/gasoline blend is swallowed, onset of serious health effects may be delayed 12 to 24 hours.

DESCRIPTION
SYSTEM OPERATION

The EEC-IV system provides accurate, instantaneous fuel metering control of fuel injection timing and duration. A potentiometer which senses the position of the vane airflow meter in the engine's air induction system, generates a voltage signal that varies with the amount of air drawn into the engine. A sensor in the area near the vane airflow meter measures the temperature of incoming air and transmits a corresponding electrical signal. Another temperature sensor, inserted into the engine coolant system, gives information on engine temperature. A switch senses throttle plate position and produces, then transmits an electrical signal to tell the control unit when the throttle is closed or in the wide-open position. An oxygen sensor in the exhaust manifold measures the amount of free oxygen remaining in the exhaust gas, which is an indication of cylinder combustion efficiency, and sends a corresponding signal to the control unit.

Crankshaft position information is transmitted by a sensor integral with the distributor.

The EEC-IV microcomputer circuit processes the input data from these sensors and produces output control signals to the fuel injectors, regulating precise fuel discharge through the injector nozzles. The microcomputer circuit also produces output signals that adjust ignition spark timing to provide a best balance between driveability and fuel economy.

The EEC-IV system also controls exhaust gas recirculation (EGR), A/C compressor cutoff at wide open throttle, knock control to eliminate detonation under adverse driving conditions, and wastegate control which regulates turbocharger boost pressure. The EEC-IV also controls fuel mixture on feedback carbureted engines.

The operating principles of all EEC-IV systems and related components are essentially the same. However, in adapting the EEC-IV system to different engines, different combinations of components are required.

SYSTEM COMPONENTS

The following EEC-IV system related components may not be used on all engines. To determine if a specific component or components are used, refer to the vacuum hose routing diagrams, EEC-IV wiring schematics, EEC-IV module connector pin usage and component locations to determine correct component usage.

AIR BYPASS VALVE SOLENOID

The air bypass valve solenoid is used on some models to control engine idle speed and is operated by the EEC-IV control module. This valve allows air to pass around the throttle plates to control, cold engine fast idle, no touch start, dashpot, over temperature idle boost and engine idle load correction.

AIR CLEANER COLD WEATHER MODULATOR

A cold weather modulator is used in addition to the air cleaner temperature control sensor to control inlet air temperature. The modulator traps vacuum in the system, so the door will not switch to cold air when the vacuum drops during deceleration.

BAROMETRIC PRESSURE (BP) SENSOR

The BP sensor, Fig. 1, measures baro-metric pressure using a frequency. This gives the PCM (ECA) information on engine load. The PCM (ECA) uses the BP sensor for spark advance, EGR flow and air/fuel ratio. It is also used for altitude compensation, updating the PCM (ECA) during the key on engine off quick test.

CONSTANT CONTROL RELAY MODULE (CCRM)

The CCRM interfaces with the powertrain control module (PCM) to provide control of the cooling fan, A/C clutch and the fuel pump. The module also incorporates the EEC power relay to provide power to the EEC system. The limits of the CCRM's operation are an operating temperature of -22°F-212°F and a storage temperature of -4°F-257°F. CCRM operating voltage is 7-17 volts.

CRANKSHAFT POSITION (CKP) SENSOR

The CKP sensor and pulse ring assembly, transmits signals according to crankshaft position. The pulse ring, Fig. 2, is pressed onto the vibration damper.

DELTA PRESSURE FEEDBACK (DPFE) SENSOR

The delta pressure feedback EGR sensor converts varying exhaust pressure signals into voltage which is digitized by the PCM (ECA). The processor uses the signal from the sensor to compute optimum EGR flow.

DUAL THERMACTOR AIR CONTROL SOLENOID VALVE

The dual thermactor air control solenoid valve assembly consists of two normally closed solenoid vacuum valves (TAB and TAD), one controlling the thermactor air bypass valve and the other controlling thermactor diverter valve operation. Both are vented when de-energized, are sourced by the intake manifold vacuum reservoir and are controlled by the EEC-IV system.

EEC POWER RELAY ASSEMBLY

EEC power relays are operated by the ignition switch and provide power to the powertrain control module. The power relays also provide reverse battery protection with internal or external series diodes and increased load handling to improve ignition switch reliability.

There are two types of relays, standard EEC power relay and the ISO relay, Fig 3. The standard relay is a single pole single throw type containing a moveable contact

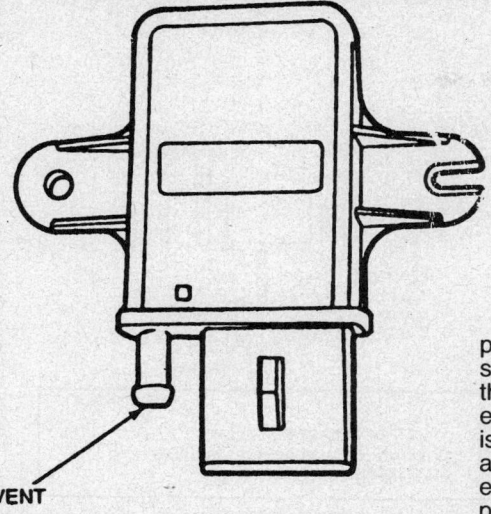

Fig. 1   Barometric pressure sensor

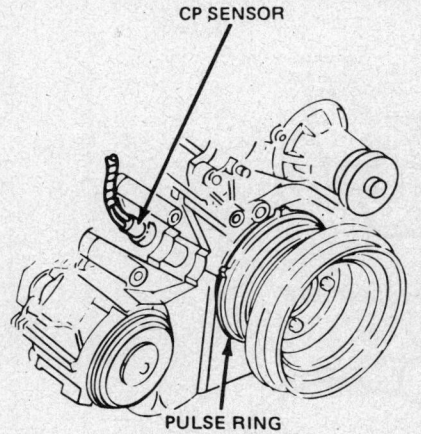

Fig. 2   Crankshaft position sensor & pulse ring

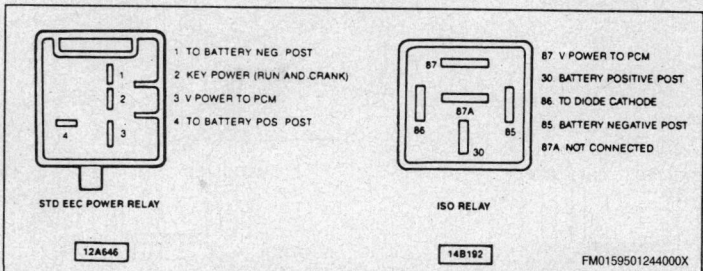

Fig. 3   EEC power relays

in the normally open position with an internal diode in series with the relay coil.

The ISO power relay is a single pole double throw type which does not have an internal diode and is used with a separate stand-alone diode. All ISO relays are identical and can be used interchangeably.

EGR SOLENOID VACUUM VALVE ASSEMBLY

The dual EGR solenoid valve assembly consists of two dithering solenoid valves, **Fig. 4.** The first is a vacuum valve which supplies vacuum to the sonic EGR valve when energized. The second is a vent valve which vents the EGR valve to the atmosphere when de-energized. Both solenoid valves receive variable duty cycle signals from the EEC system according to EGR requirements.

EGR VALVE POSITION SENSOR

The EGR valve position sensor, **Fig. 5,** provides the EEC system with an EGR valve position signal.

ENGINE COOLANT TEMPERATURE (ECT) SENSOR

The ECT, **Fig. 6,** sensor detects the temperature of engine coolant and sup-

plies information to the PCM (ECA) assembly. The ECT sensor is threaded into the heater outlet fitting on the engine. For engine control applications, the ECT signal is used to modify ignition timing, EGR flow and air/fuel mixture. On models with an electronic instrument cluster, the ECT output is used to control the coolant temperature indicator.

FLEXIBLE FUEL (FF) SENSOR

The FF sensor, **Fig. 7,** is located in the engine compartment, in the high pressure fuel supply line between the fuel mixer and the fuel rail. The sensor is a capacitive device with a signal whose frequency varies with the dielectric constant, conductivity and temperature of the methanol-gasoline mixture in the measuring cell. As the percentage of methanol increases, the output frequency of the FF sensor signal will increase.

HEATED OXYGEN SENSOR (HO2S) (HEATED EXHAUST GAS OXYGEN (HEGO) SENSOR))

The HO2S (HEGO), **Fig. 8,** sensor supplies the PCM (ECA) with a signal that indicates a rich or lean condition during engine operation. On 1993 1.9L engine, the sensor is threaded into the exhaust manifold. On the 2.3L high swirl combustion engine, it is threaded into the center rear of the exhaust manifold. On the 2.3L, 3.8L supercharged and 5.0L SEFI engines, it is threaded into both sides of the exhaust manifold. On the 3.0L EFI engine, it is threaded into the Y-pipe at the catalytic inlet. On the 3.8L Continental, Taurus and Sable models, it is threaded into the LH exhaust pipe.

IGNITION BAROMETRIC PRESSURE SWITCH

The ignition barometric pressure switch, **Fig. 9,** is used to control spark timing and/or other electrical devices in response to changes in barometric pressure (altitude).

INTAKE AIR TEMPERATURE (IAT) SENSOR (AIR CHARGE TEMPERATURE (ACT) SENSOR))

The IAT (ACT) sensor, **Fig. 10,** used on EFI models, provides the EFI system mixture (air/fuel) temperature information. The IAT (ACT) is used as both as a density correction to air flow calculation and to proportion the cold enrichment fuel flow. This sensor is mounted on an intake manifold runner or on the air cleaner.

KNOCK SENSOR (KS)

The KS, **Fig. 11,** is a piezoelectric accelerator accelerometer. The sensor uses the resonant frequency to mechanically amplify the engine knock frequency.

MANIFOLD ABSOLUTE PRESSURE (MAP) SENSOR

The MAP sensor, **Fig. 12,** measures manifold pressure using a frequency. This gives the PCM (ECA) information on engine load. The PCM (ECA) uses the MAP sensor for spark advance, EGR flow and air/fuel ratio.

MASS AIR FLOW (MAF) SENSOR

The MAF sensor, **Fig. 13,** measures the mass of air flowing into the engine. The sensor output is and analog signal ranging from .5 to 5 volts. The signal is used by the PCM to calculate injector pulse width.

POWERTRAIN CONTROL MODULE (PCM) (ELECTRONIC CONTROL ASSEMBLY (ECA))

The PCM (ECA) is the brain of the EEC-IV system and is comprised of a processor and calibration assembly, **Fig. 14.** The processor receives input signals from the various sensors. The information obtained is used by the processor to activate engine control systems to obtain optimum emission control and engine performance.

The calibration assembly is a permanent memory device that contains information. The processor applies the sensor inputs to the stored information to determine when and how long the various control systems should be applied.

THROTTLE POSITION (TP) SENSOR

The TP sensor, **Fig. 15,** is a rotary potentiometer consists of either a rigid or flexible thick film resistive substrate and a moving wiper mounted on a rotor. The blade at the end of the throttle shaft drives the rotor tangs. The TP sensor is rotated by the throttle shaft blade, the PCM determines five operating modes from the signal, closed throttle, part throttle, wide open throttle and throttle angle rate. The PCM uses the sensor output to control spark advance, EGR flow, A/F path, A/C clutch wide open throttle cutout and AIR airflow.

VANE AIR FLOW METER

The vane air flow meter measures air flowing into the engine and is mounted between the air cleaner and the throttle body assembly. The meter contains a movable

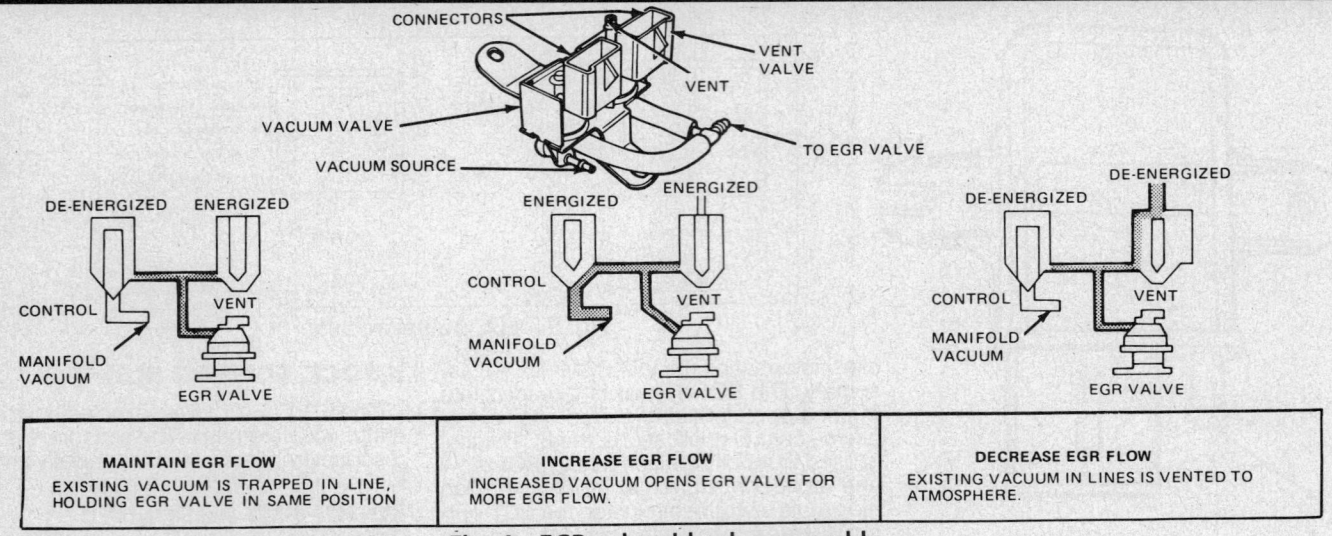

MAINTAIN EGR FLOW	INCREASE EGR FLOW	DECREASE EGR FLOW
EXISTING VACUUM IS TRAPPED IN LINE, HOLDING EGR VALVE IN SAME POSITION	INCREASED VACUUM OPENS EGR VALVE FOR MORE EGR FLOW.	EXISTING VACUUM IN LINES IS VENTED TO ATMOSPHERE.

Fig. 4   EGR solenoid valve assembly (dithering type)

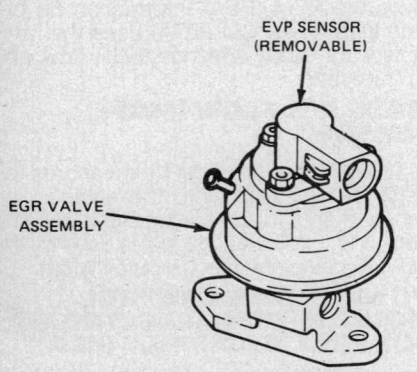

Fig. 5   EGR valve position sensor

Fig. 6   Engine coolant temperature (ECT) sensor

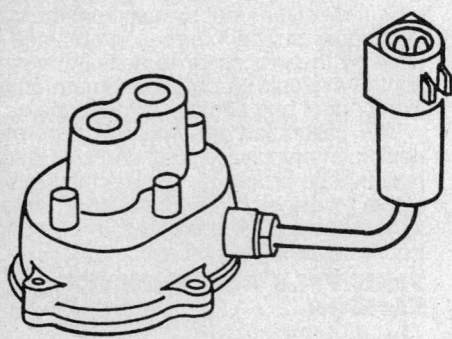

Fig. 7   Flexible fuel sensor

Fig. 8   Heated oxygen sensor (Heated exhaust gas oxygen sensor)

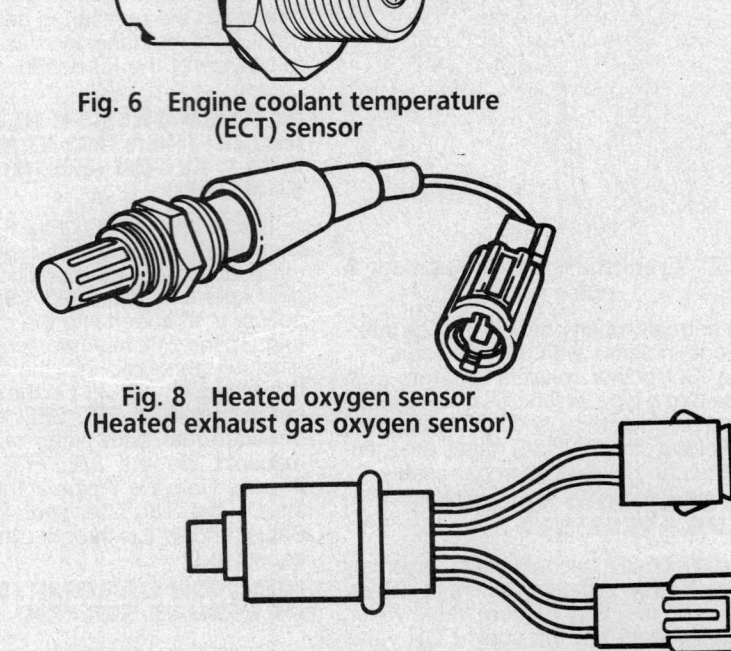

Fig. 9   Ignition barometric pressure switch

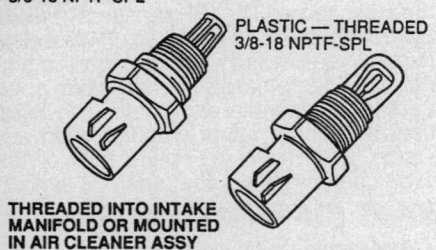

Fig. 10   Intake air temperature sensor (Air charge temperature sensor)

vane directly connected to a potentiometer. Air rushing through the vane air flow meter, changes the position of the vane and potentiometer. The potentiometer relays vane position information to the EEC-IV module. The EEC-IV module, then translates vane position information into the amount of air flowing into the engine.

An air temperature sensor is incorporated within the engine and also transmits the information to the EEC-IV module. The EEC-IV module receives, then computes the air flow and air temperature information and adjusts the fuel flow to obtain the optimum air/fuel mixture required.

VACUUM REGULATOR ASSEMBLY

Two Port

The two port vacuum regulator, **Fig. 16,** provides a constant output signal when the input signal is greater than a present level. At a lower input vacuum, the output equals the input.

Three & Four Port

The three and four port regulators, **Figs. 17 and 18,** are used to control the vacuum

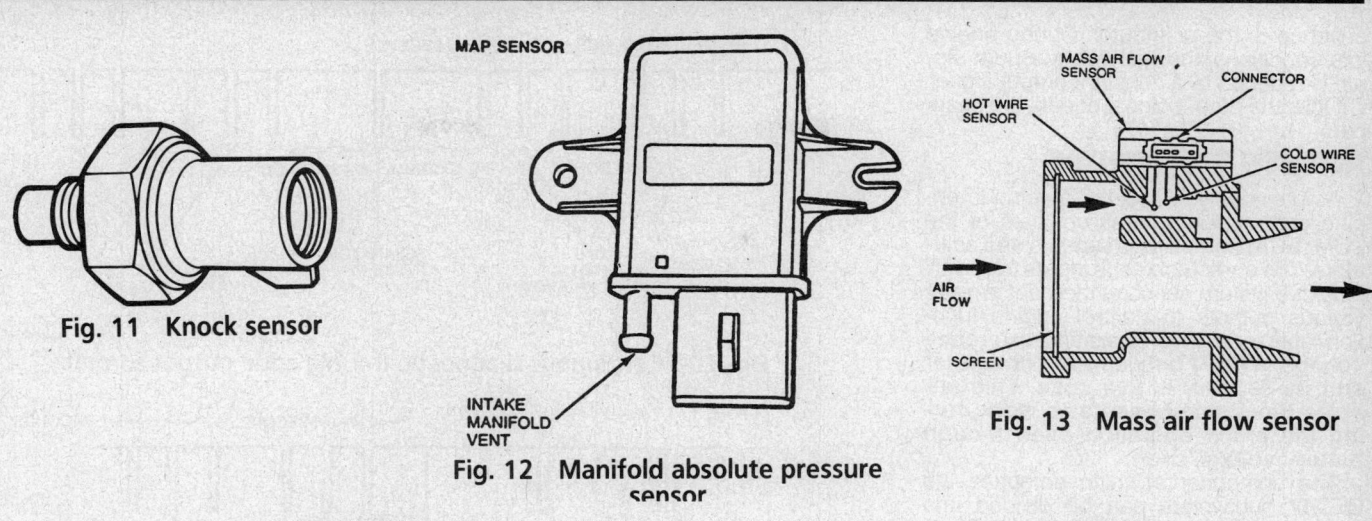

Fig. 11 Knock sensor

MAP SENSOR

INTAKE MANIFOLD VENT

Fig. 12 Manifold absolute pressure sensor

MASS AIR FLOW SENSOR

HOT WIRE SENSOR

CONNECTOR

COLD WIRE SENSOR

AIR FLOW

SCREEN

Fig. 13 Mass air flow sensor

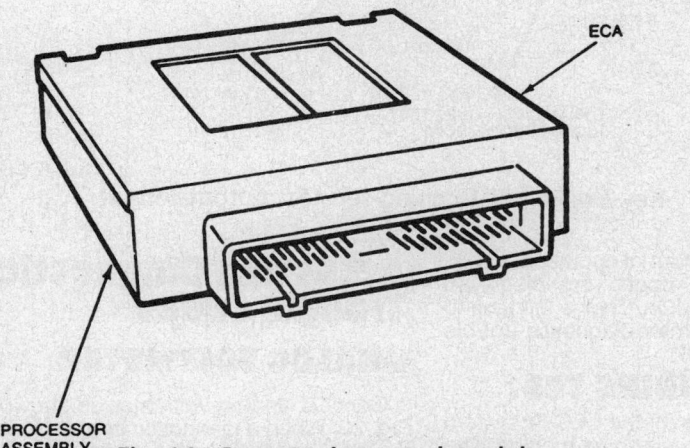

ECA

PROCESSOR ASSEMBLY

Fig. 14 Powertrain control module (Electronic control assembly)

Fig. 15 Throttle position sensor

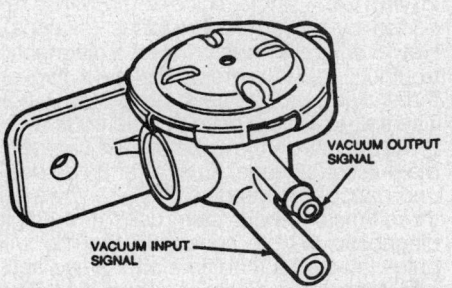

VACUUM OUTPUT SIGNAL

VACUUM INPUT SIGNAL

Fig. 16 Two port vacuum regulator

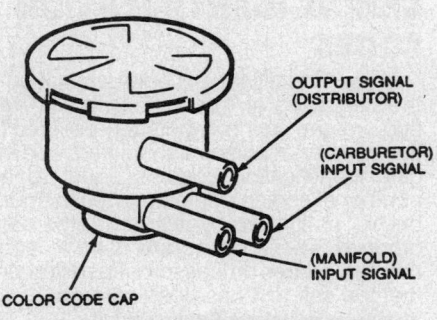

OUTPUT SIGNAL (DISTRIBUTOR)

(CARBURETOR) INPUT SIGNAL

(MANIFOLD) INPUT SIGNAL

COLOR CODE CAP

Fig. 17 Three port vacuum regulator

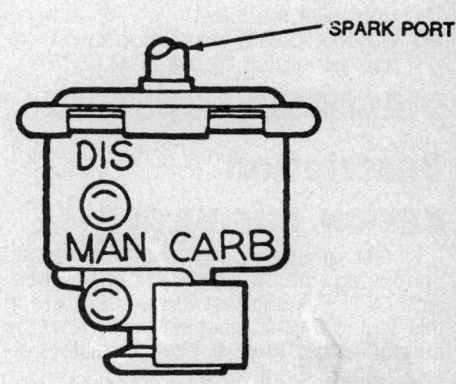

SPARK PORT

DIS

MAN CARB

Fig. 18 Four port vacuum regulator

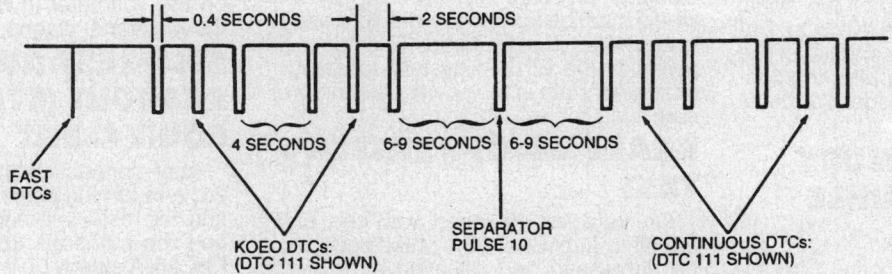

0.4 SECONDS

2 SECONDS

4 SECONDS

6-9 SECONDS

6-9 SECONDS

FAST DTCs

KOEO DTCs: (DTC 111 SHOWN)

SEPARATOR PULSE 10

CONTINUOUS DTCs: (DTC 111 SHOWN)

Fig. 19 Key-On, Engine-Off self-test output format

advance to the distributor. During engine idle conditions, the manifold vacuum signal is reduced to a constant output signal. Off idle, the output signal equals the spark port.

INPUTS & OUTPUTS

As previously stated, the electronic engine control subsystems consists of the PCM (ECA) and various sensors and actuators. The computer reads inputs from various subsystem sensors, then determines various outputs to control engine function/operation. **The operating reference voltage (VREF) between the computer and its sensors is five volts. This enables these components to work during the crank operation even though battery voltage drops.**

The components which comprise the EEC-IV subsystem can be divided into three categories: Powertrain Control Module (PCM) (Electronic Control Assembly (ECA)), System Inputs (sensors, switches or signals) and System Outputs (actuators or solenoids).

After the PCM (ECA) has determined (through inputs) the current operating condition of the engine, it will refer to operating tables in memory. Calculations will then determine the proper sequence of events in order to obtain good driveability, emissions and fuel economy. The computer will accomplish this through the use of system outputs. These outputs are electrically controlled by the PCM (ECA).

The commands from the processor are performed as outputs.

Outputs can be divided in four categories:
1. Solenoids, both normally open and normally closed.
2. Electric motors.
3. Controller modules.
4. Other outputs that are information signals generated by the PCM (ECA).

DIAGNOSIS & TESTING

Description

KEY-ON, ENGINE OFF

A test of the EEC-IV system may be conducted with the power applied and engine OFF. For self-test to detect errors in this test, the fault must be present at the time of testing, **Fig. 19.** For intermittent errors, refer to Continuous Test.

SEPARATOR PULSE

A single ½ second separator pulse is issued 6-9 seconds after the last functional test diagnostic trouble code (Key On, Engine Off only). Then, 6-9 seconds after the single ½ second separator pulse, the continuous diagnostic trouble codes will be issued.

CONTINUOUS MEMORY DIAGNOSTIC TROUBLE CODES

The continuous diagnostic trouble codes are issued as a result of information stored (memory diagnostic trouble codes) during continuous monitor testing, while

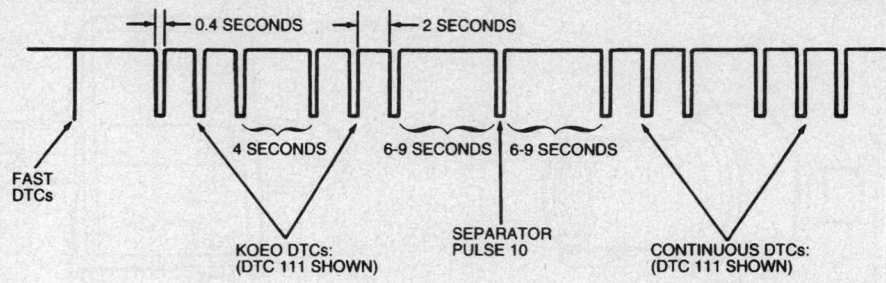

Fig. 20   Continuous diagnostic trouble code output format

Fig. 21   Key-On, Engine Running self-test output format

the vehicle was in normal operation. These diagnostic trouble codes are displayed only during the Key On, Engine Off testing and after the separator diagnostic trouble codes, **Fig. 20.**

ENGINE RUNNING TEST

At this time, a test of the EEC-IV system is conducted with the engine running. The sensors are checked under actual operating conditions and at normal operating temperature, **Fig. 21.**

ENGINE IDENTIFICATION CODES

Engine identification codes are issued at the beginning of the engine running test and are one digit numbers represented by the number of pulses transmitted. The engine identification code is equal to the number of engine cylinders when the number is multiplied by two and the zero dropped. These codes are used to verify that the proper processor is installed and that the self-test has been entered.

POWER STEERING PRESSURE SWITCH TEST

On vehicles equipped with a power steering pressure switch, the steering wheel must be turned one-half turn and released after the ID code. This tests the ability of the EEC-IV system to detect a change of state in the power steering pressure switch.

BRAKE ON/OFF SWITCH TEST

On vehicles equipped with the brake on/off switch (BOO), the brake pedal must be depressed and released after the ID code. This tests the ability of the EEC-IV system to detect a change of state in the brake on/off switch.

Accessing Diagnostic Trouble Codes

ANALOG VOLTMETER

Connect analog voltmeter as shown in **Fig. 22.** When a diagnostic trouble code is reported on the analog voltmeter for a functional test, it will represent itself as a pulsing or sweeping movement of the voltmeter's needle across the dial face, **Figs. 23 and 24.** A single digit of three will be reported by three needle pulses (sweeps). However as previously stated, a diagnostic trouble code is represented by a two or three digit number, such as 2-3 or 3-1-2. The self-test diagnostic trouble code of 2-3 will appear on the voltmeter as two needle pulses (sweeps), then after a two second pause, the needle will pulse (sweep) three times. If the system uses three-digit diagnostic trouble codes, the needle will pulse (sweep) a third time after a two second pause to indicate the third digit. The continuous testing diagnostic trouble codes are separated from the functional diagnostic trouble codes by a six-second delay, a single half-second sweep and another six-second delay. They are produced on the voltmeter in the same manner as the functional diagnostic trouble codes.

SELF-TEST AUTOMATIC READOUT (STAR) OR EQUIVALENT

After connecting the STAR tester, **Fig. 25,** and turning power switch to ON position, the tester will indicate a display check and the numerals 88 will begin to flash, **Fig. 26.** A steady 00 will then appear, signifying that the STAR tester is ready to start the self-test procedure and receive the diagnostic trouble codes.

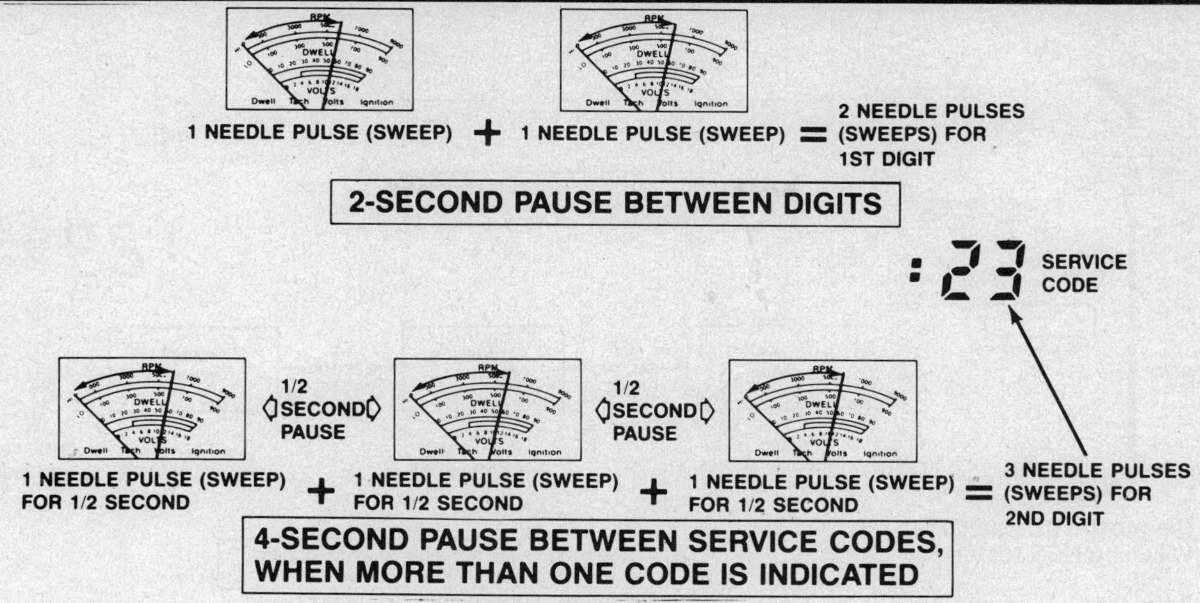

1 NEEDLE PULSE (SWEEP) **+** 1 NEEDLE PULSE (SWEEP) **=** 2 NEEDLE PULSES (SWEEPS) FOR 1ST DIGIT

2-SECOND PAUSE BETWEEN DIGITS

:23 SERVICE CODE

1 NEEDLE PULSE (SWEEP) FOR 1/2 SECOND **+** 1/2 ◊SECOND◊ PAUSE 1 NEEDLE PULSE (SWEEP) FOR 1/2 SECOND **+** 1/2 ◊SECOND◊ PAUSE 1 NEEDLE PULSE (SWEEP) FOR 1/2 SECOND **=** 3 NEEDLE PULSES (SWEEPS) FOR 2ND DIGIT

4-SECOND PAUSE BETWEEN SERVICE CODES, WHEN MORE THAN ONE CODE IS INDICATED

Fig. 23   Two-digit DTC interpretation w/analog voltmeter

VOLTMETER HOOKUP (WITH JUMPER WIRE)

TO VEHICLE HARNESS

SIGNAL RETURN PIN

DATA LINK CONNECTOR (DLC)

SELF-TEST OUTPUT (STO) PIN

SELF-TEST INPUT (STI) CONNECTOR

JUMPER WIRE

VOLT-OHM METER

VEHICLE BATTERY

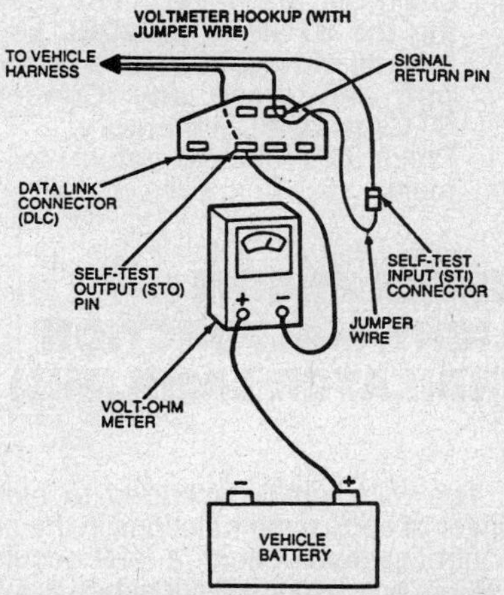

Fig. 22   Diagnostic trouble code retrieval using analog voltmeter

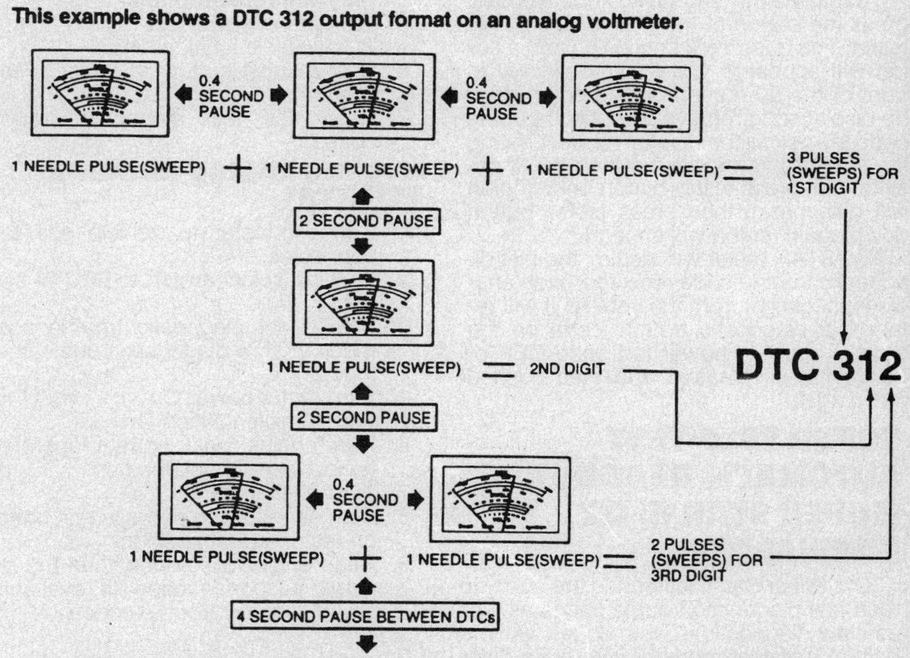

This example shows a DTC 312 output format on an analog voltmeter.

1 NEEDLE PULSE(SWEEP) ◀0.4 SECOND PAUSE▶ 1 NEEDLE PULSE(SWEEP) **+** ◀0.4 SECOND PAUSE▶ 1 NEEDLE PULSE(SWEEP) **=** 3 PULSES (SWEEPS) FOR 1ST DIGIT

2 SECOND PAUSE

1 NEEDLE PULSE(SWEEP) **=** 2ND DIGIT

2 SECOND PAUSE

DTC 312

1 NEEDLE PULSE(SWEEP) ◀0.4 SECOND PAUSE▶ 1 NEEDLE PULSE(SWEEP) **=** 2 PULSES (SWEEPS) FOR 3RD DIGIT

4 SECOND PAUSE BETWEEN DTCs

Fig. 24   Three-digit DTC interpretation w/analog voltmeter

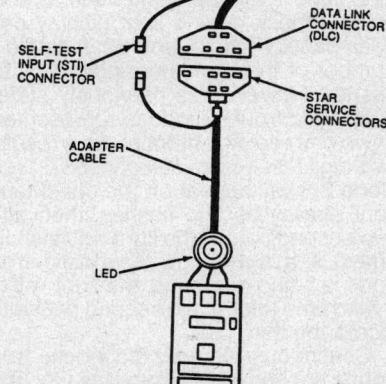

STAR HOOKUP (WITH ADAPTER CABLE ASSEMBLY)

DATA LINK CONNECTOR (DLC)

SELF-TEST INPUT (STI) CONNECTOR

STAR SERVICE CONNECTORS

ADAPTER CABLE

LED

Fig. 25   Diagnostic trouble code retrieval using STAR tester

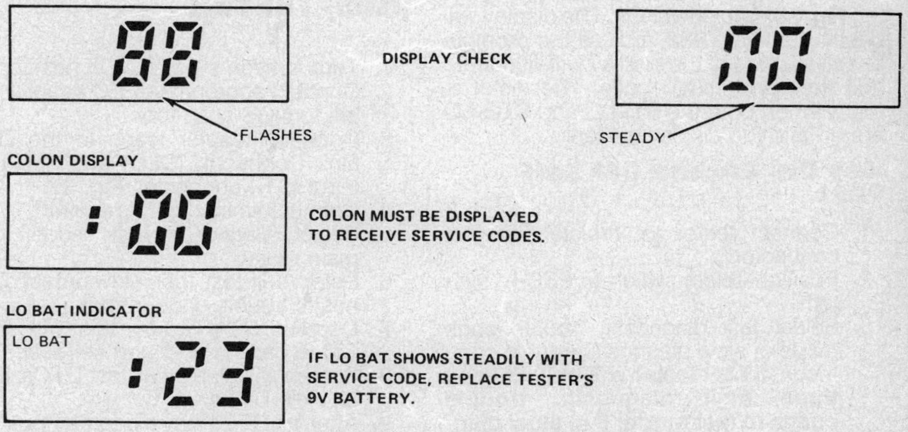

88 DISPLAY CHECK **00**

FLASHES

STEADY

COLON DISPLAY

:00

COLON MUST BE DISPLAYED TO RECEIVE SERVICE CODES.

LO BAT INDICATOR

LO BAT

:23

IF LO BAT SHOWS STEADILY WITH SERVICE CODE, REPLACE TESTER'S 9V BATTERY.

Fig. 26   STAR tester inspection

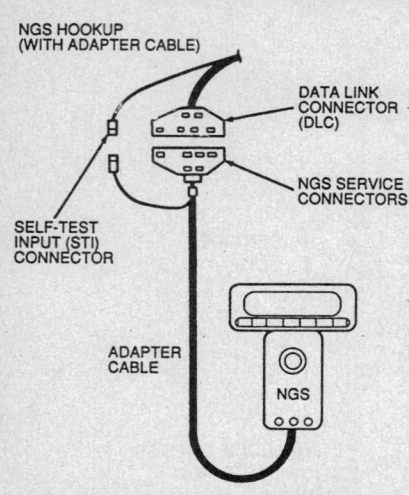

Fig. 27 Diagnostic trouble code
retrieval using NGS tester

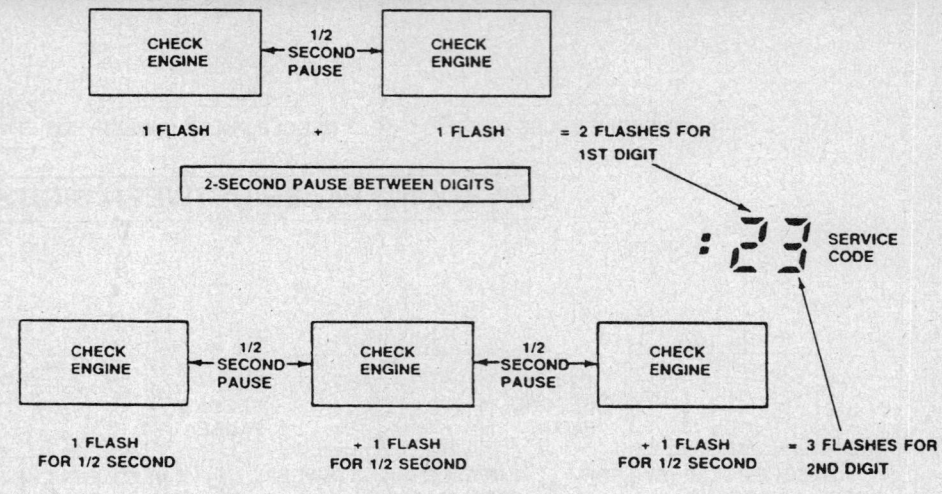

Fig. 28   Two-digit DTC
interpretation w/check engine light

To retrieve the diagnostic trouble codes, press the button at the front of the STAR tester. The button will stay down and a colon will appear in the display window in front of the 00 numerals. The colon must be displayed to retrieve diagnostic trouble codes. To clear the display window during the self-test, turn ignition switch to Off position and press tester button once (colon will disappear), then press tester button down again (colon will appear).

The STAR tester will display the last diagnostic trouble code received, even after disconnecting it from the vehicle. It will retain that diagnostic trouble code on the display until the power is turned OFF or the button is released, and then pushed down again.

SUPER SELF-TEST AUTOMATIC READOUT (SUPER STAR II) OR EQUIVALENT

The Super Star II tester has the ability to read fast diagnostic trouble codes as well as slow diagnostic trouble codes, while a built in self test memory will retain diagnostic trouble codes as they are received.

After installation of the Super Star II tester, **Fig. 25,** turn power On. The display will briefly illuminate 888, also all the prompts on the left side of the display will illuminate and the speaker will beep. The tester is ready when both the STI-LO and STO-LO are on and the display is blank.

Key On, Engine Off Self Test

1. Connect tester to vehicle self test connector.
2. Position select switch to EEC-IV system.
3. Select fast diagnostic trouble code mode or slow diagnostic trouble code mode. **STAR tester will only display three digit diagnostic trouble codes in fast mode; if in slow diagnostic trouble code display, dis-**

play will remain blank.
4. Turn tester power On.
5. Turn vehicle ignition On.
6. Depress test button on tester to test position.
7. Read self test diagnostic trouble codes.

Key On, Engine Running Self Test

1. Connect tester to vehicle self test connector.
2. Position select switch to EEC-IV system.
3. Select fast diagnostic trouble code mode or slow diagnostic trouble code mode.
4. Turn tester power On.
5. Turn vehicle ignition On.
6. Run engine until normal operating temperature is obtained.
7. Turn engine Off.
8. Start engine, then depress test button on tester to test position.
9. Read engine I.D. codes, then the dynamic response code (if available) and diagnostic trouble codes.

NEW GENERATION STAR (NGS) TESTER

1. Turn ignition switch to Off position.
2. Connect appropriate EEC adapter cable to NGS scan tool.
3. Connect adapter leads to the Data Link Connector (DLC) and Self-Test Input (STI) connector, **Fig. 27.**
4. Connect timing light if required.
5. Select diagnostic test mode from main menu.
6. Select self-test, then slow or fast diagnostic trouble code format.
7. Depress START key, this will short STI to ground and start self-test.
8. Screen will display all fast DTCs, then all slow DTCs.
9. After all DTCs have been output, depress STOP key.

10. Depress CANCEL to exit self-test to diagnostic test mode menu. **Depressing the STOP or CANCEL key before all slow DTCs have been output, will erase any Continuous DTCs from PCM memory.**
11. Press CANCEL to return to main menu.

CHECK ENGINE LIGHT/MALFUNCTION INDICATOR LAMP (MIL)

The MIL light is intended to alert the driver of certain malfunctions in the engine control system. If such a fault occurs, the EEC-IV processor will substitute a value or values and continue operating. In some cases this action may result in a slight change in vehicle driveability.

The check engine light can be used to read diagnostic trouble codes. The check engine light on the front dash panel will remain on when a hard fault is present. During the self-test sequence, a diagnostic trouble code is reported by the check engine light. It will represent itself as a flash on the check engine light display on the dash panel, **Figs. 28 and 29.** A single digit number of three will be reported by three flashes. However, as previously stated, a diagnostic trouble code is represented by a two or three digit number. As a result, the two-digit self-test Diagnostic Trouble Code 2-3 will appear on the check engine light display as two flashes, then after a two second pause, the light will flash three times. If a three-digit diagnostic trouble code is being displayed, the light will flash a third time after a two second pause to indicate the third digit.

Continuous memory diagnostic trouble codes are separated from Key On, Engine Off diagnostic trouble codes by a six second delay, a single half-second flash, then another six second delay.

THIS EXAMPLE SHOWS A DTC 312 OUTPUT FORMAT ON A MIL "CHECK ENGINE" LAMP.

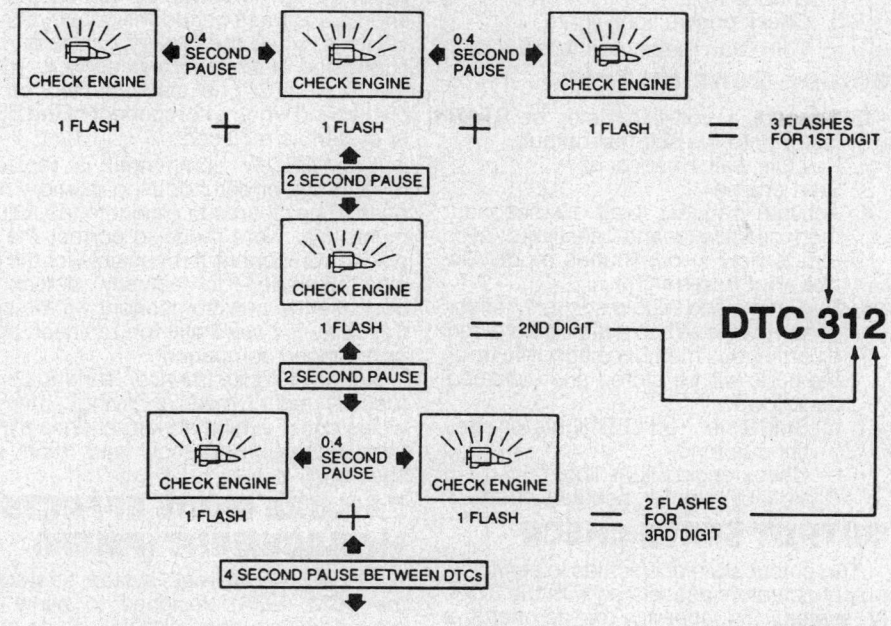

Fig. 29   Three-digit DTC interpretation w/check engine light

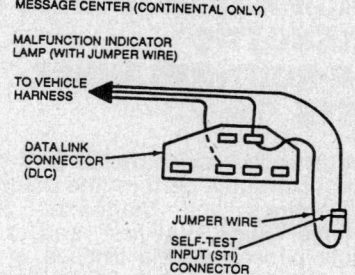

Fig. 30   Diagnostic trouble code retrieval using message center

MESSAGE CENTER

Continental

1. Install suitable jumper wire as shown in Fig. 30. Using the electronic instrument cluster, hold in all three buttons (select, checkout and reset buttons) at the same time.
2. To conduct the Key On, Engine Off self-test portion, hold in all three buttons and place ignition switch in the ON position, then release the three buttons.
3. To conduct the Key On, Engine Running self-test portion, hold in all three buttons, then place the ignition switch in the RUN position and release the three buttons.
4. Depress gauge select button three times until "dEALEr 4" is displayed.
5. To initiate the Self-test, using a jumper wire, jump self-test connectors STI to SIG RTN.
6. Diagnostic trouble codes will be displayed on message center.
7. To exit the self-test, turn ignition switch to Off position.

Diagnostic Trouble Code Interpretation

STANDARD DIAGNOSTIC TROUBLE CODES

Refer to specific year and model for quick test diagnostic trouble codes and definitions. Diagnostic trouble codes are transmitted on the self-test output (found in the self-test connector) in the form of timed pulses (as stated previously) and can be read with the use of an analog voltmeter, the STAR tester, then New Generation STAR tester, check engine light or

message center. **The numerals 20, 30 or 40 are always (and only) displayed at the beginning of the engine running test, and always refer to the number of cylinders in the engine. A Diagnostic Trouble Code 11 (system pass) will always indicate that the system checked out satisfactorily during any phase of the self-test conducted at that time. All other diagnostic trouble codes will refer to a specific problem area or component within the EEC-IV system.**

Each diagnostic trouble code has only one interpretation, wherever it appears. The same diagnostic trouble code will never mean two different things on two different engines.

The EEC-IV system transmits its information by the use of the self-test diagnostic trouble codes. These diagnostic trouble codes are two digit numbers representing the results of the self-test. They are transmitted on the self-test output (found in the self-test electrical connector) in the form of time pulses and read by the use of a voltmeter, STAR tester, NGS tester, check engine light or message center.

FAST/SLOW DIAGNOSTIC TROUBLE CODES

Fast diagnostic trouble codes are given prior to standard diagnostic trouble codes. These diagnostic trouble codes contain information identical to that provided by standard diagnostic trouble codes but are transmitted at 100 times the normal rate. After fast diagnostic trouble codes have been output, the self-test should not be exited until all slow diagnostic trouble codes have been read. Exiting system before all diagnostic trouble codes have been read will erase any continuous memory diagnostic trouble codes.

Clearing Diagnostic Trouble Codes

CONTINUOUS MEMORY

1. Perform Key On Engine Off self-test.
2. When diagnostic trouble codes begin to be displayed, deactivate self-test as follows:
   a. If using STAR tester, position center button in up position.
   b. If using analog volt/ohmmeter, remove jumper wire from self-test input connector and signal return pin of the self-test connector.
   c. If using check engine light, remove jumper wire from self-test input connector and signal return pin of the self-test connector.
   d. If using NGS tester, depress STOP button.
   e. If using message center, remove jumper wire from self-test input connector and signal return pin of the self-test connector.
3. Continuous diagnostic trouble codes should now be erased.

KEEP ALIVE MEMORY (KAM)

To clear keep alive memory, disconnect negative battery cable for a minimum of five minutes. After clearing memory, it is necessary to vehicle a minimum of 10 miles to allow processor time to relearn value.

WIRING DIAGRAMS & CONNECTOR TERMINAL IDENTIFICATION

Refer to **Figs. 31 through 121,** for wiring diagrams and connector terminal identification.

DIAGNOSTIC SUB-ROUTINES/QUICK TEST DIAGNOSTIC TROUBLE CODES & DIAGNOSTIC TROUBLE CODE DEFINITIONS

Refer to **Figs. 122 through 124** for quick test diagnostic trouble codes and diagnostic trouble code definitions.

DIAGNOSTIC ROUTINES & DIAGNOSTIC SUB-ROUTINES/QUICK TESTS

To test and service the EEC-IV subsystem correctly, perform the Diagnostic Routines and Diagnostic Sub-Routines/Quick Test first, and, if the vehicle passes all the phases of the tests, without running (performing) any Pinpoint Tests, the EEC-IV subsystem is satisfactory and the vehicles problem, if any, exists elsewhere (other than the EEC-IV subsystem). However, if a step of the diagnostic routines and diagnostic sub-routines/quick test fails, perform only the Pinpoint Tests specified by the failed step procedure. Do not begin any Pinpoint Test without following the instructions at the beginning of the Pinpoint Test procedure. After all tests and services have been completed, repeat the entire quick test procedure to ensure the EEC-IV subsystem operates satisfactory.

Refer to **Figs. 125 through 163**, for diagnostic routines, diagnostic sub-routines/quick tests and two and three digit Diagnostic Trouble Code (DTC) charts.

PINPOINT TEST

Do not perform any of the following pinpoint tests unless instructed to do so by the Diagnostic Routines or Diagnostic Sub-Routines/Quick Tests. Each pinpoint test assumes that a fault (malfunction) has been detected in the system with direction to enter a specific repair routine. Conducting any pinpoint test without direction from the quick test procedures may produce incorrect results and replacement of satisfactory components. Correct test results for quick test are dependent on the proper operation of non-related EEC components/systems. Do not replace any component unless the test result indicates that they should be replaced.

Refer to **Figs. 164 through 230**, for pinpoint tests.

Diagnostic Aids

CONTINUOUS MONITOR TEST (WIGGLE TEST)

Key On Engine Off Test

1. Connect a volt-ohmmeter or STAR tester onto the self-test output.
2. Turn ignition key to On position.
3. Activate self-test, wait 10 seconds, then deactivate and reactivate, system is now in continuous mode.
4. Tap, move and wiggle suspect sensor or harnesses. When a fault is detected a continuous memory diagnostic trouble code will be stored and indicated as follows:

a. Star tester, red LED lights or continuous tone.
b. Check engine light, lights.
c. Volt/Ohm meter, needle sweeps.

Engine Running Test

1. Connect a volt-ohmmeter or STAR tester onto the self-test output.
2. Key Off, wait 10 seconds.
3. Start engine.
4. Activate self-test, wait 10 seconds, then deactivate and reactivate, system is now in continuous mode. **Do not shut engine Off.**
5. Tap, move and wiggle suspect sensor or harnesses. When a fault is detected a continuous memory diagnostic trouble code will be stored and indicated as follows:

a. Star tester, red LED lights or continuous tone.
b. Check engine light, lights.
c. Volt/Ohmmeter, needle sweeps.

OUTPUT STATE CHECK

The output state check aids in servicing output actuators associated with the EEC-IV system. To energize or de-energize most of the system output actuators, turn EGR solenoid and self-test output (STO) ON and OFF. This mode is entered after all diagnostic trouble codes have been received from Key-ON, Engine-OFF test. During on demand and continuous testing, leave the self-test activated and depress the throttle. Each time the throttle is depressed, the output actuators will change from ON to OFF or OFF to ON.

CYLINDER BALANCE TEST

SFI Engines

The cylinder balance test is to assist in finding a weak or non-contributing cylinder. The test is entered by depressing and releasing the throttle within two minutes after the engine running self-test diagnostic trouble codes have been output.

Once the test is entered, idle speed control duty is fixed and the engine is allowed to stabilize. Engine RPM is measured and stored for later use. The fuel is shutoff to cylinder number 4, 6 or 8, after a stabilization period the engine RPM is again measured and stored. The injector is turned on again and the process is repeated for each injector down to one. If all cylinder drop the prescribed amount a diagnostic trouble code 90 will appear indicating a pass. If any cylinder is weak or non-contributing a diagnostic trouble code 10 through 80 may appear, depending upon which cylinder is at fault.

The test may now be repeated a second time if the throttle is depressed and released within two minutes of the last diagnostic trouble code output.

ADAPTIVE STRATEGY

Adaptive strategy has been added to the EEC-IV system. This feature continually adjusts the calibration strategy to correct for wear and aging calibration components. The adaptive strategy then retains the adjustments in the keep alive memory

(KAM) so they will not be lost (cancelled) when the ignition switch is turned OFF. A short adjustment period will occur: on new vehicles, when the battery has been disconnected during normal service, when the PCM (ECA) is disconnected or replaced and when a component of the EEC-IV system is replaced.

If an EEC-IV component is replaced (due to age or damage), the memory may need to be cleared to eliminate the adjustments that were made to correct the replaced component. It is possible for the engine operation to actually deteriorate because the new component will be controlled as if it were still the replaced aged or damaged component.

During the adjustment or learning period (usually under 5 miles of driving) some vehicles could exhibit abnormal drive symptoms (surge, hesitation and high idle speeds).

FAILURE MODE EFFECTS MANAGEMENT (FMEM)

FMEM is an alternate system strategy in the PCM (ECA) designed to allow improved vehicle drive should one or more sensor inputs fail.

When a sensor input is perceived to be out-of-limits by the ECA, an alternative strategy will be initiated. The computer will substitute a fixed in-limit sensor value and will continue to monitor the faulty sensor input. If the faulty sensor operates within limits, the computer will return to the normal Engine Running mode (strategy).

Diagnostic Trouble Code 98 or 998 will be displayed when FMEM is in effect.

The MIL "Check Engine" light will remain illuminated when the FMEM is in effect.

Component Locations

Refer to **Figs. 231 through 236** for power relay, electronic control assembly, constant control relay module (CCRM), integral control relay module (ICRM) or variable control relay module (VCRM) locations.

During diagnosis and troubleshooting procedures, refer to applicable model year system diagnosis and testing section for wiring diagrams and module connector pin identification.

Quick Test

To test and service the EEC-IV subsystem correctly, perform the Quick Test first, and, if the vehicle passes all three phases of the quick test (key-ON, Engine-OFF, Engine Running and Continuous Test) without running (performing) any Pinpoint Tests, the EEC-IV subsystem is satisfactory and the vehicles problem, if any, exists elsewhere (other than the EEC-IV subsystem). However, if a step of the quick test fails, perform only the Pinpoint Tests specified by the failed step procedure. Do not begin any Pinpoint Test without following the instructions at the beginning of the Pinpoint Test procedure. After all tests and services

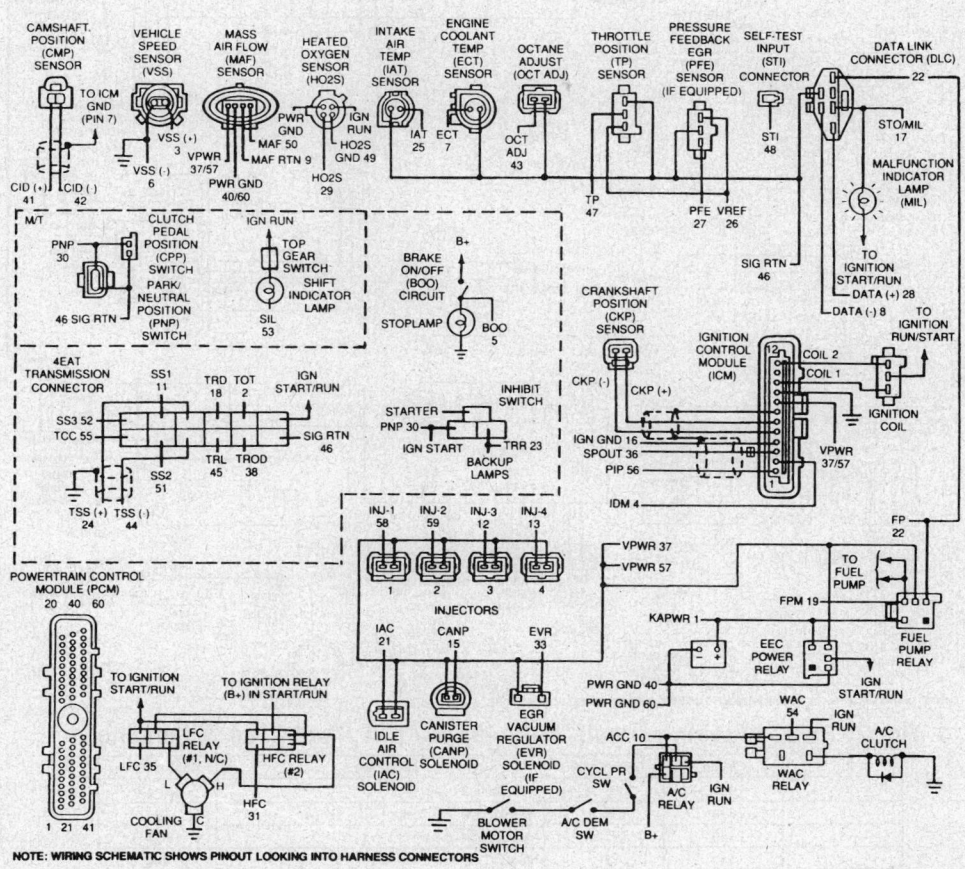

Fig. 31 EEC-IV wiring circuit. 1993 w/1.9L/4-114 MA SFI engine

have been completed, repeat the entire quick test procedure to ensure the EEC-IV subsystem operates satisfactory.

Refer to applicable model year system diagnosis and testing section for quick tests.

Pinpoint Test

Do not perform any of the following pinpoint tests unless instructed to do so by the Quick Tests. Each pinpoint test assumes that a fault (malfunction) has been detected in the system with direction to enter a specific repair routine. Conducting any pinpoint test without direction from the quick test procedures may produce incorrect results and replacement of satisfactory components. Correct test results for quick test are dependent on the proper operation of non-related EEC components/systems. Do not replace any component unless the test result indicates that they should be replaced.

Refer to applicable model year system diagnosis and testing section for pinpoint tests.

If more than one diagnostic trouble code is received, always start the service with the first diagnostic trouble code received. Do not measure voltage or resistance at the processor or connect any test lights to the processor unless specified to do so with the quick and pinpoint test procedures. Isolate both ends of a circuit, then turn ignition switch to OFF position when checking for shorts or circuit continuity, unless specified to do so with the quick or pinpoint test procedures. Disconnect solenoids and/or switches from the harness before measuring for continuity or resistance. When using the pinpoint tests, follow each step in order, starting from the first step in the appropriate test. Follow each step until the fault (malfunction) is found. After completing any repairs to the EEC-IV system, ensure all components are properly connected and repeat functional test. During the test procedure, an open is defined as any resistance obtained greater than 5 ohms, unless otherwise specified within the quick or pinpoint test charts. A short is defined as any resistance obtained of less than 10,000 ohms to ground, unless otherwise specified within the quick or pinpoint test charts.

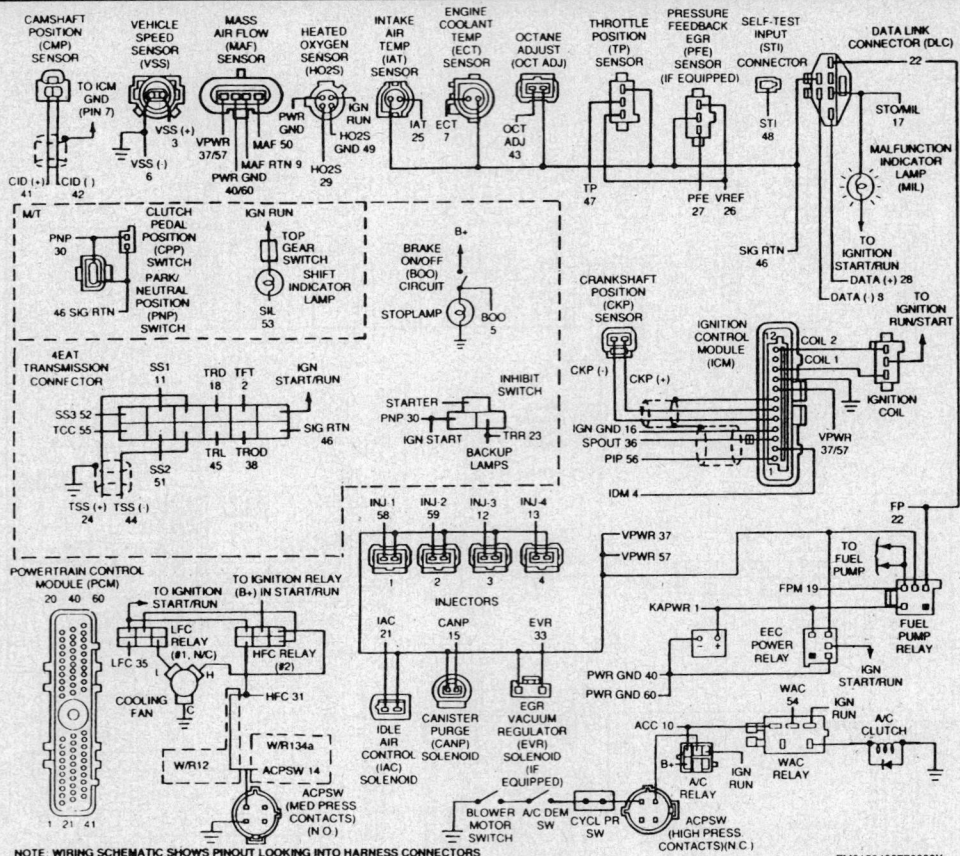

Fig. 32 EEC-IV wiring circuit. 1994–95 w/1.9L/4-114 MA SFI engine

Pin	Circuit	Wire Color	Application	Abbreviation
1	330	BL/R	Keep Alive Power	KAPWR
2	878	W	Transmission Oil Temperature Sensor	TOT
3	159	W/BK	Vehicle Speed Sensor (+)	VSS (+)
4	153	R	Ignition Diagnostic Monitor	IDM
5	351	GR	Brake On/Off	BOO
6	57	BL	Vehicle Speed Sensor (-)	VSS (-)
7	62	BL/W	Engine Coolant Temperature Sensor	ECT
8	121	Y/GR	Data(-)	DATA (-)
9	87	GR/Y	Mass Air Flow Sensor Return	MAF RTN
10	707	GR/BK	A/C Clutch	ACC
11	853	LG/BL	Shift Solenoid 1	SS1
12	105	Y/O	Injector 3	INJ 3
13	115	GR/O	Injector 4	INJ 4
15	94	O/W	Canister Purge Solenoid	CANP
16	78	R/BL	Ignition Ground	IGN GND
17	129	Y/BK	Self-Test Output/Malfunction Indicator Lamp	STO/MIL
18	857	BR/R	Transmission Range Drive	TRD
19	102	BK/PK	Fuel Pump Monitor	FPM
21	83	BL/O	Idle Air Control Solenoid	IAC
22	103	LG	Fuel Pump	FP
23	365	R/GR	Transmission Range Reverse	TRR
24	858	W/BL	Transmission Speed Sensor(+)	TSS(+)
25	109	W/GR	Intake Air Temperature Sensor	IAT
26	85	LG/W	Reference Voltage	VREF
27	145	BL/Y	Pressure Feedback EGR Sensor (if EGR equipped)	PFE
28	122	Y/BL	Data (+)	DATA (+)
29	118	GR/BL	Heated Oxygen Sensor	HO2S
30	5	BK/BL	Park/Neutral Position Switch	PNP
30	82	BR Y	Park Neutral Position Switch and Clutch Pedal Position Switch (M. T only)	PNP & CPP
31	866	R/BK	High Fan Control	HFC
33	108	W/BL	EGR Vacuum Regulator Solenoid (if EGR equipped)	EVR
35	719	Y W	Low Fan Control	LFC
36	156	LG/W	Spark Output	SPOUT
37	101	W R	Vehicle Power	VPWR
38	855	BR BL	Transmission Range Overdrive	TROD
40	999	BK GR	Power Ground	PWR GND

Fig. 33 EEC-IV PCM connector pin usage (Part 1 of 2). 1.9L/4-114 MA SFI engine

FM0159300777010X

Pin	Circuit	Wire Color	Application	Abbreviation
41	128	O	Cylinder Identification (+)	CID (+)
42	127	BL/GR	Cylinder Identification (-)	CID (-)
43	171	GR/W	Octane Adjust	OCT ADJ
44	859	Y/BL	Transmission Speed Sensor (-)	TSS (-)
45	856	BR/GR	Transmission Range Low	TRL
46	63	LG/BK	Signal Return	SIG RTN
47	71	R/W	Throttle Position Sensor	TP
48	119	LG/Y	Self-Test Input	STI
49	95	O/BK	Heated Oxygen Sensor Ground	HO2S GND
50	143	BR/BK	Mass Air Flow Sensor	MAF
51	876	PK/BK	Shift Solenoid 2	SS2
52	852	O/GR	Shift Solenoid 3	SS3
53	154	LG/R	Shift Indicator Lamp (M/T only)	SIL
54	702	BL/BK	WOT A/C Cut-out	WAC
55	851	PK/W	Torque Converter Clutch Solenoid	TCC
56	69	GR/W	Profile Ignition Pick-up	PIP
57	101	W/R	Vehicle Power	VPWR
58	106	Y	Injector 1	INJ 1
59	116	GR/R	Injector 2	INJ 2
60	999	BK/GR	Power Ground	PWR GND

Pin locations given for reference only. Probing 60-pin connector with DVOM probe will result in permanent damage to the pin connectors. Always probe as directed using the breakout box.

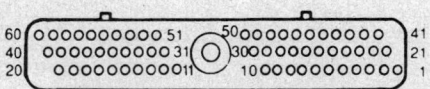

FM015930077020X

Fig. 33   EEC-IV PCM connector pin usage (Part 2 of 2). 1.9L/4-114 MA SFI engine

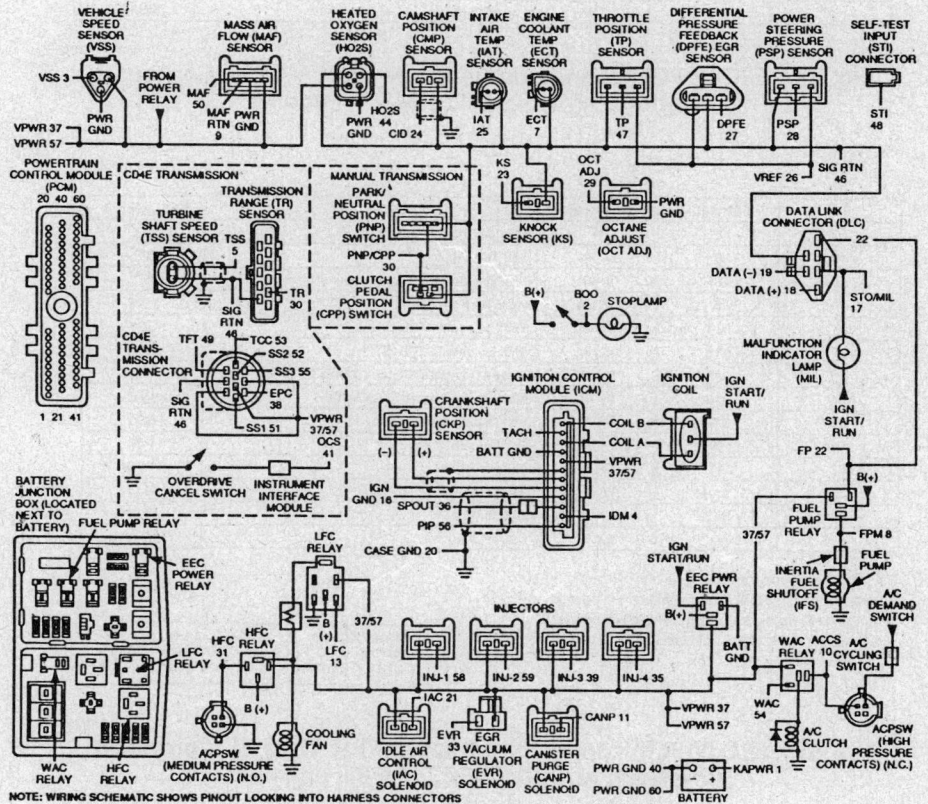

Fig. 34   EEC-IV wiring circuit.
Contour & Mystique w/2.0L/4-122
MA SFI engine

Pin	Circuit	Wire Color	Application	Abbreviation
1	89	O/Y	Keep Alive Power	KAPWR
2	29S	O	Brake On/Off	BOO
3	8	W/P	Vehicle Speed Sensor	VSS
4	8	W/GR	Ignition Diagnostic Monitor	IDM
5	8	W/P	Turbine Shaft Speed Sensor (CD4E)	TSS
7	8	W/GR	Engine Coolant Temperature Sensor	ECT
8	14S	P/BK	Fuel Pump Monitor	FPM
9	9	BR/BL	Mass Air Flow Sensor Return	MAF RTN
10	14S	P/BL	A/C Cycling Switch	ACCS
11	91S	BK/O	Canister Purge Solenoid	CANP
13	91S	BK/BL	Low Fan Control	LFC
16	91	BK/BL	Ignition Ground	IGN GND
17	91S	BK/O	Self-Test Output	STO
18	8	W/BL	Data (+)	DATA (+)
19	9	BR/BL	Data (-)	DATA (-)
20	91	BK/R	Case Ground	CSE GND
21	91S	BK/Y	Idle Air Control Solenoid	IAC
22	91S	BK/BL	Fuel Pump	FP
23	8	W/BK	Knock Sensor	KS
24	8	W/P	Cylinder Identification	CID
25	8	W/P	Intake Air Temperature Sensor	IAT
26	7	Y	Reference Voltage	VREF
27	8	W/BL	Differential Pressure Feedback EGR Sensor	DPFE
28	8	W/P	Power Steering Pressure Sensor	PSP
29	8	W/BK	Octane Adjust	OCT ADJ
30	8	W	Park/Neutral Position Switch and Clutch Pedal Position Switch (Manual Trans.)	PNP and CPP
30	8	W/GR	Transmission Range Sensor (CD4E)	TR
31	91S	BK/W	High Fan Control	HFC
33	91S	BK/O	EGR Vacuum Regulator Solenoid	EVR
35	91S	BK/O	Injector 4	INJ 4
36	8	W/P	Spark Output	SPOUT
37	95	GR/Y	Vehicle Power	VPWR
38	91S	BK/R	Electronic Pressure Control (CD4E)	EPC
39	91S	BK/BL	Injector 3	INJ 3
40	91	BK/Y	Power Ground	PWR GND
41	8	W/BK	Transmission Control Switch (CD4E)	TCS
44	8	W	Heated Oxygen Sensor	HO2S
46	9	BR	Signal Return	SIG RTN

FM0159501246010X

Fig. 35 EEC-IV PCM connector pin usage (Part 1 of 2). Contour & Mystique w/2.0L/4-122 MA SFI engine

Pin	Circuit	Wire Color	Application	Abbreviation
47	8	W	Throttle Position Sensor	TP
48	8	W/BK	Self-Test Input	STI
49	8	W/R	Transmission Fluid Temperature Sensor (CD4E)	TFT
50	8	W/BL	Mass Air Flow Sensor	MAF
51	91S	BK/Y	Shift Solenoid 1 (CD4E)	SS1
52	91S	BK/BL	Shift Solenoid 2 (CD4E)	SS2
53	91S	BK/W	Torque Converter Clutch (CD4E)	TCC
54	91S	BK/Y	Wide Open Throttle A/C Cut-Off	WAC
55	91S	BK/O	Shift Solenoid 3 (CD4E)	SS3
56	8	W/BK	Profile Ignition Pick-up	PIP
57	95	GR/Y	Vehicle Power	VPWR
58	91S	BK/W	Injector 1	INJ 1
59	91S	BK/Y	Injector 2	INJ 2
60	91	BK/Y	Power Ground	PWR GND

Pin locations given for reference only. Probing 60-pin connector with DVOM probe will result in permanent damage to the pin connectors. Always probe as directed using the breakout box.

FM0159501246020X

Fig. 35 EEC-IV PCM connector pin usage (Part 2 of 2). Contour & Mystique w/2.0L/4-122 MA SFI engine

Probe

Pin	Circuit	Wire Color	Application	Abbreviation
1	84	BL R	Keep Alive Power	KAPWR
3	684	O	Vehicle Speed Sensor (+)	VSS (+)
4	733	R BK	Ignition Diagnostic Monitor	IDM
6	687	O BK	Vehicle Speed Sensor (-)	VSS (-)
7	724	Y BK	Engine Coolant Temperature Sensor	ECT
8	703	W Y	Fuel Pump Monitor	FPM
9	721	BR	Mass Air Flow Sensor Return	MAF RTN
11	717	W BK	Canister Purge Solenoid	CANP
13	772	GR	Fuel Pressure Regulator Control Solenoid	FPRC
14	196	BL R	Blower Motor Input	BLR
15	663	BK GR	Rear Window Defroster Input	DEF
16	59	BK	Ignition Ground	IGN GND
17	746	LG R	Self Test Output Malfunction Indicator Lamp	STO and MIL
21	719	W	Idle Air Control Bypass Air Solenoid	IAC-BPA
22	704	LG	Fuel Pump	FP
23	185	GR W	A C Clutch Switch (A C Demand)	ACCS ACD
24	737	GR W	Cylinder Identification	CID
25	728	W LG	Intake Air Temperature Sensor	IAT
26	813	LG R	Reference Voltage	VREF
28	718	BR R	Power Steering Pressure Switch	PSP
29	727	GR BL	Heated Oxygen Sensor Ground	HO2S GND
30	716	LG BL	Park Neutral Position Switch	PNP
31	755	W BL	EGR Vacuum Regulator Solenoid	EVR
32	197	BK GR	Low Fan Control	LFC
33	173	BL GR	High Fan Control	HFC
35	708	Y GR	Injector 4	INJ 4
36	736	R BL	Spark Output	SPOUT
37	701	W R	Vehicle Power	VPWR
39	707	Y R	Injector 3	INJ 3
40	999	BK GR	Power Ground	PWR GND
42	272	GR	Daytime Running Lamps Input	DRL
43	725	R GR	EGR Temperature Sensor	EGRT
44	720	BL	Heated Oxygen Sensor	HO2S
45	261	W	Headlamp Input	HDL
46	66	BK BL	Signal Return	SIG RTN
47	815	LG W	Throttle Position Sensor	TP
48	711	BL W	Self Test Input	STI
50	722	R	Mass Air Flow Sensor	MAF

(Continued)

Fig. 37 EEC-IV PCM connector pin usage (Part 1 of 2). 1993 Probe w/2.0L/4-122 MA SFI engine, 1994 Probe w/2.0L/4-122 MA SFI engine & Federal emissions & 1994 Probe w/2.0L/4-122 engine, automatic transaxle & California emissions

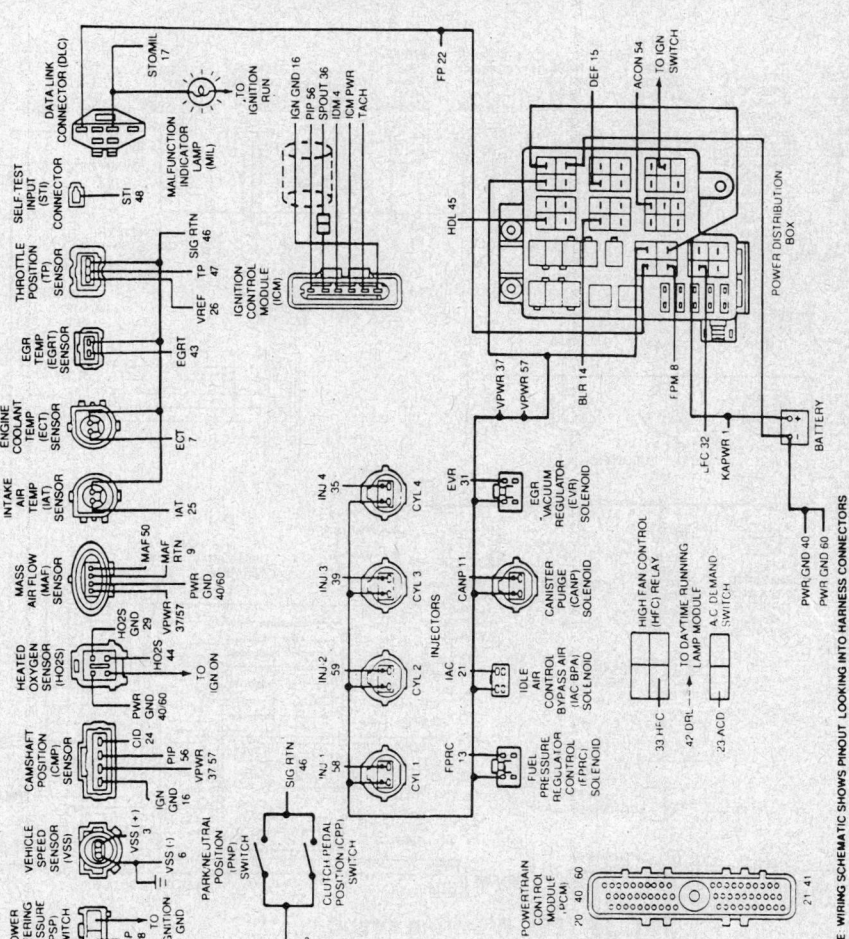

NOTE WIRING SCHEMATIC SHOWS PINOUT LOOKING INTO HARNESS CONNECTORS

Fig. 36 EEC-IV wiring circuit. 1993 Probe w/2.0L/4-122 MA SFI engine, 1994 Probe w/2.0L/4-122 MA SFI engine & Federal emissions & 1994 Probe w/2.0L/4-122 engine, automatic transaxle & California emissions

FORD–Computerized Engine Controls

Pin	Circuit	Wire Color	Application	Abbreviation
54	187	GR/BK	A/C ON Relay	ACON
56	735	R/Y	Profile Ignition Pickup	PIP
57	701	W/R	Vehicle Power	VPWR
58	705	Y/BK	Injector 1	INJ 1
59	706	Y/W	Injector 2	INJ 2
60	999	BK/GR	Power Ground	PWR GND

Pin locations given for reference only. Probing 60-pin connector with DVOM probe will result in permanent damage to the pin connectors. Always probe as directed using the breakout box.

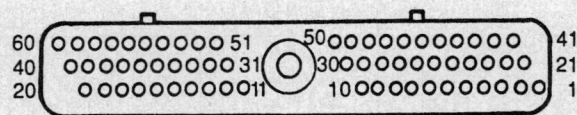

Fig. 37   EEC-IV PCM connector pin usage (Part 2 of 2). 1993 Probe w/2.0L/4-122 MA SFI engine, 1994 Probe w/2.0L/4-122 MA SFI engine & Federal emissions & 1994 Probe w/2.0L/4-122 engine, automatic transaxle & California emissions

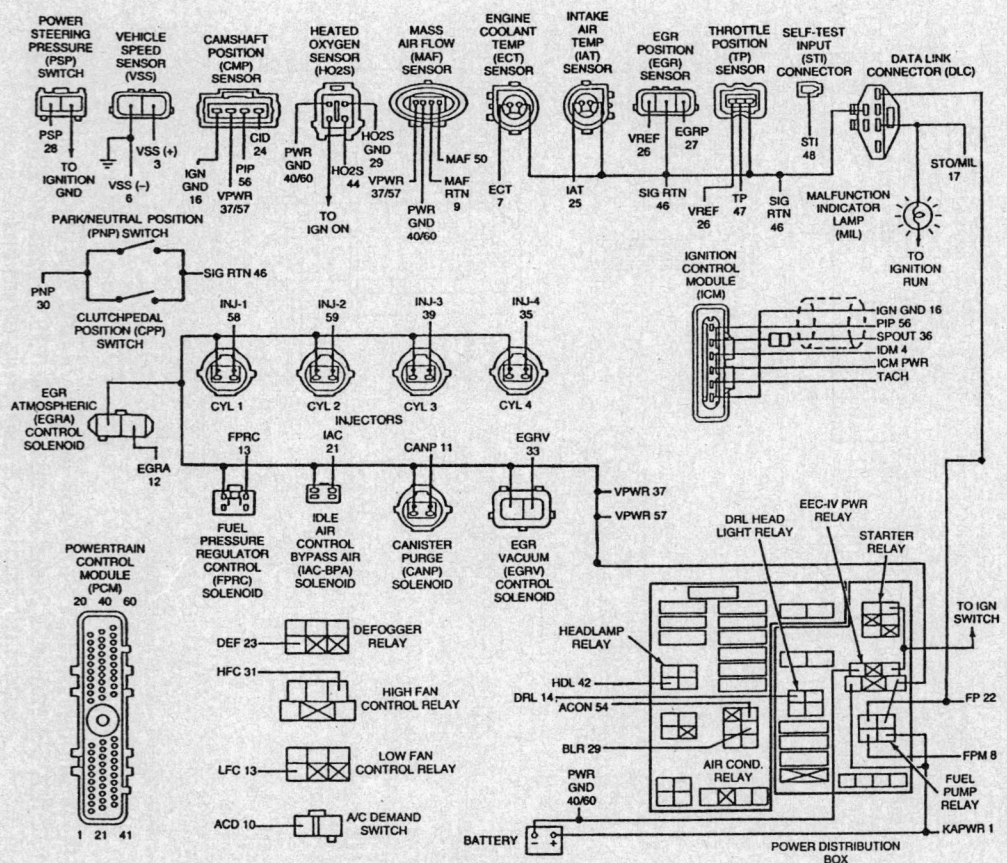

Fig. 38   EEC-IV wiring circuit. 1994–95 Probe w/2.0L/4-122 MA SFI engine, manual transaxle & California emissions

ELECTRONIC ENGINE CONTROL SYSTEM IV (EEC-IV)

Pin	Circuit	Wire Color	Application	Abbreviation
1	84	BL/R	Keep Alive Power	KAPWR
3	684	BL/W	Vehicle Speed Sensor (+)	VSSDIF(+)
4	733	BL/Y	Ignition Diagnostic Monitor	IDM
6	687	BR/G	Vehicle Speed Sensor (-)	VSSDIF(-)
7	724	O/GR	Engine Coolant Temperature Sensor	ECT
8	703	W/Y	Fuel Pump Monitor	FPM
9	721	BR	Mass Air Flow Sensor Signal Return	MAFRTN
10	185	PK/BK	A/C Demand Switch	ACD
11	717	W/BK	Canister Purge Solenoid	CANP
12	756	W/BL	EGR Atmos. Press. Control Solenoid	EGRA
13	197	BL/O	Low Fan Control	LFC
14	72	GR	Daytime Running Lamp Input	DRL
16	58	BK	Ignition Ground	IGN GND
17	746	BL	Self-Test Output / Malfunction Indicator Lamp	STO/MIL
21	719	LG/BK	Idle Air Control-Bypass Air Solenoid	IAC-BPA
22	704	LG	Fuel Pump	FP
23	663	PK/BK	Rear Window Defroster Input	DEF
24	737	GR/W	Cylinder Identification	CID
25	728	W/LG	Intake Air Temperature Sensor	IAT
26	813	LG/P	Reference Voltage	VREF
27	725	R/GR	EGR Valve Position Sensor	EGRP
28	718	BR/Y	Power Steering Pressure Switch	PSP
29	196	O/BK	Blower Motor Input	BLR
30	716	LG/BL	Park/Neutral Position Switch	PNP
31	173	BL/GR	High Fan Control	HFC
32	772	O/W	Fuel Pressure Regulator Control Solenoid	FPRC
33	755	GR/W	EGR Vacuum Control Solenoid	EGRV
35	708	Y/GR	Injector 4	INJ 4
36	736	R/BL	Spark Output	SPOUT
37	701	Y/R	Injector 3	INJ 3
39	707	Y/R	Injector 3	INJ 3
40	999	BK/GR	Power Ground	PWR GND
42	261	W	Headlamp Input	HDL
43	727	GR/BL	Heated Oxygen Sensor Ground	HO2S GND
44	720	BK/Y	Heated Oxygen Sensor / Self-Test Input	HO2S/STI
46	66	BK/BL	Signal Return	SIG RTN
47	815	LG/W	Throttle Position Sensor	TP
48	711	BL/R	Self-Test Input	STI

Fig. 39 EEC-IV PCM connector pin
usage (Part 1 of 2). 1994–95 Probe
w/2.0L/4-122 MA SFI engine,
manual transaxle & California
emissions

Pin	Circuit	Wire Color	Application	Abbreviation
50	722	R	Mass Air Flow Sensor	MAF
54	187	GR/BK	A/C ON Relay	ACON
56	735	R/Y	Profile Ignition Pickup	PIP
57	701	W/R	Vehicle Power	VPWR
58	705	Y/BK	Injector 1	INJ 1
59	706	Y/W	Injector 2	INJ 2
60	999	BK/GR	Power Ground	PWR GND

Pin locations given for reference only. Probing 60-pin connector with DVOM probe will result in permanent damage to the pin connectors. Always probe as directed using the breakout box.

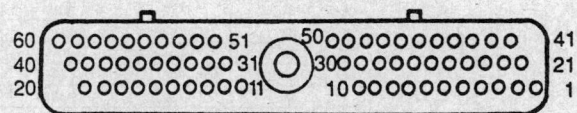

Fig. 39 EEC-IV PCM connector pin
usage (Part 2 of 2). 1994–95 Probe
w/2.0L/4-122 MA SFI engine,
manual transaxle & California
emissions

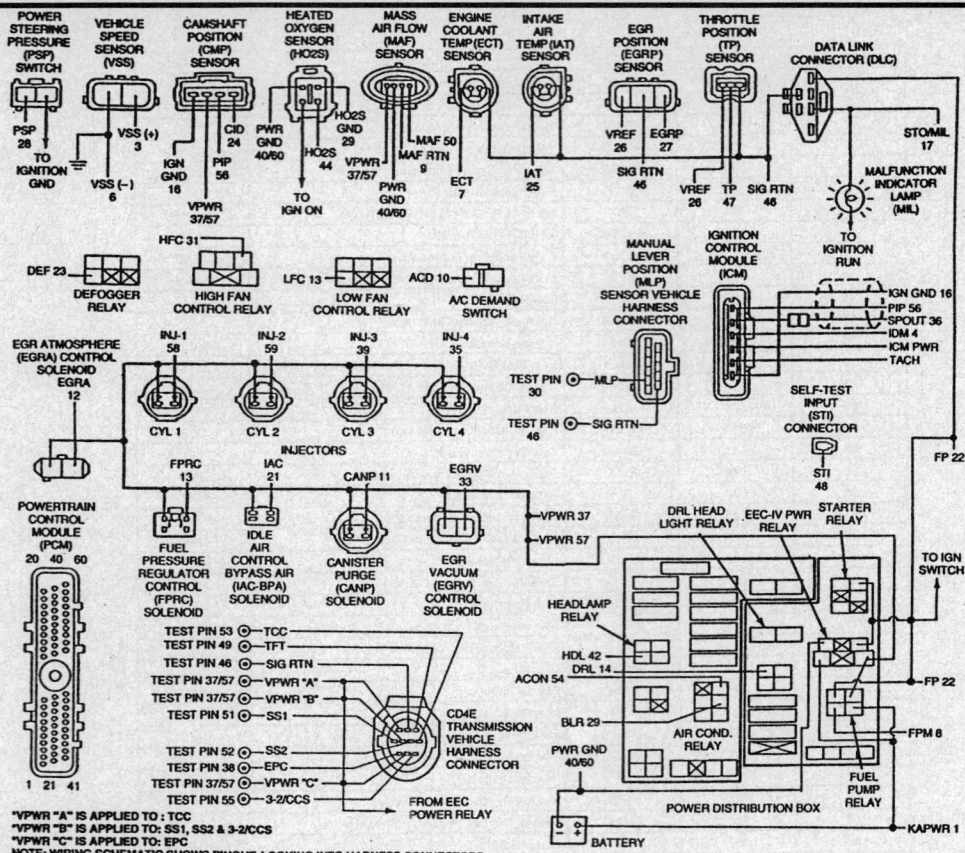

Fig. 40   EEC-IV wiring circuit. 1994-95 Probe w/2.0L/4-122 MA SFI engine & CD4E automatic transaxle

Pin	Circuit	Wire Color	Application	Abbreviation
1	84	BL/R	Keep Alive Power	KAPWR
2	321	W/BK	Brake On/Off Switch	BOO
3	684	BL/W	Vehicle Speed Sensor (+)	VSSDIF(+)
4	733	BL/Y	Ignition Diagnostic Monitor	IDM
5	805	BL/LG	Transmission Speed Sensor	TSS
6	687	BR/G	Vehicle Speed Sensor (-)	VSSDIF(-)
7	724	C/GR	Engine Coolant Temperature Sensor	ECT
8	703	W/Y	Fuel Pump Monitor	FPM
9	721	BR	Mass Air Flow Sensor Signal Return	MAFRTN
10	185	PK/BK	A/C Demand Switch	ACD
11	717	W/BK	Canister Purge Solenoid	CANP
12	756	W/BL	EGR Atmos. Press. Control Solenoid	EGRA
13	197	BL/O	Low Fan Control	LFC
14	72	GR	Daytime Running Lamp Input	DRL
16	58	BK	Ignition Ground	IGN GND
17	746	BL	Self-Test Output/Malfunction Indicator Lamp	STO/MIL
18	790	O/Y	Data(+)	DATA(+)
19	791	W/Y	Data(-)	DATA(-)
21	719	LG/BK	Idle Air Control-Bypass Air Solenoid	IAC-BPA
22	704	LG	Fuel Pump	FP
23	663	PK/BK	Rear Window Defroster Input	DEF
24	737	GR/W	Cylinder Identification	CID
25	728	W/LG	Intake Air Temperature Sensor	IAT
26	813	LG/P	Reference Voltage	VREF
27	725	R/GR	EGR Valve Position Sensor	EGRP
28	718	BR/Y	Power Steering Pressure Switch	PSP
29	196	O/BK	Blower Motor Input	BLR
30	817	R/BK	Manual Lever Position Sensor	MLP
31	173	BL/LG	High Fan Control	HFC
32	772	O/W	Fuel Pressure Regulator Control Solenoid	FPRC
33	755	GR/W	EGR Vacuum Control Solenoid	EGRV
34	824	W/Y	Manual Mode Lamp	MML
35	708	Y/GR	Injector 4	INJ 4
36	738	R/BL	Spark Output	SPOUT
37	701	W/R	Vehicle Power	VPWR
38	809	BL/BR	Electronic Pressure Control Solenoid	EPC
39	707	Y/R	Injector 3	INJ 3
40	999	BK/GR	Power Ground	PWR GND

Fig. 41   EEC-IV PCM connector pin usage (Part 1 of 2). 1994-95 Probe w/2.0L/4-122 MA SFI engine & CD4E automatic transaxle

Pin	Circuit	Wire Color	Application	Abbreviation
41	823	BR/R	Manual Mode Switch	MMS
42	261	W	Headlamp Input	HDL
43	727	GR/BL	Heated Oxygen Sensor Ground	HO2S GND
44	720	BK/Y	Heated Oxygen Sensor / Self-Test Input	HO2S/STI
46	66	BK/BL	Signal Return	SIG RTN
47	815	LG/W	Throttle Position Sensor	TP
48	711	BL/R	Self-Test Input	STI
49	806	Y/W	Transmission Fluid Temperature Sensor	TFT
50	722	R	Mass Air Flow Sensor	MAF
51	801	BL	Shift Solenoid 1	SS1
52	802	BL/BK	Shift Solenoid 2	SS2
53	804	BL/G	Torque Converter Clutch Solenoid	TCC
54	187	GR/BK	A/C ON	ACON
55	803	BL/Y	Shift Solenoid 3	SS3
56	735	R/Y	Profile Ignition Pickup	PIP
57	701	W/R	Vehicle Power	VPWR
58	705	Y/BK	Injector 1	INJ 1
59	706	Y/W	Injector 2	INJ 2
60	999	BK/GR	Power Ground	PWR GND

Pin locations given for reference only. Probing 60-pin connector with DVOM probe will result in permanent damage to the pin connectors. Always probe as directed using the breakout box.

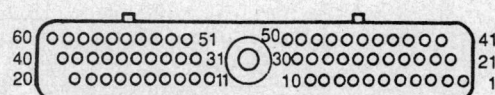

Fig. 41   EEC-IV PCM connector pin usage (Part 2 of 2). 1994–95 Probe w/2.0L/4-122 MA SFI engine & CD4E automatic transaxle

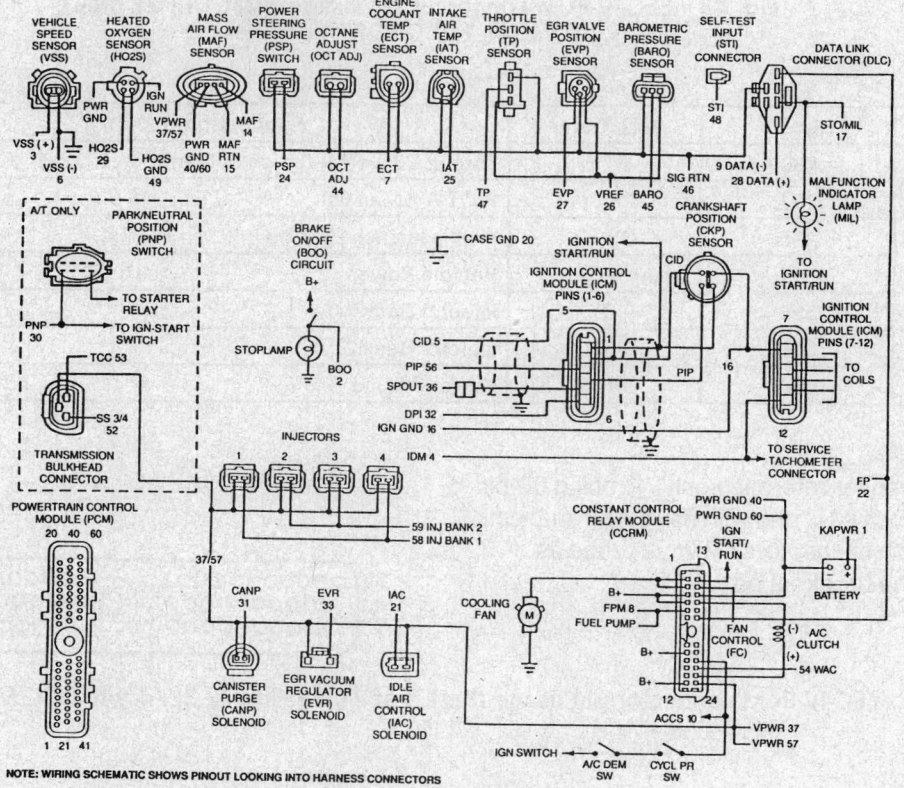

Fig. 42   EEC-IV wiring circuit. 1993 w/2.3L/4-140 OHC MFI engine

Pin	Circuit	Wire Color	Application	Abbreviation
1	37	Y	Keep Alive Power	KAPWR
2	511	LG	Brake On / Off	BOO
3	679	GY/BK	Vehicle Speed Sensor (+)	VSS (+)
4	11	T/Y	Ignition Diagnostic Monitor	IDM
5	282	DB/O	Cylinder Identification	CID
6	676	PK/O	Vehicle Speed Sensor (-)	VSS (-)
7	354	LG/R	Engine Coolant Temperature Sensor	ECT
8	238	DG/Y	Fuel Pump Monitor	FPM
9	915	PK/LB	Data (-)	DATA (-)
10	347	BK/Y	A/C Cyclic Switch	ACCS
14	967	LB/R	Mass Air Flow Sensor	MAF
15	968	T/LB	Mass Air Flow Sensor Return	MAF RTN
16	259	O/R	Ignition Ground	IGN GND
17	658	PK/LG	Self-Test Output / Malfunction Indicator Lamp	STO/MIL
20	57	BK	Case Ground	CSE GND
21	264	W/LB	Idle Air Control Solenoid	IAC
22	926	LB/O	Fuel Pump	FP
24	330	Y/LG	Power Steering Pressure Switch	PSP
25	743	GY	Intake Air Temperature Sensor	IAT
26	351	BR/W	Reference Voltage	VREF
27	352	BR/LG	EGR Valve Position Sensor	EVP
28	914	T/O	Data (+)	DATA (+)
29	74	GY/LB	Heated Oxygen Sensor	HO2S
30	199	LB/Y	Park Neutral Position (A/T Only)	PNP
31	101	GY/Y	Canister Purge Solenoid	CANP
32	283	DB/Y	Dual Plug Inhibit	DPI
33	360	BR/PK	EGR Vacuum Regulator Solenoid	EVR
36	929	PK	Spark Output	SPOUT
37	361	R	Vehicle Power	VPWR
40	570	BK/W	Power Ground	PWR GND
44	242	DG	Octane Adjust	OCT ADJ
45	358	LG/BK	Barometric Pressure Sensor	BARO
46	359	GY/R	Signal Return	SIG RTN
47	355	GY/W	Throttle Position Sensor	TP
48	209	W/P	Self-Test Input	STI
49	89	O	Heated Oxygen Sensor Ground	HO2S GND
51	639	LG/P	Fan Control	FC
52	237	O/Y	3/4 Shift Solenoid (A/T Only)	SS 3/4

FM0159300785010X

Fig. 43 EEC-IV PCM connector pin usage (Part 1 of 2). 1993 w/2.3L/4-140 OHC MFI engine

Pin	Circuit	Wire Color	Application	Abbreviation
53	480	P/Y	Torque Converter Clutch Solenoid (A/T Only)	TCC
54	331	PK/Y	WOT A/C Cut Off	WAC
56	395	GY/O	Profile Ignition Pick-Up	PIP
57	361	R	Vehicle Power	VPWR
58	555	T	Injector Bank 1	INJ BANK 1
59	556	W	Injector Bank 2	INJ BANK 2
60	570	BK/W	Power Ground	PWR GND

Pin locations given for reference only. Probing 60-pin connector with DVOM probe will result in permanent damage to the pin connectors. Always probe as directed using the breakout box.

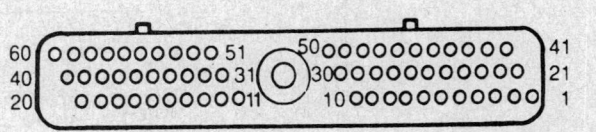

FM0159300785020X

Fig. 43 EEC-IV PCM connector pin usage (Part 2 of 2). 1993 w/2.3L/4-140 OHC MFI engine

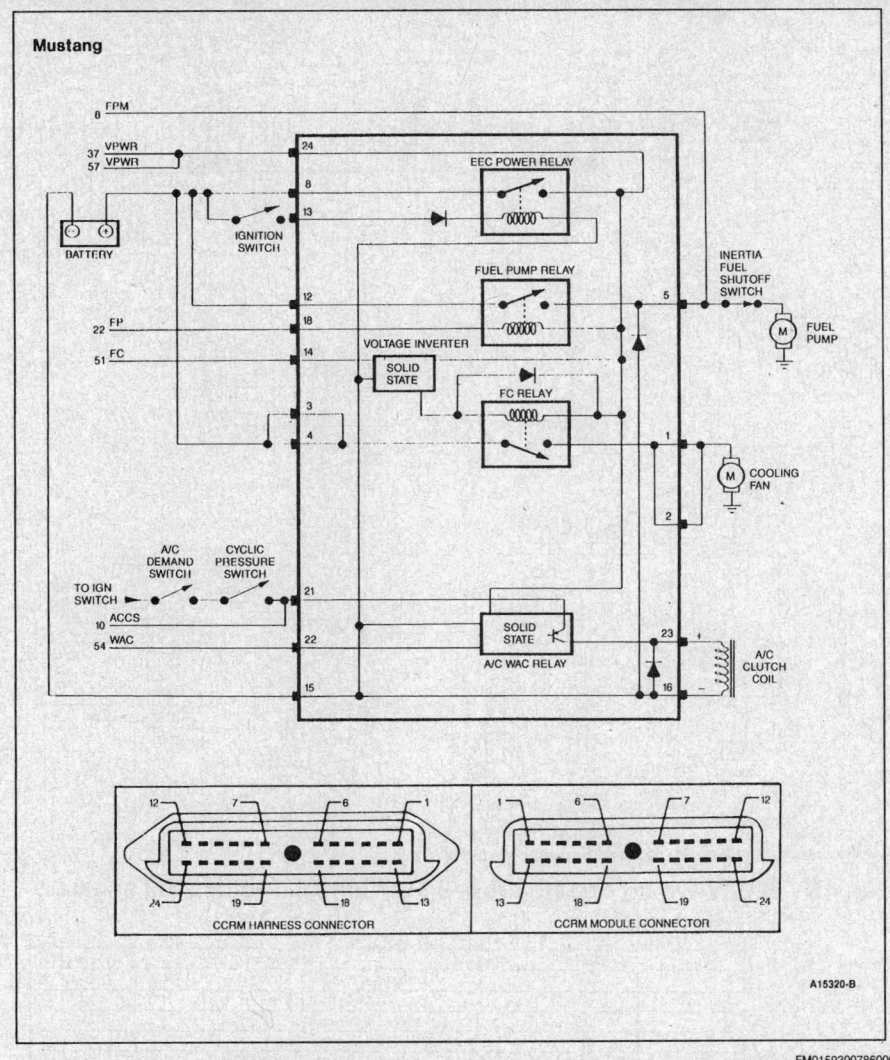

Fig. 44   EEC-IV CCRM wiring circuit. 1993 w/2.3L/4-140 OHC MFI engine

Pin	Circuit	Color	Application	Abbreviation
1	228	DB	Power to Cooling Fan	PT/CF
2	228	DB	Power to Cooling Fan	PT/CF
3	38	BK/O	B (+) to Cooling Fan Control Relay	B (+)
4	38	BK/O	B (+) to Cooling Fan Control Relay	B (+)
5	238	DG/Y	Power to Fuel Pump	PTP
8	37	Y	B (+) to EEC Power Relay	B (+)
12	787	PK/BK	B (+) to Fuel Pump Relay	B (+)
13	16	R/LG	Ignition Start/Run	KEY PWR
14	639	LG/P	Fan Control Circuit	FC
15	57	BK	Power Ground	PWR GND
16	321	GY/W	A/C Clutch Ground	A/C GND
18	926	LB/O	Fuel Pump	FP
21	883	PK/LB	A/C Cyclic Switch	ACCS
22	331	PK/Y	WOT A/C Cut Off	WAC
23	347	BK/Y	Power to A/C Clutch	PTAC
24	361	R	Vehicle Power	VPWR

FM0159300787000X

Fig. 45   EEC-IV CCRM pin usage. 1993 w/2.3L/4-140 OHC MFI engine

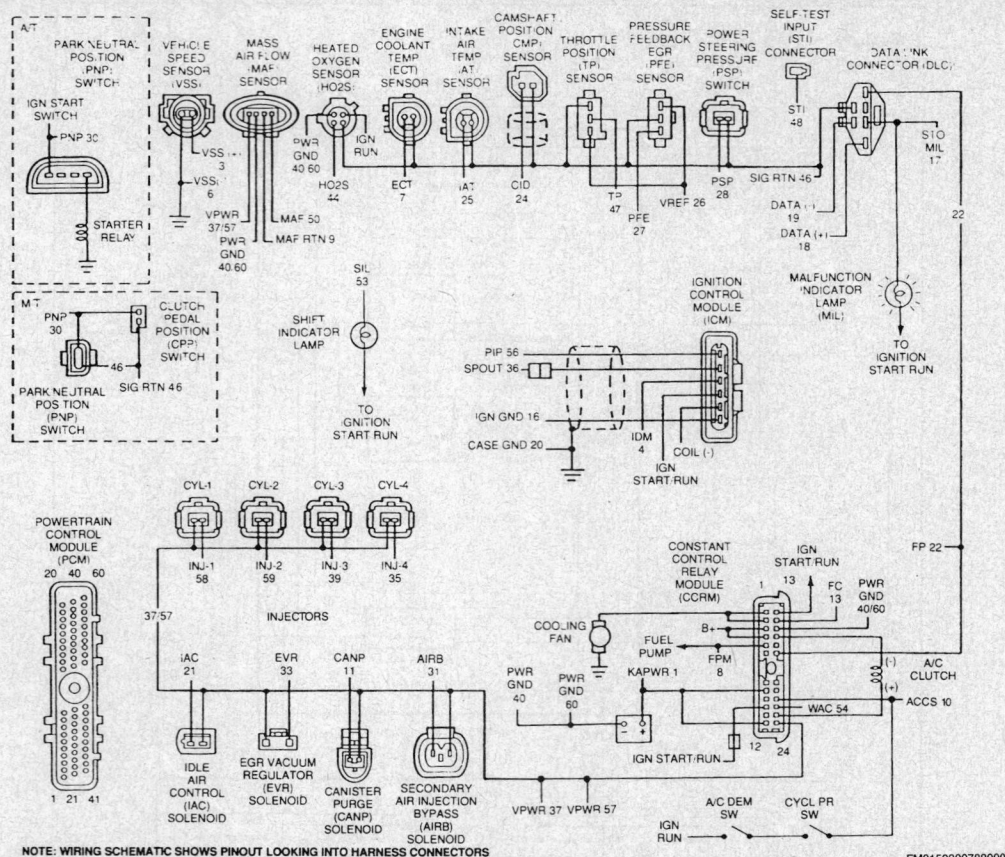

Fig. 46 EEC-IV wiring circuit. 1993–94 w/2.3L/4-140 HSC SFI engine

Tempo/Topaz

Pin	Circuit	Wire Color	Application	Abbreviation
1	37	Y	Keep Alive Power	KAPWR
3	150	DG/W	Vehicle Speed Sensor (+)	VSS (+)
4	648	W/PK	Ignition Diagnostic Monitor	IDM
6	563	O/Y	Vehicle Speed Sensor (-)	VSS (-)
7	354	LG/R	Engine Coolant Temperature Sensor	ECT
8	787	PK/BK	Fuel Pump Monitor	FPM
9	968	T/LB	Mass Air Flow Sensor Return	MAF RTN
10	883	PK/LB	A/C Cyclic Switch	ACCS
11	101	GY/Y	Canister Purge Solenoid	CANP
13	197	T/O	Fan Control	FC
16	259	O/R	Ignition Ground	IGN GND
17	201	T/R	Self-Test Output/Malfunction Indicator Lamp	STO/MIL
18	914	T/O	Data (+)	DATA (+)
19	915	PK/LB	Data (-)	DATA (-)
20	57	BK	Case Ground	CSE GND
21	264	W/LB	Idle Air Control Solenoid	IAC
22	238	DG/Y	Fuel Pump	FP
24	795	DG	Cylinder Identification	CID
25	743	GY	Intake Air Temperature Sensor	IAT
26	351	BR/W	Reference Voltage	VREF
27	352	BR/LG	Pressure Feedback EGR Sensor	PFE
28	330	Y/LG	Power Steering Pressure Switch	PSP
30	480	P/Y	Park/Neutral Position Switch/Clutch Pedal Position Switch (M/T Only)	PNP/CPP
30	480	P/Y	Park/Neutral Position Switch (A/T Only)	PNP
31	100	W/R	Secondary Air Injection Bypass (California Only)	AIRB
33	362	Y	EGR Vacuum Regulator Solenoid	EVR
35	558	BR/LB	Injector 4	INJ 4
36	929	PK	Spark Output	SPOUT
37	361	R	Vehicle Power	VPWR
39	557	BR/Y	Injector 3	INJ 3
40	60	BK/LG	Power Ground	PWR GND
44	94	R/BK	Heated Oxygen Sensor	HO2S
46	359	GY/R	Signal Return	SIG RTN
47	355	GY/W	Throttle Position Sensor	TP
48	209	W/P	Self-Test Input	STI
50	967	LB/R	Mass Air Flow Sensor	MAF
53	224	T/W	Shift Indicator Lamp	SIL
54	331	PK/Y	WOT A/C Cut Off	WAC

(Continued)

**Fig. 47 EEC-IV PCM connector pin usage (Part 1 of 2).
1993–94 w/2.3L/4-140 HSC SFI engine**

Pin	Circuit	Wire Color	Application	Abbreviation
56	349	DB	Profile Ignition Pick-Up	PIP
57	361	R	Vehicle Power	VPWR
58	555	T	Injector 1	INJ 1
59	556	W	Injector 2	INJ 2
60	60	BK/LG	Power Ground	PWR GND

Pin locations given for reference only. Probing 60-pin connector with DVOM probe will result in permanent damage to the pin connectors. Always probe as directed using the breakout box.

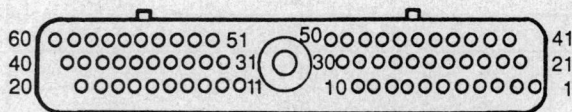

Fig. 47   EEC-IV PCM connector pin usage (Part 2 of 2). 1993–94 w/2.3L/4-140 HSC SFI engine

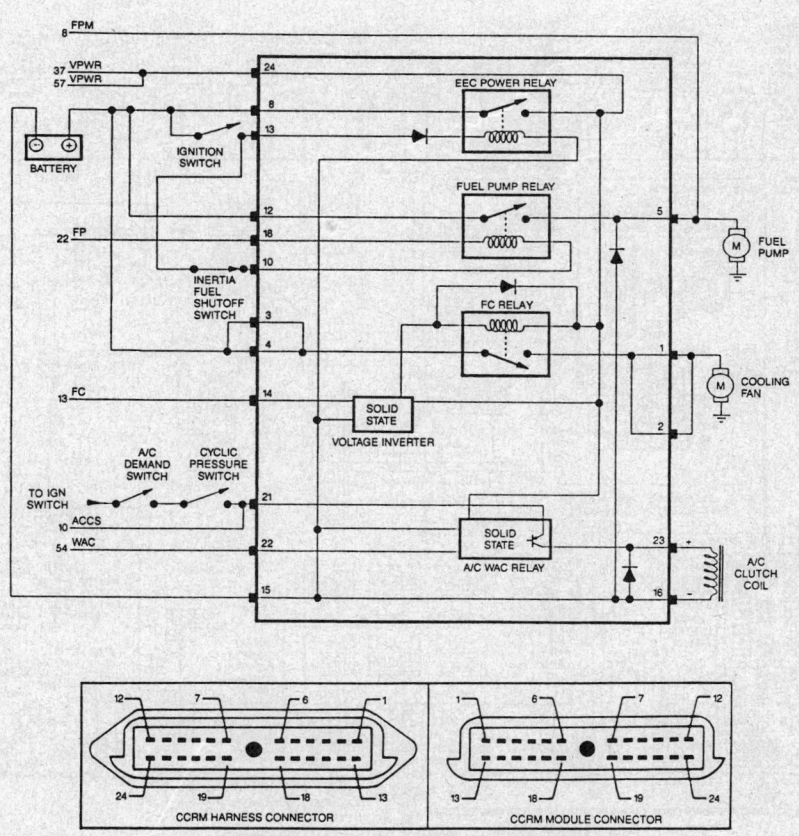

Fig. 48   EEC-IV CCRM wiring circuit. 1993–94 w/2.3L/4-140 HSC SFI engine

Pin	Circuit	Wire Color	Application	Abbreviation
1	228	DB	Cooling Fan	PTF
2	228	DB	Cooling Fan	PTF
3	37	Y	Battery (+) to FC Relay	B (+)
4	37	Y	Battery (+) to FC Relay	B (+)
5	787	PK/BK	Power to Fuel Pump	PTP
8	37	Y	Battery (+) to EEC Power Relay	B (+)
10	866	W	Ignition Start / Run	IGN
12	37	Y	Battery (+) to Fuel Pump Relay	B (+)
13	16	R/LG	Ignition Start / Run	IGN
14	197	T/O	FC Circuit	FC
15	60	BK/LG	Power Ground	PWR GND
16	321	GY/W	A/C Clutch Ground	A/C GND
18	238	DG/Y	Fuel Pump Circuit	FP
21	883	PK/LB	A/C Cyclic Switch	ACCS
22	331	PK/Y	WOT A/C Cut Off	WAC
23	347	BK/Y	Power to A/C Clutch Coil	PTAC
24	361	R	Vehicle Power	VPWR

FM0159300792000X

Fig. 49 EEC-IV CCRM pin usage. 1993–94 w/2.3L/4-140 HSC SFI engine

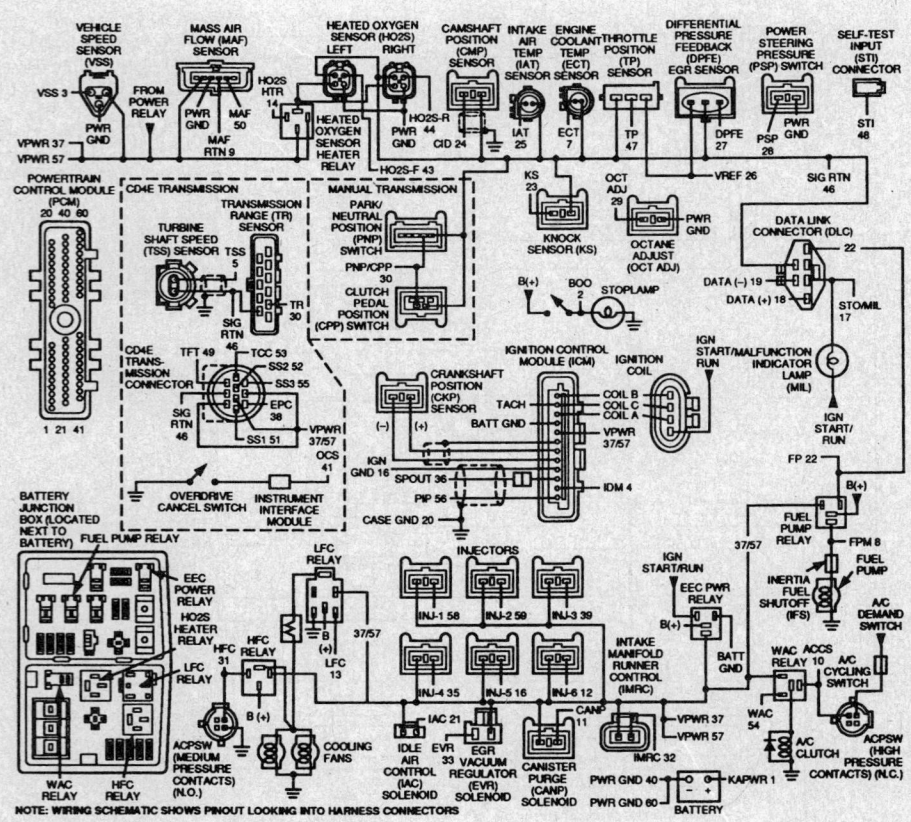

FM0159501247000X

Fig. 50 EEC-IV wiring circuit. 1995 w/2.5L/V6-153 MA SFI engine

Pin	Circuit	Wire Color	Application	Abbreviation
1	89	O/Y	Keep Alive Power	KAPWR
2	29S	O	Brake On/Off	BOO
3	8	W/P	Vehicle Speed Sensor	VSS
4	8	W/R	Ignition Diagnostic Monitor	IDM
5	8	W/P	Turbine Shaft Speed Sensor (CD4E)	TSS
7	8	W/GR	Engine Coolant Sensor	ECT
8	14S	P/BK	Fuel Pump Monitor	FPM
9	9	BR/BL	Mass Air Flow Sensor Return	MAF RTN
10	14S	P/BL	A/C Cycling Switch	ACCS
11	91S	BK/O	Canister Purge Solenoid	CANP
12	91S	BK/R	Injector 6	INJ 6
13	91S	BK/BL	Low Fan Control	LFC
14	91S	BK/BL	Heated Oxygen Sensor Heater	HO2S HTR
15	91S	BK/GR	Injector 5	INJ 5
16	91	BK/BL	Ignition Ground	IGN GND
17	91S	BK/O	Self-Test Output	STO
18	8	W/BL	Data (+)	DATA (+)
19	9	GR/BL	Data (-)	DATA (-)
20	91	BK/R	Case Ground	CSE GND
21	91S	BK/Y	Idle Air Control Solenoid	IAC
22	91S	BK/BL	Fuel Pump	FP
23	8	W/BK	Knock Sensor	KS
24	8	W/P	Cylinder Identification	CID
25	8	W/P	Intake Air Temperature Sensor	IAT
26	7	Y	Reference Voltage	VREF
27	8	W/BL	Differential Pressure Feedback EGR Sensor	DPFE
28	8	W	Power Steering Pressure Switch	PSP
29	8	W/BK	Octane Adjust	OCT ADJ
30	8	W	Park/Neutral Position Switch and Clutch Pedal Position Switch (Manual Trans.)	PNP and CPP
30	8	W/GR	Transmission Range Sensor (CD4E)	TR
31	91S	BK/W	High Fan Control	HFC
32	91S	BK/Y	Intake Manifold Runner Control	IMRC
33	91S	BK/O	EGR Vacuum Regulator Solenoid	EVR
35	91S	BK/O	Injector 4	INJ 4
36	8	W/P	Spark Output	SPOUT
37	95	GR/Y	Vehicle Power	VPWR
38	91S	BK/R	Electronic Pressure Control (CD4E)	EPC
39	91S	BK/BL	Injector 3	INJ 3

FM0159501243010X

Fig. 51   EEC-IV PCM connector pin usage (Part 1 of 2). 1995 w/2.5L/V6-153 MA SFI engine

Pin	Circuit	Wire Color	Application	Abbreviation
40	91	BK/Y	Power Ground	PWR GND
41	8	W/BK	Transmission Control Switch (CD4E)	TCS
43	8	W/R	Heated Oxygen Sensor - Front	HO2S-F
44	8	W	Heated Oxygen Sensor - Rear	HO2S-R
46	9	BR	Signal Return	SIG RTN
47	8	W	Throttle Position Sensor	TP
48	8	W/BK	Self-Test Input	STI
49	8	W/R	Transmission Fluid Temperature Sensor (CD4E)	TFT
50	8	W/BL	Mass Air Flow Sensor	MAF
51	91S	BK/Y	Shift Solenoid 1 (CD4E)	SS1
52	91S	BK/BL	Shift Solenoid 2 (CD4E)	SS2
53	91S	BK/W	Torque Converter Clutch (CD4E)	TCC
54	91S	BK/Y	Wide Open Throttle A/C Cut-Off	WAC
55	91S	BK/O	Shift Solenoid 3 (CD4E)	SS3
56	8	W/BK	Profile Ignition Pick-up	PIP
57	95	GR/Y	Vehicle Power	VPWR
58	91S	BK/W	Injector 1	INJ 1
59	91S	BK/Y	Injector 2	INJ 2
60	91	BK/Y	Power Ground	PWR GND

Pin locations given for reference only. Probing 60-pin connector with DVOM probe will result in permanent damage to the pin connectors. Always probe as directed using the breakout box.

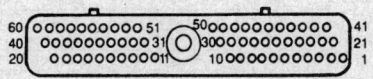

FM0159501243020X

Fig. 51   EEC-IV PCM connector pin usage (Part 2 of 2). 1995 w/2.5L/V6-153 MA SFI engine

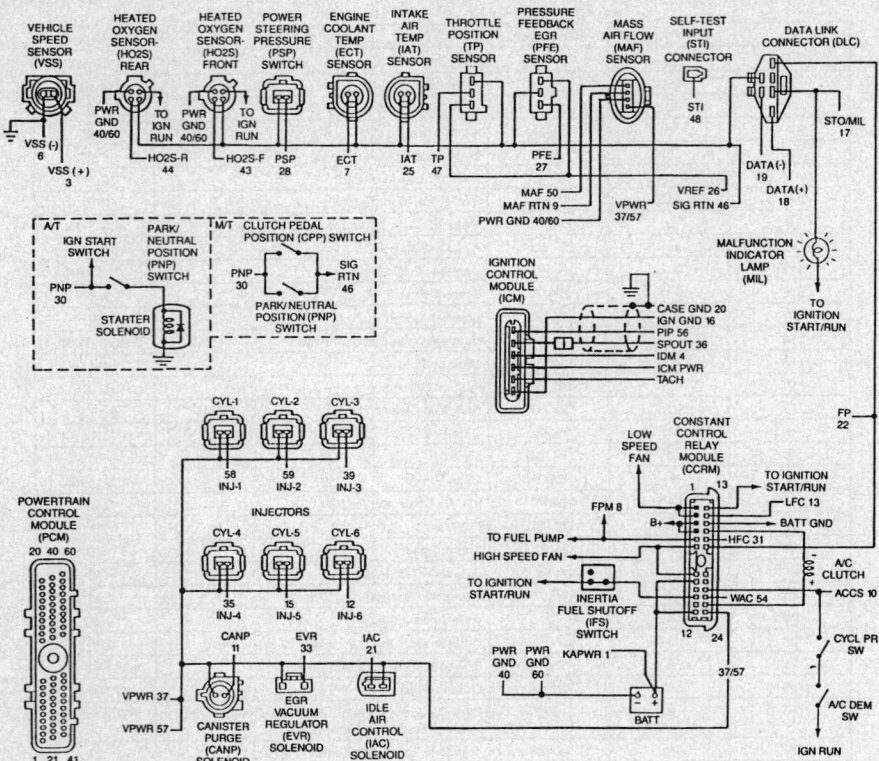

**Fig. 52 EEC-IV wiring circuit.
1993–94 w/3.0L/V6-181 MA SFI
engine**

Pin	Circuit	Wire Color	Application	Abbreviation
1	37	Y	Keep Alive Power	KAPWR
3	150	DG/W	Vehicle Speed Sensor (+)	VSS (+)
4	648	W/PK	Ignition Diagnostic Monitor	IDM
6	563	O/Y	Vehicle Speed Sensor (-)	VSS (-)
7	354	LG/R	Engine Coolant Temperature Sensor	ECT
8	787	PK/BK	Fuel Pump Monitor	FPM
9	968	T/LB	Mass Air Flow Sensor Return	MAF RTN
10	883	PK/LB	A/C Cyclic Switch	ACCS
11	101	GY/Y	Canister Purge Solenoid	CANP
12	560	LG/O	Injector 6	INJ 6
13	197	T/O	Low Fan Control	LFC
15	559	T/BK	Injector 5	INJ 5
16	259	O/R	Ignition Ground	IGN GND
17	201	T/R	Self-Test Output/Malfunction Indicator Lamp	STO/MIL
18	914	T/O	Data (+)	DATA (+)
19	915	PK/LB	Data (-)	DATA (-)
20	57	BK	Case Ground	CSE GND
21	264	W/LB	Idle Air Control Solenoid	IAC
22	238	DG/Y	Fuel Pump	FP
25	743	GY	Intake Air Temperature Sensor	IAT
26	351	BR/W	Reference Voltage	VREF
27	352	BR/LG	Pressure Feedback EGR Sensor	PFE
28	330	Y/LG	Power Steering Pressure Switch	PSP
30	480	P/Y	Park/Neutral Position Switch	PNP
31	386	LB	High Fan Control	HFC
33	362	Y	EGR Vacuum Regulator Solenoid	EVR
35	558	BR/LB	Injector 4	INJ 4
36	929	PK	Spark Output	SPOUT
37	361	R	Vehicle Power	VPWR
39	557	BR/Y	Injector 3	INJ 3
40	60	BK/LG	Power Ground	PWR GND
43	94	R/BK	Heated Oxygen Sensor - Front	HO2S - F
44	74	GY/LB	Heated Oxygen Sensor - Rear	HO2S - R
46	359	GY/R	Signal Return	SIG RTN
47	355	GY/W	Throttle Position Sensor	TP
48	209	W/P	Self-Test Input	STI
50	967	LB/R	Mass Air Flow Sensor	MAF
54	331	PK/Y	Wide Open Throttle A/C Cutout	WAC

**Fig. 53 EEC-IV PCM connector pin
usage (Part 1 of 2). 1993
w/3.0L/V6-181 MA SFI engine**

Pin	Circuit	Wire Color	Application	Abbreviation
1	37	Y	Keep Alive Power	KAPWR
3	150	DG/W	Vehicle Speed Sensor (+)	VSS (+)
4	648	W/PK	Ignition Diagnostic Monitor	IDM
6	563	O/Y	Vehicle Speed Sensor (-)	VSS (-)
7	354	LG/R	Engine Coolant Temperature Sensor	ECT
8	787	PK/BK	Fuel Pump Monitor	FPM
9	968	T/LB	Mass Air Flow Sensor Return	MAF RTN
10	883	PK/LB	A/C Cyclic Switch	ACCS
11	101	GY/Y	Canister Purge Solenoid	CANP
12	560	LG/O	Injector 6	INJ 6
13	197	T/O	Low Fan Control	LFC
15	559	T/BK	Injector 5	INJ 5
16	259	O/R	Ignition Ground	IGN GND
17	201	T/R	Self-Test Output/Malfunction Indicator Lamp	STO/MIL
18	914	T/O	Data (+)	DATA (+)
19	915	PK/LB	Data (-)	DATA (-)
20	57	BK	Case Ground	CSE GND
21	264	W/LB	Idle Air Control Solenoid	IAC
22	238	DG/Y	Fuel Pump	FP
25	743	GY	Intake Air Temperature Sensor	IAT
26	351	BR/W	Reference Voltage	VREF
27	352	BR/LG	Pressure Feedback EGR Sensor	PFE
28	330	Y/LG	Power Steering Pressure Switch	PSP
30	480	P/Y	Park/Neutral Position Switch	PNP
31	386	LB	High Fan Control	HFC
33	362	Y	EGR Vacuum Regulator Solenoid	EVR
35	558	BR/LB	Injector 4	INJ 4
36	929	PK	Spark Output	SPOUT
37	361	R	Vehicle Power	VPWR
39	557	BR/Y	Injector 3	INJ 3
40	60	BK/LG	Power Ground	PWR GND
42	439	T/LG	Dual Function A/C Pressure Switch	ACPSW
43	94	R/BK	Heated Oxygen Sensor - Front	HO2S - F
44	74	GY/LB	Heated Oxygen Sensor - Rear	HO2S - R
46	359	GY/R	Signal Return	SIG RTN
47	355	GY/W	Throttle Position Sensor	TP
48	209	W/P	Self-Test Input	STI

Fig. 53   EEC-IV PCM connector pin
usage (Part 1 of 2). 1994
w/3.0L/V6-181 MA SFI engine

Pin	Circuit	Wire Color	Application	Abbreviation
56	349	DB	Profile Ignition Pickup	PIP
57	361	R	Vehicle Power	VPWR
58	555	T	Injector 1	INJ 1
59	556	W	Injector 2	INJ 2
60	60	BK/LG	Power Ground	PWR GND

Pin locations given for reference only. Probing 60-pin
connector with DVOM probe will result in permanent
damage to the pin connectors. Always probe as
directed using the breakout box.

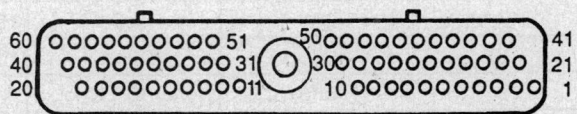

Fig. 53   EEC-IV PCM connector pin
usage (Part 2 of 2). 1994–95
w/3.0L/V6-181 MA SFI engine

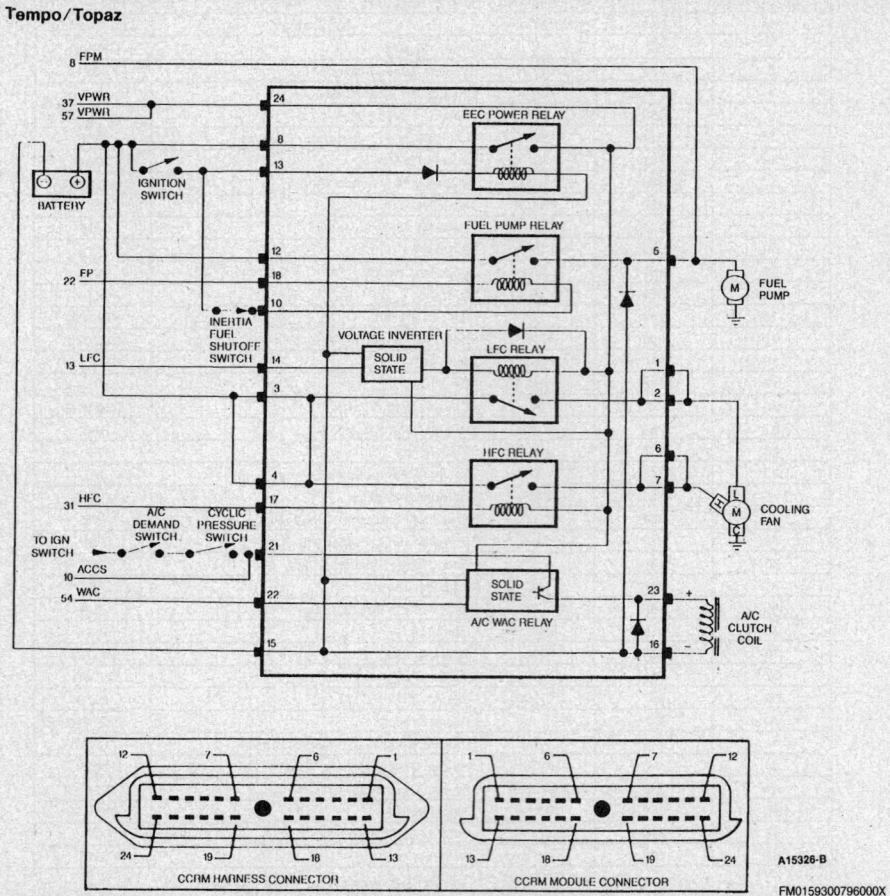

Fig. 54   EEC-IV CCRM wiring circuit. 1993–94 w/3.0L/V6-181 MA SFI engine

Pin	Circuit	Wire Color	Application	Abbreviation
1	228	DB	Power to Cooling Fan (Low Speed)	PTF
2	228	DB	Power to Cooling Fan (Low Speed)	PTF
3	37	Y	B (+) to Fan Relay	B (+)
4	37	Y	B (+) to Fan Relay	B (+)
5	787	PK/BK	Power to Fuel Pump	PTP
6	639	LG/P	Power to Cooling Fan (High Speed)	PTF
7	639	LG/P	Power to Cooling Fan (High Speed)	PTF
8	37	Y	B (+) to EEC Power Relay	B (+)
10	866	W	Ignition Start/Run	IGN
12	37	Y	B (+) to Fuel Pump Relay	B (+)
13	16	R/LG	Ignition Start/Run	IGN
14	197	T/O	LFC Circuit	LFC
15	60	BK/LG	Power Ground	PWR GND
16	321	GY/W	A/C Clutch Ground	A/C GND
17	386	LB	HFC Circuit	HFC
18	238	DG/Y	Fuel Pump Circuit	FP
21	883	PK/LB	A/C Cyclic Switch	ACCS
22	331	PK/Y	WOT A/C Cut-Off	WAC
23	347	BK/Y	Power to A/C Clutch	PTAC
24	361	R	Vehicle Power	VPWR

FM0159300797000X

Fig. 55   EEC-IV CCRM connector pin usage. 1993–94 w/3.0L/V6-181 MA SFI engine

Pin	Circuit	Wire Color	Application	Abbreviation
1	37	Y	Keep Alive Power	KAPWR
2	810	R/LG	Brake On/Off	BOO
3	150	DG/W	Vehicle Speed Sensor (+)	VSS (+)
4	648	W/PK	Ignition Diagnostic Monitor (California only)	IDM
4	11	DG/Y	Ignition Diagnostic Monitor (49 States and Canada)	IDM
5	679	GY/BK	Transmission Speed Sensor	TSS
6	563	O/Y	Vehicle Speed Sensor (-)	VSS (-)
7	354	LG/R	Engine Coolant Temperature Sensor	ECT
8	787	PK/BK	Fuel Pump Monitor	FPM
9	968	T/LB	Mass Air Flow Sensor Return	MAF RTN
10	883	PK/LB	A/C Cyclic Switch	ACCS
11	101	GY/Y	Canister Purge Solenoid	CANP
12	560	LG/O	Injector 6	INJ 6
13	197	T/O	Low Fan Control	LFC
15	559	T/BK	Injector 5	INJ 5
16	259	O/R	Ignition Ground	IGN GND
17	201	T/R	Self-Test Output / Malfunction Indicator Lamp	STO / MIL
18	914	T/O	Data (+)	DATA (+)
19	915	PK/LB	Data (-)	DATA (-)
20	57	BK	Case Ground	CSE GND
21	376	BR/W	Idle Air Control Solenoid	IAC
22	926	LB/O	Fuel Pump	FP
25	743	GY	Intake Air Temperature Sensor	IAT
26	351	BR/W	Reference Voltage	VREF
27	352	BR/LG	Pressure Feedback EGR Sensor	PFE
28	330	Y/LG	Power Steering Pressure Switch	PSP
30	199	LB/Y	Manual Lever Position Sensor	MLP
31	639	LG/P	High Fan Control	HFC
33	360	BR/PK	EGR Vacuum Regulator Solenoid	EVR
34	305	LB/PK	Data Output Line	DOL
35	558	BR/LB	Injector 4	INJ 4
36	324	Y/LG	Spark Output	SPOUT
37	361	R	Vehicle Power	VPWR
38	925	W/Y	Electronic Pressure Control	EPC
39	557	BR/Y	Injector 3	INJ 3
40	60	BK/LG	Power Ground	PWR GND
43	94	R/BK	Heated Oxygen Sensor - Front	HO2S-F
44	74	GY/LB	Heated Oxygen Sensor - Rear	HO2S-R

FM015930007990010X

Fig. 57 EEC-IV PCM connector pin usage (Part 1 of 2). 1993 w/3.0L/V6-181 SFI engine & AXODE transaxle

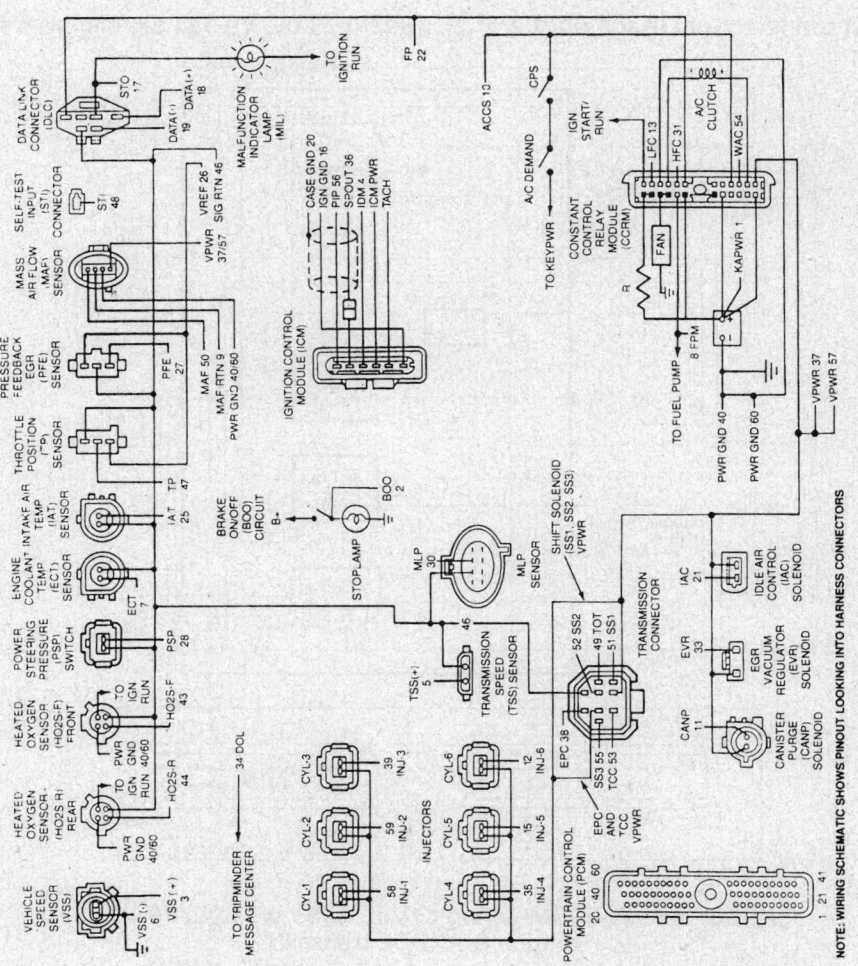

FM015930007980000X

Fig. 56 EEC-IV wiring circuit. 1993 w/3.0L/V6-181 SFI engine & AXODE transaxle

NOTE: WIRING SCHEMATIC SHOWS PINOUT LOOKING INTO HARNESS CONNECTORS

Pin	Circuit	Wire Color	Application	Abbreviation
46	359	GY/R	Signal Return	SIG RTN
47	355	GY/W	Throttle Position Sensor	TP
48	200	BR	Self-Test Input	STI
49	923	O/BK	Transmission Oil Temperature Sensor	TOT
50	967	LB/R	Mass Air Flow Sensor	MAF
51	237	O/Y	Shift Solenoid 1	SS1
52	315	P/O	Shift Solenoid 2	SS2
53	224	T/W	Torque Converter Clutch Solenoid	TCC
54	331	PK/Y	Wide Open Throttle (WOT) A/C Cut Off	WAC
55	912	W/R	Shift Solenoid 3	SS3
56	395	GY/O	Profile Ignition Pick-Up	PIP
57	361	R	Vehicle Power	VPWR
58	555	T	Injector 1	INJ 1
59	556	W	Injector 2	INJ 2
60	60	BK/LG	Power Ground	PWR GND

Pin locations given for reference only. Probing 60-pin connector with DVOM probe will result in permanent damage to the pin connectors. Always probe as directed using the breakout box.

FM0159300799020X

Fig. 57 EEC-IV PCM connector pin usage (Part 2 of 2). 1993 w/3.0L/V6-181 SFI engine & AXODE transaxle

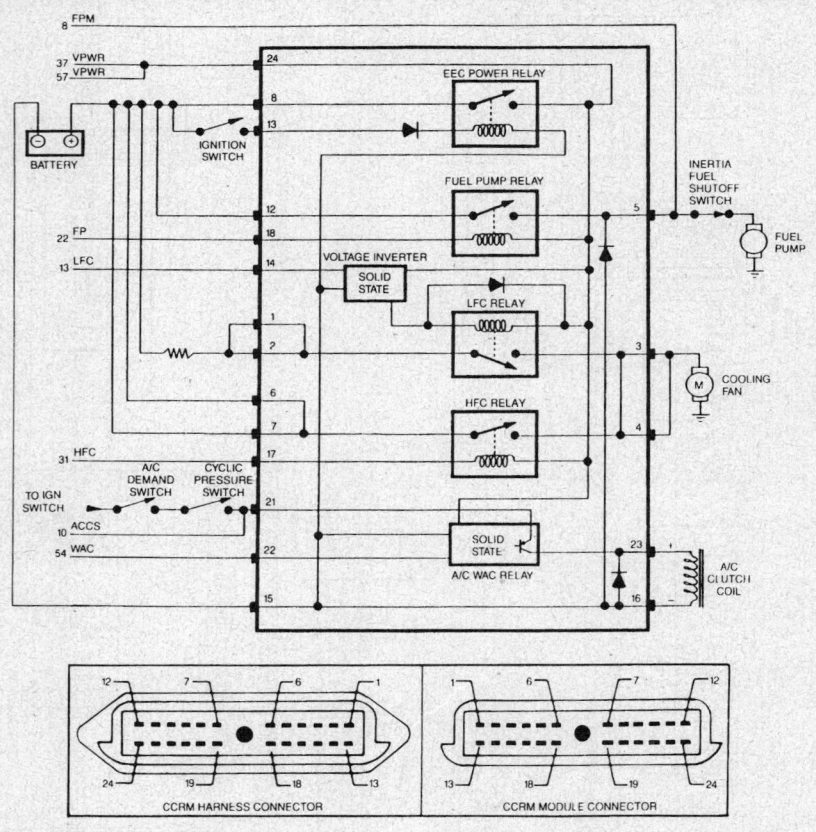

FM0159300800000X

Fig. 58 EEC-IV CCRM wiring circuit. 1993 w/3.0L/V6-181 SFI engine & AXODE transaxle

Pin	Circuit	Color	Application	Abbreviation
1	181	BR/O	Power to LFC Relay	PT/LFC
2	181	BR/O	Power to LFC Relay	PT/LFC
3	228	DB	Power to Cooling Fan	PTF
4	228	DB	Power to Cooling Fan	PTF
5	787	PK/BK	Power to Fuel Pump	PTP
6	38	BK/O	Power to HFC Relay	PT/HFC
7	38	BK/O	Power to HFC Relay	PT/HFC
8	37	Y	Battery to EEC Relay	B(+)
12	38	BK/O	Power to Fuel Pump Power Relay	PT/FPR
13	16	R/LG	Key Power	KEY PWR
14	197	T/O	LFC Circuit	LFC
15	60	BK/LG	Power Ground	PWR GND
16	57	BK	A/C Clutch Ground	PWR GND
17	639	LG/P	HFC Circuit	HFC
18	926	T/LG	Fuel Pump Circuit	FP
21	883	PK/LB	A/C Cyclic Switch	ACCS
22	331	PK/Y	WOT A/C Cut Off	WAC
23	347	BK/Y	Power to A/C Clutch	PTAC
24	361	R	Vehicle Power	VPWR

FM0159300801000X

Fig. 59   EEC-IV CCRM pin usage. 1993 w/3.0L/V6-181 SFI engine & AXODE transaxle

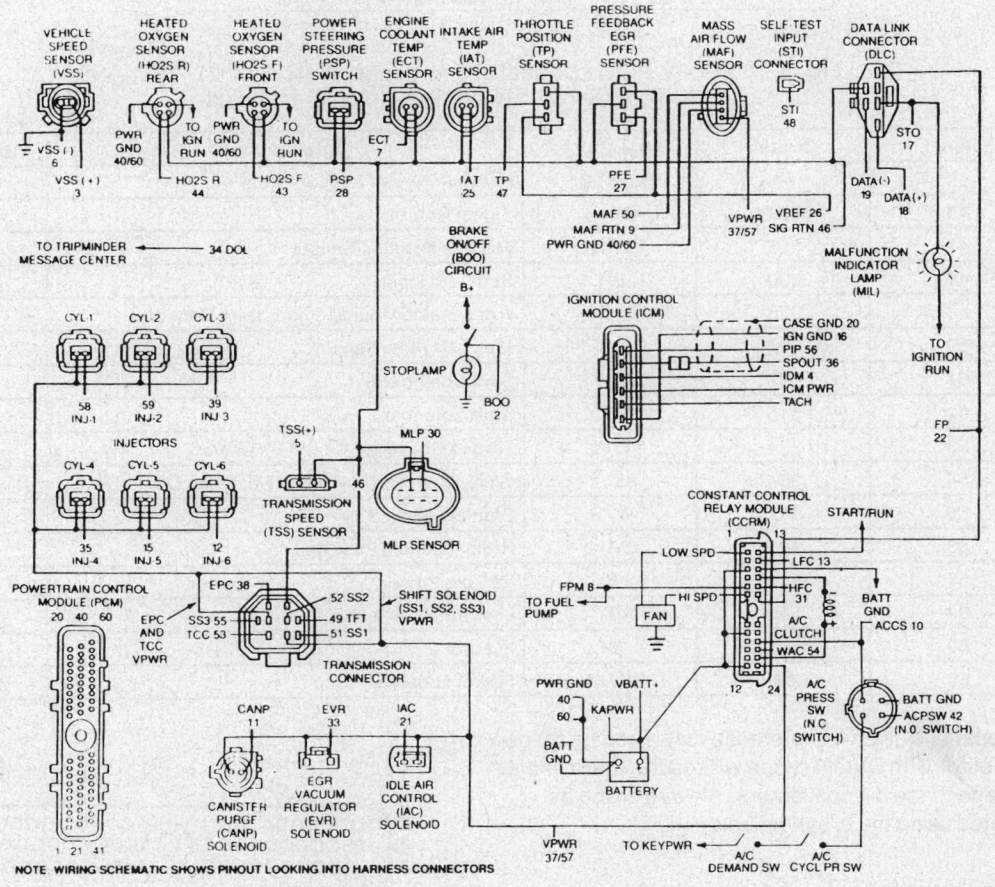

FM0159400802000X

Fig. 60   EEC-IV wiring circuit. 1994–95 w/3.0L/V6-181 SFI engine & AX4S transaxle

Pin	Circuit	Wire Color	Application	Abbreviation
1	37	Y	Keep Alive Power	KAPWR
2	810	R/LG	Brake On/Off	BOO
3	150	DG/W	Vehicle Speed Sensor (+)	VSS (+)
4	648	W/PK	Ignition Diagnostic Monitor (California only)	IDM
4	11	DG/Y	Ignition Diagnostic Monitor (49 States and Canada)	IDM
5	679	GY/BK	Transmission Speed Sensor	TSS
6	563	O/Y	Vehicle Speed Sensor (-)	VSS (-)
7	354	LG/R	Engine Coolant Temperature Sensor	ECT
8	787	PK/BK	Fuel Pump Monitor	FPM
9	968	T/LB	Mass Air Flow Sensor Return	MAF RTN
10	883	PK/LB	A/C Cyclic Switch	ACCS
11	101	GY/Y	Canister Purge Solenoid	CANP
12	560	LG/O	Injector 6	INJ 6
13	197	T/O	Low Fan Control	LFC
15	559	T/BK	Injector 5	INJ 5
16	259	O/R	Ignition Ground	IGN GND
17	201	T/R	Self-Test Output/Malfunction Indicator Lamp	STO/MIL
18	914	T/O	Data (+)	DATA (+)
19	915	PK/LB	Data (-)	DATA (-)
20	57	BK	Case Ground	CSE GND
21	376	BR/W	Idle Air Control Solenoid	IAC
22	926	LB/O	Fuel Pump	FP
25	743	GY	Intake Air Temperature Sensor	IAT
26	351	BR/W	Reference Voltage	VREF
27	352	BR/LG	Pressure Feedback EGR Sensor	PFE
28	330	Y/LG	Power Steering Pressure Switch	PSP
30	199	LB/Y	Manual Lever Position Sensor	MLP
31	639	LG/P	High Fan Control	HFC
33	360	BR/PK	EGR Vacuum Regulator Solenoid	EVR
34	305	LB/PK	Data Output Line	DOL
35	558	BR/LB	Injector 4	INJ 4
36	324	Y/LG	Spark Output	SPOUT
37	361	R	Vehicle Power	VPWR
38	925	W/Y	Electronic Pressure Control	EPC
39	557	BR/Y	Injector 3	INJ 3
40	60	BK/LG	Power Ground	PWR GND
42	439	T/LG	A/C Pressure Switch	ACPSW
43	94	R/BK	Heated Oxygen Sensor - Front	HO2S - F

FM0159400803010X

Fig. 61 EEC-IV PCM connector pin usage (Part 1 of 2). 1994–95 w/3.0L/V6-181 SFI engine & AX4S transaxle

Pin	Circuit	Wire Color	Application	Abbreviation
44	74	GY/LB	Heated Oxygen Sensor - Rear	HO2S - R
46	359	GY/R	Signal Return	SIG RTN
47	355	GY/W	Throttle Position Sensor	TP
48	200	BR	Self-Test Input	STI
49	923	O/BK	Transmission Fluid Temperature Sensor	TFT
50	967	LB/R	Mass Air Flow Sensor	MAF
51	237	O/Y	Shift Solenoid 1	SS1
52	315	P/O	Shift Solenoid 2	SS2
53	224	T/W	Torque Converter Clutch Solenoid	TCC
54	331	PK/Y	Wide Open Throttle (WOT) A/C Cut Off	WAC
55	912	W/R	Shift Solenoid 3	SS3
56	395	GY/O	Profile Ignition Pick-Up	PIP
57	361	R	Vehicle Power	VPWR
58	555	T	Injector 1	INJ 1
59	556	W	Injector 2	INJ 2
60	60	BK/LG	Power Ground	PWR GND

Pin locations given for reference only. Probing 60-pin connector with DVOM probe will result in permanent damage to the pin connectors. Always probe as directed using the breakout box.

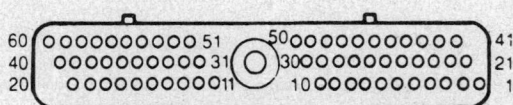

FM0159400603020X

Fig. 61 EEC-IV PCM connector pin usage (Part 2 of 2). 1994–95 w/3.0L/V6-181 SFI engine & AX4S transaxle

ELECTRONIC ENGINE CONTROL SYSTEM IV (EEC-IV)

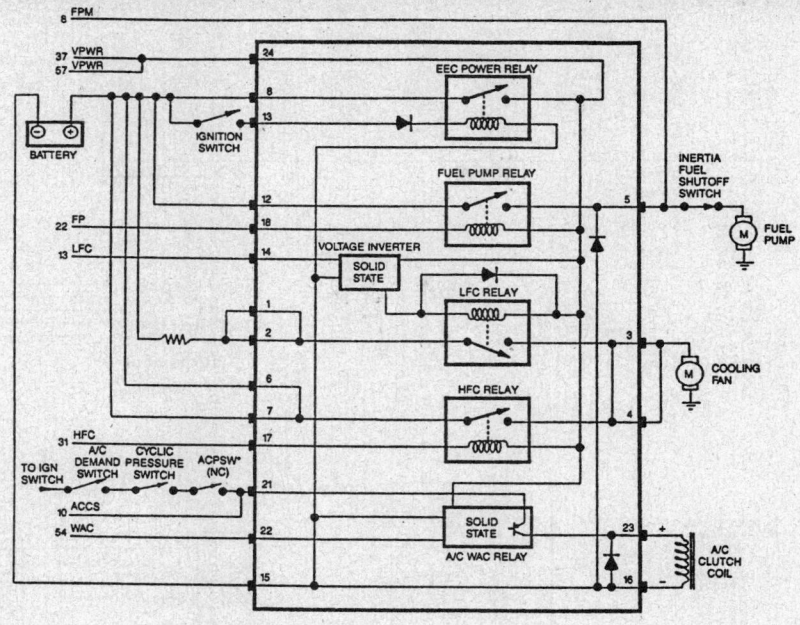

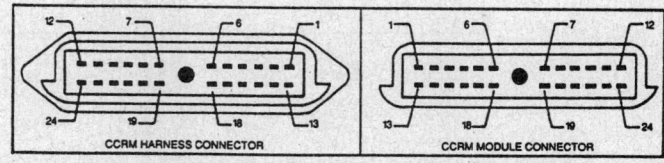

*HIGH PRESSURE CONTACTS OF THE DUAL FUNCTION A/C PRESSURE SWITCH (ACPSW)
(ALSO KNOWN AS REFRIGERANT CONTAINMENT/FAN FUNCTION SWITCH)

**Fig. 62   EEC-IV CCRM wiring circuit.
1994–95 w/3.0L/V6-181 SFI engine
& AX4S transaxle**

Pin	Circuit	Color	Application	Abbreviation
1	181	BR/O	Power to LFC Relay	PT/LFC
2	181	BR/O	Power to LFC Relay	PT/LFC
3	228	DB	Power to Cooling Fan	PTF
4	228	DB	Power to Cooling Fan	PTF
5	787	PK/BK	Power to Fuel Pump	PTP
6	38	BK/O	Power to HFC Relay	PT/HFC
7	38	BK/O	Power to HFC Relay	PT/HFC
8	37	Y	Battery to EEC Relay	B (+)
12	38	BK/O	Power to Fuel Pump Power Relay	PT/FPR
13	16	R/LG	Key Power	KEY PWR
14	197	T/O	LFC Circuit	LFC
15	60	BK/LG	Power Ground	PWR GND
16	57	BK	A/C Clutch Ground	PWR GND
17	639	LG/P	HFC Circuit	HFC
18	926	T/LG	Fuel Pump Circuit	FP
21	883	PK/LB	A/C Cyclic Switch	ACCS
22	331	PK/Y	WOT A/C Cut Off	WAC
23	347	BK/Y	Power to A/C Clutch	PTAC
24	361	R	Vehicle Power	VPWR

**Fig. 63   EEC-IV CCRM pin usage.
1994–95 w/3.0L/V6-181 SFI engine
& AX4S transaxle**

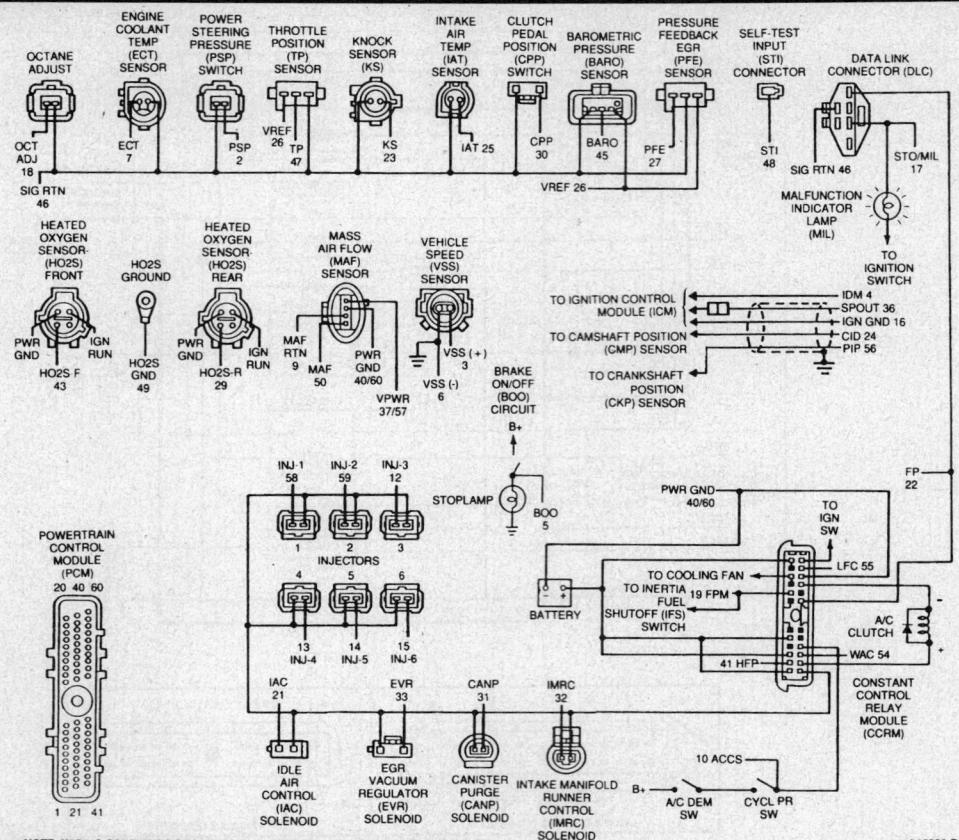

Fig. 64 EEC-IV wiring circuit. 1993 w/3.0L/V6-181 SHO SFI engine

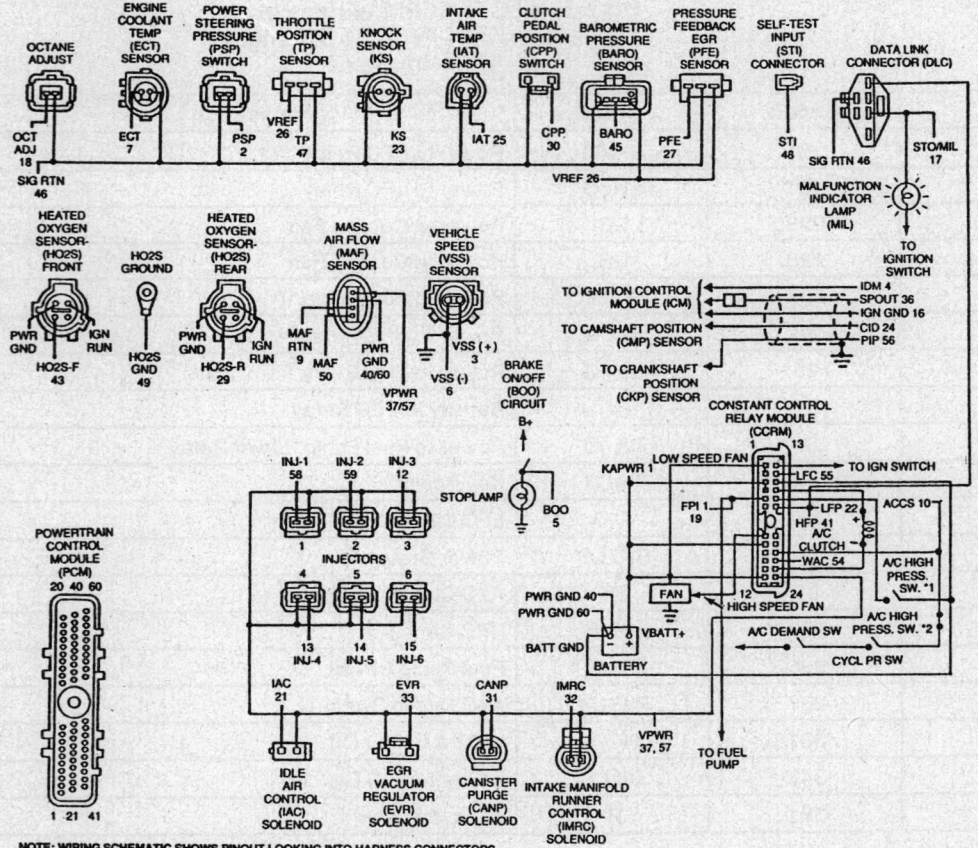

Fig. 65 EEC-IV wiring circuit.
1994–95 w/3.0L/V6-181 SHO SFI
engine

Pin	Circuit	Wire Color	Application	Abbreviation
1	37	Y	Keep Alive Power	KAPWR
2	330	Y/LG	Power Steering Pressure Switch	PSP
3	150	DG/W	Vehicle Speed Sensor (+)	VSS (+)
4	395	GY/O	Ignition Diagnostic Monitor	IDM
5	810	R/LG	Brake On/Off	BOO
6	563	O/Y	Vehicle Speed Sensor (-)	VSS (-)
7	354	LG/R	Engine Coolant Temperature Sensor	ECT
9	968	T/LB	Mass Air Flow Sensor Return	MAF RTN
10	883	PK/LB	A/C Clutch Signal	ACCS
11	144	O/Y	Vehicle Speed Control Solenoid	SOL (+)
12	557	BR/Y	Injector 3	INJ 3
13	558	BR/LB	Injector 4	INJ 4
14	559	T/BK	Injector 5	INJ 5
15	560	LG/O	Injector 6	INJ 6
16	259	O/R	Ignition Ground	IGN GND
17	201	T/R	Self-Test Output/Malfunction Indicator Lamp	STO/MIL
18	929	PK	Octane Adjust	OCT ADJ
19	787	PK/BK	Fuel Pump Monitor	FPM
20	57	BK	Case Ground	CSE GND
21	68	O/BK	Idle Air Control Solenoid	IAC
22	97	T/LG	Low Fuel Pump Relay	LFP
23	310	Y/R	Knock Sensor	KS
24	795	DG	Cylinder Identification	CID
25	743	GY	Intake Air Temperature Sensor	IAT
26	351	BR/W	Reference Voltage	VREF
27	352	BR/LG	Pressure Feedback EGR Sensor	PFE
28	151	LB/BK	Speed Control Command Switch	SCCS
29	94	R/BK	Heated Oxygen Sensor - Rear	HO2S - R
30	480	P/Y	Clutch Pedal Position Switch	CPP
31	101	GY/Y	Canister Purge Solenoid	CANP
32	965	LG/P	Intake Manifold Runner Control	IMRC
33	360	BR/PK	EGR Vacuum Regulator Solenoid	EVR
35	146	W/PK	Speed Control Vent (Solenoid)	SCVNT
36	324	Y/LG	Spark Output	SPOUT
37	361	R	Vehicle Power	VPWR
39	461	O	Speed Control Command Switch Ground	SCCS GND
40	60	BK/LG	Power Ground	PWR GND
41	926	LB/O	High Fuel Pump Relay	HFP

**Fig. 66 EEC-IV PCM connector pin
usage (Part 1 of 2). 3.0L/V6-181
SHO SFI engine**

Pin	Circuit	Wire Color	Application	Abbreviation
43	90	DB/LG	Heated Oxygen Sensor - Front	HO2S - F
45	358	LG/BK	Barometric Pressure Sensor	BARO
46	359	GY/R	Signal Return	SIG RTN
47	355	GY/W	Throttle Position Sensor	TP
48	200	BR	Self-Test Input	STI
49	89	O	HO2S Ground	HO2S GND
50	967	LB/R	Mass Air Flow Sensor	MAF
51	145	GY/BK	Speed Control Vacuum (Solenoid)	SCVAC
54	331	PK/Y	Wide Open Throttle A/C Cutoff	WAC
55	197	T/O	Fan Control	FC
56	349	DB	Profile Ignition Pick-Up	PIP
57	361	R	Vehicle Power	VPWR
58	555	T	Injector 1	INJ 1
59	556	W	Injector 2	INJ 2
60	60	BK/LG	Power Ground	PWR GND

Pin locations given for reference only. Probing 60-pin connector with DVOM probe will result in permanent damage to the pin connectors. Always probe as directed using the breakout box.

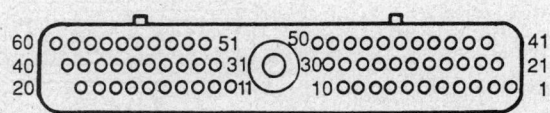

**Fig. 66 EEC-IV PCM connector pin
usage (Part 2 of 2). 1993
w/3.0L/V6-181 SHO SFI engine**

Pin	Circuit	Wire Color	Application	Abbreviation
42	439	T/LG	A/C Pressure Switch	ACPSW
43	90	DB/LG	Heated Oxygen Sensor - Front	HO2S - F
45	358	LG/BK	Barometric Pressure Sensor	BARO
46	359	GY/R	Signal Return	SIG RTN
47	355	GY/W	Throttle Position Sensor	TP
48	200	BR	Self-Test Input	STI
49	89	O	HO2S Ground	HO2S GND
50	967	LB/R	Mass Air Flow Sensor	MAF
51	145	GY/BK	Speed Control Vacuum (Solenoid)	SCVAC
54	331	PK/Y	Wide Open Throttle A/C Cutoff	WAC
55	197	T/O	Fan Control	FC
56	349	DB	Profile Ignition Pick-Up	PIP
57	361	R	Vehicle Power	VPWR
58	555	T	Injector 1	INJ 1
59	556	W	Injector 2	INJ 2
60	60	BK/LG	Power Ground	PWR GND

Pin locations given for reference only. Probing 60-pin connector with DVOM probe will result in permanent damage to the pin connectors. Always probe as directed using the breakout box.

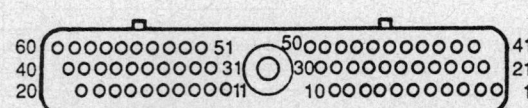

Fig. 66 EEC-IV PCM connector pin usage (Part 2 of 2). 1994–95 w/3.0L/V6-181 SHO SFI engine

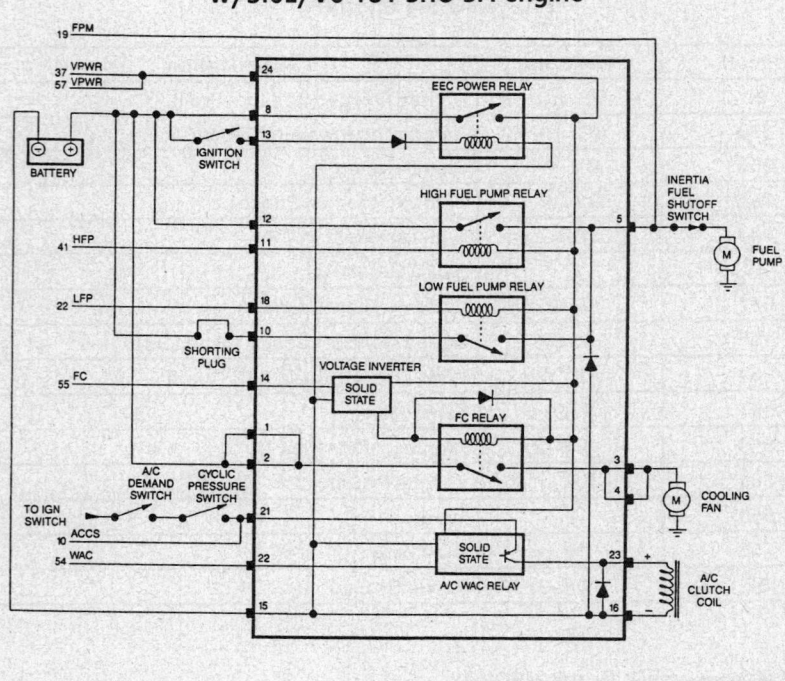

Fig. 67 EEC-IV CCRM wiring circuit. 1993 w/3.0L/V6-181 SHO SFI engine

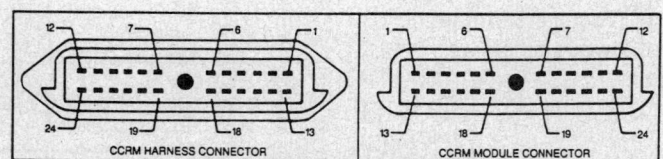

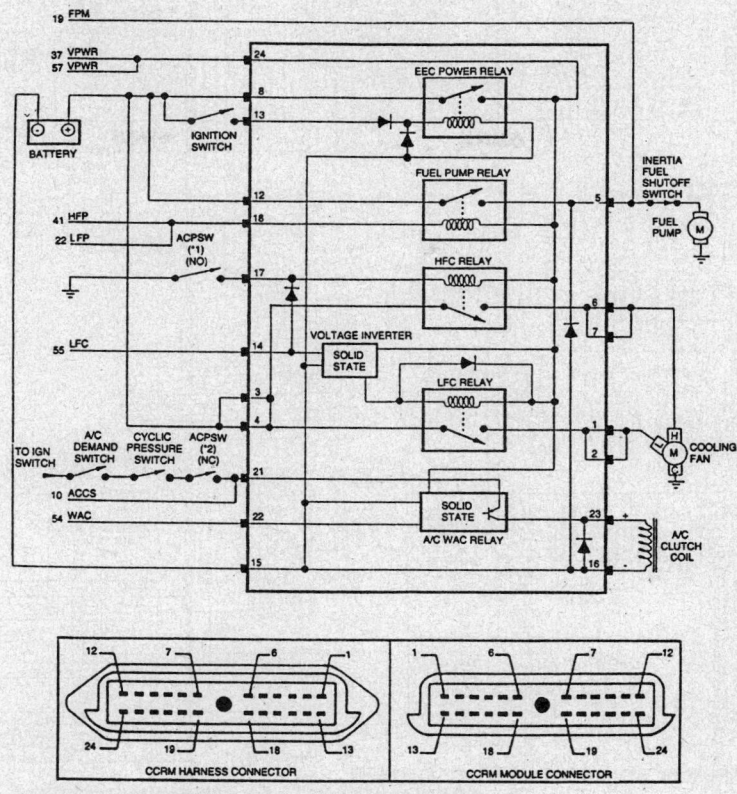

Fig. 68 EEC-IV CCRM wiring circuit.
1994–95 w/3.0L/V6-181 SHO SFI
engine

*1) MEDIUM PRESSURE CONTACTS OF THE DUAL FUNCTION A/C PRESSURE SWITCH (ACPSW)
*2) HIGH PRESSURE CONTACTS OF THE DUAL FUNCTION A/C PRESSURE SWITCH (ACPSW)
(ACPSW ALSO KNOWN AS REFRIGERANT CONTAINMENT/FAN SWITCH)

Pin	Circuit	Color	Application	Abbreviation
1	38	BK/O	Power to FC Relay	PT/FC
2	38	BK/O	Power to FC Relay	PT/FC
3	181	BR/O	Power to Cooling Fan	PTF
4	181	BR/O	Power to Cooling Fan	PTF
5	787	PK/BK	Power to Fuel Pump	PTP
8	37	Y	Battery to EEC Relay	B (+)
10	38	BK/O	Power to Low Fuel Pump Relay	PT/LFP
11	926	LB/O	High Fuel Pump	H/FP
12	38	BK/O	Power to WOT A/C Cut Off	PT/WAC
13	16	R/LG	Key Power	KEY PWR
14	197	T/O	Fan Control Circuit	FC
15	60	BK/LG	Power Ground	PWR GND
16	57	BK	A/C Clutch Ground	PWR GND
18	97	T/LG	Low Fuel Pump	L/FP
21	883	PK/LB	A/C Cyclic Switch	ACCS
22	331	PK/Y	WOT A/C Cut Off	WAC
23	347	BK/Y	Power to A/C	PTAC
24	361	R	Vehicle Power	VPWR

Fig. 69 EEC-IV CCRM pin usage.
3.0L/V6-181 SHO SFI engine

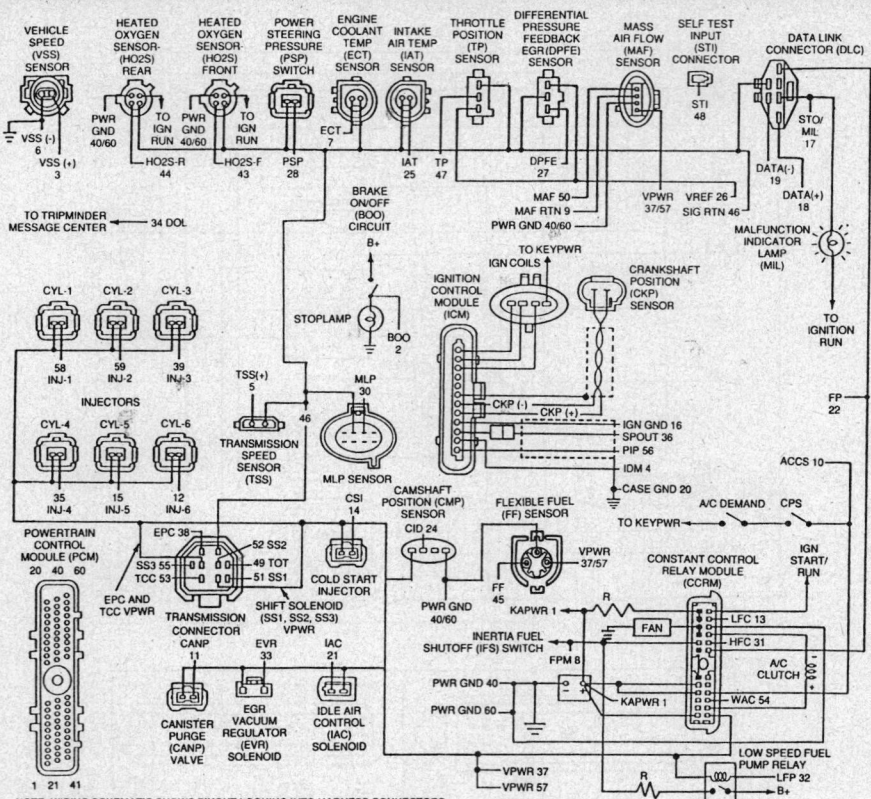

Fig. 70 EEC-IV wiring circuit. 1993 w/3.0L/V6-181 FF SFI engine & AXODE transaxle

Pin	Circuit	Wire Color	Application	Abbreviation
1	37	Y	Keep Alive Power	KAPWR
2	810	R/LG	Brake On/Off	BOO
3	150	DG/W	Vehicle Speed Sensor (+)	VSS (+)
4	648	W/PK	Ignition Diagnostic Monitor	IDM
5	679	GY/BK	Transmission Speed Sensor	TSS
6	563	O/Y	Vehicle Speed Sensor (-)	VSS (-)
7	354	LG/R	Engine Coolant Temperature Sensor	ECT
8	787	PK/BK	Fuel Pump Monitor	FPM
9	968	T/LB	Mass Air Flow Sensor Return	MAF RTN
10	883	PK/LB	A/C Cyclic Switch	ACCS
11	101	GY/Y	Canister Purge Solenoid Valve	CANP
12	560	LG/O	Injector 6	INJ 6
13	197	T/O	Low Fan Control	LFC
14	230	BK/LG	Cold Start Injector	CSI
15	559	T/BK	Injector 5	INJ 5
16	259	O/R	Ignition Ground	IGN GND
17	201	T/R	Self-Test Output/Malfunction Indicator Lamp	STO/MIL
18	914	T/O	Data (+)	DATA (+)
19	915	PK/LB	Data (-)	DATA (-)
20	57	BK	Case Ground	CSE GND
21	376	BR/W	Idle Air Control Solenoid	IAC
22	926	LB/O	Fuel Pump	FP
24	282	DB/O	Cylinder Identification	CID
25	743	GY	Intake Air Temperature Sensor	IAT
26	351	BR/W	Reference Voltage	VREF
27	352	BR/LG	Differential Pressure Feedback EGR Sensor	DPFE
28	330	Y/LG	Power Steering Pressure Switch	PSP
30	199	LB/Y	Manual Lever Position Sensor	MLP
31	639	LG/P	High Fan Control	HFC
32	27	O/LG	Low Speed Fuel Pump Relay	LFP
33	360	BR/PK	EGR Vacuum Regulator Solenoid	EVR
34	305	LB/PK	Data Output Line	DOL
35	558	BR/LB	Injector 4	INJ 4
36	929	PK	Spark Output	SPOUT
37	361	R	Vehicle Power	VPWR
38	925	W/Y	Electronic Pressure Control	EPC
39	557	BR/Y	Injector 3	INJ 3
40	60	BK/LG	Power Ground	PWR GND

Fig. 71 EEC-IV PCM connector pin usage (Part 1 of 2). 1993 w/3.0L/V6-181 FF SFI engine & AXODE transaxle

Pin	Circuit	Wire Color	Application	Abbreviation
43	94	R/BK	Heated Oxygen Sensor - Front	HO2S - F
44	74	GY/LB	Heated Oxygen Sensor - Rear	HO2S - R
45	21	DG/LG	Flexible Fuel Sensor	FF
46	359	GY/R	Signal Return	SIG RTN
47	355	GY/W	Throttle Position Sensor	TP
48	200	BR	Self-Test Input	STI
49	923	O/BK	Transmission Oil Temperature Sensor	TOT
50	967	LB/R	Mass Air Flow Sensor	MAF
51	237	O/Y	Shift Solenoid 1	SS1
52	315	P/O	Shift Solenoid 2	SS2
53	224	T/W	Torque Converter Clutch Solenoid	TCC
54	331	PK/Y	Wide Open Throttle (WOT) A/C Cut Off	WAC
55	912	W/R	Shift Solenoid 3	SS3
56	395	GY/O	Profile Ignition Pick-Up	PIP
57	361	R	Vehicle Power	VPWR
58	555	T	Injector 1	INJ 1
59	556	W	Injector 2	INJ 2
60	60	BK/LG	Power Ground	PWR GND

Pin locations given for reference only. Probing 60-pin connector with DVOM probe will result in permanent damage to the pin connectors. Always probe as directed using the breakout box.

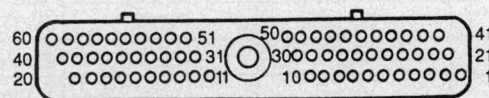

Fig. 71   EEC-IV PCM connector pin usage (Part 2 of 2). 1993 w/3.0L/V6-181 FF SFI engine & AXODE transaxle

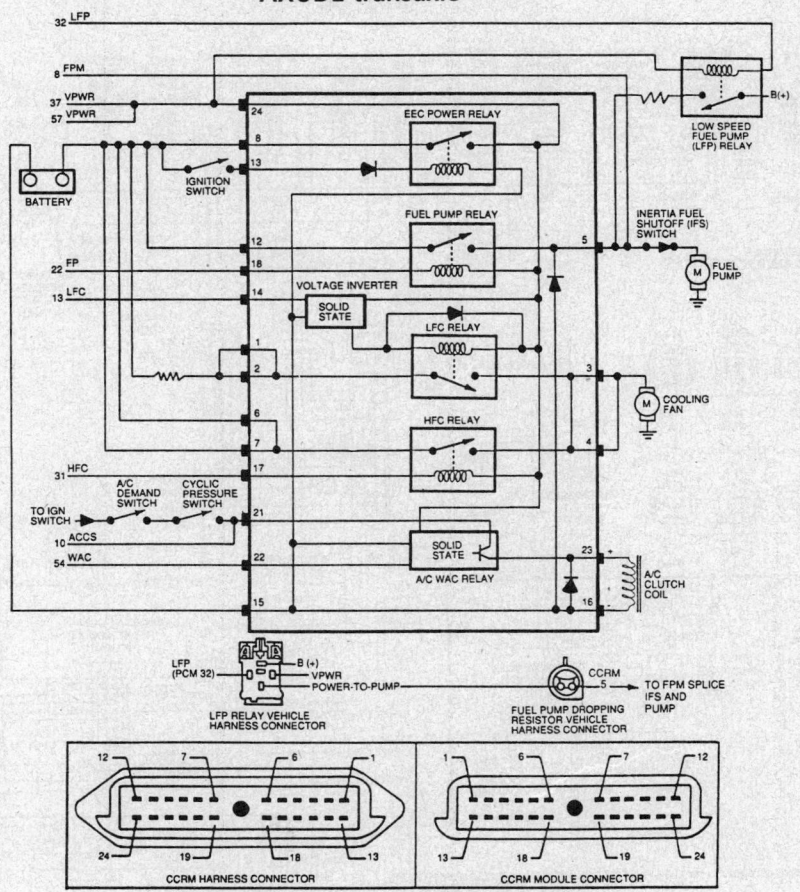

Fig. 72   EEC-IV CCRM wiring circuit. 1993 w/3.0L/V6-181 FF SFI engine & AXODE transaxle

Pin	Circuit	Color	Application	Abbreviation
1	181	BR/O	Power to LFC Relay	PT/LFC
2	181	BR/O	Power to LFC Relay	PT/LFC
3	228	DB	Power to Cooling Fan	PTF
4	228	DB	Power to Cooling Fan	PTF
5	787	PK/BK	Power to Fuel Pump	PTP
6	38	BK/O	Power to HFC Relay	PT/HFC
7	38	BK/O	Power to HFC Relay	PT/HFC
8	37	Y	Battery to EEC Relay	B (+)
12	38	BK/O	Power to Fuel Pump Power Relay	PT/FPR
13	16	R/LG	Key Power	KEY PWR
14	197	T/O	LFC Circuit	LFC
15	60	BK/LG	Power Ground	PWR GND
16	57	BK	A/C Clutch Ground	PWR GND
17	639	LG/P	HFC Circuit	HFC
18	926	LB/O	Fuel Pump Circuit	FP
21	883	PK/LB	A/C Cyclic Switch	ACCS
22	331	PK/Y	WOT A/C Cut Off	WAC
23	347	BK/Y	Power to A/C Clutch	PTAC
24	361	R	Vehicle Power	VPWR

**Fig. 73 EEC-IV CCRM pin usage.
1993 w/3.0L/V6-181 FF SFI engine
& AXODE transaxle**

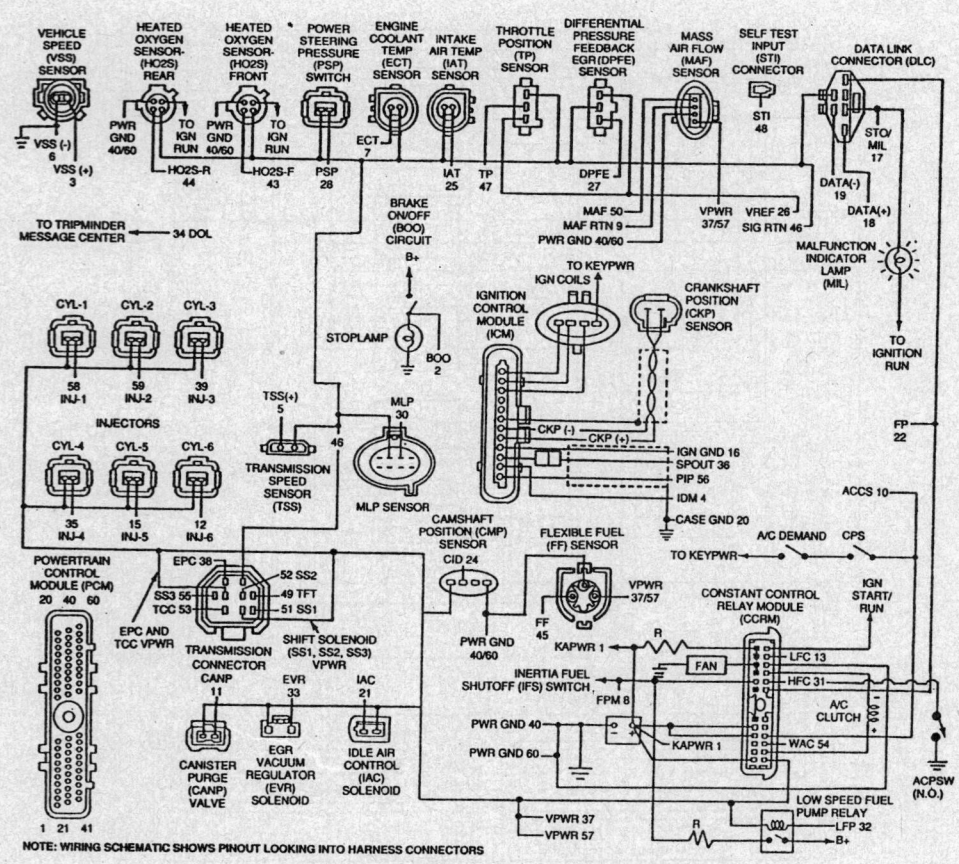

**Fig. 74 EEC-IV wiring circuit. 1994
w/3.0L/V6-181 FF SFI engine &
AX4S/N transaxle**

Electronic Engine Control System IV (EEC-IV)

Pin	Circuit	Wire Color	Application	Abbreviation
1	37	Y	Keep Alive Power	KAPWR
2	810	R/LG	Brake On/Off	BOO
3	150	DG/W	Vehicle Speed Sensor (+)	VSS (+)
4	648	W/PK	Ignition Diagnostic Monitor	IDM
5	679	GY/BK	Transmission Speed Sensor	TSS
6	563	O/Y	Vehicle Speed Sensor (-)	VSS (-)
7	354	LG/R	Engine Coolant Temperature Sensor	ECT
8	787	PK/BK	Fuel Pump Monitor	FPM
9	968	T/LB	Mass Air Flow Sensor Return	MAF RTN
10	883	PK/LB	A/C Cyclic Switch	ACCS
11	101	GY/Y	Canister Purge Solenoid Valve	CANP
12	560	LG/O	Injector 6	INJ 6
13	197	T/O	Low Fan Control	LFC
15	559	T/BK	Injector 5	INJ 5
16	259	O/R	Ignition Ground	IGN GND
17	201	T/R	Self-Test Output/Malfunction Indicator Lamp	STO/MIL
18	914	T/O	Data (+)	DATA (+)
19	915	PK/LB	Data (-)	DATA (-)
20	57	BK	Case Ground	CSE GND
21	376	BR/W	Idle Air Control Solenoid	IAC
22	926	LB/O	Fuel Pump	FP
24	282	DB/O	Cylinder Identification	CID
25	743	GY	Intake Air Temperature Sensor	IAT
26	351	BR/W	Reference Voltage	VREF
27	352	BR/LG	Differential Pressure Feedback EGR Sensor	DPFE
28	330	Y/LG	Power Steering Pressure Switch	PSP
30	199	LB/Y	Manual Lever Position Sensor	MLP
31	639	LG/P	High Fan Control	HFC
32	27	O/LG	Low Speed Fuel Pump Relay	LFP
33	360	BR/PK	EGR Vacuum Regulator Solenoid	EVR
34	305	LB/PK	Data Output Line	DOL
35	558	BR/LB	Injector 4	INJ 4
36	929	PK	Spark Output	SPOUT
37	361	R	Vehicle Power	VPWR
38	925	W/Y	Electronic Pressure Control	EPC
39	557	BR/Y	Injector 3	INJ 3
40	60	BK/LG	Power Ground	PWR GND
43	94	R/BK	Heated Oxygen Sensor - Front	HO2S - F

Fig. 75 EEC-IV PCM connector pin
usage (Part 1 of 2). 1994
w/3.0L/V6-181 FF SFI engine &
AX4S/N transaxle

Pin	Circuit	Wire Color	Application	Abbreviation
44	74	GY/LB	Heated Oxygen Sensor - Rear	HO2S - R
45	21	DG/LG	Flexible Fuel Sensor	FF
46	359	GY/R	Signal Return	SIG RTN
47	355	GY/W	Throttle Position Sensor	TP
48	200	BR	Self-Test Input	STI
49	923	O/BK	Transmission Fluid Temperature Sensor	TFT
50	967	LB/R	Mass Air Flow Sensor	MAF
51	237	O/Y	Shift Solenoid 1	SS1
52	315	P/O	Shift Solenoid 2	SS2
53	224	T/W	Torque Converter Clutch Solenoid	TCC
54	331	PK/Y	Wide Open Throttle (WOT) A/C Cut Off	WAC
55	912	W/R	Shift Solenoid 3	SS3
56	395	GY/O	Profile Ignition Pick-Up	PIP
57	361	R	Vehicle Power	VPWR
58	555	T	Injector 1	INJ 1
59	556	W	Injector 2	INJ 2
60	60	BK/LG	Power Ground	PWR GND

Pin locations given for reference only. Probing 60-pin connector with DVOM probe will result in permanent damage to the pin connectors. Always probe as directed using the breakout box.

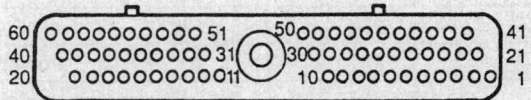

Fig. 75 EEC-IV PCM connector pin
usage (Part 2 of 2). 1994
w/3.0L/V6-181 FF SFI engine &
AX4S/N transaxle

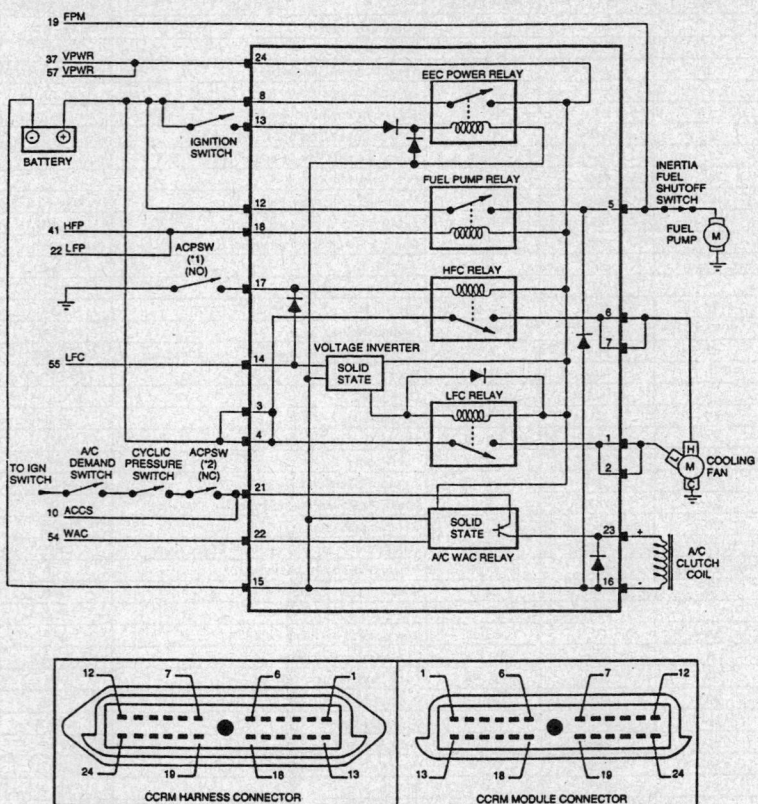

**Fig. 76 EEC-IV CCRM wiring circuit.
1994 w/3.0L/V6-181 FF SFI engine
& AX4S/N transaxle**

Pin	Circuit	Color	Application	Abbreviation
1	181	BR/O	Power to LFC Relay	PT/LFC
2	181	BR/O	Power to LFC Relay	PT/LFC
3	228	DB	Power to Cooling Fan	PTF
4	228	DB	Power to Cooling Fan	PTF
5	787	PK/BK	Power to Fuel Pump	PTP
6	38	BK/O	Power to HFC Relay	PT/HFC
7	38	BK/O	Power to HFC Relay	PT/HFC
8	37	Y	Battery to EEC Relay	B (+)
12	38	BK/O	Power to Fuel Pump Power Relay	PT/FPR
13	16	R/LG	Key Power	KEY PWR
14	197	T/O	LFC Circuit	LFC
15	60	BK/LG	Power Ground	PWR GND
16	57	BK	A/C Clutch Ground	PWR GND
17	639	LG/P	HFC Circuit	HFC
18	926	LB/O	Fuel Pump Circuit	FP
21	883	PK/LB	A/C Cyclic Switch	ACCS
22	331	PK/Y	WOT A/C Cut Off	WAC
23	347	BK/Y	Power to A/C Clutch	PTAC
24	361	R	Vehicle Power	VPWR

**Fig. 77 EEC-IV CCRM pin usage.
1994 w/3.0L/V6-181 FF SFI engine
& AX4S/N transaxle**

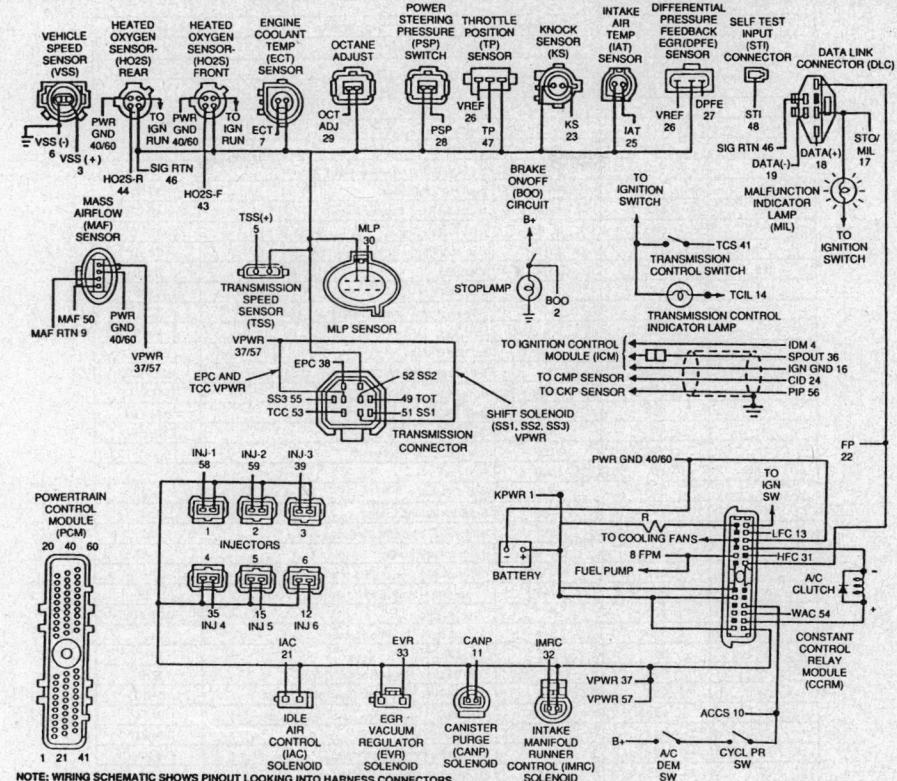

Fig. 78 EEC-IV wiring circuit. 1993 w/3.2L/V6-195 SHO SFI engine

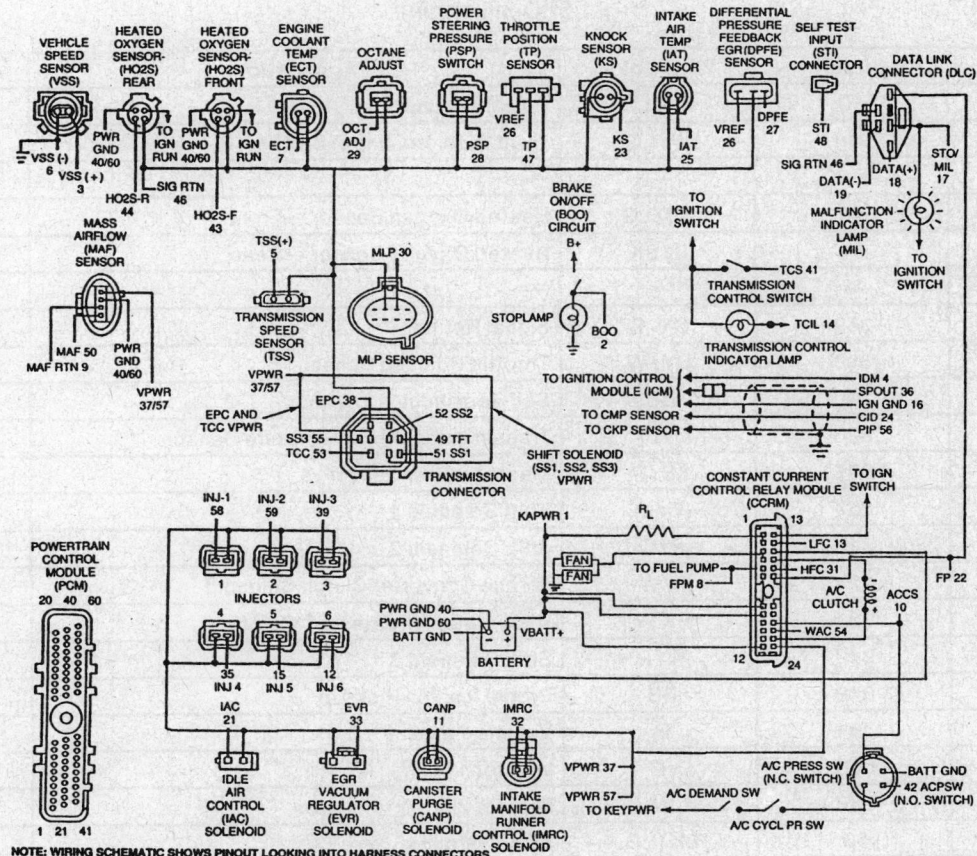

Fig. 79 EEC-IV wiring circuit. 1994-95 w/3.2L/V6-195 SHO SFI engine

Pin	Circuit	Wire Color	Application	Abbreviation
1	37	Y	Keep Alive Power	KAPWR
2	810	R/LG	Brake On/Off	BOO
3	150	DG/W	Vehicle Speed Sensor (+)	VSS (+)
4	395	GY/O	Ignition Diagnostic Monitor	IDM
5	679	GY/BK	Transmission Speed Sensor	TSS
6	563	O/Y	Vehicle Speed Sensor (-)	VSS (-)
7	354	LG/R	Engine Coolant Temperature Sensor	ECT
8	787	PK/BK	Fuel Pump Monitor	FPM
9	968	T/LB	Mass Air Flow Sensor Return	MAF RTN
10	883	PK/LB	A/C Clutch Signal	ACCS
11	101	GY/Y	Canister Purge Solenoid	CANP
12	560	LG/O	Injector 6	INJ 6
13	197	T/O	Low Fan Control	LFC
14	665	O/Y	Transmission Control Indicator Lamp	TCIL
15	559	T/BK	Injector 5	INJ 5
16	259	O/R	Ignition Ground	IGN GND
17	201	T/R	Self-Test Output/Malfunction Indicator Lamp	STO/MIL
18	696	O/BK	Data (+)	DATA (+)
19	695	BK/O	Data (-)	DATA (-)
20	57	BK	Case Ground	CSE GND
21	68	O/BK	Idle Air Control Solenoid	IAC
22	97	T/LG	Fuel Pump	FP
23	310	Y/R	Knock Sensor	KS
24	795	DG	Cylinder Indentification	CID
25	743	GY	Intake Air Temperature Sensor	IAT
26	351	BR/W	Reference Voltage	VREF
27	352	BR/LG	Differential Pressure Feedback EGR Sensor	DPFE
28	330	Y/LG	Power Steering Pressure Switch	PSP
29	929	PK	Octane Adjust	OCT ADJ
30	199	LB/Y	Manual Lever Position Sensor	MLP
31	639	LG/P	High Fan Control	HFC
33	360	BR/PK	EGR Vacuum Regulator Solenoid	EVR
34	965	LG/P	Intake Manifold Runner Control	IMRC
35	558	BR/LB	Injector 4	INJ 4
36	324	Y/LG	Spark Output	SPOUT
37	361	R	Vehicle Power	VPWR
38	925	W/Y	Electronic Pressure Control	EPC
39	557	BR/Y	Injector 3	INJ 3

Fig. 80   EEC-IV PCM connector pin usage (Part 1 of 2). 3.2L/V6-195 SHO SFI engine

Pin	Circuit	Wire Color	Application	Abbreviation
40	60	BK/LG	Power Ground	PWR GND
41	911	W/LG	Transmission Control Switch	TCS
42	—	—	—	—
43	90	DB/LG	Heated Oxygen Sensor—Front	HO2S-F
44	94	R/BK	Heated Oxygen Sensor—Rear	HO2S-R
45	—	—	—	—
46	359	GY/R	Signal Return	SIG RTN
47	355	GY/W	Throttle Position Sensor	TP
48	200	BR	Self-Test Input	STI
49	923	O/BK	Transmission Oil Temperature Sensor	TOT
50	967	LB/R	Mass Air Flow Sensor	MAF
51	237	O/Y	Shift Solenoid 1	SS1
52	315	P/O	Shift Solenoid 2	SS2
53	224	T/W	Torque Converter Clutch Solenoid	TCC
54	331	PK/Y	Wide Open Throttle A/C Cutoff	WAC
55	912	W/R	Shift Solenoid 3	SS3
56	349	DB	Profile Ignition Pick-Up	PIP
57	361	R	Vehicle Power	VPWR
58	555	T	Injector 1	INJ 1
59	556	W	Injector 2	INJ 2
60	60	BK/LG	Power Ground	PWR GND

Fig. 80   EEC-IV PCM connector pin usage (Part 2 of 2). 1993 w/3.2L/V6-195 SHO SFI engine

Pin	Circuit	Wire Color	Application	Abbreviation
40	60	BK/LG	Power Ground	PWR GND
41	911	W/LG	Transmission Control Switch	TCS
42	439	T/LG	A/C Pressure Switch	ACPSW
43	90	DB/LG	Heated Oxygen Sensor—Front	HO2S-F
44	94	R/BK	Heated Oxygen Sensor—Rear	HO2S-R
45	—	—	—	—
46	359	GY/R	Signal Return	SIG RTN
47	355	GY/W	Throttle Position Sensor	TP
48	200	BR	Self-Test Input	STI
49	923	O/BK	Transmission Fluid Temperature Sensor	TFT
50	967	LB/R	Mass Air Flow Sensor	MAF
51	237	O/Y	Shift Solenoid 1	SS1
52	315	P/O	Shift Solenoid 2	SS2
53	224	T/W	Torque Converter Clutch Solenoid	TCC
54	331	PK/Y	Wide Open Throttle A/C Cutoff	WAC
55	912	W/R	Shift Solenoid 3	SS3
56	349	DB	Profile Ignition Pick-Up	PIP
57	361	R	Vehicle Power	VPWR
58	555	T	Injector 1	INJ 1
59	556	W	Injector 2	INJ 2
60	60	BK/LG	Power Ground	PWR GND

Fig. 80 EEC-IV PCM connector pin
usage (Part 2 of 2). 1994–95
w/3.2L/V6-195 SHO SFI engine

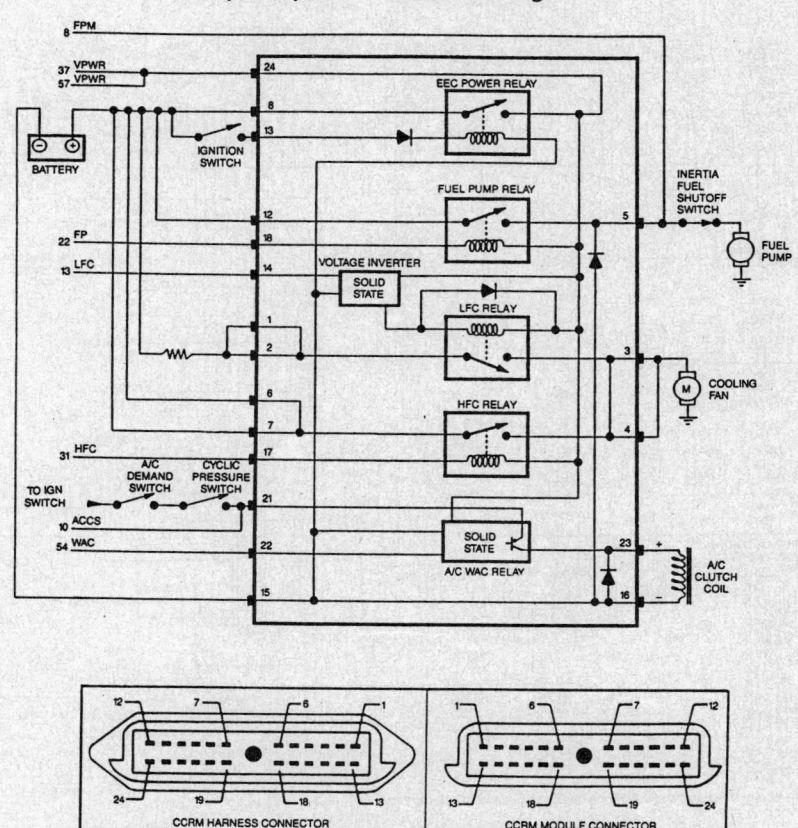

Fig. 81 EEC-IV CCRM wiring circuit.
3.2L/V6-195 SHO SFI engine

Pin	Circuit	Wire Color	Application	Abbreviation
1	181	BR/O	Power to Low Fan Control Relay	PT/LFC
2	181	BR/O	Power to Low Fan Control Relay	PT/LFC
3	228	DB	Power to Cooling Fan	PTF
4	228	DB	Power to Cooling Fan	PTF
5	787	PK/BK	Power to Fuel Pump	PTP
6	38	BK/O	Power to High Fan Control Relay	PT/HFC
7	38	BK/O	Power to High Fan Control Relay	PT/HFC
8	37	Y	Battery to EEC Relay	B (+)
9	—	—	—	—
10	—	—	—	—
11	—	—	—	—
12	38	BK/O	Power to Fuel Pump Relay	PT/FP
13	16	R/LG	Key Power	KEY PWR
14	197	T/O	Low Fan Control Circuit	LFC
15	60	BK/LG	Power Ground	PWR GND
16	57	BK	A/C Clutch Ground	PWR GND
17	639	LG/P	High Fan Control Circuit	HFC
18	97	T/LG	Fuel Pump Control Circuit	FP
19	—	—	—	—
20	—	—	—	—
21	883	PK/LB	A/C Cyclic Switch	ACCS
22	331	PK/Y	WOT A/C Cutoff	WAC
23	347	BK/Y	Power to A/C Clutch	PTAC
24	361	R	Vehicle Power	VPWR

**Fig. 82   EEC-IV CCRM pin usage.
3.2L/V6-195 SHO SFI engine**

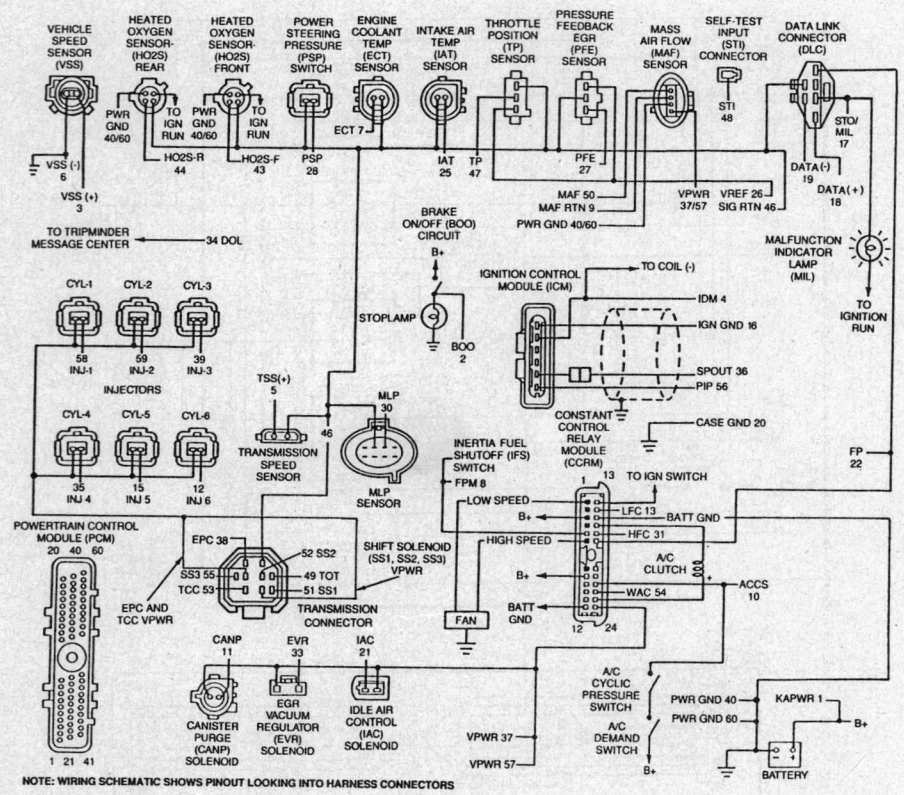

NOTE: WIRING SCHEMATIC SHOWS PINOUT LOOKING INTO HARNESS CONNECTORS

**Fig. 83   EEC-IV wiring circuit. 1993
Taurus & Sable w/3.8L/V6-232 SFI
engine & AXODE transaxle**

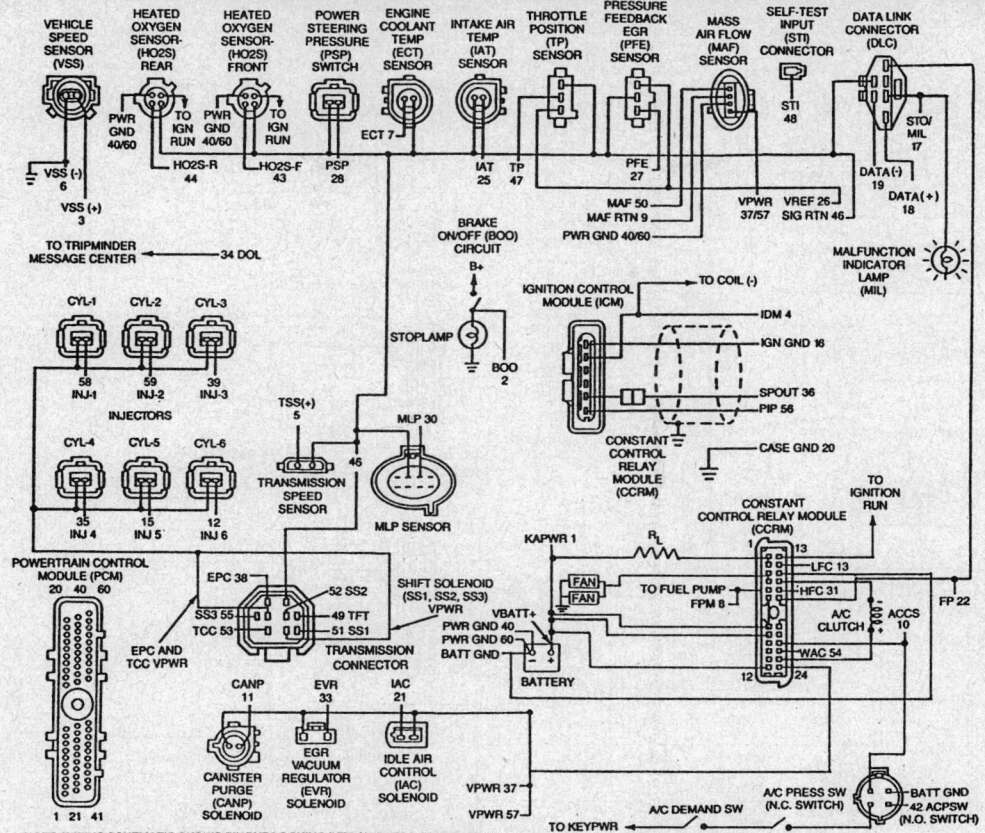

**Fig. 84 EEC-IV wiring circuit.
1994–95 Taurus & Sable
w/3.8L/V6-232 SFI engine &
AX4S/N transaxle**

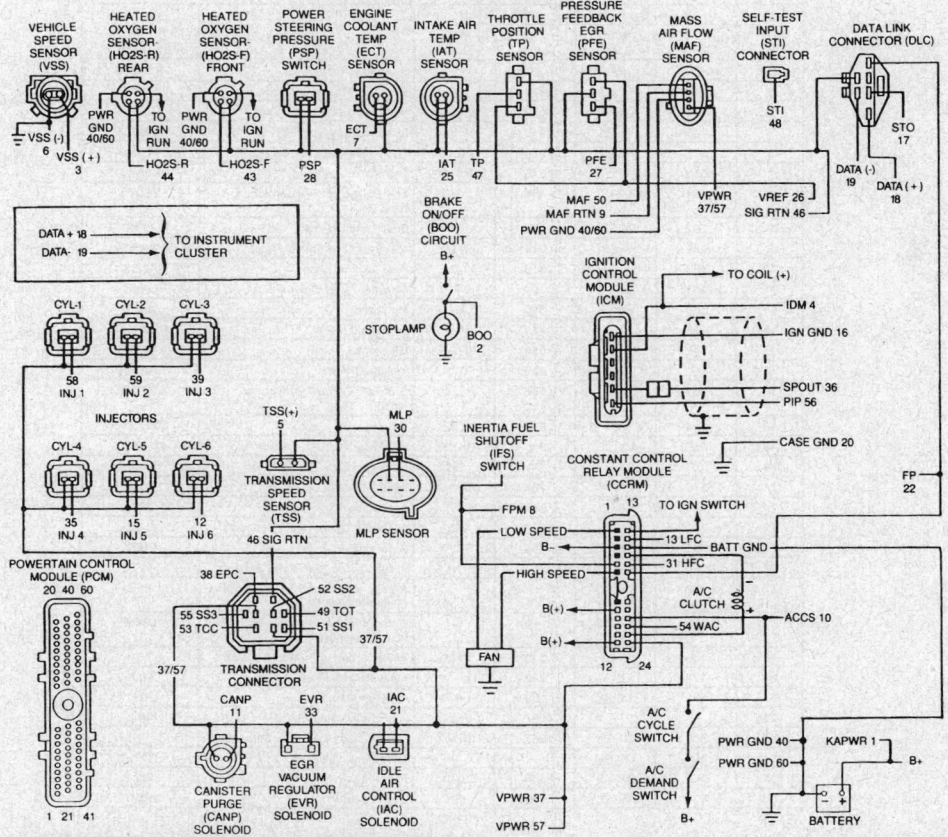

**Fig. 85 EEC-IV wiring circuit. 1993 Continental w/3.8L/V6-232 SFI engine &
AXODE transaxle**

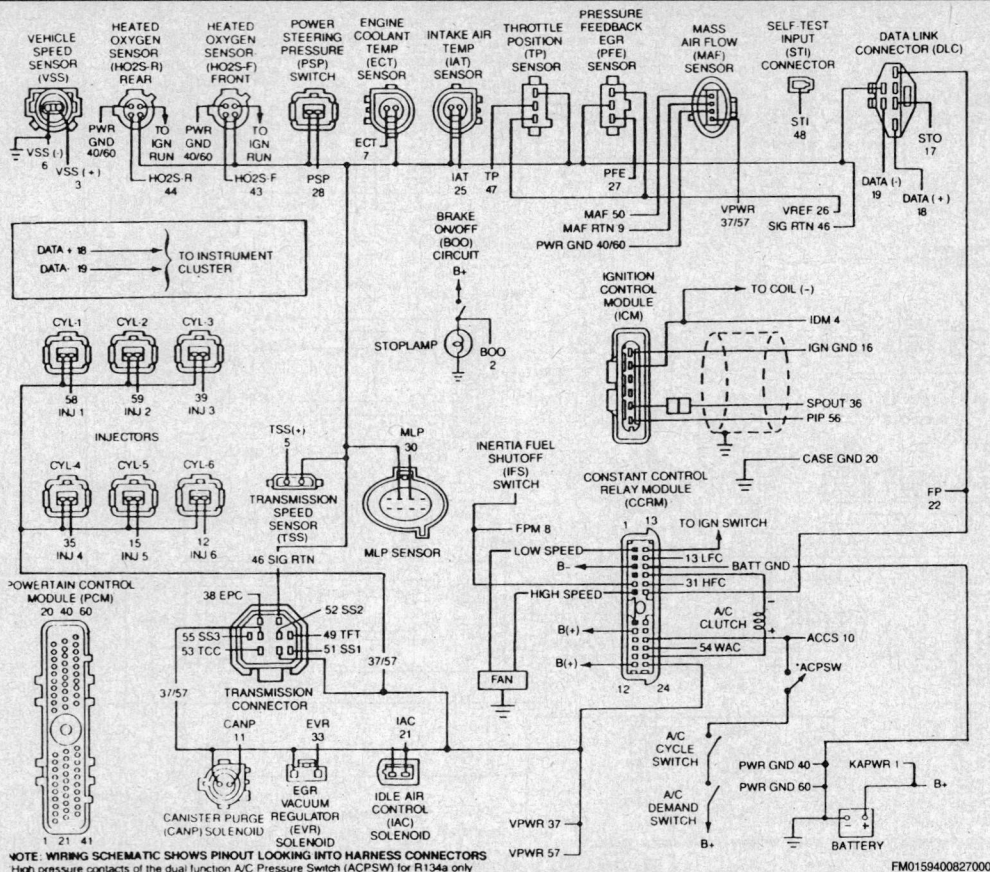

Fig. 86 EEC-IV wiring circuit. 1994 Continental w/3.8L/V6-232 SFI engine & AX4S/N transaxle

Pin	Taurus/Sable		Continental		Application	Abbreviation
	Crt. #	Wire Color	Crt. #	Wire Color		
1	37	Y	37	Y	Keep Alive Power	KAPWR
2	810	R/LG	511	LG	Brake On/Off	BOO
3	150	DG/W	679	GY/BK	Vehicle Speed Sensor (+)	VSS (+)
4	648	W/PK	648	W/PK	Ignition Diagnostic Monitor	IDM
5	679	GY/BK	970	DG/W	Transmission Speed Sensor	TSS
6	563	O/Y	676	PK/O	Vehicle Speed Sensor (-)	VSS (-)
7	354	LG/R	354	LG/R	Engine Coolant Temperature Sensor	ECT
8	787	PK/BK	238	DG/Y	Fuel Pump Monitor	FPM
9	968	T/LB	968	T/LB	Mass Air Flow Sensor Return	MAF RTN
10	883	PK/LB	348	P	A/C Cyclic Switch	ACCS
11	101	GY/Y	101	GY/Y	Canister Purge Solenoid	CANP
12	560	LG/O	560	LG/O	Injector 6	INJ 6
13	197	T/O	228	DB	Low Fan Control	LFC
15	559	T/BK	559	T/BK	Injector 5	INJ 5
16	350	GY	259	O/R	Ignition Ground	IGN GND
17	201	T/R	658	PK/LG	Self-Test Output/Malfunction Indicator Lamp	STO/MIL
18	914	T/O	914	T/O	Data (+)	DATA (+)
19	915	PK/LB	915	PK/LB	Data (-)	DATA (-)
20	57	BK	57	BK	Case Ground	CSE GND
21	376	BR/W	264	W/LB	Idle Air Control Solenoid	IAC
22	926	LB/O	926	LB/O	Fuel Pump	FP
25	743	GY	743	GY	Intake Air Temperature Sensor	IAT
26	351	BR/W	351	BR/W	Reference Voltage	VREF
27	—	—	352	BR/LG	Pressure Feedback EGR Sensor	PFE
27	352	BR/LG			Pressure Feedback EGR Sensor (California only)	PFE
27	352	BR/LG	—	—	Differential Pressure Feedback EGR Sensor (49 States)	DPFE
28	330	Y/LG	330	Y/LG	Power Steering Pressure Switch	PSP
30	199	LB/Y	199	LB/Y	Manual Lever Position Sensor	MLP
31	639	LG/P	639	LG/P	High Fan Control	HFC
32	—	—	637	DB/W	Automatic Ride Control	ARC
33	360	BR/PK	360	BR/PK	EGR Vacuum Regulator Solenoid	EVR
34	305	LB/PK	—	—	Data Output Line	DOL
35	558	BR/LB	558	BR/LB	Injector 4	INJ 4
36	324	Y/LG	929	PK	Spark Output	SPOUT

Fig. 87 EEC-IV PCM connector pin usage (Part 1 of 2).
3.8L/V6-232 SFI engine & AXODE & AX4S/N transaxles

Taurus/Sable, Continental

Pin	Taurus/Sable Crt. #	Wire Color	Continental Crt. #	Wire Color	Application	Abbreviation
37	361	R	361	R	Vehicle Power	VPWR
38	925	W/Y	925	W/Y	Electronic Pressure Control	EPC
39	557	BR/Y	557	BR/Y	Injector 3	INJ 3
40	60	BK/LG	570	BK/W	Power Ground	PWR GND
43	94	R/BK	94	R/BK	Heated Oxygen Sensor—Front	HO2S-F
44	74	GY/LB	74	GY/LB	Heated Oxygen Sensor—Rear	HO2S-R
46	359	GY/R	359	GY/R	Signal Return	SIG RTN
47	355	GY/W	355	GY/W	Throttle Position Sensor	TP
48	200	BR	209	W/P	Self-Test Input	STI
49	923	O/BK	923	O/BK	Transmission Oil Temperature Sensor	TOT
50	967	LB/R	967	LB/R	Mass Air Flow Sensor	MAF
51	237	O/Y	237	O/Y	Shift Solenoid 1	SS1
52	315	P/O	315	P/O	Shift Solenoid 2	SS2
53	224	T/W	224	T/W	Torque Converter Clutch	TCC
54	331	PK/Y	331	PK/Y	Wide Open Throttle (WOT) A/C Cut Off	WAC
55	912	W/R	971	PK/BK	Shift Solenoid 3	SS3
56	395	GY/O	395	GY/O	Profile Ignition Pick-Up	PIP
57	361	R	361	R	Vehicle Power	VPWR
58	555	T	555	T	Injector 1	INJ 1
59	556	W	556	W	Injector 2	INJ 2
60	60	BK/LG	570	BK/W	Power Ground	PWR GND

Pin locations given for reference only. Probing 60-pin connector with DVOM probe will result in permanent damage to the pin connectors. Always probe as directed using the breakout box.

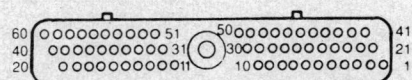

FM015930082802AX

Fig. 87   EEC-IV PCM connector pin usage (Part 2 of 2). 1993 w/3.8L/V6-232 SFI engine & AXODE transaxle

Pin	Taurus/Sable Crt. #	Wire Color	Continental Crt. #	Wire Color	Application	Abbreviation
37	361	R	361	R	Vehicle Power	VPWR
38	925	W/Y	925	W/Y	Electronic Pressure Control	EPC
39	557	BR/Y	557	BR/Y	Injector 3	INJ 3
40	60	BK/LG	570	BK/W	Power Ground	PWR GND
42	439	T/LG	439	T/LG	A/C Pressure Switch	ACPSW
43	94	R/BK	94	R/BK	Heated Oxygen Sensor—Front	HO2S-F
44	74	GY/LB	74	GY/LB	Heated Oxygen Sensor—Rear	HO2S-R
46	359	GY/R	359	GY/R	Signal Return	SIG RTN
47	355	GY/W	355	GY/W	Throttle Position Sensor	TP
48	200	BR	209	W/P	Self-Test Input	STI
49	923	O/BK	923	O/BK	Transmission Fluid Temperature Sensor	TFT
50	967	LB/R	967	LB/R	Mass Air Flow Sensor	MAF
51	237	O/Y	237	O/Y	Shift Solenoid 1	SS1
52	315	P/O	315	P/O	Shift Solenoid 2	SS2
53	224	T/W	224	T/W	Torque Converter Clutch	TCC
54	331	PK/Y	331	PK/Y	Wide Open Throttle (WOT) A/C Cut Off	WAC
55	912	W/R	971	PK/BK	Shift Solenoid 3	SS3
56	395	GY/O	395	GY/O	Profile Ignition Pick-Up	PIP
57	361	R	361	R	Vehicle Power	VPWR
58	555	T	555	T	Injector 1	INJ 1
59	556	W	556	W	Injector 2	INJ 2
60	60	BK/LG	570	BK/W	Power Ground	PWR GND

Pin locations given for reference only. Probing 60-pin connector with DVOM probe will result in permanent damage to the pin connectors. Always probe as directed using the breakout box.

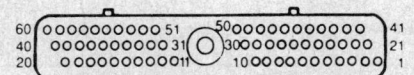

FM015940082802BX

Fig. 87   EEC-IV PCM connector pin usage (Part 2 of 2). 1994–95 w/3.8L/V6-232 SFI engine & AX4S/N transaxle

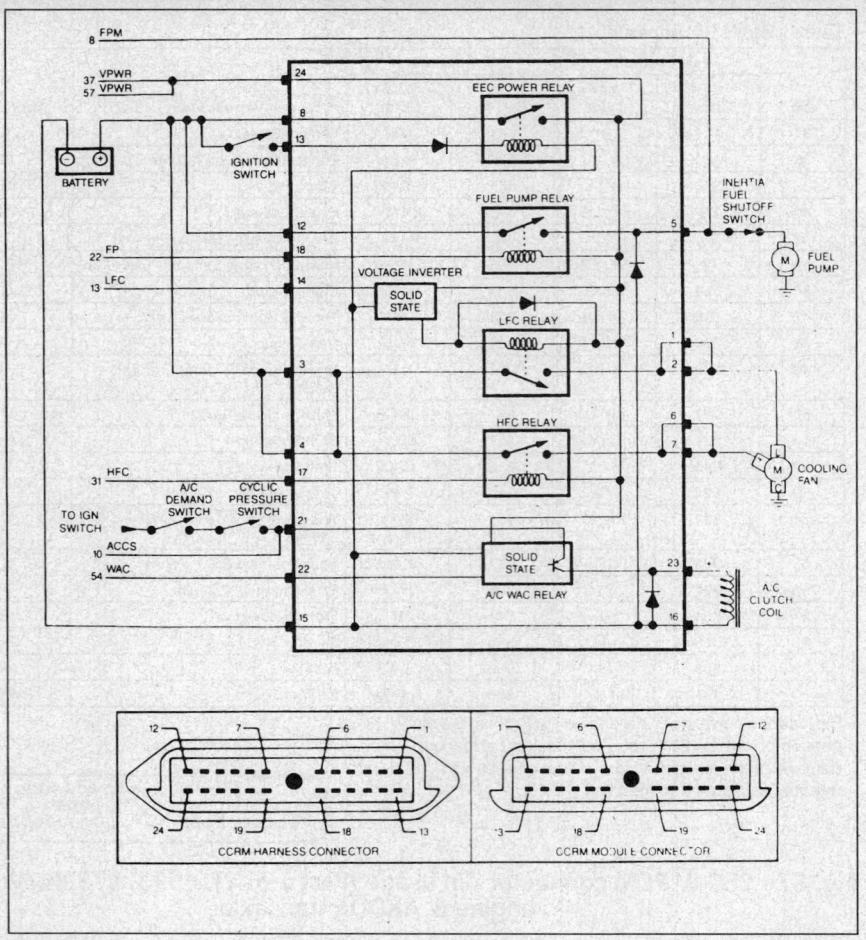

Fig. 88 EEC-IV CCRM wiring circuit. 3.8L/V6-232 SFI engine & AXODE & AX4S/N transaxles

Pin	Circuit	Color	Application	Abbreviation
1	181	BR/O	Power to Low Cooling Fan	PT/LF
2	181	BR/O	Power to Low Cooling Fan	PT/LF
3	38	BK/O	Power to Fan Relays	PTR
4	38	BK/O	Power to Fan Relays	PTR
5	787	PK/BK	Power to Fuel Pump	PTP
6	228	DB	Power to High Cooling Fan	PT/HF
7	228	DB	Power to High Cooling Fan	PT/HF
8	37	Y	Battery to EEC Power Relay	B (+)
12	38	BK/O	Power to Fuel Pump Relay	PT/FPR
13	16	R/LG	Key Power	KEY PWR
14	197	T/O	Low Fan Control Circuit	LFC
15	60	BK/LG	Power Ground	PWR GND
16	321	GY/W	A/C Clutch Ground	PWR GND
17	639	LG/P	High Fan Control Circuit	HFC
18	926	LB/O	Fuel Pump Circuit	FP
21	883	PK/LB	A/C Cyclic Switch	ACCS
22	331	PK/Y	WOT A/C Cut Off	WAC
23	347	BK/Y	Power to A/C Clutch	PTAC
24	361	R	Vehicle Power	VPWR

Fig. 89 EEC-IV CCRM pin usage. Taurus & Sable w/3.8L/V6-232 SFI engine & AXODE & AX4S/N transaxles

Pin	Circuit	Color	Application	Abbreviation
1	181	BR/O	Power to Low Cooling Fan	PT/LFC
2	181	BR/O	Power to Low Cooling Fan	PT/LFC
3	38	BK/O	Power to Fan Relays	PT/FCR
4	38	BK/O	Power to Fan Relays	PT/FCR
5	787	PK/BK	Power to Fuel Pump	PT/FP
6	536	BK/LG	Power to High Cooling Fan	PT/HFC
7	536	BK/LG	Power to High Cooling Fan	PT/HFC
8	37	Y	Battery to EEC Power Relay	B(+)
12	276	BR	Power to Fuel Pump Relay	PT/FPR
13	16	R/LG	Key Power	KEY PWR
14	228	DB	Low Fan Control Circuit	LFC
15	60	BK/LG	Power Ground	PWR GND
16	321	GY/W	A/C Clutch Ground	PWR GND
17	639	LG/P	High Fan Control Circuit	HFC
18	926	LB/O	Fuel Pump Circuit	FP
21	348	P	A/C Cyclic Switch	ACCS
22	331	PK/Y	WOT A/C Cut Off	WAC
23	347	BK/Y	Power to A/C Clutch	PT/ACC
24	361	R	Vehicle Power	VPWR

FM0159300831000X

Fig. 90 EEC-IV CCRM pin usage. 1993–94 Continental w/3.8L/V6-232 SFI engine & AXODE & AX4S/N transaxles

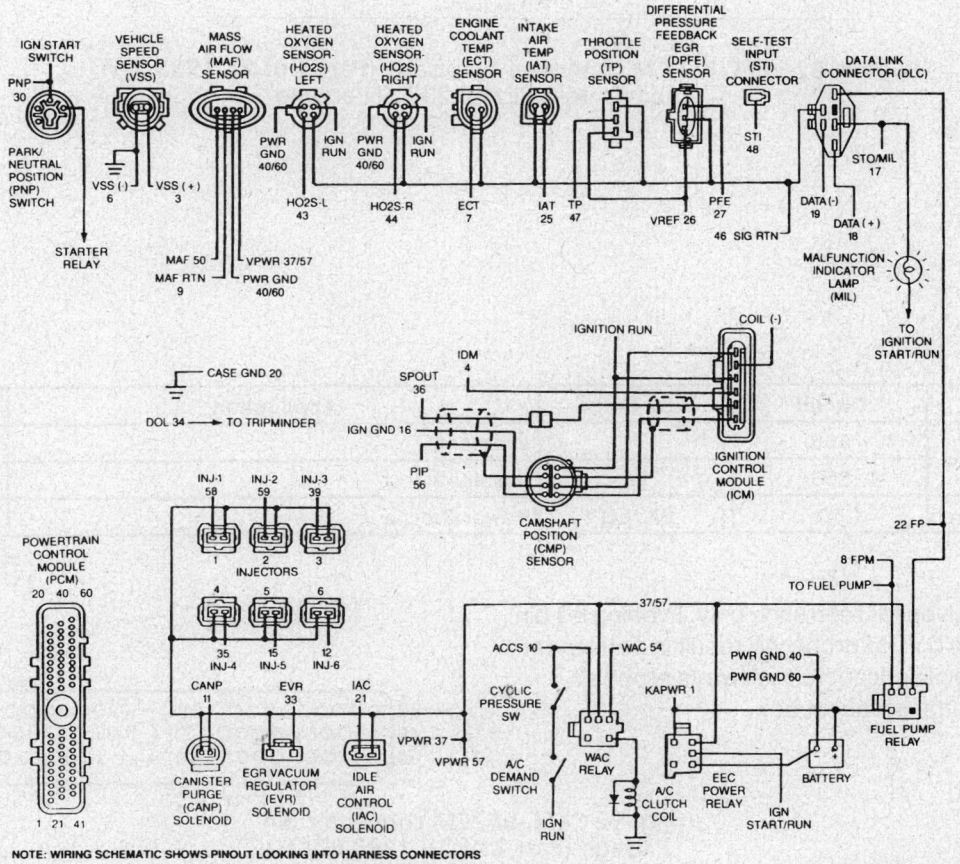

FM0159300832000X

Fig. 91 EEC-IV wiring circuit. 1993 RWD models w/3.8L/V6-232 SFI engine

Pin	Circuit	Wire Color	Application	Abbreviation
1	37	Y	Keep Alive Power	KAPWR
3	150	DG/W	Vehicle Speed Sensor (+)	VSS (+)
4	648	W/PK	Ignition Diagnostic Monitor	IDM
6	359	GY/R	Vehicle Speed Sensor (-)	VSS (-)
7	354	LG/R	Engine Coolant Temperature Sensor	ECT
8	787	PK/BK	Fuel Pump Monitor	FPM
9	968	T/LB	Mass Air Flow Sensor Return	MAF RTN
10	883	PK/LB	A/C Cyclic Switch	ACCS
11	101	GY/Y	Canister Purge Solenoid	CANP
12	560	LG/O	Injector 6	INJ 6
15	559	T/BK	Injector 5	INJ 5
16	350	GY	Ignition Ground	IGN GND
17	382	Y/BK	Self-Test Output/Malfunction Indicator Lamp	STO/MIL
18	914	T/O	Data (+)	DATA (+)
19	915	PK/LB	Data (-)	DATA (-)
20	57	BK	Case Ground	CSE GND
21	69	R/LG	Idle Air Control Solenoid	IAC
22	97	T/LG	Fuel Pump	FP
25	743	GY	Intake Air Temperature Sensor	IAT
26	351	BR/W	Reference Voltage	VREF
27	352	BR/LG	Pressure Feedback EGR Sensor	PFE
30	32	R/LB	Park/Neutral Position Switch	PNP
33	360	BR/PK	EGR Vacuum Regulator Solenoid	EVR
34	305	LB/PK	Data Output Line	DOL
35	558	BR/LB	Injector 4	INJ 4
36	324	Y/LG	Spark Output	SPOUT
37	361	R	Vehicle Power	VPWR
39	557	BR/Y	Injector 3	INJ 3
40	60	BK/LG	Power Ground	PWR GND
43	95	T/W	Heated Oxygen Sensor - Left	HO2S-L
44	96	T/O	Heated Oxygen Sensor - Right	HO2S-R
46	359	GY/R	Signal Return	SIG RTN
47	355	GY/W	Throttle Position Sensor	TP
48	209	W/P	Self-Test Input	STI
50	967	LB/R	Mass Air Flow Sensor	MAF
54	73	O/LB	WOT A/C Cut Off	WAC
56	349	DB	Profile Ignition Pick-Up	PIP
57	361	R	Vehicle Power	VPWR

FM0159300833010X

Fig. 92 EEC-IV PCM connector pin usage (Part 1 of 2). 1993 RWD models w/3.8L/V6-232 SFI engine

Pin	Circuit	Wire Color	Application	Abbreviation
58	555	T	Injector 1	INJ 1
59	556	W	Injector 2	INJ 2
60	60	BK/LG	Power Ground	PWR GND

Pin locations given for reference only. Probing 60-pin connector with DVOM probe will result in permanent damage to the pin connectors. Always probe as directed using the breakout box.

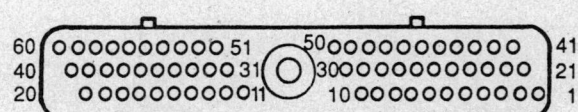

Fig. 92 EEC-IV PCM connector pin usage (Part 2 of 2). 1993 RWD models w/3.8L/V6-232 SFI engine

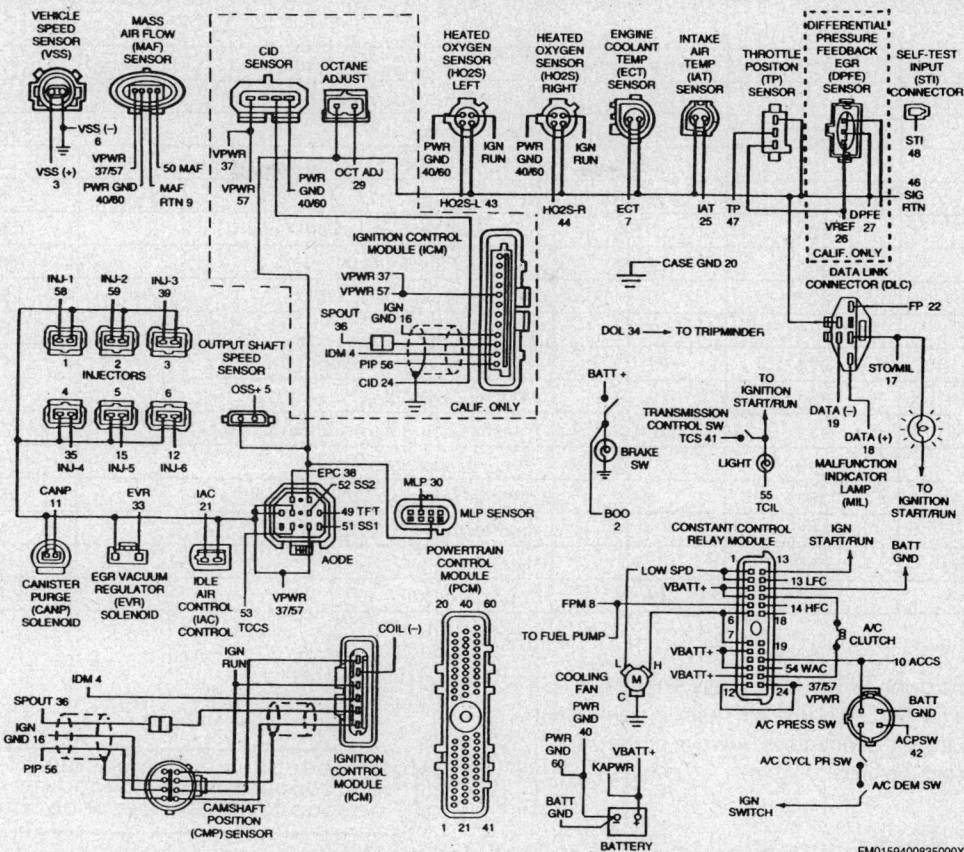

Fig. 93 EEC-IV wiring circuit. 1994–95 RWD models w/3.8L/V6-232 SFI engine

Pin	Circuit	Wire Color	Application	Abbreviation
1	37	Y	Keep Alive Power	KAPWR
2	511	LG	Brake On Off	BOO
3	679	GY/BK	Vehicle Speed Sensor (+)	VSS (+)
4	648	W/PK	Ignition Diagnostic Monitor	IDM
5	970	DG/W	Transmission Speed Sensor	TSS
6	676	PK/O	Vehicle Speed Sensor (-)	VSS (-)
7	354	LG/R	Engine Coolant Temperature Sensor	ECT
8	787	PK/BK	Fuel Pump Monitor	FPM
9	968	T/LB	Mass Air Flow Sensor Return	MAF RTN
10	883	PK/LB	A C Cyclic Switch	ACCS
11	101	GY/Y	Canister Purge Solenoid	CANP
12	560	LG/O	Injector 6	INJ 6
13	197	T/O	Low Fan Control	LFC
14	639	LG/P	High Fan Control	HFC
15	559	T/BK	Injector 5	INJ 5
16	350	GY	Ignition Ground	IGN GND
17	658	PK/LG	Self-Test Output Malfunction Indicator Lamp	STO MIL
18	914	T/O	Data (+)	DATA (+)
19	915	PK/LB	Data (-)	DATA (-)
20	57	BK	Case Ground	CSE GND
21	264	W/LB	Idle Air Control Solenoid	IAC
22	926	LB/O	Fuel Pump	FP
24	282	DB/O	Cylinder Identification	CID
25	743	GY	Intake Air Temperature Sensor	IAT
26	351	BR/W	Reference Voltage	VREF
27	352	BR/LG	Pressure Feedback EGR Sensor	PFE
29	242	DG	Octane Adjust	OCT ADJ
30	199	LB/Y	Manual Lever Position Sensor	MLP
33	360	BR/PK	EGR Vacuum Regulator Solenoid	EVR
35	558	BR/LB	Injector 4	INJ 4
36	929	PK	Spark Output	SPOUT
37	361	R	Vehicle Power	VPWR
38	925	W/Y	Electronic Pressure Control	EPC
39	557	BR/Y	Injector 3	INJ 3
40	570	BK/Y	Power Ground	PWR GND
41	224	T/W	Transmission Control Switch	TCS
42	439	T/LG	A C Pressure Switch	ACPSW
43	94	R/BK	Heated Oxygen Sensor Left	HO2S L

Fig. 94 EEC-IV PCM connector pin usage (Part 1 of 2). 1994–95 RWD models w/3.8L/V6-232 SFI engine

Pin	Circuit	Wire Color	Application	Abbreviation
44	74	GY/LB	Heated Oxygen Sensor - Right	HO2S-R
46	359	GY/R	Signal Return	SIG RTN
47	355	GY/Y	Throttle Position Sensor	TP
48	209	W/P	Self-Test Input	STI
49	923	O/BK	Transmission Fluid Temperature	TFT
50	967	LB/R	Mass Air Flow Sensor	MAF
51	237	O/Y	Shift Solenoid 1	SS1
52	315	P/O	Shift Solenoid 2	SS2
53	924	BR/O	Torque Converter Clutch	TCC
54	331	PK/Y	WOT A/C Cut Off	WAC
55	911	W/LG	Transmission Control Indicator Light	TCIL
56	349	GY/O	Profile Ignition Pick-Up	PIP
57	361	R	Vehicle Power	VPWR
58	555	T	Injector 1	INJ 1
59	556	W	Injector 2	INJ 2
60	570	BK/Y	Power Ground	PWR GND

Pin locations given for reference only. Probing 60-pin connector with DVOM probe will result in permanent damage to the pin connectors. Always probe as directed using the breakout box.

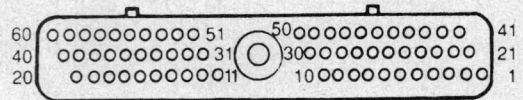

FM0159400836020X

Fig. 94   EEC-IV PCM connector pin usage (Part 2 of 2). 1994–95 RWD models w/3.8L/V6-232 SFI engine

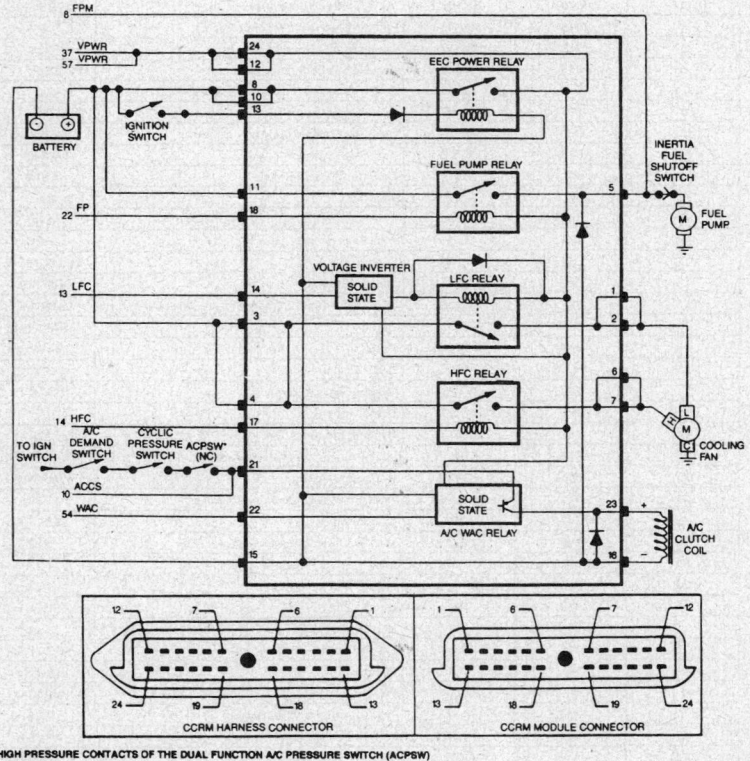

*HIGH PRESSURE CONTACTS OF THE DUAL FUNCTION A/C PRESSURE SWITCH (ACPSW)

FM0159400837000X

Fig. 95   EEC-IV CCRM wiring circuit. 1994–95 RWD models w/3.8L/V6-232 SFI engine

Pin	Circuit	Color	Application	Abbreviation
1	228	DB	Low Fan Control (output)	LFC
2	228	DB	Low Fan Control (output)	LFC
3	38	BK/O	Battery Positive	B +
4	38	BK/O	Battery Positive	B +
5	787	PK/BK	Power to Fuel Pump	PTP
6	181	BR/O	High Fan Control (output)	HFC
7	181	BR/O	High Fan Control (output)	HFC
8	37	Y	Battery to EEC Relay	B (+)
10	370	Y	Battery to EEC Relay	B+
11	175	BK/Y	Battery to Fuel Pump Relay	B+
12	361	R	Vehicle Power	VPWR
13	16	R/LG	Key Power	KEY PWR
14	197	T/O	Low Fan Control (input)	LFC
15	57	BK	Power Ground	PWR GND
16	321	GY/W	A/C Clutch Ground	PWR GND
17	639	LG/P	High Fan Control (input)	HFC
18	926	LB/O	Fuel Pump Circuit	FP
21	883	PK/LB	A/C Cyclic Switch	ACCS
22	331	PK/Y	WOT A/C Cut Off	WAC
23	347	BK/Y	Power to A/C Clutch Coil	PTAC
24	361	R	Vehicle Power	VPWR

FM0159400838000X

Fig. 96 EEC-IV CCRM pin usage. 1994–95 RWD models w/3.8L/V6-232 SFI engine

NOTE: WIRING SCHEMATIC SHOWS PINOUT LOOKING INTO HARNESS CONNECTORS

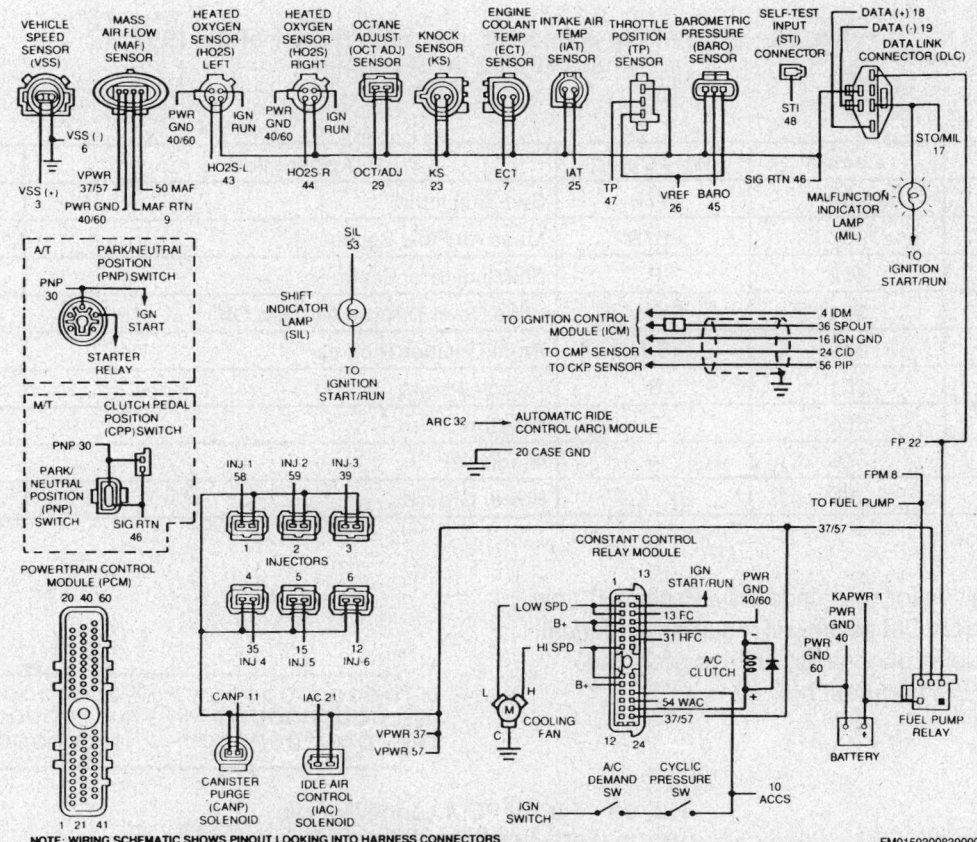

FM0159300839000X

Fig. 97 EEC-IV wiring circuit. 1993 w/3.8L/V6-232 SC SFI engine

Thunderbird SC

Pin	Circuit	Wire Color	Application	Abbreviation
1	37	Y	Keep Alive Power	KAPWR
3	150	DG/W	Vehicle Speed Sensor (+)	VSS (+)
4	11	T/Y	Ignition Diagnostic Monitor	IDM
6	359	GY/R	Vehicle Speed Sensor (-)	VSS (-)
7	354	LG/R	Engine Coolant Temperature Sensor	ECT
8	787	PK/BK	Fuel Pump Monitor	FPM
9	968	T/LB	Mass Air Flow Sensor Return	MAF RTN
10	883	PK/LB	A/C Clutch Signal	ACCS
11	101	GY/Y	Canister Purge Solenoid	CANP
12	560	LG/O	Injector 6	INJ 6
13	197	T/O	Low Fan Control	LFC
15	559	T/BK	Injector 5	INJ 5
16	796	LB	Ignition Ground	IGN GND
17	382	Y/BK	Self-Test Output/Malfunction Indicator Lamp	STO/MIL
18	914	T/O	Data (+)	DATA (+)
19	915	PK/LB	Data (-)	DATA (-)
20	57	BK	Case Ground	CSE GND
21	69	R/LG	Idle Air Control	IAC
22	97	T/LG	Fuel Pump	FP
23	310	Y/R	Knock Sensor	KS
24	795	DG	Cylinder Identification	CID
25	743	GY	Intake Air Temperature Sensor	IAT
26	351	BR/W	Reference Voltage	VREF
29	359	GY/R	Octane Adjust	OCT ADJ
30	32	R/LB	Park/Neutral Position Switch (A/T Only)	PNP
30	32	R/LB	Park/Neutral Position Switch/Clutch Pedal Position Switch (M/T Only)	PNP/CPP
31	639	LG/P	High Fan Control	HFC
32	836	O/W	Automatic Ride Control	ARC
35	558	BR/LB	Injector 4	INJ 4
36	324	Y/LG	Spark Output	SPOUT
37	361	R	Vehicle Power	VPWR
39	557	BR/Y	Injector 3	INJ 3
40	60	BK/LG	Power Ground	PWR GND
43	95	T/W	Heated Oxygen Sensor - Left	HO2S - L
44	96	T/O	Heated Oxygen Sensor - Right	HO2S - R
45	356	DB/LG	Barometric Pressure Sensor	BARO
46	359	GY/R	Signal Return	SIG RTN
47	355	GY/W	Throttle Position Sensor	TP

(Continued)

FM0159300840010X

Fig. 98 EEC-IV PCM connector pin usage (Part 1 of 2). 1993 w/ 3.8L/V6-232 SC SFI engine

Pin	Circuit	Wire Color	Application	Abbreviation
48	209	W/P	Self-Test Input	STI
50	967	LB/R	Mass Air Flow Sensor	MAF
53	462	P	Shift Indicator Lamp	SIL
54	331	PK/Y	Wide Open Throttle A/C Cut Off	WAC
56	349	DB	Profile Ignition Pick-up	PIP
57	361	R	Vehicle Power	VPWR
58	555	T	Injector 1	INJ 1
59	556	W	Injector 2	INJ 2
60	60	BK/LG	Power Ground	PWR GND

Pin locations given for reference only. Probing 60-pin connector with DVOM probe will result in permanent damage to the pin connectors. Always probe as directed using the breakout box.

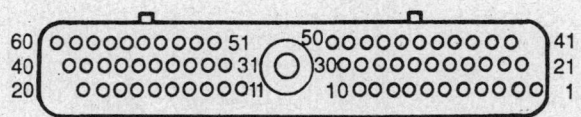

Fig. 98 EEC-IV PCM connector pin usage (Part 2 of 2). 1993 w/3.8L/ V6-232 SC SFI engine

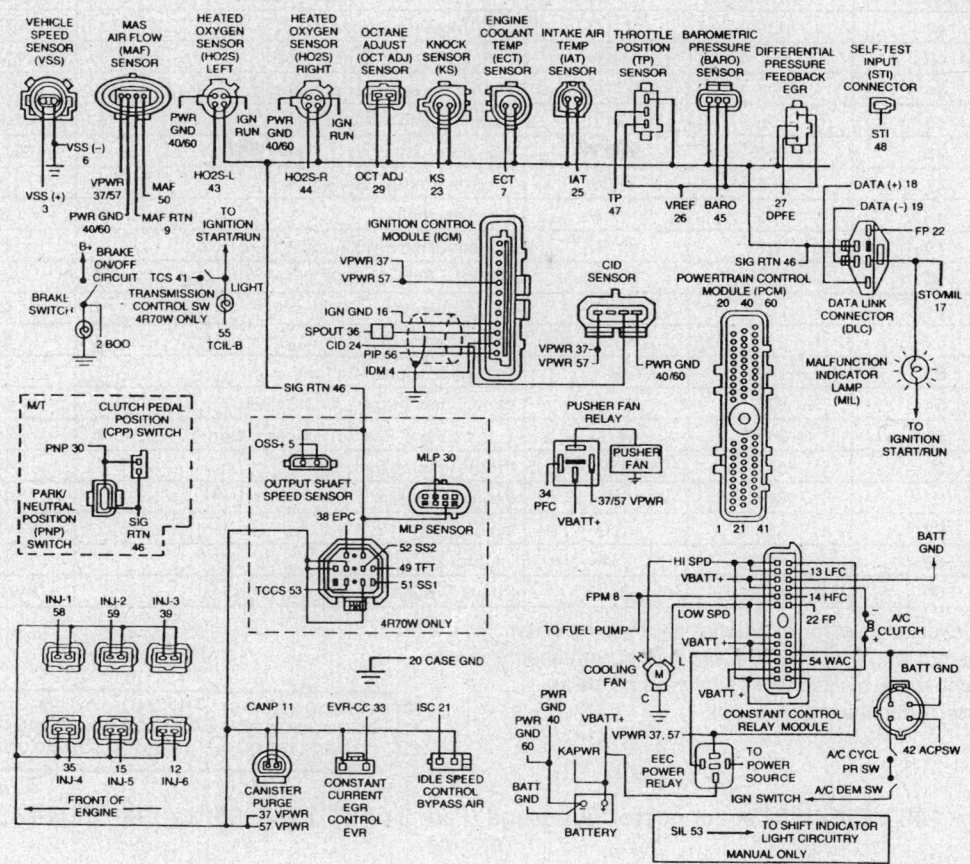

Fig. 99 EEC-IV wiring circuit. 1994–95 w/3.8L/V6-232 SC SFI engine

Pin	Circuit	Wire Color	Application	Abbreviation
1	37	Y	Keep Alive Power	KAPWR
3	679	GY/BK	Vehicle Speed Sensor (+)	VSS (+)
4	659	O/W	Ignition Diagnostic Monitor	IDM
5	970	DG/W	Transmission Speed Sensor	TSS
6	676	PK/O	Vehicle Speed Sensor (-)	VSS (-)
7	354	LG/R	Engine Coolant Temperature Sensor	ECT
8	787	PK/BK	Fuel Pump Monitor	FPM
9	968	T/LB	Mass Air Flow Sensor Return	MAF RTN
10	883	PK/LB	A/C Cyclic Switch	ACCS
11	101	GY/Y	Canister Purge Solenoid	CANP
12	560	LG/O	Injector 6	INJ 6
13	197	T/O	Low Fan Control	LFC
14	639	LG/P	High Fan Control	HFC
15	559	T/BK	Injector 5	INJ 5
16	259	O/R	Ignition Ground	IGN GND
17	658	PK/LG	Self-Test Output/Malfunction Indicator Lamp	STO MIL
18	914	T/O	Data (+)	DATA (+)
19	915	PK/LB	Data (-)	DATA (-)
20	57	BK	Case Ground	CSE GND
21	264	W/LB	Idle Air Control Solenoid	IAC
22	926	LB/O	Fuel Pump	FP
23	310	Y/R	Knock Sensor	KS
24	282	DG/O	Cylinder Identification	CID
25	743	GY	Intake Air Temperature Sensor	IAT
26	351	BR/W	Reference Voltage	VREF
27	352	BR/LG	Delta Pressure Feedback EGR Sensor	DPFE
29	242	DG	Octane Adjust	OCT ADJ
30	199	LB/Y	Manual Lever Position Sensor A·T	MLP
32	836	O/W	Automatic Ride Control	ARC
33	360	BR/PK	EGR Vacuum Regulator Solenoid	EVR
34	461	O	Pusher Fan Control	PFC
35	558	BR/LB	Injector 4	INJ 4
36	929	PK	Spark Output	SPOUT
37	361	R	Vehicle Power	VPWR
38	925	W/Y	Electronic Pressure Control	EPC
39	557	BR/Y	Injector 3	INJ 3
40	570	BK/Y	Power Ground	PWR GND
41	224	T/W	Transmission Control Switch	TCS

FM015940084301OX

**Fig. 100 EEC-IV PCM connector pin usage (Part 1 of 2).
1994–95 w/3.8L/V6-232 SC SFI engine**

Pin	Circuit	Wire Color	Application	Abbreviation
42	439	T/LG	A/C Pressure Switch	ACPSW
43	94	R/BK	Heated Oxygen Sensor - Left	HO2S-L
44	74	GY/LB	Heated Oxygen Sensor - Right	HO2S-R
45	356	DB/LG	Barometric Pressure Sensor	BARO
46	359	GY/R	Signal Return	SIG RTN
47	355	GY/Y	Throttle Position Sensor	TP
48	209	W/P	Self-Test Input	STI
49	923	O/BK	Transmission Fluid Temperature	TFT
50	967	LB/R	Mass Air Flow Sensor	MAF
51	237	O/Y	Shift Solenoid 1	SS1
52	315	P/O	Shift Solenoid 2	SS2
53	924	BR/O	Torque Converter Clutch	TCC
54	331	PK/Y	Wide Open Throttle A/C Cut Off	WAC
55	911	W/LG	Transmission Control Indicator Light	TCIL
56	395	GY/O	Profile Ignition Pick-Up	PIP
57	361	R	Vehicle Power	VPWR
58	555	T	Injector 1	INJ 1
59	556	W	Injector 2	INJ 2
60	570	BK/Y	Power Ground	PWR GND

Pin locations given for reference only. Probing 60-pin connector with DVOM probe will result in permanent damage to the pin connectors. Always probe as directed using the breakout box.

FM0159400843020X

Fig. 100 EEC-IV PCM connector pin usage (Part 2 of 2). 1994–95 w/3.8L/V6-232 SC SFI engine

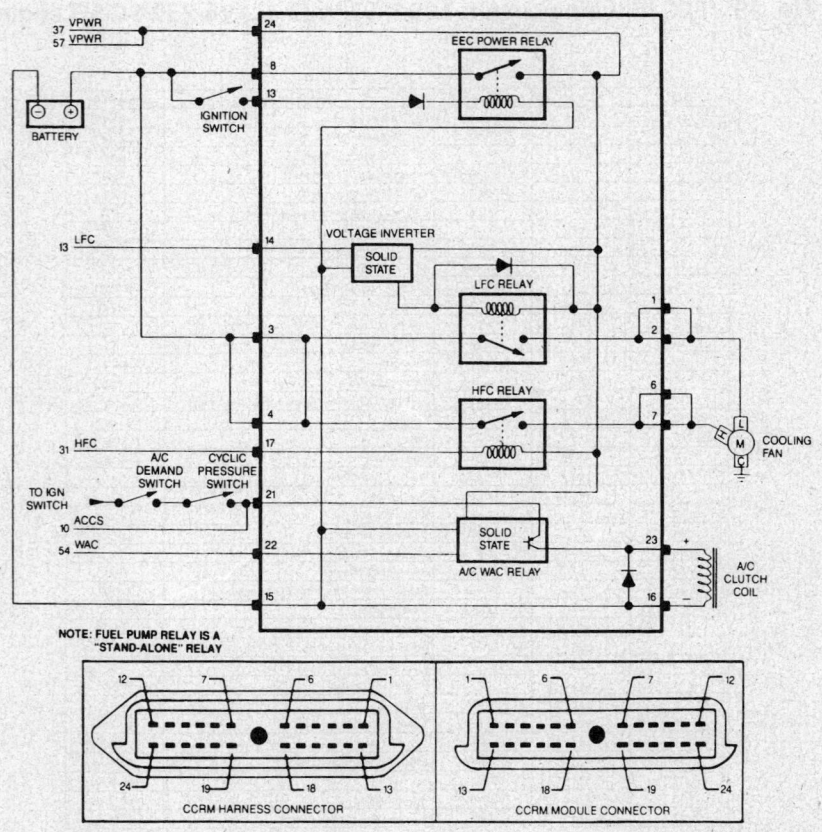

FM0159300844000X

Fig. 101 EEC-IV CCRM wiring circuit. 1993 w/3.8L/V6-232 SC SFI engine

Pin	Circuit	Color	Application	Abbreviation
1	228	DB	Low Fan Control (output)	LFC
2	228	DB	Low Fan Control (output)	LFC
3	38	BK / O	Battery Positive	B +
4	38	BK / O	Battery Positive	B +
6	181	BR / O	High Fan Control (output)	HFC
7	181	BR / O	High Fan Control (output)	HFC
8	37	Y	Battery to EEC Relay	B (+)
13	16	R / LG	Key Power	KEY PWR
14	197	T / O	Low Fan Control (input)	LFC
15	57	BK	Power Ground	PWR GND
16	321	GY / W	A / C Clutch Ground	PWR GND
17	639	LG / P	High Fan Control (input)	HFC
21	883	PK / LB	A / C Cyclic Switch	ACCS
22	331	PK / Y	WOT A / C Cut Off	WAC
23	347	BK / Y	Power to A / C Clutch Coil	PTAC
24	361	R	Vehicle Power	VPWR

FM0159300845000X

Fig. 102 EEC-IV CCRM pin usage. 1993 w/3.8L/V6-232 SC SFI engine

*HIGH PRESSURE CONTACTS OF THE DUAL FUNCTION A/C PRESSURE SWITCH (ACPSW) (ALSO KNOWN AS REFRIGERANT CONTAINMENT/FAN FUNCTION SWITCH)

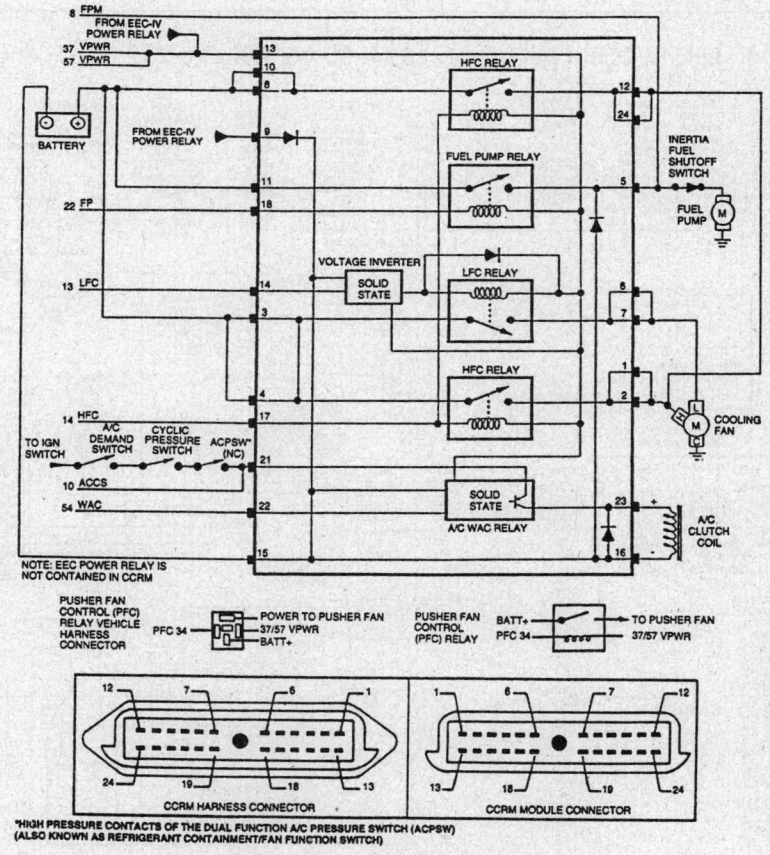

Fig. 103 EEC-IV CCRM wiring circuit. 1994–95 w/3.8L/V6-232 SC SFI engine

Thunderbird SC

Pin	Circuit	Color	Application	Abbreviation
1	228	DB	High Fan Control (output)	HFC
2	228	DB	High Fan Control (output)	HFC
3	38	BK/O	Battery Positive	B +
4	38	BK/O	Battery Positive	B +
5	787	PK/BK	Power to Fuel Pump	PTP
6	181	BR/O	Low Fan Control (output)	LFC
7	181	BR/O	Low Fan Control (output)	LFC
8	37	Y	Battery to EEC Relay	B (+)
10	370	Y	Battery to EEC Relay	B+
11	175	BK/Y	Battery to Fuel Pump Relay	B+
12	361	R	High Fan Control	HFC
13	16	R/LG	Key Power	KEY PWR
14	197	T/O	Low Fan Control (input)	LFC
15	57	BK	Power Ground	PWR GND
16	321	GY/W	A/C Clutch Ground	PWR GND
17	639	LG/P	High Fan Control (input)	HFC
18	926	LB/O	Fuel Pump Circuit	FP
21	883	PK/LB	A/C Cyclic Switch	ACCS
22	331	PK/Y	WOT A/C Cut Off	WAC
23	347	BK/Y	Power to A/C Clutch Coil	PTAC
24	361	R	High Fan Control	HFC

FM0159400846000X

Fig. 104 EEC-IV CCRM pin usage. 1994–95 w/3.8L/V6-232 SC SFI engine

NOTE: WIRING SCHEMATIC SHOWS PINOUT LOOKING INTO HARNESS CONNECTORS

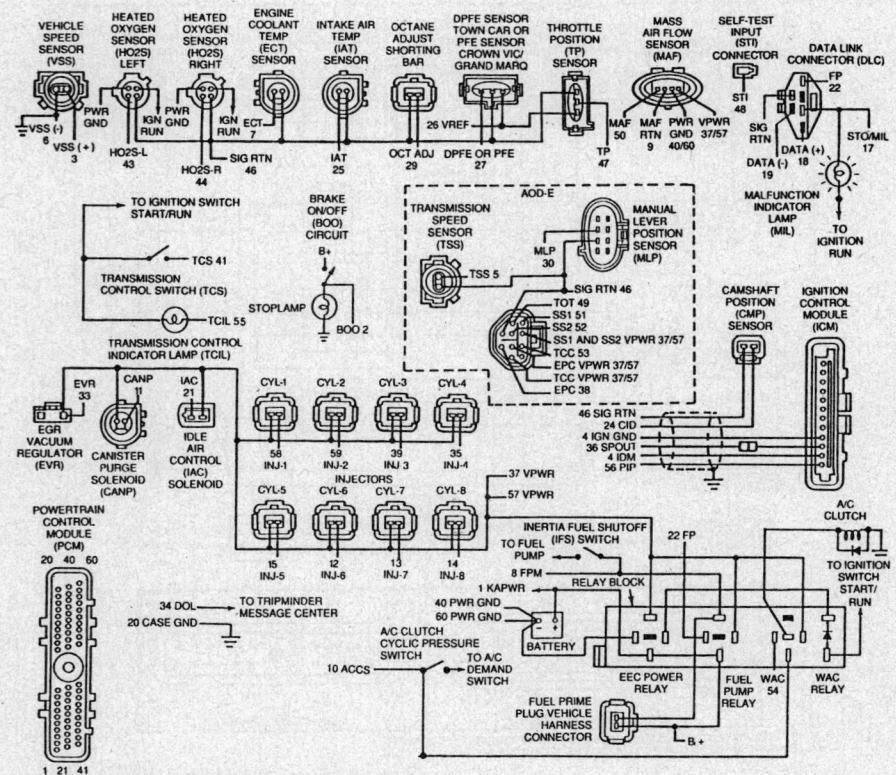

Fig. 105 EEC-IV wiring circuit. 1993 4.6L/V8-280 SFI engine

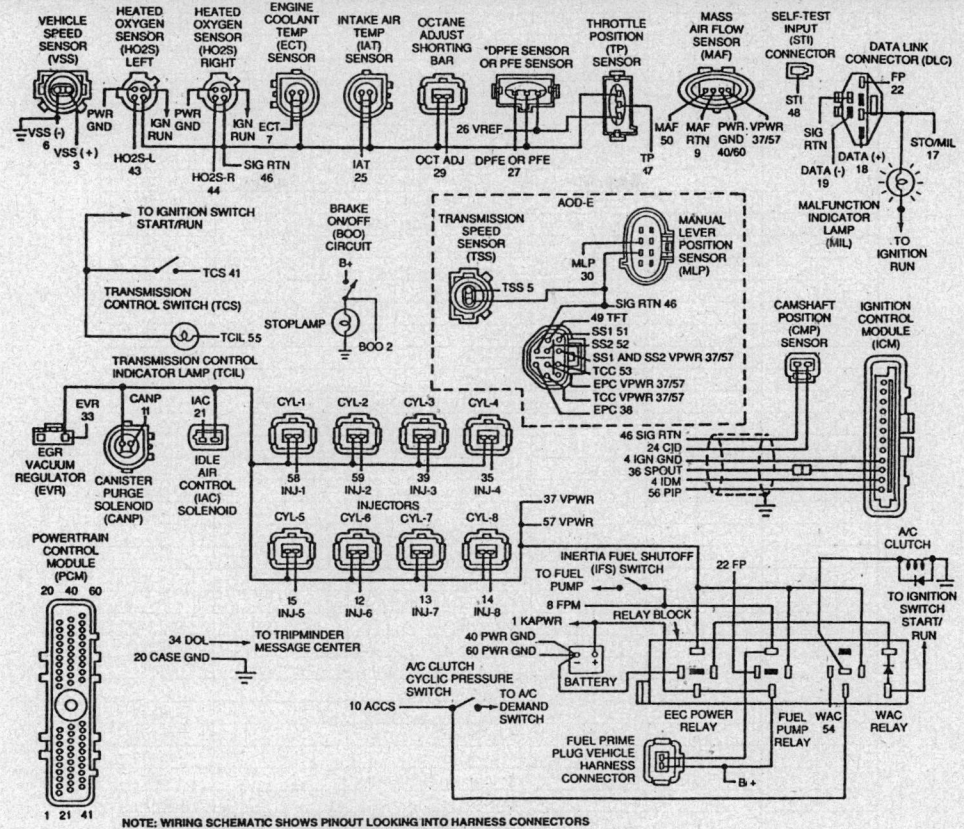

Fig. 106 EEC-IV wiring circuit. 1994
Crown Victoria & Grand Marquis
w/4.6L/V8-280 SFI engine

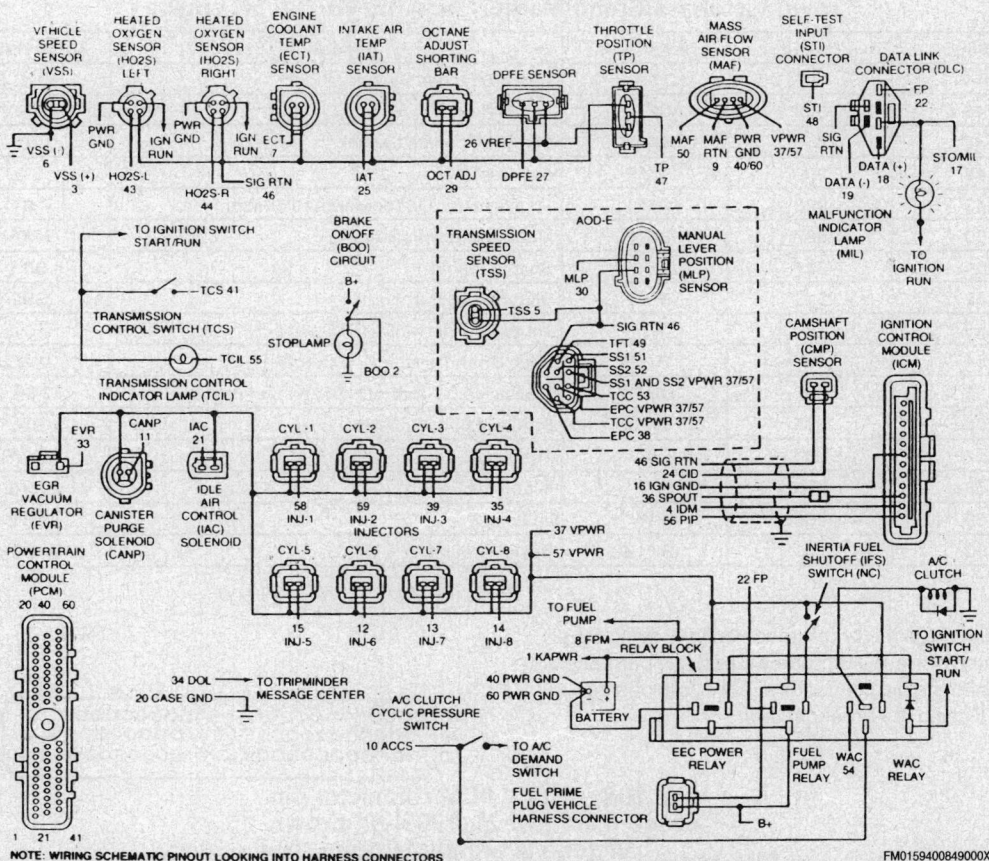

Fig. 107 EEC-IV wiring circuit. 1994 Town Car w/4.6L/V8-280 SFI engine

Pin	Circuit	Wire Color	Application	Abbreviation
1	37	Y	Keep Alive Power	KAPWR
2	511	LG	Brake On / Off	BOO
3	679	GY/BK	Vehicle Speed Sensor (+)	VSS (+)
4	11	T/Y	Ignition Diagnostic Monitor	IDM
5	683	P/LB	Transmission Speed Sensor	TSS
6	676	PK/O	Vehicle Speed Sensor (-)	VSS (-)
7	354	LG/R	Engine Coolant Temperature Sensor	ECT
8	238	DG/Y	Fuel Pump Monitor	FPM
9	968	T/LB	Mass Air Flow Sensor Return	MAF RTN
10	198	DG/O	A/C Clutch Signal	ACCS
11	101	GY/Y	Canister Purge Solenoid	CANP
12	560	LG/O	Injector 6	INJ 6
13	561	T/R	Injector 7	INJ 7
14	562	LB	Injector 8	INJ 8
15	559	T/BK	Injector 5	INJ 5
16	259	O/R	Ignition Ground	IGN GND
17	201	T/R	Self-Test Output / Malfunction Indicator Lamp	STO/MIL
18	914	T/O	Data (+)	DATA (+)
19	915	PK/LB	Data (-)	DATA (-)
20	57	BK	Case Ground	CSE GND
21	264	W/LB	Idle Air Control Solenoid	IAC
22	926	LB/O	Fuel Pump	FP
24	795	DG	Cylinder Identification	CID
25	743	GY	Intake Air Temperature Sensor	IAT
26	351	BR/W	Reference Voltage	VREF
27	352	BR/LG	Pressure Feedback EGR Sensor	PFE
29	240	W/R	Octane Adjust	OCT-ADJ
30	199	LB/Y	Manual Lever Position Sensor	MLP
33	360	BR/PK	EGR Valve Regulator Solenoid	EVR
34	205	DB/LG	Data Output Line	DOL
35	558	BR/LB	Injector 4	INJ 4
36	929	PK	Spark Output	SPOUT
37	361	R	Vehicle Power	VPWR
38	925	W/Y	Electronic Pressure Control	EPC
39	557	BR/Y	Injector 3	INJ 3
40	570	BK/W	Power Ground	PWR GND
41	224	T/W	Transmission Control Switch	TCS
43	94	R/BK	Heated Oxygen Sensor - Left	HO2S-L

FM0159300850010X

**Fig. 108   EEC-IV PCM connector pin usage (Part 1 of 2). 1993–94
Crown Victoria & Grand Marquis w/4.6L/V8-280 SFI engine**

Pin	Circuit	Wire Color	Application	Abbreviation
44	74	GY/LB	Heated Oxygen Sensor - Right	HO2S-R
46	359	GY/R	Signal Return	SIG RTN
47	355	GY/W	Throttle Position Sensor	TP
48	209	W/P	Self-Test Input	STI
49	923	O/BK	Transmission Oil Temperature Sensor	TOT
50	967	LB/R	Mass Air Flow Sensor	MAF
51	237	O/Y	Shift Solenoid 1	SS1
52	315	P/O	Shift Solenoid 2	SS2
53	480	P/Y	Torque Converter Clutch Solenoid	TCC
54	73	O/LB	Wide Open Throttle A/C Cutoff	WAC
55	637	DB/W	Transmission Control Indicator Lamp	TCIL
56	395	GY/O	Profile Ignition Pick-Up	PIP
57	361	R	Vehicle Power	VPWR
58	555	T	Injector 1	INJ 1
59	556	W	Injector 2	INJ 2
60	570	BK/W	Power Ground	PWR GND

Pin locations given for reference only. Probing 60-pin connector with DVOM probe will result in permanent damage to the pin connectors. Always probe as directed using the breakout box.

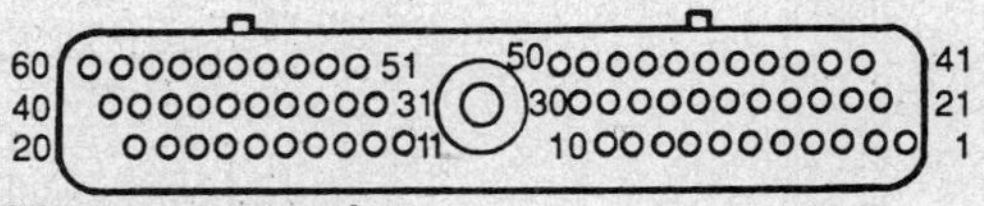

**Fig. 108   EEC-IV PCM connector pin
usage (Part 2 of 2). 1993–94 Crown
Victoria & Grand Marquis
w/4.6L/V8-280 SFI engine**

Pin	Circuit	Wire Color	Application	Abbreviation
1	554	Y	Keep Alive Power	KAPWR
2	511	LG	Brake On/Off	BOO
3	679	GY BK	Vehicle Speed Sensor (+)	VSS (+)
4	11	T Y	Ignition Diagnostic Monitor	IDM
5	970	DG W	Transmission Speed Sensor	TSS
6	676	PK O	Vehicle Speed Sensor (-)	VSS (-)
7	354	LG R	Engine Coolant Temperature Sensor	ECT
8	238	DG Y	Fuel Pump Monitor	FPM
9	968	T/LB	Mass Air Flow Sensor Return	MAF RTN
10	348	P	A/C Clutch Signal	ACCS
11	101	GY Y	Canister Purge Solenoid	CANP
12	560	LG O	Injector 6	INJ 6
13	561	T/R	Injector 7	INJ 7
14	562	LB	Injector 8	INJ 8
15	559	T BK	Injector 5	INJ 5
16	259	O R	Ignition Ground	IGN GND
17	658	PK LG	Self-Test Output/Malfunction Indicator Lamp	STO/MIL
18	914	T O	Data (+)	DATA (+)
19	915	PK LB	Data (-)	DATA (-)
20	57	BK	Case Ground	CSE GND
21	264	W LB	Idle Air Control Solenoid	IAC
22	926	LB O	Fuel Pump	FP
24	282	DB O	Camshaft Position Sensor	CMP
25	743	GY	Intake Air Temperature Sensor	IAT
26	351	BR W	Reference Voltage	VREF
27	352	BR LG	Differential Pressure Feedback EGR Sensor	DPFE
29	242	DG	Octane Adjust	OCT ADJ
30	199	LB Y	Manual Lever Position Sensor	MLP
33	360	BR PK	EGR Vacuum Regulator Solenoid	EVR
34	205	DB LG	Data Output Line	DOL
35	558	BR LB	Injector 4	INJ 4
36	929	PK	Spark Output	SPOUT
37	361	R	Vehicle Power	VPWR
38	925	W Y	Electronic Pressure Control	EPC
39	557	BR Y	Injector 3	INJ 3
40	570	BK W	Power Ground	PWR GND
41	224	T W	Transmission Control Switch	TCS
43	94	R BK	Heated Oxygen Sensor Left	HO2S L

FM0159300852010X

**Fig. 109 EEC-IV PCM connector pin usage (Part 1 of 2).
1993–94 Town Car w/4.6L/V8-280 SFI engine**

Pin	Circuit	Wire Color	Application	Abbreviation
44	74	GY/LB	Heated Oxygen Sensor - Right	HO2S-R
46	359	GY/R	Signal Return	SIG RTN
47	355	GY/W	Throttle Position Sensor	TP
48	209	W/P	Self-Test Input	STI
49	923	O/BK	Transmission Oil Temperature Sensor	TOT
50	967	LB/R	Mass Air Flow Sensor	MAF
51	237	O/Y	Shift Solenoid 1	SS1
52	315	P/O	Shift Solenoid 2	SS2
53	924	BR/O	Torque Converter Clutch Solenoid	TCC
54	331	PK/Y	Wide Open Throttle A/C Cutoff	WAC
55	911	W/LG	Transmission Control Switch	TCIL
56	395	GY/O	Profile Ignition Pick-Up	PIP
57	361	R	Vehicle Power	VPWR
58	555	T	Injector 1	INJ 1
59	556	W	Injector 2	INJ 2
60	570	BK/W	Power Ground	PWR GND

Pin locations given for reference only. Probing 60-pin connector with DVOM probe will result in permanent damage to the pin connectors. Always probe as directed using the breakout box.

FM0159300852020X

Fig. 109 EEC-IV PCM connector pin usage (Part 2 of 2). 1993–94 Town Car w/4.6L/V8-280 SFI engine

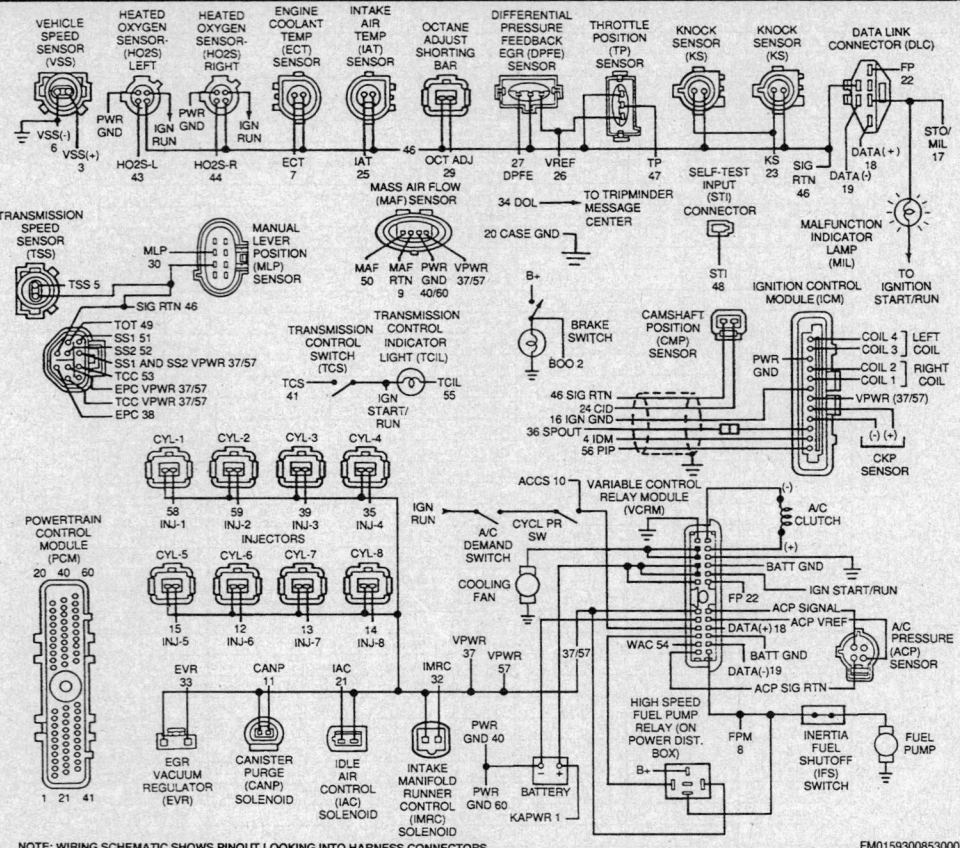

Fig. 110   EEC-IV wiring circuit. Mark VIII w/4.6L/V8-280 4V engine

Pin	Circuit	Wire Color	Application	Abbreviation
1	37	Y	Keep Alive Power	KAPWR
2	511	LG	Brake On/Off	BOO
3	679	GY/BK	Vehicle Speed Sensor (+)	VSS (+)
4	11	T/Y	Ignition Diagnostic Monitor	IDM
5	970	DG/W	Transmission Speed Sensor	TSS
6	676	PK/O	Vehicle Speed Sensor (-)	VSS (-)
7	354	LG/R	Engine Coolant Temperature Sensor	ECT
8	787	PK/BK	Fuel Pump Monitor	FPM
9	968	T/LB	Mass Air Flow Sensor Return	MAF RTN
10	347	BK/Y	A/C Cyclic Switch	ACCS
11	101	GY/Y	Canister Purge Solenoid	CANP
12	560	LG/O	Injector 6	INJ 6
13	561	T/R	Injector 7	INJ 7
14	562	LB	Injector 8	INJ 8
15	559	T/BK	Injector 5	INJ 5
16	259	O/R	Ignition Ground	IGN GND
17	658	PK/LG	Self-Test Output/Malfunction Indicator Lamp	STO/MIL
18	914	T/O	Data (+)	DATA (+)
19	915	PK/LB	Data (-)	DATA (-)
20	57	BK	Case Ground	CSE GND
21	264	W/LB	Idle Air Control Solenoid	IAC
22	926	LB/O	Fuel Pump	FP
23	310	Y/R	Knock Sensor	KS
24	282	DB/O	Cylinder Identification	CID
25	743	GY	Intake Air Temperature Sensor	IAT
26	351	BR/W	Reference Voltage	VREF
27	352	BR/LG	Differential Pressure Feedback EGR Sensor	DPFE
29	242	DG	Octane Adjust	OCT ADJ
30	199	LB/Y	Manual Lever Position Switch	MLP
32	99	LG/BK	Intake Manifold Runner Control	IMRC
33	360	BR/PK	EGR Valve Regulator Solenoid	EVR
34	305	LB/PK	Data Output Line	DOL
35	558	BR/LB	Injector 4	INJ 4
36	929	PK	Spark Output	SPOUT
37	361	R	Vehicle Power	VPWR
38	925	W/Y	Electronic Pressure Control	EPC
39	557	BR/Y	Injector 3	INJ 3
40	570	BK/W	Power Ground	PWR GND

FM015930085401 0X

Fig. 111   EEC-IV PCM connector pin usage (Part 1 of 2). Mark VIII w/4.6L/V8-280 4V engine

Pin	Circuit	Wire Color	Application	Abbreviation
41	224	T/W	Transmission Control Switch	TSC
43	94	R/BK	Heated Oxygen Sensor - Left	HO2S-L
44	74	GY/LB	Heated Oxygen Sensor - Right	HO2S-R
46	359	GY/R	Signal Return	SIG RTN
47	355	GY/W	Throttle Position Sensor	TP
48	209	W/P	Self-Test Input	STI
49	923	O/BK	Transmission Oil Temperature Sensor	TOT
50	967	LB/R	Mass Air Flow Sensor	MAF
51	237	O/Y	Shift Solenoid 1	SS1
52	315	P/O	Shift Solenoid 2	SS2
53	480	P/Y	Torque Converter Clutch Solenoid	TCC
54	331	PK/Y	Wide Open Throttle A/C Cutoff	WAC
55	911	W/LG	Transmission Control Indicator Lamp	TCIL
56	395	GY/O	Profile Ignition Pick-Up	PIP
57	361	R	Vehicle Power	VPWR
58	555	T	Injector 1	INJ 1
59	556	W	Injector 2	INJ 2
60	570	BK/W	Power Ground	PWR GND

Pin locations given for reference only. Probing 60-pin connector with DVOM probe will result in permanent damage to the pin connectors. Always probe as directed using the breakout box.

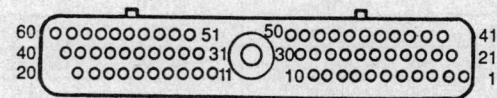

Fig. 111   EEC-IV PCM connector pin usage (Part 2 of 2). Mark VIII w/4.6L/V8-280 4V engine

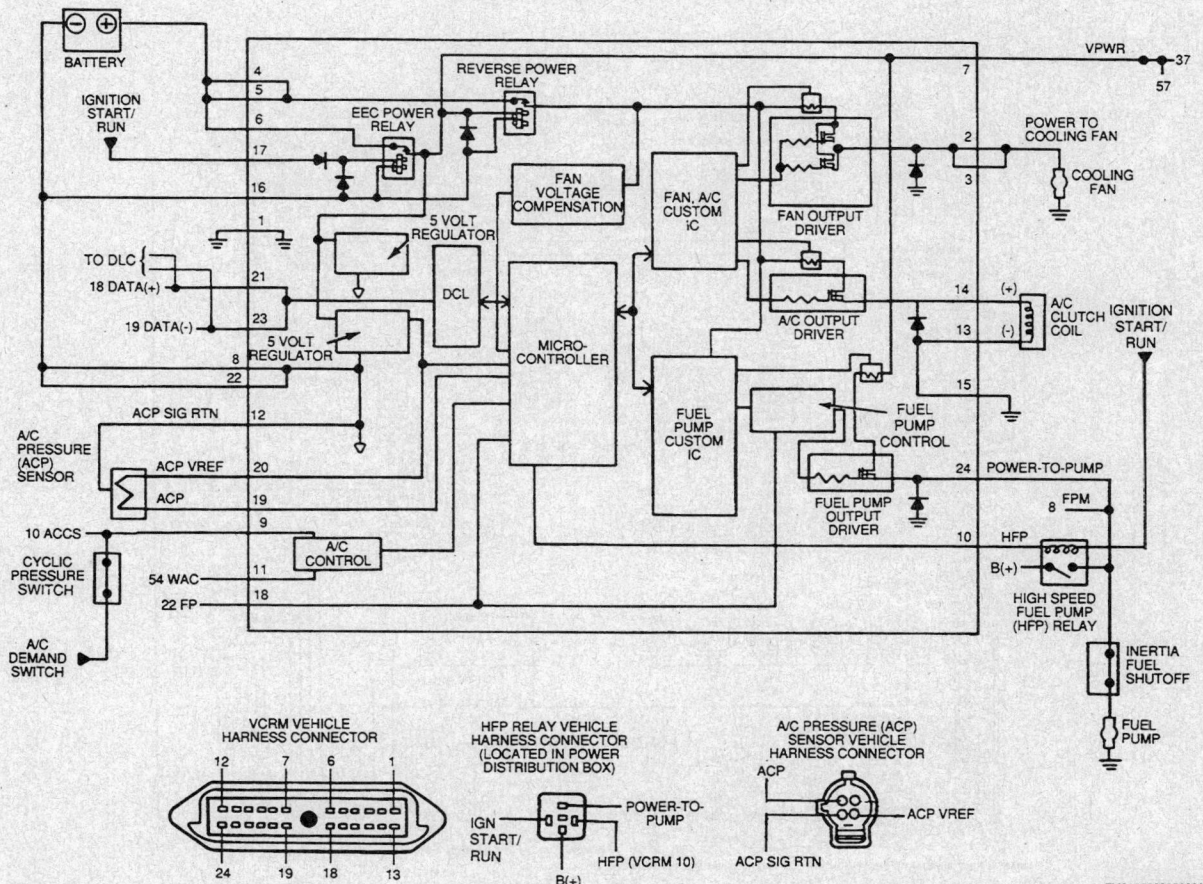

FM0159300856000X

Fig. 112   EEC-IV Variable Control Relay Module (VCRM) wiring circuit. Mark VIII w/4.6L/V8-280 4V engine

FORD–Computerized Engine Controls

Pin	Circuit	Wire Color	Application	Abbreviation
1	57	BK	Power Ground	PWR GND
2	386	LB	Power to Cooling Fan	PTF
3	386	LB	Power to Cooling Fan	PTF
4	37	Y	Battery (+) (for Fan and A/C)	B (+)
5	37	Y	Battery (+) (for Fan and A/C)	B (+)
6	37	Y	Battery (+) to EEC Power Relay	B (+)
7	361	R	Vehicle Power	VPWR
8	570	BK/W	Ground	GND
9	347	BK/Y	A/C Cyclic Switch	ACCS
10	789	BR/W	High Fuel Pump Circuit	HFP
11	331	PK/Y	WOT A/C Cut-Off	WAC
12	535	LB/R	A/C Pressure Sensor Signal Return	ACP SIG RTN
13	321	GY/W	A/C Clutch Return	ACC RTN
14	348	P	Power to A/C Clutch	PT AC
15	57	BK	A/C Clutch Ground	AC GND
16	651	BK/Y	Ground	GND
17	16	R/LG	Ignition Start/Run	IGN
18	926	LB/O	Fuel Pump Circuit	FP
19	879	DG/W	A/C Pressure Sensor Signal	ACP
20	880	O/LB	A/C Pressure Sensor VREF	ACP VREF
21	914	T/O	Data (+)	DATA (+)
22	570	BK/W	Ground	GND
23	915	PK/LB	Data (-)	DATA (-)
24	787	PK/BK	Power to Fuel Pump	PTP

FM0159300857000X

Fig. 113   EEC-IV VCRM pin usage. Mark VIII w/4.6L/V8-280 4V engine

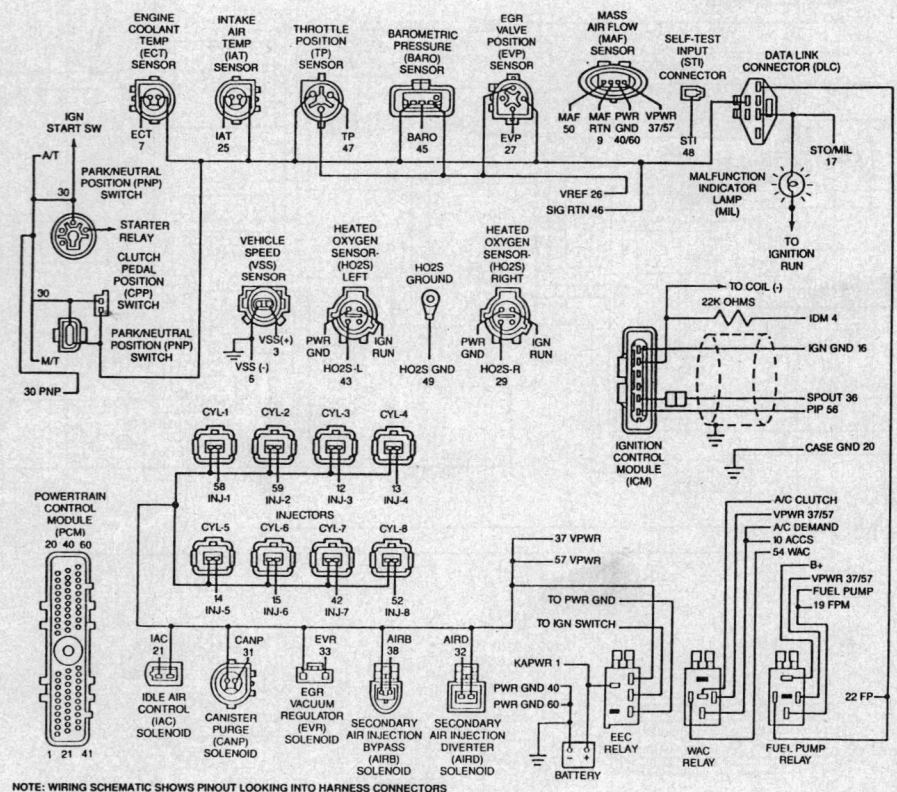

FM0159300858000X

Fig. 114   EEC-IV wiring circuit. 1993 w/5.0L/V8-302 MA SFI engine

Pin	Circuit	Wire Color	Application	Abbreviation
1	37	Y	Keep Alive Power	KAPWR
3	679	GY/BK	Vehicle Speed Sensor (+)	VSS (+)
4	11	T/Y	Ignition Diagnostic Monitor	IDM
6	676	PK/O	Vehicle Speed Sensor (-)	VSS (-)
7	354	LG/R	Engine Coolant Temperature Sensor	ECT
9	968	T/LB	Mass Air Flow Sensor Return	MAF RTN
10	347	BK/Y	A/C Clutch Signal	ACCS
12	557	BR/Y	Fuel Injector 3	INJ 3
13	558	BR/LB	Fuel Injector 4	INJ 4
14	559	T/BK	Fuel Injector 5	INJ 5
15	560	LG/O	Fuel Injector 6	INJ 6
16	259	O/R	Ignition Ground	IGN GND
17	658	PK/LG	Self-Test Output/Malfunction Indicator Lamp	STO/MIL
19	238	DG/Y	Fuel Pump Monitor	FPM
20	57	BK	Case Ground	CSE GND
21	264	W/LB	Idle Air Control Solenoid	IAC
22	926	LB/O	Fuel Pump	FP
25	743	GY	Intake Air Temperature Sensor	IAT
26	351	BR/W	Reference Voltage	VREF
27	352	BR/LG	EGR Valve Position Sensor	EVP
29	74	GY/LB	Heated Oxygen Sensor-Right	HO2S-R
30	199	LB/Y	Park/Neutral Position Switch	PNP
31	101	GY/Y	Canister Purge Solenoid	CANP
32	911	W/LG	Secondary Air Injection Diverter Solenoid	AIRD
33	360	BR/PK	EGR Vacuum Regulator Solenoid	EVR
36	929	PK	Spark Output	SPOUT
37	361	R	Vehicle Power	VPWR
38	925	W/Y	Secondary Air Injection Bypass Solenoid	AIRB
40	570	BK/W	Power Ground	PWR GND
42	561	T/R	Fuel Injector 7	INJ 7
43	94	R/BK	Heated Oxygen Sensor - Left	HO2S-L
45	358	LG/BK	Barometric Pressure Sensor	BARO
46	359	GY/R	Signal Return	SIG RTN
47	355	GY/W	Throttle Position Sensor	TP
48	209	W/P	Self-Test Input	STI
49	89	O	Heated Oxygen Sensor Ground	HO2S GND
50	967	LB/R	Mass Air Flow Sensor	MAF
52	562	LB	Injector 8	INJ 8

FM0159300859010X

Fig. 115   EEC-IV PCM connector pin usage (Part 1 of 2). 1993 Mustang w/5.0L/V8-302 MA SFI engine

Pin	Circuit	Wire Color	Application	Abbreviation
54	331	PK/Y	WOT A/C Cut Off	WAC
56	395	GY/O	Profile Ignition Pick-Up	PIP
57	361	R	Vehicle Power	VPWR
58	555	T	Injector 1	INJ 1
59	556	W	Injector 2	INJ 2
60	570	BK/W	Power Ground	PWR GND

Pin locations given for reference only. Probing 60-pin connector with DVOM probe will result in permanent damage to the pin connectors. Always probe as directed using the breakout box.

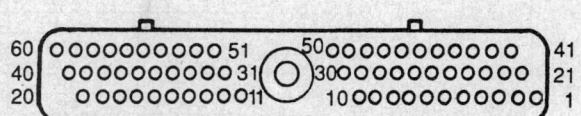

Fig. 115   EEC-IV PCM connector pin usage (Part 2 of 2). 1993 Mustang w/5.0L/V8-302 MA SFI engine

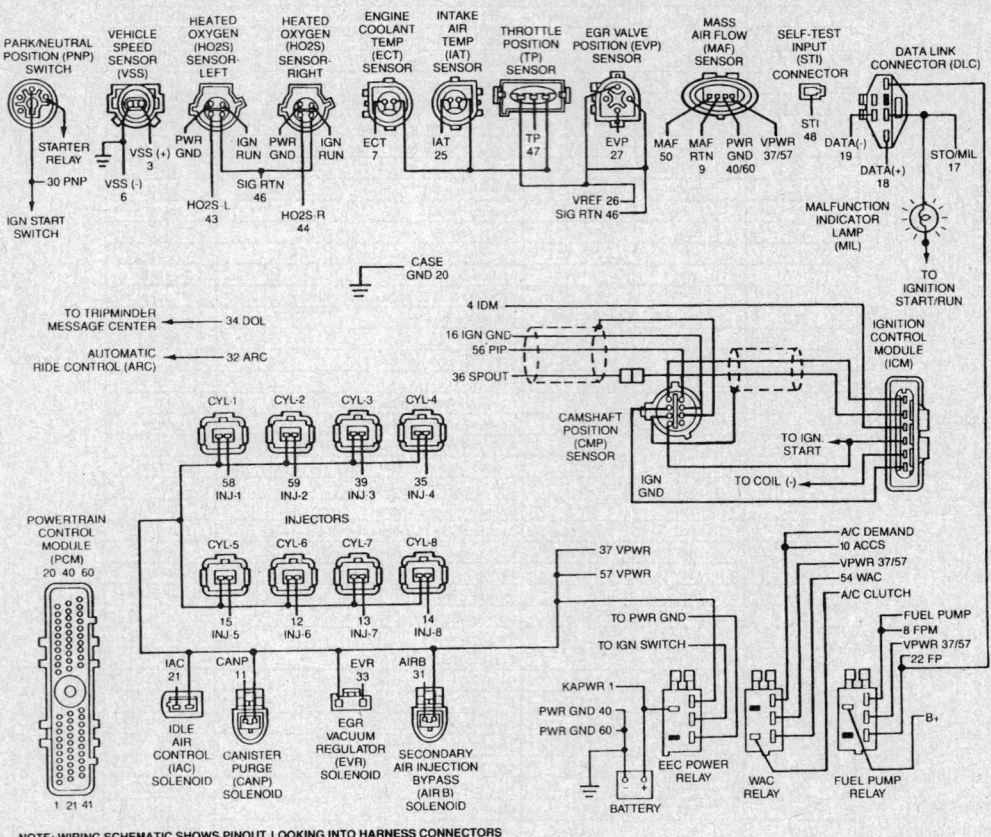

Fig. 116 EEC-IV wiring circuit. 1993 Cougar & Thunderbird w/5.0L/V8-302 MA SFI engine

Pin	Circuit	Wire Color	Application	Abbreviation
1	37	Y	Keep Alive Power	KAPWR
3	150	DG W	Vehicle Speed Sensor (+)	VSS (+)
4	648	W PK	Ignition Diagnostic Monitor	IDM
6	359	GY R	Vehicle Speed Sensor (-)	VSS (-)
7	354	LG R	Engine Coolant Temperature Sensor	ECT
8	787	PK BK	Fuel Pump Monitor	FPM
9	968	T LB	Mass Air Flow Sensor Return	MAF RTN
10	883	PK LB	A C Clutch Signal	ACCS
11	101	GY Y	Canister Purge Solenoid	CANP
12	560	LG/O	Injector 6	INJ 6
13	561	T/R	Injector 7	INJ 7
14	562	LB	Injector 8	INJ 8
15	559	T BK	Injector 5	INJ 5
16	350	GY	Ignition Ground	IGN GND
17	382	Y BK	Self-Test Output/Malfunction Indicator Lamp	STO MIL
18	914	T O	Data (+)	DATA (+)
19	915	PK LB	Data (-)	DATA (-)
20	57	BK	Case Ground	CSE GND
21	69	R/LG	Idle Air Control	IAC
22	97	T LG	Fuel Pump	FP
25	743	GY	Intake Air Temperature	IAT
26	351	BR W	Reference Voltage	VREF
27	352	BR LG	EGR Valve Position Sensor	EVP
30	32	R LB	Park Neutral Position Switch	PNP
31	100	W R	Secondary Air Injection Bypass	AIRB
32	836	O W	Automatic Ride Control	ARC
33	360	BR PK	EGR Vacuum Regulator Solenoid	EVR
34	305	LB PK	Data Output Line	DOL
35	558	BR LB	Injector 4	INJ 4
36	324	Y LG	Spark Output	SPOUT
37	361	R	Vehicle Power	VPWR
39	557	BR Y	Injector 3	INJ 3
40	60	BK LG	Power Ground	PWR GND
43	95	T W	Heated Oxygen Sensor-Left	HO2S-L
44	96	T O	Heated Oxygen Sensor-Right	HO2S-R
46	359	GY R	Signal Return	SIG RTN
47	355	GY W	Throttle Position Sensor	TP
48	209	W P	Self-Test Input	STI

FM0159300862010X

Fig. 117 EEC-IV PCM connector pin usage (Part 1 of 2). 1993 Cougar & Thunderbird w/5.0L/V8-302 MA SFI engine

Pin	Circuit	Wire Color	Application	Abbreviation
50	967	LB/R	Mass Air Flow Sensor	MAF
54	73	O/LB	WOT A/C Cut Off	WAC
56	349	DB	Profile Ignition Pick-up	PIP
57	361	R	Vehicle Power	VPWR
58	555	T	Injector 1	INJ 1
59	556	W	Injector 2	INJ 2
60	60	BK/LG	Power Ground	PWR GND

Pin locations given for reference only. Probing 60-pin connector with DVOM probe will result in permanent damage to the pin connectors. Always probe as directed using the breakout box.

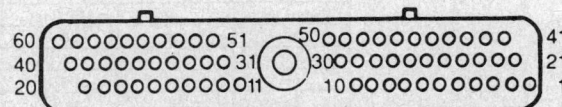

FM0159300862020X

Fig. 117   EEC-IV PCM connector pin usage (Part 2 of 2). 1993 Cougar & Thunderbird w/5.0L/V8-302 MA SFI engine

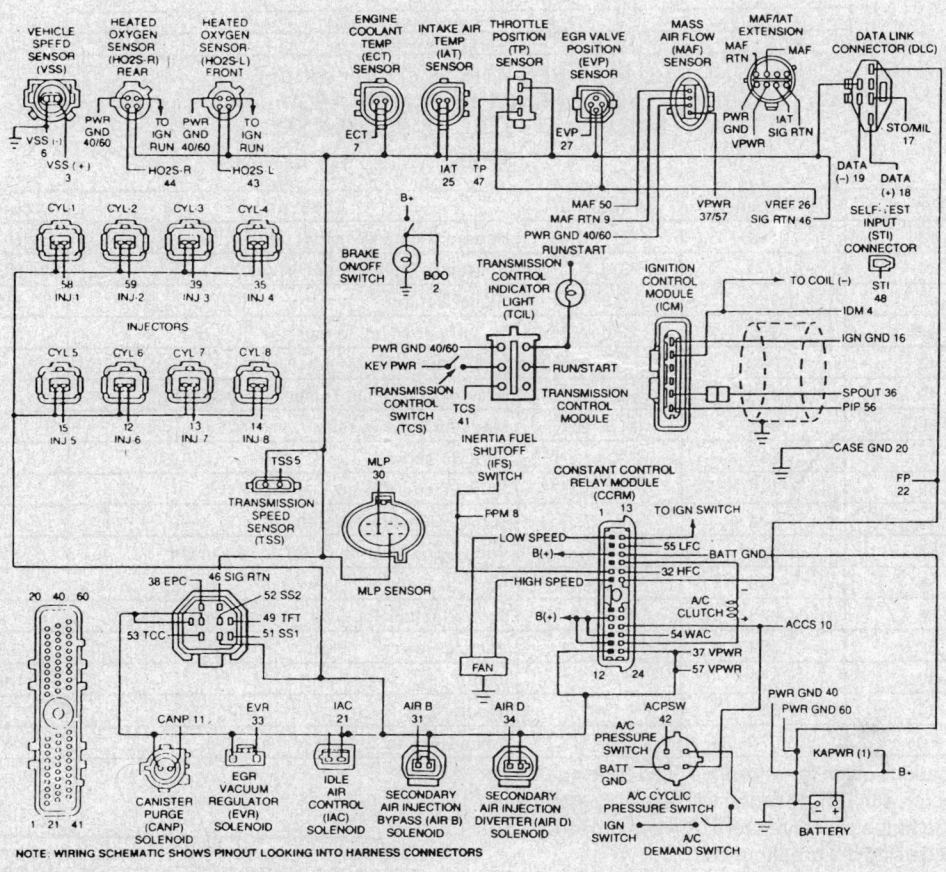

FM0159400863000X

Fig. 118   EEC-IV wiring circuit. 1994–95 Mustang w/5.0L/V8-302 MA SFI engine

Pin	Circuit	Wire Color	Application	Abbreviation
1	378	Y	Keep Alive Power	KAPWR
2	511	LG	Brake On/Off (AODE Only)	BOO
3	679	GY/BK	Vehicle Speed Sensor(+)	VSS+
4	648	W/PK	Ignition Diagnostic Monitor	IDM
5	970	DG/W	Transmission Speed Sensor	TSS
6	676	PK/O	Vehicle Speed Sensor (-)	VSS-
7	354	LG/R	Engine Coolant Temp. Sensor	ECT
8	238	DG/Y	Fuel Pump Monitor	FPM
9	968	T/LB	Mass Air Flow Sensor Return	MAF RTN
10	198	DG/O	A/C Clutch Signal	ACCS
11	101	GY/Y	Canister Purge Solenoid	CANP
12	560	LG/O	Injector 6	INJ 6
13	561	T/R	Injector 7	INJ 7
14	562	LB	Injector 8	INJ 8
15	559	T/BK	Injector 5	INJ 5
16	259	O/R	Ignition Ground	IGN GND
17	658	PK/LG	Self-Test Output/Malfunction Ind.	STO/MIL
18	914	T/O	Data (+)	DATA (+)
19	915	PK/LB	Data (-)	DATA (-)
20	57	BK	Case Ground	CASE GND
21	264	W/LB	Idle Air Control Solenoid	IAC
22	926	LB/O	Fuel Pump	FP
25	743	GY	Intake Air Temp. Sensor	IAT
26	351	BR/W	Reference Voltage	VREF
27	352	BR/LG	EGR Valve Position Sensor	EVP
30	199	LB/Y	Manual Lever Position Sensor	MLP
31	190	W/O	Secondary Air Inj. Bypass Solenoid	AIRB
32	639	LG/P	High Fan Control	HFC
33	360	BR/PK	EGR Vacuum Regulator Solenoid	EVR
34	200	BR	Secondary Air Inj. Diverter Solenoid	AIRD
35	558	BR/LB	Injector 4	INJ 4
36	929	PK	Spark Output	SPOUT
37	361	R	Vehicle Power	VPWR
38	925	W/Y	Electronic Pressure Control	EPC
39	557	BR/Y	Injector 3	INJ 3
40	570	BR/W	Power Ground	PWR GND
41	224	T/W	Transmission Control Switch	TCS
42	883	PK/LB	A/C Pressure Switch	ACPSW

Fig. 119   EEC-IV PCM connector pin
usage (Part 1 of 2). 1994–95
Mustang w/5.0L/V8-302 MA SFI
engine

Pin	Circuit	Wire Color	Application	Abbreviation
43	94	R BK	Heated Oxygen Sensor - Left	HO2S-L
44	74	GY LB	Heated Oxygen Sensor - Right	HO2S-R
46	359	GY R	Signal Return	SIG RTN
47	355	GY W	Throttle Position Sensor	TP
48	209	W P	Self-Test Input	STI
49	923	O BK	Transmission Fluid Temperature Sensor	TFT
50	967	LB R	Mass Air Flow Sensor	MAF
51	237	O Y	Shift Solenoid 1	SS1
52	315	P O	Shift Solenoid 2	SS2
53	924	BR O	Torque Converter Clutch	TCC
54	331	PK Y	Wide Open Throttle (WOT) A/C Cut Off	WAC
55	228	DB	Low Fan Control	LFC
56	395	GY O	Profile Ignition Pick-Up	PIP
57	361	R	Vehicle Power	VPWR
58	555	T	Injector 1	INJ 1
59	556	W	Injector 2	INJ 2
60	570	BK W	Power Ground	PWR GND

Pin locations given for reference only. Probing 60-pin
connector with DVOM probe will result in permanent
damage to the pin connectors. Always probe as
directed using the breakout box.

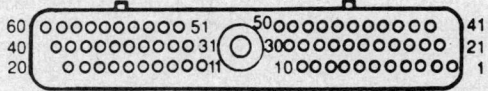

Fig. 119   EEC-IV PCM connector pin usage (Part 2 of 2). 1994–95 Mustang w/5.0L/V8-302 MA SFI
engine

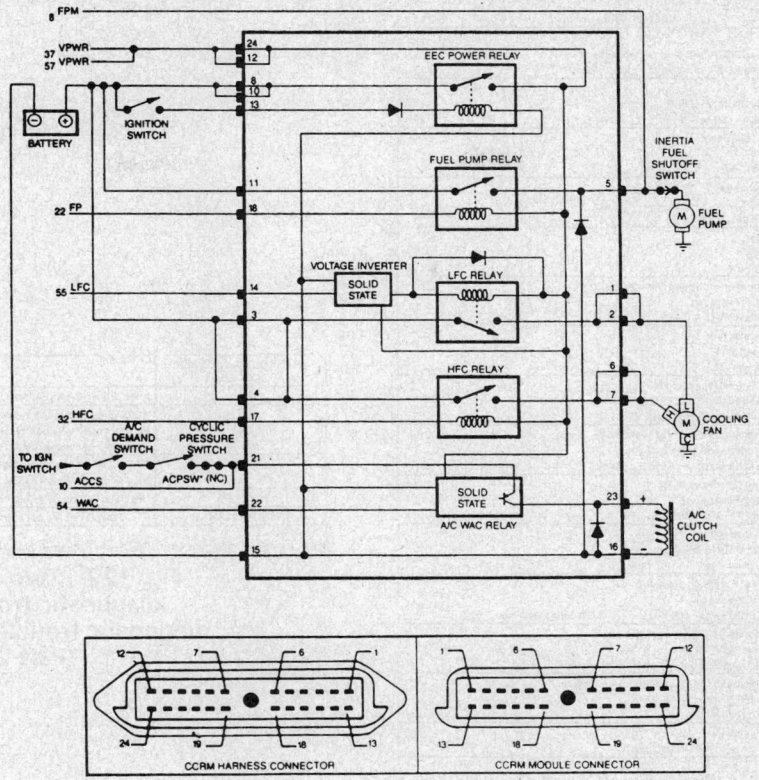

Fig. 120 EEC-IV CCRM wiring circuit. 1994–95 Mustang w/5.0L/V8-302 MA SFI engine

Pin	Circuit	Wire Color	Application	Abbreviation
1	260	R/O	Power to Cooling Fan (Low Speed)	PTF
2	260	R/O	Power to Cooling Fan (Low Speed)	PTF
3	38	BK/O	B (+) to Fan Relay	B (+)
4	38	BK/O	B (+) to Fan Relay	B (+)
5	238	DG/Y	Power to Fuel Pump	PTP
6	261	O/BK	Power to Cooling Fan (High Speed)	PTF
7	261	O/BK	Power to Cooling Fan (High Speed)	PTF
8	37	Y	B(+) to EEC Power Relay	B(+)
10	37	Y	B(+) to EEC Power Relay	B(+)
11	37	Y	B(+) to Fuel Pump Relay	B(+)
12	361	R	Vehicle Power	VPWR
13	16	R/LG	Ignition Start/Run	IGN
14	228	DB	Low Speed Fan Control	LFC
15	570	BK/W	Power Ground	PWR GND
16	57	BK	A/C Clutch Ground	A/C GND
17	639	LG/P	High Speed Fan Control	HFC
18	926	LB/O	Fuel Pump Circuit	FP
21	198	DG/O	A/C Cyclic Switch	ACCS
22	331	PK/Y	WOT A/C Cut Off	WAC
23	347	BK/Y	Power to A/C Clutch Coil	PTAC
24	361	R	Vehicle Power	VPWR

Pin locations given for reference only. Probing 60-pin connector with DVOM probe will result in permanent damage to the pin connectors. Always probe as directed using the breakout box.

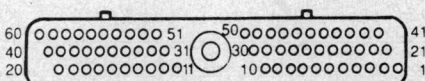

Fig. 121 EEC-IV CCRM pin usage. 1994–95 Mustang w/5.0L/V8-302 MA SFI engine

DIAGNOSTIC TROUBLE CODES	DEFINITIONS
11 orc	System PASS
12 r	Cannot control rpm during KOER Self-Test high rpm check
13 r	Cannot control rpm during KOER Self-Test low rpm check
14 c	PIP circuit failure
15 o	PCM Read Only Memory (ROM) test failed
15 c	PCM Keep Alive Memory (KAM) test failed
16 r	Rpm too low to perform HO2S test
18 r	SPOUT circuit open
18 c	IDM circuit failure / SPOUT circuit grounded
19 o	Failure in PCM internal voltage
21 or	ECT out of Self-Test range
22 orc	MAP / BARO out of Self-Test range
23 or	TP out of Self-Test range
24 or	IAT out of Self-Test range
26 or	MAF out of Self-Test range
29 c	Insufficient input from the Vehicle Speed Sensor (VSS)
31 orc	EVP circuit below minimum voltage
32 orc	EVP voltage below closed limit
33 rc	EGR valve opening not detected
34 or	EVP voltage above closed limit
35 orc	EVP circuit above maximum voltage
41 r	HO2S circuit indicates system lean (right HO2S)
41 c	No HO2S switch detected (right HO2S)
42 r	HO2S circuit indicates system rich (right HO2S)
44 r	Secondary Air Injection system inoperative (right side)
45 r	Secondary Air Injection upstream during Self-Test
46 r	Secondary Air Injection not bypassed during Self-Test
51 oc	ECT indicated -40°C (-40°F) / circuit open
53 oc	TP circuit above maximum voltage
54 oc	IAT indicated -40°C (-40°F) / circuit open
56 oc	MAF circuit above maximum voltage
61 oc	ECT indicated 123°C (254°F) / circuit grounded
63 oc	TP circuit below minimum voltage
64 oc	IAT indicated 123°C (254°F) / circuit grounded
66 c	MAF circuit below minimum voltage
67 o	Park / Neutral Position (PNP) switch circuit open - A / C ON during Self-Test
77 r	Brief WOT not sensed during Self-Test / Operator error
79 r	A / C on / Defrost on during Self-Test
81 o	Secondary Air Injection Diverter (AIRD) solenoid circuit failure
82 o	Secondary Air Injection Bypass (AIRB) solenoid circuit failure
84 o	EGR Vacuum Regulator (EVR) circuit failure
85 o	Canister Purge (CANP) circuit failure
87 oc	Fuel pump primary circuit failure
91 r	HO2S circuit indicates system lean (left HO2S)

Fig. 122 Two digit quick test diagnostic trouble codes & diagnostic trouble code definitions (Part 1 of 2)

DIAGNOSTIC TROUBLE CODES	DEFINITIONS
91 c	No HO2S switching detected (left HO2S)
92 r	HO2S circuit indicates system rich (left HO2S)
94 r	Secondary Air Injection system inoperative (left side)
95 oc	Fuel pump secondary circuit failure
96 oc	Fuel pump secondary circuit failure
98 r	Hard fault is present - FMEM mode
NO DTC's	Unable to initiate Self-Test or unable to output DTC's
DTC's NOT LISTED	DTC's displayed are not applicable to the vehicle being tested

KEY: o = Key On Engine Off (KOEO), r = Engine Running (ER), c = Continuous Memory

Fig. 122 Two digit quick test diagnostic trouble codes & diagnostic trouble code definitions (Part 2 of 2)

DIAGNOSTIC TROUBLE CODES	DEFINITIONS
211	Profile Ignition Pickup (PIP) circuit failure
212	Loss of Ignition Diagnostic Monitor (IDM) input to PCM / SPOUT circuit grounded
213	SPOUT circuit open
214	Cylinder Identification (CID) circuit failure
215	PCM detected coil 1 primary circuit failure (EI)
216	PCM detected coil 2 primary circuit failure (EI)
217	PCM detected coil 3 primary circuit failure (EI)
218	Loss of Ignition Diagnostic Monitor (IDM) signal-left side (dual plug EI)
219	Spark timing defaulted to 10 degrees-SPOUT circuit open (EI)
221	Spark timing error (EI)
222	Loss of Ignition Diagnostic Monitor (IDM) signal-right side (dual plug EI)
223	Loss of Dual Plug Inhibit (DPI) control (dual plug EI)
224	PCM detected coil 1, 2, 3 or 4 primary circuit failure (dual plug EI)
225	Knock not sensed during dynamic response test KOER
226	Ignition Diagnostic Module (IDM) signal not received (EI)
232	PCM detected coil 1, 2, 3 or 4 primary circuit failure (EI)
238	PCM detected coil 4 primary circuit failure (EI)
241	ICM to PCM IDM pulsewidth transmission error (EI)
244	CID circuit fault present when cylinder balance test requested
311	AIR system inoperative during KOER (Bank # 1 w / dual HO2S)
312	AIR misdirected during KOER
313	AIR not bypassed during KOER
314	AIR system inoperative during KOER (Bank # 2 w / dual HO2S)
326	EGR (PFE / DPFE) circuit voltage lower than expected
327	EGR (EVP / PFE / DPFE) circuit below minimum voltage
328	EGR (EVP) closed valve voltage lower than expected
332	Insufficient EGR flow detected (EVP / PFE / DPFE)
334	EGR (EVP) closed valve voltage higher than expected
335	EGR (PFE / DPFE) sensor voltage higher or lower than expected during KOEO
336	Exhaust pressure high / EGR (PFE / DPFE) circuit voltage higher than expected
337	EGR (EVP / PFE / DPFE) circuit above maximum voltage
338	Engine Coolant Temperature (ECT) lower than expected (thermostat test)
339	Engine Coolant Temperature (ECT) higher than expected (thermostat test)
341	Octane adjust service pin open
411	Cannot control RPM during KOER low RPM check
412	Cannot control RPM during KOER high RPM check
415	Idle Air Control (IAC) system at maximum adaptive lower limit
416	Idle Air Control (IAC) system at upper adaptive learning limit
452	Insufficient input from Vehicle Speed Sensor (VSS) to PCM
453	Servo leaking down (KOER IVSC test)
454	Servo leaking up (KOER IVSC test)
455	Insufficient RPM increase (KOER IVSC test)
456	Insufficient RPM decrease (KOER IVSC test)
457	Speed control command switch(s) circuit not functioning (KOEO IVSC test)

Fig. 123 Three digit diagnostic sub-routines/quick test diagnostic trouble codes & diagnostic trouble code definitions (Part 1 of 4). 1993

DIAGNOSTIC TROUBLE CODES	DEFINITIONS
111	System Pass
112	Intake Air Temp (IAT) sensor circuit below minimum voltage / 254°F indicated
113	Intake Air Temp (IAT) sensor circuit above maximum voltage / -40°F indicated
114	Intake Air Temp (IAT) higher or lower than expected
116	Engine Coolant Temp (ECT) higher or lower than expected
117	Engine Coolant Temp (ECT) sensor circuit below minimum voltage / 254°F indicated
118	Engine Coolant Temp (ECT) sensor circuit above maximum voltage / -40°F indicated
121	Closed throttle voltage higher or lower than expected
121	Indicates throttle position voltage inconsistent with the MAF sensor
122	Throttle Position (TP) sensor circuit below minimum voltage
123	Throttle Position (TP) sensor circuit above maximum voltage
124	Throttle Position (TP) sensor voltage higher than expected
125	Throttle Position (TP) sensor voltage lower than expected
126	MAP / BARO sensor higher or lower than expected
128	MAP sensor vacuum hose damaged / disconnected
129	Insufficient MAP / Mass Air Flow (MAF) change during dynamic response test KOER
136	Lack of Heated Oxygen Sensor (HO2S-2) switch during KOER, indicates lean (Bank #2)
137	Lack of Heated Oxygen Sensor (HO2S-2) switch during KOER, indicates rich (Bank #2)
138	Cold Start Injector (CSI) flow insufficient KOER
139	No Heated Oxygen Sensor (HO2S-2) switches detected (Bank #2)
144	No Heated Oxygen Sensor (HO2S-1) switches detected (Bank # 1)
157	Mass Air Flow (MAF) sensor circuit below minimum voltage
158	Mass Air Flow (MAF) sensor circuit above maximum voltage
159	Mass Air Flow (MAF) higher or lower than expected
167	Insufficient throttle position change during dynamic response test KOER
171	Fuel system at adaptive limits, Heated Oxygen Sensor (HO2S-1) unable to switch (Bank # 1)
172	Lack of Heated Oxygen Sensor (HO2S-1) switches, indicates lean (Bank # 1)
173	Lack of Heated Oxygen Sensor (HO2S-1) switches, indicates rich (Bank # 1)
175	Fuel system at adaptive limits, Heated Oxygen Sensor (HO2S-2) unable to switch (Bank #2)
176	Lack of Heated Oxygen Sensor (HO2S-2) switches, indicates lean (Bank #2)
177	Lack of Heated Oxygen Sensor (HO2S-2) switches, indicates rich (Bank #2)
179	Fuel system at lean adaptive limit at part throttle, system rich (Bank # 1)
181	Fuel system at rich adaptive limit at part throttle, system lean (Bank # 1)
184	Mass Air Flow (MAF) higher than expected
185	Mass Air Flow (MAF) lower than expected
186	Injector pulsewidth higher than expected (with BARO sensor)
186	Injector pulsewidth higher or MAF lower than expected (without BARO sensor)
187	Injector pulsewidth lower than expected (with BARO sensor)
187	Injector pulsewidth lower or MAF higher than expected (without BARO sensor)
188	Fuel system at lean adaptive limit at part throttle, system rich (Bank #2)
189	Fuel system at rich adaptive limit at part throttle, system lean (Bank #2)
193	Flexible Fuel (FF) sensor circuit failure

Fig. 123 Three digit diagnostic sub-routines/quick test diagnostic trouble codes & diagnostic trouble code definitions (Part 2 of 4). 1993

DIAGNOSTIC TROUBLE CODES	DEFINITIONS
458	Speed control command switch(s) stuck / circuit grounded (KOEO IVSC test)
459	Speed control ground circuit open (KOEO IVSC test)
511	PCM Read Only Memory (ROM) test failure KOEO
512	PCM Keep Alive Memory (KAM) test failure
513	PCM internal voltage failure (KOEO)
519	Power Steering Pressure (PSP) switch circuit open KOEO
521	Power Steering Pressure (PSP) switch circuit did not change states KOER
522	Vehicle not in PARK or NEUTRAL during KOEO / PNP switch circuit open
524	Low speed fuel pump circuit open—battery to PCM
525	Indicates vehicle in gear / A / C on
527	Park / Neutral Position (PNP) switch circuit open—A / C on KOEO
528	Clutch Pedal Position (CPP) switch circuit failure
529	Data Communication Link (DCL) or PCM circuit failure
532	Cluster Control Assembly (CCA) circuit failure
533	Data Communication Link (DCL) or Electronic Instrument Cluster (EIC) circuit failure
536	Brake On / Off (BOO) circuit failure / not actuated during KOER
538	Insufficient RPM change during PCM dynamic response test
538	Invalid cylinder balance test due to throttle movement during test (SFI only)
538	Invalid cylinder balance test due to CID circuit failure
539	A / C on / Defrost on during Self-Test
542	Fuel pump secondary circuit failure
543	Fuel pump secondary circuit failure
551	Idle Air Control (IAC) circuit failure KOEO
552	Secondary Air Injection Bypass (AIRB) circuit failure KOEO
553	Secondary Air Injection Diverter (AIRD) circuit failure KOEO
554	Fuel Pressure Regulator Control (FPRC) circuit failure
556	Fuel pump relay primary circuit failure
557	Low speed fuel pump primary circuit failure
558	EGR Vacuum Regulator (EVR) circuit failure KOEO
559	Air Conditioning On (ACON) relay circuit failure KOEO
563	High Fan Control (HFC) circuit failure KOEO
564	Fan Control (FC) circuit failure KOEO
565	Canister Purge (CANP) circuit failure KOEO
566	3-4 shift solenoid circuit failure KOEO (A4LD)
567	Speed Control Vent (SCVNT) circuit failure (KOEO IVSC test)
568	Speed Control Vacuum (SCVAC) circuit failure (KOEO IVSC test)
569	Auxiliary Canister Purge (CANP2) circuit failure KOEO
578	A / C pressure sensor circuit shorted (VCRM module)
579	Insufficient A / C pressure change (VCRM module)
581	Power to Fan circuit over current (VCRM module)
582	Fan circuit open (VCRM module)
583	Power to Fuel pump over current (VCRM module)
584	Power ground circuit open (Pin 1) (VCRM module)

Fig. 123 Three digit diagnostic sub-routines/quick test diagnostic trouble codes & diagnostic trouble code definitions (Part 3 of 4). 1993

DIAGNOSTIC TROUBLE CODES	DEFINITIONS
585	Power to A / C clutch over current (VCRM module)
586	A / C clutch circuit open (VCRM module)
587	Variable Control Relay Module (VCRM) communication failure
617	1-2 shift error
618	2-3 shift error
619	3-4 shift error
621	Shift Solenoid 1 (SS1) circuit failure KOEO
622	Shift Solenoid 2 (SS2) circuit failure KOEO
624	Electronic Pressure Control (EPC) circuit failure
625	Electronic Pressure Control (EPC) driver open in PCM
626	Coast Clutch Solenoid (CCS) circuit failure KOEO
627	Torque Converter Clutch (TCC) solenoid circuit failure
628	Excessive converter clutch slippage
629	Torque Converter Clutch (TCC) solenoid circuit failure
631	Transmission Control Indicator Lamp (TCIL) circuit failure KOEO
632	Transmission Control Switch (TCS) circuit did not change states during KOER
633	4x4L switch closed during KOEO
634	Manual Lever Position (MLP) voltage higher or lower than expected
636	Transmission Oil Temp (TOT) higher or lower than expected
637	Transmission Oil Temp (TOT) sensor circuit above maximum voltage / -40°F (-40°C) indicated / circuit open
638	Transmission Oil Temp (TOT) sensor circuit below minimum voltage / 290°F (143°C) indicated / circuit shorted
639	Insufficient input from Transmission Speed Sensor (TSS)
641	Shift Solenoid 3 (SS3) circuit failure
643	Torque Converter Clutch (TCC) circuit failure
645	Incorrect gear ratio obtained for first gear
646	Incorrect gear ratio obtained for second gear
647	Incorrect gear ratio obtained for third gear
648	Incorrect gear ratio obtained for fourth gear
649	Electronic Pressure Control (EPC) higher or lower than expected
651	Electronic Pressure Control (EPC) circuit failure
652	Torque Converter Clutch (TCC) solenoid circuit failure
654	Manual Lever Position (MLP) sensor not indicating PARK during KOEO
656	Torque Converter Clutch continuous slip error
657	Transmission over temperature condition occurred
998	Hard fault present ****FMEM MODE****

Fig. 123 Three digit diagnostic sub-routines/quick test diagnostic trouble codes & diagnostic trouble code definitions (Part 4 of 4). 1993

DIAGNOSTIC TROUBLE CODES	DEFINITIONS
582	Fan circuit open
583	Power to Fuel pump over current
584	VCRM Power ground circuit open (VCRM Pin 1)
585	Power to A / C clutch over current
586	A / C clutch circuit open
587	Variable Control Relay Module (VCRM) communication failure
617	1-2 shift error
618	2-3 shift error
619	3-4 shift error
621	Shift Solenoid 1 (SS1) circuit failure KOEO
622	Shift Solenoid 2 (SS2) circuit failure KOEO
623	Transmission Control Indicator Light (TCIL) circuit failure
624	Electronic Pressure Control (EPC) circuit failure
625	Electronic Pressure Control (EPC) driver open in PCM
626	Coast Clutch Solenoid (CCS) circuit failure KOEO
627	Torque Converter Clutch (TCC) solenoid circuit failure
628	Excessive converter clutch slippage
629	Torque Converter Clutch (TCC) solenoid circuit failure
631	Transmission Control Indicator Lamp (TCIL) circuit failure KOEO
632	Transmission Control Switch (TCS) circuit did not change states during KOER
633	4x4L switch closed during KOEO
634	Transmission Range (TR) voltage higher or lower than expected
636	Transmission Fluid Temp (TFT) higher or lower than expected
637	Transmission Fluid Temp (TFT) sensor circuit above maximum voltage / -40°F (-40°C) indicated / circuit open
638	Transmission Fluid Temp (TFT) sensor circuit below minimum voltage / 290°F (143°C) indicated / circuit shorted
639	Insufficient input from Transmission Speed Sensor (TSS)
641	Shift Solenoid 3 (SS3) circuit failure
643	Torque Converter Clutch (TCC) circuit failure
645	Incorrect gear ratio obtained for first gear
646	Incorrect gear ratio obtained for second gear
647	Incorrect gear ratio obtained for third gear
648	Incorrect gear ratio obtained for fourth gear
649	Electronic Pressure Control (EPC) higher or lower than expected
651	Electronic Pressure Control (EPC) circuit failure
652	Torque Converter Clutch (TCC) solenoid circuit failure
653	Transmission Control Switch (TCS) did not change states during KOER
654	Transmission Range (TR) sensor not indicating PARK during KOEO
656	Torque Converter Clutch continuous slip error
657	Transmission over temperature condition occurred
659	High vehicle speed in park indicated

Fig. 124 Three digit diagnostic sub-routines/quick test diagnostic trouble codes & diagnostic trouble code definitions (Part 1 of 5). 1994–95

DIAGNOSTIC TROUBLE CODES	DEFINITIONS
211	Profile Ignition Pickup (PIP) circuit failure
212	Loss of Ignition Diagnostic Monitor (IDM) input to PCM / SPOUT circuit grounded
213	SPOUT circuit open
214	Cylinder Identification (CID) circuit failure
215	PCM detected coil 1 primary circuit failure (EI)
216	PCM detected coil 2 primary circuit failure (EI)
217	PCM detected coil 3 primary circuit failure (EI)
218	Loss of Ignition Diagnostic Monitor (IDM) signal-left side (dual plug EI)
219	Spark timing defaulted to 10 degrees-SPOUT circuit open (EI)
221	Spark timing error (EI)
222	Loss of Ignition Diagnostic Monitor (IDM) signal-right side (dual plug EI)
223	Loss of Dual Plug Inhibit (DPI) control (dual plug EI)
224	PCM detected coil 1, 2, 3 or 4 primary circuit failure (dual plug EI)
225	Knock not sensed during dynamic response test KOER
226	Ignition Diagnostic Module (IDM) signal not received (EI)
232	PCM detected coil 1, 2, 3 or 4 primary circuit failure (EI)
238	PCM detected coil 4 primary circuit failure (EI)
241	ICM to PCM IDM pulsewidth transmission error (EI)
244	CID circuit fault present when cylinder balance test requested
311	AIR system inoperative during KOER (Bank #1 w / dual HO2S)
312	AIR misdirected during KOER
313	AIR not bypassed during KOER
314	AIR system inoperative during KOER (Bank #2 w / dual HO2S)
326	EGR (PFE / DPFE) circuit voltage lower than expected
327	EGR (EGRP / EVP / PFE / DPFE) circuit below minimum voltage
328	EGR (EVP) closed valve voltage lower than expected
332	Insufficient EGR flow detected (EGRP / EVP / PFE / DPFE)
334	EGR (EVP) closed valve voltage higher than expected
335	EGR (PFE / DPFE) sensor voltage higher or lower than expected during KOEO
336	Exhaust pressure high / EGR (PFE / DPFE) circuit voltage higher than expected
337	EGR (EGRP / EVP / PFE / DPFE) circuit above maximum voltage
338	Engine Coolant Temperature (ECT) lower than expected (thermostat test)
339	Engine Coolant Temperature (ECT) higher than expected (thermostat test)
341	Octane adjust service pin open
381	Frequent A / C clutch cycling
411	Cannot control RPM during KOER low RPM check
412	Cannot control RPM during KOER high RPM check
415	Idle Air Control (IAC) system at maximum adaptive lower limit
416	Idle Air Control (IAC) system at upper adaptive learning limit
452	Insufficient input from Vehicle Speed Sensor (VSS) to PCM
453	Servo leaking down (KOER IVSC test)
454	Servo leaking up (KOER IVSC test)
455	Insufficient RPM increase (KOER IVSC test)
456	Insufficient RPM decrease (KOER IVSC test)

Fig. 124 Three digit diagnostic sub-routines/quick test diagnostic trouble codes & diagnostic trouble code definitions (Part 2 of 5). 1994–95

DIAGNOSTIC TROUBLE CODES	DEFINITIONS
458	Speed control command switch(s) stuck / circuit grounded (KOEO IVSC test)
459	Speed control ground circuit open (KOEO IVSC test)
511	PCM Read Only Memory (ROM) test failure KOEO
512	PCM Keep Alive Memory (KAM) test failure
513	PCM internal voltage failure (KOEO)
519	Power Steering Pressure (PSP) switch circuit open KOEO
521	Power Steering Pressure (PSP) switch circuit did not change states KOER
522	Vehicle not in PARK or NEUTRAL during KOEO / PNP switch circuit open
524	Low speed fuel pump circuit open—battery to PCM
525	Indicates vehicle in gear / A / C on
527	Park / Neutral Position (PNP) switch circuit open—A / C on KOEO
528	Clutch Pedal Position (CPP) switch circuit failure
529	Data Communication Link (DCL) or PCM circuit failure
532	Cluster Control Assembly (CCA) circuit failure
533	Data Communication Link (DCL) or Electronic Instrument Cluster (EIC) circuit failure
536	Brake On / Off (BOO) circuit failure / not actuated during KOER
538	Insufficient RPM change during KOER dynamic response test
538	Invalid cylinder balance test due to throttle movement during test (SFI only)
538	Invalid cylinder balance test due to CID circuit failure
539	A / C on / Defrost on during Self-Test
542	Fuel pump secondary circuit failure
543	Fuel pump secondary circuit failure
551	Idle Air Control (IAC) circuit failure KOEO
552	Secondary Air Injection Bypass (AIRB) circuit failure KOEO
553	Secondary Air Injection Diverter (AIRD) circuit failure KOEO
554	Fuel Pressure Regulator Control (FPRC) circuit failure
556	Fuel pump relay primary circuit failure
557	Low speed fuel pump primary circuit failure
558	EGR Vacuum Regulator (EVR) circuit failure KOEO
559	Air Conditioning On (ACON) relay circuit failure KOEO
563	High Fan Control (HFC) circuit failure KOEO
564	Fan Control (FC) circuit failure KOEO
565	Canister Purge (CANP) circuit failure KOEO
566	3-4 shift solenoid circuit failure KOEO (A4LD)
567	Speed Control Vent (SCVNT) circuit failure (KOEO IVSC test)
568	Speed Control Vacuum (SCVAC) circuit failure (KOEO IVSC test)
569	Auxiliary Canister Purge (CANP2) circuit failure KOEO
578	A C pressure sensor circuit shorted (VCRM module)
579	Insufficient A C pressure change (VCRM module)
581	Power to Fan circuit over current (VCRM module)
582	Fan circuit open (VCRM module)
583	Power to Fuel pump over current (VCRM module)
584	Power ground circuit open (Pin 1) (VCRM module)

FM0159300668030X

Fig. 124   Three digit diagnostic sub-routines/quick test diagnostic trouble codes & diagnostic trouble code definitions (Part 3 of 5). 1994–95

DIAGNOSTIC TROUBLE CODES	DEFINITIONS
585	Power to A / C clutch over current (VCRM module)
586	A / C clutch circuit open (VCRM module)
587	Variable Control Relay Module (VCRM) communication failure
617	1-2 shift error
618	2-3 shift error
619	3-4 shift error
621	Shift Solenoid 1 (SS1) circuit failure KOEO
622	Shift Solenoid 2 (SS2) circuit failure KOEO
624	Electronic Pressure Control (EPC) circuit failure
625	Electronic Pressure Control (EPC) driver open in PCM
626	Coast Clutch Solenoid (CCS) circuit failure KOEO
627	Torque Converter Clutch (TCC) solenoid circuit failure
628	Excessive converter clutch slippage
629	Torque Converter Clutch (TCC) solenoid circuit failure
631	Transmission Control Indicator Lamp (TCIL) circuit failure KOEO
632	Transmission Control Switch (TCS) circuit did not change states during KOER
633	4x4L switch closed during KOEO
634	Manual Lever Position (MLP) voltage higher or lower than expected
636	Transmission Oil Temp (TOT) higher or lower than expected
637	Transmission Oil Temp (TOT) sensor circuit above maximum voltage / -40°F (-40°C) indicated / circuit open
638	Transmission Oil Temp (TOT) sensor circuit below minimum voltage / 290°F (143°C) indicated / circuit shorted
639	Insufficient input from Transmission Speed Sensor (TSS)
641	Shift Solenoid 3 (SS3) circuit failure
643	Torque Converter Clutch (TCC) circuit failure
645	Incorrect gear ratio obtained for first gear
646	Incorrect gear ratio obtained for second gear
647	Incorrect gear ratio obtained for third gear
648	Incorrect gear ratio obtained for fourth gear
649	Electronic Pressure Control (EPC) higher or lower than expected
651	Electronic Pressure Control (EPC) circuit failure
652	Torque Converter Clutch (TCC) solenoid circuit failure
654	Manual Lever Position (MLP) sensor not indicating PARK during KOEO
656	Torque Converter Clutch continuous slip error
657	Transmission over temperature condition occurred
998	Hard fault present * * * * FMEM MODE * * * *

Fig. 124   Three digit diagnostic sub-routines/quick test diagnostic trouble codes & diagnostic trouble code definitions (Part 3 of 5). 1994-95

DIAGNOSTIC TROUBLE CODES	DEFINITIONS
667	Transmission Range sensor circuit voltage below minimum voltage
668	Transmission Range circuit voltage above maximum voltage
675	Transmission Range sensor circuit voltage out of range
998	Hard fault present * * * * FMEM MODE * * * *

Fig. 124   Three digit diagnostic sub-routines/quick test diagnostic trouble codes & diagnostic trouble code definitions (Part 4 of 5). 1994-95

Gasoline Engines

Driveability			Chart Number
Starting Concerns		No Crank	1
		Hard Start · Long Crank · Erratic Start · Erratic Crank	2
		Stall After Start	3
		No Start · Normal Crank	4
Unique Idle Concerns		Slow Return to Idle	5
		Rolling Idle	6
		Fast Idle	7
		Low Slow Idle	8
Driveability — Performance While Driving Concerns			
Stalls Quits (607000)		Idle	3
		Acceleration	9
		Cruise	9
		Deceleration	8
Runs Rough (608000)		Idle	6
		Acceleration	9
		Cruise	9
Misses (609000)		Idle	6
		Acceleration	9
		Cruise	9
Buck Jerk (610000)		Acceleration	9
		Cruise	9
		Deceleration	9
Hesitation Stumble (611000)		Acceleration	9
Surge (612000)		Acceleration	11
		Cruise	11
Backfires (613000)		Idle	12
		Acceleration	12
		Deceleration	12
Lack Loss of Power (614000)		Acceleration	13
		Cruise	13
Spark Knock (615000)		Acceleration	14
		Cruise	14
Additional Driveability Concerns			
Diesels Runs On			7
Poor Fuel Economy			15
Emissions Compliance			16
(Continued)			

FM0159300669010X

Fig. 125   Diagnostic routines index (Part 1 of 3)

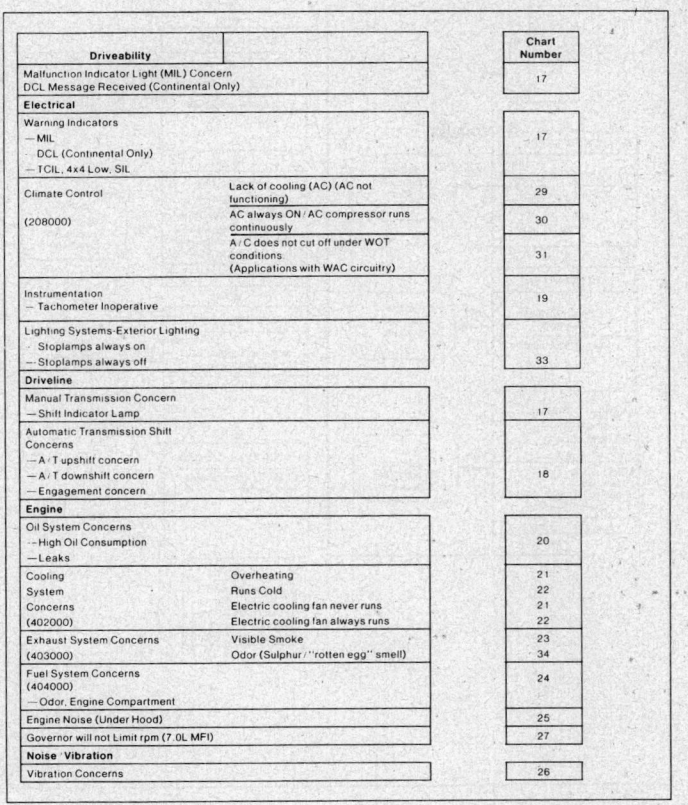

Driveability		Chart Number
Malfunction Indicator Light (MIL) Concern DCL Message Received (Continental Only)		17
Electrical		
Warning Indicators — MIL — DCL (Continental Only) — TCIL, 4x4 Low, SIL		17
Climate Control (208000)	Lack of cooling (AC) (AC not functioning)	29
	AC always ON / AC compressor runs continuously	30
	A/C does not cut off under WOT conditions. (Applications with WAC circuitry)	31
Instrumentation — Tachometer Inoperative		19
Lighting Systems-Exterior Lighting - Stoplamps always on — Stoplamps always off		33
Driveline		
Manual Transmission Concern —Shift Indicator Lamp		17
Automatic Transmission Shift Concerns — A/T upshift concern — A/T downshift concern — Engagement concern		18
Engine		
Oil System Concerns - High Oil Consumption —Leaks		20
Cooling System Concerns (402000)	Overheating	21
	Runs Cold	22
	Electric cooling fan never runs	21
	Electric cooling fan always runs	22
Exhaust System Concerns (403000)	Visible Smoke	23
	Odor (Sulphur/"rotten egg" smell)	34
Fuel System Concerns (404000) — Odor, Engine Compartment		24
Engine Noise (Under Hood)		25
Governor will not Limit rpm (7.0L MFI)		27
Noise/Vibration		
Vibration Concerns		26

FM0159300669020X

Fig. 125 Diagnostic routines index (Part 2 of 3)

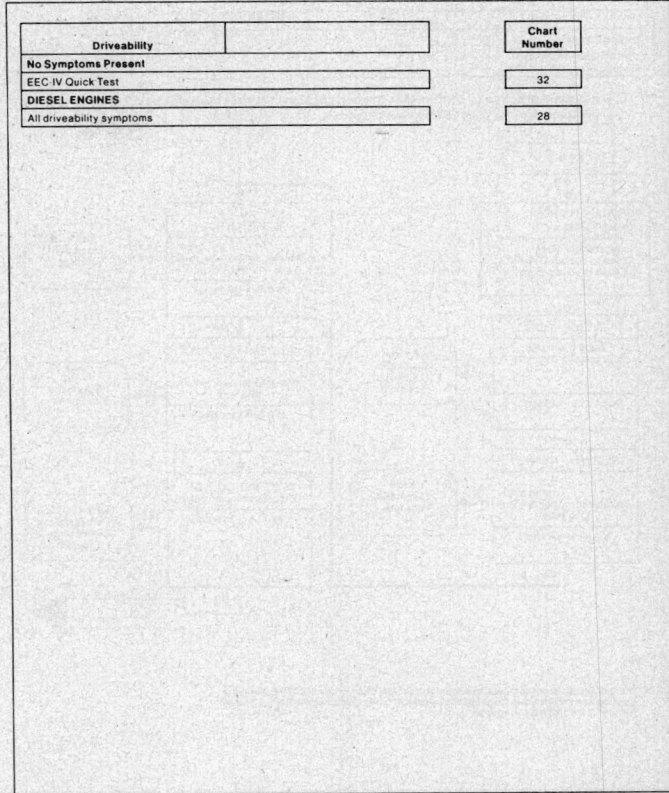

Driveability		Chart Number
No Symptoms Present		
EEC-IV Quick Test		32
DIESEL ENGINES		
All driveability symptoms		28

FM0159300669030X

Fig. 125 Diagnostic routines index (Part 3 of 3)

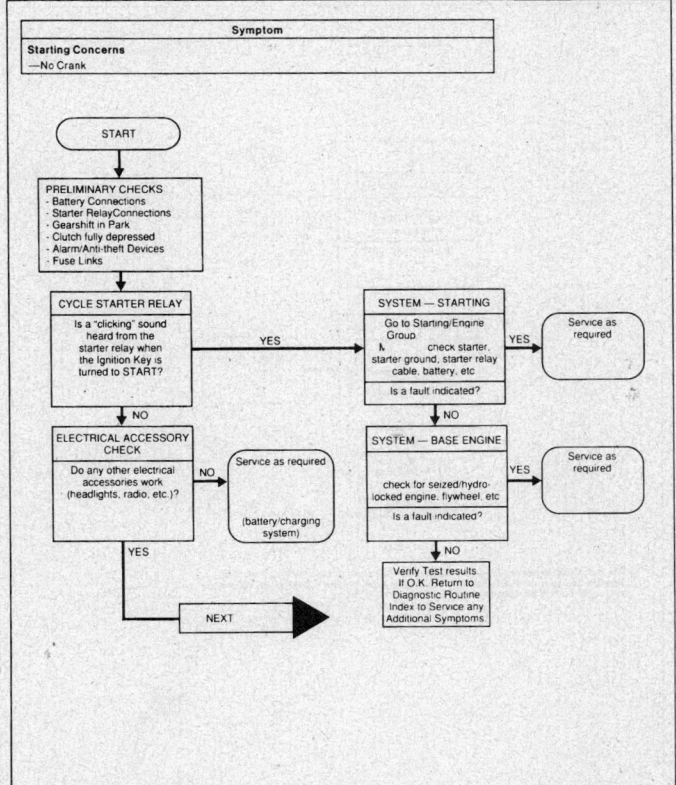

FM0159300670010X

Fig. 126 Diagnostic routines chart 1 (Part 1 of 2)

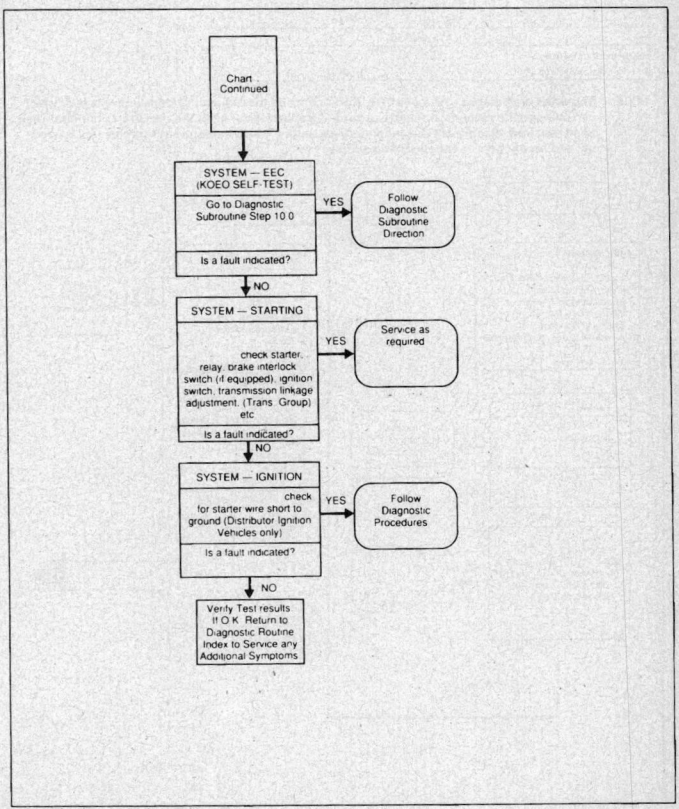

FM0159300670020X

Fig. 126 Diagnostic routines chart 1 (Part 2 of 2)

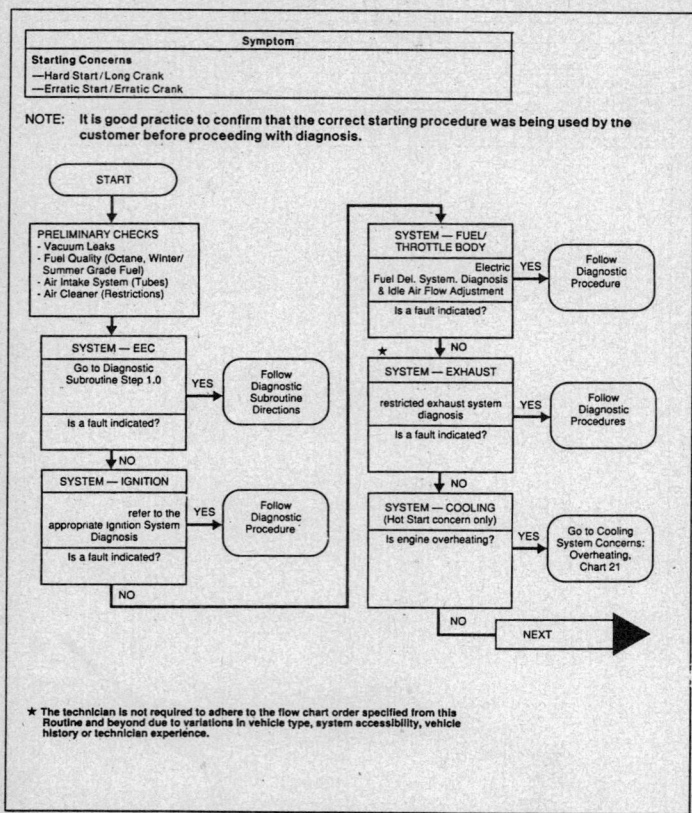

Fig. 127 Diagnostic routines chart 2 (Part 1 of 2)

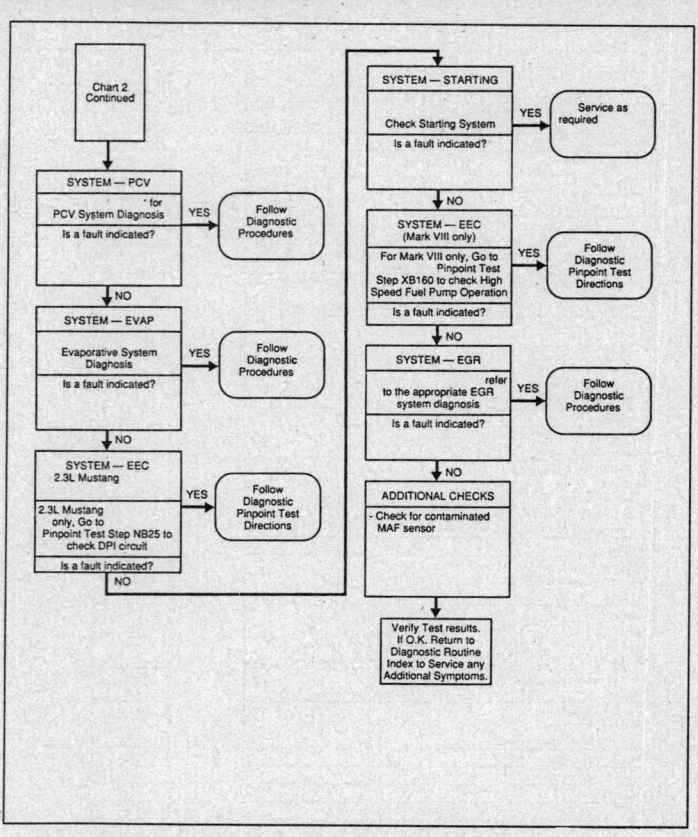

Fig. 127 Diagnostic routines chart 2 (Part 2 of 2)

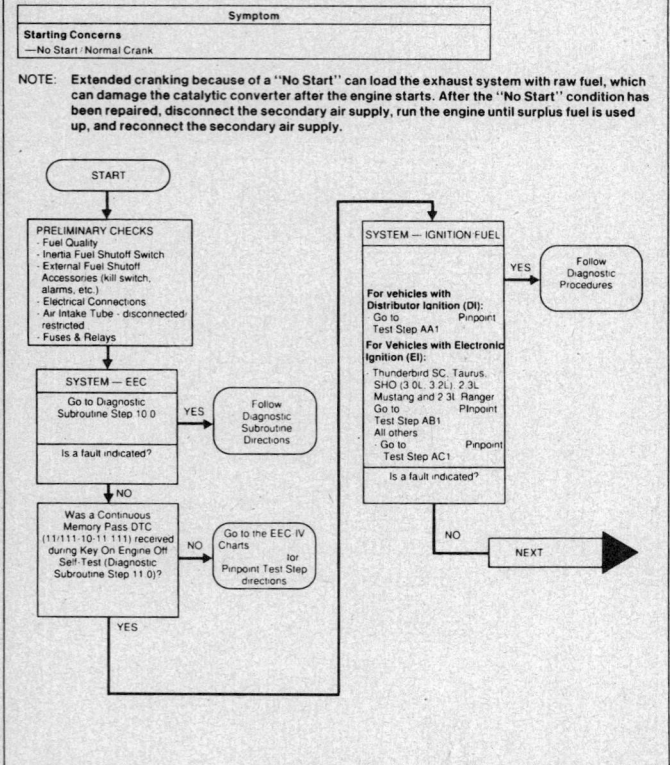

Fig. 128 Diagnostic routines chart 3 (Part 1 of 3)

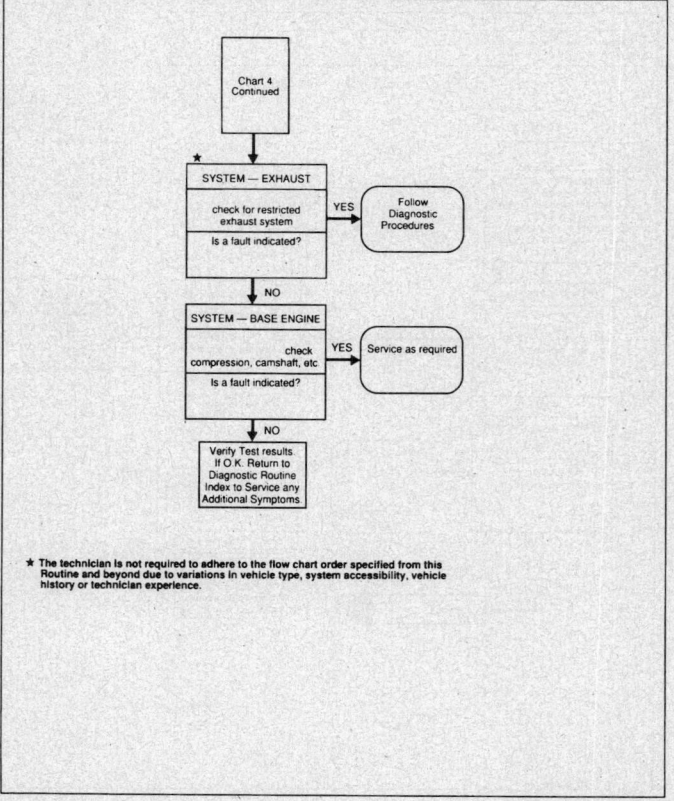

Fig. 128 Diagnostic routines chart 3 (Part 2 of 3)

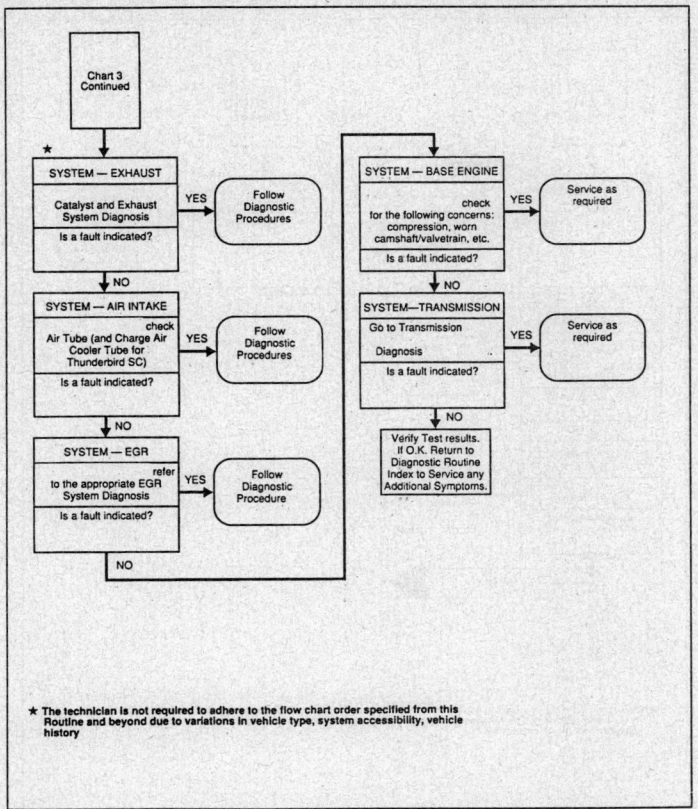

Fig. 128 Diagnostic routines chart 3 (Part 3 of 3)

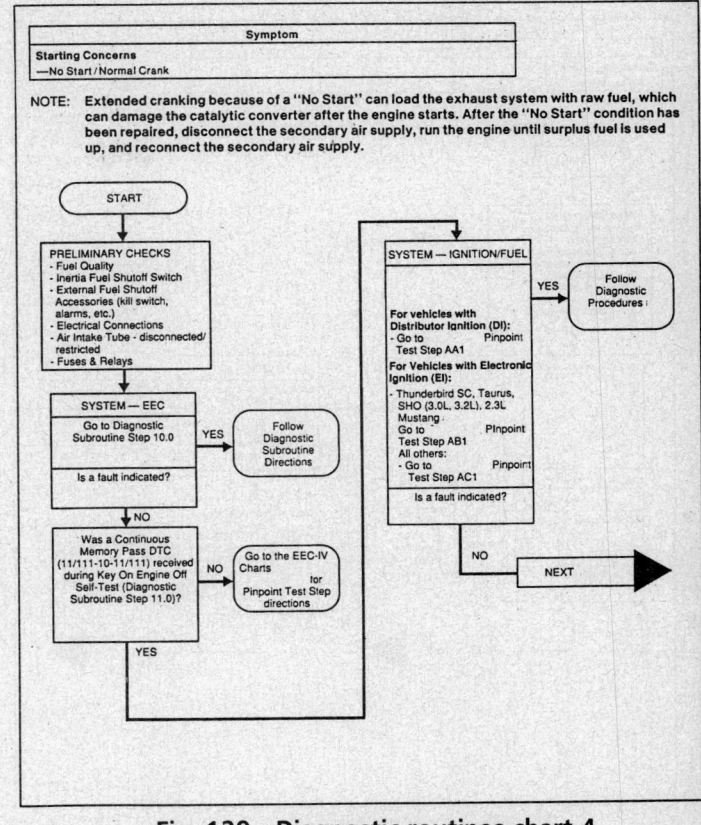

Fig. 129 Diagnostic routines chart 4 (Part 1 of 2)

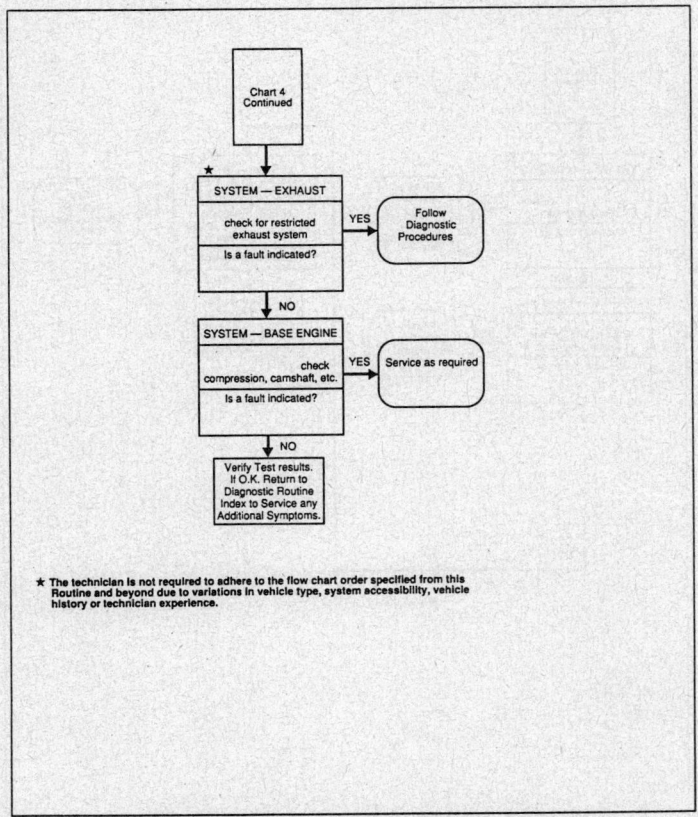

Fig. 129 Diagnostic routines chart 4 (Part 2 of 2)

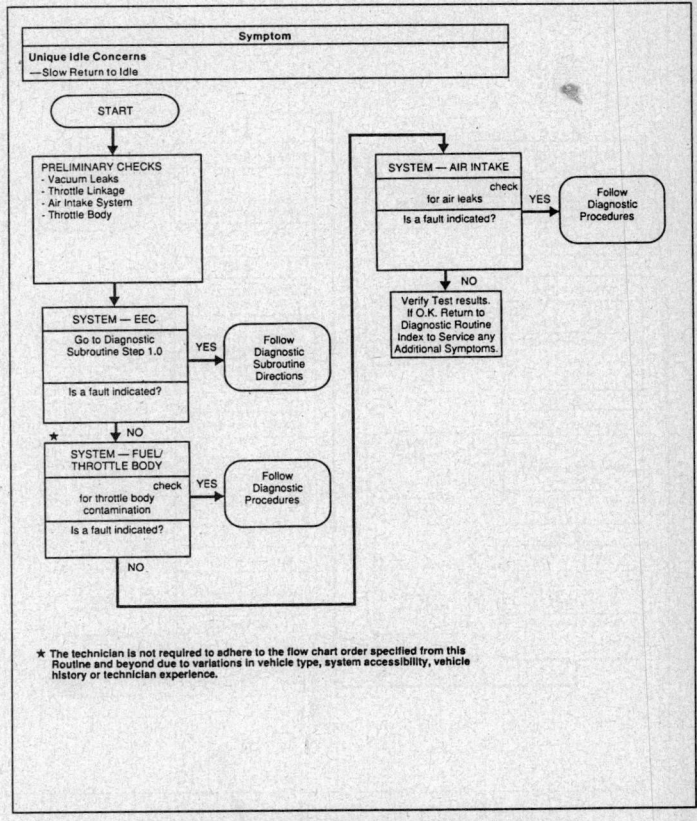

Fig. 130 Diagnostic routines chart 5

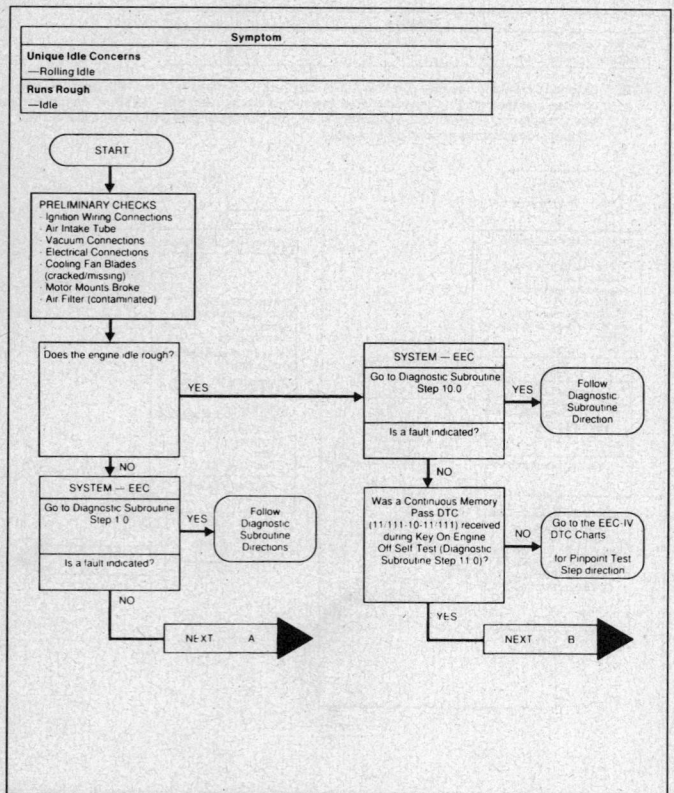

Fig. 131 Diagnostic routines chart 6 (Part 1 of 4)

FM0159300675010X

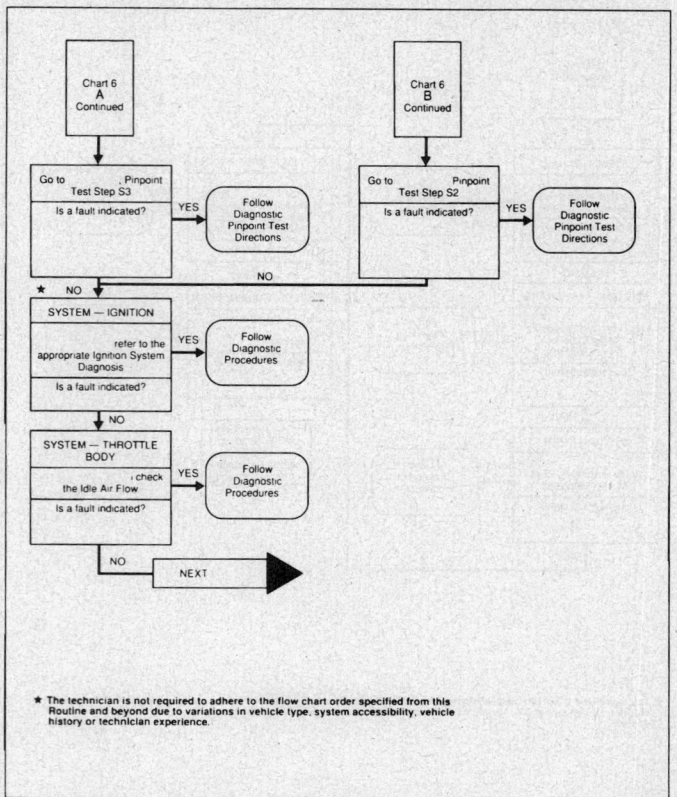

Fig. 131 Diagnostic routines chart 6 (Part 2 of 4)

FM0159300675020X

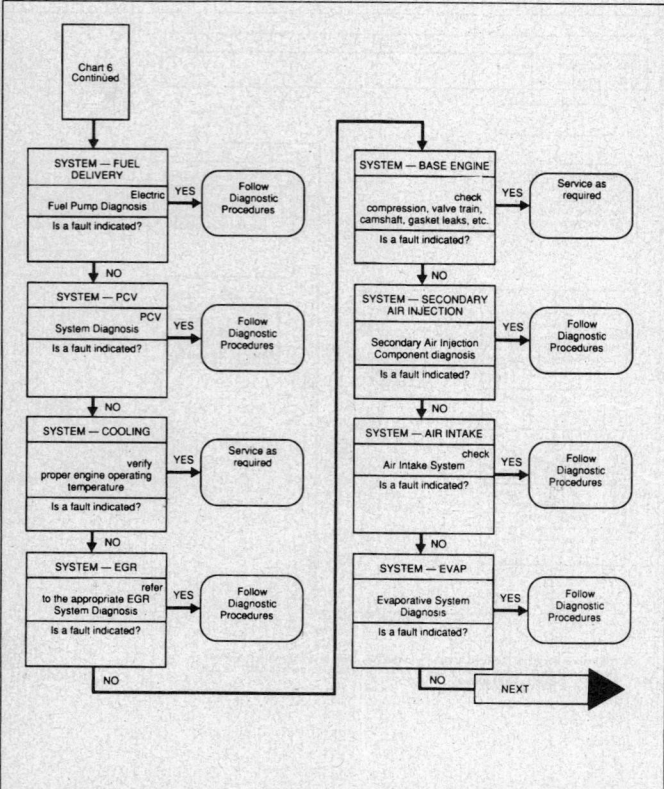

FM0159300675030X

Fig. 131 Diagnostic routines chart 6 (Part 3 of 4)

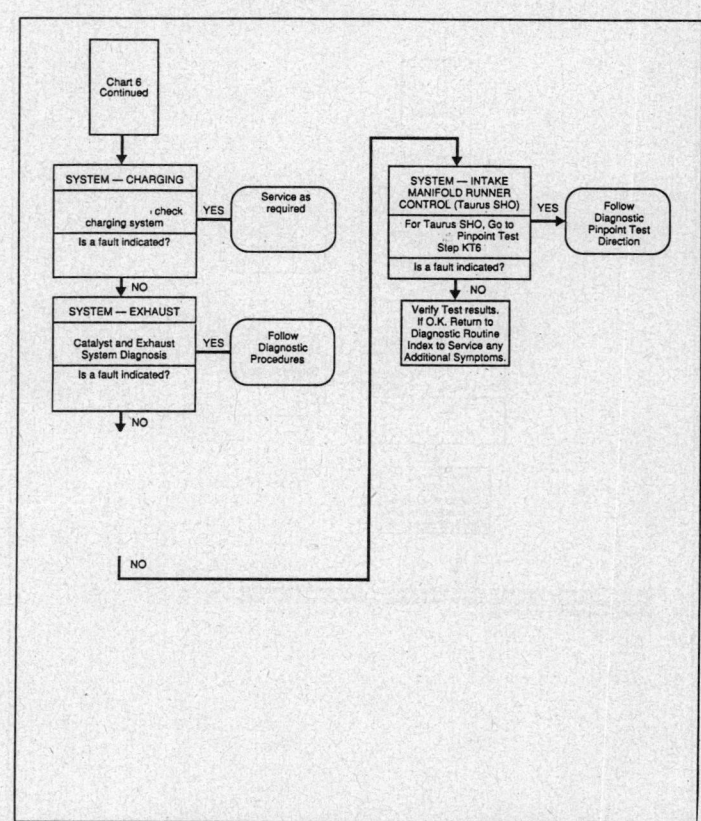

Fig. 131 Diagnostic routines chart 6 (Part 4 of 4). 1993–94

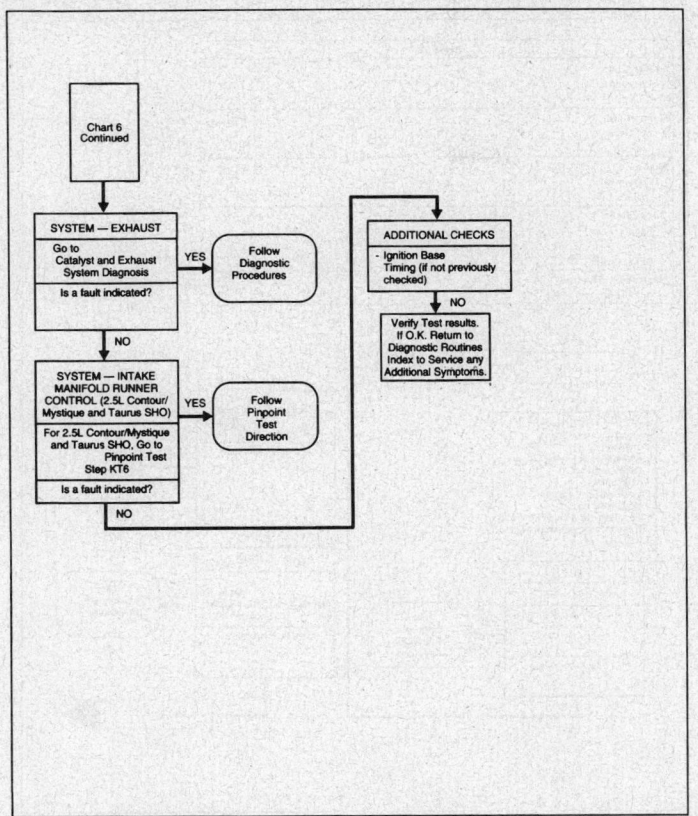

Fig. 131   Diagnostic routines chart 6 (Part 4 of 4). 1995

FM015950067504BX

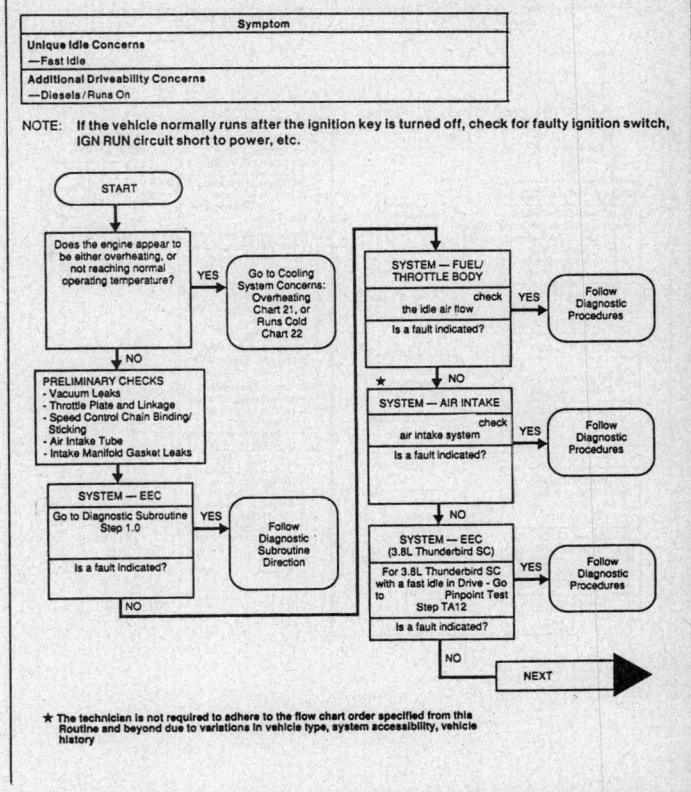

Fig. 132   Diagnostic routines chart 7
(Part 1 of 2)

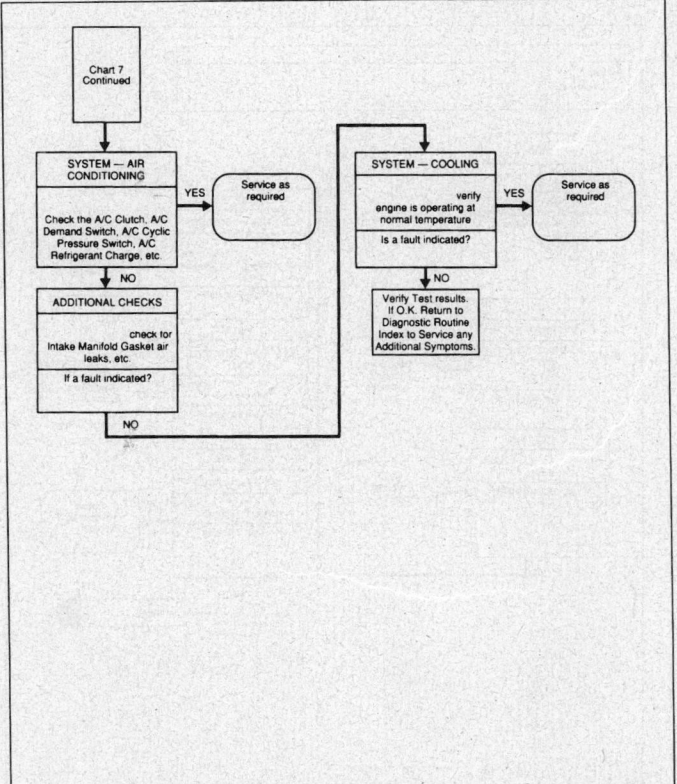

Fig. 132   Diagnostic routines chart 7 (Part 2 of 2)

FM0159300676020X

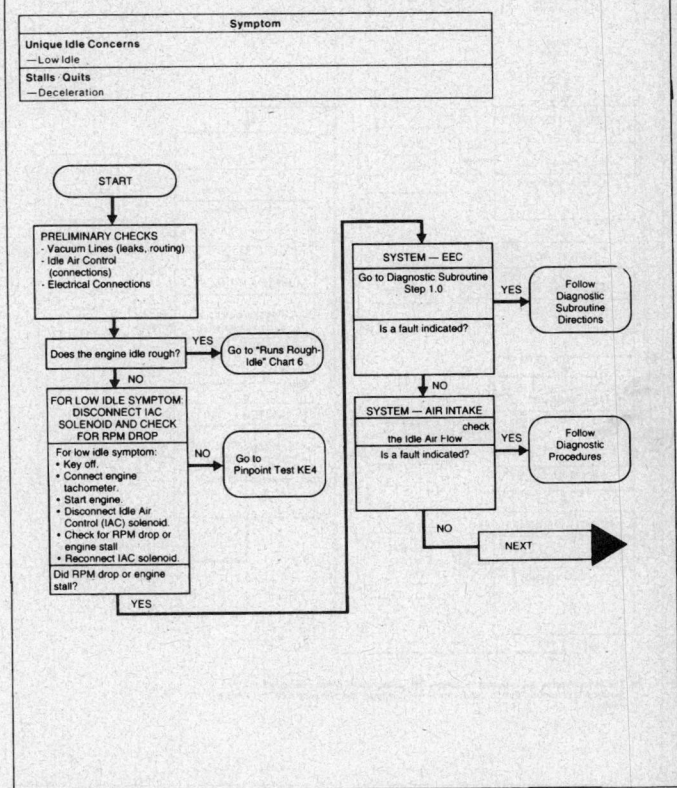

Fig. 133   Diagnostic routines chart 8 (Part 1 of 2)

FM0159300677010X

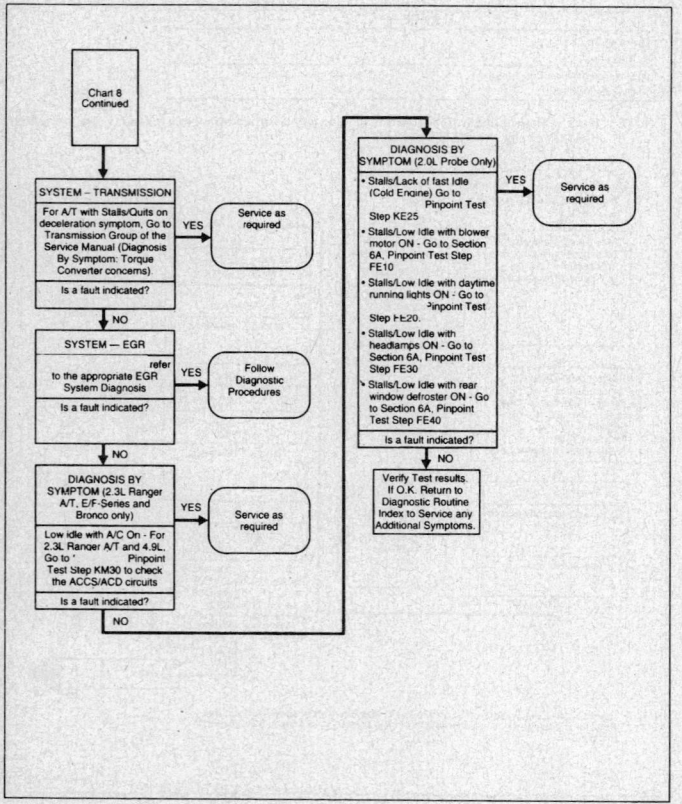

Fig. 133 Diagnostic routines chart 8 (Part 2 of 2)

Fig. 134 Diagnostic routines chart 9 (Part 1 of 2)

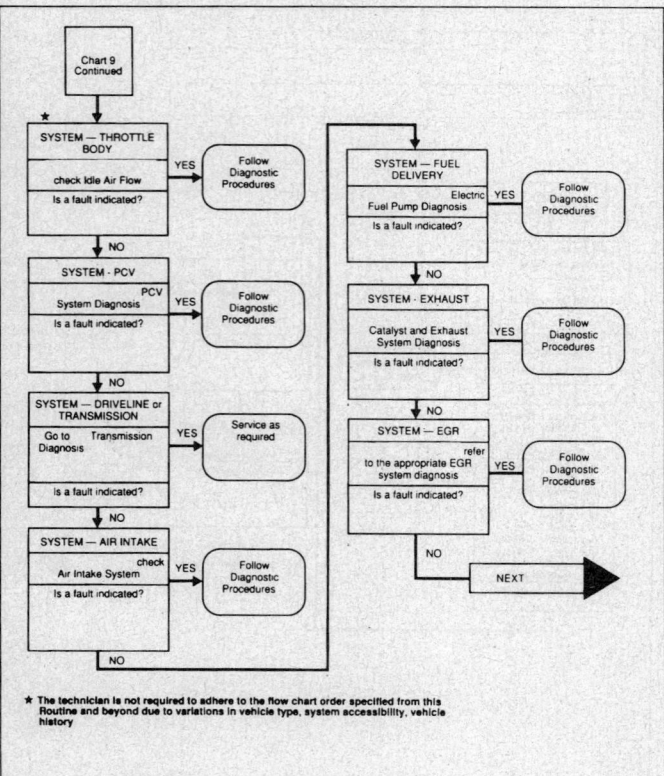

Fig. 134 Diagnostic routines chart 9 (Part 2 of 2).

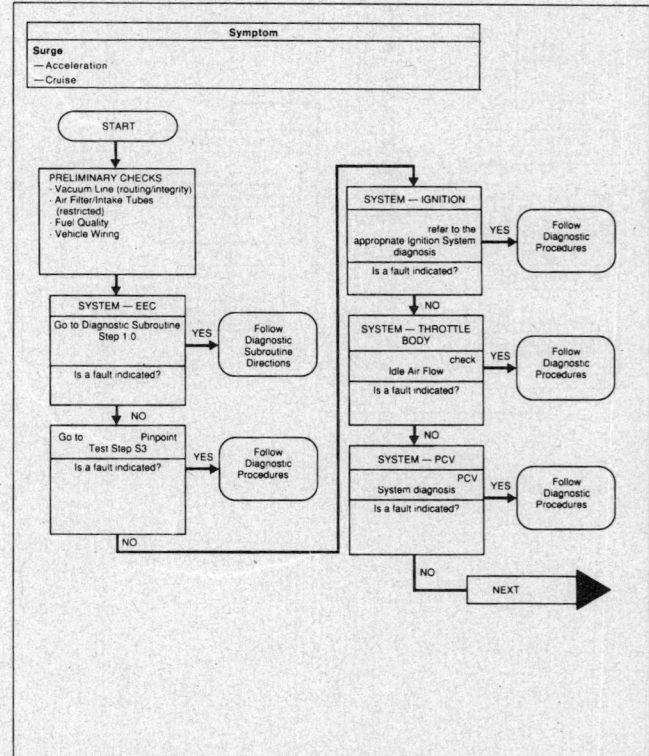

Fig. 135 Diagnostic routines chart 11 (Part 1 of 3)

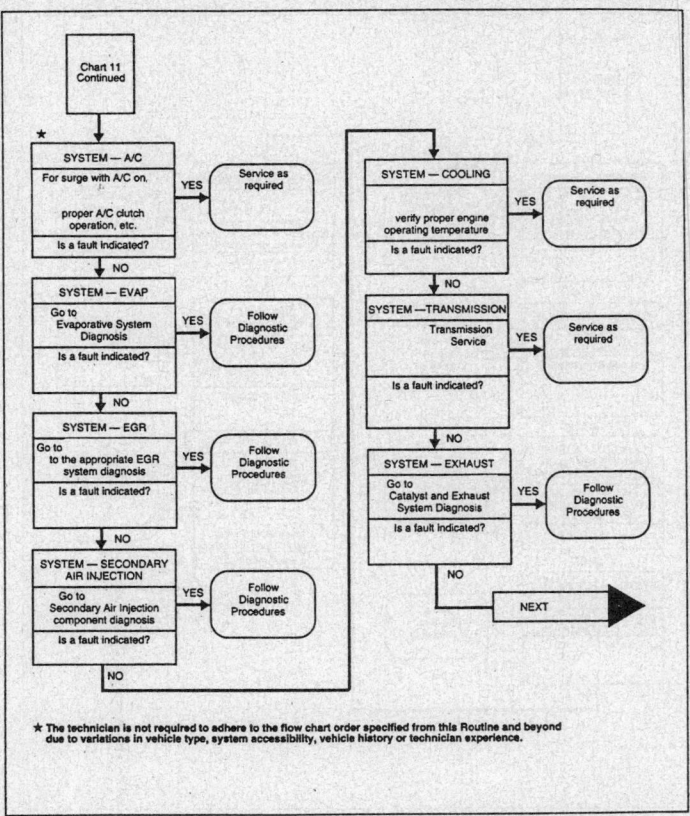

Fig. 135 Diagnostic routines chart 11 (Part 2 of 3)

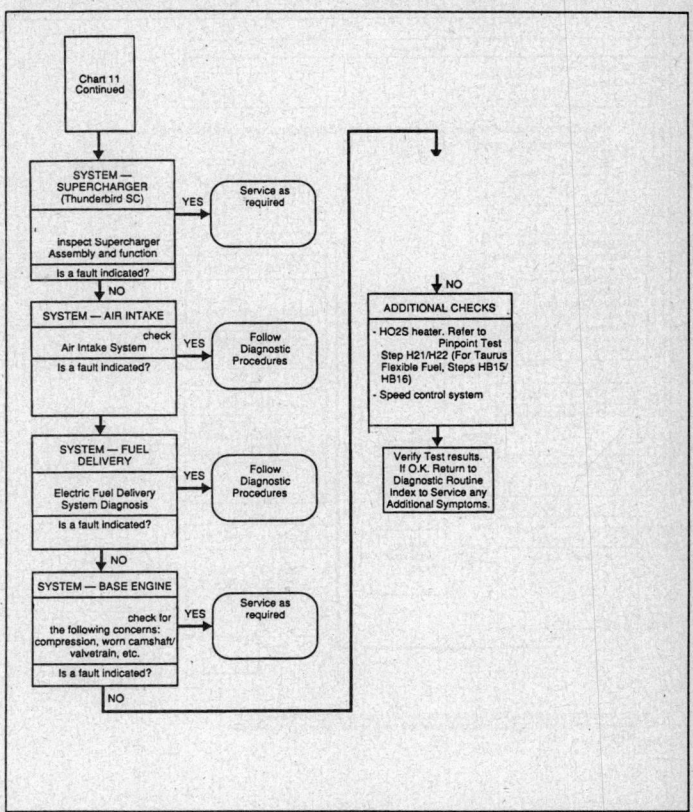

Fig. 135 Diagnostic routines chart 11 (Part 3 of 3)

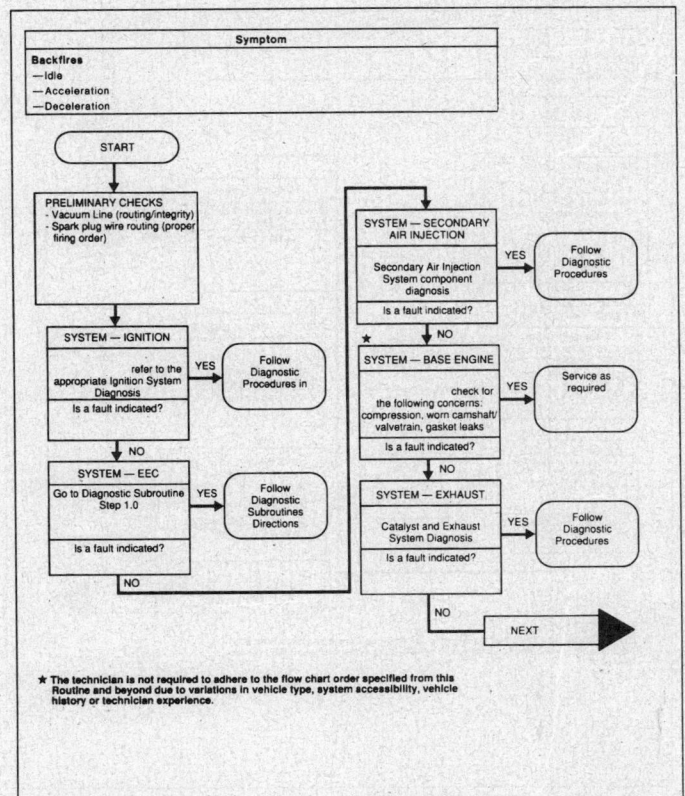

Fig. 136 Diagnostic routines chart 12 (Part 1 of 2)

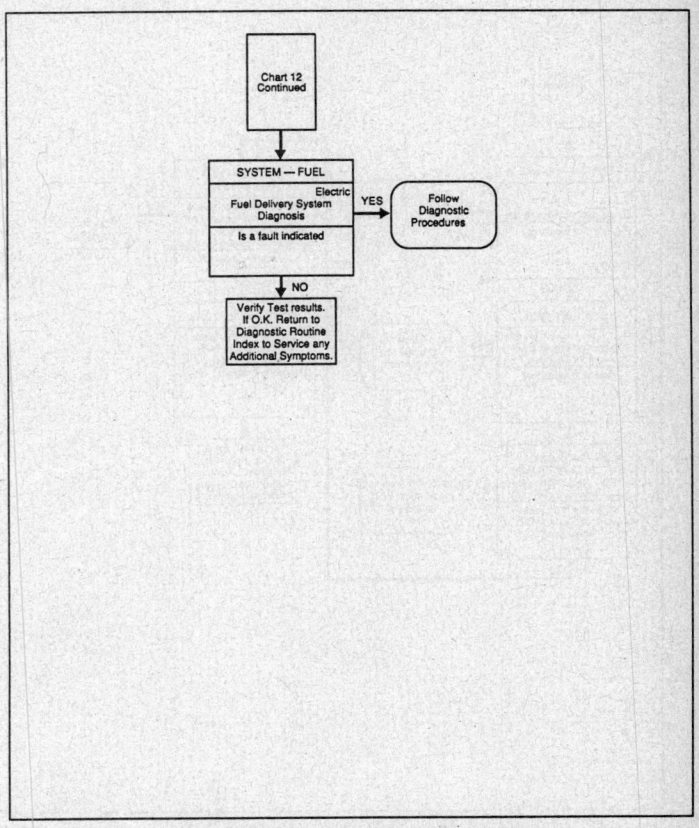

Fig. 136 Diagnostic routines chart 12 (Part 2 of 2)

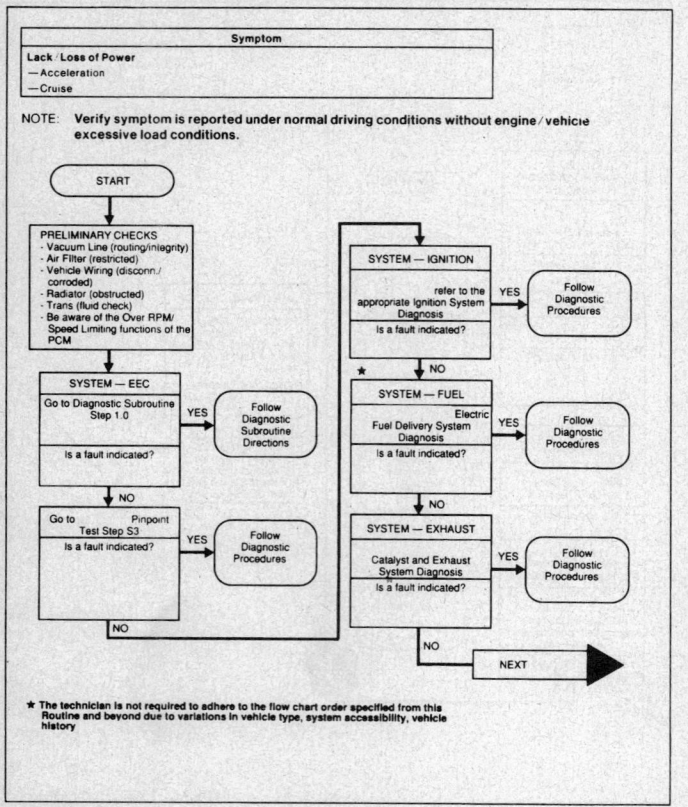

Fig. 137 Diagnostic routines chart 13 (Part 1 of 3)

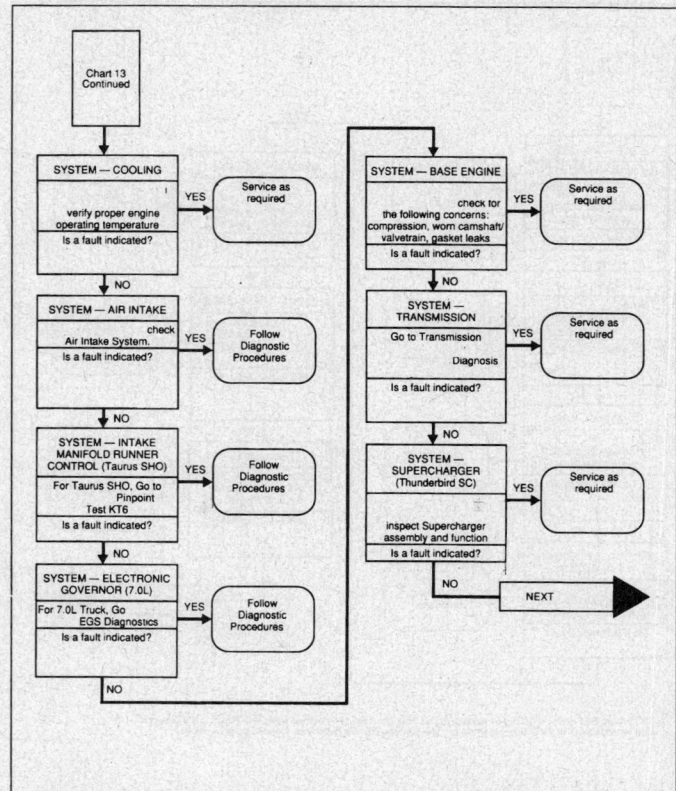

Fig. 137 Diagnostic routines chart 13 (Part 2 of 3)

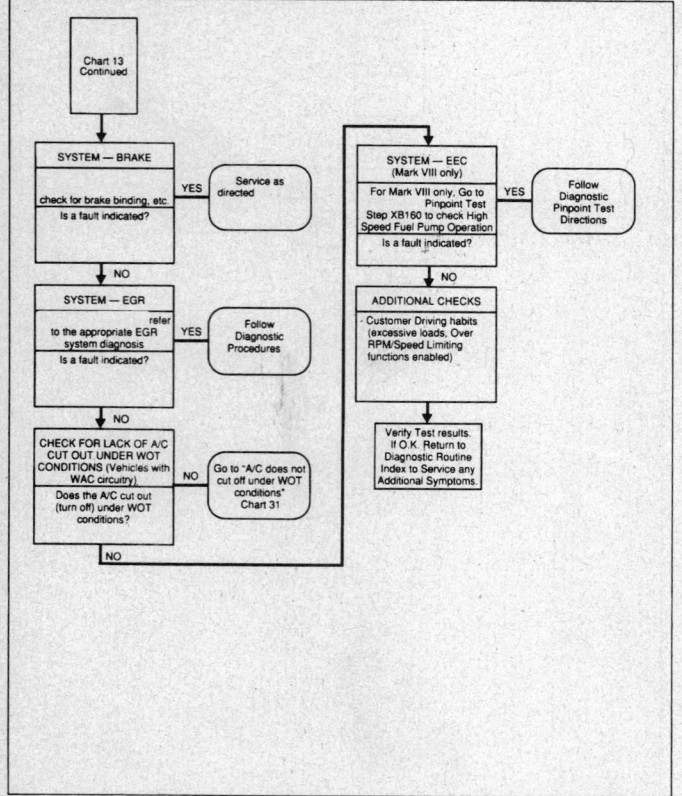

Fig. 137 Diagnostic routines chart 13 (Part 3 of 3)

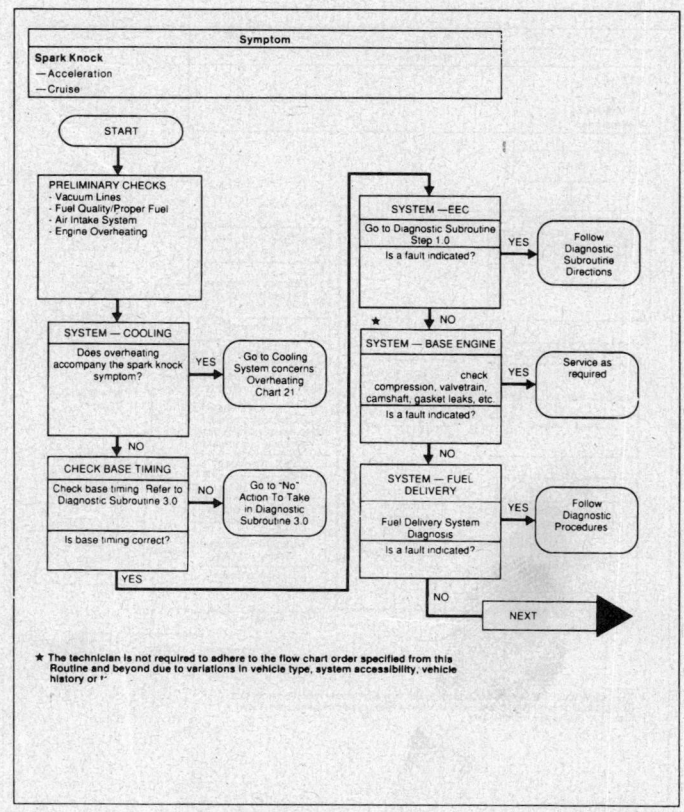

Fig. 138 Diagnostic routines chart 14 (Part 1 of 2). 1993

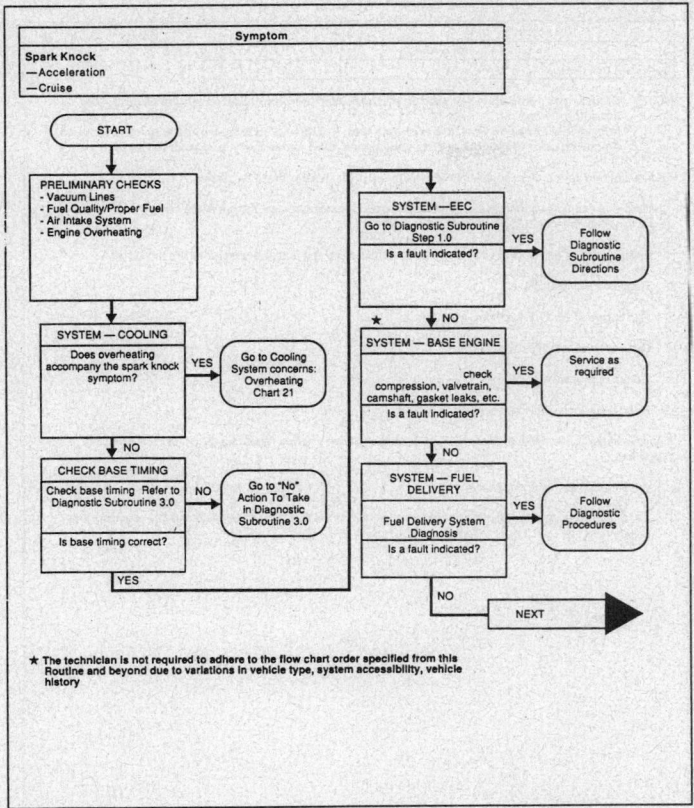

Fig. 138   Diagnostic routines chart 14 (Part 1 of 2). 1995

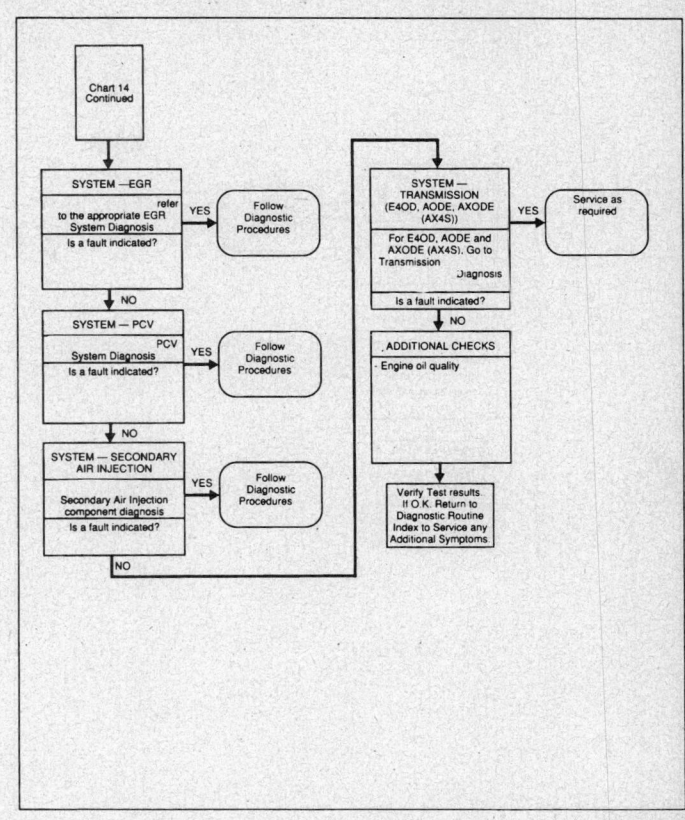

FM0159300682020X

Fig. 138   Diagnostic routines chart 14 (Part 2 of 2)

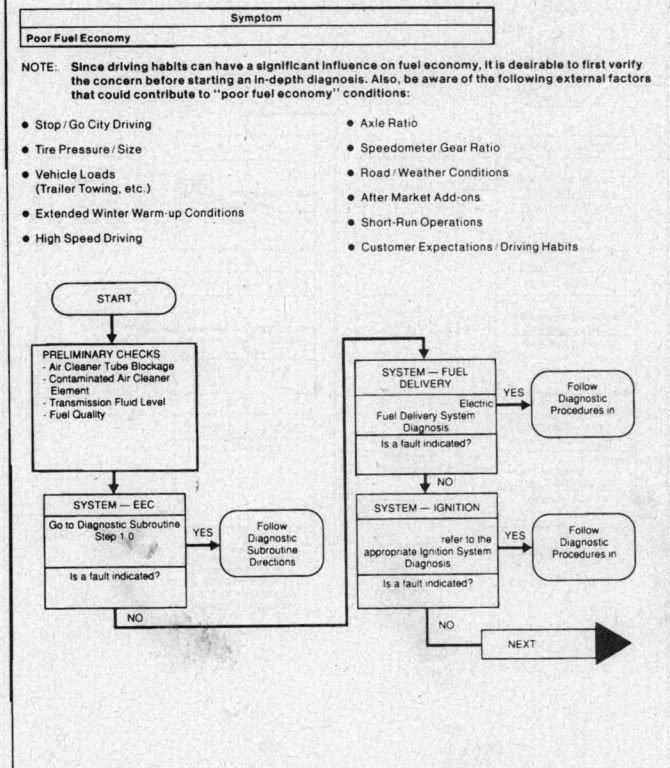

FM0159300683010X

Fig. 139   Diagnostic routines chart 15 (Part 1 of 3)

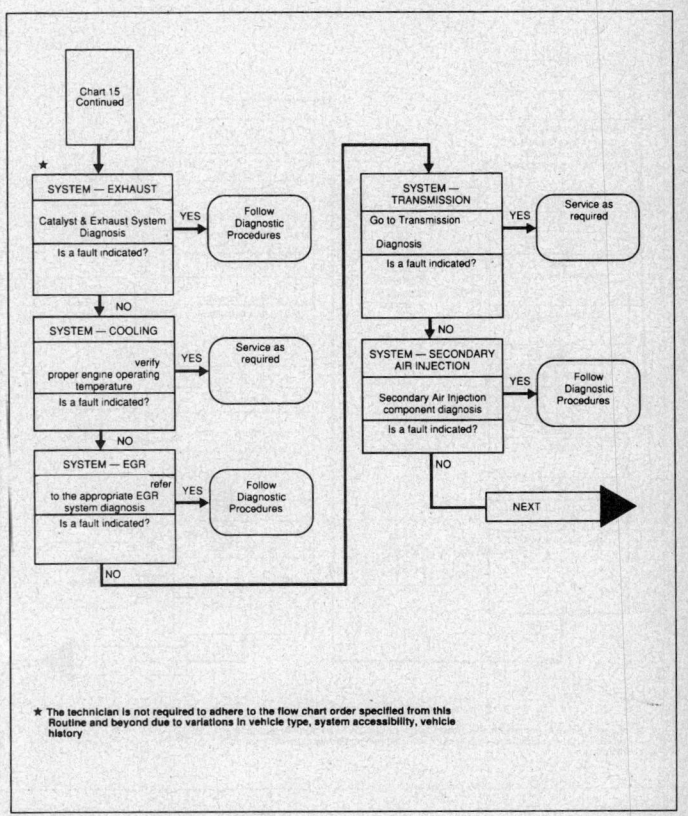

FM0159300683020X

Fig. 139   Diagnostic routines chart 15 (Part 2 of 3)

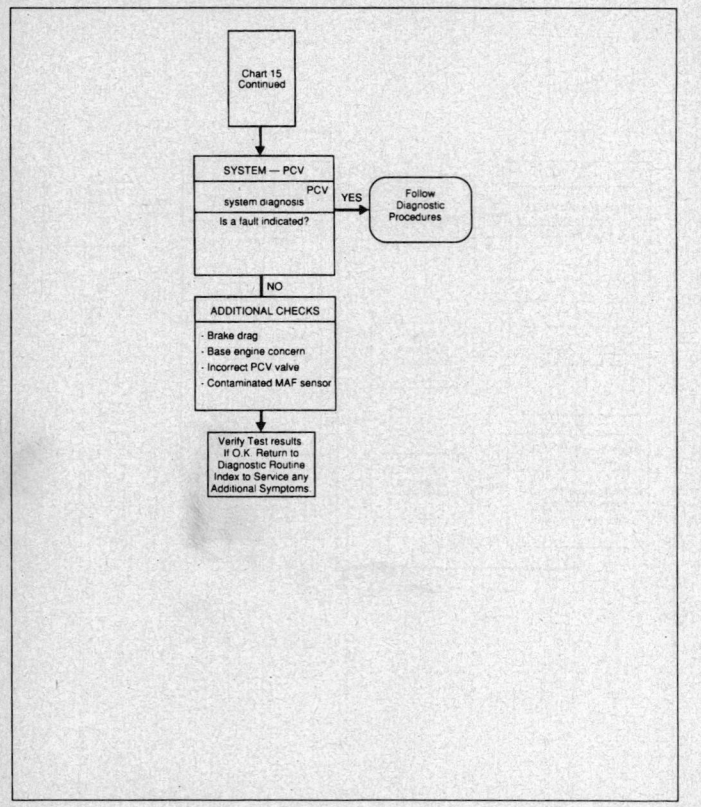

Fig. 139   Diagnostic routines chart 15 (Part 3 of 3)

FM0159300683030X

Symptom
Emissions Compliance

NOTE: **Canada and some states or metropolitan areas in the United States require periodic Idle Emission Tests.   If a product fails an Idle Emission Test, it is probable that, 1) The engine temperature was not warm and stabilized prior to the test. 2) The vehicle had idled excessively long prior to the test.**

Prior to starting any service, complaints of Idle Emission Test failure should be verified.

The following example encompasses most of the emissions measurement modes of the current state inspection / maintenance test procedures:

1.   Ensure that the engine is at normal operating temperature and that all accessories are turned off.

2.   Read emissions at idle.

3.   Run engine at 2500 ± 300 rpm.

4.   Read emissions within 30 seconds.

5.   Return engine speed to idle.

6.   Read emissions within 30 seconds.

If any emission components are replaced, perform the following before repeating the State Emission Test procedure:

1.   Clear Keep Alive Memory (KAM)

2.   To re-learn appropriate Adaptive Learning, run engine at 2500 rpm for one minute and idle engine for two minutes.

FM0159300684010X

Fig. 140   Diagnostic routines chart 16 (Part 1 of 3)

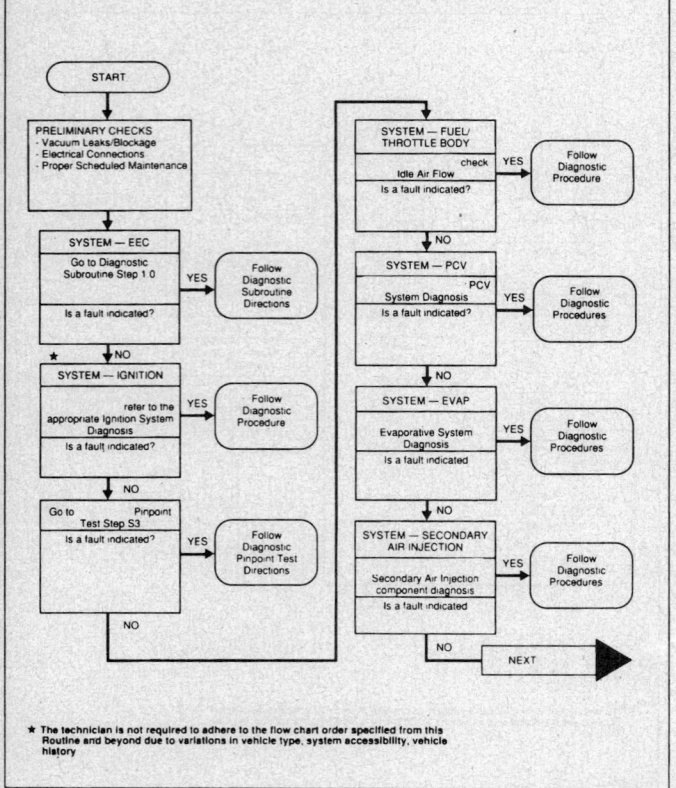

FM0159300684020X

Fig. 140   Diagnostic routines chart 16 (Part 2 of 3)

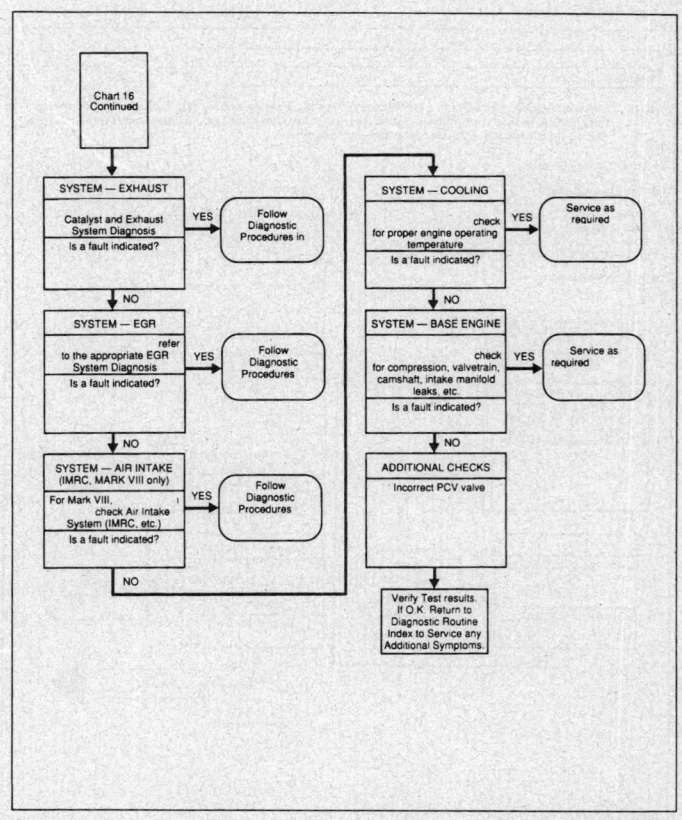

FM0159300684030X

Fig. 140   Diagnostic routines chart 16 (Part 3 of 3)

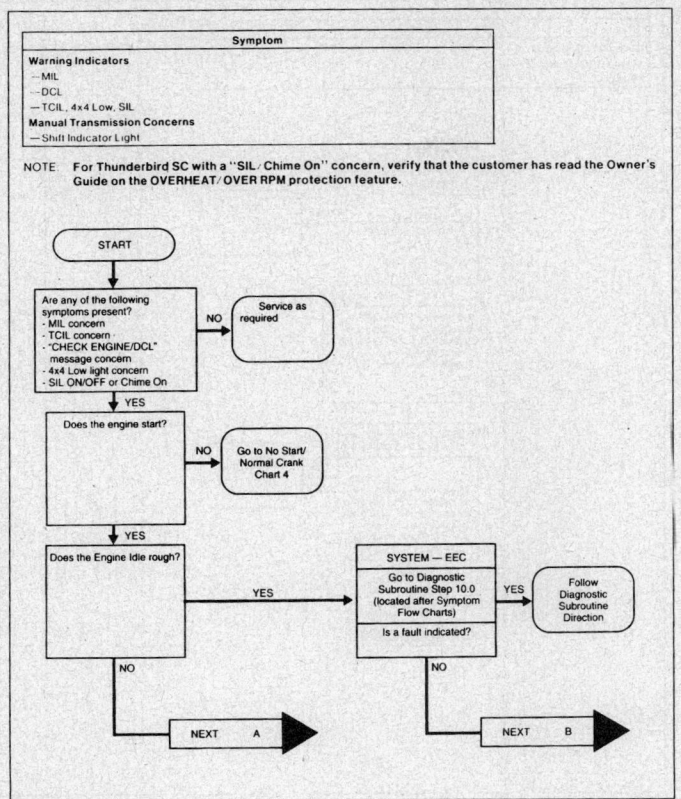

Fig. 141   Diagnostic routines chart 17 (Part 1 of 3)

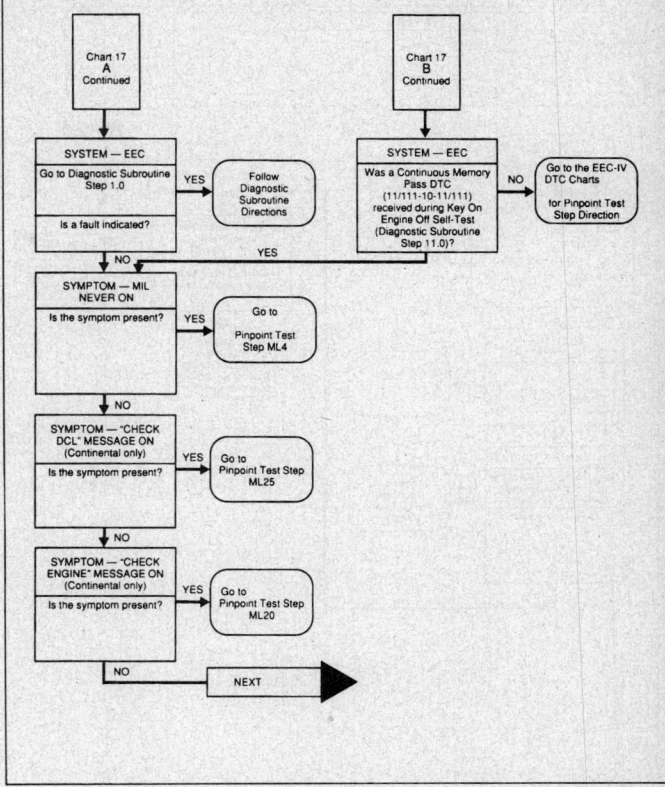

Fig. 141   Diagnostic routines chart 17 (Part 2 of 3)

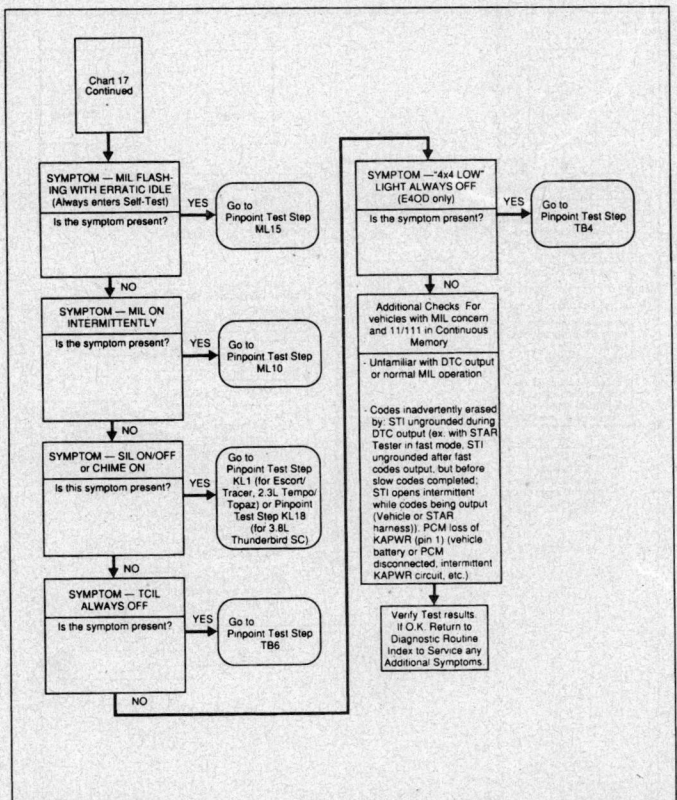

Fig. 141   Diagnostic routines chart 17 (Part 3 of 3)

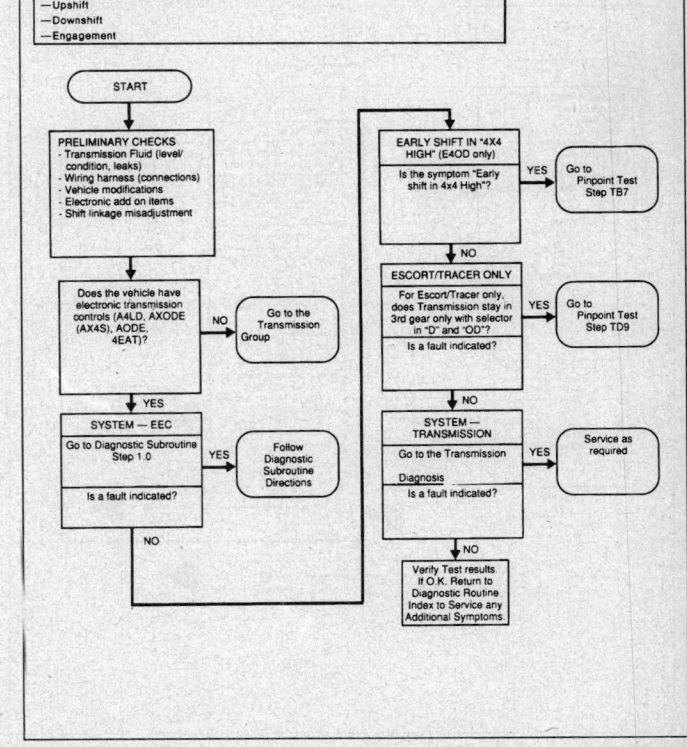

Fig. 142   Diagnostic routines chart 18

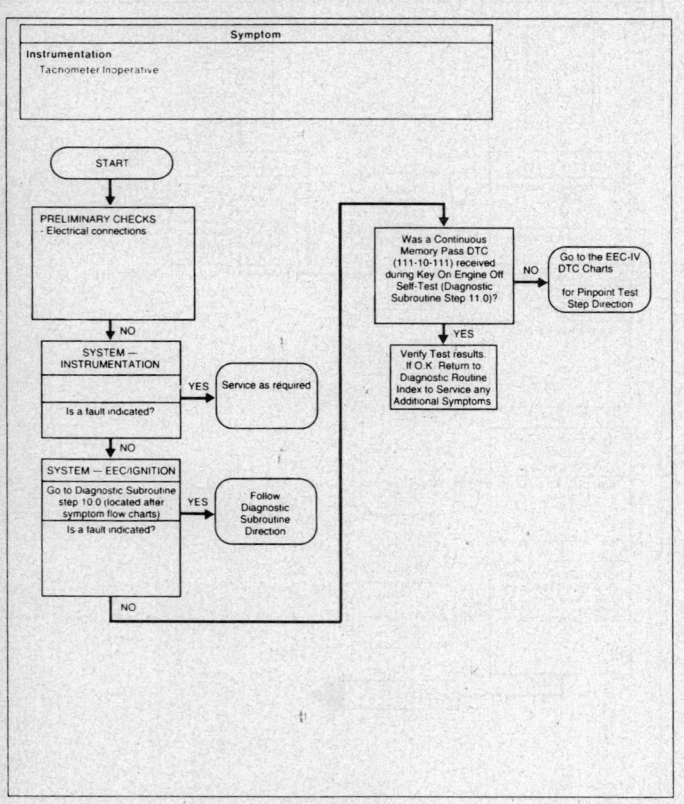

Fig. 143   Diagnostic routines chart 19. 1994–95

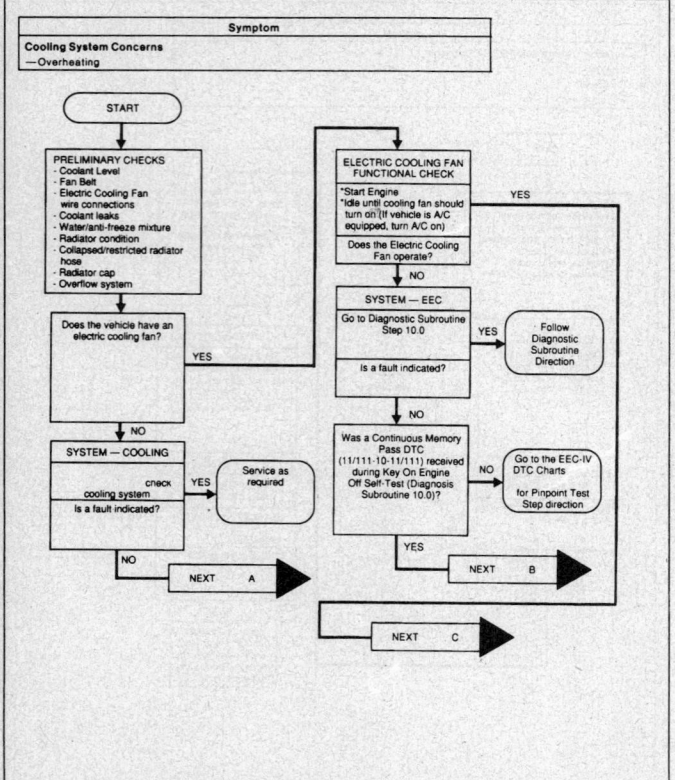

Fig. 145   Diagnostic routines chart 21 (Part 1 of 4)

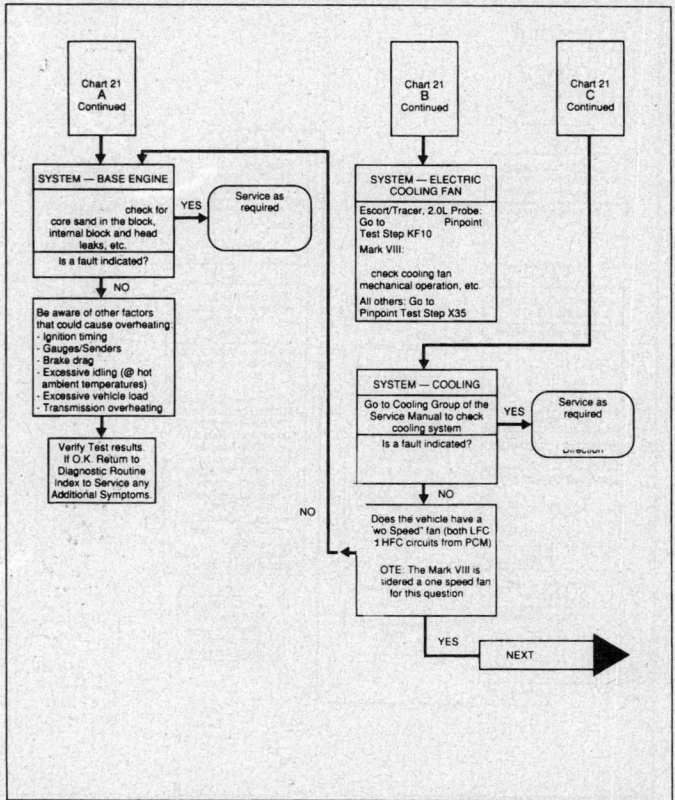

Fig. 145   Diagnostic routines chart 21 (Part 2 of 4)

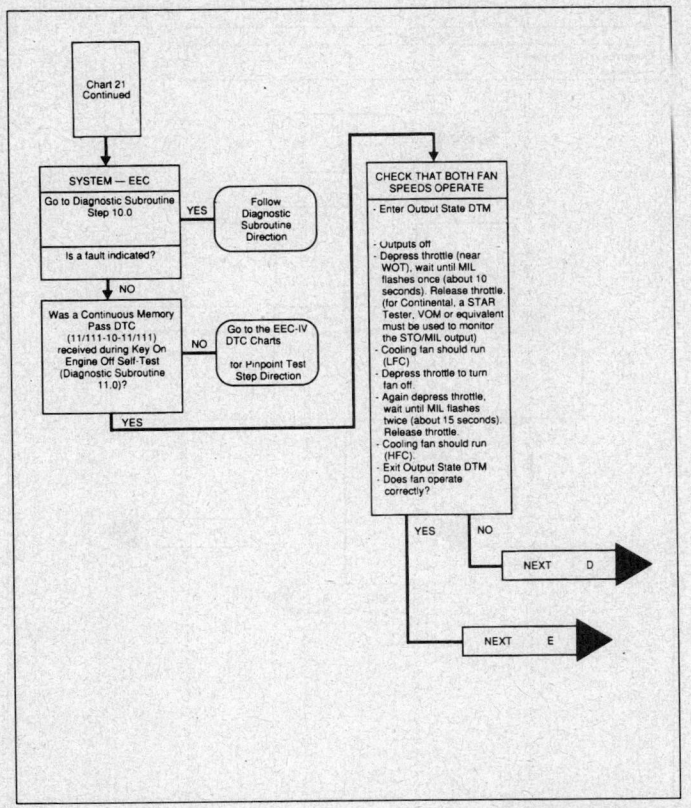

Fig. 145   Diagnostic routines chart 21 (Part 3 of 4)

FM015930068903OX

Fig. 145   Diagnostic routines chart 21 (Part 4 of 4).
1993

FM015930068904AX

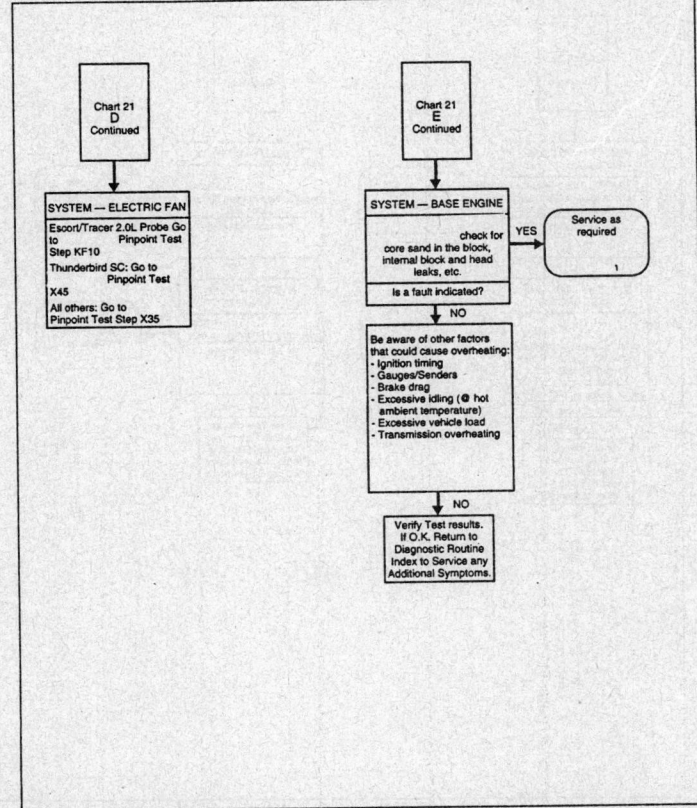

Fig. 145   Diagnostic routines chart
21 (Part 4 of 4). 1994–95

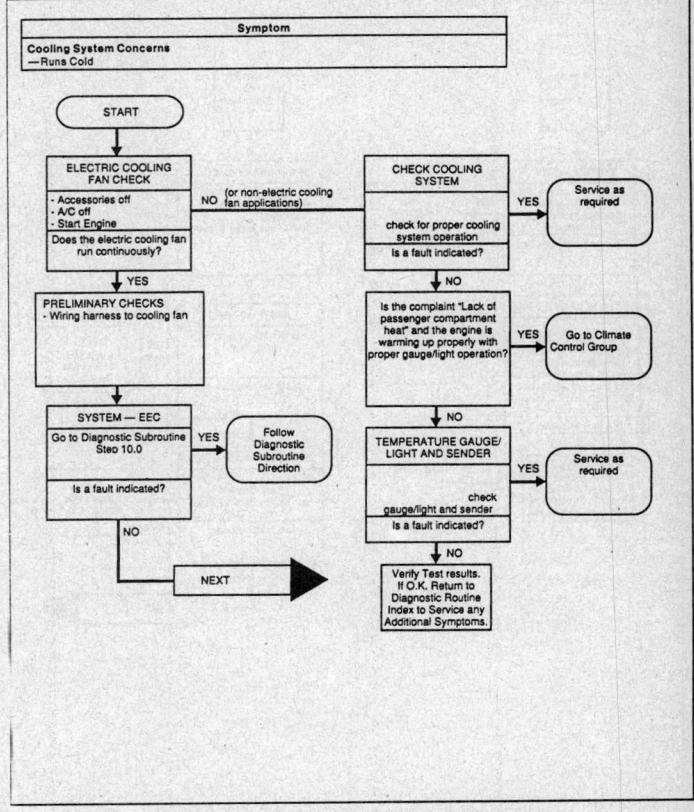

Fig. 146   Diagnostic routines chart
22 (Part 1 of 2)

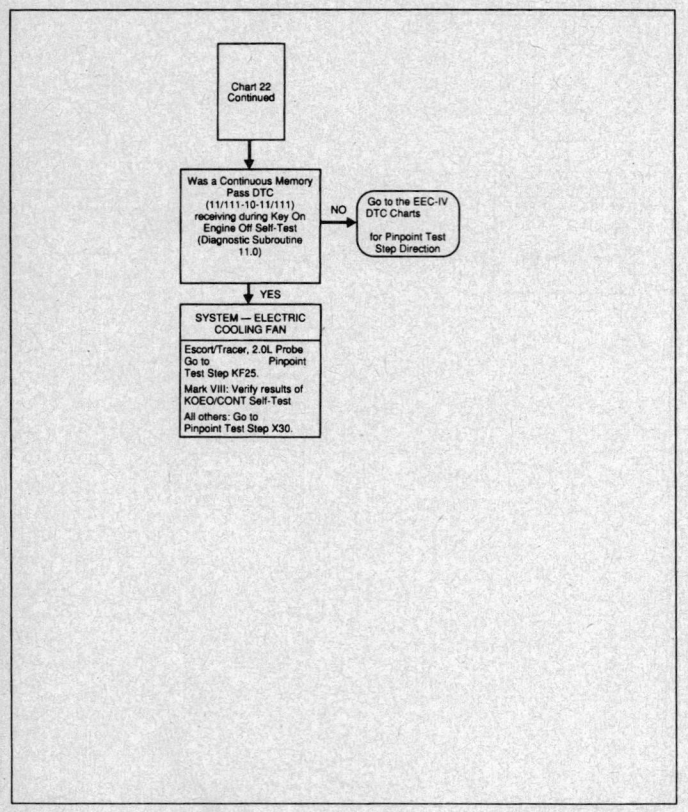

FM0159300690020X

Fig. 146   Diagnostic routines chart 22 (Part 2 of 2)

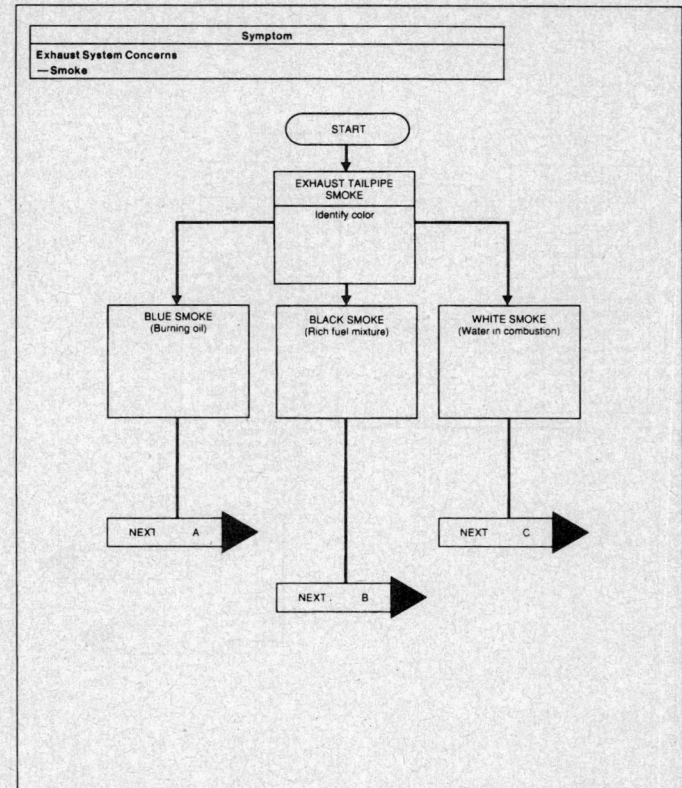

FM0159300691010X

Fig. 147   Diagnostic routines chart 23 (Part 1 of 3)

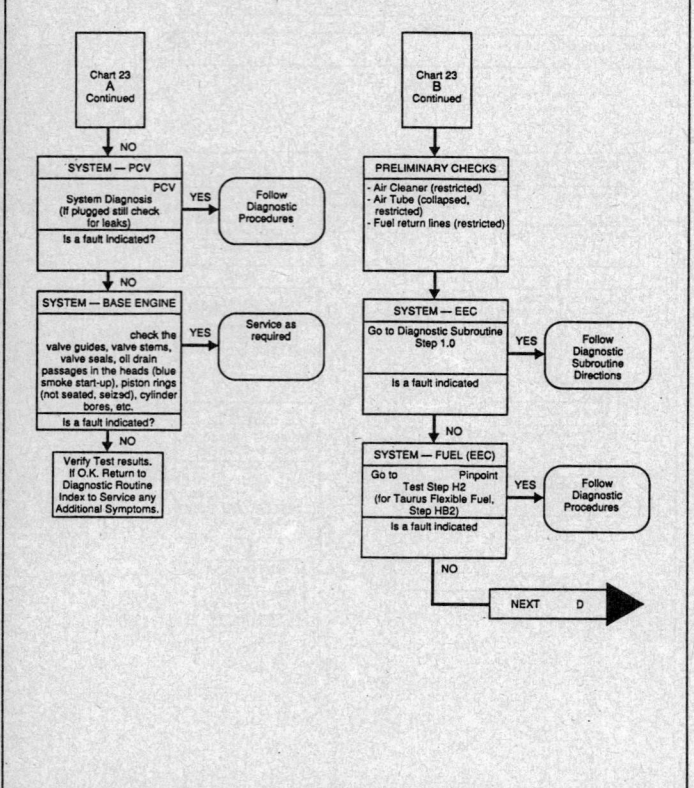

Fig. 147   Diagnostic routines chart 23 (Part 2 of 3)

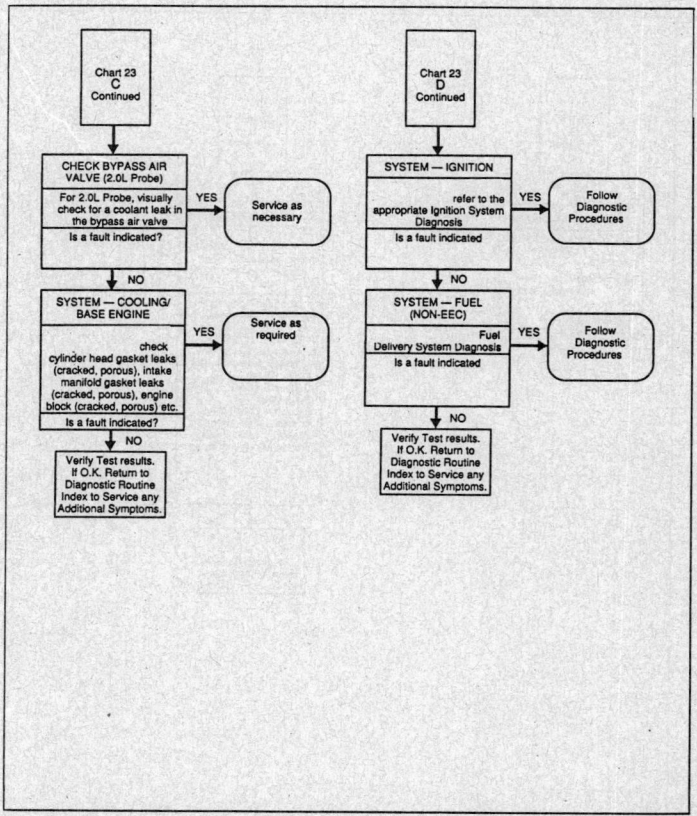

Fig. 147   Diagnostic routines chart 23 (Part 3 of 3)

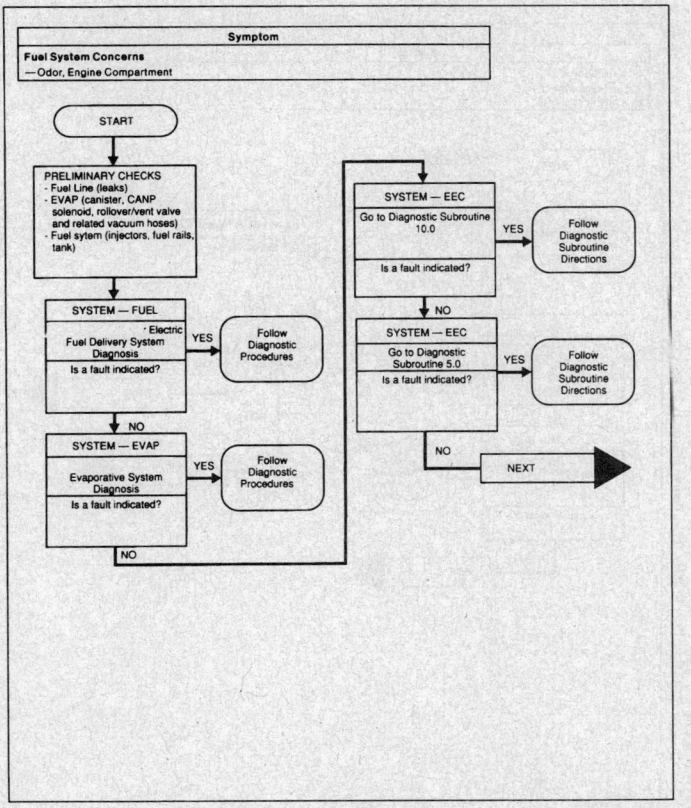

Fig. 148   Diagnostic routines chart 24 (Part 1 of 2)

FM0159300692010X

Fig. 148   Diagnostic routines chart 24 (Part 2 of 2)

FM0159300692020X

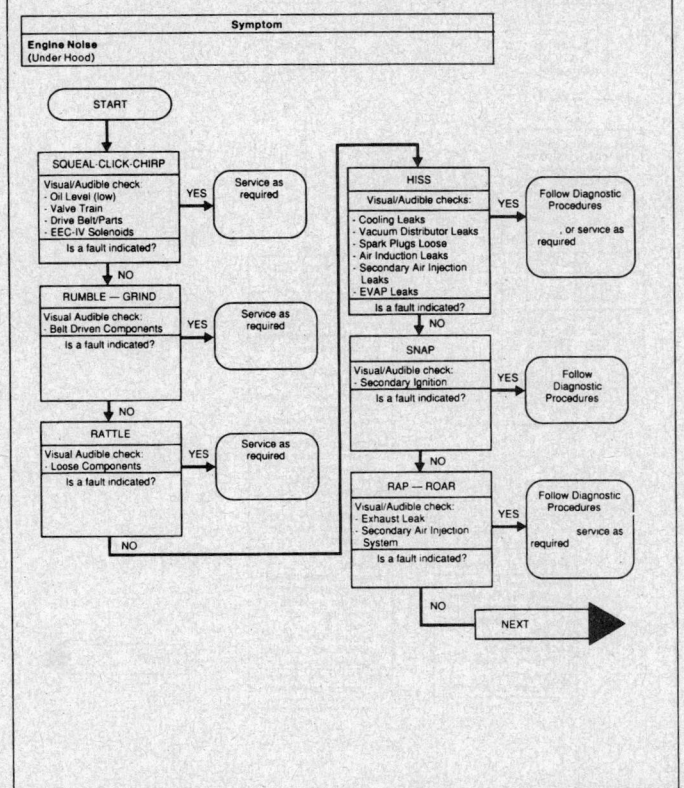

Fig. 149   Diagnostic routines chart 25 (Part 1 of 2)

FM0159300693010X

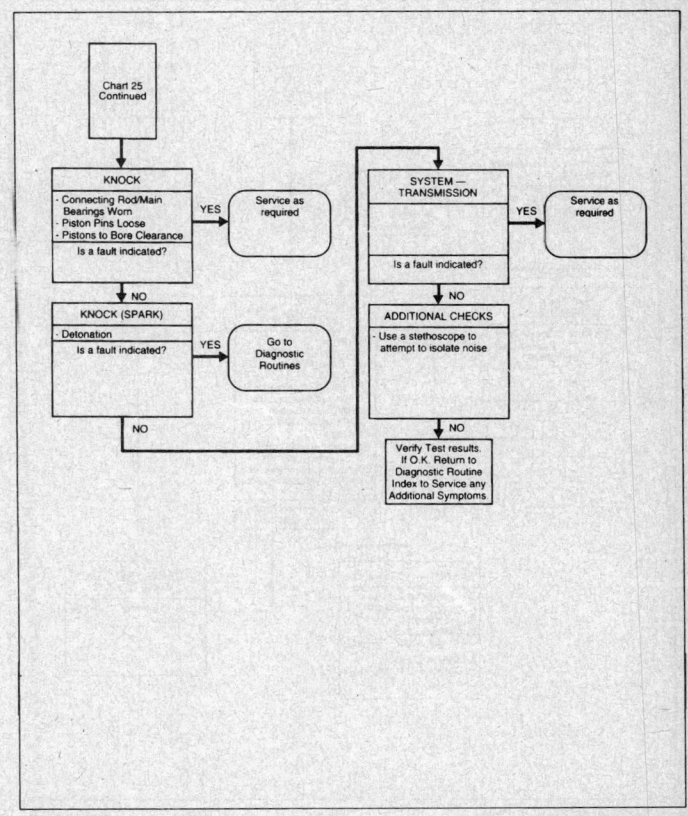

Fig. 149   Diagnostic routines chart 25 (Part 2 of 2)

FM0159300693020X

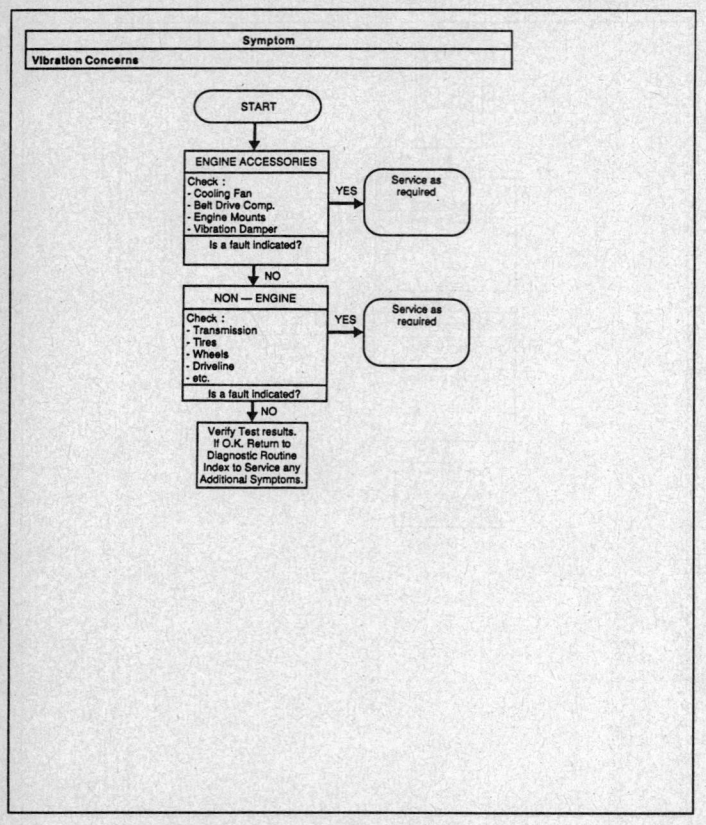

Fig. 150 Diagnostic routines chart 26

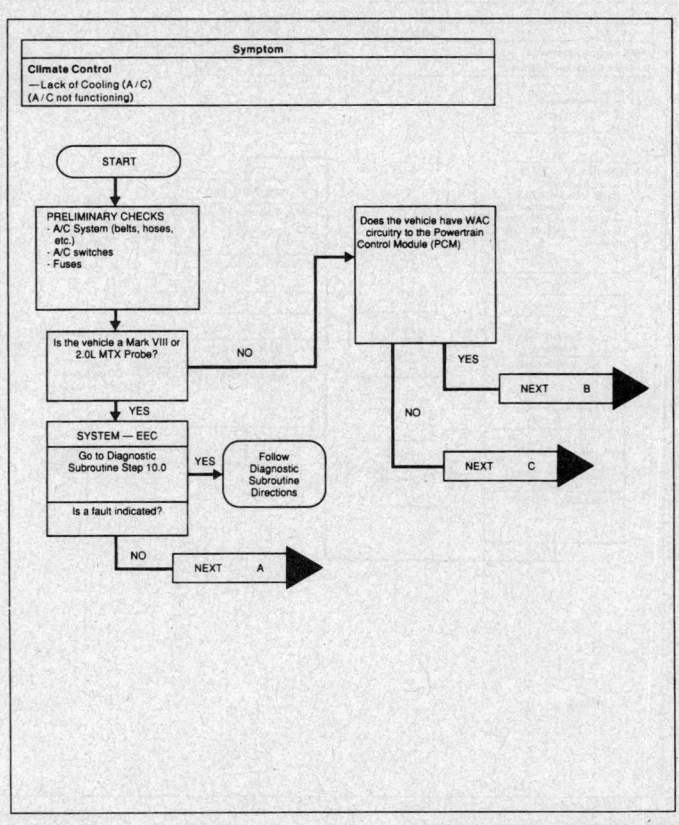

FM0159300695010X

Fig. 151 Diagnostic routines chart 29 (Part 1 of 3)

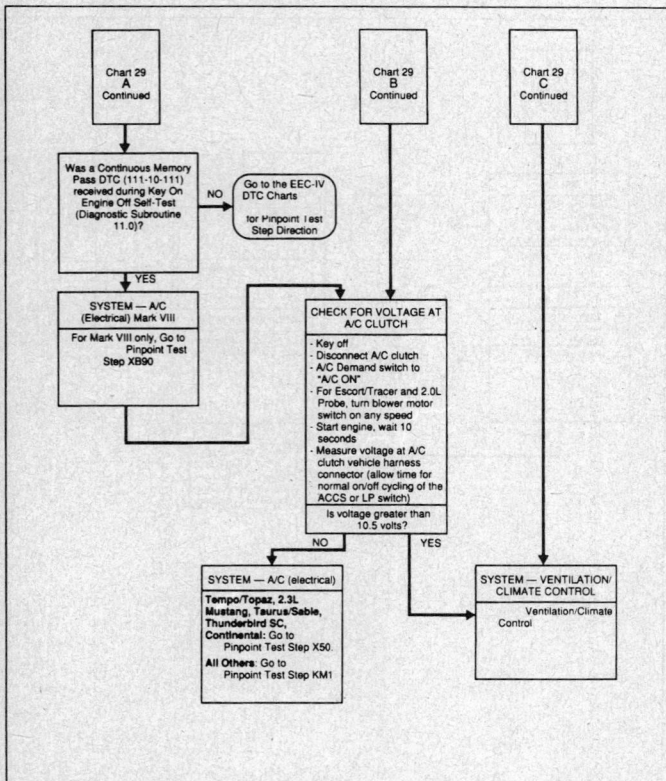

FM015930069502AX

Fig. 151 Diagnostic routines chart 29 (Part 2 of 3). 1993

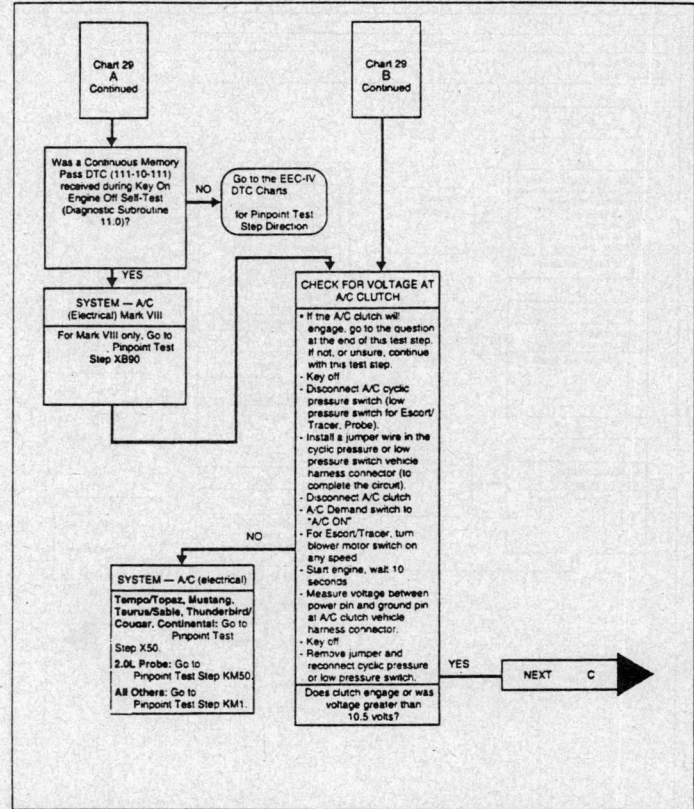

Fig. 151 Diagnostic routines chart 29 (Part 2 of 3). 1994–95

Computerized Engine Controls–FORD

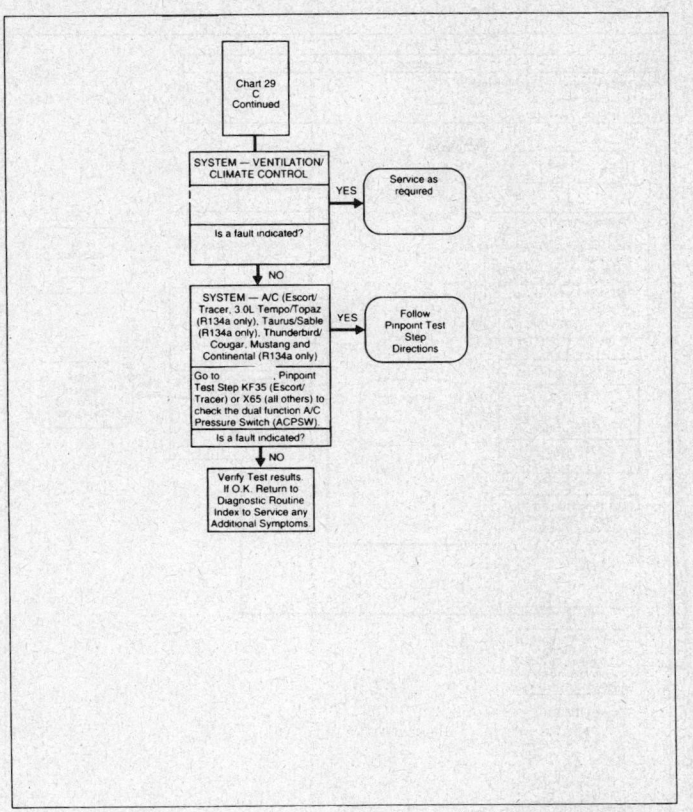

Fig. 151   Diagnostic routines chart 29 (Part 3 of 3). 1994–95

Fig. 152   Diagnostic routines chart 30

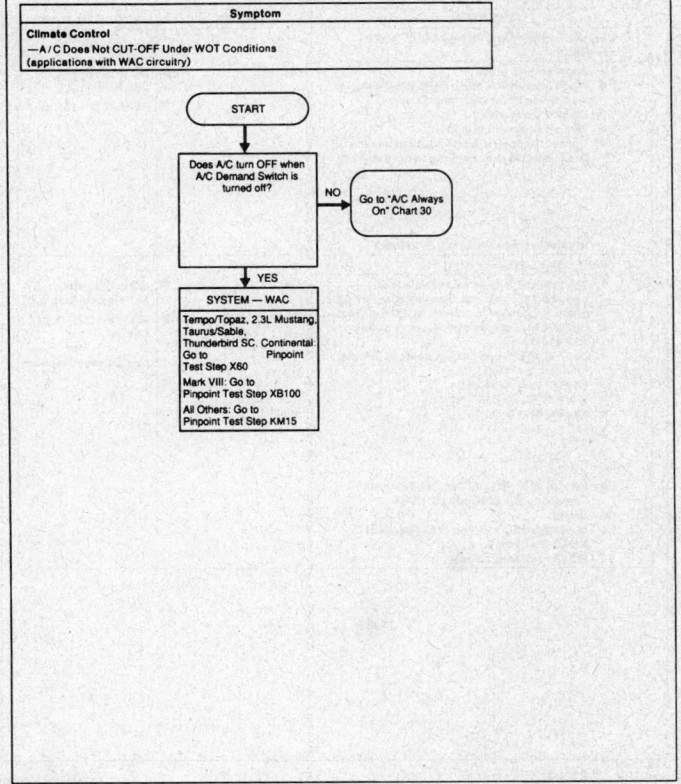

Fig. 153   Diagnostic routines chart 31. 1993

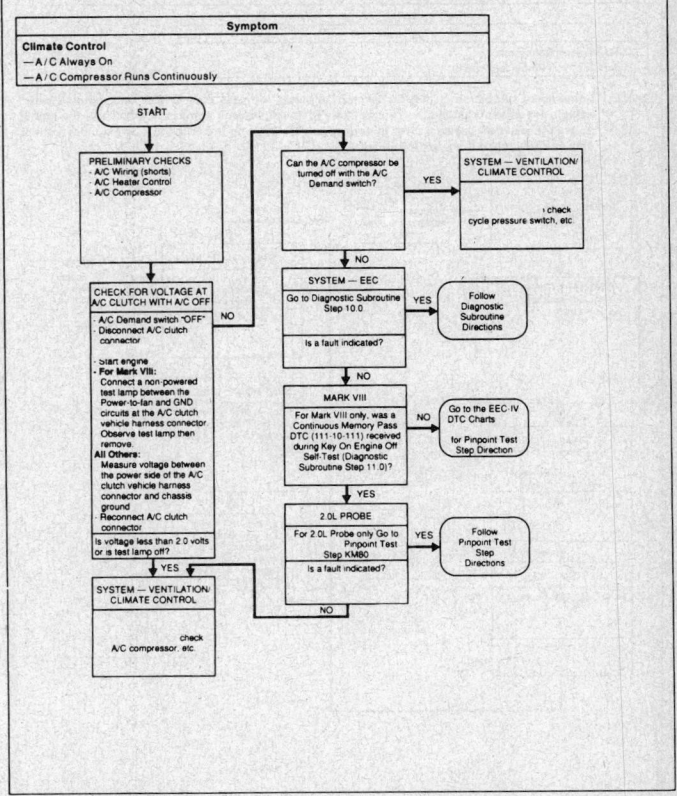

Fig. 154   Diagnostic routines chart 31. 1994–95

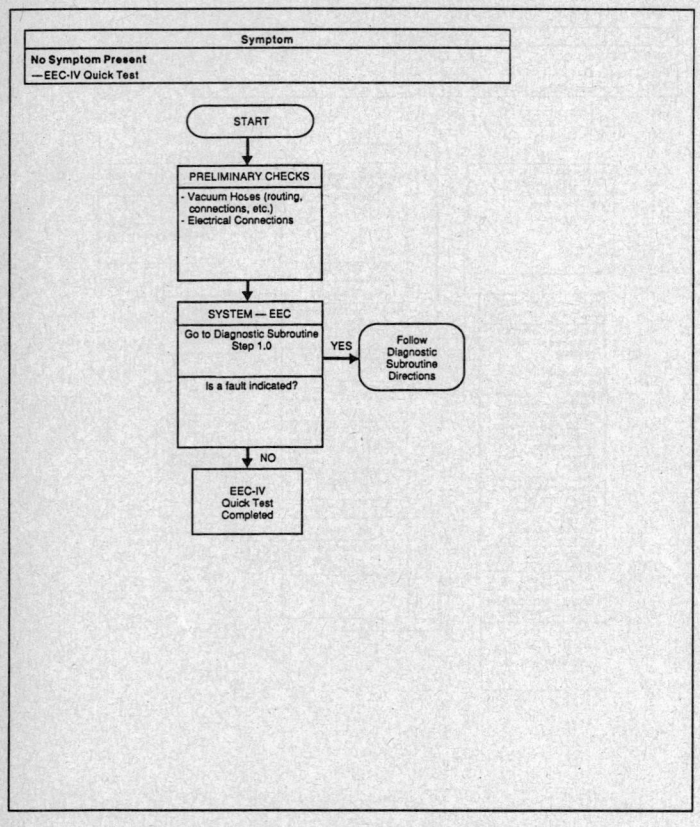

Fig. 155   Diagnostic routines chart 32

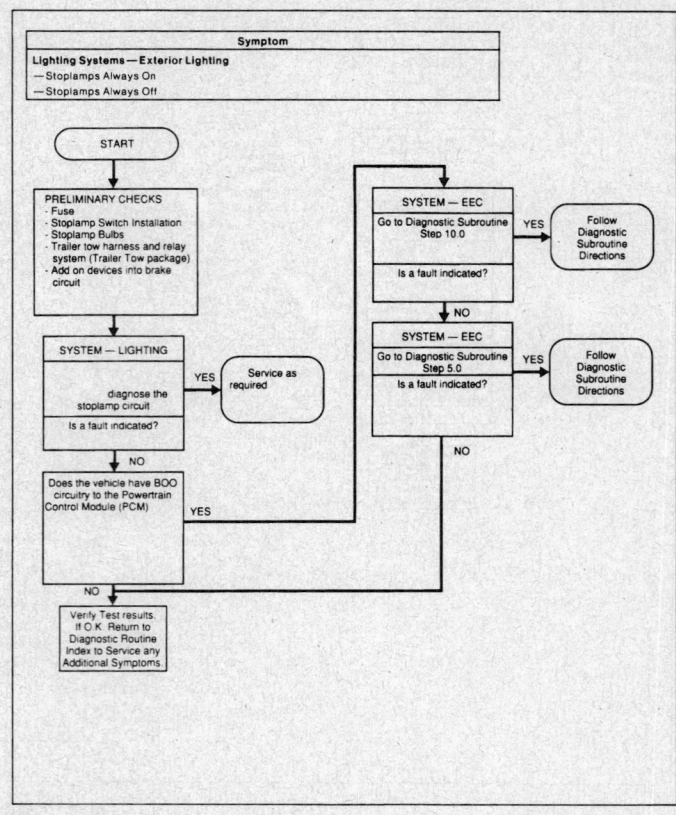

FM0159300700000X

Fig. 156   Diagnostic routines chart 33

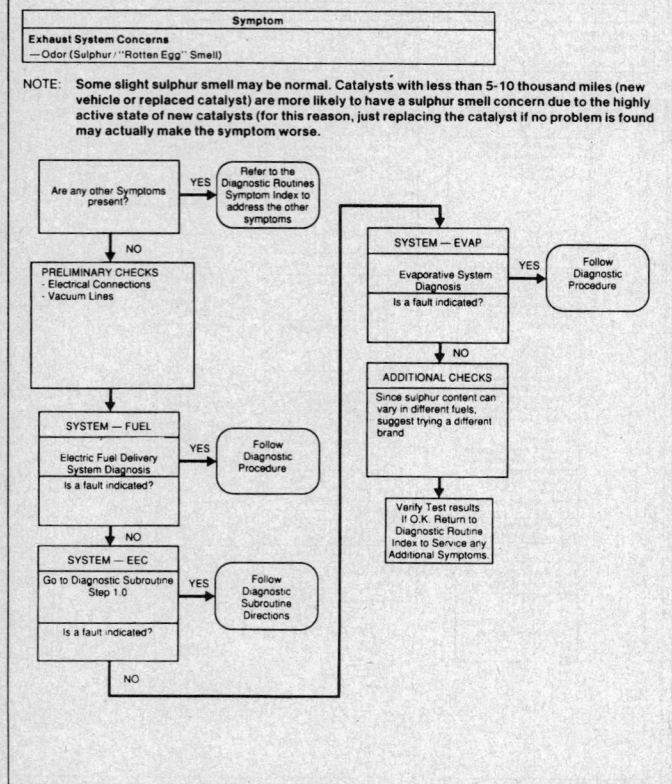

FM0159300701000X

Fig. 157   Diagnostic routines chart 34

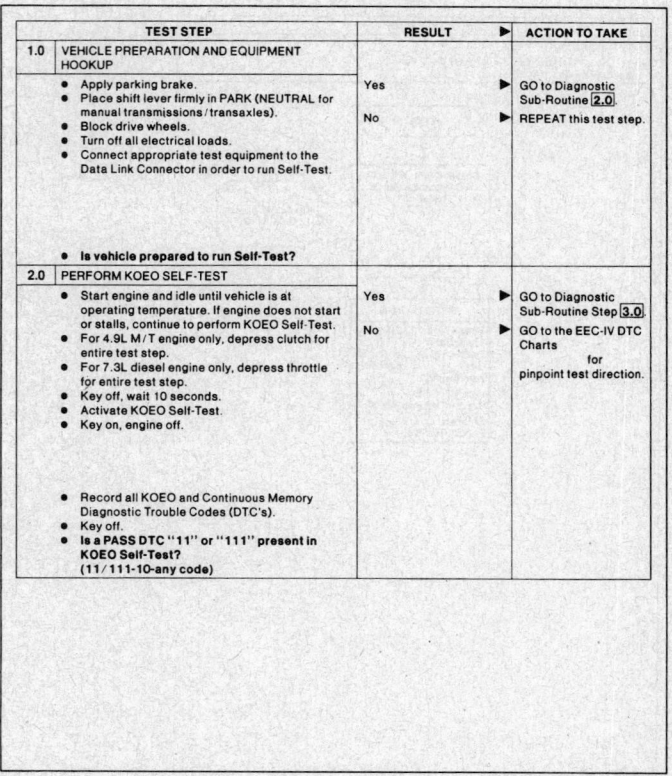

FM0159300702010X

Fig. 158   Diagnostic sub-routines/quick test 1.0 & 2.0, visual check, vehicle preparation, equipment hook-up & key On-engine Off self-test (Part 1 of 7)

Special Notes:

- The Key On Engine Off and Engine Running Self-Tests detect faults that are present at the time of testing. Faults that occur only when the vehicle is operating or intermittent faults that have occurred in the last 80 warm-up cycles are detected during Continuous Self-Test, stored in the Continuous Memory and displayed during Key On Engine Off Self-Test.

- When directed to a Pinpoint Test always read the cover page(s) for special notes and look carefully at the Pinpoint Test Schematic.

- After service, rerun Quick Test to ensure that service was effective.

- It may be necessary to disconnect or disassemble harness connector assemblies to do some of the inspections. Pin locations should be noted before disassembly.

Visual Check

1. Inspect the air cleaner and inlet ducting.

2. Check all engine vacuum hoses for damage, leaks, cracks, blockage, proper routing, etc.

3. Check EEC system wiring harness for proper connections, bent or broken pins, corrosion, loose wires, proper routing, etc.

4. Check the Powertrain Control Module (PCM), sensors and actuators for physical damage.

5. Check the engine coolant for proper level and mixture.

6. Check the transmission fluid level and quality.

7. Make all necessary repairs before continuing with QUICK TEST.

Vehicle Preparation and Equipment Hookup

Special Notes:

- Refer to the illustrations for Data Link Connector (DLC) pin orientation and VOM, STAR or Scan Tool hookup.

Vehicle Preparation

1. Perform **ALL** safety steps required to start and run vehicle tests - apply parking brake, place shift lever firmly into PARK position (NEUTRAL on manual transmission), block drive wheels, etc.

2. Turn off **ALL** electrical loads—radios, lights, A C, heater, blower, fans, etc.

Using the Star Tester

1. Turn the ignition key off.

2. Connect the color coded adapter cable to the STAR tester.

FM0159300702020X

Fig. 158 Diagnostic sub-routines/quick test 1.0 & 2.0, visual check, vehicle preparation, equipment hook-up & key On-engine Off self-test (Part 2 of 7)

3. Connect the adapter cable leads to the proper connectors

4. Connect the timing light.

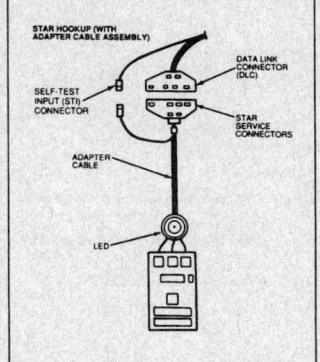 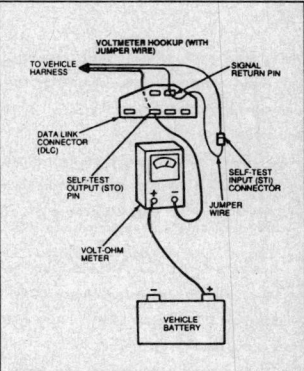

Using an Analog Volt / Ohm Meter (VOM)

1. Turn the ignition key off.

2. Set the VOM on a DC voltage range to read from 0 to 15 volts.

3. Connect the VOM from the battery positive post to the Self-Test Output pin of the large Data Link Connector (DLC)

4. Connect the timing light.

Using the Malfunction Indicator Lamp (MIL)

No special equipment hookup is required. STI is jumpered to SIG RTN at Self-Test Input (STI) connector and the Data Link Connector (DLC).

FM0159300702030X

Fig. 158 Diagnostic sub-routines/quick test 1.0 & 2.0, visual check, vehicle preparation, equipment hook-up & key On-engine Off self-test (Part 3 of 7)

Using the Message Center on Continental Applications Only

No special equipment hookup is required. STI is jumpered to SIG RTN at Self-Test Input (STI) connector and the Data Link Connector (DLC).

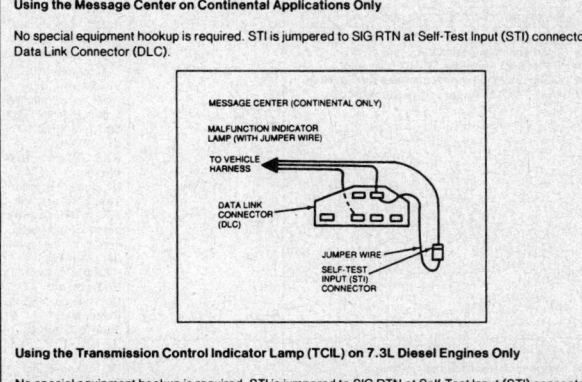

Using the Transmission Control Indicator Lamp (TCIL) on 7.3L Diesel Engines Only

No special equipment hookup is required. STI is jumpered to SIG RTN at Self-Test Input (STI) connector and the Data Link Connector (DLC).

FM0159300702040X

Fig. 158 Diagnostic sub-routines/quick test 1.0 & 2.0, visual check, vehicle preparation, equipment hook-up & key On-engine Off self-test (Part 4 of 7)

Using the New Generation STAR (NGS) Scan Tool

1. Turn the ignition switch off.

2. Connect the appropriate EEC adapter cable to the Scan Tool.

3. Connect the adapter leads to the DLC and STI connector.

4. Connect the timing light (if applicable).

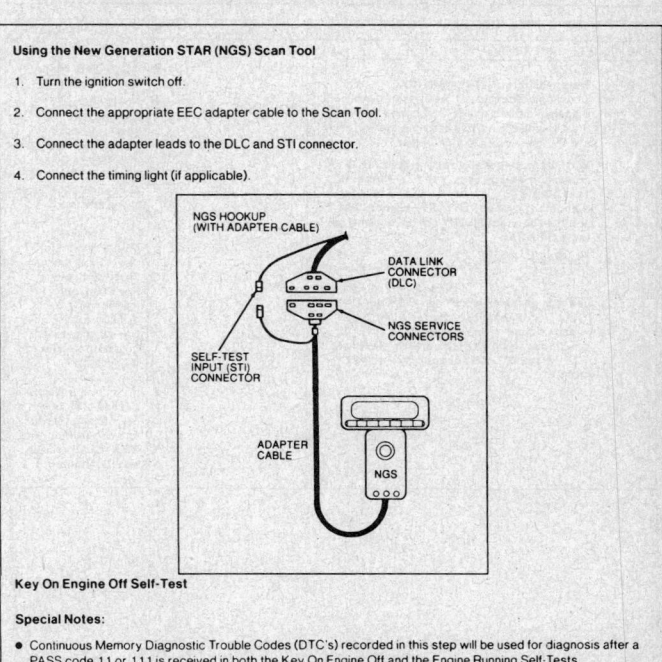

Key On Engine Off Self-Test

Special Notes:

- Continuous Memory Diagnostic Trouble Codes (DTC's) recorded in this step will be used for diagnosis after a PASS code 11 or 111 is received in both the Key On Engine Off and the Engine Running Self-Tests

- Deviation from this procedure may cause the output of false DTC's.

- On all vehicles equipped with a **4.9L ENGINE**, the clutch must be depressed during the Key On Engine Off Self-Test.

- On all vehicles equipped with a **7.3L DIESEL ENGINE**, the throttle must be depressed (WOT) during the entire Key On Engine Off Self-Test

FM0159300702050X

Fig. 158 Diagnostic sub-routines/quick test 1.0 & 2.0, visual check, vehicle preparation, equipment hook-up & key On-engine Off self-test (Part 5 of 7)

How To Run The Key On Engine Off Self-Test

DO

- Verify that the vehicle has been properly prepared.
- Start engine and run until its at operating temperature.
- Turn engine off and wait 10 seconds.
- Activate Self-Test.
  - STAR Tester: Latch the center button in the down position.
  - Analog VOM: Jumper STI to SIG RTN at the DLC and STI connectors.
  - Malfunction Indicator Lamp (MIL): Jumper STI to SIG RTN at the DLC and STI connectors. DTC's will be flashed on the Malfunction Indicator Lamp (MIL).
  - Transmission Control Indicator Lamp (TCIL) 7.3L Diesel only: Jumper STI to SIG RTN at the DLC and STI connectors. Service Codes will be flashed on the TCIL.
  - Message Center (Continental Applications Only). Refer to "Self-Test with Message Center".
  - Scan Tool: 1) Enter vehicle selection. 2) Enter KOEO Self-Test.
- Place ignition key in the ON position.
- For 7.3L Diesel vehicles only, depress the throttle.
- Record all Diagnostic Trouble Codes (DTC's) displayed.

DON'T

- Depress throttle during Key On Engine Off Self-Test on gasoline engine applications.

Self-Test with New Generation Star (NGS) Scan Tool

For a detailed description of the New Generation Star Scan Tool and the variety of tests that can be run, refer to the instruction manual provided with the tool.

The Diagnostic Test Mode Menu Selection provides access to EEC-IV format on-board Self-Tests. Self-Tests are run using STI and STO lines on the CM. Diagnostic Trouble Code (DTC) definitions are provided if a vehicle has been selected from the Vehicle Entry Menu under Vehicle and Engine Selection menu.

*For activating Key On Engine Off (KOEO) or Key on Engine Running (KOER) Self-Test

1. Connect Self-Test adapter cable to LINK connector of NGS and Data Link Connector (DLC) and Self-Test Input (STI) connector on vehicle.

2. Select Diagnostic Test Mode from the main menu.

3. Select the desired Self-Test function. Selected Self-Test will be initialized and Self-Test control screen will be displayed.

4. Select Slow or Fast coded format with the key selection.

5. Pressing the START key will short STI to ground and start Self-Test and DTC acquisition.

6. Screen will display DTC's in tabular form with definitions after all fast DTC's are received or as received using slow code format, until all DTC's have been output by the PCM.

7. Pressing the STOP key will remove STI to ground short and stop acquisition of DTC's. The first received DTC will be highlighted. As you move the highlighting through the DTC's, the definition for the selected DTC will be displayed in the lower box.

8. Press CANCEL to terminate Self-Test and to exit to the Diagnostic Test Mode menu.

9. Press CANCEL to return to the Main Menu.

NOTE: **Pressing the STOP key (unlatching STI) or CANCEL trigger before all slow DTC's have been output, will erase any Continuous DTC's from PCM memory. Although, if fast code format is used, the DTC will already be displayed for viewing, along with DTC descriptions.**

FM0159300702060X

Fig. 158 Diagnostic sub-routines/quick test 1.0 & 2.0, visual check, vehicle preparation, equipment hook-up & key On-engine Off self-test (Part 6 of 7)

FM0159300702070X

Fig. 158 Diagnostic sub-routines/quick test 1.0 & 2.0, visual check, vehicle preparation, equipment hook-up & key On-engine Off self-test (Part 7 of 7)

TEST STEP	RESULT	►	ACTION TO TAKE
3.0 CHECK BASE TIMING • Key off. • Transmission in PARK or NEUTRAL. • Turn off electrical loads (A/C, heater, etc.) • Disconnect the in-line SPOUT connector. • Start engine (do not use a remote starter, only use the ignition key to start engine). NOTE: If engine stalls, reconnect SPOUT connector and go to Pinpoint Test Step [S2]. If engine is now a NO START (will not "Fire" at all), reconnect SPOUT connector and go to Section 8A. • Check base timing. . (For 2.3L Dual Plug, use exhaust side plug. If timing light does not "light", go to Diagnostic Sub-Routine [5.0].) • Is base timing within ± 2 degrees of specification on VECI decal (base timing is 10 degrees BTDC if not specified on VECI label)?	Yes No	► ►	GO to Diagnostic Sub-Routine [4.0]. **For Distributor Ignition (DI) applications:** ADJUST as necessary and RERUN Quick Test. If unable to adjust to specification, refer to the Ignition to check proper distributor orientation, timing chain/belt, etc. **For Electronic Ignition (EI) applications:** Base timing is not adjustable. Refer to the Ignition . possible causes of incorrect base timing (timing chain/belt, incorrect CMP/Synchronizer sensor orientation, etc.).

Fig. 159 Diagnostic sub-routines/quick test 3.0, base timing

TEST STEP	RESULT	►	ACTION TO TAKE
4.0 VERIFY PCM CONTROL OF TIMING • In-line SPOUT connector disconnected. • Start engine and let idle. • Reconnect the in-line SPOUT connector. • Does timing change from base timing when the SPOUT connector is reconnected?	Yes No	► ►	GO to Diagnostic Sub-Routine [5.0]. GO to Diagnostic Sub-Routine [5.0]. While performing the Engine Running (ER) Self-Test, CHECK for DTC 213/18. **If ER DTC 213/18 is present:** Disregard any other codes. Refer to the EEC-IV DTC Charts for proper pinpoint test step direction for the DTC 213/18. **If ER DTC 213/18 is NOT present:** Continue as directed in Diagnostic Sub-Routine [5.0].
5.0 PERFORM ENGINE RUNNING SELF-TEST • Start engine and idle until vehicle is at operating temperature. • Turn engine off. • Activate Engine Running Self-Test. • Start engine. NOTE: If engine stalls during Engine Running Self-Test, go to Pinpoint Test Step [S2]. • Record all service codes displayed. NOTE: Engine Running DTC 98/998 indicates vehicle is in FMEM mode and Engine Running Self-Test cannot be performed. Go to the EEC-IV DTC charts at the end of this section for DTC 98/998 direction. • Is a PASS DTC (11 or 111) received during Engine Running Self-Test?	Yes No	► ►	GO to Diagnostic Sub-Routine Step [6.0]. GO to the EEC-IV DTC Charts for pinpoint test direction.

FM0159300704010X

Fig. 160 Diagnostic sub-routines/quick test 4.0 & 5.0, PCM timing control & engine running self-test (Part 1 of 3)

Engine Running Self-Test

Special Notes:

- On vehicles equipped with the Brake On/Off (BOO) circuit, the brake pedal MUST be depressed and released AFTER the ID code.
- On vehicles equipped with the Power Steering Pressure (PSP) switch, within 1 to 2 seconds after the ID code, the steering wheel must be turned at least one-half turn and released.
- On vehicles equipped with E4OD transmission, the Transmission Control Switch (TCS) must be cycled after the ID code.
- The Dynamic Response code is a single pulse (or a 10 code on the STAR Tester) that occurs 6-20 seconds after the engine running identification code. (See APPENDIX: DTC Output Format.)
- When/if the Dynamic Response code occurs, perform a brief wide open throttle.

Fig. 160   Diagnostic sub-routines/quick test 4.0 & 5.0, PCM timing control & engine running self-test (Part 2 of 3)

How To Run Engine Running Self-Test

DO

- Deactivate Self-Test.
- Start and run engine at 2,000 rpm for two minutes. This action warms up the HO2S.
- Turn engine off, wait 10 seconds.
- Activate Self-Test.
- Start engine.
- After the ID code, depress and release the brake pedal if appropriate. See Special Note on previous page.
- After the ID code, within 1 to 2 seconds, turn the steering wheel at least one-half turn and then release it, if appropriate. See Special Note above.
- If a Dynamic Response Code occurs, perform a brief wide-open throttle (WOT).
- Record all Diagnostic Trouble Codes (DTC's) displayed.

DON'T

- Depress the throttle unless a Dynamic Response code is displayed.

Fig. 160   Diagnostic sub-routines/quick test 4.0 & 5.0, PCM timing control & engine running self-test (Part 3 of 3)

TEST STEP		RESULT	▶	ACTION TO TAKE
6.0	ADDRESS CONTINUOUS MEMORY DTC			
	• Was a Continuous Memory PASS DTC (11/111-10-11/111) received during Key On Engine Off Self-Test?	Yes	▶	RETURN to Diagnostic Routine Symptom Flow Chart.
		No	▶	GO to the EEC-IV DTC Charts for pinpoint test direction.
10.0	VEHICLE PREPARATION AND EQUIPMENT HOOKUP			
	• Apply parking brake. • Place shift lever firmly in PARK (NEUTRAL for manual transmissions/transaxles). • Block drive wheels. • Turn off all electrical loads. • Connect appropriate test equipment to the Data Link Connector in order to run Self-Test.	Yes	▶	GO to Diagnostic Sub-Routine 11.0.
		No	▶	REPEAT this test step.
	• Is vehicle prepared to run Self-Test?			
11.0	PERFORM KOEO SELF-TEST			
	• Start engine and idle until vehicle is at operating temperature. If engine does not start or stall, continue to perform KOEO Self-Test. • For 4.9L M/T engine only, depress clutch for entire test step. • For 7.3L diesel engine only, depress throttle for entire test step. • Key off, wait 10 seconds. • Activate KOEO Self-Test. • Key on, engine off.	Yes	▶	RETURN to Diagnostic Routine Flow Chart.
		No	▶	GO to the EEC-IV DTC Charts for pinpoint test direction.
	• Record all KOEO and Continuous Memory Diagnostic Trouble Codes (DTC's). • Key off. • Is a PASS DTC "11" or "111" present in KOEO Self-Test? (11-111-10-any code)			

Fig. 161   Diagnostic sub-routines/quick test 6.0, 10.0 & 11.0, continuous memory DTC, vehicle preparation & hookup & key On-engine Off self-test (Part 1 of 2)

Key On Engine Off (KOEO) Self-Test

1. Plug in both connectors of the tester to the mating connectors of the vehicle.
2. Determine the type of system you have (EEC-IV or MECS) and set the switch to the proper type.
3. Select fast code mode or slow code mode with the mode selector switch.

    NOTE: The SUPER STAR II tester will only display 3-digit DTC's in fast code mode. If slow code mode is used on 3-digit DTC applications, the display will be blank.

4. Turn on the power to the tester.
5. Depress the test button on the tester to the test position.
6. Turn on the vehicle ignition key.

The tester will now read any DTC's in this mode.

Key On Engine Running (KOER) Self-Test

1. Start and warm up the engine until it is at a normal running temperature.
2. Turn the engine off.
3. Depress the test button to the test position, then restart the engine.

On applications with 2-digit DTC's, the tester will now display an engine I.D. code, and on certain vehicles, a Dynamic Response code. Then, service codes will be displayed. For 3-digit DTC applications, no engine ID code will be displayed. The Dynamic Response indicator will light but no Dynamic Response code will be displayed. DTC's will then be displayed.

For a detailed description of the variety of tests that can be run with the SUPER STAR II, refer to the instruction manual provided with the tester.

Fig. 161   Diagnostic sub-routines/quick test 6.0, 10.0 & 11.0, continuous memory DTC, vehicle preparation & hookup & key On-engine Off self-test (Part 2 of 2)

Service Code/ Page No.	Application	Pinpoint Test Step — Key On, Engine Off	Engine Running	Continuous Memory
NO CODES	All	QA1	QA1	QA1
Page No.	—	8-247	8-247	8-247
CODE 11	All	Pass	Pass	Pass
Page No.	—	—	—	—
CODE 12②	All	N/A	KE1	N/A
Page No.	—	—	8-203	—
CODE 13②	All	N/A	KE15	N/A
Page No.	—	—	8-204	—
CODE 14②	All	N/A	N/A	NA1
Page No.	—	—	—	8-235
CODE 15	All	①	①	QB1
Page No.	—	—	—	8-248
CODE 16②	All	N/A	KE1	N/A
Page No.	—	—	8-203	—
CODE 18②	All	N/A	PA1	NA3
Page No.	—	—	8-242	8-235
CODE 19	All	①	①	N/A
Page No.	—	—	—	—
CODE 21②	All	DA1	DA1	N/A
Page No.	—	8-124	8-124	—
CODE 22②	Mustang	DF1	DF1	DF90
Page No.	—	8-138	8-138	8-139
CODE 22②	All Others	DF1	DF7	DF90
Page No.	—	8-138	8-138	8-139Y°
CODE 22③	All	DF1	DF7	DF90
Page No.	—	8-138	8-138	8-139
CODE 23②	All	DH2	DH1	N/A
Page No.	—	8-142	8-142	—
CODE 24②	All	DA1	DA1	N/A
Page No.	—	8-124	8-124	—
CODE 25②	All	N/A	DG1	N/A
Page No.	—	—	8-140	—
CODE 26②	All	DC1	DC1	N/A
Page No.	—	8-130	8-130	—
CODE 26③	All	TE1	TE1	N/A
Page No.	—	8-267	8-267	—
CODE 29②	All	N/A	N/A	DP1
Page No.	—	—	—	8-156
CODE 29③	All	N/A	N/A	DS1
Page No.	—	—	—	8-155
CODE 31②	All	DN1	DN1	DN90
Page No.	—	8-151	8-151	8-153
CODE 32②	All	DN25	DN25	DN90
Page No.	—	8-152	8-152	8-153
CODE 33②	All	N/A	DN40	DN110
Page No.	—	—	8-153	8-154
CODE 33③	All	TB1	N/A	N/A
Page No.	—	8-254	—	—
CODE 34②	All	DN20	DN20	DN115
Page No.	—	8-152	8-152	8-154
CODE 35②	All	DN5	DN5	DN90
Page No.	—	8-151	8-151	8-153

Fig. 162 Two digit EEC-IV DTC chart (Part 1 of 4). 1993–94

Service Code/ Page No.	Application	Pinpoint Test Step — Key On, Engine Off	Engine Running	Continuous Memory
CODE 41②	All	N/A	H1	H1
Page No.	—	—	8-178	8-178
CODE 42②	All	N/A	H1	N/A
Page No.	—	—	8-178	—
CODE 44②	All	N/A	KC1	N/A
Page No.	—	—	8-199	—
CODE 45②	All	N/A	KC1	N/A
Page No.	—	—	8-199	—
CODE 46②	All	N/A	KC1	N/A
Page No.	—	—	8-199	—
CODE 47	All	TB1	N/A	N/A
Page No.	—	8-256	—	—
CODE 49②	All	N/A	N/A	TG90
Page No.	—	—	—	8-275
CODE 49③	All	N/A	N/A	TG90
Page No.	—	—	—	8-275
CODE 51②	All	DA10	N/A	DA90
Page No.	—	8-125	—	8-126
CODE 52②	All	FF1	FF5	N/A
Page No.	—	8-170	8-170	—
CODE 53②	All	DH3	N/A	DH90
Page No.	—	8-142	—	8-143
CODE 54②	All	DA10	N/A	DA90
Page No.	—	8-125	—	8-126
CODE 56②	All	DC20	N/A	DC20
Page No.	—	8-131	—	8-131
CODE 56③	All	TE10	N/A	TG90
Page No.	—	8-268	—	8-275
CODE 57②	All	KP1	N/A	N/A
Page No.	—	8-228	—	—
CODE 59②	All	N/A	N/A	TG90
Page No.	—	—	—	8-275
CODE 59③	All	N/A	N/A	TG90
Page No.	—	—	—	8-275
CODE 61②	All	DA20	N/A	DA90
Page No.	—	8-126	—	8-126
CODE 62②	All	N/A	N/A	TG90
Page No.	—	—	—	8-275
CODE 62③	All	N/A	N/A	TG90
Page No.	—	—	—	8-275
CODE 63②	All	DH10	N/A	DH94
Page No.	—	8-142	—	8-143
CODE 64②	All	DA20	N/A	DA90
Page No.	—	8-126	—	8-126
CODE 65②	All	N/A	TB2	N/A
Page No.	—	—	8-256	—
CODE 65③	All	N/A	TB2	N/A
Page No.	—	—	8-256	—
CODE 66②	All	N/A	N/A	DC10
Page No.	—	—	—	8-130
CODE 66③	All	TE10	N/A	TG90
Page No.	—	8-268	—	8-275

Fig. 162 Two digit EEC-IV DTC chart (Part 2 of 4). 1993–94

Service Code/ Page No.	Application	Pinpoint Test Step		
		Key On, Engine Off	Engine Running	Continuous Memory
CODE 67②	All	TA1	N/A	TA1
Page No.	—	8-252	—	8-252
CODE 67③	All	KM40	N/A	TG90
Page No.	—	8-218	—	8-275
CODE 68	All	N/A	N/A	TE100
Page No.	—	—	—	8-269
CODE 69②	All	N/A	N/A	TG90
Page No.	—	—	—	8-275
CODE 69③	All	N/A	N/A	TG90
Page No.	—	—	—	8-275
CODE 73②	All	N/A	DH20	N/A
Page No.	—	—	8-142	—
CODE 74	All	N/A	FD1	N/A
Page No.	—	—	8-163	—
CODE 77②	All	N/A	M1	N/A
Page No.	—	—	8-230	—
CODE 79②	All	KM40	N/A	N/A
Page No.	—	8-218	—	—
CODE 81②	All	KC8	N/A	DF11
Page No.	—	8-200	—	8-138
CODE 82②	All	KC8	N/A	N/A
Page No.	—	8-200	—	—
CODE 84②	All	DN10	N/A	N/A
Page No.	—	8-152	—	—
CODE 85②	All	KD6	N/A	N/A
Page No.	—	8-202	—	—
CODE 86	All	TC1	N/A	N/A
Page No.	—	8-260	—	—
CODE 87②	All	J1	N/A	J95
Page No.	—	8-192	—	8-194
CODE 89②	All	TC10	N/A	N/A
Page No.	—	8-260	—	—
CODE 89③	All	TC1	N/A	N/A
Page No.	—	8-260	—	—
CODE 91	All	TC1	H1	H1
Page No.	—	8-260	8-178	8-178
CODE 92	All	TC1	H1	N/A
Page No.	—	8-260	8-178	—
CODE 93	All	TC1	N/A	N/A
Page No.	—	8-260	—	—
CODE 94	All	TC1	KC1	N/A
Page No.	—	8-260	8-199	—
CODE 95②	All	J10	N/A	J90
Page No.	—	8-192	—	8-193
CODE 96②	All	J20	N/A	J93
Page No.	—	8-193	—	8-194
CODE 97②	All	TB3	N/A	N/A
Page No.	—	8-256	—	—
CODE 97③	All	TB3	N/A	N/A
Page No.	—	8-256	—	—
CODE 98	All	TC10	N/A	N/A
Page No.	—	8-260	—	—

Fig. 162 Two digit EEC-IV DTC chart (Part 3 of 4). 1993–94

Service Code/ Page No.	Application	Pinpoint Test Step		
		Key On, Engine Off	Engine Running	Continuous Memory
CODE 99	All	TC10	N/A	N/A
Page No.	—	8-260	—	—
Codes Not Listed	All	QA1	QA1	QA1
Page No.	—	8-247	8-247	8-247

① —Replace PCM.
② —1993.
③ —1994.

Fig. 162 Two digit EEC-IV DTC chart (Part 4 of 4). 1993–94

Service Code/ Page No.	Application	Pinpoint Test Step		
		Key On, Engine Off	Engine Running	Continuous Memory
NO CODES	All	QA1	QA1	QA1
Page No.	—	8-247	8-247	8-247
CODE 111	All	Pass	Pass	Pass
Page No.	—	—	—	—
CODE 112	All	DA20	N/A	DA90
Page No.	—	8-126	—	8-126
CODE 113	All	DA10	N/A	DA90
Page No.	—	8-126	—	8-126
CODE 114	All	DA1	DA1	N/A
Page No.	—	8-124	8-124	—
CODE 116	All	DA1	DA1	N/A
Page No.	—	8-124	8-124	—
CODE 117	All	DA20	N/A	DA90
Page No.	—	8-126	—	8-125
CODE 118	All	DA10	N/A	DA90
Page No.	—	8-125	—	8-126
CODE 121⑤	All	DH2	DH1	G1
Page No.	—	8-142	8-142	8-172
CODE 121⑥	All	DH2	DH1	G1
Page No.	—	8-142	8-142	8-173
CODE 122	All	DH10	N/A	DH94
Page No.	—	8-142	—	8-143
CODE 123	All	DH3	N/A	DH90
Page No.	—	8-142	—	8-143
CODE 124⑤	All	N/A	N/A	G1
Page No.	—	—	—	8-172
CODE 124⑥	All	N/A	N/A	G1
Page No.	—	—	—	8-173
CODE 125⑤	All	N/A	N/A	G1
Page No.	—	—	—	8-172
CODE 125⑥	All	N/A	N/A	G1
Page No.	—	—	—	8-173
CODE 126	All	DF1	DF1	DF90
Page No.	—	8-138	8-138	8-139
CODE 128	All	N/A	N/A	DF11
Page No.	—	—	—	8-138
CODE 129	All	N/A	DC13	N/A
Page No.	—	—	8-131	—
CODE 136	3.0L FF Taurus	N/A	HB1	N/A

Fig. 163 Three digit EEC-IV DTC chart (Part 1 of 13)

Service Code/ Page No.	Application	Key On, Engine Off	Engine Running	Continuous Memory
Page No.	—	—	8-187	—
CODE 136	All Others	N/A	H1	N/A
Page No.	—	—	8-178	—
CODE 137	3.0L FF Taurus	N/A	HB1	N/A
Page No.	—	—	8-187	—
CODE 137	All Others	N/A	H1	N/A
Page No.	—	—	8-178	—
CODE 139	All	N/A	N/A	H1
Page No.	—	—	—	8-178
CODE 141	3.0L FF Taurus	N/A	HB1	N/A
Page No.	—	—	8-187	—
CODE 144	All	N/A	N/A	H1
Page No.	—	—	—	8-178
CODE 157	All	N/A	N/A	DC10
Page No.	—	—	—	8-130
CODE 158	All	DC21	N/A	DC21
Page No.	—	8-131	—	8-131
CODE 159	All	DC1	DC1	N/A
Page No.	—	8-124	8-124	—
CODE 167	All	N/A	DH20	N/A
Page No.	—	—	8-142	—
CODE 171	3.0L FF Taurus	N/A	N/A	HB1
Page No.	—	—	—	8-187
CODE 171	All Others	N/A	N/A	H1
Page No.	—	—	—	8-178
CODE 172	3.0L FF Taurus	N/A	HB1	HB1
Page No.	—	—	8-178	8-187
CODE 172	All Others	N/A	H1	H1
Page No.	—	—	8-178	8-178
CODE 173	3.0L FF Taurus	N/A	HB1	HB1
Page No.	—	—	8-187	8-187
CODE 173	All Others	N/A	H1	H1
Page No.	—	—	8-178	8-178
CODE 174	All	N/A	N/A	H1
Page No.	—	—	—	8-178
CODE 175	3.0L FF Taurus	N/A	N/A	HB1
Page No.	—	—	—	8-187
CODE 175	All Others	N/A	N/A	H1
Page No.	—	—	—	8-178
CODE 176	3.0L FF Taurus	N/A	N/A	HB1
Page No.	—	—	—	8-187
CODE 176	All Others	N/A	N/A	H1
Page No.	—	—	—	8-178
CODE 177	3.0L FF Taurus	N/A	N/A	HB1
Page No.	—	—	—	8-187
CODE 177	All Others	N/A	N/A	H1

Fig. 163 Three digit EEC-IV DTC chart (Part 2 of 13)

Service Code/ Page No.	Application	Key On, Engine Off	Engine Running	Continuous Memory
Page No.	—	—	—	8-178
CODE 178	All	N/A	N/A	H1
Page No.	—	—	—	8-178
CODE 179	All	N/A	N/A	HA1
Page No.	—	—	—	8-184
CODE 181	All	N/A	N/A	HA1
Page No.	—	—	—	8-184
CODE 182②	All	N/A	N/A	HA15
Page No.	—	—	—	8-185
CODE 183②	All	N/A	N/A	HA1
Page No.	—	—	—	8-184
CODE 184⑤	All	N/A	N/A	G5
Page No.	—	—	—	8-172
CODE 184⑥	All	N/A	N/A	G5
Page No.	—	—	—	8-173
CODE 185⑤	All	N/A	N/A	G5
Page No.	—	—	—	8-172
CODE 185⑥	All	N/A	N/A	G5
Page No.	—	—	—	8-173
CODE 186⑤	All	N/A	N/A	G5
Page No.	—	—	—	8-172
CODE 186⑥	All	N/A	N/A	G5
Page No.	—	—	—	8-173
CODE 187⑤	All	N/A	N/A	G5
Page No.	—	—	—	8-172
CODE 187ⓒ	All	N/A	N/A	G5
Page No.	—	—	—	8-173
CODE 188	All	N/A	N/A	HA1
Page No.	—	—	—	8-184
CODE 189	All	N/A	N/A	HA1
Page No.	—	—	—	8-184
CODE 191②	All	N/A	N/A	HA15
Page No.	—	—	—	8-185
CODE 192②	All	N/A	N/A	HA1
Page No.	—	—	—	8-184
CODE 193	All	DE1	N/A	N/A
Page No.	—	8-135	—	—
CODE 194	All	N/A	N/A	H5
Page No.	—	—	—	8-178
CODE 195	All	N/A	N/A	H5
Page No.	—	—	—	8-178
CODE 211	DI	N/A	N/A	NA1
Page No.	—	—	—	8-235
CODE 211	EI-Low Data Rate	N/A	N/A	NB1
Page No.	—	—	—	8-237
CODE 211	EI-High Data Rate	N/A	N/A	NC1
Page No.	—	—	—	8-240
CODE 212	DI	N/A	N/A	NA2
Page No.	—	—	—	8-235

Fig. 163 Three digit EEC-IV DTC chart (Part 3 of 13)

Service Code/Page No.	Application	Key On, Engine Off	Engine Running	Continuous Memory
CODE 212	EI-Low Data Rate Except 2.3L Mustang & Taurus SHO	N/A	N/A	NB2
Page No.	—	—	—	8-237
CODE 212②	2.3L Mustang	N/A	N/A	③
Page No.	—	—	—	—
CODE 212	EI-High Data Rate	N/A	N/A	NC3
Page No.	—	—	—	8-240
CODE 213	TFI (DI) Ignition	N/A	PA1	N/A
Page No.	—	—	8-242	—
CODE 213	EI (DIS) Ignition & Taurus SHO	N/A	PB1	N/A
Page No.	—	—	8-243	—
CODE 213⑤	All Others	N/A	PC1	N/A
Page No.	—	—	8-245	—
CODE 213⑥	All Others	N/A	PC1	N/A
Page No.	—	—	8-246	—
CODE 214	All	N/A	N/A	DR1
Page No.	—	—	—	8-159
CODE 215	All	N/A	N/A	③
Page No.	—	—	—	—
CODE 216	All	N/A	N/A	③
Page No.	—	—	—	—
CODE 217	All	N/A	N/A	③
Page No.	—	—	—	—
CODE 218	All	N/A	N/A	③
Page No.	—	—	—	—
CODE 219	All	N/A	N/A	PB10
Page No.	—	—	—	8-243
CODE 222	All	N/A	N/A	③
Page No.	—	—	—	—
CODE 223	All	N/A	N/A	③
Page No.	—	—	—	—
CODE 224	All	N/A	N/A	③
Page No.	—	—	—	—
CODE 225	All	N/A	DG1	N/A
Page No.	—	—	8-140	—
CODE 226	All	NC2	N/A	N/A
Page No.	—	8-240	—	—
CODE 232	All	N/A	N/A	③
Page No.	—	—	—	—
CODE 238	All	N/A	N/A	③
Page No.	—	—	—	—
CODE 244	All	N/A	KC1	N/A
Page No.	—	—	8-199	—
CODE 311	All	N/A	KC1	N/A
Page No.	—	—	8-199	—

Fig. 163   Three digit EEC-IV DTC chart (Part 4 of 13)

Service Code/Page No.	Application	Key On, Engine Off	Engine Running	Continuous Memory
CODE 312	All	N/A	KC1	N/A
Page No.	—	—	8-199	—
CODE 313	All	N/A	KC1	N/A
Page No.	—	—	8-199	—
CODE 314	All	N/A	KC1	N/A
Page No.	—	—	8-199	—
CODE 326	2.0L Probe	N/A	N/A	DB10
Page No.	—	—	—	8-128Y°
CODE 326	3.0L FF Taurus, 3.8L Sable & Taurus (Calif.), 3.2L Taurus SHO & Town Car & Mark VIII	N/A	DL22	N/A
Page No.	—	—	8-146	—
CODE 326	All Others	N/A	DL20	DL90
Page No.	—	—	8-146	8-148
CODE 327	2.0L Probe (M/T & Federal)	N/A	N/A	DB1
Page No.	—	—	—	8-128
CODE 327	Probe (CD4E & M/T California)	DD1	DD1	DD90
Page No.	—	8-132	8-132	8-134
CODE 327	Mustang, 5.0L Cougar & Thunderbird	DN1	DN1	DN90
Page No.	—	8-151	8-151	8-153
CODE 327	3.0L FF Taurus, 3.8L Sable & Taurus (Calif.), 3.2L Taurus SHO & Town Car & Mark VIII	DL1	DL22	DL90
Page No.	—	8-145	8-146	8-148
CODE 327	All Others	DL1	DL21	DN90
Page No.	—	8-145	8-146	8-153
CODE 328	All	DN25	DN25	DN90
Page No.	—	8-152	8-152	8-153
CODE 332	2.0L Probe (M/T & Federal)	N/A	N/A	DB20
Page No.	—	—	—	8-128
CODE 332	Probe (CD4E & M/T California)	N/A	DD30	DD100
Page No.	—	—	8-133	8-134
CODE 332	Mustang, 5.0L Cougar & Thunderbird	N/A	DN40	DN110

Fig. 163   Three digit EEC-IV DTC chart (Part 5 of 13)

FORD–Computerized Engine Controls

Service Code/ Page No.	Application	Key On, Engine Off	Engine Running	Continuous Memory
Page No.	—	—	8-153	8-1544
CODE 332	All Others	N/A	DL30	DL100
Page No.	—	—	8-147	8-150
CODE 334	All	DN20	DN20	DN115
Page No.	—	8-152	8-152	8-154
CODE 335	All	DL8	N/A	N/A
Page No.	—	8-146	—	—
CODE 336	3.0L FF Taurus, 3.8L Sable & Taurus (Calif.), 3.2L Taurus SHO & Town Car & Mark VIII	N/A	DL50	DL90
Page No.	—	—	8-148	8-148
CODE 336	All Others	N/A	DL25	DL90
Page No.	—	—	8-147	8-148
CODE 337	2.0L Probe (M/T & Federal)	N/A	N/A	DB5
Page No.	—	—	—	8-128
CODE 337	Probe (CD4E & M/T California)	DD10	DD10	DD90
Page No.	—	8-132	8-132	8-134
CODE 337	Mustang, 5.0L Cougar & Thunderbird	DN5	DN5	DN90
Page No.	—	8-151	8-151	8-153
CODE 337	3.0L FF Taurus, 3.8L Sable & Taurus (Calif.), 3.2L Taurus SHO & Town Car & Mark VIII	DL5	DL50	DL90
Page No.	—	8-145	8-148	8-148
CODE 337	All Others	DL5	DL25	DL90
Page No.	—	8-145	8-147	8-148
CODE 338	All	N/A	N/A	DA100
Page No.	—	—	—	8-126
CODE 339	All	N/A	N/A	DA101
Page No.	—	—	—	8-127
CODE 341	All	KP1	N/A	N/A
Page No.	—	8-228	—	—
CODE 381⑥	All	N/A	N/A	X130
Page No.	—	—	—	8-299
CODE 411	All	N/A	KE15	N/A
Page No.	—	—	8-204	—
CODE 415	All	N/A	N/A	KE30
Page No.	—	—	—	8-205
CODE 416	All	N/A	N/A	KE35
Page No.	—	—	—	8-206

Fig. 163 Three digit EEC-IV DTC chart (Part 6 of 13)

Service Code/ Page No.	Application	Key On, Engine Off	Engine Running	Continuous Memory
CODE 412	All	N/A	KE1	N/A
Page No.	—	—	8-203	—
CODE 452	All	N/A	N/A	DP1
Page No.	—	—	—	8-156
CODE 511	All	①	①	①
Page No.	—	—	—	—
CODE 512	All	N/A	N/A	QB1
Page No.	—	—	—	8-248
CODE 513	All	①	①	①
Page No.	—	—	—	—
CODE 519	2.0L Probe	FF10	N/A	N/A
Page No.	—	8-170	—	—
CODE 519	All Others	FF1	N/A	N/A
Page No.	—	8-170	—	—
CODE 521	2.0L Probe	N/A	FF20	N/A
Page No.	—	—	8-171	—
CODE 521	All Others	N/A	FF5	N/A
Page No.	—	—	8-170	—
CODE 522	Continental, Cougar, Mustang, Thunderbird, Sable & Taurus Except 3.0L SHO, Crown Victoria & Grand Marquis w/AOD-E Trans., Town Car Mark VIII & Probe w/ CD4E	TD1	N/A	N/A
Page No.	—	8-264	—	—
CODE 522	All Others	TA1	N/A	N/A
Page No.	—	8-252	—	—
CODE 524⑤	3.0L Taurus SHO	X98	N/A	X110
Page No.	—	8-285	—	8-286
CODE 524⑥	3.2L Taurus SHO	X90	N/A	X110
Page No.	—	8-297	—	8-298
CODE 524	Mark VIII	XB135	N/A	XB150
Page No.	—	8-313	—	8-314
CODE 524⑥	Taurus FF	X88	N/A	X110
Page No.	—	8-296	—	8-296
CODE 524⑤	All Others	X88	N/A	X110
Page No.	—	8-284	—	8-286
CODE 525	All	TA1	N/A	TA1
Page No.	—	8-252	—	8-252
CODE 528	All	N/A	N/A	TA1
Page No.	—	—	—	8-252
CODE 529	All	N/A	N/A	ML25
Page No.	—	—	—	8-233

Fig. 163 Three digit EEC-IV DTC chart (Part 7 of 13)

ELECTRONIC ENGINE CONTROL SYSTEM IV (EEC-IV)

Service Code/ Page No.	Application	Pinpoint Test Step		
		Key On, Engine Off	Engine Running	Continuous Memory
CODE 532⑥	All	N/A	N/A	ML25
Page No.	—	—	—	8-233
CODE 533	All	N/A	N/A	ML25
Page No.	—	—	—	8-233
CODE 536	All	N/A	FD1	FD90
Page No.	—	—	8-163	8-163
CODE 538	All	N/A	M1	N/A
Page No.	—	—	8-230	—
CODE 539⑤	2.0L Probe	KM70	N/A	N/A
Page No.	—	8-219	—	—
CODE 539⑥	Probe	KM70	N/A	N/A
Page No.	—	8-224	—	—
CODE 539⑤	All Others	KM40	KM40	N/A
Page No.	—	8-218	8-2218	—
CODE 539⑥	All Others	KM40	KM40	N/A
Page No.	—	8-223	8-223	—
CODE 542⑤	Continental, Cougar, 2.3L Mustang, Sable, Tempo, Thunderbird, Topaz & Taurus	X80	N/A	X105
Page No.	—	8-284	—	8-285
CODE 542⑥	Continental, Cougar, 2.3L Mustang, Sable, Tempo, Thunderbird, Topaz & Taurus	X80	N/A	X105
Page No.	—	8-296	—	8-297
CODE 542	Mark VIII	XB120	N/A	XB155
Page No.	—	8-309	—	8-315
CODE 542	All Others	J10	N/A	J90
Page No.	—	8-192	—	8-193
CODE 543⑤	Continental, Cougar, 2.3L Mustang, Sable, Taurus, Thunderbird, Tempo & Topaz	X90	N/A	X110
Page No.	—	8-285	—	8-286
CODE 543⑥	Continental, Cougar, 2.3L Mustang, Sable, Taurus, Thunderbird, Tempo & Topaz	X90	N/A	X110
Page No.	—	8-297	—	8-298

Fig. 163 Three digit EEC-IV DTC chart (Part 8 of 13)

Service Code/ Page No.	Application	Pinpoint Test Step		
		Key On, Engine Off	Engine Running	Continuous Memory
CODE 543	Mark VIII	XB135	N/A	XB150
Page No.	—	8-313	—	8-230
CODE 543	All Others	J20	N/A	N/A
Page No.	—	8-193	—	—
CODE 551	All	KT1	N/A	N/A
Page No.	—	8-229	—	—
CODE 552⑤	All	KC8	N/A	N/A
Page No.	—	8-200	—	—
CODE 552⑥	All	KC9	N/A	N/A
Page No.	—	8-200	—	—
CODE 553⑤	All	KC8	N/A	N/A
Page No.	—	8-200	—	—
CODE 553⑥	All	KC9	N/A	N/A
Page No.	—	8-200	—	—
CODE 554	All	KN1	N/A	N/A
Page No.	—	8-225	—	—
CODE 556⑤	Continental, 2.3L Mustang, Sable, Taurus, Tempo & Topaz	X70	N/A	X115
Page No.	—	8-283	—	8-286
CODE 556⑥	Continental, 2.3L Mustang, Sable, Taurus, Tempo & Topaz	X70	N/A	X115
Page No.	—	8-295	—	8-298
CODE 556	Mark VIII	XB110	N/A	XB150
Page No.	—	8-312	—	8-314
CODE 556	All Others	J1	N/A	J95
Page No.	—	8-192	—	8-194
CODE 557⑤	3.0L FF Taurus	X70	N/A	X115
Page No.	—	8-283	—	8-286
CODE 557⑥	3.0L FF Taurus	X165	N/A	X115
Page No.	—	8-300	—	8-298
CODE 557⑤	3.0L Taurus SHO	X75	N/A	X115
Page No.	—	8-283	—	8-286
CODE 557⑥	3.0L Taurus SHO	X75	N/A	X115
Page No.	—	8-296	—	8-298
CODE 557⑤	All Others	X70	N/A	X115
Page No.	—	8-283	—	8-286
CODE 557⑥	All Others	X70	N/A	X115
Page No.	—	8-295	—	8-298
CODE 558	2.0L Probe	KA1	N/A	N/A
Page No.	—	8-196	—	—
CODE 558	Mustang & 5.0L Cougar & Thunderbird	DN10	N/A	N/A

Fig. 163 Three digit EEC-IV DTC chart (Part 9 of 13)

Service Code/ Page No.	Application	Key On, Engine Off	Engine Running	Continuous Memory
Page No.	—	8-152	—	—
CODE 558	All Others	DL11	N/A	N/A
Page No.	—	8-146	—	—
CODE 559⑤	All	KM60	N/A	N/A
Page No.	—	8-219	—	—
CODE 559⑥	All	KM60	N/A	N/A
Page No.	—	8-224	—	—
CODE 562⑥	All	X10	N/A	N/A
Page No.	—	8-290	—	—
CODE 563⑤	Escort, Tracer & 2.0L Probe	KF1	N/A	N/A
Page No.	—	8-207	—	—
CODE 563⑥	Escort, Tracer & 2.0L Probe	KF1	N/A	N/A
Page No.	—	8-210	—	—
CODE 563⑤	All Others	X15	N/A	N/A
Page No.	—	8-280	—	—
CODE 563⑥	All Others	X15	N/A	N/A
Page No.	—	8-291	—	—
CODE 564⑤	Escort, Tracer & 2.0L Probe	KF1	N/A	N/A
Page No.	—	8-207	—	—
CODE 564⑥	Escort, Tracer & 2.0L Probe	KF1	N/A	N/A
Page No.	—	8-210	—	—
CODE 564⑤	All Others	X20	N/A	N/A
Page No.	—	8-280	—	—
CODE 564⑥	All Others	X20	N/A	N/A
Page No.	—	8-291	—	—
CODE 565	3.0L FF Taurus	KB1	N/A	N/A
Page No.	—	8-197	—	—
CODE 565	All Others	KD6	N/A	N/A
Page No.	—	8-202	—	—
CODE 566	All	TC10	N/A	N/A
Page No.	—	8-260	—	—
CODE 569	All	KD6	N/A	N/A
Page No.	—	8-202	—	—
CODE 571⑥	All	DD20	N/A	N/A
Page No.	—	8-133	—	—
CODE 572⑥	All	DD20	N/A	N/A
Page No.	—	8-133	—	—
CODE 578	All	N/A	N/A	XB40
Page No.	—	—	—	8-304
CODE 579	All	N/A	N/A	XB50
Page No.	—	—	—	8-305
CODE 581	All	N/A	N/A	XB20
Page No.	—	—	—	8-303
CODE 582	All	XB30	N/A	N/A
Page No.	—	8-3304	—	—
CODE 583	All	N/A	N/A	XB135

Service Code/ Page No.	Application	Key On, Engine Off	Engine Running	Continuous Memory
Page No.	—	—	—	8-313
CODE 584	All	N/A	N/A	XB15
Page No.	—	—	—	8-303
CODE 585	All	N/A	N/A	XB70
Page No.	—	—	—	8-308
CODE 586	All	N/A	N/A	XB80
Page No.	—	—	—	8-309
CODE 587	All	XB170	N/A	XB170
Page No.	—	8-317	—	8-317
CODE 617⑤	All	N/A	N/A	TG90
Page No.	—	—	—	8-275
CODE 617⑥	All	N/A	N/A	TG90
Page No.	—	—	—	8-275
CODE 618⑤	All	N/A	N/A	TG90
Page No.	—	—	—	8-275
CODE 618⑥	All	N/A	N/A	TG90
Page No.	—	—	—	8-275
CODE 619⑤	All	N/A	N/A	TG90
Page No.	—	—	—	8-275
CODE 619⑥	All	N/A	N/A	TG90
Page No.	—	—	—	8-275
CODE 621	Escort & Tracer	TC20	N/A	TC30
Page No.	—	8-261	—	8-261
CODE 621	All Others	TC1	N/A	N/A
Page No.	—	8-260	—	—
CODE 622	Escort & Tracer	TC20	N/A	TC30
Page No.	—	8-261	—	8-261
CODE 622	All Others	TC1	N/A	N/A
Page No.	—	8-260	—	—
CODE 623⑥	All	TB3	N/A	N/A
Page No.	—	8-256	—	—
CODE 624⑤	All	TC10	N/A	TG90
Page No.	—	8-260	—	8-275
CODE 624⑥	All	TC10	N/A	TG90
Page No.	—	8-260	—	8-275
CODE 625⑤	All	TC10	N/A	TG90
Page No.	—	8-260	—	8-275
CODE 625⑥	All	TC10	N/A	TG90
Page No.	—	8-260	—	8-275
CODE 626	All	TC1	N/A	N/A
Page No.	—	8-260	—	—
CODE 627	All	TC1	N/A	N/A
Page No.	—	8-260	—	—
CODE 628⑤	All	N/A	N/A	TG90
Page No.	—	—	—	8-275
CODE 628⑥	All	N/A	N/A	TG90
Page No.	—	—	—	8-275
CODE 629	2.3L Mustang	TC10	N/A	N/A
Page No.	—	8-260	—	—
CODE 629⑤	All Others	TC1	N/A	TG90

Fig. 163 Three digit EEC-IV DTC chart (Part 10 of 13)

Fig. 163 Three digit EEC-IV DTC chart (Part 11 of 13)

Service Code/ Page No.	Application	Pinpoint Test Step		
		Key On, Engine Off	Engine Running	Continuous Memory
Page No.	—	8-260	—	8-275
CODE 629⑥	All Others	TC1	N/A	TG90
Page No.	—	8-260	—	8-275
CODE 631⑤	All	TB3	N/A	N/A
Page No.	—	8-254	—	—
CODE 631⑥	All	TB3	N/A	N/A
Page No.	—	8-256	—	—
CODE 632⑤	All	N/A	TB2	N/A
Page No.	—	—	8-254	—
CODE 632⑥	All	N/A	TB2	N/A
Page No.	—	—	8-256	—
CODE 633⑤	All	TB1	N/A	N/A
Page No.	—	8-254	—	—
CODE 633⑥	All	TB1	N/A	N/A
Page No.	—	8-256	—	—
CODE 634	Escort & Tracer	N/A	N/A	TD10
Page No.	—	—	—	8-265
CODE 634⑤	All Others	TD1	N/A	TG90
Page No.	—	8-264	—	8-275
CODE 634⑥	All Others	TD1	N/A	TG90
Page No.	—	8-264	—	8-275
CODE 636	All	TE1	TE1	N/A
Page No.	—	8-267	8-267	—
CODE 637	Escort & Tracer	TE10	N/A	TE90
Page No.	—	8-268	—	8-269
CODE 637⑤	All Others	TE10	N/A	TG90
Page No.	—	8-268	—	8-275
CODE 637⑥	All Others	TE10	N/A	TG90
Page No.	—	8-268	—	8-275
CODE 638	Escort & Tracer	TE10	N/A	TE90
Page No.	—	8-268	—	8-269
CODE 638⑤	All Others	TE10	N/A	TG90
Page No.	—	8-268	—	8-275
CODE 638⑥	All Others	TE10	N/A	TG90
Page No.	—	8-268	—	8-275
CODE 639	Escort & Tracer	N/A	TF10	TF95
Page No.	—	—	8-271	8-272
CODE 639	All Others	N/A	TF1	TF90
Page No.	—	—	8-270	8-271
CODE 641	Escort & Tracer	TC20	N/A	TC30
Page No.	—	8-261	—	8-261
CODE 641	All Others	TC1	N/A	N/A
Page No.	—	8-260	—	—
CODE 643	All	TC20	N/A	TC30
Page No.	—	8-261	—	8-261
CODE 645⑤	All	N/A	N/A	TG90
Page No.	—	—	—	8-275
CODE 645⑥	All	N/A	N/A	TG90
Page No.	—	—	—	8-275

Service Code/ Page No.	Application	Pinpoint Test Step		
		Key On, Engine Off	Engine Running	Continuous Memory
CODE 646⑤	All	N/A	N/A	TG90
Page No.	—	—	—	8-275
CODE 646⑥	All	N/A	N/A	TG90
Page No.	—	—	—	8-275
CODE 647⑤	All	N/A	N/A	TG90
Page No.	—	—	—	8-275
CODE 647⑥	All	N/A	N/A	TG90
Page No.	—	—	—	8-275
CODE 648⑤	All	N/A	N/A	TG90
Page No.	—	—	—	8-275
CODE 648⑥	All	N/A	N/A	TG90
Page No.	—	—	—	8-275
CODE 649⑤	All	N/A	N/A	TG90
Page No.	—	—	—	8-275
CODE 649⑥	All	N/A	N/A	TG90
Page No.	—	—	—	8-275
CODE 651⑤	All	N/A	N/A	TG90
Page No.	—	—	—	8-275
CODE 651⑥	All	N/A	N/A	TG90
Page No.	—	—	—	8-275
CODE 652	All	TC1	N/A	N/A
Page No.	—	8-260	—	—
CODE 653	All	N/A	TB2	N/A
Page No.	—	—	8-254	—
CODE 654	All	TD1	N/A	N/A
Page No.	—	8-264	—	—
CODE 656⑤	All	N/A	N/A	TG90
Page No.	—	—	—	8-275
CODE 656⑥	All	N/A	N/A	TG90
Page No.	—	—	—	8-275
CODE 657	All	N/A	N/A	TE100
Page No.	—	—	—	8-275
CODE 659⑥	All	N/A	N/A	TG90
Page No.	—	—	—	8-275
CODE 667⑥	All	N/A	N/A	TG90
Page No.	—	—	—	8-275
CODE 668⑥	All	N/A	N/A	TG90
Page No.	—	—	—	8-275
CODE 675⑥	All	N/A	N/A	TG90
Page No.	—	—	—	8-275
CODE 676⑥	All	④	④	④
Page No.	—	—	—	—
CODE 677⑥	All	④	④	④
Page No.	—	—	—	—
CODE 691⑥	All	N/A	N/A	TB1
Page No.	—	—	—	8-256
CODE 998	All	TC10	②	②
Page No.	—	8-260	—	—

Fig. 163 Three digit EEC-IV DTC chart (Part 12 of 13)

Service Code/ Page No.	Application	Pinpoint Test Step		
		Key On, Engine Off	Engine Running	Continuous Memory
Codes Not Listed	All	QA1	QA1	QA1
Page No.	—	8-247	8-247	8-247

① —Replace PCM.
② —Go to EEC-IV DTC charts for diagnosis of the continuous DTC received during key on engine off test.
③ —Go to "Electronic Ignition" diagnosis.
④ —Transmission/transaxle fault indicated.
⑤ —1993.
⑥ —1994—95.

Fig. 163 Three digit EEC-IV DTC chart (Part 13 of 13)

DIAGNOSTIC CHART INDEX

Test	Description	Page No. 8-	Fig. No.
Test AA	EEC-IV No Start, DI (1993)	108	164
Test AA	EEC-IV No Start, DI (1994—95)	110	165
Test AB	EEC-IV No Start, EI-Low Data Rate (1993)	113	166
Test AB	EEC-IV No Start, EI-Low Data Rate (1994—95)	115	167
Test AC	EEC-IV No Start, EI-High Data Rate	117	168
Test B	Vehicle Battery	119	169
Test C	Reference Voltage	122	170
Test DA	IAT/ECT Sensors	124	171
Test DB	EGRT Sensor	127	172
Test DC	MAF Sensor	129	173
Test DD	EGRP Sensor/EGRV Solenoid/EGRA Solenoid	132	174
Test DE	FF Sensor	134	175
Test DF	MAP/BARO Sensor	137	176
Test DG	KS	139	177
Test DH	TP Sensor	140	178
Test DL	PFE/DPFE Sensor/EVR Solenoid	144	179
Test DN	EVP Sensor/EVR Solenoid	151	180
Test DP	VSS	154	181
Test DP	VSS	156	182
Test DR	CID Circuits (1993)	158	183
Test DS	PSOM	161	184

Continued

DIAGNOSTIC CHART INDEX–Continued

Test	Description	Page No. 8-	Fig. No.
Test FD	BOO	163	185
Test FE	Electrical Load Inputs (1993)	164	186
Test FE	Electrical Load Inputs (1994—95)	166	187
Test FF	PSP Switch	169	188
Test G	MAF/TP/Injector Pulse Width (1993)	171	189
Test G	MAF/TP/Injector Pulse Width (1994—95)	173	190
Test H	Fuel Control	174	191
Test HA	Adaptive Fuel	183	192
Test HB	FF Control	185	193
Test J	Fuel Pump Circuit	190	194
Test KA	EVR Solenoid	195	195
Test KB	CANP Valve	196	196
Test KC	AIRB/AIRD Solenoids	198	197
Test KD	CANP Solenoid	201	198
Test KE	IAC Solenoid	202	199
Test KF	LFC/HFC (1993)	206	200
Test KF	LFC/HFC (1994—95)	209	201
Test KL	SIL	213	202
Test KM	WAC A/C Demand (1993)	215	203
Test KM	WAC A/C Demand (1994—95)	220	204
Test KN	FPRC Solenoid	225	205
Test KP	OCT ADJ (1993)	227	206
Test KP	OCT ADJ (1994—95)	227	206
Test KT	IMRC System	229	207
Test M	Dynamic Response Test	230	208
Test ML	STO/MIL	231	209
Test NA	IDM/DI	233	210
Test NB	IDM/EI-Low Data Rate	236	211
Test NC	IDM/EI-High Data Rate	238	212
Test PA	Spark Timing Check, DI	241	213
Test PB	Spark Timing Check, EI-Low Data Rate	242	214
Test PC	Spark Timing Check, EI-High Data Rate	244	215
Test QA	No DTC/DTC Not Listed	246	216
Test QB	Continuous Memory DTC 15/512 (1993)	248	217
Test QB	Continuous Memory DTC 15/512 (1994—95)	248	217
Test QC	Output State Check Not Functioning	249	218
Test S	System Check	249	219
Test TA	PNP/CPP Switches	250	220
Test TB	4x4 Low/TCS (1993)	253	221
Test TB	4x4 Low/TCIL/TCS/TCSM (1994—95)	255	222
Test TC	Trans Solenoids (1993)	257	223
Test TC	Trans Solenoids (1994—95)	258	223
Test TD	MLP Sensor	262	224
Test TE	TOT Sensor	266	225
Test TF	TSS	269	226
Test TG	Electronic Trans/Continuous Memory DTC	273	237
Test X	CCRM (1993)	277	228
Test X	CCRM (1994—95)	287	229
Test XB	VCRM	301	230

Note

You should enter this Pinpoint Test only when directed here from Diagnostic Routines

Remember

To prevent the replacement of good components, be aware that the following non-EEC areas may be at fault:

- Fuel: quantity and quality
- Ignition: general condition, moisture, cracks, damage, etc.
- Engine: internal, valves, timing belt, camshaft
- Starter and battery circuit
- Camshaft Position (CMP) sensor

- Ignition Control Module (ICM)
- Distributor
- Ignition coil
- Governor Control Module (GCM)

This Pinpoint Test is intended to diagnose only the following:

- Spark (as related to EEC)
- Harness circuits: PIP, SPOUT, IGN GND, VPWR
- Powertrain Control Module (PCM)

FM0159300706010X

Fig. 164 Test AA: EEC-IV No Start, DI (Part 1 of 11). 1993

Pinpoint Test Schematics

2.0L Probe

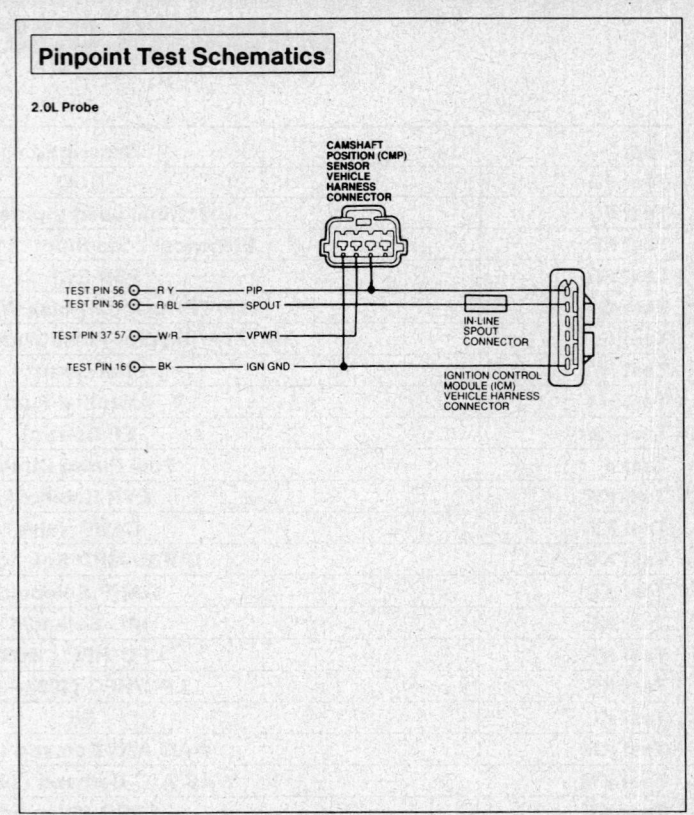

FM0159300706020X

Fig. 164 Test AA: EEC-IV No Start, DI (Part 2 of 11). 1993

3.8L SFI AX4S, 3.8L SFI Thunderbird/Cougar   5.0L Thunderbird/Cougar

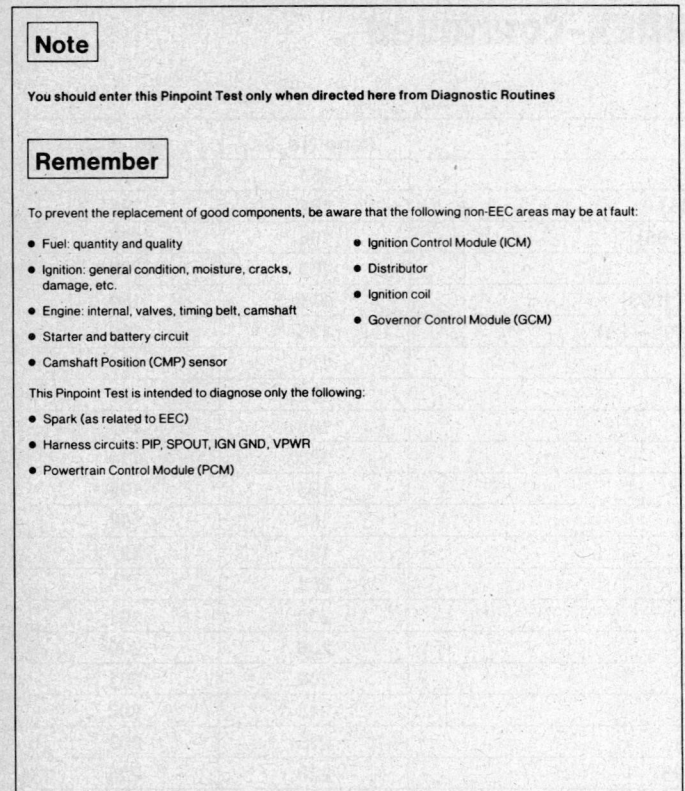

*TEST PINS LOCATED ON BREAKOUT BOX.
ALL HARNESS CONNECTORS VIEWED INTO MATING SURFACE.

Test Pin 16—IGN GND

Application	Wire Color
3.8L Continental	O/R
3.8L Taurus/Sable 3.8L Thunderbird/Cougar 5.0L Thunderbird/Cougar	GY

Test Pin 36—SPOUT

Application	Wire Color
3.8L Continental	PK
All Others	Y/LG

Test Pin 56—PIP

Application	Wire Color
3.8L Taurus/Sable 3.8L Continental	GY/O
All Others	DB

Fig. 164   Test AA: EEC-IV No Start, DI (Part 3 of 11). 1993

All Others TFI

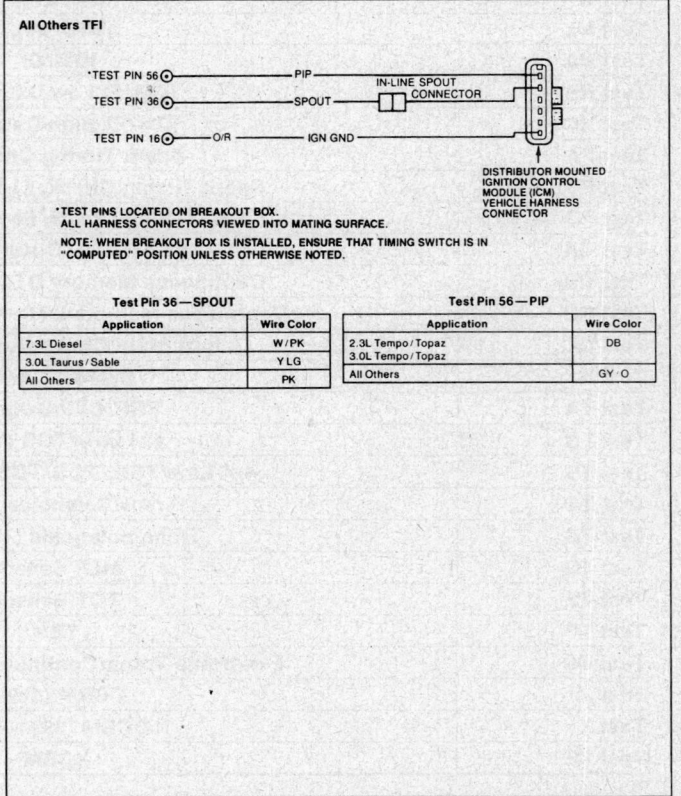

*TEST PINS LOCATED ON BREAKOUT BOX.
ALL HARNESS CONNECTORS VIEWED INTO MATING SURFACE.

NOTE: WHEN BREAKOUT BOX IS INSTALLED, ENSURE THAT TIMING SWITCH IS IN "COMPUTED" POSITION UNLESS OTHERWISE NOTED.

Test Pin 36—SPOUT

Application	Wire Color
7.3L Diesel	W/PK
3.0L Taurus/Sable	Y/LG
All Others	PK

Test Pin 56—PIP

Application	Wire Color
2.3L Tempo/Topaz 3.0L Tempo/Topaz	DB
All Others	GY/O

FM0159300706050X

Fig. 164   Test AA: EEC-IV No Start, DI (Part 4 of 11). 1993

WARNING

STOP THIS TEST AT THE FIRST SIGN OF A FUEL LEAK AND SERVICE AS REQUIRED.

CAUTION

No open flame—No smoking during fuel delivery checks.

TEST STEP	RESULT	▶	ACTION TO TAKE
AA1 ATTEMPT TO CRANK ENGINE			
NOTE: Verify Inertia Fuel Shutoff (IFS) switch is set (button pushed in). Refer to Owner Guide for location.	Yes	▶	GO to **AA2**
	No	▶	REFER to Starting / Engine Service
• Does engine crank?			
AA2 CHECK FOR VREF AT THROTTLE POSITION (TP) SENSOR			
• Key off.	Yes	▶	RECONNECT TP sensor. GO to **AA3**
• Disconnect TP sensor.			
• Key on, engine off.	No	▶	GO to Pinpoint Test Step **C1**
• Measure voltage between VREF circuit and SIG RTN circuit at the TP sensor vehicle harness connector. Refer to the illustration.			
• Is voltage between 4.0 volts and 6.0 volts?			

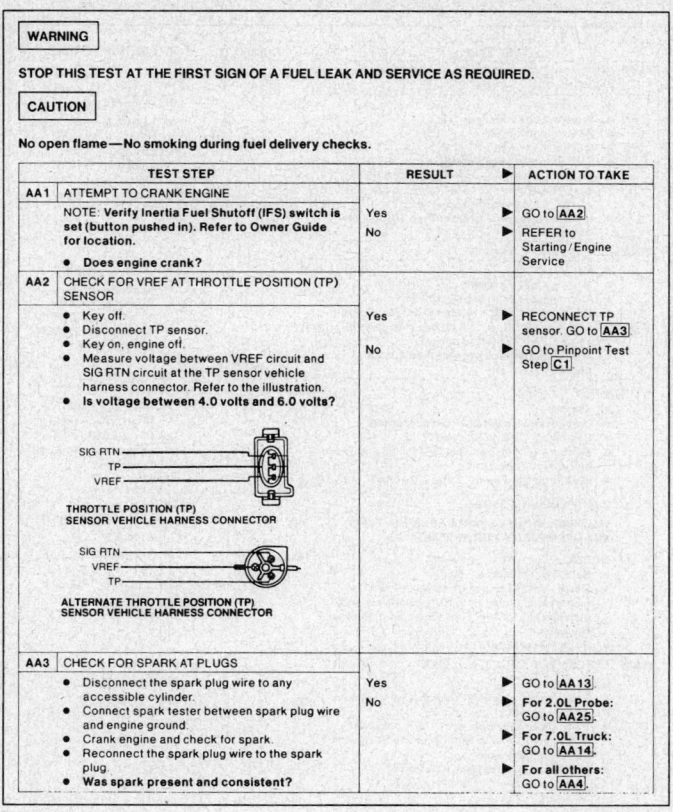

SIG RTN
TP
VREF

THROTTLE POSITION (TP) SENSOR VEHICLE HARNESS CONNECTOR

SIG RTN
VREF
TP

ALTERNATE THROTTLE POSITION (TP) SENSOR VEHICLE HARNESS CONNECTOR

TEST STEP	RESULT	▶	ACTION TO TAKE
AA3 CHECK FOR SPARK AT PLUGS			
• Disconnect the spark plug wire to any accessible cylinder.	Yes	▶	GO to **AA13**
• Connect spark tester between spark plug wire and engine ground.	No	▶	For 2.0L Probe: GO to **AA25**
• Crank engine and check for spark.		▶	For 7.0L Truck: GO to **AA14**
• Reconnect the spark plug wire to the spark plug.		▶	For all others: GO to **AA4**
• Was spark present and consistent?			

Fig. 164   Test AA: EEC-IV No Start, DI (Part 5 of 11). 1993

TEST STEP	RESULT	▶	ACTION TO TAKE
AA4 CHECK FOR SPARK AT COIL			
• Remove high tension coil wire from distributor and install spark tester.	Yes	▶	REFER to ICM, cap, rotor and wire diagnosis.
• Check for spark while cranking.	No	▶	GO to **AA5**
• Reconnect high tension coil wire to distributor.			
• Was spark present during crank?			
AA5 CHECK CONTINUITY OF IGN GND CIRCUIT			
• Key off.	Yes	▶	GO to **AA6**
• Disconnect Powertrain Control Module (PCM) 60 pin connector. Inspect for damaged or pushed out pins, corrosion, loose wires, etc. Service as necessary.	No	▶	SERVICE open circuit. REMOVE breakout box. RECONNECT all components. RERUN Quick Test.
• Install breakout box, leave PCM disconnected.			
For vehicles with distributor mounted ICM:			
— Disconnect ICM module connector.			
For 2.0L Probe:			
— Disconnect ICM and Camshaft Position (CMP) sensor.			
For vehicles with remote mount ICM:			
— Disconnect Camshaft Position (CMP) sensor.			
For 7.0L Truck:			
Disconnect Governor Control Module (GCM) and Camshaft Position (CMP) sensor.			
• Measure resistance between Test Pin 16 at breakout box and ICM or CMP sensor vehicle harness connector IGN GND circuit.			
• Is resistance less than 5.0 ohms?			
AA6 ISOLATION OF PROBLEM TO SPOUT CIRCUIT			
• Reconnect ICM and CMP sensor, as applicable.	Yes	▶	Timing switch to "Computed" position on breakout box. GO to **AA11**
• Breakout box installed.			
• Connect PCM to breakout box.	No	▶	GO to **AA7**
• Timing switch to "DIST" position on breakout box.			
• Attempt to start vehicle.			
• Does the vehicle start?			
AA7 CHECK SPOUT SIGNAL			
• Key on, engine off.	Yes	▶	EEC system OK. REMOVE breakout box. RECONNECT all components. REFER to DI system diagnosis.
• Breakout box installed, PCM connected.			
• Timing switch to "DIST" position on breakout box			
• Measure voltage between Test Pin 36 at breakout box and battery negative post during crank	No	▶	PLACE timing switch to "Computed" position and GO to **AA8**.
• Is voltage between 3.0 and 6.0 volts?			

Fig. 164   Test AA: EEC-IV No Start, DI (Part 6 of 11). 1993

TEST STEP	RESULT	▶	ACTION TO TAKE
AA8 CHECK SPOUT AND PIP CIRCUITS FOR SHORT TO POWER			
• Key off.	Yes	▶	SERVICE short circuit to the START circuit or to the VPWR circuit in the harness. REMOVE breakout box. RECONNECT all components. RERUN Quick Test.
• Breakout box installed.			
• Disconnect PCM.			
For 2.0L Probe:			
— Disconnect ICM and CMP sensor.	No	▶	GO to **AA9**.
For vehicles with remote mounted ICM:			
— Disconnect CMP and ICM sensor.			
— For 7.0L Truck also disconnect Governor Control Module (GCM).			
For all others:			
— Disconnect ICM.			
• Key on.			
• Measure voltage between Test Pin 36 (SPOUT) at breakout box and battery negative post.			
• Measure voltage between Test Pin 56 (PIP) at breakout box and battery negative post.			
• Is voltage greater than 10.5 volts?			
AA9 CHECK SPOUT AND PIP CIRCUITS FOR SHORTS TO GROUND			
• Key off.	Yes	▶	GO to **AA10**
• Breakout box installed.			
• Disconnect PCM.	No	▶	SERVICE short circuit. REMOVE breakout box. RECONNECT all components. RERUN Quick Test. If vehicle does not start, GO to **AA10**.
For 2.0L Probe:			
— Disconnect ICM and CMP sensor.			
For vehicles with remote mounted ICM:			
— Disconnect ICM and CMP sensor.			
— For 7.0L Truck, also disconnect Governor Control Module (GCM).			
For all others:			
— Disconnect ICM.			
• Measure resistance between Test Pin 36 (SPOUT) and Test Pins 16, 20, 40, 46, 60 (short to GROUND) and 56 (short to PIP) at breakout box			
• Measure resistance between Test Pin 56 (PIP) and Test Pins 16, 20, 40, 46, 60 (short to GROUND) at breakout box.			
• Is each resistance greater than 10,000 ohms?			

Fig. 164   Test AA: EEC-IV No Start, DI (Part 7 of 11). 1993

TEST STEP	RESULT	▶	ACTION TO TAKE
AA10 ISOLATE SHORT(S) IN PCM			
• Key off.	Yes	▶	RECONNECT all components. GO to **AA11**
• Breakout box installed.			
• Reconnect PCM to breakout box.	No	▶	REPLACE PCM. REMOVE breakout box. RECONNECT all components. RERUN Quick Test.
For 2.0L Probe:			
— Disconnect ICM and CMP sensor.			
For vehicles with remote mounted ICM:			
— Disconnect ICM and CMP sensor.			
— For 7.0L Truck, also disconnect GCM.			
For all others:			
— Disconnect ICM.			
• Measure resistance between Test Pin 36 (SPOUT) and Test Pins 37 and 57 (short to POWER). Also Test Pins 40 and 60 (short to GROUND) at breakout box.			
• Measure resistance between Test Pin 56 (PIP) and Test Pins 37 and 57 (short to POWER). Also Test Pins 40 and 60 (short to GROUND) at breakout box.			
• Is each resistance greater than 500 ohms?			
AA11 CHECK PIP SIGNAL			
• Key off.	Yes	▶	REPLACE PCM. REMOVE breakout box. RECONNECT all components. RERUN Quick Test.
• Breakout box installed, PCM connected.			
• Measure voltage between Test Pin 56 and Test Pin 40/60 at breakout box.	No	▶	GO to **AA12**
• Crank engine, record reading.			
• Is voltage between 3.0 and 7.0 volts?			
AA12 CHECK CONTINUITY OF PIP CIRCUIT			
• Key off.	Yes	▶	REMOVE breakout box. RECONNECT all components. REFER to DI system diagnosis.
• Breakout box installed.			
• Disconnect PCM.	No	▶	SERVICE open circuit. REMOVE breakout box. RECONNECT all components. RERUN Quick Test.
For 2.0L Probe:			
— Disconnect ICM and CMP sensor.			
For vehicles with remote mounted ICM:			
— Disconnect ICM and CMP sensor.			
— For 7.0L Truck, also disconnect GCM.			
For all others:			
— Disconnect ICM.			
• Measure resistance between Test Pin 56 at breakout box and PIP circuit at the following connectors as appropriate: ICM, CMP sensor and/or GCM.			
• Is resistance less than 5.0 ohms?			

Fig. 164   Test AA: EEC-IV No Start, DI (Part 8 of 11). 1993

TEST STEP	RESULT	▶	ACTION TO TAKE
AA13 SPOUT SIGNAL VERIFICATION • Key off. • Disconnect Powertrain Control Module (PCM). Inspect for damaged or pushed out pins, corrosion, loose wires, etc. Service as necessary. • Install breakout box and connect PCM to breakout box. • Ensure timing switch is in "Computed" position on breakout box. • Measure voltage between Test Pin 36 and Test Pins 40 and 60 at the breakout box during crank. • **Is voltage between 3.0 and 6.0 volts?**	Yes No	▶ ▶	GO to AA20. GO to AA8.
AA14 ATTEMPT TO RESTART VEHICLE • Key off. • Disconnect Governor Control Module (GCM). • Attempt to start vehicle • **Does vehicle start?**	Yes No	▶ ▶	REPLACE GCM. RERUN Quick Test. GO to AA15.
AA15 CHECK CONTINUITY OF PIP CIRCUIT • Key off. • Disconnect Powertrain Control Module (PCM). Inspect for damaged or pushed out pins, corrosion, loose wires, etc. Service as necessary. • Install breakout box, leave PCM disconnected. • GCM disconnected. • Measure resistance between Pin 17 at GCM and Test Pin 56 at breakout box. • **Is resistance less than 5.0 ohms?**	Yes No	▶ ▶	GO to AA16. SERVICE open circuit. REMOVE breakout box. RECONNECT all components. RERUN Quick Test.
AA16 CHECK CONTINUITY OF PIP CIRCUIT • Key off. • PCM disconnected. • GCM disconnected. • Disconnect Camshaft Position (CMP) sensor. • Measure resistance between PIP circuit at the CMP sensor connector and Test Pin 56 at breakout box. • **Is resistance less than 5.0 ohms?**	Yes No	▶ ▶	GO to AA17. SERVICE open circuit. REMOVE breakout box. RECONNECT all components. RERUN Quick Test.

FM0159300706100X

Fig. 164   Test AA: EEC-IV No Start, DI (Part 9 of 11). 1993

TEST STEP	RESULT	▶	ACTION TO TAKE
AA17 CHECK PIP CIRCUIT FOR SHORT TO POWER AND GROUND • Key off. • Breakout box installed. • PCM disconnected. • GCM disconnected. • CMP sensor disconnected. • Measure resistance between Test Pin 56 and Test Pins 16, 20, 40, 46, 60 (short to ground) and 26, 37, 57 (short to power). • **Is each resistance greater than 10,000 ohms?**	Yes No	▶ ▶	GO to AA18. SERVICE short circuit. REMOVE breakout box. RECONNECT all components. RERUN Quick Test.
AA18 ISOLATE SHORTS IN PCM • Key off. • Breakout box installed. • Reconnect PCM to breakout box. • Measure resistance between Test Pin 56 and Test Pins 16, 20, 40, 46, 60 (short to ground) and 26, 37, 57 (short to power). • **Is each resistance greater than 10,000 ohms?**	Yes No	▶ ▶	GO to AA19. REPLACE PCM. REMOVE breakout box. RECONNECT all components. RERUN Quick Test.
AA19 CHECK PIP SIGNAL • Key off. • Breakout box installed, PCM connected. • Reconnect CMP sensor and GCM. • Measure voltage between Test Pin 56 and Test Pin 16 at breakout box. • **Is voltage between 3.0 and 7.0 volts?**	Yes No	▶ ▶	REPLACE PCM. REMOVE breakout box. RECONNECT all components. RERUN Quick Test. GO to AA5.
AA20 CHECK FUEL PRESSURE **WARNING: IF FUEL STARTS LEAKING, TURN KEY OFF IMMEDIATELY. NO SMOKING.** • Connect fuel pressure gauge. • Note initial pressure reading. • Observe pressure gauge as you pressurize fuel system. (Turn key to RUN for one second, then turn key to OFF. Wait 10 seconds. Repeat five times.) • **Does fuel pressure increase?**	Yes No	▶ ▶	GO to Pinpoint Test Step S1. TURN key OFF. REFER to Fuel Engine Service
AA25 CHECK VPWR CIRCUIT VOLTAGE • Key off. • Disconnect Camshaft Position (CMP) sensor. • Key on, engine off. • Measure voltage between VPWR circuit at CMP sensor vehicle harness connector and battery negative post. • **Is voltage greater than 10.5 volts?**	Yes No	▶ ▶	GO to AA4. GO to AA26.

FM0159300706110X

Fig. 164   Test AA: EEC-IV No Start, DI (Part 10 of 11). 1993

TEST STEP	RESULT	▶	ACTION TO TAKE
AA26 CHECK VPWR CONTINUITY • Key off. • Disconnect Powertrain Control Module (PCM). Inspect for damaged or pushed out pins, corrosion, loose wires, etc. Service as necessary. • Install breakout box, leave PCM disconnected. • CMP sensor disconnected. • Measure resistance between VPWR circuit at CMP sensor vehicle harness connector and Test Pin 37/57 at the breakout box. • **Is resistance less than 5.0 ohms?**	Yes No	▶ ▶	GO to Pinpoint Test Step B1. SERVICE open circuit. REMOVE breakout box. Reconnect all components. RERUN Quick Test

FM0159300706120X

Fig. 164   Test AA: EEC-IV No Start, DI (Part 11 of 11). 1993

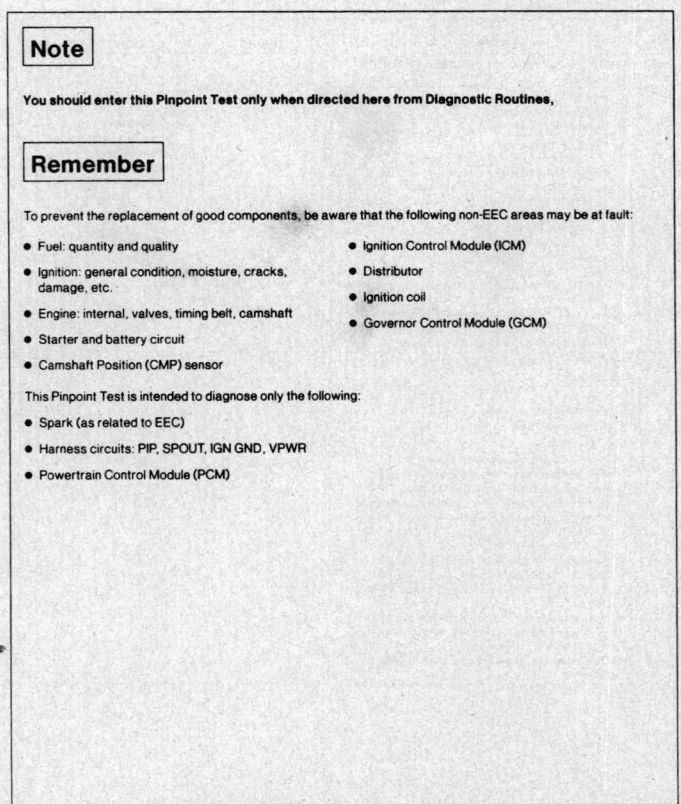

Note

You should enter this Pinpoint Test only when directed here from Diagnostic Routines.

Remember

To prevent the replacement of good components, be aware that the following non-EEC areas may be at fault:

- Fuel: quantity and quality
- Ignition: general condition, moisture, cracks, damage, etc.
- Engine: internal, valves, timing belt, camshaft
- Starter and battery circuit
- Camshaft Position (CMP) sensor

- Ignition Control Module (ICM)
- Distributor
- Ignition coil
- Governor Control Module (GCM)

This Pinpoint Test is intended to diagnose only the following:

- Spark (as related to EEC)
- Harness circuits: PIP, SPOUT, IGN GND, VPWR
- Powertrain Control Module (PCM)

FM0159400707010X

Fig. 165   Test AA: EEC-IV No Start, DI (Part 1 of 11). 1994–95

Pinpoint Test Schematics

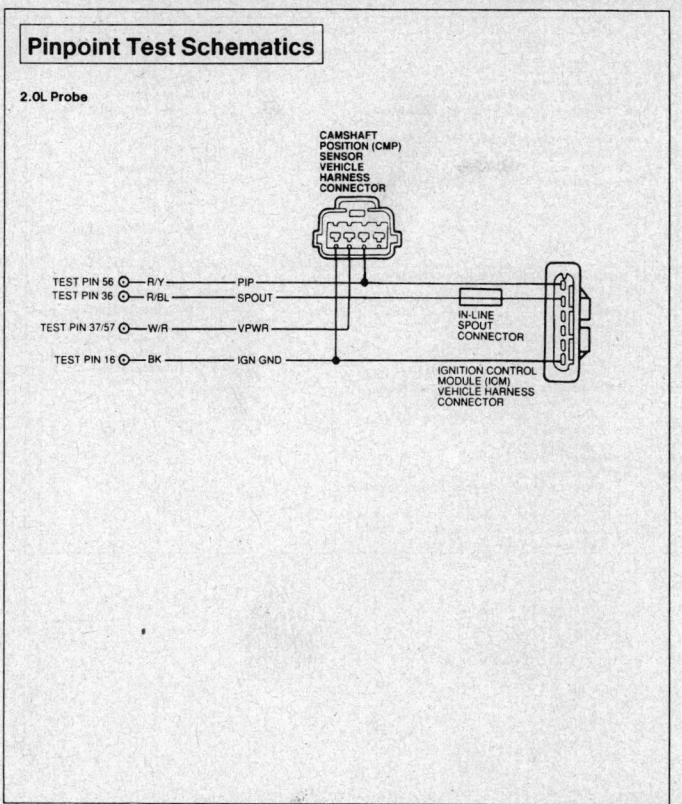

2.0L Probe

Fig. 165   Test AA: EEC-IV No Start, DI (Part 2 of 11).
1994–95

FM0159400707020X

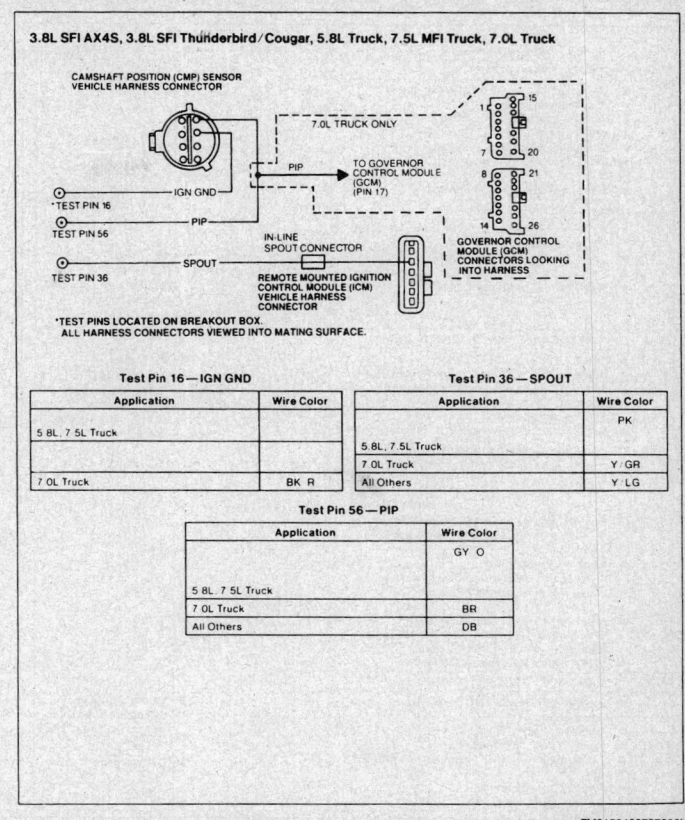

3.8L SFI AX4S, 3.8L SFI Thunderbird/Cougar, 5.8L Truck, 7.5L MFI Truck, 7.0L Truck

Test Pin 16 — IGN GND

Application	Wire Color
5.8L, 7.5L Truck	
7.0L Truck	BK R

Test Pin 36 — SPOUT

Application	Wire Color
	PK
5.8L, 7.5L Truck	
7.0L Truck	Y/GR
All Others	Y/LG

Test Pin 56 — PIP

Application	Wire Color
	GY/O
5.8L, 7.5L Truck	
7.0L Truck	BR
All Others	DB

Fig. 165   Test AA: EEC-IV No Start, DI (Part 3 of 11).
1994–95

FM0159400707030X

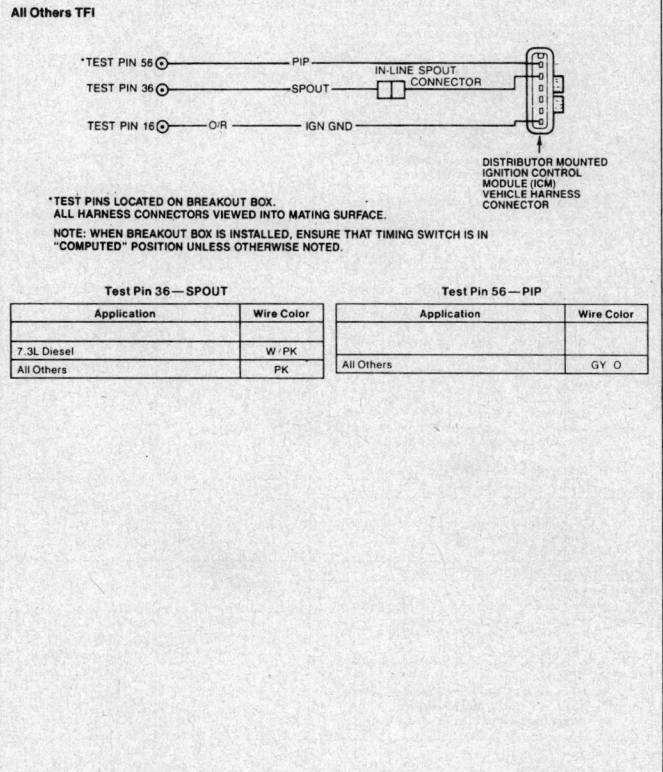

All Others TFI

Test Pin 36 — SPOUT

Application	Wire Color
7.3L Diesel	W/PK
All Others	PK

Test Pin 56 — PIP

Application	Wire Color
All Others	GY/O

Fig. 165   Test AA: EEC-IV No Start, DI (Part 4 of 11).
1994–95

FM0159400707050X

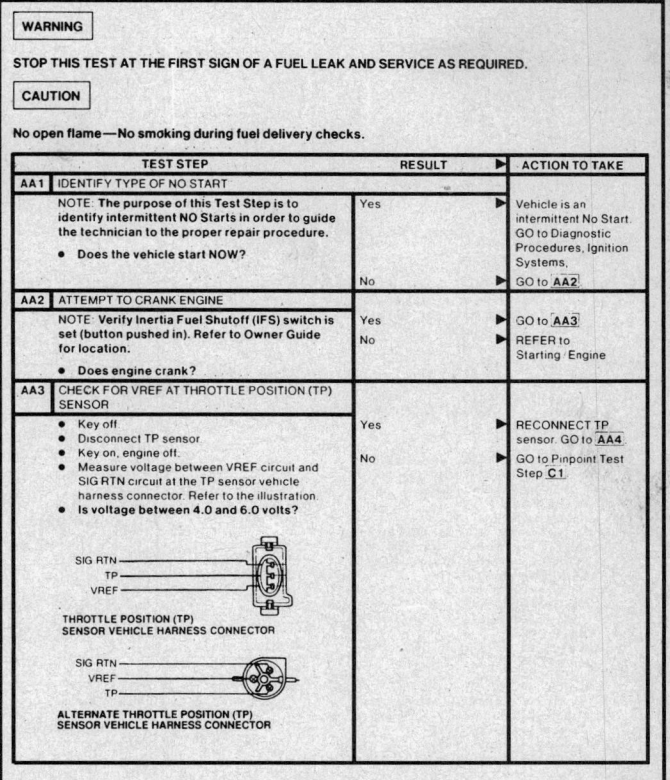

WARNING

STOP THIS TEST AT THE FIRST SIGN OF A FUEL LEAK AND SERVICE AS REQUIRED.

CAUTION

No open flame—No smoking during fuel delivery checks.

	TEST STEP	RESULT	►	ACTION TO TAKE
AA1	IDENTIFY TYPE OF NO START			
	NOTE: The purpose of this Test Step is to identify intermittent NO Starts in order to guide the technician to the proper repair procedure. ● Does the vehicle start NOW?	Yes	►	Vehicle is an intermittent No Start. GO to Diagnostic Procedures, Ignition Systems.
		No	►	GO to AA2
AA2	ATTEMPT TO CRANK ENGINE			
	NOTE: Verify Inertia Fuel Shutoff (IFS) switch is set (button pushed in). Refer to Owner Guide for location. ● Does engine crank?	Yes	►	GO to AA3
		No	►	REFER to Starting/Engine
AA3	CHECK FOR VREF AT THROTTLE POSITION (TP) SENSOR			
	● Key off. ● Disconnect TP sensor. ● Key on, engine off. ● Measure voltage between VREF circuit and SIG RTN circuit at the TP sensor vehicle harness connector. Refer to the illustration. ● Is voltage between 4.0 and 6.0 volts?	Yes	►	RECONNECT TP sensor. GO to AA4
		No	►	GO to Pinpoint Test Step C1

Fig. 165   Test AA: EEC-IV No Start, DI (Part 5 of 11).
1994–95

FM0159400707060X

TEST STEP	RESULT	▶	ACTION TO TAKE
AA4 CHECK FOR SPARK AT PLUGS • Disconnect the spark plug wire to any accessible cylinder. • Connect spark tester between spark plug wire and engine ground. • Crank engine and check for spark. • Reconnect the spark plug wire to the spark plug. • **Was spark present and consistent?**	Yes No	▶ ▶ ▶	GO to AA14 For 7.0L Truck: GO to AA15. For all others: GO to AA5.
AA5 CHECK FOR SPARK AT COIL • Remove high tension coil wire from distributor and install spark tester. • Check for spark while cranking. • Reconnect high tension coil wire to distributor. • **Was spark present during crank?**	Yes No	▶ ▶	All others: REFER to for ICM, cap, rotor and wire diagnosis. GO to AA6
AA6 CHECK CONTINUITY OF IGN GND CIRCUIT • Key off. • Disconnect Powertrain Control Module (PCM) 60 pin connector. Inspect for damaged or pushed out pins, corrosion, loose wires, etc. Service as necessary. • Install breakout box, leave PCM disconnected. **For vehicles with distributor mounted ICM:** — Disconnect ICM module connector. **For vehicles with remote mount ICM:** — Disconnect Camshaft Position (CMP) sensor. **For 7.0L Truck:** — Disconnect Governor Control Module (GCM) and Camshaft Position (CMP) sensor. • Measure resistance between Test Pin 16 at breakout box and ICM or CMP sensor vehicle harness connector IGN-GND circuit. • **Is resistance less than 5.0 ohms?**	Yes No	▶ ▶	GO to AA7 SERVICE open circuit. REMOVE breakout box. RECONNECT all components. RERUN Quick Test.
AA7 ISOLATION OF PROBLEM TO SPOUT CIRCUIT • Reconnect ICM and CMP sensor, as applicable. • Breakout box installed. • Connect PCM to breakout box. • Timing switch to "DIST" position on breakout box. • Attempt to start vehicle. • **Does the vehicle start?**	Yes No	▶ ▶	Timing switch to "Computed" position on breakout box. GO to AA12 GO to AA8

FM0159400707070X

Fig. 165   Test AA: EEC-IV No Start, DI (Part 6 of 11). 1994–95

TEST STEP	RESULT	▶	ACTION TO TAKE
AA8 CHECK SPOUT SIGNAL • Key on, engine off. • Breakout box installed, PCM connected. • Timing switch to "DIST" position on breakout box. • Measure voltage between Test Pin 36 at breakout box and battery negative post during crank. • **Is voltage between 3.0 and 6.0 volts?**	Yes No	▶ ▶	EEC system OK. REMOVE breakout box. RECONNECT all components. **All others:** REFER to DI system diagnosis. PLACE timing switch to "Computed" position and GO to AA9.
AA9 CHECK SPOUT AND PIP CIRCUITS FOR SHORT TO POWER • Key off. • Breakout box installed. • Disconnect PCM. **For vehicles with remote mounted ICM:** — Disconnect CMP and ICM sensor. — For 7.0L Truck: also disconnect GCM. **For all others:** — Disconnect ICM. • Key on. • Measure voltage between Test Pin 36 (SPOUT) at breakout box and battery negative post. • Measure voltage between Test Pin 56 (PIP) at breakout box and battery negative post. • **Is voltage greater than 10.5 volts?**	Yes No	▶ ▶	SERVICE short circuit to the START circuit or to the VPWR circuit in the harness. REMOVE breakout box. RECONNECT all components. RERUN Quick Test. GO to AA10

FM0159400707080X

Fig. 165   Test AA: EEC-IV No Start, DI (Part 7 of 11). 1994–95

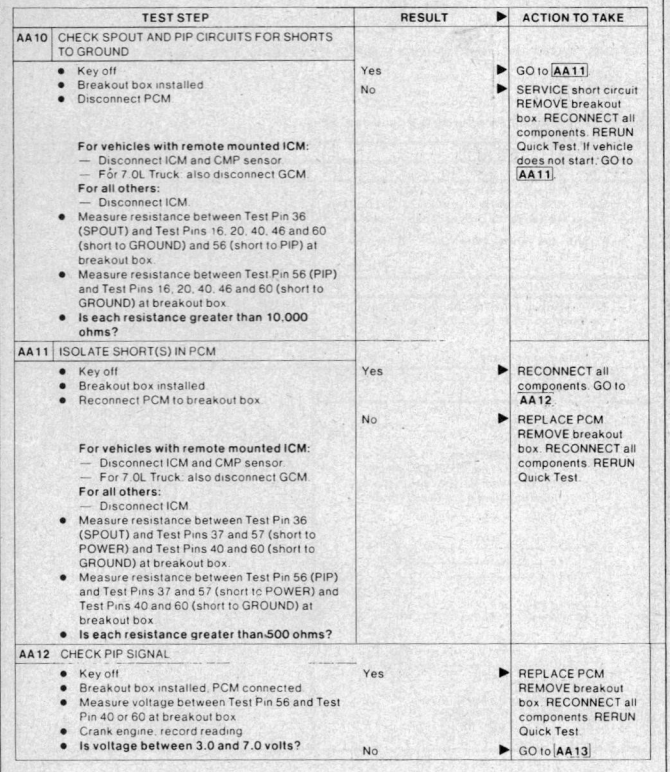

TEST STEP	RESULT	▶	ACTION TO TAKE
AA10 CHECK SPOUT AND PIP CIRCUITS FOR SHORTS TO GROUND • Key off. • Breakout box installed. • Disconnect PCM. **For vehicles with remote mounted ICM:** — Disconnect ICM and CMP sensor. — For 7.0L Truck: also disconnect GCM. **For all others:** — Disconnect ICM. • Measure resistance between Test Pin 36 (SPOUT) and Test Pins 16, 20, 40, 46 and 60 (short to GROUND) and 56 (short to PIP) at breakout box. • Measure resistance between Test Pin 56 (PIP) and Test Pins 16, 20, 40, 46 and 60 (short to GROUND) at breakout box. • **Is each resistance greater than 10,000 ohms?**	Yes No	▶ ▶	GO to AA11 SERVICE short circuit. REMOVE breakout box. RECONNECT all components. RERUN Quick Test. If vehicle does not start: GO to AA11.
AA11 ISOLATE SHORT(S) IN PCM • Key off. • Breakout box installed. • Reconnect PCM to breakout box. **For vehicles with remote mounted ICM:** — Disconnect ICM and CMP sensor. — For 7.0L Truck: also disconnect GCM. **For all others:** — Disconnect ICM. • Measure resistance between Test Pin 36 (SPOUT) and Test Pins 37 and 57 (short to POWER) and Test Pins 40 and 60 (short to GROUND) at breakout box. • Measure resistance between Test Pin 56 (PIP) and Test Pins 37 and 57 (short to POWER) and Test Pins 40 and 60 (short to GROUND) at breakout box. • **Is each resistance greater than 500 ohms?**	Yes No	▶ ▶	RECONNECT all components. GO to AA12 REPLACE PCM REMOVE breakout box. RECONNECT all components. RERUN Quick Test.
AA12 CHECK PIP SIGNAL • Key off. • Breakout box installed, PCM connected. • Measure voltage between Test Pin 56 and Test Pin 40 or 60 at breakout box. • Crank engine, record reading. • **Is voltage between 3.0 and 7.0 volts?**	Yes No	▶ ▶	REPLACE PCM REMOVE breakout box. RECONNECT all components. RERUN Quick Test. GO to AA13

FM0159400707090X

Fig. 165   Test AA: EEC-IV No Start, DI (Part 8 of 11). 1994–95

TEST STEP	RESULT	▶	ACTION TO TAKE
AA13 CHECK CONTINUITY OF PIP CIRCUIT • Key off. • Breakout box installed. • Disconnect PCM. **For vehicles with remote mounted ICM:** — Disconnect ICM and CMP sensor. — For 7.0L Truck: also disconnect GCM. **For all others:** — Disconnect ICM. • Measure resistance between Test Pin 56 at breakout box and PIP circuit at the following connectors, as appropriate: ICM, CMP sensor and/or GCM. • **Is resistance less than 5.0 ohms?**	Yes No	▶ ▶	REMOVE breakout box. RECONNECT all components. **All others:** REFER to DI system diagnosis. SERVICE open circuit. REMOVE breakout box. RECONNECT all components. RERUN Quick Test.
AA14 SPOUT SIGNAL VERIFICATION • Key off. • Disconnect Powertrain Control Module (PCM). Inspect for damaged or pushed out pins, corrosion, loose wires, etc. Service as necessary. • Install breakout box and connect PCM to breakout box. • Ensure timing switch is in "Computed" position on breakout box. • Measure voltage between Test Pin 36 and Test Pins 40 and 60 at the breakout box during crank. • **Is voltage between 3.0 and 6.0 volts?**	Yes No	▶ ▶	GO to AA21 GO to AA9
AA15 ATTEMPT TO RESTART VEHICLE • Key off. • Disconnect Governor Control Module (GCM). • Attempt to start vehicle. • **Does vehicle start?**	Yes No	▶ ▶	REPLACE GCM RERUN Quick Test. GO to AA16
AA16 CHECK CONTINUITY OF PIP CIRCUIT • Key off. • Disconnect Powertrain Control Module (PCM). Inspect for damaged or pushed out pins, corrosion, loose wires, etc. Service as necessary. • Install breakout box, leave PCM disconnected. • GCM disconnected. • Measure resistance between Pin 17 at GCM and Test Pin 56 at breakout box. • **Is resistance less than 5.0 ohms?**	Yes No	▶ ▶	GO to AA17 SERVICE open circuit. REMOVE breakout box. RECONNECT all components. RERUN Quick Test.

FM0159400707100X

Fig. 165   Test AA: EEC-IV No Start, DI (Part 9 of 11). 1994–95

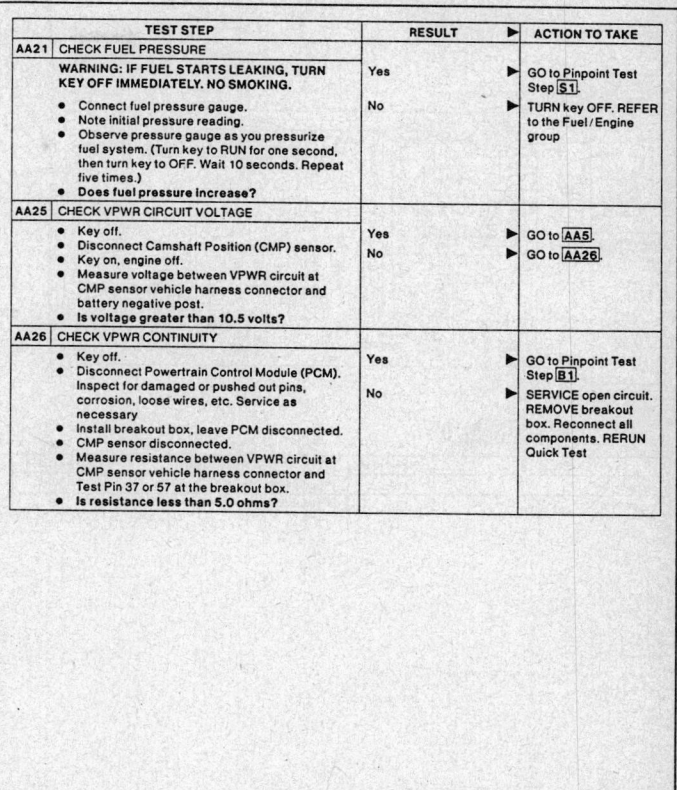

TEST STEP	RESULT	▶	ACTION TO TAKE
AA17 CHECK CONTINUITY OF PIP CIRCUIT			
• Key off • PCM disconnected • GCM disconnected • Disconnect Camshaft Position (CMP) sensor • Measure resistance between PIP circuit at the CMP sensor connector and Test Pin 56 at breakout box • **Is resistance less than 5.0 ohms?**	Yes No	▶ ▶	GO to **AA18** SERVICE open circuit. REMOVE breakout box. RECONNECT all components. RERUN Quick Test.
AA18 CHECK PIP CIRCUIT FOR SHORT TO POWER AND GROUND			
• Key off • Breakout box installed • PCM disconnected • GCM disconnected • CMP sensor disconnected • Measure resistance between Test Pin 56 and Test Pins 16, 20, 40, 46 and 60 (short to ground) and Test Pins 26, 37 and 57 (short to power) • **Is each resistance greater than 10,000 ohms?**	Yes No	▶ ▶	GO to **AA19** SERVICE short circuit. REMOVE breakout box. RECONNECT all components. RERUN Quick Test.
AA19 ISOLATE SHORTS IN PCM			
• Key off • Breakout box installed • Reconnect PCM to breakout box • Measure resistance between Test Pin 56 and Test Pins 16, 20, 40, 46 and 60 (short to ground) and Test Pins 26, 37 and 57 (short to power) • **Is each resistance greater than 10,000 ohms?**	Yes No	▶ ▶	GO to **AA20** REPLACE PCM. REMOVE breakout box. RECONNECT all components. RERUN Quick Test.
AA20 CHECK PIP SIGNAL			
• Key off • Breakout box installed. PCM connected • Reconnect CMP sensor and GCM • Measure voltage between Test Pin 56 and Test Pin 16 at breakout box • **Is voltage between 3.0 and 7.0 volts?**	Yes No	▶ ▶	REPLACE PCM. REMOVE breakout box. RECONNECT all components. RERUN Quick Test GO to **AA6**

FM0159400707110X

Fig. 165　Test AA: EEC-IV No Start, DI (Part 10 of 11). 1994–95

TEST STEP	RESULT	▶	ACTION TO TAKE
AA21 CHECK FUEL PRESSURE			
WARNING: IF FUEL STARTS LEAKING, TURN KEY OFF IMMEDIATELY. NO SMOKING. • Connect fuel pressure gauge. • Note initial pressure reading. • Observe pressure gauge as you pressurize fuel system. (Turn key to RUN for one second, then turn key to OFF. Wait 10 seconds. Repeat five times.) • **Does fuel pressure increase?**	Yes No	▶ ▶	GO to Pinpoint Test Step **S1** TURN key OFF. REFER to the Fuel/Engine group
AA25 CHECK VPWR CIRCUIT VOLTAGE			
• Key off. • Disconnect Camshaft Position (CMP) sensor. • Key on, engine off. • Measure voltage between VPWR circuit at CMP sensor vehicle harness connector and battery negative post. • **Is voltage greater than 10.5 volts?**	Yes No	▶ ▶	GO to **AA5**. GO to **AA26**.
AA26 CHECK VPWR CONTINUITY			
• Key off. • Disconnect Powertrain Control Module (PCM). Inspect for damaged or pushed out pins, corrosion, loose wires, etc. Service as necessary • Install breakout box, leave PCM disconnected. • CMP sensor disconnected. • Measure resistance between VPWR circuit at CMP sensor vehicle harness connector and Test Pin 37 or 57 at the breakout box. • **Is resistance less than 5.0 ohms?**	Yes No	▶ ▶	GO to Pinpoint Test Step **B1**. SERVICE open circuit. REMOVE breakout box. Reconnect all components. RERUN Quick Test

Fig. 165　Test AA: EEC-IV No Start, DI (Part 11 of 11). 1994–95

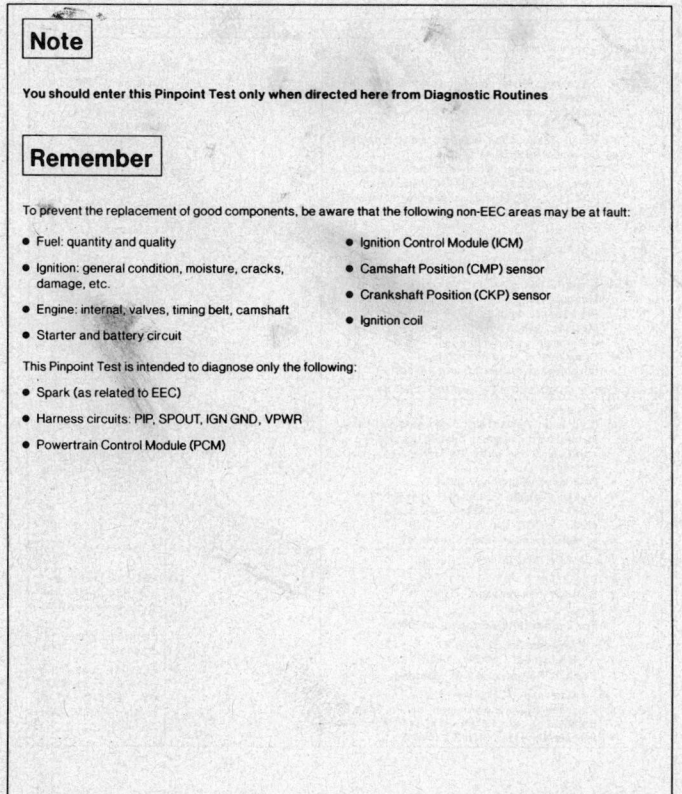

Note

You should enter this Pinpoint Test only when directed here from Diagnostic Routines

Remember

To prevent the replacement of good components, be aware that the following non-EEC areas may be at fault:

- Fuel: quantity and quality
- Ignition: general condition, moisture, cracks, damage, etc.
- Engine: internal, valves, timing belt, camshaft
- Starter and battery circuit

- Ignition Control Module (ICM)
- Camshaft Position (CMP) sensor
- Crankshaft Position (CKP) sensor
- Ignition coil

This Pinpoint Test is intended to diagnose only the following:

- Spark (as related to EEC)
- Harness circuits: PIP, SPOUT, IGN GND, VPWR
- Powertrain Control Module (PCM)

FM0159300708010X

Fig. 166　Test AB: EEC-IV No Start, EI-Low Data Rate (Part 1 of 7). 1993

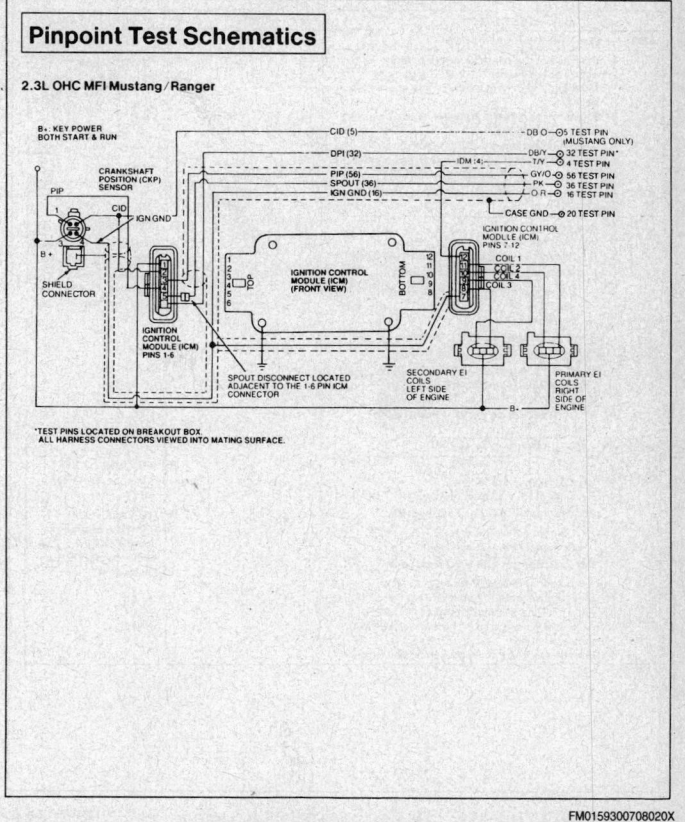

Pinpoint Test Schematics

2.3L OHC MFI Mustang/Ranger

*TEST PINS LOCATED ON BREAKOUT BOX.
ALL HARNESS CONNECTORS VIEWED INTO MATING SURFACE.

FM0159300708020X

Fig. 166　Test AB: EEC-IV No Start, EI-Low Data Rate (Part 2 of 7). 1993

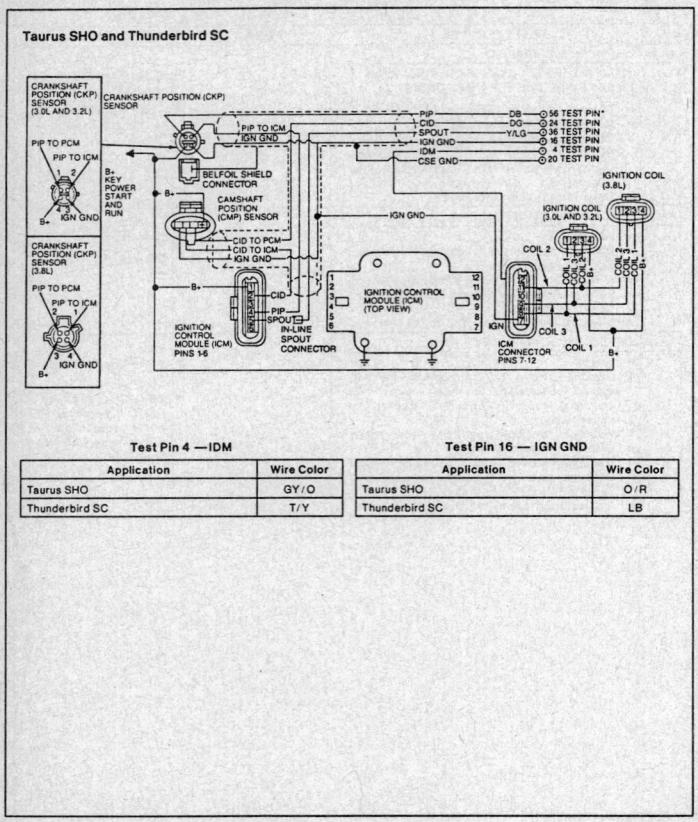

Taurus SHO and Thunderbird SC

Test Pin 4 — IDM

Application	Wire Color
Taurus SHO	GY/O
Thunderbird SC	T/Y

Test Pin 16 — IGN GND

Application	Wire Color
Taurus SHO	O/R
Thunderbird SC	LB

FM0159300708030X

Fig. 166   Test AB: EEC-IV No Start, EI-Low Data Rate (Part 3 of 7). 1993

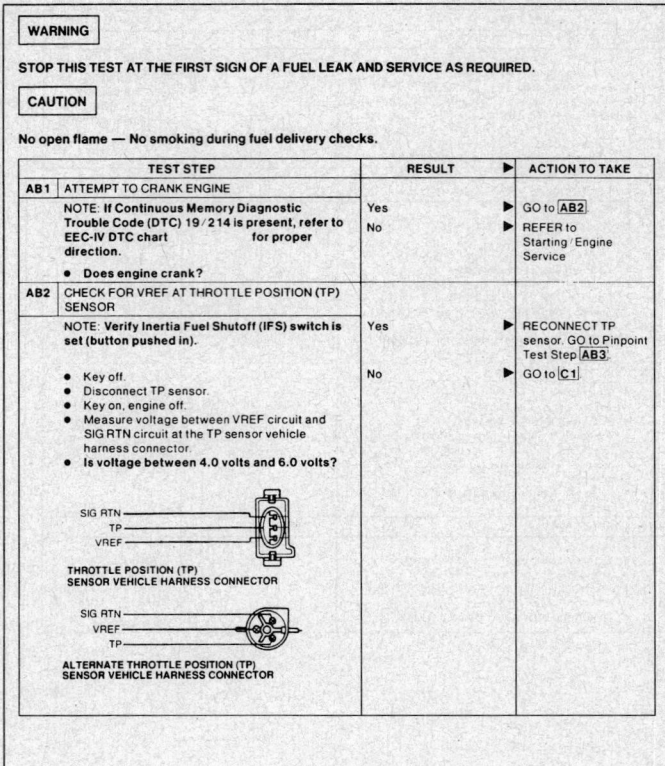

WARNING

STOP THIS TEST AT THE FIRST SIGN OF A FUEL LEAK AND SERVICE AS REQUIRED.

CAUTION

No open flame — No smoking during fuel delivery checks.

	TEST STEP	RESULT	▶	ACTION TO TAKE
AB1	ATTEMPT TO CRANK ENGINE			
	NOTE: If Continuous Memory Diagnostic Trouble Code (DTC) 19/214 is present, refer to EEC-IV DTC chart _____ for proper direction. ● **Does engine crank?**	Yes No	▶ ▶	GO to **AB2** REFER to Starting/Engine Service
AB2	CHECK FOR VREF AT THROTTLE POSITION (TP) SENSOR			
	NOTE: Verify Inertia Fuel Shutoff (IFS) switch is set (button pushed in). ● Key off. ● Disconnect TP sensor. ● Key on, engine off. ● Measure voltage between VREF circuit and SIG RTN circuit at the TP sensor vehicle harness connector. ● **Is voltage between 4.0 volts and 6.0 volts?**	Yes No	▶ ▶	RECONNECT TP sensor. GO to Pinpoint Test Step **AB3** GO to **C1**

SIG RTN
TP
VREF

THROTTLE POSITION (TP)
SENSOR VEHICLE HARNESS CONNECTOR

SIG RTN
VREF
TP

ALTERNATE THROTTLE POSITION (TP)
SENSOR VEHICLE HARNESS CONNECTOR

FM0159300708040X

Fig. 166   Test AB: EEC-IV No Start, EI-Low Data Rate (Part 4 of 7). 1993

	TEST STEP	RESULT	▶	ACTION TO TAKE
AB3	CHECK FOR SPARK AT PLUGS			
	● Disconnect the spark plug wire to any accessible cylinder (on 2.3L Ranger and Mustang disconnect exhaust side spark plug only.) ● Connect spark tester between spark plug wire and engine ground. ● Crank engine and check for spark. ● Reconnect the spark plug wire to spark plug. ● **Was spark present and consistent?**	Yes No	▶ ▶	GO to **AB7** GO to **AB4**
AB4	CHECK PIP CIRCUIT FOR SHORTS TO POWER AND GROUND			
	● Key off. ● Install breakout box. ● Disconnect Powertrain Control Module (PCM). **For Thunderbird SC or Taurus SHO:** — Disconnect Crankshaft Position (CKP) sensor. — Disconnect ICM (Pins 1-6). **For 2.3L Ranger and 2.3L Mustang:** — Disconnect ICM (Pins 1-6). ● Measure resistance between Test Pin 56 (PIP) and Test Pins 16, 20, 40, 46, 60 (short to GROUND), 26, 37, 57 (short to POWER). ● **Is each resistance greater than 10,000 ohms?**	Yes No	▶ ▶	GO to **AB5** SERVICE short circuit. REMOVE breakout box. RECONNECT all components. RERUN Quick Test.
AB5	ISOLATE SHORT(S) IN PCM			
	● Key off. ● Breakout box installed. ● Reconnect PCM to breakout box. **For Thunderbird SC or Taurus SHO:** — Disconnect CKP sensor. — Disconnect ICM (Pins 1-6). **For 2.3L Ranger and 2.3L Mustang:** — Disconnect ICM (Pins 1-6). ● Measure resistance between Test Pin 56 (PIP) and Test Pins 37 and 57 (short to POWER). Also Test Pins 40 and 60 (short to GROUND) at breakout box. ● **Is each resistance greater than 500 ohms?**	Yes No	▶ ▶	RECONNECT all components. GO to **AB6** REPLACE PCM. REMOVE breakout box. RECONNECT all components. RERUN Quick Test

FM0159300708050X

Fig. 166   Test AB: EEC-IV No Start, EI-Low Data Rate (Part 5 of 7). 1993

	TEST STEP	RESULT	▶	ACTION TO TAKE
AB6	CHECK CONTINUITY OF IGN GND CIRCUIT			
	● Key off. ● Disconnect Powertrain Control Module (PCM). Inspect for damaged or pushed out pins, corrosion, loose wires, etc. Service as necessary. ● Install breakout box, leave PCM disconnected. ● Disconnect ICM (Pins 7-12). ● Measure resistance between Test Pin 16 at the breakout box and IGN GND circuit at the ICM (Pin 7-12) vehicle harness connector. ● **Is resistance less than 5.0 ohms?**	Yes No	▶ ▶	REMOVE breakout box. RECONNECT all components. GO to Ignition System Diagnostic Procedures SERVICE open circuit. REMOVE breakout box. RECONNECT all components. RERUN Quick Test.
AB7	CHECK PIP SIGNAL			
	● Key off. ● Breakout box installed, PCM connected. ● Measure voltage between Test Pin 56 and Test Pin 16 at breakout box. (For 2.3L Ranger and Mustang, switch timing switch to "DIST" position on breakout box.) ● Crank engine, record reading. ● **Is voltage between 3.0 and 7.0 volts?**	Yes No	▶ ▶	GO to **AB8** GO to **AB9**
AB8	CHECK CONTINUITY OF IGN GND CIRCUIT			
	● Key off. ● Disconnect Powertrain Control Module (PCM). Inspect for damaged or pushed out pins, corrosion, loose wires, etc. Service as necessary. ● Disconnect ICM (Pins 7-12). ● Measure resistance between Test Pin 16 at breakout box and ICM vehicle harness connector IGN GND circuit. ● **Is resistance less than 5.0 ohms?**	Yes No	▶ ▶	GO to **AB10** SERVICE open circuit. REMOVE breakout box. RECONNECT all components. RERUN Quick Test.
AB9	CHECK CONTINUITY OF PIP CIRCUIT			
	● Key off. ● Breakout box installed. ● Disconnect PCM. **For Thunderbird SC or Taurus SHO:** — Disconnect CKP sensor. — Disconnect ICM (Pins 1-6). **For 2.3L Ranger and 2.3L Mustang:** — Disconnect ICM (Pins 1-6). ● Measure resistance between Test Pin 56 at breakout box and PIP circuit at CKP sensor. ● **Is resistance less than 5.0 ohms?**	Yes No	▶ ▶	REMOVE breakout box. RECONNECT all components. REFER to Electronic Ignition (EI) diagnosis. SERVICE open circuit. REMOVE breakout box. RECONNECT all components. RERUN Quick Test.

FM0159300708060X

Fig. 166   Test AB: EEC-IV No Start, EI-Low Data Rate (Part 6 of 7). 1993

TEST STEP	RESULT	►	ACTION TO TAKE
AB10 CHECK FUEL PRESSURE			
WARNING: IF FUEL STARTS LEAKING, TURN KEY OFF IMMEDIATELY. NO SMOKING.	Yes	►	GO to Pinpoint Test Step **S1**
• Connect fuel pressure gauge.	No	►	TURN key OFF, REFER to Fuel / Charging Service
• Note initial pressure reading.			
• Observe pressure gauge as you pressurize fuel system. (Turn key to RUN for one second, then turn key to OFF. Wait 10 seconds. Repeat five times.)			
• **Does fuel pressure increase?**			

FM0159300708070X

Fig. 166   Test AB: EEC-IV No Start, EI-Low Data Rate (Part 7 of 7). 1993

Note

You should enter this Pinpoint Test only when you have been directed here from Diagnostic Routines.

Remember

To prevent the replacement of good components, be aware that the following non-EEC areas may be at fault:

- Fuel: quantity and quality
- Ignition: general condition, moisture, cracks, damage, etc.
- Engine: internal, valves, timing belt, camshaft
- Starter and battery circuit
- Crankshaft Position (CKP) sensor
- Ignition Control Module (ICM)
- Coil Pack

This Pinpoint Test is intended to diagnose only the following:

- Spark (as related to EEC)
- Harness circuits: PIP, IGN GND, VPWR
- Powertrain Control Module (PCM)

FM0159400709010X

Fig. 167   Test AB: EEC-IV No Start, EI-Low Data Rate (Part 1 of 7). 1994–95

Pinpoint Test Schematics

Taurus SHO

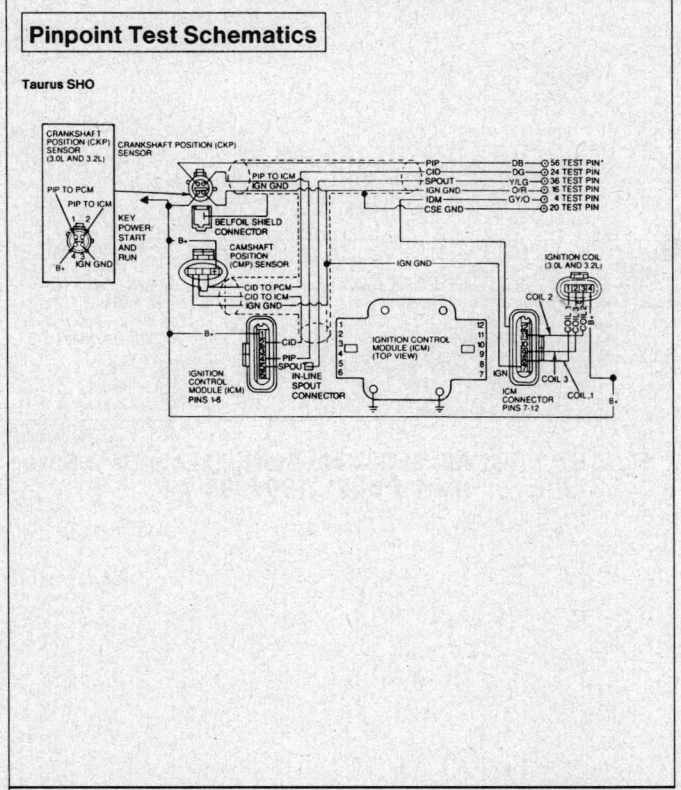

FM0159400709020X

Fig. 167   Test AB: EEC-IV No Start, EI-Low Data Rate (Part 2 of 7). 1994–95

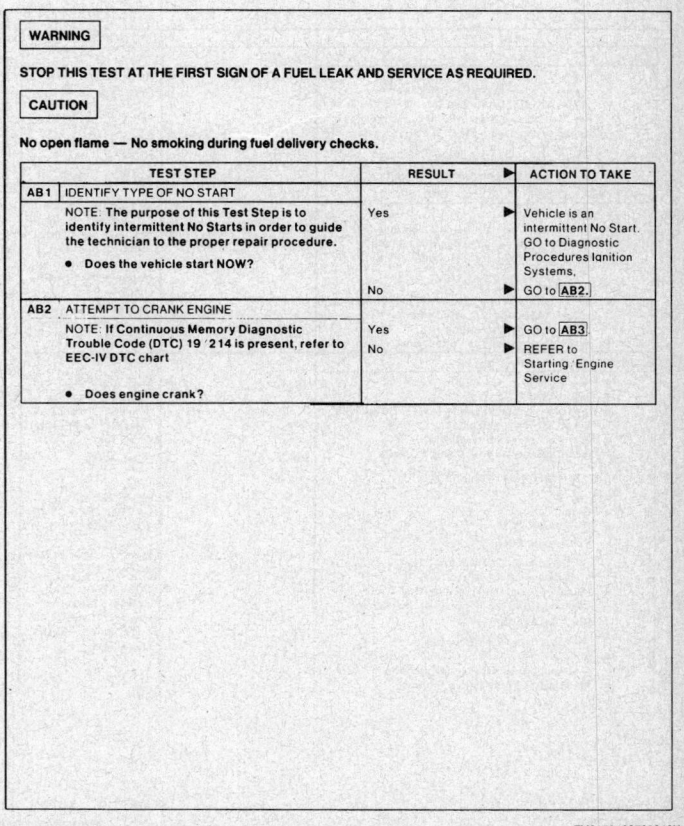

FM0159400709040X

Fig. 167   Test AB: EEC-IV No Start, EI-Low Data Rate (Part 3 of 7). 1994–95

TEST STEP	RESULT	►	ACTION TO TAKE
AB3 CHECK FOR VREF AT THROTTLE POSITION (TP) SENSOR			
NOTE: Verify Inertia Fuel Shutoff (IFS) switch is set (button pushed in). Refer to Owner Guide for location. • Key off. • Disconnect TP sensor. • Key on, engine off. • Measure voltage between VREF circuit and SIG RTN circuit at the TP sensor vehicle harness connector. • **Is voltage between 4.0 and 6.0 volts?**	Yes No	► ►	RECONNECT TP sensor. GO to Pinpoint Test Step **AB4** GO to Pinpoint Test Step **C1**

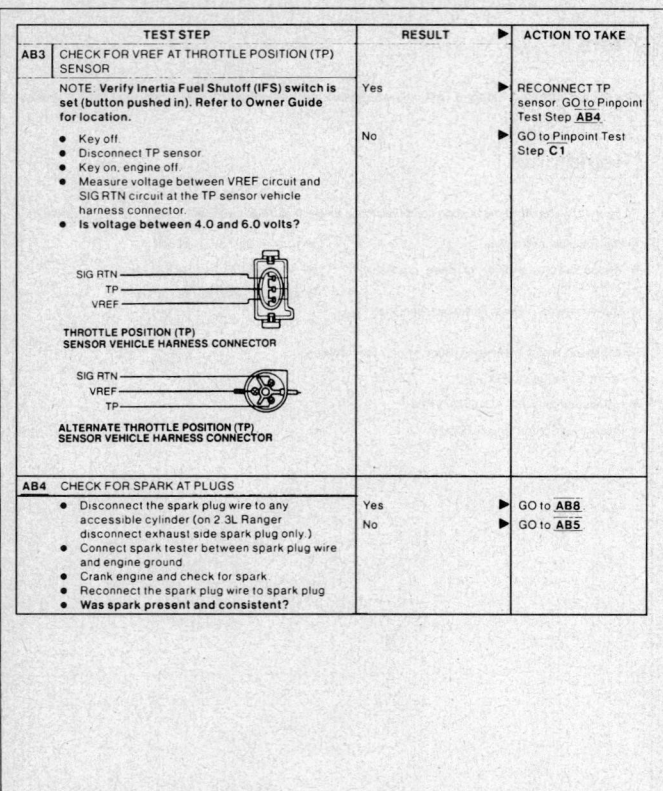

AB4 CHECK FOR SPARK AT PLUGS			
• Disconnect the spark plug wire to any accessible cylinder (on 2.3L Ranger disconnect exhaust side spark plug only.) • Connect spark tester between spark plug wire and engine ground • Crank engine and check for spark. • Reconnect the spark plug wire to spark plug • **Was spark present and consistent?**	Yes No	► ►	GO to **AB8** GO to **AB5**

FM0159400709050X

Fig. 167 Test AB: EEC-IV No Start, EI-Low Data Rate (Part 4 of 7). 1994–95

TEST STEP	RESULT	►	ACTION TO TAKE
AB5 CHECK PIP CIRCUIT FOR SHORTS TO POWER AND GROUND			

• Key off.
• Install breakout box.
• Disconnect Powertrain Control Module (PCM).
  For Taurus SHO:
  — Disconnect Crankshaft Position (CKP) sensor.
  — Disconnect ICM (Pins 1-6).
  For 2.3L Ranger:
  — Disconnect ICM (Pins 1-6).
• Measure resistance between Test Pin 56 (PIP) and Test Pins 16, 20, 40, 46, 60 (short to GROUND), 26, 37, 57 (short to POWER).
• **Is each resistance greater than 10,000 ohms?**
	Yes
	No
		►
		►
			GO to **AB6**.
			SERVICE short circuit. REMOVE breakout box. RECONNECT all components. RERUN Quick Test.

AB6 ISOLATE SHORT(S) IN PCM			

• Key off.
• Breakout box installed.
• Reconnect PCM to breakout box.
  For Taurus SHO:
  — Disconnect CKP sensor.
  — Disconnect ICM (Pins 1-6).
  For 2.3L Ranger:
  — Disconnect ICM (Pins 1-6).
• Measure resistance between Test Pin 56 (PIP) and Test Pins 37 and 57 (short to POWER). Also Test Pins 40 and 60 (short to GROUND) at breakout box.
• **Is each resistance greater than 500 ohms?**
	Yes
	
	No
		►
		
		►
			RECONNECT all components. GO to **AB7**.
			REPLACE PCM. REMOVE breakout box. RECONNECT all components. RERUN Quick Test.

AB7 CHECK CONTINUITY OF IGN GND CIRCUIT			
• Key off. • Disconnect Powertrain Control Module (PCM). Inspect for damaged or pushed out pins, corrosion, loose wires, etc. Service as necessary. • Install breakout box, leave PCM disconnected. • Disconnect ICM (Pins 7-12). • Measure resistance between Test Pin 16 at the breakout box and IGN GND circuit at the ICM (Pin 7-12) vehicle harness connector. • **Is resistance less than 5.0 ohms?**	Yes No	► ►	REMOVE breakout box. RECONNECT all components. GO to Ignition System Diagnostic SERVICE open circuit. REMOVE breakout box. RECONNECT all components. RERUN Quick Test.

FM0159400709060X

Fig. 167 Test AB: EEC-IV No Start, EI-Low Data Rate (Part 5 of 7). 1994–95

TEST STEP	RESULT	►	ACTION TO TAKE
AB8 CHECK PIP SIGNAL			
• Key off. • Breakout box installed, PCM connected. • Measure voltage between Test Pin 56 and Test Pin 16 at breakout box. (For 2.3L Ranger, switch timing switch to "DIST" position on breakout box.) • Crank engine, record reading. • **Is voltage between 3.0 and 7.0 volts?**	Yes No	► ►	GO to **AB9**. GO to **AB11**.
AB9 CHECK CONTINUITY OF IGN GND CIRCUIT			
• Key off. • Disconnect Powertrain Control Module (PCM). Inspect for damaged or pushed out pins, corrosion, loose wires, etc. Service as necessary. • Disconnect ICM (Pins 7-12). • Measure resistance between Test Pin 16 at breakout box and ICM vehicle harness connector IGN GND circuit. • **Is resistance less than 5.0 ohms?**	Yes No	► ►	GO to **AB10** SERVICE open circuit REMOVE breakout box. RECONNECT all components RERUN Quick Test
AB10 CHECK PIP SIGNAL IN PCM			
• Key off. • Disconnect PCM. • Measure voltage between Test Pin 56 and Test Pin 16 at the breakout box. • Crank engine, record reading. • **Is voltage between 3.0 and 7.0 volts?**	Yes No	► ►	REPLACE PCM. REMOVE breakout box. RECONNECT all components. RERUN Quick Test GO to **AB12**
AB11 CHECK CONTINUITY OF PIP CIRCUIT			

• Key off.
• Breakout box installed.
• Disconnect PCM.
  For Taurus SHO:
  Disconnect CKP sensor.
  Disconnect ICM (Pins 1-6).
• Measure resistance between Test Pin 56 at breakout box and PIP circuit at CKP sensor.
  For 2.3L Ranger:
  Disconnect ICM (Pins 1-6).
• Measure resistance between Test Pin 56 at breakout box and PIP circuit at ICM connector.
• Is resistance less than 5.0 ohms?
	Yes
	
	No
		►
		
		►
			REMOVE breakout box. RECONNECT all components. REFER to
			Electronic Ignition (EI) diagnosis.
			SERVICE open circuit REMOVE breakout box. RECONNECT all components RERUN Quick Test

FM015940070907OX

Fig. 167 Test AB: EEC-IV No Start, EI-Low Data Rate (Part 6 of 7). 1994–95

TEST STEP	RESULT	►	ACTION TO TAKE
AB12 CHECK FUEL PRESSURE			
WARNING: IF FUEL STARTS LEAKING, TURN KEY OFF IMMEDIATELY. NO SMOKING. • Connect fuel pressure gauge. • Note initial pressure reading. • Observe pressure gauge as fuel system is pressurized. (Turn key to RUN for one second, then turn key to OFF. Wait 10 seconds. Repeat five times.) • **Does fuel pressure increase?**	Yes No	► ►	GO to Pinpoint Test Step **S1** TURN key OFF, REFER to Fuel Charging

FM0159400709080X

Fig. 167 Test AB: EEC-IV No Start, EI-Low Data Rate (Part 7 of 7). 1994–95

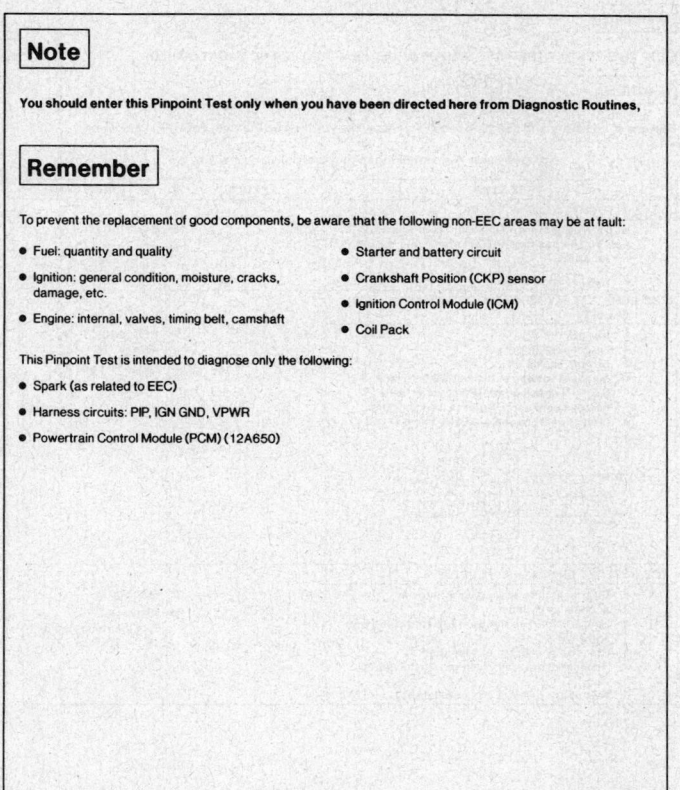

Note

You should enter this Pinpoint Test only when you have been directed here from Diagnostic Routines.

Remember

To prevent the replacement of good components, be aware that the following non-EEC areas may be at fault:

- Fuel: quantity and quality
- Ignition: general condition, moisture, cracks, damage, etc.
- Engine: internal, valves, timing belt, camshaft
- Starter and battery circuit
- Crankshaft Position (CKP) sensor
- Ignition Control Module (ICM)
- Coil Pack

This Pinpoint Test is intended to diagnose only the following:

- Spark (as related to EEC)
- Harness circuits: PIP, IGN GND, VPWR
- Powertrain Control Module (PCM) (12A650)

FM0159300710010X

Fig. 168 Test AC: EEC-IV No Start, EI-High Data Rate (Part 1 of 8)

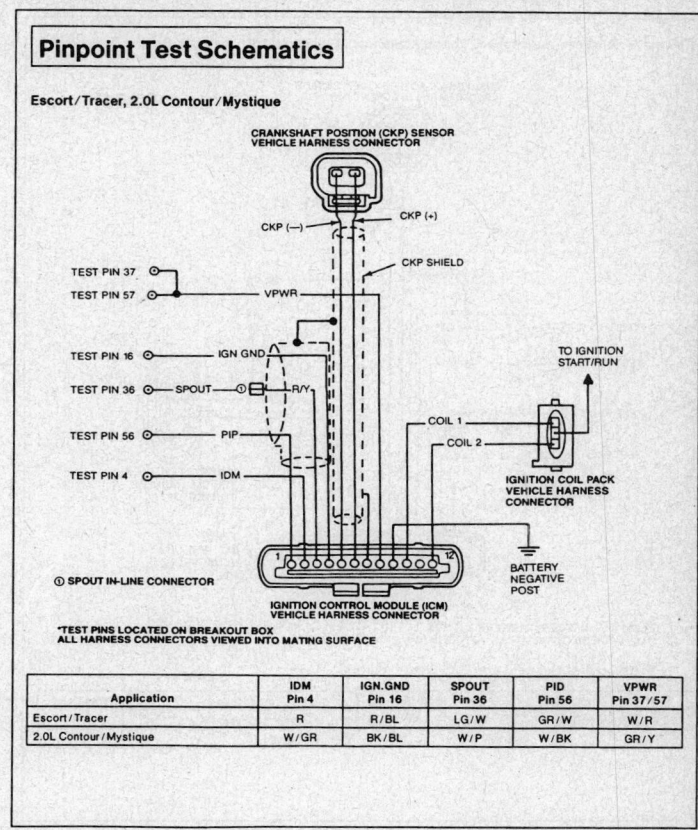

Pinpoint Test Schematics

Escort/Tracer, 2.0L Contour/Mystique

Application	IDM Pin 4	IGN.GND Pin 16	SPOUT Pin 36	PID Pin 56	VPWR Pin 37/57
Escort/Tracer	R	R/BL	LG/W	GR/W	W/R
2.0L Contour/Mystique	W/GR	BK/BL	W/P	W/BK	GR/Y

FM0159300710020A

Fig. 168 Test AC: EEC-IV No Start, EI-High Data Rate (Part 2 of 8)

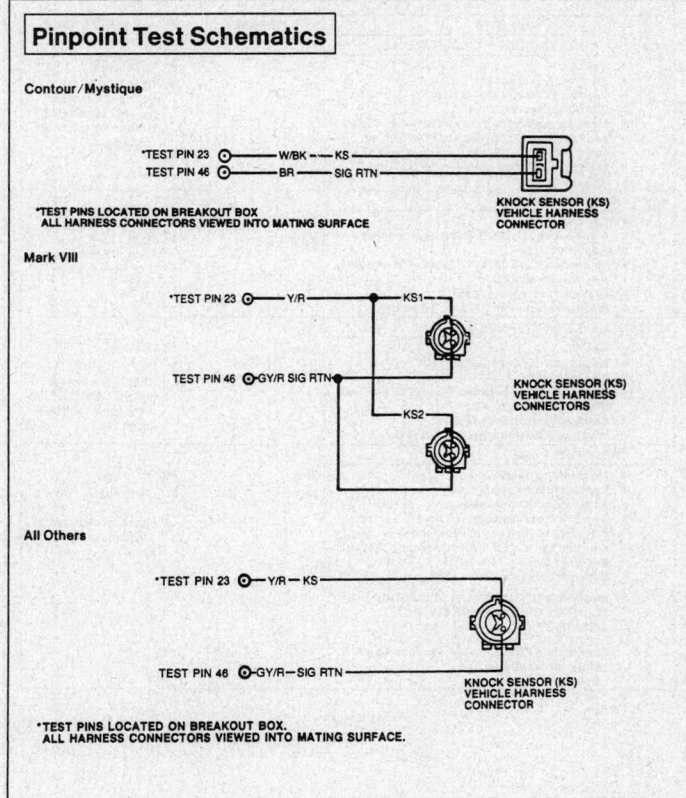

Pinpoint Test Schematics

Contour/Mystique

Mark VIII

All Others

Fig. 168 Test AC: EEC-IV No Start, EI-High Data Rate (Part 3 of 8). 1995

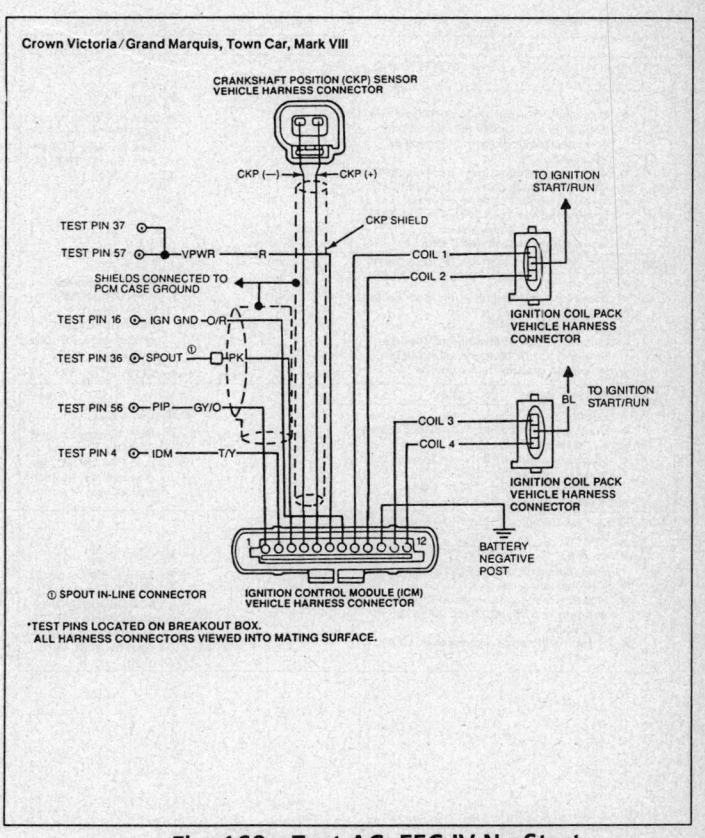

Crown Victoria/Grand Marquis, Town Car, Mark VIII

Fig. 168 Test AC: EEC-IV No Start, EI-High Data Rate (Part 4 of 8). 1993–94

Taurus Flexible Fuel, Thunderbird/Cougar (California), Thunderbird SC, Aerostar, Ranger, Explorer

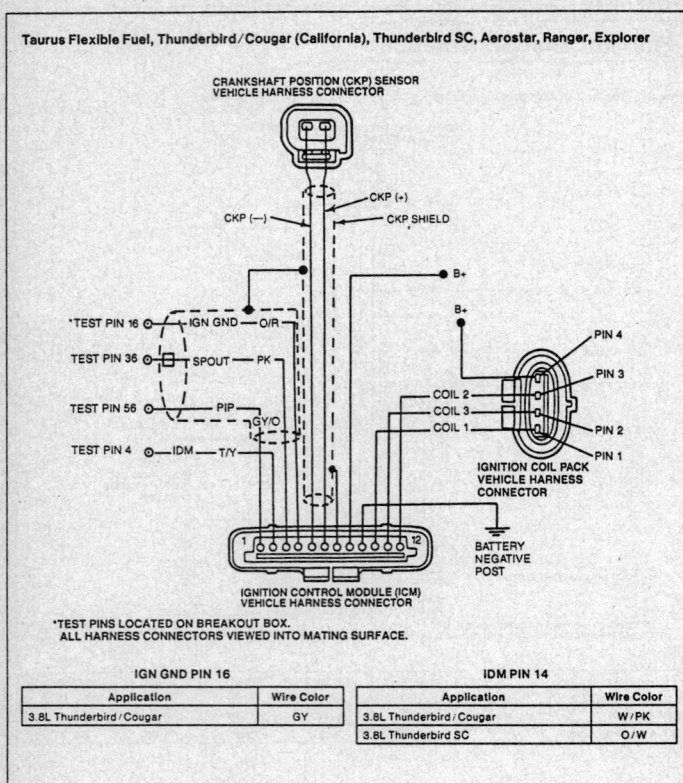

CRANKSHAFT POSITION (CKP) SENSOR VEHICLE HARNESS CONNECTOR

CKP (+)

CKP (—) — CKP SHIELD

B+

B+

PIN 4
PIN 3
PIN 2
PIN 1

COIL 2
COIL 3
COIL 1

*TEST PIN 16 — IGN GND — O/R
TEST PIN 36 — SPOUT — PK
TEST PIN 56 — PIP — GY/O
TEST PIN 4 — IDM — T/Y

IGNITION COIL PACK VEHICLE HARNESS CONNECTOR

1 12

IGNITION CONTROL MODULE (ICM) VEHICLE HARNESS CONNECTOR

BATTERY NEGATIVE POST

*TEST PINS LOCATED ON BREAKOUT BOX.
ALL HARNESS CONNECTORS VIEWED INTO MATING SURFACE.

IGN GND PIN 16	
Application	Wire Color
3.8L Thunderbird/Cougar	GY

IDM PIN 14	
Application	Wire Color
3.8L Thunderbird/Cougar	W/PK
3.8L Thunderbird SC	O/W

Fig. 168 Test AC: EEC-IV No Start, EI-High Data Rate (Part 5 of 8). 1994–95

WARNING

STOP THIS TEST AT THE FIRST SIGN OF A FUEL LEAK AND SERVICE AS REQUIRED.

CAUTION

Beware of all safety and handling requirements while working on Flexible Fuel (FF) vehicles.

No open flame—No smoking during fuel delivery checks.

TEST STEP		RESULT	▶	ACTION TO TAKE
AC1	ATTEMPT TO CRANK ENGINE			
	NOTE: Verify Inertia Fuel Shutoff (IFS) switch is set (button pushed in). Refer to Owner's Guide for location. • Does engine crank?	Yes No	▶ ▶	GO to AC2. REFER to Starting/Engine Group
AC2	CHECK FOR VREF AT THROTTLE POSITION (TP) SENSOR			
	• Key off. • Disconnect TP sensor. • Key on, engine off. • Measure voltage between VREF circuit and SIG RTN circuit at the TP sensor vehicle harness connector. Refer to the illustration. • Is voltage between 4.0 volts and 6.0 volts?	Yes No	▶ ▶	RECONNECT TP sensor. GO to AC3. GO to Pinpoint Test Step C1.
	SIG. RTN. TP VREF THROTTLE POSITION (TP) SENSOR VEHICLE HARNESS CONNECTOR			
AC3	CHECK FOR SPARK AT PLUGS			
	• Disconnect the spark plug wire to any accessible cylinder. • Connect spark tester between spark plug wire and engine ground. • Crank engine and check for spark. • Reconnect the spark plug wire to the spark plug. • Was spark present and consistent?	Yes No	▶ ▶	GO to AC4. REFER to Electronic Ignition (EI) diagnosis.

Fig. 168 Test AC: EEC-IV No Start, EI-High Data Rate (Part 6 of 8)

TEST STEP		RESULT	▶	ACTION TO TAKE
AC4	CHECK CONTINUITY OF IGNITION GROUND CIRCUIT			
	• Key off. • Disconnect Powertrain Control Module (PCM). Inspect for damaged or pushed out pins, corrosion, loose wires, etc. Service as necessary. • Install breakout box, leave PCM disconnected. • Disconnect Ignition Control Module (ICM). • Measure resistance between Test Pin 16 at breakout box and IGN GND circuit at ICM vehicle harness connector. • Is resistance less than 5.0 ohms?	Yes No	▶ ▶	GO to AC5. SERVICE open circuit. REMOVE breakout box. RECONNECT all components. RERUN Quick Test.
AC5	CHECK PIP CIRCUIT FOR SHORT TO POWER			
	• Key off. • Breakout box installed, PCM disconnected. • ICM disconnected. • Key on, engine off. • Measure voltage between Test Pin 56 at breakout box and battery negative post. • Is voltage greater than 7.0 volts?	Yes No	▶ ▶	SERVICE short to power. REMOVE breakout box. RECONNECT all components. RERUN Quick Test. GO to AC6.
AC6	CHECK PIP CIRCUIT CONTINUITY			
	• Key off. • Breakout box installed, PCM disconnected. • ICM disconnected. • Measure resistance between Test Pin 56 at breakout box and PIP circuit at the ICM vehicle harness connector. • Is resistance less than 5.0 ohms?	Yes No	▶ ▶	GO to AC7. SERVICE open circuit. REMOVE breakout box. RECONNECT all components. RERUN Quick Test.
AC7	CHECK PIP SIGNAL CIRCUIT FOR SHORTS TO GROUND			
	• Key off. • Breakout box installed, PCM disconnected. • ICM disconnected. • Measure resistance between Test Pin 56 (PIP) and Test Pins 16, 40, 46, 60 (short to GROUND). • Is each resistance greater than 10,000 ohms?	Yes No	▶ ▶	GO to AC8. SERVICE short circuit. REMOVE breakout box. RECONNECT all components. RERUN Quick Test. If vehicle does not start. GO to AC8.

Fig. 168 Test AC: EEC-IV No Start, EI-High Data Rate (Part 7 of 8)

TEST STEP		RESULT	▶	ACTION TO TAKE
AC8	ISOLATE OPEN(S) IN PIP CIRCUIT IN PCM			
	• Key off. • Breakout box installed. • Connect PCM to breakout box. • ICM disconnected. • Measure resistance between Test Pin 56 (PIP) and Test Pins 37, 57 (short to POWER), 40, and 60 (short to GROUND) at breakout box. • Is each resistance between 15,000 and 150,000 ohms?	Yes No	▶ ▶	GO to AC9. REPLACE PCM. REMOVE breakout box. RECONNECT all components. RERUN Quick Test.
AC9	CHECK PIP SIGNAL			
	• Key off. • Breakout box installed, PCM disconnected. • Reconnect ICM. • Measure voltage between Test Pin 56 and Test Pin 16 at breakout box. • Crank engine, record reading. • Is voltage between 3.0 and 7.0 volts?	Yes No	▶ ▶	GO to AC10 REPLACE ICM. REMOVE breakout box. RERUN Quick Test.
AC10	ISOLATE SHORT(S) IN PCM			
	• Key off. • Reconnect PCM to breakout box. • ICM connected. • Measure voltage between Test Pin 56 and Test Pin 16 at the breakout box. • Crank engine, record reading. • Is voltage between 3.0 and 7.0 volts?	Yes No	▶ ▶	GO to AC11. REPLACE PCM. REMOVE breakout box. RECONNECT all components. RERUN Quick Test.
AC11	CHECK FUEL PUMP			
	• No smoking nearby. • Connect fuel pressure gauge. • Note initial pressure reading. • Observe pressure gauge as you pressurize fuel system. (Turn key to RUN for one second, then turn key to OFF. Wait 10 seconds. Repeat five times.) • Does fuel pressure increase? WARNING: IF FUEL STARTS LEAKING, TURN KEY OFF IMMEDIATELY. NO SMOKING. For Flexible Fuel (FF) vehicles refer to all safety/precautions	Yes No	▶ ▶	GO to S1. GO to Fuel to check for mechanical problems in fuel system.

Fig. 168 Test AC: EEC-IV No Start, EI-High Data Rate (Part 8 of 8)

Note

You should enter this Pinpoint Test only when directed here from Pinpoint Tests C, J, PA, PB or PC.

Remember

To prevent the replacement of good components, be aware that the following non-EEC areas may be at fault:

- Ignition Switch
- Battery Cables
- Generator
- Voltage Regulator (VR)
- Ground Straps

This Pinpoint Test is intended to diagnose only the following:

- Powertrain Control Module (PCM)
- Harness circuits: SIG RTN, PWR GND, VPWR, KAPWR, IGNITION SWITCH
- Battery Positive Voltage (B+)
- EEC Power Relay

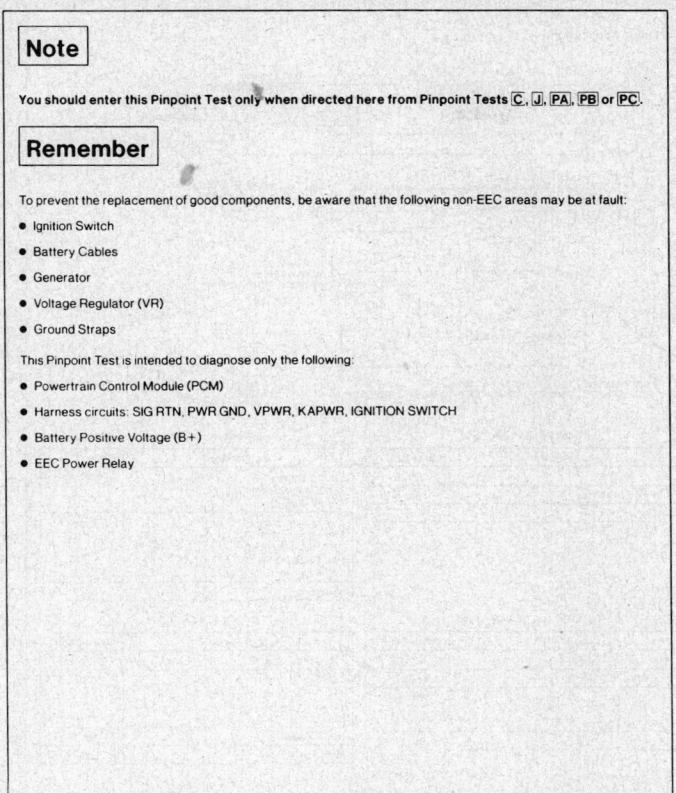

FM0159300711010X

Fig. 169   Test B: Vehicle Battery (Part 1 of 10)

Pinpoint Test Schematics

2.0L Probe

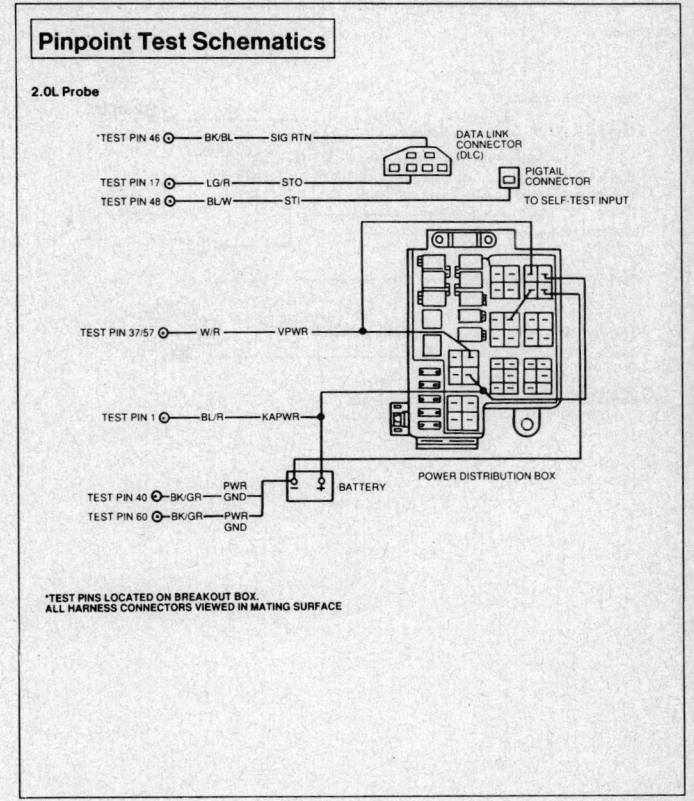

FM0159300711020X

Fig. 169   Test B: Vehicle Battery (Part 2 of 10)

Contour / Mystique

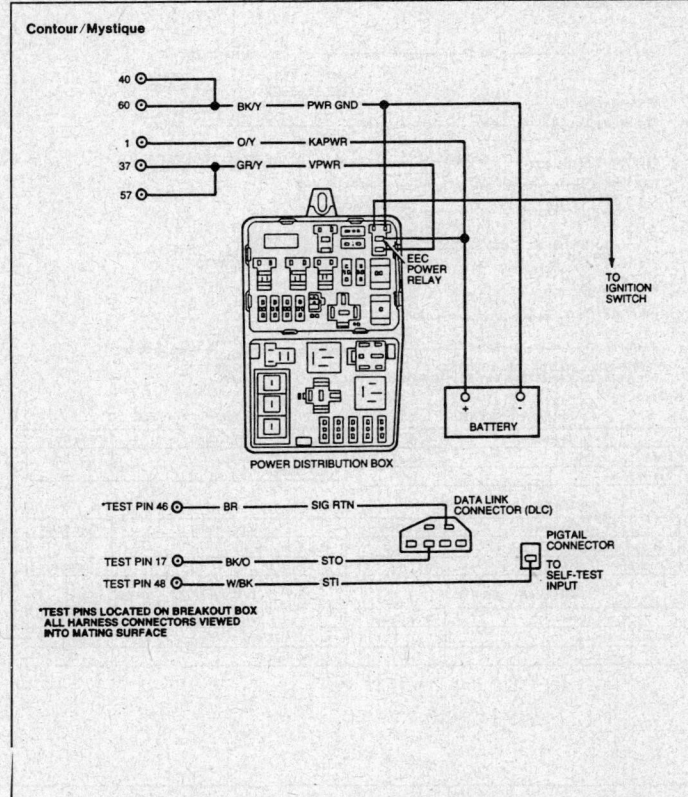

Fig. 169   Test B: Vehicle Battery (Part 3 of 10). 1995

4.6L SFI Town Car, Crown Victoria / Grand Marquis

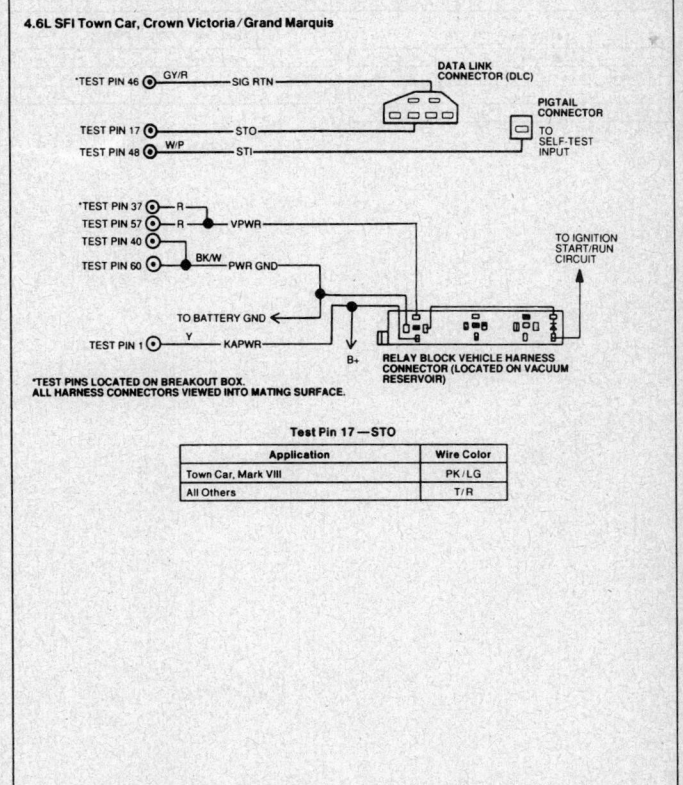

Test Pin 17—STO

Application	Wire Color
Town Car, Mark VIII	PK/LG
All Others	T/R

FM0159300711030X

Fig. 169   Test B: Vehicle Battery (Part 4 of 10). 1993–94

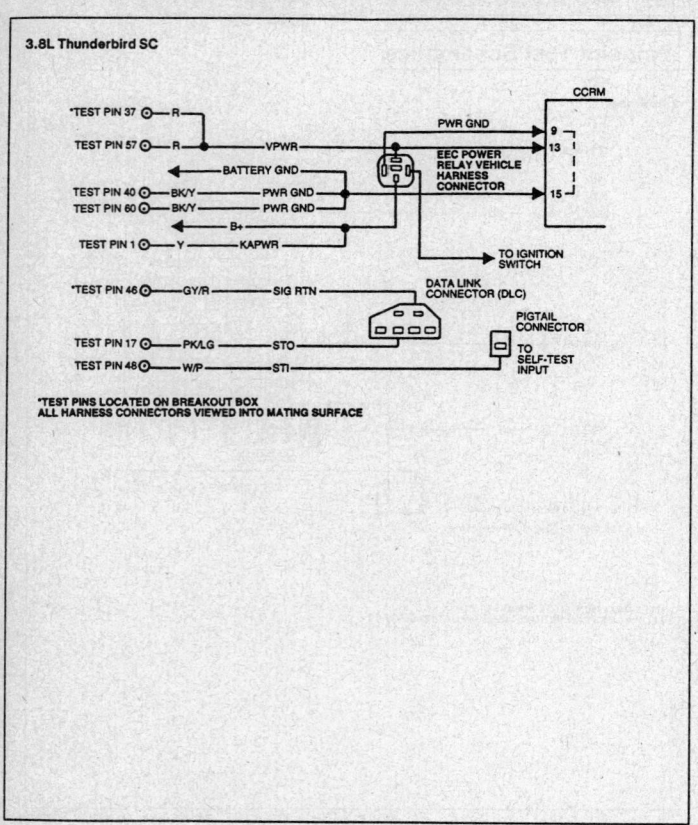

Fig. 169   Test B: Vehicle Battery (Part 5 of 10). 1994–95

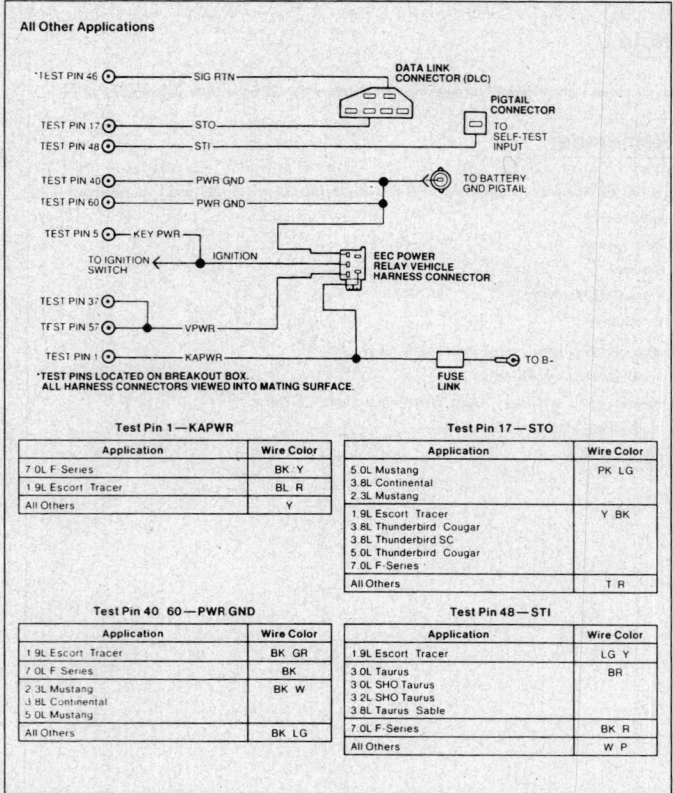

FM0159300711090X

Fig. 169   Test B: Vehicle Battery (Part 6 of 10). 1993

Test Pin 46—SIG RTN

Application	Wire Color
1.9L Escort/Tracer	LG/BK
All Others	GY/R

Test Pin 37/57—VPWR

Application	Wire Color
1.9L Escort/Tracer	W/R
All Others	R

Fig. 169   Test B: Vehicle Battery (Part 7 of 10). 1993

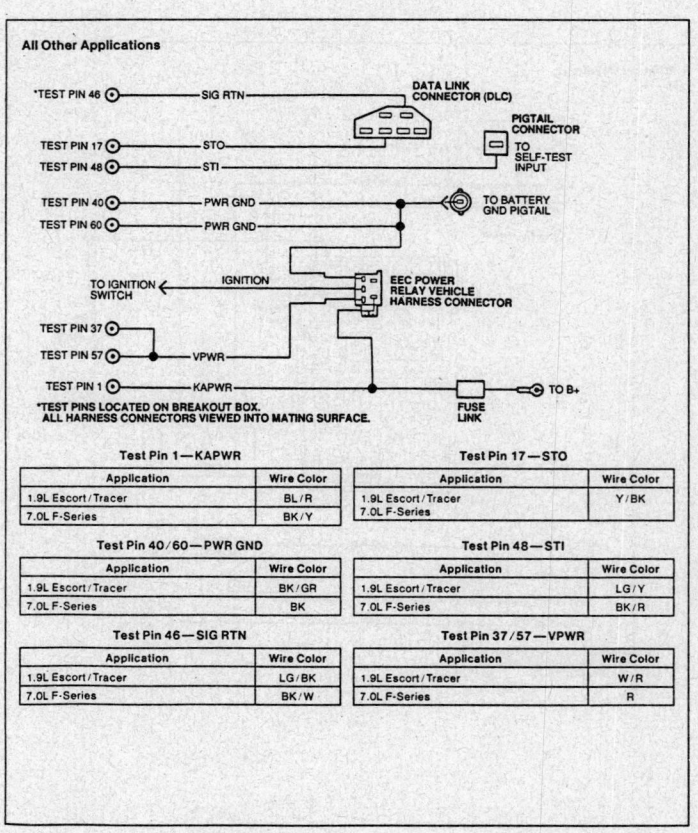

Test Pin 1—KAPWR

Application	Wire Color
1.9L Escort/Tracer	BL/R
7.0L F-Series	BK/Y

Test Pin 17—STO

Application	Wire Color
1.9L Escort/Tracer	Y/BK
7.0L F-Series	

Test Pin 40/60—PWR GND

Application	Wire Color
1.9L Escort/Tracer	BK/GR
7.0L F-Series	BK

Test Pin 48—STI

Application	Wire Color
1.9L Escort/Tracer	LG/Y
7.0L F-Series	BK/R

Test Pin 46—SIG RTN

Application	Wire Color
1.9L Escort/Tracer	LG/BK
7.0L F-Series	BK/W

Test Pin 37/57—VPWR

Application	Wire Color
1.9L Escort/Tracer	W/R
7.0L F-Series	R

Fig. 169   Test B: Vehicle Battery (Part 7 of 10). 1994–95

TEST STEP	RESULT	▶	ACTION TO TAKE
B1 CHECK BATTERY VOLTAGE • Key on, engine off. • Measure voltage across battery terminals. • **Is voltage greater than 10.5 volts?**	Yes No	▶ ▶	GO to B2. SERVICE discharged battery. REFER to Charging/Electrical Group
B2 CHECK PWR GND CIRCUIT CONTINUITY • Key off. • Disconnect Powertrain Control Module (PCM). Inspect for damaged or pushed out pins, corrosion, loose wires, etc. Service as necessary. • Install breakout box and connect PCM to breakout box. • Measure resistance between battery negative post and Test Pins 40 and 60 at the breakout box. • **Is each resistance less than 5.0 ohms?**	Yes No	▶ ▶	GO to B3. SERVICE open in PWR GND circuit. REMOVE breakout box. RECONNECT PCM. RERUN Quick Test.
B3 CHECK FOR OPEN BETWEEN SIG RTN AND PWR GND CIRCUITS AT PCM • Key off. • Breakout box installed, PCM connected. • Measure resistance between Test Pin 46 and Test Pins 40 and 60 at the breakout box. • **Is each resistance less than 5.0 ohms?**	Yes No	▶ ▶	GO to B4. REPLACE PCM. REMOVE breakout box. RERUN Quick Test.
B4 CHECK SIG RTN CIRCUIT CONTINUITY • Key off. • Breakout box installed, PCM connected. • Measure resistance between Test Pin 46 at the breakout box and SIG RTN circuit in the Data Link Connector (DLC). • **Is resistance less than 5.0 ohms?**	Yes No	▶ ▶	GO to B5. SERVICE open in SIG RTN circuit. REMOVE breakout box. RECONNECT PCM. RERUN Quick Test.
B5 CHECK KAPWR CIRCUIT VOLTAGE AT EEC POWER RELAY • Key off. • Breakout box installed, PCM connected. • Disconnect EEC power relay. • Key on, engine off. • Measure voltage between KAPWR circuit at the EEC power relay connector and battery negative post. • **Is voltage greater than 10.5 volts?**	Yes No	▶ ▶	GO to B6. SERVICE open in KAPWR circuit between EEC power relay and battery positive post. REMOVE breakout box. RECONNECT all components. RERUN Quick Test.

Fig. 169   Test B: Vehicle Battery (Part 8 of 10)

TEST STEP	RESULT	▶	ACTION TO TAKE
B6 CHECK IGNITION CIRCUIT VOLTAGE AT EEC POWER RELAY NOTE: Vehicles equipped with Power Distribution (Network) Boxes have a diode that serves as power surge protection for the Ignition Control Module (ICM) and ignition switch. A continuity check across this diode may be necessary before proceeding with this Pinpoint Test. • Key on, engine off. • Breakout box installed, PCM connected. • EEC power relay disconnected • Measure voltage between the battery negative post and ignition switch circuit at the EEC power relay connector. • **Is voltage greater than 10.5 volts?**	Yes No	▶ ▶	GO to B7. SERVICE open in ignition switch circuits. REMOVE breakout box. RECONNECT all components. RERUN Quick Test.
B7 CHECK PWR GND CIRCUIT CONTINUITY • Key off. • Breakout box installed, PCM connected. • EEC power relay disconnected. • Measure resistance between PWR GND circuit at the EEC power relay vehicle harness connector and battery negative post. • **Is the resistance less than 10 ohms?**	Yes No	▶ ▶	GO to B8. SERVICE open circuit. REMOVE breakout box. RECONNECT all components. RERUN Quick Test
B8 CHECK VPWR CIRCUIT CONTINUITY • Key off. • Breakout box installed, PCM connected. • EEC power relay disconnected. • Measure resistance between Test Pins 37/57 at the breakout box and the VPWR terminal of the EEC power relay connector. • **Is resistance less than 5.0 ohms?**	Yes No	▶ ▶	GO to B9. SERVICE open in VPWR circuit between the EEC power relay connector and PCM. REMOVE breakout box. RECONNECT all components. RERUN Quick Test.

FM0159300711120X

Fig. 169   Test B: Vehicle Battery (Part 9 of 10)

TEST STEP	RESULT	▶	ACTION TO TAKE
B9 CHECK VPWR CIRCUIT VOLTAGE • Key off • Breakout box installed, PCM connected. • Install EEC power relay. • Key on, engine off. • Measure voltage between Test Pin 37/57 and Test Pins 40/60, 46 at breakout box. • **Is voltage greater than 10.5 volts?**	Yes No	▶ ▶	SERVICE open or short to ground in VPWR circuit between PCM and EEC power relay. REMOVE breakout box. RECONNECT PCM. RERUN Quick Test. REPLACE EEC power relay. REMOVE breakout box. RECONNECT PCM. RERUN Quick Test.

FM015930071113AX

Fig. 169   Test B: Vehicle Battery (Part 10 of 10). 1993

TEST STEP	RESULT	▶	ACTION TO TAKE
B9 CHECK VPWR CIRCUIT VOLTAGE • Key off • Breakout box installed, PCM connected. • Install EEC power relay. • Key on, engine off • Measure voltage between Test Pin 37/57 and Test Pins 40/60, 46 at breakout box. • **Is voltage greater than 10.5 volts?**	Yes No	▶ ▶	SERVICE open or short to ground in VPWR circuit between PCM and EEC power relay. REMOVE breakout box. RECONNECT PCM. RERUN Quick Test REPLACE EEC power relay. REMOVE breakout box RECONNECT PCM. RERUN Quick Test
B10 CHECK CONTINUITY OF GROUND CIRCUIT BETWEEN POWER RELAY AND CCRM • Key off • EEC power relay disconnected. • Disconnect Constant Control Relay Module (CCRM) • Measure resistance between GND circuit at the EEC power relay vehicle harness connector and Pin 9 of the CCRM vehicle harness connector. • **Is resistance less than 5.0 ohms?**	Yes No	▶ ▶	GO to B11 SERVICE open GND circuit between EEC power relay and CCRM REMOVE breakout box RECONNECT all components RERUN Quick Test
B11 CHECK GROUND CIRCUIT CONTINUITY IN CCRM • Key off • CCRM disconnected. • Measure resistance of CCRM ground circuit by placing the DVOM (+) lead on Pin 9 and DVOM (-) lead on Pin 15 of the CCRM (specific DVOM (+ -) lead placement is due to diode in circuit) • **Is resistance less than 5.0 ohms?**	Yes No	▶ ▶	SERVICE open ground circuit between CCRM and battery negative post REMOVE breakout box RECONNECT all components RERUN Quick Test REPLACE CCRM REMOVE breakout box RECONNECT all components RERUN Quick Test

FM015940071113BX

Fig. 169   Test B: Vehicle Battery (Part 10 of 10). 1994–95

Note

You should enter this Pinpoint Test only when a check for VREF has failed in the sensor Pinpoint Tests (D-Series) or Pinpoint Tests AA, AB, AC, or QA.

Remember

This Pinpoint Test is intended to diagnose only the following:

- Sensor harness circuits: SIG RTN, VREF
- 3-wire sensors: TP, EVP, PFE, DPFE, MAP, BARO
- Powertrain Control Module (PCM) (12A650)

Description

Reference Voltage (VREF) is a positive voltage (about 5.0 volts) that is output by the Powertrain Control Module (PCM). This consistent voltage is used by all 3-wire sensors.

Signal Return (SIG RTN) is a dedicated ground used by most EEC sensors and some other inputs.

Fig. 170   Test C: Reference Voltage (Part 1 of 5)

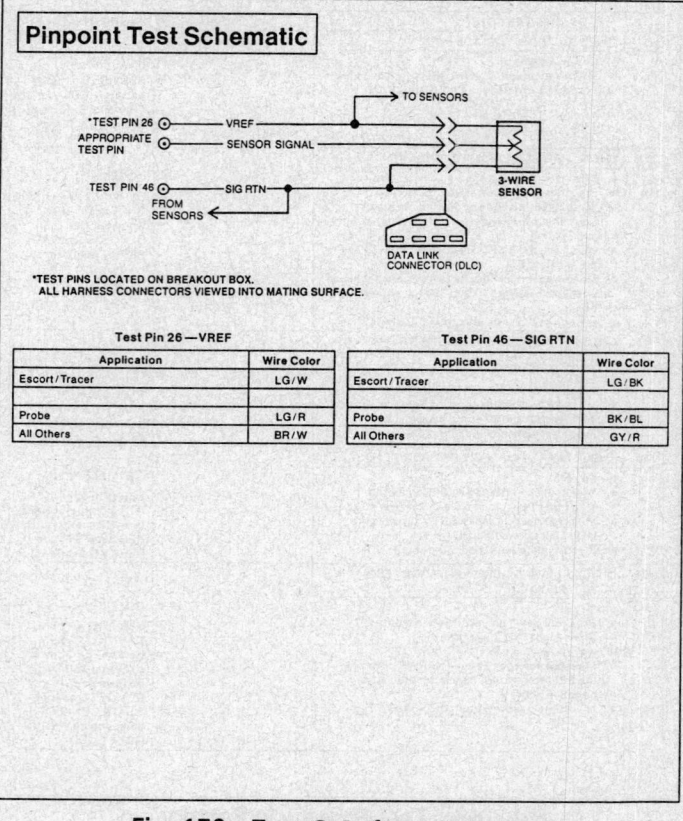

Pinpoint Test Schematic

*TEST PINS LOCATED ON BREAKOUT BOX.
ALL HARNESS CONNECTORS VIEWED INTO MATING SURFACE.

Test Pin 26 — VREF	
Application	Wire Color
Escort / Tracer	LG / W
Probe	LG / R
All Others	BR / W

Test Pin 46 — SIG RTN	
Application	Wire Color
Escort / Tracer	LG / BK
Probe	BK / BL
All Others	GY / R

Fig. 170   Test C: Reference Voltage (Part 2 of 5). 1993

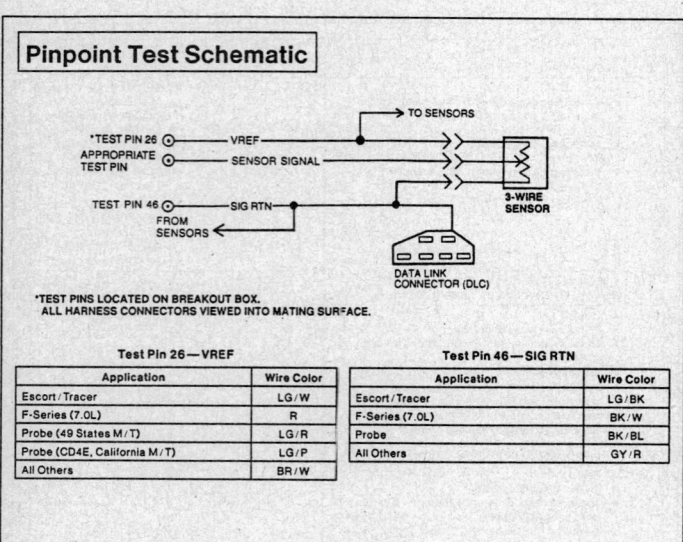

Pinpoint Test Schematic

*TEST PINS LOCATED ON BREAKOUT BOX.
ALL HARNESS CONNECTORS VIEWED INTO MATING SURFACE.

Test Pin 26 — VREF	
Application	Wire Color
Escort / Tracer	LG / W
F-Series (7.0L)	R
Probe (49 States M / T)	LG / R
Probe (CD4E, California M / T)	LG / P
All Others	BR / W

Test Pin 46 — SIG RTN	
Application	Wire Color
Escort / Tracer	LG / BK
F-Series (7.0L)	BK / W
Probe	BK / BL
All Others	GY / R

Fig. 170   Test C: Reference Voltage (Part 2 of 5). 1994

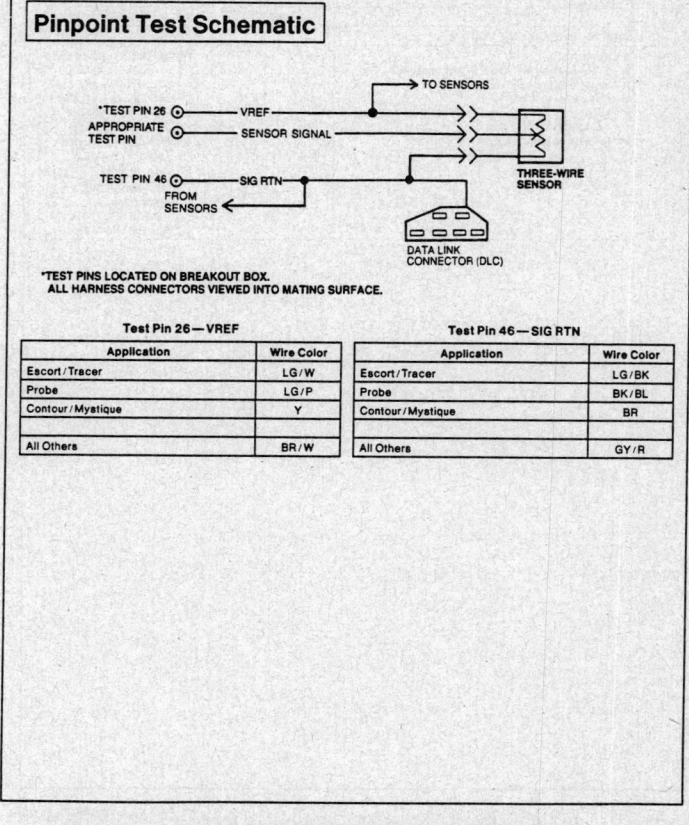

Pinpoint Test Schematic

*TEST PINS LOCATED ON BREAKOUT BOX.
ALL HARNESS CONNECTORS VIEWED INTO MATING SURFACE.

Test Pin 26 — VREF	
Application	Wire Color
Escort / Tracer	LG / W
Probe	LG / P
Contour / Mystique	Y
All Others	BR / W

Test Pin 46 — SIG RTN	
Application	Wire Color
Escort / Tracer	LG / BK
Probe	BK / BL
Contour / Mystique	BR
All Others	GY / R

Fig. 170   Test C: Reference Voltage (Part 2 of 5). 1995

TEST STEP	RESULT	▶	ACTION TO TAKE
C1 CHECK VEHICLE BATTERY POWER CIRCUIT • Key off. • Disconnect Powertrain Control Module (PCM). Inspect for damaged or pushed out pins, corrosion, loose wires, etc. Service as necessary. • Install breakout box and connect PCM to breakout box. • Key on, engine off. • Measure voltage between Test Pin 37 at the breakout box and SIG RTN circuit in the Data Link Connector (DLC). Note voltage. • Measure voltage across battery terminals. Note voltage. • **Are both voltages greater than 10.5 volts, and are both voltages within 1.0 volt of each other?**	Yes	▶	GO to C2
	No	▶	Key Off, RECONNECT sensor (if applicable). **For 2.3L Mustang, Tempo/Topaz, Taurus/Sable, Taurus SHO, Thunderbird SC and Continental:** GO to X1. **For Mark VIII:** GO to XB1. **For all others:** GO to B1.
C2 CHECK VREF VOLTAGE • Key on, engine off. • Breakout box installed, PCM connected. • Measure voltage between Test Pin 26 and Test Pin 46 at the breakout box. • **What is the voltage?**	Greater than 6.0 volts	▶	GO to C4
	Less than 4.0 volts	▶	GO to C5
	Between 4.0 volts and 6.0 volts	▶	GO to C3
C3 CHECK VREF AND SIG RTN CIRCUITS FOR CONTINUITY • Key off. • Sensor that sent you here disconnected. • Breakout box installed. • Disconnect PCM. • Measure resistance between Test Pin 26 at breakout box and VREF circuit at vehicle harness connector of the sensor that sent you here. • Measure resistance between Test Pin 46 at breakout box and SIG RTN circuit at vehicle harness connector of the sensor that sent you here. • **Is each resistance less than 5.0 ohms?**	Yes	▶	Reference voltage OK. REMOVE breakout box. RECONNECT all components. RERUN Quick Test.
	No	▶	SERVICE open in VREF or SIG RTN circuits. REMOVE breakout box. RECONNECT all components. RERUN Quick Test.

FM015930071203AX

Fig. 170   Test C: Reference Voltage (Part 3 of 5). 1993

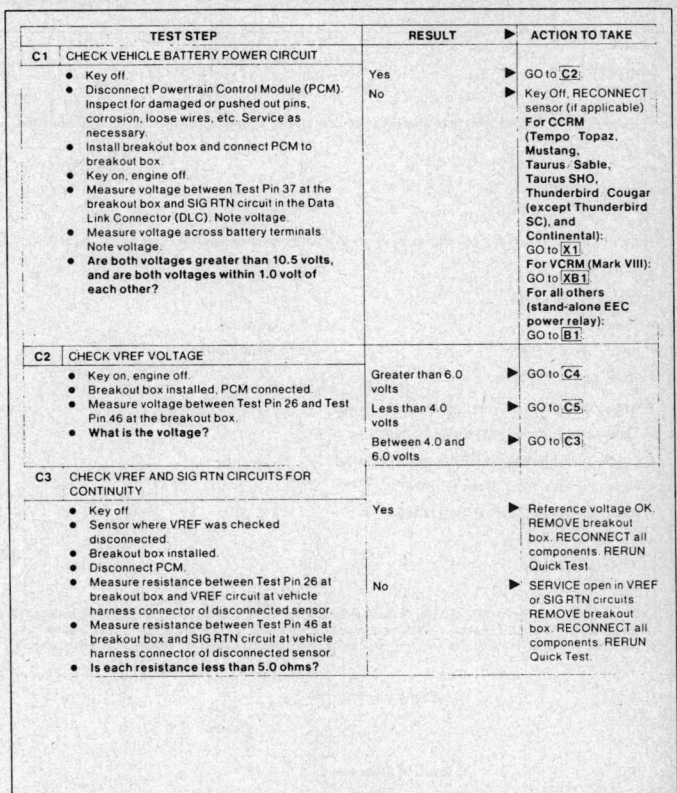

TEST STEP	RESULT	▶	ACTION TO TAKE
C1 CHECK VEHICLE BATTERY POWER CIRCUIT • Key off. • Disconnect Powertrain Control Module (PCM). Inspect for damaged or pushed out pins, corrosion, loose wires, etc. Service as necessary. • Install breakout box and connect PCM to breakout box. • Key on, engine off. • Measure voltage between Test Pin 37 at the breakout box and SIG RTN circuit in the Data Link Connector (DLC). Note voltage. • Measure voltage across battery terminals. Note voltage. • **Are both voltages greater than 10.5 volts, and are both voltages within 1.0 volt of each other?**	Yes	▶	GO to C2
	No	▶	Key Off, RECONNECT sensor (if applicable). **For CCRM (Tempo/Topaz, Mustang, Taurus/Sable, Taurus SHO, Thunderbird/Cougar (except Thunderbird SC), and Continental):** GO to X1. **For VCRM (Mark VIII):** GO to XB1. **For all others (stand-alone EEC power relay):** GO to B1.
C2 CHECK VREF VOLTAGE • Key on, engine off. • Breakout box installed, PCM connected. • Measure voltage between Test Pin 26 and Test Pin 46 at the breakout box. • **What is the voltage?**	Greater than 6.0 volts	▶	GO to C4
	Less than 4.0 volts	▶	GO to C5
	Between 4.0 and 6.0 volts	▶	GO to C3
C3 CHECK VREF AND SIG RTN CIRCUITS FOR CONTINUITY • Key off. • Sensor where VREF was checked disconnected. • Breakout box installed. • Disconnect PCM. • Measure resistance between Test Pin 26 at breakout box and VREF circuit at vehicle harness connector of disconnected sensor. • Measure resistance between Test Pin 46 at breakout box and SIG RTN circuit at vehicle harness connector of disconnected sensor. • **Is each resistance less than 5.0 ohms?**	Yes	▶	Reference voltage OK. REMOVE breakout box. RECONNECT all components. RERUN Quick Test.
	No	▶	SERVICE open in VREF or SIG RTN circuits. REMOVE breakout box. RECONNECT all components. RERUN Quick Test.

FM015940071203BX

Fig. 170   Test C: Reference Voltage (Part 3 of 5). 1994–95

TEST STEP	RESULT	▶	ACTION TO TAKE
C4 CHECK FOR EXCESS VOLTAGE ON VREF CIRCUIT • Key off. • Breakout box installed. • Disconnect PCM. • Disconnect STAR Tester or Scan Tool (ST) (if applicable). NOTE: For proper results of this test, the STAR Tester or Scan Tool must be disconnected. Due to the circuitry of the STAR Tester/Scan Tool and the vehicle, voltage can be fed to the VREF circuit giving the false indication of a short to power. • Key on, engine off. • Measure voltage between Test Pin 26 at the breakout box and battery ground. • **Is voltage less than 0.5 volt?**	Yes	▶	REPLACE PCM. REMOVE breakout box. RECONNECT all components. RERUN Quick Test.
	No	▶	SERVICE short to power in vehicle harness. REMOVE breakout box. RECONNECT PCM and sensor. RERUN Quick Test.
C5 CHECK FOR SHORTED THROTTLE POSITION (TP) SENSOR • Key off. • Breakout box installed, PCM connected. • Disconnect Throttle Position (TP) sensor from vehicle harness. • Key on, engine off. • Measure voltage between Test Pin 26 and Test Pin 46 at the breakout box. • **Is voltage less than 4.0 volts?**	Yes	▶	Key off, RECONNECT TP sensor: **For vehicles equipped with EVP/PFE/DPFE sensor:** GO to C6. **For all other vehicles:** GO to C7.
	No	▶	REPLACE TP sensor. REMOVE breakout box. RECONNECT all components. RERUN Quick Test.
C6 CHECK FOR SHORTED EVP/PFE/DPFE SENSOR • Key off. • Breakout box installed, PCM connected. • Disconnect EVP/PFE/DPFE sensor. • Key on, engine off. • Measure voltage between Test Pin 26 and Test Pin 46 at the breakout box. • **Is voltage less than 4.0 volts?**	Yes	▶	Key off, RECONNECT EVP/PFE/DPFE sensor. GO to C7.
	No	▶	REPLACE EVP/PFE/DPFE sensor. REMOVE breakout box. RECONNECT all components. RERUN Quick Test.

FM0159300712040X

Fig. 170   Test C: Reference Voltage (Part 4 of 5)

TEST STEP	RESULT	▶	ACTION TO TAKE
C7 CHECK FOR SHORTED MAP/BARO SENSOR NOTE: For vehicles not equipped with a MAP/BARO sensor, go to C8. • Key off. • Breakout box installed, PCM connected. • Disconnect MAP/BARO sensor. • Key on, engine off. • Measure voltage between Test Pin 26 and Test Pin 46 at the breakout box. • **Is voltage less than 4.0 volts?**	Yes	▶	Key off, RECONNECT MAP/BARO sensor. GO to C8.
	No	▶	REPLACE MAP/BARO sensor. REMOVE breakout box. RECONNECT PCM and sensor(s). RERUN Quick Test.
C8 CHECK VREF CIRCUIT FOR SHORT TO GROUND • Key off. • Breakout box installed. • Disconnect PCM. • Disconnect TP sensor. • Disconnect EVP/PFE/DPFE and MAP/BARO, if so equipped. • Measure resistance between Test Pin 26 and Test Pins 20, 40, 46 and 60 at the breakout box. • **Is any resistance less than 1000 ohms?**	Yes	▶	SERVICE short to ground. REMOVE breakout box. RECONNECT all components. RERUN Quick Test.
	No	▶	REPLACE PCM. REMOVE breakout box. RECONNECT all components. RERUN Quick Test.

FM0159300712050X

Fig. 170   Test C: Reference Voltage (Part 5 of 5)

Note

You should enter this Pinpoint Test only when you have been directed here from Diagnostic Routines

Remember

To prevent the replacement of good components, be aware that the following non-EEC areas may be at fault:

- Coolant level
- Cooling system
- Cooling Fan
- Water pump drive belt
- Engine operating temperature
- Engine oil level
- Thermostat
- Air cleaner duct
- Ambient temperature

This Pinpoint Test is intended to diagnose the following:

- Intake Air Temperature (IAT) sensor (12A697)
- Engine Coolant Temperature (ECT) sensor (12A648)
- Harness circuits: IAT, ECT, and SIG RTN
- Powertrain Control Module (PCM) (12A650)

Description

The Intake Air Temperature (IAT) and Engine Coolant Temperature (ECT) sensor change resistance in response to temperature. IAT and ECT sensor resistance decreases as the surrounding temperature increases providing a signal to the PCM that indicates the temperature of either the incoming intake air or engine coolant temperature.

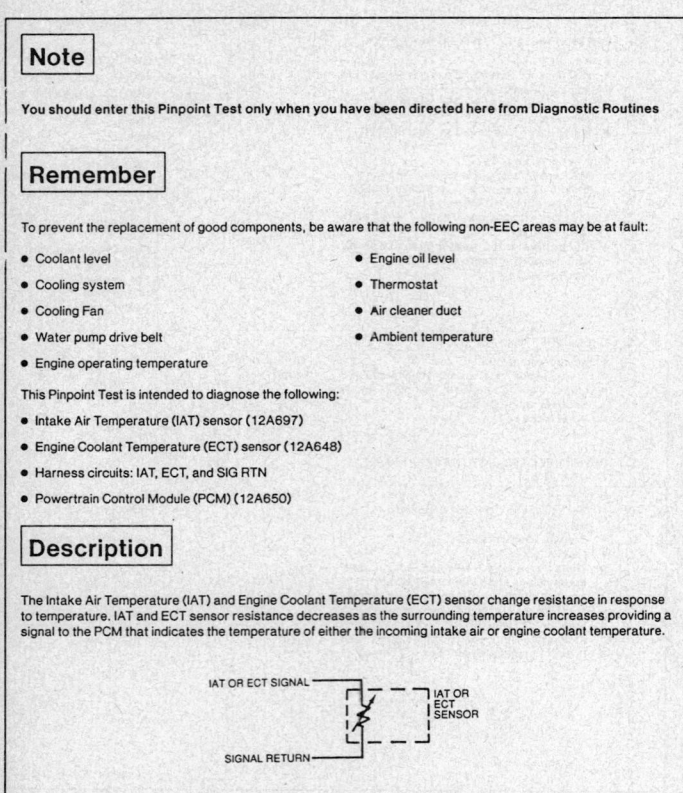

Fig. 171 Test DA: IAT/ECT Sensors (Part 1 of 10)

Pinpoint Test Schematic

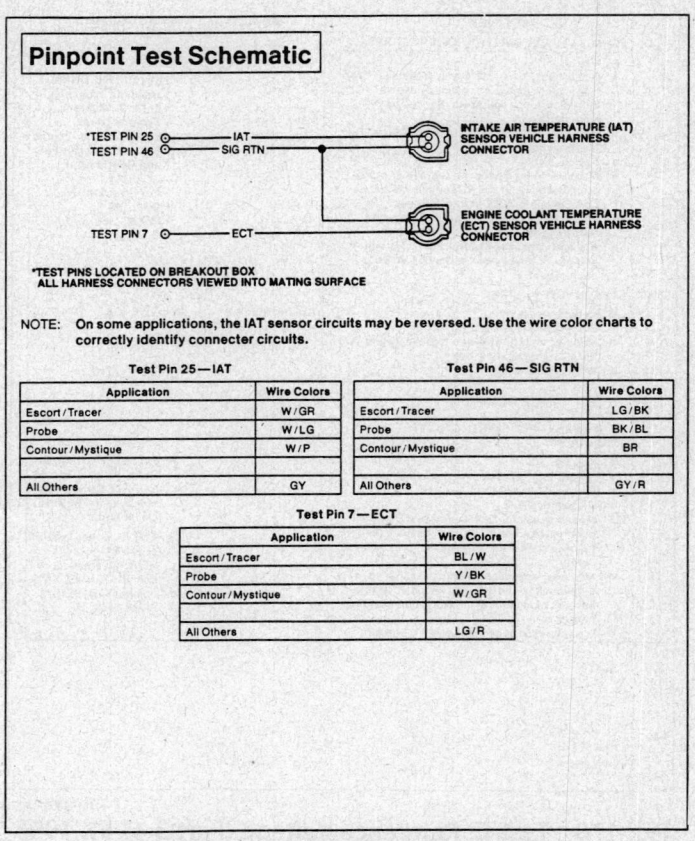

*TEST PINS LOCATED ON BREAKOUT BOX
ALL HARNESS CONNECTORS VIEWED INTO MATING SURFACE

NOTE: On some applications, the IAT sensor circuits may be reversed. Use the wire color charts to correctly identify connecter circuits.

Test Pin 25 — IAT

Application	Wire Colors
Escort/Tracer	W/GR
Probe	W/LG
Contour/Mystique	W/P
All Others	GY

Test Pin 46 — SIG RTN

Application	Wire Colors
Escort/Tracer	LG/BK
Probe	BK/BL
Contour/Mystique	BR
All Others	GY/R

Test Pin 7 — ECT

Application	Wire Colors
Escort/Tracer	BL/W
Probe	Y/BK
Contour/Mystique	W/GR
All Others	LG/R

Fig. 171 Test DA: IAT/ECT Sensors (Part 2 of 10)

Notes:

Engine coolant temperature must be greater than 10°C (50°F) to pass the KOEO Self-Test and greater than 82°C (180°F) to pass the KOER Self-Test. To accomplish this, the engine should be at normal operating temperature.

Ambient temperature should be above 10°C (50°F) to receive acceptable input from the Intake Air Temperature (IAT) sensor.

Voltage values were calculated for VREF=5.0 volts. These values may vary 15 percent due to sensor and VREF variations.

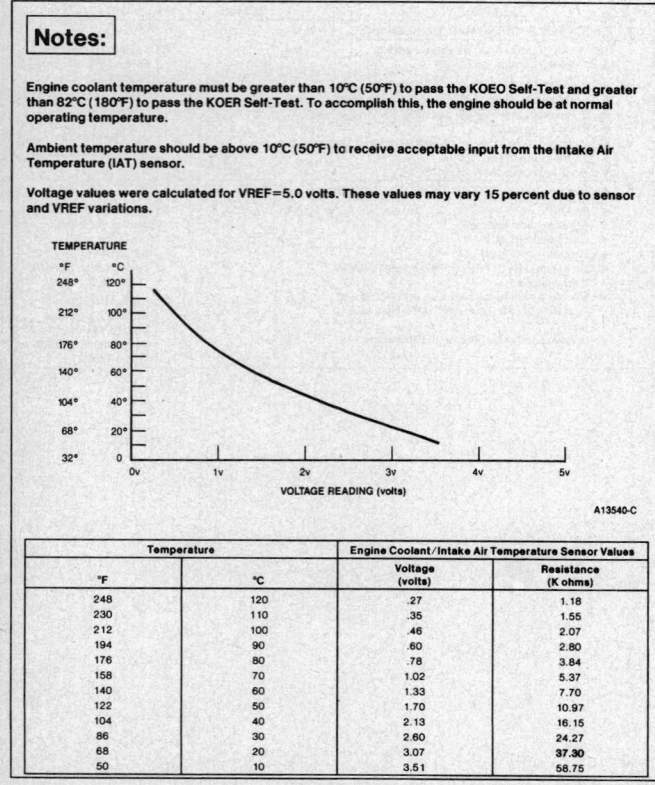

Temperature		Engine Coolant/Intake Air Temperature Sensor Values	
°F	°C	Voltage (volts)	Resistance (K ohms)
248	120	.27	1.18
230	110	.35	1.55
212	100	.46	2.07
194	90	.60	2.80
176	80	.78	3.84
158	70	1.02	5.37
140	60	1.33	7.70
122	50	1.70	10.97
104	40	2.13	16.15
86	30	2.60	24.27
68	20	3.07	37.30
50	10	3.51	58.75

FM0159300713030A

Fig. 171 Test DA: IAT/ECT Sensors (Part 3 of 10)

	TEST STEP	RESULT	▶	ACTION TO TAKE
DA1	DIAGNOSTIC TROUBLE CODE (DTC) 21/116 OR 24/114: CHECK OPERATION, INSTALLATION OF TEMPERATURE SENSOR DTC 21/116 (ECT) or 24/114 (IAT) indicates that the corresponding sensor is out of Self-Test range. Correct range of measure is 0.3 to 3.7 volts. Possible causes: — Low coolant level (ECT). — Ambient temperature below 10°C (50°F) (IAT). — Faulty harness connector. — Faulty sensor. ● Run engine for two minutes at 2000 rpm. 　NOTE: For Tempo/Topaz vehicles with DTC 114 (IAT), due to IAT sensor location, additional warm up time may be required. Run engine until under hood temperatures are warm and stabilized. 　For NO STARTS: 　— GO to DA3. 　For vehicle STALLS: 　— GO to S1. ● Check that upper radiator hose is hot and pressurized. ● Rerun Quick Test. ● Is DTC 21, 24, 114 or 116 present?	Yes No	▶ ▶	GO to DA2. SERVICE other DTCs as necessary.
DA2	CHECK VREF CIRCUIT VOLTAGE AT THROTTLE POSITION (TP) SENSOR ● Refer to schematic in Pinpoint Test DH. ● Key off. ● Disconnect TP sensor. ● Key on, engine off. ● Measure voltage between VREF circuit and SIG RTN circuit at the TP sensor vehicle harness connector. ● Is voltage between 4.0 volts and 6.0 volts?	Yes No	▶ ▶	RECONNECT TP sensor. GO to DA3. GO to Pinpoint Test Step C1.

FM0159300713040X

Fig. 171 Test DA: IAT/ECT Sensors (Part 4 of 10)

ELECTRONIC ENGINE CONTROL SYSTEM IV (EEC-IV)

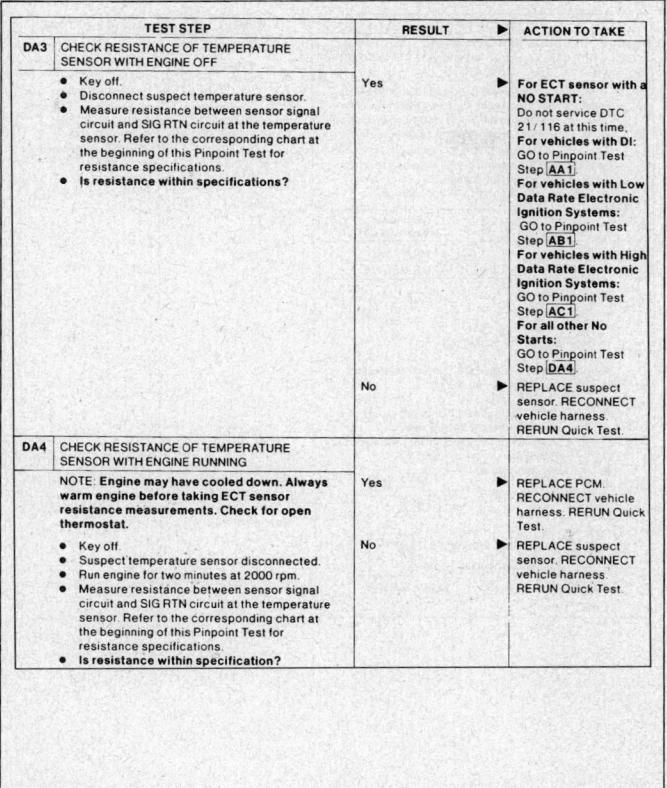

TEST STEP	RESULT	▶	ACTION TO TAKE
DA3 CHECK RESISTANCE OF TEMPERATURE SENSOR WITH ENGINE OFF • Key off. • Disconnect suspect temperature sensor. • Measure resistance between sensor signal circuit and SIG RTN circuit at the temperature sensor. Refer to the corresponding chart at the beginning of this Pinpoint Test for resistance specifications. • **Is resistance within specifications?**	Yes	▶	**For ECT sensor with a NO START:** Do not service DTC 21/116 at this time. **For vehicles with DI:** GO to Pinpoint Test Step **AA1**. **For vehicles with Low Data Rate Electronic Ignition Systems:** GO to Pinpoint Test Step **AB1**. **For vehicles with High Data Rate Electronic Ignition Systems:** GO to Pinpoint Test Step **AC1**. **For all other No Starts:** GO to Pinpoint Test Step **DA4**.
	No	▶	REPLACE suspect sensor. RECONNECT vehicle harness. RERUN Quick Test.
DA4 CHECK RESISTANCE OF TEMPERATURE SENSOR WITH ENGINE RUNNING NOTE: Engine may have cooled down. Always warm engine before taking ECT sensor resistance measurements. Check for open thermostat. • Key off. • Suspect temperature sensor disconnected. • Run engine for two minutes at 2000 rpm. • Measure resistance between sensor signal circuit and SIG RTN circuit at the temperature sensor. Refer to the corresponding chart at the beginning of this Pinpoint Test for resistance specifications. • **Is resistance within specification?**	Yes	▶	REPLACE PCM. RECONNECT vehicle harness. RERUN Quick Test.
	No	▶	REPLACE suspect sensor. RECONNECT vehicle harness. RERUN Quick Test.

FM015930071305OX

Fig. 171   Test DA: IAT/ECT Sensors (Part 5 of 10)

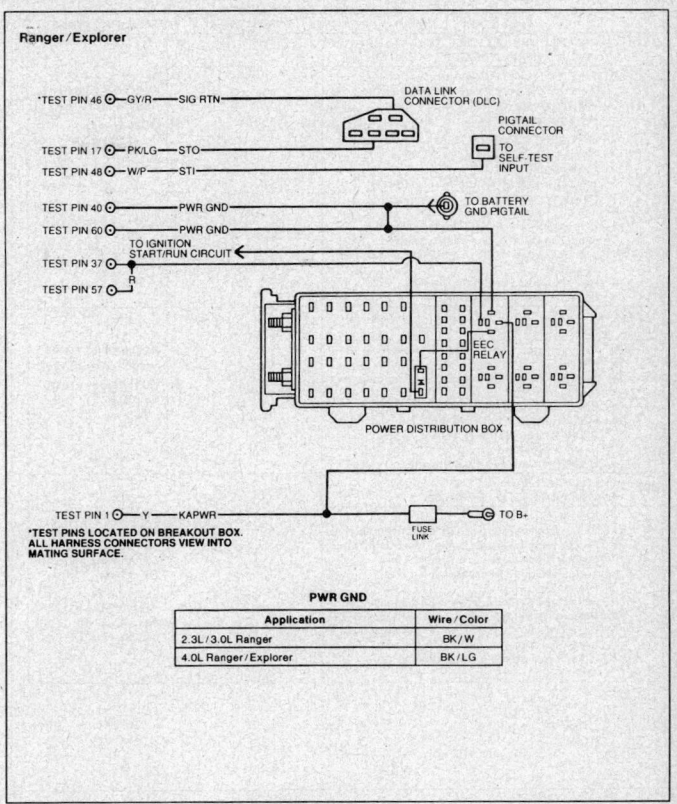

PWR GND

Application	Wire/Color
2.3L/3.0L Ranger	BK/W
4.0L Ranger/Explorer	BK/LG

FM015930071306AX

Fig. 171   Test DA: IAT/ECT Sensors (Part 6 of 10). 1993

TEST STEP	RESULT	▶	ACTION TO TAKE
DA10 DIAGNOSTIC TROUBLE CODE (DTC) 118 OR 113: INDUCE OPPOSITE DTC 117 OR 112 DTC 118 (ECT) or 113 (IAT) indicates that the corresponding sensor signal is greater then the Self-Test maximum. The maximum for ECT and IAT sensors is 4.6 volts. Possible causes: — Open in harness (IAT or ECT). — Faulty connection. — Faulty sensor. — Faulty Powertrain Control Module (PCM). • Key off. • Disconnect suspect temperature sensor. • Connect a jumper wire between the sensor signal circuit and SIG RTN circuit at the temperature sensor vehicle harness connector. • Run Key On Engine Off Self-Test. • **Is DTC 112 or 117 present?**	Yes	▶	REPLACE suspect sensor. REMOVE jumper wire. RECONNECT vehicle harness. RERUN Quick Test.
	No	▶	REMOVE jumper wire. GO to **DA11**.
DA11 CHECK CONTINUITY OF SENSOR SIGNAL AND SIG RTN CIRCUITS • Key off. • Suspect temperature sensor disconnected. • Disconnect Powertrain Control Module (PCM). Inspect for damaged or pushed out pins, corrosion, loose wires, etc. Service as necessary. • Install breakout box, leave PCM disconnected. • Measure resistance between sensor signal circuit at the temperature sensor vehicle harness connector and Test Pin 7 (ECT) or 25 (IAT) at the breakout box. • Measure resistance between SIG RTN circuit at the temperature sensor vehicle harness connector and Test Pin 46 at the breakout box. • **Is each resistance less than 5.0 ohms?**	Yes	▶	REPLACE PCM. REMOVE breakout box. RECONNECT all components. RERUN Quick Test.
	No	▶	SERVICE open circuits. REMOVE breakout box. RECONNECT all components. RERUN Quick Test.

FM015940071306BX

Fig. 171   Test DA: IAT/ECT Sensors (Part 6 of 10). 1994–95

TEST STEP	RESULT	▶	ACTION TO TAKE
DA20 DIAGNOSTIC TROUBLE CODE (DTC) 61/117 OR 64/112: INDUCE OPPOSITE CODE 51/118 OR 54/113 DTC 61/117 (ECT) or 64/112 (IAT) indicates that the corresponding sensor's signal is less than the Self-Test minimum. The IAT and ECT sensor minimum is 0.2 volts. Possible causes: — Grounded circuit in harness. — Faulty sensor. — Faulty Powertrain Control Module (PCM). — Faulty connection. • Key off. • Disconnect vehicle harness from suspect sensor. Inspect for damaged, corroded, pushed out pins or loose wires, etc. Service as necessary. • Run Key On Engine Off Self-Test. • **Is DTC 51, 54, 113 or 118 present?**	Yes	▶	REPLACE sensor. RECONNECT harness. RERUN Quick Test.
	No	▶	GO to **DA21**.
DA21 CHECK VREF CIRCUIT VOLTAGE AT THROTTLE POSITION (TP) SENSOR • Refer to schematic in Pinpoint Test **DH**. • Key off. • Suspect temperature sensor disconnected. • Disconnect TP sensor. • Key on, engine off. • Measure voltage between VREF circuit and SIG RTN circuit at the TP sensor vehicle harness connector. • **Is voltage between 4.0 volts and 6.0 volts?**	Yes	▶	RECONNECT TP sensor, GO to **DA22**.
	No	▶	GO to Pinpoint Test Step **C1**.
DA22 CHECK TEMPERATURE SENSOR SIGNAL CIRCUIT FOR SHORT TO GROUND • Key off. • Suspect temperature sensor disconnected. • Disconnect Powertrain Control Module (PCM). Inspect for damaged or pushed out pins, corrosion, loose wires, etc. Service as necessary. • Install breakout box, leave PCM disconnected. • Measure resistance between Test Pin 7 (ECT) or 25 (IAT) and Test Pins 40, 46 and 60 at the breakout box. • **Is each resistance greater than 10,000 ohms?**	Yes	▶	REPLACE PCM. REMOVE breakout box. RECONNECT all components. RERUN Quick Test.
	No	▶	SERVICE short circuit. REMOVE breakout box. RECONNECT all components. RERUN Quick Test.

FM015930071307AX

Fig. 171   Test DA: IAT/ECT Sensors (Part 7 of 10). 1993

TEST STEP	RESULT	▶	ACTION TO TAKE
DA20 DIAGNOSTIC TROUBLE CODE (DTC) 117 OR 112: INDUCE OPPOSITE CODE 118 OR 113			
DTC 117 (ECT) or 112 (IAT) indicates that the corresponding sensor's signal is less than the Self-Test minimum. The IAT and ECT sensor minimum is 0.2 volts. Possible causes: — Grounded circuit in harness. — Faulty sensor. — Faulty Powertrain Control Module (PCM). — Faulty connection. • Key off. • Disconnect vehicle harness from suspect sensor. Inspect for damaged, corroded, pushed out pins or loose wires, etc. Service as necessary. • Run Key On Engine Off Self-Test. • **Is DTC 113 or 118 present?**	Yes No	▶ ▶	REPLACE sensor. RECONNECT harness. RERUN Quick Test. GO to **DA21**.
DA21 CHECK VREF CIRCUIT VOLTAGE AT THROTTLE POSITION (TP) SENSOR			
• Refer to schematic in Pinpoint Test **DH**. • Key off. • Suspect temperature sensor disconnected. • Disconnect TP sensor. • Key on, engine off. • Measure voltage between VREF circuit and SIG RTN circuit at the TP sensor vehicle harness connector. • **Is voltage between 4.0 volts and 6.0 volts?**	Yes No	▶ ▶	RECONNECT TP sensor, GO to **DA22**. GO to Pinpoint Test Step **C1**.
DA22 CHECK TEMPERATURE SENSOR SIGNAL CIRCUIT FOR SHORT TO GROUND			
• Key off. • Suspect temperature sensor disconnected. • Disconnect Powertrain Control Module (PCM). Inspect for damaged or pushed out pins, corrosion, loose wires, etc. Service as necessary. • Install breakout box, leave PCM disconnected. • Measure resistance between Test Pin 7 (ECT) or 25 (IAT) and Test Pins 40, 46 and 60 at the breakout box. • **Is each resistance greater than 10,000 ohms?**	Yes No	▶ ▶	REPLACE PCM. REMOVE breakout box. RECONNECT all components. RERUN Quick Test. SERVICE short circuit. REMOVE breakout box. RECONNECT all components. RERUN Quick Test.

FM015940071307BX

Fig. 171   Test DA: IAT/ECT Sensors (Part 7 of 10). 1994–95

TEST STEP	RESULT	▶	ACTION TO TAKE
DA90 CONTINUOUS MEMORY DIAGNOSTIC TROUBLE CODE (DTC) 51/118, 54/113, 61/117 OR 68/112: CHECK SENSOR			
Continuous Memory DTC's 51/118 and 54/113 indicate that the sensor signal was greater than the Self-Test maximum of 4.6 volts. The DTC was generated under normal driving conditions. Continuous Memory DTC's 61/117 and 64/112 indicate that the sensor signal was less than the Self-Test minimum of 0.2 volts. The DTC was generated under normal driving conditions.	Yes No	▶ ▶	DISCONNECT and inspect connectors. If OK, REPLACE the sensor. CLEAR Continuous Memory. RERUN Quick Test. GO to **DA91**.

Sensors	Continuous Memory DTCs
IAT	54/113 and 64/112
ECT	51/118 and 61/117

Possible causes:
— Faulty sensor.
— Open circuit in harness.
— Grounded circuit in harness.
— Faulty PCM.
• Enter Key On Engine Off Continuous Monitor Diagnostic Test Mode (DTM).
• Observe VOM or STAR LED for indication of a fault while performing the following:
— Tap on the sensor to simulate road shock.
— Wiggle the sensor connector.
• **Is a fault indicated?**

FM015930071308AX

Fig. 171   Test DA: IAT/ECT Sensors (Part 8 of 10). 1993

TEST STEP	RESULT	▶	ACTION TO TAKE
DA90 CONTINUOUS MEMORY DIAGNOSTIC TROUBLE CODE (DTC) 112, 113, 117 OR 118: CHECK SENSOR			
Continuous Memory DTCs 118 and 113 indicate that the sensor signal was greater than the Self-Test maximum of 4.6 volts. The DTC was generated under normal driving conditions. Continuous Memory DTCs 117 and 112 indicate that the sensor signal was less than the Self-Test minimum of 0.2 volts. The DTC was generated under normal driving conditions.	Yes No	▶ ▶	DISCONNECT and inspect connectors. If OK, REPLACE the sensor. CLEAR Continuous Memory. RERUN Quick Test. GO to **DA91**.

Sensors	Continuous Memory DTCs
IAT	112 and 113
ECT	117 and 118

Possible causes:
— Faulty sensor.
— Open circuit in harness.
— Grounded circuit in harness.
— Faulty PCM.
• Enter Key On Engine Off Continuous Monitor Diagnostic Test Mode (DTM).
• Observe VOM or STAR LED for indication of a fault while performing the following:
— Tap on the sensor to simulate road shock.
— Wiggle the sensor connector.
• **Is a fault indicated?**

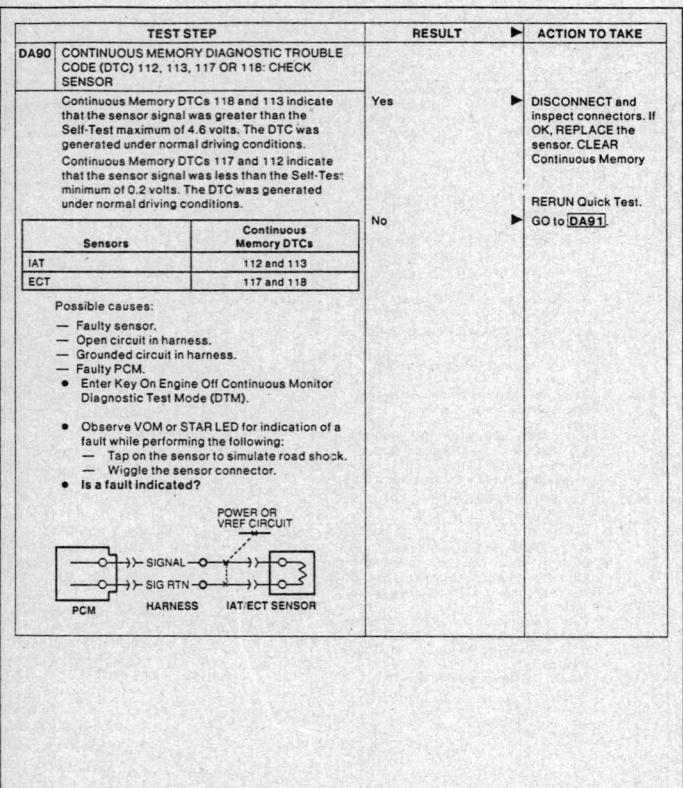

Fig. 171   Test DA: IAT/ECT Sensors (Part 8 of 10). 1994–95

TEST STEP	RESULT	▶	ACTION TO TAKE
DA91 CHECK EEC-IV VEHICLE HARNESS			
• Still in Key On Engine Off Continuous Monitor DTM. • Observe VOM or STAR LED for fault indication while performing the following: — Refer to the illustration in Step **DA90**. Grasp the vehicle harness close to the sensor connector. Wiggle, shake or bend a small section of the EEC system vehicle harness while working your way to the dash panel. Also wiggle, shake or bend the EEC system vehicle harness from the dash panel to the PCM. • **Is a fault indicated?**	Yes No	▶ ▶	ISOLATE fault and SERVICE as necessary. CLEAR Continuous Memory. RERUN Quick Test. GO to **DA92**.
DA92 CHECK PCM AND VEHICLE HARNESS CONNECTORS			
• Key off. • Disconnect Powertrain Control Module (PCM). Disconnect sensor connector. Inspect for damage, loose or pushed out pins, loose or poorly crimped wires. • **Are connectors and terminals OK?**	Yes No	▶ ▶	Unable to duplicate and/or identify fault at this time. Intermittent Diagnosis. All others, CLEAR Continuous Memory. RERUN Quick Test. SERVICE as necessary. CLEAR Continuous Memory. RERUN Quick Test.
DA100 CONTINUOUS MEMORY DIAGNOSTIC TROUBLE CODE (DTC) 338:			
DTC 338 indicates the engine had not reached the normal operating temperature or the system is not heating. The cooling system is not properly controlling the engine temperature. Possible causes: — Thermostat stuck open. — Water outlet gasket leak. — Water pump gasket leak. — Head gasket leak. — Heater hose leak. • GO directly to Cooling System for further diagnosis.		▶	

FM015930071309OX

Fig. 171   Test DA: IAT/ECT Sensors (Part 9 of 10)

TEST STEP	RESULT	▶	ACTION TO TAKE
DA101 CONTINUOUS MEMORY DIAGNOSTIC TROUBLE CODE (DTC) 339:		▶	
DTC 339 indicates the engine had exceeded the high temperature limit. the cooling system is not properly controlling the engine temperature. Possible causes: — Thermostat stuck closed — Water passages clogged — Worn or damaged water pump — Worn or damaged cooling fan — Low coolant level — Worn or damaged radiator cap — Radiator fins clogged — Coolant leakage ● GO directly to Cooling System for further diagnosis.			

FM0159300713100X

Fig. 171   Test DA: IAT/ECT Sensors (Part 10 of 10)

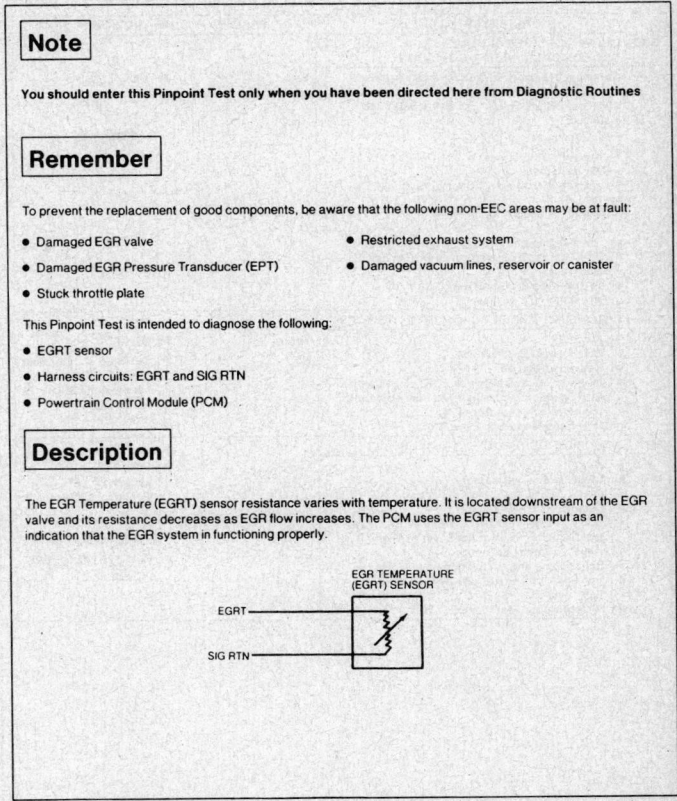

Note

You should enter this Pinpoint Test only when you have been directed here from Diagnostic Routines

Remember

To prevent the replacement of good components, be aware that the following non-EEC areas may be at fault:

● Damaged EGR valve   ● Restricted exhaust system

● Damaged EGR Pressure Transducer (EPT)   ● Damaged vacuum lines, reservoir or canister

● Stuck throttle plate

This Pinpoint Test is intended to diagnose the following:

● EGRT sensor

● Harness circuits: EGRT and SIG RTN

● Powertrain Control Module (PCM)

Description

The EGR Temperature (EGRT) sensor resistance varies with temperature. It is located downstream of the EGR valve and its resistance decreases as EGR flow increases. The PCM uses the EGRT sensor input as an indication that the EGR system in functioning properly.

FM0159300714010X

Fig. 172   Test DB: EGRT Sensor (Part 1 of 7). 1993–94

Pinpoint Test Schematic

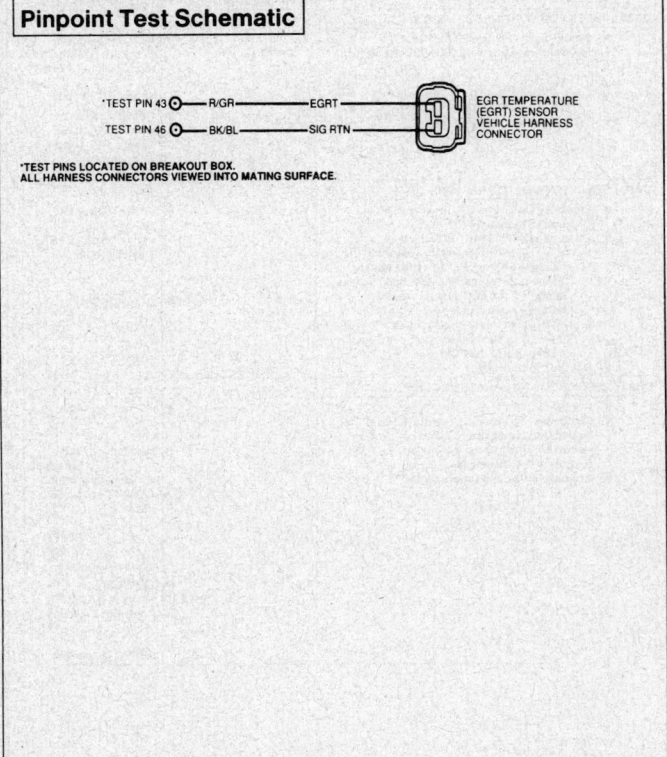

FM0159300714020X

Fig. 172   Test DB: EGRT Sensor (Part 2 of 7). 1993–94

TEST STEP	RESULT	▶	ACTION TO TAKE
DB1 CONTINUOUS MEMORY DIAGNOSTIC TROUBLE CODE (DTC) 327: VERIFY CONDITION			
Continuous Memory DTC 327 indicates that sometime in the last 80 warm-up cycles, the EGRT sensor signal was less than the Self-Test minimum. Possible Causes: — Damaged EGRT sensor — EGRT circuit shorted to ground — Damaged Powertrain Control Module (PCM) ● Key off. ● Clear Continuous Memory ● Start engine and run for at least two minutes. ● Turn engine off and rerun Key On Engine Off Self-Test. ● Is Continuous Memory DTC 327 still present?	Yes No	▶ ▶	GO to DB2. GO to DB90
DB2 INDUCE OPPOSITE DTC			
● Key off. ● Disconnect EGRT sensor. ● Clear Continuous Memory ● Start engine and run for at least two minutes. ● Turn engine off and rerun Key On Engine Off Self-Test. ● Is Continuous Memory DTC 337 present?	Yes No	▶ ▶	REPLACE EGRT sensor. CLEAR Continuous Memory RERUN Quick Test. GO to DB3.
DB3 CHECK EGRT CIRCUIT FOR SHORTS TO GROUND			
● Key off. ● Disconnect Powertrain Control Module (PCM) 60-pin connector. Inspect for damaged or pushed out pins, corrosion, loose wires, etc. Service as necessary. ● Install breakout box, leave PCM disconnected. ● EGRT sensor disconnected. ● Measure resistance between Test Pin 43 and Test Pins 40, 46 and 60 at the breakout box. ● Is each resistance greater than 10,000 ohms?	Yes No	▶ ▶	REPLACE PCM. REMOVE breakout box. RECONNECT all components. RERUN Quick Test SERVICE short circuit. REMOVE breakout box. RECONNECT all components. RERUN Quick Test.

FM0159300714030X

Fig. 172   Test DB: EGRT Sensor (Part 3 of 7). 1993–94

ELECTRONIC ENGINE CONTROL SYSTEM IV (EEC-IV)

TEST STEP		RESULT	▶	ACTION TO TAKE
DB5	CONTINUOUS MEMORY DIAGNOSTIC TROUBLE CODE (DTC) 337: VERIFY CONDITION			
	Continuous Memory DTC 337 indicates that sometime in the last 80 warm-up cycles, the EGRT sensor signal was greater than the Self-Test maximum. Possible Causes: — Damaged EGRT sensor — Open harness circuit — Damaged Powertrain Control Module (PCM). • Key off. • Clear Continuous Memory • Start engine and run for at least two minutes. • Turn engine off and rerun Key On Engine Off Self-Test. • **Is Continuous Memory DTC 337 still present?**	Yes No	▶ ▶	GO to DB6. GO to DB90.
DB6	CHECK EGRT CIRCUIT FOR SHORTS TO POWER			
	• Key off. • Disconnect EGRT sensor. • Key on, engine off. • Measure voltage between EGRT circuit at the EGRT sensor vehicle harness connector and the battery negative post. • **Is voltage less than 1.0 volt?**	Yes No	▶ ▶	GO to DB7. SERVICE short circuit. RECONNECT all components. RERUN Quick Test.
DB7	INDUCE OPPOSITE DTC			
	• Key off. • Clear Continuous Memory • Disconnect EGRT sensor. • Connect a jumper wire between EGRT circuit and SIG RTN circuit at the EGRT sensor vehicle harness connector. • Start engine and run for at least two minutes. • Turn engine off and rerun Key On Engine Off Self-Test. • **Is Continuous Memory DTC 327 present?**	Yes No	▶ ▶	REPLACE EGRT sensor. CLEAR Continuous Memory RERUN Quick Test. REMOVE jumper. GO to DB8.

Fig. 172   Test DB: EGRT Sensor (Part 4 of 7). 1993–94

TEST STEP		RESULT	▶	ACTION TO TAKE
DB8	CHECK CONTINUITY OF HARNESS CIRCUITS			
	• Key off. • Disconnect Powertrain Control Module (PCM). Inspect for damaged or pushed out pins, corrosion, loose wires, etc. Service as necessary. • Install breakout box, leave PCM disconnected. • EGRT sensor disconnected. • Measure resistance between Test Pin 43 at the breakout box and EGRT circuit at the EGRT sensor vehicle harness connector. • Measure resistance between Test Pin 46 at the breakout box and SIG RTN circuit at the EGRT sensor vehicle harness connector. • **Is each resistance less than 5.0 ohms?**	Yes No	▶ ▶	REPLACE PCM. REMOVE breakout box. RECONNECT all components. RERUN Quick Test. SERVICE open circuit. REMOVE breakout box. RECONNECT all components. RERUN Quick Test.
DB10	CONTINUOUS MEMORY DIAGNOSTIC TROUBLE CODE (DTC) 326: CHECK ENGINE IDLE			
	Continuous Memory DTC 326 indicates that sometime in the last 80 warm-up cycles, the Powertrain Control Module (PCM) detected EGR flow at idle. Possible Causes: — EGR valve stuck open — Damaged EGRT sensor — Damaged harness circuit • Key off. • Clear Continuous Memory • Start engine and let idle for at least two minutes. • **Does engine idle rough or stall?**	Yes No	▶ ▶	TURN engine off. REFER to EGR valve diagnosis. TURN engine off. GO to DB11.
DB11	VERIFY CONDITION			
	• Rerun Key On Engine Off Self-Test. • **Is Continuous Memory DTC 326 still present?**	Yes No	▶ ▶	GO to DB12. GO to DB90.

FM0159300714050X

Fig. 172   Test DB: EGRT Sensor (Part 5 of 7). 1993–94

TEST STEP		RESULT	▶	ACTION TO TAKE
DB12	CHECK CONTINUITY OF HARNESS CIRCUITS			
	• Key off. • Disconnect Powertrain Control Module (PCM). Inspect for damaged or pushed out pins, corrosion, loose wires, etc. Service as necessary. • Install breakout box, leave PCM disconnected. • Disconnect EGRT sensor. • Measure resistance between Test Pin 43 at the breakout box and EGRT circuit at the EGRT sensor vehicle harness connector. • Measure resistance between Test Pin 46 at the breakout box and SIG RTN circuit at the EGRT sensor vehicle harness connector. • **Is each resistance less than 5.0 ohms?**	Yes No	▶ ▶	REPLACE EGRT sensor. REMOVE breakout box. RECONNECT all components. RERUN Quick Test. SERVICE open circuit. REMOVE breakout box. RECONNECT all components. RERUN Quick Test.
DB20	CONTINUOUS MEMORY DIAGNOSTIC TROUBLE CODE (DTC) 332: CHECK THAT EGR VALVE HOLDS VACUUM			
	Continuous Memory DTC 332 indicates that sometime in the last 80 warm-up cycles, the Powertrain Control Module (PCM) detected no EGR flow at part throttle. Possible causes: — Damaged or plugged vacuum line. — EGR valve stuck closed. — Damaged EGR Pressure Transducer (EPT). — Damaged or plugged exhaust tube. — Damaged EGRT sensor. — Damaged harness circuit. • Key off. • Disconnect vacuum hose at EGR valve. • Connect a vacuum pump to the EGR valve. • Slowly apply 10 in-Hg (34 kPa) to the EGR valve. • **Does the EGR valve hold vacuum?**	Yes No	▶ ▶	RELEASE vacuum. GO to DB21. REMOVE vacuum pump. RECONNECT vacuum hose. REFER to EGR valve diagnosis.
DB21	CHECK EGR VALVE OPERATION			
	• Key off. • Vacuum hose disconnected at EGR valve. • Vacuum pump connected to EGR valve. • Clear Continuous Memory • Start engine. • Slowly apply 10 in-Hg (34 kPa) vacuum to the EGR valve and hold for at least two minutes. • **Does engine idle rough or stall?**	Yes No	▶ ▶	TURN engine off. GO to DB22. TURN engine off. REMOVE vacuum pump. RECONNECT vacuum hose. REFER to EGR valve diagnosis.

FM0159300714060X

Fig. 172   Test DB: EGRT Sensor (Part 6 of 7). 1993–94

TEST STEP		RESULT	▶	ACTION TO TAKE
DB22	CHECK FOR CONTINUOUS MEMORY DTC 326			
	• Rerun Key On Engine Off Self-Test. • **Is Continuous Memory DTC 326 present?**	Yes No	▶ ▶	REMOVE vacuum pump. RECONNECT vacuum hose. REFER to EGR system diagnosis. REMOVE vacuum pump. REPLACE EGRT sensor. RECONNECT all components. RERUN Quick Test.
DB90	CHECK EEC VEHICLE HARNESS			
	• Enter Key On Engine Off Continuous Monitor Diagnostic Test Mode (DTM). • Observe VOM or STAR LED for a fault indication while performing the following: — Grasp the harness close to the sensor connector. Wiggle, shake or bend a small section of the EEC system vehicle harness while working your way to the dash panel. Also wiggle, shake or bend the EEC system vehicle harness from the dash panel to the PCM. • **Is a fault indicated?**	Yes No	▶ ▶	ISOLATE fault and SERVICE as necessary. CLEAR Continuous Memory GO to DB91.
DB91	CHECK PCM AND HARNESS CONNECTORS			
	• Key off. • Disconnect Powertrain Control Module (PCM). Inspect for damaged or pushed out pins, corrosion, loose wires, etc on both the PCM and harness connectors. • **Are connector and terminals OK?**	Yes No	▶ ▶	further diagnosis. Intermittent Fault If the fault is not identified, then CLEAR Continuous Memory REFER to EGR system diagnosis. SERVICE as necessary. CLEAR Continuous Memory RERUN Quick Test.

FM0159300714070X

Fig. 172   Test DB: EGRT Sensor (Part 7 of 7). 1993–94

Note

You should enter this Pinpoint Test only when you have been directed here from Diagnostic Routines

Remember

To prevent the replacement of good components, be aware that the following non-EEC areas may be at fault:

- Air cleaner element
- Throttle body
- Inlet air duct

This Pinpoint Test is intended to diagnose only the following:

- Mass Air Flow (MAF) sensor
- Powertrain Control Module (PCM)
- Harness circuits: VPWR, PWR GND, MAF, and MAF RTN

Description

The Mass Air Flow (MAF) sensor is located between the air cleaner and the throttle body. The MAF sensor uses a hot wire sensing element to measure the amount of air entering the engine. Air passing over the hot wire causes it to cool. The MAF sensor then outputs an analog voltage signal to the PCM to determine the intake air mass. The PCM will then calculate the required fuel injector pulsewidth in order to provide the desired air/fuel ratio.

FM0159300715010X

Fig. 173   Test DC: MAF Sensor (Part 1 of 11)

Pinpoint Test Schematics

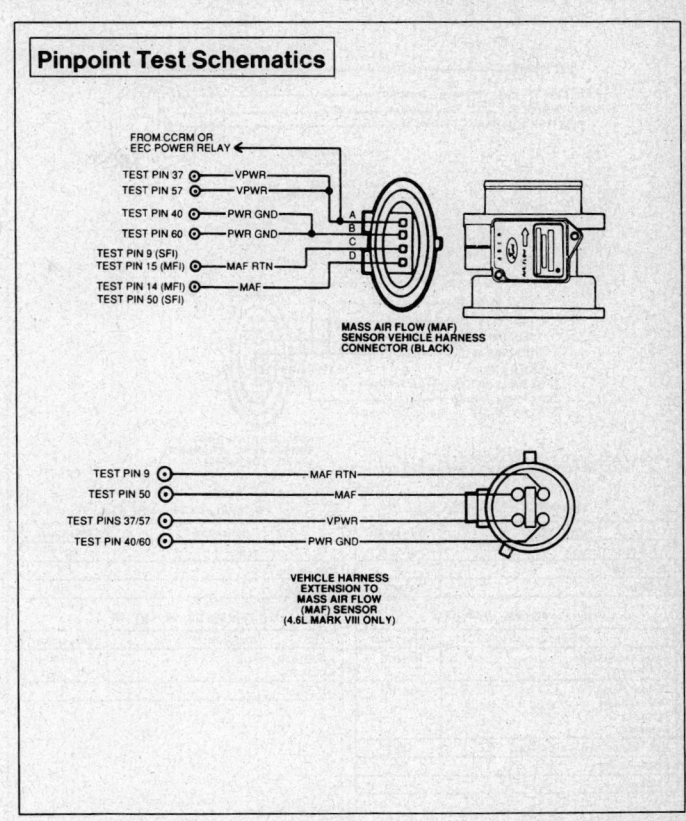

FM0159300715020X

Fig. 173   Test DC: MAF Sensor (Part 2 of 11)

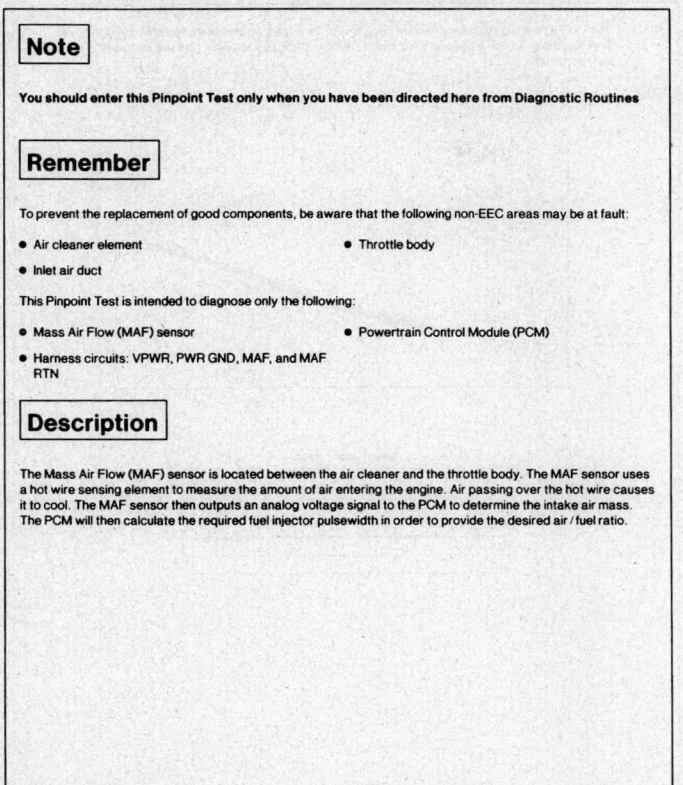

FM0159500715110A

Fig. 173   Test DC: MAF Sensor (Part 3 of 11). 1995

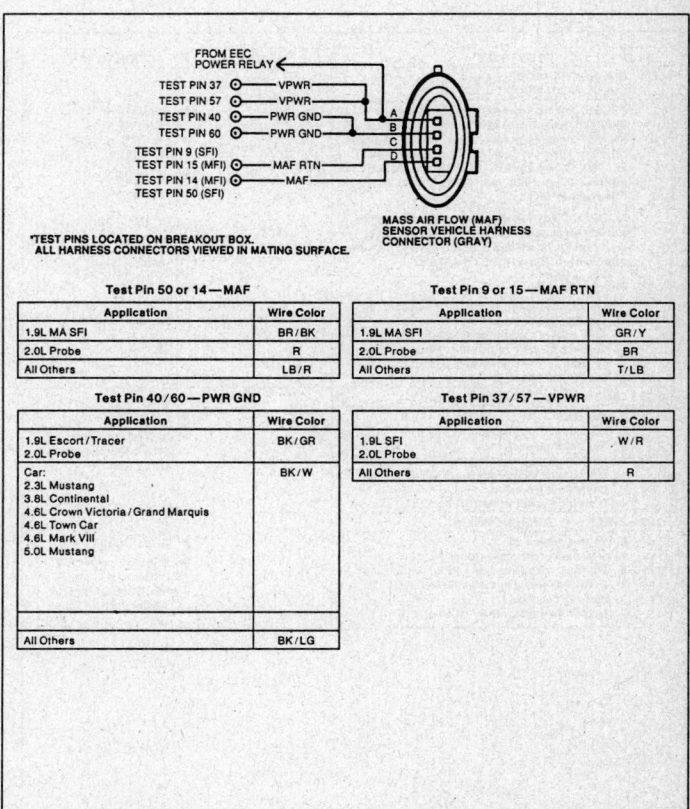

Test Pin 50 or 14 — MAF	
Application	Wire Color
1.9L MA SFI	BR/BK
2.0L Probe	R
All Others	LB/R

Test Pin 9 or 15 — MAF RTN	
Application	Wire Color
1.9L MA SFI	GR/Y
2.0L Probe	BR
All Others	T/LB

Test Pin 40/60 — PWR GND	
Application	Wire Color
1.9L Escort/Tracer 2.0L Probe	BK/GR
Car: 2.3L Mustang 3.8L Continental 4.6L Crown Victoria/Grand Marquis 4.6L Town Car 4.6L Mark VIII 5.0L Mustang	BK/W
All Others	BK/LG

Test Pin 37/57 — VPWR	
Application	Wire Color
1.9L SFI 2.0L Probe	W/R
All Others	R

Fig. 173   Test DC: MAF Sensor (Part 4 of 11). 1993

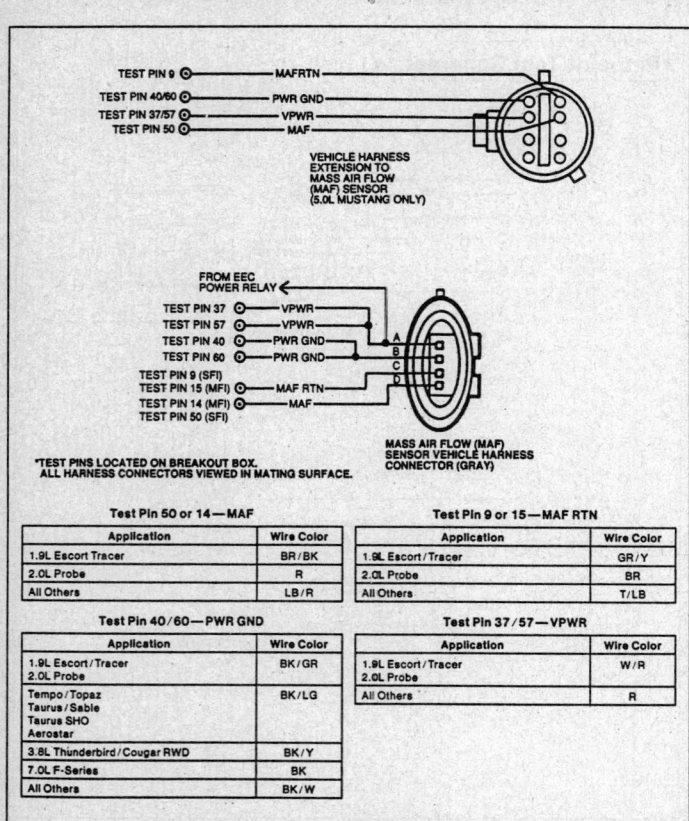

Fig. 173   Test DC: MAF Sensor (Part 4 of 11). 1994–95

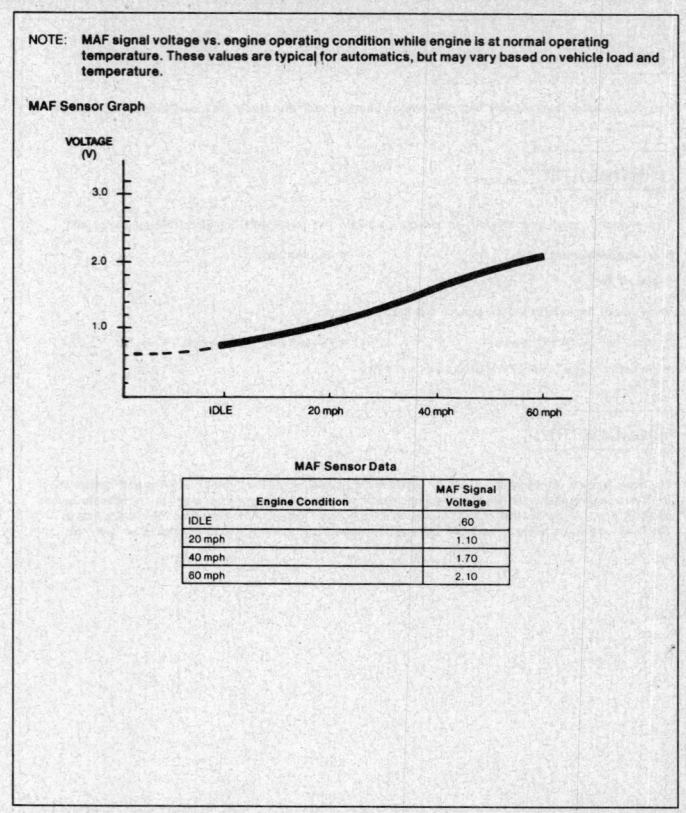

NOTE: MAF signal voltage vs. engine operating condition while engine is at normal operating temperature. These values are typical for automatics, but may vary based on vehicle load and temperature.

MAF Sensor Graph

MAF Sensor Data

Engine Condition	MAF Signal Voltage
IDLE	.60
20 mph	1.10
40 mph	1.70
60 mph	2.10

FM0159300715040X

Fig. 173   Test DC: MAF Sensor (Part 5 of 11)

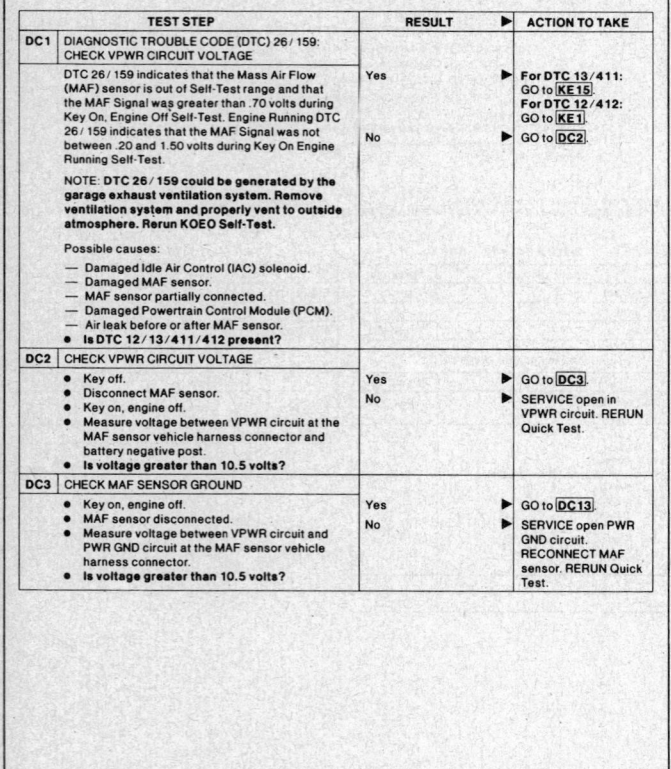

	TEST STEP	RESULT	▶	ACTION TO TAKE
DC1	DIAGNOSTIC TROUBLE CODE (DTC) 26/159: CHECK VPWR CIRCUIT VOLTAGE			
	DTC 26/159 indicates that the Mass Air Flow (MAF) sensor is out of Self-Test range and that the MAF Signal was greater than .70 volts during Key On, Engine Off Self-Test. Engine Running DTC 26/159 indicates that the MAF Signal was not between .20 and 1.50 volts during Key On Engine Running Self-Test.	Yes	▶	For DTC 13/411: GO to KE15. For DTC 12/412: GO to KE1.
		No	▶	GO to DC2.
	NOTE: DTC 26/159 could be generated by the garage exhaust ventilation system. Remove ventilation system and properly vent to outside atmosphere. Rerun KOEO Self-Test.			
	Possible causes:			
	— Damaged Idle Air Control (IAC) solenoid.			
	— Damaged MAF sensor.			
	— MAF sensor partially connected.			
	— Damaged Powertrain Control Module (PCM).			
	— Air leak before or after MAF sensor.			
	• Is DTC 12/13/411/412 present?			
DC2	CHECK VPWR CIRCUIT VOLTAGE			
	• Key off.	Yes	▶	GO to DC3.
	• Disconnect MAF sensor.	No	▶	SERVICE open in VPWR circuit. RERUN Quick Test.
	• Key on, engine off.			
	• Measure voltage between VPWR circuit at the MAF sensor vehicle harness connector and battery negative post.			
	• Is voltage greater than 10.5 volts?			
DC3	CHECK MAF SENSOR GROUND			
	• Key on, engine off.	Yes	▶	GO to DC13.
	• MAF sensor disconnected.	No	▶	SERVICE open PWR GND circuit. RECONNECT MAF sensor. RERUN Quick Test.
	• Measure voltage between VPWR circuit and PWR GND circuit at the MAF sensor vehicle harness connector.			
	• Is voltage greater than 10.5 volts?			

FM0159300715050X

Fig. 173   Test DC: MAF Sensor (Part 6 of 11)

	TEST STEP	RESULT	▶	ACTION TO TAKE
DC10	CONTINUOUS MEMORY DIAGNOSTIC TROUBLE CODE (DTC) 66/157: CHECK FOR INTERMITTENT SENSOR			
	Continuous Memory DTC 66/157 indicates that the Mass Air Flow (MAF) sensor signal went below 0.4 volt sometime during the last 80 warm-up cycles.	Yes	▶	GO to DC13.
		No	▶	GO to DC11.
	Possible causes:			
	— Poor continuity in MAF sensor harness or connectors.			
	— Intermittent open or short in MAF sensor or harness.			
	— Damaged MAF sensor.			
	— Idle Air Control (IAC) system (possible closed throttle position indication).			
	• Start engine and run at idle for approximately 5 to 10 minutes.			
	• Run Key On Engine Off Self-Test.			
	• Is Continuous Memory DTC 66/157 present?			
DC11	MONITOR MAF CIRCUIT UNDER SIMULATED ROAD SHOCK			
	• Key off.	Yes	▶	DISCONNECT and INSPECT MAF sensor connector. If OK, REPLACE MAF sensor. CLEAR Continuous Memory. RERUN Quick Test.
	• Disconnect Powertrain Control Module (PCM). Inspect for damaged or pushed out pins, corrosion, loose wires, etc. Service as necessary.			
	• Install breakout box, reconnect PCM.			
	• Connect DVOM between Test Pin 50 (SFI vehicles) or Test Pin 14 (MFI vehicles) and Test Pin 9 (SFI vehicles) or Test Pin 15 (MFI vehicles) at the breakout box.			
	• Key on, engine running.	No	▶	LEAVE DVOM and PCM connected. GO to DC12.
	• Lightly tap on MAF sensor and wiggle harness connector to simulate road shock.			
	NOTE: MAF voltage is normally above 0.4 volt. A sudden change down from this minimum limit indicates a fault.			
	• Is a fault indicated?			

FM0159300715060X

Fig. 173   Test DC: MAF Sensor (Part 7 of 11)

TEST STEP	RESULT	▶	ACTION TO TAKE
DC12 CHECK VEHICLE HARNESS FOR INTERMITTENT OPENS OR SHORTS • Key on, engine off. • DVOM connected between Test Pin 50 (SFI vehicles) or Test Pin 14 (MFI vehicles) and Test Pin 9 (SFI vehicles) or Test Pin 15 (MFI vehicles) at the breakout box. — Grasp the vehicle harness closest to the MAF sensor connector. Shake and bend a small section of the vehicle harness while working your way to the dash panel. Also wiggle, shake and bend the vehicle harness from the dash panel to the PCM. • **Is a fault indicated?**	Yes No	▶ ▶	ISOLATE fault and SERVICE as necessary. CLEAR Continuous Memory RERUN Quick Test. RECONNECT all components. Unable to duplicate and / or identify fault at this time further diagnosis, Intermittent Fault
DC13 DIAGNOSTIC TROUBLE CODE (DTC) 66 / 157 OR 72 / 129; AIR LEAK AT MAF SENSOR Engine Running DTC 72 / 129 indicates insufficient MAF change during Dynamic Response Test. Possible causes: — Open MAF circuit. — Open VPWR circuit to MAF sensor. — Open PWR GND circuit to MAF sensor. — Open MAF RTN circuit to MAF sensor. — MAF circuit shorted to ground. — Damaged Powertrain Control Module (PCM). — Damaged MAF sensor. — Air leak before or after MAF sensor. — MAF sensor disconnected. — Idle Air Control (IAC) system (possible closed throttle position indication). • Check for broken / loose air outlet tube clamps (throttle body and air cleaner assembly ends), cracks / holes in air outlet tube, worn gaskets between MAF sensor and air cleaner assembly (including intermediate tube on 3.8L SFI Taurus / Sable and 3.8L Continental). • **Is a fault indicated?**	Yes No	▶ ▶	SERVICE as necessary. RECONNECT all components. RERUN Quick Test. GO to DC14.

FM0159300715070X

Fig. 173   Test DC: MAF Sensor (Part 8 of 11)

TEST STEP	RESULT	▶	ACTION TO TAKE
DC14 CHECK CONTINUITY OF MAF AND VPWR CIRCUITS • Key off. • Disconnect MAF sensor. • Disconnect Powertrain Control Module (PCM). Inspect for damaged or pushed out pins, corrosion, loose wires, etc. Service as necessary. • Install breakout box, leave PCM disconnected. • Measure resistance between VPWR circuit at the MAF sensor vehicle harness connector and Test Pins 37 and 57 at the breakout box. **For MFI vehicles:** • Measure resistance between MAF circuit at the MAF sensor vehicle harness connector and Test Pin 14 at the breakout box. **For SFI vehicles:** • Measure resistance between MAF circuit at the MAF sensor vehicle harness connector and Test Pin 50 at the breakout box. • **Is each resistance less than 5.0 ohms?**	Yes No	▶ ▶	GO to DC15. SERVICE open circuit. REMOVE breakout box. RECONNECT all components. RERUN Quick Test.
DC15 CHECK MAF CIRCUIT FOR SHORTS TO GROUND AND MAF RTN CIRCUIT • Key off. • MAF sensor disconnected. • Breakout box installed, PCM disconnected. **For MFI vehicles** • Measure resistance between Test Pin 14 and Test Pins 15, 40 and 60 at the breakout box. **For SFI vehicles** • Measure resistance between Test Pin 50 and Test Pins 9, 40 and 60 at the breakout box. • **Is each resistance greater than 10,000 ohms?**	Yes No	▶ ▶	GO to DC16. SERVICE short circuit(s). REMOVE breakout box. RECONNECT all components. RERUN Quick Test.
DC16 CHECK PWR GND CIRCUIT CONTINUITY • Key off. • MAF sensor disconnected. • Breakout box installed, PCM disconnected. • Measure resistance between PWR GND circuit at the MAF sensor vehicle harness connector and battery negative post. • **Is resistance less than 10 ohms?**	Yes No	▶ ▶	GO to DC17. SERVICE open circuit. REMOVE breakout box. RECONNECT all components. RERUN Quick Test.

FM0159300715080X

Fig. 173   Test DC: MAF Sensor (Part 9 of 11)

TEST STEP	RESULT	▶	ACTION TO TAKE
DC17 CHECK MAF RTN CIRCUIT CONTINUITY • Key off. • MAF sensor disconnected. • Breakout box installed, PCM disconnected. **For MFI vehicles:** • Measure resistance between MAF RTN circuit at the MAF sensor vehicle harness connector and Test Pin 15 at the breakout box. **For SFI vehicles:** • Measure resistance between MAF RTN circuit at the MAF sensor vehicle harness connector and Test Pin 9 at the breakout box. • **Is resistance less than 5.0 ohms?**	Yes No	▶ ▶	GO to DC18. SERVICE open circuit. REMOVE breakout box. RECONNECT all components. RERUN Quick Test.
DC18 CHECK MAF CIRCUIT FOR SHORT TO GROUND • Key off. • MAF sensor disconnected. • Breakout box installed. • Connect PCM to breakout box. **For MFI vehicles:** • Measure resistance between Test Pin 14 and Test Pins 15, 40 and 60 at the breakout box. **For SFI vehicles:** • Measure resistance between Test Pin 50 and Test Pins 9, 40 and 60 at the breakout box. • **Is each resistance greater than 10,000 ohms?**	Yes No	▶ ▶	GO to DC19. REPLACE PCM. REMOVE breakout box. RECONNECT MAF sensor. RERUN Quick Test.
DC19 CHECK MAF CIRCUIT OUTPUT • Key off. • Reconnect MAF sensor. • Breakout box installed, PCM connected. • Key on, engine running. **For MFI vehicles:** • Measure voltage between Test Pin 14 at the breakout box and negative battery post. **For SFI vehicles:** • Measure voltage between Test Pin 50 at the breakout box and negative battery post. • **Is voltage between .36 and 1.50 volts?**	Yes No	▶ ▶	GO to DC20. REPLACE MAF sensor assembly. REMOVE breakout box. RECONNECT PCM. RERUN Quick Test.

FM0159300715090X

Fig. 173   Test DC: MAF Sensor (Part 10 of 11)

TEST STEP	RESULT	▶	ACTION TO TAKE
DC20 CHECK MAF CIRCUIT OUTPUT • Key off. • Reconnect MAF sensor. • Breakout box installed, PCM connected. • Key on, engine running. **For MFI vehicles:** • Measure voltage between Test Pin 14 and Test Pin 15 at the breakout box. **For SFI vehicles:** • Measure voltage between Test Pin 50 and Test Pin 9 at the breakout box. • **Is voltage between 0.36 and 1.50 volts?**	Yes No	▶ ▶	REPLACE PCM. REMOVE breakout box. RERUN Quick Test. REPLACE MAF sensor. REMOVE breakout box. RECONNECT PCM. RERUN Quick Test.
DC21 DIAGNOSTIC TROUBLE CODE (DTC) 56 / 158: RERUN SELF-TEST WITH MAF SENSOR DISCONNECTED DTC 56 / 158 indicates that the Mass Air Flow (MAF) sensor signal went above 4.5 volts during normal engine operation (continuous) or during Self-Test. NOTE: DTC 56 / 158 could be generated by foreign material blocking the Mass Air Flow sensor screen causing an air flow restriction. If contaminants are found on the screen, check air filter installation in air cleaner tray and proper sealing of air cleaner / tube before proceeding. • Key off. • Disconnect MAF sensor. • Start engine, idle one minute. • Key off. • Run Key On Engine Off Self-Test. • **Is DTC 66 or 157 present?**	Yes No	▶ ▶	REPLACE MAF sensor. RERUN Quick Test. GO to DC22.
DC22 CHECK MAF CIRCUIT FOR SHORT TO VPWR • Key off. • MAF sensor disconnected. • Disconnect Powertrain Control Module (PCM). Inspect for damaged or pushed out pins, corrosion, loose wires, etc. Service as necessary. • Measure resistance between MAF circuit and VPWR circuit at the MAF sensor vehicle harness connector. • **Is resistance greater than 10,000 ohms?**	Yes No	▶ ▶	REPLACE PCM. REMOVE breakout box. RECONNECT MAF sensor. RERUN Quick Test. SERVICE short circuit. REMOVE breakout box. RECONNECT all components. RERUN Quick Test.

FM0159300715100X

Fig. 173   Test DC: MAF Sensor (Part 11 of 11)

Note

You should enter this pinpoint test only when you have been directed here from Diagnostic Routines.

Remember

This pinpoint test is intended to diagnose only the following:

- EGRP sensor
- Harness circuits: EGRP, SIG RTN, VREF, EGRV, EGRA and VPWR
- EGRV solenoid
- EGRA solenoid
- EGR valve
- Powertrain Control Module (PCM)
- Vacuum lines (EGRV, EGRA, EGR)

Description

The Mazda sonic EGR system consists of an EGR valve position (EGRP) sensor, a normally closed, duty cycle controlled vacuum supply (EGRV) solenoid, a normally open, duty cycle controlled atmospheric pressure supply (EGRA) solenoid and an EGR valve.

The Powertrain Control Module (PCM) increases, decreases, and maintains the flow of EGR gases by activating and deactivating the two solenoids (EGRV and EGRA) at the proper time with a duty cycle signal. The response of the EGR valve to the activity of the two solenoids is detected and transmitted by the position (EGRP) sensor to the PCM.

FM0159400716010X

Fig. 174 Test DD: EGRP Sensor/EGRV Solenoid/EGRA Solenoid (Part 1 of 11). 1994–95

Pinpoint Test Schematic

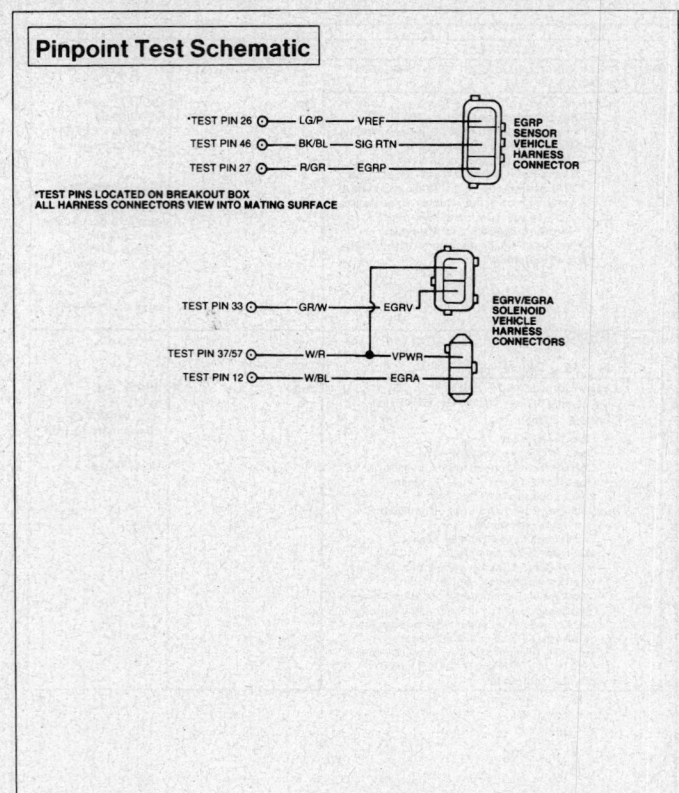

*TEST PIN 26 — LG/P — VREF
TEST PIN 46 — BK/BL — SIG RTN
TEST PIN 27 — R/GR — EGRP
EGRP SENSOR VEHICLE HARNESS CONNECTOR

*TEST PINS LOCATED ON BREAKOUT BOX
ALL HARNESS CONNECTORS VIEW INTO MATING SURFACE

TEST PIN 33 — GR/W — EGRV
TEST PIN 37/57 — W/R — VPWR
TEST PIN 12 — W/BL — EGRA
EGRV/EGRA SOLENOID VEHICLE HARNESS CONNECTORS

FM0159400716020X

Fig. 174 Test DD: EGRP Sensor/EGRV Solenoid/EGRA Solenoid (Part 2 of 11). 1994–95

TEST STEP		RESULT	▶	ACTION TO TAKE
DD1	**DIAGNOSTIC TROUBLE CODE (DTC) 327: ATTEMPT TO GENERATE DTC 337**			
	DTC 327 indicates the EGR Position (EGRP) sensor signal is less than the Self-Test minimum. NOTE: **Because the EGRP sensor is preloaded when attached to the EGR valve, a failure in the valve may cause the sensor to lose the preload and set DTC 327.** Possible Causes: — Damaged EGRP sensor/EGR valve assembly. — Open in sensor VREF circuit. — Open in sensor SIG RTN circuit. — Short to ground in sensor SIG circuit. — Damaged Powertrain Control Moduel (PCM). ● Key off. ● Disconnect the EGRP sensor. ● Jumper the VREF circuit to the EGRP sensor SIG circuit at the sensor vehicle harness connector. ● Rerun Key On Engine Off (KOEO) and Key On Engine Running (KOER) Self-Test. ● **Is DTC 337 present (ignore all other DTCs)?**	Yes No	▶ ▶	REPLACE the EGRP sensor/EGR valve assembly. REMOVE jumper. RERUN Quick Test. REMOVE jumper. GO to **DD2**.
DD2	**CHECK EGRP VREF VOLTAGE**			
	● Key on, engine off. ● EGRP sensor disconnected. ● Measure voltage between VREF circuit and SIG RTN circuit at the EGRP sensor vehicle harness connector. ● **Is voltage between 4.0 and 6.0 volts?**	Yes No	▶ ▶	GO to **DD3**. GO to Pinpoint Test Step **C1**.
DD3	**CHECK EGRP SIG RTN CIRCUIT CONTINUITY**			
	● Key off. ● EGRP sensor disconnected. ● Disconnect the PCM. Inspect for damaged or pushed out pins, corrosion, loose wires, etc. Service as necessary. ● Install breakout box, leave the PCM disconnected. ● Measure the resistance between EGRP SIG RTN circuit at the EGRP sensor vehicle harness connector and Test Pin 46 at the breakout box. ● **Is resistance less than 5 ohms?**	Yes No	▶ ▶	GO to **DD4**. SERVICE open circuit. REMOVE breakout box. RECONNECT all components. RERUN Quick Test.

FM0159400716030X

Fig. 174 Test DD: EGRP Sensor/EGRV Solenoid/EGRA Solenoid (Part 3 of 11). 1994–95

TEST STEP		RESULT	▶	ACTION TO TAKE
DD4	**CHECK EGRP SIG CIRCUIT FOR SHORT TO GROUND**			
	● Key off. ● EGRP sensor disconnected. ● Breakout box installed. PCM disconnected. ● Measure resistance between Test Pin 27 and Test Pins 40, 46, and 60 at the breakout box. ● **Is resistance greater than 10,000 ohms?**	Yes No	▶ ▶	REPLACE the PCM. REMOVE breakout box. RECONNECT all components. RERUN Quick Test. SERVICE short circuit. REMOVE the breakout box. RECONNECT all components. RERUN Quick Test.
DD10	**DIAGNOSTIC TROUBLE CODE 337: ATTEMPT TO GENERATE DTC 327**			
	DTC 337 indicates the EGR Position (EGRP) sensor signal is greater than the Self-Test maximum. Possible causes: — Open in EGRP sensor SIG circuit. — Short to power in EGRP sensor SIG circuit. — Damaged Powertrain Control Module (PCM). — Damaged EGRP sensor/EGR valve assembly. — Damaged EGR Vacuum (EGRV) solenoid valve. — Improper EGR valve vacuum hose routing. ● Key off. ● Disconnect EGRP sensor. ● Connect a jumper wire between the EGRP sensor SIG and SIG RTN circuits at the EGRP sensor vehicle harness connector. ● Rerun Key On Engine Off (KOEO) and Key On Engine Running (KOER) Self-Test. ● **Is DTC 327 present (ignore all other DTCs)?**	Yes No	▶ ▶	REMOVE the jumper wire. GO to **DD13**. RECONNECT EGRP sensor. REMOVE the jumper wire. GO to **DD11**.
DD11	**CHECK CONTINUITY OF EGRP SENSOR SIG CIRCUIT**			
	● Key off. ● EGRP sensor disconnected. ● Disconnect PCM. Inspect for damaged or pushed out pins, corrosion, loose wires, etc. Service as necessary. ● Install breakout box, leave PCM disconnected. ● Measure the resistance between the EGRP sensor SIG circuit at the EGRP sensor vehicle connector and Test Pin 27 at the breakout box. ● **Is the resistance less than 5 ohms?**	Yes No	▶ ▶	GO to **DD12**. SERVICE open circuit. REMOVE breakout box. RECONNECT all components. RERUN Quick Test.

FM0159400716040X

Fig. 174 Test DD: EGRP Sensor/EGRV Solenoid/EGRA Solenoid (Part 4 of 11). 1994–95

TEST STEP		RESULT	▶	ACTION TO TAKE
DD12	CHECK EGRP SIG CIRCUIT FOR SHORT TO POWER			
	• Key off. • EGRP sensor disconnected. • Breakout box installed, PCM disconnected. • Measure the resistance between Test Pin 27 and Test Pins 26, 37, and 57 at the breakout box. • **Is each resistance greater than 10,000 ohms?**	Yes	▶	REPLACE the PCM. REMOVE the breakout box. RECONNECT all components. RERUN Quick Test.
		No	▶	SERVICE short circuit. REMOVE the breakout box. RECONNECT all components. RERUN Quick Test.
DD13	CHECK FOR VACUUM AT EGRV SOLENOID VALVE OUTPUT PORT			
	• Key off. • Disconnect the EGRV solenoid vacuum line at the EGRV solenoid output port. • Install a vacuum gauge at the output port of the EGRV solenoid. • Key on, engine idling. • **Is a vacuum signal present as the engine idles?**	Yes	▶	REPLACE the EGRV solenoid assembly. REMOVE vacuum gauge. RECONNECT all components. RERUN Quick Test.
		No	▶	CHECK the EGR valve vacuum hose routing. If OK, REPLACE the EGRP sensor, EGR valve assembly. REMOVE the vacuum gauge. RERUN Quick Test.
DD20	DIAGNOSTIC TROUBLE CODES (DTCS) 571 AND 572. CHECK EGRV, EGRA SOLENOID RESISTANCE			
	DTC 571 indicates a failure in the EGRA solenoid circuit. DTC 572 indicates a failure in the EGRV solenoid circuit. Possible causes: – Damaged EGRA, EGRV solenoid. – Open in harness circuit. – Short in harness circuit. – Damaged Powertrain Control Module (PCM). • Key off. • Disconnect EGRA or EGRV solenoid depending on the DTC generated. • Measure solenoid resistance. • **Is resistance between 30 and 70 ohms?**	Yes	▶	GO to DD21
		No	▶	REPLACE appropriate solenoid. RERUN Quick Test.

FM0159400716050X

Fig. 174 Test DD: EGRP Sensor/EGRV Solenoid/EGRA Solenoid (Part 5 of 11). 1994–95

TEST STEP		RESULT	▶	ACTION TO TAKE
DD21	CHECK SOLENOID VPWR CIRCUIT			
	• Key on, engine off. • Solenoid disconnected. • Measure voltage between battery negative post and VPWR circuit at the solenoid vehicle harness connector. • **Is voltage greater than 10.5 volts?**	Yes	▶	GO to DD22
		No	▶	SERVICE open circuit. RECONNECT solenoid. RERUN Quick Test.
DD22	CHECK SOLENOID CIRCUIT CONTINUITY			
	• Key off. • Solenoid disconnected. • Disconnect PCM. Inspect for damaged or pushed out pins, corrosion, loose wires. Service as necessary. • Install breakout box, leave PCM disconnected. **For EGRA solenoid:** • Measure the resistance between Test Pin 12 at the breakout box and the EGRA circuit at the solenoid vehicle harness connector. **For EGRV solenoid:** • Measure the resistance between Test Pin 33 at the breakout box and the EGRV circuit at the solenoid vehicle harness connector. • **Is the resistance less than 5.0 ohms?**	Yes	▶	GO to DD23
		No	▶	SERVICE open circuit. REMOVE breakout box. RECONNECT all components. RERUN Quick Test.
DD23	CHECK SOLENOID CIRCUIT FOR SHORT TO POWER AND SHORT TO GROUND			
	• Key off. • Solenoid disconnected. • Breakout box installed, PCM disconnected. **For EGRA solenoid:** • Measure resistance between Test Pin 12 and Test Pins 37 and 57 at the breakout box. • Measure resistance between Test Pin 12 and Test Pins 40 and 60 at the breakout box. **For EGRV solenoid:** • Measure resistance between Test Pin 33 and Test Pins 37 and 57 at the breakout box. • Measure resistance between Test Pin 33 and Test Pins 40 and 60 at the breakout box. • **Is each resistance greater than 10,000 ohms?**	Yes	▶	REPLACE PCM. REMOVE breakout box. RECONNECT solenoid. RERUN Quick Test.
		No	▶	SERVICE short circuit. REMOVE breakout box. RECONNECT all components. RERUN Quick Test.

FM0159400716060X

Fig. 174 Test DD: EGRP Sensor/EGRV Solenoid/EGRA Solenoid (Part 6 of 11). 1994–95

TEST STEP		RESULT	▶	ACTION TO TAKE
DD30	DIAGNOSTIC TROUBLE CODE (DTC) 332: CHECK FOR VACUUM TO EGR VALVE			
	DTC 332 indicates that the EGRP sensor input did not change after the Powertrain Control Module (PCM) commanded the EGR valve to open. Possible Causes: – Damaged EGRP sensor, EGR valve assembly. – Damaged vacuum line(s). – Damaged EGRA solenoid. – Damaged EGRV solenoid. • Key off. • Disconnect EGR vacuum hose at the EGR valve. • Connect a vacuum gauge to the disconnected end of the EGR valve vacuum hose. • Rerun Key On Engine Running (KOER) Self-Test while observing the vacuum gauge. • **Is vacuum reading less than 1 in-Hg. throughout the KOER Self-Test (ignore all other DTCs)?**	Yes	▶	REMOVE vacuum gauge. GO to DD31
		No	▶	REPLACE the EGRP sensor, EGR valve assembly. REMOVE vacuum gauge. RECONNECT the EGR valve vacuum hose. RERUN Quick Test.
DD31	CHECK EGR VALVE VACUUM HOSE			
	• EGR valve vacuum hose disconnected. • Inspect the EGR valve vacuum hose from the EGR valve to the EGRV, EGRA solenoids for obstructions, cracks, kinks, and loose connections, etc. • **Is EGR valve vacuum hose in good condition?**	Yes	▶	RECONNECT EGR valve vacuum hose GO to DD32
		No	▶	SERVICE EGR valve vacuum hose as necessary. RERUN Quick Test.
DD32	CHECK VACUUM TO EGRV SOLENOID			
	• Key off. • Disconnect the EGRV solenoid input port vacuum source hose. • Install a vacuum gauge at the disconnected end of the input port vacuum source hose. • Key on, engine idling. • Observe the vacuum gauge reading. • **Is vacuum greater than 10 in-Hg (33 kPa)?**	Yes	▶	REMOVE vacuum gauge. RECONNECT vacuum hose. GO to DD33
		No	▶	CHECK vacuum hose to the EGRV solenoid. If OK, CHECK vacuum source for the solenoid. SERVICE as necessary. RERUN Quick Test.

FM0159400716070X

Fig. 174 Test DD: EGRP Sensor/EGRV Solenoid/EGRA Solenoid (Part 7 of 11). 1994–95

TEST STEP		RESULT	▶	ACTION TO TAKE
DD33	CHECK EGRV SOLENOID VALVE FUNCTION			
	• Key off. • Disconnect the EGRV solenoid output vacuum hose at the solenoid output port. • Install a vacuum gauge at the output port of the EGRV solenoid. • Rerun Key On Engine Running (KOER) Self-Test while observing the vacuum gauge reading. • **Does the vacuum signal decrease and then increase again?**	Yes	▶	REMOVE the vacuum gauge. GO to DD34.
		No	▶	REPLACE the EGRV solenoid assembly. REMOVE the vacuum gauge. RECONNECT all components. RERUN Quick Test.
DD34	CHECK EGRV SOLENOID OUTPUT PORT VACUUM HOSE			
	• EGRV solenoid output vacuum hose disconnected. • Inspect the EGRV solenoid output vacuum hose for obstructions, cracks, kinks and loose connections, etc. • **Is the vacuum hose in good condition?**	Yes	▶	RECONNECT the vacuum hose. Go to DD35
		No	▶	SERVICE the vacuum hose as necessary. RERUN Quick Test.
DD35	CHECK EGRA SOLENOID VACUUM HOSE			
	• Disconnect the EGRA solenoid vacuum hose. • Inspect the EGRA solenoid vacuum hose for obstructions, cracks, kinks and loose connection, etc. • **Is the vacuum hose in good condition?**	Yes	▶	REPLACE the EGRA solenoid assembly. RECONNECT the EGRA solenoid vacuum hose. RERUN Quick Test.
		No	▶	SERVICE the vacuum hose as necessary. RERUN Quick Test.

FM0159400716080X

Fig. 174 Test DD: EGRP Sensor/EGRV Solenoid/EGRA Solenoid (Part 8 of 11). 1994–95

TEST STEP	RESULT	▶	ACTION TO TAKE
DD90 CONTINUOUS MEMORY DIAGNOSTIC TROUBLE CODES (DTCS) 327 OR 337: CHECK FOR INTERMITTENT SENSOR DAMAGE			
Continuous Memory DTC 327 indicates the EGRP sensor input to the Powertrain Control Module (PCM) was below the minimum acceptable voltage sometime during vehicle operation. Continuous Memory DTC 337 indicates the EGRP sensor input to the Powertrain Control Module (PCM) was above the maximum acceptable voltage sometime during vehicle operation. Possible causes of DTC 327: — Damaged EGRP sensor/EGR valve assembly. — Intermittent open in EGRP sensor SIG RTN circuit. — Intermittent short to ground in EGRP SIG circuit. — Intermittent open in EGRP VREF circuit. Possible causes of DTC 337: — Damaged EGRP sensor/EGR valve assembly. — Intermittent open in EGRP SIG circuit. — Intermittent short to power in EGRP SIG circuit. • Enter Key On Engine Off Continuous Monitor DTM. • Observe VOM or STAR LED for indication of a fault while performing the following: — Lightly tap on the EGRP sensor and wiggle the sensor vehicle harness connector to simulate road shock. • **Is a fault indicated?**	Yes No	▶ ▶	INSPECT the EGRP sensor connector and connector terminals. If OK, REPLACE the EGRP sensor/EGR valve assembly. CLEAR Continuous memory RERUN Quick Test. GO to **DD91**.
DD91 CHECK FOR INTERMITTENT HARNESS DAMAGE			
• Still in Key On Engine Off Continuous Monitor DTM. • Observe VOM or STAR LED for indication of a fault while performing the following: — Grasp the vehicle harness closest to the EGRP sensor vehicle harness connector. Wiggle, shake or bend a small section of the EEC-IV vehicle harness while working toward the dash panel. Also, wiggle, shake and bend the EEC-IV vehicle harness from the dash panel to the PCM. • **Is a fault indicated?**	Yes No	▶ ▶	ISOLATE fault and SERVICE as necessary. CLEAR Continuous Memory RERUN Quick Test. GO to **DD92**.

FM0159400716090X

Fig. 174 Test DD: EGRP Sensor/EGRV Solenoid/EGRA Solenoid (Part 9 of 11). 1994–95

TEST STEP	RESULT	▶	ACTION TO TAKE
DD92 CHECK PCM CONNECTOR			
• Key off. • Disconnect PCM connector. • Inspect both connectors and connector terminals for damaged or pushed out pins, corrosion, loose wires, etc. • **Is damage detected?**	Yes No	▶ ▶	SERVICE as necessary. CLEAR Continuous Memory RERUN Quick Test. Unable to duplicate fault at this time. RERUN Quick Test.
DD100 CONTINUOUS MEMORY DIAGNOSTIC TROUBLE CODE (DTC) 332: CHECK EGR VALVE FUNCTION			
Continuous Memory DTC 332 indicates the EGR valve did not open when load and requested conditions had been met sometime during vehicle operation. Possible causes. — Damaged EGRP sensor/EGR valve assembly. — Damaged EGR valve vacuum line. — Damaged EGRV solenoid vacuum lines. — Damaged EGRA solenoid vacuum line. • Key off. • Disconnect and plug EGR valve vacuum line at the EGR valve. • Connect a hand vacuum pump to the EGR valve. • Apply 10 in-Hg (34 kPa) of vacuum to the EGR valve and release while observing valve for movement. • **Does the EGR valve function properly?**	Yes No	▶ ▶	REMOVE vacuum pump. UNPLUG vacuum line. GO to **DD101**. REMOVE the EGRP sensor/EGR valve assembly. INSPECT the EGR valve for blockage, binding, contamination and leakage, etc. SERVICE as necessary. CLEAR Continuous Memory RERUN Quick Test.
DD101 CHECK EGR VALVE VACUUM LINE			
• EGR valve vacuum line disconnected at both ends. • Inspect the EGR valve vacuum line from the EGR valve to the EGRV/EGRA solenoids for obstructions, cracks and kinks, etc. • **Is EGR valve vacuum line in good condition?**	Yes No	▶ ▶	RECONNECT EGR valve vacuum line. GO to **DD102**. SERVICE EGR valve vacuum line as necessary. CLEAR Continuous Memory RERUN Quick Test.

FM0159400716100X

Fig. 174 Test DD: EGRP Sensor/EGRV Solenoid/EGRA Solenoid (Part 10 of 11). 1994–95

TEST STEP	RESULT	▶	ACTION TO TAKE
DD102 CHECK EGRA SOLENOID VACUUM LINE AND EGRV SOLENOID INPUT/OUTPUT PORT VACUUM LINES			
• Vacuum lines disconnected one at a time. • Inspect the vacuum lines for obstructions, cracks and kinks, etc. • **Is each vacuum line in good condition?**	Yes No	▶ ▶	RECONNECT the vacuum lines. GO to **DD103**. SERVICE vacuum lines as necessary. CLEAR Continuous Memory RERUN Quick Test.
DD103 CHECK EGRV/EGRA SOLENOIDS AND HARNESS CIRCUITS FOR INTERMITTENT FAULT			
• Key off. • Disconnect vacuum line at the EGR valve and connect vacuum line to a vacuum gauge. • Key on, engine idling. • Look for an increase in vacuum while performing the following: — Tap the EGRV and EGRA solenoids. — Wiggle the EGRV and EGRA solenoid vehicle harness connectors and harness circuits. • **Does the EGR vacuum increase?**	Yes No	▶ ▶	ISOLATE fault and SERVICE or REPLACE as necessary. RECONNECT all components. CLEAR Continuous Memory RERUN Quick Test. Unable to duplicate and/or identify fault at this time.

FM0159400716110X

Fig. 174 Test DD: EGRP Sensor/EGRV Solenoid/EGRA Solenoid (Part 11 of 11). 1994–95

WARNING

• HANDLE METHANOL-GASOLINE FUEL BLENDS WITH EXTREME CAUTION; WEAR CHEMICAL GOGGLES AND IMPERVIOUS GLOVES.

• DO NOT EAT, SMOKE, OR DRINK WHEN THESE FUEL BLENDS ARE BEING HANDLED.

• FLAMES FROM METHANOL OR METHANOL-GASOLINE BLENDS MAY BE INVISIBLE.

• INHALING VAPORS FROM THESE FUEL BLENDS ARE HARMFUL TO YOUR HEALTH, HANDLE ONLY IN WELL-VENTILATED AREAS.

Note

You should enter this Pinpoint Test only when you have been directed here from Diagnostic Routines

Remember

To prevent the replacement of good components, be aware that this test is to be used only on vehicles that have methanol-gasoline fuel mixtures in their fuel systems. If the vehicle under observation has anything other than a methanol-gasoline fuel mixture in its fuel system, then this test procedure should not be used, since erroneous component replacement may result. The following non-EEC area may be at fault:

• Ignition system

• Fuel system

This Pinpoint Test is intended to diagnose only the following:

• FF sensor

• Harness circuits: FF sensor signal, VPWR and PWR GND

• Powertrain Control Module (PCM) assembly

FM0159300717010X

Fig. 175 Test DE: FF Sensor (Part 1 of 9)

Description

The FF sensor is a capacitive device with a signal processing stage whose frequency varies with the dielectric constant, conductivity and temperature of the fluid medium (methanol-gasoline mixture) in its measuring cell. In general, as the percentage of methanol in the fuel increases, the output frequency of the FF sensor signal will increase. For example, a fuel mixture that was determined to be 30% methanol will result in the FF sensor signal output frequency being between 60 and 100 Hz; 60% methanol results in a FF sensor signal output frequency between 90 and 130 Hz. The PCM uses the percent methanol information to calculate the correct air / fuel ratio and spark advance for the vehicle.

SAFE FUEL HANDLING PRACTICES: GASOLINE, METHANOL AND METHANOL BLENDS

FIRE

- REPORT ALL FIRES to the appropriate authorities.
- FLAMES from methanol or methanol-gasoline blends MAY BE INVISIBLE.
- Know the locations of and learn how to use PORTABLE FIRE EXTINGUISHERS, FIRE BLANKETS, FIRE ALARMS and EYE / WASH SHOWER FACILITIES.
- Use a B or AFFF (light water) type FIRE EXTINGUISHER to fight flammable liquid fires.

FIRST AID

- IF SWALLOWED:
  — If GASOLINE has been swallowed, DO NOT induce vomiting. SEEK MEDICAL ATTENTION IMMEDIATELY!
  — If METHANOL OR A METHANOL / GASOLINE BLEND has been swallowed, induce vomiting under the direction of a physician or Poison Control Center. SEEK MEDICAL ATTENTION IMMEDIATELY!
- When overcome by vapors, if safe, MOVE VICTIM TO FRESH AIR. If not breathing, give artificial respiration or CPR (Cardiopulmonary Resuscitation) as appropriate. SEEK MEDICAL ATTENTION IMMEDIATELY!
- If SPLASHED IN EYES, FLUSH with large amounts of water for 15 minutes. Remove contact lenses, if worn. SEEK MEDICAL ATTENTION.
- If SPLASHED ON SKIN, REMOVE CONTAMINATED CLOTHING. WASH SKIN thoroughly with soap and water.

HEALTH

- ALL FUELS may be HARMFUL OR FATAL IF SWALLOWED.
- BE AWARE, IF SWALLOWED, onset of serious health effects may be delayed 12 to 24 hours.
- FUELS AND PRODUCTS CONTAINING METHANOL (e.g. windshield washer fluid) may cause blindness if swallowed.

FM0159300717020X

Fig. 175   Test DE: FF Sensor (Part 2 of 9)

- ALL FUEL VAPORS may be HARMFUL BY INHALATION.
- ALL FUELS are IRRITATING to the EYES and RESPIRATORY SYSTEM.
- FUELS made with GASOLINE may contain benzene which is a cancer-causing agent.

HANDLING

- Use FLAMMABLE LIQUID HANDLING PRECAUTIONS.
- Wear CHEMICAL GOGGLES and NITRILE GLOVES (additional protective clothing and equipment may be necessary in some instances).
- Keep flammable liquids in APPROVED LABELED CLOSED CONTAINERS.
- Use in WELL-VENTILATED AREAS and CONTROL VAPORS. Be aware that vapors ARE NOT VISIBLE, are heavier than air, can travel along the floor, and will settle in lower areas.
- When transferring flammable liquids, BOND the RECEIVING CONTAINER to the SOURCE and GROUND the SOURCE to the EARTH.
- DO NOT SMOKE or use HEAT / SPARK PRODUCING EQUIPMENT near vapors.
- DO NOT eat, smoke or drink where these products are handled, processed or stored.
- NEVER SIPHON BY MOUTH.
- WASH HANDS thoroughly after HANDLING any FUEL.

SPILLS

- Notify the proper authorities in the EVENT of any spill you have NOT been trained to clean up.
- STOP, CONTAIN, AND CLEAN UP small spills with an absorbent material.

Pinpoint Test Schematic

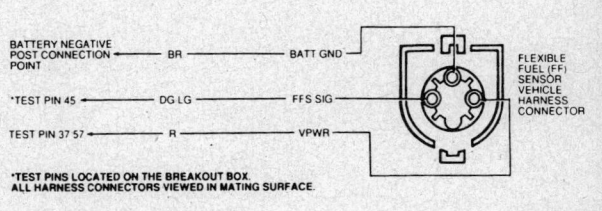

*TEST PINS LOCATED ON THE BREAKOUT BOX.
ALL HARNESS CONNECTORS VIEWED IN MATING SURFACE.

FM0159300717030X

Fig. 175   Test DE: FF Sensor (Part 3 of 9)

	TEST STEP	RESULT	▶	ACTION TO TAKE
DE 1	KEY ON ENGINE OFF DIAGNOSTIC TROUBLE CODE 193: CHECK FF SENSOR VPWR CIRCUIT			
	Diagnostic trouble code (DTC) 193 indicates a failure in the FF sensor circuit has been detected. Possible causes: — Open in FF sensor VPWR harness circuit. — Short to ground in FF sensor VPWR harness circuit. — Open in battery ground to FF sensor circuit. — Short to power in FF sensor battery ground circuit. — Open in FF sensor signal circuit. — Short to power in FF sensor signal circuit. — Short to ground in FF sensor signal circuit. — Fuel separation. — Damaged FF sensor. — Damaged Powertrain Control Module (PCM). • Key off. • Disconnect FF sensor. • Key on. • Measure VPWR voltage between the FF sensor VPWR pin at the vehicle harness connector and battery ground. • Key off. • **Is the voltage greater than 10.5 volts?**	Yes No	▶ ▶	GO to DE2. SERVICE open or short circuit in FF sensor VPWR circuit. RECONNECT all components. RERUN Quick Test.
DE 2	CHECK CONTINUITY OF FF SENSOR BATTERY GROUND CIRCUIT			
	• Key off. • FF sensor disconnected. • Measure resistance between FF sensor battery ground pin at the vehicle harness connector and battery negative post. • **Is resistance less than 10,000 ohms?**	Yes No	▶ ▶	GO to DE3. SERVICE open circuit(s). RECONNECT all components. RERUN Quick Test.
DE 3	CHECK CONTINUITY OF FF SENSOR SIGNAL CIRCUIT			
	• Key off. • FF sensor disconnected. • Disconnect powertrain control module (PCM). Inspect for damaged or pushed out pins, corrosion, loose wires, etc. Service as necessary. • Install breakout box, leave PCM disconnected. • Measure resistance between FF sensor signal circuit pin at the FF sensor vehicle harness connector and Test Pin 45 at the breakout box. • **Is resistance less than 5 ohms?**	Yes No	▶ ▶	GO to DE4. SERVICE open circuit. REMOVE breakout box. RECONNECT all components. RERUN Quick Test.

FM0159300717040X

Fig. 175   Test DE: FF Sensor (Part 4 of 9)

	TEST STEP	RESULT	▶	ACTION TO TAKE
DE4	CHECK FOR SHORT TO POWER IN FF SENSOR SIGNAL CIRCUIT			
	• Key off. • FF sensor disconnected. • Breakout box installed, PCM disconnected. • Measure resistance between Test Pin 45 and Test Pins 26, 37 and 57 at the breakout box. • **Is each resistance greater than 10,000 ohms?**	Yes No	▶ ▶	GO to DE5. SERVICE short circuit. REMOVE breakout box. RECONNECT all components. RERUN Quick Test.
DE5	CHECK FOR SHORT TO GROUND IN FF SENSOR SIGNAL CIRCUIT			
	• Key off. • FF sensor disconnected. • Breakout box installed, PCM disconnected. • Measure resistance between Test Pin 45 and Test Pins 40, 46 and 60 at the breakout box. • **Is each resistance greater than 10,000 ohms?**	Yes No	▶ ▶	RECONNECT the FF sensor. GO to DE6. SERVICE short circuit. REMOVE breakout box. RECONNECT all components. RERUN Quick Test.
DE6	CHECK STABILITY OF FF SENSOR SIGNAL OUTPUT FREQUENCY			
	• Key off. • FF sensor connected. • Breakout box installed, PCM connected. • Connect the Rotunda Megameter 014-00768 or equivalent to the breakout box in the following manner: — Red lead to Test Pin 45. — Black lead to battery negative post. — Select the frequency mode on the meter. • Key on. • Observe the frequency display of the meter. • **Does the frequency measurement fluctuate erratically within the 40 to 160 Hz range?**	Yes No	▶ ▶	GO to DE7. GO to DE9.
DE7	CHECK FOR FUEL SEPARATION			
	NOTE: In this context, fuel separation means the methanol and gasoline blend have become two distinct phases. But, under normal conditions, the methanol and gasoline parts of the fuel would not be identifiable. • Key off. • Remove the fuel filter and pour fuel within it into a clear container. • Visually inspect the fuel within the clear container for fuel separation. • Pour contents of clear container into fuel filler tube. • **Is fuel separation present?**	Yes No	▶ ▶	REINSTALL the fuel filter. DROP. DRAIN the fuel tank and refill tank with either M85 or gasoline GO to DE8 REPLACE the FF sensor. REINSTALL the fuel filter. REMOVE the breakout box. RERUN Quick Test.

FM0159300717050X

Fig. 175   Test DE: FF Sensor (Part 5 of 9)

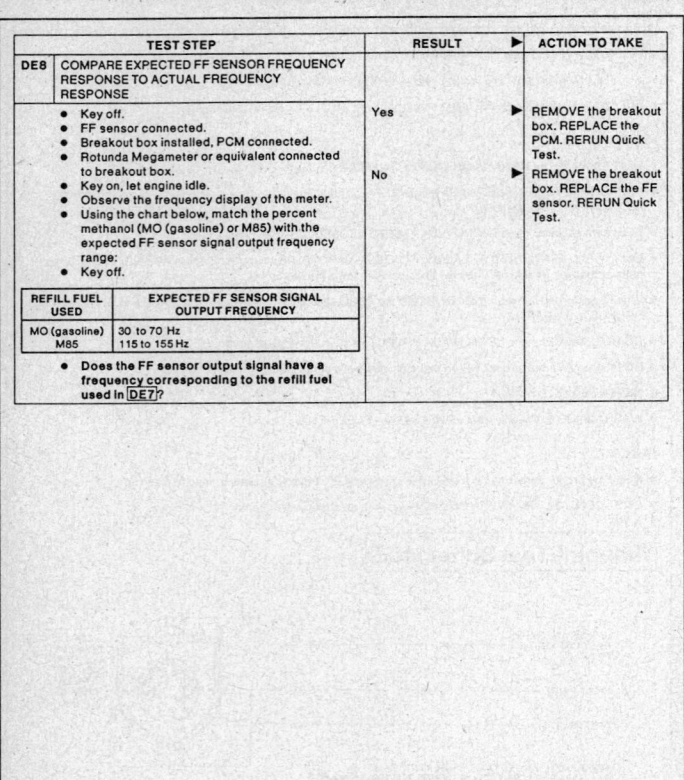

TEST STEP	RESULT	▶	ACTION TO TAKE
DE8 COMPARE EXPECTED FF SENSOR FREQUENCY RESPONSE TO ACTUAL FREQUENCY RESPONSE • Key off. • FF sensor connected. • Breakout box installed, PCM connected. • Rotunda Megameter or equivalent connected to breakout box. • Key on, let engine idle. • Observe the frequency display of the meter. • Using the chart below, match the percent methanol (MO (gasoline) or M85) with the expected FF sensor signal output frequency range. • Key off.	Yes No	▶ ▶	REMOVE the breakout box. REPLACE the PCM. RERUN Quick Test. REMOVE the breakout box. REPLACE the FF sensor. RERUN Quick Test.

REFILL FUEL USED	EXPECTED FF SENSOR SIGNAL OUTPUT FREQUENCY
MO (gasoline)	30 to 70 Hz
M85	115 to 155 Hz

• Does the FF sensor output signal have a frequency corresponding to the refill fuel used in DE7?

Fig. 175   Test DE: FF Sensor (Part 6 of 9)

DE9   PERFORM FUEL COMPOSITION TEST TO DETERMINE THE PERCENT METHANOL OF THE FUEL

This test is designed to determine the percentage of fuel methanol in the fuel. Use Rotunda FFV Fuel Test Kit 014-00770 or equivalent to test the fuel. The kit contains the following materials:

— Fuel drain hose assembly.

— Fuel pump jumper wire assembly.

— One beaker.

— One 25 ml graduated cylinder.

— One 5.71 liter gas can.

• Key off.

• FF sensor connected.

• Breakout box installed, PCM connected.

• Fill the beaker with more than 4 ml of clean water.

• Place the hose end of the fuel drain hose assembly in the gas can.

• Connect the fuel drain hose assembly to the fuel pressure relief valve on the cold start injector. Turn the connector clockwise to tighten. Turn ON/OFF valve clockwise to open.

• Connect the fuel pump jumper wire assembly to the vehicle self-test connector, refer to the illustration below.

CONNECT JUMPER WIRE HERE

• Key on.

• Depress the jumper switch to the ON position and allow slightly more than 20 ml of fuel to drain into the gas can.

• Pour exactly 20 ml of fuel into the 25 ml graduated cylinder.

• Pour enough water from the beaker into the 25 ml graduated cylinder to bring the total volume to 24 ml.

• Insert the stopper plug into the opening of the 25 ml graduated cylinder and hold the stopper firmly in place (to prevent harmful spillage and escape of vapor) as you shake the cylinder to mix water and fuel. Allow liquid to stand and separate.

• After three minutes, the methanol and water will mix together and settle to the bottom of the cylinder. The gasoline will rise to the top.

FM0159300717070X

Fig. 175   Test DE: FF Sensor (Part 7 of 9)

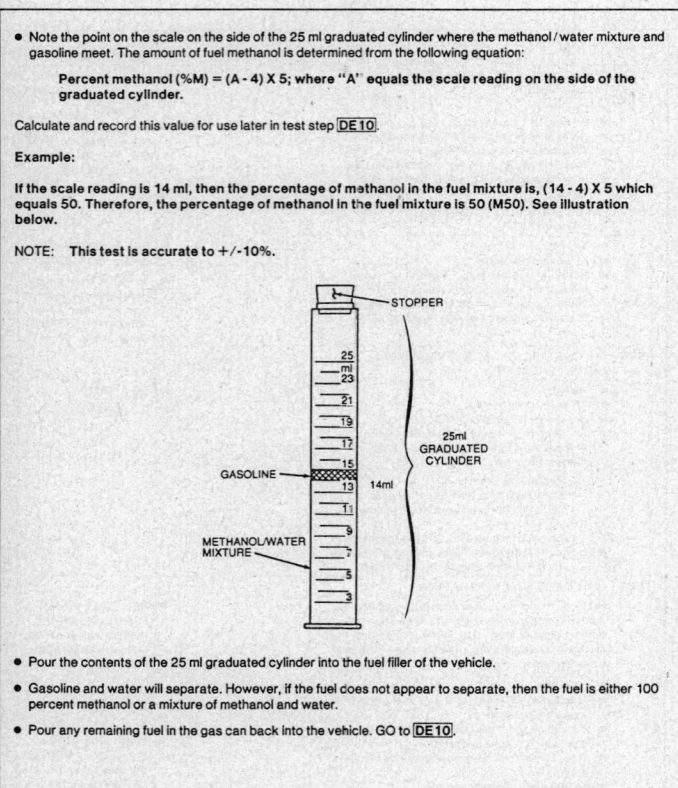

• Note the point on the scale on the side of the 25 ml graduated cylinder where the methanol/water mixture and gasoline meet. The amount of fuel methanol is determined from the following equation:

Percent methanol (%M) = (A - 4) X 5; where "A" equals the scale reading on the side of the graduated cylinder.

Calculate and record this value for use later in test step DE10.

Example:

If the scale reading is 14 ml, then the percentage of methanol in the fuel mixture is, (14 - 4) X 5 which equals 50. Therefore, the percentage of methanol in the fuel mixture is 50 (M50). See illustration below.

NOTE: This test is accurate to +/-10%.

STOPPER

25ml GRADUATED CYLINDER

GASOLINE

14ml

METHANOL/WATER MIXTURE

• Pour the contents of the 25 ml graduated cylinder into the fuel filler of the vehicle.

• Gasoline and water will separate. However, if the fuel does not appear to separate, then the fuel is either 100 percent methanol or a mixture of methanol and water.

• Pour any remaining fuel in the gas can back into the vehicle. GO to DE10.

Fig. 175   Test DE: FF Sensor (Part 8 of 9)

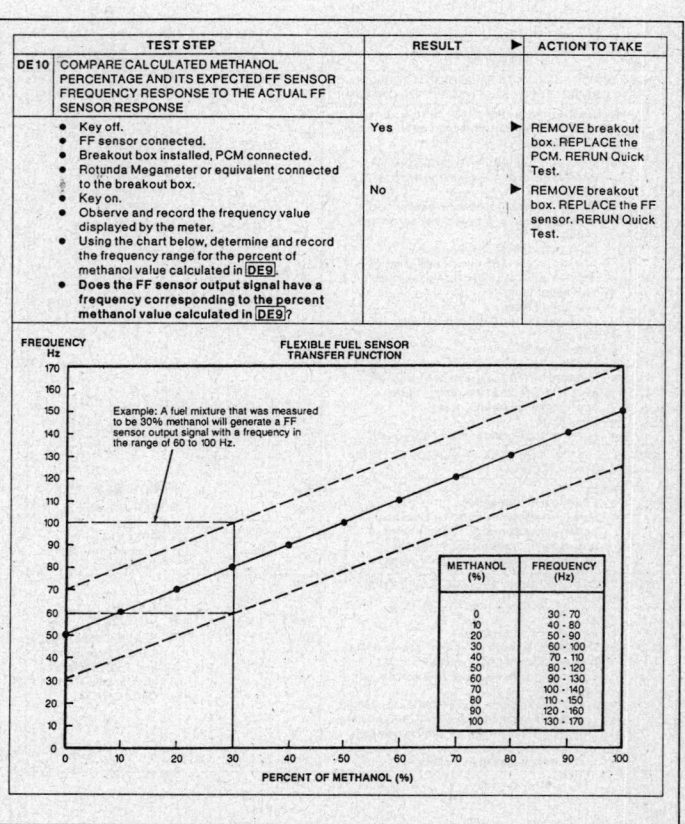

TEST STEP	RESULT	▶	ACTION TO TAKE
DE10 COMPARE CALCULATED METHANOL PERCENTAGE AND ITS EXPECTED FF SENSOR FREQUENCY RESPONSE TO THE ACTUAL FF SENSOR RESPONSE • Key off. • FF sensor connected. • Breakout box installed, PCM connected. • Rotunda Megameter or equivalent connected to the breakout box. • Key on. • Observe and record the frequency value displayed by the meter. • Using the chart below, determine and record the frequency range for the percent of methanol value calculated in DE9. • Does the FF sensor output signal have a frequency corresponding to the percent methanol value calculated in DE9?	Yes No	▶ ▶	REMOVE breakout box. REPLACE the PCM. RERUN Quick Test. REMOVE breakout box. REPLACE the FF sensor. RERUN Quick Test.

FREQUENCY Hz

FLEXIBLE FUEL SENSOR TRANSFER FUNCTION

Example: A fuel mixture that was measured to be 30% methanol will generate a FF sensor output signal with a frequency in the range of 60 to 100 Hz.

METHANOL (%)	FREQUENCY (Hz)
0	30 - 70
10	40 - 80
20	50 - 90
30	60 - 100
40	70 - 110
50	80 - 120
60	90 - 130
70	100 - 140
80	110 - 150
90	120 - 160
100	130 - 170

PERCENT OF METHANOL (%)

Fig. 175   Test DE: FF Sensor (Part 9 of 9)

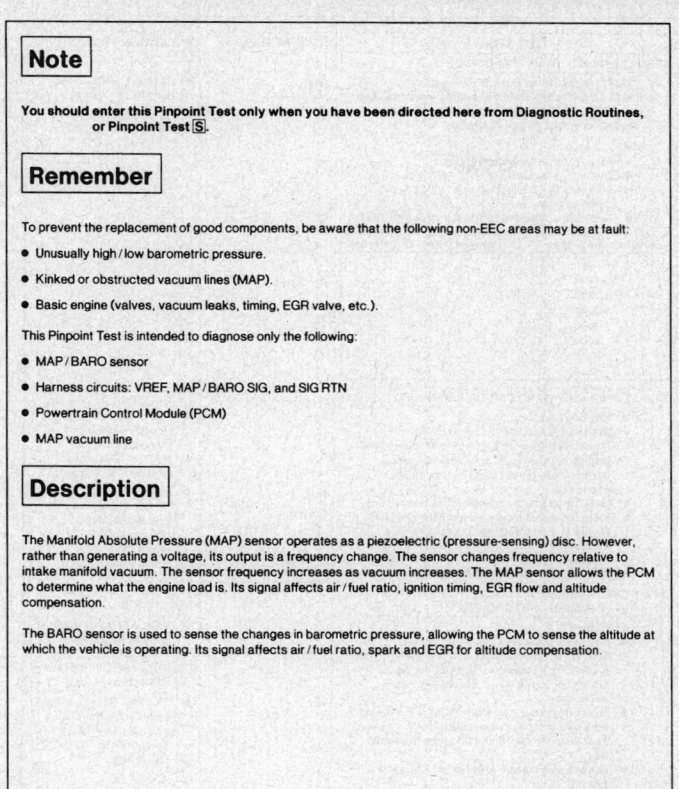

Fig. 176 Test DF: MAP/BARO Sensor (Part 1 of 10)

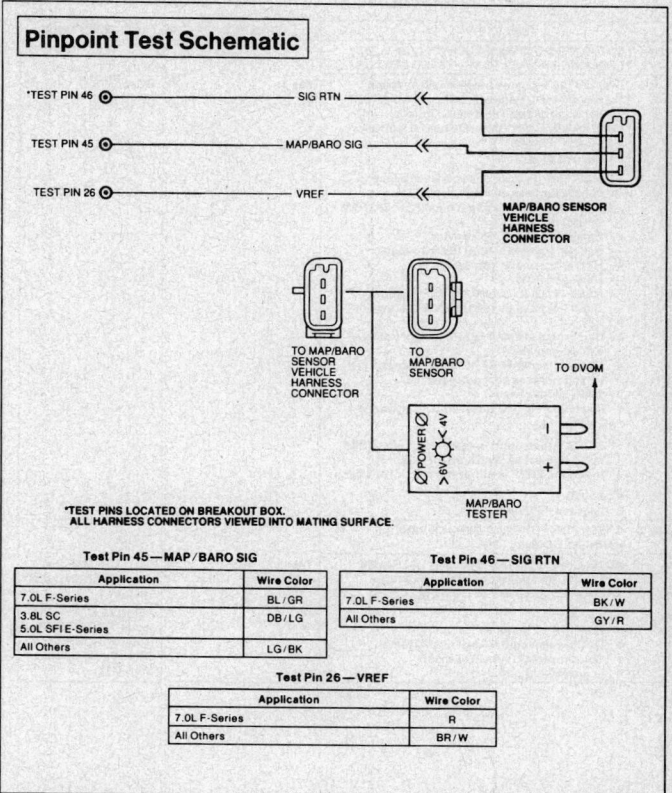

Fig. 176 Test DF: MAP/BARO Sensor (Part 2 of 10)

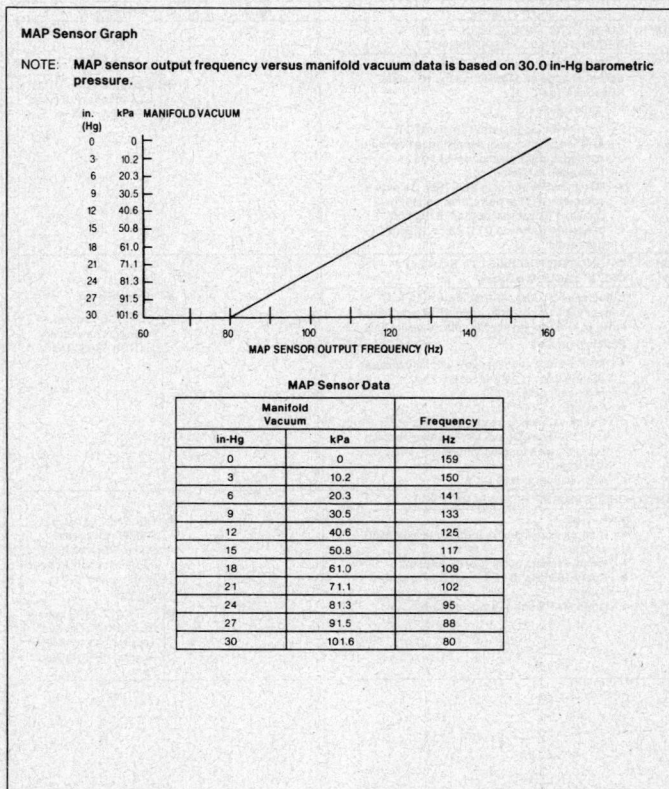

Fig. 176 Test DF: MAP/BARO Sensor (Part 3 of 10)

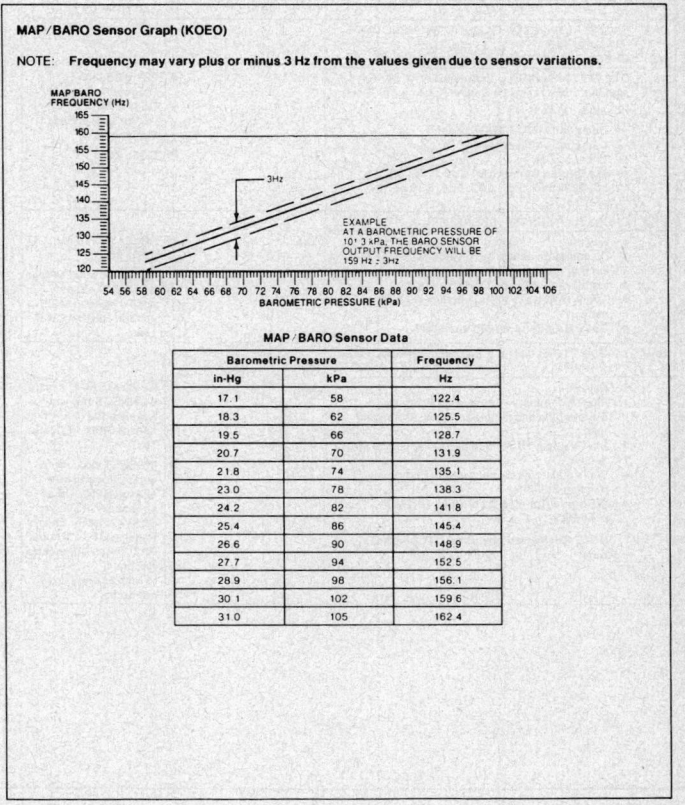

Fig. 176 Test DF: MAP/BARO Sensor (Part 4 of 10)

TEST STEP	RESULT	▶	ACTION TO TAKE
DF1 DIAGNOSTIC TROUBLE CODE (DTC) 22 / 126: CHECK FOR POWER TO MAP / BARO SENSOR			
DTC 22 / 126 indicates the Manifold Absolute Pressure (MAP) / Barometric Pressure (BARO) sensor is out of Self-Test range. Correct MAP / BARO range of measurement is typically from 1.4 to 1.6 volts. Possible causes:	Yes	▶	GO to DF3.
— MAP / BARO circuit open between sensor vehicle harness connector and PCM.	No	▶	GO to DF2.
— MAP / BARO circuit shorted to VREF, SIG RTN, or GND.			
— Damaged MAP / BARO sensor.			
— Vacuum trapped at MAP / BARO sensor.			
— High atmospheric pressure.			
— Damaged PCM.			
— VREF circuit open at MAP / BARO sensor.			
— SIG RTN circuit open at MAP / BARO sensor.			
● Key off.			
● Disconnect the MAP / BARO sensor from the vehicle harness.			
● Connect the MAP / BARO tester between the vehicle harness connector and the MAP / BARO sensor.			
● Insert MAP / BARO tester banana plugs into DVOM.			
NOTE: Green light on tester indicates VREF is OK (4-6 Volts). Red light (or no light) indicates VREF is either too low or too high.			
● Key on.			
● Is green light on?			
DF2 CHECK FOR POWER AT SENSOR VEHICLE HARNESS CONNECTOR			
NOTE: Green light reaffirms that VREF is OK (4-6 volts). Red light (or no light) indicates VREF is either too low or too high.	Yes	▶	REPLACE MAP / BARO sensor. RERUN Quick Test.
● Key on.	No	▶	REMOVE MAP / BARO tester. RECONNECT MAP / BARO sensor. GO to Pinpoint Test Step C1.
● MAP / BARO tester connected.			
● DVOM connected to MAP / BARO tester.			
● Disconnect MAP / BARO sensor.			
● Is green light on?			

Fig. 176   Test DF: MAP/BARO Sensor (Part 5 of 10)

FM0159300718060X

TEST STEP	RESULT	▶	ACTION TO TAKE
DF3 CHECK MAP / BARO SENSOR OUTPUT			
NOTE: Measure several known good MAP / BARO sensors on available vehicles. The measured voltage will be typical for your location on the day of testing.	Yes	▶	REMOVE MAP / BARO tester. GO to DF4.
● Key on.	No	▶	REMOVE MAP / BARO tester. GO to DF5.
● MAP / BARO tester connected.			
● DVOM connected to MAP / BARO tester.			
● Measure MAP / BARO sensor voltage on customer vehicle.			
● Is DVOM voltage in range for your altitude?			

Approximate Altitude (Ft.)	Voltage Output (±.04 Volts)
0	1.59
1000	1.56
2000	1.53
3000	1.50
4000	1.47
5000	1.44
6000	1.41
7000	1.39

TEST STEP	RESULT	▶	ACTION TO TAKE
DF4 CHECK MAP / BARO CIRCUIT CONTINUITY			
● Key off.	Yes	▶	REPLACE PCM. REMOVE breakout box. RECONNECT MAP / BARO sensor. RERUN Quick Test.
● MAP / BARO sensor disconnected.			
● Disconnect Powertrain Control Module (PCM). Inspect for damaged or pushed out pins, corrosion, loose wires, etc. Service as necessary.	No	▶	SERVICE open circuit. REMOVE breakout box. RECONNECT all components. RERUN Quick Test.
● Install breakout box, leave PCM disconnected.			
● Measure resistance between MAP / BARO circuit at the MAP / BARO sensor vehicle harness connector and Test Pin 45 at the breakout box.			
● Is resistance less than 5.0 ohms?			
DF5 CHECK MAP / BARO CIRCUIT FOR SHORTS TO VREF, SIG RTN AND GROUND			
● Key off.	Yes	▶	REPLACE MAP / BARO sensor. REMOVE breakout box. RECONNECT PCM. RERUN Quick Test.
● MAP / BARO sensor disconnected.			
● Disconnect Powertrain Control Module (PCM). Inspect for damaged or pushed out pins, corrosion, loose wires, etc. Service as necessary.	No	▶	SERVICE short circuit. REMOVE breakout box. RECONNECT all components. RERUN Quick Test.
● Install breakout box, leave PCM disconnected.			
● Measure resistance between Test Pin 45 and Test Pins 26, 46, 40 and 60 at the breakout box.			
● Is each resistance greater than 10,000 ohms?			

Fig. 176   Test DF: MAP/BARO Sensor (Part 6 of 10)

TEST STEP	RESULT	▶	ACTION TO TAKE
DF7 ENGINE RUNNING DIAGNOSTIC TROUBLE CODE (DTC) 22 / 126: CHECK FOR EGR DTCs			
DTC 22 / 126 (KOER) indicates the MAP / BARO signal is out of range for Engine Running Self-Test. Possible causes:	Yes	▶	GO to EEC-IV Diagnostic Trouble Code Charts for appropriate Pinpoint Test.
— Damaged MAP / BARO sensor.	No	▶	GO to DF8.
— Damaged vacuum hoses.			
— Excess EGR.			
● Are Engine Running DTCs 31, 32, 33, 34, 35, 327, 326, 328, 332, 334, 336 or 337 present?			
DF8 CHECK MAP SENSOR OPERATION			
● Key off.	Yes	▶	RELEASE vacuum. GO to DF9.
● Disconnect vacuum supply hose from MAP sensor.	No	▶	REPLACE MAP sensor. CONNECT vacuum supply hose to MAP sensor. RERUN Quick Test.
● Install vacuum pump to MAP sensor.			
● Apply 18 in-Hg (61 kPa) vacuum to MAP sensor.			
● Does MAP sensor hold vacuum?			
DF9 ATTEMPT TO ELIMINATE ENGINE RUNNING DTC 22 or 126			
● Key off.	Yes	▶	REPLACE MAP sensor. CONNECT vacuum supply hose to MAP sensor. RERUN Quick Test.
● Plug MAP sensor vacuum supply hose.			
● Start engine and maintain 1500 ± 100 engine rpm.	No	▶	INSPECT vacuum supply hose to MAP sensor. SERVICE as necessary. If OK, SERVICE other Engine Running DTCs. If none, RETURN to Diagnostic Routines to address any drive concerns.
● Slowly apply 15 in-Hg (51 kPa) vacuum to MAP sensor.			
● While maintaining rpm, perform Engine Running Self-Test.			
● Is Engine Running DTC 22 or 126 still present?			
NOTE: Disregard any other DTCs at this time.			

Fig. 176   Test DF: MAP/BARO Sensor (Part 7 of 10)

TEST STEP	RESULT	▶	ACTION TO TAKE
DF10 DIAGNOSTIC TROUBLE CODE (DTC) 72 / 129: RERUN DYNAMIC RESPONSE TEST			
DTC 72 / 129 indicates that the MAP sensor output did not change enough during the Dynamic Response Test. Possible causes:	Yes	▶	GO to DF11.
— System failed to detect partial WOT.	No	▶	SERVICE other DTCs as necessary. If none, testing complete.
— MAP sensor vacuum supply hose improper routing, blockage and / or linkage.			
— Damaged MAP sensor.			
● Rerun Engine Running Self-Test. Be sure a complete WOT is performed during the Dynamic Response portion of the test.			
● Is Engine Running DTC 72 or 129 still present?			
DF11 DIAGNOSTIC TROUBLE CODE (DTCs) 81 / 128: CHECK VACUUM HOSES			
Continuous DTC 81 / 128 indicates the MAP sensor vacuum has not changed greater than 2 in-Hg (7 kPa) during normal vehicle operation. Possible causes:	Yes	▶	GO to DF12.
— MAP sensor vacuum supply hose improper routing, blockage and / or linkage.	No	▶	SERVICE vacuum hoses as necessary. RERUN Quick Test.
— MAP sensor leak.			
● Key off.			
● Check vacuum hoses for proper routing. Refer to VECI decal. Check MAP sensor vacuum supply hoses for disconnections, kinks or blockage.			
● Are vacuum hoses OK?			
DF12 CHECK MAP SENSOR OPERATION			
● Key off.	Yes	▶	RELEASE vacuum. REMOVE vacuum pump. RECONNECT vacuum supply hose to MAP sensor. GO to DF13.
● Disconnect vacuum supply hose from MAP sensor.			
● Install vacuum pump to MAP sensor.	No	▶	REPLACE MAP sensor. RECONNECT vacuum supply hose to MAP sensor. RERUN Quick Test.
● Apply 18 in-Hg (61 kPa) vacuum to MAP sensor.			
● Does MAP sensor hold vacuum?			

Fig. 176   Test DF: MAP/BARO Sensor (Part 8 of 10)

ELECTRONIC ENGINE CONTROL SYSTEM IV (EEC-IV)

TEST STEP	RESULT	▶	ACTION TO TAKE
DF13 CHECK THAT VACUUM TO MAP SENSOR DECREASES DURING DYNAMIC RESPONSE			
• Key off. • Tee a vacuum gauge in the intake manifold vacuum supply hose at the MAP sensor. • Perform Engine Running Self-Test while observing vacuum. • **Did vacuum decrease by more than 10 in-Hg (34 kPa) vacuum during Dynamic Response test?**	Yes No	▶ ▶	REPLACE MAP sensor. REMOVE vacuum gauge. RERUN Quick Test. EEC system OK
DF90 CHECK FOR CONTINUOUS MEMORY DIAGNOSTIC TROUBLE CODE (DTC) 22 / 126: EXERCISE MAP / BARO SENSOR			
Continuous Memory DTC 22 / 126 indicates the Manifold Absolute Pressure (MAP) / Barometric Pressure (BARO) sensor was out of self-test range. The code was set during normal driving conditions. Correct range of measurement is typically from 1.4 to 1.6 volts. Possible causes: — Damaged MAP / BARO sensor. — Damaged EEC vehicle harness. — Damaged MAP / BARO sensor vehicle harness connectors and / or terminals. — Unusually high / low barometric pressure. • Using Key On, Engine Off Continuous Monitor Diagnostic Test Mode (DTM), observe VOM or STAR LED for indication of a fault while performing the following: — Connect a vacuum pump to the MAP / BARO sensor. — Slowly apply 84 kPa (25 in-Hg) vacuum to the MAP / BARO sensor. — Slowly bleed vacuum off the MAP / BARO sensor. — Lightly tap on MAP / BARO sensor (simulate road shock). — Wiggle MAP / BARO connector. • **Is fault indicated?**	Yes No	▶ ▶	DISCONNECT and INSPECT connectors. If connector and terminals are good, REPLACE MAP / BARO sensor. RERUN Quick Test. GO to DF91.

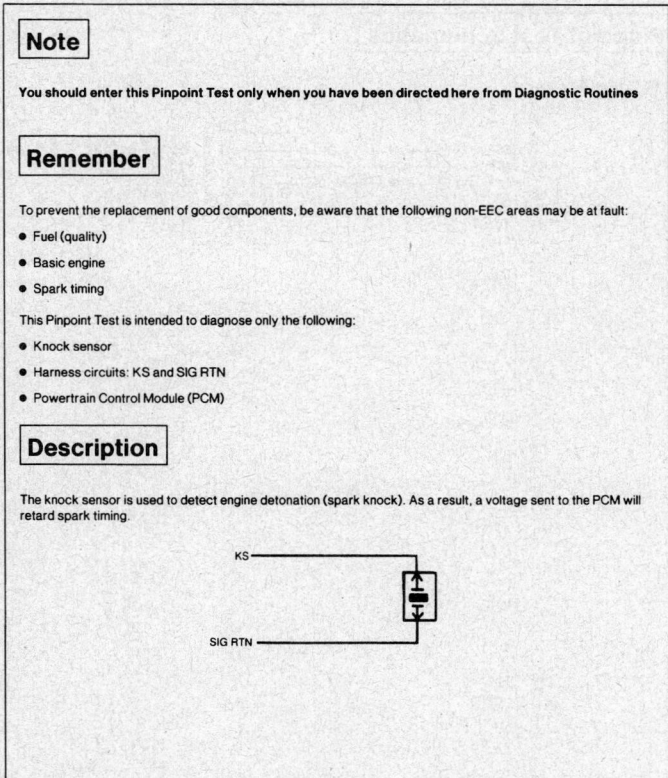

Fig. 176   Test DF: MAP/BARO Sensor (Part 9 of 10)

FM0159300718090X

TEST STEP	RESULT	▶	ACTION TO TAKE
DF91 CHECK EEC VEHICLE HARNESS			
• Remain in Key On, Engine Off Continuous Monitor DTM. • Observe VOM or STAR LED for a fault indication while performing the following: — Referring to the illustration in Step DF90, grasp the vehicle harness closest to the sensor connector. Wiggle, shake or bend a small section of the EEC system vehicle harness while working your way to the dash panel. Also wiggle, shake or bend the EEC vehicle harness from the dash panel to the PCM. • **Is a fault indicated?**	Yes No	▶ ▶	ISOLATE fault and SERVICE as necessary. CLEAR Continuous Memory Code RERUN Quick Test. GO to DF92.
DF92 CHECK PCM AND VEHICLE HARNESS CONNECTORS			
• Key off. • Disconnect PCM 60 pin connector. • Inspect connectors and connector terminals for obvious damage or faults. • **Are connectors and terminals OK?**	Yes No	▶ ▶	SERVICE as necessary. RERUN Quick Test. Unable to duplicate and / or identify fault at this time. further diagnosis, Intermittent Fault All others, CLEAR Continuous Memory RERUN Quick Test.

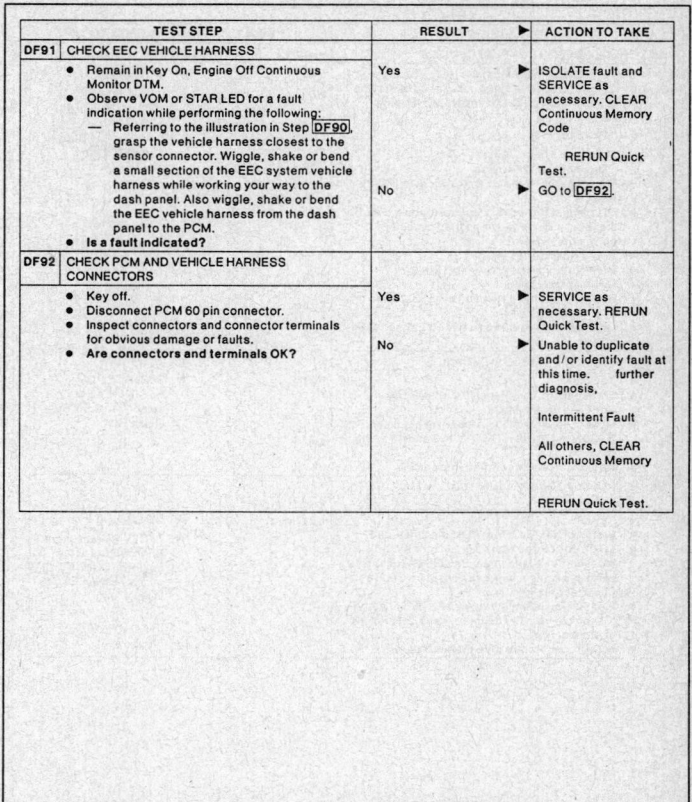

Fig. 176   Test DF: MAP/BARO Sensor (Part 10 of 10)

Note

You should enter this Pinpoint Test only when you have been directed here from Diagnostic Routines

Remember

To prevent the replacement of good components, be aware that the following non-EEC areas may be at fault:

• Fuel (quality)
• Basic engine
• Spark timing

This Pinpoint Test is intended to diagnose only the following:

• Knock sensor
• Harness circuits: KS and SIG RTN
• Powertrain Control Module (PCM)

Description

The knock sensor is used to detect engine detonation (spark knock). As a result, a voltage sent to the PCM will retard spark timing.

Fig. 177   Test DG: KS (Part 1 of 4)

FM0159300719010X

Pinpoint Test Schematics

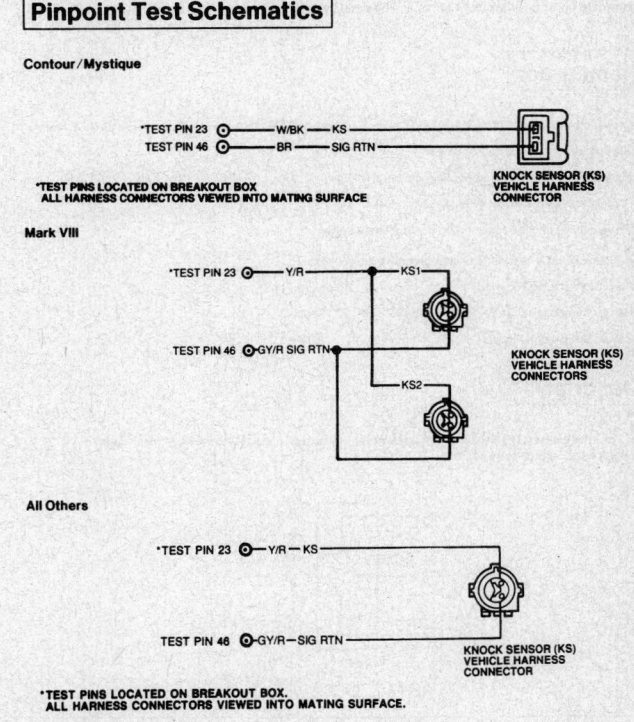

Contour / Mystique

Mark VIII

All Others

Fig. 177   Test DG: KS (Part 2 of 4)

FM0159300719020A

TEST STEP	RESULT	▶	ACTION TO TAKE
DG1 CHECK SENSOR VOLTAGE CYCLING			
DTC 25/225 indicates that the Knock Sensor (KS) signal to the PCM was not sensed during the Dynamic Response Test in the Key On Engine Running Self-Test. Possible causes are: — Damaged Knock Sensor. — Open or short in harness. — Damaged Powertrain Control Module (PCM). • Key off. • Disconnect Powertrain Control Module (PCM). Inspect for damaged or pushed out pins, corrosion, loose wires, etc. • Service as necessary. • Install breakout box, connect PCM. • Cycle the key to on. • Read DC voltage between Test Pins 23 and 46 at the breakout box. • **Is DC voltage reading between 2.4 and 2.6 volts?**	Yes No	▶ ▶	GO to **DG2**. For DC less than 2.4 volts, GO to **DG4**. For DC greater than 2.6 volt, GO to **DG5**.
DG2 CHECK FOR VOLTAGE INCREASE			
• Key off. • Breakout box installed, PCM connected. • Start and run engine. • Monitor voltage on the AC setting at idle and at 3,000 rpm between Test Pins 23 and 46 at the breakout box. • **Does AC voltage reading increase?**	Yes Nc	▶ ▶	REPLACE PCM. RECONNECT all components. RERUN Quick Test. GO to **DG3**.
DG3 CHECK CONTINUITY OF KS AND SIG RTN CIRCUITS			
• Key off. • Breakout box installed, PCM disconnected. • KS disconnected (both KS on Mark VIII). • Measure resistance between SIG RTN circuit at the KS vehicle harness connector and Test Pin 46 at breakout box. • Measure resistance between KS circuit at the KS vehicle harness connector and Test Pin 23 at breakout box. • **Is each resistance less than 5.0 ohms?**	Yes Nc	▶ ▶	GO to **DG4**. SERVICE open circuit. REMOVE breakout box. RECONNECT all components. RERUN Quick Test.

Fig. 177 Test DG: KS (Part 3 of 4)

TEST STEP	RESULT	▶	ACTION TO TAKE
DG4 CHECK KS CIRCUIT FOR SHORT TO GROUND			
• Key off. • Breakout box installed, PCM disconnected. • KS disconnected. • Measure resistance between Test Pin 23 and Test Pins 40, 46 and 60 at breakout box. • **Is each resistance greater than 10,000 ohms?**	Yes No	▶ ▶	REPLACE KS. REMOVE breakout box. RECONNECT PCM. RECONNECT all components. RERUN Quick Test, if Code 25/225 is still present, REPLACE PCM. SERVICE short circuit. REMOVE breakout box. RECONNECT all components. RERUN Quick Test.
DG5 CHECK KS CIRCUIT FOR SHORT TO POWER			
• Key off. • Breakout box installed, PCM disconnected. • KS disconnected (both KS on Mark VIII). • Key on, engine off. • Measure voltage between Test Pin 23 and Test Pin 40 at breakout box. • **Is voltage less than 0.5 volt?**	Yes No	▶ ▶	REPLACE PCM. REMOVE breakout box. RECONNECT all components. RERUN Quick Test. SERVICE short circuit. REMOVE breakout box. RECONNECT all components. RERUN Quick Test.

FM0159300719040X

Fig. 177 Test DG: KS (Part 4 of 4)

Note

You should enter this Pinpoint Test only when you have been directed here from Diagnostic Routines

Remember

To prevent the replacement of good components, be aware that the following non-EEC areas may be at fault:

• Idle speeds / throttle stop adjustment
• Binding throttle shaft / linkage or speed control linkage
• Choke / high cam system, if equipped
• TP sensor may not be seated properly (tightened down)

This Pinpoint Test is intended to diagnose only the following:

• Throttle Position (TP) sensor
• Sensor harness circuits: VREF, TP, and SIG RTN
• Powertrain Control Module (PCM)

Description

The Throttle Position (TP) Sensor is a potentiometer that provides a signal to the PCM that is directly proportional to throttle plate position.

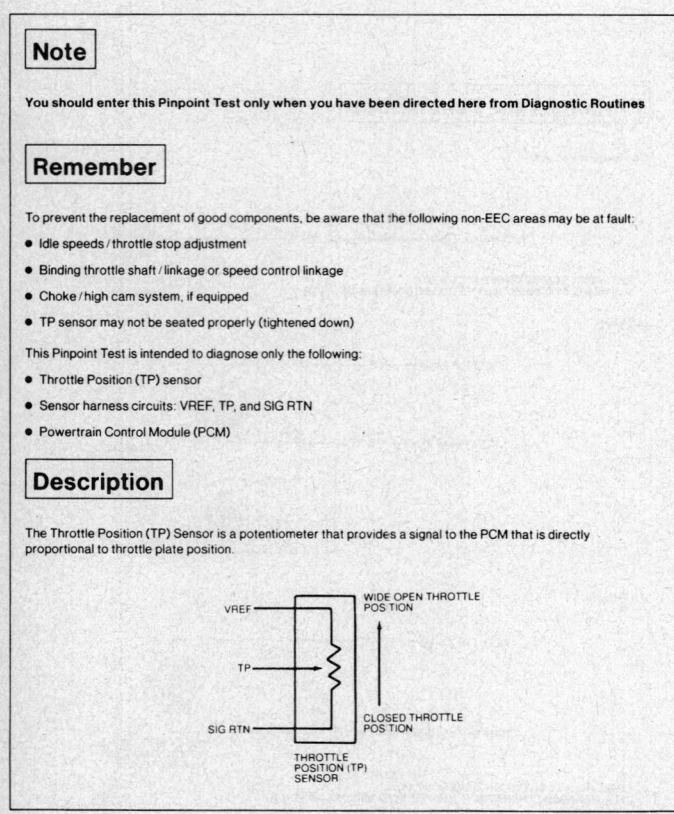

FM0159300720010X

Fig. 178 Test DH: TP Sensor (Part 1 of 12)

Pinpoint Test Schematics

2.0L SFI Probe

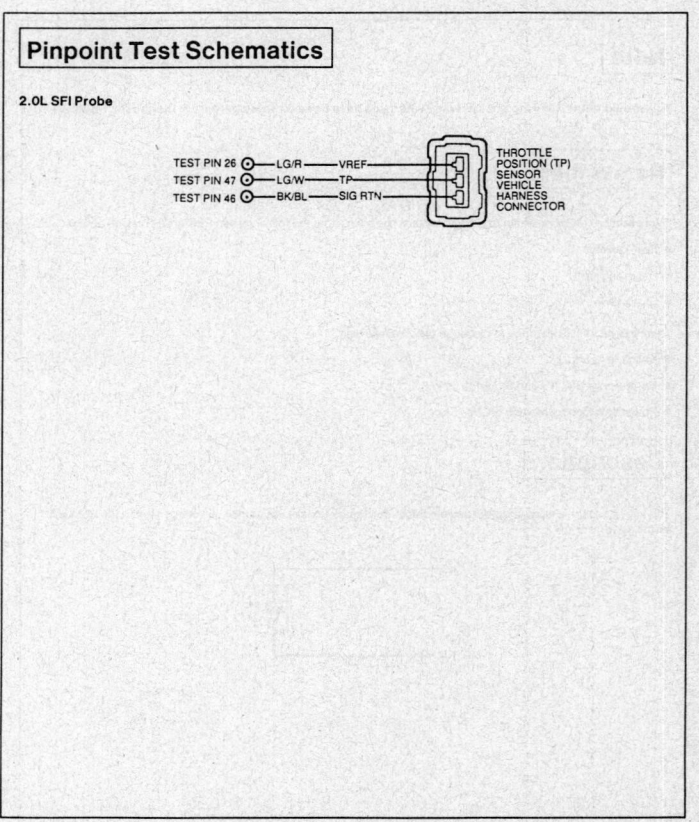

Fig. 178 Test DH: TP Sensor (Part 2 of 12). 1993

Pinpoint Test Schematics

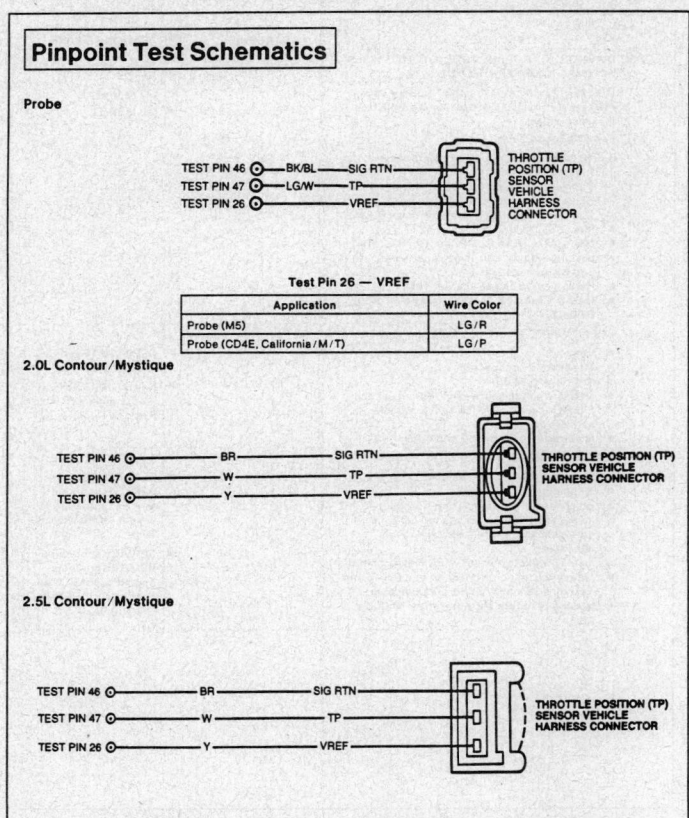

Fig. 178   Test DH: TP Sensor (Part 2 of 12). 1994–95

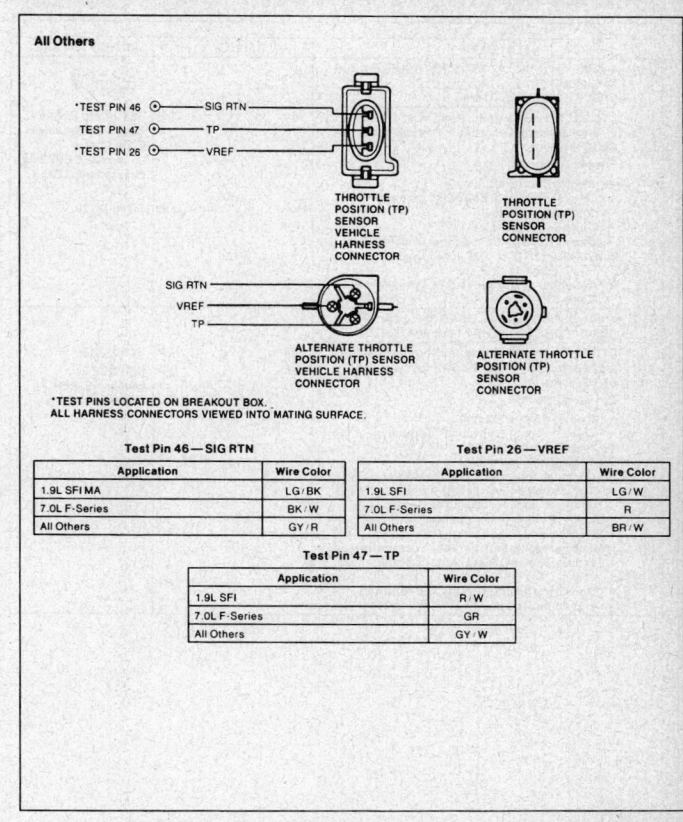

FM015930072003AX

Fig. 178   Test DH: TP Sensor (Part 3 of 12). 1993

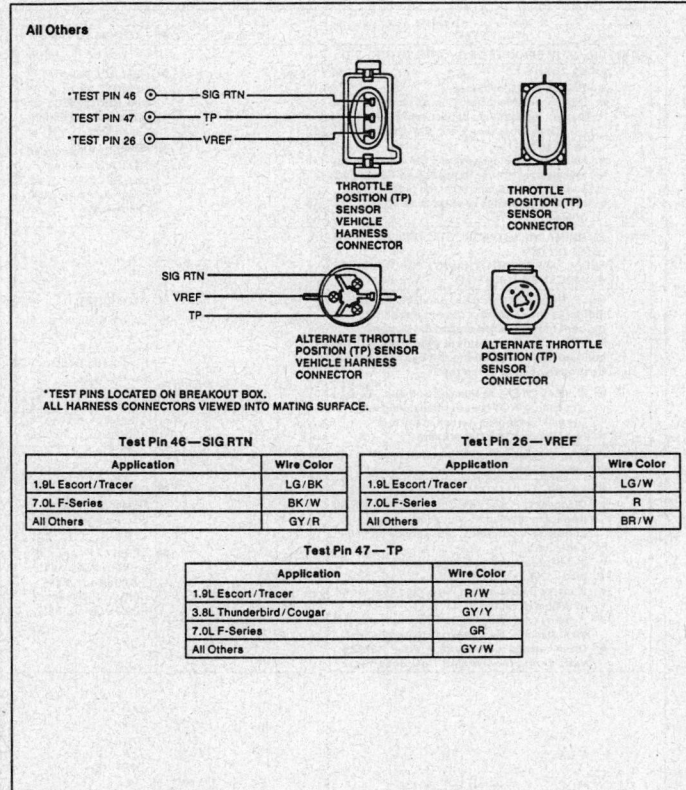

Fig. 178   Test DH: TP Sensor (Part 3 of 12). 1994–95

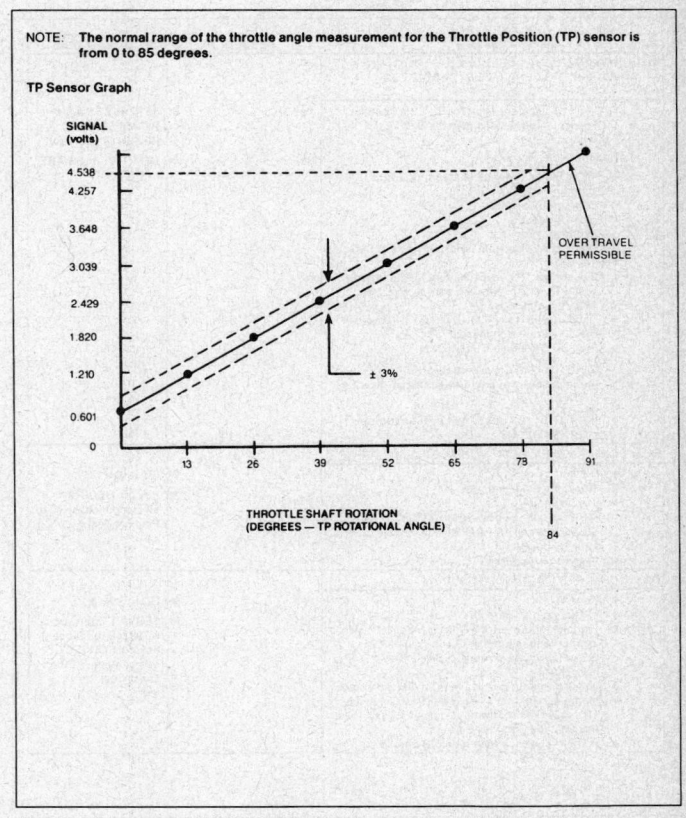

FM0159300720040X

Fig. 178   Test DH: TP Sensor (Part 4 of 12)

	TEST STEP	RESULT	▶	ACTION TO TAKE
DH1	ENGINE RUNNING DIAGNOSTIC TROUBLE CODE (DTC) 23 / 121: CHECK FOR OTHER DTCs			
	DTC 23 / 121 indicates that the Throttle Position (TP) sensor's rotational setting may be out of Self-Test range. Possible causes: — Binding throttle linkage. — TP sensor may not be seated properly (tightened down). — Damaged TP sensor. — Damaged Powertrain Control Module (PCM). ● Check for DTC 31/327 in Key On Engine Running Self-Test. ● **Are either of the above DTCs present with Code 23 or 121?**	Yes	▶	RETURN to EEC-IV Diagnostic Trouble Code Charts and PROCEED as directed with DTC 31/327.
		No	▶	GO to DH2.
DH2	DIAGNOSTIC TROUBLE CODE (DTC) 23/121: CHECK FOR STUCK THROTTLE PLATE			
	DTC 23 / 121 indicates that the Throttle Position (TP) sensor's rotational setting may be out of Self-Test range. Possible causes: — Binding throttle linkage. — TP sensor may not be seated properly (tightened down). — Damaged TP sensor. — Damaged Powertrain Control Module (PCM). ● Visually inspect carburetor / throttle body and throttle linkage for binding or sticking. ● Verify the throttle linkage is at mechanical / closed throttle. Check for: binding throttle linkage, speed control linkage, vacuum line / electrical harness interference, etc. ● **Does throttle move freely and return to closed throttle position?**	Yes	▶	GO to DH3.
		No	▶	SERVICE as necessary. RERUN Quick Test.

Fig. 178   Test DH: TP Sensor (Part 5 of 12)

	TEST STEP	RESULT	▶	ACTION TO TAKE
DH3	DIAGNOSTIC TROUBLE CODE (DTC) 53 / 123: ATTEMPT TO GENERATE DTC 63 / 122			
	DTC 53 / 123 indicates that the Throttle Position (TP) sensor signal is greater than the Self-Test maximum value. Possible causes are: — TP sensor may not be seated properly (tightened down). — Damaged TP sensor. — Short to power in harness. — Damaged Powertrain Control Module (PCM). ● Key off. ● Disconnect TP sensor. Inspect for damaged or pushed out pins, corrosion, loose wires, etc. Service as necessary. ● Rerun Key On Engine Off Self-Test. ● **Is DTC 63 or 122 present (ignore all other DTCs)?**	Yes	▶	GO to DH4.
		No	▶	GO to DH5.
DH4	CHECK VREF CIRCUIT VOLTAGE			
	● Key off. ● TP sensor disconnected. ● Key on, engine off. ● Measure voltage between VREF circuit and SIG RTN circuit at the TP sensor vehicle harness connector. ● **Is voltage between 4.0 and 6.0 volts?**	Yes	▶	REPLACE TP sensor. RERUN Quick Test.
		No	▶	Key off. RECONNECT all components. GO to Pinpoint Test Step C1.
DH5	CHECK TP CIRCUIT FOR SHORTS TO POWER			
	● Key off. ● TP sensor disconnected. ● Disconnect Powertrain Control Module (PCM). Inspect for damaged or pushed out pins, corrosion, loose wires, etc. Service as necessary. ● Install breakout box, leave PCM disconnected. ● Measure resistance between Test Pin 26 and Test Pins 26 and 57 at the breakout box. ● **Is each resistance greater than 10,000 ohms?**	Yes	▶	REPLACE PCM. REMOVE breakout box. RECONNECT TP sensor. RERUN Quick Test.
		No	▶	SERVICE short circuit. REMOVE breakout box. RECONNECT all components. RERUN Quick Test.

FM0159300720060X

Fig. 178   Test DH: TP Sensor (Part 6 of 12)

	TEST STEP	RESULT	▶	ACTION TO TAKE
DH10	DIAGNOSTIC TROUBLE CODE (DTC) 63 / 122: ATTEMPT TO GENERATE DTC 53 / 123 OR 23 / 121			
	DTC 63 / 122 indicates that the Throttle Position (TP) sensor signal is less than the Self-Test minimum value. Possible causes: — TP sensor may not be seated properly (tightened down). — Damaged TP sensor. — Open harness. — Grounded harness. — Damaged Powertrain Control Module (PCM). ● Key off. ● Disconnect TP sensor. Inspect for damaged or pushed out pins, corrosion, loose wires, etc. Service as necessary. ● Jumper VREF circuit to TP circuit at TP sensor vehicle harness connector. ● Run Key On Engine Off Self-Test. NOTE: If no DTC's are generated, immediately remove jumper and go directly to DH13. ● **Is DTC 53 / 123 or 23 / 121 present (ignore all other DTC's)?**	Yes	▶	REPLACE TP sensor. REMOVE jumper. RERUN Quick Test.
		No	▶	REMOVE jumper. GO to DH11.
DH11	CHECK VREF CIRCUIT VOLTAGE			
	● Key off. ● TP sensor disconnected. ● Key on engine off. ● Measure voltage between VREF circuit and SIG RTN circuit at the TP sensor vehicle harness connector. ● **Is voltage between 4.0 and 6.0 volts?**	Yes	▶	GO to DH12.
		No	▶	Key off. RECONNECT all components. GO to Pinpoint Test Step C1.
DH12	CHECK TP CIRCUIT CONTINUITY			
	● Key off. ● TP sensor disconnected. ● Disconnect Powertrain Control Module (PCM). Inspect for damaged or pushed out pins, corrosion, loose wires, etc. Service as necessary. ● Install breakout box, leave PCM disconnected. ● Measure resistance between TP circuit at the TP sensor vehicle harness connector and Test Pin 47 at the breakout box. ● **Is the resistance less than 5.0 ohms?**	Yes	▶	GO to DH13.
		No	▶	SERVICE open circuit. REMOVE breakout box. RECONNECT all components. RERUN Quick Test.

FM0159300720070X

Fig. 178   Test DH: TP Sensor (Part 7 of 12)

	TEST STEP	RESULT	▶	ACTION TO TAKE
DH13	CHECK TP CIRCUIT FOR SHORTS TO GROUND			
	● Key off. ● TP sensor disconnected. ● Disconnect Powertrain Control Module (PCM). Inspect for damaged or pushed out pins, corrosion, loose wires, etc. Service as necessary. ● Install breakout box, leave PCM disconnected. ● Measure resistance between Test Pin 47 and Test Pins 40, 46, and 60 at the breakout box. ● **Is each resistance greater than 10,000 ohms?**	Yes	▶	REPLACE PCM. REMOVE breakout box. RECONNECT all components. RERUN Quick Test.
		No	▶	SERVICE short circuit. REMOVE breakout box. RECONNECT all components. RERUN Quick Test.
DH20	ENGINE RUNNING DIAGNOSTIC TROUBLE CODE (DTC) 73 / 167: PERFORM PROPER DYNAMIC RESPONSE TEST AT WIDE OPEN THROTTLE			
	NOTE: Engine Running Service DTC 73 / 167 indicates the TP sensor did not exceed 25 percent of its rotation during the Dynamic Response Test. A complete wide open throttle must be performed during the Dynamic Response portion of the test. ● Run Key On Engine Running Self-Test. Be sure a complete WOT is performed during the Dynamic Response portion of the test. ● **Is DTC 73 or 167 still present?**	Yes	▶	GO to DH21.
		No	▶	Unable to duplicate DTC 73 / 167 at this time. Go to EEC-IV Diagnostic Trouble Code Charts, to service other Engine Running DTCs. Otherwise, testing completed.
DH21	CHECK TP SENSOR MOVEMENT DURING DYNAMIC RESPONSE TEST			
	● Key off. ● Disconnect Powertrain Control Module (PCM). Inspect for damaged or pushed out pins, corrosion, loose wires, etc. Service as necessary. ● Install breakout box and connect PCM to breakout box. ● Connect DVOM to Test Pin 47 and Test Pin 46 at the breakout box. ● Run Key On Engine Off Self-Test with a proper WOT Dynamic Response portion of the test. ● **Does voltage increase to greater than 3.5 volts during the Dynamic Response Test?**	Yes	▶	REPLACE PCM. REMOVE breakout box. RERUN Quick Test.
		No	▶	VERIFY TP sensor is properly installed on throttle body. If OK, REPLACE TP sensor. RERUN Quick Test.

FM0159300720080X

Fig. 178   Test DH: TP Sensor (Part 8 of 12)

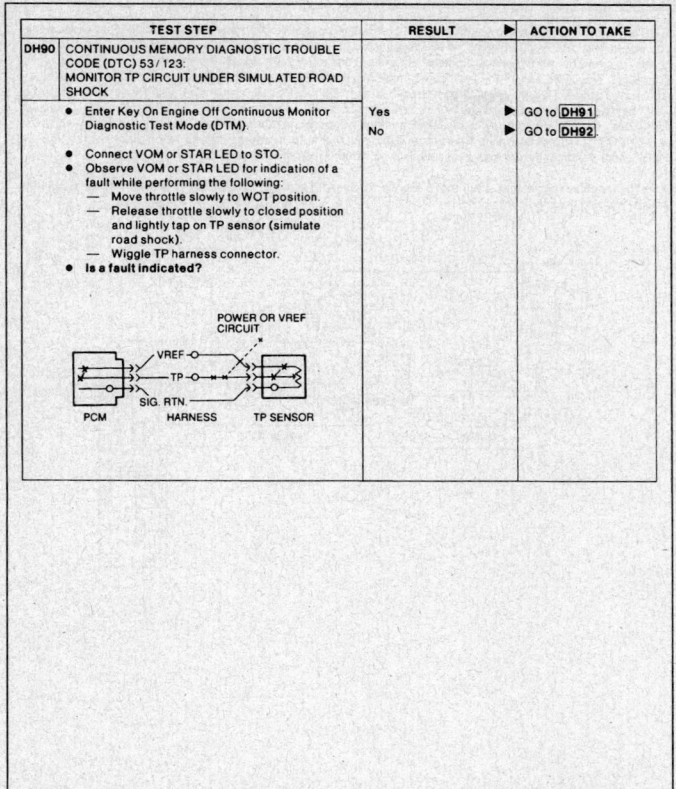

TEST STEP	RESULT	▶	ACTION TO TAKE
DH90 CONTINUOUS MEMORY DIAGNOSTIC TROUBLE CODE (DTC) 53 / 123: MONITOR TP CIRCUIT UNDER SIMULATED ROAD SHOCK			
• Enter Key On Engine Off Continuous Monitor Diagnostic Test Mode (DTM).	Yes	▶	GO to DH91.
	No	▶	GO to DH92.
• Connect VOM or STAR LED to STO. • Observe VOM or STAR LED for indication of a fault while performing the following: — Move throttle slowly to WOT position. — Release throttle slowly to closed position and lightly tap on TP sensor (simulate road shock). — Wiggle TP harness connector. • **Is a fault indicated?**			

Fig. 178   Test DH: TP Sensor (Part 9 of 12)

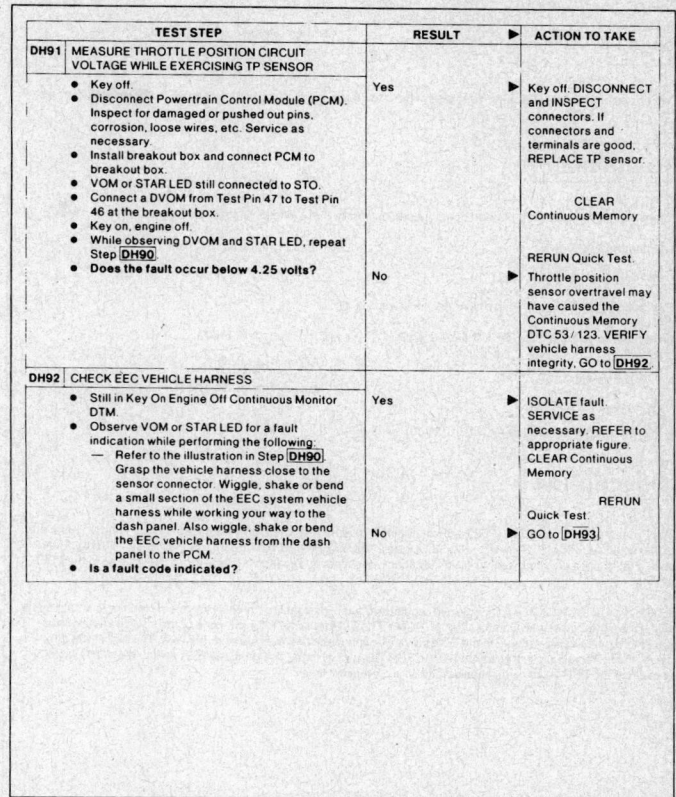

TEST STEP	RESULT	▶	ACTION TO TAKE
DH91 MEASURE THROTTLE POSITION CIRCUIT VOLTAGE WHILE EXERCISING TP SENSOR			
• Key off. • Disconnect Powertrain Control Module (PCM). Inspect for damaged or pushed out pins, corrosion, loose wires, etc. Service as necessary. • Install breakout box and connect PCM to breakout box. • VOM or STAR LED still connected to STO. • Connect a DVOM from Test Pin 47 to Test Pin 46 at the breakout box. • Key on, engine off. • While observing DVOM and STAR LED, repeat Step DH90. • **Does the fault occur below 4.25 volts?**	Yes	▶	Key off. DISCONNECT and INSPECT connectors. If connectors and terminals are good, REPLACE TP sensor. CLEAR Continuous Memory
	No	▶	RERUN Quick Test. Throttle position sensor overtravel may have caused the Continuous Memory DTC 53 / 123. VERIFY vehicle harness integrity. GO to DH92.
DH92 CHECK EEC VEHICLE HARNESS			
• Still in Key On Engine Off Continuous Monitor DTM. • Observe VOM or STAR LED for a fault indication while performing the following: — Refer to the illustration in Step DH90. Grasp the vehicle harness close to the sensor connector. Wiggle, shake or bend a small section of the EEC system vehicle harness while working your way to the dash panel. Also wiggle, shake or bend the EEC vehicle harness from the dash panel to the PCM. • **Is a fault code indicated?**	Yes	▶	ISOLATE fault. SERVICE as necessary. REFER to appropriate figure. CLEAR Continuous Memory RERUN Quick Test.
	No	▶	GO to DH93

Fig. 178   Test DH: TP Sensor (Part 10 of 12)

TEST STEP	RESULT	▶	ACTION TO TAKE
DH93 CHECK PCM AND HARNESS CONNECTORS			
• Key off. • Disconnect Powertrain Control Module (PCM). Inspect for damaged or pushed out pins, corrosion, loose wires, etc. Service as necessary. • **Are connectors and terminals OK?**	Yes	▶	SERVICE as necessary. CLEAR Continuous Memory RERUN Quick Test.
	No	▶	Unable to duplicate and / or identify fault at this time. further diagnosis. Intermittent Fault All others, CLEAR Continuous Memory RERUN Quick Test.
DH94 CONTINUOUS MEMORY DIAGNOSTIC TROUBLE CODE (DTC) 63 / 122: MONITOR TP CIRCUIT UNDER SIMULATED ROAD SHOCK			
• Enter Continuous Monitor Diagnostic Test Mode (DTM). • Connect VOM or STAR LED to STO. • Observe VOM or STAR LED for indication of a fault while performing the following: — Move throttle slowly to WOT position. — Release throttle slowly to closed position. — Lightly tap on TP sensor (simulate road shock). — Wiggle TP harness connector. • **Is a fault indicated?**	Yes	▶	Key off. INSPECT connectors. If connectors and terminals are good, REPLACE TP sensor. CLEAR Continuous Memory. RERUN Quick Test.
	No	▶	GO to DH95

Fig. 178   Test DH: TP Sensor (Part 11 of 12)

TEST STEP	RESULT	▶	ACTION TO TAKE
DH95 CHECK EEC VEHICLE HARNESS			
• Still in Key On Engine Off Continuous Monitor DTM. • Observe VOM or STAR LED for a fault indication while performing the following: — Refer to the illustration in Step DH94. Grasp the vehicle harness close to the sensor connector. Wiggle, shake or bend a small section of the EEC system vehicle harness while working your way to the dash panel. Also wiggle, shake or bend the EEC vehicle harness from the dash panel to the PCM. • **Is a fault indicated?**	Yes	▶	ISOLATE fault. SERVICE as necessary. REFER to appropriate figure. CLEAR Continuous Memory RERUN Quick Test.
	No	▶	GO to DH96.
DH96 CHECK PCM AND HARNESS CONNECTORS			
• Key off. • Disconnect PCM. Inspect for damaged or pushed out pins, corrosion, loose wires, etc. • **Are connectors and terminals OK?**	No	▶	SERVICE as necessary. CLEAR Continuous Memory.
	Yes	▶	RERUN Quick Test. Unable to duplicate and / or identify fault at this time. further diagnosis, Intermittent Fault All others, CLEAR Continuous Memory RERUN Quick Test.

Fig. 178   Test DH: TP Sensor (Part 12 of 12)

Note

You should enter this Pinpoint Test only when you have been directed here from Diagnostic Routines.

Remember

To prevent the replacement of good components, be aware that the following non-EEC areas may be at fault:

- Damaged EGR valve
- Restricted exhaust
- Damaged vacuum reservoir

This Pinpoint Test is intended to diagnose only the following:

- Harness circuits: VREF, DPFE, SIG RTN, EVR, VPWR
- PFE sensor (9D460)
- EVR solenoid (9J459)
- Powertrain Control Module (PCM) (12A650)
- DPFE sensor (9J460)
- EGR valve assembly
- Vacuum lines (EVR, PFE/DPFE)

Description

The Pressure Feedback EGR (PFE) system consists of a pressure sensor (PFE sensor), EGR Vacuum Regulator (EVR) solenoid, and a vacuum actuated EGR valve. The Differential Pressure Feedback EGR (DPFE) system uses a differential pressure sensor (DPFE sensor) which has two pressure inlets rather than one as in the PFE system.

In both type of systems, the EVR solenoid regulates a vacuum signal to the EGR valve in response to a duty cycle signal from the Powertrain Control Module (PCM). The EVR solenoid will vent some of the source vacuum and transmit the remaining vacuum to the EGR valve in response to the level of the duty cycle. The higher the duty cycle, the more vacuum is transmitted to the EGR valve. Due to the design of the EVR solenoid, the available vacuum at the EGR valve never reaches the source vacuum level.

EGR flow rate is determined by monitoring the pressure across a fixed metering orifice as exhaust gasses pass through it. The DPFE system monitors this flow across the orifice directly by supplying the DPFE sensor with a pressure signal before the orifice (upstream pressure) and a pressure signal after the orifice (downstream pressure). The DPFE sensor then evaluates these two pressure inputs and determines the pressure difference across the orifice. This pressure difference translates to a specific EGR flow which the DPFE sensor signals the PCM by means of an analog voltage signal. This signal to the PCM increases linearly as the differential pressure increases. The PFE system, unlike the DPFE system, has only one pressure signal input (downstream) and must rely on the PCM to indirectly infer the upstream exhaust pressure in order to determine the EGR flow rate. The PFE sensor transmits an analog voltage signal which decreases linearly as EGR flow increases.

With the feedback signal that either the PFE or DPFE sensors provide, the PCM can then optimize the EGR flow rate by varying the EVR duty cycle.

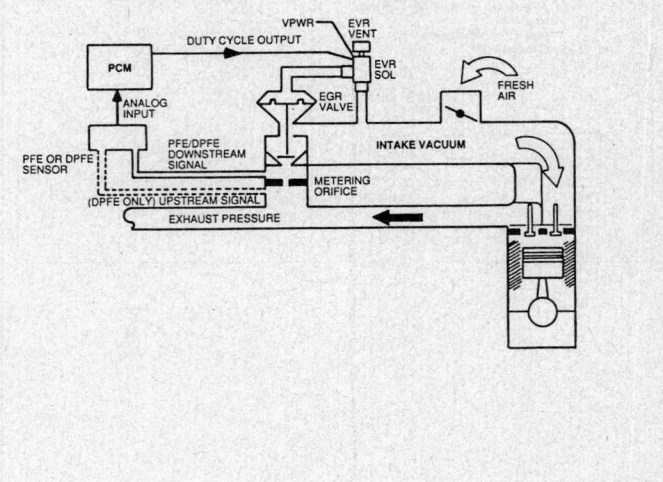

Fig. 179   Test DL: PFE/DPFE Sensor/EVR Solenoid (Part 1 of 27)

Fig. 179   Test DL: PFE/DPFE Sensor/EVR Solenoid (Part 2 of 27)

NOTE: Voltage values calculated for VREF = 5.0 volts. These values may vary ±15 percent due to sensor and VREF variations.

PFE Sensor Graph

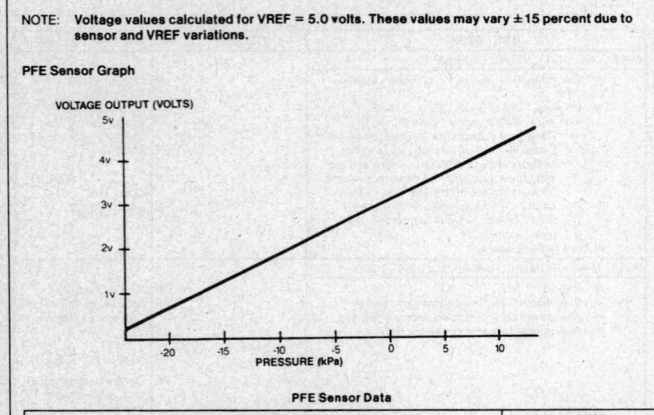

PFE Sensor Data

PRESSURE/VACUUM			VOLTAGE
PSI	in-Hg	kPa	Volts
1.82	3.70	12.5	4.75
1.36	2.79	9.42	4.38
0.91	1.85	6.25	4.0
0.46	0.94	3.17	3.63
0	0	0	3.25
-2.47	-5.03	-17.0	1.22
-3.63	-7.40	-25.0	0.25

CAUTION

To avoid possible sensor damage do not exceed pressure/vacuum range shown when testing.

NOTE: Voltage values calculated for VREF = 5.0 volts.

DPFE Sensor Graph

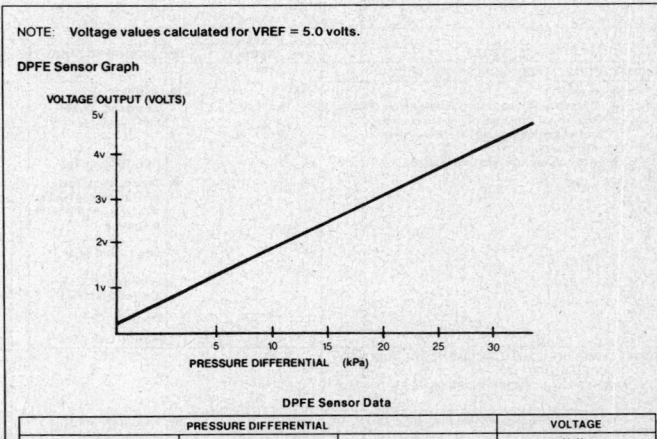

DPFE Sensor Data

PRESSURE DIFFERENTIAL			VOLTAGE
PSI	in-Hg	kPa	Volts
4.34	8.83	29.81	4.56
3.25	6.62	22.36	3.54
2.17	4.41	14.90	2.51
1.08	2.21	7.46	1.48
0	0	0	0.45

FM0159300721030X

Fig. 179   Test DL: PFE/DPFE Sensor/EVR Solenoid (Part 3 of 27)

FM0159300721040X

Fig. 179   Test DL: PFE/DPFE Sensor/EVR Solenoid (Part 4 of 27)

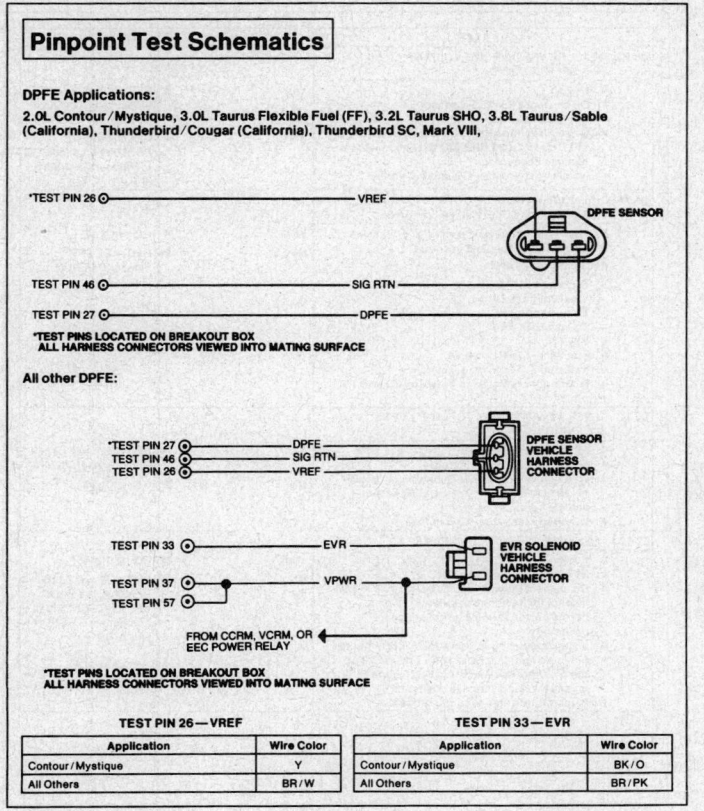

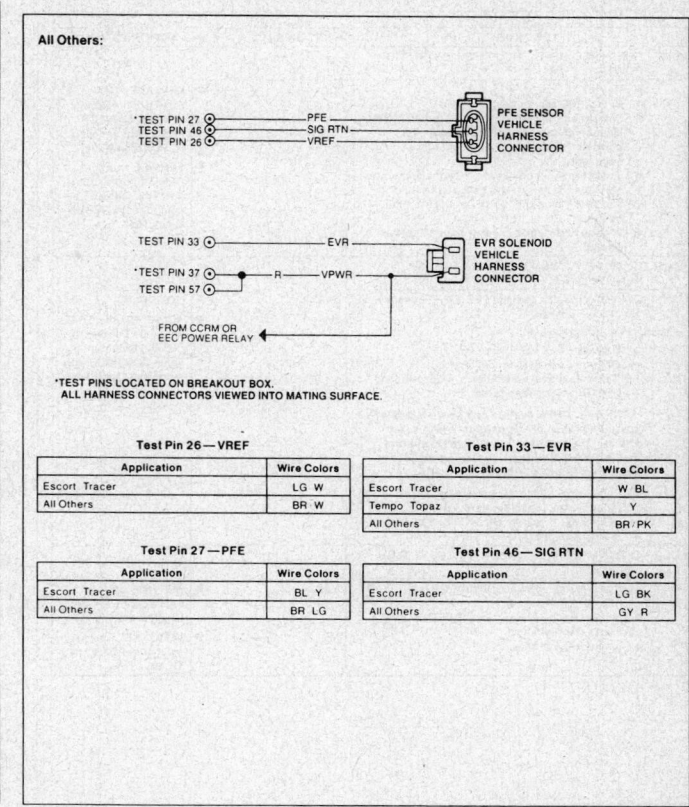

Fig. 179   Test DL: PFE/DPFE Sensor/EVR Solenoid (Part 5 of 27)

FM0159300721050A

Fig. 179   Test DL: PFE/DPFE Sensor/EVR Solenoid (Part 6 of 27)

FM0159300721060X

	TEST STEP	RESULT	▶	ACTION TO TAKE
DL1	DIAGNOSTIC TROUBLE CODE (DTC) 327: INDUCE DTC 337			
	DTC 327 indicates that the PFE/DPFE sensor signal is less than the Self Test minimum value of 0.2 volt. Possible causes: — Damaged PFE/DPFE sensor. — Open harness circuits. — Shorted harness circuits. — Damaged PCM. ● Key off. ● Disconnect PFE/DPFE sensor. ● Jumper VREF circuit to PFE/DPFE circuit at PFE/DPFE sensor vehicle harness connector. ● Rerun Key On, Engine Off (KOEO) Self-Test. NOTE: If no DTC's are generated, immediately remove jumper and go directly to Step DL4. ● **Is DTC 337 present (ignore all other DTC's)?**	Yes No	▶ ▶	REPLACE PFE/DPFE sensor. REMOVE jumper. RERUN Quick Test. REMOVE jumper. GO to DL2.
DL2	MEASURE VREF CIRCUIT VOLTAGE AT PFE/DPFE SENSOR			
	● Key off. ● PFE/DPFE sensor disconnected. ● Key on, engine off. ● Measure voltage between VREF circuit and SIG RTN circuit at the PFE/DPFE sensor vehicle harness connector. ● **Is voltage between 4.0 and 6.0 volts?**	Yes No	▶ ▶	GO to DL3. GO to Pinpoint Test Step C1.
DL3	CHECK PFE/DPFE CIRCUIT CONTINUITY			
	● Key off. ● PFE/DPFE sensor disconnected. ● Disconnect Powertrain Control Module (PCM). Inspect for damaged or pushed out pins, corrosion, loose wires, etc. Service as necessary. ● Install breakout box, leave PCM disconnected. ● Measure resistance between PFE/DPFE circuit at the PFE/DPFE sensor vehicle harness connector and Test Pin 27 at the breakout box. ● **Is resistance less than 5.0 ohms?**	Yes No	▶ ▶	GO to DL4. SERVICE open circuit. REMOVE breakout box. RECONNECT all components. RERUN Quick Test.

	TEST STEP	RESULT	▶	ACTION TO TAKE
DL4	CHECK PFE/DPFE CIRCUIT FOR SHORTS TO GROUND AND SIG RTN			
	● Key off. ● PFE/DPFE sensor disconnected. ● Breakout box installed, PCM disconnected. ● Measure resistance between Test Pin 27 and Test Pins 40, 46 and 60 at the breakout box. ● **Is each resistance greater than 10,000 ohms?**	Yes No	▶ ▶	REPLACE PCM. REMOVE breakout box. RECONNECT all components. RERUN Quick Test. SERVICE short circuit. REMOVE breakout box. RECONNECT all components. RERUN Quick Test.
DL5	DIAGNOSTIC TROUBLE CODE (DTC) 337: INDUCE DTC 327			
	DTC 337 indicates that the PFE/DPFE sensor signal is greater than the Self-Test maximum value of 4.8 volts. Possible causes are: — Damaged PFE/DPFE sensor. — Shorted harness circuits. — Open SIG RTN circuit. — Damaged PCM. ● Key off. ● Disconnect PFE/DPFE sensor. ● Rerun Key On, Engine Off (KOEO) Self Test. ● **Is DTC 327 present (ignore all other DTC's)?**	Yes No	▶ ▶	GO to DL6. GO to DL7.
DL6	MEASURE VREF CIRCUIT VOLTAGE AT PFE/DPFE SENSOR			
	● Key off. ● PFE/DPFE sensor disconnected. ● Key on, engine off. ● Measure voltage between VREF circuit and SIG RTN circuit at the PFE/DPFE sensor vehicle harness connector. ● **Is voltage between 4.0 and 6.0 volts?**	Yes No	▶ ▶	REPLACE PFE/DPFE sensor. RERUN Quick Test. GO to Pinpoint Test Step C1.

Fig. 179   Test DL: PFE/DPFE Sensor/EVR Solenoid (Part 7 of 27)

FM0159300721070X

Fig. 179   Test DL: PFE/DPFE Sensor/EVR Solenoid (Part 8 of 27)

FM0159300721080X

TEST STEP		RESULT	▶	ACTION TO TAKE
DL7	CHECK PFE/DPFE CIRCUIT FOR SHORTS TO POWER			
	• Key off. • PFE/DPFE sensor disconnected. • Disconnect Powertrain Control Module (PCM). Inspect for damaged or pushed out pins, corrosion, loose wires, etc. Service as necessary. • Install breakout box, leave PCM disconnected. • Measure the resistance between Test Pin 27 and Test Pins 26, 37 and 57 at the breakout box. • **Is each resistance greater than 10,000 ohms?**	Yes No	▶ ▶	REPLACE PCM. REMOVE breakout box. RECONNECT PFE/DPFE sensor. RERUN Quick Test. SERVICE short circuit. REMOVE breakout box. RECONNECT all components. RERUN Quick Test.
DL8	DIAGNOSTIC TROUBLE CODE (DTC) 335: REMOVE GARAGE FORCED AIR			
	DTC 335 indicates that the PFE/DPFE sensor is out of Self-Test range. Possible causes are: — Damaged PFE/DPFE sensor. — Obstructed pressure inlet hose(s). — Garage exhaust ventilation system affecting PFE/DPFE sensor operation. NOTE: PFE/DPFE system can sense a lack of pressure in the vehicle exhaust system. An efficient garage exhaust ventilation system that is installed during Key On Engine Off (KOEO) DTM may generate a DTC 335. • Remove garage forced ventilation system and properly vent to atmosphere. • Rerun Key On Engine Off (KOEO) Self-Test. • **Is DTC 335 present?**	Yes No	▶ ▶	GO to DL9. ADDRESS other DTC's in Key On Engine Off (KOEO) Self-Test. If none, CONTINUE with remaining Quick Test.
DL9	CHECK PFE/DPFE SENSOR PRESSURE INPUT HOSE(S)			
	• Remove each pressure input hose from PFE/DPFE sensor. • Inspect each hose and PFE/DPFE sensor inlet(s) for blockage. • **Is blockage present?**	Yes No	▶ ▶	SERVICE as necessary. RERUN Quick Test. RECONNECT pressure input hose(s). GO to DL10.

FM0159300721090X

Fig. 179   Test DL: PFE/DPFE Sensor/EVR Solenoid (Part 9 of 27)

TEST STEP		RESULT	▶	ACTION TO TAKE
DL10	MEASURE VREF CIRCUIT VOLTAGE AT PFE/DPFE SENSOR			
	• Key off. • Disconnect PFE/DPFE sensor. • Key on, engine off. • Measure voltage between VREF circuit and SIG RTN circuit at PFE/DPFE sensor vehicle harness connector. • **Is voltage between 4.0 and 6.0 volts?**	Yes No	▶ ▶	REPLACE PFE/DPFE sensor. RERUN Quick Test. RECONNECT PFE/DPFE sensor. GO to Pinpoint Test Step C1.
DL11	DIAGNOSTIC TROUBLE CODE (DTC) 558: MEASURE EVR SOLENOID RESISTANCE			
	DTC 558 indicates a failure in the EGR Vacuum Regulator (EVR) solenoid or circuit. Possible causes are: — Damaged EVR solenoid. — Open harness circuit. — Shorted harness. — Damaged PCM. • Key off. • Disconnect EVR solenoid. • Measure EVR solenoid resistance. • **Is solenoid resistance between 20 and 70 ohms?**	Yes No	▶ ▶	GO to DL12. REPLACE EVR solenoid. RERUN Quick Test.
DL12	CHECK VPWR CIRCUIT VOLTAGE AT EVR SOLENOID			
	• Key on, engine off. • EVR solenoid disconnected. • Measure voltage between battery negative terminal and VPWR circuit at EVR solenoid vehicle harness connector. • **Is voltage less than 10.5 volts?**	Yes No	▶ ▶	SERVICE open circuit. RERUN Quick Test. GO to DL13.
DL13	CHECK EVR CIRCUIT CONTINUITY			
	• Key off. • EVR solenoid disconnected. • Disconnect Powertrain Control Module (PCM). Inspect for damaged or pushed out pins, corrosion, loose wires, etc. Service as necessary. • Install breakout box, leave PCM disconnected. • Measure resistance between Test Pin 33 at the breakout box and EVR circuit at the EVR solenoid vehicle harness connector. • **Is resistance less than 5.0 ohms?**	Yes No	▶ ▶	GO to DL14. SERVICE open circuit. REMOVE breakout box. RECONNECT all components. RERUN Quick Test.

FM0159300721100X

Fig. 179   Test DL: PFE/DPFE Sensor/EVR Solenoid (Part 10 of 27).

TEST STEP		RESULT	▶	ACTION TO TAKE
DL14	CHECK EVR CIRCUIT FOR SHORTS TO POWER OR GROUND			
	• Key off. • EVR solenoid disconnected. • Breakout box installed, PCM disconnected. • Measure resistance between Test Pin 33 and Test Pins 37 and 57 at the breakout box. • Measure resistance between Test Pin 33 and Test Pins 40 and 60 at the breakout box. • **Is each resistance greater than 10,000 ohms?**	Yes No	▶ ▶	REPLACE PCM. REMOVE breakout box. RECONNECT all components. RERUN Quick Test. SERVICE short circuit. REMOVE breakout box. RECONNECT all components. RERUN Quick Test. If DTC 558 is repeated, REPLACE PCM.
DL20	DIAGNOSTIC TROUBLE CODE (DTC) 326: REMOVE GARAGE FORCED VENTILATION			
	DTC 326 indicates that the PFE circuit voltage is lower than expected at zero EVR duty cycle. Possible causes are: — Obstructed vacuum hose. — Contaminated EVR filter. — Damaged EGR valve. — Damaged EVR solenoid. — Garage exhaust ventilation system. NOTE: PFE system can sense a lack of pressure in the vehicle exhaust system. An efficient garage exhaust ventilation system that is installed during Key On Engine Running (KOER) Self-Test may generate a DTC 326. • Remove garage forced ventilation system and properly vent to atmosphere. • Rerun KOER Self-Test. • **Is DTC 326 present?**	Yes No	▶ ▶	GO to DL21. ADDRESS other DTC's in KOER Self-Test. If none, CONTINUE with remaining Quick-Test.
DL21	DIAGNOSTIC TROUBLE CODE (DTC) 327: RERUN SELF-TEST WITH EGR VALVE VACUUM LINE DISCONNECTED			
	DTC 327 indicates that the PFE sensor signal is less than the Self-Test minimum. • Key off. • Disconnect EGR valve vacuum line at valve and plug vacuum line. • Perform Key On Engine Running (KOER) Self-Test. • **Is DTC 327 or 326 present?**	Yes No	▶ ▶	GO to DL22. CHECK EVR vent on vacuum hose to EGR valve for obstruction. If OK, REPLACE EVR solenoid. RECONNECT all lines. RERUN Quick Test.

FM0159300721110X

Fig. 179   Test DL: PFE/DPFE Sensor/EVR Solenoid (Part 11 of 27)

TEST STEP		RESULT	▶	ACTION TO TAKE
DL22	DIAGNOSTIC TROUBLE CODE (DTC) 326 OR 327: INSPECT PFE/DPFE INPUT HOSES			
	DTC 326 or 327 indicates that DPFE circuit voltage is lower than expected at zero duty cycle. • Key off. • Check PFE/DPFE sensor pressure input hose(s) for obstruction and/or leaks? • **Are there any obstructions or leaks?**	Yes No	▶ ▶	SERVICE as necessary. RECONNECT all lines. RERUN Quick Test. GO to DL23.
DL23	CHECK PFE/DPFE SIGNAL VOLTAGE WITH ENGINE AT IDLE			
	• Key off. • Disconnect Powertrain Control Module (PCM). Inspect for damaged or pushed out pins, corrosion, loose wires, etc. Service as necessary. • Install breakout box and connect PCM to breakout box. • Start engine and idle with transmission in PARK or NEUTRAL. • Measure voltage between Test Pin 27 and Test Pin 46 at the breakout box. • **Is voltage less than 2.9 volts (PFE) or 0.2 volt (DPFE)?**	Yes No	▶ ▶	REPLACE DPFE sensor. REMOVE breakout box. RECONNECT all components. RERUN Quick Test. GO to DL24. REPLACE PCM. REMOVE breakout box. RECONNECT all components. RERUN Quick Test.
DL24	CHECK EGR VALVE FOR BINDING			
	The fault has been isolated to either the EGR valve or PFE sensor. Due to the nature of this particular fault, the EGR valve is suspect because of its vulnerability to contamination and carbon build up from the exhaust flow. If the engine runs rough at idle, this is a good indication that the EGR valve is not fully seated rather than a faulty PFE sensor. • Remove the EGR valve. • Inspect the EGR valve for signs of contamination, unusual wear, carbon deposits, binding, and other damage. Service as necessary. (Use Rotunda EGR Valve Cleaner 021-80056 or equivalent if needed) • Re-install EGR valve and rerun Key On Engine Running (KOER) Self-Test. • **Is DTC 326 or 327 still present?**	Yes No	▶ ▶	REPLACE EGR valve. REMOVE breakout box. RERUN Quick Test. If either DTC is still present, REPLACE PFE sensor. The original DTC 326 or 327 was the result of the EGR valve not fully seating. Testing complete.

FM015930072112AX

Fig. 179   Test DL: PFE/DPFE Sensor/EVR Solenoid (Part 12 of 27). 1993

TEST STEP	RESULT	▶	ACTION TO TAKE
DL22 DIAGNOSTIC TROUBLE CODE (DTC) 326 OR 327: INSPECT PFE/DPFE INPUT HOSES			
DTC 326 or 327 indicates that DPFE circuit voltage is lower than expected at zero duty cycle. • Key off. • Check PFE/DPFE sensor pressure input hose(s) for obstruction and/or leaks. • Are there any obstructions or leaks?	Yes	▶	SERVICE as necessary. RECONNECT all lines. RERUN Quick Test.
	No	▶	GO to DL23 .
DL23 CHECK PFE/DPFE SIGNAL VOLTAGE WITH ENGINE AT IDLE			
• Key off. • Disconnect Powertrain Control Module (PCM). Inspect for damaged or pushed out pins, corrosion, loose wires, etc. Service as necessary. • Install breakout box and connect PCM to breakout box. • Start engine and idle with transmission in PARK or NEUTRAL. • Measure voltage between Test Pin 27 and Test Pin 46 at the breakout box. • Is voltage less than 2.9 volts (PFE) or 0.2 volt (DPFE)?	Yes	▶	For DPFE applications: REPLACE DPFE sensor. REMOVE breakout box. RECONNECT all components. RERUN Quick Test. For PFE applications: GO to DL24 .
	No	▶	REPLACE PCM. REMOVE breakout box. RECONNECT all components. RERUN Quick Test.
DL24 CHECK EGR VALVE FOR BINDING			
The fault has been isolated to either the EGR valve or PFE sensor. Due to the nature of this particular fault, the EGR valve is suspect because of its vulnerability to contamination and carbon build-up from the exhaust flow. If the engine runs rough at idle, this is a good indication that the EGR valve is not fully seated rather than a faulty PFE sensor. • Remove the EGR valve. • Inspect the EGR valve for signs of contamination, unusual wear, carbon deposits, binding, and other damage. Service as necessary. (Use Rotunda EGR Valve Cleaner 021-80056 or equivalent if needed) • Re-install EGR valve and rerun Key On Engine Running (KOER) Self-Test. • Is DTC 326 or 327 still present?	Yes	▶	REPLACE EGR valve. REMOVE breakout box. RERUN Quick Test. If either DTC is still present, REPLACE PFE sensor.
	No	▶	The original DTC 326 or 327 was the result of the EGR valve not fully seating. Testing complete.

Fig. 179 Test DL: PFE/DPFE Sensor/EVR Solenoid (Part 12 of 27). 1994–95

TEST STEP	RESULT	▶	ACTION TO TAKE
DL25 ENGINE RUNNING DIAGNOSTIC TROUBLE CODE (DTC) 336 OR 337: CHECK FOR EXHAUST RESTRICTION:			
DTC 336 indicates that the PFE circuit voltage is higher than expected at zero EVR duty cycle. DTC 337 indicates that the PFE circuit voltage is above the Self-Test maximum. Possible causes: — Restricted exhaust system — Damaged PFE sensor or PCM — Open harness circuits — Shorted harness circuits • Attach vacuum gauge to intake manifold source. • Hook up tachometer. • Observe the vacuum gauge needle while performing the following: — Start engine and gradually increase the rpm from base idle to 2000 rpm with the transmission in NEUTRAL. — Observe the rate of speed of the vacuum gauge needle as it falls and rises while maintaining the increased engine rpm and also note final vacuum reading. NOTE: On a non-restricted system, the vacuum gauge needle will drop to zero and then quickly return to normal (above 16 in.) without delay. On a restricted system, the vacuum gauge needle will slowly drop to zero and slowly rise as rpm is maintained. The rate of speed at which the vacuum gauge needle returns to normal is much slower on a restricted system. • Is the rate of speed that the vacuum gauge needle returns to normal quick and a vacuum of 16 inches minimum is reached?	Yes	▶	No restriction in the exhaust system. GO to DL26 .
	No	▶	REFER to Catalyst and Exhaust Systems for further diagnosis.

FM0159300721130X

Fig. 179 Test DL: PFE/DPFE Sensor/EVR Solenoid (Part 13 of 27)

TEST STEP	RESULT	▶	ACTION TO TAKE
DL26 CHECK PFE SIGNAL VOLTAGE			
• Key off. • Disconnect Powertrain Control Module (PCM). Inspect for damaged or pushed out pins, corrosion, loose wires, etc. Service as necessary. • Install breakout box and connect PCM to breakout box. • Start engine and idle with transmission in PARK or NEUTRAL. • Measure voltage between Test Pin 27 and Test Pin 46 at the breakout box. • Is voltage between 3.0 and 3.5 volts?	Yes	▶	REPLACE PCM. RECONNECT all components. RERUN Quick Test.
	No	▶	GO to DL27 .
DL27 CHECK PFE AND SIG RTN HARNESS CIRCUIT CONTINUITY			
• Key off. • Breakout box connected, PCM disconnected. • PFE sensor disconnected. • Measure resistance between PFE circuit at the sensor vehicle harness connector and Test Pin 27 at the breakout box. • Measure resistance between PFE SIG RTN circuit at the sensor vehicle harness connector and Test Pin 46 at the breakout box. • Is each resistance less than 5.0 ohms?	Yes	▶	GO to DL28 .
	No	▶	SERVICE open circuit(s). REMOVE breakout box. RECONNECT all components. RERUN Quick Test.
DL28 CHECK PFE HARNESS CIRCUIT FOR SHORTS TO POWER			
• Key off. • Breakout box connected, PCM disconnected. • PFE sensor disconnected. • Measure resistance between Test Pin 27 and Test Pins 26, 37, and 57 at the breakout box. • Is each resistance greater than 10,000 ohms?	Yes	▶	REPLACE PFE sensor. REMOVE breakout box. RECONNECT all components. RERUN Quick Test.
	No	▶	SERVICE short circuit(s). REMOVE breakout box. RECONNECT all components. RERUN Quick Test.

Fig. 179 Test DL: PFE/DPFE Sensor/EVR Solenoid (Part 14 of 27)

TEST STEP	RESULT	▶	ACTION TO TAKE
DL30 DIAGNOSTIC TROUBLE CODE (DTC) 332: VERIFY VACUUM IS PRESENT AT EGR VALVE			
DTC 332 indicates that the PFE/DPFE sensor signal to the Powertrain Control Module (PCM) did not change when the PCM output a duty cycle to the EVR solenoid requesting EGR flow. Possible causes are: — Vacuum hose leaks. — Obstructed vacuum hoses. — Damaged EVR solenoid. — Damaged PFE/DPFE sensor. — Damaged EGR valve. — Damaged PCM. • Key off. • Disconnect and inspect vacuum hose between EVR solenoid and EGR valve for blockage, kinks, etc. Service as necessary and reconnect after inspection. • Disconnect vacuum hose at EGR valve and connect hose to a vacuum gauge. • Rerun Key On Engine Running (KOER) Self-Test while observing vacuum gauge. • Is vacuum reading less than 1 in-Hg (3kPa) throughout the test (disregard DTC output)?	Yes	▶	REMOVE vacuum gauge. GO to DL31 .
	No	▶	REMOVE vacuum gauge. RECONNECT EGR valve vacuum hose. RERUN Quick Test if the vacuum hose was not in good condition and service was completed. Otherwise, GO to DL34 .
DL31 CHECK VACUUM INPUT TO THE EVR SOLENOID			
• Key off. • Disconnect source vacuum hose at EVR Solenoid and connect hose to a vacuum gauge. • Start the engine and let it idle while observing the vacuum gauge. • Is vacuum above 15 inches at idle?	Yes	▶	INSPECT vacuum hose from EVR Solenoid to EGR valve. If OK, REPLACE EVR solenoid. RERUN Quick Test.
	No	▶	REPLACE the vacuum line connecting EVR solenoid to source vacuum. RERUN Quick Test.

FM0159300721150X

Fig. 179 Test DL: PFE/DPFE Sensor/EVR Solenoid (Part 15 of 27)

TEST STEP	RESULT	▶	ACTION TO TAKE
DL34 CHECK SIGNAL AT THE PFE/DPFE INLET HOSE(S)			
• Key off.	Yes	▶	REMOVE vacuum gauge. RERUN Quick Test if the inlet hose(s) needed service. If service was not needed, then GO to **DL35**.
• Disconnect and inspect the PFE/DPFE inlet hose(s) for kinks, blockages, etc. Service as necessary and reconnect after inspection.			
• Tee in a standard vacuum gauge at the PFE/DPFE inlet hose (downstream signal).			
• Rerun Key On Engine Running (KOER) Self-Test.	No	▶	REMOVE and INSPECT the EGR valve for signs of contamination, unusual wear, carbon deposits, grinding, and other damage. SERVICE as necessary (use Rotunda 021-80056 EGR valve cleaner if needed). RERUN Quick Test.
• **Is there a momentary increase in vacuum gauge reading during KOER Self-Test (indicating EGR valve is opening?**			
DL35 ATTEMPT TO GENERATE KOEO DTC 337			
• Key off.	Yes	▶	REPLACE PFE/DPFE sensor. REMOVE jumper wire. RERUN Quick Test.
• Disconnect PFE/DPFE sensor.			
• Jumper VREF circuit to PFE/DPFE circuit at the PFE/DPFE sensor vehicle harness connector.			
• Perform KOEO Self-Test.	No	▶	REMOVE jumper. GO to **DL36**.
NOTE: If no DTC's are generated, immediately remove jumper and go directly to **DL37**.			
• **Is DTC 337 present (ignore all other DTC's)?**			
DL36 MEASURE VREF CIRCUIT VOLTAGE			
• Key off.	Yes	▶	GO to **DL37**.
• PFE/DPFE disconnected.			
• Key on, engine off.	No	▶	GO to Pinpoint Test Step **C1**.
• Measure voltage between VREF circuit and SIG RTN circuit at the PFE/DPFE sensor vehicle harness connector.			
• **Is voltage between 4.0 and 6.0 volts?**			

FM015930072160X

Fig. 179 Test DL: PFE/DPFE Sensor/EVR Solenoid (Part 16 of 27)

TEST STEP	RESULT	▶	ACTION TO TAKE
DL37 CHECK PFE/DPFE HARNESS CIRCUIT CONTINUITY			
• Key off.	Yes	▶	GO to **DL38**.
• PFE/DPFE sensor disconnected.	No	▶	SERVICE open circuit. REMOVE breakout box. RECONNECT all components. RERUN Quick Test.
• Disconnect Powertrain Control Module (PCM). Inspect for damaged or pushed out pins, corrosion, loose wires, etc. Service as necessary.			
• Install breakout box, leave PCM disconnected.			
• Measure resistance between PFE/DPFE circuit at the PFE/DPFE sensor vehicle harness connector and Test Pin 27 at the breakout box.			
• **Is resistance less than 5.0 ohms?**			
DL38 CHECK PFE/DPFE HARNESS CIRCUIT FOR SHORTS TO GROUND AND SIG RTN			
• Key off.	Yes	▶	REPLACE PCM. REMOVE breakout box. RECONNECT all components. RERUN Quick Test.
• PFE/DPFE sensor disconnected.			
• Breakout box installed. PCM disconnected.			
• Measure resistance between PFE/DPFE circuit at the PFE/DPFE sensor vehicle harness connector and Test Pins 40/60 at the breakout box.	No	▶	SERVICE short circuit. REMOVE breakout box. RECONNECT all components. RERUN Quick Test.
• Measure resistance between PFE/DPFE circuit at the PFE/DPFE sensor vehicle harness connector and Test Pin 46 at the breakout box.			
• **Is each resistance greater than 10,000 ohms?**			
DL50 DIAGNOSTIC TROUBLE CODE (DTC) 336 OR 337: CHECK FOR EVR MALFUNCTION			
• DTC 336 or 337 indicates that DPFE circuit voltage is higher than expected at zero duty cycle.	Yes	▶	RECONNECT EGR vacuum line. GO to **DL51**.
Possible causes are:			
— Damaged EVR solenoid	No	▶	VERIFY vacuum line routing is correct. CHECK EVR filter for contamination or blockage. If all OK, REPLACE EVR solenoid. RECONNECT all lines. RERUN Quick Test.
— Damaged DPFE sensor			
— Damaged or contaminated EGR valve			
— Vacuum hose routing			
— Damaged PCM			
• Key off.			
• Disconnect EGR valve vacuum line at valve and plug line.			
• Rerun Key On Engine Running (KOER) Self-Test.			
• **Is DTC 336 or 337 present? (ignore all other DTC's)**			

FM015930072170X

Fig. 179 Test DL: PFE/DPFE Sensor/EVR Solenoid (Part 17 of 27)

TEST STEP	RESULT	▶	ACTION TO TAKE
DL51 CHECK DPFE SIGNAL VOLTAGE WITH ENGINE AT IDLE			
• Key off.	Yes	▶	GO to **DL52**.
• Disconnect Powertrain Control Module (PCM). Inspect for damaged or pushed out pins, corrosion, loose wires, etc. Service as necessary.	No	▶	REPLACE PCM. REMOVE breakout box. RECONNECT all components. RERUN Quick Test.
• Install breakout box and connect PCM to breakout box.			
• Start engine and idle with transmission in PARK or NEUTRAL.			
• Measure voltage between Test Pin 27 and Test Pin 46 at the breakout box.			
• **Is voltage greater than 0.7 volt at idle?**			
DL52 CHECK EGR VALVE FOR BINDING			
The fault has been isolated to either the EGR valve or DPFE sensor. Due to the nature of this particular fault, the EGR valve is suspect because of its vulnerability to contamination and carbon build-up from the exhaust flow. If the engine runs rough at idle, this is a good indication that the EGR valve is not fully seated rather than a faulty DPFE sensor.	Yes	▶	REPLACE EGR valve. REMOVE breakout box. RERUN KOER Self-Test. If DTC 336 or 337 is still present, REPLACE DPFE sensor.
• Remove the EGR valve.	No	▶	The original DTC 336 or 337 was the result of the EGR valve not fully seating. Testing complete.
• Inspect the EGR valve for signs of contamination, unusual wear, carbon deposits, binding, and other damage. Service as necessary. Use Rotunda EGR Valve Cleaner 021-80056 if needed).			
• Re-install EGR valve and rerun KOER Self-Test.			
• **Is DTC 336 or 337 still present?**			

FM015930072180X

Fig. 179 Test DL: PFE/DPFE Sensor/EVR Solenoid (Part 18 of 27)

TEST STEP	RESULT	▶	ACTION TO TAKE
DL90 ALL CONTINUOUS MEMORY EGR DIAGNOSTIC TROUBLE CODES (DTC): INTERMITTENT VERIFICATION			
NOTE: This test step verifies if the DTC is due to an intermittent or a hard fault.	Yes	▶	A hard fault is indicated. REFER to the EEC-IV DTC charts test step direction for the DTC's in question.
• Perform KOEO and KOER Self-Test if you have not already done so and make note of all codes received in KOEO, Continuous Memory and KOER modes. If unable to run KOER due to a "No Start" or "Stall", do not continue with this step but go directly to **DL101**.			
• If an EGR fault exists at the time of this test (hard fault), then an EGR DTC should also be received in KOEO or KOER or both depending on the DTC. If the EGR DTC is NOT received in KOEO or KOER but only retrieved from Continuous Memory, this could be due to an intermittent EGR system fault which occurred sometime in the past.	No	▶	An intermittent fault is indicated. GO to **DL91**.
• **Are there any EGR DTC's output in KOEO or KOER Self-Test (Ignore Continuous Memory DTC's at end of KOEO)?**			
DL91 ALL CONTINUOUS MEMORY EGR DIAGNOSTIC TROUBLE CODES (DTC): VISUAL INSPECTION			
• Key off.	Yes	▶	SERVICE fault as necessary. CLEAR Continuous Memory. RERUN Quick Test.
• Conduct a thorough visual inspection of the PFE/DPFE system for any potential failures. Use the following check list for possible causes:			
— Obvious physical damage			
— Loose connectors	No	▶	RECONNECT all components. GO to **DL92**.
— Pushed out connector pins			
— Corroded connector contacts			
— Damaged wiring insulation			
— Incorrect harness routing			
— Incorrect component mounting			
— Road salt or rust accumulation			
— Damaged vacuum hoses			
— Incorrect vacuum hose routing			
— EVR solenoid filter contamination			
— Vacuum hose restriction			
— Road splash or icing			
— Incorrect service parts			
• **Does the EGR system visual inspection reveal a potential failure?**			

FM015930072190X

Fig. 179 Test DL: PFE/DPFE Sensor/EVR Solenoid (Part 19 of 27)

TEST STEP	RESULT	▶	ACTION TO TAKE
DL92 ALL CONTINUOUS MEMORY EGR DIAGNOSTIC TROUBLE CODES (DTC): CODE DEFINITIONS AND DIRECTION			
• Select the DTC in question and follow the "Action to Take" direction.	**DTC 327 (PFE/DPFE)** PFE/DPFE signal went less than the allowable minimum voltage.	▶	GO to DL93.
	DTC 337 (PFE/DPFE) PFE/DPFE signal went greater than the allowable maximum voltage.	▶	GO to DL93.
	DTC 336 (PFE) Exhaust pressure high/PFE signal went higher than expected.	▶	GO to DL93.
	DTC 336 (DPFE) DPFE signal went higher than expected.	▶	GO to DL93.
	DTC 326 (PFE) PFE signal went lower than expected.	▶	GO to DL93.
	DTC 332 (PFE/DPFE) Insufficient EGR flow detected.	▶	GO to DL105.

FM0159300721200X

Fig. 179   Test DL: PFE/DPFE Sensor/EVR Solenoid (Part 20 of 27)

TEST STEP	RESULT	▶	ACTION TO TAKE
DL93 DTC 326, 327, 336, 337: WIGGLE TEST SENSOR			
Possible Causes: **DTC 337 (PFE/DPFE), 336 (PFE/DPFE)** — Open in PFE/DPFE SIG RTN circuit — Short to PWR or VREF in PFE/DPFE Signal circuit **DTC 336 (PFE)** — Obstructed PFE sensor inlet. **DTC 327 (PFE/DPFE), 326 (PFE)** — Open in PFE/DPFE Signal circuit — Open in PFE/DPFE VREF circuit — Short to GND in either PFE/DPFE Signal or VREF circuits **DTC 327 (PFE), 326 (PFE), 336 (DPFE), 337 (DPFE)** — EGR valve sticking open — EVR solenoid sticking open — EVR solenoid vent restricted — EVR solenoid driver shorting to GND NOTE: All circuit faults can either be in the component, harness or PCM.	Yes	▶	INSPECT connectors and terminals. If OK, REPLACE PFE/DPFE sensor. CLEAR Continuous Memory
• Enter KOEO Continuous Monitor DTM. • Observe VOM or STAR LED or indication of a fault while performing the following: — Lightly tap on PFE/DPFE sensor and wiggle the sensor vehicle harness connector (to simulate road shock). • **Is a fault indicated?**	No	▶	RERUN Quick Test. GO to DL94.
DL94 WIGGLE TEST EEC-IV VEHICLE HARNESS			
• Still in KOEO Continuous Monitor DTM. • Observe VOM or STAR LED for a fault indication while performing the following: — Grasp the vehicle harness closest to the PFE/DPFE sensor connector. Wiggle, shake or bend a small section of the EEC-IV system vehicle harness while working your way to the dash panel. Also wiggle, shake or bend the EEC-IV vehicle harness from the dash panel to the PCM. • **Is a fault indicated?**	Yes	▶	ISOLATE fault and SERVICE as necessary. CLEAR Continuous Memory
	No	▶	RERUN Quick Test. GO to DL95.

FM0159300721210X

Fig. 179   Test DL: PFE/DPFE Sensor/EVR Solenoid (Part 21 of 27)

TEST STEP	RESULT	▶	ACTION TO TAKE
DL95 CHECK PCM CONNECTOR			
• Key off. • Disconnect PCM connector. • Inspect both connectors and connector terminals for obvious damage or faults. • **Are connectors and terminals OK?**	Yes	▶	For DTC 327 (PFE), 326 (PFE), 336 (DPFE), 337 (DPFE): GO to DL96. For DTC 336 (PFE): GO to DL100. All others: Unable to duplicate and/or identify fault at this time. All others RERUN Quick Test.
	No	▶	SERVICE as necessary. CLEAR Continuous Memory RERUN Quick Test.
DL96 CHECK EGR VALVE FOR STICKING			
If customer complaint includes a rough idle or stall, the EGR valve could be sticking open or a fault in the EVR solenoid vacuum control could be forcing the EGR valve to open when not desired. • Key off. • Disconnect vacuum hose at EGR valve and plug end of hose. • Connect a hand vacuum pump to the EGR valve. • Apply (10 in-Hg) 34 kPa of vacuum to EGR valve and release while observing movement with inspection mirror if possible. Look for binding of the valve pintle. • **Does the EGR valve function in a smooth manner?** NOTE: Repeat test as necessary to ensure accurate results.	Yes	▶	GO to DL97.
	No	▶	REMOVE AND INSPECT the EGR valve for signs of contamination, unusual wear, carbon deposits, binding, and other damage. SERVICE as necessary. (Use Rotunda EGR valve cleaner 021-80056 if needed). CLEAR Continuous Memory RERUN Quick Test.

Fig. 179   Test DL: PFE/DPFE Sensor/EVR Solenoid (Part 22 of 27)

TEST STEP	RESULT	▶	ACTION TO TAKE
DL97 CHECK EVR SOLENOID AND HOSES			
An EVR solenoid that is not functioning properly can cause the EGR valve to open or remain open when EGR is NOT demanded (such as at idle). • Key off. • Inspect the EVR solenoid vacuum hoses and solenoid very closely for the following: — Look for restriction in the vacuum hoses. — Look for signs of contamination or moisture at EVR and in hoses. — Inspect the EVR filter for excessive contamination. • **Is a fault indicated?**	Yes	▶	ISOLATE fault and SERVICE as necessary. RECONNECT all components. CLEAR Continuous Memory
	No	▶	RERUN Quick Test. RECONNECT all components. GO to DL98.
DL98 CHECK EVR SOLENOID FOR SHORTS			
An EVR solenoid or EVR driver circuit short could cause the EVR to open and thereby supply the EGR valve with vacuum. • Key off. • Disconnect vacuum hose at EGR valve and connect hose to a vacuum gauge. • Run engine to operating temperature and stabilized idle. • With the engine at idle, tap the EVR solenoid and wiggle the EVR connector while noting vacuum reading. • **Does the EGR vacuum remain below 3.4 kPa (1.0 in-Hg) with no sudden increase?** NOTE: EVR leakage below 3.4 kPa (1.0 in-Hg) is normal.	Yes	▶	LEAVE vacuum gauge connected. GO to DL99.
	No	▶	INSPECT EVR solenoid connector for shorts. SERVICE as necessary. If OK, SERVICE or REPLACE EVR solenoid. RECONNECT all components. CLEAR Continuous Memory RERUN Quick Test.
DL99 CHECK EVR HARNESS CIRCUIT FOR INTERMITTENTS BETWEEN EVR AND PCM			
• Vacuum gauge connected. • Key on, engine running. • Look for an increase in EGR vacuum while performing the following: — With the engine at idle, wiggle the EVR solenoid harness between the EVR solenoid and dash panel and between dash panel and Powertrain Control Module (PCM). • **Does the EGR vacuum increase?**	Yes	▶	ISOLATE and SERVICE short in EVR circuit. REMOVE vacuum gauge. RECONNECT all components CLEAR Continuous Memory RERUN Quick Test.
	No	▶	Unable to duplicate and/or identify fault at this time.

FM0159300721230X

Fig. 179   Test DL: PFE/DPFE Sensor/EVR Solenoid (Part 23 of 27)

TEST STEP	RESULT	▶	ACTION TO TAKE
DL100 INSPECT PFE SUPPLY HOSE FOR BLOCKAGE			
• Key off. • Remove PFE sensor and inspect sensor supply inlet for liquids and/or any type of blockage. • Inspect PFE supply hose to EGR valve base for liquids and/or blockage. • **Is supply hose or sensor restricted with liquid or other blockage?**	Yes	▶	CLEAN and/or SERVICE as necessary. CLEAR Continuous Memory
	No	▶	RERUN Quick Test. Unable to duplicate and/or identify fault at this time.
			All others CLEAR Continuous Memory
			RERUN Quick Test.
DL101 CHECK VACUUM AT EGR VALVE			
This step checks if the EGR valve is receiving vacuum forcing it to open upon start-up. • Disconnect and plug vacuum hose at the EGR valve. • Start engine and let idle if possible. • **Will the engine start and idle normally?**	Yes	▶	INSPECT EVR vacuum hoses for correct routing. If OK, REPLACE EVR solenoid. RECONNECT all components. CLEAR Continuous Memory
			RERUN Quick Test.
	No	▶	GO to DL102

Fig. 179   Test DL: PFE/DPFE Sensor/EVR Solenoid (Part 24 of 27)

TEST STEP	RESULT	▶	ACTION TO TAKE
DL102 CHECK FOR STUCK OPEN EGR VALVE			
• Key off. • Connect a hand vacuum pump to the EGR valve. • Apply 34 kPa (10 in-Hg) of vacuum to EGR valve and release. Use an inspection mirror to observe valve movement or listen for valve closing shut. Repeat several times to verify valve function. The valve may have to be removed in order to determine valve functional condition. • **Is EGR valve stuck in the open position or not fully reseating?**	Yes	▶	REMOVE and INSPECT the EGR valve for signs of contamination, unusual wear, carbon deposits, binding, and other damage. SERVICE as necessary (Use Rotunda EGR valve cleaner 021-80056 if needed). CLEAR Continuous Memory
			RERUN Quick Test.
	No	▶	The "No Start" or "Stall" symptom is not due to the EGR system. RECONNECT all components. RETURN to the appropriate Diagnostic Routine Flowchart and continue to diagnose the symptom prior to servicing the EGR Continuous DTC's.

Fig. 179   Test DL: PFE/DPFE Sensor/EVR Solenoid (Part 25 of 27)

TEST STEP	RESULT	▶	ACTION TO TAKE
DL105 DTC 332 CHECK EGR VALVE OPERATION			
Possible Causes: **DTC 332 (PFE DPFE)** — EGR valve sticking closed — EGR valve diaphragm leaks — EVR solenoid sticking closed — Loss of vacuum to or from EVR — Open in EVR VPWR or driver circuits — Leak or restriction in PFE DPFE signal hoses • Key off. • Connect a vacuum pump to the EGR valve. • While observing the EGR valve, slowly apply 34 kPa (10 in-Hg) of vacuum. NOTE: EGR valve should begin to open with a very small amount of vacuum, approximately 3 to 5 kPa (1 to 1.5 in-Hg) and be fully open with about 13 kPa (4 in-Hg). EGR valve should remain open with vacuum applied or else vacuum diaphragm could be leaking if the valve closes immediately. • **Does the EGR valve open smoothly and hold vacuum?**	Yes	▶	GO to DL106
	No	▶	REMOVE and INSPECT the EGR valve for signs of diaphragm damage or leakage, contamination, unusual wear, carbon deposits, binding, and other damage. SERVICE as necessary (Use Rotunda EGR valve cleaner 021-80056 if needed). CLEAR Continuous Memory
			RERUN Quick Test.
DL106 INSPECT EVR SOLENOID HOSES			
• Key off. • Disconnect EVR vacuum hoses. • Verify that hoses are clear of any obstructions, properly routed and will hold vacuum. • **Are EVR vacuum hoses in good condition?**	Yes	▶	RECONNECT EVR hoses. GO to DL107.
	No	▶	SERVICE vacuum hoses as necessary. CLEAR Continuous Memory
			RERUN Quick Test.
DL107 INSPECT PFE DPFE SIGNAL LINE(S)			
• Key off. • Disconnect PFE DPFE signal hoses at the sensor. • Inspect sensor and signal line(s) for any signs of contamination, obstruction or leaks. • **Is there a fault indicated?**	Yes	▶	ISOLATE fault and SERVICE as necessary. CLEAR Continuous Memory
			RERUN Quick Test.
	No	▶	RECONNECT ALL COMPONENTS. GO to DL108

Fig. 179   Test DL: PFE/DPFE Sensor/EVR Solenoid (Part 26 of 27)

TEST STEP	RESULT	▶	ACTION TO TAKE
DL108 INSPECT EVR SOLENOID.			
• Key off. • Disconnect Powertrain Control Module (PCM) connector. Inspect for damaged or pushed out pins, corrosion, loose wires, etc. Service as necessary. • Install breakout box and connect PCM to breakout box. • Disconnect vacuum hose at EGR valve and connect hose to a vacuum gauge. • Run engine to operating temperature and stabilized idle. • Jumper Test Pin 40 to Test Pin 33 at the breakout box which should turn ON the EVR solenoid. • While reading the vacuum gauge, tap the EVR solenoid, wiggle the solenoid connector and solenoid vehicle harness. Look for a sudden drop in vacuum reading as you perform each action. • **Is there a fault indicated?**	Yes	▶	ISOLATE and SERVICE fault as necessary. RECONNECT all components. CLEAR Continuous Memory
	No	▶	RERUN Quick Test. Unable to duplicate and/or identify fault at this time.
			CLEAR Continuous Memory
			RERUN Quick Test.

Fig. 179   Test DL: PFE/DPFE Sensor/EVR Solenoid (Part 27 of 27)

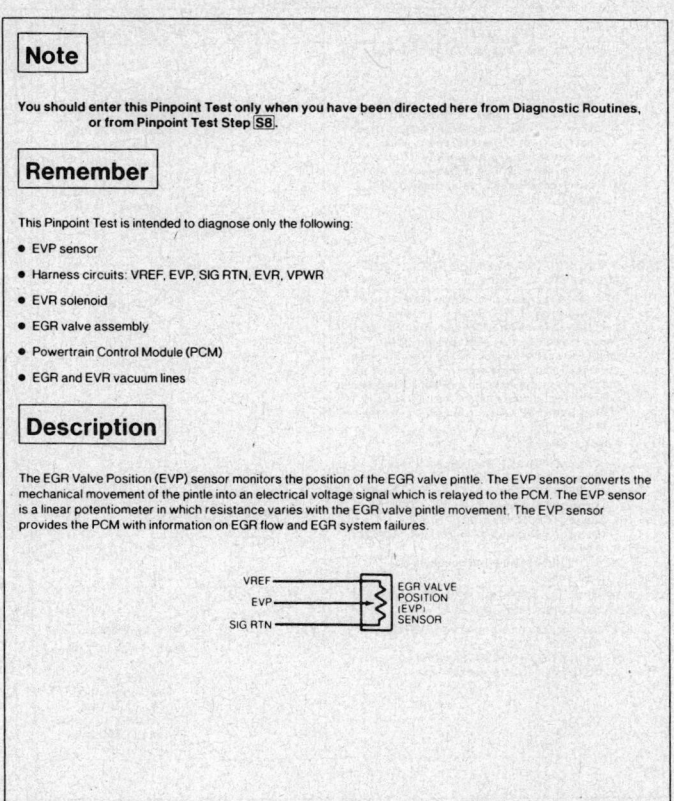

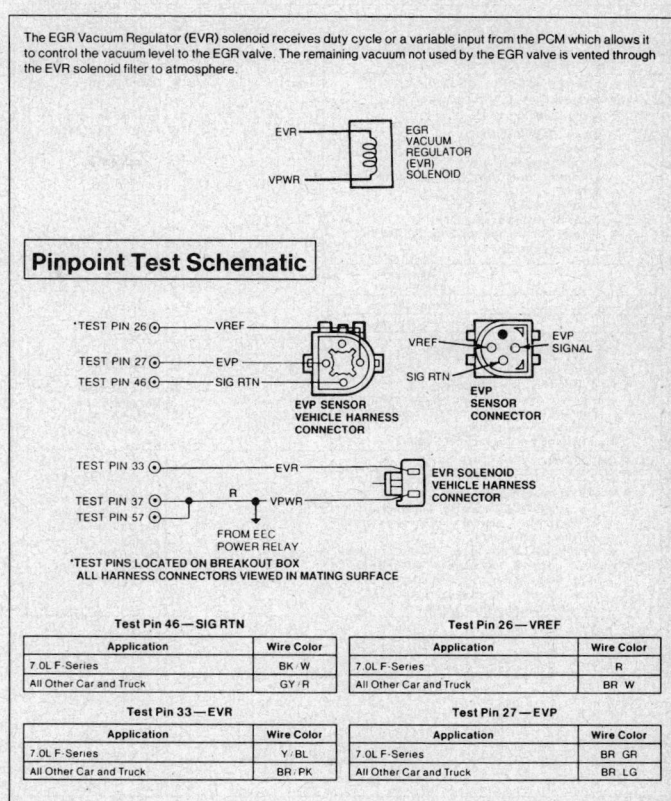

TEST STEP	RESULT	▶	ACTION TO TAKE
DN10 DIAGNOSTIC TROUBLE CODE (DTC) 84/558: CHECK RESISTANCE OF EVR SOLENOID			
DTC 84/558 indicates a failure in the EGR Vacuum Regulator (EVR) solenoid circuit. Possible causes: — Damaged EVR solenoid — Open harness — Shorted harness — Damaged Powertrain Control Module (PCM) • Key off. • Disconnect EVR solenoid. • Measure solenoid resistance. • **Is resistance within specification per the following chart?**	Yes No	▶ ▶	GO to **DN11**. REPLACE EVR solenoid assembly. RERUN Quick Test.
DN11 CHECK VPWR CIRCUIT VOLTAGE			
• Key on, engine off. • EVR solenoid disconnected. • Measure voltage between battery negative post and VPWR circuit at the EVR solenoid vehicle harness connector. • **Is voltage greater than 10.5 volts?**	Yes No	▶ ▶	GO to **DN12**. SERVICE open circuit. RECONNECT EVR solenoid. RERUN Quick Test.
DN12 CHECK EVR CIRCUIT CONTINUITY			
• Key off. • EVR solenoid disconnected. • Disconnect PCM. Inspect for damaged or pushed out pins, corrosion, loose wires, etc. Service as necessary. • Install breakout box, leave PCM disconnected. • Measure resistance between Test Pin 33 at the breakout box and EVR circuit at the EVR solenoid vehicle harness connector. • **Is resistance less than 5.0 ohms?**	Yes No	▶ ▶	GO to **DN13**. SERVICE open circuit. REMOVE breakout box. RECONNECT all components. RERUN Quick Test.

Engine resistance chart:

Engine	Resistance Specification
7.5L	100 to 135 ohms
All Others	20 to 70 ohms

FM0159300722050X

Fig. 180   Test DN: EVP Sensor/EVR Solenoid (Part 5 of 15). 1993–94

TEST STEP	RESULT	▶	ACTION TO TAKE
DN13 CHECK EVR CIRCUIT FOR SHORT TO POWER OR GROUND			
• Key off. • EVR solenoid disconnected. • Breakout box installed, PCM disconnected. • Measure resistance between Test Pin 33 and Test Pins 37 and 57 at the breakout box. • Measure resistance between Test Pin 33 and Test Pin 40, 46 and 60 at the breakout box. • **Is each resistance greater than 10,000 ohms?**	Yes No	▶ ▶	REPLACE PCM. REMOVE breakout box. RECONNECT EVR solenoid. RERUN Quick Test. SERVICE short circuit. REMOVE breakout box. RECONNECT all components. RERUN Quick Test. If DTC is repeated, REPLACE EVR solenoid.
DN20 DIAGNOSTIC TROUBLE CODE (DTC) 34/334: CHECK FOR DTC 84/558			
DTC 34/334 in Key On Engine Off (KOEO) or Engine Running (KOER) Self-Test indicates that the EGR valve and/or EGR Valve Position (EVP) sensor may not be fully seated in the closed position. The EVP sensor voltage is greater than the closed limit voltage of 0.67 volt. Because of the preload on the installed EVP sensor, it is very difficult to determine whether the EGR valve is seated or the EVP sensor is in contact with the EGR valve stem. Possible causes: — Poor continuity in EVP sensor harness. — Non-seated EGR valve. — Damaged EGR valve. — Damaged EVP sensor. — Damaged EVR solenoid. — Damaged Powertrain Control Module (PCM). • Key off. • **Is DTC 84 or 558 present in KOEO Self-Test?**	Yes No	▶ ▶	GO to **DN10**. GO to **DN21**.
DN21 RERUN KOEO AND KOER SELF-TEST WITH EGR VACUUM DISCONNECTED			
• Disconnect vacuum hose from EGR valve and plug hose. • Rerun KOEO and KOER Self-Test. • **Is DTC 34 or 334 present?**	Yes No	▶ ▶	GO to **DN22**. CHECK EVR solenoid for obstructions SERVICE as necessary. If OK, REPLACE EVR solenoid. RECONNECT all vacuum hoses RERUN Quick Test

FM0159300722060X

Fig. 180   Test DN: EVP Sensor/EVR Solenoid (Part 6 of 15). 1993–94

TEST STEP	RESULT	▶	ACTION TO TAKE
DN22 CHECK EVP SENSOR AND EGR VALVE OPERATION			
• Key off. • Disconnect EVP sensor. • Inspect the connectors on harness and sensor for damaged pins, corrosion, loose wires, etc. Service as necessary. • Remove vacuum line from EGR valve. • Exercise EGR valve by applying and releasing vacuum with a vacuum pump. • Reconnect vacuum line to EGR valve and electrical connector to EVP sensor. • Rerun Key On Engine Off (KOEO) and Key On Engine Running (KOER) Self-Test. • **Is DTC 34 or 334 still present?**	Yes No	▶ ▶	GO to **DN23**. The original DTC 34/334 was the result of poor continuity at the EVP sensor connector or binding of the EGR valve stem by contaminants. Testing complete.
DN23 CHECK EVP SIGNAL VOLTAGE			
• Key off. • Disconnect Powertrain Control Module (PCM). Inspect for damaged or pushed out pins, corrosion, loose wires, etc. Service as necessary. • Install breakout box and connect PCM to breakout box. • Key on, engine off. • Measure voltage between Test Pin 27 and Test Pin 46 at the breakout box. • **Is voltage greater than 0.67 volts?**	Yes No	▶ ▶	GO to **DN24**. REPLACE PCM. REMOVE breakout box. RERUN Quick Test.
DN24 FAULT ISOLATION CHECK			
The fault has been isolated to either the EGR valve or EVP sensor. Due to the nature of this particular fault, the EGR valve is suspect because of its vulnerability to contamination and carbon build-up from the exhaust flow. If the engine runs rough at idle, this is a good indication that the EGR valve is not fully seated rather than a worn or damaged sensor. • Remove the EGR valve and EVP sensor. • Inspect both components for contamination, unusual wear, carbon deposits, binding and other damage. Service as necessary. (Use Rotunda EGR Valve Cleaner 021-80056 or equivalent if needed.) • Re-install EGR valve and EVP assembly and run Key On Engine Off (KOEO) and Key On Engine Running (KOER) Self-Test. • **Is DTC 34 or 334 still present?**	Yes No	▶ ▶	REPLACE EGR valve. REMOVE breakout box. RERUN Quick Test. If DTC is still present, REPLACE EVP sensor. The original DTC 34/334 was the result of EGR valve contamination, binding or a worn or damaged EVP sensor. Testing complete.

FM0159300722070X

Fig. 180   Test DN: EVP Sensor/EVR Solenoid (Part 7 of 15). 1993–94

TEST STEP	RESULT	▶	ACTION TO TAKE
DN25 DIAGNOSTIC TROUBLE CODE (DTC) 32/328: CHECK EVP SENSOR AND EGR VALVE OPERATION			
DTC 32/328 in Key On Engine Off (KOEO) and Key On Engine Running (KOER) indicates that the EGR valve and/or EVP sensor voltage is lower than normal in the closed position. The EVP voltage is less than the closed limit voltage of 0.24 volts. Because of the preload of the EVP sensor it is very difficult to determine whether the EGR valve has malfunctioned or the EVP sensor has an abnormally high resistance. Possible causes: — Poor continuity in EVP sensor harness or connectors. — Damaged EGR valve. — Damaged EVP sensor. — Damaged Powertrain Control Module (PCM). • Key off. • Disconnect EVP sensor. • Inspect the connectors at harness and sensor for damaged pins, corrosion, loose wires, etc. Service as necessary. • Remove vacuum line from EGR valve. • Exercise EGR valve by applying and releasing vacuum with a vacuum pump. • Reconnect vacuum line to EGR valve and electrical connector to EVP sensor. • Rerun Key On Engine Off (KOEO) and Key On Engine Running (KOER) Self-Test. • **Is DTC 32 or 328 still present?**	Yes No	▶ ▶	GO to **DN26**. The original DTC 32/328 was the result of poor continuity at the EVP sensor connector or binding of the EGR valve stem by contaminants. Testing complete.
DN26 CHECK EVP SIGNAL VOLTAGE			
• Key off. • Disconnect Powertrain Control Module (PCM). Inspect for damaged or pushed out pins, corrosion, loose wires, etc. Service as necessary. • Install breakout box and connect PCM to breakout box. • Disconnect hose at EGR valve. • Connect a vacuum pump to the EGR valve. • Key on, engine off. • Measure voltage between Test Pin 27 and Test Pin 46 at the breakout box while performing the following: — Slowly increase vacuum at EGR valve to 6 in-Hg (20 kPa), then slowly bleed vacuum completely off. • **Does voltage drop to less than .24 volt?**	Yes No	▶ ▶	GO to **DN27**. REPLACE PCM. REMOVE breakout box. RERUN Quick Test.

FM0159300722080X

Fig. 180   Test DN: EVP Sensor/EVR Solenoid (Part 8 of 15). 1993–94

TEST STEP		RESULT	▶	ACTION TO TAKE
DN27	**SUBSTITUTE EVP SENSOR**			
	• Key off. • Install a known good EVP sensor on original EGR valve. • Reconnect EGR vacuum hose and EVP sensor connector. • Rerun Key On Engine Off (KOEO) and Key On Engine Running (KOER) Self-Test. • **Is DTC 32 or 328 still present?**	Yes No	▶ ▶	REPLACE the EGR valve. REMOVE breakout box. RERUN Quick Test. The original DTC 32 / 328 was the result of the original EVP sensor. Testing complete.
DN40	**DIAGNOSTIC TROUBLE CODE (DTC) 33 / 332: VERIFY VACUUM IS PRESENT AT EGR VALVE**			
	DTC 33 / 332 in Key On Engine Running (KOER) indicates that the EVP sensor input did not change after the EVR solenoid was instructed to open the EGR valve. Because a DTC 84 / 558 was not received in the Key On Engine Off (KOEO) Self-Test, it is known that the EVR solenoid functions electrically. It is also known that the EVP sensor is in the expected closed valve range because DTC 32 / 328 and 34 / 334 were not received in either Key On Engine Off (KOEO) or Key On Engine Running (KOER) Self-Test. Possible causes: — Vacuum hose leaks — Obstructed vacuum hose — Obstructed EVR solenoid filter — Damaged EVR solenoid. — Damaged EVP sensor. — Damaged EGR valve • Key off. • Disconnect vacuum line from EGR valve. • Connect vacuum gauge at open vacuum line. • Rerun Key On Engine Running (KOER) Self-Test while observing vacuum gauge. • **Does vacuum increase above 1.0 in-Hg (3.4 kPa)?**	Yes No	▶ ▶	REMOVE vacuum gauge. GO to **DN43**. REMOVE vacuum gauge. RECONNECT EGR valve vacuum line. GO to **DN41**.

FM015930072209OX

Fig. 180   Test DN: EVP Sensor/EVR Solenoid (Part 9 of 15). 1993–94

TEST STEP		RESULT	▶	ACTION TO TAKE
DN41	**VERIFY VACUUM SUPPLY TO EVR SOLENOID**			
	• Key off. • Disconnect the vacuum source to the EVR solenoid. • Install a vacuum gauge at source vacuum. • Start engine and check vacuum. • **Is vacuum greater than 10 in-Hg (33 kPa)?**	Yes No	▶ ▶	GO to **DN42**. CHECK source vacuum hose to EVR solenoid. SERVICE as necessary. RERUN Quick Test. For applications with a vacuum reservoir, [see] vacuum reservoir diagnosis.
DN42	**CHECK VACUUM HOSE BETWEEN EVR SOLENOID AND EGR VALVE**			
	• Carefully check EGR vacuum hose from EGR valve to EVR solenoid for obstructions, cracks, loose connectors, blockage, kinks, leaks, etc. • **Is vacuum hose in good condition?**	Yes No	▶ ▶	CHECK EVR solenoid filter for obstructions. REPLACE as necessary. If OK, REPLACE EVR solenoid assembly. RECONNECT vacuum hose. RERUN Quick Test SERVICE vacuum hose as necessary. RERUN Quick Test.
DN43	**CHECK EVP SENSOR AND EGR VALVE OPERATION**			
	• Key off. • Disconnect EVP sensor. • Inspect the connectors at harness and sensor for damaged pins, corrosion, loose wires, etc. Service as necessary. • EGR valve vacuum line disconnected. • Exercise EGR valve by applying and releasing vacuum with a vacuum pump. • Reconnect vacuum line to EGR valve and electrical connector to EVP sensor. • Rerun Key On Engine Running (KOER) Self-Test. • **Is DTC 33 or 332 still present?**	Yes No	▶ ▶	GO to **DN44**. The original DTC 33 / 332 was the result of poor continuity at the EVP sensor connector or binding of the EGR valve stem by contaminants. SERVICE as necessary. Testing complete.

FM015930072210OX

Fig. 180   Test DN: EVP Sensor/EVR Solenoid (Part 10 of 15). 1993–94

TEST STEP		RESULT	▶	ACTION TO TAKE
DN44	**CHECK EGR VALVE FUNCTION**			
	• Key off. • Install a tachometer, Rotunda 059-000 10 or equivalent. • Disconnect the Idle Air Control (IAC) solenoid electrical connector. • Remove and plug the vacuum line to the EGR valve. • Start engine, idle with transmission in NEUTRAL and observe idle speed. If necessary, adjust idle speed. • Slowly apply 5-10 in-Hg (17-34 kPa) to the EGR valve with a hand vacuum pump. • **Does the idle speed drop more than 100 rpm with vacuum applied and return to normal (± 25 rpm) after the vacuum is removed?**	Yes No	▶ ▶	The EGR valve is OK. REPLACE EVP sensor. RECONNECT all components. RERUN Quick Test. REPLACE the EGR valve if it does not hold vacuum. If the EGR valve does hold vacuum, REMOVE and inspect it for binding or other damage. SERVICE or REPLACE EGR valve as necessary. RERUN Quick Test.

FM015930072211OX

Fig. 180   Test DN: EVP Sensor/EVR Solenoid (Part 11 of 15). 1993–94

TEST STEP		RESULT	▶	ACTION TO TAKE
DN90	**CONTINUOUS MEMORY DIAGNOSTIC TROUBLE CODE (DTC) 32 / 328, 31 / 327 OR 35 / 337: CHECK FOR INTERMITTENT SENSOR**			
	Continuous Memory DTC 32 / 328 or 31 / 327 indicates that the EGR valve was closed further than normal or EVP sensor or circuit has failed with an intermittent low voltage sometime during vehicle operation. Continuous Memory DTC 35 / 337 indicates that the EVP signal to the Powertrain Control Module (PCM) was above the maximum Self-Test limit sometime during vehicle operation. Possible causes: — Poor continuity in EVP harness or connectors. — Intermittent open or short in EVP sensor or harness. — Damaged EVP sensor. • Disconnect Powertrain Control Module (PCM). Inspect for damaged or pushed out pins, corrosion, loose wires, etc. Service as necessary. • Install breakout box, reconnect PCM. • Connect DVOM between Test Pin 27 and Test Pin 46 at the breakout box. • Key on, engine off. • Lightly tap on EVP sensor and wiggle harness connector to simulate road shock. NOTE: EVP voltage with EGR valve closed is normally between .24 and .67 volt and steady. A sudden change in voltage indicates a fault. • **Is a fault indicated?**	Yes No	▶ ▶	REMOVE and INSPECT EVP sensor connector. If OK, REPLACE EVP sensor. CLEAR Continuous Memory. RERUN Quick Test. LEAVE DVOM connected, RECONNECT PCM and GO to **DN91**.
DN91	**CHECK EEC-IV VEHICLE HARNESS FOR INTERMITTENT OPENS OR SHORTS**			
	• Key on, engine off. • DVOM connected between Test Pin 27 and Test Pin 46 at breakout box. — Grasp the vehicle harness closest to the EVP sensor connector. Shake and bend a small section of the EEC-IV harness while working your way to the dash panel. Also wiggle, shake and bend the EEC-IV harness from the dash panel to the PCM. • **Is a fault indicated?**	Yes No	▶ ▶	ISOLATE fault and SERVICE as necessary. CLEAR Continuous Memory. RERUN Quick Test. LEAVE DVOM connected and GO to **DN92**.

FM015930072212OX

Fig. 180   Test DN: EVP Sensor/EVR Solenoid (Part 12 of 15). 1993–94

TEST STEP	RESULT	▶	ACTION TO TAKE
DN92 CHECK VOLTAGE WHILE EXERCISING EGR VALVE			
• Disconnect vacuum hose at EGR valve and connect a vacuum pump. • Key on, engine off. • Measure voltage between Test Pin 27 and Test Pin 46 at the breakout box while performing the following: — Slowly apply 5-10 in-Hg (17-34 kPa) of vacuum to EGR valve, then slowly bleed vacuum off. • **Does the voltage increase and decrease steadily from no more than 4.81 volts to no less than .24 volt?**	Yes No	▶ ▶	Unable to duplicate and/or identify fault at this time. REPLACE EVP sensor. REMOVE breakout box. RECONNECT all components. RERUN Quick Test.
DN110 CONTINUOUS MEMORY DIAGNOSTIC TROUBLE CODE (DTC) 33/332: CHECK EGR VALVE FUNCTION			
Continuous Memory DTC 33/332 indicates that the EGR valve did not open with the engine stabilized and with EVR solenoid duty cycle present sometime during vehicle operation. Possible cause: — Obstructed or cracked hose to EGR valve. — Damaged EGR valve. — Damaged EVR solenoid harness. • Key off. • Disconnect vacuum hose at EGR valve and connect a hand vacuum pump. • Apply 10-20 in-Hg (34-67 kPa) to EGR valve. • **Does EGR valve open and maintain vacuum?**	Yes No	▶ ▶	REMOVE vacuum pump. RECONNECT vacuum hose. GO to **DN111**. REMOVE and INSPECT the EGR valve assembly for blockage, binding, contamination and leakage. SERVICE EGR valve as necessary. CLEAR Continuous Memory. RERUN Quick Test.
DN111 CHECK VACUUM HOSE TO AND FROM EVR SOLENOID			
• Carefully check EGR vacuum hose from EGR valve to EVR solenoid and from EVR solenoid to vacuum source for obstructions, cracks, loose connection, kinks, leaks, etc. • **Are vacuum hoses in good condition?**	Yes No	▶ ▶	GO to **DN112**. SERVICE as necessary. CLEAR Continuous Memory. RERUN Quick Test.

FM0159300722130X

Fig. 180   Test DN: EVP Sensor/EVR Solenoid (Part 13 of 15). 1993–94

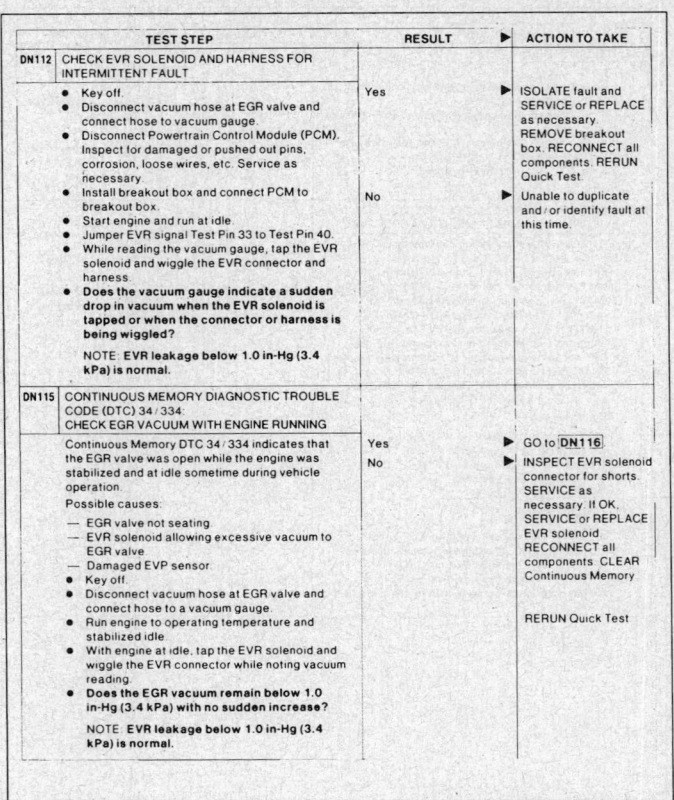

TEST STEP	RESULT	▶	ACTION TO TAKE
DN112 CHECK EVR SOLENOID AND HARNESS FOR INTERMITTENT FAULT			
• Key off. • Disconnect vacuum hose at EGR valve and connect hose to vacuum gauge. • Disconnect Powertrain Control Module (PCM). Inspect for damaged or pushed out pins, corrosion, loose wires, etc. Service as necessary. • Install breakout box and connect PCM to breakout box. • Start engine and run at idle. • Jumper EVR signal Test Pin 33 to Test Pin 40. • While reading the vacuum gauge, tap the EVR solenoid and wiggle the EVR connector and harness. • **Does the vacuum gauge indicate a sudden drop in vacuum when the EVR solenoid is tapped or when the connector or harness is being wiggled?** NOTE: EVR leakage below 1.0 in-Hg (3.4 kPa) is normal.	Yes No	▶ ▶	ISOLATE fault and SERVICE or REPLACE as necessary. REMOVE breakout box. RECONNECT all components. RERUN Quick Test. Unable to duplicate and/or identify fault at this time.
DN115 CONTINUOUS MEMORY DIAGNOSTIC TROUBLE CODE (DTC) 34/334: CHECK EGR VACUUM WITH ENGINE RUNNING			
Continuous Memory DTC 34/334 indicates that the EGR valve was open while the engine was stabilized and at idle sometime during vehicle operation. Possible causes: — EGR valve not seating. — EVR solenoid allowing excessive vacuum to EGR valve. — Damaged EVP sensor. • Key off. • Disconnect vacuum hose at EGR valve and connect hose to a vacuum gauge. • Run engine to operating temperature and stabilized idle. • With engine at idle, tap the EVR solenoid and wiggle the EVR connector while noting vacuum reading. • **Does the EGR vacuum remain below 1.0 in-Hg (3.4 kPa) with no sudden increase?** NOTE: EVR leakage below 1.0 in-Hg (3.4 kPa) is normal.	Yes No	▶ ▶	GO to **DN116**. INSPECT EVR solenoid connector for shorts. SERVICE as necessary. If OK, SERVICE or REPLACE EVR solenoid. RECONNECT all components. CLEAR Continuous Memory. RERUN Quick Test.

FM0159300722140X

Fig. 180   Test DN: EVP Sensor/EVR Solenoid (Part 14 of 15). 1993–94

TEST STEP	RESULT	▶	ACTION TO TAKE
DN116 CHECK EVR SIGNAL FOR INTERMITTENT SHORT			
• Vacuum gauge connected. • Key on, engine running. • Look for an increase in EGR valve vacuum while performing the following: — With the engine at idle, wiggle the EVR solenoid harness between the EVR solenoid and dash panel and between dash panel and PCM. • **Does the EGR vacuum increase?**	Yes No	▶ ▶	ISOLATE and SERVICE short in EVR circuit. REMOVE vacuum gauge. RECONNECT all components. CLEAR Continuous Memory. RERUN Quick Test. RECONNECT vacuum hose to EGR valve. GO to **DN117**.
DN117 CHECK EVP SIGNAL AT POWERTRAIN CONTROL MODULE (PCM) WITH ENGINE IDLING			
• Key off. • Disconnect Powertrain Control Module (PCM). Inspect for damaged or pushed out pins, corrosion, loose wires, etc. Service as necessary. • Install breakout box and connect PCM to breakout box. • Key on, engine running. • Measure voltage between Test Pin 27 and Test Pin 46 at the breakout box while performing the following: — With engine at idle, tap and wiggle the EVP sensor and connector. • **Does the voltage increase above .67 volt?**	Yes No	▶ ▶	REMOVE EGR assembly and inspect for contamination, carbon deposits, binding and other damage. SERVICE as necessary. If EGR valve is OK, REPLACE EVP sensor. CLEAR Continuous Memory. RERUN Quick Test. Unable to duplicate and/or identify fault at this time.

FM0159300722150X

Fig. 180   Test DN: EVP Sensor/EVR Solenoid (Part 15 of 15). 1993–94

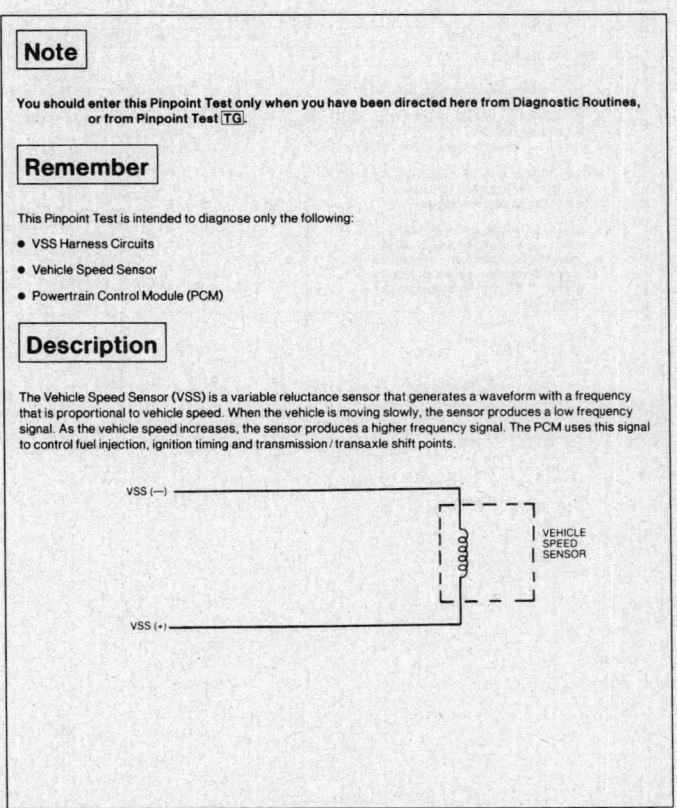

Note

You should enter this Pinpoint Test only when you have been directed here from Diagnostic Routines, or from Pinpoint Test **TG**.

Remember

This Pinpoint Test is intended to diagnose only the following:

• VSS Harness Circuits
• Vehicle Speed Sensor
• Powertrain Control Module (PCM)

Description

The Vehicle Speed Sensor (VSS) is a variable reluctance sensor that generates a waveform with a frequency that is proportional to vehicle speed. When the vehicle is moving slowly, the sensor produces a low frequency signal. As the vehicle speed increases, the sensor produces a higher frequency signal. The PCM uses this signal to control fuel injection, ignition timing and transmission/transaxle shift points.

FM0159300723010X

Fig. 181   Test DP: VSS (Part 1 of 4). 1993–94

Pinpoint Test Schematic

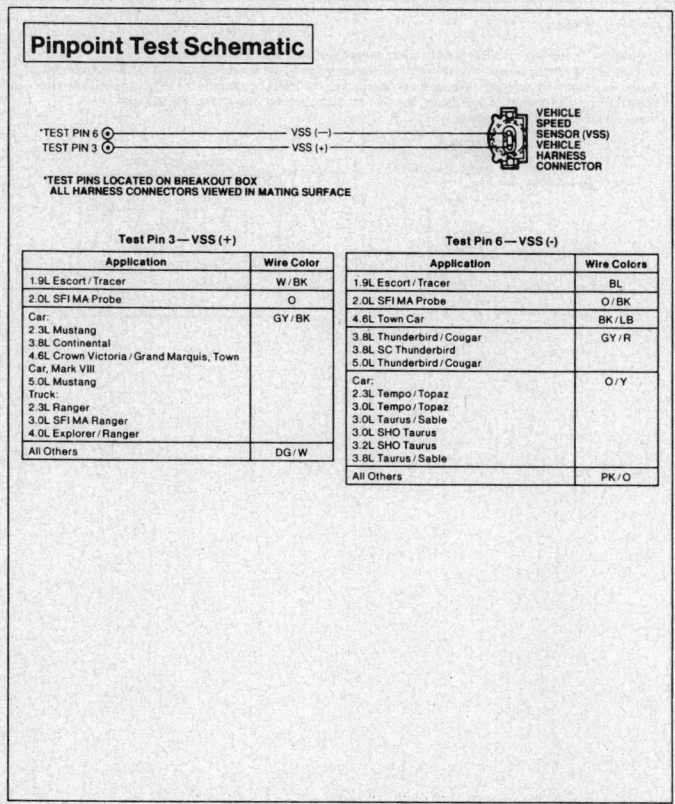

Fig. 181   Test DP: VSS (Part 2 of 4). 1993

*TEST PIN 6 — VSS (−)
TEST PIN 3 — VSS (+)

*TEST PINS LOCATED ON BREAKOUT BOX
ALL HARNESS CONNECTORS VIEWED IN MATING SURFACE

VEHICLE SPEED SENSOR (VSS) VEHICLE HARNESS CONNECTOR

Test Pin 3 — VSS (+)

Application	Wire Color
1.9L Escort / Tracer	W / BK
2.0L SFI MA Probe	O
Car: 2.3L Mustang 3.8L Continental 4.6L Crown Victoria / Grand Marquis, Town Car, Mark VIII 5.0L Mustang Truck: 2.3L Ranger 3.0L SFI MA Ranger 4.0L Explorer / Ranger	GY / BK
All Others	DG / W

Test Pin 6 — VSS (-)

Application	Wire Colors
1.9L Escort / Tracer	BL
2.0L SFI MA Probe	O / BK
4.6L Town Car	BK / LB
3.8L Thunderbird / Cougar 3.8L SC Thunderbird 5.0L Thunderbird / Cougar	GY / R
Car: 2.3L Tempo / Topaz 3.0L Tempo / Topaz 3.0L Taurus / Sable 3.0L SHO Taurus 3.2L SHO Taurus 3.8L Taurus / Sable	O / Y
All Others	PK / O

FM015930072302AX

Pinpoint Test Schematic

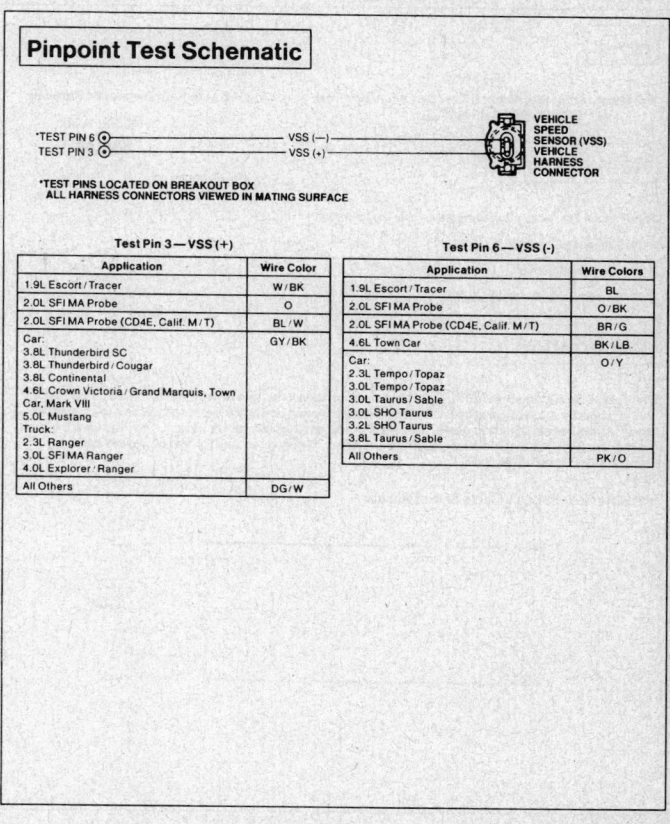

Fig. 181   Test DP: VSS (Part 2 of 4). 1994

*TEST PIN 6 — VSS (−)
TEST PIN 3 — VSS (+)

*TEST PINS LOCATED ON BREAKOUT BOX
ALL HARNESS CONNECTORS VIEWED IN MATING SURFACE

VEHICLE SPEED SENSOR (VSS) VEHICLE HARNESS CONNECTOR

Test Pin 3 — VSS (+)

Application	Wire Color
1.9L Escort / Tracer	W / BK
2.0L SFI MA Probe	O
2.0L SFI MA Probe (CD4E, Calif. M / T)	BL / W
Car: 3.8L Thunderbird SC 3.8L Thunderbird / Cougar 3.8L Continental 4.6L Crown Victoria / Grand Marquis, Town Car, Mark VIII 5.0L Mustang Truck: 2.3L Ranger 3.0L SFI MA Ranger 4.0L Explorer / Ranger	GY / BK
All Others	DG / W

Test Pin 6 — VSS (-)

Application	Wire Colors
1.9L Escort / Tracer	BL
2.0L SFI MA Probe	O / BK
2.0L SFI MA Probe (CD4E, Calif. M / T)	BR / G
4.6L Town Car	BK / LB
Car: 2.3L Tempo / Topaz 3.0L Tempo / Topaz 3.0L Taurus / Sable 3.0L SHO Taurus 3.2L SHO Taurus 3.8L Taurus / Sable	O / Y
All Others	PK / O

FM015940072302BX

	TEST STEP	RESULT	▶	ACTION TO TAKE
DP1	CONTINUOUS MEMORY DIAGNOSTIC TROUBLE CODE (DTC) 29 / 452: COMPLETE VSS DRIVE CYCLE: VERIFY DTC OR DRIVE COMPLAINT			
	Continuous Memory DTC 29 or 452 indicates that sometime during the last 40 or 80 warm-up cycles, the Powertrain Control Module (PCM) detected an error in the vehicle speed sensor output signal. Possible causes: — Damaged Vehicle Speed Sensor. — Damaged harness circuits. — Damaged Powertrain Control Module (PCM). ● Perform VSS Drive Cycle at least three times as outlined below. **VEHICLE SPEED SENSOR (VSS) DRIVE CYCLE:** — Record and clear Continuous Memory DTCs. — Warm engine to operating temperature. **AUTOMATIC TRANSMISSIONS:** — Place gear selector in DRIVE range. — Obey all local traffic laws. Accelerate heavily to 35 mph. — Coast down to an idle and stop the vehicle. — Shut the engine off. — After the drive cycle is completed, run Key On Engine Off Self-Test and record the Continuous Memory DTCs displayed. **MANUAL TRANSMISSIONS:** — From first gear, shift to second. — Obey all local traffic laws. Accelerate moderately to 40 mph. — Coast down to an idle and stop the vehicle. — Shut the engine off. — After the drive cycle is completed, run Key On Engine Off Self-Test and record the Continuous Memory DTCs displayed. ● **Did Continuous Memory DTC 29 or 452 repeat?**	Yes No	▶ ▶	GO to DP2. Unable to duplicate and / or identify fault at this time. All others, CLEAR Continuous Memory

FM01593007230300X

Fig. 181   Test DP: VSS (Part 3 of 4). 1993–94

	TEST STEP	RESULT	▶	ACTION TO TAKE
DP2	CHECK CONTINUITY OF VSS HARNESS CIRCUITS			
	● Key off. ● Disconnect Powertrain Control Module (PCM). Inspect for damaged or pushed out pins, corrosion, loose wires, etc. Service as necessary. ● Install breakout box, PCM disconnected. ● Disconnect VSS. ● Measure resistance between Test Pin 3 at the breakout box and VSS (+) circuit at the VSS vehicle harness connector. ● Measure resistance between Test Pin 6 at the breakout box and VSS (-) circuit at the VSS vehicle harness connector. ● **Is each resistance less than 5.0 ohms?**	Yes No	▶ ▶	GO to DP3. SERVICE open circuit. REMOVE breakout box. RECONNECT all components. REPEAT Test Step DP1 to verify elimination of DTC or drive complaint.
DP3	CHECK VSS SIGNAL HARNESS CIRCUITS FOR SHORTS TO POWER OR GROUND			
	● Key off. ● VSS disconnected. ● Breakout box installed, PCM disconnected. ● Measure resistance between Test Pin 3 and Test Pins 6, 37 and 40 at the breakout box. ● **Is each resistance greater than 500 ohms?**	Yes No	▶ ▶	RECONNECT the PCM. GO to DP4. SERVICE short circuit. REMOVE breakout box. RECONNECT all components. REPEAT Test Step DP1 to verify elimination of DTC or the drive complaint.
DP4	CHECK VSS RESISTANCE			
	● Key off. ● VSS disconnected. ● Measure the resistance of the VSS. ● **Is resistance between 190 and 250 ohms?**	Yes No	▶ ▶	REMOVE breakout box. REPLACE PCM. RECONNECT VSS. REPEAT Test Step DP1 to verify elimination of DTC or drive complaint. REPLACE VSS. REMOVE breakout box. REPEAT Test Step DP1 to verify the elimination of DTC or drive complaint.

FM01593007230400X

Fig. 181   Test DP: VSS (Part 4 of 4). 1993–94

Note

You should enter this Pinpoint Test only when you have been directed here from Diagnostic Routines or from Pinpoint Test TG.

Remember

This Pinpoint Test is intended to diagnose only the following:

- VSS Harness Circuits
- Vehicle Speed Sensor
- Powertrain Control Module (PCM)

Description

The Vehicle Speed Sensor (VSS) is a variable reluctance sensor that generates a waveform with a frequency that is proportional to vehicle speed. When the vehicle is moving slowly, the sensor produces a low frequency signal. As the vehicle speed increases, the sensor produces a higher frequency signal. The PCM uses this signal for idle speed control, fuel control for lean cruise, fuel shut off during deceleration and overspeed and transmission/transaxle shift points.

Variable Reluctance Vehicle Speed Sensor

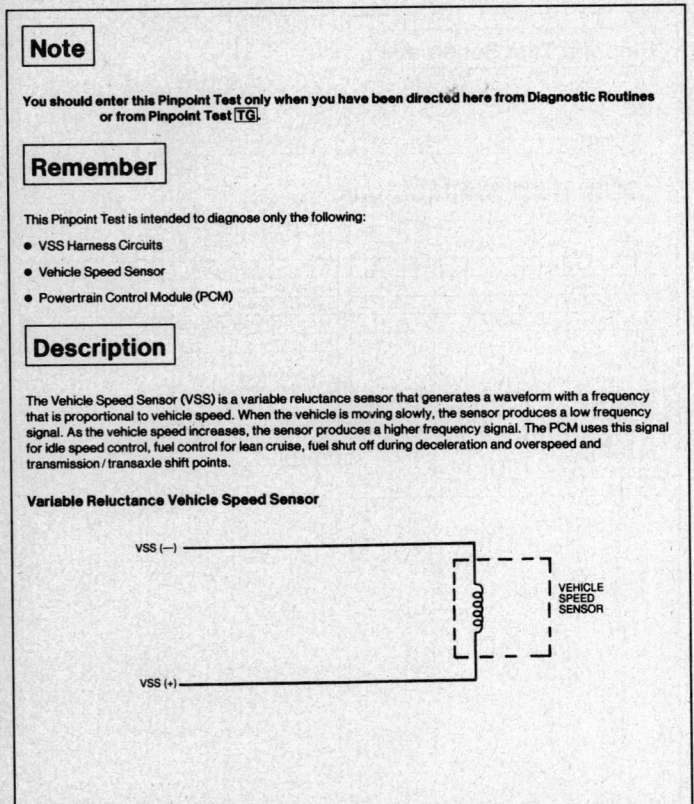

Fig. 182   Test DP: VSS (Part 1 of 7). 1995

Contour/Mystique

The Vehicle Speed Sensor (VSS) is a hall effect sensor that generates a waveform with a frequency that is proportional to vehicle speed. When the vehicle is moving slowly, the sensor produces a low frequency signal. As the vehicle speed increases, the sensor produces a higher frequency signal. The PCM uses this signal for idle speed control, fuel control for lean cruise, fuel shut-off during deceleration and overspeed and transmission/transaxle shift points.

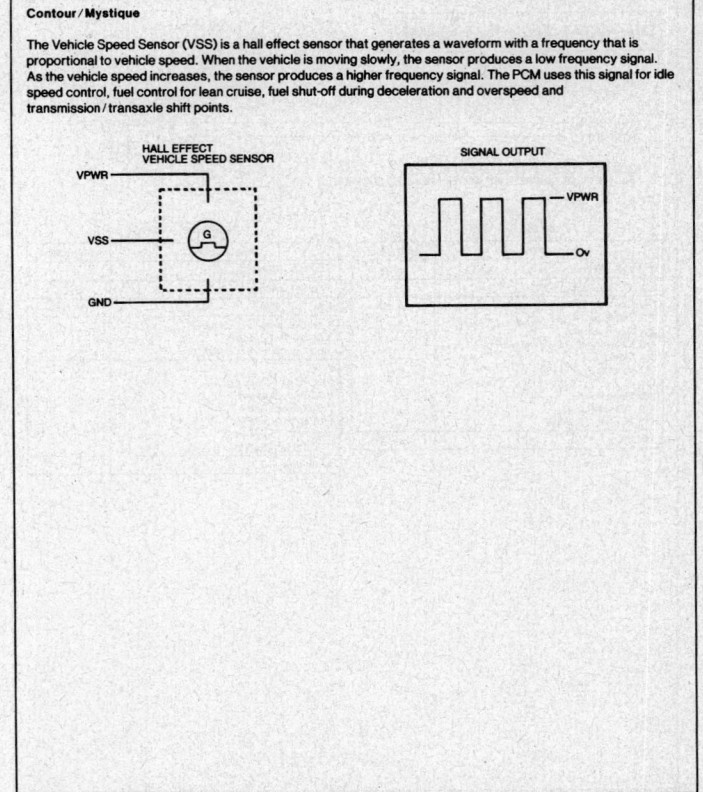

Fig. 182   Test DP: VSS (Part 2 of 7). 1995

Pinpoint Test Schematic

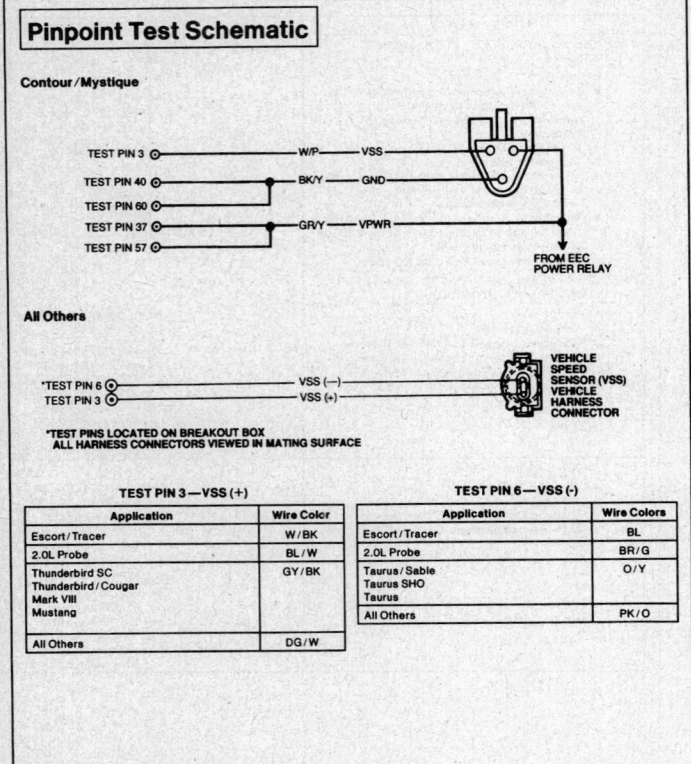

TEST PIN 3 — VSS (+)

Application	Wire Color
Escort/Tracer	W/BK
2.0L Probe	BL/W
Thunderbird SC Thunderbird/Cougar Mark VIII Mustang	GY/BK
All Others	DG/W

TEST PIN 6 — VSS (−)

Application	Wire Colors
Escort/Tracer	BL
2.0L Probe	BR/G
Taurus/Sable Taurus SHO Taurus	O/Y
All Others	PK/O

Fig. 182   Test DP: VSS (Part 3 of 7). 1995

	TEST STEP	RESULT	▶	ACTION TO TAKE
DP1	CONTINUOUS MEMORY DIAGNOSTIC TROUBLE CODE (DTC) 452: COMPLETE VSS DRIVE CYCLE, VERIFY DTC OR DRIVE COMPLAINT			
	Continuous Memory DTC 452 indicates that sometime during the last 40 or 80 warm-up cycles, the Powertrain Control Module (PCM) detected an error in the Vehicle Speed Sensor (VSS) output signal. Possible causes: — Damaged VSS. — Damaged harness circuits. — Damaged Powertrain Control Module (PCM). ● Perform VSS Drive Cycle at least three times as outlined below. **VEHICLE SPEED SENSOR (VSS) DRIVE CYCLE:** — Record and clear Continuous Memory DTCs. — Warm engine to operating temperature. **AUTOMATIC TRANSMISSIONS:** — Place gear selector in DRIVE range. — Obey all local traffic laws. Accelerate heavily to 56 km/h (35 mph). — Coast down to an idle and stop the vehicle. — Shut the engine off. — After the drive cycle is completed, run Key On Engine Off (KOEO) Self-Test and record the Continuous Memory DTCs displayed. **MANUAL TRANSMISSIONS:** — From first gear, shift to second. — Obey all local traffic laws. Accelerate moderately to 64 km/h (40 mph). — Decelerate to 40 km/h (25 mph). — Shift into third gear. — Accelerate moderately to 72 km/h (45 mph). — Coast down to an idle and stop the vehicle. — Shut the engine off. — After the drive cycle is completed, run KOEO Self-Test and record the Continuous Memory DTCs displayed. ● Did Continuous Memory DTC 452 repeat?	Yes No	▶ ▶	For Contour/Mystique: GO to DP5. All others: GO to DP2. Unable to duplicate and/or identify fault at this time. For further diagnosis, REFER to EEC-IV Intermittent Fault Diagnosis. All others, CLEAR Continuous Memory (REFER to Quick Test Appendix.

Fig. 182   Test DP: VSS (Part 4 of 7). 1995

TEST STEP		RESULT	▶	ACTION TO TAKE
DP2	CHECK CONTINUITY OF VSS HARNESS CIRCUITS • Key off. • Disconnect Powertrain Control Module (PCM). Inspect for damaged or pushed out pins, corrosion, loose wires, etc. Service as necessary. • Install breakout box, PCM disconnected. • Disconnect VSS. • Measure resistance between Test Pin 3 at the breakout box and VSS (+) circuit at the VSS vehicle harness connector. • Measure resistance between Test Pin 6 at the breakout box and VSS (-) circuit at the VSS vehicle harness connector. • **Is each resistance less than 5.0 ohms?**	Yes No	▶ ▶	GO to DP3. SERVICE open circuit. REMOVE breakout box. RECONNECT all components. REPEAT DP1 drive cycle to verify elimination of DTC or drive complaint.
DP3	CHECK VSS SIGNAL HARNESS CIRCUITS FOR SHORTS TO POWER OR GROUND • Key off. • VSS disconnected. • Breakout box installed, PCM disconnected. • Measure resistance between Test Pin 3 and Test Pins 6, 37 and 40 at the breakout box. • **Is each resistance greater than 500 ohms?**	Yes No	▶ ▶	RECONNECT the PCM. GO to DP4. SERVICE short circuit. REMOVE breakout box. RECONNECT all components. REPEAT DP1 drive cycle to verify elimination of DTC or the drive complaint.
DP4	CHECK VSS RESISTANCE • Key off. • VSS disconnected. • Measure the resistance of the VSS. • **Is resistance between 190 and 250 ohms?**	Yes No	▶ ▶	REMOVE breakout box. REPLACE PCM. RECONNECT VSS. REPEAT DP1 drive cycle to verify elimination of DTC or drive complaint. REPLACE VSS. REMOVE breakout box. REPEAT DP1 drive cycle to verify the elimination of DTC or drive complaint.

FM0159501290050X

Fig. 182   Test DP: VSS (Part 5 of 7). 1995

TEST STEP		RESULT	▶	ACTION TO TAKE
DP5	CHECK VSS SIGNAL OUTPUT TO POWERTRAIN CONTROL MODULE (PCM) • Key off. • Disconnect Powertrain Control Module (PCM). Inspect for damaged or pushed out pins, corrosion, loose wires, etc. Service as necessary. • Install breakout box, PCM disconnected. • Key on. • Observe voltage reading between Test Pin 3 and Test Pin 40 at breakout box while slowly rotating the drive wheel(s). • The voltage should rise above 5.0 volts and fall below 1.0 volt in a regular cycle. Observe several cycles. • **Does the VSS output voltage rise and fall as specified while slowly rotating the drive wheel(s)?**	Yes No	▶ ▶	REMOVE breakout box. REPLACE PCM. RECONNECT VSS. REPEAT DP1 to verify elimination of DTC or drive complaint. GO to DP6.
DP6	CHECK FOR BATTERY VOLTAGE TO VSS • Key off. • Disconnect VSS. • Key on. • Measure voltage at VPWR pin to GND pin at the VSS vehicle harness connector. • **Is the voltage greater than 10.5 volts?**	Yes No	▶ ▶	GO to DP7. GO to DP10.
DP7	CHECK VSS CIRCUIT SHORT TO POWER • VSS disconnected. • Key on, PCM disconnected. • Measure voltage between Test Pin 3 and Test Pin 40 at the breakout box. • **Is voltage less than 1.0 volt?**	Yes No	▶ ▶	GO to DP8. SERVICE short to power. REMOVE breakout box. RECONNECT all components. REPEAT DP1 to verify elimination of DTC or drive complaint.
DP8	CHECK VSS CIRCUIT SHORT TO GROUND • Key off. • VSS disconnected. • Measure resistance between Test Pin 3 and Test Pin 40 at the breakout box. • **Is resistance greater than 3,000 ohms?**	Yes No	▶ ▶	GO to DP9. SERVICE short to ground. REMOVE breakout box. RECONNECT all components. REPEAT DP1 to verify elimination of DTC or drive complaint.

FM0159501290060X

Fig. 182   Test DP: VSS (Part 6 of 7). 1995

TEST STEP		RESULT	▶	ACTION TO TAKE
DP9	CHECK CONTINUITY OF VSS HARNESS CIRCUIT • Key off, VSS disconnected. • PCM disconnected. • Measure resistance between Test Pin 3 at the breakout box and the VSS circuit at the VSS vehicle harness connector. • **Is resistance less than 5.0 ohms?**	Yes No	▶ ▶	REPLACE VSS. REMOVE the breakout box. RECONNECT all components. REPEAT DP1 to verify elimination of DTC or drive complaint. SERVICE open circuit. REMOVE breakout box. RECONNECT all components. REPEAT DP1 drive cycle to verify elimination of DTC or drive complaint.
DP10	CHECK CONTINUITY OF VSS GROUND HARNESS CIRCUIT • Key off, VSS disconnected. • PCM disconnected. • Measure resistance between GND Pin at the VSS vehicle harness connector and chassis ground. • **Is resistance less than 5.0 ohms?**	Yes No	▶ ▶	SERVICE open VPWR to VSS. REMOVE breakout box. RECONNECT all components. REPEAT DP1 to verify elimination of DTC or drive complaint. SERVICE open VSS GND circuit. REMOVE breakout box. RECONNECT all components. REPEAT DP1 to verify elimination of DTC or drive complaint.

FM0159501290070X

Fig. 182   Test DP: VSS (Part 7 of 7). 1995

Note

You should enter this Pinpoint Test only when you have been directed here from Diagnostic Routines.

Remember

This Pinpoint Test is intended to diagnose only the following:

- Harness circuits: CID(+), CID(-), CID, SIG RTN, VPWR
- Camshaft Position (CMP) sensor   Crankshaft Position (CKP) sensor
- Powertrain Control Module (PCM)

Description

The PCM uses the CID signal information for fuel injector synchronization.

For the Escort/Tracer, 2.3L Tempo/Topaz, Crown Victoria/Grand Marquis, Town Car, and Mark VIII the CID signal is generated by a variable reluctance-type Camshaft Position (CMP) sensor.

For the 2.0L Probe, the CID signal is generated by an optical Camshaft Position (CMP) sensor built into the distributor and consists of an LED, photo diode and a photo interrupter (rotor plate).

For the 2.3L Mustang and 2.3L Ranger, the CID signal is generated by a dual hall-type Crankshaft Position (CKP) sensor with a 50% duty cycle and an amplitude that varies from 0.4 volts to B(+).

All other applications, the CID signal is generated by a hall-type Camshaft Position (CMP) sensor with a 50% duty cycle and an amplitude that varies from 0.4 volts to B(+).

Pinpoint Test Schematics

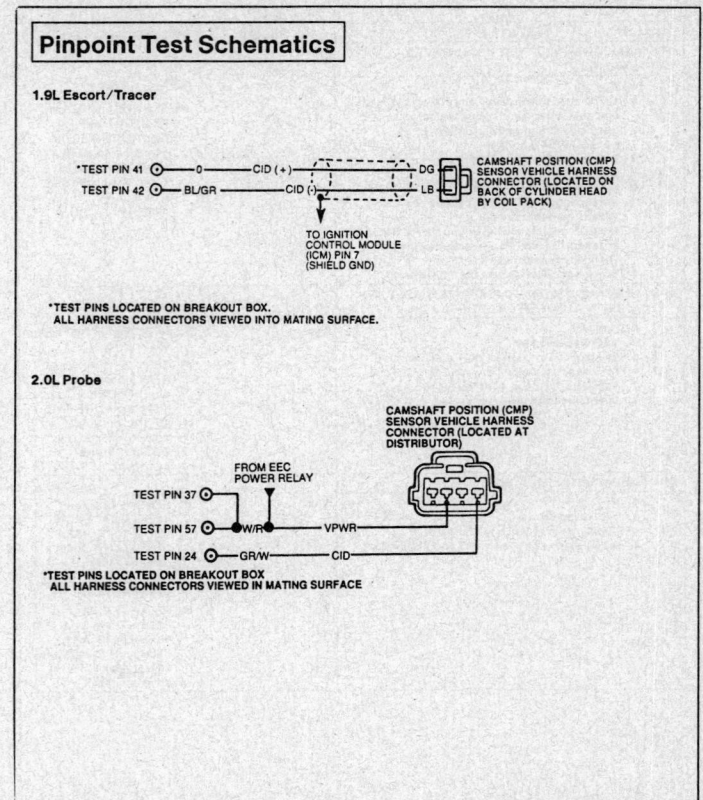

Fig. 183   Test DR: CID Circuits (Part 1 of 11). 1993

FM015930072401AX

Fig. 183   Test DR: CID Circuits (Part 2 of 11)

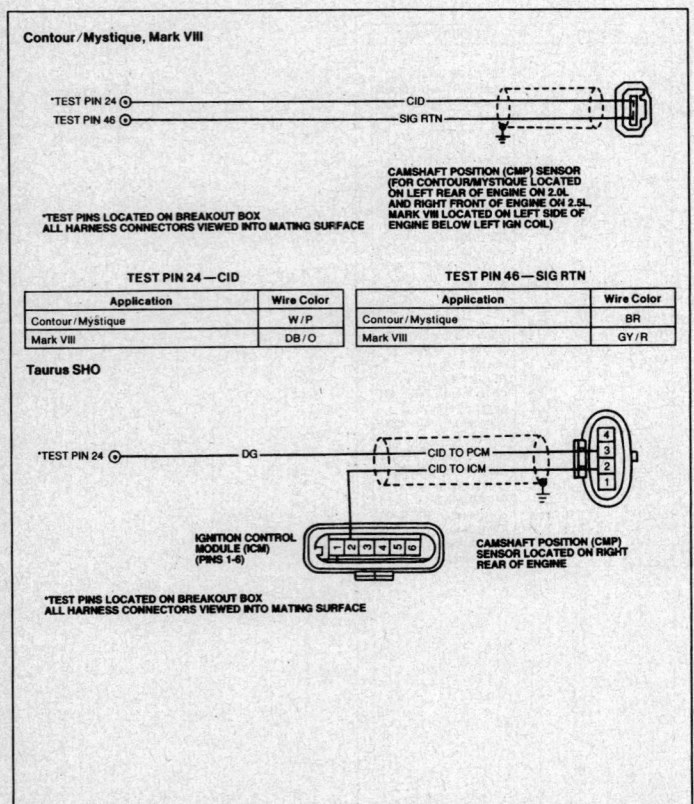

Fig. 183   Test DR: CID Circuits (Part 3 of 11). 1993–94

FM015950072403BA

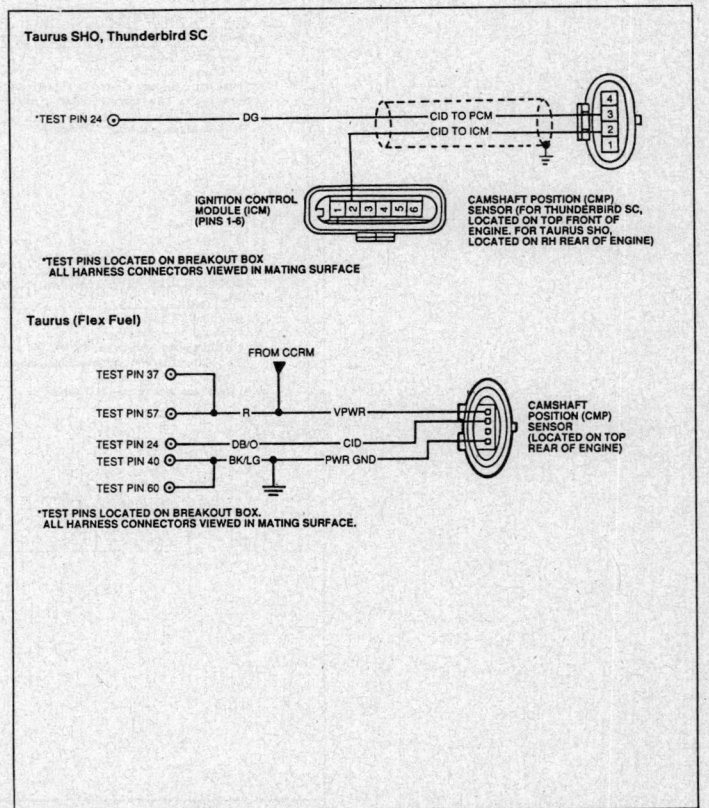

Fig. 183   Test DR: CID Circuits (Part 4 of 11). 1993

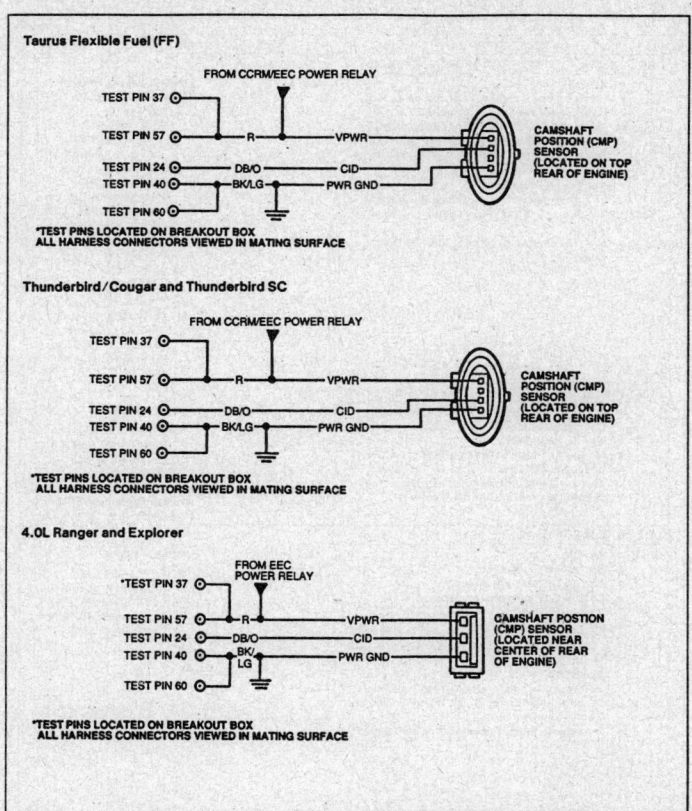

Taurus Flexible Fuel (FF)

FROM CCRM/EEC POWER RELAY

TEST PIN 37
TEST PIN 57 — R — VPWR
TEST PIN 24 — DB/O — CID
TEST PIN 40 — BK/LG — PWR GND
TEST PIN 60

CAMSHAFT POSITION (CMP) SENSOR (LOCATED ON TOP REAR OF ENGINE)

*TEST PINS LOCATED ON BREAKOUT BOX
ALL HARNESS CONNECTORS VIEWED IN MATING SURFACE

Thunderbird/Cougar and Thunderbird SC

FROM CCRM/EEC POWER RELAY

TEST PIN 37
TEST PIN 57 — R — VPWR
TEST PIN 24 — DB/O — CID
TEST PIN 40 — BK/LG — PWR GND
TEST PIN 60

CAMSHAFT POSITION (CMP) SENSOR (LOCATED ON TOP REAR OF ENGINE)

*TEST PINS LOCATED ON BREAKOUT BOX
ALL HARNESS CONNECTORS VIEWED IN MATING SURFACE

4.0L Ranger and Explorer

FROM EEC POWER RELAY

*TEST PIN 37
TEST PIN 57 — R — VPWR
TEST PIN 24 — DB/O — CID
TEST PIN 40 — BK/LG — PWR GND
TEST PIN 60

CAMSHAFT POSITION (CMP) SENSOR (LOCATED NEAR CENTER OF REAR OF ENGINE)

*TEST PINS LOCATED ON BREAKOUT BOX
ALL HARNESS CONNECTORS VIEWED IN MATING SURFACE

Fig. 183   Test DR: CID Circuits (Part 4 of 11). 1994–95

	TEST STEP	RESULT	►	ACTION TO TAKE
DR1	CONTINUOUS MEMORY DIAGNOSTIC TROUBLE CODE (DTC) 214: WILL ENGINE START?			
	NOTE: Key On Engine Running (KOER) DTC 244 (for Probe only) indicates a Camshaft Position (CMP) Sensor DTC 214 has been stored in Keep Alive Memory. This was detected during Cylinder Balance DTM.	Yes	►	GO to DR2.
		No	►	For Probe: GO to DR10. All others: GO to Electronic Ignition (EI) Diagnostics.
	Continuous Memory DTC 214 indicates an error has been detected in the Cylinder Identification (CID) input signal. The error could be due to a hard fault or an intermittent condition. Possible causes:			
	— Open or shorted harness.			
	— Damaged Camshaft Position (CMP)/Crankshaft Position (CKP) sensor.			
	— Damaged Ignition Control Module (ICM) (if equipped).			
	— Damaged Powertrain Control Module (PCM).			
	• Will engine start?			
DR2	CLEAR AND ATTEMPT TO REGENERATE DTC 214			
	• Clear Continuous Memory	Yes	►	GO to DR3.
	• Start engine.	No	►	DTC 214 is intermittent. GO to DR20.
	• Increase rpm to greater than 1500 rpm for 10 seconds. Repeat two times.			
	• Key off.			
	• Rerun KOEO Self-Test.			
	• Is Continuous Memory DTC 214 present?			

Fig. 183   Test DR: CID Circuits (Part 5 of 11). 1994–95

	TEST STEP	RESULT	►	ACTION TO TAKE
DR1	CONTINUOUS MEMORY DIAGNOSTIC TROUBLE CODE (DTC) 214: WILL ENGINE START?			
	Continuous Memory DTC 214 indicates an error has been detected in the Cylinder Identification (CID) input signal. The error could be due to a "hard fault" or an intermittent condition. Possible causes:	Yes	►	GO to DR2.
		No	►	For 2.0L Probe: GO to DR10. All others: GO to Electronic Ignition (EI) Diagnostics.
	— Open or shorted harness.			
	— Damaged Camshaft Position (CMP)/Crankshaft Position (CKP) sensor.			
	— Damaged Ignition Control Module (ICM) (if equipped).			
	— Damaged Powertrain Control Module (PCM).			
	• Will engine start?			
DR2	CLEAR AND ATTEMPT TO RE-GENERATE DTC 214			
	• Clear Continuous Memory	Yes	►	GO to DR3.
	• Start engine.	No	►	DTC 214 is intermittent. GO to DR20.
	• Increase rpm to greater than 1500 rpm for 10 seconds. Repeat two times.			
	• Key off.			
	• Rerun Key On Engine Off Self-Test.			
	• Is Continuous Memory DTC 214 present?			

FM015930072406AX

Fig. 183   Test DR: CID Circuits (Part 5 of 11). 1993

	TEST STEP	RESULT	►	ACTION TO TAKE
DR3	CHECK CID CIRCUIT CONTINUITY TO PCM			
	• Key off.	Yes	►	GO to DR4.
	• Disconnect Powertrain Control Module (PCM). Inspect for damaged or pushed out pins, corrosion, loose wires, etc. Service as necessary.	No	►	SERVICE open circuit. REMOVE breakout box. RECONNECT all components. RERUN Quick Test.
	• Install breakout box. Leave PCM disconnected.			
	• Disconnect Camshaft Position (CMP) sensor or Crankshaft Position (CKP) sensor (refer to DR cover pages for proper sensor test pin number and sensor location).			
	• Measure resistance between the CID/CID(+) Signal Test Pin at the breakout box and the CID/CID(+) circuit at the CMP or CKP sensor vehicle harness connector.			
	For Tempo/Topaz, Crown Victoria/Grand Marquis, Mark VIII and Town Car:			
	— Also measure resistance between Test Pin 46 and SIG RTN circuit at the CMP sensor vehicle harness connector.			
	For Taurus (FF):			
	— Also measure resistance between Test Pin 40 and PWR GND circuit at the CMP sensor vehicle harness connector.			
	For Escort/Tracer:			
	— Also measure resistance between Test Pin 42 and CID(–) circuit at the CMP sensor vehicle harness connector.			
	• Is each resistance less than 5.0 ohms?			
DR4	CHECK CID CIRCUIT FOR SHORT TO POWER			
	• Key off.	Yes	►	Key off. GO to DR5.
	• Breakout box installed, PCM disconnected.	No	►	SERVICE short to power. REMOVE breakout box. RECONNECT all components. RERUN Quick Test.
	• CMP or CKP sensor disconnected.			
	• Disconnect STAR Tester (if applicable).			
	NOTE: For proper results of this test, the STAR Tester must be disconnected. Due to the circuitry of the STAR Tester and the vehicle, a CID signal short to SIG RTN could appear as a CID short to power.			
	For Mustang, Taurus SHO, Thunderbird			
	— Disconnect ICM Pins 1-6.			
	• Key on.			
	• Measure voltage between the CID/CID(+) Signal Test Pin and Test Pin 40 at the breakout box.			
	• Is voltage less than 1.0 volt?			

Fig. 183   Test DR: CID Circuits (Part 6 of 11)

TEST STEP		RESULT	▶	ACTION TO TAKE
DR5	CHECK CID CIRCUIT FOR SHORT TO GROUND			
	• Key off. • Breakout box installed, PCM disconnected. • CMP or CKP sensor disconnected. • ICM (Pins 1-6) disconnected (if applicable). • Measure resistance between the CID/CID(+) Signal Test Pin and Test Pins 16, 40 and 46 at the breakout box. **For Escort/Tracer:** — Also measure resistance between Test Pin 41 and Test Pin 42 at the breakout box. • Is each resistance greater than 10,000 ohms?	Yes	▶	For Mustang, Taurus SHO, Thunderbird SC RECONNECT all components. GO to Electronic Ignition diagnostics. For Taurus (FF) GO to DR6. For all others: GO to DR7.
		No	▶	SERVICE short circuit. REMOVE breakout box. RECONNECT PCM. RERUN Quick Test.
DR6	CHECK VPWR CIRCUIT VOLTAGE			
	• Breakout box installed, PCM disconnected. • CMP sensor disconnected. • Key on, engine off. • Measure voltage between VPWR circuit at CMP sensor vehicle harness connector and battery negative post. • Is voltage greater than 10.5 volts?	Yes	▶	GO to DR7.
		No	▶	SERVICE open in VPWR circuit. REMOVE breakout box. RECONNECT all components. RERUN Quick Test.
DR7	CHECK FOR SHORTS IN PCM			
	• Key off. • Breakout box installed. • Connect PCM to breakout box. • CMP or CKP sensor disconnected. **For Escort/Tracer:** — Measure resistance between Test Pin 41 and Test Pins 42, 37, 57, 40 and 60 at the breakout box. **All others:** — Measure resistance between Test Pin 24 and Test Pins 37, 57, 40, 46 and 60 at the breakout box. • Is each resistance greater than 500 ohms?	Yes	▶	GO to DR8.
		No	▶	REPLACE PCM. REMOVE breakout box. RECONNECT all components. RERUN Quick Test.

Fig. 183 Test DR: CID Circuits (Part 7 of 11). 1993

TEST STEP		RESULT	▶	ACTION TO TAKE
DR5	CHECK CID CIRCUIT FOR SHORT TO GROUND			
	• Key off. • Breakout box installed, PCM disconnected. • CMP or CKP sensor disconnected. • ICM (Pins 1-6) disconnected (if applicable). • Measure resistance between the CID/CID(+) Signal Test Pin and Test Pins 16, 40 and 46 at the breakout box. **For Escort/Tracer:** — Also measure resistance between Test Pin 41 and Test Pin 42 at the breakout box. • Is each resistance greater than 10,000 ohms?	Yes	▶	For Taurus SHO and 2.3L Ranger (49 States): RECONNECT all components. GO to Electronic Ignition diagnostics. For Taurus (FF), Thunderbird/Cougar, Thunderbird SC, 2.3L Ranger (Calif.), Explorer and 4.0L Ranger: GO to DR6. For all others: GO to DR7.
		No	▶	SERVICE short circuit. REMOVE breakout box. RECONNECT PCM. RERUN Quick Test.
DR6	CHECK PWR CIRCUIT VOLTAGE TO CMP			
	• Breakout box installed, PCM disconnected. • CMP sensor disconnected. • Key on, engine off. • Measure voltage between VPWR or KEYPWR circuit at CMP sensor vehicle harness connector and battery negative post. • Is voltage greater than 10.5 volts?	Yes	▶	GO to DR7.
		No	▶	SERVICE open in VPWR or KEYPWR circuit. REMOVE breakout box. RECONNECT all components. RERUN Quick Test.
DR7	CHECK FOR SHORTS IN PCM			
	• Key off. • Breakout box installed. • Connect PCM to breakout box. • CMP or CKP sensor disconnected. **For Escort/Tracer:** — Measure resistance between Test Pin 41 and Test Pins 16, 42, 37, 57, 40 and 60 at the breakout box. **All others:** — Measure resistance between Test Pin 24 and Test Pins 16, 37, 57, 40, 46 and 60 at the breakout box. • Is each resistance greater than 500 ohms?	Yes	▶	GO to DR8.
		No	▶	REPLACE PCM REMOVE breakout box. RECONNECT all components. RERUN Quick Test.

FM015940072407BX

Fig. 183 Test DR: CID Circuits (Part 7 of 11). 1994–95

TEST STEP		RESULT	▶	ACTION TO TAKE
DR8	CHECK CMP OR CKP SENSOR OUTPUT			
	• Key off. • Breakout box installed, PCM connected. • Reconnect CMP or CKP sensor. • DVOM on AC scale (to monitor less than 5.0 volts). **For Escort/Tracer:** — Measure voltage between Test Pins 41 and 42 at the breakout box while varying engine rpm. **For all others:** — Measure voltage between Test Pins 24 and 40 at the breakout box while varying engine rpm. • Does AC voltage vary greater than 0.1 volt AC?	Yes	▶	REPLACE PCM. REMOVE breakout box. RECONNECT all components. RERUN Quick Test.
		No	▶	REPLACE CMP or CKP sensor. REMOVE breakout box. RECONNECT all components. RERUN Quick Test.
DR10	CHECK FOR VPWR TO CAMSHAFT POSITION (CMP) SENSOR			
	• Key off. • Disconnect CMP sensor. • Key on, engine off. • Measure voltage between the VPWR circuit at the CMP sensor vehicle harness connector and the battery negative post. • Is voltage greater than 10.5 volts?	Yes	▶	RECONNECT CMP sensor. REFER to Electronic Ignition System Diagnosis.
		No	▶	SERVICE open VPWR circuit between CMP sensor and power relay. RECONNECT CMP sensor. RERUN Quick Test.

Fig. 183 Test DR: CID Circuits (Part 8 of 11)

TEST STEP		RESULT	▶	ACTION TO TAKE
DR20	CHECK CID WIRING			
	• Enter Engine Running (Continuous Monitor Diagnostic Test Mode (DTM) • Observe VOM or STAR LED for a fault indication while performing the following: **CAUTION: While performing this test, do not touch any moving engine parts.** — Shake, wiggle, bend the CMP or CKP sensor wiring from the PCM to as close as possible to the CMP or CKP sensor. — If possible, lightly tap on the CMP or CKP sensor/connector (to simulate road shock). • Is a fault indicated?	Yes	▶	ISOLATE fault and SERVICE as necessary. CLEAR Continuous Memory. RERUN Quick Test.
		No	▶	Key off. If an EEC-IV monitor box or Scan Tool is not available, GO to DR21.

Fig. 183 Test DR: CID Circuits (Part 9 of 11)

DR21   ROAD TEST (OPTIONAL)

The purpose of the road test is to identify an area of concern by monitoring certain controlled parameters while trying to re-create a driveability or MIL symptom.

Note

A basic working knowledge of the EEC-IV system is critical to effectively analyze road test data.

WARNING

THIS ROAD TEST IS A SUGGESTED BUT OPTIONAL PROCEDURE. ALL APPLICABLE SAFETY PROCEDURES AND TRAFFIC LAWS MUST BE FOLLOWED. IN ORDER FOR A ROAD TEST TO BE PERFORMED IT IS REQUIRED THAT ANOTHER PERSON ACCOMPANY THE DRIVER. THE ACCOMPANYING PERSON CAN MAKE MEASUREMENTS, OBSERVE CHANGES AND RECORD NOTES. IF FOR SOME REASON THIS TEST IS NOT PERFORMED, RETURN TC   OTHER POSSIBLE CAUSES.

Prepare Vehicle For a Road Test

- Breakout box installed, PCM connected.
- Install fuel pressure gauge and MAP / BARO tester (optional).
- Other materials needed; DVOM, pencil, paper, appropriate schematic / pin usage sheet

Preliminary Power / Ground Checks

- With the key ON and a DVOM referenced to the battery negative post, check the following signals for correct values.

POWERS: KAPWR > 10.5V (Pin 1), VPWR > 10.5V (Pins 37 / 57), VREF 5 ± 1V (Pin 26).
GROUNDS (all = 0 ± .5V): PWR GND (Pins 40 / 60), SIG RTN (Pin 46), IGN GND (Pin 16).
OPTIONAL GROUNDS: HO2S GND (Pin 49), CSE GND (Pin 20), MAF RTN (Pin 9 or 15).

Obtaining Other Needed Information and Materials Before the Road Test

-
                                         Before the road test perform
Visual / Mechanical Checks   the EEC-IV sensors and actuators
            along with the CID signal(s), are the main circuits that will be monitored.

-
         a DVOM (with the DVOM referenced to ground all values in DCV units can be used; other values may also be helpful, ex., MAP Hz using the MAP / BARO tester).

Fig. 183   Test DR: CID Circuits (Part 10 of 11)

DR21   ROAD TEST (OPTIONAL) (Continued)

- After starting the engine for the road test, enter Engine Running Continuous Monitor Diagnostic Test Mode (DTM)
- Drive the vehicle to create the conditions so that the symptom will occur.

- When the symptom occurs, the accompanying passenger should observe changes in listed EEC signals. Information about the symptom, operating condition value of the EEC signal or other notes should be recorded onto paper.
- If you are unable to duplicate the symptom, it may still be helpful to verify that the EEC values are in the expected range.

Analyzing the Data

- Once the road test is completed, the results need to be analyzed to locate and service the exact fault which caused the symptom (if, for example, a Continuous Memory Diagnostic Trouble Code 214 is set again and the CID signal stayed within specification, the PCM would be suspect; if the signal went out of specification, harness or sensor would be suspect).
- If no problem is identified, return to   diagnostic procedures.

Fig. 183   Test DR: CID Circuits (Part 11 of 11)

Note

You should enter this Pinpoint Test only when you have been directed here from Diagnostic Routines.

Remember

To prevent the replacement of good components, the following non-EEC areas may be at fault:

- Vehicle speed control system.
- Rear anti-lock brake system.
- Ring gear inside differential.
- Instrumentation system.

This Pinpoint Test is intended to diagnose the following

- PSOM output to the Powertrain Control Module (PCM).
- Harness circuits: PSOM(+) PSOM(-).
- Powertrain Control Module (PCM).

Description

The Programmable Speedometer Odometer Module (PSOM) receives input from the Rear Anti-Lock Brake Sensor (RABS), which is mounted on the rear axle differential. The PSOM takes this input signal information to the Speed Control module and the Powertrain Control Module (PCM).

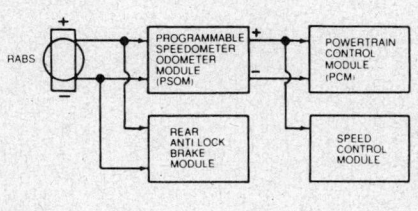

FM0159300725010X

Fig. 184   Test DS: PSOM (Part 1 of 4)

Pinpoint Test Schematic

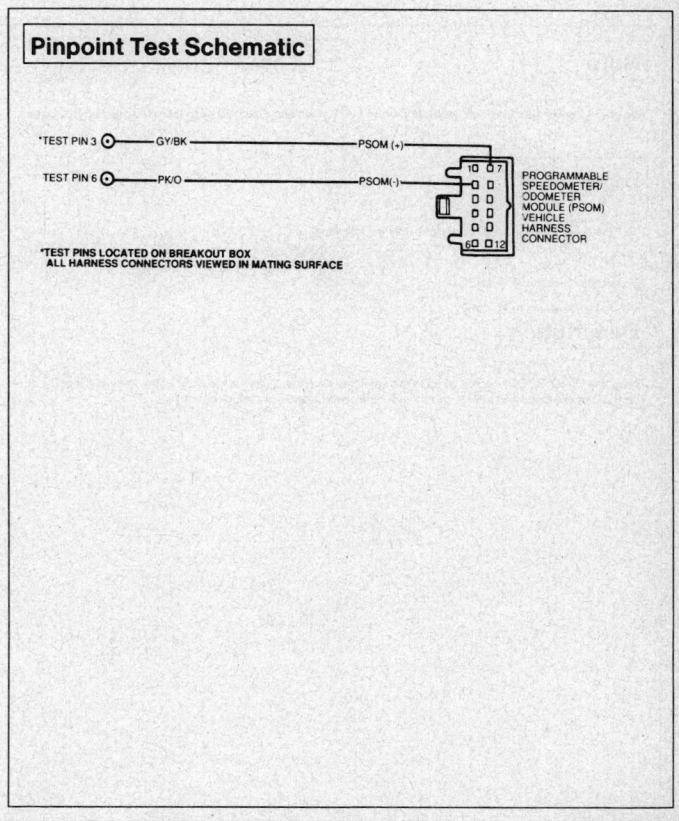

FM0159300725020X

Fig. 184   Test DS: PSOM (Part 2 of 4)

	TEST STEP	RESULT	▶	ACTION TO TAKE
DS1	DIAGNOSTIC TROUBLE CODE (DTC) 29 / 452: CHECK PSOM RESISTANCE			
	Continuous Memory DTC 29 indicates that during the last 80 warm-up cycles, (DTC 452 indicates that during the last 40 warm-up cycles), the PCM detected an error in the PSOM output signal.	Yes	▶	GO to **DS4**.
		No	▶	GO to **DS2**.
	Possible Causes:			
	— Damaged Rear Anti-Lock Brake System (RABS).			
	— Damaged PSOM.			
	— Damaged harness circuits.			
	— Damaged PCM.			
	● Key off.			
	● Disconnect Powertrain Control Module (PCM). Inspect for damaged or pushed out pins, corrosion, loose wires, etc. Service as necessary.			
	● Install breakout box, leave PCM disconnected.			
	● Measure resistance between Test Pin 3 and Test Pin 6 at the breakout box.			
	● **Is resistance between 21,000 and 55,000 ohms?**			
DS2	CHECK CONTINUITY OF THE HARNESS CIRCUITS			
	● Key off.	Yes	▶	GO to **DS3**.
	● Breakout box installed, PCM disconnected.	No	▶	SERVICE open circuit. REMOVE breakout box. RECONNECT all components. RERUN Quick Test.
	● Disconnect PSOM.			
	● Measure resistance between Test Pin 3 at the breakout box and PSOM(+) circuit at the PSOM vehicle harness connector.			
	● Measure resistance between Test Pin 6 at the breakout box and PSOM(-) circuit at the PSOM vehicle harness connector.			
	● **Is each resistance less than 5.0 ohms?**			
DS3	CHECK HARNESS CIRCUITS FOR SHORTS TO POWER AND GROUND			
	● Key off.	Yes	▶	GO to **DS4**.
	● Breakout box installed, PCM disconnected.	No	▶	SERVICE short circuit. REMOVE breakout box. RECONNECT all components. RERUN Quick Test.
	● PSOM disconnected.			
	● Measure resistance between Test Pin 3 and Test Pins 6, 37 and 40 at the breakout box.			
	● **Is each resistance greater than 10,000 ohms?**			

FM0159300725030X

Fig. 184   Test DS: PSOM (Part 3 of 4)

	TEST STEP	RESULT	▶	ACTION TO TAKE
DS4	CHECK RABS SENSOR RESISTANCE			
	● Key off.	Yes	▶	GO to **DS5**.
	● RABS disconnected.	No	▶	REPLACE the RABS. REMOVE breakout box. RECONNECT all components. RERUN Quick Test.
	● Measure the resistance of the RABS.			
	● **Is resistance between 1300 and 1550 ohms?**			
DS5	CHECK PSOM OUTPUT VOLTAGE			
	WARNING: THIS TEST STEP REQUIRES ANOTHER PERSON TO ACCOMPANY THE DRIVER TO MAKE MEASUREMENTS AND RECORD DATA. ALL APPLICABLE SAFETY PROCEDURES AND TRAFFIC LAWS MUST BE FOLLOWED.	Yes	▶	REPLACE PCM. REMOVE breakout box. RERUN Quick Test.
	● Key off.	No	▶	REMOVE breakout box. RECONNECT components. REFER to the Instrument Cluster, Speed Control or Brake for further diagnosis.
	● Breakout box installed.			
	● Reconnect PCM to breakout box.			
	● Reconnect PSOM.			
	● DVOM on 20 volt AC scale.			
	● Warm engine to operating temperature.			
	● Measure AC voltage between Test Pin 3 and Test Pin 6 while gradually increasing vehicle speed to 50 mph.			
	● **Is the maximum voltage received greater than 4.5 volts?**			

FM0159300725040X

Fig. 184   Test DS: PSOM (Part 4 of 4)

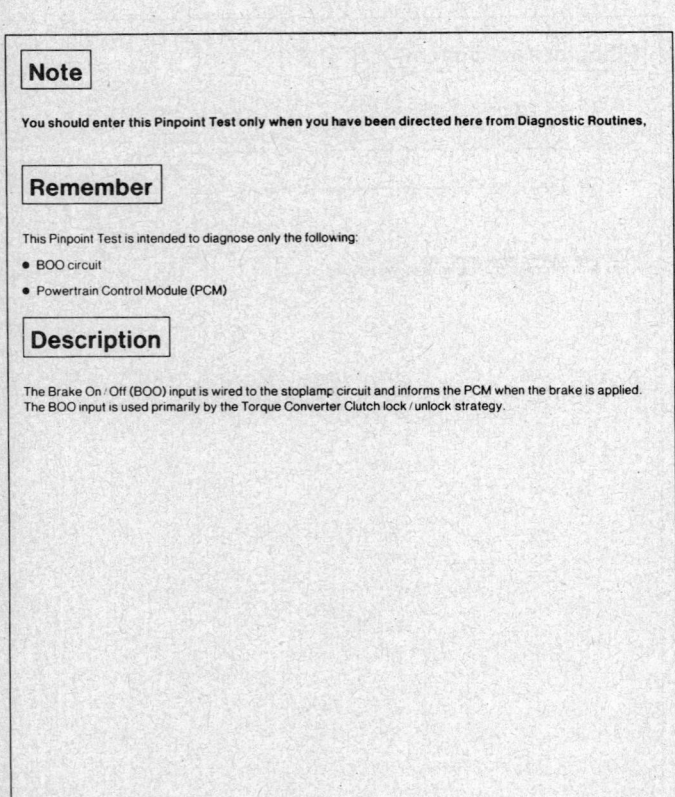

Note

You should enter this Pinpoint Test only when you have been directed here from Diagnostic Routines,

Remember

This Pinpoint Test is intended to diagnose only the following:
● BOO circuit
● Powertrain Control Module (PCM)

Description

The Brake On / Off (BOO) input is wired to the stoplamp circuit and informs the PCM when the brake is applied. The BOO input is used primarily by the Torque Converter Clutch lock / unlock strategy.

FM0159300726010X

Fig. 185   Test FD: BOO (Part 1 of 8)

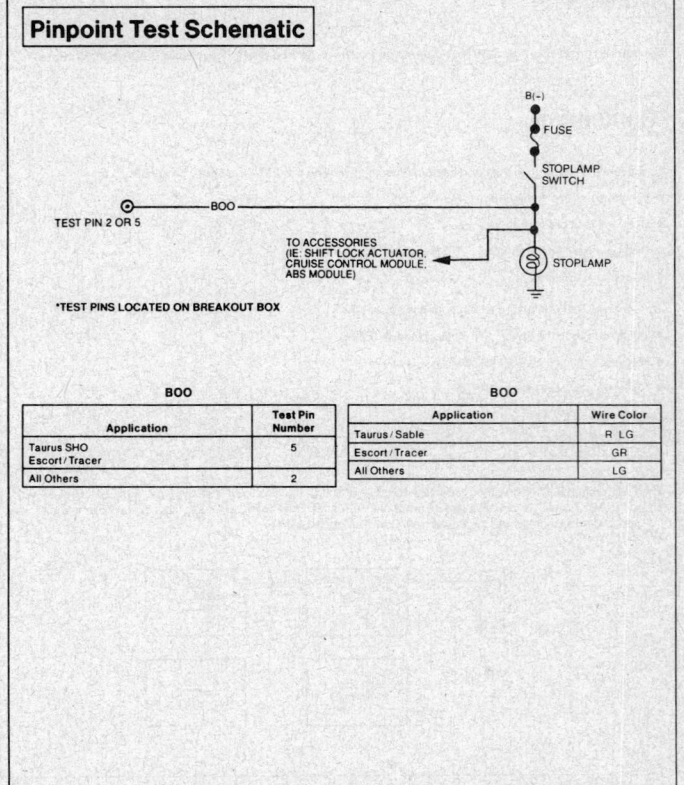

Pinpoint Test Schematic

B(-)

FUSE

STOPLAMP SWITCH

TEST PIN 2 OR 5 — BOO

TO ACCESSORIES (IE: SHIFT LOCK ACTUATOR, CRUISE CONTROL MODULE, ABS MODULE)

STOPLAMP

*TEST PINS LOCATED ON BREAKOUT BOX

BOO	
Application	Test Pin Number
Taurus SHO Escort / Tracer	5
All Others	2

BOO	
Application	Wire Color
Taurus / Sable	R LG
Escort / Tracer	GR
All Others	LG

FM0159300726020X

Fig. 185   Test FD: BOO (Part 2 of 8)

FD1 — Part 3 of 8

TEST STEP	RESULT	▶	ACTION TO TAKE
FD1 DIAGNOSTIC TROUBLE CODE (DTC) 74 / 536 VERIFY BRAKE WAS PRESSED DTC 74 / 536 indicates that when the brake pedal was depressed and released during the Engine Running Self-Test, the BOO signal did not cycle high and low. Possible causes: — Brake pedal not depressed and released during the Engine Running Self-Test. — Brake pedal depressed during entire Engine Running Self-Test. — Open BOO / stoplamp circuit. — Short to GROUND or POWER. — Damaged brake switch. — Damaged Powertrain Control Module (PCM). • **Did you press brake during the Engine Running Self-Test?** NOTE: On some vehicles it is necessary to depress and release the brake after the Dynamic Response Code 1(0) but before the brief WOT.	Yes No	▶ ▶	GO to **FD2**. RERUN Engine Running Self-Test. PRESS brake once during test.
FD2 CHECK OPERATION OF STOPLAMPS • Key on. • Check stoplamp operation.	Stoplamps operate normally Stoplamps never on Stoplamps always on	▶ ▶ ▶	GO to **FD3**. GO to **FD4**. GO to **FD5**.
FD3 CHECK FOR BOO CIRCUIT CYCLING • Key off. • Disconnect Powertrain Control Module (PCM). Inspect for damaged or pushed out pins, corrosion, loose wires, etc. Service as necessary. • Install breakout box, leave PCM disconnected. • DVOM on 20 volt scale. • Measure voltage between BOO Test Pin (refer to chart on **FD** cover page) and Test Pin 40 at the breakout box while depressing and releasing brake. • **Does the voltage cycle?**	Yes No	▶ ▶	REPLACE PCM. REMOVE breakout box. RERUN Quick Test. SERVICE open in BOO circuit between PCM and BOO connection to stoplamp circuit. RERUN Quick Test.

Fig. 185 Test FD: BOO (Part 3 of 8)

FM0159300726030X

Part 4 of 8

TEST STEP	RESULT	▶	ACTION TO TAKE
FD4 CHECK FOR POWER TO BRAKE SWITCH NOTE: Using a 12V test lamp, verify integrity of related fuses in fuse panel and check condition of stoplamp bulbs. • Key off. • Disconnect brake switch (located on brake pedal). • Measure voltage between B+ input to brake switch and chassis ground. • **Is voltage greater than 10 volts?**	Yes No	▶ ▶	VERIFY operation of brake switch. If OK, SERVICE open circuit between brake switch and stoplamp ground. RECONNECT brake switch connector. RERUN Quick Test. SERVICE open B+ circuit to brake switch. RECONNECT brake switch connector. RERUN Quick Test.
FD5 VERIFY BRAKE SWITCH IS NOT ALWAYS CLOSED • Key off. • Brake switch disconnected. • Key on, engine off. • **Are stoplamps still on?**	Yes No	▶ ▶	GO to **FD6**. VERIFY proper installation of brake switch. If OK, REPLACE brake switch. RECONNECT harness connector. RERUN Quick Test.
FD6 CHECK FOR SHORT TO POWER IN PCM • Key off. • Brake switch disconnected. • Disconnect Powertrain Control Module (PCM). • Key on, engine off. • **Are stoplamps still on?**	Yes No	▶ ▶	GO to **FD7**. REPLACE PCM. RECONNECT brake switch. RERUN Quick Test.
FD7 CHECK FOR SHORT TO POWER IN SHIFTLOCK ACTUATOR • Key off. • PCM disconnected. • Brake switch disconnected. • Disconnect shiftlock actuator, cruise control module and ABS module (if equipped) to isolate brake switch wiring. • Key on, engine off. • **Are stoplights still on?**	Yes No	▶ ▶	SERVICE short to power in BOO / Stoplamp circuit. RECONNECT PCM, brake switch and accessories. RERUN Quick Test. SERVICE short in accessories (i.e., shiftlock actuator, ABS module, etc). RECONNECT all components. RERUN Quick Test.

Fig. 185 Test FD: BOO (Part 4 of 8)

FM0159300726040X

Part 5 of 8

TEST STEP	RESULT	▶	ACTION TO TAKE
FD90 CONTINUOUS MEMORY CODE 536: CHECK FOR PROPER STOPLAMP SWITCH INSTALLATION Continuous Memory Code 536 indicates a BOO circuit failure. If the BOO input does not cycle after a predetermined number of transitions from 0 mph to a specific speed, the BOO input is assumed to be damaged and Continuous Memory Code 536 is set. Possible causes: — Stoplamp switch improperly installed. — Open stoplamp / BOO circuit. — Stoplamp / BOO circuit shorted to power. — Damaged stoplamp switch. — Damaged stoplamp ground connection. • Check stoplamp switch for proper installation (alignment with pedal), corrosion, frayed wires, etc. • **Is stoplamp switch in good condition and properly installed?**	Yes No	▶ ▶	GO to **FD91**. SERVICE as necessary. CLEAR Continuous Memory (refer to Quick Test Appendix). RERUN Quick Test.
FD91 CHECK STOPLAMP GROUND • Check stoplamp ground connection for corrosion or other damage. • Check stoplamp connector and wires for corrosion or other damage. • **Are stoplamp wires, connector, and ground connection OK?**	Yes No	▶ ▶	GO to **FD92**. SERVICE as necessary. CLEAR Continuous Memory. RERUN Quick Test.
FD92 CHECK STOPLAMP / BOO CIRCUITS FOR SHORT TO POWER • Key on, engine off. • Brake pedal NOT depressed. • Wiggle stoplamp / BOO circuit wires and connectors while observing stoplamps. • **Do stoplamps flash on while wiggling?**	Yes No	▶ ▶	ISOLATE short to power and SERVICE as necessary. CLEAR Continuous Memory. RERUN Quick Test. GO to **FD93**
FD93 CHECK STOPLAMP CIRCUIT CONTINUITY • Key off. • Depress brake pedal and hold. • Wiggle stoplamp circuit wires and connectors while observing stoplamps. • Lightly tap stoplamp switch (simulate road shock) while observing stoplamps. • **Do stoplamps ever go off?**	Yes No	▶ ▶	ISOLATE open in stoplamp circuit and SERVICE as necessary. CLEAR Continuous Memory. RERUN Quick Test. GO to **FD94**

Fig. 185 Test FD: BOO (Part 5 of 8). 1994–95

FM0159400726050X

Part 6 of 8

TEST STEP	RESULT	▶	ACTION TO TAKE
FD94 CHECK BOO CIRCUIT CONTINUITY • Key off. • Release brake pedal. • Disconnect processor 60 pin connector. Inspect for damaged or pushed out pins, corrosion, loose wires, etc. Service as necessary. • Install breakout box, leave processor disconnected. • Connect DVOM between BOO Test Pin (refer to schematic) at the breakout box and stoplamp circuit at the stoplamp switch. • DVOM on 200 ohm scale. • Wiggle BOO circuit wires and connectors while observing DVOM. • **Is resistance ever greater than 5.0 ohms while wiggling?**	Yes No	▶ ▶	ISOLATE open in BOO circuit and SERVICE as necessary. REMOVE breakout box. RECONNECT processor. RERUN Quick Test. further diagnosis using the EEC-IV monitor box. If an EEC-IV monitor box is not available, GO to **FD99**.

Fig. 185 Test FD: BOO (Part 6 of 8). 1994–95

FM0159400726060X

FD99 ROAD TEST

The purpose of the road test is to identify an area of concern by monitoring certain controlled parameters while trying to recreate a driveability or MIL symptom.

Note

A basic working knowledge of the EEC-IV system is critical to effectively analyze road test data.

WARNING

THIS ROAD TEST IS A SUGGESTED BUT OPTIONAL PROCEDURE. ALL APPLICABLE SAFETY PROCEDURES AND TRAFFIC LAWS MUST BE FOLLOWED. IN ORDER FOR A ROAD TEST TO BE PERFORMED IT IS REQUIRED THAT ANOTHER PERSON ACCOMPANY THE DRIVER. THE ACCOMPANYING PERSON CAN MAKE MEASUREMENTS, OBSERVE CHANGES AND RECORD NOTES.

Prepare Vehicle for a Road Test

- Breakout box installed, processor connected.
- Install fuel pressure gauge and MAP/BP tester (optional).
- Other materials needed: DVOM, pencil, paper, appropriate schematic/pin usage sheet

Preliminary Power/Ground Checks

- With the key ON and a DVOM referenced to the battery negative post, check the following signals for correct values.

POWERS: KAPWR > 10.5V (Pin 1), VPWR > 10.5V (Pins 37/57), VREF 5 ± 1V (Pin 26).
GROUNDS (all = 0 ± .5V): PWR GND (Pins 40/60), SIG RTN (Pin 46), IGN GND (Pin 16).
OPTIONAL GROUNDS: HEGO GND (Pin 49), CSE GND (Pin 20), MAF RTN (Pin 9 or 15).

Obtaining Other Information and Materials Before the Road Test

- Refer to the Symptom Charts in   (EEC-IV Monitor Box: Intermittent Fault Diagnosis) that most resemble driveability or MIL symptom. Before the road test, perform the Visual/Mechanical Checks that are listed. Next, list the EEC-IV sensors and actuators in the order given. These circuits, along with the BOO signal, are the main circuits that will be monitored.

-            most of the values can be read using the breakout box and a DVOM (with the DVOM referenced to ground all values in DCV units can be used; other values may also be helpful, ex., MAP Hz using the MAP/BP tester).

FM0159400726070X

Fig. 185   Test FD: BOO (Part 7 of 8). 1994–95

FD99 ROAD TEST (Continued)

- The use of test lamps may also aid diagnosis. For example, a test lamp could be connected at the stop lamp switch between BATT (+) and ground with another connected between the power to bulbs pin and ground. The BATT (+) lamp should always stay. The power to bulbs lamp will only be on when the brake is depressed. Also, with a DVOM connected between the BOO Test Pin and Test Pin 40 at the breakout box, if 6-7 volts is shown with the brake pedal released, this could indicate an open circuit between the processor and stop lamp ground (the processor supplies 6-7 volts on the BOO circuit, but this voltage is not strong enough to light the stoplamps or most test lamps).

Road Test

- After starting the engine for the road test, enter Engine Running Continuous Monitor Mode
- Drive the vehicle to create the conditions in which the symptom occurs.
- When the symptom occurs, the passenger should observe changes in listed EEC-IV signals. Information about the symptom, operating condition, value of the EEC-IV signal or other notes should be recorded.
- If the symptom cannot be duplicated, verify that the EEC-IV values are in the expected range.

Analyzing the Data

- Once the road test is completed, the results should be analyzed to locate and service the fault which caused the symptom.

FM0159400726080X

Fig. 185   Test FD: BOO (Part 8 of 8). 1994–95

Note

You should enter this Pinpoint Test only when you have been directed here from Diagnostic Routines or Pinpoint Test S.

Remember

This Pinpoint Test is intended to diagnose only the following:

- Blower (BLR) motor input circuit.
- Daytime Running Lamps (DRL) input circuit.
- Headlamp (HDL) input circuit.
- Rear window Defroster (DEF) input circuit.
- Powertrain Control Module (PCM)

Description

The electrical load inputs are used by idle speed control strategy to prevent idle speed fluctuations when loads are demanded or turned off by the driver. Four circuits are used by the PCM to detect the ON and OFF status of the blower motor, daytime running lamps (Canadian vehicles), headlamps and the rear window defroster.

Input Logic:

INPUT	OFF STATE	ON STATE
Blower motor	Position 1 or 2: Between 10 and 17 volts	Position 3 or 4: Less than 1.5 volts
Daytime running lamps	Between 10 and 17 volts	Less than 1.5 volts
Headlamps	Less than 1.5 volts	Between 10 and 17 volts
Rear window defroster	Between 10 and 17 volts	Less than 3.0 volts

FM0159300727010X

Fig. 186   Test FE: Electrical Load Inputs (Part 1 of 9). 1993

Pinpoint Test Schematic

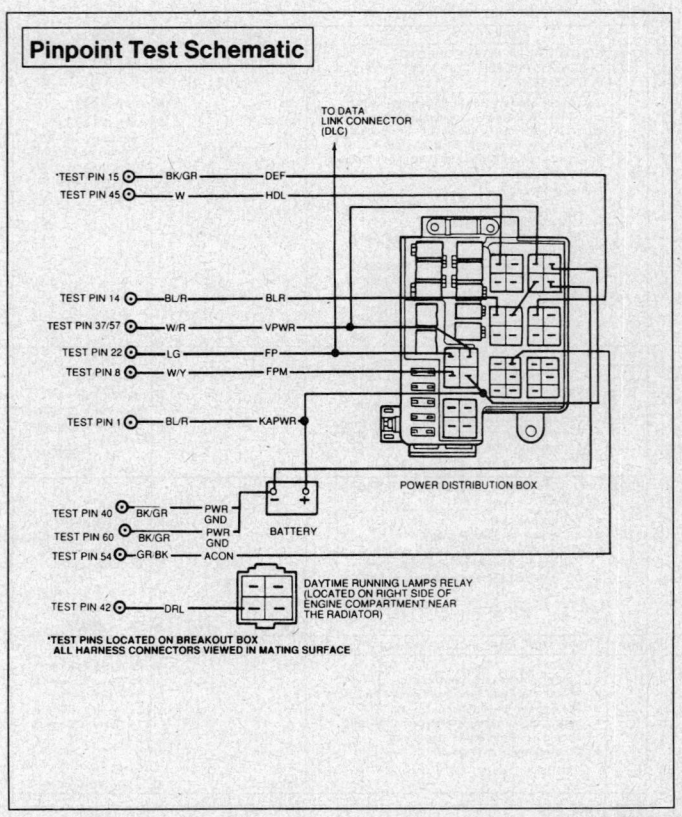

FM0159300727020X

Fig. 186   Test FE: Electrical Load Inputs (Part 2 of 9). 1993

TEST STEP	RESULT	▶	ACTION TO TAKE
FE1 ELECTRICAL LOAD SWITCH TEST DIRECTIONS			
• If the idle speed symptom is observed when the Blower (BLR) Motor is ON, then		▶	GO to FE10
• If the idle speed symptom is observed when the Daytime Running Lamps (DRL) are ON, then		▶	GO to FE20
• If the idle speed symptom is observed when the Headlamp (HDL) switch is turned ON, then		▶	GO to FE30
• If the idle speed symptom is observed when the Rear Window Defroster (DEF) switch is turned ON, then		▶	GO to FE40
• If the idle speed symptom is observed at any other time, then		▶	RETURN to Diagnostic Routines to continue symptom diagnosis
FE10 CHECK VOLTAGE OF BLR CIRCUIT, SWITCH IN LOW SPEED POSITION			
• Key off.	Yes	▶	GO to FE11
• Disconnect Powertrain Control Module (PCM). Inspect for damaged or pushed out pins, corrosion, loose wires, etc. Service as necessary.	No	▶	GO to FE13
• Install breakout box, leave PCM disconnected.			
• Key on, engine off.			
• Push the climate control blower motor switch to low speed position 1 or 2.			
• Turn all other accessories off.			
• Measure the voltage between Test Pin 14 at the breakout box and chassis ground.			
• **Is the voltage between 10 and 17 volts?**			
FE11 CHECK VOLTAGE OF BLR CIRCUIT, SWITCH IN HIGH SPEED POSITION			
• Key off.	Yes	▶	REPLACE the PCM. REMOVE breakout box. VERIFY elimination of idle speed concern.
• Breakout box installed, PCM disconnected.			
• Push the climate control blower motor switch to high speed position 3 or 4.			
• Turn all other accessories off.			
• Key on, engine off.	No	▶	GO to FE12
• Measure the voltage between Test Pin 14 at the breakout box and chassis ground.			
• **Is voltage less than 1.5 volts?**			

FM0159300727030X

Fig. 186 Test FE: Electrical Load Inputs (Part 3 of 9). 1993

TEST STEP	RESULT	▶	ACTION TO TAKE
FE12 CHECK BLR CIRCUIT FOR SHORT TO POWER			
• Key off.	Yes	▶	REMOVE breakout box. RECONNECT all components.
• Disconnect blower motor relay (refer to Pinpoint Test schematic).			check for damaged blower motor switch or relay.
• Breakout box installed, PCM disconnected.			
• Measure resistance between Test Pin 14 and Test Pins 37 / 57 at the breakout box.	No	▶	SERVICE short circuit. REMOVE breakout box. RECONNECT all components. VERIFY elimination of idle speed concern.
• **Is resistance greater than 10,000 ohms?**			
FE13 CHECK BLR CIRCUIT CONTINUITY			
• Key off.	Yes	▶	GO to FE14
• Disconnect blower motor relay (refer to Pinpoint Test schematic).	No	▶	SERVICE open circuit. REMOVE breakout box. RECONNECT all components. VERIFY elimination of idle speed concern.
• Breakout box installed, PCM disconnected.			
• Measure resistance between Test Pin 14 at breakout box and BLR circuit at Power Distribution box (refer to the Pinpoint Test schematic).			
• **Is resistance less than 5.0 ohms?**			
FE14 CHECK BLR CIRCUIT FOR SHORT TO GROUND			
• Key off.	Yes	▶	REMOVE breakout box. RECONNECT all components.
• Blower motor relay disconnected.			check for damaged blower motor switch or relay.
• Breakout box installed, PCM disconnected.			
• Measure resistance between Test Pin 14 and Test Pins 40, 46 and 60 at breakout box.	No	▶	SERVICE short circuit. REMOVE breakout box. RECONNECT all components. VERIFY elimination of idle speed concern.
• **Is resistance greater than 10,000 ohms?**			

FM0159300727040X

Fig. 186 Test FE: Electrical Load Inputs (Part 4 of 9). 1993

TEST STEP	RESULT	▶	ACTION TO TAKE
FE20 CHECK VOLTAGE OF DRL CIRCUIT, PARKING BRAKE AND HEADLAMPS ON			
• Key off.	Yes	▶	GO to FE21
• Disconnect Powertrain Control Module (PCM). Inspect for damaged or pushed out pins, corrosion, loose wires, etc. Service as necessary.	No	▶	GO to FE23
• Install breakout box, leave PCM disconnected.			
• Apply parking brake.			
• Key on, engine off.			
• Turn headlamps on.			
• Turn all other accessories off.			
• Measure voltage between Test Pin 42 at breakout box and chassis ground.			
• **Is voltage between 10 and 17 volts?**			
FE21 CHECK VOLTAGE OF DRL CIRCUIT, PARKING BRAKE AND HEADLAMPS OFF			
• Key off.	Yes	▶	REPLACE PCM. REMOVE breakout box. VERIFY elimination of idle speed concern.
• Breakout box installed, PCM disconnected.			
• Release parking brake.			
• Key on, engine off.			
• Turn headlamps off.	No	▶	GO to FE22
• Measure voltage between Test Pin 42 at breakout box and chassis ground.			
• **Is voltage less than 1.5 volts?**			
FE22 CHECK DRL CIRCUIT FOR SHORT TO POWER			
• Key off.	Yes	▶	REMOVE breakout box. RECONNECT all components.
• Breakout box installed, PCM disconnected.			check DRL module.
• Disconnect Daytime Running Lamps relay (refer to Pinpoint Test schematic).			
• Measure resistance between Test Pin 42 and Test Pins 37 57 at breakout box.	No	▶	SERVICE short circuit. REMOVE breakout box. RECONNECT all components. VERIFY elimination of idle speed concern.
• **Is resistance greater than 10,000 ohms?**			
FE23 CHECK DRL CIRCUIT CONTINUITY			
• Key off.	Yes	▶	GO to FE24
• Breakout box installed, PCM disconnected.	No	▶	SERVICE open circuit. REMOVE breakout box. RECONNECT all components. VERIFY elimination of idle speed concern.
• Disconnect Daytime Running Lamps relay (refer to Pinpoint Test schematic).			
• Measure resistance between Test Pin 42 at breakout box and Daytime Running Lamps relay signal pin cavity at DRL relay female connector.			
• **Is resistance less than 5.0 ohms?**			

FM0159300727050X

Fig. 186 Test FE: Electrical Load Inputs (Part 5 of 9). 1993

TEST STEP	RESULT	▶	ACTION TO TAKE
FE24 CHECK DRL CIRCUIT FOR SHORT TO GROUND			
• Key off.	Yes	▶	REMOVE breakout box. RECONNECT all components.
• Daytime Running Lamps relay disconnected.			
• Breakout box installed, PCM disconnected.			check for damaged DRL module.
• Measure resistance between Test Pin 42 and Test Pins 40, 46 and 60 at breakout box.	No	▶	SERVICE short circuit. REMOVE breakout box. RECONNECT all components. VERIFY elimination of idle speed concern.
• **Is resistance greater than 10,000 ohms?**			
FE30 CHECK VOLTAGE OF HDL CIRCUIT, HEADLAMPS OFF			
• Key off.	Yes	▶	GO to FE31
• Disconnect Powertrain Control Module (PCM). Inspect for damaged or pushed out pins, corrosion, loose wires, etc. Service as necessary.	No	▶	GO to FE34
• Install breakout box, leave PCM disconnected.			
• Key on, engine off.			
• Turn headlamps and all other accessories off.			
• Measure voltage between Test Pin 45 at Breakout box and chassis ground.			
• **Is voltage less than 1.5 volts?**			
FE31 CHECK VOLTAGE OF HDL CIRCUIT, HEADLAMPS ON			
• Key off.	Yes	▶	REPLACE PCM. REMOVE breakout box. VERIFY elimination of idle speed concern.
• Breakout box installed, PCM disconnected.			
• Key on, engine off.			
• All accessories off.			
• Turn headlamps on.	No	▶	GO to FE32
• Measure voltage between Test Pin 45 at breakout box and chassis ground.			
• **Is voltage between 10 and 17 volts?**			
FE32 CHECK HDL CIRCUIT CONTINUITY			
• Key off.	Yes	▶	GO to FE33
• Disconnect headlamp relay (refer to Pinpoint Test schematic).	No	▶	SERVICE open circuit. REMOVE breakout box. RECONNECT all components. VERIFY elimination of idle speed concern.
• Breakout box installed, PCM disconnected.			
• Measure resistance between Test Pin 45 at breakout box and HDL circuit at Power Distribution box (refer to Pinpoint Test schematic).			
• **Is resistance less than 5.0 ohms?**			

FM0159300727060X

Fig. 186 Test FE: Electrical Load Inputs (Part 6 of 9). 1993

TEST STEP	RESULT	▶	ACTION TO TAKE
FE33 CHECK HDL CIRCUIT FOR SHORT TO GROUND • Key off. • Headlamp relay disconnected. • Breakout box installed, PCM disconnected. • Measure resistance between Test Pin 45 and Test Pins 40, 46 and 60 at breakout box. • Is each resistance greater than 10,000 ohms?	Yes	▶	REMOVE breakout box. RECONNECT all components. check for damaged HDL switch.
	No	▶	SERVICE short circuit. REMOVE breakout box. RECONNECT all components. VERIFY elimination of idle speed concern.
FE34 CHECK HDL CIRCUIT FOR SHORT TO POWER • Key off. • Disconnect headlamp relay (refer to Pinpoint Test schematic). • Breakout box installed, PCM disconnected. • Measure resistance between Test Pin 45 and Test Pins 37/57 at breakout box. • Is each resistance greater than 10,000 ohms?	Yes	▶	REMOVE breakout box. RECONNECT all components. check for damaged HDL switch.
	No	▶	SERVICE short circuit. REMOVE breakout box. RECONNECT all components. VERIFY elimination of idle speed concern.
FE40 CHECK VOLTAGE OF DEF CIRCUIT, DEFROSTER OFF • Key off. • Disconnect Powertrain Control Module (PCM). Inspect for damaged or pushed out pins, corrosion, loose wires, etc. Service as necessary. • Install breakout box, leave PCM disconnected. • Key on, engine off. • Turn rear window defroster and all other accessories off. • Measure voltage between Test Pin 15 at breakout box and chassis ground. • Is voltage between 10 and 17 volts?	Yes	▶	GO to FE41.
	No	▶	GO to FE43.

Fig. 186 Test FE: Electrical Load Inputs (Part 7 of 9). 1993

TEST STEP	RESULT	▶	ACTION TO TAKE
FE41 CHECK VOLTAGE OF DEF CIRCUIT, DEFROSTER ON • Key off. • Breakout box installed, PCM disconnected. • Key on, engine off. • Turn all accessories off. • Turn rear window defroster on. • Measure voltage between Test Pin 15 at breakout box and chassis ground. • Is voltage less than 3.0 volts?	Yes	▶	REPLACE PCM. REMOVE breakout box. VERIFY elimination of idle speed concern.
	No	▶	GO to FE42.
FE42 CHECK DEF CIRCUIT FOR SHORT TO POWER • Key off. • Disconnect rear window defroster relay (refer to Pinpoint Test schematic). • Breakout box installed, PCM disconnected. • Measure resistance between Test Pin 15 and Test Pins 37/57 at breakout box. • Is each resistance greater than 10,000 ohms?	Yes	▶	REMOVE breakout box. RECONNECT all components. check for fault in DEF switch and relay circuit.
	No	▶	SERVICE short circuit. REMOVE breakout box. RECONNECT all components. VERIFY elimination of idle speed concern.
FE43 CHECK DEF CIRCUIT CONTINUITY • Key off. • Disconnect rear window defroster switch (refer to Pinpoint Test schematic). • Breakout box installed, PCM disconnected. • Measure resistance between Test Pin 15 at breakout box and DEF circuit at Power Distribution box (refer to Pinpoint Test schematic). • Is resistance less than 5.0 ohms?	Yes	▶	GO to FE44.
	No	▶	SERVICE open circuit. REMOVE breakout box. RECONNECT all components. VERIFY elimination of idle speed concern.

Fig. 186 Test FE: Electrical Load Inputs (Part 8 of 9). 1993

TEST STEP	RESULT	▶	ACTION TO TAKE
FE44 CHECK DEF CIRCUIT FOR SHORT TO GROUND • Key off. • Rear window defroster relay disconnected. • Breakout box installed, PCM disconnected. • Measure resistance between Test Pin 15 and Test Pin 40, 46 and 60 at breakout box. • Is resistance greater than 10,000 ohms?	Yes	▶	REMOVE breakout box. RECONNECT all components. check for fault in DEF switch and relay circuit.
	No	▶	SERVICE short circuit. REMOVE breakout box. RECONNECT all components. VERIFY elimination of idle speed concern.

Fig. 186 Test FE: Electrical Load Inputs (Part 9 of 9). 1993

Note

You should enter this Pinpoint Test only when you have been directed here from Diagnostic Routines, or Pinpoint Test **S**.

Remember

This Pinpoint Test is intended to diagnose only the following:

• Blower (BLR) motor input circuit
• Daytime Running Lamps (DRL) input circuit
• Headlamp (HDL) input circuit
• Rear window Defroster (DEF) input circuit
• Powertrain Control Module (PCM)

Description

The electrical load inputs are used by idle speed control strategy to prevent idle speed fluctuations when loads are demanded or turned off by the driver. Four circuits are used by the PCM to detect the ON and OFF status of the blower motor, daytime running lamps (Canadian vehicles), headlamps and the rear window defroster.

Input Logic:

INPUT	OFF	ON
Blower motor	Position 1 or 2 Between 10 and 17 volts	Position 3 or 4 Less than 1.5 volts
Daytime running lamps	Between 10 and 17 volts	Less than 1.5 volts
Headlamps	Less than 1.5 volts	Between 10 and 17 volts
Rear window defroster	Between 10 and 17 volts	Less than 3.0 volts

FM015940072901 0X

Fig. 187 Test FE: Electrical Load Inputs (Part 1 of 10). 1994–95

Pinpoint Test Schematic

Probe CD4E and Calif. M/T

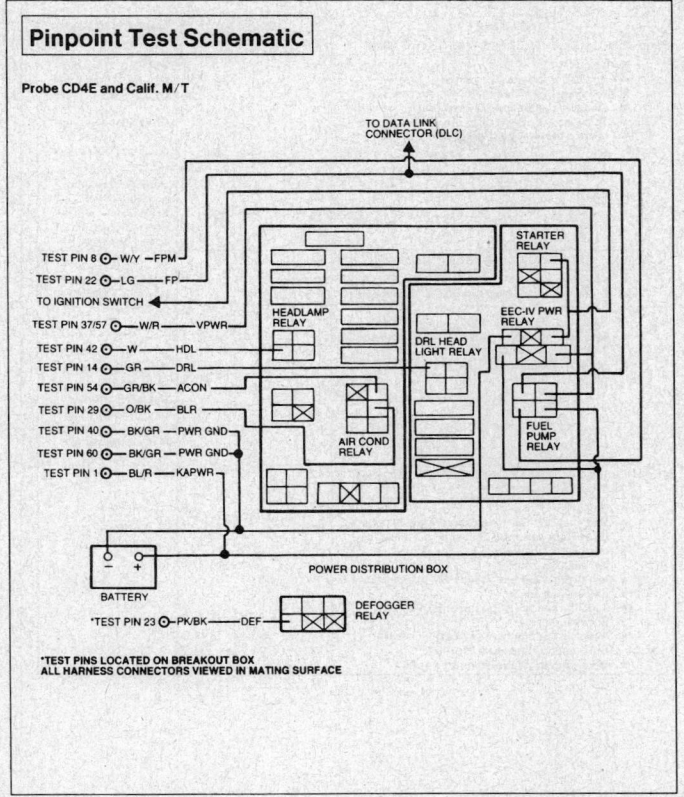

FM0159400729020X

Fig. 187 Test FE: Electrical Load Inputs (Part 2 of 10). 1994–95

All others

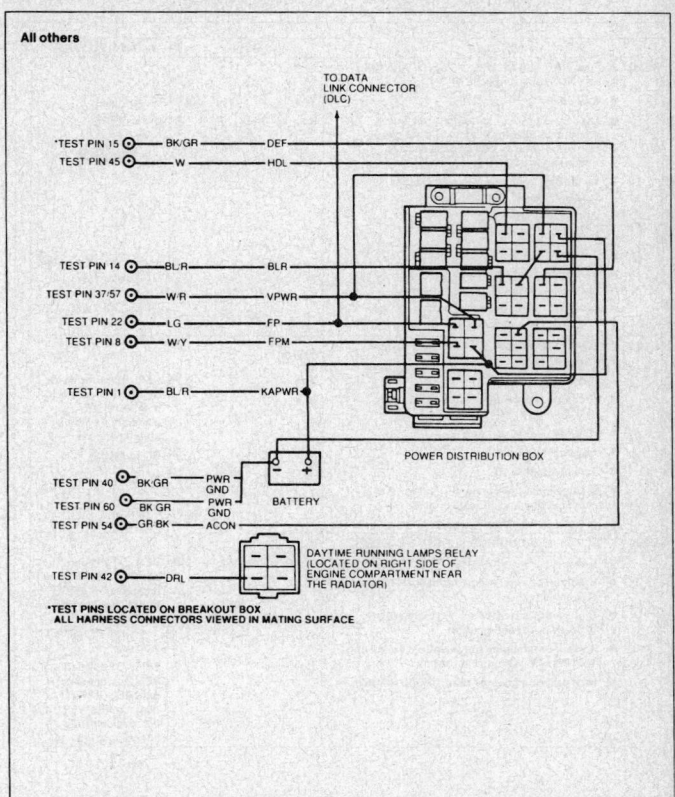

FM0159400729030X

Fig. 187 Test FE: Electrical Load Inputs (Part 3 of 10). 1994–95

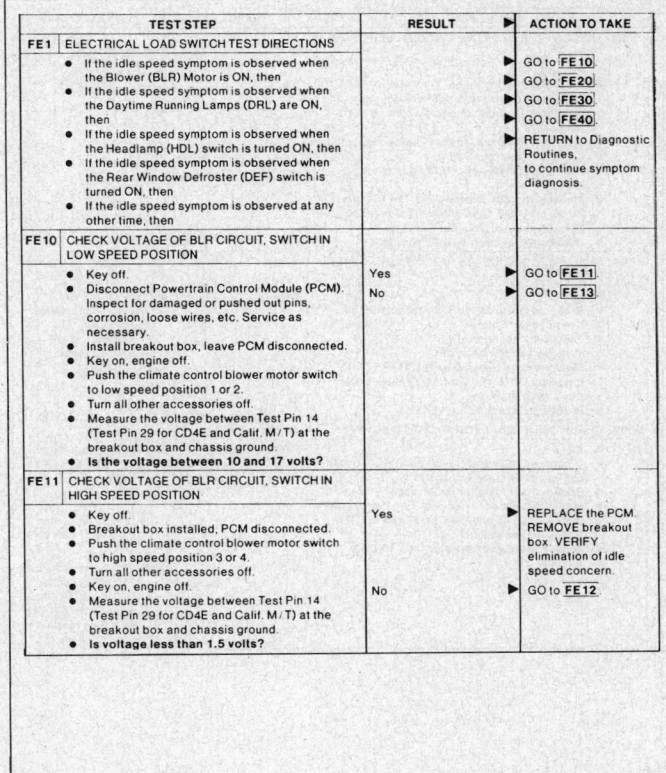

TEST STEP		RESULT	▶	ACTION TO TAKE
FE1	**ELECTRICAL LOAD SWITCH TEST DIRECTIONS**			
	• If the idle speed symptom is observed when the Blower (BLR) Motor is ON, then		▶	GO to FE10.
	• If the idle speed symptom is observed when the Daytime Running Lamps (DRL) are ON, then		▶	GO to FE20.
	• If the idle speed symptom is observed when the Headlamp (HDL) switch is turned ON, then		▶	GO to FE30.
	• If the idle speed symptom is observed when the Rear Window Defroster (DEF) switch is turned ON, then		▶	GO to FE40.
	• If the idle speed symptom is observed at any other time, then			RETURN to Diagnostic Routines, to continue symptom diagnosis.
FE10	**CHECK VOLTAGE OF BLR CIRCUIT, SWITCH IN LOW SPEED POSITION**			
	• Key off.	Yes	▶	GO to FE11.
	• Disconnect Powertrain Control Module (PCM). Inspect for damaged or pushed out pins, corrosion, loose wires, etc. Service as necessary.	No	▶	GO to FE13.
	• Install breakout box, leave PCM disconnected.			
	• Key on, engine off.			
	• Push the climate control blower motor switch to low speed position 1 or 2.			
	• Turn all other accessories off.			
	• Measure the voltage between Test Pin 14 (Test Pin 29 for CD4E and Calif. M/T) at the breakout box and chassis ground.			
	• **Is the voltage between 10 and 17 volts?**			
FE11	**CHECK VOLTAGE OF BLR CIRCUIT, SWITCH IN HIGH SPEED POSITION**			
	• Key off.	Yes	▶	REPLACE the PCM. REMOVE breakout box. VERIFY elimination of idle speed concern.
	• Breakout box installed, PCM disconnected.			
	• Push the climate control blower motor switch to high speed position 3 or 4.			
	• Turn all other accessories off.			
	• Key on, engine off.	No	▶	GO to FE12.
	• Measure the voltage between Test Pin 14 (Test Pin 29 for CD4E and Calif. M/T) at the breakout box and chassis ground.			
	• **Is voltage less than 1.5 volts?**			

FM0159400729040X

Fig. 187 Test FE: Electrical Load Inputs (Part 4 of 10). 1994–95

TEST STEP		RESULT	▶	ACTION TO TAKE
FE12	**CHECK BLR CIRCUIT FOR SHORT TO POWER**			
	• Key off.	Yes	▶	REMOVE breakout box. RECONNECT all components. REFER to Climate Control Group to check for damaged blower motor switch or relay.
	• Disconnect blower motor relay (refer to Pinpoint Test schematic).			
	• Breakout box installed, PCM disconnected.			
	• Measure resistance between Test Pin 14 (Test Pin 29 for CD4E and Calif. M/T) and Test Pins 37/57 at the breakout box.	No	▶	SERVICE short circuit. REMOVE breakout box. RECONNECT all components. VERIFY elimination of idle speed concern.
	• **Is resistance greater than 10,000 ohms?**			
FE13	**CHECK BLR CIRCUIT CONTINUITY**			
	• Key off.	Yes	▶	GO to FE14.
	• Disconnect blower motor relay (refer to Pinpoint Test schematic).	No	▶	SERVICE open circuit. REMOVE breakout box. RECONNECT all components. VERIFY elimination of idle speed concern.
	• Breakout box installed, PCM disconnected.			
	• Measure resistance between Test Pin 14 (Test Pin 29 for CD4E and Calif. M/T) at breakout box and BLR circuit at Power Distribution box (refer to the Pinpoint Test schematic).			
	• **Is resistance less than 5.0 ohms?**			
FE14	**CHECK BLR CIRCUIT FOR SHORT TO GROUND**			
	• Key off.	Yes	▶	REMOVE breakout box. RECONNECT all components. REFER to Climate Control Group to check for damaged blower motor switch or relay.
	• Blower motor relay disconnected.			
	• Breakout box installed, PCM disconnected.			
	• Measure resistance between Test Pin 14 (Test Pin 29 for CD4E and Calif. M/T) and Test Pins 40, 46 and 60 at breakout box.	No	▶	SERVICE short circuit. REMOVE breakout box. RECONNECT all components. VERIFY elimination of idle speed concern.
	• **Is resistance greater than 10,000 ohms?**			

FM0159400729050X

Fig. 187 Test FE: Electrical Load Inputs (Part 5 of 10). 1994–95

TEST STEP		RESULT	▶	ACTION TO TAKE
FE20	CHECK VOLTAGE OF DRL CIRCUIT, PARKING BRAKE AND HEADLAMPS ON			
	• Key off.	Yes	▶	GO to **FE21**.
	• Disconnect processor 60-pin connector. Inspect for damaged or pushed out pins, corrosion, loose wires, etc. Service as necessary.	No	▶	GO to **FE23**.
	• Install breakout box, leave processor disconnected.			
	• Apply parking brake.			
	• Key on, engine off.			
	• Turn headlights on.			
	• Turn all other accessories off.			
	• Measure voltage between Test Pin 42 at breakout box and chassis ground.			
	• **Is voltage between 10 and 17 volts?**			
FE21	CHECK VOLTAGE OF DRL CIRCUIT, PARKING BRAKE AND HEADLAMPS OFF			
	• Key off.	Yes	▶	REPLACE processor. REMOVE breakout box. VERIFY elimination of idle speed concern.
	• Breakout box installed, processor disconnected.			
	• Release parking brakes.			
	• Key on, engine off.	No	▶	GO to **FE22**.
	• Turn headlights off.			
	• Measure voltage between Test Pin 42 at breakout box and chassis ground.			
	• **Is voltage less than 1.5 volts?**			
FE22	CHECK DRL CIRCUIT FOR SHORT TO POWER			
	• Key off.	Yes	▶	REMOVE breakout box. RECONNECT all components. REFER to Headlamp/Illumination to check DRL module.
	• Breakout box installed, processor disconnected.			
	• Disconnect Daytime Running Lights relay (refer to cover schematic).			
	• Measure resistance between Test Pin 42 and Test Pins 37/57 at breakout box.	No	▶	SERVICE short circuit. REMOVE breakout box. RECONNECT all components. VERIFY elimination of idle speed concern.
	• **Is resistance greater than 10,000 ohms?**			

FM0159400729060X

Fig. 187 Test FE: Electrical Load Inputs (Part 6 of 10). 1994–95

TEST STEP		RESULT	▶	ACTION TO TAKE
FE33	CHECK HDL CIRCUIT FOR SHORT TO GROUND			
	• Key off.	Yes	▶	REMOVE breakout box. RECONNECT all components.
	• Headlamp relay disconnected.			
	• Breakout box installed, PCM disconnected.			Group in the Service check for damaged HDL switch.
	• Measure resistance between Test Pin 45 and Test Pins 40, 46 and 60 at breakout box.			
	• **Is each resistance greater than 10,000 ohms?**	No	▶	SERVICE short circuit. REMOVE breakout box. RECONNECT all components. VERIFY elimination of idle speed concern.
FE34	CHECK HDL CIRCUIT FOR SHORT TO POWER			
	• Key off.	Yes	▶	REMOVE breakout box. RECONNECT all components.
	• Disconnect headlamp relay (refer to Pinpoint Test schematic).			
	• Breakout box installed, PCM disconnected.			check for damaged HDL switch.
	• Measure resistance between Test Pin 45 and Test Pins 37/57 at breakout box.			
	• **Is each resistance greater than 10,000 ohms?**	No	▶	SERVICE short circuit. REMOVE breakout box. RECONNECT all components. VERIFY elimination of idle speed concern.
FE40	CHECK VOLTAGE OF DEF CIRCUIT, DEFROSTER OFF			
	• Key off.	Yes	▶	GO to **FE41**
	• Disconnect Powertrain Control Module (PCM). Inspect for damaged or pushed out pins, corrosion, loose wires, etc. Service as necessary.	No	▶	GO to **FE43**
	• Install breakout box, leave PCM disconnected.			
	• Key on, engine off.			
	• Turn rear window defroster and all other accessories off.			
	• Measure voltage between Test Pin 15 at breakout box and chassis ground.			
	• **Is voltage between 10 and 17 volts?**			

FM0159400729070X

Fig. 187 Test FE: Electrical Load Inputs (Part 7 of 10). 1994–95

TEST STEP		RESULT	▶	ACTION TO TAKE
FE32	CHECK HDL CIRCUIT CONTINUITY			
	• Key off.	Yes	▶	GO to **FE33**.
	• Disconnect headlamp relay (refer to Pinpoint Test schematic).	No	▶	SERVICE open circuit. REMOVE breakout box. RECONNECT all components. VERIFY elimination of idle speed concern.
	• Breakout box installed, PCM disconnected.			
	• Measure resistance between Test Pin 45 (Test Pin 42 for CD4E and Calif. M/T) at breakout box and HDL circuit at Power Distribution box (refer to Pinpoint Test schematic).			
	• **Is resistance less than 5.0 ohms?**			
FE33	CHECK HDL CIRCUIT FOR SHORT TO GROUND			
	• Key off.	Yes	▶	REMOVE breakout box. RECONNECT all components
	• Headlamp relay disconnected.			
	• Breakout box installed, PCM disconnected.			check for damaged HDL switch.
	• Measure resistance between Test Pin 45 (Test Pin 42 for CD4E and Calif. M/T) and Test Pins 40, 46 and 60 at breakout box.			
	• **Is each resistance greater than 10,000 ohms?**	No	▶	SERVICE short circuit. REMOVE breakout box. RECONNECT all components. VERIFY elimination of idle speed concern.
FE34	CHECK HDL CIRCUIT FOR SHORT TO POWER			
	• Key off.	Yes	▶	REMOVE breakout box. RECONNECT all components
	• Disconnect headlamp relay (refer to Pinpoint Test schematic).			
	• Breakout box installed, PCM disconnected.			check for damaged HDL switch.
	• Measure resistance between Test Pin 45 (Test Pin 42 for CD4E and Calif. M/T) and Test Pins 37/57 at breakout box.			
	• **Is each resistance greater than 10,000 ohms?**	No	▶	SERVICE short circuit. REMOVE breakout box. RECONNECT all components. VERIFY elimination of idle speed concern.

FM0159400729080X

Fig. 187 Test FE: Electrical Load Inputs (Part 8 of 10). 1994–95

TEST STEP		RESULT	▶	ACTION TO TAKE
FE40	CHECK VOLTAGE OF DEF CIRCUIT, DEFROSTER OFF			
	• Key off.	Yes	▶	GO to **FE41**.
	• Disconnect Powertrain Control Module (PCM). Inspect for damaged or pushed out pins, corrosion, loose wires, etc. Service as necessary.	No	▶	GO to **FE43**.
	• Install breakout box, leave PCM disconnected.			
	• Key on, engine off.			
	• Turn rear window defroster and all other accessories off.			
	• Measure voltage between Test Pin 15 (Test Pin 23 for CD4E and Calif. M/T) at breakout box and chassis ground.			
	• **Is voltage between 10 and 17 volts?**			
FE41	CHECK VOLTAGE OF DEF CIRCUIT, DEFROSTER ON			
	• Key off.	Yes	▶	REPLACE PCM. REMOVE breakout box. VERIFY elimination of idle speed concern.
	• Breakout box installed, PCM disconnected.			
	• Key on, engine off.			
	• Turn all accessories off.			
	• Turn rear window defroster on.	No	▶	GO to **FE42**.
	• Measure voltage between Test Pin 15 (Test Pin 23 for CD4E and Calif. M/T) at breakout box and chassis ground.			
	• **Is voltage less than 3.0 volts?**			
FE42	CHECK DEF CIRCUIT FOR SHORT TO POWER			
	• Key off.	Yes	▶	REMOVE breakout box. RECONNECT all components.
	• Disconnect rear window defroster relay (refer to Pinpoint Test schematic).			
	• Breakout box installed, PCM disconnected.			check for fault in DEF switch and relay circuit.
	• Measure resistance between Test Pin 15 (Test Pin 23 for CD4E and Calif. M/T) and Test Pins 37/57 at breakout box.			
	• **Is resistance greater than 10,000 ohms?**	No	▶	SERVICE short circuit. REMOVE breakout box. RECONNECT all components. VERIFY elimination of idle speed concern.

FM0159400729090X

Fig. 187 Test FE: Electrical Load Inputs (Part 9 of 10). 1994–95

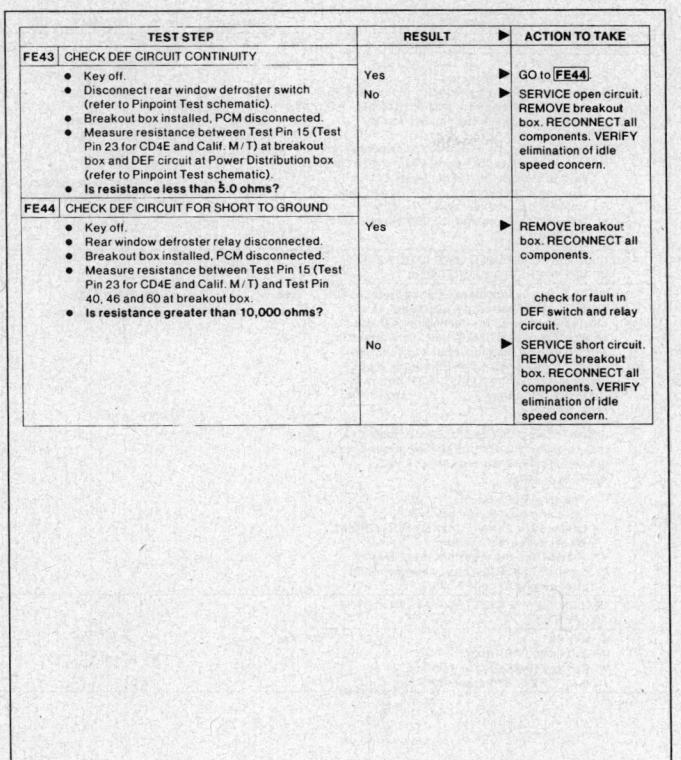

TEST STEP		RESULT	▶	ACTION TO TAKE
FE43	CHECK DEF CIRCUIT CONTINUITY			
	● Key off.	Yes	▶	GO to **FE44**.
	● Disconnect rear window defroster switch (refer to Pinpoint Test schematic).	No	▶	SERVICE open circuit. REMOVE breakout box. RECONNECT all components. VERIFY elimination of idle speed concern.
	● Breakout box installed, PCM disconnected.			
	● Measure resistance between Test Pin 15 (Test Pin 23 for CD4E and Calif. M/T) at breakout box and DEF circuit at Power Distribution box (refer to Pinpoint Test schematic).			
	● **Is resistance less than 5.0 ohms?**			
FE44	CHECK DEF CIRCUIT FOR SHORT TO GROUND			
	● Key off.	Yes	▶	REMOVE breakout box. RECONNECT all components.
	● Rear window defroster relay disconnected.			
	● Breakout box installed, PCM disconnected.			check for fault in DEF switch and relay circuit.
	● Measure resistance between Test Pin 15 (Test Pin 23 for CD4E and Calif. M/T) and Test Pin 40, 46 and 60 at breakout box.			
	● **Is resistance greater than 10,000 ohms?**	No	▶	SERVICE short circuit. REMOVE breakout box. RECONNECT all components. VERIFY elimination of idle speed concern.

FM01594C0729100X

Fig. 187 Test FE: Electrical Load Inputs (Part 10 of 10). 1994–95

Note

You should enter this Pinpoint Test only when you have been directed here from Diagnostic Routines,

Remember

To prevent the replacement of good components, be aware that the following non-EEC areas may be at fault:

● Idle Air Control throttle stop adjustment
● Binding throttle shaft/linkage or speed control linkage
● Power steering hydraulic system

This Pinpoint Test is intended to diagnose only the following:

● Power Steering Pressure (PSP) switch (3N824)
● Harness circuits: PSP and SIG RTN
● Powertrain Control Module (PCM) (12A650)

Description

The Power Steering Pressure (PSP) switch on the 2.0L Probe is a normally open switch that closes when power steering pressure increases as the wheels are being turned. The PSP switch on all other applications is a normally closed switch that opens as pressure increases. The PCM uses the signal from the PSP switch to adjust idle speed to compensate for the additional load on the engine.

Fig. 188 Test FF: PSP Switch (Part 1 of 8)

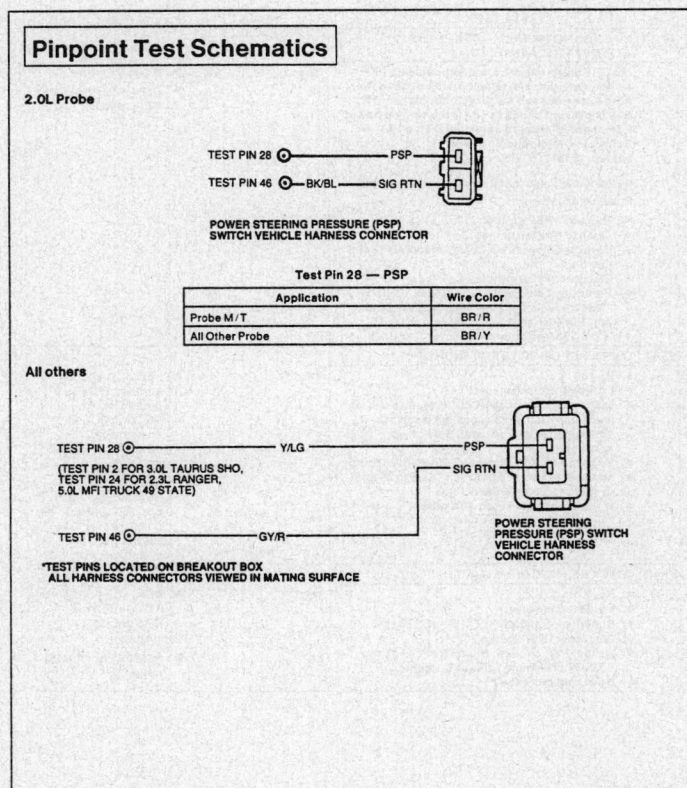

Fig. 188 Test FF: PSP Switch (Part 2 of 8). 1993–94

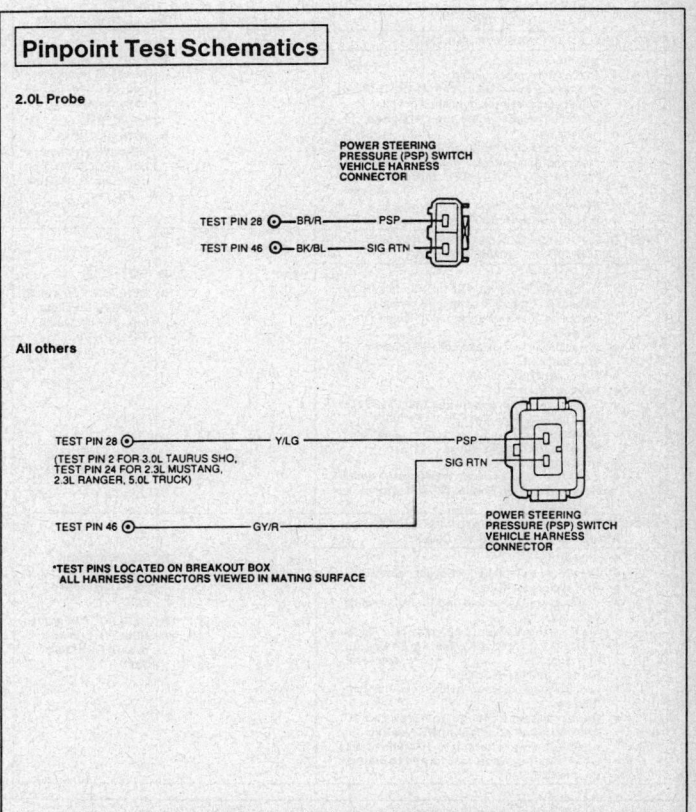

Fig. 188 Test FF: PSP Switch (Part 2 of 8). 1995

Fig. 188 Test FF: PSP Switch (Part 3 of 8)

TEST STEP		RESULT	▶	ACTION TO TAKE
FF1	DIAGNOSTIC TROUBLE CODE (DTC) 52/519: ATTEMPT TO ELIMINATE DTC 52/519			
	NOTE: Some vehicles are equipped with a PSP switch software strategy, but do not have hardware released for the engine/vehicle application. When DTC 52/519 is received in Key On Engine Off, check to see if the vehicle is equipped with PSP switch. If not, disregard servicing DTC 52/519. Return to Diagnostic Routines, to service other DTCs.	Yes	▶	GO to FF2 .
		No	▶	REPLACE PSP switch. RERUN Quick Test.
	DTC 52/519 indicates that the PSP circuit is open. Possible causes:			
	— Damaged PSP switch.			
	— Open harness.			
	— Damaged Powertrain Control Module (PCM).			
	• Key off.			
	• Disconnect PSP switch.			
	• Jumper PSP circuit to SIG RTN circuit at the PSP switch vehicle harness connector.			
	• Rerun Key On or Engine Off Self-Test.			
	• **Is DTC 52 or 519 still present?**			
FF2	CHECK CONTINUITY OF PSP CIRCUITS			
	• Key off.	Yes	▶	REPLACE PCM. REMOVE breakout box. RECONNECT all components. RERUN Quick Test.
	• PSP switch disconnected.			
	• Disconnect Powertrain Control Module (PCM). Inspect for damaged or pushed out pins, corrosion, loose wires, etc. Service as necessary.			
	• Install breakout box, leave PCM disconnected.	No	▶	SERVICE open circuit. REMOVE breakout box. RECONNECT all components. RERUN Quick Test.
	• Measure resistance between Test Pin 46 at the breakout box and SIG RTN circuit at the PSP switch vehicle harness connector.			
	• Measure resistance between Test Pin 28 (Test Pin 2 for 3.0L SHO; Test Pin 24 for 2.3L Mustang, at the breakout box and PSP circuit at the PSP switch vehicle harness connector.			
	• **Is each resistance less than 5.0 ohms?**			
FF3	CHECK PSP SWITCH OPERATION			
	• Key off.	Yes	▶	REPLACE PSP switch. RE-EVALUATE symptom.
	• Install tachometer.			
	• Start engine, allow to idle in NEUTRAL/PARK.	No	▶	GO to FF4 .
	• Disconnect PSP switch.			
	• **Does rpm increase?**			

Fig. 188 Test FF: PSP Switch (Part 4 of 8)

TEST STEP		RESULT	▶	ACTION TO TAKE
FF4	CHECK PSP CIRCUITS FOR SHORTS			
	• Key off.	Yes	▶	SERVICE short in harness. REMOVE breakout box. RECONNECT all components. RE-EVALUATE symptom.
	• PSP switch disconnected.			
	• Disconnect Powertrain Control Module (PCM). Inspect for damaged or pushed out pins, corrosion, loose wires, etc. Service as necessary.			
	• Install breakout box, leave PCM disconnected.	No	▶	REPLACE PCM. REMOVE breakout box. RECONNECT all components. RE-EVALUATE symptom.
	• Measure resistance between Test Pin 2 for 3.0L SHO; Test Pin 24 for 2.3L Mustang, 2.3L Ranger and Test Pin 46 at the breakout box.			
	• **Is resistance less than 10,000 ohms?**			
FF5	DIAGNOSTIC TROUBLE CODE (DTC) 52/521 VERIFY OPERATOR INTERACTION			
	NOTE: Some vehicles are equipped with a PSP switch software strategy, but do not have hardware released for the engine/vehicle application. When DTC 52/521 is received in Key On Engine Running, check to see if the vehicle is equipped with PSP switch. If not, disregard servicing DTC 52/521. Return to Diagnostic Routines to service other DTCs.	Yes	▶	GO to FF6 .
		No	▶	RERUN Self Test.
	Engine Running Service DTC 52/521 indicates that the PSP switch did not change states due to the switch staying either open or closed. Possible causes:			
	— Damaged PSP switch.			
	— Open or grounded harness circuit.			
	— Damaged Powertrain Control Module (PCM).			
	— Wheel turned, not centered.			
	• **Did you turn the steering wheel at least one-half turn within one to two seconds after engine ID code?**			
FF6	DETERMINE WHETHER THE PCM CAN IDENTIFY AN OPEN CIRCUIT			
	• Key off.	Yes	▶	GO to FF8 .
	• Disconnect PSP switch.	No	▶	GO to FF7 .
	• Run Key On Engine Off Self-Test.			
	• **Is DTC 52 or 519 present?**			

Fig. 188 Test FF: PSP Switch (Part 5 of 8)

TEST STEP		RESULT	▶	ACTION TO TAKE
FF7	CHECK PSP CIRCUITS FOR SHORTS			
	• Key off.	Yes	▶	SERVICE short circuit. REMOVE breakout box. RECONNECT all components. RERUN Quick Test.
	• PSP switch disconnected.			
	• Disconnect Powertrain Control Module (PCM). Inspect for damaged or pushed out pins, corrosion or loose wires, etc. Service as necessary.			
	• Install breakout box, leave PCM disconnected.	No	▶	REPLACE PCM. REMOVE breakout box. RECONNECT all components. RERUN Quick Test.
	• Measure resistance between Test Pin 28 (Test Pin 2 for 3.0L SHO; Test Pin 24 for 2.3L Mustang, and Test Pin 46 at the breakout box.			
	• **Is resistance 10,000 ohms or less?**			
FF8	CHECK PSP SWITCH STATE WITH KEY ON ENGINE OFF VS. ENGINE RUNNING			
	• Key off.	Yes	▶	GO to FF9 .
	• Disconnect Powertrain Control Module (PCM). Inspect for damaged or pushed out pins, corrosion, loose wires, etc. Service as necessary.	No	▶	REPLACE PSP switch. REMOVE breakout box. RERUN Quick Test.
	• Install breakout box and connect PCM to breakout box.			
	• Reconnect PSP switch.			
	• Key on, engine off.			
	• Measure resistance between Test Pin 28 (Test Pin 2 for 3.0L SHO; Test Pin 24 for 2.3L Mustang, and Test Pin 46 at the breakout box.			
	• Start engine.			
	• **Does resistance remain less than 10 ohms between Key On Engine Off and Engine Running?**			
FF9	CHECK PSP SWITCH STATE WITH ENGINE RUNNING AND LOAD VS. NO LOAD			
	• Engine idling.	Yes	▶	PSP system OK. Testing completed. REMOVE breakout box.
	• Breakout box installed, PCM connected.			
	• PSP switch connected.			
	• Clutch is not depressed on 3.0L SHO manual vehicles.	No	▶	REPLACE PSP switch. REMOVE breakout box. RERUN Quick Test.
	• Measure the resistance between Test Pin 28 (Test Pin 2 for 3.0L SHO; Test Pin 24 for 2.3L Mustang, and Test Pin 46 at the breakout box.			
	• Turn the steering wheel at least one-half turn then return.			
	• **Does resistance change from less than 10 ohms to infinity (indicating PSP switch opening), then returning to 10 ohms or less when steering wheel is returned to center position?**			

Fig. 188 Test FF: PSP Switch (Part 6 of 8)

TEST STEP		RESULT	▶	ACTION TO TAKE
FF10	DIAGNOSTIC TROUBLE CODE (DTC) 519: ATTEMPT TO ELIMINATE DTC 519			
	NOTE: Some vehicles are equipped with PSP switch software strategy, but do not have the hardware released for production. When DTC 519 is present check to see if the vehicle has a PSP. If not, disregard servicing DTC 519. Return to Diagnostic Routines to service other DTCs.	Yes	▶	GO to FF11 .
		No	▶	REPLACE PSP switch. RERUN Quick Test.
	DTC 519 indicates that the PSP circuit is closed. Possible causes:			
	— Damaged PSP switch.			
	— Open or shorted harness.			
	— Damaged Powertrain Control Module (PCM).			
	• Key off.			
	• Disconnect PSP switch.			
	• Rerun Key On Engine Off Self-Test.			
	• Measure resistance between Test Pin 28 and Test Pin 46 at the breakout box.			
	• **Is DTC 519 still present?**			
FF11	CHECK PSP CIRCUITS FOR SHORTS			
	• Key off.	Yes	▶	SERVICE short in harness. REMOVE breakout box. RECONNECT all components. RE-EVALUATE symptom.
	• PSP switch disconnected.			
	• Disconnect Powertrain Control Module (PCM). Inspect for damaged or pushed out pins, corrosion, loose wires, etc. Service as necessary.			
	• Install breakout box, leave PCM disconnected.	No	▶	REPLACE PCM. REMOVE breakout box. RECONNECT all components. RE-EVALUATE symptom.
	• Measure resistance between Test Pin 28 and Test Pin 46 at the breakout box.			
	• **Is resistance less than 10K ohms?**			
FF15	CHECK PSP SWITCH OPERATION			
	• Key off.	Yes	▶	REPLACE PSP switch. REMOVE jumper. RE-EVALUATE symptom.
	• Install tachometer.			
	• Start engine and idle in PARK/NEUTRAL.			
	• Disconnect PSP switch.	No	▶	REMOVE jumper. GO to FF16 .
	• Jumper PSP circuit to SIG RTN circuit at the PSP switch vehicle harness connector.			
	• **Does rpm increase?**			

TEST STEP	RESULT	▶	ACTION TO TAKE
FF 16 CHECK CONTINUITY OF PSP CIRCUITS • Key off. • PSP switch disconnected. • Disconnect Powertrain Control Module (PCM). Inspect for damaged or pushed out pins, corrosion, loose wires, etc. Service as necessary. • Install breakout box, leave PCM connected. • Measure resistance between Test Pin 28 at the breakout box and PSP circuit at the PSP switch vehicle harness connector. • Measure resistance between Test Pin 46 at the breakout box and SIG RTN circuit at the PSP vehicle harness connected. • Is each resistance less than 5.0 ohms?	Yes No	▶ ▶	REPLACE PCM. REMOVE breakout box. RECONNECT all components. RE-EVALUATE symptom. SERVICE open in harness. REMOVE breakout box. RECONNECT all components. RERUN Quick Test.
FF 20 DIAGNOSTIC TROUBLE CODE (DTC) 521: VERIFY OPERATOR INTERACTION	Yes No	▶ ▶	GO to FF21. RERUN Quick Test.
NOTE: Some vehicles are equipped with PSP switch software strategy, but do not have the hardware released for production. When DTC 519 is present, check to see if the vehicle has a PSP switch; if not, disregard servicing DTC 519. Return to Diagnostic Routines, to service other DTCs. DTC 521 indicates that the PSP switch did not change state due to the switch staying either open or closed. Possible Causes: — Damaged PSP switch. — Open or shorted harness. — Damaged Powertrain Control Module (PCM). — Wheels turned, not centered. • Did you turn the steering wheel at least one-half turn within one to two seconds after engine ID DTC?			
FF 21 DETERMINE IF THE PCM CAN IDENTIFY A CLOSED CIRCUIT • Key off. • Disconnect PSP switch. • Jumper PSP circuit to SIG RTN circuit at the PSP switch vehicle harness connector. • Run Key On Engine Off Self Test. • Is DTC 519 present?	Yes No	▶ ▶	REMOVE jumper. GO to FF23. REMOVE jumper. GO to FF22.

TEST STEP	RESULT	▶	ACTION TO TAKE
FF22 CHECK CONTINUITY OF PSP CIRCUITS • Key off. • PSP disconnected. • Disconnect Powertrain Control Module (PCM). Inspect for damaged or pushed out pins, corrosion, loose wires, etc. Service as necessary. • Install breakout box, leave PCM disconnected. • Measure resistance between Test Pin 28 at the breakout box and PSP circuit at the PSP switch vehicle harness connector. • Measure resistance between Test Pin 46 at the breakout box and SIG RTN circuit at the PSP switch vehicle harness connector. • Is each resistance less than 5.0 ohms?	Yes No	▶ ▶	REPLACE PCM. REMOVE breakout box. RECONNECT all components. RE-EVALUATE symptom. SERVICE open in harness. REMOVE breakout box. RECONNECT all components. RERUN Quick Test.
FF23 CHECK PSP STATE WITH KEY ON ENGINE OFF VS. ENGINE RUNNING • Key off. • Disconnect Powertrain Control Module (PCM). Inspect for damaged or pushed out pins, corrosion, loose wires, etc. Service as necessary. • Install breakout box and connect PCM to breakout box. • Reconnect PSP switch. • Key on, engine off. • Measure resistance between Test Pin 28 and Test Pin 46 at the breakout box. • Start Engine. • Does resistance remain greater than 10 ohms between Key On, Engine Off and Engine Running?	Yes No	▶ ▶	GO to FF24. REPLACE PSP switch. REMOVE breakout box. RERUN Quick Test.
FF24 CHECK PSP SWITCH STATE WITH ENGINE RUNNING AND LOAD VS. NO LOAD • Engine speed at idle. • Breakout box installed, PCM connected. • PSP switch connected. • Measure resistance between Test Pin 28 and Test Pin 46 at the breakout box. • Turn the steering wheel at least one-half turn then back to center position. • Does resistance change from infinity to less than 30 ohms indicating PSP closing then changing back to infinity?	Yes No	▶ ▶	PSP system OK. REMOVE breakout box. Testing completed. REPLACE PSP switch. REMOVE breakout box. RERUN Quick Test.

Fig. 188 Test FF: PSP Switch (Part 7 of 8)

Fig. 188 Test FF: PSP Switch (Part 8 of 8)

Note

You should enter this Pinpoint Test only when you have been directed here from Diagnostic Routines.

Remember

To prevent the replacement of good components, be aware that the following non-EEC areas may be at fault:

• Excessive blow-by
• PCV malfunction
• Vacuum leaks
• Fuel pressure
• Throttle sticking or linkage binding

This Pinpoint Test is intended to diagnose only the following:

• MAP/BARO sensor (9F479)
• Throttle Position (TP) sensor (9B989)
• Mass Air Flow (MAF) sensor (12B579)
• Intake Air Temperature (IAT) sensor (12A697)
• Fuel Injectors

Description

This In-Range Self-Test was designed to detect in-range failures of the MAF sensor, TP sensor or the fuel delivery system. The PCM will use information from these three areas based on vehicle load to generate three independent values. The three independent values will be continuously monitored by the PCM and if one of the values differs significantly from the others during normal vehicle operation, a Continuous Memory Diagnostic Trouble Code (DTC) will be displayed..

TEST STEP	RESULT	▶	ACTION TO TAKE
G1 THROTTLE POSITION SENSOR INTEGRITY	Yes No	▶ ▶	For Continuous Memory DTC 121: GO to G7. For all others: GO to G2. VERIFY TP sensor is properly installed to the throttle body. If OK, REPLACE TP sensor. REMOVE breakout box. RECONNECT PCM. RERUN Quick Test.
Continuous Memory Diagnostic Trouble Code (DTC) 121 indicates TP was inconsistent with MAF value. Continuous Memory DTC 124 indicates TP value was higher than expected. Continuous Memory DTC 125 indicates TP value was lower than expected. • Key off. • Disconnect Powertrain Control Module (PCM). Inspect for damaged or pushed out pins, corrosion, loose wires, etc. Service as necessary. • Install breakout box and connect PCM to breakout box. • Connect DVOM from Test Pin 47 to Test Pin 46 at the breakout box. • Key on, engine off. • Rotate throttle slowly to WOT, release throttle slowly to closed position. • Does the voltage change smoothly between 0.4 and 4.5 volts? NOTE: Refer to Pinpoint Test DH for schematics and specific engine values.			
G2 CHECK IDLE • Verify engine idle speed is normal. • Is idle normal?	Yes No	▶ ▶	GO to G3. RESET idle airflow to specification. REFER to idle airflow adjust procedure. If unable to adjust, GO to G3.
G3 CHECK THROTTLE BODY • Check throttle linkage and/or speed control linkage for binding. • Inspect throttle body for contamination • Check engine vacuum hoses. Refer to VECI decal. • Check for leaks around IAC solenoid mounting gasket. • Check for air leaks between IAC solenoid and MAF sensor. • Are all of the above checks OK?	Yes No	▶ ▶	GO to G4. SERVICE as necessary. REMOVE breakout box. RECONNECT PCM. RERUN Quick Test.

Fig. 189 Test G: MAF/TP/Injector Pulse Width (Part 1 of 6). 1993

Fig. 189 Test G: MAF/TP/Injector Pulse Width (Part 2 of 6). 1993

TEST STEP		RESULT	▶	ACTION TO TAKE
G4	**CHECK MAP/BARO SENSOR OUTPUT**			
	NOTE: For vehicles without a MAP/BARO sensor, go to G5. Measure several known good MAP/BARO sensors on available vehicles. The measured voltage will be typical for your location on the day of testing. Refer to Pinpoint Test DF for schematic. • Key off. • Disconnect MAP/BARO sensor from vehicle harness. • Connect MAP/BARO tester between the vehicle harness connector and MAP/BARO sensor. • Insert MAP/BARO tester banana plugs into DVOM. • DVOM on 20 volt scale. • Key on, engine off. • Measure MAP/BARO sensor voltage on vehicle. • **Is DVOM voltage in range for your altitude?**	Yes No	▶ ▶	REMOVE MAP/BARO tester. RECONNECT MAP/BARO sensor. GO to G5. REPLACE MAP/BARO sensor. REMOVE MAP/BARO tester and breakout box. RECONNECT all components. RERUN Quick Test.

Approximate Altitude (Ft.)	Voltage Output (+/-.04 Volt)
0	1.59
1000	1.56
2000	1.53
3000	1.50
4000	1.47
5000	1.44
6000	1.41
7000	1.39

Fig. 189   Test G: MAF/TP/Injector Pulse Width (Part 3 of 6). 1993

TEST STEP		RESULT	▶	ACTION TO TAKE
G5	**CHECK INTAKE AIR TEMPERATURE (IAT) SENSOR**			
	NOTE: Ambient temperature should be at least 10°C (50°F) before performing this test. Also check for air leaks in front of the IAT sensor. Service as necessary. • Key off. • Breakout box installed, PCM connected. • Connect DVOM between Test Pin 25 and Test Pin 46 at breakout box. • DVOM on 20 volt scale. • Monitor voltage as engine warms up. • **Does voltage decrease smoothly and stabilize after engine has reached operating conditions?** NOTE: Refer to voltage chart in Pinpoint Test DA for engine specific values.	Yes No	▶ ▶	Sometime during the last 80 warm-up cycles the TP sensor signal indicated out of range. However, at this time EEC system is operating OK. REMOVE breakout box. RECONNECT PCM. RERUN Quick Test. REPLACE IAT sensor. REMOVE breakout box. RERUN Quick Test.
G6	**VISUALLY INSPECT MAF SENSOR**			

	Continuous Memory DTC 184 indicates MAF value is higher than expected.
	Continuous Memory DTC 185 indicates MAF value is lower than expected.
	
	• Key off.
	• Check for air leaks between IAC solenoid and MAF sensor.
	• Inspect MAF sensor for oil contamination.
	  — Excessive blow-by
	  — PCV malfunction
	• **Are the above checks OK?**
		Yes
		No
			▶
			▶
				GO to G9.
				SERVICE as necessary. CLEAR Continuous Memory
				
				RERUN Quick Test.

Fig. 189   Test G: MAF/TP/Injector Pulse Width (Part 4 of 6). 1993

TEST STEP		RESULT	▶	ACTION TO TAKE
G7	**CHECK MAF SENSOR**			
	• Key off. • Disconnect Powertrain Control Module (PCM). Inspect for damaged or pushed out pins, corrosion, loose wires, etc. Service as necessary. • Install breakout box, and connect PCM to breakout box. • Start engine and allow to idle until engine is at normal operating temperature. • Measure voltage between MAF signal and Test Pin 40/60. • **Is voltage within the acceptable range?**	Yes No	▶ ▶	Sometime during the last 80 warm-up cycles the MAF sensor signal indicated out of range. However, at this time EEC system is operating OK. REMOVE breakout box. RECONNECT PCM. RERUN Quick Test. REPLACE MAF sensor. REMOVE breakout box. RECONNECT PCM. RERUN Quick Test.
G8	**VISUAL VACUUM CHECKS**			
	Continuous Memory DTC 186 indicates pulse width lower than expected (rich). Continuous Memory DTC 187 indicates pulse width higher than expected (lean). • Inspect the air cleaner and air inlet ducting. • Check for unmetered air between MAF sensor and IAC solenoid. • Check all engine vacuum hoses for damage, leaks, cracks, blockage, proper routing, etc. • **Are all the above vacuum checks OK?**	Yes No	▶ ▶	GO to G9. SERVICE as necessary. RERUN Quick Test.
G9	**CHECK FUEL PRESSURE**			
	• Key off. • Install fuel pressure gauge. • Verify manifold vacuum is connected to the fuel pressure regulator if applicable. • Start and run engine at idle. • Refer to fuel specification table in Pinpoint Test H. • **Is fuel pressure within specification for the engine being tested?**	Yes No	▶ ▶	GO to G10. GO to Electric Fuel pump and fuel pressure regulator checks.

Fig. 189   Test G: MAF/TP/Injector Pulse Width (Part 5 of 6). 1993

TEST STEP		RESULT	▶	ACTION TO TAKE
G10	**CHECK SYSTEM'S ABILITY TO HOLD FUEL PRESSURE**			
	• Key on, engine off. • **Does fuel pressure remain at specification for 60 seconds?**	Yes No	▶ ▶	For Flexible Fuel vehicles: GO to HB2. FOR MFI: GO to Pinpoint Test Step H7. FOR SFI: GO to G11. GO to Fuel Delivery Systems.
G11	**CYLINDER BALANCE TEST**			
	• Run the Engine Running Self-Test. • After the last repeated DTC, wait 5-10 seconds. • "Goose" throttle lighty (not wide-open-throttle). • Cylinder Balance Diagnostic Test Mode (DTM) will be performed. Time of test is approximately 2-3 minutes. • **Is Code 90 present?**	Yes No	▶ ▶	GO to G6. For Flexible Fuel vehicles: GO to HB5. All others: GO to Pinpoint Test Step H4.

Fig. 189   Test G: MAF/TP/Injector Pulse Width (Part 6 of 6). 1993

Note

You should enter this Pinpoint Test only when you have been directed here from Diagnostic Routines.

Remember

To prevent the replacement of good components, be aware that the following non-EEC areas may be at fault:

- Excessive blow-by
- PCV malfunction
- Vacuum leaks
- Fuel pressure
- Throttle sticking or linkage binding
- Idle Air Control Solenoid

This Pinpoint Test is intended to diagnose only the following:

- MAP / BARO sensor
- Throttle Position (TP) sensor
- Mass Air Flow (MAF) sensor
- Intake Air Temperature (IAT) sensor
- Fuel Injectors

Description

This In-Range Self-Test was designed to detect in-range failures of the MAF sensor, TP sensor or the fuel delivery system. The PCM will use information from these three areas based on vehicle load to generate three independent values. The three independent values will be continuously monitored by the PCM and if one of the values differs significantly from the others during normal vehicle operation, a Continuous Memory Diagnostic Trouble Code (DTC) will be displayed.

Fig. 190   Test G: MAF/TP/Injector Pulse Width (Part 1 of 6). 1994–95

	TEST STEP	RESULT	▶	ACTION TO TAKE
G1	CHECK FOR IDLE AIR DTCS. INITIATE KEY ON ENGINE RUNNING SELF-TEST			
	Continuous Memory Diagnostic Trouble Code (DTC) 121 indicates TP was inconsistent with MAF value. Continuous Memory DTC 124 indicates TP value was higher than expected. Continuous Memory DTC 125 indicates TP value was lower than expected. • Key ON. • Initiate Key On Engine Running (KOER) Self-Test. • Are DTCs 411 or 412 present?	Yes No	▶ ▶	RETURN to Diagnostic Routines, for appropriate Pinpoint Test GO to G2
G2	THROTTLE POSITION SENSOR INTEGRITY			
	• Key off. • Disconnect Powertrain Control Module (PCM). Inspect for damaged or pushed out pins, corrosion, loose wires, etc. Service as necessary. • Install breakout box and connect PCM to breakout box. • Connect DVOM from Test Pin 47 to Test Pin 46 at the breakout box. • Key on, engine off. • Rotate throttle slowly to WOT, release throttle slowly to closed position. • Does the voltage change smoothly between 0.4 and 4.5 volts? NOTE: Refer to Pinpoint Test DH for schematics and specific engine values.	Yes No	▶ ▶	For Continuous Memory DTC 121: GO to G8 For all others: GO to G3 VERIFY TP sensor is properly installed to the throttle body. If OK, REPLACE TP sensor. REMOVE breakout box. RECONNECT PCM. RERUN Quick Test
G3	CHECK IDLE			
	• Verify engine idle speed is normal. • Refer to Section 12A. • Is idle normal?	Yes No	▶ ▶	GO to G4 RESET idle airflow to specification. REFER to idle airflow adjust procedure. If unable to adjust, GO to G4

Fig. 190   Test G: MAF/TP/Injector Pulse Width (Part 2 of 6). 1994–95

	TEST STEP	RESULT	▶	ACTION TO TAKE
G4	CHECK THROTTLE BODY			
	• Check throttle linkage and / or speed control linkage for binding. • Inspect throttle body for contamination. determine if Idle Air Control (IAC) solenoid can be cleaned. • Check engine vacuum hoses. Refer to VECI decal. • Check for leaks around IAC solenoid mounting gasket. • Check for air leaks between IAC solenoid and MAF sensor. • Are all of the above checks OK?	Yes No	▶ ▶	GO to G5 SERVICE as necessary. REMOVE breakout box. RECONNECT PCM. RERUN Quick Test.
G5	CHECK MAP / BARO SENSOR OUTPUT			
	NOTE: For vehicles without a MAP / BARO sensor, go to G6. Measure several known good MAP / BARO sensors on available vehicles. The measured voltage will be typical for your location on the day of testing. Refer to Pinpoint Test DF for schematic. • Key off. • Disconnect MAP / BARO sensor from vehicle harness. • Connect MAP / BARO tester between the vehicle harness connector and MAP / BARO sensor. • Insert MAP / BARO tester banana plugs into DVOM. • DVOM on 20 volt scale. • Key on, engine off. • Measure MAP / BARO sensor voltage on vehicle. • Is DVOM voltage in range for area altitude?	Yes No	▶ ▶	REMOVE MAP / BARO tester. RECONNECT MAP / BARO sensor. GO to G6. REPLACE MAP / BARO sensor. REMOVE MAP / BARO tester and breakout box. RECONNECT all components. RERUN Quick Test.

Approximate Altitude (Ft.)	Voltage Output (+ / -.04 Volt)
0	1.59
1000	1.56
2000	1.53
3000	1.50
4000	1.47
5000	1.44
6000	1.41
7000	1.39

Fig. 190   Test G: MAF/TP/Injector Pulse Width (Part 3 of 6). 1994–95

	TEST STEP	RESULT	▶	ACTION TO TAKE
G6	CHECK INTAKE AIR TEMPERATURE (IAT) SENSOR			
	NOTE: Ambient temperature should be at least 10°C (50°F) before performing this test. Also check for air leaks in front of the IAT sensor. Service as necessary. • Key off. • Breakout box installed, PCM connected. • Connect DVOM between Test Pin 25 and Test Pin 46 at breakout box. • DVOM on 20 volt scale. • Monitor voltage as engine warms up. • Does voltage decrease smoothly and stabilize after engine has reached operating conditions? NOTE: Refer to voltage chart in Pinpoint Test DA for engine specific values.	Yes No	▶ ▶	Sometime during the last 80 warm-up cycles the TP sensor signal indicated out of range. However, at this time EEC system is operating OK. REMOVE breakout box. RECONNECT PCM. RERUN Quick Test. REPLACE IAT sensor. REMOVE breakout box. RERUN Quick Test.
G7	VISUALLY INSPECT MAF SENSOR			
	Continuous Memory DTC 184 indicates MAF value is higher than expected. Continuous Memory DTC 185 indicates MAF value is lower than expected. • Key off. • Check for air leaks between IAC solenoid and MAF sensor. • Inspect MAF sensor for oil contamination. — Excessive blow-by — PCV malfunction • Are the above checks OK?	Yes No	▶ ▶	GO to G10. SERVICE as necessary. CLEAR Continuous Memory RERUN Quick Test.

Fig. 190   Test G: MAF/TP/Injector Pulse Width (Part 4 of 6). 1994–95

TEST STEP		RESULT ▶	ACTION TO TAKE
G8	CHECK MAF SENSOR		
	• Key off. • Disconnect Powertrain Control Module (PCM). Inspect for damaged or pushed out pins, corrosion, loose wires, etc. Service as necessary. • Install breakout box, and connect PCM to breakout box. • Start engine and allow to idle until engine is at normal operating temperature. • Measure voltage between MAF signal and Test Pin 40 or 60.	Yes ▶	Sometime during the last 80 warm-up cycles the MAF sensor signal indicated out of range. However, at this time EEC system is operating OK. REMOVE breakout box. RECONNECT PCM. RERUN Quick Test.
	• **Is voltage within the acceptable range?**	No ▶	REPLACE MAF sensor. REMOVE breakout box. RECONNECT PCM. RERUN Quick Test.
G9	VISUAL VACUUM CHECKS		
	Continuous Memory DTC 186 indicates pulse width lower than expected (rich). Continuous Memory DTC 187 indicates pulse width higher than expected (lean). • Inspect the air cleaner and air inlet ducting. • Check for unmetered air between MAF sensor and IAC solenoid. • Check all engine vacuum hoses for damage, leaks, cracks, blockage, proper routing, etc. • **Are all the above vacuum checks OK?**	Yes ▶ No ▶	GO to G10. SERVICE as necessary. RERUN Quick Test.
G10	CHECK FUEL PRESSURE		
	• Key off. • Install fuel pressure gauge. • Verify manifold vacuum is connected to the fuel pressure regulator if applicable. • Start and run engine at idle. • Refer to fuel specification table in Pinpoint Test H. • **Is fuel pressure within specification for the engine being tested?**	Yes ▶ No ▶	GO to G11. GO to Fuel Delivery Systems.

FM0159400731050X

Fig. 190 Test G: MAF/TP/Injector Pulse Width (Part 5 of 6). 1994–95

TEST STEP		RESULT ▶	ACTION TO TAKE
G11	CHECK SYSTEM'S ABILITY TO HOLD FUEL PRESSURE		
	• Key on, engine off. • **Does fuel pressure remain at specification for 60 seconds?**	Yes ▶	**For Flexible Fuel vehicles:** GO to HB2. **FOR MFI:** GO to Pinpoint Test Step H7. **FOR SFI:** GO to G12.
		No ▶	GO to Fuel Delivery Systems.
G12	CYLINDER BALANCE TEST		
	• Run the Key On Engine Running Self-Test. • After the last repeated DTC, wait 5-10 seconds. • "Goose" throttle lightly (not wide-open-throttle). • Cylinder Balance Diagnostic Test Mode (DTM) will be performed. Time of test is 2-3 minutes. • **Is Code 90 present?**	Yes ▶ No ▶	GO to G7. **For Flexible Fuel vehicles:** GO to HB5. **All others:** GO to Pinpoint Test Step H4.

FM0159400731060X

Fig. 190 Test G: MAF/TP/Injector Pulse Width (Part 6 of 6). 1994–95

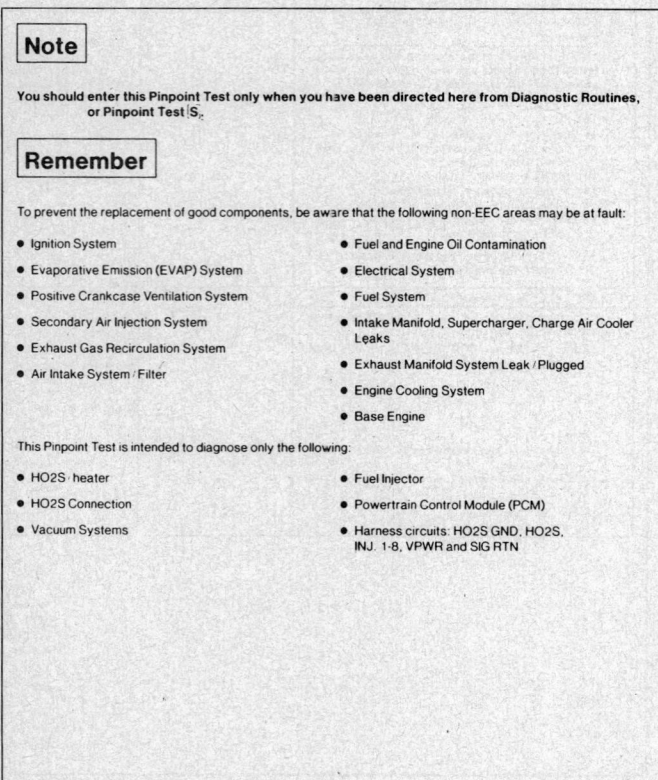

Note

You should enter this Pinpoint Test only when you have been directed here from Diagnostic Routines, or Pinpoint Test S.

Remember

To prevent the replacement of good components, be aware that the following non-EEC areas may be at fault:

- Ignition System
- Evaporative Emission (EVAP) System
- Positive Crankcase Ventilation System
- Secondary Air Injection System
- Exhaust Gas Recirculation System
- Air Intake System / Filter
- Fuel and Engine Oil Contamination
- Electrical System
- Fuel System
- Intake Manifold, Supercharger, Charge Air Cooler Leaks
- Exhaust Manifold System Leak / Plugged
- Engine Cooling System
- Base Engine

This Pinpoint Test is intended to diagnose only the following:

- HO2S heater
- HO2S Connection
- Vacuum Systems
- Fuel Injector
- Powertrain Control Module (PCM)
- Harness circuits: HO2S GND, HO2S, INJ. 1-8, VPWR and SIG RTN

FM0159300732010X

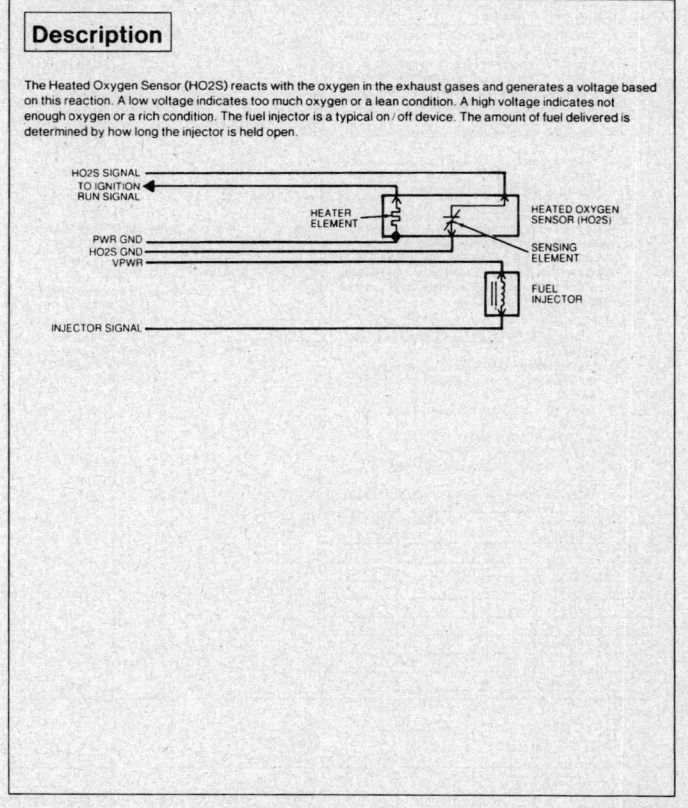

Fig. 191 Test H: Fuel Control (Part 1 of 33)

Description

The Heated Oxygen Sensor (HO2S) reacts with the oxygen in the exhaust gases and generates a voltage based on this reaction. A low voltage indicates too much oxygen or a lean condition. A high voltage indicates not enough oxygen or a rich condition. The fuel injector is a typical on / off device. The amount of fuel delivered is determined by how long the injector is held open.

HO2S SIGNAL
TO IGNITION RUN SIGNAL
HEATER ELEMENT
HEATED OXYGEN SENSOR (HO2S)
PWR GND
HO2S GND
VPWR
SENSING ELEMENT
FUEL INJECTOR
INJECTOR SIGNAL

FM0159300732020X

Fig. 191 Test H: Fuel Control (Part 2 of 33)

Pinpoint Test Schematics

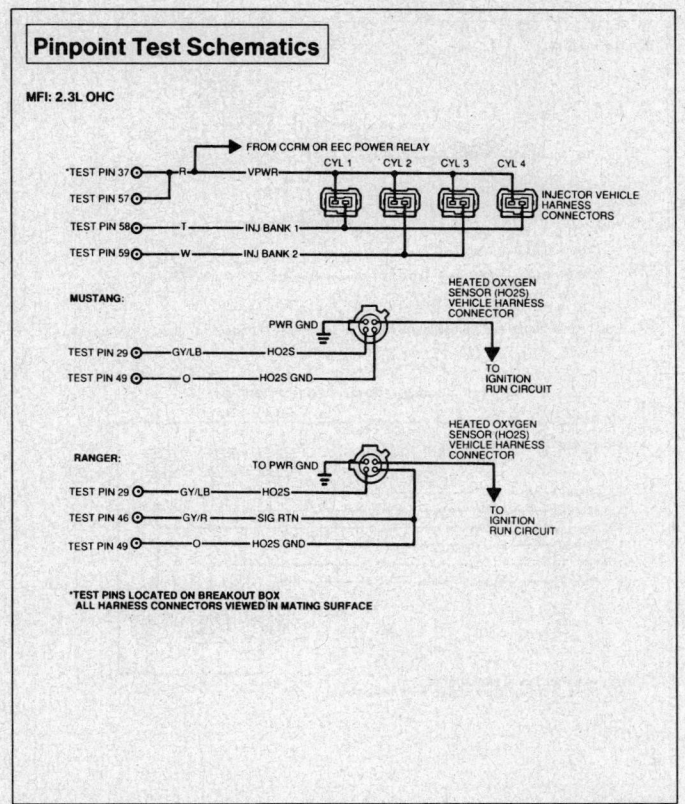

Fig. 191 Test H: Fuel Control (Part 3 of 33)

FM0159300732030X

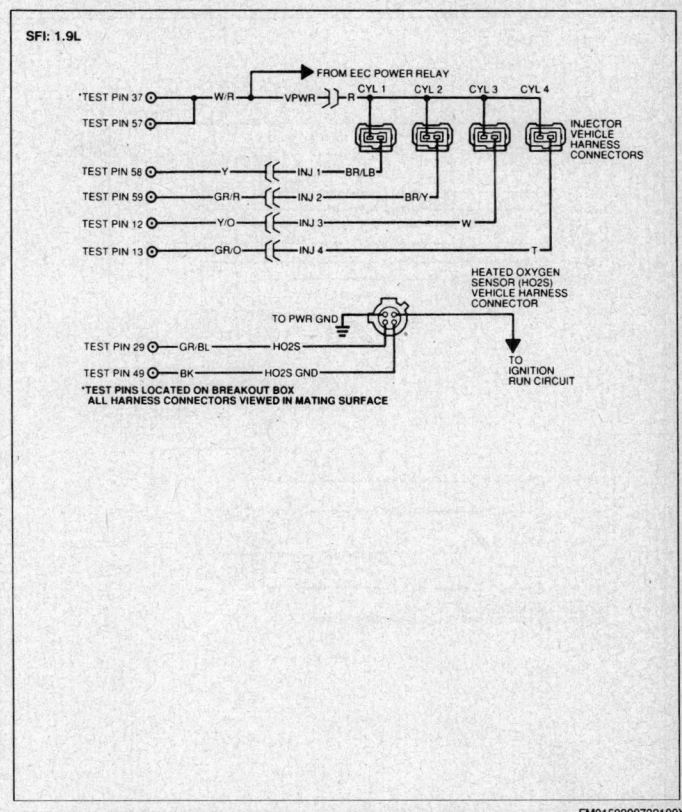

Fig. 191 Test H: Fuel Control (Part 4 of 33)

FM0159300732100X

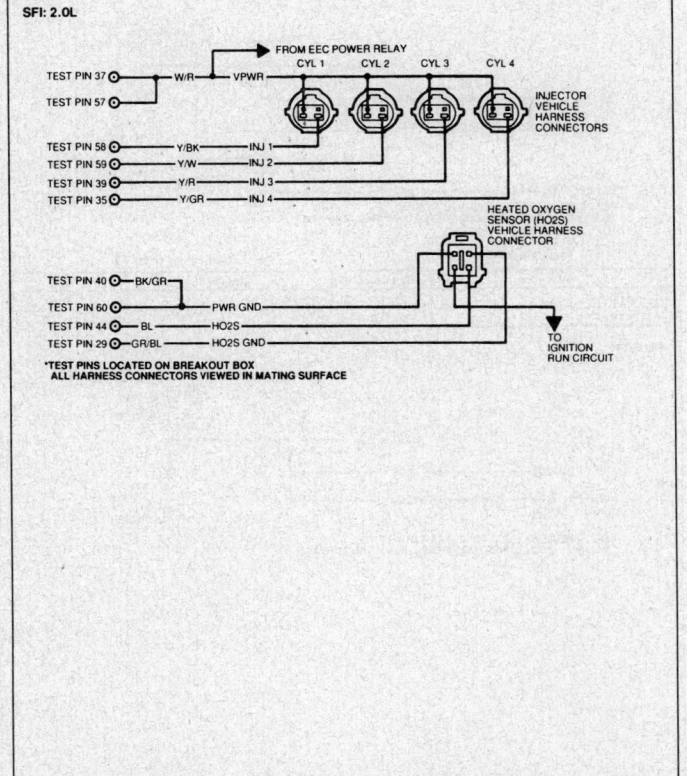

Fig. 191 Test H: Fuel Control (Part 5 of 33)

FM0159300732110X

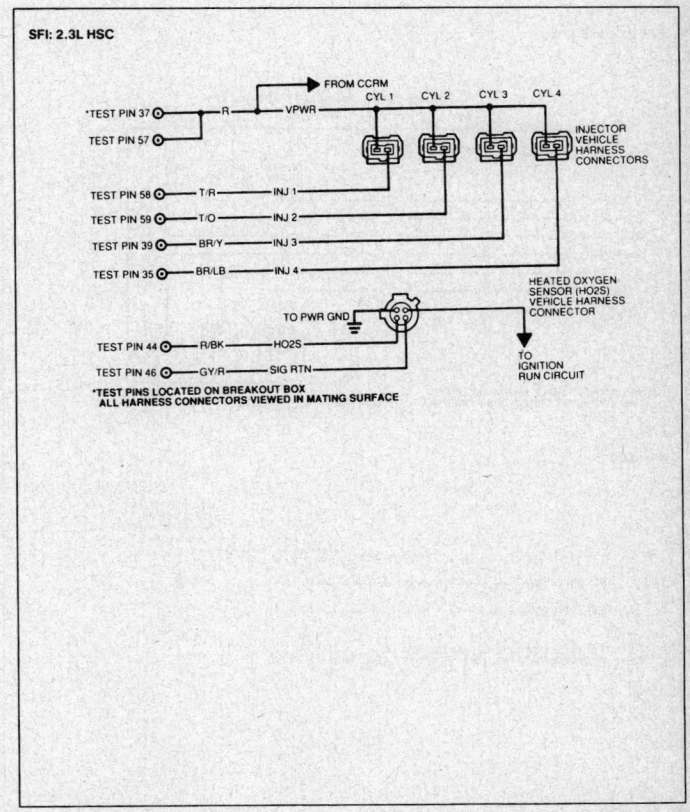

Fig. 191 Test H: Fuel Control (Part 6 of 33)

FM0159300732120X

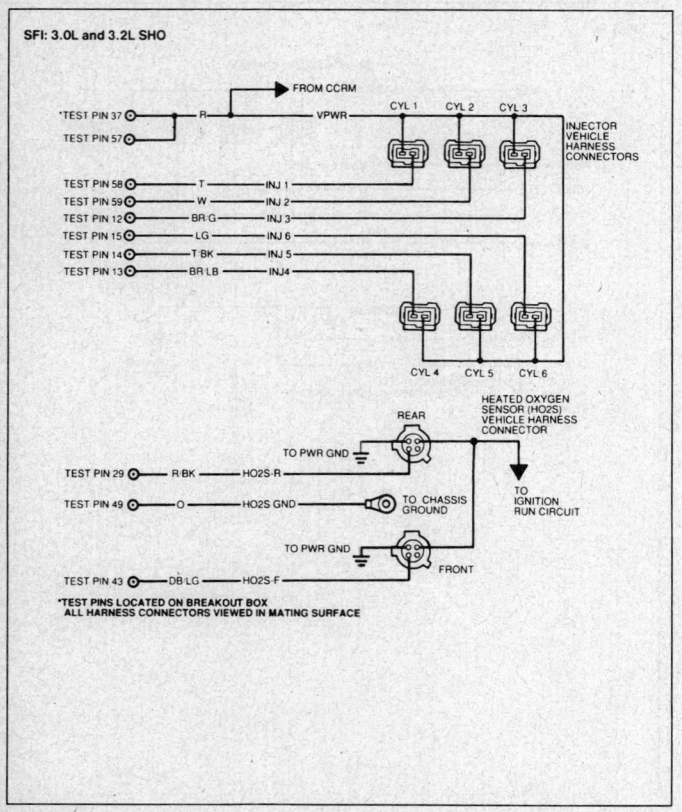

Fig. 191   Test H: Fuel Control (Part 7 of 33). 1993

FM015930073213AX

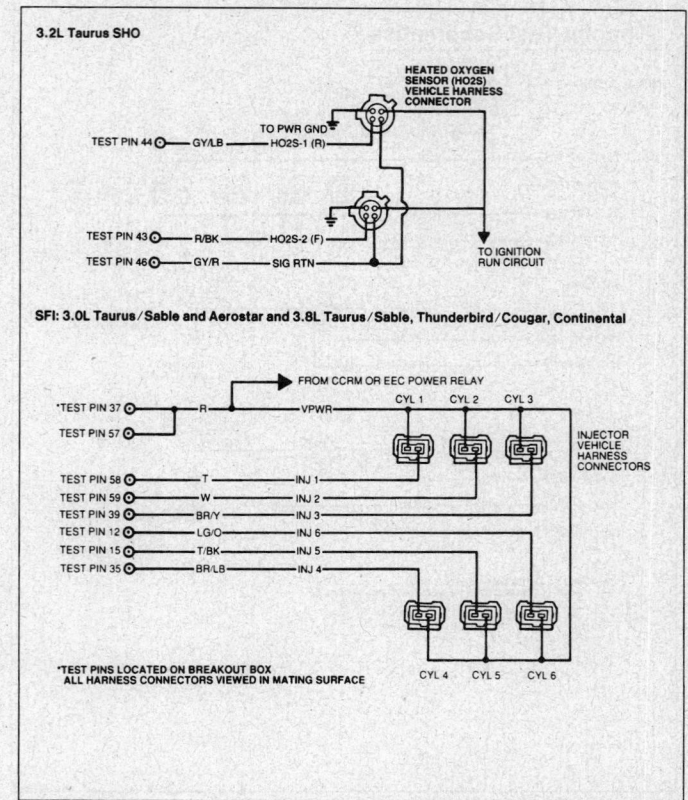

Fig. 191   Test H: Fuel Control (Part 7 of 33). 1994–95

FM015940073213BX

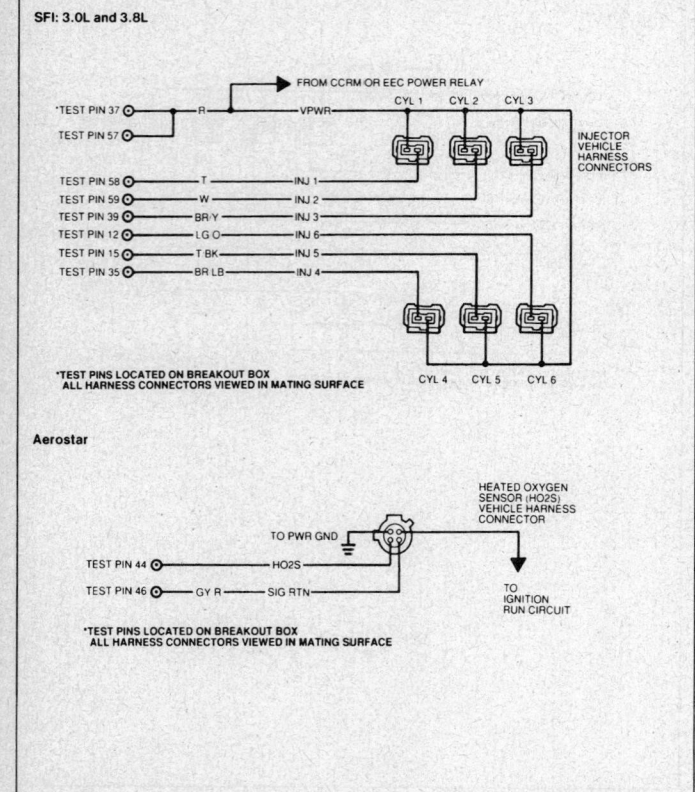

Fig. 191   Test H: Fuel Control (Part 8 of 33). 1993

FM015930073214AX

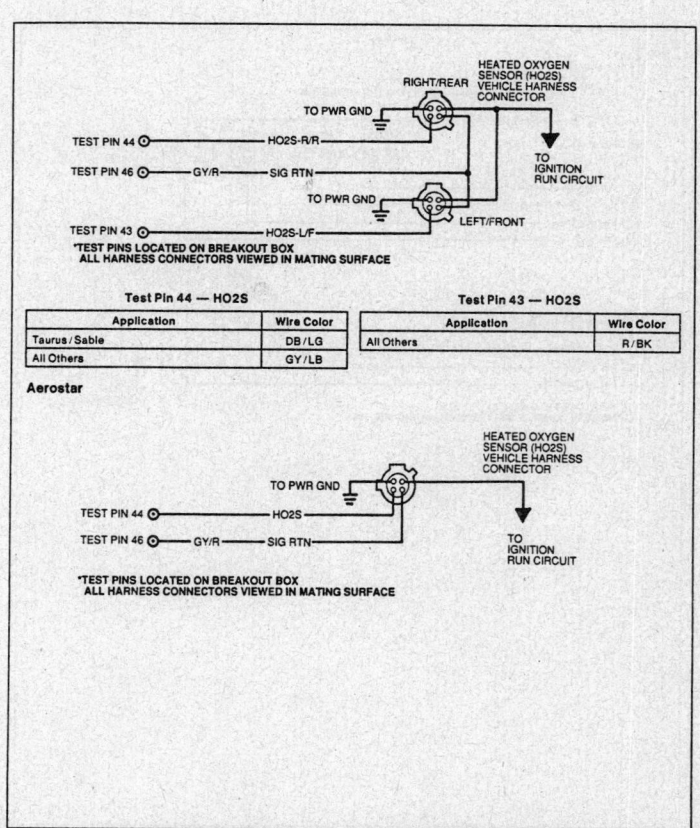

Fig. 191   Test H: Fuel Control (Part 8 of 33). 1994–95

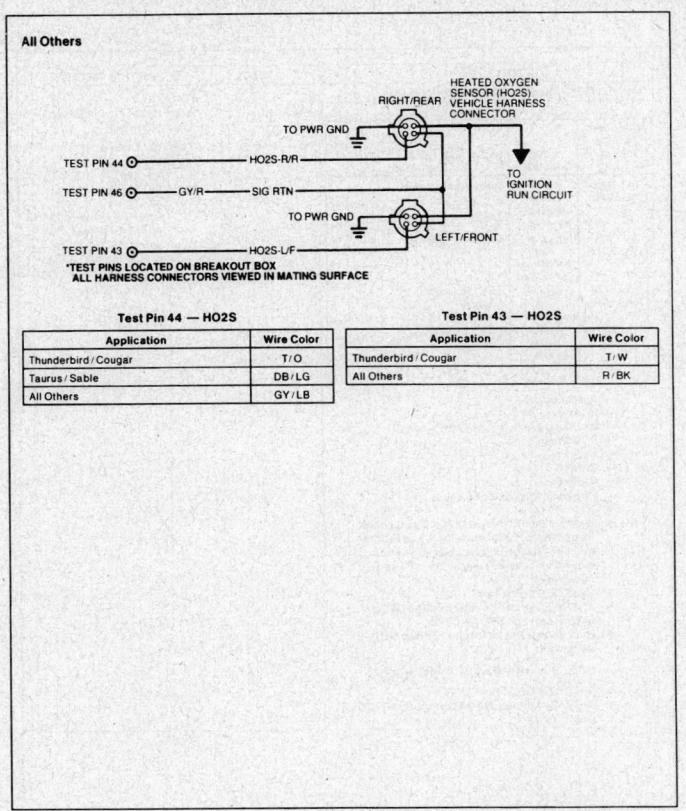

Fig. 191 Test H: Fuel Control (Part 9 of 33)

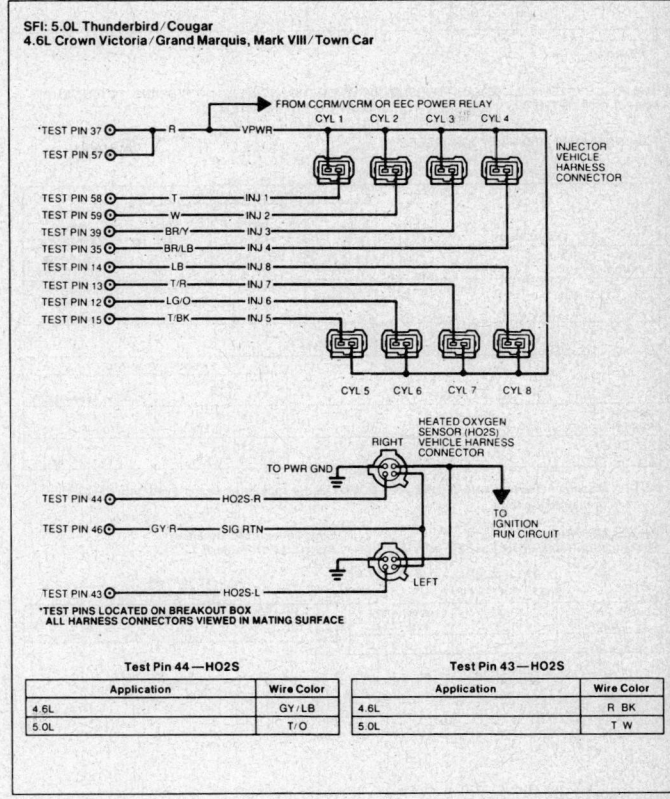

Fig. 191 Test H: Fuel Control (Part 10 of 33). 1993

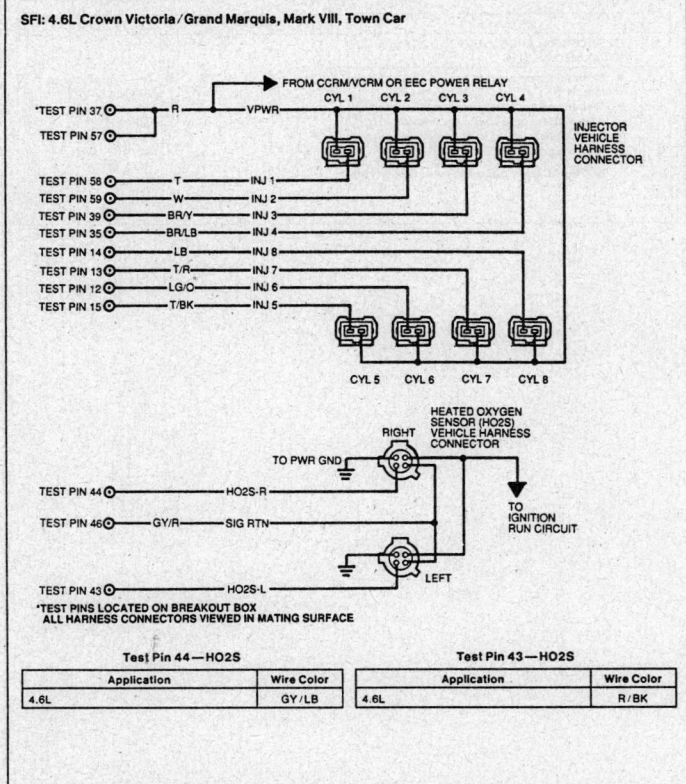

Fig. 191 Test H: Fuel Control (Part 10 of 33). 1994–95

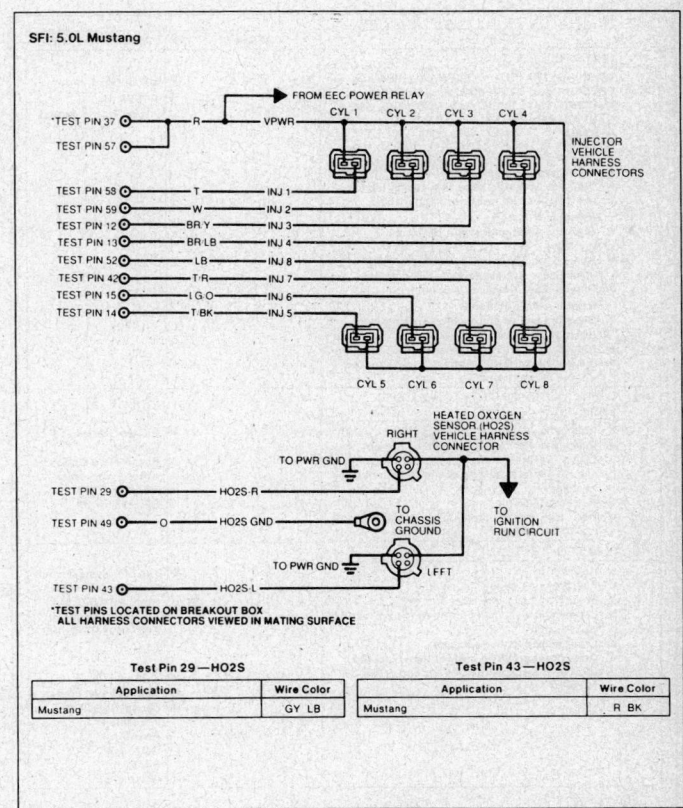

Fig. 191 Test H: Fuel Control (Part 11 of 33)

WARNING

THE FUEL SYSTEM WILL REMAIN PRESSURIZED WHEN THE ENGINE IS NOT RUNNING. TO PREVENT INJURY OR FIRE USE CAUTION WHEN WORKING ON THE FUEL SYSTEM.

FUEL PRESSURE SPECIFICATION TABLES

Car Engines

ENGINE MODE	ENGINE APPLICATION			
	2.3L HSC MFI	3.0L SHO SFI	3.8L SC SFI	All Other Applications
ENGINE RUNNING	45-60 PSI 310-415 kPa	28-33 PSI 193-227 kPa	30-40 PSI 210-280 kPa	30-45 PSI 210-310 kPa
KEY ON ENGINE OFF	50-60 PSI 345-415 kPa	30-45 PSI 210-310 kPa	35-40 PSI 240-280 kPa	35-40 PSI 240-280 kPa

Truck Engines

ENGINE MODE	ENGINE APPLICATION	
	4.9L MFI	All Other Applications
ENGINE RUNNING	45-60 PSI 310-415 kPa	30-45 PSI 210-310 kPa
KEY ON ENGINE OFF	50-60 PSI 345-415 kPa	35-45 PSI 240-310 kPa

NOTE: Maximum fuel pressure is obtainable at WOT or the vacuum hose removed from the fuel pressure regulator.

Injector Bank Resistance Specification Table 1 (Not For SFI)

All Engines Values Are In Ohms

2.3L	3.0L 4.0L 4.9L	5.0L 5.8L 7.0L 7.5L
6.0-8.5	4.0-5.5	3.0-4.0

Single Injector Resistance Specification Table 2

All Engines Values Are In Ohms

ALL ENGINES
11.0-18.0

Fig. 191 Test H: Fuel Control (Part 12 of 33)

FM0159300732180X

TEST STEP			RESULT	▶	ACTION TO TAKE
H1	CHECK FOR FUEL DILUTED ENGINE OIL				

Diagnostic Trouble Code (DTC)	HO2S Orientation	Fault Definition
41/172r 91/136r 176c	right or rear left or front	system indicates lean
42/173r 92/137r 177c	right or rear left or front	system indicates rich
144/41c 139/91c	right or rear left or front	no HO2S switch detected
171c 175c	right or rear left or front	adaptive fuel limit reached

RESULT	▶	ACTION TO TAKE
Yes	▶	REINSTALL PCV valve. GO to **H2**.
No	▶	For Continuous Memory DTC's 41/144, 91/139, 176 GO to **H2**. All Others: CHANGE engine oil and filter. REINSTALL PCV valve. DRIVE vehicle 5 miles/55mph. RERUN Quick Test.

Possible Causes:
- Fuel injectors.
- HO2S.
- Secondary Air Injection (AIR) system.
- PCV/Hose.
- Vacuum.
- CANP.
- MAP sensor.
- Electronic Ignition Coil Failure.
- Key off.
- Remove the PCV valve from the valve cover. Inspect both rocker cover hole and PCV for damage, sludge build up, blockage and movement of valve plunger. Service as necessary.
- Run KOEO Quick Test.
- Address any continuous ignition DTC's before servicing KOER DTCs.
- Start engine and let idle for two minutes minimum.

  NOTE: For a No Start GO directly to **H2**.

- Run KOER Quick Test.
- Are any of the above DTC's present in KOER Quick Test?

Fig. 191 Test H: Fuel Control (Part 13 of 33)

FM0159300732190A

TEST STEP		RESULT	▶	ACTION TO TAKE
H2	CHECK FUEL PRESSURE	Yes	▶	GO to **H3**.
WARNING: THE FUEL SYSTEM WILL REMAIN PRESSURIZED WHEN ENGINE IS NOT RUNNING. TO PREVENT INJURY OR FIRE USE CAUTION WHEN WORKING ON THE FUEL SYSTEM.		No	▶	REFER to Diagnostic Routines
• Key off. • Install fuel pressure gauge. • Verify that manifold vacuum is connected to the fuel pressure regulator if applicable. **If engine will start:** • Start and run engine at idle. Note fuel pressure. • Increase engine speed to 2500 rpms and maintain for one minute. Note fuel pressure. • Refer to Fuel Pressure Specification Table. **If engine will not start:** • Cycle the key off and on several times. Note fuel pressure. • Refer to Fuel Pressure Specification Table. • **Is fuel pressure within specification for the engine being tested?**				
H3	CHECK SYSTEM'S ABILITY TO HOLD FUEL PRESSURE	Yes	▶	For No Starts: GO to **H4**. For Service Codes or other Symptoms: MFI: GO to **H5**; SFI: GO to **H6**
• Pressurize fuel system per step **H2**. • Visually look for fuel leaking at the injector O-ring, fuel pressure regulator, and the fuel lines to the fuel charging assembly. Service as necessary. • Key on, engine off. • **Does fuel pressure remain at specification for 60 seconds?**				
H4	FUEL DELIVERY TEST	Yes	▶	The EEC system is not the cause of the No Start. REMOVE the fuel pressure gauge. RECONNECT the IFS switch.
• Key off. • Fuel pressure gauge installed. • Pressurize fuel system per step **H2**. • Locate and disconnect the Inertia Fuel Shutoff (IFS) switch. • Crank engine for five seconds. • **Does pressure drop greater than 5 psi (34 kPa) by the end of the five second crank cycle?**		No	▶	REMOVE fuel pressure gauge. RECONNECT IFS switch. For MFI: GO to **H7** For SFI: GO to **H8**.

Fig. 191 Test H: Fuel Control (Part 14 of 33)

FM0159300732200X

TEST STEP		RESULT	▶	ACTION TO TAKE
H5	CYLINDER BALANCE DIAGNOSTIC TEST MODE (DTM): MFI ENGINES	Yes	▶	For Symptoms or DTCs 41/172, 91/136, 176: GO to **H13**. For DTCs 42/173, 92/137, 177: GO to **H24**. For all others: GO to **H14**.
• Connect tachometer to engine. Run engine at idle. • Disconnect and reconnect the injectors one at a time: Note rpm drop for each injector. • **Does each injector produce a momentary drop in rpm?** NOTE: IAC will attempt to re-establish rpm.		No	▶	GO to **H7**.

Fig. 191 Test H: Fuel Control (Part 15 of 33)

TEST STEP	RESULT	► ACTION TO TAKE
H6 CYLINDER BALANCE DIAGNOSTIC TEST MODE (DTM) SFI ENGINES The DTM switches each injector OFF and ON one at a time. Diagnostic Trouble Codes (DTC) correspond to the cylinder number (i.e., Service DTC 30 indicates a problem with cylinder No. 3, a DTC 90 indicates a pass). The Cylinder Balance (DTM) is designed to aid in the detection of a weak or non-contributing cylinder. The Pinpoint Test Steps are designed to isolate only EEC related problems. • Run the Engine Running Quick Test. • After the last repeated code, wait 5-10 seconds. • "Goose" throttle lightly (not wide-open-throttle). • Cylinder Balance (DTM) will be performed. Time of test is approximately 2-3 minutes. • **Are there any DTCs requiring service?**	Yes No	► GO to **H8** ► For Symptoms or DTC 41/172, 91/136, 176: GO to **H13** For DTC 42/173, 92/137, 177: GO to **H24** For all others: GO to **H14**

DTC TABLE VS. CYLINDER

DIAGNOSTIC TROUBLE CODES	90	10	20	30	40	50	60	70	80	77 538
CYLINDER INJECTOR NUMBER	PASS	1	2	3	4	5	6	7	8	RERUN TEST*

*If throttle is touched (moved) during the Cylinder Balance (DTM) DTC 77.538 will appear, indicating test was not completed. Service DTM Code 538 could also be output if a Continuous Memory DTC 214(CID) is present. If Continuous Memory DTC 214 is present refer to the appropriate code chart in Quick Test for service direction.

Fig. 191 Test H: Fuel Control (Part 16 of 33)

TEST STEP	RESULT	► ACTION TO TAKE
H7 CHECK RESISTANCE OF INJECTOR(S) AND HARNESS MFI ENGINES • Key off. • Disconnect Powertrain Control Module (PCM). Inspect for damaged or pushed out pins, corrosion, loose wires, etc. Service as necessary. NOTE: This erases Continuous Memory. • Install breakout box, leave PCM disconnected. • Measure resistance of INJECTOR BANK 1 between Test Pin 37 and Test Pin 58 at the breakout box. Record resistance. • Measure resistance of INJECTOR BANK 2 between Test Pin 37 and Test Pin 59 at the breakout box. Record resistance. • Refer to Injector Resistance Specification Table 1. • **Is each resistance within specification for the appropriate engine?**	Yes No	► GO to **H12** ► For NO START: SERVICE open in VPWR circuit. For others: GO to **H9**
H8 CHECK RESISTANCE OF INJECTOR(S) AND HARNESS SFI ENGINES • Key off. • Disconnect Powertrain Control Module (PCM). Inspect for damaged or pushed out pins, corrosion, loose wires, etc. Service as necessary. NOTE: This erases Continuous Memory. • Install breakout box, leave PCM disconnected. • Measure resistance between the suspect INJECTOR circuit Test Pin and Test Pin 37 at the breakout box. Record resistance. • For No Starts: — Pick any injector and measure resistance between that INJECTOR circuit's Test Pin and Test Pin 37 at the breakout box. Record resistance. • Refer to Injector Resistance Specification Table 2. • **Is each resistance within specification for the appropriate engine?**	Yes No	► GO to **H12** ► For NO START: SERVICE open in VPWR circuit. For others: GO to **H9**

Fig. 191 Test H: Fuel Control (Part 17 of 33)

TEST STEP	RESULT	► ACTION TO TAKE
H9 CHECK CONTINUITY OF FUEL INJECTOR HARNESS • Key off. • Breakout box installed, PCM disconnected. • Disconnect injector vehicle harness connector at the suspect injector. • Measure resistance between Test Pin 37/57 at the breakout box and the VPWR pin at the injector vehicle harness connector. • Refer to the Pinpoint Test Schematic for the appropriate injector pin identification. • Measure resistance between the injector test pin(s) at the breakout box and the same injector circuit signal pin at the each injector vehicle harness connector. • **Is each resistance less than 5.0 ohms?**	Yes No	► GO to **H10** ► SERVICE open circuit. REMOVE breakout box. RECONNECT PCM and injectors DRIVE vehicle 5 miles/55 mph. RERUN Quick Test
H10 CHECK INJECTOR HARNESS CIRCUIT FOR SHORT TO POWER OR GROUND • Key off. • Breakout box installed, PCM disconnected. • Suspect fuel injector vehicle harness disconnected. • Refer to the Pinpoint Test Schematic for the appropriate injector pin identification. • Measure resistance between the injector test pin(s) and Test Pin 37/57, 40, 46 and 60 at the breakout box. • Measure resistance between the injector test pin(s) at the breakout box and chassis ground. • **Is each resistance greater than 10,000 ohms?**	Yes No	► For SFI: REPLACE injector per Cylinder Balance DTM fault code RERUN Quick Test For MFI: GO to **H11** ► SERVICE short circuit. REMOVE breakout box. RECONNECT PCM and injectors. DRIVE vehicle 5 miles/55 mph. RERUN Quick Test
H11 ISOLATE FAULTY INJECTOR CIRCUIT • Key off. • Breakout box installed, PCM disconnected. • Disconnect all injectors on suspect bank. • DVOM on 200 ohm scale. • Connect one injector and measure resistance between Test Pin 37 and either Test Pin 58 or 59 as appropriate. • Disconnect that injector and repeat process for each of the remaining injectors. • Refer to Injector Resistance Specification Table 2. • **Is each resistance within specification for the appropriate engine?**	Yes No	► GO to **H12** ► REPLACE injector. REMOVE breakout box. RECONNECT PCM and injectors. DRIVE vehicle 5 miles/55 mph. RERUN Quick Test

Fig. 191 Test H: Fuel Control (Part 18 of 33)

TEST STEP	RESULT	► ACTION TO TAKE
H12 CHECK INJECTOR DRIVER SIGNAL Requires standard non-powered 12 volt test lamp. • Key off. • Breakout box installed. • Connect PCM to breakout box. • For MFI: — Connect test lamp between Test Pin 37 and Test Pin 58 at the breakout box. — Connect test lamp between Test Pin 37 and 59 at the breakout box. • For SFI: — Connect test lamp between Test Pin 37 and the suspect injectors Test Pin at the breakout box. • Crank or start engine. NOTE: Properly operating systems will show a dim glow on the lamp. • **Is glow on lamp dim?**	Yes No	► REMOVE breakout box. RECONNECT PCM. refer to Ignition for other possible causes. After any servicing, DRIVE vehicle 5 miles/55 mph. RERUN Quick Test and Cylinder Balance DTM. ► No light/Bright light: REPLACE PCM. REMOVE breakout box. DRIVE vehicle 5 miles/55 mph. RERUN Quick Test.
H13 CHECK SECONDARY AIR INJECTION (AIR) OPERATION NOTE: If vehicle is equipped with Pulsed-Secondary Air Injection (PAIR) or no AIR, ignore this step and GO to **H14**. With dual HO2S, DTC 41/172 refers to right or rear HO2S; DTC 91/136, 176 refers to left or front HO2S. HO2S always lean could be caused by: — Thermactor air being diverted upstream from the HO2S. • Key off. • Disconnect the AIR hose(s) from the AIR pump so that secondary air is bypassed to atmosphere during testing. • Run Engine Running Quick Test. • **Are Codes 41/172, 91/136, 176 present?**	Yes No	► RECONNECT AIR Hose. GO to **H14** ► For Continuous Memory DTC's 41/144, 91/139, 176. GO to **H90**. All Others: GO to AIR systems diagnosis.

Fig. 191 Test H: Fuel Control (Part 19 of 33)

TEST STEP		RESULT	▶	ACTION TO TAKE
H14 CHECK HO2S INTEGRITY				

HO2S always lean, slow to switch or lack of switching; fuel at adaptive limit could be caused by:
  — Moisture inside the HO2S harness connector resulting in a short to ground.
  — HO2S coated with contaminants.
  — HO2S circuit open.
  — HO2S circuit shorted to ground.
• Key off.
• Inspect the HO2S harness for chafing, burns or other indications of damage. Service as necessary.
• Inspect HO2S and connector for indication of submerging in water, oil, coolant, etc. Service as necessary.
• Run engine at 2000 rpm for two minutes.
• Key off.
• Run Engine Running Self Test.
• **Are fault codes present?**
		Yes
		
		No
			▶
			
			▶
				For engines with
				— **MAP sensor:** GO to **H15**
				— **MAF sensor:** GO to **H16**
				
				GO to **H21**

Fig. 191 Test H: Fuel Control (Part 20 of 33)

FM015930073226OX

TEST STEP		RESULT	▶	ACTION TO TAKE
H15 CHECK HO2S ON ENGINES WITH MAP SENSORS				

NOTE: Vacuum/air leaks in non-EEC areas could also cause DTC 41, 91, 136, 172 or 176. Check for:
  — Leaking vacuum actuator (e.g. A/C control motor).
  — Engine sealing.
  — EGR system.
  — PCV system.
  — Lead contaminated HO2S
• Key off.
• Verify MAP sensor output voltage (refer to procedure in Pinpoint Test **DF3**).
• Disconnect appropriate HO2S from vehicle harness.
For 4 wire HO2S (refer to schematic):
  — Connect DVOM to HO2S circuit and HO2S GND or SIG RTN at the HO2S connector.
For 3 wire HO2S (refer to schematic):
  — Connect DVOM to HO2S circuit at the sensor and battery negative post.
• Disconnect and plug vacuum line at MAP sensor.
• DVOM on 20 volt scale.
• Start engine and apply 10-14 in-Hg (33-46 kPa) to MAP sensor.
• Run engine at approximately 2000 rpm for two minutes.
• **Does the DVOM indicate greater than 0.5 volt within two minutes?**
		Yes
		No
			▶
			▶
				GO to **H17**.
				REPLACE HO2S. RECONNECT MAP sensor vacuum line. RERUN Quick Test.

Fig. 191 Test H: Fuel Control (Part 21 of 33)

TEST STEP		RESULT	▶	ACTION TO TAKE
H16 CHECK HO2S ON ENGINES WITH MAF SENSOR				

NOTE: The purpose of this test is to verify the HO2S can generate greater than 0.5 volt during Engine Running Quick Test.
 	
Any vacuum/air leaks in non-EEC areas could also cause DTC 41, 91, 136, 172 or 176. Check for:
  — Leaking vacuum actuator (e.g. A/C control motor).
  — Engine sealing.
  — EGR system.
  — PCV system.
  — Unmetered air leak between Mass Air Flow (MAF) sensor and throttle body.
  — Lead contaminated HO2S.
• Key off.
• Disconnect appropriate HO2S from vehicle harness.
For 4 wire HO2S (refer to schematic):
  — Connect DVOM to HO2S circuit and HO2S SIG RTN or HO2S GND at the HO2S connector.
For 3 wire HO2S (refer to schematic):
  — Connect DVOM to HO2S circuit at the sensor and battery negative post.
• DVOM on 20 volt scale.
• Run engine at approximately 2000 rpm for two minutes.
• Rerun Engine Running Quick Test and monitor HO2S voltage.
• **Does DVOM indicate greater than 0.5 volt at the end of Quick Test?**
		Yes
		No
			▶
			▶
				GO to **H17**
				REPLACE HO2S. RERUN Quick Test.

Fig. 191   Test H: Fuel Control (Part 22 of 33)

FM015930073228OX

TEST STEP		RESULT	▶	ACTION TO TAKE
H17 CHECK CONTINUITY OF HO2S AND HO2S GROUND CIRCUITS				

• Key off.
• Breakout box installed, PCM disconnected.
• Disconnect suspect HO2S from vehicle harness. Inspect both ends of connector for damaged or pushed out pins, moisture, corrosion, loose wires, etc. Service as necessary.
• Measure resistance between HO2S circuit Test Pin at the breakout box and HO2S circuit at the vehicle harness connector.
For 3-wire HO2S (refer to schematic):
  — Measure resistance between HO2S GND Test Pin at the breakout box and battery negative post.
 	
For 4-wire HO2S (refer to schematic):
  — Measure resistance between SIG RTN Test Pin at the breakout box and HO2S SIG RTN at the vehicle harness connector.
  — Where applicable measure resistance between HO2S GND and SIG RTN at the breakout box.
• **Is each resistance less than 5.0 ohms?**
		Yes
		No
			▶
			▶
				GO to **H18**
				SERVICE open circuit. REMOVE breakout box. RECONNECT PCM, HO2S, and any other components that have been disconnected. DRIVE vehicle 5 miles/55 mph. RERUN Quick Test.

H18 CHECK HO2S CIRCUIT FOR SHORT TO GROUND				
• Key off. • Breakout box installed, PCM disconnected. • HO2S disconnected. • Measure resistance between the HO2S circuit Test Pin at the breakout box and Test Pins 40, 46 or 49 where applicable at the breakout box. • **Is each resistance greater than 10,000 ohms?**		Yes No	▶ ▶	GO to **H19** SERVICE short circuit. REMOVE breakout box. RECONNECT PCM, HO2S, and any other components that are disconnected. DRIVE vehicle 5 miles 55 mph. RERUN Quick Test.

Fig. 191   Test H: Fuel Control (Part 23 of 33)

FM015930073229OX

TEST STEP		RESULT	▶	ACTION TO TAKE
H19	**CHECK HO2S FOR SHORT TO GROUND**			
	• Key off. • Breakout box installed, PCM disconnected. • HO2S disconnected. • Measure resistance between PWR GND and HO2S circuit at the HO2S connector. • For 4-wire HO2S (refer to schematic). Also measure resistance between HO2S GND and / or SIG RTN at the HO2S connector. • **Is resistance greater than 10,000 ohms?**	Yes	▶	For DTCs: 144 / 41C, 139 / 91C, 171, 174, 175 or 178, GO to **H90**. ▶ For other DTCs: — MAP sensor: GO to **H20**. — MAF Sensor: REMOVE breakout box. RECONNECT HO2S. REPLACE PCM. DRIVE vehicle 5 miles / 55 mph. RERUN Quick Test.
		No	▶	REPLACE HO2S. REMOVE breakout box. RECONNECT PCM. DRIVE vehicle 5 miles / 55 mph. RERUN Quick Test.
H20	**ATTEMPT TO ELIMINATE DTC 41 / 172, 91 / 136 or 176 ON ENGINES WITH MAP SENSOR**			
	• Key off. • Breakout box installed. • Disconnect and plug MAP sensor vacuum line. • Connect PCM to breakout box. • Reconnect HO2S. • Start engine and apply 10- 14 in-Hg (34-47 kPa) vacuum to MAP sensor. • Run engine at approximately 2000 rpm for two minutes. Allow engine to return to idle. • Rerun Engine Running Quick Test. NOTE: If you are here for Continuous Memory DTCs the vehicle has to be driven 5 miles / 55 mph. • **Is DTC 41 / 172, 91 / 136 or 176 still present (ignore all other DTCs)?**	Yes	▶	REMOVE breakout box. RECONNECT MAP sensor vacuum line. If engine runs rough, GO to **S2**. All others REPLACE PCM. DRIVE vehicle 5 miles / 55 mph. RERUN Quick Test.
		No	▶	REMOVE breakout box. RECONNECT PCM and MAP sensor vacuum line. HO2S input OK. Fuel delivery is OK. Problem is in an area common to all cylinders, i.e. air vacuum leak, fuel contamination, EGR, AIR, CHECK MAP frequency, IGN System, etc. (SERVICE as necessary.)

FM0159300732300X

Fig. 191   Test H: Fuel Control (Part 24 of 33)

TEST STEP		RESULT	▶	ACTION TO TAKE
H21	**CHECK RESISTANCE OF HEATER ELEMENT ON HO2S**			

	• Key off.
	• Disconnect suspect HO2S from vehicle harness.
	• Inspect both ends of the connector for damaged or pushed out pins, moisture, corrosion, loose wires, etc. Service as necessary.
	• Measure resistance between KEY PWR circuit and PWR GND circuit at HO2S connector (refer to schematic).
	  — Hot to warm resistance specification is 5.0 to 30.0 ohms.
	  — Room temperature resistance specification is 2.0 to 5.0 ohms.
	• **Is resistance within specification?**
		Yes	▶	GO to **H22**.

		No	▶	REPLACE HO2S. RERUN Quick Test.
H22	**CHECK FOR POWER AT HO2S HARNESS CONNECTOR**			
	• Key on, engine off. • HO2S disconnected. • Measure voltage between KEY POWER circuit and PWR GND circuit at the HO2S vehicle harness connector (refer to schematic). • **Is voltage greater than 10.5 volts?**	Yes	▶	RECONNECT HO2S. HO2S system OK. Fuel delivery is OK. HO2S sensor may have cooled prior to Engine Running Quick Test. If symptom persists, problem is in an area common to all cylinders, i.e. air / vacuum leak, fuel contamination, EGR AIR, MAP. CHECK MAP frequency, ignition system. etc. SERVICE as necessary.
		No	▶	GO to **H23**.
H23	**CHECK CONTINUITY OF POWER GROUND CIRCUIT**			
	• Key off. • HO2S disconnected. • Measure resistance between PWR GND circuit at the HO2S vehicle harness connector and battery negative post. • **Is resistance less than 5.0 ohms?**	Yes	▶	SERVICE open in KEY PWR circuit. RECONNECT HO2S sensor. RERUN Quick Test.
		No	▶	SERVICE open in PWR GND circuit. RECONNECT HO2S sensor. RERUN Quick Test.

FM0159300732310X

Fig. 191   Test H: Fuel Control (Part 25 of 33)

TEST STEP		RESULT	▶	ACTION TO TAKE
H24	**CHECK HO2S SIGNAL FOR SHORT TO POWER**			
	With dual HO2S, DTC 42 / 173 refers to right or rear HO2S; DTC 92 / 137, 177 refers to left or front HO2S. HO2S always rich could be caused by: — Moisture inside HO2S harness connector resulting in a short to power. — HO2S circuit shorted to power. • Key off. • Disconnect the suspect HO2S from vehicle harness. • Inspect both ends of the connector for damaged or pushed out pins, moisture, corrosion, loose wires, etc. Service as necessary. • Key on, engine off. • Measure voltage between HO2S circuit and PWR GND at the HO2S vehicle harness connector (refer to schematic). • **Is voltage less than 0.5 volt?**	Yes	▶	GO to **H26**.
		No	▶	GO to **H25**.
H25	**CHECK FOR SHORT TO POWER**			
	• Key off. • Inspect HO2S GND and HO2S circuit harness for chaffing, burns or other indications of short to power. Service as necessary. • Disconnect Powertrain Control Module (PCM). Inspect for damaged, or pushed out pins, corrosion, loose wires etc. Service as necessary. • Install breakout box, leave PCM disconnected. • Suspect HO2S disconnected. • Measure resistance between HO2S circuit, and KEYPWR at the breakout box. • **Is the resistance greater than 10,000 ohms?**	Yes	▶	REPLACE PCM. REMOVE breakout box. RECONNECT HO2S. DRIVE vehicle 5 miles / 55 mph. RERUN Quick Test.
		No	▶	SERVICE short to power. REMOVE breakout box. RECONNECT PCM. DRIVE vehicle 5 miles / 55 mph. RERUN Quick Test.

FM0159300732320X

Fig. 191   Test H: Fuel Control (Part 26 of 33)

TEST STEP		RESULT	▶	ACTION TO TAKE
H26	**CHECK HO2S FOR SHORT TO IGNITION RUN CIRCUIT**			
	• Key off. • HO2S disconnected. • Measure resistance between KEY PWR circuit and HO2S SIG circuit at the HO2S connector (refer to schematic). • **Is resistance greater than 10,000 ohms?**	Yes	▶	For DTCs 42 / 173, 92 / 137, 177: GO to **H27**; ▶ For DTCs 171, 174, 175, 178: MAP sensor: GO to **H28**. ▶ MAF sensor: GO to **H30**.
		No	▶	REPLACE HO2S. DRIVE vehicle 5 miles / 55 mph. RERUN Quick Test.
H27	**ATTEMPT TO GENERATE DTC 41 / 172, 91 / 136, 176**			
	• Key off. • HO2S disconnected. • Jumper HO2S circuit at the HO2S vehicle harness connector to battery negative post. • Rerun Engine Running Quick Test. • **Is DTC 41 / 172, 91, 136 or 176 present?**	Yes	▶	REMOVE jumper. For Engines With MAP Sensor: GO to **H28**. ▶ MAF sensor: GO to **H30**.
		No	▶	REMOVE jumper. RECONNECT HO2S. DISCONNECT PCM 60 pin connector. Inspect for damaged or pushed out pins, corrosion, loose wires, etc. SERVICE as necessary. If OK REPLACE PCM. DRIVE vehicle 5 miles / 55 mph. RERUN Quick Test.

Fig. 191   Test H: Fuel Control (Part 27 of 33)

TEST STEP	RESULT	▶	ACTION TO TAKE
H28 CHECK MAP SENSOR FOR VACUUM LEAK			
NOTE: Due to the MAP sensor's large influence on fuel control, there is a possibility that MAP could be at fault without a DTC 22 / 126. Therefore the next two Test Steps will verify proper vacuum to the MAP sensor and its ability to hold vacuum. • Key off. • Disconnect vacuum line from MAP sensor. • Inspect hose for blockage (kinks or gel build up), damage from wear or aging. Service as necessary. • Plug vacuum hose at the MAP side. • Connect a vacuum pump to the MAP sensor and apply 18 in-Hg (60 kPa) vacuum to MAP sensor. • **Does MAP sensor hold vacuum?**	Yes Nc	▶ ▶	RELEASE vacuum. GO to **H29**. REPLACE MAP sensor. REMOVE vacuum pump. RECONNECT HO2S. DRIVE vehicle 5 miles / 55 mph. RERUN Quick Test.
H29 CHECK FOR LOSS OF VACUUM TO MAP SENSOR			
• Tee a vacuum gauge into the manifold vacuum line at MAP sensor. • Start the engine and let rpm stabilize. Note vacuum level. • Key off. • REMOVE vacuum gauge and Tee and reconnect vacuum line to MAP sensor. • Tee in vacuum gauge at a different source of intake manifold vacuum and restart the engine. Note vacuum level. • **Does the vacuum level differ greater than 1.0 in-Hg (3.4 kPa)?**	Yes No	▶ ▶	INSPECT engine vacuum integrity. SERVICE as necessary. REMOVE vacuum gauge and Tee. RECONNECT HO2S. DRIVE vehicle 5 miles / 55 mph. RERUN Quick Test. GO to **H30**

Fig. 191   Test H: Fuel Control (Part 28 of 33)

FM0159300732340X

TEST STEP	RESULT	▶	ACTION TO TAKE
H30 HO2S CHECK			
• Key off. • HO2S disconnected. **For 4-wire HO2S (refer to schematic):** — Connect DVOM to HO2S circuit and HO2S GND or SIG RTN at the HO2S connector. **For 3-wire HO2S (refer to schematic):** — Connect DVOM to HO2S circuit at the HO2S connector and to battery negative post. • DVOM on 20 volt scale. • Create a vacuum leak to cause HO2S to go lean. **For all engines with MAF sensors:** — Disconnect any vacuum hose from the manifold vacuum tree. **For all other applications:** • Disconnect the PCV valve hose from the PCV valve. • Start engine and run at approximately 2000 rpm. • **Does the DVOM indicate less than 0.4 volt within 30 seconds?**	Yes No	▶ ▶	GO to **H90**. REPLACE HO2S. RECONNECT vacuum hoses. DRIVE vehicle 5 miles / 55 mph. RERUN Quick Test.
H90 CHECK CONTINUOUS MONITOR DIAGNOSTIC TEST MODE (DTM)			
• Key off. • Verify engine at operating temperature. • Start engine and run at 2000 rpm for two minutes. • With engine rpm at idle enter Engine Running Continuous Monitor (DTM). • Observe VOM or STAR LED for indication of fault. • Wiggle, shake or bend a small section of the EEC harness while working your way from the HO2S to the PCM. • Wiggle, shake or bend a small section of the EEC harness while working your way from the HO2S GND to the PCM. • **is a fault indicated?**	Yes No	▶ ▶	ISOLATE fault and SERVICE as necessary. REMOVE breakout box. CLEAR Continuous Memory RERUN Quick Test. REMAIN in Engine Running Continuous Monitor DTM. GO to **H91**.

Fig. 191   Test H: Fuel Control (Part 29 of 33)

FM0159300732350X

TEST STEP	RESULT	▶	ACTION TO TAKE
H40 DIAGNOSTIC TROUBLE CODE (DTC) 593: CHECK HO2S HEATER RELAY ELECTRICAL OPERATION			
DTC 593 indicates that a primary HO2S Heater circuit failure has been detected. Possible causes: — Damaged HO2S HTR Relay. — Open VPWR circuit. — Open in relay control signal circuit. — Short to power in relay control signal circuit. — Short to ground in relay control signal circuit. — Damaged Powertrain Control Module (PCM). • Key off. • Disconnect both HO2S. Inspect for damaged or pushed out pins, corrosion, loose wires, etc. Service as necessary. • Connect VOM / DVOM positive test lead to VPWR circuit and negative test lead to PWR GND circuit at the HO2S vehicle harness connector. • Enter Output State Diagnostic Test Mode (DTM) (refer to Quick Test Appendix). • While observing VOM / DVOM depress and release throttle several times to cycle outputs (take this reading at both HO2S vehicle harness connectors). • **Does the voltage cycle from 10.5 or greater volts to less than 0.5 volts?**	Yes No	▶ ▶	For symptom: GO to **H21**. For DTC 593: Concern may be intermittent. RECONNECT all components. RERUN Quick Test. For DTC 593: GO to **H41**. For symptom: GO to **H46**.
H41 CHECK VPWR CIRCUIT VOLTAGE			
• Key on, engine off. • HO2S heater relay disconnected. • Measure the voltage between VPWR at the HO2S heater relay socket (located in the power distribution box) and battery ground (refer to schematic at the beginning of test). • **Is the voltage greater than 10.5 volts?**	Yes No	▶ ▶	For DTC 593: GO to **H42**. For symptoms: GO to **H46**. SERVICE open in harness. RECONNECT all components. RERUN Quick Test.
H42 CHECK CONTINUITY OF HO2S HEATER RELAY CIRCUIT			
• Key off. • HO2S heater relay removed from power distribution box. • Disconnect Powertrain Control Module (PCM). Inspect for damaged or pushed out pins, corrosion, loose wires, etc. Service as necessary. • Measure the resistance between the HO2S heater relay circuit and the HO2S heater relay socket and Test Pin 14 at the breakout box. • **Is the resistance less than 5.0 ohms?**	Yes No	▶ ▶	GO to **H43**. SERVICE open in harness. REMOVE breakout box. RECONNECT all components. RERUN Quick Test.

Fig. 191   Test H: Fuel Control (Part 30 of 33). 1995

FM0159500732370X

TEST STEP	RESULT	▶	ACTION TO TAKE
H43 CHECK HO2S HEATER RELAY CIRCUIT FOR SHORT TO POWER			
• Key off. • HO2S heater relay disconnected. • Breakout box installed, leave PCM disconnected. • Measure the resistance between Test Pin 14 and Test Pins 37 / 57 at the breakout box. • **Is the resistance greater than 10,000 ohms?**	Yes No	▶ ▶	GO to **H44**. SERVICE short in harness. REMOVE breakout box. RECONNECT all components. RERUN Quick Test.
H44 CHECK HO2S HEATER RELAY CIRCUIT FOR SHORT TO GROUND			
• Key off. • HO2S heater relay disconnected. • Breakout box installed, leave PCM disconnected. • Measure the resistance between Test Pin 14 and Test Pins 40, 46 and 60 at the breakout box. • **Is the resistance greater than 10,000 ohms?**	Yes No	▶ ▶	GO to **H45**. SERVICE short in harness. REMOVE breakout box. RECONNECT all components. RERUN Quick Test.
H45 CHECK HO2S HEATER RELAY COIL RESISTANCE			
• Key off. • HO2S heater relay removed from power distribution box. • Measure the resistance of the HO2S heater relay coil (refer to schematic). • **Is the resistance between 90 and 110 ohms?**	Yes No	▶ ▶	REPLACE PCM. REMOVE breakout box. RECONNECT all components. RERUN Quick Test. REPLACE HO2S HEATER RELAY. REMOVE breakout box. RECONNECT all components. RERUN Quick Test.

VPWR (FROM POWER RELAY)

TO HO2S HTR

TAKE READINGS AT THESE PINS

HTR CONTROL EEC TEST PIN 14

NOTE: VIEW LOOKING AT HTR RELAY TERMINALS.

Fig. 191   Test H: Fuel Control (Part 31 of 33). 1995

FM0159500732380X

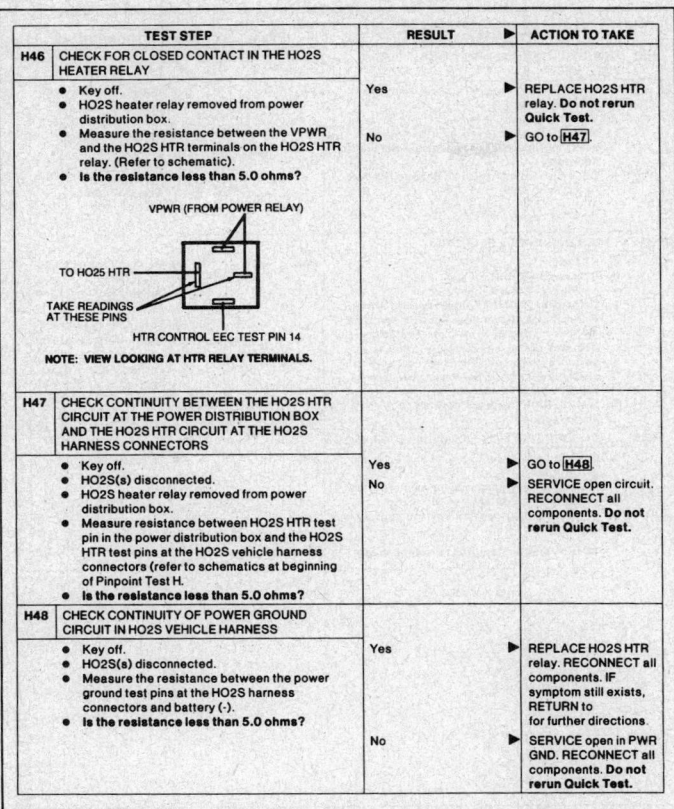

	TEST STEP	RESULT	▶	ACTION TO TAKE
H46	CHECK FOR CLOSED CONTACT IN THE HO2S HEATER RELAY			
	• Key off. • HO2S heater relay removed from power distribution box. • Measure the resistance between the VPWR and the HO2S HTR terminals on the HO2S HTR relay. (Refer to schematic.) • Is the resistance less than 5.0 ohms?	Yes No	▶ ▶	REPLACE HO2S HTR relay. Do not rerun Quick Test. GO to H47.
H47	CHECK CONTINUITY BETWEEN THE HO2S HTR CIRCUIT AT THE POWER DISTRIBUTION BOX AND THE HO2S HTR CIRCUIT AT THE HO2S HARNESS CONNECTORS			
	• Key off. • HO2S(s) disconnected. • HO2S heater relay removed from power distribution box. • Measure resistance between HO2S HTR test pin in the power distribution box and the HO2S HTR test pins at the HO2S vehicle harness connectors (refer to schematics at beginning of Pinpoint Test H. • Is the resistance less than 5.0 ohms?	Yes No	▶ ▶	GO to H48. SERVICE open circuit. RECONNECT all components. Do not rerun Quick Test.
H48	CHECK CONTINUITY OF POWER GROUND CIRCUIT IN HO2S VEHICLE HARNESS			
	• Key off. • HO2S(s) disconnected. • Measure the resistance between the power ground test pins at the HO2S harness connectors and battery (-). • Is the resistance less than 5.0 ohms?	Yes No	▶ ▶	REPLACE HO2S HTR relay. RECONNECT all components. IF symptom still exists, RETURN to for further directions. SERVICE open in PWR GND. RECONNECT all components. Do not rerun Quick Test.

FM0159300732390X

Fig. 191   Test H: Fuel Control (Part 32 of 33). 1995

	TEST STEP	RESULT	▶	ACTION TO TAKE
H91	CONTINUOUS MONITOR DTM TEST DRIVE CHECK			
	• Remain in Engine Running Continuous Monitor DTM. • Test drive vehicle at 55 mph with minimum road load for five miles. • Continue to drive on a rough road at 55 mph for five miles. • If possible drive vehicle through a pool of water on the road to shower the HO2S and/or connector. • Is a fault indicated?	Yes No	▶ ▶	ISOLATE fault and SERVICE as necessary. REMOVE breakout box. CLEAR Continuous Memory Code. RERUN Quick Test. EXIT Engine Running Continuous Monitor DTM. GO to H92.
H92	CHECK HO2S SWITCHING			
	• Key off. • Inspect EEC wire harness for proper routing and insulation; burnt, chafed, intermittently shorted or open. Service as necessary. • Disconnect PCM 60 pin connector and inspect for damaged or pushed out pins, corrosion, loose wires, etc. Service as necessary. • Install breakout box and connect PCM to breakout box. • Connect analog voltmeter to the suspect HO2S test pin and HO2S GND at the breakout box. • Test drive vehicle at 55 mph with minimum roadload for five miles. • Observe voltmeter for HO2S switching from .3 to .9 volts within three seconds. • Did HO2S voltage switch?	Yes No	▶ ▶	Unable to duplicate or identify fault at this time. Clear Continuous Memory DTCs REPLACE HO2S. REMOVE breakout box. RECONNECT PCM. RERUN Quick Test.

FM0159300732360X

Fig. 191   Test H: Fuel Control (Part 33 of 33)

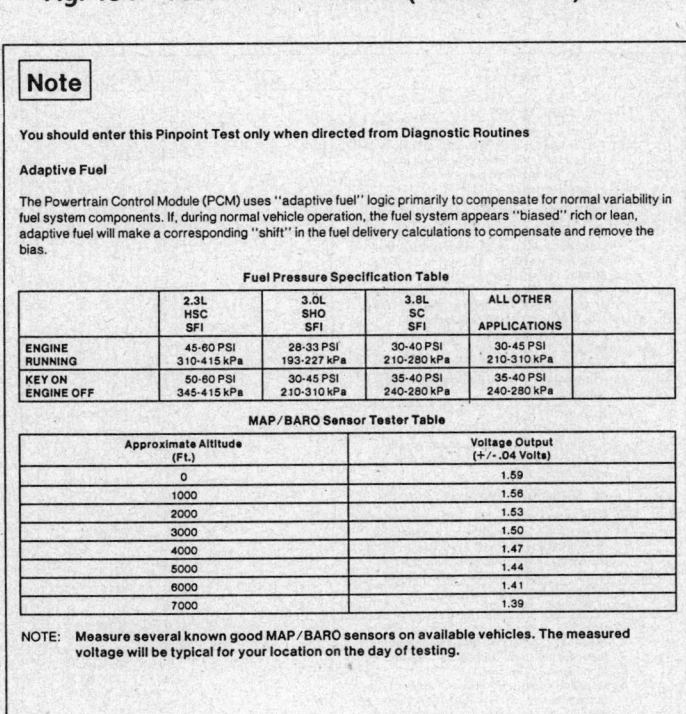

Note

You should enter this Pinpoint Test only when directed from Diagnostic Routines

Adaptive Fuel

The Powertrain Control Module (PCM) uses "adaptive fuel" logic primarily to compensate for normal variability in fuel system components. If, during normal vehicle operation, the fuel system appears "biased" rich or lean, adaptive fuel will make a corresponding "shift" in the fuel delivery calculations to compensate and remove the bias.

Fuel Pressure Specification Table

	2.3L HSC SFI	3.0L SHO SFI	3.8L SC SFI	ALL OTHER APPLICATIONS
ENGINE RUNNING	45-60 PSI 310-415 kPa	28-33 PSI 193-227 kPa	30-40 PSI 210-280 kPa	30-45 PSI 210-310 kPa
KEY ON ENGINE OFF	50-60 PSI 345-415 kPa	30-45 PSI 210-310 kPa	35-40 PSI 240-280 kPa	35-40 PSI 240-280 kPa

MAP/BARO Sensor Tester Table

Approximate Altitude (Ft.)	Voltage Output (+/-.04 Volts)
0	1.59
1000	1.56
2000	1.53
3000	1.50
4000	1.47
5000	1.44
6000	1.41
7000	1.39

NOTE: Measure several known good MAP/BARO sensors on available vehicles. The measured voltage will be typical for your location on the day of testing.

Fig. 192   Test HA: Adaptive Fuel (Part 1 of 8)

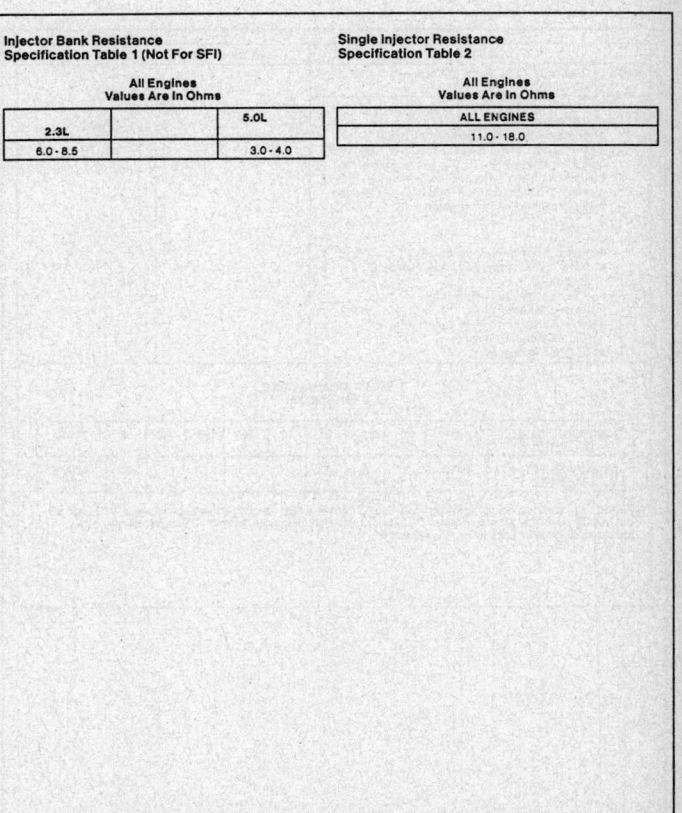

Injector Bank Resistance
Specification Table 1 (Not For SFI)

All Engines Values Are In Ohms			
2.3L		5.0L	
6.0 - 8.5		3.0 - 4.0	

Single Injector Resistance
Specification Table 2

All Engines Values Are In Ohms
ALL ENGINES
11.0 - 18.0

Fig. 192   Test HA: Adaptive Fuel (Part 2 of 8)

TEST STEP			RESULT	▶	ACTION TO TAKE
HA1 CHECK FOR OTHER DIAGNOSTIC TROUBLE CODES (DTCS)					
			Yes	▶	SERVICE them as required.
			No	▶	GO to **HA2**.
DTC	HO2S Orientation	Fault Definition			
181	Right or Rear	Rich limit reached.			
183	Right or Rear	Rich limit reached at idle.			
189	Left or Front	Rich limit reached.			
192	Left or Front	Rich limit reached at idle.			
These DTCs indicate that the system is running lean, although strategy adjusted it to Max. rich.					
179	Right or Rear	Lean limit reached.			
182	Right or Rear	Lean limit reached at idle.			
188	Left or Front	Lean limit reached.			
191	Left or Front	Lean limit reached at idle.			
These DTCs indicate that the system is running rich, although strategy adjusted it to Max. lean.					

Possible Causes:
— Fuel pressure
— Fuel injector
— Air intake
— MAP sensor
— Fuel injector electrical circuit
— Fuel filter
— Vacuum
— Air filter
● Are any other DTCs present?

TEST STEP	RESULT	▶	ACTION TO TAKE
HA2 CHECK FUEL PRESSURE			
WARNING: THE FUEL SYSTEM WILL REMAIN PRESSURIZED WHEN ENGINE IS NOT RUNNING. TO PREVENT INJURY OR FIRE USE CAUTION WHEN WORKING ON THE FUEL SYSTEM. ● Key off. ● Install fuel pressure gauge. ● Verify that manifold vacuum is connected to the fuel pressure regulator if applicable. ● Start and run engine at idle. Note fuel pressure. ● Refer to Fuel Pressure Specification Table. ● Is fuel pressure within specification?	Yes No	▶ ▶	GO to **HA3**. VERIFY integrity of fuel pressure regulator, vacuum line, fuel filter and fuel lines

FM0159300733030X

Fig. 192 Test HA: Adaptive Fuel (Part 3 of 8)

TEST STEP	RESULT	▶	ACTION TO TAKE
HA3 CHECK SYSTEM'S ABILITY TO HOLD FUEL PRESSURE			
● Cycle the key on and off several times. Note the fuel pressure. ● Visually look for fuel leaking at the injector O-ring, fuel pressure regulator, and the fuel lines to the fuel charging assembly. Service as necessary. ● Does fuel pressure remain at specification for 60 seconds?	Yes	▶	VERIFY integrity of air intake, air filter, no vacuum leaks, EGR valve closed. **For vehicles with MAP/BARO:** GO to **HA4**. **For all others:** GO to **HA6**.
HA4 CHECK MAP/BARO FREQUENCY			
● Key off. ● Connect MAP/BARO tester. ● Key on. ● Refer to MAP/BARO Frequency Charts on this Pinpoint Test's cover page (also Pinpoint Test **DF's** cover pages) to check MAP/BARO frequency. It may be necessary to measure several known good MAP/BARO sensors on available vehicles to determine your area's typical reading for that day. ● Is MAP/BARO frequency within specification?	Yes No	▶ ▶	For vehicles with MFI: GO to **HA5**. All others: GO to **HA6**. CHECK wiring to MAP/BARO sensor for corrosion, high resistance, etc. If OK, REPLACE MAP/BARO sensor. CLEAR KAM. RERUN Quick Test.
HA5 DIAGNOSTIC TEST MODE (DTM): MFI ENGINES			
● Connect tachometer to engine. Run engine at idle. ● Disconnect and reconnect the injectors one at a time. Note rpm drop for each injector. ● Does each injector produce a momentary drop in rpm? NOTE: IAC will attempt to re-establish rpm.	Yes No	▶ ▶	GO to Ignition GO to **HA7**.

FM0159300733040X

Fig. 192 Test HA: Adaptive Fuel (Part 4 of 8)

TEST STEP	RESULT	▶	ACTION TO TAKE
HA6 DIAGNOSTIC TEST MODE (DTM): SFI ENGINES			
The DTM switches each injector OFF and ON one at a time. Diagnostic Trouble Codes (DTC) correspond to the cylinder number, (i.e. DTC 30 indicates a problem with cylinder No. 3, a DTC 90 indicates a pass.) The DTM is designed to aid in the detection of a weak or non-contributing cylinder. The Pinpoint Test Steps are designed to isolate only EEC related problems. ● Run the Engine Running Self-Test. ● After the last repeated code, wait 5-10 seconds. ● "Goose" throttle lightly (not wide-open-throttle). ● DTM will be performed. Time of test is approximately 2-3 minutes. ● Is Code 90 present?	Yes No	▶ ▶	GO to Ignition GO to **HA8**.

CYLINDER BALANCE TABLE
DTC VS. CYLINDER

DIAGNOSTIC TROUBLE CODE (DTC)	90	10	20	30	40	50	60	70	80	77/538
CYLINDER/INJECTOR NUMBER	PASS	1	2	3	4	5	6	7	8	RERUN TEST*

*If throttle is touched (moved) during the Test, DTC Code 77/538 will appear, indicating test was not completed. DTC Code 538 could also be output if a Continuous Memory DTC 214 (CID) is present. If Continuous Memory DTC is present refer to the appropriate code chart in Self Test for service direction.

FM0159300733050X

Fig. 192 Test HA: Adaptive Fuel (Part 5 of 8)

TEST STEP	RESULT	▶	ACTION TO TAKE
HA7 CHECK RESISTANCE OF INJECTOR(S) AND HARNESS MFI ENGINES.			
● Key off. ● Disconnect Powertrain Control Module (PCM). Inspect for damaged or pushed out pins, corrosion, loose wires, etc. Service as necessary. NOTE: This erases Continuous Memory. ● Install breakout box, leave PCM disconnected. ● Measure resistance of INJECTOR BANK 1 between Test Pin 37 and Test Pin 58 at the breakout box. Record resistance. ● Measure resistance of INJECTOR BANK 2 between Test Pin 37 and Test Pin 59 at the breakout box. Record resistance. ● Refer to Injector Resistance Specification Table 1. ● Is each resistance within specification?	Yes No	▶ ▶	GO to **HA12**. GO to **HA9**.
HA8 CHECK RESISTANCE OF INJECTOR(S) AND HARNESS SFI ENGINES			
● Key off. ● Disconnect Powertrain Control Module (PCM). Inspect for damaged or pushed out pins, corrosion, loose wires, etc. Service as necessary. NOTE: This erases Continuous Memory. ● Install breakout box, leave PCM disconnected. ● Measure resistance between the suspect INJECTOR circuit Test Pin and Test Pin 37 at the breakout box. Record resistance. ● Is each resistance within specification?	Yes No	▶ ▶	GO to **HA12**. GO to **HA9**.
HA9 CHECK CONTINUITY OF FUEL INJECTOR HARNESS			
● Key off. ● Breakout box installed, PCM disconnected. ● Disconnect injector vehicle harness connector at the suspect injector. ● Measure resistance between Test Pin 37/57 at the breakout box and the VPWR pin at the injector vehicle harness connector. ● Refer to the Pinpoint Test H Schematic for the appropriate injector pin identification. ● Measure resistance between the injector test pin(s) at the breakout box and the same injector circuit signal pin at the each injector vehicle harness connector. ● Is each resistance less than 5.0 ohms?	Yes No	▶ ▶	GO to **HA10**. SERVICE open circuit. REMOVE breakout box. RECONNECT PCM and injectors. DRIVE vehicle 5 miles/55 mph. RERUN Quick Test.

FM0159300733060X

Fig. 192 Test HA: Adaptive Fuel (Part 6 of 8)

TEST STEP	RESULT	▶	ACTION TO TAKE
HA10 CHECK INJECTOR HARNESS CIRCUIT FOR SHORT TO POWER OR GROUND			
• Key off. • Breakout box installed, PCM disconnected. • Suspect fuel injector vehicle harness disconnected. • Refer to the Pinpoint Test H Schematic for the appropriate injector pin identification. • Measure resistance between the injector test pin(s) and Test Pin 37 / 57, 40, 46 and 60 at the breakout box. • Measure resistance between the injector test pin(s) at the breakout box and chassis ground. • Is each resistance greater than 10,000 ohms?	Yes	▶	For SFI: REPLACE injector per Cylinder Balance DTM fault code. RERUN Quick Test. For MFI: GO to **HA11**
	No	▶	SERVICE short circuit. REMOVE breakout box. RECONNECT PCM and injectors. DRIVE vehicle 5 miles / 55 mph. RERUN Quick Test.
HA11 ISOLATE FAULTY INJECTOR CIRCUIT			
• Key off. • Breakout box installed, PCM disconnected. • Disconnect all injectors on suspect bank. • DVOM on 200 ohm scale. • Connect one injector and measure resistance between Test Pin 37 and either Test Pin 58 or 59 as appropriate. • Disconnect that injector and repeat process for each of the remaining injectors. • Refer to Injector Resistance Specification Table 2. • Is each resistance within specification for the appropriate engine?	Yes	▶	GO to **HA12**.
	No	▶	REPLACE injector. REMOVE breakout box. RECONNECT PCM and injectors. DRIVE vehicle 5 miles / 55 mph. RERUN Quick Test.

FM0159300733070X

Fig. 192   Test HA: Adaptive Fuel (Part 7 of 8)

TEST STEP	RESULT	▶	ACTION TO TAKE
HA12 CHECK INJECTOR DRIVER SIGNAL			
Requires standard non-powered 12 volt test lamp. • Key off. • Breakout box installed. • Connect PCM to breakout box. • For MFI: — Connect test lamp between Test Pin 37 and Test Pin 58 at the breakout box. — Connect test lamp between Test Pin 37 and 59 at the breakout box. • For SFI: — Connect test lamp between Test Pin 37 and the suspect injectors Test Pin at the breakout box. • Crank or start engine. NOTE: Properly operating systems will show a dim glow on the lamp. • Is glow on lamp dim?	Yes	▶	REMOVE breakout box. RECONNECT PCM. injector test Also refer to Ignition Section for other possible causes. After any servicing, DRIVE vehicle 5 miles / 55 mph. RERUN Quick Test and Cylinder Balance DTM.
	No	▶	No light / Bright light: REPLACE PCM. REMOVE breakout box. DRIVE vehicle 5 miles / 55 mph. RERUN Quick Test.

Fig. 192   Test HA: Adaptive Fuel (Part 8 of 8)

WARNING

SAFE FUEL HANDLING PRACTICES:
GASOLINE, METHANOL AND METHANOL BLENDS

FIRE

• FLAMES from methanol or methanol-gasoline blends may be invisible.

• Know the locations of and learn how to use PORTABLE FIRE EXTINGUISHERS, FIRE BLANKETS, FIRE ALARMS and EYE / WASH SHOWER FACILITIES.

• Use a B or AFFF (light water) type FIRE EXTINGUISHER to fight flammable liquid fires.

FIRST AID

• IF SWALLOWED:

— If GASOLINE has been swallowed, DO NOT induce vomiting. SEEK MEDICAL ATTENTION IMMEDIATELY!

— If METHANOL OR A METHANOL / GASOLINE BLEND has been swallowed, induce vomiting under the direction of a physician or Poison Control Center. SEEK MEDICAL ATTENTION IMMEDIATELY!

• When overcome by vapors, if safe, MOVE VICTIM TO FRESH AIR. If not breathing, give artificial respiration or CPR (Cardiopulmonary Resuscitation) as appropriate. SEEK MEDICAL ATTENTION IMMEDIATELY!

• If SPLASHED IN EYES, FLUSH with large amounts of water for 15 minutes. Remove contact lenses, if worn. SEEK MEDICAL ATTENTION.

• If SPLASHED ON SKIN, REMOVE CONTAMINATED CLOTHING. WASH SKIN thoroughly with soap and water.

HEALTH

• ALL FUELS may be HARMFUL OR FATAL IF SWALLOWED.

• BE AWARE, IF SWALLOWED, onset of serious health effects may be delayed 12 to 24 hours.

• FUELS AND PRODUCTS containing methanol (e.g. windshield washer fluid) may cause blindness if swallowed.

• ALL FUEL VAPORS may be HARMFUL BY INHALATION.

• ALL FUELS may be HARMFUL BY SKIN ABSORPTION.

• ALL FUELS are IRRITATING to the EYES and RESPIRATORY SYSTEM.

• FUELS made with GASOLINE may contain benzene which is a cancer-causing agent.

Fig. 193   Test HB: FF Control (Part 1 of 17)

HANDLING

• Use FLAMMABLE LIQUID HANDLING PRECAUTIONS.

• Wear CHEMICAL GOGGLES and NITRILE GLOVES (additional protective clothing and equipment may be necessary in some instances).

• Keep flammable liquids in APPROVED LABELED CLOSED CONTAINERS.

• Use in WELL-VENTILATED AREAS and CONTROL VAPORS. (Be aware that vapors ARE NOT VISIBLE, are heavier than air, can travel along the floor, and will settle in lower areas.)

• When transferring flammable liquids, BOND the RECEIVING CONTAINER to the SOURCE and GROUND the SOURCE to the EARTH.

• DO NOT SMOKE or use HEAT / SPARK PRODUCING EQUIPMENT near vapors.

• DO NOT eat, smoke or drink where these products are handled, processed or stored.

• NEVER SIPHON BY MOUTH.

• WASH HANDS thoroughly after HANDLING any fuel.

SPILLS

• STOP, CONTAIN, AND CLEAN UP small spills with an absorbent material.

Description

The Heated Oxygen Sensor (HO2S) reacts with the oxygen in the exhaust gases and generates a voltage based on this reaction. A low voltage indicates too much oxygen or a lean condition. A high voltage indicates not enough oxygen or a rich condition. The fuel injector is a typical on / off device. The amount of fuel delivered is determined by how long the injector is held open.

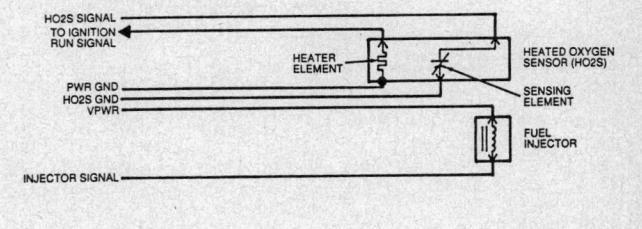

Fig. 193   Test HB: FF Control (Part 2 of 17)

Note

You should enter this Pinpoint Test only when you have been directed here from Diagnostic Routines, or Pinpoint Test [S].

Remember

To prevent the replacement of good components, be aware that the following non-EEC areas may be at fault:

- Ignition System
- Evaporative Emission (EVAP) System
- Positive Crankcase Ventilation (PCV) System
- Exhaust Gas Recirculation System
- Air Intake System / Filter
- Fuel and Engine Oil Contamination
- Electrical System
- Fuel System
- Intake Manifold Leaks
- Exhaust Manifold System Leak / Plugged
- Engine Cooling System
- Base Engine

This Pinpoint Test is intended to diagnose only the following:

- HO2S / heater
- HO2S Connection
- Vacuum Systems
- Cold Start Injector
- Fuel Injector
- Powertrain Control Module (PCM)
- Harness circuits: HO2S GND, HO2S, INJ. 1-6, VPWR and SIG RTN

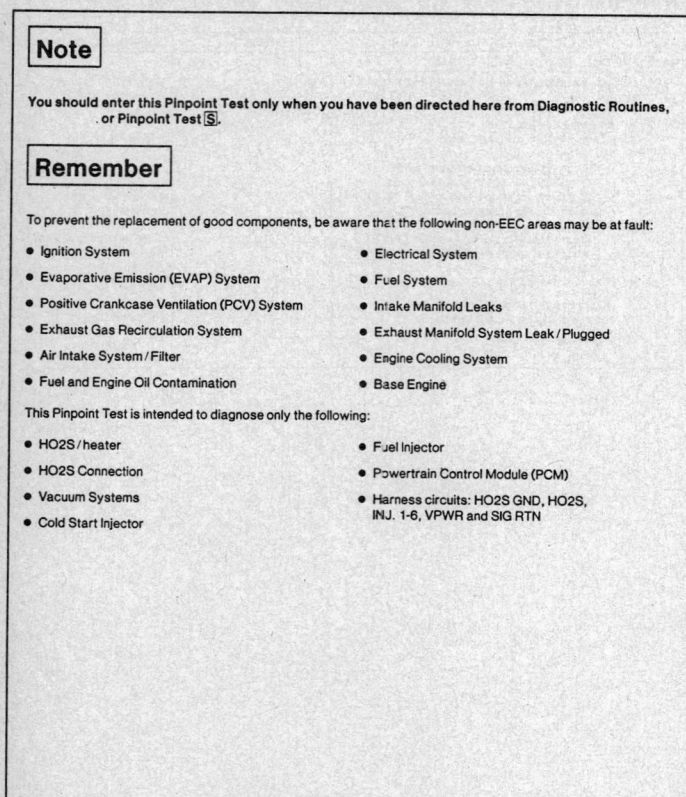

Fig. 193   Test HB: FF Control (Part 3 of 17)

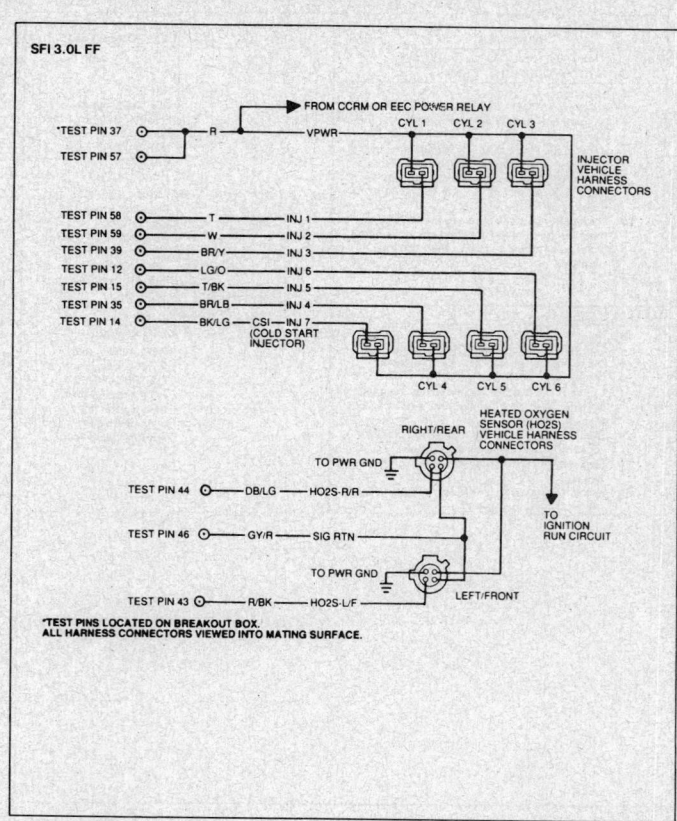

Fig. 193   Test HB: FF Control (Part 4 of 17). 1993

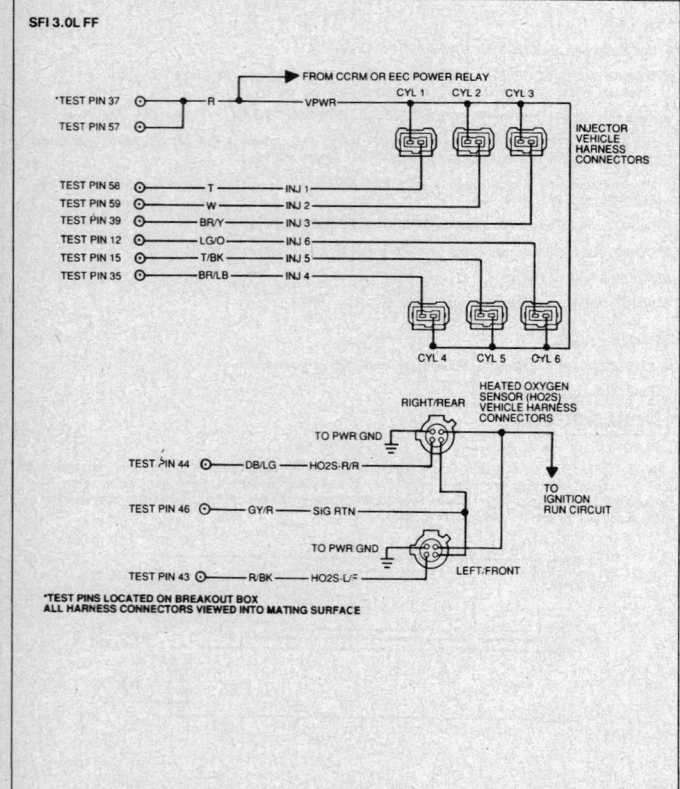

Fig. 193   Test HB: FF Control (Part 4 of 17). 1994–95

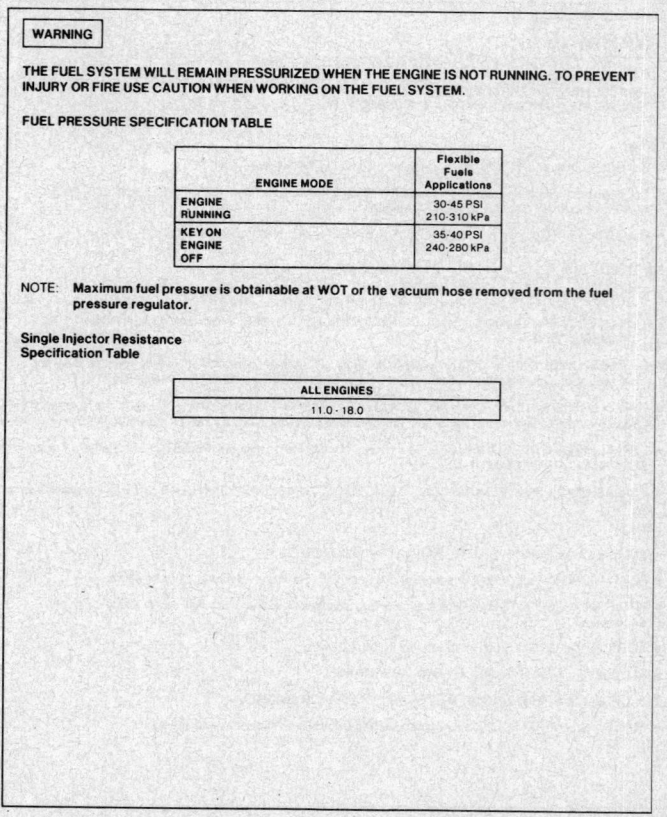

WARNING

THE FUEL SYSTEM WILL REMAIN PRESSURIZED WHEN THE ENGINE IS NOT RUNNING. TO PREVENT INJURY OR FIRE USE CAUTION WHEN WORKING ON THE FUEL SYSTEM.

FUEL PRESSURE SPECIFICATION TABLE

ENGINE MODE	Flexible Fuels Applications
ENGINE RUNNING	30-45 PSI 210-310 kPa
KEY ON ENGINE OFF	35-40 PSI 240-280 kPa

NOTE: Maximum fuel pressure is obtainable at WOT or the vacuum hose removed from the fuel pressure regulator.

Single Injector Resistance Specification Table

ALL ENGINES
11.0 - 18.0

Fig. 193   Test HB: FF Control (Part 5 of 17)

Part 6 of 17

TEST STEP	RESULT	▶	ACTION TO TAKE
HB1 CHECK FOR FUEL DILUTED ENGINE OIL	Yes	▶	REINSTALL PCV valve. GO to **HB2**.
	No	▶	For Continuous Memory DTCs **139, 141, 144,** 176 GO to **HB2**. All Others: CHANGE engine oil and filter with FF grade oil. REINSTALL PCV valve. DRIVE vehicle 5 miles / 55mph. RERUN Self Test.

Diagnostic Trouble Code (DTC)	HO2S Orientation	Fault Definition
172r 136o 176c	right or rear left or front left or front	System indicates lean
173r 137r 177c	right or rear left or front left or front	System indicates rich
144c 139o	right or rear left or front	No HO2S switch detected
171c 175c	right or rear left or front	Adaptive fuel limit reached
141c		System indicates lean

Possible Causes:
— Fuel injectors.
— HO2S.
— PCV/Hose.
— Vacuum.
— Plugged fuel filter.
— Fuel pump.
— CANP.
— Electronic Ignition Coil Failure.
- Key off.
- Remove the PCV valve from the valve cover. Inspect both rocker cover hole and PCV for damage, sludge build up, blockage and movement of valve plunger. Service as necessary.
- Run KOEO, KOER Self-Tests.
- **Address any continuous ignition DTCs before servicing KOER DTCs.**
NOTE: For a No Start, GO directly to **HB2**.
- **Are any of the above DTCs present in KOER Self-Test?**

FM0159300734060A

Fig. 193   Test HB: FF Control (Part 6 of 17)

Part 7 of 17

TEST STEP	RESULT	▶	ACTION TO TAKE
HB2 CHECK FUEL PRESSURE **WARNING: THE FUEL SYSTEM WILL REMAIN PRESSURIZED WHEN ENGINE IS NOT RUNNING. TO PREVENT INJURY OR FIRE, USE CAUTION WHEN WORKING ON THE FUEL SYSTEM.** - Key off. - Install fuel pressure gauge. - Verify that manifold vacuum is connected to the fuel pressure regulator. **If engine will start:** - Start and run engine at idle. Note fuel pressure. - While under load, increase engine speed to 2500 rpm's and maintain for one minute (test drive). Note fuel pressure. - Refer to Fuel Pressure Specification Table. **If engine will not start:** - Cycle the key off and on several times. Note fuel pressure gauge. - Refer to Fuel Pressure Specification Table. - **Is fuel pressure within specification for the engine being tested?**	Yes	▶	GO to **HB3**
HB3 CHECK SYSTEM'S ABILITY TO HOLD FUEL PRESSURE - Pressurize fuel system per step **HB2**. - Visually look for fuel leaking at the injector O-ring, fuel pressure regulator, and the fuel lines to the fuel charging assembly. Service as necessary. - Key on, engine off. - **Does fuel pressure remain at specification for 60 seconds?**	Yes	▶	For No Starts: GO to **HB4** For DTCs or other Symptoms: GO to **HB5**.
HB4 FUEL DELIVERY TEST - Key off. - Fuel pressure gauge installed. - Pressurize fuel system per step **HB2**. - Locate and disconnect the Inertia Fuel Shutoff (IFS) switch. - Crank engine for five seconds. - **Does pressure drop greater than 5 psi (34 kPa) by the end of the five second crank cycle?**	Yes	▶	The EEC system is not the cause of the No Start. REMOVE the fuel pressure gauge. RECONNECT the IFS switch.
	No	▶	REMOVE fuel pressure gauge. RECONNECT IFS switch. GO to **HB6**.

FM0159300734070X

Fig. 193   Test HB: FF Control (Part 7 of 17)

Part 8 of 17

TEST STEP	RESULT	▶	ACTION TO TAKE
HB5 CYLINDER BALANCE DIAGNOSTIC TEST MODE (DTM) The DTM switches each injector OFF and ON one at a time. Diagnostic Trouble Codes (DTC) correspond to the cylinder number (i.e., DTC 30 indicates a problem with cylinder No. 3, a DTC 90 indicates a pass.) The Cylinder Balance DTM is designed to aid in the detection of a weak or non-contributing cylinder. The Pinpoint Test Steps are designed to isolate only EEC related problems. Refer to Quick Test Appendix, Section 5A, for detailed information about Cylinder Balance (DTM). - Run the Engine Running Self-Test. - After the last repeated code, wait 5-10 seconds. - "Goose" throttle lightly (not wide-open-throttle). - Cylinder Balance (DTM) will be performed. Time of test is approximately 2-3 minutes. - **Are there any Cylinder Balance DTC's requiring service?**	Yes	▶	GO to **HB6**
	No	▶	For Symptoms or DTC **136, 172, 176:** GO to **HB10**. For DTC 137, 173, 177: GO to **HB18**. For Continuous Memory DTC's **139, 141, 144,** 176 GO to **HB23**.

CYLINDER BALANCE TABLE
DTC VS. CYLINDER

DIAGNOSTIC TROUBLE CODE (DTC)	90	10	20	30	40	50	60	538
CYLINDER/INJECTOR NUMBER	PASS	1	2	3	4	5	6	RERUN TEST

* If throttle is touched (moved) during the Test, DTC Code 538 will appear, indicating test was not completed. DTC Code 538 could also be output if a Continuous Memory DTC 214 (CID) is present. If Continuous Memory DTC is present, refer to the appropriate code chart in Self Test for service direction.

FM0159300734080X

Fig. 193   Test HB: FF Control (Part 8 of 17)

Part 9 of 17

TEST STEP	RESULT	▶	ACTION TO TAKE
HB6 CHECK RESISTANCE OF INJECTOR(S) AND HARNESS - Key off. - Disconnect Powertrain Control Module (PCM). Inspect for damaged or pushed out pins, corrosion, loose wires, etc. Service as necessary. NOTE: This erases Continuous Memory. - Install breakout box, leave PCM disconnected. - Measure resistance between the suspect INJECTOR circuit Test Pin and Test Pin 37 at the breakout box. Record resistance. - For No Starts: — Pick any injector and measure resistance between that INJECTOR circuit's Test Pin and Test Pin 37 at the breakout box. Record resistance. - Refer to Injector Resistance Specification. - **Is each resistance within specification for the appropriate engine?**	Yes	▶	GO to **HB9**
	No	▶	For NO START: SERVICE open in VPWR circuit. For others: GO to **HB7**.
HB7 CHECK CONTINUITY OF FUEL INJECTOR HARNESS - Key off. - Breakout box installed, PCM disconnected. - Disconnect injector vehicle harness connector at the suspect injector. - Measure resistance between Test Pin 37 / 57 at the breakout box and the VPWR pin at the injector vehicle harness connector. - Refer to the Pinpoint Test Schematic for the appropriate injector pin identification. - Measure resistance between the injector test pin(s) at the breakout box and the same injector circuit signal pin at the each injector vehicle harness connector. - **Is each resistance less than 5.0 ohms?**	Yes	▶	GO to **HB8**
	No	▶	SERVICE open circuit. REMOVE breakout box. RECONNECT PCM and injectors. DRIVE vehicle 5 miles / 55 mph. RERUN Quick Test.

FM0159300734090X

Fig. 193   Test HB: FF Control (Part 9 of 17)

TEST STEP	RESULT	▶	ACTION TO TAKE
HB8 CHECK INJECTOR HARNESS CIRCUIT FOR SHORT TO POWER OR GROUND			
• Key off. • Breakout box installed, PCM disconnected. • Suspect fuel injector vehicle harness disconnected. • Refer to the Pinpoint Test Schematic for the appropriate injector pin identification. • Measure resistance between the injector test pin(s) and Test Pin 37/57, 40, 46 and 60 at the breakout box. • Measure resistance between the injector test pin(s) at the breakout box and chassis ground. • **Is each resistance greater than 10,000 ohms?**	Yes No	▶ ▶	REPLACE injector per Cylinder Balance DTM fault code. RERUN Quick Test. SERVICE short circuit. REMOVE breakout box. RECONNECT PCM and injectors. DRIVE vehicle 5 miles/55 mph. RERUN Quick Test.
HB9 CHECK INJECTOR DRIVER SIGNAL			
Requires standard non-powered 12 volt test lamp. • Key off. • Breakout box installed. • Connect PCM to breakout box. • Connect test lamp between Test Pin 37 and the suspect injector Test Pins at the breakout box. • Crank or start engine. NOTE: Properly operating systems will show a dim glow on the lamp. • **Is glow on lamp dim?**	Yes No	▶ ▶	REMOVE breakout box. RECONNECT PCM. Follow instructions of the injector test equipment. Also refer to Ignition Section for other possible causes. After any servicing, DRIVE vehicle 5 miles/55 mph. RERUN Quick Test and Cylinder Balance DTM. No light/Bright light: REPLACE PCM. REMOVE breakout box. DRIVE vehicle 5 miles/55 mph. RERUN Quick Test.

Fig. 193   Test HB: FF Control (Part 10 of 17)

FM0159300734100X

TEST STEP	RESULT	▶	ACTION TO TAKE
HB10 CHECK HO2S INTEGRITY			
HO2S always lean, slow to switch or lack of switching; fuel at adaptive limit could be caused by: — Moisture inside the HO2S harness connector resulting in a short to ground. — HO2S coated with contaminants. — HO2S circuit open. — HO2S circuit shorted to ground. • Key off. • Inspect the HO2S harness for chafing, burns or other indications of damage. Service as necessary. • Inspect HO2S and connector for indication of submerging in water, oil, coolant, etc. Service as necessary. • Run engine at 2000 rpm for two minutes. • Key off. • Run Engine Running Self Test. • **Are DTCs present?**	Yes No	▶ ▶	GO to **HB11**. GO to **HB15**.
HB11 CHECK HO2S ON ENGINES WITH MAF SENSOR			
NOTE: The purpose of this test is to verify the HO2S can generate greater than 0.5 volt during Engine Running Self-Test. Any Vacuum/air leaks in non-EEC areas could also cause DTC 136, 172 or 176. Check for: — Leaking vacuum actuator (e.g. A/C control motor). — Engine sealing. — EGR system. — PCV system. — Unmetered air leak between Mass Air Flow (MAF) sensor and throttle body. — Lead contaminated HO2S. • Key off. • Disconnect appropriate HO2S sensor from vehicle harness. **For 4-wire HO2S (refer to schematic):** — Connect DVOM to HO2S circuit and HO2S SIG RTN or HO2S GND at the HO2S connector. • DVOM on 20 volt scale. • Run engine at approximately 2000 rpm for two minutes. • Rerun Engine Running Self-Test and monitor HO2S voltage. • **Does DVOM indicate greater than 0.5 volt at the end of Self-Test?**	Yes No	▶ ▶	GO to **HB12**. REPLACE HO2S. RERUN Quick Test.

Fig. 193   Test HB: FF Control (Part 11 of 17)

FM0159300734110X

TEST STEP	RESULT	▶	ACTION TO TAKE
HB12 CHECK CONTINUITY OF HO2S AND HO2S GROUND			
• Key off. • Breakout box installed, PCM disconnected. • Disconnect suspect HO2S from vehicle harness. Inspect both ends of connector for damaged or pushed out pins, moisture, corrosion, loose wires, etc. Service as necessary. • Measure resistance between HO2S circuit Test Pin at the breakout box and HO2S circuit at the vehicle harness connector. — Measure resistance between Test Pin 46 at the breakout box and HO2S SIG RTN at the vehicle harness connector. — Where applicable measure resistance between HO2S GND and SIG RTN at the breakout box. • **Is each resistance less than 5.0 ohms?**	Yes No	▶ ▶	GO to **HB13**. SERVICE open circuit. REMOVE breakout box. RECONNECT PCM, HO2S, and any other components that have been disconnected. DRIVE vehicle 5 miles/55 mph. RERUN Quick Test.
HB13 CHECK HO2S CIRCUIT FOR SHORT TO GROUND			
• Key off. • Breakout box installed, PCM disconnected. • HO2S disconnected. • Measure resistance between the HO2S SIGNAL Test Pin at the breakout box and Test Pins 40 and 46 at the breakout box. • **Is each resistance greater than 10,000 ohms?**	Yes No	▶ ▶	GO to **HB14**. SERVICE short circuit. REMOVE breakout box. RECONNECT PCM, HO2S, and any other components that are disconnected. DRIVE vehicle 5 miles/55 mph. RERUN Quick Test.
HB14 CHECK HO2S FOR SHORT TO GROUND			
• Key off. • Breakout box installed, PCM disconnected. • HO2S disconnected. • Measure resistance between PWR GND and HO2S circuit at the HO2S connector. (Refer to schematic). Also measure resistance between PWR GND and SIG RTN at the HO2S connector. • **Is resistance greater than 10,000 ohms?**	Yes No	▶ ▶	For DTCs: 144C, 139C, 171, 174, 175 or 178, GO to **HB23**. For other DTCs: — MAF Sensor. REMOVE breakout box. RECONNECT HO2S. REPLACE PCM. DRIVE vehicle 5 miles/55 mph. RERUN Quick Test. REPLACE HO2S. REMOVE breakout box. RECONNECT PCM. DRIVE vehicle 5 miles/55 mph. RERUN Quick Test.

Fig. 193   Test HB: FF Control (Part 12 of 17)

FM0159300734120X

TEST STEP	RESULT	▶	ACTION TO TAKE
HB15 CHECK RESISTANCE OF HEATER ELEMENT ON HO2S			
• Key off. • Disconnect suspect HO2S from vehicle harness. • Inspect both ends of the connector for damaged or pushed out pins, moisture, corrosion, loose wires, etc. Service as necessary. • Measure resistance between KEY PWR circuit and PWR GND circuit at HO2S connector (refer to schematic). — Hot to warm resistance specification is 5.0 to 30.0 ohms. — Room temperature resistance specification is 2.0 to 5.0 ohms. • **Is resistance within specification?**	Yes No	▶ ▶	GO to **HB16**. REPLACE HO2S. RERUN Quick Test.
HB16 CHECK FOR POWER AT HO2S HARNESS CONNECTOR			
• Key on, engine off. • HO2S disconnected. • Measure voltage between KEY POWER circuit and PWR GND circuit at the HO2S vehicle harness connector (refer to schematic). • **Is voltage greater than 10.5 volts?**	Yes No	▶ ▶	RECONNECT HO2S. HO2S system OK. Fuel delivery is OK. HO2S may have cooled prior to Engine Running Self-Test. If symptom persists, problem is in an area common to all cylinders, i.e. air/vacuum leak, fuel contamination, EGR. SERVICE as necessary. GO to **HB17**.
HB17 CHECK CONTINUITY OF POWER GROUND CIRCUIT			
• Key off. • HO2S disconnected. • Measure resistance between PWR GND circuit at the HO2S vehicle harness connector and battery negative post. • **Is resistance less than 5.0 ohms?**	Yes No	▶ ▶	SERVICE open in KEY PWR circuit. RECONNECT HO2S sensor. RERUN Quick Test. SERVICE open in PWR GND circuit. RECONNECT HO2S sensor. RERUN Quick Test.

Fig. 193   Test HB: FF Control (Part 13 of 17)

FM0159300734130X

TEST STEP	RESULT	▶	ACTION TO TAKE
HB18 CHECK HO2S SIGNAL FOR SHORT TO POWER			
DTC 173 refers to rear HO2S. DTCs 137 and 177 refer to front HO2S. HO2S always rich could be caused by: — Moisture inside HO2S harness connector resulting in a short to power. — HO2S circuit shorted to power. • Key off. • Disconnect the suspect HO2S from vehicle harness. • Inspect both ends of the connector for damaged or pushed out pins, moisture, corrosion, loose wires, etc. Service as necessary. • Key on, engine off. • Measure voltage between HO2S circuit and PWR GND at the HO2S vehicle harness connector (refer to schematic). • **Is voltage less than 0.5 volts?**	Yes No	▶ ▶	GO to HB20. GO to HB19.
HB19 CHECK FOR SHORT TO POWER			
• Key off. • Inspect HO2S GND and HO2S circuit harness for chafing, burns or other indications of short to power. Service as necessary. • Disconnect PCM. Inspect for damaged, or pushed out pins, corrosion, loose wires etc. Service as necessary. • Install breakout box, leave PCM disconnected. • Suspect HO2S disconnected. • Measure resistance between HO2S SIG, and KEYPWR at the breakout box. • **Is the resistance greater than 10,000 ohms?**	Yes No	▶ ▶	REPLACE PCM. REMOVE breakout box. RECONNECT HO2S. DRIVE vehicle 5 miles / 55 mph. RERUN Quick Test. SERVICE short to power. REMOVE breakout box. RECONNECT PCM. DRIVE vehicle 5 miles 55 mph. RERUN Quick Test.
HB20 CHECK HO2S FOR SHORT TO IGNITION RUN CIRCUIT			
• Key off. • HO2S disconnected. • Measure resistance between KEY PWR circuit and HO2S SIG circuit at the HO2S connector (refer to schematic). • **Is resistance greater than 10,000 ohms?**	Yes No	▶ ▶	For DTCs 137, 173, 177: GO to HB21. For DTCs 171, 174, 175, 178: GO to HB22. REPLACE HO2S. DRIVE vehicle 5 miles 55 mph. RERUN Quick Test

Fig. 193   Test HB: FF Control (Part 14 of 17)

FM0159300734140X

TEST STEP	RESULT	▶	ACTION TO TAKE
HB21 ATTEMPT TO GENERATE DTC 172, 136, 176			
• Key off. • HO2S disconnected. • Jumper HO2S circuit at the HO2S vehicle harness connector to battery negative post. • Rerun Engine Running Self-Test. • **Is DTC 172, 136 or 176 present?**	Yes No	▶ ▶	REMOVE jumper. GO to HB22. REMOVE jumper. RECONNECT HO2S. DISCONNECT PCM. Inspect for damaged or pushed out pins, corrosion, loose wires, etc. SERVICE as necessary. If OK REPLACE PCM. DRIVE vehicle 5 miles / 55 mph. RERUN Quick Test.
HB22 HO2S CHECK			
• Key off. • HO2S disconnected: **(Refer to schematic)** — Connect DVOM to HO2S SIGNAL and SIG RTN at the HO2S connector. • DVOM on 20 volt scale. • Disconnect the PCV valve hose from the PCV valve. • Start engine and run at approximately 2000 rpm. • **Does the DVOM indicate less than 0.4 volt within 30 seconds?**	Yes No	▶ ▶	GO to HB23. REPLACE HO2S. RECONNECT vacuum hoses. DRIVE vehicle 5 miles / 55 mph. RERUN Quick Test.
HB23 CHECK CONTINUOUS MONITOR DIAGNOSTIC TEST MODE (DTM)			
• Key off. • Verify engine at operating temperature. • Start engine and run at 2000 rpm for two minutes. • With engine rpm at idle enter Engine Running Continuous Monitor (DTM). • Observe VOM or STAR LED for indication of fault. • Wiggle, shake or bend a small section of the EEC harness while working your way from the HO2S to the PCM. • Wiggle, shake or bend a small section of the EEC harness while working your way from the HO2S GND to the PCM. • **Is a fault indicated?**	Yes No	▶ ▶	ISOLATE fault and SERVICE as necessary. REMOVE breakout box. CLEAR Continuous Memory RERUN Quick Test. REMAIN in Engine Running Continuous Monitor DTM. GO to HB24.

Fig. 193   Test HB: FF Control (Part 15 of 17)

FM0159300734150X

TEST STEP	RESULT	▶	ACTION TO TAKE
HB24 CONTINUOUS MONITOR DTM TEST DRIVE CHECK			
• Remain in Engine Running Continuous Monitor DTM. • Test drive vehicle at 55 mph with minimum road load for five miles. • Continue to drive on a rough road at 55 mph for five miles. • If possible, drive vehicle through a pool of water on the road to shower the HO2S and / or connector. • **Is a fault indicated?**	Yes No	▶ ▶	ISOLATE fault and SERVICE as necessary. REMOVE breakout box. CLEAR Continuous Memory DTC. RERUN Quick Test. EXIT Engine Running Continuous Monitor DTM. GO to HB25.
HB25 CHECK HO2S SWITCHING			
• Key off. • Inspect EEC wire harness for proper routing and for insulation that is burnt or chafed or intermittently shorted or open. Service as necessary. • Disconnect PCM and inspect for damaged or pushed out pins, corrosion, loose wires, etc. Service as necessary. • Install breakout box and connect PCM to breakout box. • Connect a DVOM to the suspect sensor test pin and SIG RTN at the breakout box. • Test drive vehicle at 55 mph with minimum roadload for five miles. • Observe voltmeter for HO2S switching from .3 to .9 volt within three seconds. • **Did HO2S voltage switch?**	Yes No	▶ ▶	Unable to duplicate or identify fault at this time. CLEAR Continuous Memory. REPLACE HO2S. REMOVE breakout box. RECONNECT PCM. RERUN Quick Test.

Fig. 193   Test HB: FF Control (Part 16 of 17)

FM0159300734160X

TEST STEP	RESULT	▶	ACTION TO TAKE
HB27 CHECK CONTINUITY OF CSI CONTROL CIRCUIT			
• Key off. • CSI disconnected. • Disconnect the PCM. Inspect for damaged or pushed out pins, corrosion, loose wires, etc. Service as necessary. • Install breakout box, leave PCM disconnected. • Measure resistance between Test Pin 14 at the breakout box and CSI control pin at the CSI vehicle harness connector. • **Is resistance less than 5 ohms?**	Yes No	▶ ▶	GO to HB28. SERVICE open circuit. REMOVE breakout box. RECONNECT all components. RERUN Quick Test.
HB28 CHECK FOR SHORT TO POWER IN CSI CONTROL CIRCUIT			
• Key off. • CSI disconnected. • Breakout box installed, PCM disconnected. • Measure resistance between Test Pin 14 and Test Pins 37 / 57 at the breakout box. • **Is resistance greater than 10,000 ohms?**	Yes No	▶ ▶	REMOVE breakout box. REINSTALL the PCM. GO to HB29. SERVICE short circuit. REMOVE breakout box. RECONNECT all components. RERUN Quick Test.
HB29 CHECK CSI OPERATION			
• Key off. • CSI disconnected. • Connect an Injector Tester J34730-3A and OTC Pulse Tester / Generator OTC-3398 or equivalent to the electrical terminals. • Connect Pulse Tester / Generator power cable to battery positive post and the Pulse Tester / Generator ground cable to a clean ground. • Key on, engine running. • Select 1 pulse of 500 milliseconds on the Pulse Tester / Generator. • Turn the Pulse Tester / Generator on. • **Does the engine: idle rough, drop in RPM or stall as a result of energizing the CSI?**	Yes No	▶ ▶	REPLACE the PCM. REMOVE the Injector Tester and the Pulse Tester / Generator. RECONNECT all components. RERUN Quick Test. REPLACE the CSI assembly. REMOVE the Injector Tester and the Pulse Tester / Generator. RECONNECT all components. RERUN Quick Test.

Fig. 193   Test HB: FF Control (Part 17 of 17)

FM0159300734170X

Note

You should enter this Pinpoint Test only when you have been directed here from Diagnostic Routines.

Remember

This Pinpoint Test is intended to diagnose only the following:

- Fuel Pump Relay
- Inertia Fuel Shutoff (IFS) switch
- Harness circuits: B(+), VPWR, FP, GND and Power-To-Pump(s)
- Powertrain Control Module (PCM)

Description

The Fuel Pump Relay is a normally open relay that is used to supply voltage to the electric fuel pump. When the ignition key is turned to START or RUN position, the Powertrain Control Module (PCM) grounds Pin 22 (FP), which activates the relay (closes the contacts) and sends voltage to the fuel pump. If, within 1-2 seconds, the PCM does not receive an ignition PIP signal (indicating the engine is not turning), Pin 22 will be ungrounded and the fuel pump will turn off.

The Inertia Fuel Shutoff (IFS) switch is a safety device that is wired into either the primary circuit (coil side) or secondary circuit (contact side). In the event of a collision the IFS switch will open and voltage will be cut off to the fuel pump.

The fuel pump monitor circuit is wired into the power-to-pump circuit and is used by the PCM to monitor the fuel pump secondary circuit.

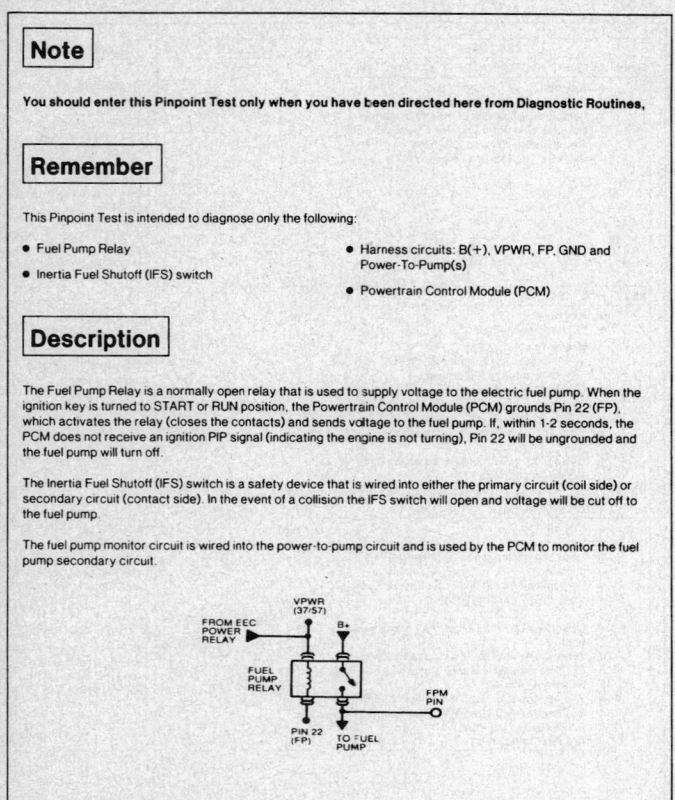

Fig. 194   Test J: Fuel Pump Circuit (Part 1 of 20)

FM0159300735010X

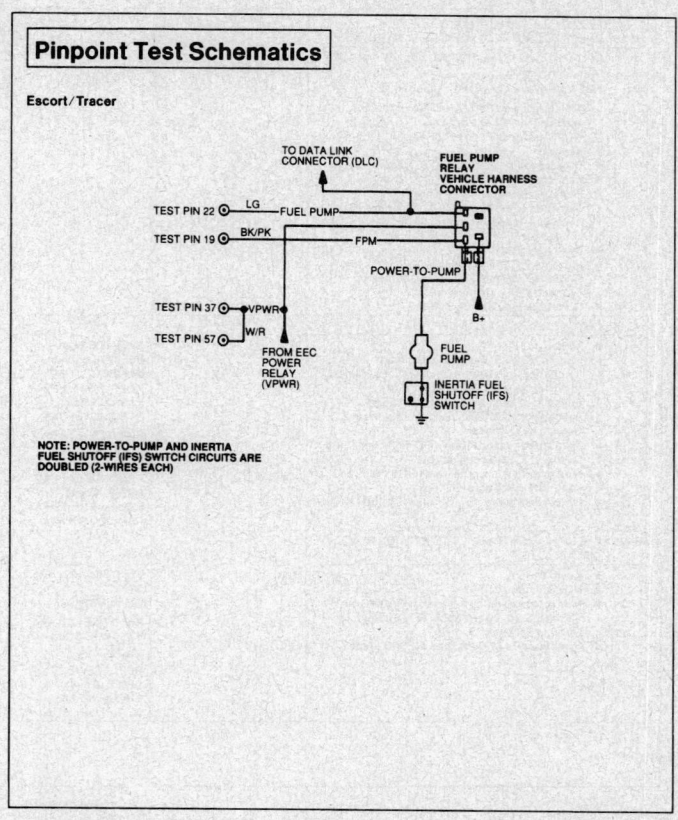

Fig. 194   Test J: Fuel Pump Circuit (Part 2 of 20)

FM0159300735020X

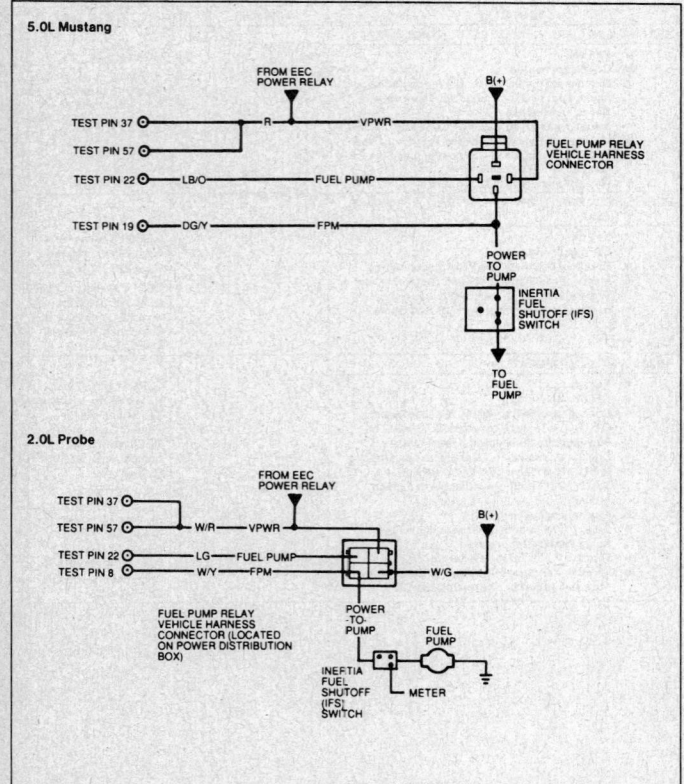

Fig. 194   Test J: Fuel Pump Circuit (Part 3 of 20). 1993

FM015930073503AX

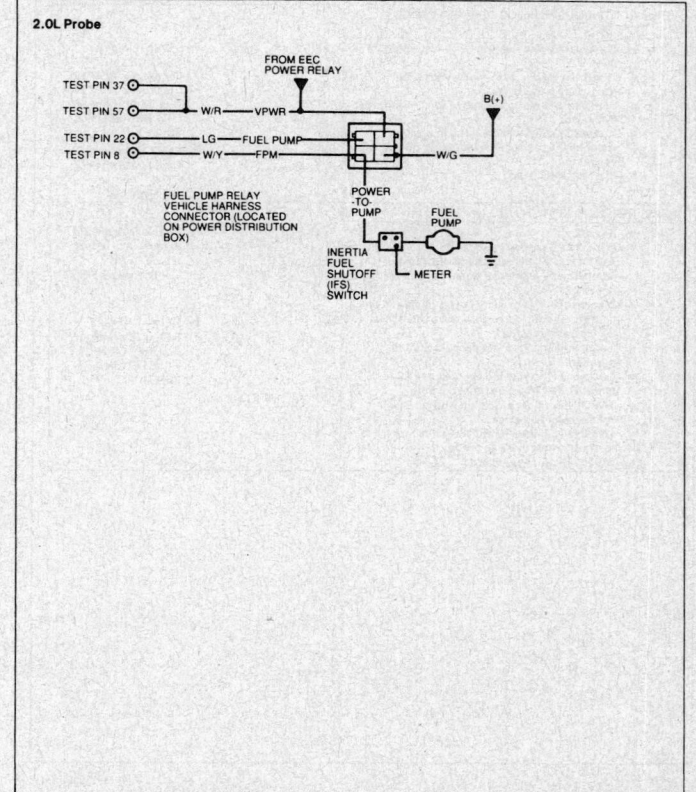

Fig. 194   Test J: Fuel Pump Circuit (Part 3 of 20). 1994–95

FM015940073503BX

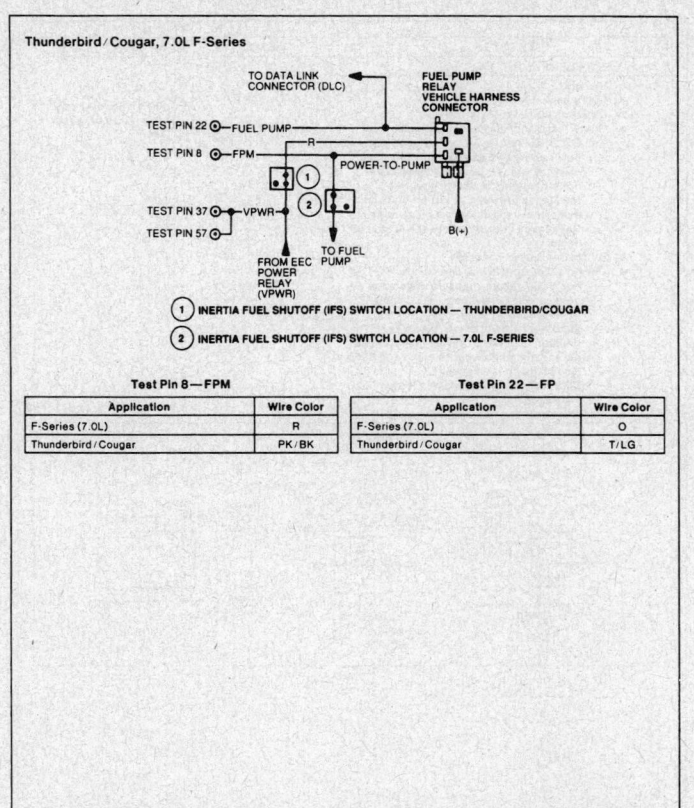

Fig. 194   Test J: Fuel Pump Circuit (Part 4 of 20)

FM015930073504 0X

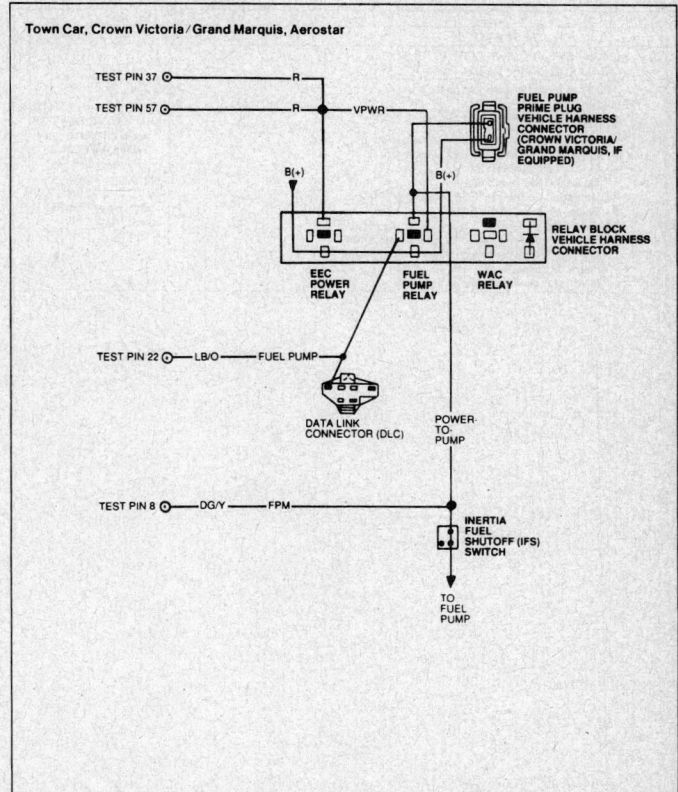

Fig. 194   Test J: Fuel Pump Circuit (Part 5 of 20). 1993

FM015930073505AX

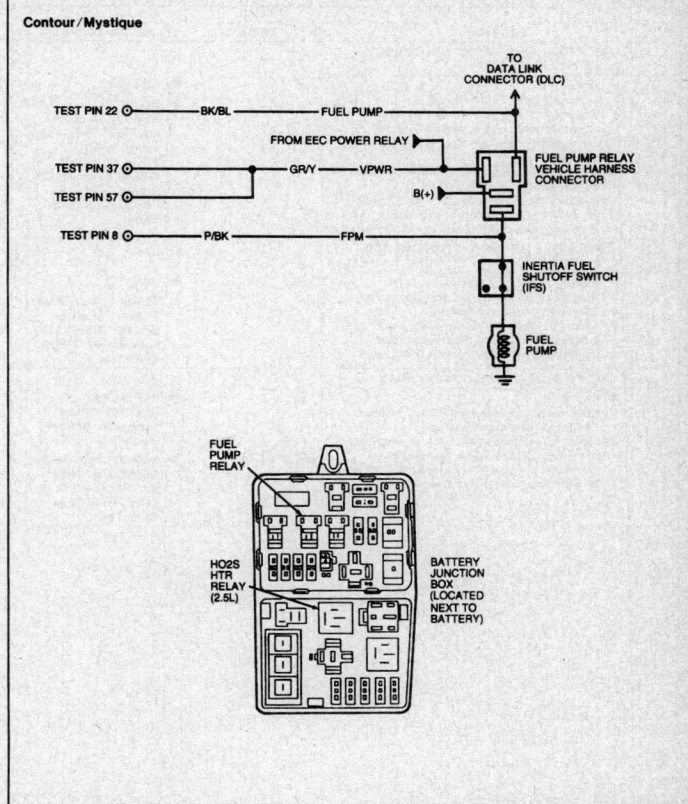

Fig. 194   Test J: Fuel Pump Circuit (Part 5 of 20). 1994

FM015940073505BX

Fig. 194   Test J: Fuel Pump Circuit (Part 6 of 20). 1995

FM015950073523 0X

TEST STEP	RESULT	▶	ACTION TO TAKE
J1 DIAGNOSTIC TROUBLE CODE (DTC) 87 / 556: CHECK FOR VPWR TO FUEL PUMP RELAY			
DTC 87 / 556 indicates a fuel pump primary circuit failure. Possible causes: — Inertia Fuel Shutoff (IFS) switch not reset or electrically open (if in primary circuit). — Open or shorted circuit. — Damaged fuel pump relay. — Damaged Powertrain Control Module (PCM). • Disconnect fuel pump relay. • Key on, engine off. • Measure voltage between VPWR circuit at the fuel pump relay vehicle harness connector and chassis ground. • **Is voltage greater than 10.5 volts?**	Yes No	▶ ▶	GO to **J2**. VERIFY integrity of IFS switch. If OK, SERVICE open in VPWR circuit between the EEC power relay and the fuel pump relay. RECONNECT fuel pump relay. RERUN Quick Test.

Fig. 194   Test J: Fuel Pump Circuit (Part 7 of 20)

FM0159300735090X

TEST STEP	RESULT	▶	ACTION TO TAKE
J2 CHECK FUEL PUMP RELAY			
• Key off. • Fuel pump relay disconnected. • DVOM on 200 ohm scale. • Check fuel pump relay coil resistance: — For "ISO" relays, measure resistance between Pins 85 and 86 at the fuel pump relay (pin numbers molded on relay). — For other types of relays, measure resistance between VPWR pin and fuel pump circuit pin at the fuel pump relay. — Resistance should be between 40 and 85 ohms. • DVOM on 10,000 ohm scale. • Check fuel pump relay for internal shorts. — For "ISO" relays, measure resistance between Pin 85 and both Pins 30 and 87 at the fuel pump relay. — For other types of relays, measure resistance between the fuel pump circuit pin and both the power-to-pump and B(+) pins at the fuel pump relay. — Both resistances should be greater than 10,000 ohms. • **Are all resistance checks OK?**	Yes No	▶ ▶	GO to **J3**. REPLACE fuel pump relay. RERUN Quick Test.

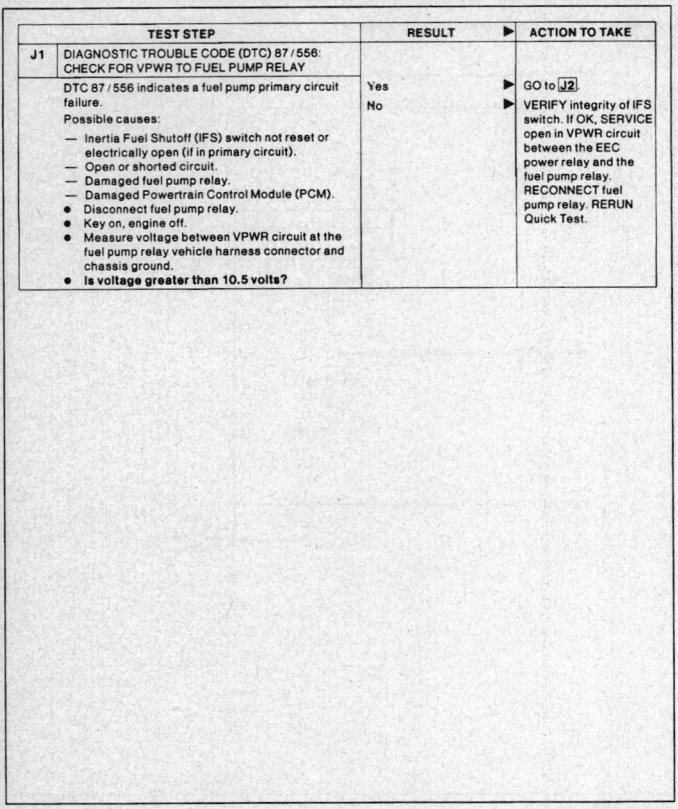

FUEL PUMP RELAY

"MINI" RELAY   ISO RELAY (5.0L MUSTANG, CR. VICTORIA/ GR. MARQUIS, TOWN CAR, RANGER, EXPLORER, AEROSTAR, E/F-SERIES (EXCEPT 7.0L), BRONCO)   PROBE

COIL - 85 AND 86
COMMON - 30
NO-87
NC -87A

Fig. 194   Test J: Fuel Pump Circuit (Part 8 of 20)

FM0159300735100X

TEST STEP	RESULT	▶	ACTION TO TAKE
J3 CHECK FUEL PUMP CIRCUIT FOR SHORT TO POWER			
• Key off. • Fuel pump relay disconnected. • Disconnect Powertrain Control Module (PCM). Inspect for damaged or pushed out pins, corrosion, loose wires, etc. Service as necessary. • Install breakout box, leave PCM disconnected. • Key on, engine off. • Measure voltage between Test Pin 22 at the breakout box and battery negative post. • **Is voltage less than 1.0 volt?**	Yes No	▶ ▶	GO to **J4**. SERVICE short circuit. REMOVE breakout box. RECONNECT all components. ATTEMPT to start vehicle. If vehicle fails to start, REPLACE PCM. RERUN Quick Test.
J4 CHECK FUEL PUMP CIRCUIT FOR SHORT TO GROUND			
• Key off. • Breakout box installed, PCM disconnected. • Fuel pump relay disconnected. • Measure resistance between Test Pin 22 and Test Pins 40 and 60 at the breakout box. • **Is resistance greater than 10,000 ohms?**	Yes No	▶ ▶	GO to **J5**. SERVICE short circuit. REMOVE breakout box. RECONNECT all components. RERUN Quick Test.
J5 CHECK FUEL PUMP CIRCUIT CONTINUITY			
• Key off. • Breakout box installed, PCM disconnected. • Fuel pump relay disconnected. • Measure resistance between fuel pump circuit at the fuel pump relay vehicle harness connector and Test Pin 22 at the breakout box. • **Is resistance less than 5.0 ohms?**	Yes No	▶ ▶	REPLACE PCM. RECONNECT fuel pump relay. RERUN Quick Test. SERVICE open circuit. REMOVE breakout box. RECONNECT all components. RERUN Quick Test.

Fig. 194   Test J: Fuel Pump Circuit (Part 9 of 20)

FM0159300735110X

TEST STEP	RESULT	▶	ACTION TO TAKE
J10 DIAGNOSTIC TROUBLE CODE (DTC) 95 / 542: DOES ENGINE START			
DTC 95 / 542 indicates that one of the following has occurred: No Start: — Inertia Fuel Shutoff (IFS) switch not reset or electrically open (if in secondary circuit). — Open circuit between the fuel pump and FPM circuit connection to the power-to-pump circuit. — Poor fuel pump ground. — Fuel pump electrically open. Engine Starts: — Fuel pump secondary circuit short to power. — Fuel pump relay contacts always closed. — Open in FPM circuit between PCM and connection to the power-to-pump circuit. — Left / front HO2S short to power (dual HO2S applications). — Damaged Powertrain Control Module (PCM). • **Does the engine start (For trucks with dual fuel tanks, verify tank selector is in the same position it was when KOEO DTC 542 was received)?**	Yes No	▶ ▶	GO to **J11**. GO to **J15**.
J11 VERIFY THAT FUEL PUMP IS OFF			
• Key on, wait five seconds. • Listen for motor noise from fuel pump. • **Is fuel pump off?**	Yes No	▶ ▶	GO to **J13**. GO to **J12**.
J12 CHECK FOR FUEL PUMP RELAY ALWAYS CLOSED			
• Key off. • Locate and disconnect fuel pump relay. • Key on. • **Is fuel pump off with relay disconnected?**	Yes No	▶ ▶	REPLACE fuel pump relay. RERUN Quick Test. SERVICE short to power in power-to-pump / FPM circuit. (For applications with Relay Block, also CHECK fuel pump prime plug circuit (if equipped). REFER to schematic). RECONNECT fuel pump relay. RERUN Quick Test.

Fig. 194   Test J: Fuel Pump Circuit (Part 10 of 20)

FM0159300735120X

	TEST STEP	RESULT	▶	ACTION TO TAKE
J13	CHECK FPM CIRCUIT CONTINUITY			
	• Key off. • Disconnect Powertrain Control Module (PCM). Inspect for damaged or pushed out pins, corrosion, loose wires, etc. Service as necessary. • Install breakout box, leave PCM disconnected. • Disconnect fuel pump relay. • Measure resistance between Test Pin 8 (Test Pin 19 for Escort / Tracer and Mustang) at the breakout box and power-to-pump circuit at the fuel pump relay vehicle harness connector. • **Is resistance less than 5.0 ohms?**	Yes	▶	For dual HO2S applications: RECONNECT fuel pump relay. GO to [J25]. All others: REPLACE PCM. REMOVE breakout box. RECONNECT fuel pump relay. RERUN Quick Test.
		No	▶	SERVICE open circuit. REMOVE breakout box. RECONNECT all components. RERUN Quick Test.
J15	CHECK INERTIA FUEL SHUTOFF (IFS) SWITCH			
	• Key off. • Locate and disconnect Inertia Fuel Shutoff (IFS) switch (verify that switch is reset). • Measure resistance between the C and NC pins of the IFS switch. (For Escort / Tracer and Probe, measure between GND pin and FP pin.) • **Is resistance less than 5.0 ohms?**	Yes	▶	RECONNECT IFS switch. REFER to Fuel / Engine (Electric Fuel Pump) for open in power-to-pump circuit, poor fuel pump ground, open in fuel pump, etc.
		No	▶	REPLACE or RESET IFS switch. RERUN Quick Test.

FP ☐ METER
PASSIVE C/U
GND
ESCORT/TRACER, PROBE (IFS) SWITCH

FM0159300735130X

Fig. 194   Test J: Fuel Pump Circuit (Part 11 of 20)

	TEST STEP	RESULT	▶	ACTION TO TAKE
J20	DIAGNOSTIC TROUBLE CODE (DTC) 96/543: DOES ENGINE START			
	DTC 96/543 indicates a fuel pump secondary circuit failure between the B(+) supply and the FPM connection to the power-to-pump circuit. Possible causes: No Start: — Open circuit between the B(+) supply and the FPM connection to the power-to-pump circuit. — Fuel pump relay contacts always open. Engine Starts: — HO2S short to power (dual HO2S applications). — Damaged Powertrain Control Module (PCM). • **Does the engine start?**	Yes	▶	For dual HO2S applications: GO to [J25]. All others: REPLACE PCM. RERUN Quick Test.
		No	▶	GO to [J21].
J21	CHECK FOR B(+) TO FUEL PUMP RELAY			
	• Key off. • Disconnect fuel pump relay. • Measure voltage between B(+) circuit at the fuel pump relay vehicle harness connector and battery negative post. • **Is voltage greater than 10.5 volts?**	Yes	▶	GO to [J22].
		No	▶	VERIFY integrity of fuse / fuse link for B(+) supply to fuel pump relay. If OK, SERVICE open in B(+) circuit. RECONNECT fuel pump relay. RERUN Quick Test.
J22	CHECK POWER-TO-PUMP CIRCUIT CONTINUITY			
	• Key off. • Fuel pump relay disconnected. • Measure resistance between power-to-pump circuit at the fuel pump relay vehicle harness connector and the battery negative post. • **Is resistance less than 10.0 ohms?**	Yes	▶	REPLACE fuel pump relay. RERUN Quick Test.
		No	▶	SERVICE open in power-to-pump circuit between FPM splice and fuel pump relay. REFER to schematic. RECONNECT fuel pump relay. RERUN Quick Test.

FM0159300735140X

Fig. 194   Test J: Fuel Pump Circuit (Part 12 of 20)

	TEST STEP	RESULT	▶	ACTION TO TAKE
J25	CHECK LEFT/FRONT HEATED OXYGEN SENSOR (HO2S) FOR SHORT TO POWER	Yes	▶	GO to [J26].
	NOTE: Due to the internal circuitry of the PCM, a left/front HO2S signal short to power could produce a DTC 95/542 or 96/543.	No	▶	REPLACE HO2S. RERUN Quick Test. CLEAR Keep Alive Memory
	• Key off. • Disconnect left or front HO2S sensor. • Measure resistance between HO2S signal pin and KEY POWER pin at the HO2S sensor connector. • **Is resistance greater than 10,000 ohms?**			

HO2S SIGNAL
KEY POWER
4-WIRE HO2S
3-WIRE HO2S

	TEST STEP	RESULT	▶	ACTION TO TAKE
J26	CHECK HO2S CIRCUIT FOR SHORT TO POWER	Yes	▶	REPLACE PCM. RECONNECT HO2S. RERUN Quick Test.
	• Key off. • Left or front HO2S disconnected. • Disconnect Powertrain Control Module (PCM). Inspect for damaged or pushed out pins, corrosion, loose wires, etc. Service as necessary. Leave PCM disconnected. • Key on. • Measure voltage between the HO2S signal at the HO2S vehicle harness connector and chassis ground. • **Is voltage less than 2.0 volts?**	No	▶	SERVICE short circuit. RECONNECT PCM and HO2S. RERUN Quick Test. CLEAR Keep Alive Memory

HO2S SIGNAL
KEY POWER
3-WIRE HO2S
4-WIRE HO2S

Fig. 194   Test J: Fuel Pump Circuit (Part 13 of 20)

	TEST STEP	RESULT	▶	ACTION TO TAKE
J90	CONTINUOUS MEMORY DIAGNOSTIC TROUBLE CODE (DTC) 95/542: CHECK EEC-IV HARNESS			
	A Continuous Memory DTC 95/542 indicates that one of the following intermittent conditions has occurred: — Fuel pump circuit activated when PCM expected circuit to be off (i.e. fuel system test or prime procedure). — Inertia fuel shutoff switch reset (if in power-to-pump circuit). — Open circuit in or between the fuel pump and FPM circuit at the PCM (refer to schematic). — Poor fuel pump ground. — FPM or power-to-pump circuit short to power. — Fuel pump relay contacts stuck closed. — Left / Front HO2S circuit short to power (with / dual HO2S). — Engine stall due to excessive load. NOTE: For trucks with dual fuel tanks, perform Key On Engine Off (KOEO) Self-Test twice, once with the front tank selected and once with the rear tank selected. If KOEO DTC 11/111 and Continuous DTC 95/542 is present both times, continue with this test (intermittent concern). If KOEO DTC 543 is present in only one test, refer to Fuel/Engine to check for open circuit between select switch and suspect pump circuit ground. • Start engine. • Check for engine stall / stumble while performing the following (also, if possible, listen for fuel pump turning off): — Shake, wiggle, bend the power-to-pump circuit between the power-to-pump pin at the fuel pump relay and the fuel pump. — Shake, wiggle, bend the fuel pump ground circuit from the fuel pump to the fuel pump ground. — Lightly tap the fuel pump to simulate road shock. — For vehicles with the Inertia Fuel Shutoff switch in the power-to-pump circuit (refer to schematic), lightly tap Inertia Fuel Shutoff switch to simulate road shock. • Key off. • Inspect the fuel pump vehicle harness connector and the fuel pump ground for corrosion, damaged pins, etc. • **Is fault indicated found?**	Yes	▶	ISOLATE fault and SERVICE as necessary. CLEAR Continuous Memory DTC RERUN Quick Test.
		No	▶	GO to [J91].

FM0159300735160X

Fig. 194   Test J: Fuel Pump Circuit (Part 14 of 20)

TEST STEP	RESULT	▶	ACTION TO TAKE
J91 CHECK FPM CIRCUIT			
• Key off. • Disconnect PCM. Inspect for damaged or pushed out pins, corrosion, loose wires, etc. Service as necessary. • Install breakout box, leave PCM disconnected. • Key on, engine off. • Connect a test lamp between Test Pin 8 (Test Pin 19 for Escort/Tracer, and Mustang) and Test Pin 37 at the breakout box. • Observe test lamp for an indication of a fault while performing the following (The light will go out when a fault is found, indicating an open): — Shake, wiggle, bend the Fuel Pump Monitor circuit between the fuel pump relay (or splice if applicable, refer to schematic) and the PCM. • **Is fault indicated?**	Yes No	▶ ▶	ISOLATE fault and SERVICE as necessary. REMOVE breakout box. RECONNECT PCM. RERUN Quick Test. GO to **J92**.
J92 CHECK FOR SHORTS TO POWER			
• Key on, engine off. • Breakout box installed, PCM disconnected. • Connect a test lamp between Test Pin 8 (Test Pin 19 for Escort/Tracer, and Mustang) and Test Pin 40. • Observe test lamp for an indication of a fault while performing the following (The lamp will turn on when a fault is detected, indicating a short to power.): — Shake, wiggle, bend the Fuel Pump monitor circuit and power-to-pump circuit, especially where there may be in the vicinity of a power circuit. • Lightly tap the fuel pump relay (to simulate road shock). • **Is fault indicated?**	Yes No	▶ ▶	ISOLATE fault and SERVICE as necessary. REMOVE breakout box. RECONNECT PCM. RERUN Quick Test. For dual HO2S applications: GO to **J96**. All others: further diagnosis using an EEC-IV monitor box or Scan Tool. If an EEC-IV monitor box or Scan Tool is not available, GO to **J99**.
J93 CONTINUOUS MEMORY DIAGNOSTIC TROUBLE CODE (DTC) 96/543: CHECK FOR CONTINUOUS MEMORY DTC 87/556			
• Is Continuous Memory DTC 87 or 556 also present?	Yes No	▶ ▶	GO to **J95**. GO to **J94**.

Fig. 194   Test J: Fuel Pump Circuit (Part 15 of 20)

TEST STEP	RESULT	▶	ACTION TO TAKE
J94 CHECK EEC-IV HARNESS			
A Continuous Memory DTC 96/543, without the presence of a Continuous Memory DTC 87/556, indicates that during vehicle operation, one of the following has occurred: — Open in the B(+) circuit between B(+) and the fuel pump relay. — Fuel pump relay contacts opened. — Open in the power-to-pump circuit from the fuel pump relay to the FPM splice, if applicable (refer to schematic). — Left/Front HO2S circuit short to power (with/dual HO2S). • Start engine. • Check for engine stall/stumble while performing the following (also, if possible, listen for fuel pump turning off): — Shake, wiggle, bend the B(+) circuit from B(+) to the fuel pump relay. — Lightly tap the fuel pump relay (to simulate road shock). — Shake, wiggle, bend the power-to-pump circuit from the fuel pump relay to the FPM splice, if applicable (refer to schematic). • Key off. • Inspect the fuel pump relay connectors and B(+) connector terminal for corrosion, damaged pins, etc. • **Is fault indicated/found?**	Yes No	▶ ▶	ISOLATE fault and SERVICE as necessary. CLEAR Continuous Memory RERUN Quick Test. Under certain conditions, a Continuous Memory DTC 96/543 may have been set without a Continuous Memory DTC 87/556, even though a fault has occurred in the fuel pump primary circuit. GO to **J95** to check the fuel pump primary circuit.

Fig. 194   Test J: Fuel Pump Circuit (Part 16 of 20)

TEST STEP	RESULT	▶	ACTION TO TAKE
J95 CONTINUOUS MEMORY DIAGNOSTIC TROUBLE CODE (DTC) 87/556: CHECK EEC-IV HARNESS			
A Continuous Memory DTC 87/556 indicates that a fuel pump primary circuit failure has occurred during vehicle operation. Possible causes are: — Open in VPWR circuit between the PCM power relay and the fuel pump relay. — Open coil in fuel pump relay. — Open in fuel pump circuit (Pin 22). — Inertia Fuel Shutoff (IFS) switch reset (if in VPWR circuit). • Start engine. • Check for engine stall/stumble while performing the following (also, if possible, listen for fuel pump turning off): — Shake, wiggle, bend the VPWR circuit between the EEC power relay and the fuel pump relay. For vehicles with the Inertia Fuel Shutoff (IFS) switch in the VPWR circuit (refer to schematic), lightly tap the Inertia Fuel Shutoff (IFS) switch to simulate road shock. — Shake, wiggle, bend the PCM vehicle harness fuel pump circuit (Pin 22) between the PCM and the fuel pump relay. — Lightly tap the fuel pump relay to simulate road shock. • Key off. • Inspect the PCM connector and the fuel pump relay connectors for corrosion, damaged pins, etc. • **Is fault indicated/found?**	Yes No	▶ ▶	ISOLATE fault and SERVICE as necessary. CLEAR Continuous Memory RERUN Quick Test. For dual HO2S applications with a DTC 96/543 only: GO to **J96**. ALL others: further diagnosis using an EEC-IV monitor box or Scan Tool. If an EEC-IV monitor box or Scan Tool is not available, GO to **J99**.

Fig. 194   Test J: Fuel Pump Circuit (Part 17 of 20)

TEST STEP	RESULT	▶	ACTION TO TAKE
J96 CHECK LEFT/FRONT HO2S CIRCUIT FOR SHORT TO POWER			
NOTE: Due to the internal circuitry of the PCM, an intermittent left/front HO2S signal short to power could produce a Continuous Memory DTC 95/542 or 96/543. • Key off. • Install breakout box, if applicable. • Breakout box installed, PCM disconnected. • Connect a test lamp between the left/front HO2S test pin and test pin 40 at the breakout box (Refer to pinpoint test **H** cover page for appropriate HO2S test pin). • Observe test lamp for an indication of a fault while performing the following (the light will turn on bright when a fault is detected): — Shake, wiggle, bend the left/front HO2S circuit from the HO2S sensor to the PCM. — Lightly tap the HO2S sensor (to simulate road shock). • **Is fault indicated?**	Yes No	▶ ▶	ISOLATE fault and SERVICE as necessary. REMOVE breakout box. RECONNECT PCM. RERUN Quick Test. further diagnosis using an EEC-IV monitor box or Scan Tool. If an EEC-IV monitor box or Scan Tool is not available, GO to **J99**.

Fig. 194   Test J: Fuel Pump Circuit (Part 18 of 20)

J99 ROAD TEST

The purpose of the road test is to identify an area of concern by monitoring certain controlled parameters while trying to re-create a driveability or MIL symptom.

Note

A basic working knowledge of the EEC system is critical to effectively analyze road test data.

WARNING

THIS ROAD TEST IS A SUGGESTED BUT OPTIONAL PROCEDURE. ALL APPLICABLE SAFETY PROCEDURES AND TRAFFIC LAWS MUST BE FOLLOWED. IN ORDER FOR A ROAD TEST TO BE PERFORMED IT IS REQUIRED THAT ANOTHER PERSON ACCOMPANY THE DRIVER. THE ACCOMPANYING PERSON CAN MAKE MEASUREMENTS, OBSERVE CHANGES AND RECORD NOTES. IF FOR SOME REASON THIS TEST IS NOT PERFORMED, RETURN TO Diagnostic Routines

Prepare Vehicle For A Road Test

- Install breakout box, if applicable.
- Breakout box installed, PCM connected.
- Install fuel pressure gauge and MAP / BARO tester (optional).
- Other materials needed; DVOM, pencil, paper, appropriate schematic / pin usage sheet

Preliminary Power Ground Checks

- With the key ON and a DVOM referenced to the battery negative post, check the following signals for correct values.

  POWERS: KAPWR > 10.5V (Pin 1), VPWR > 10.5V (Pins 37 57), VREF 5 ± 1V (Pin 26). GROUNDS: (all = 0 ± .5V) PWR GND (Pins 40 60), SIG RTN (Pin 46), IGN GND (Pin 16) OPTIONAL GROUNDS: HO2S GND (Pin 49), CSE GND (Pin 20), MAF RTN (Pin 9 or 15)

Obtaining Other Needed Information And Materials Before The Road Test

- Refer to the Symptom Charts that most resembles the vehicle's driveability or MIL symptom. Before the road test perform the Visual Mechanical Checks that are listed. Next, list the EEC-IV sensors and actuators in the order given. These circuits, along with the FP FPM signal(s), are the main signals that will be monitored.

Fig. 194 Test J: Fuel Pump Circuit (Part 19 of 20)

FM0159300735210X

J99 ROAD TEST (Continued)

- Refer to the proper Diagnostic Reference Value Sheet Although these charts were designed for use with the EEC-IV monitor box, most of the values can be read using the breakout box and a DVOM (with the DVOM referenced to ground all values in DCV units can be used; other values may also be helpful, ex., MAP Hz using the MAP / BARO tester). Also refer to EEC Graphs and Charts.

- The use of test lamp(s) and a DVOM may also aid diagnosis. For example, with a Continuous Memory DTC 87 / 556 (fuel pump primary circuit failure) and a surge / stall symptom, a test lamp could be connected at the fuel pump relay between the VPWR circuit and ground, with a DVOM connected between the Fuel Pump (FP) circuit at the relay and Test Pin 1 (KAPWR) at the breakout box. Under normal drive conditions the lamp will be on and the DVOM will read battery voltage (if the vehicle stalls, the processor will "unground" the FP circuit and the DVOM voltage will be low. If the problem is in the fuel pump wiring the lamp / voltage should change just before the symptom occurs). If the VPWR lamp goes out, the problem is in the VPWR supply to the relay. If the lamp stayed on, the DVOM voltage remained high and a Continuous Memory DTC 87 / 556 was set again, REPLACE the fuel pump relay. If only the FP voltage went low, the problem is either in the FP circuit or the PCM. The DVOM could now be connected between Test Pin 22 (FP) and Test Pin 1 (KAPWR) at the breakout box. If, just before the symptom occurs, the voltage goes low, REPLACE the PCM; if the voltage stays high, the problem is in the FP circuit wiring. For the fuel pump secondary circuit DTCs (95 / 542, 96 / 543), the B(+), Power-to-Pump and FPM circuits could be similarly monitored.

NOTE: Due to the low resistance of some test lamps, it is recommended that a DVOM or equivalent high resistance testing device be used when monitoring PCM output circuits.

Road Test

- After starting the engine for the road test, enter Engine Running Continuous Monitor Diagnostic Test Mode

- Drive the vehicle to create the conditions so that the symptom will occur. If the Customer Information Worksheet has been completed, this information may help when trying to re-create the symptom.

- When the symptom occurs, the accompanying passenger should observe changes in listed PCM signals. Information about the symptom, operating condition, value of the PCM signal or other notes should be recorded onto paper.

- If you are unable to duplicate the symptom, it may still be helpful to verify that the PCM values are in the expected range.

Analyzing The Data

- Once the road test is completed, the results need to be analyzed to locate and service the exact fault which caused the symptom.

- If no problem is identified, return to possible causes of the symptom.

Fig. 194 Test J: Fuel Pump Circuit (Part 20 of 20)

FM0159300735220X

Note

You should enter this Pinpoint Test only when you have been directed here from Diagnostic Routines,

Remember

To prevent the replacement of good components, be aware that the following non-EEC areas may be at fault:

- Damaged vacuum hoses
- EGR Pressure Transducer (EPT)
- EGR valve

This Pinpoint Test is intended to diagnose only the following:

- EGR Vacuum Regulator (EVR) solenoid
- Harness circuits: EVR and VPWR
- Powertrain Control Module (PCM)

Description

The EGR Vacuum Regulator (EVR) solenoid regulates the vacuum supply to the EGR valve via the EGR Pressure Transducer (EPT). If the EVR solenoid is energized, the solenoid valve opens a path for the manifold vacuum to be applied to the EGR valve via the EPT. If the EVR solenoid is not energized, then the solenoid valve closes the vacuum path to the EGR valve and vacuum is vented to the atmosphere.

Fig. 195 Test KA: EVR Solenoid (Part 1 of 5). 1993–94

FM0159300736010X

Pinpoint Test Schematic

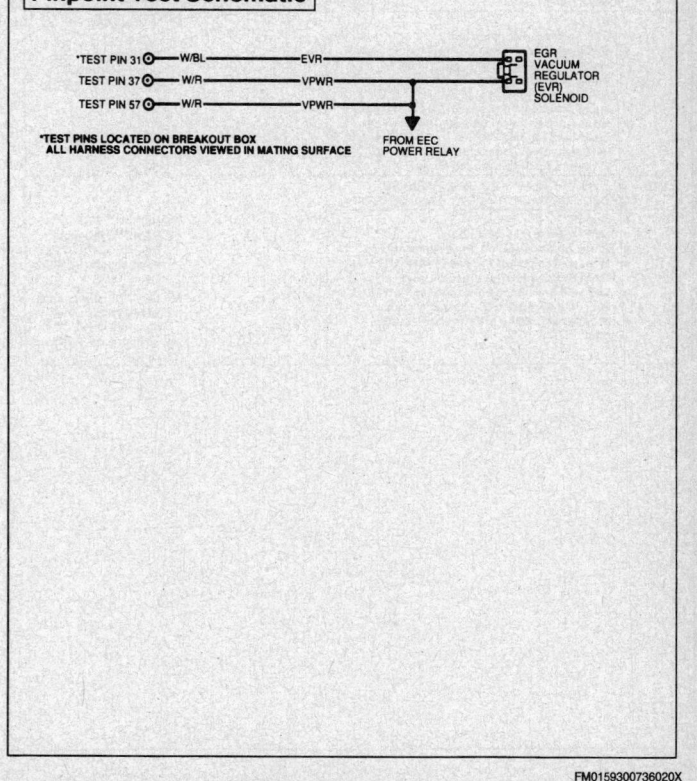

*TEST PIN 31 — W/BL — EVR —
TEST PIN 37 — W/R — VPWR —
TEST PIN 57 — W/R — VPWR —

*TEST PINS LOCATED ON BREAKOUT BOX
ALL HARNESS CONNECTORS VIEWED IN MATING SURFACE

EGR VACUUM REGULATOR (EVR) SOLENOID

FROM EEC POWER RELAY

Fig. 195 Test KA: EVR Solenoid (Part 2 of 5). 1993–94

FM0159300736020X

TEST STEP		RESULT	▶	ACTION TO TAKE
KA1	KOEO DIAGNOSTIC TROUBLE CODE (DTC) 558: ENTER OUTPUT STATE DIAGNOSTIC TEST MODE (DTM)			
	DTC 558 indicates a failure in the EVR solenoid circuit. Possible causes:	Yes	▶	REMAIN in Output State DTM. GO to **KA2.**
	— Damaged EVR solenoid. — Damaged vacuum hose(s). — Open in harness. — Short in harness. — Damaged PCM.	No	▶	DEPRESS throttle to WOT and release. If STO voltage does not go high leave equipment hooked up and GO to **QC1**
	NOTE: Do not use STAR Tester for this step. Use a VOM/DVOM. ● Key off. ● Disconnect electrical connector on the speed control servo, if equipped. ● DVOM on 20 volt scale. ● Connect DVOM negative test lead to STO circuit at Data Link Connector (DLC) and positive test lead to battery positive. ● Jumper STI circuit to SIG RTN at the DLC. ● Perform Key On Engine Off Self-Test until the completion of the Continuous Test DTC's. ● DVOM will indicate less than 1.0 volt when test is completed. ● Depress and release the throttle. ● **Does voltage increase?**			
KA2	CHECK EVR SOLENOID ELECTRICAL OPERATION			
	● Key on, engine off. ● Disconnect EVR solenoid. ● Connect DVOM positive test lead to VPWR pin and negative test lead to EVR circuit at the EVR solenoid vehicle harness connector. ● DVOM at 20 volt scale. ● While observing DVOM, depress and release the throttle several times to cycle the solenoid output. ● **Does the EVR solenoid output voltage change greater than 0.5 volt?**	Yes	▶	GO to **KA3**.
		No	▶	REMOVE jumper. GO to **KA6**.

FM0159300736030X

Fig. 195   Test KA: EVR Solenoid (Part 3 of 5). 1993–94

TEST STEP		RESULT	▶	ACTION TO TAKE
KA3	CHECK EVR SOLENOID VALVE OPERATION			
	● Key on, engine off. ● Disconnect both source port and output port vacuum hoses at the EVR solenoid. ● Install a vacuum pump at the source port and a vacuum gauge at the output port of the EVR solenoid. ● Maintain a minimum vacuum of 20.2 kPa (6 in-Hg) at the solenoid source port. ● Cycle the solenoid state by depressing and releasing the throttle several times. ● Key off. ● **Does the vacuum gauge needle show that the vacuum at the output port cycles?**	Yes	▶	REMOVE jumper wire. REMOVE vacuum pump and vacuum gauge. RECONNECT output port vacuum hose. GO to **KA4**
		No	▶	REMOVE jumper wire. REMOVE vacuum pump and vacuum gauge. REMOVE EVR solenoid. RERUN Quick Test.
KA4	CHECK VACUUM HOSE FROM THE EVR SOLENOID SOURCE PORT TO THE THROTTLE BODY			
	● Key off. ● Source port vacuum hose between EVR solenoid and throttle body disconnected. ● Plug one end of the hose and install a vacuum/pressure pump at the other end. ● Apply and maintain a steady pressure through the hose, while observing the pump gauge needle. ● **Does the pump gauge needle show a pressure drop?**	Yes	▶	REMOVE vacuum pump and hose plug. REPLACE vacuum hose. RERUN Quick Test.
		No	▶	Remove vacuum pump and vacuum gauge. RECONNECT vacuum hose. GO to **KA5**.
KA5	CHECK VACUUM HOSE FROM EVR SOLENOID TO EGR PRESSURE TRANSDUCER (EPT)			
	● Key off. ● Disconnect vacuum hose between EVR solenoid and EGR Pressure Transducer (EPT). ● Plug one end of the hose and install a vacuum/pressure pump at the other end. ● Apply and maintain a steady pressure through the hose while observing pump gauge needle. ● **Does the pump gauge needle show a pressure drop?**	Yes	▶	REMOVE vacuum pump and hose plug. REPLACE vacuum hose. RERUN Quick Test.
		No	▶	REMOVE vacuum pump and hose. check the EPT to EGR valve vacuum path.
KA6	CHECK EVR SOLENOID VPWR			
	● Key off. ● EVR solenoid disconnected. ● Key on, engine off. ● Measure voltage between VPWR at the EVR solenoid vehicle harness connector and battery ground. ● **Is voltage greater than 10.5 volts?**	Yes	▶	GO to **KA7**
		No	▶	SERVICE open in VPWR harness circuit. RECONNECT EVR solenoid. RERUN Quick Test.

FM0159300736040X

Fig. 195   Test KA: EVR Solenoid (Part 4 of 5). 1993–94

TEST STEP		RESULT	▶	ACTION TO TAKE
KA7	CHECK CONTINUITY OF EVR SOLENOID SIGNAL HARNESS CIRCUIT			
	● Key off. ● EVR solenoid disconnected. ● Disconnect Powertrain Control Module (PCM). Inspect for damaged or pushed out pins, corrosion, loose wires, etc. Service as necessary. ● Install breakout box, leave PCM disconnected. ● Measure resistance between Test Pin 31 at breakout box and EVR circuit at EVR solenoid vehicle harness connector. ● **Is resistance less than 5.0 ohms?**	Yes	▶	GO to **KA8**.
		No	▶	SERVICE open circuit. REMOVE breakout box. RECONNECT all components. RERUN Quick Test.
KA8	CHECK EVR SOLENOID SIGNAL HARNESS CIRCUIT FOR SHORT TO POWER AND GROUND			
	● Key off. ● EVR solenoid disconnected. ● Breakout box installed, PCM disconnected. ● Measure resistance between Test Pin 31 and Test Pins 37 and 57 at breakout box. ● Measure resistance between Test Pin 31 and Test Pins 40, 46 and 60 at breakout box. ● **Is each resistance greater than 10,000 ohms?**	Yes	▶	REPLACE PCM. REMOVE breakout box. RECONNECT all components. RERUN Quick Test.
		No	▶	SERVICE short circuit. REMOVE breakout box. RECONNECT all components. RERUN Quick Test.

Fig. 195   Test KA: EVR Solenoid (Part 5 of 5). 1993–94

Note

You should enter this Pinpoint Test only when you have been directed here from Diagnostic Routines.

Remember

This Pinpoint Test is intended to diagnose only the following:

● CANP valve
● Harness circuits: CANP and VPWR
● Powertrain Control Module (PCM)

Description

The CANP valve is a part solenoid, part valve output component that is used by the PCM to regulate the flow of fuel vapors from the EVAP canister to the fuel system. The CANP valve regulates the flow as a function of manifold vacuum and duty cycle signal from the PCM, which controls the CANP valve solenoid.

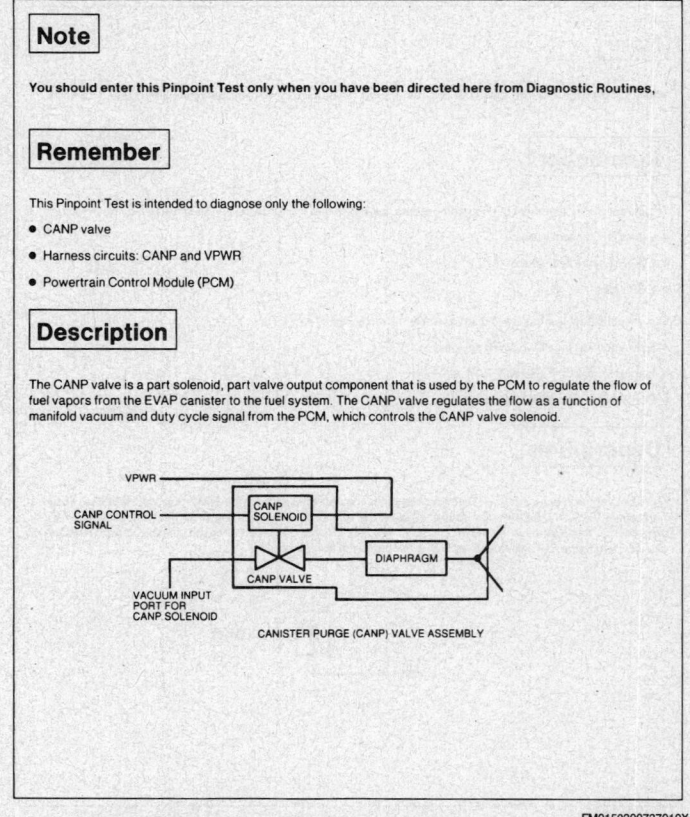

FM0159300737010X

Fig. 196   Test KB: CANP Valve (Part 1 of 6)

Pinpoint Test Schematic

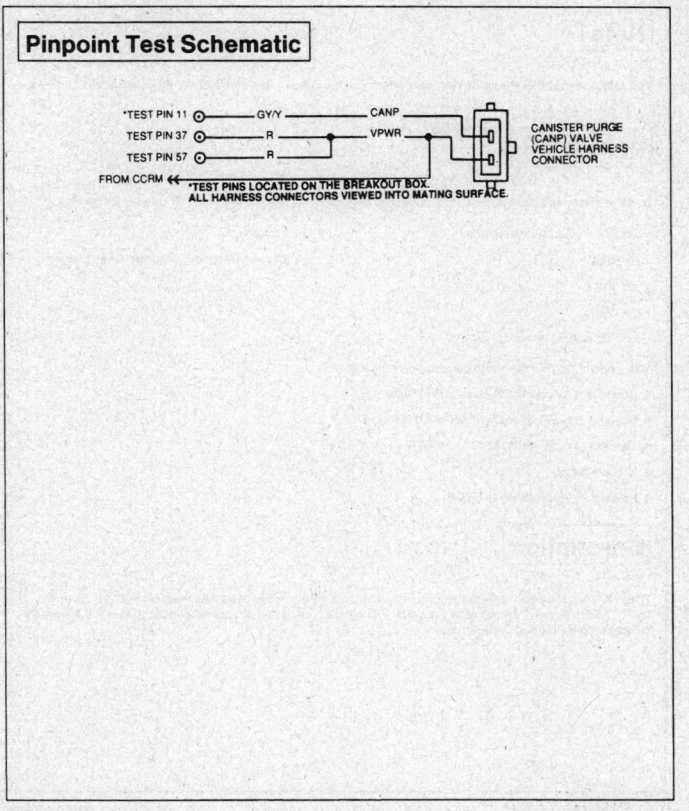

*TEST PIN 11 — GY/Y ———— CANP
TEST PIN 37 — R ———— VPWR
TEST PIN 57 — R
FROM CCRM ← *TEST PINS LOCATED ON THE BREAKOUT BOX.
ALL HARNESS CONNECTORS VIEWED INTO MATING SURFACE.

CANISTER PURGE
(CANP) VALVE
VEHICLE HARNESS
CONNECTOR

FM0159300737020X

Fig. 196   Test KB: CANP Valve (Part 2 of 6)

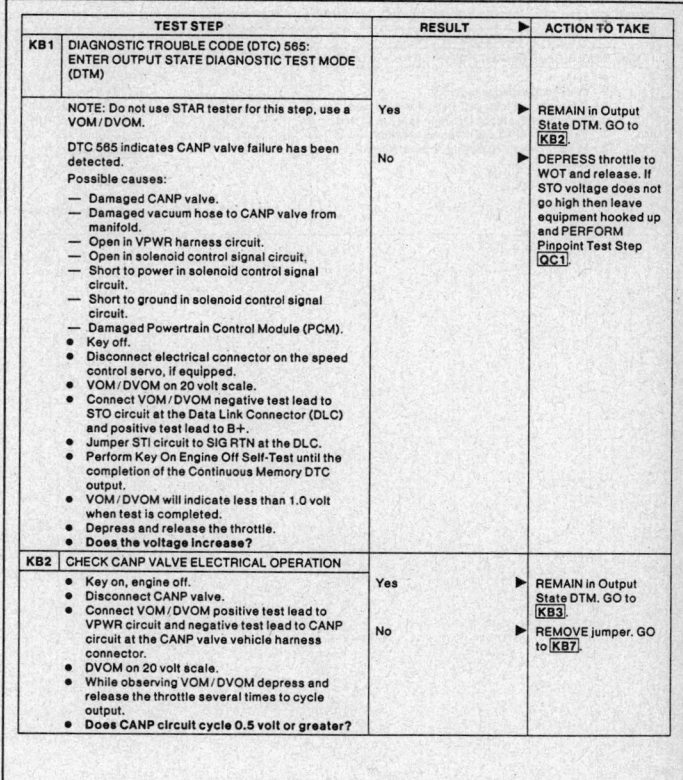

	TEST STEP	RESULT	▶	ACTION TO TAKE
KB1	DIAGNOSTIC TROUBLE CODE (DTC) 565: ENTER OUTPUT STATE DIAGNOSTIC TEST MODE (DTM)			
	NOTE: Do not use STAR tester for this step, use a VOM/DVOM. DTC 565 indicates CANP valve failure has been detected. Possible causes: — Damaged CANP valve. — Damaged vacuum hose to CANP valve from manifold. — Open in VPWR harness circuit. — Open in solenoid control signal circuit. — Short to power in solenoid control signal circuit. — Short to ground in solenoid control signal circuit. — Damaged Powertrain Control Module (PCM). • Key off. • Disconnect electrical connector on the speed control servo, if equipped. • VOM/DVOM on 20 volt scale. • Connect VOM/DVOM negative test lead to STO circuit at the Data Link Connector (DLC) and positive test lead to B+. • Jumper STI circuit to SIG RTN at the DLC. • Perform Key On Engine Off Self-Test until the completion of the Continuous Memory DTC output. • VOM/DVOM will indicate less than 1.0 volt when test is completed. • Depress and release the throttle. • **Does the voltage increase?**	Yes No	▶ ▶	REMAIN in Output State DTM. GO to **KB2**. DEPRESS throttle to WOT and release. If STO voltage does not go high then leave equipment hooked up and PERFORM Pinpoint Test Step **QC1**.
KB2	CHECK CANP VALVE ELECTRICAL OPERATION			
	• Key on, engine off. • Disconnect CANP valve. • Connect VOM/DVOM positive test lead to VPWR circuit and negative test lead to CANP circuit at the CANP valve vehicle harness connector. • DVOM on 20 volt scale. • While observing VOM/DVOM depress and release the throttle several times to cycle output. • **Does CANP circuit cycle 0.5 volt or greater?**	Yes No	▶ ▶	REMAIN in Output State DTM. GO to **KB3**. REMOVE jumper. GO to **KB7**.

FM0159300737030X

Fig. 196   Test KB: CANP Valve (Part 3 of 6)

	TEST STEP	RESULT	▶	ACTION TO TAKE
KB3	CHECK CANP VALVE RESISTANCE			
	• Key on, engine off. • CANP valve disconnected. • Measure CANP valve resistance. • **Is resistance between 30 and 36 ohms?**	Yes No	▶ ▶	REMAIN in Output State DTM. GO to **KB4**. REPLACE CANP valve assembly. REMOVE jumper wire. RERUN Quick Test.
KB4	CHECK CANP VALVE FOR VACUUM LEAKS			
	• Key on, engine off. • CANP valve disconnected. • Disconnect vacuum hose at input port of CANP valve (Refer to illustration.) • Apply 16 in-Hg of vacuum to CANP valve input port. • **Does CANP valve hold vacuum for 20 seconds?**	Yes No	▶ ▶	REMAIN in Output State DTM. GO to **KB5**. REPLACE CANP valve assembly. REMOVE jumper wire. RERUN Quick Test.
KB5	CHECK CANP VALVE ELECTRO-MECHANICAL OPERATION			
	• Still in Output State DTM, reconnect the CANP valve. • Vacuum (16 in-Hg) applied to CANP solenoid input port. • Depress and release throttle. • **Is vacuum released?**	Yes No	▶ ▶	REMOVE jumper wire. REMOVE vacuum pump. GO to **KB6**. REMOVE jumper wire. REPLACE CANP valve assembly. RERUN Quick Test.

FM0159300737040X

Fig. 196   Test KB: CANP Valve (Part 4 of 6)

	TEST STEP	RESULT	▶	ACTION TO TAKE
KB6	CHECK FOR VACUUM TO CANP VALVE INPUT PORT			
	• Key on, engine running. • CANP valve connected. • Place finger on vacuum hose end that attaches to the input port of the CANP valve. • **Is vacuum present at vacuum hose end?**	Yes No	▶ ▶	RECONNECT CANP input port vacuum hose. EEC system is OK. REFER to Evaporative Emission Systems Diagnosis. CHECK CANP valve input port vacuum hose for proper routing, kinks, leaks or blockage. If OK, REFER to Engine for items that may affect engine vacuum.
KB7	CHECK VPWR CIRCUIT VOLTAGE			
	• Key on, engine off. • CANP valve disconnected. • Measure voltage between VPWR at the CANP valve vehicle harness connector and battery ground. • **Is voltage greater than 10.5 volts?**	Yes No	▶ ▶	GO to **KB8**. SERVICE open in harness. RECONNECT CANP valve. RERUN Quick Test.
KB8	CHECK CONTINUITY OF CANP CIRCUIT			
	• Key off. • CANP valve disconnected. • Disconnect Powertrain Control Module (PCM). Inspect for damaged or pushed out pins, corrosion, loose wires, etc. Service as necessary. • Install breakout box, leave PCM disconnected. • Measure resistance between CANP circuit at the CANP valve vehicle harness connector and Test Pin 11 at the breakout box. • **Is resistance less than 5.0 ohms?**	Yes No	▶ ▶	GO to **KB9**. SERVICE open in harness. REMOVE breakout box. RECONNECT all components. RERUN Quick Test.
KB9	CHECK CANP CIRCUIT FOR SHORT TO POWER			
	• Key off. • CANP valve disconnected. • Breakout box installed, PCM disconnected. • Measure resistance between Test Pin 11 and Test Pins 37 and 57 at the breakout box. • **Is each resistance greater than 10,000 ohms?**	Yes No	▶ ▶	GO to **KB10**. SERVICE short in harness. REMOVE breakout box. RECONNECT all components. RERUN Quick Test.

Fig. 196   Test KB: CANP Valve (Part 5 of 6)

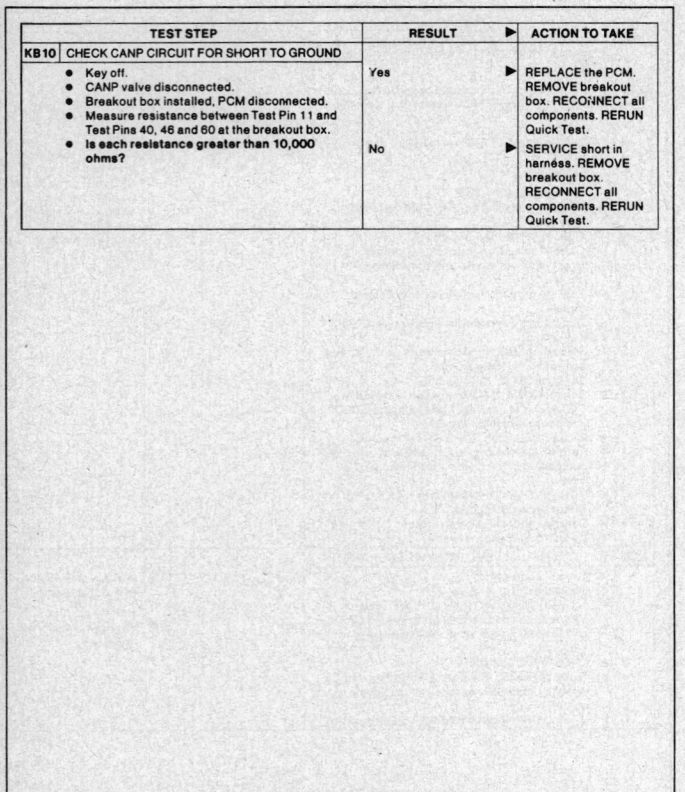

	TEST STEP	RESULT	▶	ACTION TO TAKE
KB10	CHECK CANP CIRCUIT FOR SHORT TO GROUND			
	• Key off. • CANP valve disconnected. • Breakout box installed, PCM disconnected. • Measure resistance between Test Pin 11 and Test Pins 40, 46 and 60 at the breakout box. • Is each resistance greater than 10,000 ohms?	Yes	▶	REPLACE the PCM. REMOVE breakout box. RECONNECT all components. RERUN Quick Test.
		No	▶	SERVICE short in harness. REMOVE breakout box. RECONNECT all components. RERUN Quick Test.

FM0159300737060X

Fig. 196 Test KB: CANP Valve (Part 6 of 6)

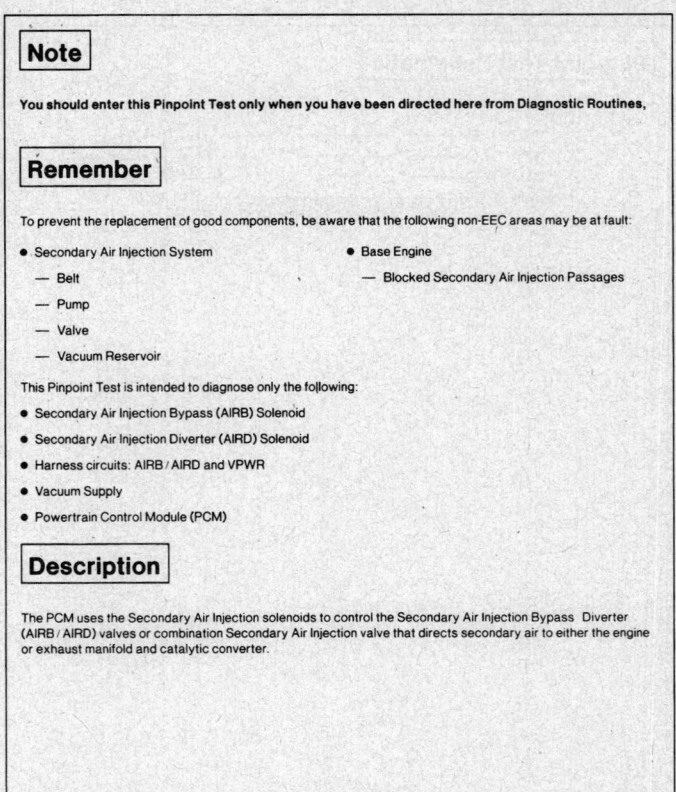

Note

You should enter this Pinpoint Test only when you have been directed here from Diagnostic Routines.

Remember

To prevent the replacement of good components, be aware that the following non-EEC areas may be at fault:

- Secondary Air Injection System
  - Belt
  - Pump
  - Valve
  - Vacuum Reservoir
- Base Engine
  - Blocked Secondary Air Injection Passages

This Pinpoint Test is intended to diagnose only the following:

- Secondary Air Injection Bypass (AIRB) Solenoid
- Secondary Air Injection Diverter (AIRD) Solenoid
- Harness circuits: AIRB / AIRD and VPWR
- Vacuum Supply
- Powertrain Control Module (PCM)

Description

The PCM uses the Secondary Air Injection solenoids to control the Secondary Air Injection Bypass Diverter (AIRB / AIRD) valves or combination Secondary Air Injection valve that directs secondary air to either the engine or exhaust manifold and catalytic converter.

FM0159300738010X

Fig. 197 Test KC: AIRB/AIRD Solenoids (Part 1 of 7)

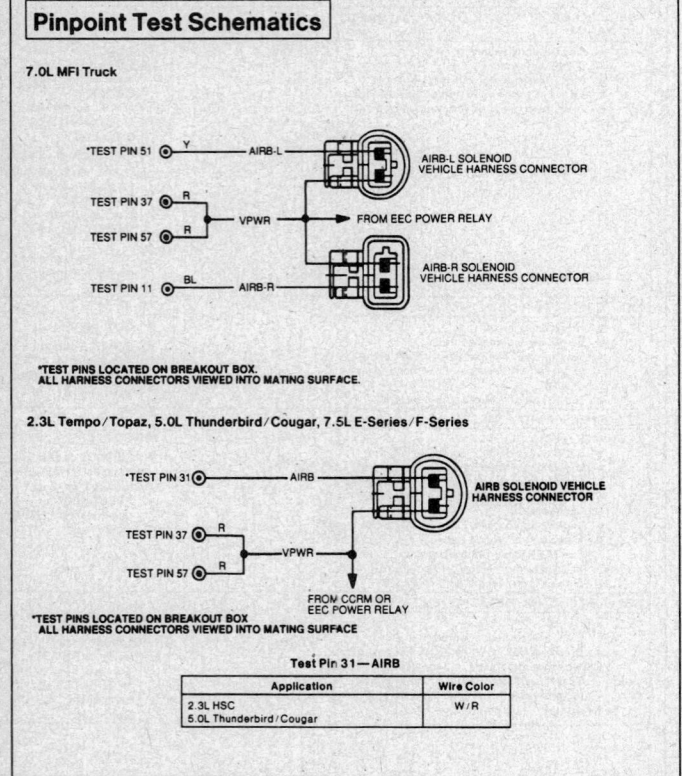

Pinpoint Test Schematics

7.0L MFI Truck

*TEST PINS LOCATED ON BREAKOUT BOX.
ALL HARNESS CONNECTORS VIEWED INTO MATING SURFACE.

2.3L Tempo / Topaz, 5.0L Thunderbird / Cougar, 7.5L E-Series / F-Series

*TEST PINS LOCATED ON BREAKOUT BOX
ALL HARNESS CONNECTORS VIEWED INTO MATING SURFACE

Test Pin 31—AIRB

Application	Wire Color
2.3L HSC 5.0L Thunderbird / Cougar	W / R

FM0159300738020X

Fig. 197 Test KC: AIRB/AIRD Solenoids (Part 2 of 7)

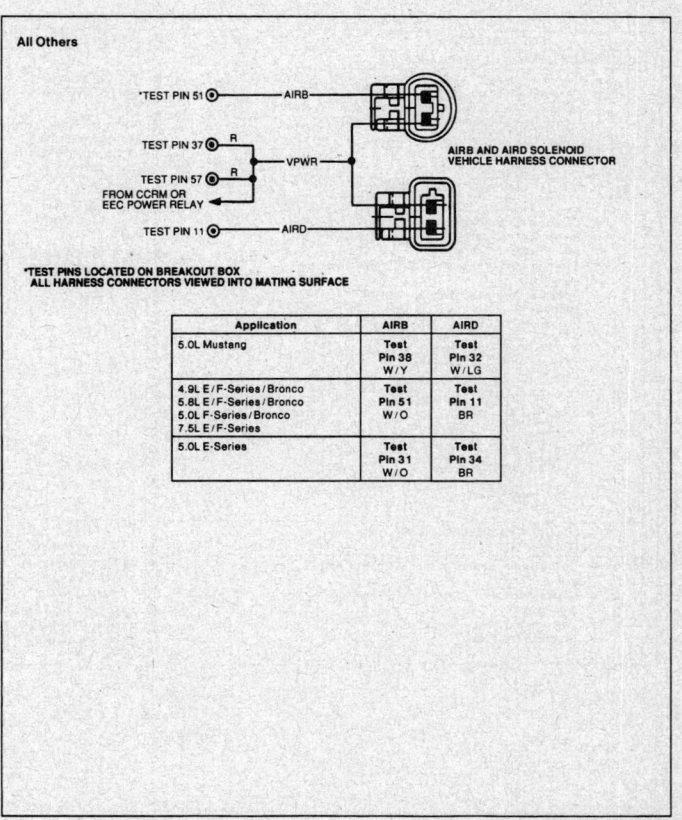

All Others

*TEST PINS LOCATED ON BREAKOUT BOX
ALL HARNESS CONNECTORS VIEWED INTO MATING SURFACE

Application	AIRB	AIRD
5.0L Mustang	Test Pin 38 W / Y	Test Pin 32 W / LG
4.9L E / F-Series / Bronco 5.8L E / F-Series / Bronco 5.0L F-Series / Bronco 7.5L E / F-Series	Test Pin 51 W / O	Test Pin 11 BR
5.0L E-Series	Test Pin 31 W / O	Test Pin 34 BR

FM015930073803AX

Fig. 197 Test KC: AIRB/AIRD Solenoids (Part 3 of 7). 1993

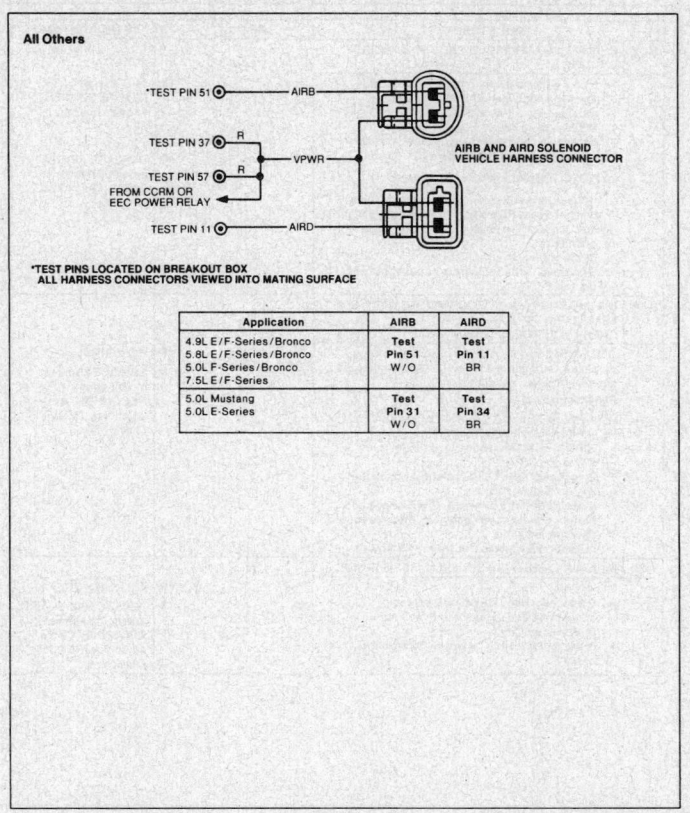

All Others

*TEST PIN 51 — AIRB

TEST PIN 37 — R

VPWR — AIRB AND AIRD SOLENOID VEHICLE HARNESS CONNECTOR

TEST PIN 57 — R
FROM CCRM OR
EEC POWER RELAY

TEST PIN 11 — AIRD

*TEST PINS LOCATED ON BREAKOUT BOX
ALL HARNESS CONNECTORS VIEWED INTO MATING SURFACE

Application	AIRB	AIRD
4.9L E/F-Series/Bronco	Test Pin 51	Test Pin 11
5.8L E/F-Series/Bronco		
5.0L F-Series/Bronco	W/O	BR
7.5L E/F-Series		
5.0L Mustang	Test Pin 31	Test Pin 34
5.0L E-Series	W/O	BR

FM015940073803BX

Fig. 197 Test KC: AIRB/AIRD Solenoids (Part 3 of 7). 1994–95

	TEST STEP	RESULT	▶	ACTION TO TAKE
KC1	DIAGNOSTIC TROUBLE CODES (DTC's) 44/311, 45/312, 46/313 AND 94/314: VERIFY VACUUM LINE ROUTING			
	DTC 44/311 and 94/314 indicate that Secondary Air Injection (AIR) system is inoperative. DTC 45/312 indicates that secondary air is misdirected. DTC 46/313 indicates that secondary air is not being bypassed when requested. Possible causes: — Vacuum hoses leaking, blocked or kinked. — AIRB/AIRD valve, AIR pump inoperative. — AIRB/AIRD solenoid(s) damaged, blocked. • Verify proper vacuum line routing in the Secondary Air Injection (AIR) system, including vacuum reservoir. Refer to VECI decal. • Check for kinked or blocked vacuum lines. • Check for kinked or blocked air hoses. • Check for disconnected or cracked vacuum lines. • Were any problems found?	Yes No	▶ ▶	SERVICE vacuum lines as necessary. RERUN Quick Test. For DTC's 44/311, 94/314: GO to KC4. For DTC's 45/312: GO to KC2. For DTC's 46/313: GO to KC3.
KC2	ATTEMPT TO ELIMINATE DTC 45/312			
	• Disconnect vacuum line on AIRD valve (or left AIRB2 valve on 7.0L) and cap vacuum line. • Key off. • Repeat Engine Running Self-Test and record service codes. • Is Code 45 or 312 present?	Yes No	▶ ▶	EEC system OK. GO to KC4.
KC3	ATTEMPT TO ELIMINATE DTC 46/313			
	• Disconnect vacuum line on AIRB (or right AIRB1 valve on 7.0L) and cap vacuum line. • Key off. • Repeat Engine Running Self-Test and record DTCs. • Is DTC 46 or 313 present?	Yes No	▶ ▶	EEC-IV system OK. RECONNECT vacuum line. GO to KC4.

Fig. 197 Test KC: AIRB/AIRD Solenoids (Part 4 of 7). 1993

	TEST STEP	RESULT	▶	ACTION TO TAKE
KC1	DIAGNOSTIC TROUBLE CODES (DTCs) 311 AND 314: VISUALLY INSPECT VACUUM HOSES			
	DTC 311 and 314 indicate the Secondary Air Injection system is inoperative. DTC 312 indicates that Secondary Air is misdirected. DTC 313 indicates that Secondary Air is not being bypassed when requested. Possible causes: — Vacuum hoses damaged. — AIRB/AIRD valve inoperative. — Air Pump inoperative. — AIRB/AIRD solenoids damaged. • Visually inspect vacuum lines for disconnects in the AIR system. • Visually inspect for proper vacuum line routing. Refer to VECI decal. • Visually inspect Air Pump for broken or loose Air Pump Belt. • Were any problems found?	Yes No	▶ ▶	SERVICE as necessary. RERUN Quick Test. GO to KC2.
KC2	CHECK AIR VACUUM LINES			
	• Carefully check AIR vacuum lines; — From AIRB solenoid to AIRB valve. — From AIRD solenoid to AIRD valve. — From Manifold Vacuum TREE to AIRB/AIRD solenoids. • Check for obstructions, cracks, kinks, and leaks, etc. • Are vacuum lines in good condition?	Yes No	▶ ▶	For DTCs 311 and 314: GO to KC5 For DTC 312: GO to KC3. For DTC 313: GO to KC4. SERVICE as necessary. RERUN Quick Test.
KC3	ATTEMPT TO ELIMINATE DTC 312			
	• Disconnect vacuum line on AIRD valve (or left AIRB2 valve on 7.0L) and cap vacuum line. • Key off. • Repeat Engine Running Self-Test and record service codes. • Is Code 312 present?	Yes No	▶ ▶	EEC system OK. GO to KC5.
KC4	ATTEMPT TO ELIMINATE DTC 313			
	• Disconnect vacuum line on AIRB (or right AIRB1 valve on 7.0L) and cap vacuum line. • Key off. • Repeat Engine Running Self-Test and record DTCs. • Is DTC 313 present?	Yes No	▶ ▶	EEC-IV system OK. RECONNECT vacuum line. GO to KC5.

Fig. 197 Test KC: AIRB/AIRD Solenoids (Part 4 of 7). 1994–95

	TEST STEP	RESULT	▶	ACTION TO TAKE
KC4	ENTER OUTPUT STATE DIAGNOSTIC TEST MODE (DTM)			
	NOTE: Do not use STAR tester for this Step. Use a VOM/DVOM. • Key off. • Disconnect electrical connector on the speed control servo, if equipped. • DVOM on 20 volt scale. • Connect DVOM negative test lead to STO circuit at the Data Link Connector (DLC) and positive test lead to battery positive. • Jumper STI circuit to SIG RTN at the DLC. • Perform Key On Engine Off Self-Test until complete output of all Continuous Memory Diagnostic Trouble Codes (DTCs). • DVOM will indicate less than 1.0 volt when test is complete. • Depress and release the throttle. • Does voltage increase?	Yes No	▶ ▶	REMAIN in Output State DTM. GO to KC5. DEPRESS throttle to WOT and RELEASE. If STO voltage does not go high, leave equipment hooked up and GO to Pinpoint Test Step QC1.
KC5	CHECK AIRB AND AIRD SOLENOIDS ELECTRICAL OPERATION			
	• DVOM on 20 volt scale. • Disconnect both AIRB and AIRD solenoids. • Connect DVOM positive test lead to VPWR circuit and negative test lead to one solenoid vehicle harness connector. • While observing DVOM depress and release the throttle several times (to cycle output On and Off). • Repeat for the other solenoid. Connect positive test lead to VPWR circuit and negative test lead to the solenoid vehicle harness connector. • Does each solenoid circuit cycle 0.5 volt or greater?	Yes No	▶ ▶	REMAIN in Output State DTM. RECONNECT solenoids. GO to KC6. REMOVE jumper. GO to KC9.
KC6	CHECK AIRB/AIRD SOLENOIDS FOR INTERNAL VACUUM LEAKS			
	• Vacuum pump connected to the supply port and vacuum gauge connected to the output port of one solenoid. • Apply 15 in-Hg (51 kPa) vacuum and observe gauge. • Repeat steps above for the other solenoid. • Does vacuum gauge reading hold for each solenoid?	Yes No	▶ ▶	GO to KC7. REPLACE AIRB/AIRD solenoid assembly. RERUN Quick Test.

FM015930073805AX

Fig. 197 Test KC: AIRB/AIRD Solenoids (Part 5 of 7). 1993

FORD—Computerized Engine Controls

TEST STEP	RESULT	▶	ACTION TO TAKE
KC5 ENTER OUTPUT STATE DIAGNOSTIC TEST MODE (DTM) NOTE: Do not use STAR tester for this Step. Use a VOM/DVOM. • Key off. • Disconnect electrical connector on the speed control servo, if equipped. • DVOM on 20 volt scale. • Connect DVOM negative test lead to STO circuit at the Data Link Connector (DLC) and positive test lead to battery positive. • Jumper STI circuit to SIG RTN at the DLC. • Perform Key On Engine Off Self-Test until complete output of all Continuous Memory Diagnostic Trouble Codes (DTCs). • DVOM will indicate less than 1.0 volt when test is complete. • Depress and release the throttle. • **Does voltage increase?**	Yes No	▶ ▶	REMAIN in Output State DTM. GO to **KC6**. DEPRESS throttle to WOT and RELEASE. If STO voltage does not go high, leave equipment hooked up and GO to Pinpoint Test Step **QC1**.
KC6 CHECK AIRB AND AIRD SOLENOIDS ELECTRICAL OPERATION • DVOM on 20 volt scale. • Disconnect both AIRB and AIRD solenoids. • Connect DVOM positive test lead to VPWR circuit and negative test lead to one solenoid vehicle harness connector. • While observing DVOM, depress and release the throttle several times (to cycle output On and Off). • Repeat for the other solenoid. Connect positive test lead to VPWR circuit and negative test lead to the solenoid vehicle harness connector. • **Does each solenoid circuit cycle 0.5 volt or greater?**	Yes No	▶ ▶	REMAIN in Output State DTM. RECONNECT solenoids. GO to **KC7**. REMOVE jumper. GO to **KC10**.
KC7 CHECK AIRB/AIRD SOLENOIDS FOR INTERNAL VACUUM LEAKS • Vacuum pump connected to the supply port and vacuum gauge connected to the output port of one solenoid. • Apply 15 in-Hg (51 kPa) vacuum and observe gauge. • Repeat steps above for the other solenoid. • **Does vacuum gauge reading hold for each solenoid?**	Yes No	▶ ▶	GO to **KC8**. REPLACE AIRB/AIRD solenoid assembly. RERUN Quick Test.

Fig. 197 Test KC: AIRB/AIRD Solenoids (Part 5 of 7). 1994–95

TEST STEP	RESULT	▶	ACTION TO TAKE
KC7 CHECK AIRB/AIRD SOLENOIDS FOR VACUUM CYCLING • Install vacuum pump to the AIRB solenoid vacuum supply port and install a vacuum gauge to the AIRB output port. • While cycling outputs On and Off (by depressing and releasing throttle), observe the vacuum gauge at the output. NOTE: Maintain vacuum at source. • Repeat for AIRD solenoid. Connect vacuum pump to the AIRD solenoid vacuum supply port and connect a vacuum gauge to the AIRD output port. • Cycle output On and Off. • **Does each solenoid cycle vacuum output On and Off?**	Yes No	▶ ▶	EXIT Output State DTM, RECONNECT vacuum hoses. REPLACE AIRB/AIRD solenoid assembly. RERUN Quick Test.
KC8 DIAGNOSTIC TROUBLE CODES (DTC'S) 81/553, 82/552: CHECK VOLTAGE OF VPWR CIRCUIT DTC 81/553 and 82/552 indicate that voltage output for Secondary Air Injection solenoid(s) did not change when activated. Possible causes: — AIRB/AIRD circuits shorted to power. — AIRB/AIRD circuits open or grounded. — AIRB/AIRD resistance out of range. — Damaged PCM. • Disconnect AIRB/AIRD solenoid connector. • Key on, engine off. • Measure voltage between VPWR circuit and battery ground of one solenoid, then repeat for the other solenoid. • **Is each voltage greater than 10.5 volts?**	Yes No	▶ ▶	GO to **KC9**. SERVICE harness circuit open. RECONNECT both solenoids. RERUN Quick Test.
KC9 MEASURE AIRB/AIRD SOLENOID RESISTANCE • Key off. • Disconnect both AIRB/AIRD solenoid connectors and measure both solenoid resistances. • **Is each resistance between 50 and 100 ohms?**	Yes No	▶ ▶	GO to **KC10**. REPLACE AIRB/AIRD solenoid assembly. RECONNECT both solenoids. RERUN Quick Test.

Fig. 197 Test KC: AIRB/AIRD Solenoids (Part 6 of 7). 1993

TEST STEP	RESULT	▶	ACTION TO TAKE
KC8 CHECK AIRB/AIRD SOLENOIDS FOR VACUUM CYCLING • Install vacuum pump to the AIRB solenoid vacuum supply port and install a vacuum gauge to the AIRB output port. • While cycling outputs On and Off (by depressing and releasing throttle), observe the vacuum gauge at the output. NOTE: Maintain vacuum at source. • Repeat for AIRD solenoid. Connect vacuum pump to the AIRD solenoid vacuum supply port and connect a vacuum gauge to the AIRD output port. • Cycle output on and off. • **Does each solenoid cycle vacuum output on and off?**	Yes No	▶ ▶	EXIT Output State DTM, RECONNECT vacuum hoses. REFER to Diagnosis Index. REPLACE AIRB/AIRD solenoid assembly. RERUN Quick Test.
KC9 DIAGNOSTIC TROUBLE CODES (DTCS) 553 AND 552: CHECK VOLTAGE OF VPWR CIRCUIT DTC 553 and 552 indicate that voltage output for Secondary Air Injection solenoid(s) did not change when activated. Possible causes: — AIRB/AIRD circuits shorted to power. — AIRB/AIRD circuits open or grounded. — AIRB/AIRD resistance out of range. — Damaged PCM. • Disconnect AIRB/AIRD solenoid connector. • Key on, engine off. • Measure voltage between VPWR circuit and battery ground of one solenoid, then repeat for the other solenoid. • **Is each voltage greater than 10.5 volts?**	Yes No	▶ ▶	GO to **KC10**. SERVICE harness circuit open. RECONNECT both solenoids. RERUN Quick Test.
KC10 MEASURE AIRB/AIRD SOLENOID RESISTANCE • Key off. • Disconnect both AIRB/AIRD solenoid connectors and measure both solenoid resistances. • **Is each resistance between 50 and 100 ohms?**	Yes No	▶ ▶	GO to **KC11**. REPLACE AIRB/AIRD solenoid assembly. RECONNECT both solenoids. RERUN Quick Test.

Fig. 197 Test KC: AIRB/AIRD Solenoids (Part 6 of 7). 1994–95

TEST STEP	RESULT	▶	ACTION TO TAKE
KC10 CHECK CIRCUIT CONTINUITY • Key off. • Disconnect Powertrain Control Module (PCM). Inspect for damaged or pushed out pins, corrosion, loose wires, etc. Service as necessary. • Install breakout box, leave PCM disconnected. • Measure resistance between Test Pin 51 (Test Pin 38 for 5.0L Mustang, Test Pin 31 on 5.0L Thunderbird/Cougar and 2.3L Tempo/Topaz) at breakout box and AIRB circuit at vehicle harness connector. • Measure resistance between Test Pin 11 (Test Pin 32 for 5.0L Mustang) at the breakout box and AIRD circuit at vehicle harness connector. • **Is each resistance less than 5.0 ohms?**	Yes No	▶ ▶	GO to **KC11**. SERVICE harness open circuit. REMOVE breakout box. RECONNECT PCM and both solenoids. RERUN Quick Test.
KC11 CHECK FOR SHORT TO GROUND • Key off. • Breakout box installed, PCM disconnected. • Disconnect both AIRB/AIRD solenoids. • Measure resistance between Test Pin 51 (Test Pin 38 for 5.0L Mustang, Test Pin 31 on 5.0L Thunderbird/Cougar and 2.3L Tempo/Topaz) and Test Pins 40, 46 and 60 and between Test Pin 11 (Test Pin 32 for 5.0L Mustang) and Test Pins 40, 46 and 60 at the breakout box. • **Is each resistance greater than 10,000 ohms?**	Yes No	▶ ▶	GO to **KC12**. SERVICE short to ground. REMOVE breakout box. RECONNECT PCM and AIRB/AIRD solenoids. RERUN Quick Test.
KC12 CHECK FOR SHORT TO POWER • Key off. • Breakout box installed, PCM disconnected. • Both AIRB/AIRD solenoids disconnected. • Measure resistance between Test Pin 51 (Test Pin 38 for 5.0L Mustang, Test Pin 31 on 5.0L Thunderbird/Cougar and 2.3L Tempo/Topaz) and Test Pins 37 and 57, and between Test Pin 11 (Test Pin 32 for 5.0L Mustang) and Test Pins 37 and 57 at the breakout box. • **Is each resistance greater than 10,000 ohms?**	Yes No	▶ ▶	REPLACE PCM. REMOVE breakout box. RECONNECT both solenoids. RERUN Quick Test. SERVICE short to power. REMOVE breakout box. RECONNECT PCM and AIRB/AIRD solenoids. RERUN Quick Test. If DTC is present, REPLACE PCM.

Fig. 197 Test KC: AIRB/AIRD Solenoids (Part 7 of 7). 1993

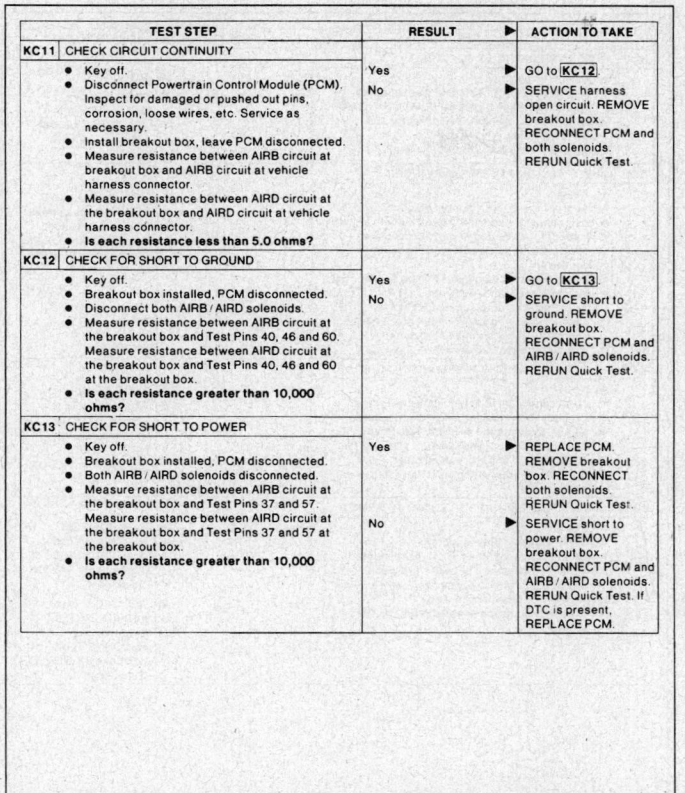

TEST STEP		RESULT	▶	ACTION TO TAKE
KC11	CHECK CIRCUIT CONTINUITY			
	• Key off. • Disconnect Powertrain Control Module (PCM). Inspect for damaged or pushed out pins, corrosion, loose wires, etc. Service as necessary. • Install breakout box, leave PCM disconnected. • Measure resistance between AIRB circuit at breakout box and AIRB circuit at vehicle harness connector. • Measure resistance between AIRD circuit at the breakout box and AIRD circuit at vehicle harness connector. • **Is each resistance less than 5.0 ohms?**	Yes No	▶ ▶	GO to **KC12**. SERVICE harness open circuit. REMOVE breakout box. RECONNECT PCM and both solenoids. RERUN Quick Test.
KC12	CHECK FOR SHORT TO GROUND			
	• Key off. • Breakout box installed, PCM disconnected. • Disconnect both AIRB / AIRD solenoids. • Measure resistance between AIRB circuit at the breakout box and Test Pins 40, 46 and 60. • Measure resistance between AIRD circuit at the breakout box and Test Pins 40, 46 and 60 at the breakout box. • **Is each resistance greater than 10,000 ohms?**	Yes No	▶ ▶	GO to **KC13**. SERVICE short to ground. REMOVE breakout box. RECONNECT PCM and AIRB / AIRD solenoids. RERUN Quick Test.
KC13	CHECK FOR SHORT TO POWER			
	• Key off. • Breakout box installed, PCM disconnected. • Both AIRB / AIRD solenoids disconnected. • Measure resistance between AIRB circuit at the breakout box and Test Pins 37 and 57. • Measure resistance between AIRD circuit at the breakout box and Test Pins 37 and 57 at the breakout box. • **Is each resistance greater than 10,000 ohms?**	Yes No	▶ ▶	REPLACE PCM. REMOVE breakout box. RECONNECT both solenoids. RERUN Quick Test. SERVICE short to power. REMOVE breakout box. RECONNECT PCM and AIRB / AIRD solenoids. RERUN Quick Test. If DTC is present, REPLACE PCM.

FM015940073807BX

Fig. 197   Test KC: AIRB/AIRD Solenoids (Part 7 of 7). 1994–95

Note

You should enter this Pinpoint Test only when you have been directed here from Diagnostic Routines.

Remember

This Pinpoint Test is intended to diagnose only the following:

• CANP solenoid(s) (9C915)
• Harness circuits: CANP and VPWR
• Powertrain Control Module (PCM)

Description

The Canister Purge (CANP) solenoid is an output control which allows venting of the EVAP carbon canister back into the fuel (intake) system. This output may be an on / off or constant frequency varying duty cycle type control.

Pinpoint Test Schematics

7.0L MFI Truck:

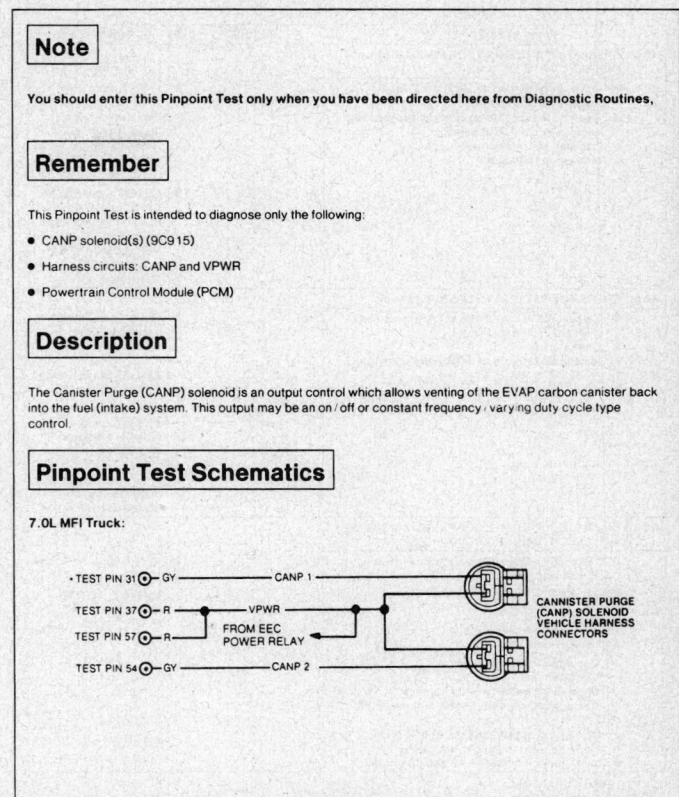

FM0159300739010X

Fig. 198   Test KD: CANP Solenoid (Part 1 of 5)

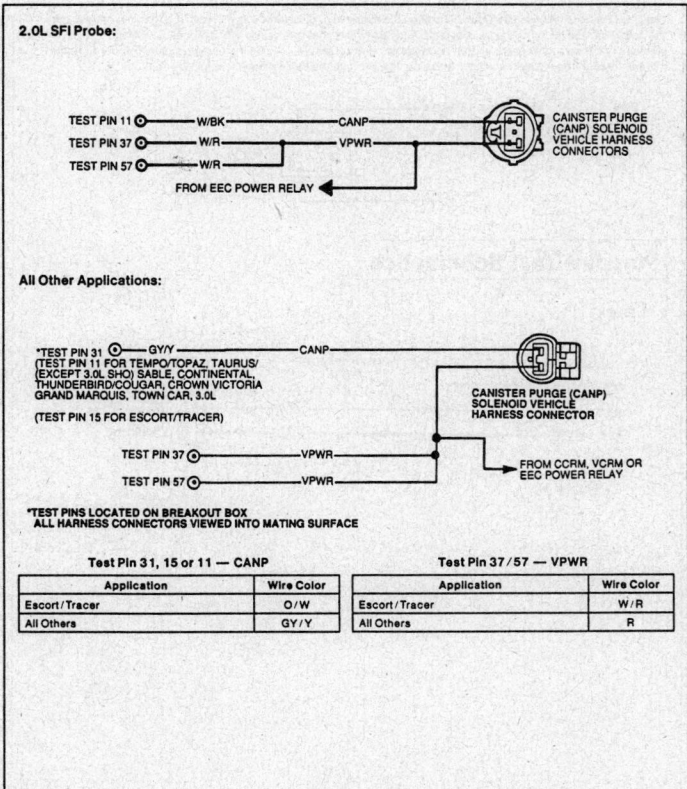

Fig. 198   Test KD: CANP Solenoid (Part 2 of 5). 1993–95

	TEST STEP	RESULT	▶	ACTION TO TAKE
KD1	ENTER OUTPUT STATE DIAGNOSTIC TEST MODE (DTM)			
	NOTE: Do not use STAR tester for this step, use VOM/DVOM. • Key off. • Disconnect electrical connector on the speed control servo, if equipped. • DVOM on 20 volt scale. • Connect DVOM negative test lead to STO circuit at Data Link Connector (DLC) and positive test lead to B+. • Jumper STI circuit to SIG RTN at the Self-Test connector. • Perform Key On Engine Off Self-Test until the completion of the Continuous Memory DTC. DVOM will indicate less than 1.0 volt when test is completed. • Depress and release the throttle. • **Does voltage increase?**	Yes No	▶ ▶	REMAIN in Output State DTM. GO to **KD2**. DEPRESS throttle to WOT and release. If STO voltage does not go high, leave equipment hooked up and PERFORM Pinpoint Test Step **QC1**.
KD2	CHECK CANP SOLENOID ELECTRICAL OPERATION			
	• Key on, engine off. • Disconnect CANP solenoid (on 7.0L MFI do one at a time). • Connect DVOM positive test lead to VPWR circuit and negative test lead to CANP circuit at the CANP solenoid vehicle harness connector. • DVOM on 20 volt scale. • While observing DVOM depress and release the throttle several times to cycle output. • **Does CANP circuit cycle 0.5 volt or greater?**	Yes No	▶ ▶	REMAIN in Output State DTM. GO to **KD3**. REMOVE jumper. GO to **KD7**.
KD3	CHECK CANP SOLENOID FOR VACUUM LEAKS			
	• Key on, engine off. • CANP solenoid disconnected. • Disconnect vacuum hose at CANP solenoid on manifold vacuum side of CANP solenoid. • Apply 16 in-Hg (53 kPa) of vacuum to manifold vacuum side of CANP solenoid. • **Does CANP solenoid hold vacuum for 20 seconds?**	Yes No	▶ ▶	REMAIN in Output State DTM. Leave vacuum pump setup in place. GO to **KD4**. REPLACE CANP solenoid. RERUN Quick Test. If symptom is still present, REFER to Evaporative Emission System Diagnosis.

FM0159300739030X

Fig. 198   Test KD: CANP Solenoid (Part 3 of 5)

TEST STEP	RESULT	▶	ACTION TO TAKE
KD4 CHECK CANP SOLENOID FOR MECHANICAL OPERATION			
• While remaining in Output State DTM, reconnect CANP solenoid. • Apply 16 in-Hg (53 kPa) of vacuum to manifold vacuum side of CANP solenoid. • Depress and release throttle. • **Is vacuum released?**	Yes	▶	CHECK hose from CANP solenoid to canister for cracks, leaks, etc. If OK, REMOVE jumper from STI to SIG RTN. GO to **KD5**.
	No	▶	CHECK hose from CANP solenoid to canister for blockage or kinks. If OK, REPLACE CANP solenoid. RERUN Quick Test.
KD5 CHECK FOR VACUUM TO CANP SOLENOID			
• Disconnect vacuum hose at CANP solenoid at manifold vacuum side. • Start engine. • **Is vacuum present at engine vacuum hose?**	Yes	▶	EEC system OK. If a symptom is still present, REFER to Evaporative Emission Systems Diagnosis.
	No	▶	CHECK vacuum line for proper routing, kinks, leaks or blockage. If OK, REFER to Engine for probable subjects affecting engine vacuum.
KD6 DIAGNOSTIC TROUBLE CODE (DTC) 85/565 OR 569: CHECK CANP RESISTANCE			
DTC 85/565 or 569 indicates a failure in the CANP solenoid circuit. With Dual CANP system (7.0L Truck): DTC 565 refers to CANP 1. DTC 569 refers to CANP 2. Possible causes are: — Damaged CANP solenoid — Open harness — Shorted (power or ground) harness — Damaged Powertrain Control Module (PCM). • Key off. • Disconnect appropriate CANP solenoid. • Measure CANP solenoid resistance. • **Is resistance between 40 and 90 ohms?**	Yes	▶	GO to **KD7**.
	No	▶	REPLACE CANP solenoid. RERUN Quick Test.

FM0159300739040X

Fig. 198 Test KD: CANP Solenoid (Part 4 of 5)

TEST STEP	RESULT	▶	ACTION TO TAKE
KD7 CHECK VPWR CIRCUIT VOLTAGE			
• Key on, engine off. • Appropriate CANP solenoid disconnected. • Measure voltage between VPWR at the CANP solenoid vehicle harness connector and battery ground. • **Is voltage greater than 10.5 volts?**	Yes	▶	GO to **KD8**.
	No	▶	SERVICE open harness circuit. RECONNECT CANP solenoid. RERUN Quick Test.
KD8 CHECK CONTINUITY OF CANP CIRCUIT			
• Key off. • Appropriate CANP solenoid disconnected. • Disconnect Powertrain Control Module (PCM). Inspect for damaged or pushed out pins, corrosion, loose wires, etc. Service as necessary. • Install breakout box, leave PCM disconnected. • Measure resistance between Test Pin 11, (15, 31 or Pin 54 refer to schematic) at the breakout box and CANP circuit at the CANP solenoid vehicle harness connector. • **Is resistance less than 5.0 ohms?**	Yes	▶	GO to **KD9**.
	No	▶	SERVICE open circuit. REMOVE breakout box. RECONNECT all components. RERUN Quick Test.
KD9 CHECK CANP CIRCUIT FOR SHORT TO GROUND			
• Key off. • Appropriate CANP solenoid disconnected. • Breakout box installed, PCM disconnected. • Measure resistance between Test Pin 11 (15, 31 or Pin 54 refer to schematic) and Test Pins 40, 46 and 60 at the breakout box. • **Is each resistance greater than 10,000 ohms?**	Yes	▶	GO to **KD10**.
	No	▶	SERVICE short to ground. REMOVE breakout box. RECONNECT all components. RERUN Quick Test.
KD10 CHECK CANP CIRCUIT FOR SHORT TO POWER			
• Key off. • CANP solenoid disconnected. • Breakout box installed, PCM disconnected. • Measure resistance between Test Pin 11 (15, 31 or Pin 54 refer to schematic) and Test Pins 37 and 57 at the breakout box. • **Is each resistance greater than 10,000 ohms?**	Yes	▶	REPLACE PCM. REMOVE breakout box. RECONNECT all components. RERUN Quick Test.
	No	▶	SERVICE short to power. REMOVE breakout box. RECONNECT all components. RERUN Quick Test.

FM0159300739050X

Fig. 198 Test KD: CANP Solenoid (Part 5 of 5)

Note

You should enter this Pinpoint Test only when you have been directed here from Diagnostic Routines, or Pinpoint Test ⑤.

Remember

To prevent the replacement of good components, be aware that the following non-EEC areas may be at fault:

• Engine not up to operating temperature
• Engine over operating temperature
• A/C input (electrical problem)
• Throttle Speed Control Linkage
• Throttle Linkage

This Pinpoint Test is intended to diagnose only the following:

• Rpm in Self-Test only
• IAC Solenoid
• Harness Circuits: IAC and VPWR
• Powertrain Control Module (PCM)

Description

The Idle Air Control (IAC) solenoid is used to control engine idle speed and dashpot functions. The IAC solenoid is mounted on the throttle body and allows air to bypass the throttle plate. The amount of air allowed to bypass is determined by the PCM and controlled by a duty cycle signal.

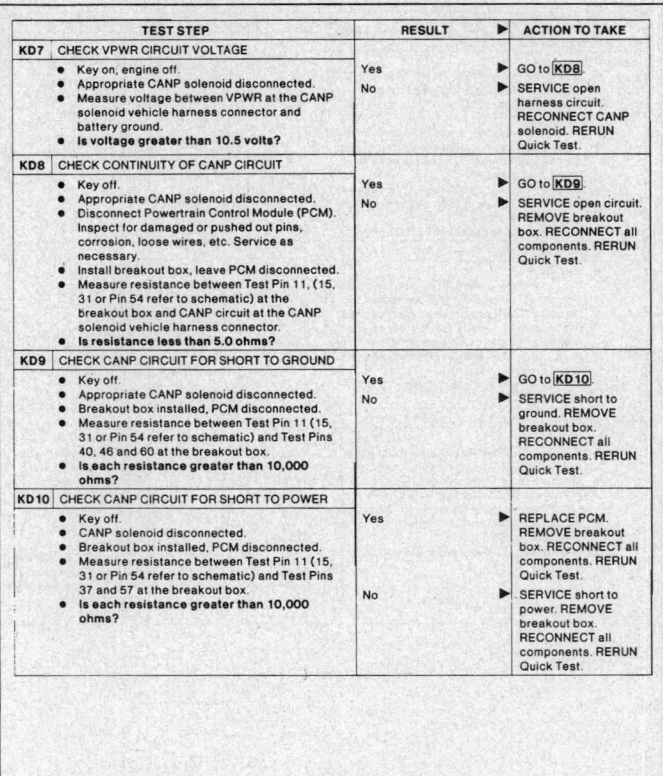

The 2.0L Probe is unique in that the IAC solenoid's ability to control airflow is more limited than the others, and the cold/high idle is controlled by a Bypass Air (BPA) valve that is built into the component. The BPA valve consists of a thermowax material that expands or contracts depending on the engine coolant temperature that passes through the valve, resulting in extra air flow through the valve when the engine is cold.

Pinpoint Test Schematics

2.0L Probe

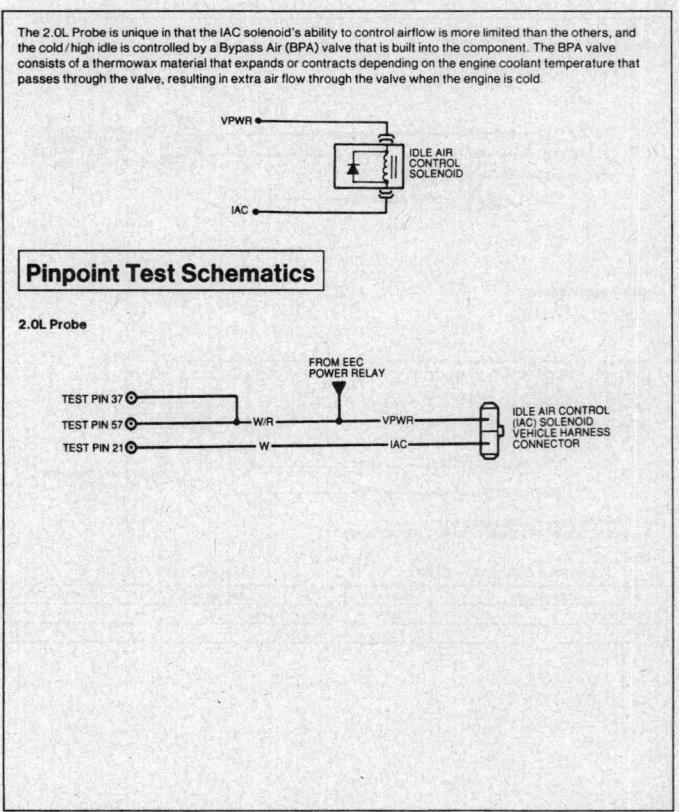

FM0159300740010X

Fig. 199 Test KE: IAC Solenoid (Part 1 of 16)

FM0159300740020X

Fig. 199 Test KE: IAC Solenoid (Part 2 of 16)

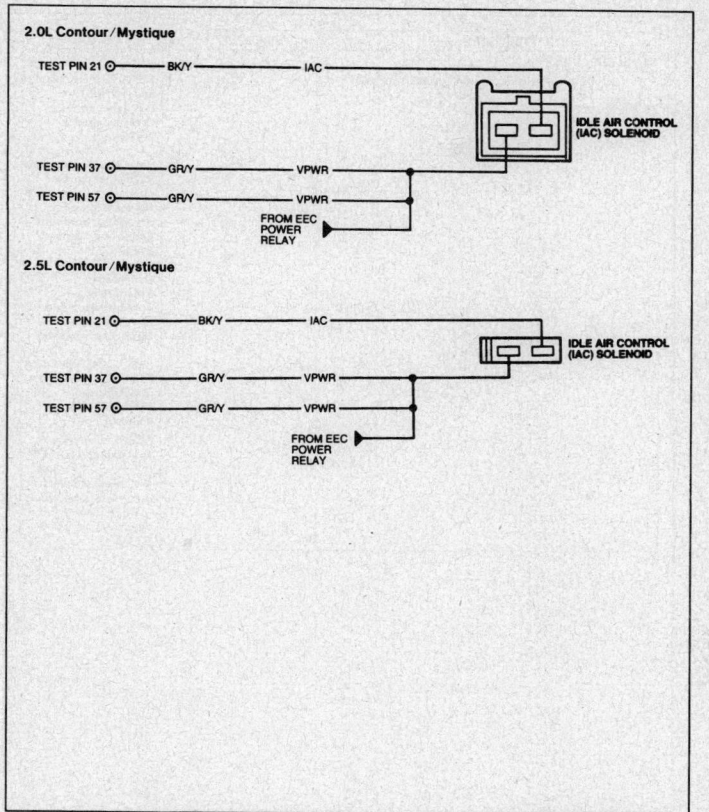

Fig. 199   Test KE: IAC Solenoid (Part 3 of 16). 1995

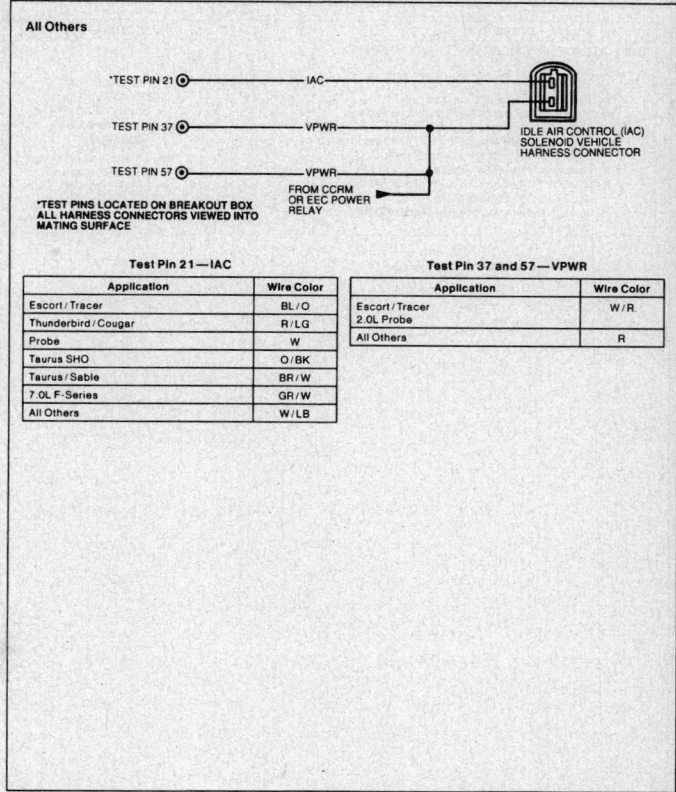

Fig. 199   Test KE: IAC Solenoid (Part 4 of 16)

TEST STEP	RESULT	▶	ACTION TO TAKE
KE1 DIAGNOSTIC TROUBLE CODE (DTC) 12/412, 16: CHECK FOR RPM DROP			
DTC 12/412 indicates that during Engine Running Self-Test, engine rpm could not be controlled within the Self-Test upper limit band. DTC 16 indicates that during Engine Running Self-Test, engine rpm was too low to perform the HO2S test. Possible causes: — Open or shorted circuit — Throttle linkage binding — Improper idle airflow set — IAC solenoid contamination — Items external to Idle Air Control system that could affect engine rpm — Damaged IAC solenoid — Damaged Powertrain Control Module (PCM). ● Key off. ● Connect engine tachometer. ● Start engine. ● Disconnect IAC harness connector. ● **Does rpm drop or stall?**	Yes No	▶ ▶	GO to **KE2**. GO to **KE3**.
KE2 CHECK FOR EGR DTCS			
● Are DTCs 31/327, 32/326/328, 33/332, 34/336/334/232 or 213 present?	Yes	▶	RECONNECT IAC solenoid. RETURN to Diagnostic Routines, appropriate Pinpoint Test.
	No	▶	GO to **KE3**.
KE3 CHECK FOR OTHER EEC DTCS			
● Are DTCs 22/126, 41/172, 42/173, 91/136 or 92/137 present?	Yes	▶	RECONNECT IAC solenoid. RETURN to Diagnostic Routines, for appropriate Pinpoint Test.
	No	▶	GO to **KE4**.

Fig. 199   Test KE: IAC Solenoid (Part 5 of 16)

TEST STEP	RESULT	▶	ACTION TO TAKE
KE4 MEASURE IAC SOLENOID RESISTANCE			
● Key off. ● IAC solenoid disconnected. ● Measure solenoid resistance. NOTE: Due to diode in solenoid, place DVOM(+) lead on VPWR pin and (−) lead on IAC pin. ● **Is resistance between 6.0 and 13.0 ohms?**	Yes No	▶ ▶	GO to **KE5**. REPLACE IAC solenoid. RERUN Quick Test.
KE5 CHECK FOR INTERNAL SHORT TO IAC SOLENOID CASE			
● Key off. ● IAC solenoid disconnected. ● Measure resistance from either IAC solenoid pin to IAC housing. ● **Is resistance greater than 10,000 ohms?**	Yes No	▶ ▶	GO to **KE6**. REPLACE IAC solenoid. RERUN Quick Test.
KE6 CHECK VPWR CIRCUIT VOLTAGE			
● Key on, engine off. ● IAC solenoid disconnected. ● Measure voltage between VPWR circuit at the IAC solenoid vehicle harness connector and battery ground. ● **Is voltage greater than 10.5 volts?**	Yes No	▶ ▶	GO to **KE7**. SERVICE open circuit. RERUN Quick Test.
KE7 CHECK IAC CIRCUIT CONTINUITY			
● Key off. ● IAC solenoid disconnected. ● Disconnect Powertrain Control Module (PCM) and inspect both 60 pin connectors for damaged or pushed out pins, corrosion, loose wires, etc. Service as necessary. ● Install breakout box, leave PCM disconnected. ● Measure resistance between Test Pin 21 at the breakout box and IAC circuit at IAC solenoid vehicle harness connector. ● **Is resistance less than 5.0 ohms?**	Yes No	▶ ▶	GO to **KE8**. SERVICE open circuit. REMOVE breakout box. RECONNECT all components. RERUN Quick Test.

FM015930074005OX

Fig. 199   Test KE: IAC Solenoid (Part 6 of 16)

FORD–Computerized Engine Controls

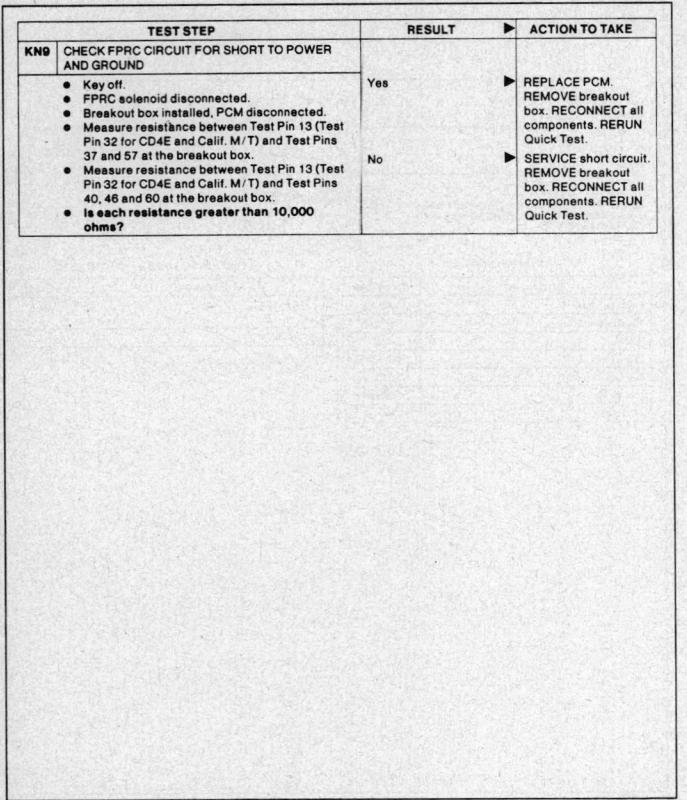

TEST STEP		RESULT	▶	ACTION TO TAKE
KN9	CHECK FPRC CIRCUIT FOR SHORT TO POWER AND GROUND			
	• Key off. • FPRC solenoid disconnected. • Breakout box installed, PCM disconnected. • Measure resistance between Test Pin 13 (Test Pin 32 for CD4E and Calif. M/T) and Test Pins 37 and 57 at the breakout box. • Measure resistance between Test Pin 13 (Test Pin 32 for CD4E and Calif. M/T) and Test Pins 40, 46 and 60 at the breakout box. • Is each resistance greater than 10,000 ohms?	Yes	▶	REPLACE PCM. REMOVE breakout box. RECONNECT all components. RERUN Quick Test.
		No	▶	SERVICE short circuit. REMOVE breakout box. RECONNECT all components. RERUN Quick Test.

FM0159300740060X

Fig. 199   Test KE: IAC Solenoid (Part 7 of 16)

TEST STEP		RESULT	▶	ACTION TO TAKE
KE11	CHECK IDLE			
	• Does engine idle speed appear normal?	Yes	▶	REMOVE IAC solenoid and INSPECT for contamination. If contamination is present, determine if solenoid is a type that can be cleaned. **No contamination present or solenoid cannot be cleaned:** REPLACE IAC solenoid. RERUN Quick Test. **Solenoid is contaminated and can be cleaned:** CLEAN as necessary RERUN Quick Test. If DTC/symptom is still present, REPLACE IAC solenoid.
		No	▶	RESET idle airflow to specification. REFER idle airflow adjustment procedure. If UNABLE to RESET idle to specification, GO to KE12.

FM0159300740070X

Fig. 199   Test KE: IAC Solenoid (Part 8 of 16)

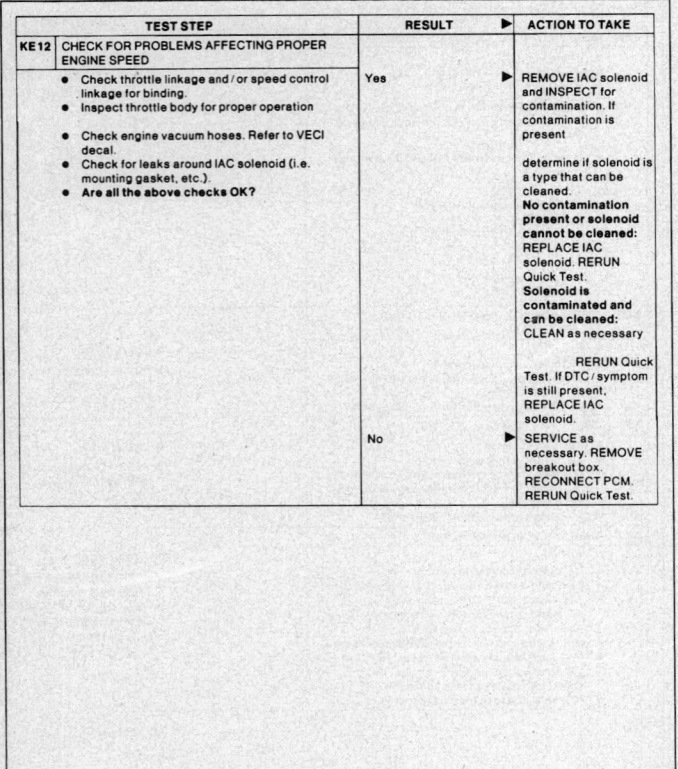

TEST STEP		RESULT	▶	ACTION TO TAKE
KE12	CHECK FOR PROBLEMS AFFECTING PROPER ENGINE SPEED			
	• Check throttle linkage and/or speed control linkage for binding. • Inspect throttle body for proper operation • Check engine vacuum hoses. Refer to VECI decal. • Check for leaks around IAC solenoid (i.e. mounting gasket, etc.). • Are all the above checks OK?	Yes	▶	REMOVE IAC solenoid and INSPECT for contamination. If contamination is present determine if solenoid is a type that can be cleaned. **No contamination present or solenoid cannot be cleaned:** REPLACE IAC solenoid. RERUN Quick Test. **Solenoid is contaminated and can be cleaned:** CLEAN as necessary RERUN Quick Test. If DTC/symptom is still present, REPLACE IAC solenoid.
		No	▶	SERVICE as necessary. REMOVE breakout box. RECONNECT PCM. RERUN Quick Test.

FM0159300740080X

Fig. 199   Test KE: IAC Solenoid (Part 9 of 16)

TEST STEP		RESULT	▶	ACTION TO TAKE
KE15	DIAGNOSTIC TROUBLE CODE (DTC) 13/411:			
	DTC 13/411 indicates that during Engine Running Self-Test, engine rpm could not be controlled within the Self-Test lower limit band. Possible causes: — Improper idle air flow set. — Vacuum leaks. — Throttle linkage binding. — Throttle plates open. — Improper ignition timing (Distributor Ignition vehicles only). — IAC solenoid contamination. — IAC circuit short to ground. — Damaged IAC solenoid. • Does engine idle speed appear normal?	Yes	▶	REMOVE IAC solenoid and INSPECT for contamination. If contamination is present, determine if solenoid is a type that can be cleaned. **No contamination present or solenoid cannot be cleaned:** REPLACE IAC solenoid. RERUN Quick Test. **Solenoid is contaminated and can be cleaned:** CLEAN as necessary RERUN Quick Test. If DTC/symptom is still present, REPLACE IAC solenoid.
		No	▶	RESET idle airflow to specification. REFER for idle airflow adjust procedure. If UNABLE to RESET idle to specification, GO to KE16.
KE16	CHECK FOR CONDITIONS AFFECTING IDLE			
	• Check engine vacuum hoses for leaks. Refer to VECI decal. • Check throttle linkage and/or speed control linkage for binding. • Check that throttle plates are closed. • Check for induction system leaks. (i.e. IAC solenoid to throttle body gasket, EGR flange gasket, loose IAC/EGR/PCV, etc.) • Check throttle body for proper operation • Verify base timing is to specification (Distributor Ignition vehicles only). Refer to VECI decal. • Verify that CANP solenoid(s) is not stuck open (if equipped). • Are all the above checks OK?	Yes	▶	GO to KE17.
		No	▶	SERVICE as necessary. RERUN Quick Test.

FM0159300740090X

Fig. 199   Test KE: IAC Solenoid (Part 10 of 16)

TEST STEP	RESULT	▶	ACTION TO TAKE
KE17 CHECK FOR INTERNAL SHORT TO IAC SOLENOID CASE			
• Key off. • Disconnect IAC solenoid. • Measure resistance from either IAC solenoid pin to IAC housing. • **Is resistance greater than 10,000 ohms?**	Yes No	▶ ▶	GO to **KE18**. REPLACE IAC solenoid. RERUN Quick Test.
KE18 CHECK IAC CIRCUIT FOR SHORT TO GROUND			
• Key off. • IAC solenoid disconnected. • Disconnect the Powertrain Control Module (PCM). Inspect for damaged or pushed out pins, corrosion, loose wires, etc. Service as necessary. • Install breakout box, leave PCM disconnected. • Measure resistance between Test Pin 21 and Test Pins 40, 46 and 60 at the breakout box. • **Are all resistances greater than 10,000 ohms?**	Yes No	▶ ▶	GO to **KE19**. SERVICE short circuit. REMOVE breakout box. RECONNECT all components. RERUN Quick Test.

FM015930074010 0X

Fig. 199 Test KE: IAC Solenoid (Part 11 of 16)

TEST STEP	RESULT	▶	ACTION TO TAKE
KE19 CHECK PCM OUTPUT			
• Key off. • Breakout box installed. • Reconnect PCM to breakout box. • Reconnect IAC solenoid. • Connect DVOM between Test Pin 21 and Test Pin 40 at the breakout box. • Start engine. • Slowly increase rpm to 3000 rpm. • **Is voltage between 3.0 and 11.5 volts?**	Yes	▶	For 2.0L Probe: GO to **KE20**. For all others: REMOVE IAC solenoid and INSPECT for contamination. If contamination is present, determine if solenoid is a type that can be cleaned. **No contamination present or solenoid cannot be cleaned:** REPLACE IAC solenoid. RERUN Quick Test. **Solenoid is contaminated and can be cleaned:** CLEAN as necessary RERUN Quick Test. If DTC symptom is still present, REPLACE IAC solenoid.
	No	▶	REPLACE PCM. REMOVE breakout box. RERUN Quick Test.

FM015930074011 0X

Fig. 199 Test KE: IAC Solenoid (Part 12 of 16)

TEST STEP	RESULT	▶	ACTION TO TAKE
KE20 CHECK FOR PROPER ENGINE COOLANT FLOW TO BYPASS AIR (BPA) VALVE			
• Verify that engine coolant is warming up properly. • Check for proper engine coolant level. • Check engine coolant hoses to and from the AIRB valve for kinks, leaks, blockage, etc. • **Are the above checks OK?**	Yes	▶	REMOVE IAC-BPA solenoid and INSPECT for contamination. If contamination is present, determine if solenoid is a type that can be cleaned. **No contamination present or solenoid cannot be cleaned:** REPLACE IAC-BPA solenoid. RERUN Quick Test. **Solenoid is contaminated and can be cleaned:** CLEAN as necessary RERUN Quick Test. If DTC/symptom is still present, REPLACE IAC-BPA solenoid.
	No	▶	SERVICE as necessary. REMOVE breakout box. RECONNECT PCM.
KE25 LACK OF HIGH IDLE WITH COLD ENGINE: VERIFY THAT IAC-BPA VALVE IS NOT STUCK CLOSED			
• Key off. • Remove the IAC-BPA valve from the engine. • When the valve is cold (room temperature), blow through the air passage and check if air flows freely. • **Does air flow freely through the valve when it is at room temperature?**	Yes No	▶ ▶	RETURN to Diagnostic Routines. REPLACE IAC-BPA valve. RE-EVALUATE symptom.

Fig. 199 Test KE: IAC Solenoid (Part 13 of 16)

TEST STEP	RESULT	▶	ACTION TO TAKE
KE30 DIAGNOSTIC TROUBLE CODE (DTC) 415: CHECK FOR AIR LEAKS			
DTC 415 indicates the IAC the adaptive learning has reached minimum learning limit. NOTE: For a brief description of a IAC adaptive strategy, refer to the front cover of this test. Possible Causes: — Air leaks. — Throttle body/linkage binding. — Damaged IAC solenoid. • Key OFF. • Inspect the entire inlet air system for leaks such as loose connection at throttle body or air cleaner, cracked or punctured ducting, etc. • **Is an air leak detected in the air inlet system?**	Yes No	▶ ▶	SERVICE as necessary. CLEAR Keep Alive Memory RERUN Quick Test. GO to **KE31**
KE31 CHECK FOR VACUUM LEAKS AT IDLE			
• Key on, engine running. • With engine at idle, listen for a vacuum leak. • Inspect IAC valve assembly, throttle body, EGR valve, vacuum hoses, and other intake connections for leaks or loose connection. • **Is a fault indicated?**	Yes No	▶ ▶	SERVICE as necessary. CLEAR Keep Alive Memory RERUN Quick Test. GO to **KE32**
KE32 INSPECT THROTTLE BODY AND LINKAGE			
• Key off. • Disconnect linkage from throttle body. • Exercise both throttle plate and throttle body linkage separately while looking for binding or interference. • **Is a fault indicated?**	Yes No	▶ ▶	SERVICE as necessary. CLEAR Keep Alive Memory RERUN Quick Test. GO to **KE33**.

FM015930074013 0X

Fig. 199 Test KE: IAC Solenoid (Part 14 of 16)

TEST STEP		RESULT	▶	ACTION TO TAKE
KE33 CHECK IDLE SPEED				
• Key off. • Install a tachometer. • Check engine rpm while engine is at operating temperature and at idle.		Yes	▶	CLEAR Keep Alive Memory CHECK idle speed and ADJUST if applicable RERUN Quick Test.
Application	**RPM**	No	▶	CLEAR Keep Alive Memory
Ranger / Explorer	Auto 800 ± 50 Drive 720 ± 50 Neutral Manual 750 ± 50 Neutral			RESET idle speed to specification
• **Is idle rpm within range?**				If unable to reset idle or system is nonadjustable, REPLACE IAC solenoid or throttle body assembly as necessary. RERUN Quick Test.
KE35 DIAGNOSTIC TROUBLE CODE (DTC) 416: CHECK FOR A PLUGGED AIR FILTER				
DTC 416 indicates the IAC adaptive learning has reached the maximum learning limit. NOTE: For a brief description of the IAC adaptive strategy, refer to the front cover of this test.		Yes	▶	SERVICE as necessary. CLEAR Keep Alive Memory RERUN Quick Test.
Possible Causes: — Plugged air filter. — Sludged or damaged throttle body. — Sludged or damaged IAC solenoid. • Key OFF. • Remove air filter and verify it is not plugged by excessive dirt, water, snow, debris, etc. • **Is the air filter plugged?**		No	▶	GO to KE36
KE36 CHECK IAC SOLENOID AND THROTTLE BODY FOR DAMAGED OR CONTAMINATION				
• Key OFF. • Inspect IAC and throttle body for obvious damage. Verify that throttle plate moves without binding and is not bent. • Inspect IAC and throttle body for excessive contamination. REFER to the appropriate cleaning procedure and clean if applicable. • **Was any damage or excessive contamination found?**		Yes	▶	SERVICE as necessary. CLEAR Keep Alive Memory RERUN Quick Test.
		No	▶	GO to KE37.

FM0159300740140X

Fig. 199 Test KE: IAC Solenoid (Part 15 of 16)

TEST STEP		RESULT	▶	ACTION TO TAKE
KE37 CHECK IDLE SPEED				
• Key off. • Install a tachometer. • Check engine rpm while engine is at operating temperature and at idle.		Yes	▶	**Idle is OK with no drive symptom:** Testing complete CLEAR Keep Alive Memory RERUN Quick Test **Idle is OK with a drive symptom:** GO to Diagnostic Routines, and follow chart for symptom.
Application	**RPM**			
Ranger / Explorer	Auto 800 ± 50 Drive 720 ± 50 Neutral Manual 750 ± 50 Neutral	No	▶	GO to Diagnostic Routines, and follow chart for the idle concern.
• **Is idle rpm within range?**				

FM0159300740150X

Fig. 199 Test KE: IAC Solenoid (Part 16 of 16)

Note

You should enter this Pinpoint Test only when you have been directed here from Diagnostic Routines,

Remember

This Pinpoint Test is intended to diagnose only the following:

• Harness circuits: LFC, HFC, LFC Power-To-Fan, HFC Power-To-Fan, IGN Start / Run and GND.
• LFC Relay
• HFC Relay
• Cooling Fan
• Powertrain Control Module (PCM) (12A650)

Description

The PCM determines engine cooling fan requirements and controls the fan operation through the LFC and HFC outputs. The HFC relay is a normally open relay. The LFC relay is normally closed for the Escort / Tracer and normally open for the Probe.

Both Fans Off

The HFC output is off. For the Escort / Tracer, the LFC output is on (grounded) which opens the normally closed relay. For the Probe, the LFC output is off.

Low Speed Fan On

For the Escort / Tracer, the LFC output is turned off which closes the normally closed LFC relay. For the Probe, the LFC output is turned on closing the normally open LFC relay. For both applications, the HFC output is off, and B(+) is supplied to the LFC relay through the HFC relay.

High Speed Fan On

The HFC output is on which closes the HFC relay. With the HFC relay contacts closed, B(+) is not supplied to the LFC relay preventing both fan speeds from being activated at the same time.

FM015930074101OX

Fig. 200 Test KF: LFC/HFC (Part 1 of 11). 1993

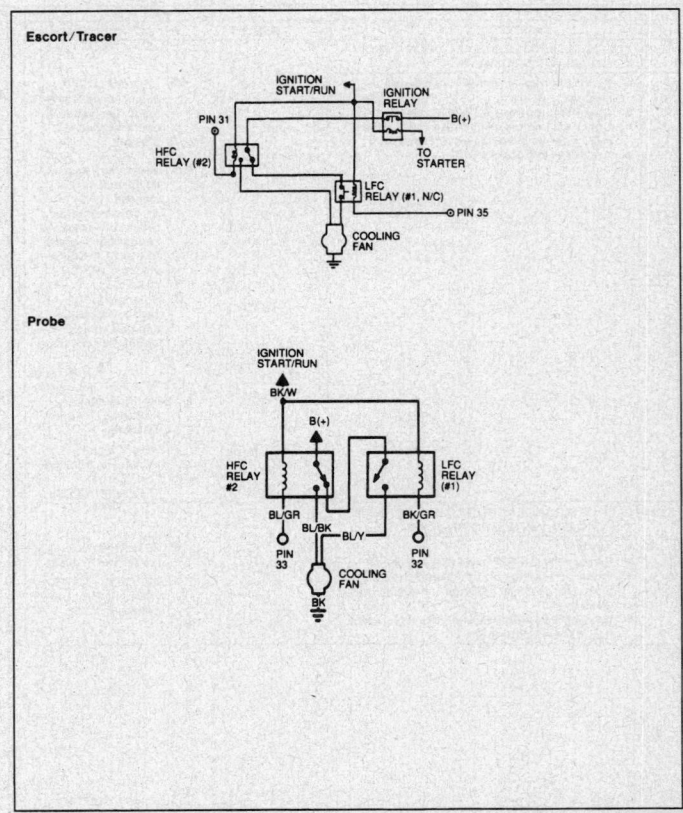

FM015930074102OX

Fig. 200 Test KF: LFC/HFC (Part 2 of 11). 1993

Pinpoint Test Schematic

Escort / Tracer

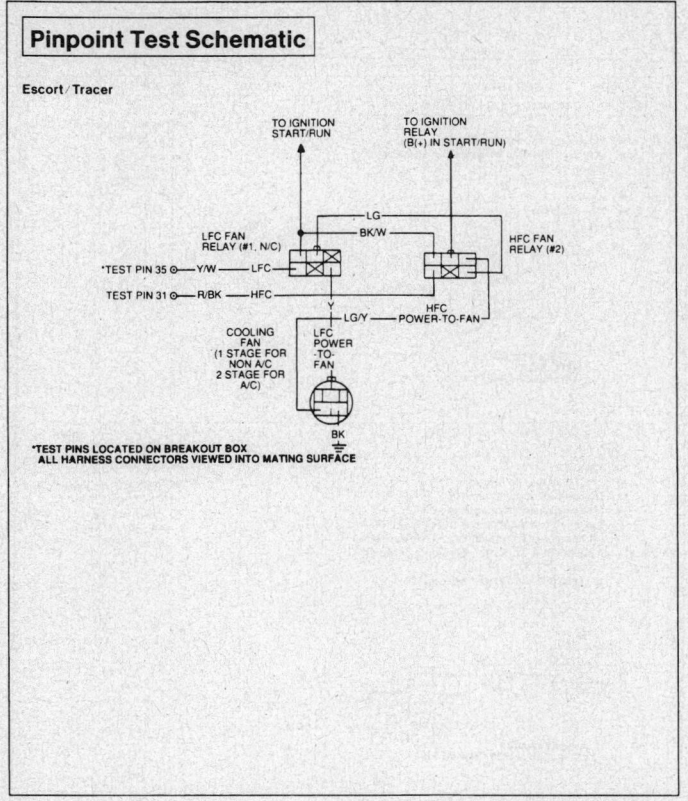

TO IGNITION START/RUN

TO IGNITION RELAY (B(+) IN START/RUN)

LFC FAN RELAY (#1, N/C)

HFC FAN RELAY (#2)

LG

BK/W

*TEST PIN 35 — Y/W — LFC

TEST PIN 31 — R/BK — HFC

Y

LG/Y

HFC POWER-TO-FAN

COOLING FAN (1 STAGE FOR NON A/C 2 STAGE FOR A/C)

LFC POWER -TO -FAN

BK

*TEST PINS LOCATED ON BREAKOUT BOX
ALL HARNESS CONNECTORS VIEWED INTO MATING SURFACE

1993 Powertrain Control Emissions Diagnosis July, 1992

FM0159300741030X

Fig. 200 Test KF: LFC/HFC (Part 3 of 11). 1993

TEST STEP		RESULT	▶	ACTION TO TAKE
KF1	DIAGNOSTIC TROUBLE CODE (DTC) 563 or 564: CHECK FOR IGNITION START/RUN CIRCUIT VOLTAGE AT LFC/HFC RELAY			
	DTC 563 indicates an HFC primary circuit failure. DTC 564 indicates an LFC primary circuit failure. Possible causes are: — Open or shorted circuit. — Damaged fan relay. — Damaged Powertrain Control Module (PCM).	Yes	▶	GO to **KF2**.
		No	▶	VERIFY integrity of fuse / fuse link for IGN Start / Run voltage supply to LFC/HFC relay. If OK, SERVICE open circuit. RECONNECT LFC/HFC relay. RERUN Quick Test.

NOTE: During diagnosis, use the chart below to determine the correct pin number, circuit and relay being tested.

Code	Circuit	Test Pin Number		Fan Relay
		Escort/Tracer	Probe	
563	HFC	31	33	HFC (2)
564	LFC	35	32	LFC (1)

TEST STEP		RESULT	▶	ACTION TO TAKE
	• Key off. • Disconnect LFC or HFC relay. • Key on. • Measure voltage between IGN Start / Run circuit at the LFC/HFC relay vehicle harness connector and chassis ground. • **Is voltage greater than 10.5 volts?**			
KF2	ENTER OUTPUT STATE DIAGNOSTIC TEST MODE (DTM)			
	NOTE: Use VOM / DVOM for this Step. • Key off, wait 10 seconds. • DVOM on 20 volt scale. • Disconnect electrical connector on the speed control servo, if equipped. • Connect DVOM negative test lead to STO at the Data Link Connector (DLC) and positive test lead to the battery positive post. • Jumper STI to SIG RTN at the Data Link Connector. • Perform Key On Engine Off Self-Test until the completion of the Continuous Memory DTCs. • DVOM will indicate less than 1.0 volt when test is complete. • Depress and release throttle. • **Does voltage increase to greater than 10.5 volts?**	Yes	▶	REMAIN in Output State DTM. GO to **KF3**.
		No	▶	DEPRESS throttle to WOT and RELEASE. If STO voltage does not go high, leave equipment hooked up and GO to Pinpoint Test Step **QC2**.

FM0159300741040X

Fig. 200 Test KF: LFC/HFC (Part 4 of 11). 1993

TEST STEP		RESULT	▶	ACTION TO TAKE
KF3	CHECK FOR LFC/HFC CIRCUIT CYCLING			
	• Still in Output State DTM. • LFC or HFC relay disconnected. • DVOM on 20 volt scale. • Connect DVOM positive test lead to the IGN Start / Run circuit and the negative test lead to the LFC or HFC circuit at the LFC/HFC relay vehicle harness connector. • Depress and release throttle to cycle outputs off. • While observing DVOM, depress throttle again. For LFC, wait until the MIL flashes once (10 seconds). For HFC, wait until the MIL flashes twice (15 seconds). Release throttle. The LFC or HFC output is now "on". To cycle "off", depress and release throttle. • **Does voltage cycle high and low (about 1.0 volt change)?**	Yes	▶	REPLACE LFC or HFC relay. REMOVE jumper. RERUN Quick Test.
		No	▶	REMOVE jumper. GO to **KF4**.
KF4	CHECK CONTINUITY OF LFC/HFC CIRCUIT			
	• Key off. • LFC or HFC relay disconnected. • Disconnect Powertrain Control Module (PCM). Inspect for damaged or pushed out pins, corrosion, loose wires, etc. Service as necessary. • Install breakout box, leave PCM disconnected. • For DTC 563: — Measure resistance between applicable Test Pin at the breakout box and HFC circuit at the HFC relay vehicle harness connector. • For DTC 564: — Measure resistance between applicable Test Pin at the breakout box and LFC circuit at the LFC relay vehicle harness connector. • **Is resistance less than 5.0 ohms?**	Yes	▶	GO to **KF5**.
		No	▶	SERVICE open circuit. REMOVE breakout box. RECONNECT all components. RERUN Quick Test.
KF5	CHECK LFC/HFC CIRCUIT FOR SHORT TO POWER			
	• Key on. • Breakout box installed, PCM disconnected. • LFC or HFC relay disconnected. • Measure voltage between applicable Test Pin (HFC or LFC) at the breakout box and battery negative post. • **Is voltage less than 1.0 volts?**	Yes	▶	GO to **KF6**.
		No	▶	SERVICE short circuit. REMOVE breakout box. RECONNECT all components. RERUN Quick Test. If DTC is still present, REPLACE PCM.

FM0159300741050X

Fig. 200 Test KF: LFC/HFC (Part 5 of 11). 1993

TEST STEP		RESULT	▶	ACTION TO TAKE
KF6	CHECK LFC/HFC CIRCUIT FOR SHORT TO GROUND			
	• Key off. • Breakout box installed, PCM disconnected. • LFC or HFC relay disconnected. • Measure resistance between applicable Test Pin (LFC or HFC) and Test Pins 40 and 60 at the breakout box. • **Is resistance greater than 10,000 ohms?**	Yes	▶	REPLACE PCM. REMOVE breakout box. RECONNECT all components. RERUN Quick Test.
		No	▶	SERVICE short circuit. REMOVE breakout box. RECONNECT all components. RERUN Quick Test.
KF10	LOW SPEED AND / OR HIGH SPEED COOLING FAN DOES NOT OPERATE: CHECK FOR VOLTAGE TO LFC RELAY			
	• Key off. • Disconnect LFC relay. • Key on. • Measure voltage from HFC RELAY pin at the LFC relay vehicle harness connector and battery negative post. • **Is voltage greater than 10.5 volts?**	Yes	▶	GO to **KF13**.
		No	▶	GO to **KF11**.

FROM HFC RELAY

ESCORT/TRACER
LFC RELAY
VEHICLE HARNESS
CONNECTOR

FM0159300741060X

Fig. 200 Test KF: LFC/HFC (Part 6 of 11). 1993

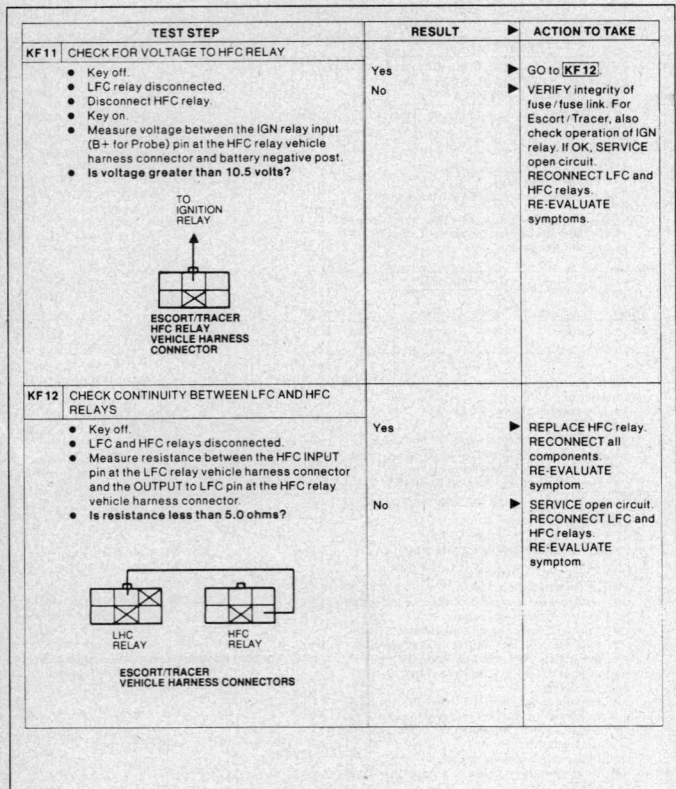

TEST STEP	RESULT	▶	ACTION TO TAKE
KF11 CHECK FOR VOLTAGE TO HFC RELAY • Key off. • LFC relay disconnected. • Disconnect HFC relay. • Key on. • Measure voltage between the IGN relay input (B+ for Probe) pin at the HFC relay vehicle harness connector and battery negative post. • **Is voltage greater than 10.5 volts?**	Yes No	▶ ▶	GO to **KF12**. VERIFY integrity of fuse / fuse link. For Escort / Tracer, also check operation of IGN relay. If OK, SERVICE open circuit. RECONNECT LFC and HFC relays. RE-EVALUATE symptoms.
KF12 CHECK CONTINUITY BETWEEN LFC AND HFC RELAYS • Key off. • LFC and HFC relays disconnected. • Measure resistance between the HFC INPUT pin at the LFC relay vehicle harness connector and the OUTPUT to LFC pin at the HFC relay vehicle harness connector. • **Is resistance less than 5.0 ohms?**	Yes No	▶ ▶	REPLACE HFC relay. RECONNECT all components. RE-EVALUATE symptom. SERVICE open circuit. RECONNECT LFC and HFC relays. RE-EVALUATE symptom.

FM0159300741070X

Fig. 200   Test KF: LFC/HFC (Part 7 of 11). 1993

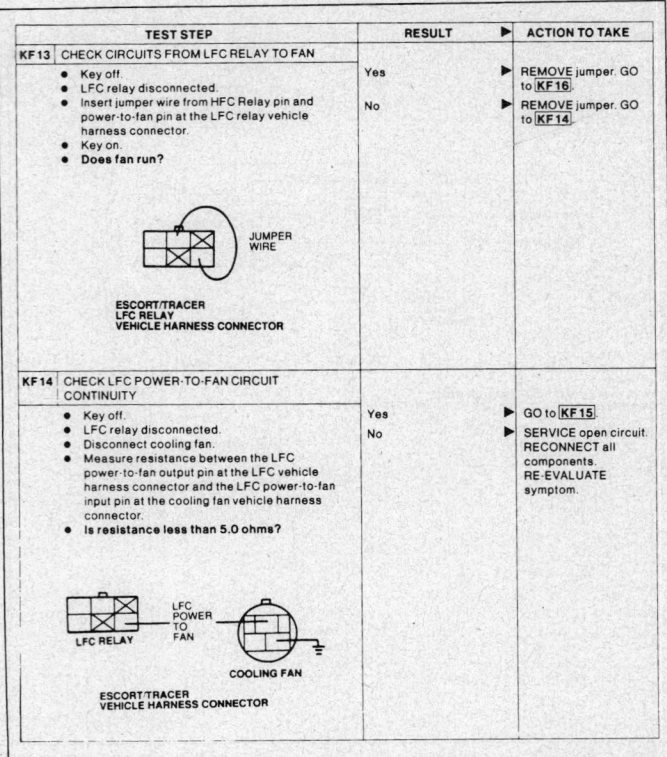

TEST STEP	RESULT	▶	ACTION TO TAKE
KF13 CHECK CIRCUITS FROM LFC RELAY TO FAN • Key off. • LFC relay disconnected. • Insert jumper wire from HFC Relay pin and power-to-fan pin at the LFC relay vehicle harness connector. • Key on. • **Does fan run?**	Yes No	▶ ▶	REMOVE jumper. GO to **KF16**. REMOVE jumper. GO to **KF14**.
KF14 CHECK LFC POWER-TO-FAN CIRCUIT CONTINUITY • Key off. • LFC relay disconnected. • Disconnect cooling fan. • Measure resistance between the LFC power-to-fan output pin at the LFC vehicle harness connector and the LFC power-to-fan input pin at the cooling fan vehicle harness connector. • **Is resistance less than 5.0 ohms?**	Yes No	▶ ▶	GO to **KF15**. SERVICE open circuit. RECONNECT all components. RE-EVALUATE symptom.

FM0159300741080X

Fig. 200   Test KF: LFC/HFC (Part 8 of 11). 1993

TEST STEP	RESULT	▶	ACTION TO TAKE
KF15 CHECK COOLING FAN GROUND CIRCUIT • Key off. • LFC relay disconnected. • Cooling fan disconnected. • Measure resistance between GND circuit at the cooling fan vehicle harness connector and battery negative post. • **Is resistance less than 5.0 ohms?**	Yes No	▶ ▶	REPLACE cooling fan. RECONNECT all components. RE-EVALUATE symptom. SERVICE open circuit. RECONNECT all components. RE-EVALUATE symptom.
KF16 CHECK CIRCUITS FROM HFC RELAY TO FAN • Key off. • LFC relay disconnected. • Disconnect Powertrain Control Module (PCM). Inspect for damaged or pushed out pins, corrosion, loose wires, etc. Service as necessary. • Install breakout box, leave PCM disconnected. **For Escort / Tracer:** — Insert a jumper wire between Test Pin 31 and Test Pin 40 at the breakout box. **For Probe:** — Insert a jumper wire between Test Pin 33 and Test Pin 40 at the breakout box. • Key on. • **Does fan run at high speed?**	Yes No	▶ ▶	REPLACE LFC relay. REMOVE breakout box. RE-EVALUATE symptom. REMOVE jumper. GO to **KF17**.

FM0159300741090X

Fig. 200   Test KF: LFC/HFC (Part 9 of 11). 1993

TEST STEP	RESULT	▶	ACTION TO TAKE
KF17 CHECK HFC POWER-TO-FAN VOLTAGE AT FAN • Key off. • Breakout box installed, PCM disconnected. • LFC relay disconnected. • Disconnect cooling fan. • Again insert a jumper wire between Test Pin 31 (Escort / Tracer) or Test Pin 33 (Probe) and Test Pin 40 at the breakout box. • Key on. • Measure voltage between HFC power-to-fan circuit at the cooling fan vehicle harness connector and battery negative post. • **Is voltage greater than 10.5 volts?**	Yes No	▶ ▶	REPLACE cooling fan. REMOVE breakout box. RECONNECT all components. RE-EVALUATE symptom. REMOVE jumper. GO to **KF18**.
KF18 CHECK HFC POWER-TO-FAN CIRCUIT CONTINUITY • Key off. • Breakout box installed, PCM disconnected. • LFC relay disconnected. • Cooling fan disconnected. • Disconnect HFC relay. • Measure resistance between the HFC power-to-fan output pin at the HFC vehicle harness connector and the HFC power-to-fan input pin at the cooling fan vehicle harness connector. • **Is resistance less than 5.0 ohms?**	Yes No	▶ ▶	REPLACE HFC relay. REMOVE breakout box. RECONNECT all components. RE-EVALUATE symptom. SERVICE open circuit. REMOVE breakout box. RECONNECT all components. RE-EVALUATE symptom.

Fig. 200   Test KF: LFC/HFC (Part 10 of 11). 1993

TEST STEP	RESULT	▶	ACTION TO TAKE
KF25 LOW SPEED OR HIGH SPEED COOLING FAN ALWAYS ON: VERIFY IGNITION RELAY IS OPENING			
NOTE: Verify that A/C is off during testing. ● For Probe, go directly to **KF26**. ● Is cooling fan always on with key off, but operating normally with key on?	Yes	▶	VERIFY that IGN relay contacts are not always closed. If OK, CHECK circuit from IGN relay to fan relay(s) for short to B(+).
	No	▶	GO to **KF26**.
KF26 CHECK FOR LFC RELAY ALWAYS CLOSED	Yes	▶	GO to **KF27**.
● Key off. ● Disconnect LFC relay. ● Key on. ● **Does fan continue to run?**	No	▶	REPLACE LFC relay. RE-EVALUATE symptom.
KF27 CHECK HFC RELAY	Yes	▶	GO to **KF28**.
● Key off. ● LFC relay disconnected. ● Disconnect HFC relay. ● Key on. ● **Does fan continue to run?**	No	▶	REPLACE HFC relay. RECONNECT LFC relay. RE-EVALUATE symptom.
KF28 CHECK LFC POWER-TO-FAN CIRCUIT FOR SHORT TO POWER			
● Key off. ● LFC and HFC relay disconnected. ● Disconnect cooling fan. ● Key on. ● Measure voltage between LFC power-to-fan circuit at the cooling fan vehicle harness connector and battery negative post. ● **Is voltage greater than 1.0 volt?**	Yes	▶	SERVICE short to power in LFC power to fan circuit. RECONNECT all components. RE-EVALUATE symptom.
	No	▶	SERVICE short to power in HFC power-to-fan circuit. RECONNECT all components. RE-EVALUATE symptom.

LFC POWER-TO-FAN

HFC POWER-TO-FAN

ESCORT/TRACER COOLING FAN VEHICLE HARNESS CONNECTOR

FM0159300741110X

Fig. 200 Test KF: LFC/HFC (Part 11 of 11). 1993

Note

You should enter this Pinpoint Test only when you have been directed here from Diagnostic Routines,

Remember

This Pinpoint Test is intended to diagnose only the following:

● Harness circuits: LFC, HFC, LFC Power-To-Fan, HFC Power-To-Fan, IGN Start/Run and GND.
● LFC Relay
● HFC Relay
● Cooling Fan
● Powertrain Control Module (PCM) (12A650)

Description

The PCM determines engine cooling fan requirements and controls the fan operation through the LFC and HFC outputs. The HFC relay is a normally open relay. The LFC relay is normally closed for the Escort/Tracer and normally open for the Probe.

Both Fans Off

The HFC output is off. For the Escort/Tracer, the LFC output is on (grounded) which opens the normally closed relay. For the Probe, the LFC output is off.

Low Speed Fan On

For the Escort/Tracer, the LFC output is turned off which closes the normally closed LFC relay. For the Probe, the LFC output is turned on closing the normally open LFC relay. For both applications, the HFC output is off, and B(+) is supplied to the LFC relay through the HFC relay.

High Speed Fan On

The HFC output is on which closes the HFC relay. With the HFC relay contacts closed, B(+) is not supplied to the LFC relay preventing both fan speeds from being activated at the same time.

Fig. 201 Test KF: LFC/HFC (Part 1 of 17). 1994–95

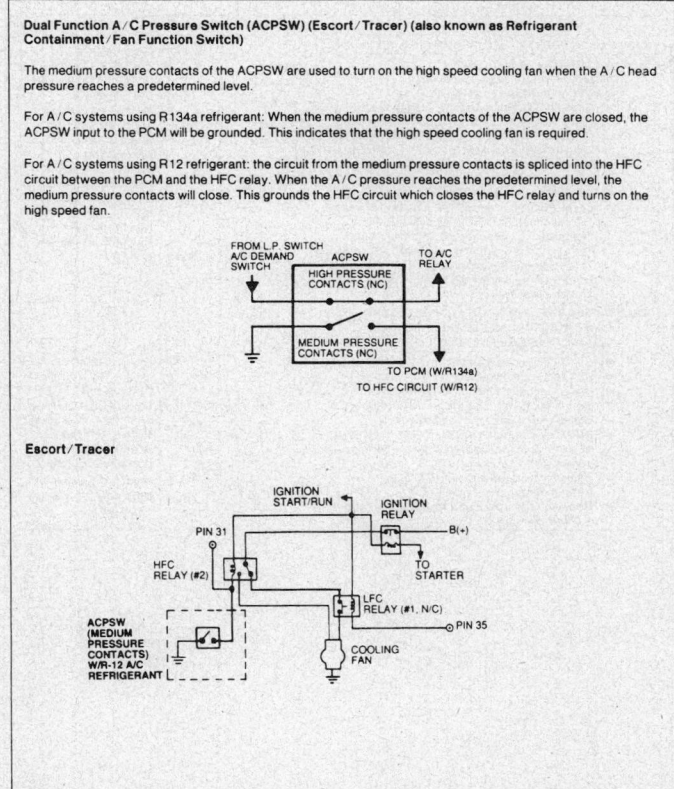

Dual Function A/C Pressure Switch (ACPSW) (Escort/Tracer) (also known as Refrigerant Containment/Fan Function Switch)

The medium pressure contacts of the ACPSW are used to turn on the high speed cooling fan when the A/C head pressure reaches a predetermined level.

For A/C systems using R134a refrigerant: When the medium pressure contacts of the ACPSW are closed, the ACPSW input to the PCM will be grounded. This indicates that the high speed cooling fan is required.

For A/C systems using R12 refrigerant: the circuit from the medium pressure contacts is spliced into the HFC circuit between the PCM and the HFC relay. When the A/C pressure reaches the predetermined level, the medium pressure contacts will close. This grounds the HFC circuit which closes the HFC relay and turns on the high speed fan.

FM0159400742020X

Fig. 201 Test KF: LFC/HFC (Part 2 of 17). 1994–95

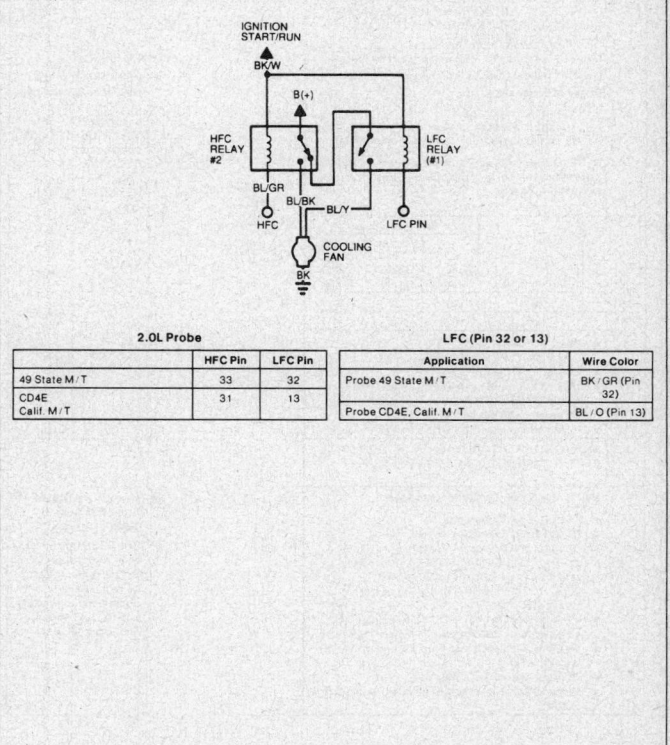

Probe

2.0L Probe	HFC Pin	LFC Pin
49 State M/T	33	32
CD4E	31	13
Calif. M/T		

LFC (Pin 32 or 13)	
Application	Wire Color
Probe 49 State M/T	BK/GR (Pin 32)
Probe CD4E, Calif. M/T	BL/O (Pin 13)

FM0159400742030X

Fig. 201 Test KF: LFC/HFC (Part 3 of 17). 1994–95

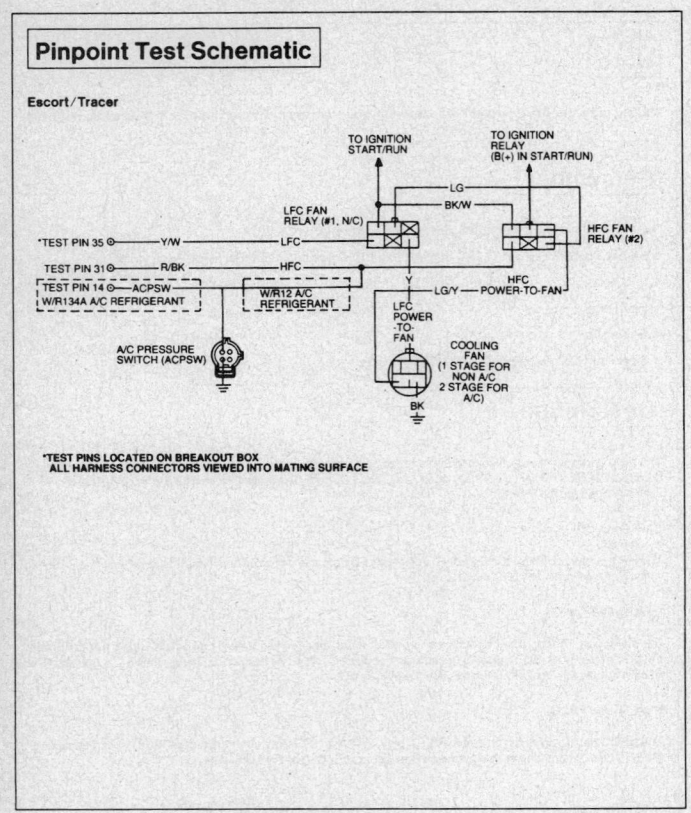

Fig. 201 Test KF: LFC/HFC (Part 4 of 17). 1994–95

FM015940074204OX

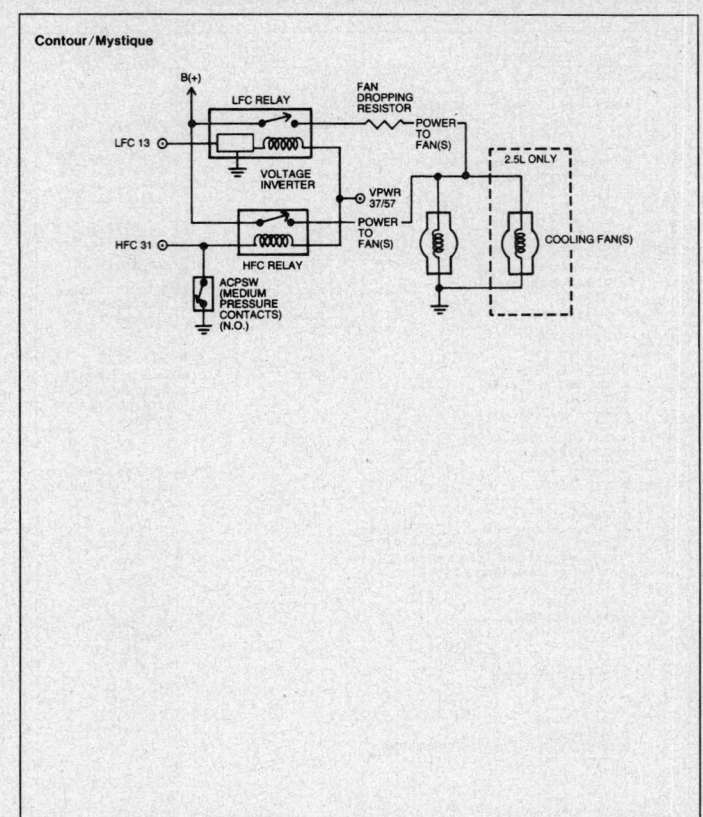

Fig. 201 Test KF: LFC/HFC (Part 5 of 17). 1995

FM015950074217OX

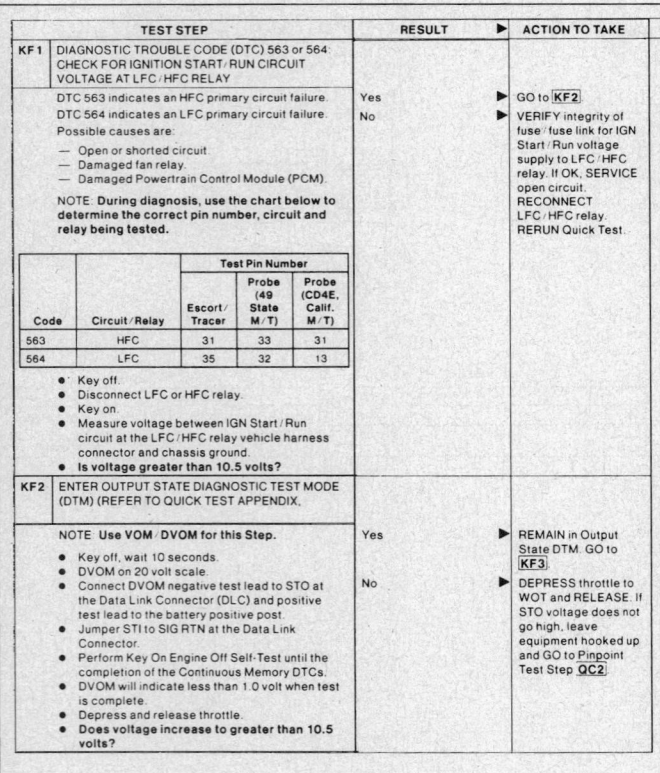

Fig. 201 Test KF: LFC/HFC (Part 6 of 17). 1994–95

FM015940074205OX

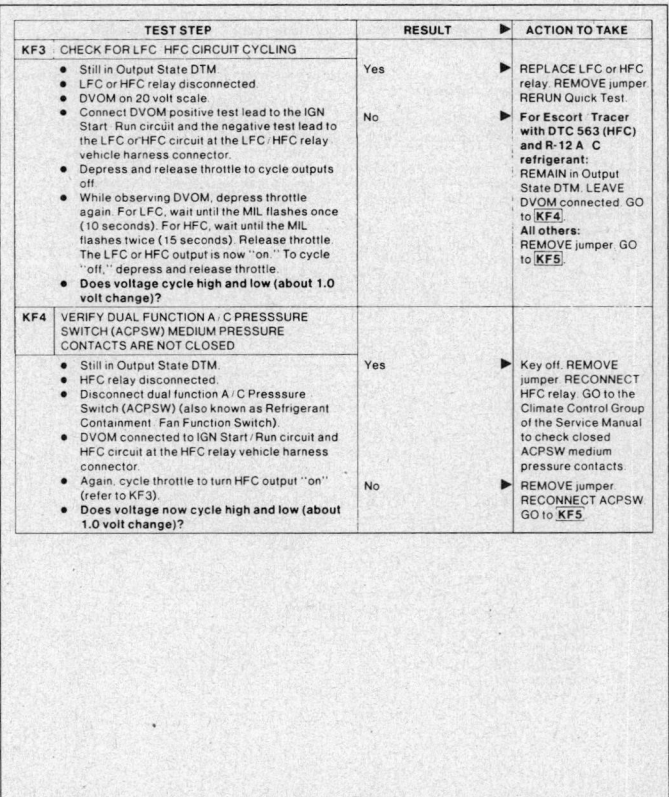

Fig. 201 Test KF: LFC/HFC (Part 7 of 17). 1994–95

FM015940074206OX

TEST STEP	RESULT	▶	ACTION TO TAKE

KF5 CHECK CONTINUITY OF LFC HFC CIRCUIT
• Key off.
• LFC or HFC relay disconnected.
• Disconnect Powertrain Control Module (PCM). Inspect for damaged or pushed out pins, corrosion, loose wires, etc. Service as necessary.
• Install breakout box, leave PCM disconnected.
• **For DTC 563:**
  — Measure resistance between applicable Test Pin at the breakout box and HFC circuit at the HFC relay vehicle harness connector.
• **For DTC 564:**
  — Measure resistance between applicable Test Pin at the breakout box and LFC circuit at the LFC relay vehicle harness connector.
• **Is resistance less than 5.0 ohms?**
	Yes
	No
		▶
		▶
			GO to KF6.
			SERVICE open circuit. REMOVE breakout box. RECONNECT all components. RERUN Quick Test.

KF6 CHECK LFC HFC CIRCUIT FOR SHORT TO POWER • Key on. • Breakout box installed, PCM disconnected. • LFC or HFC relay disconnected. • Measure voltage between applicable Test Pin (HFC or LFC) at the breakout box and battery negative post. • **Is voltage less than 1.0 volts?**	Yes No	▶ ▶	GO to KF7. SERVICE short circuit. REMOVE breakout box. RECONNECT all components. RERUN Quick Test. If DTC is still present, REPLACE PCM
KF7 CHECK LFC HFC CIRCUIT FOR SHORT TO GROUND • Key off. • Breakout box installed, PCM disconnected. • LFC or HFC relay disconnected. • Measure resistance between applicable Test Pin (LFC or HFC) and Test Pins 40 and 60 at the breakout box. • **Is resistance greater than 10,000 ohms?**	Yes No	▶ ▶	REPLACE PCM. REMOVE breakout box. RECONNECT all components. RERUN Quick Test. SERVICE short circuit. REMOVE breakout box. RECONNECT all components. RERUN Quick Test.

Fig. 201   Test KF: LFC/HFC (Part 8 of 17). 1994–95

FM0159400742070X

TEST STEP	RESULT	▶	ACTION TO TAKE
KF10 LOW SPEED AND/OR HIGH SPEED COOLING FAN DOES NOT OPERATE: CHECK FOR VOLTAGE TO LFC RELAY • Key off. • Disconnect LFC relay. • Key on. • Measure voltage from HFC RELAY pin at the LFC relay vehicle harness connector and battery negative post. • **Is voltage greater than 10.5 volts?**	Yes No	▶ ▶	GO to KF13. GO to KF11.
KF11 CHECK FOR VOLTAGE TO HFC RELAY • Key off. • LFC relay disconnected. • Disconnect HFC relay. • Key on. • Measure voltage between the IGN relay input (B+ for Probe) pin at the HFC relay vehicle harness connector and battery negative post. • **Is voltage greater than 10.5 volts?**	Yes No	▶ ▶	GO to KF12. VERIFY integrity of fuse/fuse link. For Escort/Tracer, also check operation of IGN relay. If OK, SERVICE open circuit. RECONNECT LFC and HFC relays. RE-EVALUATE symptoms.

Fig. 201   Test KF: LFC/HFC (Part 9 of 17). 1994–95

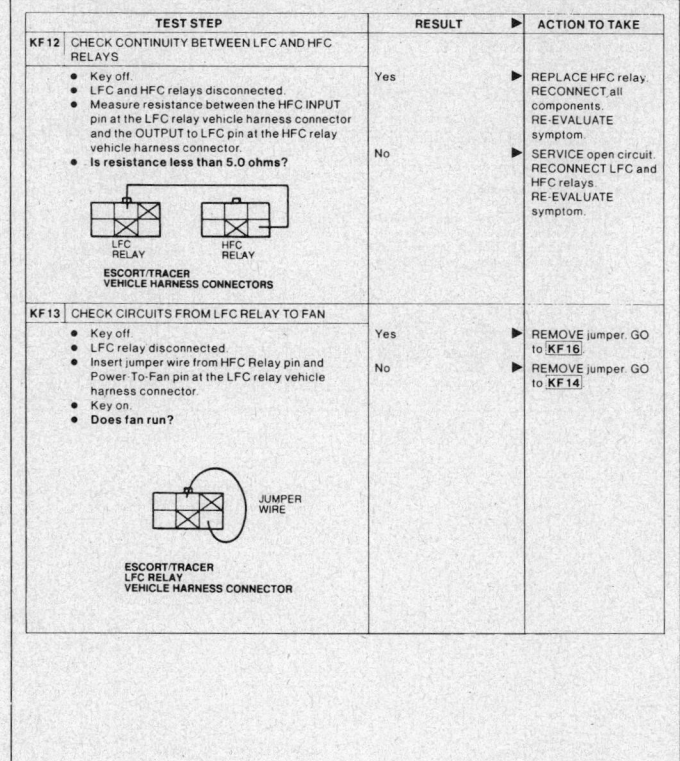

TEST STEP	RESULT	▶	ACTION TO TAKE
KF12 CHECK CONTINUITY BETWEEN LFC AND HFC RELAYS • Key off. • LFC and HFC relays disconnected. • Measure resistance between the HFC INPUT pin at the LFC relay vehicle harness connector and the OUTPUT to LFC pin at the HFC relay vehicle harness connector. • **Is resistance less than 5.0 ohms?**	Yes No	▶ ▶	REPLACE HFC relay. RECONNECT all components. RE-EVALUATE symptom. SERVICE open circuit. RECONNECT LFC and HFC relays. RE-EVALUATE symptom.
KF13 CHECK CIRCUITS FROM LFC RELAY TO FAN • Key off. • LFC relay disconnected. • Insert jumper wire from HFC Relay pin and Power-To-Fan pin at the LFC relay vehicle harness connector. • Key on. • **Does fan run?**	Yes No	▶ ▶	REMOVE jumper. GO to KF16. REMOVE jumper. GO to KF14.

Fig. 201   Test KF: LFC/HFC (Part 10 of 17). 1994–95

FM0159400742090X

TEST STEP	RESULT	▶	ACTION TO TAKE
KF14 CHECK LFC POWER-TO-FAN CIRCUIT CONTINUITY • Key off. • LFC relay disconnected. • Disconnect cooling fan. • Measure resistance between the LFC Power-To-Fan output pin at the LFC vehicle harness connector and the LFC Power-To-Fan input pin at the cooling fan vehicle harness connector. • **Is resistance less than 5.0 ohms?**	Yes No	▶ ▶	GO to KF15. SERVICE open circuit. RECONNECT all components. RE-EVALUATE symptom.
KF15 CHECK COOLING FAN GROUND CIRCUIT • Key off. • LFC relay disconnected. • Cooling fan disconnected. • Measure resistance between GND circuit at the cooling fan vehicle harness connector and battery negative post. • **Is resistance less than 5.0 ohms?**	Yes No	▶ ▶	REPLACE cooling fan. RECONNECT all components. RE-EVALUATE symptom. SERVICE open circuit. RECONNECT all components. RE-EVALUATE symptom.

Fig. 201   Test KF: LFC/HFC (Part 11 of 17). 1994–95

FM0159400742100X

TEST STEP	RESULT	►	ACTION TO TAKE
KF16 CHECK CIRCUITS FROM HFC RELAY TO FAN • Key off. • LFC relay disconnected. • Disconnect Powertrain Control Module (PCM). Inspect for damaged or pushed out pins, corrosion, loose wires, etc. Service as necessary. • Install breakout box, leave PCM disconnected. **For Escort / Tracer:** — Insert a jumper wire between HFC Test Pin 31 and Test Pin 40 at the breakout box. **For Probe:** — Insert a jumper wire between HFC Test Pin (33 for 49 state M / T, 31 for CD4E and Calif. M / T) and Test Pin 40 at the breakout box. • Key on. • **Does fan run at high speed?**	Yes No	► ►	REPLACE LFC relay. REMOVE breakout box. RE-EVALUATE symptom. REMOVE jumper. GO to **KF17**.
KF17 CHECK HFC POWER-TO-FAN VOLTAGE AT FAN • Key off. • Breakout box installed, PCM disconnected. • LFC relay disconnected. • Disconnect cooling fan. • Again insert a jumper wire between HFC Test Pin 31 and Test Pin 40 at the breakout box. • Key on. • Measure voltage between HFC Power-To-Fan circuit at the cooling fan vehicle harness connector and battery negative post. • **Is voltage greater than 10.5 volts?**	Yes No	► ►	REPLACE cooling fan. REMOVE breakout box. RECONNECT all components. RE-EVALUATE symptom. REMOVE jumper. GO to **KF18**.

HFC POWER-TO-FAN

ESCORT/TRACER
COOLING FAN VEHICLE HARNESS CONNECTOR

Fig. 201 Test KF: LFC/HFC (Part 12 of 17). 1994–95

FM0159400742110X

TEST STEP	RESULT	►	ACTION TO TAKE
KF18 CHECK HFC POWER-TO-FAN CIRCUIT CONTINUITY • Key off. • Breakout box installed, PCM disconnected. • LFC relay disconnected. • Cooling fan disconnected. • Disconnect HFC relay. • Measure resistance between the HFC Power-To-Fan output pin at the HFC vehicle harness connector and the HFC Power-To-Fan input pin at the cooling fan vehicle harness connector. • **Is resistance less than 5.0 ohms?**	Yes No	► ►	REPLACE HFC relay. REMOVE breakout box. RECONNECT all components. RE-EVALUATE symptom. SERVICE open circuit. REMOVE breakout box. RECONNECT all components. RE-EVALUATE symptom.

HFC POWER-TO-FAN

ESCORT/TRACER
HFC RELAY
VEHICLE HARNESS CONNECTOR

KF25 LOW SPEED OR HIGH SPEED COOLING FAN ALWAYS ON. VERIFY IGNITION RELAY IS OPENING NOTE: Verify that A / C is off during testing. • For Probe, go directly to **KF26**. • Is cooling fan always on with key off, but operating normally with key on?	Yes No	► ►	VERIFY that IGN relay contacts are not always closed. If OK, CHECK circuit from IGN relay to fan relay(s) for short to B(+). GO to **KF26**.
KF26 CHECK FOR LFC RELAY ALWAYS CLOSED • Key off. • Disconnect LFC relay. • Key on. • **Does fan continue to run?**	Yes No	► ►	GO to **KF27**. REPLACE LFC relay RE-EVALUATE symptom.

Fig. 201 Test KF: LFC/HFC (Part 13 of 17). 1994–95

FM0159400742120X

TEST STEP	RESULT	►	ACTION TO TAKE
KF27 CHECK HFC RELAY • Key off. • LFC relay disconnected. • Disconnect HFC relay. • Key on. • **Does fan continue to run?**	Yes No	► ►	GO to **KF28**. If A/C system uses R134a refrigerant: Key off. GO to **KF30**. If no A/C, or A/C system uses R-12 refrigerant: REPLACE HFC relay. RECONNECT LFC relay. RE-EVALUATE symptom.
KF28 CHECK LFC POWER-TO-FAN CIRCUIT FOR SHORT TO POWER • Key off. • LFC and HFC relay disconnected. • Disconnect cooling fan. • Key on. • Measure voltage between LFC Power-To-Fan circuit at the cooling fan vehicle harness connector and battery negative post. • **Is voltage greater than 1.0 volt?**	Yes No	► ►	SERVICE short to power in LFC Power-To-Fan circuit. RECONNECT all components. RE-EVALUATE symptom. SERVICE short to power in HFC Power-To-Fan circuit. RECONNECT all components. RE-EVALUATE symptom.

LFC POWER-TO-FAN

HFC POWER-TO-FAN

ESCORT/TRACER
COOLING FAN VEHICLE HARNESS CONNECTOR

KF30 CHECK DUAL FUNCTION A/C PRESSURE SWITCH (ACPSW) • Key off. • LFC relay disconnected. • Reconnect HFC relay. • Disconnect ACPSW (also known as Refrigerant Containment / Fan Function switch). • Start engine. • **Does fan run?**	Yes No	► ►	Key off. GO to **KF31**. Key off. RECONNECT LFC and HFC relays. check ACPSW operation.

Fig. 201 Test KF: LFC/HFC (Part 14 of 17). 1994–95

TEST STEP	RESULT	►	ACTION TO TAKE
KF31 CHECK PCM • Key off. • LFC relay disconnected. • HFC relay connected. • Disconnect Powertrain Control Module (PCM). • Key on, engine off. • **Does fan run?**	Yes No	► ►	Key off. REPLACE HFC relay. RECONNECT all components. RE-EVALUATE symptom. Key off. GO to **KF32**.
KF32 CHECK ACPSW CIRCUIT FOR SHORT TO GROUND • Key off. • ACPSW disconnected. • PCM disconnected. • Measure resistance between the ACPSW circuit at the ACPSW vehicle harness connector and the battery negative post. • **Is resistance greater than 10,000 ohms?**	Yes No	► ►	REPLACE PCM. RECONNECT all components. RE-EVALUATE symptom. SERVICE ACPSW circuit short to ground. RECONNECT all components. RE-EVALUATE symptom.

TEST PIN 14 — ACPSW

ACPSW
VEHICLE HARNESS CONNECTOR

Fig. 201 Test KF: LFC/HFC (Part 15 of 17). 1994–95

FM0159400742140X

TEST STEP	RESULT	▶	ACTION TO TAKE
KF35 CHECK A/C PRESSURE SWITCH (ACPSW) MEDIUM PRESSURE CIRCUITS • Key off. • Disconnect ACPSW (also known as the Refrigerant Containment / Fan Function Switch). • A/C off (to prevent short circuits) • Connect a jumper wire between the HFC circuit and the GND circuit at the ACPSW vehicle harness connector. • Start engine. • Does the high speed fan come on?	Yes No	▶ ▶	Key off. ACPSW medium pressure circuits are OK. REMOVE jumper. RECONNECT ACPSW. check operation of the medium pressure function of the ACPSW. If OK, return for other possible causes of symptom. GO to **KF36**
KF36 CHECK GND CIRCUIT TO ACPSW • Key on, engine off. • ACPSW disconnected • Connect jumper wire between the HFC circuit at the ACPSW vehicle harness connector and the battery negative post. • Does the high speed fan come on now?	Yes No	▶ ▶	Key off. SERVICE open GND circuit to the ACPSW. REMOVE jumper wire and RECONNECT ACPSW. RE-EVALUATE symptom. If A/C system uses R134a refrigerant: Key off. REMOVE jumper wire. GO to **X37** If A/C system uses R-12 refrigerant: Key off. SERVICE open HFC circuit between the ACPSW and splice. REMOVE jumper wire and RECONNECT ACPSW. RE-EVALUATE symptom.

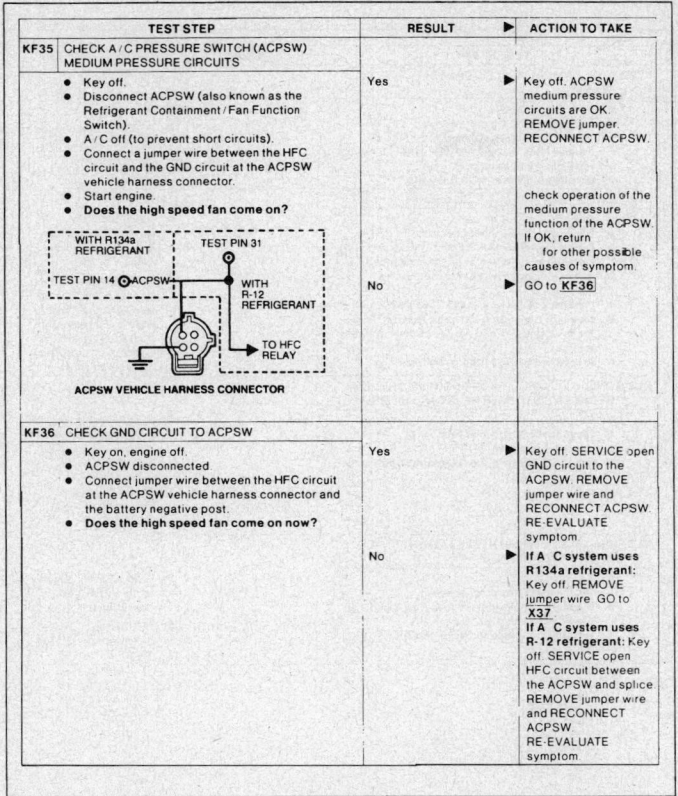

FM0159400742150X

Fig. 201   Test KF: LFC/HFC (Part 16 of 17). 1994–95

TEST STEP	RESULT	▶	ACTION TO TAKE
KF37 CHECK ACPSW CIRCUIT CONTINUITY TO PCM • Key off. • ACPSW disconnected. • Disconnect Powertrain Control Module (PCM). Inspect for damaged or pushed out pins, corrosion, loose wires, etc. Service as necessary. • Install breakout box, leave PCM disconnected. • Measure resistance between Test Pin 14 at the breakout box and the ACPSW circuit at the ACPSW vehicle harness connector. • Is resistance less than 5.0 ohms?	Yes No	▶ ▶	REPLACE PCM. REMOVE breakout box. RECONNECT all components. RE-EVALUATE symptom. SERVICE open circuit. REMOVE breakout box. RECONNECT all components. RE-EVALUATE symptom.

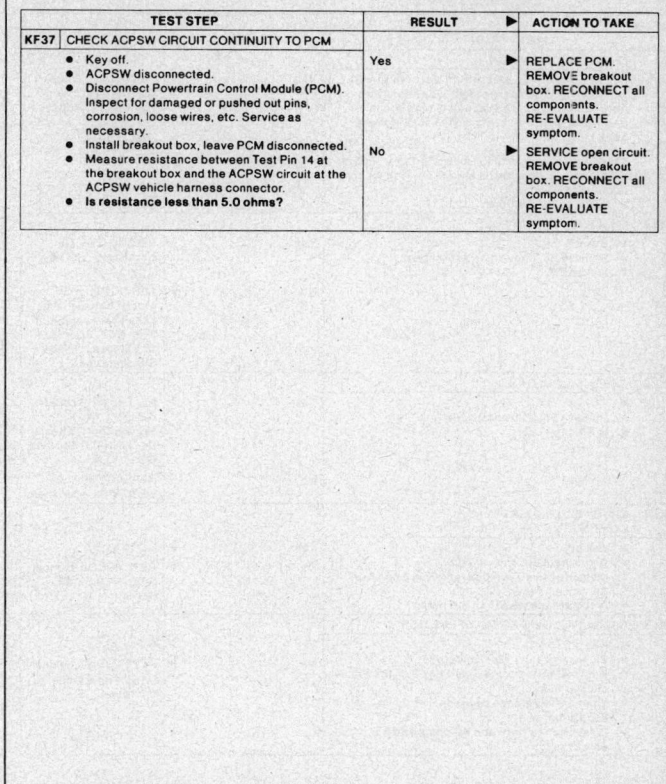

FM0159400742160X

Fig. 201   Test KF: LFC/HFC (Part 17 of 17). 1994–95

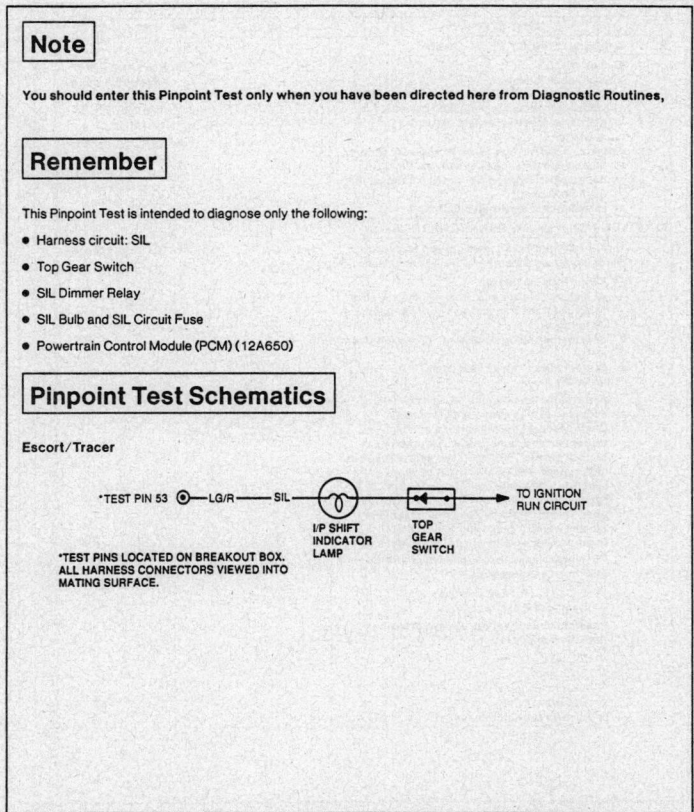

Note

You should enter this Pinpoint Test only when you have been directed here from Diagnostic Routines.

Remember

This Pinpoint Test is intended to diagnose only the following:

• Harness circuit: SIL
• Top Gear Switch
• SIL Dimmer Relay
• SIL Bulb and SIL Circuit Fuse
• Powertrain Control Module (PCM) (12A650)

Pinpoint Test Schematics

Escort/Tracer

Fig. 202   Test KL: SIL (Part 1 of 7)

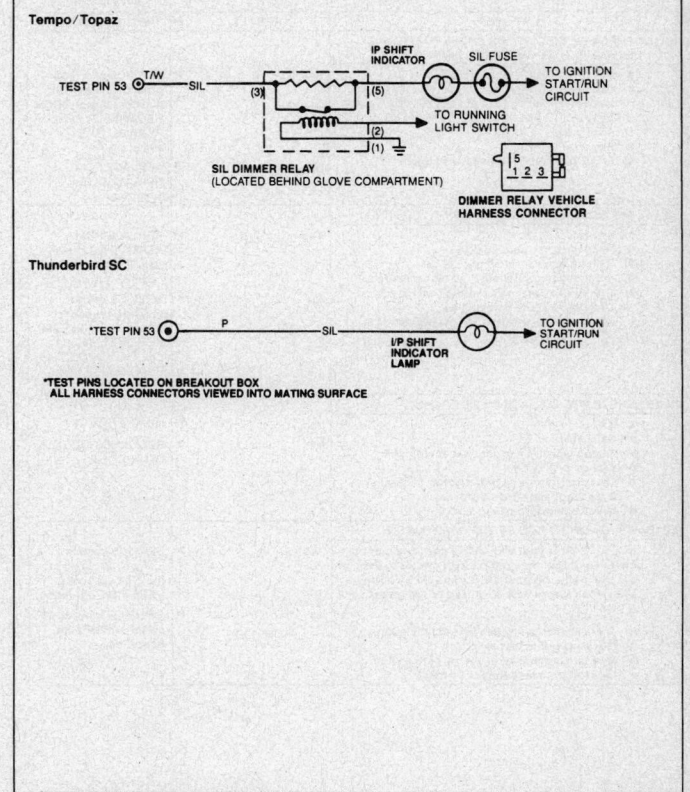

FM0159300743020X

Fig. 202   Test KL: SIL (Part 2 of 7)

TEST STEP	RESULT	►	ACTION TO TAKE
KL1 CHECK SIL OPERATION NOTE: To verify SIL operation, observe the SIL while driving the vehicle. The SIL should turn on when optimum shift speed is reached in each gear and remain off while in the highest gear. If the SIL is always on, look for a short to ground in the SIL circuit. If the SIL is always off, look for an open in the SIL circuit. • **Is SIL on all the time?**	Yes No	► ►	For Escort/Tracer: GO to KL11. For Tempo/Topaz: GO to KL8. GO to KL2.
KL2 CHECK SIL CIRCUIT FUSE • Key off. • Remove SIL circuit fuse and inspect. • **Is fuse OK?**	Yes No	► ►	RECONNECT SIL circuit fuse. GO TO KL3. SERVICE short to ground between SIL circuit fuse and SIL bulb. REPLACE SIL circuit fuse. VERIFY SIL operation.
KL3 CHECK SIL BULB • Key off. • Remove SIL bulb and inspect. • **Is SIL bulb OK?**	Yes No	► ►	For Escort/Tracer: GO to KL15. For Tempo/Topaz: RECONNECT SIL bulb. GO to KL4. REPLACE SIL bulb. VERIFY SIL operation.
KL4 CHECK SIL DIMMER RELAY CONTINUITY • Key off. • Disconnect SIL dimmer relay. • Measure resistance between Pins 3 and 5 on SIL dimmer relay. • **Is resistance less than 5.0 ohms?**	Yes No	► ►	GO to KL5. REPLACE SIL dimmer relay. VERIFY SIL operation.
KL5 CHECK SIL DIMMER RELAY FUNCTION • Key off. • SIL dimmer relay disconnected. • Apply 12 volts across Pins 1 and 2 on the SIL dimmer relay. • Measure resistance between Pins 3 and 5 on SIL dimmer relay. • **Is resistance between 40 ohms and 55 ohms?**	Yes No	► ►	GO to KL6. REPLACE SIL dimmer relay. VERIFY SIL operation.

Fig. 202   Test KL: SIL (Part 3 of 7)

TEST STEP	RESULT	►	ACTION TO TAKE
KL6 CHECK VOLTAGE AT SIL DIMMER RELAY • Key on, engine off. • Disconnect SIL dimmer relay. • Measure voltage between Pin 5 at the SIL dimmer relay vehicle harness connector and the battery negative post. • **Is voltage greater than 5.0 volts?**	Yes No	► ►	GO to KL7. SERVICE open circuit between SIL dimmer relay and SIL fuse. VERIFY SIL operation.
KL7 CHECK CONTINUITY OF SIL CIRCUIT • Key off. • SIL dimmer relay disconnected. • Disconnect Powertrain Control Module (PCM). Inspect for damaged or pushed out pins, corrosion, loose wires, etc. Service as necessary. • Install breakout box, leave PCM disconnected. • Measure resistance between Test Pin 53 at the breakout box and the SIL circuit connector for Pin 3. • **Is resistance less than 5.0 ohms?**	Yes No	► ►	REPLACE PCM. REMOVE breakout box. RERUN Quick Test. SERVICE open circuit between SIL dimmer relay and the PCM. REMOVE breakout box. RECONNECT all components. VERIFY SIL operation.
KL8 CHECK SIL CIRCUIT FOR SHORT TO GROUND BETWEEN SIL DIMMER RELAY AND SIL BULB • Key off. • Disconnect SIL dimmer relay. • Key on, engine off. • **Is the SIL ON with the SIL dimmer relay disconnected?**	Yes No	► ►	SERVICE short to ground between SIL dimmer relay and SIL bulb. RECONNECT SIL dimmer relay. RE-EVALUATE symptom. GO to KL9.
KL9 CHECK SIL DIMMER RELAY FOR INTERNAL SHORT TO GROUND • Key off. • SIL dimmer relay disconnected. • Measure resistance between Pins 3 and 1 on the SIL dimmer relay. • **Is resistance less than 5.0 ohms?**	Yes No	► ►	REPLACE SIL dimmer relay. VERIFY SIL operation. RECONNECT SIL dimmer relay. GO to KL10.

FM0159300743040X

Fig. 202   Test KL: SIL (Part 4 of 7)

TEST STEP	RESULT	►	ACTION TO TAKE
KL10 CHECK SIL CIRCUIT FOR SHORT TO GROUND BETWEEN THE PCM AND SIL DIMMER RELAY • Key off. • Disconnect Powertrain Control Module (PCM). Inspect for damaged or pushed out pins, corrosion, loose wires, etc. Service as necessary. • Key on, engine off. • **Is SIL ON with PCM disconnected?**	Yes No	► ►	SERVICE short to ground between SIL dimmer relay and PCM. RECONNECT PCM. RE-EVALUATE symptom. REPLACE PCM. RE-EVALUATE symptom.
KL11 CHECK SIL CIRCUIT FOR SHORT TO GROUND • Key off. • Reconnect top gear switch. • Shift transmission to highest gear. • Breakout box installed, PCM disconnected. • Measure resistance between Test Pin 53 and Test Pin 60 at the breakout box. • **Is resistance greater than 10,000 ohms?**	Yes No	► ►	REPLACE PCM. REMOVE breakout box. RERUN Quick Test. SERVICE short to ground between top gear switch and PCM. REMOVE breakout box. RECONNECT PCM. VERIFY SIL operation.
KL15 CHECK FOR VOLTAGE TO SIL SOCKET • Key off. • SIL bulb removed. • Transmission in any gear except top gear. • Key on, engine off. • Measure voltage between power contact at SIL socket and chassis ground. • **Is voltage greater than 10.5 volts?**	Yes No	► ►	GO to KL17. RECONNECT SIL bulb. GO to KL16.
KL16 CHECK OPERATION OF TOP GEAR SWITCH NOTE: The top gear switch is a normally closed switch and is in the ignition RUN circuit to the SIL bulb. The top gear switch should be open only when the vehicle is shifted to top gear. • Key off. • Transmission in any gear except top gear. • Disconnect top gear switch. • Measure resistance of the top gear switch. • **Is resistance less than 5.0 ohms?**	Yes No	► ►	SERVICE open in ignition run circuit to the SIL bulb. VERIFY SIL operation. REPLACE top gear switch. VERIFY SIL operation.

Fig. 202   Test KL: SIL (Part 5 of 7)

TEST STEP	RESULT	►	ACTION TO TAKE
KL17 CHECK CONTINUITY OF SIL CIRCUIT • Key off. • SIL bulb removed. • Disconnect Powertrain Control Module (PCM). Inspect for damaged or pushed out pins, corrosion, loose wires, etc. Service as necessary. • Install breakout box, leave PCM disconnected. • Measure resistance between Test Pin 53 at the breakout box and SIL circuit contact at the SIL bulb socket. • **Is resistance less than 5.0 ohms?**	Yes No	► ►	REPLACE PCM. REMOVE breakout box. RECONNECT SIL bulb. VERIFY SIL operation. SERVICE open circuit. REMOVE breakout box. RECONNECT all components. VERIFY SIL operation.
KL18 OPERATION OF THE THUNDERBIRD SC SIL The Thunderbird SC SIL will light and an audible chime will sound under the following conditions: — Key in RUN, engine off. — At high vehicle speeds, when engine speed is too high for the transmission gear selected, as follows: • Greater than 93 mph (4000 rpm) in 3rd gear for A/T. • Greater than 121 mph (4300 rpm) in 4th gear for M/T. At the same time that the SIL and chime are activated at high speed, the Powertrain Control Module (PCM) will take action to prevent engine damage from overheating. If coolant gets too hot, or 60 seconds elapses at high speeds, the PCM will shut off three injectors until a safe operating speed is reached or transmission is upshifted to top gear. This PCM action is independent of the SIL and warning chime and will occur regardless of a malfunction in these circuits. **Possible causes for SIL always on (other than normal operation):** — SIL circuit to PCM shorted — Damaged PCM **Possible causes for SIL always off (other than normal operation):** — SIL fuse — SIL bulb — SIL circuit open — Damaged PCM • **Is SIL always on or always off?**	Always On Always Off	► ►	GO to KL23. GO to KL19.

FM0159300743060X

Fig. 202   Test KL: SIL (Part 6 of 7)

TEST STEP	RESULT	▶	ACTION TO TAKE
KL19 CHECK SIL CIRCUIT FUSE • Key off. • Remove SIL circuit fuse and inspect. • **Is fuse OK?**	Yes No	▶ ▶	GO to **KL20**. SERVICE short to ground between SIL circuit fuse and SIL bulb. REPLACE SIL circuit fuse.
KL20 CHECK SIL BULB • Key off. • Remove the SIL bulb and inspect. • **Is SIL bulb OK?**	Yes No	▶ ▶	GO to **KL21**. REPLACE SIL bulb.
KL21 CHECK FOR VOLTAGE TO SIL SOCKET • Key off. • SIL bulb removed. • Key on, engine off. • Measure voltage between power contact at SIL socket and chassis ground. • **Is voltage greater than 10.5 volts?**	Yes No	▶ ▶	GO to **KL22**. SERVICE open in ignition START/RUN circuit to the SIL bulb socket.
KL22 CHECK CONTINUITY OF SIL CIRCUIT • Key off. • SIL bulb removed. • Disconnect Powertrain Control Module (PCM). Inspect for damaged or pushed out pins, corrosion, loose wires, etc. Service as necessary. • Install breakout box, leave PCM disconnected. • Measure resistance between Test Pin 53 at the breakout box and SIL circuit contact at the SIL bulb socket. • **Is resistance less than 5.0 ohms?**	Yes No	▶ ▶	REPLACE PCM. REMOVE breakout box. RECONNECT SIL bulb. SERVICE open circuit. REMOVE breakout box. RECONNECT all components.
KL23 CHECK SIL CIRCUIT FOR SHORT TO GROUND • Key off. • Disconnect Powertrain Control Module (PCM). Inspect for damaged or pushed out pins, corrosion, loose wires, etc. Service as necessary. • Key on, engine off. • **Is the SIL ON with the PCM disconnected?**	Yes No	▶ ▶	SERVICE short to ground between SIL bulb and PCM. RECONNECT PCM. RE-EVALUATE symptom. REPLACE PCM. RE-EVALUATE symptom.

FM0159300743070X

Fig. 202 Test KL: SIL (Part 7 of 7)

Note

You should enter this Pinpoint Test only when directed here from Diagnostic Routines, Pinpoint Test **TA.**

Remember

To prevent the replacement of good components, be aware that the following non-EEC areas may be at fault:

– Refrigerant charge

– Ambient temperature less than 7°C (45°F)

This Pinpoint Test is intended to diagnose only the following:

– Harness circuits: WAC, VPWR, GND, POWER-TO-CLUTCH, ACD

– WAC relay (11433 or 13A025)

– Powertrain Control Module (PCM) (12A650)

Fig. 203 Test KM: WAC A/C Demand (Part 1 of 20). 1993

Description

2.0L Probe

When the A/C demand switch is turned on and the Low Pressure (LP) switch is closed, the ACD input (Pin 23) to the Powertrain Control Module (PCM) is low, indicating that A/C is requested. The PCM will then ground the A/C ON output (Pin 54) which will energize the coil in the A/C relay. This will close the normally open contacts, sending B(+) voltage to the A/C Clutch. The PCM will also adjust idle as necessary.

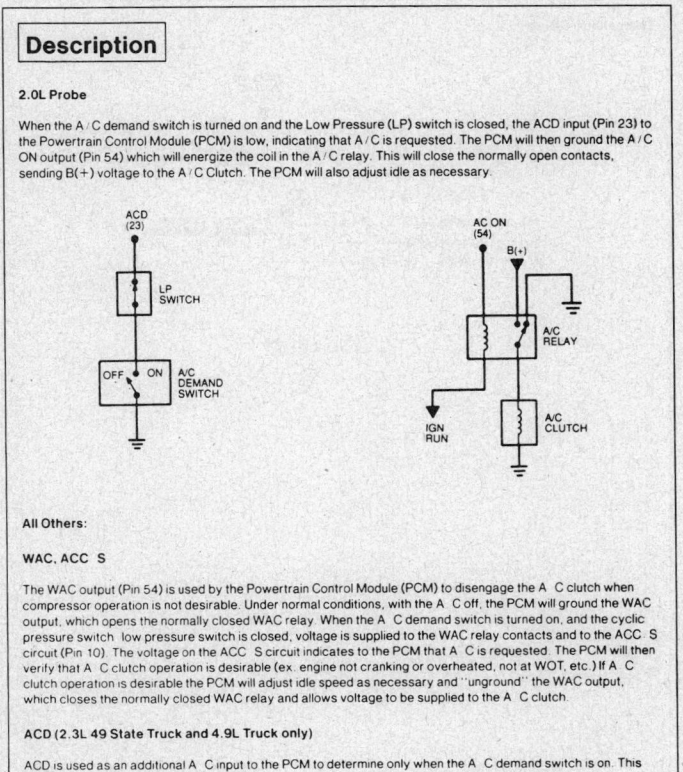

All Others:

WAC, ACC S

The WAC output (Pin 54) is used by the Powertrain Control Module (PCM) to disengage the A/C clutch when compressor operation is not desirable. Under normal conditions, with the A/C off, the PCM will ground the WAC output, which opens the normally closed WAC relay. When the A/C demand switch is turned on, and the cyclic pressure switch (low pressure switch) is closed, voltage is supplied to the WAC relay contacts and to the ACC S circuit (Pin 10). The voltage on the ACC S circuit indicates to the PCM that A/C is requested. The PCM will then verify that A/C clutch operation is desirable (ex. engine not cranking or overheated, not at WOT, etc.) If A/C clutch operation is desirable the PCM will adjust idle speed as necessary and "unground" the WAC output, which closes the normally closed WAC relay and allows voltage to be supplied to the A/C clutch.

ACD (2.3L 49 State Truck and 4.9L Truck only)

ACD is used as an additional A/C input to the PCM to determine only when the A/C demand switch is on. This information is used primarily for idle control.

FM0159300744020X

Fig. 203 Test KM: WAC A/C Demand (Part 2 of 20). 1993

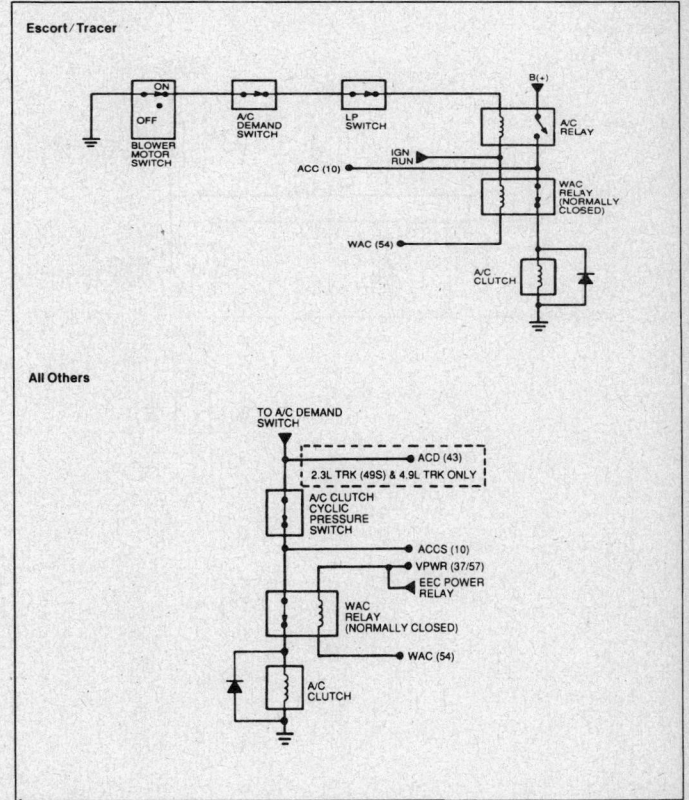

FM0159300744030X

Fig. 203 Test KM: WAC A/C Demand (Part 3 of 20). 1993

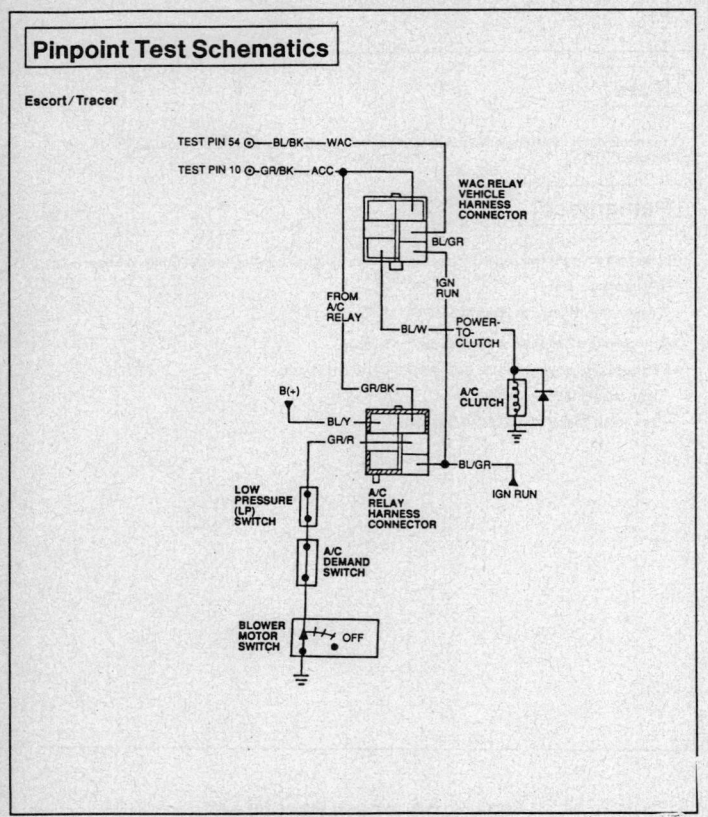

Fig. 203   Test KM: WAC A/C Demand (Part 4 of 20). 1993

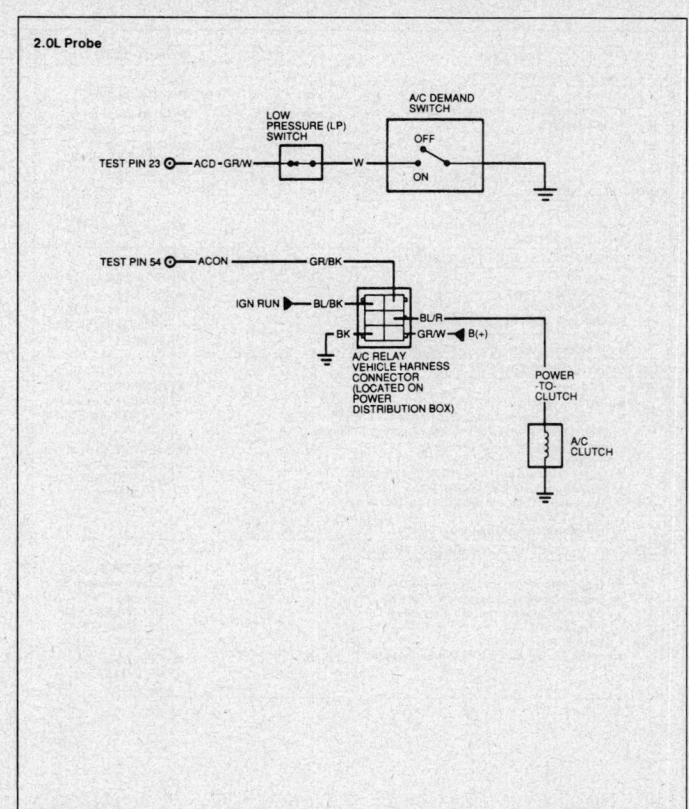

Fig. 203   Test KM: WAC A/C Demand (Part 5 of 20). 1993

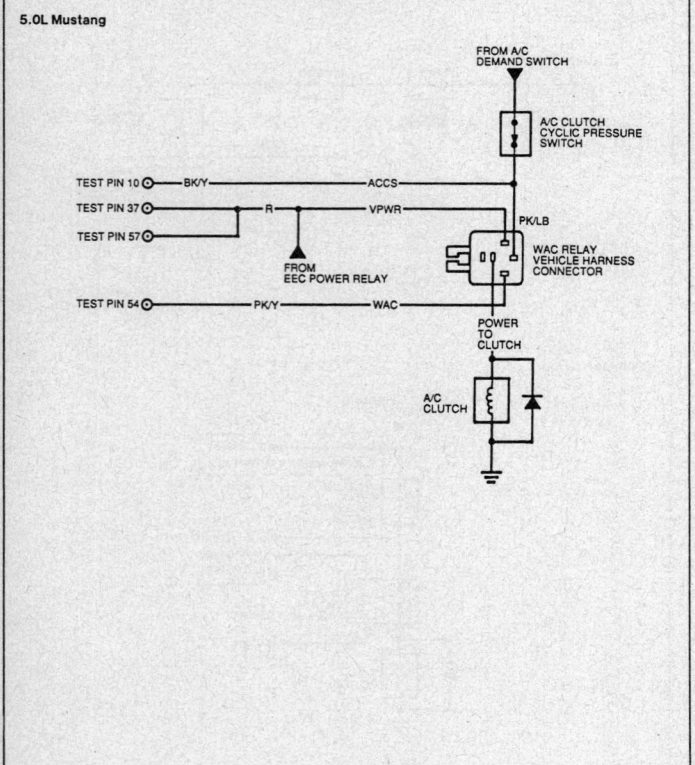

Fig. 203   Test KM: WAC A/C Demand (Part 6 of 20). 1993

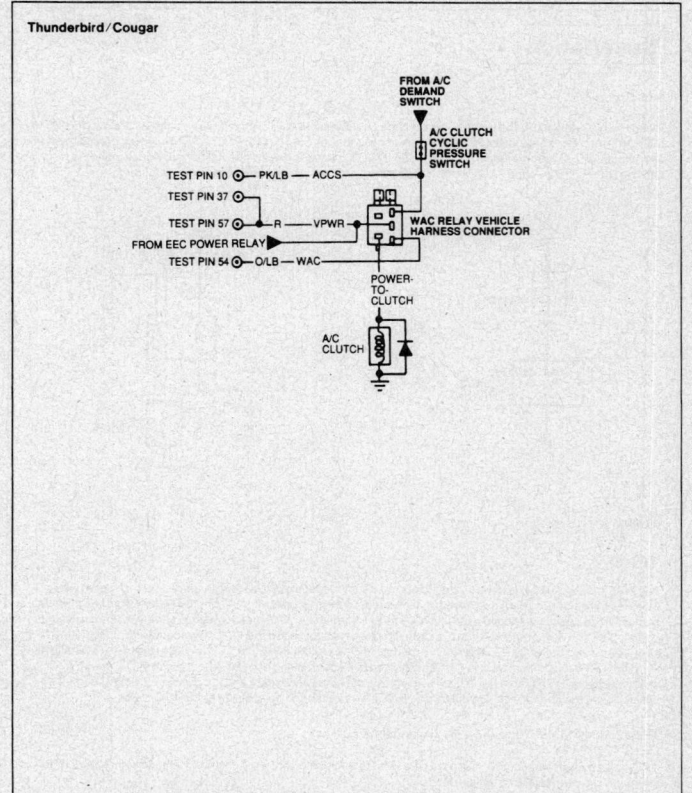

Fig. 203   Test KM: WAC A/C Demand (Part 7 of 20). 1993

Town Car, Crown Victoria / Grand Marquis, Aerostar

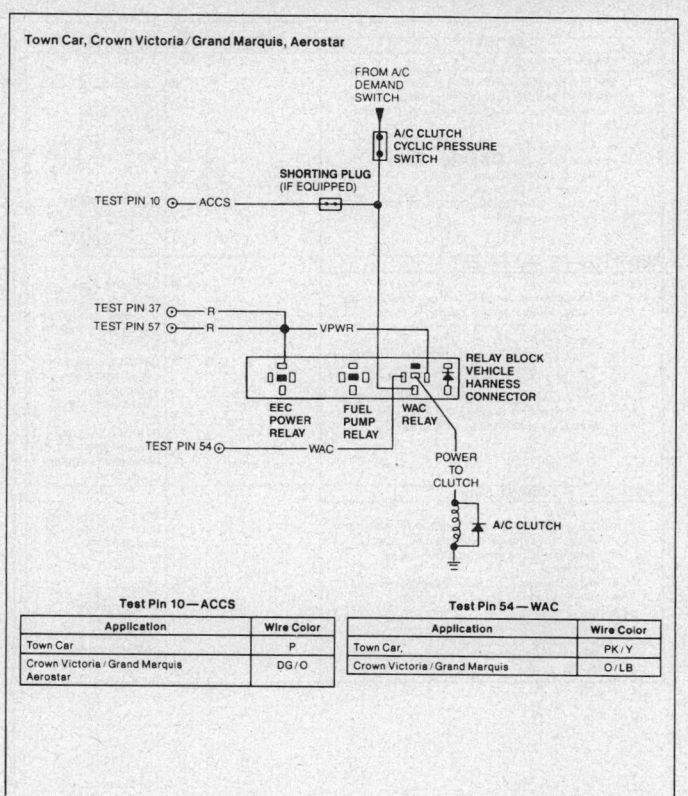

Test Pin 10—ACCS	
Application	Wire Color
Town Car	P
Crown Victoria / Grand Marquis Aerostar	DG / O

Test Pin 54—WAC	
Application	Wire Color
Town Car,	PK / Y
Crown Victoria / Grand Marquis	O / LB

FM0159300744080X

Fig. 203   Test KM: WAC A/C Demand (Part 8 of 20). 1993

	TEST STEP	RESULT	▶	ACTION TO TAKE
KM1	NO A/C: CHECK FOR VOLTAGE AT A/C CLUTCH			
	NOTE: Before proceeding with "NO A/C" diagnostics, verify integrity of related fuses in fuse box. • Key off. • Disconnect A/C clutch. • A/C demand switch to A/C on. • For Escort/Tracer and Probe, turn blower motor switch on (any speed). • Start engine, wait 10 seconds. • Measure voltage between the power side of the A/C clutch vehicle harness connector and battery negative post (allow time for normal ON/OFF cycling of the ACC/S or LP switch). • Is voltage greater than 10.5 volts?	Yes	▶	EEC system OK. REFER to Ventilation/Climate Control Group A/C Diagnosis in the Service Manual, to check for poor ground, open circuit in clutch, mechanical problems, etc.
		No	▶	For 2.0L Probe: GO to KM50. All others: GO to KM2.
KM2	CHECK POWER-TO-CLUTCH CIRCUIT CONTINUITY			
	• Key off. • A/C clutch disconnected. • Disconnect WAC relay. • Measure resistance between power side of the A/C clutch vehicle harness connector and power-to-clutch pin at the WAC relay vehicle harness connector. • Is resistance less than 5.0 ohms?	Yes	▶	RECONNECT A/C clutch. GO to KM3.
		No	▶	SERVICE open circuit. RECONNECT all components. RE-EVALUATE symptom.
KM3	CHECK FOR POWER ON A/C DEMAND CIRCUIT			
	• Key on, engine off. • WAC relay disconnected. • A/C demand switch to A/C on. **For Escort/Tracer:** — Blower motor switch on (any speed). — Measure voltage between A/C relay input pin at WAC relay vehicle harness connector and chassis ground. **All Others:** — Measure voltage between A/C demand input pin at WAC relay vehicle harness connector and chassis ground. • Is voltage greater than 10.5 volts?	Yes	▶	GO to KM5.
		No	▶	For Escort/Tracer: GO to KM4. For all others: VERIFY operation of A/C clutch cyclic pressure switch and A/C demand switch. Ventilation/Climate If OK, SERVICE open circuit. RECONNECT all components. RE-EVALUATE symptom.

Fig. 203   Test KM: WAC A/C Demand (Part 9 of 20). 1993

	TEST STEP	RESULT	▶	ACTION TO TAKE
KM4	CHECK CONTINUITY BETWEEN WAC RELAY AND A/C RELAY			
	• Key off. • WAC relay disconnected. • Disconnect A/C relay. • Measure resistance between the A/C relay output to the WAC relay at the A/C relay vehicle harness connector and the A/C relay input at the WAC relay vehicle harness connector. • Is resistance less than 5.0 ohms?	Yes	▶	RECONNECT WAC relay. REFER to Ventilation/Climate Control to check for proper input to A/C relay from B+, IGN RUN and A/C demand circuits; proper A/C relay operation, etc.
		No	▶	SERVICE open circuit. RECONNECT WAC relay and A/C relay. RE-EVALUATE symptom.
KM5	CHECK WAC CIRCUIT FOR SHORT TO GROUND			
	• Key off. • WAC relay disconnected. • Disconnect Powertrain Control Module (PCM). Inspect for damaged or pushed out pins, corrosion, loose wires, etc. Service as necessary. Leave PCM disconnected. • Measure resistance between WAC circuit at the WAC relay vehicle harness connector and chassis ground. • Is resistance greater than 10,000 ohms?	Yes	▶	GO to KM6.
		No	▶	SERVICE short circuit. RECONNECT all components. RE-EVALUATE symptom.
KM6	CHECK FOR VOLTAGE AT ACCS/ACD INPUT TO PCM			
	• Key off. • WAC relay disconnected. • PCM disconnected. • Install breakout box, leave PCM disconnected. • Key on, engine off. • A/C demand switch to A/C on. • For Escort/Tracer, turn blower motor switch on (any speed). • Measure voltage between Test Pin 10 and Test Pin 40 at the breakout box. • For 2.3L Ranger, also measure voltage between Test Pin 43 (ACD) and Test Pin 40 at the breakout box. • Is voltage(s) greater than 10.5 volts?	Yes	▶	GO to KM7.
		No	▶	SERVICE open in ACCS/ACD circuit. REMOVE breakout box. RECONNECT all components. RE-EVALUATE symptom.

1993 Powertrain Control Emissions Diagnosis July, 1992

FM0159300744120X

Fig. 203   Test KM: WAC A/C Demand (Part 10 of 20). 1993

	TEST STEP	RESULT	▶	ACTION TO TAKE
KM7	CHECK WAC RELAY			
	• Key off. • Breakout box installed, PCM disconnected. • Reconnect WAC relay. • Disconnect A/C clutch. • Key on, engine off. • A/C demand switch to A/C on. • For Escort/Tracer turn blower motor switch on (any speed). • Measure voltage between the power side of the A/C clutch vehicle harness connector and the battery negative post. • Is voltage greater than 10.5 volts?	Yes	▶	REPLACE PCM. RECONNECT A/C clutch. RE-EVALUATE symptom.
		No	▶	REPLACE WAC relay. REMOVE breakout box. RECONNECT all components. RE-EVALUATE symptom.
KM15	NO A/C CUTOUT AT WOT: ENTER OUTPUT STATE DIAGNOSTIC TEST MODE (DTM)			
	NOTE: Use VOM/DVOM for this Step. • Key off, wait 10 seconds. • Disconnect electrical connector on the speed control servo, if equipped. • Connect DVOM negative test lead to STO at the Data Link Connector (DLC) and positive test lead to battery positive post. • Jumper STI to SIG RTN at the DLC. • Perform Key On Engine Off Self-Test until the completion of the Continuous Memory Diagnostic Trouble Codes. • DVOM will indicate less than 1.0 volt when test is complete. • Depress and release the throttle. • Does voltage increase to greater than 10.5 volts?	Yes	▶	REMAIN in Output State DTM. GO to KM16.
		No	▶	DEPRESS throttle to WOT and RELEASE. If STO voltage does not go high, leave equipment hooked up and GO to Pinpoint Test Step QC2.
KM16	CHECK FOR VPWR TO WAC RELAY			
	• Still in Output State DTM. • Disconnect harness from WAC relay. • Measure voltage between VPWR circuit (IGN RUN for Escort/Tracer) at the WAC relay vehicle harness connector and chassis ground. • Is voltage greater than 10.5 volts?	Yes	▶	GO to KM17.
		No	▶	SERVICE open in VPWR circuit between EEC power relay and WAC relay (for Escort/Tracer, IGN RUN circuit between WAC relay and joint box). RECONNECT all components and REMOVE jumper. RE-EVALUATE symptom.

FM0159300744130X

Fig. 203   Test KM: WAC A/C Demand (Part 11 of 20). 1993

TEST STEP		RESULT	▶	ACTION TO TAKE
KM17 CHECK FOR WAC CYCLING				
• Still in Output State DTM. • WAC relay disconnected. • DVOM on 20 volt scale. • Connect DVOM positive test lead to the VPWR circuit (IGN RUN for Escort/Tracer) and the negative test lead to the WAC circuit at the WAC relay vehicle harness connector. • While observing DVOM, depress and release throttle several times (to cycle output on and off). • **Does voltage cycle high and low (about one volt change)?**		Yes No	▶ ▶	REPLACE WAC relay. REMOVE jumper. RECONNECT speed control servo. RE-EVALUATE symptom. REMOVE jumper. RECONNECT speed control servo. GO to **KM18**.
KM18 CHECK WAC CIRCUIT CONTINUITY				
• Key off. • Disconnect Powertrain Control Module (PCM). Inspect for damaged or pushed out pins, corrosion, loose wires, etc. Service as necessary. • Install breakout box, leave PCM disconnected. • WAC relay disconnected. • Measure resistance between Test Pin 54 at the breakout box and WAC circuit at the WAC relay vehicle harness connector. • **Is resistance less than 5.0 ohms?**		Yes No	▶ ▶	GO to **KM19**. SERVICE open circuit. REMOVE breakout box. RECONNECT all components. RE-EVALUATE symptom.
KM19 CHECK WAC CIRCUIT FOR SHORT TO POWER				
• Key off. • Breakout box installed, PCM disconnected. • WAC relay disconnected. • Key on, engine off. • Measure voltage between Test Pin 54 and chassis ground. • **Is voltage less than 1.0 volt?**		Yes No	▶ ▶	REPLACE PCM. RECONNECT WAC relay. RE-EVALUATE symptom. SERVICE short circuit. REMOVE breakout box. RECONNECT all components. RE-EVALUATE symptom. If symptom is still present, REPLACE PCM.

FM0159300744140X

Fig. 203   Test KM: WAC A/C Demand (Part 12 of 20). 1993

TEST STEP		RESULT	▶	ACTION TO TAKE
KM30 CHECK A/C INPUT CIRCUITRY				
NOTE: A low idle with A/C on could be the result of the Powertrain Control Module (PCM) not receiving, or recognizing, the A/C input on Pin 10. • A/C demand switch to A/C on. • For Escort/Tracer and Probe, turn blower motor switch on lowest speed. • Perform Key On Engine Off Self-Test. • **Is Diagnostic Trouble Code (DTC) 67 or 79/539 present?**		Yes No	▶ ▶	2.3L Ranger and 4.9L Truck: GO to **KM32**. All others: The PCM is receiving and recognizing the A/C input on Pin 10. other possible causes of a low idle. A/C demand switch off. GO to **KM31**.
KM31 CHECK A/C INPUT CIRCUIT				
• Key off. • Disconnect Powertrain Control Module (PCM). Inspect for damaged or pushed out pins, corrosion, loose wires, etc. Service as necessary. • Install breakout box, leave PCM disconnected. • Key on, engine off. • A/C on. • Measure voltage between Test Pin 10 and Test Pin 40 at the breakout box. • **Is voltage greater than 10.5 volts?**		Yes No	▶ ▶	REPLACE PCM. REMOVE breakout box. RECONNECT all components. RERUN Quick Test. SERVICE open in A/C circuit. REFER to the appropriate schematic. REMOVE breakout box. RECONNECT all components. RERUN Quick Test.
KM32 CYCLE A/C DEMAND SWITCH				
• Key off. • Disconnect Powertrain Control Module (PCM). Inspect for damaged or pushed out pins, corrosion, loose wires, etc. Service as necessary. • Install breakout box, leave PCM disconnected. • DVOM on 20 volt scale. • Key on, engine off. • Connect DVOM positive test lead to Test Pin 43 and negative test lead to Test Pin 40. • **Does voltage cycle high and low when A/C demand switch is cycled?**		Yes No	▶ ▶	The PCM is receiving the A/C inputs on Pin 10 and Pin 43. SERVICE open in ACD circuit. REMOVE breakout box. RECONNECT all components. RERUN Quick Test.

FM0159300744150X

Fig. 203   Test KM: WAC A/C Demand (Part 13 of 20). 1993

TEST STEP		RESULT	▶	ACTION TO TAKE
KM40 DIAGNOSTIC TROUBLE CODE (DTC) 67, 79/539: CHECK A/C INPUT				
DTC 79/539 indicates that the ACCS input to the Powertrain Control Module (PCM) was high during KOEO/KOER Self-Test. DTC 67 indicates that during KOEO Self-Test, voltage was high on NDS (Pin 30) or ACCS (Pin 10) circuit. **NOTE:** Before entering this test, verify A/C selector is off (and shift selector is in PARK for AXODE and E4OD vehicles). If A/C was on, turn off and rerun Self-Test. If DTC 67 or 79/539 is present, continue with this test. • Disconnect Powertrain Control Module (PCM). Inspect for damaged or pushed out pins, corrosion, loose wires, etc. Service as necessary. • Install breakout box, leave PCM disconnected. • Key on, engine off. • Measure voltage between Test Pin 10 at the breakout box and chassis ground. • **Is voltage greater than 1.0 volt?**		Yes No	▶ ▶	VERIFY operation of A/C demand switch. If OK, SERVICE short to power in A/C circuit. REMOVE breakout box. RECONNECT all components. RERUN Quick Test. For trucks with two-digit DTCs and E4OD transmission: GO to **KM41**. For all others: REPLACE PCM. REMOVE breakout box. RECONNECT all components. RERUN Quick Test.
KM41 CHECK FOR SHORT TO POWER IN PCM				
• Key off. • Breakout box installed. • Connect PCM to breakout box. • Disconnect A/C clutch. • Key on, engine off. • Measure voltage between Test Pin 10 and Test Pin 40 at the breakout box. • **Is voltage greater than 5.0 volts?**		Yes No	▶ ▶	REPLACE PCM. RECONNECT A/C clutch. RERUN Quick Test. RECONNECT A/C clutch. GO to Pinpoint Test Step **TD1**.
KM50 NO A/C — ATTEMPT TO GENERATE KOEO DTC 539				
• Key off. • A/C demand switch to A/C on. • Perform KOEO Self-Test. • **Is KOEO DTC 539 present?**		Yes No	▶ ▶	GO to **KM51**. GO to **KM55**.
KM51 CHECK FOR B+ VOLTAGE TO A/C RELAY				
• Key off. • Disconnect A/C relay. • Key on. • Measure voltage between B+ circuit at A/C relay vehicle harness connector and chassis ground. • **Is voltage greater than 10.5 volts?**		Yes No	▶ ▶	Key off. GO to **KM52**. Key off. VERIFY condition of related fuses. If OK, SERVICE open circuit. RECONNECT all components. RE-EVALUATE symptom.

FM0159300744160X

Fig. 203   Test KM: WAC A/C Demand (Part 14 of 20). 1993

TEST STEP		RESULT	▶	ACTION TO TAKE
KM52 CHECK POWER TO CLUTCH CIRCUIT CONTINUITY				
• Key off. • A/C relay disconnected. • Disconnect A/C clutch. • Measure resistance between power side of A/C clutch vehicle harness connector and power-to-clutch circuit at A/C relay vehicle harness connector. • **Is resistance less than 5.0 ohms?**		Yes No	▶ ▶	GO to **KM53**. SERVICE open circuit. RECONNECT all components. RE-EVALUATE symptom.
KM53 CHECK A/C RELAY				
• Key off. • A/C clutch disconnected. • Reconnect A/C relay. • Jumper AC ON circuit at A/C relay vehicle harness connector to battery ground. • Key on. • Measure voltage between power side of A/C clutch vehicle harness connector and chassis ground. • **Is voltage greater than 10.5 volts?**		Yes No	▶ ▶	Key off. REMOVE jumper. EEC system OK. REFER to Ventilation/Climate Control A/C Diagnosis, to check for proper ground, open circuit in clutch, mechanical concerns, etc. REPLACE A/C relay. RECONNECT all components. RE-EVALUATE symptom.
KM55 CHECK ACD CIRCUIT CONTINUITY TO LOW PRESSURE (LP) SWITCH				
• Key off. • A/C demand switch to A/C on. • Disconnect LP switch. • Measure resistance between A/C demand switch side of LP switch vehicle harness connector and chassis ground. • **Is resistance less than 5.0 ohms?**		Yes No	▶ ▶	GO to **KM56**. VERIFY operation of A/C demand switch. REFER to Ventilation/Climate Control. If OK, SERVICE open circuit. RECONNECT all components. RE-EVALUATE symptom.

FM0159300744170X

Fig. 203   Test KM: WAC A/C Demand (Part 15 of 20). 1993

TEST STEP	RESULT	▶	ACTION TO TAKE
KM56 MEASURE RESISTANCE OF LP SWITCH • Key off. • LP switch disconnected. • Measure resistance of LP switch. • **Is resistance less than 5.0 ohms?**	Yes No	▶ ▶	GO to **KM57**. REFER to Ventilation / Climate Control RECONNECT all components. RE-EVALUATE symptom.
KM57 CHECK ACD CIRCUIT CONTINUITY FROM LP SWITCH TO POWERTRAIN CONTROL MODULE (PCM) • Key off. • LP switch disconnected. • Disconnect Powertrain Control Module (PCM). Inspect for damaged or pushed out pins, corrosion, loose wires, etc. Service as necessary. • Install breakout box, leave PCM disconnected. • Measure resistance between Test Pin 23 at the breakout box and PCM side of LP switch vehicle harness connector. • **Is resistance less than 5.0 ohms?**	Yes No	▶ ▶	REPLACE PCM. REMOVE breakout box. RECONNECT all components. RE-EVALUATE symptom. SERVICE open circuit. RECONNECT all components. RE-EVALUATE symptom.

Fig. 203 Test KM: WAC A/C Demand (Part 16 of 20). 1993

FM0159300744180X

TEST STEP	RESULT	▶	ACTION TO TAKE
KM61 CHECK A/C RELAY • Key off. • A/C relay disconnected. • Check A/C relay coil resistance: — Measure resistance between ACON pin and IGN RUN pin at the A/C relay. — Resistance should be between 50 and 100 ohms. • Check A/C relay for internal shorts: — Measure resistance between ACON pin and the following pins at the A/C relay; B+, power-to-clutch, ground. — Resistances should be greater than 10,000 ohms. • **Are all resistance checks OK?**	Yes No	▶ ▶	GO to **KM62**. REPLACE A/C relay. RECONNECT all components. RERUN Quick Test.

IGN RUN
ACON (PIN 54) — GROUND — B(+) — POWER-TO-CLUTCH
A/C RELAY

TEST STEP	RESULT	▶	ACTION TO TAKE
KM62 CHECK ACON CIRCUIT FOR SHORT TO POWER • Key off. • A/C relay disconnected. • Disconnect Powertrain Control Module (PCM). Inspect for damaged or pushed out pins, corrosion, loose wire, etc. Service as necessary. • Install breakout box, leave PCM disconnected. • Key on, engine off. • Measure voltage between Test Pin 54 at the breakout box and chassis ground. • **Is voltage less than 1.0 volt?**	Yes No	▶ ▶	GO to **KM63**. SERVICE short to power. REMOVE breakout box. RECONNECT all components. RERUN Quick Test.
KM63 CHECK ACON CIRCUIT FOR SHORT TO GROUND. • Key off. • A/C relay disconnected. • Breakout box installed, PCM disconnected. • Measure resistance between Test Pin 54 at the breakout box and chassis ground. • **Is resistance greater than 10,000 ohms?**	Yes No	▶ ▶	GO to **KM64**. SERVICE short to ground. REMOVE breakout box. RECONNECT all components. RERUN Quick Test.

Fig. 203 Test KM: WAC A/C Demand (Part 18 of 20). 1993

TEST STEP	RESULT	▶	ACTION TO TAKE
KM60 DIAGNOSTIC TROUBLE CODE (DTC) 559: CHECK FOR IGN RUN VOLTAGE TO A/C RELAY DTC 559 indicates an A/C relay primary circuit fault. Possible causes: — Open or shorted circuit — Damaged A/C relay — Damaged Powertrain Control Module (PCM) • Key off. • Disconnect A/C relay. • Key on. • Measure voltage between IGN RUN circuit at A/C relay vehicle harness connector and chassis ground. • **Is voltage greater than 10.5 volts?**	Yes No	▶ ▶	GO to **KM61**. VERIFY condition of related fuses. If OK, SERVICE open circuit. RECONNECT all components. RERUN Quick Test.

IGN RUN — ACON (PIN 54) — POWER-TO-CLUTCH — B(+)
A/C RELAY VEHICLE HARNESS CONNECTOR

Fig. 203 Test KM: WAC A/C Demand (Part 17 of 20). 1993

FM0159300744190X

TEST STEP	RESULT	▶	ACTION TO TAKE
KM64 CHECK ACON CIRCUIT CONTINUITY • Key off. • A/C relay disconnected. • Breakout box installed, PCM disconnected. • Measure resistance between Test Pin 54 at breakout box and ACON circuit at A/C relay vehicle harness connector. • **Is resistance less than 5.0 ohms?**	Yes No	▶ ▶	REPLACE PCM. REMOVE breakout box. RECONNECT all components. RERUN Quick Test. SERVICE open circuit. REMOVE breakout box. RECONNECT all components. RERUN Quick Test.
KM70 DIAGNOSTIC TROUBLE CODE (DTC) 539: CHECK A/C INPUT DTC 539 indicates that the A/C demand input to the Powertrain Control Module (PCM) was low (A/C on) during KOEO Self-Test. **NOTE: Before entering this test, verify A/C selector is off. If A/C was on, rerun KOEO Self-Test. If DTC 539 is present, continue with this test.** • Key off. • A/C off. • Disconnect Low Pressure (LP) switch. • Measure resistance between A/C demand switch side of LP switch vehicle harness connector and chassis ground. • **Is resistance greater than 10,000 ohms?**	Yes No	▶ ▶	GO to **KM71**. VERIFY operation of A/C demand switch. REFER to Ventilation / Climate Control If OK, SERVICE short to ground. RECONNECT all components. RE-EVALUATE symptom.
KM71 CHECK LOW PRESSURE (LP) SWITCH • Key off. • LP switch disconnected. • Measure resistance between chassis ground and both pins of LP switch. • **Are both resistances greater than 10,000 ohms?**	Yes No	▶ ▶	GO to **KM72**. REPLACE LP switch. RECONNECT all components. RE-EVALUATE symptom.
KM72 CHECK ACD CIRCUIT TO PCM FOR SHORT TO GROUND • Key off. • LP switch disconnected. • Disconnect Powertrain Control Module (PCM). Inspect for damaged or pushed out pins, corrosion, loose wires, etc. Service as necessary. • Measure resistance between PCM side of the LP switch vehicle harness connector and chassis ground. • **Is resistance greater than 10,000 ohms?**	Yes No	▶ ▶	REPLACE PCM. RECONNECT all components. RE-EVALUATE symptom. SERVICE short to ground. RECONNECT all components. RE-EVALUATE symptom.

Fig. 203 Test KM: WAC A/C Demand (Part 19 of 20). 1993

FM0159300744210X

	TEST STEP	RESULT	▶	ACTION TO TAKE
KM80	A/C ALWAYS ON: CHECK POWER TO CLUTCH CIRCUIT FOR SHORT TO POWER			
	NOTE: Before entering this test, verify KOEO DTC 539 or 559 was not received. If DTC 539 or 559 is present, refer to EEC-IV Diagnostic Trouble Code Charts, for proper Pinpoint Test direction. • Key off. • Disconnect A/C relay. • Disconnect A/C clutch. • Key on. • Measure voltage between power side of A/C Clutch vehicle harness connector and battery negative post. • **Is voltage less than 1.0 volt?**	Yes No	▶ ▶	GO to KM81 SERVICE short to power. RECONNECT all components. RE-EVALUATE symptom.
KM81	CHECK A/C RELAY			
	• Key off. • A/C relay disconnected. • Measure resistance between power-to-clutch pin and both the IGN RUN and B+ pins at the A/C relay. • **Are both resistances greater than 10,000 ohms?**	Yes No	▶ ▶	EEC system OK. REFER to Ventilation/Climate Control A/C Diagnosis. REPLACE A/C relay. RECONNECT all components. RE-EVALUATE symptom.

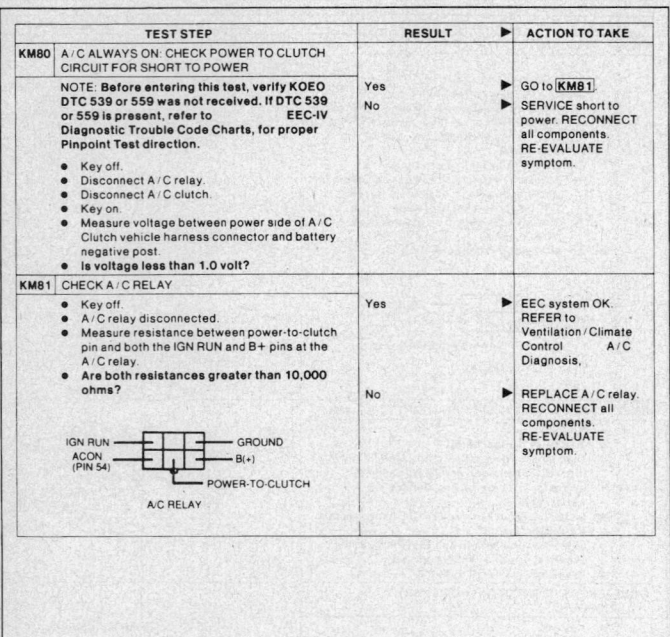

FM0159300744220X

Fig. 203 Test KM: WAC A/C Demand (Part 20 of 20). 1993

Note

You should enter this Pinpoint Test only when directed here from Diagnostic Routines,   or Pinpoint Test TA.

Remember

To prevent the replacement of good components, be aware that the following non-EEC areas may be at fault:

— Refrigerant charge
— Ambient temperature less than 7°C (45°F)

This Pinpoint Test is intended to diagnose only the following:

— Harness circuits: WAC, VPWR, GND, POWER-TO-CLUTCH, ACD
— WAC relay
— Powertrain Control Module (PCM)

FM0159400745010X

Fig. 204 Test KM: WAC A/C Demand (Part 1 of 19). 1994–95

Description

2.0L Probe

When the A/C demand switch is turned on and the Low Pressure (LP) switch is closed, the ACD input (Pin 23 or 10) to the Powertrain Control Module (PCM) is low, indicating that A/C is requested. The PCM will ground the A/C ON output (Pin 54) which will energize the coil in the A/C relay. This will close the normally open contacts, sending B(+) voltage to the A/C Clutch. The PCM will also adjust idle as necessary.

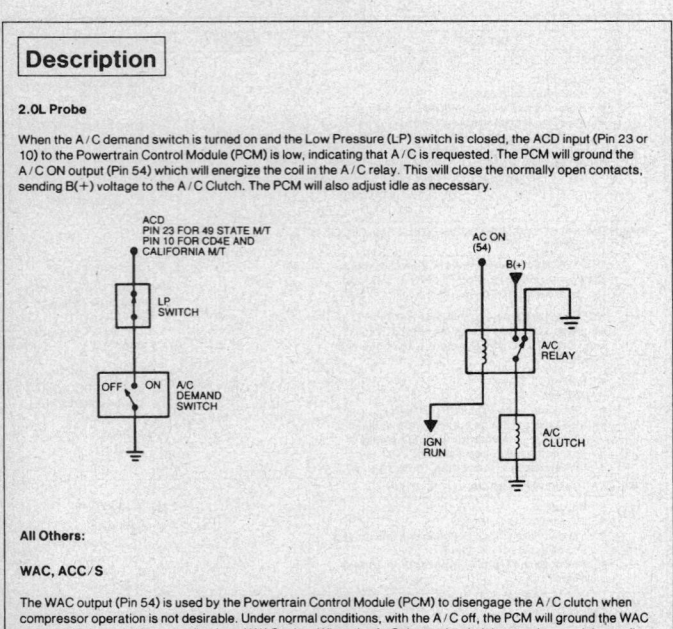

All Others:

WAC, ACC/S

The WAC output (Pin 54) is used by the Powertrain Control Module (PCM) to disengage the A/C clutch when compressor operation is not desirable. Under normal conditions, with the A/C off, the PCM will ground the WAC output, which opens the normally closed WAC relay. When the A/C demand switch is turned on, and the cyclic pressure switch/low pressure switch is closed, voltage is supplied to the WAC relay contacts and to the ACC/S circuit (Pin 10). (For Escort/Tracer, the A/C Pressure Switch (ACPSW) high pressure contacts, and the A/C relay must also be closed (see schematic). The voltage on the ACC/S circuit indicates to the PCM that A/C is requested. The PCM will then verify that A/C clutch operation is desirable (ex. engine not cranking or overheated, not at WOT, etc.) If A/C clutch operation is desirable, the PCM will adjust idle speed as necessary and "unground" the WAC output, which closes the normally closed WAC relay and allows voltage to be supplied to the A/C clutch.

FM0159400745020X

Fig. 204 Test KM: WAC A/C Demand (Part 2 of 19). 1994–95

ACD (2.3L A/T Ranger and 4.9L Truck only)

ACD is used as an additional A/C input to the PCM to determine only when the A/C demand switch is on. This information is used primarily for idle control.

Escort/Tracer

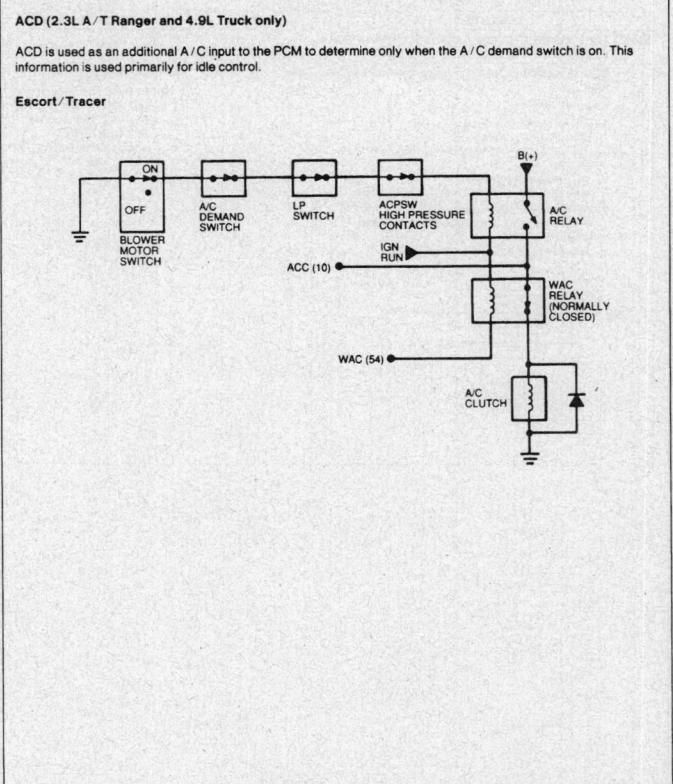

FM0159400745030X

Fig. 204 Test KM: WAC A/C Demand (Part 3 of 19). 1994–95

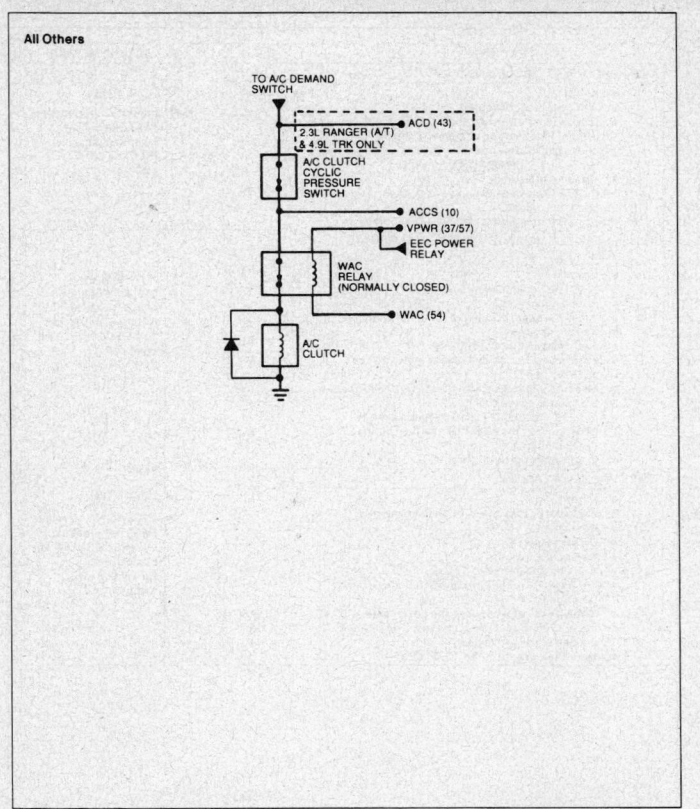

Fig. 204   Test KM: WAC A/C Demand (Part 4 of 19).
1994–95

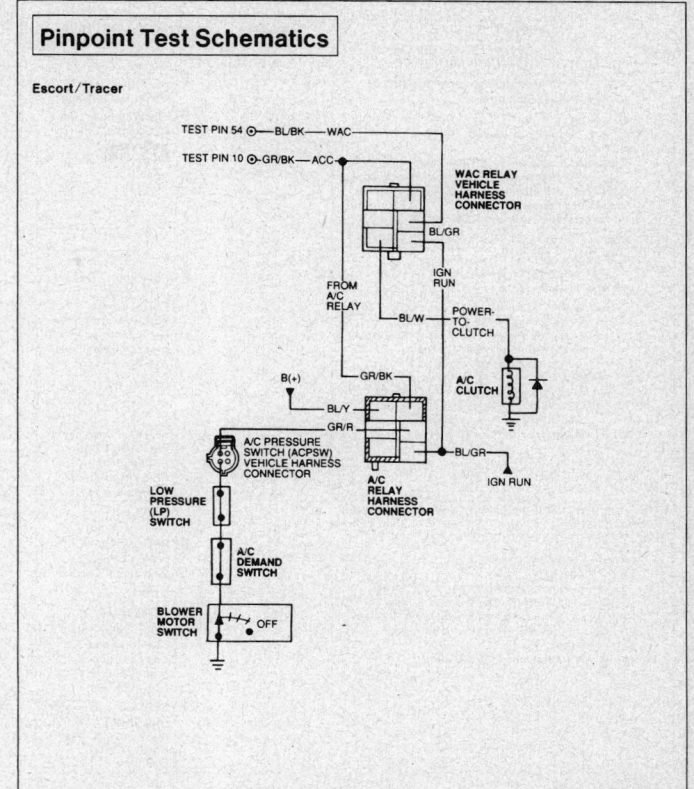

Fig. 204   Test KM: WAC A/C Demand (Part 5 of 19).
1994–95

2.0L Probe

ACD (Pin 10 or 23)

Application	Wire Color
Probe 49 States M/T	GR/W (Pin 23)
Probe CD4E, Calif M/T	PK/BK (Pin 10)

Fig. 204   Test KM: WAC A/C Demand (Part 6 of 19).
1994–95

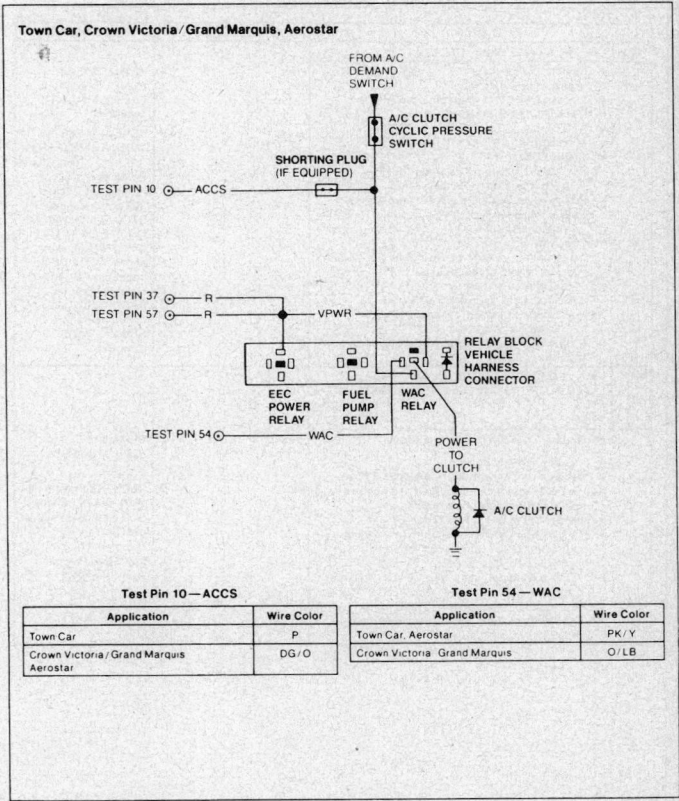

Town Car, Crown Victoria/Grand Marquis, Aerostar

Test Pin 10 — ACCS	
Application	Wire Color
Town Car	P
Crown Victoria/Grand Marquis Aerostar	DG/O

Test Pin 54 — WAC	
Application	Wire Color
Town Car, Aerostar	PK/Y
Crown Victoria Grand Marquis	O/LB

Fig. 204   Test KM: WAC A/C Demand (Part 7 of 19).
1994–95

TEST STEP	RESULT	▶	ACTION TO TAKE
KM1 LOW/NO VOLTAGE TO A/C CLUTCH: CHECK POWER-TO-CLUTCH CIRCUIT CONTINUITY			
NOTE: Before proceeding, verify integrity of related fuses in fuse box. • Key off. • A/C clutch disconnected. • Disconnect WAC relay. • Measure resistance between power side of the A/C clutch vehicle harness connector and Power-To-Clutch pin at the WAC relay vehicle harness connector. • Is resistance less than 5.0 ohms?	Yes No	▶ ▶	RECONNECT A/C clutch. GO to **KM2**. SERVICE open circuit. RECONNECT all components. RE-EVALUATE symptom.
KM2 CHECK FOR POWER ON A/C DEMAND CIRCUIT			
• Key on, engine off. • WAC relay disconnected. • A/C demand switch to A/C on. **For Escort/Tracer:** — Blower motor switch on (any speed). — Measure voltage between A/C relay input pin at WAC relay vehicle harness connector and chassis ground. **All Others:** — Measure voltage between A/C demand input pin at WAC relay vehicle harness connector and chassis ground. • Is voltage greater than 10.5 volts?	Yes No	▶ ▶	GO to **KM5**. For Escort/Tracer: GO to **KM3**. For all others: VERIFY operation of A/C clutch cyclic pressure switch and A/C demand switch. If OK, SERVICE open circuit. RECONNECT all components. RE-EVALUATE symptom.
KM3 CHECK CONTINUITY BETWEEN WAC RELAY AND A/C RELAY			
• Key on. • WAC relay disconnected. • Disconnect A/C relay. • Measure resistance between the A/C relay output to the WAC relay at the A/C relay vehicle harness connector and the A/C relay input at the WAC relay vehicle harness connector. • Is resistance less than 5.0 ohms?	Yes No	▶ ▶	RECONNECT WAC relay. REFER to Ventilation Climate Control to check for proper input to A/C relay from B+. IGN RUN and A/C demand circuits; proper A/C relay operation, etc. SERVICE open circuit. RECONNECT WAC relay and A/C relay. RE-EVALUATE symptom.

FM0159400745100X

Fig. 204 Test KM: WAC A/C Demand (Part 8 of 19). 1994–95

TEST STEP	RESULT	▶	ACTION TO TAKE
KM5 CHECK WAC CIRCUIT FOR SHORT TO GROUND			
• Key off. • WAC relay disconnected. • Disconnect Powertrain Control Module (PCM). Inspect for damaged or pushed out pins, corrosion, loose wires, etc. Service as necessary. Leave PCM disconnected. • Measure resistance between WAC circuit at the WAC relay vehicle harness connector and chassis ground. • Is resistance greater than 10,000 ohms?	Yes No	▶ ▶	GO to **KM6**. SERVICE short circuit. RECONNECT all components. RE-EVALUATE symptom.
KM6 CHECK FOR VOLTAGE AT ACCS/ACD INPUT TO PCM			
• Key off. • WAC relay disconnected. • PCM disconnected. • Install breakout box, leave PCM disconnected. • Key on, engine off. • A/C demand switch to A/C on. • For Escort/Tracer, turn blower motor switch on (any speed). • Measure voltage between Test Pin 10 and Test Pin 40 at the breakout box. • For 2.3L Ranger A/T, also measure voltage between Test Pin 43 (ACD) and Test Pin 40 at the breakout box. • Is voltage(s) greater than 10.5 volts?	Yes No	▶ ▶	GO to **KM7**. SERVICE open in ACCS/ACD circuit. REMOVE breakout box. RECONNECT all components. RE-EVALUATE symptom.
KM7 CHECK WAC RELAY			
• Key off. • Breakout box installed, PCM disconnected. • Reconnect WAC relay. • Disconnect A/C clutch. • Key on, engine off. • A/C demand switch to A/C on. • For Escort/Tracer turn blower motor switch on (any speed). • Measure voltage between the power side of the A/C clutch vehicle harness connector and the battery negative post. • Is voltage greater than 10.5 volts?	Yes No	▶ ▶	GO to **KM8**. REPLACE WAC relay. REMOVE breakout box. RECONNECT all components. RE-EVALUATE symptom.

FM0159400745110X

Fig. 204 Test KM: WAC A/C Demand (Part 9 of 19). 1994–95

TEST STEP	RESULT	▶	ACTION TO TAKE
KM8 CHECK ECT AND TP INPUTS			
• Key off. • Breakout box installed. • Reconnect PCM to breakout box. • Reconnect A/C clutch. • A/C on. • Start engine. • Check ECT input: — Measure voltage between Test Pin 7 and Test Pin 40 at the breakout box. • ECT voltage should be greater than 0.3 volt (refer to Pinpoint Test **DA** cover sheet for ECT voltage chart). • Check TP input: — Measure voltage between Test Pin 47 and Test Pin 40 at the breakout box. — At closed and part throttle, the TP voltage should stay below 4.5 volts (refer to Pinpoint Test **DH** cover sheet for TP voltage chart). • Do the ECT and TP input voltages check out OK?	Yes No	▶ ▶	REPLACE PCM. REMOVE breakout box. RE-EVALUATE symptom. PERFORM EEC-IV Quick Test (REFER to Diagnostic Routines Symptom Flow Chart, number 32). SERVICE any DTCs as directed. If OK, CHECK ECT/TP wiring for opens or shorts. SERVICE as necessary. REMOVE breakout box. RECONNECT all components. RE-EVALUATE symptom.
KM15 NO A/C CUTOUT AT WOT: ENTER OUTPUT STATE DIAGNOSTIC TEST MODE (DTM)			
NOTE: Use VOM/DVOM for this Step. • Key off, wait 10 seconds. • Connect DVOM negative test lead to STO at the Data Link Connector (DLC) and positive test lead to battery positive post. • Jumper STI to SIG RTN at the DLC. • Perform Key On Engine Off Self-Test until the completion of the Continuous Memory Diagnostic Trouble Codes. • DVOM will indicate less than 1.0 volt when test is complete. • Depress and release the throttle. • Does voltage increase to greater than 10.5 volts?	Yes No	▶ ▶	REMAIN in Output State DTM. GO to **KM16**. DEPRESS throttle to WOT and RELEASE. If STO voltage does not go high, leave equipment hooked up and GO to Pinpoint Test Step **QC2**.

FM0159400745120X

Fig. 204 Test KM: WAC A/C Demand (Part 10 of 19). 1994–95

TEST STEP	RESULT	▶	ACTION TO TAKE
KM16 CHECK FOR VPWR TO WAC RELAY			
• Still in Output State DTM. • Disconnect harness from WAC relay. • Measure voltage between VPWR circuit (IGN RUN for Escort/Tracer) at the WAC relay vehicle harness connector and chassis ground. • Is voltage greater than 10.5 volts?	Yes No	▶ ▶	GO to **KM17**. SERVICE open in VPWR circuit between EEC power relay and WAC relay (for Escort/Tracer, IGN RUN circuit between WAC relay and joint box). RECONNECT all components and REMOVE jumper. RE-EVALUATE symptom.
KM17 CHECK FOR WAC CYCLING			
• Still in Output State DTM. • WAC relay disconnected. • DVOM on 20 volt scale. • Connect DVOM positive test lead to the VPWR circuit (IGN RUN for Escort/Tracer) and the negative test lead to the WAC circuit at the WAC relay vehicle harness connector. • While observing DVOM, depress and release throttle several times (to cycle output on and off). • Does voltage cycle high and low (about one volt change)?	Yes No	▶ ▶	REPLACE WAC relay. REMOVE jumper. RE-EVALUATE symptom. REMOVE jumper. RECONNECT speed control servo. GO to **KM18**.
KM18 CHECK WAC CIRCUIT CONTINUITY			
• Key off. • Disconnect Powertrain Control Module (PCM). Inspect for damaged or pushed out pins, corrosion, loose wires, etc. Service as necessary. • Install breakout box, leave PCM disconnected. • WAC relay disconnected. • Measure resistance between Test Pin 54 at the breakout box and WAC circuit at the WAC relay vehicle harness connector. • Is resistance less than 5.0 ohms?	Yes No	▶ ▶	GO to **KM19**. SERVICE open circuit. REMOVE breakout box. RECONNECT all components. RE-EVALUATE symptom.

FM0159400745130X

Fig. 204 Test KM: WAC A/C Demand (Part 11 of 19). 1994–95

Fig. 204 Test KM: WAC A/C Demand (Part 12 of 19). 1994–95

TEST STEP	RESULT	▶	ACTION TO TAKE
KM19 CHECK WAC CIRCUIT FOR SHORT TO POWER • Key off. • Breakout box installed, PCM disconnected. • WAC relay disconnected. • Key on, engine off. • Measure voltage between Test Pin 54 and chassis ground. • **Is voltage less than 1.0 volt?**	Yes No	▶ ▶	REPLACE PCM. RECONNECT WAC relay. RE-EVALUATE symptom. SERVICE short circuit. REMOVE breakout box. RECONNECT all components. RE-EVALUATE symptom. If symptom is still present, REPLACE PCM.
KM30 CHECK A/C INPUT CIRCUITRY • A/C demand switch to A/C on. • For Escort/Tracer, turn blower motor switch on lowest speed. • Perform Key On Engine Off Self-Test. • **Is Diagnostic Trouble Code (DTC) 67 or 79/539 present?**	Yes No	▶ ▶	2.3L Ranger (A/T) and 4.9L Truck: GO to KM32. All others: The PCM is receiving and recognizing the A/C input on Pin 10. RETURN for other possible causes of a low idle. A/C demand switch off. GO to KM31.
KM31 CHECK A/C INPUT CIRCUIT • Key off. • Disconnect Powertrain Control Module (PCM). Inspect for damaged or pushed out pins, corrosion, loose wires, etc. Service as necessary. • Install breakout box, leave PCM disconnected. • Key on, engine off. • A/C on. • For Escort/Tracer, turn blower motor switch on. • Measure voltage between Test Pin 10 and Test Pin 40 at the breakout box. • **Is voltage greater than 10.5 volts?**	Yes No	▶ ▶	REPLACE PCM. REMOVE breakout box. RECONNECT all components. RERUN Quick Test. SERVICE open in A/C circuit. REFER to the appropriate engine schematic. REMOVE breakout box. RECONNECT all components. RERUN Quick Test.

FM0159400745140X

Fig. 204 Test KM: WAC A/C Demand (Part 13 of 19). 1994–95

TEST STEP	RESULT	▶	ACTION TO TAKE
KM32 CYCLE A/C DEMAND SWITCH • Key off. • Disconnect Powertrain Control Module (PCM). Inspect for damaged or pushed out pins, corrosion, loose wires, etc. Service as necessary. • Install breakout box, leave PCM disconnected. • DVOM on 20 volt scale. • Key on, engine off. • Connect DVOM positive test lead to Test Pin 43 and negative test lead to Test Pin 40. • **Does voltage cycle high and low when A/C demand switch is cycled?**	Yes No	▶ ▶	The PCM is receiving the A/C inputs on Pin 10 and Pin 43. SERVICE open in ACD circuit. REMOVE breakout box. RECONNECT all components. RERUN Quick Test.
KM40 DIAGNOSTIC TROUBLE CODES (DTCS) 67, 79/539 CHECK A/C INPUT DTC 79/539 indicates the ACCS input to the Powertrain Control Module (PCM) was high during KOEO/KOER Self-Test. DTC 67 indicates that during KOEO Self-Test, voltage was high on NDS (Pin 30) or ACCS (Pin 1C) circuit. NOTE: Before entering this test, verify A/C selector is off (and shift selector is in PARK for AXODE and E4OD vehicles). If A/C was on, turn off and rerun Self-Test. If DTC 67 or 79/539 is present, continue with this test. • Disconnect Powertrain Control Module (PCM). Inspect for damaged or pushed out pins, corrosion, loose wires, etc. Service as necessary. • Install breakout box, leave PCM disconnected. • Key on, engine off. • Measure voltage between Test Pin 10 at the breakout box and chassis ground. • **Is voltage greater than 1.0 volt?**	Yes No	▶ ▶	VERIFY operation of A/C demand switch. If OK, SERVICE short to power in A/C circuit (A/C demand or Power-to-A/C clutch). REMOVE breakout box. RECONNECT all components. RERUN Quick Test. For 7.3L diesel: GO to KM41. For all others: REPLACE PCM. REMOVE breakout box. RECONNECT all components. RERUN Quick Test.
KM41 CHECK FOR SHORT TO POWER IN PCM • Key off. • Breakout box installed. • Connect PCM to breakout box. • Disconnect A/C clutch. • Key on, engine off. • Measure voltage between Test Pin 10 and Test Pin 40 at the breakout box. • **Is voltage greater than 5.0 volts?**	Yes No	▶ ▶	REPLACE PCM. RECONNECT A/C clutch. RERUN Quick Test. RECONNECT A/C clutch. GO to Pinpoint Test Step TD1.

FM0159400745150X

Fig. 204 Test KM: WAC A/C Demand (Part 14 of 19). 1994–95

TEST STEP	RESULT	▶	ACTION TO TAKE
KM50 LOW/NO VOLTAGE TO A/C CLUTCH (2.0L PROBE): ATTEMPT TO GENERATE KOEO DTC 539 • Key off. • A/C demand switch to A/C on. • Perform KOEO Self-Test. • **Is KOEO DTC 539 present?**	Yes No	▶ ▶	GO to KM51. GO to KM55.
KM51 CHECK FOR B+ VOLTAGE TO A/C RELAY • Key off. • Disconnect A/C relay. • Key on. • Measure voltage between B+ circuit at A/C relay vehicle harness connector and chassis ground. • **Is voltage greater than 10.5 volts?**	Yes No	▶ ▶	Key off. GO to KM52. Key off. VERIFY condition of related fuses. If OK, SERVICE open circuit. RECONNECT all components. RE-EVALUATE symptom.
KM52 CHECK POWER TO CLUTCH CIRCUIT CONTINUITY • Key off. • A/C relay disconnected. • Disconnect A/C clutch. • Measure resistance between power side of A/C clutch vehicle harness connector and Power-To-Clutch circuit at A/C relay vehicle harness connector. • **Is resistance less than 5.0 ohms?**	Yes No	▶ ▶	GO to KM53. SERVICE open circuit. RECONNECT all components. RE-EVALUATE symptom.
KM53 CHECK A/C RELAY • Key off. • A/C clutch disconnected. • Reconnect A/C relay. • Jumper AC ON circuit at A/C relay vehicle harness connector to battery ground. • Key on. • Measure voltage between power side of A/C clutch vehicle harness connector and chassis ground. • **Is voltage greater than 10.5 volts?**	Yes No	▶ ▶	Key off. REMOVE jumper. EEC system OK. check for proper ground, open circuit in clutch, mechanical concerns, etc. REPLACE A/C relay. RECONNECT all components. RE-EVALUATE symptom.

FM0159400745160X

Fig. 204 Test KM: WAC A/C Demand (Part 15 of 19). 1994–95

TEST STEP	RESULT	▶	ACTION TO TAKE
KM55 CHECK ACD CIRCUIT CONTINUITY TO LOW PRESSURE (LP) SWITCH • Key off. • A/C demand switch to A/C on. • Disconnect LP switch. • Measure resistance between A/C demand switch side of LP switch vehicle harness connector and chassis ground. • **Is resistance less than 5.0 ohms?**	Yes No	▶ ▶	GO to KM56. VERIFY operation of A/C demand switch. If OK, SERVICE open circuit. RECONNECT all components RE-EVALUATE symptom.
KM56 MEASURE RESISTANCE OF LP SWITCH • Key off. • LP switch disconnected. • Measure resistance of LP switch. • **Is resistance less than 5.0 ohms?**	Yes No	▶ ▶	GO to KM57. REFER to Ventilation/Climate Control. RECONNECT all components RE-EVALUATE symptom.
KM57 CHECK ACD CIRCUIT CONTINUITY FROM LP SWITCH TO POWERTRAIN CONTROL MODULE (PCM) • Key off. • LP switch disconnected. • Disconnect Powertrain Control Module (PCM). Inspect for damaged or pushed out pins, corrosion, loose wires, etc. Service as necessary. • Install breakout box, leave PCM disconnected. • Measure resistance between Test Pin 23 (49 state M/T) or Test Pin 10 (CD4E, Calif. M/T) at the breakout box and PCM side of LP switch vehicle harness connector. • **Is resistance less than 5.0 ohms?**	Yes No	▶ ▶	REPLACE PCM. REMOVE breakout box. RECONNECT all components. RE-EVALUATE symptom. SERVICE open circuit. RECONNECT all components. RE-EVALUATE symptom.

FM0159400745170X

TEST STEP	RESULT	▶	ACTION TO TAKE
KM60 DIAGNOSTIC TROUBLE CODE (DTC) 559: CHECK FOR IGN RUN VOLTAGE TO A/C RELAY			
DTC 559 indicates an A/C relay primary circuit fault.	Yes	▶	GO to **KM61**.
Possible causes:	No	▶	VERIFY condition of related fuses. If OK, SERVICE open circuit. RECONNECT all components. RERUN Quick Test.
— Open or shorted circuit — Damaged A/C relay — Damaged Powertrain Control Module (PCM) • Key off. • Disconnect A/C relay. • Key on. • Measure voltage between IGN RUN circuit at A/C relay vehicle harness connector and chassis ground. • **Is voltage greater than 10.5 volts?**			

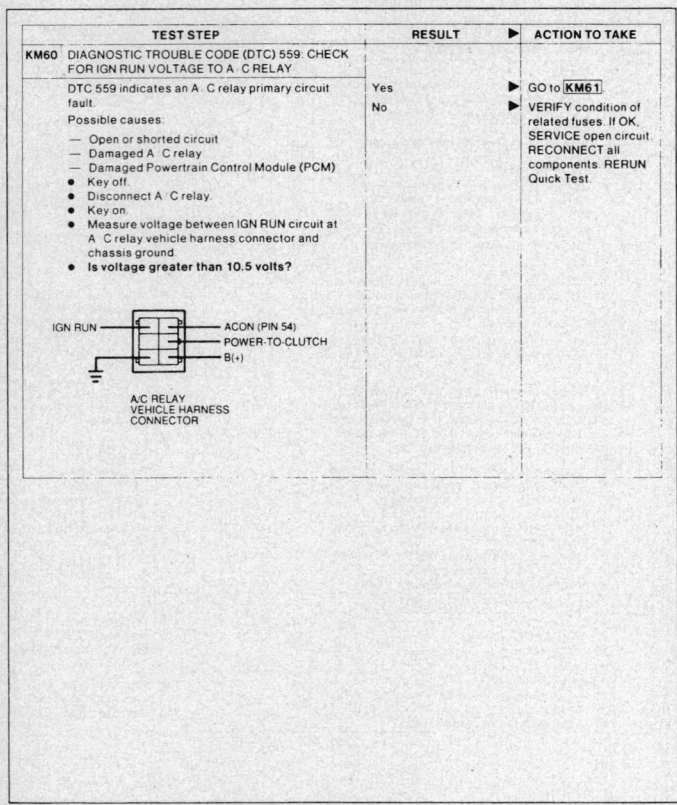

TEST STEP	RESULT	▶	ACTION TO TAKE
KM61 CHECK A/C RELAY			

• Key off.
 • A/C relay disconnected.
 • Check A/C relay coil resistance:
  — Measure resistance between ACON pin and IGN RUN pin at the A/C relay.
  — Resistance should be between 50 and 100 ohms.
 • Check A/C relay for internal shorts:
  — Measure resistance between ACON pin and the following pins at the A/C relay: B+, power-to-clutch, ground.
  — Resistances should be greater than 10,000 ohms.
 • **Are all resistance checks OK?**
	Yes	▶	GO to **KM62**.

	No	▶	REPLACE A/C relay. RECONNECT all components. RERUN Quick Test.
KM62 CHECK ACON CIRCUIT FOR SHORT TO POWER			
• Key off. • A/C relay disconnected. • Disconnect Powertrain Control Module (PCM). Inspect for damaged or pushed out pins, corrosion, loose wire, etc. Service as necessary. • Install breakout box, leave PCM disconnected. • Key on, engine off. • Measure voltage between Test Pin 54 at the breakout box and chassis ground. • **Is voltage less than 1.0 volt?**	Yes	▶	GO to **KM63**.
	No	▶	SERVICE short to power. REMOVE breakout box. RECONNECT all components. RERUN Quick Test.
KM63 CHECK ACON CIRCUIT FOR SHORT TO GROUND			
• Key off. • A/C relay disconnected. • Breakout box installed, PCM disconnected. • Measure resistance between Test Pin 54 at the breakout box and chassis ground. • **Is resistance greater than 10,000 ohms?**	Yes	▶	GO to **KM64**.
	No	▶	SERVICE short to ground. REMOVE breakout box. RECONNECT all components. RERUN Quick Test.

Fig. 204 Test KM: WAC A/C Demand (Part 16 of 19). 1994–95

Fig. 204 Test KM: WAC A/C Demand (Part 17 of 19). 1994–95

TEST STEP	RESULT	▶	ACTION TO TAKE
KM64 CHECK ACON CIRCUIT CONTINUITY			
• Key off. • A/C relay disconnected. • Breakout box installed, PCM disconnected. • Measure resistance between Test Pin 54 at breakout box and ACON circuit at A/C relay vehicle harness connector. • **Is resistance less than 5.0 ohms?**	Yes	▶	REPLACE PCM. REMOVE breakout box. RECONNECT all components. RERUN Quick Test.
	No	▶	SERVICE open circuit. REMOVE breakout box. RECONNECT all components. RERUN Quick Test.
KM70 DIAGNOSTIC TROUBLE CODE (DTC) 539: CHECK A/C INPUT			
DTC 539 indicates the A/C demand input to the Powertrain Control Module (PCM) was low (A/C on) during KOEO Self-Test.	Yes	▶	GO to **KM71**.
	No	▶	VERIFY operation of A/C demand switch.
NOTE: Before entering this test, verify A/C selector is off. If A/C was on, rerun KOEO Self-Test. If DTC 539 is present, continue with this test. • Key off. • A/C off. • Disconnect Low Pressure (LP) switch. • Measure resistance between A/C demand switch side of LP switch vehicle harness connector and chassis ground. • **Is resistance greater than 10,000 ohms?**			If OK, SERVICE short to ground. RECONNECT all components. RE-EVALUATE symptom.
KM71 CHECK LOW PRESSURE (LP) SWITCH			
• Key off. • LP switch disconnected. • Measure resistance between chassis ground and both pins of LP switch. • **Are both resistances greater than 10,000 ohms?**	Yes	▶	GO to **KM72**.
	No	▶	REPLACE LP switch. RECONNECT all components. RE-EVALUATE symptom.
KM72 CHECK ACD CIRCUIT TO PCM FOR SHORT TO GROUND			
• Key off. • LP switch disconnected. • Disconnect Powertrain Control Module (PCM). Inspect for damaged or pushed out pins, corrosion, loose wires, etc. Service as necessary. • Measure resistance between PCM side of the LP switch vehicle harness connector and chassis ground. • **Is resistance greater than 10,000 ohms?**	Yes	▶	REPLACE PCM. RECONNECT all components. RE-EVALUATE symptom.
	No	▶	SERVICE short to ground. RECONNECT all components. RE-EVALUATE symptom.

TEST STEP	RESULT	▶	ACTION TO TAKE
KM80 A/C ALWAYS ON: CHECK POWER TO CLUTCH CIRCUIT FOR SHORT TO POWER			
NOTE: Before entering this test, verify KOEO DTC 539 or 559 was not received. If DTC 539 or 559 is present, refer to EEC-IV Diagnostic Trouble Code Charts for proper Pinpoint Test direction.	Yes	▶	GO to **KM81**.
	No	▶	SERVICE short to power. RECONNECT all components. RE-EVALUATE symptom.
• Key off. • Disconnect A/C relay. • Disconnect A/C clutch. • Key on. • Measure voltage between power side of A/C Clutch vehicle harness connector and battery negative post. • **Is voltage less than 1.0 volt?**			
KM81 CHECK A/C RELAY			
• Key off. • A/C relay disconnected. • Measure resistance between power-to-clutch pin and both the IGN RUN and B+ pins at the A/C relay. • **Are both resistances greater than 10,000 ohms?**	Yes	▶	EEC system OK. A/C Diagnosis.
	No	▶	REPLACE A/C relay. RECONNECT all components. RE-EVALUATE symptom.

IGN RUN
 ACON (PIN 54) — GROUND
 — B(+)
 — POWER-TO-CLUTCH
 A/C RELAY

Fig. 204 Test KM: WAC A/C Demand (Part 18 of 19). 1994–95

Fig. 204 Test KM: WAC A/C Demand (Part 19 of 19). 1994–95

Note

You should enter this Pinpoint Test only when you have been directed here from Diagnostic Routines.

Remember

To prevent the replacement of good components, be aware that the following non-EEC areas may be at fault:

- Damaged fuel pressure regulator
- Damaged vacuum hoses
- Engine operating temperatures
- Base engine (valves, vacuum leaks, timing, etc.)

This Pinpoint Test is intended to diagnose only the following:

- FPRC solenoid
- Harness Circuits: FPRC, and VPWR
- Powertrain Control Module (PCM)

Description

The Fuel Pressure Regulator Control (FPRC) solenoid controls the vacuum applied to the fuel pressure regulator. The FPRC solenoid contains a valve with two ports. One port is connected to the manifold vacuum. The second port is connected to the fuel pressure regulator. The FPRC solenoid also has an air filter cap (vent) on it. If the solenoid is energized, then the solenoid valve closes the vacuum path to the second port which leads to the fuel pressure regulator. This results in a higher fuel pressure during crank, idle, neutral and wide open throttle drive modes for a predetermined time and engine temperature. If the solenoid is not energized, then the solenoid valve opens the vacuum path to the second port, allowing the manifold vacuum signal to be applied as input to the fuel pressure regulator.

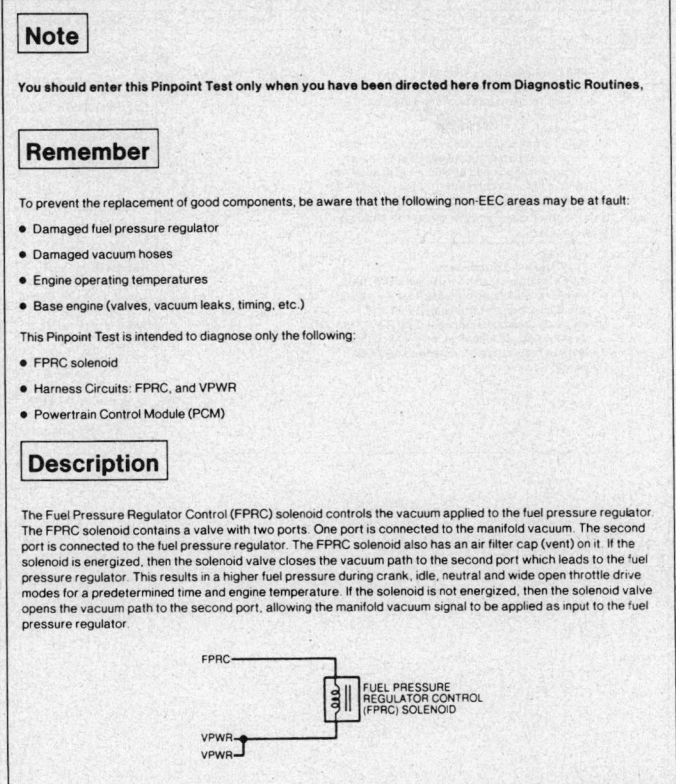

FM015930074601OX

Fig. 205   Test KN: FPRC Solenoid (Part 1 of 6)

Pinpoint Test Schematic

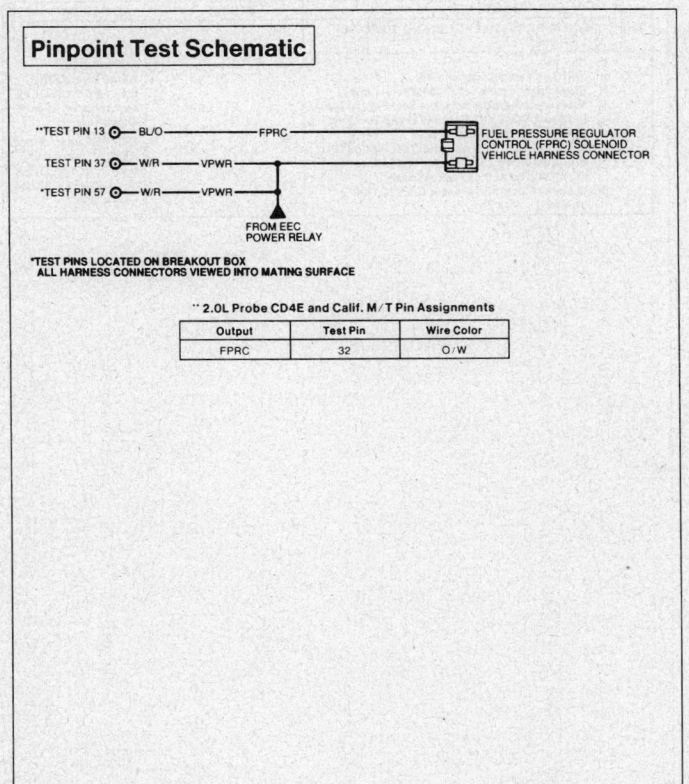

Fig. 205   Test KN: FPRC Solenoid (Part 2 of 6). 1993

Pinpoint Test Schematic

FM015940074602BX

Fig. 205   Test KN: FPRC Solenoid (Part 2 of 6). 1994–95

	TEST STEP	RESULT	▶	ACTION TO TAKE
KN1	KOEO DIAGNOSTIC TROUBLE CODE (DTC) 554: ENTER OUTPUT STATE DIAGNOSTIC TEST MODE (DTM)			
	DTC 554 indicates a failure in the Fuel Pressure Regulator Control (FPRC) solenoid circuit. Possible causes: — Damaged FPRC solenoid — Damaged vacuum hose(s) — Open in harness — Short (to power or ground) in harness — Damaged Powertrain Control Module (PCM) NOTE: Do not use STAR Tester for this step. Use a VOM/DVOM. • Key off. • Disconnect electrical connector on the speed control servo, if equipped. • DVOM on 20 volt scale. • Connect DVOM negative test lead to STO circuit at Data Link Connector (DLC) and positive test lead to battery positive. • Jumper STI circuit to SIG RTN at DLC. • Perform Key On Engine Off Self-Test until completion of Continuous Test Memory DTCs. • DVOM will indicate less than 1.0 volt when test is completed. • Depress and release throttle. • **Does voltage increase?**	Yes No	▶ ▶	REMAIN in Output State DTM. GO to **KN2**. DEPRESS throttle to WOT and RELEASE. If STO voltage does not go high leave equipment hooked up and GO to Pinpoint Test Step **QC1**.
KN2	CHECK FUEL PRESSURE REGULATOR CONTROL SOLENOID ELECTRICAL OPERATION			
	• Key on, engine off. • Disconnect FPRC solenoid. • Connect DVOM positive test lead to VPWR pin and negative test lead to FPRC circuit at the FPRC solenoid vehicle harness connector. • DVOM on 20 volt scale. • While observing DVOM depress and release throttle several times to cycle solenoid output. • **Does FPRC solenoid output voltage change greater than 1.0 volt?**	Yes No	▶ ▶	RECONNECT FPRC solenoid. REMOVE jumper. GO to **KN3**. REMOVE jumper. GO to **KN5**.

FM015930074603OX

Fig. 205   Test KN: FPRC Solenoid (Part 3 of 6)

TEST STEP	RESULT	▶	ACTION TO TAKE
KN3 CHECK VACUUM SIGNAL BETWEEN FUEL PRESSURE REGULATOR AND FPRC SOLENOID			
• Key off. • Disconnect and inspect vacuum hose between fuel pressure regulator and FPRC solenoid for blockage, kinks, etc. Service as necessary. • Start and idle engine for about five minutes to allow it to reach normal operating temperature. • Key off. • Tee in a standard vacuum gauge between fuel pressure regulator and FPRC solenoid. • Start and idle engine while observing vacuum gauge needle. Observe vacuum gauge needle for about five minutes. • **Did vacuum signal appear after about two minutes of engine idle?**	Yes No	▶ ▶	REMOVE vacuum gauge. REFER to Fuel Pressure Regulator diagnostics. REMOVE vacuum gauge. GO to **KN4**.
KN4 CHECK VACUUM SIGNAL BETWEEN FPRC SOLENOID AND MANIFOLD VACUUM SOURCE			
• Key off. • Tee in a standard vacuum gauge between the FPRC solenoid and manifold vacuum source. • Start and idle engine while observing the vacuum gauge needle. • **Was any vacuum signal present?**	Yes No	▶ ▶	REPLACE FPRC solenoid. REMOVE vacuum gauge. RERUN Quick Test and/or VERIFY elimination of drive symptom. REPLACE vacuum hose between FPRC solenoid and source vacuum. REMOVE vacuum gauge. RERUN Quick Test and/or VERIFY elimination of drive symptom.
KN5 CHECK FPRC SOLENOID VPWR			
• Key off. • FPRC solenoid disconnected. • Key on, engine off. • Measure voltage between VPWR at FPRC solenoid vehicle harness connector and battery ground. • **Is voltage greater than 10.5 volts?**	Yes No	▶ ▶	GO to **KN6** SERVICE open in VPWR harness circuit. RECONNECT FPRC solenoid. RERUN Quick Test and/or VERIFY elimination of drive symptom.

FM015930074 6040X

Fig. 205   Test KN: FPRC Solenoid (Part 4 of 6)

TEST STEP	RESULT	▶	ACTION TO TAKE
KN6 CHECK FPRC CIRCUIT CONTINUITY			
• Key off. • FPRC solenoid disconnected. • Disconnect Powertrain Control Module (PCM). Inspect for damaged or pushed out pins, corrosion, loose wires, etc. Service as necessary. • Install breakout box, leave PCM disconnected. • Measure resistance between Test Pin 13 at the breakout box and FPRC circuit at solenoid vehicle harness connector. • **Is resistance less and 5.0 ohms?**	Yes No	▶ ▶	GO to **KN7** SERVICE open circuit. REMOVE breakout box. RECONNECT all components. RERUN Quick Test and/or VERIFY elimination of drive symptom.
KN7 CHECK FPRC CIRCUIT FOR SHORT TO POWER AND GROUND			
• Key off. • FPRC solenoid disconnected. • Breakout box installed, PCM disconnected. • Measure resistance between Test Pin 13 and Test Pins 37 and 57 at the breakout box. • Measure resistance between Test Pin 13 and Test Pins 40, 46 and 60 at the breakout box. • **Is each resistance greater than 10,000 ohms?**	Yes No	▶ ▶	REPLACE PCM. REMOVE breakout box. RECONNECT all components. RERUN Quick Test and/or VERIFY elimination of drive symptom. SERVICE short circuit. REMOVE breakout box. RECONNECT all components. RERUN Quick Test and/or VERIFY elimination of drive symptom.

FM015930074605AX

Fig. 205   Test KN: FPRC Solenoid (Part 5 of 6). 1993

TEST STEP	RESULT	▶	ACTION TO TAKE
KN6 EXERCISE THE FPRC SOLENOID VALVE			

• Key off.
 • Install vacuum gauge between the FPRC solenoid output port and the fuel pressure regulator.
 • Perform the road test as outlined below:
   — Warm engine to operating temperature.
   — Obey all local traffic laws.
   — Observe the vacuum gauge while
     (1) Accelerating heavily to 40 mph and
     (2) Decelerating to a steady cruise below 20 mph.
 	
 NOTE: Gauge should indicate a low vacuum (FPRC solenoid valve closed) during the heavy acceleration and a higher vacuum (FPRC solenoid valve open) during the steady cruise if the FPRC solenoid valve is functioning properly. Repeat the test as necessary to confirm status of the FPRC solenoid valve operation.
 	
 • **Did vacuum signal to fuel pressure regulator fall and rise as expected?**
	Yes
	
	 No
		▶
		
		 ▶
			REMOVE the vacuum gauge pressure regulator diagnostics.
			 REMOVE the vacuum gauge. REPLACE the FPRC solenoid assembly. RERUN Quick Test.

KN7 CHECK FPRC SOLENOID VPWR			
• Key off. • FPRC solenoid disconnected. • Key on, engine off. • Measure voltage between VPWR at FPRC solenoid vehicle harness connector and battery ground. • **Is voltage greater than 10.5 volts?**	Yes No	▶ ▶	GO to **KN8**. SERVICE open in VPWR harness circuit. RECONNECT FPRC solenoid. RERUN Quick Test and/or VERIFY elimination of drive symptom.
KN8 CHECK FPRC CIRCUIT CONTINUITY			
• Key off. • FPRC solenoid disconnected. • Disconnect Powertrain Control Module (PCM). Inspect for damaged or pushed out pins, corrosion, loose wires, etc. Service as necessary. • Install breakout box, leave PCM disconnected. • Measure resistance between Test Pin 13 (Test Pin 32 for CD4E and Calif. M/T) at the breakout box and FPRC circuit at solenoid vehicle harness connector. • **Is resistance less and 5.0 ohms?**	Yes No	▶ ▶	GO to **KN9**. SERVICE open circuit. REMOVE breakout box. RECONNECT all components. RERUN Quick Test and/or VERIFY elimination of drive symptom.

Fig. 205   Test KN: FPRC Solenoid (Part 5 of 6). 1994–95

TEST STEP	RESULT	▶	ACTION TO TAKE
KN9 CHECK FPRC CIRCUIT FOR SHORT TO POWER AND GROUND			
• Key off. • FPRC solenoid disconnected. • Breakout box installed, PCM disconnected. • Measure resistance between Test Pin 13 (Test Pin 32 for CD4E and Calif. M/T) and Test Pins 37 and 57 at the breakout box. • Measure resistance between Test Pin 13 (Test Pin 32 for CD4E and Calif. M/T) and Test Pins 40, 46 and 60 at the breakout box. • **Is each resistance greater than 10,000 ohms?**	Yes No	▶ ▶	REPLACE PCM. REMOVE breakout box. RECONNECT all components. RERUN Quick Test. SERVICE short circuit. REMOVE breakout box. RECONNECT all components. RERUN Quick Test.

Fig. 205   Test KN: FPRC Solenoid (Part 6 of 6). 1994–95

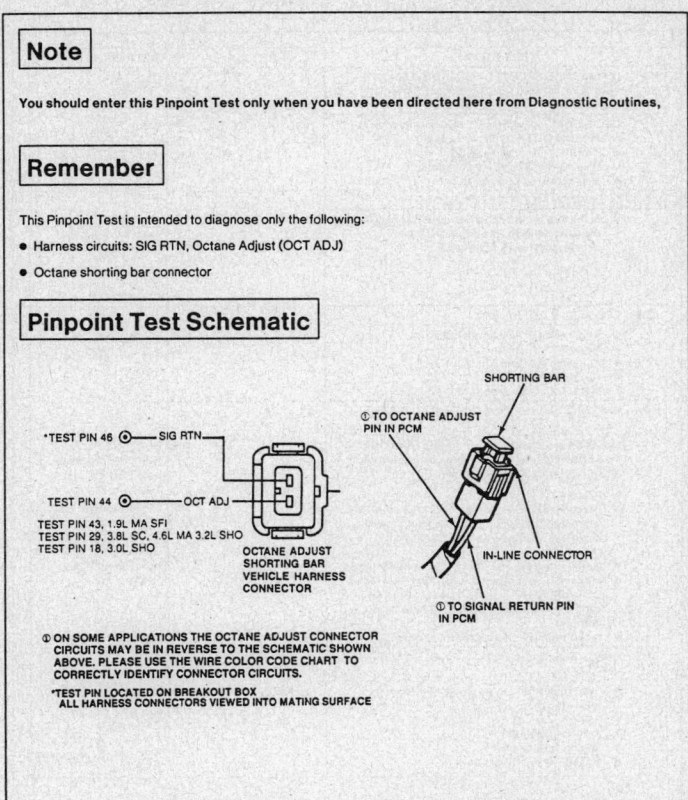

Note

You should enter this Pinpoint Test only when you have been directed here from Diagnostic Routines,

Remember

This Pinpoint Test is intended to diagnose only the following:

- Harness circuits: SIG RTN, Octane Adjust (OCT ADJ)
- Octane shorting bar connector

Pinpoint Test Schematic

Fig. 206   Test KP: OCT ADJ (Part 1 of 6). 1993

Note

You should enter this Pinpoint Test only when you have been directed here from Diagnostic Routines,

Remember

This Pinpoint Test is intended to diagnose only the following:

- Harness circuits: SIG RTN, Octane Adjust (OCT ADJ)
- Octane shorting bar connector

Fig. 206   Test KP: OCT ADJ (Part 1 of 6). 1994–95

NOTE: The Octane Adjust (OCT ADJ) shorting bar is similar in shape to the SPOUT in-line connector and on some applications the PSP circuit will also have a similar shorting bar connector. DO NOT remove the shorting bar unless you have been directed by a specific application or Technical Service Bulletin (TSB).

Test Pin 18, 29 or 44 — OCT ADJ

Application	Wire Color
1.9L Escort / Tracer	GR / W
Car: 2.3L Mustang 4.6L Town Car 4.6L Mark VIII	DG
3.0L Taurus SHO 3.2L Taurus SHO	PK
3.8L Thunderbird SC	GY / R
4.6L Crown Victoria / Grand Marquis	W / R

Test Pin 46 — SIG RTN

Application	Wire Color
1.9L MA SFI Escort / Tracer	LG / BK
All Others	GY / R

Fig. 206   Test KP: OCT ADJ (Part 2 of 6). 1993

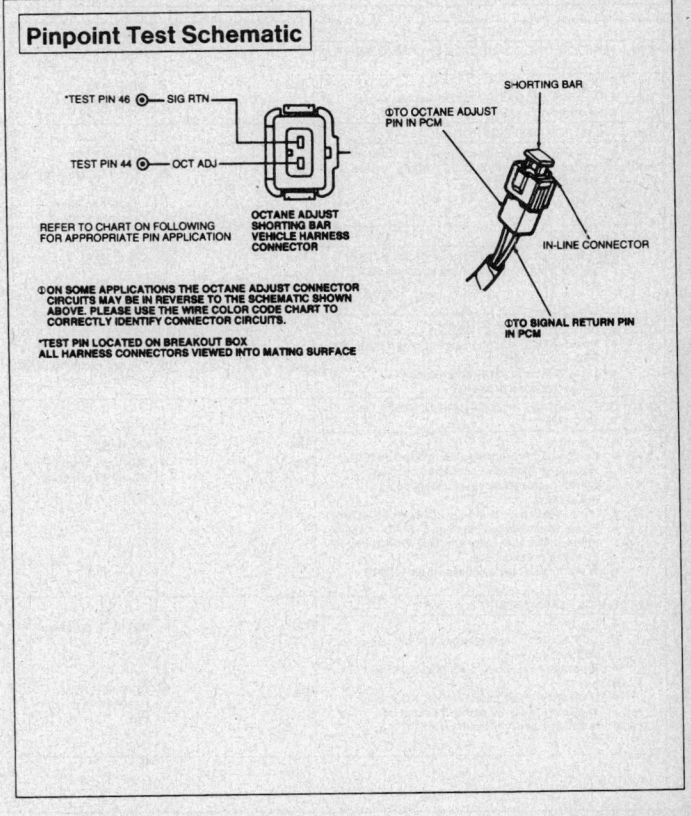

Pinpoint Test Schematic

Fig. 206   Test KP: OCT ADJ (Part 3 of 6). 1994–95

FM015940074702BX

NOTE: The Octane Adjust (OCT ADJ) shorting bar is similar in shape to the SPOUT in-line connector and on some applications the PSP circuit will also have a similar shorting bar connector. DO NOT remove the shorting bar unless you have been directed by a specific application or Technical Service Bulletin (TSB).

Octane Adjust Circuit

Application	Pin Number	Wire Color
1.9L Escort/Tracer	43	GR/W
3.0L Taurus SHO	18	PK
3.2L Taurus SHO	29	
3.8L Thunderbird SC	29	DG
3.8L Thunderbird/Cougar	29	
4.6L Crown Victoria/Grand Marquis	29	W/R
4.6L Mark VIII	29	DG
4.6L Town Car	29	DG
2.3L Ranger (49 States)	44	DG
2.3L Ranger (Calif.)	29	
4.0L Aerostar	44	DG
4.0L Ranger (49 States)	44	
4.0L Ranger (Calif.)	29	
4.0L Explorer	29	

Test Pin 46—SIG RTN

Application	Wire Color
1.9L Escort/Tracer	LG/BK
All Others	GY/R

Fig. 206   Test KP: OCT ADJ (Part 4 of 6). 1994–95

	TEST STEP	RESULT	▶	ACTION TO TAKE
KP1	DIAGNOSTIC TROUBLE CODE (DTC) 57/341: VISUALLY INSPECT OCTANE ADJUST IN-LINE CONNECTOR DTC 57/341 indicates OCT ADJ shorting bar is not in or the OCT ADJ circuit is open. • Key off. • Visually inspect in-line connector. • Is shorting bar removed?	Yes No	▶ ▶	GO to KP2. GO to KP4.
KP2	CHECK FOR MODIFICATION DECAL • Is there a modification decal attached to the vehicle indicating that OCT ADJ shorting bar was removed?	Yes No	▶ ▶	Testing complete. If vehicle has spark knock concern, GO to KP3.
KP3	CHECK FOR DTC 57/341 • Replace OCT ADJ shorting bar. • Key off. • Activate Self-Test. • Key on, engine off. • Is DTC 57/341 present?	Yes No	▶ ▶	GO to KP4. Testing complete. EEC system OK.
KP4	CHECK CONTINUITY OF OCTANE ADJUST CIRCUIT NOTE: There should be continuity from OCT ADJ circuit through the in-line connector and shorting bar to SIG RTN circuit. • Key off. • Disconnect Powertrain Control Module (PCM). Inspect for damaged or pushed out pins, corrosion, loose wires, etc. Service as necessary. • Install breakout box, leave PCM disconnected. • Measure resistance between Test Pin 46 and OCT ADJ Test Pin at the breakout box (refer to schematic for appropriate OCT ADJ circuit test pin). • Is the resistance less than 5.0 ohms?	Yes No	▶ ▶	REPLACE PCM. REMOVE breakout box. RERUN Quick Test. SERVICE open OCT ADJ circuit or shorting bar or SIG RTN circuit. REMOVE breakout box. RERUN Quick Test.
KP5	CHECK FOR DIAGNOSTIC TROUBLE CODE (DTC) 11 • Start engine and idle vehicle at operating temperature. • Key off. • Activate Self-Test. • Key on, engine off. • Is DTC 11 or 111 present?	Yes No	▶ ▶	GO to KP6. For DTC 57 341: GO to KP1. For all other DTC's: RETURN to Diagnostic Routines.

FM0159300747040X

Fig. 206   Test KP: OCT ADJ (Part 5 of 6)

	TEST STEP	RESULT	▶	ACTION TO TAKE
KP6	VERIFY IN-LINE CONNECTOR SHORTING BAR IS INSTALLED • Key off. • Visually inspect OCT ADJ in-line connector. • Is shorting bar installed?	Yes No	▶ ▶	GO to KP8. GO to KP7.
KP7	CHECK FOR MODIFICATION DECAL • Is there a decal attached to vehicle indicating that OCT ADJ shorting bar was removed?	Yes No	▶ ▶	GO to KP10. REPLACE shorting bar. address spark knock concern.
KP8	CHECK FOR TSB • Is there a Technical Service Bulletin (TSB) authorizing removal of the shorting OCT ADJ bar?	Yes No	▶ ▶	GO to KP9. address spark knock concern.
KP9	REMOVE OCT ADJ SHORTING BAR • Remove OCT ADJ shorting bar only if there is a TSB authorization. • Drive vehicle to verify spark knock. • Is spark knock present?	Yes No	▶ ▶	GO to KP10. Testing complete. EEC system OK.
KP10	CHECK OCTANE ADJUST CIRCUIT FOR A SHORT TO GROUND • Key off. • Disconnect Powertrain Control Module (PCM). Inspect for damaged or pushed out pins, corrosion, loose wires, etc. Service as necessary. • Install breakout box; leave PCM disconnected. • Measure resistance between OCT ADJ circuit at the in-line connector and Test Pin 40, 46 and 60 at the breakout box. • Is each resistance greater than 10,000 ohms?	Yes No	▶ ▶	GO to KP11. SERVICE short circuit. REMOVE breakout box.
KP11	CHECK PCM INTEGRITY • Key off. • OCT ADJ shorting bar removed because of TSB authorization. • Breakout box installed, PCM connected. • Key on. • Measure voltage between OCT ADJ circuit and Test Pin 40/60 at the breakout box. • Is voltage greater than 4.0 volts?	Yes No	▶ ▶	REMOVE breakout box. REPLACE PCM. REMOVE breakout box.

Fig. 206   Test KP: OCT ADJ (Part 6 of 6)

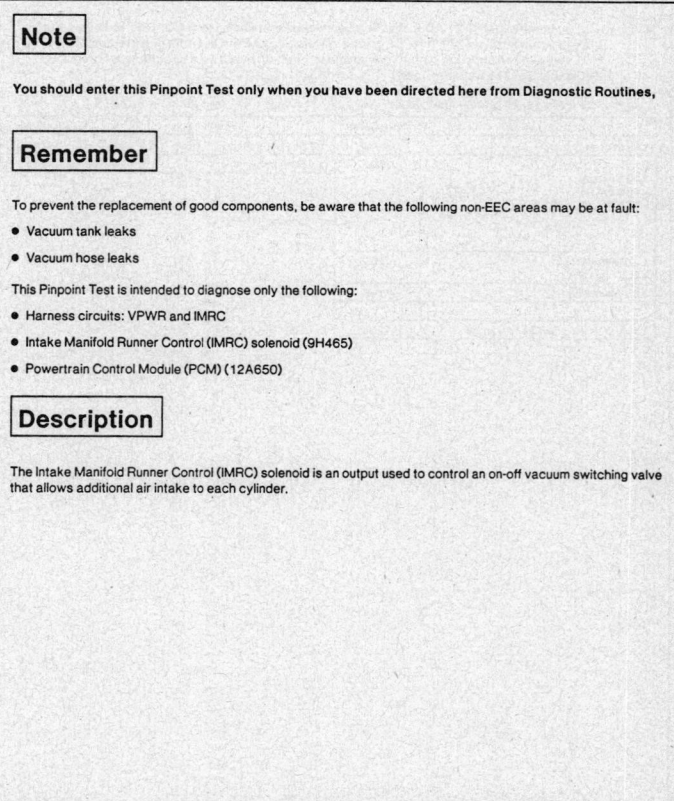

Note

You should enter this Pinpoint Test only when you have been directed here from Diagnostic Routines,

Remember

To prevent the replacement of good components, be aware that the following non-EEC areas may be at fault:
• Vacuum tank leaks
• Vacuum hose leaks

This Pinpoint Test is intended to diagnose only the following:
• Harness circuits: VPWR and IMRC
• Intake Manifold Runner Control (IMRC) solenoid (9H465)
• Powertrain Control Module (PCM) (12A650)

Description

The Intake Manifold Runner Control (IMRC) solenoid is an output used to control an on-off vacuum switching valve that allows additional air intake to each cylinder.

Fig. 207   Test KT: IMRC System (Part 1 of 6)

Pinpoint Test Schematic

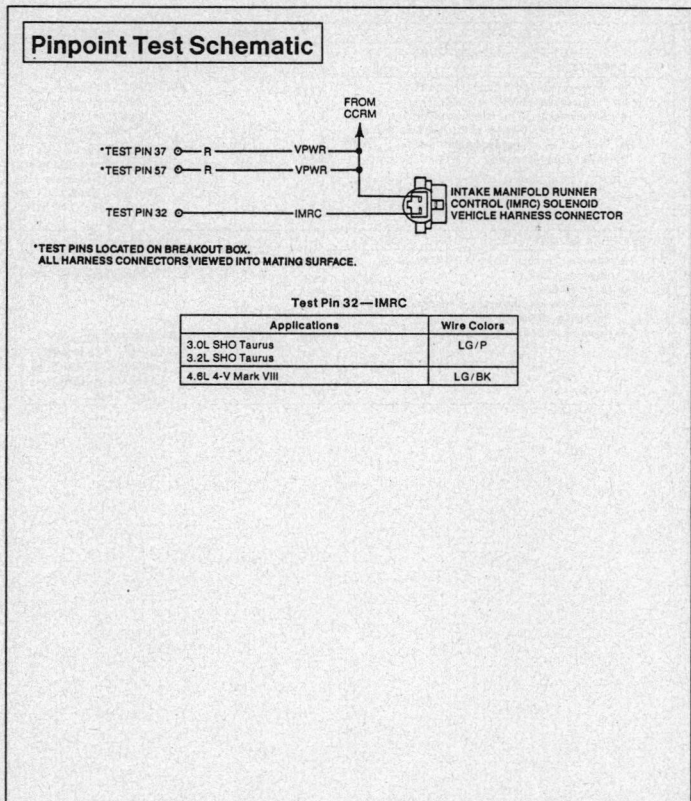

Fig. 207 Test KT: IMRC System
(Part 2 of 6). 1993–94

Pinpoint Test Schematic

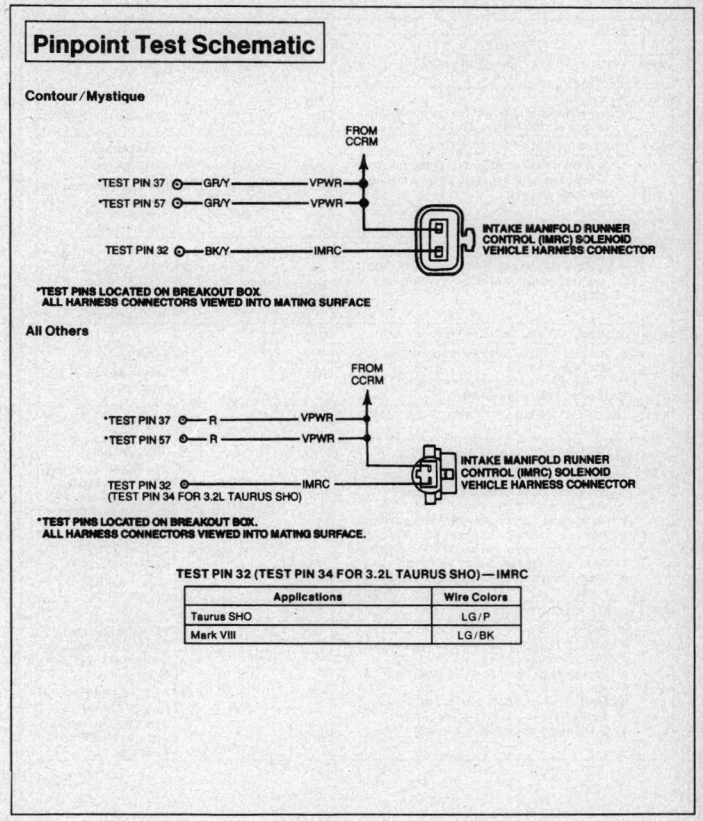

FM015950074802B)

Fig. 207 Test KT: IMRC System (Part 2 of 6). 1995

	TEST STEP	RESULT	▶	ACTION TO TAKE
KT1	DIAGNOSTIC TROUBLE CODE (DTC) 81/551: CHECK IMRC SOLENOID RESISTANCE			
	DTC 81/551 indicates that the IMRC solenoid output voltage did not change when activated during Key On Engine Off Self-Test. Possible causes: — IMRC circuit open — IMRC circuit short — IMRC solenoid — IMRC valve(s) assembly — Powertrain Control Module (PCM) output driver open/grounded • Key off. • Disconnect IMRC solenoid. • Measure resistance between IMRC circuit and VPWR circuit at the IMRC solenoid. • **Is solenoid resistance between 50 and 100 ohms?**	Yes No	▶ ▶	GO to **KT2** REPLACE IMRC solenoid. RERUN Quick Test.
KT2	CHECK VPWR CIRCUIT VOLTAGE			
	• Key on, engine off. • IMRC solenoid disconnected. • Measure voltage between VPWR circuit of IMRC solenoid vehicle harness connector and battery negative post. • **Is voltage greater than 10.5 volts?**	Yes No	▶ ▶	GO to **KT3** SERVICE open circuit. RECONNECT IMRC solenoid. RERUN Quick Test.
KT3	CHECK IMRC CIRCUIT CONTINUITY			
	• Key off. • IMRC solenoid disconnected. • Disconnect Powertrain Control Module (PCM). Inspect for damaged pins, corrosion, loose wires etc. Service as necessary. • Install breakout box, leave PCM disconnected. • Measure resistance between Test Pin 32 at the breakout box and IMRC circuit at the IMRC solenoid vehicle harness connector. • **Is resistance less than 5.0 ohms?**	Yes No	▶ ▶	GO to **KT4** SERVICE open circuit. REMOVE breakout box. RECONNECT all components. RERUN Quick Test.
KT4	CHECK IMRC CIRCUIT FOR SHORT TO GROUND			
	• Key off. • IMRC solenoid disconnected. • Breakout box installed. PCM disconnected. • Measure resistance between Test Pin 32 and Test Pins 40, 46 and 60 at the breakout box. • **Is each resistance greater than 100,000 ohms?**	Yes No	▶ ▶	GO to **KT5** SERVICE short circuit. REMOVE breakout box. RECONNECT all components. RERUN Quick Test.

FM0159300748030X

Fig. 207 Test KT: IMRC System (Part 3 of 6)

	TEST STEP	RESULT	▶	ACTION TO TAKE
KT5	CHECK IMRC CIRCUIT FOR SHORT TO POWER			
	• Key off. • IMRC solenoid disconnected. • Breakout box installed, PCM disconnected. • Measure resistance between Test Pin 32 and Test Pins 37 and 57 at the breakout box. • **Is each resistance greater than 100,000 ohms?**	Yes No	▶ ▶	REPLACE PCM. REMOVE breakout box. RECONNECT all components. RERUN Quick Test. SERVICE short circuit. REMOVE breakout box. RECONNECT all components. RERUN Quick Test. If symptom is still present, REPLACE PCM.
KT6	CHECK BOTH IMRC VALVES			
	• Key off. • Disconnect vacuum lines from both IMRC valves. • Install vacuum pump at each IMRC valve. • Apply 10 in-Hg (34 kPa) vacuum to each of the IMRC valves. • **Did both IMRC valves hold vacuum?**	Yes No	▶ ▶	GO to **KT7**. REPLACE IMRC valve assembly as necessary. REMOVE vacuum pumps. RECONNECT vacuum lines to both IMRC valves. RERUN Quick Test.
KT7	CHECK OPERATION OF BOTH IMRC VALVES AND LINKAGES			
	• Key off. • Apply 10 in-Hg (34 kPa) vacuum to both IMRC valves. • **Did both valves and valve mechanical linkages move in response to the applied vacuum?**	Yes No	▶ ▶	GO to **KT8**. SERVICE as necessary. INSPECT for contamination, if none then REPLACE appropriate IMRC valve assembly. RERUN Quick Test.
KT8	CHECK VACUUM HOSES TO BOTH IMRC VALVES			
	• Key off. • Check the vacuum hose from the front and rear IMRC valves to the IMRC solenoid. Inspect for holes, kinks, disconnections and blockages. • **Are vacuum hoses OK?**	Yes No	▶ ▶	GO to **KT9**. SERVICE vacuum hose(s) as necessary. RERUN Quick Test.

Fig. 207 Test KT: IMRC System (Part 4 of 6)

TEST STEP	RESULT	▶	ACTION TO TAKE
KP6 VERIFY IN-LINE CONNECTOR SHORTING BAR IS INSTALLED			
• Key off. • Visually inspect OCT ADJ in-line connector. • **Is shorting bar installed?**	Yes No	▶ ▶	GO to KP8. GO to KP7.
KP7 CHECK FOR MODIFICATION DECAL			
• **Is there a modification decal attached to vehicle indicating that OCT ADJ shorting bar was removed?**	Yes No	▶ ▶	GO to KP10 REPLACE shorting bar. address spark knock concern.
KP8 CHECK FOR TSB			
• **Is there a Technical Service Bulletin (TSB) authorizing removal of the shorting OCT ADJ bar?**	Yes No	▶ ▶	GO to KP9. address spark knock concern.
KP9 REMOVE OCT ADJ SHORTING BAR			
• Remove OCT ADJ shorting bar only if there is a TSB authorization. • Drive vehicle to verify spark knock. • **Is spark knock present?**	Yes No	▶ ▶	GO to KP10. Testing complete. EEC system OK.
KP10 CHECK OCTANE ADJUST CIRCUIT FOR A SHORT TO GROUND			
• Key off. • Disconnect Powertrain Control Module (PCM). Inspect for damaged or pushed out pins, corrosion, loose wires, etc. Service as necessary. • Install breakout box; leave PCM disconnected. • Measure resistance between OCT ADJ circuit at the in-line connector and Test Pin 40, 46 and 60 at the breakout box. • **Is each resistance greater than 10,000 ohms?**	Yes No	▶ ▶	GO to KP11. SERVICE short circuit. REMOVE breakout box. If spark knock is still present, RETURN to Section
KP11 CHECK PCM INTEGRITY			
• Key off. • OCT ADJ shorting bar removed because of TSB authorization. • Breakout box installed, PCM connected. • Key on. • Measure voltage between OCT ADJ circuit and Test Pin 40 / 60 at the breakout box. • **Is voltage greater than 4.0 volts?**	Yes No	▶ ▶	REMOVE breakout box. If spark knock is still present, RETURN to Section REPLACE PCM. REMOVE breakout box. If spark knock is still present, RETURN to Section

FM0159300748050X

Fig. 207 Test KT: IMRC System (Part 5 of 6)

TEST STEP	RESULT	▶	ACTION TO TAKE
KT12 CHECK IMRC SOLENOID MECHANICAL OPERATION			
• While remaining in Output State DTM, reconnect the IMRC solenoid. • Slowly apply 16 in-Hg of vacuum to the manifold vacuum port of the IMRC solenoid. • Depress and release the throttle. • **Is vacuum released?**	Yes No	▶ ▶	REMOVE vacuum pump setup and jumper from STI to SIGNAL RETURN. GO to KT13. REMOVE vacuum pump setup and jumper from STI to SIGNAL RETURN. REPLACE IMRC solenoid. RERUN Quick Test.
KT13 CHECK SOURCE VACUUM TO IMRC SOLENOID			
• Manifold vacuum hose at IMRC solenoid disconnected. • Start engine. • Check for vacuum at the disconnected manifold vacuum hose. • **Is vacuum present at the hose?**	Yes No	▶ ▶	RECONNECT all components. RETURN INSPECT vacuum supply hose to IMRC solenoid. SERVICE as necessary. RERUN Quick Test.

Fig. 207 Test KT: IMRC System (Part 6 of 6)

Note

You should enter this Pinpoint Test only when you have been directed here from Diagnostic Routines.

Remember

This Pinpoint Test is intended to diagnose only the following:

— Throttle movement (greater than 3/4 throttle)

— Rpm increase (greater than 2000 rpm)

Pinpoint Test Illustration

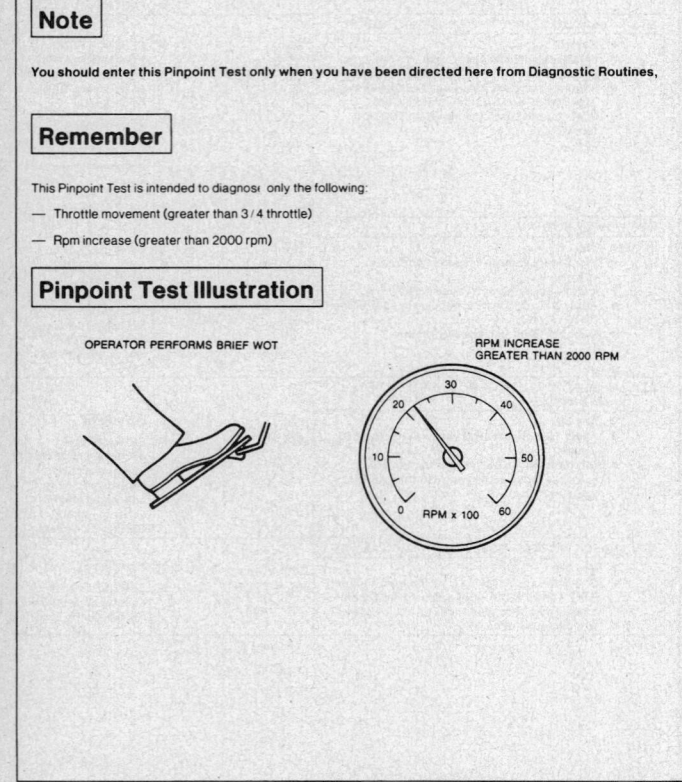

OPERATOR PERFORMS BRIEF WOT

RPM INCREASE GREATER THAN 2000 RPM

FM0159300749010X

Fig. 208 Test M: Dynamic Response Test (Part 1 of 2)

TEST STEP	RESULT	▶	ACTION TO TAKE
M1 DIAGNOSTIC TROUBLE CODE (DTC) 77 / 538: SYSTEM FAILED TO RECOGNIZE BRIEF WOT			
NOTE: A brief snap of the throttle may not be sufficient to pass this test. Be sure to go to WOT and return. • Rerun Engine Running Self-Test. Be sure operator is familiar with the Engine Running format which proceeds as follows: — Activate Engine Running Self-Test. — Start engine. — ID Code start of test. — Dynamic Response code 1 (0); perform brief WOT. — Testing over. — DTC output begins. • **Is DTC 77 or 538 still present?**	Yes No	▶ ▶	GO to M2. Dynamic Response Test passed. SERVICE any other DTC(s) received as necessary.
M2 DID ENGINE ACHIEVE GREATER THAN 2000 RPM			
• **During the WOT in the Dynamic Response Test, did the engine achieve greater than 2000 rpm?**	Yes No	▶ ▶	REPLACE PCM. RERUN Quick Test. CHECK for conditions that would prevent engine from achieving greater than 2000 rpm (binding throttle linkage, etc.).

FM0159300749020X

Fig. 208 Test M: Dynamic Response Test (Part 2 of 2)

Note

You should enter this Pinpoint Test only when you have been directed here from Diagnostic Routines, or Pinpoint Test QA.

Remember

To prevent the replacement of good components, be aware that the following non-EEC areas may be at fault:

• Fuse, bulb or socket.

This Pinpoint Test is intended to diagnose only the following:

• STO/MIL Circuit
• Powertrain Control Module (PCM)

Description

The Malfunction Indicator Lamp (MIL) is intended to alert the driver of certain malfunctions in the EEC system. The MIL output is turned on when the strategy detects a fault in input/output circuits. The lamp will remain on as long as the fault causing it is present. Regulations governing this lamp also require that the Diagnostic Trouble Codes (DTCs) be displayed by the flashing of this lamp.

FM015930075010X

Fig. 209   Test ML: STO/MIL (Part 1 of 7). 1993–94

Pinpoint Test Schematic

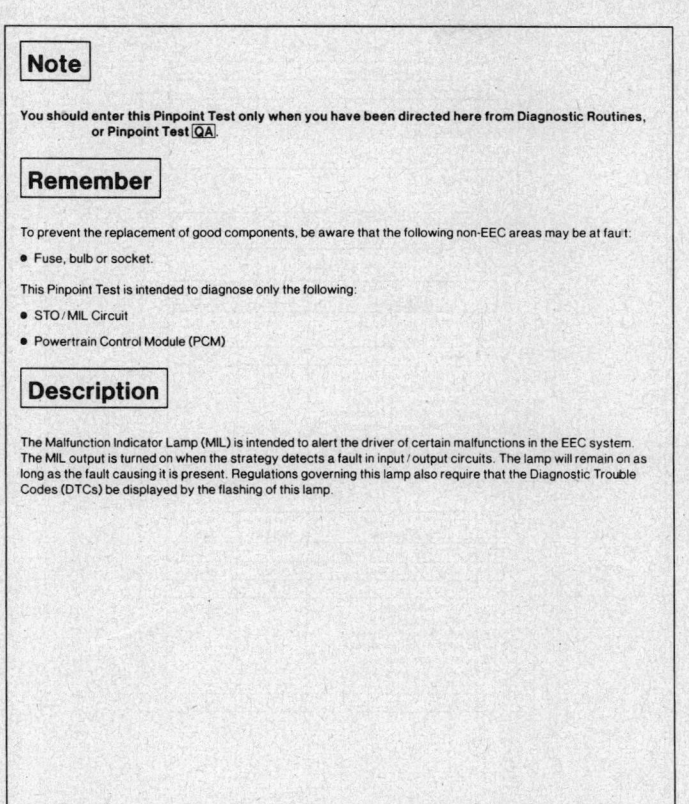

*TEST PINS LOCATED ON BREAKOUT BOX
ALL HARNESS CONNECTORS VIEWED INTO MATING SURFACE

Test Pin 17 — STO/MIL

Application	Wire Color
2.3L OHC MFI 3.8L SFI, Continental 4.6L SFI, Town Car 5.0L SFI-MA, Mustang	PK/LG
2.0L SFI-MA, Probe	LG/R
1.9L SFI-MA, Escort/Tracer 3.8L SFI-MA, Thunderbird/Cougar 5.0L SFI-MA, Thunderbird/Cougar 7.0L MFI F-Series	Y/BK
2.3L SFI Tempo/Topaz 3.0L SFI Tempo/Topaz 3.0L SFI SHO Taurus 3.2L SFI SHO Taurus 3.0L SFI Taurus FF 3.8L SFI Taurus/Sable 3.0L SFI Taurus/Sable 4.6L SFI Crown Victoria/Grand Marquis 5.0L SFI Mustang	T/R
All Others	PK/LG

FM015930075002AX

Fig. 209   Test ML: STO/MIL (Part 2 of 7). 1993

Pinpoint Test Schematic

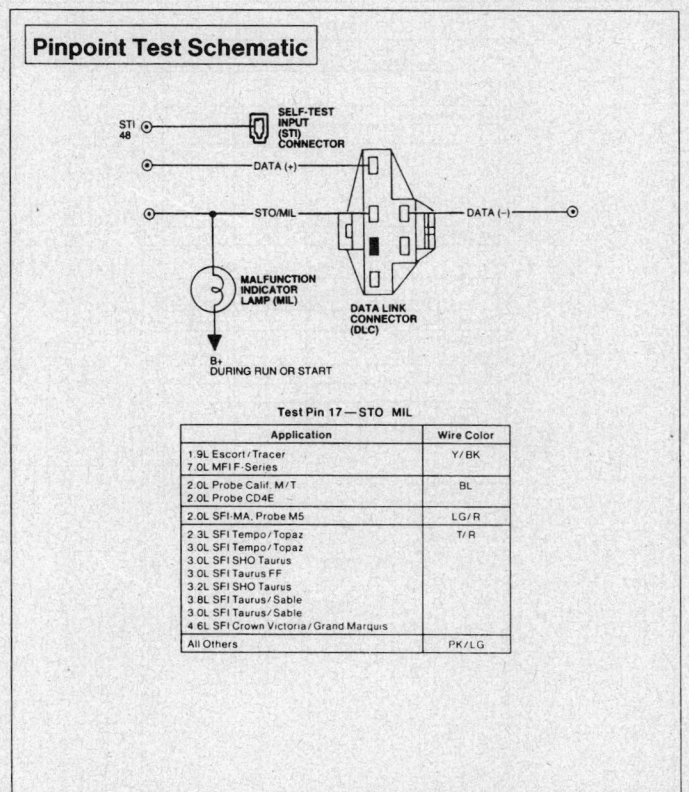

Test Pin 17 — STO/MIL

Application	Wire Color
1.9L Escort/Tracer 7.0L MFI F-Series	Y/BK
2.0L Probe Calif. M/T 2.0L Probe CD4E	BL
2.0L SFI-MA, Probe M5	LG/R
2.3L SFI Tempo/Topaz 3.0L SFI Tempo/Topaz 3.0L SFI SHO Taurus 3.0L SFI Taurus FF 3.2L SFI SHO Taurus 3.8L SFI Taurus/Sable 3.0L SFI Taurus/Sable 4.6L SFI Crown Victoria/Grand Marquis	T/R
All Others	PK/LG

FM015940075002BX

Fig. 209   Test ML: STO/MIL (Part 2 of 7). 1994

Pinpoint Test Schematic

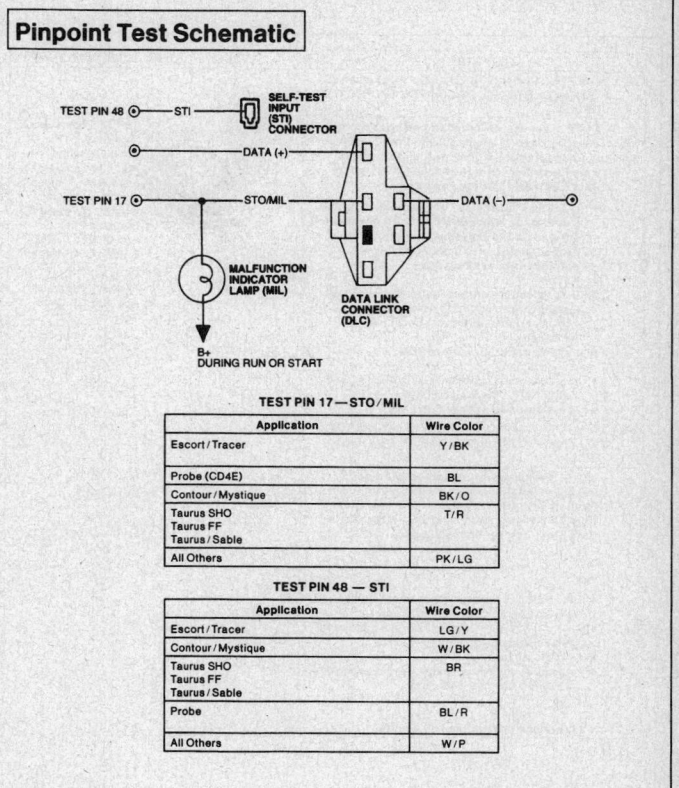

TEST PIN 17 — STO/MIL

Application	Wire Color
Escort/Tracer	Y/BK
Probe (CD4E)	BL
Contour/Mystique	BK/O
Taurus SHO Taurus FF Taurus/Sable	T/R
All Others	PK/LG

TEST PIN 48 — STI

Application	Wire Color
Escort/Tracer	LG/Y
Contour/Mystique	W/BK
Taurus SHO Taurus FF Taurus/Sable	BR
Probe	BL/R
All Others	W/P

FM015950075002CX

Fig. 209   Test ML: STO/MIL (Part 2 of 7). 1995

DATA(+)

Application	Pin Number	Wire Color
1.9L SFI-MA Escort/Tracer	28	Y/BL
2.3L MFI OHC Mustang	28	T/O
All Others	18	T/O

DATA(-)

Application	Pin Number	Wire Color
1.9L SFI-MA Escort/Tracer	8	Y/GR
3.2L SFI-MA Taurus SHO	19	BK/O
2.3L MFI OHC Mustang	9	PK/LB
All Others	19	PK/LB

Fig. 209   Test ML: STO/MIL (Part 3 of 7). 1993

Test Pin 48 — STI

Application	Wire Color
1.9L Escort·Tracer	LG/Y
3.0L Taurus/Sable, 3.0L SHO Taurus, 3.0L SFI Taurus FF, 3.2L SHO Taurus, 3.8L Taurus/Sable	BR
2.0L Probe MTX, 2.0L Probe CD4E, 7.0L F-Series	BL/R
2.0L Probe MS	BL/W
All Others	W/P

DATA(+)

Application	Pin Number	Wire Color
1.9L SFI-MA Escort/Tracer	28	Y/BL
3.2L SFI-MA Taurus SHO	18	O/BK
7.0L MFI F-Series	28	O/BK
2.3L MFI OHC Ranger, 4.0L MFI Aerostar, 4.0L MFI Ranger (49 States), 4.9L MFI E·F-Series·Bronco, 5.0L MFI F-Series·Bronco, 5.8L MFI E·F-Series·Bronco, 7.5L MFI E·F-Series	28	T/O
All Others	18	T/O

DATA(-)

Application	Pin Number	Wire Color
1.9L SFI-MA Escort/Tracer	8	Y/GR
3.2L SFI-MA Taurus SHO	19	BK/O
7.0L MFI F-Series	9	BK/O
2.3L MFI OHC Ranger, 4.0L MFI Aerostar, 4.0L MFI Ranger (49 States), 4.9L MFI E·F-Series·Bronco, 5.0L MFI F-Series·Bronco, 5.8L MFI E·F-Series·Bronco, 7.5L MFI E·F-Series	9	PK/LB
All Others	19	PK/LB

FM015940075003BX

Fig. 209   Test ML: STO/MIL (Part 3 of 7). 1994

TEST STEP		RESULT	▶	ACTION TO TAKE
ML1	MALFUNCTION INDICATOR LAMP (MIL) ALWAYS ON: CHECK STO/MIL CIRCUIT FOR SHORTS TO GROUND			
	NOTE: If vehicle will not start perform Pinpoint Test Step [AA1] if equipped with Distributorless Ignition (DI), [AB1] if equipped with Low Data Rate Electronic Ignition and [AC1] if High Data Rate Electronic Ignition equipped.	Yes	▶	SERVICE short circuit between Test Pin 17 and Malfunction Indicator Lamp (MIL), or between Test Pin 17 and the Data Link Connector. REMOVE Breakout Box. RECONNECT PCM. RERUN Quick Test.
	• If any Key On Engine Off Diagnostic Trouble Codes or Continuous Memory Diagnostic Trouble Codes are present, service before proceeding. If pass codes are present, continue with this Test Step. • Key off. • Disconnect Powertrain Control Module (PCM). Inspect for damaged or pushed out pins, corrosion, loose wires, etc. Service as necessary. • Install Breakout Box, leave PCM disconnected. • Measure resistance between Test Pin 17 and Test Pin 40 at the Breakout Box. • **Is resistance less than 5.0 ohms?**	No	▶	REPLACE PCM. REMOVE Breakout Box. RERUN Quick Test.
ML4	MALFUNCTION INDICATOR LAMP (MIL) NEVER ON: CHECK FOR B(+) AT MIL FUSE (GROUND SIDE)			
	NOTE: If vehicle will not start go to Pinpoint Test Step [AA1] if equipped with Distributorless Ignition (DI), [AB1] if equipped with Low Data Rate Electronic Ignition and [AC1] if High Data Rate Electronic Ignition equipped.	Yes	▶	GO to [ML6].
		No	▶	GO to [ML5].
	• If vehicle has electronic instrument cluster, refer to Electronic Instrument Cluster Malfunction Indicator Lamp (MIL) diagnostic procedure. • Key on, engine off. • Measure voltage from battery negative post to "Ground" side of the MIL fuse. • **Is voltage greater than 10.5 volts?**			

FM015930075040X

Fig. 209   Test ML: STO/MIL (Part 4 of 7)

DATA(+)

Application	Pin Number	Wire Color
Escort/Tracer	28	Y/BL
3.2L Taurus SHO	18	O/BK
Contour/Mystique	18	W/BL
All Others	18	T/O

DATA(-)

Application	Pin Number	Wire Color
Escort/Tracer	8	Y/GR
2.0L Contour/Mystique	19	BR/BL
2.5L Contour/Mystique	19	GR/BL
3.2L Taurus SHO	19	BK/O
All Others	19	PK/LB

FM015950075003CX

Fig. 209   Test ML: STO/MIL (Part 3 of 7). 1995

	TEST STEP	RESULT	▶	ACTION TO TAKE
ML5	CHECK FOR B+ MIL FUSE			
	• Key on, engine off. • Measure voltage from battery negative post to B+ side of the MIL fuse. • **Is voltage greater than 10.5 volts?**	Yes No	▶ ▶	REPLACE the MIL fuse. VERIFY service by turning ignition key to the RUN position. SERVICE open in the MIL / B+ circuit. VERIFY service by turning ignition key to the RUN position.
ML6	CHECK FOR B+ AT MIL BULB / SOCKET			
	• Key on, engine off. • Measure voltage from battery negative post to B+ side of MIL bulb / socket. • **Is voltage greater than 10.5 volts?**	Yes No	▶ ▶	GO to ML7. SERVICE open between MIL fuse and MIL bulb. VERIFY service by turning ignition key to RUN position.
ML7	CHECK MIL BULB RESPONSE TO GROUNDING			
	• Key off. • Attach one end of jumper wire to battery negative post or chassis ground. • Attach other end of jumper wire to ground side of the MIL bulb / socket. • Turn ignition key to RUN position. • **Is the MIL on?**	Yes No	▶ ▶	Turn ignition key to the OFF position. Remove jumper wire. GO to ML8. Turn ignition key to OFF position. REMOVE jumper wire. REPLACE MIL bulb / socket. VERIFY service by turning ignition key to RUN position.
ML8	CHECK MIL CIRCUIT CONTINUITY			
	• Key off. • Disconnect powertrain control module (PCM). Inspect for damaged or pushed out pins, corrosion, loose wires, etc. Service as necessary. • Install breakout box, leave PCM disconnected. • Measure resistance between Test Pin 17 at breakout box and MIL. • **Is resistance less than 5.0 ohms?**	Yes No	▶ ▶	REPLACE PCM. REMOVE breakout box. VERIFY the service by turning ignition key to the RUN position. SERVICE open in ground side of MIL circuit. REMOVE breakout box. RECONNECT PCM. VERIFY service by turning ignition key to RUN position.

FM0159300750050X

Fig. 209   Test ML: STO/MIL (Part 5 of 7)

	TEST STEP	RESULT	▶	ACTION TO TAKE
ML10	MALFUNCTION INDICATOR LAMP (MIL) INTERMITTENTLY ON: CHECK FOR INTERMITTENT STO SHORT TO GROUND			
	NOTE: If vehicle will not start go to Pinpoint Test Step AA1 if equipped with Distributorless Ignition (DI), AB1 if equipped with Low Data Rate, Electronic Ignition and AC1 if equipped with High Data Rate, Electronic Ignition. The MIL will come ON when there is a Continuous Memory Diagnostic Trouble Code present. Service any Continuous Memory Diagnostic Trouble Codes before proceeding. If pass codes are output, continue with this Test Step. • Enter Key On Engine Off Continuous Monitor Diagnostic Test Mode (DTM). • Observe VOM or STAR LED for indication of a fault while you wiggle, shake or bend a small section of the EEC-IV system harness in the following locations: — Harness closest to Data Link Connector to the dash panel — Dash panel to the PCM — Dash panel to the MIL • **Is a fault indicated?**	Yes No	▶ ▶	SERVICE short to ground. RERUN Quick Test. UNABLE to duplicate fault at this time. If the MIL flashec on intermittently with pass codes (11-10-11 or 111-10-11), then testing is complete. The fault occurred over 40 / 80 warm-up cycles ago. Diagnostic Trouble Codes are not stored in memory beyond 40 / 80 warm-up cycles.
ML15	MALFUNCTION INDICATOR LAMP (MIL) FLASHING WITH ERRATIC IDLE: CHECK FOR STI SHORT TO GROUND			
	NOTE: Vehicle symptoms indicate that STI is grounded and the vehicle is actually performing Self-Test without a tester installed. • Key off. • Disconnect powertrain control module (PCM) connector. Inspect for damaged or pushed out pins, corrosion, loose wires, etc. Service as necessary. • Measure resistance between the STI circuit at the Data Link Connector and engine block ground. • **Is resistance less than 10,000 ohms?**	Yes No	▶ ▶	SERVICE short circuit. RECONNECT PCM. VERIFY symptom eliminatec. RECONNECT PCM. VERIFY symptom eliminated. RETURN to rough idle diagnosis.

FM0159300750060X

Fig. 209   Test ML: STO/MIL (Part 6 of 7)

	TEST STEP	RESULT	▶	ACTION TO TAKE
ML20	"CHECK ENGINE" MESSAGE DISPLAYED			
	NOTE: If vehicle will not start go to Pinpoint Test Step AA1 if equipped with Distributorless Ignition (DI), AB1 if equipped with Low Data Rate Electronic Ignition and AC1 if equipped with High Data Rate Electronic Ignition. • Run Key On Engine Off Self-Test. • **Is result 11-10-11 or 111-10-111 (Pass Codes)?**	Yes No	▶ ▶	GO to Instruments / Gauges for DCL diagnosis. Self-Test indicates a fault. GO to EEC-IV Diagnostic Trouble Code Chart
ML25	CONTINUOUS MEMORY DIAGNOSTIC TROUBLE CODE (DTC) 529, "CHECK ENGINE" / "CHECK DCL" MESSAGE DISPLAYED			
	Continuous Memory Diagnostic Trouble Codes 529 and 533 indicate that a circuit failure has occurred on the Data Communications Link (DCL). These codes can appear alone or in conjunction with one another. The messages "CHECK ENGINE" and / or "CHECK DCL" will also be on. — Code 529 indicates the PCM or Data Communications Link (DCL) circuit failure. — Code 533 indicates a Data Communication Link to Electronic Instrument Cluster circuit failure. NOTE: If vehicle will not start go to Pinpoint Test Step AA1 if equipped with Distributorless Ignition (DI), AB1 if equipped with Low Data Rate Electronic Ignition and AC1 if equipped with High Data Rate Electronic Ignition. • Clear Continuous Memory • Wait five minutes. • Rerun Key On Engine Off Self-Test with a STAR tester or volt / ohmmeter. • **Is result 11-10-11 or 111-10-111 (Pass Codes)?**	Yes No	▶ ▶	REFER to Instruments / Gauges DCL diagnosis. Self-Test indicates a fault. GO to EEC-IV Diagnostic Trouble Code Chart

FM0159300750070X

Fig. 209   Test ML: STO/MIL (Part 7 of 7)

Note

You should enter this Pinpoint Test only when you have been directed here from Diagnostic Routines.

Remember

To prevent the replacement of good components, be aware that the following non-EEC areas may be at fault:

• Ignition Control Module (ICM)
• Ignition coil
• Spark plugs and high tension cables
• Distributor
• Arcing of secondary ignition components

This Pinpoint Test is intended to diagnose only the following:

• Harness circuit: IDM
• Powertrain Control Module (PCM)

Description

The Ignition Diagnostic Monitor (IDM) is an input signal to the PCM that verifies spark function based on the flyback voltage created by the ignition coil primary discharge. This signal is transmitted from the ICM to the PCM. The IDM signal consists of a single pulse for each successful ignition event. Lack of an IDM pulse is used as an indication of intermittent and / or missing spark events.

FM0159300751010X

Fig. 210   Test NA: IDM/DI (Part 1 of 8)

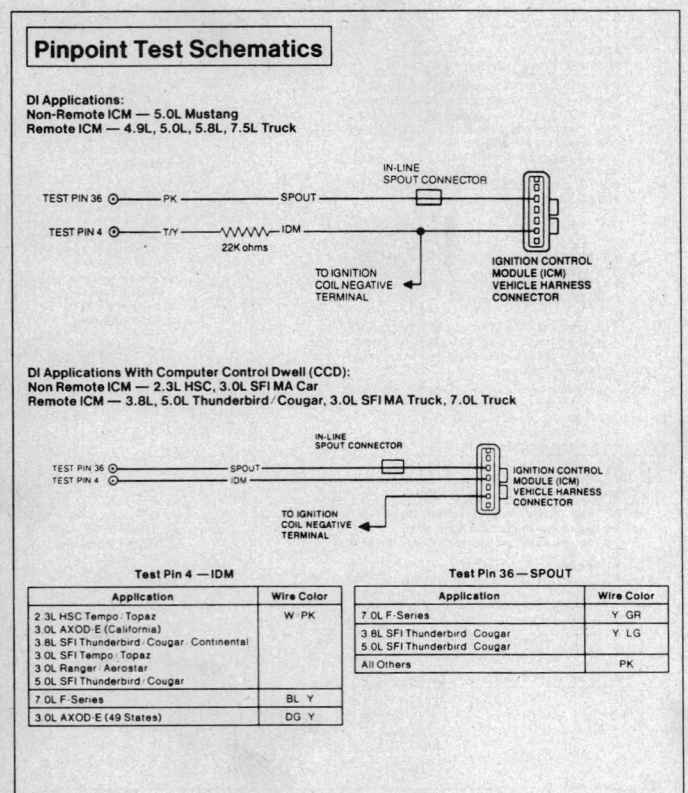

Pinpoint Test Schematics

DI Applications:
Non-Remote ICM — 5.0L Mustang
Remote ICM — 4.9L, 5.0L, 5.8L, 7.5L Truck

DI Applications With Computer Control Dwell (CCD):
Non Remote ICM — 2.3L HSC, 3.0L SFI MA Car
Remote ICM — 3.8L, 5.0L Thunderbird/Cougar, 3.0L SFI MA Truck, 7.0L Truck

Test Pin 4 — IDM

Application	Wire Color
2.3L HSC Tempo/Topaz	W/PK
3.0L AXOD-E (California)	
3.8L SFI Thunderbird/Cougar/Continental	
3.0L SFI Tempo/Topaz	
3.0L Ranger/Aerostar	
5.0L SFI Thunderbird/Cougar	
7.0L F-Series	BL/Y
3.0L AXOD-E (49 States)	DG/Y

Test Pin 36 — SPOUT

Application	Wire Color
7.0L F-Series	Y/GR
3.8L SFI Thunderbird/Cougar	Y/LG
5.0L SFI Thunderbird/Cougar	
All Others	PK

FM015930075102AX

Fig. 210   Test NA: IDM/DI (Part 2 of 8). 1993

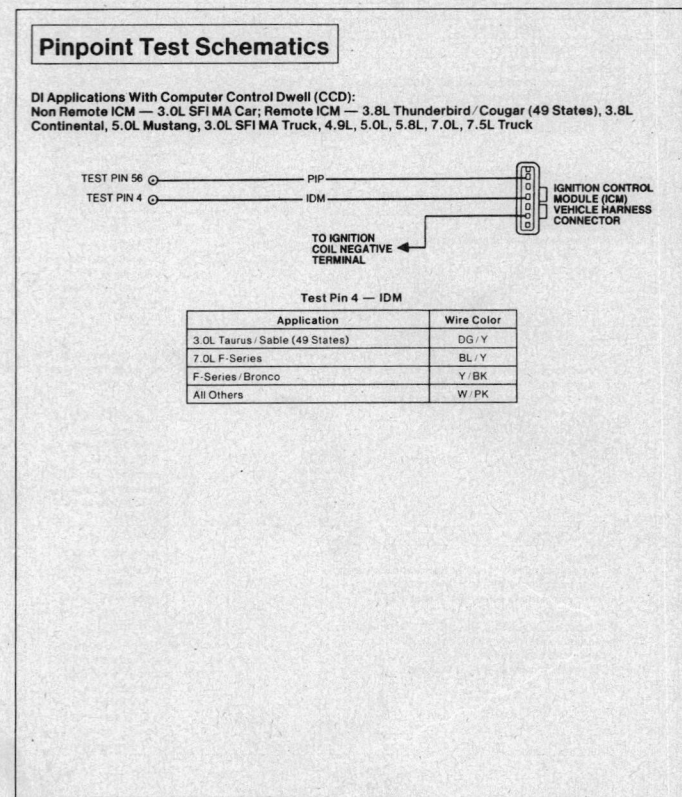

Pinpoint Test Schematics

DI Applications With Computer Control Dwell (CCD):
Non Remote ICM — 3.0L SFI MA Car; Remote ICM — 3.8L Thunderbird/Cougar (49 States), 3.8L
Continental, 5.0L Mustang, 3.0L SFI MA Truck, 4.9L, 5.0L, 5.8L, 7.0L, 7.5L Truck

Test Pin 4 — IDM

Application	Wire Color
3.0L Taurus/Sable (49 States)	DG/Y
7.0L F-Series	BL/Y
F-Series/Bronco	Y/BK
All Others	W/PK

FM015940075102BX

Fig. 210   Test NA: IDM/DI (Part 2 of 8). 1994–95

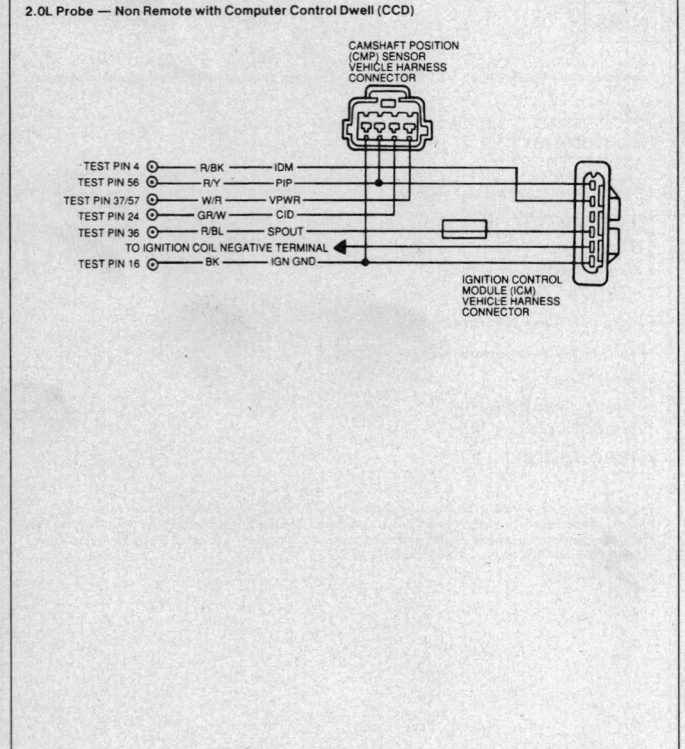

2.0L Probe — Non Remote with Computer Control Dwell (CCD)

FM015930075103AX

Fig. 210   Test NA: IDM/DI (Part 3 of 8). 1993

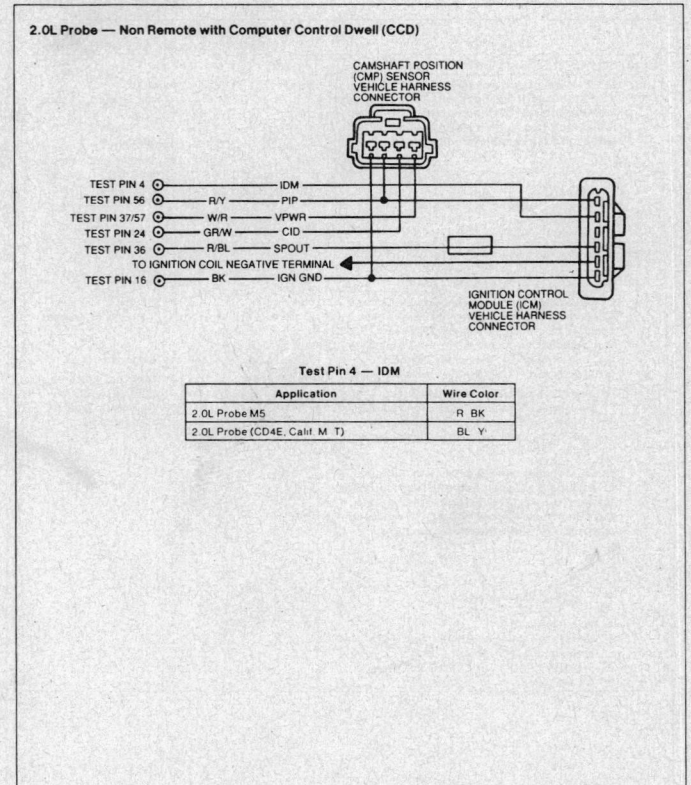

2.0L Probe — Non Remote with Computer Control Dwell (CCD)

Test Pin 4 — IDM

Application	Wire Color
2.0L Probe M5	R/BK
2.0L Probe (CD4E, Calif M/T)	BL/Y

FM015940075103BX

Fig. 210   Test NA: IDM/DI (Part 3 of 8). 1994–95

TEST STEP		RESULT	▶	ACTION TO TAKE
NA1	CONTINUOUS MEMORY DIAGNOSTIC TROUBLE CODE (DTC) 14/211: ERRATIC IGNITION			
	DTC 14/211 indicates two successive erratic Profile Ignition Pickup (PIP) pulses occurred, resulting in a possible engine miss or stall.	Yes	▶	SERVICE as necessary. CLEAR Continuous Memory
	Possible causes: — Loose wires/connectors. — Arcing secondary ignition components (coil, cap, rotor, wires, plugs, etc.). — On-board transmitter (2-way radio).* • Verify all radio and condenser installations. Carefully follow manufacturer's installation instructions regarding the routing of antenna and power leads. • **Are any of the above present?**	No	▶	RERUN Quick Test. **For No Starts on 2.0L Probe:** GO to **AA1**. **For all other No Starts:** REFER to for DI diagnostics. All others: GO to **NA2**.
NA2	CONTINUOUS MEMORY DIAGNOSTIC TROUBLE CODE (DTC) 18/212			
	DTC 18/212 indicates a loss of IDM input to the PCM.	Yes	▶	REFER to DI Diagnostics.
	Possible Causes: — Open harness circuit. — Shorted harness circuit. — Damaged Ignition Control Module (ICM). — Damaged Powertrain Control Module (PCM). • **Is vehicle a No Start?**	No	▶	For vehicles with Computer Control Dwell (refer to Pinpoint Test Schematic): GO to **NA3**. For all others: GO to **NA4**.
NA3	CONTINUOUS MEMORY DIAGNOSTIC TROUBLE CODE (DTC) 18/212: CHECK IDM CIRCUIT CONTINUITY			
	• Key off. • Disconnect Powertrain Control Module (PCM). Inspect for damaged or pushed out pins, corrosion, loose wires, etc. Service as necessary. • Install breakout box, leave PCM disconnected. • Disconnect Ignition Control Module (ICM). • Measure resistance between Test Pin 4 at the breakout box and IDM circuit at the ICM vehicle harness connector. • **Is resistance less than 5.0 ohms?**	Yes No	▶ ▶	GO to **NA5**. SERVICE open circuit. REMOVE breakout box. RECONNECT PCM. CLEAR Continuous Memory. RECONNECT all components. RERUN Quick Test.

FM015930075104AX

Fig. 210   Test NA: IDM/DI (Part 4 of 8). 1993

TEST STEP		RESULT	▶	ACTION TO TAKE
NA1	CONTINUOUS MEMORY DIAGNOSTIC TROUBLE CODE (DTC) 211: ERRATIC IGNITION			
	DTC 211 indicates two successive erratic Profile Ignition Pickup (PIP) pulses occurred, resulting in a possible engine miss or stall.	Yes	▶	SERVICE as necessary. CLEAR Continuous Memory
	Possible causes: — Loose wires/connectors. — Arcing secondary ignition components (coil, cap, rotor, wires, plugs, etc.). — On-board transmitter (2-way radio).* • Verify all radio and condenser installations. Carefully follow manufacturer's installation instructions regarding the routing of antenna and power leads. • **Are any of the above present?**	No	▶	RERUN Quick Test. **For No Starts on 2.0L Probe:** GO to **AA1**. **For all other No Starts:** REFER to DI Diagnostics. All others: GO to **NA2**.
NA2	CONTINUOUS MEMORY DIAGNOSTIC TROUBLE CODE (DTC) 212			
	DTC 212 indicates a loss of IDM input to the PCM.	Yes	▶	REFER to DI Diagnostics
	Possible Causes: — Open harness circuit. — Shorted harness circuit. — Damaged Ignition Control Module (ICM). — Damaged Powertrain Control Module (PCM). • **Is vehicle a No Start?**	No	▶	GO to **NA3**
NA3	CONTINUOUS MEMORY DIAGNOSTIC TROUBLE CODE (DTC) 212: CHECK IDM CIRCUIT CONTINUITY			
	• Key off. • Disconnect Powertrain Control Module (PCM). Inspect for damaged or pushed out pins, corrosion, loose wires, etc. Service as necessary. • Install breakout box, leave PCM disconnected. • Disconnect Ignition Control Module (ICM). • Measure resistance between Test Pin 4 at the breakout box and IDM circuit at the ICM vehicle harness connector. • **Is resistance less than 5.0 ohms?**	Yes No	▶ ▶	GO to **NA5** SERVICE open circuit. REMOVE breakout box. RECONNECT PCM. CLEAR Continuous Memory. RECONNECT all components. RERUN Quick Test.

FM015940075104BX

Fig. 210   Test NA: IDM/DI (Part 4 of 8). 1994–95

TEST STEP		RESULT	▶	ACTION TO TAKE
NA4	CONTINUOUS MEMORY DIAGNOSTIC TROUBLE CODE (DTC) 18/212: CHECK IDM CIRCUIT CONTINUITY			
	• Key off. • Disconnect Powertrain Control Module (PCM). Inspect for damaged or pushed out pins, corrosion, loose wires, etc. Service as necessary. • Install breakout box, leave PCM disconnected. • Disconnect ignition coil and Ignition Control Module (ICM). • Measure resistance between Test Pin 4 at the breakout box and IDM circuit at ICM vehicle harness connector. • **Is resistance between 20,000 and 24,000 ohms?**	Yes No	▶ ▶	GO to **NA5**. SERVICE open circuit. REMOVE breakout box. RECONNECT PCM. CLEAR Continuous Memory. RECONNECT all components. RERUN Quick Test.
NA5	CHECK IDM CIRCUIT FOR SHORTS TO POWER (EXCLUDING VREF)			
	• Key off. • Breakout box installed. • PCM and ICM disconnected. • Measure voltage between Test Pin 4 at the breakout box and battery negative post. • Key on, engine off. • Measure voltage between Test Pin 4 and Test Pins 40 and 60 at the breakout box. • **Is any voltage reading greater than 10.5 volts?**	Yes No	▶ ▶	SERVICE short circuit. REMOVE breakout box. RECONNECT all components. RERUN Quick Test. GO to **NA6**.

Fig. 210   Test NA: IDM/DI (Part 5 of 8)

TEST STEP		RESULT	▶	ACTION TO TAKE
NA6	CHECK IDM CIRCUIT FOR SHORTS TO VREF AND PIP			
	• Key off. • Breakout box installed, PCM disconnected. • ICM disconnected. • Ignition coil disconnected on Non-CCD vehicles (refer to Pinpoint Test Schematic). • Disconnect Scan Tool from Data Link Connector (if applicable). NOTE: For proper results of this test, the Scan Tool must be disconnected. Due to the circuitry of the Scan Tool and the vehicle, voltage can be fed to the VREF circuit giving the false indication of a short to power. **For Shorts To VREF:** — Measure resistance between Test Pin 4 and Test Pin 26 at the breakout box. **For Shorts To PIP circuit:** — Measure resistance between Test Pin 4 and Test Pin 56 at the breakout box. • **Is each resistance greater than 10,000 ohms?**	Yes No	▶ ▶	RECONNECT Scan Tool. GO to **NA7.** SERVICE short circuits. REMOVE breakout box. RECONNECT all components and SCAN Tool (if applicable). RERUN Quick Test.
NA7	CHECK IDM CIRCUIT FOR SHORT TO GROUND			
	NOTE: During this check when 4-wire HO2S is connected to the vehicle harness on DI vehicles, a short to SIG RTN (Pin 46) may be indicated in conjunction with an actual PWR GND short. • Key off. • Breakout box installed, PCM disconnected. • **Scan Tool disconnected from Data Link Connector.** • ICM disconnected. • Ignition coil disconnected on Non-CCD vehicles (refer to Pinpoint Test Schematic). • Measure resistance between Test Pin 4 and Test Pins 20, 40, 46 and 60 at the breakout box. • **Is each resistance above 10,000 ohms?**	Yes No	▶ ▶	RECONNECT Scan Tool. GO to **NA8**. REMOVE breakout box. SERVICE short to ground in IDM circuit. RECONNECT all components. CLEAR Continuous Memory. RERUN Quick Test.

FM0159300751060A

Fig. 210   Test NA: IDM/DI (Part 6 of 8)

TEST STEP	RESULT	▶	ACTION TO TAKE
NA8 CHECK ICM			
• Key off.	Yes	▶	DISCONNECT and INSPECT connectors. If connector and terminals are good, REMOVE breakout box, RECONNECT all components and REFER to Ignition Diagnostics.
• Breakout box installed.			
• Connect PCM to breakout box.			
• Reconnect ignition coil and ICM.			
• Connect DVOM between Test Pin 4 and Test Pin 16 at the breakout box.			
• Start engine.			
• Observe DVOM when voltage is allowed to stabilize.	No	▶	GO to **NA9**
• Lightly tap on ICM to simulate road shock.			
• Wiggle ICM connector (for 3.8L AXODE, 3.8L RWD, 5.0L Thunderbird / Cougar; 3.0L, 7.0L and 7.5L Trucks, wiggle ICM, GCM and CMP sensor connectors).			
• A sudden change in voltage indicates a fault.			
• **Is a fault indicated?**			
NA9 CHECK EEC HARNESS			
• DVOM still connected between Test Pin 4 and Test Pin 16 at the breakout box.	Yes	▶	ISOLATE fault and SERVICE as necessary. REMOVE breakout box. RECONNECT all components. CLEAR Continuous Memory. RERUN Quick Test.
• Key on, engine running.			
• While observing a voltage change like in **NA7**, perform the following:			
— Grasp vehicle harness closest to ICM connector (for 3.8L AXODE, 3.8L RWD, 5.0L Thunderbird / Cougar; 3.0L, 7.5L Trucks, wiggle ICM, GCM and CMP sensor connectors). Shake and bend a small section of the EEC harness while working your way to the dash panel. Also wiggle, shake and bend the EEC harness from dash panel to PCM.	No	▶	GO to **NA10**.
• **Is a fault indicated?**			
NA10 CHECK PCM AND HARNESS CONNECTORS			
• Key off.	Yes	▶	GO to **NA11**
• Disconnect Powertrain Control Module (PCM). Inspect for damaged or pushed out pins, corrosion, loose wires, etc.	No	▶	SERVICE as necessary. REMOVE breakout box. RECONNECT all components. CLEAR Continuous Memory. RERUN Quick Test.
• **Are connectors and terminals OK?**			

FM0159300751070X

Fig. 210   Test NA: IDM/DI (Part 7 of 8)

TEST STEP	RESULT	▶	ACTION TO TAKE
NA11 CHECK PCM FOR SHORT TO POWER			
• Key off.	Yes	▶	REPLACE PCM. REMOVE breakout box. RECONNECT all components. RERUN Quick Test.
• Breakout box installed.			
• PCM connected to breakout box.			
For vehicles with Remote Mounted ICM and Camshaft Position (CMP) sensor:			
— Disconnect ICM and CMP.	No	▶	GO to **NA12**.
For 7.0L Truck:			
— Disconnect Governor Control Module (GCM).			
For 2.0L Probe:			
— Disconnect Camshaft Position (CMP) sensor.			
For all others:			
— Disconnect ICM.			
• Measure voltage between Test Pin 4 and chassis ground.			
• Key on, engine off.			
• Measure voltage between Test Pin 4 and Test Pins 40 and 60 at the breakout box.			
• **Is any voltage reading greater than 10.5 volts?**			
NA12 CHECK PCM FOR SHORT TO GROUND			
• Key off.	Yes	▶	REMOVE breakout box. RECONNECT all components. For further diagnosis, Ignition Diagnostics.
• Breakout box installed.			
• PCM connected to breakout box.			
• Ignition coil (Non-CCD only), ICM and CMP sensor disconnected.	No	▶	REPLACE PCM. REMOVE breakout box. RECONNECT all components. RERUN Quick Test.
• Measure resistance between Test Pin 4 and Test Pins 40, 46 and 60 at breakout box.			
• **Is each resistance greater than 10,000 ohms?**			

FM0159300751080X

Fig. 210   Test NA: IDM/DI (Part 8 of 8)

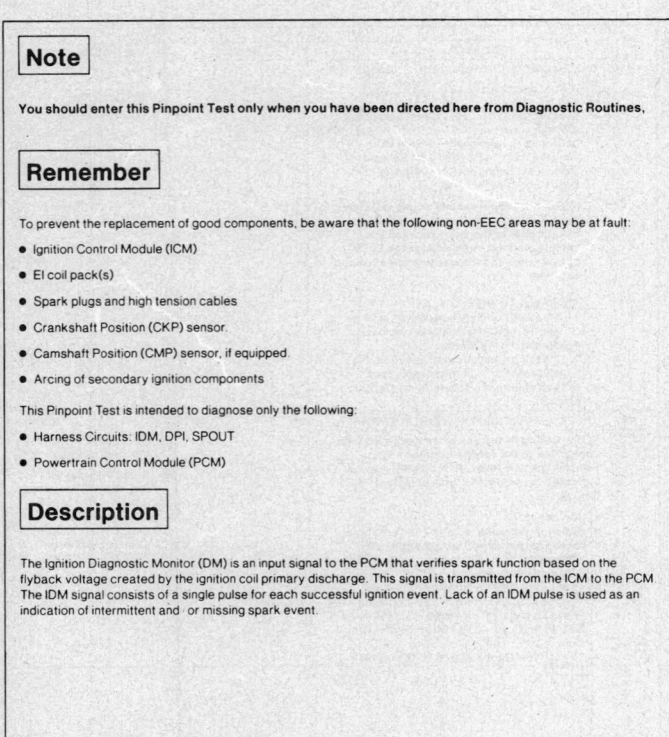

Note

You should enter this Pinpoint Test only when you have been directed here from Diagnostic Routines.

Remember

To prevent the replacement of good components, be aware that the following non-EEC areas may be at fault:

• Ignition Control Module (ICM)
• EI coil pack(s)
• Spark plugs and high tension cables
• Crankshaft Position (CKP) sensor.
• Camshaft Position (CMP) sensor, if equipped.
• Arcing of secondary ignition components

This Pinpoint Test is intended to diagnose only the following:
• Harness Circuits: IDM, DPI, SPOUT
• Powertrain Control Module (PCM)

Description

The Ignition Diagnostic Monitor (DM) is an input signal to the PCM that verifies spark function based on the flyback voltage created by the ignition coil primary discharge. This signal is transmitted from the ICM to the PCM. The IDM signal consists of a single pulse for each successful ignition event. Lack of an IDM pulse is used as an indication of intermittent and / or missing spark event.

FM0159300752010X

Fig. 211   Test NB: IDM/EI-Low Data Rate (Part 1 of 8)

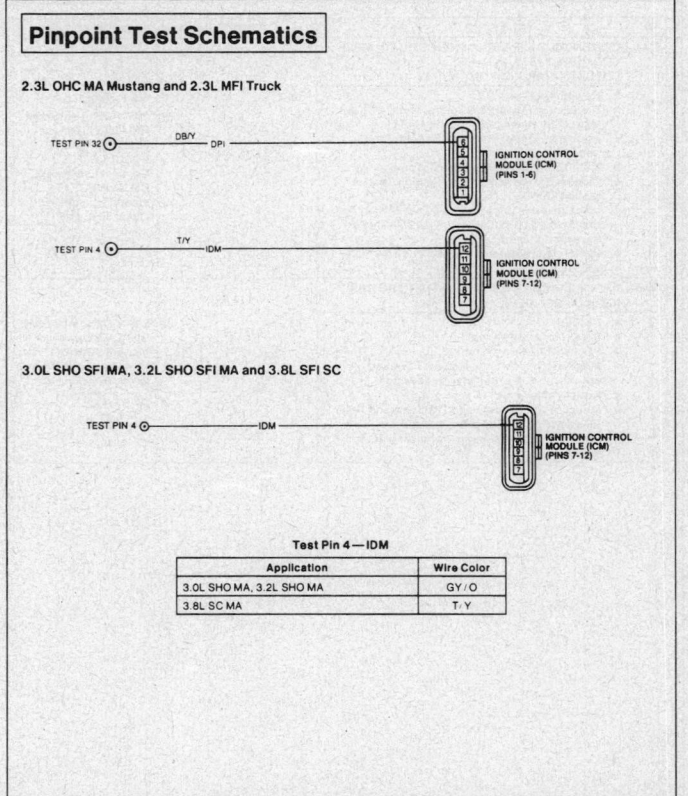

Pinpoint Test Schematics

2.3L OHC MA Mustang and 2.3L MFI Truck

3.0L SHO SFI MA, 3.2L SHO SFI MA and 3.8L SFI SC

Test Pin 4 — IDM

Application	Wire Color
3.0L SHO MA, 3.2L SHO MA	GY / O
3.8L SC MA	T / Y

FM0159300752020AX

Fig. 211   Test NB: IDM/EI-Low Data Rate (Part 2 of 8).
1993

Pinpoint Test Schematics

2.3L MFI and SFI Ranger

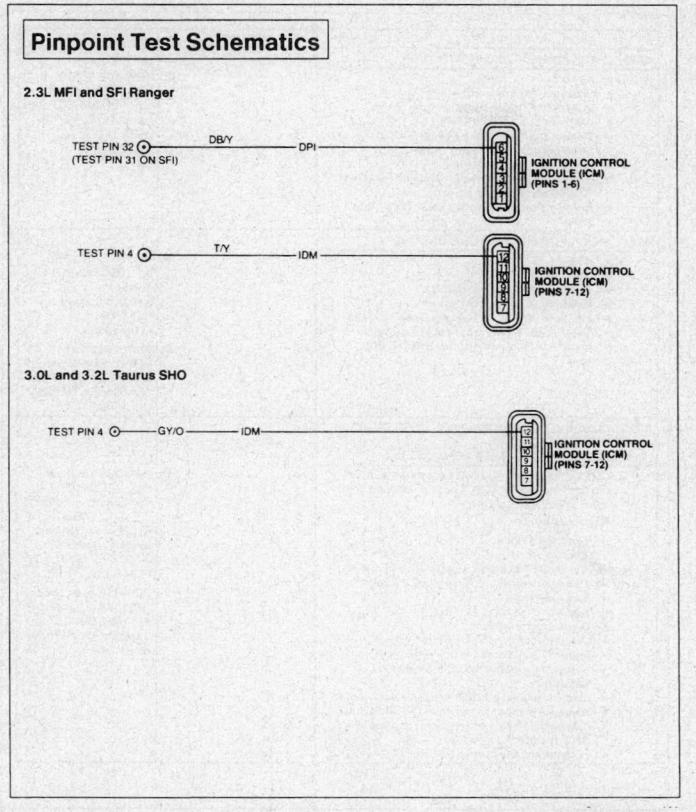

TEST PIN 32 ⊙ —— DB/Y —— DPI
(TEST PIN 31 ON SFI)
IGNITION CONTROL MODULE (ICM) (PINS 1-6)

TEST PIN 4 ⊙ —— T/Y —— IDM
IGNITION CONTROL MODULE (ICM) (PINS 7-12)

3.0L and 3.2L Taurus SHO

TEST PIN 4 ⊙ —— GY/O —— IDM
IGNITION CONTROL MODULE (ICM) (PINS 7-12)

FM015940075202BX

Fig. 211   Test NB: IDM/EI-Low Data Rate (Part 2 of 8). 1994–95

	TEST STEP	RESULT	▶	ACTION TO TAKE
NB1	CONTINUOUS MEMORY DIAGNOSTIC TROUBLE CODE (DTC) 211: ERRATIC IGNITION			
	DTC 211 indicates two successive erratic Profile Ignition Pickup (PIP) pulses occurred, resulting in a possible engine miss or stall. Possible causes: — Loose wires / connectors. — Arcing secondary ignition components (coil, cap, rotor, wires, plugs, etc.). — On-board transmitter (2-way radio). * • Are any of the above present? * Verify all radio and condenser installations. Carefully follow manufacturer's installation instructions regarding the routing of antenna and power leads.	Yes No	▶ ▶	SERVICE as necessary. CLEAR Continuous Memory. RERUN Quick Test. GO to NB4
NB2	CONTINUOUS MEMORY DIAGNOSTIC TROUBLE CODE (DTC) 212: CHECK FOR OTHER DTC's			
	DTC 212 indicates a loss of IDM input to the PCM. Possible causes: — Open harness circuit. — Shorted harness circuit. — Damaged Ignition Control Module (ICM). — Damaged Powertrain Control Module (PCM). • Is vehicle a No Start or is Continuous Memory Service DTC 214, 215, 216 or 217 present?	Yes No	▶ ▶ ▶	For DTC 214: GO to Pinpoint Test Step DR1. For all others: REFER to EI Diagnostics. GO to NB3

FM015930075O2030X

Fig. 211   Test NB: IDM/EI-Low Data Rate (Part 3 of 8)

	TEST STEP	RESULT	▶	ACTION TO TAKE
NB3	CONTINUOUS MEMORY DIAGNOSTIC TROUBLE CODES (DTCS) 212, 222 OR 218: CHECK CONTINUITY OF IDM CIRCUIT			
	Continuous Memory DTC 212 indicates a loss of IDM input to the PCM. Possible causes: — Open harness circuit. — Shorted harness circuit. — Damaged Ignition Control Module (ICM). — Damaged Powertrain Control Module (PCM). Continuous Memory DTC 222 indicates IDM input to the PCM is always low. Possible causes: — Open harness circuit. — Shorted harness circuit. — Damaged Crankshaft Position (CKP) or Camshaft Position (CMP) sensor. — Damaged Ignition Control Module (ICM). — Damaged Powertrain Control Module (PCM). — B+ low at ICM. Continuous Memory DTC 218 indicates IDM input to the PCM is always high. Possible causes: — Open harness. — B+ open at secondary coil. — B+ low at secondary coil • Key off, wait 10 seconds. • Disconnect Powertrain Control Module (PCM). Inspect for damaged or pushed out pins, corrosion, loose wires, etc. Service as necessary. • Install breakout box, leave PCM disconnected. • Disconnect ICM (Pins 7-12). • Measure resistance between Test Pin 4 at the breakout box and IDM Pin 12 at the ICM vehicle harness connector. • Is resistance less than 5.0 ohms?	Yes No	▶ ▶	GO to NB4 SERVICE open circuit. REMOVE breakout box. RECONNECT PCM. CLEAR Continuous Memory. RECONNECT all components. RERUN Quick Test.
NB4	CHECK IDM CIRCUIT FOR SHORTS TO POWER (EXCLUDING VREF)			
	• Key off. • Breakout box installed. • PCM and ICM (Pins 1-6) disconnected. • Disconnect Camshaft Position (CMP) sensor on 3.0L and 3.2L Taurus SHO. • Key on. • Measure voltage between Test Pin 4 and Test Pin 40 or 60 at the breakout box. • Is voltage reading greater than 10.5 volts?	Yes No	▶ ▶	SERVICE short circuit. REMOVE breakout box. RECONNECT all components. RERUN Quick Test GO to NB5

FM015930075O2040X

Fig. 211   Test NB: IDM/EI-Low Data Rate (Part 4 of 8)

	TEST STEP	RESULT	▶	ACTION TO TAKE
NB5	CHECK IDM CIRCUIT FOR SHORTS TO VREF AND PIP			
	• Key off. • Breakout box installed, PCM disconnected. • ICM (Pins 1-6) disconnected. • CMP sensor disconnected on 3.0L and 3.2L Taurus SHO. • Disconnect Scan Tool from Data Link Connector (if applicable). NOTE: For proper results of this test, the Scan Tool must be disconnected. Due to the circuitry of the Scan Tool and the vehicle, voltage can be fed to the VREF circuit giving a false indication of a short to power. • For Shorts To VREF: — Measure resistance between Test Pin 4 and Test Pin 26 at the breakout box. • For Shorts To PIP circuit: — Measure resistance between Test Pin 4 and Test Pin 56 at the breakout box. • Is each resistance greater than 10,000 ohms?	Yes No	▶ ▶	GO to NB6 SERVICE short circuit. REMOVE breakout box. RECONNECT all components and Scan Tool (if applicable). RERUN Quick Test.
NB6	CHECK IDM CIRCUIT FOR SHORT TO GROUND			
	• Key off. • Breakout box installed, PCM disconnected. • ICM (Pins 7-12) disconnected. • Scan tool disconnected from Data Link Connector. NOTE: During this check when the 4-wire HO2S is connected to the vehicle harness on EI vehicles, a short to SIG RTN (Pin 46) may be indicated in conjunction with an actual PWR GND short. • Measure resistance between Test Pin 4 and Test Pins 16, 20, 40, 46 and 60 at the breakout box. • Is each resistance above 10,000 ohms?	Yes No	▶ ▶	RECONNECT Scan Tool. RECONNECT all components. GO to NB7 REMOVE breakout box. SERVICE short to ground in IDM circuit. RECONNECT all components. CLEAR Continuous Memory. RERUN Quick Test.

FM015930075O2050X

Fig. 211   Test NB: IDM/EI-Low Data Rate (Part 5 of 8)

TEST STEP	RESULT	▶	ACTION TO TAKE
NB7 CHECK ICM • Key off. • Breakout box installed. • Connect PCM to breakout box. • Reconnect ICM, • Connect DVOM between Test Pin 4 (also Test Pin 32 on 2.3L Mustang and Ranger) and Test Pin 16 at the breakout box. • Start engine. • Observe DVOM when voltage is allowed to stabilize. • Lightly tap on ignition components (to simulate road shock). • Wiggle both ICM connectors. • A sudden change in voltage indicates a fault. • **Is a fault indicated?**	Yes No	▶ ▶	DISCONNECT and INSPECT connectors. If connector and terminals are good, REMOVE breakout box, RECONNECT all components and GO to Electronic Ignition Diagnostics. GO to **NB8**
NB8 CHECK EEC HARNESS • DVOM still connected between Test Pin 4 (also, Test Pin 32 on 2.3L Mustang and Ranger) and Test Pin 16 at the breakout box. • Key on, engine running. • While observing a voltage change like in **NB7**, perform the following: — Grasp vehicle harness closest to both ICM connectors. Wiggle, shake and bend a small section of the EEC harness while working your way to the ignition system components and to the dash panel. Also wiggle, shake and bend the EEC harness from dash panel to PCM. • **Is a fault indicated?**	Yes No	▶ ▶	ISOLATE fault and SERVICE as necessary. REMOVE breakout box. RECONNECT all components. CLEAR Continuous Memory. RERUN Quick Test. GO to **NB9**
NB9 CHECK PCM AND HARNESS CONNECTORS • Key off. • Disconnect Powertrain Control Module (PCM). Inspect for damaged or pushed out pins, corrosion, loose wires, etc. • **Are connectors and terminals OK?**	Yes No	▶ ▶	GO to **NB10**. SERVICE as necessary. REMOVE breakout box. RECONNECT all components. CLEAR Continuous Memory. RERUN Quick Test.

FM0159300752060X

Fig. 211   Test NB: IDM/EI-Low Data Rate (Part 6 of 8)

TEST STEP	RESULT	▶	ACTION TO TAKE
NB10 CHECK PCM FOR SHORT TO POWER • Key off. • Breakout box installed. • PCM connected to breakout box. • Disconnect ICM (Pins 7-12). • Measure voltage between Test Pin 4 at the breakout box and chassis ground. • Key on, engine off. • Measure voltage between Test Pin 4 and Test Pins 40 and 60 at the breakout box. • **Is any voltage reading greater than 10.5 volts?**	Yes No	▶ ▶	REPLACE PCM. REMOVE breakout box. RECONNECT all components. RERUN Quick Test. GO to **NB11**.
NB11 CHECK PCM FOR SHORT TO GROUND • Key off. • Install breakout box. • Connect PCM to breakout box. • ICM (Pins 7-12) disconnected. • Measure resistance between Test Pin 4 and Test Pin 40, 46 and 60 at breakout box. • **Is each resistance greater than 10,000 ohms?**	Yes No	▶ ▶	REMOVE breakout box. RECONNECT all components. For further diagnosis, REFER to EI Diagnosis. REPLACE PCM. REMOVE breakout box. RECONNECT all components. RERUN Quick Test.
NB20 CONTINUOUS MEMORY DIAGNOSTIC TROUBLE CODE (DTC) 223 CHECK CONTINUITY OF DPI CIRCUIT Continuous Memory DTC 223 indicates an open in the Dual Plug Inhibit (DPI) circuit or an open or short to ground in coil 4. Possible causes: — Open in harness. — Short in harness. — Damaged Powertrain Control Module (PCM). — Damaged Ignition Control Module (ICM). — Coil 4 damage. • Key off. • Disconnect ICM (Pins 1-6). • Disconnect Powertrain Control Module (PCM). Inspect for damaged or pushed out pins, corrosion, loose wires, etc. Service as necessary. • Install breakout box, leave PCM disconnected. • Measure resistance between DPI pin at the ICM vehicle harness connector and Test Pin 32 at the breakout box. • **Is resistance less than 5.0 ohms?**	Yes No	▶ ▶	REMOVE breakout box. RECONNECT all components. REFER to EI Diagnosis. If ignition system checks OK REPLACE PCM. SERVICE open circuit. REMOVE breakout box. RECONNECT all components. RERUN Quick Test.

FM0159300752070X

Fig. 211   Test NB: IDM/EI-Low Data Rate (Part 7 of 8)

TEST STEP	RESULT	▶	ACTION TO TAKE
NB25 HARD TO START: CHECK FOR SPARK DURING CRANK • Using a neon Bulb Spark Tester (OTC D89P-6666-A) or Air Gap Spark Tester (D81P-6666-A), check for spark at all spark plug wires while cranking. • **Was spark present on ALL spark plug wires and consistent (one spark per crankshaft revolution)?**	Yes No	▶ ▶	GO to **NB26** SERVICE or REPLACE damaged spark plug. RERUN Quick Test.
NB26 HARD TO START: CHECK DPI CIRCUIT FOR SHORT TO GROUND • Key off. • Disconnect ICM (Pins 1-6). • Disconnect Powertrain Control Module (PCM). Inspect for damaged or pushed out pins, corrosion, loose wires, etc. Service as necessary. • Install breakout box, leave PCM disconnected. • Measure resistance between Test Pin 32 and Test Pins 40 and 60 at the breakout box. • **Is resistance greater than 100,000 ohms?**	Yes No	▶ ▶	GO to **NB27**. SERVICE short circuit. REMOVE breakout box. RECONNECT all components. RERUN Quick Test.
NB27 CHECK PCM FOR SHORT TO GROUND • Key off. • ICM (Pins 1-6) disconnected. • Breakout box installed. • Connect PCM to breakout box. • Measure resistance between Test Pin 32 and Test Pins 40 and 60 at the breakout box. • **Is resistance greater than 500 ohms?**	Yes No	▶ ▶	REMOVE breakout box. RECONNECT all components. GO to EI Diagnosis. REPLACE PCM. REMOVE breakout box. RECONNECT all components. RERUN Quick Test.

Fig. 211   Test NB: IDM/EI-Low Data Rate (Part 8 of 8)

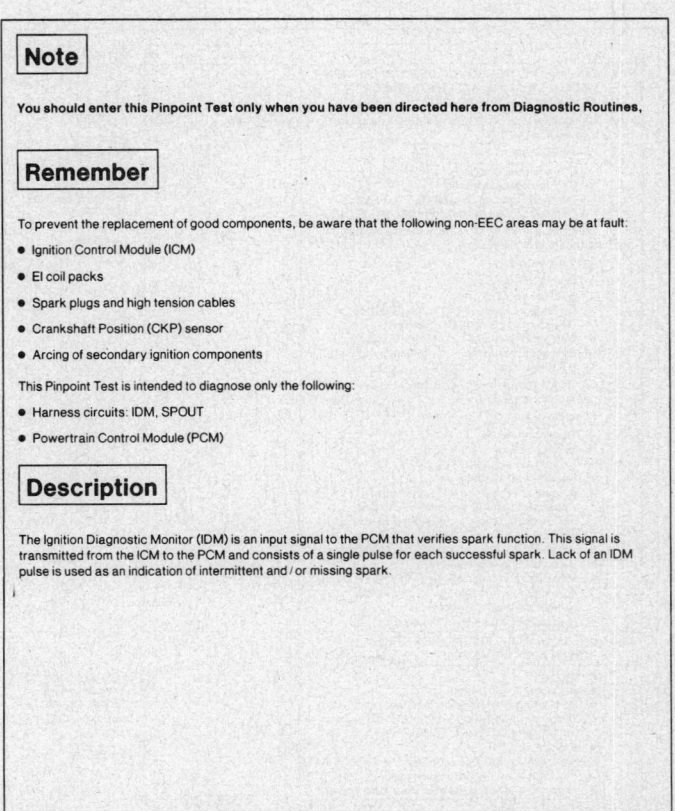

Note

You should enter this Pinpoint Test only when you have been directed here from Diagnostic Routines,

Remember

To prevent the replacement of good components, be aware that the following non-EEC areas may be at fault:

• Ignition Control Module (ICM)
• EI coil packs
• Spark plugs and high tension cables
• Crankshaft Position (CKP) sensor
• Arcing of secondary ignition components

This Pinpoint Test is intended to diagnose only the following:

• Harness circuits: IDM, SPOUT
• Powertrain Control Module (PCM)

Description

The Ignition Diagnostic Monitor (IDM) is an input signal to the PCM that verifies spark function. This signal is transmitted from the ICM to the PCM and consists of a single pulse for each successful spark. Lack of an IDM pulse is used as an indication of intermittent and/or missing spark.

FM0159300753010X

Fig. 212   Test NC: IDM/EI-High Data Rate (Part 1 of 9)

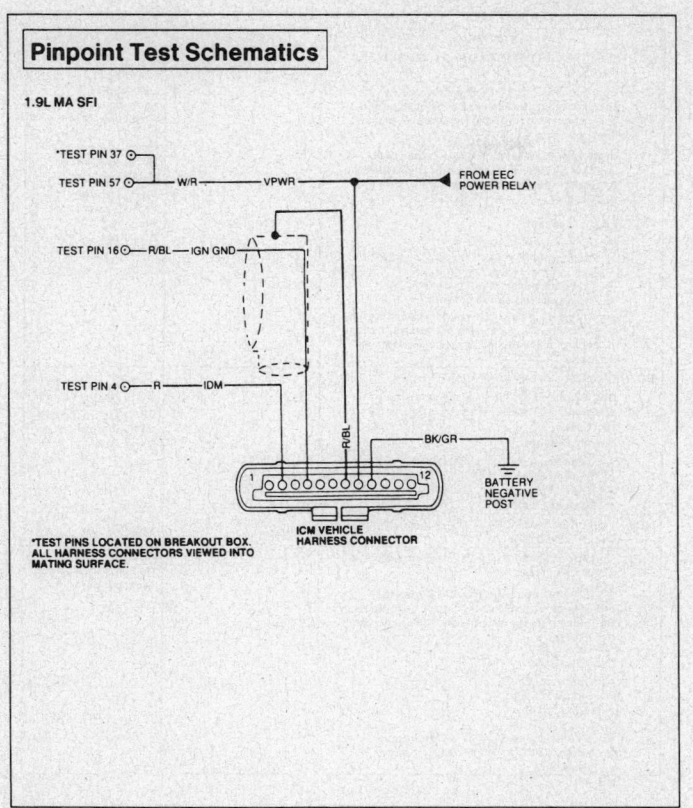

Fig. 212   Test NC: IDM/EI-High Data Rate (Part 2 of 9)

Fig. 212   Test NC: IDM/EI-High Data Rate (Part 3 of 9). 1993

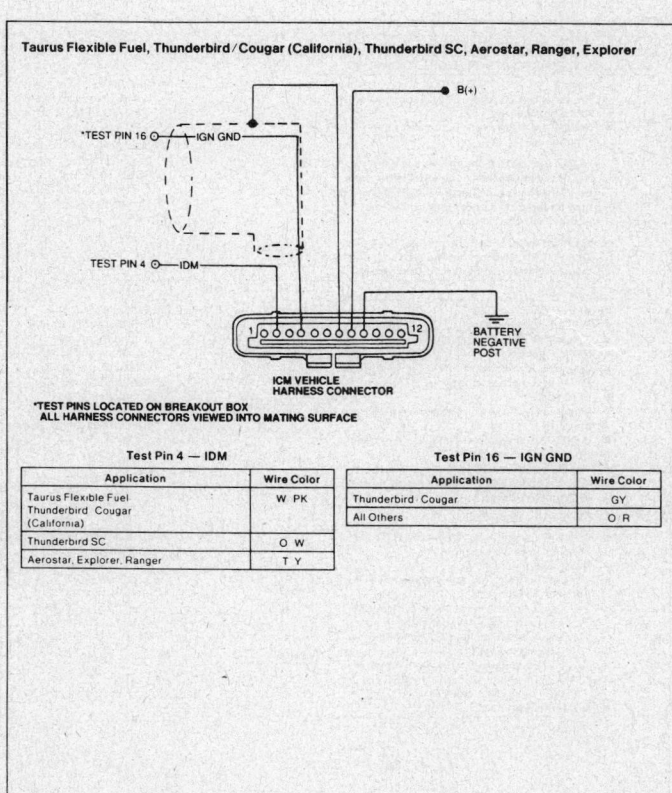

Fig. 212   Test NC: IDM/EI-High Data Rate (Part 3 of 9). 1994–95

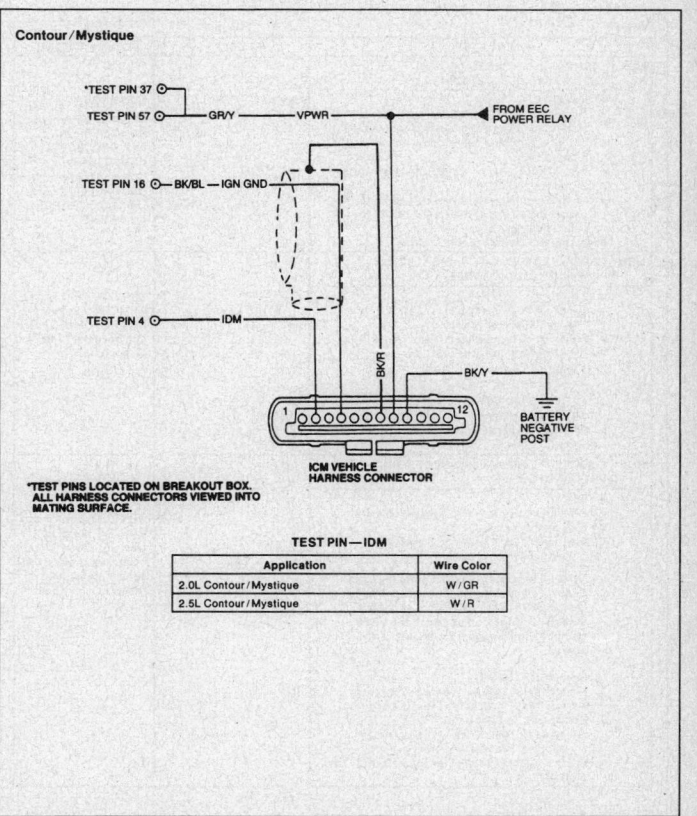

Fig. 212   Test NC: IDM/EI-High Data Rate (Part 4 of 9). 1995

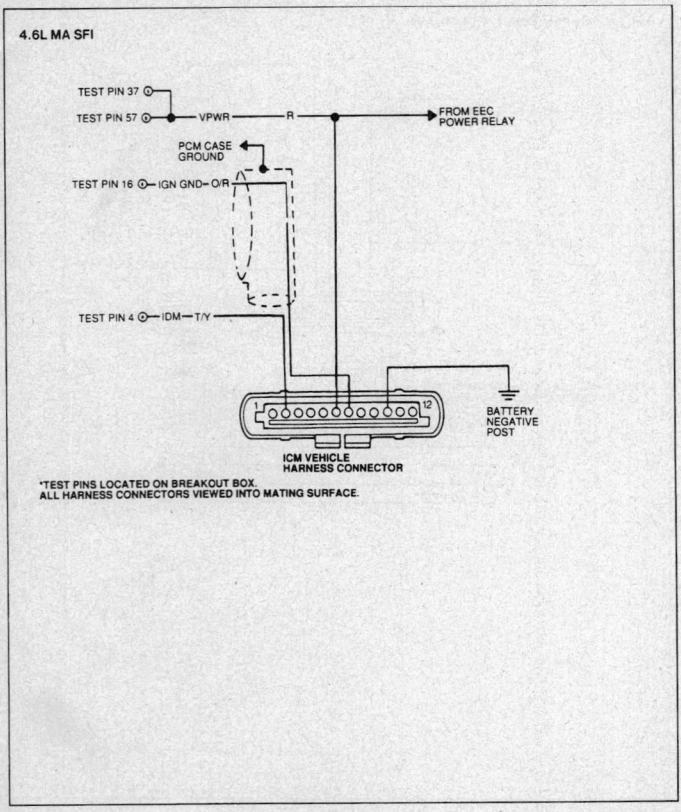

4.6L MA SFI

TEST PIN 37 ○——
TEST PIN 57 ○—— VPWR —— R ——→ FROM EEC
POWER RELAY
PCM CASE
GROUND
TEST PIN 16 ○— IGN GND—O/R ——

TEST PIN 4 ○— IDM—T/Y

1 12
ICM VEHICLE
HARNESS CONNECTOR

→ BATTERY
NEGATIVE
POST

*TEST PINS LOCATED ON BREAKOUT BOX.
ALL HARNESS CONNECTORS VIEWED INTO MATING SURFACE.

FM0159300753040X

**Fig. 212 Test NC: IDM/EI-High Data Rate (Part 5 of 9).
1993–94**

	TEST STEP	RESULT	▶	ACTION TO TAKE
NC1	CONTINUOUS MEMORY DTC 211: ERRATIC IGNITION			
	Continuous Memory DTC 211 indicates two successive erratic Profile Ignition Pickup (PIP) pulses occurred, resulting in a possible engine miss or stall.	Yes	▶	SERVICE as necessary. CLEAR Continuous Memory DTC 211 (REFER to Quick Test Appendix, Section 5A). RERUN Quick Test.
	NOTE: For Diagnostic Trouble Codes that indicate an intermittent, go directly to Section 8A, Electronic Ignition Diagnostics, with the DIST tester. Possible causes: — Loose wires/connectors. — Arcing secondary ignition components (coil, cap, rotor, wires, plugs, etc.). — On-board transmitter (2-way radio). * ● **Are any of the above present?** *Verify all 2-way radio installations. Carefully follow manufacturer's installation instructions regarding the routing of antenna and power leads.	No	▶	For No Starts: GO to Pinpoint Test Step AC1. All others: GO to NC4.
NC2	DTC 226: IDM CIRCUIT FAILURE			
	DTC 226 indicates the PCM did not receive the IDM signal from the ICM in Key On Engine Off Self-Test. Possible causes: — Open harness (IDM or IGN GND circuit). — Shorted harness. — ICM. ● **Does engine start?**	Yes	▶	GO to NC4.
		No	▶	REFER to Section 8A for Electronic Ignition Diagnostics.
NC3	CONTINOUS MEMORY DTC 212: CHECK FOR OTHER EEC DTCS			
	Continuous Memory DTC 212 indicates a loss of IDM input to the PCM. NOTE: For Diagnostic Trouble Codes that indicate an intermittent, go directly to Section 8A, Electronic Ignition Diagnostics, with the DIST tester. Possible causes — Open circuit — Shorted circuit — Damaged ICM — Damaged PCM ● **Is vehicle a No Start or is Continuous Memory DTC 215, 216, 217, or 232 present?**	Yes	▶	REFER to Section 8A for Electronic Ignition Diagnostics.
		No	▶	GO to NC4.

FM0159300753050X

Fig. 212 Test NC: IDM/EI-High Data Rate (Part 6 of 9)

	TEST STEP	RESULT	▶	ACTION TO TAKE
NC4	CONTINUOUS MEMORY DTC 212: CHECK IDM CIRCUIT CONTINUITY			
	● Key off. ● Disconnect Powertrain Control Module (PCM). Inspect for damaged or pushed out pins, corrosion, loose wires, etc. Service as necessary. ● Install breakout box, leave PCM disconnected. ● Disconnect ICM. ● Measure resistance between Test Pin 4 at the breakout box and at IDM circuit the ICM vehicle harness connector. ● **Is resistance less than 5.0 ohms?**	Yes	▶	GO to NC5.
		No	▶	SERVICE open circuit. REMOVE breakout box. RECONNECT PCM. CLEAR Continuous Memory. RECONNECT E-core ignition coil. RERUN Quick Test.
NC5	CHECK IDM CIRCUIT FOR SHORTS TO POWER (EXCLUDING VREF)			
	● Key off. ● Breakout box installed. ● PCM and ICM disconnected. ● Measure voltage between Test Pin 4 and Test Pin 40 or 60 at the breakout box. For Short To B+: — Key off. For Short To Keypower or VPWR: — Key on, engine off. ● **Is any voltage reading greater than 10.5 volts?**	Yes	▶	SERVICE short circuit. REMOVE breakout box. RECONNECT all components. RERUN Quick Test.
		No	▶	GO to NC6.
NC6	CHECK IDM CIRCUIT FOR SHORT TO VREF AND PIP			
	● Key off. ● Breakout box installed, PCM disconnected. ● ICM disconnected. ● Disconnect Scan Tool from Data Link Connector (if applicable). NOTE: For proper results of this test, the Scan Tool must be disconnected. Due to the circuitry of the Scan Tool and the vehicle, voltage can be fed to the VREF circuit giving a false indication of a short to power. For Shorts To VREF: — Measure resistance between Test Pin 4 and Test Pin 26 at the breakout box. For Shorts To PIP circuit: — Measure resistance between Test Pin 4 and Test Pin 56 at the breakout box. ● **Is each resistance greater than 10,000 ohms?**	Yes	▶	GO to NC7.
		No	▶	SERVICE short circuit. REMOVE breakout box. RECONNECT all components and SCAN Tool (if applicable). RERUN Quick Test.

FM0159300753060X

Fig. 212 Test NC: IDM/EI-High Data Rate (Part 7 of 9)

	TEST STEP	RESULT	▶	ACTION TO TAKE
NC7	CHECK IDM CIRCUIT FOR SHORT TO GROUND			
	● Key off. ● Breakout box installed, PCM disconnected. ● ICM disconnected. ● SCAN Tool disconnected from Data Link Connector. NOTE: During this check when the 4-wire HO2S is connected to the vehicle harness on ICM vehicles, a short to SIG RTN (Pin 46) may be indicated in conjunction with an actual PWR GND short. ● Measure resistance between Test Pin 4 and Test Pins 40, 46 and 60 at the breakout box. ● **Is each resistance above 10,000 ohms?**	Yes	▶	RECONNECT all components and SCAN Tool. GO to NC8.
		No	▶	REMOVE breakout box. SERVICE short to ground in IDM circuit. RECONNECT all components. CLEAR Continuous Memory. RERUN Quick Test.
NC8	CHECK ICM			
	● Key off. ● Breakout box installed. ● Connect PCM to breakout box. ● ICM connected. ● Connect DVOM between Test Pin 4 and Test Pin 16 at the breakout box. ● Start engine. ● Observe DVOM when voltage is allowed to stabilize. ● Lightly tap on electronic ignition components (to simulate road shock). ● Wiggle both ICM connectors. ● A sudden change in voltage indicates a fault. ● **Is a fault indicated?**	Yes	▶	DISCONNECT and INSPECT connectors. If connector and terminals are good, REMOVE breakout box, RECONNECT all components and REFER to Electronic Ignition Diagnostics.
		No	▶	GO to NC9.
NC9	CHECK EEC-IV HARNESS			
	● DVOM still connected between Test Pin 4 and Test Pin 16 at the breakout box. ● Key on, engine running. ● While observing a voltage change like in NC8, perform the following: — Grasp vehicle harness closest to ICM connector. Wiggle, shake and bend a small section of the EEC harness while working toward the other ignition system components and to the dash panel. Also wiggle, shake and bend the EEC harness from dash panel to PCM. ● **Is a fault indicated?**	Yes	▶	ISOLATE fault and SERVICE as necessary. REMOVE breakout box. RECONNECT all components. CLEAR Continuous Memory. RERUN Quick Test.
		No	▶	GO to NC10.

FM0159300753070X

Fig. 212 Test NC: IDM/EI-High Data Rate (Part 8 of 9)

TEST STEP	RESULT	▶	ACTION TO TAKE
NC10 CHECK PCM AND HARNESS CONNECTORS			
• Key off. • Disconnect Powertrain Control Module (PCM) 60 pin connector. Inspect for damaged or pushed out pins, corrosion, loose wires, etc. • **Are connectors and terminals OK?**	Yes No	▶ ▶	GO to **NC11**. SERVICE as necessary. REMOVE breakout box. RECONNECT all components. CLEAR Continuous Memory. RERUN Quick Test.
NC11 CHECK PCM FOR SHORT TO POWER			
• Key off. • Breakout box installed. • PCM connected to breakout box. • Disconnect ICM. • Measure voltage between Test Pin 4 at breakout box and chassis ground. • Key on, engine off. • Measure voltage between Test Pin 4 and Test Pins 40 and 60 at the breakout box. • **Is any voltage reading greater than 10.5 volts?**	Yes No	▶ ▶	REPLACE PCM. REMOVE breakout box. RECONNECT all components. RERUN Quick Test. GO to **NC12**.
NC12 CHECK PCM FOR SHORT TO GROUND			
• Key off. • Install breakout box. • Connect PCM to breakout box. • ICM disconnected. • Measure resistance between Test Pin 4 and Test Pins 16, 20, 40, 46 and 60 at breakout box. • **Is each resistance greater than 10,000 ohms?**	Yes No	▶ ▶	REMOVE breakout box. RECONNECT all components. For further diagnosis, REFER to EI Diagnosis. REPLACE PCM. REMOVE breakout box. RECONNECT all components. RERUN Quick Test.

FM0159300753080X

Fig. 212   Test NC: IDM/EI-High Data Rate (Part 9 of 9)

Note

You should enter this Pinpoint Test only when checking computed timing, or you have been directed here from Diagnostic Routines,

Remember

To prevent the replacement of good components, be aware that the following non-EEC areas may be at fault:

• Base engine
• Distributor
• Ignition Control Module (ICM)

This Pinpoint Test is intended to diagnose only the following:

• Harness circuit: SPOUT
• Base timing
• Powertrain Control Module (PCM)

Description

The Spark Output (SPOUT) is a digital signal generated by the PCM which supplies desired spark timing and, in some instances dwell information to the ICM. Normally there will be one and only one SPOUT pulse for each PIP period.

FM0159300754010X

Fig. 213   Test PA: Spark Timing Check, DI (Part 1 of 4)

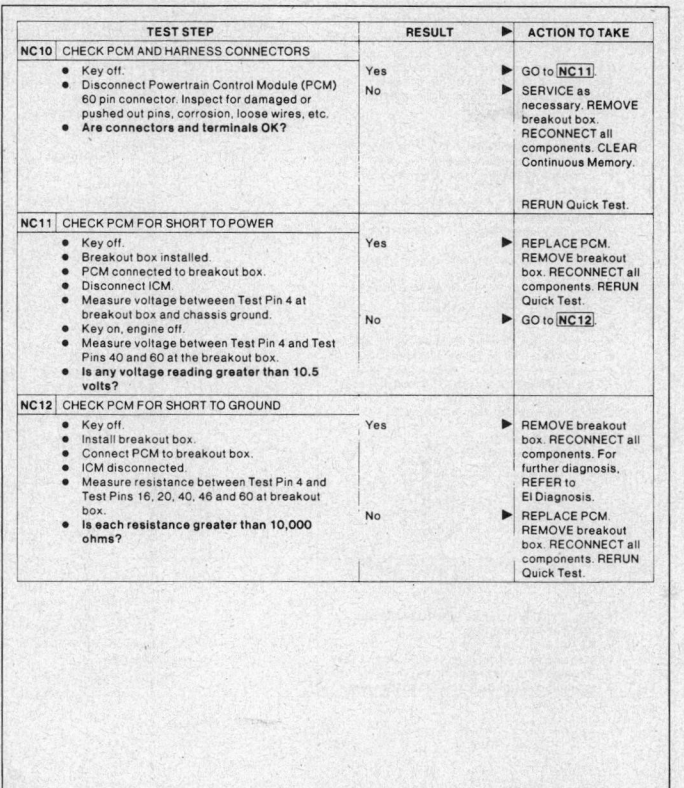

FM015930075402AX

Fig. 213   Test PA: Spark Timing Check, DI (Part 2 of 4). 1993

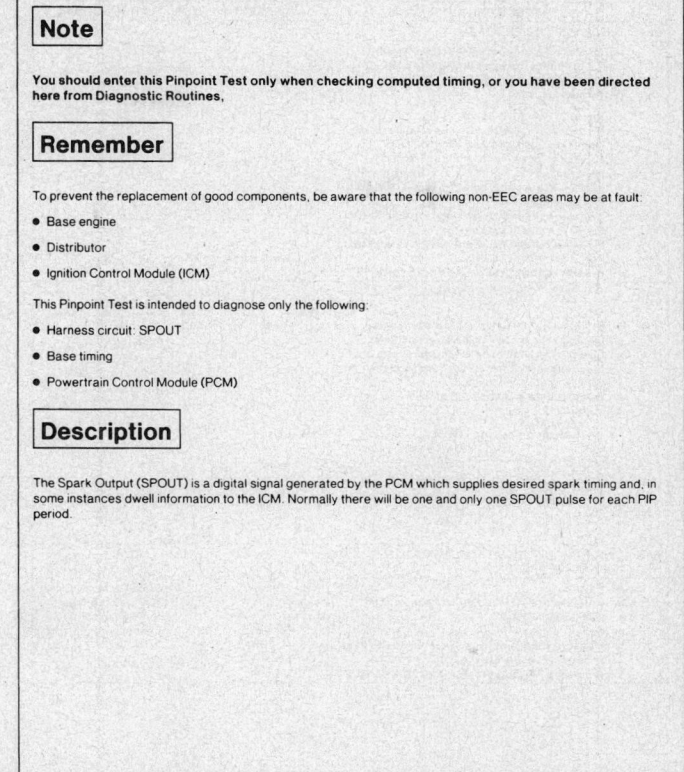
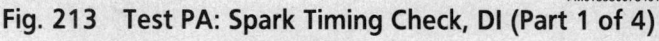
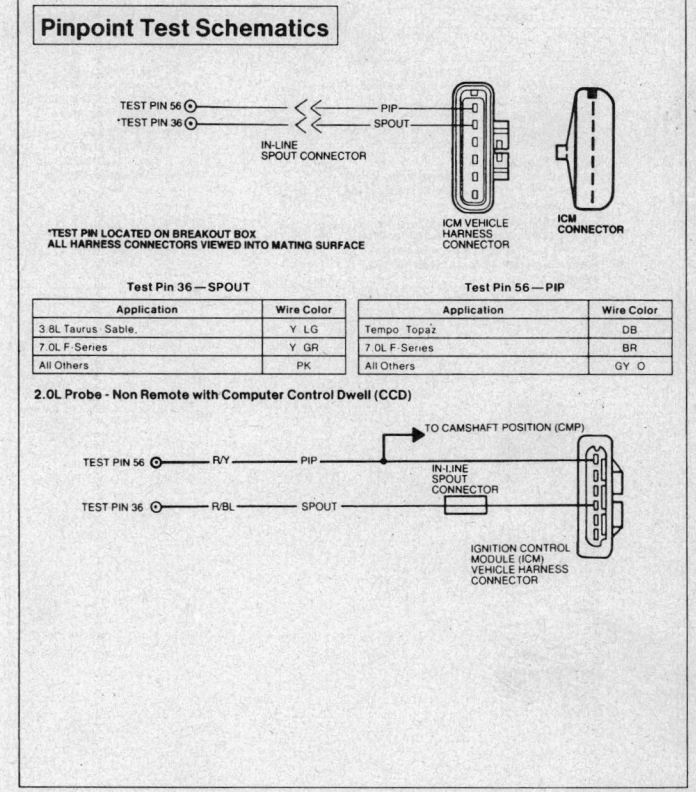

FM015940075402BX

Fig. 213   Test PA: Spark Timing Check, DI (Part 2 of 4). 1994–95

TEST STEP		RESULT	▶	ACTION TO TAKE
PA1	CHECK FOR POWER TO PCM			
	NOTE: **Before proceeding with this Pinpoint Test, verify that the base timing check in Diagnostic Subroutine Step `4.0` has been performed.** • Key off. • Disconnect Powertrain Control Module (PCM). Inspect for damaged or pushed out pins, corrosion, loose wires, etc. Service as necessary. • Install breakout box, leave PCM disconnected. • Key on, engine off. • Measure voltage between Test Pin 37 and Test Pin 40 at the breakout box. • Measure voltage between Test Pin 57 and Test Pin 60 at the breakout box. • **Is each voltage greater than 10.5 volts?**	Yes No	▶ ▶	GO to `PA2`. **For Tempo / Topaz, Taurus / Sable, Continental:** GO to Pinpoint Test Step `X1`. **For all others:** GO to Pinpoint Test Step `B1`.
PA2	CHECK SPOUT CIRCUIT CONTINUITY			
	• Key off. • Breakout box installed, PCM disconnected. • Disconnect Ignition Control Module (ICM). • Measure resistance between Test Pin 36 at the breakout box and SPOUT circuit at the ICM vehicle harness connector. • **Is resistance less than 5.0 ohms?**	Yes No	▶ ▶	GO to `PA3`. SERVICE open circuit. REMOVE breakout box. RECONNECT all components. CHECK timing as in Diagnostic Subroutine Step `4.0`.

ICM VEHICLE HARNESS CONNECTOR

TEST PIN 36 ⊙——□ SPOUT

IN LINE SPOUT CONNECTOR

PA3	CHECK SPOUT CIRCUIT FOR SHORT TO B+ (EXCLUDING VREF)			
	• Key off. • Breakout box installed, PCM disconnected. • ICM disconnected. • Key on, engine off. • Measure voltage between Test Pin 36 and Test Pin 40 or 60 at the breakout box. • **Is voltage reading greater than 10.5 volts?**	Yes No	▶ ▶	SERVICE short circuit. REMOVE breakout box. RECONNECT all components. RERUN Quick Test. GO to `PA4`.

FM015930075403AX

Fig. 213   Test PA: Spark Timing Check, DI (Part 3 of 4). 1993

TEST STEP		RESULT	▶	ACTION TO TAKE
PA1	CHECK FOR POWER TO PCM			
	NOTE: **Before proceeding with this Pinpoint Test, verify that the base timing check in Diagnostic Subroutine Step `4.0` has been performed.** • Key off. • Disconnect Powertrain Control Module (PCM). Inspect for damaged or pushed out pins, corrosion, loose wires, etc. Service as necessary. • Install breakout box, leave PCM disconnected. • Key on, engine off. • Measure voltage between Test Pin 37 and Test Pin 40 at the breakout box. • Measure voltage between Test Pin 57 and Test Pin 60 at the breakout box. • **Is each voltage greater than 10.5 volts?**	Yes No	▶ ▶	GO to `PA2`. **For Tempo / Topaz, Taurus / Sable, Thunderbird / Cougar, Continental, Mustang:** GO to Pinpoint Test Step `X1`. **For all others:** GO to Pinpoint Test Step `B1`.
PA2	CHECK SPOUT CIRCUIT CONTINUITY			
	• Key off. • Breakout box installed, PCM disconnected. • Disconnect Ignition Control Module (ICM). • Measure resistance between Test Pin 36 at the breakout box and SPOUT circuit at the ICM vehicle harness connector. • **Is resistance less than 5.0 ohms?**	Yes No	▶ ▶	GO to `PA3`. SERVICE open circuit. REMOVE breakout box. RECONNECT all components. CHECK timing as in Diagnostic Subroutine Step `4.0`.

ICM VEHICLE HARNESS CONNECTOR

TEST PIN 36 ⊙——□ SPOUT

IN LINE SPOUT CONNECTOR

PA3	CHECK SPOUT CIRCUIT FOR SHORT TO B+ (EXCLUDING VREF)			
	• Key off. • Breakout box installed, PCM disconnected. • ICM disconnected. • Key on, engine off. • Measure voltage between Test Pin 36 and Test Pin 40 or 60 at the breakout box. • **Is voltage reading greater than 10.5 volts?**	Yes No	▶ ▶	SERVICE short circuit. REMOVE breakout box. RECONNECT all components. RERUN Quick Test. GO to `PA4`.

FM015940075403BX

Fig. 213   Test PA: Spark Timing Check, DI (Part 3 of 4). 1994–95

TEST STEP		RESULT	▶	ACTION TO TAKE
PA4	CHECK SPOUT CIRCUIT FOR SHORT TO VREF, GROUND AND PIP			
	• Key off. • Breakout box installed, PCM disconnected. • ICM disconnected. **For Short to VREF:** — Measure resistance between Test Pin 36 and Test Pin 26 at the breakout box. **For Short to Ground:** — Measure resistance between Test Pin 36 and Test Pins 16, 20, 40, 46 and 60 at the breakout box. **For Short to PIP:** — Measure resistance between Test Pin 36 and Test Pin 56 at the breakout box. • **Is each resistance greater than 10,000 ohms?**	Yes No	▶ ▶	RECONNECT all components. GO to Distributor Ignition Diagnosis. SERVICE short circuit. REMOVE breakout box. RECONNECT all components. RERUN Quick Test.

FM0159300754040X

Fig. 213   Test PA: Spark Timing Check, DI (Part 4 of 4)

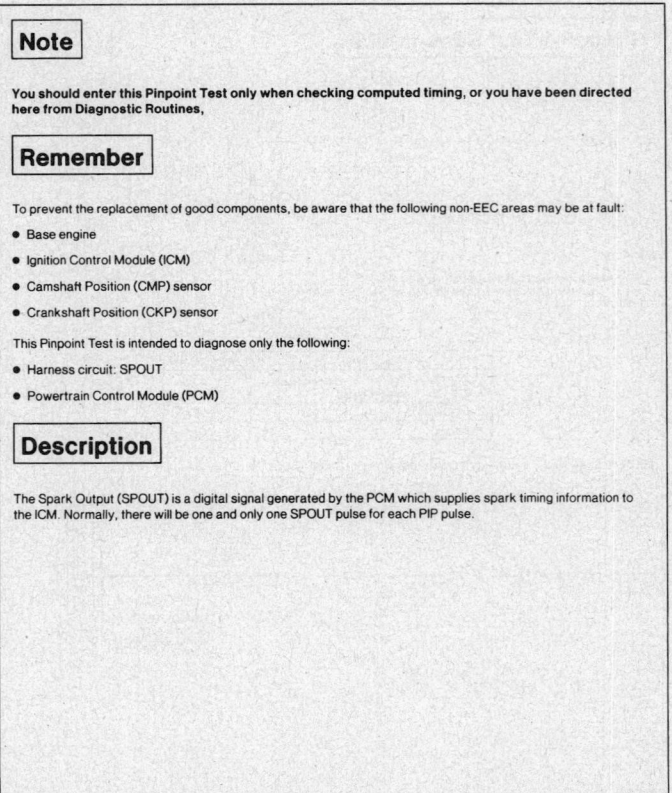

Note

You should enter this Pinpoint Test only when checking computed timing, or you have been directed here from Diagnostic Routines.

Remember

To prevent the replacement of good components, be aware that the following non-EEC areas may be at fault:

• Base engine
• Ignition Control Module (ICM)
• Camshaft Position (CMP) sensor
• Crankshaft Position (CKP) sensor

This Pinpoint Test is intended to diagnose only the following:

• Harness circuit: SPOUT
• Powertrain Control Module (PCM)

Description

The Spark Output (SPOUT) is a digital signal generated by the PCM which supplies spark timing information to the ICM. Normally, there will be one and only one SPOUT pulse for each PIP pulse.

FM0159300755010X

Fig. 214   Test PB: Spark Timing Check, EI-Low Data Rate (Part 1 of 5)

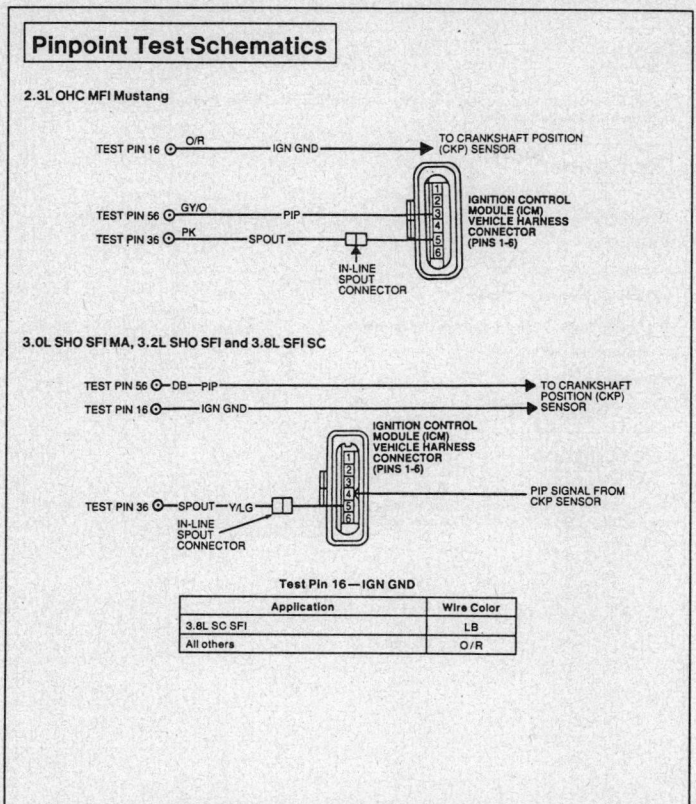

Fig. 214 Test PB: Spark Timing Check, EI-Low Data Rate (Part 2 of 5). 1993

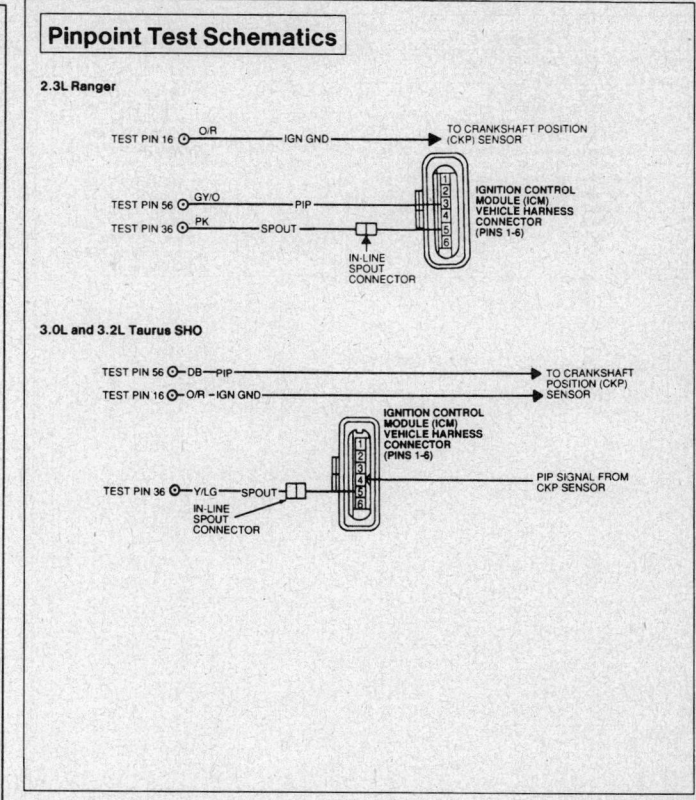

FM015940075502BX

Fig. 214 Test PB: Spark Timing Check, EI-Low Data Rate (Part 2 of 5). 1994–95

TEST STEP	RESULT	▶	ACTION TO TAKE
PB1 CHECK FOR POWER TO PCM			
NOTE: Before proceeding with this Pinpoint Test, verify that the base timing check in Diagnostic Subroutine Step **4.0** has been performed. • Key off. • Disconnect Powertrain Control Module (PCM). Inspect for damaged or pushed out pins, corrosion, loose wires. Service as necessary. • Install breakout box, leave PCM disconnected. • Key on, engine off. • Measure voltage between Test Pin 37 and Test Pin 40 at the breakout box. • Measure voltage between Test Pin 57 and Test Pin 60 at the breakout box. • **Is each voltage greater than 10.5 volts?**	Yes No	▶ ▶	GO to **PB2**. **For all others:** GO to Pinpoint Test Step **X1**.
PB2 CHECK SPOUT CIRCUIT CONTINUITY			
• Key off. • Breakout box installed, PCM disconnected. • Disconnect Ignition Control Module (ICM) (Pins 1-6). • Measure resistance between Test Pin 36 at the breakout box and SPOUT circuit at the ICM vehicle harness connector. • **Is resistance less than 5.0 ohms?**	Yes No	▶ ▶	GO to **PB3**. SERVICE open circuit. REMOVE breakout box. RECONNECT all components. CHECK timing as in Diagnostic Subroutine Step **4.0**.
PB3 CHECK SPOUT CIRCUIT FOR SHORT TO B+ (EXCLUDING VREF)			
• Key off. • Breakout box installed, PCM disconnected. • ICM (Pins 1-6) disconnected. • Key on, engine off. • Measure voltage between Test Pin 36 and Test Pin 40 or 60 at the breakout box. • **Is voltage reading greater than 10.5 volts?**	Yes No	▶ ▶	SERVICE short circuit. REMOVE breakout box. RECONNECT all components. RERUN Quick Test. GO to **PB4**.

FM015930075030X

Fig. 214 Test PB: Spark Timing Check, EI-Low Data Rate (Part 3 of 5)

TEST STEP	RESULT	▶	ACTION TO TAKE
PB4 CHECK SPOUT CIRCUIT FOR SHORT TO VREF, GROUND AND PIP			
• Key off. • Breakout box installed, PCM disconnected. • ICM (Pins 1-6) disconnected. **For Short to VREF:** — Measure resistance between Test Pin 36 and Test Pin 26 at the breakout box. **For Short to Ground:** — Measure resistance between Test Pin 36 and Test Pins 16, 20, 40, 46 and 60 at the breakout box. **For Short to PIP:** — Measure resistance between Test Pin 36 and Test Pin 56 at the breakout box. • **Is each resistance greater than 10,000 ohms?**	Yes No	▶ ▶	RECONNECT all components. GO to Distributor Ignition Diagnosis. SERVICE short circuit. REMOVE breakout box. RECONNECT all components. RERUN Quick Test.
PB10 CONTINUOUS MEMORY DIAGNOSTIC TROUBLE CODE (DTC) 219: CHECK SPOUT CIRCUIT CONTINUITY			
DTC 219 indicates the spark timing has defaulted to 10 degrees BTDC. The SPOUT signal has a variable duty cycle with amplitude that varies from 0.4 volt to B+. In the event of a SPOUT failure, the ICM will generate a fixed dwell and constant spark angle based on CID and PIP signals (FMEM mode). Possible causes: — Damaged ICM. — Damaged SPOUT circuit. • Key off. • Disconnect Powertrain Control Module (PCM). Inspect for damaged or pushed out pins, corrosion, loose wires, etc. Service as necessary. • Breakout box installed, leave PCM disconnected. • Disconnect Ignition Control Module (ICM) (Pins 1-6). • Measure resistance between Test Pin 36 at the breakout box and SPOUT circuit at the ICM vehicle harness connector. • **Is resistance less than 5.0 ohms?**	Yes No	▶ ▶	GO to **PB11**. VERIFY in-line SPOUT connector is properly connected. If OK, SERVICE open circuit. RECONNECT all components. RERUN Quick Test.

FM015930075040X

Fig. 214 Test PB: Spark Timing Check, EI-Low Data Rate (Part 4 of 5)

FORD—Computerized Engine Controls

TEST STEP	RESULT	▶	ACTION TO TAKE
PB11 CHECK SPOUT CIRCUIT FOR SHORT TO POWER AND GROUND • Key off. • ICM disconnected. • Breakout box installed, leave PCM disconnected. • Measure resistance between Test Pin 36 and Test Pins 16 and 40 at the breakout box. • Measure resistance between Test Pin 36 at the breakout box and battery positive post. • **Is each resistance greater than 10,000 ohms?**	Yes	▶	REPLACE ICM. EEC system OK. REMOVE breakout box. RECONNECT all components. RERUN Quick Test.
	No	▶	SERVICE SPOUT circuit for short to power or ground. REMOVE breakout box. RECONNECT all components. RERUN Quick Test.

FM0159300756050X

Fig. 214 Test PB: Spark Timing Check, EI-Low Data Rate (Part 5 of 5)

Note

You should enter this Pinpoint Test only when checking computed timing, or you have been directed here from Diagnostic Routines.

Remember

To prevent the replacement of good components, be aware that the following non-EEC areas may be at fault:
• Base engine
• Ignition Control Module (ICM)
• Crankshaft Position (CKP) sensor

This Pinpoint Test is intended to diagnose only the following:
• Harness Circuit: SPOUT
• Base Timing
• Powertrain Control Module (PCM)

Description

The SPOUT is a digital signal generated by the PCM which supplies spark timing information to the ICM. Normally there will be one and only one SPOUT pulse for each PIP pulse.

FM0159300756010X

Fig. 215 Test PC: Spark Timing Check, EI-High Data Rate (Part 1 of 7)

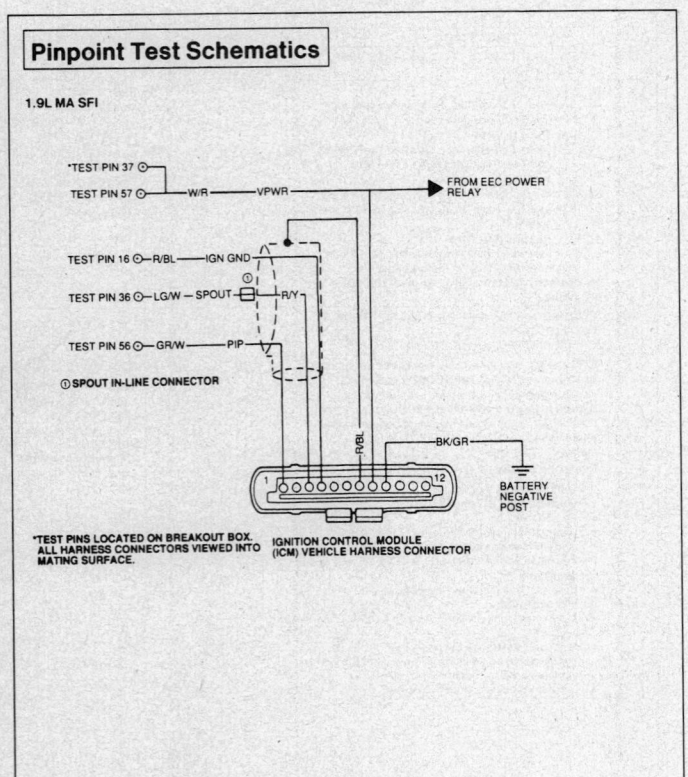

FM0159300756020X

Fig. 215 Test PC: Spark Timing Check, EI-High Data Rate (Part 2 of 7)

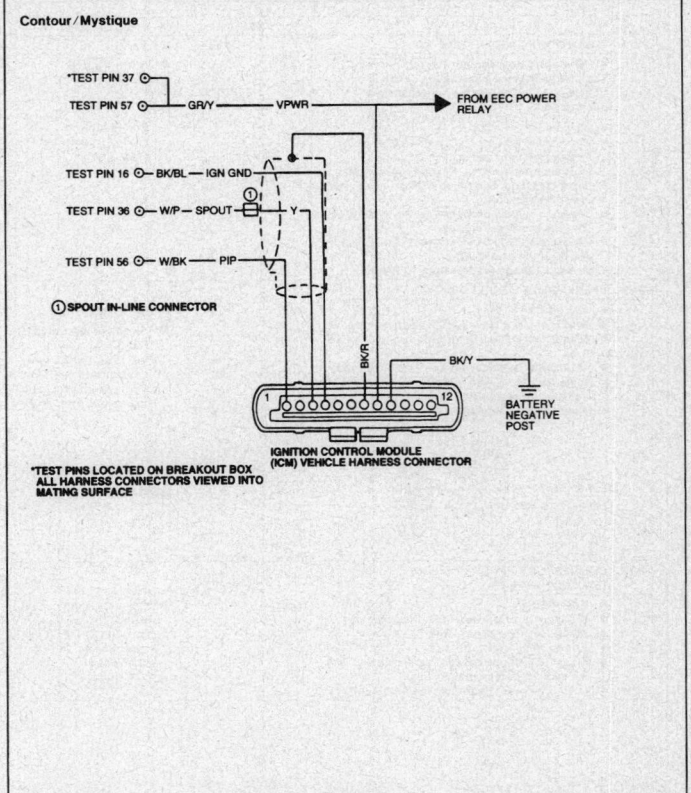

FM0159500756070X

Fig. 215 Test PC: Spark Timing Check, EI-High Data Rate (Part 3 of 7). 1995

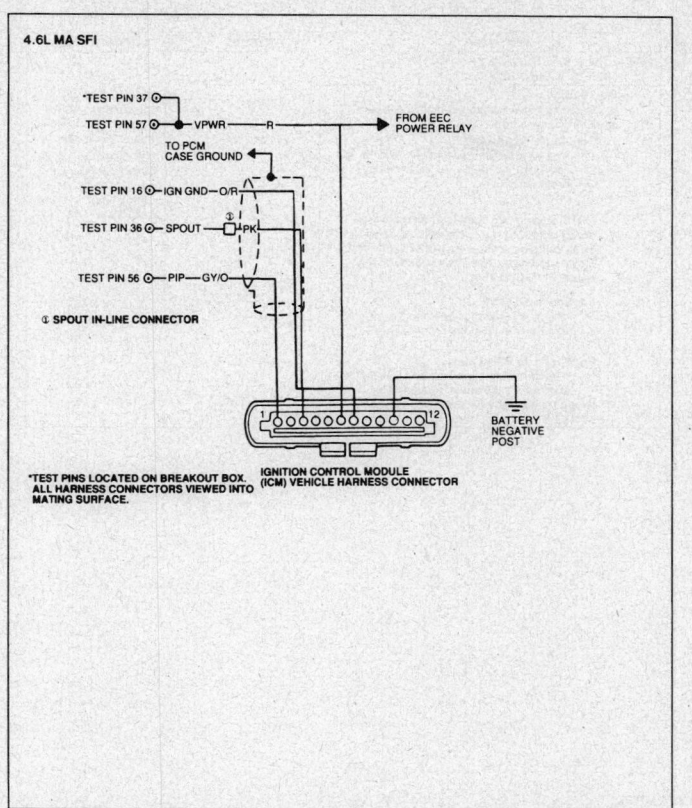

Fig. 215 Test PC: Spark Timing Check, EI-High Data Rate (Part 4 of 7)

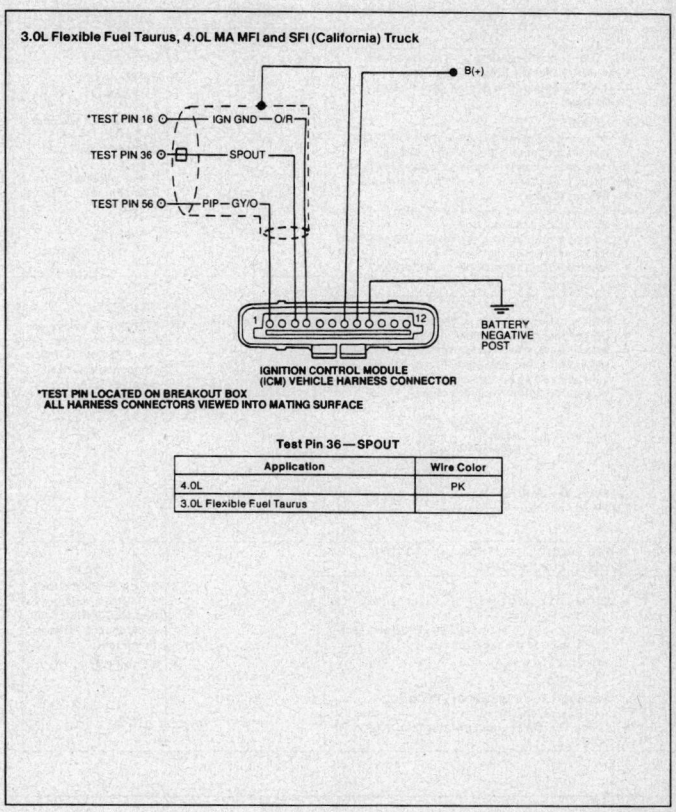

Fig. 215 Test PC: Spark Timing Check, EI-High Data Rate (Part 5 of 7). 1993

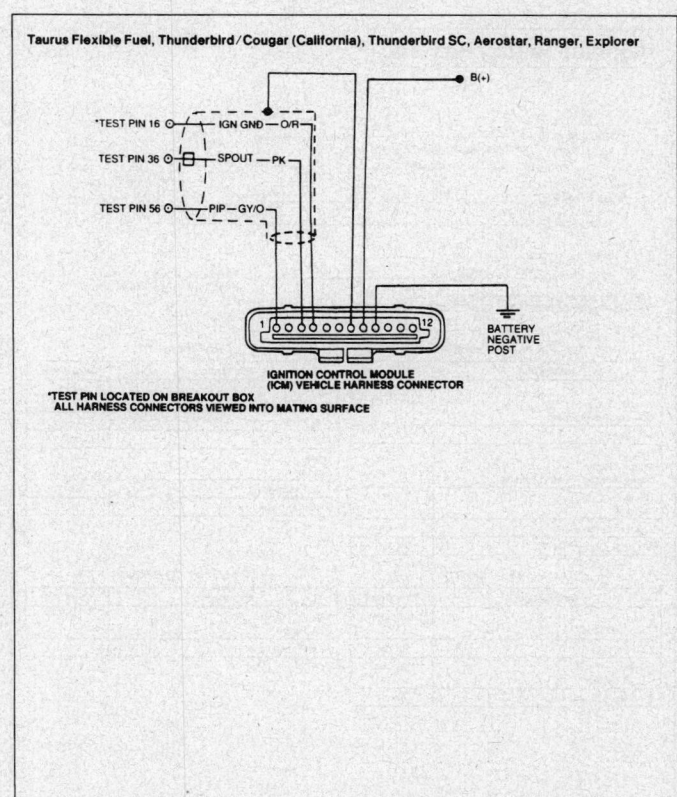

Fig. 215 Test PC: Spark Timing Check, EI-High Data Rate (Part 5 of 7). 1994–95

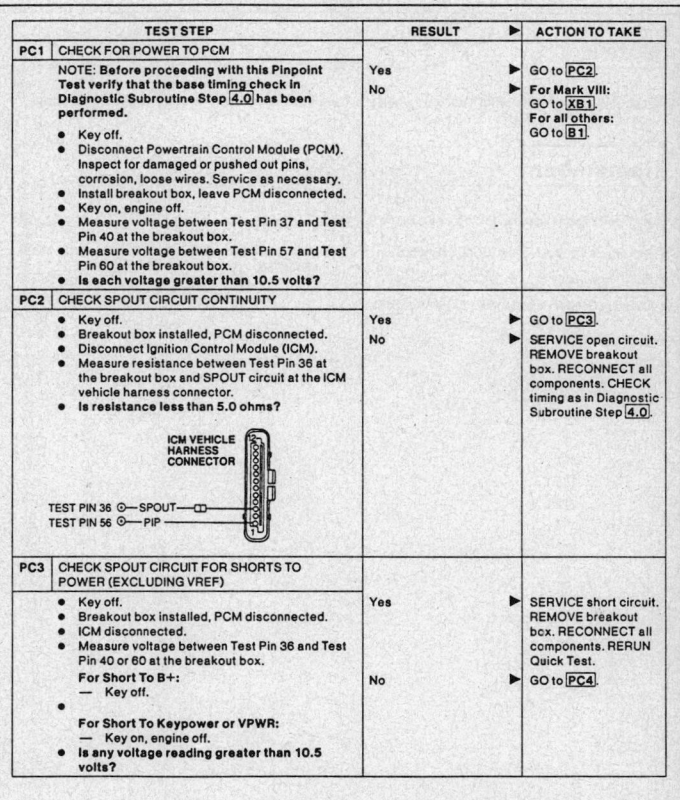

Fig. 215 Test PC: Spark Timing Check, EI-High Data Rate (Part 6 of 7). 1993

FORD—Computerized Engine Controls

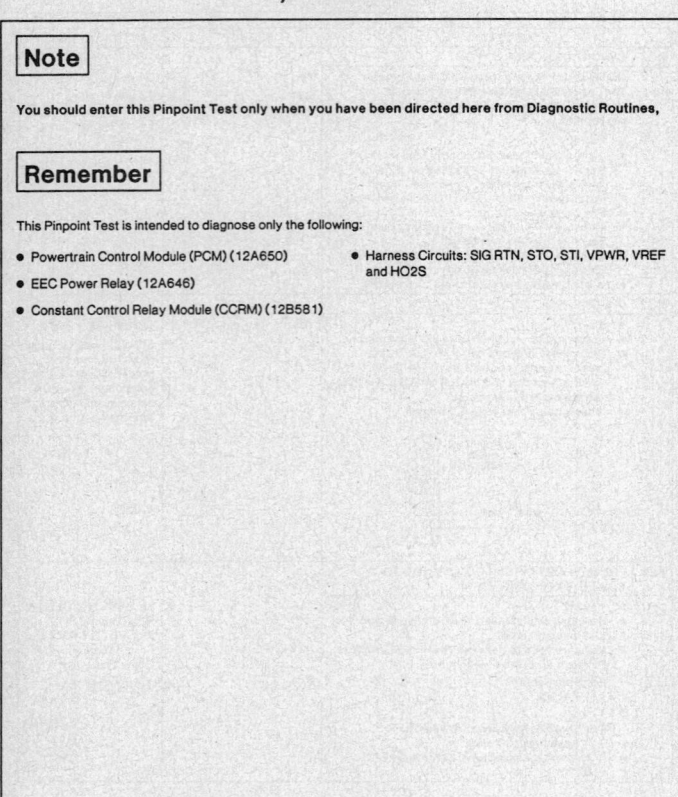

TEST STEP	RESULT	▶	ACTION TO TAKE
PC1 CHECK FOR POWER TO PCM			
NOTE: Before proceeding with this Pinpoint Test, verify that the base timing check in Diagnostic Subroutine Step 4.0 has been performed. • Key off. • Disconnect Powertrain Control Module (PCM). Inspect for damaged or pushed out pins, corrosion, loose wires. Service as necessary. • Install breakout box, leave PCM disconnected. • Key on, engine off. • Measure voltage between Test Pin 37 and Test Pin 40 at the breakout box. • Measure voltage between Test Pin 57 and Test Pin 60 at the breakout box. • Is each voltage greater than 10.5 volts?	Yes No	▶ ▶	GO to PC2. For Mark VIII: GO to XB1. For Thunderbird / Cougar (not SC): GO to Pinpoint Test Step X1. For all others: GO to Pinpoint Test Step B1.
PC2 CHECK SPOUT CIRCUIT CONTINUITY			
• Key off. • Breakout box installed, PCM disconnected. • Disconnect Ignition Control Module (ICM). • Measure resistance between Test Pin 36 at the breakout box and SPOUT circuit at the ICM vehicle harness connector. • Is resistance less than 5.0 ohms?	Yes No	▶ ▶	GO to PC3. SERVICE open circuit. REMOVE breakout box. RECONNECT all components. CHECK timing as in Diagnostic Subroutine Step 4.0.
PC3 CHECK SPOUT CIRCUIT FOR SHORTS TO POWER (EXCLUDING VREF)			
• Key off. • Breakout box installed, PCM disconnected. • ICM disconnected. • Measure voltage between Test Pin 36 and Test Pin 40 or 60 at the breakout box. For Short To B+: — Key off. For Short To Keypower or VPWR: — Key on, engine off. • Is any voltage reading greater than 10.5 volts?	Yes No	▶ ▶	SERVICE short circuit. REMOVE breakout box. RECONNECT all components. RERUN Quick Test. GO to PC4.

Fig. 215 Test PC: Spark Timing Check, EI-High Data Rate (Part 6 of 7). 1994–95

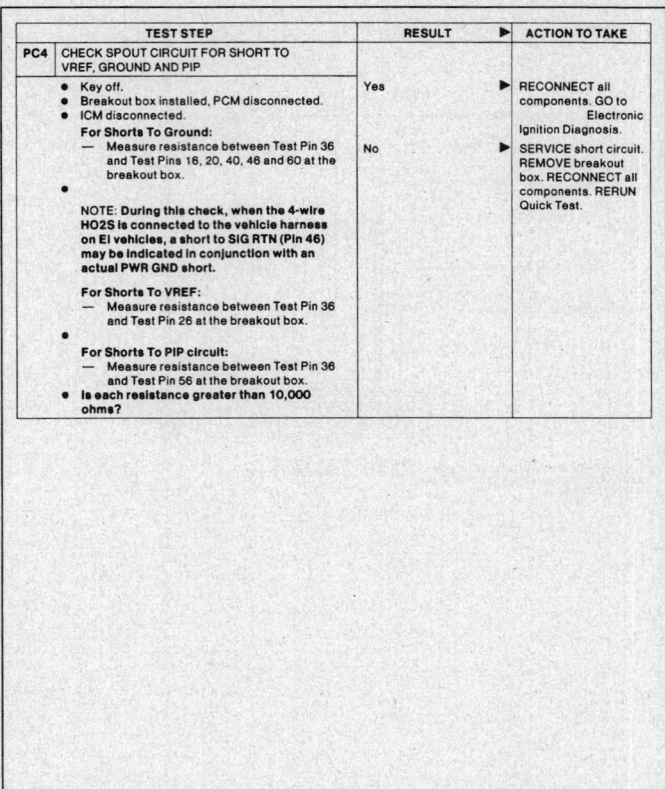

TEST STEP	RESULT	▶	ACTION TO TAKE
PC4 CHECK SPOUT CIRCUIT FOR SHORT TO VREF, GROUND AND PIP			
• Key off. • Breakout box installed, PCM disconnected. • ICM disconnected. **For Shorts To Ground:** — Measure resistance between Test Pin 36 and Test Pins 16, 20, 40, 46 and 60 at the breakout box. • NOTE: During this check, when the 4-wire HO2S is connected to the vehicle harness on EI vehicles, a short to SIG RTN (Pin 46) may be indicated in conjunction with an actual PWR GND short. **For Shorts To VREF:** — Measure resistance between Test Pin 36 and Test Pin 26 at the breakout box. **For Shorts To PIP circuit:** — Measure resistance between Test Pin 36 and Test Pin 56 at the breakout box. • Is each resistance greater than 10,000 ohms?	Yes No	▶ ▶	RECONNECT all components. GO to Electronic Ignition Diagnosis. SERVICE short circuit. REMOVE breakout box. RECONNECT all components. RERUN Quick Test.

FM0159300756060X

Fig. 215 Test PC: Spark Timing Check, EI-High Data Rate (Part 7 of 7)

Note

You should enter this Pinpoint Test only when you have been directed here from Diagnostic Routines.

Remember

This Pinpoint Test is intended to diagnose only the following:

• Powertrain Control Module (PCM) (12A650)
• EEC Power Relay (12A646)
• Constant Control Relay Module (CCRM) (12B581)

• Harness Circuits: SIG RTN, STO, STI, VPWR, VREF and HO2S

Fig. 216 Test QA: No DTC/DTC Not Listed (Part 1 of 5)

Pinpoint Test Schematic

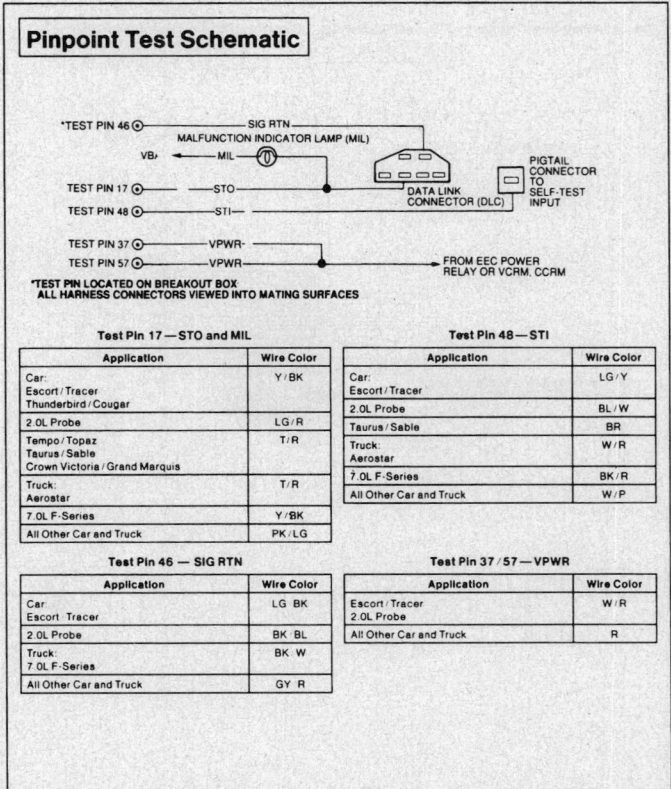

*TEST PIN LOCATED ON BREAKOUT BOX
ALL HARNESS CONNECTORS VIEWED INTO MATING SURFACES

Test Pin 17 — STO and MIL

Application	Wire Color
Car: Escort / Tracer Thunderbird / Cougar	Y / BK
2.0L Probe	LG / R
Tempo / Topaz Taurus / Sable Crown Victoria / Grand Marquis	T / R
Truck: Aerostar	T / R
7.0L F-Series	Y / BK
All Other Car and Truck	PK / LG

Test Pin 48 — STI

Application	Wire Color
Car: Escort / Tracer	LG / Y
2.0L Probe	BL / W
Taurus / Sable	BR
Truck: Aerostar	W / R
7.0L F-Series	BK / R
All Other Car and Truck	W / P

Test Pin 46 — SIG RTN

Application	Wire Color
Car: Escort / Tracer	LG / BK
2.0L Probe	BK / BL
Truck: 7.0L F-Series	BK / W
All Other Car and Truck	GY / R

Test Pin 37 / 57 — VPWR

Application	Wire Color
Escort / Tracer 2.0L Probe	W / R
All Other Car and Truck	R

FM015930007575702AX

Fig. 216 Test QA: No DTC/DTC Not Listed (Part 2 of 5). 1993

Pinpoint Test Schematic

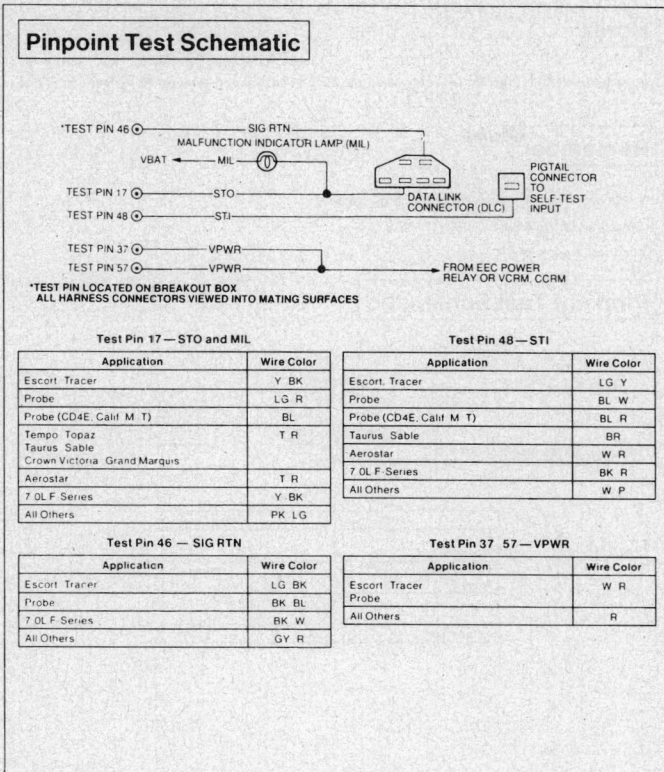

*TEST PIN 46 — SIG RTN
MALFUNCTION INDICATOR LAMP (MIL)
VBAT — MIL
TEST PIN 17 — STO
TEST PIN 48 — STI
TEST PIN 37 — VPWR
TEST PIN 57 — VPWR — FROM EEC POWER RELAY OR VCRM, CCRM

DATA LINK CONNECTOR (DLC)
PIGTAIL CONNECTOR TO SELF-TEST INPUT

*TEST PIN LOCATED ON BREAKOUT BOX
ALL HARNESS CONNECTORS VIEWED INTO MATING SURFACES

Test Pin 17 — STO and MIL

Application	Wire Color
Escort, Tracer	Y BK
Probe	LG R
Probe (CD4E, Calif M T)	BL
Tempo, Topaz Taurus, Sable Crown Victoria, Grand Marquis	T R
Aerostar	T R
7.0L F-Series	Y BK
All Others	PK LG

Test Pin 48 — STI

Application	Wire Color
Escort, Tracer	LG Y
Probe	BL W
Probe (CD4E, Calif M T)	BL R
Taurus, Sable	BR
Aerostar	W R
7.0L F-Series	BK R
All Others	W P

Test Pin 46 — SIG RTN

Application	Wire Color
Escort, Tracer	LG BK
Probe	BK BL
7.0L F-Series	BK W
All Others	GY R

Test Pin 37, 57 — VPWR

Application	Wire Color
Escort, Tracer Probe	W R
All Others	R

FM015940075702BX

Fig. 216   Test QA: No DTC/DTC Not Listed (Part 2 of 5). 1994–95

	TEST STEP	RESULT	▶	ACTION TO TAKE
QA1	CHECK VREF VOLTAGE AT DATA LINK CONNECTOR (DLC)			
	NOTE: Aftermarket devices such as an alarm system may cause Self-Test to abort if wiring is connected to certain EEC components. PRIOR TO SERVICING VEHICLE, inform customer that disconnection of the device is necessary for the proper diagnosis and function of the EEC system. Restore EEC system to original configuration before proceeding with this Pinpoint Test.	Yes	▶	GO to QA3.
		No	▶	GO to QA2.
	If using a STAR Tester to run Self-Test, verify that correct procedure is used for your application. • Key off. • Disconnect Powertrain Control Module (PCM). Inspect for damaged or pushed out pins, corrosion, loose wires, etc. Service as necessary. • Install breakout box and connect PCM to breakout box. • Key on, engine off. • Measure voltage between Test Pin 26 at the breakout box and SIG RTN circuit in the DLC. • **Is voltage between 4.0 and 6.0 volts?**			
QA2	CHECK SIG RTN CIRCUIT CONTINUITY			
	• Key off. • Breakout box installed, PCM disconnected. • Measure resistance between SIG RTN circuit in the DLC and Test Pin 46 at the breakout box. • **Is resistance less than 5.0 ohms?**	Yes	▶	GO to Pinpoint Test Step C1.
		No	▶	SERVICE open circuit. RECONNECT PCM. RERUN Quick Test.
QA3	CHECK STI CIRCUIT CONTINUITY			
	• Key off. • Breakout box installed. • Disconnect PCM. • Measure resistance between STI circuit in the Self-Test single pin pigtail connector and Test Pin 48 at the breakout box. • **Is resistance less than 5.0 ohms?**	Yes	▶	GO to QA4.
		No	▶	SERVICE open circuit. REMOVE breakout box. RECONNECT PCM. RERUN Quick Test.

Fig. 216   Test QA: No DTC/DTC Not Listed (Part 3 of 5). 1993

	TEST STEP	RESULT	▶	ACTION TO TAKE
QA1	CHECK VREF VOLTAGE AT DATA LINK CONNECTOR (DLC)			
	NOTE: Aftermarket devices such as an alarm system may cause Self-Test to abort if wiring is connected to certain EEC components. BEFORE SERVICING VEHICLE, inform customer that disconnection of the device is necessary for the proper diagnosis and function of the EEC system. Restore EEC system to original configuration before proceeding with this Pinpoint Test. NOTE: For OBD I Thunderbird/Cougar, it may be possible to have two DLC connectors. For the 3.8L and 3.8L SC use the DLC that is in the engine compartment. NOTE: For the 3.8L Thunderbird/Cougar, DO NOT use the DLC located under the dash; it does not function. • Key off. • Disconnect Powertrain Control Module (PCM). Inspect for damaged or pushed out pins, corrosion, loose wires, etc. Service as necessary. • Install breakout box and connect PCM to breakout box. • Key on, engine off. • Measure voltage between Test Pin 26 at the breakout box and SIG RTN circuit in the DLC. • **Is voltage between 4.0 and 6.0 volts?**	Yes	▶	GO to QA3.
		No	▶	GO to QA2.
QA2	CHECK SIG RTN CIRCUIT CONTINUITY			
	• Key off. • Breakout box installed, PCM disconnected. • Measure resistance between SIG RTN circuit in the DLC and Test Pin 46 at the breakout box. • **Is resistance less than 5.0 ohms?**	Yes	▶	GO to Pinpoint Test Step C1.
		No	▶	SERVICE open circuit. RECONNECT PCM. RERUN Quick Test.
QA3	CHECK STI CIRCUIT CONTINUITY			
	• Key off. • Breakout box installed. • Disconnect PCM. • Measure resistance between STI circuit in the Self-Test single pin pigtail connector and Test Pin 48 at the breakout box. • **Is resistance less than 5.0 ohms?**	Yes	▶	GO to QA4.
		No	▶	SERVICE open circuit. REMOVE breakout box. RECONNECT PCM. RERUN Quick Test.

Fig. 216   Test QA: No DTC/DTC Not Listed (Part 3 of 5). 1994–95

	TEST STEP	RESULT	▶	ACTION TO TAKE
QA4	CHECK STO CIRCUIT CONTINUITY			
	• Key off. • Breakout box installed, PCM disconnected. • Measure resistance between STO circuit in the DLC and Test Pin 17 at the breakout box. • **Is resistance less than 5.0 ohms?**	Yes	▶	For 7.3L Diesel: GO to QA7. For all others: GO to QA5.
		No	▶	SERVICE open circuit. REMOVE breakout box. RECONNECT PCM. RERUN Quick Test.
QA5	CHECK HO2S SIGNAL FOR SHORT TO POWER			
	NOTE: Due to the internal circuitry of the PCM, a right/rear HO2S signal short to power could cause EEC strategy NOT to enter on-demand Self-Test. • Breakout box installed, PCM disconnected. • Key on, engine off. • Measure voltage between HO2S signal Test Pin 29 or 44 (refer to Pinpoint Test HB schematic for flexible fuel vehicles, Pinpoint Test H schematic for all other vehicles) and Test Pin 40 or 60 at the breakout box. • **Is voltage greater than 2.0 volts?**	Yes	▶	GO to QA6.
		No	▶	GO to QA7.
QA6	ISOLATE SHORT TO HARNESS OR HO2S			
	• Breakout box installed, PCM disconnected. • Disconnect right/rear HO2S. • Key on, engine off. • Measure voltage between HO2S signal Test Pin 29 or 44 (refer to Pinpoint Test HB schematic for flexible fuel vehicles, Pinpoint Test H schematic for all other vehicles) and Test Pin 40 or 60 at the breakout box. • **Is voltage greater than 2.0 volts?**	Yes	▶	SERVICE HO2S signal circuit for shorts to power. REMOVE breakout box. RECONNECT all components. RERUN Quick Test.
		No	▶	REPLACE right/rear HO2S. REMOVE breakout box. RECONNECT all components. RERUN Quick Test.
QA7	CHECK STO CIRCUIT FOR SHORT TO GROUND			
	• Key off. • Breakout box installed, PCM disconnected. • Measure resistance between STO circuit in the DLC and engine block ground. • **Is resistance less than 5.0 ohms?**	Yes	▶	SERVICE STO or MIL circuit for short to ground. REMOVE breakout box. RECONNECT PCM. RERUN Quick Test.
		No	▶	GO to QA8

FM015930007570040X

Fig. 216   Test QA: No DTC/DTC Not Listed (Part 4 of 5)

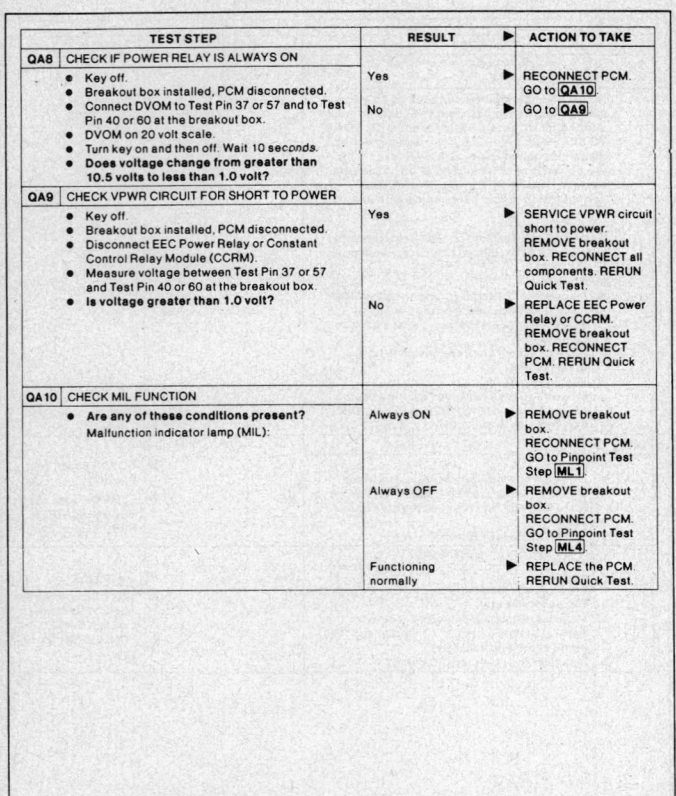

Fig. 216   Test QA: No DTC/DTC Not Listed (Part 5 of 5)

FM0159300757050X

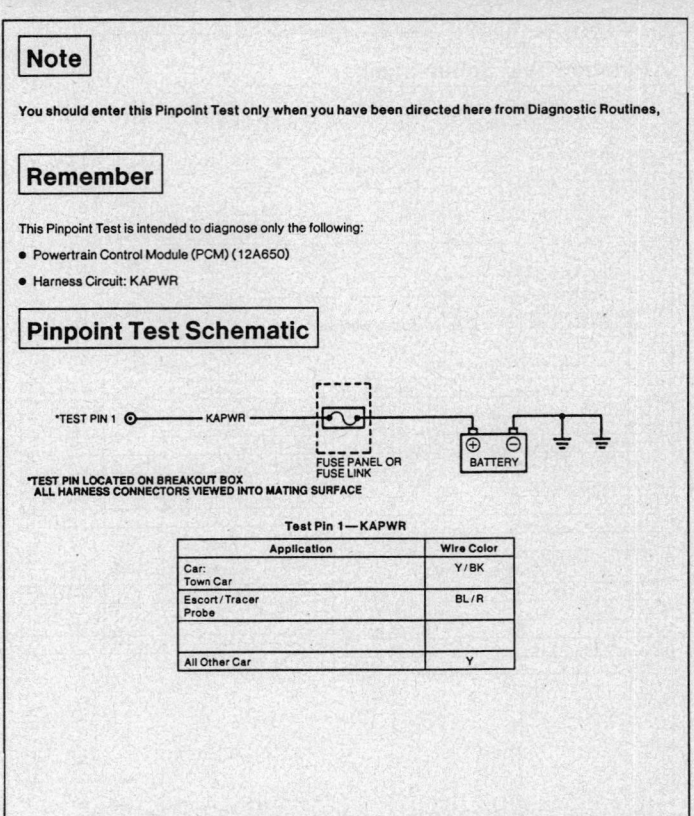

Fig. 217   Test QB: Continuous Memory DTC 15/512 (Part 1 of 2). 1993

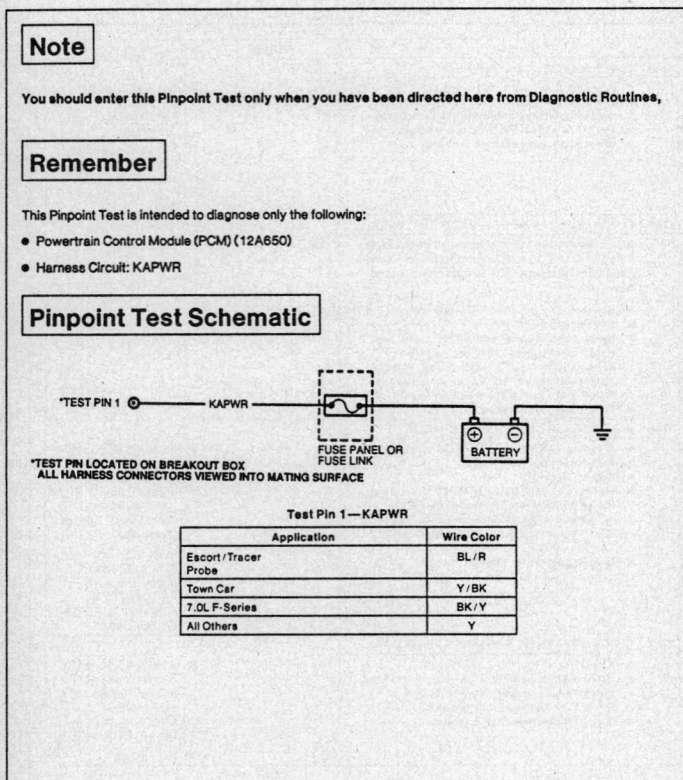

Fig. 217   Test QB: Continuous Memory DTC 15/512 (Part 1 of 2). 1994–95

FM0159300758020X

Fig. 217   Test QB: Continuous Memory DTC 15/512 (Part 2 of 2)

Note

You should enter this Pinpoint Test only when you have been directed here from other Pinpoint Tests.

Remember

This Pinpoint Test is intended to diagnose only the following:

- Test Conditions
- Throttle Plate Linkage

TEST STEP	RESULT	▶	ACTION TO TAKE
QC1 CHECK FOR DIAGNOSTIC TROUBLE CODES (DTC) 23, 53, 63, 121, 122 or 123			
NOTE: If vehicle is equipped with speed control, the speed control servo must be electrically disconnected. This prevents the speed control system from affecting the throttle plate movement during Output State DTM. Rerun Quick Test or Output State DTM.	Yes	▶	GO to Quick Test and SERVICE appropriate DTC as instructed.
• Key off.	DTC 11 or 111	▶	GO to QC2.
• Perform Key On Engine Off Self-Test.	No DTCs	▶	GO to Pinpoint Test Step QA1.
NOTE: If additional information is required on Output State DTM, refer to Diagnostic Aids			
• Are any of these DTC's (23, 53, 63, 121, 122 or 123) present?			
QC2 CHECK THROTTLE LINKAGE			
• Check throttle and throttle linkages for sticking and binding.	Yes	▶	REPLACE TP sensor. RERUN Quick Test.
• Is throttle OK?	No	▶	SERVICE as necessary. RERUN Quick Test.

FM0159300759000X

Fig. 218   Test QC: Output State Check Not Functioning

Note

You should enter this Pinpoint Test only when you have been directed here from Diagnostic Routines, or Pinpoint Test AA, AB or AC.

Remember

To prevent the replacement of good components, be aware that the following Non-EEC areas may be at fault:

- Poor power / ground connections
- Ignition system distributor cap, rotor, wires, coil, plugs
- Base engine valves, cam timing, compression, etc.

This Pinpoint Test is intended only as a quick check for the basic functioning of the following:

- Idle Air Control (IAC) system
- MAP / BARO system
- EGR system
- MAF system

FM0159300760010X

Fig. 219   Test S: System Check (Part 1 of 5)

TEST STEP	RESULT	▶	ACTION TO TAKE
S1 IAC CHECK			
• Attempt to start engine at part throttle.	Yes	▶	GO to Pinpoint Test Step KE4.
• Will engine run smooth at part throttle?	No	▶	GO to S3.
S2 CHECK FOR RPM DROP			
• Key off.			
• Connect engine tachometer.	Yes	▶	RECONNECT IAC solenoid. GO to S3.
• Start engine.	No	▶	GO to Pinpoint Test Step KE4.
• Disconnect IAC solenoid.			
• Does rpm drop or stall?			

FM0159300760020X

Fig. 219   Test S: System Check (Part 2 of 5)

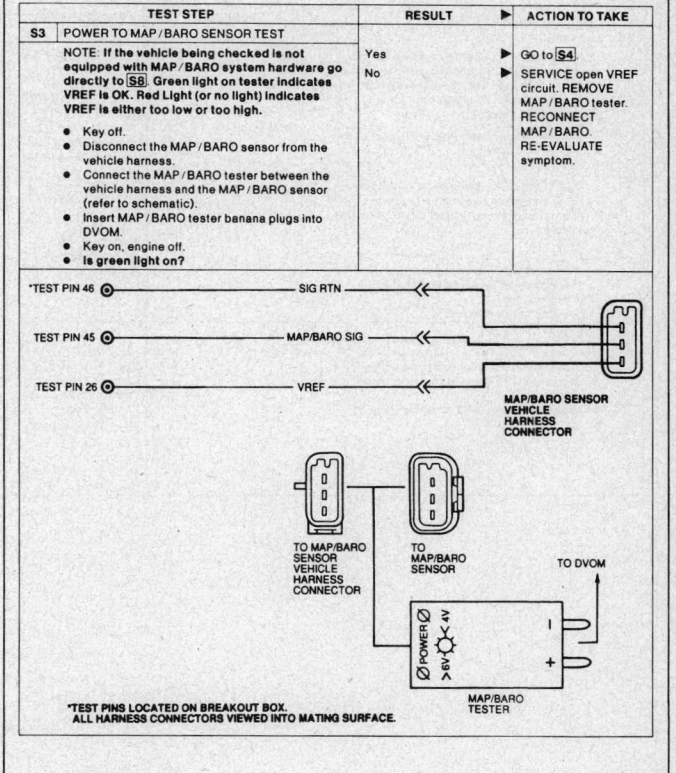

TEST STEP	RESULT	▶	ACTION TO TAKE
S3 POWER TO MAP / BARO SENSOR TEST			
NOTE: If the vehicle being checked is not equipped with MAP / BARO system hardware go directly to S8. Green light on tester indicates VREF is OK. Red Light (or no light) indicates VREF is either too low or too high.	Yes	▶	GO to S4.
• Key off.	No	▶	SERVICE open VREF circuit. REMOVE MAP / BARO tester. RECONNECT MAP / BARO. RE-EVALUATE symptom.
• Disconnect the MAP / BARO sensor from the vehicle harness.			
• Connect the MAP / BARO tester between the vehicle harness and the MAP / BARO sensor (refer to schematic).			
• Insert MAP / BARO tester banana plugs into DVOM.			
• Key on, engine off.			
• Is green light on?			

FM0159300760030X

Fig. 219   Test S: System Check (Part 3 of 5)

TEST STEP		RESULT	▶	ACTION TO TAKE
S4	**MAP/BARO TESTER OUTPUT READING**	Yes	▶	**REMOVE MAP/BARO Tester. RECONNECT all components. For vehicles with Mass Air Flow sensors: GO to S8. For all others: GO to S5.**
	NOTE: Measure several known good MAP/BARO sensors on available vehicles. The measured voltage will be typical for your location on the day of testing.			
	● MAP/BARO Tester and DVOM connected. ● Key on.			

Approximate Altitude (Ft.)	Voltage Output (+/-.04 Volts)
0	1.59
1000	1.56
2000	1.53
3000	1.50
4000	1.47
5000	1.44
6000	1.41
7000	1.39

TEST STEP		RESULT	▶	ACTION TO TAKE
	● Is voltage in range for your altitude?	No (Sensor output is out-of-range)	▶	**REPLACE MAP/BARO sensor.**
S5	**CHECK VACUUM LINES**	Yes	▶	**GO to S6.**
	● Check vacuum lines for proper routing. Refer to VECI decal. Check MAP sensor vacuum line for holes, disconnections, kinks or blockage. ● **Are vacuum lines OK?**	No	▶	**SERVICE vacuum lines as necessary. RERUN Quick Test.**
S6	**CHECK MAP SENSOR**	Yes	▶	**RELEASE vacuum. REMOVE vacuum pump. GO to S7.**
	● Key off. ● Disconnect MAP vacuum hose from manifold tee. ● Install vacuum pump to MAP vacuum hose. ● Apply 18 in-Hg (61 kPa) vacuum to MAP sensor. ● **Does MAP sensor and vacuum hose hold vacuum?**	No	▶	**REPLACE MAP sensor. RECONNECT vacuum line to MAP sensor. RERUN Quick Test.**
S7	**CHECK VACUUM MANIFOLD SOURCE**	Yes	▶	**REMOVE vacuum gauge. RECONNECT vacuum line to MAP sensor and manifold vacuum tee. GO to S8.**
	● Key off. ● MAP vacuum hose from manifold vacuum tee disconnected. ● Install vacuum gauge to manifold vacuum tee. ● Start/crank engine. ● Is manifold vacuum present at the vacuum tee?	No	▶	**REMOVE obstruction in manifold vacuum tee or REPLACE damaged manifold vacuum tee. RERUN Quick Test.**

FM0159300760040)

Fig. 219   Test S: System Check (Part 4 of 5)

TEST STEP		RESULT	▶	ACTION TO TAKE
S8	**CHECK EGR VACUUM**	Yes	▶	**For vehicles with EVP sensors: GO to Pinpoint Test Step DN42. For all others: GO to Pinpoint Test Step DL21.**
	NOTE: If the vehicle being checked is not equipped with EGR system hardware, go directly to H2. The next two test steps will attempt to determine if the EGR system is the cause of the current symptom and/or NO START.			
	● Disconnect vacuum line at EGR valve, and plug the vacuum line. ● Start engine.	No	▶	**GO to S9.**
	NOTE: When verifying drive symptom, a DTC may possibly be stored in memory; erase Continuous Memory before proceeding with procedure.			
	For Drive Symptom: — Was drive symptom eliminated? **For No Start:** — Does engine start?			
S9	**CHECK EGR VALVE**	Yes	▶	**RECONNECT original EGR valve. For 2.0L Probe: GO to Pinpoint Test Step FE1. For 3.0L Flexible Fuel: GO to Pinpoint Test Step HB2. For all others: GO to Pinpoint Test Step H2.**
	● Check EGR valve for housing leaks or EGR gasket blow-by. Service as necessary. ● Remove EGR valve and check for proper seating. ● **Does EGR valve seat properly (fully closed)?**	No	▶	**RECONNECT oringinal EGR valve. REFER to EGR valve diagnosis.**

Fig. 219   Test S: System Check (Part 5 of 5). 1993

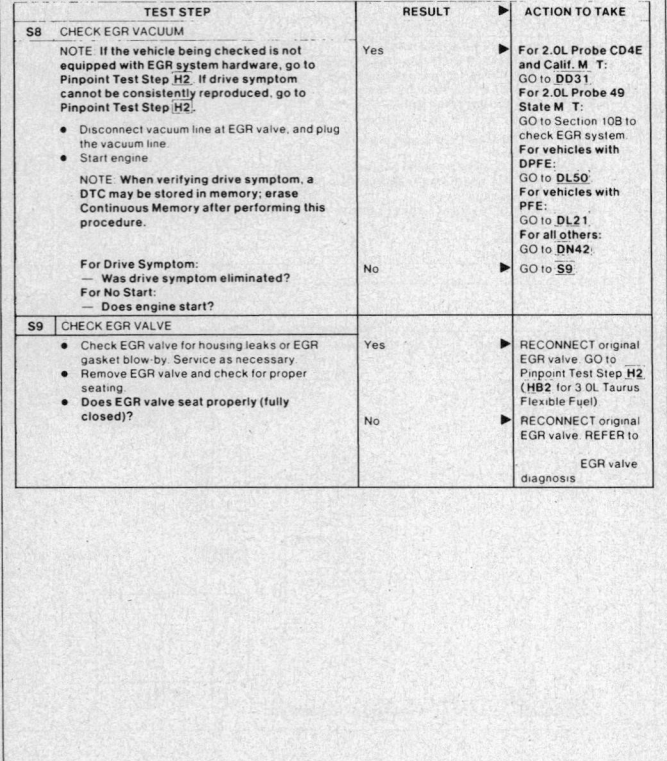

TEST STEP		RESULT	▶	ACTION TO TAKE
S8	**CHECK EGR VACUUM**	Yes	▶	**For 2.0L Probe CD4E and Calif. M T: GO to DD31 For 2.0L Probe 49 State M T: GO to Section 10B to check EGR system. For vehicles with DPFE: GO to DL50 For vehicles with PFE: GO to DL21 For all others: GO to DN42.**
	NOTE: If the vehicle being checked is not equipped with EGR system hardware, go to Pinpoint Test Step H2. If drive symptom cannot be consistently reproduced, go to Pinpoint Test Step H2.			
	● Disconnect vacuum line at EGR valve, and plug the vacuum line. ● Start engine.			
	NOTE: When verifying drive symptom, a DTC may be stored in memory; erase Continuous Memory after performing this procedure.			
	For Drive Symptom: — Was drive symptom eliminated? **For No Start:** — Does engine start?	No	▶	**GO to S9.**
S9	**CHECK EGR VALVE**	Yes	▶	**RECONNECT original EGR valve. GO to Pinpoint Test Step H2. (HB2 for 3.0L Taurus Flexible Fuel)**
	● Check EGR valve for housing leaks or EGR gasket blow-by. Service as necessary. ● Remove EGR valve and check for proper seating. ● **Does EGR valve seat properly (fully closed)?**	No	▶	**RECONNECT original EGR valve. REFER to EGR valve diagnosis**

FM0159400760005BX

Fig. 219   Test S: System Check (Part 5 of 5). 1994–95

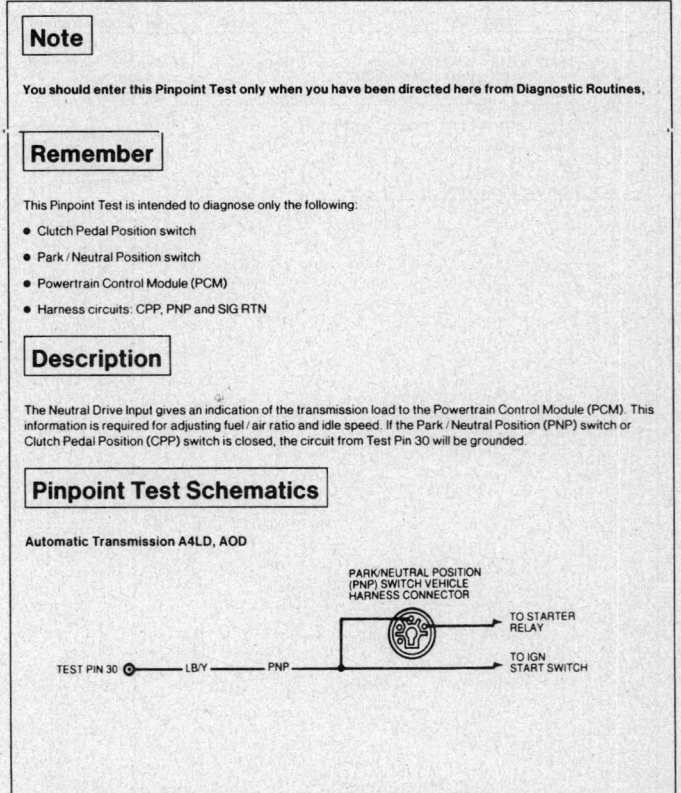

Note

You should enter this Pinpoint Test only when you have been directed here from Diagnostic Routines,

Remember

This Pinpoint Test is intended to diagnose only the following:
● Clutch Pedal Position switch
● Park/Neutral Position switch
● Powertrain Control Module (PCM)
● Harness circuits: CPP, PNP and SIG RTN

Description

The Neutral Drive Input gives an indication of the transmission load to the Powertrain Control Module (PCM). This information is required for adjusting fuel/air ratio and idle speed. If the Park/Neutral Position (PNP) switch or Clutch Pedal Position (CPP) switch is closed, the circuit from Test Pin 30 will be grounded.

Pinpoint Test Schematics

Automatic Transmission A4LD, AOD

PARK/NEUTRAL POSITION (PNP) SWITCH VEHICLE HARNESS CONNECTOR

TEST PIN 30 —— LB/Y —— PNP

TO STARTER RELAY

TO IGN START SWITCH

FM0159300761010X

Fig. 220   Test TA: PNP/CPP Switches (Part 1 of 11)

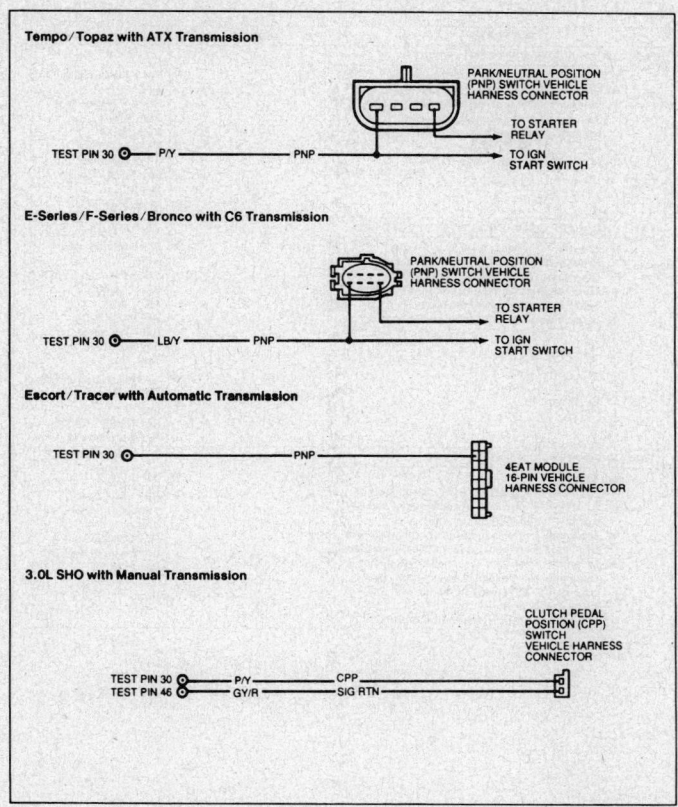

Fig. 220 Test TA: PNP/CPP Switches (Part 2 of 11). 1993–94

FM0159300761020X

(Part 3 of 11)

4.9L E-Series/F-Series/Bronco with Manual Transmission

3.8L SC Thunderbird, 4.0L Ranger/Aerostar/Explorer with Manual Transmission

Fig. 220 Test TA: PNP/CPP Switches (Part 3 of 11). 1993–94

FM0159300761030X

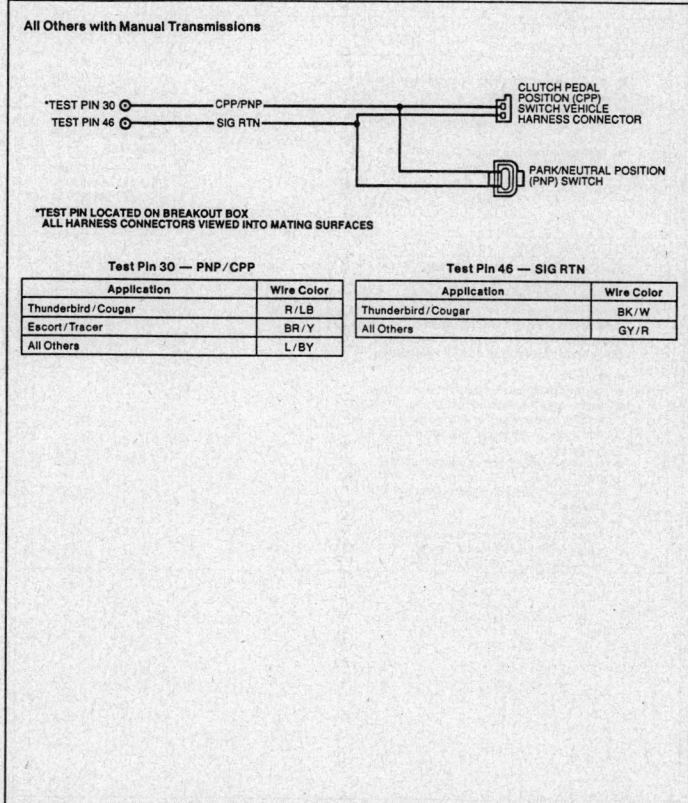

Test Pin 30 — PNP/CPP

Application	Wire Color
Thunderbird/Cougar	R/LB
Escort/Tracer	BR/Y
All Others	L/BY

Test Pin 46 — SIG RTN

Application	Wire Color
Thunderbird/Cougar	BK/W
All Others	GY/R

Fig. 220 Test TA: PNP/CPP
Switches (Part 4 of 11). 1993–94

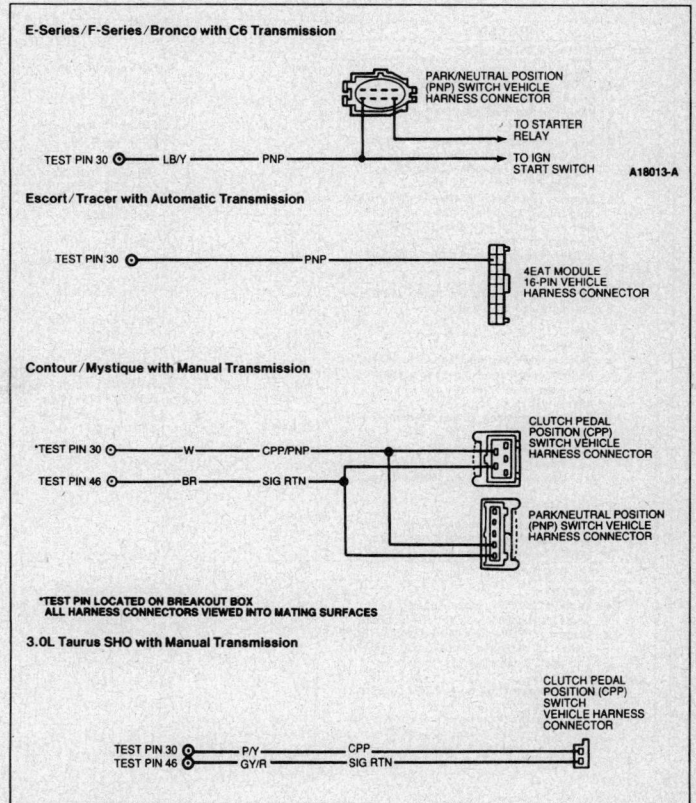

Fig. 220 Test TA: PNP/CPP Switches (Part 4 of 11). 1995

FM015950076104BX

Table TA1–TA2 (Part 5)

TEST STEP	RESULT	▶	ACTION TO TAKE
TA1 DIAGNOSTIC TROUBLE CODE (DTC) 67/522, 525 or 528 / SYSTEM IDENTIFICATION DTC 67/522, 525, or 528 resulted from the voltage being high at either: — Pin 10 = A/C input — Pin 30 = PNP/CPP input while cranking the engine or during KOEO Diagnostic Test Mode (DTM). Possible causes: — A/C circuit shorted to power — CPP circuit open — PNP open — Damaged PCM — Starter relay disconnected during Self-Test.	**For Manual Transmissions:** 3.0L SHO: 1.9L SFI, 2.3L, 3.0L, 3.8L SFI Super Charged, 4.0L and 5.0L SFI MAF **For Automatic Transmissions:** 1.9L SFI **For all other engines:**	▶ ▶ ▶ ▶	**GO to** TA7 **GO to** TA2 **GO to** TA10 **GO to** TA8
TA2 CHECK PNP/CPP INPUT • Key off. • Verify A/C is off, if so equipped. • Disconnect Powertrain Control Module (PCM). Inspect for damaged or pushed out pins, corrosion, loose wires, etc. Service as necessary. • Install breakout box, leave PCM disconnected. • Measure resistance between Test Pin 30 and Test Pin 46 at the breakout box: 1. With transmission in NEUTRAL and the clutch pedal up. 2. With transmission in GEAR and the clutch pedal down. • **Is each resistance less than 5.0 ohms?**	Yes No	▶ ▶	**GO to** TA3 **GO to** TA5

PNP SWITCH OPEN IN ANY GEAR
 TEST PIN 30 ⊙
 PNP CIRCUIT
 CPP SWITCH OPEN WHEN PEDAL IS UP
 TEST PIN 46 ⊙ — BK/W — SIG. RTN.

Fig. 220 Test TA: PNP/CPP Switches (Part 5 of 11)

Table TA3–TA5 (Part 6)

TEST STEP	RESULT	▶	ACTION TO TAKE
TA3 CHECK CPP/PNP SWITCH INTEGRITY • Key off. • Breakout box installed, PCM disconnected. • Measure resistance between Test Pin 30 and Test Pin 46 at the breakout box with transmission in any gear and the clutch pedal up. • **Is resistance less than 5.0 ohms?**	Yes No	▶ ▶	**For vehicles with A/C:** GO to Pinpoint Test Step KM40. **All others:** REPLACE PCM. REMOVE breakout box. RERUN Quick Test. **GO to** TA4
TA4 CHECK CPP CIRCUIT FOR SHORT TO GROUND • Key off. • Breakout box installed, PCM disconnected. • Disconnect CPP switch. • Measure resistance between Test Pin 30 and Test Pin 46 at the breakout box. • **Is resistance greater than 10,000 ohms?**	Yes No	▶ ▶	**For vehicles with A/C:** GO to Pinpoint Test Step KM40. **All others:** REPLACE PCM. REMOVE breakout box. RERUN Quick Test. SERVICE short circuit. REMOVE breakout box. RECONNECT PCM. RERUN Quick Test.
TA5 CHECK PNP/CPP SWITCH • Key off. • Breakout box installed, PCM disconnected. • Locate PNP switch (on transmission) and CPP switch (at clutch pedal linkage). • Disconnect vehicle harness at both switches and inspect connectors for pushed back pins. • Measure resistance across the PNP switch terminals with transmission in neutral and across the CPP switch terminals with the clutch pedal down. • **Is each resistance less than 5.0 ohms?**	Yes No	▶ ▶	**GO to** TA6 REPLACE open switch(es). REMOVE breakout box. RECONNECT all components. RERUN Quick Test.

Fig. 220 Test TA: PNP/CPP Switches (Part 6 of 11)

Table TA6–TA8 (Part 7)

TEST STEP	RESULT	▶	ACTION TO TAKE
TA6 CHECK PNP/CPP HARNESS • Key off. • DVOM on 200 ohm scale. • Breakout box installed, PCM disconnected. • Vehicle harness disconnected at both switches. • Measure resistance between Test Pin 30 and PNP switch harness connector and between Test Pin 30 and the CPP switch harness connector. • Measure resistance between Test Pin 46 and the PNP switch harness connector and between Test Pin 46 and the CPP switch harness connector. • **Is each resistance less than 5.0 ohms?**	Yes No	▶ ▶	**For vehicles with A/C:** GO to Pinpoint Test Step KM40. **For all others:** REPLACE PCM. SERVICE open circuit. REMOVE breakout box. RECONNECT all components. RERUN Quick Test.
TA7 CHECK CPP SWITCH NOTE: For 4.9L engines, the clutch pedal must be down during KOEO test. • Key off. • A/C off. • Disconnect Powertrain Control Module (PCM). Inspect for damaged or pushed out pins, corrosion, loose wires, etc. Service as necessary. • Install breakout box, leave PCM disconnected. • Clutch pedal down. **For 3.0L SHO:** — Measure resistance between Test Pin 30 and Test Pin 46 at the breakout box. **For 4.9L:** — Measure resistance between Test Pin 30 at the breakout box and starter relay. • **Is each resistance less than 5.0 ohms?**	Yes No	▶ ▶	**For vehicles with A/C:** GO to Pinpoint Test Step KM40. **For all others:** REPLACE PCM. SERVICE open circuit. REMOVE breakout box. RECONNECT all components.
TA8 CHECK PNP INPUT • Key off. • Verify A/C is OFF, if so equipped. • Verify transmission is in NEUTRAL or PARK. • Disconnect Powertrain Control Module (PCM). Inspect for damaged or pushed out pins, corrosion, loose wires, etc. Service as necessary. • Install breakout box, leave PCM connected. • Key on, engine off. • Measure voltage between Test Pin 30 at the breakout box and chassis ground. • **Is voltage less than 1.0 volt?**	Yes No	▶ ▶	**For vehicles with A/C:** GO to Pinpoint Test Step KM40. **For all others:** REPLACE PCM. **GO to** TA9

Fig. 220 Test TA: PNP/CPP Switches (Part 7 of 11)

Table TA9–TA10 (Part 8)

TEST STEP	RESULT	▶	ACTION TO TAKE
TA9 CHECK PNP SWITCH • Key off. • Breakout box installed, PCM disconnected. • Locate the PNP switch. • Disconnect vehicle harness from the PNP switch and measure resistance across the switch. • **Is resistance less than 5.0 ohms?**	Yes No	▶ ▶	SERVICE open in vehicle harness PNP circuit. REMOVE breakout box. RECONNECT all components. RERUN Quick Test. REPLACE PNP switch. REMOVE breakout box. RECONNECT all components. RERUN Quick Test.
TA10 CHECK PNP INPUT NOTE: For Escort/Tracer with EEC-IV "Integrated 4EAT", go to TA15. "Stand-Alone" application can be identified by looking for the 4EAT module under the driver's side dash between steering column and the kick panel. The 4EAT module will not be present on "Integrated 4EAT" application. • Key off. • Verify transmission is in PARK or NEUTRAL. • Disconnect Powertrain Control Module (PCM). Inspect for damaged or pushed out pins, corrosion, loose wires, etc. Service as necessary. • Install breakout box and connect PCM to breakout box. • Disconnect 16 pin connector from the 4EAT module. • Key on, engine off. • Measure voltage between Test Pin 30 at the breakout box and chassis ground. • **Is voltage less than 1.0 volt?**	Yes No	▶ ▶	REPLACE PCM. REMOVE breakout box. RECONNECT all components. RERUN Quick Test. Key off. GO to TA11

Fig. 220 Test TA: PNP/CPP Switches (Part 8 of 11)

TEST STEP	RESULT	▶	ACTION TO TAKE
TA11 CHECK PNP CIRCUIT CONTINUITY BETWEEN PROCESSOR AND 4EAT MODULE • Key off. • 4EAT module 16 pin connector disconnected. • Breakout box installed. • Disconnect PCM. • Measure resistance between Test Pin 30 at the breakout box and the PNP pin at the 4EAT module vehicle harness connector. • Is resistance less than 5.0 ohms?	Yes No	▶ ▶	REFER to the Transmission Service 4EAT system diagnosis. REMOVE breakout box and RECONNECT all components when testing is complete. SERVICE open circuit. REMOVE breakout box. RECONNECT all components. RERUN Quick Test.
TA12 CHECK PNP CIRCUIT FOR SHORT TO GROUND OR CLOSED SWITCH • Key off. • Disconnect Powertrain Control Module (PCM). Inspect for damaged or pushed out pins, corrosion, loose wires, etc. Service as necessary. • Install breakout box, leave PCM disconnected. • Place transmission in DRIVE. • DVOM on 200,000 ohm scale. • Measure resistance between Test Pin 30 and Test Pin 40/60 at the breakout box. • Is resistance greater than 10,000 ohms?	Yes No	▶ ▶	REFER to other possible causes. SERVICE short circuit or closed PNP switch. REMOVE breakout box. RECONNECT PCM. RE-EVALUATE symptom.

Fig. 220 Test TA: PNP/CPP Switches (Part 9 of 11)

TEST STEP	RESULT	▶	ACTION TO TAKE
TA15 DIAGNOSTIC TROUBLE CODE (DTC) 522: DOES ENGINE START? Key On Engine Off DTC 522 indicates that during Self-Test, high voltage was sensed at Pin 30 (PNP). Possible causes: Engine starts: — Transmission not in PARK during Self-Test. — Open PNP circuit between PCM and connection to START circuit. — PNP / START circuit short to power. — Damaged PCM. No start: — Damaged starter relay. — Open START circuit between PNP switch and PNP connection to circuit, PNP switch and starter relay or starter relay and ground. **NOTE:** Verify that transmission was in PARK during Self Test. If transmission was not in PARK, rerun Self Test and proceed as directed. • Does engine start?	Yes No	▶ ▶	GO to **TA16**. REFER to Starting System possible causes - No Starts within this Pinpoint Test).
TA16 CHECK PNP / START CIRCUIT FOR SHORT TO POWER • Key off. • Disconnect Powertrain Control Module (PCM). Inspect for damaged or pushed out pins, corrosion, loose wires, etc. Service as necessary. • Install breakout box, leave PCM disconnected. • Key on. • Measure voltage between Test Pin 30 and Test Pin 40 (GND) at the breakout box. • Is voltage less than 0.5 volt?	Yes No	▶ ▶	Key off. GO to **TA17**. SERVICE short to power (a direct short to power would always activate starter when PNP switch was closed. This would prevent KOEO Self-Test from being entered. Short to power is most likely a high resistance short). REMOVE breakout box. RERUN Quick Test.

Fig. 220 Test TA: PNP/CPP Switches (Part 10 of 11)

TEST STEP	RESULT	▶	ACTION TO TAKE
TA17 CHECK PNP CIRCUIT CONTINUITY • Key off. • Breakout box installed, PCM disconnected. • Disconnect PNP switch (3 pin at transmission). • Measure resistance between Test Pin 30 at the breakout box and PNP/IGN START circuit at PNP switch vehicle harness connector. • Is resistance less than 5.0 ohms?	Yes No	▶ ▶	REPLACE PCM. REMOVE breakout box. RECONNECT all components. RERUN Quick Test. SERVICE open between PCM and PNP circuit connection to START circuit. REMOVE breakout box. RECONNECT all components. RERUN Quick Test.

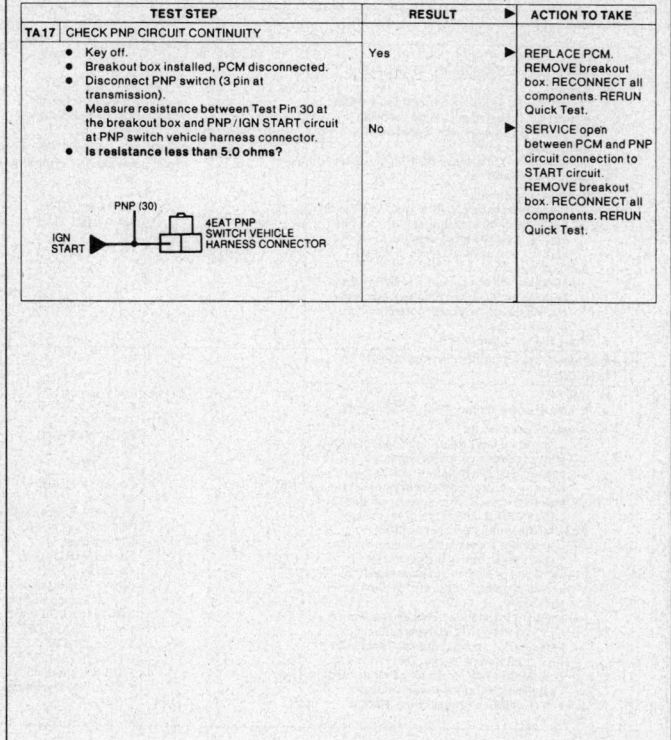

Fig. 220 Test TA: PNP/CPP Switches (Part 11 of 11)

Note

You should enter this Pinpoint Test only when you have been directed here from Diagnostic Routines.

Remember

This Pinpoint Test is not intended to diagnose components internal to the transmission. To prevent the replacement of good components, be aware that the following non-EEC areas may be at fault:

• Engine
 — Performance, vacuum, cooling.
• Electrical
 — Charging system.
• Transmission
 — Hydraulic fluid, friction elements, cooling.
 — Transfer case linkage.
 — Transfer case internal damage.

This Pinpoint Test is intended to diagnose only the following:

• Harness Circuits: 4x4 LOW, TCIL, TCS.
• Powertrain Control Module (PCM)

Description

The 4x4 Low Switch is an input used by the Powertrain Control Module, which, when closed allows the use of a secondary shift schedule while in the low range.

The Transmission Control Switch (TCS) allows the vehicle operator to disengage the overdrive feature when desired

Fig. 221 Test TB: 4x4 Low/TCS (Part 1 of 7). 1993

Pinpoint Test Schematics

Touchdrive Option

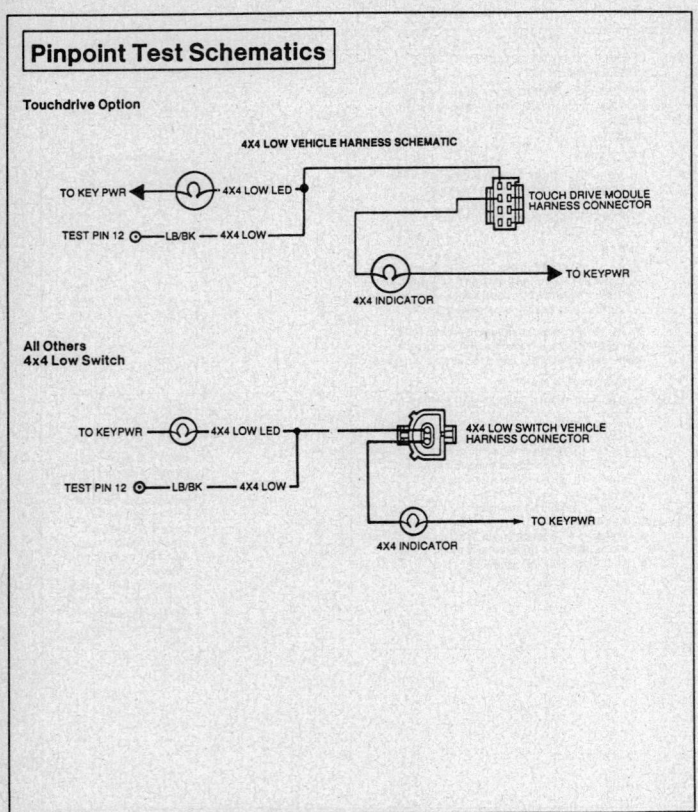

Transmission Control Switch

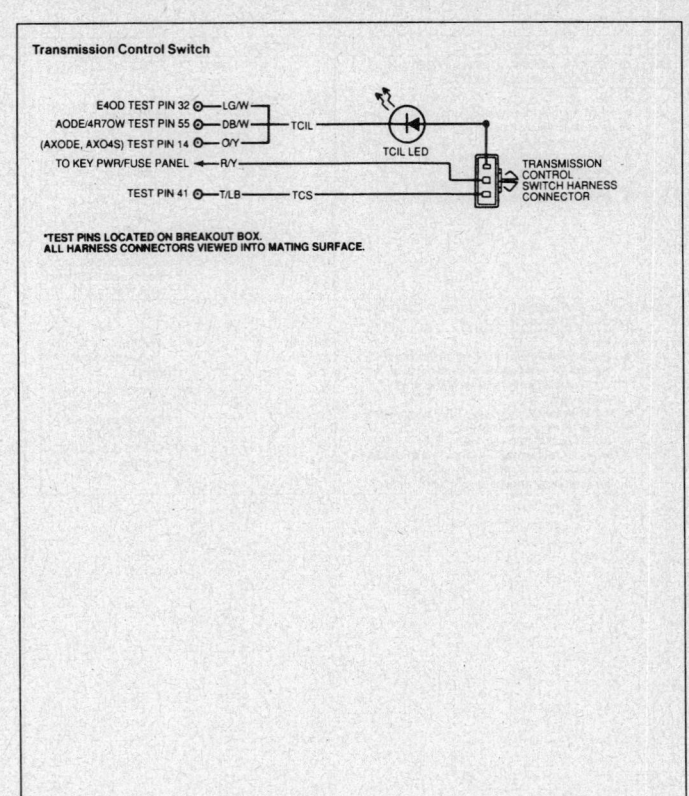

Fig. 221 Test TB: 4x4 Low/TCS (Part 2 of 7). 1993

Fig. 221 Test TB: 4x4 Low/TCS (Part 3 of 7). 1993

FM0159300762030X

TEST STEP	RESULT	▶	ACTION TO TAKE
TB1 DIAGNOSTIC TROUBLE CODE (DTC) 47/633			
DTC 47/633 indicates the 4x4 Low Selector Lever is not in the 4x2 or 4x4 high position (observed in Key On Engine Off Self-Test). A change in the automatic transmission shift cycle will occur. **Possible Causes:** — Damaged 4x4 Low switch or 4x4 selector lever position. — Shorted harness — Damaged PCM — Internal damage to transfer case ● **Is the 4x4 lever positioned in 4x2/4x4 high?**	Yes No	▶ ▶	GO to **TB4**. RERUN Self-Test positioning selector in 4x2/4x4 high.
TB2 DIAGNOSTIC TROUBLE CODE (DTC) 65/632			
DTC 65/632 indicates that the Transmission Control Switch (TCS) was not cycled between engine "ID Code" and the "Goose Test" in Key On Engine Running Self-Test. **Possible Causes:** — TCS damaged or switch not cycled during self-test. — Shorted harness. — Damaged Powertrain Control Module (PCM). — Open harness or fuse. ● **Was TCS cycled during Self-Test?**	Yes No	▶ ▶	GO to **TB4**. RERUN Self-Test cycling the TCS.
TB3 DIAGNOSTIC TROUBLE CODE (DTC) 97/631			
DTC 97/631 indicates a transmission control light circuit concern (observed during Key On Engine Off Self-Test). **Possible Causes:** — Burned out bulb. — Shorted harness. — Open harness/fuse. ● **Was the TCS cycled during Self-Test?**	Yes No	▶ ▶	GO to **TB5**. RERUN Self-Test cycling the TCS.

TEST STEP	RESULT	▶	ACTION TO TAKE
TB4 CYCLE THE APPROPRIATE CIRCUIT: (4x4 LOW OR TRANSMISSION CONTROL)			
● Key off. ● Disconnect Powertrain Control Module (PCM). Inspect for damaged or pushed out pins, corrosion, loose wires, etc. Service as necessary. ● Install breakout box, leave PCM disconnected. ● Key on, engine off. **For 4x4 Low circuit:** — Measure voltage between Test Pin 12 and Test Pin 40/60 at the breakout box while moving the 4x4 select lever between 4x2 and 4x4 Low several times. **For TCS circuit:** — Measure voltage between Test Pin 41 and Test Pin 40/60 at the breakout box while cycling the transmission control switch several times. ● **Does the voltage cycle?**	Yes No	▶ ▶	REPLACE PCM. REMOVE breakout box. RERUN Quick Test. If you are here for a driveability symptom only: GO to **TB7**. If here for a DTC: GO to **TB5**.
TB5 CHECK HARNESS CIRCUIT(S) FOR SHORT TO GROUND			
● Key off. ● Breakout box installed, PCM disconnected. **For 4x4 Low circuit:** — Disconnect 4x4 Low switch. Inspect both ends of the connector for damaged or pushed out pins, moisture, corrosion, loose wires, etc. Service as necessary. — Measure resistance between Test Pin 12 and Test Pin 40/60 at the breakout box. **For Transmission Control circuits:** — Disconnect Transmission Control Switch. Inspect both ends of the connector for damaged or pushed out pins, moisture, corrosion, loose wires, etc. Service as necessary. — Measure resistance between Test Pin 41 and Test Pin 40/60 at the breakout box. — Measure resistance between Test Pin 32 for E/F/B Series Trucks, Test Pin 14 for 3.2L SHO or Test Pin 55 for all others and Test Pin 40/60 at the breakout box. ● **Is each resistance greater than 10,000 ohms?**	Yes No	▶ ▶	For original DTC 47/633 or 65/632: GO to **TB8**. For original DTC 97/631: GO to **TB6**. For original DTC 47/633: SERVICE short circuit. RERUN Key On, Engine Off Self-Test. For original DTC 65/632: SERVICE short circuit. RERUN Engine Running Self-Test. If DTC is still present, GO to **TB7**. For original DTC 97/631: SERVICE short circuit. RERUN Key On, Engine Off Self-Test.

Fig. 221 Test TB: 4x4 Low/TCS (Part 4 of 7). 1993

FM0159300762040?

Fig. 221 Test TB: 4x4 Low/TCS (Part 5 of 7). 1993

TEST STEP	RESULT	►	ACTION TO TAKE
TB6 CHECK KEYPOWER THROUGH TCIL CIRCUIT • Key on, engine off. • Breakout box installed, PCM disconnected. • Measure voltage between Test Pin 32 for E/F/B Series Trucks, Test Pin 14 for 3.2L SHO or Test Pin 55 for all others and Test Pin 40/60 at the breakout box. • Is voltage greater than 10.5 volts?	Yes No	► ►	REPLACE PCM. REMOVE breakout box. RERUN Quick Test. GO to TB7.
TB7 CHECK OUTPUT DRIVER SIGNAL NOTE: When entering this Test Step with a symptom or a Self-Test Pass code, first disconnect Powertrain Control Module (PCM). Inspect for damaged pins, pushed out pins, loose wires, etc. Service as necessary. • Key off. • Breakout box installed, PCM disconnected. **For 4x4 Low circuit:** — Switch disconnected. — Measure voltage between keypower at the fuse panel and Test Pin 12 at the breakout box (ohmmeter negative probe) **For TCIL circuit:** — Measure voltage between keypower at the fuse panel and Test Pin 32 for E/F/B Series Trucks, Test Pin 14 for 3.2L SHO or Test Pin 55 for all others at the breakout box (ohmmeter negative probe). • Are both voltage readings at least 2.0 volts? Fuse Locations and Fuse Amperages for TCIL Application.	Yes No	► ►	GO to TB8. INSPECT for damaged indicator bulb (4x4 Low LED or TCIL) or damaged fuse in fuse panel. If OK, SERVICE open circuit. REMOVE breakout box. RECONNECT all components. RERUN Quick Test.

Car: (AODE)	Fuse Number	Amp. Fuse
Crown Victoria	13	10
Grand Marquis	13	10
Mark VIII	15	10
Town Car	4	10
Truck: (E4OD)		
E Series	5	15
F/B Series	17	10

FM0159300762060X

Fig. 221   Test TB: 4x4 Low/TCS (Part 6 of 7). 1993

TEST STEP	RESULT	►	ACTION TO TAKE
TB8 CHECK CONTINUITY OF THE 4x4 LOW OR TRANSMISSION CONTROL SWITCH HARNESS • Key off. • Breakout box connected, PCM disconnected. • Appropriate switch disconnected **For 4x4 Low circuit:** — Measure the resistance between Test Pin 12 at the breakout box and 4x4 Low circuit at 4x4 Low switch touch drive module vehicle harness connector **For TCS/TCIL circuit:** — Measure the resistance between keypower at the fuse panel (fuses) (ohmmeter positive probe) and power side of transmission control switch vehicle harness connector (ohmmeter negative probe). — Measure the resistance between Test Pin 41 at the breakout box and signal side of transmission control switch vehicle harness connector. • Are both resistances less than 5.0 ohms?	Yes No	► ►	GO to TB9. SERVICE open circuit(s). REMOVE breakout box. RECONNECT all components. RERUN Quick Test.
TB9 CHECK HARNESS CIRCUIT(S) FOR SHORTS TO POWER • Key off. • Breakout box installed, PCM disconnected. • Appropriate switch disconnected. **For 4x4 Low circuit:** — Measure resistance between Test Pin 12 and Test Pin 37/57 at the breakout box **For TCS/TCIL circuits:** — Measure resistance between Test Pin 41 and Test Pins 37/57 at the breakout box — Measure resistance between Test Pin 32 for E/F/B Series Trucks, Test Pin 14 for 3.2L SHO or Test Pin 55 for all others and Test Pins 37/57 at the breakout box • Is each resistance greater than 10,000 ohms?	Yes No	► ►	REPLACE damaged switch, either 4x4L range switch or transmission control switch (TCS) due to DTC received. REMOVE breakout box. RECONNECT PCM. RERUN Quick Test SERVICE short circuit(s). REMOVE breakout box. RECONNECT all components. RERUN Quick Test

FM0159300762070X

Fig. 221   Test TB: 4x4 Low/TCS (Part 7 of 7). 1993

Note

You should enter this Pinpoint Test only when you have been directed here from Diagnostic Routines.

Remember

This Pinpoint Test is not intended to diagnose components in the transmission. To prevent the replacement of good components, be aware that the following non-EEC areas may be at fault:

• Engine
— Performance, vacuum, cooling
• Electrical
— Charging system
• Transmission
— Hydraulic fluid, friction elements, cooling
— Transfer case linkage
— Transfer case internal damage

This Pinpoint Test is intended to diagnose only the following:
• Harness Circuits: 4x4 LOW, TCIL, TCS, TCSM
• Powertrain Control Module (PCM)

Description

The **4x4 Low Switch** is an input used by the Powertrain Control Module, which, when closed, allows the use of a secondary shift schedule while in the low range.

The **Transmission Control Switch (TCS)** allows the vehicle operator to disengage the overdrive feature when desired.

The **Transmission Control Switch Module (TCSM)** monitors the Transmission Control Switch (TCS) on the 5.0L AODE Mustang. The TCSM informs the PCM of the vehicle operator's request to disengage the overdrive feature and also controls the Transmission Control Indicator Light (TCIL).

FM0159400763010X

Fig. 222   Test TB: 4x4 Low/TCIL/TCS/TCSM (Part 1 of 9). 1994–95

The **Transmission Control Indicator Lamp (TCIL)** informs the vehicle operator of the Overdrive Range Status "ON" or "OFF" and also informs the operator of certain transmission sensor/actuator malfunctions by flashing the TCIL.

Pinpoint Test Schematics

Touchdrive Option

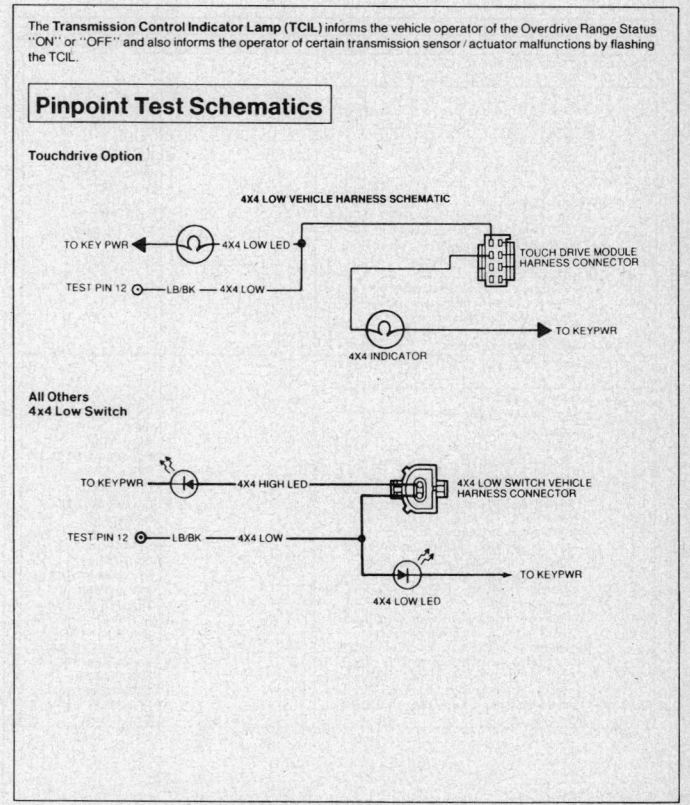

All Others
4x4 Low Switch

FM0159400763020X

Fig. 222   Test TB: 4x4 Low/TCIL/TCS/TCSM (Part 2 of 9). 1994–95

FORD—Computerized Engine Controls

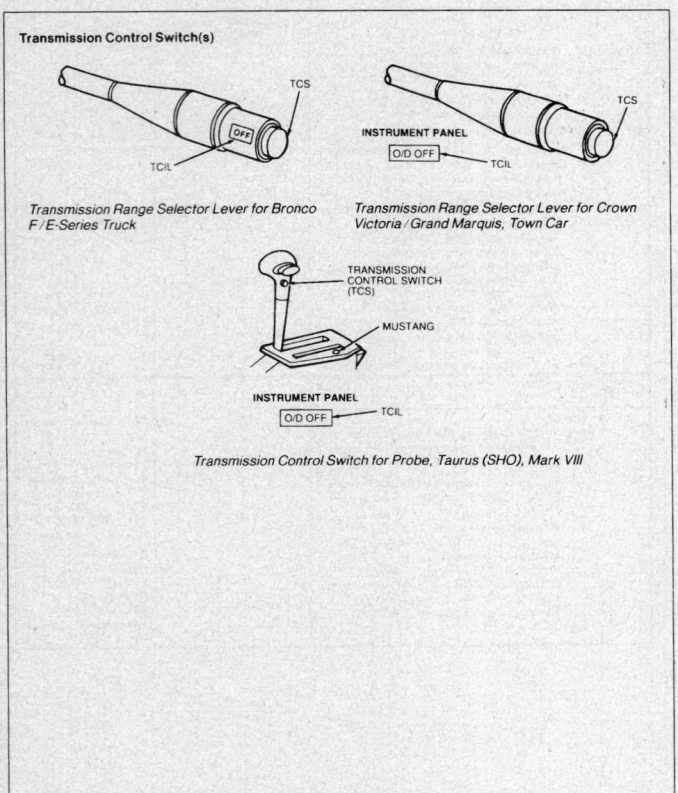

Transmission Control Switch(s)

Transmission Range Selector Lever for Bronco F/E-Series Truck

Transmission Range Selector Lever for Crown Victoria / Grand Marquis, Town Car

Transmission Control Switch for Probe, Taurus (SHO), Mark VIII

Fig. 222   Test TB: 4x4 Low/TCIL/TCS/TCSM (Part 3 of 9). 1994–95

TEST STEP	RESULT	▶	ACTION TO TAKE
TB1 DIAGNOSTIC TROUBLE CODES (DTCS) 47, 633 AND 691			
DTCs 47 and 633 indicate the 4x4 Low Selector Lever is not in the 4x2 or 4x4 high position (observed in Key On Engine Off (KOEO) Self-Test). A change in the automatic transmission shift cycle will occur. DTC 691 4x4 selector fault (observed in Continuous Self-Test) is set when a stored Kam value for N V (engine rpm vehicle speed) is compared to a calculated N V for the current switch position and driving condition. If these checks disagree, DTC 691 is set. Possible Causes: — Damaged 4x4 Low switch or 4x4 selector lever position. — Shorted harness — Damaged PCM — Internal damage to transfer case. ● Is the 4x4 lever positioned in 4x2 4x4 high?	Yes	▶	GO to **TB4**
	No	▶	RERUN KOEO Self-Test with positioning selector in 4x2 / 4x4 high.
TB2 DIAGNOSTIC TROUBLE CODES (DTCS) 65, 632 and 653			
DTCs 65, 632 and 653 indicate the Transmission Control Switch (TCS) was not cycled between engine "ID Code" and the "Goose Test" in Key On Engine Running (KOER) Self-Test. Possible Causes: — TCS damaged or switch not cycled during self-test. — Shorted harness — Damaged Powertrain Control Module (PCM). — Open harness or fuse. ● Was TCS cycled during KOER Self-Test?	Yes	▶	GO to **TB4**
	No	▶	RERUN KOER Self-Test cycling the TCS.
TB3 DIAGNOSTIC TROUBLE CODES (DTCS) 97, 623 AND 631			
DTCs 97, 623 and 631 indicates a transmission control light circuit concern (observed during Key On Engine Off (KOEO) Self-Test). Possible Causes: — Burned out bulb — Shorted harness — Open harness fuse. ● Was the TCS cycled during KOEO Self-Test?	Yes	▶	GO to **TB5**
	No	▶	RERUN KOEO Self-Test cycling the TCS.

Fig. 222   Test TB: 4x4 Low/TCIL/TCS/TCSM (Part 4 of 9). 1994–95

TEST STEP	RESULT	▶	ACTION TO TAKE
TB4 CYCLE THE APPROPRIATE CIRCUIT: (4x4 LOW OR TRANSMISSION CONTROL)			
● Key off. ● Disconnect Powertrain Control Module (PCM). Inspect for damaged or pushed out pins, corrosion, loose wires, etc. Service as necessary. ● Install breakout box, leave PCM disconnected. ● Key on, engine off. **For 4x4 Low circuit:** — Measure voltage between Test Pin 12 and Test Pin 40 60 at the breakout box while moving the 4x4 select lever between 4x2 and 4x4 Low several times. **For TCS circuit:** — Measure voltage between Test Pin 41 and Test Pin 40 60 at the breakout box while cycling the transmission control switch several times. ● Does the voltage cycle?	Yes	▶	REPLACE PCM. REMOVE breakout box. RERUN Quick Test.
	No	▶	For a driveability symptom only: GO to **TB7** For a DTC: GO to **TB5** For 5.0L Mustang only: GO to **TB20**
TB5 CHECK HARNESS CIRCUIT(S) FOR SHORT TO GROUND			
● Key off. ● Breakout box installed, PCM disconnected. **For 4x4 Low circuit:** — Disconnect 4x4 Low switch. Inspect both ends of the connector for damaged or pushed out pins, moisture, corrosion, loose wires, etc. Service as necessary. — Measure resistance between Test Pin 12 and Test Pin 40 60 at the breakout box. **For Transmission Control circuits:** — Disconnect Transmission Control Switch. Inspect the connector for damaged or pushed out pins, moisture, corrosion, loose wires, etc. Service as necessary. — Measure resistance between Test Pin 41 and Test Pin 40 60 at the breakout box. — Measure resistance between Test Pin 32 for E F B Series Trucks, Test Pin 14 for 3.2L SHO or Test Pin 55 for all others and Test Pin 40 60 at the breakout box. ● Is each resistance greater than 10,000 ohms?	Yes	▶	For original DTCs 47, 65, 632, 633, 653 and 691: GO to **TB8** For original DTCs 97, 623 and 631: GO to **TB6**
	No	▶	For original DTCs 47, 633 and 691: SERVICE short circuit. RERUN Key On, Engine Off Self-Test. For original DTCs 65, 632 and 653: SERVICE short circuit. RERUN Engine Running Self-Test. If DTC is still present, GO to **TB7** For original DTCs 97, 623 and 631: SERVICE short circuit. RERUN Key On, Engine Off Self-Test

Fig. 222   Test TB: 4x4 Low/TCIL/TCS/TCSM (Part 5 of 9). 1994–95

TEST STEP	RESULT	▶	ACTION TO TAKE
TB6 CHECK KEYPOWER THROUGH TCIL CIRCUIT			
● Key on, engine off. ● Breakout box installed, PCM disconnected. ● Measure voltage between Test Pin 32 for E F B Series Trucks, Test Pin 14 for 3.2L SHO or Test Pin 55 for all others and Test Pin 40 60 at the breakout box. ● Is voltage greater than 10.5 volts?	Yes	▶	REPLACE PCM. REMOVE breakout box. RERUN Quick Test.
	No	▶	GO to **TB7**
TB7 CHECK OUTPUT DRIVER SIGNAL			
NOTE: When entering this Test Step with a symptom or a Self-Test Pass code, first disconnect Powertrain Control Module (PCM). Inspect for damaged or pushed out pins, loose wires, etc. Service as necessary. ● Key off. ● Breakout box installed, PCM disconnected. ● Key on, engine off. **For 4x4 Low circuit:** — Switch disconnected. — Measure voltage between Test Pin 12 and PWR GND at the breakout box (ohmmeter negative probe) **For TCIL circuit:** — Measure voltage between Test Pin 32 for E F B Series Trucks, Test Pin 14 for 3.2L SHO or Test Pin 55 for all others and PWR GND at the breakout box (ohmmeter negative probe) ● Are both voltage readings at least 2.0 volts?	Yes	▶	GO to **TB8**
	No	▶	INSPECT for damaged indicator bulb (4x4 Low LED or TCIL) or damaged fuse in fuse panel. If OK, SERVICE open circuit. REMOVE breakout box. RECONNECT all components. RERUN Quick Test.

Fig. 222   Test TB: 4x4 Low/TCIL/TCS/TCSM (Part 6 of 9). 1994–95

ELECTRONIC ENGINE CONTROL SYSTEM IV (EEC-IV)

TEST STEP	RESULT	▶	ACTION TO TAKE
TB8 CHECK CONTINUITY OF THE 4x4 LOW OR TRANSMISSION CONTROL SWITCH HARNESS • Key off. • Breakout box connected, PCM disconnected. • Appropriate switch disconnected. **For 4x4 Low circuit:** — Measure the resistance between Test Pin 12 at the breakout box and 4x4 Low circuit at 4x4 Low switch touch drive module vehicle harness connector. **For TCS circuit:** — Measure the resistance between keypower at the fuse panel (fuses) (ohmmeter positive probe) and power side of transmission control switch vehicle harness connector (ohmmeter negative probe). — Measure the resistance between Test Pin 41 at the breakout box and signal side of transmission control switch vehicle harness connector. • **Are both resistances less than 5.0 ohms?**	Yes No	▶ ▶	GO to **TB9**. SERVICE open circuit(s). REMOVE breakout box. RECONNECT all components. RERUN Quick Test.
TB9 CHECK HARNESS CIRCUIT(S) FOR SHORTS TO POWER • Key off. • Breakout box installed, PCM disconnected. • Appropriate switch disconnected. **For 4x4 Low circuit:** — Measure resistance between Test Pin 12 and Test Pin 37/57 at the breakout box. **For TCS circuits:** — Measure resistance between Test Pin 41 and Test Pins 37/57 at the breakout box. — Measure resistance between Test Pin 32 for E/F/B Series Trucks, Test Pin 14 for 3.2L SHO or Test Pin 55 for all others and Test Pins 37/57 at the breakout box. • **Is each resistance greater than 10,000 ohms?**	Yes No	▶ ▶	REPLACE damaged switch, either 4x4L range switch or transmission control switch (TCS) due to DTC received. REMOVE breakout box. RECONNECT PCM. RERUN Quick Test. SERVICE short circuit(s). REMOVE breakout box. RECONNECT all components. RERUN Quick Test.

FM0159400763070X

Fig. 222   Test TB: 4x4 Low/TCIL/TCS/TCSM (Part 7 of 9). 1994–95

TEST STEP	RESULT	▶	ACTION TO TAKE
TB20 CHECK THE TRANSMISSION CONTROL SWITCH MODULE (TCSM) NOTE: This test step is for 5.0L Mustang AODE only. • Key off. • Breakout box installed, PCM disconnected. • Access the TCSM harness connector. (Refer to Mustang Electrical Vacuum Trouble Shooting Manual (EVTSM) for location.) • Remove TCSM from its mounting location to gain access to harness connector. • Key on, engine off. • Measure the voltage between the orange-black wire and the black-white wire of the TCSM connector while cycling the Transmission Control Switch (TCS) several times (refer to schematic). • **Does the voltage cycle?**	Yes No	▶ ▶	SERVICE the open circuit from the TCSM connector to PCM. CHECK orange/black wire to Test Pin 41. CHECK black/white wire to Test Pin 40/60. RECONNECT PCM. RERUN Self-Test. NOTE: If voltage cycles and the TCIL does not, GO to **TB25**. GO to **TB21**.
TB21 CHECK WIRING OF THE TRANSMISSION CONTROL SWITCH MODULE (TCSM) • Key off. • Breakout box installed, PCM disconnected. • TCSM connected. • Measure the voltage supply to the TCSM between the red-light green (+) wire and the black-white (-) wire. • **Is the voltage greater than 10.5V?**	Yes No	▶ ▶	GO to **TB22** SERVICE open circuit or fuse from the TCSM connector to the ignition switch. REMOVE breakout box. RECONNECT all components. RERUN Self-Test.
TB22 CHECK TRANSMISSION CONTROL MODULE SWITCH INPUT FROM TRANSMISSION CONTROL SWITCH • Key on, engine off. • Breakout box installed, PCM disconnected. • Measure the voltage between the tan-white wire and the black-white wire while cycling the TCS several times. • **Does the voltage cycle?**	Yes No	▶ ▶	REPLACE TCSM. REMOVE breakout box. RECONNECT PCM. RERUN Quick Test. CHECK TCS circuit.
TB23 TRANSMISSION CONTROL INDICATOR LIGHT (TCIL) ALWAYS ON • Key on, engine off. • Cycle the Transmission Control Switch (TCS). • **Does the TCIL turn on and off?**	Yes No	▶ ▶	Concern may be intermittent. CHECK pin fit, wire crimps, pushed out pins. GO to **TB24**

FM0159400763080X

Fig. 222   Test TB: 4x4 Low/TCIL/TCS/TCSM (Part 8 of 9). 1994–95

TEST STEP	RESULT	▶	ACTION TO TAKE
TB24 TRANSMISSION CONTROL SWITCH MODULE SHORT CIRCUIT CHECK • Key off. • Locate and unplug TCSM. • Key on, engine off. • **Does the TCIL remain on?**	Yes No	▶ ▶	Short to ground is in the 911 circuit (W·LG). REPAIR short. RECONNECT all components. VERIFY TCIL turns on and off. TCIL turns off when TCSM is disconnected. REPLACE TCSM.
TB25 TRANSMISSION CONTROL INDICATOR LIGHT (TCIL) NEVER ON • Verify over drive is functional. • Run Key On Engine Running (KOER) Self-Test. • **Is DTC 631 present?**	Yes No	▶ ▶	GO to **TB3**. GO to **TB26**.
TB26 CHECK FOR VOLTAGE AT FUSE PANEL • Key on, engine off. • Using the EVTM, locate the fuse that supplies 12V to the TCIL. • DVOM connected, measure the voltage at both sides of the fuse. • **Is the voltage greater than 10.5V?**	Yes No	▶ ▶	GO to **TB27**. REPLACE fuse. RECHECK TCIL operation.
TB27 CHECK WIRING FROM FUSE PANEL TO TCSM CONNECTOR • Key off. • Disconnect TCSM. • Locate circuit (911) on the vehicle harness side of the TCSM connector and ground pin (911). • Key on, engine off. • **Does TCIL light?**	Yes No	▶ ▶	Concern may be intermittent. CHECK pin fit, wire crimps, pushed out pins. CHECK bulb, if OK, open is in the wiring between the fuse panel and the TCSM connector. SERVICE open.

FM0159400763090X

Fig. 222   Test TB: 4x4 Low/TCIL/TCS/TCSM (Part 9 of 9). 1994–95

Note

You should enter this Pinpoint Test only when you have been directed here from Diagnostic Routines.

Remember

This Pinpoint Test is not intended to diagnose components interior to the transmission. To prevent the replacement of good components, be aware that the following non-EEC areas may be at fault:

- Engine
  - Performance, Vacuum, Cooling, Brakes.
- Electrical
  - Generator, Battery integrity.
- Transmission
  - Internal Transmission Components, Linkage, Cooling.

This Pinpoint Test is intended to diagnose only the following:

- Harness Circuits: TCC, CCS, EPC, SS3/4-4/3 SS1, SS2, SS3, SIG RTN, EPC PWR, and VPWR.
- Powertrain Control Module (PCM)

Description

2.3L Mustang, Ranger/Aerostar/Explorer (A4LD)
Taurus/Sable, Continental AX4S (AXODE)
Crown Victoria/Grand Marquis, Town Car, E-Series (AODE/4R70W)
E-Series/F-Series/Bronco (E4OD)
Escort/Tracer (4EAT)

The A4LD, AXODE, AODE and E4OD transmissions use solenoids to shift transmission gear ratios, connect both turbine and impeller in the torque converter, and provide coasting on deceleration. The ground signal is controlled by the PCM and 12 volts VPWR is supplied to the solenoids from the EEC power relay. On 4EAT transmissions, the solenoids are controlled by a positive voltage from the PCM.

FM015930076401AX

Fig. 223   Test TC: Trans Solenoids (Part 1 of 13). 1993

Note

You should enter this Pinpoint Test only when you have been directed here from Diagnostic Routines.

Remember

This Pinpoint Test is not intended to diagnose components in the transmission. To prevent the replacement of good components, be aware that the following non-EEC areas may be at fault:

- Engine
  — Performance, Vacuum, Cooling, Brakes
- Electrical
  — Generator, Battery integrity, Brake Switch
- Transmission
  — Internal Transmission Components, Linkage, Cooling

This Pinpoint Test is intended to diagnose only the following:

- Harness Circuits: TCC, CCS, EPC, SS3/4-4/3 SS1, SS2, SS3, SIG RTN, EPC PWR, and VPWR
- Powertrain Control Module (PCM) (12A650) or (12B565 on 7.3L Diesel)

Description

Ranger · Aerostar · Explorer (A4LD)
Taurus · Sable, Continental (AX4S)
Crown Victoria · Grand Marquis, Mark VIII, Town Car,
Mustang, E-Series · F-Series · Bronco (AODE/4R70W) E-Series · F-Series · Bronco (E4OD)
Escort · Tracer (4EAT)
2.0L Probe, California (CD4E)

The A4LD, AX4S, AODE, E4OD and CD4E transmissions use solenoids to shift transmission gear ratios, connect both turbine and impeller in the torque converter, and provide coasting on deceleration. The ground signal is controlled by the PCM and 12 volts VPWR is supplied to the solenoids from the EEC power relay. On 4EAT transmissions, the solenoids are controlled by a positive voltage from the PCM.

FM015940076401BX

Fig. 223   Test TC: Trans Solenoids (Part 1 of 13). 1994–95

Pinpoint Test Schematic

2.3L Mustang, Ranger / Aerostar / Explorer (A4LD)

Test Pin 53		
Application		Wire Color
3.0L SFI Aerostar		PK/BK
All Others		P/Y

Solenoid	PCM Signal Output Pin	KOEO DTC
TCC	53 or 14	89/629
SS 3/4	52 or 51	86/586

TCC - Torque Converter Clutch solenoid
SS 3/4 - Shift Solenoid 3/4-4/3

FM015930076402AX

Fig. 223   Test TC: Trans Solenoids (Part 2 of 13). 1993

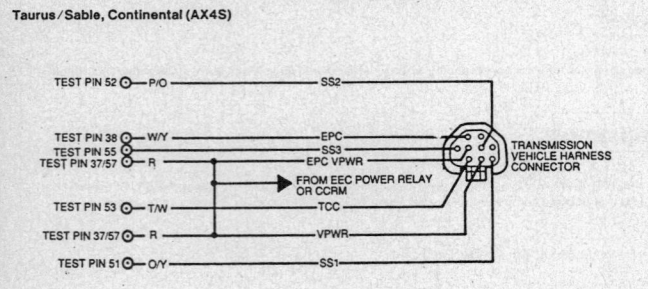

Taurus / Sable, Continental (AX4S)

Test Pin 55—SS-3		
Application		Wire Color
Taurus/Sable		W/R
Continental		PK/BK

Solenoid	PCM Signal Output Pin	KOEO DTC
SS1	51	621
SS2	52	622
SS3	55	641
TCC	53	652
EPC	38	624,625

Fig. 223   Test TC: Trans Solenoids (Part 2 of 13). 1994

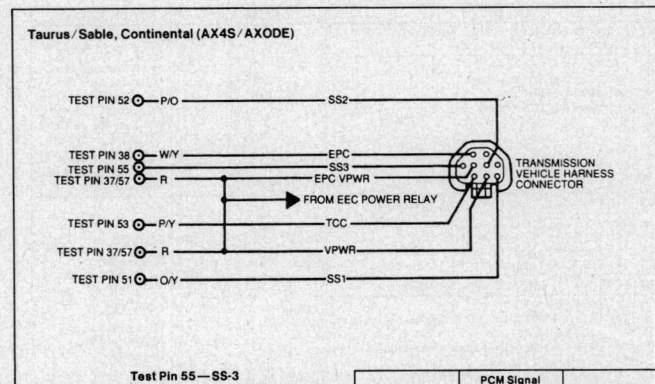

Taurus / Sable, Continental (AX4S/AXODE)

Test Pin 55—SS-3		
Application		Wire Color
Taurus/Sable		W/R
Continental		PK/BK

Solenoid	PCM Signal Output Pin	KOEO DTC
SS1	51	621
SS2	52	622
SS3	55	641
TCC	53	629, 652
EPC	38	624,625

SS1 = Shift Solenoid #1

SS2 = Shift Solenoid #2

SS3 = Shift Solenoid #3

TCC = Torque Converter Clutch

EPC = Electronic Pressure Control

FM015930076403AX

Fig. 223   Test TC: Trans Solenoids (Part 3 of 13). 1993

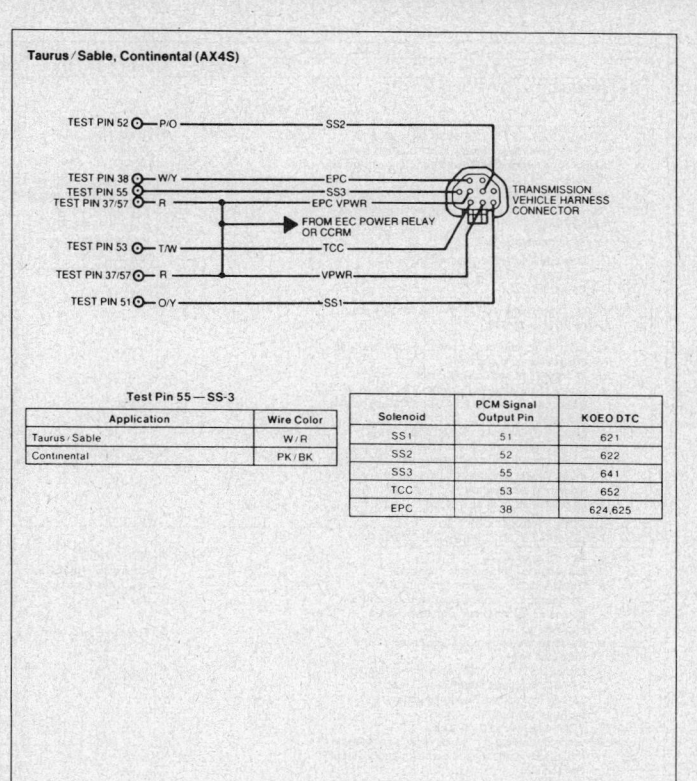

Test Pin 55 — SS-3

Application	Wire Color
Taurus/Sable	W/R
Continental	PK/BK

Solenoid	PCM Signal Output Pin	KOEO DTC
SS1	51	621
SS2	52	622
SS3	55	641
TCC	53	652
EPC	38	624,625

Fig. 223   Test TC: Trans Solenoids (Part 3 of 13). 1994

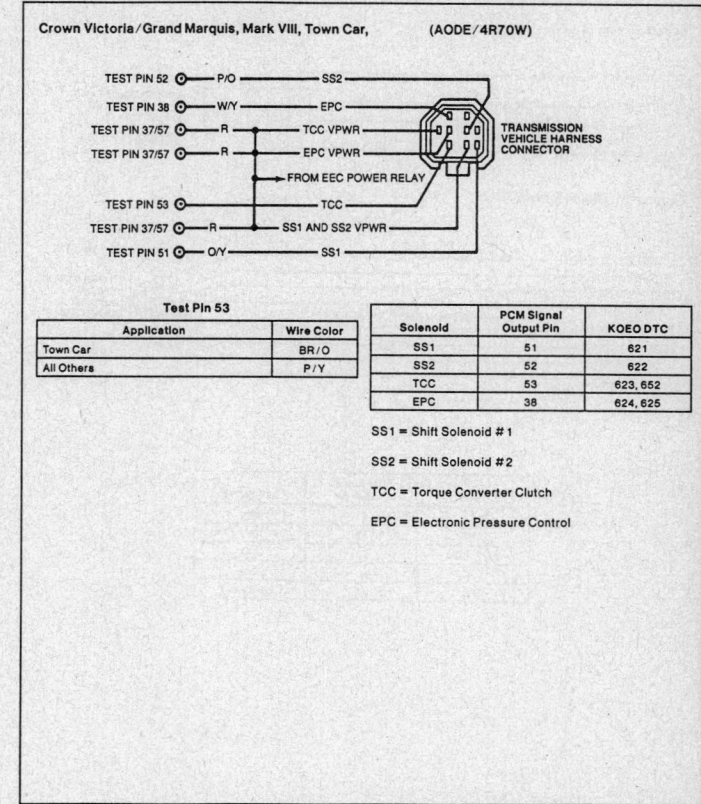

Test Pin 53

Application	Wire Color
Town Car	BR/O
All Others	P/Y

Solenoid	PCM Signal Output Pin	KOEO DTC
SS1	51	621
SS2	52	622
TCC	53	623, 652
EPC	38	624, 625

SS1 = Shift Solenoid #1

SS2 = Shift Solenoid #2

TCC = Torque Converter Clutch

EPC = Electronic Pressure Control

Fig. 223   Test TC: Trans Solenoids (Part 4 of 13). 1993

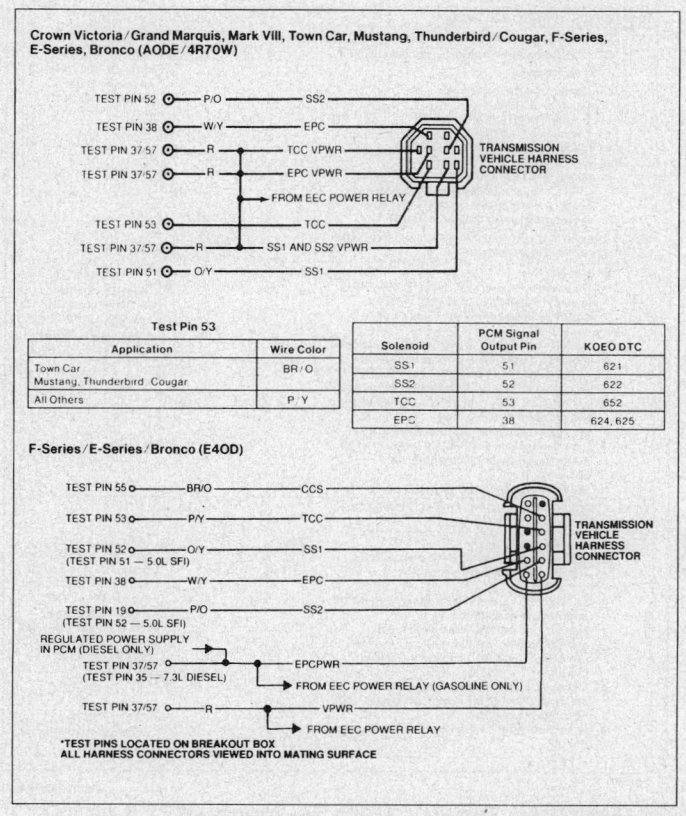

Test Pin 53

Application	Wire Color
Town Car	BR/O
Mustang, Thunderbird/Cougar	
All Others	P/Y

Solenoid	PCM Signal Output Pin	KOEO DTC
SS1	51	621
SS2	52	622
TCC	53	652
EPC	38	624, 625

Fig. 223   Test TC: Trans Solenoids (Part 4 of 13). 1994

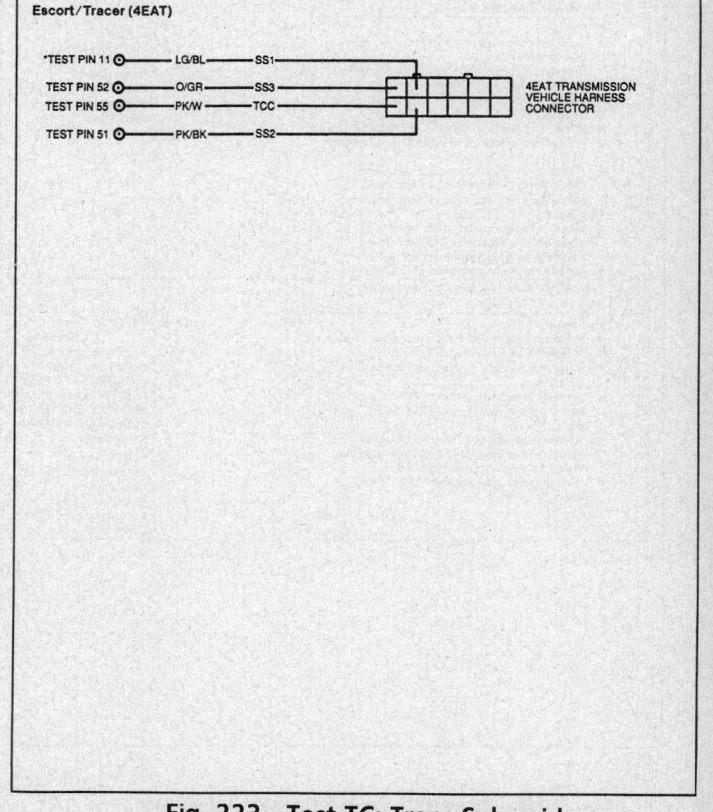

Fig. 223   Test TC: Trans Solenoids (Part 5 of 13). 1993

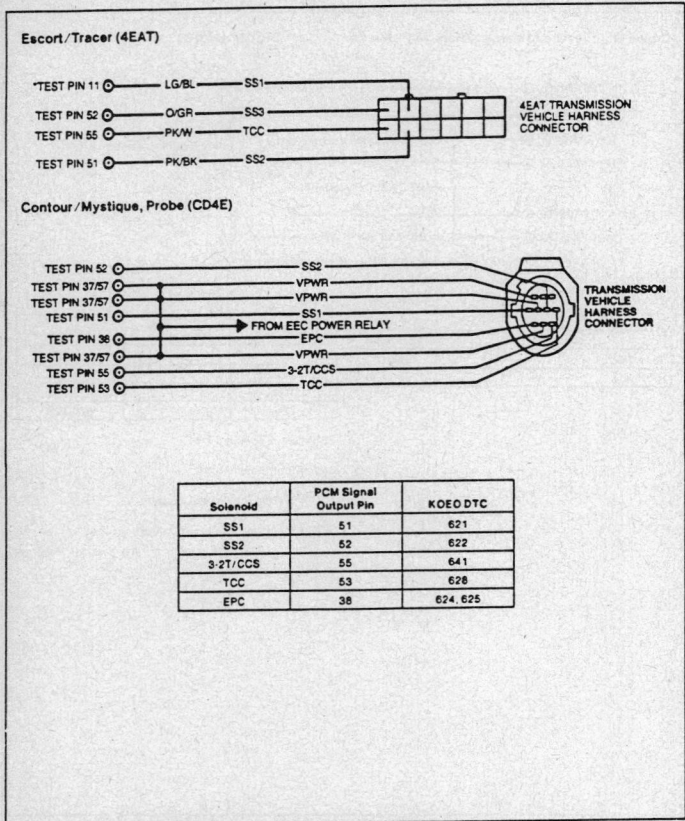

Fig. 223 Test TC: Trans Solenoids (Part 5 of 13). 1994–95

	TEST STEP	RESULT	►	ACTION TO TAKE
TC1	ENTER OUTPUT STATE DIAGNOSTIC TEST MODE (DTM)			
	DTCs 91 / 621, 92 / 622, 93 / 626, 94 / 627, 629, 641, 652 indicate solenoid did not change state when requested by the Powertrain Control Module (PCM). DTC 86 / 566 or 89 / 629 indicates that the CCO or 553 / 4-4 / 3 did not change state when requested by the PCM. Possible causes: — Damaged solenoid / assembly — Open or shorted harness (internal / external) — Damaged PCM **NOTE: Do not use a STAR Tester for this step. Use a VOM or DVOM.** • Disconnect electrical connector on the speed control servo, if equipped. • VOM / DVOM on 20 volt scale. • Connect negative test lead to STO circuit at Data Link Connector (DLC) and meter positive test lead to B+. • Jumper STI circuit to SIG RTN at the DLC. • Perform Key On Engine Off Self-Test until Continuous Memory DTC have been displayed. • VOM / DVOM will indicate less than 1.0 volt when test is complete. • Depress and release throttle. • **Does voltage increase?**	Yes No	► ►	REMAIN in Output State DTM. GO to TC2. DEPRESS throttle to WOT and RELEASE. If STO voltage does not go high PERFORM Pinpoint Test Step QC1. Leave equipment hooked up.
TC2	CHECK SOLENOID ELECTRICAL OPERATION			
	• Key on, engine off. • Disconnect transmission connector. • Using a mirror, inspect both ends of the connector for damaged or pushed out pins, corrosion, loose wires, etc. Service as necessary. • **Refer to the schematic and table of this Pinpoint Test.** • Connect VOM / DVOM positive test lead to VPWR circuit and negative test lead to solenoid circuit of the transmission vehicle harness connector. • VOM / DVOM on 20 volt scale. • While observing DVOM, depress and release throttle several times to cycle solenoid output ON and OFF. • **Does the suspect solenoid output voltage change at least 0.5 volt?**	Yes No	► ►	RECONNECT connector. REFER to Transmission REMOVE jumper wire. GO to TC3.

Fig. 223 Test TC: Trans Solenoids (Part 6 of 13)

FM0159300764070X

	TEST STEP	RESULT	►	ACTION TO TAKE
TC3	CHECK CONTINUITY OF SOLENOID SIGNAL AND VPWR HARNESS CIRCUITS			
	• Key off. • Solenoid transmission connector disconnected. • Disconnect Powertrain Control Module (PCM). Inspect for damaged or pushed out pins, corrosion, loose wires, etc. Service as necessary. • Install breakout box, leave PCM disconnected. • **Refer to schematic and table in this Pinpoint Test.** • Measure resistance between PCM signal output pin at the breakout box and signal output pin at transmission vehicle harness connector. • Measure resistance between Test Pin 37 / 57 at the breakout box and VPWR pin at transmission vehicle harness connector. • **Is each resistance less than 5.0 ohms?**	Yes No	► ►	GO to TC4. SERVICE open circuit(s). REMOVE breakout box. RECONNECT all components. RERUN Quick Test.
TC4	CHECK SOLENOID HARNESS FOR SHORTS TO POWER OR GROUND			
	• Key off. • Breakout box installed, PCM disconnected. • Transmission connector disconnected. • Refer to schematic and table in this Pinpoint Test. • Measure resistance between PCM signal output pin and Test Pin 37 / 57 at the breakout box. • Measure resistance between PCM signal output pin and Test Pins 40 / 60 and 46 at the breakout box and chassis ground. • **Is each resistance greater than 10,000 ohms?**	Yes No	► ►	REFER to Transmission Diagnosis for internal harness and solenoids. IF OK, REPLACE PCM. REMOVE breakout box. RECONNECT all components. RERUN Quick Test. SERVICE short circuits. REMOVE breakout box. RECONNECT all components. RERUN Quick Test.

FM0159300764080X

Fig. 223 Test TC: Trans Solenoids (Part 7 of 13)

	TEST STEP	RESULT	►	ACTION TO TAKE
TC10	CHECK VPWR TO SOLENOID			
	DTC 99 / 624 indicates a failure of EPC circuit. DTC 625 indicates an opening in the driver circuit. Possible causes: — Open or short harnesses (internal / external). — Solenoid damaged electrically. • Key off. • Disconnect transmission connector. • Key on, engine off. • Measure the voltage between VPWR, EPC PWR circuit at transmission vehicle harness connector and chassis / battery ground. • **Is voltage greater than 10.5 volts?**	Yes No	► ►	GO to TC11. SERVICE open in harness. RECONNECT all components. RERUN Quick Test.
TC11	CHECK CONTINUITY OF SOLENOID SIGNAL AND VPWR HARNESS CIRCUIT			
	• Key off. • Disconnect Powertrain Control Module (PCM). Inspect for damaged or pushed out pins, corrosion, loose wires, etc. Service as necessary. • Install breakout box, leave PCM disconnected. • Measure the resistance between Test Pin 37 / 57 (Test Pin 35 on 7.3L Diesel for EPC solenoid check only) at the breakout box and VPWR / EPC PWR circuit at the transmission vehicle harness connector. • Measure resistance between Test Pin 38 at the breakout box and EPC solenoid signal pin at the transmission vehicle harness connector. • **Is each resistance less than 5.0 ohms?**	Yes No	► ►	GO to TC12. SERVICE open circuit. REMOVE breakout box. RECONNECT all components. RERUN Quick Test.
TC12	CHECK HARNESS FOR SHORT TO POWER OR GROUND			
	• Key off. • Breakout box installed, PCM disconnected. • Transmission bulkhead connector disconnected. • **Refer to the schematic for the transmission and vehicle application.** • Measure resistance between suspect solenoid circuit Test Pin and Test Pin 37 / 57 (Test Pin 35 on 7.3L Diesel) at the breakout box. • Measure resistance between suspect solenoid circuit Test Pin and Test Pins 40 / 60, 46 at the breakout box. • **Is each resistance greater than 10,000 ohms?**	Yes No	► ►	REFER to Service Manual Transmission Diagnosis for internal harness and solenoids. If OK, REPLACE PCM. REMOVE breakout box. RECONNECT EPC solenoid. RERUN Quick Test. SERVICE short circuits. REMOVE breakout box. RECONNECT all components. RERUN Quick Test.

FM0159300764090X

Fig. 223 Test TC: Trans Solenoids (Part 8 of 13)

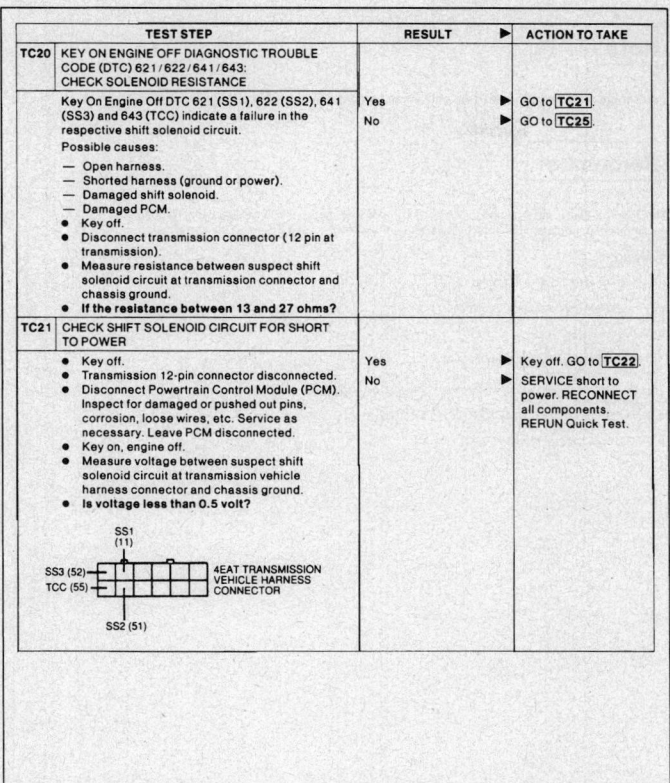

TEST STEP	RESULT	▶	ACTION TO TAKE
TC20 KEY ON ENGINE OFF DIAGNOSTIC TROUBLE CODE (DTC) 621/622/641/643: CHECK SOLENOID RESISTANCE			
Key On Engine Off DTC 621 (SS1), 622 (SS2), 641 (SS3) and 643 (TCC) indicate a failure in the respective shift solenoid circuit.	Yes	▶	GO to **TC21**
Possible causes:	No	▶	GO to **TC25**
— Open harness. — Shorted harness (ground or power). — Damaged shift solenoid. — Damaged PCM.			
• Key off. • Disconnect transmission connector (12 pin at transmission). • Measure resistance between suspect shift solenoid circuit at transmission connector and chassis ground. • **If the resistance between 13 and 27 ohms?**			
TC21 CHECK SHIFT SOLENOID CIRCUIT FOR SHORT TO POWER			
• Key off. • Transmission 12-pin connector disconnected. • Disconnect Powertrain Control Module (PCM). Inspect for damaged or pushed out pins, corrosion, loose wires, etc. Service as necessary. Leave PCM disconnected. • Key on, engine off. • Measure voltage between suspect shift solenoid circuit at transmission vehicle harness connector and chassis ground. • **Is voltage less than 0.5 volt?**	Yes No	▶ ▶	Key off. GO to **TC22**. SERVICE short to power. RECONNECT all components. RERUN Quick Test.

SS1 (11)
SS3 (52)
TCC (55)
SS2 (51)
4EAT TRANSMISSION VEHICLE HARNESS CONNECTOR

FM0159300764100X

Fig. 223 Test TC: Trans Solenoids (Part 9 of 13)

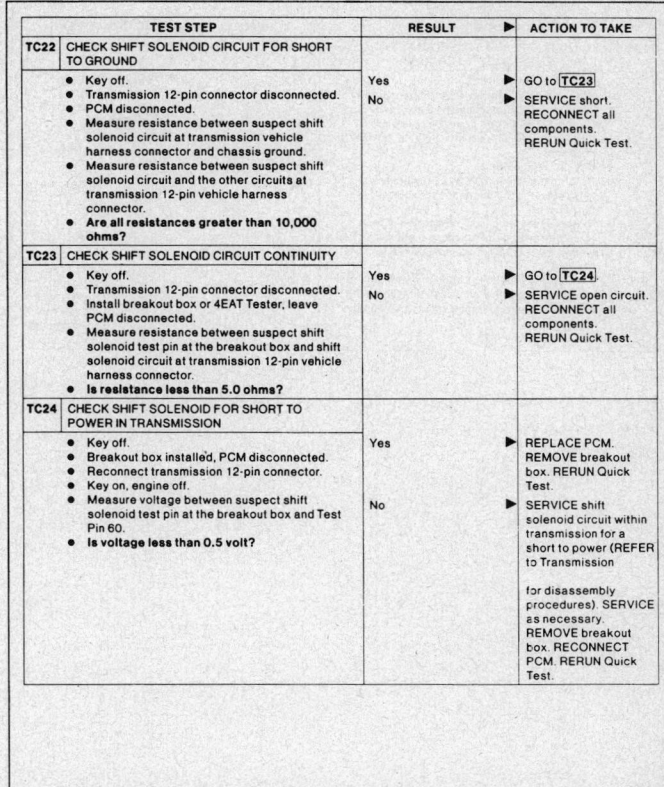

TEST STEP	RESULT	▶	ACTION TO TAKE
TC22 CHECK SHIFT SOLENOID CIRCUIT FOR SHORT TO GROUND			
• Key off. • Transmission 12-pin connector disconnected. • PCM disconnected. • Measure resistance between suspect shift solenoid circuit at transmission vehicle harness connector and chassis ground. • Measure resistance between suspect shift solenoid circuit and the other circuits at transmission 12-pin vehicle harness connector. • **Are all resistances greater than 10,000 ohms?**	Yes No	▶ ▶	GO to **TC23** SERVICE short. RECONNECT all components. RERUN Quick Test.
TC23 CHECK SHIFT SOLENOID CIRCUIT CONTINUITY			
• Key off. • Transmission 12-pin connector disconnected. • Install breakout box or 4EAT Tester, leave PCM disconnected. • Measure resistance between suspect shift solenoid test pin at the breakout box and shift solenoid circuit at transmission 12-pin vehicle harness connector. • **Is resistance less than 5.0 ohms?**	Yes No	▶ ▶	GO to **TC24**. SERVICE open circuit. RECONNECT all components. RERUN Quick Test.
TC24 CHECK SHIFT SOLENOID FOR SHORT TO POWER IN TRANSMISSION			
• Key off. • Breakout box installed, PCM disconnected. • Reconnect transmission 12-pin connector. • Key on, engine off. • Measure voltage between suspect shift solenoid test pin at the breakout box and Test Pin 60. • **Is voltage less than 0.5 volt?**	Yes No	▶ ▶	REPLACE PCM. REMOVE breakout box. RERUN Quick Test. SERVICE shift solenoid circuit within transmission for a short to power (REFER to Transmission for disassembly procedures). SERVICE as necessary. REMOVE breakout box. RECONNECT PCM. RERUN Quick Test.

FM0159300764110X

Fig. 223 Test TC: Trans Solenoids (Part 10 of 13)

TEST STEP	RESULT	▶	ACTION TO TAKE
TC25 INSPECT TRANSMISSION WIRING			
• Key off. • Check transmission connector/external wiring for open or shorts. Service as necessary. • Check internal transmission wiring for opens or shorts. Refer to Transmission for disassembly procedures. • **Is the transmission wiring OK?**	Yes No	▶ ▶	REPLACE suspect shift solenoid. REASSEMBLE/ RECONNECT all components. RERUN Quick Test. SERVICE as necessary. REASSEMBLE/ RECONNECT all components. RERUN Quick Test.
TC30 CONTINUOUS MEMORY DIAGNOSTIC TROUBLE CODE (DTC) 621/622/641/643: VISUALLY CHECK SHIFT SOLENOID HARNESS			
Continuous Memory DTC 621 (SS1), 622 (SS2), 641 (SS3) and 643 (TCC) indicate that sometime during the last 80 warm-up cycles, a failure was detected in the respective shift solenoid circuit.	Yes No	▶ ▶	GO to **TC31**. SERVICE as necessary. CLEAR Continuous Memory RERUN Quick Test.
Possible causes:			
— Intermittent open/shorted harness. — Intermittent fault in shift solenoid.			
• Check shift solenoid wires between transmission and Powertrain Control Module (PCM). • **Do the shift solenoid wires appear OK?**			

FM0159300764120X

Fig. 223 Test TC: Trans Solenoids (Part 11 of 13)

TEST STEP	RESULT	▶	ACTION TO TAKE
TC31 CHECK HARNESS AND CONNECTORS FOR INTERMITTENT OPENS OR SHORTS			
• Key off. • Disconnect Powertrain Control Module (PCM). Inspect for damaged or pushed out pins, corrosion, loose wires, etc. Service as necessary. • Install breakout box or 4EAT Tester. Leave PCM disconnected. • Key on, engine off. • Refer to the chart below. Connect a test lamp between suspect shift solenoid test pins and Test Pin 37 (VPWR) at the breakout box. • Observe test lamp for an indication of a fault while performing the following (the lamp will normally be on, but not to full brightness due to the 12-25 ohm resistance to ground through the shift solenoid. An open or short to power will be indicated by the light turning off. A short to ground may be detected by the light getting brighter). — Shake, wiggle and bend the shift solenoid circuit from the transmission to PCM. Lightly excercise harness connectors. • Key off.	Yes No	▶ ▶	ISOLATE fault and SERVICE as necessary. REMOVE breakout box. RECONNECT all components. RERUN Quick Test. GO to **TC32**.

Shift Solenoid	Test Pin
SS1	11
SS2	51
SS3	52
TCC	55

• Is a fault indicated?

FM0159300764130X

Fig. 223 Test TC: Trans Solenoids (Part 12 of 13)

	TEST STEP	RESULT	▶	ACTION TO TAKE
TC32	CHECK HARNESS AND CONNECTORS FOR INTERMITTENT SHORTS TO GROUND			
	• Key off.	Yes	▶	ISOLATE fault and SERVICE as necessary. REMOVE breakout box. RECONNECT all components. RERUN Quick Test.
	• Breakout box installed, PCM disconnected.			
	• Disconnected transmission 12-pin connector. Inspect for damaged or pushed out pins, corrosion, loose wires, etc. Service as necessary.			
	• Key on, engine off.	No	▶	For further diagnosis using the EEC-IV monitor box
	• Refer to the chart in TC31. Connect a test lamp between the suspect shift solenoid test pins and Test Pin 37.			If an EEC-IV monitor box is not available, GO to Pinpoint Test Step TD22 (even though TD is the MLP Pinpoint Test, we will mainly be checking the shift solenoid circuits).
	• Observe test lamp for an indication of fault while performing the following (light will turn on when a fault is detected, indicating a short to ground):			
	— Shake, wiggle and bend the shift solenoid circuit from the transmission to the PCM.			
	• Repeat the test for remaining shift solenoid circuits.			
	• **Is a fault indicated?**			

FM0159300764140X

Fig. 223   Test TC: Trans Solenoids (Part 13 of 13)

Note

You should enter this Pinpoint Test only when you been directed here from Diagnostic Routines,

Remember

This Pinpoint Test is not intended to diagnose components interior to the transmission. To prevent the replacement of good components, be aware that the following non-EEC areas may be at fault:

● Electrical

  — Generator, battery integrity.

  — Add-on devices (back-up alarm)

● Transmission

  — Shift linkage internal components.

This Pinpoint Test is intended to diagnose only the following:

● Harness Circuits: SIG RTN, MLP, TRR, TRL, TRD and TROD

● Powertrain Control Module (PCM)

FM0159300765010X

Fig. 224   Test TD: MLP Sensor (Part 1 of 15)

Description

Crown Victoria/Grand Marquis, Town Car,
Taurus/Sable, Continental (AXODE/AX4S)   **(AODE/4R70W)**

The Manual Lever Position (MLP) sensor is a ratiometric rotary switch mounted on the transmission shift linkage. It indicates the position of the shift lever by way of a variable resistance.

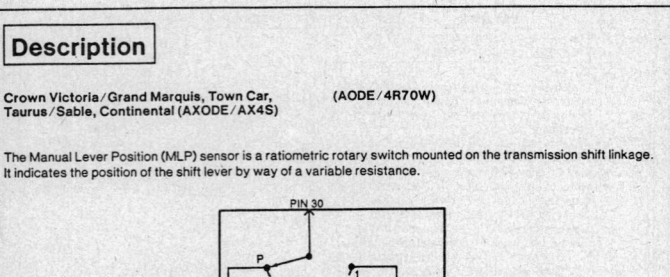
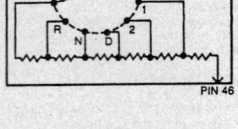

Manual Lever Position (MLP) Sensor
Resistance Specification Table

Transmission Shift Position	Resistance (ohms)	
	Minimum	Maximum
Park	3770	4607
Reverse	1304	1593
Neutral	660	807
Overdrive	361	442
Drive	190	232
First	78	95

Fig. 224   Test TD: MLP Sensor (Part 2 of 15). 1993–94

Description

Mark VIII, Mustang, Thunderbird/Cougar, E-Series/F-Series/Bronco (AODE/4R70W)
Explorer (4R55E), Taurus/Sable (AX4S/AX4N)
Contour/Mystique, Probe (CD4E)
E-Series/F-Series/Bronco (E4OD)

The Transmission Range (TR) sensor is a ratiometric rotary switch mounted on the transmission range selector linkage. It indicates the position of the shift lever by way of a variable resistance.

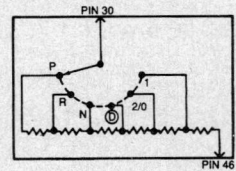

RESISTANCE SPECIFICATION TABLE

Transmission Shift Position	Resistance (ohms)	
	Minimum	Maximum
Park	3770	4607
Reverse	1304	1593
Neutral	660	807
Overdrive	361	442
Second/Drive	190	232
First	78	95

FM015950076502BX

Fig. 224   Test TD: MLP Sensor (Part 2 of 15). 1995

Pinpoint Test Schematics

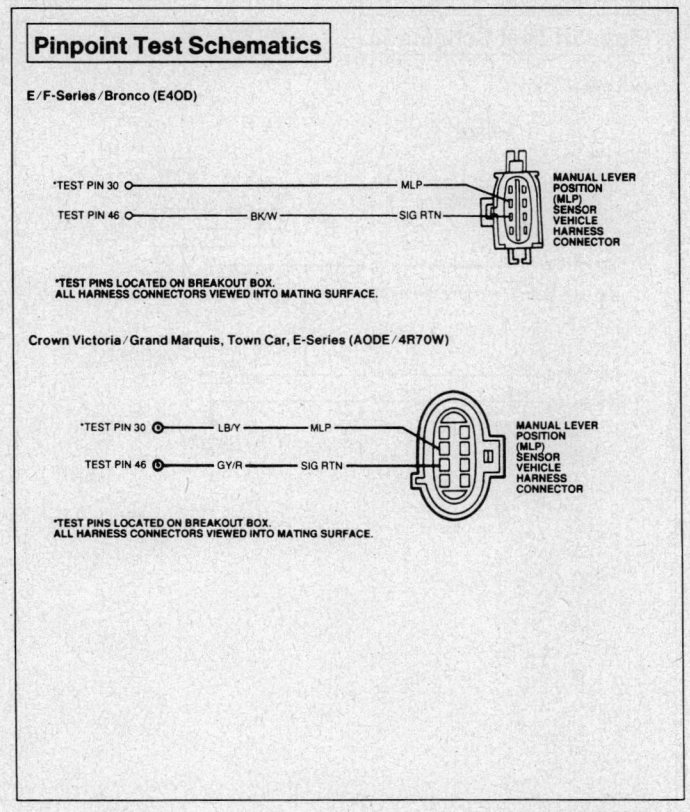

Fig. 224   Test TD: MLP Sensor (Part 3 of 15). 1993–94

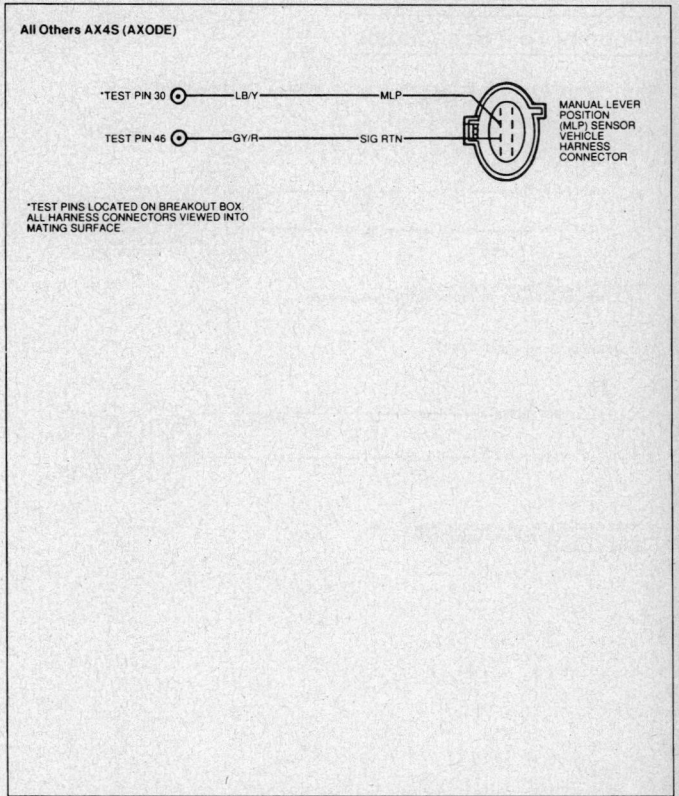

Fig. 224   Test TD: MLP Sensor (Part 4 of 15)

Description

Escort/Tracer (4EAT)

The transmission range switch inputs are used by the Powertrain Control Module (PCM) to determine the position of the gear shift selector.

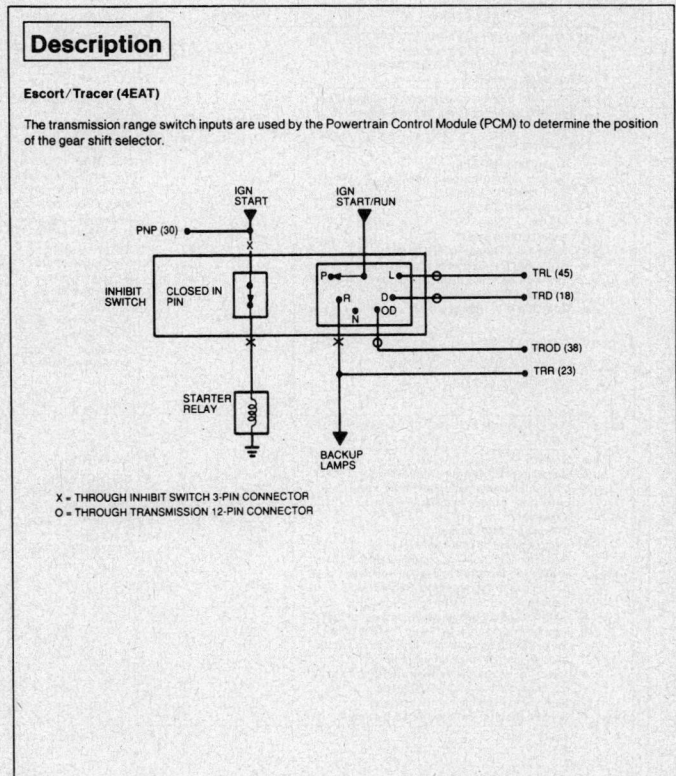

X = THROUGH INHIBIT SWITCH 3-PIN CONNECTOR
O = THROUGH TRANSMISSION 12-PIN CONNECTOR

Fig. 224   Test TD: MLP Sensor (Part 5 of 15). 1993

4EAT Transmission Range Switch State

Transmission Switch (at transmission connector)		Switch State
Switch (at transmission 12-pin connector)	Reference (at transmission 12-pin connector)	(Closed: Less than 5.0 ohms Open: Greater than 10,000 ohms)
TROD	IGN START/RUN	Closed in "OD", open in all other positions
TRD	IGN START/RUN	Closed in "D", open in all other positions
TRL	IGN START/RUN	Closed in "L", open in all other positions
Switch (at inhibit SW3-pin connector)	Reference (at trans 12-pin connector)	
TRR	IGN START/RUN	Closed in "R", open in all other positions
Switch (at inhibit SW3-pin connector)	Reference (at 12-pin connector)	
PNP	To Starter	Closed in "P" and "N", open in all other positions

4EAT Transmission Range Switch Voltage at EEC-IV Breakout Box

Circuit	Pin	Reference (Pin)	Voltage at EEC-IV Breakout Box (Key on) (All voltages ± 0.5 volts)
TRR	23	GND (40)	VBAT in "R", 0V in all other positions
TRL	45	GND (40)	VBAT in "L", 0V in all other positions
TRD	18	GND (40)	VBAT in "D", 0V in all other positions
TROD	38	GND (40)	VBAT in "OD", 0V in all other positions

Fig. 224   Test TD: MLP Sensor (Part 6 of 15). 1993

Pinpoint Test Schematics

Crown Victoria/Grand Marquis, Mark VIII, Town Car, Mustang, Thunderbird/Cougar, E-Series/F-Series/Bronco (AODE/4R70W)

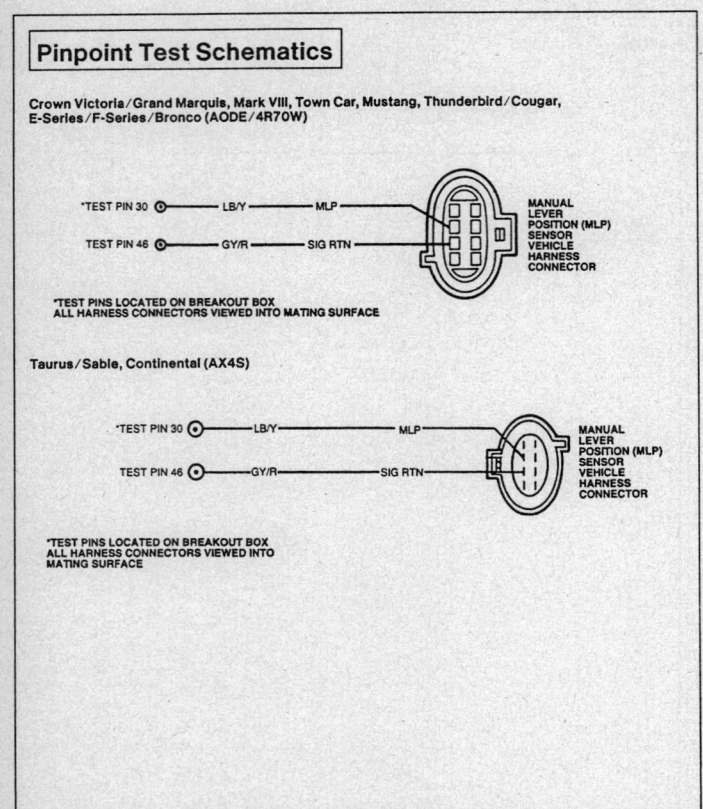

*TEST PINS LOCATED ON BREAKOUT BOX
ALL HARNESS CONNECTORS VIEWED INTO MATING SURFACE

Taurus/Sable, Continental (AX4S)

*TEST PINS LOCATED ON BREAKOUT BOX
ALL HARNESS CONNECTORS VIEWED INTO MATING SURFACE

Fig. 224 Test TD: MLP Sensor (Part 6 of 15). 1994

Pinpoint Test Schematic

Escort/Tracer (4EAT)

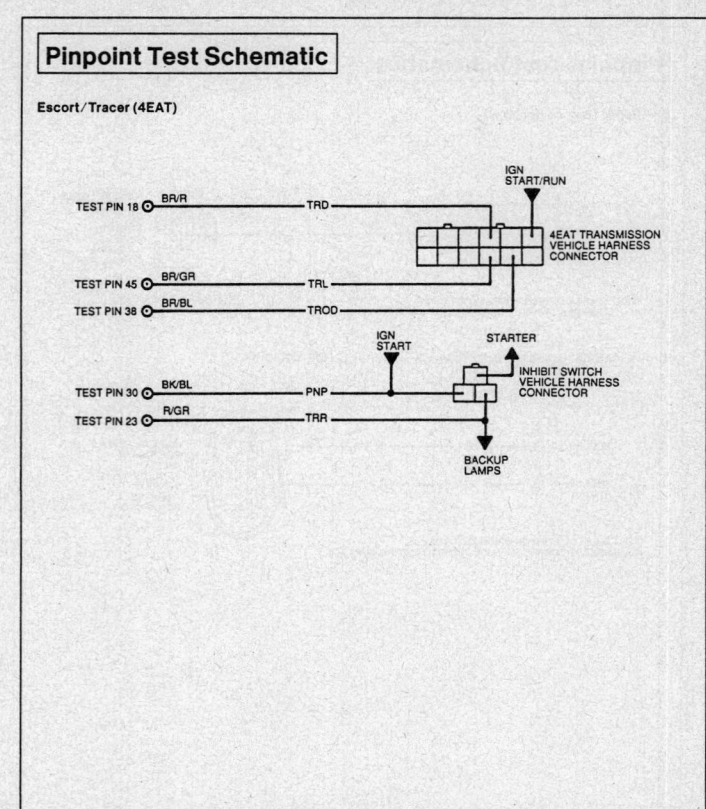

Fig. 224 Test TD: MLP Sensor (Part 7 of 15). 1993–94

Pinpoint Test Schematic

Escort/Tracer (4EAT)

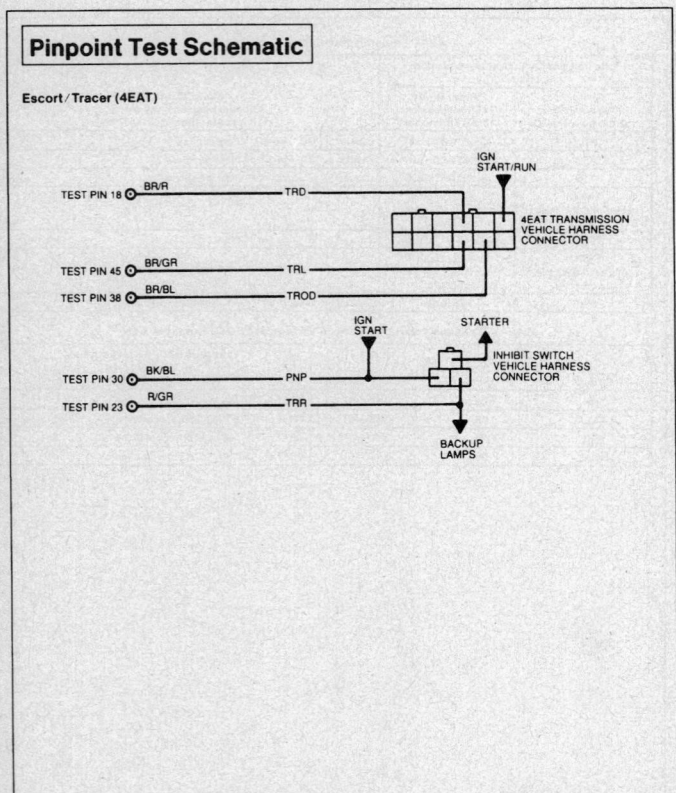

FM0159300765080X

Fig. 224 Test TD: MLP Sensor (Part 8 of 15)

	TEST STEP	RESULT	▶	ACTION TO TAKE
TD1	KEY ON ENGINE OFF DIAGNOSTIC TROUBLE CODE (DTC) 67/634 522 AND 654: CHECK MANUAL LEVER POSITION (MLP) SENSOR ALIGNMENT			
	DTC 67, 634, 522 indicates the MLP sensor is out of Self-Test range when the gear selector is in PARK. Possible causes: — Misadjusted linkage. — Open or short in harness circuits. — Damaged MLP sensor. — Damaged PCM. • Key off. • Apply parking brake. • Place transmission in NEUTRAL. • Verify that Manual Lever Position Sensor Tool (Rotunda T91P-7010-AHT) or equivalent fits in the appropriate slot. • **Does the tool fit properly?**	Yes No	▶ ▶	REMOVE tool. GO to TD2. PLACE the transmission in NEUTRAL. LOOSEN the two MLP sensor mounting bolts. MOVE the sensor about to allow insertion of the Manual Lever Position Sensor Tool in the appropriate slots. TIGHTEN the two mounting bolts to specification. REMOVE tool. VERIFY shift linkage adjustment. CLEAR Continuous Memory RERUN Quick Test.
TD2	CHECK CONTINUITY OF MLP SENSOR HARNESS CIRCUITS			
	• Key off. • Disconnect Powertrain Control Module (PCM). Inspect for damaged or pushed out pins, corrosion, loose wires, etc. Service as necessary. • Disconnect MLP sensor. • Using a mirror, inspect both ends of transmission harness connector at MLP sensor for damaged or pushed out pins, corrosion, loose wires, etc. Service as necessary. • Install breakout box, leave PCM disconnected. • Measure resistance between Test Pin 30 at the breakout box and MLP signal circuit at the MLP sensor vehicle harness connector. • Measure resistance between Test Pin 46 at the breakout box and SIG RTN circuit at the MLP sensor vehicle harness connector. • **Is each resistance less than 5.0 ohms?**	Yes No	▶ ▶	GO to TD3. SERVICE open circuit(s). REMOVE breakout box. RECONNECT all components. RERUN Quick Test.

FM0159300765090X

Fig. 224 Test TD: MLP Sensor (Part 9 of 15)

TEST STEP	RESULT	▶	ACTION TO TAKE
TD3 CHECK MLP CIRCUIT FOR SHORT TO POWER AND GROUND • Key off. • MLP sensor disconnected. • Breakout box installed, PCM disconnected. • Measure resistance between Test Pins 37 / 57, 40 / 60 and 46 at the breakout box. • Measure resistance between Test Pin 30 at the breakout box and chassis ground. • **Is each resistance greater than 10,000 ohms?**	Yes No	▶ ▶	GO to **TD4**. SERVICE short circuit(s). REMOVE breakout box. RECONNECT all components. RERUN Self Test.
TD4 CHECK MLP SENSOR RESISTANCE • Key off. • Connect MLP sensor. • Breakout box installed, PCM disconnected. • Unlock steering column. • Measure resistance between Test Pin 30 and Test Pin 46 at the breakout box in each gear selector position. Refer to the MLP sensor resistance specification table. • **Is each resistance within specification?**	Yes No	▶ ▶	REPLACE PCM. REMOVE breakout box. RERUN Self Test. REPLACE MLP sensor. REMOVE breakout box. RERUN Self Test.
TD9 TRANSMISSION IN 3RD GEAR ONLY WITH SELECTOR IN "D" AND "OD" PRELIMINARY CHECKS • Check transmission fluid level and fluid condition. Service as necessary. • Test drive vehicle to check / verify symptom. During the test drive: — Drive vehicle with gear selector in both DRIVE (D) and OVERDRIVE (OD) positions. Check to see if symptom can be consistently reproduced, or if it is an intermittent concern. • **Can the symptom be consistently reproduced?**	Yes No	▶ ▶	GO to **TD11**. GO to **TD20** (intermittent concern).

FM0159300765100X

Fig. 224 Test TD: MLP Sensor (Part 10 of 15)

TEST STEP	RESULT	▶	ACTION TO TAKE
TD10 DIAGNOSTIC TROUBLE CODE (DTC) 634: CHECK SYMPTOM Continuous Memory DTC 634 indicates that the PCM has detected an invalid combination of transmission range switch states. NOTE: Park / Neutral Position (PNP) switch is considered a transmission range switch in this Pinpoint Test. • Test drive vehicle with gear selector in both DRIVE (D) and OVERDRIVE (OD) positions. Check to see if transmission is always in 3rd gear with selector in the D or OD position. • **With the gear selector in D and OD position, is transmission ALWAYS in 3rd gear?**	Yes No	▶ ▶	GO to **TD11**. If symptom is "Transmission stays in 3rd gear occasionally", GO to **TD20**. For all other symptoms, DISREGARD Continuous DTC 634. CLEAR Continuous Memory.
TD11 CHECK FOR IGN START / RUN CIRCUIT VOLTAGE AT TRANSMISSION • Key off. • Disconnect 4EAT transmission connector (12-pin at transmission). • Key on. • Measure voltage between IGN START / RUN circuit at transmission vehicle harness connector and chassis ground. • **Is voltage greater than 10.5 volts?**	Yes No	▶ ▶	Key off. GO to **TD12**. SERVICE open circuit (verify condition of related fuse). RECONNECT transmission connector. RERUN Quick Test. RE-EVALUATE symptom.

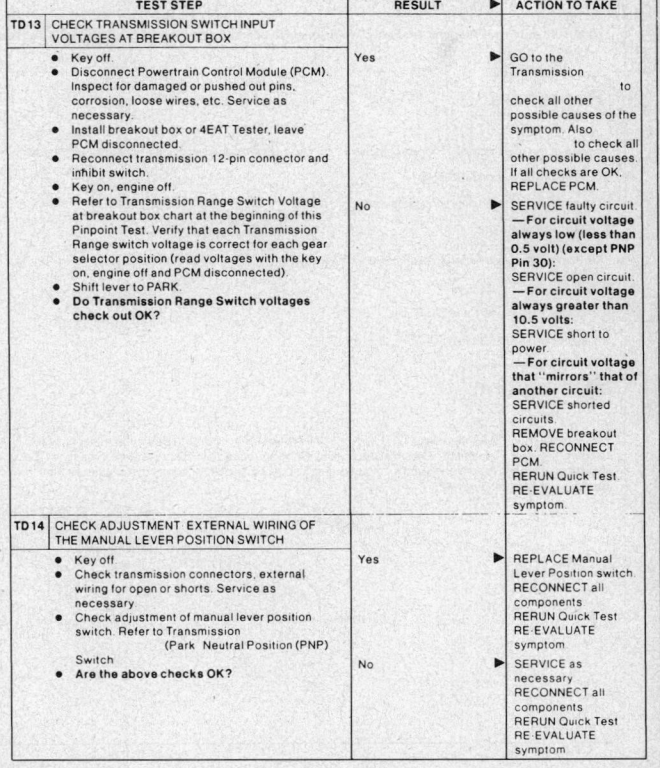

IGN START/RUN

4EAT TRANSMISSION VEHICLE HARNESS CONNECTOR

FM0159300765110X

Fig. 224 Test TD: MLP Sensor (Part 11 of 15)

TEST STEP	RESULT	▶	ACTION TO TAKE
TD12 CHECK FUNCTION OF THE TRANSMISSION RANGE SWITCHES • Key off. • Transmission 12-pin connector disconnected. • Disconnect inhibit (PNP) switch (3-pin at transmission). • Refer to Transmission Range Switch State chart at the beginning of this Pinpoint Test. Verify that each Transmission Range switch state is correct for each gear selector position. (Open is defined as greater than 10,000 ohms. Closed is defined as less than 5.0 ohms.) • Shift lever to PARK. • **Do the Transmission Range switches check out OK?**	Yes No	▶ ▶	GO to **TD13**. GO to **TD14**.

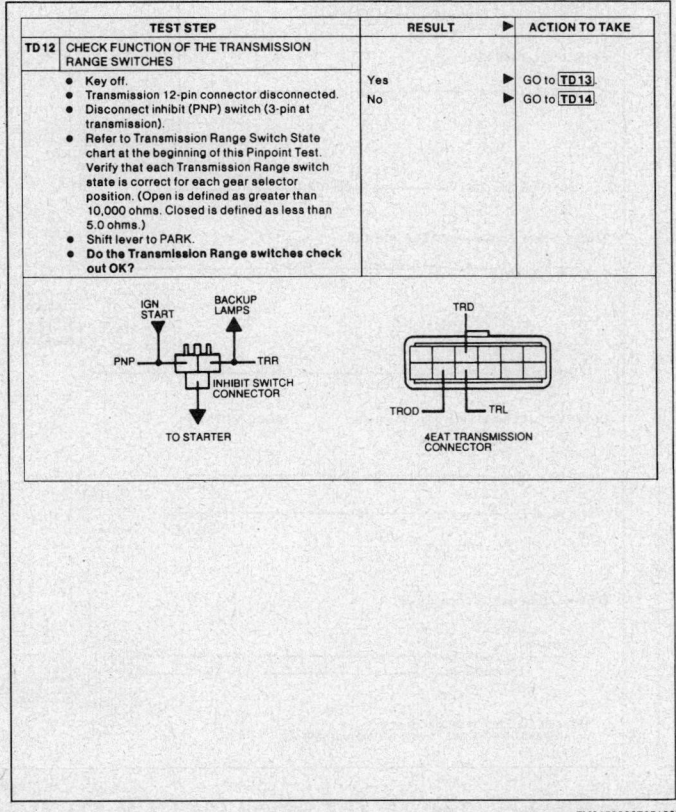

4EAT TRANSMISSION CONNECTOR

FM0159300765120X

Fig. 224 Test TD: MLP Sensor (Part 12 of 15)

TEST STEP	RESULT	▶	ACTION TO TAKE
TD13 CHECK TRANSMISSION SWITCH INPUT VOLTAGES AT BREAKOUT BOX • Key off. • Disconnect Powertrain Control Module (PCM). Inspect for damaged or pushed out pins, corrosion, loose wires, etc. Service as necessary. • Install breakout box or 4EAT Tester, leave PCM disconnected. • Reconnect transmission 12-pin connector and inhibit switch. • Key on, engine off. • Refer to Transmission Range Switch Voltage at breakout box chart at the beginning of this Pinpoint Test. Verify that each Transmission Range switch voltage is correct for each gear selector position (read voltages with the key on, engine off and PCM disconnected). • Shift lever to PARK. • **Do Transmission Range Switch voltages check out OK?**	Yes No	▶ ▶	GO to the Transmission ___ to check all other possible causes of the symptom. Also ___ to check all other possible causes. If all checks are OK, REPLACE PCM. SERVICE faulty circuit. —For circuit voltage always low (less than 0.5 volt) (except PNP Pin 30): SERVICE open circuit. —For circuit voltage always greater than 10.5 volts: SERVICE short to power. —For circuit voltage that "mirrors" that of another circuit: SERVICE shorted circuits. REMOVE breakout box. RECONNECT PCM. RERUN Quick Test. RE-EVALUATE symptom.
TD14 CHECK ADJUSTMENT EXTERNAL WIRING OF THE MANUAL LEVER POSITION SWITCH • Key off. • Check transmission connectors, external wiring for open or shorts. Service as necessary. • Check adjustment of manual lever position switch. Refer to Transmission ___ (Park Neutral Position (PNP) Switch • **Are the above checks OK?**	Yes No	▶ ▶	REPLACE Manual Lever Position switch. RECONNECT all components RERUN Quick Test RE-EVALUATE symptom. SERVICE as necessary RECONNECT all components RERUN Quick Test RE-EVALUATE symptom

FM0159300765130X

Fig. 224 Test TD: MLP Sensor (Part 13 of 15)

TEST STEP	RESULT	▶	ACTION TO TAKE
TD20 VISUALLY CHECK EEC-IV HARNESS BETWEEN EEC-IV AND TRANSMISSION			
• Visually check Transmission Range switch and shift solenoid wires between Powertrain Control Module and transmission.	Yes	▶	GO to **TD21**.
• **Do Transmission Range switch and shift solenoid wires appear OK?**	No	▶	SERVICE as necessary. RE-EVALUATE symptom.
TD21 CHECK HARNESS AND CONNECTORS FOR INTERMITTENT OPENS OR SHORTS			
NOTE: This Pinpoint Test Step is included to help isolate a possible intermittent Transmission Range switch circuit concern.	Yes	▶	ISOLATE fault and SERVICE as necessary. REMOVE breakout box. RECONNECT all components. RE-EVALUATE symptom.
• Key off. • Disconnect Powertrain Control Module (PCM). Inspect for damaged or pushed out pins, corrosion, loose wires, etc. Service as necessary.			
• Install breakout box or 4EAT tester. Leave PCM disconnected.	No	▶	address this, or any other symptom as necessary.
• Key on. • Refer to the ''4EAT Transmission Range Switch Voltage at EEC-IV Breakout Box'' chart at the start of this Pinpoint Test. Connect a test lamp between Test Pin 23 (TRR) and Test Pin 40 (GND). Observe test lamp for an indication of a fault while performing the following (the light will be normally on when the gear selector is in the same position as the circuit being tested (i.e., TRR=Reverse), and off in all other selector positions. A fault will be indicated by the light going off when it should be on (open in Transmission Range switch circuit or IGN START/RUN circuit), or on when it should be off (short to power or the ''activated'' circuit, switch contact closing). — Shake, wiggle, bend the Transmission Range switch circuit between the PCM and the transmission. — Shake, wiggle, bend the IGN START/RUN circuit. — Lightly tap on the Inhibit Switch to simulate road shock. — After completing testing on the TRR circuit, repeat the testing for the other Transmission Range Switch circuits (TRL, TRD, TROD). • Key off. • **Is a fault indicated?**			

FM0159300765140X

Fig. 224   Test TD: MLP Sensor (Part 14 of 15)

TD22   ROAD TEST (ESCORT/TRACER ONLY)

The purpose of the road test is to identify an area of concern by monitoring certain controlled parameters while trying to re-create a driveability or MIL symptom.

Note

A basic working knowledge of the EEC-IV system is critical to effectively analyze road test data.

WARNING

THIS ROAD TEST IS A SUGGESTED BUT OPTIONAL PROCEDURE. ALL APPLICABLE SAFETY PROCEDURES AND TRAFFIC LAWS MUST BE FOLLOWED. IN ORDER FOR A ROAD TEST TO BE PERFORMED IT IS REQUIRED THAT ANOTHER PERSON ACCOMPANY THE DRIVER. THE ACCOMPANYING PERSON CAN MAKE MEASUREMENTS, OBSERVE CHANGES AND RECORD NOTES. IF FOR SOME REASON THIS TEST IS NOT PERFORMED, RETURN TO Diagnostic Routines

Prepare Vehicle For a Road Test

• Disconnect Powertrain Control Module (PCM). Inspect for damaged or pushed out pins, corrosion, loose wires, etc. Service as necessary.

• Install breakout box/4EAT tester and connect PCM to breakout box/4EAT tester.

• Other materials needed: DVOM, pencil, paper, appropriate schematic/pin usage sheet

• Optional equipment:

— Fuel pressure gauge, manifold vacuum gauge, MAP/BARO tester.

Preliminary Power/Ground Checks

• With the key ON and a DVOM referenced to the battery negative post, check the following signals for correct values.

POWERS: KAPWR > 10.5V (Pin 1), VPWR > 10.5V (Pins 37/57), VREF 5 ± 1V (Pin 26). GROUNDS: (all = 0 ± .5V): PWR GND (Pins 40/60), SIG RTN (Pin 46), IGN GND (Pin 16). OPTIONAL GROUNDS: HO2S GND (Pin 49) CSE GND (Pin 20) MAF RTN (Pin 9 or 15).

Obtaining Other Needed Information and Materials Before the Road Test

• Refer to the Transmission Range Switch Voltage at EEC-IV breakout box chart at the beginning of this Pinpoint Test. These are the main signals that will be monitored. The PNP input (Pin 30) should also be monitored (with the PNP switch referenced to GND, the voltage should be about zero volts in Park or Neutral and greater than 3.0 volts in all other gearshift positions).

FM0159300765150X

Fig. 224   Test TD: MLP Sensor (Part 15 of 15)

Note

You should enter this Pinpoint Test only when you have been directed here from Diagnostic Routines.

Remember

To prevent the replacement of good components, be aware that the following non-EEC areas may at fault:

• Engine/transmission fluid levels
• Engine/transmission operating temperature
• Ambient temperature

This Pinpoint Test is intended to diagnose only the following:

• TOT sensor
• Harness circuits: TOT and SIG RTN
• Powertrain Control Module (PCM)

Description

The Transmission Oil Temperature (TOT) sensor is a thermistor that changes resistance in response to temperature. The TOT sensor resistance decreases as the surrounding fluid temperature increases. The resistance variation is converted into a voltage signal and sent to the PCM to give an indication of the transmission fluid temperature.

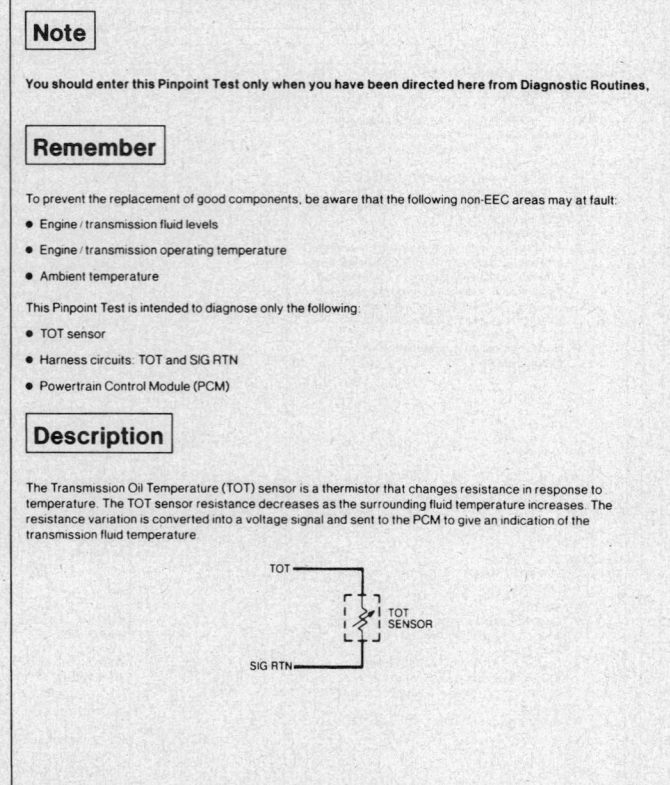

FM0159300766010X

Fig. 225   Test TE: TOT Sensor (Part 1 of 11)

Pinpoint Test Schematics

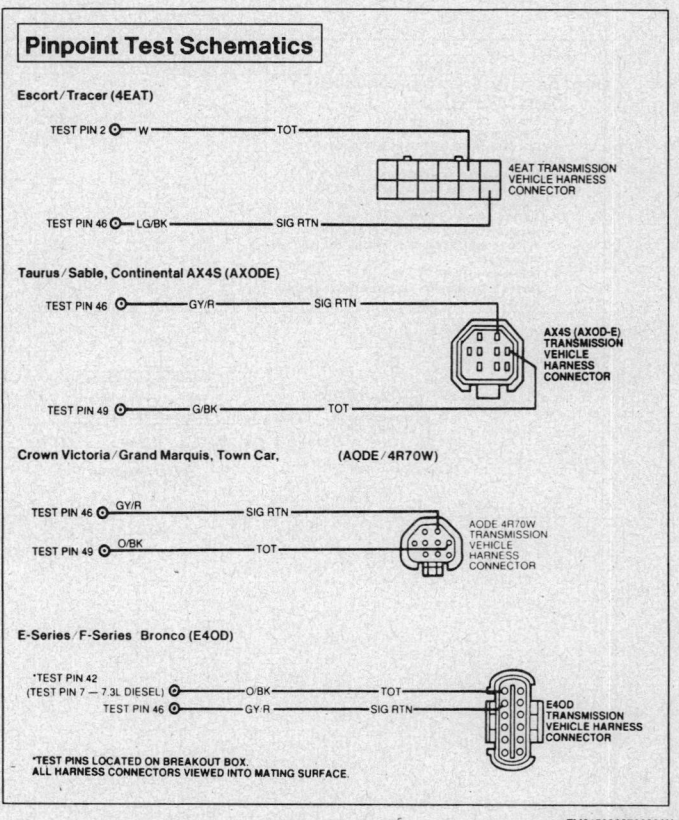

Escort/Tracer (4EAT)

TEST PIN 2 — W — TOT — 4EAT TRANSMISSION VEHICLE HARNESS CONNECTOR
TEST PIN 46 — LG/BK — SIG RTN

Taurus/Sable, Continental AX4S (AXODE)

TEST PIN 46 — GY/R — SIG RTN — AX4S (AXOD-E) TRANSMISSION VEHICLE HARNESS CONNECTOR
TEST PIN 49 — G/BK — TOT

Crown Victoria/Grand Marquis, Town Car,   (AQDE/4R70W)

TEST PIN 46 — GY/R — SIG RTN — AODE 4R70W TRANSMISSION VEHICLE HARNESS CONNECTOR
TEST PIN 49 — O/BK — TOT

E-Series/F-Series Bronco (E4OD)

*TEST PIN 42 (TEST PIN 7 — 7.3L DIESEL) — O/BK — TOT — E4OD TRANSMISSION VEHICLE HARNESS CONNECTOR
TEST PIN 46 — GY/R — SIG RTN

*TEST PINS LOCATED ON BREAKOUT BOX. ALL HARNESS CONNECTORS VIEWED INTO MATING SURFACE.

FM015930076602AX

Fig. 225   Test TE: TOT Sensor (Part 2 of 11). 1993

Pinpoint Test Schematics

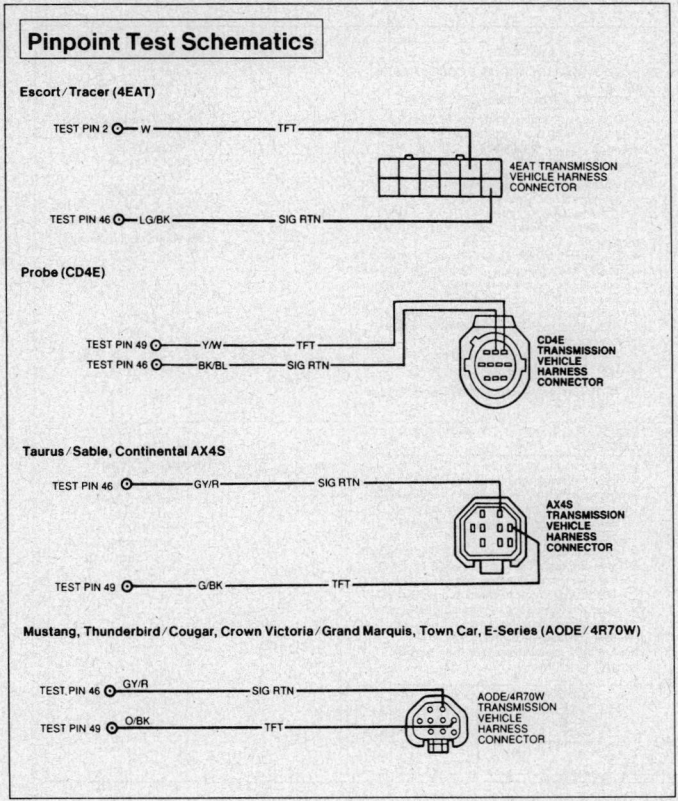

Escort/Tracer (4EAT)

Probe (CD4E)

Taurus/Sable, Continental AX4S

Mustang, Thunderbird/Cougar, Crown Victoria/Grand Marquis, Town Car, E-Series (AODE/4R70W)

FM015940076602BX

Fig. 225   Test TE: TOT Sensor (Part 2 of 11). 1994–95

Escort/Tracer (4EAT)

NOTE: Voltage and resistance values may vary ± 15%.

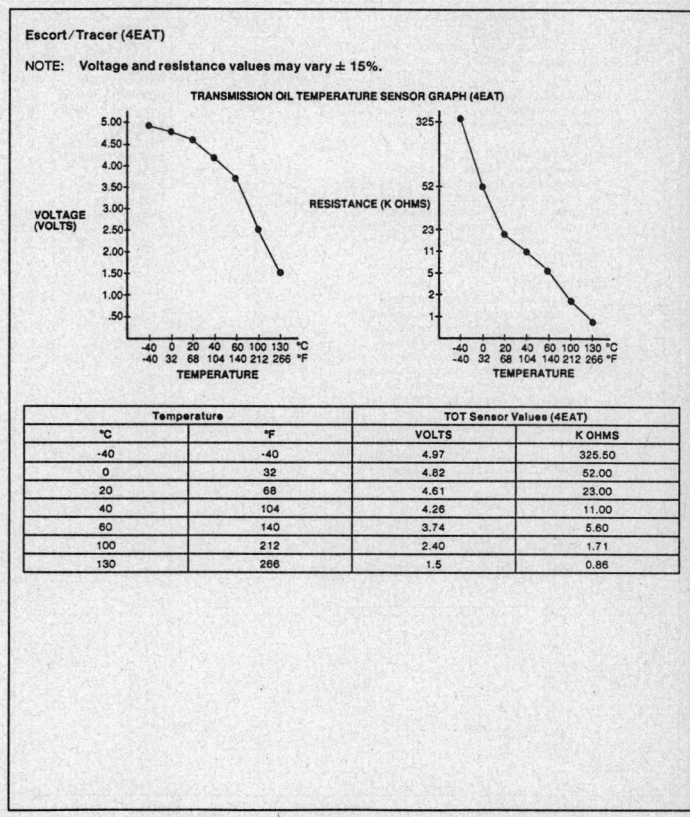

Temperature		TOT Sensor Values (4EAT)	
°C	°F	VOLTS	K OHMS
-40	-40	4.97	325.50
0	32	4.82	52.00
20	68	4.61	23.00
40	104	4.26	11.00
60	140	3.74	5.60
100	212	2.40	1.71
130	266	1.5	0.86

Fig. 225   Test TE: TOT Sensor (Part 3 of 11)

All Others

NOTE: Voltage values are calculated for VREF = 5.0 volts: These values may vary 15 percent due to sensor and VREF variations. Transmission oil temperature must be minimum of 10°C (50°F) before taking transmission oil temperature sensor resistance measurements.

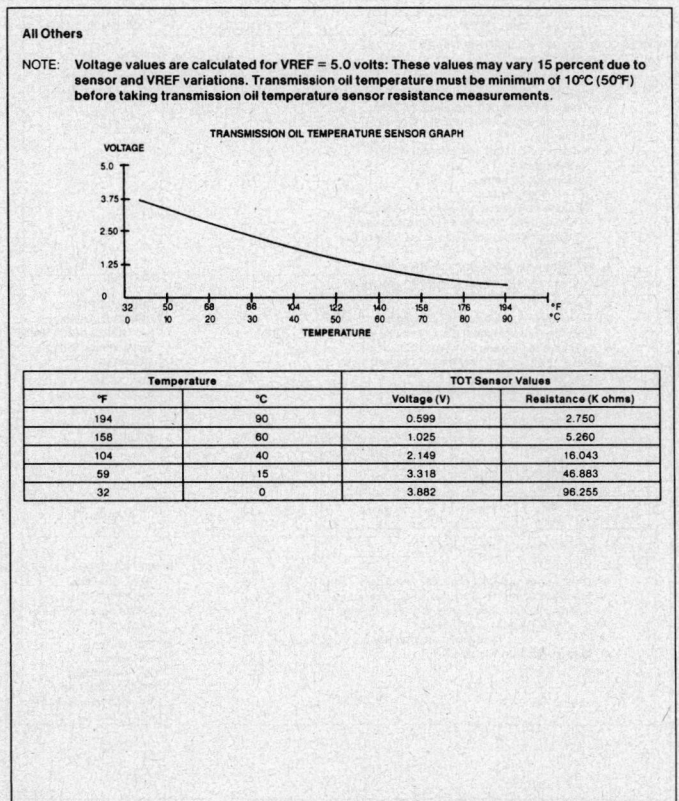

TRANSMISSION OIL TEMPERATURE SENSOR GRAPH

Temperature		TOT Sensor Values	
°F	°C	Voltage (V)	Resistance (K ohms)
194	90	0.599	2.750
158	60	1.025	5.260
104	40	2.149	16.043
59	15	3.318	46.883
32	0	3.882	96.255

FM0159300766040X

Fig. 225   Test TE: TOT Sensor (Part 4 of 11)

	TEST STEP	RESULT	▶	ACTION TO TAKE
TE1	KOEO AND KOER DIAGNOSTIC TROUBLE CODE (DTC) 26 OR 636: INCREASE/DECREASE TRANSMISSION OIL TEMPERATURE			
	DTC 26/636 indicates the output of the Transmission Oil Temperature (TOT) sensor was out of Self-Test range. The sensor output shows a failure occurred at either the low or high end of the acceptable range. The correct range of measurement is from 0.76 to 4.69 volts for Escort/Tracer and from 0.21 to 3.50 volts for all others. Possible causes: — Fluid levels not to specification — Transmission fluid not at operating temperature. — Sensor resistance out of limits. — Damaged Powertrain Control Module (PCM). ● Drive vehicle through normal city traffic to bring transmission oil temperature to at least 10°C (50°F). ● Rerun Quick Test. ● Is DTC 26 or 636 present?	Yes No	▶ ▶	GO to TE2 TOT sensor OK. SERVICE other DTC's as necessary. RETURN to Quick Test to SERVICE other DTC's as necessary.
TE2	CHECK FOR VREF AT THROTTLE POSITION SENSOR			
	● Key off. ● Disconnect Powertrain Control Module (PCM). Inspect for damaged or pushed out pins, corrosion, loose wires, etc. Service as necessary. ● Install breakout box and connect PCM to breakout box. ● Disconnect TP sensor. ● Key on, engine off. ● Measure voltage between VREF and SIG RTN at the sensor vehicle harness connector. Refer to schematic in Pinpoint Test DH or DQ. ● Is the voltage between 4.0 and 6.0 volts?	Yes No	▶ ▶	RECONNECT TP sensor. GO to TE3. GO to Pinpoint Test Step C1.

FM0159300766050X

Fig. 225   Test TE: TOT Sensor (Part 5 of 11)

Fig. 225 Test TE: TOT Sensor (Part 6 of 11)

TEST STEP	RESULT	▶	ACTION TO TAKE
TE3 CHECK TOT SENSOR RESISTANCE CHANGE AS TRANSMISSION OIL TEMPERATURE VARIES • Key off. • Breakout box installed, PCM disconnected. • Key on, engine off. • Verify that transmission oil pan is warm to the touch. **IF IT IS TOO HOT TO TOUCH:** — Measure and record TOT sensor resistance between TOT test pin (refer to chart) and Test Pin 46 at breakout box, then let transmission cool down and repeat measurement. The last resistance measurement should be greater than the first. • **IF IT IS COLD:** — Measure and record the TOT sensor resistance between TOT test pin (refer to chart) and Test Pin 46 at the breakout box, then reconnect PCM and drive vehicle for short time to elevate oil temperature. Disconnect PCM and repeat the measurements at the breakout box. The last resistance should be less than the first. • **Did resistance measurement differ and was last measurement within specifications?** Refer to applicable chart at the beginning of this Pinpoint Test for the resistance specifications.	Yes No	▶ ▶	REPLACE PCM. REMOVE breakout box. RERUN Quick Test. REMOVE breakout box. RECONNECT PCM. **For Escort/Tracer:** GO to TE25. **For all others:**

TOT TEST PIN

	4R70W AODE AXODE (AX4S)	E4OD (except 7.3L diesel)	E4OD (7.3L diesel)	4EAT
TOT TEST PIN	49	42	7	2

Fig. 225 Test TE: TOT Sensor (Part 7 of 11)

TEST STEP	RESULT	▶	ACTION TO TAKE
TE10 KOEO DIAGNOSTIC TROUBLE CODE (DTC) 56 OR 637: ATTEMPT TO GENERATE DTC 66 OR 638 DTC 56 and 637 indicate that the TOT sensor output is greater than Self-Test maximum value of 4.8 volts. Possible causes: — Fluid levels not to specification. — Damaged TOT sensor. — Open harness circuit(s). — Damaged Powertrain Control Module (PCM). • Key off. • Disconnect transmission bulkhead connector at TOT sensor. Inspect for damaged or pushed out pins, corrosion, loose wires, etc. Service as necessary. • Insert a jumper wire from the TOT circuit to SIG RTN circuit at transmission vehicle harness connector. • Run Key On Engine Off Self-Test. • **Is DTC 66 or 638 present?** NOTE: Disregard any other DTC generated at this time.	Yes No	▶ ▶	REMOVE jumper wire. **For Escort/Tracer:** GO to TE25. **For all others:** REFER to Transmission for TOT sensor service. REMOVE jumper wire. GO to TE11.
TE11 CHECK CONTINUITY OF TOT AND SIG RTN CIRCUITS • Key off. • Transmission connector disconnected. • Disconnect Powertrain Control Module (PCM). Inspect for damaged or pushed out pins, corrosion, loose wires, etc. Service as necessary. • Install breakout box, leave PCM disconnected. • Measure resistance between TOT circuit at transmission vehicle harness connector and TOT test pin (refer to chart) at breakout box. • Measure resistance between SIG RTN circuit at transmission vehicle harness connector and Test Pin 46 at the breakout box. • **Are both resistances less than 5.0 ohms?**	Yes No	▶ ▶	GO to TE12. SERVICE open circuit(s). REMOVE breakout box. RECONNECT all components. RERUN Quick Test.

TOT TEST PIN

	4R70W AODE AXODE (AX4S)	E4OD (except 7.3L diesel)	E4OD (7.3L diesel)	4EAT
TOT TEST PIN	49	42	7	2

Fig. 225 Test TE: TOT Sensor (Part 8 of 11)

TEST STEP	RESULT	▶	ACTION TO TAKE
TE12 CHECK TOT CIRCUIT FOR SHORT TO VPWR • Key off. • Transmission connector disconnected. • Breakout box installed, PCM disconnected. • Measure resistance between TOT test pin (refer to chart in Test Step TE11) and Test Pins 37/57 at breakout box. • **Is each resistance greater than 10,000 ohms?**	Yes No	▶ ▶	REPLACE PCM. REMOVE breakout box. RECONNECT all components. RERUN Quick Test. SERVICE short circuit(s). REMOVE breakout box. RECONNECT all components. RERUN Quick Test.
TE20 KOEO DIAGNOSTIC TROUBLE CODE (DTC) 66 OR 638: ATTEMPT TO GENERATE DTC 56 OR 637 DTC 66 and 638 indicate that TOT sensor output was less than the allowed Self-Test minimum value of 0.57 volts for Escort/Tracer and 0.15 volts for all others. Possible causes: — Fluid levels not to specification. — Damaged TOT sensor. — TOT shorted to ground. — Damaged Powertrain Control Module (PCM). • Key off. • Disconnect transmission connector. Inspect for damaged or pushed out pins, corrosion, loose wires, etc. Service as necessary. • Run Key On Engine Off Self-Test (transmission connector remains disconnected for KOEO Self-Test). • **Is DTC 56 or 637 present?** NOTE: Disregard any other DTC generated at this time.	Yes No	▶ ▶	**For Escort/Tracer:** GO to TE25. **For all others:** REFER to Transmission for TOT sensor service. GO to TE21.

Fig. 225 Test TE: TOT Sensor (Part 9 of 11)

TEST STEP	RESULT	▶	ACTION TO TAKE
TE21 CHECK VREF AT THE THROTTLE POSITION SENSOR • Key off. • Disconnect Powertrain Control Module (PCM). Inspect for damaged or pushed out pins, corrosion, loose wires, etc. Service as necessary. • Install breakout box and connect PCM to breakout box. • Disconnect TP sensor. • Key on, engine off. • Measure resistance between VREF and SIG RTN circuits at TP sensor vehicle harness connector. Refer to schematic in Pinpoint Test DH or DQ. • **Is voltage between 4.0 and 6.0 volts?**	Yes No	▶ ▶	RECONNECT TP sensor. GO to TE22. GO to Pinpoint Test Step C1.
TE22 CHECK TOT CIRCUIT FOR SHORT TO GROUND • Key off. • Transmission connector disconnected. • Breakout box installed, disconnect PCM. • Measure resistance between TOT test pin (refer to chart) and Test Pins 40, 60 and 46 at the breakout box. • **Is each resistance greater than 10,000 ohms?**	Yes No	▶ ▶	REPLACE PCM. REMOVE breakout box. RECONNECT all components. RERUN Quick Test. SERVICE short circuit. REMOVE breakout box. RECONNECT all components. RERUN Quick Test.

TOT TEST PIN

	4R70W AODE AXODE (AX4S)	E4OD (except 7.3L diesel)	E4OD (7.3L diesel)	4EAT
TOT TEST PIN	49	42	7	2

TEST STEP	RESULT	▶	ACTION TO TAKE
TE25 CHECK TRANSMISSION WIRING • Key off. • Check transmission connector/external wiring for opens or shorts. Service as necessary. • Check internal transmission wiring for opens or shorts. Refer to Transmission for disassembly procedures. • **Is transmission wiring OK?**	Yes No	▶ ▶	REPLACE TOT sensor. REASSEMBLE/RECONNECT all components. RERUN Quick Test. SERVICE as necessary. REASSEMBLE/RECONNECT all components. RERUN Quick Test.

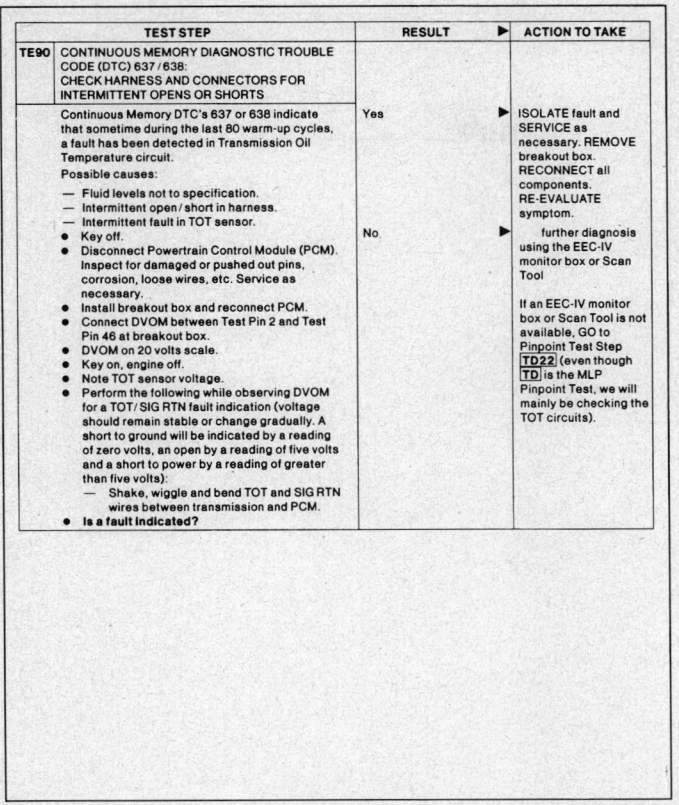

TEST STEP	RESULT	▶	ACTION TO TAKE
TE90 CONTINUOUS MEMORY DIAGNOSTIC TROUBLE CODE (DTC) 637/638: CHECK HARNESS AND CONNECTORS FOR INTERMITTENT OPENS OR SHORTS			
Continuous Memory DTC's 637 or 638 indicate that sometime during the last 80 warm-up cycles, a fault has been detected in Transmission Oil Temperature circuit. Possible causes: — Fluid levels not to specification. — Intermittent open/short in harness. — Intermittent fault in TOT sensor. • Key off. • Disconnect Powertrain Control Module (PCM). Inspect for damaged or pushed out pins, corrosion, loose wires, etc. Service as necessary. • Install breakout box and reconnect PCM. • Connect DVOM between Test Pin 2 and Test Pin 46 at breakout box. • DVOM on 20 volts scale. • Key on, engine off. • Note TOT sensor voltage. • Perform the following while observing DVOM for a TOT/SIG RTN fault indication (voltage should remain stable or change gradually. A short to ground will be indicated by a reading of zero volts, an open by a reading of five volts and a short to power by a reading of greater than five volts): — Shake, wiggle and bend TOT and SIG RTN wires between transmission and PCM. • **Is a fault indicated?**	Yes No	▶ ▶	ISOLATE fault and SERVICE as necessary. REMOVE breakout box. RECONNECT all components. RE-EVALUATE symptom. further diagnosis using the EEC-IV monitor box or Scan Tool If an EEC-IV monitor box or Scan Tool is not available, GO to Pinpoint Test Step **TD22** (even though **TD** is the MLP Pinpoint Test, we will mainly be checking the TOT circuits).

FM0159300766100X

Fig. 225   Test TE: TOT Sensor (Part 10 of 11)

TEST STEP	RESULT	▶	ACTION TO TAKE
TE100 CONTINUOUS MEMORY DIAGNOSTIC TROUBLE CODE (DTC) 68/657: RERUN KEY ON ENGINE OFF SELF-TEST			
DTC 68/657 indicates a transmission over temperature condition occurred. Possible causes: — Damaged transmission cooling system. — Excessive loading, e.g. trailer towing. — Damaged clutch. — Improper transmission fluid level. — Damaged transmission connector. — Damaged TOT sensor circuit. • Key off. • Disconnect transmission connector. Inspect for damaged or pushed out pins, corrosion, loose wires, etc. Service as necessary and reconnect. • Run Key On Engine Off Self-Test, record all DTC's. • **Any transmission related DTC generated?** NOTE: If DTC 68/657 repeats and no other DTC is generated, refer to Transmission for transmission over temperature condition.	Yes No	▶ ▶	ADDRESS any transmission related DTC by referring to the DTC charts in Dianostic Routines. REFER to Transmission for over temperature condition (check clutch transmission fluid level etc.).

FM0159300766110X

Fig. 225   Test TE: TOT Sensor (Part 11 of 11)

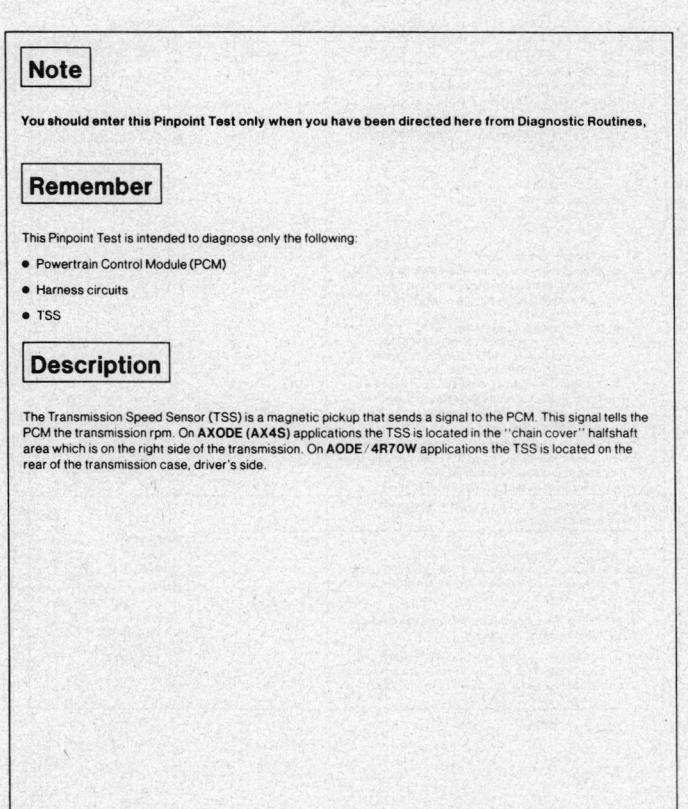

Note

You should enter this Pinpoint Test only when you have been directed here from Diagnostic Routines.

Remember

This Pinpoint Test is intended to diagnose only the following:
• Powertrain Control Module (PCM)
• Harness circuits
• TSS

Description

The Transmission Speed Sensor (TSS) is a magnetic pickup that sends a signal to the PCM. This signal tells the PCM the transmission rpm. On AXODE (AX4S) applications the TSS is located in the "chain cover" halfshaft area which is on the right side of the transmission. On AODE/4R70W applications the TSS is located on the rear of the transmission case, driver's side.

FM0159300767010X

Fig. 226   Test TF: TSS (Part 1 of 12)

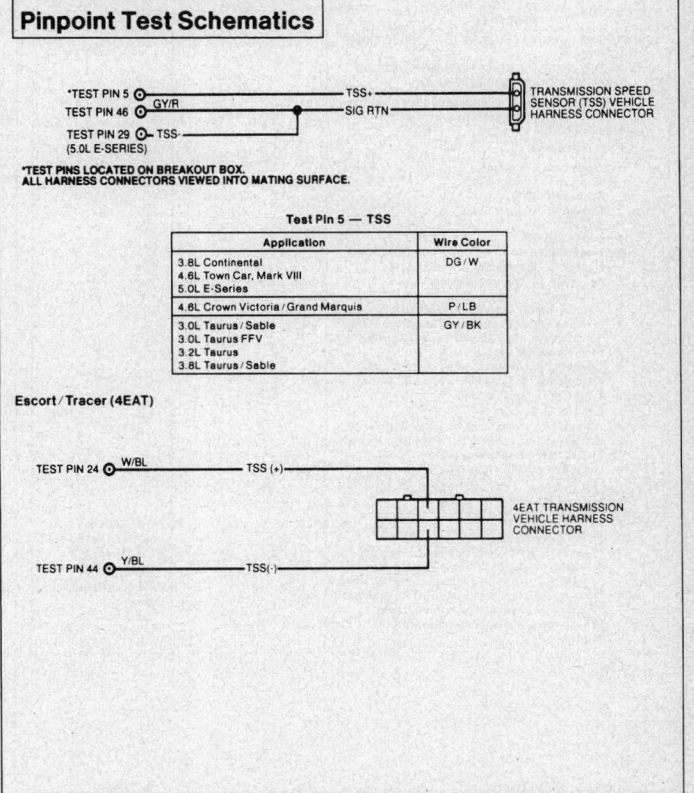

Pinpoint Test Schematics

Test Pin 5 — TSS

Application	Wire Color
3.8L Continental 4.6L Town Car, Mark VIII 5.0L E-Series	DG/W
4.6L Crown Victoria/Grand Marquis	P/LB
3.0L Taurus/Sable 3.0L Taurus FFV 3.2L Taurus 3.8L Taurus/Sable	GY/BK

FM0159300767702AX

Fig. 226   Test TF: TSS (Part 2 of 12). 1993

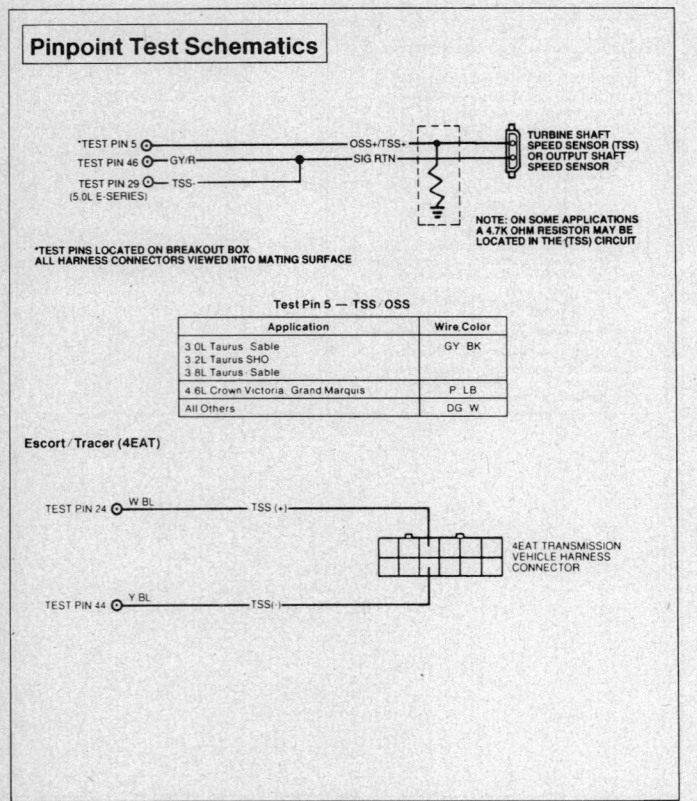

Fig. 226   Test TF: TSS (Part 2 of 12). 1994–95

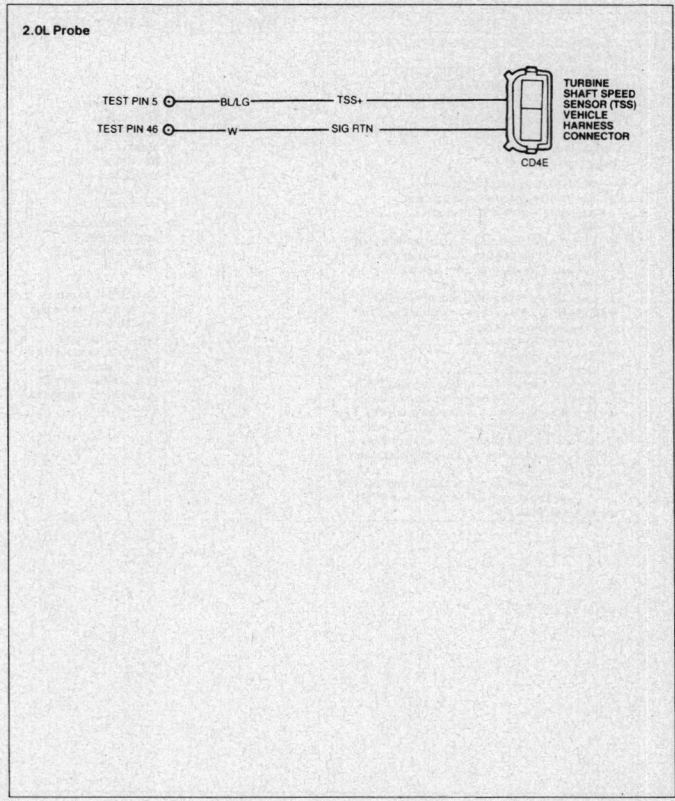

Fig. 226   Test TF: TSS (Part 3 of 12). 1994–95

TEST STEP		RESULT	▶	ACTION TO TAKE
TF 1	ENGINE RUNNING DIAGNOSTIC TROUBLE CODE (DTC) 639: CHECK TRANSMISSION SPEED SENSOR (TSS) HARNESS CONNECTOR CONTINUITY			
	DTC 639 indicates frequency or voltage of the TSS is insufficient to the Powertrain Control Module (PCM).	Yes	▶	GO to TF2
		No	▶	SERVICE open circuit. REMOVE breakout box. RECONNECT all components. RERUN Quick Test.
	Possible causes:			
	— Open circuit in harness.			
	— Short circuit in harness.			
	— Damaged TSS.			
	— Damaged PCM.			
	• Key off.			
	• Disconnect TSS.			
	• Disconnect Powertrain Control Module (PCM). Inspect for damaged or pushed out pins, corrosion, loose wires, etc. Service as necessary.			
	• Install breakout box, leave PCM disconnected.			
	• Measure resistance between Test Pin 5 at the breakout box and TSS+ circuit at TSS vehicle harness connector.			
	• Measure resistance between Test Pin 46 at the breakout box and SIG RTN circuit at the TSS vehicle harness connector.			
	For 5.0L E-Series:			
	• Also measure resistance between Test Pin 29 at the breakout box and SIG RTN circuit at the TSS vehicle harness connector.			
	• **Is each resistance less than 5.0 ohms?**			
TF 2	CHECK TSS CIRCUIT FOR SHORT TO POWER AND GROUND			
	• Key off.	Yes	▶	REMOVE breakout box. RECONNECT PCM. GO to TF3
	• TSS disconnected.			
	• Breakout box installed, PCM disconnected.	No	▶	SERVICE short circuit(s). REMOVE breakout box. RECONNECT all components. RERUN Quick Test.
	• Measure resistance between Test Pin 5 and Test Pins 37/57 at breakout box.			
	• Measure resistance between Test Pin 5 and Test Pins 40/60 and 46 at breakout box.			
	• **Is each resistance greater than 10,000 ohms?**			

Fig. 226   Test TF: TSS (Part 4 of 12). 1993

TEST STEP		RESULT	▶	ACTION TO TAKE
TF 1	ENGINE RUNNING DIAGNOSTIC TROUBLE CODE (DTC) 639: CHECK TSS/OSS HARNESS CONNECTOR CONTINUITY			
	DTC 639 indicates frequency or voltage of the TSS/OSS is insufficient to the Powertrain Control Module (PCM).	Yes	▶	GO to TF2
		No	▶	SERVICE open circuit. REMOVE breakout box. RECONNECT all components. RERUN Quick Test.
	Possible causes:			
	— Open circuit in harness.			
	— Short circuit in harness.			
	— Damaged TSS/OSS.			
	— Damaged PCM.			
	• Key off.			
	• Disconnect TSS/OSS.			
	• Disconnect Powertrain Control Module (PCM). Inspect for damaged or pushed out pins, corrosion, loose wires, etc. Service as necessary.			
	• Install breakout box, leave PCM disconnected.			
	• Measure resistance between Test Pin 5 at the breakout box and TSS+/OSS+ circuit at TSS/OSS vehicle harness connector.			
	• Measure resistance between Test Pin 46 at the breakout box and SIG RTN circuit at the TSS vehicle harness connector.			
	For 5.0L E-Series:			
	• Also measure resistance between Test Pin 29 at the breakout box and SIG RTN circuit at the TSS vehicle harness connector.			
	• **Is each resistance less than 5.0 ohms?**			
TF 2	CHECK TSS+/OSS+ CIRCUIT FOR SHORT TO POWER OR GROUND			
	• Key off.	Yes	▶	REMOVE breakout box. RECONNECT PCM. GO to TF3
	• TSS/OSS disconnected.			
	• Breakout box installed, PCM disconnected.	No	▶	SERVICE short circuit(s). REMOVE breakout box. RECONNECT all components. RERUN Quick Test.
	• Measure resistance between Test Pin 5 and Test Pins 37/57 at breakout box.			
	NOTE: Some applications may have a 4.7K ohm resistor to ground.			
	• Measure resistance between Test Pin 5 and Test Pins 40/60 and 46 at breakout box.			
	• **Is each resistance greater than 10,000 ohms?**			

Fig. 226   Test TF: TSS (Part 4 of 12). 1994–95

TEST STEP	RESULT	▶	ACTION TO TAKE
TF3 CHECK TSS RESISTANCE • Key off. • TSS disconnected. • Measure resistance of TSS sensor. **For AXODE (AX4S) Transmission:** • Is resistance between 80 and 200 ohms? **For AODE/4R70W Transmission:** • Is the resistance between 450 and 750 ohms?	Yes No	▶ ▶	GO to Transmission to verify internal components. If OK, then replace PCM. REMOVE breakout box. RERUN Quick Test. REPLACE TSS. REMOVE breakout box. RERUN Quick Test.
TF10 ENGINE RUNNING DTC 639: CHECK TSS RESISTANCE Engine Running DTC 639 indicates an error has been detected in the Transmission Speed Sensor (TSS) input signal. Possible causes: — Open or shorted harness. — Damaged transmission speed sensor. — Damaged Powertrain Control Module (PCM). • Key off. • Disconnect transmission connector (12 pin at transmission). • Measure resistance between TSS(+) and TSS(-) pins at transmission 12 pin connector. • **Is resistance between 200 and 600 ohms?**	Yes No	▶ ▶	GO to **TF11**. INSPECT transmission wiring for opens/shorts. If OK, REPLACE transmission speed sensor. RERUN Quick Test.

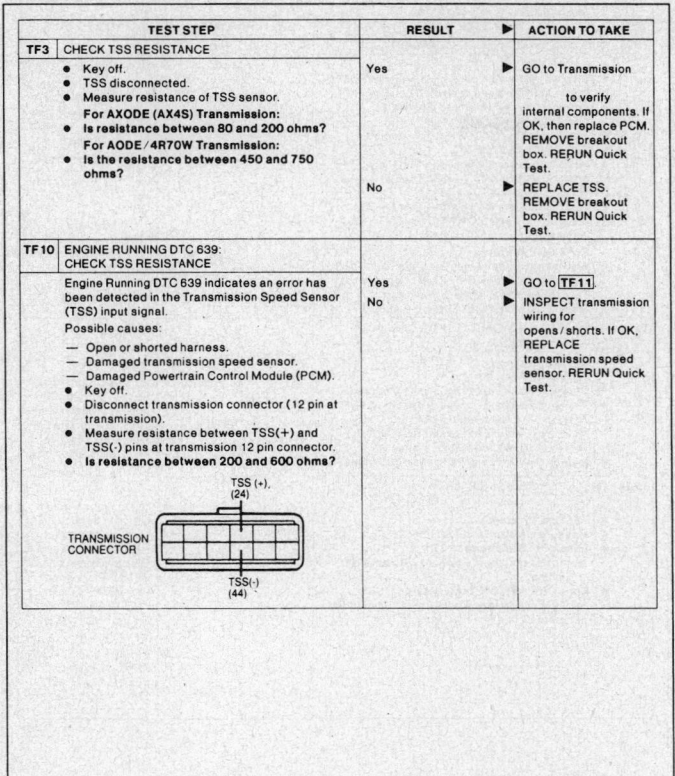

Fig. 226   Test TF: TSS (Part 5 of 12). 1993

FM015930076705AX

TEST STEP	RESULT	▶	ACTION TO TAKE
TF3 CHECK TSS OSS RESISTANCE • Key off. • TSS OSS disconnected. • Measure resistance of TSS/OSS sensor. **For AX4S CD4E Transmission:** • Is resistance between 80 and 200 ohms? **For AODE 4R70W Transmission:** • Is the resistance between 450 and 750 ohms?	Yes No	▶ ▶	verify internal components. If OK, then replace PCM. REMOVE breakout box. RERUN Quick Test. REPLACE TSS. REMOVE breakout box. RERUN Quick Test.
TF10 ENGINE RUNNING DTC 639: CHECK TSS RESISTANCE Engine Running DTC 639 indicates an error has been detected in the Transmission Speed Sensor (TSS) input signal. Possible causes: — Open or shorted harness. — Damaged transmission speed sensor. — Damaged Powertrain Control Module (PCM). • Key off. • Disconnect transmission connector (12 pin at transmission). • Measure resistance between TSS(+) and TSS(-) pins at transmission 12 pin connector. • **Is resistance between 200 and 600 ohms?**	Yes No	▶ ▶	GO to **TF11**. INSPECT transmission wiring for opens/shorts. If OK, REPLACE transmission speed sensor. RERUN Quick Test.

Fig. 226   Test TF: TSS (Part 5 of 12). 1994–95

FM015940076705BX

TEST STEP	RESULT	▶	ACTION TO TAKE
TF11 CHECK TSS CIRCUITS FOR SHORT TO POWER • Key off. • Transmission 12 pin connector disconnected. • Disconnect Powertrain Control Module (PCM). Inspect for damaged or pushed out pins, corrosion, loose wires, etc. Service as necessary. • Key on. • Measure voltage between TSS (+) circuit at the transmission 12 pin vehicle harness connector and chassis ground. • Measure voltage between TSS(-) circuit at the transmission 12 pin vehicle harness connector and chassis ground. • **Are both voltages less than 0.5 volt?**	Yes No	▶ ▶	Key off. GO to **TF12**. SERVICE short circuit. RECONNECT all components. RERUN Quick Test.
TF12 CHECK TSS CIRCUITS FOR SHORT TO GROUND OR EACH OTHER • Key off. • Transmission 12 pin connector disconnected. • PCM disconnected. • Measure resistance between TSS (+) circuit at transmission 12 pin vehicle harness connector and chassis ground. • Measure resistance between TSS(-) circuit at transmission 12 pin vehicle harness connector and chassis ground. • Measure resistance between TSS (+) and TSS(-) circuits at transmission 12 pin vehicle harness connector. • **Are all resistances greater than 10,000 ohms?**	Yes No	▶ ▶	GO to **TF13**. SERVICE short circuit. RECONNECT all components. RERUN Quick Test.
TF13 CHECK TSS CIRCUIT CONTINUITY • Key off. • Transmission 12 pin connector disconnected. • Install breakout box or 4EAT tester. Leave PCM disconnected. • Measure resistance between Test Pin 24 and TSS (+) circuit at transmission 12 pin vehicle harness connector. • Measure resistance between Test Pin 44 and TSS(-) circuit at transmission 12 pin vehicle harness connector. • **Are both resistances less than 5.0 ohms?**	Yes No	▶ ▶	GO to **TF14**. SERVICE open circuit. REMOVE breakout box. RECONNECT all components. RERUN Quick Test.

Fig. 226   Test TF: TSS (Part 6 of 12)

FM015930076706OX

TEST STEP	RESULT	▶	ACTION TO TAKE
TF14 CHECK PCM FOR INTERNAL SHORTS • Key off. • Breakout box installed. • Connect PCM to breakout box. • Transmission 12 pin connector disconnected. • Measure resistance between Test Pin 24 and Test Pins 44, 37, 57, 40 and 60. • **Is each resistance greater than 500 ohms?**	Yes No	▶ ▶	GO to **TF15**. REPLACE PCM. REMOVE breakout box. RECONNECT all components. RERUN Quick Test.
TF15 CHECK TSS OUTPUT • Key off. • PCM connected to breakout box. • Reconnect transmission 12 pin connector. • DVOM on AC scale (to monitor less than 5.0 volts AC). • Start engine. • Measure voltage between Test Pins 24 and 44 at breakout box while varying engine rpm. • **Does AC voltage vary greater than 0.5 volt?**	Yes No	▶ ▶	REPLACE PCM. REMOVE breakout box. RERUN Quick Test. REPLACE TSS. REMOVE breakout box. RERUN Quick Test.
TF90 CONTINUOUS MEMORY DIAGNOSTIC TROUBLE CODE (DTC) 639: COMPLETE TRANSMISSION DRIVE CYCLE. VERIFY DTC Continuous Memory DTC 639 indicates that sometime during the last 40 or 80 warm-up cycles, the PCM detected an error in the TSS output signal. Possible causes: — Transmission (internal components) — Damaged TSS. — Damaged harness circuits. — Damaged PCM. • Perform transmission Drive Cycle outlined: **TRANSMISSION DRIVE CYCLE:** — Record and clear Continuous Memory DTC's. — Warm engine to operating temperature. — Place gear selector in DRIVE. — Obey all local traffic laws. Accelerate heavily to 35 mph. — Return to idle. — Shut the engine off. — After drive cycle is completed, run Key On Engine Off Self-Test and record Continuous Memory DTC's displayed. • **Did Continuous Memory DTC 639 repeat?**	Yes No	▶ ▶	GO to **TF91**. Unable to duplicate and/or identify fault at this time. further EEC-IV monitor box or Scan Tool For all others, CLEAR Continuous Memory.

Fig. 226   Test TF: TSS (Part 7 of 12)

FM015930076707OX

TEST STEP	RESULT	▶	ACTION TO TAKE
TF91 CHECK TSS CIRCUIT CONTINUITY • Key off. • Disconnect Powertrain Control Module (PCM). Inspect for damaged or pushed out pins, corrosion, loose wires, etc. Service as necessary. • Install breakout box, PCM disconnected. • Disconnect TSS. • Measure resistance between Test Pin 5 at breakout box and TSS circuit at sensor vehicle harness connector. • Measure resistance between Test Pin 46 at breakout box and SIG RTN at the TSS vehicle harness connector. **For 5.0L E-Series:** • Also measure resistance between Test Pin 29 at the breakout box and SIG RTN circuit at the TSS vehicle harness connector. • **Is each resistance less than 5.0 ohms?**	Yes No	▶ ▶	GO to TF92. SERVICE open circuit. REMOVE breakout box. RECONNECT all components. REPEAT Test Step TF90 to verify elimination of DTC.
TF92 CHECK TSS CIRCUITS FOR SHORT TO POWER OR GROUND • Key off. • TSS disconnected. • Breakout box installed, PCM disconnected. • Measure resistance between Test Pin 5 and Test Pin 37/57 at breakout box. • Measure resistance between Test Pin 5 and Test Pins 40/60 and 46 at breakout box. • **Is each resistance greater than 500 ohms?**	Yes No	▶ ▶	GO to TF93. SERVICE short circuit. REMOVE breakout box. RECONNECT all components. REPEAT Test Step TF90 to verify elimination of DTC.
TF93 CHECK TSS RESISTANCE • Key off. • TSS disconnected. • Measure resistance of TSS. • For AXODE (AX4S) Transmission (TSS): — Is the resistance between 80 and 200 ohms? • For AODE/4R70W Transmission (TSS): — Is the resistance between 450 and 750 ohms?	Yes No	▶ ▶	GO to Transmission to verify internal components. If OK, then replace PCM. REMOVE breakout box. RECONNECT TSS. REPEAT Test Step TF90 to verify elimination of DTC. REPLACE TSS. REMOVE breakout box. REPEAT Test Step TF90 to verify elimination of DTC.

FM015930076708AX

Fig. 226   Test TF: TSS (Part 8 of 12). 1993

TEST STEP	RESULT	▶	ACTION TO TAKE
TF91 CHECK TSS/OSS CIRCUIT CONTINUITY • Key off. • Disconnect Powertrain Control Module (PCM). Inspect for damaged or pushed out pins, corrosion, loose wires, etc. Service as necessary. • Install breakout box, PCM disconnected. • Disconnect TSS/OSS. • Measure resistance between Test Pin 5 at breakout box and TSS/OSS circuit at sensor vehicle harness connector. • Measure resistance between Test Pin 46 at breakout box and SIG RTN at the TSS/OSS vehicle harness connector. **For 5.0L E-Series:** • Also measure resistance between Test Pin 29 at the breakout box and SIG RTN circuit at the TSS/OSS vehicle harness connector. • **Is each resistance less than 5.0 ohms?**	Yes No	▶ ▶	GO to TF92. SERVICE open circuit. REMOVE breakout box. RECONNECT all components. REPEAT Test Step TF90 to verify elimination of DTC.
TF92 CHECK TSS/OSS CIRCUITS FOR SHORT TO POWER OR GROUND • Key off. • TSS disconnected. • Breakout box installed, PCM disconnected. • Measure resistance between Test Pin 5 and Test Pin 37/57 at breakout box. • Measure resistance between Test Pin 5 and Test Pins 40/60 and 46 at breakout box. • **Is each resistance greater than 500 ohms?**	Yes No	▶ ▶	GO to TF93. SERVICE short circuit. REMOVE breakout box. RECONNECT all components. REPEAT Test Step TF90 to verify elimination of DTC.
TF93 CHECK TSS/OSS RESISTANCE • Key off. • TSS disconnected. • Measure resistance of TSS/OSS. • For CD4E Transmission TSS: — Is the resistance between 80 and 200 ohms? • For AODE/4R70W Transmission OSS: — Is the resistance between 450 and 750 ohms?	Yes No	▶ ▶	GO to Transmission Group in Service Manual to verify internal components. If OK, then replace PCM. REMOVE breakout box. RECONNECT TSS. REPEAT Test Step TF90 to verify elimination of DTC. REPLACE TSS/OSS. REMOVE breakout box. REPEAT Test Step TF90 to verify elimination of DTC.

FM015940076708BX

Fig. 226   Test TF: TSS (Part 8 of 12). 1994–95

TEST STEP	RESULT	▶	ACTION TO TAKE
TF95 CONTINUOUS MEMORY DIAGNOSTIC TROUBLE CODE (DTC) 639: CHECK TSS WIRING Continuous Memory DTC 639 indicates that sometime during the last 80 warm-up cycles an error was detected in the Transmission Speed Sensor (TSS) input signal. Possible causes: — Intermittent open or shorted harness. — Intermittent fault in Transmission Speed Sensor. — Transmission fluid drained and refilled (if, within one minute of the first start after a transmission fluid change, the vehicle is put in gear, a Continuous Memory DTC 639 could be set due to an insufficient time for the new transmission fluid to fill all the ''cavities''. • Key off. • Visually check the TSS wires for obvious concerns. Service as necessary. • Disconnect Powertrain Control Module (PCM). Inspect for damaged or pushed out pins, corrosion, loose wires, etc. Service as necessary. • Install breakout box. Connect PCM to breakout box. • DVOM to 20 volts scale. • Connect DVOM between Test Pin 24 and Test Pin 44 at breakout box. • Start engine. • Observe DVOM for a fault indication while performing the following (the voltage should remain stable. A fault will be indicated by the voltage becoming erratic or dropping to zero): **CAUTION: While performing this Diagnostic Test Mode (DTM), use caution not to touch any moving engine parts.** — Shake, wiggle, bend the TSS (+) and TSS(-) circuits from the transmission to the PCM. — Lightly shake and tap the transmission connector, EEC-IV connector and other related harness connectors. • **Is a fault indicated?**	Yes No	▶ ▶	ISOLATE fault and SERVICE as necessary. CLEAR Continuous Memory RERUN Quick Test. Key off. GO to TF96.

FM015930076709OX

Fig. 226   Test TF: TSS (Part 9 of 12)

TEST STEP	RESULT	▶	ACTION TO TAKE
TF96 CHECK PCM AND HARNESS CONNECTORS • Key off. • Disconnect the transmission 12 pin connector and all other connectors related to the TSS one at a time. Inspect the connectors for damaged or pushed out pins, corrosion, loose wires, etc. Reconnect each connector after inspection. • **Are connectors and terminals OK?**	Yes No	▶ ▶	further diagnosis using the EEC-IV monitor box or Scan Tool If an EEC-IV monitor box or Scan Tool is not available, GO to TF97. SERVICE as necessary. RECONNECT all connectors/components. RERUN Quick Test.

FM015930076710OX

Fig. 226   Test TF: TSS (Part 10 of 12)

TF97 ROAD TEST (ESCORT/TRACER ONLY)

The purpose of the road test is to identify an area of concern by monitoring certain controlled parameters while trying to re-create a driveability or MIL symptom.

Note

A basic working knowledge of the EEC-IV system is critical to effectively analyze road test data.

WARNING

THIS ROAD TEST IS A SUGGESTED BUT OPTIONAL PROCEDURE. ALL APPLICABLE SAFETY PROCEDURES AND TRAFFIC LAWS MUST BE FOLLOWED. IN ORDER FOR A ROAD TEST TO BE PERFORMED IT IS REQUIRED THAT ANOTHER PERSON ACCOMPANY THE DRIVER. THE ACCOMPANYING PERSON CAN MAKE MEASUREMENTS, OBSERVE CHANGES AND RECORD NOTES. IF FOR SOME REASON THIS TEST IS NOT PERFORMED, RETURN TO **Diagnostic Routines**

Prepare Vehicle For a Road Test

- Disconnect Powertrain Control Module (PCM) connector. Inspect for damaged or pushed out pins, corrosion, loose wires, etc. Service as necessary.

- Install breakout box/4EAT tester and reconnect PCM to breakout box/4EAT tester.

- Other materials needed; DVOM, pencil, paper, appropriate schematic/pin usage sheet

- Optional equipment:

  — Fuel pressure gauge, manifold vacuum gauge, MAP/BARO tester.

Preliminary Power/Ground Checks

- With the key ON and a DVOM referenced to the battery negative post, check the following signals for correct values.

POWERS: KAPWR > 10.5V (Pin 1), VPWR > 10.5V (Pins 37/57), VREF 5 ± 1V (Pin 26).
GROUNDS (all = 0 ± .5V): PWR GND (Pins 40/60), SIG RTN (Pin 46), IGN GND (Pin 16).
OPTIONAL GROUNDS: HO2S GND (Pin 49), CSE GND (Pin 20) MAF RTN. (Pin 9 or 15).

Obtaining Other Needed Information and Materials Before the Road Test

- Refer to the Symptom Charts EEC-IV Monitor Box/Intermittent Fault Diagnosis, looking at the chart(s) that most resembles the vehicle's driveability or MIL symptom. Before the road test perform the Visual/Mechanical Checks that are listed. Next, list the EEC-IV sensors and actuators in the order given. These are the main signals that will be monitored.

FM0159300767110X

Fig. 226   Test TF: TSS (Part 11 of 12)

TF97 ROAD TEST (ESCORT/TRACER ONLY) (Continued)

- Refer to the proper Diagnostic Reference Value Sheet Although these charts were designed for use with the EEC-IV Monitor Box, most of the values can be read using the breakout box and a DVOM (with the DVOM referenced to ground all values in DCV units can be used; other values may also be helpful, ex., MAP Hz using the MAP/BARO tester).

- After starting the engine for the road test, enter Engine Running Continuous Monitor Diagnostic Test Mode

- Drive the vehicle to create the conditions so that the symptom will occur. If the Customer Information Worksheet has been completed, this information may help when trying to re-create the symptom.

- When the symptom occurs, the accompanying passenger should observe changes in listed EEC-IV signals. Information about the symptom, operating condition value of the EEC-IV signal or other notes should be recorded onto paper.

- If you are unable to duplicate the symptom, it may still be helpful to verify that the EEC-IV values are in the expected range.

Analyzing the Data

- Once the road test is completed, the results need to be analyzed to locate and service the exact fault which caused the symptom (if, for example, a Continuous Memory Diagnostic Trouble Code 639 is set again and the TSS signal stayed within specification, the PCM would be suspect; if the signal went out of specification, the harness or sensor would be suspect).

FM0159300767120X

Fig. 226   Test TF: TSS (Part 12 of 12)

Note

You should enter this Pinpoint Test only when you have been directed here from Diagnostic Routines,

Remember

To prevent the replacement of good components, be aware that the following non-EEC areas may be at fault:

- Other aftermarket modifications
- Incorrect transmission fluid level
- Transmission operating temperature
- Engine operating temperature
- Ambient temperature
- Faulty connections
- Engine Sensors (i.e. TP Sensor)

The transmission solenoids and the MLP sensor are not analyzed in this Pinpoint Test

This Pinpoint Test is intended to diagnose only the following:

- Harness Circuits: CCS, SS1, SS2, SS3, EPC, TCC, TOT and MLP
- Powertrain Control Module (PCM)

FM0159300768010X

Fig. 227   Test TG: Electronic Trans/Continuous Memory DTC (Part 1 of 13)

Pinpoint Test Schematics

Taurus/Sable, Continental (AX4S/AXODE)

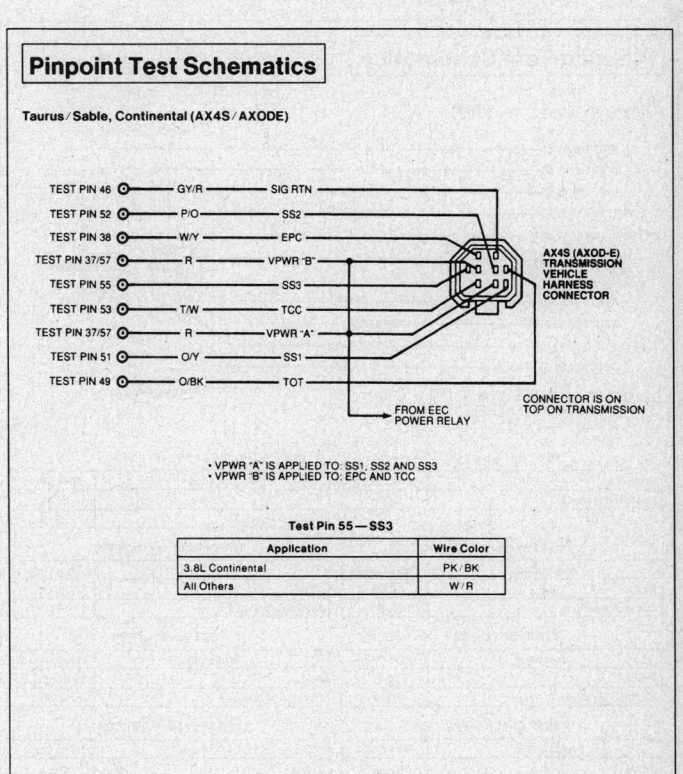

- VPWR "A" IS APPLIED TO: SS1, SS2 AND SS3
- VPWR "B" IS APPLIED TO: EPC AND TCC

Test Pin 55 — SS3

Application	Wire Color
3.8L Continental	PK/BK
All Others	W/R

FM0159300768020X

Fig. 227   Test TG: Electronic Trans/Continuous Memory DTC (Part 2 of 13)

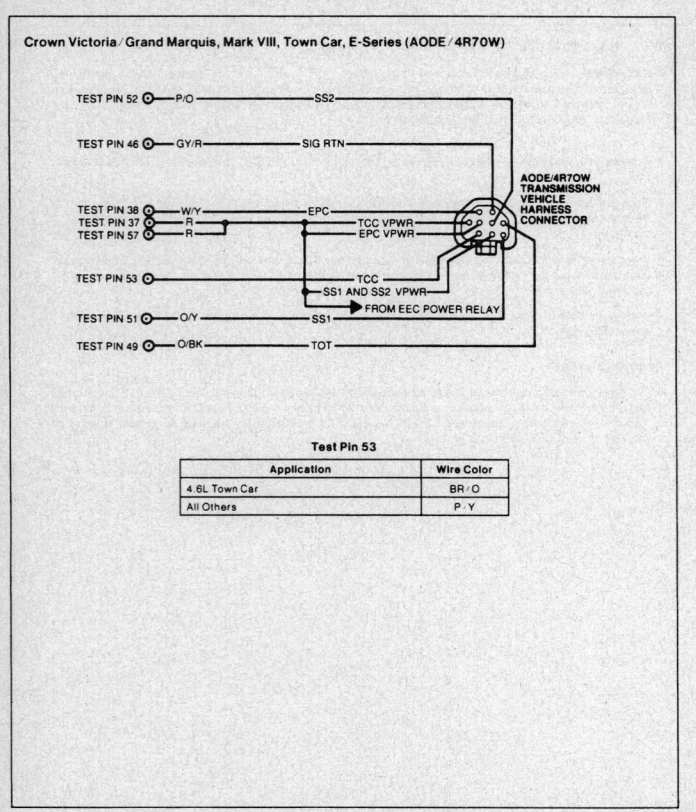

Fig. 227   Test TG: Electronic Trans/Continuous Memory DTC (Part 3 of 13). 1993

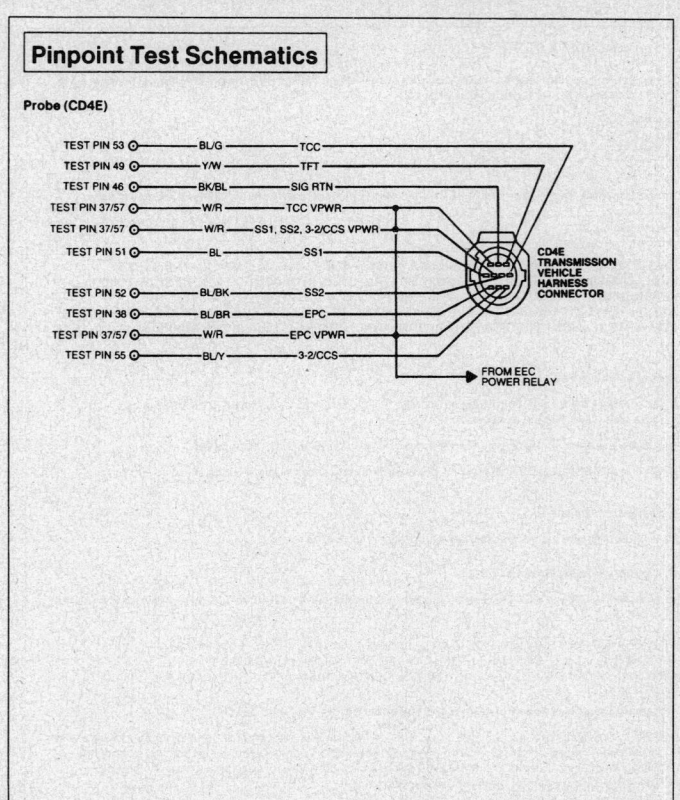

Fig. 227   Test TG: Electronic Trans/Continuous Memory DTC (Part 3 of 13). 1994

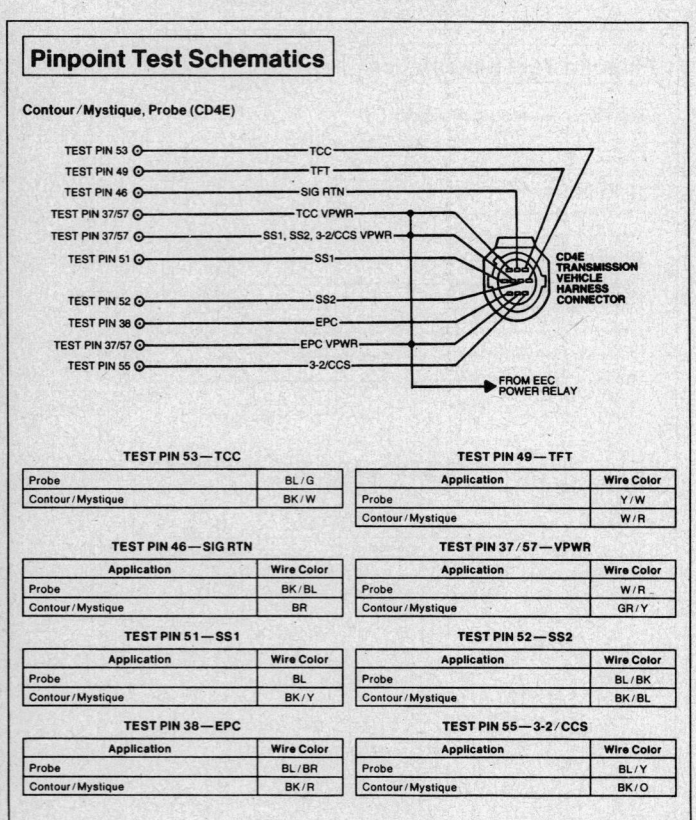

Fig. 227   Test TG: Electronic Trans/Continuous Memory DTC (Part 3 of 13). 1995

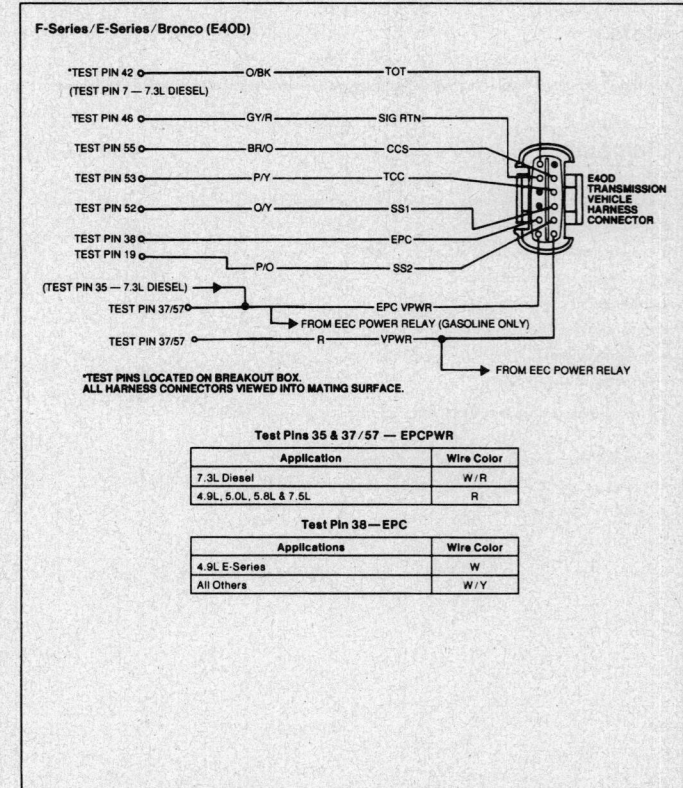

Fig. 227   Test TG: Electronic Trans/Continuous Memory DTC (Part 4 of 13). 1993

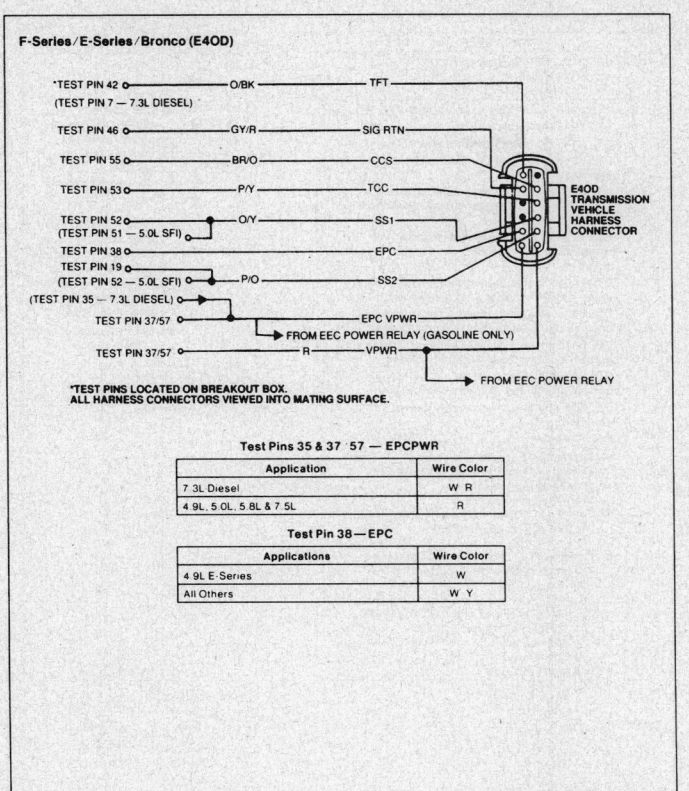

Fig. 227 Test TG: Electronic Trans/Continuous Memory DTC (Part 4 of 13). 1994

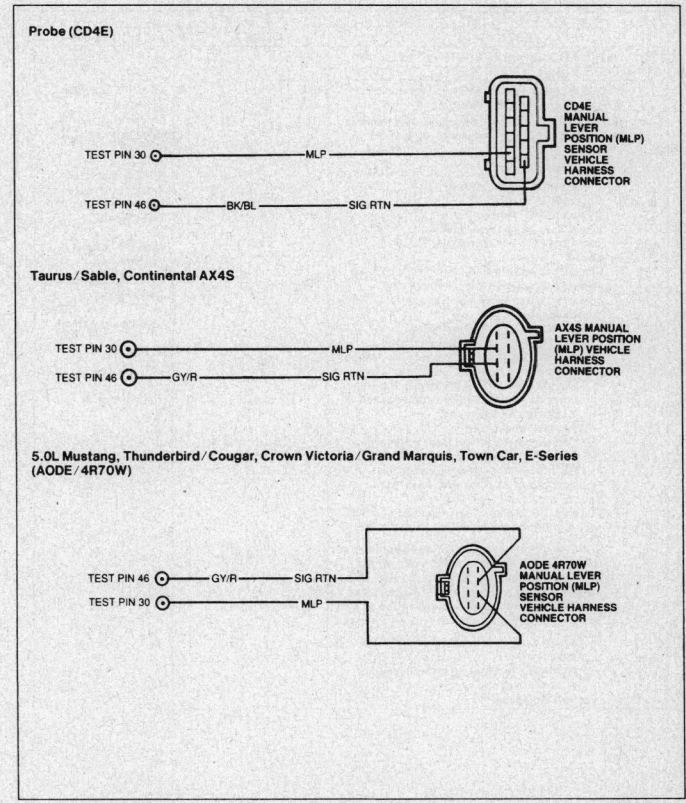

Fig. 227 Test TG: Electronic Trans/Continuous Memory DTC (Part 5 of 13). 1994-95

TEST STEP	RESULT	▶	ACTION TO TAKE
TG90 PERFORM DRIVE CYCLE TEST			
• Run Key On Engine Off Self-Test and record all Continuous Memory DTCs displayed. • Clear Continuous Memory NOTE: Obey all traffic laws. • **AX4S (AXODE) Drive Cycle (except 3.2L SHO):** — Gear position in OVERDRIVE range, moderately accelerate from stop to 50 MPH. This allows transmission to shift into fourth gear. Hold speed and throttle steady for a minimum of 15 seconds. — With transmission in fourth gear and holding speed and throttle opening steady, lightly apply and release brake. Then hold speed and throttle steady for at least five seconds. — Brake to a stop and remain stopped for a minimum of 20 seconds. Repeat drive cycle at least five times. • **4R70W, AODE, E4OD and 3.2L SHO Drive Cycle:** — Gear position in DRIVE range, press the Transmission Control Switch (TCS) (the Transmission Control Indicator (TCIL) should light) and moderately accelerate from stop to 40 mph. This will allow the transmission to shift into third gear. Hold speed and throttle opening steady for a minimum of 15 seconds (30 seconds for altitudes above 4000 feet). — Press TCS (the TCIL should turn off) and accelerate from 40 mph to 50 mph. This will allow the transmission to shift into fourth gear. Hold speed and throttle steady for a minimum of 15 seconds. — With transmission in fourth gear and maintaining steady speed and throttle opening, lightly apply and release brake (to operate stop lamps). Then hold speed and throttle steady for at least an additional five seconds. — Brake to a stop and remain stopped for a minimum of 20 seconds with transmission in drive. Repeat drive cycle at least five times. • Rerun Key On Engine Off Self-Test and record all Continuous Memory DTCs. — Are pass codes present in Continuous Memory (any code 10-11/111)?	Yes No	▶ ▶	Unable to duplicate fault at this time; For further diagnosis using EEC-IV Monitor Box or Scan Tool, REFER to EEC-IV Monitor Box: Intermittent Fault Diagnosis. If further diagnosis is not performed, then CLEAR Continuous Memory and REFER to appropriate Transmission for possible internal transmission damage. For DTC 99/624, 651 or 67/634: GO to **TG91** For DTC 29/452: GO to **DS1** (for all other vehicles). For any other DTC: GO to **TG92**.

Fig. 227 Test TG: Electronic Trans/Continuous Memory DTC (Part 6 of 13). 1993

TEST STEP	RESULT	▶	ACTION TO TAKE
TG90 PERFORM DRIVE CYCLE TEST			
• Run Key On Engine Off (KOEO) Self-Test and record all Continuous Memory DTCs displayed. • Clear Continuous Memory NOTE: Obey all traffic laws. • **AX4S Drive Cycle (except 3.2L SHO):** — Gear position in OVERDRIVE range, moderately accelerate from stop to 50 MPH. This allows transmission to shift into fourth gear. Hold speed and throttle steady for a minimum of 15 seconds. — With transmission in fourth gear and holding speed and throttle opening steady, lightly apply and release brake. Then hold speed and throttle steady for at least five seconds. — Brake to a stop and remain stopped for a minimum of 20 seconds. Repeat drive cycle at least five times. • **4R70W, AODE, CD4E, E4OD and AX4S-3.2L SHO Drive Cycle:** — Gear position in DRIVE range, press the Transmission Control Switch (TCS) (the Transmission Control Indicator (TCIL) should light) and moderately accelerate from stop to 40 mph. This will allow the transmission to shift into third gear. Hold speed and throttle opening steady for a minimum of 15 seconds (30 seconds for altitudes above 4000 feet). — Press TCS (the TCIL should turn off) and accelerate from 40 mph to 50 mph. This will allow the transmission to shift into fourth gear. Hold speed and throttle steady for a minimum of 15 seconds. — With transmission in fourth gear and maintaining steady speed and throttle opening, lightly apply and release brake (to operate stop lamps). Then hold speed and throttle steady for at least an additional five seconds. — Brake to a stop and remain stopped for a minimum of 20 seconds with transmission in drive. Repeat drive cycle at least five times. • Rerun KOEO Self-Test and record all Continuous Memory DTCs. — Are pass codes present in Continuous Memory (any code 10-11/111)?	Yes No	▶ ▶	Unable to duplicate fault at this time further diagnosis using EEC-IV Monitor Box or Scan tool Intermittent Fault Diagnosis. If further diagnosis is not performed, then CLEAR Continuous Memory and possible internal transmission damage. For DTCs 99/624, 651 or 67/634: GO to **TG91** For DTCs 29/452: GO to Pinpoint Test Step **DS1** (E/F Series Bronco) or GO to **DP1** (for all other vehicles). For DTCs 659, 667, 668 and 675: GO to **TG93**. For any other DTC: GO to **TG92**.

Fig. 227 Test TG: Electronic Trans/Continuous Memory DTC (Part 6 of 13). 1994-95

TEST STEP		RESULT	▶	ACTION TO TAKE
TG91	CHECK CIRCUIT FOR INTERMITTENT FAULT IN HARNESS AND CONNECTORS.			
	DTC 99/624 and 651 indicates an Electronic Pressure Control (EPC) circuit failure.	Yes	▶	ISOLATE fault and SERVICE as necessary. CLEAR Continuous Memory
	Code 67/634 indicates the Manual Lever Position Sensor (MLP) voltage is higher or lower than expected.			
	Possible causes:			RERUN Quick Test. If the concern still exists, REFER to appropriate Transmission for possible internal transmission damage.
	— Damaged harness connector.			
	— Damaged EPC solenoid.			
	— Damaged MLP sensor.			
	— Intermittent harness continuity.			
	— Damaged PCM connector pins.	No	▶	GO to the appropriate Transmission CLEAR Continuous Memory
	● Key off.			
	● Disconnect Powertrain Control Module (PCM). Inspect for damaged or pushed out pins, corrosion, loose wires, etc. Service as necessary.			
	● Install breakout box, connect PCM.			
	● Connect DVOM to test pins as indicated:			
	— **For EPC solenoid:** Connect one test lead to EPC signal pin and the other to EPC VPWR pin. Refer to cover page schematics per application for correct EPC test pin.			
	— **For MLP sensor:** Connect one test lead to MLP signal pin and the other test lead to Test Pin 46. Refer to cover page schematics per application for correct MLP test pin.			
	● Key on, engine off.			
	● Observe DVOM display for indication of a fault while performing the following:			
	NOTE: In either case, the voltage should remain steady (less than 10.0 volts for the EPC and less than 5.0 volts for the MLP with vehicle in PARK). A changing voltage or one greater than expected is an indication of a fault.			
	— Shake, wiggle and bend the harness of the component.			
	— Lightly tap on the component connector to simulate a road shock.			
	● Is a fault indicated?			

FM0159300768090X

Fig. 227   Test TG: Electronic Trans/Continuous Memory DTC (Part 7 of 13)

TEST STEP		RESULT	▶	ACTION TO TAKE
TG92	ENTER KEY ON ENGINE OFF CONTINUOUS MONITOR MODE: CHECK HARNESS CIRCUITS			
	DTC 49/617 indicates an improper 1-2 shift.	Yes	▶	DISCONNECT and INSPECT connector and harness wires. SERVICE as necessary. CLEAR Continuous Memory
	DTC 59/618 indicates an improper 2-3 shift.			
	DTC 69/619 indicates an improper 3-4 shift.			
	DTC 62/628 indicates excessive converter clutch slip detected.			
	DTC 56/637 indicates transmission oil temperature (TOT) sensor circuit above maximum voltage.			RERUN Quick Test. If the concern remains, REFER to appropriate Transmission for possible internal transmission damage.
	DTC 66/638 indicates transmission oil temperature (TOT) sensor circuit below minimum voltage.			
	DTC 645 indicates an incorrect gear ratio was present after first gear was commanded.			
	DTC 646 indicates an incorrect gear ratio was present after second gear was commanded.	No	▶	REFER to appropriate Transmission
	DTC 647 indicates an incorrect gear ratio was present after third gear was commanded.			
	DTC 648 indicates an incorrect gear ratio was present after fourth gear was commanded.			
	DTC 656 indicates continuous slip error was detected.			
	Possible causes:			
	— Intermittent harness continuity.			
	— Damaged manual lever position sensor.			
	— Damaged shift solenoid.			
	— Worn friction elements.			
	● Enter Key On Engine Off Continuous Monitor Diagnostic Test Mode (DTM)			
	● Observe VOM or STAR Tester LED for an indication of a fault while performing the following:			
	— Wiggle, shake or bend a small section of the Powertrain Control Module (PCM) vehicle harness while working toward the dash panel, PCM and transmission connectors.			
	● Is a fault indicated?			

FM0159300768100X

Fig. 227   Test TG: Electronic Trans/Continuous Memory DTC (Part 8 of 13)

TEST STEP		RESULT	▶	ACTION TO TAKE
TG93	CHECK FOR DTC 659			
	DTC 659 indicates high vehicle speed detected while the vehicle was in PARK.	Yes	▶	GO to TG103.
	Possible causes:	No	▶	GO to TG94.
	— Damaged Manual Lever Position (MLP) Sensor.			
	— Damaged PCM.			
	● Did DTC 659 repeat during the drive cycle test?			
TG94	CHECK FOR DTC 675			
	DTC 675 indicates the MLP circuit voltage was out of the expected range.	Yes	▶	GO to TG95.
	Possible causes:	No	▶	GO to TG98.
	— Damaged MLP sensor.			
	— Open in MLP harness SIG circuit.			
	— Open in MLP harness SIG RTN circuit.			
	— Short to ground in MLP harness SIG circuit.			
	— Short to power in MLP harness SIG circuit.			
	— Damaged PCM.			
	● Did DTC 675 repeat during the drive cycle test?			
TG95	CHECK FOR DTC 675 WITH DTC 667			
	DTC 667 indicates the MLP circuit voltage was below the allowed minimum voltage.	Yes	▶	GO to TG99.
	Possible causes:	No	▶	GO to TG96.
	— Damaged MLP sensor.			
	— Short to ground in MLP harness SIG circuit.			
	— Open in MLP harness SIG circuit.			
	— Damaged PCM.			
	● Did DTC 675 repeat with DTC 667 during the drive cycle test?			
TG96	CHECK FOR DTC 675 GENERATED WITH DTC 668			
	DTC 668 indicates the MLP circuit voltage was above the allowed maximum voltage.	Yes	▶	GO to TG101.
	Possible causes:	No	▶	GO to TG97.
	— Open in MLP harness SIG RTN circuit.			
	— Damaged MLP sensor.			
	— Damaged PCM.			
	— Short to power in MLP harness SIG circuit.			
	● Did DTC 675 repeat with DTC 668 during the drive cycle test?			

Fig. 227   Test TG: Electronic Trans/Continuous Memory DTC (Part 9 of 13). 1994–95

TEST STEP		RESULT	▶	ACTION TO TAKE
TG97	CHECK MLP ALIGNMENT			
	● Key off.	Yes	▶	REMOVE tool. GO to TG103.
	● Apply parking brake.	No	▶	PLACE the transmission in NEUTRAL, loosen the two MLP sensor mounting bolts. MOVE the sensor about to allow insertion of the MLP sensor tool in the appropriate slots. TIGHTEN the two mounting bolts to specification. REMOVE the tool. VERIFY shift linkage adjustment
	● Place transmission in NEUTRAL.			
	● Verify the MLP tool (Rotunda T92P-7010-AH or equivalent) fits in the appropriate slot.			
	● Does the tool fit properly?			
				CLEAR Continuous Memory
				RERUN Quick Test.
TG98	CHECK FOR DTC 667			
	DTC 667 indicates the MLP circuit voltage was below the allowed minimum voltage.	Yes	▶	GO to TG99
	Possible causes:	No	▶	GO to TG101
	— Damaged MLP sensor.			
	— Short to ground in MLP harness SIG circuit.			
	— Open in MLP harness SIG circuit.			
	— Damaged PCM.			
	● Did DTC 667 repeat during the drive cycle test?			

FM0159400768120X

Fig. 227   Test TG: Electronic Trans/Continuous Memory DTC (Part 10 of 13). 1994–95

TEST STEP	RESULT	▶	ACTION TO TAKE
TG99 CHECK CONTINUITY OF THE TR HARNESS SIG CIRCUIT • Key off. • Disconnect Powertrain Control Module (PCM). Inspect for damaged or pushed out pins, corrosion or loose wires, etc. Service as necessary. • Disconnect MLP sensor. • Using a mirror, inspect both ends of transmission harness connector at MLP sensor for damaged or pushed out pins, corrosion, loose wires, etc. Service as necessary. • Install breakout box, leave PCM disconnected. • Measure resistance between Test Pin 30 at the breakout box and MLP SIG circuit at the MLP sensor vehicle harness connector. • **Is resistance less than 5.0 ohms?**	Yes No	▶ ▶	GO to **TG100** SERVICE open circuit. REMOVE breakout box. RECONNECT all components. RERUN Quick Test.
TG100 CHECK FOR SHORT TO GROUND IN MLP HARNESS SIG CIRCUIT • Key off. • MLP sensor disconnected. • Breakout box installed, PCM disconnected. • Measure resistance between Test Pins 30 at the breakout box and chassis ground. • **Is resistance greater than 10,000 ohms?**	Yes No	▶ ▶	GO to **TG103** SERVICE short circuit. REMOVE breakout box. RECONNECT all components. RERUN Quick Test.

FM0159400768130X

Fig. 227 Test TG: Electronic Trans/Continuous Memory DTC (Part 11 of 13). 1994–95

TEST STEP	RESULT	▶	ACTION TO TAKE
TG101 DTC 668 WAS GENERATED DURING THE DRIVE CYCLE TEST- CHECK FOR CONTINUITY OF THE MLP HARNESS SIG RTN CIRCUIT DTC 668 indicates the MLP circuit voltage was above the allowed maximum voltage. Possible causes: — Open in MLP harness SIG RTN circuit. — Damaged MLP sensor. — Damaged PCM. — Short to power in MLP harness SIG circuit. • Key off. • Disconnect Powertrain Control Module (PCM). Inspect for damaged or pushed out pins, corrosion or loose wires, etc. Service as necessary. • Disconnect MLP sensor. • Using a mirror, inspect both ends of transmission harness connector at MLP sensor for damaged or pushed out pins, corrosion or loose wires, etc. Service as necessary. • Install breakout box, leave PCM disconnected. • Measure resistance between Test Pin 46 at the breakout box and SIG RTN circuit at the MLP sensor vehicle harness connector. • **Is resistance less than 5.0 ohms?**	Yes No	▶ ▶	GO to **TG102** SERVICE open circuit. REMOVE breakout box. RECONNECT all components. RERUN Quick Test.
TG102 CHECK FOR SHORT TO POWER IN MLP SIG HARNESS CIRCUIT • Key off. • MLP sensor disconnected. • Breakout box installed, PCM disconnected. • Measure resistance between Test Pin 30 and Test Pins 37, 57, 40, 60 and 46 at the breakout box. • **Is each resistance greater than 10,000 ohms?**	Yes No	▶ ▶	GO to **TG103** SERVICE short circuit. REMOVE breakout box. RECONNECT all components. RERUN Quick Test.

FM0159400768140X

Fig. 227 Test TG: Electronic Trans/Continuous Memory DTC (Part 12 of 13). 1994–95

TEST STEP	RESULT	▶	ACTION TO TAKE
TG103 CHECK MLP SENSOR RESISTANCE • Key off. • Connect MLP sensor. • Breakout box installed, PCM disconnected. • Unlock steering column. • Measure resistance between Test Pin 30 and Test Pin 46 at the breakout box in each gear selector position. Refer to the MLP sensor resistance specification table below:	Yes No	▶ ▶	REPLACE the PCM. REMOVE the breakout box. RERUN Quick Test. REPLACE MLP sensor. REMOVE breakout box. RERUN Quick Test.

Transmission Shift Position	Minimum (ohms)	Maximum (ohms)
Park	3770	4607
Reverse	1304	1593
Neutral	660	807
Overdrive	361	442
2: Drive*	190	232
First	78	95

* Drive for AX4S except SHO applications
• **Is each resistance within specification?**

FM0159300768150X

Fig. 227 Test TG: Electronic Trans/Continuous Memory DTC (Part 13 of 13). 1994–95

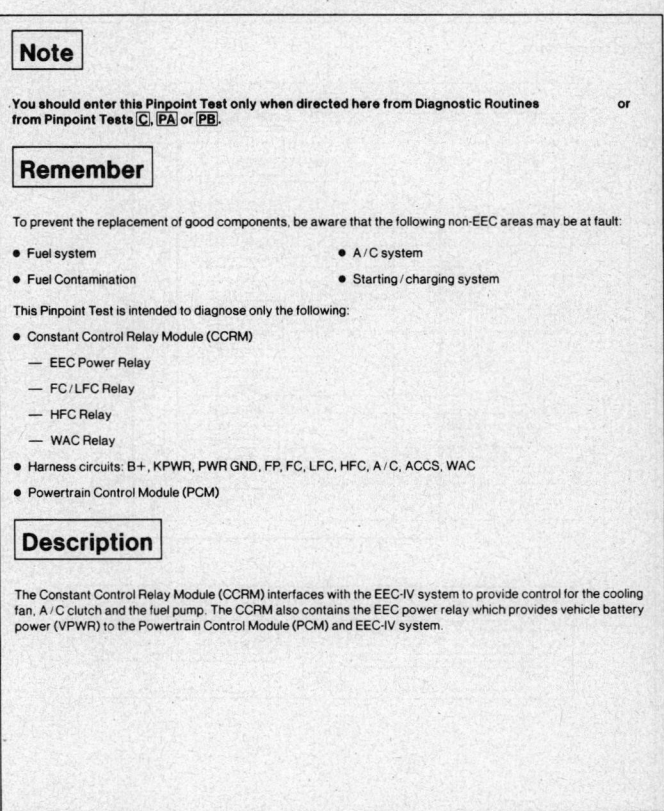

Note

You should enter this Pinpoint Test only when directed here from Diagnostic Routines   or from Pinpoint Tests **C**, **PA** or **PB**.

Remember

To prevent the replacement of good components, be aware that the following non-EEC areas may be at fault:

• Fuel system
• Fuel Contamination
• A/C system
• Starting/charging system

This Pinpoint Test is intended to diagnose only the following:

• Constant Control Relay Module (CCRM)
  — EEC Power Relay
  — FC/LFC Relay
  — HFC Relay
  — WAC Relay
• Harness circuits: B+, KPWR, PWR GND, FP, FC, LFC, HFC, A/C, ACCS, WAC
• Powertrain Control Module (PCM)

Description

The Constant Control Relay Module (CCRM) interfaces with the EEC-IV system to provide control for the cooling fan, A/C clutch and the fuel pump. The CCRM also contains the EEC power relay which provides vehicle battery power (VPWR) to the Powertrain Control Module (PCM) and EEC-IV system.

FM0159300769010X

Fig. 228 Test X: CCRM (Part 1 of 39). 1993

Pinpoint Test Schematics

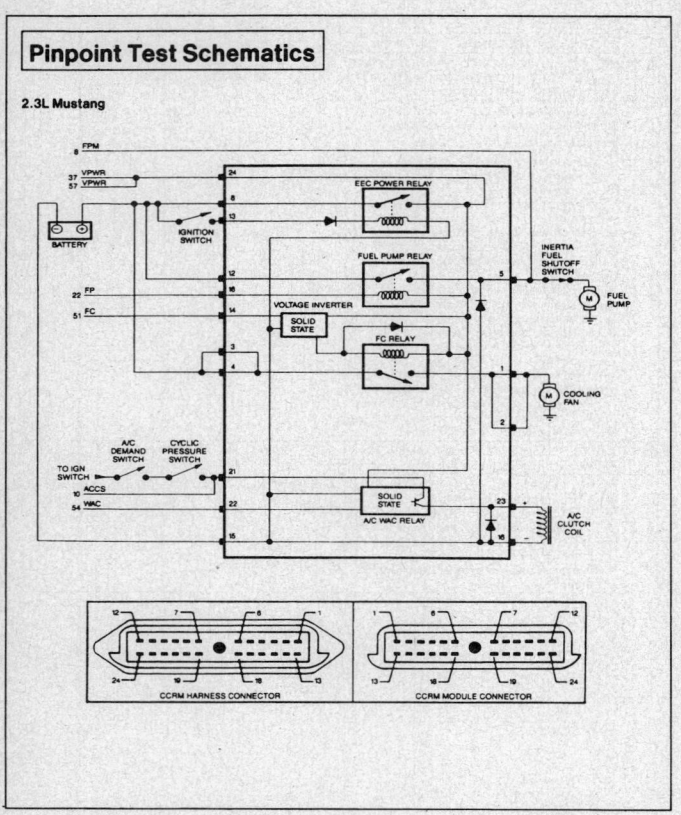

2.3L Mustang

FM0159300769020X

Fig. 228   Test X: CCRM (Part 2 of 39). 1993

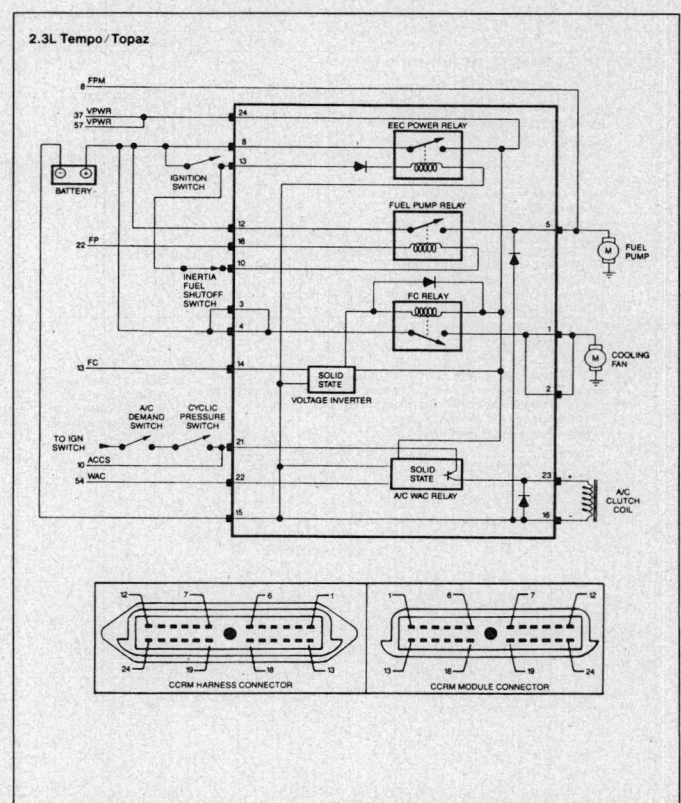

2.3L Tempo/Topaz

FM0159300769030X

Fig. 228   Test X: CCRM (Part 3 of 39). 1993

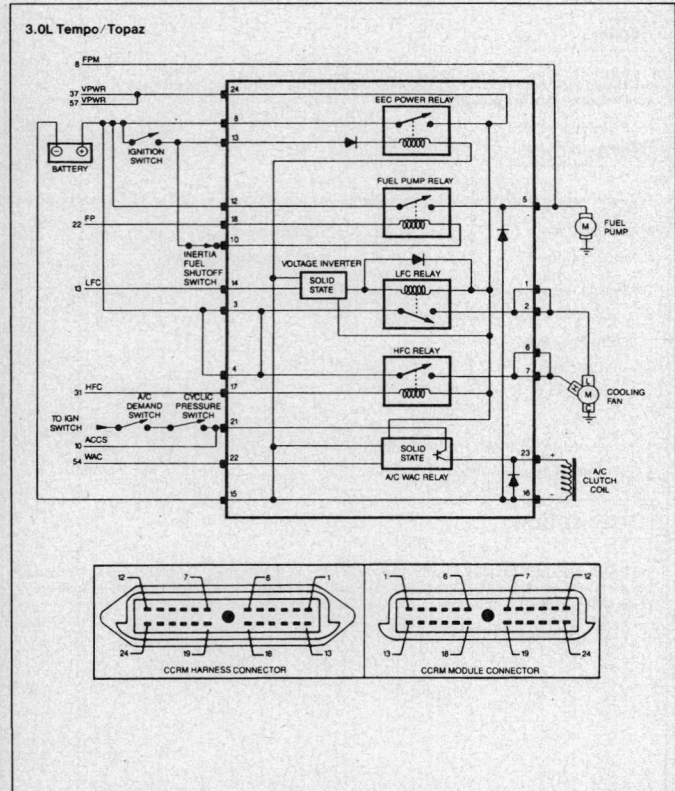

3.0L Tempo/Topaz

FM0159300769040X

Fig. 228   Test X: CCRM (Part 4 of 39). 1993

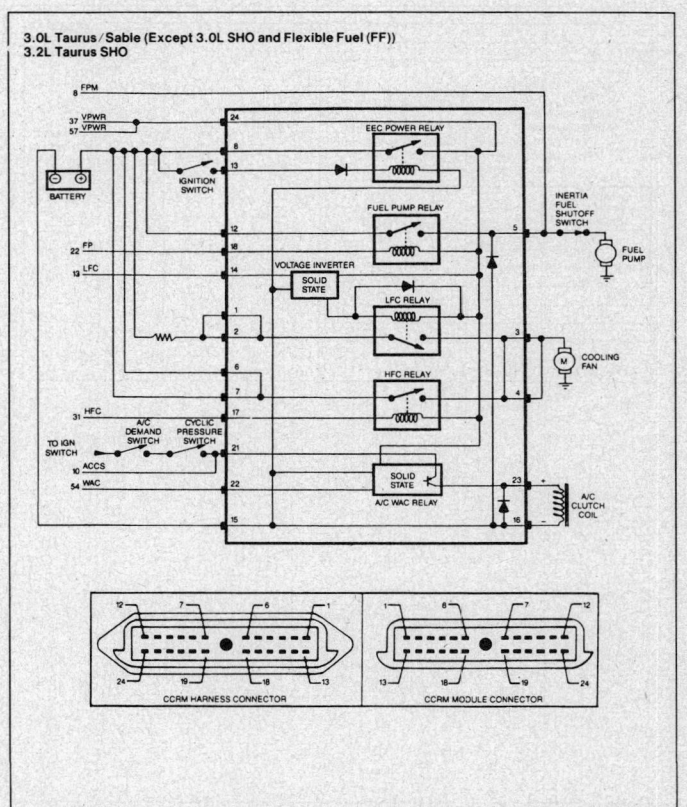

3.0L Taurus/Sable (Except 3.0L SHO and Flexible Fuel (FF))
3.2L Taurus SHO

FM0159300769050X

Fig. 228   Test X: CCRM (Part 5 of 39). 1993

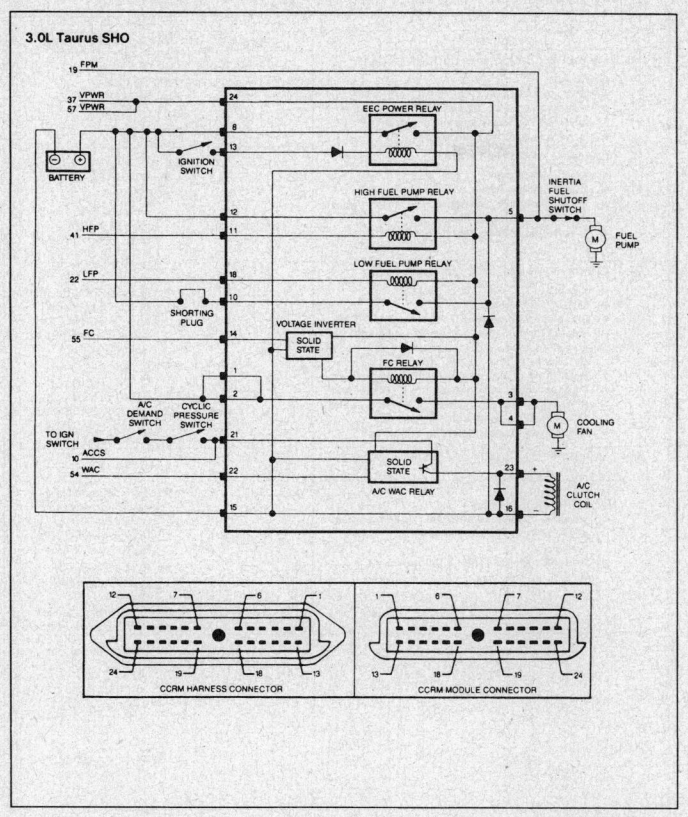

Fig. 228   Test X: CCRM (Part 6 of 39). 1993

FM0159300769060X

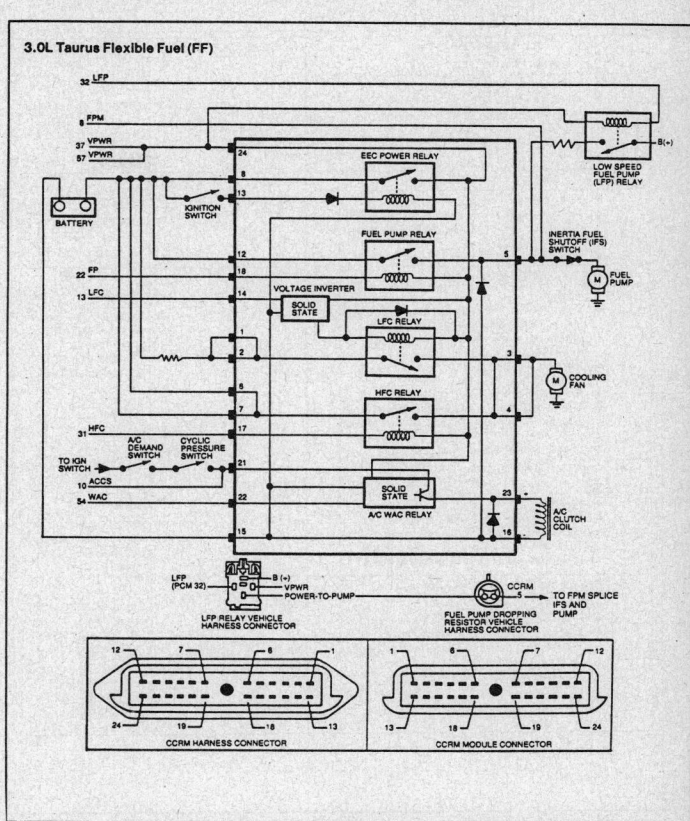

Fig. 228   Test X: CCRM (Part 7 of 39). 1993

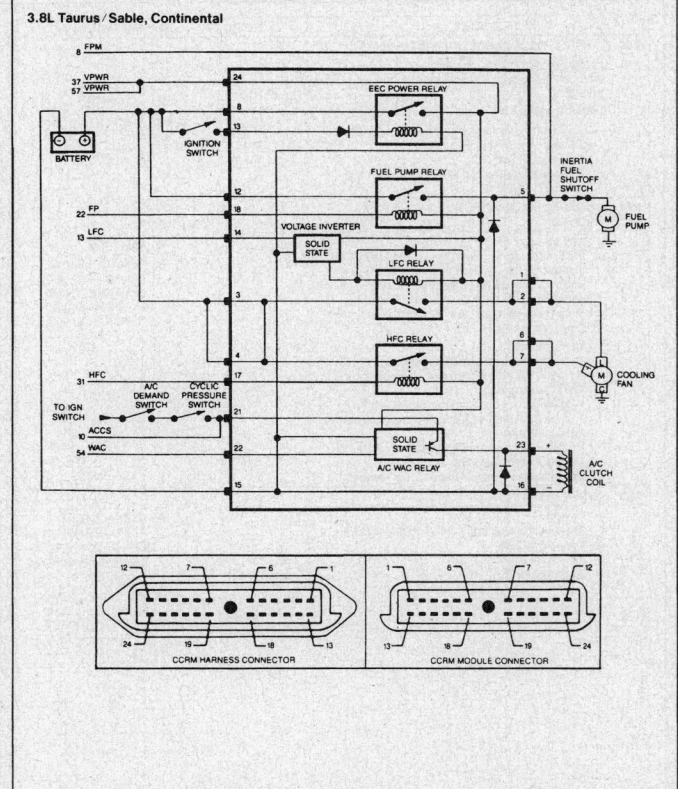

Fig. 228   Test X: CCRM (Part 8 of 39). 1993

FM0159300769080X

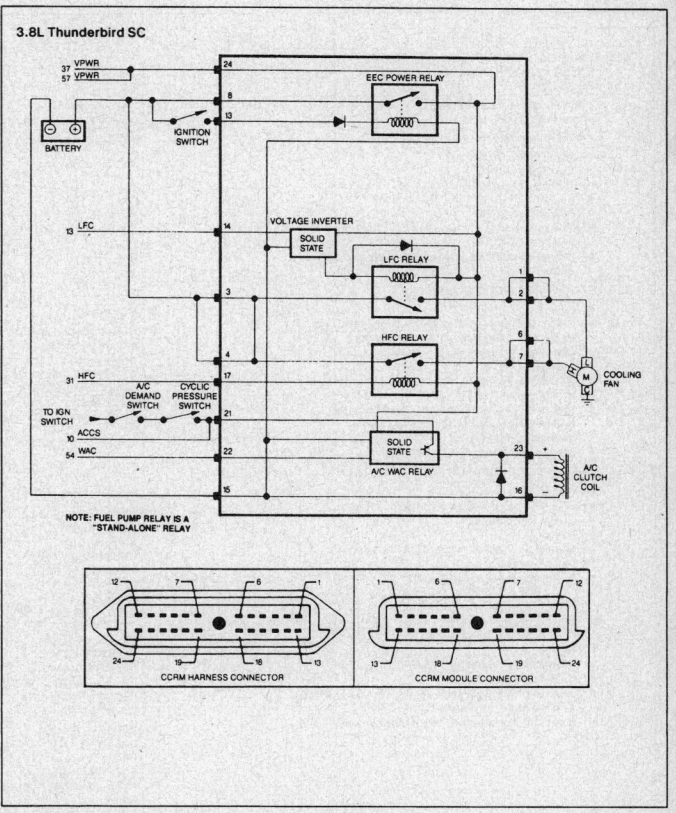

Fig. 228   Test X: CCRM (Part 9 of 39). 1993

FM0159300769090X

TEST STEP	RESULT	▶	ACTION TO TAKE
X1 CHECK BATTERY VOLTAGE • Key on, engine off. • Measure voltage across battery terminals. • **Is voltage greater than 10.5 volts?**	Yes No	▶ ▶	GO to X2 SERVICE discharged battery. REFER to Charging Electrical
X2 CHECK BATTERY GROUND • Key on, engine off. • Measure voltage between SIG RTN circuit in the Data Link Connector and battery negative post. • **Is voltage greater than 0.5 volt?**	Yes No	▶ ▶	GO to X3 GO to X6
X3 GROUND FAULT ISOLATION • Key off. • Disconnect Powertrain Control Module (PCM). Inspect for damaged or pushed out pins, corrosion, loose wires etc. Service as necessary. • Install breakout box and connect PCM to breakout box. • Key on, engine off. • Measure voltage between battery negative post and Test Pins 40 and 60 at the breakout box. • **Is each voltage less than 0.5 volt?**	Yes No	▶ ▶	GO to X4 SERVICE open ground circuit. REMOVE breakout box. RECONNECT PCM. RERUN Quick Test.
X4 POWERTRAIN CONTROL MODULE (PCM) GROUND FAULT ISOLATION • Key off. • Breakout box installed, PCM connected. • Measure resistance between Test Pin 46 and Test Pins 40 and 60 at the breakout box. • **Is each resistance less than 5.0 ohms?**	Yes No	▶ ▶	GO to X5. REPLACE PCM. REMOVE breakout box RERUN Quick Test.
X5 CHECK SIG RTN CIRCUIT CONTINUITY • Key off. • Breakout box installed, PCM disconnected. • Measure resistance between Test Pin 46 at the breakout box and SIG RTN circuit in the Data Link Connector. • **Is resistance less than 5.0 ohms?**	Yes No	▶ ▶	System OK REMOVE breakout box. RECONNECT PCM. RERUN Quick Test. SERVICE open circuit REMOVE breakout box RECONNECT PCM RERUN Quick Test

Fig. 228   Test X: CCRM (Part 10 of 39). 1993

TEST STEP	RESULT	▶	ACTION TO TAKE
X6 MEASURE VOLTAGE AND GROUND TO CCRM • Key off. • Disconnect CCRM. • Measure voltage between Pin 8 and Pin 15 at the CCRM vehicle harness connector. • **Is voltage greater than 10.5 volts?**	Yes No	▶ ▶	GO to X7 GO to X9
X7 CHECK KEY POWER TO CCRM • Key on, engine off. • CCRM disconnected. • Measure voltage between Pin 13 and Pin 15 at the CCRM vehicle harness connector. • **Is voltage greater than 10.5 volts?**	Yes No	▶ ▶	GO to X8 SERVICE open between Pin 13 and ignition switch. RECONNECT CCRM. RERUN Quick Test.
X8 CHECK VPWR CIRCUIT CONTINUITY • Key off. • CCRM disconnected. • Disconnect Powertrain Control Module (PCM). Inspect for damaged or pushed out pins, corrosion, loose wires, etc. Service as necessary. • Install breakout box, leave PCM disconnected. • Measure resistance between Test Pins 37 and 57 at the breakout box and Pin 24 at the CCRM vehicle harness connector. • **Is each resistance less than 5.0 ohms?**	Yes No	▶ ▶	REPLACE CCRM. REMOVE breakout box. RECONNECT all components. RERUN Quick Test. SERVICE open in VPWR circuit. REMOVE breakout box. RECONNECT all components. RERUN Quick Test.
X9 MEASURE CONTINUITY OF POWER GROUND TO CCRM • Key off. • CCRM disconnected. • Measure resistance between battery negative post and Pin 15 at the CCRM vehicle harness connector. • **Is resistance less than 5.0 ohms?**	Yes No	▶ ▶	SERVICE open in battery positive to CCRM Pin 8. RECONNECT CCRM. RERUN Quick Test. SERVICE open in battery ground to CCRM Pin 15. RECONNECT CCRM. RERUN Quick Test.

Fig. 228   Test X: CCRM (Part 11 of 39). 1993

TEST STEP	RESULT	▶	ACTION TO TAKE
X15 DIAGNOSTIC TROUBLE CODE (DTC) 563: CHECK HIGH FAN CONTROL (HFC) RELAY RESISTANCE DTC 563 indicates a High Fan Control (HFC) primary circuit failure. Possible causes are: — Open or shorted circuit. — Damaged CCRM. — Damaged Powertrain Control Module (PCM). • Key off. • Disconnect CCRM. • Measure resistance between Pin 17 and Pin 24 at the CCRM. • **Is the resistance between 50 ohms and 100 ohms?**	Yes No	▶ ▶	GO to X16. REPLACE CCRM. RERUN Quick Test.
X16 CHECK HFC CIRCUIT CONTINUITY • Key off. • Disconnect Powertrain Control Module (PCM). Inspect for damaged or pushed out pins, corrosion, loose wires, etc. Service as necessary. • Install breakout box, leave PCM disconnected. • CCRM disconnected. • Measure resistance between Test Pin 31 at breakout box and Pin 17 of CCRM vehicle harness connector. • **Is resistance less than 5.0 ohms?**	Yes No	▶ ▶	GO to X17. SERVICE open in HFC circuit. REMOVE breakout box. RECONNECT all components. RERUN Quick Test.
X17 CHECK HFC CIRCUIT FOR SHORT TO POWER • Key off. • Breakout box installed, PCM disconnected. • CCRM disconnected. • Key on. • Measure voltage between Test Pin 31 and battery negative post. • **Is voltage less than 1.0 volt?**	Yes No	▶ ▶	Key off. GO to X18. SERVICE short to power. REMOVE breakout box. RECONNECT all components. RERUN Quick Test. If DTC 563 is still present, REPLACE PCM.
X18 CHECK HFC CIRCUIT FOR SHORTS TO GROUND • Key off. • Breakout box installed, PCM disconnected. • CCRM disconnected. • Measure resistance between Test Pin 31 and Test Pin 40 at the breakout box. • **Is resistance greater than 10,000 ohms?**	Yes No	▶ ▶	REPLACE PCM REMOVE breakout box RECONNECT all components RERUN Quick Test SERVICE short to ground in HFC circuit REMOVE breakout box RECONNECT all components RERUN Quick Test

Fig. 228   Test X: CCRM (Part 12 of 39). 1993

TEST STEP	RESULT	▶	ACTION TO TAKE
X20 DIAGNOSTIC TROUBLE CODE (DTC) 564: DOES FAN RUN WITH KEY ON? DTC 564 indicates a FC/LFC primary circuit failure. Possible causes are: — Open or shorted circuit. — Damaged CCRM. — Damaged PCM. • Does the cooling fan always run with the key on?	Yes No	▶ ▶	GO to X23. GO to X21.
X21 CHECK FC/LFC SIGNAL FOR SHORT TO GROUND • Key off. • Disconnect Powertrain Control Module (PCM). Inspect for damaged or pushed out pins, corrosion, loose wires, etc. Service as necessary. • Install breakout box, leave PCM disconnected. • Disconnect CCRM. For 3.0L SHO: — Measure resistance between Test Pin 55 and Test Pins 40/60 at the breakout box. For 2.3L Mustang: — Measure resistance between Test Pin 51 and Test Pins 40/60 at the breakout box. For all others: — Measure resistance between Test Pin 13 and Test Pins 40/60 at the breakout box. • **Is resistance greater than 10,000 ohms?**	Yes No	▶ ▶	GO to X22. SERVICE short to ground in FC/LFC circuit. RECONNECT all components. RERUN Quick Test.
X22 CHECK FAN RUNNING MODE • Key off. • Breakout box installed, PCM disconnected. • Connect CCRM. • Key on, engine off. • **Does fan run?**	Yes No	▶ ▶	REPLACE PCM. REMOVE breakout box. RECONNECT all components. RERUN Quick Test. REPLACE CCRM. REMOVE breakout box. RECONNECT all components. RERUN Quick Test.

Fig. 228   Test X: CCRM (Part 13 of 39). 1993

ELECTRONIC ENGINE CONTROL SYSTEM IV (EEC-IV)

	TEST STEP	RESULT	►	ACTION TO TAKE
X23	CHECK FC/LFC CIRCUIT CONTINUITY			

	• Key off.
	• Disconnect Powertrain Control Module (PCM). Inspect for damaged or pushed out pins, corrosion, and loose wires, etc. Service as necessary.
	• Install breakout box, leave PCM disconnected.
	• Disconnect CCRM.
	  For 3.0L SHO:
	  — Measure resistance between Test Pin 55 at the breakout box and Pin 14 at the CCRM vehicle harness connector.
	  For 2.3L Mustang:
	  — Measure resistance between Test Pin 51 at the breakout box and Pin 14 at the CCRM vehicle harness connector.
	  For all others:
	  — Measure resistance between Test Pin 13 at the breakout box and Pin 14 at the CCRM vehicle harness connector.
	• **Is resistance less than 5.0 ohms?**
		Yes
		
		No
			►
			
			►
				GO to X24.
				
				SERVICE open in FC/LFC circuit. REMOVE breakout box. RECONNECT all components. RERUN Quick Test.

X24	CHECK FC/LFC CIRCUIT FOR SHORT TO POWER			

	• Key off.
	• Breakout box installed, PCM disconnected.
	• CCRM disconnected.
	• Key on, engine off.
	  For 3.0L SHO:
	  — Measure voltage between Test Pin 55 and battery negative post.
	  For 2.3L Mustang:
	  — Measure voltage between Test Pin 51 and battery negative post.
	  For all others:
	  — Measure voltage between Test Pin 13 and battery negative post.
	• **Is voltage less than 1.0 volt?**
		Yes
		
		No
			►
			
			►
				GO to X25.
				
				SERVICE short to power in FC/LFC circuit. REMOVE breakout box. RECONNECT all components. RERUN Quick Test.

Fig. 228   Test X: CCRM (Part 14 of 39). 1993

	TEST STEP	RESULT	►	ACTION TO TAKE
X25	FC/LFC CIRCUIT FAULT ISOLATION CHECK			

	• Key off.
	• Breakout box installed, PCM disconnected.
	• Reconnect CCRM.
	• Key on, engine off.
	  For 3.0L SHO:
	  — Jumper Test Pin 55 to Test Pin 40 or 60 at the breakout box.
	  For 2.3L Mustang:
	  — Jumper Test Pin 51 to Test Pin 40 or 60 at the breakout box.
	  For all others:
	  — Jumper Test Pin 13 to Test Pin 40 or 60 at the breakout box.
	• **Does fan continue to run?**
		Yes
		
		No
			►
			
			►
				REPLACE CCRM. REMOVE breakout box. RECONNECT all components. RERUN Quick Test.
				
				REPLACE PCM. REMOVE breakout box. RECONNECT all components. RERUN Quick Test.

X30	COOLING FAN ALWAYS ON (ANY SPEED): DISCONNECT CCRM AND CHECK IF FAN IS ON			
	NOTE: For proper results of this Test Step, a "pass" Diagnostic Trouble Code (DTC) 111 must have been received during EEC-IV Self-Test. • Accessories off (A/C, etc.) • Key on, verify "cooling fan always on" symptom. • Key off. • Disconnect CCRM. • Key on. • **Is cooling fan still on?**	Yes No	► ►	Key off. For 3.0L Tempo/Topaz, 3.8L Taurus/Sable, Continental and Thunderbird SC: GO to X31. All others: SERVICE short to power on power-to-fan circuit (between CCRM and cooling fan). RECONNECT CCRM. RE-EVALUATE symptom. Key off. REPLACE CCRM. RE-EVALUATE symptom.

Fig. 228   Test X: CCRM (Part 15 of 39). 1993

	TEST STEP	RESULT	►	ACTION TO TAKE
X31	CHECK LOW SPEED POWER-TO-FAN CIRCUIT FOR SHORT TO POWER			
	• Key off. • CCRM disconnected. • Disconnect cooling fan. • Measure voltage between Pin 1 of the CCRM vehicle harness connector and the battery negative post. • **Is voltage less than 1.0 volt?**	Yes No	► ►	SERVICE short to power in high speed power-to-fan circuit. RECONNECT all components. RE-EVALUATE symptom. SERVICE short to power in low speed power-to-fan circuit. RECONNECT all components. RE-EVALUATE symptom.
X35	NO ENGINE COOLING FAN (LOW SPEED AND/OR HIGH SPEED): CHECK POWER SUPPLY TO CCRM			

	• Key off.
	• Disconnect CCRM.
	• Connect negative probe of DVOM to battery negative post.
	  For 3.0L SHO:
	  — Check for voltage on Pins 1 and 2 at the CCRM vehicle harness connector.
	  For 3.0L Taurus/Sable and 3.2L SHO:
	  — Check for voltage on Pins 1, 2, 6, and 7 at the CCRM vehicle harness connector.
	  For all others:
	  — Check for voltage on Pins 3 and 4 at the CCRM vehicle harness connector.
	• **Is each voltage greater than 10.0 volts?**
		Yes
		No
			►
			►
				GO to X36.
				SERVICE open in battery power circuit. RECONNECT CCRM. RE-EVALUATE symptom.

X36	CHECK FAN MOTOR OPERATION			

	• Key off.
	• CCRM disconnected.
	  For 3.0L SHO, 2.3L Mustang and 2.3L Tempo/Topaz:
	  — Jumper Pin 1 to Pin 3 at the CCRM vehicle harness connector.
	  For all others:
	  — Jumper Pin 3 to Pin 6 at the CCRM vehicle harness connector.
	• **Does fan run?**
		Yes
		
		No
			►
			
			►
				For 3.0L SHO, 2.3L Mustang and 2.3L Tempo/Topaz: GO to X42.
				For all others: GO to X37.
				
				GO to X38.

Fig. 228   Test X: CCRM (Part 16 of 39). 1993

	TEST STEP	RESULT	►	ACTION TO TAKE
X37	CHECK FAN MOTOR OPERATION			
	• Key off. • CCRM disconnected. • Jumper Pin 3 to Pin 2 at CCRM vehicle harness connector. • **Does fan run?**	Yes No	► ►	GO to X42. GO to X40.
X38	MEASURE BATTERY VOLTAGE SUPPLY AT FAN—BYPASSING CCRM			

	• Key off.
	• Disconnect cooling fan.
	• CCRM disconnected.
	  For 3.0L SHO, 2.3L Mustang and 2.3L Tempo/Topaz:
	  — Jumper Pin 1 to Pin 3 at the CCRM vehicle harness connector.
	  For all others:
	  — Jumper Pin 3 to Pin 6 at the CCRM vehicle harness connector.
	• Measure voltage at cooling fan vehicle harness connector between power (HFC power for two speed fans) and ground pins.
	• **Is voltage greater than 8.0 volts?**
		Yes
		
		No
			►
			
			►
				REPLACE fan motor. RECONNECT CCRM. RE-EVALUATE symptom.
				
				GO to X39.

X39	VERIFY COOLING FAN GROUND			

	• Key off.
	• Cooling fan disconnected.
	• CCRM disconnected.
	  For 3.0L SHO, 2.3L Mustang and 2.3L Tempo/Topaz:
	  — Jumper Pin 1 to Pin 3 at the CCRM vehicle harness connector.
	  For all others:
	  — Jumper Pin 3 to Pin 6 at the CCRM vehicle harness connector.
	• Measure voltage between positive voltage pin (HFC power for two speed fans) at the cooling fan vehicle harness connector and battery negative post.
	• **Is voltage greater than 8.0 volts?**
		Yes
		
		No
			►
			
			►
				SERVICE open in ground circuit to fan. RECONNECT all components. RE-EVALUATE symptom.
				
				SERVICE open in power-to-fan circuit from CCRM vehicle harness connector to cooling fan vehicle harness connector. RECONNECT all components. RE-EVALUATE symptom.

Fig. 228   Test X: CCRM (Part 17 of 39). 1993

FORD—Computerized Engine Controls

Fig. 228 Test X: CCRM (Part 18 of 39). 1993

TEST STEP	RESULT	►	ACTION TO TAKE
X40 MEASURE BATTERY VOLTAGE SUPPLY AT FAN—BYPASSING CCRM • Key off. • Disconnect cooling fan. • CCRM disconnected. • Jumper Pin 3 to Pin 2 at CCRM vehicle harness connector. • Measure voltage at cooling fan vehicle harness connector between power (HFC power for two speed fans) and ground pins. • **Is voltage greater than 8.0 volts?**	Yes No	► ►	REPLACE fan motor. RECONNECT CCRM. RE-EVALUATE symptom. SERVICE open in power-to-fan circuit from Pin 1 and Pin 2 of CCRM vehicle harness connector to cooling fan vehicle harness connector. RECONNECT all components. RE-EVALUATE symptom.
X42 CHECK FAN RUNNING MODE (LOW) • Key off. • Disconnect Powertrain Control Module (PCM). • Reconnect CCRM. • Key on, engine off. • **Does fan run?**	Yes No	► ►	For 3.0L SHO, 2.3L Mustang and 2.3L Tempo / Topaz: GO to **X44** For all others: GO to **X43** REPLACE CCRM. RECONNECT PCM. RE-EVALUATE symptom.
X43 JUMPER HIGH FAN CONTROL (HFC) SIGNAL TO GROUND • Key off. • Inspect PCM for damaged or pushed out pins, corrosion, loose wires, etc. Service as necessary. • Install breakout box, leave PCM disconnected. • CCRM connected. • Key on, engine off. • Jumper Test Pin 31 to Test Pin 40 at the breakout box. • **Does fan speed change from low to high?**	Yes No	► ►	GO to **X44**. REPLACE CCRM. REMOVE breakout box. RECONNECT PCM. RE-EVALUATE symptom.

Fig. 228 Test X: CCRM (Part 19 of 39). 1993

TEST STEP	RESULT	►	ACTION TO TAKE
X44 CHECK ECT SENSOR • Key off. • Breakout box installed. • Connect PCM to breakout box. • Check engine coolant level. • While measuring the voltage between Test Pin 7 and Test Pin 46, start engine and warm engine to operating temperature. Continue to let engine idle. • **Will the voltage drop below .45 volt (allow sufficient time for voltage to drop, being careful not to overheat engine. If cooling fan turns on, other possible causes of symptom.)?**	Yes No	► ►	REPLACE PCM. REMOVE breakout box. RECONNECT all components. RE-EVALUATE symptom. CHECK ECT sensor wires and connector for high resistance. VERIFY cooling system is operating properly. If OK, REPLACE ECT sensor. REMOVE breakout box. RECONNECT all components. RE-EVALUATE symptom.
X50 A/C NOT FUNCTIONING: CHECK FOR VOLTAGE AT A/C CLUTCH • Disconnect A/C clutch. • Key on, engine off. • A/C demand switch to A/C ON position. • Start engine. • Measure voltage between power pin and ground pin of the A/C clutch vehicle harness connector (allow time for normal on / off cycling of the cyclic pressure switch). • **Is voltage greater than 10.5 volts?**	Yes No	► ►	REFER to Ventilating, Heating and Air Conditioning GO to **X51**
X51 CHECK FOR CONTINUITY FROM CCRM TO A/C CLUTCH • Key off. • A/C clutch disconnected. • Disconnect CCRM. • Measure resistance between Pin 23 of the CCRM vehicle harness connector and power side of the A/C clutch vehicle harness connector. • Measure resistance between Pin 16 of the CCRM vehicle harness connector and ground side of the A/C clutch vehicle harness connector. • **Is each resistance less than 5.0 ohms?**	Yes No	► ►	RECONNECT A/C clutch. GO to **X52** SERVICE open in power or ground to A/C circuit. RECONNECT CCRM and A/C clutch. RE-EVALUATE symptom.

Fig. 228 Test X: CCRM (Part 20 of 39). 1993

TEST STEP	RESULT	►	ACTION TO TAKE
X52 CHECK FOR A/C DEMAND SWITCH VOLTAGE TO CCRM • CCRM disconnected. • Key on, engine off. • A/C demand switch to A/C ON. • Measure voltage between Pin 21 of the CCRM vehicle harness connector and battery negative post. • **Is voltage greater than 10.5 volts?**	Yes No	► ►	Key off. GO to **X54** GO to **X53**
X53 CHECK VOLTAGE TO CYCLIC PRESSURE SWITCH • Key on, engine off. • Disconnect cyclic pressure switch. • A/C demand switch to A/C ON position. • Measure voltage between the A/C demand switch side of the cyclic pressure switch vehicle harness connector and battery negative post. • **Is voltage greater than 10.5 volts?**	Yes No	► ►	VERIFY operation of the A/C cyclic pressure switch (REFER to Ventilation / Climate Control If OK, SERVICE open between the cyclic pressure switch and CCRM. REMOVE breakout box. RECONNECT all components. RE-EVALUATE symptom. EEC-IV system OK. REMOVE breakout box. RECONNECT all components. REFER to Ventilation / Climate Control (Inspect A/C Demand Switch, applicable fuses, wiring to cyclic pressure switch, etc.)

Fig. 228 Test X: CCRM (Part 21 of 39). 1993

TEST STEP	RESULT	►	ACTION TO TAKE
X54 CHECK FOR A/C DEMAND SWITCH VOLTAGE TO POWERTRAIN CONTROL MODULE (PCM) • Key off. • Disconnect Powertrain Control Module (PCM). Inspect for damaged or pushed out pins, corrosion, loose wires, etc. Service as necessary. • Install breakout box, leave PCM disconnected. • CCRM disconnected. • Key on, engine off. • A/C demand switch to A/C ON. • Measure voltage between Test Pin 10 and chassis ground. • **Is voltage greater than 10.5 volts?**	Yes No	► ►	Key off. GO to **X55**. Key off. SERVICE open in ACCS circuit between PCM and its connection to the A/C demand circuit. REMOVE breakout box. RECONNECT all components. RE-EVALUATE symptom.
X55 CHECK WAC CIRCUIT FOR SHORTS TO GROUND • Key off. • Breakout box installed, PCM disconnected. • CCRM disconnected. • Measure resistance between Test Pin 54 and chassis ground. • **Is resistance greater than 10,000 ohms?**	Yes No	► ►	GO to **X62**. SERVICE short to ground in WAC circuit. REMOVE breakout box. RECONNECT all components. RE-EVALUATE symptom.
X60 NO A/C CUTOFF: CHECK WAC CIRCUIT CONTINUITY • Key off. • Disconnect Powertrain Control Module (PCM). Inspect for damaged or pushed out pins, corrosion, loose wires, etc. Service as necessary. • Install breakout box, leave PCM disconnected. • Disconnect CCRM. • Measure resistance between Test Pin 54 at the breakout box and Pin 22 at the CCRM vehicle harness connector. • **Is resistance less than 5.0 ohms?**	Yes No	► ►	GO to **X61**. SERVICE open in WAC circuit. REMOVE breakout box. RECONNECT all components. RE-EVALUATE symptom.
X61 CHECK WAC CIRCUIT FOR SHORTS TO POWER • Key off. • Breakout box installed, PCM disconnected. • CCRM disconnected. • Key on, engine off. • Measure voltage between Test Pin 54 and battery negative post. • **Is voltage less than 1.0 volt?**	Yes No	► ►	Key off. GO to **X62**. Key off. SERVICE short to power in WAC circuit. REMOVE breakout box. RECONNECT all components. RE-EVALUATE symptom.

ELECTRONIC ENGINE CONTROL SYSTEM IV (EEC-IV)

TEST STEP	RESULT	▶	ACTION TO TAKE
X62 ISOLATE FAULT TO PCM OR CCRM			
• Key off. • Breakout box installed, PCM disconnected. • Reconnect CCRM and A/C clutch. • Key on, engine off. • A/C demand switch to A/C on position. • Connect jumper between Test Pins 54 and 40 at the breakout box. • Disconnect and reconnect jumper several times while listening to the A/C clutch. • **Does the A/C clutch engage and disengage as the jumper is disconnected and reconnected?**	Yes	▶	REPLACE PCM. REMOVE breakout box. RECONNECT all components. RE-EVALUATE symptom.
	No	▶	REPLACE CCRM. INSPECT the A/C clutch circuit for possible shorts to GND. SERVICE as necessary. REMOVE breakout box. RECONNECT all components. RE-EVALUATE symptom.
X70 DIAGNOSTIC TROUBLE CODE (DTC) 556 OR 557: CHECK FUEL PUMP RELAY COIL RESISTANCE			
DTC 556 for the 3.0L SHO indicates a high speed fuel pump primary circuit fault. DTC 556 for ALL OTHERS indicates a fuel pump primary circuit fault. DTC 557 indicates a low speed fuel pump primary circuit fault. Possible causes: — Open or shorted circuit. — Open Inertia Fuel Shutoff (IFS) switch (Tempo/Topaz). — Damaged CCRM. — Damaged Powertrain Control Module (PCM). • Key off. • Disconnected CCRM. For 3.0L SHO: • Measure resistance of CCRM from Pin 18 to 24, and from Pin 11 to 24. For Tempo/Topaz: • Measure resistance of CCRM from Pin 18 to Pin 10. For all others: • Measure resistance of CCRM from Pin 18 to Pin 24. • **Is resistance between 65 and 120 ohms?**	Yes	▶	For Tempo/Topaz: GO to **X71**. For all others: GO to **X72**.
	No	▶	REPLACE CCRM. REMOVE breakout box. RECONNECT PCM. RERUN Quick Test.

Fig. 228   Test X: CCRM (Part 22 of 39). 1993

TEST STEP	RESULT	▶	ACTION TO TAKE
X71 CHECK VOLTAGE TO FUEL PUMP RELAY			
• CCRM disconnected. • Key on. • Measure voltage between CCRM Pin 10 at vehicle harness connector and battery negative post. • **Is voltage greater than 10.5 volts?**	Yes	▶	GO to **X72**.
	No	▶	CHECK Inertia Fuel Shutoff switch for open or reset. If OK, SERVICE open in ignition START/RUN circuit to CCRM.
X72 CHECK CONTINUITY OF FUEL PUMP CIRCUIT			
• Key off. • CCRM disconnected. • Disconnect Powertrain Control Module (PCM). Inspect for damaged or pushed out pins, corrosion, loose wires, etc. Service as necessary. • Install breakout box, leave PCM disconnected. For 3.0L SHO with DTC 556: — Measure resistance between Test Pin 41 at the breakout box and Pin 11 at the CCRM vehicle harness connector. • For all others: — Measure resistance between Test Pin 22 at the breakout box and Pin 18 at the CCRM vehicle harness connector. • **Is resistance less than 5.0 ohms?**	Yes	▶	GO to **X73**.
	No	▶	SERVICE open in fuel pump circuit. REMOVE breakout box. RECONNECT all components. RERUN Quick Test.
X73 CHECK APPROPRIATE FUEL PUMP CIRCUIT FOR SHORT TO POWER			
• Key off. • Breakout box installed, PCM disconnected. • CCRM disconnected. • Key on. For 3.0L SHO with DTC 556: — Measure voltage between Test Pin 41 and the battery negative post. • For all others: — Measure voltage between Test Pin 22 and the battery negative post. • **Is voltage less than 1.0 volt?**	Yes	▶	GO to **X74**.
	No	▶	SERVICE short to power. REMOVE breakout box. RECONNECT all components. RERUN Quick Test. If DTC 556/557 is still present, REPLACE PCM.

Fig. 228   Test X: CCRM (Part 23 of 39). 1993

TEST STEP	RESULT	▶	ACTION TO TAKE
X74 CHECK APPROPRIATE FUEL PUMP CIRCUIT FOR SHORT TO GROUND			
• Key off. • Breakout box installed, PCM disconnected. • CCRM disconnected. • Key on. For 3.0L SHO with DTC 556: — Measure voltage between Test Pin 41 and the battery negative post. • For all others: — Measure voltage between Test Pin 22 and the battery negative post. • **Is resistance greater than 10,000 ohms?**	Yes	▶	REPLACE PCM. REMOVE breakout box. RECONNECT all components. RERUN Quick Test.
	No	▶	SERVICE the appropriate fuel pump circuit short to ground. REMOVE breakout box. RECONNECT all components. RERUN Quick Test.
X75 DIAGNOSTIC TROUBLE CODE (DTC) 557: CHECK FOR VPWR TO LOW SPEED FUEL PUMP (LFP) RELAY			
DTC 557 indicates a low speed fuel pump primary circuit failure. Possible causes: — Open or shorted circuit. — Damaged LFP relay. — Damaged Powertrain Control Module (PCM). • Disconnect LFP relay. • Key on, engine off. • Measure voltage between the VPWR circuit at the LFP relay vehicle harness connector and the battery negative post. • Key off. • **Was voltage greater than 10.5 volts?**	Yes	▶	GO to **X76**.
	No	▶	SERVICE open in VPWR circuit between CCRM and LFP relay. RERUN Quick Test.

LFP (PCM 32)   B(+)
VPWR
POWER-TO-PUMP (AND DROPPING RESISTOR)
LFP RELAY
VEHICLE HARNESS CONNECTOR

Fig. 228   Test X: CCRM (Part 24 of 39). 1993

TEST STEP	RESULT	▶	ACTION TO TAKE
X76 CHECK LFP RELAY			
• Key off. • LFP relay disconnected. • DVOM on 200 ohm scale. • Measure LFP relay coil resistance between the LFP pin and VPWR pin at the fuel pump relay. Resistance should be between 40 and 85 ohms. • DVOM on 10,000 ohm scale. • Check LFP relay for internal shorts: Measure resistance between the LFP pin and both the power-to-pump and B(+) pins. Both resistances should be greater than 10,000 ohms. • **Are all resistance checks OK?**	Yes	▶	GO to **X77**.
	No	▶	REPLACE LFP relay. RERUN Quick Test.

87   B(+)
VPWR   87A
LFP
30
POWER-TO-PUMP

TEST STEP	RESULT	▶	ACTION TO TAKE
X77 CHECK LFP CIRCUIT FOR SHORT TO POWER			
• Key off. • LFP relay disconnected. • Disconnect PCM. Inspect for damaged or pushed out pins, corrosion, loose wires, etc. Service as necessary. • Install breakout box, leave PCM disconnected. • Key on, engine off. • Measure voltage between Test Pin 32 at the breakout box and battery negative post. • **Is voltage less than 1.0 volt?**	Yes	▶	GO to **X78**.
	No	▶	SERVICE short circuit. REMOVE breakout box. RECONNECT all components. RERUN Quick Test.
X78 CHECK LFP CIRCUIT FOR SHORT TO GROUND			
• Key off. • Breakout box installed, PCM disconnected. • LFP relay disconnected. • Measure resistance between Test Pin 32 and Test Pins 40 and 60 at the breakout box. • **Is resistance greater than 10,000 ohms?**	Yes	▶	GO to **X79**.
	No	▶	SERVICE short circuit. REMOVE breakout box. RECONNECT all components. RERUN Quick Test.

Fig. 228   Test X: CCRM (Part 25 of 39). 1993

TEST STEP	RESULT	▶	ACTION TO TAKE
X79 CHECK LFP CIRCUIT CONTINUITY • Key off. • Breakout box installed, PCM disconnected. • LFP relay disconnected. • Measure resistance between the LFP circuit at the LFP relay vehicle harness connector and Test Pin 32 at the breakout box. • **Is resistance less than 5.0 ohms?**	Yes No	▶ ▶	REPLACE PCM. RECONNECT LFP relay. RERUN Quick Test. SERVICE open circuit. REMOVE breakout box. RECONNECT all components. RERUN Quick Test.
X80 DIAGNOSTIC TROUBLE CODE (DTC) 542: DOES ENGINE START Diagnostic Trouble Code (DTC) 542 indicates that one of the following has occurred: No Start: — Inertia Fuel Shutoff (IFS) switch not reset or electrically open (if in secondary circuit). — Open circuit between the fuel pump and FPM circuit connection to power-to-pump circuit. — Poor fuel pump ground. — Fuel pump electrically open. Engine Starts: — Fuel pump secondary circuit short to power. — Fuel pump relay contacts always closed. — Open in FPM circuit between PCM and connection to power-to-pump circuit. — Left / Front HO2S short to power (dual HO2S applications). — Damaged PCM. • **Does the engine start?**	Yes No	▶ ▶	GO to **X81**. For Tempo / Topaz: REFER to Fuel / Engine (Electric Fuel Pump) for open in power-to-pump circuit, poor fuel pump ground, open in fuel pump, etc. All others: GO to **X85**.
X81 VERIFY THAT FUEL PUMP IS OFF • Key on, wait 5 seconds. • Listen for motor noise from fuel pump. • **Is fuel pump off?**	Yes No	▶ ▶	GO to **X84** For 3.0L Taurus Flexible Fuel (FF): GO to **X82** All others: GO to **X83**.
X82 CHECK FOR LOW SPEED FUEL PUMP (LFP) RELAY ALWAYS CLOSED • Key off. • Disconnect LFP relay. • Key on, wait 5 seconds. • **Does fuel pump shut off when LFP relay is disconnected?**	Yes No	▶ ▶	REPLACE LFP relay. RERUN Quick Test. Key off, GO to **X83**

Fig. 228   Test X: CCRM (Part 26 of 39). 1993

TEST STEP	RESULT	▶	ACTION TO TAKE
X83 CHECK FOR FUEL PUMP RELAY ALWAYS CLOSED • Key off. • Disconnect CCRM. • Key on, wait 5 seconds. • **Does fuel pump shut off when CCRM is disconnected?**	Yes No	▶ ▶	REPLACE CCRM. RERUN Quick Test. SERVICE short to power in power-to-pump/FPM circuit. RECONNECT CCRM. RERUN Quick Test.
X84 CHECK FPM CIRCUIT CONTINUITY • Key off. • Disconnect Powertrain Control Module (PCM). Inspect for damaged or pushed out pins, corrosion, loose wires, etc. Service as necessary. • Install breakout box, leave PCM disconnected. • Disconnect CCRM. • Measure resistance between Test Pin 8 (Test Pin 19 for 3.0L SHO) at the breakout box and Pin 5 at the CCRM vehicle harness connector. • **Is resistance less than 5.0 ohms?**	Yes No	▶ ▶	For dual HO2S applications: GO to **X86**. All others: REPLACE PCM. RECONNECT CCRM. RERUN Quick Test. SERVICE open circuit. REMOVE breakout box. RECONNECT all components. RERUN Quick Test.
X85 CHECK INERTIA FUEL SHUTOFF SWITCH • Key off. • Locate and disconnect Inertia Fuel Shutoff (IFS) switch (verify that switch is reset). • Measure resistance between the "C" and "NC" pins of the IFS switch. • **Is resistance less than 5.0 ohms?**	Yes No	▶ ▶	RECONNECT IFS switch. REFER to Fuel / Engine (Electric Fuel Pump) for open in power-to-pump circuit, poor fuel pump ground, open in fuel pump, etc. REPLACE or RESET IFS switch. RERUN Quick Test.

1993 Powertrain Control Emissions Diagnosis July, 1992

Fig. 228   Test X: CCRM (Part 27 of 39). 1993

TEST STEP	RESULT	▶	ACTION TO TAKE
X86 CHECK FRONT / LEFT HO2S FOR SHORT TO POWER **NOTE: Due to the internal circuitry of the PCM, a Left / Front HO2S signal short to power could produce a DTC 542 / 543.** • Key off. • Disconnect left or front HO2S. • Measure resistance between HO2S signal pin and KEY POWER pin at the HO2S connector. • **Is resistance greater than 10,000 ohms?**	Yes No	▶ ▶	GO to **X87**. REPLACE HO2S. REMOVE breakout box. RECONNECT all components. RERUN Quick Test.

TEST STEP	RESULT	▶	ACTION TO TAKE
X87 CHECK HO2S CIRCUIT FOR SHORT TO POWER • Key off. • Left or Front HO2S disconnected. • Disconnect Powertrain Control Module (PCM). Inspect for damaged or pushed out pins, corrosion, loose wires, etc. Service as necessary. Leave PCM disconnected. • Key on. • Measure voltage between the HO2S signal at the HO2S vehicle harness connector and chassis ground. • **Is voltage less than 1.0 volt?**	Yes No	▶ ▶	REPLACE PCM. RECONNECT HO2S. RERUN Quick Test. SERVICE short circuit. RECONNECT PCM and HO2S. RERUN Quick Test.

Fig. 228   Test X: CCRM (Part 28 of 39). 1993

TEST STEP	RESULT	▶	ACTION TO TAKE
X88 DIAGNOSTIC TROUBLE CODE (DTC) 524: CHECK B(+) TO LOW SPEED FUEL PUMP (LFP) RELAY NOTE: If Key On Engine Off DTC 543 is also present, GO to **X90**. DTC 524 indicates a Low Speed Fuel Pump (LFP) secondary circuit failure. Possible causes (without DTC 543): — Open B(+) circuit to LFP relay. — Open power-to-pump circuit between LFP relay and splice to "common" power-to-pump circuit. — Damaged fuel pump dropping resistor. — Damaged LFP relay. — Damaged PCM. • Key off. • Disconnect LFP relay. • Measure voltage between the B(+) circuit at the LFP relay vehicle harness connector and the battery negative post. • **Is voltage greater than 10.5 volts?**	Yes No	▶ ▶	GO to **X89**. VERIFY condition of related fuses. If OK, SERVICE open in B(+) circuit to LFP relay. RECONNECT LFP relay. RERUN Quick Test.
X89 CHECK POWER-TO-PUMP CIRCUIT CONTINUITY BETWEEN LFP RELAY AND CCRM • Key off. • LFP relay disconnected. • Disconnect CCRM. • Measure resistance between Pin 5 of the CCRM vehicle harness connector and the power-to-pump circuit at the LFP relay vehicle harness connector. • **Is resistance less than 10.0 ohms?**	Yes No	▶ ▶	REPLACE LFP relay. RECONNECT all components. RERUN Quick Test. VERIFY condition of Fuel Pump Dropping Resistor (about 1 ohm resistance). If OK, SERVICE open in power-to-pump circuit between LFP relay and splice to "common" power-to-pump circuit. RECONNECT all components. RERUN Quick Test.

Fig. 228   Test X: CCRM (Part 29 of 39). 1993

Fig. 228 Test X: CCRM (Part 30 of 39). 1993

TEST STEP		RESULT	▶	ACTION TO TAKE
X90	**DIAGNOSTIC TROUBLE CODE (DTC) 543: DOES ENGINE START**			
	Diagnostic Trouble Code (DTC) 543 indicates a fuel pump secondary circuit between the B(+) supply and the FPM connection to the power-to-pump circuit. Possible causes: No Starts:	Yes	▶	For 3.0L Taurus SHO and 3.0L Taurus Flexible Fuel (FF): GO TO **X93**. For all other dual HO2S applications: GO TO **X86**. For single HO2S applications: REPLACE PCM. RERUN Quick Test.
	— Open circuit between the B(+) supply and the FPM connection to the power-to-pump circuit. — Fuel pump relay contacts alway open. Engine Starts: — Left / Front HO2S short to power — Damaged Powertrain Control Module (PCM). — High Speed Fuel Pump relay contacts always open (3.0L SHO, 3.0L FF) — B(+) open to high speed fuel pump relay (3.0L SHO, 3.0L FF) — Power-to-pump open between CCRM and splice to LFP relay (3.0L FF) ● **Does the engine start?**	No	▶	GO to **X91**.
X91	**CHECK B(+) SUPPLY TO FUEL PUMP RELAY(S)**			
	● Key off. ● Disconnect CCRM. ● Measure voltage between Pin 12 at the CCRM vehicle harness connector and battery negative post. ● **Is voltage greater than 10.5 volts?**	Yes	▶	GO to **X92**.
		No	▶	VERIFY integrity of fuse / fuse link for B(+) supply to CCRM (fuel pump relay). If OK, SERVICE open in B(+) supply to CCRM. RECONNECT CCRM. RERUN Quick Test.
X92	**CHECK POWER-TO-PUMP CIRCUIT CONTINUITY**			
	● Key off. ● CCRM disconnected. ● Measure resistance between Pin 5 at the CCRM vehicle harness connector and the battery negative post. ● **Is resistance less than 10.0 ohms?**	Yes	▶	REPLACE CCRM. RERUN Quick Test.
		No	▶	SERVICE open in power-to-pump circuit between FPM splice and CCRM. RECONNECT CCRM. RERUN Quick Test.

FM0159300769300X

Fig. 228   Test X: CCRM (Part 30 of 39). 1993

Fig. 228 Test X: CCRM (Part 31 of 39). 1993

TEST STEP		RESULT	▶	ACTION TO TAKE
X93	**CHECK B(+) SUPPLY TO HIGH SPEED FUEL PUMP RELAY**			
	● Key off. ● Disconnect CCRM. ● Measure voltage between Pin 12 at the CCRM vehicle harness connector and battery negative post. ● **Is voltage greater than 10.5 volts?**	Yes	▶	For 3.0L Taurus FF: GO TO **X94**. For 3.0L Taurus SHO: GO TO **X95**.
		No	▶	SERVICE open in B(+) circuit between CCRM and B(+) splice to the High Speed and Low Speed Fuel Pump relays. RECONNECT CCRM. RERUN Quick Test.
X94	**CHECK POWER-TO-PUMP CONTINUITY BETWEEN CCRM AND IFS SWITCH**			
	● Key off. ● CCRM disconnected. ● Disconnect Inertia Fuel Shutoff (IFS) switch. ● Measure resistance between Pin 5 at the CCRM vehicle harness connector and the power-to-pump circuit from the CCRM circuit at the IFS switch vehicle harness connector. ● **Is resistance less than 5.0 ohms?**	Yes	▶	GO to **X95**.
		No	▶	SERVICE open in power-to-pump circuit between CCRM and splice to LFP relay. RECONNECT all components. RERUN Quick Test.
X95	**CHECK PCM ABILITY TO MONITOR FPM**			
	● Key off. ● Reconnect CCRM. ● Disconnect Inertia Fuel Shutoff switch (if applicable). ● Rerun Key On Engine Off Self-Test. ● **Is KOEO DTC 542 present?**	Yes	▶	REPLACE CCRM. RECONNECT Inertia Fuel Shutoff switch. RERUN Quick Test.
		No	▶	REPLACE PCM. RECONNECT Inertia Fuel Shutoff switch. RERUN Quick Test.

FM0159300769310X

Fig. 228   Test X: CCRM (Part 31 of 39). 1993

Fig. 228 Test X: CCRM (Part 32 of 39). 1993

TEST STEP		RESULT	▶	ACTION TO TAKE
X98	**DIAGNOSTIC TROUBLE CODE (DTC) 524: CHECK FOR B(+) SUPPLY TO LOW SPEED FUEL PUMP RELAY**			
	NOTE: If Key On Engine Off Diagnostic Trouble Code (DTC) 543 is also present, go to **X90**. DTC 524 indicates a Low Speed Fuel Pump secondary circuit failure. Possible causes (without DTC 543): — Open B(+) circuit to Low Speed Fuel Pump relay. — Damaged CCRM. ● Key off. ● Disconnect CCRM. ● Measure voltage between Pin 10 at the CCRM vehicle harness connector and battery negative post. ● **Is voltage greater than 10.5 volts?**	Yes	▶	REPLACE CCRM. RERUN Quick Test.
		No	▶	SERVICE open in B(+) circuit between the CCRM and B(+) splice to Low Speed and High Speed Fuel Pump relays. RECONNECT CCRM. RERUN Quick Test.

FM0159300769320X

Fig. 228   Test X: CCRM (Part 32 of 39). 1993

Fig. 228 Test X: CCRM (Part 33 of 39). 1993

TEST STEP		RESULT	▶	ACTION TO TAKE
X105	**CONTINUOUS MEMORY DIAGNOSTIC TROUBLE CODE (DTC) 542: CHECK EEC-IV HARNESS**			
	A Continuous Memory DTC 542 indicates that one of the following intermittent conditions has occurred:	Yes	▶	ISOLATE fault and SERVICE as necessary. CLEAR Continuous Memory DTC RERUN Quick Test.
	— Fuel pump circuit activated when PCM expected circuit to be off (i.e. fuel system test or prime procedure). — Inertia Fuel Shutoff switch reset (except Tempo / Topaz). — Open circuit in or between the fuel pump and FPM circuit at the PCM (refer to schematic). — Poor fuel pump ground. — FPM or power-to-pump circuit short to power. — Fuel pump relay contacts stuck closed. — Left / Front HO2S circuit short to power (w / dual HO2S). — Engine stall due to excessive load. ● Start engine. ● Check for engine stall / stumble while performing the following (also, if possible, listen for fuel pump turning off.) — Shake, wiggle, bend the Power-To-Pump circuit between the CCRM Pin 5 and the fuel pump. — Shake, wiggle, bend the fuel pump ground circuit from the fuel pump to ground. — Lightly tap the fuel pump to simulate road shock. — For all except Tempo / Topaz, lightly tap Inertia Fuel Shutoff switch to simulate road shock. — For 3.0L Taurus Flexible Fuel (FF), also shake, wiggle, bend the power-to-pump circuit to the Low Speed Fuel Pump (LFP) relay and lightly tap the LFP relay to simulate road shock. ● Key off. ● Inspect the fuel pump vehicle harness connector and the fuel pump ground for corrosion, damaged pins, etc. ● **Is fault indicated found?**	No	▶	GO to **X106**.

FM0159300769330X

Fig. 228   Test X: CCRM (Part 33 of 39). 1993

TEST STEP	RESULT	▶	ACTION TO TAKE
X106 CHECK FPM CIRCUIT			
• Key off. • Disconnect PCM. Inspect for damaged or pushed out pins, corrosion, loose wires, etc. Service as necessary. • Install breakout box, leave PCM disconnected. • Key on, engine off. • Connect a test lamp between Test Pin 8 (Test Pin 19 for 3.0L SHO) and Test Pin 37 at the breakout box. • Observe test lamp for an indication of a fault while performing the following (The light will go out when a fault is found, indicating an open): — Shake, wiggle, bend the Fuel Pump Monitor circuit between the splice into the power-to-pump circuit and the PCM. • **Is fault indicated?**	Yes No	▶ ▶	ISOLATE fault and SERVICE as necessary. REMOVE breakout box. RECONNECT PCM. RERUN Quick Test. GO to X107
X107 CHECK FOR SHORTS TO POWER			

• Key on, engine off.
 • Breakout box installed, PCM disconnected.
 • Connect a test lamp between Test Pin 8 (Test Pin 19 for 3.0L SHO) and Test Pin 40.
 • Observe test lamp for an indication of a fault while performing the following (The lamp will turn on when a fault is detected, indicating a short to power. Also, if possible, listen for fuel pump turning on.):
   — Shake, wiggle, bend the Fuel Pump Monitor circuit and power-to-pump circuit, especially where they may be in the vicinity of a power circuit.
   — For 3.0L FF, also shake, wiggle, bend the power-to-pump circuit to the Low Speed Fuel Pump (LFP) relay and lightly tap the LFP relay to simulate road shock.
 • Lightly tap the CCRM (to simulate road shock).
 • **Is fault indicated?**
	Yes
	
	 No
		▶
		
		 ▶
			ISOLATE fault and SERVICE as necessary. REMOVE breakout box. RECONNECT PCM. RERUN Quick Test.
			
			 For dual HO2S applications: GO to X116. All others: further diagnosis using the EEC-IV monitor box or Scan Tool
			
			 If an EEC-IV monitor box or Scan Tool is not available, GO to X120.

X110 CONTINUOUS MEMORY DIAGNOSTIC TROUBLE CODE (DTC) 524/543: CHECK FOR CONTINUOUS MEMORY DTC 556/557			
• Is Continuous Memory DTC 556 or 557 also present?	Yes No	▶ ▶	GO to X115. GO to X111.

FM0159300769340X

Fig. 228 Test X: CCRM (Part 34 of 39). 1993

TEST STEP	RESULT	▶	ACTION TO TAKE
X111 CHECK EEC-IV HARNESS			

A Continuous Memory DTC 524/543, without the presence of a Continuous Memory DTC 556/557, indicates that during vehicle operation, one of the following has occurred (For the 3.0L SHO and 3.0L Taurus Flexible Fuel (FF), DTC 524 refers to the Low Speed Fuel Pump circuit and DTC 543 refers to the High Speed Fuel Pump circuit. Also, for the 3.0L FF the Low Speed Fuel Pump (LFP) relay is external to the CCRM):
   — Open in the B(+) circuit between B(+) and the fuel pump relay.
   — Fuel pump relay contacts opened.
   — Open in the power-to-pump circuit from the CCRM/LFP relay to the FPM splice.
   — Left/Front HO2S circuit short to power (w/ dual HO2S).
 • Start engine.
 • Check for engine stall/stumble while performing the following (also, if possible, listen for fuel pump turning off):
   — Shake, wiggle, bend the B(+) circuit from B(+) to the CCRM/LFP relay.
   — Lightly tap the CCRM/LFP relay (to simulate road shock).
   — Shake, wiggle, bend the power-to-pump circuit from the fuel CCRM/LFP relay to the FPM splice.
 • Key off.
 • Inspect the CCRM/LFP relay connectors and B(+) connector terminal for corrosion, damaged pins, etc.
 • **Is fault indicated/found?**
	Yes
	
	 No
		▶
		
		 ▶
			ISOLATE fault and SERVICE as necessary. CLEAR Continuous Memory DTC. RERUN Quick Test.
			
			 Under certain conditions, a Continuous Memory DTC 524/543 may have been set without a Continuous Memory DTC 556/557, even though a fault has occurred in the fuel pump primary circuit. GO to X115 to check the fuel pump primary circuit.

FM0159300769350X

Fig. 228 Test X: CCRM (Part 35 of 39). 1993

TEST STEP	RESULT	▶	ACTION TO TAKE
X115 CONTINUOUS MEMORY DIAGNOSTIC TROUBLE CODE (DTC) 556/557: CHECK EEC-IV HARNESS			

A Continuous Memory DTC 556/557 indicates that a fuel pump primary circuit failure has occurred during vehicle operation (for the 3.0L SHO and 3.0L Taurus Flexible Fuel (FF), DTC 556 refers to the High Speed Fuel Pump primary circuit and DTC 557 refers to the Low Speed Fuel Pump primary circuit). Possible causes are:
   — Open VPWR in the CCRM.
   — Open coil in fuel pump relay.
   — Open in fuel pump circuit (PCM Pin 22, 32 or 41).
   — Inertia Fuel Shutoff switch reset (Tempo/Topaz).
   — Open VPWR to LFP relay (3.0L FF).
 • Start engine.
 • Check for engine stall/stumble while performing the following (also, if possible, listen for fuel pump turning off):
   — Shake, wiggle, bend the EEC-IV vehicle harness fuel pump circuit (Pin 22 or 32) between the PCM and the CCRM.
   — Lightly tap the Inertia Fuel Shutoff (IFS) switch to simulate road shock (Tempo/Topaz).
   — Lightly tap the CCRM to simulate road shock.
   — For 3.0L FF with DTC 557, shake, wiggle, bend the VPWR circuit between the CCRM and LFP relay. Also tap on the LFP relay to simulate road shock.
 • Key off.
 • Inspect the PCM connector and the fuel pump relay connectors for corrosion, damaged pins, etc.
 • **Is fault indicated/found?**
	Yes
	
	 No
		▶
		
		 ▶
			ISOLATE fault and SERVICE as necessary. CLEAR Continuous Memory RERUN Quick Test.
			
			 For dual HO2S applications with a DTC 524/543 only: GO to X116. ALL others: further diagnosis using the EEC-IV monitor box or Scan Tool
			
			 If an EEC-IV monitor box or Scan Tool is not available, GO to X120.

FM0159300769360X

Fig. 228 Test X: CCRM (Part 36 of 39). 1993

TEST STEP	RESULT	▶	ACTION TO TAKE
X116 CHECK LEFT/FRONT HO2S CIRCUIT FOR SHORT TO POWER			

NOTE: Due to the internal circuitry of the PCM, an intermittent left/front HO2S signal short to power could produce a Continuous Memory DTC 542 or 524/543.
 • Key off.
 • Install breakout box, if applicable.
 • Breakout box installed, PCM disconnected.
 • Connect a test lamp between the left/front HO2S test pin and test pin 40 at the breakout box (Refer to pinpoint test **H** cover page for appropriate HO2S test pin).
 • Key on, engine off.
 • Observe test lamp for an indication of a fault while performing the following (the light will turn on bright when a fault is detected):
   — Shake, wiggle, bend the left/front HO2S circuit from the HO2S sensor to the PCM.
   — Lightly tap the HO2S sensor (to simulate road shock).
 • **Is fault indicated?**
	Yes
	
	 No
		▶
		
		 ▶
			ISOLATE fault and SERVICE as necessary. REMOVE breakout box. RECONNECT PCM. RERUN Quick Test.
			
			 further diagnosis using an EEC-IV monitor box or Scan Tool
			
			 If an EEC-IV monitor box or Scan Tool is not available, GO to X120.

FM0159300769370X

Fig. 228 Test X: CCRM (Part 37 of 39). 1993

X120 ROAD TEST

The purpose of the road test is to identify an area of concern by monitoring certain controlled parameters while trying to re-create a driveability or MIL symptom.

Note

A basic working knowledge of the EEC-IV system is critical to effectively analyze road test data.

WARNING

THIS ROAD TEST IS A SUGGESTED BUT OPTIONAL PROCEDURE. ALL APPLICABLE SAFETY PROCEDURES AND TRAFFIC LAWS MUST BE FOLLOWED. IN ORDER FOR A ROAD TEST TO BE PERFORMED IT IS REQUIRED THAT ANOTHER PERSON ACCOMPANY THE DRIVER. THE ACCOMPANYING PERSON CAN MAKE MEASUREMENTS, OBSERVE CHANGES AND RECORD NOTES. IF FOR SOME REASON THIS TEST IS NOT PERFORMED, RETURN TO **Diagnostic Routines**

Prepare Vehicle For A Road Test

- Install breakout box, if applicable.
- Breakout box installed, PCM connected.
- Install fuel pressure gauge and MAP BARO tester (optional).
- Other materials needed: DVOM, pencil, paper, appropriate schematic pin usage sheet

Preliminary Power Ground Checks

- With the key ON and a DVOM referenced to the battery negative post, check the following signals for correct values.

POWERS: KAPWR > 10.5V (Pin 1), VPWR > 10.5V (Pins 37 57), VREF 5 ± 1V (Pin 26)
GROUNDS: (all = 0 ± .5V) PWR GND (Pins 40 60), SIG RTN (Pin 46), IGN GND (Pin 16)
OPTIONAL GROUNDS: HO2S GND (Pin 49), CSE GND (Pin 20), MAF RTN (Pin 9 or 15)

Obtaining Other Needed Information And Materials Before The Road Test

- Refer to the Symptom Charts looking at the chart(s) that most resembles the vehicle's driveability or MIL symptom Before the road test, perform the Visual Mechanical Checks that are listed Next, list the PCM sensors and actuators in the order given. These circuits, along with the FP FPM signal(s), are the main signals that will be monitored

Fig. 228 Test X: CCRM (Part 38 of 39). 1993

X120 ROAD TEST (Continued)

- Refer to the proper Diagnostic Reference Value Sheet   Although these charts were designed for use with the EEC-IV monitor box, most of the values can be read using the breakout box and a DVOM (with the DVOM referenced to ground all values in DCV units can be used; other values may also be helpful, ex., MAP Hz using the MAP / BARO tester).

- The use of test lamp(s) and a DVOM may also aid diagnosis. Depending on the DTC being diagnosed, the FP / FPM circuits could be monitored as well as the circuits to / from the Inertia Fuel Shutoff switch, the Left / Front HO2S circuit, etc. Remember, if the vehicle stalls the PCM will "unground" the FP circuit and turn off the fuel pump. If the problem is in the fuel pump wiring the lamp / voltage should change just BEFORE the symptom occurs.

NOTE: Due to the low resistance of some test lamps, it is recommended that a DVOM or equivalent high resistance testing device be used when monitoring PCM output circuits.

Road Test

- After starting the engine for the road test, enter Engine Running Continuous Monitor Diagnostic Test Mode

- Drive the vehicle to create the conditions so that the symptom will occur. If the Customer Information Worksheet   has been completed, this information may help when trying to re-create the symptom.

- When the symptom occurs, the accompanying passenger should observe changes in listed PCM signals. Information about the symptom, operating condition value of the PCM signal or other notes should be recorded onto paper.

- If you are unable to duplicate the symptom, it may still be helpful to verify that the PCM values are in the expected range.

Analyzing The Data

- Once the road test is completed, the results need to be analyzed to locate and service the exact fault which caused the symptom.

Fig. 228 Test X: CCRM (Part 39 of 39). 1993

Note

You should enter this Pinpoint Test only when directed here from Diagnostic Routines   or from Pinpoint Tests C, PA or PB.

Remember

To prevent the replacement of good components, be aware that the following non-EEC areas may be at fault:

- Fuel system
- Fuel Contamination
- A/C system
- Starting / charging system

This Pinpoint Test is intended to diagnose only the following:

- Constant Control Relay Module (CCRM)
  — EEC Power Relay
  — FC / LFC Relay
  — HFC Relay
  — WAC Relay
  — FP Relay
- Pusher Fan Control Relay
- Harness circuits: B+, KPWR, PWR GND, FP, LFP, HFP, FC, LFC, HFC, PFC, A/C, ACCS, ACPSW, WAC
- Powertrain Control Module (PCM)

Description

Constant Control Relay Module (CCRM)

The Constant Control Relay Module (CCRM) interfaces with the EEC-IV system to provide control for the cooling fan, A/C clutch and the fuel pump. The CCRM also contains the EEC power relay which provides vehicle battery power (VPWR) to the Powertrain Control Module (PCM) and EEC-IV system. Refer to the following schematics for specific CCRM relay control.

Fig. 229 Test X: CCRM (Part 1 of 55). 1994–95

Pusher Fan (Thunderbird SC)

The Thunderbird SC has a pusher fan for additional cooling. The pusher fan is located in front of the radiator and uses a stand-alone relay that is controlled by the PCM.

Dual and Single Function A/C Pressure Switch (ACPSW) (also known as Refrigerant Containment Switch)

The ACPSW is used on some applications for additional A/C system pressure control and is also known as the refrigerant containment switch. The normally open medium pressure contacts close at a predetermined A/C head pressure and are used on all CCRM applications except the 2.3L Tempo / Topaz. This grounds the input to the PCM indicating that the high speed cooling fan is required. For the 3.0L SHO and Taurus Flex Fuel, the medium pressure ACPSW circuit is not wired to the PCM, but is wired directly to the CCRM for high speed cooling fan control. The normally closed high pressure contracts are used on all CCRM applications and open at a predetermined A/C head pressure. This turns off the A/C by opening the A/C demand circuit preventing the A/C pressure from rising to a level that would open the A/C high pressure relief valve. For additional information, refer to the Ventilation / Climate Control group of the service manual.

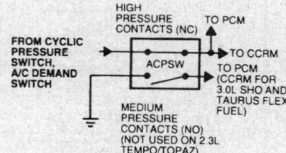

Fig. 229 Test X: CCRM (Part 2 of 55). 1994

Pinpoint Test Schematics

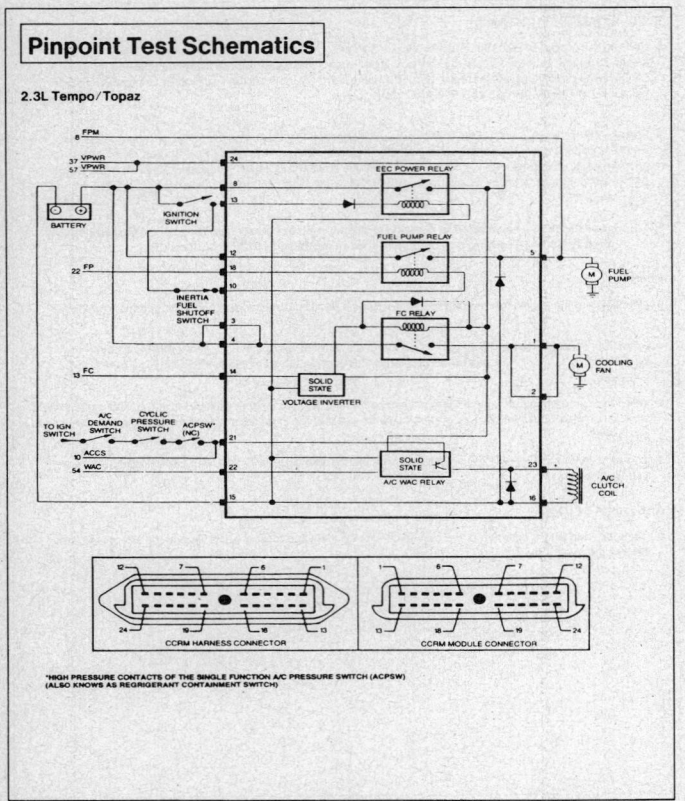

Fig. 229   Test X: CCRM (Part 3 of 55). 1994

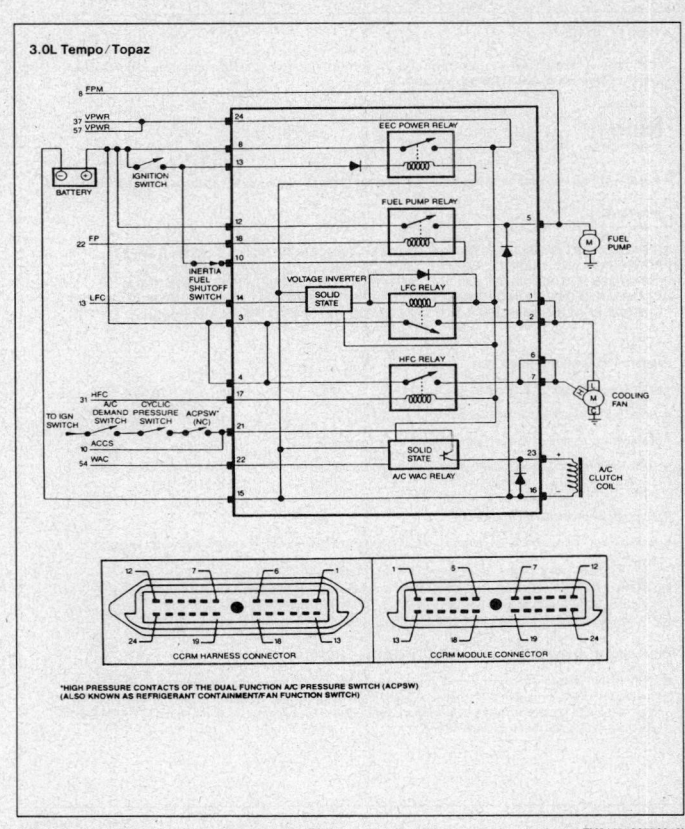

Fig. 229   Test X: CCRM (Part 4 of 55). 1994

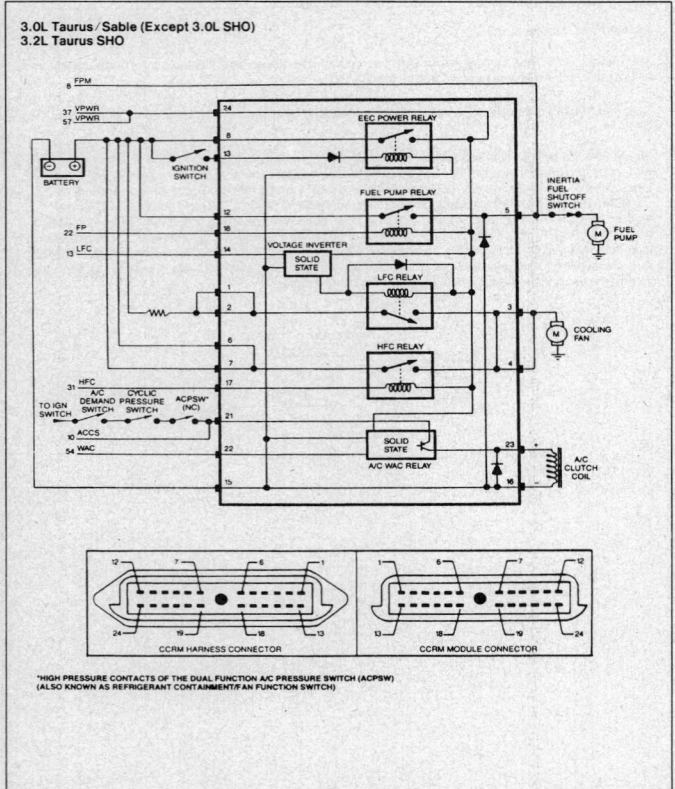

Fig. 229   Test X: CCRM (Part 5 of 55). 1994–95

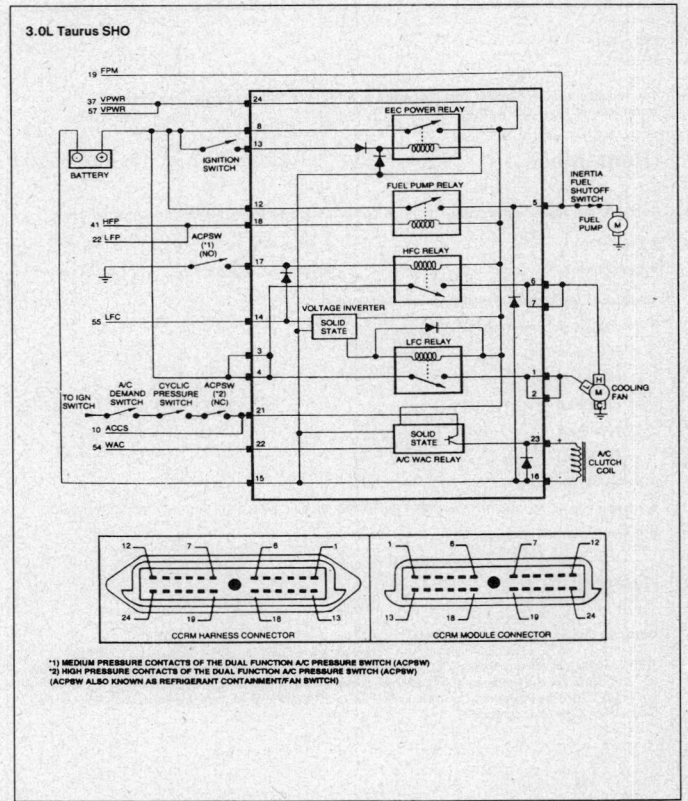

Fig. 229   Test X: CCRM (Part 6 of 55). 1994–95

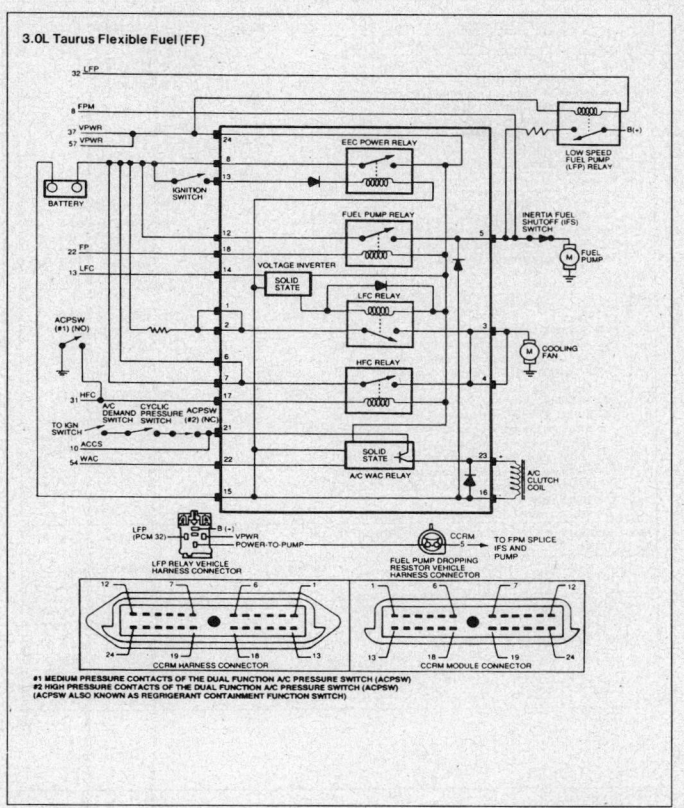

Fig. 229 Test X: CCRM (Part 7 of 55). 1994–95

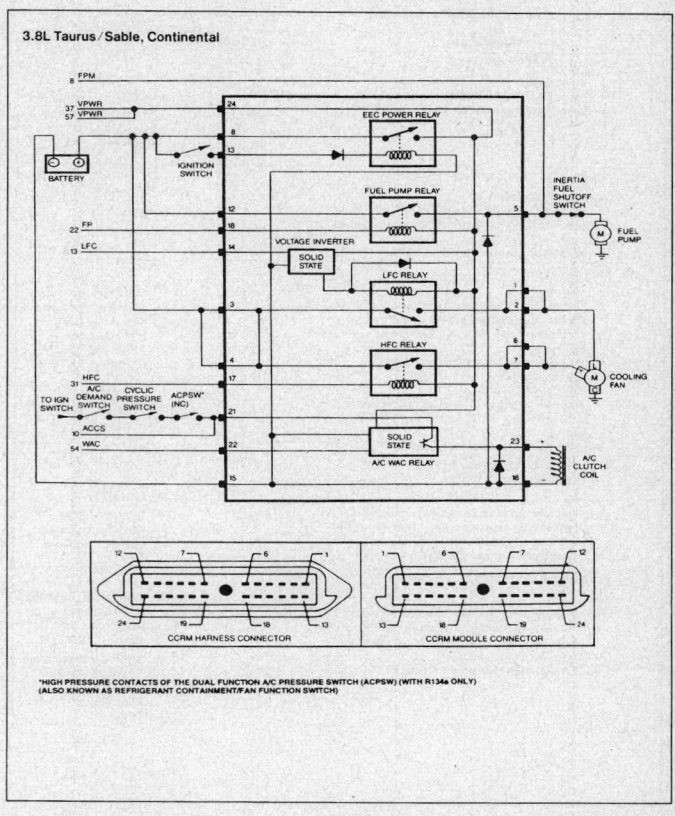

Fig. 229 Test X: CCRM (Part 8 of 55). 1994–95

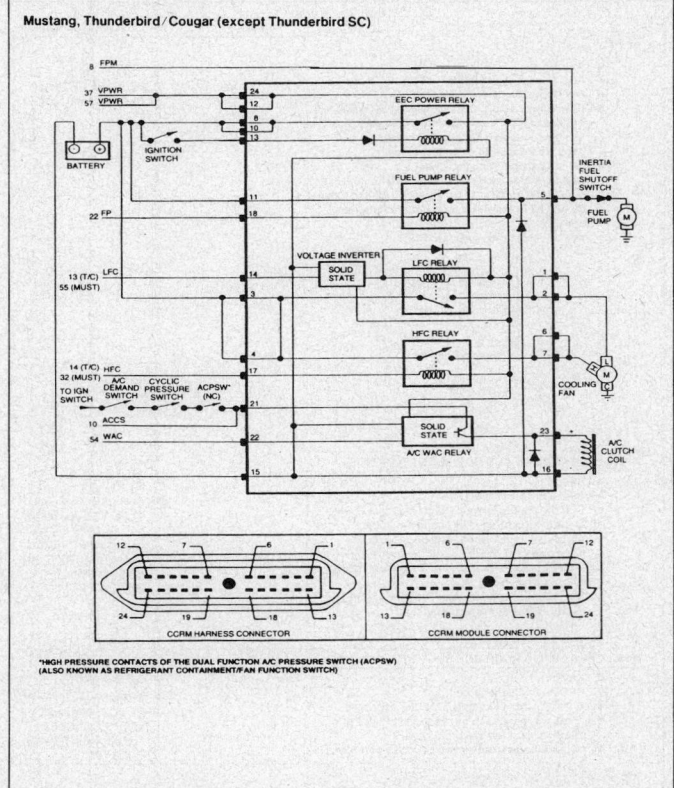

Fig. 229 Test X: CCRM (Part 9 of 55). 1994–95

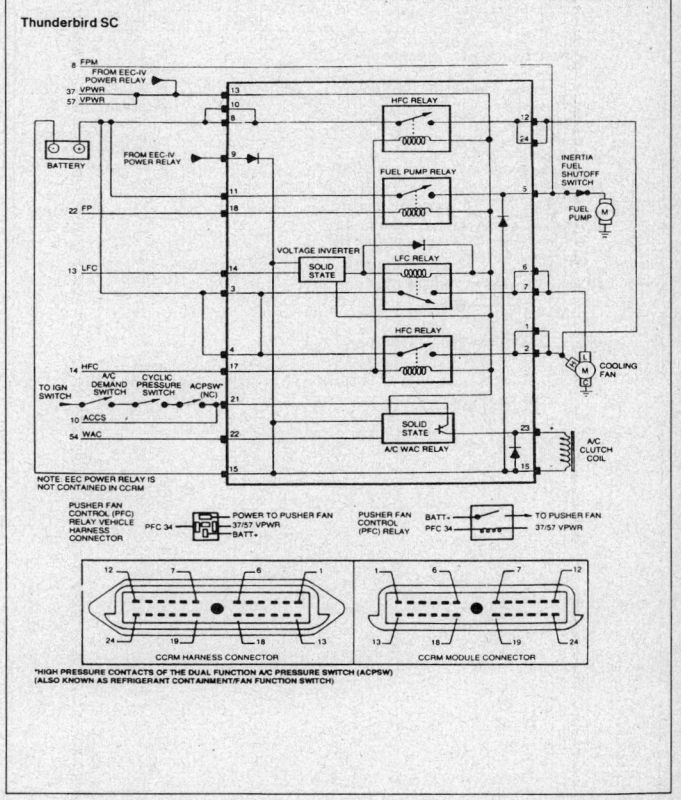

Fig. 229 Test X: CCRM (Part 10 of 55). 1994–95

TEST STEP		RESULT	▶	ACTION TO TAKE
X1	CHECK BATTERY VOLTAGE • Key on, engine off. • Measure voltage across battery terminals. • **Is voltage greater than 10.5 volts?**	Yes No	▶ ▶	GO to **X2**. SERVICE discharged battery
X2	CHECK BATTERY GROUND • Key on, engine off. • Measure voltage between SIG RTN circuit in the Data Link Connector and battery negative post. • **Is voltage greater than 0.5 volt?**	Yes No	▶ ▶	GO to **X3**. GO to **X6**.
X3	GROUND FAULT ISOLATION • Key off. • Disconnect Powertrain Control Module (PCM). Inspect for damaged or pushed out pins, corrosion, loose wires etc. Service as necessary. • Install breakout box and connect PCM to breakout box. • Key on, engine off. • Measure voltage between battery negative post and Test Pins 40 and 60 at the breakout box. • **Is each voltage less than 0.5 volt?**	Yes No	▶ ▶	GO to **X4**. SERVICE open ground circuit. REMOVE breakout box. RECONNECT PCM. RERUN Quick Test.
X4	POWERTRAIN CONTROL MODULE (PCM) GROUND FAULT ISOLATION • Key off. • Breakout box installed, PCM connected. • Measure resistance between Test Pin 46 and Test Pins 40 and 60 at the breakout box. • **Is each resistance less than 5.0 ohms?**	Yes No	▶ ▶	GO to **X5**. REPLACE PCM. REMOVE breakout box. RERUN Quick Test.
X5	CHECK SIG RTN CIRCUIT CONTINUITY • Key off. • Breakout box installed, PCM disconnected. • Measure resistance between Test Pin 46 at the breakout box and SIG RTN circuit in the Data Link Connector. • **Is resistance less than 5.0 ohms?**	Yes No	▶ ▶	System OK. REMOVE breakout box. RECONNECT PCM. RERUN Quick Test. SERVICE open circuit. REMOVE breakout box. RECONNECT PCM. RERUN Quick Test.

FM015940077011 0X

Fig. 229   Test X: CCRM (Part 11 of 55). 1994–95

TEST STEP		RESULT	▶	ACTION TO TAKE
X6	MEASURE VOLTAGE AND GROUND TO CCRM • Key off. • Disconnect CCRM. • Measure voltage between Pin 8 and Pin 15 at the CCRM vehicle harness connector. • For Mustang and Thunderbird/Cougar also measure voltage between Pin 10 and Pin 15 at the CCRM vehicle harness connector. • **Is voltage greater than 10.5 volts?**	Yes No	▶ ▶	GO to **X7**. GO to **X9**.
X7	CHECK KEY POWER TO CCRM • Key on, engine off. • CCRM disconnected. • Measure voltage between Pin 13 and Pin 15 at the CCRM vehicle harness connector. • **Is voltage greater than 10.5 volts?**	Yes No	▶ ▶	GO to **X8**. SERVICE open between Pin 13 and ignition switch. RECONNECT CCRM. RERUN Quick Test.
X8	CHECK VPWR CIRCUIT CONTINUITY • Key off. • CCRM disconnected. • Disconnect Powertrain Control Module (PCM). Inspect for damaged or pushed out pins, corrosion, loose wires, etc. Service as necessary. • Install breakout box, leave PCM disconnected. • Measure resistance between Test Pins 37 and 57 at the breakout box and Pin 24 at the CCRM vehicle harness connector. • For Mustang and Thunderbird/Cougar, also measure resistance between Test Pins 37 and 57 at the breakout box and Pin 12 at the CCRM vehicle harness connector. • **Is each resistance less than 5.0 ohms?**	Yes No	▶ ▶	REPLACE CCRM. REMOVE breakout box. RECONNECT all components. RERUN Quick Test. SERVICE open in VPWR circuit. REMOVE breakout box. RECONNECT all components. RERUN Quick Test.
X9	MEASURE CONTINUITY OF POWER GROUND TO CCRM • Key off. • CCRM disconnected. • Measure resistance between battery negative post and Pin 15 at the CCRM vehicle harness connector. • **Is resistance less than 5.0 ohms?**	Yes No	▶ ▶	SERVICE open in battery positive to CCRM Pin 8/Pin 10. RECONNECT CCRM. RERUN Quick Test. SERVICE open in battery ground to CCRM Pin 15. RECONNECT CCRM. RERUN Quick Test.

FM015940077012 0X

Fig. 229   Test X: CCRM (Part 12 of 55). 1994–95

TEST STEP		RESULT	▶	ACTION TO TAKE
X10	DIAGNOSTIC TROUBLE CODE (DTC) 562: CHECK FOR VPWR TO PUSHER FAN CONTROL (PFC) RELAY DTC 562 indicates a Pusher Fan Control (PFC) primary circuit failure. Possible causes: — Open or shorted circuit. — Damaged PFC relay. — Damaged Powertrain Control Module (PCM). • Key off. • Disconnect PFC relay. • Key on. • Measure voltage between the VPWR pin at the PFC relay vehicle harness connector and the battery negative post. • Key off. • **Was voltage greater than 10.5 volts?**	Yes No	▶ ▶	GO to **X11**. SERVICE open in VPWR circuit to PFC relay. RECONNECT PFC relay. RERUN Quick Test.

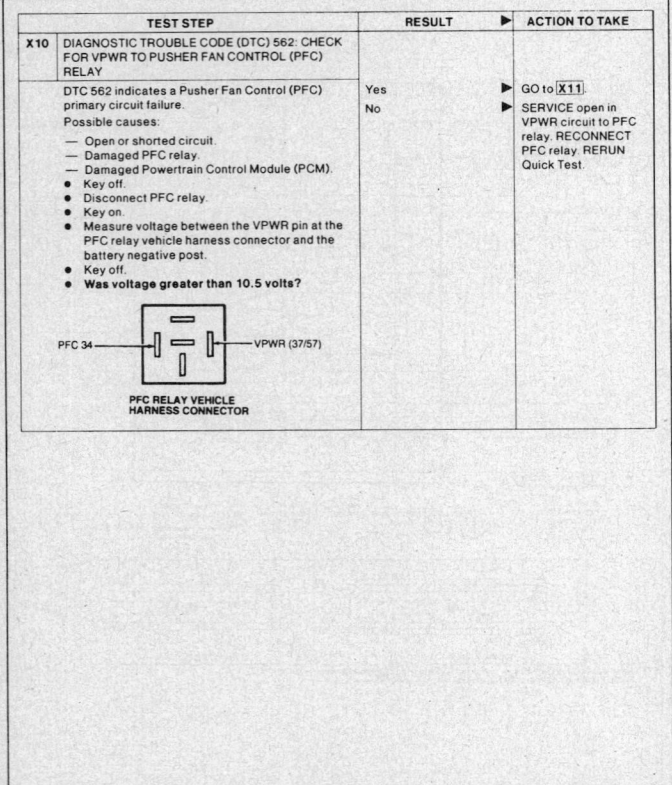

FM015940077013 0X

Fig. 229   Test X: CCRM (Part 13 of 55). 1994–95

TEST STEP		RESULT	▶	ACTION TO TAKE
X11	CHECK PFC RELAY • Key off. • PFC relay disconnected. • DVOM on 200 ohm scale. • Check PFC relay coil by measuring resistance between Pins 85 and 86 of the PFC relay (pin numbers moulded on relay). Resistance should be between 40 and 85 ohms. • DVOM on 10,000 ohms scale. • Check PFC relay for internal shorts by measuring resistance between Pin 85 and Pins 30 and 87 of the PFC relay. Both resistances should be greater than 10,000 ohms. • **Are all resistance checks OK?**	Yes No	▶ ▶	GO to **X12**. REPLACE PFC relay. RERUN Quick Test.
	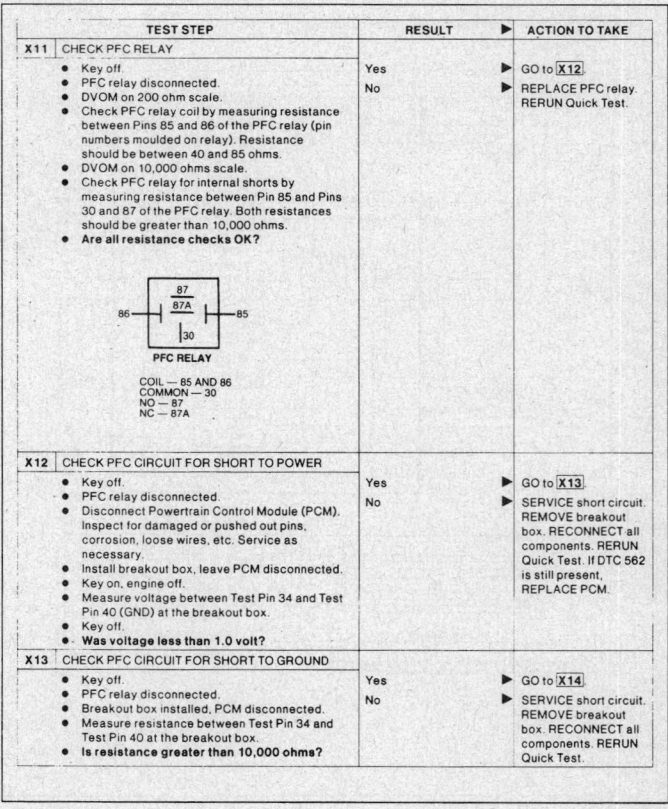			
X12	CHECK PFC CIRCUIT FOR SHORT TO POWER • Key off. • PFC relay disconnected. • Disconnect Powertrain Control Module (PCM). Inspect for damaged or pushed out pins, corrosion, loose wires, etc. Service as necessary. • Install breakout box, leave PCM disconnected. • Key on, engine off. • Measure voltage between Test Pin 34 and Test Pin 40 (GND) at the breakout box. • Key off. • **Was voltage less than 1.0 volt?**	Yes No	▶ ▶	GO to **X13**. SERVICE short circuit. REMOVE breakout box. RECONNECT all components. RERUN Quick Test. If DTC 562 is still present, REPLACE PCM.
X13	CHECK PFC CIRCUIT FOR SHORT TO GROUND • Key off. • PFC relay disconnected. • Breakout box installed, PCM disconnected. • Measure resistance between Test Pin 34 and Test Pin 40 at the breakout box. • **Is resistance greater than 10,000 ohms?**	Yes No	▶ ▶	GO to **X14**. SERVICE short circuit. REMOVE breakout box. RECONNECT all components. RERUN Quick Test.

FM015940077014 0X

Fig. 229   Test X: CCRM (Part 14 of 55). 1994–95

TEST STEP	RESULT	▶	ACTION TO TAKE
X14 CHECK PFC CIRCUIT CONTINUITY • Key off. • PFC relay disconnected. • Breakout box installed, PCM disconnected. • Measure resistance between the PFC circuit at the PFC relay vehicle harness connector and Test Pin 34 at the breakout box. • **Is resistance less than 5.0 ohms?**	Yes No	▶ ▶	REPLACE PCM. RECONNECT PFC relay. RERUN Quick Test. SERVICE open circuit. REMOVE breakout box. RECONNECT all components. RERUN Quick Test.
X15 DIAGNOSTIC TROUBLE CODE (DTC) 563: CHECK HIGH FAN CONTROL (HFC) RELAY RESISTANCE DTC 563 indicates a High Fan Control (HFC) primary circuit failure. Possible causes are: — Open or shorted circuit. — Damaged CCRM. — Damaged Powertrain Control Module (PCM). — ACPSW medium pressure contacts closed (3.0L Flex Fuel Taurus only). • Key off. • Disconnect CCRM. • Measure resistance between Pin 17 and Pin 24 (Pin 13 for Thunderbird SC) at the CCRM. • **Is the resistance between 50 ohms and 100 ohms?**	Yes No	▶ ▶	For Thunderbird SC: GO to X16. All others: GO to X17. REPLACE CCRM. RERUN Quick Test.
X16 CHECK FOR VPWR TO CCRM • Key off. • CCRM disconnected. • Key on, engine off. • Measure voltage between Pin 13 of CCRM vehicle harness connector and the battery negative post. • Key off. • **Was voltage greater than 10.5 volts?**	Yes No	▶ ▶	GO to X17. SERVICE open in VPWR circuit between EEC-IV power relay and CCRM. RECONNECT CCRM. RERUN Quick Test.

FM0159400770150X

Fig. 229   Test X: CCRM (Part 15 of 55). 1994–95

TEST STEP	RESULT	▶	ACTION TO TAKE
X17 CHECK HFC CIRCUIT CONTINUITY • Key off. • Disconnect Powertrain Control Module (PCM). Inspect for damaged or pushed out pins, corrosion, loose wires, etc. Service as necessary. • Install breakout box, leave PCM disconnected. • CCRM disconnected. • Measure resistance between the HFC Test Pin at breakout box and Pin 17 of CCRM vehicle harness connector. • **Is resistance less than 5.0 ohms?**	Yes No	▶ ▶	GO to X18. SERVICE open in HFC circuit. REMOVE breakout box. RECONNECT all components. RERUN Quick Test.

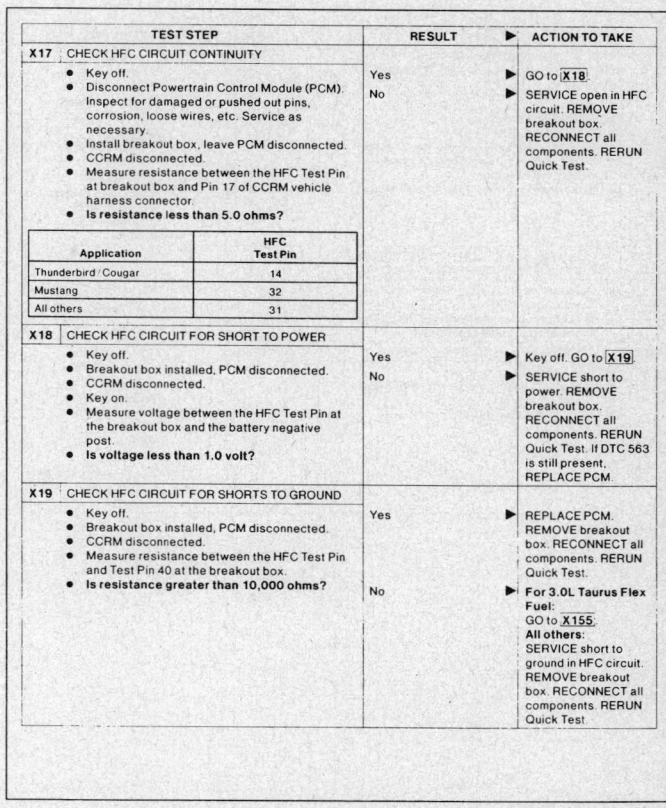

Application	HFC Test Pin
Thunderbird / Cougar	14
Mustang	32
All others	31

TEST STEP	RESULT	▶	ACTION TO TAKE
X18 CHECK HFC CIRCUIT FOR SHORT TO POWER • Key off. • Breakout box installed, PCM disconnected. • CCRM disconnected. • Key on. • Measure voltage between the HFC Test Pin at the breakout box and the battery negative post. • **Is voltage less than 1.0 volt?**	Yes No	▶ ▶	Key off. GO to X19. SERVICE short to power. REMOVE breakout box. RECONNECT all components. RERUN Quick Test. If DTC 563 is still present, REPLACE PCM.
X19 CHECK HFC CIRCUIT FOR SHORTS TO GROUND • Key off. • Breakout box installed, PCM disconnected. • CCRM disconnected. • Measure resistance between the HFC Test Pin and Test Pin 40 at the breakout box. • **Is resistance greater than 10,000 ohms?**	Yes No	▶ ▶	REPLACE PCM. REMOVE breakout box. RECONNECT all components. RERUN Quick Test. **For 3.0L Taurus Flex Fuel:** GO to X155. **All others:** SERVICE short to ground in HFC circuit. REMOVE breakout box. RECONNECT all components. RERUN Quick Test.

FM0159400770160X

Fig. 229   Test X: CCRM (Part 16 of 55). 1994–95

TEST STEP	RESULT	▶	ACTION TO TAKE
X20 DIAGNOSTIC TROUBLE CODE (DTC) 564: DOES FAN RUN WITH KEY ON? DTC 564 indicates a FC/LFC primary circuit failure. Possible causes are: — Open or shorted circuit. — Damaged CCRM. — Damaged PCM. • **Does the cooling fan always run with the key on?**	Yes No	▶ ▶	GO to X24. For Thunderbird SC: GO to X21. All others: GO to X22.
X21 CHECK FOR VPWR TO CCRM • Key off. • Disconnect CCRM. • Key on, engine off. • Measure voltage between Pin 13 at the CCRM vehicle harness connector and the battery negative post. • Key off. • **Was voltage greater than 10.5 volts?**	Yes No	▶ ▶	GO to X22. SERVICE open VPWR circuit between the EEC-IV Power Relay and the CCRM. RECONNECT CCRM. RERUN Quick Test.
X22 CHECK FC/LFC SIGNAL FOR SHORT TO GROUND • Key off. • Disconnect Powertrain Control Module (PCM). Inspect for damaged or pushed out pins, corrosion, loose wires, etc. Service as necessary. • Install breakout box, leave PCM disconnected. • Disconnect CCRM. **For 3.0L SHO and Mustang:** — Measure resistance between Test Pin 55 and Test Pins 40/60 at the breakout box. **For all others:** — Measure resistance between Test Pin 13 and Test Pins 40/60 at the breakout box. • **Is resistance greater than 10,000 ohms?**	Yes No	▶ ▶	GO to X23. SERVICE short to ground in FC/LFC circuit. RECONNECT all components. RERUN Quick Test.
X23 CHECK FAN RUNNING MODE • Key off. • Breakout box installed, PCM disconnected. • Connect CCRM. • Key on, engine off. • **Does fan run?**	Yes No	▶ ▶	REPLACE PCM. REMOVE breakout box. RECONNECT all components. RERUN Quick Test. REPLACE CCRM. REMOVE breakout box. RECONNECT all components. RERUN Quick Test.

FM0159400770170X

Fig. 229   Test X: CCRM (Part 17 of 55). 1994–95

TEST STEP	RESULT	▶	ACTION TO TAKE
X24 CHECK FC/LFC CIRCUIT CONTINUITY • Key off. • Disconnect Powertrain Control Module (PCM). Inspect for damaged or pushed out pins, corrosion, and loose wires, etc. Service as necessary. • Install breakout box, leave PCM disconnected. • Disconnect CCRM. **For 3.0L SHO and Mustang:** — Measure resistance between Test Pin 55 at the breakout box and Pin 14 at the CCRM vehicle harness connector. **For all others:** — Measure resistance between Test Pin 13 at the breakout box and Pin 14 at the CCRM vehicle harness connector. • **Is resistance less than 5.0 ohms?**	Yes No	▶ ▶	GO to X25. SERVICE open in FC/LFC circuit. REMOVE breakout box. RECONNECT all components. RERUN Quick Test.
X25 CHECK FC/LFC CIRCUIT FOR SHORT TO POWER • Key off. • Breakout box installed, PCM disconnected. • CCRM disconnected. • Key on, engine off. **For 3.0L SHO and Mustang:** — Measure voltage between Test Pin 55 at the breakout box and battery negative post. **For all others:** — Measure voltage between Test Pin 13 at the breakout box and battery negative post. • **Is voltage less than 1.0 volt?**	Yes No	▶ ▶	GO to X26. SERVICE short to power in FC/LFC circuit. REMOVE breakout box. RECONNECT all components. RERUN Quick Test.
X26 FC/LFC CIRCUIT FAULT ISOLATION CHECK • Key off. • Breakout box installed, PCM disconnected. • Reconnect CCRM. • Key on, engine off. **For 3.0L SHO and Mustang:** — Jumper Test Pin 55 to Test Pin 40 or 60 at the breakout box. **For all others:** — Jumper Test Pin 13 to Test Pin 40 or 60 at the breakout box. • **Does fan continue to run?**	Yes No	▶ ▶	Key off. REMOVE jumper. If DTC 563 was also present with the 564, GO to X150. If not, REPLACE CCRM. REMOVE breakout box. RECONNECT all components. RERUN Quick Test. REPLACE PCM. REMOVE breakout box and jumper. RECONNECT all components. RERUN Quick Test.

FM0159400770180X

Fig. 229   Test X: CCRM (Part 18 of 55). 1994–95

TEST STEP	RESULT	▶	ACTION TO TAKE
X27 CHECK ACPSW MEDIUM PRESSURE CONTACT CIRCUIT TO CCRM FOR SHORT TO GND (3.0L SHO)			
• Key off. • ACPSW disconnected. • Disconnect CCRM. • Measure resistance between Pin 17 at the CCRM vehicle harness connector and the battery negative post. • **Is resistance greater than 10,000 ohms?**	Yes	▶	REPLACE CCRM. RECONNECT all components. RE-EVALUATE symptom.
	No	▶	SERVICE short to ground. RECONNECT all components. RE-EVALUATE symptom.
X28 COOLING FAN ALWAYS ON (ANY SPEED) (3.8L SC): CHECK IF PUSHER FAN IS ALWAYS ON			
• Accessories off (A/C, defroster, etc.) • Key on, engine off. • **Is the pusher fan always on? (The pusher fan is in front of the radiator.)**	Yes	▶	Key off, GO to X29.
	No	▶	Key off, GO to X30.
X29 CHECK PUSHER FAN CONTROL RELAY			
• Key off. • Disconnect Pusher Fan Control (PFC) Relay. • Key on, engine off. • **Is the pusher fan still on?**	Yes	▶	Key off. SERVICE short to power on Power-To-Pusher Fan circuit. RECONNECT PFC relay. RE-EVALUATE symptom.
	No	▶	Key off. REPLACE PFC relay. RE-EVALUATE symptom.

FM0159400770190X

Fig. 229   Test X: CCRM (Part 19 of 55). 1994–95

TEST STEP	RESULT	▶	ACTION TO TAKE
X30 COOLING FAN ALWAYS ON (ANY SPEED): DISCONNECT CCRM AND CHECK IF FAN IS ON			
NOTE: For proper results of this Test Step, a "pass" Diagnostic Trouble Code (DTC) 111 must have been received during EEC-IV Self-Test. • Accessories off (A/C, etc.). • Key on, verify "cooling fan always on" symptom. • Key off. • Disconnect CCRM. • Key on, engine off. • **Is cooling fan still on?**	Yes	▶	Key off. For 2.3L Tempo/Topaz, 3.0L Taurus/Sable (except 3.0L SHO) and 3.2L SHO: SERVICE short to power on power-to-fan circuit (between CCRM and cooling fan). RECONNECT CCRM. RE-EVALUATE symptom. All others: GO to X31.
	No	▶	For vehicles that use R134a A/C refrigerant (except 2.3L Tempo/Topaz and 3.0L Taurus Flex Fuel): GO to X32. All others: Key off. REPLACE CCRM. RE-EVALUATE symptom.
X31 CHECK LOW SPEED POWER-TO-FAN CIRCUIT FOR SHORT TO POWER			
• Key off. • CCRM disconnected. • Disconnect cooling fan. • Measure voltage between Pin 1 (Pin 6 for Thunderbird SC) of the CCRM vehicle harness connector and the battery negative post. • **Is voltage less than 1.0 volt?**	Yes	▶	SERVICE short to power in high speed power-to-fan circuit. RECONNECT all components. RE-EVALUATE symptom.
	No	▶	SERVICE short to power in low speed power-to-fan circuit. RECONNECT all components. RE-EVALUATE symptom.

FM0159400770200X

Fig. 229   Test X: CCRM (Part 20 of 55). 1994–95

TEST STEP	RESULT	▶	ACTION TO TAKE
X32 CHECK DUAL FUNCTION A/C PRESSURE SWITCH (ACPSW)			
• Key off. • Reconnect CCRM. • Disconnect dual function A/C Pressure Switch (ACPSW) (also known as Refrigerant Containment/Fan Function Switch). • Start engine. • **Is cooling fan on?**	Yes	▶	Key off. For 3.0L SHO: GO to X27. All others: GO to X33.
	No	▶	Key off. check ACPSW operation.
X33 CHECK PCM			
• Key off. • CCRM disconnected. • ACPSW disconnected. • Disconnect Powertrain Control Module (PCM). • Key on, engine off. • **Is cooling fan on?**	Yes	▶	Key off. REPLACE CCRM. RECONNECT all components. RE-EVALUATE symptom.
	No	▶	Key off. GO to X34.
X34 CHECK ACPSW CIRCUIT FOR SHORT TO GROUND			
• Key off. • ACPSW disconnected. • PCM disconnected. • Measure resistance between the ACPSW circuit at the ACPSW vehicle harness connector and the battery negative post. • **Is resistance greater than 10,000 ohms?**	Yes	▶	REPLACE PCM. RECONNECT all components. RE-EVALUATE SYMPTOM.
	No	▶	SERVICE ACPSW circuit short to ground. RECONNECT all components. RE-EVALUATE symptom.

TO CCRM/PCM — GND — ACPSW 42 — A/C PRESSURE SWITCH (ACPSW) VEHICLE HARNESS CONNECTOR — TO A/C DEMAND SW, CYCLIC PRESSURE SW

FM0159400770210X

Fig. 229   Test X: CCRM (Part 21 of 55). 1994–95

TEST STEP	RESULT	▶	ACTION TO TAKE
X35 NO ENGINE COOLING FAN (LOW SPEED AND/OR HIGH SPEED): CHECK POWER SUPPLY TO CCRM			
• Key off. • Disconnect CCRM. • Connect negative probe of DVOM to battery negative post. For 3.0L Taurus/Sable (except 3.0L SHO) and 3.2L SHO: — Check for voltage on Pins 1, 2, 6, and 7 at the CCRM vehicle harness connector. For all others: — Check for voltage on Pins 3 and 4 at the CCRM vehicle harness connector. — For Thunderbird SC, also check for voltage on Pins 8 and 10 at the CCRM vehicle harness connector. • **Is each voltage greater than 10.0 volts?**	Yes	▶	GO to X36.
	No	▶	SERVICE open in battery power circuit. For Thunderbird SC, if B+ was open to only two pins (3/4 or 8/10), SERVICE open and GO to X141. RECONNECT CCRM. RE-EVALUATE symptom.
X36 CHECK FAN MOTOR OPERATION			
• Key off. • CCRM disconnected. For 3.0L SHO, 2.3L Tempo/Topaz and Thunderbird SC: — Jumper Pin 1 to Pin 3 at the CCRM vehicle harness connector. For all others: — Jumper Pin 3 to Pin 6 at the CCRM vehicle harness connector. • **Does fan run?**	Yes	▶	For 3.0L SHO and 2.3L Tempo/Topaz: GO to X41. For all others: GO to X37.
	No	▶	GO to X38.
X37 CHECK FAN MOTOR OPERATION			
• Key off. • CCRM disconnected. For Thunderbird SC: — Jumper Pin 3 to Pin 6 at CCRM vehicle harness connector. All others: — Jumper Pin 3 to Pin 2 at CCRM vehicle harness connector. • **Does fan run?**	Yes	▶	GO to X41.
	No	▶	GO to X40.

FM0159400770220X

Fig. 229   Test X: CCRM (Part 22 of 55). 1994–95

TEST STEP		RESULT	▶	ACTION TO TAKE
X38	MEASURE BATTERY VOLTAGE SUPPLY AT FAN—BYPASSING CCRM			
	• Key off. • Disconnect cooling fan. • CCRM disconnected. **For 3.0L SHO, 2.3L Tempo/Topaz and Thunderbird SC:** — Jumper Pin 1 to Pin 3 at the CCRM vehicle harness connector. **For all others:** — Jumper Pin 3 to Pin 6 at the CCRM vehicle harness connector. • Negative probe of DVOM connected to the ground pin of the cooling fan vehicle harness connector • Check for voltage to the cooling fan vehicle harness connector (for 3.0L SHO, check Power-To-Low Fan pin, for all other two-speed fan applications, check Power-To-High Fan pin) • **Is voltage greater than 8.0 volts?**	Yes No	▶ ▶	REPLACE fan motor. RECONNECT CCRM. RE-EVALUATE symptom. GO to X39
X39	VERIFY COOLING FAN GROUND			
	• Key off. • Cooling fan disconnected. • CCRM disconnected. **For 3.0L SHO, 2.3L Tempo/Topaz and Thunderbird SC:** — Jumper Pin 1 to Pin 3 at the CCRM vehicle harness connector. **For all others:** — Jumper Pin 3 to Pin 6 at the CCRM vehicle harness connector. • Connect negative probe of DVOM to the battery negative post. • Check for voltage to the cooling fan vehicle harness connector (for 3.0L SHO, check Power-To-Low Fan pin, for all other two-speed fan applications, check Power-To-High Fan pin) • **Is voltage greater than 8.0 volts?**	Yes No	▶ ▶	SERVICE open in ground circuit to fan. RECONNECT all components. RE-EVALUATE symptom. **For Thunderbird SC:** GO to X140 **All others:** SERVICE open in power-to-fan circuit from CCRM vehicle harness connector to cooling fan vehicle harness connector. RECONNECT all components. RE-EVALUATE symptom.

Fig. 229 Test X: CCRM (Part 23 of 55). 1994–95

FM0159400770230X

TEST STEP		RESULT	▶	ACTION TO TAKE
X40	MEASURE BATTERY VOLTAGE SUPPLY AT FAN—BYPASSING CCRM			
	• Key off. • Disconnect cooling fan. • CCRM disconnected. **For Thunderbird SC:** — Jumper Pin 3 to Pin 6 at CCRM vehicle harness connector. **All others:** — Jumper Pin 3 to Pin 2 at the CCRM vehicle harness connector. • Measure voltage at cooling fan vehicle harness connector between power (HFC power for two speed fans) and ground pins. • **Is voltage greater than 8.0 volts?**	Yes No	▶ ▶	REPLACE fan motor. RECONNECT CCRM. RE-EVALUATE symptom. SERVICE open in power-to-fan circuit from Pins 1 and 2 (6 and 7 for Thunderbird SC) of CCRM vehicle harness connector to cooling fan vehicle harness connector. RECONNECT all components. RE-EVALUATE symptom.
X41	CHECK FAN RUNNING MODE (LOW)			
	• Key off. • Disconnect Powertrain Control Module (PCM). • Reconnect CCRM. • Key on, engine off. • **Does fan run?**	Yes No	▶ ▶	For 3.0L SHO and 2.3L Tempo/Topaz: GO to X44 For all others: GO to X42 REPLACE CCRM. RECONNECT PCM. RE-EVALUATE symptom.
X42	JUMPER HIGH FAN CONTROL (HFC) SIGNAL TO GROUND			
	• Key off. • Inspect PCM for damaged or pushed out pins, corrosion, loose wires, etc. Service as necessary • Install breakout box, leave PCM disconnected. • CCRM connected. • Key on, engine off. **For Mustang:** — Jumper Test Pin 32 to Test Pin 40 at the breakout box. **For Thunderbird/Cougar:** — Jumper Test Pin 14 to Test Pin 40 at the breakout box. **All others:** — Jumper Test Pin 31 to Test Pin 40 at the breakout box. • **Does fan speed change from low to high?**	Yes No	▶ ▶	GO to X44 **For Thunderbird SC:** GO to X43 **All others:** REPLACE CCRM. REMOVE breakout box. RECONNECT PCM. RE-EVALUATE symptom.

Fig. 229 Test X: CCRM (Part 24 of 55). 1994–95

FM0159400770240X

TEST STEP		RESULT	▶	ACTION TO TAKE
X43	CHECK CONTINUITY OF HIGH SPEED POWER-TO-FAN CIRCUIT			
	• Key off. • Disconnect CCRM. • Disconnect the 2 speed cooling fan. • Measure resistance between Pin 1 and Pin 12 of the CCRM vehicle harness connector. • **Is resistance less than 5.0 ohms?**	Yes No	▶ ▶	REPLACE CCRM. REMOVE breakout box. RECONNECT PCM. RE-EVALUATE symptom. SERVICE open circuit and REPLACE CCRM. REMOVE breakout box. RECONNECT all components. RE-EVALUATE symptom.
X44	CHECK ECT SENSOR			
	• Key off. • Breakout box installed. • Connect PCM to breakout box. • Check engine coolant level. • While measuring the voltage between Test Pin 7 and Test Pin 46, start engine and warm engine to operating temperature. Continue to let engine idle. • **Will the voltage drop below .45 volt?** (Allow sufficient time for voltage to drop, being careful not to overheat engine. If cooling fan turns on, return to other possible causes of symptom.)	Yes No	▶ ▶	REPLACE PCM. REMOVE breakout box. RECONNECT all components. RE-EVALUATE symptom. CHECK ECT sensor wires and connector for high resistance. VERIFY cooling system is operating properly. If OK, REPLACE ECT sensor. REMOVE breakout box. RECONNECT all components. RE-EVALUATE symptom.
X45	NO ENGINE COOLING FAN (ANY SPEED) (3.8L S/C): DOES THE PUSHER FAN OPERATE?			
	• During the functional check of each cooling fan speed in chart 21 (the "CHECK THAT ALL FAN SPEEDS OPERATE" box), did the Pusher Fan operate?	Yes No	▶ ▶	GO to X35 GO to X46

Fig. 229 Test X: CCRM (Part 25 of 55). 1994–95

FM0159400770250X

TEST STEP		RESULT	▶	ACTION TO TAKE
X46	CHECK B+ TO PUSHER FAN CONTROL RELAY			
	• Key off. • Disconnect Pusher Fan Control (PFC) relay. • Measure voltage between the B+ circuit at the PFC relay vehicle harness connector and the battery negative post. • **Is voltage greater than 10.5 volts?** POWER-TO-PUSHER FAN B+ **PFC RELAY VEHICLE HARNESS CONNECTOR**	Yes No	▶ ▶	GO to X47 SERVICE open in B+ circuit. RECONNECT PFC relay. RE-EVALUATE symptom.
X47	CHECK PUSHER FAN GROUND CIRCUIT			
	• Key off. • PFC relay disconnected. • Disconnect pusher fan. • Measure resistance between the ground circuit at the pusher fan vehicle harness connector and the battery negative post. • **Is resistance less than 5.0 ohms?**	Yes No	▶ ▶	GO to X48 SERVICE open in ground circuit. RECONNECT all components. RE-EVALUATE symptom.
X48	CHECK POWER-TO-PUSHER FAN CIRCUIT CONTINUITY			
	• Key off. • PFC relay disconnected. • Pusher fan disconnected. • Measure resistance between the Power-To-Pusher Fan circuit at the PFC relay vehicle harness connector and the Power-To-Pusher Fan circuit at the pusher fan vehicle harness connector. • **Is resistance less than 5.0 ohms?**	Yes No	▶ ▶	GO to X49 SERVICE open in Power-To-Pusher Fan circuit. RECONNECT all components. RE-EVALUATE symptom.

Fig. 229 Test X: CCRM (Part 26 of 55). 1994–95

FM0159400770260X

TEST STEP	RESULT	►	ACTION TO TAKE
X49 CHECK OPERATION OF PFC RELAY • Key off. • Reconnect PFC relay. • Pusher fan disconnected. • Again, enter Output State Diagnostic Test Mode (DTM) • Outputs off. • Command the PFC output on by depressing the throttle (near WOT), waiting for the MIL to flash three consecutive times (about 20 seconds), then releasing the throttle. • Measure voltage between the Power-To-Pusher Fan circuit at the pusher fan vehicle harness connector and the battery negative post. • **Is voltage greater than 10.5 volts?**	Yes No	► ►	EXIT Output State DTM. Key off. REPLACE pusher fan. RE-EVALUATE symptom. VERIFY test results. If voltage is still less than 10.5 volts, EXIT Output State DTM. Key off. REPLACE PFC relay. RECONNECT pusher fan. RE-EVALUATE symptom.
X50 LOW / NO VOLTAGE TO A / C CLUTCH: CHECK FOR CONTINUITY FROM CCRM TO A / C CLUTCH • Key off. • A / C clutch disconnected. • Disconnect CCRM. • Measure resistance between Pin 23 of the CCRM vehicle harness connector and power side of the A / C clutch vehicle harness connector. • Measure resistance between Pin 16 of the CCRM vehicle harness connector and ground side of the A / C clutch vehicle harness connector. • **Is each resistance less than 5.0 ohms?**	Yes No	► ►	RECONNECT A / C clutch. GO to X51. SERVICE open in power or ground to A / C clutch. RECONNECT CCRM and A / C clutch. RE-EVALUATE symptom.
X51 CHECK FOR A / C DEMAND SWITCH VOLTAGE TO CCRM • CCRM disconnected. • Key on, engine off. • A / C demand switch to A / C ON. • Measure voltage between Pin 21 of the CCRM vehicle harness connector and battery negative post. • **Is voltage greater than 10.5 volts?**	Yes No	► ►	Key off. GO to X57. For vehicles that use R-12 A / C refrigerant: GO to X54. All others: GO to X52.

Fig. 229   Test X: CCRM (Part 27 of 55). 1994–95

TEST STEP	RESULT	►	ACTION TO TAKE
X52 CHECK VOLTAGE TO A / C PRESSURE SWITCH (ACPSW) • Key off. • Disconnect A / C Pressure Switch (ACPSW) (also known as Refrigerant Containment / Fan Function Switch). • Key on, engine off. • A / C demand switch to A / C ON position. • Measure voltage between the A / C Demand / Cyclic Pressure Switch Input pin at the ACPSW vehicle harness connector and the battery negative post. • Key off. • **Was voltage greater than 10.5 volts?**	Yes No	► ►	GO to X53. GO to X54.

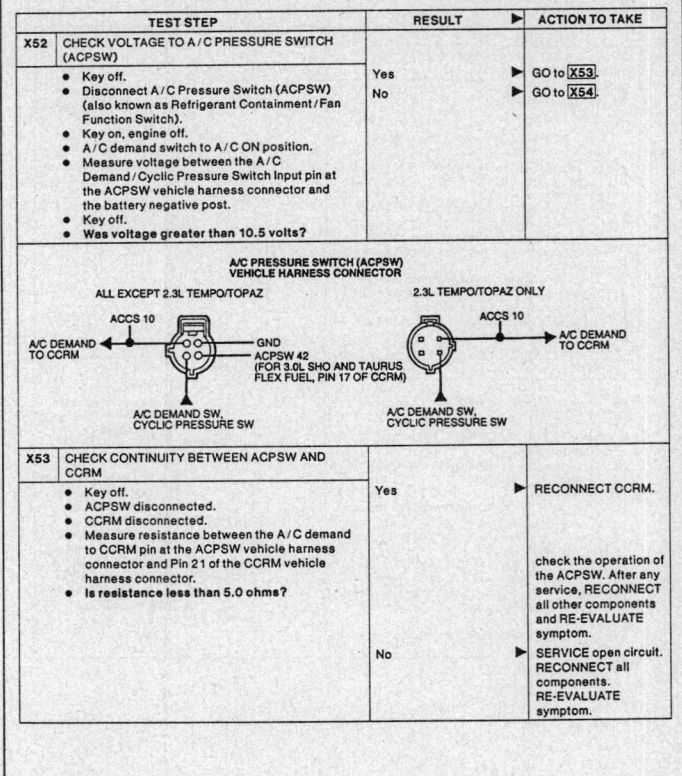

A/C PRESSURE SWITCH (ACPSW) VEHICLE HARNESS CONNECTOR

TEST STEP	RESULT	►	ACTION TO TAKE
X53 CHECK CONTINUITY BETWEEN ACPSW AND CCRM • Key off. • ACPSW disconnected. • CCRM disconnected. • Measure resistance between the A / C demand to CCRM pin at the ACPSW vehicle harness connector and Pin 21 of the CCRM vehicle harness connector. • **Is resistance less than 5.0 ohms?**	Yes No	► ►	RECONNECT CCRM. check the operation of the ACPSW. After any service, RECONNECT all other components and RE-EVALUATE symptom. SERVICE open circuit. RECONNECT all components. RE-EVALUATE symptom.

Fig. 229   Test X: CCRM (Part 28 of 55). 1994–95

TEST STEP	RESULT	►	ACTION TO TAKE
X54 CHECK VOLTAGE TO CYCLIC PRESSURE SWITCH • Key off. • Disconnect cyclic pressure switch. • Key on, engine off. • A / C demand switch to A / C ON position. • Measure voltage between the A / C demand switch side of the cyclic pressure switch vehicle harness connector and battery negative post. • **Is voltage greater than 10.5 volts?**	Yes No	► ►	GO to X55. EEC-IV system OK. REMOVE breakout box. RECONNECT all components A / C diagnosis. (Inspect A / C Demand Switch, applicable fuses, wiring to cyclic pressure switch, etc.)

X55 CHECK CONTINUITY BETWEEN CYCLIC PRESSURE SWITCH AND CCRM OR ACPSW
• Key off.
• Cyclic pressure switch disconnected.
• CCRM disconnected.
• ACPSW disconnected (if applicable).
  • For vehicles that use R-12 refrigerant:
  — Measure resistance between the A / C demand circuit to CCRM pin at the cyclic pressure switch vehicle harness connector and Pin 21 of the CCRM vehicle harness connector.
  All others:
  — Measure resistance between the A / C demand circuit to ACPSW at the cyclic pressure switch vehicle harness connector and the A / C demand / cyclic pressure switch input pin at the ACPSW vehicle harness connector.
• **Is resistance less than 5.0 ohms?**
	Yes
	
	No
		►
		
		►
			RECONNECT CCRM.
			
			check the operation of the cyclic pressure switch. After any service, RECONNECT all components and RE-EVALUATE symptom.
			
			SERVICE open circuit. RECONNECT all components. RE-EVALUATE symptom.

X57 CHECK FOR A / C DEMAND SWITCH VOLTAGE TO POWERTRAIN CONTROL MODULE (PCM) • Key off. • Disconnect Powertrain Control Module (PCM). Inspect for damaged or pushed out pins, corrosion, loose wires, etc. Service as necessary. • Install breakout box, leave PCM disconnected. • CCRM disconnected. • Key on, engine off. • A / C demand switch to A / C ON. • Measure voltage between Test Pin 10 and chassis ground. • **Is voltage greater than 10.5 volts?**	Yes No	► ►	Key off. GO to X58. Key off. SERVICE open in ACCS circuit between PCM and its connection to the A / C demand circuit. REMOVE breakout box. RECONNECT all components. RE-EVALUATE symptom.

Fig. 229   Test X: CCRM (Part 29 of 55). 1994–95

TEST STEP	RESULT	►	ACTION TO TAKE
X58 CHECK WAC CIRCUIT FOR SHORTS TO GROUND • Key off. • Breakout box installed, PCM disconnected. • CCRM disconnected. • Measure resistance between Test Pin 54 and chassis ground. • **Is resistance greater than 10,000 ohms?**	Yes No	► ►	GO to X62. SERVICE short to ground in WAC circuit. REMOVE breakout box. RECONNECT all components. RE-EVALUATE symptom.
X60 NO A / C CUTOFF: CHECK WAC CIRCUIT CONTINUITY • Key off. • Disconnect Powertrain Control Module (PCM). Inspect for damaged or pushed out pins, corrosion, loose wires, etc. Service as necessary. • Install breakout box, leave PCM disconnected. • Disconnect CCRM. • Measure resistance between Test Pin 54 at the breakout box and Pin 22 at the CCRM vehicle harness connector. • **Is resistance less than 5.0 ohms?**	Yes No	► ►	GO to X61. SERVICE open in WAC circuit. REMOVE breakout box. RECONNECT all components. RE-EVALUATE symptom.
X61 CHECK WAC CIRCUIT FOR SHORTS TO POWER • Key off. • Breakout box installed, PCM disconnected. • CCRM disconnected. • Key on, engine off. • Measure voltage between Test Pin 54 and battery negative post. • **Is voltage less than 1.0 volt?**	Yes No	► ►	Key off. GO to X62. Key off. SERVICE short to power in WAC circuit. REMOVE breakout box. RECONNECT all components. RE-EVALUATE symptom.

Fig. 229   Test X: CCRM (Part 30 of 55). 1994–95

Fig. 229 Test X: CCRM (Part 31 of 55). 1994–95

TEST STEP	RESULT	▶	ACTION TO TAKE
X62 ISOLATE FAULT TO PCM OR CCRM • Key off. • Breakout box installed, PCM disconnected. • Reconnect CCRM and A/C clutch. • Key on, engine off. • A/C demand switch to A/C on position. • Connect jumper between Test Pins 54 and 40 at the breakout box. • Disconnect and reconnect jumper several times while listening to the A/C clutch. • **Does the A/C clutch engage and disengage as the jumper is disconnected and reconnected?**	Yes	▶	**For No A/C symptom:** REMOVE jumper. GO to **X63**. **For No WAC symptom:** REPLACE PCM. REMOVE breakout box. RECONNECT all components. RE-EVALUATE symptom.
	No	▶	REPLACE CCRM. INSPECT the A/C clutch circuit for possible shorts to GND. SERVICE as necessary. REMOVE breakout box. RECONNECT all components. RE-EVALUATE symptom.

X63 CHECK ECT AND TP INPUTS
• Key off.
• Breakout box installed.
• Reconnect PCM to breakout box.
• A/C on.
• Start engine.
• Check ECT input:
  — Measure voltage between Test Pin 7 and Test Pin 40 at the breakout box.
  — ECT voltage should be greater than 0.3 volt (refer to Pinpoint Test DA cover sheet for ECT voltage chart).
• Check TP input:
  — Measure voltage between Test Pin 47 and Test Pin 40 at the breakout box.
  — At closed and part throttle, the TP voltage should stay below 4.5 volts (refer to Pinpoint Test DH cover sheet for TP voltage chart).
• **Do the ECT and TP input voltages check out OK?**
	Yes	▶	REPLACE PCM. REMOVE breakout box. RECONNECT all components. RE-EVALUATE symptom.

	No	▶	PERFORM EEC-IV Quick Test (REFER to Diagnostic Routines Symptom Flow Chart, number 32). SERVICE any DTCs as directed. If OK, CHECK ECT·TP wiring for opens or shorts. SERVICE as necessary. REMOVE breakout box. RECONNECT all components. RE-EVALUATE symptom.

Fig. 229 Test X: CCRM (Part 32 of 55). 1994–95

TEST STEP	RESULT	▶	ACTION TO TAKE
X65 CHECK DUAL FUNCTION A/C PRESSURE SWITCH (ACPSW) INPUT • Key off. • Unplug dual function A/C Pressure Switch (ACPSW) (also known as Refrigerant Containment/Fan Function Switch). • A/C off (to prevent chance of short circuit). • Start engine. • Jumper ACPSW circuit to GND circuit at the ACPSW vehicle harness connector. • **Does the high speed fan come on?**	Yes	▶	Key off. ACPSW circuit is OK. REMOVE jumper. RECONNECT ACPSW check operation of the medium pressure function of the dual function A/C pressure switch. If OK, RETURN to other possible causes.
 A/C PRESSURE SWITCH VEHICLE HARNESS CONNECTOR	No	▶	GO to **X66**.
X66 CHECK GND CIRCUIT TO ACPSW • Engine running. • ACPSW disconnected. • Connect jumper wire between ACPSW circuit at the ACPSW vehicle harness connector and the battery negative post. • **Does the high speed fan now come on?**	Yes	▶	Key off. SERVICE open GND circuit to ACPSW. RECONNECT ACPSW. RE-EVALUATE symptom.
	No	▶	Key off. **For 3.0L SHO and 3.0L Flex Fuel Taurus:** GO to **X68**. **All others:** GO to **X67**.
X67 CHECK ACPSW CIRCUIT CONTINUITY TO PCM • Key off. • ACPSW disconnected. • Disconnect Powertrain Control Module (PCM). Inspect for damaged or pushed out pins, corrosion, loose wires, etc. Service as necessary. • Install breakout box, leave PCM disconnected. • Measure resistance between Test Pin 42 at the breakout box and the ACPSW circuit at the ACPSW vehicle harness connector. • **Is resistance less than 5.0 ohms?**	Yes	▶	REPLACE PCM. REMOVE breakout box. RECONNECT all components. RE-EVALUATE symptom.
	No	▶	SERVICE open circuit. REMOVE breakout box. RECONNECT all components. RE-EVALUATE symptom.

Fig. 229 Test X: CCRM (Part 33 of 55). 1994–95

TEST STEP	RESULT	▶	ACTION TO TAKE
X68 CHECK ACPSW CIRCUIT CONTINUITY TO CCRM • Key off. • ACPSW disconnected. • Disconnect CCRM. • Measure resistance between Pin 17 of the CCRM vehicle harness connector and the ACPSW circuit at the ACPSW vehicle harness connector. • **Is resistance less than 5.0 ohms?**	Yes	▶	**For 3.0L Flex Fuel Taurus:** GO to **X160**. **For 3.0L SHO:** GO to **X69**.
	No	▶	SERVICE open circuit. RECONNECT all components. RE-EVALUATE symptom.
X69 CHECK HIGH SPEED FAN OPERATION, BYPASSING CCRM • Key off. • ACPSW disconnected. • CCRM disconnected. • Jumper Pin 3 to Pin 6 at the CCRM vehicle harness connector. • **Does fan run?**	Yes	▶	REPLACE CCRM. RECONNECT all components. RE-EVALUATE symptom.
	No	▶	CHECK continuity of Power-To-High Speed Fan circuit between CCRM and cooling fan. SERVICE as necessary. If OK, REPLACE cooling fan. RECONNECT all components. RE-EVALUATE symptom.

Fig. 229 Test X: CCRM (Part 34 of 55). 1994–95

TEST STEP	RESULT	▶	ACTION TO TAKE

X70 DIAGNOSTIC TROUBLE CODE (DTC) 556 OR 557:
CHECK FUEL PUMP RELAY COIL RESISTANCE
 	
DTC 556 for the 3.0L SHO indicates a high speed fuel pump primary circuit fault.
DTC 556 for ALL OTHERS indicates a fuel pump primary circuit fault.
DTC 557 indicates a low speed fuel pump primary circuit fault.
Possible causes:
— Open or shorted circuit.
— Open Inertia Fuel Shutoff (IFS) switch (Tempo/Topaz).
— Damaged CCRM.
— Damaged Powertrain Control Module (PCM).
• Key off.
• Disconnected CCRM.
  For Tempo/Topaz:
  — Measure resistance of CCRM from Pin 18 to Pin 10.
  For Thunderbird SC:
  — Measure resistance of CCRM from Pin 18 to Pin 13.
  For all others:
  — Measure resistance of CCRM from Pin 18 to Pin 24.
• **Is resistance between 65 and 120 ohms?**
	Yes	▶	**For Tempo/Topaz:**
			GO to **X72**.
			For Thunderbird SC:
			GO to **X71**.
			For all others:
			GO to **X73**.

	No	▶	REPLACE CCRM. REMOVE breakout box. RECONNECT PCM. RERUN Quick Test.
X71 CHECK VOLTAGE TO FUEL PUMP RELAY • CCRM disconnected. • Key on. • Measure voltage between CCRM Pin 10 at vehicle harness connector and battery negative post. • **Is voltage greater than 10.5 volts?**	Yes	▶	GO to **X73**.
	No	▶	CHECK Inertia Fuel Shutoff switch for open or reset. If OK, SERVICE open in ignition START/RUN circuit to CCRM. RECONNECT CCRM. RERUN Quick Test.
X72 CHECK FOR VPWR TO CCRM • CCRM disconnected. • Key on, engine off. • Measure voltage between Pin 13 of the CCRM vehicle harness connector and the battery negative post. • Key off. • **Was the voltage greater than 10.5 volts?**	Yes	▶	GO to **X73**.
	No	▶	SERVICE open in VPWR circuit between EEC-IV power relay and CCRM. RECONNECT CCRM. RERUN Quick Test.

TEST STEP		RESULT	▶	ACTION TO TAKE
X73	CHECK CONTINUITY OF FUEL PUMP CIRCUIT			
	• Key off. • CCRM disconnected. • Disconnect Powertrain Control Module (PCM). Inspect for damaged or pushed out pins, corrosion, loose wires, etc. Service as necessary. • Install breakout box, leave PCM disconnected. • Measure resistance between Test Pin 22 at the breakout box and Pin 18 at the CCRM vehicle harness connector. • For 3.0L SHO, also measure resistance between Test Pin 41 at the breakout box and Pin 18 at the CCRM vehicle harness connector. • **Is resistance less than 5.0 ohms?**	Yes No	▶ ▶	GO to X74. SERVICE open in fuel pump circuit. REMOVE breakout box. RECONNECT all components. RERUN Quick Test.
X74	CHECK FUEL PUMP CIRCUIT FOR SHORT TO POWER			
	• Key off. • Breakout box installed, PCM disconnected. • CCRM disconnected. • Key on. • Measure voltage between Test Pin 22 and the battery negative post. • **Is voltage less than 1.0 volt?**	Yes No	▶ ▶	GO to X75. SERVICE short to power. REMOVE breakout box. RECONNECT all components. RERUN Quick Test. If DTC 556 / 557 is still present, REPLACE PCM.
X75	CHECK FUEL PUMP CIRCUIT FOR SHORT TO GROUND			
	• Key off. • Breakout box installed, PCM disconnected. • CCRM disconnected. • Measure resistance between Test Pin 22 and the battery negative post. • **Is resistance greater than 10,000 ohms?**	Yes No	▶ ▶	REPLACE PCM. REMOVE breakout box. RECONNECT all components. RERUN Quick Test. SERVICE fuel pump circuit short to ground. REMOVE breakout box. RECONNECT all components. RERUN Quick Test.

FM0159400770350X

Fig. 229   Test X: CCRM (Part 35 of 55). 1994–95

TEST STEP		RESULT	▶	ACTION TO TAKE
X80	DIAGNOSTIC TROUBLE CODE (DTC) 542: DOES ENGINE START			
	Diagnostic Trouble Code (DTC) 542 indicates that one of the following has occurred: **No Start:** — Inertia Fuel Shutoff (IFS) switch not reset or electrically open (if in secondary circuit). — Open circuit between the fuel pump and FPM circuit connection to power-to-pump circuit. — Poor fuel pump ground. — Fuel pump electrically open. **Engine Starts:** — Fuel pump secondary circuit short to power. — Fuel pump relay contacts always closed. — Open in FPM circuit between PCM and connection to power-to-pump circuit. — Left / Front HO2S short to power (dual HO2S applications). — Damaged PCM. • **Does the engine start?**	Yes No	▶ ▶	GO to X81. For Tempo / Topaz: REFER to the (Electric Fuel Pump) for open in power-to-pump circuit, poor fuel pump ground, open in fuel pump, etc. **All others:** GO to X85.
X81	VERIFY THAT FUEL PUMP IS OFF			
	• Key on, wait 5 seconds. • Listen for motor noise from fuel pump (it may be necessary to listen by fuel tank). • **Is fuel pump off?**	Yes No	▶ ▶	GO to X84. For 3.0L Flex Fuel Taurus: GO to X82. All others: GO to X83.
X82	CHECK FOR LOW SPEED FUEL PUMP (LFP) RELAY ALWAYS CLOSED			
	• Key off. • Disconnect LFP relay. • Key on, wait 5 seconds. • **Does fuel pump shut off when LFP relay is disconnected?**	Yes No	▶ ▶	REPLACE LFP relay. RERUN Quick Test. Key off. GO to X83.
X83	CHECK FOR FUEL PUMP RELAY ALWAYS CLOSED			
	• Key off. • Disconnect CCRM. • Key on. • **Does fuel pump shut off when CCRM is disconnected?**	Yes No	▶ ▶	REPLACE CCRM. RERUN Quick Test SERVICE short to power in power-to-pump / FPM circuit. RECONNECT CCRM. RERUN Quick Test.

FM0159400770360X

Fig. 229   Test X: CCRM (Part 36 of 55). 1994–95

TEST STEP		RESULT	▶	ACTION TO TAKE
X84	CHECK FPM CIRCUIT CONTINUITY			
	• Key off. • Disconnect Powertrain Control Module (PCM). Inspect for damaged or pushed out pins, corrosion, loose wires, etc. Service as necessary. • Install breakout box, leave PCM disconnected. • Disconnect CCRM. • Measure resistance between Test Pin 8 (Test Pin 19 for 3.0L SHO) at the breakout box and Pin 5 at the CCRM vehicle harness connector. • **Is resistance less than 5.0 ohms?**	Yes No	▶ ▶	**For dual HO2S applications:** GO to X86. **All others:** REPLACE PCM. RECONNECT CCRM. RERUN Quick Test. SERVICE open circuit. REMOVE breakout box. RECONNECT all components. RERUN Quick Test.
X85	CHECK INERTIA FUEL SHUTOFF SWITCH			
	• Key off. • Locate and disconnect Inertia Fuel Shutoff (IFS) switch (verify that switch is reset). • Measure resistance between the "C" and "NC" pins of the IFS switch. • **Is resistance less than 5.0 ohms?**	Yes No	▶ ▶	RECONNECT IFS switch. REFER to the (Electric Fuel Pump) for open in power-to-pump circuit, poor fuel pump ground, open in fuel pump, etc. REPLACE or RESET IFS switch. RERUN Quick Test.
X86	CHECK FRONT / LEFT HO2S FOR SHORT TO POWER			
	NOTE: Due to the internal circuitry of the PCM, a Left / Front HO2S signal short to power could produce a DTC 542 / 543. • Key off. • Disconnect left or front HO2S. • Measure resistance between HO2S signal pin and KEY POWER pin at the HO2S connector. • **Is resistance greater than 10,000 ohms?**	Yes No	▶ ▶	GO to X87. REPLACE HO2S. REMOVE breakout box. RECONNECT all components. RERUN Quick Test.

FM0159400770370X

Fig. 229   Test X: CCRM (Part 37 of 55). 1994–95

TEST STEP		RESULT	▶	ACTION TO TAKE
X87	CHECK HO2S CIRCUIT FOR SHORT TO POWER			
	• Key off. • Left or Front HO2S disconnected. • Disconnect Powertrain Control Module (PCM). Inspect for damaged or pushed out pins, corrosion, loose wires, etc. Service as necessary. Leave PCM disconnected. • Key on. • Measure voltage between the HO2S signal at the HO2S vehicle harness connector and chassis ground. • **Is voltage less than 1.0 volt?**	Yes No	▶ ▶	REPLACE PCM. RECONNECT PCM. RERUN Quick Test. SERVICE short circuit. RECONNECT PCM and HO2S. RERUN Quick Test.
X88	DIAGNOSTIC TROUBLE CODE (DTC) 524: CHECK B(+) TO LOW SPEED FUEL PUMP (LFP) RELAY			
	NOTE: If Key On Engine Off DTC 543 is also present, GO to X90. DTC 524 indicates a Low Speed Fuel Pump (LFP) secondary circuit failure. Possible causes (without DTC 543): — Open B(+) circuit to LFP relay. — Open power-to-pump circuit between LFP relay and splice to "common" power-to-pump circuit. — Damaged fuel pump dropping resistor. — Damaged LFP relay. • Key off. • Disconnect LFP relay. • Measure voltage between B(+) circuit at the LFP relay vehicle harness connector and the battery negative post. • **Is voltage greater than 10.5 volts?**	Yes No	▶ ▶	GO to X89. VERIFY condition of related fuses. If OK, SERVICE open in B(+) circuit to LFP relay. RECONNECT LFP relay. RERUN Quick Test.

FM0159400770380X

Fig. 229   Test X: CCRM (Part 38 of 55). 1994–95

TEST STEP		RESULT	▶	ACTION TO TAKE
X89	CHECK POWER-TO-PUMP CIRCUIT CONTINUITY BETWEEN LFP RELAY AND CCRM			
	• Key off. • LFP relay disconnected. • Disconnect CCRM. • Measure resistance between Pin 5 of the CCRM vehicle harness connector and the power-to-pump circuit at the LFP relay vehicle harness connector. • **Is resistance less than 10.0 ohms?**	Yes	▶	REPLACE LFP relay. RECONNECT all components. RERUN Quick Test.
		No	▶	VERIFY condition of Fuel Pump Dropping Resistor (about 1 ohm resistance). If OK, SERVICE open in power-to-pump circuit between LFP relay and splice to "common" power-to-pump circuit. RECONNECT all components. RERUN Quick Test.

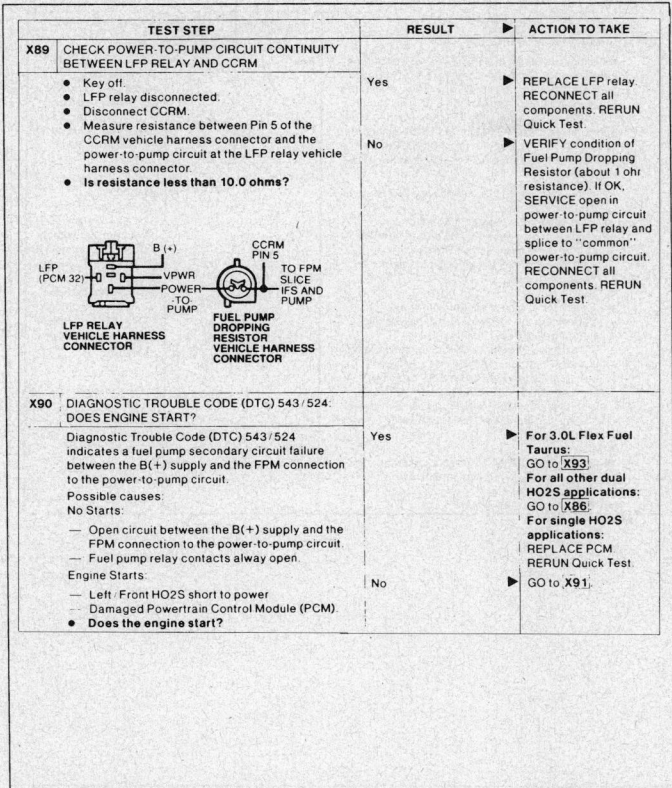

TEST STEP		RESULT	▶	ACTION TO TAKE
X90	DIAGNOSTIC TROUBLE CODE (DTC) 543/524: DOES ENGINE START?			
	Diagnostic Trouble Code (DTC) 543/524 indicates a fuel pump secondary circuit failure between the B(+) supply and the FPM connection to the power-to-pump circuit. Possible causes: No Starts: — Open circuit between the B(+) supply and the FPM connection to the power-to-pump circuit. — Fuel pump relay contacts alway open. Engine Starts: — Left/Front HO2S short to power — Damaged Powertrain Control Module (PCM). • **Does the engine start?**	Yes	▶	For 3.0L Flex Fuel Taurus: GO to X93 For all other dual HO2S applications: GO to X86. For single HO2S applications: REPLACE PCM. RERUN Quick Test.
		No	▶	GO to X91.

Fig. 229 Test X: CCRM (Part 39 of 55). 1994–95

FM0159400770390X

TEST STEP		RESULT	▶	ACTION TO TAKE
X91	CHECK B(+) SUPPLY TO FUEL PUMP RELAY			
	• Key off. • Disconnect CCRM. **For Mustang and Thunderbird/Cougar:** — Measure voltage between Pin 11 at the CCRM vehicle harness connector and the battery negative post. **All others:** — Measure voltage between Pin 12 at the CCRM vehicle harness connector and battery negative post. **Is voltage greater than 10.5 volts?**	Yes	▶	GO to X92
		No	▶	VERIFY integrity of fuse/fuse link for B(+) supply to CCRM (fuel pump relay). If OK, SERVICE open in B(+) supply to CCRM. RECONNECT CCRM. RERUN Quick Test.
X92	CHECK POWER-TO-PUMP CIRCUIT CONTINUITY			
	• Key off. • CCRM disconnected. • Measure resistance between Pin 5 at the CCRM vehicle harness connector and the battery negative post. • **Is resistance less than 10.0 ohms?**	Yes	▶	REPLACE CCRM. RERUN Quick Test.
		No	▶	SERVICE open in power-to-pump circuit between FPM splice and CCRM. RECONNECT CCRM. RERUN Quick Test.
X93	CHECK B(+) SUPPLY TO HIGH SPEED FUEL PUMP RELAY			
	• Key off. • Disconnect CCRM. • Measure voltage between Pin 12 at the CCRM vehicle harness connector and battery negative post. • **Is voltage greater than 10.5 volts?**	Yes	▶	GO to X94
		No	▶	SERVICE open in B(+) circuit between CCRM and B(+) splice to the High Speed and Low Speed Fuel Pump relays. RECONNECT CCRM. RERUN Quick Test.
X94	CHECK POWER-TO-PUMP CONTINUITY BETWEEN CCRM AND IFS SWITCH			
	• Key off. • CCRM disconnected. • Disconnect Inertia Fuel Shutoff (IFS) switch. • Measure resistance between Pin 5 at the CCRM vehicle harness connector and the power-to-pump circuit from the CCRM circuit at the IFS switch vehicle harness connector. • **Is resistance less than 5.0 ohms?**	Yes	▶	GO to X95
		No	▶	SERVICE open in power-to-pump circuit between CCRM and splice to LFP relay. RECONNECT all components. RERUN Quick Test.

Fig. 229 Test X: CCRM (Part 40 of 55). 1994–95

FM0159400770400X

TEST STEP		RESULT	▶	ACTION TO TAKE
X95	CHECK PCM ABILITY TO MONITOR FPM			
	• Key off. • Reconnect CCRM. • Inertia Fuel Shutoff switch disconnected. • Rerun Key On Engine Off Self-Test. • **Is KOEO DTC 542 present?**	Yes	▶	REPLACE CCRM. RECONNECT Inertia Fuel Shutoff switch. RERUN Quick Test.
		No	▶	REPLACE PCM. RECONNECT Inertia Fuel Shutoff switch. RERUN Quick Test.

Fig. 229 Test X: CCRM (Part 41 of 55). 1994–95

FM0159400770410X

TEST STEP		RESULT	▶	ACTION TO TAKE
X105	CONTINUOUS MEMORY DIAGNOSTIC TROUBLE CODE (DTC) 542: CHECK EEC-IV HARNESS			
	A Continuous Memory DTC 542 indicates that one of the following intermittent conditions has occurred: — Fuel pump circuit activated when PCM expected circuit to be off (i.e. fuel system test or prime procedure). — Inertia Fuel Shutoff switch was tripped, then reset (except Tempo/Topaz). — Open circuit in or between the fuel pump and FPM circuit at the PCM (refer to schematic). — Poor fuel pump ground. — FPM or power-to-pump circuit short to power. — Fuel pump relay contacts stuck closed. — Left/Front HO2S circuit short to power (w/dual HO2S). — Engine stall due to excessive load. • Start engine. • Check for engine stall/stumble while performing the following (also, if possible, listen for fuel pump turning off): — Shake, wiggle, bend the Power-To-Pump circuit between the CCRM Pin 5 and the fuel pump. — Shake, wiggle, bend the fuel pump ground circuit from the fuel pump to ground. — Lightly tap the fuel pump to simulate road shock. — For all except Tempo/Topaz, lightly tap Inertia Fuel Shutoff switch to simulate road shock. — For 3.0L Flex Fuel (FF) Taurus, also shake, wiggle, bend the power-to-pump circuit to the Low Speed Fuel Pump (LFP) relay and lightly tap the LFP relay to simulate road shock. • Key off. • Inspect the fuel pump vehicle harness connector and the fuel pump ground for corrosion, damaged pins, etc. • **Is fault indicated/found?**	Yes	▶	ISOLATE fault and SERVICE as necessary. CLEAR Continuous Memory DTC RERUN Quick Test.
		No	▶	GO to X106.

Fig. 229 Test X: CCRM (Part 42 of 55). 1994–95

FM0159400770420X

TEST STEP	RESULT	▶	ACTION TO TAKE
X106 CHECK FPM CIRCUIT			
• Key off. • Disconnect PCM. Inspect for damaged or pushed out pins, corrosion, loose wires, etc. Service as necessary. • Install breakout box, leave PCM disconnected. • Key on, engine off. • Connect a test lamp between Test Pin 8 (Test Pin 19 for 3.0L SHO) and Test Pin 37 at the breakout box. • Observe test lamp for an indication of a fault while performing the following (the light will go out when a fault is found, indicating an open): — Shake, wiggle, bend the Fuel Pump Monitor circuit between the splice into the power-to-pump circuit and the PCM. • **Is fault indicated?**	Yes	▶	ISOLATE fault and SERVICE as necessary. REMOVE breakout box. RECONNECT PCM. RERUN Quick Test.
	No	▶	GO to X107.
X107 CHECK FOR SHORTS TO POWER			
• Key on, engine off. • Breakout box installed, PCM disconnected. • Connect a test lamp between Test Pin 8 (Test Pin 19 for 3.0L SHO) and Test Pin 40. • Observe test lamp for an indication of a fault while performing the following (The lamp will turn on when a fault is detected, indicating a short to power. Also, if possible, listen for fuel pump turning on.) — Shake, wiggle, bend the Fuel Pump Monitor circuit and power-to-pump circuit, especially where they may be in the vicinity of a power circuit. — For 3.0L FF Taurus, also shake, wiggle, bend the power-to-pump circuit to the LFP relay and lightly tap the LFP relay to simulate road shock. • Lightly tap the CCRM (to simulate road shock). • **Is fault indicated?**	Yes	▶	ISOLATE fault and SERVICE as necessary. REMOVE breakout box. RECONNECT PCM. RERUN Quick Test.
	No	▶	**For dual HO2S applications:** GO to X116. **All others:** further diagnosis using the EEC-IV monitor box or Scan Tool. If an EEC-IV monitor box or Scan Tool is not available, GO to X120.
X110 CONTINUOUS MEMORY DIAGNOSTIC TROUBLE CODE (DTC) 524/543: CHECK FOR CONTINUOUS MEMORY DTC 556/557			
• **Is Continuous Memory DTC 556 or 557 also present?**	Yes	▶	GO to X115.
	No	▶	GO to X111.

FM0159400770430X

Fig. 229   Test X: CCRM (Part 43 of 55). 1994–95

TEST STEP	RESULT	▶	ACTION TO TAKE
X111 CHECK EEC-IV HARNESS			
A Continuous Memory DTC 524/543, without the presence of a Continuous Memory DTC 556/557, indicates that during vehicle operation, one of the following has occurred (for the 3.0L Flex Fuel (FF) Taurus, DTC 524 refers to the low speed fuel pump circuit and DTC 543 refers to the high speed fuel pump circuit. Also, for the 3.0L FF Taurus, the Low Speed Fuel Pump (LFP) relay is external to the CCRM): — Open in the B(+) circuit between B(+) and the fuel pump relay. — Fuel pump relay contacts opened. — Open in the power-to-pump circuit from the CCRM/LFP relay to the FPM splice. — Left/Front HO2S circuit short to power (w/dual HO2S). • Start engine. • Check for engine stall/stumble while performing the following (also, if possible, listen for fuel pump turning off): — Shake, wiggle, bend the fuel pump relay B(+) circuit to the CCRM/LFP relay. — Lightly tap the CCRM/LFP relay (to simulate road shock). — Shake, wiggle, bend the power-to-pump circuit from the CCRM/LFP relay to the FPM splice. • Key off. • Inspect the CCRM/LFP relay connector and B(+) connector terminal for corrosion, damaged pins, etc. • **Is fault indicated/found?**	Yes	▶	ISOLATE fault and SERVICE as necessary. CLEAR Continuous Memory DTC (REFER to Quick Test Appendix, Section 5A). RERUN Quick Test.
	No	▶	Under certain conditions, a Continuous Memory DTC 524/543 may have been set without a Continuous Memory DTC 556/557, even though a fault has occurred in the fuel pump primary circuit. GO to X115 to check the fuel pump primary circuit.

FM0159400770440X

Fig. 229   Test X: CCRM (Part 44 of 55). 1994–95

TEST STEP	RESULT	▶	ACTION TO TAKE
X115 CONTINUOUS MEMORY DIAGNOSTIC TROUBLE CODE (DTC) 556/557: CHECK EEC-IV HARNESS			
A Continuous Memory DTC 556/557 indicates a fuel pump primary circuit failure has occurred during vehicle operation (for the 3.0L SHO and 3.0L Flex Fuel Taurus. DTC 556 refers to the High Speed Fuel Pump primary circuit and DTC 557 refers to the Low Speed Fuel Pump primary circuit). Possible causes are: — Open VPWR in the CCRM. — Open coil in fuel pump relay. — Open in fuel pump circuit (PCM Pin 22 or 41). — Inertia Fuel Shutoff switch was tripped, then reset (Tempo/Topaz). — Open VPWR circuit to CCRM (Thunderbird SC). — Open VPWR to LFP relay (3.0L FF). • Start engine. • Check for engine stall/stumble while performing the following (also, if possible, listen for fuel pump turning off): — Shake, wiggle, bend the EEC-IV vehicle harness fuel pump circuit (Pin 22) between the PCM and the CCRM. — For Thunderbird SC, also shake, wiggle, bend the VPWR circuit between the EEC-IV power relay and the CCRM (Pin 13). — Lightly tap the Inertia Fuel Shutoff (IFS) switch to simulate road shock (Tempo/Topaz). — Lightly tap the CCRM to simulate road shock. — For 3.0L FF Taurus with DTC 557, shake, wiggle, bend the VPWR circuit between the CCRM and LFP relay. Also lightly tap on the LFP relay to simulate road shock. • Key off. • Inspect the PCM connector and the fuel pump relay connectors for corrosion, damaged pins, etc. • **Is fault indicated/found?**	Yes	▶	ISOLATE fault and SERVICE as necessary. CLEAR Continuous Memory RERUN Quick Test.
	No	▶	**For dual HO2S applications with a DTC 524/543 only:** GO to X116. **ALL others:** further diagnosis using the EEC-IV monitor box or Scan Tool. If an EEC-IV monitor box or Scan Tool is not available, GO to X120.

FM0159400770450X

Fig. 229   Test X: CCRM (Part 45 of 55). 1994–95

TEST STEP	RESULT	▶	ACTION TO TAKE
X116 CHECK LEFT/FRONT HO2S CIRCUIT FOR SHORT TO POWER			
NOTE: **Due to the internal circuitry of the PCM, an intermittent left/front HO2S signal short to power could produce a Continuous Memory DTC 542 or 524/543.** • Key off. • Install breakout box, if applicable. • Breakout box installed, PCM disconnected. • Connect a test lamp between the left/front HO2S test pin and test pin 40 at the breakout box (refer to Pinpoint Test H cover page for appropriate HO2S test pin). • Key on, engine off. • Observe test lamp for an indication of a fault while performing the following (the light will turn on bright when a fault is detected): — Shake, wiggle, bend the left/front HO2S circuit from the HO2S sensor to the PCM. — Lightly tap the HO2S sensor (to simulate road shock). • **Is fault indicated?**	Yes	▶	ISOLATE fault and SERVICE as necessary. REMOVE breakout box. RECONNECT PCM. RERUN Quick Test.
	No	▶	further diagnosis using an EEC-IV monitor box or Scan Tool. If an EEC-IV monitor box or Scan Tool is not available, GO to X120.

FM0159400770460X

Fig. 229   Test X: CCRM (Part 46 of 55). 1994–95

X120 ROAD TEST

The purpose of the road test is to identify an area of concern by monitoring certain controlled parameters while trying to recreate a driveability or MIL symptom.

Note

A basic working knowledge of the EEC-IV system is critical to effectively analyze road test data.

WARNING

THIS ROAD TEST IS A SUGGESTED BUT OPTIONAL PROCEDURE. ALL APPLICABLE SAFETY PROCEDURES AND TRAFFIC LAWS MUST BE FOLLOWED. IN ORDER FOR A ROAD TEST TO BE PERFORMED, IT IS REQUIRED THAT ANOTHER PERSON ACCOMPANY THE DRIVER. THE ACCOMPANYING PERSON CAN MAKE MEASUREMENTS, OBSERVE CHANGES AND RECORD NOTES.

Prepare Vehicle For A Road Test

- Install breakout box, if applicable.
- Breakout box installed, PCM connected.
- Install fuel pressure gauge and MAP / BARO tester (optional)
- Other materials needed; DVOM, pencil, paper, appropriate schematic / pin usage sheet.

Preliminary Power Ground Checks

- With the key ON and a DVOM referenced to the battery negative post, check the following signals for correct values.

POWERS: KAPWR > 10.5V (Pin 1), VPWR > 10.5V (Pins 37 / 57), VREF 5 ± 1V (Pin 26).
GROUNDS: (all = 0 ± .5V) PWR GND (Pins 40 60), SIG RTN (Pin 46), IGN GND (Pin 16)
OPTIONAL GROUNDS: HO2S GND (Pin 49), CSE GND (Pin 20), MAF RTN (Pin 9 or 15)

Obtaining Other Information And Materials Before The Road Test

- Before the road test, perform the Visual Mechanical Checks Next, list the PCM sensors and actuators in the order given. These circuits and the FP FPM signal(s) are the main signals that will be monitored.

FM0159400770470X
Fig. 229 Test X: CCRM (Part 47 of 55). 1994–95

X120 ROAD TEST (Continued)

- The use of test lamp(s) and a DVOM may also aid diagnosis. Depending on the DTC being diagnosed, the FP/FPM circuits could be monitored, as well as the circuits to / from the Inertia Fuel Shutoff switch, the Left / Front HO2S circuit, etc. Remember, if the vehicle stalls, the PCM will "unground" the FP circuit and turn off the fuel pump. If the problem is in the fuel pump wiring, the lamp / voltage should change just BEFORE the symptom occurs.

- NOTE: Due to the low resistance of some test lamps, it is required that a DVOM or equivalent high resistance testing device be used when monitoring PCM output circuits.

Road Test

- After starting the engine for the road test, enter Engine Running Continuous Monitor Diagnostic Test Mode

- Drive the vehicle to create the conditions in which the symptom occurs

- When the symptom occurs, the passenger should observe changes in listed PCM signals. Information about the symptom, operating condition, value of the PCM signal or other notes should be recorded.

- If the symptom cannot be duplicated, verify that the PCM values are in the expected range.

Analyzing The Data

- Once the road test is completed, the results should be analyzed to locate and service the fault which caused the symptom.

- If no problem is identified, return to   other possible causes of the symptom.

FM0159400770480X
Fig. 229 Test X: CCRM (Part 48 of 55). 1994–95

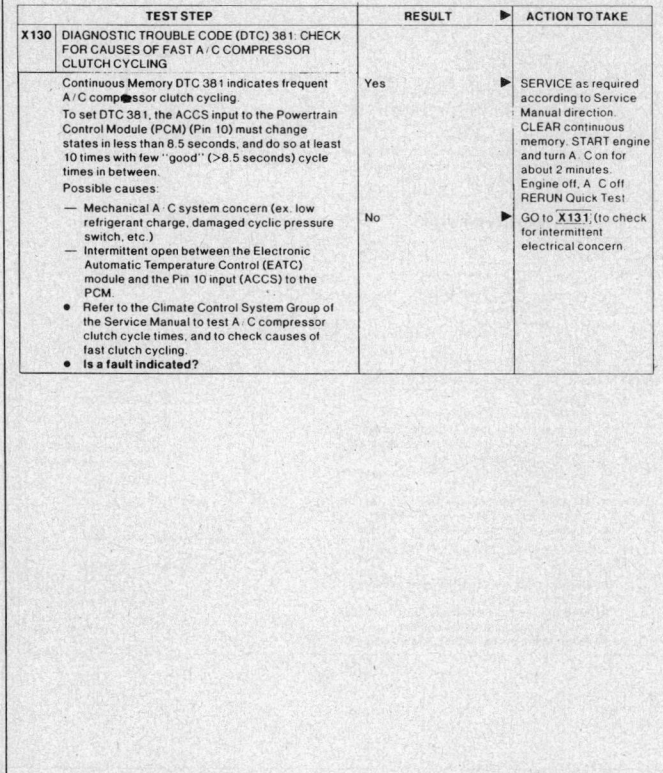

FM0159400770490X
Fig. 229 Test X: CCRM (Part 49 of 55). 1994–95

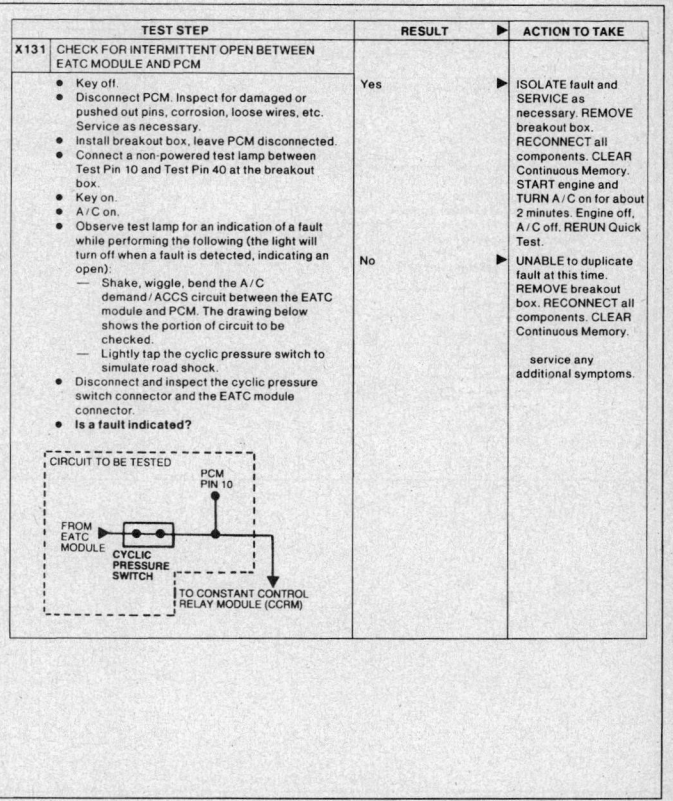

FM0159400770500X
Fig. 229 Test X: CCRM (Part 50 of 55). 1994–95

TEST STEP		RESULT	▶	ACTION TO TAKE
X140	CHECK HARNESS CONTINUITY OF HIGH SPEED POWER TO FAN CIRCUITS			
	• Key off. • Cooling fan disconnected. • CCRM disconnected. • Measure resistance between Pin 1 and Pin 12 of the CCRM vehicle harness connector. • **Is resistance less than 5.0 ohms?**	Yes	▶	SERVICE open in high speed Power-To-Fan circuit between Pins 1/2/12/24 splice and the cooling fan. RECONNECT all components. RE-EVALUATE symptom.
		No	▶	SERVICE open in high speed Power-To-Fan circuit between Pins 1/2/12/24 splice and CCRM. After service, GO to **X141** to verify proper operation of both HFC relays in CCRM.
X141	VERIFY OPERATION OF BOTH HFC RELAYS IN CCRM			
	• Key off. • CCRM disconnected. • Connect a jumper wire between Pin 13 of the CCRM and the battery positive (+) post. • Connect another jumper wire between Pin 17 of the CCRM and the battery negative (-) post. • Measure resistance between Pin 10 and both Pins 12 and 24. • Measure resistance between Pin 4 and both Pins 1 and 2. • **Are all resistances less than 5.0 ohms?**	Yes	▶	Both HFC relays are OK. REMOVE jumpers. After original service, RECONNECT all components. RE-EVALUATE symptom.
		No	▶	REPLACE CCRM. After also performing original service, RECONNECT all components. RE-EVALUATE symptom.
X150	CHECK HFC CIRCUIT FOR SHORT TO GROUND			
	• Key off. • Breakout box installed, PCM disconnected. • Disconnect CCRM. • Measure resistance between the HFC Test Pin (refer to **X** cover page schematics) and Test Pin 40 at the breakout box. • **Is resistance greater than 10,000 ohms?**	Yes	▶	REPLACE CCRM. REMOVE breakout box. RECONNECT all components. RERUN Quick Test.
		No	▶	SERVICE short to ground in HFC circuit. REMOVE breakout box. RECONNECT all components. RERUN Quick Test.

FM0159400770510X

Fig. 229 Test X: CCRM (Part 51 of 55). 1994–95

TEST STEP		RESULT	▶	ACTION TO TAKE
X155	CHECK DUAL FUNCTION A/C PRESSURE SWITCH (ACPSW) MEDIUM PRESSURE CONTACTS (3.0L FF TAURUS)			
	• Key off. • Breakout box installed, PCM disconnected. • CCRM disconnected. • Disconnect the dual function A/C Pressure Switch (ACPSW) (also known as the Refrigerant Containment/Fan Function Switch). • Again, measure resistance between Test Pin 31 and Test Pin 40 at the breakout box. • **Is resistance now greater than 10,000 ohms?**	Yes	▶	
		No	▶	check ACPSW operation. SERVICE short to ground in HFC circuit. REMOVE breakout box. RECONNECT all components. RERUN Quick Test.
X160	CHECK HFC RELAY PRIMARY CIRCUIT FOR OPEN IN CCRM (3.0L FF TAURUS)			
	• Key off. • ACPSW disconnected. • CCRM disconnected. • Measure resistance between Pin 17 and Pin 24 of the CCRM. • **Is resistance between 50 and 100 ohms?**	Yes	▶	No fault found. VERIFY test results. If all OK, RECONNECT all components. continue diagnosis.
		No	▶	REPLACE CCRM. RECONNECT all components. RE-EVALUATE symptom.

FM0159400770520X

Fig. 229 Test X: CCRM (Part 52 of 55). 1994–95

TEST STEP		RESULT	▶	ACTION TO TAKE
X165	DIAGNOSTIC TROUBLE CODE (DTC) 557: CHECK FOR VPWR TO LOW SPEED FUEL PUMP (LFP) RELAY			
	DTC 557 indicates a low speed fuel pump primary circuit failure. Possible causes: — Open or shorted circuit. — Damaged LFP relay. — Damaged Powertrain Control Module (PCM). • Disconnect LFP relay. • Key on, engine off. • Measure voltage between the VPWR circuit at the LFP relay vehicle harness connector and the battery negative post. • Key off. • **Was voltage greater than 10.5 volts?**	Yes	▶	GO to **X166**
		No	▶	SERVICE open in VPWR circuit between CCRM and LFP relay. RERUN Quick Test.

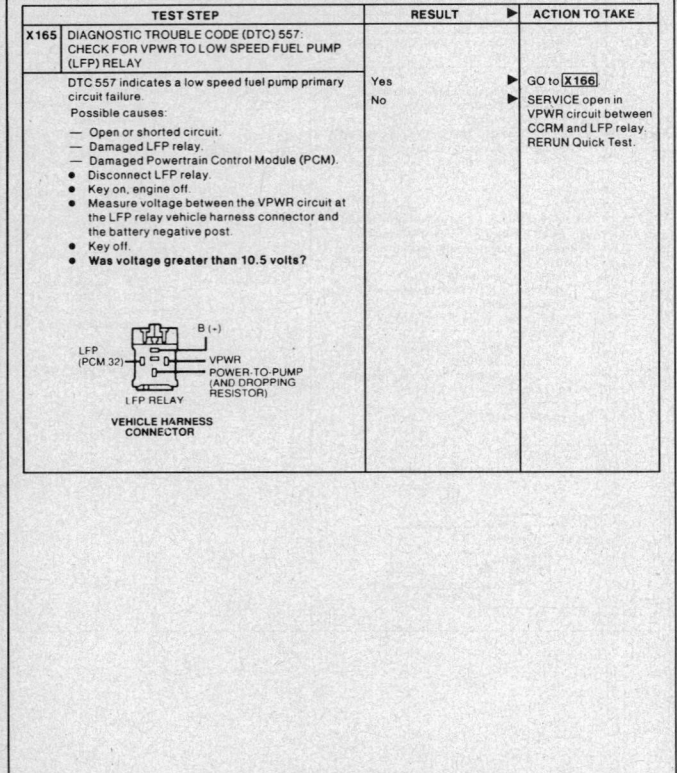

FM0159400770530X

Fig. 229 Test X: CCRM (Part 53 of 55). 1994–95

TEST STEP		RESULT	▶	ACTION TO TAKE
X166	CHECK LFP RELAY			
	• Key off. • LFP relay disconnected. • DVOM on 200 ohm scale. • Measure LFP relay coil resistance between the LFP pin and VPWR pin at the fuel pump relay. Resistance should be between 40 and 85 ohms. • DVOM on 10,000 ohm scale. • Check LFP relay for internal shorts: Measure resistance between the LFP pin and both the power-to-pump and B(+) pins. Both resistances should be greater than 10,000 ohms. • **Are all resistance checks OK?**	Yes	▶	GO to **X167**
		No	▶	REPLACE LFP relay. RERUN Quick Test.
	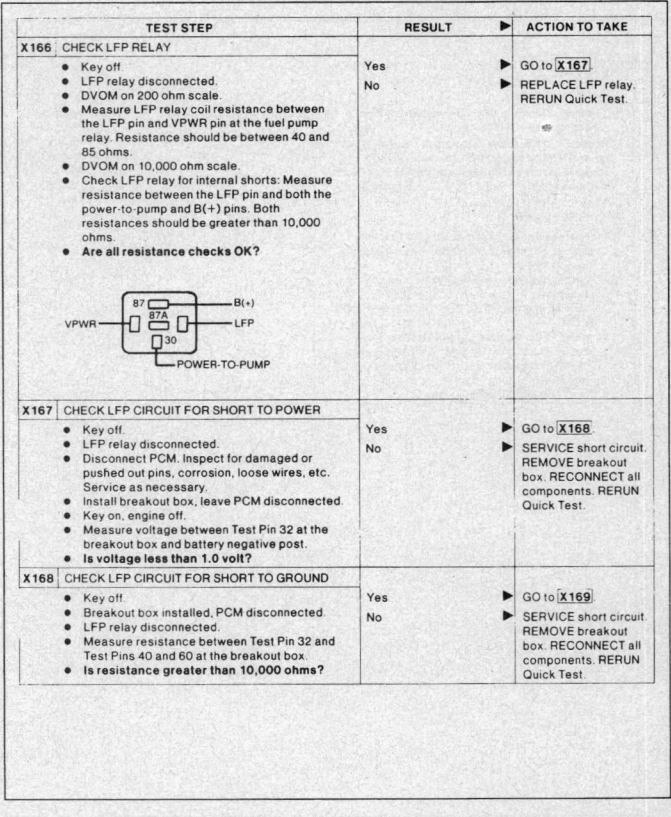			
X167	CHECK LFP CIRCUIT FOR SHORT TO POWER			
	• Key off. • LFP relay disconnected. • Disconnect PCM. Inspect for damaged or pushed out pins, corrosion, loose wires, etc. Service as necessary. • Install breakout box, leave PCM disconnected. • Key on, engine off. • Measure voltage between Test Pin 32 at the breakout box and battery negative post. • **Is voltage less than 1.0 volt?**	Yes	▶	GO to **X168**
		No	▶	SERVICE short circuit. REMOVE breakout box. RECONNECT all components. RERUN Quick Test.
X168	CHECK LFP CIRCUIT FOR SHORT TO GROUND			
	• Key off. • Breakout box installed, PCM disconnected. • LFP relay disconnected. • Measure resistance between Test Pin 32 and Test Pins 40 and 60 at the breakout box. • **Is resistance greater than 10,000 ohms?**	Yes	▶	GO to **X169**
		No	▶	SERVICE short circuit. REMOVE breakout box. RECONNECT all components. RERUN Quick Test.

FM0159400770540X

Fig. 229 Test X: CCRM (Part 54 of 55). 1994–95

TEST STEP	RESULT	▶	ACTION TO TAKE
X169 CHECK LFP CIRCUIT CONTINUITY • Key off. • Breakout box installed, PCM disconnected. • LFP relay disconnected. • Measure resistance between the LFP circuit at the LFP relay vehicle harness connector and Test Pin 32 at the breakout box. • **Is resistance less than 5.0 ohms?**	Yes No	▶ ▶	REPLACE PCM. RECONNECT LFP relay. RERUN Quick Test. SERVICE open circuit. REMOVE breakout box. RECONNECT all components. RERUN Quick Test.

Fig. 229   Test X: CCRM (Part 55 of 55). 1994

TEST STEP	RESULT	▶	ACTION TO TAKE
X169 CHECK LFP CIRCUIT CONTINUITY • Key off. • Breakout box installed, PCM disconnected. • LFP relay disconnected. • Measure resistance between the LFP circuit at the LFP relay vehicle harness connector and Test Pin 32 at the breakout box. • **Is resistance less than 5.0 ohms?**	Yes No	▶ ▶	REPLACE PCM. RECONNECT LFP relay. RERUN Quick Test. SERVICE open circuit. REMOVE breakout box. RECONNECT all components. RERUN Quick Test.
X175 ONE COOLING FAN MOTOR INOPERATIVE WHEN THE OTHER FAN MOTOR OPERATES (3.2L SHO ONLY): CHECK GROUND CIRCUIT TO INOPERATIVE FAN • Key off. • Disconnect inoperative cooling fan. • Measure resistance between the ground pin at the inoperative cooling fan vehicle harness connector and the battery negative post. • **Is resistance less than 5.0 ohms?**	Yes No	▶ ▶	GO to **X176**. SERVICE open ground circuit. RECONNECT cooling fan. RE-EVALUATE symptom.
X176 CHECK POWER-TO-FAN CIRCUIT CONTINUITY BETWEEN BOTH COOLING FANS • Key off. • Inoperative cooling fan disconnected. • Disconnect the cooling fan that operates. • Measure resistance of the power-to-fan circuit between the operative and inoperative cooling fan's vehicle harness connectors. • **Is resistance less than 5.0 ohms?**	Yes No	▶ ▶	REPLACE inoperative cooling fan. RECONNECT both cooling fans. RE-EVALUATE symptom. SERVICE open circuit between cooling fans. RECONNECT both cooling fans. RE-EVALUATE symptom.

FM015950077055BX

Fig. 229   Test X: CCRM (Part 55 of 55). 1995

Note

You should enter this Pinpoint Test only when directed here from Diagnostic Routines,   or Pinpoint Test **C** or **PC**.

Remember

This pinpoint test is intended to diagnose only the following:

• Harness circuits: All associated with VCRM.
• Variable Control Relay Module (VCRM)
• Powertrain Control Module (PCM)

Description

The Variable Control Relay Module (VCRM) is used to perform the following functions: fuel pump control; engine cooling fan control; A/C clutch control; A/C head pressure control; supply VPWR to the EEC-IV system and Powertrain Control Module (PCM). In addition to these functions, the VCRM performs diagnostic checks of its system. Information on any failure that is detected by the VCRM is sent via DCL (DATA+ and DATA- circuits) to the Powertrain Control Module (PCM). This failure information is output as Diagnostic Trouble Codes (DTC) during EEC-IV Self-Test. Each function is described in more detail below.

Fuel Pump Control

The Mark VIII uses a two speed fuel pump control strategy. The fuel pump receives either B(+) voltage (High Speed Fuel Pump), or a voltage less than B(+) (Low Speed Fuel Pump). The vehicle normally runs on the Low Speed Fuel Pump (FP), with the High Speed Fuel Pump (HFP) being activated during engine start-up and during certain high load conditions.

For low speed pump operation, the PCM grounds the Fuel Pump (FP) circuit. The VCRM receives this request for the low speed pump and activates the fuel pump output driver, sending voltage to the pump through the power-to-pump circuit. The power-to-pump circuit from the VCRM is designed so that the full B(+) voltage will not reach the pump, resulting in low speed pump operation.

For high speed pump operation, the PCM grounds the FP circuit and also sends a message, through DCL, indicating that the high speed pump is requested. With the FP circuit grounded the VCRM will activate the fuel pump output driver, the same as is done in low speed operation. With the high speed pump requested the VCRM will also ground its HFP output, which closes the normally open contacts of the HFP relay. This sends full B(+) voltage to the pump, resulting in high speed pump operation.

Engine Cooling Fan Control

The PCM monitors certain engine parameters (ECT sensor, vehicle speed, A/C demand, A/C head pressure, etc.) to determine engine cooling fan needs. The PCM will send the desired fan speed to the VCRM via DCL. The VCRM then adjusts the fan speed according to vehicle battery voltage, and outputs the appropriate voltage through the fan output driver with a pulse width modulated duty cycle.

A/C Head Pressure Control

The VCRM receives the A/C pressure reading from the A/C Head Pressure (ACP) sensor. This information is supplied to the PCM through the DCL, and is used to help determine the desired fan speed. The PCM also has the ability to turn off A/C (through WAC) if the A/C head pressure has, or could, exceed the safe limits of the system. The A/C Cyclic Pressure Switch is also used to help control A/C pressure.

Vehicle Power

When the ignition switch is turned to the start or run position, the VCRM supplies Vehicle Power (VPWR) to the EEC system and the PCM.

FM015930077101OX

Fig. 230   Test XB: VCRM (Part 1 of 63)

FM015930077102OX

Fig. 230   Test XB: VCRM (Part 2 of 63)

Pinpoint Test Schematic

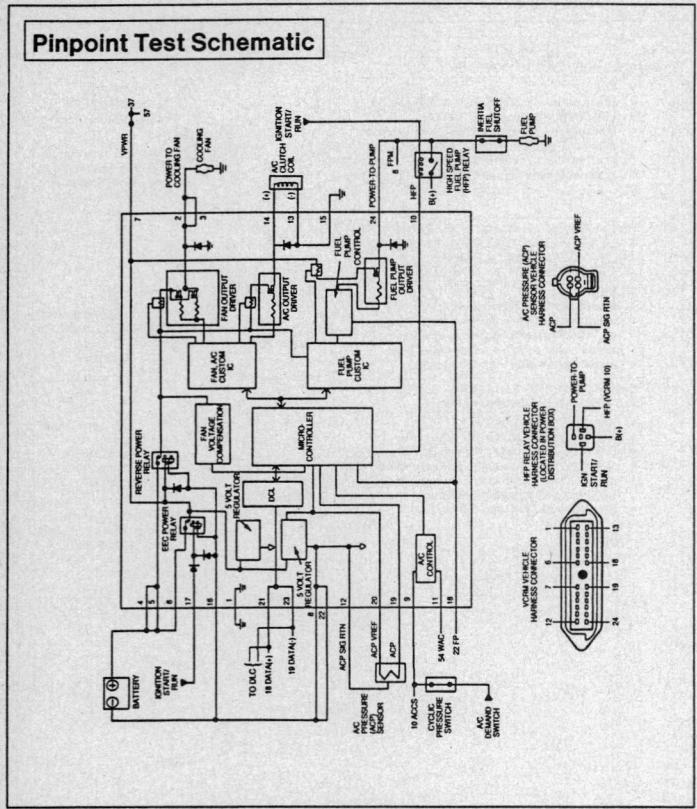

Fig. 230   Test XB: VCRM (Part 3 of 63)

VCRM Pin Usage and Wire Colors

Pin	Pin Usage	Wire Color	Pin	Pin Usage	Wire Color
1	Power Ground	BK	13	A/C Clutch Return	GY/W
2	Power-to-Cooling Fan	LB	14	Power-to-A/C Clutch	P
3	Power-to-Cooling Fan	LB	15	A/C Clutch Ground	BK
4	B(+)	Y	16	Ground	BK/Y
5	B(+)	Y	17	IGN Start/Run	R/LG
6	B(+)	Y	18	Fuel Pump Circuit	LB/O
7	VPWR	R	19	ACP Signal	DG/W
8	Ground	BK/W	20	ACP VREF	O/LB
9	A/C Cyclic Switch	BK/Y	21	DATA(+)	T/O
10	High Fuel Pump	BR/W	22	Ground	BK/W
11	WOT A/C Cut-Off	PK/Y	23	DATA(-)	PK/LB
12	ACP SIG RTN	LB/R	24	Power-to-Fuel Pump	PK/BK

FM0159300771040X

Fig. 230   Test XB: VCRM (Part 4 of 63)

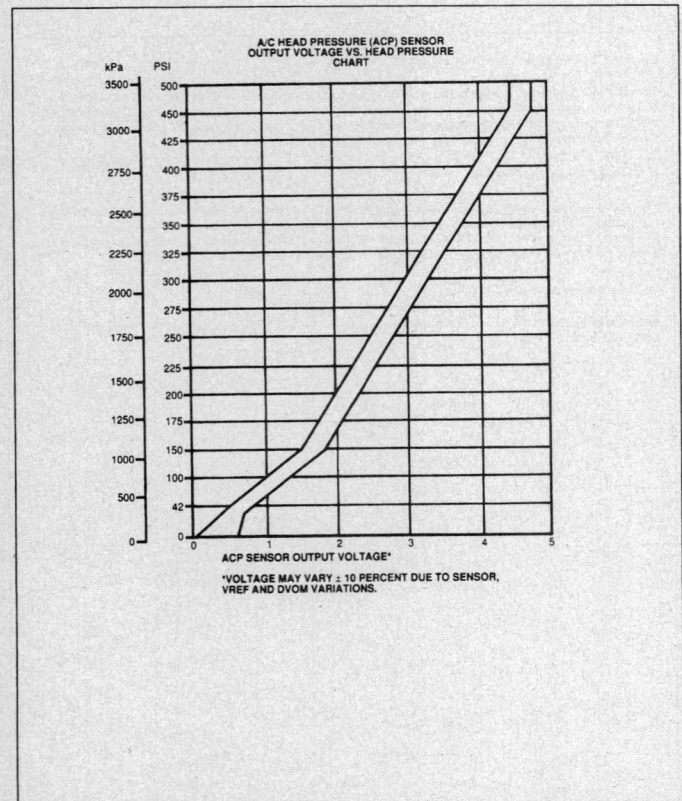

FM0159300771050X

Fig. 230   Test XB: VCRM (Part 5 of 63)

FM0159300771060X

Fig. 230   Test XB: VCRM (Part 6 of 63)

TEST STEP	RESULT	▶	ACTION TO TAKE
XB10 CHECK VPWR CIRCUIT CONTINUITY BETWEEN PCM AND VCRM			
• Key off. • Breakout box installed, PCM disconnected. • Disconnect VCRM. Inspect for damaged or pushed out pins, corrosion, loose wires, etc. Service as necessary. • Measure resistance between Pin 7 of the VCRM vehicle harness connector and Test Pins 37 and 57 at the breakout box. • **Is resistance less than 5.0 ohms?**	Yes No	▶ ▶	GO to **XB11**. SERVICE open in VPWR circuit between PCM and VCRM. REMOVE breakout box. RECONNECT all components. RERUN Quick Test.
XB11 CHECK FOR B(+) AND IGN START/RUN VOLTAGE TO VCRM			
• Key off. • Breakout box installed, PCM disconnected. • VCRM disconnected. • Measure voltage between Pin 6 of the VCRM vehicle harness connector and the battery negative post. • Key on. • Measure voltage between Pin 17 of the VCRM vehicle harness connector and the battery negative post. • **Are both voltages greater than 10.5 volts?**	Yes No	▶ ▶	Key off. GO to **XB12**. Key off. SERVICE open in B(+) or IGN START/RUN circuit. REMOVE breakout box. RECONNECT all components. RERUN Quick Test.
XB12 CHECK VCRM GROUND (PIN 16)			
• Key off. • Breakout box installed, PCM disconnected. • VCRM disconnected. • Measure resistance between Pin 16 of the VCRM vehicle harness connector and the battery negative post. • **Is resistance less than 5.0 ohms?**	Yes No	▶ ▶	REPLACE VCRM. REMOVE breakout box. RECONNECT all components. RERUN Quick Test. SERVICE open GND circuit. REMOVE breakout box. RECONNECT all components. RERUN Quick Test.

FM0159300771070X

Fig. 230 Test XB: VCRM (Part 7 of 63)

TEST STEP	RESULT	▶	ACTION TO TAKE
XB15 CONTINUOUS MEMORY DIAGNOSTIC TROUBLE CODE (DTC) 584: CLEAR AND ATTEMPT TO REGENERATE DTC			
Continuous Memory DTC 584 indicates that the VCRM PWR GND (Pin 1) is open. This could be due to a "hard fault" or an intermittent condition. Possible causes: — Open VCRM PWR GND circuit. — Damaged VCRM. • Clear Continuous Memory • Start engine. • Turn A/C on, wait 15 seconds. • A/C off. • Engine off. • Rerun Key On Engine Off Self-Test. • **Is Continuous Memory DTC 584 present?**	Yes No	▶ ▶	DTC 584 is a "hard fault". GO to **XB16**. DTC 584 is intermittent. GO to **XB18**.
XB16 CHECK VCRM PWR GND CIRCUIT CONTINUITY			
• Key off. • Disconnect VCRM. Inspect for damaged or pushed out pins, corrosion, loose wires, etc. Service as necessary. • Measure resistance between Pin 1 of the VCRM vehicle harness connector and the battery negative post. • **Is resistance less than 5.0 ohms?**	Yes No	▶ ▶	REPLACE VCRM. RECONNECT all components. CLEAR Continuous Memory. START engine. A/C on, WAIT 15 seconds. Key off, A/C off. RERUN Quick Test. SERVICE open in VCRM PWR GND circuit. RECONNECT all components. CLEAR Continuous Memory. START engine. A/C on, WAIT 15 seconds. Key off, A/C off. RERUN Quick Test.

FM0159300771080X

Fig. 230 Test XB: VCRM (Part 8 of 63)

TEST STEP	RESULT	▶	ACTION TO TAKE
XB18 CHECK VCRM PWR GND CIRCUIT			
• Key off. • Visually check the VCRM PWR GND circuit (VCRM Pin 1) from the VCRM to the circuit's ground point. The VCRM PWR GND circuit is grounded to the RH side radiator support to a weld nut. • Start engine. • A/C on (to turn cooling fan on). **CAUTION: While performing this test, do not touch any moving/hot engine parts.** • Shake, wiggle, bend the VCRM PWR GND circuit, between the VCRM and the circuit's ground point. An open circuit will be indicated by the fan speed increasing to 100% (although the open must be present for at least 5 seconds). • Lightly tap on VCRM to simulate road shock. • **Is a fault indicated?**	Yes No	▶ ▶	ISOLATE fault and SERVICE as necessary. CLEAR Continuous memory (DTC 584 should have been set). START engine. A/C on, WAIT 15 seconds. Key off, A/C off. RERUN Quick Test. Key off, A/C off. GO to **XB19**.
XB19 CHECK VCRM PWR GND CIRCUIT			
• Key off. • Disconnect VCRM. Inspect for damaged or pushed out pins, corrosion, loose wires, etc. Service as necessary. • Connect a test lamp between Pin 5 and Pin 1 of the VCRM vehicle harness connector. • Observe test lamp for an indication of a fault while performing the following (the lamp will go out when a fault is found, indicating an open): — Shake, wiggle, bend the VCRM PWR GND circuit between the VCRM vehicle harness connector and the circuit's ground point. • **Is fault indicated?**	Yes No	▶ ▶	ISOLATE fault and SERVICE as necessary. RECONNECT all components. START engine. A/C on, WAIT 15 seconds. A/C off, key off. RERUN Quick Test. Unable to isolate fault at this time. RECONNECT all components. further diagnosis using the EEC-IV Monitor Box or Scan Tool RETURN to Diagnostic Routines

FM0159300771090X

Fig. 230 Test XB: VCRM (Part 9 of 63)

TEST STEP	RESULT	▶	ACTION TO TAKE
XB20 CONTINUOUS MEMORY DIAGNOSTIC TROUBLE CODE (DTC) 581: CLEAR AND ATTEMPT TO RE-GENERATE DTC			
Continuous Memory DTC 581 indicates that when the cooling fan was activated, the Power-to-Cooling Fan circuit exceeded the normal current draw. This could be due to a "hard fault" or an intermittent condition. Possible causes: — Power-to-Cooling Fan circuit short to ground. — Damaged cooling fan motor. — Damaged VCRM. • Clear Continuous Memory • Start engine. • Turn A/C on, wait 15 seconds. • A/C off. • Engine off. • Rerun Key On Engine Off Self-Test. • **Is Continuous Memory DTC 581 present?**	Yes No	▶ ▶	DTC 581 is a "hard fault". GO to **XB21**. DTC 581 is intermittent. GO to **XB24**.
XB21 CHECK COOLING FAN MOTOR			
• Again clear Continuous Memory. • Disconnect cooling fan motor. • Start engine. • Turn A/C on, wait 15 seconds (but no more than 20 seconds). • A/C off. • Engine off. • Rerun Key On Engine Off Self-Test. • **Is Continuous Memory DTC 581 present (disregard any other codes)?**	Yes No	▶ ▶	GO to **XB22**. REPLACE cooling fan motor. RECONNECT all components. RERUN Quick Test.

FM0159300771100X

Fig. 230 Test XB: VCRM (Part 10 of 63)

FORD—Computerized Engine Controls

Fig. 230 Test XB: VCRM (Part 11 of 63)

TEST STEP	RESULT	▶	ACTION TO TAKE
XB22 CHECK POWER-TO-COOLING FAN CIRCUIT FOR SHORT TO GROUND • Key off. • Cooling fan motor disconnected. • Disconnect VCRM. Inspect for damaged or pushed out pins, corrosion, loose wires, etc. Service as necessary. • Measure resistance between the power-to-cooling fan circuit at the cooling fan vehicle harness connector and the battery negative post. • **Is resistance greater than 10,000 ohms?**	Yes No	▶ ▶	REPLACE VCRM. RECONNECT all components. CLEAR Continuous Memory. START engine. TURN A/C on, wait 15 seconds. A/C off, key off. RERUN Quick Test. SERVICE power-to-cooling fan circuit short to ground. RECONNECT all components. CLEAR Continuous Memory. START engine. TURN A/C on, WAIT 15 seconds. A/C off, key off. RERUN Quick Test.
XB24 CHECK POWER-TO-COOLING FAN CIRCUIT FOR INTERMITTENT SHORT TO GROUND • Key off. • Visually check the power-to-cooling fan circuit from the VCRM to the cooling fan. • Start engine. • A/C on (to turn cooling fan on). **CAUTION: While performing this test, do not touch any moving/hot engine parts.** • Shake, wiggle, bend the power-to-cooling fan circuit from the VCRM to the cooling fan (as close as practical). A short to ground will be indicated by the fan turning off (the VCRM FMEM will turn the fan off when an "overcurrent" condition exists). • Key off. A/C off. • **Is a fault indicated?**	Yes No	▶ ▶	ISOLATE fault and SERVICE as necessary. CLEAR Continuous Memory (DTC 581 should have been set). START engine. A/C on, WAIT 5 seconds. A/C off, key off. RERUN Quick Test. GO to XB25

Fig. 230 Test XB: VCRM (Part 12 of 63)

TEST STEP	RESULT	▶	ACTION TO TAKE
XB25 CHECK VCRM CONNECTOR AND POWER-TO-COOLING FAN CIRCUIT • Key off. • Disconnect VCRM. Inspect for damaged or pushed out pins, corrosion, loose wires, etc. Service as necessary. • Connect a test lamp between Pin 2 and Pin 4 of the VCRM vehicle harness connector. • Observe test lamp for an indication of a fault while performing the following (the lamp will be on, but not to full brightness. A short to ground will be indicated by the lamp getting brighter): — Shake, wiggle, bend the power-to-cooling fan circuit near the cooling fan. • Disconnect cooling fan. Inspect for damaged or pushed out pins, corrosion, loose wires, etc. Service as necessary. • Test lamp still connected between Pin 2 and Pin 4 of the VCRM vehicle harness connector. • Observe test lamp for an indication of a fault while performing the following (the lamp will turn on, indicating a short to ground): — Again shake, wiggle, bend the power-to-cooling fan circuit from the VCRM vehicle harness connector to the cooling fan vehicle harness connector. • **Is a fault indicated?**	Yes No	▶ ▶	ISOLATE fault and SERVICE as necessary. RECONNECT all components. START engine. A/C on, WAIT 5 seconds. A/C off, key off. RERUN Quick Test. Unable to isolate fault at this time. RECONNECT all components. further diagnosis using the EEC-IV Monitor Box or Scan Tool RETURN to *Diagnostic Routines*

Fig. 230 Test XB: VCRM (Part 13 of 63)

TEST STEP	RESULT	▶	ACTION TO TAKE
XB30 KEY ON ENGINE OFF DIAGNOSTIC TROUBLE CODE (DTC) 582: VERIFY COOLING FAN IS NOT ALWAYS ON Key On Engine Off DTC 582 indicates an open or short to power in the power-to-cooling fan circuit. Possible causes: — Open or short to power in the power-to-cooling fan circuit (harness). — Open cooling fan motor ground circuit. — Open circuit in cooling fan. — Damaged VCRM. NOTE: If Key On Engine Off DTC 587 is also present, refer to the EEC-IV DTC charts to address the 587 first. Also verify that the cooling fan was not turning during Key On Engine Off Self-Test. If the fan was turning, "back voltage" could be sent to the VCRM thru the power-to-cooling fan circuit resulting in an invalid 582 DTC. • Engine cooled down (so cooling fan would normally be off). • A/C and defroster off. • Key on, engine off. • **Is cooling fan on?**	Yes No	▶ ▶	Key off. GO to XB35 (to check for short to power). Key off. GO to XB31 (to check for opens).
XB31 CHECK FOR VOLTAGE TO COOLING FAN • Key off. • Disconnect cooling fan. • Start engine. • Turn A/C on. • Measure voltage between the power-to-cooling fan circuit and ground circuit at the cooling fan vehicle harness connector. • **Is voltage greater than 6.0 volts?**	Yes No	▶ ▶	Key off. REPLACE cooling fan. RERUN Quick Test. Key off. GO to XB32.
XB32 CHECK COOLING FAN GROUND CIRCUIT CONTINUITY • Key off. • Cooling fan disconnected. • Measure resistance between the ground circuit at the cooling fan vehicle harness connector and the battery negative post. • **Is resistance less than 5.0 ohms?**	Yes No	▶ ▶	GO to XB33. SERVICE open in cooling fan ground circuit. RECONNECT cooling fan. RERUN Quick Test.

Fig. 230 Test XB: VCRM (Part 14 of 63)

TEST STEP	RESULT	▶	ACTION TO TAKE
XB33 CHECK POWER-TO-COOLING FAN CIRCUIT CONTINUITY • Key off. • Cooling fan disconnected. • Disconnect VCRM. Inspect for damaged or pushed out pins, corrosion, loose wires, etc. Service as necessary. • Measure resistance between the power-to-cooling fan circuit at the cooling fan vehicle harness connector and Pins 2 and 3 of the VCRM vehicle harness connector. • **Is resistance less than 5.0 ohms?**	Yes No	▶ ▶	REPLACE VCRM. RECONNECT all components. RERUN Quick Test. SERVICE open in power-to-cooling fan circuit. RECONNECT all components. RERUN Quick Test.
XB35 CHECK POWER-TO-COOLING FAN CIRCUIT FOR SHORT TO POWER • Key off. • Disconnect cooling fan. • Disconnect VCRM. Inspect for damaged or pushed out pins, corrosion, loose wires, etc. Service as necessary. • Key on, engine off. • Measure voltage between the power-to-cooling fan circuit at the cooling fan vehicle harness connector and the battery negative post. • **Is voltage less than 1.0 volt?**	Yes No	▶ ▶	REPLACE VCRM. RECONNECT all components. RERUN Quick Test. SERVICE short to power in the power-to-cooling fan circuit. RECONNECT all components. RERUN Quick Test.
XB40 CONTINUOUS MEMORY DIAGNOSTIC TROUBLE CODE (DTC) 578: CLEAR AND ATTEMPT TO RE-GENERATE DTC Continuous Memory DTC 578 indicates that the A/C Pressure (ACP) sensor VREF circuit is short to ground. This could be due to a "hard fault" or an intermittent condition. Possible causes: — ACP sensor VREF circuit short to ground. — Damaged ACP sensor. — Damaged VCRM. • Clear Continuous Memory • Start engine, wait 15 seconds. • Engine off. • Rerun Key On Engine Off Self-Test. • **Is Continuous Memory DTC 578 present?**	Yes No	▶ ▶	DTC 578 is a "hard fault". GO to XB41 DTC 578 is intermittent. GO to XB44.

TEST STEP	RESULT	▶	ACTION TO TAKE
XB41 CHECK ACP SENSOR			
• Again, clear Continuous Memory.	Yes	▶	GO to XB42.
• Key off.	No	▶	REPLACE ACP sensor.
• Disconnect ACP sensor.			RECONNECT all
• Start engine, wait 15 seconds.			components. CLEAR
• Engine off.			Continuous Memory.
• Rerun Key On Engine Off Self-Test.			START engine, WAIT
• **Is Continuous Memory DTC 578 present (disregard any other codes)?**			15 seconds. Key off. RERUN Quick Test.
XB42 CHECK ACP VREF CIRCUIT FOR SHORT TO GND			
• Key off.	Yes	▶	REPLACE VCRM.
• ACP sensor disconnected.			RECONNECT all
• Disconnect VCRM. Inspect for damaged or pushed out pins, corrosion, loose wires, etc. Service as necessary.			components. CLEAR Continuous Memory. START engine, WAIT 15 seconds. Key off.
• Measure resistance between the ACP VREF circuit at the ACP sensor vehicle harness connector and the battery ground post.	No	▶	RERUN Quick Test. SERVICE ACP VREF circuit short to ground.
• **Is resistance greater than 10,000 ohms?**			RECONNECT all components. CLEAR Continuous Memory. START engine, WAIT 15 seconds. Key off. RERUN Quick Test.
XB44 CHECK ACP VREF FOR INTERMITTENT SHORT TO GROUND			
• Key off.	Yes	▶	ISOLATE fault and
• Visually check the ACP VREF circuit from the ACP sensor to the VCRM.			SERVICE as necessary. RECONNECT all
• Disconnect the ACP sensor. Inspect for damaged or pushed out pins, corrosion, loose wires, etc. Service as necessary.			components. START engine, WAIT 15 seconds. Key off.
• Disconnect VCRM. Inspect for damaged or pushed out pins, corrosion, loose wires, etc. Service as necessary.	No	▶	RERUN Quick Test. Unable to isolate fault at this time.
• Connect test lamp between Pin 6 and Pin 20 of the VCRM vehicle harness connector.			RECONNECT all components
• Observe test lamp for an indication of a fault while performing the following (the lamp will come on when a fault is found, indicating a short to ground):			further diagnosis using the EEC-IV Monitor Box or Scan Tool
— Shake, wiggle, bend the ACP VREF circuit from the ACP sensor vehicle harness connector and the VCRM vehicle harness connector.			
• **Is a fault indicated?**			RETURN to Diagnostic Routines

FM0159300771150X

Fig. 230   Test XB: VCRM (Part 15 of 63)

TEST STEP	RESULT	▶	ACTION TO TAKE
XB50 CONTINUOUS MEMORY DIAGNOSTIC TROUBLE CODE (DTC) 579: CHECK ACP VREF AND ACP SIG RTN CIRCUITS			
Continuous Memory DTC 579 indicates the A/C Pressure (ACP) sensor did not detect a sufficient change in A/C system pressure when the A/C was turned on or the ACP circuit is above maximum voltage. This could be due to a problem in the ACP sensor circuits or the A/C system, and could be a hard fault or an intermittent concern.	Greater than 6.0 volts	▶	GO to XB62 (to check ACP VREF for short to power).
Possible causes:	Less than 4.0 volts	▶	GO to XB63 (to check ACP VREF and ACP SIG RTN circuits).
— Open or shorted ACP sensor circuit. — A/C system mechanical concern. — Damaged ACP sensor. — Damaged VCRM. — Power-to-A/C clutch circuit open (DTC 586 also present).	Between 4.0 and 6.0 volts	▶	GO to XB51 (ACP VREF and ACP SIG RTN circuits OK to sensor).
NOTE: If Continuous Memory DTC 586 is also present, address the 586.			
• Key off. • Disconnect ACP sensor. • Key on. • Measure voltage between the ACP VREF and the ACP SIG RTN circuits at the ACP sensor vehicle harness connector. • Key off. • **What was the voltage?**			

A/C PRESSURE (ACP) SENSOR VEHICLE HARNESS CONNECTOR
ACP
ACP SIG RTN
ACP VREF

FM0159300771160X

Fig. 230   Test XB: VCRM (Part 16 of 63)

TEST STEP	RESULT	▶	ACTION TO TAKE
XB51 CHECK IF A/C CLUTCH WILL ENGAGE (ACP SENSOR CONNECTED)			
• Key off.	Yes	▶	Key off, A/C off. GO to XB52 (ACP circuit is not open or short to power).
• Reconnect ACP sensor.			
• Start engine.			
• Turn A/C on, wait 30 seconds.	No	▶	Key off, A/C off. GO to XB57 (to check if ACP circuit is OK).
• **Does the A/C clutch "click" on?**			
XB52 CLEAR AND ATTEMPT TO RE-GENERATE DTC			
• Clear Continuous Memory (refer to Quick Test Appendix in Section 5A).	Yes	▶	DTC 579 is a "hard fault". GO to XB53.
• Attempt to reset DTC 579 by performing the following:	No	▶	The ACP sensor is now able to detect an A/C system pressure change. Either an intermittent ACP sensor circuit fault exists, or an A/C system intermittent or "marginal" mechanical condition exists. GO to XB66.
(1) Start engine. (2) A/C on, wait 20 seconds after A/C clutch engagement is heard ("click"). (3) A/C off, wait 5 seconds. (4) Repeat steps 2 and 3 four more times (a total of five A/C clutch engagements, with each engagement lasting about 20 seconds, must be seen by the VCRM during the same "power-up" to set DTC 579 for insufficient A/C pressure change).			
• A/C off. • Engine off. • Rerun Key On Engine Off Self-Test. • **Is Continuous Memory DTC 579 present?**			NOTE: For VCRM module number F3LF-12B577-AG (early 1993 production) if DTC 579 cannot be reset and there are no symptoms reported that are associated with the A/C system, be aware that DTC 579 could have been set due to a "sensitive" strategy.

FM0159300771170X

Fig. 230   Test XB: VCRM (Part 17 of 63)

TEST STEP	RESULT	▶	ACTION TO TAKE
XB53 CHECK A/C SYSTEM PRESSURE AND PRESSURE CHANGE			
• Key off.	Yes	▶	GO to XB54 (the A/C pressure changed as expected. ACP sensor and circuit will now be checked).
• Install A/C System Manifold Gauge Set			
• A/C off.	No	▶	A/C system pressure did not change as expected. Go to the Climate Control Group of the Service Manual to check for A/C system mechanical concerns.
• Start engine.			
• Note the A/C high pressure gauge reading.			
• While monitoring the A/C high pressure gauge reading, turn the A/C on. Ten seconds after clutch engagement, note the pressure (the pressure should increase).			
• Key off.			After any service,
• A/C off.			CLEAR Continuous
• **Did the A/C high pressure gauge reading change more than 20 psi within 10 seconds of clutch engagement?**			Memory. ATTEMPT to reset DTC 579 (refer to XB52 for procedure only). RERUN Quick Test.

FM0159300771180X

Fig. 230   Test XB: VCRM (Part 18 of 63)

TEST STEP	RESULT	▶	ACTION TO TAKE
XB54 CHECK ACP SENSOR OUTPUT			
• Key off. • Disconnect ACP sensor. • A/C system Manifold Gauge Set installed. • Jumper the ACP SIG RTN circuit between the ACP sensor vehicle harness connector and the ACP sensor connector. • Jumper the ACP VREF circuit between the ACP sensor vehicle harness connector and the ACP sensor connector. • Jumper the ACP signal circuit at the ACP sensor vehicle harness connector to the battery negative post. • Connect a DVOM between the ACP signal circuit at the ACP sensor connector and the ACP SIG RTN circuit jumper wire. • A/C off. • Start engine. • Note the A/C high pressure gauge reading and the ACP sensor voltage. • While monitoring the ACP sensor voltage, turn the A/C on. Ten seconds after clutch engagement, note the voltage. • A/C off. • Key off. • **Did the ACP sensor voltage change more than 0.2 volts within 10 seconds of turning the A/C on?** NOTE: By listening to the A/C clutch, verify that it does not disengage during the 10 seconds of testing. If it does disengage, retest.	Yes	▶	REMOVE jumper wires. GO to XB55. (ACP sensor is operational.)
	No	▶	REPLACE ACP sensor. REMOVE A/C system Manifold Gauge Set. REMOVE jumper wires. RECONNECT all components. CLEAR Continuous Memory. ATTEMPT to reset DTC 579 (REFER to XB52 for procedure only). RERUN Quick Test.

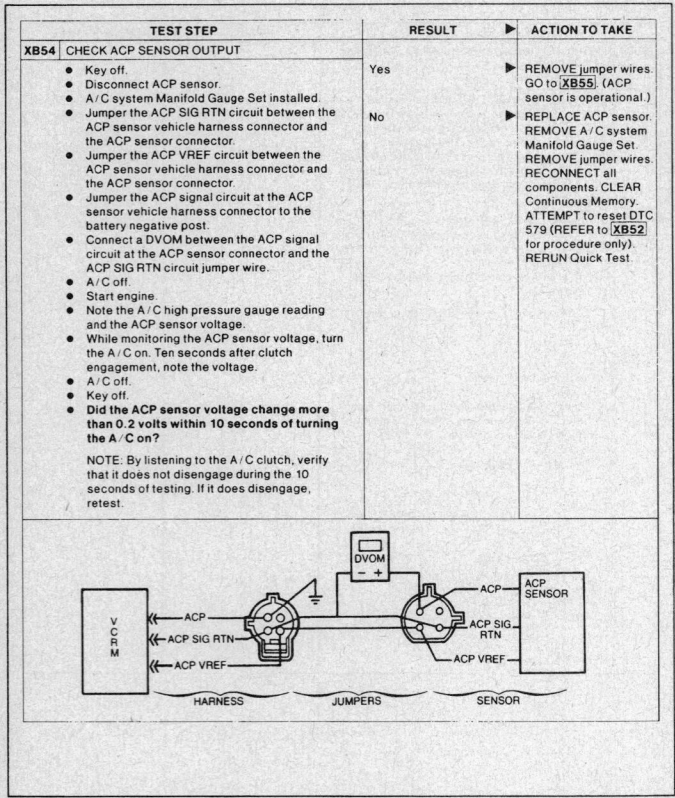

Fig. 230   Test XB: VCRM (Part 19 of 63)

FM015930077119OX

TEST STEP	RESULT	▶	ACTION TO TAKE
XB55 CHECK ACP CIRCUIT FOR SHORT TO GROUND			
• Key off. • ACP sensor disconnected. • Disconnect VCRM. • Measure resistance between the ACP circuit at the ACP sensor vehicle harness connector and the battery negative post. • Measure resistance between the ACP circuit and the ACP SIG RTN circuit at the ACP sensor vehicle harness connector. • **Are both resistances greater than 10,000 ohms?**	Yes	▶	REPLACE VCRM. REMOVE A/C system Manifold Gauge Set. RECONNECT all components. CLEAR Continuous Memory. Attempt to reset DTC 579 (refer to XB52 for procedure only). RERUN Quick Test.
	No	▶	SERVICE ACP circuit short to ground or ACP SIG RTN. REMOVE A/C system Manifold Gauge Set. RECONNECT all components. CLEAR Continuous Memory. Attempt to reset DTC 579 (refer to XB52 for procedure only). RERUN Quick Test.

FM015930077120OX

Fig. 230   Test XB: VCRM (Part 20 of 63). 1993

TEST STEP	RESULT	▶	ACTION TO TAKE
XB57 CHECK FOR VOLTAGE TO A/C CLUTCH (USING TEST LAMP)			
• Key off. • Disconnect A/C Cyclic Pressure Switch. Install a jumper wire in the A/C Cyclic Pressure Switch vehicle harness connector (to complete the circuit). • Disconnect A/C clutch. • Connect a non-powered test lamp between the power-to-A/C clutch circuit and the A/C clutch ground circuit at the A/C clutch vehicle harness connector. • Start engine. • A/C on, wait 10 seconds. • **Is test lamp on?**	Yes	▶	REMOVE test lamp and jumper. RECONNECT all components. GO to the Air Conditioing Group of the Service Manual to check for A/C system "mechanical" concerns (ex. A/C clutch air gap etc.). After any service, CLEAR Continuous Memory. Attempt to reset DTC 579 (REFER to XB52 for procedure only). RERUN Quick Test.
	No	▶	REMOVE test lamp and jumper. RECONNECT all components. **FOR VCRM MODULE NUMBERS F3LF-12B577-AG:** REPLACE VCRM. CLEAR Continuous Memory. Attempt to reset DTC 579 (refer to XB52 for procedure only). RERUN Quick Test. **FOR ALL OTHER VCRM MODULE NUMBERS:** GO to XB58 (to check ACP circuits).

FM015930077121AX

Fig. 230   Test XB: VCRM (Part 21 of 63). 1993

TEST STEP	RESULT	▶	ACTION TO TAKE
XB55 CHECK ACP CIRCUIT FOR SHORT TO GROUND			
• Key off. • ACP sensor disconnected. • Disconnect VCRM. • Measure resistance between the ACP circuit at the ACP sensor vehicle harness connector and the battery negative post. • Measure resistance between the ACP circuit and the ACP SIG RTN circuit at the ACP sensor vehicle harness connector. • **Are both resistances greater than 10,000 ohms?**	Yes	▶	REPLACE VCRM. REMOVE A/C system Manifold Gauge set. RECONNECT all components. CLEAR Continuous Memory. ATTEMPT to reset DTC 579 (refer to XB52 for procedure only). RERUN Quick Test.
	No	▶	SERVICE ACP circuit short to ground or SIG RTN. REMOVE A/C system Manifold Gauge Set. RECONNECT all components. CLEAR Continuous Memory. ATTEMPT to reset DTC 579 (refer to XB52 for procedure only). RERUN Quick Test.
XB57 CHECK FOR VOLTAGE TO A/C CLUTCH (USING TEST LAMP)			
• Key off. • Disconnect A/C Cyclic Pressure Switch. Install a jumper wire in the A/C Cyclic Pressure Switch vehicle harness connector (to complete the circuit). • Disconnect A/C clutch. • Connect a non-powered test lamp between the Power-to-A/C Clutch circuit and the A/C clutch ground circuit at the A/C clutch vehicle harness connector. • Start engine. • A/C on, wait 10 seconds. • **Is test lamp on?**	Yes	▶	REMOVE test lamp and jumper. RECONNECT all components. GO to the Climate Control Group of the Service Manual to check for A/C system mechanical concerns (ex. A/C clutch air gap, etc.). After any service, CLEAR Continuous Memory. Attempt to reset DTC 579 (REFER to XB52 for procedure only). RERUN Quick Test.
	No	▶	GO to XB58 (to check ACP circuits)

FM015940077121BX

Fig. 230   Test XB: VCRM (Part 21 of 63). 1994–95

TEST STEP	RESULT	▶	ACTION TO TAKE
XB58 CHECK CONTINUITY OF ACP CIRCUIT • Key off. • Disconnect ACP sensor. • Disconnect VCRM. Inspect for damaged or pushed out pins, corrosion, loose wires, etc. Service as necessary. • Measure resistance between the ACP circuit at the ACP sensor vehicle harness connector and Pin 19 at the VCRM vehicle harness connector. • **Is resistance less than 5.0 ohms?**	Yes No	▶ ▶	GO TO XB59. SERVICE open ACP circuit. REMOVE test lamp and jumper. RECONNECT all components. CLEAR Continuous Memory. A/C off, START engine. TURN A/C on, WAIT 20 seconds, Key off, A/C off. RERUN Quick Test.
XB59 CHECK ACP CIRCUIT FOR SHORT TO POWER • Key off. • ACP sensor disconnected. • VCRM disconnected. • Key on. • Measure voltage between the ACP circuit at the ACP sensor vehicle harness connector and the battery negative post. • Key off. • **Was the voltage less than 1.0 volt?**	Yes No	▶ ▶	GO to XB60. SERVICE ACP circuit short to power. REMOVE test lamp and jumper. RECONNECT all components. CLEAR Continuous Memory. A/C off, START engine. TURN A/C on, WAIT 20 seconds. Key off, A/C off. RERUN Quick Test.

FM0159300771220X

Fig. 230   Test XB: VCRM (Part 22 of 63)

TEST STEP	RESULT	▶	ACTION TO TAKE
XB60 CHECK IF TEST LAMP AT A/C CLUTCH WILL TURN ON WITH ACP CIRCUIT GROUNDED • Key off. • ACP sensor disconnected. • Reconnect VCRM. • A/C Cyclic Pressure Switch disconnected. Jumper wire installed in vehicle harness connector. • A/C clutch disconnected. • Non-powered test lamp connected between the Power-To-A/C clutch circuit and A/C clutch ground circuit at the A/C clutch vehicle harness connector. • Connect a jumper wire between the ACP signal circuit at the ACP sensor vehicle harness connector and the battery negative post. • Start engine. • A/C on, wait 10 seconds. • **Is test lamp on?** 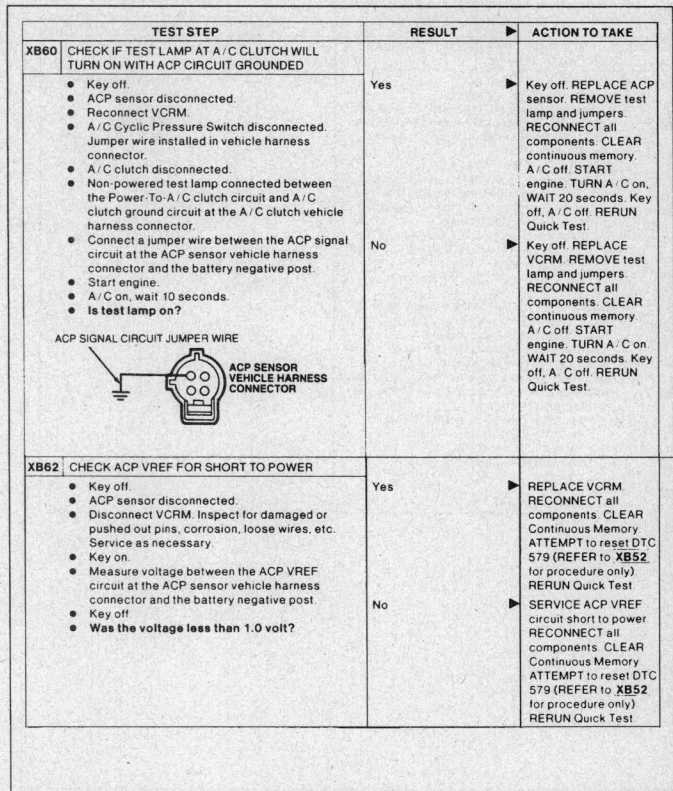 ACP SIGNAL CIRCUIT JUMPER WIRE ACP SENSOR VEHICLE HARNESS CONNECTOR	Yes No	▶ ▶	Key off. REPLACE ACP sensor. REMOVE test lamp and jumpers. RECONNECT all components. CLEAR continuous memory. A/C off. START engine. TURN A/C on, WAIT 20 seconds. Key off, A/C off. RERUN Quick Test. Key off. REPLACE VCRM. REMOVE test lamp and jumpers. RECONNECT all components. CLEAR continuous memory. A/C off. START engine. TURN A/C on, WAIT 20 seconds. Key off, A/C off. RERUN Quick Test.
XB62 CHECK ACP VREF FOR SHORT TO POWER • Key off. • ACP sensor disconnected. • Disconnect VCRM. Inspect for damaged or pushed out pins, corrosion, loose wires, etc. Service as necessary. • Key on. • Measure voltage between the ACP VREF circuit at the ACP sensor vehicle harness connector and the battery negative post. • Key off. • **Was the voltage less than 1.0 volt?**	Yes No	▶ ▶	REPLACE VCRM. RECONNECT all components. CLEAR Continuous Memory. ATTEMPT to reset DTC 579 (REFER to XB52 for procedure only) RERUN Quick Test SERVICE ACP VREF circuit short to power. RECONNECT all components. CLEAR Continuous Memory ATTEMPT to reset DTC 579 (REFER to XB52 for procedure only) RERUN Quick Test

FM0159300771230X

Fig. 230   Test XB: VCRM (Part 23 of 63)

TEST STEP	RESULT	▶	ACTION TO TAKE
XB63 CHECK ACP SIG RTN AND ACP VREF CIRCUIT CONTINUITY • Key off. • ACP sensor disconnected. • Disconnect VCRM. Inspect for damaged or pushed out pins, corrosion, loose wires, etc. Service as necessary. • Measure resistance between the ACP SIG RTN circuit at the ACP sensor vehicle harness connector and Pin 12 of the VCRM vehicle harness connector. • Measure resistance between the ACP VREF circuit at the ACP sensor vehicle harness connector and Pin 20 of the VCRM vehicle harness connector. • **Are both resistances less than 5.0 ohms?**	Yes No	▶ ▶	GO to XB64. SERVICE open in ACP VREF or ACP SIG RTN circuit. RECONNECT all components. CLEAR Continuous Memory. ATTEMPT to reset DTC 579 (REFER to XB52 for procedure only). RERUN Quick Test.
XB64 CHECK ACP SIG RTN FOR SHORT TO VREF • Key off. • ACP sensor disconnected. • VCRM disconnected. • Measure resistance between the ACP SIG RTN circuit and the ACP VREF circuit at the ACP sensor vehicle harness connector. • **Is resistance greater than 10,000 ohms?**	Yes No	▶ ▶	GO to XB65. SERVICE ACP SIG RTN short to ACP VREF. RECONNECT all components. CLEAR Continuous Memory. ATTEMPT to reset DTC 579 (REFER to XB52 for procedure only). RERUN Quick Test.
XB65 CHECK ACP SIG RTN FOR SHORT TO POWER • Key off. • ACP sensor disconnected. • VCRM disconnected. • Key on. • Measure voltage between the ACP SIG RTN circuit and the battery negative post. • Key off. • **Was voltage less than 1.0 volt?**	Yes No	▶ ▶	REPLACE VCRM. RECONNECT all components. CLEAR Continuous Memory. ATTEMPT to reset DTC 579 (REFER to XB52 for procedure only). RERUN Quick Test. SERVICE ACP SIG RTN circuit short to power. RECONNECT all components. CLEAR Continuous Memory. ATTEMPT to reset DTC 579 (REFER to XB52 for procedure only). RERUN Quick Test.

FM0159300771240X

Fig. 230   Test XB: VCRM (Part 24 of 63)

TEST STEP	RESULT	▶	ACTION TO TAKE
XB66 DOES THE A/C APPEAR TO COOL PROPERLY • **Does the A/C appear to cool properly?**	Yes No	▶ ▶	GO to XB67 (to check for intermittent ACP circuits). check the mechanical operation of the A/C system (low refrigerant charge, intermittent concerns, etc). If all checks are OK, RETURN to XB67 to check for intermittent ACP circuits
XB67 CHECK ACP VREF AND ACP SIG RTN CIRCUITS FOR INTERMITTENT OPENS • Key off. • A/C off. • Disconnect ACP sensor. Inspect for damaged or pushed out pins, corrosion, loose wires, etc. Service as necessary. • Key on. • Connect test lamp between ACP VREF and ACP SIG RTN circuits at the ACP sensor vehicle harness connector (if test lamp will not light sufficiently, use DVOM to monitor 5 volts). • Observe test lamp/DVOM for an indication of a fault while performing the following (the test lamp will go out, or the DVOM voltage will drop, indicating an open circuit): — Shake, wiggle, bend the ACP VREF and ACP SIG RTN circuits between the ACP sensor vehicle harness connector and the VCRM. — Lightly tap the VCRM (to simulate road shock). • Key off. • **Is a fault indicated?**	Yes No	▶ ▶	ISOLATE fault and SERVICE as necessary. RECONNECT all components. START engine, A/C on. WAIT 20 seconds. Key off. RERUN Quick Test. GO to XB68.

FM0159300771250X

Fig. 230   Test XB: VCRM (Part 25 of 63)

TEST STEP	RESULT	▶	ACTION TO TAKE
XB68 CHECK ACP SIGNAL FOR INTERMITTENT SHORT TO GROUND OR POWER			
• Key off. • ACP sensor disconnected. • Connect test lamp or DVOM (which ever was used in previous step) between ACP VREF and ACP signal circuit at the ACP sensor vehicle harness connector. • Key on. • Observe test lamp / DVOM for an indication of a fault while performing the following (the lamp will come on, or DVOM will read 5V, indicating an ACP signal short to ground): — Shake, wiggle, bend the ACP signal from the ACP sensor vehicle harness connector to the VCRM. — Lightly tap the VCRM (to simulate road shock). • Reconnect test lamp / DVOM between ACP SIG RTN and ACP signal circuit at the ACP sensor vehicle harness connector. • Again, observe test lamp / DVOM for an indication of a fault while performing the following (the test lamp will come on, or DVOM voltage will increase, indicating an ACP signal short to power): — Shake, wiggle, bend the ACP signal from the ACP sensor vehicle harness connector to the VCRM — Lightly tap the VCRM (to simulate road shock). • Key off • **Is a fault indicated?**	Yes No	▶ ▶	ISOLATE fault and SERVICE as necessary. RECONNECT all components. START engine. A / C on, WAIT 20 seconds. A / C off, key off. RERUN Quick Test. GO to **XB69**

Fig. 230   Test XB: VCRM (Part 26 of 63)

FM0159300771260X

TEST STEP	RESULT	▶	ACTION TO TAKE
XB69 CHECK ACP SIGNAL FOR INTERMITTENT OPEN			
• Key off. • ACP sensor disconnected. • Disconnect VCRM. Inspect for damaged or pushed out pins, corrosion, loose wires, etc. Service as necessary. • Connect DVOM (to measure resistance) between Pin 19 at the VCRM vehicle harness connector and the ACP signal circuit at the ACP sensor vehicle harness connector. Resistance reading should be less than 5.0 ohms. • Observe DVOM for an indication of a fault while performing the following (the DVOM will read greater than 5.0 ohms when a fault is detected, indicating an open circuit). — Shake, wiggle, bend the ACP signal circuit from the VCRM vehicle harness connector to the ACP sensor vehicle harness connector. • **Is a fault indicated?**	Yes No	▶ ▶	ISOLATE fault and SERVICE as necessary. RECONNECT all components. START engine. A / C on, WAIT 20 seconds. Key off. RERUN Quick Test. Unable to isolate fault at this time. RECONNECT all components. further diagnosis using the EEC-IV Monitor Box or Scan Tool.
XB70 CONTINUOUS MEMORY DIAGNOSTIC TROUBLE CODE (DTC) 585: CLEAR AND ATTEMPT TO REGENERATE DTC			
Continuous Memory DTC 585 indicates that when the A / C was turned on, the power-to-A / C clutch circuit exceeded the normal current draw. This could be due to a hard fault or an intermittent condition. Possible causes: — Power-to-A / C clutch circuit short to ground. — Damaged A / C clutch. — Damaged VCRM. • Clear Continuous Memory (refer to Quick Test Appendix in Section 5A). • Start engine • Turn A / C on, wait 15 seconds. • A / C off. • Engine off • Rerun Key On Engine Off (KOEO) Self-Test. • **Is Continuous Memory DTC 585 present?**	Yes No	▶ ▶	DTC 585 is a hard fault. GO to **XB71** DTC 585 is intermittent. GO to **XB74**

Fig. 230   Test XB: VCRM (Part 27 of 63)

FM0159300771270X

TEST STEP	RESULT	▶	ACTION TO TAKE
XB71 CHECK A/C CLUTCH			
• Again clear Continuous Memory. • Disconnect A / C clutch. • Start engine. • Turn A / C on, wait 15 seconds. • A / C off. • Engine off. • Rerun Key On Engine Off Self-Test. • **Is Continuous Memory DTC 585 present (ignore DTC 586, if received)?**	Yes No	▶	GO to **XB72** CHECK any A/C clutch external wiring for shorts to ground. If OK, REPLACE A/C clutch (refer to Air Conditioning RECONNECT all components. CLEAR Continuous Memory (if necessary). RERUN Quick Test.
XB72 CHECK POWER-TO-A/C CLUTCH CIRCUIT FOR SHORT TO GROUND			
• Key off. • A / C clutch disconnected. • Disconnect VCRM. Inspect for damaged or pushed out pins, corrosion, loose wires, etc. Service as necessary. • Measure resistance between the power-to-A / C clutch circuit at the A / C clutch vehicle harness connector and the battery negative post. • **Is resistance greater than 10,000 ohms?**	Yes No	▶ ▶	REPLACE VCRM. RECONNECT all components. CLEAR Continuous Memory. START engine. TURN A / C on, WAIT 15 seconds. A / C off. Key off. RERUN Quick Test. SERVICE power-to-A / C clutch circuit short to ground. RECONNECT all components. CLEAR Continuous Memory. START engine. TURN A / C on, WAIT 15 seconds. A / C off. Key off. RERUN Quick Test.

Fig. 230   Test XB: VCRM (Part 28 of 63)

FM0159300771280X

TEST STEP	RESULT	▶	ACTION TO TAKE
XB74 CHECK POWER-TO-A/C CLUTCH CIRCUIT FOR INTERMITTENT SHORT TO GROUND			
• Key off. • Visually check the power-to-A/C clutch circuit from the VCRM to the A/C clutch. • Start engine. • A / C on. **CAUTION: While performing this test, do not touch any moving/hot engine parts.** • Shake, wiggle, bend the power-to-A/C clutch from the A/C clutch to the VCRM. A short to ground will be indicated by the A/C clutch disengaging for other than normal cyclic pressure switch operation (the VCRM FMEM will turn the A/C off when an "overcurrent" condition exists). • Key off, A/C off. • **Is a fault indicated?**	Yes No	▶ ▶	ISOLATE fault and SERVICE as necessary. CLEAR Continuous Memory (DTC 585 should have been set). START engine. A / C on, WAIT 5 seconds. A / C off, key off. RERUN Quick Test. GO to **XB75**
XB75 CHECK POWER-TO-A/C CLUTCH CIRCUIT FOR INTERMITTENT SHORT TO GROUND			
• Key off. • Disconnect VCRM. Inspect for damaged or pushed out pins, corrosion, loose wires, etc. Service as necessary. • Disconnect A/C clutch. Inspect for damaged or pushed out pins, corrosion, loose wires, etc. Service as necessary. • Connect a test lamp between Pin 4 and Pin 14 of the VCRM vehicle harness connector. • Observe test lamp for an indication of a fault while performing the following (the lamp will turn on when a fault is detected, indicating a short to ground): — Shake, wiggle, bend the power-to-A/C clutch circuit from the A/C clutch vehicle harness connector to the VCRM vehicle harness connector. • **Is a fault indicated?**	Yes No	▶ ▶	ISOLATE fault and SERVICE as necessary. RECONNECT all components. START engine. A / C on, WAIT 5 seconds. A / C off, key off. RERUN Quick Test. Unable to isolate fault at this time. RECONNECT all components. further diagnosis using the EEC-IV Monitor Box or Scan Tool RETURN to Diagnostic Routines

Fig. 230   Test XB: VCRM (Part 29 of 63)

FM0159300771290X

TEST STEP	RESULT	▶	ACTION TO TAKE
XB80 CONTINUOUS MEMORY DIAGNOSTIC TROUBLE CODE (DTC) 586: CLEAR AND ATTEMPT TO RE-GENERATE DTC			
Continuous Memory DTC 586 indicates an open or short to power in the power-to-A/C clutch circuit. This could be due to a "hard fault" or an intermittent condition. Possible causes: — Open or short to power in the power-to-A/C clutch circuit (harness). — Open A/C clutch ground circuit (to VCRM Pin 13). — Open VCRM A/C ground (VCRM Pin 15 to weld nut on LH side radiator support). — Open circuit in A/C clutch. — Damaged VCRM. • Clear Continuous Memory • A/C off, defroster off (testing for DTC 586 is done only with the A/C off). • Start engine, wait 15 seconds. • Engine off. • Rerun Key On Engine Off Self-Test. • **Is Continuous Memory DTC 586 present?**	Yes No	▶ ▶	DTC 586 is a "hard fault". GO TO **XB81**. DTC 586 is intermittent. GO TO **XB85**.
XB81 CHECK POWER-TO-A/C CLUTCH CIRCUIT FOR SHORT TO POWER			
• Key off. • Disconnect A/C clutch. • Disconnect VCRM. Inspect for damaged or pushed out pins, corrosion, loose wires, etc. Service as necessary. • Key on. • Measure voltage between the power-to-A/C clutch circuit at the A/C clutch vehicle harness connector and the battery negative post. • Key off. • **Was the voltage less than 1.0 volt?**	Yes No	▶ ▶	GO to **XB82**. SERVICE power-to-A/C clutch circuit for short to power. RECONNECT all components. CLEAR Continuous Memory. A/C off, defroster off. START engine. WAIT 15 seconds. Key off. RERUN Quick Test.

FM0159300771300X

Fig. 230   Test XB: VCRM (Part 30 of 63)

TEST STEP	RESULT	▶	ACTION TO TAKE
XB82 CHECK CONTINUITY OF POWER-TO-A/C CLUTCH, A/C CLUTCH GROUND AND VCRM A/C GROUND CIRCUITS			
• Key off. • A/C clutch disconnected. • VCRM disconnected. • Measure resistance between Pin 14 of the VCRM vehicle harness connector and the power-to-A/C clutch circuit at the A/C clutch vehicle harness connector. • Measure resistance between Pin 13 of the VCRM vehicle harness connector and the A/C clutch ground circuit at the A/C clutch vehicle harness connector. • Measure resistance between Pin 15 of the VCRM vehicle harness connector and the battery negative post. • **Are all resistances less than 5.0 ohms?**	Yes No	▶ ▶	GO to **XB83**. SERVICE open in applicable circuit. RECONNECT all components. CLEAR Continuous Memory. A/C off, defroster off. START engine, WAIT 15 seconds. Key off. RERUN Quick Test.
XB83 CHECK CONTINUITY OF A/C CLUTCH			
• Key off. • A/C clutch disconnected. • VCRM disconnected. • Measure resistance of the A/C clutch coil (between the power-to-A/C clutch and A/C clutch ground pins at the A/C clutch connector). • **Is resistance less than 10 ohms?**	Yes No	▶ ▶	REPLACE VCRM. RECONNECT all components. CLEAR Continuous Memory. A/C off, defroster off. START engine, WAIT 15 seconds. Key off. RERUN Quick Test. REPLACE A/C clutch (refer to Air Conditioning RECONNECT all components. CLEAR Continuous Memory. A/C off, defroster off. START engine, WAIT 15 seconds. Key off. RERUN Quick Test.

FM0159300771310X

Fig. 230   Test XB: VCRM (Part 31 of 63)

TEST STEP	RESULT	▶	ACTION TO TAKE
XB85 CHECK POWER-TO-A/C CLUTCH, A/C CLUTCH GROUND AND VCRM A/C GROUND CIRCUITS FOR INTERMITTENT OPENS			
• Key off. • Visually check the power-to-A/C clutch and A/C clutch ground (Pin 13) circuits from the VCRM to the A/C clutch. Also check the VCRM A/C ground circuit (Pin 15) from the VCRM to its ground point (weld nut on LH side radiator support). • Start engine. • A/C on. **CAUTION: While performing this test, do not touch any moving/hot engine parts.** • Shake, wiggle, bend the power-to-A/C clutch, A/C clutch ground and VCRM A/C ground circuits. An open will be indicated by the A/C clutch disengaging for other than normal cyclic pressure switch operation. • Key off, A/C off. • **Is a fault indicated?**	Yes No	▶ ▶	ISOLATE fault and SERVICE as necessary. RERUN Quick Test. GO to **XB86**.
XB86 CHECK POWER-TO-A/C CLUTCH CIRCUIT FOR INTERMITTENT SHORT TO POWER			
• A/C off. • Key on. • Shake, wiggle, bend the power-to-A/C clutch circuit between the VCRM and A/C clutch (especially in the vicinity of power circuits). A short to power will be indicated by the A/C clutch engaging. • Key off. • **Is a fault indicated?**	Yes No	▶ ▶	ISOLATE fault and SERVICE as necessary. RERUN Quick Test. GO to **XB87**.

FM0159300771320X

Fig. 230   Test XB: VCRM (Part 32 of 63)

TEST STEP	RESULT	▶	ACTION TO TAKE
XB87 AGAIN CHECK POWER-TO-A/C CLUTCH, A/C CLUTCH GROUND AND VCRM A/C GROUND CIRCUITS FOR INTERMITTENT OPENS			
• Key off. • Disconnect A/C clutch. Inspect for damaged or pushed out pins, corrosion, loose wires, etc. Service as necessary. • Connect a test lamp between the power-to-A/C clutch and A/C clutch ground circuits at the A/C clutch vehicle harness connector. • Start engine. • A/C on. **CAUTION: While performing this test, do not touch any moving/hot engine parts.** • Observe test lamp for an indication of a fault while performing the following (the lamp will go out when a fault is detected, indicating an open circuit): — Shake, wiggle, bend the power-to-A/C clutch, A/C clutch ground and VCRM A/C ground circuits. — Lightly tap on the VCRM (to simulate road shock). • Key off, A/C off. • **Is a fault indicated?**	Yes No	▶ ▶	ISOLATE fault and SERVICE as necessary. RECONNECT all components. RERUN Quick Test. Disconnect VCRM. Inspect for damaged or pushed out pins, corrosion, loose wires, etc. Service as necessary. If OK, unable to isolate fault at this time. RECONNECT all components. further diagnosis using the EEC-IV Monitor Box or Scan Tool RETURN to *Diagnostic Routines*
XB90 NO A/C (WITH DTC 111'S): CHECK FOR VOLTAGE AT A/C CLUTCH			
NOTE: Before proceeding with "No A/C" diagnostics, verify integrity of related fuse(s) in fuse panel. • Key off. • Disconnect A/C clutch. • Connect a non-powered test lamp between the power-to-A/C clutch circuit and the A/C clutch ground circuit at the A/C clutch vehicle harness connector. • A/C on. • Start engine, wait 10 seconds. • **Is test lamp on (allow time for normal on/off cycling of the Cyclic Pressure Switch)?**	Yes No	▶ ▶	EEC-IV system OK. RECONNECT A/C clutch. REFER to Air Conditioning to check for A/C system mechanical problems, etc. GO to **XB91**.

FM0159300771330X

Fig. 230   Test XB: VCRM (Part 33 of 63)

TEST STEP	RESULT	▶	ACTION TO TAKE
XB91 CHECK IF PCM IS RECEIVING AND RECOGNIZING ACCS (PIN 10) INPUT • Key off. • Remove test lamp. • Reconnect A/C clutch. • A/C on. • Perform Key On Engine Off Self-Test. • **Is Key On Engine Off DTC 539 present?**	Yes	▶	The PCM is receiving and recognizing the ACCS input. GO to **XB92** (to verify the VCRM is receiving the A/C demand voltage).
	No	▶	The PCM is not receiving or recognizing the ACCS input. GO to **XB98**.
XB92 CHECK A/C DEMAND SWITCH VOLTAGE AT VCRM • Key off. • Disconnect VCRM. Inspect for damaged or pushed out pins, corrosion, loose wires, etc. Service as necessary. • A/C on. • Key on. • Measure voltage between Pin 9 of the VCRM vehicle harness connector and the battery negative post. • Key off. • **Was voltage greater than 10.5 volts?**	Yes	▶	**FOR VCRM MODULE NUMBERS F3LF-12B577-AG:** GO to **XB93** (to check ACP circuits). **FOR ALL OTHER VCRM MODULE NUMBERS:** GO to **XB96** (to check for WAC circuit short to ground).
	No	▶	SERVICE open in A/C demand switch circuit between VCRM and splice to PCM. RECONNECT all components. RE-EVALUATE symptom.

FM015930077134QX

Fig. 230   Test XB: VCRM (Part 34 of 63). 1993

TEST STEP	RESULT	▶	ACTION TO TAKE
XB93 CHECK ACP AND ACP SIG RTN HARNESS CIRCUITS • Key off. • VCRM disconnected. • Disconnect A/C Pressure (ACP) sensor (verify connector was seated and orientated correctly). • Check continuity of ACP and ACP SIG RTN harness circuits: — Measure resistance between the ACP circuit at the ACP sensor vehicle harness connector and Pin 19 of the VCRM vehicle harness connector. — Measure resistance between the ACP SIG RTN circuit at the ACP sensor vehicle harness connector and Pin 12 of the VCRM vehicle harness connector. — Both resistance readings should be less than 5.0 ohms. • Check ACP circuit for short to power: — Key on, engine off. — Measure voltage between the ACP circuit at the ACP sensor vehicle harness connector and the battery negative post. — Key off. — Voltage should have read less than 1.0 volt? • **Do the ACP and ACP SIG RTN harness circuits check out OK?**	Yes	▶	GO to **XB94**.
	No	▶	SERVICE open or shorted circuit. RECONNECT all components. RE-EVALUATE symptom.

A/C PRESSURE (ACP) SENSOR VEHICLE HARNESS CONNECTOR

ACP

ACP VREF

ACP SIG RTN

FM015930077135QX

Fig. 230   Test XB: VCRM (Part 35 of 63). 1993

TEST STEP	RESULT	▶	ACTION TO TAKE
XB94 VERIFY ACP SENSOR IS NOT AT FAULT • Key off. • ACP sensor disconnected. • Reconnect VCRM. • Disconnect A/C clutch. • Again connect a non-powered test lamp between the power-to-A/C clutch and A/C clutch ground circuit at the A/C clutch vehicle harness connector. • Connect a jumper wire between the ACP circuit and the ACP SIG RTN circuit at the ACP sensor vehicle harness connector. • A/C on. • Start engine, wait 10 seconds. • **Is test lamp on (allow time for normal cycling of the Cyclic Pressure Switch)?**	Yes	▶	Key off. REPLACE ACP sensor. REMOVE test lamp and jumper wire. RECONNECT all components. RE-EVALUATE symptom.
	No	▶	Key off. REMOVE jumper wire and RECONNECT ACP sensor. GO to **XB95**.

FM015930077136AX

Fig. 230   Test XB: VCRM (Part 36 of 63). 1993

TEST STEP	RESULT	▶	ACTION TO TAKE
XB91 CHECK IF PCM IS RECEIVING AND RECOGNIZING ACCS (PIN 10) INPUT • Key off. • Remove test lamp. • Reconnect A/C clutch. • A/C on. • Perform Key On Engine Off Self-Test. • **Is Key On Engine Off DTC 539 present?**	Yes	▶	The PCM is receiving and recognizing the ACCS input. GO to **XB92** (to verify the VCRM is receiving the A/C demand voltage).
	No	▶	The PCM is not receiving or recognizing the ACCS input. GO to **XB96**.
XB92 CHECK FOR A/C DEMAND VOLTAGE AT VCRM • Key off. • Disconnect VCRM. Inspect for damaged or pushed out pins, corrosion, loose wires, etc. Service as necessary. • A/C on. • Key on. • Measure voltage between Pin 9 of the VCRM vehicle harness connector and the battery negative post. • Key off. • **Was voltage greater than 10.5 volts?**	Yes	▶	GO to **XB93** (to check for WAC circuit short to ground).
	No	▶	SERVICE open in A/C demand circuit between VCRM and splice to PCM. RECONNECT all components. RE-EVALUATE symptom.
XB93 CHECK WAC CIRCUIT FOR SHORT TO GROUND • Key off. • VCRM disconnected. • Disconnect PCM. Inspect for damaged or pushed out pins, corrosion, loose wires, etc. Service as necessary. • Measure resistance between Pin 11 of the VCRM vehicle harness connector and the battery negative post. • **Is resistance greater than 10,000 ohms?**	Yes	▶	GO to **XB94**.
	No	▶	SERVICE WAC circuit short to ground. RECONNECT all components. RE-EVALUATE symptom.
XB94 VERIFY WAC CIRCUIT IS NOT SHORT TO GROUND IN PCM • Key off. • PCM disconnected. • Reconnect VCRM. • Disconnect A/C clutch. • Again, connect a non-powered test lamp between the power-to-A/C clutch circuit and the A/C clutch ground circuit at the A/C clutch vehicle harness connector. • A/C on. • Key on. • **Is test lamp on?**	Yes	▶	REPLACE PCM. RECONNECT all components. RE-EVALUATE symptom.
	No	▶	REPLACE VCRM. RECONNECT all components. RE-EVALUATE symptom.

FM015940077136BX

Fig. 230   Test XB: VCRM (Part 36 of 63). 1994–95

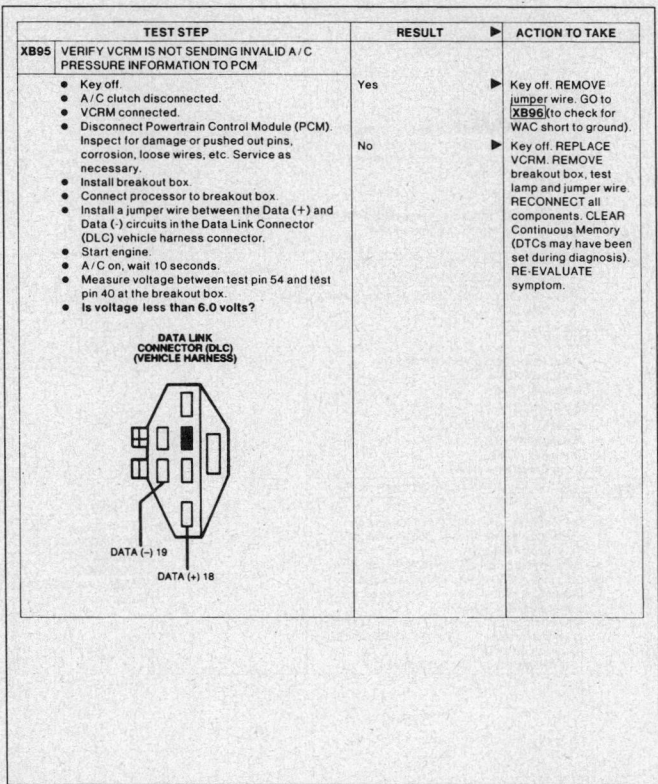

TEST STEP	RESULT	▶	ACTION TO TAKE
XB95 VERIFY VCRM IS NOT SENDING INVALID A/C PRESSURE INFORMATION TO PCM • Key off. • A/C clutch disconnected. • VCRM connected. • Disconnect Powertrain Control Module (PCM). Inspect for damage or pushed out pins, corrosion, loose wires, etc. Service as necessary. • Install breakout box. • Connect processor to breakout box. • Install a jumper wire between the Data (+) and Data (-) circuits in the Data Link Connector (DLC) vehicle harness connector. • Start engine. • A/C on, wait 10 seconds. • Measure voltage between test pin 54 and test pin 40 at the breakout box. • **Is voltage less than 6.0 volts?**	Yes No	▶ ▶	Key off. REMOVE jumper wire. GO to **XB96** (to check for WAC short to ground). Key off. REPLACE VCRM. REMOVE breakout box, test lamp and jumper wire. RECONNECT all components. CLEAR Continuous Memory (DTCs may have been set during diagnosis). RE-EVALUATE symptom.

DATA LINK CONNECTOR (DLC) (VEHICLE HARNESS)

DATA (−) 19
DATA (+) 18

FM015930077137OX

Fig. 230   Test XB: VCRM (Part 37 of 63). 1993

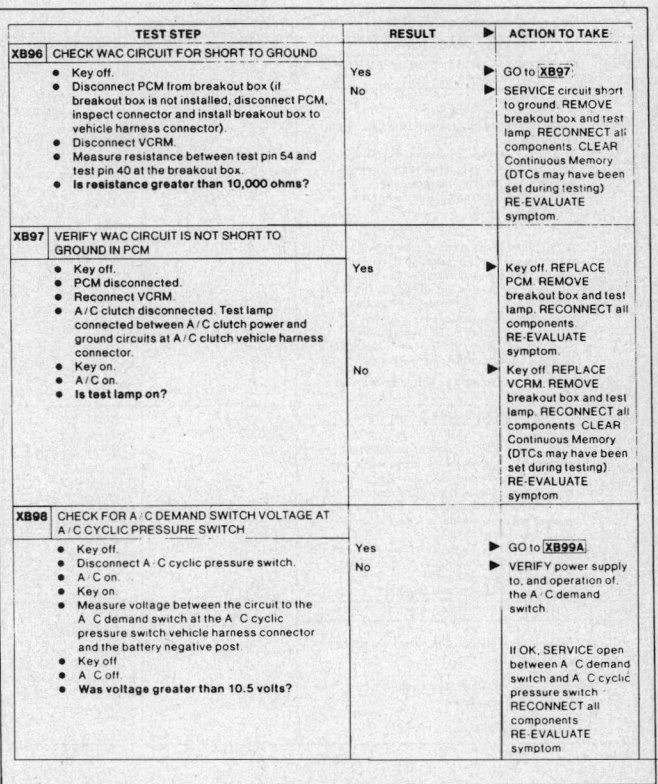

TEST STEP	RESULT	▶	ACTION TO TAKE
XB96 CHECK WAC CIRCUIT FOR SHORT TO GROUND • Key off. • Disconnect PCM from breakout box (if breakout box is not installed, disconnect PCM, inspect connector and install breakout box to vehicle harness connector). • Disconnect VCRM. • Measure resistance between test pin 54 and test pin 40 at the breakout box. • **Is resistance greater than 10,000 ohms?**	Yes No	▶ ▶	GO to **XB97**. SERVICE circuit short to ground. REMOVE breakout box and test lamp. RECONNECT all components. CLEAR Continuous Memory (DTCs may have been set during testing). RE-EVALUATE symptom.
XB97 VERIFY WAC CIRCUIT IS NOT SHORT TO GROUND IN PCM • Key off. • PCM disconnected. • Reconnect VCRM. • A/C clutch disconnected. Test lamp connected between A/C clutch power and ground circuits at the A/C clutch vehicle harness connector. • Key on. • A/C on. • **Is test lamp on?**	Yes No	▶ ▶	Key off. REPLACE PCM. REMOVE breakout box and test lamp. RECONNECT all components. RE-EVALUATE symptom. Key off. REPLACE VCRM. REMOVE breakout box and test lamp. RECONNECT all components. CLEAR Continuous Memory (DTCs may have been set during testing). RE-EVALUATE symptom.
XB98 CHECK FOR A/C DEMAND SWITCH VOLTAGE AT A/C CYCLIC PRESSURE SWITCH • Key off. • Disconnect A/C cyclic pressure switch. • A/C on. • Key on. • Measure voltage between the circuit to the A/C demand switch at the A/C cyclic pressure switch vehicle harness connector and the battery negative post. • Key off. • A/C off. • **Was voltage greater than 10.5 volts?**	Yes No	▶ ▶	GO to **XB99A**. VERIFY power supply to, and operation of, the A/C demand switch. If OK, SERVICE open between A/C demand switch and A/C cyclic pressure switch. RECONNECT all components. RE-EVALUATE symptom.

FM015930077138AX

Fig. 230   Test XB: VCRM (Part 38 of 63). 1993

TEST STEP	RESULT	▶	ACTION TO TAKE
XB96 CHECK FOR A/C DEMAND VOLTAGE FROM ELECTRONIC AUTOMATIC TEMPERATURE CONTROL (EATC) MODULE AT A/C CYCLIC PRESSURE SWITCH • Key off. • Disconnect A/C cyclic pressure switch. • A/C on. • Key on. • Measure voltage between the circuit from the EATC module at the A/C cyclic pressure switch vehicle harness connector and the battery negative post. • Key off. • A/C off. • **Was voltage greater than 10.5 volts?**	Yes No	▶ ▶	GO to **XB97**. VERIFY power supply to, and operation of, the EATC module. REFER to the Climate Control Group of the Service Manual. If OK, SERVICE open between EATC module and A/C cyclic pressure switch. RECONNECT all components. RE-EVALUATE symptom.
XB97 CHECK A/C CYCLIC PRESSURE SWITCH CONTINUITY • Key off. • A/C cyclic pressure switch disconnected. • Measure continuity of the A/C cyclic pressure switch. • **Is resistance less than 5.0 ohms?**	Yes No	▶ ▶	GO to **XB98**. check A/C system pressure, A/C cyclic pressure switch operation, etc.
XB98 CHECK CONTINUITY BETWEEN A/C CYCLIC PRESSURE SWITCH AND PCM (PIN 10) • Key off. • A/C cyclic pressure switch disconnected. • Disconnect PCM. Inspect for damaged or pushed out pins, corrosion, loose wires, etc. Service as necessary. • Install breakout box, leave PCM disconnected. • Measure continuity between test Pin 10 at the breakout box and the circuit to the PCM/VCRM at the A/C Cyclic Pressure Switch vehicle harness connector. • **Is resistance less than 5.0 ohms?**	Yes No	▶ ▶	REPLACE PCM. REMOVE breakout box. RECONNECT all components. RE-EVALUATE symptom. SERVICE open circuit between the A/C cyclic pressure switch and the PCM. REMOVE breakout box. RECONNECT all components. RERUN Quick Test.

FM015940077138BX

Fig. 230   Test XB: VCRM (Part 38 of 63). 1994–95

TEST STEP	RESULT	▶	ACTION TO TAKE
XB99A CHECK A/C CYCLIC PRESSURE SWITCH CONTINUITY • Key off. • A/C cyclic pressure switch disconnected. • Measure continuity of the A/C cyclic pressure switch. • **Is resistance less than 5.0 ohms?**	Yes No	▶ ▶	GO to **XB99B**. check A/C system pressure, A/C cyclic pressure switch operation, etc.
XB99B CHECK CONTINUITY BETWEEN A/C CYCLIC PRESSURE SWITCH AND PCM (PIN 10) • Key off. • A/C cyclic pressure switch disconnected. • Disconnect PCM. Inspect for damaged or pushed out pins, corrosion, loose wires, etc. Service as necessary. • Install breakout box, leave PCM disconnected. • Measure continuity between test Pin 10 at the breakout box and the circuit to the PCM/VCRM at the A/C Cyclic Pressure Switch vehicle harness connector. • **Is resistance less than 5.0 ohms?**	Yes No	▶ ▶	REPLACE PCM. REMOVE breakout box. RECONNECT all components. RE-EVALUATE symptom. SERVICE open circuit between the A/C cyclic pressure switch and the PCM. REMOVE breakout box. RECONNECT all components. RERUN Quick Test.

FM015930077139OX

Fig. 230   Test XB: VCRM (Part 39 of 63). 1993

TEST STEP	RESULT	▶	ACTION TO TAKE
XB100 LACK OF POWER (WITH A/C ON): VERIFY WAC IS ABLE TO TURN OFF A/C CLUTCH • Start engine. • A/C on. • Perform a brief wide open throttle (WOT) and return to idle. • The A/C clutch should disengage during the WOT, then a few seconds after returning to idle, the A/C clutch should re-engage (a "click" sound should be heard when the clutch re-engages). • Repeat test if necessary to verify results. NOTE: If the clicking sound cannot be heard, it may be necessary to disconnect the A/C clutch. With a test lamp connected to the Power-to-A/C clutch circuit and the GND circuit at the A/C clutch vehicle harness connector, observe the test lamp while performing the brief WOT. The test lamp should go off during the WOT, then come back on a few seconds after returning to idle. • **Does the A/C clutch or test lamp work as indicated?**	Yes No	▶ ▶	The WAC circuit is operating properly. RETURN to *Diagnostic Routines* The WAC circuit is not turning the A/C clutch off. GO to **XB101**
XB101 CHECK WAC CIRCUIT HARNESS CONTINUITY • Key off. • Disconnect PCM. Inspect for damaged or pushed out pins, corrosion, loose wires, etc. Service as necessary. • Install breakout box, leave PCM disconnected. • Disconnect VCRM. Inspect for damaged or pushed out pins, corrosion, loose wires, etc. Service as necessary. • Measure resistance between Test Pin 54 at the breakout box and Pin 11 of the VCRM vehicle harness connector. • **Is resistance less than 5.0 ohms?**	Yes No	▶ ▶	GO to **XB102**. SERVICE open WAC circuit. REMOVE breakout box. RECONNECT all components. RE-EVALUATE symptom.
XB102 CHECK WAC CIRCUIT FOR SHORT TO POWER • Key off. • Breakout box installed, PCM disconnected. • VCRM disconnected. • Key on. • Measure voltage between Test Pin 54 and Test Pin 40 at the breakout box. • Key off. • **Was voltage less than 1.0 volt?**	Yes No	▶ ▶	GO to **XB103**. SERVICE short to power in WAC circuit. REMOVE breakout box. RECONNECT all components. RE-EVALUATE symptom.

FM0159300771400X

Fig. 230   Test XB: VCRM (Part 40 of 63)

TEST STEP	RESULT	▶	ACTION TO TAKE
XB103 CHECK VCRM WAC CIRCUITRY • Key off. • Breakout box installed, PCM disconnected. • Reconnect VCRM. • Key on. • A/C on. • Connect a jumper wire to Test Pin 54. While listening to the A/C clutch, connect and disconnect the other end of the jumper to Test Pin 40 a couple times. • Key off. • A/C off. • **Does the A/C clutch disengage and engage as the jumper wire is connected and disconnected?**	Yes No	▶ ▶	REPLACE PCM. REMOVE breakout box. RECONNECT all components. RE-EVALUATE symptom. REPLACE VCRM. REMOVE breakout box. RECONNECT all components. RE-EVALUATE symptom.
XB110 KEY ON ENGINE OFF DIAGNOSTIC TROUBLE CODE (DTC) 556: DOES ENGINE START? Key On Engine Off DTC 556 indicates a fuel pump primary circuit failure. Possible causes: No Start: — Open or short to power in FP circuit. — Damaged VCRM. — Damaged PCM. Engine Starts: — Short to ground in FP circuit. — Damaged VCRM. — Damaged PCM. • **Does the engine start?**	Yes No	▶ ▶	GO to **XB115** (to check for short to ground). GO to **XB111** (to check for opens and short to power).
XB111 CHECK FUEL PUMP (FP) CIRCUIT CONTINUITY • Key off. • Disconnect PCM. Inspect for damaged or pushed out pins, corrosion, loose wires, etc. Service as necessary. • Install breakout box, leave PCM disconnected. • Disconnect VCRM. Inspect for damaged or pushed out pins, corrosion, loose wires, etc. Service as necessary. • Measure continuity between Test Pin 22 at the breakout box and Pin 18 of the VCRM vehicle harness connector. • **Is resistance less than 5.0 ohms?**	Yes No	▶ ▶	GO to **XB112**. SERVICE open in FP circuit. REMOVE breakout box. RECONNECT all components. RERUN Quick Test.

FM0159300771410X

Fig. 230   Test XB: VCRM (Part 41 of 63)

TEST STEP	RESULT	▶	ACTION TO TAKE
XB112 CHECK FP CIRCUIT FOR SHORT TO POWER • Key off. • Breakout box installed, PCM disconnected. • VCRM disconnected. • Key on. • Measure voltage between Test Pin 22 and Test Pin 40. • Key off. • **Was voltage less than 1.0 volt?**	Yes No	▶ ▶	GO to **XB113**. SERVICE FP circuit short to power. REMOVE breakout box. RECONNECT all components. RERUN Quick Test.
XB113 CHECK VCRM FP CIRCUIT • Key off. • Breakout box installed, PCM disconnected. • Reconnect VCRM. • Jumper Test Pin 22 to Test Pin 40 at the breakout box. • Key on. • **Does the fuel pump run?**	Yes No	▶ ▶	Key off. REMOVE jumper. REPLACE PCM. REMOVE breakout box. RECONNECT all components. RERUN Quick Test. Key off. REMOVE jumper. REPLACE VCRM. REMOVE breakout box. RECONNECT all components. RERUN Quick Test.
XB115 CHECK PCM FOR SHORT TO GND • Key off. • Disconnect PCM. Inspect for damaged or pushed out pins, corrosion, loose wires, etc. Service as necessary. • Key on. • **Does the fuel pump run?**	Yes No	▶ ▶	Key off. GO to **XB116**. Key off. REPLACE PCM. RECONNECT all components. RERUN Quick Test.
XB116 CHECK FUEL PUMP (FP) CIRCUIT FOR SHORT TO GROUND • Key off. • Install breakout box, leave PCM disconnected. • Disconnect VCRM. Inspect for damaged or pushed out pins, corrosion, loose wires, etc. Service as necessary. • Measure resistance between Test Pin 22 and Test Pin 40 at the breakout box. • **Is resistance greater than 10,000 ohms?**	Yes No	▶ ▶	REPLACE VCRM. REMOVE breakout box. RECONNECT all components. RERUN Quick Test. SERVICE FP circuit short to ground. REMOVE breakout box. RECONNECT all components. RERUN Quick Test.

FM0159300771420X

Fig. 230   Test XB: VCRM (Part 42 of 63)

TEST STEP	RESULT	▶	ACTION TO TAKE
XB120 KEY ON ENGINE OFF DIAGNOSTIC TROUBLE CODE (DTC) 542: WILL ENGINE START AND IDLE Key On Engine Off DTC 542 indicates that one of the following has occurred: No Start: — Inertia Fuel Shutoff (IFS) switch not reset or electrically open. — Open in power-to-pump circuit between the FPM splice and the fuel pump. — Poor fuel pump ground. — Open circuit in fuel pump. Engine Starts: — Power-to-pump/FMP circuit short to power. — High Speed Fuel Pump (HFP) relay contacts stuck closed. — HFP circuit (VCRM Pin 10) short to ground. — Open FPM circuit between PCM and power-to-pump splice. — Left HO2S short to power. — Damaged VCRM. — Damaged PCM. • **Will the engine start and idle for one minute?**	Yes No	▶ ▶	GO to **XB121**. GO to **XB130** (to check for open in power-to-pump circuit between FPM splice and fuel pump ground. If engine starts but stalls, open is between FPM splice and HFP relay splice).
XB121 VERIFY THAT FUEL PUMP IS OFF • Key on, wait 5 seconds. • Listen for motor noise from fuel pump. • **Is fuel pump off?**	Yes No	▶ ▶	Key off. GO to **XB126** (to check FPM circuit continuity and HO2S for short to power). Key off. GO to **XB122** (to check power-to-pump FPM circuit short to power or HFP circuit short to ground).
XB122 CHECK VCRM • Key off. • Disconnect VCRM. Inspect for damaged or pushed out pins, corrosion, loose wires, etc. Service as necessary. • Key on. • **Is fuel pump off?**	Yes No	▶ ▶	Key off. REPLACE VCRM. RECONNECT all components RERUN Quick Test. Key off. GO to **XB123**

FM0159300771430X

Fig. 230   Test XB: VCRM (Part 43 of 63)

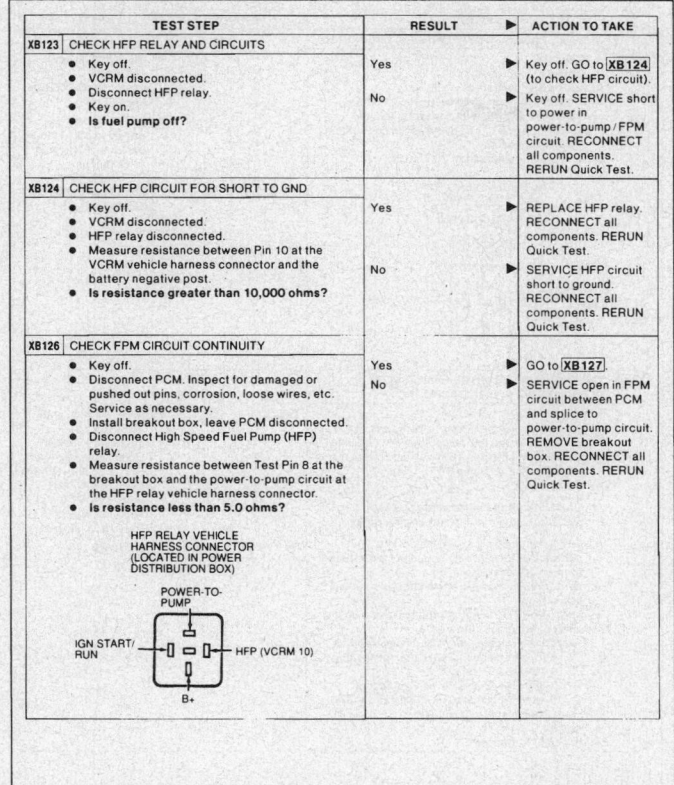

TEST STEP	RESULT	▶	ACTION TO TAKE
XB123 CHECK HFP RELAY AND CIRCUITS			
• Key off. • VCRM disconnected. • Disconnect HFP relay. • Key on. • **Is fuel pump off?**	Yes No	▶ ▶	Key off. GO to **XB124** (to check HFP circuit). Key off. SERVICE short to power in power-to-pump / FPM circuit. RECONNECT all components. RERUN Quick Test.
XB124 CHECK HFP CIRCUIT FOR SHORT TO GND			
• Key off. • VCRM disconnected. • HFP relay disconnected. • Measure resistance between Pin 10 at the VCRM vehicle harness connector and the battery negative post. • **Is resistance greater than 10,000 ohms?**	Yes No	▶ ▶	REPLACE HFP relay. RECONNECT all components. RERUN Quick Test. SERVICE HFP circuit short to ground. RECONNECT all components. RERUN Quick Test.
XB126 CHECK FPM CIRCUIT CONTINUITY			
• Key off. • Disconnect PCM. Inspect for damaged or pushed out pins, corrosion, loose wires, etc. Service as necessary. • Install breakout box, leave PCM disconnected. • Disconnect High Speed Fuel Pump (HFP) relay. • Measure resistance between Test Pin 8 at the breakout box and the power-to-pump circuit at the HFP relay vehicle harness connector. • **Is resistance less than 5.0 ohms?**	Yes No	▶ ▶	GO to **XB127**. SERVICE open in FPM circuit between PCM and splice to power-to-pump circuit. REMOVE breakout box. RECONNECT all components. RERUN Quick Test.

Fig. 230   Test XB: VCRM (Part 44 of 63)

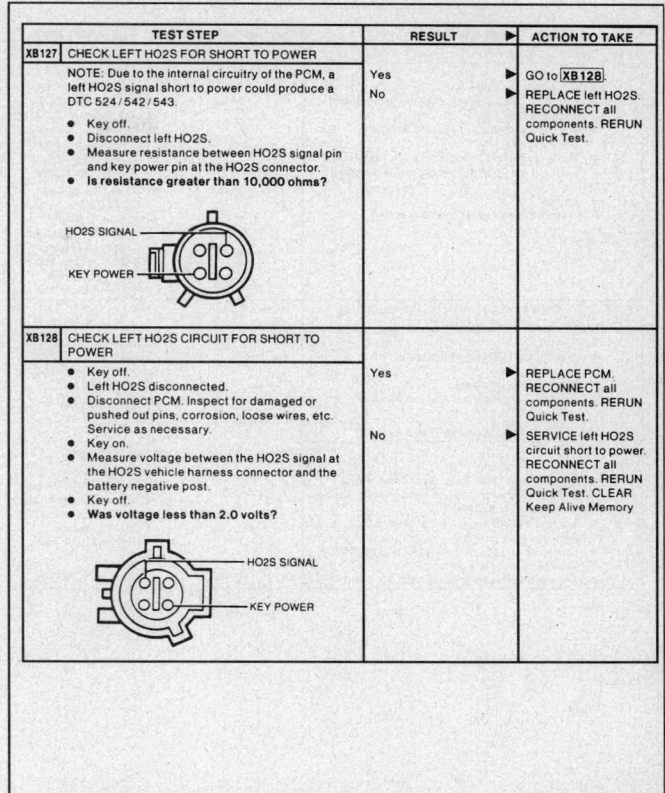

TEST STEP	RESULT	▶	ACTION TO TAKE
XB127 CHECK LEFT HO2S FOR SHORT TO POWER			
NOTE: Due to the internal circuitry of the PCM, a left HO2S signal short to power could produce a DTC 524/542/543. • Key off. • Disconnect left HO2S. • Measure resistance between HO2S signal pin and key power pin at the HO2S connector. • **Is resistance greater than 10,000 ohms?**	Yes No	▶ ▶	GO to **XB128**. REPLACE left HO2S. RECONNECT all components. RERUN Quick Test.
XB128 CHECK LEFT HO2S CIRCUIT FOR SHORT TO POWER			
• Key off. • Left HO2S disconnected. • Disconnect PCM. Inspect for damaged or pushed out pins, corrosion, loose wires, etc. Service as necessary. • Key on. • Measure voltage between the HO2S signal at the HO2S vehicle harness connector and the battery negative post. • Key off. • **Was voltage less than 2.0 volts?**	Yes No	▶ ▶	REPLACE PCM. RECONNECT all components. RERUN Quick Test. SERVICE left HO2S circuit short to power. RECONNECT all components. RERUN Quick Test. CLEAR Keep Alive Memory.

Fig. 230   Test XB: VCRM (Part 45 of 63)

TEST STEP	RESULT	▶	ACTION TO TAKE
XB130 CHECK INERTIA FUEL SHUTOFF (IFS) SWITCH			
• Key off. • Disconnect IFS switch (verify switch is reset). • Measure resistance between the C (common) and NC (normally closed) pins of the IFS switch. • **Is resistance less than 5.0 ohms?**	Yes No	▶ ▶	RECONNECT IFS switch. REFER to Fuel/Engine to check for; open in power-to-pump circuit from FPM splice to fuel pump, open circuit in fuel pump, poor fuel pump ground, etc. After service, RERUN Quick Test. RESET or REPLACE IFS switch. RECONNECT all components. RERUN Quick Test.
XB135 KEY ON ENGINE OFF DIAGNOSTIC TROUBLE CODE (DTC) 524/543: CONTINUOUS MEMORY DTC 583: IS CONTINUOUS MEMORY DTC 583 PRESENT?			
Key On Engine Off DTC 524/543 indicates that when the PCM commanded the fuel pump on, voltage was not detected on FPM (PCM Pin 8). Although DTC 524 refers to the low speed output (VCRM Pin 24) and DTC 543 refers to the high speed output, it is not possible to distinguish between circuits, due to the vehicle wiring and fuel pump operating strategy. Continuous Memory DTC 583 indicates that when the fuel pump was activated, the power-to-pump circuit exceeded the normal current draw. This could be due to a "hard fault" or an intermittent condition. Possible causes are: Without DTC 583: — Open in power-to-pump circuit between VCRM and FPM splice. — Open in B(+) supply to VCRM (Pins 4 and 5). — Left HO2S short to power. With DTC 583: — Power-to-pump / FPM circuit short to ground. • **Is Continuous Memory DTC 583 present?**	Yes No	▶ ▶	GO to **XB136**. GO to **XB144**.

Fig. 230   Test XB: VCRM (Part 46 of 63)

TEST STEP	RESULT	▶	ACTION TO TAKE
XB136 CLEAR AND ATTEMPT TO RE-GENERATE DTC 583			
• Key off. • Clear Continuous Memory. • Start or attempt to start engine (if engine will not start, crank for 5 seconds). • Rerun Key On Engine Off (KOEO) Self-Test. • **Is Continuous Memory DTC 583 present?**	Yes No	▶ ▶	DTC 583 is a "hard fault". GO to **XB139** (to check power-to-pump/FPM for short to ground). DTC 583 is intermittent. GO to **XB137**.
XB137 WERE KOEO DTC 524 AND/OR 543 PRESENT IN XB136			
• Were KOEO DTC 524 and/or 543 received from KOEO Self-Test in XB136?	Yes No	▶ ▶	GO to **XB144**. Be aware that an overcurrent condition (short to GND) was present sometime during the last 80 warm-up cycles. GO to **XB147**.
XB139 ATTEMPT TO ISOLATE SHORT TO GROUND			
• Key off. • Again clear Continuous Memory. • Unplug Inertia Fuel Shutoff (IFS) switch. • Crank engine for 5 seconds. • Rerun KOEO Self-Test. • **Is Continuous Memory DTC 583 present (disregard other codes)?**	Yes No	▶ ▶	GO to **XB140**. GO to Fuel/Engine to check for short to ground in power-to-pump circuit (IFS switch to pump) or short to ground in fuel pump. After service, RERUN Quick Test.
XB140 CHECK POWER-TO-PUMP / FPM CIRCUIT FOR SHORT TO GROUND			
• Key off. • IFS switch disconnected. • Disconnect PCM. Inspect for damaged or pushed out pins, corrosion, loose wires, etc. Service as necessary. • Install breakout box, leave PCM disconnected. • Disconnect VCRM. Inspect for damaged or pushed out pins, corrosion, loose wires, etc. Service as necessary. • Measure resistance between Test Pin 8 and Test Pin 40 at the breakout box. • **Is resistance greater than 10,000 ohms?**	Yes No	▶ ▶	GO to **XB141**. SERVICE power-to-pump / FPM circuit for short to ground. REMOVE breakout box. RECONNECT all components. CLEAR Continuous Memory. START engine, WAIT 5 seconds. Key off. RERUN Quick Test.

Fig. 230   Test XB: VCRM (Part 47 of 63)

TEST STEP		RESULT	▶	ACTION TO TAKE
XB141	**CHECK VCRM**			
	• Key off. • IFS switch disconnected. • Breakout box installed, PCM disconnected. • Reconnect VCRM. • Jumper Test Pin 22 to Test Pin 40 at the breakout box. • While measuring voltage between Test Pin 8 and Test Pin 60 at the breakout box, turn key on. • Key off. • **Was voltage greater than 8.5 volts?**	Yes	▶	REPLACE PCM. REMOVE breakout box. RECONNECT all components. CLEAR Continuous Memory. START engine, WAIT 5 seconds. Key off. RERUN Quick Test.
		No	▶	REPLACE VCRM. REMOVE breakout box. RECONNECT all components. CLEAR Continuous Memory. START engine, WAIT 5 seconds. Key off. RERUN Quick Test.
XB144	**DOES ENGINE START WITH HIGH SPEED FUEL PUMP (HFP) RELAY DISCONNECTED**			
	• Key off. • Disconnect HFP relay (located in Power Distribution Box). • Attempt to start engine. • **Does the engine start and run for one minute?**	Yes	▶	RECONNECT HFP relay. GO to **XB127** (to check left HO2S for short to power).
		No	▶	GO to **XB145**
XB145	**CHECK FOR B(+) TO VCRM (PINS 4 AND 5)**			
	• Key off. • HFP relay disconnected. • Disconnect VCRM. Inspect for damaged or pushed out pins, corrosion, loose wires, etc. Service as necessary. • Connect DVOM negative test lead to the battery negative post. • Check for voltage on Pins 4 and 5 at the VCRM vehicle harness connector. • **Are both voltages greater than 10.5 volts?**	Yes	▶	GO to **XB146**
		No	▶	SERVICE open in B(+) supply to VCRM (verify integrity of any related fuses). RECONNECT all components. RERUN Quick Test.

TEST STEP		RESULT	▶	ACTION TO TAKE
XB146	**CHECK POWER-TO-PUMP CIRCUIT CONTINUITY**			
	• Key off. • HFP relay disconnected. • VCRM disconnected. • Measure resistance between Pin 24 of the VCRM vehicle harness connector and the power-to-pump circuit at the HFP relay vehicle harness connector. • **Is resistance less than 10 ohms?**	Yes	▶	REPLACE VCRM. RECONNECT all components. RERUN Quick Test.
		No	▶	SERVICE open in power-to-pump circuit between VCRM and FPM splice. RECONNECT all components. RERUN Quick Test.
	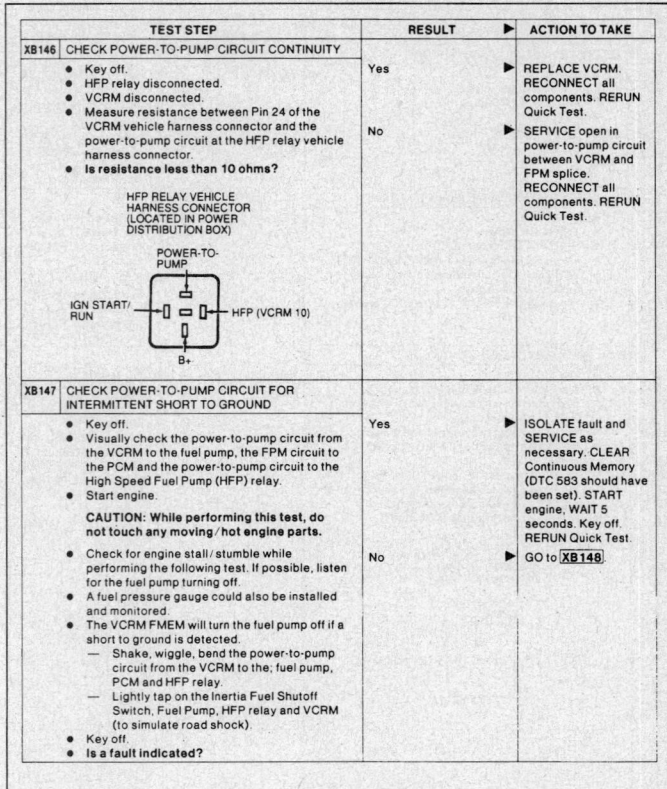 HFP RELAY VEHICLE HARNESS CONNECTOR (LOCATED IN POWER DISTRIBUTION BOX)			
XB147	**CHECK POWER-TO-PUMP CIRCUIT FOR INTERMITTENT SHORT TO GROUND**			
	• Key off. • Visually check the power-to-pump circuit from the VCRM to the fuel pump, the FPM circuit to the PCM and the power-to-pump circuit to the High Speed Fuel Pump (HFP) relay. • Start engine. **CAUTION: While performing this test, do not touch any moving/hot engine parts.** • Check for engine stall/stumble while performing the following test. If possible, listen for the fuel pump turning off. • A fuel pressure gauge could also be installed and monitored. • The VCRM FMEM will turn the fuel pump off if a short to ground is detected. — Shake, wiggle, bend the power-to-pump circuit from the VCRM to the; fuel pump, PCM and HFP relay. — Lightly tap on the Inertia Fuel Shutoff Switch, Fuel Pump, HFP relay and VCRM (to simulate road shock). • Key off. • **Is a fault indicated?**	Yes	▶	ISOLATE fault and SERVICE as necessary. CLEAR Continuous Memory (DTC 583 should have been set). START engine, WAIT 5 seconds. Key off. RERUN Quick Test.
		No	▶	GO to **XB148**.

TEST STEP		RESULT	▶	ACTION TO TAKE
XB148	**AGAIN, CHECK POWER-TO-PUMP CIRCUIT FOR INTERMITTENT SHORT TO GROUND**			
	• Key off. • Disconnect PCM, VCRM and fuel pump. Inspect each connector for damaged or pushed out pins, corrosion, loose wires, etc. Service as necessary. • Install breakout box. Leave the PCM, VCRM and fuel pump disconnected. • Connect a test lamp between Test Pin 1 (KAPWR) and Test Pin 8 (FPM). • Observe test lamp for an indication of a fault while performing the following (the light will turn on when a fault is detected, indicating a short to ground): — Shake, wiggle, bend the power-to-pump circuit from the VCRM to the; fuel pump, PCM and HFP relay. — Lightly tap on the Inertia Fuel Shutoff Switch and HFP relay (to simulate road shock). • **Is a fault indicated?**	Yes	▶	ISOLATE fault and SERVICE as necessary. REMOVE breakout box. RECONNECT all components. START engine, WAIT 5 seconds. Key off. RERUN Quick Test.
		No	▶	Unable to isolate fault at this time. RECONNECT all components. further diagnosis using the EEC-IV Monitor Box or Scan Tool RETURN to Diagnostic Routines
XB150	**CONTINUOUS MEMORY DIAGNOSTIC TROUBLE CODE (DTC) 524/543/556: IS CONTINUOUS MEMORY DTC 583 PRESENT?**			
	Continuous Memory DTC 524/543 indicate that, sometime during vehicle operation, when the PCM commanded the fuel pump on, voltage was not detected on the power-to-pump circuit (through FPM, PCM Pin 8). Although DTC 524 refers to the "low" speed output (VCRM Pin 24) and DTC 543 refers to the high speed output, it is not possible to distinguish between circuits due to the vehicle wiring and fuel pump operating strategy. Possible causes: — Open in power-to-pump circuit between the VCRM and FPM splice. — Open in B(+) supply to VCRM (Pins 4 and 5). — Left HO2S short to power. Continuous Memory DTC 556 indicates that, sometime during vehicle operation, a fuel pump primary circuit failure occurred. Possible causes: — Open or short in FP circuit (PCM Pin 22). • **Is Continuous Memory DTC 583 also present?**	Yes	▶	Continuous DTC 583 indicates that an "overcurrent" (short to ground) occurred on the power-to-pump/FPM circuit. This could also result in DTC 524/543 being set. GO to **XB136**
		No	▶	GO to **XB151**

TEST STEP	RESULT	▶	ACTION TO TAKE
XB151 CHECK POWER-TO-PUMP AND FP CIRCUITS			
• Start engine. **CAUTION: While performing this test, do not touch any moving / hot engine parts.** • Disconnect High Speed Fuel Pump (HFP) relay (located in power distribution box). • Connect a test lamp between the power-to-pump circuit at the HFP relay vehicle harness connector and chassis ground. • Observe test lamp for an indication of a fault while performing the following (the lamp will go out if an open; or FP circuit short to power, is detected. Also listen for engine stall / stumble or the fuel pump turning off. A fuel pressure gauge could also be installed and monitored): — For DTC 524 / 543; shake, wiggle, bend the power-to-pump circuit from the VCRM to the FPM splice and the B(+) circuit to Pins 4 and 5 at the VCRM. — For DTC 556; shake, wiggle, bend the FP circuit from the VCRM to PCM. • Key off. • Reconnect HFP relay. • **Is fault indicated?**	Yes No	▶ ▶	ISOLATE fault and SERVICE as necessary. CLEAR Continuous Memory RECONNECT all components. RERUN Quick Test. If DTC 556 was present: GO to XB152. If DTC 556 was not present: GO to XB158.
XB152 CHECK FP CIRCUIT FOR INTERMITTENT SHORT TO GROUND			
• Key off. • Disconnect PCM. Inspect for damaged or pushed out pins, corrosion, loose wires, etc. Service as necessary. • Disconnect VCRM. Inspect for damaged or pushed out pins, corrosion, loose wires, etc. Service as necessary. • Connect a DVOM between Pin 18 and Pin 1 of the VCRM vehicle harness connector. • While monitoring the DVOM resistance reading for an indication of a short to ground, perform the following: — Shake, wiggle, bend the FP circuit between the VCRM vehicle harness connector and the PCM vehicle harness connector. Also check the FP circuit to the Data Link Connector (DLC). • **Is a short to ground indicated?**	Yes No	▶ ▶	ISOLATE fault and SERVICE as necessary. RECONNECT all components. CLEAR Continuous Memory RERUN Quick Test. Unable to isolate fault at this time. RECONNECT all components. further diagnosis using the EEC-IV Monitor Box or Scan Tool RETURN to Diagnostic Routines

FM0159300771510X

Fig. 230   Test XB: VCRM (Part 51 of 63)

TEST STEP	RESULT	▶	ACTION TO TAKE
XB155 CONTINUOUS MEMORY DIAGNOSTIC TROUBLE CODE (DTC) 542: CHECK POWER-TO-PUMP AND FUEL PUMP GROUND CIRCUITS FOR INTERMITTENT OPEN			
Continuous Memory DTC 542 indicates that one of the following intermittent conditions has occurred: — Fuel pump circuit activated when PCM expected circuit to be off (ex. fuel pump prime or test procedure). — Open in the FPM, power-to-pump (FPM splice to fuel pump), fuel pump or fuel pump ground circuit. — FPM or power-to-pump circuit short to power. — VCRM output driver, or HFP relay contacts stuck closed. — HFP circuit short to ground. — Left HO2S signal circuit short to power. — Engine stall due to excessive load. • Start engine. **CAUTION: While performing this test, do not touch any moving / hot engine parts.** • Check for engine stall / stumble while performing the following (if possible listen for fuel pump turning off, or install and monitor a fuel pressure gauge): — Shake, wiggle, bend the power-to-pump circuit from the fuel pump to FPM splice. — Lightly tap on the fuel pump, Inertia Fuel Shutoff switch and VCRM (to simulate road shock). • Key off. • **Is fault indicated?**	Yes No	▶ ▶	ISOLATE fault and SERVICE as necessary. CLEAR Continuous Memory RERUN Quick Test. GO to XB156

FM0159300771520X

Fig. 230   Test XB: VCRM (Part 52 of 63)

TEST STEP	RESULT	▶	ACTION TO TAKE
XB156 CHECK FPM, POWER-TO-PUMP AND FUEL PUMP GROUND CIRCUITS FOR INTERMITTENT OPENS OR SHORTS TO POWER, AND HFP CIRCUIT FOR SHORT TO GND			
• Key off. • Disconnect PCM. Inspect for damaged or pushed out pins, corrosion, loose wires, etc. Service as necessary. • Install breakout box, leave PCM disconnected. • Connect a test lamp between Test Pin 8 and Test Pin 37 at the breakout box. • Key on, engine off. • Observe test lamp for an indication of a fault while performing the following (the light will go out if an open circuit is detected. The light will also go out, and the fuel pump will run, if a short to power or HFP circuit short to ground is detected): — Shake, wiggle, bend the following circuits: FPM, power-to-pump (VCRM to fuel pump, including circuit to HFP relay), fuel pump ground and HFP circuit between the HFP relay and VCRM. — Lightly tap on the Inertia Fuel Shutoff switch, HFP relay and VCRM (to simulate road shock). • **Is a fault indicated?**	Yes No	▶ ▶	ISOLATE fault and SERVICE as necessary. REMOVE breakout box. RECONNECT all components. RERUN Quick Test. GO to XB158 (to check left HO2S for intermittent short to power).
XB158 CHECK LEFT HO2S CIRCUIT FOR INTERMITTENT SHORT TO POWER			
NOTE: Due to the internal circuitry of the PCM, an intermittent left HO2S signal short to power could produce a Continuous Memory DTC 524, 542 or 543. • Key off. • Install breakout box, if applicable. • Breakout box installed, PCM disconnected. • Connect a test lamp between Test Pin 43 (HO2S-L) and Test Pin 40 at the breakout box. • Key on. • Observe test lamp for an indication of a fault while performing the following (the light will turn on bright if a fault is detected): — Shake, wiggle, bend the left HO2S circuit from the HO2S to the PCM. — Lightly tap on the HO2S (to simulate road shock). • **Is a fault indicated?**	Yes No	▶ ▶	ISOLATE fault and SERVICE as necessary. REMOVE breakout box. RECONNECT all components. RERUN Quick Test. Unable to isolate fault at this time. REMOVE breakout box. RECONNECT all components. further diagnosis using the EEC-IV Monitor Box or Scan Tool RETURN to Diagnostic Routines

FM0159300771530X

Fig. 230   Test XB: VCRM (Part 53 of 63)

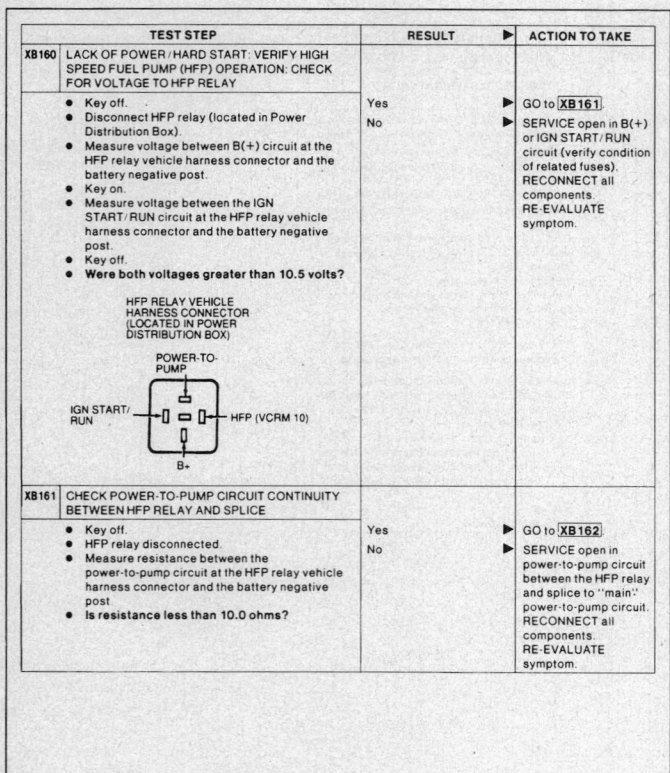

Fig. 230   Test XB: VCRM (Part 54 of 63)

TEST STEP	RESULT	▶	ACTION TO TAKE
XB160 LACK OF POWER/HARD START: VERIFY HIGH SPEED FUEL PUMP (HFP) OPERATION: CHECK FOR VOLTAGE TO HFP RELAY • Key off. • Disconnect HFP relay (located in Power Distribution Box). • Measure voltage between B(+) circuit at the HFP relay vehicle harness connector and the battery negative post. • Key on. • Measure voltage between the IGN START/RUN circuit at the HFP relay vehicle harness connector and the battery negative post. • Key off. • **Were both voltages greater than 10.5 volts?**	Yes No	▶ ▶	GO to XB161. SERVICE open in B(+) or IGN START/RUN circuit (verify condition of related fuses). RECONNECT all components. RE-EVALUATE symptom.
XB161 CHECK POWER-TO-PUMP CIRCUIT CONTINUITY BETWEEN HFP RELAY AND SPLICE • Key off. • HFP relay disconnected. • Measure resistance between the power-to-pump circuit at the HFP relay vehicle harness connector and the battery negative post. • **Is resistance less than 10.0 ohms?**	Yes No	▶ ▶	GO to XB162. SERVICE open in power-to-pump circuit between the HFP relay and splice to "main" power-to-pump circuit. RECONNECT all components. RE-EVALUATE symptom.

FM0159300771540X

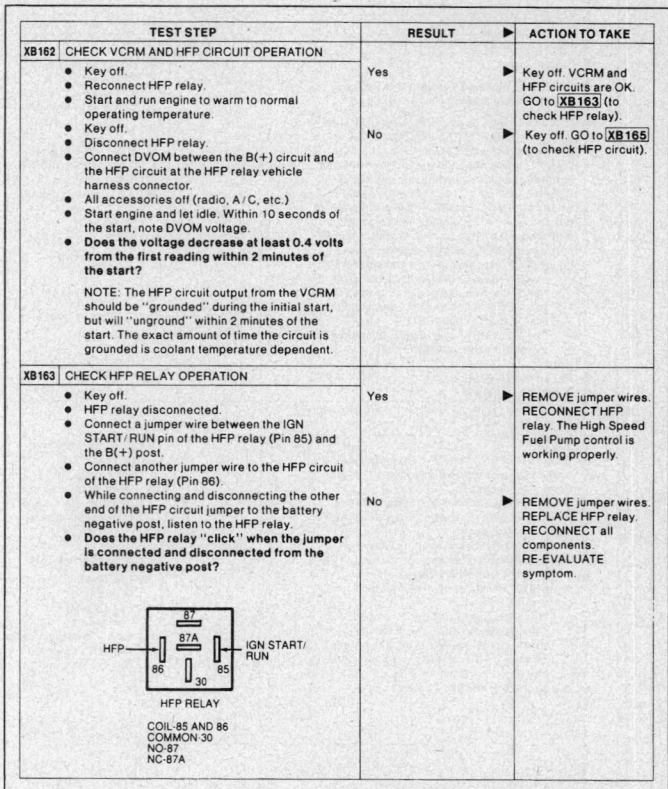

Fig. 230   Test XB: VCRM (Part 55 of 63)

TEST STEP	RESULT	▶	ACTION TO TAKE
XB162 CHECK VCRM AND HFP CIRCUIT OPERATION • Key off. • Reconnect HFP relay. • Start and run engine to warm to normal operating temperature. • Key off. • Disconnect HFP relay. • Connect DVOM between the B(+) circuit and the HFP circuit at the HFP relay vehicle harness connector. • All accessories off (radio, A/C, etc.). • Start engine and let idle. Within 10 seconds of the start, note DVOM voltage. • **Does the voltage decrease at least 0.4 volts from the first reading within 2 minutes of the start?** NOTE: The HFP circuit output from the VCRM should be "grounded" during the initial start, but will "unground" within 2 minutes of the start. The exact amount of time the circuit is grounded is coolant temperature dependent.	Yes No	▶ ▶	Key off. VCRM and HFP circuits are OK. GO to XB163 (to check HFP relay). Key off. GO to XB165 (to check HFP circuit).
XB163 CHECK HFP RELAY OPERATION • Key off. • HFP relay disconnected. • Connect a jumper wire between the IGN START/RUN pin of the HFP relay (Pin 85) and the B(+) post. • Connect another jumper wire to the HFP circuit of the HFP relay (Pin 86). • While connecting and disconnecting the other end of the HFP circuit jumper to the battery negative post, listen to the HFP relay. • **Does the HFP relay "click" when the jumper is connected and disconnected from the battery negative post?**	Yes No	▶ ▶	REMOVE jumper wires. RECONNECT HFP relay. The High Speed Fuel Pump control is working properly. REMOVE jumper wires. REPLACE HFP relay. RECONNECT all components. RE-EVALUATE symptom.

FM0159300771550X

TEST STEP	RESULT	▶	ACTION TO TAKE
XB165 CHECK HFP CIRCUIT CONTINUITY • Key off. • HFP relay disconnected. • Disconnect VCRM. Inspect for damaged or pushed out pins, corrosion, loose wires, etc. Service as necessary. • Measure resistance between Pin 10 of the VCRM vehicle harness connector and the HFP circuit at the HFP relay vehicle harness connector. • **Is resistance less than 5.0 ohms?**	Yes No	▶ ▶	GO to XB166. SERVICE open in HFP circuit. RECONNECT all components. RE-EVALUATE symptom.
XB166 CHECK HFP CIRCUIT FOR SHORT TO POWER • Key off. • HFP relay disconnected. • VCRM disconnected. • Key on. • Measure voltage between the HFP circuit at the HFP relay vehicle harness connector and the battery negative post. • Key off. • **Was voltage less than 1.0 volt?**	Yes No	▶ ▶	GO to XB167. SERVICE HFP circuit short to power. RECONNECT all components. RE-EVALUATE symptom.
XB167 CHECK HFP CIRCUIT FOR SHORT TO GROUND • Key off. • HFP relay disconnected. • VCRM disconnected. • Measure resistance between the HFP circuit at the HFP relay vehicle harness connector and the battery negative post. • **Is resistance greater than 10,000 ohms?**	Yes No	▶ ▶	REPLACE VCRM. RECONNECT all components. RE-EVALUATE symptom. SERVICE HFP circuit short to ground. RECONNECT all components. RE-EVALUATE symptom.

FM0159300771560X

Fig. 230   Test XB: VCRM (Part 56 of 63)

TEST STEP		RESULT	▶	ACTION TO TAKE
XB170	DIAGNOSTIC TROUBLE CODE (DTC) 587: CHECK WIRING HARNESS			
	DTC 587 indicates a Data Communications Link (DCL) error between the PCM and VCRM (DCL includes the DATA (+) and DATA (-) circuits). Possible causes: — Open or short in DATA (+) or DATA (-) circuit. — Damaged VCRM. — Damaged PCM. • Check vehicle harness that contains the DATA (+) and DATA (-) circuits (Powertrain Control Module (PCM) to VCRM and Data Link Connector (DLC) for: Close proximity to high voltage wires, aftermarket modifications, etc. • **Are the above checks OK?**	Yes No	▶ ▶	If Key On, Engine Off DTC 587 is present: GO to **XB171** For Continuous Memory DTC 587 only: GO to **XB180** SERVICE as necessary. CLEAR Continuous Memory START engine. TURN A/C on, WAIT 15 seconds. A/C off. Engine off. RERUN Quick Test.
XB171	CHECK DATA (+) AND DATA (-) CIRCUIT CONTINUITY			
	• Key off. • Disconnect any test equipment connected to the Data Link Connector (DLC) (leave equipment disconnected throughout procedure unless otherwise instructed). • Disconnect VCRM. Inspect for damaged or pushed out pins, corrosion, loose wires, etc. Service as necessary. • Disconnect Powertrain Control Module (PCM). Inspect for damaged or pushed out pins, corrosion, loose wires, etc. Service as necessary. • Install breakout box, leave PCM disconnected. • Measure continuity between Test Pin 18 at the breakout box and Pin 21 at the VCRM vehicle harness connector. • Measure continuity between Test Pin 19 at the breakout box and Pin 23 at the VCRM vehicle harness connector. • **Are both resistances less than 5.0 ohms?**	Yes No	▶ ▶	GO to **XB172**. SERVICE open in DATA (+) or DATA (-) circuit. REMOVE breakout box. RECONNECT all components. START engine. TURN A/C on, WAIT 15 seconds. A/C off. Engine off. RERUN Quick Test.

FM0159300771570X

Fig. 230   Test XB: VCRM (Part 57 of 63)

TEST STEP		RESULT	▶	ACTION TO TAKE
XB172	CHECK DATA (+) AND DATA (-) FOR SHORT TO POWER			
	• Breakout box installed, PCM disconnected. • VCRM disconnected. • Key on. • Measure voltage between Test Pin 18 and Test Pin 40 at the breakout box. • Measure voltage between Test Pin 19 and Test Pin 40 at the breakout box. • Key off. • **Were both voltages less than 1.0 volt?**	Yes No	▶ ▶	GO to **XB173**. SERVICE DATA (+) or DATA (-) circuit short to power. REMOVE breakout box. RECONNECT all components. START engine. TURN A/C on, WAIT 15 seconds. A/C off. Engine off. RERUN Quick Test.
XB173	CHECK DATA (+) AND DATA (-) FOR SHORT TO GROUND OR EACH OTHER			
	• Key off. • Breakout box installed, PCM disconnected. • VCRM disconnected. • Measure resistance between Test Pin 18 and Test Pin 40 at the breakout box. • Measure resistance between Test Pin 19 and Test Pin 40 at the breakout box. • Measure resistance between Test Pin 18 and Test Pin 19 at the breakout box. • **Are all resistances greater than 10,000 ohms?**	Yes No	▶ ▶	GO to **XB174**. SERVICE short circuit. REMOVE breakout box. RECONNECT all components. START engine. A/C on, WAIT 15 seconds. A/C off. Engine off. RERUN Quick Test.
XB174	CHECK DCL IN VCRM			
	• Key off. • All test equipment disconnected from DLC. • Breakout box installed, PCM disconnected. • Reconnect VCRM. • Key on. • Measure voltage between Test Pin 18 (DATA +) and Test Pin 19 (DATA -) at the breakout box. • **Is voltage between 3.5 and 5.3 volts?**	Yes No	▶ ▶	Key off. GO to **XB175**. Key off. REPLACE VCRM. REMOVE breakout box. RECONNECT all components. START engine. A/C on, WAIT 15 seconds. A/C off. Engine off. RERUN Quick Test.
XB175	CHECK DATA(-) CIRCUIT IN VCRM			
	• Key off. • All test equipment disconnected from DLC. • Breakout box installed, PCM disconnected. • VCRM connected. • Measure resistance between Test Pin 19 (DATA -) and Test Pin 40 (GND). • **Is resistance between 1500 and 2500 ohms?**	Yes No	▶ ▶	GO to **XB176**. Key off. REPLACE VCRM. REMOVE breakout box. RECONNECT all components. START engine. A/C on, wait 15 seconds. A/C off. Engine off.

FM0159300771580X

Fig. 230   Test XB: VCRM (Part 58 of 63)

TEST STEP		RESULT	▶	ACTION TO TAKE
XB176	VERIFY THAT PCM CAN COMMUNICATE ON DCL			
	NOTE: The purpose of this test is to verify that the PCM can communicate on DCL. A Scan Tool (ST) is required for this test step (ex. New Generation Star (NGS)). Refer to the ST operating instructions for specific operating procedure. • Key off. • Remove breakout box. • Reconnect PCM. • Connect ST to DLC. • Start engine. • While in DCL display, view the RPM Parameter Identification (PID). • While monitoring RPM, change engine speed. • **Does the RPM PID display and can the value change?**	Yes No	▶ ▶	Key off. GO to **XB177**. Key off. GO to **XB179**.
XB177	VERIFY DCL IN VCRM			
	• Key off. • PCM connected. • VCRM connected. • A/C off. • Enter Output State Diagnostic Test Mode (OS DTM). • Outputs off. • Depress throttle (near WOT), wait until the MIL flashes once (about 10 seconds). Release throttle. • Cooling fan should come on. • Depress throttle to turn fan off. • **Does fan come on and turn off as requested during Output State check?** NOTE: The cooling fan can only be cycled once while in Output State DTM. To re-test, exit and re-enter OS DTM.	Yes No	▶ ▶	EXIT OS DTM. GO to **XB178**. VERIFY OS DTM is operating properly (The MIL can be viewed and should change when the throttle is depressed and released. If the MIL does not change, check throttle linkage, DLC connections, etc.) If OS DTM is operating properly, REPLACE VCRM. RECONNECT all components. START engine. A/C on, WAIT 15 seconds. A/C off. Engine off. RERUN Quick Test.

FM0159300771590X

Fig. 230   Test XB: VCRM (Part 59 of 63)

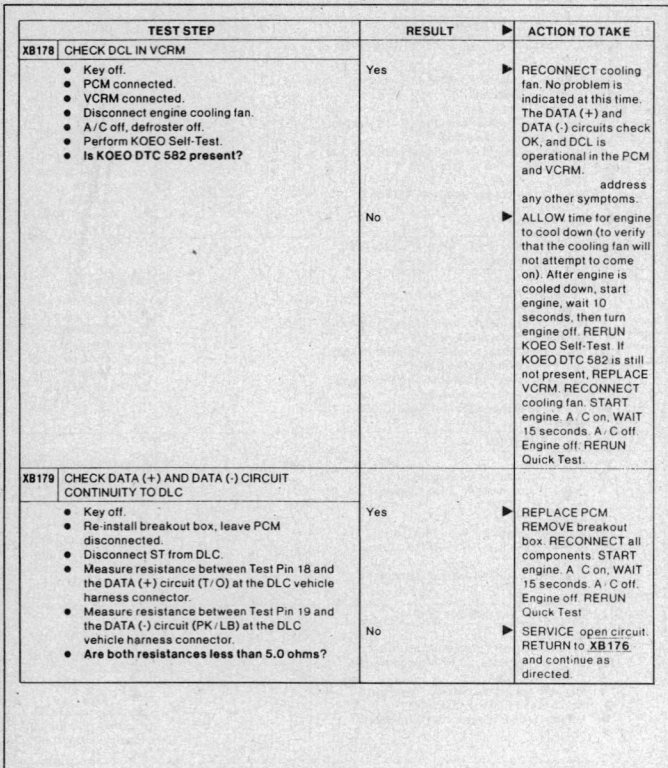

TEST STEP	RESULT	▶	ACTION TO TAKE
XB178 CHECK DCL IN VCRM			
• Key off. • PCM connected. • VCRM connected. • Disconnect engine cooling fan. • A/C off, defroster off. • Perform KOEO Self-Test. • **Is KOEO DTC 582 present?**	Yes	▶	RECONNECT cooling fan. No problem is indicated at this time. The DATA (+) and DATA (-) circuits check OK, and DCL is operational in the PCM and VCRM. address any other symptoms.
	No	▶	ALLOW time for engine to cool down (to verify that the cooling fan will not attempt to come on). After engine is cooled down, start engine, wait 10 seconds, then turn engine off. RERUN KOEO Self-Test. If KOEO DTC 582 is still not present, REPLACE VCRM. RECONNECT cooling fan. START engine. A/C on, WAIT 15 seconds. A/C off. Engine off. RERUN Quick Test.
XB179 CHECK DATA (+) AND DATA (-) CIRCUIT CONTINUITY TO DLC			
• Key off. • Re-install breakout box, leave PCM disconnected. • Disconnect ST from DLC. • Measure resistance between Test Pin 18 and the DATA (+) circuit (T/O) at the DLC vehicle harness connector. • Measure resistance between Test Pin 19 and the DATA (-) circuit (PK/LB) at the DLC vehicle harness connector. • **Are both resistances less than 5.0 ohms?**	Yes	▶	REPLACE PCM. REMOVE breakout box. RECONNECT all components. START engine. A/C on, WAIT 15 seconds. A/C off. Engine off. RERUN Quick Test
	No	▶	SERVICE open circuit. RETURN to **XB176** and continue as directed.

FM0159300771600X

Fig. 230   Test XB: VCRM (Part 60 of 63)

TEST STEP	RESULT	▶	ACTION TO TAKE
XB180 CHECK DATA (+) AND DATA (-) CIRCUITS FOR INTERMITTENT CONCERNS			
WARNING: WHILE PERFORMING THIS TEST STEP, THE ENGINE COOLING FAN MAY TURN ON. KEEP CLEAR OF THE ENGINE COOLING FAN. • Start engine. • A/C off. • Engine cooling fan off. (This test is to be performed while the cooling fan is off, during its normal cooling operation.) • Check for cooling fan coming on (for other than normal operation) while performing the following, (the VCRM will turn the fan on if a DCL communication fault is detected): — Shake, wiggle, bend the DATA (+) and DATA (-) circuits between the PCM and VCRM, and between the DLC and splice. — Lightly tap on the VCRM to simulate road shock. • **Did the cooling fan come on for other than normal operation?**	Yes	▶	ISOLATE fault and SERVICE as necessary. CLEAR Continuous Memory START engine. TURN A/C on, WAIT 15 seconds. A/C off. Engine off. RERUN Quick Test.
	No	▶	Key off. GO to **XB181**.

FM0159300771610X

Fig. 230   Test XB: VCRM (Part 61 of 63)

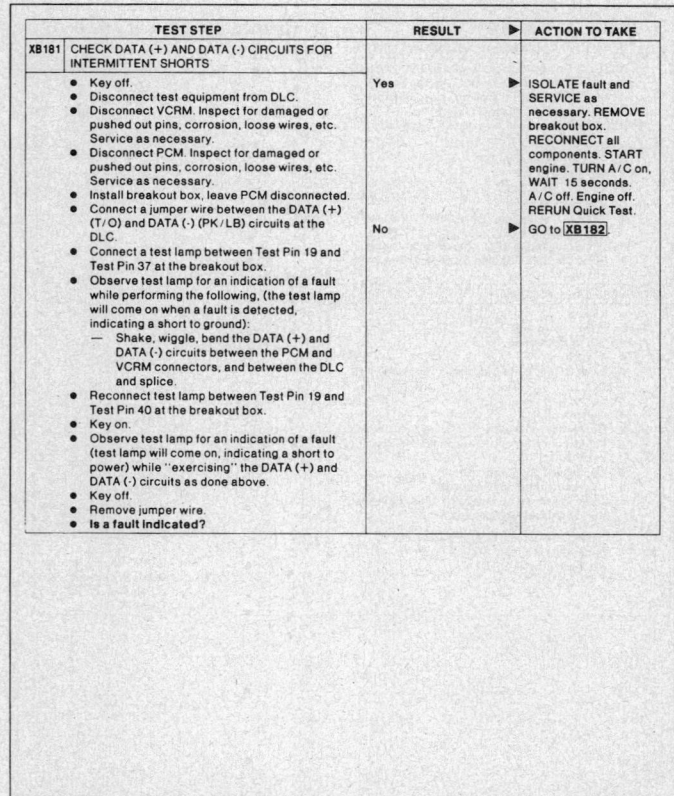

TEST STEP	RESULT	▶	ACTION TO TAKE
XB181 CHECK DATA (+) AND DATA (-) CIRCUITS FOR INTERMITTENT SHORTS			
• Key off. • Disconnect test equipment from DLC. • Disconnect VCRM. Inspect for damaged or pushed out pins, corrosion, loose wires, etc. Service as necessary. • Disconnect PCM. Inspect for damaged or pushed out pins, corrosion, loose wires, etc. Service as necessary. • Install breakout box, leave PCM disconnected. • Connect a jumper wire between the DATA (+) (T/O) and DATA (-) (PK/LB) circuits at the DLC. • Connect a test lamp between Test Pin 19 and Test Pin 37 at the breakout box. • Observe test lamp for an indication of a fault while performing the following, (the test lamp will come on when a fault is detected, indicating a short to ground): — Shake, wiggle, bend the DATA (+) and DATA (-) circuits between the PCM and VCRM connectors, and between the DLC and splice. • Reconnect test lamp between Test Pin 19 and Test Pin 40 at the breakout box. • Key on. • Observe test lamp for an indication of a fault (test lamp will come on, indicating a short to power) while "exercising" the DATA (+) and DATA (-) circuits as done above. • Key off. • Remove jumper wire. • **Is a fault indicated?**	Yes	▶	ISOLATE fault and SERVICE as necessary. REMOVE breakout box. RECONNECT all components. START engine. TURN A/C on, WAIT 15 seconds. A/C off. Engine off. RERUN Quick Test.
	No	▶	GO to **XB182**.

FM0159300771620X

Fig. 230   Test XB: VCRM (Part 62 of 63)

TEST STEP	RESULT	▶	ACTION TO TAKE
XB182 CHECK DATA (+) AND DATA (-) CIRCUITS FOR INTERMITTENT OPENS			
• Key off.	Yes	▶	ISOLATE fault and SERVICE as necessary. REMOVE jumper wire and breakout box. RECONNECT all components. START engine. A/C on, WAIT 15 seconds. A/C off. Engine off. RERUN Quick Test.
• Breakout box installed, PCM disconnected.			
• VCRM disconnected.			
• Connect a jumper wire between Pin 21 and Pin 23 at the VCRM vehicle harness connector (be careful that jumper wire does not contact other pins).			
• Connect DVOM between Test Pin 18 and Test Pin 19 at the breakout box.			
• While monitoring the resistance reading, shake, wiggle, bend the DATA (+) and DATA (-) circuits between the PCM and VCRM connectors.	No	▶	Unable to isolate fault at this time. REMOVE jumper wire and breakout box. RECONNECT all components.
• **Does resistance reading go above 5.0 ohms (indicating an open)?**			
			RETURN to Diagnostic Routines

FM0159300771630X

Fig. 230   Test XB: VCRM (Part 63 of 63)

Vehicle	Location
Mark VIII / Continental, Thunderbird / Cougar, Mustang, Ranger	RH dash panel behind kick panel
Tempo / Topaz, Escort / Tracer	Under instrument panel left of steering column
Taurus / Sable	Ahead of glove compartment
Town Car, Crown Victoria / Grand Marquis, Probe	LH dash panel in passenger compartment

**Fig. 231   Electronic control
assembly locations & applications.
1993–94**

Vehicle	Location
Mark VIII, Thunderbird / Cougar, Mustang	RH dash panel behind kick panel
Escort / Tracer	Under instrument panel, center console, right side
Taurus / Sable	Ahead of glove compartment
Probe	LH dash panel in passenger compartment

FM0159501250000X

Fig. 232   Electronic control assembly locations & applications. 1995

Part Number And Relay Type (Power or ISO)	System Application(s)	Location(s)
E6EF-12A646-B1A/B2A Power Relay (Std.)	Escort/Tracer 1.9L	Passenger compartment under dash on PCM bracket.
E3UF-12A646-B1A/B2A Power Relay (Std.)	5.0L SFI	Passenger compartment on PCM bracket in right cowl area.
E3AF-12A646-B1A/B2A Power Relay (Std.)	Thunderbird/Cougar 3.8/5.0L MFI (Base)	Engine compartment fuse/relay box.
F0AB-14B192-AA Power Relay (ISO)	Lincoln Town Car 4.6L Ford/Mercury 4.6L SFI	Engine compartment relay box; attached to vacuum reservoir.

Fig. 233   Power relay locations & applications. 1993–94

Part Number And Relay Type (Power or ISO)	System Application(s)	Location(s)
E6EF-12A646-B1A/B2A Power Relay (Std.)	Escort/Tracer	Passenger compartment under dash on PCM bracket.
F0AB-14B192-AA Power Relay (ISO)	All Other Cars	Engine compartment relay box; attached to vacuum reservoir.

FM0159501251000X

Fig. 234   Power relay locations & applications. 1995

Powertrain Model Application	Module -12B577-	Bracket and Module Assembly -12B581-	Vehicle Location
3.0L A/T Taurus/Sable	F1DF-AA	F1DF-AA	Radiator Support
3.0L, 3.2L SHO	F1DF-BA	F1DF-BA	Radiator Support
3.8L Supercharged	F1SF-AA	F1SF-AA	Radiator Support
3.8L A/T Taurus/Sable	F1DF-AA	F1DF-CA	Radiator Support
2.3L Mustang	F1ZF-AA	F1ZF-AA	Right Hand Shock Tower
2.3L Tempo/Topaz	F23F-BA	F23F-BA	Left Hand Shock Tower
3.0L Tempo/Topaz	F23F-AA	F23F-AA	Left Hand Shock Tower

NOTE: Fuel pump relay on the 3.8L supercharged package is not part of the CCRM.

Fig. 235   Constant control relay module locations & applications. 1993–95

Powertrain Model Application	Module -12B577-	Bracket and Module Assy -12B581-	Location
4.6L Mark VIII	F3LF-CE	F3LF-BE	Radiator Support

Fig. 236   Variable control relay module locations & applications. 1993–95

Electronic Engine Control System V (EEC-V)

If Unsure Of The System Used On The Vehicle Being Serviced, Refer To The "Engine Systems Identification Chart." Further Assistance For The Proper Use Of Information Contained In This Section Can Also Be Found In The Front Of This Tabbed Section Under "How To Use This Manual."

Prior To Performing Any Service Operations Listed In This Section, Consult The Technical Service Bulletin Section For Related Information.

Electrical Symbol & Wire Color Code Identification Located In The Front Of This Manual May Be Used As An Aid When Using Wiring Circuits Found In This Section.

INDEX

Page No.

Description: 9-2
  EEC-V & OBD II Systems 9-2
  System Components 9-2
Diagnosis & Testing: 9-5
  Accessing Diagnostic Trouble Codes. 9-5
    Emission Related Continuous
    DTCS 9-6
    Key On Engine Off (KOEO) Self
    Test....................... 9-6
    Key On Engine Running (KOER)
    Self Test..................... 9-6

Page No.

Mode 1 (Parameter Identification
  (PID) Access) 9-6
Mode 2 (Freeze Frame Data
  Access)...................... 9-7
Mode 3 (Emission Related
  Continuous DTCS)............. 9-7
Mode 4 (PCM Reset)............. 9-7
On-Board System Readiness Test
  Access 9-6
Powertrain Continuous DTCS
  (Enhanced Mode).............. 9-6

Page No.

Clearing Diagnostic Trouble Codes .. 9-7
Diagnostic Trouble Code
  Interpretation 9-7
Drive Cycles.................... 9-7
Pinpoint Tests 9-7
Quick Tests 9-7
Symptom Diagnosis 9-7
Wiring Circuits & Terminal
  Identification................... 9-7
Diagnostic Chart Index.......... 9-105
Sensor & Fuel Injector Specifications 9-1

SENSOR & FUEL INJECTOR SPECIFICATIONS

Sensor	Shift Position	Temperature°F	Voltage	Resistance ①	MPH	Throttle Angle°
Engine Coolant Temperature (ECT)	—	248	.28	1.18	—	—
	—	230	.36	1.55	—	—
	—	212	.47	2.07	—	—
	—	194	.61	2.80	—	—
	—	176	.80	3.84	—	—
	—	158	1.04	5.37	—	—
	—	140	1.35	7.60	—	—
	—	144	2.16	16.15	—	—
	—	86	2.62	24.27	—	—
	—	68	3.06	37.30	—	—
	—	50	3.52	58.75	—	—
Intake Air Temperature (IAT)	—	248	.28	1.18	—	—
	—	230	.36	1.55	—	—
	—	212	.47	2.07	—	—
	—	194	.61	2.80	—	—
	—	176	.80	3.84	—	—
	—	158	1.04	5.37	—	—
	—	140	1.35	7.60	—	—
	—	144	2.16	16.15	—	—
	—	86	2.62	24.27	—	—
	—	68	3.06	37.30	—	—
	—	50	3.52	58.75	—	—

Continued

SENSOR & FUEL INJECTOR SPECIFICATIONS—Continued

Sensor	Shift Position	Temperature°F	Voltage	Resistance ①	MPH	Throttle Angle°
Transmission Fluid Temperature (TFT)	—	248	.28	1.18	—	—
	—	230	.36	1.55	—	—
	—	212	.47	2.07	—	—
	—	194	.61	2.80	—	—
	—	176	.80	3.84	—	—
	—	158	1.04	5.37	—	—
	—	140	1.35	7.60	—	—
	—	144	2.16	16.15	—	—
	—	86	2.62	24.27	—	—
	—	68	3.06	37.30	—	—
	—	50	3.52	58.75	—	—
Mass Air Flow (MAF)	—	—	.80	—	0	—
	—	—	1.00	—	20	—
	—	—	1.70	—	40	—
	—	—	2.10	—	60	—
Delta Pressure Feedback EGR (DPFE)	—	—	4.56	—	—	4.34
	—	—	3.54	—	—	3.25
	—	—	2.51	—	—	2.17
	—	—	1.48	—	—	1.08
	—	—	.45	—	—	0
Manual Lever Position (MLP)	P	—	4.41	4.16	—	—
	R	—	3.60	1.44	—	—
	N	—	2.83	733 ②	—	—
	D	—	2.09	401 ②	—	—
	2	—	1.37	211 ②	—	—
	1	—	.68	81 ②	—	—

①—Kilo-ohms.
②—Ohms.

DESCRIPTION
EEC-V & OBD II SYSTEMS

The EEC-V system provides optimum control of the engine and transmission through enhanced capability of the microprocessor. The EEC-V system also has an on board diagnostic system (OBD II) with expanded features and functions.

The EEC-V has two major divisions, hardware and software. The hardware includes the Powertrain Control Module (PCM), Constant Control Relay Module (CCRM), sensors, switches, actuators, solenoids and interconnecting terminals. The software in the PCM provides strategy control for outputs (engine and transmission hardware) based on the values of the inputs to the PCM.

The PCM receives information from a variety of sensor and switch inputs. Based on the strategy and calibrations stored within the memory chip, the PCM generates the appropriate output. The system is designed to minimize emissions and optimize fuel economy and driveability. The software strategy controls basic operation of the engine and transmission, provides the OBD II strategy, controls the Malfunction Indicator Lamp (MIL), communicates to the scan tool (New Generation Star

(NGS), etc.) via the Standard Protocol (SCP), allows for Flash Electrically Erasable and Programmable Read-Only-Memory (EPROM), provides adaptive idle air and fuel control and controls Failure Mode Effects Management (FMEM).

The On Board Diagnostic (OBD II) System monitors the emission control system. When a component exceeds emission specifications or a component operates outside of tolerance, a Diagnostic Trouble Code (DTC) will be stored and the Malfunction Indicator Lamp (MIL) will be illuminated.

Fault detection strategy and MIL operation are associated with Tips and drive cycles. Each monitor has requirements for setting and clearing DTCs and for controlling the MIL. The Diagnostic Executive is the computer program in the EEC-V PCM that coordinates the OBD II self-monitoring system. This program controls all the monitors and interactions, DTC and MIL operation, Freeze Frame data and scan tool interface.

Freeze Frame data describes stored engine conditions such as state of the engine, state of fuel control, SPARK, RPM, load and warm-up status at the point the first malfunction is detected. Previously stored conditions will be replaced only if a

fuel or misfire malfunction is detected. This data is accessible by the scan tool to assist in repairing the vehicle.

OBD II inspection Maintenance (IM) Readiness Code P1000 is the DTC that identifies the monitors that have not completed since the computer memory was cleared. In certain states, it may be necessary to operate the vehicle until this code is erased from the PCM in order to purchase a vehicle license.

SYSTEM COMPONENTS
Powertrain Control Module (PCM)

The PCM is a microprocessor that controls the EEC-V system. On Mustang, Cougar and Thunderbird, the PCM is located behind the kick panel cover on the right hand passenger area near the dash panel. On Crown Victoria and Grand Marquis, the PCM is located behind the kick panel cover on the left hand passenger area near the dash panel. On Continental and Town Car models, the PCM is located behind the dash panel almost center to the passenger and driver but accessible from the engine compartment. It has a 104-pin electrical connector, **Fig. 1,** and receives inputs from sensors and other electronic components (switches, relays, etc.). The PCM gener-

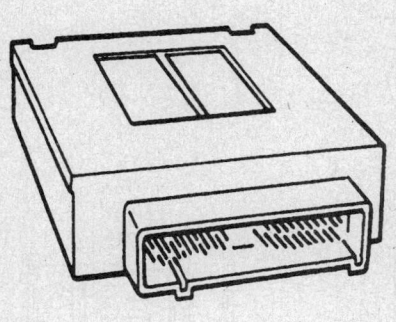

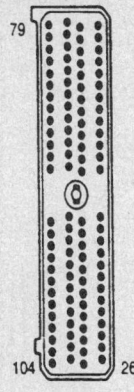

Fig. 1 Powertrain control module (PCM)

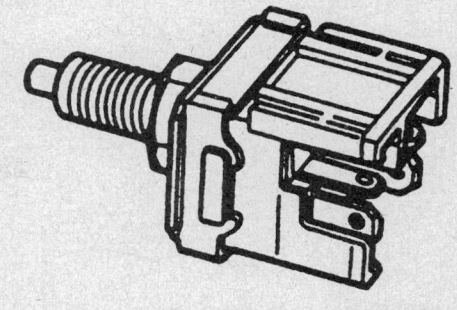

FM0159401119000X

Fig. 2 Brake On/Off (BOO) switch

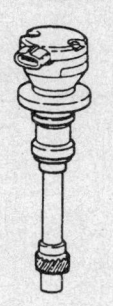

HALL TYPE (SHOWN)

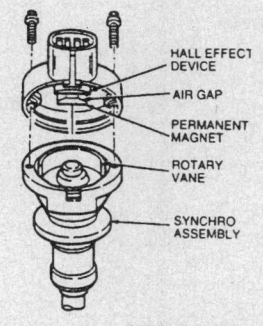

HALL EFFECT DEVICE
AIR GAP
PERMANENT MAGNET
ROTARY VANE
SYNCHRO ASSEMBLY

FM0159401120000X

Fig. 3 Camshaft position (CMP) sensor.
3.8L/V6-232 Mustang

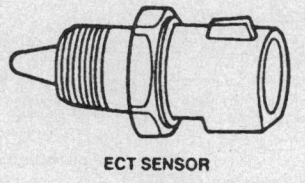

ECT SENSOR

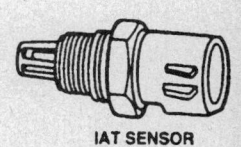

IAT SENSOR

FM0159401121000X

Fig. 4 Engine coolant temperature (ECT) sensor &
intake air temperature (IAT) sensor

ates output signals stored in its memory, based on information received, to control the various relays, solenoids and actuators.

Keep Alive Memory (KAM)

The PCM stores information in KAM (a memory integrated circuit chip) about vehicle operating conditions, then uses this information to compensate for component tolerances. KAM remains powered when the vehicle ignition key is Off so the information stored in the PCM is not lost.

Hardware Limited Operation Strategy (HLOS)

This is a system of special circuitry that provides minimal operation should the PCM (mainly the CPU or EPROM) stop functioning properly. All modes of Self-Test are not functional at this time. Electronic hardware is in control of the system while in HLOS. HLOS allows the following output functions:
1. Spark output controlled directly by the PIP signal.
2. Fixed fuel pulse width synchronized with the PIP signal.
3. Fuel pump relay energized.
4. Idle Speed Control output signal functional.

The HLOS disables the following outputs to default state:
1. EGR solenoids.
2. No converter lock-up.

Brake On/Off (BOO) Switch

The brake on/off switch, **Fig. 2**, signals the PCM with a battery voltage (B+) signal whenever the vehicle brakes are on.

On certain applications, the PCM adjusts engine idle speed with the brakes applied and the A/C on, or turns the A/C off after a calibrated time.

On vehicles with locking torque converters, the signal informs the PCM to unlock the torque converter.

If the stop lamp bulb is burned out (open), a high voltage is present at the PCM due to a pull-up resistor in the PCM. This provides fail safe operation in the event the circuit in the BOO switch has failed.

Camshaft Position (CMP) Sensor

The camshaft position (CMP) sensor, **Fig. 3**, is used to identify when piston No. 1 is at a specific top dead center (ATDC) point of the compression stroke. The signal is then supplied to the PCM and used for synchronizing the firing of sequential fuel injectors. The input circuit supplied to the PCM is referred to as the Cylinder Identification (CID) input or circuit.

There are two different types of camshaft sensors. The 3.8L/V6-232 Mustang uses a hall device, **Fig. 3**, and the 4.6L/V8-281 Thunderbird/Cougar uses a variable reluctance type.

Engine Coolant Temperature Sensor (ECT) & Intake Air Temperature (IAT) Sensor

These sensors, **Fig. 4**, are thermistor devices in which resistance changes with temperature. The electrical resistance of a thermistor decreases as temperature increases, and increases as temperature decreases. The varying resistance affects the

voltage drop across the sensor terminals and provides electrical signals to the PCM corresponding to temperature. Thermistor-type sensors are considered passive sensors. A passive sensor is connected to a voltage divider network so varying the resistance of the passive sensor causes a variation in total current flow.

Voltage that is dropped across a fixed resistor, in a series with the sensor resistor determines the voltage sign at the PCM. This voltage signal is equal to the reference voltage minus the voltage drop across the fixed resistor.

The ECT measures coolant temperature of the engine and is threaded into an engine coolant passage.

The IAT provides air temperature information to the PCM. The PCM uses this information as correction factors in the calculation of fuel, spark and mass air flow (MAF).

The IAT provides a quicker temperature change response time than the ECT, though similar in construction.

Heated Oxygen Sensor (HO2S)

The heated oxygen sensor (HO2S), **Fig. 5**, detects the presence of oxygen in the exhaust and produces a variable voltage according to the amount of oxygen detected. A high concentration of oxygen (lean air/fuel ratio) in the exhaust produces a low voltage signal (less than .4 volt). A low concentration of oxygen (rich air/fuel ratio) in the exhaust produces a high voltage signal (greater than .6 volt). The HO2S provides feedback to the processor indicating air/fuel ratio in order to achieve a near stoichiometric air/fuel ratio of 14.7:1 during closed loop operation. In closed loop operation, HO2S generates a voltage between 0-1.1 volts. During leaner then stoichiometric ratio, HO2S generates a voltage between 0-0.4 volt. During richer then stoichiometric ratio, HO2S generates a voltage between .6-0.1 volt at HO2S top temperature of 662°F.

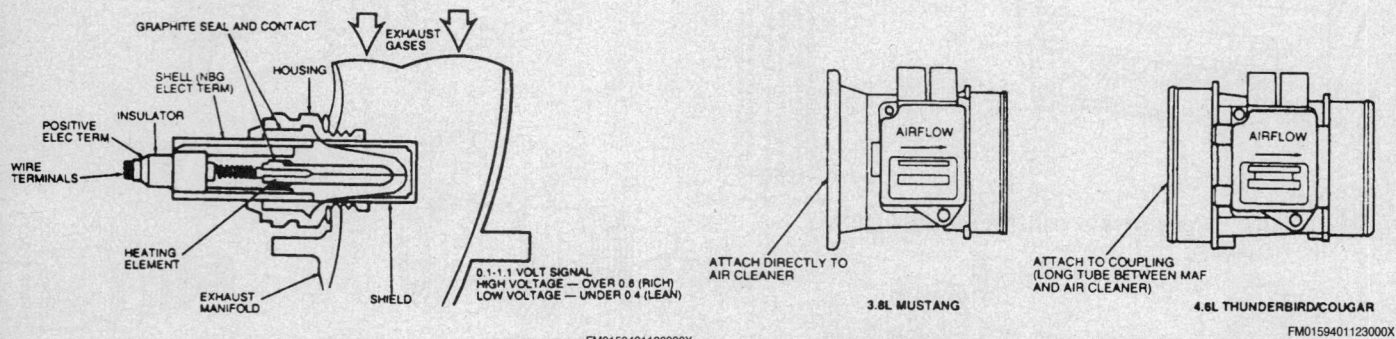

Fig. 5   Heated oxygen sensor (HO2S)

Fig. 6   Mass air flow (MAF) sensor

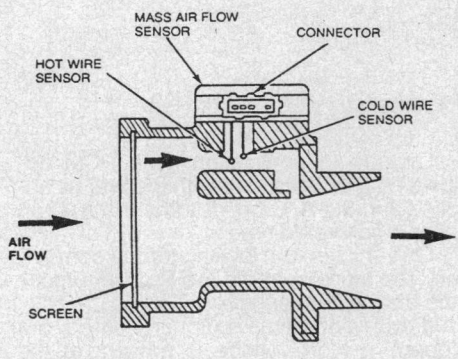

Fig. 7   Air flow through throttle body contacting MAF
sensor hot & cold wire terminals

Mass Air Flow (MAF) Sensor

The MAF sensor , **Fig. 6,** uses a hot wire sensing element to measure the amount of air entering the engine. Air passing over the hot wire causes it to cool. This hot wire is maintained at 392°F above ambient temperature as measured by a constant cold wire. The current required to maintain the hot wire at its 392°F is proportional to the mass air flow. The MAF sensor then outputs an analog voltage signal to the PCM proportional to the intake air mass. The PCM calculates the required fuel injector pulse-width in order to provide the desired air/fuel ratio, **Fig. 7.**

Knock Sensor

The knock sensor is a tuned accelerometer on the engine which converts engine vibration to an electrical signal. The PCM uses this signal to determine the presence of engine knock and to retard spark timing.

Octane Adjust (OCT ADJ) Shorting Bar

The OCT ADJ, **Fig. 8,** is used to retard spark. Removal of the in-line connector will typically retard spark three degrees. The purpose of the OCT ADJ self-test is to check the state of the OCT ADJ shorting bar. A diagnostic trouble code (DTC) will be present if the shorting bar is removed or if there is an open circuit. The OCT ADJ shorting bar is similar in shape to th SPOUT in-line connector. On some applications, the power steering pressure (PSP) circuit will also have a similar shorting bar connector. **Do not remove the shorting bar unless directed.**

Output Shaft Speed (OSS) Sensor

The OSS sensor, **Fig. 9,** is a magnetic pick-up that sends a voltage signal to the PCM. This signal tells the PCM the transmission output shaft RPM. The signal is also used for shift schedules, modulated converter clutch control and determining EPC pressure. On AODE transmissions, the OSS is located on the left rear of the transmission case. Some of the control functions are limiting vehicle speed, converter clutch control and shift quality.

Throttle Position (TP) Sensor

The integral TP sensor (mounted on the throttle body), **Fig. 10,** is a rotary potentiometer that provides a signal to the PCM that is linearly proportional to the throttle plate/shaft position. The sensor housing

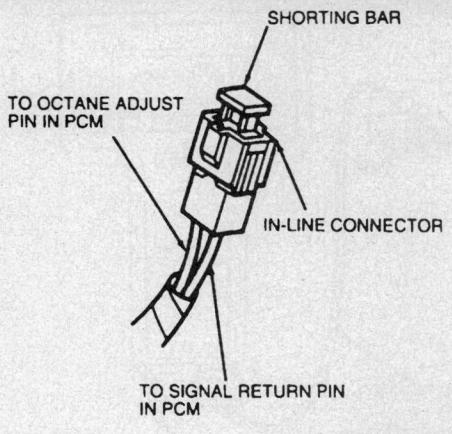

Fig. 8 Octane adjusting (OCT ADJ) shorting bar

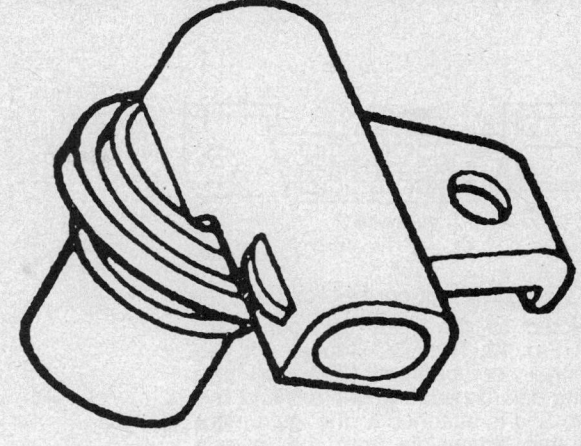

Fig. 9 Output shaft speed (OSS) sensor

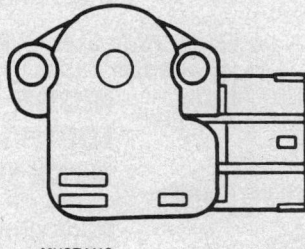

Fig. 10 Throttle position (TP) sensor

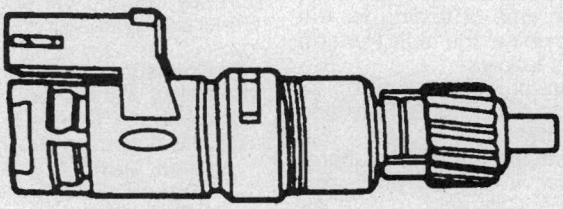

Fig. 12 Vehicle speed sensor (VSS)

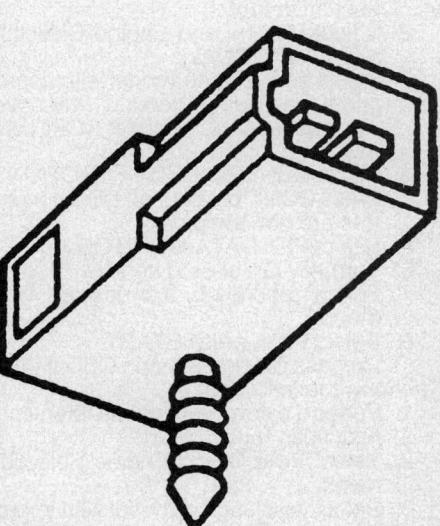

Fig. 11 Transmission fluid temperature (TFT) sensor

has a three blade gold plated electrical connector. The gold plating decreases corrosion resistance on terminals and increases connector durability. As the TP sensor is rotated by the throttle shaft, four operating modes are determined by the PCM from the TP. Those modes are closed throttle (includes idle or deceleration), part throttle (includes cruise or moderate acceleration), wide open throttle (includes maximum acceleration or de-choke on crank) and throttle angle rate.

Transmission Fluid Temperature (TFT) Sensor

The TFT sensor, **Fig. 11,** is a thermistor that changes resistance in response to temperature. The electrical resistance of a thermistor decreases as temperature increases, and increases as temperature decreases. The varying resistance is converted into a corresponding voltage signal and input to the PCM.

Vehicle Speed Sensor (VSS)

The VSS, **Fig. 12,** is a variable reluctance sensor that generates a sine wave type waveform with a frequency that is proportional to the speed of the vehicle. If the vehicle is moving at a relatively low velocity, the signal produces a signal with a low voltage. As vehicle speed increases, the sensor generates a signal with a higher frequency. The PCM uses the frequency signal generated by the VSS (and other inputs) to control such parameters as fuel injection, ignition timing and transaxle/transmission shift points.

Cooling Fan Control

The PCM determines engine cooling fan requirements and controls the fan operation through the Fan Control (FC) output (single speed fan applications) or Low Fan Control (LFC) and High Fan Control (HFC) outputs. Although the FC, LFC and HFC Relays are normally open relays, the FC/LFC circuit is wired through a voltage inverter inside the CCRM. The voltage inverter ensures the PCM must turn on (ground) the FC/LFC output to turn the fan off. This is done so the cooling fan will operate in the event of an open FC/LFC circuit.

Constant Control Relay Module (CCRM)

The CCRM interfaces with the EEC-V system to provide control for the cooling fan, A/C clutch and electric fuel pump. The CCRM also contains the EEC-V Power Relay which provides Vehicle Power (VPWR) to the PCM and the EEC-V system. If any of the internal components of the CCRM fail, the entire unit must be replaced.

DIAGNOSIS & TESTING
Accessing Diagnostic Trouble Codes

To access codes, the scan tool must be

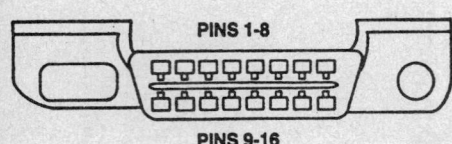

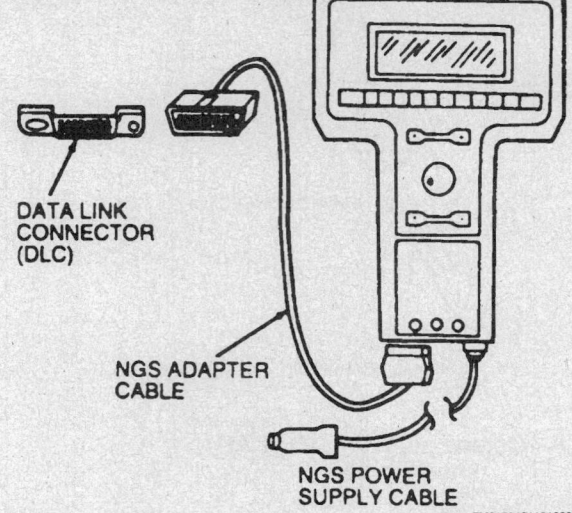

Fig. 13 Data link connector (DLC)

connected to the data link connector (DLC), **Fig. 13**. The DLC is located in the passenger compartment between the steering column and the centerlink of the vehicle and is attached to the instrument panel and accessible from the driver's seat. It can accommodate up to sixteen terminals. If the New Generation Star (NGS) is used for communication with the vehicle, an OBD II adapter cable must be connected to the tool, **Fig. 14**. It may be possible to have two DLCs. One is under the instrument panel, the other is inside the engine compartment. Use the one under the instrument panel for OBD II vehicles.

KEY ON ENGINE OFF (KOEO) SELF TEST

This is a functional test of the powertrain control system performed on-demand with the key on and the engine off. A fault must be present at the time of testing for the KOEO self test to detect the fault. Perform KOEO self test as follows:

1. Connect scan tool to DLC.
2. Select Vehicle and Engine Selection menu (OPTIONAL).
3. Select year, engine, model with appropriate qualifier, if needed (transmission, 49 state, California) (OPTIONAL).
4. Select DIAGNOSTIC DATA LINK.
5. Select PCM-POWERTRAIN CTRL MODULE.
6. Select DIAGNOSTIC TEST MODE.
7. Select KOEO ON-DEMAND SELF-TEST.
8. Turn key On.
9. Follow operating instructions from the menu.

KEY ON ENGINE RUNNING (KOER) SELF TEST

This is a functional test of the powertrain control system performed on-demand with the engine running and the vehicle stopped. A check of the vehicle inputs and outputs is made during operating conditions and at normal temperature. A fault must be present at the time of testing for the KOER self test to detect the fault. Perform KOER self test as follows:

1. Connect scan tool to DLC.
2. Select Vehicle and Engine Selection menu (OPTIONAL).
3. Select year, engine, model with appropriate qualifier, if needed (transmission, 49 state, California) (OPTIONAL).
4. Select DIAGNOSTIC DATA LINK.
5. Select PCM-POWERTRAIN CTRL MODULE.

6. Select DIAGNOSTIC TEST MODE.
7. Select KOER ON-DEMAND SELF-TEST.
8. Turn key On.
9. Follow operating instructions from the menu.

EMISSION RELATED CONTINUOUS DTCs

DTC retrieval is conducted with the ignition key On and the engine Off. On New Generation Star scan tools, proceed as follows:

1. Connect scan tool to DLC.
2. Select Vehicle and Engine Selection menu (OPTIONAL).
3. Select year, engine, model with appropriate qualifier, if needed (transmission, 49 state, California) (OPTIONAL).
4. Select GENERIC OBD II FUNCTIONS. Press CONT button if all OBD II monitors are not complete.
5. Select DIAGNOSTIC TROUBLE CODES. Press
6. Turn key On.
7. Follow operating instructions from the menu.

POWERTRAIN CONTINUOUS DTCs (ENHANCED MODE)

DTC retrieval is conducted with the ignition key On and the engine Off. On New Generation Star scan tools, proceed as follows:

1. Connect scan tool to DLC.
2. Select Vehicle and Engine Selection menu.
3. Select year, engine, model with appropriate qualifier, if needed (transmission, 49 state, California).
4. Select DIAGNOSTIC DATA LINK.
5. Select PCM-POWERTRAIN CTRL MODULE.
6. Select DIAGNOSTIC TEST MODES.
7. Select RETRIEVE/CLEAR CONTINUOUS DTCs.
8. Turn key On.
9. Follow operating instructions from menu.

MODE 1 (PARAMETER IDENTIFICATION (PID) ACCESS)

The Parameter Identification (PID) mode allows access to certain data values, analog and digital inputs and outputs, calculated values and system status information. To access the generic OBD II PIDs, perform the following:

1. Perform safety precautions, then connect scan tool.
2. Select Vehicle and Engine Selection menu (OPTIONAL).
3. Select year, engine, model with appropriate qualifier, if needed (transmission, 49 state, California) (OPTIONAL).
4. Select GENERIC OBD II FUNCTIONS. Press CONT button if all OBD II monitors are not complete.
5. Select PID/DATA MONITOR.
6. Turn key On or start vehicle.
7. Follow operating instructions from menu.
8. Select PIDs, press START.

To access the non-generic OBD II PIDs, perform the following:

1. Perform safety precautions, then connect scan tool.
2. Select Vehicle and Engine Selection menu.
3. Select year, engine, model with appropriate qualifier, if needed (transmission, 49 state, California).
4. Select DIAGNOSTIC DATA LINK.
5. Select PCM-POWERTRAIN CTRL MODULE.
6. Select PID DATA MONITOR AND RECORD.
7. Turn key On or start vehicle.
8. Follow operating instructions from menu.
9. Select PIDs, press START.

ON-BOARD SYSTEM READINESS TEST ACCESS

All OBD II scan tools must display the On-Board System Readiness (OSR) Test. The OSR will display the monitors on the vehicle and the status of all monitors (complete and not complete) at that time. If any monitor is not complete, the scan tools will identify which monitor has not completed. To access the OSR Test, perform the following:

1. Connect scan tool to DLC.
2. Select Vehicle and Engine Selection menu (OPTIONAL).
3. Select year, engine, model with appropriate qualifier, if needed (transmission, 49 state, California).
4. Follow the operating instructions from menu.
5. Select GENERIC OBD II FUNCTIONS. Press TEST button if all monitors are not complete.
6. Start vehicle.
7. Select ON-BOARD SYSTEM READINESS.

MODE 2 (FREEZE FRAME DATA ACCESS)

Freeze Frame Data allows access to emission related data values from specific generic PIDs. These values are stored the instant an emission related DTC is stored in Continuous Memory. This provides a snapshot of the conditions that were present when the DTC was stored. Once one set of freeze fame data is stored, this data will remain in memory even if another emission related DTC is stored, with the exception of Misfire or Fuel System DTCs. Once freeze frame data for Misfire or Fuel System DTCs is stored, it will overwrite any previous data and freeze frame will not be further overwritten. When a DTC associated with the freeze frame is erased or a PCM memory reset is performed, new freeze frame data can be stored again. In the event of multiple emission related DTCs in memory, always note the DTC for the freeze frame data. To access freeze frame data, perform the following:

1. Connect scan tool to DLC.
2. Select Vehicle and Engine Selection menu (OPTIONAL).
3. Select year, engine, model with appropriate qualifier, if needed (transmission, 49 state, California).
4. Follow the operating instructions from menu.
5. Select GENERIC OBD II FUNCTIONS. Press CONT button if monitors are not complete.
6. Turn key On.
7. Select FREEZE FAME PID REQUEST.

MODE 3 (EMISSION RELATED CONTINUOUS DTCs)

Refer to Emission Related Continuous DTCs as outlined.

Output Test Mode (Enhanced Mode)

The Output Test Mode (OTP) aids in servicing output actuators associated with the PCM. It allows energizing and de-energizing of most of the system output actuators on command. When entering OTM, the outputs can be turned off and on without controlling the cooling fans. The low and high speed cooling fans may be turned on separately without energizing

the other outputs. To enter OTM with the ignition key On and the engine Off, perform the following:

1. Connect scan tool to DLC.
2. Select Vehicle and Engine Selection menu.
3. Select year, model with appropriate qualifier, if needed (transmission, 499 state, California).
4. Follow operating instructions from menu (turn key On).
5. Select DIAGNOSTIC DATA LINK.
6. Select PCM-POWERTRAIN CTRL MODULE.
7. Select DIAGNOSTIC TEST MODE.
8. Select ACTIVE COMMAND MODES.
9. Select OUTPUT TEST MODE.
10. Turn key On, then follow instructions from menu.
11. Select mode (ALL ON, HIGH SPEED FAN or LOW SPEED FAN).
12. Select START to turn outputs ON (may link up to PIDs).
13. Select STOP to turn outputs OFF.

MODE 4 (PCM RESET)
PCM Reset

The PCM Reset allows the scan tool to command the PCM to clear all emission-related diagnostic information. When resetting the PCM, a DTC P1000 will be stored in the PCM until all the OBD II system monitors or components have been tested to satisfy a Trip without any other faults occurring.

1. The following results occur when resetting the PCM:
   a. Clears the number of DTCs.
   b. Clears the DTCs.
   c. Clears the freeze frame data.
   d. Clears oxygen sensor test data.
   e. Resets status of the OBD II system monitors.
   f. Sets DTC P1000.
2. To reset the PCM, perform the following:
   a. Connect scan tool to DLC.
   b. Select Vehicle and Engine Selection menu (OPTIONAL).
   c. Select year, model with appropriate qualifier, if needed (transmission, 499 state, California) (OPTIONAL).
   d. Follow operating instructions from menu (turn key On).
   e. Select GENERIC OBD II FUNCTIONS. Press CONT button if all OBD II monitors are not complete,
   f. Turn key On.
   g. Select CLEAR DIAGNOSTIC CODES.

KAM Reset

Disconnect the battery ground cable for a minimum of five minutes (this will also result in PCM reset). Resetting KAM will also clear learned values the PCM has stored for adaptive systems such as idle and Fuel systems. Once the vehicle is driven, the PCM will relearn new adaptive values. It will take a few miles and may run rough until the values are relearned.

Mode 5 (Oxygen Sensor Monitoring Test Results)

The Oxygen Sensor Monitoring Test Results allows access to the on-board sensor fault limits and actual values during

the test cycle. The test cycle has specified operating conditions that must be met (engine temperature, load, etc.) for completion. This information helps to determine the efficiency of the exhaust catalyst. To access the Oxygen Sensor Monitoring Test Results, perform the following:

1. Connect scan tool to DLC.
2. Select Vehicle and Engine Selection menu (OPTIONAL).
3. Select year, model with appropriate qualifier, if needed (transmission, 499 state, California) (OPTIONAL).
4. Follow operating instructions from menu (turn key On).
5. Select GENERIC OBD II FUNCTIONS.
6. Select OXYGEN SENSOR REQUEST.
7. Select appropriate oxygen sensor test. To enter a Ford specific test:
   a. Enter MANUFACTURER SPECIFIC TEST ID.
   b. Turn ignition key On.
   c. Scroll up to test number and trigger (Test Nos. 41, 61 and 81 are manufacturer specific tests and require test number be entered into scan tool manually).

Clearing Diagnostic Trouble Codes

Refer to PCM Reset and KAM Reset for clearing of DTCs.

Wiring Circuits & Terminal Identification

Refer to **Figs. 15 through 89** for PCM and CCRM wiring circuits and terminal identification.

Diagnostic Trouble Code Interpretation

Refer to **Figs. 90 through 92** for DTC identification.

Quick Tests

Refer to **Figs. 93 through 103** for diagnostic subroutines/quick tests. Refer to **Figs. 104 through 106** for diagnostic trouble code pinpoint test reference charts.

Symptom Diagnosis

Refer to **Figs. 107 and 108** for symptom index and **Figs. 109 through 171** for symptom diagnosis.

Pinpoint Tests

Refer to **Figs. 172 through 305** for pinpoint tests.

Drive Cycles

The drive cycle assists in identifying an OBD II system problem through total monitor testing. The primary intention of the OBD II drive cycle is to clear the DTC P1000. A scan tool can be installed in the vehicle before the drive cycle test to observe diagnostic trouble code output.

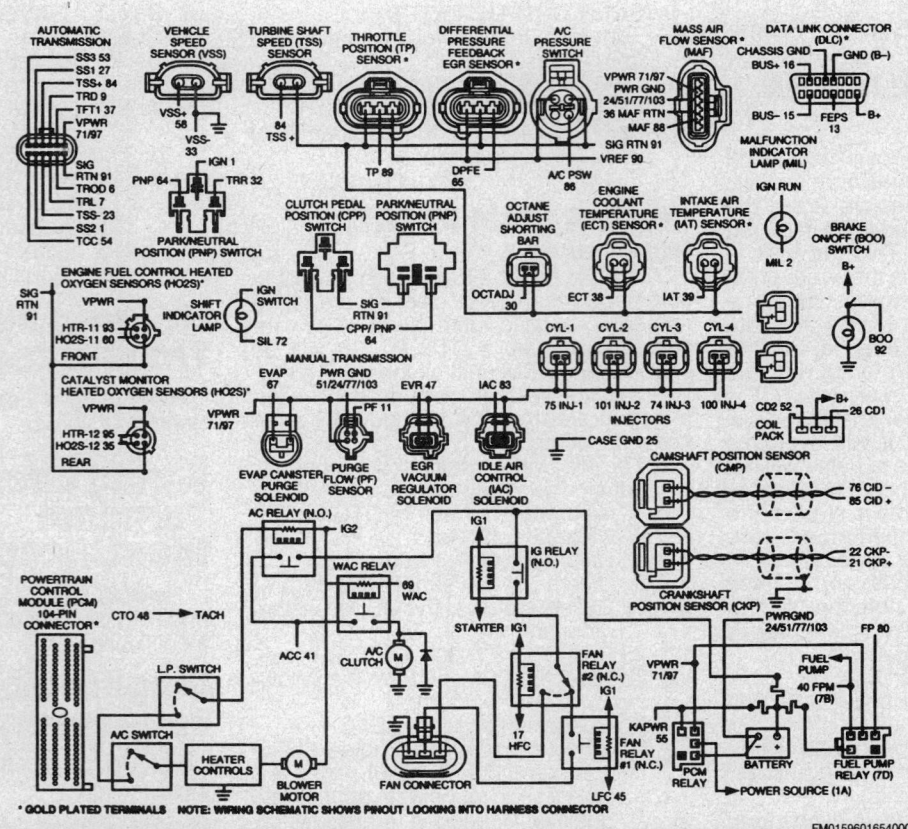

Fig. 15   PCM wiring circuit. 1996 Escort & Tracer w/1.9L/4-116

Complete drive cycle test as follows:
1. Start engine.
2. Drive vehicle for 4 to 6 minutes until engine is at operating temperature of approximately 180°F or greater.
3. Idle for 45 seconds.
4. Accelerate to 45 mph at ¼ throttle (approximately 10 seconds).
5. Drive to accumulate at least 4 minutes in 30-45 mph range. No wide open throttle conditions should be encountered.
6. Drive vehicle at speed between 30 and 40 mph maintaining steady throttle position for at least one minute.
7. Decelerate at idle for at least one minute.
8. Accelerate to 55 mph at ½ throttle (elapsed time about 10 seconds).
9. Cruise at speed between 40 and 65 maintaining steady throttle position for at least 80 seconds.
10. Bring vehicle down to idle.
11. While ignition key is on, check for continuous memory diagnostic trouble codes using scan tool.

Pin	Circuit	Wire Color	Application	Abbreviation
64	5B	R	Park/Neutral Position Automatic Transmission	PNP
65	145	BL/Y	Differential Pressure Feedback EGR Sensor	DPFE
67	94	O/W	EVAP Canister Purge Solenoid	EVAP CANP
69	702	BL/BK	Wide Open Throttle A/C Cut-off	WOT
71	101H	W/R	Vehicle Power	VPWR
72	125	PK	Shift Indicator Lamp	SIL
74	105	BR/W	Injector 3	INJ 3
75	106	Y	Injector 1	INJ 1
76	127	BL	Cylinder Identification (-)	CID-
77	999F	BK/Y	Power Ground	PWR GND
80	103	LG	Fuel Pump Control	FP
83	83	BL/O	Intake Air Control Solenoid	IAC
84	858	W/BL	Turbine Shaft Speed Sensor	TSS +
85	128	DG	Cylinder Identification (+)	CID +
86	133	DG/BK	Air Conditioning Pressure Sensor	ACP
88	143	BR/BK	Mass Air Flow Sensor	MAF
89	71A	R/W	Throttle Position Sensor	TP
90	85A	LG/W	Vehicle Reference Voltage	VREF
91	63	LG/BK	Signal Return	SIG RTN
92	351G	DG	Brake On/Off Switch	BOO
93	95	O/BK	Heater - 11 Front Oxygen Sensor	HTR - 11
95	97	P	Heater - 12 Rear Oxygen Sensor	HTR - 12
97	101P	W/R	Vehicle Power	VPWR
100	115	DG/O	Injector 4	INJ 4
101	116	P/Y	Injector 2	INJ 2
103	999G	BK/Y	Power Ground	PWR GND

Fig. 16 PCM connector pin identification (Part 2 of 2). 1996 Escort & Tracer w/1.9L/4-116

Pin	Circuit	Wire Color	Application	Abbreviation
1	876	PK/BK	Shift Solenoid 2	SS2
2	129	Y/BK	Malfunction Indicator Lamp	MIL
6	855	BR/BK	Transmission Range Overdrive	TROD
7	856	BR/DG	Transmission Range Low	TRL
9	857	BR/Y	Transmission Range Drive	TRD
11	93	BL/PK	Purge Flow Sensor	PF
13	130	PK/DG	Flash EPROM Power Supply	FEPS
15	132	BK/BL	BUS 1 (-)	BUS 1 -
16	131	W/BL	BUS 2 (+)	BUS 2 +
17	866	R/BK	High Fan Control	HFC
21	138	BL/DG	Crankshaft Position Sensor (+)	CKP +
22	141	O	Crankshaft Position Sensor (-)	CKP-
23	859	Y/BL	Transmission Shaft Speed Sensor 1 (-)	TSS1 -
24	999H	BK/Y	Power Ground	PWR GND
25	135B	R/BL	Case Ground	CSE GND
26	147	GY/Y	Coil Driver 1	CD 1
27	853	LG/BL	Shift Solenoid 1	SS1
30	171	DG/W	Octane Adjust	OCT ADJ
32	365	R/G	Transmission Range Reverse	TRR
33	57	BL	Vehicle Speed Sensor	VSS-
35	98	GY	Heated Oxygen Sensor - 12 (Rear)	HO2S-12
36	87	O/BL	Mass Air Flow Sensor Return	MAF RTN
37	878	W	Transmission Fluid Temperature	TFT
38	62	BL/W	Engine Coolant Temperature Sensor	ECT
39	109	W/G	Intake Air Temperature Sensor	IAT
40	102C	BK/PK	Fuel Pump Monitor	FPM
41	716A	G/R	A/C Cycling Switch	ACCS
45	719	PK/W	Low Fan Control	LFC
47	108	P/R	EGR Vacuum Regulator Solenoid	EVR
48	73	LG/R	Tachometer	TACH
51	999I	BK/Y	Power Ground	PWR GND
52	146	BR/R	Coil Driver 2	CD 2
53	852	O/G	Shift Solenoid 3	SS3
54	851	GY/W	Torque Converter Clutch Solenoid	TCC
55	330E	BL/R	Keep Alive Power	KAPWR
58	159	W/BK	Vehicle Speed Sensor (+)	VSS +
60	96	GY/DG	Heated Oxygen Sensor - 11 (Front)	HO2S - 11
64	82A	BR/Y	Park/Neutral Position Manual Transmission	PNP

Fig. 16 PCM connector pin identification (Part 1 of 2). 1996 Escort & Tracer w/1.9L/4-116

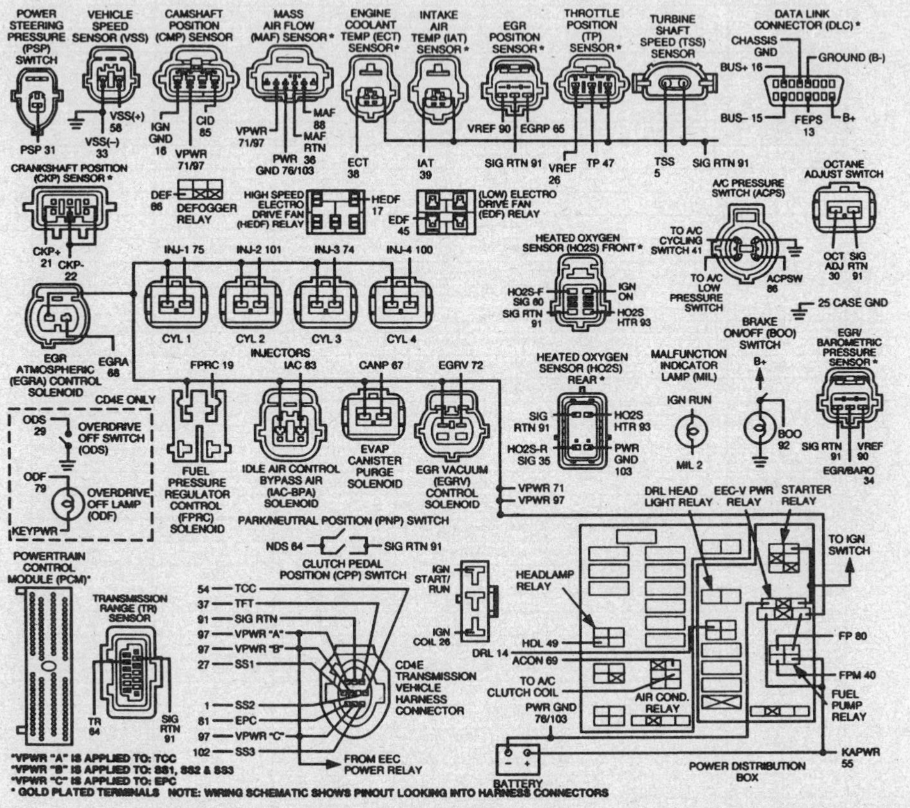

Pin	Circuit	Wire Color	Application	Abbreviation
1	802	BL/BK	Shift Solenoid 2	SS2
2	746	BL	Malfunction Indicator Light	MIL
10	196	Y/BK	Blower Switch	BLR
13	39	GR/Y	Flash EPROM Power Supply	FEPS
14	272	GR	Daytime Running Lights	DRL
15	38	W/R	BUS (-)	BUS -
16	37	O/GR	BUS (+)	BUS +
17	173	BL/GR	High Speed Electro - Drive Fan	HEDF
19	755	GR/W	Fuel Pressure Regulator Control Solenoid	FPRC
21	727	GR	Crankshaft Position Sensor (+)	CAS +
22	728	BL	Crankshaft Position Sensor (-)	CAS -
23	999	BK/Y	Power Ground	PWR GND
24	999	BK/Y	Power Ground	PWR GND
26	731	GR	Ignition Coil	IGN COIL
27	801	BL	Shift Solenoid 1	SS1
29	823	BR/BK	Transmission Control Switch	TCS
30	880	O/BL	Octane Adjust Switch	OCT ADJ
31	718	BR/Y	Power Steering Pressure Switch	PSP
33	687	O/BK	Vehicle Speed Sensor (-)	VSS -
34	775	LG	EGR / Barometric Pressure Sensor	EGR / BARO
35	720	BK/Y	Heated Oxygen Sensor - Rear	HO2S-R
36	721	BR	Mass Air Flow Sensor Signal Return	MAF RTN
37	806	V/W	Transmission Fluid Temperature Sensor	TFT
38	724	O/GR	Engine Coolant Temperature Sensor	ECT
39	723	W/GR	Intake Air Temperature Sensor	IAT
40	703	W/Y	Fuel Pump Monitor	FPM
41	185	P/BK	A/C Cyclic Switch	ACCS
45	174	BL/O	Electro - Drive Fan (Low Speed)	EDF
49	261	W	Head Lamp Switch	HDL
51	999	BK/GR	Power Ground	PWR GND
54	804	BL/LG	Modulated Converter Clutch Solenoid	MCC
55	84	BL/W	Keep Alive Power	KAPWR
58	684	BL/W	Vehicle Speed Sensor (+)	VSS +
60	726	BL/W	Heated Oxygen Sensor - Front	HO2S-F
64	817	R/BK	Transmission Range Sensor (CD4E only)	TR
64	817	R/BK	Neutral Drive Switch (5MT only)	NDS
65	725	R/GR	EGR Position Sensor	EGRP
66	663	V	Defroster Switch	DEF

(Continued)

Fig. 18 PCM connector pin identification (Part 1 of 2). 1996 Probe w/2.0L/4-122

Fig. 17 PCM wiring circuit. 1996 Probe w/2.0L/4-122

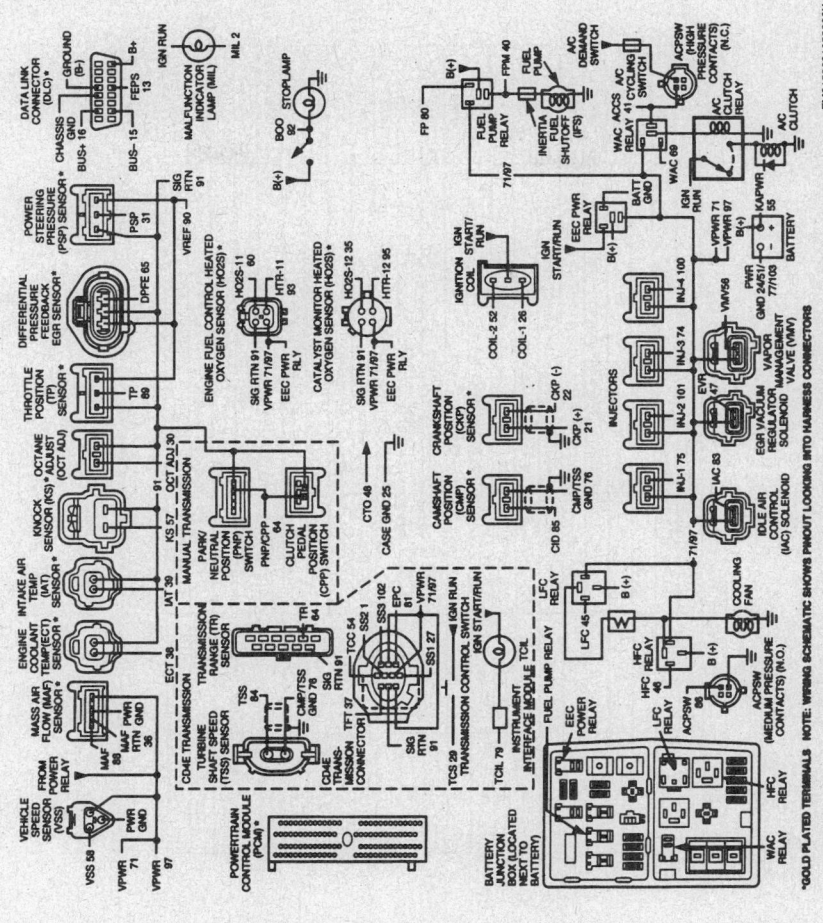

Fig. 19 PCM Wiring circuit. 1996 Contour & Mystique w/2.0L/4-122

*GOLD PLATED TERMINALS   NOTE: WIRING SCHEMATIC SHOWS PINOUT LOOKING INTO HARNESS CONNECTORS

Pin	Circuit	Wire Color	Application	Abbreviation
67	717	W/BK	EVAP Canister Purge Solenoid	EVAP CANP
68	756	W/BL	EGR Atmospheric Solenoid	EGRA
69	187	GR/BK	A/C Relay	ACON
71	701	W/R	Vehicle Power	VPWR
72	767	GR/BL	EGR Vacuum Solenoid	EGRV
74	707	Y/R	Injector 3	INJ-3
75	705	Y/BK	Injector 1	INJ-1
76	999	BK/GR	Power Ground	PWR GND
77	999	BK/GR	Power Ground	PWR GND
79	824	BR/Y	Transmission Control Indicator Lamp	TCIL
80	704	LG	Fuel Pump Control	FP
81	809	BL/BR	Electronic Pressure Control	EPC
83	719	LG/BK	Idle Speed Control Bypass Air Solenoid	ISC-BPA
84	805	BL/GR	Turbine Shaft Speed Sensor (+)	TSS +
85	737	GR/W	Cylinder Identification	CID
86	195	P/Y	A/C Pressure Switch	ACPSW
88	722	R	Mass Air Flow Sensor	MAF
89	815	LG/W	Throttle Position Sensor	TP
90	813	LG/V	Reference Voltage	VREF
91	66	BK/BL	Signal Return	SIG RTN
92	321	W/BK	Brake On/Off Switch	BOO
93	762	Y	Heated Oxygen Sensor Heater - Front	HTR-F
97	701	W/R	Vehicle Power	VPWR
98	772	O/W	EGR Check Solenoid	EGRCS
100	708	Y/G	Injector 4	INJ-4
101	706	Y/W	Injector 2	INJ-2
102	803	BL/V	Shift Solenoid 3	SS3
103	999	BK/GR	Power Ground	PWR GND

Fig. 18 PCM connector pin identification (Part 2 of 2). 1996 Probe w/2.0L/4-122

Pin	Circuit	Wire Color	Application	Abbreviation
74	91S	BK/BL	Injector 3	INJ-3
75	91S	BK/W	Injector 1	INJ-1
76	91	BK/Y	CMP/TSS Ground	CMP/TSS GND
77	91	BK/Y	Power Ground	PWR GND
79	8	W/BL	Transmission Control Indicator Lamp (CD4E)	TCIL
80	91S	BK/BL	Fuel Pump	FP
81	91S	BK/R	Electronic Pressure Control (CD4E)	EPC
83	91S	BK/Y	Idle Air Control Solenoid	IAC
84	8	W/P	Turbine Shaft Speed Sensor (CD4E)	TSS
85	8	W/P	Cylinder Identification	CID
86	91S	BK/W	A/C Pressure Switch	ACPSW
88	8	W/BL	Mass Air Flow Sensor	MAF
89	8	W	Throttle Position Sensor	TP
90	7	Y	Vehicle Reference Voltage	VREF
91	9	BR	Signal Return	SIG RTN
92	29S	O	Brake On/Off Switch	BOO
93	91S	BK/Y	HO2S Heater - 11	HTR-11
95	91S	BK/O	HO2S Heater - 12	HTR-12
97	95	GR/Y	Vehicle Power	VPWR
100	91S	BK/O	Injector 4	INJ-4
101	91S	BK/Y	Injector 2	INJ-2
102	91S	BK/O	Shift Solenoid 3	SS3
103	91	BK/Y	Power Ground	PWR GND

Fig. 20 PCM connector pin identification (Part 2 of 2). 1996 Contour & Mystique w/2.0L/4-122

Pin	Circuit	Wire Color	Application	Abbreviation
1	91S	BK/BL	Shift Solenoid 2	SS2
2	91S	BK/O	Malfunction Indicator Lamp	MIL
13	8	W/BL	Flash EPROM Power Supply	FEPS
15	9	BR/BL	BUS (-)	BUS-
16	8	W/BL	BUS (+)	BUS+
21	8	W/R	Crankshaft Position Sensor (+)	CKP+
22	9	BR/R	Crankshaft Position Sensor (-)	CKP-
24	91	BK/Y	Power Ground	PWR GND
25	91	BK/R	Case Ground	CASE GND
26	9	BR/BL	Ignition Coil 1	COIL 1
27	91S	BK/Y	Shift Solenoid 1 (CD4E)	SS1
29	14S	P/BK	Transmission Control Switch (CD4E)	TCS
30	8	W/BK	Octane Adjust	OCT ADJ
31	8	W/P	Power Steering Pressure Sensor	PSP
35	8	W/BL	Heated Oxygen Sensor - 12	HO2S-12
36	9	BR/BL	Mass Air Flow Sensor Return	MAF RTN
37	8	W/R	Transmission Fluid Temperature Sensor	TFT
38	8	W/GR	Engine Coolant Temperature Sensor	ECT
39	8	W/P	Intake Air Temperature Sensor	IAT
40	14S	P/BK	Fuel Pump Monitor	FPM
41	14S	P/BL	A/C Cycling Switch	ACCS
45	91S	BK/BL	Low Fan Control	LFC
46	91S	BK/W	High Fan Control	HFC
47	91S	BK/GR	EGR Electronic Vacuum Regulator	EVR
48	8	W/BK	Clean Tach Output	CTO
51	91	BK/Y	Power Ground	PWR GND
52	9	BR/GR	Ignition Coil 2	COIL-2
54	91S	BK/W	Torque Converter Clutch Solenoid	TCC
55	89	O/Y	Keep Alive Power	KAPWR
56	91S	BK/O	Vapor Management Valve	VMV
57	8	W/BK	Knock Sensor	KS
58	8	W/P	Vehicle Speed Sensor	VSS
60	8	W	Heated Oxygen Sensor - 11	HO2S-11
64	8	W/GR	Transmission Range Sensor (CD4E)	TR
64	8	W	Neutral Gear Switch/Clutch Pedal Position Switch (Manual Transmission)	NGS/CPP
65	8	W/BL	Differential Pressure Feedback EGR Sensor	DPFE
69	91S	BK/Y	Wide Open Throttle A/C Cutoff	WAC
71	95	GR/Y	Vehicle Power	VPWR

(Continued)

Fig. 20 PCM connector pin identification (Part 1 of 2). 1996 Contour & Mystique w/2.0L/4-122

Pin	Circuit	Wire Color	Application	Abbreviation
1	91S	BK/BL	Shift Solenoid 2	SS2
2	91S	BK/O	Malfunction Indicator Lamp	MIL
8	91S	BK/BL	Intake Manifold Runner Control Monitor	IMRCM
13	8	W/BL	Flash EPROM Power Supply	FEPS
15	9	BR/BL	BUS (-)	BUS-
16	8	W/BL	BUS (+)	BUS+
21	8	W/R	Crankshaft Position Sensor (+)	CKP+
22	9	BR/R	Crankshaft Position Sensor (-)	CKP-
24	91	BK/Y	Power Ground	PWR GND
25	91	BK/R	Case Ground	CASE GND
26	9	BR/BL	Ignition Coil 1	COIL-1
27	91S	BK/Y	Shift Solenoid 1 (CD4E)	SS1
29	14S	P/BK	Transmission Control Switch (CD4E)	TCS
30	8	W/BL	Octane Adjust	OCT ADJ
31	8	W	Power Steering Pressure Switch	PSP
35	8	W/BL	Heated Oxygen Sensor - 12	HO2S-12
36	9	BR/BL	Mass Air Flow Sensor Return	MAF RTN
37	8	W/R	Transmission Fluid Temperature Sensor	TFT
38	8	W/GR	Engine Coolant Temperature Sensor	ECT
39	8	W/P	Intake Air Temperature Sensor	IAT
40	14S	P/BK	Fuel Pump Monitor	FPM
41	91S	P/BL	A/C Cycling Switch	ACCS
42	91S	BK/R	Intake Manifold Runner Control	IMRC
45	91S	BK/BL	Low Fan Control	LFC
46	91S	BK/W	High Fan Control	HFC
47	91S	BK/GR	EGR Electronic Vacuum Regulator	EVR
48	8	W/BK	Clean Tach Output	CTO
51	91	BK/Y	Power Ground	PWR GND
52	9	BR/GR	Ignition Coil 2	COIL-2
54	91S	BK/W	Torque Converter Clutch Solenoid	TCC
55	89	O/Y	Keep Alive Power	KAPWR
56	91S	BK/O	Vapor Management Valve	VMV
57	8	W/BK	Knock Sensor	KS
58	8	W/P	Vehicle Speed Sensor	VSS
60	8	W/R	Heated Oxygen Sensor - 11	HO2S-11
61	8	W/GR	Heated Oxygen Sensor - 22	HO2S-22
64	8	W/GR	Transmission Range Sensor (CD4E)	TR
64	8	W	Neutral Gear Switch / Clutch Pedal Position Switch (Manual Transmission)	NGS/CPP

(Continued)

Fig. 22 PCM connector pin identification (Part 1 of 2). 1996 Contour & Mystique w/2.5L/V6-153

FM0159601661010X

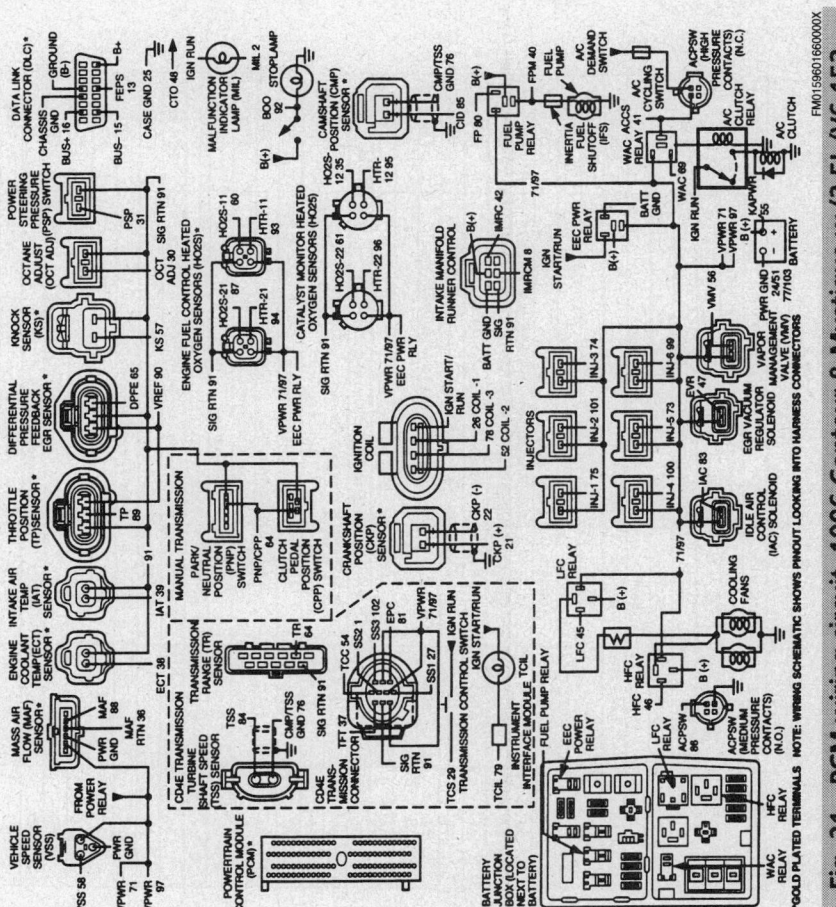

Fig. 21 PCM wiring circuit. 1996 Contour & Mystique w/2.5L/V6-153

FM0159601660000X

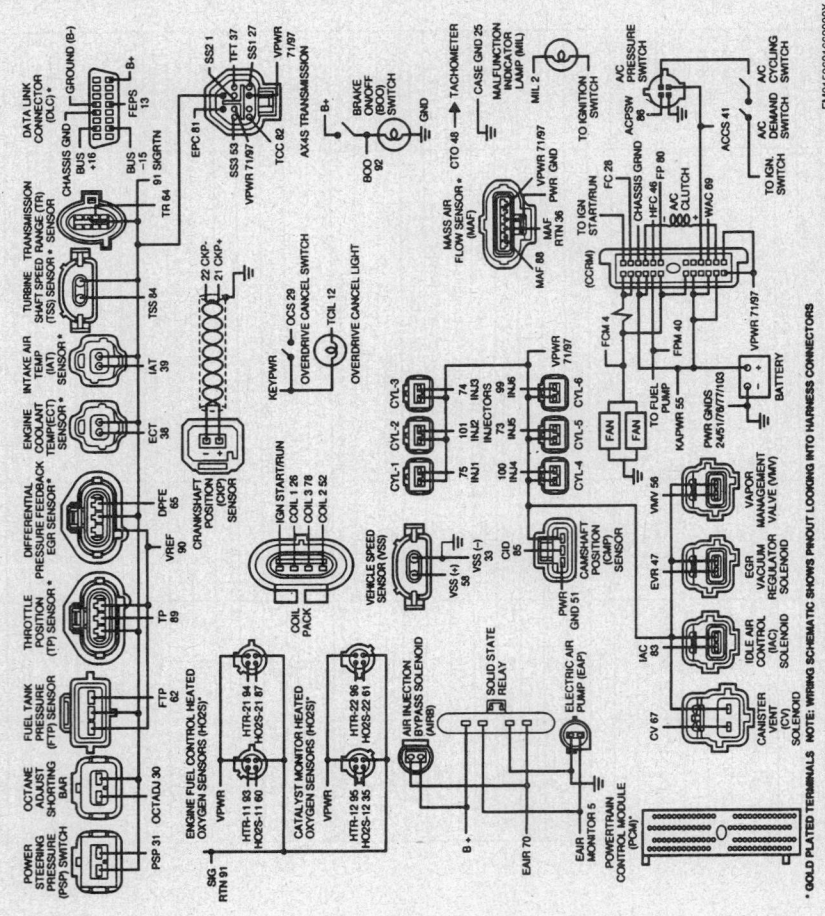

Fig. 23 PCM wiring circuit. 1996 Sable & Taurus w/3.0L/V6-182 (12 Valve)

Pin	Circuit	Wire Color	Application	Abbreviation
65	8	W/BL	Differential Pressure Feedback EGR Sensor	DPFE
69	91S	BK/Y	Wide Open Throttle A/C Cutoff	WAC
71	95	GR/Y	Vehicle Power	VPWR
73	91S	BK/GR	Injector 5	INJ-5
74	91S	BK/BL	Injector 3	INJ-3
75	91S	BK/W	Injector 1	INJ-1
76	91	BK/Y	CMP/TSS Ground	CMP/TSS GND
77	91	BK/Y	Power Ground	PWR GND
78	9	BR/Y	Ignition Coil 3	COIL-3
79	8	W/BL	Transmission Control Indicator Lamp (CD4E)	TCIL
80	91S	BK/BL	Fuel Pump	FP
81	91S	BK/R	Electronic Pressure Control (CD4E)	EPC
83	91S	BK/Y	Idle Air Control Solenoid	IAC
84	8	W/P	Turbine Shaft Speed Sensor (CD4E)	TSS
85	8	W/P	Cylinder Identification	CID
86	91S	BK/W	A/C Pressure Switch	ACPSW
87	8	W/R	Heated Oxygen Sensor - 21	HO2S-21
88	8	W/BL	Mass Air Flow Sensor	MAF
89	8	W	Throttle Position Sensor	TP
90	7	Y	Vehicle Reference Voltage	VREF
91	9	BR	Signal Return	SIG RTN
92	29S	O	Brake On/Off Switch	BOO
93	91S	BK/Y	HO2S Heater - 11	HTR-11
94	91S	BK/BL	HO2S Heater - 21	HTR-21
95	91S	BK/O	HO2S Heater - 12	HTR-12
96	91S	BK/GR	HO2S Heater - 22	HTR-22
97	95	GR/Y	Vehicle Power	VPWR
99	91S	BK/R	Injector 6	INJ-6
100	91S	BK/O	Injector 4	INJ-4
101	91S	BK/Y	Injector 2	INJ-2
102	91S	BK/O	Shift Solenoid 3	SS3
103	91	BK/Y	Power Ground	PWR GND

Fig. 22 PCM connector pin identification (Part 2 of 2). 1996 Contour & Mystique w/2.5L/V6-153

Pin	Circuit	Wire Color	Application	Abbreviation
71	361	R	Vehicle Power	VPWR
73	559	T/BK	Injector 5	INJ-5
74	557	BR/Y	Injector 3	INJ-3
75	555	T	Injector 1	INJ-1
76	570	BK/W	Power Ground	PWR GND
77	570	BK/W	Power Ground	PWR GND
78	852	Y/W	Coil Driver 3	CD3
80	926	LB/O	Fuel Pump Control	FP
81	925	W/Y	Electronic Pressure Control Solenoid	EPC
82	480	P/Y	Transmission Converter Clutch Solenoid	TCC
83	264	W/LB	Intake Air Control Solenoid	IAC
84	970	DG/W	Turbine Shaft Speed Sensor	TSS
85	282	DB/O	Cylinder Identification	CID-1
86	347	BK/Y	A/C Pressure Switch	ACPSW
87	392	R/LG	Heated Oxygen Sensor - 21 (Front)	HO2S-21
88	967	LB/R	Mass Air Flow Sensor	MAF
89	355	GY/W	Throttle Position Sensor	TP
90	351	BR/W	Reference Voltage	VREF
91	359	GY/R	Signal Return	SIG RTN
92	810	R/LG	Brake On / Off Switch	BOO
93	387	R/W	HO2S - 11 Heater (Front)	HTR-11
94	389	W/BK	HO2S - 21 Heater (Front)	HTR-21
95	388	Y/LB	HO2S - 12 Heater (Rear)	HTR-12
96	390	T/Y	HO2S - 22 Heater (Rear)	HTR-22
97	361	R	Vehicle Power	VPWR
99	560	LG/O	Injector 6	INJ-6
100	558	BR/LB	Injector 4	INJ-4
101	556	W	Injector 2	INJ-2
103	507	BK/W	Power Ground	PWR GND

Fig. 24 PCM connector pin identification (Part 2 of 2), 1996 Sable & Taurus w/3.0L/V6-182 (12 Valve)

Pin	Circuit	Wire Color	Application	Abbreviation
1	315	P/O	Shift Solenoid 2	SS2
2	658	PK/LG	Malfunction Indicator Light	MIL
13	107	P	Flash EPROM Power Supply	FEPS
15	915	PK/LB	BUS (-)	BUS -
16	914	T/O	BUS (+)	BUS +
21	350	GY	Crankshaft Position Sensor (+)	CKP+
22	349	DB	Crankshaft Position Sensor (-)	CKP-
24	570	BK/W	Power Ground	PWR GND
25	57	BK	Chassis Ground	CGND
26	850	Y/BK	Coil Driver 1	CD1
27	237	BK	Shift Solenoid1	SS1
28	197	O/Y	Low Speed Fan Control	LFC
30	242	T/O	Octane Adjust	OCT ADJ
31	330	DG	Power Steering Pressure Switch	PSP
33	676	Y/LG	Vehicle Speed Sensor (-)	VSS -
35	94	PK/O	Heated Oxygen Sensor - 12 (Rear)	HO2S-12
36	968	R/BK	Mass Air Flow Sensor Signal Return	MAF RTN
37	923	T/LB	Transmission Fluid Temperature Sensor	TFT
38	354	O/BK	Engine Coolant Temperature Sensor	ECT
39	743	LG/R	Intake Air Temperature Sensor	IAT
40	238	GY	Fuel Pump Monitor	FPM
41	883	DG/Y	A/C Cyclic Switch	ACCS
46	639	PK/LB	High Speed Fan Control	HFC
47	360	LG/P	EGR Vacuum Regulator Solenoid	EVR
48	11	BR/PK	Clean Tachometer Output	CTO
51	570	T/Y	Power Ground	PWR GND
52	851	BK/W	Coil Driver 2	CD2
53	971	Y/R	Shift Solenoid 3	SS3
55	107	PK/BK	Keep Alive Power	KAPWR
56	101	P	Vapor Management Valve Solenoid	VMV - CC
58	679	GY/Y	Vehicle Speed Sensor (+)	VSS +
60	74	GY/BK	Heated Oxygen Sensor - 11 (Front)	HO2S-11
61	393	GY/LB	Heated Oxygen Sensor - 22 (Rear)	HO2S-22
62	791	P/LG	Fuel Tank Pressure Sensor	FTP
64	199	R/PK	Transmission Range Sensor	TR
65	352	LB/Y	Differential Pressure Feedback EGR Sensor	DPFE
67	91	BR/LG	Canister Vent Solenoid	CV
69	331	P/W	Wide Open Throttle A/C Cut-off	WAC

(Continued)

Fig. 24 PCM connector pin identification (Part 1 of 2), 1996 Sable & Taurus w/3.0L/V6-182 (12 Valve)

Pin	Circuit	Wire Color	Application	Abbreviation
1	229	R/O	Power to Low Speed Fan	PTLSF
2	229	R/O	Power to Low Speed Fan	PTLSF
3	228	DB	Battery Positive	B+
4	228	DB	Battery Positive	B+
5	238	DG/Y	Power to Fuel Pump	PTP
6	538	GY/R	Power to High Speed Fan	PTHSF
7	538	GY/R	Power to High Speed Fan	PTHSF
8	1075	DG/O	Battery to EEC Power Relay	B+
10	1075	DG/O	Battery Positive	B+
11	931	O	Battery Positive	B+
12	361	R	Vehicle Power	VPWR
13	20	W/LB	Key Power	KEY PWR
14	386	LB	Low Fan Control	LFC
15	57	BK	Power Ground	PWR GND
16	321	GY/W	A/C Clutch Ground	ACC GND
17	639	LG/P	High Fan Control	HFC
18	926	LB/O	Fuel Pump Control	FP
21	879	DG/W	A/C Cycling Switch	ACCS
22	331	PK/Y	Wide Open Throttle A/C Cutoff	WAC
23	347	BK/Y	Power to A/C Clutch	PTAC
24	361	R	Vehicle Power	VPWR

Fig. 26 CCRM connector pin identification. 1996 Sable & Taurus w/3.0L/V6-182 (12 Valve)

FM015960166S0000X

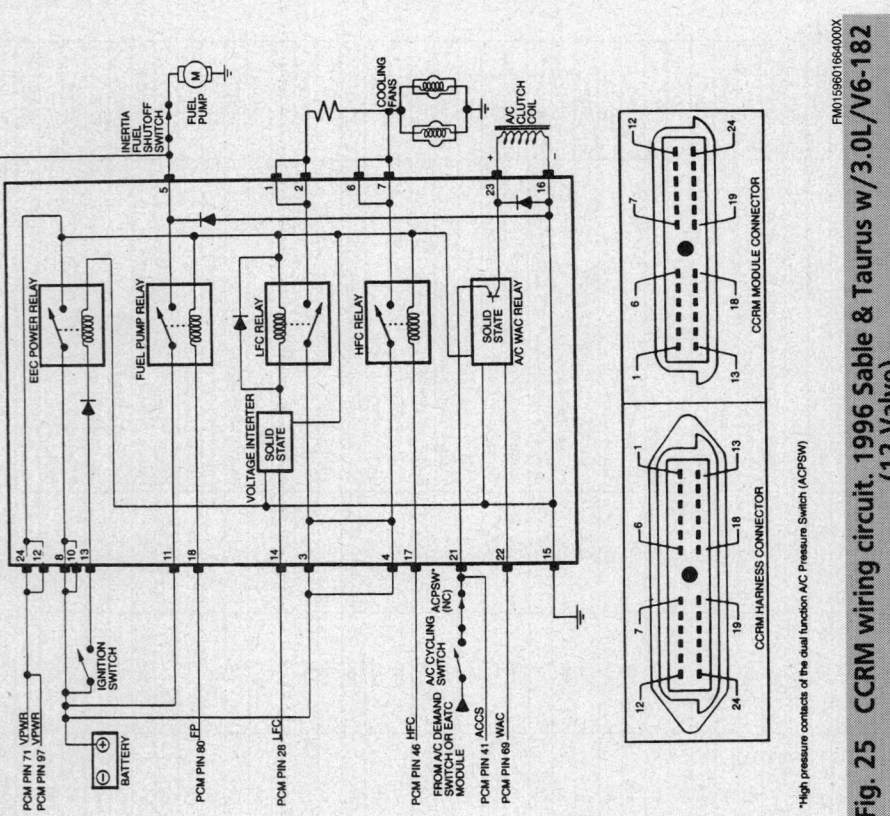

Fig. 25 CCRM wiring circuit. 1996 Sable & Taurus w/3.0L/V6-182 (12 Valve)

*High pressure contacts of the dual function A/C Pressure Switch (ACPSW)

FM015960164000X

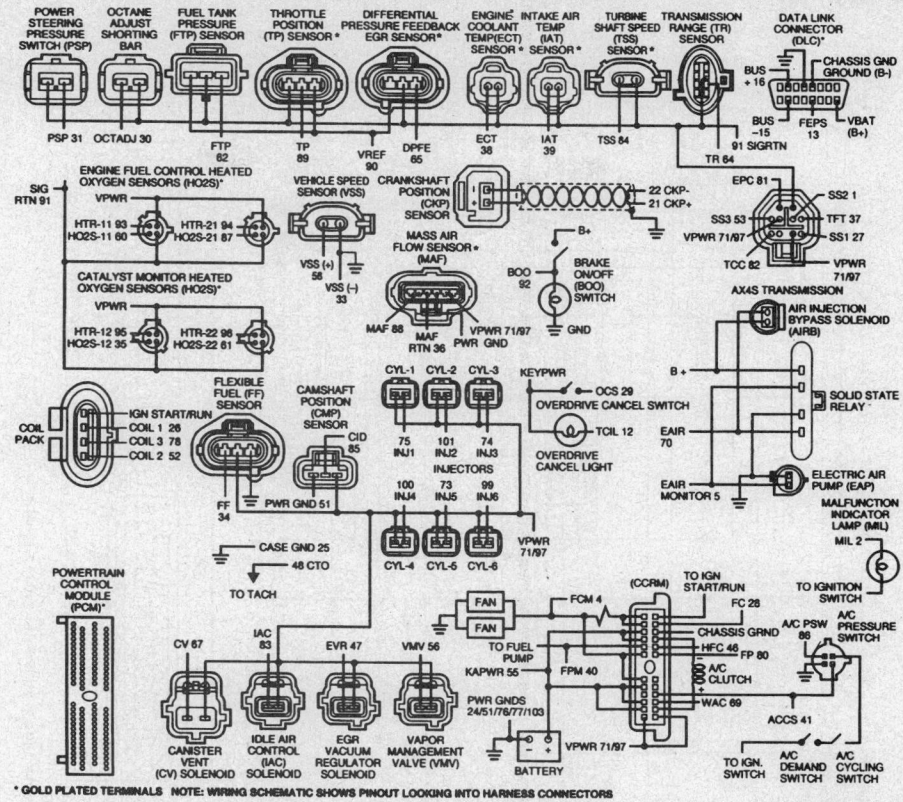

Fig. 27   PCM wiring circuit. 1996 Taurus w/3.0L/V6-182 engine & flexible fuel

Pin	Circuit	Wire Color	Application	Abbreviation
1	315	P/O	Shift Solenoid 2	SS2
2	658	PK/LG	Malfunction Indicator Light	MIL
13	190	W/O	Flash EPROM Power Supply	FEPS
15	107	P	BUS (-)	BUS -
16	915	PK/LB	BUS (+)	BUS +
21	914	T/O	Crankshaft Position Sensor (+)	CKP+
22	350	GY	Crankshaft Position Sensor (-)	CKP-
24	349	DB	Power Ground	PWR GND
25	570	BK/W	Chassis Ground	CGND
26	57	BK	Coil Driver 1	CD1
27	850	Y/BK	Shift Solenoid 1	SS1
28	237	O/Y	Low Speed Fan Control	LFC
30	197	T/O	Octane Adjust	OCT ADJ
31	242	DG	Power Steering Pressure Switch	PSP
33	330	Y/LG	Vehicle Speed Sensor (-)	VSS -
34	676	PK/O	Flexible Fuel Sensor	FFS
35	21	DG/LG	Heated Oxygen Sensor - 12 (Rear)	HO2S-12
36	94	R/BK	Mass Air Flow Sensor Signal Return	MAF RTN
37	968	T/LB	Transmission Fluid Temperature Sensor	TFT
38	923	O/BK	Engine Coolant Temperature Sensor	ECT
39	354	LG/R	Intake Air Temperature Sensor	IAT
40	743	GY	Fuel Pump Monitor	FPM
41	238	DG/Y	A/C Cyclic Switch	ACCS
43	71	O/LG	Data Output Link	DOL
46	639	LG/P	High Speed Fan Control	HFC
47	360	BR/PK	EGR Vacuum Regulator Solenoid	EVR
48	11	T/Y	Clean Tachometer Output	CTO
51	570	BK/W	Power Ground	PWR GND
52	851	Y/R	Coil Driver 2	CD2
53	971	PK/BK	Shift Solenoid 3	SS3
55	107	P	Keep Alive Power	KAPWR
56	101	GY/Y	Vapor Management Valve Solenoid	VMV - CC
58	679	GY/BK	Vehicle Speed Sensor (+)	VSS +
60	74	GY/LB	Heated Oxygen Sensor - 11 (Front)	HO2S-11
61	393	P/LG	Heated Oxygen Sensor - 22 (Rear)	HO2S-22
62	791	R/PK	Fuel Tank Pressure Sensor	FTP
64	199	LB/Y	Transmission Range Sensor	TR
65	352	BR/LG	Differential Pressure Feedback EGR Sensor	DPFE

Fig. 28   PCM connector pin identification (Part 1 of 2). 1996 Taurus w/3.0L/V6-182 engine & flexible fuel

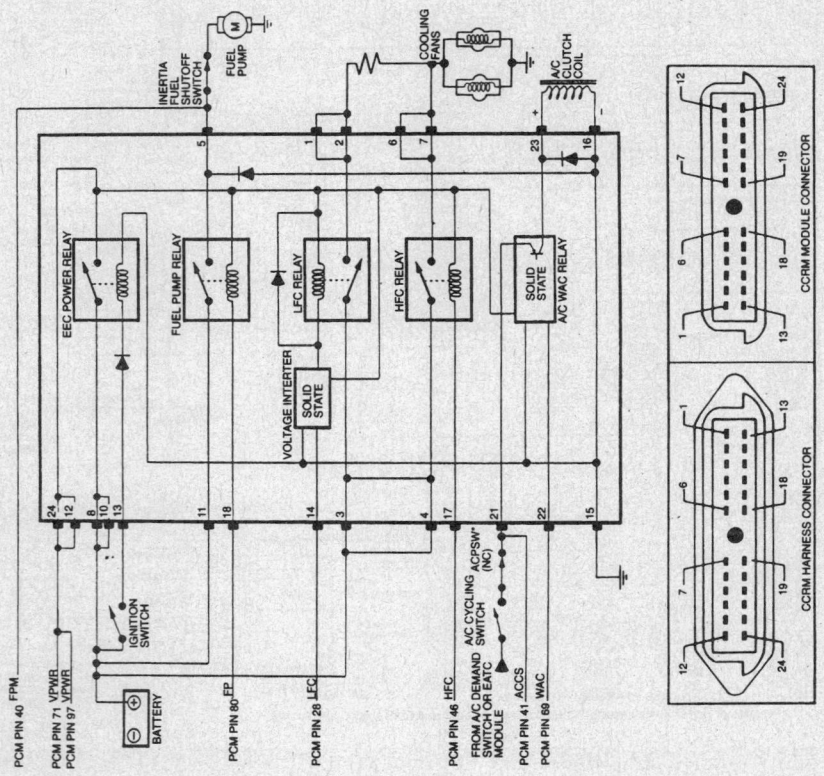

Fig. 29 CCRM wiring circuit. 1996 Taurus w/3.0L/V6-182 engine & flexible fuel

*High pressure contacts of the dual function A/C Pressure Switch (ACPSW)

Pin	Circuit	Wire Color	Application	Abbreviation
67	91	P/W	Canister Vent Solenoid	CV
69	331	PK/Y	Wide Open Throttle A/C Cut-off	WAC
70	200	BR	Electronic Secondary Air Injection	EAIR
71	361	R	Vehicle Power	VPWR
73	559	T/BK	Injector 5	INJ-5
74	557	BR/Y	Injector 3	INJ-3
75	555	T	Injector 1	INJ-1
76	570	BK/W	Power Ground	PWR GND
77	570	BK/W	Power Ground	PWR GND
78	852	Y/W	Coil Driver 3	CD3
80	926	LB/O	Fuel Pump Control	FP
81	925	W/Y	Electronic Pressure Control Solenoid	EPC
82	480	P/Y	Transmission Converter Clutch Solenoid	TCC
83	264	W/LB	Intake Air Control Solenoid	IAC
84	970	DG/W	Turbine Shaft Speed Sensor	TSS
85	282	DB/O	Cylinder Identification	CID 1
86	347	BK/Y	A/C Pressure Switch	ACPSW
87	392	R/LG	Heated Oxygen Sensor - 21 (Front)	HO2S-21
88	967	LB/R	Mass Air Flow Sensor	MAF
89	355	GY/W	Throttle Position Sensor	TP
90	351	BR/W	Reference Voltage	VREF
91	359	GY/R	Signal Return	SIG RTN
92	810	R/LG	Brake On/Off Switch	BOO
93	387	R/W	HO2S - 11 Heater (Front)	HTR-11
94	389	W/BK	HO2S - 21 Heater (Front)	HTR-21
95	388	Y/LB	HO2S - 12 Heater (Rear)	HTR-12
96	390	T/Y	HO2S - 22 Heater (Rear)	HTR-22
97	361	R	Vehicle Power	VPWR
99	560	LG/O	Injector 6	INJ-6
100	558	BR/LB	Injector 4	INJ-4
101	556	W	Injector 2	INJ-2
103	570	BK/W	Power Ground	PWR GND

Fig. 28 PCM connector pin identification (Part 2 of 2). 1996 Taurus w/3.0L/V6-182 engine & flexible fuel

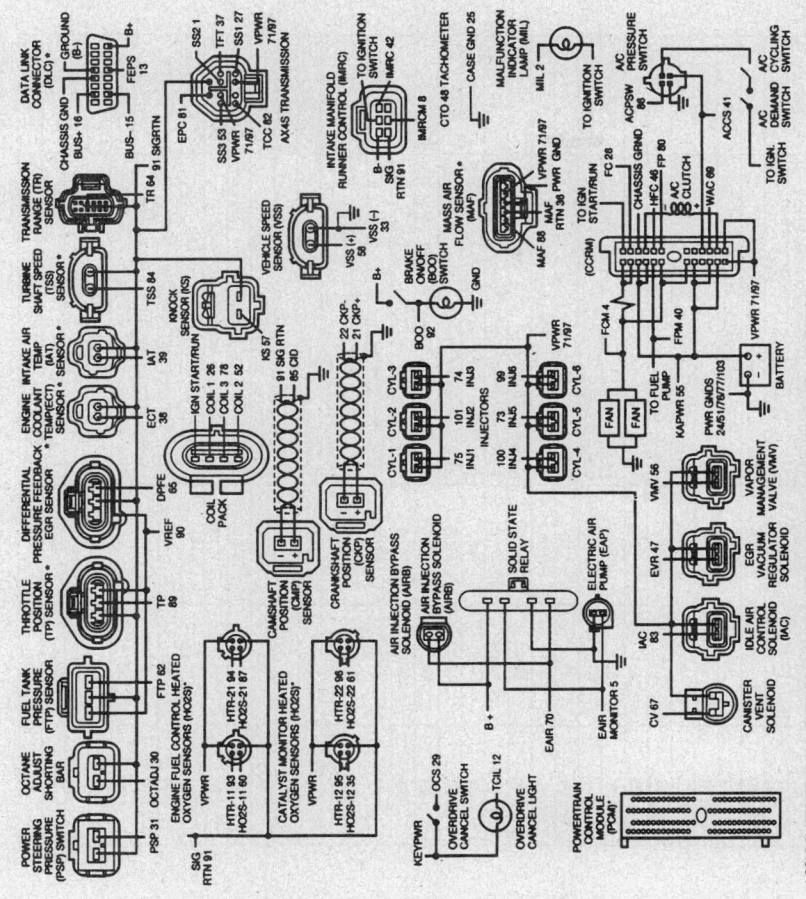

Fig. 31 PCM wiring circuit. 1996 Sable & Taurus w/3.0L/V6-182 (24 Valve)

Pin	Circuit	Wire Color	Application	Abbreviation
1	229	R/O	Power to Low Speed Fan	PTLSF
2	229	R/O	Power to Low Speed Fan	PTLSF
3	228	DB	Battery Positive	B+
4	228	DB	Battery Positive	B+
5	238	DG/Y	Power to Fuel Pump	PTP
6	538	GY/R	Power to High Speed Fan	PTHSF
7	538	GY/R	Power to High Speed Fan	PTHSF
8	1075	DG/O	Battery to EEC Power Relay	B+
10	1075	DG/O	Battery Positive	B+
11	931	O	Battery Positive	B+
12	361	R	Vehicle Power	VPWR
13	20	W/LB	Key Power	KEY PWR
14	386	LB	Low Fan Control	LFC
15	57	BK	Power Ground	PWR GND
16	321	GY/W	A/C Clutch Ground	ACC GND
17	639	LG/P	High Fan Control	HFC
18	926	LB/O	Fuel Pump Control	FP
21	879	DG/W	A/C Cycling Switch	ACCS
22	331	PK/Y	Wide Open Throttle A/C Cutoff	WAC
23	347	BK/Y	Power to A/C Clutch	PTAC
24	361	R	Vehicle Power	VPWR

Fig. 30 CCRM connector pin identification. 1996 Taurus w/3.0L/V6-182 engine & flexible fuel

Pin	Circuit	Wire Color	Application	Abbreviation
62	791	R/PK	Fuel Tank Pressure Sensor	FTP
64	199	LB/Y	Transmission Range Sensor	TR
65	352	BR/LG	Differential Pressure Feedback EGR Sensor	DPFE
67	91	P/W	Canister Vent Solenoid	CV
69	331	PK/Y	Wide Open Throttle A/C Cut-off	WAC
70	200	BR	Electronic Secondary Air Injection	EAIR
71	361	R	Vehicle Power	VPWR
73	559	T/BK	Injector 5	INJ-5
74	557	BR/Y	Injector 3	INJ-3
75	555	T	Injector 1	INJ-1
76	570	BK/W	Power Ground	PWR GND
77	570	BK/W	Power Ground	PWR GND
78	852	Y/W	Coil Driver 3	CD3
79	911	W/LG	Transmission Control Indicator Lamp	TCIL-B
80	926	LB/O	Fuel Pump Control	FP
81	925	W/Y	Electronic Pressure Control Solenoid	EPC
82	480	P/Y	Transmission Converter Clutch Solenoid	TCC
83	264	W/LB	Intake Air Control Solenoid	IAC
84	970	DG/W	Turbine Shaft Speed Sensor	TSS
85	282	DB/O	Cylinder Identification	CID
86	347	BK/Y	A/C Pressure Switch	ACPSW
87	392	R/LG	Heated Oxygen Sensor - 21 (Front)	HO2S-21
88	967	LB/R	Mass Air Flow Sensor	MAF
89	355	GY/W	Throttle Position Sensor	TP
90	351	BR/W	Reference Voltage	VREF
91	359	GY/R	Signal Return	SIG RTN
92	810	R/LG	Brake On/Off	BOO
93	387	R/W	Heater Oxygen Sensor HTR - 11 (Front)	HTR-11
94	389	W/BK	Heater Oxygen Sensor HTR - 21 (Front)	HTR-21
95	388	Y/LG	Heater Oxygen Sensor HTR - 12 (Rear)	HTR-12
96	390	T/Y	Heater Oxygen Sensor HTR - 22 (Rear)	HTR-22
97	361	R	Vehicle Power	VPWR
99	560	LG/O	Injector 6	INJ-6
100	558	BR/LB	Injector 4	INJ-4
101	556	W	Injector 2	INJ-2
103	507	BK/W	Power Ground	PWR GND

FM01596016710 20X

Fig. 32 PCM connector pin identification (Part 2 of 2). 1996 Sable & Taurus w/3.0L/V6-182 (24 Valve)

Pin	Circuit	Wire Color	Application	Abbreviation
1	315	P/O	Shift Solenoid 2	SS2
2	658	PK/LG	Malfunction Indicator Lamp	MIL
5	190	W/O	Electronic Secondary Air Injection Monitor	EAIRM
8	1022	DB/Y	Intake Manifold Runner Control Monitor	IMRCM
13	107	P	Flash EPROM Power Supply	FEPS
15	915	PK/LB	BUS (-)	BUS -
16	914	T/O	BUS (+)	BUS +
21	350	GY	Crankshaft Position Sensor (+)	CKP +
22	349	DB	Crankshaft Position Sensor (-)	CKP -
24	570	BK/W	Power Ground	PWR GND
25	57	BK	Chassis Ground	CGND
26	850	Y/BK	Coil Driver 1	CD1
27	237	O/Y	Shift Solenoid 1	SS1
28	197	T/O	Low Speed Fan Control	LFC
29	224	T/W	Overdrive Cancel Switch	OCS
30	242	DG	Octane Adjust Switch	OCT ADJ
31	330	Y/LG	Power Steering Pressure Switch	PSP
33	676	PK/O	Vehicle Speed Sensor (-)	VSS -
35	94	R/BK	Heated Oxygen Sensor - 12 (Rear)	HO2S-12
36	968	T/LB	Mass Air Flow Sensor Signal Return	MAF RTN
37	923	O/BK	Transmission Fluid Temperature Sensor	TFT
38	354	LG/R	Engine Coolant Temperature Sensor	ECT
39	743	GY	Intake Air Temperature Sensor	IAT
40	238	DG/Y	Fuel Pump Monitor	FPM
41	883	PK/LB	A/C Cycling Switch	ACCS
42	367	BR	Intake Manifold Runner Control	IMRC
46	639	LG/P	High Speed Fan Control	HFC
47	360	BP/PK	EGR Vacuum Regulator	EVR
48	11	T/Y	Clean Tachometer Out	CTO
51	570	BK/W	Power Ground	PWR GND
52	851	Y/R	Coil Driver 2	CD2
53	971	PK/BK	Shift Solenoid 3	SS3
55	1076	DG/O	Keep Alive Power	KAPWR
56	101	GY/Y	Vapor Management Valve - Solenoid	VMV
57	310	Y/R	Knock Sensor	KS
58	679	GY/BK	Vehicle Speed Sensor (+)	VSS +
60	74	GY/LB	Heated Oxygen Sensor - 11 (Front)	HO2S-11
61	393	P/LG	Heated Oxygen Sensor - 22 (Rear)	HO2S-22

(Continued)

FM01596016710 10X

Fig. 32 PCM connector pin identification (Part 1 of 2). 1996 Sable & Taurus w/3.0L/V6-182 (24 Valve)

Pin	Circuit	Wire Color	Application	Abbreviation
1	229	R/O	Power to Low Speed Fan	PTLSF
2	229	R/O	Power to Low Speed Fan	PTLSF
3	228	DB	Battery Positive	B+
4	228	DB	Battery Positive	B+
5	238	DG/Y	Power to Fuel Pump	PTP
6	538	GY/R	Power to High Speed Fan	PTHSF
7	538	GY/R	Power to High Speed Fan	PTHSF
8	1075	DG/O	Battery to EEC Power Relay	B+
10	1075	DG/O	Battery Positive	B+
11	931	O	Battery Positive	B+
12	361	R	Vehicle Power	VPWR
13	20	W/LB	Key Power	KEY PWR
14	386	LB	Low Fan Control	LFC
15	57	BK	Power Ground	PWR GND
16	321	GY/W	A/C Clutch Ground	ACC GND
17	639	LG/P	High Fan Control	HFC
18	926	LB/O	Fuel Pump Control	FP
21	879	DG/W	A/C Cycling Switch	ACCS
22	331	PK/Y	Wide Open Throttle A/C Cut-off	WAC
23	347	BK/Y	Power to A/C Clutch	PTAC
24	361	R	Vehicle Power	VPWR

FM0159601673000X

Fig. 34   CCRM connector pin identification. 1996 Sable & Taurus w/ 3.0L/V6-182 (24 Valve)

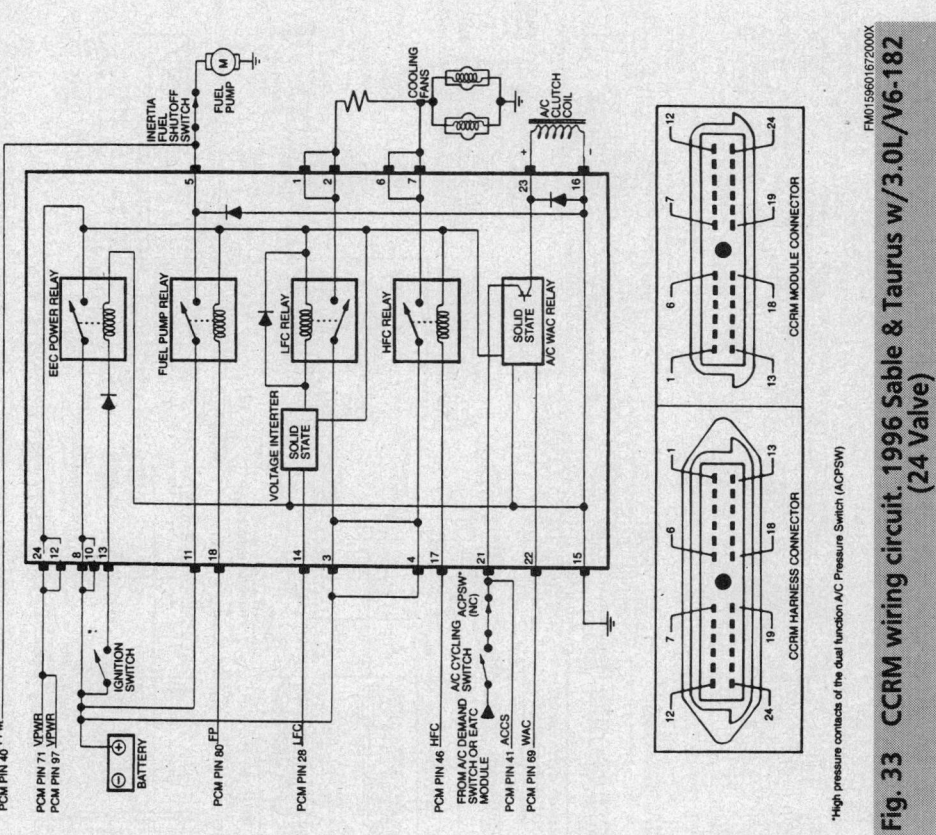

FM0159601672000X

Fig. 33   CCRM wiring circuit. 1996 Sable & Taurus w/3.0L/V6-182 (24 Valve)

*High pressure contacts of the dual function A/C Pressure Switch (ACPSW).

Pin	Circuit	Wire Color	Application	Abbreviation
1	1025	O/Y	Coil Driver 5	CD5
2	658	PK/LG	Malfunction Indicator Lamp	MIL
3	570	BK/W	Power Ground	PWR GND
5	190	W/O	Electronic Secondary Air Injection Monitor	EAIRM
6	237	O/Y	Shift Solenoid 1	SS1
8	1022	DB/Y	Intake Manifold Runner Control Monitor	IMRCM
11	315	P/O	Shift Solenoid 2	SS2
12	911	W/LG	Transmission Control Indicator Lamp	TCIL
13	107	P	Flash EPROM Power Supply	FEPS
15	915	PK/LG	BUS (-)	BUS -
16	914	T/O	BUS (+)	BUS +
20	971	PK/BK	Shift Solenoid 3	SS3
21	350	GY	Crankshaft Position Sensor (+)	CKP +
22	349	DB	Crankshaft Position Sensor (-)	CKP -
23	570	BK/W	Power Ground	PWR GND
24	570	BK/W	Power Ground	PWR GND
25	57	BK	Chassis Ground	CGND
26	1024	LG/W	Coil Driver 1	CD1
27	1028	W/PK	Coil Driver 6	CD6
28	197	T/O	Low Speed Fan Control	LFC
29	224	T/W	Overdrive Cancel Switch	OCS
30	242	DG	Octane Adjust	OCT ADJ
31	330	Y/LG	Power Steering Pressure Switch	PSP
32	311	DG/P	Knock Sensor 2	KS2
33	676	PK/O	Vehicle Speed Circuit Ground	VSC GND
35	94	R/BK	Heated Oxygen Sensor - 12 (Rear)	HO2S-12
36	968	T/LB	Mass Air Flow Sensor Signal Return	MAF RTN
37	923	O/BK	Transmission Fluid Temperature Sensor	TFT
38	354	LG/R	Engine Coolant Temperature Sensor	ECT
39	743	GY	Intake Air Temperature Sensor	IAT
40	238	DG/Y	Fuel Pump Monitor	FPM
41	883	PK/LB	A/C Cycling Switch	ACCS
42	367	BR	Intake Manifold Runner Control	IMRC
46	639	LG/P	High Speed Fan Control	HFC
47	360	BR/PK	EGR Vacuum Regulator Solenoid	EVR
48	11	T/Y	Clean Tachometer Output	CTO
51	570	BK/W	Power Ground	PWR GND
52	1021	LG/Y	Coil Driver 2	CD2

(Continued)

Fig. 36 PCM connector pin identification (Part 1 of 3). 1996 Taurus SHO w/3.4L/V6-204

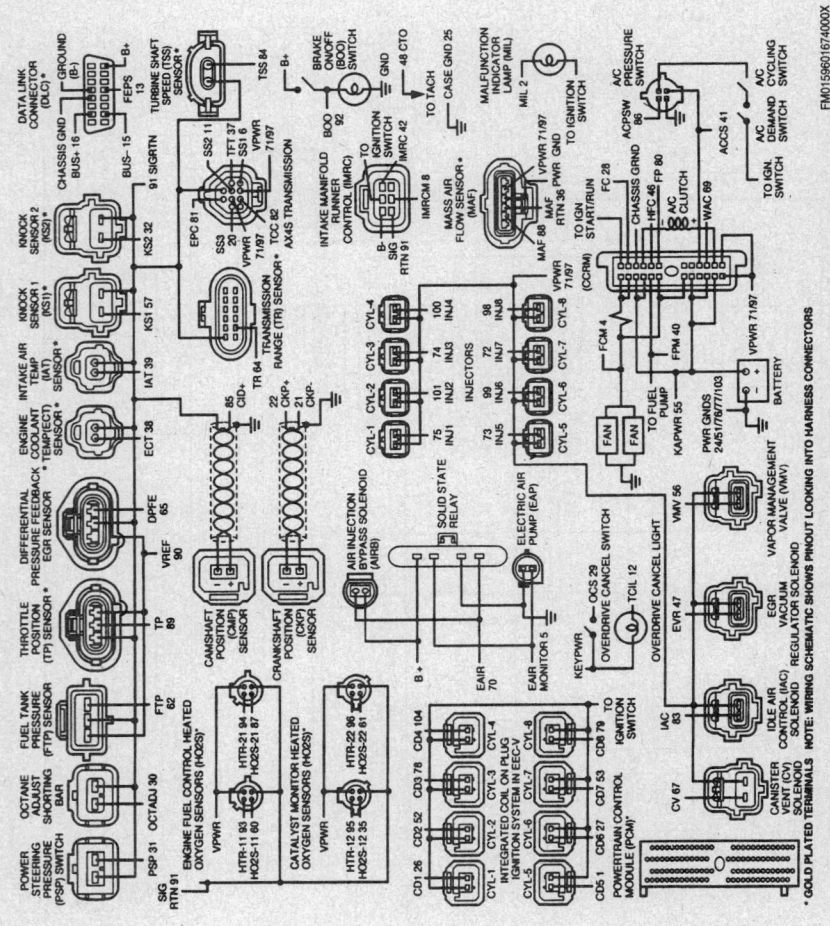

Fig. 35 PCM wiring circuit. 1996 Taurus SHO w/3.4L/V6-204

Pin	Circuit	Wire Color	Application	Abbreviation
98	562	LB	Injector 8	INJ-8
99	560	LG/O	Injector 6	INJ-6
100	558	BR/LB	Injector 4	INJ-4
101	556	W	Injector 2	INJ-2
103	570	BK/W	Power Ground	PWR GND
104	1026	PK/W	Coil Driver 4	CD4

FM01596016750030X

Fig. 36 PCM connector pin identification (Part 3 of 3). 1996 Taurus SHO w/3.4L/V6-204

Fig. 37 CCRM wiring circuit. 1996 Taurus SHO w/3.4L/V6-204

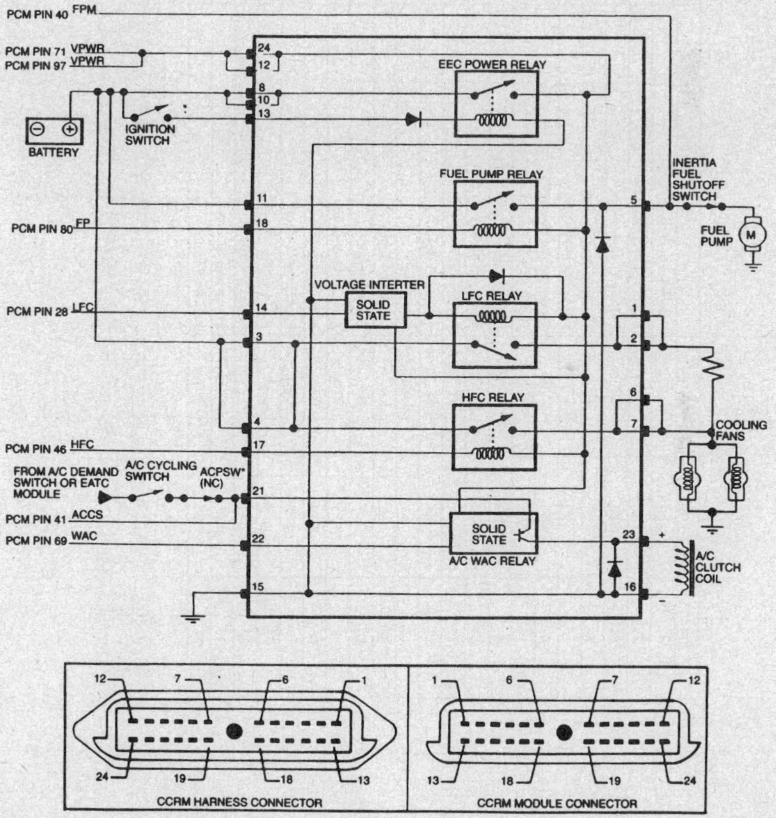

*High pressure contacts of the dual function A/C Pressure Switch (ACPSW).

Pin	Circuit	Wire Color	Application	Abbreviation
53	1027	PK/LB	Coil Driver 7	CD7
55	1076	DG/O	Keep Alive Power	KAPWR
56	101	GY/Y	Vapor Management Valve	VMV
57	310	Y/R	Knock Sensor 1	KS1
58	679	GY/BK	Vehicle Speed Circuit Signal	VSC SIG
60	74	GY/LB	Heated Oxygen Sensor - 11 (Front)	HO2S-11
61	393	P/LG	Heated Oxygen Sensor - 22 (Rear)	HO2S-22
62	791	R/PK	Fuel Tank Pressure Sensor	FTP
64	199	LB/Y	Transmission Range Sensor	TR
65	352	BR/LG	Differential Pressure Feedback EGR Sensor	DPFE
67	91	P/W	Canister Vent Solenoid	CV
69	331	PK/Y	Wide Open Throttle A/C Cut-off	WAC
70	200	BR	Electronic Secondary Air Injection	EAIR
71	361	R	Vehicle Power	VPWR
72	561	T/R	Injector 7	INJ-7
73	559	T/BK	Injector 5	INJ-5
74	557	BR/Y	Injector 3	INJ-3
75	555	T	Injector 1	INJ-1
76	570	BK/W	Power Ground	PWR GND
77	570	BK/W	Power Ground	PWR GND
78	1030	DG/P	Coil Driver 3	CD3
79	1029	W/R	Coil Driver 8	CD8
80	926	LB/O	Fuel Pump	FP
81	925	W/Y	Electronic Pressure Control Solenoid	EPC
82	480	P/Y	Transmission Converter Clutch Solenoid	TCC
83	264	W/LB	Intake Air Control Solenoid	IAC
84	970	DG/W	Turbine Shaft Speed Sensor	TSS
85	282	DB/O	Cylinder Identification	CID
86	347	BK/Y	A/C Pressure Switch	ACPSW
87	392	R/LG	Heated Oxygen Sensor - 21 (Front)	HO2S-21
88	967	LB/R	Mass Air Flow Sensor	MAF
89	355	GY/W	Throttle Position Sensor	TP
90	351	BR/W	Reference voltage	VREF
91	359	GY/R	Signal Return	SIG RTN
92	810	R/LG	Brake On/Off	BOO
93	387	R/W	Heated Oxygen Sensor Heater - 11 (Front)	HTR-11
94	389	W/BK	Heated Oxygen Sensor Heater - 21 (Front)	HTR-21
95	388	Y/LB	Heated Oxygen Sensor Heater - 12 (Rear)	HTR-12
96	390	T/Y	Heated Oxygen Sensor Heater - 22 (Rear)	HTR-22
97	361	R	Vehicle Power	VPWR

(Continued)

FM01596016750020X

Fig. 36 PCM connector pin identification (Part 2 of 3). 1996 Taurus SHO w/3.4L/V6-204

Pin	Circuit	Wire Color	Application	Abbreviation
1	229	R/O	Power to Low Speed Fan	PTLSF
2	229	R/O	Power to Low Speed Fan	PTLSF
3	228	DB	Battery Positive	B+
4	228	DB	Battery Positive	B+
5	238	DG/Y	Power to Fuel Pump	PTP
6	538	GY/R	Power to High Speed Fan	PTHSF
7	538	GY/R	Power to High Speed Fan	PTHSF
8	1075	DG/O	Battery to EEC Power Relay	B+
10	1075	DG/O	Battery Positive	B+
11	931	O	Battery Positive	B+
12	361	R	Vehicle Power	VPWR
13	20	W/LB	Key Power	KEY PWR
14	386	LB	Low Fan Control	LFC
15	57	BK	Power Ground	PWR GND
16	321	GY/W	A/C Clutch Ground	ACC GND
17	639	LG/P	High Fan Control	HFC
18	926	LB/O	Fuel Pump Control	FP
21	879	DG/W	A/C Cycling Switch	ACCS
22	331	PK/Y	Wide Open Throttle A/C Cut-off	WAC
23	347	BK/Y	Power to A/C Clutch	PTAC
24	361	R	Vehicle Power	VPWR

FM0159601677000X.

Fig. 38   CCRM connector pin identification. 1996 Taurus SHO w/ 3.4L/V6-204

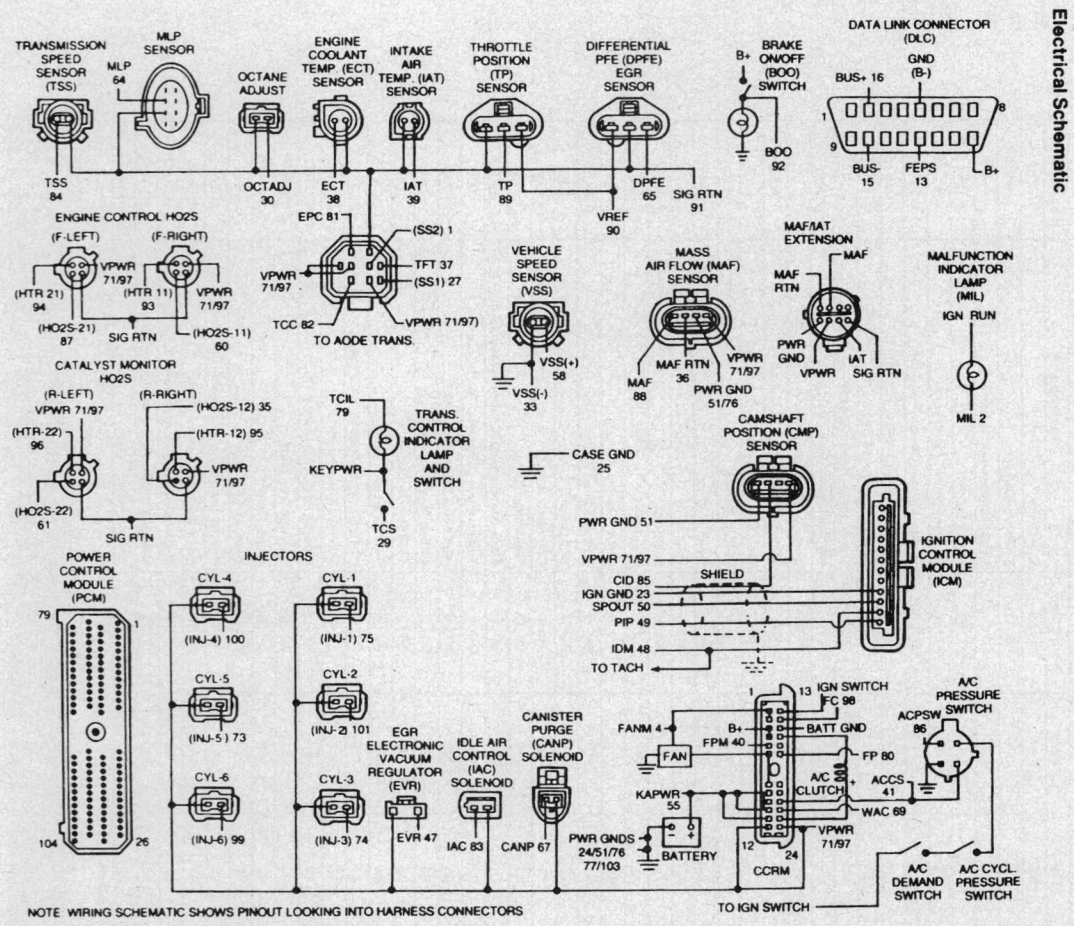

NOTE: WIRING SCHEMATIC SHOWS PINOUT LOOKING INTO HARNESS CONNECTORS

FM0159401132000X

Fig. 39   PCM wiring circuit. 1994–95 Mustang w/3.8L/V6-232

Pin	CKT	Wire Color	Application	Abbreviation
1	315	P/O	Shift Solenoid 2	SS2
2	658	PK/LG	Malfunction Indicator Lamp	MIL
4	229	R/O	Fan Monitor	FANM
13	107	P	Flash EPROM Power Supply	FEPS
15	915	PK/LB	BUS (-)	BUS -
16	914	T/O	BUS (+)	BUS +
23	259	O/R	Ignition Ground	IGN GND
24	570	BK/W	Power Ground	PWR GND
25	57	BK	Case Ground	CASE GND
27	237	O/Y	Shift Solenoid 1	SS1
29	224	T/W	Transmission Control Switch	TCS
30	242	DG	Octane Adjust	OCT ADJ
33	676	PK/O	Vehicle Speed Sensor (-)	VSS-
35	392	R/LG	Heated Oxygen Sensor-12 (R-Right)	HO2S-12
36	968	T/LB	Mass Air Flow Sensor Return	MAF RTN
37	923	O/BK	Transmission Fluid Temperature Sensor	TFT
38	354	LG/R	Engine Coolant Temperature Sensor	ECT
39	743	GY	Intake Air Temperature Sensor	IAT
40	238	DG/Y	Fuel Pump Monitor	FPM
41	198	DG/O	A/C Cyclic Switch	ACCS
47	360	BR/PK	EGR Electronic Vacuum Regulator	EVR
48	659	O/W	Ignition Diagnostic Monitor	IDM
49	395	GY/O	Profile Ignition Pickup	PIP
50	929	PK	Spark Output	SPOUT
51	570	BK/W	Power Ground	PWR GND
55	37	Y	Keep Alive Power	KAPWR
58	679	GY/BK	Vehicle Speed Sensor (+)	VSS+
60	74	GY/LB	Heated Oxygen Sensor-11 (F-Right)	HO2S-11
61	393	P/LG	Heated Oxygen Sensor-22 (R-Left)	HO2S-22
64	199	LB/Y	Manual Lever Position Switch	MLP
65	352	BR/LG	Differential PFE EGR Sensor	DPFE
67	101	GY/Y	Canister Purge Solenoid	CANP
69	331	PK/Y	Wide Open Throttle A/C Cutout	WAC
71	361	R	Vehicle Power	VPWR
73	559	T/BK	Injector 5	INJ-5
74	557	BR/Y	Injector 3	INJ-3
75	555	T	Injector 1	INJ-1
76	570	BK/W	Power Ground	PWR GND

(Continued)

**Fig. 40 PCM connector pin
identification (Part 1 of 2). 1994–95
Mustang w/3.8L/V6-232**

Pin	CKT	Wire Color	Application	Abbreviation
77	570	BK/W	Power Ground	PWR GND
79	911	W/LG	Transmission Control Indicator Lamp	TCIL
80	926	LB/O	Fuel Pump Control	FP
81	925	W/Y	Electronic Pressure Control	EPC
82	125	DB/W	Torque Converter Clutch Solenoid	TCC
83	264	W/LB	Idle Air Control Solenoid	IAC
84	970	DG/W	Transmission Speed Sensor	TSS
85	282	DB/O	Cylinder Identification	CID
86	439	T/LG	A/C Pressure Switch	ACPSW
87	94	R/BK	Heated Oxygen Sensor-21 (F-Left)	HO2S-21
88	967	LB/R	Mass Air Flow Sensor	MAF
89	355	GY/W	Throttle Position Sensor	TP
90	351	BR/W	Vehicle Reference Voltage	VREF
91	359	GY/R	Signal Return	SIG RTN
92	511	LG	Brake On/Off Switch	BOO
93	387	R/W	HO2S Heater-11 (F-Right)	HTR-11
94	388	Y/LB	HO2S Heater-21 (F-Left)	HTR-21
95	389	W/BK	HO2S Heater-12 (R-Right)	HTR-12
96	390	T/Y	HO2S Heater-22 (R-Left)	HTR-22
97	361	R	Vehicle Power	VPWR
98	228	DB	Fan Control	FC
99	560	LG/O	Injector-6	INJ-6
100	558	BR/LB	Injector-4	INJ-4
101	556	W	Injector-2	INJ-2
103	570	BK/W	Power Ground	PWR GND

**Fig. 40 PCM connector pin
identification (Part 2 of 2). 1994–95
Mustang w/3.8L/V6-232**

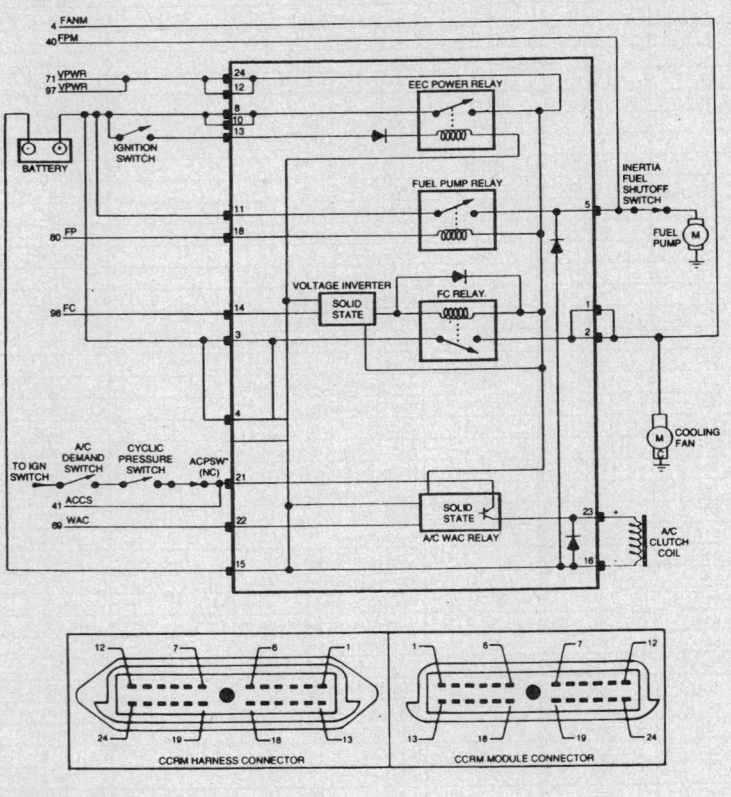

Fig. 41   CCRM wiring circuit. 1994–95 Mustang w/3.8L/V6-232

*High pressure contacts of the dual function A/C Pressure Switch (ACPSW)

FM0159401135000X

Pin	CKT	Wire Color	Application	Abbreviation
1	229	R/O	Power to Fan	PTF
2	229	R/O	Power to Fan	PTF
3	38	BK/O	Battery Positive	B+
4	38	BK/O	Battery Positive	B+
5	238	DG/Y	Power to Fuel Pump	PTP
8	37	Y	Battery Positive	B+
10	37	Y	Battery Positive	B+
11	37	Y	Battery Positive	B+
12	361	R	Vehicle Power	VPWR
13	16	R/LG	Key Power	KEYPWR
14	228	DB	Fan Control	FC
15	570	BK/W	Power Ground	PWR GND
16	570	BK/W	A/C Clutch Ground	ACC GND
18	926	LB/O	Fuel Pump Control	FP
21	198	DG/O	A/C Cyclic Switch	ACCS
22	331	PK/Y	WOT A/C Cutoff	WAC
23	347	BK/Y	Power to A/C Clutch	PTAC
24	361	R	Vehicle Power	VPWR

FM0159401136000X

Fig. 42   CCRM connector pin identification. 1994–95 Mustang w/3.8L/V6-232

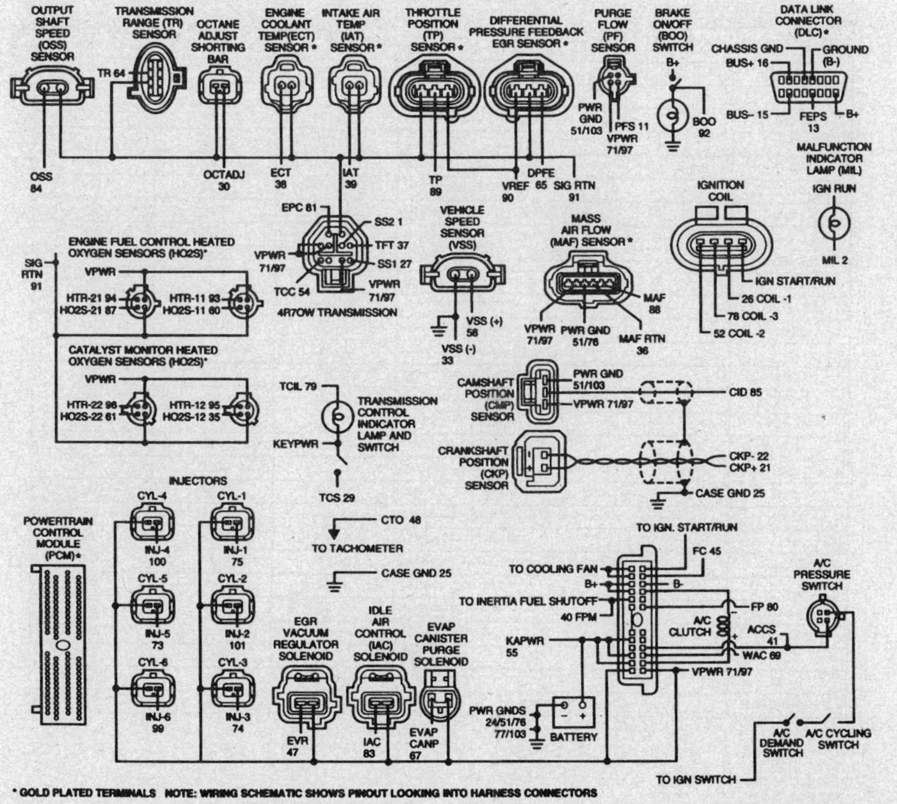

Pin	CKT	Wire Color	Application	Abbreviation
1	315	P/O	Shift Solenoid 2	SS2
2	658	PK/LG	Malfunction Indicator Lamp	MIL
11	91	P/W	Purge Flow Sensor	PFS
13	107	P	Flash EPROM Power Supply	FEPS
15	915	PK/LB	BUS (-)	BUS-
16	914	T/O	BUS (+)	BUS+
21	349	DB	Crankshaft Position Sensor (+)	CKP+
22	350	GY	Crankshaft Position Sensor (-)	CKP-
24	570	BK/W	Power Ground	PWR GND
25	57	BK	Case Ground	CASE GND
26	526	DB/LG	Ignition Coil 1	COIL-1
27	237	O/Y	Shift Solenoid 1	SS1
29	224	T/W	Transmission Control Switch	TCS
30	242	DG	Octane Adjust Shorting Bar	OCT ADJ
33	676	PK/O	Vehicle Speed Sensor (-)	VSS-
35	392	R/LG	Heated Oxygen Sensor-12 (R-Right)	HO2S-12
36	968	T/LB	Mass Air Flow Sensor Return	MAF RTN
37	923	O/BK	Transmission Fluid Temperature Sensor	TFT
38	354	LG/R	Engine Coolant Temperature Sensor	ECT
39	743	GY	Intake Air Temperature Sensor	IAT
40	238	DG/Y	Fuel Pump Monitor	FPM
41	198	DG/O	A/C Cycling Switch	ACCS
45	228	DB	Fan Control	FC
47	360	BR/PK	EGR Vacuum Regulator Solenoid	EVR
48	659	O/W	Ignition Diagnostic Monitor	IDM
51	570	BK/W	Power Ground	PWR GND
52	527	R/LB	Ignition Coil 2	COIL-2
54	924	BR/O	Torque Converter Clutch Solenoid	TCC
55	37	Y	Keep Alive Power	KAPWR
58	679	GY/BK	Vehicle Speed Sensor (+)	VSS+
60	74	GY/LG	Heated Oxygen Sensor-11 (F-Right)	HO2S-11
61	393	P/LG	Heated Oxygen Sensor-22 (R-Left)	HO2S-22
64	199	LB/Y	Transmission Range Sensor	TR
65	352	BR/LG	Differential Pressure Feedback EGR Sensor	DPFE
67	101	GY/Y	Canister Purge Solenoid	EVAP CANP
69	331	PK/Y	Wide Open Throttle A/C Cut-off	WAC
71	361	R	Vehicle Power	VPWR
73	559	T/BK	Injector 5	INJ-5

(Continued)

Fig. 44 PCM connector pin identification (Part 1 of 2). 1996 Mustang w/3.8L/V8-232

Fig. 43 PCM wiring circuit. 1996 Mustang w/3.8L/V8-232

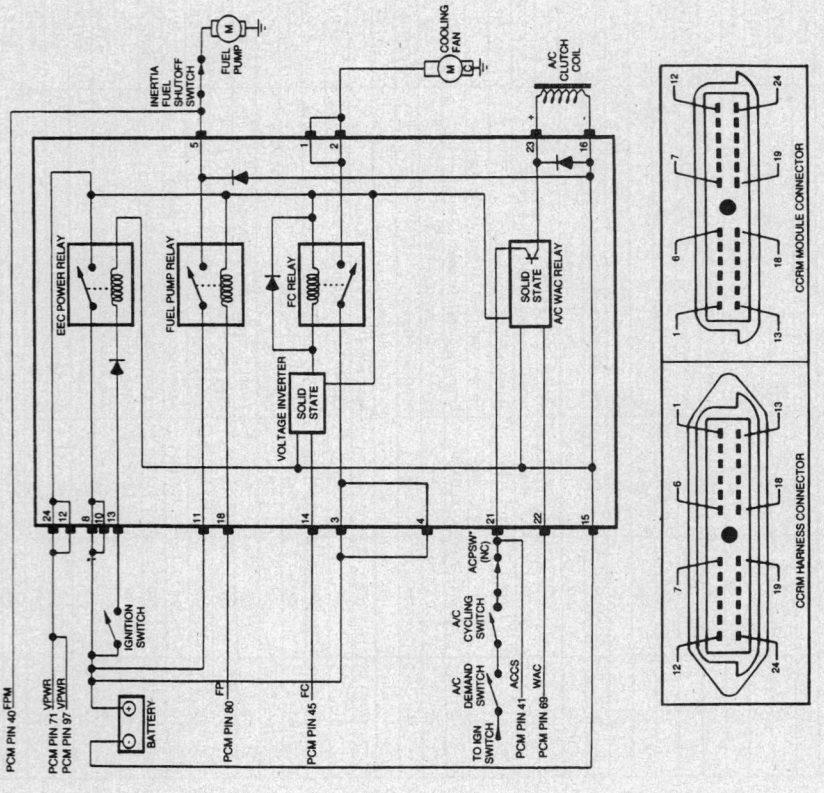

Fig. 45 CCRM wiring circuit. 1996 Mustang w/3.8L/V8-232

*High pressure contacts of the dual function A/C Pressure Switch (ACPSW)

Pin	CKT	Wire Color	Application	Abbreviation
74	557	BR/Y	Injector 3	INJ-3
75	555	T	Injector 1	INJ-1
76	570	BK/W	Power Ground	PWR GND
77	570	BK/W	Power Ground	PWR GND
78	528	PK/W	Ignition Coil 3	COIL-3
79	911	W/LG	Transmission Control Indicator Lamp	TCIL
80	926	LB/O	Fuel Pump Control	FP
81	925	W/Y	Electronic Pressure Control	EPC
83	264	W/LB	Idle Air Control Solenoid	IAC
84	970	DG/W	Turbine Shaft Speed Sensor	TSS
85	282	DB/O	Cylinder Identification	CID
86	439	T/LG	A/C Pressure Switch	ACPSW
87	94	R/BK	Heated Oxygen Sensor-21 (F-Left)	HO2S-21
88	967	LB/R	Mass Air Flow Sensor	MAF
89	355	GY/W	Throttle Position Sensor	TP
90	351	BR/W	Vehicle Reference Voltage	VREF
91	359	GY/R	Signal Return	SIG RTN
92	511	LG	Brake On / Off Switch	BOO
93	387	R/W	HO2S Heater-11 (F-Right)	HTR-11
94	388	Y/LB	HO2S Heater-21 (F-Left)	HTR-21
95	389	W/BK	HO2S Heater-12 (R-Right)	HTR-12
96	390	T/Y	HO2S Heater-22 (R-Left)	HTR-22
97	361	R	Vehicle Power	VPWR
99	560	LG/O	Injector-6	INJ-6
100	558	BR/LB	Injector-4	INJ-4
101	556	W	Injector-2	INJ-2
103	570	BK/W	Power Ground	PWR GND

Fig. 44 PCM connector pin identification (Part 2 of 2). 1996 Mustang w/3.8L/V8-232

Pin	Circuit	Wire Color	Application	Abbreviation
1	229	R/O	Power to Fan	PTF
2	229	R/O	Power to Fan	PTF
3	38	BK/O	Battery Positive	B+
4	38	BK/O	Battery Positive	B+
5	238	DG/Y	Power to Fuel Pump	PTP
8	37	Y	Battery Positive	B+
10	37	Y	Battery Positive	B+
11	37	Y	Battery Positive	B+
12	361	R	Vehicle Power	VPWR
13	16	R/LG	Key Power	KEYPWR
14	228	DB	Fan Control	FC
15	570	BK/W	Power Ground	PWR GND
16	57	BK	A/C Clutch Ground	ACC GND
18	926	LB/O	Fuel Pump Control	FP
21	198	DG/O	A/C Cycling Switch	ACCS
22	331	PK/Y	Wide Open Throttle A/C Cut-off	WAC
23	347	BK/Y	Power to A/C Clutch	PTAC
24	361	R	Vehicle Power	VPWR

FM0159601681000X

Fig. 46 CCRM connector pin identification. 1996 Mustang w/3.8L/V8-232

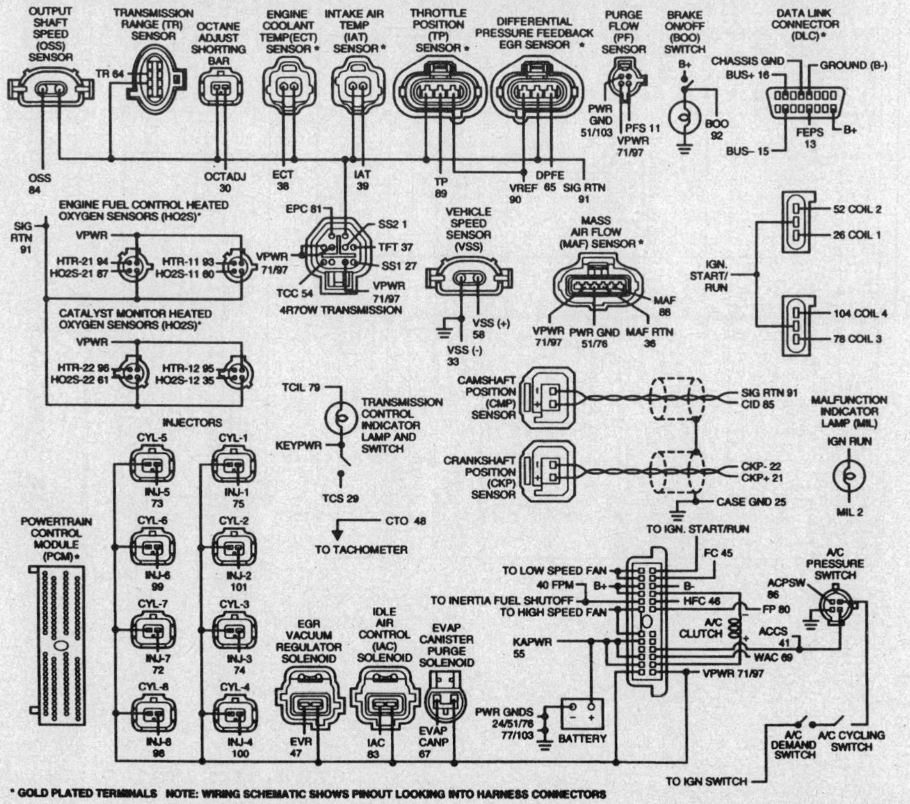

* GOLD PLATED TERMINALS NOTE: WIRING SCHEMATIC SHOWS PINOUT LOOKING INTO HARNESS CONNECTORS

FM0159601682000X

Fig. 47 PCM wiring circuit. 1996 Mustang w/4.6L/V8-281 (16 Valve)

Pin	Circuit	Wire Color	Application	Abbreviation
1	315	P/O	Shift Solenoid 2	SS2
2	658	PK/LG	Malfunction Indicator Lamp	MIL
11	91	P/W	Purge Flow Sensor	PFS
13	107	P	Flash EPROM Power Supply	FEPS
15	915	PK/LB	BUS (-)	BUS -
16	914	T/O	BUS (+)	BUS +
21	349	DB	Crankshaft Position Sensor (+)	CKP +
22	350	GY	Crankshaft Position Sensor (-)	CKP -
24	570	BK/W	Power Ground	PWR GND
25	57	BK	Case Ground	CASE GND
26	526	DG/LG	Ignition Coil 1	COIL-1
27	237	O/Y	Shift Solenoid 1	SS-1
29	224	T/W	Transmission Control Switch	TCS
30	242	DG	Octane Adjust	OCT ADJ
33	676	PK/O	Vehicle Speed Sensor (-)	VSS-
35	392	R/LG	Heated Oxygen Sensor-12 (R-Right)	HO2S-12
36	968	T/LB	Mass Air Flow Sensor Return	MAF RTN
37	923	O/BK	Transmission Fluid Temperature Sensor	TFT
38	354	LG/R	Engine Coolant Temperature Sensor	ECT
39	743	GY	Intake Air Temperature Sensor	IAT
40	238	DG/Y	Fuel Pump Monitor	FPM
41	198	DG/O	A/C Cycling Switch	ACCS
45	228	DB	Low Fan Control	LFC
46	639	LG/P	High Fan Control	HFC
47	360	BR/PK	EGR Vacuum Regulator Solenoid	EVR
48	659	O/W	Clean Tachometer Output	CTO
51	570	BK/W	Power Ground	PWR GND
52	527	R/LB	Ignition Coil 2	COIL 2
54	924	BR/O	Torque Converter Clutch Solenoid	TCC
55	37	Y	Keep Alive Power	KAPWR
58	679	GY/BK	Vehicle Speed Sensor (+)	VSS+
60	74	GY/LB	Heated Oxygen Sensor-11 (F-Right)	HO2S-11
61	393	P/LG	Heated Oxygen Sensor-22 (R-Left)	HO2S-22
64	199	LB/Y	Transmission Range Sensor	TR
65	352	BR/LG	Differential Pressure Feedback EGR Sensor	DPFE
67	101	GY/Y	Canister Purge Solenoid	CANP
69	331	PK/Y	Wide Open Throttle A/C Cut-off	WAC
71	361	R	Vehicle Power	VPWR

(Continued)

FM0159601683010X

Fig. 48 PCM connector pin identification (Part 1 of 2). 1996 Mustang w/4.6L/V8-281 (16 Valve)

Pin	Circuit	Wire Color	Application	Abbreviation
72	561	T/R	Injector 7	INJ-7
73	559	T/BK	Injector 5	INJ-5
74	557	BR/Y	Injector 3	INJ-3
75	555	T	Injector 1	INJ-1
76	570	BK/W	Power Ground	PWR GND
77	570	BK/W	Power Ground	PWR GND
78	528	PK/W	Ignition Coil 3	COIL-3
79	911	W/LG	Transmission Control Indicator Lamp	TCIL
80	926	LB/O	Fuel Pump Control	FP
81	925	W/Y	Electronic Pressure Control	EPC
83	264	W/LB	Idle Air Control Solenoid	IAC
84	970	DG/W	Output Shaft Speed Sensor	OSS
85	282	DB/O	Cylinder Identification	CID
86	439	T/LG	A/C Pressure Switch	ACPSW
87	94	R/BK	Heated Oxygen Sensor-21 (F-Left)	HO2S-21
88	967	LB/R	Mass Air Flow Sensor	MAF
89	355	GY/W	Throttle Position Sensor	TP
90	351	BR/W	Vehicle Reference Voltage	VREF
91	359	GY/R	Signal Return	SIG RTN
92	511	LG	Brake On/Off Switch	BOO
93	387	R/W	HO2S Heater-11 (F-Right)	HTR-11
94	388	Y/LB	HO2S Heater-21 (F-Left)	HTR-21
95	389	W/BK	HO2S Heater-12 (R-Right)	HTR-12
96	390	T/Y	HO2S Heater-22 (R-Left)	HTR-22
97	361	R	Vehicle Power	VPWR
98	562	LB	Injector 8	INJ-8
99	560	LG/O	Injector-6	INJ-6
100	558	BR/LB	Injector-4	INJ-4
101	556	W	Injector-2	INJ-2
103	570	BK/W	Power Ground	PWR GND
104	529	R/Y	Ignition Coil 4	COIL-4

FM0159601683020X

Fig. 48   PCM connector pin identification (Part 2 of 2). 1996 Mustang w/4.6L/V8-281 (16 Valve)

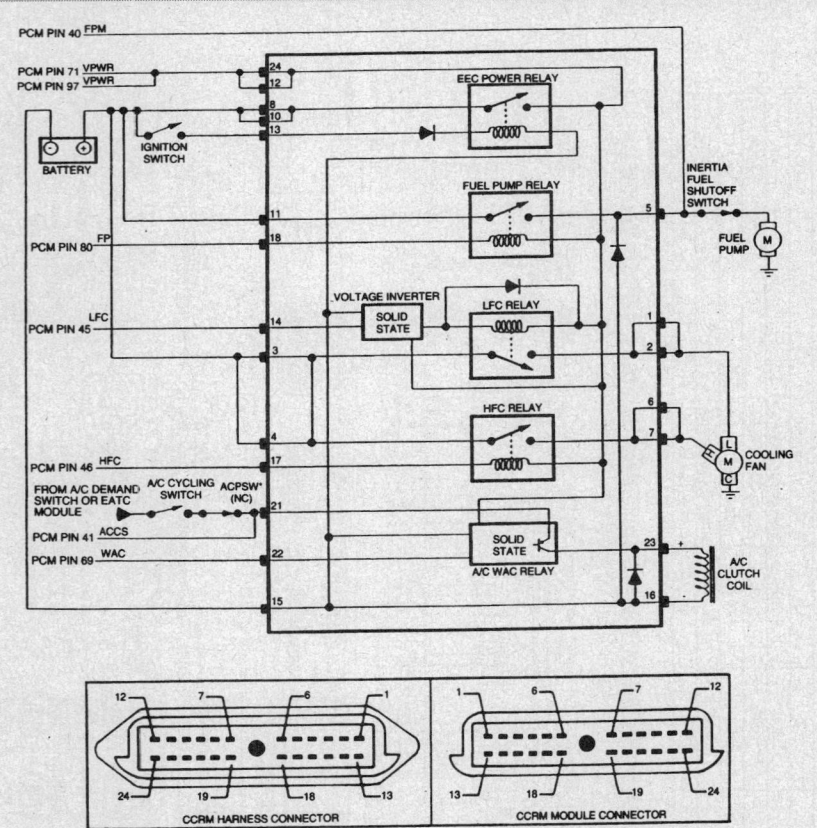

FM0159601684000X

Fig. 49   CCRM wiring circuit. 1996 Mustang w/4.6L/V8-281 (16 Valve)

ELECTRONIC ENGINE CONTROL SYSTEM (EEC-V)

Pin	Circuit	Wire Color	Application	Abbreviation
1	229	R/O	Power to Fan	PTF
2	229	R/O	Power to Fan	PTF
3	38	BK/O	Battery Positive	B+
4	38	BK/O	Battery Positive	B+
5	238	DG/Y	Power to Fuel Pump	PTP
6	638	O/LB	Power to High Speed Fan	PTHSF
7	638	O/LB	Power to High Speed Fan	PTHSF
8	37	Y	Battery Positive	B+
10	37	Y	Battery Positive	B+
11	37	Y	Battery Positive	B+
12	361	R	Vehicle Power	VPWR
13	16	R/LG	Key Power	KEYPWR
14	228	DB	Low Fan Control	LFC
15	570	BK/W	Power Ground	B-
16	57	BK	A/C Clutch Ground	ACC GND
17	639	LG/P	High Fan Control	HFC
18	926	LB/O	Fuel Pump Control	FP
21	198	DG/O	A/C Cycling Switch	ACCS
22	331	PK/Y	Wide Open Throttle A/C Cut-off	WAC
23	347	BK/Y	Power to A/C Clutch	PTAC
24	361	R	Vehicle Power	VPWR

FM0159601685000X

Fig. 50 CCRM connector pin identification. 1996 Mustang w/4.6L/V8-281 (16 Valve)

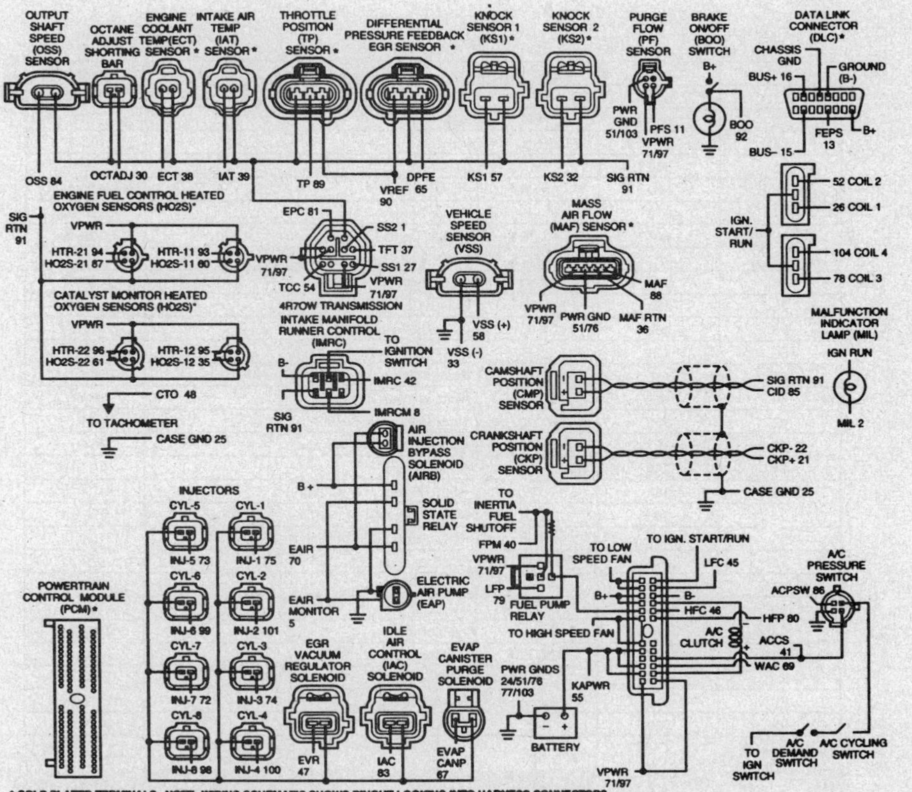

* GOLD PLATED TERMINALS NOTE: WIRING SCHEMATIC SHOWS PINOUT LOOKING INTO HARNESS CONNECTORS

FM0159601686000X

Fig. 51 PCM wiring circuit. 1996 Mustang w/4.6L/V8-281 (32 Valve)

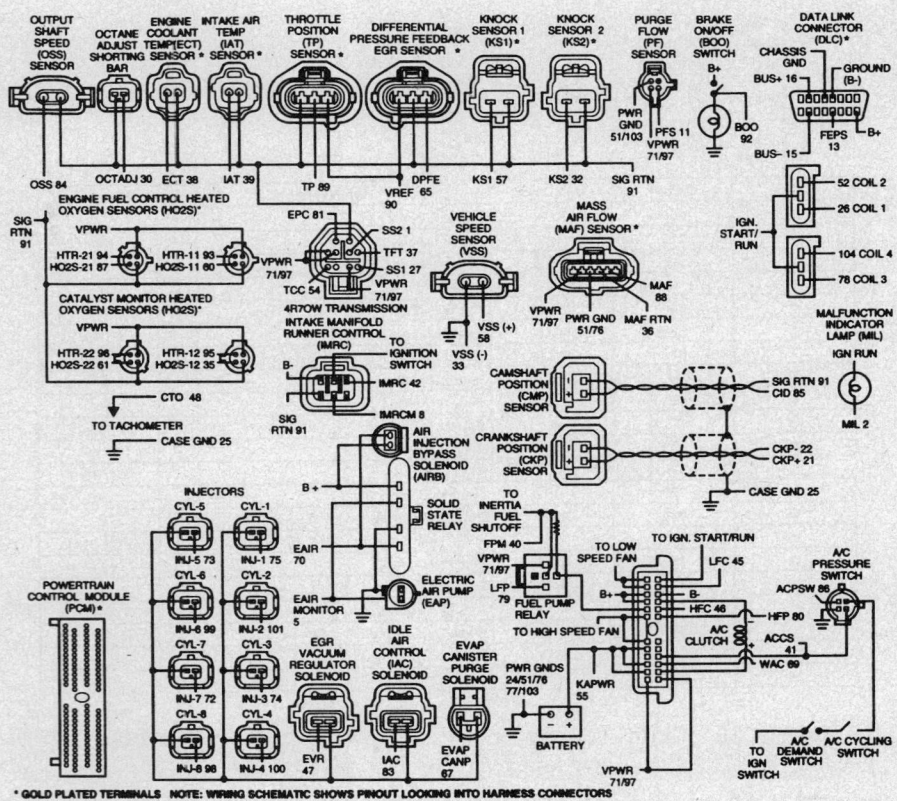

Fig. 52   PCM connector pin identification (Part 1 of 2). 1996 Mustang w/4.6L/V8-281 (32 Valve)

Pin	Circuit	Wire Color	Application	Abbreviation
72	561	T/R	Injector 7	INJ-7
73	559	T/BK	Injector 5	INJ-5
74	557	BR/Y	Injector 3	INJ-3
75	555	T	Injector 1	INJ-1
76	570	BK/W	Power Ground	PWR GND
77	570	BK/W	Power Ground	PWR GND
78	528	PK/W	Ignition Coil 3	COIL-3
79	922	W/R	Low Fuel Pump Control	LFP
80	926	LB/O	High Fuel Pump Control	HFP
83	264	W/LB	Idle Air Control Solenoid	IAC
85	282	DB/O	Cylinder Identification	CID
86	439	T/LG	A/C Pressure Switch	ACPSW
87	94	R/BK	Heated Oxygen Sensor-21 (F-Left)	HO2S-21
88	967	LB/R	Mass Air Flow Sensor	MAF
89	355	GY/W	Throttle Position Sensor	TP
90	351	BR/W	Vehicle Reference Voltage	VREF
91	359	GY/R	Signal Return	SIG RTN
93	387	R/W	HO2S Heater-11 (F-Right)	HTR-11
94	388	Y/LB	HO2S Heater-21 (F-Left)	HTR-21
95	389	W/BK	HO2S Heater-12 (R-Right)	HTR-12
96	390	T/Y	HO2S Heater-22 (R-Left)	HTR-22
97	361	R	Vehicle Power	VPWR
98	562	LB	Injector 8	INJ-8
99	560	LG/O	Injector-6	INJ-6
100	558	BR/LB	Injector-4	INJ-4
101	556	W	Injector-2	INJ-2
103	570	BK/W	Power Ground	PWR GND
104	529	R/Y	Ignition Coil 4	COIL-4

FM0159601712020X

Fig. 52   PCM connector pin identification (Part 2 of 2). 1996 Mustang w/4.6L/V8-281 (32 Valve)

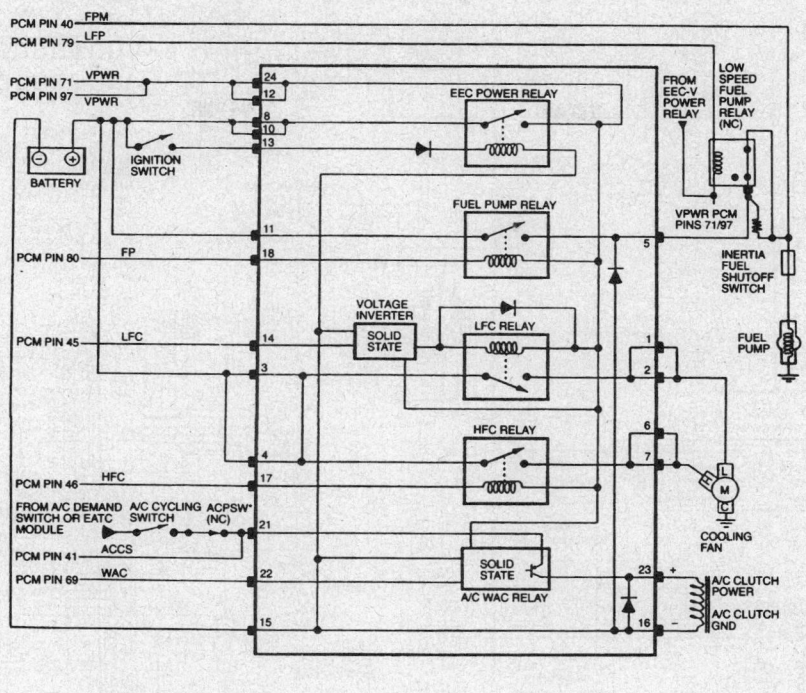

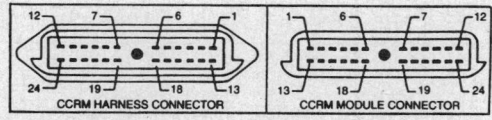

*HIGH PRESSURE CONTACTS OF THE DUAL FUNCTION A/C PRESSURE SWITCH (ACPSW)

FM0159601687000X

Fig. 53   CCRM wiring circuit. 1996 Mustang w/4.6L/V8-281 (32 Valve)

Pin	Circuit	Wire Color	Application	Abbreviation
1	229	R/O	Power to Fan	PTF
2	229	R/O	Power to Fan	PTF
3	38	BK/O	Battery Positive	B+
4	38	BK/O	Battery Positive	B+
5	238	DG/Y	Power to Fuel Pump	PTP
6	638	O/LB	Power to High Speed Fan	PTHSF
7	638	O/LB	Power to High Speed Fan	PTHSF
8	37	Y	Battery Positive	B+
10	37	Y	Battery Positive	B+
11	37	Y	Battery Positive	B+
12	361	R	Vehicle Power	VPWR
13	16	R/LG	Key Power	KEYPWR
14	228	DB	Low Fan Control	LFC
15	570	BK/W	Power Ground	B-
16	57	BK	A/C Clutch Ground	ACC GND
17	639	LG/P	High Fan Control	HFC
18	926	LB/O	Fuel Pump Control	FP
21	198	DG/O	A/C Cycling Switch	ACCS
22	331	PK/Y	Wide Open Throttle A/C Cut-off	WAC
23	347	BK/Y	Power to A/C Clutch	PTAC
24	361	R	Vehicle Power	VPWR

FM0159601688000X

Fig. 54   CCRM connector pin identification. 1996 Mustang w/4.6L/V8-281 (32 Valve)

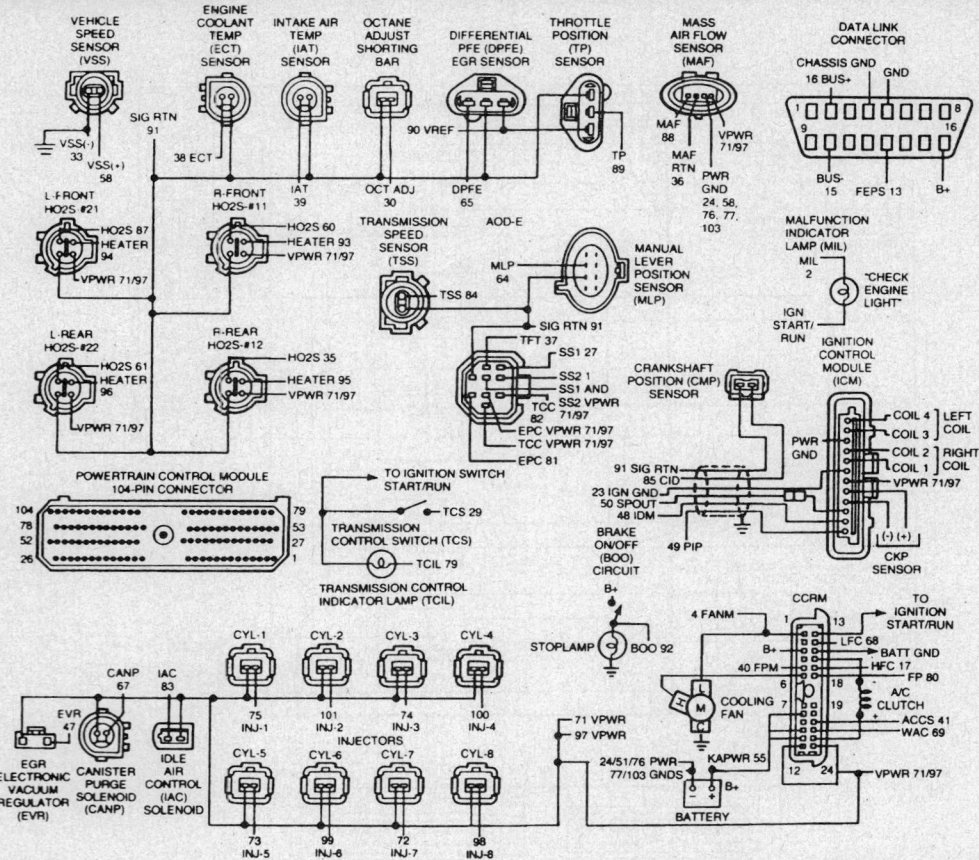

Fig. 55 PCM wiring circuit. 1994 Cougar & Thunderbird w/4.6L/V8-281

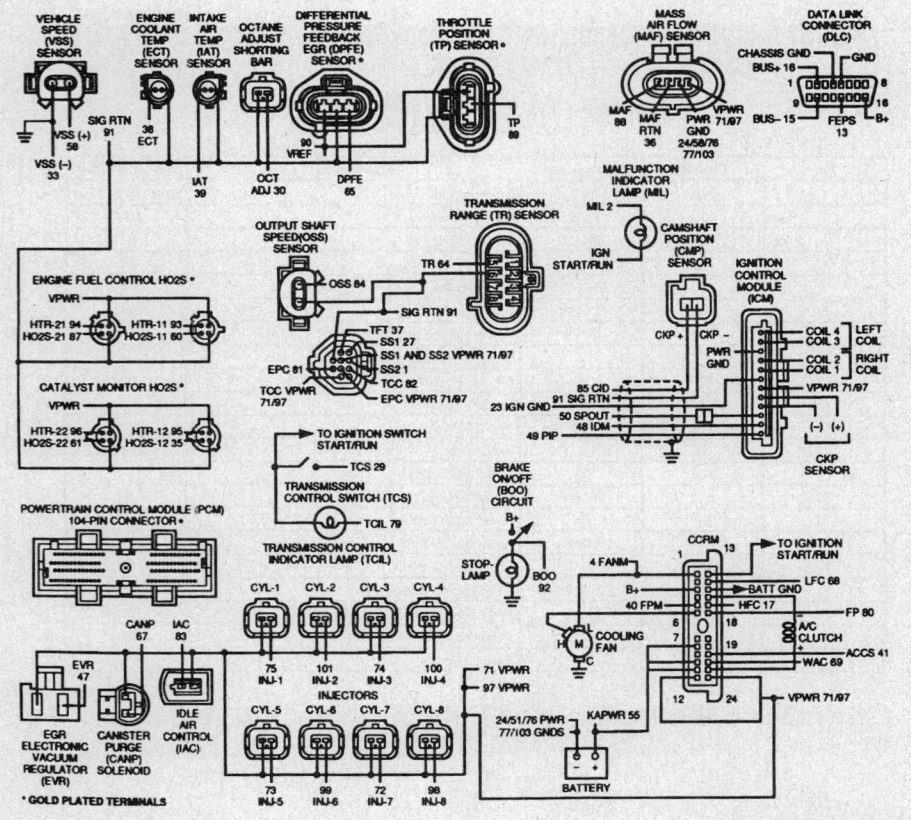

Fig. 56 PCM wiring circuit. 1995 Cougar & Thunderbird w/4.6L/V8-281

Pin	CKT	Wire Color	Application	Abbreviation
1	315	P/O	Shift Solenoid 2	SS2
2	658	PK/LG	Malfunction Indicator Lamp	MIL
4	229	R/O	Fan Monitor	FANM
13	107	P	Flash EPROM power supply	FEPROM
15	915	PK/LB	BUS (-)	BUS-
16	914	T/O	BUS (+)	BUS+
17	639	LG/P	High Fan Control	HFC
23	259	O/R	Ignition Ground	Ign Gnd
24	570	BK/W	Power Ground	PWR GND
25	57	BK	Case Ground	Case Gnd
27	237	O/Y	Shift Solenoid 1	SS1
29	224	T/W	Transmission Control Switch	TCS
30	242	DG	Octane Adjust	OCT ADJ
33	676	PK/O	Vehicle Speed Sensor (-)	VSS-
35	392	R/LG	Heated Oxygen Sensor-12 (R-Right)	HO2S-12
36	968	T/LB	Mass Air Flow Sensor Return	MAF RTN
37	923	O/BK	Transmission Fluid Temperature Sensor	TFT
38	354	LG/R	Engine Coolant Temperature Sensor	ECT
39	743	GY	Intake Air Temperature Sensor	IAT
40	787	PK/BK	Fuel Pump Monitor	FPM
41	883	PK/LB	A/C Cyclic Switch	ACCS
47	360	BR/PK	EGR Electronic Vacuum Regulator	EVR
48	659	O/W	Ignition Diagnostic Monitor	IDM
49	395	GY/O	Profile Ignition Pickup	PIP
50	929	PK	Spark Output	SPOUT
51	570	BK/W	Power Ground	PWR GND
55	37	Y	Keep Alive Power	KAPWR
58	679	GY/BK	Vehicle Speed Sensor (+)	VSS +
60	74	GY/LB	Heated Oxygen Sensor -11 (F-Right)	HO2S-11
61	393	P/LG	Heated Oxygen Sensor -22 (R-Left)	HO2S-22
64	199	LB/Y	Manual Lever Position Switch	MLPS
65	352	BR/LG	Differential PFE EGR Sensor	DPFE
67	107	GY/Y	Canister Purge Solenoid	CANP
68	197	T/O	Low Fan Control	LFC
69	331	PK/Y	Wide Open Throttle A/C Cutoff	WAC
71	361	R	Vehicle Power	VPWR
72	561	T/R	Injector-7	INJ 7
73	559	T/BK	Injector-5	INJ 5

(Continued)

Fig. 57 PCM connector pin identification (Part 1 of 2). 1994–95 Cougar & Thunderbird w/4.6L/V8-281

Pin	CKT	Wire Color	Application	Abbreviation
74	557	BR/Y	Injector-3	INJ 3
75	555	T	Injector-1	INJ 1
76	570	BK/W	Power Ground	PWR GND
77	570	BK/W	Power Ground	PWR GND
79	911	W/LG	Transmission Control Indicator Lamp	TCIL
80	926	LB/O	Fuel Pump Control	FP
81	925	W/Y	Electronic Pressure Control	EPC
82	924	BR/O	Torque Converter Clutch Solenoid	TCC
83	264	W/LB	Idle Air Control Solenoid	IAC
84	970	DG/W	Transmission Speed Sensor	TSS
85	282	DB/O	Cylinder Identification	CID
86	439	T/LG	A/C Pressure Switch	ACPSW
87	94	R/BK	Heated Oxygen Sensor -21 (F-Left)	HO2S-21
88	967	LB/R	Mass Air Flow Sensor	MAF
89	355	GY/W	Throttle Position Sensor	TP
90	351	BR/W	Vehicle Reference Voltage	VREF
91	359	GY/R	Signal Return	SIG RTN
92	511	LG	Brake On/Off Switch	BOO
93	387	R/W	Heater-11 HO2S (F-Right)	HTR-11
94	388	Y/LB	Heater-21 HO2S (F-Left)	HTR-21
95	389	W/BK	Heater-12 HO2S (R-Right)	HTR-12
96	390	T/Y	Heater-22 HO2S (R-Left)	HTR-22
97	361	R	Vehicle Power	VPWR
98	562	LB	Injector-8	INJ 8
99	560	LG/O	Injector-6	INJ 6
100	558	BR/LB	Injector-4	INJ 4
101	556	W	Injector-2	INJ 2
103	570	BK/W	Power Ground	PWR GND

Fig. 57 PCM connector pin identification (Part 2 of 2). 1994–95 Cougar & Thunderbird w/4.6L/V8-281

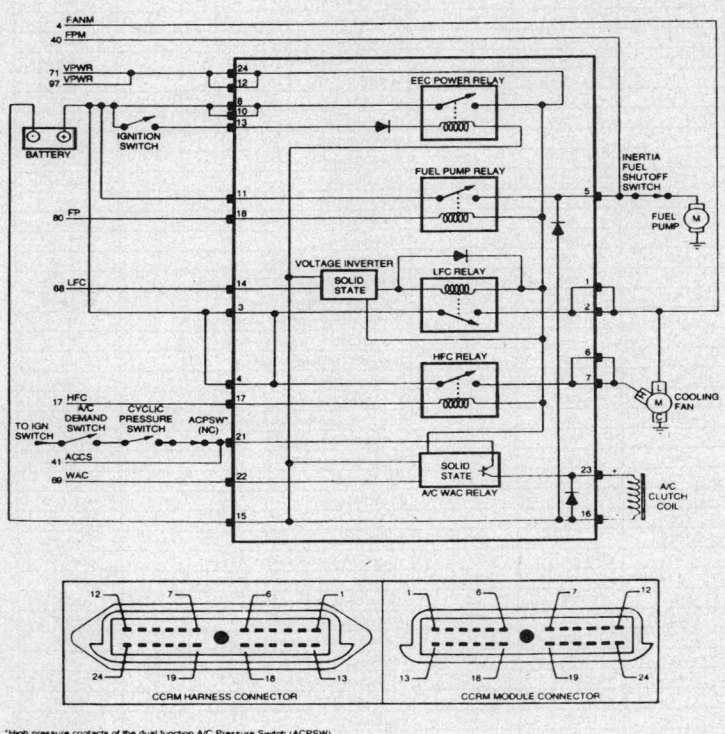

Fig. 58   CCRM wiring circuit. 1994–95 Cougar & Thunderbird w/4.6L/V8-281

Pin	CKT	Wire Color	Application	Abbreviation
1	228	DB	Power to Low Speed Fan	PTLSF
2	228	DB	Power to Low Speed Fan	PTLSF
3	38	BK/O	Battery Positive	B+
4	38	BK/O	Battery Positive	B+
5	787	PK/BK	Power to Fuel Pumps	PTP
6	181	BR/O	Power to High Speed Fan	PTHSF
7	181	BR/O	Power to High Speed Fan	PTHSF
8	97	T/LG	Battery to EEC Relay	B+
12	361	R	Vehicle Power	VPWR
13	16	R/LG	Key Power	KEY PWR
14	197	T/O	Low Fan Control	LFC
15	57	BK	Power Ground	PWR GND
16	321	GY/W	A/C Clutch Ground	ACC GND
17	639	LG/P	High Fan Control	HFC
18	926	LB/O	Fuel Pump Control	FP
21	883	PK/LB	A/C Cyclic Switch	ACCS
22	331	PK/Y	WOT A/C Cutoff	WAC
23	347	BK/Y	Power to A/C Clutch	PTAC
24	361	R	Vehicle Power	VPWR

Fig. 59   CCRM connector pin identification. 1994–95 Cougar & Thunderbird w/4.6L/V8-281

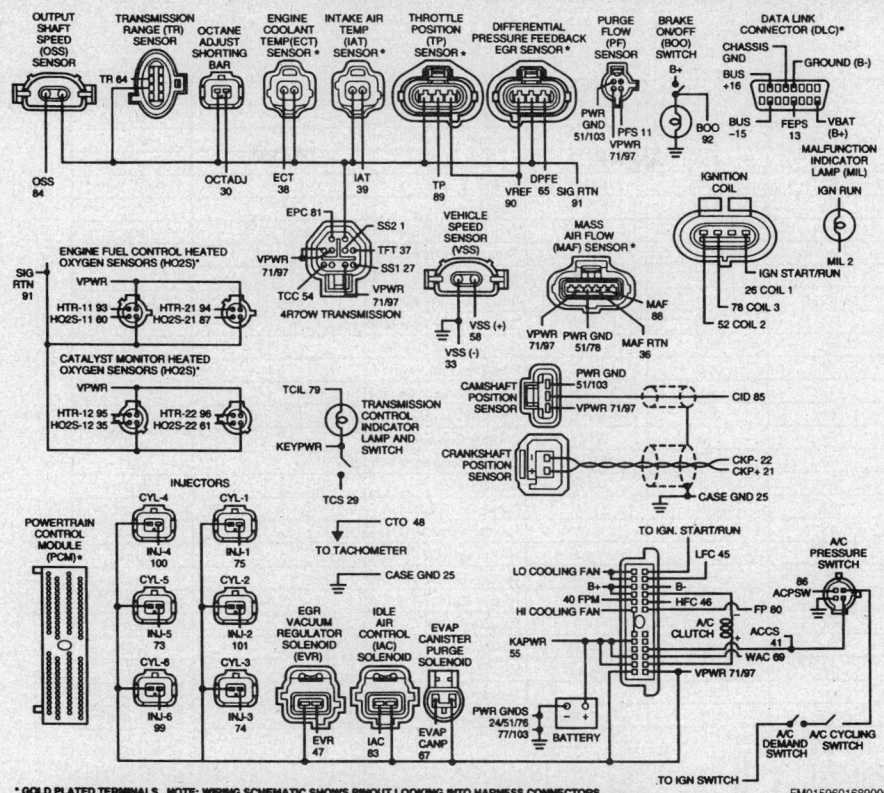

* GOLD PLATED TERMINALS   NOTE: WIRING SCHEMATIC SHOWS PINOUT LOOKING INTO HARNESS CONNECTORS   FM0159601689000X

Fig. 60   PCM wiring circuit. 1996 Cougar & Thunderbird w/3.8/V6-232

Pin	CKT	Wire Color	Application	Abbreviation
1	315	P/O	Shift Solenoid 2	SS2
2	658	PK/LG	Malfunction Indicator Lamp	MIL
11	91	P/W	Purge Flow Sensor	PFS
13	107	P	Flash EPROM power supply	FEPS
15	915	PK/LB	BUS (-)	BUS-
16	914	T/O	BUS (+)	BUS+
21	349	DB	Crankshaft Position Sensor	CKP +
22	350	GY	Crankshaft Position Sensor	CKP -
24	570	BK/W	Power Ground	PWR GND
25	57	BK	Case Ground	Case Gnd
26	526	DB/LG	Coil Driver 1	CD1
27	237	O/Y	Shift Solenoid 1	SS1
29	224	T/W	Transmission Control Switch	TCS
30	242	DG	Octane Adjust	OCT ADJ
33	676	PK/O	Vehicle Speed Sensor (-)	VSS-
35	392	R/LG	Heated Oxygen Sensor-12 (R-Right)	HO2S-12
36	968	T/LB	Mass Air Flow Sensor Return	MAF RTN
37	923	O/BK	Transmission Fluid Temperature Sensor	TFT
38	354	LG/R	Engine Coolant Temperature Sensor	ECT
39	743	GY	Intake Air Temperature Sensor	IAT
40	787	PK/BK	Fuel Pump Monitor	FPM
41	883	PK/LB	A/C Cycling Switch	ACCS
45	197	T/O	Low Fan Control	LFC
46	639	LG/P	High Fan Control	HFC
47	360	BR/PK	EGR Vacuum Regulator Solenoid	EVR
51	570	BK/W	Power Ground	PWR GND
52	527	R/LB	Coil Driver 2	CD2
54	924	BR/O	Torque Converter Clutch Solenoid	TCC
55	37	Y	Keep Alive Power	KAPWR
58	679	GY/BK	Vehicle Speed Sensor (+)	VSS +
60	74	GY/LB	Heated Oxygen Sensor -11 (F-Right)	HO2S-11
61	393	P/LG	Heated Oxygen Sensor -22 (R-Left)	HO2S-22
64	199	LB/Y	Transmission Range Sensor	TR
65	352	BR/LG	Differential Pressure Feedback EGR Sensor	DPFE
67	101	GY/Y	Canister Purge Solenoid	CANP
69	331	PK/Y	Wide Open Throttle A/C Cut-off	WAC
71	361	R	Vehicle Power	VPWR
73	559	T/BK	Injector-5	INJ 5

(Continued)   FM0159601690010X

Fig. 61   PCM connector pin identification (Part 1 of 2). 1996 Cougar & Thunderbird w/3.8/V6-232

Pin	CKT	Wire Color	Application	Abbreviation
74	557	BR / Y	Injector-3	INJ 3
75	555	T	Injector-1	INJ 1
76	570	BK / W	Power Ground	PWR GND
77	570	BK / W	Power Ground	PWR GND
78	528	PK / W	Coil Driver 3	CD3
79	911	W / LG	Transmission Control Indicator Lamp	TCIL
80	926	LB / O	Fuel Pump Control	FP
81	925	W / Y	Electronic Pressure Control	EPC
83	264	W / LB	Idle Air Control Solenoid	IAC
84	970	DG / W	Turbine Shaft Speed Sensor	TSS
85	795	DG	Cylinder Identification	CID
86	439	T / LG	A / C Pressure Switch	ACPSW
87	94	R / BK	Heated Oxygen Sensor -21 (F-Left)	HO2S-21
88	967	LB / R	Mass Air Flow Sensor	MAF
89	355	GY / W	Throttle Position Sensor	TP
90	351	BR / W	Vehicle Reference Voltage	VREF
91	359	GY / R	Signal Return	SIG RTN
92	511	LG	Brake On / Off Switch	BOO
93	387	R / W	Heater-11 HO2S (F-Right)	HTR-11
94	388	Y / LB	Heater-21 HO2S (F-Left)	HTR-21
95	389	W / BK	Heater-12 HO2S (R-Right)	HTR-12
96	390	T / Y	Heater-22 HO2S (R-Left)	HTR-22
97	361	R	Vehicle Power	VPWR
99	560	LG / O	Injector-6	INJ 6
100	558	BR / LB	Injector-4	INJ 4
101	556	W	Injector-2	INJ 2
103	570	BK / W	Power Ground	PWR GND

FM0159601690020X

Fig. 61 PCM connector pin identification (Part 2 of 2). 1996 Cougar & Thunderbird w/3.8/V6-232

*High pressure contacts of the dual function A/C Pressure Switch (ACPSW)

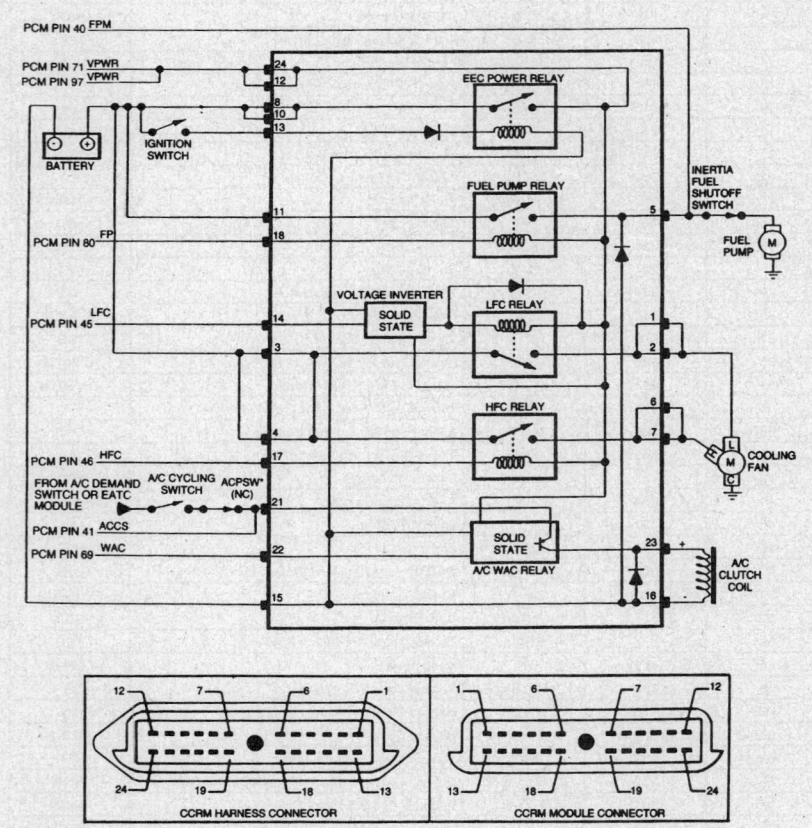

FM0159601691000X

Fig. 62 CCRM wiring circuit. 1996 Cougar & Thunderbird w/3.8/V6-232

Pin	CKT	Wire Color	Application	Abbreviation
1	228	DB	Power to Low Speed Fan	PTLSF
2	228	DB	Power to Low Speed Fan	PTLSF
3	38	BK/O	Battery Positive	B+
4	38	BK/O	Battery Positive	B+
5	787	PK/BK	Power to Fuel Pumps	PTP
6	181	BR/O	Power to High Speed Fan	PTHSF
7	181	BR/O	Power to High Speed Fan	PTHSF
8	37	Y	Battery to EEC Relay	B+
11	175	BK/Y	Battery to Fuel Pump Relay	B+
12	361	R	Vehicle Power	VPWR
13	16	R/LG	Key Power	KEY PWR
14	197	T/O	Low Fan Control	LFC
15	57	BK	Power Ground	PWR GND
16	321	GY/W	A/C Clutch Ground	ACC GND
17	639	LG/P	High Fan Control	HFC
18	926	LB/O	Fuel Pump Control	FP
21	883	PK/LB	A/C Cycling Switch	ACCS
22	331	PK/Y	WOT A/C Cut-off	WAC
23	347	BK/Y	Power to A/C Clutch	PTAC
24	361	R	Vehicle Power	VPWR

FM0159601692000X

Fig. 63 CCRM connector pin identification. 1996 Cougar & Thunderbird w/3.8/V6-232

* GOLD PLATED TERMINALS NOTE: WIRING SCHEMATIC SHOWS PINOUT LOOKING INTO HARNESS CONNECTORS

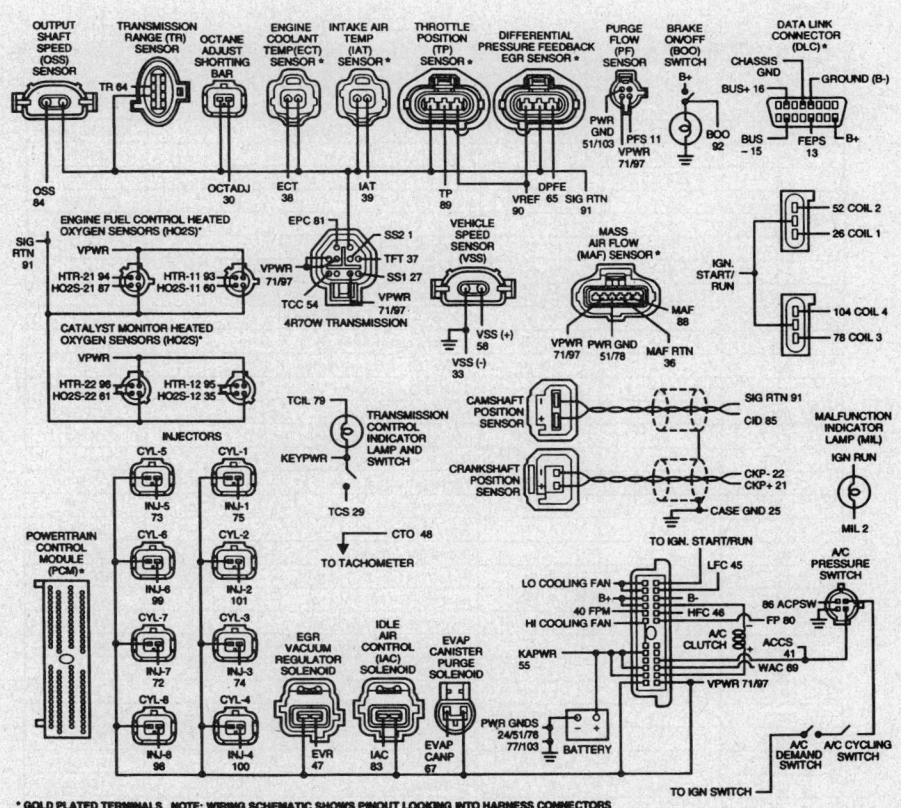

FM0159601693000X

Fig. 64 PCM wiring circuit. 1996 Cougar & Thunderbird w/4.6L/V8-281

Pin	CKT	Wire Color	Application	Abbreviation
1	315	P/O	Shift Solenoid 2	SS2
2	658	PK/LG	Malfunction Indicator Lamp	MIL
11	91	P/W	Purge Flow Sensor	PF
13	107	P	Flash EPROM power supply	FEPS
15	915	PK/LB	BUS (-)	BUS-
16	914	T/O	BUS (+)	BUS+
21	349	DB	Crankshaft Position Sensor	CKP +
22	350	GY	Crankshaft Position Sensor	CKP -
24	570	BK/W	Power Ground	PWR GND
25	57	BK	Case Ground	Case Gnd
26	526	DB/LG	Coil Driver 1	CD1
27	237	O/Y	Shift Solenoid 1	SS1
29	224	T/W	Transmission Control Switch	TCS
30	242	DG	Octane Adjust	OCT ADJ
33	676	PK/O	Vehicle Speed Sensor (-)	VSS-
35	392	R/LG	Heated Oxygen Sensor-12 (R-Right)	HO2S-12
36	968	T/LB	Mass Air Flow Sensor Return	MAF RTN
37	923	O/BK	Transmission Fluid Temperature Sensor	TFT
38	354	LG/R	Engine Coolant Temperature Sensor	ECT
39	743	GY	Intake Air Temperature Sensor	IAT
40	787	PK/BK	Fuel Pump Monitor	FPM
41	883	PK/LB	A/C Cycling Switch	ACCS
45	197	T/O	Low Fan Control	LFC
46	639	LG/P	High Fan Control	HFC
47	360	BR/PK	EGR Vacuum Regulator Solenoid	EVR
51	570	BK/W	Power Ground	PWR GND
52	527	R/LB	Coil Driver 2	CD2
54	924	BR/O	Torque Converter Clutch Solenoid	TCC
55	37	Y	Keep Alive Power	KAPWR
58	679	GY/BK	Vehicle Speed Sensor (+)	VSS +
60	74	GY/LB	Heated Oxygen Sensor -11 (F-Right)	HO2S-11
61	393	P/LG	Heated Oxygen Sensor -22 (R-Left)	HO2S-22
64	199	LB/Y	Transmission Range Sensor	TR
65	352	BR/LG	Differential Pressure Feedback EGR Sensor	DPFE
67	101	GY/Y	Canister Purge Solenoid	CANP
69	331	PK/Y	Wide Open Throttle A/C Cut-off	WAC
71	361	R	Vehicle Power	VPWR
73	559	T/BK	Injector-5	INJ 5

(Continued)

FM0159601694010X

Fig. 65   PCM connector pin identification (Part 1 of 2). 1996 Cougar & Thunderbird w/4.6L/V8-281

Pin	CKT	Wire Color	Application	Abbreviation
74	557	BR/Y	Injector-3	INJ 3
75	555	T	Injector-1	INJ 1
76	570	BK/W	Power Ground	PWR GND
77	570	BK/W	Power Ground	PWR GND
78	528	PK/W	Coil Driver 3	CD3
79	911	W/LG	Transmission Control Indicator Lamp	TCIL
80	926	LB/O	Fuel Pump Control	FP
81	925	W/Y	Electronic Pressure Control	EPC
83	264	W/LB	Idle Air Control Solenoid	IAC
84	970	DG/W	Turbine Shaft Speed Sensor	TSS
85	795	DG	Cylinder Identification	CID
86	439	T/LG	A/C Pressure Switch	ACPSW
87	94	R/BK	Heated Oxygen Sensor -21 (F-Left)	HO2S-21
88	967	LB/R	Mass Air Flow Sensor	MAF
89	355	GY/W	Throttle Position Sensor	TP
90	351	BR/W	Vehicle Reference Voltage	VREF
91	359	GY/R	Signal Return	SIG RTN
92	511	LG	Brake On/Off Switch	BOO
93	387	R/W	Heater-11 HO2S (F-Right)	HTR-11
94	388	Y/LB	Heater-21 HO2S (F-Left)	HTR-21
95	389	W/BK	Heater-12 HO2S (R-Right)	HTR-12
96	390	T/Y	Heater-22 HO2S (R-Left)	HTR-22
97	361	R	Vehicle Power	VPWR
99	560	LG/O	Injector-6	INJ 6
100	558	BR/LB	Injector-4	INJ 4
101	556	W	Injector-2	INJ 2
103	570	BK/W	Power Ground	PWR GND
104	529	R/Y	Coil Driver 4	CD4

FM0159601694020X

Fig. 65   PCM connector pin identification (Part 2 of 2). 1996 Cougar & Thunderbird w/4.6L/V8-281

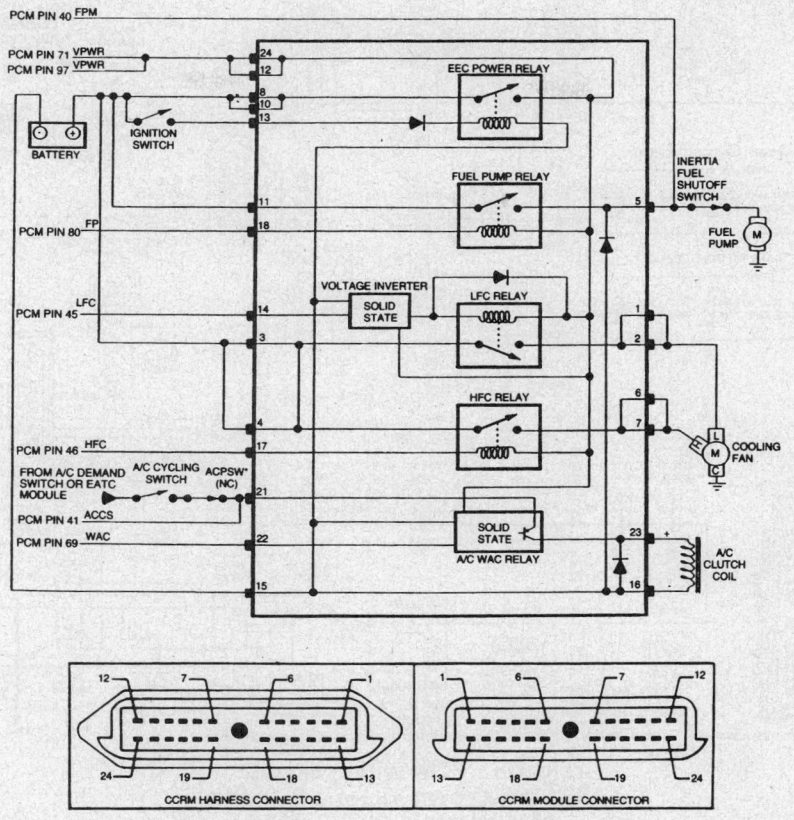

Fig. 66 CCRM wiring circuit. 1996 Cougar & Thunderbird w/4.6L/V8-281

*High pressure contacts of the dual function A/C Pressure Switch (ACPSW)

FM0159601695000X

Pin	CKT	Wire Color	Application	Abbreviation
1	228	DB	Power to Low Speed Fan	PTLSF
2	228	DB	Power to Low Speed Fan	PTLSF
3	38	BK/O	Battery Positive	B+
4	38	BK/O	Battery Positive	B+
5	787	PK/BK	Power to Fuel Pumps	PTP
6	181	BR/O	Power to High Speed Fan	PTHSF
7	181	BR/O	Power to High Speed Fan	PTHSF
8	37	Y	Battery to EEC Relay	B+
11	175	BK/Y	Battery to Fuel Pump Relay	B+
12	361	R	Vehicle Power	VPWR
13	16	R/LG	Key Power	KEY PWR
14	197	T/O	Low Fan Control	LFC
15	57	BK	Power Ground	PWR GND
16	321	GY/W	A/C Clutch Ground	ACC GND
17	639	LG/P	High Fan Control	HFC
18	926	LB/O	Fuel Pump Control	FP
21	883	PK/LB	A/C Cycling Switch	ACCS
22	331	PK/Y	WOT A/C Cut-off	WAC
23	347	BK/Y	Power to A/C Clutch	PTAC
24	361	R	Vehicle Power	VPWR

FM0159601696000X

Fig. 67 CCRM connector pin identification. 1996 Cougar & Thunderbird w/4.6L/V8-281

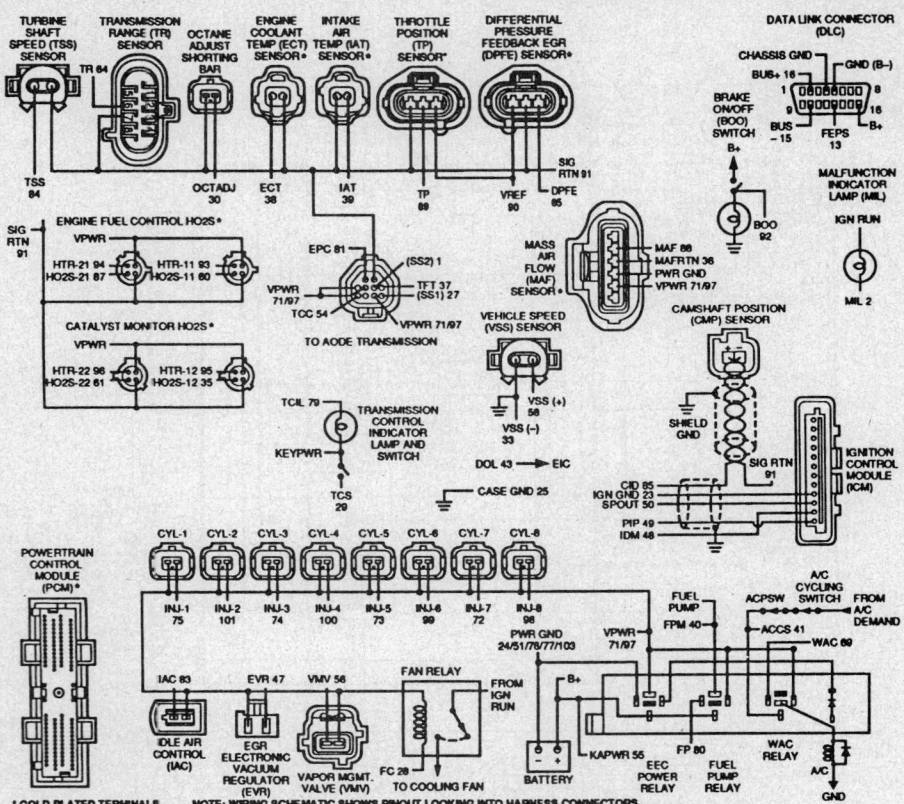

Fig. 68 PCM wiring circuit.
1994–95 Crown Victoria & Grand
Marquis w/4.6L/V8-281

Pin	CKT	Wire Color	Application	Abbreviation
1	315	P/O	Shift Solenoid 2	SS2
2	658	PK/LG	Malfunction Indicator Lamp	MIL
13	67	LG/Y	Flash EPROM Power Supply	FEPS
15	915	PK/LB	BUS (-)	BUS-
16	914	T/O	BUS (+)	BUS+
23	259	O/R	Ignition Ground	IGN GND
24	570	BK/W	Power Ground	PWR GND
25	57	BK	Case Ground	CASE GND
27	237	O/Y	Shift Solenoid 1	SS1
28	229	R/O	Fan Control	FC
29	224	T/W	Transmission Control Switch	TCS
30	240	W/R	Octane Adjust	OCT ADJ
33	676	PK/O	Vehicle Speed Sensor (-)	VSS-
35	392	R/LG	Heated Oxygen Sensor -12 (R-Right)	HO2S-12
36	968	T/LB	Mass Air Flow Sensor Return	MAF RTN
37	923	O/BK	Transmission Fluid Temperature Sensor	TFT
38	354	LG/R	Engine Coolant Temperature Sensor	ECT
39	743	GY	Intake Air Temperature Sensor	IAT
40	238	DG/Y	Fuel Pump Monitor	FPM
41	198	DG/O	A/C Cycling Switch	ACCS
43	205	DB/LG	Data Output Link	DOL
47	360	BR/PK	EGR Electronic Vacuum Regulator	EVR
48	11	T/Y	Ignition Diagnostic Monitor	IDM
49	395	GY/O	Profile Ignition Pickup	PIP
50	929	PK	Spark Output	SPOUT
51	570	BK/W	Power Ground	PWR GND
54	473	R/LB	Torque Converter Clutch Solenoid	TCC
55	554	Y/BK	Keep Alive Power	KAPWR
56	191	LG/BK	Vapor Management Valve	VMV
58	679	GY/BK	Vehicle Speed Sensor (+)	VSS +
60	74	GY/LB	Heated Oxygen Sensor -11 (F-Right)	HO2S-11
61	393	P/LG	Heated Oxygen Sensor -22 (R-Left)	HO2S-22
64	199	LB/Y	Transmission Range Sensor	TR
65	352	BR/LG	Differential Pressure Feedback EGR Sensor	DPFE
69	73	O/LB	Wide Open Throttle A C Cut-off	WAC
71	361	R	Vehicle Power	VPWR
72	561	T/R	Injector-7	INJ 7
73	559	T/BK	Injector-5	INJ 5
74	557	BR/Y	Injector-3	INJ 3

FM0159501258010X

Fig. 69 PCM connector pin identification (Part 1 of 2).
1994–95 Crown Victoria & Grand Marquis
w/4.6L/V8-281

Pin	CKT	Wire Color	Application	Abbreviation
75	555	T	Injector-1	INJ 1
76	570	BK/W	Power Ground	PWR GND
77	570	BK/W	Power Ground	PWR GND
79	911	W/LG	Transmission Control Indicator Lamp	TCIL
80	926	LB/O	Fuel Pump Control	FP
81	925	W/Y	Electronic Pressure Control	EPC
83	264	W/LB	Idle Air Control Solenoid	IAC
84	683	P/LB	Turbine Shaft Speed Sensor	TSS
85	795	DG	Cylinder Identification	CID
87	94	R/BK	Heated Oxygen Sensor -21 (F-Left)	HO2S-21
88	967	LB/R	Mass Air Flow Sensor	MAF
89	355	GY/W	Throttle Position Sensor	TP
90	351	BR/W	Vehicle Reference Voltage	VREF
91	359	GY/R	Signal Return	SIG RTN
92	511	LG	Brake On/Off Switch	BOO
93	387	R/W	Heater-11 HO2S (F-Right)	HTR-11
94	388	Y/LB	Heater-21 HO2S (F-Left)	HTR-21
95	389	W/BK	Heater-12 HO2S (R-Right)	HTR-12
96	390	T/Y	Heater-22 HO2S (R-Left)	HTR-22
97	361	R	Vehicle Power	VPWR
98	562	LB	Injector-8	INJ 8
99	560	LG/O	Injector-6	INJ 6
100	558	BR/LB	Injector-4	INJ 4
101	556	W	Injector-2	INJ 2
103	570	BK/W	Power Ground	PWR GND

Fig. 69   PCM connector pin identification (Part 2 of 2). 1994–95 Crown Victoria & Grand Marquis w/4.6L/V8-281

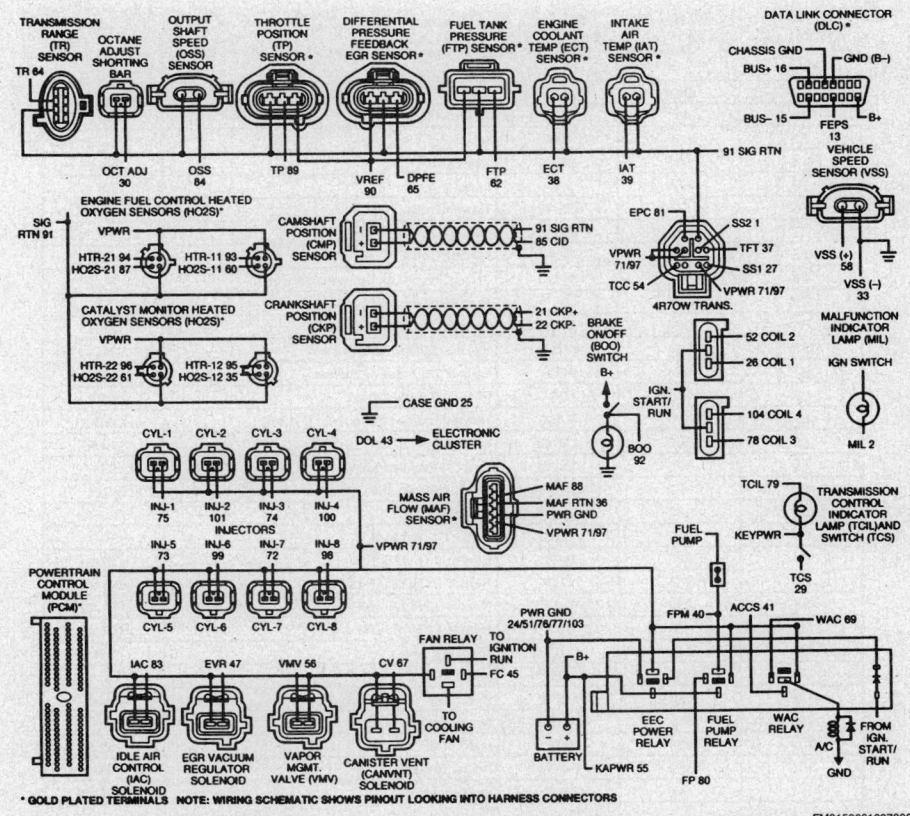

FM0159601697000X

Fig. 70   PCM wiring circuit. 1996 Crown Victoria & Grand Marquis w/4.6L/V8-281

FORD–Electronic Engine Controls

Pin	CKT	Wire Color	Application	Abbreviation
1	315	P/O	Shift Solenoid 2	SS2
2	658	PK/LG	Malfunction Indicator Lamp	MIL
13	67	LG/Y	Flash EPROM Power Supply	FEPS
15	915	PK/LB	BUS (-)	BUS-
16	914	T/O	BUS (+)	BUS+
21	349	DB	Crankshaft Position Sensor (+)	CKP +
22	350	GY	Crankshaft Position Sensor (-)	CKP -
24	570	BK/W	Power Ground	PWR GND
25	57	BK	Case Ground	CASE GND
26	95	TW	Ignition Coil 1	COIL-1
27	237	O/Y	Shift Solenoid 1	SS1
29	224	T/W	Transmission Control Switch	TCS
30	240	W/R	Octane Adjust	OCT ADJ
33	676	PK/O	Vehicle Speed Sensor (-)	VSS-
35	392	R/LG	Heated Oxygen Sensor-12 (R-Right)	HO2S-12
36	968	T/LB	Mass Air Flow Sensor Return	MAF RTN
37	923	O/BK	Transmission Fluid Temperature Sensor	TFT
38	354	LG/R	Engine Coolant Temperature Sensor	ECT
39	743	GY	Intake Air Temperature Sensor	IAT
40	238	DG/Y	Fuel Pump Monitor	FPM
41	198	DG/O	A/C Cycling Switch	ACCS
43	205	DB/LG	Data Output Link	DOL
45	228	R/O	Fan Control	FC
47	360	BR/PK	EGR Vacuum Regulator Solenoid	EVR
51	570	BK/W	Power Ground	PWR GND
52	96	T/O	Ignition Coil 2	COIL-2
54	473	R/LB	Torque Converter Clutch Solenoid	TCC
55	554	Y/BK	Keep Alive Power	KAPWR
56	191	LG/BK	Vapor Management Valve	VMV
58	679	GY/BK	Vehicle Speed Sensor (+)	VSS +
60	74	GY/LB	Heated Oxygen Sensor -11 (F-Right)	HO2S-11
61	393	P/LG	Heated Oxygen Sensor -22 (R-Left)	HO2S-22
62	791	R/PK	Fuel Tank Pressure Sensor	FTP
64	199	LB/Y	Transmission Range Sensor	TR
65	352	BR/LG	Differential Pressure Feedback EGR Sensor	DPFE
67	91	P/W	Canister Vent Solenoid	CV
69	73	O/LB	Wide Open Throttle A/C Cut-off	WAC
71	361	R	Vehicle Power	VPWR

(Continued)

FM0159601698010X

Fig. 71 PCM connector pin identification (Part 1 of 2). 1996 Crown Victoria & Grand Marquis w/4.6L/V8-281

Pin	CKT	Wire Color	Application	Abbreviation
72	561	T/R	Injector-7	INJ 7
73	559	T/BK	Injector-5	INJ 5
74	557	BR/Y	Injector-3	INJ 3
75	555	T	Injector-1	INJ 1
76	570	BK/W	Power Ground	PWR GND
77	570	BK/W	Power Ground	PWR GND
78	97	T/LG	Ignition Coil 3	COIL-3
79	911	W/LG	Transmission Control Indicator Lamp	TCIL
80	926	LB/O	Fuel Pump Control	FP
81	925	W/Y	Electronic Pressure Control	EPC
83	264	W/LB	Idle Air Control Solenoid	IAC
84	683	P/LB	Output Shaft Speed Sensor	OSS
85	795	DG	Cylinder Identification	CID
87	94	R/BK	Heated Oxygen Sensor -21 (F-Left)	HO2S-21
88	967	LB/R	Mass Air Flow Sensor	MAF
89	355	GY/W	Throttle Position Sensor	TP
90	351	BR/W	Vehicle Reference Voltage	VREF
91	359	GY/R	Signal Return	SIG RTN
92	511	LG	Brake On/Off Switch	BOO
93	387	R/W	Heater-11 HO2S (F-Right)	HTR-11
94	388	Y/LB	Heater-21 HO2S (F-Left)	HTR-21
95	389	W/BK	Heater-12 HO2S (R-Right)	HTR-12
96	390	T/Y	Heater-22 HO2S (R-Left)	HTR-22
97	361	R	Vehicle Power	VPWR
98	562	LB	Injector-8	INJ 8
99	560	LG/O	Injector-6	INJ 6
100	558	BR/LB	Injector-4	INJ 4
101	556	W	Injector-2	INJ 2
103	570	BK/W	Power Ground	PWR GND
104	98	T/LB	Ignition Coil 4	COIL-4

FM0159601698020X

Fig. 71 PCM connector pin identification (Part 2 of 2). 1996 Crown Victoria & Grand Marquis w/4.6L/V8-281

ELECTRONIC ENGINE CONTROL SYSTEM (EEC-V)

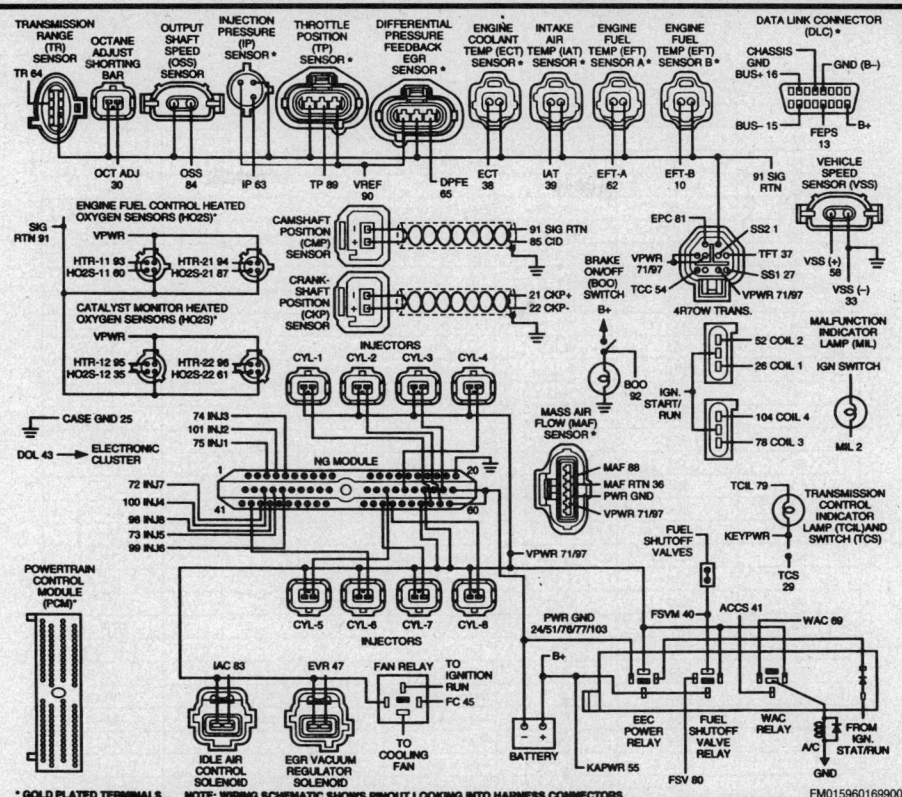

Fig. 72   PCM wiring circuit. 1996 Crown Victoria w/4.6L/V8-281 natural gas engine

Pin	Circuit	Wire Color	Application	Abbreviation
1	315	P/O	Shift Solenoid 2	SS2
2	658	PK/LG	Malfunction Indicator Lamp	MIL
10	241	LB/W	Engine Fuel Temperature Sensor B	EFT-B
13	67	LG/Y	Flash EPROM Power Supply	FEPS
15	915	PK/LB	BUS (-)	BUS -
16	914	T/O	BUS (+)	BUS +
21	349	DB	Crankshaft Position Sensor (+)	CKP +
22	350	GY	Crankshaft Position Sensor (-)	CKP -
24	570	BK/W	Power Ground	PWR GND
25	57	BK	Case Ground	CASE GND
26	95	T/W	Ignition Coil 1	COIL-1
27	237	O/Y	Shift Solenoid 1	SS1
29	224	T/W	Transmission Control Switch	TCS
30	240	W/R	Octane Adjust	OCT ADJ
33	676	PK/O	Vehicle Speed Sensor (-)	VSS -
35	392	R/LG	Heated Oxygen Sensor - 12 (R-Right)	HO2S-12
36	968	T/LB	Mass Air Flow Sensor Return	MAF RTN
37	923	O/BK	Transmission Fluid Temperature Sensor	TFT
38	354	LG/R	Engine Coolant Temperature Sensor	ECT
39	743	GY	Intake Air Temperature Sensor	IAT
40	238	DG/Y	Fuel Shutoff Valve Monitor	FSVM
41	198	DG/O	A/C Cycling Switch	ACCS
45	229	R/O	Fan Control	FC
47	360	BR/PK	EGR Vacuum Regulator Solenoid	EVR
51	570	BK/W	Power Ground	PWR GND
52	96	T/O	Ignition Coil 2	COIL-2
54	473	R/LB	Torque Converter Clutch Solenoid	TCC
55	554	Y/BK	Keep Alive Power	KAPWR
58	679	GY/BK	Vehicle Speed Sensor (+)	VSS +
60	74	GY/LB	Heated Oxygen Sensor - 11 (F-Right)	HO2S-11
61	393	P/LG	Heated Oxygen Sensor - 22 (R-Left)	HO2S-22
62	225	BK/Y	Engine Fuel Temperature Sensor A	EFT-A
63	141	R/PK	Injection Pressure Sensor	IPS
64	199	LB/Y	Transmission Range Sensor	TR
65	352	BR/LG	Differential Pressure Feedback EGR Sensor	DPFE
69	73	O/LB	Wide Open Throttle A/C Cut-off	WAC
71	361	R	Vehicle Power	VPWR
72	561	T/R	Injector 7	INJ-7

(Continued)   FM0159601700010X

Fig. 73   PCM connector pin identification (Part 1 of 2). 1996 Crown Victoria w/4.6L/V8-281 natural gas engine

Pin	Circuit	Wire Color	Application	Abbreviation
73	559	T/BK	Injector 5	INJ-5
74	557	BR/Y	Injector 3	INJ-3
75	555	T	Injector 1	INJ-1
76	570	BK/W	Power Ground	PWR GND
77	570	BK/W	Power Ground	PWR GND
78	97	T/LG	Ignition Coil 3	COIL-3
79	911	W/LG	Transmission Control Indicator Lamp	TCIL
80	926	LB/O	Fuel Shutoff Valve Control	FSV
81	925	W/Y	Electronic Pressure Control	EPC
83	264	W/LB	Idle Air Control Solenoid	IAC
84	683	P/LB	Output Shaft Speed Sensor	OSS
85	795	DG	Cylinder Identification	CID
87	94	R/BK	Heated Oxygen Sensor -21 (F-Left)	HO2S-21
88	967	LB/R	Mass Air Flow Sensor	MAF
89	355	GY/W	Throttle Position Sensor	TP
90	351	BR/W	Vehicle Reference Voltage	VREF
91	359	GY/R	Signal Return	SIG RTN
92	511	LG	Brake On/Off Switch	BOO
93	387	R/W	Heater -11 HO2S (F-Right)	HTR-11
94	388	Y/LB	Heater -21 HO2S (F-Left)	HTR-21
95	389	W/BK	Heater -12 HO2S (R-Right)	HTR-12
96	390	T/Y	Heater -22 HO2S (R-Left)	HTR-22
97	361	R	Vehicle Power	VPWR
98	562	LB	Injector 8	INJ-8
99	560	LG/O	Injector 6	INJ-6
100	558	BR/LB	Injector 4	INJ-4
101	556	W	Injector 2	INJ-2
103	570	BK/W	Power Ground	PWR GND
104	98	T/LB	Ignition Coil 4	COIL-4

FM015960170020X

Fig. 73   PCM connector pin identification (Part 2 of 2). 1996 Crown Victoria w/4.6L/V8-281 natural gas engine

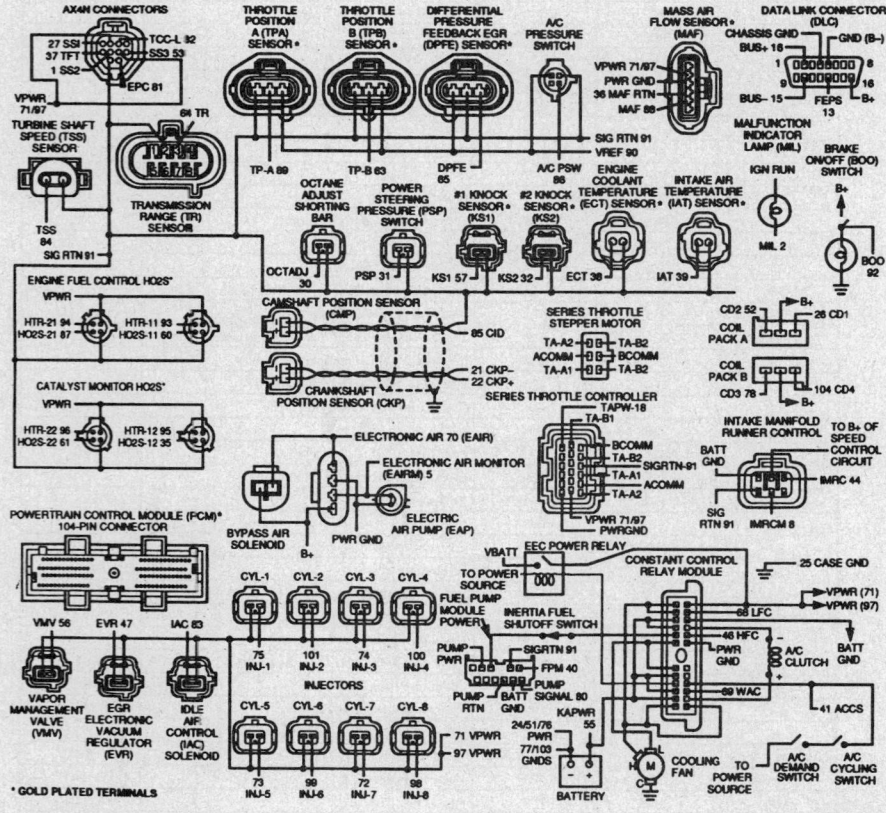

FM015950125300X

Fig. 74   PCM wiring circuit. 1994–95 Continental w/4.6L/V8-281

Pin	CKT	Wire Color	Application	Abbreviation
1	315	P/O	Shift Solenoid 2	SS2
2	658	PK/LG	Malfunction Indicator Lamp	MIL
5	111	BK/O	Electronic Air Management Monitor	EAIRM
8	358	LG/BK	Intake Manifold Runner Control Monitor	IMRCM
13	107	P	Flash EPROM Power Supply	FEPROM
15	915	PK/LB	BUS (-)	BUS-
16	914	T/O	BUS (+)	BUS+
18	961	W/PK	Traction Assist Pulsewidth Modulator	TAPW
21	138	BK/PK	Crankshaft Position Sensor+	CKP+
22	139	GY/Y	Crankshaft Position Sensor-	CKP-
24	570	BK/W	Power Ground	PWR GND
25	57	BK	Case Ground	CASE GND
26	526	DB/LG	Coil Driver 1	CD1
27	237	O/Y	Shift Solenoid 1	SS1
30	242	DG	Octane Adjust	OCT ADJ
31	330	Y/LG	Power Steering Pressure Switch	PSP
32	311	DG/P	Knock Sensor 2	KS2
35	392	R/LG	Heated Oxygen Sensor-12 (R-Right)	HO2S-12
36	968	T/LB	Mass Air Flow Sensor Return	MAF RTN
37	923	O/BK	Transmission Fluid Temperature Sensor	TFT
38	354	LG/R	Engine Coolant Temperature Sensor	ECT
39	743	GY	Intake Air Temperature Sensor	IAT
40	238	DG/Y	Fuel Pump Monitor	FPM
41	348	P	A/C Cycling Switch	ACCS
44	387	BR	Intake Manifold Runner Control	IMRC
46	639	LG/P	High Speed Fan Control	HFC
47	360	BR/PK	EGR Electronic Vacuum Regulator	EVR
51	570	BK/W	Power Ground	PWR GND
52	527	R/LB	Coil Driver 2	CD2
53	971	PK/BK	Shift Solenoid 3	SS3
55	37	Y	Keep Alive Power	KAPWR
57	310	Y/R	Knock Sensor 1	KS1
60	74	GY/LB	Heated Oxygen Sensor -11	HO2S-11
61	393	P/LG	Heated Oxygen Sensor -22 (R-Left)	HO2S-22
63	357	Y/W	Throttle Position Sensor B	TP-B
64	199	LB/Y	Transmission Range Sensor	TR
65	352	BR/LG	Differential Pressure Feedback EGR Sensor	DPFE
68	228	DB	Low Fan Control	LFC
69	331	PK/Y	Wide Open Throttle A/C Cut-off	WAC

FM0159501254010X

Fig. 75 PCM connector pin identification (Part 1 of 2). 1994–95 Continental w/4.6L/V8-281

Pin	CKT	Wire Color	Application	Abbreviation
70	369	W/O	Electronic Air Management Control	EAIR
71	361	R	Vehicle Power	VPWR
72	561	T/R	Injector-7	INJ 7
73	559	T/BK	Injector-5	INJ 5
74	557	BR/Y	Injector-3	INJ 3
75	555	T	Injector-1	INJ 1
76	570	BK/W	Power Ground	PWR GND
77	570	BK/W	Power Ground	PWR GND
78	528	PK/W	Coil Driver 3	CD3
80	926	LB/O	Fuel Pump Control	FP
81	925	W/Y	Electronic Pressure Control	EPC
82	125	DB/W	Transmission Converter Clutch Lock-up	TCCL
83	264	W/LB	Idle Air Control Solenoid	IAC
84	970	DG/W	Turbine Shaft Speed Sensor	TSS
85	282	DB/O	Cylinder Identification	CID
86	440	T/LG	Air Conditioning Pressure Switch	ACPSW
87	94	R/BK	Heated Oxygen Sensor -21	HO2S-21
88	967	LB/R	Mass Air Flow Sensor	MAF
89	355	GY/W	Throttle Position Sensor A	TP-A
90	351	BR/W	Vehicle Reference Voltage	VREF
91	359	GY/R	Signal Return	SIG RTN
92	511	LG	Brake On/Off Switch	BOO
93	387	R/W	HO2S Heater-11	HTR-11
94	388	Y/LB	HO2S Heater-21	HTR-21
95	389	W/BK	HO2S Heater-12	HTR-12
96	390	T/Y	HO2S Heater-22	HTR-22
97	361	R	Vehicle Power	VPWR
98	562	LB	Injector-8	INJ 8
99	560	LG/O	Injector-6	INJ 6
100	558	BR/LB	Injector-4	INJ 4
101	556	W	Injector-2	INJ 2
103	570	BK/W	Power Ground	PWR GND
104	529	R/Y	Coil Driver 4	CD4

FM0159501254020X

Fig. 75 PCM connector pin identification (Part 2 of 2). 1994–95 Continental w/4.6L/V8-281

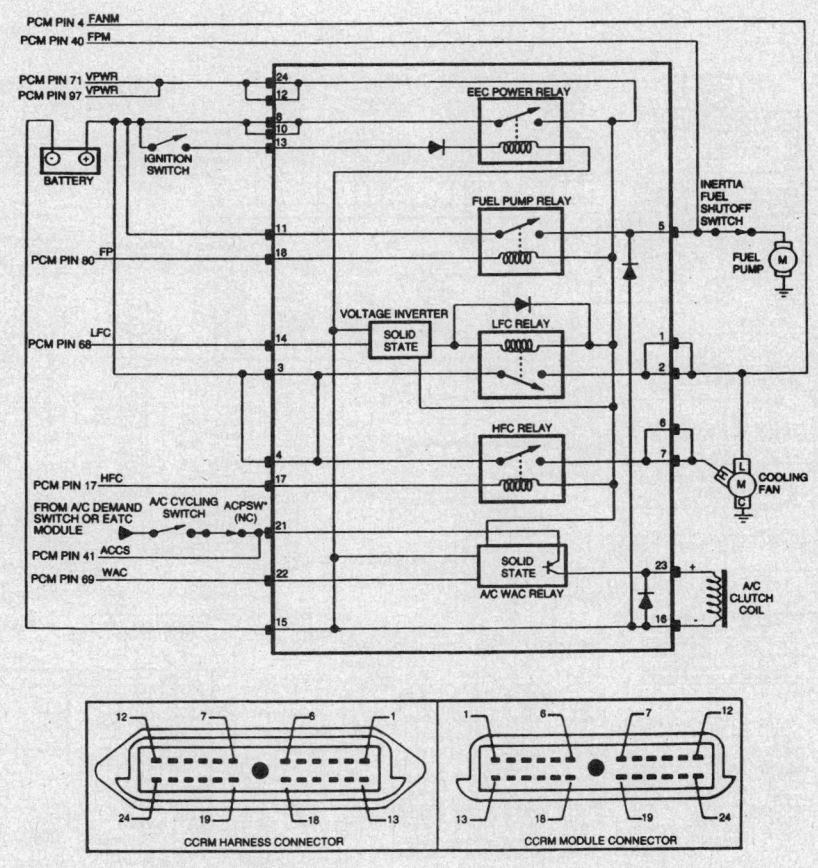

FM0159501255000X

Fig. 76 CCRM wiring circuit. 1994–95 Continental w/4.6L/V8-281

Pin	CKT	Wire Color	Application	Abbreviation
1	638	O/LB	Power to High Speed Fan	
2	638	O/LB	Power to High Speed Fan	
3	38	BK/O	Power to LFC Relay/HFC Relay #2	B+
4	38	BK/O	Power to LFC Relay/HFC Relay #2	B+
5	366	R/BK	Power to Fuel Pump Driver Module	
6	229	R/O	Power to Low Speed Fan	
7	229	R/O	Power to Low Speed Fan	
8	38	BK/O	Power to HFC Relay #1	B+
9	37	Y	From EEC-V Power Relay	
10	38	BK/O	Power to HFC Relay #1	B+
11	1059	LB/O	Battery to Fuel Pump Relay	B+
12	638	O/LB	Power to High Speed Fan	
13	361	R	Key Power	KEY PWR
14	228	DB	Low Fan Control Circuit	LFC
15	57	BK	Power Ground	PWR GND
16	321	GY/W	A/C Clutch Ground	ACC GND
17	639	LG/P	High Fan Control Circuit	HFC
18	57	BK	Power Ground	PWR GND
21	348	B	A/C Cycling Switch	ACCS
22	331	PK/Y	Wide Open Throttle A/C Cut-off	WAC
23	347	BK/Y	Power to A/C Clutch Coil	
24	638	O/LB	Power to High Speed Fan	

FM0159501256000X

Fig. 77   CCRM connector pin identification. 1994–95 Continental w/4.6L/V8-281

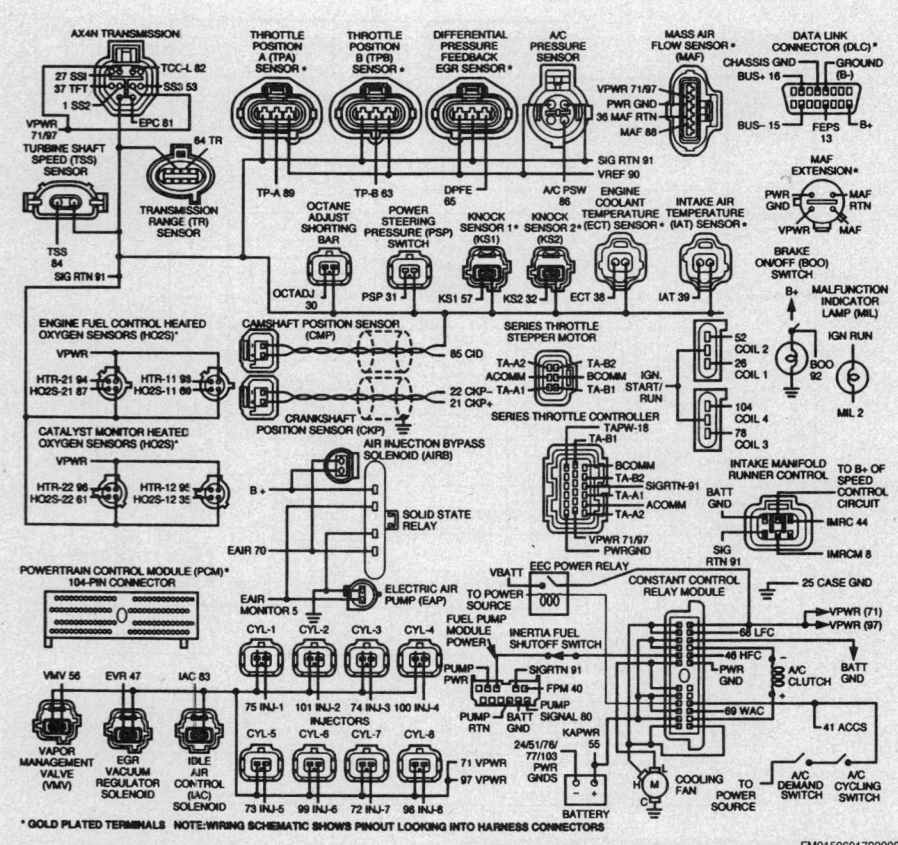

FM0159601702000X

Fig. 78   PCM wiring circuit. 1996 Continental w/4.6L/V8-281

Pin	CKT	Wire Color	Application	Abbreviation
68	228	DB	Low Fan Control	LFC
69	331	PK/Y	Wide Open Throttle A/C Cut-off	WAC
70	369	W/O	Electronic Air Management Control	EAIR
71	361	R	Vehicle Power	VPWR
72	561	T/R	Injector-7	INJ 7
73	559	T/BK	Injector-5	INJ 5
74	557	BR/Y	Injector-3	INJ 3
75	555	T	Injector-1	INJ 1
76	570	BK/W	Power Ground	PWR GND
77	570	BK/W	Power Ground	PWR GND
78	528	PK/W	Coil Driver 3	CD3
80	926	LB/O	Fuel Pump Control	FP
81	925	W/Y	Electronic Pressure Control	EPC
82	125	DB/W	Transmission Converter Clutch Lock-up	TCCL
83	264	W/LB	Idle Air Control Solenoid	IAC
84	970	DG/W	Turbine Shaft Speed Sensor	TSS
85	282	DB/O	Cylinder Identification	CID
86	440	T/LG	Air Conditioning Pressure Sensor	ACPS
87	94	R/BK	Heated Oxygen Sensor -21	HO2S-21
88	967	LB/R	Mass Air Flow Sensor	MAF
89	355	GY/W	Throttle Position Sensor A	TP-A
90	351	BR/W	Vehicle Reference Voltage	VREF
91	359	GY/R	Signal Return	SIG RTN
92	511	LG	Brake On/Off Switch	BOO
93	387	R/W	HO2S Heater-11	HTR-11
94	388	Y/LB	HO2S Heater-21	HTR-21
95	389	W/BK	HO2S Heater-12	HTR-12
96	390	T/Y	HO2S Heater-22	HTR-22
97	361	R	Vehicle Power	VPWR
98	562	LB	Injector-8	INJ 8
99	560	LG/O	Injector-6	INJ 6
100	558	BR/LB	Injector-4	INJ 4
101	556	W	Injector-2	INJ 2
103	570	BK/W	Power Ground	PWR GND
104	529	R/Y	Coil Driver 4	CD4

FM0159601703020X

Fig. 79 PCM connector pin identification (Part 2 of 2). 1996 Continental w/4.6L/V8-281

Pin	CKT	Wire Color	Application	Abbreviation
1	315	P/O	Shift Solenoid 2	SS2
2	658	PK/LG	Malfunction Indicator Lamp	MIL
5	111	BK/O	Electronic Air Management Monitor	EAIRM
8	358	LG/BK	Intake Manifold Runner Control Monitor	IMRCM
13	107	P	Flash EPROM Power Supply	FEPS
15	915	PK/LB	BUS (-)	BUS-
16	914	T/O	BUS (+)	BUS+
18	961	W/PK	Traction Assist Pulsewidth Modulator	TAPW
21	138	BK/PK	Crankshaft Position Sensor+	CKP+
22	139	GY/Y	Crankshaft Position Sensor-	CKP-
24	570	BK/W	Power Ground	PWR GND
25	57	BK	Case Ground	CASE GND
26	526	DB/LG	Coil Driver 1	CD1
27	237	O/Y	Shift Solenoid 1	SS1
30	242	DG	Octane Adjust	OCT ADJ
31	330	Y/LG	Power Steering Pressure Switch	PSP
32	311	DG/P	Knock Sensor 2	KS2
35	392	R/LG	Heated Oxygen Sensor-12	HO2S-12
36	968	T/LB	Mass Air Flow Sensor Return	MAF RTN
37	923	O/BK	Transmission Fluid Temperature Sensor	TFT
38	354	LG/R	Engine Coolant Temperature Sensor	ECT
39	743	GY	Intake Air Temperature Sensor	IAT
40	238	DG/Y	Fuel Pump Monitor	FPM
41	348	P	A/C Cycling Switch	ACCS
44	367	BR	Intake Manifold Runner Control	IMRC
46	639	LG/P	High Speed Fan Control	HFC
47	360	BR/PK	EGR Vacuum Regulator Solenoid	EVR
51	570	BK/W	Power Ground	PWR GND
52	527	R/LB	Coil Driver 2	CD2
53	971	PK/BK	Shift Solenoid 3	SS3
55	37	Y	Keep Alive Power	KAPWR
56	191	LG/BK	Vapor Management Valve	VMV
57	310	Y/R	Knock Sensor 1	KS1
60	74	GY/LB	Heated Oxygen Sensor -11	HO2S-11
61	393	P/LG	Heated Oxygen Sensor -22	HO2S-22
63	357	Y/W	Throttle Position Sensor B	TP-B
64	199	LB/Y	Transmission Range Sensor	TR
65	352	BR/LG	Differential Pressure Feedback EGR Sensor	DPFE

(Continued)

FM0159601703010X

Fig. 79 PCM connector pin identification (Part 1 of 2). 1996 Continental w/4.6L/V8-281

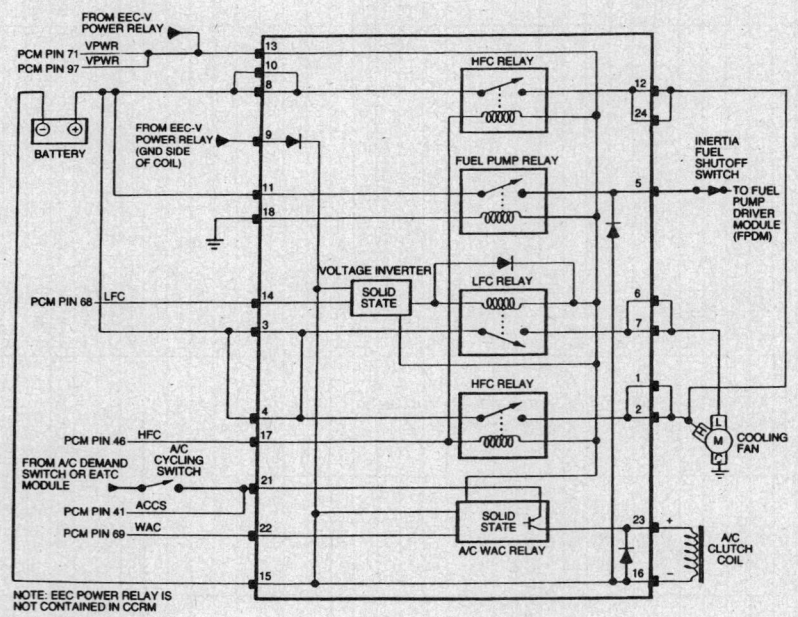

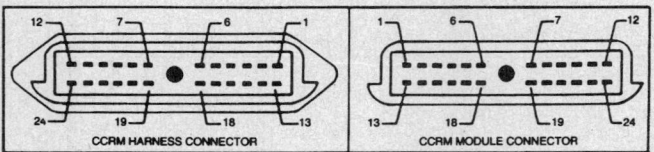

Fig. 80 CCRM wiring circuit. 1996 Continental w/4.6L/V8-281

Pin	CKT	Wire Color	Application	Abbreviation
1	638	O/LB	Power to High Speed Fan	
2	638	O/LB	Power to High Speed Fan	
3	38	BK/O	Power to LFC Relay/HFC Relay #2	B+
4	38	BK/O	Power to LFC Relay/HFC Relay #2	B+
5	366	R/BK	Power to Fuel Pump Driver Module	
6	229	R/O	Power to Low Speed Fan	
7	229	R/O	Power to Low Speed Fan	
8	38	BK/O	Power to HFC Relay #1	B+
9	37	Y	From EEC-V Power Relay	
10	38	BK/O	Power to HFC Relay #1	B+
11	1059	LB/O	Battery to Fuel Pump Relay	B+
12	638	O/LB	Power to High Speed Fan	
13	361	R	Key Power	KEY PWR
14	228	DB	Low Fan Control Circuit	LFC
15	57	BK	Power Ground	PWR GND
16	321	GY/W	A/C Clutch Ground	ACC GND
17	639	LG/P	High Fan Control Circuit	HFC
18	57	BK	Power Ground	PWR GND
21	348	B	A/C Cycling Switch	ACCS
22	331	PK/Y	Wide Open Throttle A/C Cut-off	WAC
23	347	BK/Y	Power to A/C Clutch Coil	
24	638	O/LB	Power to High Speed Fan	

FM0159601705000X

Fig. 81 CCRM connector pin identification. 1996 Continental w/4.6L/V8-281

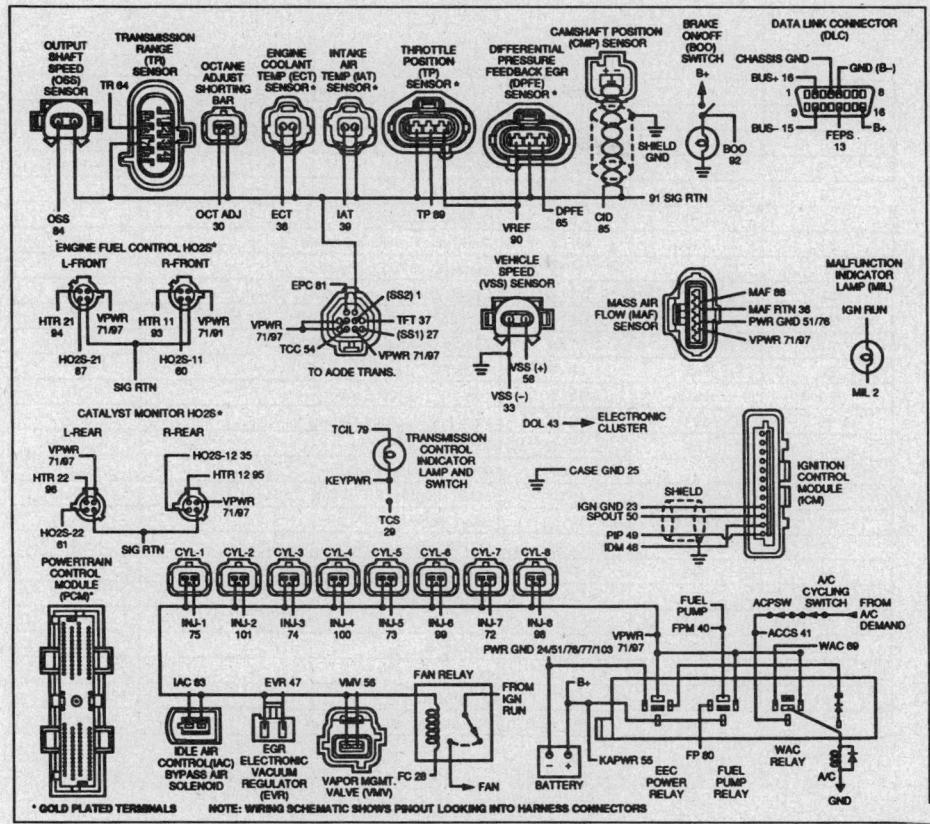

Fig. 82   PCM wiring circuit. 1994–95 Town Car w/4.6L/V8-281

Pin	CKT	Wire Color	Application	Abbreviation
1	315	P/O	Shift Solenoid 2	SS2
2	658	PK/LG	Malfunction Indicator Lamp	MIL
13	107	P	Flash EPROM Power Supply	FEPS
15	915	PK/LB	BUS (-)	BUS
16	914	T/O	BUS (+)	BUS+
23	259	O/R	Ignition Ground	IGN GND
24	570	BK/W	Power Ground	PWR GND
25	57	BK	Case Ground	CASE GND
27	237	O/Y	Shift Solenoid 1	SS1
28	228	DB	Fan Control	FC
29	224	T/W	Transmission Control Switch	TCS
30	242	DG	Octane Adjust	OCT ADJ
33	676	PK/O	Vehicle Speed Sensor (-)	VSS-
35	392	R/LG	Heated Oxygen Sensor-12 (R-Right)	HO2S-12
36	968	T/LB	Mass Air Flow Sensor Return	MAF RTN
37	923	O/BK	Transmission Fluid Temperature Sensor	TFT
38	354	LG/R	Engine Coolant Temperature Sensor	ECT
39	743	GY	Intake Air Temperature Sensor	IAT
40	238	DG/Y	Fuel Pump Monitor	FPM
41	347	BK/Y	A/C Cycling Switch	ACCS
43	205	DB/LG	Data Output Link	DOL
47	360	BR/PK	EGR Electronic Vacuum Regulator	EVR
48	659	O/W	Ignition Diagnostic Monitor	IDM
49	395	GY/O	Profile Ignition Pickup	PIP
50	929	PK	Spark Output	SPOUT
51	570	BK/W	Power Ground	PWR GND
54	924	BR/O	Torque Converter Clutch Solenoid	TCC
55	554	Y/BK	Keep Alive Power	KAPWR
56	191	LG/BK	Vapor Management Valve Solenoid	VMV
58	679	GY/BK	Vehicle Speed Sensor (+)	VSS+
60	74	GY/LB	Heated Oxygen Sensor-11 (F-Right)	HO2S-11
61	393	P/LG	Heated Oxygen Sensor-22 (R-Left)	HO2S-22
64	199	LB/Y	Transmission Range Sensor	TR
65	352	BR/LG	Differential Pressure Feedback EGR Sensor	DPFE
69	331	PK/Y	Wide Open Throttle A/C Cutoff	WAC
71	361	R	Vehicle Power	VPWR
72	561	T/R	Injector-7	INJ 7
73	559	T/BK	Injector-5	INJ 5
74	557	BR/Y	Injector-3	INJ 3

**Fig. 83   PCM connector pin identification (Part 1 of 2).
1994–95 Town Car w/4.6L/V8-281**

Pin	CKT	Wire Color	Application	Abbreviation
75	555	T	Injector-1	INJ 1
76	570	BK/W	Power Ground	PWR GND
77	570	BK/W	Power Ground	PWR GND
79	911	W/LG	Transmission Control Indicator Lamp	TCIL
80	926	LB/O	Fuel Pump Control	FP
81	925	W/Y	Electronic Pressure Control	EPC
83	264	W/LB	Idle Air Control Solenoid	IAC
84	970	DG/W	Output Shaft Speed Sensor	OSS
85	282	DB/O	Cylinder Identification	CID
87	94	R/BK	Heated Oxygen Sensor -21 (F-Left)	HO2S-21
88	967	LB/R	Mass Air Flow Sensor	MAF
89	355	GY/W	Throttle Position Sensor	TP
90	351	BR/W	Vehicle Reference Voltage	VREF
91	359	GY/R	Signal Return	SIG RTN
92	511	LG	Brake On/Off Switch	BOO
93	387	R/W	HO2S Heater-11 (F-Right)	HTR-11
94	388	Y/LB	HO2S Heater-21 (F-Left)	HTR-21
95	389	W/BK	HO2S Heater-12 (R-Right)	HTR-12
96	390	T/Y	HO2S Heater-22 (R-Left)	HTR-22
97	361	R	Vehicle Power	VPWR
98	562	LB	Injector-8	INJ 8
99	560	LG/O	Injector-6	INJ 6
100	558	BR/LB	Injector-4	INJ 4
101	556	W	Injector-2	INJ 2
103	570	BK/W	Power Ground	PWR GND

FM0159501260020X

Fig. 83   PCM connector pin identification (Part 2 of 2). Town Car w/4.6L/V8-281

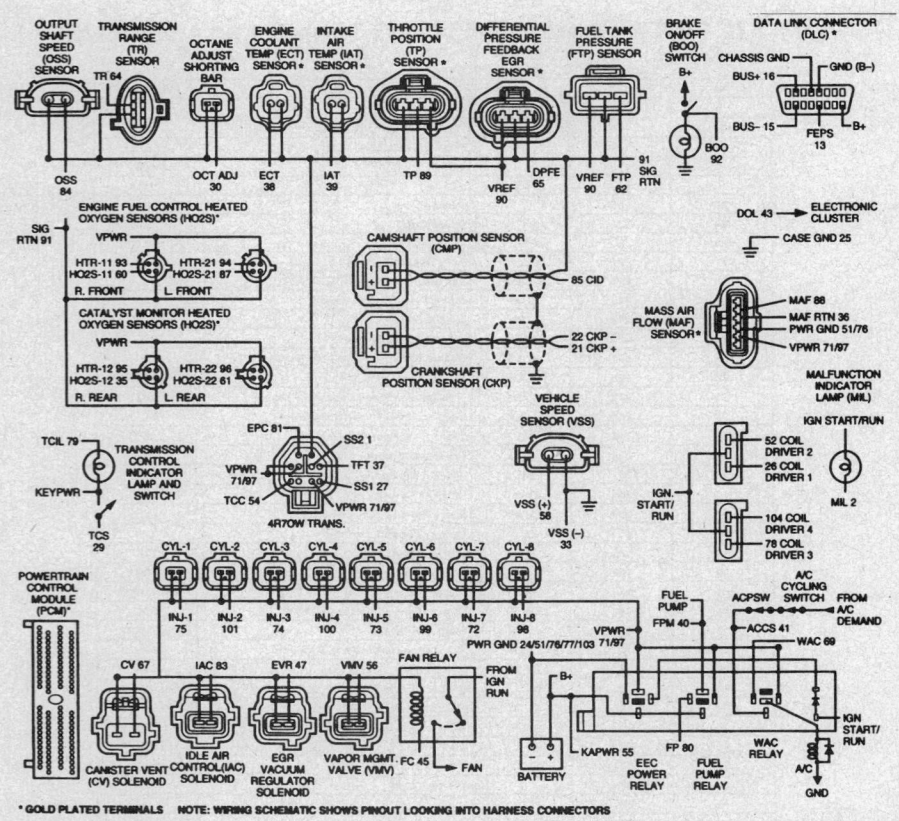

FM0159601706000X

Fig. 84   PCM wiring circuit. 1996 Town Car w/4.6L/V8-281

Pin	CKT	Wire Color	Application	Abbreviation
1	315	P/B	Shift Solenoid 2	SS2
2	658	PK/LG	Malfunction Indicator Lamp	MIL
13	107	P	Flash EPROM Power Supply	FEPS
15	915	PK/LB	BUS (-)	BUS-
16	914	T/O	BUS (+)	BUS+
21	349	BD	Crankshaft Position Sensor (+)	CKP +
22	350	GY	Crankshaft Position Sensor (-)	CKP -
24	570	BK/W	Power-Ground	PWR GND
25	57	BK	Case Ground	CASE GND
26	95	T/W	Coil Driver 1	CD1
27	237	O/Y	Shift Solenoid 1	SS1
29	224	T/W	Transmission Control Switch	TCS
30	242	DG	Octane Adjust	OCT ADJ
33	676	PK/O	Vehicle Speed Sensor (-)	VSS-
35	392	R/LG	Heated Oxygen Sensor-12 (R. Rear)	HO2S-12
36	968	T/LB	Mass Air Flow Sensor Return	MAF RTN
37	923	O/BK	Transmission Fluid Temperature Sensor	TFT
38	354	LG/R	Engine Coolant Temperature Sensor	ECT
39	743	GY	Intake Air Temperature Sensor	IAT
40	238	DG/Y	Fuel Pump Monitor	FPM
41	347	BK/Y	A/C Cycling Switch	ACCS
43	205	DB/LG	Data Output Link	DOL
45	228	DB	Fan Control Relay	FC
47	360	BR/PK	EGR Vacuum Regulator Solenoid	EVR
51	570	BK/W	Power Ground	PWR GND
52	96	T/O	Coil Driver 2	CD2
54	480	P/Y	Torque Converter Clutch Solenoid	TCC
55	554	Y/BK	Keep Alive Power	KAPWR
56	191	LG/BK	Vapor Management Valve Solenoid	VMV
58	679	GY/BK	Vehicle Speed Sensor (+)	VSS +
60	74	GY/LB	Heated Oxygen Sensor -11 (R. Front)	HO2S-11
61	393	P/LG	Heated Oxygen Sensor -22 (L. Rear)	HO2S-22
62	791	R/PK	Fuel Tank Pressure Sensor	FTP
64	199	LB/Y	Transmission Range Sensor	TR
65	352	BR/LG	Differential Pressure Feedback EGR Sensor	DPFE
67	91	P/W	Canister Vent Solenoid	CAN VNT
69	331	PK/Y	Wide Open Throttle A/C Cut-off	WAC
71	361	R	Vehicle Power	VPWR

(Continued)

FM0159601707010X

Fig. 85 PCM connector pin identification (Part 1 of 2). 1996 Town Car w/4.6L/V8-281

Pin	CKT	Wire Color	Application	Abbreviation
72	561	T/R	Injector-7	INJ 7
73	559	T/BK	Injector-5	INJ 5
74	557	BR/Y	Injector-3	INJ 3
75	555	T	Injector-1	INJ 1
76	570	BK/W	Power Ground	PWR GND
77	570	BK/W	Power Ground	PWR GND
78	97	T/LG	Coil Driver 3	CD 3
79	911	W/LG	Transmission Control Indicator Lamp	TCIL
80	926	LB/O	Fuel Pump Control	FP
81	925	W/Y	Electronic Pressure Control	EPC
83	264	W/LB	Idle Air Control Solenoid	IAC
84	970	DG/W	Output Shaft Speed Sensor	OSS
85	795	DG	Cylinder Identification	CID
87	94	R/BK	Heated Oxygen Sensor -21 (L. Front)	HO2S-21
88	967	LB/R	Mass Air Flow Sensor	MAF
89	355	GY/W	Throttle Position Sensor	TP
90	351	BR/W	Vehicle Reference Voltage	VREF
91	359	GY/R	Signal Return	SIG RTN
92	511	LG	Brake On/Off Switch	BOO
93	387	R/W	HO2S Heater-11 (R. Front)	HTR-11
94	388	Y/LB	HO2S Heater-21 (L. Front)	HTR-21
95	389	W/BK	HO2S Heater-12 (R. Rear)	HTR-12
96	390	T/Y	HO2S Heater-22 (L. Rear)	HTR-22
97	361	R	Vehicle Power	VPWR
98	562	LB	Injector-8	INJ 8
99	560	LG/O	Injector-6	INJ 6
100	558	BR/LB	Injector-4	INJ 4
101	556	W	Injector-2	INJ 2
103	570	BK/W	Power Ground	PWR GND
104	98	T/LB	Coil Driver 4	CD4

FM0159601707020X

Fig. 85 PCM connector pin identification (Part 2 of 2). 1996 Town Car w/4.6L/V8-281

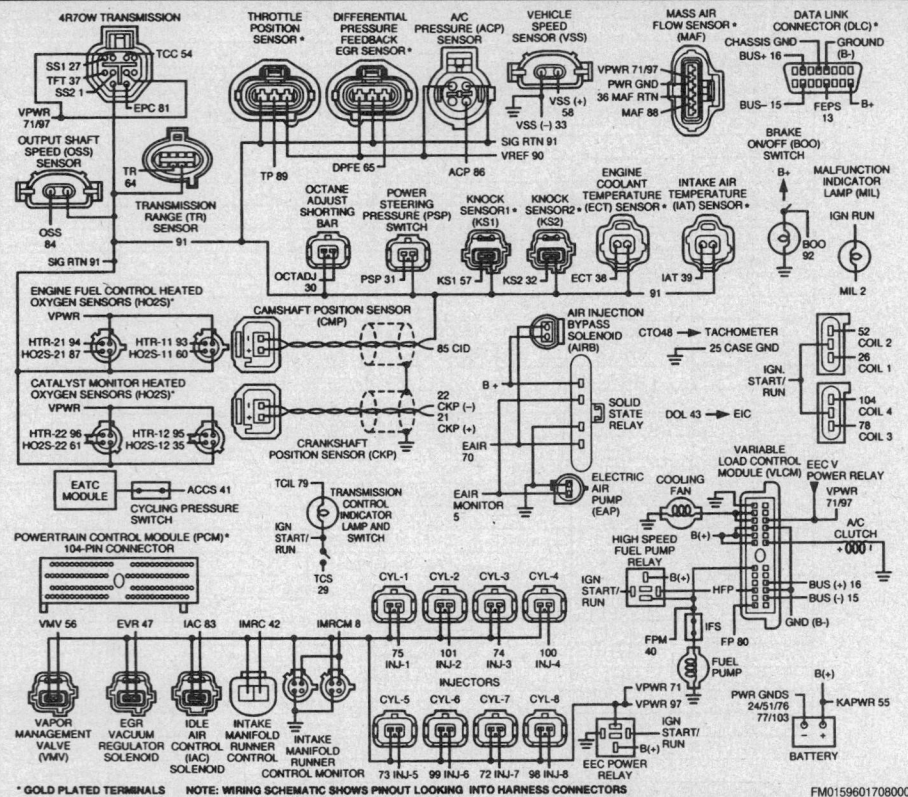

Fig. 86 PCM wiring circuit. 1996 Mark VIII w/4.6L/V8-281

Pin	Circuit	Wire Color	Application	Abbreviation
1	315	P/O	Shift Solenoid 2	SS2
2	658	PK/LG	Malfunction Indicator Lamp	MIL
5	17	W	Electronic Air Management Monitor	EAMM
8	75	DG/LG	Intake Manifold Runner Control Monitor	IMRCM
13	382	Y/BK	Flash EPROM Power Supply	FEPS
15	915	PK/LB	BUS (-)	BUS -
16	914	T/O	BUS (+)	BUS +
21	349	DB	Crankshaft Position Sensor (+)	CKP +
22	350	GY	Crankshaft Position Sensor (-)	CKP -
24	570	BK/W	Power Ground	PWR GND
25	57	BK	Case Ground	CASE GND
26	95	T/W	Ignition Coil 1	COIL-1
27	237	O/Y	Shift Solenoid 1	SS1
29	224	T/W	Transmission Control Switch	TCS
30	242	DG	Octane Adjust	OCT ADJ
32	311	DG/P	Knock Sensor 2	KS2
33	676	PK/O	Vehicle Speed Sensor (-)	VSS -
35	392	R/LG	Heated Oxygen Sensor - 12 (Right-Rear)	HO2S-12
36	968	T/LB	Mass Air Flow Sensor Return	MAF RTN
37	923	O/BK	Transmission Fluid Temperature Sensor	TFT
38	354	LG/R	Engine Coolant Temperature Sensor	ECT
39	743	GY	Intake Air Temperature Sensor	IAT
40	787	PK/BK	Fuel Pump Monitor	FPM
41	347	BK/Y	A/C Cycling Switch	ACCS
42	99	LG/BK	Intake Manifold Runner Control	IMRC
43	305	LB/PK	Data Output Line	DOL
47	360	BR/PK	EGR Electronic Vacuum Regulator	EVR
48	11	T/Y	Clean Tachometer Output	CTO
51	570	BK/W	Power Ground	PWR GND
52	96	T/O	Ignition Coil 2	COIL-2
54	480	P/Y	Torque Converter Clutch Solenoid	TCC
55	37	Y	Keep Alive Power	KAPWR
56	191	LG/BK	Vapor Management Valve	VMV
57	310	Y/R	Knock Sensor 1	KS1
58	150	DG/W	Vehicle Speed Sensor (+)	VSS +
60	74	GY/LB	Heated Oxygen Sensor - 11 (Right-Front)	HO2S-11
61	393	P/LG	Heated Oxygen Sensor - 22 (Left-Rear)	HO2S-22
64	199	LB/Y	Transmission Range Sensor	TR

(Continued)

FM0159601709010X

Fig. 87 PCM connector pin identification (Part 1 of 2). 1996 Mark VIII w/4.6L/V8-281

PIN	Circuit	Wire Color	Application	Abbreviation
65	352	BR/LG	Differential Pressure Feedback EGR Sensor	DPFE
70	18	O/Y	Electronic Air Management	EAM
71	361	R	Vehicle Power	VPWR
72	561	T/R	Injector 7	INJ-7
73	559	T/BK	Injector 5	INJ-5
74	557	BR/Y	Injector 3	INJ-3
75	555	T	Injector 1	INJ-1
76	570	BK/W	Power Ground	PWR GND
77	570	BK/W	Power Ground	PWR GND
78	97	T/LG	Ignition Coil 3	COIL-3
79	911	W/LG	Transmission Control Indicator Lamp	TCIL
80	926	LB/O	Fuel Pump Control	FP
81	925	W/Y	Electronic Pressure Control Solenoid	EPC
83	264	W/LB	Idle Air Control Solenoid	IAC
84	970	DG/W	Output Shaft Speed Sensor	OSS
85	282	DB/O	Cylinder Identification	CID
86	879	DG/W	A/C Pressure Sensor	ACP
87	94	R/BK	Heated Oxygen Sensor - 21 (Left-Front)	HO2S-21
88	967	LB/R	Mass Air Flow Sensor	MAF
89	355	GY/W	Throttle Position Sensor	TP
90	351	BR/W	Vehicle Reference Voltage	VREF
91	359	GY/R	Signal Return	SIG RTN
92	511	LG	Brake On/Off Switch	BOO
93	387	R/W	Heater Oxygen Sensor HTR - 11 (Right-Front)	HTR-11
94	388	Y/LB	Heater Oxygen Sensor HTR - 21 (Left-Front)	HTR-21
95	389	W/BK	Heater Oxygen Sensor HTR - 12 (Right-Rear)	HTR-12
96	390	T/Y	Heater Oxygen Sensor HTR - 22 (Left-Rear)	HTR-22
97	361	R	Vehicle Power	VPWR
98	562	LB	Injector 8	INJ-8
99	560	LG/O	Injector 6	INJ-6
100	558	BR/LB	Injector 4	INJ-4
101	556	W	Injector 2	INJ-2
103	570	BK/W	Power Ground	PWR GND
104	98	T/LB	Ignition Coil 4	COIL 4

FM0159601709020X

Fig. 87 PCM connector pin identification (Part 2 of 2). 1996 Mark VIII w/4.6L/V8-281

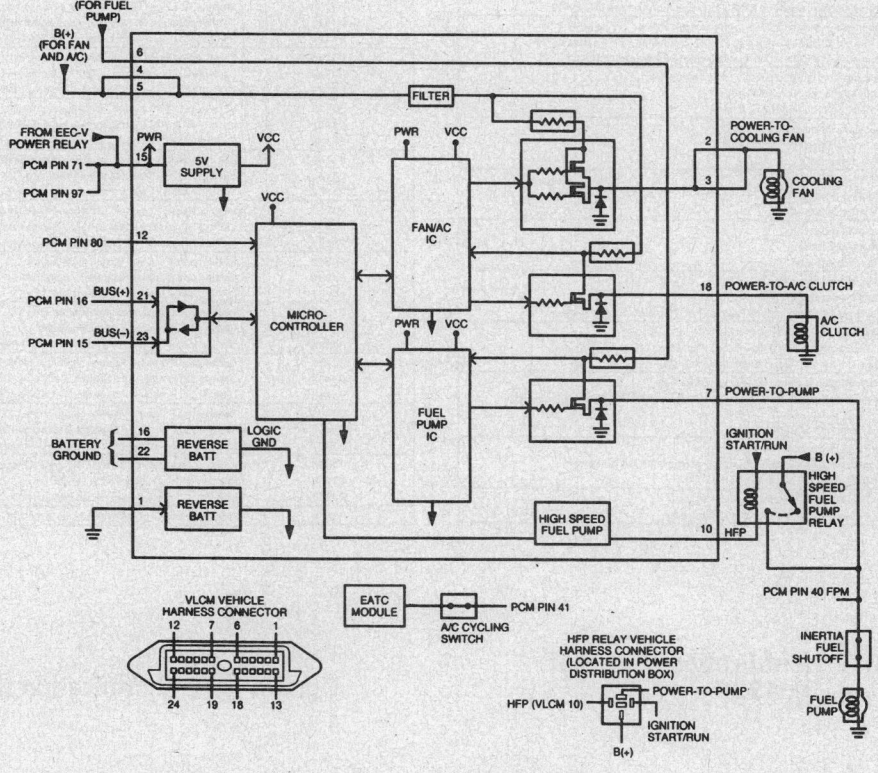

FM0159601710000X

Fig. 88 VLCM wiring circuit. 1996 Mark VIII w/4.6L/V8-281

Pin	Circuit	Wire Color	Application	Abbreviation
1	57	BK	Power Ground	PWR GND
2	386	LB	Power-to-Cooling Fan	Power-to-Fan
3	386	LB	Power-to-Cooling Fan	Power-to-Fan
4	37	Y	B (+) for Fan and A/C Output Driver	B (+)
5	37	Y	B (+) for Fan and A/C Output Driver	B (+)
6	37	Y	B (+) for Fuel Pump Output Driver	B (+)
7	787	PK/BK	Power-to-Fuel Pump	Power-to-Pump
10	789	BR/W	High Speed Fuel Pump Control	HFP
12	926	LB/O	Fuel Pump Control	FP
15	361	R	VPWR (for VLCM logic)	VPWR
16	570	BK/W	Ground	GND
18	348	P	Power-to-A/C Clutch	Power-to-Clutch
21	914	T/O	BUS (+)	BUS +
22	570	BK/W	Ground	GND
23	915	PK/LB	BUS (-)	BUS -

FM0159601711000X

Fig. 89   VLCM connector pin identification. 1996 Mark VIII w/4.6L/V8-281

DTC	Definitions
P0102	Mass Air Flow (MAF) sensor circuit low input
P0103	Mass Air Flow (MAF) sensor circuit high input
P0112	Intake Air Temperature (IAT) sensor circuit low input
P0113	Intake Air Temperature (IAT) sensor circuit high input
P0117	Engine Coolant Temperature (ECT) sensor circuit low input
P0118	Engine Coolant Temperature (ECT) sensor circuit high input
P0122	Throttle Position (TP) sensor circuit low input
P0123	Throttle Position (TP) sensor circuit high input
P0125	Insufficient Coolant Temperature to enter closed loop fuel control
P0132	Upstream Heated Oxygen sensor (HO2S 11) circuit high voltage (Bank # 1)
P0135	Heated Oxygen sensor heater (HTR 11) circuit malfunction
P0138	Downstream Heated Oxygen sensor (HO2S 12) circuit high voltage (Bank # 1)
P0140	Heated Oxygen sensor (HO2S 12) circuit no activity detected (Bank # 1)
P0141	Heated Oxygen sensor heater (HTR 12) circuit malfunction
P0152	Upstream Heated Oxygen sensor (HO2S 21) circuit high voltage (Bank # 2)
P0155	Heated Oxygen sensor heater (HTR 21) circuit malfunction
P0158	Downstream Heated Oxygen sensor (HO2S 22) circuit high voltage (Bank # 2)
P0160	Heated Oxygen sensor (HO2S 22) circuit no activity detected (Bank # 2)
P0161	Heated Oxygen sensor heater (HTR 22) circuit malfunction
P0171	System (adaptive fuel) too lean (Bank # 1)
P0172	System (adaptive fuel) too rich (Bank # 1)
P0174	System (adaptive fuel) too lean (Bank # 2)
P0175	System (adaptive fuel) too rich (Bank # 2)
P0300	Random Misfire detected
P0301	Cylinder # 1 Misfire detected
P0302	Cylinder # 2 Misfire detected
P0303	Cylinder # 3 Misfire detected
P0304	Cylinder # 4 Misfire detected
P0305	Cylinder # 5 Misfire detected
P0306	Cylinder # 6 Misfire detected
P0307	Cylinder # 7 Misfire detected
P0308	Cylinder # 8 Misfire detected
P0320	Ignition Engine Speed (Profile Ignition Pickup (PIP)) input circuit malfunction
P0340	Camshaft Position (CMP) sensor circuit malfunction (CID)
P0402	Exhaust Gas Recirculation (EGR) flow excess detected (valve open at idle)
P0420	Catalyst system efficiency below threshold (Bank # 1)
P0430	Catalyst system efficiency below threshold (Bank # 2)
P0443	Evaporative emission control system Canister Purge Control Valve (CANP) circuit malfunction
P0500	Vehicle Speed Sensor (VSS) malfunction
P0505	Idle Air Control (IAC) system malfunction
P0605	Powertrain Control Module (PCM) - Read Only Memory (ROM) test error
P0703	Brake On/Off switch (BOO) input malfunction
P0707	Manual Lever Position (MLP) sensor circuit low input
P0708	Manual Lever Position (MLP) sensor circuit high input

DTC	Definitions
P0720	Output Shaft Speed (OSS) sensor circuit malfunction
P0741	Torque Converter Clutch (TCC) system incorrect mechanical performance
P0743	Torque Converter Clutch (TCC) system electrical failure
P0750	Shift Solenoid # 1 (SS1) circuit malfunction
P0751	Shift Solenoid # 1 (SS1) performance
P0755	Shift Solenoid # 2 (SS2) circuit malfunction
P0756	Shift Solenoid # 2 (SS2) performance
P1000	OBD II Monitor Testing not complete
P1100	Mass Air Flow (MAF) sensor intermittent
P1101	Mass Air Flow (MAF) sensor out of Self-Test range
P1112	Intake Air Temperature (IAT) sensor intermittent
P1116	Engine Coolant Temperature (ECT) sensor out of Self-Test range
P1117	Engine Coolant Temperature (ECT) sensor intermittent
P1120	Throttle Position (TP) sensor out of range low
P1121	Throttle Position (TP) sensor inconsistent with MAF sensor
P1124	Throttle Position (TP) sensor out of Self-Test range
P1125	Throttle Position (TP) sensor circuit intermittent
P1130	Lack of HO2S 11 switch, adaptive fuel at limit
P1131	Lack of HO2S 11 switch, sensor indicates lean (Bank # 1)
P1132	Lack of HO2S 11 switch, sensor indicates rich (Bank # 1)
P1137	Lack of HO2S 12 switch, sensor indicates lean (Bank # 1)
P1138	Lack of HO2S 12 switch, sensor indicates rich (Bank # 1)
P1150	Lack of HO2S 21 switch, adaptive fuel at limit
P1151	Lack of HO2S 21 switch, sensor indicates lean (Bank # 2)
P1152	Lack of HO2S 21 switch, sensor indicates rich (Bank # 2)
P1157	Lack of HO2S 22 switch, sensor indicates lean (Bank # 2)
P1158	Lack of HO2S 22 switch, sensor indicates rich (Bank # 2)
P1351	Ignition Diagnostic Monitor (IDM) circuit input malfunction
P1352	Ignition coil A primary circuit malfunction
P1353	Ignition coil B primary circuit malfunction
P1354	Ignition coil C primary circuit malfunction
P1355	Ignition coil D primary circuit malfunction
P1364	Ignition coil primary circuit malfunction
P1390	Octane Adjust (OCT ADJ) out of Self-Test range
P1400	Differential Pressure Feedback Electronic (DPFE) sensor circuit low voltage detected
P1401	Differential Pressure Feedback Electronic (DPFE) sensor circuit high voltage detected
P1403	Differential Pressure Feedback Electronic (DPFE) sensor hoses reversed
P1405	Differential Pressure Feedback Electronic (DPFE) sensor upstream hose off or plugged
P1406	Differential Pressure Feedback Electronic (DPFE) sensor downstream hose off or plugged
P1407	Exhaust Gas Recirculation (EGR) no flow detected (valve stuck closed or inoperative)
P1408	Exhaust Gas Recirculation (EGR) flow out of Self-Test range
P1473	Fan Secondary High with Fan(s) Off
P1474	Low Fan Control primary circuit malfunction
P1479	High Fan Control primary circuit malfunction

FM0159401142020X

Fig. 90   DTC identification (Part 1 of 3). 1994

Fig. 90   DTC identification (Part 2 of 3). 1994

DTC	Definitions
P1480	Fan Secondary Low with Low Fan On
P1481	Fan Secondary Low with High Fan On
P1500	Vehicle Speed Sensor (VSS) circuit intermittent
P1505	Idle Air Control (IAC) system at adaptive clip
P1605	Powertrain Control Module (PCM) - Keep Alive Memory (KAM) test error
P1703	Brake On/Off (BOO) switch out of Self-Test range
P1705	Manual Lever Position (MLP) sensor out of Self-Test range
P1711	Transmission Fluid Temperature (TFT) sensor out of Self-Test range
P1742	Torque Converter Clutch (TCC) solenoid mechanically failed on (turns on MIL)
P1743	Torque Converter Clutch (TCC) solenoid mechanically failed on (turns on TCIL)
P1744	Torque Converter Clutch (TCC) system mechanically stuck in off position
P1746	Electronic Pressure Control (EPC) solenoid circuit low input (open circuit)
P1747	Electronic Pressure Control (EPC) solenoid circuit high input (short circuit)
P1751	Shift Solenoid #1 (SS1) performance
P1756	Shift Solenoid #2 (SS2) performance
P1780	Transmission Control Switch (TCS) circuit out of Self-Test range

FM015940114203OX

Fig. 90   DTC identification (Part 3 of 3). 1994

DTC	Definitions
P0102	Mass Air Flow (MAF) sensor circuit low input
P0103	Mass Air Flow (MAF) sensor circuit high input
P0112	Intake Air Temperature (IAT) sensor circuit low input
P0113	Intake Air Temperature (IAT) sensor circuit high input
P0117	Engine Coolant Temperature (ECT) sensor circuit low input
P0118	Engine Coolant Temperature (ECT) sensor circuit high input
P0121	In-range operating Throttle Position (TP) sensor circuit failure
P0122	Throttle Position (TP) sensor circuit low input
P0123	Throttle Position (TP) sensor circuit high input
P0125	Insufficient coolant temperature to enter closed loop fuel control
P0126	Insufficient coolant temperature for stable operation
P0131	Upstream Heated Oxygen Sensor (HO2S 11) circuit out of range low voltage (Bank #1)
P0132	Upstream Heated Oxygen Sensor (HO2S 11) circuit high voltage (Bank #1)
P0133	Upstream Heated Oxygen Sensor (HO2S 11) circuit slow response (Bank #1)
P0135	Upstream Heated Oxygen Sensor Heater (HTR 11) circuit malfunction (Bank #1)
P0136	Downstream Heated Oxygen Sensor (HO2S 12) circuit malfunction (Bank #1)
P0138	Downstream Heated Oxygen Sensor (HO2S 12) circuit high voltage (Bank #1)
P0141	Downstream Heated Oxygen Sensor Heater (HTR 12) circuit malfunction (Bank #1)
P0151	Upstream Heated Oxygen Sensor (HO2S 21) circuit out of range low voltage (Bank #2)
P0152	Upstream Heated Oxygen Sensor (HO2S 21) circuit high voltage (Bank #2)
P0153	Upstream Heated Oxygen Sensor (HO2S 21) circuit slow response (Bank #2)
P0155	Upstream Heated Oxygen Sensor Heater (HTR 21) circuit malfunction (Bank #2)
P0156	Downstream Heated Oxygen Sensor (HO2S 22) circuit malfunction (Bank #2)
P0158	Downstream Heated Oxygen Sensor (HO2S 22) circuit high voltage (Bank #2)
P0161	Downstream Heated Oxygen Sensor Heater (HTR 22) circuit malfunction (Bank #2)
P0171	System (adaptive fuel) too lean (Bank #1)
P0172	System (adaptive fuel) too rich (Bank #1)
P0174	System (adaptive fuel) too lean (Bank #2)
P0175	System (adaptive fuel) too rich (Bank #2)
P0222	Throttle Position Sensor B (TP-B) circuit low input
P0223	Throttle Position Sensor B (TP-B) circuit high input
P0230	Fuel Pump primary circuit malfunction
P0231	Fuel Pump secondary circuit low
P0232	Fuel Pump secondary circuit high
P0300	Random Misfire detected
P0301	Cylinder #1 Misfire detected
P0302	Cylinder #2 Misfire detected
P0303	Cylinder #3 Misfire detected
P0304	Cylinder #4 Misfire detected
P0305	Cylinder #5 Misfire detected
P0306	Cylinder #6 Misfire detected
P0307	Cylinder #7 Misfire detected
P0308	Cylinder #8 Misfire detected
P0320	Ignition Engine Speed (Profile Ignition Pickup (PIP)) input circuit malfunction

Fig. 91   DTC identification (Part 1 of 5). 1995

DTC	Definitions
PC340	Camshaft Position (CMP) Sensor circuit malfunction (CID)
P0350	Ignition Coil primary circuit malfunction
P0351	Ignition Coil A primary circuit malfunction
P0352	Ignition Coil B primary circuit malfunction
P0353	Ignition Coil C primary circuit malfunction
P0354	Ignition Coil D primary circuit malfunction
P0400	Exhaust Gas Recirculation (EGR) flow malfunction
P0401	Exhaust Gas Recirculation (EGR) flow insufficient detected
P0402	Exhaust Gas Recirculation (EGR) flow excess detected
P0411	Secondary Air Injection system incorrect flow detected
P0412	Secondary Air Injection system control valve malfunction
P0420	Catalyst system efficiency below threshold (Bank #1)
P0430	Catalyst system efficiency below threshold (Bank #2)
P0443	Evaporative emission control system purge control solenoid or valve circuit malfunction
P0500	Vehicle Speed Sensor (VSS) malfunction
P0505	Idle Air Control (IAC) system malfunction
P0603	Powertrain Control Module (PCM) - Keep Alive Memory (KAM) test error
P0605	Powertrain Control Module (PCM) - Read Only Memory (ROM) test error
P0703	Brake On/Off (BOO) switch input malfunction
P0704	Clutch Pedal Position (CPP) switch input circuit malfunction
P0707	Transmission Range (TR) Sensor circuit low input
P0708	Transmission Range (TR) Sensor circuit high input
P0712	Transmission Fluid Temperature (TFT) Sensor circuit low input
P0713	Transmission Fluid Temperature (TFT) Sensor circuit high input
P0715	Turbine Shaft Speed (TSS) Sensor circuit malfunction
P0720	Output Shaft Speed (OSS) Sensor circuit malfunction
P0731	Incorrect ratio for first gear
P0732	Incorrect ratio for second gear
P0733	Incorrect ratio for third gear
P0734	Incorrect ratio for fourth gear
P0736	Reverse incorrect gear ratio
P0741	Torque Converter Clutch (TCC) mechanical system performance
P0743	Torque Converter Clutch (TCC) electrical system malfunction
P0746	Electronic Pressure Control (EPC) solenoid performance
P0750	Shift Solenoid #1 (SS1) circuit malfunction
P0751	Shift Solenoid #1 (SS1) performance
P0755	Shift Solenoid #2 (SS2) circuit malfunction
P0756	Shift Solenoid #2 (SS2) performance
P0760	Shift Solenoid #3 (SS3) circuit malfunction
P0761	Shift Solenoid #3 (SS3) performance
P0781	1 to 2 shift error
P0782	2 to 3 shift error
P0783	3 to 4 shift error
P0784	4 to 5 shift error

Fig. 91   DTC identification (Part 2 of 5). 1995

DTC	Definitions
P1000	OBD II Monitor Testing not complete
U1039	Vehicle speed signal missing or incorrect
U1051	Brake switch signal missing or incorrect
P1100	Mass Air Flow (MAF) Sensor intermittent
P1101	Mass Air Flow (MAF) Sensor out of Self-Test range
P1112	Intake Air Temperature (IAT) Sensor intermittent
P1116	Engine Coolant Temperature (ECT) Sensor out of Self-Test range
P1117	Engine Coolant Temperature (ECT) Sensor intermittent
P1120	Throttle Position (TP) Sensor out of range low
P1121	Throttle Position (TP) Sensor inconsistent with MAF Sensor
P1124	Throttle Position (TP) Sensor out of Self-Test range
P1125	Throttle Position (TP) Sensor circuit intermittent
P1130	Lack of upstream Heated Oxygen Sensor (HO2S 11) switch, adaptive fuel at limit (Bank #1)
P1131	Lack of upstream Heated Oxygen Sensor (HO2S 11) switch, sensor indicates lean (Bank #1)
P1132	Lack of upstream Heated Oxygen Sensor (HO2S 11) switch, sensor indicates rich (Bank #1)
U1135	Ignition switch signal missing or incorrect
P1150	Lack of upstream Heated Oxygen Sensor (HO2S 21) switch, adaptive fuel at limit (Bank #2)
P1151	Lack of upstream Heated Oxygen Sensor (HO2S 21) switch, sensor indicates lean (Bank #2)
P1152	Lack of upstream Heated Oxygen Sensor (HO2S 21) switch, sensor indicates rich (Bank #2)
P1157	Lack of downstream Heated Oxygen Sensor (HO2S 22) switch, sensor indicates lean (Bank #2)
P1158	Lack of downstream Heated Oxygen Sensor (HO2S 22) switch, sensor indicates rich (Bank #2)
P1220	Series Throttle Control malfunction
P1224	Throttle Position Sensor B (TP-B) out of Self-Test range
P1233	Fuel Pump Driver Module offline
P1234	Fuel Pump Driver Module offline
P1235	Fuel Pump control out of range
P1236	Fuel Pump control out of range
P1237	Fuel Pump secondary circuit malfunction
P1238	Fuel Pump secondary circuit malfunction
P1260	THEFT detected - engine disabled
P1270	Engine RPM or vehicle speed limiter reached
P1351	Ignition Diagnostic Monitor (IDM) circuit input malfunction
P1358	Ignition Diagnostic Monitor (IDM) signal out of Self-Test range
P1359	Spark output circuit malfunction
P1390	Octane Adjust (OCT ADJ) out of Self-Test range
P1400	Differential Pressure Feedback EGR (DPFE) Sensor circuit low voltage detected
P1401	Differential Pressure Feedback EGR (DPFE) Sensor circuit high voltage detected
P1403	Differential Pressure Feedback EGR (DPFE) Sensor hoses reversed
P1405	Differential Pressure Feedback EGR (DPFE) Sensor upstream hose off or plugged
P1406	Differential Pressure Feedback EGR (DPFE) Sensor downstream hose off or plugged

Fig. 91   DTC identification (Part 3 of 5). 1995

DTC	Definitions
P1407	Exhaust Gas Recirculation (EGR) no flow detected (valve stuck closed or inoperative)
P1408	Exhaust Gas Recirculation (EGR) flow out of Self-Test range
P1409	Electronic Vacuum Regulator (EVR) control circuit malfunction
P1413	Secondary Air Injection system monitor circuit low voltage
P1414	Secondary Air Injection system monitor circuit high voltage
P1443	Evaporative emission control system - vacuum system, purge control solenoid or purge control valve malfunction
P1444	Purge Flow Sensor (PFS) circuit low input
P1445	Purge Flow Sensor (PFS) circuit high input
U1451	Lack of response from Passive Anti-Theft system (PATS) module - engine disabled
P1460	Wide Open Throttle Air Conditioning Cut-off (WAC) circuit malfunction
P1461	Air Conditioning Pressure (ACP) Sensor circuit low input
P1462	Air Conditioning Pressure (ACP) Sensor circuit high input
P1463	Air Conditioning Pressure (ACP) Sensor insufficient pressure change
P1469	Low air conditioning cycling period
P1473	Fan secondary high with fan(s) off
P1474	Low Fan Control primary circuit malfunction
P1479	High Fan Control primary circuit malfunction
P1480	Fan secondary low with low fan on
P1481	Fan secondary low with high fan on
P1500	Vehicle Speed Sensor (VSS) circuit intermittent
P1505	Idle Air Control (IAC) system at adaptive clip
P1506	Idle Air Control (IAC) overspeed error
P1507	Idle Air Control (IAC) underspeed error
P1518	Intake Manifold Runner Control (IMRC) malfunction (stuck open)
P1519	Intake Manifold Runner Control (IMRC) malfunction (stuck closed)
P1520	Intake Manifold Runner Control (IMRC) circuit malfunction
P1605	Powertrain Control Module (PCM) - Keep Alive Memory (KAM) test error
P1650	Power Steering Pressure (PSP) switch out of Self-Test range
P1651	Power Steering Pressure (PSP) switch input malfunction
P1701	Reverse engagement error
P1703	Brake On / Off (BOO) switch out of Self-Test range
P1705	Transmission Range (TR) Sensor out of Self-Test range
P1709	Park or Neutral Position (PNP) switch out of Self-Test range
P1711	Transmission Fluid Temperature (TFT) Sensor out of Self-Test range
P1729	4x4 Low switch error
P1741	Torque Converter Clutch (TCC) control error
P1742	Torque Converter Clutch (TCC) solenoid failed on (turns on MIL)
P1743	Torque Converter Clutch (TCC) solenoid failed on (turns on TCIL)
P1744	Torque Converter Clutch (TCC) system mechanically stuck in off position
P1746	Electronic Pressure Control (EPC) solenoid open circuit (low input)
P1747	Electronic Pressure Control (EPC) solenoid short circuit (high input)
P1749	Electronic Pressure Control (EPC) solenoid failed low
P1751	Shift Solenoid # 1 (SS1) performance

FM0159501261040X

Fig. 91   DTC identification (Part 4 of 5). 1995

DTC	Definitions
P1754	Coast Clutch Solenoid (CCS) circuit malfunction
P1756	Shift Solenoid #2 (SS2) performance
P1761	Shift Solenoid #3 (SS3) performance
P1780	Transmission Control switch (TCS) circuit out of Self-Test range
P1781	4x4 Low switch out of Self-Test range
P1783	Transmission overtemperature condition

FM0159501261050X

Fig. 91   DTC identification (Part 5 of 5). 1995

DTC	Definitions
P0102	Mass Air Flow (MAF) sensor circuit low input
P0103	Mass Air Flow (MAF) sensor circuit high input
P0106	Barometric Pressure (BP) sensor circuit performance
P0107	Barometric Pressure (BP) sensor circuit low input
P0108	Barometric Pressure (BP) sensor circuit high input
P0112	Intake Air Temperature (IAT) sensor circuit low input
P0113	Intake Air Temperature (IAT) sensor circuit high input
P0117	Engine Coolant Temperature (ECT) sensor circuit low input
P0118	Engine Coolant Temperature (ECT) sensor circuit high input
P0121	In-range operating Throttle Position (TP) sensor circuit failure
P0122	Throttle Position (TP) sensor circuit low input
P0123	Throttle Position (TP) sensor circuit high input
P0125	Insufficient coolant temperature to enter closed loop fuel control
P0131	Upstream Heated Oxygen Sensor (HO2S 11) circuit out of range low voltage (Bank # 1)
P0133	Upstream Heated Oxygen Sensor (HO2S 11) circuit slow response (Bank # 1)
P0135	Upstream Heated Oxygen Sensor Heater (HTR 11) circuit malfunction (Bank # 1)
P0136	Downstream Heated Oxygen Sensor (HO2S 12) circuit malfunction (Bank # 1)
P0141	Downstream Heated Oxygen Sensor Heater (HTR 12) circuit malfunction (Bank # 1)
P0151	Upstream Heated Oxygen Sensor (HO2S 21) circuit out of range low voltage (Bank #2)
P0153	Upstream Heated Oxygen Sensor (HO2S 21) circuit slow response (Bank #2)
P0155	Upstream Heated Oxygen Sensor Heater (HTR 21) circuit malfunction (Bank #2)
P0156	Downstream Heated Oxygen Sensor (HO2S 22) circuit malfunction (Bank #2)
P0161	Downstream Heated Oxygen Sensor Heater (HTR 22) circuit malfunction (Bank #2)
P0171	System (adaptive fuel) too lean (Bank # 1)
P0172	System (adaptive fuel) too rich (Bank # 1)
P0174	System (adaptive fuel) too lean (Bank #2)
P0175	System (adaptive fuel) too rich (Bank #2)
P0176	Fuel Composition sensor (FCS) circuit malfunction
P0182	Fuel Temperature sensor A circuit low input
P0183	Fuel Temperature sensor A circuit high input
P0187	Fuel Temperature sensor B circuit low input
P0188	Fuel Temperature sensor B circuit high input
P0191	Injector Pressure sensor circuit performance
P0192	Injector Pressure sensor circuit low input
P0193	Injector Pressure sensor circuit high input
P0222	Throttle Position Sensor B (TP-B) circuit low input
P0223	Throttle Position Sensor B (TP-B) circuit high input
P0230	Fuel Pump primary circuit malfunction
P0231	Fuel Pump secondary circuit low
P0232	Fuel Pump secondary circuit high
P0300	Random Misfire detected
P0301	Cylinder # 1 Misfire detected
P0302	Cylinder #2 Misfire detected
P0303	Cylinder #3 Misfire detected

(Continued)

FM0159601611010X

Fig. 92   DTC identification (Part 1 of 6). 1996

DTC	Definitions
P0304	Cylinder # 4 Misfire detected
P0305	Cylinder # 5 Misfire detected
P0306	Cylinder # 6 Misfire detected
P0307	Cylinder # 7 Misfire detected
P0308	Cylinder # 8 Misfire detected
P0320	Ignition Engine Speed (Profile Ignition Pickup (PIP)) input circuit malfunction
P0325	Knock Sensor (KS) 1 circuit malfunction
P0326	Knock Sensor (KS) 1 circuit performance
P0331	Knock Sensor (KS) 2 circuit malfunction
P0331	Knock Sensor (KS) 2 circuit performance
P0340	Camshaft Position (CMP) sensor circuit malfunction (CID)
P0350	Ignition Coil primary circuit malfunction
P0351	Ignition Coil A primary circuit malfunction
P0352	Ignition Coil B primary circuit malfunction
P0353	Ignition Coil C primary circuit malfunction
P0354	Ignition Coil D primary circuit malfunction
P0385	Crankshaft Position (CKP) sensor malfunction
P0400	Exhaust Gas Recirculation (EGR) flow malfunction
P0401	Exhaust Gas Recirculation (EGR) flow insufficient detected
P0402	Exhaust Gas Recirculation (EGR) flow excess detected
P0411	Secondary Air Injection system incorrect upstream flow detected
P0412	Secondary Air Injection system switching valve A malfunction
P0413	Secondary Air Injection system switching valve A circuit open
P0414	Secondary Air Injection system switching valve A circuit shorted
P0416	Secondary Air Injection system switching valve B circuit open
P0417	Secondary Air Injection system switching valve B circuit shorted
P0420	Catalyst system efficiency below threshold (Bank # 1)
P0430	Catalyst system efficiency below threshold (Bank #2)
P0440	Evaporative emission control system malfunction (Probe)
P0442	Evaporative emission control system small leak detected
P0443	Evaporative emission control system purge control solenoid or vapor management valve circuit malfunction
P0446	Evaporative emission control system Canister Vent (CV) solenoid control malfunction
P0452	Evaporative emission control system Fuel Tank Pressure (FTP) sensor low input
P0453	Evaporative emission control system Fuel Tank Pressure (FTP) sensor high input
P0455	Evaporative emission control system control leak detected (gross leak)
P0500	Vehicle Speed Sensor (VSS) malfunction
P0503	Vehicle Speed Sensor (VSS) circuit intermittent
P0505	Idle Air Control (IAC) system malfunction
P0552	Power Steering Pressure (PSP) sensor circuit low input
P0553	Power Steering Pressure (PSP) sensor circuit high input
P0603	Powertrain Control Module (PCM) - Keep Alive Memory (KAM) test error
P0605	Powertrain Control Module (PCM) - Read Only Memory (ROM) test error
P0703	Brake On / Off (BOO) switch input malfunction

(Continued)

FM0159601611020X

Fig. 92   DTC identification (Part 2 of 6). 1996

DTC	Definitions
P0704	Clutch Pedal Position (CPP) switch input circuit malfunction
P0707	Transmission Range (TR) sensor circuit low input
P0708	Transmission Range (TR) sensor circuit high input
P0712	Transmission Fluid Temperature (TFT) sensor circuit low input
P0713	Transmission Fluid Temperature (TFT) sensor circuit high input
P0715	Turbine Shaft Speed (TSS) sensor circuit malfunction
P0720	Output Shaft Speed (OSS) sensor circuit malfunction
P0721	Output Shaft Speed (OSS) sensor performance (noise)
P0731	Incorrect ratio for first gear
P0732	Incorrect ratio for second gear
P0733	Incorrect ratio for third gear
P0734	Incorrect ratio for fourth gear
P0736	Reverse incorrect gear ratio
P0741	Torque Converter Clutch (TCC) mechanical system performance
P0743	Torque Converter Clutch (TCC) electrical system malfunction
P0746	Electronic Pressure Control (EPC) solenoid performance
P0750	Shift Solenoid #1 (SS1) circuit malfunction
P0751	Shift Solenoid #1 (SS1) performance
P0755	Shift Solenoid #2 (SS2) circuit malfunction
P0756	Shift Solenoid #2 (SS2) performance
P0760	Shift Solenoid #3 (SS3) circuit malfunction
P0761	Shift Solenoid #3 (SS3) performance
P0781	1 to 2 shift error
P0782	2 to 3 shift error
P0783	3 to 4 shift error
P0784	4 to 5 shift error
P1000	OBD II Monitor Testing not complete
P1001	Key On Engine Running (KOER) Self-Test not able to complete. KOER aborted
P1100	Mass Air Flow (MAF) sensor intermittent
P1101	Mass Air Flow (MAF) sensor out of Self-Test range
P1112	Intake Air Temperature (IAT) sensor intermittent
P1116	Engine Coolant Temperature (ECT) sensor out of Self-Test range
P1117	Engine Coolant Temperature (ECT) sensor intermittent
P1120	Throttle Position (TP) sensor out of range low
P1121	Throttle Position (TP) sensor inconsistent with MAF Sensor
P1124	Throttle Position (TP) sensor out of Self-Test range
P1125	Throttle Position (TP) sensor circuit intermittent
P1127	Exhaust not warm enough, downstream Heated Oxygen Sensors (HO2Ss) not tested
P1128	Upstream Heated Oxygen Sensors (HO2Ss) swapped from bank to bank
P1129	Downstream Heated Oxygen Sensors (HO2Ss) swapped from bank to bank
P1130	Lack of upstream Heated Oxygen Sensor (HO2S 11) switch, adaptive fuel at limit (Bank #1)
P1131	Lack of upstream Heated Oxygen Sensor (HO2S 11) switch, sensor indicates lean (Bank #1)
P1132	Lack of upstream Heated Oxygen Sensor (HO2S 11) switch, sensor indicates rich (Bank #1)

(Continued)

FM0159601611030X

Fig. 92   DTC identification (Part 3 of 6). 1996

DTC	Definitions
P1137	Lack of downstream Heated Oxygen Sensor (HO2S 12) switch, sensor indicates lean (Bank #1)
P1138	Lack of downstream Heated Oxygen Sensor (HO2S 12) switch, sensor indicates rich (Bank #1)
P1150	Lack of upstream Heated Oxygen Sensor (HO2S 21) switch, adaptive fuel at limit (Bank #2)
P1151	Lack of upstream Heated Oxygen Sensor (HO2S 21) switch, sensor indicates lean (Bank #2)
P1152	Lack of upstream Heated Oxygen Sensor (HO2S 21) switch, sensor indicates rich (Bank #2)
P1157	Lack of downstream Heated Oxygen Sensor (HO2S 22) switch, sensor indicates lean (Bank #2)
P1158	Lack of downstream Heated Oxygen Sensor (HO2S 22) switch, sensor indicates rich (Bank #2)
P1220	Series Throttle Control system malfunction
P1224	Throttle Position Sensor B (TP-B) out of Self-Test range
P1230	Fuel Pump low speed malfunction
P1231	Fuel Pump secondary circuit low with high speed pump on
P1232	Low speed Fuel Pump primary circuit malfunction
P1233	Fuel Pump Driver Module disabled or offline
P1234	Fuel Pump Driver Module disabled or offline
P1235	Fuel Pump control out of Self-Test range
P1236	Fuel Pump control out of Self-Test range
P1237	Fuel Pump secondary circuit malfunction
P1238	Fuel Pump secondary circuit malfunction
P1260	THEFT detected - engine disabled
P1270	Engine RPM or vehicle speed limiter reached
P1285	Cylinder Head over temperature sensed
P1288	Cylinder Head Temperature (CHT) sensor out of Self-Teat range
P1289	Cylinder Head Temperature (CHT) sensor circuit low input
P1290	Cylinder Head Temperature (CHT) sensor circuit high input
P1299	Engine over temperature condition
P1351	Ignition Diagnostic Monitor (IDM) circuit input malfunction
P1356	PIPs occurred while IDM indicates engine not turning
P1357	Ignition Diagnostic Monitor (IDM) pulsewidth not defined
P1358	Ignition Diagnostic Monitor (IDM) signal out of Self-Test range
P1359	Spark output circuit malfunction
P1390	Octane Adjust (OCT ADJ) out of Self-Test range
P1400	Differential Pressure Feedback EGR (DPFE) sensor circuit low voltage detected
P1401	Differential Pressure Feedback EGR (DPFE) sensor circuit high voltage detected
P1405	Differential Pressure Feedback EGR (DPFE) sensor upstream hose off or plugged
P1406	Differential Pressure Feedback EGR (DPFE) sensor downstream hose off or plugged
P1408	Exhaust Gas Recirculation (EGR) flow out of Self-Test range
P1409	Electronic Vacuum Regulator (EVR) control circuit malfunction
P1411	Secondary Air Injection system incorrect downstream flow detected
P1413	Secondary Air Injection system monitor circuit low voltage
P1414	Secondary Air Injection system monitor circuit high voltage

(Continued)

FM0159601611040X

Fig. 92   DTC identification (Part 4 of 6). 1996

DTC	Definitions
P1442	Evaporative emission control system small leak detected
P1443	Evaporative emission control system - vacuum system, purge control solenoid or vapor management valve malfunction
P1444	Purge Flow (PF) Sensor circuit low input
P1445	Purge Flow (PF) Sensor circuit high input
P1449	Evaporative emission control system unable to hold vacuum (Probe)
P1450	Unable to bleed up fuel tank vacuum
P1452	Unable to bleed up fuel tank vacuum
P1455	Evaporative emission control system control leak detected (gross leak)
P1460	Wide Open Throttle Air Conditioning Cut-off (WAC) circuit malfunction
P1461	Air Conditioning Pressure (ACP) sensor circuit low input
P1462	Air Conditioning Pressure (ACP) sensor circuit high input
P1463	Air Conditioning Pressure (ACP) sensor insufficient pressure change
P1464	Air condition (A/C) demand out of Self-Test range
P1469	Low air conditioning cycling period
P1473	Fan secondary high with fan(s) off
P1474	Low Fan Control primary circuit malfunction
P1479	High Fan Control primary circuit malfunction
P1480	Fan secondary low with low fan on
P1481	Fan secondary low with high fan on
P1483	Power to fan circuit overcurrent
P1484	Open power ground to Variable Load Control Module (VLCM)
P1500	Vehicle Speed Sensor (VSS) circuit intermittent
P1501	Vehicle Speed Sensor (VSS) out of Self-Test range
P1504	Idle Air Control (IAC) circuit malfunction
P1505	Idle Air Control (IAC) system at adaptive clip
P1506	Idle Air Control (IAC) overspeed error
P1507	Idle Air Control (IAC) underspeed error
P1512	Intake Manifold Runner Control (IMRC) malfunction (Bank #1 stuck closed)
P1513	Intake Manifold Runner Control (IMRC) malfunction (Bank #2 stuck closed)
P1516	Intake Manifold Runner Control (IMRC) input error (Bank #1)
P1517	Intake Manifold Runner Control (IMRC) input error (Bank #2)
P1518	Intake Manifold Runner Control (IMRC) malfunction (stuck open)
P1519	Intake Manifold Runner Control (IMRC) malfunction (stuck closed)
P1520	Intake Manifold Runner Control (IMRC) circuit malfunction
P1530	Air Condition (A/C) clutch circuit malfunction
P1537	Intake Manifold Runner Control (IMRC) malfunction (Bank #1 stuck open)
P1538	Intake Manifold Runner Control (IMRC) malfunction (Bank #2 stuck open)
P1539	Power to Air Condition (A/C) clutch circuit overcurrent
P1550	Power Steering Pressure (PSP) sensor out of Self-Test range
P1605	Powertrain Control Module (PCM) - Keep Alive Memory (KAM) test error
P1625	B(+) supply to Variable Load Control Module (VLCM) fan circuit malfunction
P1626	B(+) supply to Variable Load Control Module (VLCM) Air Condition (A/C) circuit malfunction
P1650	Power Steering Pressure (PSP) switch out of Self-Test range

(Continued)

FM0159601611050X

Fig. 92   DTC identification (Part 5 of 6). 1996

DTC	Definitions
P1651	Power Steering Pressure (PSP) switch input malfunction
P1701	Reverse engagement error
P1703	Brake On/Off (BOO) switch out of Self-Test range
P1705	Transmission Range (TR) Sensor out of Self-Test range
P1709	Park or Neutral Position (PNP) switch is not indicating neutral during KOEO Self-Test
P1711	Transmission Fluid Temperature (TFT) sensor out of Self-Test range
P1728	Transmission slip fault
P1729	4x4 Low switch error
P1741	Torque Converter Clutch (TCC) control error
P1742	Torque Converter Clutch (TCC) solenoid failed on (turns on MIL)
P1743	Torque Converter Clutch (TCC) solenoid failed on (turns on TCIL)
P1744	Torque Converter Clutch (TCC) system mechanically stuck in off position
P1746	Electronic Pressure Control (EPC) solenoid open circuit (low input)
P1747	Electronic Pressure Control (EPC) solenoid short circuit (high input)
P1749	Electronic Pressure Control (EPC) solenoid failed low
P1751	Shift Solenoid #1 (SS1) performance
P1754	Coast Clutch Solenoid (CCS) circuit malfunction
P1756	Shift Solenoid #2 (SS2) performance
P1761	Shift Solenoid #3 (SS3) performance
P1780	Transmission Control switch (TCS) circuit out of Self-Test range
P1781	4x4 Low switch out of Self-Test range
P1783	Transmission overtemperature condition
P1788	3-2 Timing/Coast Clutch Solenoid (3-2/CCS) circuit open
P1789	3-2 Timing/Coast Clutch Solenoid (3-2/CCS) circuit shorted
U1021	SCP indicating the lack of Air Condition (A/C) clutch status response
U1039	SCP indicating the vehicle speed signal missing or incorrect
U1051	SCP indicating the brake switch signal missing or incorrect
U1073	SCP indicating the lack of engine coolant fan status response
U1131	SCP indicating the lack of Fuel Pump status response
U1135	SCP indicating the ignition switch signal missing or incorrect
U1256	SCP indicating a communications error
U1451	Lack of response from Passive Anti-Theft system (PATS) module - engine disabled

FM0159601611060X

Fig. 92   DTC identification (Part 6 of 6). 1996

TEST STEP	RESULT	▶	ACTION TO TAKE
1.0 VEHICLE PREPARATION			
• Apply parking brake.	Yes	▶	GO to Diagnostic Subroutines [2.0].
• Place shift lever firmly in PARK (NEUTRAL for manual transmission).	No	▶	REPEAT this test step.
• Block all drive wheels.			
• Turn off all electrical loads.			
• **Is vehicle prepared to run Quick Test?**			

TEST STEP	RESULT	▶	ACTION TO TAKE
2.0 RETRIEVE AND RECORD ANY CONTINUOUS MEMORY DTCS			
NOTE: The purpose of recording any Continuous Memory Diagnostic Trouble Codes (DTCs) at this time is to ensure that they will not be unintentionally cleared during any Key On Engine Off (KOEO) or Key On Engine Running (KOER) DTC service (by disconnecting the PCM, vehicle battery, etc.). As always, KOEO and KOER DTCs will be addressed before Continuous Memory DTCs.	Yes	▶	RECORD (on a piece of paper, etc.) the Continuous Memory DTC(s). These DTC(s) will be addressed after KOEO and KOER Self-Tests. GO to Diagnostic Subroutine [3.0].
• Key off.			
• Connect Scan Tool to Data Link Connector (DLC).	No	▶	GO to Diagnostic Subroutine [3.0].
• Key on, engine off.			
• Retrieve and record any Continuous Memory DTCs (MIL and non-MIL).			
NOTE: If unable to access Continuous Memory DTCs or any Scan Tool Communication problem exists, go to Pinpoint Test Step [QA1].			
• **Are any Continuous Memory DTCs present?**			

Fig. 93   Diagnostic subroutines/quick tests 1.0 & 2.0. 1994–95

FM0159501262000X

TEST STEP	RESULT	▶	ACTION TO TAKE
3.0 PERFORM KEY ON ENGINE OFF (KOEO) SELF-TEST			
• Key off.	Yes	▶	Key off. GO to the Powertrain DTC Charts (located after the Diagnostic Subroutines) for Pinpoint Test direction (begin diagnosis with first DTC output).
• Scan Tool connected.			
• Start engine, if possible, and idle until it is at normal operating temperature.			
• Key off.			
• Key on, engine off.			
• Activate KOEO Self-Test.	No	▶	For Mustang, Thunderbird/Cougar GO to Diagnostic Subroutine [4.0]. All others: GO to Diagnostic Subroutine [5.0].
NOTE: If unable to activate KOEO Self-Test or any Scan Tool Communication problem exists, go to Pinpoint Test Step [QA1].			
• After the completion of KOEO Self-Test, retrieve and record any KOEO DTCs.			
• If DTC P1000 is present, ignore it at this time.			
• **Are any KOEO DTCs (except P1000) present?**			

TEST STEP	RESULT	▶	ACTION TO TAKE
4.0 VERIFY PCM CONTROL OF TIMING			
NOTE: This test is performed because, for the applications that are sent here, PCM control of timing is not checked by Self-Test.	Yes	▶	The PCM is controlling timing. GO to Diagnostic Subroutine [5.0].
• Scan Tool connected.			
• Start engine.	No	▶	GO to Diagnostic Subroutine [4.5].
• Engine at normal operating temperature.			
• Access "IAC" PID on Scan Tool.			
• While monitoring IAC duty cycle (%), disconnect the in-line SPOUT connector. Allow IAC duty cycle to stabilize, then reconnect SPOUT connector.			
• **Does the IAC duty cycle change at least 2% when the SPOUT connector is disconnected and connected?**			

Fig. 94   Diagnostic subroutines/quick tests 3.0 & 4.0. 1994–95

FM0159501263000X

TEST STEP	RESULT	▶	ACTION TO TAKE
4.5 CHECK TIMING USING A TIMING LIGHT			
• Key off.	Yes	▶	GO to Diagnostic Subroutine [5.0].
• Electrical loads off (A/C, heater, etc.)			
• Engine at normal operating temperature.	No	▶	If base timing was not 8-12 degrees BTDC: Base timing is not adjustable.
• Shift lever in PARK (A/T) or NEUTRAL (M/T).			
• Connect timing light.			
• Start engine. (Use the ignition key to start engine, do not use a remote starter.)			check possible causes of incorrect base timing (damaged, loose, misaligned CKP sensor or Trigger Wheel, etc.).
• Disconnect SPOUT connector.			
• Check base timing.			**If base timing was OK, but timing did not change as expected:** Verify results by checking computed timing while revving the engine a few times. If timing still remains at base timing, GO to Pinpoint Test Step [MC1].
— Refer to the Ignition/Engine Group in the Service Manual for specific instructions for checking base timing.			
— Base timing should be 8-12 degrees BTDC.			
• Check for computed timing.			
— Reconnect SPOUT connector.			
— Timing should change from base timing.			
• **Are the base timing and computed timing checks OK?**			

TEST STEP	RESULT	▶	ACTION TO TAKE
5.0 PERFORM KEY ON ENGINE RUNNING (KOER) SELF-TEST			
• Scan Tool connected.	Yes	▶	Key off. GO to the Powertrain DTC Charts (located after the Diagnostic Subroutines) for Pinpoint Test direction (begin diagnosis with first DTC output).
• Start engine.			
• Engine at normal operating temperature.			
• Shift lever in PARK (A/T) or NEUTRAL (M/T).			
• Activate KOER Self-Test.			
NOTE: If engine stalls during KOER Self-Test, discontinue test and go to Diagnostic Subroutine [6.0]. If unable to activate or complete KOER Self-Test, or any Scan Tool Communication problem exists, go to Pinpoint Test Step [QA1].	No	▶	GO to Diagnostic Subroutine [6.0].
• After the completion of KOER Self-Test, retrieve and record any KOER DTCs.			
• If DTC P1000 is present, ignore it at this time.			
• **Are any KOER DTCs (except P1000) present?**			

Fig. 95   Diagnostic subroutines/quick tests 4.5 & 5.0. 1994–95

FM0159501264000X

TEST STEP	RESULT	▶	ACTION TO TAKE
6.0 WERE ANY CONTINUOUS MEMORY DTCS RECEIVED IN DIAGNOSTIC SUBROUTINE 2.0?			
• Previous Diagnostic Subroutines performed as directed.	Yes	▶	GO to Diagnostic Subroutine [7.0].
• **Were any Continuous Memory DTCs received in Diagnostic Subroutine 2.0?**	No	▶	Quick Test complete. Key off. RETURN to Symptom Flow Chart.

TEST STEP	RESULT	▶	ACTION TO TAKE
7.0 WERE ANY IDENTICAL/RELATED DTCS SERVICED DURING THIS REPAIR PROCESS?			
• **Were any identical/related DTCs serviced during this repair process?**	Yes	▶	DISREGARD the identical/related DTC(s). GO to Diagnostic Subroutine [8.0].
	No	▶	Key off. GO to the Powertrain DTC Charts (located after the Diagnostic Subroutines) for Pinpoint Test direction (begin diagnosis with first DTC output).

TEST STEP	RESULT	▶	ACTION TO TAKE
8.0 ARE THERE ANY ADDITIONAL (UNRELATED) CONTINUOUS MEMORY DTCS?			
• **Are there any additional (unrelated) Continuous Memory DTCs?**	Yes	▶	Key off. GO to the Powertrain DTC Charts (located after the Diagnostic Subroutines) for Pinpoint Test direction (begin diagnosis with first unrelated DTC output).
	No	▶	COMPLETE PCM. RESET to clear DTCs

Fig. 96   Diagnostic subroutines/quick tests 6.0, 7.0 & 8.0. 1994–95

FM0159501265000X

TEST STEP	RESULT	▶	ACTION TO TAKE
10.0 VEHICLE PREPARATION • Apply parking brake. • Place shift lever firmly in PARK (NEUTRAL for manual transmissions). • Block all drive wheels. • Turn off all electrical loads. • **Is vehicle prepared to run Self-Test?**	Yes No	▶ ▶	GO to Diagnostic Subroutine **11.0**. REPEAT this step.

TEST STEP	RESULT	▶	ACTION TO TAKE
11.0 RETRIEVE AND RECORD ANY CONTINUOUS MEMORY DTCS NOTE: The purpose of recording any Continuous Memory Diagnostic Trouble Codes (DTCs) at this time is to ensure that they will not be unintentionally cleared during any Key On Engine Off (KOEO) DTC service (by disconnecting the PCM, vehicle battery, etc.). As always, KOEO DTCs will be addressed before Continuous Memory DTCs. • Key off. • Connect Scan Tool to Data Link Connector (DLC). • Key on, engine off. • Retrieve and record any Continuous Memory DTCs (MIL and non-MIL). NOTE: If unable to access Continuous Memory DTCs, or any Scan Tool Communication problem exists, go to Pinpoint Test Step QA1. • **Are any Continuous Memory DTCs present?**	Yes No	▶ ▶	RECORD (on a piece of paper, etc.) the Continuous Memory DTC(s). These DTC(s) will be addressed after KOEO Self-Test. GO to Diagnostic Subroutine **12.0**. GO to Diagnostic Subroutine **12.0**.

Fig. 97 Diagnostic subroutines/quick tests 10.0 & 11.0. 1994–95

TEST STEP	RESULT	▶	ACTION TO TAKE
12.0 PERFORM KEY ON ENGINE OFF (KOEO) SELF-TEST • Scan Tool connected. • Start engine, if possible, and idle until it is at normal operating temperature. • Key off. • Key on, engine off. • Activate KOEO Self-Test. NOTE: If unable to access KOEO Self-Test, or any Scan Tool Communication problem exists, go to Pinpoint Test Step QA1. If additional information is required for KOEO Self-Test, refer to Diagnostic Methods. • After the completion of KOEO Self-Test, retrieve and record any KOEO DTCs. • If DTC P1000 is present, ignore it at this time. • **Are any KOEO DTCs (except P1000) present?**	Yes No	▶ ▶	Key off. GO to the Powertrain DTC Charts (located after the Diagnostic Subroutines) for Pinpoint Test direction (begin diagnosis with first DTC output). GO to Diagnostic Subroutine **13.0**.

TEST STEP	RESULT	▶	ACTION TO TAKE
13.0 WERE ANY CONTINUOUS MEMORY DTCS RECEIVED IN DIAGNOSTIC SUBROUTINE 11.0? • Previous Diagnostic Subroutines performed as directed. • **Were any Continuous Memory DTCs received in Diagnostic Subroutine 11.0?**	Yes No	▶ ▶	GO to Diagnostic Subroutine **14.0**. Quick Test complete. Key off. RETURN to Symptom Flow Chart.

TEST STEP	RESULT	▶	ACTION TO TAKE
14.0 WERE ANY IDENTICAL/RELATED DTCS SERVICED DURING THIS REPAIR PROCESS? • **Were any identical/related DTCs serviced during this repair process?**	Yes No	▶ ▶	DISREGARD the identical/related DTC(s). GO to Diagnostic Subroutine **15.0**. Key off. GO to the Powertrain DTC Charts (located after the Diagnostic Subroutines) for Pinpoint Test direction (begin diagnosis with first DTC output).

Fig. 98 Diagnostic subroutines/quick tests 12.0, 13.0 & 14.0. 1994–95

TEST STEP	RESULT	▶	ACTION TO TAKE
15.0 ARE THERE ANY ADDITIONAL (UNRELATED) CONTINUOUS MEMORY DTCS? • **Are there any additional (unrelated) Continuous Memory DTCs?**	Yes No	▶ ▶	Key off. GO to the Powertrain DTC Charts (located after the Diagnostic Subroutines) for Pinpoint Test direction (begin diagnosis with first unrelated DTC output). COMPLETE PCM reset to clear DTCs.

Fig. 99 Diagnostic subroutines/quick test 15.0. 1994–95

TEST STEP	RESULT	▶	ACTION TO TAKE
20.0 CHECK/COMPARE PID VALUES • Scan Tool connected. • Accessories off (A/C, heater, etc.). • Start engine and warm to normal operating temperature. • Access each PID listed in the chart below. Check to see if all PID values are in the range given. • **Are PID values within range?**	Yes No	▶ ▶	RETURN to Symptom Flow Chart FOLLOW direction given in chart.

PID	RANGE		IF OUT OF RANGE (If value is noisy/erratic, GO to Diagnostic Subroutine 21.0.)
	KOEO	HOT IDLE	
DPFEGR	.2–.7V	within .15V of KOEO value	GO to Pinpoint Test Step HE100.
ECT	—	.35V (232°F)–.75V (180°F)	GO to Cooling Group of the Service Manual to CHECK cooling system.
IAC	—	20-45%	RETURN to Symptom Flow Charts, focusing diagnosis in the following areas: If value is low: CHECK areas that would cause engine speed to increase (ex. vacuum/air leak, binding throttle linkage). If value is high: CHECK areas that would cause engine speed to decrease.
LONGFT1 LONGFT2 (Formerly LFT1/LFT2)	—	(-)20% - (+)20%	RETURN to Symptom Flow Charts, focusing diagnosis in the following areas: If value is low (-): CHECK areas that would cause engine to run rich. If value is high (+): CHECK areas that would cause engine to run lean.
VPWR	Between 10.5 and 17.0 volts, and within .5 volts of Batt. volt	Between 10.5 and 17.0 volts, and within .5 volts of Batt. volt	If not between 10.5 and 17.0 volts: GO to the Charging/Electrical Group fo the Service Manual. If greater than 10.5V but not +/-.5V: CHECK B(+) supply to power relay (or CCRM pins 8/10). CHECK resistance of VPWR circuit between PCM pins 71/97 and power relay or CCRM. CHECK PWR GND circuits (PCM pins 51, 76, 77, 103).
VREF (If PID is available)	4.0-6.0V	4.0-6.0V	GO to Pinpoint Test Step C1.

Fig. 100 Diagnostic subroutines/quick test 20.0. 1994–95

TEST STEP	RESULT	▶	ACTION TO TAKE
21.0 **ISOLATE CAUSE OF NOISY PID VALUE**			
• If only one PID value is noisy/erratic: Check harness circuit/component for intermittent opens/shorts (refer to Pinpoint Test Step [Z1]), proper harness routing away from spark plug wires, battery cables, high voltage or high current aftermarket add-on wiring, etc. If all checks are OK, perform the Circuit/Component Noise Isolation Test below.	Yes	▶	ISOLATE fault and SERVICE as necessary. RE-EVALUATE symptom.
• If multiple PID values are noisy/erratic: Check for proper harness routing away from spark plug wires, battery cables, high voltage or high current aftermarket add-on wiring, etc. Check any common power or ground circuits. If harness appears OK, perform the CIRCUIT/COMPONENT NOISE ISOLATION TEST below.	No	▶	GO to Pinpoint Test Step [Z1] to check for intermittent harness concerns, or RETURN to Symptom Flow Chart to continue diagnosis.
• Circuit/Component Noise Isolation Test			
— Engine in same mode (key on, engine off or engine running) as it was when noisy/erratic PID value detected.			
— While monitoring PIDs, disconnect fuses/fuse links one at a time.			
— If noise is eliminated by pulling a specific fuse, all circuits/components supplied by the fuse need to be checked for excessive noise generation. Disconnect each module/component on the fuse circuit, one at a time, to help isolate the fault.			
• **Is fault indicated?**			

FM0159501270000X

Fig. 101 Diagnostic subroutines/quick test 21.0. 1994–95

	TEST STEP	RESULT	▶	ACTION TO TAKE
25.0	**CONTINENTAL WITH TRACTION ASSIST:** **INSPECT SERIES THROTTLE ASSEMBLY**			
	• Key off.	Yes	▶	If symptom is no traction assist or poor/erratic traction assist: GO to Pinpoint Test Step [HT22]. If symptom is lack/loss of power: RETURN to Symptom Flow Chart.
	• Remove air tube from Series Throttle Body.			
	• Visually inspect the throttle body assembly for obstruction; loose stepper motor, electrical connector or Throttle Position Sensor B (TP-B); or any other damage.			
	• Determine if the Series Throttle plate is binding or stuck. The throttle plate is normally wide open. Push the throttle plate closed, then release several times. The throttle plates should spring back open when released.			
	• Key on, engine off.	No	▶	GO to Pinpoint Test Step [HT21] (to help isolate concern).
	— As part of the Traction Assist initialization, the Series Throttle plate will be commanded closed briefly while the PCM reads the TP-B voltage. Look for binding while the throttle plate is being exercised.			
	• **Are the above Series Throttle checks OK?**			

FM0159501271000X

Fig. 102 Diagnostic subroutine/quick tests 25.0. 1994–95

	Test Step	Result	▶	Action to Take
DSR1	**QUICK TEST: VEHICLE PREPARATION**			
	• Apply parking brake.	Yes	▶	GO to [DSR2].
	• Place shift lever firmly in PARK (NEUTRAL for manual transmission).	No	▶	REPEAT this test step.
	• Block all drive wheels.			
	• Turn off all electrical loads.			
	• **Is vehicle prepared to run Quick Test?**			
DSR2	**RETRIEVE AND RECORD ANY CONTINUOUS MEMORY DTCS**			
	NOTE: The purpose of recording any Continuous Memory Diagnostic Trouble Codes (DTCs) at this time is to ensure that they will not be unintentionally cleared during any Key On Engine Off (KOEO) or Key On Engine Running (KOER) DTC service (by disconnecting the PCM, vehicle battery, etc.). As always, KOEO and KOER DTCs will be addressed before Continuous Memory DTCs.	Yes	▶	RECORD (on a piece of paper, etc.) the Continuous Memory DTC(s). These DTC(s) will be addressed after KOEO and KOER Self-Tests. GO to [DSR3].
	• Key off.	No	▶	GO to [DSR3].
	• Connect Scan Tool to Data Link Connector (DLC).			
	• Key on, engine off.			
	• Retrieve and record any Continuous Memory DTCs (MIL and non-MIL).			
	NOTE: If unable to access Continuous Memory DTCs or any Scan Tool Communication problem exists, go to Pinpoint Test Step [QA1]. For more information on retrieving MIL and non-MIL DTCs, refer to Diagnostic Methods (Continuous Memory Self-Test).			
	• **Are any Continuous Memory DTCs present?**			

FM0159601578010X

Fig. 103 Diagnostic subroutines/quick test (Part 1 of 9). 1996

	Test Step	Result	▶	Action to Take
DSR3	**PERFORM KEY ON ENGINE OFF (KOEO) SELF-TEST**			
	• Key off.	Yes	▶	Key off. GO to the Powertrain DTC Charts (located after the Diagnostic Subroutines) for Pinpoint Test direction (begin diagnosis with first DTC output).
	• Scan Tool connected.			
	• Start engine, if possible, and idle until it is at normal operating temperature.			
	• Key off.			
	• Key on, engine off.	No	▶	For Electronic Ignition (EI) Applications and Probe: GO to [DSR5]. All others: GO to [DSR4].
	• Activate KOEO Self-Test.			
	NOTE: If unable to activate KOEO Self-Test or any Scan Tool Communication problem exists, go to Pinpoint Test Step [QA1]. If additional information is required for KOEO Self-Test, refer to Diagnostic Methods.			
	• After the completion of KOEO Self-Test, retrieve and record any KOEO DTCs.			
	• If DTC P1000 is present, ignore it at this time.			
	• **Are any KOEO DTCs (except P1000) present?**			
DSR4	**CHECK TIMING USING A TIMING LIGHT (DI APPLICATIONS)**			
	• Key off.	Yes	▶	GO to [DSR5].
	• Electrical loads off (A/C, heater, etc.).	No	▶	If base timing was not within ± 3 degrees of specification: ADJUST as necessary and RERUN Quick Test. If unable to adjust to specification, check proper distributor orientation, timing chain/belt, etc. If base timing was OK, but timing did not change as expected: Verify results by checking computed timing while revving the engine a few times. If timing still remains at base timing, GO to Pinpoint Test Step [JG63].
	• Engine at normal operating temperature.			
	• Shift lever in PARK (A/T) or NEUTRAL (M/T).			
	• Connect timing light.			
	• Start engine. (Use the ignition key to start engine, do not use a remote starter.)			
	• Disconnect SPOUT connector.			
	NOTE: If engine stalls when spout connector is disconnected, GO to Pinpoint Test Step [JG40].			
	• Check base timing.			
	— Base timing should be within ± 3 degrees of specification on VECI decal.			
	• Check for computed timing.			
	— Reconnect SPOUT connector.			
	— Timing should change from base timing (engine RPM may have to be increased to about 1500 rpm to see change).			
	• **Are the base timing and computed timing checks OK?**			

FM0159601578020X

Fig. 103 Diagnostic subroutines/quick test (Part 2 of 9). 1996

Part 3 of 9

Test Step		Result	▶	Action to Take
DSR5	PERFORM KEY ON ENGINE RUNNING (KOER) SELF-TEST			
	• Scan Tool connected. • Shift lever in PARK (A/T) or NEUTRAL (M/T). • Start engine. • Warm engine to normal operating temperature. After warming engine, leave engine running. • Activate KOER Self-Test. NOTE: If engine stalls during KOER Self-Test, discontinue test and go to DSR6 . If unable to activate or complete KOER Self-Test, or any Scan Tool Communication problem exists, go to Pinpoint Test Step QA1 . If additional information is required for KOER Self-Test, refer to Diagnostic Methods. • After the completion of KOER Self-Test, retrieve and record any KOER DTCs. • If DTC P1000 is present, ignore it at this time. • **Are any KOER DTCs (except P1000) present?**	Yes No	▶ ▶	Key off. GO to the Powertrain DTC Charts (located after the Diagnostic Subroutines) for Pinpoint Test direction (begin diagnosis with first DTC output). GO to DSR6 .
DSR6	WERE ANY CONTINUOUS MEMORY DTCS RECEIVED IN DSR2 ?			
	• Previous Diagnostic Subroutines performed as directed. • **Were any Continuous Memory DTCs received in DSR2 ?**	Yes No	▶ ▶	GO to DSR7 . Quick Test complete. Key off. RETURN to Symptom Flowchart
DSR7	WERE ANY IDENTICAL/RELATED DTCS SERVICED DURING THIS VEHICLE'S DIAGNOSIS?			
	• NOTE: If no DTCs have been serviced during this vehicle's diagnosis, Go to "NO" Action to Take. The cause of some Continuous Memory DTCs may have been eliminated during previous DTC service. This step is included so identical/related DTCs that were serviced will be disregarded. • **Were any identical/related DTCs serviced during this vehicles diagnosis process?**	Yes No	▶ ▶	DISREGARD the identical/related DTC(s). GO to DSR8 . Key off. GO to the Powertrain DTC Charts (located after the Diagnostic Subroutines) for Pinpoint Test direction (begin diagnosis with first DTC output).

FM0159601578030X

Fig. 103 Diagnostic subroutines/quick test (Part 3 of 9). 1996

Part 4 of 9

Test Step		Result	▶	Action to Take
DSR8	ARE THERE ANY ADDITIONAL (UNRELATED) CONTINUOUS MEMORY DTCS?			
	• **Are there any additional (unrelated) Continuous Memory DTCs?**	Yes No	▶ ▶	Key off. GO to the Powertrain DTC Charts (located after the Diagnostic Subroutines) for Pinpoint Test direction (begin diagnosis with first unrelated DTC output). COMPLETE PCM RESET to clear DTCs (REFER to Powertrain Control Module (PCM) Reset). VERIFY repair.
DSR10	VEHICLE PREPARATION			
	• Apply parking brake. • Place shift lever firmly in PARK (NEUTRAL for manual transmissions). • Block all drive wheels. • Turn off all electrical loads. • Is vehicle prepared to run Self-Test?	Yes No	▶ ▶	GO to DSR11 . REPEAT this step.
DSR11	RETRIEVE AND RECORD ANY CONTINUOUS MEMORY DTCS			
	NOTE: The purpose of recording any Continuous Memory Diagnostic Trouble Codes (DTCs) at this time is to ensure that they will not be unintentionally cleared during any Key On Engine Off (KOEO) DTC service (by disconnecting the PCM, vehicle battery, etc.). As always, KOEO DTCs will be addressed before Continuous Memory DTCs. • Key off. • Connect Scan Tool to Data Link Connector (DLC). • Key on, engine off. • Retrieve and record any Continuous Memory DTCs (MIL and non-MIL). NOTE: If unable to access Continuous Memory DTCs, or any Scan Tool Communication problem exists, go to Pinpoint Test Step QA1 . For more information on retrieving MIL and non-MIL DTCs, refer to Diagnostic Methods (Continuous Memory Self-Test). • **Are any Continuous Memory DTCs present?**	Yes No	▶ ▶	RECORD (on a piece of paper, etc.) the Continuous Memory DTC(s). These DTC(s) will be addressed after KOEO Self-Test. GO to DSR12 . GO to DSR12 .

FM0159601578040X

Fig. 103 Diagnostic subroutines/quick test (Part 4 of 9). 1996

Part 5 of 9

Test Step		Result	▶	Action to Take
DSR12	PERFORM KEY ON ENGINE OFF (KOEO) SELF-TEST			
	• Scan Tool connected. • Start engine, if possible, and idle until it is at normal operating temperature. • Key off. • Key on, engine off. • Activate KOEO Self-Test. NOTE: If unable to access KOEO Self-Test, or any Scan Tool Communication problem exists, go to Pinpoint Test Step QA1 . If additional information is required for KOEO Self-Test, refer to Diagnostic Methods. • After the completion of KOEO Self-Test, retrieve and record any KOEO DTCs. • If DTC P1000 is present, ignore it at this time. • **Are any KOEO DTCs (except P1000) present?**	Yes No	▶ ▶	Key off. GO to the Powertrain DTC Charts (located after the Diagnostic Subroutines) for Pinpoint Test direction (begin diagnosis with first DTC output). GO to DSR13 .
DSR13	WERE ANY CONTINUOUS MEMORY DTCS RECEIVED IN DSR11 ?			
	• Previous Diagnostic Subroutines performed as directed. • **Were any Continuous Memory DTCs received in DSR11 ?**	Yes No	▶ ▶	GO to DSR14 . Quick Test complete. Key off. RETURN to Symptom Flow Chart
DSR14	WERE ANY IDENTICAL/RELATED DTCS SERVICED DURING THIS VEHICLE'S DIAGNOSIS?			
	• NOTE: If no DTCs have been serviced during this vehicle's diagnosis, Go to "NO" Action to Take. The cause of some Continuous Memory DTCs may have been eliminated during previous DTC service. This step is included so identical/related DTCs that were serviced will be disregarded. • **Were any identical/related DTCs serviced during this vehicle's diagnosis?**	Yes No	▶ ▶	DISREGARD the identical/related DTC(s). GO to DSR15 . Key off. GO to the Powertrain DTC Charts (located after the Diagnostic Subroutines) for Pinpoint Test direction (begin diagnosis with first DTC output).

FM0159601578050X

Fig. 103 Diagnostic subroutines/quick test (Part 5 of 9). 1996

Part 6 of 9

Test Step		Result	▶	Action to Take
DSR15	ARE THERE ANY ADDITIONAL (UNRELATED) CONTINUOUS MEMORY DTCS?			
	• **Are there any additional (unrelated) Continuous Memory DTCs?**	Yes No	▶ ▶	Key off. GO to the Powertrain DTC Charts (located after the Diagnostic Subroutines) for Pinpoint Test direction (begin diagnosis with first unrelated DTC output). COMPLETE PCM reset to clear DTCs (REFER to Powertrain Control Module (PCM) Reset). VERIFY repair.

FM0159601578060X

Fig. 103 Diagnostic subroutines/quick test (Part 6 of 9). 1996

Test Step	Result	▶	Action to Take
DSR20 CHECK/COMPARE PID VALUES			
• Scan Tool connected. • Accessories off (A/C, heater, etc.). • Start engine and warm to normal operating temperature. • Access each PID listed in the chart below. Check to see if all PID values are in the range given. • **Are PID values within range?**	Yes No	▶ ▶	RETURN to Symptom Flowchart FOLLOW direction given in chart.

PID	Range KOEO	Range Hot Idle	If Out Of Range (If value is noisy/erratic, GO to DSR21.)
DPFEGR (If Equipped)	.2-.7V	within .15V of KOEO value	GO to Pinpoint Test Step **HE100**
ECT	—	.35V (232°F)-.75V (180°F)	CHECK cooling system.
IAC	—	15-50%	RETURN to Symptom Flowcharts, focusing diagnosis in the following areas: **If value is low:** CHECK areas that would cause engine speed to increase (ex. vacuum/air leak, binding throttle linkage). **If value is high:** CHECK areas that would cause engine speed to decrease.
LONGFT1 LONGFT2	—	(-)20% - (+)20%	RETURN to Symptom Flowcharts, focusing diagnosis in the following areas: **If value is low (-):** CHECK areas that would cause engine to run rich. **If value is high (+):** CHECK areas that would cause engine to run lean.
VPWR	Between 10.5 and 17.0 volts, and within .5 volts of Batt. volt	Between 10.5 and 17.0 volts, and within .5 volts of Batt. volt	**If not between 10.5 and 17.0 volts:** GO to the Charging/Electrical **If greater than 10.5V but not +/-.5V:** CHECK B(+) supply to power relay (or CCRM pins 8/10). CHECK resistance of VPWR circuit between PCM pins 71/97 and power relay or CCRM. CHECK PCM "PWR GND" circuits.
VREF (If PID is available)	4.0-6.0V	4.0-6.0V	Check voltage between VREF and SIG RTN circuits at TP vehicle harness connector. Voltage should be 4.0-6.0 V. If not ok, GO to Pinpoint Test Step **C1**

Fig. 103 Diagnostic subroutines/quick test (Part 7 of 9). 1996

Test Step	Result	▶	Action to Take
DSR21 ISOLATE CAUSE OF NOISY PID VALUE			
• **If only one PID value is noisy/erratic:** Check harness circuit/component for intermittent opens/shorts (refer to Pinpoint Test Step **Z1**), proper harness routing away from spark plug wires, battery cables, high voltage or high current aftermarket add-on wiring, etc. If all checks are OK, perform the Circuit/Component Noise Isolation Test below. • **If multiple PID values are noisy/erratic:** Check for proper harness routing away from spark plug wires, battery cables, high voltage or high current aftermarket add-on wiring, etc. Check any common power or ground circuits. If harness appears OK, perform the CIRCUIT/COMPONENT NOISE ISOLATION TEST below. • Circuit/Component Noise Isolation Test — Engine in same mode (key on, engine off or engine running) as it was when noisy/erratic PID value detected. — While monitoring PIDs, disconnect fuses/fuse links one at a time. — If noise is eliminated by pulling a specific fuse, all circuits/components supplied by the fuse need to be checked for excessive noise generation. Disconnect each module/component on the fuse circuit, one at a time, to help isolate the fault. • **Is fault indicated?**	Yes No	▶ ▶	ISOLATE fault and SERVICE as necessary. VERIFY a symptom no longer exists. GO to Pinpoint Test Step **Z1** to check for intermittent harness concerns, or RETURN to Symptom Flowchart continue diagnosis.

Fig. 103 Diagnostic subroutines/quick test (Part 8 of 9). 1996

Test Step	Result	▶	Action to Take
DSR25 CONTINENTAL WITH TRACTION CONTROL: INSPECT SERIES THROTTLE ASSEMBLY			
• Key off. • Remove air tube from Series Throttle Body. • Visually inspect the throttle body assembly for obstruction; loose stepper motor, electrical connector or Throttle Position Sensor B (TP-B); or any other damage. • Determine if the Series Throttle plate is binding or stuck. The throttle plate is normally wide open. Push the throttle plate closed, then release several times. The throttle plates should spring back open when released. • Key on, engine off. — As part of the Traction Control initialization, the Series Throttle plate will be commanded closed briefly while the PCM reads the TP-B voltage. Look for binding while the throttle plate is being exercised. • **Are the above Series Throttle checks OK?**	Yes No	▶ ▶	**If symptom is no traction control or poor/erratic traction control:** GO to Pinpoint Test Step **HT23**. **If symptom is lack/loss of power:** RETURN to Symptom Flowchart. GO to Pinpoint Test Step **HT21** (to help isolate concern).

Fig. 103 Diagnostic subroutines/quick test (Part 9 of 9). 1996

Service Code/Page No.	Application	Pinpoint Test Step			Service Code/Page No.	Application	Pinpoint Test Step		
		Key On, Engine Off	Engine Running	Continuous Memory			Key On, Engine Off	Engine Running	Continuous Memory
CODE P0102	All	N/A	DC6	DC6	CODE P0301	All	N/A	HD1	HD1
Page No.	—	—	9-117	9-117	Page No.	—	—	9-140	9-140
CODE P0103	All	DC20	DC20	DC20	CODE P0302	All	N/A	HD1	HD1
Page No.	—	9-118	9-118	9-118	Page No.	—	—	9-140	9-140
CODE P0112	All	DA202	DA20	DA90	CODE P0303	All	N/A	HD1	HD1
Page No.	—	9-115	9-115	9-115	Page No.	—	—	9-140	9-140
CODE P0113	All	DA10	DA10	DA90	CODE P0304	All	N/A	HD1	HD1
Page No.	—	9-115	9-115	9-115	Page No.	—	—	9-140	9-140
CODE P0117	All	DA20	DA20	DA90	CODE P0305	All	N/A	HD1	HD1
Page No.	—	9-115	9-115	9-115	Page No.	—	—	9-140	9-140
CODE P0118	All	DA10	DA10	DA90	CODE P0306	All	N/A	HD1	HD1
Page No.	—	9-115	9-115	9-115	Page No.	—	—	9-140	9-140
CODE P0122	All	DH8	DH8	DH8	CODE P0307	All	N/A	HD1	HD1
Page No.	—	9-121	9-121	9-121	Page No.	—	—	9-140	9-140
CODE P0123	All	DH5	DH5	DH5	CODE P0308	All	N/A	HD1	HD1
Page No.	—	9-120	9-120	9-120	Page No.	—	—	9-140	9-140
CODE P0125	All	N/A	N/A	DA100	CODE P0320	All	N/A	N/A	NA1
Page No.	—	—	—	9-116	Page No.	—	—	—	9-203
CODE P0132	All	H10	H10	H10	CODE P0340	All	N/A	N/A	DR1
Page No.	—	9-126	9-126	9-126	Page No.	—	—	—	9-123
CODE P0133	All	N/A	N/A	H20	CODE P0402	All	N/A	HE20	HE20
Page No.	—	—	—	9-127	Page No.	—	—	9-143	9-143
CODE P0135	All	H30	H30	H30	CODE P0420	All	N/A	N/A	HF1
Page No.	—	9-127	9-127	9-127	Page No.	—	—	—	9-152
CODE P0136	All	N/A	N/A	H80	CODE P0430	All	N/A	N/A	HF1
Page No.	—	—	—	9-130	Page No.	—	—	—	9-152
CODE P0138	All	H10	H10	H10	CODE P0443	All	HV9	HV9	HV14
Page No.	—	9-126	9-126	9-126	Page No.	—	9-165	9-165	9-165
CODE P0141	All	H30	H30	H30	CODE P0500	All	N/A	N/A	DP1
Page No.	—	9-127	9-127	9-127	Page No.	—	—	—	9-122
CODE P0152	All	H10	H10	H10	CODE P0703	All	N/A	FD1	FD1
Page No.	—	9-126	9-126	9-126	Page No.	—	—	9-125	9-125
CODE P0153	All	N/A	N/A	H20	CODE P0705	All	N/A	N/A	TG90
Page No.	—	—	—	9-127	Page No.	—	—	—	9-214
CODE P0155	All	H30	H30	H30	CODE P0707	All	N/A	N/A	TG90
Page No.	—	9-127	9-127	9-127	Page No.	—	—	—	9-214
CODE P0156	All	N/A	N/A	H80	CODE P0708	All	N/A	N/A	TG90
Page No.	—	—	—	9-130	Page No.	—	—	—	9-212
CODE P0158	All	H10	H10	H10	CODE P0712	All	TE1	TE1	TE90
Page No.	—	9-126	9-126	9-126	Page No.	—	9-	9-	9-212
CODE P0161	All	H30	H30	H30	CODE P0713	All	TE10	TE10	TE100
Page No.	—	9-127	9-127	9-127	Page No.	—		9-	9-213
CODE P0171	All	N/A	N/A	HB1	CODE P0720	All	N/A	N/A	TF1
Page No.	—	—	—	9-137	Page No.	—	—	—	9-213
CODE P0172	All	N/A	N/A	HB1	CODE P0731	All	N/A	N/A	TG90
Page No.	—	—	—	9-137	Page No.	—	—	—	9-214
CODE P0174	All	N/A	N/A	HB1	CODE P0732	All	N/A	N/A	TG90
Page No.	—	—	—	9-137	Page No.	—	—	—	9-214
CODE P0175	All	N/A	N/A	HB1	CODE P0733	All	N/A	N/A	TG90
Page No.	—	—	—	9-137	Page No.	—	—	—	9-214
CODE P0300	All	N/A	HD1	HD1					
Page No.	—	—	9-140	9-140					

Fig. 104 Diagnostic trouble code & pinpoint test reference chart (Part 1 of 3). 1994

Service Code/Page No.	Application	Pinpoint Test Step Key On, Engine Off	Engine Running	Continuous Memory
CODE P0734	All	N/A	N/A	TG90
Page No.	—	—	—	9-214
CODE P0735	All	N/A	N/A	TG90
Page No.	—	—	—	9-214
CODE P0741	All	N/A	N/A	TG90
Page No.	—	—	—	9-214
CODE P0743	All	TC1	N/A	TG90
Page No.	—	9-208	—	9-214
CODE P0750	All	TC1	N/A	TG90
Page No.	—	9-208	—	9-214
CODE P0751	All	N/A	N/A	TG90
Page No.	—	—	—	9-214
CODE P0755	All	TC1	N/A	TG90
Page No.	—	9-208	—	9-214
CODE P0756	All	N/A	N/A	TG90
Page No.	—	—	—	9-214
CODE P1000	All	①	①	QC1
Page No.	—	—	—	9-207
CODE P1100	All	N/A	N/A	DC2
Page No.	—	—	—	9-117
CODE P1101	All	DC1	DC1	N/A
Page No.	—	9-116	9-116	—
CODE P1112	All	N/A	N/A	DA90
Page No.	—	—	—	9-115
CODE P1116	All	DA1	DA1	N/A
Page No.	—	9-114	9-114	—
CODE P1117	All	N/A	N/A	DA90
Page No.	—	—	—	9-115
CODE P1120	All	DH2	DH2	DH2
Page No.	—	9-120	9-120	9-120
CODE P1121	All	N/A	N/A	DH12
Page No.	—	—	—	9-121
CODE P1124	All	DH1	DH1	N/A
Page No.	—	9-120	9-120	—
CODE P1125	All	N/A	N/A	DH17
Page No.	—	—	—	9-121
CODE P1130	All	N/A	N/A	H40
Page No.	—	—	—	9-128
CODE P1131	All	N/A	H40	H40
Page No.	—	—	9-128	9-128
CODE P1132	All	N/A	H40	H40
Page No.	—	—	9-128	9-128
CODE P1137	All	N/A	H80	N/A
Page No.	—	—	9-130	—
CODE P1138	All	N/A	H80	N/A
Page No.	—	—	9-130	—
CODE P1150	All	N/A	N/A	H40
Page No.	—	—	—	9-128
CODE P1151	All	N/A	H40	H40
Page No.	—	—	9-128	9-128
CODE P1152	All	N/A	H40	H40
Page No.	—	—	9-128	9-128
CODE P1157	All	N/A	H80	N/A
Page No.	—	—	9-130	—
CODE P1158	All	N/A	H80	N/A
Page No.	—	—	9-130	—
CODE P1351	All	N/A	N/A	NA2
Page No.	—	—	—	9-203
CODE P1352	6 Cylinder	N/A	N/A	JC1
Page No.	—	—	—	9-181
CODE P1352	8 Cylinder	N/A	N/A	JC30
Page No.	—	—	—	9-183
CODE P1353	6 Cylinder	N/A	N/A	JC1
Page No.	—	—	—	9-181
CODE P1353	8 Cylinder	N/A	N/A	JC30
Page No.	—	—	—	9-183
CODE P1354	6 Cylinder	N/A	N/A	JC1
Page No.	—	—	—	9-181
CODE P1354	8 Cylinder	N/A	N/A	JC30
Page No.	—	—	—	9-183
CODE P1355	All	N/A	N/A	JC30
Page No.	—	—	—	9-183
CODE P1364	6 Cylinder	N/A	N/A	JC1
Page No.	—	—	—	9-181
CODE P1364	8 Cylinder	N/A	N/A	JC30
Page No.	—	—	—	9-183
CODE P1390	All	FG1	N/A	N/A
Page No.	—	9-125	—	—
CODE P1400	All	HE1	HE1	HE1
Page No.	—	9-142	9-142	9-142
CODE P1401	All	HE10	HE10	HE10
Page No.	—	9-142	9-142	9-142
CODE P1403	All	N/A	N/A	HE40
Page No.	—	—	—	9-144
CODE P1405	All	N/A	N/A	HE50
Page No.	—	—	—	9-145
CODE P1406	All	N/A	N/A	HE60
Page No.	—	—	—	9-145
CODE P1407	All	N/A	N/A	HE70
Page No.	—	—	—	9-146
CODE P1408	All	N/A	HE71	N/A
Page No.	—	—	9-146	—
CODE P1460	All	X105	X105	X120
Page No.	—	9-222	9-222	9-223
CODE P1473	All	X30	X30	X30
Page No.	—	9-219	9-219	9-219
CODE P1474	All	X20	X20	X60
Page No.	—	9-218	9-218	9-220
CODE P1479	All	X15	X15	X65
Page No.	—	9-218	9-218	9-221
CODE P1480	All	X45	X45	X75
Page No.	—	9-220	9-220	9-221
CODE P1481	All	X50	X50	X50
Page No.	—	9-220	9-220	9-220

Fig. 104 Diagnostic trouble code & pinpoint test reference chart (Part 2 of 3). 1994

Service Code/Page No.	Application	Pinpoint Test Step		
		Key On, Engine Off	Engine Running	Continuous Memory
CODE P1500	All	N/A	N/A	DP10
Page No.	—	—	—	9-122
CODE P1505	All	N/A	KE15	KE15
Page No.	—	—	9-197	9-197
CODE P1605	All	QB1	N/A	N/A
Page No.	—	9-206	—	—
CODE P1650	All	FG1	N/A	N/A
Page No.	—	9-125	—	—
CODE P1651	All	N/A	FG4	FG4
Page No.	—	—	9-125	9-125
CODE P1703	All	FD2	N/A	N/A
Page No.	—	9-125	—	—
CODE P1705	All	TD1	N/A	N/A
Page No.	—	9-210	—	—
CODE P1706	All	N/A	N/A	TG90
Page No.	—	—	—	9-214
CODE P1711	All	TE20	TE20	N/A
Page No.	—	9-212	9-212	—
CODE P1731	All	N/A	N/A	TG90
Page No.	—	—	—	9-214
CODE P1732	All	N/A	N/A	TG90
Page No.	—	—	—	9-214
CODE P1733	All	N/A	N/A	TG90
Page No.	—	—	—	9-214
CODE P1734	All	N/A	N/A	TG90
Page No.	—	—	—	9-214
CODE P1741	All	N/A	N/A	TG90
Page No.	—	—	—	9-214
CODE P1742	All	N/A	N/A	②
Page No.	—	—	—	—
CODE P1743	All	N/A	N/A	②
Page No.	—	—	—	—
CODE P1744	All	N/A	N/A	TG90
Page No.	—	—	—	9-214
CODE P1746	All	TC1	N/A	TG90
Page No.	—	9-208	—	9-214
CODE P1747	All	TC1	N/A	TG90
Page No.	—	9-208	—	9-214
CODE P1780	All	N/A	TB1	N/A
Page No.	—	—	9-207	—
CODE P1783	All	N/A	N/A	TE110
Page No.	—	—	—	9-213
CODE P1784	All	N/A	N/A	②
Page No.	—	—	—	—
CODE P1785	All	N/A	N/A	②
Page No.	—	—	—	—
CODE P1786	All	N/A	N/A	TG90
Page No.	—	—	—	9-214
CODE P1787	All	N/A	N/A	TG90
Page No.	—	—	—	9-214

①—Ignore DTC P1000 during KOEO & KOER Self-Test.
②—Transmission fault indicated.

Fig. 104 Diagnostic trouble code & pinpoint test reference chart (Part 3 of 3). 1994

Service Code/Page No.	Application	Pinpoint Test Step		
		Key On, Engine Off	Engine Running	Continuous Memory
CODE P0102	All	N/A	DC6	DC6
Page No.	—	—	9-117	9-117
CODE P0103	All	DC20	DC20	DC20
Page No.	—	9-118	9-118	9-118
CODE P0112	All	DA20	DA20	DA90
Page No.	—	9-115	9-115	9-115
CODE P0113	All	DA10	DA10	DA90
Page No.	—	9-115	9-115	9-115
CODE P0117	All	DA20	DA20	DA90
Page No.	—	9-115	9-115	9-115
CODE P0118	All	DA10	DA10	DA90
Page No.	—	9-115	9-115	9-115
CODE P0122	All	DH8	DH8	DH8
Page No.	—	9-121	9-121	9-121
CODE P0123	All	DH5	DH5	DH5
Page No.	—	9-120	9-120	9-120
CODE P0125	All	N/A	N/A	DA100
Page No.	—	—	—	9-116
CODE P0126	All	N/A	N/A	DA100
Page No.	—	—	—	9-116
CODE P0131	All	N/A	N/A	H27
Page No.	—	—	—	9-132
CODE P0132	All	H10	H10	H10
Page No.	—	9-132	9-132	9-132
CODE P0133	All	N/A	N/A	H20
Page No.	—	—	—	9-132
CODE P0135	All	H30	H30	H30
Page No.	—	9-133	9-133	9-133
CODE P0136	All	N/A	N/A	H80
Page No.	—	—	—	9-136
CODE P0138	All	H10	H10	H10
Page No.	—	9-132	9-132	9-132
CODE P0141	All	H30	H30	H30
Page No.	—	9-133	9-133	9-133
CODE P0151	All	N/A	N/A	H27
Page No.	—	—	—	9-132
CODE P0152	All	H10	H10	H10
Page No.	—	9-132	9-132	9-132
CODE P0153	All	N/A	N/A	H20
Page No.	—	—	—	9-133
CODE P0155	All	H30	H30	H30
Page No.	—	9-133	9-133	9-133
CODE P0156	All	N/A	N/A	H80
Page No.	—	—	—	9-136
CODE P0158	All	H10	H10	H10
Page No.	—	9-132	9-132	9-132
CODE P0161	All	H30	H30	H30
Page No.	—	9-133	9-133	9-133
CODE P0171	All	N/A	N/A	H40
Page No.	—	—	—	9-134

Fig. 105 Diagnostic trouble code & pinpoint test reference chart (Part 1 of 5). 1995

| Service Code/ Page No. | Application | Pinpoint Test Step | | | Service Code/ Page No. | Application | Pinpoint Test Step | | |
		Key On, Engine Off	Engine Running	Continuous Memory			Key On, Engine Off	Engine Running	Continuous Memory
CODE P0172	All	N/A	N/A	H40	CODE P0352	6 Cylinder	N/A	N/A	JC1
Page No.	—	—	—	9-133	Page No.	—	—	—	9-181
CODE P0174	All	N/A	N/A	H40	CODE P0352	8 Cylinder	N/A	N/A	JC30
Page No.	—	—	—	9-133	Page No.	—	—	—	9-183
CODE P0175	All	N/A	N/A	H40	CODE P0353	6 Cylinder	N/A	N/A	JC1
Page No.	—	—	—	9-133	Page No.	—	—	—	9-181
CODE P0230	③	KB30	KB30	KB30	CODE P0353	8 Cylinder	N/A	N/A	JC30
Page No.	—	9-194	9-194	9-194	Page No.	—	—	—	9-183
CODE P0230	④	KA1	KA1	KA40	CODE P0354	8 Cylinder	N/A	N/A	JC30
Page No.	—	9-135	9-135	9-137	Page No.	—	—	—	9-183
CODE P0231	All	KA20	KA20	KA35	CODE P0400	All	HE130	HE130	HE180
Page No.	—	9-189	9-189	9-137	Page No.	—	9-148	9-148	9-151
CODE P0232	All	KA10	KA10	KA30	CODE P0401	All	N/A	N/A	HE70
Page No.	—	9-136	9-136	9-137	Page No.	—	—	—	9-146
CODE P0300	All	N/A	HD1	HD1	CODE P0402	All	N/A	HE20	HE20
Page No.	—	—	9-140	9-140	Page No.	—	—	9-143	9-143
CODE P0301	All	N/A	HD1	HD1	CODE P0411	All	HM10	HM10	HM10
Page No.	—	—	9-140	9-140	Page No.	—	9-155	9-155	9-155
CODE P0302	All	N/A	HD1	HD1	CODE P0412	All	HM1	HM1	HM1
Page No.	—	—	9-140	9-140	Page No.	—	9-154	9-154	9-154
CODE P0303	All	N/A	HD1	HD1	CODE P0420	All	N/A	N/A	HF1
Page No.	—	—	9-140	9-140	Page No.	—	—	—	9-152
CODE P0304	All	N/A	HD1	HD1	CODE P0430	All	N/A	N/A	HF1
Page No.	—	—	9-140	9-140	Page No.	—	—	—	9-152
CODE P0305	All	N/A	HD1	HD1	CODE P0443	⑤	HV17	HV17	HV22
Page No.	—	—	9-140	9-140	Page No.	—	9-168	9-168	9-169
CODE P0306	All	N/A	HD1	HD1	CODE P0443	⑥	HW1	HW1	HW33
Page No.	—	—	9-140	9-140	Page No.	—	9-170	9-170	9-173
CODE P0307	All	N/A	HD1	HD1	CODE P0500	All	N/A	N/A	DP1
Page No.	—	—	9-140	9-140	Page No.	—	—	—	9-122
CODE P0308	All	N/A	HD1	HD1	CODE P0505	All	N/A	KE2	N/A
Page No.	—	—	9-140	9-140	Page No.	—	—	9-196	—
CODE P0320	All	N/A	N/A	NA1	CODE P0603	All	QB1	N/A	N/A
Page No.	—	—	—	9-203	Page No.	—	9-206	—	—
CODE P0325	All	N/A	DG1	DG1	CODE P0605	All	⑧	⑧	⑧
Page No.	—	—	9-119	9-119	Page No.	—	—	—	—
CODE P0326	All	N/A	DG1	DG1	CODE P0703	All	N/A	FD1	FD1
Page No.	—	—	9-119	9-119	Page No.	—	—	9-125	9-125
CODE P0330	All	N/A	DG1	DG1	CODE P0707	All	N/A	N/A	TD1
Page No.	—	—	9-119	9-119	Page No.	—	—	—	9-210
CODE P0331	All	N/A	DG1	DG1	CODE P0708	All	N/A	N/A	TD1
Page No.	—	—	9-119	9-119	Page No.	—	—	—	9-210
CODE P0340	All	N/A	N/A	DR1	CODE P0712	All	TE1	TE1	TE90
Page No.	—	—	—	9-124	Page No.	—	9-211	9-211	9-212
CODE P0350	6 Cylinder	N/A	N/A	JC1	CODE P0713	All	TE10	TE10	TE100
Page No.	—	—	—	9-181	Page No.	—	9-212	9-212	9-213
CODE P0350	8 Cylinder	N/A	N/A	JC30	CODE P0715	All	N/A	N/A	TF1
Page No.	—	—	—	9-183	Page No.	—	—	—	9-213
CODE P0351	6 Cylinder	N/A	N/A	JC1	CODE P0720	All	N/A	N/A	TF1
Page No.	—	—	—	9-181	Page No.	—	—	—	9-213
CODE P0351	8 Cylinder	N/A	N/A	JC30	CODE P0731	All	N/A	N/A	TC1
Page No.	—	—	—	9-183	Page No.	—	—	—	9-208

Fig. 105   Diagnostic trouble code & pinpoint test reference chart (Part 2 of 5). 1995

Service Code/ Page No.	Application	Key On, Engine Off	Engine Running	Continuous Memory
		Pinpoint Test Step		
CODE P0732	All	N/A	N/A	TC1
Page No.	—	—	—	9-208
CODE P0733	All	N/A	N/A	TC1
Page No.	—	—	—	9-208
CODE P0734	All	N/A	N/A	TC1
Page No.	—	—	—	9-208
CODE P0736	All	N/A	N/A	TD1
Page No.	—	—	—	9-210
CODE P0741	All	N/A	N/A	TC5
Page No.	—	—	—	9-209
CODE P0743	All	TC5	TC5	TC5
Page No.	—	9-209	9-209	9-209
CODE P0746	All	N/A	N/A	TC5
Page No.	—	9-209	—	9-209
CODE P0750	All	TC1	TC1	TC1
Page No.	—	9-208	9-208	9-208
CODE P0751	All	N/A	N/A	TC1
Page No.	—	—	—	9-208
CODE P0755	All	TC1	TC1	TC1
Page No.	—	9-208	9-208	9-208
CODE P0756	All	N/A	N/A	TC1
Page No.	—	—	—	9-208
CODE P0760	All	TC1	TC1	TC1
Page No.	—	9-208	9-208	9-208
CODE P0761	All	N/A	N/A	TC1
Page No.	—	—	—	9-208
CODE P0781	All	N/A	N/A	TC1
Page No.	—	—	—	9-208
CODE P0782	All	N/A	N/A	TC1
Page No.	—	—	—	9-208
CODE P0783	All	N/A	N/A	TC1
Page No.	—	—	—	9-208
CODE P0784	All	N/A	N/A	TC1
Page No.	—	—	—	9-208
CODE P1000	All	①	①	QC1
Page No.	—	—	—	9-207
CODE P1100	All	N/A	N/A	DC2
Page No.	—	—	—	9-117
CODE P1101	All	DC1	DC1	N/A
Page No.	—	—	—	—
CODE P1112	All	N/A	N/A	DA90
Page No.	—	—	—	9-115
CODE P1116	All	DA1	DA1	N/A
Page No.	—	9-114	9-114	—
CODE P1117	All	N/A	N/A	DA90
Page No.	—	—	—	9-115
CODE P1120	All	DH2	DH2	DH2
Page No.	—	9-120	9-120	9-120
CODE P1121	All	N/A	N/A	DH12
Page No.	—	—	—	9-121
CODE P1124	All	DH1	DH1	N/A
Page No.	—	9-120	9-120	—

Service Code/ Page No.	Application	Key On, Engine Off	Engine Running	Continuous Memory
		Pinpoint Test Step		
CODE P1125	All	N/A	N/A	DH17
Page No.	—	—	—	9-121
CODE P1130	All	N/A	N/A	H40
Page No.	—	—	—	9-128
CODE P1131	All	N/A	H40	H40
Page No.	—	—	9-128	9-128
CODE P1132	All	N/A	H40	H40
Page No.	—	—	9-128	9-128
CODE P1137	All	N/A	H80	N/A
Page No.	—	—	9-130	—
CODE P1138	All	N/A	H80	N/A
Page No.	—	—	9-130	—
CODE P1150	All	N/A	N/A	H40
Page No.	—	—	—	9-128
CODE P1151	All	N/A	H40	H40
Page No.	—	—	9-128	9-128
CODE P1152	All	N/A	H40	H40
Page No.	—	—	9-128	9-128
CODE P1157	All	N/A	H80	N/A
Page No.	—	—	9-130	—
CODE P1158	All	N/A	H80	N/A
Page No.	—	—	9-130	—
CODE P1233	All	KB1	KB1	KB1
Page No.	—	9-193	9-193	9-193
CODE P1234	All	KB1	KB1	KB1
Page No.	—	9-193	9-193	9-193
CODE P1235	All	KB30	KB30	KB30
Page No.	—	9-194	9-194	9-194
CODE P1236	All	KB30	KB30	KB30
Page No.	—	9-194	9-194	9-194
CODE P1237	All	KB47	KB47	KB47
Page No.	—	9-195	9-195	9-195
CODE P1238	All	KB47	KB47	KB47
Page No.	—	9-195	9-195	9-195
CODE P1351	All	N/A	N/A	NA2
Page No.	—	—	—	9-203
CODE P1352	6 Cylinder	N/A	N/A	JC1
Page No.	—	—	—	9-181
CODE P1352	8 Cylinder	N/A	N/A	JC30
Page No.	—	—	—	9-183
CODE P1353	6 Cylinder	N/A	N/A	JC1
Page No.	—	—	—	9-181
CODE P1353	8 Cylinder	N/A	N/A	JC30
Page No.	—	—	—	9-183
CODE P1354	6 Cylinder	N/A	N/A	JC1
Page No.	—	—	—	9-181
CODE P1354	8 Cylinder	N/A	N/A	JC30
Page No.	—	—	—	9-183
CODE P1355	8 Cylinder	N/A	N/A	JC30
Page No.	—	—	—	9-183
CODE P1359	All	N/A	MC1	MC1
Page No.	—	—	9-201	9-201

Fig. 105 Diagnostic trouble code & pinpoint test reference chart (Part 3 of 5). 1995

Service Code/ Page No.	Application	Pinpoint Test Step			Service Code/ Page No.	Application	Pinpoint Test Step		
		Key On, Engine Off	Engine Running	Continuous Memory			Key On, Engine Off	Engine Running	Continuous Memory
CODE P1364	6 Cylinder	N/A	N/A	JC1	CODE P1518	All	HU15	HU15	HU15
Page No.	—	—	—	9-181	Page No.	—	9-161	9-161	9-161
CODE P1364	8 Cylinder	N/A	N/A	JC30	CODE P1519	All	—	—	HU15
Page No.	—	—	—	9-183	Page No.	—	—	—	9-161
CODE P1390	All	FG1	N/A	N/A	CODE P1520	All	HU15	HU15	HU15
Page No.	—	—	—	—	Page No.	—	9-161	9-161	9-161
CODE P1400	All	HE1	HE1	HE1	CODE P1605	All	QB1	N/A	N/A
Page No.	—	9-142	9-142	9-142	Page No.	—	9-206	—	—
CODE P1401	All	HE10	HE10	HE10	CODE P1701	All	N/A	N/A	TD1
Page No.	—	9-142	9-142	9-142	Page No.	—	—	—	9-210
CODE P1403	All	N/A	N/A	HE40	CODE P1703	All	FD2	FD2	N/A
Page No.	—	—	—	9-144	Page No.	—	9-125	9-125	—
CODE P1405	All	N/A	N/A	HE50	CODE P1705	All	TD1	TD1	N/A
Page No.	—	—	—	9-145	Page No.	—	9-210	9-210	—
CODE P1406	All	N/A	N/A	HE60	CODE P1711	All	TE20	TE20	N/A
Page No.	—	—	—	9-145	Page No.	—	9-212	9-212	—
CODE P1407	All	N/A	N/A	HE70	CODE P1729	All	N/A	N/A	②
Page No.	—	—	—	9-146	Page No.	—	—	—	—
CODE P1408	All	N/A	HE71	N/A	CODE P1742	All	N/A	N/A	②
Page No.	—	—	9-146	—	Page No.	—	—	—	—
CODE P1409	All	HE110	HE110	HE120	CODE P1743	All	N/A	N/A	②
Page No.	—	9-148	9-148	9-148	Page No.	—	—	—	—
CODE P1413	All	HM20	HM20	HM20	CODE P1746	All	TC5	TC5	TC5
Page No.	—	9-155	9-155	9-155	Page No.	—	9-209	9-209	9-209
CODE P1414	All	HM26	HM26	HM26	CODE P1747	All	TC5	TC5	TC5
Page No.	—	9-156	9-156	9-156	Page No.	—	9-209	9-209	9-209
CODE P1443	All	N/A	N/A	HW5	CODE P1749	All	N/A	N/A	TC5
Page No.	—	—	—	—	Page No.	—	—	—	9-209
CODE P1444	All	N/A	N/A	HW21	CODE P1751	All	N/A	N/A	TC1
Page No.	—	—	—	9-171	Page No.	—	—	—	9-208
CODE P1445	All	N/A	N/A	HW25	CODE P1754	All	TC5	TC5	TC5
Page No.	—	—	—	9-172	Page No.	—	9-209	9-209	9-209
CODE P1460	⑤	X105	X105	X120	CODE P1756	All	N/A	N/A	TC1
Page No.	—	9-222	9-222	9-223	Page No.	—	—	—	9-208
CODE P1460	⑥	KM1	KM1	KM30	CODE P1761	All	N/A	N/A	TC1
Page No.	—	9-198	9-198	9-199	Page No.	—	—	—	9-208
CODE P1473	All	X30	X30	X30	CODE P1780	All	N/A	TB1	N/A
Page No.	—	9-219	9-219	9-219	Page No.	—	—	9-201	—
CODE P1474	⑦	X20	X20	X60	CODE P1781	All	②	N/A	N/A
Page No.	—	9-218	9-218	9-220	Page No.	—	—	—	—
CODE P1479	All	X15	X15	X65	CODE P1783	All	N/A	N/A	TE110
Page No.	—	9-218	9-218	9-221	Page No.	—	—	—	9-213
CODE P1480	All	X45	X45	X75	CODE P1784	All	N/A	N/A	②
Page No.	—	9-220	9-220	9-221	Page No.	—	—	—	—
CODE P1481	All	X50	X50	X50					
Page No.	—	9-220	9-220	9-220					
CODE P1500	All	N/A	N/A	DP10					
Page No.	—	—	—	9-122					
CODE P1505	All	N/A	KE15	KE15					
Page No.	—	—	9-197	9-197					
CODE P1506	All	N/A	KE10	KE20					
Page No.	—	—	—	9-197					

Fig. 105   Diagnostic trouble code & pinpoint test reference chart (Part 4 of 5). 1995

Service Code/ Page No.	Application	Pinpoint Test Step		
		Key On, Engine Off	Engine Running	Continuous Memory
CODE P1785	All	N/A	N/A	②
Page No.	—	—	—	—

① —Ignore DTC P1000 during KOEO & KOER Self-Test.
② —Transmission fault indicated.
③ —Continental.
④ —Except continental.
⑤ —Cougar, Mustang & Thunderbird.
⑥ —Continental, Crown Victoria, Grand Marquis & Town Car.
⑦ —Continental, Cougar, Mustang & Thunderbird.
⑧ —Replace PCM.

Fig. 105 Diagnostic trouble code & pinpoint test reference chart (Part 5 of 5). 1995

Service Code/ Page No.	Application	Pinpoint Test Step		
		Key On, Engine Off	Engine Running	Continuous Memory
CODE P0102	All	N/A	DC6	DC6
Page No.	—	—	9-251	9-251
CODE P0103	All	DC20	DC20	DC20
Page No.	—	9-252	9-252	9-252
CODE P0106	Probe	N/A	N/A	HH1
Page No.	—	—	—	9-310
CODE P0107	Probe	N/A	N/A	HH10
Page No.	—	—	—	9-311
CODE P0108	Probe	N/A	N/A	HH20
Page No.	—	—	—	9-311
CODE P0112	All	DA20	DA20	DA90
Page No.	—	9-247	9-247	9-247
CODE P0113	All	DA10	DA10	DA90
Page No.	—	9-246	9-246	9-247
CODE P0117	All	DA20	DA20	DA90
Page No.	—	9-247	9-247	9-247
CODE P0118	All	DA10	DA10	DA90
Page No.	—	9-246	9-246	9-247
CODE P0121	All	N/A	DH22	DH22
Page No.	—	—	9-262	9-262
CODE P0122	All	DH11	DH11	DH11
Page No.	—	9-261	9-261	9-261
CODE P0123	All	DH8	DH8	DH8
Page No.	—	9-260	9-260	9-260
CODE P0125	All	N/A	N/A	DA100
Page No.	—	—	—	9-247
CODE P0131	All	N/A	N/A	H27
Page No.	—	—	—	9-279
CODE P0132	All	H10	H10	H10
Page No.	—	—	—	—
CODE P0133	All	N/A	N/A	H20
Page No.	—	—	—	9-279
CODE P0135	⑨	HA30	HA30	HA30
Page No.	—	9-286	9-286	9-286

Fig. 106 Diagnostic trouble code & pinpoint test reference chart (Part 1 of 8). 1996

Service Code/ Page No.	Application	Pinpoint Test Step		
		Key On, Engine Off	Engine Running	Continuous Memory
CODE P0135	Others	H30	H30	H30
Page No.	—	9-279	9-279	9-279
CODE P0136	③	N/A	N/A	H90
Page No.	—	—	—	9-284
CODE P0136	Others	N/A	N/A	H80
Page No.	—	—	—	9-283
CODE P0138	All	H10	H10	H10
Page No.	—	—	—	—
CODE P0141	⑨	HA30	HA30	HA30
Page No.	—	9-286	9-286	9-286
CODE P0141	Others	H30	H30	H30
Page No.	—	9-279	9-279	9-279
CODE P0151	All	N/A	N/A	H27
Page No.	—	—	—	9-279
CODE P0152	All	H10	H10	H10
Page No.	—	—	—	—
CODE P0153	All	N/A	N/A	H20
Page No.	—	—	—	9-279
CODE P0155	⑨	HA30	HA30	HA30
Page No.	—	9-286	9-286	9-286
CODE P0155	All	H30	H30	H30
Page No.	—	9-279	9-279	9-279
CODE P0156	③	N/A	N/A	H90
Page No.	—	—	—	9-284
CODE P0156	Others	N/A	N/A	H80
Page No.	—	—	—	9-283
CODE P0158	All	H10	H10	H10
Page No.	—	—	—	—
CODE P0161	⑨	HA30	HA30	HA30
Page No.	—	9-286	9-286	9-286
CODE P0161	Others	H30	H30	H30
Page No.	—	9-279	9-279	9-279
CODE P0171	All	N/A	N/A	H40
Page No.	—	—	—	9-280
CODE P0171	⑨	HA41	HA41	HA41
Page No.	—	9-287	9-287	9-287
CODE P0172	Others	N/A	N/A	H41
Page No.	—	—	—	9-281
CODE P0174	⑨	HA41	HA41	HA41
Page No.	—	9-287	9-287	9-287
CODE P0174	Others	N/A	N/A	H41
Page No.	—	—	—	9-281
CODE P0175	⑨	HA41	HA41	HA41
Page No.	—	9-287	9-287	9-287
CODE P0175	Others	N/A	N/A	H41
Page No.	—	—	—	9-281
CODE P0176	All	N/A	DE1	DE20
Page No.	—	—	9-255	9-257

Fig. 106 Diagnostic trouble code & pinpoint test reference chart (Part 2 of 8). 1996

Service Code/Page No.	Application	Key On, Engine Off	Engine Running	Continuous Memory
CODE P0182	⑨	DB4	DB4	DB7
Page No.	—	9-248	9-248	9-249
CODE P0183	⑨	DB1	DB1	DB7
Page No.	—	9-248	9-248	9-249
CODE P0187	⑨	DB4	DB4	DB7
Page No.	—	9-248	9-247	9-249
CODE P0188	⑨	DB1	DB1	DB7
Page No.	—	9-248	9-248	9-249
CODE P0191	⑨	DD11	DD11	N/A
Page No.	—	9-254	9-254	—
CODE P0192	⑨	DD1	DD1	DD9
Page No.	—	9-253	9-253	9-254
CODE P0193	⑨	DD6	DD6	DD9
Page No.	—	9-254	9-254	9-254
CODE P0222	All	HT1	HT1	HT1
Page No.	—	9-322	9-322	9-322
CODE P0223	All	HT10	HT10	HT10
Page No.	—	9-322	9-322	9-322
CODE P0230	③	KB30	KB30	KB30
Page No.	—	9-379	9-379	9-379
CODE P0230	④	KA1	KA1	KA40
Page No.	—	9-373	9-373	9-376
CODE P0230	⑨	KC1	KC1	KC40
Page No.	—	9-381	9-381	9-383
CODE P0231	⑨	KA20	KA20	KA35
Page No.	—	9-375	9-375	9-376
CODE P0231	⑩	X180	X180	X195
Page No.	—	9-426	9-426	9-428
CODE P0231	⑪	X180	X180	X194
Page No.	—	9-426	9-426	9-427
CODE P0231	⑫	XB115	XB115	XB150
Page No.	—	9-434	9-434	9-435
CODE P0232	⑨	KC10	KC10	KC30
Page No.	—	9-382	9-382	9-383
CODE P0232	⑩	X170	X170	X190
Page No.	—	9-426	9-426	9-427
CODE P0232	⑫	XB100	XB100	XB155
Page No.	—	9-433	9-433	9-435
CODE P0300	All	N/A	HD1	HD1
Page No.	—	—	9-296	9-296
CODE P0301	All	N/A	HD1	HD1
Page No.	—	—	9-296	9-296
CODE P0302	All	N/A	HD1	HD1
Page No.	—	—	9-296	9-296
CODE P0303	All	N/A	HD1	HD1
Page No.	—	—	9-296	9-296
CODE P0304	All	N/A	HD1	HD1
Page No.	—	—	9-296	9-296
CODE P0305	All	N/A	HD1	HD1
Page No.	—	—	9-296	9-296
CODE P0306	All	N/A	HD1	HD1
Page No.	—	—	9-296	9-296
CODE P0307	All	N/A	HD1	HD1
Page No.	—	—	9-296	9-296
CODE P0308	All	N/A	HD1	HD1
Page No.	—	—	9-296	9-296
CODE P0320	DI	N/A	N/A	JG1
Page No.	—	—	—	9-368
CODE P0320	Others	N/A	N/A	N/A
Page No.	—	—	—	—
CODE P0325	All	N/A	DG1	DG1
Page No.	—	—	9-259	9-259
CODE P0326	All	N/A	DG1	DG1
Page No.	—	—	9-259	9-259
CODE P0330	All	N/A	DG1	DG1
Page No.	—	—	9-259	9-259
CODE P0331	All	N/A	DG1	DG1
Page No.	—	—	9-259	9-259
CODE P0340	All	N/A	N/A	DR1
Page No.	—	—	—	9-268
CODE P0350	6 Cylinder	N/A	N/A	JE60
Page No.	—	—	—	9-357
CODE P0350	8 Cylinder	N/A	N/A	JE90
Page No.	—	—	—	9-359
CODE P0351	6 Cylinder	N/A	N/A	JE60
Page No.	—	—	—	9-357
CODE P0351	8 Cylinder	N/A	N/A	JE90
Page No.	—	—	—	9-359
CODE P0352	6 Cylinder	N/A	N/A	JE60
Page No.	—	—	—	9-357
CODE P0352	8 Cylinder	N/A	N/A	JE90
Page No.	—	—	—	9-359
CODE P0353	6 Cylinder	N/A	N/A	JE60
Page No.	—	—	—	9-357
CODE P0353	8 Cylinder	N/A	N/A	JE90
Page No.	—	—	—	9-359
CODE P0354	8 Cylinder	N/A	N/A	JE90
Page No.	—	—	—	9-359
CODE P0355	⑬	N/A	N/A	JF1
Page No.	—	—	—	9-362
CODE P0356	⑬	N/A	N/A	JF1
Page No.	—	—	—	9-362
CODE P0357	⑬	N/A	N/A	JF1
Page No.	—	—	—	9-362
CODE P0358	⑬	N/A	N/A	JF1
Page No.	—	—	—	9-362
CODE P0385	DI	N/A	DK1	DK1
Page No.	—	—	9-263	9-263
CODE P0400	⑭	N/A	N/A	HH70
Page No.	—	—	—	9-315
CODE P0400	Others	HE130	HE130	HE130
Page No.	—	9-304	9-304	9-304

Fig. 106 Diagnostic trouble code & pinpoint test reference chart (Part 3 of 8). 1996

Service Code/ Page No.	Application	Pinpoint Test Step		
		Key On, Engine Off	Engine Running	Continuous Memory
CODE P0401	All	N/A	N/A	HE70
Page No.	—	—	—	9-302
CODE P0402	All	N/A	HE20	HE20
Page No.	—	—	9-300	9-300
CODE P0411	All	HM7	HM7	HM7
Page No.	—	9-317	9-317	9-317
CODE P0413	All	HM75	HM75	HM75
Page No.	—	9-320	9-320	9-320
CODE P0414	All	HM75	HM75	HM75
Page No.	—	9-320	9-320	9-320
CODE P0416	All	HM75	HM75	HM75
Page No.	—	9-320	9-320	9-320
CODE P0417	All	HM75	HM75	HM75
Page No.	—	9-320	9-320	9-320
CODE P0420	All	N/A	N/A	HF1
Page No.	—	—	—	9-307
CODE P0421	⑭	N/A	N/A	HF1
Page No.	—	—	—	9-307
CODE P0430	All	N/A	N/A	HF1
Page No.	—	—	—	9-307
CODE P0431	⑭	N/A	N/A	HF1
Page No.	—	—	—	9-307
CODE P0440	⑭	N/A	N/A	HV10
Page No.	—	—	—	9-334
CODE P0442	All	N/A	N/A	HX1
Page No.	—	—	—	9-343
CODE P0443	⑤	HX7	HX7	HX6
Page No.	—	9-344	9-344	9-344
CODE P0443	⑭	HV1	HV1	HV1
Page No.	—	9-334	9-334	9-334
CODE P0443	Others	HW1	HW1	HW38
Page No.	—	9-337	9-337	9-342
CODE P0446	All	N/A	N/A	HX13
Page No.	—	—	—	9-345
CODE P0452	All	N/A	HX22	HX22
Page No.	—	—	9-346	9-346
CODE P0453	All	N/A	HX28	HX28
Page No.	—	—	9-346	9-346
CODE P0455	All	N/A	N/A	HX40
Page No.	—	—	—	9-347
CODE P0500	④	N/A	N/A	DP5
Page No.	—	—	—	9-266
CODE P0500	⑤	HX7	HX7	HX6
Page No.	—	9-344	9-344	9-344
CODE P0500	Others	N/A	N/A	DP1
Page No.	—	—	—	9-266
CODE P0505	All	N/A	KE2	N/A
Page No.	—	—	9-384	—
CODE P0552	All	N/A	DT1	DT1
Page No.	—	—	9-272	9-272
CODE P0553	All	N/A	DT1	DT1
Page No.	—	—	9-272	9-272
CODE P0603	All	QB1	N/A	N/A
Page No.	—	9-404	—	—

Service Code/ Page No.	Application	Pinpoint Test Step		
		Key On, Engine Off	Engine Running	Continuous Memory
CODE P0605	All	⑧	⑧	⑧
Page No.	—	—	—	—
CODE P0703	All	N/A	N/A	FD3
Page No.	—	—	—	9-273
CODE P0705	⑥	TD7	TD7	N/A
Page No.	—	9-411	9-411	—
CODE P0705	Others	TD1	TD1	N/A
Page No.	—	9-411	9-411	—
CODE P0707	⑥	N/A	N/A	TD7
Page No.	—	—	—	9-411
CODE P0707	Others	N/A	N/A	TD1
Page No.	—	—	—	9-410
CODE P0708	⑥	N/A	N/A	TD7
Page No.	—	—	—	9-411
CODE P0708	Others	N/A	N/A	TD1
Page No.	—	—	—	9-410
CODE P0712	All	TE1	TE1	TE90
Page No.	—	9-413	9-413	9-414
CODE P0713	All	TE10	TE10	TE100
Page No.	—	9-413	9-413	9-414
CODE P0715	⑥	N/A	N/A	TF1
Page No.	—	—	—	9-415
CODE P0715	Others	N/A	N/A	TF1
Page No.	—	—	—	9-415
CODE P0720	All	N/A	N/A	TF1
Page No.	—	—	—	9-415
CODE P0721	All	N/A	N/A	TF7
Page No.	—	—	—	9-415
CODE P0731	⑥	N/A	N/A	TC9
Page No.	—	—	—	9-409
CODE P0731	Others	N/A	N/A	TC1
Page No.	—	—	—	9-408
CODE P0732	⑥	N/A	N/A	TC9
Page No.	—	—	—	9-409
CODE P0732	Others	N/A	N/A	TC1
Page No.	—	—	—	9-408
CODE P0733	⑥	N/A	N/A	TC9
Page No.	—	—	—	9-409
CODE P0733	Others	N/A	N/A	TC1
Page No.	—	—	—	9-408
CODE P0734	⑥	N/A	N/A	TC9
Page No.	—	—	—	9-409
CODE P0734	Others	N/A	N/A	TC1
Page No.	—	—	—	9-408
CODE P0736	All	N/A	N/A	TD1
Page No.	—	—	—	9-411
CODE P0741	⑥	N/A	N/A	TC9
Page No.	—	—	—	9-409
CODE P0741	Others	N/A	N/A	TC5
Page No.	—	—	—	9-408
CODE P0743	⑥	TC9	TC9	TC9
Page No.	—	9-409	9-409	9-409
CODE P0743	Others	TC5	TC5	TC5
Page No.	—	9-408	9-408	9-408

Fig. 106   Diagnostic trouble code & pinpoint test reference chart (Part 4 of 8). 1996

FORD–Electronic Engine Controls

Service Code/ Page No.	Application	Pinpoint Test Step Key On, Engine Off	Engine Running	Continuous Memory
CODE P0746	All	N/A	N/A	TC5
Page No.	—	9-408	—	9-408
CODE P0750	⑥	TC9	TC9	TC9
Page No.	—	9-409	9-409	9-409
CODE P0750	Others	TC1	TC1	TC1
Page No.	—	9-408	9-408	9-408
CODE P0751	⑥	N/A	N/A	TC9
Page No.	—	—	—	9-409
CODE P0751	Others	N/A	N/A	TC1
Page No.	—	—	—	9-408
CODE P0755	⑥	TC9	TC9	TC9
Page No.	—	9-409	9-409	9-409
CODE P0755	Others	TC1	TC1	TC1
Page No.	—	9-408	9-408	9-408
CODE P0756	⑥	N/A	N/A	TC9
Page No.	—	—	—	9-409
CODE P0756	Others	N/A	N/A	TC1
Page No.	—	—	—	9-408
CODE P0760	⑥	TC9	TC9	TC9
Page No.	—	9-409	9-409	9-409
CODE P0760	Others	TC1	TC1	TC1
Page No.	—	9-408	9-408	9-408
CODE P0761	⑥	N/A	N/A	TC9
Page No.	—	—	—	9-409
CODE P0761	Others	N/A	N/A	TC1
Page No.	—	—	—	9-408
CODE P0781	⑥	N/A	N/A	TC9
Page No.	—	—	—	9-409
CODE P0781	Others	N/A	N/A	TC1
Page No.	—	—	—	9-408
CODE P0782	⑥	N/A	N/A	TC9
Page No.	—	—	—	9-409
CODE P0782	Others	N/A	N/A	TC1
Page No.	—	—	—	9-408
CODE P0783	⑥	N/A	N/A	TC9
Page No.	—	—	—	9-409
CODE P0783	Others	N/A	N/A	TC1
Page No.	—	—	—	9-408
CODE P0784	⑥	N/A	N/A	TC9
Page No.	—	—	—	9-409
CODE P0784	Others	N/A	N/A	TC1
Page No.	—	—	—	9-408
CODE P1000	All	①	①	QC1
Page No.	—	—	—	9-404
CODE P1100	All	N/A	N/A	DC2
Page No.	—	—	—	9-250
CODE P1101	All	DC2	DC1	N/A
Page No.	—	9-250	9-250	—
CODE P1112	All	N/A	N/A	DA90
Page No.	—	—	—	9-247
CODE P1116	All	DA1	DA1	N/A
Page No.	—	9-246	9-246	—
CODE P1117	All	N/A	N/A	DA90
Page No.	—	—	—	9-247

Service Code/ Page No.	Application	Pinpoint Test Step Key On, Engine Off	Engine Running	Continuous Memory
CODE P1120	All	DH3	DH3	DH3
Page No.	—	9-260	9-260	9-260
CODE P1121	All	N/A	N/A	DH15
Page No.	—	—	—	9-261
CODE P1124	All	DH1	DH1	N/A
Page No.	—	9-260	9-260	—
CODE P1125	All	N/A	N/A	DH20
Page No.	—	—	—	9-261
CODE P1127	⑨	HA90	HA90	HA90
Page No.	—	9-291	9-291	9-291
CODE P1127	Others	N/A	H100	N/A
Page No.	—	—	—	—
CODE P1128	⑨	HA100	HA100	HA100
Page No.	—	9-291	9-291	9-291
CODE P1128	Others	N/A	H110	N/A
Page No.	—	—	9-285	—
CODE P1129	⑨	HA100	HA100	HA100
Page No.	—	9-291	9-291	9-291
CODE P1129	Others	N/A	H110	N/A
Page No.	—	—	9-285	—
CODE P1130	⑨	HA40	HA40	HA40
Page No.	—	9-287	9-287	9-287
CODE P1130	Others	H40	H40	H40
Page No.	—	9-280	9-280	9-280
CODE P1131	⑨	HA40	HA40	HA40
Page No.	—	9-287	9-287	9-287
CODE P1131	Others	H40	H40	H40
Page No.	—	9-280	9-280	9-280
CODE P1132	⑨	HA40	HA40	HA40
Page No.	—	9-287	9-287	9-287
CODE P1132	Others	H40	H40	H40
Page No.	—	9-280	9-280	9-280
CODE P1137	⑨	N/A	HA80	N/A
Page No.	—	—	9-290	—
CODE P1137	Others	N/A	H80	N/A
Page No.	—	—	9-280	—
CODE P1138	⑨	N/A	HA80	N/A
Page No.	—	—	9-290	—
CODE P1138	Others	N/A	H80	N/A
Page No.	—	—	9-280	—
CODE P1150	⑨	HA40	HA40	HA40
Page No.	—	9-287	9-287	9-287
CODE P1150	Others	H40	H40	H40
Page No.	—	9-280	9-280	9-280
CODE P1151	⑨	HA40	HA40	HA40
Page No.	—	9-287	9-287	9-287
CODE P1151	Others	H40	H40	H40
Page No.	—	9-280	9-280	9-280
CODE P1152	⑨	HA40	HA40	HA40
Page No.	—	9-287	9-287	9-287
CODE P1152	Others	H40	H40	H40
Page No.	—	9-280	9-280	9-280

Fig. 106 Diagnostic trouble code & pinpoint test reference chart (Part 5 of 8). 1996

ELECTRONIC ENGINE CONTROL SYSTEM (EEC-V)

Service Code/ Page No.	Application	Pinpoint Test Step Key On, Engine Off	Engine Running	Continuous Memory	Service Code/ Page No.	Application	Pinpoint Test Step Key On, Engine Off	Engine Running	Continuous Memory
CODE P1157	⑨	N/A	HA80	N/A	CODE P1364	8 Cylinder	N/A	N/A	JC30
Page No.	—	—	9-290	—	Page No.	—	—	—	—
CODE P1157	Others	N/A	H80	N/A	CODE P1390	All	FG1	N/A	N/A
Page No.	—	—	9-280	—	Page No.	—	—	—	—
CODE P1158	⑨	N/A	HA80	N/A	CODE P1400	⑭	HH30	HH30	HH30
Page No.	—	—	9-290	—	Page No.	—	9-312	9-312	9-312
CODE P1158	Others	N/A	H80	N/A	CODE P1400	Others	HE1	HE1	HE1
Page No.	—	—	9-280	—	Page No.	—	9-299	9-299	9-299
CODE P1220	All	HT20	HT20	HT20	CODE P1401	⑭	HE40	HE40	HE40
Page No.	—	9-323	9-323	9-323	Page No.	—	9-301	9-301	9-301
CODE P1224	All	HT40	HT40	HT40	CODE P1401	Others	HE10	HE10	HE10
Page No.	—	9-324	9-324	9-324	Page No.	—	9-299	9-299	9-299
CODE P1230	All	HT20	HT20	HT20	CODE P1405	All	N/A	N/A	HE50
Page No.	—	9-323	9-323	9-323	Page No.	—	—	—	9-301
CODE P1231	All	XB135	N/A	N/A	CODE P1406	All	N/A	N/A	HE60
Page No.	—	9-434	—	—	Page No.	—	—	—	9-302
CODE P1232	All	X160	X160	X205	CODE P1407	All	N/A	N/A	HE70
Page No.	—	9-425	9-425	9-428	Page No.	—	—	—	9-302
CODE P1233	All	KB1	KB1	KB1	CODE P1408	⑭	N/A	HE50	N/A
Page No.	—	9-377	9-377	9-377	Page No.	—	—	9-301	—
CODE P1234	All	KB1	KB1	KB1	CODE P1408	Others	N/A	HE71	N/A
Page No.	—	9-377	9-377	9-377	Page No.	—	—	9-302	—
CODE P1235	③	KB30	KB30	KB30	CODE P1409	All	HE110	HE110	HE120
Page No.	—	9-379	9-379	9-379	Page No.	—	9-304	9-304	9-304
CODE P1235	⑫	XB140	XB140	XB170	CODE P1411	All	HE110	HE110	HE120
Page No.	—	9-435	9-435	9-436	Page No.	—	9-304	9-304	9-304
CODE P1236	③	KB30	KB30	KB30	CODE P1413	All	HM18	HM18	HM18
Page No.	—	9-379	9-379	9-379	Page No.	—	9-317	9-317	9-317
CODE P1236	⑫	XB140	XB140	XB170	CODE P1414	All	HM25	HM25	HM25
Page No.	—	9-435	9-435	9-436	Page No.	—	9-318	9-318	9-318
CODE P1237	All	KB47	KB47	KB47	CODE P1442	All	N/A	N/A	HX1
Page No.	—	9-379	9-379	9-379	Page No.	—	—	—	9-343
CODE P1238	All	KB47	KB47	KB47	CODE P1443	All	N/A	N/A	HW6
Page No.	—	9-379	9-379	9-379	Page No.	—	—	—	9-337
CODE P1351	All	N/A	N/A	NA2	CODE P1444	All	N/A	N/A	HW27
Page No.	—	—	—	—	Page No.	—	—	—	9-341
CODE P1352	6 Cylinder	N/A	N/A	JC1	CODE P1445	All	N/A	N/A	HW31
Page No.	—	—	—	—	Page No.	—	—	—	9-341
CODE P1352	8 Cylinder	N/A	N/A	JC30	CODE P1460	⑩	X105	X105	X120
Page No.	—	—	—	—	Page No.	—	9-423	9-423	9-424
CODE P1353	6 Cylinder	N/A	N/A	JC1	CODE P1460	⑭	KM60	KM60	KM30
Page No.	—	—	—	—	Page No.	—	9-397	9-397	9-396
CODE P1353	8 Cylinder	N/A	N/A	JC30	CODE P1460	Others	KM1	KM1	KM30
Page No.	—	—	—	—	Page No.	—	9-394	9-394	9-396
CODE P1354	6 Cylinder	N/A	N/A	JC1	CODE P1461	All	DS1	DS1	DS1
Page No.	—	—	—	—	Page No.	—	9-269	9-269	9-269
CODE P1354	8 Cylinder	N/A	N/A	JC30	CODE P1462	All	DS10	DS10	DS10
Page No.	—	—	—	—	Page No.	—	9-270	9-270	9-270
CODE P1355	8 Cylinder	N/A	N/A	JC30	CODE P1463	All	N/A	N/A	DS20
Page No.	—	—	—	—	Page No.	—	—	—	9-271
CODE P1359	All	N/A	MC1	MC1	CODE P1464	All	X124	X124	N/A
Page No.	—	—	—	—	Page No.	—	9-424	9-424	—
CODE P1364	6 Cylinder	N/A	N/A	JC1	CODE P1469	All	N/A	N/A	X115
Page No.	—	—	—	—	Page No.	—	—	—	9-423

Fig. 106   Diagnostic trouble code & pinpoint test reference chart (Part 6 of 8). 1996

Service Code/Page No.	Application	Key On, Engine Off	Engine Running	Continuous Memory
CODE P1473	All	XB20	N/A	N/A
Page No.	—	9-430	—	—
CODE P1474	⑦	X20	X20	X60
Page No.	—	9-418	9-418	9-421
CODE P1479	⑦	X15	X15	X65
Page No.	—	9-418	9-418	9-422
CODE P1480	All	X45	X45	X75
Page No.	—	9-420	9-420	9-422
CODE P1481	All	X50	X50	X50
Page No.	—	9-421	9-421	9-421
CODE P1483	All	XB10	XB10	XB10
Page No.	—	9-429	9-429	9-429
CODE P1500	All	N/A	N/A	DP25
Page No.	—	—	—	9-267
CODE P1501	All	N/A	DP15	N/A
Page No.	—	—	9-267	—
CODE P1504	All	KE2	KE2	KE2
Page No.	—	9-384	9-384	9-384
CODE P1505	All	KE25	KE25	KE25
Page No.	—	9-385	9-385	9-385
CODE P1506	All	N/A	KE10	KE20
Page No.	—	—	9-385	9-385
CODE P1507	All	N/A	KE2	KE2
Page No.	—	—	9-384	9-384
CODE P1512	All	N/A	N/A	HU15
Page No.	—	—	—	9-327
CODE P1513	All	N/A	N/A	HU15
Page No.	—	—	—	9-327
CODE P1516	All	HU15	N/A	HU15
Page No.	—	9-327	—	9-327
CODE P1517	All	HU15	N/A	HU15
Page No.	—	9-327	—	9-327
CODE P1518	All	HU15	HU15	HU15
Page No.	—	9-327	9-327	9-327
CODE P1519	All	HU15		HU15
Page No.	—	9-327	—	9-327
CODE P1520	All	HU15	HU15	HU15
Page No.	—	9-327	9-327	9-327
CODE P1530	All	XB50	XB50	XB50
Page No.	—	9-431	9-431	9-431
CODE P1537	All	HU15	HU15	HU15
Page No.	—	9-327	9-327	9-327
CODE P1538	All	HU15	HU15	HU15
Page No.	—	9-327	9-327	9-327
CODE P1539	All	HB40	HB40	HB40
Page No.	—	—	—	—
CODE P1550	All	N/A	DT1	DT1
Page No.	—	—	9-272	9-272
CODE P1605	All	QB1	N/A	N/A
Page No.	—	9-404	—	—
CODE P1625	All	XB60	XB60	XB65
Page No.	—	9-431	9-431	9-432
CODE P1626	All	XB60	XB60	XB65
Page No.	—	9-431	9-431	9-432

Service Code/Page No.	Application	Key On, Engine Off	Engine Running	Continuous Memory
CODE P1650	All	FF1	FF1	N/A
Page No.	—	9-277	9-277	—
CODE P1651	All	N/A	FF1	FF1
Page No.	—	—	9-277	9-277
CODE P1701	All	N/A	N/A	TD1
Page No.	—	—	—	9-410
CODE P1703	All	FD2	FD1	N/A
Page No.	—	9-273	9-273	—
CODE P1705	⑥	TD1	TD1	N/A
Page No.	—	9-410	9-410	—
CODE P1705	Others	TD7	TD7	N/A
Page No.	—	9-411	9-411	—
CODE P1709	M/T	TA5	N/A	N/A
Page No.	—	9-406	—	—
CODE P1709	A/T	TA1	N/A	N/A
Page No.	—	9-405	—	—
CODE P1711	All	TE20	TE20	N/A
Page No.	—	9-413	9-413	—
CODE P1728	All	N/A	N/A	②
Page No.	—	—	—	—
CODE P1729	All	N/A	N/A	TG6
Page No.	—	—	—	—
CODE P1741	All	N/A	N/A	②
Page No.	—	—	—	—
CODE P1742	All	N/A	N/A	②
Page No.	—	—	—	—
CODE P1743	All	N/A	N/A	②
Page No.	—	—	—	—
CODE P1744	All	N/A	N/A	②
Page No.	—	—	—	—
CODE P1746	All	TC1	N/A	TC1
Page No.	—	9-408	—	9-408
CODE P1747	All	TC1	N/A	TC1
Page No.	—	9-408	—	9-408
CODE P1749	All	N/A	N/A	TC1
Page No.	—	—	—	9-408
CODE P1751	⑥	N/A	N/A	TC9
Page No.	—	—	—	9-409
CODE P1751	Others	N/A	N/A	TC1
Page No.	—	—	—	9-408
CODE P1754	All	TC1	N/A	TC1
Page No.	—	9-408	—	9-408
CODE P1756	⑥	N/A	N/A	TC9
Page No.	—	—	—	9-409
CODE P1756	Others	N/A	N/A	TC1
Page No.	—	—	—	9-408
CODE P1761	⑥	N/A	N/A	TC9
Page No.	—	—	—	9-409
CODE P1761	Others	N/A	N/A	TC1
Page No.	—	—	—	9-408
CODE P1780	All	N/A	TB1	N/A
Page No.	—	—	9-406	—
CODE P1781	All	TG6	N/A	N/A
Page No.	—	—	—	—

Fig. 106 Diagnostic trouble code & pinpoint test reference chart (Part 7 of 8). 1996

ELECTRONIC ENGINE CONTROL SYSTEM (EEC-V)

		Pinpoint Test Step		
CODE P1783	All	N/A	N/A	TE110
Page No.	—	—	—	9-414
CODE P1784	All	N/A	N/A	②
Page No.	—	—	—	—
CODE P1785	All	N/A	N/A	②
Page No.	—	—	—	—
CODE P1786	All	N/A	N/A	②
Page No.	—	—	—	—
CODE P1787	All	N/A	N/A	②
Page No.	—	—	—	—
CODE P1788	All	TC1	N/A	TC1
Page No.	—	9-408	—	9-408
CODE P1789	All	TC1	N/A	TC1
Page No.	—	9-408	—	9-408
CODE U1021	All	XB180	XB180	XB180
Page No.	—	9-437	9-437	9-437
CODE U1039	All	N/A	N/A	①
Page No.	—	—	—	—
CODE U1051	All	N/A	N/A	①
Page No.	—	—	—	—
CODE U1073	All	XB180	XB180	XB180
Page No.	—	9-437	9-437	9-437
CODE U1131	All	XB180	XB180	XB180
Page No.	—	9-437	9-437	9-437
CODE U1135	All	N/A	N/A	①
Page No.	—	—	—	—
CODE U1256	All	XB180	XB180	XB180
Page No.	—	9-437	9-437	9-437
CODE U1135	All	N/A	N/A	①
Page No.	—	—	—	—

①—Fault in 1996 Continental module communications network.
②—Transmission fault indicated.
③—Continental.
④—Contour & Mystique.
⑤—Sable & Taurus.
⑥—Escort & Tracer.
⑦—w/CCRM.
⑧—Replace PCM.
⑨—Crown Victoria w/natural gas engine.
⑩—w/CCRM except Mustang.
⑪—Mustang.
⑫—Mark VIII.
⑬—Taurus SHO.
⑭—Probe.

Fig. 106 Diagnostic trouble code & pinpoint test reference chart (Part 8 of 8). 1996

Driveability		Chart Number
Starting Concerns	No Crank	1
	Hard Start / Long Crank / Erratic Start / Erratic Crank	2
	Stall After Start	7
	No Start / Normal Crank	3
Unique Idle Concerns	Slow Return to Idle	4
	Rolling Idle	7
	Fast Idle	5
	Low / Slow Idle	6
Driveability — Performance While Driving Concerns		
Stalls / Quits (607000)	Idle	7
	Acceleration	7
	Cruise	7
	Deceleration	6
Runs Rough (608000)	Idle	7
	Acceleration	7
	Cruise	7
Misses (609000)	Idle	7
	Acceleration	7
	Cruise	7
Buck / Jerk (610000)	Acceleration	7
	Cruise	7
	Deceleration	7
Hesitation / Stumble (611000)	Acceleration	7
Surge (612000)	Acceleration	7
	Cruise	7
Backfires (613000)	Idle	8
	Acceleration	8
	Deceleration	8
Lack / Loss of Power (614000)	Acceleration	9
	Cruise	9
Spark Knock (615000)	Acceleration	10
	Cruise	10
Additional Driveability Concerns		
Diesels / Runs On		5
Poor Fuel Economy		11
Emissions Compliance		12
Malfunction Indicator Lamp (MIL) Concern		13
DTC P1000 received during Emission Test / All Supported On Board System Readiness Tests not completed		29
Electrical		
Warning Indicators		13
—MIL		
—TCIL		
—"CHECK TRACTION ASSIST" message on message center (Continental)		
Climate Control (208000)	Lack of cooling (A/C) (A/C not functioning)	23
	A/C always ON/AC compressor runs continuously	24
	A/C does not cut off under WOT conditions	25
Instrumentation		15
—Tachometer Inoperative		
—Speedometer Inoperative		
Lighting Systems-Exterior Lighting		27
—Stoplamps always on		
—Stoplamps always off		
Chassis		
Traction Assist Concerns (Continental only) (300000)		31
—No Traction Assist		
—Poor / Erratic Traction Assist		
Engine		
Oil System Concerns		16
—High Oil Consumption		
—Leaks		
Cooling System Concerns (402000)	Overheating	17
	Runs Cold	18
	Electric cooling fan never runs	17
	Electric cooling fan always runs	18
Exhaust System Concerns (403000)	Visible Smoke	19
	Odor (Sulphur / "rotten egg" smell)	28
Fuel System Concerns (404000)	Odor, Engine Compartment	20
	Fuel pump always runs	30
Engine Noise (Under Hood)	Electric Secondary Air Injection air pump always runs (Continental)	32
	Other Noises	21
Driveline		
Manual Transmission Concern		13
—Shift Indicator Lamp		
Automatic Transmission Shift Concerns		14
—A/T upshift concern		
—A/T downshift concern		
—Engagement concern		
Noise / Vibration		
Vibration Concerns		22
No Symptoms Present		
EEC-V Quick Test		26

Fig. 107 Symptom index. 1994-95

System / Symptom		Chart Number
Driveability		
Starting Concerns	No Crank	1
	Hard Start/Long Crank/Erratic Start/Erratic Crank	2
	Stall After Start	7
	No Start/Normal Crank	3
Unique Idle Concerns	Slow Return to Idle	4
	Rolling Idle	7
	Fast Idle	5
	Low/Slow Idle	6
Driveability — Performance While Driving Concerns		
Stalls/Quits (607000)	Idle	7
	Acceleration	7
	Cruise	7
	Deceleration	6
Runs Rough (608000)	Idle	7
	Acceleration	7
	Cruise	7
Misses (609000)	Idle	7
	Acceleration	7
	Cruise	7
Buck/Jerk (610000)	Acceleration	7
	Cruise	7
	Deceleration	7
Hesitation/Stumble (611000)	Acceleration	7
Surge (612000)	Acceleration	7
	Cruise	7
Backfires (613000)	Idle	8
	Acceleration	8
	Deceleration	8
Lack/Loss of Power (614000)	Acceleration	9
	Cruise	9
(Continued)		

Fig. 108   Symptom index (Part 1 of 3). 1996

System / Symptom		Chart Number
Driveability — Performance While Driving Concerns (continued)		
Spark Knock (615000)	Acceleration	10
	Cruise	10
Additional Driveability Concerns		
Diesels/Runs On		5
Poor Fuel Economy		11
Emissions Compliance		12
Malfunction Indicator Lamp (MIL) Concern		13
DTC P1000 received during Emission Test/All Supported On Board System Readiness Tests not completed		29
Electrical		
Warning Indicators (206000)	MIL	13
	TCIL	13
	4x4 Low Lamp	13
	CHTIL Concern (4.6L F-Series)	13
	SIL	13
	"CHECK TRACTION CONTROL" message on message center (Continental)	13
Climate Control (208000)	Lack of A/C cooling, A/C not functioning (applications with WAC relay, A/C relay, CCRM or VLCM)	23
	A/C always ON/AC compressor runs continuously	24
	A/C does not cut off under WOT conditions (applications with WAC relay, A/C relay or CCRM)	25
Instrumentation (204000)	Tachometer Inoperative	15
	Speedometer Inoperative	15
Lighting Systems-Exterior Lighting (201000)	Stoplamps always on	27
	Stoplamps always off	27
Chassis		
Traction Control Concerns (Continental only) (300000)	No Traction Control	31
	Poor/Erratic Traction Control	31
(Continued)		

Fig. 108   Symptom index (Part 2 of 3). 1996

System / Symptom		Chart Number
Engine		
Oil System Concerns (401000)	High Oil Consumption	16
	Leaks	16
Cooling System Concerns (402000)	Overheating	17
	Electric cooling fan does not run (low and/or high speed)	17
	Electric cooling fan always runs	18
Exhaust System Concerns (403000)	Visible Smoke	19
	Odor (Sulphur/"rotten egg" smell)	28
Fuel System Concerns (404000)	Odor, Engine Compartment	20
	Fuel pump always runs	30
Engine Noise (Under Hood)	Electric Secondary Air Injection air pump always runs	22
	Other Noises	21
Driveline		
Manual Transmission Concern	Shift Indicator Lamp (SIL)	13
Automatic Transmission Shift Concerns (501000)	A/T upshift concern	14
	A/T downshift concern	14
	Engagement concern	14
No Symptoms Present		
EEC-V Quick Test		26

Fig. 108   Symptom index (Part 3 of 3). 1996

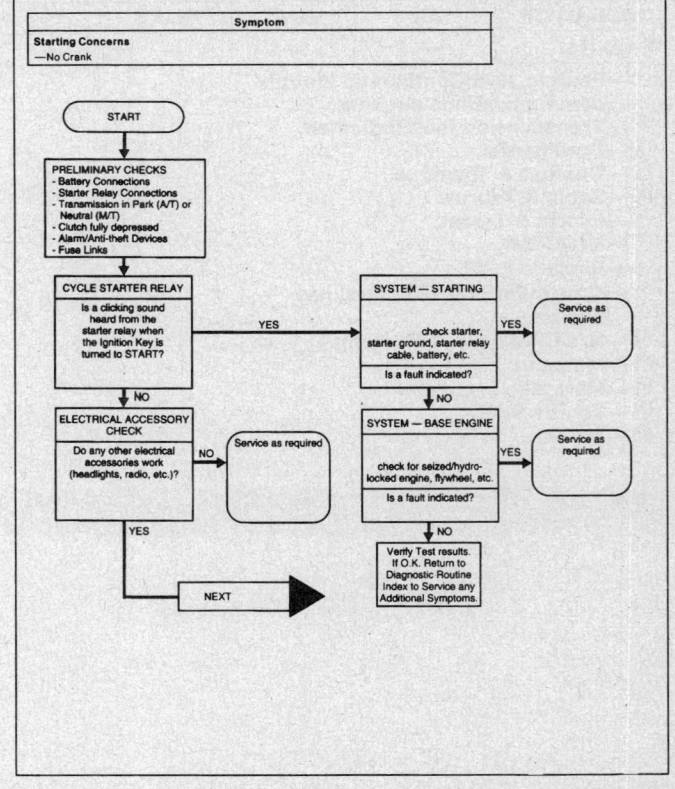

Fig. 109   Symptom flowchart 1 (Part 1 of 2). 1994–95

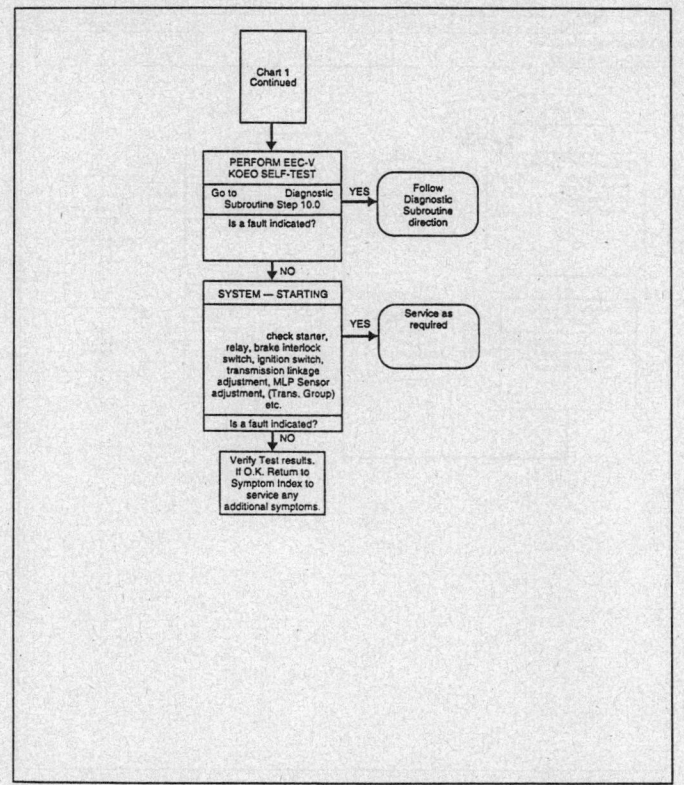

Fig. 109   Symptom flowchart 1 (Part 2 of 2). 1994–95

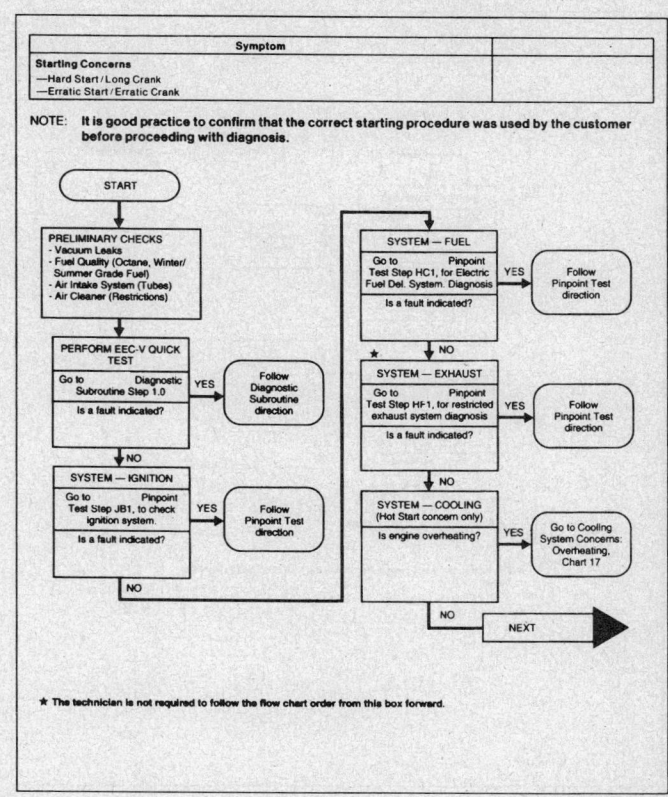

Fig. 110   Symptom flowchart 2 (Part 1 of 2). 1994–95

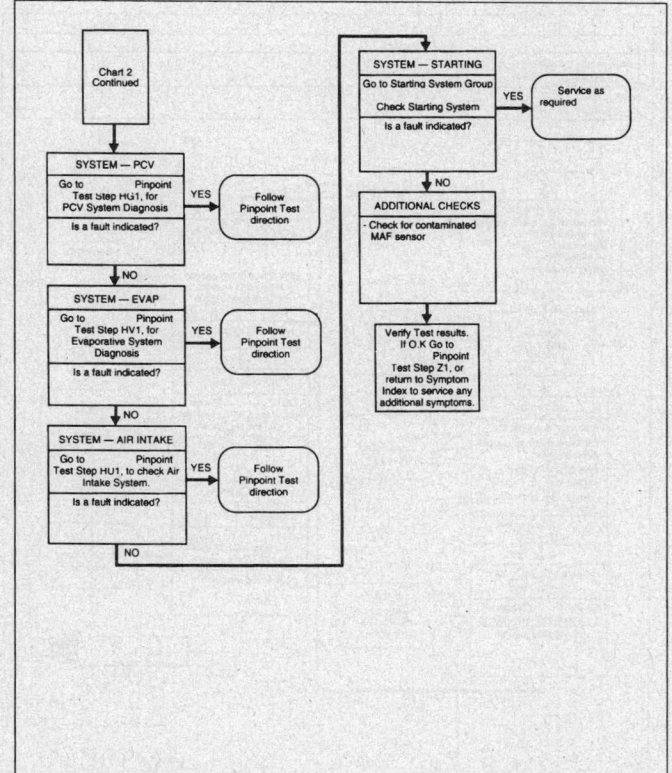

Fig. 110   Symptom flowchart 2 (Part 2 of 2). 1994–95

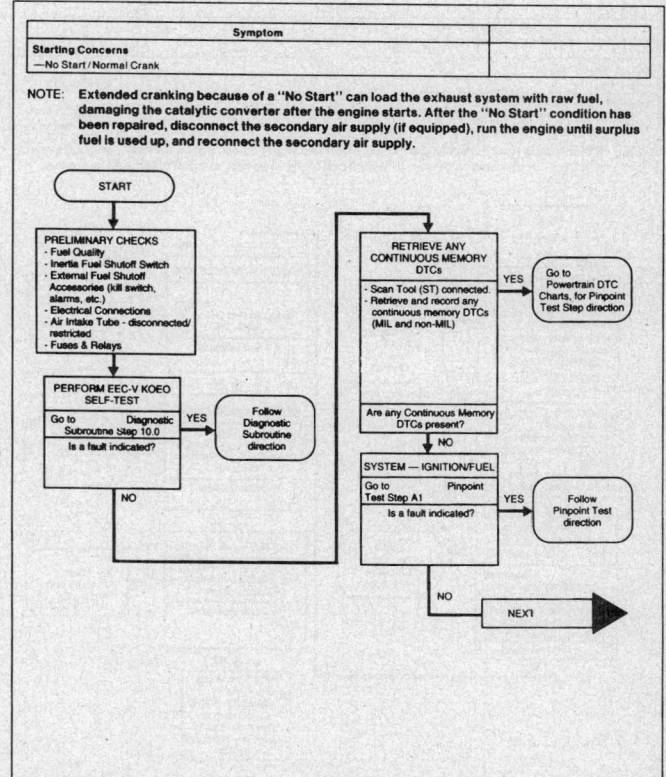

Fig. 111   Symptom flowchart 3 (Part 1 of 2). 1994–95

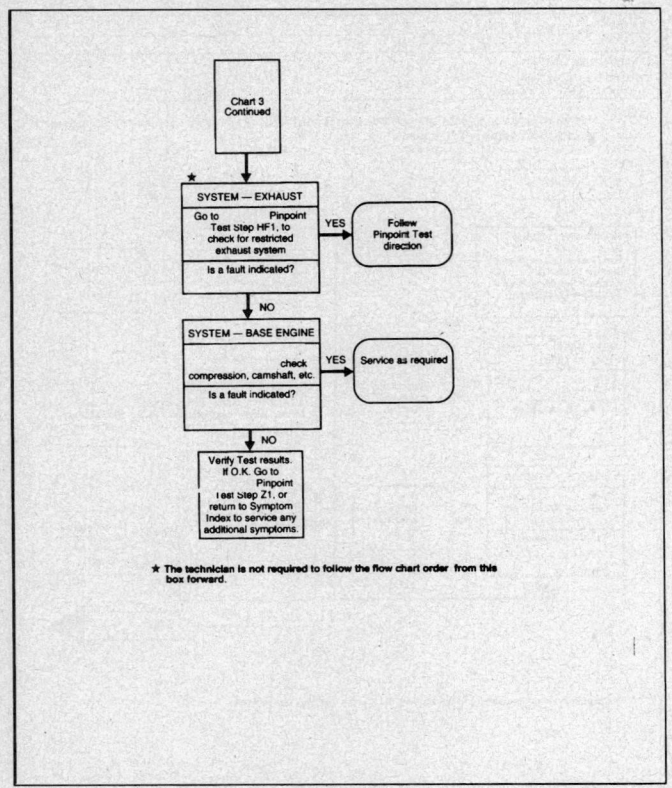

Fig. 111 Symptom flowchart 3 (Part 2 of 2). 1994–95

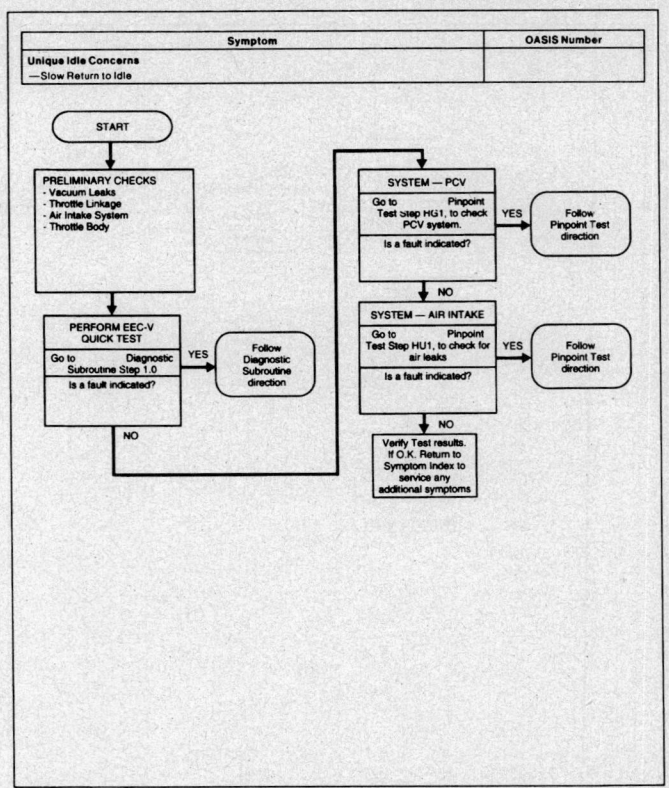

Fig. 112 Symptom flowchart 4. 1994–95

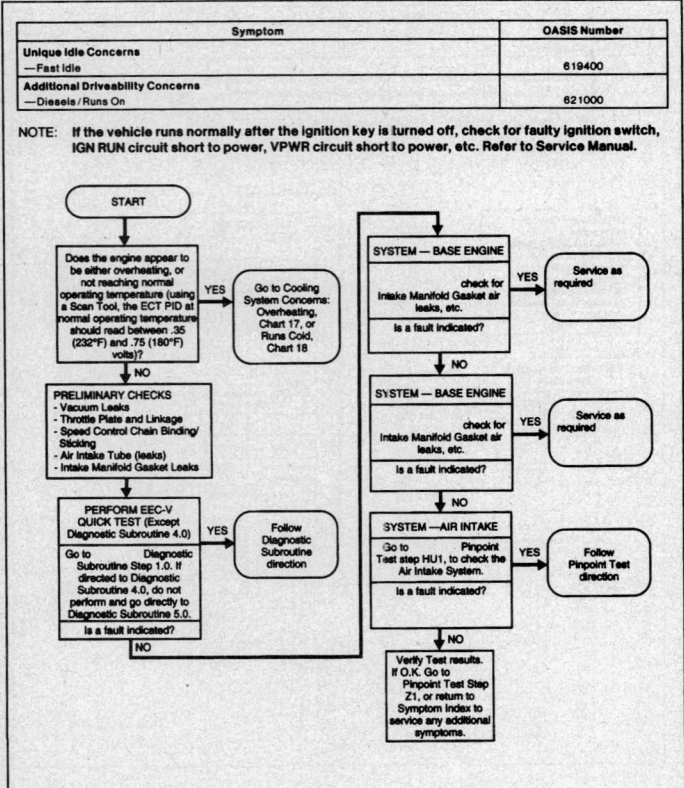

Fig. 113 Symptom flowchart 5. 1994–95

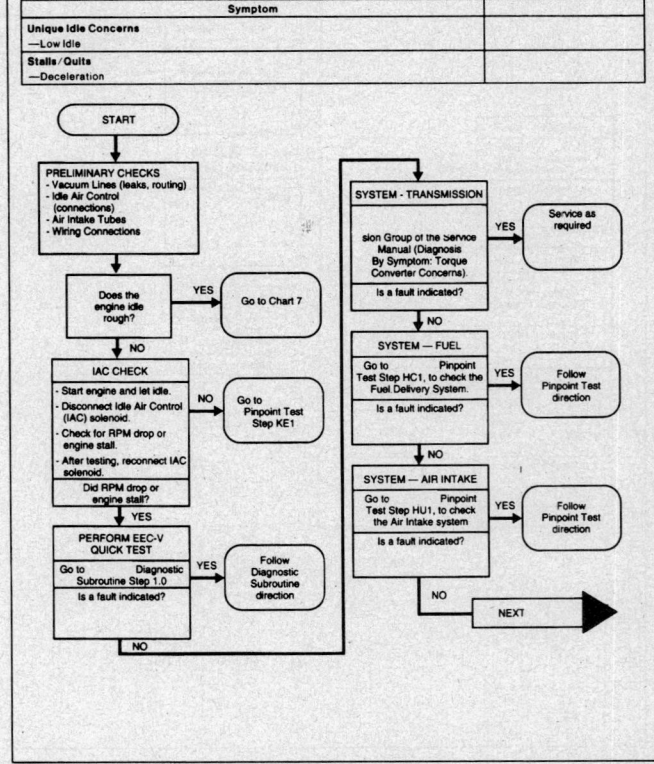

Fig. 114 Symptom flowchart 6 (Part 1 of 2). 1994–95

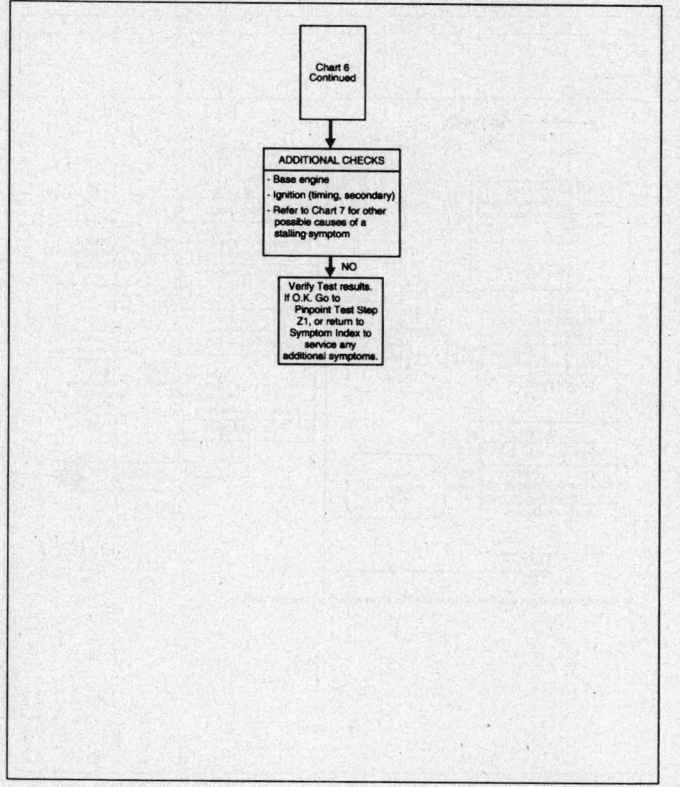

Fig. 114   Symptom flowchart 6 (Part 2 of 2). 1994–95

FM0159401154020X

Symptom
Starting Concerns
—Stalls After Start
Stalls/Quits
—Idle
—Acceleration
—Cruise
Runs Rough
—Idle
—Acceleration
—Cruise
Misses
—Idle
—Acceleration
—Cruise
Buck/Jerk
—Acceleration
—Cruise
—Deceleration
Hesitation/Stumble
—Acceleration
Surge
—Acceleration
—Cruise
Unique Idle Concerns
—Rolling Idle

FM0159401155010X

Fig. 115   Symptom flowchart 7 (Part 1 of 4). 1994–95

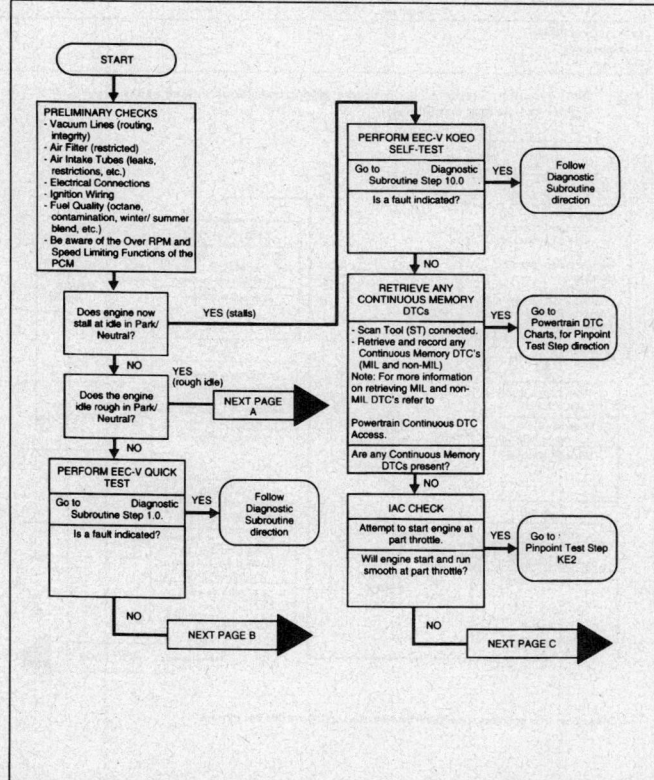

FM0159401155020X

Fig. 115   Symptom flowchart 7 (Part 2 of 4). 1994–95

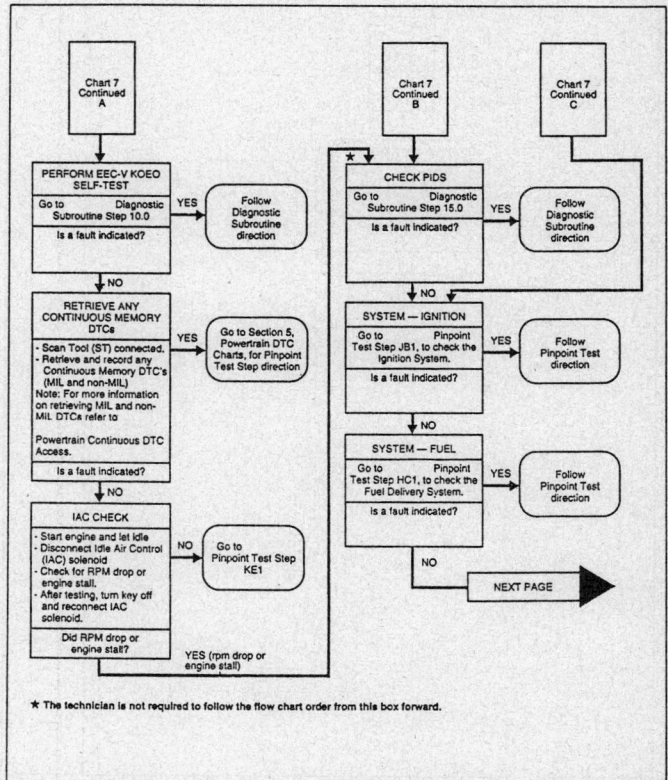

Fig. 115   Symptom flowchart 7
(Part 3 of 4). 1994–95

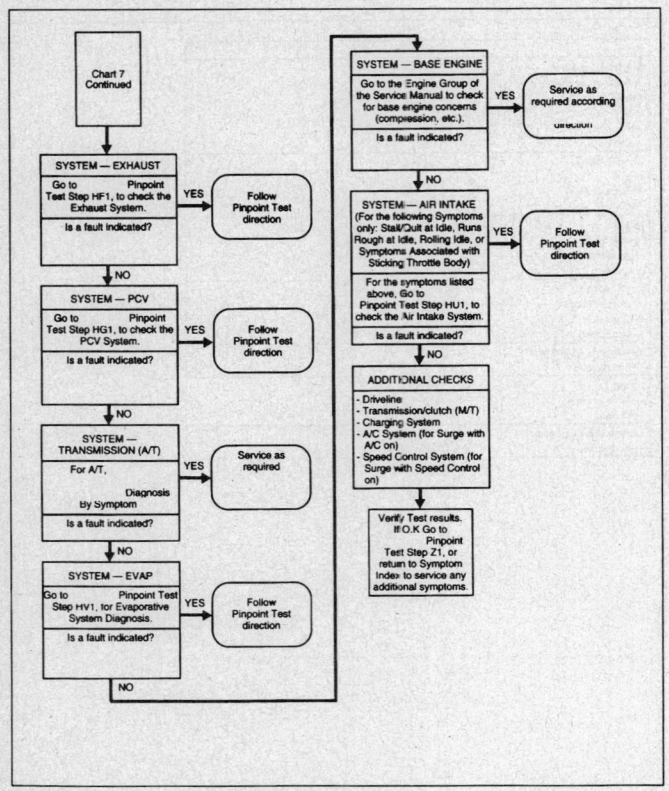

Fig. 115 Symptom flowchart 7 (Part 4 of 4). 1994–95

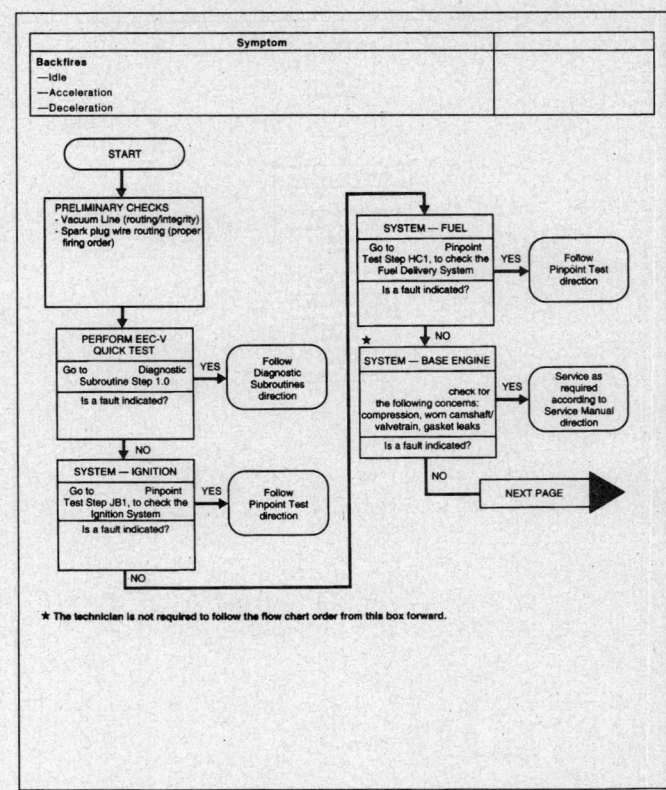

Fig. 116 Symptom flowchart 8 (Part 1 of 2). 1994–95

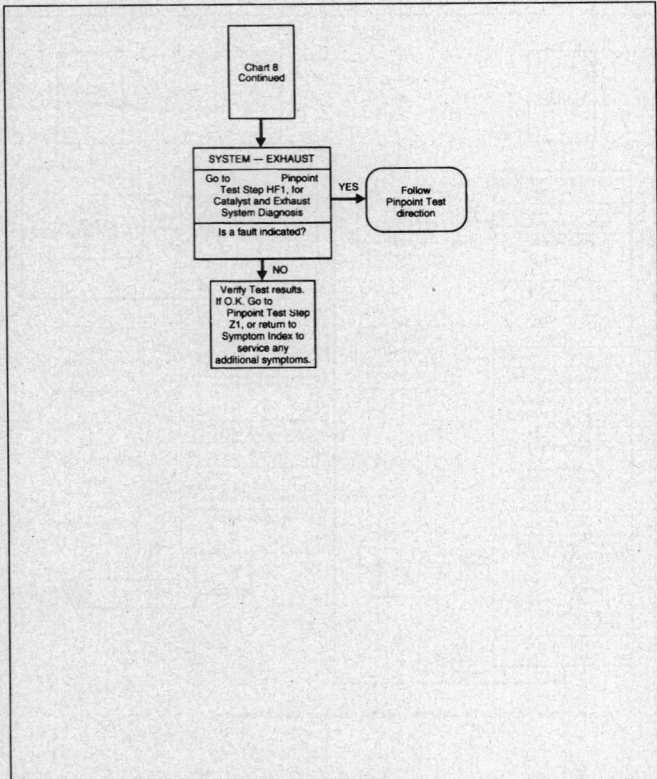

Fig. 116 Symptom flowchart 8 (Part 2 of 2). 1994–95

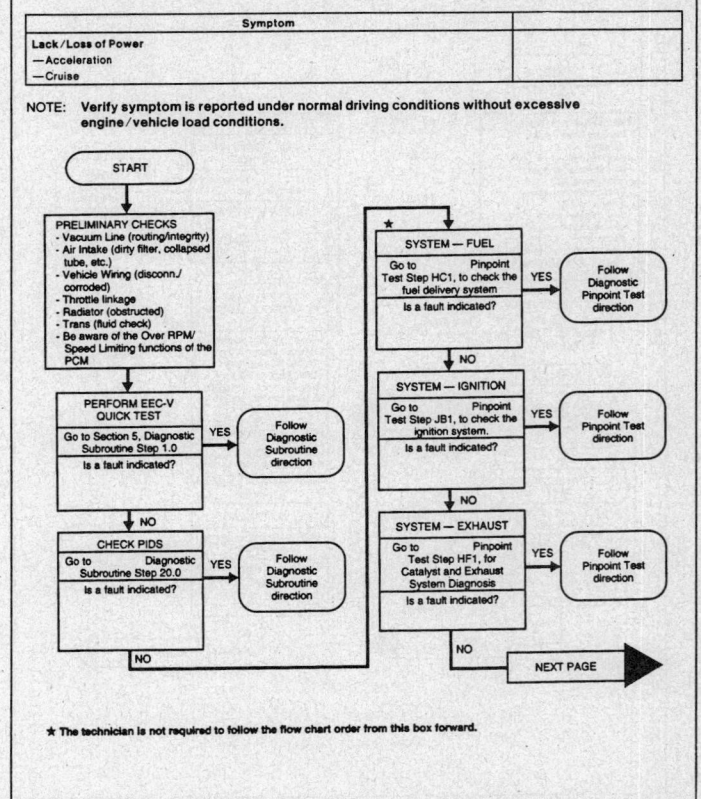

Fig. 117 Symptom flowchart 9
(Part 1 of 2). 1994–95

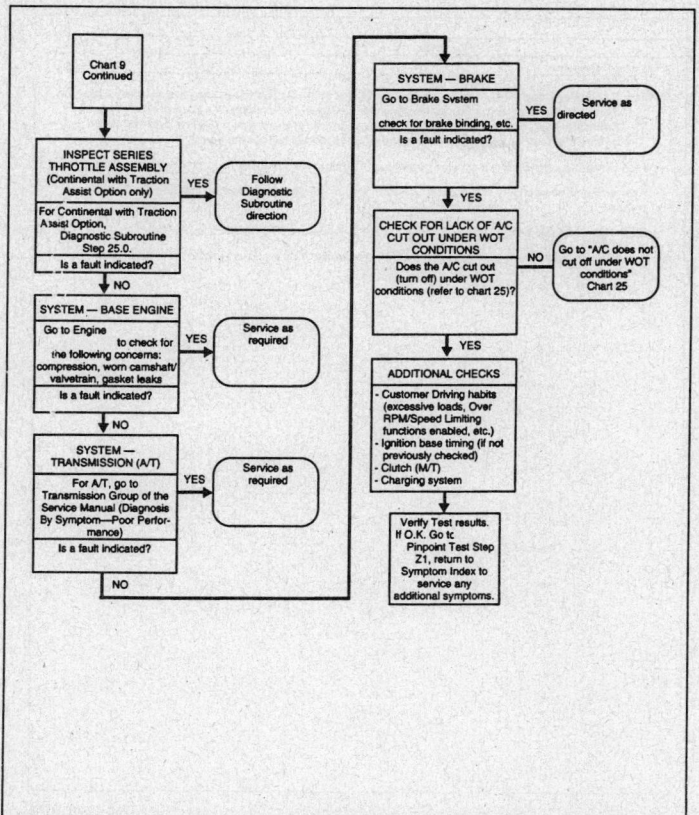

Fig. 117   Symptom flowchart 9 (Part 2 of 2). 1994–95

FM0159401158010X

Fig. 118   Symptom flowchart 10 (Part 1 of 2). 1994–95

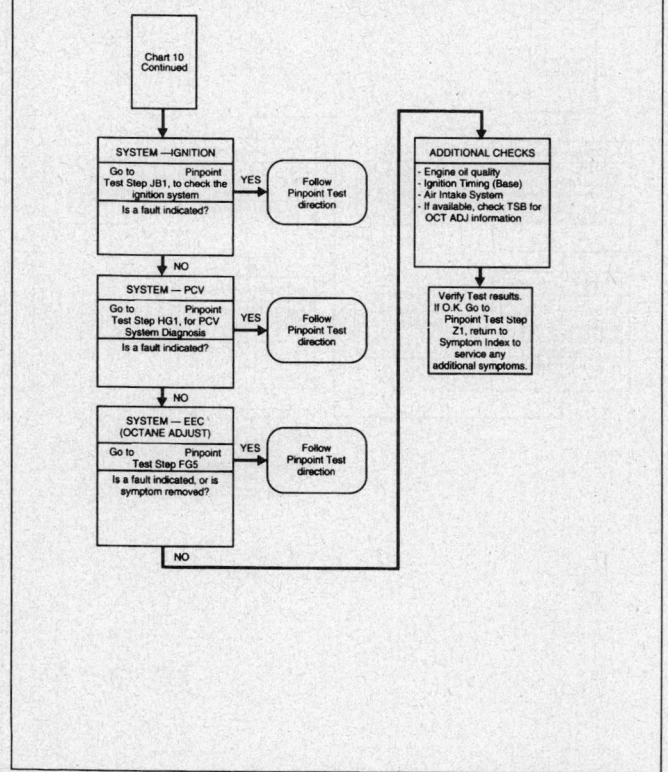

FM0159401158020X

Fig. 118   Symptom flowchart 10 (Part 2 of 2). 1994–95

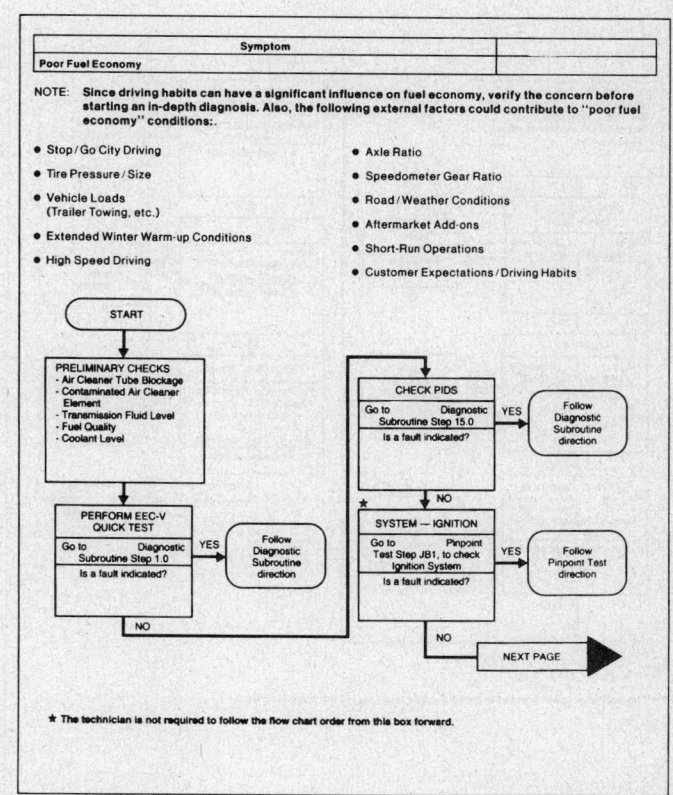

FM0159401159010X

Fig. 119   Symptom flowchart 11 (Part 1 of 2). 1994–95

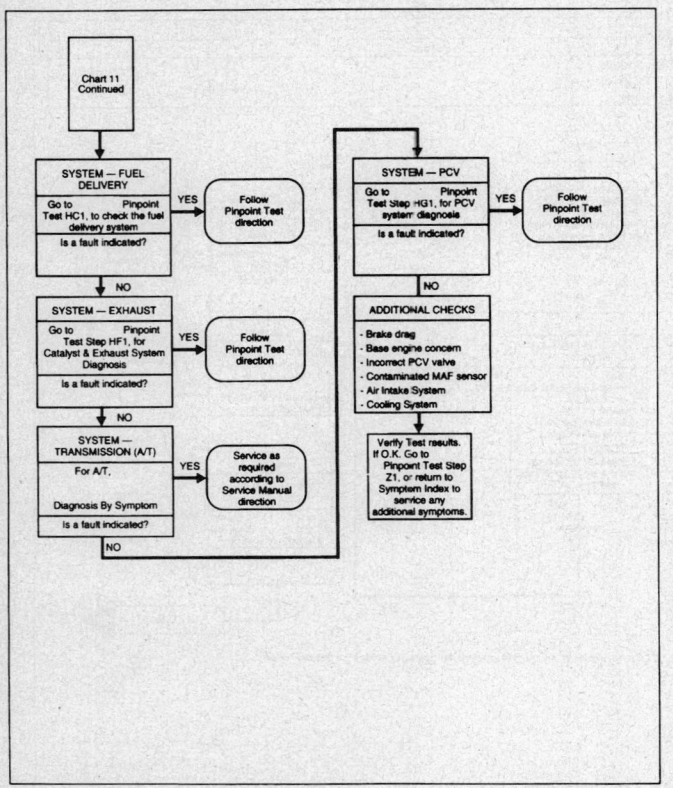

Fig. 119 Symptom flowchart 11 (Part 2 of 2). 1994–95

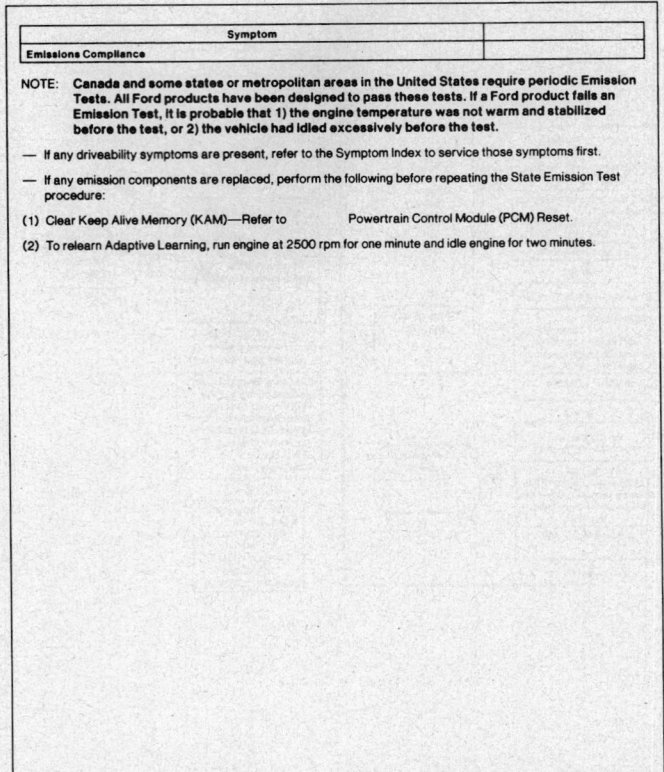

Fig. 120 Symptom flowchart 12 (Part 1 of 3). 1994–95

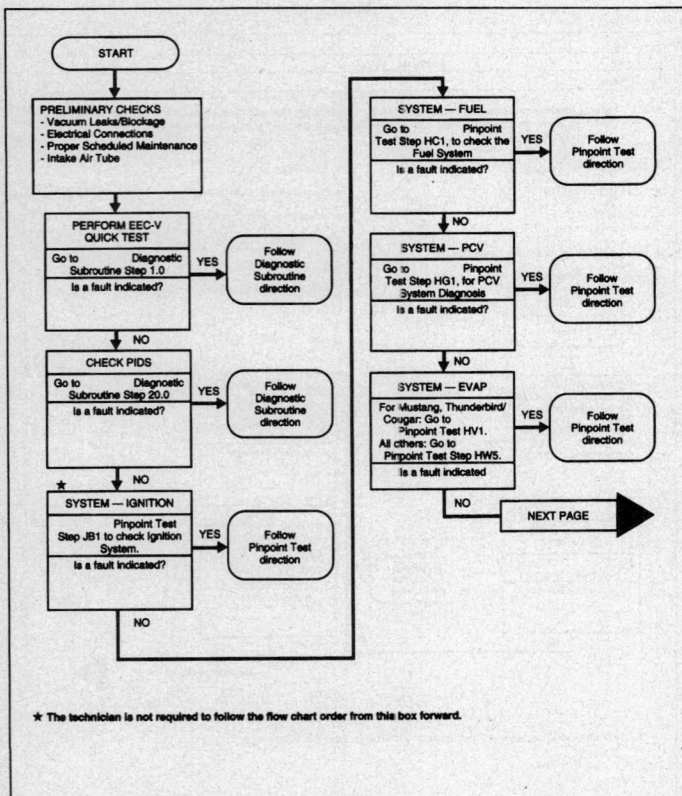

Fig. 120 Symptom flowchart 12 (Part 2 of 3). 1995

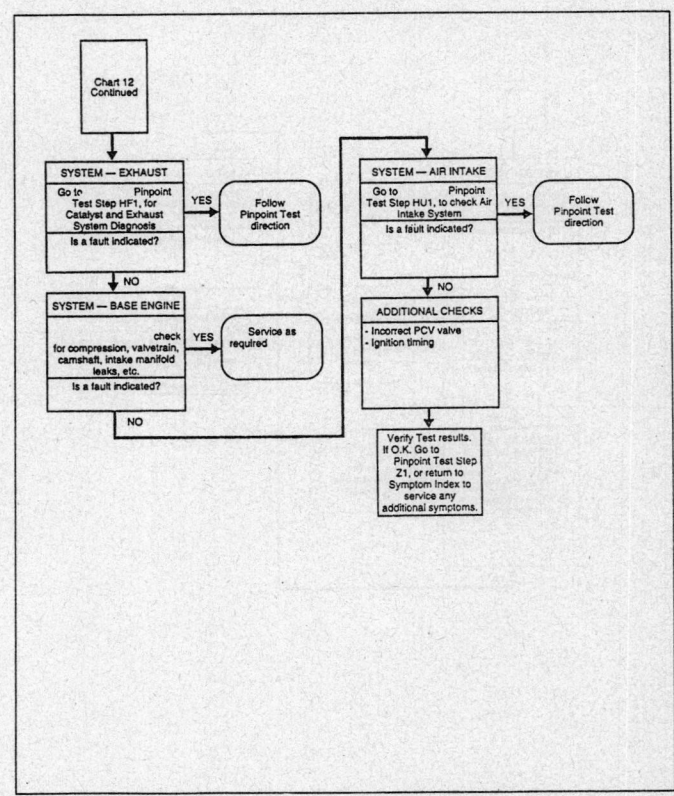

Fig. 120 Symptom flowchart 12 (Part 3 of 3). 1994–95

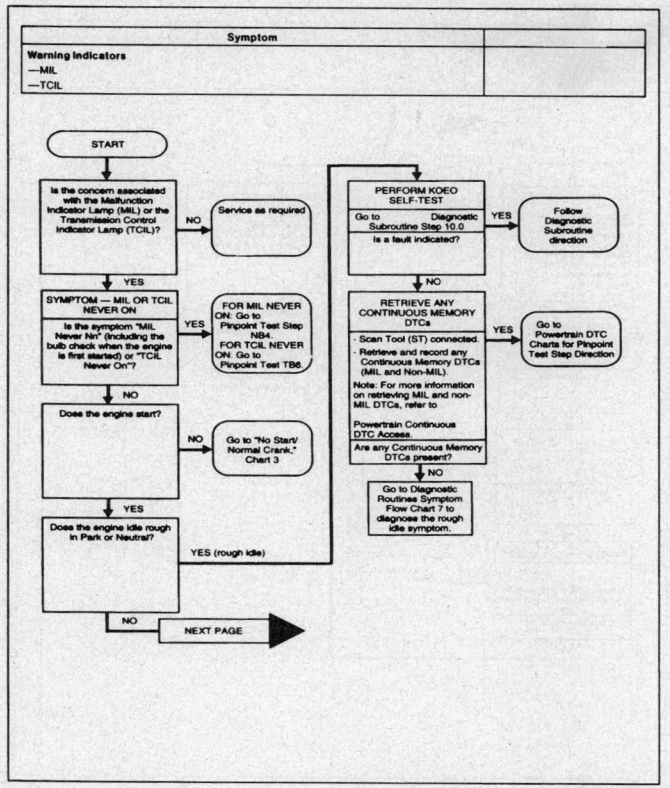

Fig. 121 Symptom flowchart 13 (Part 1 of 2). 1994–95

FM0159401161010X

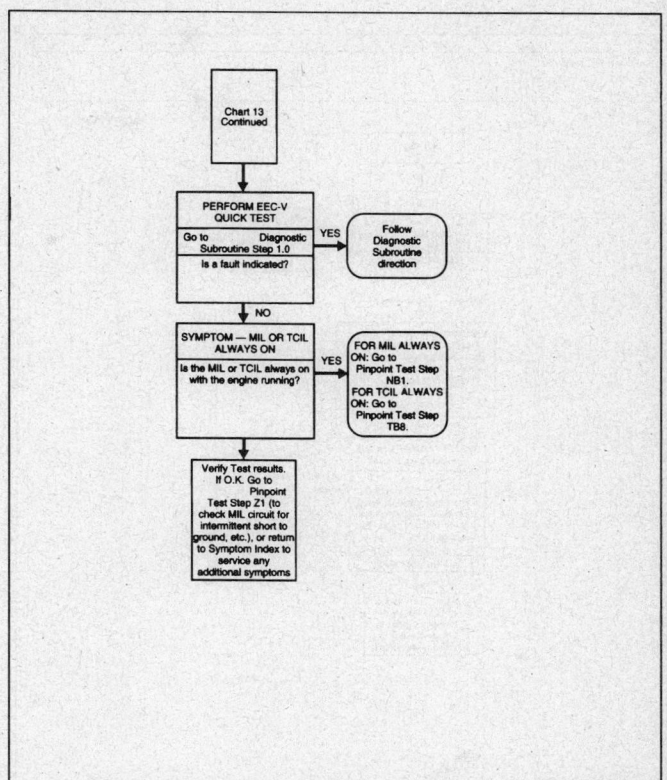

Fig. 121 Symptom flowchart 13 (Part 2 of 2). 1994–95

FM0159401161020X

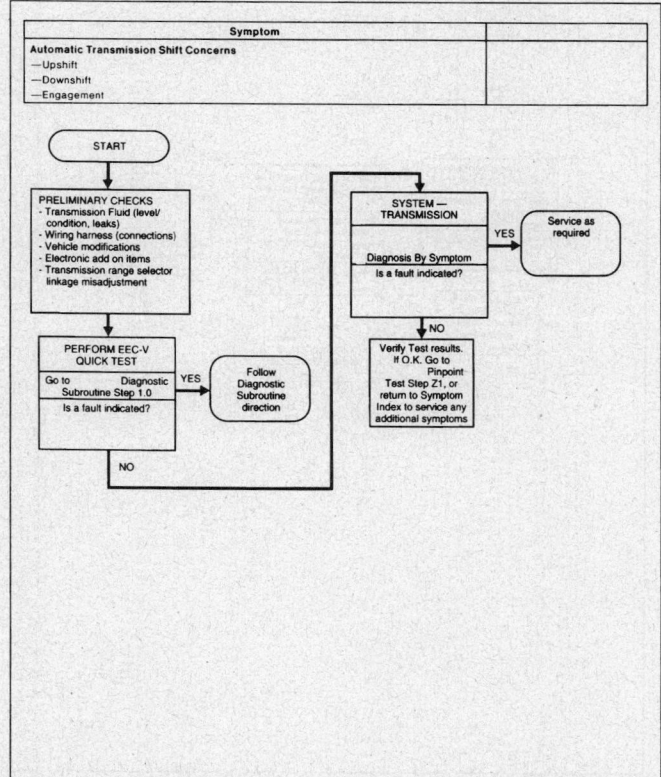

Fig. 122 Symptom flowchart 14. 1994–95

FM0159401162000X

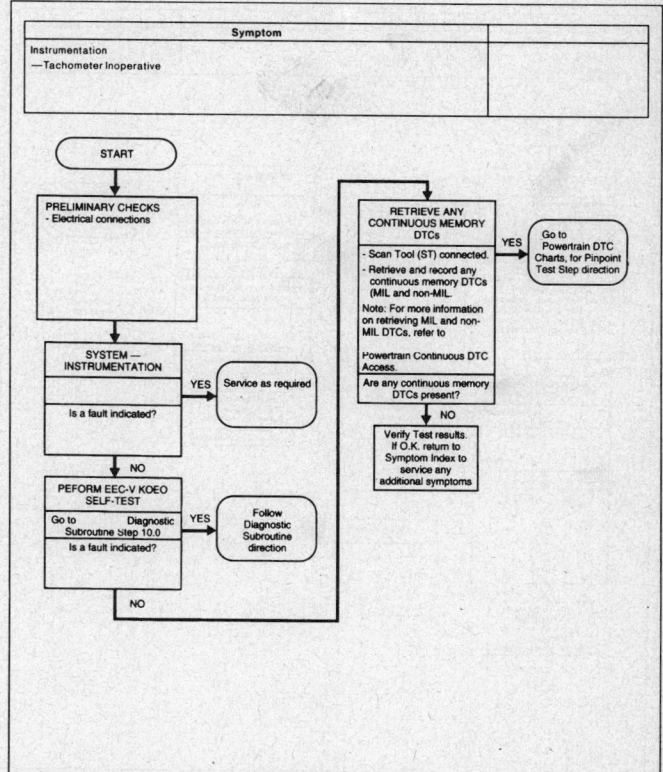

Fig. 123 Symptom flowchart 15. 1994–95

FM0159401163000X

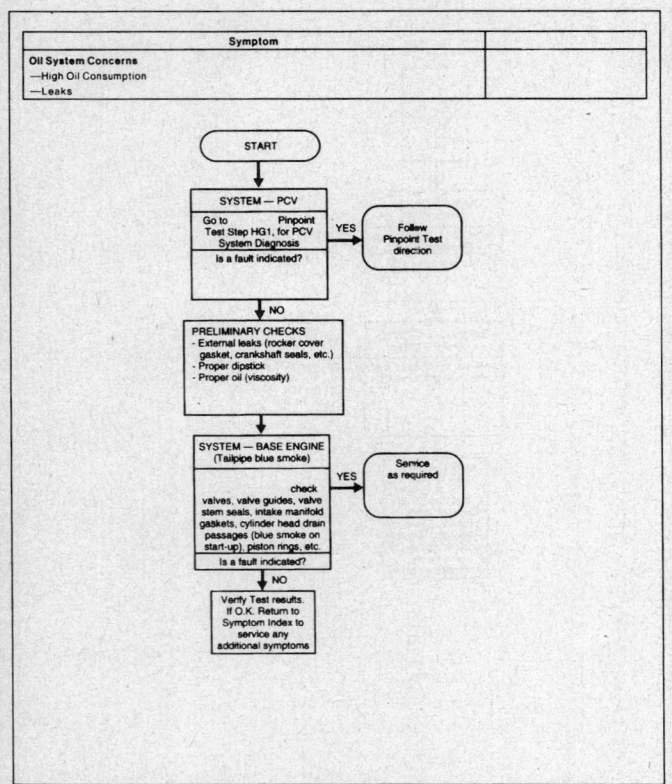

Fig. 124   Symptom flowchart 16. 1994–95

FM0159401164000X

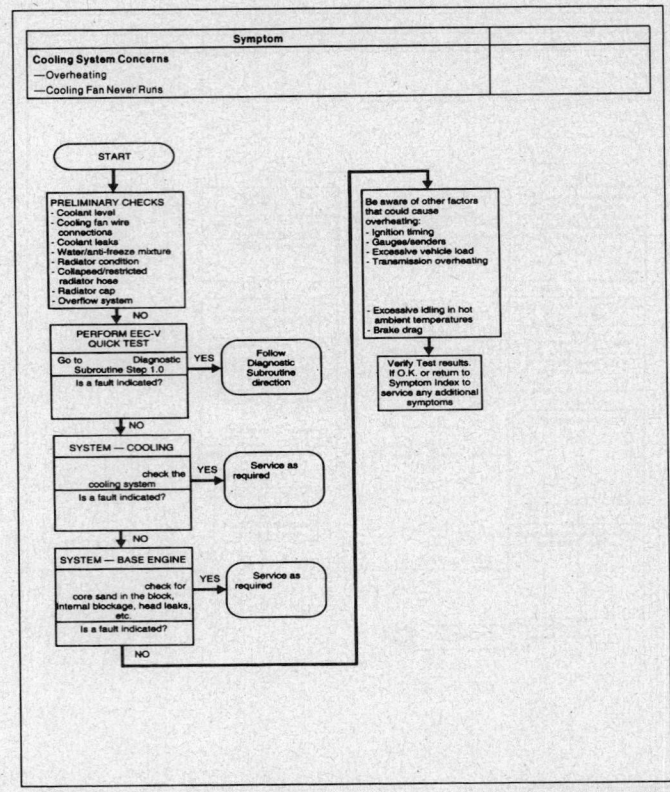

Fig. 125   Symptom flowchart 17. 1994–95

FM0159401165000X

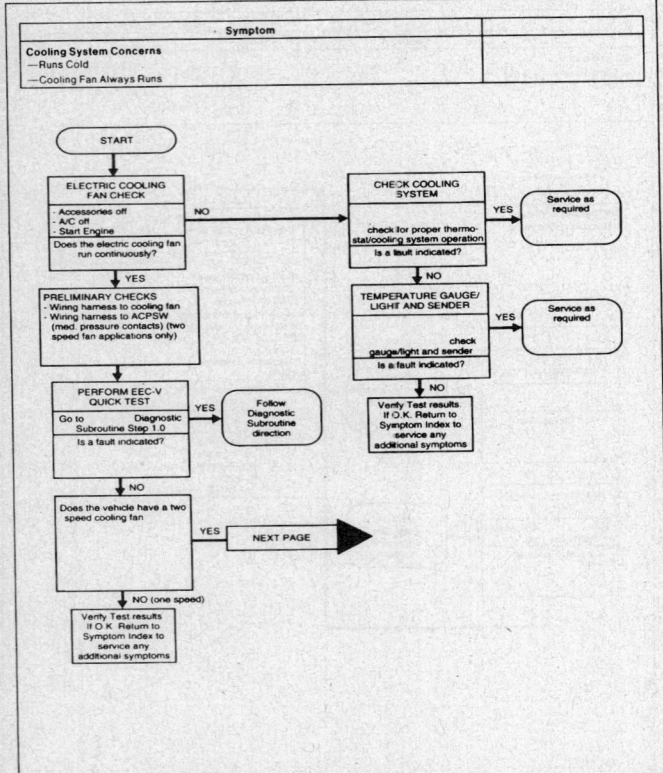

**Fig. 126   Symptom flowchart 18 (Part 1 of 2).
1994–95**

FM0159401166010X

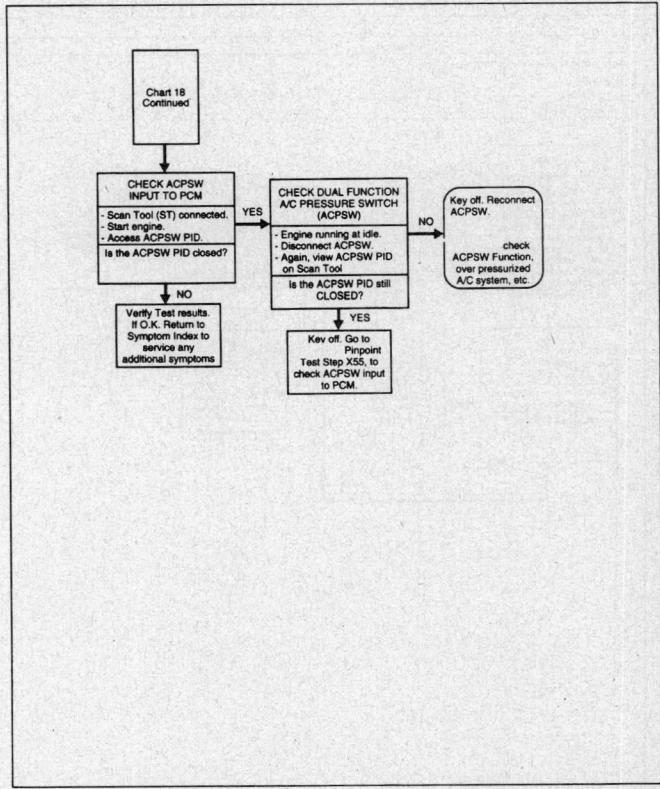

**Fig. 126   Symptom flowchart 18 (Part 2 of 2).
1994–95**

FM0159401166020X

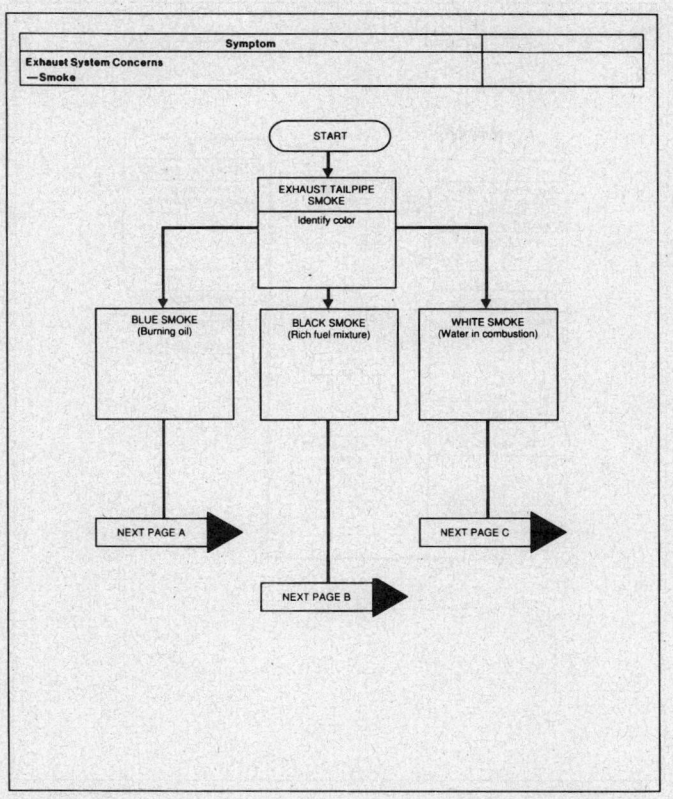

Fig. 127 Symptom flowchart 19 (Part 1 of 3). 1994–95

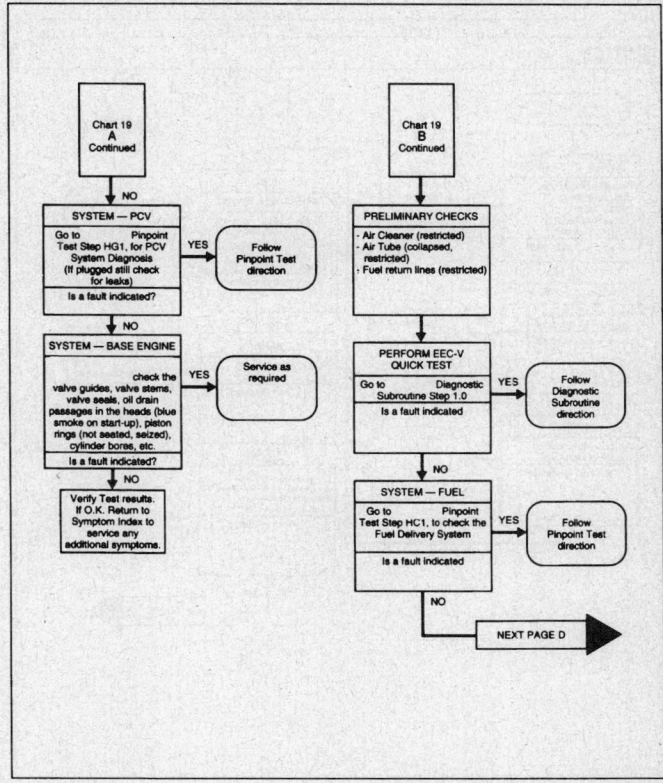

Fig. 127 Symptom flowchart 19 (Part 2 of 3). 1994–95

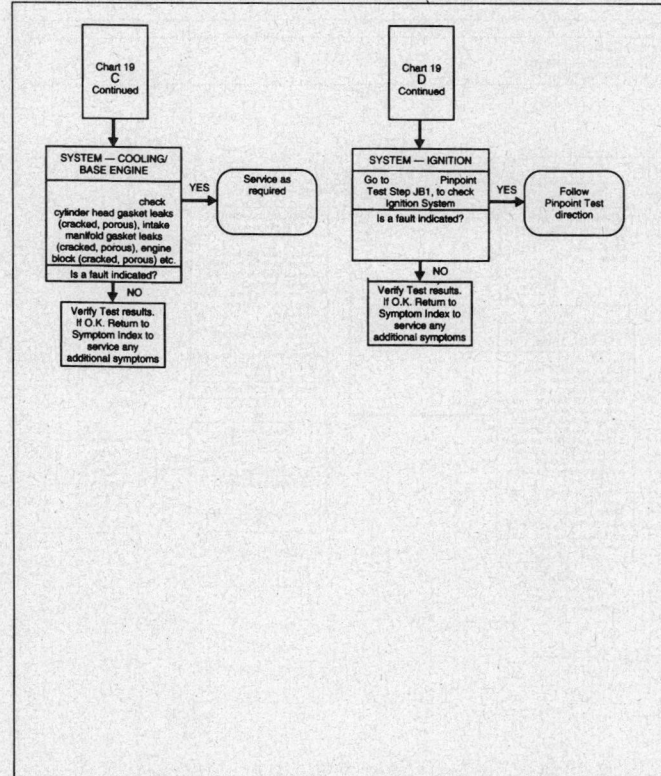

Fig. 127 Symptom flowchart 19 (Part 3 of 3). 1994–95

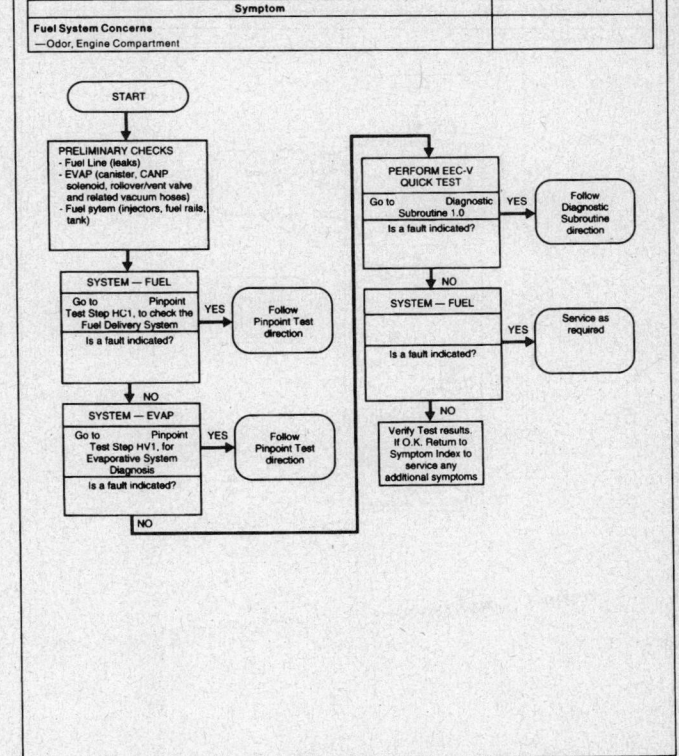

Fig. 128 Symptom flowchart 20. 1994–95

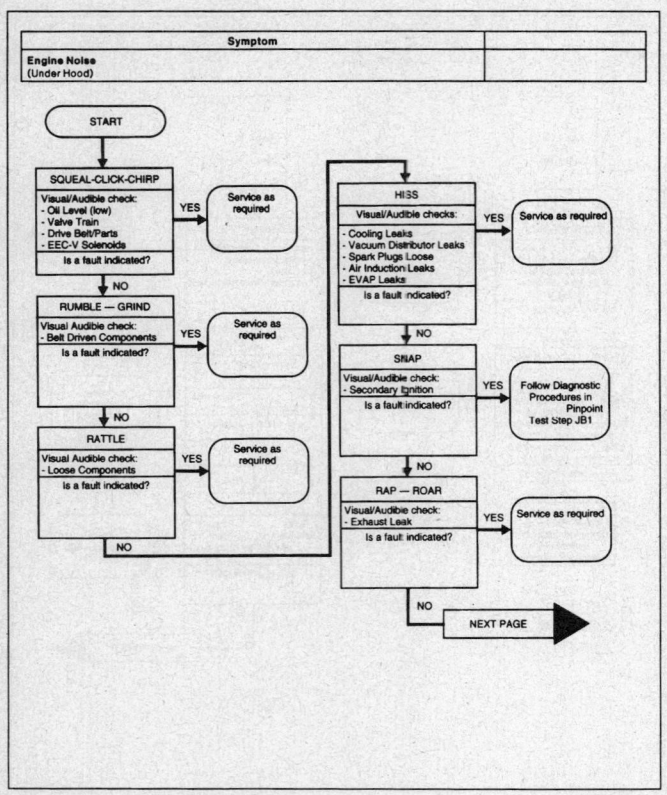

**Fig. 129   Symptom flowchart 21 (Part 1 of 2).
1994–95**

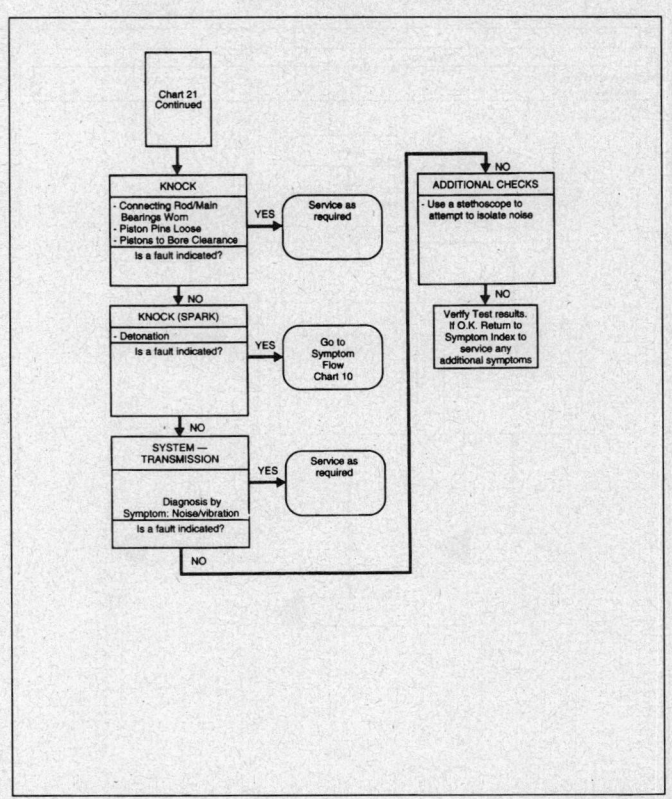

**Fig. 129   Symptom flowchart 21 (Part 2 of 2).
1994–95**

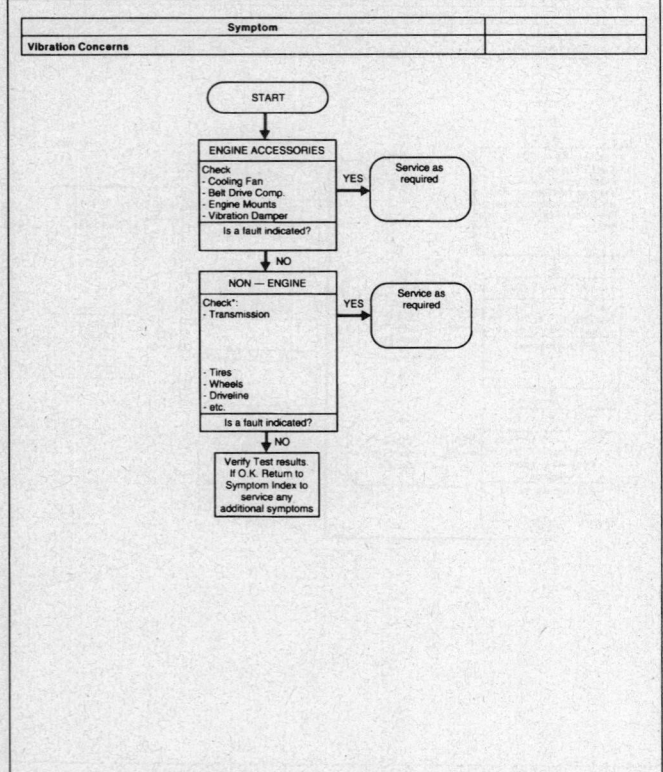

Fig. 130   Symptom flowchart 22. 1994–95

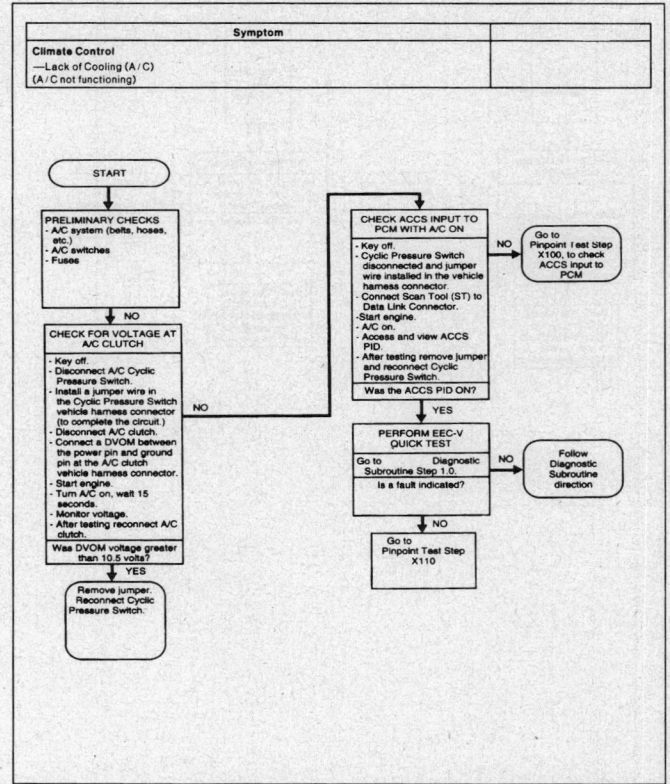

Fig. 131   Symptom flowchart 23. 1994–95

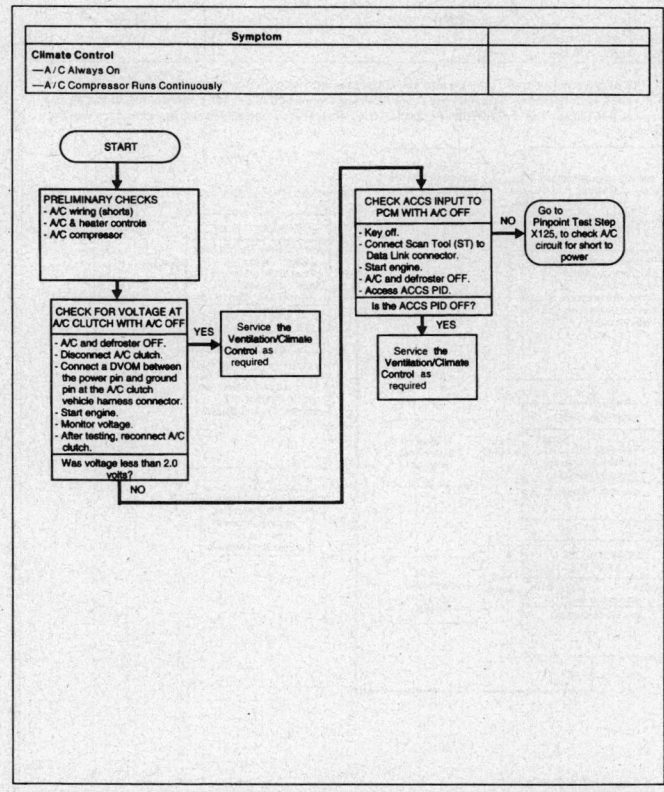

Fig. 132 Symptom flowchart 24. 1994–95

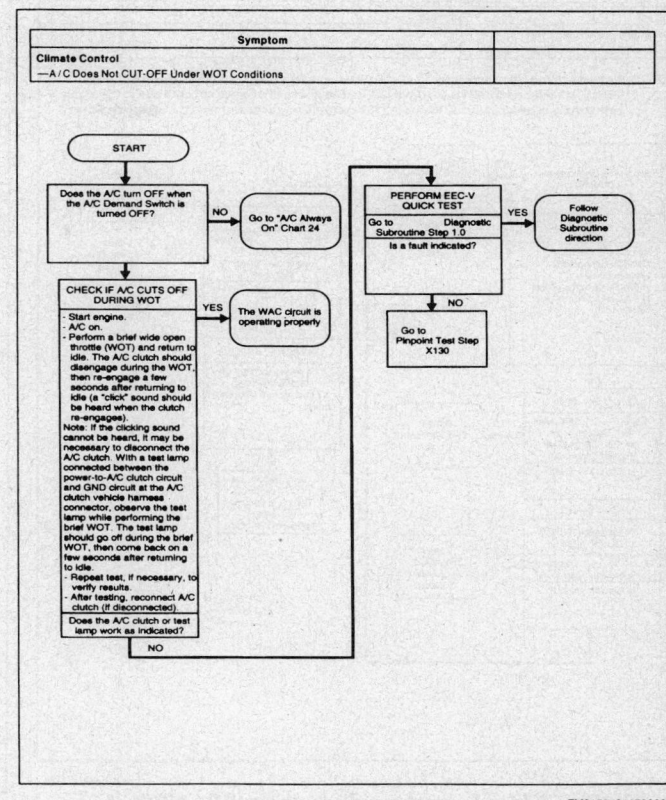

Fig. 133 Symptom flowchart 25. 1994–95

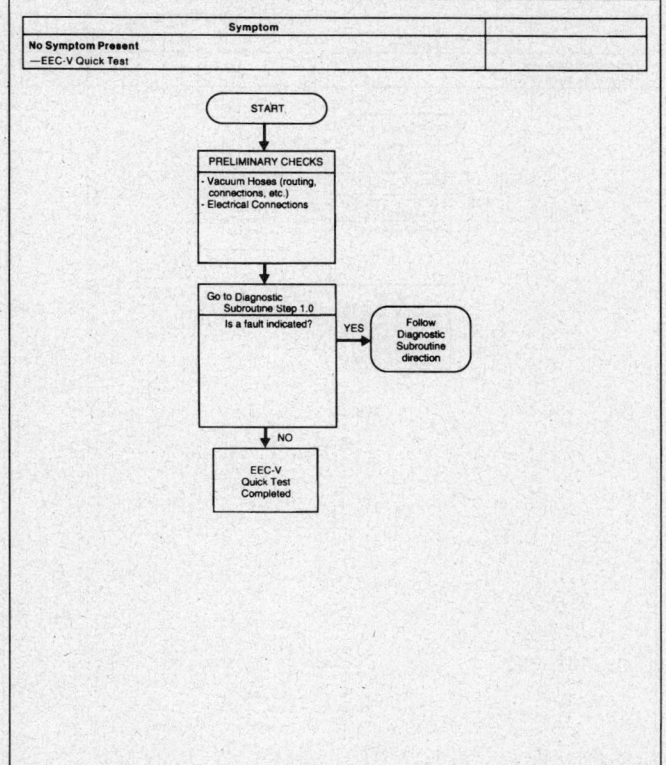

Fig. 134 Symptom flowchart 26. 1994–95

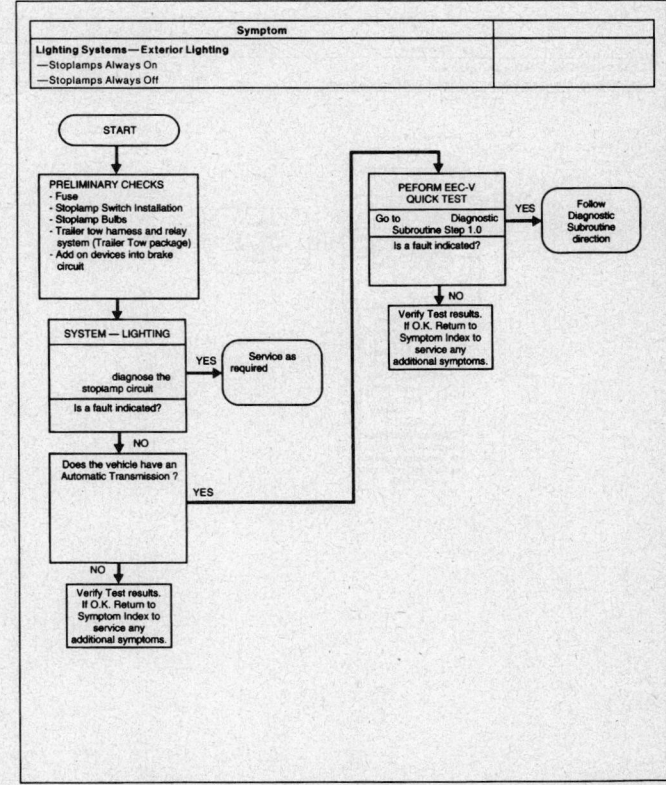

Fig. 135 Symptom flowchart 27. 1994–95

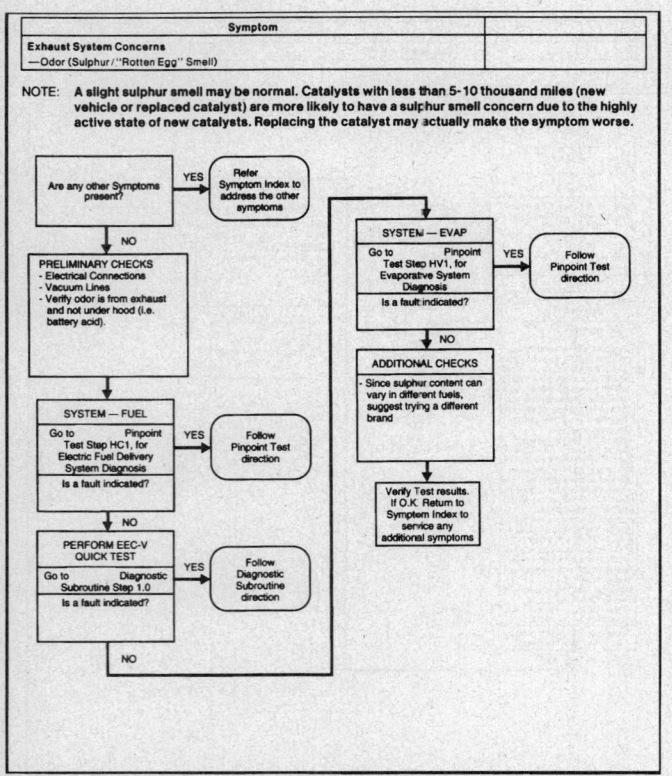

Fig. 136 Symptom flowchart 28. 1994

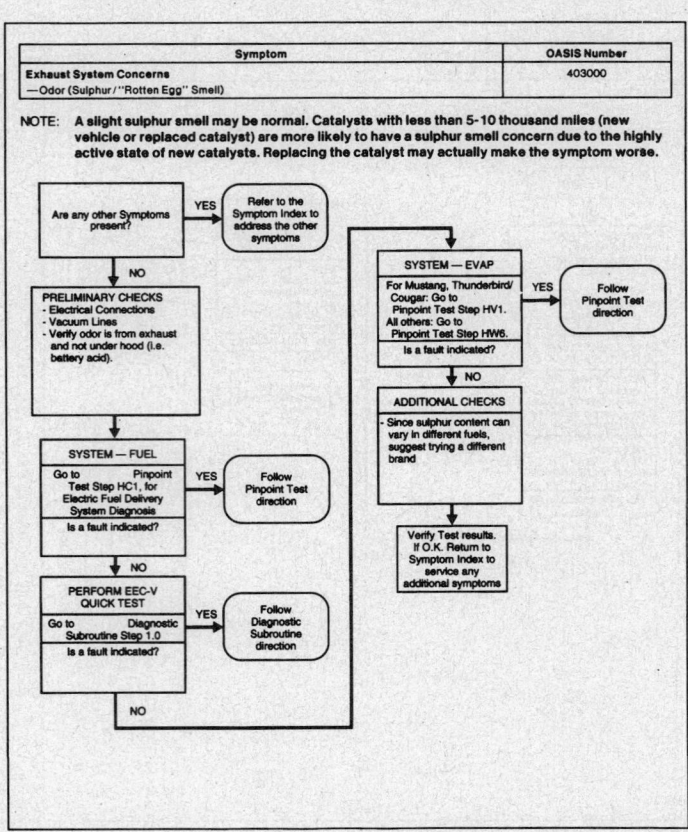

Fig. 137 Symptom flowchart 28. 1995

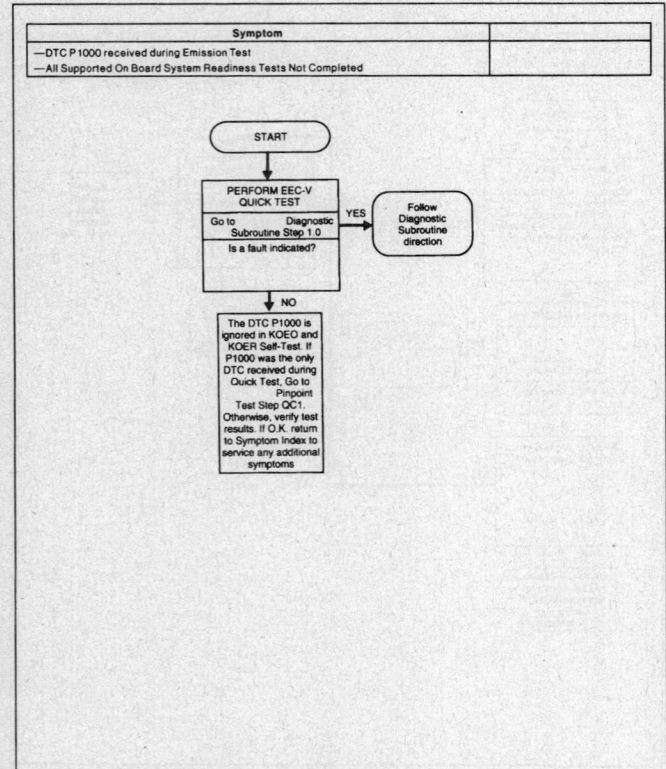

Fig. 138 Symptom flowchart 29. 1994–95

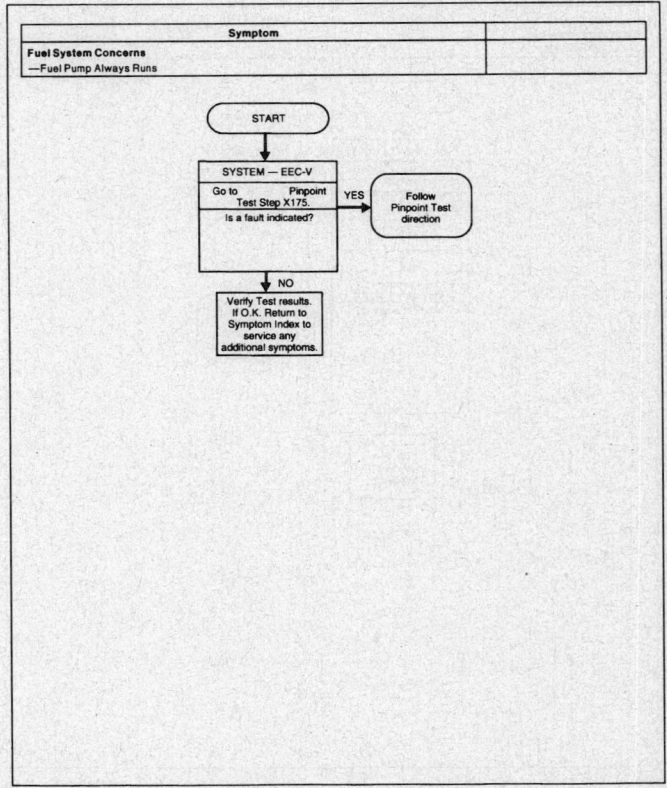

Fig. 139 Symptom flowchart 30. 1994

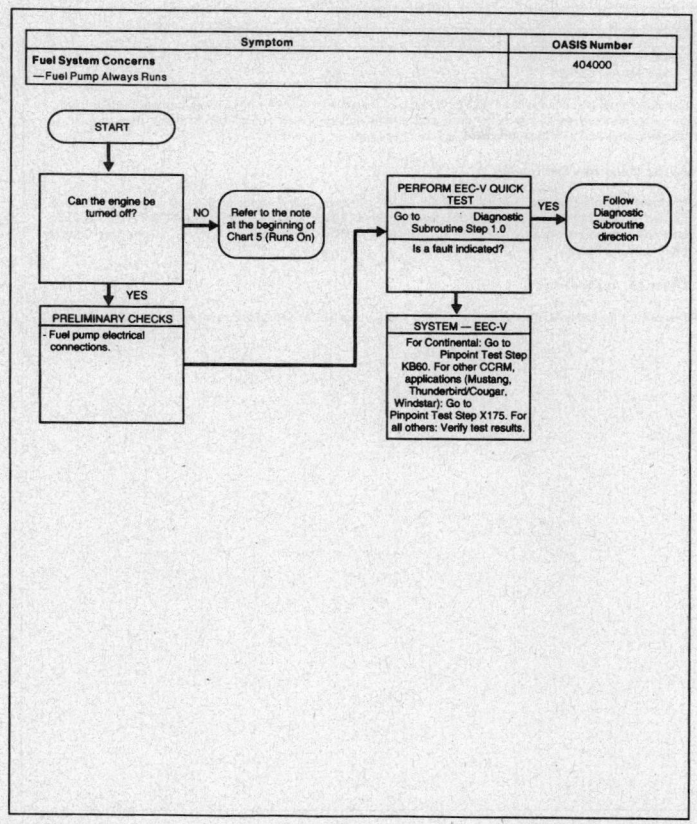

Fig. 140   Symptom flowchart 30. 1995

FM015950127300X

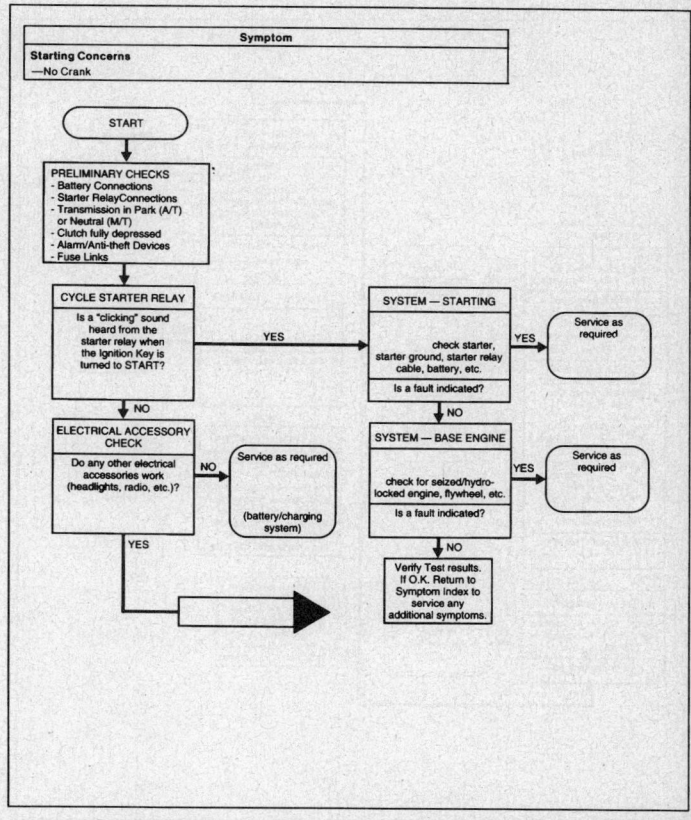

FM0159601580010X

Fig. 141   Symptom flowchart 1 (Part 1 of 2). 1996

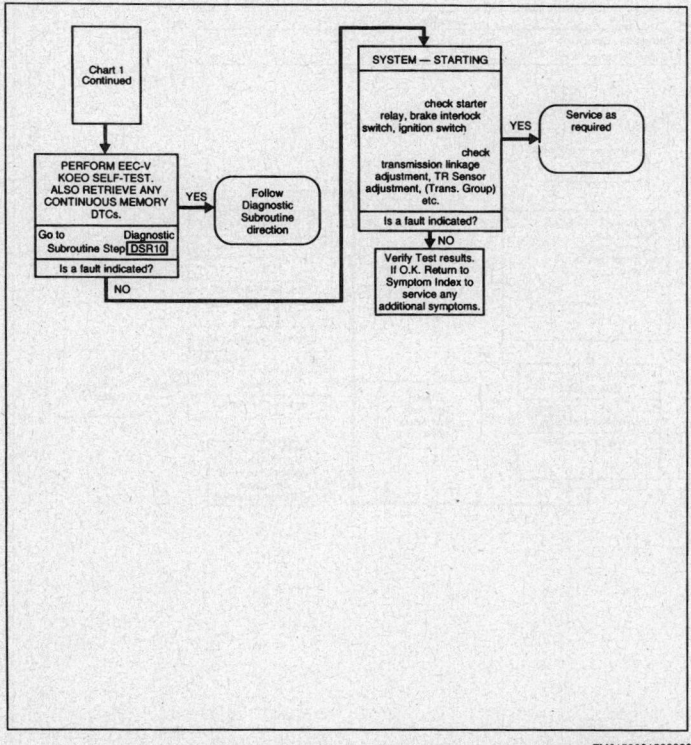

FM0159601580020X

Fig. 141   Symptom flowchart 1 (Part 2 of 2). 1996

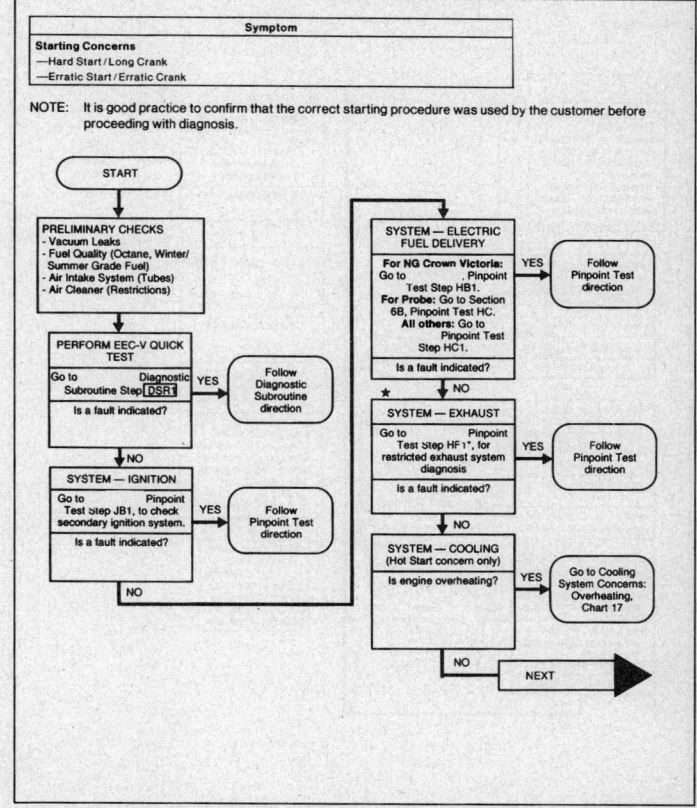

FM0159601581010X

Fig. 142   Symptom flowchart 2 (Part 1 of 2). 1996

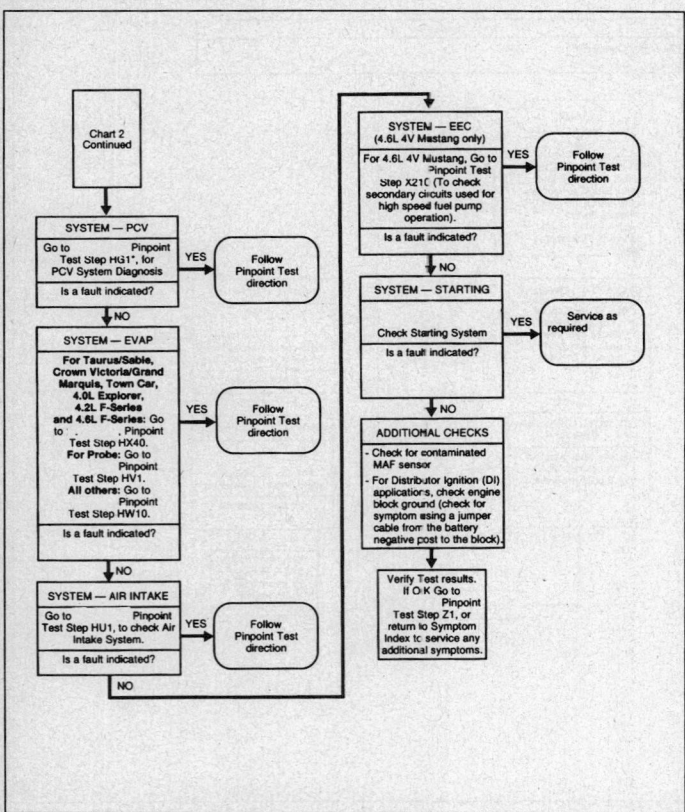

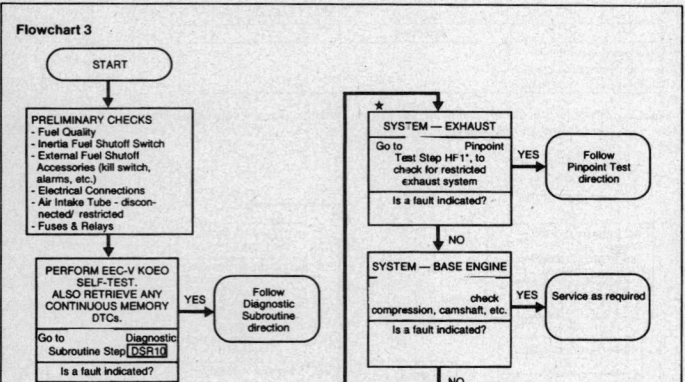

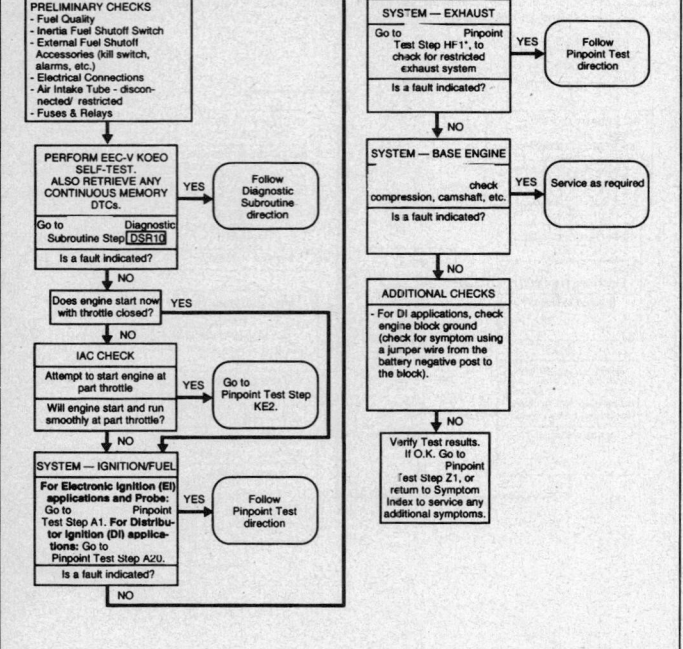

Fig. 142   Symptom flowchart 2 (Part 2 of 2). 1996

FM0159601581020X

Fig. 143   Symptom flowchart 3 (Part 2 of 2). 1996

FM01596O1582020X

Symptom

Starting Concerns
—No Start / Normal Crank

Extended cranking because of a "No Start" can load the exhaust system with raw fuel, damaging the catalytic converter after the engine starts. For applications with Secondary Air Injection (AIR) Systems, perform the following after the "No Start" condition has been repaired.

Applications with Electric AIR

Disconnect the Electric Secondary Air Injection (AIR) Solid State Relay, run the engine until surplus fuel is used up, and reconnect the relay. Disconnecting the Electric AIR Solid State Relay may set an EEC-V DTC. After all service has been completed, clear the PCM Continuous Memory DTCs (refer to   Powertrain Control Module (PCM) Reset).

Other AIR Applications

Disconnect the secondary air supply, run engine until surplus fuel is used up and reconnect secondary air supply.

FM0159601582010X

Fig. 143   Symptom flowchart 3 (Part 1 of 2). 1996

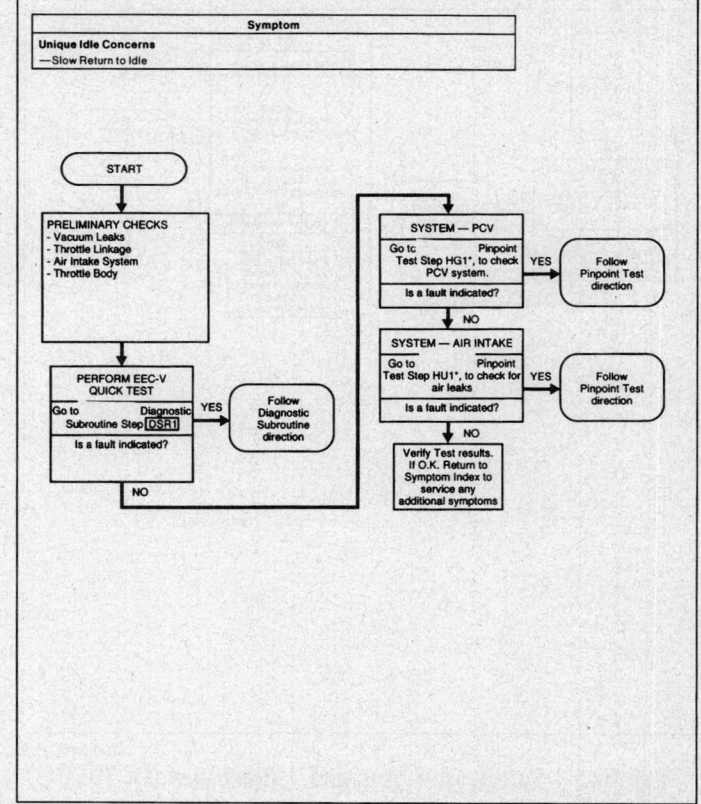

Fig. 144   Symptom flowchart 4. 1996

FM01596O1583000X

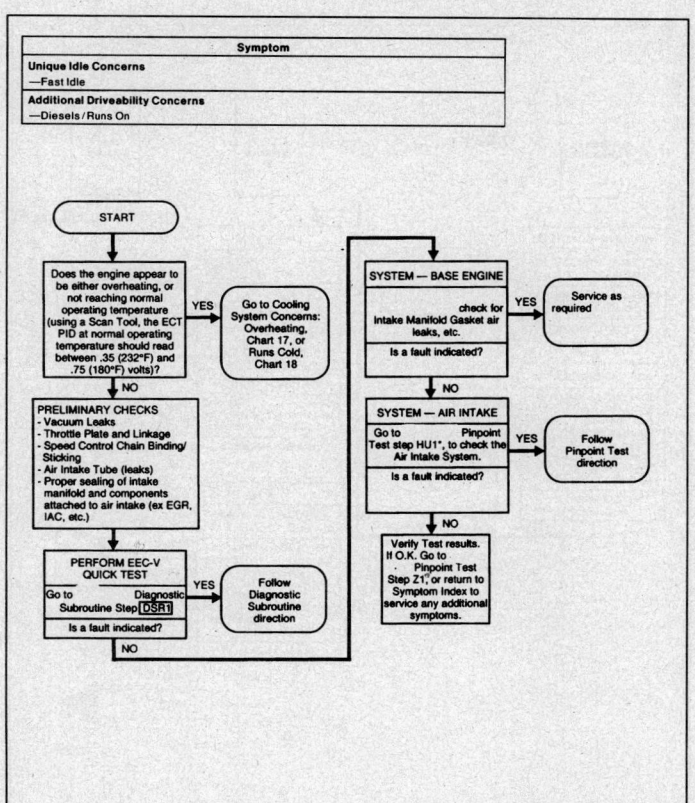

Fig. 145   Symptom flowchart 5. 1996

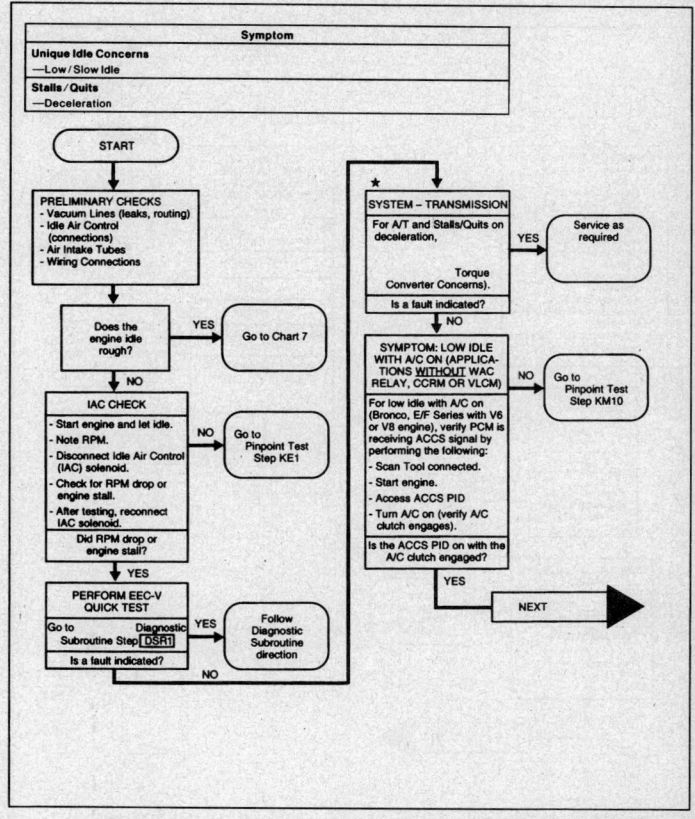

Fig. 146   Symptom flowchart 6 (Part 1 of 2). 1996

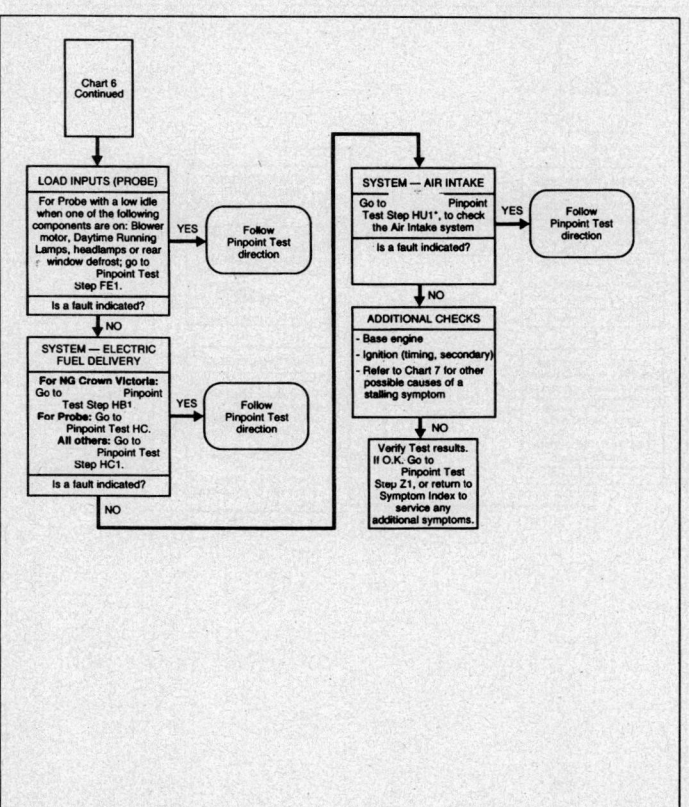

Fig. 146   Symptom flowchart 6 (Part 2 of 2). 1996

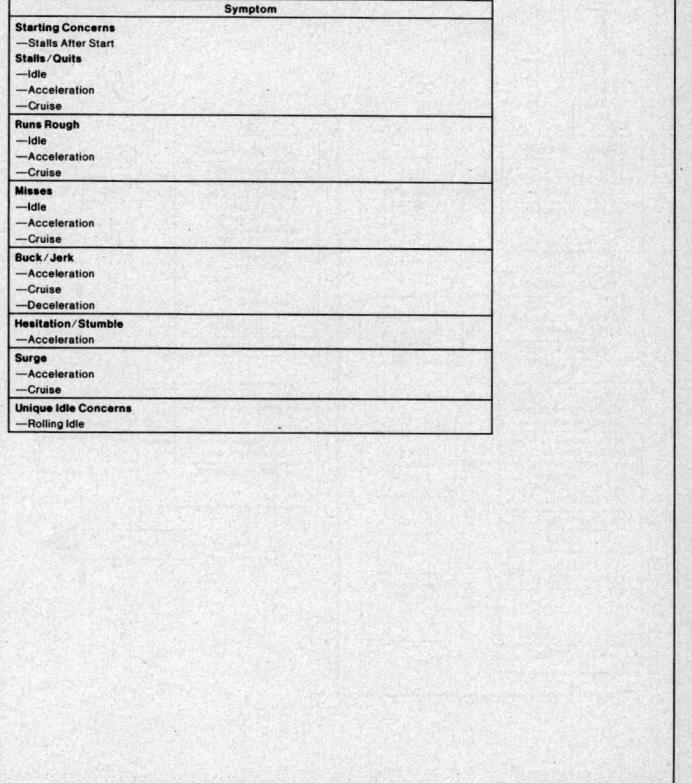

Fig. 147   Symptom flowchart 7 (Part 1 of 5). 1996

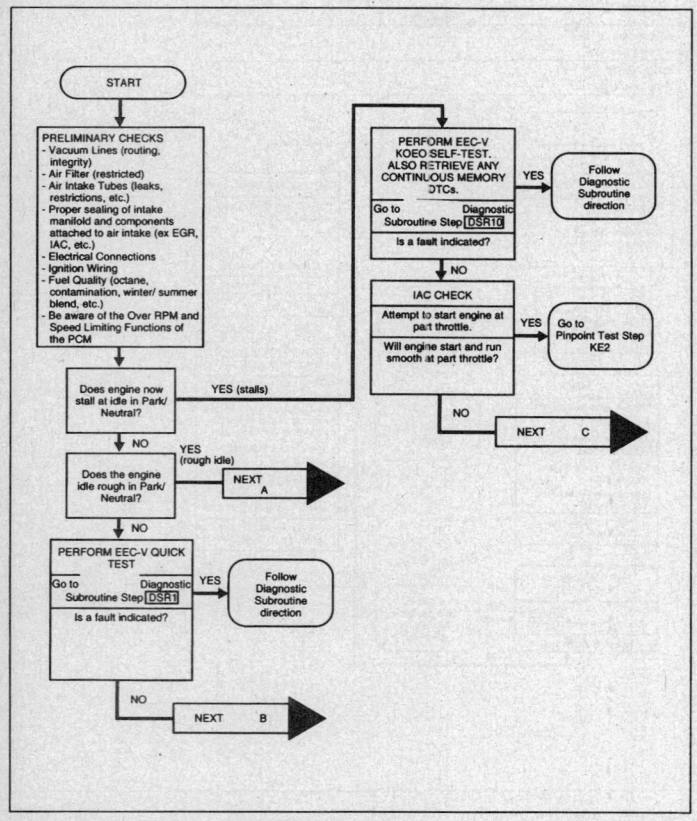

Fig. 147 Symptom flowchart 7 (Part 2 of 5). 1996

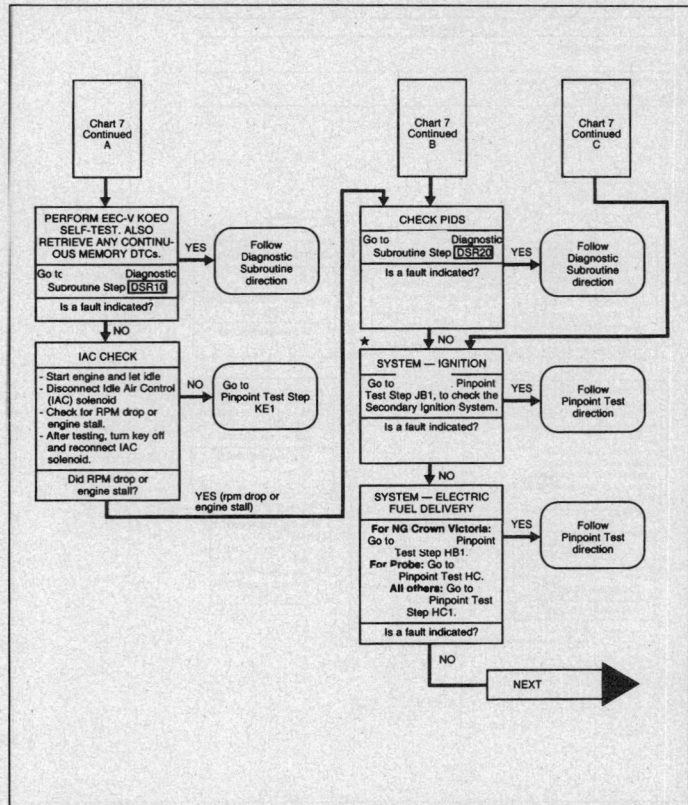

Fig. 147 Symptom flowchart 7 (Part 3 of 5). 1996

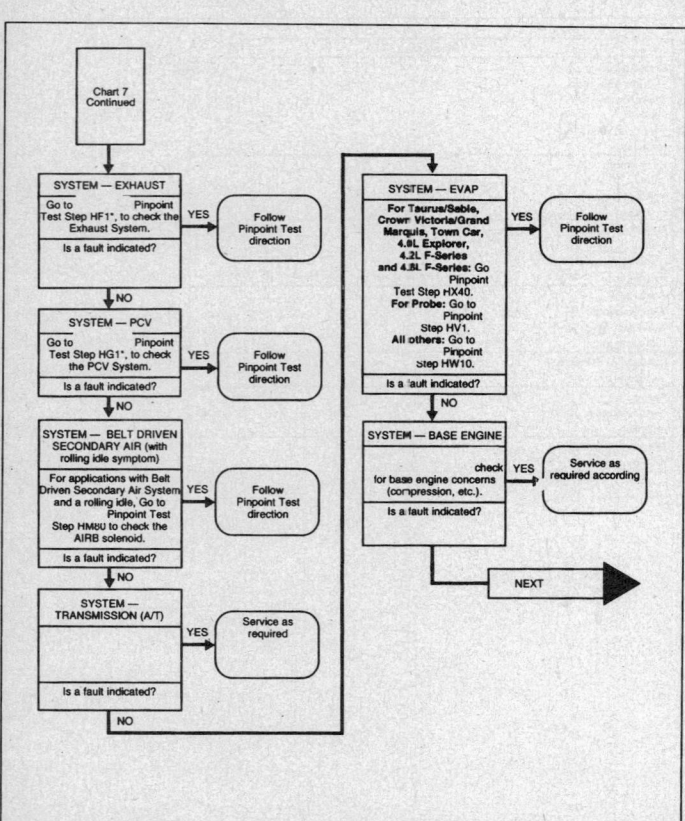

Fig. 147 Symptom flowchart 7 (Part 4 of 5). 1996

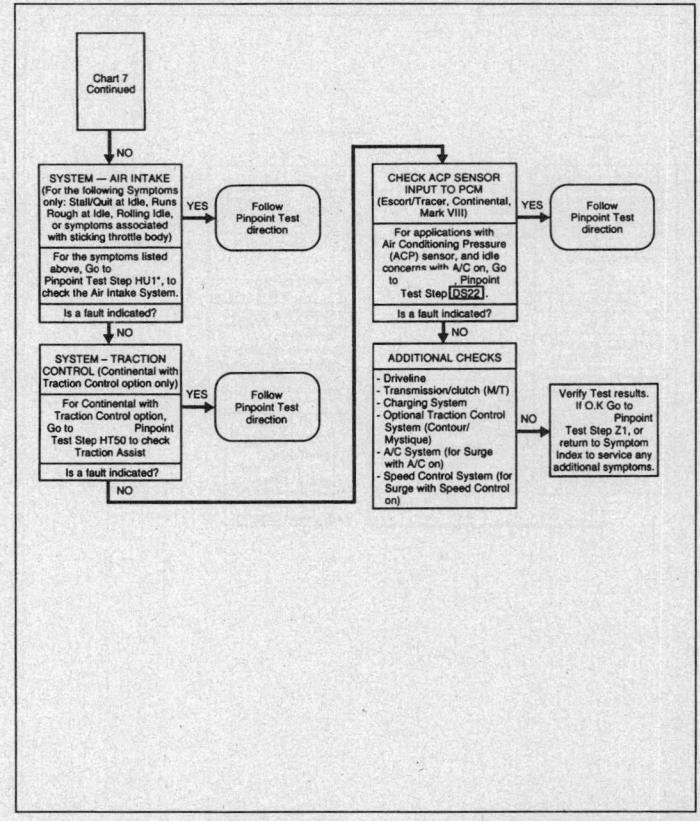

Fig. 147 Symptom flowchart 7 (Part 5 of 5). 1996

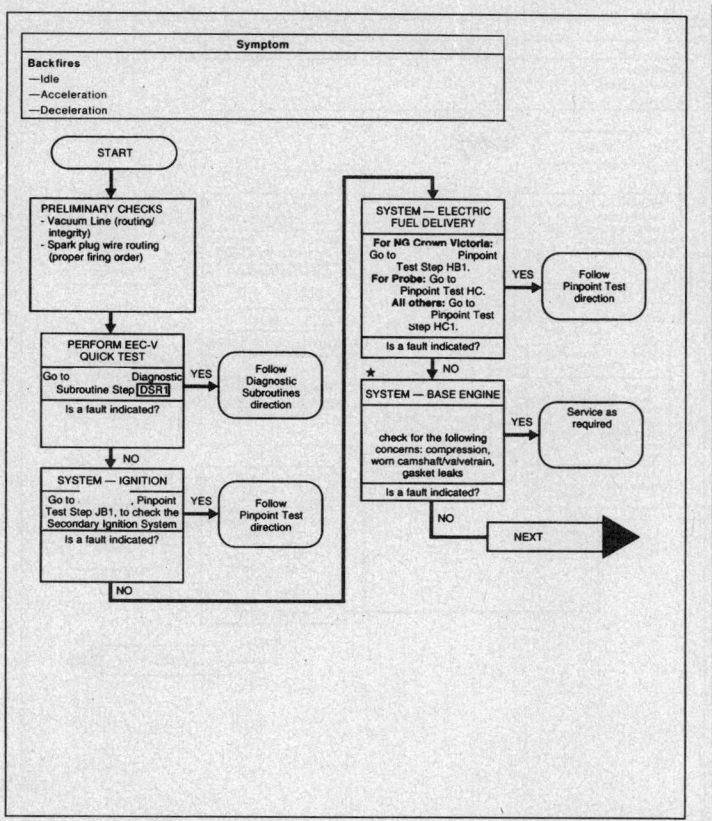

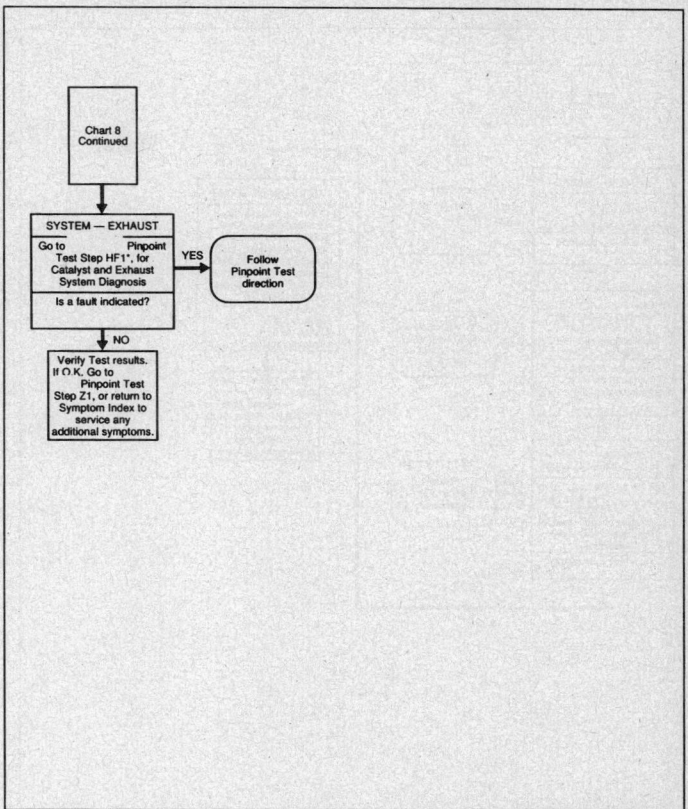

Fig. 148 Symptom flowchart 8 (Part 1 of 2). 1996

Fig. 148 Symptom flowchart 8 (Part 2 of 2). 1996

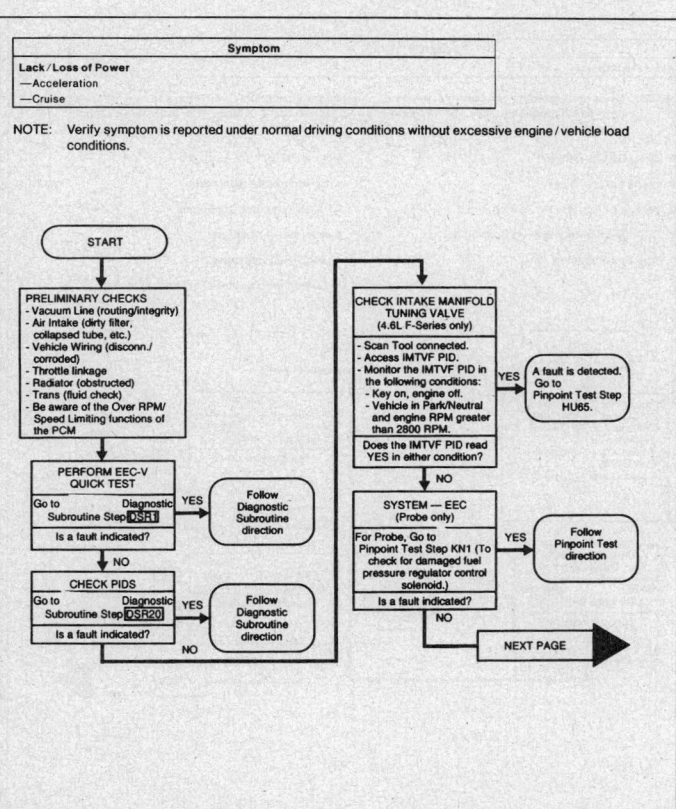

Fig. 149 Symptom flowchart 9 (Part 1 of 3). 1996

Fig. 149 Symptom flowchart 9 (Part 2 of 3). 1996

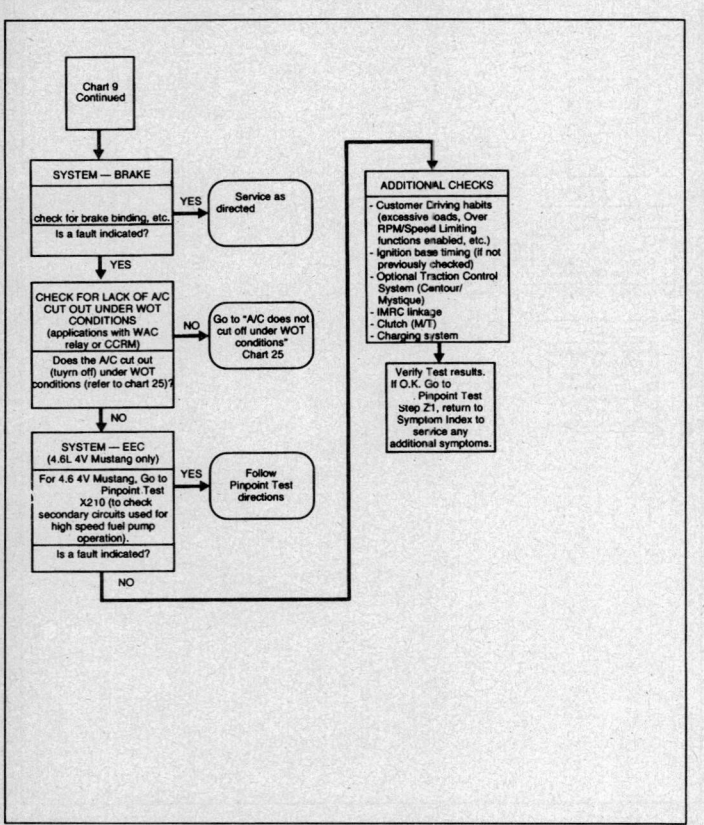

Fig. 149   Symptom flowchart 9 (Part 3 of 3). 1996

FM0159601588030X

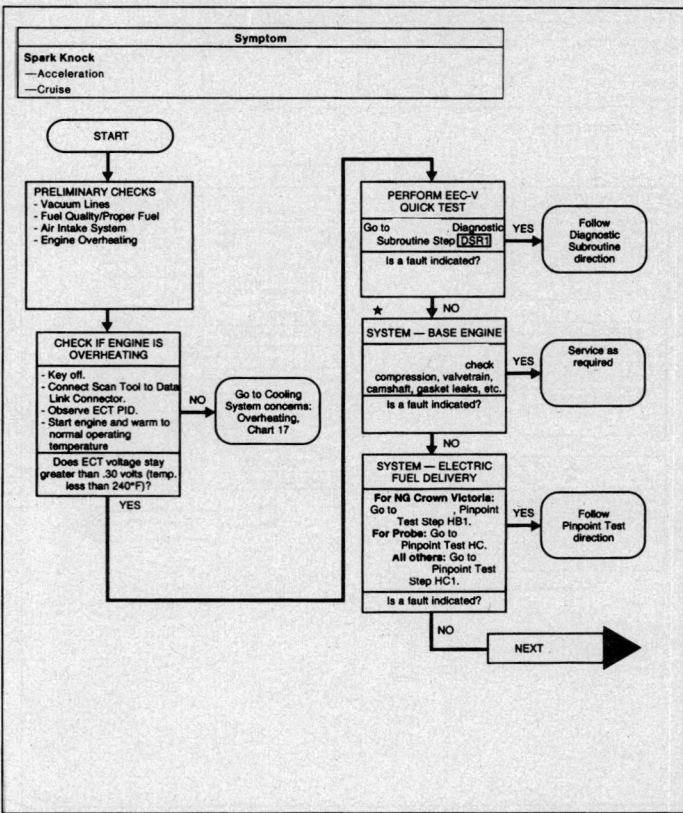

Fig. 150   Symptom flowchart 10 (Part 1 of 2). 1996

FM0159601589010X

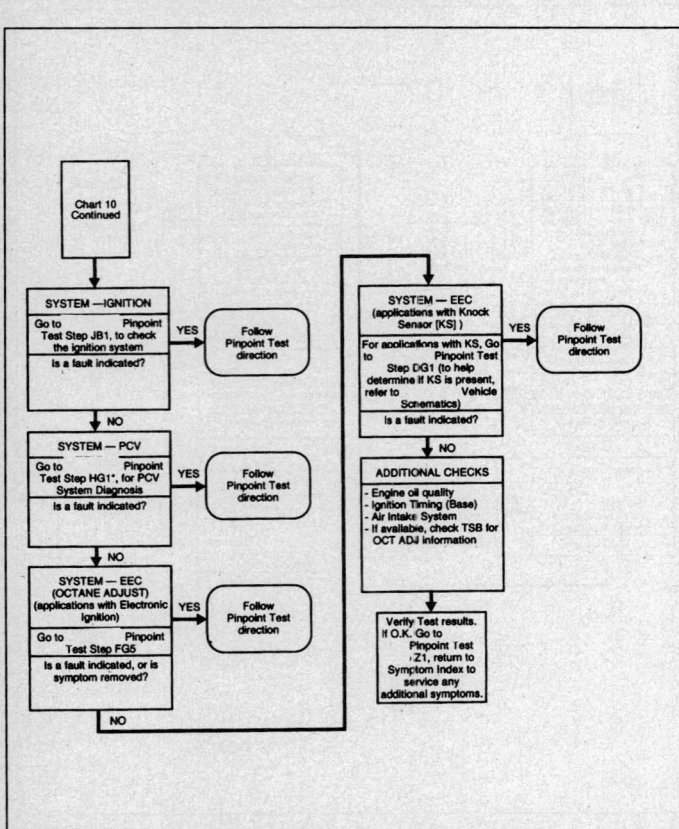

Fig. 150   Symptom flowchart 10 (Part 2 of 2). 1996

FM0159601589020X

Fig. 151   Symptom flowchart 11 (Part 1 of 2). 1996

Symptom

Poor Fuel Economy

NOTE: Since driving habits can have a significant influence on fuel economy, verify the concern before starting an in-depth diagnosis. Also, the following external factors could contribute to "poor fuel economy" conditions:

- Stop / Go City Driving
- Tire Pressure / Size
- Vehicle Loads (Trailer Towing, etc.)
- Extended Winter Warm-up Conditions
- High Speed Driving
- Axle Ratio
- Speedometer Gear Ratio
- Road / Weather Conditions
- Aftermarket Add-ons
- Short-Run Operations
- Customer Expectations / Driving Habits

FM0159601590010X

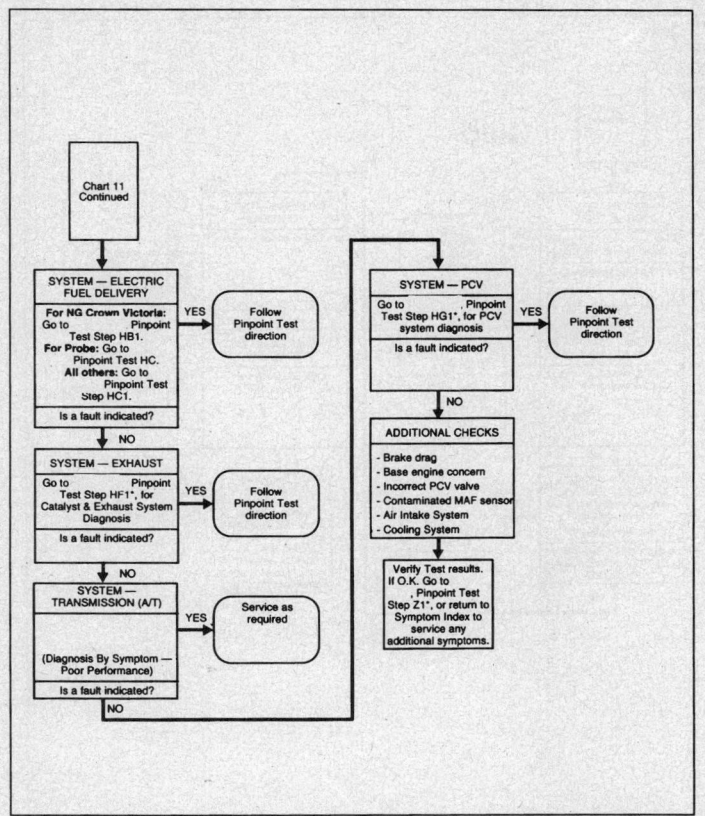

Fig. 151   Symptom flowchart 11 (Part 2 of 2). 1996

FM0159601590020X

Symptom
Emissions Compliance

NOTE: Canada and some states or metropolitan areas in the United States require periodic Emission Tests. All Ford products have been designed to pass these tests. If a Ford product fails an Emission Test, it is probable that 1) the engine temperature was not warm and stabilized before the test, or 2) the vehicle had idled excessively before the test.

— If any driveability symptoms are present, refer to the Symptom Index to service those symptoms first.

— If any emission components are replaced, perform the following before repeating the State Emission Test procedure:

(1) Clear Keep Alive Memory (KAM)—Refer to   Powertrain Control Module (PCM) Reset.

(2) To relearn Adaptive Learning, run engine at 2500 rpm for one minute and idle engine for two minutes.

Fig. 152   Symptom flowchart 12 (Part 1 of 3). 1996

FM0159601591010X

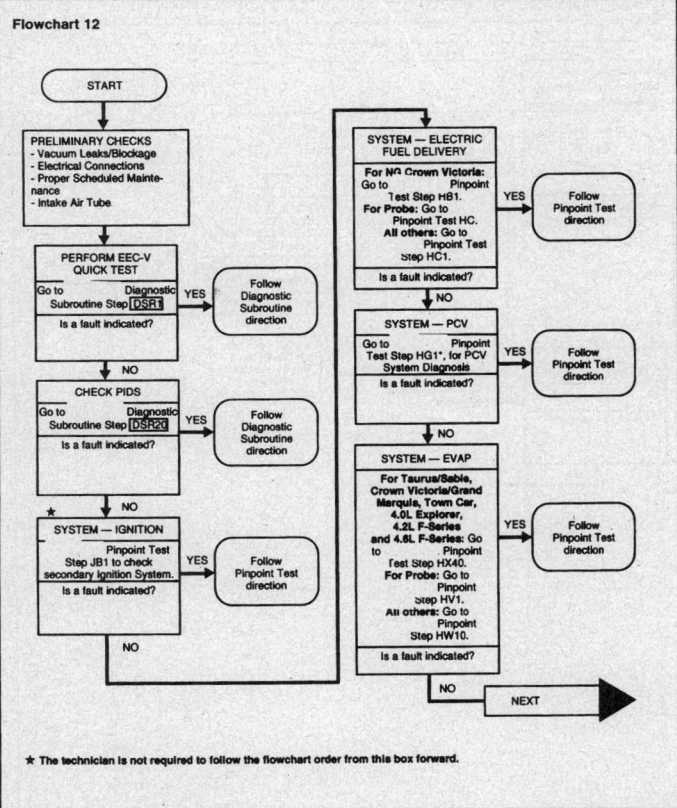

Fig. 152   Symptom flowchart 12 (Part 2 of 3). 1996

FM0159601591020X

Fig. 152   Symptom flowchart 12 (Part 3 of 3). 1996

FM0159601591030X

ELECTRONIC ENGINE CONTROL SYSTEM (EEC-V)

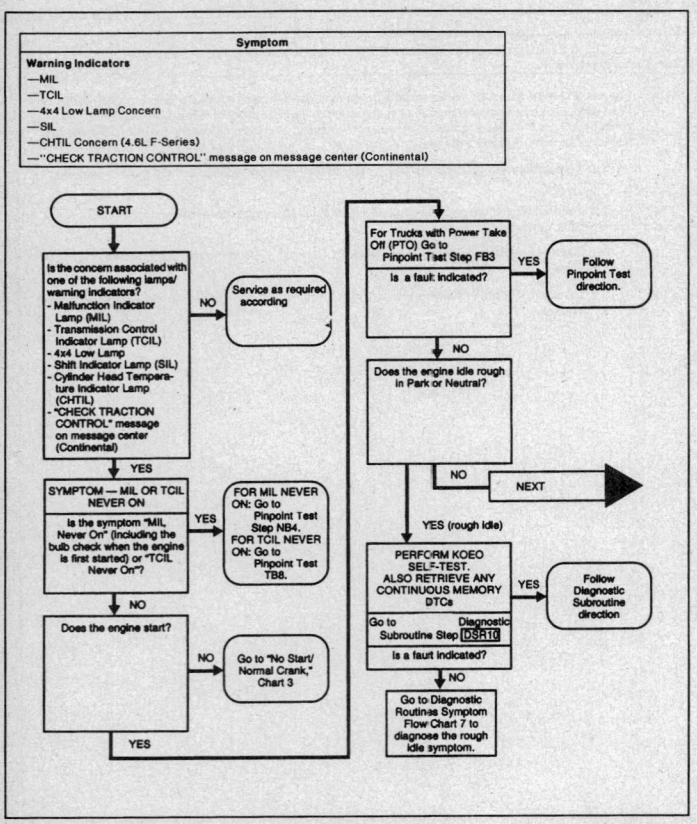

Fig. 153 Symptom flowchart 13 (Part 1 of 2). 1996

FM015960159201 0X

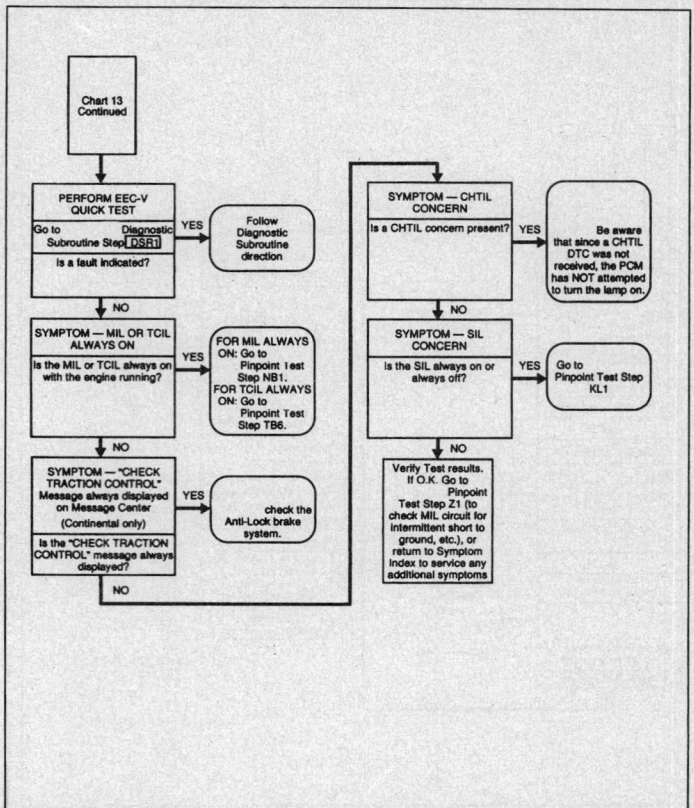

Fig. 153 Symptom flowchart 13 (Part 2 of 2). 1996

FM0159601592020X

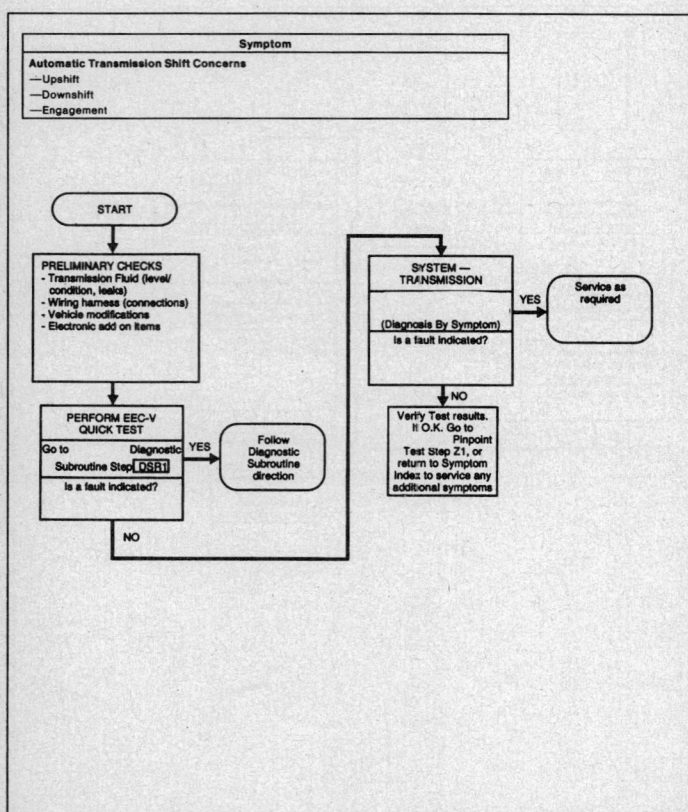

Fig. 154 Symptom flowchart 14. 1996

FM0159601593000X

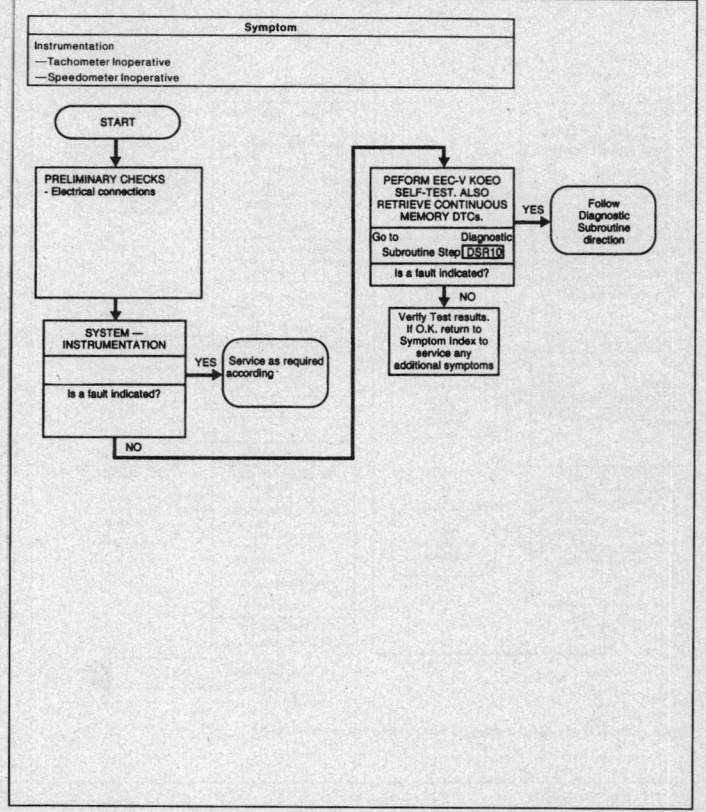

Fig. 155 Symptom flowchart 15. 1996

FM0159601594000X

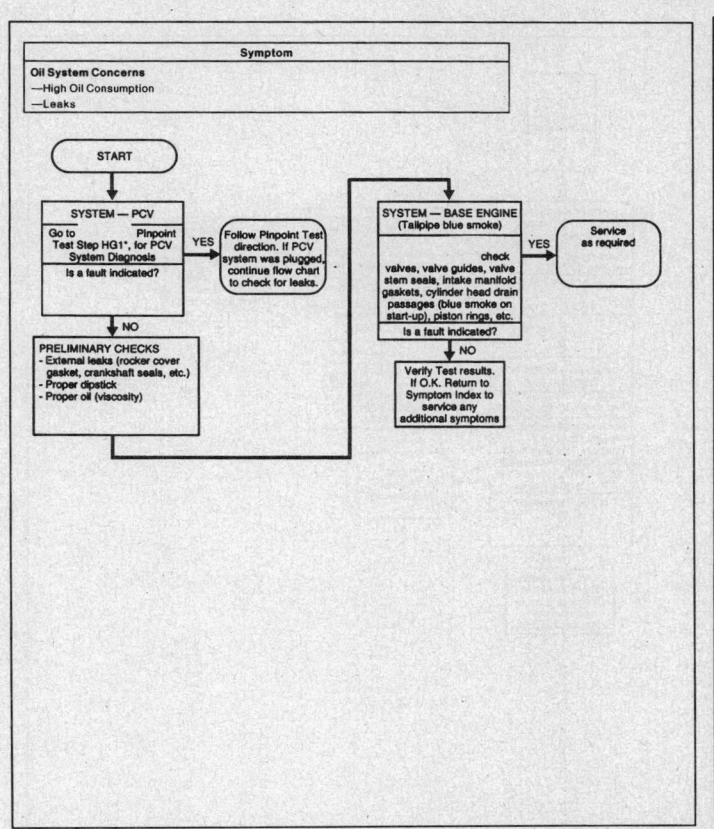

Fig. 156 Symptom flowchart 16. 1996

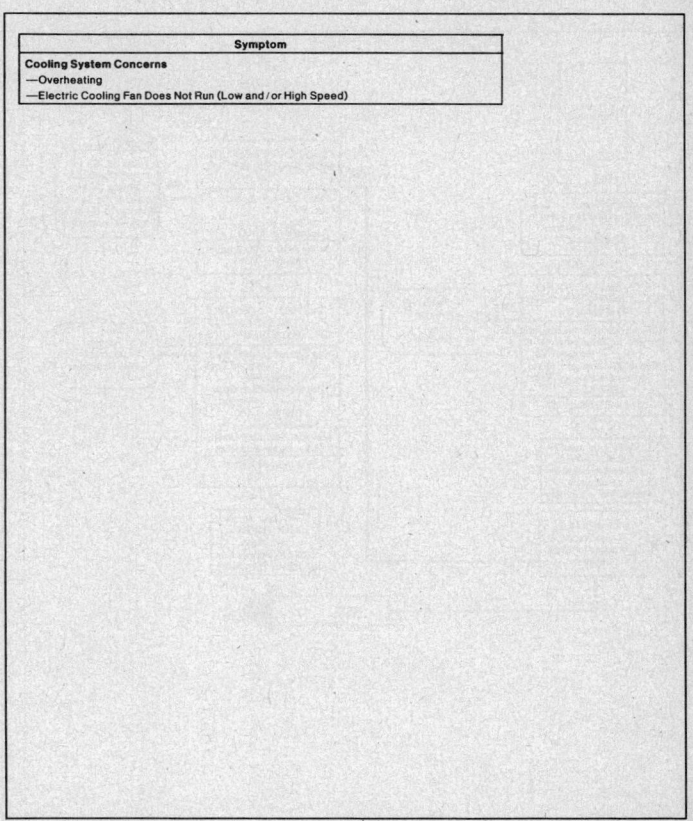

Fig. 157 Symptom flowchart 17 (Part 1 of 2). 1996

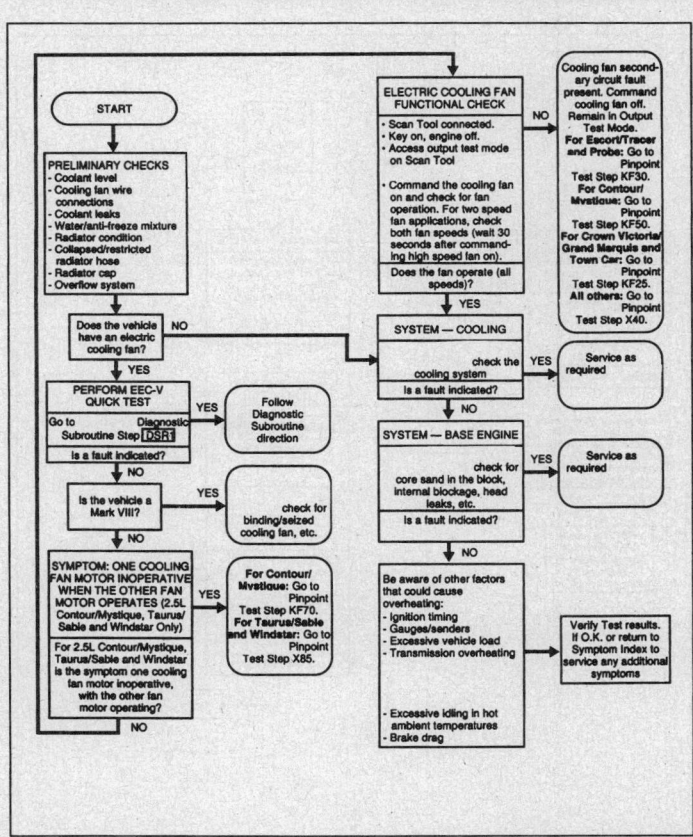

Fig. 157 Symptom flowchart 17 (Part 2 of 2). 1996

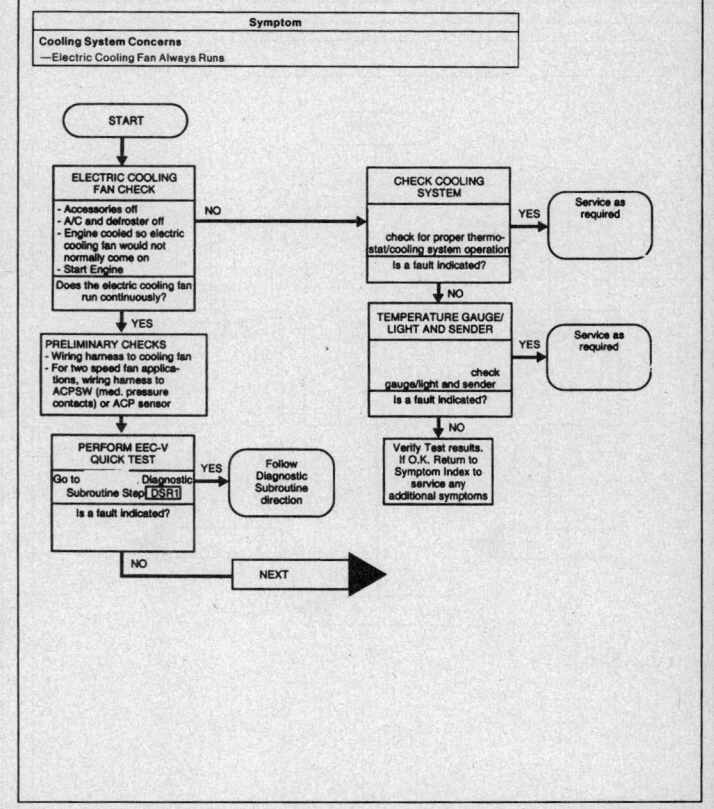

Fig. 158 Symptom flowchart 18 (Part 1 of 3). 1996

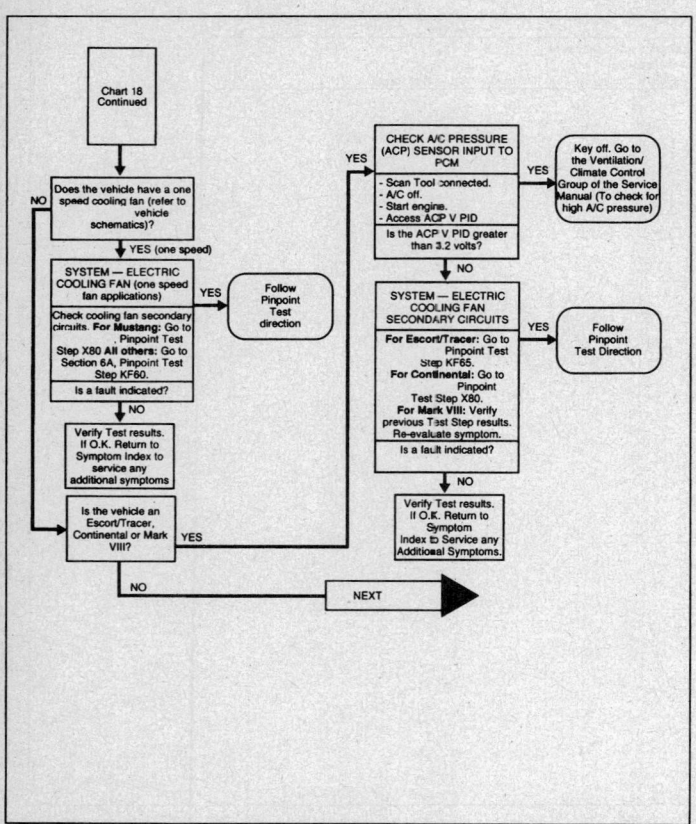

FM0159601597020X

Fig. 158 Symptom flowchart 18 (Part 2 of 3). 1996

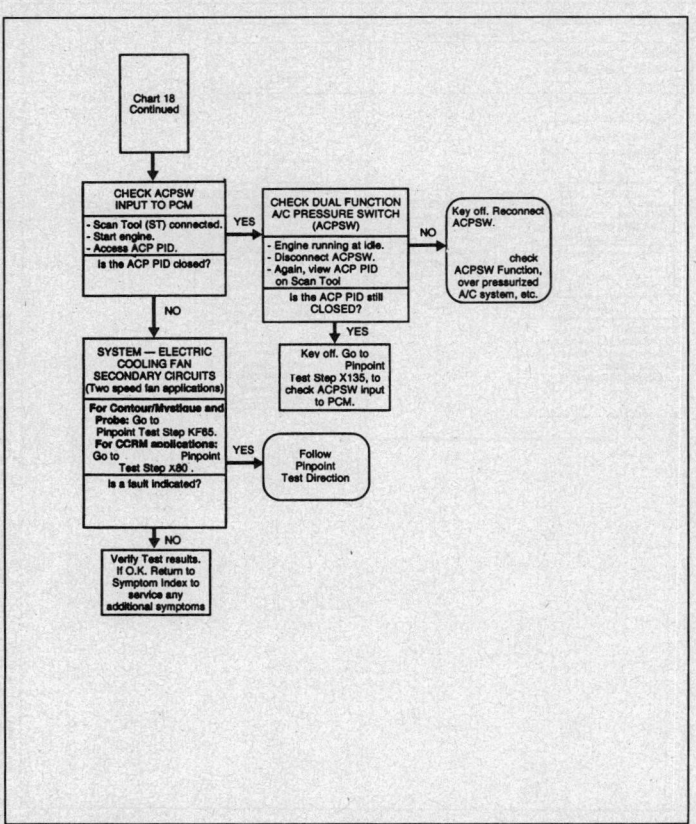

FM0159601597030X

Fig. 158 Symptom flowchart 18 (Part 3 of 3). 1996

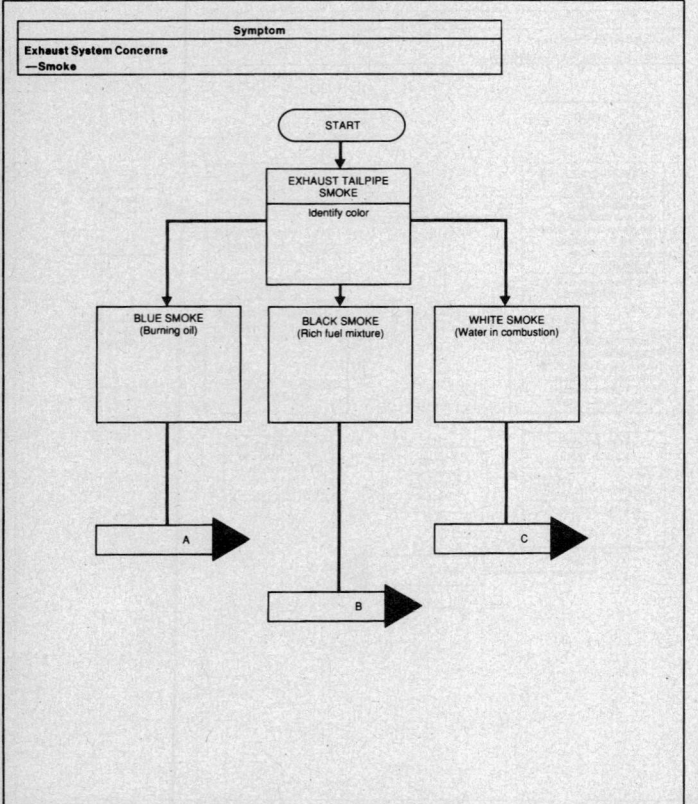

FM0159601598010X

Fig. 159 Symptom flowchart 19 (Part 1 of 3). 1996

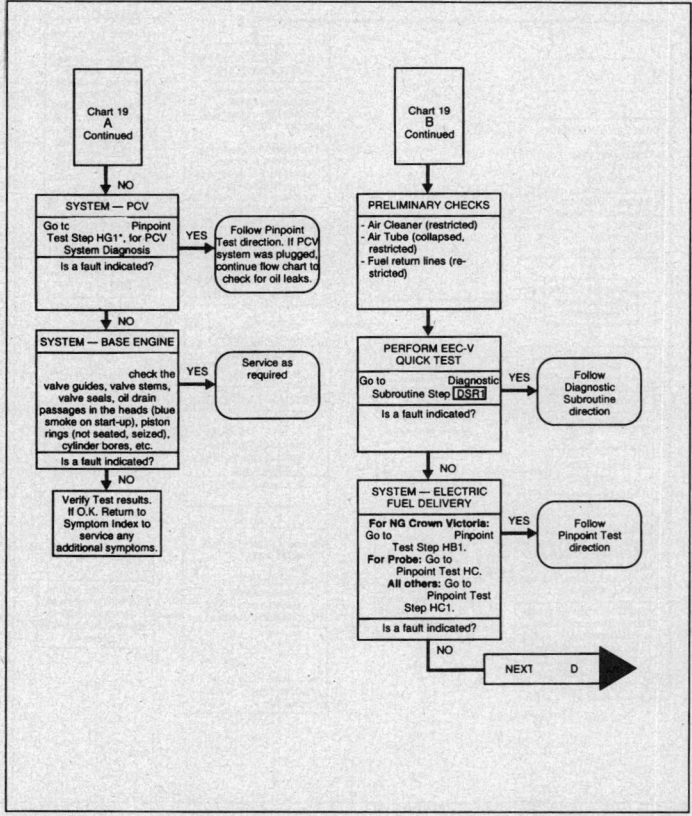

FM0159601598020X

Fig. 159 Symptom flowchart 19 (Part 2 of 3). 1996

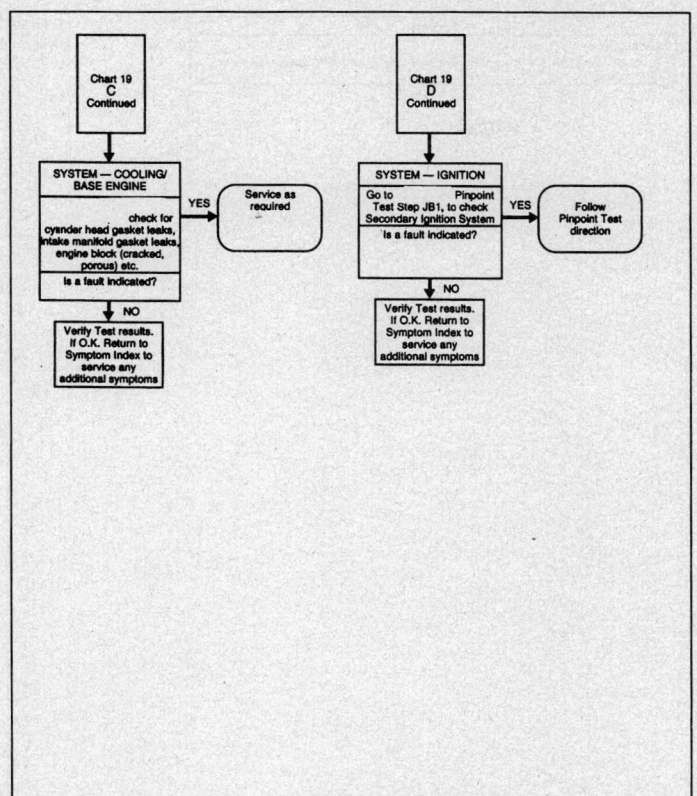

Fig. 159   Symptom flowchart 19 (Part 3 of 3). 1996

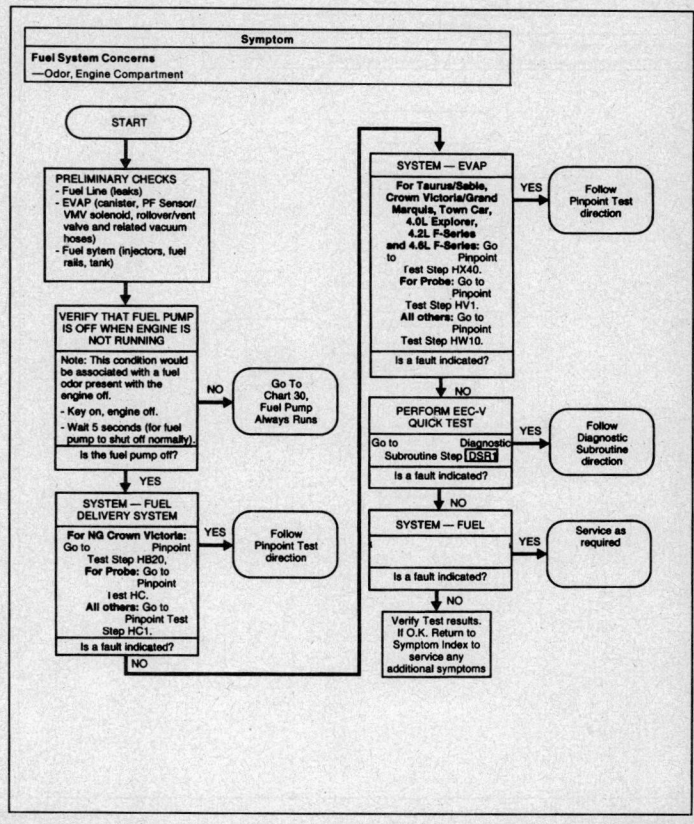

Fig. 160   Symptom flowchart 20. 1996

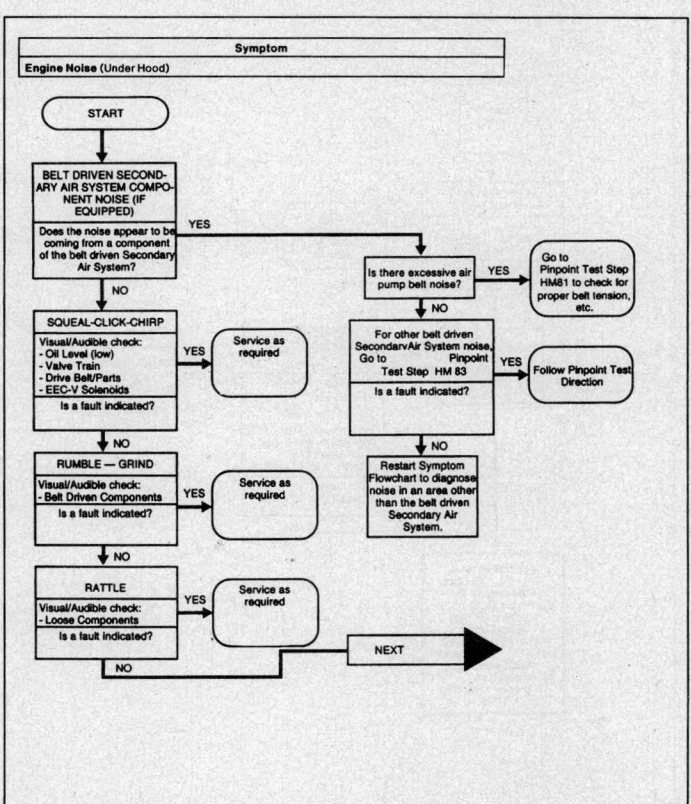

Fig. 161   Symptom flowchart 21 (Part 1 of 2). 1996

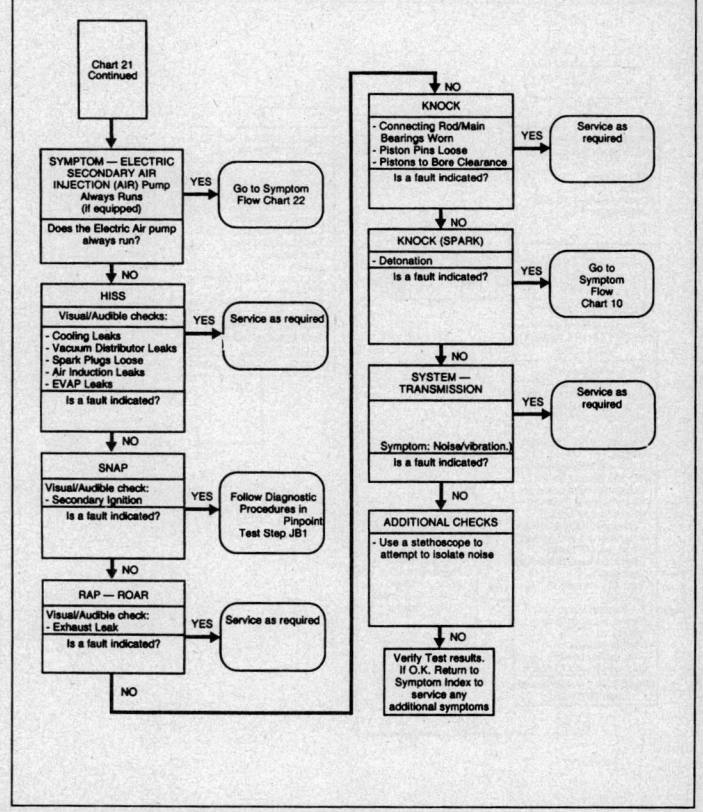

Fig. 161   Symptom flowchart 21 (Part 2 of 2). 1996

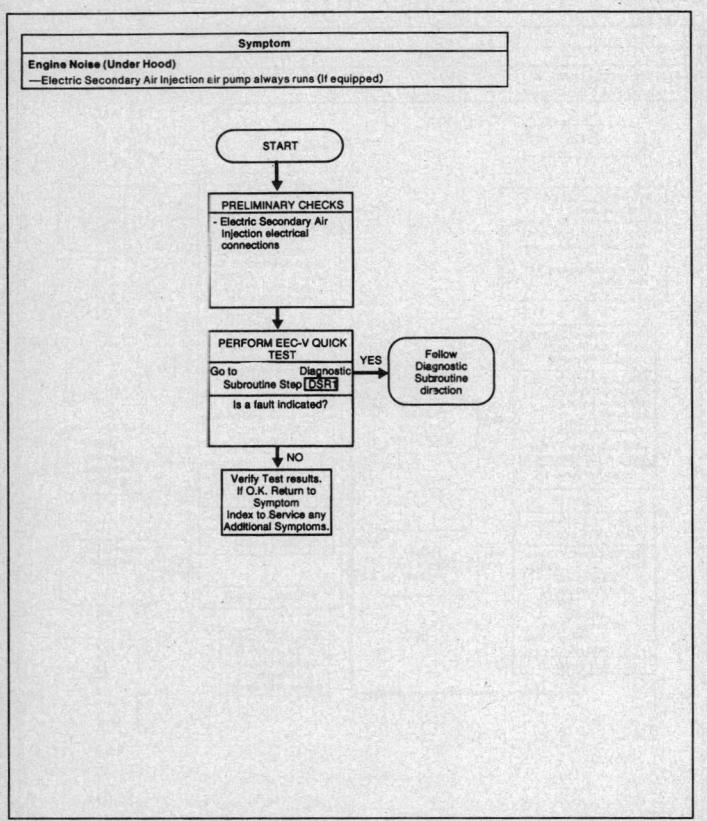

Fig. 162 Symptom flowchart 22. 1996

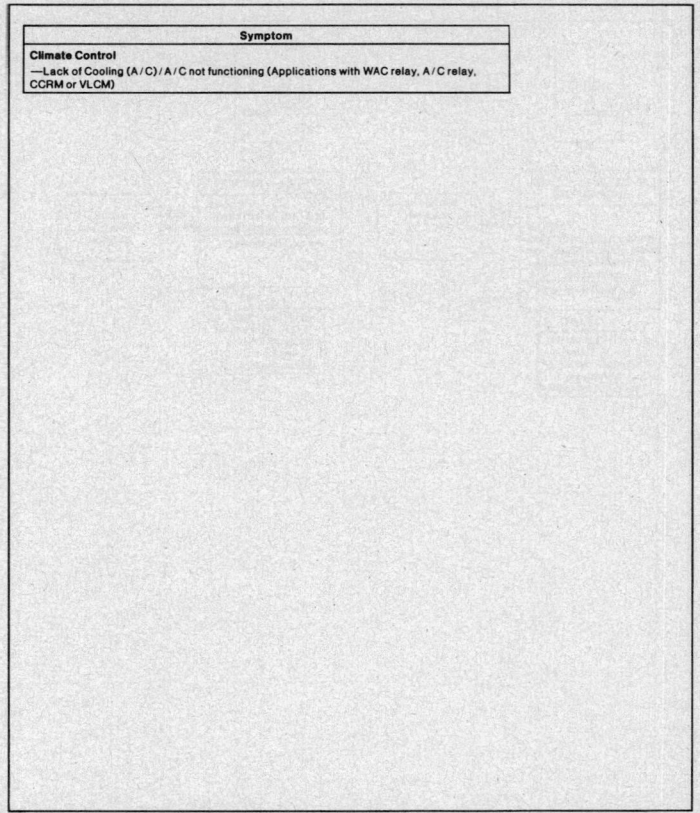

Fig. 163 Symptom flowchart 23 (Part 1 of 3). 1996

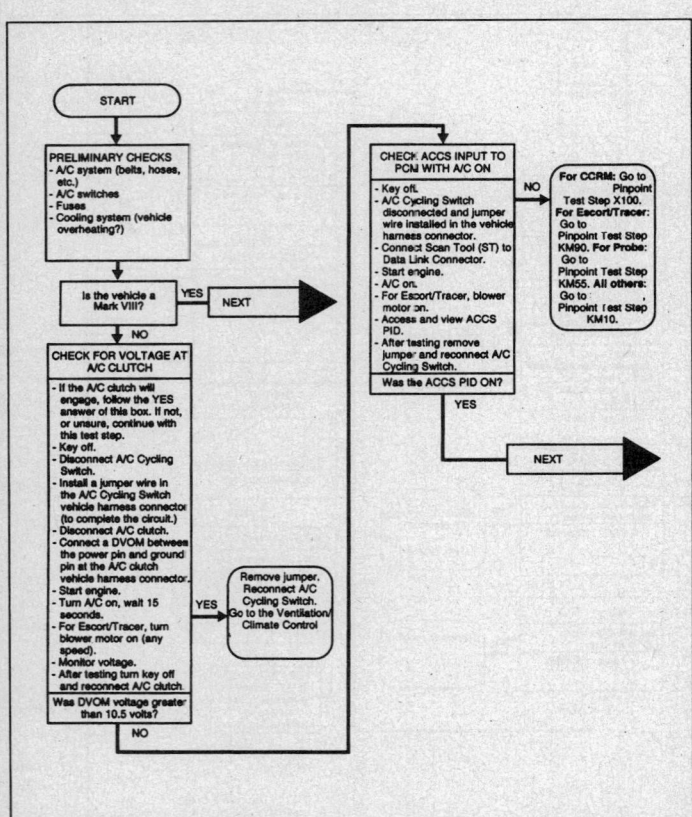

Fig. 163 Symptom flowchart 23 (Part 2 of 3). 1996

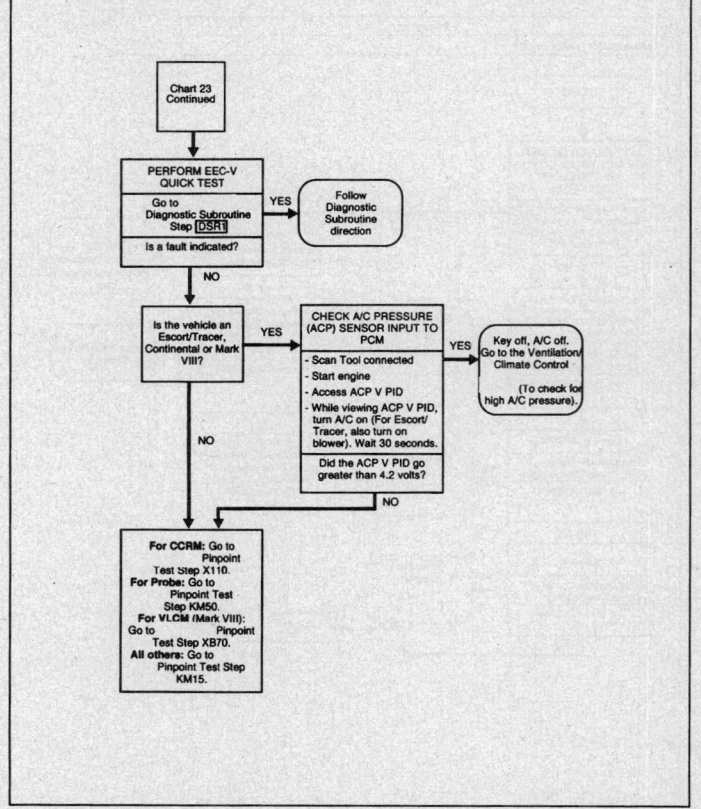

Fig. 163 Symptom flowchart 23 (Part 3 of 3). 1996

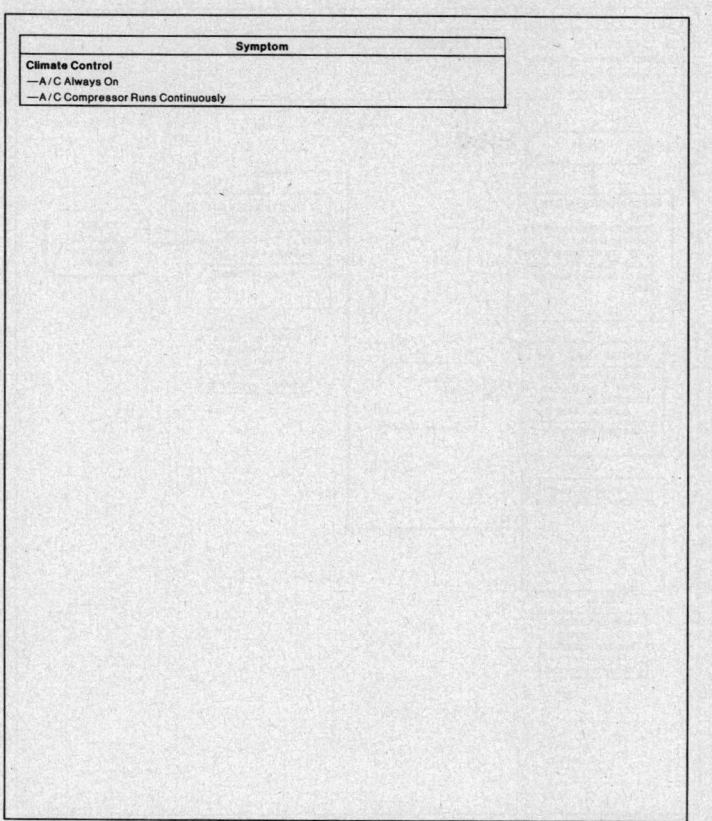

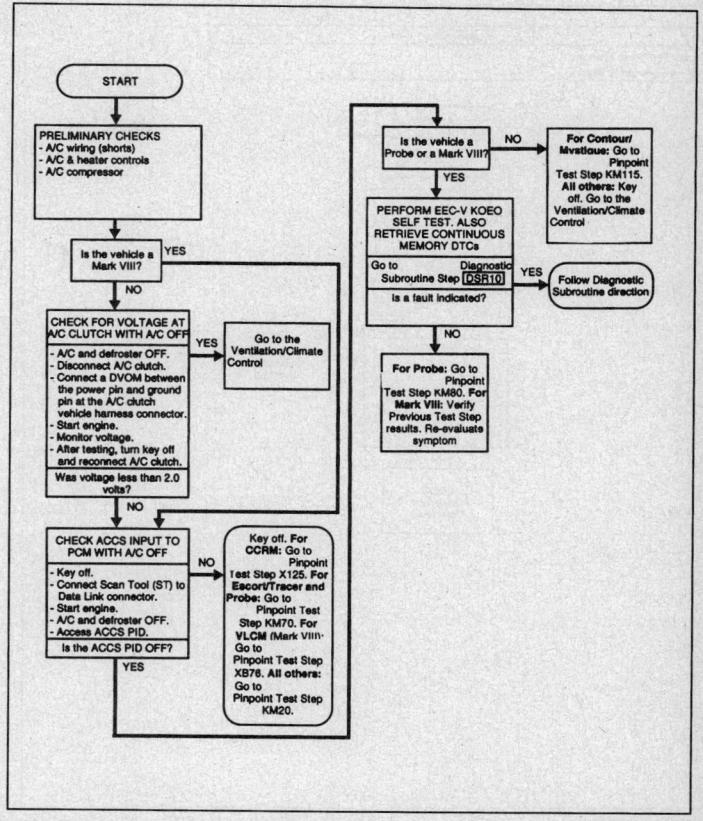

Fig. 164   Symptom flowchart 24 (Part 1 of 2). 1996

Fig. 164   Symptom flowchart 24 (Part 2 of 2). 1996

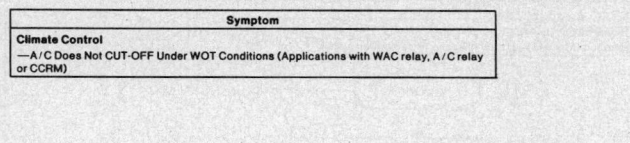

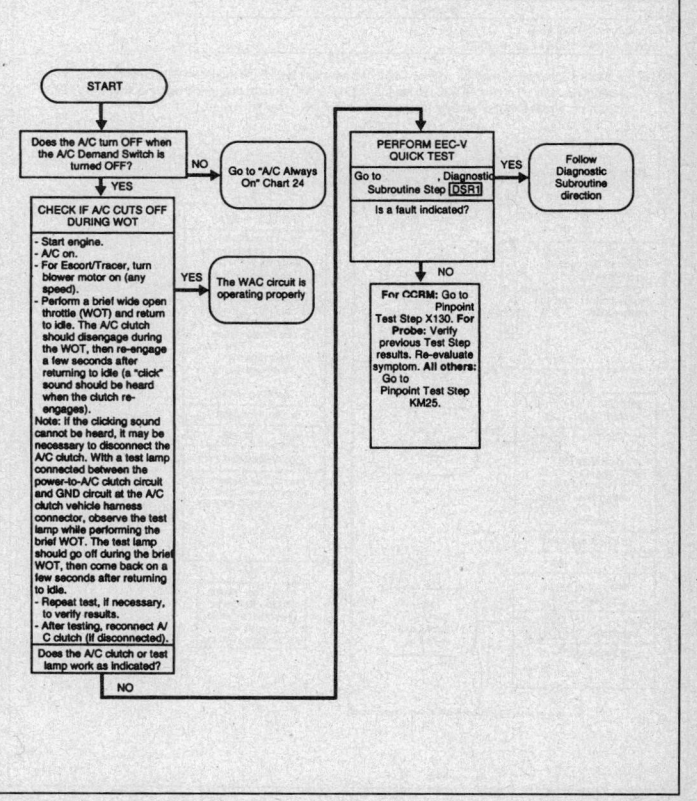

Fig. 165   Symptom flowchart 25 (Part 1 of 2). 1996

Fig. 165   Symptom flowchart 25 (Part 2 of 2). 1996

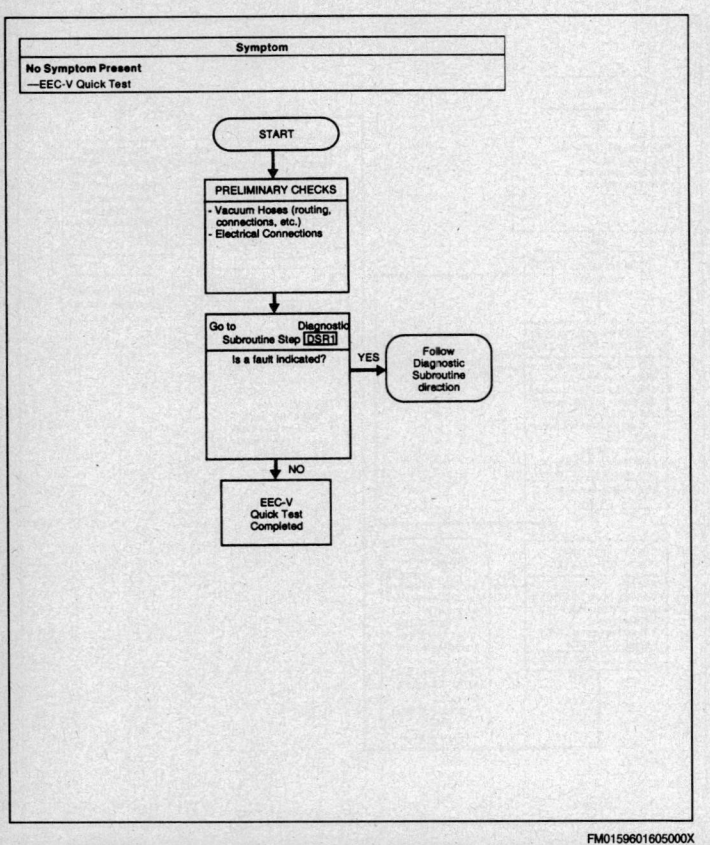

Fig. 166   Symptom flowchart 26. 1996

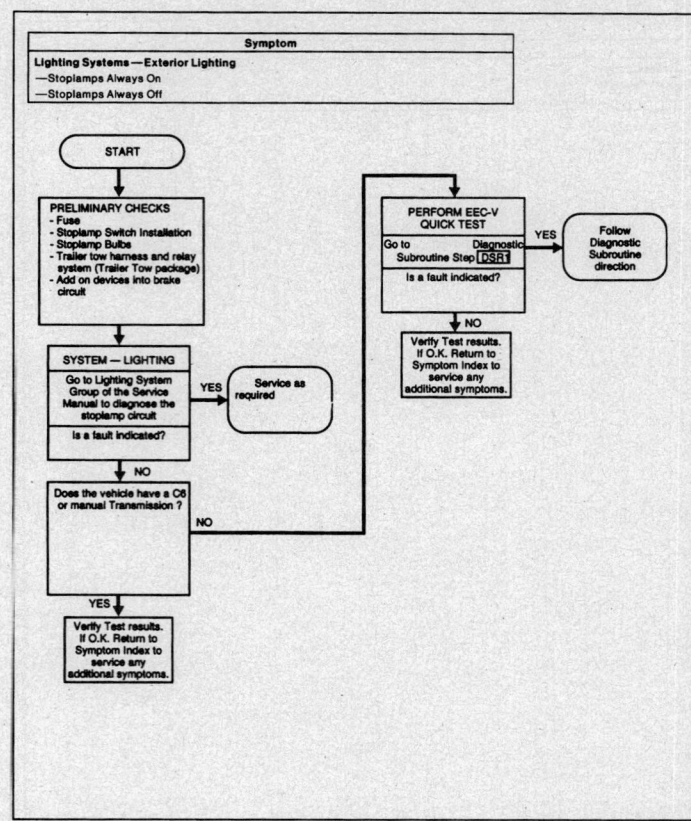

Fig. 167   Symptom flowchart 27. 1996

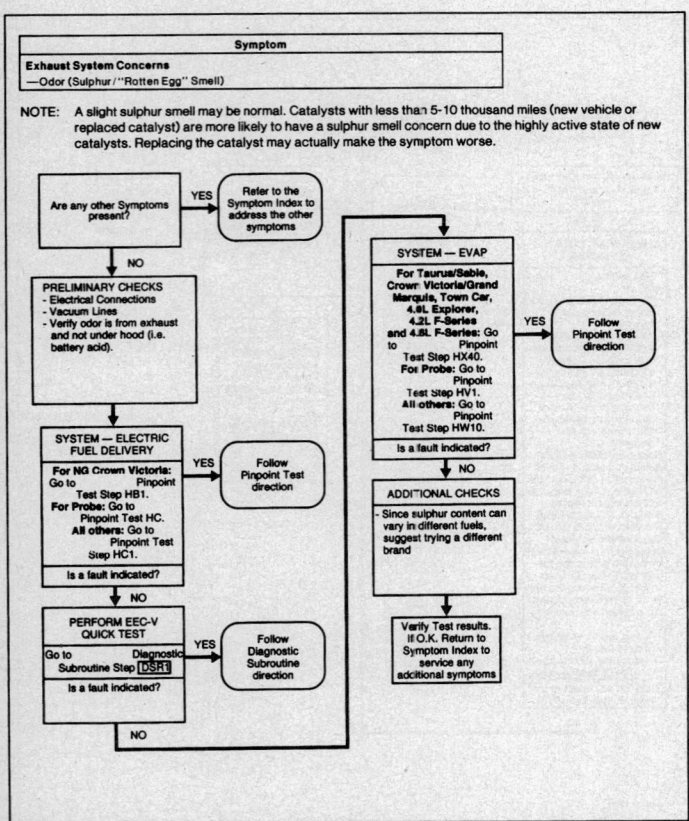

Fig. 168   Elsymptom flowchart 28. 1996

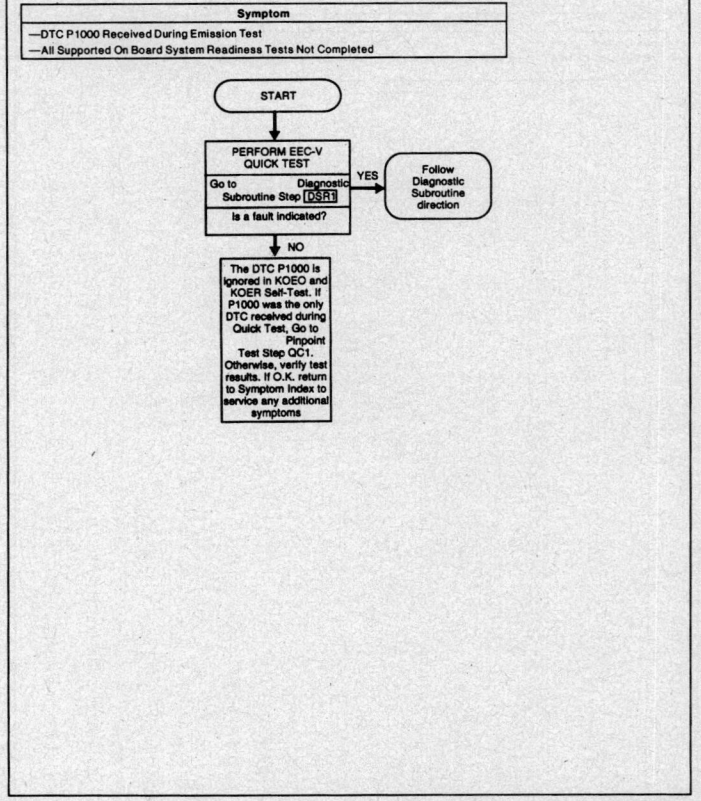

Fig. 169   Symptom flowchart 29. 1996

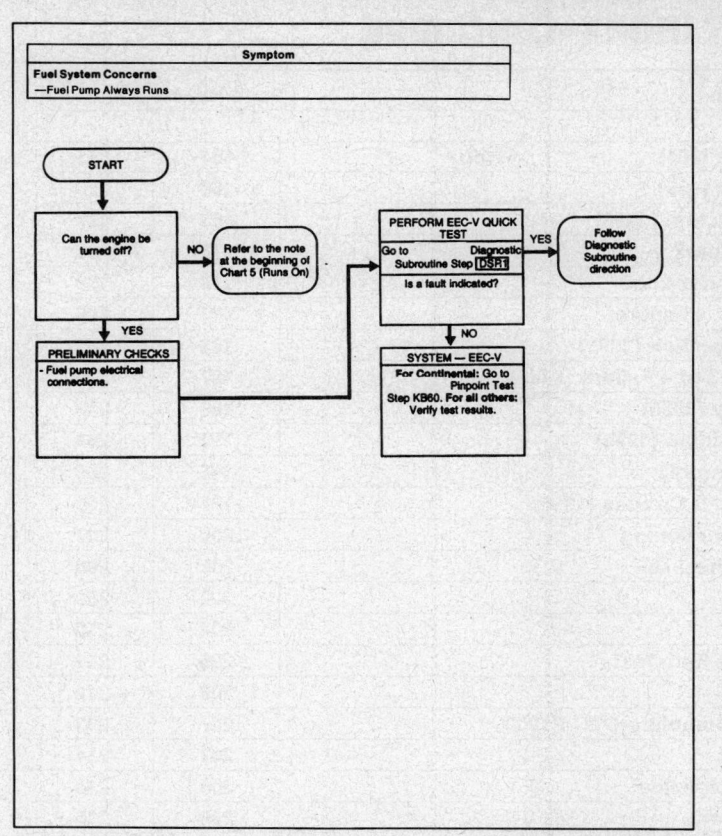

Fig. 170   Symptom flowchart 30. 1996

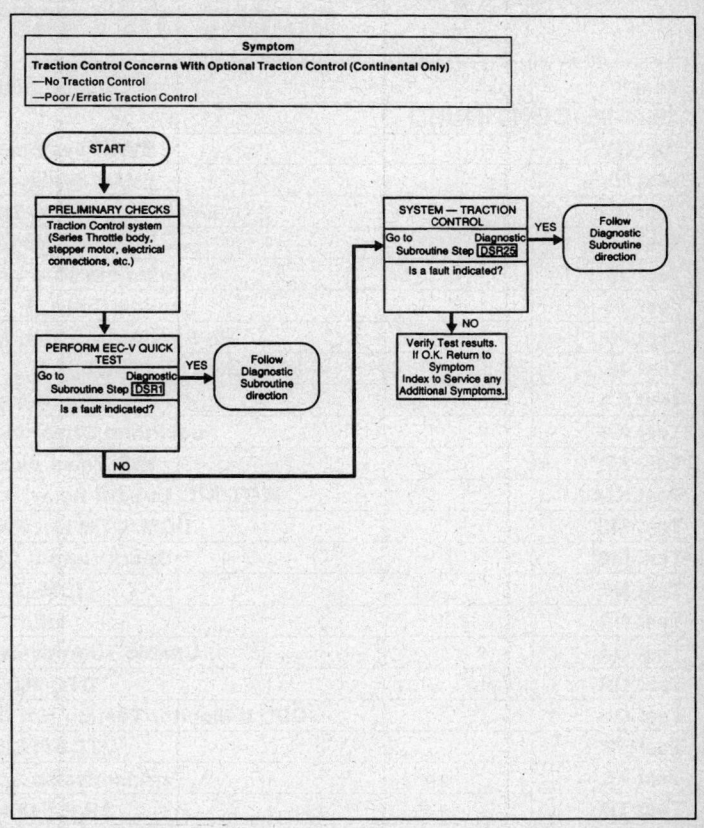

Fig. 171   Symptom flowchart 31. 1996

DIAGNOSTIC CHART INDEX

Test	Description	Page No. 9-	Fig. No.
1994-95			
Test A	No Start	108	172
Test B	EEC-V Power Relay (1995)	110	172
Test C	Reference Voltage (1994)	111	174
Test C	Reference Voltage (1995)	112	175
Test DA	IAT/ECT Sensor	114	176
Test DC	MAF Sensor	116	177
Test DG	Knock Sensor	119	178
Test DH	TP Sensor	119	179
Test DP	VSS	122	180
Test DR	CID Circuit	123	181
Test FD	BOO Switch	124	182
Test FG	OCT ADJ	125	183
Test H	Fuel Control (1994)	126	184
Test H	Fuel Control (1995)	131	185
Test HB	Adaptive Fuel (1994)	137	186
Test HC	Fuel Delivery System	138	187
Test HD	Misfire Monitor	140	188
Test HE	EGR System	141	189
Test HF	Catalyst Efficiency Monitor & Exhaust Systems	151	190
Test HG	PCV System	153	191
Test HM	Secondary Air Injection System (1995)	154	192
Test HU	Air Intake & Throttle Body (1994)	154	193
Test HU	Air Intake & Throttle Body (1995)	154	194

Continued

DIAGNOSTIC CHART INDEX—Continued

Test	Description	Page No. 9-	Fig. No.
1994-95-CONTINUED			
Test HV	EVAP System (1994)	164	195
Test HV	EVAP System (1995)	166	196
Test HW	EVAP Purge Flow System (1995)	169	197
Test JA	Ignition No Spark	173	198
Test JB	Ignition Misfire Under Load	178	199
Test JC	Ignition Coil 1, 2, 3, 4 Failure	181	200
Test JD	No Spark-Integrated Ignition (1995)	186	201
Test JE	Integrated Ignition-Coil 1, 2, 3 or 4 Failure (1995)	187	202
Test KA	Fuel Pump Relay (1995)	190	203
Test KB	Fuel Pump Driver Module (1995)	192	204
Test KE	IAC Valve Assembly	196	205
Test KM	WOT A/C Cut-Off Relay, A/C Circuits (1995)	197	206
Test MB	DCM/OTM Not Functioning	200	207
Test MC	Spark Output Check-EI	200	208
Test NA	IDM-EI	202	209
Test NB	MIL	204	210
Test QA	Unable To Activate Self-Test	205	211
Test QB	DTC 1605	206	212
Test QC	OBD II Monitor Testing Not Complete-DTC P1000	207	213
Test TB	TCS/TCIL	207	214
Test TC	Transmission Solenoids	208	215
Test TD	MLP Sensor	209	216
Test TE	TFT Sensor (1994)	210	217
Test TF	OSS Sensor	213	218
Test TG	Electronic Transmission-Continuous Memory DTC (1994)	214	219
Test X	CCRM	217	220
Test Z	Intermittents	230	221
1996			
Test A	No Start	239	223
Test B	EEC-V Power Relay	242	224
Test C	Reference Voltage	243	225
Test DA	Intake Air Temperature/Engine Coolant Temperature Sensors	245	226
Test DB	Engine Fuel Temperature Sensor	247	227
Test DC	Mass Air Flow Sensor	249	228
Test DD	Injection Pressure Sensor	253	229
Test DE	Flexible Fuel Sensor	255	230
Test DF	Vehicle Speed Circuit check	257	231
Test DG	Knock Sensor	258	232
Test DH	Throttle Position Sensor	259	233
Test DJ	Programmable Speedometer/Odometer Module	262	234
Test DK	Misfire Detection Sensor	263	235
Test DL	Cylinder Head Temperature Sensor	263	236
Test DP	Vehicle Speed Sensor	266	237
Test DR	Cylinder Identification Circuit	268	238
Test DS	A/C Pressure Sensor	269	239
Test DT	Power Steering Pressure Sensor	271	240
Test FB	Power Take Off	272	241
Test FD	Brake On/Off Switch	273	242
Test FE	Electrical Load Inputs	274	243
Test FF	Power Steering Pressure Switch	276	244
Test FG	Octane Adjust	277	245

Continued

Test	Description	Page No. 9-	Fig. No.
1996 -CONTINUED			
Test H	Fuel Control	278	246
Test HA	Natural Gas Fuel Control	285	247
Test HB	Natural Gas Fuel Delivery System	291	248
Test HC	Fuel Delivery System	294	249
Test HD	Misfire Detection Monitor	296	250
Test HE	Exhaust Gas Recirculation Systems	298	251
Test HF	Catalyst Efficiency Monitor & Exhaust Systems	307	252
Test HG	Positive Crankcase Ventilation System	309	253
Test HH	EGR Monitor & System ①	310	254
Test HM	Secondary Air Injection System	316	255
Test HT	Traction Control System	321	256
Test HU	Air Intake Systems	325	257
Test HV	EVAP Monitor & System ①	333	258
Test HW	EVAP Purge System	335	259
Test HX	EVAP Monitor & System ②	342	260
Test JD	Integrated Ignition/No Spark	350	261
Test JE	Integrated Ignition Coil 1, 2, 3 or 4 Failure	352	262
Test JF	Integrated Ignition Coil On Plug Coil 1 Through 8 Failure	362	263
Test JG	Distributor Ignition	368	264
Test JK	Distributor Ignition No Spark ①	371	265
Test KA	Fuel Pump Relay	372	266
Test KB	Fuel Pump Driver Module	377	267
Test KC	Fuel Shutoff Valve Relay	380	268
Test KE	IAC Valve Assembly	383	269
Test KF	Fan Control Relay	386	270
Test KL	Shift Indicator Lamp	391	271
Test KM	WOT A/C Cut-Off (WAC) Relay, A/C Circuits	392	272
Test KN	Fuel Pressure Regulator Control Solenoid ①	399	273
Test MB	Output Test Mode Not Functioning	400	274
Test MD	Spark Output Check/Integrated Electronic Ignition	401	275
Test NB	Malfunction Indicator Lamp	401	276
Test NC	Ignition Diagnostic Monitor/Integrated Electronic Ignition	402	277
Test ND	Engine RPM/Vehicle Speed Limiter	402	278
Test QA	Unable To Activate Self-Test/SCP Communication Error/DTC Not Listed	402	279
Test QB	DTC P0603/P1605	403	280
Test QC	OBD II Monitor Testing Not Complete/DTC P1000	404	281
Test QD	DTC P1260	404	282
Test TA	Park/Neutral Position Switch & Clutch Pedal Position Switch	405	283
Test TB	Transmission Control Switch & Indicator Lamp	406	284
Test TC	Transmission Solenoids	407	285
Test TD	Transmission Range Sensor	409	286
Test TE	Transmission Fluid Temperature Sensor	411	287
Test TF	Output Shaft/Turbine Shaft Speed Sensor	414	288
Test X	Constant Control Relay Module	416	289
Test XB	Variable Load Control Module	429	290
Test Z	Intermittent	438	291

①—Probe.
②—Except Probe.

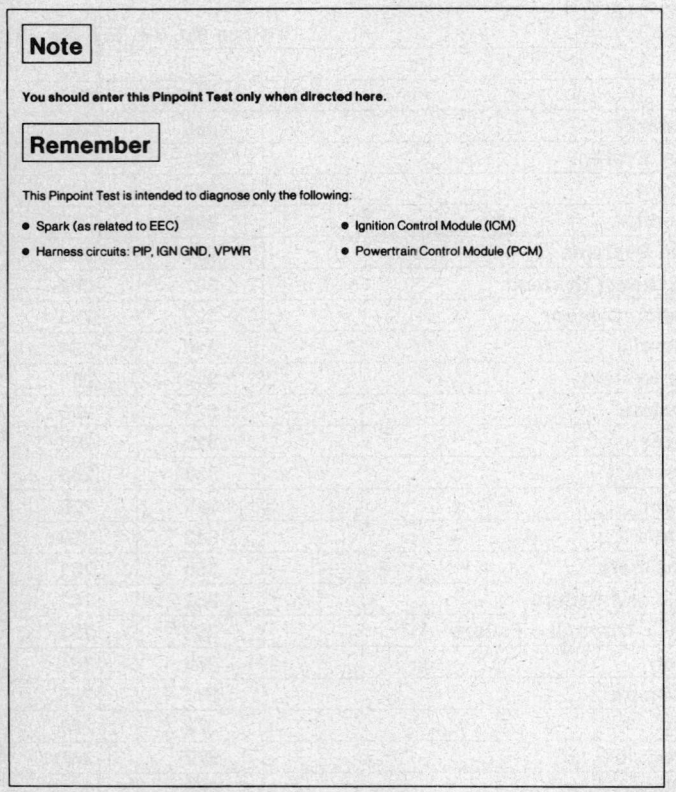

Note

You should enter this Pinpoint Test only when directed here.

Remember

This Pinpoint Test is intended to diagnose only the following:

- Spark (as related to EEC)
- Harness circuits: PIP, IGN GND, VPWR
- Ignition Control Module (ICM)
- Powertrain Control Module (PCM)

FM0159401179010X

Fig. 172   Test A: No Start (Part 1 of 9). 1994-95

FM0159401179030X

Fig. 172   Test A: No Start (Part 2 of 9). 1994-95

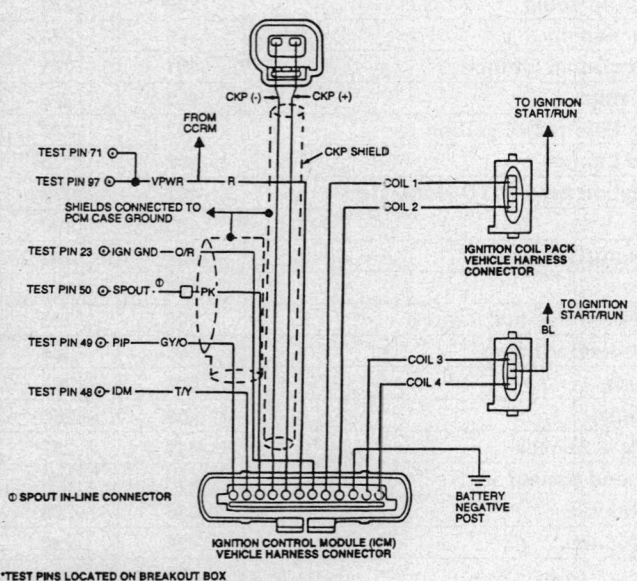

Fig. 172   Test A: No Start (Part 3 of 9). 1994-95

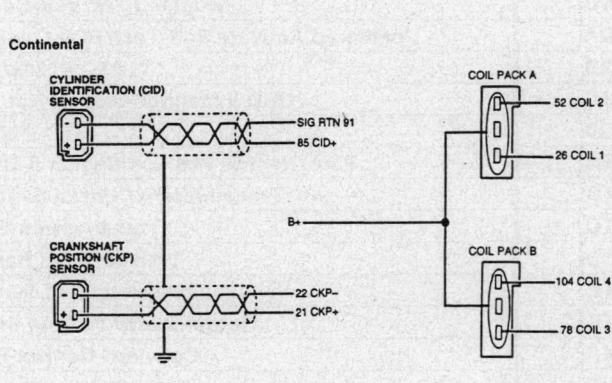

Fig. 172   Test A: No Start (Part 4 of 9). 1994-95

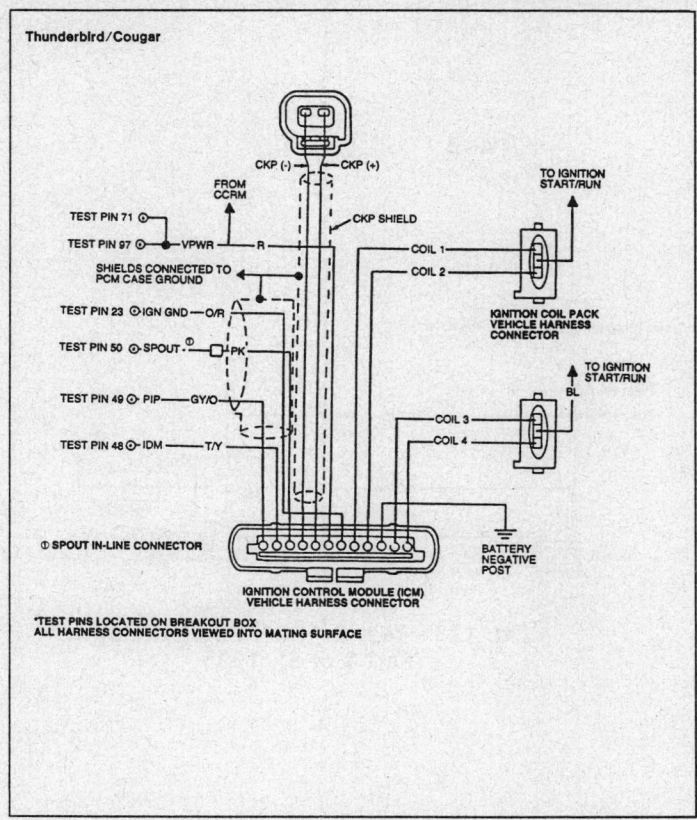

Fig. 172 Test A: No Start (Part 5 of 9). 1994-95

WARNING

STOP THIS TEST AT THE FIRST SIGN OF A FUEL LEAK AND SERVICE AS REQUIRED.

CAUTION

No open flame — No smoking during fuel delivery checks.

TEST STEP	RESULT	▶	ACTION TO TAKE
A1 ATTEMPT TO CRANK ENGINE			
NOTE: Verify Inertia Fuel Shutoff (IFS) switch is set (button pushed in). Refer to Owner's Guide for location. • **Does engine crank?**	Yes No	▶ ▶	GO to A2. REFER to Starting/Engine
A2 IDENTIFY TYPE OF NO START			
NOTE: The purpose of this Test Step is to identify intermittent No Starts in order to guide the technician to the proper repair procedure. • **Does the vehicle start now?**	Yes No	▶ ▶	Vehicle is an intermittent No Start. GO to Pinpoint Test Step Z50 and prepare to use the Ignition Intermittent Analyzer, DIST tool. GO to A3.
A3 CHECK MIL DURING CRANK			
• Key off. • Key on, observe Malfunction Indicator Lamp (MIL). MIL should be on, if not, go to Pinpoint Test Step ML1. • Turn key to start position and observe MIL while cranking the engine. • **Did the MIL turn off during crank?**	Yes No	▶ ▶	MIL turning off during crank indicates PIP circuit is OK. GO to A4. GO to A7.
A4 CHECK FUEL PRESSURE			
WARNING: IF FUEL STARTS LEAKING, TURN KEY OFF IMMEDIATELY. NO SMOKING. • Key off. • Install fuel pressure gauge. • Note initial pressure reading. • Observe pressure gauge as fuel system is pressurized. • Turn key to on for one second, then turn key off. Wait 10 seconds. Repeat five times. • **Does the fuel pressure increase?**	Yes No	▶ ▶	GO to A5. GO to Pinpoint Test Step X150.

Fig. 172 Test A: No Start (Part 6 of 9). 1994-95

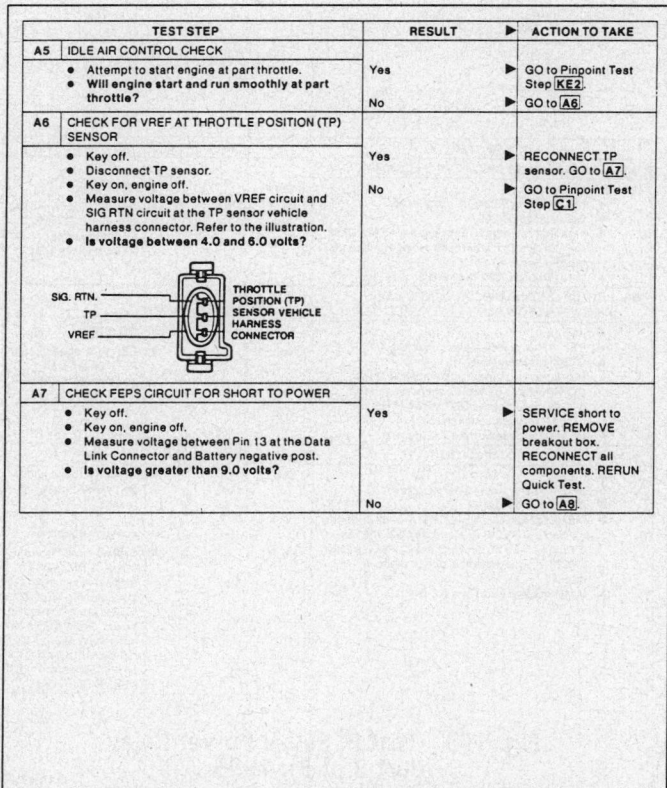

Fig. 172 Test A: No Start (Part 7 of 9). 1994-95

TEST STEP	RESULT	▶	ACTION TO TAKE
A8 CHECK FOR SPARK AT THE PLUGS			
• Disconnect the spark plug wire to any accessible cylinder. • Connect spark tester between spark plug wire and engine ground. • Connect Spark Plug Firing Indicator D81P-6666-A or D89P-6666-A or equivalent. • Crank engine and check for spark. • Reconnect the spark plug wire to the spark plug. • **Was spark present and consistent?**	Yes No	▶ ▶	If MIL turned off during crank in A3: RETURN to Section 4, Symptom Charts. If MIL stayed on during crank in A3: GO to A9. If MIL turned off during crank in A3: SERVICE or REPLACE spark plug wires for insulation damage, looseness or other damage. SERVICE or REPLACE spark plugs for wear, carbon deposits and proper plug gap. If MIL stayed on during crank in A3: GO to Pinpoint Test Step JA1 for 3.8L Mustang. GO to Pinpoint Test Step JA30 for 4.6L Thunderbird/Cougar.
A9 CHECK CONTINUITY OF IGNITION GROUND CIRCUIT			
• Key off. • Disconnect PCM. Inspect for damaged or pushed out pins, corrosion, loose wires, etc. Service as necessary. • Install breakout box, leave PCM disconnected. • Install EI diagnostic harness (Rotunda 007-00059) to breakout box and leave ICM disconnected. • Install ICM overlay. • Measure resistance between Test Pin 23 at breakout box and IGN GND circuit at the EI diagnostic harness. • **Is resistance less than 5.0 ohms?**	Yes No	▶ ▶	GO to A10. SERVICE open circuit. REMOVE breakout box. RECONNECT all components. RERUN Quick Test.
A10 CHECK PIP CIRCUIT CONTINUITY			
• Key off. • Breakout box installed, PCM disconnected. • EI harness installed, ICM disconnected. • Measure resistance between Test Pin 49 at breakout box and PIP circuit at the EI diagnostic harness. • **Is resistance less than 5.0 ohms?**	Yes No	▶ ▶	GO to A11. SERVICE open circuit. REMOVE breakout box. RECONNECT all components. RERUN Quick Test.

Fig. 172 Test A: No Start (Part 8 of 9). 1994-95

TEST STEP	RESULT	▶	ACTION TO TAKE
A11 CHECK PIP CIRCUIT FOR SHORT TO POWER • Key off. • Breakout box installed, PCM disconnected. • ICM disconnected. • EI harness installed. • Key on, engine off. • Measure voltage between Test Pin 49 at breakout box and battery negative post. • **Is voltage greater than 1.0 volts?**	Yes No	▶ ▶	SERVICE short to power. REMOVE breakout box. RECONNECT all components. RERUN Quick Test. GO to A12.
A12 CHECK PIP SIGNAL CIRCUIT FOR SHORTS TO GROUND • Key off. • Breakout box installed, PCM disconnected. • ICM disconnected. • Measure resistance between Test Pin 49 (PIP) and Test Pins 23, 51, 91 and 103 (short to GROUND). • **Is each resistance greater than 10,000 ohms?**	Yes No	▶ ▶	GO to A13. SERVICE short circuit. REMOVE breakout box. RECONNECT all components. RERUN Quick Test. If vehicle does not start, GO to A13.
A13 CHECK PIP SIGNAL • Key off. • Breakout box installed, PCM disconnected. • Reconnect ICM. • Measure voltage between Test Pin 49 and Test Pin 23 at breakout box. • Crank engine, record reading. • **Is voltage between 3.0 and 7.0 volts?**	Yes No	▶ ▶	REPLACE PCM. REMOVE breakout box. RERUN Quick Test. REPLACE ICM. REMOVE breakout box. RERUN Quick Test.

Fig. 172 Test A: No Start (Part 9 of 9)

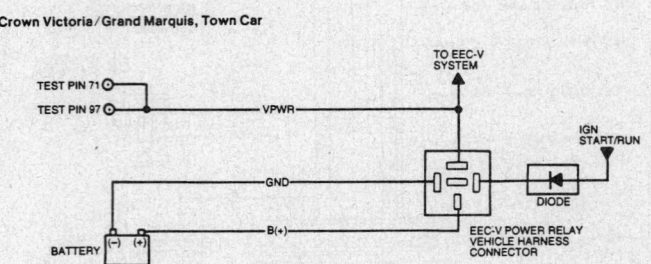

Crown Victoria/Grand Marquis, Town Car

Fig. 173 Test B: EEC-V Power Relay (Part 1 of 3). 1995

TEST STEP	RESULT	▶	ACTION TO TAKE
B1 CHECK VPWR CIRCUIT CONTINUITY • Key off. • Idle Air Control (IAC) solenoid disconnected. • Disconnect Scan Tool from DLC. • Disconnect EEC-V Power Relay. • Measure resistance between the VPWR circuit at the IAC solenoid vehicle harness connector and the VPWR circuit at the EEC-V Power Relay vehicle harness connector. • **Is resistance less than 5.0 ohms?**	Yes No	▶ ▶	RECONNECT IAC solenoid. GO to B2. SERVICE open VPWR circuit between the EEC-V Power Relay and the splice to the IAC solenoid. RECONNECT all components. RERUN Quick Test.
B2 CHECK GROUND CIRCUIT TO EEC-V POWER RELAY • Key off. • EEC-V Power Relay disconnected. • Measure resistance between the ground circuit at the EEC-V Power Relay vehicle harness connector and the battery negative post. • **Is resistance less than 5.0 ohms?**	Yes No	▶ ▶	GO to B3. Ground circuit fault to EEC-V Power Relay. For applications with CCRM (Continental, Windstar): GO to B5. All others: SERVICE open ground circuit. RECONNECT all components. RERUN Quick Test.
B3 CHECK B+ AND IGN START/RUN VOLTAGE TO EEC-V POWER RELAY • Key off. • EEC-V Power Relay disconnected. • Connect the DVOM negative (-) test lead to the battery negative post. • Check for voltage on the B(+) circuit at the EEC-V Power Relay vehicle harness connector. • Key on, engine off. • Check for voltage on the IGN START/RUN circuit at the EEC-V Power Relay vehicle harness connector. • Key off. • **Were both voltages greater than 10.5 volts?**	Yes No	▶ ▶	REPLACE EEC-V Power Relay. RECONNECT all components. RERUN Quick Test. SERVICE open in B+ or IGN START/RUN circuit. (If open was in IGN START/RUN circuit, verify condition of diode (if equipped), see schematic.) RECONNECT all components. RERUN Quick Test.

Fig. 173 Test B: EEC-V Power Relay (Part 2 of 3). 1995

TEST STEP	RESULT	▶	ACTION TO TAKE
B5 CHECK GROUND CIRCUIT FROM CCRM • Key off. • EEC-V Power Relay disconnected. • Disconnect CCRM. • Measure resistance between pin 15 (GND) of the CCRM vehicle harness connector and the battery negative post. • **Is resistance less than 5.0 ohms?**	Yes No	▶ ▶	GO to B6. SERVICE open ground circuit. RECONNECT all components. RERUN Quick Test.
B6 CHECK GROUND CIRCUIT CONTINUITY BETWEEN EEC-V POWER RELAY AND CCRM • Key off. • EEC-V Power Relay disconnected. • CCRM disconnected. • Measure resistance between pin 9 of the CCRM vehicle harness connector and the ground circuit at the EEC-V Power Relay vehicle harness connector. • **Is resistance less than 5.0 ohms?**	Yes No	▶ ▶	GO to B7. SERVICE open circuit. RECONNECT all components. RERUN Quick Test.
B7 CHECK GROUND CIRCUIT IN CCRM • Key off. • EEC-V Power Relay disconnected. • CCRM disconnected. • Measure resistance of CCRM ground circuit by placing the DVOM (+) lead on pin 9 and the DVOM (-) lead on pin 15 of the CCRM (specific DVOM +/- placement is due to diode in circuit). • **Is resistance less than 5.0 ohms?**	Yes No	▶ ▶	Ground circuits check OK. VERIFY test results. continue diagnosis. Ground circuit is open in the CCRM. VERIFY that harness circuits to pin 9 and pin 15 of the CCRM are not short to power. SERVICE as necessary. REPLACE CCRM. RECONNECT all components. RERUN Quick Test.

Fig. 173 Test B: EEC-V Power Relay (Part 3 of 3). 1995

Note

You should enter this Pinpoint Test only when directed.

Remember

This Pinpoint Test is intended to diagnose only the following:

- Sensor harness circuits: SIG RTN, VREF
- 3-wire sensors: Throttle Position (TP) sensor and Differential Pressure Feedback Electronic EGR (DPFE) sensor
- Powertrain Control Module (PCM)

Pinpoint Test Schematic

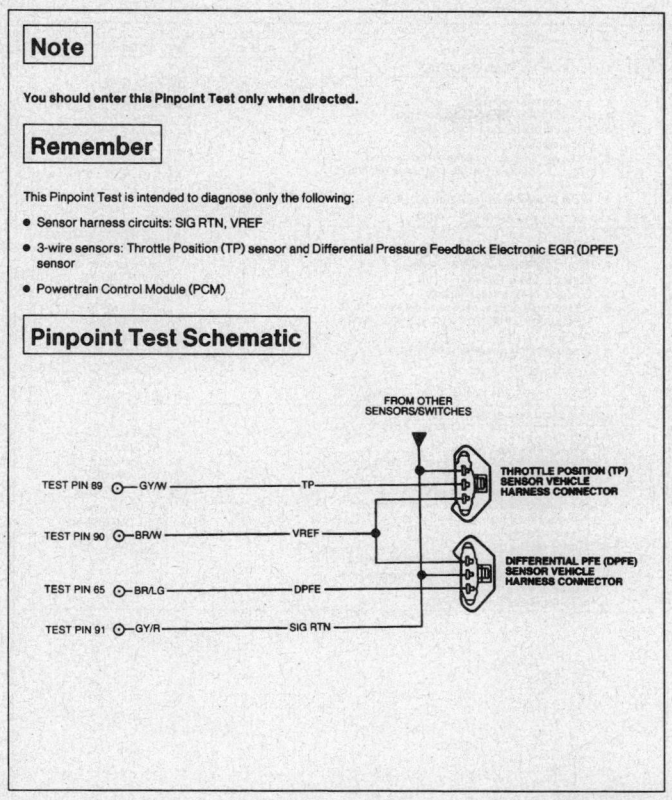

FM0159401180010X

Fig. 174   Test C: Reference Voltage (Part 1 of 6). 1994

TEST STEP		RESULT	►	ACTION TO TAKE
C1	**CHECK BATTERY VOLTAGE**			
• Key on, engine off. • Measure voltage across battery terminals. • **Is voltage greater than 10.5 volts?**		Yes No	► ►	GO to C2 Key off. service discharged battery.
C2	**CHECK SIG RTN TO TP OR DPFE SENSOR**			
• Key on, engine off. • For DPFE DTC: — DPFE sensor disconnected. — Measure voltage between battery positive post and SIG RTN circuit in the DPFE sensor vehicle harness connector. All others: — TP sensor disconnected. — Measure voltage between battery positive post and SIG RTN circuit in the TP sensor vehicle harness connector. • **Is voltage greater than 10.5 volts and within 1.0 volt of battery voltage?**		Yes No	► ►	Key off. GO to C3. Key off. SIG RTN / PWR GND fault present. GO to C11
C3	**CHECK FOR VPWR TO IAC SOLENOID**			
• Key off. • TP or DPFE sensor disconnected. • Disconnect Idle Air Control (IAC) solenoid. • Key on, engine off. • Measure voltage between the VPWR circuit at the IAC vehicle harness connector and the battery negative post. • Key off. • **Was voltage greater than 10.5 volts?**		Yes No	► ►	RECONNECT IAC solenoid. GO to C4. VPWR is not present. RECONNECT TP or DPFE sensor. GO to Pinpoint Test Step X1

**IDLE AIR CONTROL (IAC)
VEHICLE HARNESS CONNECTOR**

VPWR (R)

FM0159401180020X

Fig. 174   Test C: Reference Voltage (Part 2 of 6). 1994

TEST STEP		RESULT	►	ACTION TO TAKE
C4	**CHECK FOR SHORTED TP OR DPFE SENSOR**			
• Key off. • TP or DPFE sensor disconnected. • For DPFE DTC: — Disconnect TP sensor. — Key on. — Measure voltage between VREF and SIG RTN circuits at the DPFE sensor vehicle harness connector. All others: — Disconnect DPFE sensor. — Key on. — Measure voltage between VREF and SIG RTN circuits at the TP sensor vehicle harness connector. • **Is voltage between 4.0 and 6.0 volts?**		Yes No	► ►	Key off. — For DPFE DTC: REPLACE TP sensor. — All others: REPLACE DPFE sensor. RECONNECT all components. RERUN Quick Test. — For voltage less than 4.0 volts: GO to C5. — For voltage greater than 6.0 volts: GO to C16 (to check VREF short to power).
C5	**CHECK FOR VREF AT OTHER SENSOR**			
• TP and DPFE sensors disconnected. • Key on, engine off. • For DPFE DTC: — Measure voltage between the VREF and SIG RTN circuits at the TP sensor vehicle harness connector. All others: — Measure voltage between the VREF and SIG RTN circuits at the DPFE sensor vehicle harness connector. • **Is voltage between 4.0 and 6.0 volts?**		Yes No	► ►	Key off. SERVICE open VREF circuit to other sensor (TP or DPFE). RECONNECT all components. RERUN Quick Test. Key off. GO to C6 (to check VPWR to PCM, and VREF for short to ground and continuity from PCM).
C6	**CHECK VPWR TO PCM**			
• Key off. • TP and DPFE sensors disconnected. • Disconnect PCM. Inspect for damaged or pushed out pins, corrosion, loose wires, etc. Service as necessary. • Install breakout box, leave PCM disconnected. • Key on, engine off. • Measure voltage between Test Pin 71 (VPWR) and Test Pin 77 (PWR GND). • **Is voltage greater than 10.5 volts?**		Yes No	► ►	GO to C7. SERVICE open VPWR circuit between PCM and splice to IAC solenoid. REMOVE breakout box. RECONNECT all components. RERUN Quick Test.

FM0159401180030X

Fig. 174   Test C: Reference Voltage (Part 3 of 6). 1994

TEST STEP		RESULT	►	ACTION TO TAKE
C7	**CHECK VREF CONTINUITY TO PCM**			
• Key off. • TP and DPFE sensors disconnected. • Breakout box installed, PCM disconnected. • Measure resistance between Test Pin 90 (VREF) and the VREF circuit at the TP sensor vehicle harness connector. • **Is resistance less than 5.0 ohms?**		Yes No	► ►	GO to C8. SERVICE open VREF circuit between PCM and splice to TP / DPFE sensors. REMOVE breakout box. RECONNECT all components. RERUN Quick Test.
C8	**CHECK VREF CIRCUIT FOR SHORT TO GROUND OR SIG RTN**			
• Key off. • TP and DPFE sensors disconnected. • Breakout box installed, PCM disconnected. • Disconnect Scan Tool from DLC. • Measure resistance between Test Pin 90 (VREF) and Test Pins 51, 103 (PWR GND) and 91 (SIG RTN). • **Is each resistance greater than 10,000 ohms?**		Yes No	► ►	REPLACE PCM. REMOVE breakout box. RECONNECT all components. RERUN Quick Test. SERVICE VREF short to ground. REMOVE breakout box. RECONNECT all components. RERUN Quick Test.

FM0159401180040X

Fig. 174   Test C: Reference Voltage (Part 4 of 6). 1994

TEST STEP	RESULT	▶	ACTION TO TAKE
C11 CHECK SIG RTN CIRCUIT CONTINUITY TO GROUND AT TP AND DPFE SENSORS • Key off. • TP or DPFE sensors disconnected. • Disconnect the DPFE or TP sensor (so both are disconnected). • Disconnect Scan Tool from DLC. • Measure resistance between the SIG RTN circuit at the TP sensor vehicle harness connector and the battery negative post. Note resistance. • Measure resistance between the SIG RTN circuit at the DPFE sensor vehicle harness connector and the battery negative post. Note resistance. • **Are both resistances less than 5.0 ohms?**	Yes No	▶ ▶	SIG RTN/PWR GND circuits are OK. VERIFY results of **C1** and **C2** (the battery must be at the same state of charge for those tests). RERUN Quick Test to verify DTC/symptom. If BOTH resistance readings were GREATER than 5.0 ohms: — GO to **C12** (to check common SIG RTN/PWR GND circuits. If only ONE resistance reading was GREATER than 5.0 ohms: — SERVICE open SIG RTN circuit to the appropriate sensor. RECONNECT all components. RERUN Quick Test.
C12 CHECK SIG RTN CIRCUIT CONTINUITY TO PCM • Key off. • Scan Tool disconnected. • TP and DPFE sensors disconnected. • Disconnect PCM. Inspect for damaged or pushed out pins, corrosion, loose wires, etc. Service as necessary. • Install breakout box, leave PCM disconnected. • Measure resistance between the SIG RTN circuit at the TP sensor vehicle harness connector and Test Pin 91 (SIG RTN) at the breakout box. • **Is resistance less than 5.0 ohms?**	Yes No	▶ ▶	GO to **C13**. SERVICE open SIG RTN circuit between the PCM and splice to TP/DPFE sensors. REMOVE breakout box. RECONNECT all components. RERUN Quick Test.

Fig. 174   Test C: Reference Voltage (Part 5 of 6). 1994

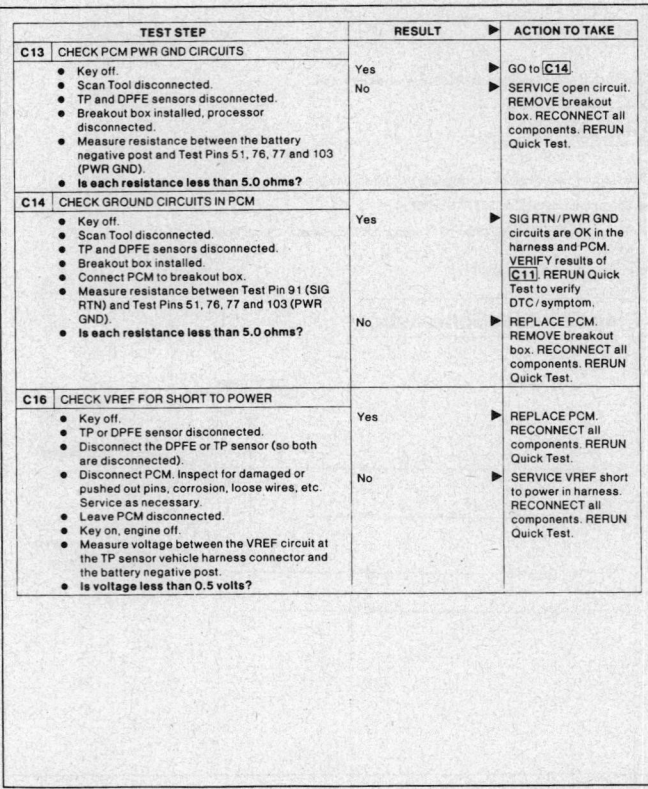

TEST STEP	RESULT	▶	ACTION TO TAKE
C13 CHECK PCM PWR GND CIRCUITS • Key off. • Scan Tool disconnected. • TP and DPFE sensors disconnected. • Breakout box installed, processor disconnected. • Measure resistance between the battery negative post and Test Pins 51, 76, 77 and 103 (PWR GND). • **Is each resistance less than 5.0 ohms?**	Yes No	▶ ▶	GO to **C14**. SERVICE open circuit. REMOVE breakout box. RECONNECT all components. RERUN Quick Test.
C14 CHECK GROUND CIRCUITS IN PCM • Key off. • Scan Tool disconnected. • TP and DPFE sensors disconnected. • Breakout box installed. • Connect PCM to breakout box. • Measure resistance between Test Pin 91 (SIG RTN) and Test Pins 51, 76, 77 and 103 (PWR GND). • **Is each resistance less than 5.0 ohms?**	Yes No	▶ ▶	SIG RTN/PWR GND circuits are OK in the harness and PCM. VERIFY results of **C11**. RERUN Quick Test to verify DTC/symptom. REPLACE PCM. REMOVE breakout box. RECONNECT all components. RERUN Quick Test.
C16 CHECK VREF FOR SHORT TO POWER • Key off. • TP or DPFE sensor disconnected. • Disconnect the DPFE or TP sensor (so both are disconnected). • Disconnect PCM. Inspect for damaged or pushed out pins, corrosion, loose wires, etc. Service as necessary. • Leave DPFE sensor disconnected. • Key on, engine off. • Measure voltage between the VREF circuit at the TP sensor vehicle harness connector and the battery negative post. • **Is voltage less than 0.5 volts?**	Yes No	▶ ▶	REPLACE PCM. RECONNECT all components. RERUN Quick Test. SERVICE VREF short to power in harness. RECONNECT all components. RERUN Quick Test.

FM0159401180060X

Fig. 174   Test C: Reference Voltage (Part 6 of 6). 1994

Pinpoint Test Schematic

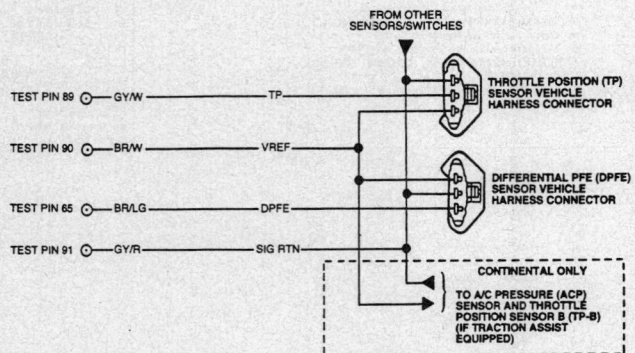

Fig. 175   Test C: Reference Voltage (Part 1 of 6). 1995

TEST STEP	RESULT	▶	ACTION TO TAKE
C1 WAS VREF GREATER THAN 6.0 VOLTS? • Was VREF greater than 6.0 volts when measured in the previous test step?	Yes No	▶ ▶	GO to **C24** (to check VREF for short to power). GO to **C2**.
C2 CHECK BATTERY VOLTAGE • Key on, engine off. • Measure voltage across battery terminals. • **Is voltage greater than 10.5 volts?**	Yes No	▶ ▶	GO to **C3**. Key off. REFER to the Charging/Electrical Group in the Service Manual to service discharged battery.
C3 CHECK SIG RTN TO TP, DPFE, ACP OR TP-B SENSOR • Key on, engine off. • Sensor where VREF check failed disconnected. • Measure voltage between battery positive post and SIG RTN circuit at the appropriate sensor vehicle harness connector. • **Is voltage greater than 10.5 volts and within 1.0 volt of battery voltage?**	Yes No	▶ ▶	GO to **C4**. SIG RTN/PWR GND fault present. GO to **C16**.
C4 CAN THE ECT PID BE ACCESSED? NOTE: The purpose of this test step is to determine if the Scan Tool is able to communicate with the PCM. • Key on, engine off. • Attempt to access the ECT PID. • **Can the ECT PID be accessed?**	Yes No	▶ ▶	GO to **C12** (to check VREF for opens). GO to **C5** (to check for VPWR, and VREF for shorts).

Fig. 175   Test C: Reference Voltage (Part 2 of 6). 1995

Fig. 175 Test C: Reference Voltage (Part 3 of 6). 1995

TEST STEP	RESULT	▶	ACTION TO TAKE
C5 CHECK FOR VPWR TO IAC SOLENOID			
• Key off. • TP sensor disconnected. • Disconnect Idle Air Control (IAC) solenoid. • Key on, engine off. • Measure voltage between the VPWR circuit at the IAC vehicle harness connector and the battery negative post. • Key off. • Was voltage greater than 10.5 volts? IDLE AIR CONTROL (IAC) VEHICLE HARNESS CONNECTOR — VPWR (R)	Yes No	▶ ▶	RECONNECT IAC solenoid. GO to C6. VPWR is not present. RECONNECT TP sensor. For applications with EEC-V Power Relay inside CCRM (Mustang, Thunderbird/Cougar): GO to Pinpoint Test Step X1. All others: GO to Pinpoint Test Step B1.
C6 CHECK FOR SHORTED DPFE SENSOR			
• Key off. • Disconnect DPFE sensor. • Key on, engine off. • TP sensor disconnected. • Again measure voltage between VREF and SIG RTN circuits at the TP sensor vehicle harness connector. • Key off. • Was voltage between 4.0 and 6.0 volts?	Yes No	▶ ▶	REPLACE DPFE sensor. RECONNECT all components. RERUN Quick Test. For Continental: GO to C7. For all others: GO to C9.
C7 CHECK FOR SHORTED ACP SENSOR (CONTINENTAL)			
• Key off. • TP and DPFE sensors disconnected. • Disconnect ACP sensor. • Key on, engine off. • Again measure voltage between the VREF and SIG RTN circuits at the TP sensor vehicle harness connector. • Key off. • Was voltage between 4.0 and 6.0 volts?	Yes No	▶ ▶	REPLACE ACP sensor. RECONNECT all components. RERUN Quick Test. If vehicle is equipped with optional Traction Assist (with TP-B sensor): GO to C8. All others: GO to C9.

Fig. 175 Test C: Reference Voltage (Part 4 of 6). 1995

TEST STEP	RESULT	▶	ACTION TO TAKE
C8 CHECK FOR SHORTED TP-B SENSOR			
• Key off. • TP, DPFE and ACP sensors disconnected. • Disconnect Throttle Position sensor B (TP-B). • Key on, engine off. • Again measure voltage between VREF and SIG RTN circuits at the TP sensor vehicle harness connector. • Key off. • Was voltage between 4.0 and 6.0 volts?	Yes No	▶ ▶	REPLACE TP-B sensor. RECONNECT all components. RERUN Quick Test. GO to C9.
C9 CHECK VPWR TO PCM			
• Key off. • TP and DPFE sensors disconnected. • ACP and TP-B sensors disconnected (Continental only, if equipped). • Disconnect PCM. Inspect for damaged or pushed out pins, corrosion, loose wires, etc. Service as necessary. • Install breakout box, leave PCM disconnected. • Key on, engine off. • Measure voltage between Test Pin 71 (VPWR) and Test Pin 77 (PWR GND). • Is voltage greater than 10.5 volts?	Yes No	▶ ▶	GO to C10. SERVICE open VPWR circuit between PCM and splice to IAC solenoid. REMOVE breakout box. RECONNECT all components. RERUN Quick Test.
C10 CHECK VREF CIRCUIT FOR SHORT TO GROUND OR SIG RTN			
• Key off. • TP and DPFE sensors disconnected. • ACP and TP-B sensors disconnected (Continental, if equipped). • Breakout box installed, PCM disconnected. • Disconnect Scan Tool from DLC. • Measure resistance between Test Pin 90 (VREF) and Test Pins 51 or 103 (PWR GND) and 91 (SIG RTN). • Is each resistance greater than 10,000 ohms?	Yes No	▶ ▶	REPLACE PCM. REMOVE breakout box. RECONNECT all components. RERUN Quick Test. SERVICE VREF short to ground. REMOVE breakout box. RECONNECT all components. RERUN Quick Test.

Fig. 175 Test C: Reference Voltage (Part 5 of 6). 1995

TEST STEP	RESULT	▶	ACTION TO TAKE
C12 CHECK VREF CONTINUITY TO PCM			
• Key off. • Sensor where VREF check failed disconnected. • Disconnect PCM. Inspect for damaged or pushed out pins, corrosion, loose wires, etc. Service as necessary. • Install breakout box, leave PCM disconnected. • Measure resistance between Test Pin 90 (VREF) and the VREF circuit at the appropriate sensor vehicle harness connector. • Is resistance less than 5.0 ohms?	Yes No	▶ ▶	REPLACE PCM. REMOVE breakout box. RECONNECT all components. RERUN Quick Test. SERVICE open VREF circuit. USE the vehicle wiring schematic and DTCs received to help pinpoint the location of the open. REMOVE breakout box. RECONNECT all components. RERUN Quick Test.
C16 CAN THE ECT PID BE ACCESSED?			
NOTE: The purpose of this test step is to determine if the Scan Tool is able to communicate with the PCM. • Key on, engine off. • Attempt to access the ECT PID. • Can the ECT PID be accessed?	Yes No	▶ ▶	GO to C17. GO to C19.
C17 ARE KOEO DTCs PRESENT FOR TWO OR MORE SENSORS/SWITCHES CONNECTED TO THE SIG RTN CIRCUIT?			
• Are KOEO DTCs present for two or more sensors connected to the SIG RTN circuit (refer to the EEC-V schematic in	Yes No	▶ ▶	GO to C18. SERVICE open SIG RTN circuit to the sensor where the VREF check failed. RECONNECT all components. RERUN Quick Test.
C18 CHECK SIG RTN CIRCUIT CONTINUITY TO PCM			
• Key off. • Scan Tool disconnected. • Sensor where VREF check failed disconnected. • Disconnect PCM. Inspect for damaged or pushed out pins, corrosion, loose wires, etc. Service as necessary. • Install breakout box, leave PCM disconnected. • Measure resistance between the SIG RTN circuit at the appropriate sensor vehicle harness connector and Test Pin 91 (SIG RTN) at the breakout box. • Is resistance less than 5.0 ohms?	Yes No	▶ ▶	RECONNECT sensor. GO to C19. SERVICE open SIG RTN circuit. USE the vehicle wiring schematic and DTCs received to help pinpoint the location of the open. REMOVE breakout box. RECONNECT all components. RERUN Quick Test.

Fig. 175 Test C: Reference Voltage (Part 6 of 6). 1995

TEST STEP	RESULT	▶	ACTION TO TAKE
C19 CHECK PCM PWR GND CIRCUITS			
• Key off. • Disconnect Scan Tool from DLC. • Breakout box installed, processor disconnected. • Measure resistance between the battery negative post and Test Pins 51, 76, 77 and 103 (PWR GND). • Is each resistance less than 5.0 ohms?	Yes No	▶ ▶	GO to C20. SERVICE open circuit. REMOVE breakout box. RECONNECT all components. RERUN Quick Test.
C20 CHECK GROUND CIRCUITS IN PCM			
• Key off. • Scan Tool disconnected. • Breakout box installed. • Connect PCM to breakout box. • Measure resistance between Test Pin 91 (SIG RTN) and Test Pins 51, 76, 77 and 103 (PWR GND). • Is each resistance less than 5.0 ohms?	Yes No	▶ ▶	SIG RTN/PWR GND circuits are OK in the harness and PCM. VERIFY results of previous test steps. RERUN Quick Test to verify DTC/symptom. REPLACE PCM. REMOVE breakout box. RECONNECT all components. RERUN Quick Test.
C24 CHECK VREF FOR SHORT TO POWER			
• Key off. • Sensor where VREF check failed disconnected. • Disconnect the DPFE and/or TP sensor (so both are disconnected). • For Continental, also disconnect the ACP sensor, and if Traction Assist equipped, the TP-B sensor. • Disconnect PCM. Inspect for damaged or pushed out pins, corrosion, loose wires, etc. Service as necessary. • Leave PCM disconnected. • Key on, engine off. • Measure voltage between the VREF circuit at the TP sensor vehicle harness connector and the battery negative post. • Is voltage less than 0.5 volts?	Yes No	▶ ▶	REPLACE PCM. RECONNECT all components. RERUN Quick Test. SERVICE VREF short to power in harness. RECONNECT all components. RERUN Quick Test.

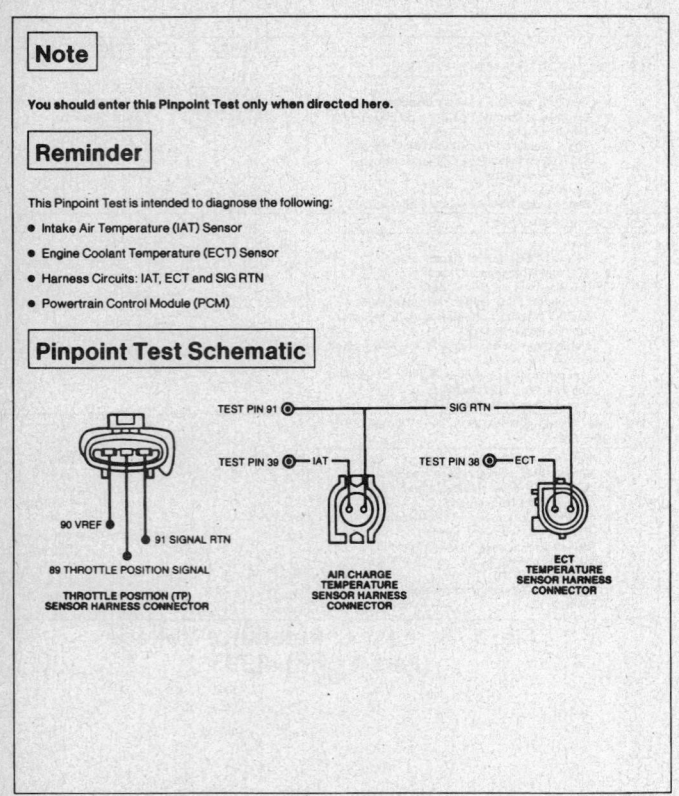

Note

You should enter this Pinpoint Test only when directed here.

Reminder

This Pinpoint Test is intended to diagnose the following:

- Intake Air Temperature (IAT) Sensor
- Engine Coolant Temperature (ECT) Sensor
- Harness Circuits: IAT, ECT and SIG RTN
- Powertrain Control Module (PCM)

Pinpoint Test Schematic

FM0159401181010X

Fig. 176 Test DA: IAT/ECT Sensors (Part 1 of 10). 1994-95

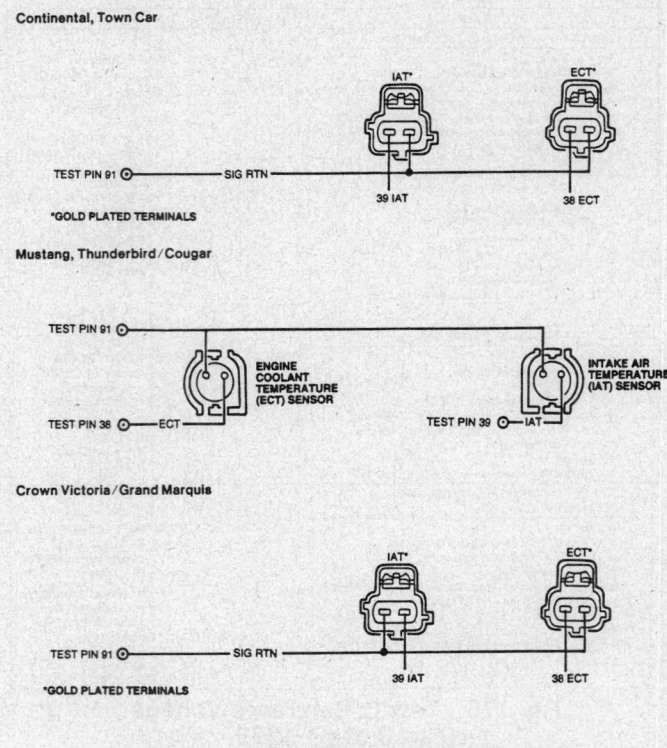

Fig. 176 Test DA: IAT/ECT Sensors (Part 2 of 10). 1994-95

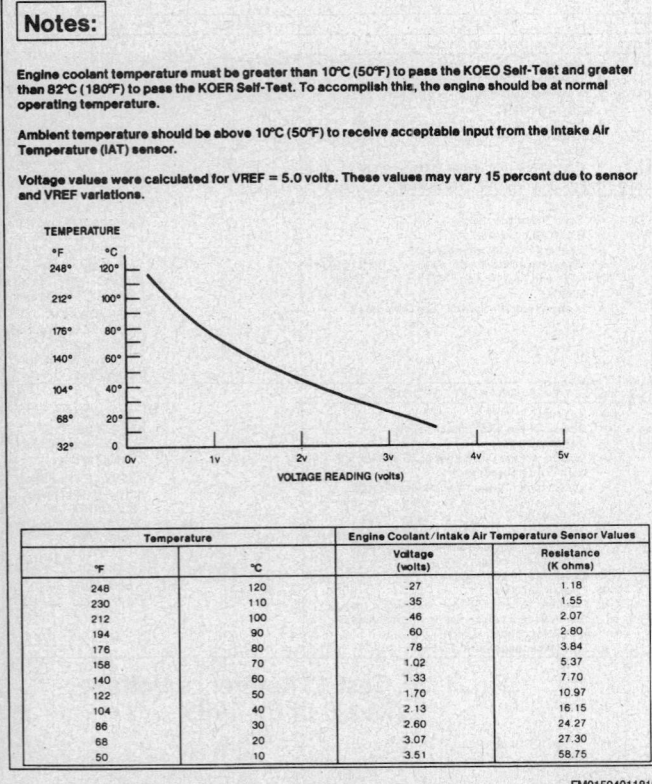

Notes:

Engine coolant temperature must be greater than 10°C (50°F) to pass the KOEO Self-Test and greater than 82°C (180°F) to pass the KOER Self-Test. To accomplish this, the engine should be at normal operating temperature.

Ambient temperature should be above 10°C (50°F) to receive acceptable input from the Intake Air Temperature (IAT) sensor.

Voltage values were calculated for VREF = 5.0 volts. These values may vary 15 percent due to sensor and VREF variations.

Temperature		Engine Coolant/Intake Air Temperature Sensor Values	
°F	°C	Voltage (volts)	Resistance (K ohms)
248	120	.27	1.18
230	110	.35	1.55
212	100	.46	2.07
194	90	.60	2.80
176	80	.78	3.84
158	70	1.02	5.37
140	60	1.33	7.70
122	50	1.70	10.97
104	40	2.13	16.15
86	30	2.60	24.27
68	20	3.07	27.30
50	10	3.51	58.75

FM0159401181020X

Fig. 176 Test DA: IAT/ECT Sensors (Part 3 of 10). 1994-95

	TEST STEP	RESULT	▶	ACTION TO TAKE
DA1	DTC 1116: CHECK OPERATION AND INSTALLATION OF TEMPERATURE SENSOR			
	Diagnostic Trouble Code (DTC) 1116 ECT indicates the temperature sensor is out of Self-Test range. Correct range is 0.3 to 3.7 volts. Possible Causes: — Low coolant level ECT. — Damaged harness connector. — Damaged sensor. • Run engine at 2000 rpm until engine temperature becomes stabilized. For No Starts: — Go to DA3 For vehicles that stall: — Return to Symptom Flow Charts. • Check that upper radiator hose is hot and pressurized. • Rerun Key On Engine Running (KOER) Self-Test. • Is DTC 1116 present?	Yes ▶ No ▶		GO to DA2. Engine was not at closed loop operating conditions. SERVICE any other DTCs as necessary.
DA2	CHECK VREF CIRCUIT VOLTAGE AT TP SENSOR			
	• Refer to schematic at beginning of test. • Key off. • Disconnect Throttle Position (TP) sensor. • Key on, engine off. • Measure the voltage between VREF circuit and SIG RTN circuit at the TP sensor vehicle harness connector. • Is voltage between 4.0 volts and 6.0 volts?	Yes ▶ No ▶		There is sufficient VREF voltage. RECONNECT TP sensor. GO to DA3. GO to Pinpoint Test Step C1.
DA3	CHECK RESISTANCE OF TEMPERATURE SENSOR WITH ENGINE OFF			
	• Key off. • Disconnect suspect temperature sensor. • Measure resistance between sensor Signal Circuit and SIG RTN circuit at the temperature sensor. Refer to the corresponding charts at the beginning of this Pinpoint Test for resistance specifications. • Is resistance within specification?	Yes ▶ No ▶		For ECT sensor with a No Start: Do not service DTC 1116 at this time. RETURN to Symptom Flow Charts. All others: GO to DA4. REPLACE suspect sensor. RECONNECT vehicle harness. RERUN Quick Test.

FM0159401181030X

Fig. 176 Test DA: IAT/ECT Sensors (Part 4 of 10). 1994-95

TEST STEP		RESULT	▶	ACTION TO TAKE
DA4	**CHECK RESISTANCE OF TEMPERATURE SENSOR WITH ENGINE RUNNING**			
	NOTE: **Verify that engine is at operating temperature before taking ECT readings.** • Key off. • Suspect temperature sensor disconnected. • Run engine for two minutes at 2000 rpms. • Measure resistance between sensor Signal Circuit and SIG RTN circuit at the temperature sensor. Refer to the corresponding chart at the beginning of this Pinpoint Test for resistance specification. • **Is resistance within specification?**	Yes No	▶ ▶	REPLACE PCM. RECONNECT vehicle harness. RERUN Quick Test. REPLACE suspect sensor. RECONNECT vehicle harness. RERUN Quick Test.
DA10	**DTC 0118 OR 0113: SIMULATE OPPOSITE SIGNAL TO PCM**			
	Diagnostic Trouble Code (DTC) 0118 (ECT) or 0113 (IAT) indicates the sensor signal is greater than the Self-Test maximum. The maximum for ECT and IAT sensor is 4.6 volts or -46°F (-50°C). Possible Causes: — Open in harness (IAT or ECT). — Improper harness connection. — Damaged sensor. — Damaged PCM. • Key off. • Disconnect suspect temperature sensor. • Connect a jumper wire between the sensor signal circuit and SIG RTN circuit at the temperature sensor vehicle harness connector. • Scan Tool installed. • Key on. NOTE: If a communication link error is displayed, remove jumper wire immediately and go to DA12. • Access ECT or IAT PID. • Is the ECT or IAT PID less than 0.2 volts (greater than 248°F / 120°C)?	Yes No	▶ ▶	REPLACE suspect sensor. REMOVE jumper wire. RECONNECT vehicle harness. RERUN Quick Test. REMOVE jumper wire. GO to DA11.

Fig. 176   Test DA: IAT/ECT Sensors (Part 5 of 10). 1994-95

TEST STEP		RESULT	▶	ACTION TO TAKE
DA11	**CHECK CONTINUITY OF SENSOR SIGNAL AND SIG RTN CIRCUITS**			
	• Key off. • Suspect temperature sensor disconnected. • Disconnect PCM. Inspect for damaged or pushed out pins, corrosion, loose wires, etc. Service as necessary. • Install breakout box, leave PCM disconnected. • Measure resistance between sensor signal circuit at the temperature sensor vehicle harness connector and Test Pin 38 (ECT) or 39 (IAT) at the breakout box. • Measure resistance between SIG RTN circuit at the temperature sensor vehicle harness connector and Test Pin 91 (SIG RTN) at the breakout box. • Is each resistance less than 5.0 ohms?	Yes No	▶ ▶	REPLACE PCM. REMOVE breakout box. RECONNECT components. RERUN Quick Test. SERVICE open circuits. REMOVE breakout box. RECONNECT all components. RERUN Quick Test.
DA12	**CHECK FOR SENSOR SIGNAL SHORTED TO VREF**			
	• Key off. • Suspect temperature sensor disconnected. • Disconnect PCM. Inspect for damaged or pushed out pins, corrosion, loose wires, etc. Service as necessary. • Install breakout box, leave PCM disconnected. • Measure resistance between sensor signal circuit Test Pin 38 (ECT) or 39 (IAT) and VREF at the breakout box. • Is each resistance greater than 10,000 ohms?	Yes No	▶ ▶	REPLACE PCM. RERUN Quick Test. LOCATE and REPAIR short to VREF. RERUN Quick Test.

Fig. 176   Test DA: IAT/ECT Sensors (Part 6 of 10). 1994-95

TEST STEP		RESULT	▶	ACTION TO TAKE
DA20	**DTC 0112 OR 0117: SIMULATE OPPOSITE SIGNAL TO PCM**			
	Diagnostic Trouble Code (DTC) 0117 ECT or 0112 IAT indicates the sensor signal is less than Self-Test minimum. The IAT and ECT sensor minimum is 0.2 volt 250°F (121°C). Possible Causes: — Grounded circuit in harness. — Damaged sensor. — Improper harness connection. — Damaged PCM. • Key off. • Disconnect vehicle harness from suspect sensor. Inspect for damaged or pushed out pins, corrosion, loose wires, etc. Service as necessary. • Scan Tool installed. • Key on. • Access ECT or IAT PID. • **Is the ECT or IAT PID more than 4.2 volts (less than -40°F/°C)?**	Yes No	▶ ▶	REPLACE sensor. RECONNECT harness. RERUN Quick Test. GO to DA21.
DA21	**CHECK VREF CIRCUIT VOLTAGE AT TP SENSOR**			
	• Refer to schematic at beginning of test. • Key off. • Disconnect TP sensor. • Key on, engine off. • Measure the voltage between VREF circuit and SIG RTN circuit at the TP sensor vehicle harness connector. • **Is voltage between 4.0 and 6.0 volts?**	Yes No	▶ ▶	There is sufficient VREF voltage. RECONNECT TP sensor. GO to DA22. GO to Pinpoint Test Step C1.
DA22	**SIGNAL CIRCUIT FOR SHORT TO GROUND**			
	• Key off. • Suspect temperature sensor disconnected. • Disconnect PCM. Inspect for damaged or pushed out pins, corrosion, loose wires, etc. Service as necessary. • Install breakout box, PCM disconnected. • Measure resistance between Test Pin 38 (ECT) or 39 (IAT) and Test Pin 24 or 51 (PWR GND) at the breakout box. • **Is each resistance greater than 10,000 ohms?**	Yes No	▶ ▶	REPLACE PCM. REMOVE breakout box. RECONNECT all components. RERUN Quick Test. SERVICE short circuit. REMOVE breakout box. RECONNECT all components. RERUN Quick Test.

Fig. 176   Test DA: IAT/ECT Sensors (Part 7 of 10). 1994-95

TEST STEP		RESULT	▶	ACTION TO TAKE
DA90	**DTCS 0112, 1112, 0113, 0117, 1117 OR 0118: INTERMITTENT CHECK**			
	Diagnostic Trouble Codes (DTCa) 0112, 1112 or 0113 (IAT) and 0117, 1117 or 0118 (ECT) that are not received during On-Demand Self-Test, but are accessible during the monitor code retrieval may be intermittent and should be diagnosed as follows: Possible causes: — Damaged harness. — Damaged harness connector. — Damaged IAT or ECT sensor. — Low coolant (ECT). — Damaged PCM. • Key off. • Scan Tool connected. • Key on. • Monitor the ECT or IAT PID. • While observing the appropriate PID, perform the following: — Tap on the sensor to simulate road shock. — Wiggle the sensor connector. • **Is there any large change in the temperature reading?**	Yes No	▶ ▶	DISCONNECT and INSPECT connectors. If OK, REPLACE the sensor. COMPLETE PCM reset to clear DTCs (REFER to Powertrain Control Module (PCM) Reset). RERUN Quick Test. For Continuous DTCs 1112 and 1117, COMPLETE Comprehensive Component Monitor Drive Cycle (REFER to Drive Cycles). GO to DA91.
DA91	**CHECK EEC-V WIRING HARNESS**			
	• Still monitoring PID. • While observing the appropriate PID, perform the following: — Hold the vehicle harness close to the sensor connector. Wiggle, shake and bend small sections of wiring harness while working toward the PCM. • **Is there any change in the temperature reading?**	Yes No	▶ ▶	ISOLATE fault. SERVICE as necessary. COMPLETE PCM reset to clear DTCs (REFER to Powertrain Control Module (PCM) Reset). RERUN Quick Test. For Continuous DTCs 1112 and 1117, COMPLETE Comprehensive Component Monitor Drive Cycle (REFER to Drive Cycles). GO to DA92.

Fig. 176   Test DA: IAT/ECT Sensors (Part 8 of 10). 1994-95

	TEST STEP	RESULT	▶	ACTION TO TAKE
DA92	CHECK PCM AND VEHICLE HARNESS CONNECTOR • Key off. • Disconnect PCM. • Disconnect sensor connector. Inspect for spread terminals, pushed out pins and loose or crimped wires. • **Are connectors and terminals OK?**	Yes	▶	Fault is not present at this time. COMPLETE PCM reset to clear DTCs (REFER to Powertrain Control Module (PCM) Reset). RERUN Quick Test. For Continuous DTCs 1112 and 1117, COMPLETE Comprehensive Component Monitor Drive Cycle (REFER to Drive Cycles).
		No	▶	SERVICE as necessary. COMPLETE PCM reset to clear DTCs (REFER to Powertrain Control Module (PCM) Reset). RERUN Quick Test. For Continuous DTCs 1112 or 1117, COMPLETE Comprehensive Component Monitor Drive Cycle (REFER to Drive Cycles).

FM0159401181080X

Fig. 176   Test DA: IAT/ECT Sensors (Part 9 of 10). 1994-95

	TEST STEP	RESULT	▶	ACTION TO TAKE
DA100	DTC 0125: EXCESSIVE TIME TO ENTER CLOSED LOOP FUEL CONTROL Diagnostic Trouble Code (DTC) 0125 indicates the ECT sensor has not achieved the required temperature level to enter closed loop operating conditions within a specified amount of time after starting engine. Possible Causes: — Leaky or stuck open thermostat. — Low coolant. • Check coolant level. • **Is the coolant level fill correct?**	Yes	▶	Thermostat Diagnostics
		No	▶	FILL to proper level. COMPLETE PCM reset to clear DTCs (REFER to Powertrain Control Module (PCM) Reset). COMPLETE Comprehensive Component Monitor Drive Cycle (REFER to Drive Cycles). CHECK for DTCs.

FM0159401181090X

Fig. 176   Test DA: IAT/ECT Sensors (Part 10 of 10). 1994-95

Note

You should enter this Pinpoint Test only when directed here.

Remember

This Pinpoint Test is intended to diagnose the following:

• Mass Air Flow (MAF) Sensor (12B579)
• Harness Circuits:

 MAF SIG, MAF RTN (signal return to MAF sensor), Vehicle Power (VPWR), and Power Ground (PWR GND)

• Powertrain Control Module (PCM) (12A650)

Tables and Charts

	VOLTAGE TO MASS AIR FLOW CONVERSION TABLE					
volts	2.3L Ranger 3.0L Ranger 3.0L Windstar	Mustang Crown Victoria/ Grand Marquis Town Car	3.8L Windstar 4.0L Ranger	Continental	Thunderbird/ Cougar
3.90v	78.41 gm/sec	151.15 gm/sec	133.30 gm/sec	165.00 gm/sec	137.21 gm/sec
1.96v	16.90 gm/sec	30.94 gm/sec	25.78 gm/sec	61.84 gm/sec	29.44 gm/sec
1.00v	4.83 gm/sec	9.57 gm/sec	6.99 gm/sec	8.45 gm/sec	8.39 gm/sec
0.60v	1.55 gm/sec	3.32 gm/sec	2.21 gm/sec	2.57 gm/sec	2.66 gm/sec
0.39v	0.85 gm/sec	2.28 gm/sec	1.40 gm/sec	1.60 gm/sec	1.73 gm/sec
0.34v	0.74 gm/sec	1.99 gm/sec	1.22 gm/sec	1.39 gm/sec	1.51 gm/sec

FM0159501182010A

Fig. 177   Test DC: MAF Sensor (Part 1 of 10). 1994-95

Pinpoint Test Schematics

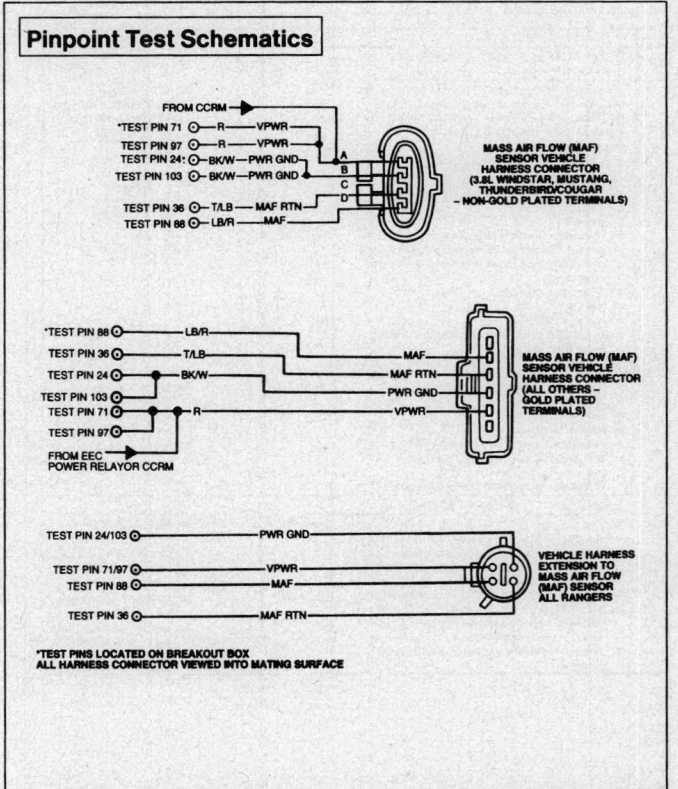

FM0159501182020A

Fig. 177   Test DC: MAF Sensor (Part 2 of 10). 1994-95

TEST STEP		RESULT	▶	ACTION TO TAKE
DC2	CONTINUOUS MEMORY DTC P1100: CHECK FOR MAF CIRCUIT INTERMITTENT VOLTAGE INPUT			
Continuous Memory DTC P1100 indicates the MAF sensor signal went below 0.39 volts or above ▓▓▓ volts (refer to Voltage to Mass Air Flow Conversion Table at beginning of this Pinpoint Test) sometime during the last 40 warm-up cycles.		Yes	▶	DISCONNECT and INSPECT the MAF sensor connector. If OK, REPLACE the MAF sensor. RESET KAM
Possible causes: — MAF sensor connector with poor continuity. — MAF harness with poor continuity. — MAF harness intermittent short. — MAF sensor internal intermittent open or short. ● Start engine and bring to idle.		No	▶	RERUN Quick Test. GO to DC3.
NOTE: If a stabilized idle is not at least 700 rpm, go to Section 4, Symptom Flow Charts. ● Scan Tool connected. ● Run throttle up to 1500 rpm for 5 seconds, and bring back to idle. ● Access MAF V PID (MAF PID) for a fault indication while performing the following: — Lightly tap on MAF sensor and wiggle harness connector to simulate road shock. ● Is the MAF V PID (MAF PID) changing below the minimum 0.39 volts or above a maximum ▓▓ volts (refer to Voltage to Mass Air Flow Conversion Table at beginning of this Pinpoint Test)?				

Fig. 177 Test DC: MAF Sensor (Part 3 of 10). 1994-95

FM0159501182030A

TEST STEP		RESULT	▶	ACTION TO TAKE
DC3	CHECK MAF HARNESS TO PCM FOR INTERMITTENT OPENS OR SHORTS			
● Key off. ● Disconnect PCM. Inspect for damaged or pushed out pins, corrosion, loose wires, etc. Service as necessary. ● Install breakout box, reconnect PCM. ● Key on, engine off. ● Connect DVOM between Test Pin 88 (MAF SIG) and Test Pin 36 (MAF RTN) at the breakout box.		Yes	▶	ISOLATE fault and SERVICE as necessary. RECONNECT all components. RESET KAM RERUN Quick Test.
● While viewing DVOM, do the following: — Grasp the vehicle harness closest to the MAF sensor connector. — Shake and bend a small section of the harness all the way to the dash panel. — Wiggle, shake and bend the harness from the dash panel to the PCM. ● Is the voltage changing below the minimum 0.39 volts or above the maximum 4.60 volts?		No	▶	Unable to duplicate and / or identify fault at this time. GO to Pinpoint Test Step Z1 with the following data: MAF V PID (MAF PID) and list of Possible Causes.

Fig. 177 Test DC: MAF Sensor (Part 4 of 10). 1994-95

FM0159501182040A

TEST STEP		RESULT	▶	ACTION TO TAKE
DC6	CONTINUOUS MEMORY AND KOER DTC P0102: CHECK MAF SIGNAL LOW INPUT TO PCM			
Diagnostic Trouble Code (DTC) P0102 indicates the MAF signal went below 0.39 volts (refer to Voltage to Mass Air Flow Conversion Table at beginning of this Pinpoint Test) sometime during normal engine operation (Continuous) or during Key On Engine Running (KOER) Self-Test.		Yes	▶	The MAF SIG voltage is lower than acceptable minimum. GO to DC7.
Possible causes: — Damaged MAF sensor. — MAF sensor disconnected. — MAF circuit open. — VPWR circuit open. — PWR GND circuit open. — MAF RTN circuit open. — MAF circuit shorted to ground. — Air Intake Leak (near MAF sensor). — Throttle Position (TP) system (possible closed throttle indication). — Damaged PCM.		No	▶	For KOER reading between 0.60 and 1.00 (refer to Voltage to Mass Air Flow Conversion Table at beginning of this Pinpoint Test) : GO to DC15. All others: GO to DC2.
● Check broken / loose air outlet tube clamps (throttle body and air cleaner assembly ends), cracks / holes in air outlet tube, worn gaskets between MAF sensor and air cleaner assembly. Service as necessary. ● Start engine and bring to idle.				
NOTE: If a KOER DTC P0505 is present, go to Section 5, Powertrain Diagnostic Trouble Code Charts. If a stabilized idle is not at least 700 rpm, go to Symptom Flow Charts. For 2.3L A/T Rangers, if the ▓▓▓▓▓▓ and cannot maintain an idle, go to DC8.				
● Run engine up 1500 rpm for 5 seconds, then bring it back to idle. ● Access MAF V PID (MAF PID) with a Scan Tool. ● Is the MAF V PID (MAF PID) less than 0.39 volts (refer to Voltage to Mass Air Flow Conversion Table at beginning of this Pinpoint Test)?				

Fig. 177 Test DC: MAF Sensor (Part 5 of 10). 1994-95

FM0159501182050A

TEST STEP		RESULT	▶	ACTION TO TAKE
DC7	CHECK VPWR CIRCUIT VOLTAGE			
● Key off. ● Disconnect MAF sensor. ● Key on, engine off. ● Measure the voltage between VPWR circuit at the MAF sensor vehicle harness connector and the battery negative post. ● Is the voltage greater than 10.5 volts?		Yes	▶	VPWR harness circuit from CCRM to MAF sensor OK. GO to DC8.
		No	▶	Service open VPWR circuit. RESET KAM RERUN Quick Test.
DC8	CHECK CONTINUITY OF VPWR CIRCUIT			
● Key off. ● MAF sensor disconnected. ● Disconnect PCM. Inspect for damaged or pushed out pins, corrosion, loose wires, etc. Service as necessary. ● Install breakout box, leave PCM disconnected. ● Measure resistance between VPWR circuit at the MAF sensor vehicle harness connector and Test Pin 71 or 97 (VPWR) at the breakout box. ● Is resistance less than 5.0 ohms?		Yes	▶	VPWR harness circuit to PCM is OK. GO to DC9.
		No	▶	Service open in VPWR harness circuit. REMOVE breakout box. RECONNECT all components. RESET KAM RERUN Quick Test.
DC9	CHECK MAF CIRCUIT FOR SHORTS TO GROUND AND MAF RTN CIRCUIT			
● Key off. ● MAF sensor disconnected. ● Breakout box installed, PCM disconnected. ● Disconnect Scan Tool from Data Link Connector (DLC). ● Measure the resistance between Test Pin 88 (MAF SIG) and Test Pins 36 (MAF RTN) and 24 or 103 (PWR GND) at the breakout box. ● Is each resistance greater than 10,000 ohms?		Yes	▶	MAF SIG, MAF RTN and GROUND harness circuits to PCM are OK. RECONNECT Scan Tool. GO to DC10.
		No	▶	Service short circuit between MAF SIG and GROUND or MAF RTN. REMOVE breakout box. RECONNECT all components. RESET KAM RERUN Quick Test.

Fig. 177 Test DC: MAF Sensor (Part 6 of 10). 1994-95

FM0159501182060A

TEST STEP	RESULT	▶	ACTION TO TAKE
DC10 CHECK CONTINUITY OF MAF SIG CIRCUIT • Key off. • MAF sensor disconnected. • Breakout box installed, PCM disconnected. • Measure resistance between MAF circuit at the MAF sensor vehicle harness connector and Test Pin 88 (MAF SIG) at the breakout box. • Is resistance less than 5.0 ohms?	Yes No	▶ ▶	MAF SIG harness circuit to PCM is OK. GO to DC11. SERVICE open in MAF SIG harness circuit. REMOVE breakout box. RECONNECT all components. RESET KAM RERUN Quick Test.
DC11 CHECK PWR GND CIRCUIT TO MAF SENSOR • Key off. • MAF sensor disconnected. • Breakout box installed. • PCM connected to breakout box. • Key on, engine off. • Measure the voltage between VPWR circuit and PWR GND circuit at the MAF sensor vehicle harness connector. • Is the voltage greater than 10.5 volts?	Yes No	▶ ▶	PWR GND harness circuit from battery negative post to MAF sensor is OK. GO to DC13. GO to DC12.
DC12 CHECK PWR GND CIRCUIT CONTINUITY • Key off. • MAF sensor disconnected. • Breakout box installed. • Disconnect PCM. • Disconnect Scan Tool from DLC. • Measure the resistance between PWR GND circuit at the MAF sensor vehicle harness connector and battery negative post. • Is the resistance less than 10 ohms?	Yes No	▶ ▶	PWR GND harness circuit to MAF sensor is OK. RECONNECT Scan Tool. GO to DC13. SERVICE open in PWR GND harness circuit. REMOVE breakout box. RECONNECT all components. RESET KAM RERUN Quick Test.

FM0159501182070A

Fig. 177   Test DC: MAF Sensor (Part 7 of 10). 1994-95

TEST STEP	RESULT	▶	ACTION TO TAKE
DC13 CHECK MAF RTN CIRCUIT CONTINUITY • Key off. • MAF sensor disconnected. • Breakout box installed, PCM disconnected. • Measure the resistance between MAF RTN circuit at the MAF sensor vehicle harness connector and Test Pin 36 (MAF RTN) at the breakout box. • Is the resistance less than 5.0 ohms?	Yes No	▶ ▶	MAF RTN harness circuit to PCM is OK. GO to DC14. SERVICE open in MAF RTN harness circuit. REMOVE breakout box. RECONNECT all components. RESET KAM RERUN Quick Test.
DC14 CHECK MAF CIRCUIT FOR SHORT TO GROUND IN PCM • Key off. • MAF sensor disconnected. • Breakout box installed. • Reconnect PCM to breakout box. • Disconnect Scan Tool from DLC (if applicable). • Measure the resistance between Test Pin 88 (MAF SIG) and Test Pins 36 (MAF RTN) and 24 or 103 (PWR GND) at the breakout box. • Is each resistance greater than 10,000 ohms?	Yes No	▶ ▶	RECONNECT Scan Tool. GO to DC15. MAF SIG shorted to PWR GND or MAF RTN in the PCM. REPLACE the PCM. REMOVE breakout box. RECONNECT MAF sensor. RESET KAM RERUN Quick Test.
DC15 CHECK MAF CIRCUIT OUTPUT • Key off. • MAF sensor connected. • Breakout box installed, PCM connected. • Key on, engine running. NOTE: If a stabilized idle is not at least 700 rpm, go to Symptom Flow Charts. For 2.3L A/T Rangers, if the vehicle stalls and cannot maintain an idle, replace PCM. • Measure the voltage between Test Pin 88 (MAF SIG) at the breakout box and battery negative post. • Is the voltage at idle between 0.34 and 1.96 volts?	Yes No	▶ ▶	MAF SIG to the PCM is OK. GO to DC16. MAF SIG is open or shorted to MAF RTN in the MAF sensor. REPLACE MAF sensor. REMOVE breakout box. RECONNECT PCM. RESET KAM RERUN Quick Test.

FM0159501182080A

Fig. 177   Test DC: MAF Sensor (Part 8 of 10). 1994-95

TEST STEP	RESULT	▶	ACTION TO TAKE
DC16 VERIFY MAF CIRCUIT INPUT AND OUTPUT • Key off. • MAF sensor connected. • Breakout box installed, PCM connected. • Key on, engine running. • Measure the voltage between Test Pin 88 (MAF SIG) and Test Pin 36 (MAF RTN) at the breakout box. • Is the voltage between 0.34 and 1.96 volts?	Yes No	▶ ▶	MAF RTN in the MAF sensor is OK. GO to DC17. MAF RTN is open in the PCM. REPLACE MAF sensor. REMOVE breakout box. RECONNECT PCM. RESET KAM RERUN Quick Test.
DC17 CHECK MAF CIRCUIT OUTPUT WITH SCAN TOOL • Key off. • MAF sensor connected. • Breakout box installed, PCM connected. • Key on, engine running. • Access MAF V PID (MAF PID) with a Scan Tool at idle. • Is the MAF V PID (MAF PID) between 0.34 and 1.96 volts (refer to Voltage to Mass Air Flow Conversion Table at the beginning of this Pinpoint Test)?	Yes No	▶ ▶	UNABLE to duplicate and/or identify fault at this time. GO to Pinpoint Test Step Z1 with the following data: MAF V PID (MAF PID) and list of possible causes. MAF SIG or MAF RTN is open or shorted in the PCM. REPLACE PCM. REMOVE breakout box. RECONNECT PCM. RESET KAM RERUN Quick Test.

FM0159501182090A

Fig. 177   Test DC: MAF Sensor (Part 9 of 10). 1994-95

TEST STEP	RESULT	▶	ACTION TO TAKE
DC20 DTC P0103: CHECK MAF SIGNAL HIGH INPUT TO PCM Diagnostic Trouble Code (DTC) P0103 indicates the MAF Signal went above 3.90 volts (refer to Voltage to Mass Air Flow Conversion Table at the beginning of this Pinpoint Test) sometime during normal engine operation (Continuous), during Key On Engine Off Self-Test, or during Key On Engine Running Self-Test. NOTE: DTC P0103 could be generated by foreign material blocking the MAF sensor screen causing an air flow restriction. If contaminants are found on the screen, check air filter installation in air cleaner tray and proper sealing of air cleaner and air tubes before proceeding. Rerun Quick Test after repair. Possible causes: — Blocked MAF sensor screen. — Damaged MAF sensor. — MAF SIG harness short to VPWR. — Damaged PCM. • Start engine and bring to idle. NOTE: If a KOER DTC P0505 is present, go to Powertrain Diagnostic Trouble Code Charts. If stabilized idle is not at least 700 rpm, go directly to Symptom Flow Charts. • Run throttle up to 1500 rpm for 5 seconds, and bring it back to idle. • Access MAF V PID (MAF PID) with a Scan Tool. NOTE: MAF V PID (MAF PID) should be greater than 3.90 volts (refer to Voltage to Mass Air Flow Conversion Table at the beginning of this Pinpoint Test). • Key off. • Disconnect MAF sensor. • Key on, engine running. • Again access MAF V PID (MAF PID) with a Scan Tool. • Did the MAF V PID (MAF PID) drop from the previous reading to below 0.39 volts (refer to Voltage to Mass Air Flow Conversion Table at the beginning of this Pinpoint Test)?	Yes No	▶ ▶	MAF SIG shorted to VPWR in MAF sensor. REPLACE MAF sensor. RESET KAM RERUN Quick Test. Power short in circuit but not in MAF sensor. GO to DC21.

FM0159501182100A

Fig. 177   Test DC: MAF Sensor (Part 10 of 10). 1994-95

You should enter this Pinpoint Test only when directed here.

| Remember |

This Pinpoint Test is intended to diagnose the following:

● Knock sensor

● Harness circuits: KS and SIG RTN

● Powertrain Control Module (PCM)

| Description |

For additional information on the Knock Sensor (KS), refer to   EEC-V Hardware

Pinpoint Test Schematic

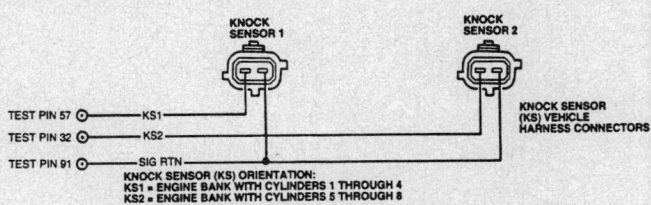

KNOCK SENSOR (KS) ORIENTATION:
KS1 = ENGINE BANK WITH CYLINDERS 1 THROUGH 4
KS2 = ENGINE BANK WITH CYLINDERS 5 THROUGH 8

Fig. 178 Test DG: Knock Sensor (Part 1 of 3). 1994-95

	TEST STEP	RESULT	▶	ACTION TO TAKE
DG1	CHECK SENSOR VOLTAGE			
	Ignition spark knock has occurred and the Knock Sensor has failed to respond by adjusting spark timing.	Yes	▶	GO to DG2
	Possible causes:	No	▶	Less than 2.4 volts: GO to DG5. Greater than 2.6 volts: GO to DG6.
	— PCM not receiving the signal at high altitude. — Open or short in harness. — Damaged knock sensor. — Damaged PCM. ● Key off. ● Disconnect PCM. Inspect for damaged or pushed out pins, corrosion, loose wires, etc. Service as necessary. ● Install breakout box, connect PCM. ● Key on. ● Read DC voltage between suspect Knock Sensor signal Test Pin and the SIG RTN Test Pin at the breakout box. ● Is the reading between 2.4 and 2.6 volts?			
DG2	CHECK FOR INTERMITTENT CIRCUIT FAULT			
	● Key on. ● While viewing the voltmeter, grasp the vehicle harness as close to the knock sensor(s) as possible. Shake and bend a small section of the harness from the KS sensor to the PCM. ● Tap the PCM and KS connectors if possible. ● Is KS reading changing?	Yes	▶	ISOLATE fault and SERVICE as required. VERIFY symptom has been repaired. RETURN to Symptom Flow Charts.
		No	▶	GO to DG3
DG3	CHECK FOR VOLTAGE INCREASE			
	● Key off. ● Disconnect PCM. ● Inspect for damaged or pushed out pins, corrosion, loose wires, etc. Service as necessary. ● Install breakout box, connect PCM. ● Disconnect Scan Tool. ● Start and run engine. ● Monitor voltage on the AC setting at idle and at 3,000 rpm between the suspect Knock Sensor Test Pin and SIG RTN Test Pin at the breakout box. ● Does the AC voltage reading increase?	Yes	▶	REPLACE PCM. RECONNECT all components. RERUN Quick Test.
		No	▶	GO to DG4.

Fig. 178 Test DG: Knock Sensor (Part 2 of 3). 1994-95

	TEST STEP	RESULT	▶	ACTION TO TAKE
DG4	CHECK CONTINUITY OF KS AND SIG RTN CIRCUITS			
	● Key off. ● Breakout box installed, PCM disconnected. ● Disconnect suspect KS. ● Measure resistance of the KS signal circuit between the KS signal Test Pin at the breakout box and the same signal pin at the vehicle harness connector. ● Measure resistance of the SIG RTN between Test Pin at the breakout box and the same SIG RTN pin at the vehicle harness connector. ● Is each resistance less than 5.0 ohms?	Yes	▶	GO to DG5.
		No	▶	SERVICE open circuit. REMOVE breakout box. RECONNECT all components. RERUN Quick Test.
DG5	CHECK KS CIRCUIT FOR SHORT TO GROUND			
	● Key off. ● Breakout box installed, PCM disconnected. KS disconnected. ● Measure resistance between KS signal Test Pins and SIG RTN, PWR GND at the breakout box and chassis GND. ● Is each resistance greater than 10,000 ohms?	Yes	▶	REPLACE suspect KS. REMOVE breakout box. RECONNECT all components. RERUN Quick Test.
		No	▶	SERVICE short circuit. REMOVE breakout box. RECONNECT all components. RERUN Quick Test.
DG6	CHECK KS CIRCUITS FOR SHORT TO POWER			
	● Key off. ● Breakout box installed, PCM disconnected. KS disconnected. ● Key on, engine off. ● Measure voltage between the KS signal Test Pins and PWR GND Test Pins at the breakout box. ● Is voltage less than 0.5 volts?	Yes	▶	REPLACE PCM. REMOVE breakout box. RECONNECT all components. RERUN Quick Test.
		No	▶	SERVICE short circuit. REMOVE breakout box. RECONNECT all components. RERUN Quick Test.

Fig. 178 Test DG: Knock Sensor (Part 3 of 3). 1994-95

You should enter this Pinpoint Test only when directed here.

| Reminder |

This Pinpoint Test is intended to diagnose the following:

● Throttle Position (TP) Sensor (9B989)

● Binding and Sticking Throttle Linkage

● Harness Circuits:

    TP SIG, SIG RTN, VREF, Vehicle Power (VPWR), Power Ground (PWR GND)

● Powertrain Control Module (PCM) (12A650)

| Reminder |

NOTE: The normal range of the throttle angle measurement for the Throttle Position (TP) sensor is 0 to 85 degrees.

FM0159401183010X

Fig. 179 Test DH: TP Sensor (Part 1 of 10). 1994-95

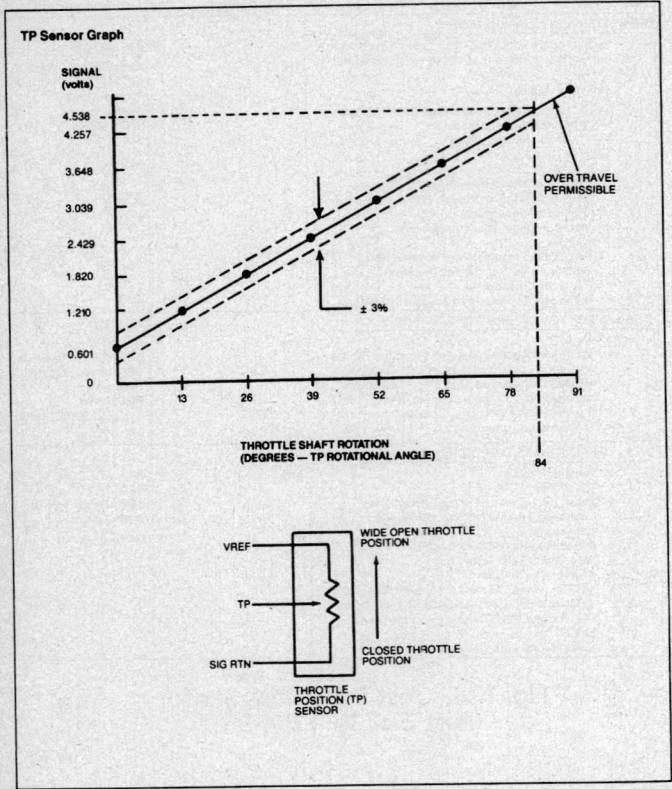

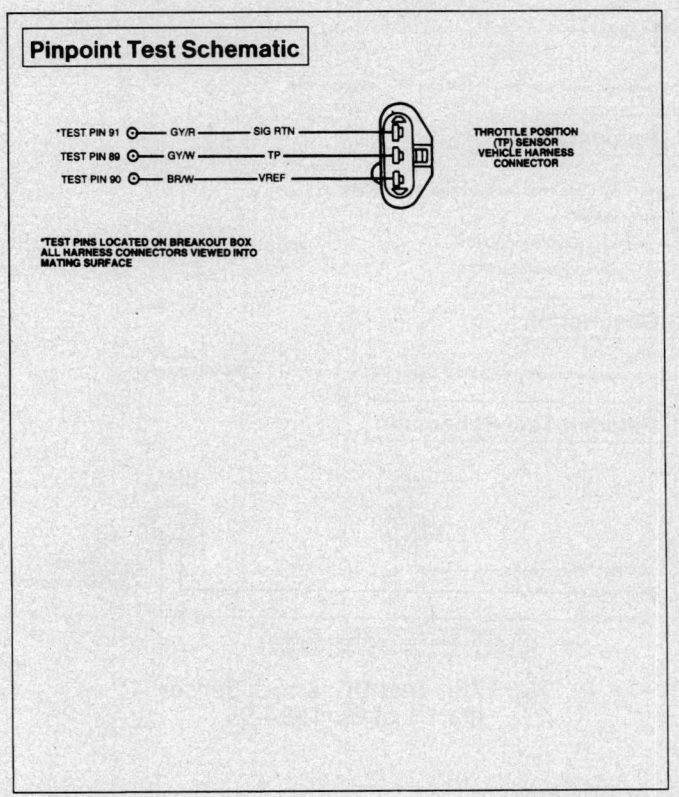

Fig. 179 Test DH: TP Sensor (Part 2 of 10). 1994-95

FM0159401183020X

Fig. 179 Test DH: TP Sensor (Part 3 of 10). 1994-95

FM0159401183030X

	TEST STEP	RESULT	▶	ACTION TO TAKE
DH1	**KOEO AND KOER DTC 1124: CHECK FOR OTHER DTCS**			
	Key On Engine Off (KOEO) and Key On Engine Running (KOER) Diagnostic-Trouble Code (DTC) 1124 indicates the Throttle Position (TP) sensor's rotational setting and signal are not in the Self-Test range of 13.23% to 24.02% (0.66 to 1.20 volts). Possible Causes: — Binding throttle linkage. — TP sensor not seated properly (tightened down). — Throttle plate / screw misadjusted. — Damaged TP sensor. — Damaged PCM. • Check for DTC 1400 in KOEO or KOER Self-Test. • **Is KOEO or KOER DTC 1400 present with KOEO DTC 1124?**	Yes No	▶ ▶	RETURN to Powertrain Diagnostic Trouble Code Charts, for DTC 1400. GO to **DH2**.
DH2	**DTC 1120: CHECK FOR STUCK TP SENSOR AND THROTTLE PLATE OR LINKAGE**			
	Diagnostic Trouble Code (DTC) 1120 indicates the TP signal is below the closed throttle position range of 9.80% (0.49 volts). Possible Causes: — Binding or bent throttle linkage. — Damaged TP sensor. — Throttle plate below closed throttle position. — Damaged PCM. • Visually inspect the throttle linkage and throttle plate for binding or sticking. • Verify the throttle plate and linkage is at closed throttle position. • **Does the throttle move freely and return to closed throttle position?**	Yes No	▶ ▶	Throttle plate and linkage are OK. **For DTC 1124:** GO to **DH5**. **For DTC 1120:** GO to **DH3**. SERVICE as necessary. RERUN Quick Test.
DH3	**CHECK FOR STUCK TP SENSOR**			
	• Key on, engine off. • Access TP PID with the Scan Tool. • Slowly move throttle from closed throttle position to wide open throttle position and observe the TP PID. • **While opening the throttle, is there a sudden drop in the TP PID to below 9.80% (0.49 volts)?**	Yes No	▶ ▶	TP sensor has internal substrate problem. REPLACE TP sensor. RERUN Quick Test. GO to **DH4**.

Fig. 179 Test DH: TP Sensor (Part 4 of 10). 1994-95

FM0159401183040X

	TEST STEP	RESULT	▶	ACTION TO TAKE
DH4	**CHECK TP SENSOR SIGNAL TO PCM**			
	• Key off. • Disconnect PCM. Inspect for damaged or pushed out pins, corrosion, loose wires, etc. Service necessary. • Install breakout box, connect PCM to breakout box. • Start engine and idle for 2 minutes. • Slowly open the throttle from closed position, while doing next step. • Measure the voltage between Test Pin 89 (TP SIG) and Test Pin 91 (SIG RTN) at the breakout box. • **Is the voltage at any time between 0.17 to 0.40 volts?**	Yes No	▶ ▶	TP sensor is damaged. REPLACE TP sensor. REMOVE breakout box. RERUN Quick Test. RERUN Quick Test. If DTC 1120 is still present, GO to **DH8**.
DH5	**DTC 0123: GENERATE OPPOSITE DTC 0122**			
	Diagnostic Trouble Code (DTC) 0123 indicates the TP sensor signal is greater than the Self-Test maximum value of 92.27% (4.60 volts). NOTE: An intermittent fault can cause a Continuous Memory DTC 0123. If Continuous Memory DTC 0123 is still present after DH5 through DH7, go to DH15. Possible Causes: — Damaged TP sensor. — TP not seated properly (tightened down). — TP SIG harness short to VREF or VPWR. — VREF harness short to VPWR. — Open SIG RTN harness circuit. — Damaged PCM. • Key off. • Disconnect TP sensor. Inspect for damaged or pushed out pins, corrosion, loose wires, etc. Service as necessary. • Key on, engine off. • Access TP PID with the Scan Tool. • **Is the TP PID less than 3.43% (0.17 volts)?**	Yes No	▶ ▶	TP SIG is either shorted to VREF in TP sensor or SIG RTN is open in the TP sensor or harness. GO to **DH6**. TP SIG circuit is shorted to VPWR or VREF. GO to **DH7**.
DH6	**CHECK VREF CIRCUIT VOLTAGE**			
	• Key off. • TP sensor disconnected. • Key on, engine off. • Measure voltage between VREF circuit and SIG RTN circuit at the TP sensor vehicle harness connector. • **Is the voltage between 4.0 and 6.0 volts?**	Yes No	▶ ▶	TP SIG shorted to VREF or SIG RTN open in the TP sensor. REPLACE TP sensor. RERUN Quick Test. Key off. RECONNECT all components. GO to Pinpoint Test Step **C1**.

Fig. 179 Test DH: TP Sensor (Part 5 of 10). 1994-95

FM0159401183050X

TEST STEP	RESULT	▶	ACTION TO TAKE
DH7 CHECK TP CIRCUIT FOR SHORTS TO VREF OR VPWR • Key off. • TP sensor disconnected. • Disconnect PCM. Inspect for damaged or pushed out pins, corrosion, loose wires, etc. Service as necessary. • Install breakout box, leave PCM disconnected. • Measure the resistance between Test Pin 89 (TP SIG) and Test Pins 90 (VREF) and 71 or 97 (VPWR) at the breakout box. • **Is each resistance greater than 10,000 ohms?**	Yes	▶	TP SIG is shorted to VREF or VPWR in PCM. REPLACE PCM. REMOVE breakout box. RECONNECT TP sensor. RERUN Quick Test.
	No	▶	TP SIG is shorted to VREF in the harness. SERVICE short in harness circuit between TP SIG and VREF. REMOVE breakout box. RECONNECT all components. RERUN Quick Test.
DH8 DTC 0122: GENERATE OPPOSITE DTC 0123 Diagnostic Trouble Code (DTC) 0122 indicates the TP sensor signal is less than the Self-Test minimum value of 3.43% (0.17 volts). NOTE: An intermittent fault can cause a Continuous Memory DTC 0122. If a Continuous Memory DTC 0122 **is still** present after DH8 through DH11, go to **DH15**. Possible Causes: — Damaged TP sensor. — TP not seated properly (tightened down). — Open TP SIG or VREF harness. — TP SIG harness short to SIG RTN or PWR GND. — Damaged PCM. • Key off. • Disconnect TP sensor. Inspect for damaged or pushed out pins, corrosion, loose wires, etc. Service as necessary. • Jumper VREF circuit to TP circuit at the TP sensor vehicle harness connector. • Key on, engine off. NOTE: If a communication error message is present, immediately remove jumper and go directly to DH11. • Access TP PID with the Scan Tool. • **Is the TP PID greater than 92.27% (4.60 volts)?**	Yes	▶	TP shorted to SIG RTN in TP sensor, or TP SIG or VREF open in TP sensor. REPLACE TP sensor. REMOVE jumper. RERUN Quick Test.
	No	▶	VREF or TP SIG open in harness or PCM, or TP SIG shorted to SIG RTN (or PWR GND) in harness or PCM. REMOVE jumper. GO to **DH9**.

FM0159401183060X

Fig. 179 Test DH: TP Sensor (Part 6 of 10). 1994-95

TEST STEP	RESULT	▶	ACTION TO TAKE
DH9 CHECK VREF CIRCUIT VOLTAGE • Key off. • TP sensor disconnected. • Key on, engine off. • Measure voltage between VREF circuit and SIG RTN circuit at the TP sensor vehicle harness connector. • **Is the voltage between 4.0 and 6.0 volts?**	Yes	▶	TP SIG open or shorted to SIG RTN (or PWR GND) in the harness or PCM. GO to **D10**.
	No	▶	Key off. RECONNECT all components. GO to Pinpoint Test Step **C1**.
DH10 CHECK TP CIRCUIT CONTINUITY • Key off. • TP sensor disconnected. • Disconnect PCM. Inspect for damaged or pushed out pins, corrosion, loose wires, etc. Service as necessary. • Install breakout, leave PCM disconnected. • Measure the resistance between TP circuit at the TP sensor vehicle harness connector and Test Pin 89 (TP SIG) at the breakout box. • **Is the resistance less than 5.0 ohms?**	Yes	▶	TP SIG harness circuit to PCM is OK. GO to **DH11**.
	No	▶	SERVICE open in TP SIG harness circuit. REMOVE breakout box. RECONNECT all components. RERUN Quick Test.
DH11 CHECK TP CIRCUIT FOR SHORTS TO SIG RTN OR PWR GND • Key off. • TP sensor disconnected. • Breakout box installed. • PCM disconnected. • Measure the resistance between Test Pin 89 (TP SIG) and Test Pins 91 (SIG RTN) and 24 or 103 (PWR GND) at the breakout box. • **Is each resistance greater than 10,000 ohms?**	Yes	▶	TP SIG open or shorted to SIG RTN (or PWR GND) in the PCM. REPLACE PCM. REMOVE breakout box. RECONNECT all components. RERUN Quick Test.
	No	▶	SERVICE TP SIG shorted to SIG RTN (or PWR GND) in the harness. REMOVE breakout box. RECONNECT all components. RERUN Quick Test.
DH12 CONTINUOUS MEMORY DTC 1121: TP SENSOR AND MAF SENSOR RATIONALITY CHECK Continuous Memory DTC 1121 indicates the TP sensor is inconsistent with the MAF sensor. Possible Causes: — Damaged TP sensor. — TP sensor not seated properly (almost completely detached from throttle body). — Air leak between MAF sensor and throttle body. • Attempt to start engine. • **Does the engine run?**	Yes	▶	GO to **DH13**.
	No	▶	CHECK for major leaks, cracks, and openings between MAF sensor and throttle body. If OK, GO to Pinpoint Test Step **A1**.

FM0159401183070X

Fig. 179 Test DH: TP Sensor (Part 7 of 10). 1994-95

TEST STEP	RESULT	▶	ACTION TO TAKE
DH13 CHECK MECHANICAL OPERATION OF TP SENSOR • Key on, engine off. • Access TP PID with the Scan Tool. • Slowly move throttle from closed throttle position to wide open throttle position and observe the TP PID for smooth reading change. • **While opening and closing the throttle, is there a sudden drop in the TP PID below 13.23% (0.66 volts) or a sudden jump in the TP PID above 24.02% (1.20 volts)?**	Yes	▶	TP sensor has internal substrate problem. REPLACE TP sensor. RERUN Quick Test.
	No	▶	GO to **DH14**.
DH14 CHECK TP SENSOR SIGNAL HIGH VERSUS THE ENGINE LOAD WHILE DRIVING VEHICLE • Key on, engine running. • Do normal drive, exercising the throttle and TP sensor while accessing PIDS. • Access TP PID and LOAD PID with the Scan Tool and record readings. • **Is the TP PID reading greater than 49.02% (2.44 volts) and the LOAD PID reading less than 25%?**	Yes	▶	CHECK for air leaks between the MAF sensor and the throttle body, including air noise sounds while engine is running. SERVICE as necessary. If OK, REPLACE the TP sensor. RERUN Quick Test.
	No	▶	GO to **DH15**.
DH15 CHECK TP SENSOR SIGNAL LOW VERSUS THE ENGINE LOAD • Key on, engine running. NOTE: If the vehicle is a No Start, go to Pinpoint Test Step **A1**. • Access TP PID and LOAD PID with the Scan Tool and record readings. • **Is the TP PID reading less than 4.90% (0.24 volts) and the LOAD PID reading greater than 60%?**	Yes	▶	CHECK for TP sensor loosely connected to the throttle body (screws not securely tightened down). SERVICE as necessary. COMPLETE PCM reset to clear DTCs (REFER to Powertrain Control Module (PCM) Reset). DRIVE vehicle exercising the throttle. RERUN Quick Test. If Continuous Memory 1121 is now present, REPLACE MAF sensor.
	No	▶	GO to **DH16**.

FM0159401183080X

Fig. 179 Test DH: TP Sensor (Part 8 of 10). 1994-95

TEST STEP	RESULT	▶	ACTION TO TAKE
DH16 CHECK TP SENSOR SIGNAL LOW VERSUS THE ENGINE LOAD WHILE DRIVING VEHICLE • Key on, engine running. • Do normal drive, exercising the throttle and TP sensor near higher gears (preferably overdrive) while accessing PIDS. • Access TP PID and LOAD PID with the Scan Tool and record readings. • **Is the TP PID reading less than 4.90% (0.24 volts) and the LOAD PID reading greater than 60%?**	Yes	▶	CHECK if the TP sensor is loosely connected to the throttle body (screws not securely tightened down). SERVICE as necessary. COMPLETE PCM reset to clear DTCs (REFER to Powertrain Control Module (PCM) Reset). DRIVE vehicle exercising the throttle. RERUN Quick Test. If Continuous Memory 1121 is now present, REPLACE MAF sensor.
	No	▶	Unable to identify the fault at this time. If vehicle is still a No Start, GO to Pinpoint Test Step **A1**.
DH17 CONTINUOUS MEMORY DTC 1125: CHECK FOR TP CIRCUIT INTERMITTENT VOLTAGE INPUT Continuous Memory DTC 1125 indicates the TP sensor signal went below 9.80% (0.49 volts) or above 92.27% (4.60 volts) sometime during the last 80 warm-up cycles. Possible Causes: — TP sensor connector with poor continuity. — TP harness with poor continuity. — TP harness intermittent short. — TP sensor internal electrical or substrate open or electrical short. • Start engine and bring to idle. • Run throttle up to 1500 rpm for 5 seconds. • Key on, engine running. • Access TP PID for a fault indication with a Scan Tool while performing the following: — Lightly tap on TP sensor and wiggle harness connector to simulate road shock. • **Is the TP PID changing below the minimum 9.80% (0.49 volts) or above the maximum 92.27% (4.60 volts)?**	Yes	▶	DISCONNECT and INSPECT the TP sensor connector. If OK, REPLACE the TP sensor. COMPLETE PCM reset to clear DTCs (REFER to Powertrain Control Module (PCM) Reset). RERUN Quick Test.
	No	▶	GO to **DH18**.

FM0159401183090X

Fig. 179 Test DH: TP Sensor (Part 9 of 10). 1994-95

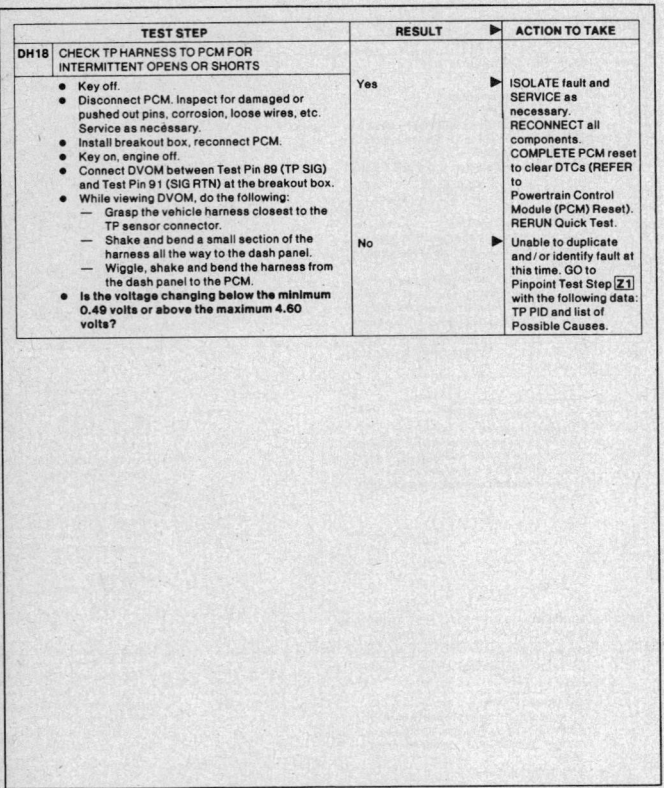

TEST STEP	RESULT	▶	ACTION TO TAKE
DH18 CHECK TP HARNESS TO PCM FOR INTERMITTENT OPENS OR SHORTS			
• Key off. • Disconnect PCM. Inspect for damaged or pushed out pins, corrosion, loose wires, etc. Service as necessary. • Install breakout box, reconnect PCM. • Key on, engine off. • Connect DVOM between Test Pin 89 (TP SIG) and Test Pin 91 (SIG RTN) at the breakout box. • While viewing DVOM, do the following: — Grasp the vehicle harness closest to the TP sensor connector. — Shake and bend a small section of the harness all the way to the dash panel. — Wiggle, shake and bend the harness from the dash panel to the PCM. • Is the voltage changing below the minimum 0.49 volts or above the maximum 4.60 volts?	Yes	▶	ISOLATE fault and SERVICE as necessary. RECONNECT all components. COMPLETE PCM reset to clear DTCs (REFER to Powertrain Control Module (PCM) Reset). RERUN Quick Test.
	No	▶	Unable to duplicate and/or identify fault at this time. GO to Pinpoint Test Step Z1 with the following data: TP PID and list of Possible Causes.

Fig. 179   Test DH: TP Sensor (Part 10 of 10). 1994-95

FM0159401183100X

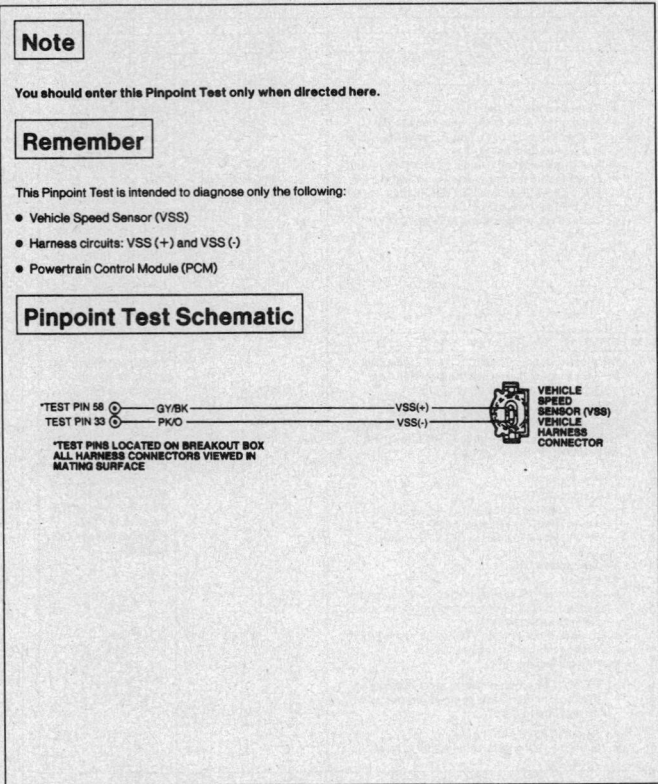

Note

You should enter this Pinpoint Test only when directed here.

Remember

This Pinpoint Test is intended to diagnose only the following:

• Vehicle Speed Sensor (VSS)
• Harness circuits: VSS (+) and VSS (-)
• Powertrain Control Module (PCM)

Pinpoint Test Schematic

*TEST PIN 58 — GY/BK — VSS(+)
TEST PIN 33 — PK/O — VSS(-)

VEHICLE SPEED SENSOR (VSS) VEHICLE HARNESS CONNECTOR

*TEST PINS LOCATED ON BREAKOUT BOX
ALL HARNESS CONNECTORS VIEWED IN
MATING SURFACE

Fig. 180   Test DP: VSS (Part 1 of 4). 1994-95

FM0159401184010X

TEST STEP	RESULT	▶	ACTION TO TAKE
DP1 DTC 0500: CHECK CONTINUITY OF VSS HARNESS CIRCUITS			
Diagnostic Trouble Code (DTC) 0500 indicates the VSS input signal has been detected out of Self-Test range. Possible Causes: — Open in VSS (+)/VSS (-) harness circuit. — Short to GND or SIG RTN in VSS (+)/VSS(-) harness circuit. — Short to PWR in VSS(+)/VSS(-) harness circuit. — Damaged VSS. — Damaged PCM. • Key off. • Disconnect PCM. Inspect for damaged or pushed out pins, corrosion, loose wires, etc. Service as necessary. • Install breakout box, PCM disconnected. • Disconnect VSS. • Measure resistance between Test Pin 58 [VSS (+)] at the breakout box and VSS (+) circuit at the VSS vehicle harness connector. • Measure resistance between Test Pin 33 [VSS (-)] at the breakout box and VSS(-) circuit at the VSS vehicle harness connector. • Is each resistance less than 5.0 ohms?	Yes	▶	GO to DP2.
	No	▶	SERVICE open in harness circuit. REMOVE breakout box. RECONNECT all components. COMPLETE PCM reset to clear DTCs (REFER to Powertrain Control Module (PCM) Reset). RUN VSS Drive Cycle in DP20 to verify repair.
DP2 CHECK VSS HARNESS CIRCUITS FOR SHORTS TO GROUND, SIG RTN AND POWER			
• Key off. • VSS disconnected. • Breakout box installed, PCM disconnected. • Measure resistance between Test Pin 58 [VSS (+)] and Test Pins 51, 103 (PWR GND), 33 [VSS (-)], 91 (SIG RTN) and 71 (VPWR) at the breakout box. • Measure resistance between Test Pin 33 [VSS (-)] and Test Pins 51 or 103 (PWR GND), 91 (SIG RTN) and 71 (VPWR) at the breakout box. • Is each resistance greater than 500 ohms?	Yes	▶	GO to DP3.
	No	▶	SERVICE short circuit. REMOVE the breakout box. RECONNECT all components. COMPLETE PCM reset to clear DTCs (REFER to Powertrain Control Module (PCM) Reset). RUN VSS Drive Cycle in DP20 to verify the repair.

Fig. 180   Test DP: VSS (Part 2 of 4). 1994-95

FM0159401184020X

TEST STEP	RESULT	▶	ACTION TO TAKE
DP3 CHECK VSS RESISTANCE			
• Key off. • VSS disconnected. • Measure the resistance of the VSS. • Is resistance between 190 and 250 ohms?	Yes	▶	REMOVE breakout box. REPLACE the PCM. RECONNECT the VSS. COMPLETE PCM reset to clear DTCs (REFER to Powertrain Control Module (PCM) Reset). RUN VSS Drive Cycle in DP20 to verify the repair.
	No	▶	REPLACE the VSS. REMOVE breakout box. RECONNECT the PCM. RUN VSS Drive Cycle in DP20 to verify the repair.
DP10 DTC 1500: VISUAL INSPECTION			
Diagnostic Trouble Code (DTC) 1500 indicates the VSS input signal was intermittent. Possible Causes: — Intermittent VSS connections. — Intermittent open in VSS harness circuit(s). — Intermittent short in VSS harness circuit(s). — Damaged VSS. — Damaged PCM. • Key off. • Visually inspect the VSS and VSS harness circuits for any potential failures. Use the following check list for reference: — Loose VSS connector. — Pushed out VSS connector pins. — Damaged VSS wiring harness insulation. — Incorrect harness routing. — Incorrect VSS mounting. • Did the visual inspection reveal a potential failure?	Yes	▶	SERVICE fault as necessary. COMPLETE PCM reset to clear DTCs (REFER to Powertrain Control Module (PCM) Reset). RUN VSS Drive Cycle in DP20 to verify the repair.
	No	▶	RECONNECT all components. Unable to duplicate or identify fault at this time. GO to Pinpoint Test Step Z1 with the following data: the VSS check list and list of Possible Causes.

Fig. 180   Test DP: VSS (Part 3 of 4). 1994-95

FM0159401184030X

TEST STEP	RESULT ▶	ACTION TO TAKE
DP20 VSS DRIVE CYCLE TEST		
• Warm engine to operating temperature. • Perform the VSS Drive Cycle at least three times as outlined below: **AUTOMATIC TRANSMISSIONS:** • Place gear selector in DRIVE range. • Obey all local traffic laws. • Accelerate heavily to 35 mph. • Coast down to an idle and stop the vehicle. • Shut the engine off. • After the drive cycle is completed, retrieve and record any Continuous Memory DTCs, address the DTCs in _____ Diagnostic Subroutines. • If no DTCs are generated, testing is complete. **MANUAL TRANSMISSIONS:** • Shift to second from first gear. • Obey all traffic laws. • Accelerate moderately to 40 mph. • Coast down to an idle and stop the vehicle. • After the drive cycle is completed, retrieve and record any Continuous Memory DTCs, address the DTCs in _____ Diagnostic Subroutines. • If no DTCs are generated, testing is complete		

FM0159401184040X

Fig. 180   Test DP: VSS (Part 4 of 4). 1994-95

Note

You should enter this Pinpoint Test only when directed here.

Remember

This Pinpoint Test is intended to diagnose the following:

• Camshaft Position (CMP) Sensor (6B288)
• Harness Circuits: CID, VPWR, SIG RTN, PWR GND
• Powertrain Control Module (PCM)

FM0159401185010X

Fig. 181   Test DR: CID Circuit (Part 1 of 5). 1994-95

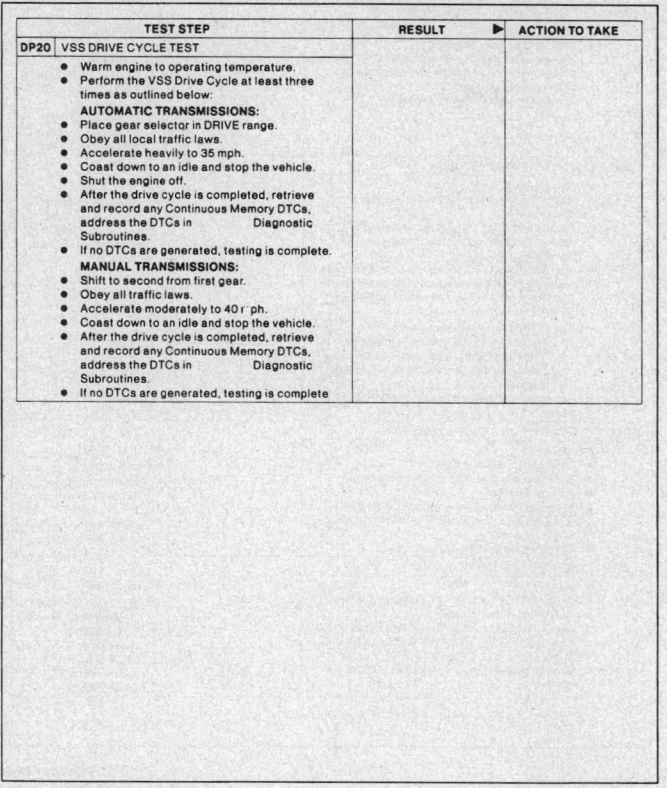

Fig. 181   Test DR: CID Circuit (Part 2 of 5). 1994

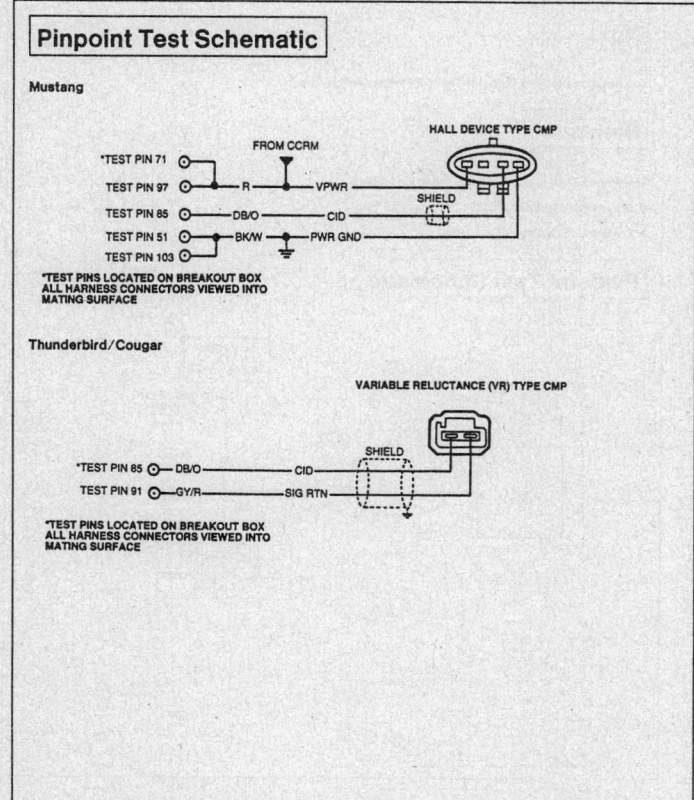

Fig. 181   Test DR: CID Circuit (Part 2 of 5). 1994

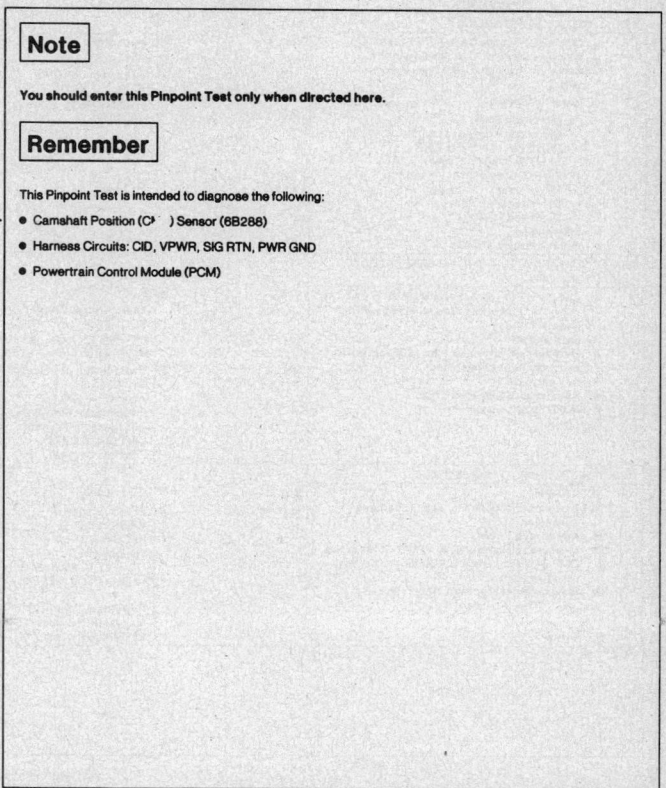
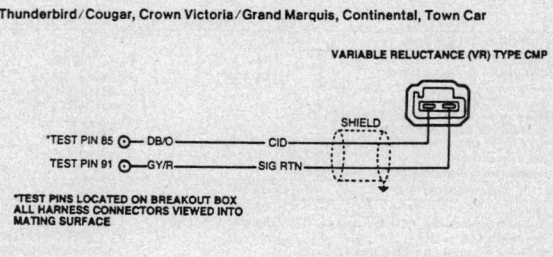

Fig. 181   Test DR: CID Circuit (Part 2 of 5). 1995

TEST STEP		RESULT	▶	ACTION TO TAKE
DR1	**DTC 0340: START ENGINE**			
	• Diagnostic Trouble Code (DTC) 0340 indicates that Self-Test has detected a Camshaft Position (CMP) Sensor circuit failure. Possible Causes: — CID circuit open. — CID circuit shorted to GND. — CID circuit shorted to PWR. — SIG RTN open (VR type). — PWR GND open (HALL type). — VPWR open (HALL type). — Damaged CMP Sensor. — Damaged PCM. • Start engine. • **Will the engine start?**	Yes No	▶ ▶	GO to **DR2**. DTC 0340 is not the cause of the No Start. GO to diagnose the No Start symptom.
DR2	**CLEAR AND ATTEMPT TO RE-GENERATE DTC 0340**			
	• Complete PCM reset to clear DTCs Powertrain Control Module (PCM) Reset). • Start engine. • Increase rpm to greater than 1500 rpm for 10 seconds. Repeat two times. • Key off. • Retrieve all Continuous DTCs. • **Is DTC 0340 present?**	Yes No	▶ ▶	For Thunderbird/Cougar: GO to **DR5**. All Others: GO to **DR3**. The fault that produced DTC 0340 is intermittent. GO to Pinpoint Test Step **Z1** with the following data: CID PID and list of Possible Causes.
DR3	**CHECK VPWR TO CMP SENSOR**			
	• Key off. • Disconnect CMP sensor vehicle harness connector. • Key on, engine off. • Measure voltage between VPWR circuit at the CMP vehicle harness connector and battery negative post. • **Is voltage greater than 10.5 volts?**	Yes No	▶ ▶	GO to **DR4**. SERVICE open in VPWR circuit. RECONNECT all components. COMPLETE PCM reset to clear DTCs (REFER to Powertrain Control Module (PCM) Reset). RERUN Quick Test.

Fig. 181 Test DR: CID Circuit (Part 3 of 5). 1994-95

FM0159401185030X

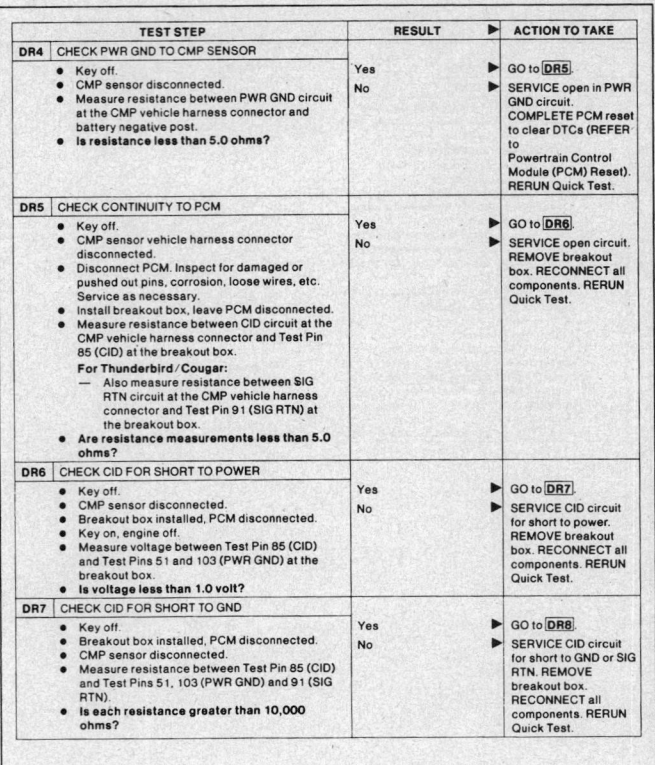

TEST STEP		RESULT	▶	ACTION TO TAKE
DR4	**CHECK PWR GND TO CMP SENSOR**			
	• Key off. • CMP sensor disconnected. • Measure resistance between PWR GND circuit at the CMP vehicle harness connector and battery negative post. • **Is resistance less than 5.0 ohms?**	Yes No	▶ ▶	GO to **DR5**. SERVICE open in PWR GND circuit. COMPLETE PCM reset to clear DTCs (REFER to Powertrain Control Module (PCM) Reset). RERUN Quick Test.
DR5	**CHECK CONTINUITY TO PCM**			
	• Key off. • CMP sensor vehicle harness connector disconnected. • Disconnect PCM. Inspect for damaged or pushed out pins, corrosion, loose wires, etc. Service as necessary. • Install breakout box, leave PCM disconnected. • Measure resistance between CID circuit at the CMP vehicle harness connector and Test Pin 85 (CID) at the breakout box. For Thunderbird/Cougar: — Also measure resistance between SIG RTN circuit at the CMP vehicle harness connector and Test Pin 91 (SIG RTN) at the breakout box. • **Are resistance measurements less than 5.0 ohms?**	Yes No	▶ ▶	GO to **DR6**. SERVICE open circuit. REMOVE breakout box. RECONNECT all components. RERUN Quick Test.
DR6	**CHECK CID FOR SHORT TO POWER**			
	• Key off. • CMP sensor disconnected. • Breakout box installed, PCM disconnected. • Key on, engine off. • Measure voltage between Test Pin 85 (CID) and Test Pins 51 and 103 (PWR GND) at the breakout box. • **Is voltage less than 1.0 volt?**	Yes No	▶ ▶	GO to **DR7**. SERVICE CID circuit for short to power. REMOVE breakout box. RECONNECT all components. RERUN Quick Test.
DR7	**CHECK CID FOR SHORT TO GND**			
	• Key off. • Breakout box installed, PCM disconnected. • CMP sensor disconnected. • Measure resistance between Test Pin 85 (CID) and Test Pins 51, 103 (PWR GND) and 91 (SIG RTN). • **Is each resistance greater than 10,000 ohms?**	Yes No	▶ ▶	GO to **DR8**. SERVICE CID circuit for short to GND or SIG RTN. REMOVE breakout box. RECONNECT all components. RERUN Quick Test.

Fig. 181 Test DR: CID Circuit (Part 4 of 5). 1994-95

FM0159401185040X

TEST STEP		RESULT	▶	ACTION TO TAKE
DR8	**CHECK FOR SHORTS IN PCM**			
	• Key off. • CMP sensor disconnected. • Breakout box installed. • Connect PCM to breakout box. • Measure resistance between Test Pin 85 (CID) and Test Pins 51, 103 (PWR GND), 71, 97 (VPWR), 91 (SIG RTN), and 23 (IGN GND) at the breakout box. • **Is each resistance greater than 500 ohms?**	Yes No	▶ ▶	GO to **DR9**. REPLACE PCM. REMOVE breakout box. RECONNECT all components. RERUN Quick Test.
DR9	**CHECK CMP SENSOR OUTPUT**			
	• Key off. • Breakout box installed, PCM connected. • Reconnect CMP sensor. • DVOM on AC scale (to monitor less 5.0 volts). • Measure voltage between Test Pin 85 (CID) and Test Pins 51 and 103 (PWR GND) at the breakout box while running engine at varying rpm. • **Does AC voltage vary greater than 0.1 volt AC?**	Yes No	▶ ▶	REPLACE PCM. REMOVE breakout box. RECONNECT all components. RERUN Quick Test. REPLACE CMP sensor. REMOVE breakout box. RECONNECT all components. RERUN Quick Test.

Fig. 181 Test DR: CID Circuit (Part 5 of 5). 1994-95

FM0159401185050X

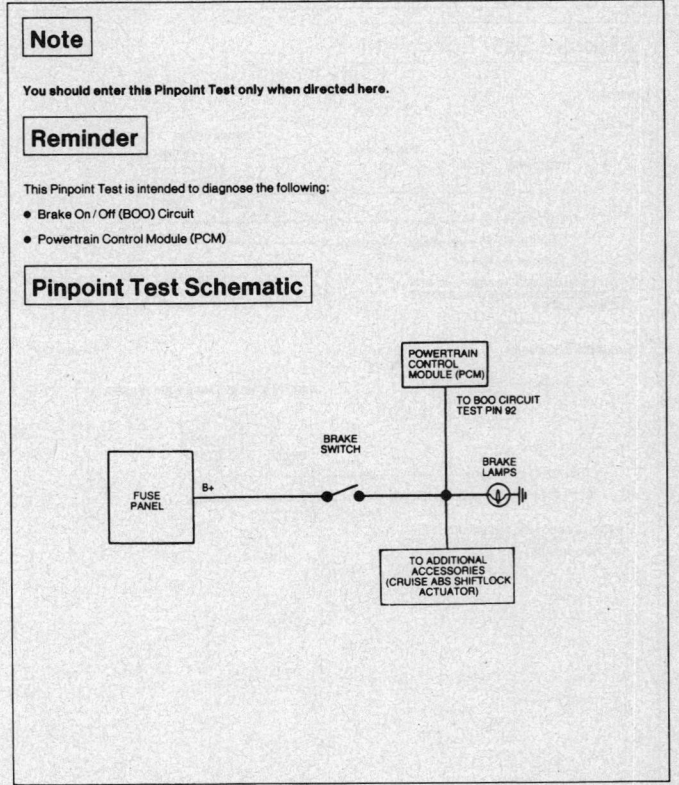

Note

You should enter this Pinpoint Test only when directed here.

Reminder

This Pinpoint Test is intended to diagnose the following:
• Brake On/Off (BOO) Circuit
• Powertrain Control Module (PCM)

Pinpoint Test Schematic

Fig. 182 Test FD: BOO Switch (Part 1 of 3). 1994-95

FM0159401186010X

TEST STEP	RESULT	▶	ACTION TO TAKE
FD1 DTC 0703: VERIFY BRAKE PEDAL WAS PRESSED			
Diagnostic Trouble Code (DTC) 0703 indicates that when the brake pedal was pressed and released during the Key On Engine Running (KOER) Self-Test, the BOO signal did not cycle high and low. Possible causes: — Brake pedal not pressed and released during the KOER Self-Test. — Brake pedal pressed during entire KOER Self-Test. — Open to ground or power. — Damaged brake switch. — Damaged PCM. ● **Was the brake pedal pressed and released during KOER Self-Test?**	Yes No	▶ ▶	GO to FD3. RERUN KOER Self-Test. PRESS and RELEASE brake pedal.
FD2 KOEO DTC 1703			
Diagnostic Trouble Code (DTC) 1703 indicates that during Key On Engine Off (KOEO) Self-Test, voltage was seen on the BOO Test Pin at the PCM. Possible Causes: — Brake pedal pressed during KOEO Self-Test. — BOO Test Pin shorted to B+. — Defective brake switch. ● **Was brake pedal pressed during KOEO Self-Test?**	Yes No	▶ ▶	RERUN KOEO Self-Test. Avoid pressing brake pedal during test. GO to FD3.
FD3 CHECK OPERATION OF STOPLAMPS			
● Key on. ● Check stoplamp operation.	Stoplamps operate normally Stoplamps never on Stoplamps always on	▶ ▶ ▶	GO to FD4. GO to FD5. GO to FD6.
FD4 CHECK FOR BOO CIRCUIT CYCLING			
● Key off. ● Disconnect PCM. Inspect for damaged or pushed out pins, corrosion, loose wires, etc. Service as necessary. ● Install breakout box, leave PCM disconnected. ● DVOM on 20 volt scale. ● Measure the voltage between BOO Test Pin (refer to chart on FD cover page) and Test Pins 76 and 77 at the breakout box while pressing and releasing the brake. ● Does the voltage cycle?	Yes No	▶ ▶	REPLACE PCM. REMOVE breakout box. RERUN Self-Test. SERVICE open in BOO circuit between PCM and BOO connection to stoplamp circuit. RERUN Self-Test.

FM0159401186020X

Fig. 182   Test FD: BOO Switch (Part 2 of 3). 1994-95

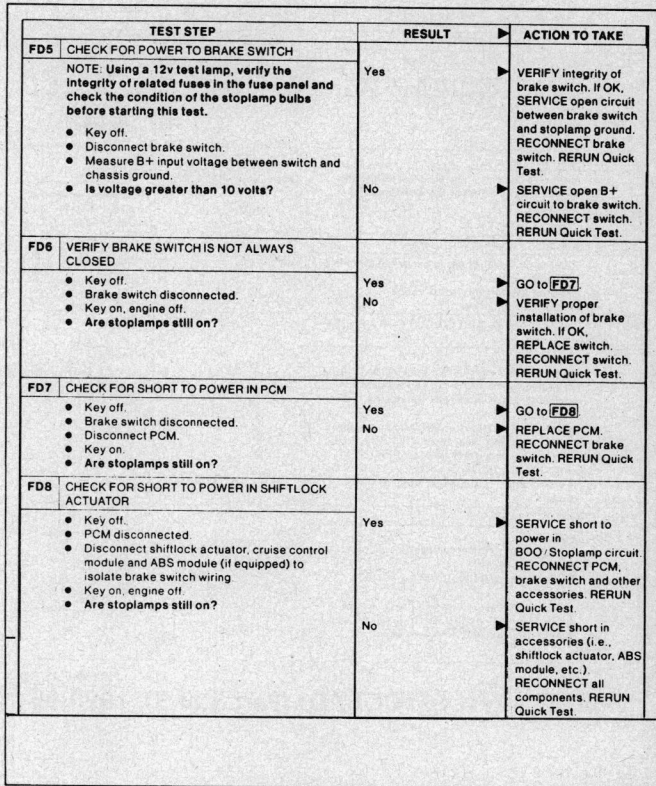

TEST STEP	RESULT	▶	ACTION TO TAKE
FD5 CHECK FOR POWER TO BRAKE SWITCH			
NOTE: Using a 12v test lamp, verify the integrity of related fuses in the fuse panel and check the condition of the stoplamp bulbs before starting this test. ● Key off. ● Disconnect brake switch. ● Measure B+ input voltage between switch and chassis ground. ● Is voltage greater than 10 volts?	Yes No	▶ ▶	VERIFY integrity of brake switch. If OK, SERVICE open circuit between brake switch and stoplamp ground. RECONNECT brake switch. RERUN Quick Test. SERVICE open B+ circuit to brake switch. RECONNECT switch. RERUN Quick Test.
FD6 VERIFY BRAKE SWITCH IS NOT ALWAYS CLOSED			
● Key off. ● Brake switch disconnected. ● Key on, engine off. ● Are stoplamps still on?	Yes No	▶ ▶	GO to FD7. VERIFY proper installation of brake switch. If OK, REPLACE switch. RECONNECT switch. RERUN Quick Test.
FD7 CHECK FOR SHORT TO POWER IN PCM			
● Key off. ● Brake switch disconnected. ● Disconnect PCM. ● Key on. ● Are stoplamps still on?	Yes No	▶ ▶	GO to FD8. REPLACE PCM. RECONNECT brake switch. RERUN Quick Test.
FD8 CHECK FOR SHORT TO POWER IN SHIFTLOCK ACTUATOR			
● Key off. ● PCM disconnected. ● Disconnect shiftlock actuator, cruise control module and ABS module (if equipped) to isolate brake switch wiring. ● Key on, engine off. ● Are stoplamps still on?	Yes No	▶ ▶	SERVICE short to power in BOO/Stoplamp circuit. RECONNECT PCM, brake switch and other accessories. RERUN Quick Test. SERVICE short in accessories (i.e., shiftlock actuator, ABS module, etc.) RECONNECT all components. RERUN Quick Test.

FM0159401186030X

Fig. 182   Test FD: BOO Switch (Part 3 of 3). 1994-95

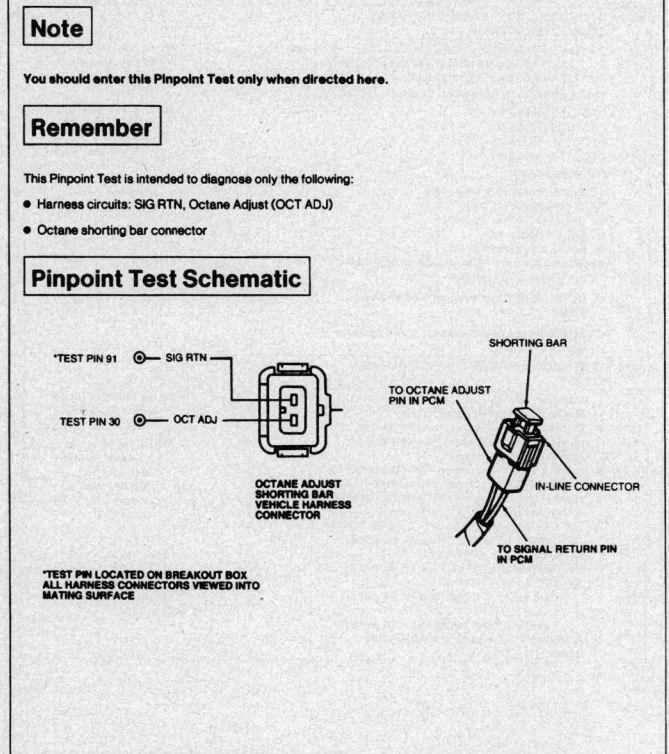

Note

You should enter this Pinpoint Test only when directed here.

Remember

This Pinpoint Test is intended to diagnose only the following:
● Harness circuits: SIG RTN, Octane Adjust (OCT ADJ)
● Octane shorting bar connector

Pinpoint Test Schematic

FM0159401187010X

Fig. 183   Test FG: OCT ADJ (Part 1 of 3). 1994-95

TEST STEP	RESULT	▶	ACTION TO TAKE
FG1 DTC 1390: VISUALLY INSPECT OCTANE ADJUST IN-LINE CONNECTOR			
Diagnostic Trouble Code (DTC) 1390 indicates OCT ADJ shorting bar is not in or the OCT ADJ circuit is open. ● Key off. ● Visually inspect in-line connector. ● Is shorting bar removed?	Yes No	▶ ▶	GO to FG2. GO to FG4.
FG2 CHECK FOR MODIFICATION DECAL			
● Is there a modification decal attached to the vehicle indicating that OCT ADJ shorting bar was removed?	Yes No	▶ ▶	Testing complete. GO to FG3.
FG3 CHECK FOR DTC 1390			
● Replace OCT ADJ shorting bar. ● Key off. ● Connect Scan Tool. ● Activate Key On Engine Off Self-Test. ● Is DTC 1390 present?	Yes No	▶ ▶	GO to FG4. Testing complete. EEC system OK.
FG4 CHECK CONTINUITY OF OCTANE ADJUST CIRCUIT			
NOTE: There should be continuity from OCT ADJ circuit through the in-line connector and shorting bar to SIG RTN circuit. ● Key off. ● Disconnect Powertrain Control Module (PCM). Inspect for damaged or pushed out pins, corrosion, loose wires, etc. Service as necessary. ● Install breakout box, leave PCM disconnected. ● Measure resistance between Test Pin 91 and OCT ADJ Test Pin 30 at the breakout box. ● Is the resistance less than 5.0 ohms?	Yes No	▶ ▶	REPLACE PCM. REMOVE breakout box. RERUN Quick Test. SERVICE open OCT ADJ circuit or shorting bar or SIG RTN circuit. REMOVE breakout box. RERUN Quick Test.
FG5 CHECK FOR DTC 1390			
● Start engine and idle vehicle at operating temperature. ● Key off. ● Connect Scan Tool. ● Activate Key On Engine Off Self-Test. ● Is DTC 1390 present?	Yes No	▶ ▶	GO to FG1. GO to FG6.
FG6 VERIFY IN-LINE CONNECTOR SHORTING BAR IS INSTALLED			
● Key off. ● Visually inspect OCT ADJ in-line connector. ● Is shorting bar installed?	Yes No	▶ ▶	GO to FG8. GO to FG7.

Fig. 183   Test FG: OCT ADJ (Part 2 of 3). 1994-95

TEST STEP		RESULT	▶	ACTION TO TAKE
FG7	CHECK FOR MODIFICATION DECAL			
	• Is there a modification decal attached to vehicle indicating that OCT ADJ shorting bar was removed?	Yes	▶	GO to FG10.
		No	▶	REPLACE shorting bar.
FG8	CHECK FOR TSB			
	• Is there a Technical Service Bulletin (TSB) authorizing removal of the shorting OCT ADJ bar?	Yes	▶	GO to FG9.
		No	▶	RETURN to Section 4 to address spark knock concern.
FG9	REMOVE OCT ADJ SHORTING BAR			
	• Remove OCT ADJ shorting bar only if there is a TSB authorization.	Yes	▶	GO to FG10.
	• Drive vehicle to verify spark knock.	No	▶	Testing complete. EEC system OK.
	• Is spark knock present?			
FG10	CHECK OCTANE ADJUST CIRCUIT FOR A SHORT TO GROUND			
	• Key off.	Yes	▶	GO to FG11.
	• Disconnect Powertrain Control Module (PCM). Inspect for damaged or pushed out pins, corrosion, loose wires, etc. Service as necessary.	No	▶	SERVICE short circuit. REMOVE breakout box.
	• Install breakout box; leave PCM disconnected.			
	• Measure resistance between OCT ADJ circuit at the in-line connector and Test Pins 51, 91 and 103 at the breakout box.			
	• Is each resistance greater than 10,000 ohms?			
FG11	CHECK PCM INTEGRITY			
	• Key off.	Yes	▶	REMOVE breakout box
	• OCT ADJ shorting bar removed because of TSB authorization.			
	• Breakout box installed, PCM connected.			
	• Key on.	No	▶	REPLACE PCM REMOVE breakout box.
	• Measure voltage between OCT ADJ circuit and Test Pins 51 and 103 at the breakout box.			
	• Is voltage greater than 4.0 volts?			

FM0159401187030X

Fig. 183   Test FG: OCT ADJ (Part 3 of 3). 1994-95

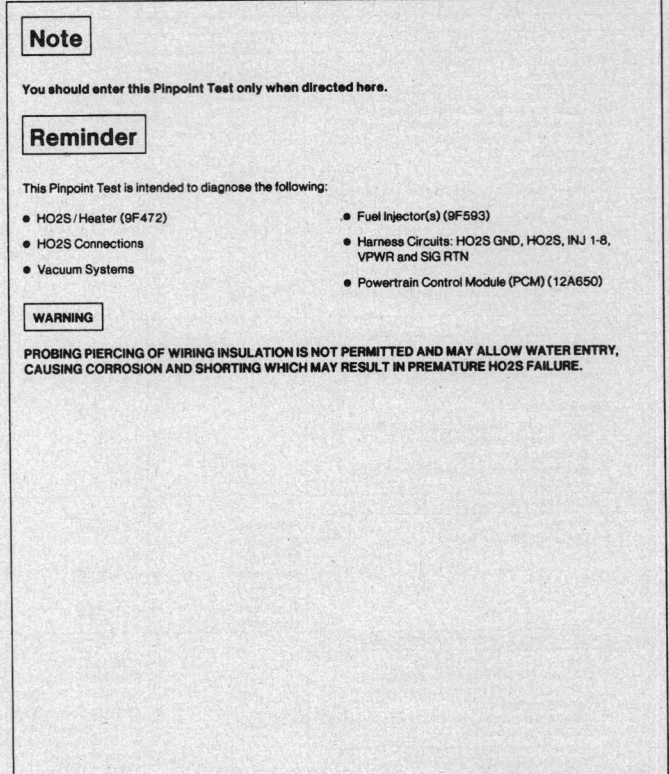

Fig. 184   Test H: Fuel Control (Part 1 of 21). 1994

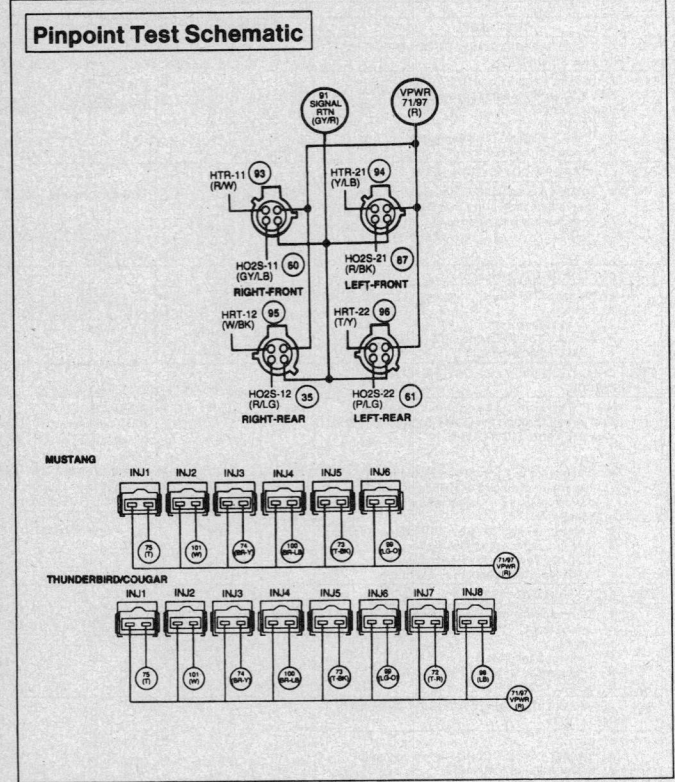

Fig. 184   Test H: Fuel Control (Part 2 of 21). 1994

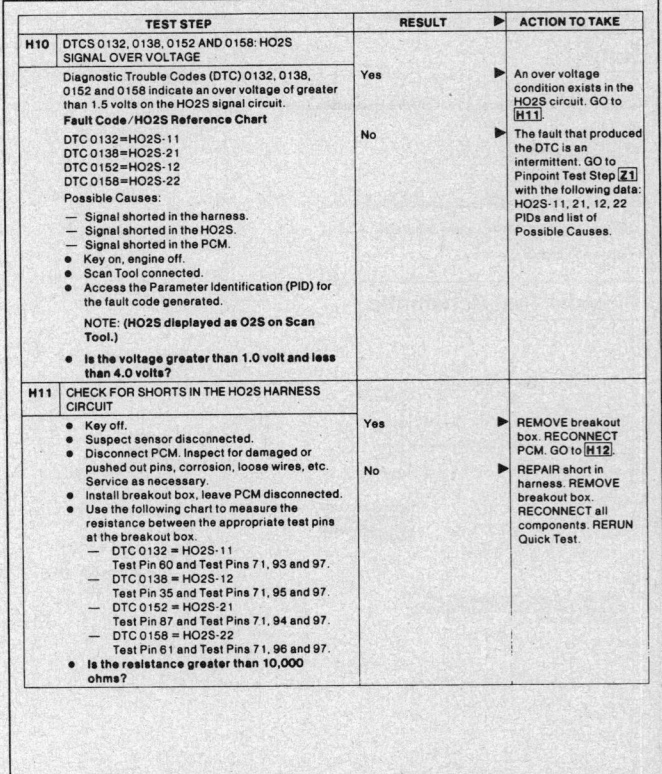

Fig. 184   Test H: Fuel Control (Part 3 of 21). 1994

TEST STEP		RESULT	▶	ACTION TO TAKE
H12	**CHECK FOR HO2S SIGNAL SHORT TO HO2S HEATER CIRCUIT IN THE SENSOR** • Key off. • Suspect HO2S sensor disconnected. • Scan Tool connected. • Key on, engine off. • View HO2S (PID) corresponding to DTCs received. NOTE: (HO2S displayed as O2S on Scan Tool.) • Is the HO2S voltage less than 0.2 volts?	Yes No	▶ ▶	REPLACE HO2S. RECONNECT all components. RERUN Quick Test. REPLACE PCM. RECONNECT all components. RERUN Quick Test.
H20	**DTCS 0133 AND 0153: HO2S RESPONSE TEST** DTCs 0133 and 0153 indicate the response rate of the HO2S is below some calibrated window. **Fault Code/HO2S reference chart:** DTC 0133 = HO2S-11 DTC 0153 = HO2S-21 Possible Causes: — Contaminated HO2S. — Exhaust leaks. — Shorted / open wires. — Excessive fueling. — MAF meter. — Air leaks. • Key off. • Scan Tool connected. • Key on, engine off. • Access Generic OBD II functions and trigger. • Scroll to Oxygen Sensor Test and trigger. • Scroll to Manufacturer Specific Test ID and trigger. • Scroll to Test ID: (41H) and trigger. • **Is the measurement for the HO2S fault greater than 0.6 volts?**	Yes No	▶ ▶	COMPLETE PCM reset to clear DTCs (refer to Powertrain Control Module (PCM) Reset.) COMPLETE a HO2S monitor drive cycle. (REFER to Drive Cycles.) REPEAT Test Step H20. If test results are greater than 0.6 volts, testing is complete. Oxygen Sensor test results are out of an acceptable range. GO to H21.

Fig. 184   Test H: Fuel Control (Part 4 of 21). 1994

FM0159401188040X

TEST STEP		RESULT	▶	ACTION TO TAKE

H21	**CHECK FOR SOURCE OF POTENTIAL HO2S CONTAMINATION**
	• Investigate the following items as a potential source of HO2S contamination.
	  — Use of unapproved Silicon sealers.
	  — Fuel contaminated by silicon additives.
	  — Excessive oil burning (i.e. rings, valve seals and oil overfill).
	  — Glycol (antifreeze) leaking internally in the engine.
	  — Lead contaminated fuel.
	  — Use of unapproved cleaning agents.
	• **Are any of the above conditions present?**
		Yes
		
		No
			▶
			
			▶
				REPAIR source of contamination. REPLACE HO2S and oil / filter. COMPLETE PCM reset to clear DTCs (REFER to Powertrain Control Module (PCM) Reset.) COMPLETE a HO2S monitor drive cycle (REFER to Drive Cycles).
				GO to H22.

H22	**CHECK FOR UNMETERED AIR LEAKS**
	Fuel calculations can be affected by unmetered air leaks.
	• Carefully inspect the following areas for potential air leaks.
	  — Hoses connecting to MAF.
	  — Hoses connecting to Throttle Body.
	  — Intake manifold gasket leaks.
	  — PCV disconnected.
	  — Vacuum lines disconnected.
	  — Improperly seated dip stick and tube.
	• **Are there any air leaks?**
		Yes
		
		No
			▶
			
			▶
				Air leaks located. REPAIR source of air leak. COMPLETE PCM reset to clear DTCs (REFER Powertrain Control Module (PCM) Reset.) COMPLETE a HO2S monitor drive cycle (REFER to Drive Cycles.)
				GO to H23.

H23	**CHECK OF HO2S CIRCUIT WIRING WITH PCM CONNECTED** • Key off. • PCM connected. • Suspect HO2S disconnected. • Jumper HO2S Signal to VPWR at the HO2S harness connector. • Scan Tool connected. • Key on, engine off. • Access the correct HO2S PID. NOTE: (HO2S displayed as O2S on Scan Tool.) • **Is the voltage greater than 3.50 volts?**	Yes No	▶ ▶	HO2S signal circuit is not faulty. REPLACE HO2S, change oil / filter, COMPLETE PCM reset to clear DTCs (REFER to Powertrain Control Module (PCM) Reset.) COMPLETE a HO2S monitor drive cycle (REFER to Drive Cycles.) GO to H24.

Fig. 184   Test H: Fuel Control (Part 5 of 21). 1994

FM0159401188050X

TEST STEP		RESULT	▶	ACTION TO TAKE

H24	**CHECK RESISTANCE OF HO2S SIGNAL CIRCUIT**
	• Key off.
	• PCM disconnected, breakout box installed.
	• Measure the resistance between HO2S Signal Test Pin at the breakout box and the HO2S harness connector.
	• Measure the resistance between Signal RTN test pin at the breakout box and the HO2S harness connector.
	  — HO2S-11 = Sig. Pin 60
	  — HO2S-21 = Sig. Pin 87
	  — HO2S-11 = Sig. RTN Pin 91
	  — HO2S-21 = Sig. RTN Pin 91
	• **Is the resistance less than 5.0 ohms?**
		Yes
		
		No
			▶
			
			▶
				GO to H25.
				Resistance is high. SERVICE open circuit. REMOVE breakout box. RECONNECT all components. COMPLETE a HO2S monitor drive cycle (REFER to Drive Cycles.)

H25	**CHECK FOR SHORT IN HO2S CIRCUIT**
	• Key off.
	• Breakout box installed. PCM disconnected.
	• Measure the resistance between the HO2S Signal Test Pin and VPWR circuit and HO2S Signal Test Pin and Signal return circuit.
	  — HO2S-11 = Sig. Pin 60
	  — HO2S-21 = Sig. Pin 87
	  — VPWR = 71/97
	  — Signal RTN = 91
	• **Is the resistance greater than 10,000 ohms?**
		Yes
		
		No
			▶
			
			▶
				PCM is at fault. REPLACE PCM. COMPLETE a HO2S monitor drive cycle (REFER to Drive Cycles.)
				SERVICE short circuit. REMOVE breakout box. RECONNECT all components. COMPLETE a HO2S monitor drive cycle (REFER to Drive Cycles.)

Fig. 184   Test H: Fuel Control (Part 6 of 21). 1994

FM0159401188060X

TEST STEP		RESULT	▶	ACTION TO TAKE
H30	**DTCS 0135, 0141, 0155 AND 0161: HO2S HEATER SIGNAL CIRCUIT OPEN, SHORTED TO GND OR SHORTED TO B+** Diagnostic Trouble Codes (DTCs) 0135, 0141, 0155 and 0161 received separately indicate a short to ground or open in the HO2S heater circuit. DTCs received in pairs (0135 and 0155) (0141 and 0161) indicate the HO2S Heater Signal circuit shorted to a power source greater than 2.0 volts. DTCs received in pairs with one upstream heater code and one downstream heater code are treated as separate codes. **Fault Code/HO2S Reference Chart:** DTC 0135 = HO2S HTR - 11 DTC 0141 = HO2S HTR - 12 DTC 0155 = HO2S HTR - 21 DTC 0161 = HO2S HTR - 22 Possible Causes: — Shorts to B+ in harness or HO2S. — Water in connectors. — Cut or pulled wires. — Disconnected wiring. — Open VPWR circuit. — Open PWR GND. • Visually inspect the HO2S connectors for proper assembly, contamination and exposed wiring. NOTE: On some applications, a vehicle hoist may be required to access the HO2S harness. • **Were any concerns found during the visual inspection?**	Yes No	▶ ▶	REPAIR any concerns found in the visual inspection. RERUN Quick Test. For codes received individually: a short to GND or an open exists in the HO2S HTR circuit. GO to H31. For codes (0135 and 0155) received in pairs: a short to power exists in the HO2S HTR circuit. GO to H35. For codes (0141 and 0161) received in pairs: a short to power exists in the HO2S HTR circuit. GO to H35.
H31	**CHECK FOR VOLTAGE AT THE HO2S HEATER HARNESS CONNECTOR** • Key off. • Disconnect the appropriate HO2S. • Inspect both ends of the connector for damaged or pushed out pins, moisture, contamination, etc. Service as necessary. • Key on, engine off. • Measure the voltage between VPWR circuit and SIG RTN at the HO2S vehicle harness connector (refer to schematic at the beginning of H.) • **Is the voltage greater than 10.5 volts?**	Yes No	▶ ▶	There is sufficient VPWR. GO to H32. Insufficient VPWR. REPAIR VPWR circuit. RECONNECT all components. RERUN Quick Test.

Fig. 184   Test H: Fuel Control (Part 7 of 21). 1994

FM0159401188070X

TEST STEP		RESULT	▶	ACTION TO TAKE
H32	**CHECK HO2S HEATER RESISTANCE**			
	• Suspect sensor disconnected. • Inspect sensor end of the connector for damaged or pushed out pins, moisture, contamination, etc. Service as necessary. • Measure the resistance between VPWR circuit and Heater Sig. circuit at the HO2S connector. • **Is the resistance between 2.0 and 30.0 ohms?**	Yes No	▶ ▶	GO to **H33** REPLACE HO2S. RECONNECT all components. RERUN Quick Test.
H33	**CHECK FOR SHORTS TO GND IN THE HO2S HEATER HARNESS CIRCUIT**			
	• Key off. • Suspect sensor disconnected. • Disconnect PCM. Inspect for damaged or pushed out pins, corrosion, loose wires, etc. Service as necessary. • Install breakout box, leave PCM disconnected. • Use the following chart to measure the resistance between the appropriate test pins at the breakout box. — DTC 0135 = HO2S HTR-11 Test Pin 93 and Test Pins 24, 76, 103 and 91. — DTC 0141 = HO2S HTR-12 Test Pin 95 and Test Pins 24, 76, 103 and 91. — DTC 0155 = HO2S HTR-21 Test Pin 94 and Test Pins 24, 76, 103 and 91. — DTC 0161 = HO2S HTR-22 Test Pin 96 and Test Pins 24, 76, 103 and 91. • **Is the resistance greater 10,000 ohms?**	Yes No	▶ ▶	Resistance is within specification. GO to **H34** Reading indicates a short in the harness. REPAIR short circuit. RECONNECT all components. RERUN Quick Test.
H34	**CHECK FOR OPEN HO2S HEATER HARNESS CIRCUIT**			
	• Key off. • Suspect sensor disconnected. • Breakout box installed, PCM disconnected. • Use the following chart to measure the resistance between the appropriate test pins at the breakout box and the HO2S heater harness connector. HO2S-11 Test Pin 93 (Heater Sig) HO2S-12 Test Pin 95 (Heater Sig) HO2S-21 Test Pin 94 (Heater Sig) HO2S-22 Test Pin 96 (Heater Sig) • **Is the resistance less 5.0 ohms?**	Yes No	▶ ▶	OPEN heater circuit in the PCM. REPLACE PCM. REMOVE breakout box. RECONNECT all components. RERUN Quick Test OPEN in the wiring harness. REPAIR open in harness. REMOVE breakout box. RECONNECT all components. RERUN Quick Test

FM0159401188080X

Fig. 184   Test H: Fuel Control (Part 8 of 21). 1994

TEST STEP		RESULT	▶	ACTION TO TAKE
H35	**CHECK FOR HO2S HEATER SIGNAL SHORTED TO VPWR**			
	Upstream DTCs 0135 and 0155 and downstream DTCs 0141 and 0161 are received in pairs and indicate the HO2S heater signal is shorted to a voltage source greater than 2.0 volts. Possible Causes: — HO2S HTR SIG shorted to VPWR in the sensor. — Short in the harness. — Short in the PCM. — Both upstream sensors are disconnected. — Both downstream sensors are disconnected. • Use codes and inspect the upstream or downstream HO2S connectors for proper connection. • **Were the HO2S sensors connected during Self-Test?**	Yes No	▶ ▶	GO to **H36**. RECONNECT sensors. RERUN Quick Test.
H36	**CHECK HO2S HEATER RESISTANCE**			
	• Suspect sensors disconnected. • Inspect sensor end of the connector for damaged or pushed out pins, moisture, contamination, etc. Service as necessary. • Measure the resistance between VPWR circuit and HO2S heater signal at the HO2S connectors. • **Are both heater resistance readings between 2.0 and 30.0 ohms?**	Yes No	▶ ▶	GO to **H37**. Resistance out of specification. REPLACE HO2S(s). RECONNECT all components. RERUN Quick Test.
H37	**CHECK FOR SHORTS IN THE HO2S HEATER HARNESS CIRCUIT**			
	• Key off. • Suspect sensors disconnected. • Disconnect PCM. Inspect for damaged or pushed out pins, corrosion, loose wires, etc. Service as necessary. • Install breakout box, leave PCM disconnected. • Use the following chart to measure the resistance between the appropriate test pins at the breakout box. — DTC 0135 = HO2S HTR-11 Test Pin 93 and Test Pin 71 and 97. — DTC 0141 = HO2S HTR-12 Test Pin 95 and Test Pin 71 and 97. — DTC 0155 = HO2S HTR-21 Test Pin 94 and Test Pin 71 and 97. — DTC 0161 = HO2S HTR-22 Test Pin 91 and Test Pin 71 and 97. • **Is the resistance greater than 10,000 ohms?**	Yes No	▶ ▶	REPLACE PCM. REMOVE breakout box. RECONNECT all components. RERUN Quick Test. REPAIR shorted wiring in harness. REMOVE breakout box. RECONNECT all components. RERUN Quick Test.

FM0159401188090X

Fig. 184   Test H: Fuel Control (Part 9 of 21). 1994

TEST STEP		RESULT	▶	ACTION TO TAKE
H40	**DTCS 1131, 1151, 1132 AND 1152: DETERMINE CAUSE OF UPSTREAM HO2S(S) NOT SWITCHING. DTCS 1130 AND 1150: HO2S NOT SWITCHING FUEL SYSTEM AT THE ADAPTIVE LIMITS (RICH OR LEAN)**			
	• Diagnostic Trouble Codes (DTCs) 1131 and 1151 indicate the system is correcting RICH for an overly LEAN condition. HO2S voltage less than .45 volts. DTCs 1132 and 1152 indicate the system is correcting LEAN for an overly RICH condition. HO2S voltage greater than .45 volts. DTCs 1130 and 1150 indicate the fuel control system has reached its maximum compensation for a lean or rich condition. Possible Causes: • Fuel System — Excessive fuel pressure. — Leaking fuel injector(s). — Leaking pressure regulator. — Low fuel pressure. — Plugged injector(s). • Induction System — Air leaks after MAF. — Vacuum leaks. — Restricted air inlet. — PCV system. • Base Engine — Oil over fill. — Cam timing. — Compression. • Ignition — Coil and secondary side of ignition system. • **Are there any obvious concerns?**	Yes No	▶ ▶	REPAIR any of the problems found in the visual inspection. RERUN Quick Test. For DTCs 1130 and 1150: GO to **H42**. All others: GO to **H41**.
H41	**INITIATE KOER SELF-TEST**			
	• Key off. • Scan Tool connected. • Enter Key On Engine Running (KOER) Self-Test. • **Are any of the above HO2S codes from test step H40 present?**	Yes No	▶ ▶	GO to **H42**. The fault that produced the DTC is an intermittent. GO to Pinpoint Test Step **Z1** with the following data: HO2S-11, 21, 12, 22 PIDs and list of Possible Causes

FM0159401188100X

Fig. 184   Test H: Fuel Control (Part 10 of 21). 1994

TEST STEP		RESULT	▶	ACTION TO TAKE
H42	**CHECK FUEL PRESSURE**			
	WARNING: THE FUEL SYSTEM IS PRESSURIZED WHEN THE ENGINE IS NOT RUNNING. TO PREVENT INJURY OR FIRE, USE CAUTION WHEN WORKING ON THE FUEL SYSTEM. • Key off. • Install fuel pressure gauge. • Verify vacuum source to fuel regulator. **If engine will start:** • Start engine and idle. Record fuel pressure. • Increase engine speed to 2500 rpms and maintain for one minute. Record fuel pressure. **No Start:** • Cycle key on and off several times. Record fuel pressure. • **Is the fuel pressure between 30-45 psi (210-310 kPa)?**	Yes No	▶ ▶	Fuel system is capable of required fuel pressure. GO to **H43**. Fuel pressure out of specification.
H43	**CHECK SYSTEM ABILITY TO HOLD FUEL PRESSURE**			
	• Fuel pressure gauge installed. • Cycle key several times. • Verify there are no external leaks (repair as necessary). • **Does the fuel pressure remain within 5 psi of the highest reading after one minute?**	Yes No	▶ ▶	For No Starts: GO to **H44**. For all other DTCs: GO to **H49**. Excessive pressure loss. Follow fuel system diagnostic procedure
H44	**CHECK ABILITY OF INJECTOR(S) TO DELIVER FUEL**			
	• Pressure gauge installed. • Cycle key several times. • Locate and disconnect the Inertia Fuel Switch (IFS). • Monitor pressure gauge while cranking the engine for at least five seconds. • **Was there a pressure drop greater than 5 psi (34 kPa)?**	Yes No	▶ ▶	The EEC-V System is not the cause of the no start. REMOVE the fuel pressure gauge. RECONNECT the IFS switch. REMOVE fuel pressure gauge. RECONNECT IFS switch. GO to **H45**

FM0159401188110X

Fig. 184   Test H: Fuel Control (Part 11 of 21). 1994

Fig. 184 Test H: Fuel Control (Part 12 of 21). 1994

TEST STEP	RESULT	▶	ACTION TO TAKE
H45 CHECK RESISTANCE OF INJECTOR(S) AND HARNESS • Key off. • Disconnect PCM. Inspect for damaged or pushed out pins, corrosion, loose wires etc. Service as necessary. NOTE: **This erases Continuous Codes.** • Install breakout box, leave PCM disconnected. • Measure resistance between suspect injector Test Pin(s) and Test Pin 71 or 97 at the breakout using the chart below.	Yes No	▶ ▶	Injector and harness resistance is OK. For No Start and DTCs: GO to **H48**. For all others: GO to **H46**.

Cyl. No.	Test Pin	Cyl. No.	Test Pin
1	75	5	73
2	101	6	99
3	74	7	72
4	100	8	98

TEST STEP	RESULT	▶	ACTION TO TAKE
• For No Starts: Pick any injector and measure resistance between injector Test Pin and Test Pin 71 or 97 at the breakout box. • **Is the resistance between 11.0–18.0 ohms?**			
H46 CHECK CONTINUITY OF FUEL INJECTOR HARNESS • Key off. • Breakout box installed, PCM disconnected. • Disconnect injector harness connector at the suspect injector. • Measure the resistance between Test Pin 71 or 97 at the breakout box and the VPWR pin at the injector harness connector. • Measure resistance between the injector Test Pin(s) at the breakout box and the injector signal pin at the injector connector. (Refer to chart in H45 for injector pin location.) • **Is each resistance less than 5.0 ohms?**	Yes No	▶ ▶	GO to **H47**. SERVICE open harness circuit. REMOVE breakout box. RECONNECT PCM and injectors. DRIVE vehicle for 5 miles / 55 mph. RERUN Quick Test.

FM0159401188120X

Fig. 184 Test H: Fuel Control (Part 13 of 21). 1994

TEST STEP	RESULT	▶	ACTION TO TAKE
H47 CHECK INJECTOR HARNESS CIRCUIT FOR SHORT TO POWER OR GROUND • Key off. • Breakout box installed, PCM disconnected. • Suspect fuel injector harness disconnected. • Measure resistance between the injector Test Pin(s) and Test Pin 71 or 97, 24, 76 and 103 at the breakout box. • Measure the resistance between the injector Test Pin(s) at the breakout box and chassis ground. • **Is each resistance greater than 10,000 ohms?**	Yes No	▶ ▶	REPLACE injector. REMOVE breakout box. RECONNECT PCM and all injector(s). RERUN Quick Test. SERVICE short circuit. REMOVE breakout box. RECONNECT PCM and all injector(s). DRIVE vehicle 5 miles / 55 mph. RERUN Quick Test.
H48 CHECK INJECTOR DRIVER SIGNAL Requires standard 12 volt test lamp. • Key off. • Breakout box installed. • Connect PCM to breakout box. • Connect test lamp between Test Pin 71 or 97 and each injector. • Crank or start engine. NOTE: A properly operating system will show a dim glow at idle on the test lamp. • **Does test lamp have a dim glow while cranking or running engine?**	Yes No	▶ ▶	REMOVE breakout box. RECONNECT PCM. GO to **H49**. No light / Continuous bright light. REPLACE PCM. REMOVE breakout box. DRIVE vehicle 5 miles / 55 mph. RERUN Quick Test.
H49 FLOW TEST INJECTOR(S) • Flow test injector(s). • **Is the leakage and flow within specification?**	Yes No	▶ ▶	DTCs **1130** and **1150**: GO to **H51**. All others: GO to **H50**. CLEAN or REPLACE as instructed. DRIVE vehicle for 5 miles / 55 mph. RERUN Quick Test

FM0159401188130X

Fig. 184 Test H: Fuel Control (Part 14 of 21). 1994

TEST STEP	RESULT	▶	ACTION TO TAKE
H50 CHECK CYLINDER COMPRESSION • Check cylinder compression. • **Are cylinder compression readings within specification?**	Yes No	▶ ▶	For DTCs 1131, 1151, 1130 and 1150: GO to **H51**. For DTCs 1132, 1152, 1130 AND 1150: GO to **H56**. REPAIR as necessary. COMPLETE PCM reset to clear DTCs (REFER to Powertrain Control Module (PCM) Reset.) RERUN Quick Test.
H51 CHECK HO2S INTEGRITY Diagnostic Trouble Codes (DTCs) 1131 and 1151 and / or 1130 and 1150 indicate HO2S always lean, slow to switch, lack of switching or fuel at adaptive limit. Possible Causes: — Moisture inside the HO2S harness connector resulting in a short to ground. — HO2S coated with contaminates. — HO2S circuit open. — HO2S circuit shorted to ground. • Key off. • Inspect HO2S harness for chaffing, burnt wires or other damage and service. • Inspect HO2S and connector for indications of submersions in water, oil, coolant, etc., and service. • Run engine at 2000 rpm for two minutes. • Key off. • Activate Key On Engine Running (KOER) Self-Test. • **Are there codes present?**	Yes No	▶ ▶	GO to **H52**. HO2S system is OK. Fuel delivery system is OK. Faults may have been repaired while doing inspection. Testing is complete at this time.

FM0159401188140X

Fig. 184 Test H: Fuel Control (Part 15 of 21). 1994

TEST STEP	RESULT	▶	ACTION TO TAKE
H52 CHECK HO2S ABILITY TO GENERATE A VOLTAGE GREATER THAN 0.5 VOLTS Any vacuum or air leaks in non-EEC areas could cause DTCs 1131, 1151, 1130 and 1150. Possible Causes: — Leaking vacuum actuators. — Engine sealing. — EGR system. — PCV system. — Unmetered air leaks between throttle body and Mass Air Flow (MAF). — Silicon contaminated HO2S. • Key off. • Disconnect the suspect HO2S from vehicle harness. • Connect DVOM to the HO2S Signal and HO2S SIG RTN or HO2S GND at the HO2S connector. DVOM on 20 volt scale. • Run engine at 2000 rpm for two minutes. • Rerun KOER Self-Test and monitor HO2S voltage. • **Does DVOM indicate greater than 0.5 volt at the end of Self-Test?**	Yes No	▶ ▶	GO to **H53**. REPLACE HO2S. RERUN Quick Test.
H53 CHECK CONTINUITY OF HO2S AND HO2S GROUND CIRCUITS • Key off. • Breakout box installed, PCM disconnected. • Disconnect suspect HO2S from harness. Inspect both ends or connector for damaged or pushed out pins, moisture, corrosion, loose pins etc. and service. • Measure the resistance between HO2S Signal Test Pin at the breakout box and the HO2S harness connector. Use the Pin assignment below and record the reading. • Measure resistance between SIG RTN test pin at the breakout box and HO2S SIG RTN harness connector. Record readings. — HO2S-11 SIG = Test Pin 60 — HO2S-21 SIG = Test Pin 87 — HO2S SIG RTN = Test Pin 91 • **Is the resistance reading less than 5.0 ohms?**	Yes No	▶ ▶	GO to **H54**. SERVICE open circuit. REMOVE breakout box. RECONNECT PCM and HO2S. DRIVE 5 miles / 55 mph. RERUN Quick Test.

FM0159401188150X

TEST STEP	RESULT	▶	ACTION TO TAKE
H54 CHECK HO2S CIRCUIT WIRING HARNESS FOR SHORT TO GROUND			
• Key off. • Breakout box installed, PCM disconnected. • HO2S disconnected. • Measure resistance between the HO2S Signal Test Pin and Test Pins 24, 51, 76, 77 and 103 at the breakout box. • **Is each resistance greater than 10,000 ohms?**	Yes No	▶ ▶	GO to **H55**. SERVICE short circuit. REMOVE breakout box. RECONNECT PCM and HO2S. DRIVE 5 miles / 55 mph. RERUN Quick Test.
H55 CHECK HO2S FOR SHORT TO GROUND			
• Key off. • Breakout box installed, PCM disconnected. • HO2S connected. • Measure resistance between PWR GND / SIG RTN Test Pin and HO2S Signal Test Pin at the breakout box. HO2S-11 SIG = Test Pin 60 HO2S-21 SIG = Test Pin 87 HO2S PWR GND = Test Pin 24, 76 and 103 HO2S SIG RTN = Test Pin 91 • **Is resistance greater than 10,000 ohms?**	Yes No	▶ ▶	For DTCs 1131C, 1151C, 1130 and 1150: GO to **H61**. For other HO2S DTCs: REMOVE breakout box. RECONNECT HO2S. REPLACE PCM. REPLACE HO2S. REMOVE breakout box. RECONNECT PCM. DRIVE 5 miles / 55 mph. RERUN Quick Test.
H56 CHECK FOR DTCS 1132 AND 1152 WITH 1130 AND 1150			
• Key off. • Scan Tool connected. • Activate Key On Engine Running (KOER) Self-Test. • **Is DTCs 1132 or 1152 present?**	Yes No	▶ ▶	GO to **H57**. The fault that produced the DTC is an intermittent. GO to Pinpoint Test Step **Z1** with the following data: HO2S-11, 21, 12, 22 PIDs and list of possible causes.

FM0159401188160X

Fig. 184   Test H: Fuel Control (Part 16 of 21). 1994

TEST STEP	RESULT	▶	ACTION TO TAKE
H57 CHECK FOR HO2S SIGNAL SHORTED TO POWER			
Diagnostic Trouble Codes (DTCs) 1132 and 1152 and / or 1130 indicate HO2S always rich. — Moisture inside the HO2S harness connector resulting in a short to power. — HO2S circuit shorted to power. • Key off. • Disconnect the suspect HO2S from vehicle harness. • Inspect both ends of the connector for damaged or pushed out pins, moisture, corrosion, loose wires, etc. and service as necessary. • Key on, engine off. • Measure the voltage between HO2S circuit and PWR GND at the HO2S harness connector (refer to schematic before pinpoint test). • **Is the voltage less than 0.5 volts?**	Yes No	▶ ▶	GO to **H59**. An over voltage condition exists on the HO2S circuit. GO to **H58**.
H58 CHECK FOR SHORT TO POWER			
• Key off. • Inspect HO2S harness for chaffing, burnt wires or other damage and service as necessary. • Disconnect PCM from harness. Inspect both ends of connector for damaged or pushed out pins, moisture, corrosion, loose pins, etc. and service. • Install breakout box, leave PCM disconnected. • Suspect HO2S disconnected. • Measure the resistance between HO2S Signal and Test Pins 71 at the breakout box. • **Is the resistance greater than 10,000 ohms?**	Yes No	▶ ▶	REPLACE PCM. REMOVE breakout box. DRIVE 5 miles / 55 mph. RERUN Quick Test. SERVICE short to power. REMOVE breakout box. RECONNECT PCM. DRIVE 5 miles / 55 mph. RERUN Quick Test.
H59 CHECK HO2S FOR SHORT TO IGNITION RUN CIRCUIT			
• Key off. • HO2S disconnected. • Measure resistance between Test Pins 71 and 97 and HO2S Signal at the HO2S harness connector. • **Is resistance greater than 10,000 ohms?**	Yes No	▶ ▶	For DTCs 1132, 1152, 1130 AND 1150: GO to **H60**. REPLACE HO2S. DRIVE vehicle 5 miles / 55 mph. RERUN Quick Test.

FM0159401188170X

Fig. 184   Test H: Fuel Control (Part 17 of 21). 1994

TEST STEP	RESULT	▶	ACTION TO TAKE
H60 ATTEMPT TO GENERATE DTCS 1131 AND 1151			
• Key off. • HO2S disconnected. • Jumper HO2S Signal at the HO2S harness connector to the battery negative post. • Activate Key On Engine Running (KOER) Self-Test. • **Are DTCs 1131 or 1151 present?**	Yes No	▶ ▶	REMOVE jumper. GO to **H61**. REMOVE jumper. RECONNECT HO2S. DISCONNECT 104 pin connector. INSPECT both ends of connector for damaged or pushed out pins, moisture, corrosion, loose pins etc. and service as necessary. If OK, REPLACE PCM. RERUN KOER Self-Test.
H61 HO2S CHECK			
• Key off. • Suspect HO2S disconnected. • Connect DVOM to HO2S Signal circuit and HO2S SIG RTN at the HO2S sensor connector. • DVOM on 20 volt scale. • Disconnect vacuum hose from vacuum tree. • Start engine and run at 2000 rpm. • **Does the DVOM indicate less than 0.4 volts within 30 seconds?**	Yes No	▶ ▶	GO to **H70**. REPLACE HO2S. RECONNECT vacuum hose. DRIVE 5 miles / 55 mph. RERUN Quick Test.
H70 MONITOR HO2S (PID)			
• Key on, engine running. • Engine at operating temperature. • Access suspect HO2S PID using Scan Tool. NOTE: (HO2S displayed as O2S on Scan Tool.) • View HO2S PID while wiggling, bending, and shaking small sections of the EEC harness from the PCM to the HO2S. • **Did the HO2S voltage stay high (greater than 0.45 volts) or low (less than 0.45 volts)?**	Yes No	▶ ▶	ISOLATE cause of lack of HO2S switches and service. COMPLETE PCM reset to clear DTCs (REFER to Powertrain Control Module (PCM) Reset). RERUN Quick Test. GO to H71.

FM0159401188180X

Fig. 184   Test H: Fuel Control (Part 18 of 21). 1994

TEST STEP	RESULT	▶	ACTION TO TAKE
H71 TEST DRIVE WHILE MONITORING HO2S PID			
NOTE: This test step requires an observer to monitor PID for proper operation. • Scan Tool still attached. • Access HO2S PID. • While observer views PID, test drive vehicle under different road conditions in an attempt to simulate the original fault. • **Does HO2S appear to switch properly?**	Yes No	▶ ▶	UNABLE to duplicate fault. CLEAR any codes. Testing complete at this time. REPLACE HO2S. COMPLETE PCM reset to clear DTCs (REFER to Powertrain Control Module (PCM) Reset). RERUN Quick Test.
H80 DTCS 0136 AND 0156 MONITOR DOWNSTREAM HO2S OUTPUT VOLTAGE FOR ACTIVITY. 1137, 1138, 1157, 1158 LACK OF HO2S SWITCHING			
DTC 0136 and 0156 indicate the output voltage of the downstream HO2S is within some calibratable functional window. KOER DTCs 1137, 1138, 1157 and 1158 can only be retrieved during KOER Self-Test when the fuel control is ramped rich and lean and monitored for a voltage change on the downstream HO2S. Possible Causes: • Wiring Concerns — Pinched, shorted, and corroded wiring and pins. — Crossed sensor wires • Other Concerns — Exhaust leaks — Contaminated or defective sensor • **Are any of the above concerns present?**	Yes No	▶ ▶	SERVICE as necessary. COMPLETE PCM reset to clear DTCs (REFER to Powertrain Control Module (PCM) Reset). COMPLETE a HO2S monitor drive cycle (REFER to Drive Cycles). GO to **H81**.
H81 CHECK FOR KOER DTCS 1137, 1138, 1157 OR 1158			
• Key off. • Scan Tool connected. • Key on, engine idling and stabilized. • Activate KOER Self-Test. • Check for DTCs. • **Are DTCs 1137, 1138, 1157 and 1158 present?**	Yes No	▶ ▶	GO to **H83**. For codes 0136, 0156: GO to **H82**. For DTCs 1137, 1138, 1157 and 1158: The fault that produced the DTC is an intermittent. GO to Pinpoint Test Step **Z1** with the following data: HO2S-11, 21, 12, 22 PIDs and list of possible causes.

FM0159401188190X

Fig. 184   Test H: Fuel Control (Part 19 of 21). 1994

Fig. 184 Test H: Fuel Control (Part 20 of 21). 1994

TEST STEP	RESULT	▶	ACTION TO TAKE
H82 CHECK FOR CROSSED HO2S HARNESS CONNECTOR • Key off. • Disconnect the HO2S that corresponds to the DTCs.	Yes	▶	DTCs correspond to correct HO2S location indicating HO2S are not crossed. GO to **H83**.
HO2S / Original DTC / Heater DTC HO2S-12 / 0136 / 0141 HO2S-22 / 0156 / 0161 • Activate KOER Self-Test. • Is a corresponding HO2S HTR fault code generated? NOTE: Disregard any codes other than HO2S HTR codes.	No	▶	CHECK for crossed HO2S and wiring. REFER to schematic for correct HO2S pin location. COMPLETE a HO2S Monitor Drive Cycle (REFER to Drive Cycles).
H83 CHECK EXHAUST SYSTEM FOR LEAKS NOTE: Any exhaust leaks between the engine and the end of the Catalyst may cause DTC 0136, 0156. • Key off. • Place vehicle on a hoist, transmission in park, emergency brake applied, raise vehicle. • Inspect the following: — Exhaust flanges for leaks. — HO2S torque. — Check for punctures and cracks in Catalyst and pipes leading to them. • Are there any exhaust leaks?	Yes	▶	REPLACE or REPAIR as required. COMPLETE PCM reset to clear DTCs (REFER to Powertrain Control Module (PCM) Reset). COMPLETE a HO2S Monitor Drive Cycle (REFER to Drive Cycles).
	No	▶	GO to **H84**.
H84 CHECK HO2S CIRCUIT CONTINUITY • Key off. • PCM connected. • Suspect HO2S disconnected. • Jumper HO2S Signal to VPWR at the HO2S harness connector. • Scan Tool connected. • Key on, engine off. • Access the correct HO2S PID. NOTE: (HO2S displayed as O2S on Scan Tool.)	Yes	▶	REPLACE HO2S. COMPLETE PCM reset to clear DTCs (REFER to Powertrain Control Module (PCM) Reset). COMPLETE a HO2S Monitor Drive Cycle (REFER to Drive Cycles).
DTC / HO2S / PINS 0136 / HO2S-12 / 35 and 91 0156 / HO2S-22 / 61 and 91 • Is the voltage reading greater than 3.50 volts?	No	▶	GO to **H85**.

FM0159401188200X

Fig. 184 Test H: Fuel Control (Part 20 of 21). 1994

TEST STEP	RESULT	▶	ACTION TO TAKE
H85 CHECK HO2S HARNESS CIRCUIT FOR SHORT TO VPWR AND GROUND • Key off. • Breakout box installed, PCM disconnected. Inspect both ends of connector for damaged or pushed out pins, moisture, corrosion, loose pins, etc. and service. • HO2S disconnected. • Measure the resistance between HO2S Signal Test Pin and SIG RTN Test Pin at the breakout box. • Measure the resistance between HO2S Signal Test Pin and VPWR Test Pin at the breakout box. HO2S-12 SIG = Test Pin 35 HO2S-22 SIG = Test Pin 61 HO2S SIG RTN = Test Pin 91 PWR GND = Test Pins 24, 76 and 103 VPWR = Test Pins 71 and 97 • Is resistance greater than 10,000 ohms?	Yes No	▶ ▶	GO to **H86**. SERVICE short in harness. COMPLETE PCM reset to clear DTCs (REFER to Powertrain Control Module (PCM) Reset). COMPLETE a HO2S Monitor Drive Cycle (REFER to Drive Cycles).
H86 CHECK CONTINUITY OF HO2S AND HO2S GROUND CIRCUITS • Key off. • Breakout box installed, PCM disconnected. • Disconnect suspect HO2S from harness. • Measure the resistance between HO2S Signal Test Pin at the breakout box and the HO2S harness connector. Record readings. • Measure resistance between SIG RTN Test Pin at the breakout box and HO2S SIG RTN harness connector. Record readings. — HO2S-12 SIG = Test Pin 35 — HO2S-22 SIG = Test Pin 61 — HO2S SIG RTN = Test Pin 91 • Is the resistance reading less than 5.0 ohms?	Yes	▶	If sent here from Pinpoint Test Step **HF2**, HO2S testing is complete. RETURN to **HF3** for additional testing. Otherwise: REPLACE PCM. REMOVE breakout box. RECONNECT all components. COMPLETE a HO2S Monitor Drive Cycle (REFER to Drive Cycles).
	No	▶	REPAIR open circuit in harness. REMOVE breakout box. RECONNECT all components. COMPLETE a HO2S Monitor Drive Cycle (REFER to Drive Cycles).

FM0159401188210X

Fig. 184 Test H: Fuel Control (Part 21 of 21). 1994

Pinpoint Test Schematic

71/91 VPWR

GND TO PCM

INJECTOR VEHICLE HARNESS CONNECTOR

HEATED OXYGEN SENSOR (HO2S) VEHICLE HARNESS CONNECTOR (PIN LOCATIONS REFERENCED FROM LARGE TAB)

HO2S HEATER GND (FROM PCM)

LARGE TAB

*VPWR

*HO2S SIGNAL

SIGNAL RETURN

*GOLD PLATED TERMINALS

HO2S Connector Pin Assignment

Signal	Pin #	Wire Color	HO2S Heater Ground	Pin #	Wire Color	Heater VPWR	Pin #	Wire Color	HO2S SIG RTN	Pin #	Wire Color
HO2S-11	60	GY/LB	HO2S HTR-11 (GND)	93	R/W	VPWR	71/97	R	SIG RTN	91	GY/R
HO2S-12	35	R/LG	HO2S HTR-12 (GND)	95	W/BR	VPWR	71/97	R	SIG RTN	91	GY/R
HO2S-21	87	R/BK	HO2S HTR-21 (GND)	94	Y/LB	VPWR	71/97	R	SIG RTN	91	GY/R
HO2S-22	61	P/LG	HO2S HTR-22 (GND)	96	T/Y	VPWR	71/97	R	SIG RTN	91	GY/R

Fig. 185 Test H: Fuel Control (Part 1 of 24). 1995

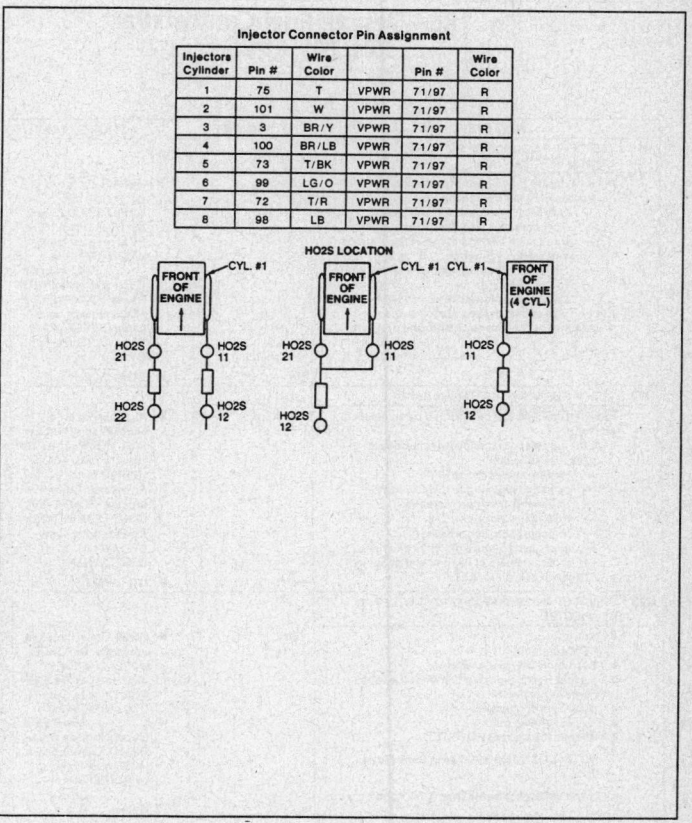

Injector Connector Pin Assignment

Injectors Cylinder	Pin #	Wire Color		Pin #	Wire Color
1	75	T	VPWR	71/97	R
2	101	W	VPWR	71/97	R
3	3	BR/Y	VPWR	71/97	R
4	100	BR/LB	VPWR	71/97	R
5	73	T/BK	VPWR	71/97	R
6	99	LG/O	VPWR	71/97	R
7	72	T/R	VPWR	71/97	R
8	98	LB	VPWR	71/97	R

HO2S LOCATION

Fig. 185 Test H: Fuel Control (Part 2 of 24). 1995

TEST STEP	RESULT	▶	ACTION TO TAKE
H10 DTCs P0132, P0138, P0152 AND P0158: HO2S SIGNAL OVER VOLTAGE			
Diagnostic Trouble Codes (DTC) P0132, P0138, P0152 and P0158 indicate an over voltage greater than 1.5 volts on the HO2S signal circuit. **DTC/HO2S Reference List:** DTC P0132 = HO2S-11 DTC P0138 = HO2S-12 DTC P0152 = HO2S-21 DTC P0158 = HO2S-22 Possible causes: — Signal shorted in the harness. — Signal shorted in the HO2S. — Signal shorted in the PCM. ● Key on, engine off. ● Scan Tool connected. ● Access the Parameter Identification (PID) for the DTC. NOTE: (HO2S displayed as O2S on Scan Tool.) ● Is the voltage greater than 1.0 volt and less than 4.0 volts?	Yes No	▶ ▶	An over voltage condition exists in the HO2S circuit. GO to H11. The fault that produced the DTC is an intermittent. GO to Pinpoint Test Step Z1 with the following data: HO2S-11, 21, 12, 22 PIDs and list of Possible Causes.
H11 CHECK FOR SHORTS IN THE HO2S HARNESS CIRCUIT			

● Key off.
● Suspect sensor disconnected.
● Disconnect PCM. Inspect for damaged or pushed out pins, corrosion, loose wires, etc. Service as necessary.
● Install breakout box, leave PCM disconnected.
● Use the following list to measure the resistance between the appropriate test pins at the breakout box.
— DTC P0132 = HO2S-11
  Test Pin 60 and Test Pins 71, 90, 93 and 97.
— DTC P0138 = HO2S-12
  Test Pin 35 and Test Pins 71, 90, 95 and 97.
— DTC P0152 = HO2S-21
  Test Pin 87 and Test Pins 71, 90, 94 and 97.
— DTC P0158 = HO2S-22
  Test Pin 61 and Test Pins 71, 90, 96 and 97.
● Is the resistance greater than 10,000 ohms?
	Yes
	
	No
		▶
		
		▶
			REMOVE breakout box. RECONNECT PCM. GO to H12.
			REPAIR short in harness. REMOVE breakout box. RECONNECT all components. RERUN Quick Test.

Fig. 185 Test H: Fuel Control (Part 3 of 24). 1995

TEST STEP	RESULT	▶	ACTION TO TAKE
H12 CHECK FOR HO2S SIGNAL SHORT TO HO2S HEATER CIRCUIT IN THE SENSOR			
● Key off. ● Suspect HO2S sensor disconnected. ● Scan Tool connected. ● Key on, engine off. ● Access HO2S (PID) corresponding to DTCs received. NOTE: HO2S displayed as O2S on Scan Tool. ● Is the HO2S voltage less than 0.2 volt?	Yes No	▶ ▶	REPLACE HO2S. RECONNECT all components. RERUN Quick Test. REPLACE PCM. RECONNECT all components. RERUN Quick Test.
H20 DIAGNOSTIC TROUBLE CODES (DTCS) P0133 AND P0153: HO2S RESPONSE TEST			
Diagnostic Trouble Codes (DTCs) P0133 and P0153 indicate the response rate of the HO2S is below some calibrated window. **DTC/HO2S Reference List:** DTC P0133 = HO2S-11 DTC P0153 = HO2S-21 Possible causes: — Contaminated HO2S. — Exhaust leaks. — Shorted / open wires. — Excessive fueling. — MAF meter. — Air leaks. ● Key off. ● Scan Tool connected. ● Key on, engine off. ● Access Generic OBD II functions and trigger. ● Scroll to Oxygen Sensor Test and trigger. ● Scroll to Manufacturer Specific Test ID and trigger. ● Scroll to Test ID: (41H) and trigger. ● Is the measurement for the HO2S fault greater than 0.6 volt?	Yes No	▶ ▶	COMPLETE PCM reset to clear DTCs (refer to Powertrain Control Module (PCM) Reset.) COMPLETE a HO2S monitor drive cycle (REFER to Drive Cycles). REPEAT Test Step H20. If test results are greater than 0.6 volt, testing is complete. Oxygen Sensor test results are out of an acceptable range. GO to H21.

Fig. 185 Test H: Fuel Control (Part 4 of 24). 1995

TEST STEP	RESULT	▶	ACTION TO TAKE
H21 CHECK FOR SOURCE OF POTENTIAL HO2S CONTAMINATION			
● Investigate the following items as a potential source of HO2S contamination. — Use of unapproved silicon sealers. — Fuel contaminated by silicon additives. — Excessive oil burning (i.e. rings, valve seals and oil overfill). — Glycol (antifreeze) leaking internally in the engine. — Lead contaminated fuel. — Use of unapproved cleaning agents. ● Are any of the above conditions present?	Yes No	▶ ▶	REPAIR source of contamination. REPLACE HO2S and oil / filter. COMPLETE PCM reset to clear DTCs (REFER to Powertrain Control Module (PCM) Reset.) COMPLETE a HO2S monitor drive cycle (REFER to Drive Cycles). GO to H22.
H22 CHECK FOR UNMETERED AIR LEAKS			
Fuel calculations can be affected by unmetered air leaks. ● Carefully inspect the following areas for potential air leaks. — Hoses connecting to MAF. — Hoses connecting to throttle body. — Intake manifold gasket leaks. — PCV disconnected. — Vacuum lines disconnected. — Improperly seated dip stick and tube. — Exhaust leaks at flanges and gaskets. ● Are there any air leaks?	Yes No	▶ ▶	Air leaks located. REPAIR source of air leak. COMPLETE PCM reset to clear DTCs (REFER to Powertrain Control Module (PCM) Reset.) COMPLETE a HO2S monitor drive cycle (REFER to Drive Cycles). GO to H23.
H23 CHECK OF HO2S CIRCUIT WIRING WITH PCM CONNECTED			
● Key off. ● PCM connected. ● Suspect HO2S disconnected. ● Jumper HO2S Signal to VPWR at the HO2S harness connector. ● Scan Tool connected. ● Key on, engine off. ● Access the correct HO2S PID. NOTE: HO2S displayed as O2S on Scan Tool. ● Is the voltage greater than 1.50 volts?	Yes No	▶ ▶	HO2S signal circuit is not faulty. REPLACE HO2S. CHANGE oil / filter. COMPLETE PCM reset to clear DTCs (REFER to Powertrain Control Module (PCM) Reset.) COMPLETE a HO2S monitor drive cycle (REFER to Drive Cycles). GO to H24.

Fig. 185 Test H: Fuel Control (Part 5 of 24). 1995

TEST STEP	RESULT	▶	ACTION TO TAKE
H24 CHECK RESISTANCE OF HO2S SIGNAL CIRCUIT			
● Key off. ● PCM disconnected, breakout box installed. ● Measure the resistance between HO2S Signal Test Pin at the breakout box and the HO2S harness connector. ● Measure the resistance between Signal RTN test pin at the breakout box and the HO2S harness connector. — HO2S-11 = Sig. Pin 60 — HO2S-21 = Sig. Pin 87 — HO2S-11 = Sig. RTN Pin 91 — HO2S-21 = Sig. RTN Pin 91 ● Is the resistance less than 5.0 ohms?	Yes No	▶ ▶	GO to H25. Resistance is high. SERVICE open circuit. REMOVE breakout box. RECONNECT all components. COMPLETE a HO2S monitor drive cycle (REFER to Drive Cycles).
H25 CHECK FOR SHORT IN HO2S CIRCUIT			
● Key off. ● Breakout box installed. PCM disconnected. ● Measure the resistance between the HO2S Signal Test Pin at the breakout box and VPWR circuit and HO2S Signal Test Pin and Signal return circuit at the breakout box. — HO2S-11 = Sig. Pin 60 — HO2S-21 = Sig. Pin 87 — VPWR = 71/97 — Signal RTN = 91 ● Is the resistance greater than 10,000 ohms?	Yes No	▶ ▶	REPLACE PCM. COMPLETE a HO2S monitor drive cycle (REFER to Drive Cycles). SERVICE short circuit. REMOVE breakout box. RECONNECT all components. COMPLETE a HO2S monitor drive cycle (REFER to Drive Cycles).
H27 DTCS P0131 AND P0151: CONTAMINATED HO2S / VOLTAGE SHIFT			
Diagnostic Trouble Codes (DTCs) P0131 and P0151 are set when the HO2S generates a negative voltage. — DTC P0131 = HO2S-11 — DTC P0151 = HO2S-21 Possible causes: — Contaminated HO2S (water, fuel, etc.). — Crossed HO2S signal / signal return wiring. ● Check for water in HO2S connector. ● Is there water in the HO2S connector?	Yes No	▶ ▶	REPAIR source of water entry. Dry out connector. REPLACE HO2S. RERUN Quick Test. GO to H28.

Fig. 185 Test H: Fuel Control (Part 6 of 24). 1995

TEST STEP		RESULT	►	ACTION TO TAKE
H28	VERIFY WIRING IS IN PROPER PIN LOCATION			
	• Key off. • Suspect sensor disconnected. • Install breakout box, leave PCM disconnected. • Use the following list to measure the resistance between the appropriate test pins at the breakout box and the HO2S Signal and Signal RTN at the harness connector(s). — HO2S-11 = P0131 — HO2S Signal Test Pin 60 — HO2S-21 = P0151 — HO2S Signal Test Pin 87 — HO2S Signal RTN Test Pin 91 • Is the resistance less than 5.0 ohms?	Yes No	► ►	REPLACE HO2S. REMOVE breakout box. RECONNECT all components. RERUN Quick Test. REPAIR wiring as necessary. REMOVE breakout box. RECONNECT all components. RERUN Quick Test.
H30	DTCS P0135, P0141, P0155 AND P0161: HO2S HEATER SIGNAL CIRCUIT IS OPEN, SHORTED TO GROUND, SHORTED TO B+ OR EXCESSIVE CURRENT DRAW			
	Diagnostic Trouble Codes (DTCs) P0135, P0141, P0155 and P0161 indicate a short to ground, or open, or short to VPWR in the HO2S heater circuit. **DTC/HO2S Reference List** DTC P0135 = HO2S HTR-11 DTC P0141 = HO2S HTR-12 DTC P0155 = HO2S HTR-21 DTC P0161 = HO2S HTR-22 Possible causes: — Shorts to B+ in harness or HO2S. — Water in connectors. — Cut or pulled wires. — Disconnected wiring. — Open VPWR circuit. — Open GND circuit. — Corrosion or poor mating terminals. — Damaged PCM. • Visually inspect the HO2S circuit for exposed wiring, contamination, corrosion and proper assembly. NOTE: On some applications, a vehicle hoist may be required to access the HO2S harness. • Were any concerns found during the visual inspection?	Yes No	► ►	REPAIR any concerns found in the visual inspection. RERUN Quick Test. GO to **H31**.

Fig. 185   Test H: Fuel Control (Part 7 of 24). 1995

TEST STEP		RESULT	►	ACTION TO TAKE
H31	PERFORM KEY ON KOER SELF TEST			
	• Key off. • Scan tool connected. • Key on, engine on. • Engine at idle for 10 minutes. • Activate key on, engine running (KOER) self test. • Are DTCs P0135, P0141, P0155 or P0161 present?	Yes No	► ►	GO to **H32**. Fault may be intermittent. GO to Pinpoint Test Step **Z1** with the following data: HO2S PIDs and a list of possible causes.
H32	CHECK FOR VPWR AT THE VEHICLE HO2S HARNESS CONNECTOR			
	• Key off. • Disconnect the appropriate HO2S(s). • Inspect both ends of the connector(s) for damaged or pushed out pins, moisture, corrosion, contamination, etc. Service as necessary. • Key on, engine off. • Measure the voltage between VPWR and SIG RTN circuit at the HO2S vehicle harness connector (refer to schematic at the beginning of this pinpoint test). • Is the voltage greater than 10.5 volts?	Yes No	► ►	GO to **H34**. GO to **H33**.
H33	CHECK FOR OPEN VPWR CIRCUIT			
	• Key off. • Install breakout box, PCM disconnected. • Suspect sensor disconnected. • Measure the resistance between the VPWR Test Pin at the breakout box and VPWR at the HO2S vehicle harness connector. • Is the resistance less than 4.0 ohms?	Yes No	► ►	GO to **H34**. REPAIR open circuit. REMOVE breakout box. RECONNECT all components. RERUN Quick Test.
H34	CHECK HO2S HEATER RESISTANCE			
	• Key off. • HO2S disconnected. • Connect DVOM to HO2S HTR GND and VPWR Test Pins at the HO2S sensor connector, and measure the resistance. • Is the resistance between 3 and 30 ohms?	Yes No	► ►	GO to **H35**. REPLACE HO2S. REMOVE breakout box. RECONNECT all components. RERUN Quick Test.
H35	CHECK FOR HEATER GND AND VPWR SHORTED TO HO2S CASE			
	• Suspect sensor disconnected. • Measure the resistance between the HO2S Heater GND at the HO2S connector and the HO2S case. • Measure the resistance between the HO2S VPWR at the HO2S sensor connector and the HO2S sensor case. • Is the resistance greater than 10,000 ohms?	Yes No	► ►	GO to **H36**. REPLACE HO2S. REMOVE breakout box. RECONNECT all components. RERUN Quick Test.

Fig. 185   Test H: Fuel Control (Part 8 of 24). 1995

TEST STEP		RESULT	►	ACTION TO TAKE
H36	CHECK FOR SHORTS TO OTHER GROUNDS AND VPWR IN THE HO2S HEATER GROUND HARNESS CIRCUITS			
	• Key off. • Suspect sensor disconnected. • Disconnect PCM. • Breakout box installed, leave PCM disconnected. • Use the following list to measure the resistance between the appropriate test pins at the breakout box. — DTC P0135 = HO2S HTR-11 (HTR GND) Test Pin 93 and Test Pins 24, 76, 91 and 97. — DTC P0141 = HO2S HTR-12 (HTR GND) Test Pin 95 and Test Pins 24, 76, 103, 91 and 97. — DTC P0155 = HO2S HTR-21 (HTR GND) Test Pin 94 and Test Pins 24, 76, 103, 91 and 97. — DTC P0161 = HO2S HTR-22 (HTR GND) Test Pin 96 and Test Pins 24, 76, 103, 91 and 97. • Is the resistance greater than 10,000 ohms?	Yes No	► ►	GO to **H37**. REPAIR shorted circuit. REMOVE breakout box. RECONNECT all components. RERUN Quick Test.
H37	CHECK FOR OPEN HO2S HEATER GROUND HARNESS CIRCUIT			
	• Key off. • Suspect sensor disconnected. • Breakout box installed, PCM disconnected. • Use the following list to measure the resistance between the appropriate test pins at the breakout box and the HO2S HTR GND at the vehicle harness connector. — HO2S HTR-11 Test Pin 93 (HTR GND) — HO2S HTR-12 Test Pin 95 (HTR GND) — HO2S HTR-21 Test Pin 94 (HTR GND) — HO2S HTR-22 Test Pin 96 (HTR GND) • Is the resistance less than 4.0 ohms?	Yes No	► ►	Open or shorted circuit in the PCM. REPLACE PCM. REMOVE breakout box. RECONNECT all components. RERUN Quick Test. REPAIR open in harness. REMOVE breakout box. RECONNECT all components. RERUN Quick Test.

Fig. 185   Test H: Fuel Control (Part 9 of 24). 1995

TEST STEP		RESULT	►	ACTION TO TAKE
H40	DTCS P1131, P1151, P1132 AND P1152: UPSTREAM HO2S(S) NOT SWITCHING. DTCS P1130 AND P1150: HO2S NOT SWITCHING. DTCS P0172, P0174, P0171 AND P0175: FUEL SYSTEM AT ADAPTIVE LIMITS			
	NOTE: Before servicing DTCs P0171, P0172, P0174 and P0175, verify with the customer that before the "Check Engine Light" came on, the vehicle did not run out of fuel. Diagnostic Trouble Codes (DTCs) P1131 and P1151 indicate the system is correcting rich for an overly lean condition. The HO2S voltage is less than 0.45 volt. DTCs P1132 and P1152 indicate the system is correcting lean for an overly rich condition. The HO2S voltage is greater than 0.45 volt. DTCs P1130 and P1150 indicate the fuel control system has reached its maximum compensation for a lean or rich condition and HO2S is not switching. DTC P0171, left bank, and DTC P0174, right bank, indicate the fuel/air ratio is too lean. The system is at the rich limit. DTC P0172, left bank, and DTC P0175, right bank, indicate the fuel/air ratio is too rich. The system is at the lean limit. **DTC/HO2S Reference List** — HO2S-11 = DTCs P1130, P1131, P1132, P0171 and P0172. — HO2S-21 = DTCs P1150, P1151, P1152, P0174 and P0175. Possible causes: **Fuel System** — Excessive fuel pressure. — Leaking fuel injector(s). — Leaking fuel pressure regulator. — Low fuel pressure. — Plugged injector(s). — Damaged/disconnected HO2S circuit. **Induction System** — Air leaks after MAF. — Vacuum leaks. — Restricted air inlet. — PCV system.			

Fig. 185   Test H: Fuel Control (Part 10 of 24). 1995

TEST STEP	RESULT	▶	ACTION TO TAKE
H40 DTCS P1131, P1151, P1132 AND P1152: UPSTREAM HO2S(S) NOT SWITCHING. DTCS P1130 AND P1150: HO2S NOT SWITCHING, FUEL SYSTEM AT THE ADAPTIVE LIMITS (RICH OR LEAN) P0172, P0174 AND P0171 AND P0175: FUEL SYSTEM AT ADAPTIVE LIMITS (CONTINUED)			
Base Engine — Oil overfill. — Cam timing. — Compression. Ignition — Coil and secondary side of ignition system. • Check air intake for leaks, obstructions, and damage. • Check air filter, air filter housing for blockage. • Check positive crankcase ventilation system integrity. • Check engine vacuum integrity? • **Are there any obvious concerns?**	Yes No	▶ ▶	REPAIR any of the problems found in the visual inspection. RERUN Quick Test. GO to **H41**.
H41 INITIATE KOER SELF-TEST • Key off. • Scan Tool connected. • Enter Key On Engine Running (KOER) Self-Test. • **Are HO2S DTCs P1131, P1132, P1151 or P1152 present?**	Yes No	▶ ▶	GO to **H42** For DTCs P1130, P1150, P0171, P0174 and P0172 and P0175: GO to **H42**. All others: The fault that produced the DTC is an intermittent. GO to Pinpoint Test Step **Z1** with the following data: HO2S-11, 21, 12, 22 PIDs and list of Possible Causes.

Fig. 185   Test H: Fuel Control (Part 11 of 24). 1995

TEST STEP	RESULT	▶	ACTION TO TAKE
H42 CHECK FUEL PRESSURE **WARNING: THE FUEL SYSTEM IS PRESSURIZED WHEN THE ENGINE IS NOT RUNNING. TO PREVENT INJURY OR FIRE, USE CAUTION WHEN WORKING ON THE FUEL SYSTEM.** • Key off. • Install fuel pressure gauge. • Verify vacuum source to fuel pressure regulator. **If engine will start:** • Start engine and idle. Record fuel pressure. • Increase engine speed to 2500 rpm and maintain for one minute. Record fuel pressure. **No Start:** • Cycle key on and off several times. Record fuel pressure. • **Is the fuel pressure between 30-45 psi (210-310 kPa)?**	Yes No	▶ ▶	Fuel system is capable of required fuel pressure. GO to **H43**. Fuel pressure out of specification.
H43 CHECK SYSTEM ABILITY TO HOLD FUEL PRESSURE • Fuel pressure gauge installed. • Cycle key on and off several times. • Verify there are no external leaks (repair as necessary). • **Does the fuel pressure remain within 5 psi of the highest reading after one minute?**	Yes No	▶ ▶	For DTCs P1130, P1150, P0172, P0174 and P0175: GO to **H44**. For No Starts: GO to **H45**. All other DTCs: GO to **H50**. Excessive pressure loss. Follow fuel system diagnostic procedure
H44 CHECK SYSTEM ABILITY TO HOLD FUEL PRESSURE WITH KEY ON • Fuel pressure gauge installed. • Cycle key on then off several times. • Turn key on and engine off, monitor fuel pressure gauge. • **Does the fuel pressure remain within 5 psi of the highest reading after 10 seconds?**	Yes No	▶ ▶	For DTCs P1130, P1150, P0171 and P0174: GO to **H46**. For DTCs P0172 and P0175: GO to **H48**.

Fig. 185   Test H: Fuel Control (Part 12 of 24). 1995

TEST STEP	RESULT	▶	ACTION TO TAKE
H45 CHECK ABILITY OF INJECTOR(S) TO DELIVER FUEL • Pressure gauge installed. • Cycle key several times. • Locate and disconnect the Inertia Fuel Shutoff (IFS) Switch. • Monitor pressure gauge while cranking the engine for at least five seconds. • **Was there a pressure drop greater than 5 psi (34 kPa)?**	Yes No	▶ ▶	The EEC-V System is not the cause of the no start. REMOVE the fuel pressure gauge. RECONNECT the IFS switch. REMOVE fuel pressure gauge. RECONNECT IFS switch. GO to **H46**.
H46 CHECK RESISTANCE OF INJECTOR(S) AND HARNESS • Key off. • Disconnect PCM. Inspect for damaged or pushed out pins, corrosion, loose wires, etc. Service as necessary. NOTE: This erases Continuous Memory DTCs. • Install breakout box, leave PCM disconnected. • Measure resistance between suspect injector Test Pin(s) and Test Pin 71 or 97 at the breakout box using the chart below. NOTE: If a misfire DTC(s) are displayed with the Fuel Control DTC(s), use the misfire DTC(s) to determine the injector(s) requiring testing.	Yes No	▶ ▶	Fuel injector and harness resistance is OK. For No Start and DTCs: GO to **H49**. GO to **H47**.

Cyl. No.	Test Pin	Cyl. No.	Test Pin
1	75	5	73
2	101	6	99
3	74	7	72
4	100	8	98

• For No Starts:
Pick any fuel injector and measure resistance between injector Test Pin and Test Pin 71 or 97 at the breakout box.
• **Is the resistance between 11.0-18.0 ohms?**

Fig. 185   Test H: Fuel Control (Part 13 of 24). 1995

TEST STEP	RESULT	▶	ACTION TO TAKE
H47 CHECK CONTINUITY OF FUEL INJECTOR HARNESS • Key off. • Breakout box installed, PCM disconnected. • Disconnect injector harness connector at the suspect injector. • Measure the resistance between Test Pin 71 or 97 at the breakout box and the VPWR pin at the injector harness connector. • Measure resistance between the Injector Test Pin(s) at the breakout box and the Injector Signal Pin at the injector connector. (Refer to chart in H46 for Injector Pin location.) • **Is each resistance less than 5.0 ohms?**	Yes No	▶ ▶	GO to **H48**. SERVICE open harness circuit. REMOVE breakout box. RECONNECT PCM and fuel injectors. RERUN Quick Test.
H48 CHECK INJECTOR HARNESS CIRCUIT FOR SHORT TO POWER OR GROUND • Key off. • Breakout box installed, PCM disconnected. • Suspect fuel injector harness disconnected. • Measure resistance between the injector Test Pin(s) and Test Pin 71 or 97, 24, 76 and 103 at the breakout box (refer to chart in H46). • Measure the resistance between the Injector Test Pin(s) at the breakout box and chassis ground. • **Is each resistance greater than 10,000 ohms?**	Yes No	▶ ▶	GO to **H49**. SERVICE short circuit. REMOVE breakout box. RECONNECT PCM and all fuel injector(s). RERUN Quick Test.
H49 CHECK INJECTOR DRIVER SIGNAL Requires standard 12 volt test lamp. • Key off. • Breakout box installed. • Connect PCM to breakout box. • Connect test lamp between Test Pin 71 or 97 and each injector Test Pin (refer to chart in H46). • Crank or start engine. NOTE: Properly operating system will show a dim glow at idle on the test lamp. • **Does test lamp have a dim glow while cranking or running engine?**	Yes No	▶ ▶	REMOVE breakout box. RECONNECT PCM. GO to **H50**. No light / Continuous bright light. REPLACE PCM. REMOVE breakout box. RERUN Quick Test.

Fig. 185   Test H: Fuel Control (Part 14 of 24). 1995

TEST STEP	RESULT	►	ACTION TO TAKE
H50 FLOW TEST FUEL INJECTOR(S)			DTCs P0171, P0172, P0174 and P0175: The fault that produced the DTC is an intermittent. GO to Pinpoint Test Step Z1 with the following data: SF1, SF2, LFT1, LFT2 PIDs and list of possible causes. DTCs P1130 and P1150: GO to H52. All others: GO to H51.
• Flow test fuel injector(s). • Use the Rotunda Injector Tester 113-00001, SBDS Injector Tester or equivalent to flow test the injectors according to the instructions for the injector tester. • **Is the leakage and flow within specification?**	Yes	►	
	No	►	REPLACE injector. RERUN Quick Test.
H51 CHECK CYLINDER COMPRESSION			For DTCs P1131, P1130, P1151 and P1150: GO to H52. For DTCs P1132 and P1152: GO to H57.
• Check cylinder compression. Refer to (Engine) of the Service Manual. • **Are cylinder compression readings within specification?**	Yes	►	
	No	►	REPAIR as necessary. COMPLETE PCM Reset to clear DTCs (REFER to Powertrain Control Module (PCM) Reset). RERUN Quick Test.

Fig. 185   Test H: Fuel Control (Part 15 of 24). 1995

TEST STEP	RESULT	►	ACTION TO TAKE
H52 CHECK HO2S INTEGRITY			GO to H53.
Diagnostic Trouble Codes (DTCs) P1131 and P1151 and/or P1130 and P1150 indicate HO2S always lean, slow to switch, lack of switching or fuel at adaptive limit. Possible causes: — Moisture inside the HO2S harness connector resulting in a short to ground. — HO2S coated with contaminants. — HO2S circuit open. — HO2S circuit shorted to ground. • Key off. • Inspect HO2S harness for chafing, burned out wires or other damage and service. • Inspect HO2S and connector for indications of submersions in water, oil, coolant, etc., and service. • Run engine at 2000 rpm for two minutes. • Key off. • Activate Key On Engine Running (KOER) Self-Test. • **Are DTCs P1131 and/or P1151 present?**	Yes	►	
	No	►	HO2S system is OK. Fuel delivery system is OK. Faults may have been repaired while doing inspection. Testing is complete at this time.
H53 CHECK HO2S ABILITY TO GENERATE A VOLTAGE GREATER THAN 0.5 VOLT			GO to H54.
Any vacuum or air leaks in non-EEC areas could cause DTCs P1131, P1151, P1130 and P1150. Possible causes: — Leaking vacuum actuators. — Engine sealing. — EGR system. — PCV system. — Unmetered air leaks between throttle body and Mass Air Flow (MAF) sensor assembly. — Silicone contaminated HO2S. • Key off. • Disconnect the suspect HO2S from vehicle harness. • Connect DVOM to the HO2S Signal and HO2S SIG RTN or HO2S GND at the HO2S sensor connector. • DVOM on 20 volt scale. • Run engine at 2000 rpm for two minutes. • Rerun KOER Self-Test and monitor HO2S voltage. • **Does DVOM indicate greater than 0.5 volt during or at the end of Self-Test?**	Yes	►	
	No	►	REPLACE HO2S. RERUN Quick Test.

Fig. 185   Test H: Fuel Control (Part 16 of 24). 1995

TEST STEP	RESULT	►	ACTION TO TAKE
H54 CHECK CONTINUITY OF HO2S AND HO2S GROUND CIRCUITS			GO to H55.
• Key off. • Breakout box installed, PCM disconnected. • Disconnect suspect HO2S from harness. Inspect both ends of connector for damaged or pushed out pins, moisture, corrosion, loose pins, etc., and service. • Measure the resistance between HO2S Signal Test Pin at the breakout box and the HO2S vehicle harness connector. Use the Pin assignment below and record the reading. • Measure resistance between SIG RTN test pin at the breakout box and HO2S SIG RTN vehicle harness connector. Record readings. — HO2S-11 SIG = Test Pin 60 — HO2S-21 SIG = Test Pin 87 — HO2S SIG RTN = Test Pin 91 • **Is the resistance reading less than 5.0 ohms?**	Yes	►	
	No	►	SERVICE open circuit. REMOVE breakout box. RECONNECT PCM and HO2S. RERUN Quick Test.
H55 CHECK HO2S CIRCUIT WIRING HARNESS FOR SHORT TO GROUND			GO to H56.
• Key off. • Breakout box installed, PCM disconnected. • HO2S disconnected. • Measure resistance between the HO2S Signal Test Pin and Test Pins 24, 51, 76, 77 and 103 at the breakout box. • **Is each resistance greater than 10,000 ohms?**	Yes	►	
	No	►	SERVICE short circuit. REMOVE breakout box. RECONNECT PCM and HO2S. RERUN Quick Test.
H56 CHECK HO2S FOR SHORT TO GROUND			For DTCs 1130 and 1150: GO to H57. For DTCs 1131C and 1151C: GO to H62. For KOER DTCs P1131 and P1151: REMOVE breakout box. RECONNECT HO2S. REPLACE PCM.
• Key off. • Breakout box installed, PCM disconnected. • HO2S connected. • Measure resistance between PWR GND/SIG RTN Test Pin and HO2S Signal Test Pin at the breakout box. HO2S-11 SIG = Test Pin 60 HO2S-21 SIG = Test Pin 87 HO2S PWR GND = Test Pin 24, 76 and 103 HO2S SIG RTN = Test Pin 91 • **Is resistance greater than 10,000 ohms?**	Yes	►	
	No	►	REPLACE HO2S. REMOVE breakout box. RECONNECT PCM. RERUN Quick Test.

Fig. 185   Test H: Fuel Control (Part 17 of 24). 1995

TEST STEP	RESULT	►	ACTION TO TAKE
H57 CHECK FOR DTCS P1132 AND P1152 WITH P1130 AND P1150			GO to H58.
• Key off. • Scan Tool connected. • Activate Key On Engine Running (KOER) Self-Test. • **Are DTCs P1132 or P1152 present?**	Yes	►	
	No	►	The fault that produced the DTC is an intermittent. GO to Pinpoint Test Step Z1 with the following data: HO2S-11, 21, 12, 22 PIDs and list of possible causes.
H58 CHECK FOR HO2S SIGNAL SHORTED TO POWER			An over voltage condition exists in the HO2S circuit. GO to H59.
Diagnostic Trouble Codes (DTCs) P1132 and/or P1152 and/or P1130 and P1150 indicate HO2S always rich. Possible causes: — Moisture inside the HO2S harness connector resulting in a short to power. — HO2S circuit shorted to power. DTC P1130, P1132=HO2S-11 DTC P1150, P1152=HO2S-21 • Key on, engine off. • Scan Tool connected. • Access the Parameter Identification (PID) for the DTC generated. NOTE: HO2S displayed as O2S on Scan Tool. • **Is the voltage greater than 1.0 volt and less than 4.0 volts?**	Yes	►	
	No	►	GO to H61.
H59 CHECK FOR SHORTS TO VOLTAGE SOURCE IN THE HARNESS CIRCUIT			REMOVE breakout box. RECONNECT PCM. GO to H60.
• Key off. • Suspect sensor disconnected. • Disconnect PCM. Inspect for damaged or pushed out pins, corrosion, loose wires, etc. Service as necessary. • Install breakout box, leave PCM disconnected. • Use the following list to measure the resistance between the appropriate test pins at the breakout box. — DTC P1130, P1132=HO2S-11 Test Pin 60 and Test Pins 71, 93 and 97. — DTC P1150, P1152=HO2S-21 Test Pin 87 and Test Pins 71, 93 and 97. • **Is the resistance greater than 10,000 ohms?**	Yes	►	
	No	►	REPAIR short to power. REMOVE breakout box. RECONNECT all components. RERUN Quick Test.

Fig. 185   Test H: Fuel Control (Part 18 of 24). 1995

TEST STEP		RESULT	▶	ACTION TO TAKE
H60	CHECK FOR HO2S SIGNAL SHORTED TO HO2S HEATER CIRCUIT IN THE SENSOR			
	• Key off. • Suspect HO2S sensor disconnected. • Scan Tool connected. • Key on, engine off. • Access HO2S PID corresponding to DTCs received. NOTE: HO2S displayed as O2S on Scan Tool. • Is the HO2S voltage less than 0.2 volt?	Yes	▶	REPLACE HO2S. RECONNECT all components. RERUN Quick Test.
		No	▶	REPLACE PCM. RECONNECT all components. RERUN Quick Test.
H61	ATTEMPT TO GENERATE DTCS P1131 AND P1151			
	• Key off. • HO2S disconnected. • Jumper HO2S Signal at the HO2S harness vehicle connector to the battery negative post. • Activate Key On Engine Running (KOER) Self-Test. • Are DTCs P1131 or P1151 present?	Yes	▶	REMOVE jumper. GO to H62.
		No	▶	REMOVE jumper. RECONNECT HO2S. DISCONNECT PCM. INSPECT both ends of connector for damaged or pushed out pins, moisture, corrosion, loose pins, etc. and service as necessary. If OK, REPLACE PCM. RERUN KOER Self-Test.
H62	HO2S CHECK			
	• Key off. • Suspect HO2S disconnected. • Connect DVOM to HO2S Signal circuit and HO2S SIG RTN at the HO2S sensor connector. • DVOM on 20 volt scale. • Disconnect vacuum hose from vacuum tree. • Start engine and run at 2000 rpm. • Does the DVOM indicate less than 0.4 volt within 30 seconds?	Yes	▶	RECONNECT vacuum hose and HO2S. GO to H70.
		No	▶	REPLACE HO2S. RECONNECT vacuum hose. RERUN Quick Test.

Fig. 185 Test H: Fuel Control (Part 19 of 24). 1995

TEST STEP		RESULT	▶	ACTION TO TAKE
H70	MONITOR HO2S (PID) FOR NORMAL SWITCHING			
	• Key on, engine running. • Engine at operating temperature. • Access suspect HO2S PID using Scan Tool. NOTE: HO2S displayed as O2S on Scan Tool. • Access HO2S PID while wiggling, bending, and shaking small sections of the EEC harness from the PCM to the HO2S. • Did the HO2S voltage stay high (greater than 0.45 volt) or low (less than 0.45 volt)?	Yes	▶	ISOLATE cause of lack of HO2S switches and service. COMPLETE PCM Reset to clear DTCs (REFER to Powertrain Control Module (PCM) Reset). RERUN Quick Test.
		No	▶	GO to H71.
H71	TEST DRIVE WHILE MONITORING HO2S PID FOR NORMAL SWITCHING			
	NOTE: This test step requires an observer to monitor PID for proper operation. • Scan Tool still attached. • Access HO2S PID. • While observer views PID, test drive vehicle under different road conditions in an attempt to simulate the original fault. • Does HO2S appear to switch properly?	Yes	▶	UNABLE to duplicate fault. CLEAR any DTCs. Testing complete at this time.
		No	▶	REPLACE HO2S. COMPLETE PCM reset to clear DTCs (REFER to Powertrain Control Module (PCM) Reset). RERUN Quick Test.
H80	DTCS P0136 AND P0156 MONITOR DOWNSTREAM HO2S OUTPUT VOLTAGE FOR ACTIVITY			
	DTC P0136 and P0156 indicate the output voltage of the downstream HO2S is within some calibratable functional window. Possible causes: • Wiring Concerns — Pinched, shorted, and corroded wiring and pins — Crossed sensor wires • Other Concerns — Exhaust leaks — Contaminated or damaged sensor • Are any of the above concerns present?	Yes	▶	SERVICE as necessary. COMPLETE PCM reset to clear DTCs (REFER to Powertrain Control Module (PCM) Reset). COMPLETE a HO2S monitor drive cycle (REFER to Drive Cycles). RERUN Continuous Memory Self-Test.
		No	▶	GO to H81.

Fig. 185 Test H: Fuel Control (Part 20 of 24). 1995

TEST STEP		RESULT	▶	ACTION TO TAKE
H81	CHECK FOR CROSSED HO2S HARNESS CONNECTOR			
	• Key off. • Disconnect the HO2S that corresponds to the DTCs.	Yes	▶	DTCs correspond to correct HO2S location indicating HO2S are not crossed. GO to H82.

HO2S	Original DTC	Heater DTC
HO2S-12	P0136	P0141
HO2S-22	P0156	P0161

	• Activate KOEO Self-Test. • Is a corresponding HO2S HTR DTC generated? NOTE: Disregard any DTCs other than HO2S HTR codes.	No	▶	CHECK for crossed HO2S and wiring. REFER to schematic for correct HO2S pin location. COMPLETE an HO2S Monitor Drive Cycle (REFER to Drive Cycles). RERUN Continuous Memory Self-Test.
H82	CHECK EXHAUST SYSTEM FOR LEAKS			
	NOTE: Any exhaust leaks between the engine and the end of the catalyst may cause DTCs P0136 and P0156. • Key off. • Place vehicle on a hoist, transmission in park, emergency brake applied, raise vehicle. • Inspect the following: — Exhaust flanges for leaks. — HO2S torque. — Check for punctures and cracks in catalyst and pipes leading to them. • Are there any exhaust leaks?	Yes	▶	REPLACE or REPAIR as required. COMPLETE PCM reset to clear DTCs (REFER to Powertrain Control Module (PCM) Reset). COMPLETE a HO2S Monitor Drive Cycle (REFER to Drive Cycles). RERUN Continuous Memory Self-Test.
		No	▶	GO to H83.

Fig. 185 Test H: Fuel Control (Part 21 of 24). 1995

TEST STEP		RESULT	▶	ACTION TO TAKE
H83	CHECK HO2S HARNESS CIRCUIT FOR SHORT TO VPWR AND GROUND			
	• Key off. • Breakout box installed, PCM disconnected. Inspect both ends of connector for damaged or pushed out pins, moisture, corrosion, loose pins, etc. and service. • HO2S disconnected. • Measure the resistance between HO2S Signal Test Pin and SIG RTN Test Pin at the breakout box. • Measure the resistance between HO2S Signal Test Pin and VPWR and VREF Test Pin at the breakout box. • Measure the resistance between HO2S Signal Test Pin and PWR GND Test Pin at the breakout box. HO2S-12 SIG = Test Pin 35 HO2S-22 SIG = Test Pin 61 HO2S SIG RTN = Test Pin 91 PWR GND = Test Pins 24, 76 and 103 VPWR = Test Pins 71 and 97 VREF = Test Pin 90 • Is resistance greater than 10,000 ohms?	Yes	▶	GO to H84.
		No	▶	SERVICE short in harness. COMPLETE PCM reset to clear DTCs (REFER to Powertrain Control Module (PCM) Reset). COMPLETE a HO2S Monitor Drive Cycle (REFER to Drive Cycles). RERUN Continuous Memory Self-Test.
H84	CHECK CONTINUITY OF HO2S AND HO2S GROUND CIRCUITS			
	• Key off. • Breakout box installed, PCM disconnected. • Disconnect suspect HO2S from harness. • Measure the resistance between HO2S Signal Test Pin at the breakout box and the HO2S vehicle harness connector. Record readings. • Measure resistance between SIG RTN Test Pin at the breakout box and HO2S SIG RTN vehicle harness connector. Record readings. — HO2S-12 SIG = Test Pin 35 — HO2S-22 SIG = Test Pin 61 — HO2S SIG RTN = Test Pin 91 • Is the resistance reading less than 5.0 ohms?	Yes	▶	GO to H85.
		No	▶	REPAIR open circuit in harness. REMOVE breakout box. RECONNECT all components. COMPLETE an HO2S Monitor Drive Cycle (REFER to Drive Cycles). RERUN Continuous Memory Self-Test.

Fig. 185 Test H: Fuel Control (Part 22 of 24). 1995

TEST STEP	RESULT	▶	ACTION TO TAKE
H85 CHECK HO2S CIRCUIT CONTINUITY			
• Key off. • PCM connected. • Suspect HO2S connected. • Scan Tool connected. • Key on, engine off. • Access the correct HO2S PID. NOTE: HO2S displayed as O2S on Scan Tool.	Greater than 1.5 volts	▶	GO to **H87**.
	Less than 1.5 volts	▶	GO to **H86**.

DTC	HO2S	PINS
P0136	HO2S-12	35 and 97
P0156	HO2S-22	61 and 97

TEST STEP	RESULT	▶	ACTION TO TAKE
• Is the voltage reading?			
H86 CHECK CONTINUITY OF HO2S GROUND CIRCUIT IN THE PCM			
• Key off. • PCM connected to breakout box. Vehicle harness disconnected from breakout box. • Measure the resistance between SIG RTN Test Pin and PWR GND Test Pin at the breakout box. • Is the resistance reading less than 5.0 ohms?	Yes	▶	REPLACE HO2S. REMOVE breakout box. RECONNECT all components. COMPLETE an HO2S Monitor Drive Cycle. (REFER to Drive Cycles). RERUN Continuous Memory Self-Test.
	No	▶	REPLACE PCM. REMOVE breakout box. RECONNECT all components. COMPLETE an HO2S Monitor Drive Cycle. (REFER to Drive Cycles). RERUN Continuous Memory Self-Test.

Fig. 185   Test H: Fuel Control (Part 23 of 24). 1995

TEST STEP	RESULT	▶	ACTION TO TAKE
H87 CHECK FOR OVER VOLTAGE ON THE HO2S CIRCUIT IN THE PCM			
• Key on. • PCM connected to vehicle harness. • HO2S disconnected. • Measure the voltage between SIG RTN Test Pin at the HO2S vehicle harness connector and battery negative post. • Measure the voltage between HO2S Signal Test Pin at the HO2S vehicle harness connector and battery negative post. • Are the voltage readings greater than 1.5 volts?	Yes	▶	REPLACE PCM. RECONNECT all components. COMPLETE an HO2S Monitor Drive Cycle (REFER to Drive Cycles). RERUN Continuous Memory Self-Test.
	No	▶	REPLACE HO2S. RECONNECT all components. COMPLETE an HO2S Monitor Drive Cycle (REFER to Drive Cycles). RERUN Continuous Memory Self-Test.

Fig. 185   Test H: Fuel Control (Part 24 of 24). 1995

Note

You should enter this Pinpoint Test only when directed here.

Reminder

This Pinpoint Test is intended to diagnose the following:

• Fuel Pressure System
• Air Intake System
• Crankcase Ventilation
• Engine Vacuum
• HO2S Injector Harness

TEST STEP	RESULT	▶	ACTION TO TAKE
HB1 CONTINUOUS MEMORY DTCS 0171, 0172, 0174 AND 0175. CHECK FOR OTHER DTCS			
Diagnostic Trouble Codes (DTCs) 0171, left bank, and DTC 0174, right bank, indicate the fuel / air ratio is too lean. The system is at the rich limit. DTC 0172, left bank, and DTC 0175, right bank, indicate the fuel / air ratio is too rich. The system is at the lean limit. Possible Causes: — Fuel pressure. — Air Intake / System. — Crankcase ventilation. — Engine vacuum. — HO2S / Injector harness. • Are other DTCs present?	Yes	▶	SERVICE as required.
	No	▶	GO to **HB2**.
HB2 CHECK AIR INTAKE SYSTEM			
• Check air intake for leaks, obstructions, and damage. • Check air filter, air filter box for blockage. • Check crankcase ventilation system integrity. • Check engine vacuum integrity. • Are problems indicated?	Yes	▶	SERVICE as required.
	No	▶	GO to **HB3**.

FM0159401189010X

Fig. 186   Test HB: Adaptive Fuel (Part 1 of 3). 1994

TEST STEP	RESULT	▶	ACTION TO TAKE
HB3 CHECK FUEL TRIM PID STATUS			
• Key on, engine running. • Verify engine at operating temperature. • Scan Tool connected. • Access Fuel B1 and Fuel B2 PIDs. • Verify PIDs, read CL and O2S indicating closed loop and oxygen sensor signal. • Access LFT 1, LFT 2, SFT 1, and SFT 2 PIDs. • While at idle, view PIDs. • Increase engine speed to 2,000 rpm and return to idle. • Do the PID numbers change from positive to negative, or visa versa at least once on LFT and at a faster rate on SFT?	Yes	▶	Problem may be intermittent. GO to Pinpoint Test Step **Z1** with the following data: FPW, HO2S, LFT, MAF and SFT PIDs and list of Possible Causes.
	No	▶	GO to **HB4**.
HB4 CHECK CONTINUITY OF INJECTOR HARNESS			
• Key off. • Disconnect Powertrain Control Module (PCM) and injector vehicle harness connectors. Inspect connectors and harness for damaged or pushed out pins, corrosion, loose wires, chafing or burns. Service as necessary. • Install breakout box, leave PCM disconnected. • Measure resistance between VPWR pin at the injector vehicle harness connector and the VPWR pin at the breakout box. • Measure resistance between the injector signal pins at the vehicle harness connector and injector pins at the breakout box? • Is each resistance less than 5.0 ohms?	Yes	▶	GO to **HB5**.
	No	▶	SERVICE open in harness. REMOVE breakout box. RECONNECT all components. RERUN Quick Test.
HB5 CHECK INJECTOR HARNESS FOR SHORT TO POWER OR GROUND			
• Key off. • Breakout box installed, PCM disconnected. • Injectors disconnected. • Measure resistance between Test Pin 71 and the injector signal pins at the breakout box. • Measure resistance between the injector signal pins at the breakout box and chassis ground. • Is each resistance greater than 10,000 ohms?	Yes	▶	GO to **HB6**.
	No	▶	SERVICE short circuit. REMOVE breakout box. RECONNECT all components. RERUN Quick Test.

FM0159401189020X

Fig. 186   Test HB: Adaptive Fuel (Part 2 of 3). 1994

TEST STEP	RESULT	▶	ACTION TO TAKE
HB6 CHECK INJECTOR DRIVER SIGNAL			
• Key off. • Breakout box installed. • Connect PCM to breakout box. • Connect test lamp between VPWR Test Pin 7.1 and injector signal.Test Pin at the breakout box. • Crank engine. There should be a dim glow. • Is a dim glow present at each test pin?	Yes	▶	REMOVE breakout box. RECONNECT all components. GO to Pinpoint Test Step **HC1**.
	No	▶	REPLACE PCM. REMOVE breakout box. RECONNECT all components. RERUN Quick Test.

FM0159401189030X

Fig. 186   Test HB: Adaptive Fuel (Part 3 of 3). 1994

Note

You should enter this Pinpoint Test only when directed here.

Remember

This Pinpoint Test is intended to diagnose the following:

- Chassis Components
- Engine Vacuum
- Fuel Pressure
- Fuel Filter
- Fuel Return
- Fuel Supply
- Fuel Injector

Tables and Charts

FUEL INJECTOR APPLICATION CHART

Engine Application	Part Number 9F593	Electrical Connector Color	Resistance Ohms	Flow # /Hr	Rotunda Injector Tester Information	
					Flow Tube	Color Scale
Car:						
3.8L	F3DE-BD	Gray	11-18	14	1A	Gray
4.6L SOHC	F4SE-AB	Gold	11-18	19	1A	Yellow
4.6L SOHC	FOTE-DA	Gold	11-18	19	1A	Yellow
4.6L DOHC	F2LE-BA	Dk. Blue	11-18	24	2B	Lt. Blue
4.6L DOHC	F55E-AD	Dk. Blue	11-18	24	2B	Lt. Blue

FM0159401190030X

Fig. 187   Test HC: Fuel Delivery System (Part 1 of 7). 1994-95

CAUTION

Use care to prevent combustion from fuel spillage. No smoking, open flames or any kind of arcing.

SAFE FUEL HANDLING PRACTICES: GASOLINE, METHANOL AND METHANOL BLENDS

FIRE

- REPORT ALL FIRES to the appropriate authorities.
- FLAMES from methanol or methanol-gasoline blends MAY BE INVISIBLE.
- Know the locations of PORTABLE FIRE EXTINGUISHERS, FIRE BLANKETS, FIRE ALARMS and EYE / WASH SHOWER FACILITIES. Learn how to use them.
- Use a B or AFFF (light water) type FIRE EXTINGUISHER to fight flammable liquid fires.

FIRST AID

- IF SWALLOWED:
  - If GASOLINE has been swallowed, DO NOT induce vomiting. SEEK MEDICAL ATTENTION IMMEDIATELY!
  - If METHANOL OR A METHANOL / GASOLINE BLEND has been swallowed, induce vomiting under the direction of a physician or Poison Control Center. SEEK MEDICAL ATTENTION IMMEDIATELY!
- When overcome by vapors, if safe, MOVE VICTIM TO FRESH AIR. If not breathing, give artificial respiration or CPR (Cardiopulmonary Resuscitation) as appropriate. SEEK MEDICAL ATTENTION IMMEDIATELY!
- If SPLASHED IN EYES, FLUSH with large amounts of water for 15 minutes. Remove contact lenses, if worn. SEEK MEDICAL ATTENTION.
- If SPLASHED ON SKIN, REMOVE CONTAMINATED CLOTHING. WASH SKIN thoroughly with soap and water.

HEALTH

- ALL FUELS may be HARMFUL OR FATAL IF SWALLOWED.
- BE AWARE, IF SWALLOWED, onset of serious health effects may be delayed 12 to 24 hours.
- FUELS AND PRODUCTS containing methanol (e.g. windshield washer fluid) may cause blindness if swallowed.
- ALL FUEL VAPORS may be HARMFUL BY INHALATION.
- ALL FUELS may be HARMFUL BY SKIN ABSORPTION.
- ALL FUELS are IRRITATING to the EYES and RESPIRATORY SYSTEM.
- FUELS made with GASOLINE may contain benzene which is a cancer-causing agent.

FM0159401190020X

Fig. 187   Test HC: Fuel Delivery System (Part 2 of 7). 1994-95

HANDLING

- Use FLAMMABLE LIQUID HANDLING PRECAUTIONS.
- Wear CHEMICAL GOGGLES and NITRILE GLOVES (additional protective clothing and equipment may be necessary in some instances).
- Keep flammable liquids in APPROVED, LABELED, CLOSED CONTAINERS.
- Use in WELL-VENTILATED AREAS and CONTROL VAPORS. Be aware that vapors ARE NOT VISIBLE, are heavier than air, can travel along the floor, and will settle in lower areas.
- When transferring flammable liquids, BOND the RECEIVING CONTAINER to the SOURCE and GROUND the SOURCE to the EARTH.
- DO NOT SMOKE or use HEAT / SPARK PRODUCING EQUIPMENT near vapors.
- DO NOT eat, smoke or drink where these products are handled, processed or stored.
- NEVER SIPHON BY MOUTH.
- WASH HANDS thoroughly after HANDLING any FUEL.

SPILLS

- Notify the proper authorities in the EVENT of any spill you have NOT been trained to clean up.
- STOP, CONTAIN, AND CLEAN UP small spills with an absorbent material.

WARNING

FUEL IN THE FUEL SYSTEM REMAINS UNDER HIGH PRESSURE EVEN WHEN THE ENGINE IS NOT RUNNING. TO AVOID INJURY OR FIRE, RELEASE THE FUEL PRESSURE FROM THE FUEL SYSTEM BEFORE DISCONNECTING ANY FUEL LINE. TO RELEASE THE PRESSURE FROM THE SYSTEM PERFORM THE FOLLOWING:

- CONNECT THE ROTUNDA FUEL PRESSURE TESTING KIT 014-00447 OR EQUIVALENT AT THE SCHRADER VALVE LOCATED ON THE FUEL RAIL. TESTING KIT VALVE SHOULD BE CLOSED.
- GRADUALLY OPEN THE TESTING KIT VALVE TO RELIEVE FUEL PRESSURE IN THE VEHICLE FUEL SYSTEM AND DRAIN THE FUEL INTO A SUITABLE CONTAINER OR RETURN IT TO THE FUEL TANK.
- TO AVOID UNNECESSARY FUEL SPILLAGE AND FIRE HAZARD ANY TIME FUEL LINES ARE DISCONNECTED, THE IGNITION SWITCH SHOULD BE IN THE OFF POSITION UNLESS FUEL PUMP OPERATION IS REQUIRED FOR TEST PURPOSES.

FM0159401190030X

Fig. 187   Test HC: Fuel Delivery System (Part 3 of 7). 1994-95

TEST STEP		RESULT	▶	ACTION TO TAKE
HC1	**CHECK SYSTEM INTEGRITY**			
	• Key off.	Yes	▶	SERVICE as necessary. RERUN Quick Test.
	• Visually inspect the complete fuel delivery system, including fuel lines, connections, pump, pressure regulator and injector areas for leaks, looseness, cracks, kinks, pinching, or abrasion caused by accident, collision, mishandling, etc.	No	▶	GO to **HC2**.
	• Visually inspect electrical harness and connectors for loose pins, corrosion, abrasion, or other damage from accident, abrasion, or mishandling, etc.			
	• Verify vehicle has followed maintenance schedule.			
	• Verify Inertia Fuel Shutoff (IFS) switch set.			
	• Verify vehicle battery is fully charged.			
	• Verify electrical / fuse integrity.			
	• Verify sufficient fuel in the tank.			
	• **Has any problem been found?**			
HC2	**CHECK FUEL PRESSURE**			
	WARNING: BEFORE SERVICING OR REPLACING ANY COMPONENTS IN THE FUEL SYSTEM, REDUCE THE POSSIBILITY OF INJURY OR FIRE BY FOLLOWING DIRECTIONS IN FUEL SYSTEM ''CAUTION, HANDLING AND WARNING'' AT THE BEGINNING OF THIS PINPOINT TEST.	Yes	▶	GO to **HC3**.
	• Key off.	No	▶	GO to **HC9**.
	• Release the fuel pressure.			
	• Install fuel pressure tester.			
	• Scan Tool connected.			
	• Key on, engine off.			
	• Enter Output Test Mode and run the fuel pump to obtain maximum fuel pressure.			
	• **Is fuel pressure between 35 and 40 psi (240-280 kPa)?**			
HC3	**CHECK FUEL PRESSURE LEAKDOWN**			
	• Observe ''NOTES, CAUTION AND WARNING.''	Yes	▶	GO to **HC5**.
	• Fuel pressure tester installed.	No	▶	GO to **HC4**.
	• Scan Tool connected.			
	• Key on, engine off.			
	• Enter Output Test Mode and run fuel pump to obtain maximum fuel pressure.			
	• Exit Output Test Mode, key off.			
	• Verify fuel pressure remains within 5 psi of the maximum pressure for 1 minute after turning pump off.			
	• **Does fuel pressure remain within 5 psi?**			

FM0159401190040X

Fig. 187 Test HC: Fuel Delivery System (Part 4 of 7). 1994-95

TEST STEP		RESULT	▶	ACTION TO TAKE
HC4	**CHECK PRESSURE REGULATOR DIAPHRAGM**			
	• Key off.	Yes	▶	GO to **HC11**.
	• Fuel pressure tester installed.	No	▶	REPLACE fuel pressure regulator. RERUN Quick Test.
	• Start and run engine for 10 seconds.			
	• Key off, wait 10 seconds.			
	• Start and run engine for 10 seconds.			
	• Key off, remove vacuum hose from fuel pressure regulator.			
	• Inspect for fuel in the vacuum hose or regulator port.			
	• **Is vacuum hose and regulator port free of fuel?**			
HC5	**CHECK FUEL PRESSURE, ENGINE RUNNING**			
	• Key off.	Yes	▶	UNPLUG vacuum hose and RECONNECT to the regulator. GO to **HC6**.
	• Fuel pressure tester installed.	No	▶	GO to **HC8**.
	• Disconnect vacuum hose at the fuel pressure regulator and plug it.			
	• Drive vehicle with heavy accelerations while observing fuel pressure gauge reading.			
	• **Does fuel pressure reading hold steady within 3 psi during test?**			
HC6	**CHECK FUEL PRESSURE REGULATOR RESPONSE TO VACUUM**			
	• Key off.	Yes	▶	REMOVE vacuum gauge and fuel pressure tester. Problem is elsewhere. RETURN to Symptom Flow Charts, for further direction.
	• Fuel pressure tester installed.			
	• Install vacuum gauge to intake manifold.			
	• Start engine and observe both gauges.	No	▶	GO to **HC7**.
	• Accelerate and decelerate engine speed to vary the vacuum gauge reading.			
	• **Does fuel pressure gauge reading increase as vacuum gauge reading decreases, or does fuel pressure gauge reading decrease as vacuum gauge reading increases?**			
HC7	**CHECK VACUUM SUPPLY**			
	• Key off.	Yes	▶	SERVICE vacuum system. UNPLUG vacuum hose and RECONNECT to the pressure regulator. RERUN Quick Test.
	• Fuel pressure tester installed.			
	• Vacuum hose disconnected and plugged at the regulator.	No	▶	REPLACE fuel pressure regulator. RERUN Quick Test.
	• Install hand held vacuum pump to the fuel pressure regulator.			
	• Start engine, run at idle.			
	• Observe fuel pressure while applying vacuum.			
	• **Does the fuel pressure change as the vacuum changes?**			

FM0159401190050X

Fig. 187 Test HC: Fuel Delivery System (Part 5 of 7). 1994-95

TEST STEP		RESULT	▶	ACTION TO TAKE
HC8	**CHECK FUEL FILTER**			
	• Observe ''CAUTION, HANDLING AND WARNING.''	Yes	▶	GO to the Fuel Group of the Service Manual.
	• Key off.	No	▶	REPLACE fuel filter. RECHECK fuel pressure as in HC2 and HC3. If problem still exists, RECHECK as in HC1.
	• Scan Tool connected.			
	• Fuel pressure tester installed.			
	• Disconnect fuel line at the filters inlet side and install fuel pressure tester adapter and fuel pressure gauge between the filter and fuel pump.			
	• Key on, engine off.			
	• Enter OSM mode to run the fuel pump.			
	• Compare fuel pressure reading between both gauges.			
	• **Is fuel pressure at the pump side within 5 psi of the fuel rail side?**			
	NOTE: Both gauges should read the same when the pump is not running. If readings differ, there may be gauge problems.			
HC9	**CHECK REGULATOR FOR HIGH PRESSURE CAUSE**			
	• Key off.	Yes	▶	GO to **HC10**.
	• Scan Tool connected.	No	▶	REPLACE fuel pressure regulator. RERUN Quick Test.
	• Remove fuel return line at the fuel rail and connect a short hose from rail to a measured container of at least one quart capacity.			
	• Key off.			
	• Enter OSM mode and run the fuel pump.			
	• Record fuel pressure and note whether fuel is being returned to the measured container.			
	• Exit OSM mode to shut off the fuel pump, key off.			
	• **Is fuel pressure between 35 and 40 psi (240-280 kPa) and is fuel returning to the container?**			
HC10	**CHECK FUEL RETURN SYSTEM**			
	• Key off.	Yes	▶	REPLACE the fuel pump assembly. RERUN Quick Test.
	• Observe ''CAUTION, HANDLING AND WARNING.''	No	▶	SERVICE the fuel return line. RERUN Quick Test.
	• Fuel line disconnected at the fuel pressure regulator.			
	• Check the fuel return system for restriction due to blockage, kinking, or pinching.			
	• Disconnect the fuel return line near the fuel tank.			
	• Apply 3-5 psi regulated shop air to the return line at the pressure regulator side.			
	• **Does air flow freely through the line?**			

FM0159401190060X

Fig. 187 Test HC: Fuel Delivery System (Part 6 of 7). 1994-95

TEST STEP		RESULT	▶	ACTION TO TAKE
HC11	**CHECK FUEL INJECTOR FLOW AND LEAKAGE**			
	• Key off.	Yes	▶	VERIFY no other leaks. If none are found, REPLACE fuel pump assembly. RERUN Quick Test.
	• Observe ''CAUTION, HANDLING AND WARNING.''	No	▶	REPLACE the defective injector. RECONNECT all components. RERUN Quick Test.
	• Use the Rotunda Injector Tester 113-00001, SBDS Injector Tester or equivalent to flow test the injectors according to the instructions for the injector tester.			
	• **Is the flow rate for each injector within specification?**			

FM0159401190070X

Fig. 187 Test HC: Fuel Delivery System (Part 7 of 7). 1994-95

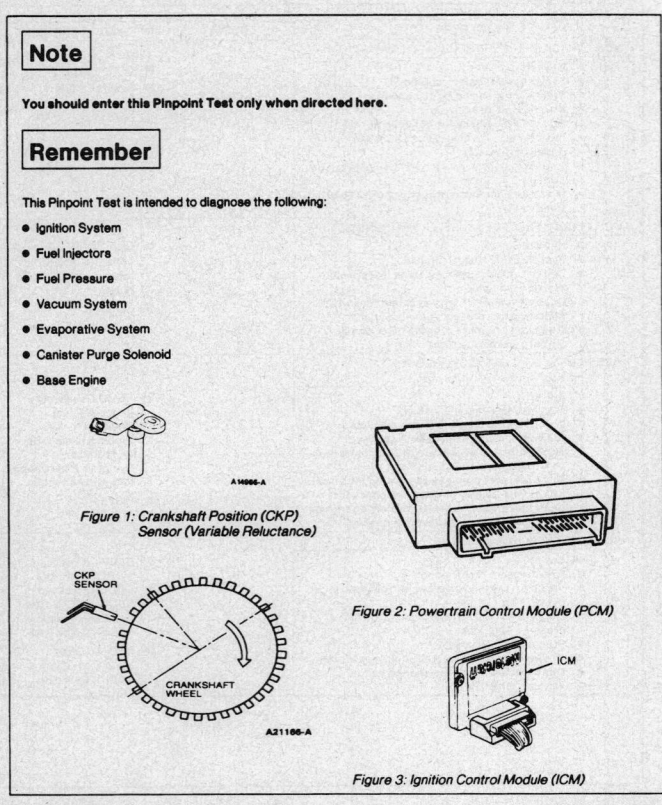

Note

You should enter this Pinpoint Test only when directed here.

Remember

This Pinpoint Test is intended to diagnose the following:

- Ignition System
- Fuel Injectors
- Fuel Pressure
- Vacuum System
- Evaporative System
- Canister Purge Solenoid
- Base Engine

A 14065-A

Figure 1: Crankshaft Position (CKP) Sensor (Variable Reluctance)

CKP SENSOR

CRANKSHAFT WHEEL

A21166-A

Figure 2: Powertrain Control Module (PCM)

ICM

Figure 3: Ignition Control Module (ICM)

FM0159401191010X

Fig. 188   Test HD: Misfire Monitor (Part 1 of 6). 1994-95

TEST STEP	RESULT	▶	ACTION TO TAKE
HD3 CHECK FOR ON-DEMAND SELF-TEST DTCS			
• Are any Key On Engine Off or Key On Engine Running DTCs displayed on the Scan Tool?	Yes	▶	REFER to Section 5, Powertrain DTC Charts and PROCEED as required.
	No	▶	GO to Pinpoint Test Step **JB1** to evaluate spark plugs and secondary wires. If OK, GO to **HD8**.
HD8 CHECK RESISTANCE OF INJECTOR(S) AND HARNESS			
• Key off. • Disconnect PCM. Inspect for damaged or pushed out pins, corrosion, loose wires etc. Service as necessary. NOTE: This erases Continuous Memory DTCs. • Install breakout box, leave PCM disconnected. • Measure resistance between suspect injector test pin and Test Pin 71 or 97 at the breakout box. Refer to the list in **HD1**. • Is the resistance between 11.0-18.0 ohms?	Yes	▶	Injector and harness resistance is OK, GO to **HD9**.
	No	▶	GO to Pinpoint Test Step **H42** to evaluate fuel injectors.
HD9 CHECK INJECTOR DRIVER SIGNAL			
NOTE: Requires a standard 12 volt test lamp. • Key off. • Breakout box installed. • Connect PCM to breakout box. • Connect Test Lamp between Test Pin 71 or 97 and suspect injector test pin. • Start engine. • Does test lamp have a dim glow while running engine? NOTE: Properly operating system will show a dim glow on the Test Lamp.	Yes	▶	GO to **HD10**.
	No	▶	No light or bright light. REPLACE PCM. REMOVE breakout box. RERUN Quick Test.

Fig. 188   Test HD: Misfire Monitor (Part 3 of 6). 1994-95

TEST STEP	RESULT	▶	ACTION TO TAKE
HD1 CHECK POSSIBLE CAUSES TO MISFIRE			
Misfire Continuous Memory Diagnostic Trouble Codes (DTCs): P0301 - Cyl # 1, Inj Test Pin 75 P0302 - Cyl # 2, Inj Test Pin 101 P0303 - Cyl # 3, Inj Test Pin 74 P0304 - Cyl # 4, Inj Test Pin 100 P0305 - Cyl # 5, Inj Test Pin 73 P0306 - Cyl # 6, Inj Test Pin 99 P0307 - Cyl # 7, Inj Test Pin 72 P0308 - Cyl # 8, Inj Test Pin 98 P0300 - multiple cylinders misfiring, or cannot identify cylinder due to Crankshaft Position sensor failure. Possible Causes: — Ignition System. — Fuel Injectors. — Fuel Pressure. — Evaporative System. — Canister Purge. — Base Engine. — Running out of fuel. NOTE: Running out of fuel may turn on the MIL and possibly store a Continuous Misfire DTC. • Has the vehicle recently run out of fuel?	Yes	▶	CLEAR Diagnostic Trouble Codes, MIL will turn off. OBD II system OK. RETURN vehicle to customer.
	No	▶	GO to **HD2**.
HD2 CHECK FOR OTHER CONTINUOUS MEMORY (DTCS)			
• Check for other Continuous Memory DTCs. • Are there any other Continuous Memory DTCs present?	Yes	▶	ADDRESS the next Continuous DTC. DISREGARD Misfire code at this time. GO to Powertrain DTC Charts.
	No	▶	GO to **HD3**.

FM0159401191020X

Fig. 188   Test HD: Misfire Monitor (Part 2 of 6). 1994-95

TEST STEP	RESULT	▶	ACTION TO TAKE
HD10 CHECK FUEL PRESSURE			
WARNING: THE FUEL SYSTEM WILL REMAIN PRESSURIZED WHEN ENGINE IS NOT RUNNING. TO PREVENT INJURY OR FIRE, USE CAUTION WHILE WORKING ON THE FUEL SYSTEM. • Key off. • Install fuel pressure gauge. • Start and run engine at idle. Record fuel pressure. • Increase engine speed to 2500 rpms and maintain for one minute. Note and compare fuel pressure. • Is fuel pressure between 30-45 psi (210-310 kPa)?	Yes	▶	GO to **HD11**.
	No	▶	GO to Pinpoint Test Step **HC9** to check the integrity of the Fuel Delivery System.
HD11 CHECK ABILITY OF FUEL SYSTEM TO HOLD FUEL PRESSURE			
• Start and run engine at idle. Note fuel pressure. • Increase engine speed to 2500 rpms and maintain for one minute. • Visually look for fuel leaking at the injector O-ring, fuel pressure regulator and the fuel lines to the fuel charging assembly. Service as necessary. • Turn engine off. • Key on, engine off. • Does fuel pressure remain at specification for 60 seconds?	Yes	▶	GO to **HD12**.
	No	▶	GO to Pinpoint Test Step **HC9** to determine which area within the Fuel Delivery System is at fault.
HD12 CHECK FUEL INJECTOR FOR FLOW AND LEAKAGE			
• Refer to "CAUTION, HANDLING AND WARNING" at the beginning of Pinpoint Test **HC** to avoid fuel spillage and injury. • Verify that the flow rate for each fuel injector is within specification using Rotunda Injector Tester 113-00001, SBDS Injector Flow Tester or equivalent. • Is flow rate for each injector within specification?	Yes	▶	Fuel Delivery System is not considered the likely area to have caused the Misfire DTC. GO to **HD20** to evaluate the Vacuum System.
	No	▶	REPLACE or CLEAN the defective injector(s) as required. RERUN Quick Test.

Fig. 188   Test HD: Misfire Monitor (Part 4 of 6). 1994-95

	TEST STEP	RESULT	▶	ACTION TO TAKE
HD20	**CHECK VACUUM SYSTEM**	Yes	▶	GO to **HD21**.
	• Visually inspect all vacuum lines for damage, such as pinched lines, cracks, proper routing and assembly.	No	▶	SERVICE the vacuum system. RERUN Quick Test.
	• Refer to the Electrical and Vacuum Troubleshooting Manual (EVTM) for vacuum service information and repair.			
	NOTE: Some vacuum leaks can be found audibly.			
	• Is the vehicle vacuum system OK?			
HD21	**CHECK EVAPORATIVE EMISSION SYSTEM**	Yes	▶	REPLACE carbon canister. RERUN Quick Test.
	The Misfire Monitor can be influenced by Evaporative Emission System. The next four pinpoint test steps will evaluate the Evaporative Emission System.	No	▶	GO to **HD22**. CHECK fuel tank vent system.
	• Check the carbon canister for fuel saturation.			
	• Is there an excess amount of liquid fuel present in the canister?			
HD22	**PRESSURE TEST EVAPORATIVE SYSTEM**	Yes	▶	RECONNECT canister line, GO to **HD23**.
	• Remove vapor line at canister.	No	▶	SERVICE as necessary. RERUN Quick Test.
	• Install a TEE in the line.			
	• Install a pressure gauge to one side of TEE.			
	• Supply air to the other side of TEE, up to a maximum of .75 psi.			
	• Is evaporative emission system holding pressure?			
HD23	**CHECK VACUUM IN EVAPORATIVE SYSTEM**	Yes	▶	REPLACE damaged vacuum hoses, or REMOVE blockage/restrictions. RERUN Quick Test.
	• Check for blockage/restrictions or cut hoses between engine vacuum port and carbon canister.			
	• Check for blockage in fuel tank vent system.			
	• Is there a fault indicated?	No	▶	GO to **HD24**.

FM0159401191050X

Fig. 188   Test HD: Misfire Monitor (Part 5 of 6). 1994-95

	TEST STEP	RESULT	▶	ACTION TO TAKE
HD24	**CHECK CANISTER PURGE SOLENOID (CANP)**	Yes	▶	Evaporative System is functioning properly. GO to **HD25** for Base Engine concerns.
	This pinpoint test step will verify the mechanical integrity of (CANP). The solenoid and circuit have been checked electrically and reported during KOEO Self-Test.	No	▶	REPLACE Canister Purge solenoid. RERUN Quick Test.
	• Key off.			
	• Disconnect (CANP) solenoid.			
	• Connect 12 volt DC power source to solenoid. CAUTION must be observed for proper pin orientation. Refer to the vehicle electrical schematic.			
	• Connect positive power source to VPWR circuit and negative lead to CANP circuit at the CANP solenoid harness connector.			
	• Apply 53 kPa (16 in-Hg) of vacuum to the manifold side of the CANP solenoid. Apply power source.			
	• Does the solenoid open and pass air freely?			
HD25	**CHECK FOR BASE ENGINE CONCERNS**	Yes	▶	
	The purpose of this pinpoint test step is to determine if there are any Base Engine concerns that may have caused the Misfire DTC or drive concern.			make repairs.
	Perform the following tests in order to evaluate Base Engine integrity.	No	▶	The cause of the Misfire DTC is intermittent and diagnosis will be in the Ignition System. GO to the Intermittent Ignition procedure in Pinpoint Test Step **Z50**. FOLLOW instructions for using the Ignition Intermittent Analyzer, also known as the DIST tool.
	• Perform an Engine Compression test.			
	• Perform Dynamic Valve Train analysis.			
	• Check Positive Crankcase Ventilation System.			
	• Check possible leakage points.			
	• Is any service required?			

FM0159401191060X

Fig. 188   Test HD: Misfire Monitor (Part 6 of 6). 1994-95

Note

You should enter this Pinpoint Test only when directed here.

Remember

This Pinpoint Test is intended to diagnose the following:

• Differential Pressure Feedback Electronic (DPFE) EGR Sensor (9J460)
• Exhaust Gas Recirculation (EGR) Valve (9D480) (9D475)
• Electronic Vacuum Regulator (EVR) (9J459)
• Orifice Tube Assembly (9D477)
• DPFE Sensor Pressure Hoses
• Vacuum Lines
• Harness Circuits: VREF, DPFE, SIG, SIG RTN, EVR, EVR PWR
• Powertrain Control Module (PCM) (12A650)

FM0159401192010X

Fig. 189   Test HE: EGR System (Part 1 of 41). 1994-95

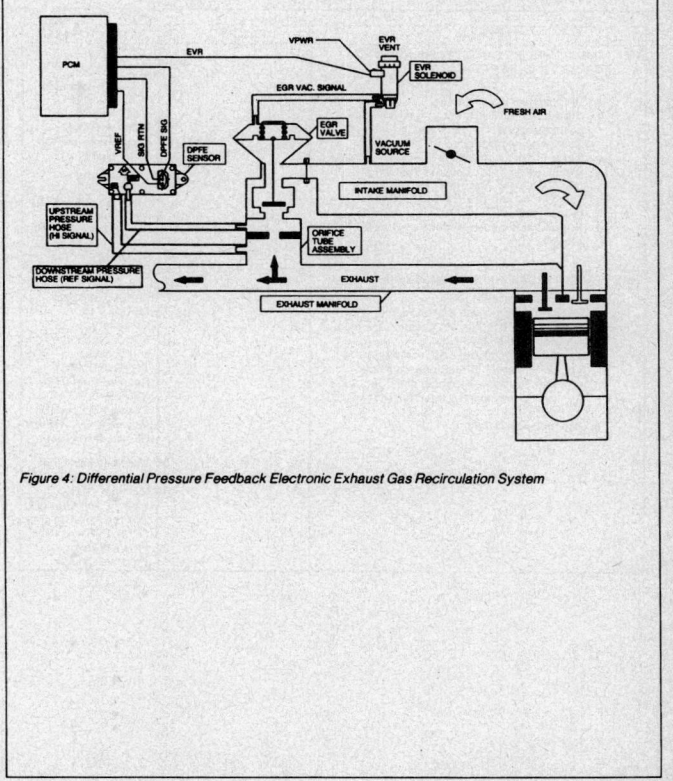

Figure 4: Differential Pressure Feedback Electronic Exhaust Gas Recirculation System

FM0159401192020X

Fig. 189   Test HE: EGR System (Part 2 of 41). 1994-95

Pinpoint Test Schematic

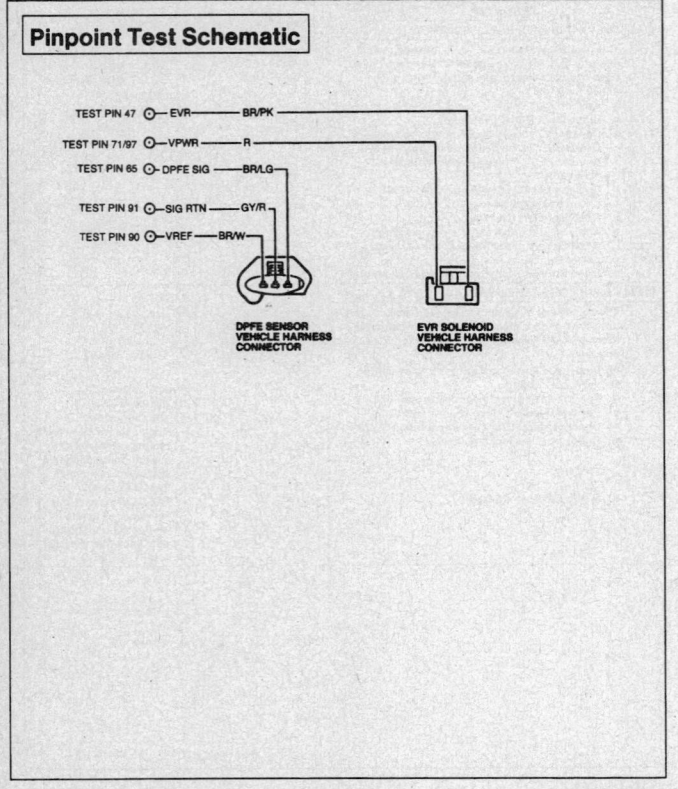

TEST PIN 47 ⊙— EVR ——— BR/PK
TEST PIN 71/97 ⊙— VPWR ——— R
TEST PIN 65 ⊙— DPFE SIG ——— BR/LG
TEST PIN 91 ⊙— SIG RTN ——— GY/R
TEST PIN 90 ⊙— VREF ——— BR/W

DPFE SENSOR
VEHICLE HARNESS
CONNECTOR

EVR SOLENOID
VEHICLE HARNESS
CONNECTOR

FM0159401192030X

Fig. 189   Test HE: EGR System (Part 3 of 41). 1994-95

	TEST STEP	RESULT	▶	ACTION TO TAKE
HE1	DTC 1400: VERIFY DPFE SIG VOLTAGE			
	Diagnostic Trouble Code (DTC) 1400 indicates that self-test has detected DPFE SIG circuit input below the minimum. Possible Causes: — Leaking upstream pressure hose. — DPFE SIG shorted to GND or SIG RTN. — VREF shorted to GND or SIG RTN. — Damaged DPFE sensor. — Damaged PCM. ● Key on, engine off. ● Access DPFE PID with a Scan Tool. NOTE: DPFE sensor input with no EGR flow is 0.45 volts ± 0.25 volts. ● Is DPFE SIG PID voltage less than 0.2 volts?	Yes	▶	The DPFE SIG voltage is less than the acceptable minimum. GO to **HE2**
		No	▶	INSPECT pressure signal hoses for leaks. SERVICE as necessary. If OK, fault that produced DTC 1400 is intermittent. GO to **HE6**
HE2	INDUCE OPPOSITE DPFE SIGNAL			
	● Key off. ● Disconnect DPFE sensor vehicle harness connector. ● Connect a jumper wire between the sensor VREF circuit and DPFE SIG circuit at the DPFE sensor vehicle harness connector. ● Key on, engine off. NOTE: If a Scan Tool error occurs, remove jumper immediately and go directly to **HE3** ● Access DPFE PID with a Scan Tool. ● Is DPFE SIG PID value between 4.0 and 6.0 volts?	Yes	▶	REPLACE damaged DPFE sensor. RECONNECT all components. COMPLETE PCM Reset to clear DTCs (REFER to Powertrain Control Module (PCM) Reset). RERUN Quick Test.
		No	▶	REMOVE jumper. GO to **HE3**
HE3	MEASURE VREF VOLTAGE AT DPFE SENSOR VEHICLE HARNESS CONNECTOR			
	● DPFE sensor disconnected. ● Key on, engine off. ● Measure voltage between the sensor VREF circuit and SIG RTN circuit at the DPFE sensor vehicle harness connector. ● Is VREF voltage between 4.0 and 6.0 volts?	Yes	▶	GO to **HE4**
		No	▶	VREF voltage is out of range. GO to Pinpoint Test Step **C1**

FM0159401192040X

Fig. 189   Test HE: EGR System (Part 4 of 41). 1994-95

	TEST STEP	RESULT	▶	ACTION TO TAKE
HE4	CHECK DPFE SIG CIRCUIT FOR SHORTS TO GROUND AND SIG RTN			
	● Key off. ● DPFE sensor disconnected. ● Disconnect PCM. Inspect for damaged or pushed out pins, corrosion, loose wires, etc. Service as necessary. ● Install breakout box, leave PCM disconnected. ● Measure resistance between Test Pin 65 (DPFE SIG) and Test Pin 91 (SIG RTN) and Test Pins 51 and 103 (PWR GND) at the breakout box. ● Is each resistance greater than 10,000 ohms?	Yes	▶	REPLACE damaged PCM. REMOVE breakout box. RECONNECT all components. RERUN Quick Test.
		No	▶	SERVICE short circuit between DPFE SIG and GROUND or SIG RTN. REMOVE breakout box. RECONNECT all components. RERUN Quick Test.
HE6	WIGGLE TEST SENSOR AND HARNESS			
	● Key on, engine off. ● Access DPFE PID with a Scan Tool. ● Observe DPFE PID for an indication of a fault while performing the following: — Lightly tap on DPFE sensor; wiggle the DPFE sensor connector and vehicle harness between sensor and PCM. A fault is indicated by a sudden change in DPFE PID voltage. ● Is a fault indicated?	Yes	▶	ISOLATE fault and SERVICE as necessary. RECONNECT all components. COMPLETE PCM Reset to clear DTCs (REFER to Powertrain Control Module (PCM) Reset). RERUN Quick Test
		No	▶	Unable to duplicate and·or identify fault at this time. GO to Pinpoint Test Step **Z1** with the following data: DPFE, EVR and VREF PIDs and list of Possible Causes.

FM0159401192050X

Fig. 189   Test HE: EGR System (Part 5 of 41). 1994-95

	TEST STEP	RESULT	▶	ACTION TO TAKE
HE10	DTC 1401: VERIFY DPFE SIGNAL VOLTAGE			
	Diagnostic Trouble Code (DTC) 1401 indicates that self-test has detected DPFE SIG circuit input above the maximum. Possible Causes: — DPFE SIG open. — DPFE SIG shorted to VREF or PWR. — VREF shorted to PWR. — SIG RTN open. — Damaged DPFE sensor. — Damaged PCM. ● Key on, engine off. ● Access DPFE PID with a Scan Tool. NOTE: DPFE sensor input with no EGR flow is 0.45 volts ± 0.25 volts. ● Is DPFE SIG PID voltage greater than 4.0 volts?	Yes	▶	The DPFE SIG voltage is greater than the acceptable maximum. GO to **HE11**
		No	▶	The fault that produced DTC 1401 is intermittent. GO to **HE19**
HE11	CHECK DPFE SIG FOR SHORT TO PWR			
	● Key off. ● Disconnect DPFE sensor vehicle harness connector. ● Key on, engine off. ● Measure voltage between DPFE SIG circuit at the DPFE sensor vehicle harness connector and battery ground. ● Is voltage greater than 10.5 volts?	Yes	▶	The DPFE SIG input is indicating a short to PWR. GO to **HE12**
		No	▶	GO to **HE13**
HE12	CHECK DPFE SIG FOR SHORT TO PWR IN HARNESS			
	● Key off. ● DPFE sensor disconnected. ● Disconnect PCM. Inspect for damaged or pushed out pins, corrosion, loose wires, etc. Service as necessary. ● Install breakout box, leave PCM disconnected. ● Key on, engine off. ● Measure voltage between Test Pin 65 (DPFE SIG) and Test Pins 51 and 103 (PWR GND) at the breakout box. ● Is voltage greater than 10.5 volts?	Yes	▶	SERVICE short between DPFE SIG and PWR circuit. REMOVE breakout box. RECONNECT all components. RERUN Quick Test.
		No	▶	REPLACE damaged PCM. REMOVE breakout box. RECONNECT all components. RERUN Quick Test.

Fig. 189   Test HE: EGR System (Part 6 of 41). 1994-95

TEST STEP		RESULT	▶	ACTION TO TAKE
HE13	**INDUCE OPPOSITE DPFE SIGNAL** • Key off. • Disconnect DPFE sensor vehicle harness connector. • Connect a jumper wire between the sensor DPFE SIG circuit and SIG RTN circuit at the DPFE sensor vehicle harness connector. • Key on, engine off. NOTE: If a Scan Tool error occurs, remove jumper immediately and go directly to HE18. • Access DPFE PID with a Scan Tool. • **Is DPFE SIG PID value less than 0.05 volts?**	Yes No	▶ ▶	REMOVE jumper. GO to HE14. Unable to induce opposite signal. GO to HE16.
HE14	**VERIFY THAT VREF IS IN RANGE** • DPFE sensor disconnected. • Key on, engine off. • Measure voltage between the sensor VREF circuit and SIG RTN circuit at the DPFE sensor vehicle harness connector. • **Is VREF voltage between 4.0 and 6.0 volts?**	Yes No	▶ ▶	GO to HE15. VREF voltage is out of range. GO to Pinpoint Test Step C1.
HE15	**CHECK DPFE SIG FOR SHORT TO VREF IN HARNESS** • Key off. • DPFE sensor disconnected. • Disconnect PCM. Inspect for damaged or pushed out pins, corrosion, loose wires, etc. Service as necessary. • Install breakout box, leave PCM disconnected. • Measure resistance between Test Pin 65 (DPFE SIG) and Test Pin 90 (VREF) at the breakout box. • **Is resistance greater than 10,000 ohms?**	Yes No	▶ ▶	REPLACE damaged DPFE sensor. REMOVE breakout box. RECONNECT all components. RERUN Quick Test. SERVICE short between DPFE SIG and VREF circuit. REMOVE breakout box. RECONNECT all components. RERUN Quick Test.
HE16	**CHECK DPFE SIG FOR OPEN IN HARNESS** • Key off. • DPFE sensor disconnected. • Disconnect PCM. Inspect for damaged or pushed out pins, corrosion, loose wires, etc. Service as necessary. • Install breakout box, leave PCM disconnected. • Measure resistance between Test Pin 65 (DPFE SIG) and DPFE SIG circuit at the DPFE sensor vehicle harness connector. • **Is resistance less than 5.0 ohms?**	Yes No	▶ ▶	GO to HE17. SERVICE open in DPFE SIG circuit. REMOVE breakout box. RECONNECT all components. RERUN Quick Test

Fig. 189   Test HE: EGR System (Part 7 of 41). 1994-95

FM0159401192070X

TEST STEP		RESULT	▶	ACTION TO TAKE
HE17	**CHECK SIG RTN FOR OPEN IN HARNESS** • Key off. • DPFE sensor disconnected. • Breakout box installed, PCM disconnected. • Measure resistance between Test Pin 91 (SIG RTN) and SIG RTN circuit at the DPFE sensor vehicle harness connector. • **Is resistance less than 5.0 ohms?**	Yes No	▶ ▶	REPLACE damaged PCM. REMOVE breakout box. RECONNECT all components. RERUN Quick Test. SERVICE open in SIG RTN circuit. REMOVE breakout box. RECONNECT all components. RERUN Quick Test.
HE18	**CHECK DPFE SIG FOR SHORT TO VREF IN HARNESS** • Key off. • DPFE sensor disconnected. • Disconnect PCM. Inspect for damaged or pushed out pins, corrosion, loose wires, etc. Service as necessary. • Install breakout box, leave PCM disconnected. • Measure resistance between Test Pin 65 (DPFE SIG) and Test Pin 90 (VREF) at the breakout box. • **Is resistance greater than 10,000 ohms?**	Yes No	▶ ▶	REPLACE damaged PCM. REMOVE breakout box. RECONNECT all components. RERUN Quick Test. SERVICE short between DPFE SIG and VREF circuit. REMOVE breakout box. RECONNECT all components. RERUN Quick Test.
HE19	**WIGGLE TEST SENSOR AND HARNESS** • Key on, engine off. • Access DPFE PID with a Scan Tool. • Observe DPFE PID for an indication of a fault while performing the following: — Lightly tap on DPFE sensor; wiggle the DPFE sensor connector and vehicle harness between sensor and PCM. A fault is indicated by a sudden change in DPFE PID voltage. • **Is a fault indicated?**	Yes No	▶ ▶	ISOLATE fault and SERVICE as necessary. RECONNECT all components. COMPLETE PCM Reset to clear DTCs (REFER to Powertrain Control Module (PCM) Reset). RERUN Quick Test. Unable to duplicate and/or identify fault at this time. GO to Pinpoint Test Step Z1 with the following data: DPFE, EVR and VREF PIDS and list of Possible Causes.

Fig. 189   Test HE: EGR System (Part 8 of 41). 1994-95

FM0159401192080X

TEST STEP		RESULT	▶	ACTION TO TAKE
HE20	**DTC 0402: CHECK FOR EGR FLOW AT IDLE WITH EGR VACUUM HOSE DISCONNECTED** Diagnostic Trouble Code (DTC) 0402 indicates that self-test has detected EGR flow at idle. NOTE: If DTC 1405 is in Continuous Memory, diagnose that first starting with HE50. Possible Causes: — EGR valve stuck open. — EVR solenoid vent plugged or iced. — EVR circuit shorted to GND. — Improper vacuum hose connection. — Plugged/pinched EGR vacuum hose. — Damaged EVR solenoid. — Damaged PCM. • Key off. • Disconnect vacuum hose at EGR valve and plug hose. • Run Key On Engine Running (KOER) Self-Test. • **Is KOER DTC 0402 output?**	Yes No	▶ ▶	The KOER Self-Test has detected EGR flow at idle. REMOVE and INSPECT the EGR valve for signs of contamination, unusual wear, carbon deposits, binding and other damage. SERVICE as necessary (use Rotunda EGR Valve Cleaner 021-00056, if needed). RECONNECT all components. COMPLETE PCM Reset to clear DTCs (REFER to Powertrain Control Module (PCM) Reset). RERUN Quick Test. RECONNECT vacuum hose to EGR valve. GO to HE21.
HE21	**CHECK FOR EGR FLOW AT IDLE WITH EGR VACUUM HOSE CONNECTED** • Key off. • EGR vacuum hose connected. • Run KOER Self-Test. • **Is KOER DTC 0402 output?**	Yes No	▶ ▶	The KOER Self-Test has detected EGR flow at idle. GO to HE22. The fault that produced DTC 0402 is intermittent. GO to HE30.
HE22	**CHECK EGR SYSTEM VACUUM HOSES FOR INTEGRITY AND CONNECTION** NOTE: A pinched or plugged EGR vacuum hose can trap vacuum between the EVR solenoid and EGR valve not allowing the EGR valve to close. • Key off. • Trace each vacuum hose from EVR solenoid and verify that each is connected correctly. (Refer to vehicle's vacuum diagram label.) • Verify that the EGR valve vacuum hose is not pinched or plugged and routed properly. • **Are vacuum hoses OK?**	Yes No	▶ ▶	RECONNECT vacuum hoses. GO to HE23. SERVICE vacuum hoses as necessary. RECONNECT all components. COMPLETE PCM Reset to clear DTCs (REFER to Powertrain Control Module (PCM) Reset). RERUN Quick Test.

Fig. 189   Test HE: EGR System (Part 9 of 41). 1994-95

FM0159401192090X

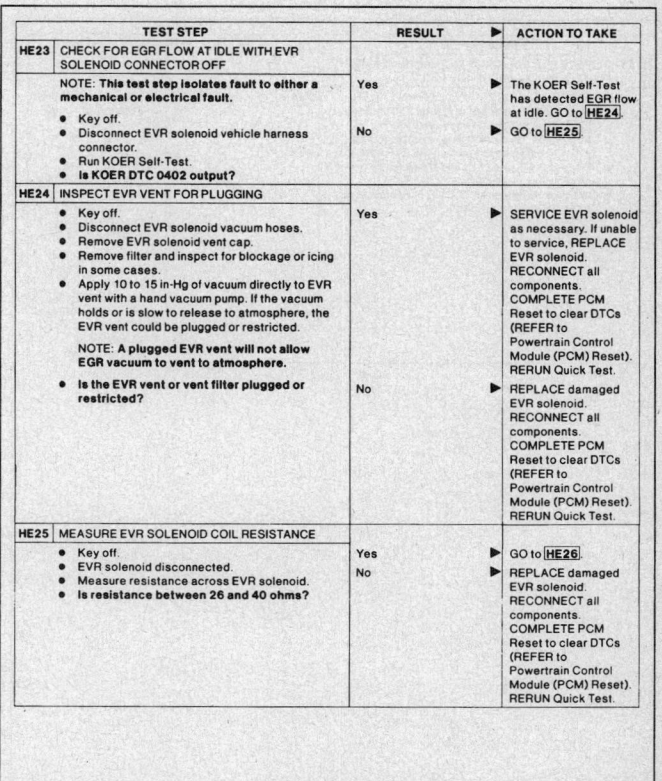

TEST STEP		RESULT	▶	ACTION TO TAKE
HE23	**CHECK FOR EGR FLOW AT IDLE WITH EVR SOLENOID CONNECTOR OFF** NOTE: This test step isolates fault to either a mechanical or electrical fault. • Key off. • Disconnect EVR solenoid vehicle harness connector. • Run KOER Self-Test. • **Is KOER DTC 0402 output?**	Yes No	▶ ▶	The KOER Self-Test has detected EGR flow at idle. GO to HE24. GO to HE25.
HE24	**INSPECT EVR VENT FOR PLUGGING** • Key off. • Disconnect EVR solenoid vacuum hoses. • Remove EVR solenoid vent cap. • Remove filter and inspect for blockage or icing in some cases. • Apply 10 to 15 in-Hg of vacuum directly to EVR vent with a hand vacuum pump. If the vacuum holds or is slow to release to atmosphere, the EVR vent could be plugged or restricted. NOTE: A plugged EVR vent will not allow EGR vacuum to vent to atmosphere. • **Is the EVR vent or vent filter plugged or restricted?**	Yes No	▶ ▶	SERVICE EVR solenoid as necessary. If unable to service, REPLACE EVR solenoid. RECONNECT all components. COMPLETE PCM Reset to clear DTCs (REFER to Powertrain Control Module (PCM) Reset). RERUN Quick Test. REPLACE damaged EVR solenoid. RECONNECT all components. COMPLETE PCM Reset to clear DTCs (REFER to Powertrain Control Module (PCM) Reset). RERUN Quick Test.
HE25	**MEASURE EVR SOLENOID COIL RESISTANCE** • Key off. • EVR solenoid disconnected. • Measure resistance across EVR solenoid. • **Is resistance between 26 and 40 ohms?**	Yes No	▶ ▶	GO to HE26. REPLACE damaged EVR solenoid. RECONNECT all components. COMPLETE PCM Reset to clear DTCs (REFER to Powertrain Control Module (PCM) Reset). RERUN Quick Test.

Fig. 189   Test HE: EGR System (Part 10 of 41). 1994-95

FM0159401192100X

TEST STEP	RESULT	▶	ACTION TO TAKE
HE26 CHECK EVR CIRCUIT FOR SHORT TO GROUND IN HARNESS			
• Key off. • EVR solenoid disconnected. • Disconnect PCM. Inspect for damaged or pushed out pins, corrosion, loose wires, etc. Service as necessary. • Install breakout box, leave PCM disconnected. • Measure resistance between Test Pin 47 (EVR) and Test Pins 51 and 103 (PWR GND) at the breakout box. • **Is resistance greater than 10,000 ohms?**	Yes	▶	REPLACE damaged PCM. REMOVE breakout box. RECONNECT all components. RERUN Quick Test.
	No	▶	SERVICE short between EVR and GROUND. REMOVE breakout box. RECONNECT all components. RERUN Quick Test.
HE30 CHECK DPFE SENSOR OUTPUT BY APPLYING VACUUM WITH HAND PUMP			
• Key off. • Disconnect pressure hoses at DPFE sensor. • Connect a hand vacuum pump to the downstream pickup marked "REF" on the DPFE. • Key on, engine off. • Access DPFE PID with a Scan Tool. PID voltage should be 0.45 ± 0.25 volts. • Apply 8-9 in-Hg vacuum to the DPFE sensor. The DPFE voltage should be above 4.0 volts. Quickly release vacuum from sensor. PID voltage should drop to less than 1 volt in less than 3 seconds. • **Does the DPFE PID voltage indicate a fault in the DPFE sensor?**	Yes	▶	REPLACE damaged DPFE sensor. RECONNECT all components. COMPLETE PCM Reset to clear DTCs (REFER to Powertrain Control Module (PCM) Reset). RERUN Quick Test.
	No	▶	RECONNECT DPFE sensor. GO to **HE31**.

Fig. 189   Test HE: EGR System (Part 11 of 41). 1994-95

TEST STEP	RESULT	▶	ACTION TO TAKE
HE31 CHECK DPFE SIG VOLTAGE WHILE EXERCISING EGR VALVE			
• Key on, engine off. • View DPFE PID with a Scan Tool and make note of voltage. NOTE: Typical DPFE SIG voltage with no EGR flow is 0.45 volts ± 0.25 volts. • Disconnect vacuum hose at EGR valve and plug hose. • Connect a hand vacuum pump to EGR valve. • Start engine and bring to idle. • Observe DPFE PID at idle and compare to the key on engine off voltage. (A higher voltage at idle could be due to a non-seating EGR valve.) • Apply just enough vacuum to EGR valve to open it (2 to 3 in-Hg) without stalling engine and release vacuum. Repeat several times while observing DPFE PID on Scan Tool. (DPFE PID voltage should increase as valve begins to open and return to initial value as vacuum is released. A slow to return voltage could be an indication of a binding or a slow closing EGR valve.) • **Does the DPFE PID voltage indicate an open, binding or slow closing EGR valve?**	Yes	▶	REMOVE and INSPECT the EGR valve for signs of contamination, unusual wear, carbon deposits, binding and other damage. SERVICE as necessary (use Rotunda EGR Valve Cleaner 021-00056, if needed). RECONNECT all components. COMPLETE PCM Reset to clear DTCs (REFER to Powertrain Control Module (PCM) Reset). RERUN Quick Test.
	No	▶	RECONNECT EGR vacuum hose. GO to **HE32**.
HE32 MONITOR EGR VALVE VACUUM WHILE WIGGLING EVR CIRCUIT			
NOTE: An intermittent short to GND in the EVR circuit will cause the vacuum applied to the EGR valve to be higher than normal while the short is present. The vacuum available at the EGR valve at idle is normally below 1.0 in-Hg and it takes about 1.6 in-Hg for the valve to begin to open. • Key off. • Disconnect vacuum hose at EGR valve and connect hose to a vacuum gauge. • Key on, engine running. • Observe vacuum gauge for an indication of a fault while performing the following: — Lightly tap on the EVR solenoid; wiggle the EVR solenoid connector and vehicle harness between solenoid and PCM. A fault is indicated by a sudden jump in vacuum reading. • **Is a fault indicated?**	Yes	▶	ISOLATE fault and SERVICE as necessary. RECONNECT all components. COMPLETE PCM Reset to clear DTCs (REFER to Powertrain Control Module (PCM) Reset). RERUN Quick Test.
	No	▶	RECONNECT vacuum hose. GO to **HE33**.

Fig. 189   Test HE: EGR System (Part 12 of 41). 1994-95

TEST STEP	RESULT	▶	ACTION TO TAKE
HE33 INSPECT EVR SOLENOID AND VACUUM HOSES FOR POTENTIAL PLUGGING			
• Key off. • Remove EVR solenoid vent filter and inspect for contamination and excessive water absorption. (In cold climate, excessive water in filter could freeze and plug the EVR vent.) • Inspect EGR vacuum hose for possible blockage or pinching. • **Is EVR solenoid vent or filter contaminated or vacuum line plugged?**	Yes	▶	SERVICE EVR solenoid or EGR vacuum hose as necessary. RECONNECT all components. COMPLETE PCM Reset to clear DTCs (REFER to Powertrain Control Module (PCM) Reset). RERUN Quick Test.
	No	▶	Unable to duplicate and/or identify fault at this time. GO to Pinpoint Test Step **Z1** with the following data: DPFE, EVR and VREF PIDs and list of Possible Causes.

Fig. 189   Test HE: EGR System (Part 13 of 41). 1994-95

TEST STEP	RESULT	▶	ACTION TO TAKE
HE40 DTC 1403: CHECK FOR REVERSED PRESSURE HOSES			
Diagnostic Trouble Code (DTC) 1403 indicates that continuous self-test has detected reversed DPFE sensor pressure hoses. NOTE: If the fault is currently present, DTC 1408 will be output in Key On Engine Running (KOER) Self-Test. Possible Cause: — Reversed DPFE sensor pressure hoses. • Key off. • Visually inspect hoses for proper connection between DPFE sensor and EGR orifice tube assembly. — The hose connection marked "HI" on the DPFE sensor should connect to the exhaust side of the orifice tube and the connection marked "REF" connects to the intake manifold side of the orifice tube. The HI side hose has a larger inside diameter than the REF side hose. • **Are the DPFE sensor pressure hoses connected properly?**	Yes	▶	Fault may have been recently serviced without clearing DTCs. RECONNECT all components. COMPLETE PCM Reset to clear DTCs (REFER to Powertrain Control Module (PCM) Reset). RERUN Quick Test.
	No	▶	SERVICE hoses as necessary (if hoses are replaced, USE only the service part and not a substitute). COMPLETE PCM Reset to clear DTCs (REFER to Powertrain Control Module (PCM) Reset). RERUN Quick Test.

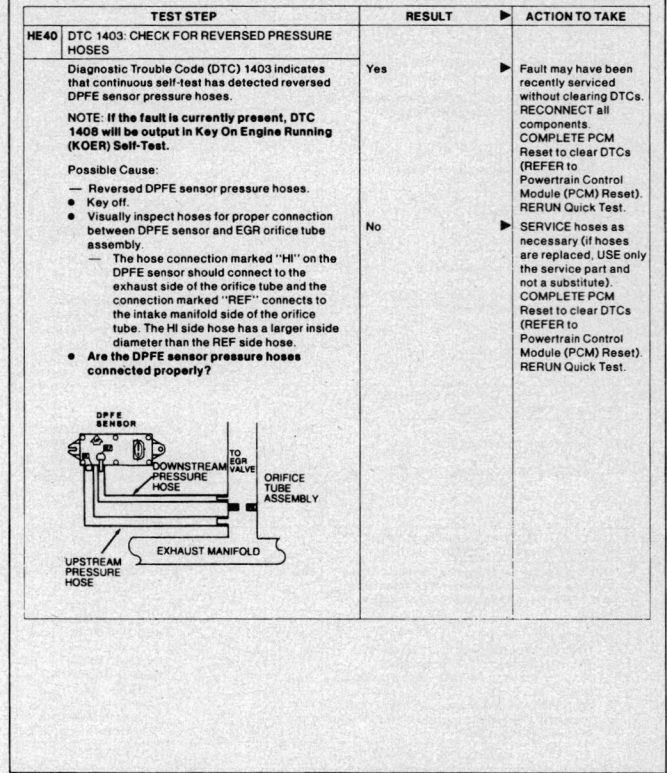

Fig. 189   Test HE: EGR System (Part 14 of 41). 1994-95

TEST STEP	RESULT	▶	ACTION TO TAKE
HE50 DTC 1405: INSPECT UPSTREAM PRESSURE HOSE CONNECTIONS Diagnostic Trouble Code (DTC) 1405 indicates that continuous self-test has detected the exhaust manifold side (upstream) DPFE pressure hose is off or plugged. Possible Causes: — Upstream pressure hose off. — Upstream pressure hose plugged. — Plugged or damaged pressure pickup tubes. ● Key off. ● Inspect upstream hose at DPFE sensor and orifice tube assembly for disconnect or poor connection. ● **Is hose off or poorly connected?** 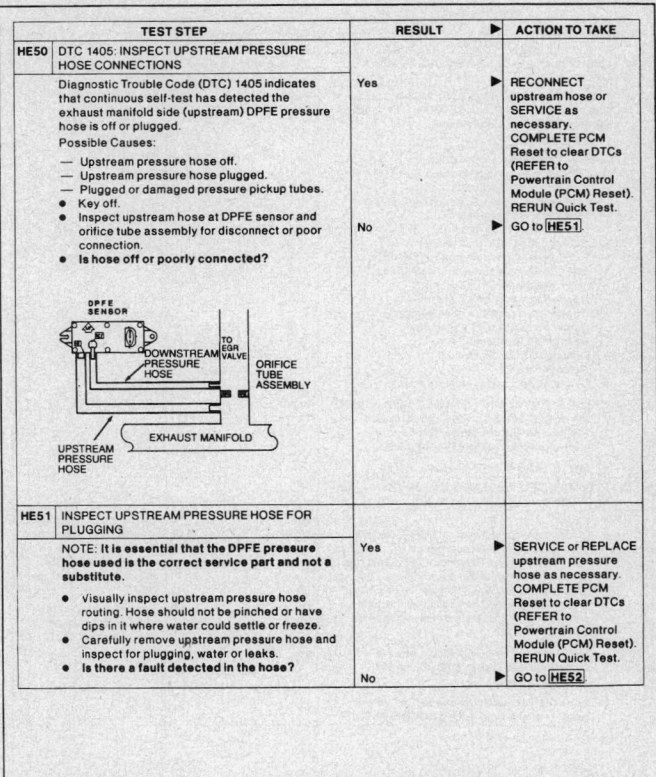	Yes No	▶ ▶	RECONNECT upstream hose or SERVICE as necessary. COMPLETE PCM Reset to clear DTCs (REFER to Powertrain Control Module (PCM) Reset). RERUN Quick Test. GO to **HE51**.
HE51 INSPECT UPSTREAM PRESSURE HOSE FOR PLUGGING NOTE: It is essential that the DPFE pressure hose used is the correct service part and not a substitute. ● Visually inspect upstream pressure hose routing. Hose should not be pinched or have dips in it where water could settle or freeze. ● Carefully remove upstream pressure hose and inspect for plugging, water or leaks. ● **Is there a fault detected in the hose?**	Yes No	▶ ▶	SERVICE or REPLACE upstream pressure hose as necessary. COMPLETE PCM Reset to clear DTCs (REFER to Powertrain Control Module (PCM) Reset). RERUN Quick Test. GO to **HE52**.

FM0159401192150X

Fig. 189   Test HE: EGR System (Part 15 of 41). 1994-95

TEST STEP	RESULT	▶	ACTION TO TAKE
HE52 CHECK ORIFICE TUBE ASSEMBLY AND DPFE SENSOR ● Inspect the connection marked "HI" on the DPFE sensor for plugging or damage at the sensor. ● Inspect the exhaust manifold side pressure pickup tube at the orifice tube assembly for plugging or damage. ● **Is the DPFE sensor or orifice tube assembly plugged or damaged?**	Yes No	▶ ▶	SERVICE or REPLACE DPFE sensor or orifice tube assembly as necessary. COMPLETE PCM Reset to clear DTCs RERUN Quick Test. Fault may have been recently serviced without clearing DTCs. COMPLETE PCM Reset to clear DTCs RERUN Quick Test.

FM0159401192160X

Fig. 189   Test HE: EGR System (Part 16 of 41). 1994-95

TEST STEP	RESULT	▶	ACTION TO TAKE
HE60 DTC 1406: INSPECT DOWNSTREAM PRESSURE HOSE CONNECTIONS Diagnostic Trouble Code (DTC) 1406 indicates that continuous self-test has detected the intake manifold side (downstream) DPFE pressure hose is off or plugged. NOTE: If the fault is currently present, DTC 1408 will be output in Key On Engine Running (KOER) Self-Test. Possible Causes: — Downstream pressure hose off. — Downstream pressure hose plugged. — Orifice tube assembly loose. — Orifice tube assembly broken. — Plugged or damaged pressure pickup tubes. — Slow responding DPFE sensor. ● Key off. ● Inspect downstream hose at DPFE sensor and orifice tube assembly for disconnect or poor connection. ● **Is hose OFF or poorly connected?** 	Yes No	▶ ▶	RECONNECT downstream hose or SERVICE as necessary. COMPLETE PCM Reset to clear DTCs (REFER to Powertrain Control Module (PCM) Reset). RERUN Quick Test. GO to **HE61**.

FM0159401192170X

Fig. 189   Test HE: EGR System (Part 17 of 41). 1994-95

TEST STEP	RESULT	▶	ACTION TO TAKE
HE61 INSPECT DOWNSTREAM PRESSURE HOSE FOR PLUGGING NOTE: It is essential that the DPFE pressure hose is the correct service part and not a substitute. ● Visually inspect downstream pressure hose routing. Hose should not be pinched or have dips in it where water could settle or freeze. ● Carefully remove downstream pressure hose and inspect for plugging, water or leaks. ● **Is there a fault detected in the hose?**	Yes No	▶ ▶	SERVICE or REPLACE downstream pressure hose as necessary. COMPLETE PCM Reset to clear DTCs (REFER to Powertrain Control Module (PCM) Reset). RERUN Quick Test. GO to **HE62**.
HE62 CHECK ORIFICE TUBE ASSEMBLY AND DPFE SENSOR ● Inspect the connection marked "REF" on the DPFE sensor for plugging or damage at the sensor. ● Inspect the intake manifold side pressure pickup tube and orifice tube assembly for plugging, loose connection or damage. ● **Is the DPFE sensor or orifice tube assembly plugged, loose or damaged?**	Yes No	▶ ▶	SERVICE or REPLACE DPFE sensor or orifice tube assembly as necessary. COMPLETE PCM Reset to clear DTCs (REFER to Powertrain Control Module (PCM) Reset). RERUN Quick Test. RECONNECT all components. GO to **HE63**.

FM0159401192180X

Fig. 189   Test HE: EGR System (Part 18 of 41). 1994-95

TEST STEP	RESULT	►	ACTION TO TAKE
HE63 CHECK DPFE SENSOR OUTPUT BY APPLYING VACUUM WITH HAND PUMP			
• Key off. • Disconnect pressure hoses at DPFE sensor. • Connect a hand vacuum pump to the downstream pickup marked "REF" on the DPFE sensor. • Key on, engine off. • Access DPFE PID with a Scan Tool. PID voltage should be 0.45 volt ± 0.25 volt. • Apply 8-9 in-Hg vacuum to the DPFE sensor. The PID voltage should be above 4.0 volts. Quickly release vacuum from sensor. PID voltage should drop to less than 1 volt in less than 3 seconds. • **Does the DPFE PID voltage indicate a fault in the DPFE sensor?**	Yes No	► ►	REPLACE damaged DPFE sensor. RECONNECT all components. COMPLETE PCM Reset to clear DTCs (REFER to Powertrain Control Module (PCM) Reset). RERUN Quick Test. Fault may have been recently serviced without clearing DTCs. RECONNECT all components. COMPLETE PCM Reset to clear DTCs (REFER to Powertrain Control Module (PCM) Reset). RERUN Quick Test.
HE70 DTC 1407: RUN KOER SELF-TEST			
Diagnostic Trouble Code (DTC) 1407 indicates that continuous self-test has detected no EGR flow. NOTE: If the fault is currently present, DTC 1408 will be output in Key On Engine Running (KOER) Self-Test. Possible Causes: — EGR valve stuck closed or iced. — EGR valve diaphragm leaks. — EGR flow path restricted. — EGR vacuum hose off, plugged or leaks. — EVR VPWR circuit open. — EVR circuit to PCM open. — EVR circuit to PCM shorted to PWR. — DPFE sensor pressure hoses both off. — DPFE sensor VREF circuit open. — Damaged EVR solenoid. — Damaged DPFE sensor. — Damaged PCM. • Run KOER Self-Test. • **Is KOER DTC 1408 output?**	Yes No	► ►	The KOER Self-Test has detected an EGR fault that is currently present. GO to HE71. The fault that produced DTC 1407 is intermittent. GO to HE90.

Fig. 189   Test HE: EGR System (Part 19 of 41). 1994-95

TEST STEP	RESULT	►	ACTION TO TAKE
HE71 DTC 1408: OUTPUT CONTINUOUS MEMORY DTCS			
Diagnostic Trouble Code (DTC) 1408 indicates that Key On Engine Running (KOER) Self-Test has detected EGR flow out of range. Possible Causes: — EGR valve stuck closed or iced. — EGR valve diaphragm leaks. — EGR flow path restricted. — EGR vacuum hose off, plugged or leaks. — EVR VPWR circuit open. — EVR circuit to PCM open. — EVR circuit to PCM shorted to PWR. — DPFE sensor pressure hoses both off. — DPFE sensor pressure hoses reversed. — DPFE sensor VREF circuit open. — Downstream pressure hose off. — Downstream pressure hose plugged. — Damaged orifice tube assembly. — Damaged EVR solenoid. — Damaged DPFE sensor. — Damaged PCM. • Output all continuous memory codes. NOTE: If DTCs other than DTC 1403 or 1406 are output, record codes and refer to Diagnostic Trouble Code Charts after completing this Pinpoint Test. • **Is DTC 1403 or 1406 output?**	Yes No	► ►	For DTC 1403: GO to HE40. For DTC 1406: GO to HE60. GO to HE72.
HE72 RUN KOER SELF-TEST WHILE MONITORING EGR VACUUM			
• Key off. • Disconnect vacuum hose at EGR valve and connect hose to a vacuum gauge. • Run Key On Engine Running (KOER) Self-Test while monitoring gauge. Approximately 30 seconds into test, EGR flow will be requested for a few seconds. The vacuum at this time should increase above 1.6 in-Hg to open the valve. NOTE: Since the EGR vacuum hose is disconnected, ignore DTCs during this KOER Self-Test. • **Does the vacuum increase to 1.6 in-Hg or greater at any time during KOER Self-Test?**	Yes No	► ►	The vacuum indicated is sufficient to open the EGR valve. Fault is unlikely to be in EGR vacuum control. GO to HE73. The vacuum indicated is insufficient to open the EGR valve. GO to HE80.

Fig. 189   Test HE: EGR System (Part 20 of 41). 1994-95

TEST STEP	RESULT	►	ACTION TO TAKE
HE73 INSPECT DPFE SENSOR PRESSURE HOSES			
• Key off. • Visually inspect both pressure hoses for reversed connection at DPFE sensor or at orifice tube assembly. • Inspect both hoses for improper routing. Hoses should not be pinched or have dips where water could settle or freeze. • Inspect both hoses for leaks and blockage. • Inspect DPFE sensor and orifice tube assembly for blockage or damage at the pick up tubes. • **Is there a fault detected?**	Yes No	► ►	SERVICE pressure hoses as necessary. RECONNECT all components. COMPLETE PCM Reset to clear DTCs (REFER to Powertrain Control Module (PCM) Reset). RERUN Quick Test. RECONNECT all components. GO to HE74.
HE74 MEASURE VREF VOLTAGE AT DPFE SENSOR VEHICLE HARNESS CONNECTOR			
• DPFE sensor disconnected. • Key on, engine off. • Measure voltage between the sensor VREF circuit and SIG RTN circuit at the DPFE sensor vehicle harness connector. • **Is VREF voltage between 4.0 and 6.0 volts?**	Yes No	► ►	RECONNECT DPFE sensor. GO to HE75. VREF voltage is out of range. GO to Pinpoint Test Step C1.

Fig. 189   Test HE: EGR System (Part 21 of 41). 1994-95

TEST STEP	RESULT	►	ACTION TO TAKE
HE75 CHECK DPFE SENSOR OUTPUT BY APPLYING VACUUM WITH HAND PUMP			
• Key off. • Disconnect pressure hoses at DPFE sensor. • Connect a hand vacuum pump to the downstream pickup marked "REF" on the DPFE sensor. • Key on, engine off. • Access DPFE PID with a Scan Tool. PID voltage should be 0.45 volt ± 0.25 volt. • Apply 8-9 in-Hg vacuum to the DPFE sensor. The PID voltage should be above 4.0 volts. Quickly release vacuum from sensor. PID voltage should drop to less than 1.0 volt in less than 3 seconds. • **Does the DPFE PID voltage indicate a fault in the DPFE sensor?**	Yes No	► ►	REPLACE damaged DPFE sensor. RECONNECT all components. COMPLETE PCM Reset to clear DTCs (REFER to Powertrain Control Module (PCM) Reset). RERUN Quick Test. RECONNECT pressure hoses. GO to HE76.
HE76 CHECK EGR VALVE FUNCTION BY APPLYING VACUUM WITH HAND PUMP			
• Key off. • Disconnect vacuum hose at EGR valve and plug hose. • Connect a hand vacuum pump to to EGR valve. • Start engine and bring to idle. • Access DPFE and RPM PIDs with a Scan Tool. • Slowly apply 5-10 in-Hg of vacuum to the EGR valve and hold it for 10 seconds. If engine wants to stall, increase rpm with throttle just enough to maintain idle rpm. • Look for the following: — EGR valve starts opening at about 1.6 in-Hg vacuum indicated by increasing DPFE PID voltage. — DPFE PID voltage increasing until EGR valve is fully open. DPFE PID should read 2.5 volts minimum with full vacuum applied. — DPFE PID voltage steady when vacuum is held. If voltage drops within a few seconds, the EGR valve or vacuum source could be leaking. • **Does the DPFE PID voltage indicate that the EGR valve is functioning as described in this test?**	Yes No	► ►	RECONNECT all components. GO to HE85. REMOVE and INSPECT the EGR valve for signs of contamination, unusual wear, carbon deposits, binding and other damage. SERVICE as necessary (use Rotunda EGR Valve Cleaner 021-00056, if needed). RECONNECT all components. COMPLETE PCM Reset to clear DTCs (REFER to Powertrain Control Module (PCM) Reset). RERUN Quick Test.

Fig. 189   Test HE: EGR System (Part 22 of 41). 1994-95

TEST STEP	RESULT	▶	ACTION TO TAKE
HE80 CHECK VACUUM SOURCE AND VACUUM HOSES TO AND FROM EVR SOLENOID • Key off. • Disconnect vacuum hoses at EVR solenoid. • Connect EVR vacuum supply hose to a vacuum gauge. • With engine warm and at idle, take vacuum gauge reading. • Inspect vacuum lines between vacuum source and EVR and between EVR and EGR valve for leaks, kinks, disconnects, blockage, routing or any damage. • **Is the vacuum gauge reading a minimum of 15 in-Hg at idle and vacuum lines OK?**	Yes No	▶ ▶	RECONNECT all components. GO to **HE81**. ISOLATE fault and SERVICE as necessary. RECONNECT all components. COMPLETE PCM Reset to clear DTCs (REFER to Powertrain Control Module (PCM) Reset). RERUN Quick Test.
HE81 CHECK VPWR TO EVR SOLENOID • Key off. • EVR solenoid disconnected. • Key on, engine off. • Measure voltage between VPWR circuit and chassis ground at the EVR solenoid vehicle harness connector. • **Is EVR VPWR voltage greater than 10.5 volts?**	Yes No	▶ ▶	GO to **HE82**. SERVICE open in EVR VPWR circuit. RECONNECT all components. COMPLETE PCM Reset to clear DTCs (REFER to Powertrain Control Module (PCM) Reset). RERUN Quick Test.
HE82 MEASURE RESISTANCE ACROSS EVR SOLENOID • Key off. • EVR solenoid disconnected. • Measure resistance across EVR solenoid. • **Is solenoid resistance between 26 and 40 ohms?**	Yes No	▶ ▶	GO to **HE83**. REPLACE damaged EVR solenoid. RECONNECT all components. COMPLETE PCM Reset to clear DTCs (REFER to Powertrain Control Module (PCM) Reset). RERUN Quick Test.

FM0159401192230X

Fig. 189 Test HE: EGR System (Part 23 of 41). 1994-95

TEST STEP	RESULT	▶	ACTION TO TAKE
HE83 CHECK EVR FOR SHORT TO PWR • Key off. • EVR solenoid disconnected. • Disconnect PCM. Inspect for damaged or pushed out pins, corrosion, loose pins, etc. Service as necessary. • Install breakout box, leave PCM disconnected. • Key on, engine off. • Measure voltage between Test Pin 47 (EVR) and chassis ground. • **Is voltage greater than 1.0 volt?**	Yes No	▶ ▶	SERVICE EVR circuit for short to PWR. RECONNECT all components. COMPLETE PCM Reset to clear DTCs (REFER to Powertrain Control Module (PCM) Reset). RERUN Quick Test. GO to **HE84**.
HE84 CHECK EVR CIRCUIT FOR OPEN IN HARNESS • Key off. • EVR solenoid disconnected. • Breakout box installed, PCM disconnected. • Measure resistance between Test Pin 47 (EVR) and EVR circuit at the EVR solenoid vehicle harness connector. • **Is resistance less than 5.0 ohms?**	Yes No	▶ ▶	RECONNECT EVR solenoid. GO to **HE85**. SERVICE open in EVR circuit. RECONNECT all components. COMPLETE PCM Reset to clear DTCs (REFER to Powertrain Control Module (PCM) Reset). RERUN Quick Test.
HE85 CHECK EVR VACUUM OUTPUT CAPABILITY BY GROUNDING EVR CIRCUIT • Key off. • Breakout box installed, PCM connected. • EVR solenoid connected. • Disconnect vacuum hose at the EGR valve and connect to a vacuum gauge. • Key on, engine running. • With engine at idle, jumper Test Pin 47 (EVR) to chassis ground. • **Is vacuum gauge reading 4.0 in-Hg or greater?**	Yes No	▶ ▶	REPLACE damaged PCM. RECONNECT all components. RERUN Quick Test. REPLACE damaged EVR solenoid. RECONNECT all components. COMPLETE PCM Reset to clear DTCs (REFER to Powertrain Control Module (PCM) Reset). RERUN Quick Test.

FM0159401192240X

Fig. 189 Test HE: EGR System (Part 24 of 41). 1994-95

TEST STEP	RESULT	▶	ACTION TO TAKE
HE90 INSPECT EGR SYSTEM FOR AN INTERMITTENT FAILURE • Key off. • Visually inspect the EGR system for signs of intermittent failure. • **Is a fault found?**	Yes No	▶ ▶	SERVICE fault as necessary. RECONNECT all components. COMPLETE PCM Reset to clear DTCs (REFER to Powertrain Control Module (PCM) Reset). RERUN Quick Test. GO to **HE91**.
HE91 CHECK EGR VALVE OPERATION • Key off. • Disconnect vacuum hose at EGR valve and connect a hand vacuum pump to EGR valve. • View DPFE PID with a Scan Tool. • Key on, engine running. • Slowly apply 5 to 10 in-Hg of vacuum to the EGR valve, hold vacuum for 5 seconds and release. (Increase rpm slightly if engine begins to stall.) — Look for a smooth operation of the EGR valve without binding. The DPFE PID voltage should increase once the EGR valve begins to open and until its fully open. — While holding vacuum to EGR valve, look for a vacuum leakage causing the valve to close. • **Does the EGR valve open smoothly and hold vacuum?**	Yes No	▶ ▶	GO to **HE92**. REMOVE and INSPECT EGR valve for signs of damage, leakage, contamination, icing, unusual wear, carbon deposits, binding and other damage. SERVICE as necessary (use Rotunda EGR Valve Cleaner 021-00056, if needed). RECONNECT all components. COMPLETE PCM Reset to clear DTCs (REFER to Powertrain Control Module (PCM) Reset). RERUN Quick Test.

FM0159401192250X

Fig. 189 Test HE: EGR System (Part 25 of 41). 1994-95

TEST STEP	RESULT	▶	ACTION TO TAKE
HE92 INSPECT EGR VACUUM SIGNAL SUPPLY FOR INTERMITTENT FAILURE • Key off. • Disconnect PCM. Inspect for damaged or pushed out pins, corrosion, loose wires, etc. Service as necessary. • Install breakout box and connect PCM to breakout box. • Disconnect hose at EGR valve and connect to a vacuum gauge. • Key on, engine running. • Jumper Test Pin 47 (EVR) to chassis ground to activate the EVR to full ON. At idle, the vacuum gauge should read above 4.0 in-Hg. • Observe vacuum gauge for an indication of a fault while performing the following: — Lightly tap on the EVR solenoid and wiggle the EVR solenoid connector, vacuum lines and vehicle harness between the solenoid and PCM. A fault is indicated by a sudden drop in vacuum reading. • **Is a fault indicated?**	Yes No	▶ ▶	ISOLATE fault and SERVICE as necessary. RECONNECT all components. COMPLETE PCM Reset to clear DTCs (REFER to Powertrain Control Module (PCM) Reset). RERUN Quick Test. Unable to duplicate and/or identify fault at this time. (In cold climates, the EGR valve may temporarily freeze shut and thaw when the engine warms up causing the intermittent DTC.) GO to Pinpoint Test Step **Z1** with the following data: DPFE, EVR and VREF PIDs and list of Possible Causes.

FM0159401192260X

Fig. 189 Test HE: EGR System (Part 26 of 41). 1994-95

TEST STEP	RESULT	▶	ACTION TO TAKE
HE100 EGR DIAGNOSIS BY SYMPTOM: CHECK FOR EGR FLOW WITH EGR VACUUM HOSE DISCONNECTED AND PLUGGED			
NOTE: Perform KOER Self-Test and service any DTCs before proceeding with this test. The symptom flowcharts have indicated possible EGR flow at idle with no EGR Diagnostic Trouble Codes output. Possible Causes: — EGR valve not fully seating. — EVR solenoid vent restricted. — Damaged EVR solenoid. • Disconnect vacuum hose at EGR valve and plug hose. • Key on, engine off. • Access DPFE PID with a Scan Tool and note voltage. **NOTE: DPFE sensor input with no EGR flow is 0.45 volt ± 0.25 volt.** • Start engine and bring to idle. • With engine at idle, look at the DPFE PID voltage and compare to the engine off reading. An increase in the voltage at idle indicates that the DPFE sensor is sensing EGR flow. • **Is the DPFE PID voltage greater at idle by a minimum of 0.15 volts than with the engine off?**	Yes No	▶ ▶	The DPFE PID voltage is indicating EGR flow at idle. Since the EGR vacuum hose is disconnected and plugged, the fault is most likely in the EGR valve. REMOVE and INSPECT the EGR valve for signs of contamination, unusual wear, carbon deposits, binding and other damage. SERVICE as necessary (use Rotunda EGR Valve Cleaner 021-00056, if needed). RECONNECT all components. RE-EVALUATE symptom. This indicates a fault in the EGR valve vacuum supply. INSPECT the EVR solenoid vent and vent filter for restrictions. SERVICE as necessary. If OK, REPLACE EVR solenoid. RE-EVALUATE symptom.

Fig. 189   Test HE: EGR System (Part 27 of 41). 1994-95

TEST STEP	RESULT	▶	ACTION TO TAKE
HE110 DTC P1409: OUTPUT ALL DTCs			
Diagnostic Trouble Code (DTC) P1409 indicates that Self-Test has detected an electrical malfunction in the EVR circuit. Possible causes: — Open EVR circuit. — Open VPWR circuit to EVR. — EVR circuit shorted to VPWR. — EVR circuit shorted to GND. — Damaged EVR solenoid. — Damaged PCM. • Key off. • Disconnect EVR solenoid. • Measure EVR solenoid resistance. • **Is solenoid resistance between 26 and 40 ohms?**	Yes No	▶ ▶	The EVR solenoid resistance is within specification. GO to **HE111**. REPLACE EVR solenoid. RECONNECT all components. COMPLETE PCM Reset to clear DTCs (Refer to Powertrain Control Module (PCM) Reset). RERUN Quick Test.
HE111 CHECK VPWR CIRCUIT VOLTAGE AT EVR SOLENOID			
• Key off. • EVR solenoid disconnected. • Measure voltage between VPWR circuit at the EVR solenoid vehicle harness connector and chassis GND. • **Is voltage less than 10.5 volts?**	Yes No	▶ ▶	SERVICE open in VPWR circuit to EVR solenoid. RECONNECT all components. COMPLETE PCM Reset to clear DTCs (Refer to Powertrain Control Module (PCM) Reset). RERUN Quick Test. GO to **HE112**.
HE112 CHECK EVR CIRCUIT CONTINUITY			
• Key on, engine off. • EVR solenoid disconnected. • Disconnect PCM. Inspect for damaged or pushed out pins, corrosion, loose wires, etc. Service as necessary. • Install breakout box and leave PCM disconnected. • Measure resistance between Test Pin 47 (EVR) and EVR circuit at the EVR solenoid vehicle harness connector. • **Is resistance less than 5.0 ohms?**	Yes No	▶ ▶	GO to **HE113**. SERVICE open in EVR circuit. RECONNECT all components. RERUN Quick Test.

Fig. 189   Test HE: EGR System (Part 28 of 41). 1995

TEST STEP	RESULT	▶	ACTION TO TAKE
HE113 CHECK EVR CIRCUIT FOR SHORTS TO POWER OR GROUND			
• Key off. • EVR solenoid disconnected. • Breakout box installed, leave PCM disconnected. • Measure resistance between Test Pin 47 (EVR) and Test Pins 71 and 97 (VPWR) at the breakout box. • Measure resistance between Test Pin 47 (EVR) and Test Pins 24 and 103 (PWR GND) at the breakout box. • **Is each resistance greater than 10,000 ohms?**	Yes No	▶ ▶	REPLACE damaged PCM. RECONNECT all components. RERUN Quick Test. SERVICE EVR circuit for short to PWR or PWR GND. RECONNECT all components. RERUN Quick Test.
HE120 CONTINUOUS DTC P1409: WIGGLE EVR WHILE MONITORING VPWR			
Continuous DTC P1409 indicates that Continuous Self-Test has detected an electrical malfunction in the EVR circuit sometime during vehicle operation. NOTE: If DTC P1409 was output in Key On Engine Off (KOEO) or Key On Engine Running (KOER) Self-Test, go to **HE110** to diagnose present fault. Possible causes: — Open EVR circuit. — Open VPWR circuit to EVR. — EVR shorted to VPWR. — EVR shorted to GND. — Damaged EVR solenoid. — Damaged PCM. • Disconnect PCM. Inspect for damaged or pushed out pins, corrosion, loose wires, etc. • Install breakout box, leave PCM disconnected. • Measure voltage between Test Pin 47 (EVR) and Test Pins 24 (PWR GND) at the breakout box. • Key on. • Voltage should read greater than 10.5 volts. For an indication of a fault, look for this voltage to drop while performing the following: — Lightly tap on the EVR solenoid. — Wiggle the EVR solenoid connector. — Grasp the EVR solenoid vehicle harness connector and wiggle wires between solenoid and PCM. • **Is a fault indicated?**	Yes No	▶ ▶	ISOLATE fault and SERVICE as necessary. RECONNECT all components. RERUN Quick Test. Unable to duplicate and/or identify fault at this time. GO to Pinpoint Test Step **Z1** with the following data: DPFEGR (formerly DPFE) and EGRVR (formerly EVR) PIDs and list of Possible Causes.

Fig. 189   Test HE: EGR System (Part 29 of 41). 1995

TEST STEP	RESULT	▶	ACTION TO TAKE
HE130 DTC P0400: ACCESS DPFEGR PID WITH SCAN TOOL			
Diagnostic Trouble Code (DTC) P0400 indicates that Self-Test has detected an EGR system malfunction. Possible causes: — Any EGR system failure. • Key on, engine off. • Access DPFEGR PID (formerly DPFE) with a Scan Tool. NOTE: DPFE sensor input with no EGR flow is 0.45 volts ± 0.25 volts. • **Is DPFEGR PID voltage less than 0.2 volts?**	Yes No	▶ ▶	The DPFE SIG voltage is less than the acceptable minimum. GO to **HE134**. GO to **HE131**.
HE131 CHECK FOR HIGH DPFE SIG VOLTAGE			
• Key on, engine off. • **Is DPFEGR PID voltage greater than 4.0 volts?**	Yes No	▶ ▶	The DPFE SIG voltage is greater than the acceptable maximum. GO to **HE137**. GO to **HE132**.
HE132 COMPARE DPFEGR PID VOLTAGE WITH THE ENGINE OFF AND ENGINE AT IDLE			
• Key on, engine off. • Note the DPFEGR PID voltage with the key on and engine off. • Start engine and bring to idle. • With the engine at idle, look at DPFEGR PID voltage and compare it to the engine off reading. An increase in the voltage at idle indicates that the DPFE sensor is sensing EGR flow. • **Is the DPFEGR PID voltage greater at idle by a minimum of 0.15 volts than with the engine off?**	Yes No	▶ ▶	The DPFEGR PID voltage is indicating EGR flow at idle. GO to **HE133**. GO to **HE160**.

Fig. 189   Test HE: EGR System (Part 30 of 41). 1995

TEST STEP		RESULT	►	ACTION TO TAKE
HE133	CHECK DPFEGR PID VOLTAGE WITH EGR VACUUM HOSE DISCONNECTED			
	• Key off. • Disconnect vacuum hose at EGR valve and plug hose. • Compare DPFEGR PID voltage with engine off and engine at idle as described in step HE132 but with the EGR vacuum hose disconnected this time. • Is the DPFEGR PID voltage greater at idle by a minimum of 0.15 volts than with the engine off?	Yes	►	The DPFEGR PID voltage is indicating EGR flow at idle. REMOVE and INSPECT the EGR valve for signs of contamination, unusual wear, carbon deposits, binding and other damage. SERVICE as necessary (use Rotunda EGR Valve Cleaner 021-00056, if needed). RECONNECT all components. RERUN Quick Test.
		No	►	GO to HE150.
HE134	INDUCE OPPOSITE DPFE SIGNAL			
	• Key off. • Disconnect DPFE sensor vehicle harness connector. • Connect a jumper wire between the sensor VREF circuit and DPFE SIG circuit at the DPFE sensor vehicle harness connector. • Key on, engine off. NOTE: If a Scan Tool communication problem exists, remove jumper immediately and go directly to HE135. • Access DPFEGR PID with a Scan Tool. • Is DPFEGR PID value between 4.0 and 6.0 volts?	Yes	►	REPLACE damaged DPFE sensor. RECONNECT all components. COMPLETE PCM Reset to clear DTCs (REFER to Powertrain Control Module (PCM) Reset). RERUN Quick Test.
		No	►	REMOVE jumper. GO to HE135.
HE135	MEASURE VREF VOLTAGE AT DPFE SENSOR VEHICLE HARNESS CONNECTOR			
	• DPFE sensor disconnected. • Key on, engine off. • Measure voltage between the sensor VREF circuit and SIG RTN circuit at the DPFE sensor vehicle harness connector. • Is VREF voltage between 4.0 and 6.0 volts?	Yes	►	GO to HE136.
		No	►	VREF voltage is out of range. GO to Pinpoint Test Step C1.

Fig. 189   Test HE: EGR System (Part 31 of 41). 1995

TEST STEP		RESULT	►	ACTION TO TAKE
HE136	CHECK DPFE SIG CIRCUIT FOR SHORTS TO GROUND AND SIG RTN			
	• Key off. • DPFE sensor disconnected. • Disconnect PCM. Inspect for damaged or pushed out pins, corrosion, loose wires, etc. Service as necessary. • Install breakout box, leave PCM disconnected. • Measure resistance between Test Pin 65 (DPFE SIG) and Test Pin 91 (SIG RTN) and Test Pins 51 and 103 (PWR GND) at the breakout box. • Is each resistance greater than 10,000 ohms?	Yes	►	REPLACE damaged PCM. REMOVE breakout box. RECONNECT all components. RERUN Quick Test.
		No	►	SERVICE short circuit between DPFE SIG and GROUND or SIG RTN. REMOVE breakout box. RECONNECT all components. RERUN Quick Test.
HE137	CHECK DPFE SIG FOR SHORT TO PWR			
	• Key off. • Disconnect DPFE sensor vehicle harness connector. • Key on, engine off. • Measure voltage between DPFE SIG circuit at the DPFE sensor vehicle harness connector and battery ground. • Is voltage greater than 10.5 volts?	Yes	►	The DPFE SIG input is indicating a short to PWR. GO to HE138.
		No	►	GO to HE139.
HE138	CHECK DPFE SIG FOR SHORT TO PWR IN HARNESS			
	• Key off. • DPFE sensor disconnected. • Disconnect PCM. Inspect for damaged or pushed out pins, corrosion, loose wires, etc. Service as necessary. • Install breakout box, leave PCM disconnected. • Key on, engine off. • Measure voltage between Test Pin 65 (DPFE SIG) and Test Pins 51 and 103 (PWR GND) at the breakout box. • Is voltage greater than 10.5 volts?	Yes	►	SERVICE short between DPFE SIG and PWR circuit. REMOVE breakout box. RECONNECT all components. RERUN Quick Test.
		No	►	REPLACE damaged PCM. REMOVE breakout box. RECONNECT all components. RERUN Quick Test.

Fig. 189   Test HE: EGR System (Part 32 of 41). 1995

TEST STEP		RESULT	►	ACTION TO TAKE
HE139	INDUCE OPPOSITE DPFE SIGNAL			
	• Key off. • Disconnect DPFE sensor vehicle harness connector. • Connect a jumper wire between the sensor DPFE SIG circuit and SIG RTN circuit at the DPFE sensor vehicle harness connector. • Key on, engine off. NOTE: If a Scan Tool communication problem exists, remove jumper immediately and go directly to HE144. • Access DPFEGR PID with a Scan Tool. • Is DPFEGR PID voltage less than 0.05 volts?	Yes	►	REMOVE jumper. GO to HE140.
		No	►	Unable to induce opposite signal. GO to HE142.
HE140	VERIFY THAT VREF IS IN RANGE			
	• DPFE sensor disconnected. • Key on, engine off. • Measure voltage between the sensor VREF circuit and SIG RTN circuit at the DPFE sensor vehicle harness connector. • Is VREF voltage between 4.0 and 6.0 volts?	Yes	►	GO to HE141.
		No	►	VREF voltage is out of range. GO to Pinpoint Test Step C1.
HE141	CHECK DPFE SIG FOR SHORT TO VREF IN HARNESS			
	• Key off. • DPFE sensor disconnected. • Disconnect PCM. Inspect for damaged or pushed out pins, corrosion, loose wires, etc. Service as necessary. • Install breakout box, leave PCM disconnected. • Measure resistance between Test Pin 65 (DPFE SIG) and Test Pin 90 (VREF) at the breakout box. • Is resistance greater than 10,000 ohms?	Yes	►	REPLACE damaged DPFE sensor. REMOVE breakout box. RECONNECT all components. RERUN Quick Test.
		No	►	SERVICE short between DPFE SIG and VREF circuit. REMOVE breakout box. RECONNECT all components. RERUN Quick Test.
HE142	CHECK DPFE SIG FOR OPEN IN HARNESS			
	• Key off. • DPFE sensor disconnected. • Disconnect PCM. Inspect for damaged or pushed out pins, corrosion, loose wires, etc. Service as necessary. • Install breakout box, leave PCM disconnected. • Measure resistance between Test Pin 65 (DPFE SIG) and DPFE SIG circuit at the DPFE sensor vehicle harness connector. • Is resistance less than 5.0 ohms?	Yes	►	GO to HE143.
		No	►	SERVICE open in DPFE SIG circuit. REMOVE breakout box. RECONNECT all components. RERUN Quick Test.

Fig. 189   Test HE: EGR System (Part 33 of 41). 1995

TEST STEP		RESULT	►	ACTION TO TAKE
HE143	CHECK SIG RTN FOR OPEN IN HARNESS			
	• Key off. • DPFE sensor disconnected. • Breakout box installed, PCM disconnected. • Measure resistance between Test Pin 91 (SIG RTN) and SIG RTN circuit at the DPFE sensor vehicle harness connector. • Is resistance less than 5.0 ohms?	Yes	►	REPLACE damaged PCM. REMOVE breakout box. RECONNECT all components. RERUN Quick Test.
		No	►	SERVICE open in SIG RTN circuit. REMOVE breakout box. RECONNECT all components. RERUN Quick Test.
HE144	CHECK DPFE SIG FOR SHORT TO VREF IN HARNESS			
	• Key off. • DPFE sensor disconnected. • Disconnect PCM. Inspect for damaged or pushed out pins, corrosion, loose wires, etc. Service as necessary. • Install breakout box, leave PCM disconnected. • Measure resistance between Test Pin 65 (DPFE SIG) and Test Pin 90 (VREF) at the breakout box. • Is resistance greater than 10,000 ohms?	Yes	►	REPLACE damaged PCM. REMOVE breakout box. RECONNECT all components. RERUN Quick Test.
		No	►	SERVICE short between DPFE SIG and VREF circuit. REMOVE breakout box. RECONNECT all components. RERUN Quick Test.
HE150	CHECK EGR SYSTEM VACUUM HOSES FOR INTEGRITY AND CONNECTION			
	NOTE: A pinched or plugged EGR vacuum hose can trap vacuum between the EVR solenoid and EGR valve not allowing the EGR valve to close. • Key off. • Trace each vacuum hose from EVR solenoid and verify that each hose is connected correctly. (Refer to vehicle's vacuum diagram label.) • Verify that the EGR valve vacuum hose is not pinched or plugged and routed properly. • Are vacuum hoses OK?	Yes	►	RECONNECT vacuum hoses. GO to HE151.
		No	►	SERVICE vacuum hoses as necessary. RECONNECT all components. COMPLETE PCM Reset to clear DTCs (REFER to Powertrain Control Module (PCM) Reset). RERUN Quick Test.

Fig. 189   Test HE: EGR System (Part 34 of 41). 1995

TEST STEP	RESULT	▶	ACTION TO TAKE
HE151 CHECK FOR EGR FLOW AT IDLE WITH EVR SOLENOID CONNECTOR OFF • Key on, engine off. • Note the DPFEGR PID voltage with the key on and engine off. • Disconnect EVR solenoid vehicle harness connector. • Start engine and bring to idle. • Compare DPFEGR PID voltage at idle to the engine off voltage. • Is the DPFEGR PID voltage greater at idle by a minimum of 0.15 volts than with the engine off?	Yes No	▶ ▶	This indicates an EVR solenoid mechanical fault. GO to HE152. GO to HE153.
HE152 INSPECT EVR VENT FOR PLUGGING • Key off. • Disconnect EVR solenoid vacuum hoses. • Remove EVR solenoid vent cap. • Remove filter and inspect for blockage or icing in some cases. • Apply 10 to 15 in-Hg of vacuum directly to EVR vent with a hand vacuum pump. If the vacuum holds or is slow to release to atmosphere, the EVR vent could be plugged or restricted. NOTE: A plugged EVR vent will not allow EGR vacuum to vent to atmosphere. • Is the EVR vent or vent filter plugged or restricted?	Yes No	▶ ▶	SERVICE EVR solenoid as necessary. If unable to service, REPLACE EVR solenoid. RECONNECT all components. COMPLETE PCM Reset to clear DTCs (REFER to Section 2, Powertrain Control Module (PCM) Reset). RERUN Quick Test. REPLACE damaged EVR solenoid. RECONNECT all components. COMPLETE PCM Reset to clear DTCs (REFER to Powertrain Control Module (PCM) Reset). RERUN Quick Test.
HE153 MEASURE EVR SOLENOID COIL RESISTANCE • Key off. • EVR solenoid disconnected. • Measure resistance across EVR solenoid. • Is resistance between 26 and 40 ohms?	Yes No	▶ ▶	GO to HE154. REPLACE damaged EVR solenoid. RECONNECT all components. COMPLETE PCM Reset to clear DTCs (REFER to Powertrain Control Module (PCM) Reset). RERUN Quick Test.

Fig. 189 Test HE: EGR System (Part 35 of 41). 1995

TEST STEP	RESULT	▶	ACTION TO TAKE
HE154 CHECK DPFE SENSOR OUTPUT BY APPLYING VACUUM WITH HAND PUMP • Key off. • Disconnect pressure hoses at DPFE sensor. • Connect a hand vacuum pump to the downstream pickup marked "REF" on the DPFE. • Key on, engine off. • Access DPFEGR PID with a Scan Tool. PID voltage should be 0.45 ± 0.25 volts. • Apply 8-9 in-Hg vacuum to the DPFE sensor. The PID voltage should be above 4.0 volts. Quickly release vacuum from sensor. PID voltage should drop to less than 1 volt in less than 3 seconds. • Does the DPFEGR PID voltage indicate a fault in the DPFE sensor?	Yes No	▶ ▶	REPLACE damaged DPFE sensor. RECONNECT all components. COMPLETE PCM Reset to clear DTCs (REFER to Powertrain Control Module (PCM) Reset). RERUN Quick Test. RECONNECT DPFE sensor. GO to HE155.
HE155 CHECK EVR CIRCUIT FOR SHORT TO GROUND IN HARNESS • Key off. • EVR solenoid disconnected. • Disconnect PCM. Inspect for damaged or pushed out pins, corrosion, loose wires, etc. Service as necessary. • Install breakout box, leave PCM disconnected. • Measure resistance between Test Pin 47 (EVR) and Test Pins 51 and 103 (PWR GND) at the breakout box. • Is resistance greater than 10,000 ohms?	Yes No	▶ ▶	REPLACE damaged PCM. REMOVE breakout box. RECONNECT all components. RERUN Quick Test. SERVICE short between EVR and GROUND. REMOVE breakout box. RECONNECT all components. RERUN Quick Test.

Fig. 189 Test HE: EGR System (Part 36 of 41). 1995

TEST STEP	RESULT	▶	ACTION TO TAKE
HE160 CHECK FOR REVERSED PRESSURE HOSES • Key off. • Visually inspect hoses for proper connection between DPFE sensor and EGR orifice tube assembly. — The hose connection marked "HI" on the DPFE sensor should connect to the exhaust side of the orifice tube and the connection marked "REF" connects to the intake manifold side of the orifice tube. The HI side hose has a larger inside diameter than the REF side hose. • Are the DPFE sensor pressure hoses connected properly?	Yes No	▶ ▶	GO to HE161. SERVICE hoses as necessary (if hoses are replaced, USE only the service part and not a substitute). COMPLETE PCM Reset to clear DTCs (REFER to Powertrain Control Module (PCM) Reset). RERUN Quick Test.
HE161 CHECK UPSTREAM AND DOWNSTREAM PRESSURE SIGNAL HOSES • Key off. • Remove and inspect both pressure signal hoses between DPFE sensor and EGR orifice tube. • Look for disconnects, leaks, pinching, plugging, poor routing, incorrect hose substitution, and possible freezing in cold weather. • Check both the DPFE sensor and orifice tube connections for plugging or damage. • Is a fault found?	Yes No	▶ ▶	SERVICE as necessary. Use only the service replacement hoses if new hoses are needed. COMPLETE PCM Reset (REFER to , Powertrain Control Module (PCM) Reset). RERUN Quick Test. RECONNECT all components. GO to HE162.

Fig. 189 Test HE: EGR System (Part 37 of 41). 1995

TEST STEP	RESULT	▶	ACTION TO TAKE
HE162 CHECK DPFE SENSOR OUTPUT BY APPLYING VACUUM WITH HAND PUMP • Key off. • Disconnect pressure hoses at DPFE sensor. • Connect a hand vacuum pump to the downstream pickup marked "REF" on the DPFE sensor. • Key on, engine off. • Access DPFEGR PID with a Scan Tool. PID voltage should be 0.45 volt ± 0.25 volt. • Apply 8-9 in-Hg vacuum to the DPFE sensor. The PID voltage should be above 4.0 volts. Quickly release vacuum from sensor. PID voltage should drop to less than 1.0 volt in less than 3 seconds. • Does the DPFEGR PID voltage indicate a fault in the DPFE sensor?	Yes No	▶ ▶	REPLACE damaged DPFE sensor. RECONNECT all components. COMPLETE PCM Reset to clear DTCs (REFER to Powertrain Control Module (PCM) Reset). RERUN Quick Test. RECONNECT pressure hoses. GO to HE163.
HE163 CHECK EGR VALVE FUNCTION BY APPLYING VACUUM WITH HAND PUMP • Key off. • Disconnect vacuum hose at EGR valve and plug hose. • Connect a hand vacuum pump to EGR valve. • Start engine and bring to idle. • Access DPFEGR and RPM PIDs with a Scan Tool. • Slowly apply 5-10 in-Hg of vacuum to the EGR valve and hold it for 10 seconds. If engine wants to stall, increase rpm with throttle just enough to maintain idle rpm. • Look for the following: — EGR valve starts opening at about 1.6 in-Hg vacuum indicated by increasing DPFEGR PID voltage. — DPFEGR PID voltage increasing until EGR valve is fully open. DPFEGR PID should read 2.5 volts minimum with full vacuum applied. — DPFEGR PID voltage steady when vacuum is held. If voltage drops within a few seconds, the EGR valve or vacuum source could be leaking. • Does the DPFEGR PID voltage indicate that the EGR valve is functioning as described in this test?	Yes No	▶ ▶	RECONNECT all components. GO to HE164. REMOVE and INSPECT the EGR valve for signs of contamination, unusual wear, carbon deposits, binding, leaking diaphragm and other damage. If EGR valve is OK, look for an obstructed EGR port in the intake manifold. SERVICE as necessary (use Rotunda EGR Valve Cleaner 021-00056, if needed). RECONNECT all components. COMPLETE PCM Reset to clear DTCs (REFER to Powertrain Control Module (PCM) Reset). RERUN Quick Test.

Fig. 189 Test HE: EGR System (Part 38 of 41). 1995

ELECTRONIC ENGINE CONTROL SYSTEM (EEC-V)

TEST STEP	RESULT	▶	ACTION TO TAKE
HE164 CHECK VACUUM SOURCE AND VACUUM HOSES TO AND FROM EVR SOLENOID • Key off. • Disconnect vacuum hoses at EVR solenoid. • Connect EVR vacuum supply hose to a vacuum gauge. • With engine warm and at idle, take vacuum gauge reading. • Inspect vacuum lines between vacuum source and EVR and between EVR and EGR valve for leaks, kinks, disconnects, blockage, routing or any damage. • **Is the vacuum gauge reading a minimum of 15 in-Hg at idle and vacuum lines OK?**	Yes No	▶ ▶	RECONNECT all components. GO to **HE165**. ISOLATE fault and SERVICE as necessary. RECONNECT all components. COMPLETE PCM Reset to clear DTCs (REFER to Powertrain Control Module (PCM) Reset). RERUN Quick Test.
HE165 CHECK VPWR TO EVR SOLENOID • Key off. • EVR solenoid disconnected. • Key on, engine off. • Measure voltage between VPWR circuit and chassis ground at the EVR solenoid vehicle harness connector. • **Is EVR VPWR voltage greater than 10.5 volts?**	Yes No	▶ ▶	GO to **HE166**. SERVICE open in EVR VPWR circuit. RECONNECT all components. COMPLETE PCM Reset to clear DTCs (REFER to Powertrain Control Module (PCM) Reset). RERUN Quick Test.
HE166 MEASURE RESISTANCE ACROSS EVR SOLENOID • Key off. • EVR solenoid disconnected. • Measure resistance across EVR solenoid. • **Is solenoid resistance between 26 and 40 ohms?**	Yes No	▶ ▶	GO to **HE167**. REPLACE damaged EVR solenoid. RECONNECT all components. COMPLETE PCM Reset to clear DTCs (REFER to Powertrain Control Module (PCM) Reset). RERUN Quick Test.

Fig. 189   Test HE: EGR System (Part 39 of 41). 1995

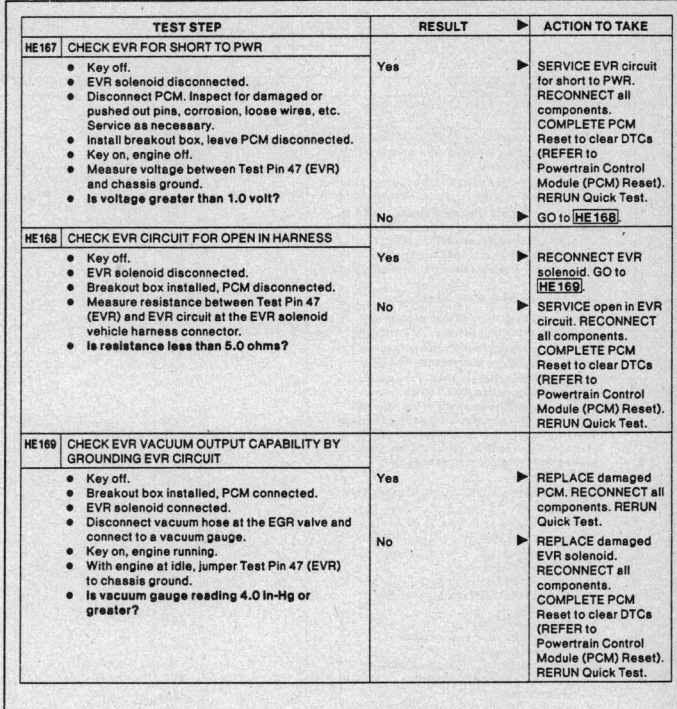

TEST STEP	RESULT	▶	ACTION TO TAKE
HE167 CHECK EVR FOR SHORT TO PWR • Key off. • EVR solenoid disconnected. • Disconnect PCM. Inspect for damaged or pushed out pins, corrosion, loose wires, etc. Service as necessary. • Install breakout box, leave PCM disconnected. • Key on, engine off. • Measure voltage between Test Pin 47 (EVR) and chassis ground. • **Is voltage greater than 1.0 volt?**	Yes No	▶ ▶	SERVICE EVR circuit for short to PWR. RECONNECT all components. COMPLETE PCM Reset to clear DTCs (REFER to Powertrain Control Module (PCM) Reset). RERUN Quick Test. GO to **HE168**.
HE168 CHECK EVR CIRCUIT FOR OPEN IN HARNESS • Key off. • EVR solenoid disconnected. • Breakout box installed, PCM disconnected. • Measure resistance between Test Pin 47 (EVR) and EVR circuit at the EVR solenoid vehicle harness connector. • **Is resistance less than 5.0 ohms?**	Yes No	▶ ▶	RECONNECT EVR solenoid. GO to **HE169**. SERVICE open in EVR circuit. RECONNECT all components. COMPLETE PCM Reset to clear DTCs (REFER to Powertrain Control Module (PCM) Reset). RERUN Quick Test.
HE169 CHECK EVR VACUUM OUTPUT CAPABILITY BY GROUNDING EVR CIRCUIT • Key off. • Breakout box installed, PCM connected. • EVR solenoid connected. • Disconnect vacuum hose at the EGR valve and connect to a vacuum gauge. • Key on, engine running. • With engine at idle, jumper Test Pin 47 (EVR) to chassis ground. • **Is vacuum gauge reading 4.0 in-Hg or greater?**	Yes No	▶ ▶	REPLACE damaged PCM. RECONNECT all components. RERUN Quick Test. REPLACE damaged EVR solenoid. RECONNECT all components. COMPLETE PCM Reset to clear DTCs (REFER to Powertrain Control Module (PCM) Reset). RERUN Quick Test.

Fig. 189   Test HE: EGR System (Part 40 of 41). 1995

TEST STEP	RESULT	▶	ACTION TO TAKE
HE180 CONTINUOUS DTC P0400: PERFORM EGR DRIVE CYCLE Continuous Diagnostic Trouble Code (DTC) P0400 indicates that Self-Test has detected an EGR system malfunction sometime during vehicle operation. NOTE: If DTC P0400 is output in either Key On Engine Off (KOEO) or Key On Engine Running (KOER) Self-Test, go directly to step **HE130**. Possible causes: — Restricted EGR valve or EGR port. — Any EGR system failure occuring intermittently. • Record all DTCs received for reference. Complete a PCM reset to clear DTCs • Complete the EGR monitor drive cycle (refer to Section 2 Drive Cycles). • Output all DTCs and perform both KOEO and KOER Self-Tests (refer to Diagnostic Subroutines). • **Is DTC P0400 output?**	Yes No	▶ ▶	If DTC P0400 is output in either KOEO or KOER Self-Test: GO to **HE130**. If DTC P0400 is only output from continuous memory: REMOVE and INSPECT the EGR valve and intake manifold for contamination and restriction. SERVICE as necessary (Use Rotunda EGR Valve Cleaner 021-00056, if needed). If no restriction is found, GO to Pinpoint Test Step **Z1** with the following data: DPFEGR and EGRVR (formerly EVR) PIDs and list of Possible Causes. DTC P0400 is intermittent. GO to Pinpoint Test Step **Z1** with the following data: DPFEGR and EGRVR (formerly EVR) PIDs and list of Possible Causes.

Fig. 189   Test HE: EGR System (Part 41 of 41). 1995

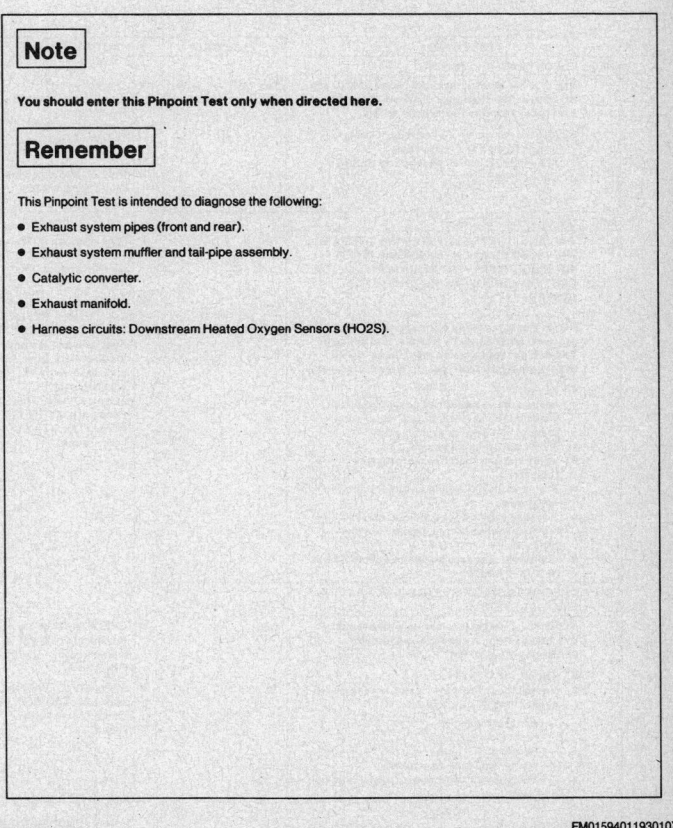

Fig. 190   Test HF: Catalyst Efficiency Monitor & Exhaust Systems (Part 1 of 8). 1994-95

TEST STEP	RESULT	▶	ACTION TO TAKE
HF1 DTC 0420 OR 0430: CHECK FOR MISFIRE MONITOR DTCS			
Diagnostic Trouble Code (DTC) 0420 indicates that Bank 1 catalyst system efficiency is below the acceptable threshold. DTC 0430 indicates that Bank 2 catalyst system efficiency is below the acceptable threshold. **NOTE 1: Complete the spark timing check in Quick Test before proceeding with this test step. Spark timing retarded below specification may increase exhaust gas temperature and decrease catalyst efficiency over time. NOTE 2: Be sure customer has not:** (1) Refueled vehicle with leaded gasoline. (2) Experienced high vehicle oil consumption. **NOTE 3: If entering this Pinpoint Test for symptoms only, go immediately to HF6. NOTE 4: Internal deterioration of a catalytic converter is usually caused by abnormal engine operation upstream of the catalyst. Events that may produce higher than normal temperatures in the catalyst are particularly suspect. For example, misfiring can cause higher than normal catalyst operating temperatures.** Possible Causes: (Catalyst and Exhaust System Concerns.) — Use of leaded fuel. — Oil contamination. — Cylinder misfiring. — Damaged HO2S. — Damaged ECT sensor. — Downstream HO2S wires improperly connected. — Fuel pressure too high. — Damaged exhaust system pipe. — Damaged exhaust manifold. — Damaged muffler/tail-pipe assembly. — Damaged catalytic converter. ● Key on, engine off. ● Retrieve and record all Continuous Memory DTCs (MIL and non-MIL). ● Were any of the following misfire monitor DTCs recorded: 0300, 0301, 0302, 0303, 0304, 0305, 0306, 0307 and 0308?	Yes No	▶ ▶	GO to Diagnostic Subroutines, to address the misfire monitor DTCs present. After repair, RETRIEVE and record all Continuous Memory DTCs to verify the repair. GO to HF2.

FM0159401193020X

Fig. 190 Test HF: Catalyst Efficiency Monitor & Exhaust Systems (Part 2 of 8). 1994-95

TEST STEP	RESULT	▶	ACTION TO TAKE
HF2 CHECK FOR HO2S MONITOR DTCS			
NOTE 1: Incorrect HO2S signal input (e.g. rich/lean input signal when the engine is operating under lean/rich conditions) may cause an abnormal temperature increase in the catalyst. NOTE 2: Non-California applications will not have an active HO2S monitor. As a result, a Catalyst Efficiency Monitor DTC can be generated for a rear HO2S concern. To check for a rear HO2S concern on these applications, go to the HO2S monitor Pinpoint Test Step H82. If any repair actions are necessary in Pinpoint Test H, run KOER Self-Test, to verify the repair. Otherwise, go to HF3. ● Were any of the following HO2S monitor DTCs recorded in HF1: 0136, 0138, 0140 and 0141 (Bank 1, rear HO2S) or 0156, 0158, 0160 and 0161 (Bank 2, rear HO2S)?	Yes No	▶ ▶	GO to Diagnostic Subroutines, to address the HO2S Monitor DTCs. RERUN Quick Test to verify repair. GO to HF3.
HF3 CHECK FOR ECT SENSOR DTCS			
NOTE: ECT sensor DTCs can be an indication that the thermostat is not operating correctly or that the coolant level is not filled to specifications producing above normal operating temperatures. ● Were any of the following ECT sensor DTCs recorded in HF1: 0117, 0118, 0125 and 1117?	Yes No	▶ ▶	GO to Diagnostic Subroutines, to address the ECT sensor DTCs present. RERUN Quick Test to verify repair. GO to HF4.
HF4 CHECK FOR ANY OTHER DTCS			
● Were any other DTCs recorded in HF1 (not including the initial 0420 and/or 0430 DTCs)?	Yes No	▶ ▶	GO to Diagnostic Subroutines, to address the DTCs. RERUN Quick Test to verify repair. Non-California applications: GO to HF6. All others: GO to HF5.

FM0159401193030X

Fig. 190 Test HF: Catalyst Efficiency Monitor & Exhaust Systems (Part 3 of 8). 1994-95

TEST STEP	RESULT	▶	ACTION TO TAKE
HF5 CHECK REAR HO2S WIRING			
NOTE: If the electrical connections of the rear HO2S are interchanged/crossed, the Catalyst Efficiency Monitor Test will be failed. ● Inspect the wiring of each rear HO2S for proper routing and connection. ● Are the HO2S wires improperly routed or connected?	Yes No	▶ ▶	Correctly route/connect the rear HO2S harness circuit(s). RERUN Quick Test to verify repair. No EEC-V root causes related to the DTCs. GO to HF6.
HF6 CHECK FUEL PRESSURE			
WARNING: THE FUEL SYSTEM WILL REMAIN PRESSURIZED WHEN THE ENGINE IS NOT RUNNING. TO PREVENT INJURY OR FIRE, USE CAUTION WHEN WORKING ON THE FUEL SYSTEM. **NOTE: Fuel pressures above specification may produce an abnormally rich air/fuel mixture. The rich air/fuel mixture may cause higher than normal catalyst operating temperatures.** ● Key off. ● Inspect the vacuum hose going to the fuel pressure regulator for proper installation, cracks, etc. Service as necessary. ● Install fuel pressure gauge. ● Verify vacuum source to fuel pressure regulator. ● Start and run the engine at idle. Record the fuel pressure. ● Increase engine speed to 2500 rpm and maintain for one minute. Record the fuel pressure. ● Is the fuel pressure between 30 and 40 psi (210-310 kPa)?	Yes No	▶ ▶	Fuel pressure is OK. REMOVE the fuel pressure gauge. GO to HF7. Fuel pressure is out of specification. REFER to Pinpoint Test HC, Fuel Delivery Systems for diagnosis. Drive vehicle to verify elimination of symptom. Also, if here because of a DTC, RERUN Quick Test to verify repair.
HF7 CHECK FOR OBVIOUS LEAK SOURCES IN THE EXHAUST SYSTEM			
NOTE: If a catalyst is in series with a leaking exhaust system, it can fail the Catalyst Efficiency Monitor test. ● Key off. ● Inspect the following for leaks, cracks, loose connections or punctures: — Exhaust manifold. — Front exhaust pipe. — Rear exhaust pipe. — Muffler/tail-pipe assembly. ● Are the above components free of cracks and punctures, etc.?	Yes No	▶ ▶	CHECK the exhaust manifold to catalyst inlet pipe joint is tight. GO to HF8. REPLACE/REPAIR the leak source(s). RERUN Quick Test to verify repair.

FM0159401193040X

Fig. 190 Test HF: Catalyst Efficiency Monitor & Exhaust Systems (Part 4 of 8). 1994-95

TEST STEP	RESULT	▶	ACTION TO TAKE
HF8 CHECK FOR OBVIOUS RESTRICTIONS IN THE EXHAUST SYSTEM			
● Inspect the following for dents, areas of collapsed material and unusual bending: — Front exhaust pipe. — Rear exhaust pipe. — Muffler/tail-pipe assembly. ● Are the above components free of dents and areas of collapsed material or unusual bending, etc.?	Yes No	▶ ▶	GO to HF9. REPLACE/REPAIR the restricted component(s) as necessary. Drive vehicle to verify elimination of symptom. Also, if here because of a DTC, RERUN Quick Test to verify repair.
HF9 CHECK MANIFOLD VACUUM FOR INDICATION OF EXCESSIVE EXHAUST SYSTEM RESTRICTION			
● Attach a vacuum gauge to the intake manifold vacuum source. ● Install a tachometer. ● Observe the vacuum gauge needle while performing the following: — Start the engine and gradually increase the rpm to 2000 with the transmission in NEUTRAL. **NOTE: The vacuum gauge reading may be normal when the engine is first started and idled. However, excessive restriction in the exhaust system will cause the vacuum gauge needle to drop to a low point even while the engine is idled.** ● Decrease engine speed to base idle rpm. ● Key off. ● Did manifold vacuum rise above 16 inches Hg with the engine rpm at 2000?	Yes No	▶ ▶	GO to HF10. Manifold vacuum did not reach an acceptable level. An excessive restriction may be present. GO to HF11.

FM0159401193050X

Fig. 190 Test HF: Catalyst Efficiency Monitor & Exhaust Systems (Part 5 of 8). 1994-95

TEST STEP	RESULT	▶	ACTION TO TAKE
HF 10 CHECK MANIFOLD VACUUM FOR INDICATION OF MODERATE EXHAUST SYSTEM RESTRICTION			
• Vacuum gauge installed. • Tachometer installed. • Key on, engine idling. • Increase the engine speed gradually from base idle rpm to 2000 rpm with the transmission in NEUTRAL. • Observe the speed the vacuum gauge needle rises, while maintaining the increased engine rpm. NOTE 1: On a non-restricted exhaust system, the vacuum gauge needle will rise quickly to the normal range as the increased rpm is maintained. NOTE 2: On a restricted exhaust system, the vacuum gauge needle will rise slowly to the normal range as the increased rpm is maintained. NOTE 3: The rate of speed the vacuum gauge needle rises to the normal range is slower on a restricted system than on a non-restricted system as the increased rpm is maintained. • Decrease engine speed to base idle rpm. • Key off. • Is the rate of speed that the vacuum gauge needle rises back to the normal range (above 16 inches Hg) much slower than that of a non-restricted system?	Yes No	▶ ▶	A moderate restriction may be present. GO to **HF11**. No indications of restrictions or leaks have been detected in the exhaust system. REMOVE the vacuum gauge and tachometer. For further diagnosis of symptom (e.g. Lack of Power, Loss of Power, or No Start) REFER to Symptom Flow Charts.

FM0159401193060X

Fig. 190   Test HF: Catalyst Efficiency Monitor & Exhaust Systems (Part 6 of 8). 1994-95

TEST STEP	RESULT	▶	ACTION TO TAKE
HF11 CHECK MANIFOLD VACUUM WITH EXHAUST MANIFOLD DISCONNECTED FOR INDICATION OF A RESTRICTION			
• Key off. • Disconnect exhaust system immediately after the exhaust manifold. • Repeat the vacuum measurement found in test step H10. • Did the vacuum needle QUICKLY rise above 16 inches Hg with the engine rpm at 2000? NOTE: An intake manifold gasket leak can also cause the vacuum gauge needle to remain well below the normal range.	Yes No	▶ ▶	The exhaust system restriction is downstream of the exhaust manifold. RECONNECT exhaust system at exhaust manifold. GO to **HF12**. A restriction is present in the exhaust manifold. REMOVE the vacuum gauge and tachometer. INSPECT each exhaust port for casting flash/restrictions by dropping a length of chain into it (NOTE: Do not use a wire or lamp to check the ports. The restriction may be large enough for either to pass through, but small enough to cause excessive back pressure at high engine rpm.). REPLACE the exhaust manifold if unable to remove the casting flash/restriction. Drive the vehicle to verify elimination of symptom. Also, if here because of a DTC, RERUN Quick Test to verify repair.

FM0159401193070X

Fig. 190   Test HF: Catalyst Efficiency Monitor & Exhaust Systems (Part 7 of 8). 1994-95

TEST STEP	RESULT	▶	ACTION TO TAKE
HF12 CHECK MANIFOLD VACUUM WITH MUFFLER/TAIL-PIPE ASSEMBLY DISCONNECTED FOR INDICATION OF A RESTRICTION			
• Key off. • Disconnect muffler/tail-pipe assembly located after the catalytic converter. • Repeat the vacuum measurement found in test step **HF10**. • Did the vacuum needle QUICKLY rise above 16 inches Hg with the engine rpm at 2000?	Yes No	▶ ▶	There is a restriction in the muffler/tail-pipe assembly. REPLACE the muffler/tail-pipe assembly. REMOVE the vacuum gauge and tachometer. DRIVE the vehicle to verify elimination of the symptom. Also, if here because of a DTC, RERUN Quick Test to verify repair. There is a restriction in the catalytic converter. REMOVE the vacuum gauge and tachometer. REPLACE the catalytic converter and INSPECT the muffler to be certain converter debris has not entered. RECONNECT muffler/tail-pipe assembly. DRIVE the vehicle to verify elimination of symptom. Also, if here because of a DTC, RERUN Quick Test to verify repair.

FM0159401193080X

Fig. 190   Test HF: Catalyst Efficiency Monitor & Exhaust Systems (Part 8 of 8). 1994-95

Note

You should enter this Pinpoint Test only when directed here.

Remember

This Pinpoint Test is intended to diagnose only the following.

• Positive Crankcase Ventilation (PCV) valve and related vacuum lines.

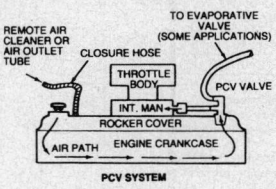

PCV SYSTEM

TEST STEP	RESULT	▶	ACTION TO TAKE
HG1 STUCK PCV VALVE CHECK			
NOTE: Set parking brake and block wheels. Place transmission/transaxle in NEUTRAL or PARK. Place the A/C-Heat selector in the OFF position. • Remove PCV valve. • Shake the PCV valve. • Does PCV valve rattle when shaken?	Yes No	▶ ▶	REINSTALL PCV valve. GO to **HG2**. PCV valve is sticking. REPLACE PCV valve.
HG2 PCV SYSTEM CHECK			
• Start engine and bring to normal operating temperature. • Disconnect hose from remote air cleaner or air outlet tube (tube connecting mass air meter and throttle body). • Place a stiff piece of paper over the hose end. Wait one minute. • Does vacuum hold the paper in place?	Yes No	▶ ▶	System is OK. RECONNECT hose. System is plugged or Evaporative Emission Valve is leaking (if equipped). GO to **HG3**.

FM0159401194010X

Fig. 191   Test HG: PCV System (Part 1 of 2). 1994-95

TEST STEP		RESULT	▶	ACTION TO TAKE
HG3	EVAPORATIVE EMISSION SYSTEM CHECK			
NOTE: If the evaporative hose is not connected to the PCV hose, follow the "No" Action to take in this test step. • Disconnect evaporative hose at connection to PCV hose (if equipped). Cap the connector. • Place a stiff piece of paper over the hose/nipple, as in HG2. Wait one minute. • **Does vacuum hold the paper in place?**		Yes	▶	GO to Evaporative Emission System, Pinpoint Test Step HV1 .
		No	▶	CHECK for vacuum leaks/obstruction in the system (e.g. oil cap, PCV valve, hoses, cut grommets, rocker cover bolt torque/gasket leak, etc). SERVICE as necessary.

FM0159401194020X

Fig. 191 Test HG: PCV System (Part 2 of 2). 1994-95

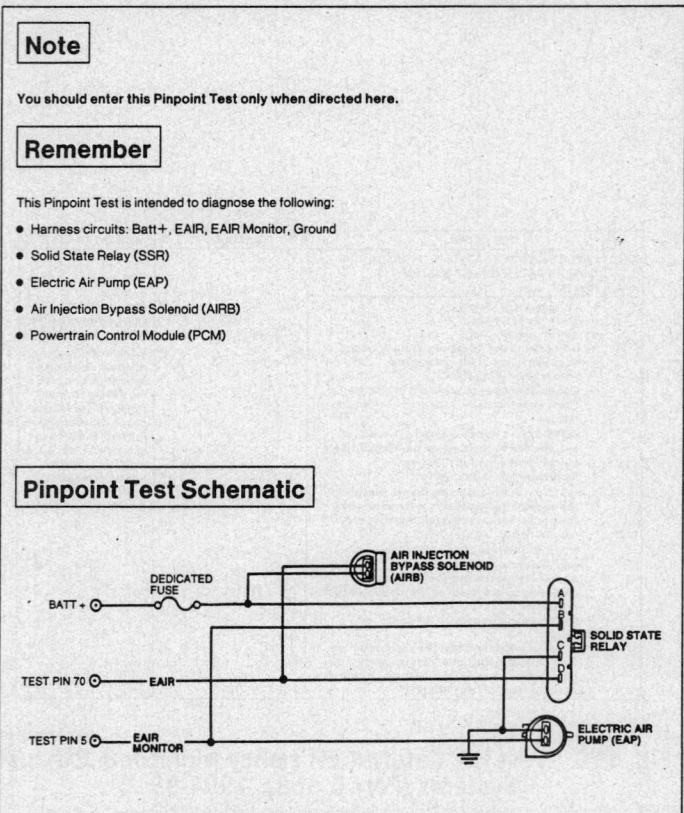

Note

You should enter this Pinpoint Test only when directed here.

Remember

This Pinpoint Test is intended to diagnose the following:

● Harness circuits: Batt+, EAIR, EAIR Monitor, Ground
● Solid State Relay (SSR)
● Electric Air Pump (EAP)
● Air Injection Bypass Solenoid (AIRB)
● Powertrain Control Module (PCM)

Pinpoint Test Schematic

Fig. 192 Test HM: Secondary Air Injection System (Part 1 of 13). 1995

TEST STEP		RESULT	▶	ACTION TO TAKE
HM1	CHECK B+ AT SOLID STATE RELAY			
DTC P0412 indicates EAIR primary circuit malfunction. Possible causes: — EAIR circuit open. — EAIR circuit short to power. — AIR bypass solenoid malfunction. — Solid State Relay malfunction. — Damaged PCM. • Key off. • Disconnect SSR. • Key on, engine off. • Measure voltage between B+ circuit at SSR vehicle harness connector and battery negative post. • **Is voltage greater than 10.5 volts?**		Yes	▶	Supplied voltage is OK, GO to HM2 .
		No	▶	GO to HM7 .
HM2	CHECK CONTINUITY OF EAIR CIRCUIT			
• Key off. • Solid State Relay disconnected. • Disconnect AIR bypass solenoid. • Remove Secondary Air dedicated fuse temporarily. • Disconnect PCM. Inspect for damaged or pushed out pins, corrosion, loose wires, etc. Service as necessary. • Install breakout box, leave PCM disconnected. • Measure resistance between EAIR circuit at SSR vehicle harness connector and Test Pin 70 at the breakout box. • Measure resistance between EAIR circuit at the AIR bypass vehicle harness connector and Test Pin 70 at the breakout box. • **Is resistance less than 5.0 ohms?**		Yes	▶	GO to HM3 .
		No	▶	SERVICE open EAIR circuit. REMOVE breakout box. RECONNECT all components. COMPLETE PCM Reset to clear DTCs. (REFER to Powertrain Control Module (PCM) Reset.) RERUN Quick Test.
HM3	CHECK EAIR CIRCUIT FOR SHORT TO POWER			
• Key off. • AIR bypass solenoid disconnected. • Solid State Relay disconnected. • PCM disconnected, breakout box installed. • Measure resistance between Test Pins 70 and Test Pins 71, 97 and 90 at the breakout box. • **Is each resistance greater than 10,000 ohms?**		Yes	▶	The EAIR harness is OK. GO to HM4 .
		No	▶	SERVICE EAIR circuit for short. REMOVE breakout box. RECONNECT all components. COMPLETE PCM Reset to clear DTCs. (REFER to Powertrain Control Module (PCM) Reset.) RERUN Quick Test.

Fig. 192 Test HM: Secondary Air Injection System (Part 2 of 13). 1995

TEST STEP		RESULT	▶	ACTION TO TAKE
HM4	CHECK EAIR CIRCUIT FOR SHORT TO POWER			
• Key off. • Reconnect AIR bypass solenoid. • Solid State Relay and PCM disconnected, breakout box installed. • Measure resistance between Test Pin 70 and Test Pins 71, 97 and 90 at the breakout box. • **Is each resistance greater than 10,000 ohms?**		Yes	▶	EAIR circuit with AIR bypass solenoid OK. GO to HM5 .
		No	▶	REPLACE AIR bypass solenoid. REMOVE breakout box. RECONNECT components. COMPLETE PCM Reset to clear DTCs. (REFER to Powertrain Control Module (PCM) Reset.) RERUN Quick Test.
HM5	CHECK EAIR CIRCUIT FOR SHORT TO POWER			
• Key off. • AIR bypass solenoid disconnected. • Reconnect Solid State Relay. • PCM disconnected, breakout box installed. • Measure resistance between Test Pin 70 and Test Pins 71, 97 and 90 at the breakout box. • **Is each resistance greater than 10,000 ohms?**		Yes	▶	REPLACE PCM. RECONNECT all components. COMPLETE PCM Reset to clear DTCs. (REFER to Powertrain Control Module (PCM) Reset.) RERUN Quick Test.
		No	▶	REPLACE Solid State Relay. REMOVE breakout box. RECONNECT components. COMPLETE PCM Reset to clear DTCs. (REFER to Powertrain Control Module (PCM) Reset.) RERUN Quick Test.

Fig. 192 Test HM: Secondary Air Injection System (Part 3 of 13). 1995

TEST STEP	RESULT	▶	ACTION TO TAKE
HM7 CHECK CONTINUITY OF B+ CIRCUIT • Key off. • Disconnect Solid State Relay. • Measure resistance between Solid State Relay vehicle harness connector and Secondary Air dedicated fuse. • **Is resistance less than 5.0 ohms?**	Yes	▶	SERVICE Secondary Air dedicated fuse. RECONNECT Solid State Relay. RERUN Quick Test.
	No	▶	SERVICE open in B+ circuit. RECONNECT Solid State Relay. COMPLETE PCM Reset to clear DTCs. (REFER to Powertrain Control Module (PCM) Reset.) RERUN Quick Test.
HM8 CHECK EAIR MONITOR CIRCUIT FOR SHORT TO POWER • Key off. • Disconnect Solid State Relay (SSR). • Disconnect Powertrain Control Module (PCM). • Install breakout box. • Key on. • Measure voltage between Test Pin 5 at the breakout box and chassis ground. • **Is voltage greater than 10.5 volts?**	Yes	▶	SERVICE EAIR monitor for short to power. RECONNECT all components. COMPLETE PCM Reset to clear DTCs. (REFER to Powertrain Control Module (PCM) Reset.) RERUN Quick Test.
	No	▶	EAMM circuit is OK. GO to HM9.
HM9 CHECK EAIR MONITOR CIRCUIT FOR SHORT TO POWER • Key off. • Reconnect Solid State Relay. • Breakout box installed. • PCM disconnected. • Key on. • Measure voltage between Test Pin 5 at the breakout box and chassis ground. • **Is voltage greater than 10.5 volts?**	Yes	▶	GO to HM10.
	No	▶	EAMM circuit with Solid State Relay OK. REPLACE PCM. RECONNECT all components. COMPLETE PCM Reset to clear DTCs. (REFER to Powertrain Control Module (PCM) Reset.) RERUN Quick Test.

Fig. 192 Test HM: Secondary Air Injection System (Part 4 of 13). 1995

TEST STEP	RESULT	▶	ACTION TO TAKE
HM10 CHECK EAIR MONITOR CIRCUIT FOR SHORT TO POWER • Key off. • Reconnect Solid State Relay. • Breakout box installed, PCM disconnected. • Key on. • Measure voltage between Test Pin 5 at the breakout box and chassis ground. • Measure voltage between Test Pin 70 at the breakout box and chassis ground. • **Are both greater than 10.5 volts?**	Yes	▶	REPLACE Solid State Relay. REMOVE breakout box. RECONNECT all components. COMPLETE PCM Reset to clear DTCs. (REFER to Powertrain Control Module (PCM) Reset.) RERUN Quick Test.
	No	▶	GO to HM13.
HM11 VISUALLY INSPECT EAP HOSES DTC P0411 indicates Secondary Air not detected. In order to test the pump, it must be capable of driving the HO2S lean. • Key off. • Visually inspect EAP hoses from the EAP to both Air Control Valves (ACV). • Inspect air hose for cracks, binding and obstructions. • **Are EAP hoses OK?**	Yes	▶	GO to HM12.
	No	▶	SERVICE or REPLACE damaged parts. COMPLETE PCM Reset to clear DTCs. (REFER to Powertrain Control Module (PCM) Reset.) RERUN Quick Test.
HM12 CHECK ELECTRIC AIR PUMP OPERATION • Key off. • Disconnect air hose from either ACV. • Check air flow at the open hose by placing a hand over the outlet of the hose. Caution must be observed while performing this test. Beware of moving vehicle components and heat. • Key on, engine running. • After a 5 second delay, air will be present between 30-90 seconds. • **Is air flow present?**	Yes	▶	GO to HM8.
	No	▶	SERVICE air hose to ACV for leaks or blockage. If OK, GO to HM17.
HM13 CHECK FOR VACUUM AT BOTH ACV • Key off. • Disconnect vacuum control line from both ACVs. • Key on, engine running. • After a 5 second delay, vacuum will be present between 30-90 seconds. • **Is vacuum present at both ACVs?**	Yes	▶	GO to HM14.
	No	▶	GO to HM30.

Fig. 192 Test HM: Secondary Air Injection System (Part 5 of 13). 1995

TEST STEP	RESULT	▶	ACTION TO TAKE
HM14 CHECK ACV INTEGRITY • Key off. • Disconnect air tube from both ACVs outlet side. • Cork off both air tubes to prevent exhaust gases from escaping. • Inspect both ACV outlets for damage from hot exhaust gases. Service as necessary. Caution must be observed while performing this test. • Key on, engine running. • After a 5 second delay, air will be present between 30-90 seconds. • **Is air present at both ACVs?**	Yes	▶	GO to HM15.
	No	▶	REPLACE appropriate ACV. RECONNECT all components. COMPLETE PCM Reset to clear DTCs. (REFER to Powertrain Control Module (PCM) Reset.) RERUN Quick Test.
HM17 CHECK ELECTRIC AIR PUMP OPERATION • Key off. • Disconnect EAP. • Measure voltage between EAIR monitor circuit and ground at the EAP vehicle harness connector. • Key on, engine running. • **Is voltage greater than 10.5 volts for 20-30 seconds after a 5 to 10 second delay?**	Yes	▶	GO to HM18.
	No	▶	GO to HM21.
HM18 CHECK EAP GROUND INTEGRITY • Key off. • EAP disconnected. • Measure resistance between EAP ground circuit at the vehicle harness connector and chassis ground. • **Is resistance less than 5 ohms?**	Yes	▶	GO to HM19.
	No	▶	SERVICE open ground circuit. RECONNECT all components. COMPLETE PCM Reset to clear DTCs. (REFER to Powertrain Control Module (PCM) Reset.) RERUN Quick Test.

Fig. 192 Test HM: Secondary Air Injection System (Part 6 of 13). 1995

TEST STEP	RESULT	▶	ACTION TO TAKE
HM19 CHECK AIR HOSE TO EAP • Key off. • Disconnect inlet air hose. • Visually inspect inlet air hose for binding and obstructions to the EAP. • **Is the hose integrity OK?**	Yes	▶	REPLACE EAP. RECONNECT all components. COMPLETE PCM Reset to clear DTCs. (REFER to Powertrain Control Module (PCM) Reset.) RERUN Quick Test.
	No	▶	SERVICE air hose. COMPLETE PCM Reset to clear DTCs. (REFER to Powertrain Control Module (PCM) Reset.) RERUN Quick Test.
HM20 CHECK FOR VOLTAGE AT SOLID STATE RELAY DTC P1413 indicates EAIR monitor circuit is low while the EAP was commanded ON. • Key off. • Disconnect Solid State Relay. • Key on. • Measure voltage between B+ circuit at Solid State Relay vehicle harness connector and chassis ground. • **Is voltage greater than 10.5 volts?**	Yes	▶	GO to HM21.
	No	▶	GO to HM25.
HM21 CHECK EAIR MONITOR CIRCUIT FOR VOLTAGE • Key off. • Reconnect Solid State Relay. • Disconnect EAP. • Measure voltage between EAIR monitor circuit at the EAP vehicle harness connector and chassis ground. • Key on, engine running. • **Is voltage greater than 10.5 volts?**	Yes	▶	IF DTC P0411 is present, REPLACE EAP. If not, GO to HM24.
	No	▶	GO to HM22.
HM22 CHECK CONTINUITY OF EAIR MONITOR CIRCUIT • Key off. • Disconnect Solid State Relay. • Disconnect PCM. Install breakout box. • EAP disconnected. • Measure resistance between Test Pin 5 at the breakout box and EAIR monitor circuit at the Solid State Relay vehicle harness connector. • Measure resistance between EAIR monitor circuit at the Solid State Relay vehicle harness connector and EAIR monitor circuit at the EAP vehicle harness connector. • **Is each resistance less than 5.0 ohms?**	Yes	▶	GO to HM23.
	No	▶	SERVICE open EAIR monitor circuit. RECONNECT all components. COMPLETE PCM Reset to clear DTCs. (REFER to Powertrain Control Module (PCM) Reset.) RERUN Quick Test.

Fig. 192 Test HM: Secondary Air Injection System (Part 7 of 13). 1995

TEST STEP		RESULT	▶	ACTION TO TAKE
HM23	CHECK EAIR MONITOR CIRCUIT FOR SHORT TO GROUND			
	• Key off. • Solid State Relay disconnected. • EAP disconnected. • Breakout box installed, PCM disconnected. • Measure resistance between Test Pin 5 and Test Pin 51, 76 and 91 at the breakout box. • **Is each resistance greater than 10,000 ohms?**	Yes	▶	REPLACE Solid State Relay. RECONNECT all components. COMPLETE PCM Reset to clear DTCs. (REFER to Powertrain Control Module (PCM) Reset.) RERUN Quick Test.
		No	▶	SERVICE EAIR monitor circuit for short to ground. RECONNECT all components. COMPLETE PCM Reset to clear DTCs. (REFER to Powertrain Control Module (PCM) Reset.) RERUN Quick Test.
HM24	CHECK EAIR MONITOR CIRCUIT FOR VOLTAGE			
	• Key off. • Reconnect EAP. • Install breakout box. PCM connected. • Key on, engine running. • Measure voltage between Test Pin 5 at the breakout box and chassis ground. • **Is voltage greater than 10.5 after the 5 second delay?**	Yes	▶	REPLACE PCM. REMOVE breakout box. COMPLETE PCM Reset to clear DTCs. (REFER to Powertrain Control Module (PCM) Reset.) RERUN Quick Test.
		No	▶	SERVICE open EAIR monitor circuit. REMOVE breakout box. COMPLETE PCM Reset to clear DTCs. (REFER to Powertrain Control Module (PCM) Reset.) RERUN Quick Test.

Fig. 192   Test HM: Secondary Air Injection System (Part 8 of 13). 1995

TEST STEP		RESULT	▶	ACTION TO TAKE
HM25	CHECK CONTINUITY OF B+ CIRCUIT			
	• Key off. • Solid State Relay disconnected. • Measure resistance between Solid State Relay vehicle harness connector B+ circuit and Solid State Relay dedicated fuse B+ circuit. • **Is resistance less than 5 ohms?**	Yes	▶	SERVICE Solid State Relay dedicated B+ fuse. RECONNECT all components. COMPLETE PCM Reset to clear DTCs. (REFER to Powertrain Control Module (PCM) Reset.) RERUN Quick Test.
		No	▶	SERVICE open B+ circuit. RECONNECT all components. COMPLETE PCM Reset to clear DTCs. (REFER to Powertrain Control Module (PCM) Reset.) RERUN Quick Test.
HM26	CHECK EAIR MONITOR CIRCUIT FOR CONTINUITY			
	DTC P1414 indicates EAP commanded off, but PCM indicates EAP is on. • Key off. • Disconnect Solid State Relay. • Disconnect PCM, install breakout box. • Disconnect Electric Air Pump (EAP). • Measure resistance between Test Pin 5 at the breakout box and EAP harness connector. • **Is resistance less than 5 ohms?**	Yes	▶	GO to HM27.
		No	▶	SERVICE EAIR monitor circuit for open. RECONNECT all components. COMPLETE PCM Reset to clear DTCs. (REFER to Powertrain Control Module (PCM) Reset.) RERUN Quick Test.
HM27	CHECK EAP FOR OPEN			
	• Key off. • Disconnect EAP vehicle harness. • Measure resistance across EAP terminals at EAP. • **Is resistance between 0.5-5.0 ohms?**	Yes	▶	GO to HM28.
		No	▶	REPLACE EAP. RECONNECT all components. COMPLETE PCM Reset to clear DTCs. (REFER to Powertrain Control Module (PCM) Reset.) RERUN Quick Test.

Fig. 192   Test HM: Secondary Air Injection System (Part 9 of 13). 1995

TEST STEP		RESULT	▶	ACTION TO TAKE
HM28	CHECK EAIR CIRCUIT FOR SHORT TO GROUND			
	• Key off. • Disconnect AIR bypass solenoid. • Solid State Relay disconnected. • Breakout box installed, PCM disconnected. • Measure resistance between Test Pin 70 and Test Pin 51, 76, and 91 at the breakout box. • **Is each resistance greater than 10,000 ohms?**	Yes	▶	GO to HM29.
		No	▶	SERVICE short to ground. RECONNECT all components. COMPLETE PCM Reset to clear DTCs. (REFER to Powertrain Control Module (PCM) Reset.) RERUN Quick Test.
HM29	CHECK EAIR MONITOR CIRCUIT FOR SHORT TO POWER			
	• Key off. • Solid State Relay disconnected. • Breakout box installed, PCM disconnected. • Reconnect EAP. • Key on. • Measure voltage between Test Pin 5 at the breakout box and chassis ground. • **Is voltage greater than 5.0 volts?**	Yes	▶	SERVICE EAIR monitor circuit for short to power. RECONNECT all components. COMPLETE PCM Reset to clear DTCs. (REFER to Powertrain Control Module (PCM) Reset.) RERUN Quick Test.
		No	▶	REPLACE PCM. RECONNECT all components. COMPLETE PCM Reset to clear DTCs. (REFER to Powertrain Control Module (PCM) Reset.) RERUN Quick Test.
HM30	CHECK VACUUM HOSE AIR BYPASS SOLENOID			
	• Key off. • Disconnect source vacuum hose at AIR bypass solenoid. • Connect a vacuum gauge to the hose. • Start the engine and let it idle while observing the vacuum gauge. • **Is vacuum above 15 inches at idle?**	Yes	▶	GO to HM31.
		No	▶	REPLACE the vacuum line connecting the AIR bypass solenoid to source vacuum. COMPLETE PCM Reset to clear DTCs. (REFER to Powertrain Control Module (PCM) Reset.) RERUN Quick Test.

Fig. 192   Test HM: Secondary Air Injection System (Part 10 of 13). 1995

TEST STEP		RESULT	▶	ACTION TO TAKE
HM31	CHECK AIR BYPASS SOLENOID ELECTRICAL OPERATION			
	• Key on, engine off. • Enter Output Test Mode (OTM). Refer to Diagnostic Methods. • Disconnect AIR bypass solenoid. • Connect DVOM to AIR bypass solenoid vehicle harness connector. • While observing DVOM, depress and release the throttle several times to cycle output. • **Does EAIR circuit voltage cycle greater than .5 volt?**	Yes	▶	REMAIN in Output Test Mode. GO to HM32.
		No	▶	GO to HM35.
HM32	CHECK AIR BYPASS SOLENOID FOR MECHANICAL OPERATION			
	• While remaining in Output Test Mode, reconnect AIR bypass solenoid. • Disconnect source vacuum hose from AIR bypass solenoid. • Apply 16 in-Hg. (53 kPa) of vacuum to source side of AIR bypass solenoid. • Depress and release throttle. • **Was vacuum released?**	Yes	▶	REPAIR vacuum hose from AIR bypass solenoid to ACV. RECONNECT all components. COMPLETE PCM Reset to clear DTCs. (REFER to Powertrain Control Module (PCM) Reset.) RERUN Quick Test.
		No	▶	REPAIR vacuum hose from AIR bypass solenoid to manifold vacuum tree. If OK, replace AIR bypass solenoid. RECONNECT all components. COMPLETE PCM Reset to clear DTCs. (REFER to Powertrain Control Module (PCM) Reset.) RERUN Quick Test.
HM35	CHECK AIR BYPASS SOLENOID RESISTANCE			
	• Key off. • Disconnect AIR bypass solenoid vehicle harness connector. • Measure AIR bypass solenoid resistance. • **Is resistance between 50-100 ohms?**	Yes	▶	GO to HM36.
		No	▶	REPLACE AIR bypass solenoid. RECONNECT all components. COMPLETE PCM Reset to clear DTCs. (REFER to Powertrain Control Module (PCM) Reset.) RERUN Quick Test.

Fig. 192   Test HM: Secondary Air Injection System (Part 11 of 13). 1995

TEST STEP	RESULT	▶	ACTION TO TAKE
HM36 CHECK VPWR CIRCUIT VOLTAGE			
• Key on, engine off. • AIR bypass solenoid disconnected. • Measure voltage between VPWR at the AIR bypass solenoid vehicle harness connector and battery ground. • Is voltage greater than 10.5 volts?	Yes No	▶ ▶	GO to **HM37**. SERVICE open VPWR circuit. RECONNECT AIR bypass. COMPLETE PCM Reset to clear DTCs. (REFER to Powertrain Control Module (PCM) Reset.) RERUN Quick Test.
HM37 CHECK CONTINUITY OF EAIR CIRCUIT			
• Key off. • AIR bypass solenoid disconnected. • Disconnect Solid State Relay. • Install breakout box, leave PCM disconnected. • Measure resistance between Test Pin 70 at the breakout box and EAIR circuit at the AIR solenoid bypass vehicle harness connector and at the Solid State Relay vehicle harness connector. • Is resistance less than 5.0 ohms?	Yes No	▶ ▶	GO to **HM38**. SERVICE open EAIR circuit. RECONNECT components. COMPLETE PCM Reset to clear DTCs. (REFER to Powertrain Control Module (PCM) Reset.) RERUN Quick Test.
HM38 CHECK EAIR CIRCUIT FOR SHORT TO GROUND			
• Key off. • AIR bypass solenoid disconnected. • Solid State Relay disconnected. • Breakout box installed, PCM disconnected. • Measure resistance between Test Pin 70 and Test Pins 51, 76 and 91 at the breakout box. • Is each resistance greater than 10,000 ohms?	Yes No	▶ ▶	GO to **HM39**. SERVICE short to ground. RECONNECT components. COMPLETE PCM Reset to clear DTCs. (REFER to Powertrain Control Module (PCM) Reset.) RERUN Quick Test.

Fig. 192   Test HM: Secondary Air Injection System (Part 12 of 13). 1995

TEST STEP	RESULT	▶	ACTION TO TAKE
HM39 CHECK EAIR CIRCUIT FOR SHORT TO POWER			
• Key off. • AIR bypass solenoid disconnected. • Solid State Relay disconnected. • Breakout box installed, PCM disconnected. • Measure resistance between Test Pin 70 and Test Pins 71 and 97 at the breakout box. • Is each resistance greater than 10,000 ohms?	Yes No	▶ ▶	REPLACE PCM. RECONNECT components. COMPLETE PCM Reset to clear DTCs. (REFER to Powertrain Control Module (PCM) Reset.) RERUN Quick Test. SERVICE short to power. RECONNECT components. COMPLETE PCM Reset to clear DTCs. (REFER to Powertrain Control Module (PCM) Reset.) RERUN Quick Test.

Fig. 192   Test HM: Secondary Air Injection System (Part 13 of 13). 1995

Note

You should enter this Pinpoint Test only when directed here.

Reminder

This Pinpoint Test is intended to diagnose the following:

• Throttle Body Assembly
• Accelerator Cable - Linkage to Throttle Body
• Air Cleaner Assembly (including air filter)
 — 3.8L Mustang
 — 4.6L Thunderbird / Cougar
• Air Inlet Tube - 4.6L Thunderbird / Cougar only
• Clean Air Tube (Hose) and Resonator

FM0159401195010X

Fig. 193   Test HU: Air Intake & Throttle Body (Part 1 of 8). 1994

Mustang

IDLE AIR CONTROL VALVE

THROTTLE BODY ASSEMBLY

AIR CLEANER ASSEMBLY

FM0159401195020X

Fig. 193   Test HU: Air Intake & Throttle Body (Part 2 of 8). 1994

Thunderbird/Cougar

MASS AIR FLOW SENSOR

AIR CLEANER ASSEMBLY

AIR INLET TUBE & RESONATOR

FM015940195030X

Fig. 193   Test HU: Air Intake & Throttle Body (Part 3 of 8). 1994

	TEST STEP	RESULT	▶	ACTION TO TAKE
HU1	CONFIRM PROPER DRIVE SYMPTOM TO PINPOINT TEST PROCEDURE			
	• This pinpoint test addresses the following drive symptoms only: — Stick, bind, grab feeling in accelerator pedal. — Hard start / long crank. — Slow return to idle. — Rolling idle. — Fast idle. — Lack of power. • Is the drive symptom one of the above?	Yes No	▶ ▶	GO to HU2. RETURN to address other drive symptoms.
HU2	SELECT PROPER DIAGNOSTIC SYMPTOM ROUTINE			
	• Does the air intake system symptom relate to stick, bind, grab conditions on the throttle body?	Yes No	▶ ▶	GO to HU3. GO to HU8.
HU3	CHECK ACCELERATOR CABLE FREEDOM OF TRAVEL			
	• Key off. • Disconnect accelerator cable from throttle body linkage. • Inspect cable for freedom of travel from accelerator pedal to throttle body linkage cable connector. • Does cable travel freely?	Yes No	▶ ▶	GO to HU4. SERVICE accelerator cable as necessary.
HU4	VERIFY THROTTLE RETURN SCREW			
	• Key off. • Accelerator cable removed from throttle body linkage per HU3. • Remove the clean air tube from the throttle body and verify that there is no foreign material or debris preventing the throttle plate from rotating to the fully closed position. • Verify that the Throttle Return Screw (TRC) is in contact with the throttle linkage lever arm when the throttle is in the closed plate (idle) position. • Does the TRC screw contact lever arm?	Yes No	▶ ▶	GO to HU6. The following adjustment should be made only in the event the TRC screw does not contact the throttle lever arm. Do not adjust TRC screw to try to correct idle quality concerns. 1.) PLACE a 0.002 inch feeler gauge between the TRC screw and lever arm. ADJUST TRC screw until it just contacts the feeler gauge. 2.) REMOVE the feeler gauge and turn the screw clockwise a half turn. 3.) GO to HU5.

FM015940195040X

Fig. 193   Test HU: Air Intake & Throttle Body (Part 4 of 8). 1994

	TEST STEP	RESULT	▶	ACTION TO TAKE
HU5	VERIFY TP SENSOR IN RANGE			
	• Key on, engine off. • Access TP PID with the Scan Tool. • Slowly move throttle from closed to wide open throttle position and observe the TP PID for smooth reading change. • Release throttle and allow to return to fully closed position. • While at closed throttle position, is the TP PID reading between 13% (0.66 volt) and 24% (1.20 volts)?	Yes No	▶ ▶	REMOVE Scan Tool. GO to HU6. REMOVE Scan Tool. REPLACE throttle body assembly.
HU6	CHECK FOR THROTTLE BODY STICKING, BINDING, GRABBING			
	• Key off. • Accelerator cable removed from throttle body linkage per HU3. • Clean air tube removed from throttle body per HU4. • Snap throttle from open to closed position several times. • Gently cycle throttle by hand from closed to wide open position. Inspect for freedom of travel particularly during the initial throttle opening. • Check for foreign material or debris in the throttle bore and plate area that can cause sticking or binding. NOTE: The Mustang and Thunderbird/Cougar throttle bodies use a special coating/sealant on the throttle bore and plate area to make them tolerant to engine sludge accumulation. Sludge or oil film deposits in this area do not cause a sticking or binding condition and do not require servicing. DO NOT CLEAN THE THROTTLE BORE AND PLATE AREA, THIS WILL DAMAGE THE THROTTLE BODY ASSEMBLY. • Does the throttle rotate freely without sticking, binding or grabbing condition?	Yes No	▶ ▶	RECONNECT accelerator cable and clean air tube to the throttle body assembly. GO to HU7.

FM015940195050X

Fig. 193   Test HU: Air Intake & Throttle Body (Part 5 of 8). 1994

	TEST STEP	RESULT	▶	ACTION TO TAKE
HU7	VERIFY FREE THROTTLE MOVEMENT WITH SPEED CONTROL DISCONNECT			
	• Key off. • Remove speed control cable. • Repeat pinpoint test procedures in HU6. • Does the throttle rotate freely without sticking, binding or grabbing condition?	Yes No	▶ ▶	RECONNECT all components. SERVICE speed control cable as necessary. RECONNECT all components. REPLACE the throttle body assembly.
HU8	CHECK AIR FILTER ELEMENT			
	• Inspect air filter element. • Is the air filter excessively dirty?	Yes No	▶ ▶	REPLACE air filter. RETURN if drive symptom persists. GO to HU9.
HU9	CHECK FOR PROPER OPERATION OF RELATED ENGINE SYSTEMS			
	• Verify that the following engine systems have been properly diagnosed and corrected before proceeding with the Air Intake system diagnostics: — Positive Crankcase Ventilation (PCV) System. — Exhaust System. — Engine Cooling System (engine coolant temperature is above 160 degrees F). — Incorrect fuel pressure, plugged fuel filter, fuel quality (contamination). • Have the above systems been properly checked and are they functioning correctly?	Yes No	▶ ▶	GO to HU10. For PCV System: GO to Pinpoint Test Step HG1. For Exhaust System: GO to Pinpoint Test Step HF1. For Engine Cooling System: GO to the Cooling System. For Fuel System: GO to Pinpoint Test Step HC.
HU10	CHECK FOR VACUUM LEAKS			
	• Key on, engine running. • With engine at idle, listen for vacuum leaks. • Inspect the entire inlet air system from the Mass Air Flow (MAF) sensor to the intake manifold for leaks such as: — Cracked or punctured inlet air tube. — Loose connections on the inlet air tube at the air cleaner housing or throttle body. — Idle Air Control (IAC) valve assembly or gasket seal. — Intake manifold assembly or gasket seal. — EGR valve diaphragm or control solenoid. — Vacuum supply connectors and hose. — PCV connectors and hose. • Are any leaks detected in the above areas?	Yes No	▶ ▶	SERVICE as necessary. GO to HU11.

FM015940195060X

Fig. 193   Test HU: Air Intake & Throttle Body (Part 6 of 8). 1994

TEST STEP		RESULT	▶	ACTION TO TAKE
HU11 CHECK IDLE				
• Key off.		Yes	▶	GO to **HU12**.
• Transmission in Park (wheels blocked and parking brake engaged).		No	▶	GO to **HU13**.
• A/C, heater and all accessories are off.				
• Key on, engine running.				
• Engine at normal operating temperature and cooling fan off.				
WARNING: DO NOT UNPLUG COOLING FAN. IT MAY CAUSE ENGINE OVERHEATING.				
• Connect Scan Tool				
• Access engine RPM PID.				
NOTE: Engine idle RPM is controlled by the PCM and can not be adjusted. The PCM is calibrated to control idle at the speeds listed below. When performing this test, verify the RPM is within the specification. If the engine is allowed to idle for an extended period of time, or if the engine temperature is hot enough to require cooling fan operation, it may be necessary to turn the engine off and repeat this test procedure.				
— Mustang 3.8L with A/T at 700 +/- 25 RPM.				
— Mustang 3.8L with M/T at 720 +/- 25 RPM.				
— Thunderbird/Cougar 4.6L at 768 +/- 25 RPM.				
• Access IAC PID, idle air percent duty cycle.				
• Is the IAC PID reading 20% to 45% duty cycle?				
HU12 CHECK IDLE CONTROL PRESSURE				
• Transmission still in Park.		Yes	▶	GO to **HU13**.
• A/C, heater and all accessories off.		No	▶	Air intake system is OK. DISCONNECT Scan Tool. RETURN to check other possible causes of the drive symptoms.
• Engine at normal operating temperature and cooling fan off, but not unplugged.				
WARNING: DO NOT UNPLUG COOLING FAN. IT MAY CAUSE ENGINE OVERHEATING.				
• Key on, engine running.				
• Goose throttle and let it return to the idle position				
• Does the engine stall or does the RPM fluctuate excessively before returning to the idle speed specified in HU11?				

FM0159401195070X

Fig. 193   Test HU: Air Intake & Throttle Body (Part 7 of 8). 1994

TEST STEP		RESULT	▶	ACTION TO TAKE
HU13 CHECK IAC SOLENOID FOR PROPER FUNCTION				
• Transmission still in Park.		Yes	▶	For Fast Idle Symptom: GO to **HU14**. For All Other Symptoms: Throttle body is defective, REPLACE the entire throttle body assembly. CLEAR Keep Alive Memory (REFER to Powertrain Control Module (PCM) Reset).
• A/C, heater and all accessories off.				
• Engine at normal operating temperature and cooling fan off, but not unplugged.				
WARNING: DO NOT UNPLUG COOLING FAN. IT MAY CAUSE ENGINE OVERHEATING.				
• Key on, engine running.				NOTE: Do not attempt to clean throttle bore or throttle plate area. Do not adjust air flow.
• Disconnect IAC solenoid vehicle harness connector.				
• Does the RPM drop or engine stall?		No	▶	IAC solenoid is defective, REPLACE IAC solenoid only. CLEAR Keep Alive Memory
				NOTE: Do not attempt to clean the IAC solenoid.
HU14 CHECK IAC CIRCUIT FOR SHORT TO GROUND				
• Key off.		Yes	▶	REPLACE damaged PCM. REMOVE breakout box. RECONNECT all components. RERUN Quick Test.
• IAC solenoid disconnected.				
• Disconnect PCM. Inspect for damaged or pushed out pins, corrosion, loose wires, etc. Service as necessary.				
• Install breakout box, leave PCM disconnected.		No	▶	SERVICE short circuit. RECONNECT all components. RERUN Quick Test.
• Measure resistance between Test Pin 83 (IAC) and Test Pins 51 or 103 (PWR GND) at the breakout box and chassis ground.				
• Is each resistance greater than 10,000 ohms?				

FM0159401195080X

Fig. 193   Test HU: Air Intake & Throttle Body (Part 8 of 8). 1994

Note

You should enter this Pinpoint Test only when directed here.

Remember

This Pinpoint Test is intended to diagnose the following:

• Throttle Body Assembly (9E926)
• Speed Control Cable
• Accelerator Cable - Linkage to Throttle Body (9C799)
• Air Cleaner Assembly (including air filter)
 — Mustang, Thunderbird/Cougar (F4ZE)
 — Crown Victoria/Grand Marquis, Continental, Town Car (F50E)

• Air Inlet Tube
• Clean Air Tube (Hose) and Resonator (9R504)
• Intake Manifold Runner Control Housing Assembly (IMRC) (9U531)
• IMRC Actuator Assembly (9J559)
• Powertrain Control Module (PCM) (12A650)
• Harness Circuits: IMRC, IMRC Monitor, SIG RTN, PWR GND, VPWR

Fig. 194   Test HU: Air Intake & Throttle Body (Part 1 of 18). 1995

Description

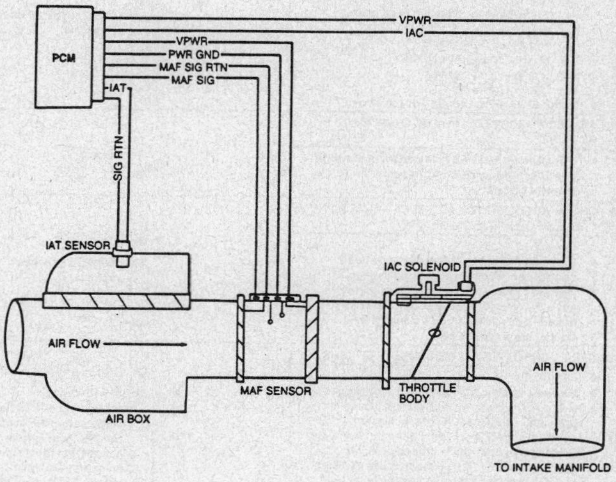

Air Intake and Throttle Body System

Fig. 194   Test HU: Air Intake & Throttle Body (Part 2 of 18). 1995

Tables and Charts

HOT IDLE PID VALUE TABLE

VEHICLE	ENGINE	TRANS	RPM	IAC %	ECT
Mustang	3.8L	AODE	700±25	21-45	180°F
Mustang	3.8L	T50D	720±25	20-44	180°F
Thunderbird / Cougar	4.6L	4R70W	768±25	20-44	180°F
Crown Victoria / Grand Marquis	4.6L	AODE	800±25	19-43	180°F
Continental	4.6L	AX4N	800±25	19-43	180°F
Town Car	4.6L	AODE	800±25	20-44	180°F

Continental:

During some Intake Manifold Runner Control repair procedures, it may be necessary to perform a drive cycle for verification of the IMRC and PCM operation. The table lists RPM, IMRCM and IMRC PID values during an acceleration and de-acceleration.

INTAKE MANIFOLD DRIVE CYCLE PID TABLE

RPM	IMRCM VDC	IMRC ON/OFF
2500	4.6 ± .2	OFF
2700	4.6 ± .2	OFF
2900	4.6 ± .2	OFF
3100	4.6 ± .2	OFF
3300	4.6 ± .2	OFF
3500	0.7 ± .2	ON
3700	0.7 ± .2	ON
3900	0.7 ± .2	ON
4100	0.7 ± .2	ON
3900	0.7 ± .2	ON
3700	0.7 ± .2	ON
3500	0.7 ± .2	ON
3300	4.6 ± .2	OFF
3100	4.6 ± .2	OFF

Fig. 194   Test HU: Air Intake & Throttle Body (Part 3 of 18). 1995

Pinpoint Test Schematic

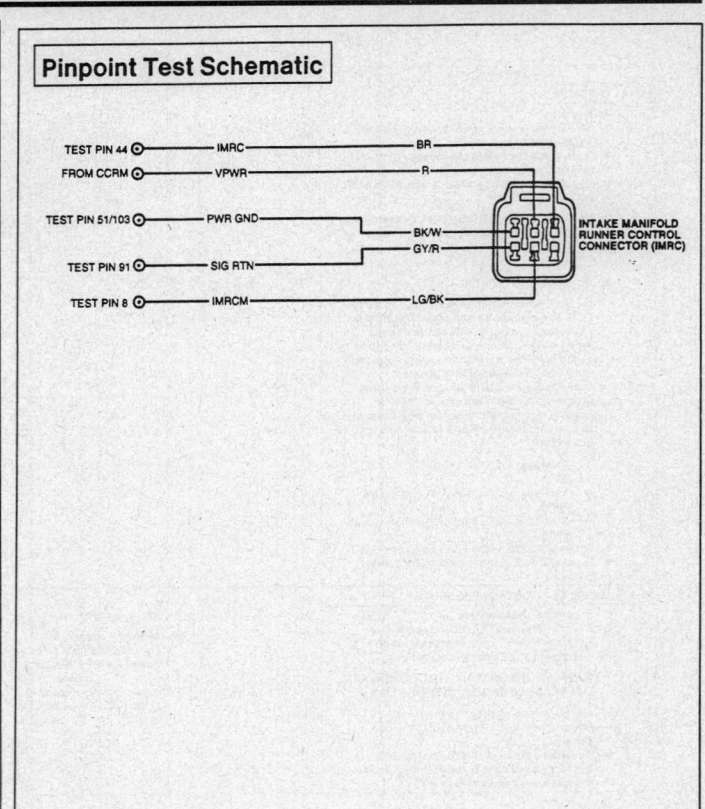

Fig. 194   Test HU: Air Intake & Throttle Body (Part 4 of 18). 1995

TEST STEP		RESULT	▶	ACTION TO TAKE
HU1	CONFIRM PROPER DRIVE SYMPTOM TO PINPOINT TEST PROCEDURE			
	• This pinpoint test addresses the following drive symptoms only: — Stick, bind, grab feeling in accelerator pedal. — Hard start/long crank. — Hesitation or stalls at idle. — Idle quality symptoms. — Lack of power. • Is the drive symptom one of the above?	Yes No	▶	GO to HU2. address other drive symptoms.
HU2	SELECT PROPER DIAGNOSTIC SYMPTOM ROUTINE			
	• Does the air intake system symptom relate to stick, bind, grab conditions on the throttle body?	Yes No	▶ ▶	GO to HU3. GO to HU7.
HU3	CHECK ACCELERATOR AND SPEED CONTROL CABLES FOR FREEDOM OF TRAVEL			
	• Key off. • Disconnect accelerator cable and speed control cable from throttle body linkage. • Inspect cables for freedom of travel from accelerator pedal/speed control device to throttle body linkage cable connector. • Do cables travel freely?	Yes No	▶ ▶	GO to HU4. SERVICE cable as necessary.
HU4	VERIFY THROTTLE RETURN SCREW SETTING			
	• Key off. • Cables removed from throttle body linkage. • Remove the clean air tube from the throttle body and verify that there is no foreign material or debris preventing the throttle plate from rotating to the fully closed position. • Verify that the Throttle Return Screw (TRC) is in contact with the throttle linkage lever arm when the throttle is in the closed plate (idle) position. Refer to the Air Intake and Throttle Body Systems in Section 1 for TRC screw description. • Does the TRC screw contact lever arm?	Yes No	▶ ▶	GO to HU6. The following adjustment should be made only in the event the TRC screw does not contact the throttle lever arm. Do not adjust TRC screw to try to correct idle quality concerns. 1.) PLACE a 0.002 inch feeler gauge between the TRC screw and lever arm. ADJUST TRC screw until it just contacts the feeler gauge. 2.) REMOVE the feeler gauge and turn the screw clockwise a half turn. 3.) GO to HU5.

Fig. 194   Test HU: Air Intake & Throttle Body (Part 5 of 18). 1995

TEST STEP		RESULT	▶	ACTION TO TAKE
HU5	VERIFY TP SENSOR IN RANGE			
	• Key on, engine off. • Access TP PID with the Scan Tool. • Slowly move throttle from closed to wide open position and observe the TP PID for smooth reading change. • Release throttle and allow to return to fully closed position. • While at closed throttle position, is the TP PID reading between 13% (0.66 volt) and 24% (1.20 volts)?	Yes No	▶ ▶	REMOVE Scan Tool. GO to HU6. REMOVE Scan Tool. REPLACE throttle body assembly.
HU6	CHECK FOR THROTTLE BODY STICKING, BINDING, GRABBING			
	• Key off. • Cables removed from throttle body linkage. • Clean air tube removed from throttle body. • Snap throttle from open to closed position several times. • Gently cycle throttle by hand from closed to wide open position. Inspect for freedom of travel particularly during the initial throttle opening. • Check for foreign material or debris in the throttle bore and plate area that can cause sticking or binding. NOTE: Throttle bodies use a special coating/sealant on the throttle bore and plate area to make them tolerant to engine sludge accumulation. Sludge or oil film deposits in this area do not cause a sticking or binding condition and do not require servicing. DO NOT CLEAN THE THROTTLE BORE AND PLATE AREA. CLEANING WILL DAMAGE THE THROTTLE BODY ASSEMBLY. • Does the throttle rotate freely without sticking, binding or grabbing condition?	Yes No	▶ ▶	RECONNECT accelerator cable and clean air tube to the throttle body assembly. REPLACE throttle body assembly. RECONNECT all components.
HU7	CHECK AIR FILTER ELEMENT			
	• Inspect air filter element. • Is the air filter excessively dirty?	Yes No	▶ ▶	REPLACE air filter. persists. GO to HU8.

Fig. 194   Test HU: Air Intake & Throttle Body (Part 6 of 18). 1995

TEST STEP	RESULT	▶	ACTION TO TAKE
HU8 CHECK FOR PROPER OPERATION OF RELATED ENGINE SYSTEMS NOTE: If here from Pinpoint Test QA, go directly to HU9. • Verify that the following engine systems have been properly diagnosed and corrected before proceeding with the Air Intake system diagnostics: — Positive Crankcase Ventilation (PCV) System. — Ignition System. — Exhaust System. — Engine Cooling System (engine coolant temperature is above 180 degrees F). — Incorrect fuel pressure, plugged fuel filter, fuel quality (contamination). • Have the systems been properly checked and are they functioning correctly?	Yes No	▶ ▶	GO to HU9. GO to Symptom Flow Charts, with the symptom, for direction.
HU9 CHECK FOR VACUUM LEAKS • Key on, engine running. • With engine at idle, listen for vacuum leaks. • Inspect the entire inlet air system from the Mass Air Flow (MAF) sensor to the intake manifold for leaks such as: — Cracked or punctured inlet air tube. — Loose connections on the inlet air tube at the air cleaner housing or throttle body. — Idle Air Control (IAC) valve assembly or gasket seal. — EGR valve gasket seal leak to intake manifold. — Intake manifold assembly or gasket seal. — EGR valve diaphragm or control solenoid. — Vacuum supply connectors and hose. — PCV connectors and hose. • Are any leaks detected in the above areas?	Yes No	▶ ▶	SERVICE as necessary. GO to HU10.

Fig. 194   Test HU: Air Intake & Throttle Body (Part 7 of 18). 1995

TEST STEP	RESULT	▶	ACTION TO TAKE
HU10 CHECK IDLE • Key on, engine running. • Transmission in Park (wheels blocked and parking brake engaged). • A/C, heater and all accessories are off. • Key on, engine running. • Engine at normal operating temperature and cooling fan off. WARNING: DO NOT UNPLUG COOLING FAN. IT MAY CAUSE ENGINE OVERHEATING. • Connect Scan Tool • Access engine RPM PID. NOTE: Engine Idle RPM is controlled by the PCM and cannot be adjusted. The PCM is calibrated to control idle at the speeds listed in the Hot Idle PID Value Table at the beginning of the pinpoint test. When performing this test, verify the RPM is within the specification. If the engine is allowed to idle for an extended period of time, or if the engine temperature is hot enough to require cooling fan operation, it may be necessary to turn the engine off and repeat this test procedure. • Access IAC PID, idle air percent duty cycle. • Do the RPM and IAC PID readings match the values in the Hot Idle PID Value Table at the beginning of the pinpoint test?	Yes No	▶ ▶	GO to HU11. GO to HU12.
HU11 CHECK IDLE CONTROL RESPONSE • Transmission still in Park. • A/C, heater and all accessories off. • Engine at normal operating temperature and cooling fan off, but not unplugged. WARNING: DO NOT UNPLUG COOLING FAN. IT MAY CAUSE ENGINE OVERHEATING. • Key on, engine running. • Goose throttle and let it return to the idle position. • Does the engine stall or does the RPM fluctuate excessively before returning to the idle speed specified in HU10?	Yes No	▶ ▶	GO to HU12. Air Intake system is OK. DISCONNECT Scan Tool.

Fig. 194   Test HU: Air Intake & Throttle Body (Part 8 of 18). 1995

TEST STEP	RESULT	▶	ACTION TO TAKE
HU12 CHECK IAC SOLENOID FOR PROPER FUNCTION • Transmission still in Park. • A/C, heater and all accessories off. • Engine at normal operating temperature and cooling fan off, but not unplugged. WARNING: DO NOT UNPLUG COOLING FAN. IT MAY CAUSE ENGINE OVERHEATING. • Key on, engine running. • Disconnect IAC solenoid vehicle harness connector. • Does the RPM drop or engine stall?	Yes No	▶ ▶	Fast Idle Symptom: GO to HU14. All Other Symptoms: GO to HU13. IAC solenoid is defective, REPLACE IAC solenoid only. RESET KAM (REFER to Powertrain Control Module (PCM) Reset). NOTE: Do not attempt to clean the IAC solenoid.
HU13 THROTTLE BODY VISUAL/FUNCTIONAL CHECK • Key off. • Remove throttle body assembly • Hold throttle body up to a light source. With the throttle plate closed, no light should be visible between the plate and bore (sludge tolerant coating intact). The hole in the throttle plate (in some applications only) should be visible and unobstructed. • Rotate the throttle lever and allow it to return. It should not stick or bind and should return to the closed plate position (TRC screw contacting lever) freely when released. • Does the throttle body pass these visual/functional checks?	Yes No	▶ ▶	Throttle body is functioning properly. REINSTALL throttle body assembly. Throttle body is defective. REPLACE entire throttle body assembly. RESET KAM (REFER to Powertrain Control Module (PCM) Reset).
HU14 CHECK IAC CIRCUIT FOR SHORT TO GROUND • Key off. • IAC solenoid disconnected. • Disconnect PCM. Inspect for damaged or pushed out pins, corrosion, loose wires, etc. Service as necessary. • Install breakout box, leave PCM disconnected. • Measure resistance between Test Pin 83 (IAC) and Test Pins 51 or 103 (PWR GND) at the breakout box. • Is each resistance greater than 10,000 ohms?	Yes No	▶ ▶	REPLACE damaged PCM. REMOVE breakout box. RECONNECT all components. RERUN Quick Test. SERVICE short circuit. REMOVE breakout box. RECONNECT all components. RERUN Quick Test.

Fig. 194   Test HU: Air Intake & Throttle Body (Part 9 of 18). 1995

TEST STEP	RESULT	▶	ACTION TO TAKE
HU15 DTCs P1518, P1519 AND P1520: PERFORM VISUAL INSPECTION DTC P1518 indicates IMRC may be stuck open. DTC P1519 indicates IMRC may be stuck closed. DTC P1520 indicates IMRC control circuit malfunction. Possible causes: — Cables improperly routed (binding) or seized. — Damaged/disconnected IMRC housing return springs. — Lever/shaft return stop obstructed/bent. — Lever/shaft wide open stop obstructed/bent. — IMRC lever/shaft stick/bind. — IMRC actuator cable/gears seized. • View cable routing. Make sure cables are not binding or improperly routed. With engine off or at idle, cable core wire at IMRC housing attachment should have slack and lever should contact Closed Plate Stop Screw. Refer to the IMRC System Description in Section 1, Air Intake and Throttle Body, for illustrations. • Manually open and close IMRC plates at intake manifold, feel for sticking/binding. NOTE: IMRC return spring is strong. Make sure return springs operate properly and plates open and close fully. • Is fault indicated?	Yes No	▶ ▶	SERVICE as necessary. Passed visual inspection, GO to HU16.
HU16 PERFORM IMRC FUNCTIONAL TEST • Key off. • Connect Scan Tool to Data Link Connector (DLC). • Key on, engine off. • Access Output Test Mode CAUTION: Keep fingers clear of IMRC lever/cable mechanism. • Turn all outputs on (IMRC included). • When IMRC is commanded on, both levers should rotate to full open position. At least one of the levers should contact the wide open stop, the other may be slightly off the wide open stop. This is normal. • Did the IMRC levers cycle from fully close to fully open?	Yes No	▶ ▶	Passed check. Exit OTM. NOTE: Always service P1520 first. For DTC P1518: GO to HU26. For DTC P1519: GO to HU29. For DTC P1520: GO to HU19. Exit OTM. GO to HU17.

Fig. 194   Test HU: Air Intake & Throttle Body (Part 10 of 18). 1995

TEST STEP	RESULT	▶	ACTION TO TAKE
HU17 PERFORM IMRC OPERATIONAL TEST			
• Perform the necessary safety precautions to start engine. • Apply parking brake and block wheels. • Key on, engine running. • Rev engine to above 3500 RPM. CAUTION: Keep fingers clear of IMRC lever/cable mechanism. • When engine speed is above 3500 RPM, both levers should rotate to full open position. At least one lever should contact the wide open stop, the other may be slightly off the wide open stop. This is normal. When engine returns to idle (or below 3000 RPM), both levers must contact Closed Plate Stop Screw. • Did the IMRC levers cycle from fully closed to fully open when the RPM was above 3500?	Yes No	▶ ▶	Passed operational test. NOTE: Always service P1520 first. For DTC P1518: GO to **HU26**. For DTC P1519: GO to **HU29**. For DTC P1520: GO to **HU19**. Failed operational test. GO to **HU18**.
HU18 PERFORM IMRC PHYSICAL TEST			
• Disconnect IMRC cables from both left and right intake runners. procedure. • Rotate by hand both the left and right bank IMRC housing lever assembly fully open and then closed. NOTE: IMRC return springs are strong. • Feel for sticking or binding plate rotation. • Feel for return string tension (3-4 inch lbs). • Do the IMRC plates open and close completely (lever contacting Closed Plate Stop Screw) without obstruction?	Yes No	▶ ▶	Passed physical check, RECONNECT IMRC cables. NOTE: Always service P1520 first. For DTC P1518: GO to **HU26**. For DTC P1519: GO to **HU29**. For DTC P1520: GO to **HU19**. Failed physical test. clean and inspect IMRC runner plates for sludge contaminants, warping, misaligned, etc.

Fig. 194   Test HU: Air Intake & Throttle Body (Part 11 of 18). 1995

TEST STEP	RESULT	▶	ACTION TO TAKE
HU19 DTC P1520: VERIFY IMRC CIRCUIT VOLTAGE			
Diagnostic Trouble Code (DTC) P1520 indicates Intake Manifold Runner Control circuit malfunction. Possible causes: — IMRC control circuit open. — IMRC control circuit shorted to PWR GND or SIG RTN. — IMRC control circuit shorted to VPWR. — Damaged IMRC module. — Damaged PCM. • Key off. • Connect Scan Tool to DLC. • Key on, engine off. • Run Key On Engine Off (KOEO) self-test. • Is KOEO DTC P1520 output?	Yes No	▶ ▶	Fault is present. GO to **HU20**. Fault is intermittent. GO to **HU36**.
HU20 IMRC VOLTAGE CHECK			
• Key off. • Disconnect IMRC module connector from vehicle harness. • Key on, engine off. • Measure voltage between VPWR circuit at the IMRC module vehicle harness connector and BATT(-). • Is IMRC VPWR voltage greater than 10.5 volts?	Yes No	▶ ▶	VPWR OK. GO to **HU21**. SERVICE open in IMRC VPWR circuit. RECONNECT all components. RERUN Quick Test.
HU21 CHECK IMRC PWR GND CIRCUIT			
• Key off. • IMRC module disconnected. • Key on, engine off. • Measure voltage between PWR GND circuit and VPWR circuit at the IMRC module vehicle harness connector. • Is voltage greater than 10.5 volts?	Yes No	▶ ▶	Passed PWR GND check. GO to **HU22**. SERVICE open in IMRC PWR GND circuit. RECONNECT all components. RERUN Quick Test.
HU22 CHECK IMRC CIRCUIT DRIVER FOR SHORT TO GROUND			
• Key off. • IMRC module disconnected. • Measure resistance from IMRC control circuit at the vehicle harness connector to BATT(-). • Is resistance greater than 10,000 ohms?	Yes No	▶ ▶	Passed check. GO to **HU23**. SERVICE short to BATT(-) in IMRC control circuit. RECONNECT all components. RERUN Quick Test.

Fig. 194   Test HU: Air Intake & Throttle Body (Part 12 of 18). 1995

TEST STEP	RESULT	▶	ACTION TO TAKE
HU23 CHECK IMRC CIRCUIT DRIVER FOR SHORT TO VPWR/VREF			
• Key off. • IMRC module disconnected. • Disconnect PCM. Inspect for damaged or pushed out pins, corrosion, loose wires, etc. Service as necessary. • Install breakout box, leave PCM disconnected. • Measure voltage between Test Pin 44 (IMRC) and Test Pins 51 or 103 (PWR GND) at the breakout box. • Is voltage less than 1.0 volt?	Yes No	▶ ▶	GO to **HU24**. REPAIR IMRC control circuit short to VPWR. REMOVE breakout box. RECONNECT all components. RERUN Quick Test.
HU24 CHECK IMRC CIRCUIT DRIVER FOR OPEN			
• Key off. • IMRC Module and PCM disconnected, breakout box connected. • Measure resistance from Test Pin 44 (IMRC) and IMRC control circuit at IMRC module vehicle harness connector. • Is resistance less than 5.0 ohms?	Yes No	▶ ▶	GO to **HU25**. REPAIR open IMRC control circuit. REMOVE breakout box. RECONNECT all components. RERUN Quick Test.
HU25 VERIFY PCM IMRC DRIVER			
• Key off. • Reconnect IMRC module. • Breakout box installed, PCM disconnected. • Key on, engine off. • Jumper Test Pin 44 (IMRC) to Test Pins 51 or 103 (PWR GND) at the breakout box. • Do the IMRC plates open?	Yes No	▶ ▶	REPLACE PCM. REMOVE breakout box. RECONNECT all components. RERUN Quick Test. REPLACE IMRC module. REMOVE breakout box. RECONNECT all components. RERUN Quick Test.
HU26 DTC P1518: VERIFY IMRC MONITOR (IMRCM) VOLTAGE			
DTC P1518 IMRCM indicates the voltage is less than expected. Possible causes: — IMRCM signal circuit shorted to PWR GND or SIG RTN. — Damaged IMRC module. — Damaged PCM. • Key off. • Connect Scan Tool to Diagnostic Link Connector (DLC). • Key on, engine off. • Access IMRCM PID. • Is IMRCM PID reading with the plates closed greater than 1.6 volts?	Yes No	▶ ▶	Fault is intermittent. GO to **HU34**. Failed IMRCM check. GO to **HU27**.

Fig. 194   Test HU: Air Intake & Throttle Body (Part 13 of 18). 1995

TEST STEP	RESULT	▶	ACTION TO TAKE
HU27 CHECK IMRCM CIRCUIT			
• Key off. • Disconnect IMRC module connector from vehicle harness. • Key on, engine off. • Access IMRCM PID. • Did IMRCM PID reading increase to greater than 1.6 volts when the IMRC module was disconnected?	Yes No	▶ ▶	Make sure IMRC plates are closed and DTC P1520 is not present. Then REPLACE IMRC module. COMPLETE PCM Reset to clear DTCs Powertrain Control Module (PCM Reset). RECONNECT all components. RERUN Quick Test. GO to **HU28**.
HU28 RESISTANCE CHECK ON IMRCM CIRCUIT P1518			
• Key off. • IMRC module disconnected. • Measure resistance from IMRC Monitor circuit at the vehicle harness connector to BATT(-). • Is resistance greater than 10,000 ohms?	Yes No	▶ ▶	REPLACE damaged PCM. REMOVE breakout box. RECONNECT all components. COMPLETE PCM Reset to clear DTCs Powertrain Control Module (PCM) Reset). RERUN Quick Test. SERVICE short in IMRCM circuit to BATT(-). RECONNECT all components. COMPLETE PCM Reset to clear DTCs (REFER to Powertrain Control Module (PCM) Reset). RERUN Quick Test.

Fig. 194   Test HU: Air Intake & Throttle Body (Part 14 of 18). 1995

ELECTRONIC ENGINE CONTROL SYSTEM (EEC-V)

TEST STEP	RESULT	▶	ACTION TO TAKE
HU29 CONTINUOUS MEMORY DTC P1519: IMRC INPUT GREATER THAN EXPECTED			
NOTE: If DTC P1520 is present, service before entering this pinpoint. Possible causes: — IMRCM signal circuit open. — IMRCM signal return circuit open. — Damaged IMRC module. — Damaged PCM. • Connect Scan Tool to Diagnostic Link Connector (DLC). • Key on, engine off. • Disconnect IMRC module connector from vehicle harness. • Connect a wire jumper from IMRC Monitor pin to SIG RTN pin at IMRC vehicle harness connector. • Access IMRCM PID. • Is IMRCM PID reading less than 0.2 volt?	Yes No	▶ ▶	Expected reading. REMOVE jumper wire. GO to HU32. REMOVE jumper wire. GO to HU30.
HU30 SIG RTN CIRCUIT CONTINUITY CHECK			
• Key off. • IMRC module disconnected. • Measure resistance between BATT(-) and SIG RTN circuit at the IMRC vehicle harness connector. • Is reading less than 55.0 ohms?	Yes No	▶ ▶	Expected reading. GO to HU31. SERVICE open SIG RTN circuit. RECONNECT all components. PERFORM IMRC Drive Cycle Test Step HU33 to verify repair.
HU31 IMRCM CIRCUIT CONTINUITY CHECK			
• Key off. • Disconnect PCM. Inspect for damaged or pushed out pins, corrosion, loose wires, etc. Service as necessary. • Install breakout box, leave PCM disconnected. • Measure resistance between Test Pin 8 (IMRC Monitor) and IMRC Monitor circuit at the IMRC module vehicle harness connector. • Is resistance less than 5.0 ohms?	Yes No	▶ ▶	REPLACE damaged PCM. RECONNECT all components. PERFORM IMRC Drive Cycle Test Step HU33 to verify repair. SERVICE open in IMRC Monitor circuit. RECONNECT all components. PERFORM IMRC Drive Cycle Test Step HU33 to verify repair.

Fig. 194 Test HU: Air Intake & Throttle Body (Part 15 of 18). 1995

TEST STEP	RESULT	▶	ACTION TO TAKE
HU32 DTC P1519: ENTER OTM TO CHECK CIRCUIT OPERATION			
• Key off. • Reconnect all components. • Connect Scan Tool to DLC. • Key on, engine off. • Access Output Test Mode (OTM) • While in Output Test Mode, access the IMRC and IMRCM PIDs. If the Scan Tool will not allow access to PIDs while in Output Test Mode, disconnect PCM, install a breakout box, reconnect PCM and connect a DVOM between Test Pin 8 (IMRC Monitor) and Test Pins 51 or 103 (PWR GND). • Command the outputs on. The IMRCM PID value should be less than 1.6 volts (the DVOM voltage should have the same reading). Also, the IMRC PID should be in the ON state. • Is the IMRC PID/DVOM reading less than 1.6 volts?	Yes No	▶ ▶	Fault is intermittent. GO to HU34. REPLACE damaged IMRC module. REMOVE breakout box. RECONNECT all components. PERFORM IMRC Drive Cycle Test Step HU33 to verify service.
HU33 IMRC DRIVE CYCLE			
• Key on, engine off. • Connect Scan Tool to Diagnostic Link Connector (DLC). • Complete PCM Reset to clear DTCs (refer to Section 2, Powertrain Control Module (PCM) Reset). • Access IMRC, IMRCM and RPM PIDs. • Vehicle at operating temperature and condition. • Drive vehicle, obey all traffic and safety laws. • Transmission in OVERDRIVE RANGE. • SAFELY perform three (3) accelerations from a stop to greater than 3500 rpms (IMRC, IMRCM and RPM PIDs should change. Refer to IMRC Drive Cycle PID Table at the beginning of the Pinpoint Test). • Retrieve all Continuous Memory DTCs. • Is DTC P1519 present?	Yes No	▶ ▶	Fault is present. GO to HU29. PASSED IMRC Drive Cycle. NO IMRC fault is present at this time.

Fig. 194 Test HU: Air Intake & Throttle Body (Part 16 of 18). 1995

TEST STEP	RESULT	▶	ACTION TO TAKE
HU34 IMRC MONITOR WIGGLE TEST			
• Key on, engine off. • Connect Scan Tool to data link connector (DLC). • IMRC module disconnected. • Connect a wire jumper from IMRC Monitor pin to SIG RTN pin at IMRC connector. • Access IMRCM PID (with jumper connected, reading should be less than 0.2 volt). • While viewing the IMRCM PID, wiggle wiring from IMRC connector to PCM connector. • Did IMRCM PID reading jump from less than 0.2 volt to greater than 1.6 volts?	Yes No	▶	Intermittent fault area has been identified. ISOLATE and SERVICE as necessary. REMOVE jumper wire. RECONNECT all components. COMPLETE PCM Reset to DTCs (REFER to Powertrain Control Module (PCM) Reset). RERUN Quick Test. GO to HU35.
HU35 IMRCM WIGGLE TEST			
• Key off. • Scan Tool connected. • Key on, engine off. • IMRC module disconnected. • Access IMRCM PID. • While viewing the IMRCM PID, wiggle wiring from IMRC connector to PCM connector. • Did IMRCM PID reading jump to less than 1.6 volts?	Yes No	▶ ▶	Intermittent fault area has been identified. ISOLATE and SERVICE as necessary. PERFORM this test step again to verify repair. Unable to duplicate and/or identify fault at this time. GO to Pinpoint Test Step Z1 with the following data: IMRCM, IMRC PIDs and list of Possible Causes.

Fig. 194 Test HU: Air Intake & Throttle Body (Part 17 of 18). 1995

TEST STEP	RESULT	▶	ACTION TO TAKE
HU36 CONTINUOUS MEMORY DTC P1520: INTERMITTENT CIRCUIT MALFUNCTION			
• Key off. • Reconnect all components. • Connect Scan Tool to DLC. • Key on, engine off. • Access Output Test Mode • While in Output Test Mode, access the IMRC and IMRCM PIDs. If the Scan Tool will not allow access to PIDs while in Output Test Mode, disconnect PCM, install a breakout box, reconnect PCM and connect a DVOM between Test Pin 44 (IMRC Control Circuit) and Test Pins 51 or 103 (PWR GND). • Command the outputs on. The IMRC PID value should be ON (the DVOM voltage should be less than 1.0 volt) and the IMRCM PID value should be less than 1.6 volts. — Shake, wiggle and bend the IMRC Control Circuit wiring from the IMRC Module back to the PCM while viewing the IMRC DVOM reading or IMRCM PID reading. — Look for a sudden change in the IMRCM PID reading or in the DVOM reading to indicate when a fault is detected. • Is fault indicated?	Yes No	▶ ▶	Possible open in IMRC Control Circuit or VPWR Circuit to the IMRC module. ISOLATE fault and SERVICE as necessary. PERFORM this test step over to verify service. GO to HU37.
HU37 CONTINUOUS MEMORY DTC P1520: INTERMITTENT CIRCUIT MALFUNCTION			
This step is used to check if the IMRC Control Circuit is intermittently shorting to ground and causing the IMRC plates to open. • Key on, engine off. • All components connected. • While viewing IMRC plates, wiggle wiring and connectors from IMRC module to PCM. • Did the IMRC plates open while wiggling/pulling on the wiring?	Yes No	▶ ▶	Possible short to ground in the IMRC Control Circuit. ISOLATE fault and SERVICE as necessary. PERFORM this test step over to verify service. Unable to duplicate and/or identify fault at this time. GO to Pinpoint Test Step Z1 with the following data: IMRCM, IMRC PIDs and list of Possible Causes.

Fig. 194 Test HU: Air Intake & Throttle Body (Part 18 of 18). 1995

Note

You should enter this Pinpoint Test only when directed here.

Reminder

This Pinpoint Test is intended to diagnose the following:

- Canister Purge (CANP) Solenoid
- Carbon Canister
- Leaks in Fuel Vapor Hoses
- Vapor Orifice Rollover Valve
- Vacuum or vapor leaks caused by loose gas cap
- Possible fuel tank air vapor leaks
- Harness Circuits: CANP SIG, SIG RTN (short in PCM), Vehicle Power (VPWR), and Power Ground (PWR GND)
- Powertrain Control Module (PCM)

FM0159401196010X

Fig. 195   Test HV: EVAP System (Part 1 of 9). 1994

Evaporative Emission System

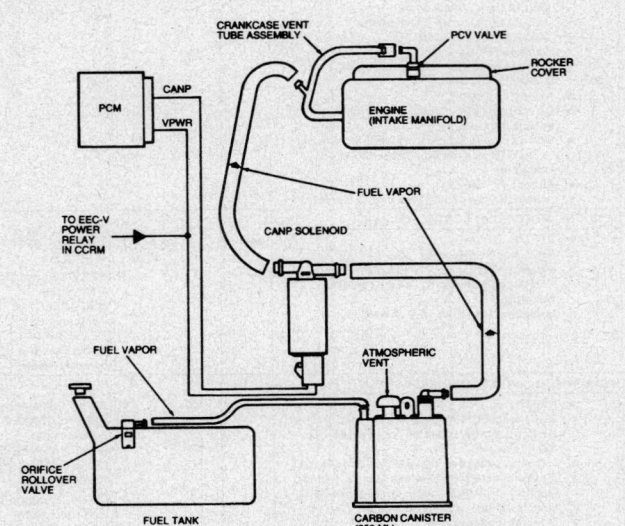

FM0159401196020X

Fig. 195   Test HV: EVAP System (Part 2 of 9). 1994

Pinpoint Test Schematic

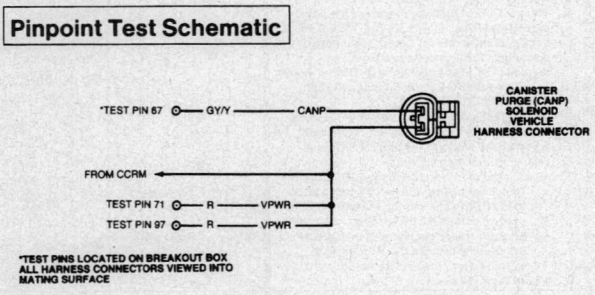

*TEST PINS LOCATED ON BREAKOUT BOX
ALL HARNESS CONNECTORS VIEWED INTO
MATING SURFACE

FM0159401196030X

Fig. 195   Test HV: EVAP System (Part 3 of 9). 1994

	TEST STEP	RESULT	▶	ACTION TO TAKE
HV1	**ENTER OUTPUT STATE DIAGNOSTIC TEST MODE: CHECK CANP SOLENOID ELECTRICAL OPERATION**			
	• Key off. • Install a Scan Tool. • Disconnect CANP solenoid. • Disconnect electrical connector on the speed control servo, if equipped. • Connect DVOM positive test lead to the VPWR circuit and negative test lead to the CANP circuit at the CANP solenoid vehicle harness connector. • Key on, engine off. • Turn on the Scan Tool outputs with the trigger button. • Observe CANP voltage reading on the DVOM and record. • Turn the outputs off with the Scan Tool trigger button. • Observe CANP voltage reading on the DVOM and record. • Cycle the Scan Tool trigger button on and off several times. • **Does the CANP circuit cycle 0.5 volts or greater on the DVOM?**	Yes No	▶ ▶	PCM capable of detecting CANP output signal change. LEAVE CANP solenoid disconnected. EXIT Output State DTM. GO to HV2. GO to HV9.
HV2	**CHECK CARBON CANISTER**			
	NOTE: Fuel saturation of carbon canister cannot be effectively checked by the canister weight or intensity of odor or smell. Vehicle must run over an extended period of time to purge fuel (or vapor) build-up in carbon canister. • Check for cracks or other damage to carbon canister. • **Is the canister cracked or damaged?**	Yes No	▶ ▶	REPLACE carbon canister(s). Carbon canister is not contaminated. GO to HV3.

FM0159401196040X

Fig. 195   Test HV: EVAP System (Part 4 of 9). 1994

TEST STEP	RESULT	▶	ACTION TO TAKE
HV3 CHECK VACUUM FUEL TANK TO CANISTER			
• Remove fuel vapor hose at canister. • Install a vacuum tee in the hose and add small pieces of vacuum hose to the other two ends of tee. • Install a vacuum gauge in the second end of the tee. • Install a vacuum shut off valve in the third end of the tee. • Add a small piece of hose (with a plastic straight fitting at one end) to free end of the shut off valve. • Apply 0.75 psi maximum vacuum to the plastic straight end with a hand held vacuum pump. • Close the shut off valve and monitor the vacuum gauge. • **Is the fuel tank to canister system holding vacuum or fuel pressure?**	Yes No	▶ ▶	Fuel tank, fuel vapor hose and gas cap indicate no leaks. REMOVE vacuum gauge and vacuum pump. RECONNECT carbon canister. GO to **HV4**. SERVICE as necessary the fuel pressure leak or EVAP vacuum leak (gas cap, vapor orifice rollover valve, fuel vapor hose or fuel tank). REPEAT vacuum check on this part of the system to verify repair.
HV4 CHECK CANP SOLENOID FOR VACUUM LEAKS - CLOSED VACUUM POSITION			
• Key on, engine off. • CANP solenoid disconnected. • Disconnect vacuum hose at CANP solenoid on the manifold vacuum side of the CANP solenoid. • Apply 16 in-Hg (53 kPa) of vacuum to the manifold vacuum side of the CANP solenoid. • **Does the CANP solenoid hold vacuum for 20 seconds?**	Yes No	▶ ▶	LEAVE the vacuum pump connected. GO to **HV5**. REPLACE CANP solenoid. RERUN Quick Test.
HV5 CHECK CANP SOLENOID MECHANICAL OPERATION - OPEN VACUUM POSITION			
• Key off. • Reconnect CANP solenoid (electrical). • Disconnect manifold vacuum side of CANP solenoid. • Apply 16 in-Hg (53 kPa) of vacuum to the CANP solenoid with a vacuum pump. • Key on, engine off. • **Does the CANP solenoid open and vacuum reading on the pump drop (air passes freely)?**	Yes No	▶ ▶	REMOVE vacuum pump. GO to **HV6**. CHECK hose from CANP solenoid to canister for blockage or kinks. SERVICE as necessary. If no fault is indicated, REPLACE CANP solenoid. RERUN Quick Test.

Fig. 195   Test HV: EVAP System (Part 5 of 9). 1994

FM0159401196050X

TEST STEP	RESULT	▶	ACTION TO TAKE
HV6 CHECK VACUUM HOSE LEAK BETWEEN CANP SOLENOID AND CARBON CANISTER			
• Check for cracks, splits and holes in the vacuum hose between the CANP solenoid and the carbon canister. • **Is a fault indicated?**	Yes No	▶ ▶	REPLACE damaged vacuum hose (cracks, splits and holes). RERUN Quick Test. CANP solenoid is OK. GO to **HV7**.
HV7 CHECK FOR MANIFOLD VACUUM TO CANP SOLENOID			
• Key off. • Vacuum hose disconnected from manifold vacuum side of CANP solenoid. • Start engine. • Place thumb on open end of vacuum hose at CANP solenoid. • **Is vacuum present at the engine vacuum hose to CANP solenoid?**	Yes No	▶ ▶	Evaporative Emission System is OK. RECONNECT all components. DRIVE vehicle. If symptom is still present, RETURN to Symptom Flow Charts. CHECK vacuum hose to engine from CANP solenoid for proper routing, kinks, leaks or blockage. If OK, REFER to Engine
HV9 DTC 0443: CHECK CANP RESISTANCE			
Diagnostic Trouble Code (DTC) 0443 indicates a failure in the CANP solenoid circuit. Possible Causes: — Damaged CANP solenoid. — CANP SIG harness circuit open. — VPWR harness circuit open. — CANP SIG harness circuit short to VPWR. — CANP SIG harness circuit short to PWR GND or SIG RTN. — Damaged PCM. • Key off. • Disconnect the CANP solenoid. • Measure CANP solenoid resistance. • **Is the resistance between 30 and 90 ohms?**	Yes No	▶ ▶	CANP solenoid is OK electrically. GO to **HV10**. CANP solenoid is out of specification. REPLACE CANP solenoid. COMPLETE PCM reset to clear DTCs (REFER to Powertrain Control Module (PCM) Reset). RERUN Quick Test.

Fig. 195   Test HV: EVAP System (Part 6 of 9). 1994

FM0159401196060X

TEST STEP	RESULT	▶	ACTION TO TAKE
HV10 CHECK VPWR CIRCUIT VOLTAGE			
• Key on, engine off. • CANP solenoid disconnected. • Measure the voltage between VPWR at the CANP solenoid vehicle harness connector and battery ground. • **Is the voltage greater than 10.5 volts?**	Yes No	▶ ▶	VPWR circuit is OK. GO to **HV11**. SERVICE open in VPWR circuit. RECONNECT CANP solenoid. RERUN Quick Test.
HV11 CHECK CANP SIG HARNESS CONTINUITY			
• Key on, engine off. • CANP solenoid disconnected. • Disconnect PCM. Inspect for damaged or pushed out pins, corrosion, loose wires, etc. Service as necessary. • Install breakout box, leave PCM disconnected. • Measure the resistance between Test Pin 67 (CANP SIG) at the breakout box and CANP SIG circuit at the CANP solenoid vehicle harness connector. • **Is the resistance less than 5.0 ohms?**	Yes No	▶ ▶	CANP SIG harness circuit is OK. GO to **HV12**. SERVICE open in CANP SIG harness circuit. REMOVE breakout box. RECONNECT all components. COMPLETE PCM reset to clear DTCs (REFER to Powertrain Control Module (PCM) Reset). RERUN Quick Test.
HV12 CHECK CANP SIG CIRCUIT FOR SHORT TO GROUND			
• Key off. • Breakout box installed, PCM disconnected. • Disconnect Scan Tool from Data Link Connector (DLC). • Measure the resistance between Test Pin 67 (CANP SIG) and Test Pins 91 (SIG RTN) and 24 or 103 (PWR GND) at the breakout box. • **Is each resistance greater than 10,000 ohms?**	Yes No	▶ ▶	CANP SIG possibly shorted to ground in PCM. GO to **HV13**. SERVICE short to ground in CANP SIG harness circuit. REMOVE breakout box. RECONNECT all components. COMPLETE PCM reset to clear DTCs (REFER to Powertrain Control Module (PCM) Reset). RERUN Quick Test.

Fig. 195   Test HV: EVAP System (Part 7 of 9). 1994

FM0159401196070X

TEST STEP	RESULT	▶	ACTION TO TAKE
HV13 CHECK CANP SIG CIRCUIT FOR SHORT TO VPWR			
• Key off. • CANP disconnected. • Breakout box installed, PCM disconnected. • Scan Tool disconnected from DLC. • Measure the resistance between Test Pin 67 (CANP SIG) and Test Pins 71 or 97 (VPWR) at the breakout box. • **Is each resistance greater than 10,000 ohms?**	Yes No	▶ ▶	CANP SIG is either shorted to VPWR, PWR GND or SIG RTN in the PCM. REPLACE PCM. REMOVE breakout box and Scan Tool. RECONNECT all components. COMPLETE PCM reset to clear DTCs (REFER to Powertrain Control Module (PCM) Reset). RERUN Quick Test. SERVICE short to VPWR in the CANP harness circuit. REMOVE breakout box and scan tool. RECONNECT all components. COMPLETE PCM reset to clear DTCs (REFER to Powertrain Control Module (PCM) Reset). RERUN Quick Test.
HV14 CONTINUOUS MEMORY DTC 0443: INSPECT CANP CIRCUIT FOR INTERMITTENT FAILURE			
Continous Memory Diagnostic Trouble Code (DTC) 0443 may indicate a CANP solenoid circuit failure. Possible Causes: — Damaged CANP solenoid. — CANP SIG or VPWR harness circuit open. • Rerun KOEO, KOER and Continuous Self-Test. • **Is DTC 0443 only present in Continuous Self-Test?**	Yes No	▶ ▶	GO to **HV15**. GO to **HV9**.

Fig. 195   Test HV: EVAP System (Part 8 of 9). 1994

TEST STEP		RESULT	▶	ACTION TO TAKE
HV15	**WIGGLE TEST SOLENOID AND HARNESS**			
	• Key off.	Yes	▶	ISOLATE fault and SERVICE as necessary. RECONNECT all components. COMPLETE PCM. RESET to clear DTCs (REFER to Powertrain Control Module (PCM) Reset). RERUN Quick Test.
	• Disconnect PCM. Inspect for damaged or pushed out pins, corrosion, loose wires, etc. Service as necessary.			
	• Install breakout box, leave PCM disconnected.			
	• Measure the resistance between Test Pin 67 (CANP SIG) and Test Pins 71 or 97 (VPWR), while performing the following:			
	— Lightly tap on the CANP solenoid, and observe a resistance change.			
	— Wiggle the CANP solenoid connector and vehicle harness between the solenoid and the PCM, and observe a resistance change.	No	▶	Unable to duplicate and / or identify fault at this time. GO to Pinpoint Test Step Z1 with the resistance readings and list of Possible Causes.
	• Does the resistance reading change to below 30 ohms or above 90 ohms?			

Fig. 195   Test HV: EVAP System (Part 9 of 9). 1994

Note

You should enter this Pinpoint Test only when directed here.

Remember

This Pinpoint Test is intended to diagnose the following:

- Canister Purge (CANP) Solenoid (9C915)
- Vapor Management Valve (VMV) (9C915)
- Carbon Canister (9D653)
- Leaks in Fuel Vapor Hoses
- Vapor Orifice Rollover Valve (9B593)
- Vacuum or vapor leaks caused by loose gas cap
- Possible fuel tank air vapor leaks
- Harness Circuits: CANP SIG, VMV SIG, SIG RTN (short in PCM), Vehicle Power (VPWR), and Power Ground (PWR GND)
- Powertrain Control Module (PCM) (12A650)

FM0159501280010X

Fig. 196   Test HV: EVAP System (Part 1 of 12). 1995

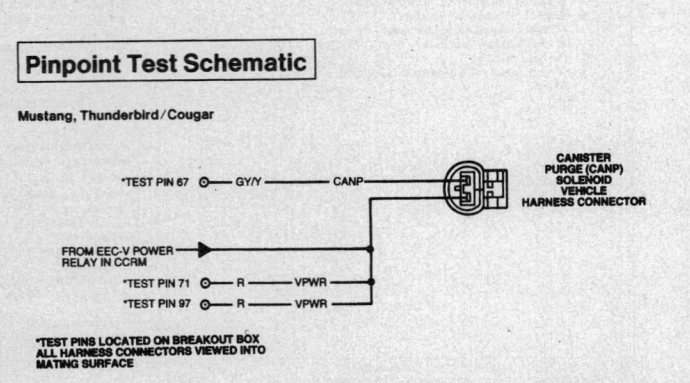

Pinpoint Test Schematic

Mustang, Thunderbird / Cougar

*TEST PINS LOCATED ON BREAKOUT BOX
ALL HARNESS CONNECTORS VIEWED INTO
MATING SURFACE

FM0159501280020X

Fig. 196   Test HV: EVAP System (Part 2 of 12). 1995

TEST STEP		RESULT	▶	ACTION TO TAKE
HV1	**ENTER OUTPUT TEST MODE: CHECK CANP SOLENOID OR VMV ELECTRICAL OPERATION**			
	• Key off.	Yes	▶	PCM capable of detecting CANP (or VMV) output signal change. EXIT Output Test Mode. GO to **HV2**.
	• Install a Scan Tool.			
	• Disconnect CANP solenoid or Vapor Management Valve (VMV).			
	• Disconnect electrical connector on the speed control servo, if equipped.	No	▶	GO to **HV17**.
	• Connect DVOM positive test lead to the VPWR circuit and negative test lead to the CANP circuit at the CANP solenoid (or VMV) vehicle harness connector.			
	• Key on, engine off.			
	• Turn on the Scan Tool outputs with the trigger button.			
	• Observe CANP (or VMV) voltage reading on the DVOM and record.			
	• Turn the outputs off with the Scan Tool trigger button.			
	• Observe CANP (or VMV) voltage reading on the DVOM and record.			
	• Cycle the Scan Tool trigger button on and off several times.			
	• Does the CANP (or VMV) circuit cycle 0.2 volt or greater on the DVOM?			
HV2	**CHECK CANP (OR VMV) RESISTANCE**			
	• Key off.	Yes	▶	CANP solenoid (or VMV) is OK electrically. GO to **HV3**.
	• CANP solenoid (or VMV) disconnected.			
	• Measure CANP solenoid resistance.			
	• Is the resistance between 30 and 90 ohms (or VMV resistance between 30 and 36 ohms)?	No	▶	CANP solenoid (or VMV) is out of specification. REPLACE CANP solenoid (or VMV). DRIVE vehicle to verify correction of driveability symptom. COMPLETE PCM Reset to clear DTCs

FM0159501280030X

Fig. 196   Test HV: EVAP System (Part 3 of 12). 1995

Fig. 196 Test HV: EVAP System (Part 4 of 12). 1995

TEST STEP	RESULT	▶	ACTION TO TAKE
HV3 CHECK CARBON CANISTER			
NOTE: Fuel saturation of carbon canister cannot be effectively checked by the canister weight or intensity of odor or smell. Vehicle must run over an extended period of time to purge fuel (or vapor) build-up in carbon canister. • Check for cracks or other damage to carbon canister. • **Is the canister cracked or damaged?**	Yes No	▶ ▶	REPLACE carbon canister(s). Carbon canister is not contaminated. For Mustang and Thunderbird/Cougar: GO to **HV4**. For 3.8L Windstar: GO to **HV10**.
HV4 CHECK VACUUM: FUEL TANK TO CARBON CANISTER			
• Remove the fuel vapor hoses from the fuel tank at the carbon canister. • Install a hand held pressure pump with gauge at the open end of the fuel vapor hose. • Apply 1.0 in-Hg (0.5 psi) maximum pressure to the fuel vapor hose with the pressure pump. • Monitor the pressure gauge on the pump. • **Is the fuel tank to carbon canister system holding a constant pressure?**	Yes No	▶ ▶	CHECK for possible blockage in fuel vapor hose between fuel tank and carbon canister(s). If blockage is found, SERVICE as necessary. REMOVE pressure pump (gauge). RECONNECT carbon canister. DRIVE vehicle. If symptom is still present, RETURN to Symptom Flow Charts. If blockage is not present, REMOVE pressure pump (gauge). RECONNECT carbon canister. GO to **HV6**. GO to **HV5**.
HV5 CHECK FUEL TANK-GAS CAP-ROLLOVER VALVE			
• Check for holes, cracks and leaks in fuel vapor hose between fuel tank and carbon canister. • Check for fuel tank damage. • Check for damaged rollover valve. • **Is a fault indicated?**	Yes No	▶ ▶	SERVICE as necessary. REMOVE pressure pump (gauge). RECONNECT carbon canister. DRIVE vehicle. If symptom is still present, RETURN to Symptom Flow Charts. REMOVE pressure pump (gauge). GO to **HV6**.

FM0159501280040X

Fig. 196   Test HV: EVAP System (Part 4 of 12). 1995

TEST STEP	RESULT	▶	ACTION TO TAKE
HV6 CHECK CANP SOLENOID FOR VACUUM LEAKS - CLOSED VACUUM POSITION			
• Key off. • Disconnect the vacuum hose at both ends of the CANP solenoid. • Install a hand held vacuum pump to the intake manifold vacuum side of the CANP solenoid. • Disconnect the CANP solenoid electrically. • Apply 16 in-Hg (53 kPa) of vacuum to the CANP solenoid. • **Does the CANP solenoid hold vacuum for 20 seconds?**	Yes No	▶ ▶	LEAVE the vacuum pump connected. GO to **HV7**. REMOVE vacuum pump. REPLACE CANP solenoid. RECONNECT all components. COMPLETE PCM Reset to clear DTCs (REFER to Powertrain Control Module (PCM) Reset). RERUN Quick Test.
HV7 CHECK CANP SOLENOID MECHANICAL OPERATION - OPEN VACUUM POSITION			
• Key off. • Reconnect CANP solenoid electrically. • Vacuum hose at both ends of the CANP solenoid disconnected. • Connect Scan Tool. • Apply 16 in.-Hg. (53 kPa) of vacuum to the CANP solenoid on the intake manifold side with a vacuum pump. • Access Output Test Mode on Scan Tool • Key on, engine off. • **Does the CANP solenoid open and vacuum reading on the pump drop (air passes freely) when commanding the output on?**	Yes No	▶ ▶	CHECK fuel vapor hose between carbon canister and CANP solenoid for blockage or kinks. SERVICE as necessary. If no fault is indicated, REMOVE vacuum pump. GO to **HV8**. REPLACE CANP solenoid. COMPLETE PCM Reset to clear DTCs
HV8 CHECK VACUUM HOSE LEAK BETWEEN CANP SOLENOID AND CARBON CANISTER			
• Check for cracks, splits and holes in the vacuum hose between the CANP solenoid and the carbon canister. • **Is a fault indicated?**	Yes No	▶ ▶	REPLACE damaged vacuum hose (cracks, splits and holes). RERUN Quick Test. CANP solenoid is OK. GO to **HV9**.

FM0159501280050X

Fig. 196   Test HV: EVAP System (Part 5 of 12). 1995

TEST STEP	RESULT	▶	ACTION TO TAKE
HV9 CHECK FOR MANIFOLD VACUUM TO CANP SOLENOID			
• Key off. • Vacuum hose disconnected from manifold vacuum side of CANP solenoid. • Start engine. • Place thumb on open end of vacuum hose at CANP solenoid. • **Is vacuum present at the engine vacuum hose to CANP solenoid?**	Yes No	▶ ▶	Evaporative Emission System is OK. RECONNECT all components. DRIVE vehicle. If symptom is still present, RETURN to Symptom Flow Charts. CHECK vacuum hose to engine from CANP solenoid for proper routing, kinks, leaks or blockage. If OK, Engine conditions affecting vacuum.
HV10 CHECK FOR VACUUM AT VMV VACUUM INPUT PORT HOSE TO INTAKE MANIFOLD			
• Key off. • VMV solenoid disconnected. • VMV input port vacuum hose disconnected at the VMV. • Start engine. • Place thumb on open end of vacuum hose. • Key off. • **Was vacuum present at the input port hose?**	Yes No	▶ ▶	RECONNECT VMV input port vacuum hose. GO to **HV11**. EXIT Output Test Mode. RECONNECT VMV assembly. CHECK fuel vacuum hose for proper routing, kinks, leaks or blockage. If OK, REFER to Engine subjects affecting engine vacuum.

FM0159501280060X

Fig. 196   Test HV: EVAP System (Part 6 of 12). 1995

TEST STEP	RESULT	▶	ACTION TO TAKE
HV11 CHECK VACUUM: FUEL VAPOR HOSE FROM VMV TO INTAKE MANIFOLD			
• Key off. • VMV solenoid disconnected. • Disconnect VMV fuel vapor hose that runs from the VMV to the intake manifold vacuum tree. • Start engine. • Place thumb at one end of fuel vapor hose. • Key off. • **Was vacuum present at the fuel vapor hose?**	Yes No	▶ ▶	RECONNECT fuel vapor hose. GO to **HV12**. EXIT Output Test Mode. RECONNECT VMV assembly. CHECK fuel vapor hose for proper routing, kinks, leaks or blockage. If OK, REFER to Engine subjects affecting engine vacuum.
HV12 CHECK VMV ELECTRO-MECHANICAL OPERATION			
• Key off. • Reconnect VMV. • Apply 16 in-Hg (53 kPa) of vacuum to the VMV solenoid (fuel vapor port to intake manifold) with a vacuum pump. • Key on, engine off. • Turn the outputs on and off with the Scan Tool trigger button. • Observe the vacuum reading. • Release vacuum applied by the pump. • Key off. • **Did the vacuum reading on the pump drop (air passes freely)?**	Yes No	▶ ▶	EXIT Output Test Mode. REMOVE the vacuum pump. GO to **HV13**. EXIT Output Test Mode. REPLACE the VMV assembly. REMOVE the vacuum pump. RERUN Quick Test.

FUEL VAPOR TO INTAKE MANIFOLD

FUEL VAPOR TO CARBON CANISTER

INPUT PORT VACUUM (TO INTAKE MANIFOLD)

FM0159501280070X

Fig. 196   Test HV: EVAP System (Part 7 of 12). 1995

TEST STEP	RESULT	▶	ACTION TO TAKE
HV13 CHECK VMV HOUSING FOR LEAKS			
• Key on, engine off. • VMV solenoid disconnected. • Disconnect input port hose of VMV. • Apply 16 in-Hg (53 kPa) of vacuum to VMV (vacuum input port to intake manifold) with a vacuum pump. • Observe the vacuum reading. • Key off. • **Did all vacuum applied to VMV bleed off immediately?**	Yes No	▶ ▶	GO to **HV14**. EXIT Output Test Mode. REPLACE VMV assembly. REMOVE vacuum pump. RERUN Quick Test.
HV14 CHECK FOR LEAK: FUEL VAPOR HOSE FROM CARBON CANISTER TO VMV			
• Key off. • Disconnect fuel vapor hose between the carbon canister and the VMV. • Plug one end of the hose and install a vacuum pump at the remaining end. • Apply 16 in-Hg (53 kPa) of vacuum to the hose. • Observe the vacuum reading for at least 15 seconds. • Release vacuum applied by the pump. • **Did the fuel vapor hose hold the vacuum applied?**	Yes No	▶ ▶	REMOVE the vacuum pump. RECONNECT the fuel vapor hose. GO to **HV15**. REMOVE the vacuum pump. REPLACE the damaged fuel vapor hose. RERUN Quick Test.
HV15 CHECK VACUUM: FUEL TANK TO CARBON CANISTER			
• Remove the fuel vapor hoses from the fuel tank at the carbon canister. • Install a hand held pressure pump with gauge to the open end of the fuel vapor hose. • Apply 1.0 in-Hg (0.5 psi) maximum pressure to the fuel vapor hose with the pressure pump. • Monitor the pressure gauge on the pump. • **Is the fuel tank to carbon canister system holding a constant pressure?**	Yes No	▶ ▶	CHECK for possible blockage in fuel vapor hose between fuel tank and carbon canister(s). If blockage is found, SERVICE as necessary. If blockage is not present, REMOVE pressure pump (gauge). RECONNECT carbon canister. DRIVE vehicle. If symptom is still present, RETURN to Symptom Flow Charts. GO to **HV16**.

FM015950128 0080X

Fig. 196 Test HV: EVAP System (Part 8 of 12). 1995

TEST STEP	RESULT	▶	ACTION TO TAKE
HV16 CHECK FUEL TANK-GAS CAP-ROLLOVER VALVE			
• Check for holes, cracks and leaks in fuel vapor hose between fuel tank and carbon canister(s). • Check for fuel tank damage. • Check for damaged rollover valve. • **Is a fault indicated?**	Yes No	▶ ▶	SERVICE as necessary. REPEAT pressure check on this part of the system to verify the service. REMOVE pressure pump (gauge). RECONNECT carbon canister. REMOVE pressure pump (gauge). RECONNECT carbon canister. DRIVE vehicle. If symptom is still present, RETURN to Symptom Flow Charts.
HV17 DTC P0443: CHECK VPWR TO CANP SOLENOID			
Diagnostic Trouble Code (DTC) P0443 indicates a failure in the CANP solenoid (or VMV) circuit. Possible causes: — VPWR harness circuit open. — Damaged CANP solenoid or Vapor Management Valve (VMV). — CANP SIG (or VMV) harness circuit open. — CANP SIG (or VMV) harness circuit short to PWR GND or SIG RTN. — CANP SIG (or VMV) harness circuit short to VPWR. — Damaged PCM. • Key on, engine off. • CANP solenoid (or VMV) disconnected. • Measure the voltage between VPWR at the CANP solenoid (or VMV) vehicle harness connector and battery ground. • **Is the voltage greater than 10.5 volts?**	Yes No	▶ ▶	VPWR circuit is OK. GO to **HV18**. SERVICE open in VPWR circuit. RECONNECT CANP solenoid (or VMV). RERUN Quick Test.

Fig. 196 Test HV: EVAP System (Part 9 of 12). 1995

TEST STEP	RESULT	▶	ACTION TO TAKE
HV18 CHECK CANP RESISTANCE			
• Key off. • CANP solenoid (or VMV) disconnected. • Measure CANP solenoid (or VMV) resistance. • **Is the resistance between 30 and 90 ohms (36 ohms for VMV applications)?**	Yes No	▶ ▶	CANP solenoid (or VMV) is OK electrically. GO to **HV19**. CANP solenoid (or VMV) is out of specification. REPLACE CANP solenoid (or VMV). COMPLETE PCM Reset to clear DTCs (REFER to Powertrain Control Module (PCM) Reset). RERUN Quick Test.
HV19 CHECK CANP SIG OR VMV SIG HARNESS CONTINUITY			
• Key on, engine off. • CANP solenoid disconnected. • Disconnect PCM. Inspect for damaged or pushed out pins, corrosion, loose wires, etc. Service as necessary. • Install breakout box, leave PCM disconnected. • Measure the resistance between Test Pin 67 (CANP SIG) or Test Pin 56 (VMV SIG) at the breakout box and CANP SIG circuit at the CANP solenoid (or VMV) vehicle harness connector. • **Is the resistance less than 5.0 ohms?**	Yes No	▶ ▶	CANP SIG (or VMV SIG) harness circuit is OK. GO to **HV20**. SERVICE open in CANP SIG (or VMV SIG) harness circuit. REMOVE breakout box. RECONNECT all components. COMPLETE PCM Reset to clear DTCs (REFER to Powertrain Control Module (PCM) Reset). RERUN Quick Test.

Fig. 196 Test HV: EVAP System (Part 10 of 12). 1995

TEST STEP	RESULT	▶	ACTION TO TAKE
HV20 CHECK CANP SIG OR VMV SIG CIRCUIT FOR SHORT TO GROUND			
• Key off. • CANP solenoid (or VMV) disconnected. • Breakout box installed, PCM disconnected. • Disconnect Scan Tool from Data Link Connector (DLC). • Measure the resistance between Test Pin 67 (CANP SIG) or Test Pin 56 (VMV SIG) and Test Pins 91 (SIG RTN) and 24 or 103 (PWR GND) at the breakout box. • **Is each resistance greater than 10,000 ohms?**	Yes No	▶ ▶	CANP SIG (or VMV SIG) possibly shorted to ground in PCM. GO to **HV21**. SERVICE short to ground in CANP SIG (or VMV SIG) harness circuit. REMOVE breakout box. RECONNECT all components. COMPLETE PCM Reset to clear DTCs (REFER to Powertrain Control Module (PCM) Reset). RERUN Quick Test.
HV21 CHECK CANP SIG OR VMV SIG CIRCUIT FOR SHORT TO VPWR			
• Key off. • CANP (or VMV) disconnected. • Breakout box installed, PCM disconnected. • Scan Tool disconnected from DLC. • Measure the resistance between Test Pin 67 (CANP SIG) or Test Pin 56 (VMV SIG) and Test Pins 71 or 97 (VPWR) at the breakout box. • **Is each resistance greater than 10,000 ohms?**	Yes No	▶ ▶	CANP SIG (or VMV SIG) is either shorted to VPWR, PWR GND or SIG RTN in the PCM. REPLACE PCM. REMOVE breakout box and Scan Tool. RECONNECT all components. COMPLETE PCM Reset to clear DTCs (REFER to Powertrain Control Module (PCM) Reset). RERUN Quick Test. SERVICE short to VPWR in the CANP (or VMV) harness circuit. REMOVE breakout box and scan tool. RECONNECT all components. COMPLETE PCM Reset to clear DTCs (REFER to Powertrain Control Module (PCM) Reset). RERUN Quick Test.

FM015950128 0110X

Fig. 196 Test HV: EVAP System (Part 11 of 12). 1995

TEST STEP	RESULT	▶	ACTION TO TAKE
HV22 CONTINUOUS MEMORY DTC P0443: INSPECT CANP (OR VMV) CIRCUIT FOR INTERMITTENT FAILURE			
Continuous Memory Diagnostic Trouble Code (DTC) P0443 may indicate a CANP solenoid (or VMV) circuit failure. Possible causes: — Damaged CANP solenoid. — Damaged VMV. — CANP SIG, VMV SIG or VPWR harness circuit open. • Rerun Key On Engine Off (KOEO), Key On Engine Running (KOER) and Continuous Memory Self-Tests. • **Is DTC P0443 present in Continuous Memory Self-Test only?**	Yes No	▶ ▶	GO to **HV23**. GO to **HV17**.
HV23 WIGGLE TEST SOLENOID AND HARNESS			

• Key off.
• Disconnect PCM. Inspect for damaged or pushed out pins, corrosion, loose wires, etc. Service as necessary.
• Install breakout box, leave PCM disconnected.
• Measure the resistance between Test Pin 67 (CANP SIG) or Test Pin 56 (VMV SIG) and Test Pins 71 or 97 (VPWR), while performing the following:
  — Lightly tap on the CANP solenoid or VMV, and observe a resistance change.
  — Wiggle the CANP solenoid or VMV connector and vehicle harness between the solenoid (or valve) and the PCM, and observe a resistance change.
• **Does the resistance reading change to below 30 ohms or above 90 ohms (36 ohms for VMV)?**
	Yes
	
	No
		▶
		
		▶
			ISOLATE fault and SERVICE as necessary. RECONNECT all components. COMPLETE PCM Reset to clear DTCs (REFER to Powertrain Control Module (PCM) Reset). RERUN Quick Test.
			UNABLE to duplicate and/or identify fault at this time. GO to Pinpoint Test Step **Z1** with the resistance readings and list of Possible Causes.

Fig. 196 Test HV: EVAP System (Part 12 of 12). 1995

You should enter this Pinpoint Test only when directed here.

Remember

This Pinpoint Test is intended to diagnose the following:

- Canister Purge (CANP) Solenoid (9C915)
- Purge Flow Sensor (PFS) (14A606)
- Vapor Management Valve (VMV) solenoid (9C915)
- Carbon canister (9D653)
- Fuel vapor hoses
- Vapor orifice roll-over valve (9B593)
- Vacuum or vapor leaks caused by loose gas cap
- Possible fuel tank air / vapor leaks
- Harness circuits: CANP SIG, PFS SIG, VMV SIG, Vehicle Power (VPWR), and Power Ground (PWR GND)
- Powertrain Control Module (PCM) (12A650)

Fig. 197   Test HW: EVAP Purge Flow System (Part 1 of 25). 1995

Evaporative Emission System with Vapor Management Valve

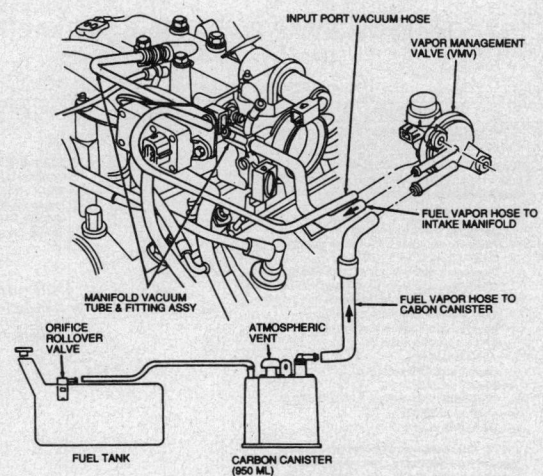

Fig. 197   Test HW: EVAP Purge Flow System (Part 3 of 25). 1995

Evaporative Emission System with Canister Purge Solenoid and Purge Flow System

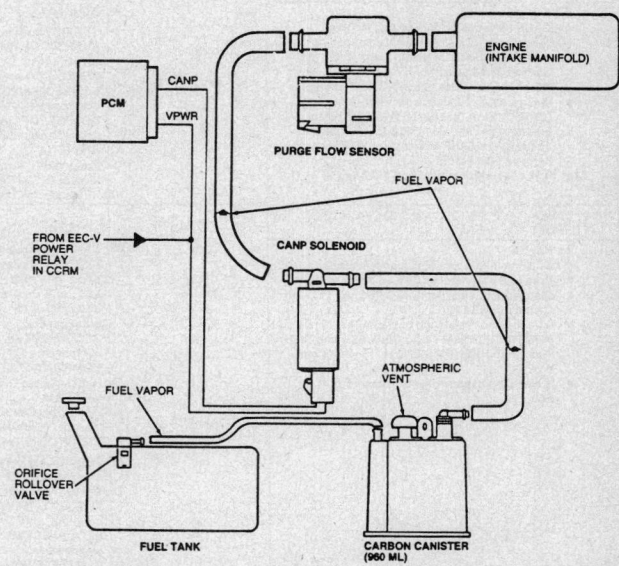

Fig. 197   Test HW: EVAP Purge Flow System (Part 2 of 25). 1995

Ranger

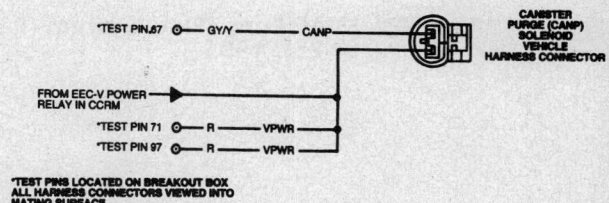

Fig. 197   Test HW: EVAP Purge Flow System (Part 4 of 25). 1995

Continental, Crown Victoria/Grand Marquis

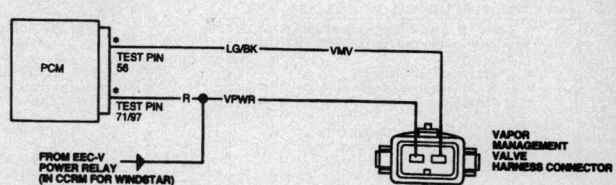

Ranger

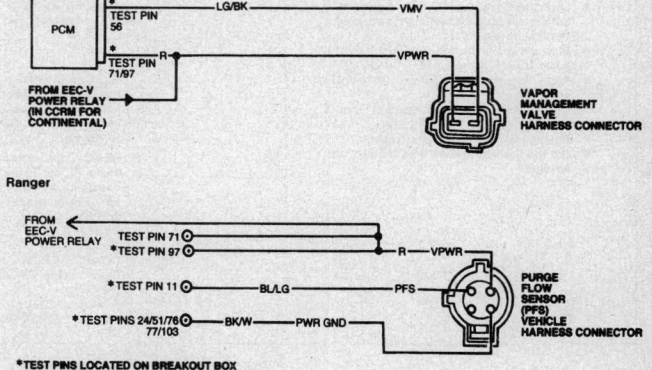

Fig. 197   Test HW: EVAP Purge Flow System (Part 5 of 25). 1995

TEST STEP		RESULT	▶	ACTION TO TAKE
HW1	DTC P0443: CHECK VPWR TO CANISTER PURGE (CANP) SOLENOID OR VAPOR MANAGEMENT (VMV) VALVE			
	Diagnostic Trouble Code (DTC) P0443 indicates a failure in the CANP solenoid (or VMV) circuit. Possible causes: — VPWR circuit open. — CANP SIG (or VMV SIG) open. — CANP SIG (or VMV SIG)) shorted to PWR GND or SIG RTN. — Damaged CANP solenoid or Vapor Management Valve (VMV). — Damaged PCM. • Key off. • Disconnect CANP solenoid (or VMV). • Key on, engine off. • Measure the voltage between VPWR at the CANP solenoid (or VMV) vehicle harness connector and battery ground. • Is the voltage greater than 10.5 volts?	Yes No	▶ ▶	GO to **HW2**. SERVICE open in VPWR harness. RECONNECT all components. COMPLETE PCM Reset to clear DTCs RERUN Quick Test.
HW2	CHECK CANP SOLENOID (OR VMV) RESISTANCE			
	• Key off. • CANP solenoid (or VMV) disconnected. • Measure the resistance between CANP SIG (or VMV SIG) and VPWR on the CANP solenoid (or VMV). • Is resistance between 30 and 90 ohms (or VMV resistance between 30 and 36 ohms)?	Yes No	▶ ▶	For Rangers: GO to **HW2M**. All Others: GO to **HW3**. REPLACE damaged CANP solenoid (or VMV). DRIVE vehicle to check for a driveability symptom. If driveability symptom is still present, RETURN to Symptom Flow Charts. COMPLETE PCM Reset to clear DTCs RERUN Quick Test.

Fig. 197   Test HW: EVAP Purge Flow System (Part 6 of 25). 1995

TEST STEP	RESULT	▶	ACTION TO TAKE
HW3 CHECK CANP SIG OR VMV SIG FOR OPEN IN HARNESS • Key off. • CANP solenoid (or VMV) disconnected. • Disconnect PCM. Inspect for damaged or pushed out pins, corrosion, loose wires, etc. Service as necessary. • Install breakout box, leave PCM disconnected. • Measure the resistance between Test Pin 67 (CANP SIG) or Test Pin 56 (VMV SIG) at the breakout box and CANP SIG (or VMV) circuit at the CANP solenoid (or VMV) vehicle harness connector. • Is the resistance less than 5.0 ohms?	Yes No	▶ ▶	GO to **HW4**. SERVICE open in CANP SIG (or VMV SIG) harness. REMOVE breakout box. RECONNECT all components. COMPLETE PCM Reset to clear DTCs (REFER to Powertrain Control Module (PCM) Reset). RERUN Quick Test.
HW4 CHECK CANP SIG (OR VMV SIG) CIRCUIT FOR SHORT TO PWR GND • Key off. • CANP solenoid (or VMV) disconnected. • Breakout box installed, PCM disconnected. • Disconnect Scan Tool from Data Link Connector (DLC). • Measure the resistance between Test Pin 67 (CANP SIG) or Test Pin 56 (VMV SIG) and Test Pins 24 and 103 (PWR GND) at the breakout box. • Is each resistance greater than 10,000 ohms?	Yes No	▶ ▶	CANP SIG (or VMV SIG) is shorted to PWR GND in the PCM. REPLACE damaged PCM. REMOVE breakout box. RECONNECT all components. COMPLETE PCM Reset to clear DTCs (REFER to Powertrain Control Module (PCM) Reset). RERUN Quick Test. SERVICE harness short between CANP SIG (or VMV SIG) and PWR GND. REMOVE breakout box. RECONNECT all components. COMPLETE PCM Reset to clear DTCs (REFER to Powertrain Control Module (PCM) Reset). RERUN Quick Test.

Fig. 197   Test HW: EVAP Purge Flow System (Part 7 of 25). 1995

TEST STEP	RESULT	▶	ACTION TO TAKE
HW8 CHECK FUEL TANK-GAS CAP-ROLLOVER VALVE • Check for holes, cracks and leaks in fuel vapor hose between fuel tank and carbon canister(s). • Check for fuel tank damage. • Check for damaged rollover valve. • Is a fault indicated?	Yes No	▶ ▶	SERVICE as necessary. REMOVE pressure pump (gauge). RECONNECT carbon canister(s). COMPLETE PCM Reset to clear DTCs (REFER to Powertrain Control Module (PCM) Reset). RERUN Quick Test. DRIVE vehicle. If a fuel or sulphur odor is still present, RETURN to Symptom Flow Charts. REMOVE pressure pump (gauge). GO to **HW9**.
HW9 CHECK VACUUM HOSE LEAK BETWEEN CANP SOLENOID (OR VMV) AND CARBON CANISTER • Key off. • Disconnect fuel vapor hose between the carbon canister and the CANP solenoid (or VMV) at both ends. • Plug one end of the hose and install a vacuum pump at the remaining end. • Apply 16 in-Hg (53 kPa) of vacuum to the fuel vapor hose. • Observe the vacuum reading for at least 15 seconds. • Release vacuum applied by the pump. • Did the fuel vapor hose hold the vacuum applied?	Yes No	▶ ▶	REMOVE the vacuum pump. RECONNECT the fuel vapor hose. CHECK fuel vapor hose for blockage or kinks. SERVICE as necessary. If OK, GO to **HW15**. REMOVE the vacuum pump. REPLACE the damaged fuel vapor hose (visible cracks, splits or holes). RECONNECT all components. COMPLETE PCM Reset to clear DTCs (REFER to Powertrain Control Module (PCM) Reset). RERUN Quick Test.

Fig. 197   Test HW: EVAP Purge Flow System (Part 11 of 25). 1995

TEST STEP	RESULT	▶	ACTION TO TAKE
HW5 CONTINUOUS DTC P1443: MONITOR IDLE AIR CONTROL DUTY CYCLE (IAC AT IDLE) - VMV PURGE SYSTEMS Continuous Diagnostic Trouble Code (DTC) P1443 can be initiated by an IAC valve speed error sometime during vehicle operation. If a Continuous DTC P1507 is received with the DTC P1443 in Self-Test, GO directly to Pinpoint Test Step **KE30**. NOTE: The following overspeed check is to be done on 3.0L Windstar, Crown Victoria/Grand Marquis, Continental and Town Car. • Key on, engine off. • Access IAC, TP, and RPM PIDs with a Scan Tool. • With engine at normal operating temperature, accessories off and at idle, the IAC duty cycle should be between 20% to 45%. • Observe the IAC and RPM PIDs for an indication of a fault while performing the following: — While at idle, wiggle the IAC connector and vehicle harness between the IAC and PCM. A fault is indicated by a sudden increase in rpm and decrease in duty cycle. — Goose the engine several times while looking for slow return to idle (observing the TP PID). This may indicate a sticking IAC valve. • Is a fault indicated?	Yes No	▶ ▶	ISOLATE fault and SERVICE as necessary. RECONNECT all components. COMPLETE PCM Reset to clear DTCs (REFER to Powertrain Control Module (PCM) Reset). RERUN Quick Test. If driveability symptom is still present, RETURN to Symptom Flow Charts. GO to **HW6**.

Fig. 197   Test HW: EVAP Purge Flow System (Part 8 of 25). 1995

TEST STEP	RESULT	▶	ACTION TO TAKE
HW6 CONTINUOUS DTC P1443: CHECK CARBON CANISTER Continuous Diagnostic Trouble Code (DTC) P1443 indicates an Evaporative Emission System Purge Control Valve malfunction. Possible causes: — Damaged carbon canister. — Plugged vapor line between canister and CANP solenoid (or VMV). — Plugged or disconnected vapor line between CANP solenoid and Purge Flow Sensor (PFS). — Plugged or disconnected vapor line between VMV and intake manifold. — Plugged or disconnected vapor line between PFS and intake manifold. — Damaged VMV. — Damaged CANP solenoid. — Damaged PFS. — CANP SIG, VMV SIG, or PFS SIG circuit shorted to VPWR. — Damaged PCM. NOTE: Fuel saturation of carbon canister cannot be effectively checked by the canister weight or intensity of odor (smell). Vehicle must run over an extended period of time to purge fuel (or vapor) build-up in carbon canister. • Check for cracks or other damage to the carbon canister(s). • Is the canister(s) cracked or damaged?	Yes No	▶ ▶	REPLACE the carbon canister(s). RECONNECT all components. COMPLETE PCM Reset to clear DTCs RERUN Quick Test. Carbon canister(s) is not contaminated. GO to **HW7**.

Fig. 197   Test HW: EVAP Purge Flow System (Part 9 of 25). 1995

TEST STEP	RESULT	▶	ACTION TO TAKE
HW7 CHECK VACUUM: FUEL TANK TO CARBON CANISTER (SINGLE OR DUAL CANISTER SYSTEM) • Remove the fuel vapor hoses from the fuel tank at all carbon canisters. (Vehicle may have multiple canisters.) • Plug the fuel vapor hose at one carbon canister for dual canister systems. • Install a hand held pressure pump with gauge to the open end of the remaining fuel vapor hose. • Apply 1.0 in-Hg (0.5 psi) maximum pressure to the fuel vapor hose with the pressure pump. • Monitor the pressure gauge on the pump. • Is the fuel tank to carbon canister(s) system holding a constant pressure?	Yes No	▶ ▶	CHECK for possible blockage in fuel vapor hose between fuel tank and carbon canister(s). If blockage is found, SERVICE as necessary. REMOVE pressure pump (gauge). RECONNECT carbon canister. COMPLETE PCM Reset to clear DTCs RERUN Quick Test. DRIVE vehicle. If a fuel or sulphur odor is still present, RETURN to , Symptom Flow Charts. If blockage is not present, REMOVE pressure pump (gauge). RECONNECT carbon canister(s). GO to **HW9**. GO to **HW8**.

Fig. 197   Test HW: EVAP Purge Flow System (Part 10 of 25). 1995

TEST STEP	RESULT	▶	ACTION TO TAKE
HW10 CHECK CANP SOLENOID FOR VACUUM LEAKS - CLOSED VACUUM POSITION • Key off. • Disconnect the vacuum hose at both ends of the CANP solenoid. • Install a hand held vacuum pump to the intake manifold vacuum side of the CANP solenoid. • Disconnect the CANP solenoid electrically. • Apply 16 in-Hg (53 kPa) of vacuum to the CANP solenoid. • **Does the CANP solenoid hold vacuum for 20 seconds?**	Yes No	▶ ▶	LEAVE the vacuum pump connected. GO to **HW11**. REMOVE vacuum pump. REPLACE CANP solenoid. RECONNECT all components. COMPLETE PCM Reset to clear DTCs (REFER to Powertrain Control Module (PCM) Reset). RERUN Quick Test.
HW11 CHECK CANP SOLENOID MECHANICAL OPERATION - OPEN VACUUM POSITION • Key off. • Reconnect CANP solenoid electrically. • Vacuum hose at both ends of the CANP solenoid disconnected. • Connect Scan Tool. • Apply 16 in-Hg (53 kPa) of vacuum to the CANP solenoid on the intake manifold side with a vacuum pump. • Access Output Test Mode on Scan Tool • Key on, engine off. • **Does the CANP solenoid open and vacuum reading on the pump drop (air passes freely) when commanding the output on?**	Yes No	▶ ▶	CHECK fuel vapor hose between carbon canister and CANP solenoid for blockage or kinks. SERVICE as necessary. If no fault is indicated, REMOVE vacuum pump. GO to **HW12**. REPLACE CANP solenoid. COMPLETE PCM Reset to clear DTCs (REFER to Powertrain Control Module (PCM) Reset). RERUN Quick Test.

Fig. 197 Test HW: EVAP Purge Flow System (Part 12 of 25). 1995

TEST STEP	RESULT	▶	ACTION TO TAKE
HW14 CHECK FOR INTAKE MANIFOLD VACUUM AT PFS • Key off. • CANP solenoid and PFS connected electrically. • Intake manifold vacuum side of PFS disconnected. • Start engine. • Place thumb on open end of vacuum hose at PFS. • **Is vacuum present at the vacuum hose opening?**	Yes No	▶ ▶	CHECK for small vacuum leak between PFS and the engine intake manifold. SERVICE as necessary. RECONNECT all vacuum hoses. GO to **HW19**. CHECK for large vacuum leak or open in vacuum line between PFS and engine intake manifold. If OK, COMPLETE PCM Reset to clear DTCs RERUN Quick Test. If a fuel or sulphur odor is still present. RETURN to Symptom Flow Charts.

Fig. 197 Test HW: EVAP Purge Flow System (Part 14 of 25). 1995

TEST STEP	RESULT	▶	ACTION TO TAKE
HW17 CHECK FOR VACUUM AT VMV VACUUM INPUT PORT HOSE TO INTAKE MANIFOLD • Key off. • VMV solenoid connected. • VMV input port vacuum hose disconnected at the VMV. • Start engine. • Place thumb on open end of vacuum hose. • **Is vacuum present at the input port hose?**	Yes No	▶ ▶	RECONNECT VMV input port vacuum hose. GO to **HW18**. RECONNECT VMV assembly. CHECK VMV input port vacuum routing, kinks, leaks, or blockage. SERVICE as necessary. For no manifold vacuum on engine restart, GO to Engine Group Service Manual for engine vacuum loss. If OK, COMPLETE PCM Reset to clear DTCs (REFER to Powertrain Control Module (PCM) Reset). RERUN Quick Test. If fuel or sulphur odor is still present, RETURN to Symptom Flow Charts.

Fig. 197 Test HW: EVAP Purge Flow System (Part 16 of 25). 1995

TEST STEP	RESULT	▶	ACTION TO TAKE
HW12 CHECK FOR INTAKE MANIFOLD VACUUM AT THE CANP SOLENOID • Key off. • CANP solenoid and PFS connected electrically. • Intake manifold vacuum side of CANP solenoid disconnected. • Start engine. • Place thumb on open end of vacuum hose at CANP solenoid. • **Is vacuum present at the vacuum hose opening?**	Yes No	▶ ▶	LEAVE intake manifold vacuum hose to CANP solenoid disconnected. GO to **HW13**. RECONNECT intake manifold vacuum hose to CANP solenoid. CHECK vacuum hoses between CANP solenoid, PFS and intake manifold for proper routing, leaks, cracks, blockage and kinks. CHECK for PFS cracked housing. REPLACE vacuum hoses or damaged PFS as necessary. COMPLETE PCM Reset to clear DTCs (REFER to Powertrain Control Module (PCM) Reset). RERUN Quick Test.
HW13 CHECK PFS SEAL LEAK DOWN • Key off. • Purge Flow Sensor (PFS) connected electrically. • Plug open end of intake manifold vacuum hose to CANP solenoid or PFS vacuum port to CANP solenoid. • Disconnect vacuum hose at the intake manifold port on the PFS. • Install hand held vacuum pump at the intake manifold port on the PFS. • Apply 4.1 in-Hg (13.6 kPa) vacuum to the PFS. • **Does the PFS bleed off all the vacuum in less than 2.5 seconds?**	Yes No	▶ ▶	Excessive leak on PFS seal is detected. REPLACE PFS. REMOVE vacuum pump. RECONNECT all vacuum hoses. COMPLETE PCM Reset to clear DTCs (REFER to Powertrain Control Module (PCM) Reset). RERUN Quick Test. REMOVE vacuum pump. RECONNECT vacuum hose to CANP solenoid. LEAVE vacuum hose to intake manifold port on PFS disconnected. GO to **HW14**.

Fig. 197 Test HW: EVAP Purge Flow System (Part 13 of 25). 1995

TEST STEP	RESULT	▶	ACTION TO TAKE
HW15 CHECK VMV ELECTRO-MECHANICAL OPERATION • Key off. • Scan Tool installed. • VMV connected electrically. • Disconnect the fuel vapor port to intake manifold at the VMV. • Install the vacuum pump to the VMV (fuel vapor port to intake manifold side). • Apply 16 in-Hg (53 kPa) of vacuum to the VMV solenoid with the vacuum pump. • Key on, engine off. • Turn the outputs on and off with the Scan Tool trigger button. • Observe the vacuum reading. • Release vacuum applied by the pump. • Key off. • **Did the vacuum reading on the pump drop (air passes freely)?** FUEL VAPOR TO INTAKE MANIFOLD FUEL VAPOR TO CARBON CANISTER INPUT PORT VACUUM (TO INTAKE MANIFOLD)	Yes No	▶ ▶	EXIT Output Test Mode. REMOVE the vacuum pump. GO to **HW16**. EXIT Test Mode. REPLACE the VMV assembly. REMOVE the vacuum pump. RECONNECT all components. COMPLETE PCM Reset to clear DTCs (REFER to Powertrain Control Module (PCM) Reset). RERUN Quick Test.
HW16 CHECK VMV HOUSING FOR LEAKS • Key on, engine off. • VMV solenoid connected. • Disconnect input port hose of VMV solenoid. • Apply 16 in-Hg (53 kPa) of vacuum to VMV (vacuum input port to intake manifold) with a vacuum pump. • Observe the vacuum reading. • Key off. • **Did all vacuum applied to VMV bleed off immediately?**	Yes No	▶ ▶	GO to **HW17**. EXIT Test Mode. REPLACE VMV assembly. REMOVE vacuum pump. RECONNECT all components. COMPLETE PCM Reset to clear DTCs (REFER to Powertrain Control Module (PCM) Reset). RERUN Quick Test.

Fig. 197 Test HW: EVAP Purge Flow System (Part 15 of 25). 1995

TEST STEP	RESULT	▶	ACTION TO TAKE
HW18 CHECK VACUUM: FUEL VAPOR HOSE FROM VMV TO INTAKE MANIFOLD • Key off. • VMV solenoid connected. • Disconnect VMV fuel vapor hose that runs from the VMV to the intake manifold vacuum tree. • Start engine. • Place thumb at one end of fuel vapor hose. • Is vacuum present at the fuel vapor hose?	Yes No	▶ ▶	RECONNECT fuel vapor hose. GO to **HW19**. RECONNECT VMV assembly. CHECK fuel vapor hose routing, kinks, leaks or blockage. SERVICE as necessary. For no manifold vacuum on engine restart RERUN Quick Test. If fuel or sulphur odor is still present, RETURN to Symptom Flow Charts.
HW19 CHECK CANP SOLENOID (OR VMV) RESISTANCE • Key off. • CANP solenoid (or VMV) disconnected. • Measure the resistance between CANP SIG (or VMV SIG) and VPWR on the CANP solenoid (or VMV). • Is the resistance between 30 and 90 ohms (or VMV resistance between 30 and 36 ohms)?	Yes No	▶ ▶	CANP solenoid (or VMV) is OK electrically. GO to **HW20**. REPLACE damaged CANP solenoid (or VMV). DRIVE vehicle to check for a driveability symptom. If driveability symptom is still present, RETURN to Symptom Flow Charts. COMPLETE PCM Module (PCM) Reset). RERUN Quick Test.

Fig. 197   Test HW: EVAP Purge Flow System (Part 17 of 25). 1995

TEST STEP	RESULT	▶	ACTION TO TAKE
HW20 CHECK CANP SIG (OR VMV SIG) FOR SHORT TO VPWR • Key off. • Disconnect CANP solenoid (or VMV). • Disconnect PCM. Inspect for damaged or pushed out pins, corrosion, loose wires, etc. Service as necessary. • Install breakout box, leave PCM disconnected. • Disconnect Scan Tool from the Data Link Connector (DLC). • Measure the resistance between Test Pin 67 (CANP SIG) or Test Pin 56 (VMV SIG) and Test Pins 71 and 97 (VPWR) at the breakout box. • Is each resistance greater than 10,000 ohms?	Yes No	▶ ▶	CANP SIG (or VMV SIG) is shorted to VPWR in the PCM. REPLACE damaged PCM. REMOVE breakout box and Scan Tool. RECONNECT all components. RERUN Quick Test. SERVICE harness short between CANP SIG (or VMV SIG) and VPWR. REMOVE breakout box and Scan Tool. RECONNECT all components. COMPLETE PCM Module (PCM) Reset). RERUN Quick Test.
HW21 CONTINUOUS DTC P1444: VERIFY PFS SIG VOLTAGE Continuous Diagnostic Trouble Code (DTC) P1444 indicates that Self-Test has detected a PFS SIG circuit input below the minimum. Possible causes: — PFS SIG shorted to PWR GND. — VPWR open circuit. — Damaged Purge Flow Sensor (PFS). — Damaged PCM. • Key on, engine off. • Access PF PID with a Scan Tool. NOTE: PFS Input to the PCM is 0.14 to 4.89 volts. • Is PF SIG PID voltage less than 0.14 volts?	Yes No	▶ ▶	The PFS SIG voltage is less than the acceptable minimum. GO to **HW22**. Fault may have been an intermittent DTC P1444. GO to **HW24**.

Fig. 197   Test HW: EVAP Purge Flow System (Part 18 of 25). 1995

TEST STEP	RESULT	▶	ACTION TO TAKE
HW22 MEASURE PURGE FLOW SENSOR (PFS) RESISTANCE (POWER GROUND CIRCUIT) • Key off. • Disconnect PFS vehicle harness connector. • Measure the resistance between PFS SIG (Pin 2) and PWR GND (Pin 3) on the Purge Flow Sensor (PFS). VPWR (PIN 1) PFS SIG (PIN 2) PWR GND (PIN 3) • Is the resistance less than 25.60 ohms?	Yes No	▶ ▶	PFS SIG shorted to PWR GND in PFS. REPLACE damaged PFS. RECONNECT all components. COMPLETE PCM Reset to clear DTCs RERUN Quick Test. GO to **HW31**.
HW23 CHECK PFS SIG CIRCUIT FOR SHORTS TO PWR GND • Key off. • PFS disconnected. • Disconnect PCM. Inspect for damaged or pushed out pins, corrosion, loose wires, etc. Service as necessary. • Install breakout box, leave PCM disconnected. • Disconnect Scan Tool from Data Link Connector (DLC). • Measure the resistance between Test Pin 11 (PFS SIG) and Test Pins 24 and 103 (PWR GND) at the breakout box. • Is each resistance greater than 10,000 ohms?	Yes No	▶ ▶	VPWR is open in the PCM or PFS SIG is shorted to PWR GND in the PCM. REPLACE damaged PCM. REMOVE breakout box. RECONNECT all components. RERUN Quick Test. SERVICE harness short between PFS SIG and PWR GND. REMOVE breakout box. RECONNECT all components. COMPLETE PCM Reset to clear DTCs RERUN Quick Test.

Fig. 197   Test HW: EVAP Purge Flow System (Part 19 of 25). 1995

TEST STEP	RESULT	▶	ACTION TO TAKE
HW24 WIGGLE TEST PURGE FLOW SENSOR AND HARNESS • Key on, engine off. • Access PF PID with a Scan Tool. • Observe PF PID for an indication of a fault while performing the following: — Lightly tap on PFS; wiggle the PFS connector and vehicle harness between the sensor and the PCM. A fault is indicated by a sudden change in PF PID voltage (less than 0.14 volts). • Is a fault indicated?	Yes No	▶ ▶	ISOLATE fault and SERVICE as necessary. RECONNECT all components. COMPLETE PCM Reset to clear DTCs RERUN Quick Test. Unable to duplicate and / or identify fault at this time. GO to Pinpoint Test Step **Z1** with the following data: PF PID and a list of possible causes.
HW25 CONTINUOUS DTC P1445: VERIFY PFS SIG VOLTAGE Continuous Diagnostic Trouble Code (DTC) P1445 indicates that Self-Test has detected a PFS SIG circuit input above the maximum. Possible causes: — PFS SIG shorted to VPWR. — PFS SIG open circuit. — Damaged Purge Flow Sensor (PFS). — Damaged PCM. • Key on, engine off. • Access PF PID with a Scan Tool. NOTE: PFS input to the PCM is 0.14 to 4.89 volts. • Is PF PID voltage greater than 4.89 volts?	Yes No	▶ ▶	The PFS SIG voltage is greater than the acceptable maximum. GO to **HW26**. Fault may have been an intermittent DTC P1445. GO to **HW33**.
HW26 MEASURE PFS RESISTANCE • Key off. • Disconnect PFS vehicle harness connector. • Measure the resistance between PFS SIG (Pin 2) and VPWR (Pin 1) on the Purge Flow Sensor (PFS) at room temperature (55 to 80°F). (Refer to schematic in Pinpoint Test Step **HW22**.) • Is the resistance between 25.65 and 28.35 ohms?	Yes No	▶ ▶	GO to **HW27**. REPLACE damaged PFS. RECONNECT all components. COMPLETE PCM Reset to clear DTCs RERUN Quick Test.

Fig. 197   Test HW: EVAP Purge Flow System (Part 20 of 25). 1995

TEST STEP	RESULT	▶	ACTION TO TAKE
HW27 CHECK PFS SHORT TO VPWR • Key off. • PFS disconnected. • Key on, engine off. • Measure the voltage between PFS SIG circuit at the PFS vehicle harness connector and battery ground. • Is the voltage greater than 10.5 volts?	Yes No	▶ ▶	The PFS SIG input is indicating a short to VPWR. GO TO HW28. GO to HW29
HW28 CHECK PFS SIG CIRCUIT FOR SHORT TO VPWR • Key off. • PFS disconnected. • Disconnect PCM. Inspect for damaged or pushed out pins, corrosion, loose wires, etc. Service as necessary. • Install breakout box, leave PCM disconnected. • Key on, engine off. • Measure the resistance between Test Pin 11 (PFS SIG) and Test Pins 24 and 103 (PWR GND) at the breakout box. • Is the voltage greater than 10.5 volts?	Yes No	▶ ▶	SERVICE harness short between PFS SIG and VPWR. REMOVE breakout box. RECONNECT all components. COMPLETE PCM Reset to clear DTCs RERUN Quick Test. REPLACE damaged PCM. REMOVE breakout box. RECONNECT all components. RERUN Quick Test.
HW29 CHECK PFS SIG FOR OPEN IN HARNESS • Key off. • PFS disconnected. • Disconnect PCM. Inspect for damaged or pushed out pins, corrosion, loose wires, etc. Service as necessary. • Install breakout box, leave PCM disconnected. • Measure the resistance between Test Pin 11 (PFS SIG) at the breakout box and PFS SIG circuit at the PFS vehicle harness connector. • Is the resistance less than 5.0 ohms?	Yes No	▶ ▶	GO to HW30 SERVICE open in PFS SIG harness. REMOVE breakout box. RECONNECT all components. COMPLETE PCM Reset to clear DTCs RERUN Quick Test.

Fig. 197   Test HW: EVAP Purge Flow System (Part 21 of 25). 1995

TEST STEP	RESULT	▶	ACTION TO TAKE
HW30 CHECK PWR GND FOR OPEN IN HARNESS • Key off. • PFS disconnected. • PCM disconnected. • Measure the resistance between Test Pins 24 and 103 (PWR GND) at the breakout box and PWR GND circuit at the PFS vehicle harness connector. • Is the resistance less than 5.0 ohms?	Yes No	▶ ▶	REPLACE damaged PCM. REMOVE breakout box. RECONNECT all components. RERUN Quick Test. SERVICE open in PWR GND harness. REMOVE breakout box. RECONNECT all components. COMPLETE PCM Reset to clear DTCs RERUN Quick Test.
HW31 MEASURE PFS RESISTANCE (VPWR CIRCUIT) • Key off. • PFS disconnected. • Measure the resistance between PFS SIG (Pin 2) and VPWR (Pin 1) on the Purge Flow Sensor (PFS). • Measure the resistance between PWR GND (Pin 3) and VPWR (Pin 1) on the PFS. • Is the resistance greater than 100 ohms between Pin 1 and Pin 2 and greater than 130 ohms between Pin 1 and Pin 3?	Yes No	▶ ▶	VPWR is open in the PFS. REPLACE damaged PFS. RECONNECT all components. COMPLETE PCM Reset to clear DTCs RERUN Quick Test. GO to HW32.
HW32 CHECK VPWR FOR OPEN IN HARNESS • Key off. • PFS disconnected. • PCM disconnected. • Measure the resistance between Test Pins 71 and 97 at the breakout box and VPWR circuit at the PFS vehicle harness connector. • Is the resistance less than 5.0 ohms?	Yes No	▶ ▶	GO to HW23 SERVICE open in VPWR harness. REMOVE breakout box. RECONNECT all components. COMPLETE PCM Reset to clear DTCs RERUN Quick Test.

Fig. 197   Test HW: EVAP Purge Flow System (Part 22 of 25). 1995

TEST STEP	RESULT	▶	ACTION TO TAKE
HW33 WIGGLE TEST PURGE FLOW SENSOR AND HARNESS • Key on, engine off. • Access PF PID with a Scan Tool. • Observe PF PID for an indication of a fault while performing the following: — Lightly tap on PFS; wiggle the PFS connector and vehicle harness between the sensor and the PCM. A fault is indicated by a sudden change in PF PID voltage (greater than 4.89 volts). • Is a fault indicated?	Yes No	▶ ▶	ISOLATE fault and SERVICE as necessary. RECONNECT all components. COMPLETE PCM Reset to clear DTCs RERUN Quick Test. UNABLE to duplicate and/or identify fault at this time. GO to Pinpoint Test Step Z1 with the following data: PF PID and a list of Possible Causes.
HW34 CONTINUOUS DTC P0443: INSPECT CANP (OR VMV) CIRCUIT FOR INTERMITTENT FAILURE Continuous Diagnostic Trouble Code (DTC) P0443 may indicate a CANP solenoid (or VMV) circuit failure. Possible causes: — Damaged CANP solenoid. — Damaged VMV. — CANP SIG, VMV SIG or VPWR harness circuit open. • Rerun KOEO, KOER and Continuous Memory Self-Tests. • Is DTC P0443 present in Continuous Memory Self-Test only?	Yes No	▶ ▶	GO to HW35. GO to HW1.

Fig. 197   Test HW: EVAP Purge Flow System (Part 23 of 25). 1995

TEST STEP	RESULT	▶	ACTION TO TAKE
HW35 WIGGLE TEST SOLENOID AND HARNESS • Key off. • Disconnect PCM. Inspect for damaged or pushed out pins, corrosion, loose wires, etc. Service as necessary. • Install breakout box, leave PCM disconnected. • Measure the resistance between Test Pin 67 (CANP SIG) or Test Pin 56 (VMV SIG) and Test Pins 71 and 97 (VPWR), while performing the following: — Lightly tap on the CANP solenoid or VMV, and observe a resistance change. — Wiggle the CANP solenoid or VMV connector and vehicle harness between the solenoid (or valve) and the PCM, observe a resistance change. • Does the resistance reading change to below 30 ohms or above 90 ohms (36 ohms for VMV)?	Yes No	▶ ▶	ISOLATE fault and SERVICE as necessary. RECONNECT all components. COMPLETE PCM Reset to clear DTCs RERUN Quick Test. UNABLE to duplicate and/or identify fault at this time. GO to Pinpoint Test Step Z1 with the resistance readings and list of Possible Causes.
HW36 CHECK CANP SOLENOID SHORT TO CASE GROUND • Key off. • CANP solenoid disconnected. • Measure the resistance between the CANP SIG pin on the solenoid and the CANP solenoid casing. • Measure resistance between the VPWR pin on the solenoid and the CANP solenoid casing. • Are both resistance readings greater than 90 ohms?	Yes No	▶ ▶	CANP solenoid is OK. GO to HW35 REPLACE damaged CANP solenoid. DRIVE vehicle to check for a driveability symptom. If a driveability symptom is still present, RETURN to Symptom Flow Charts. COMPLETE PCM Reset to clear DTCs RERUN Quick Test.

Fig. 197   Test HW: EVAP Purge Flow System (Part 24 of 25). 1995

TEST STEP	RESULT	▶	ACTION TO TAKE
HW37 CONTINUOUS DTC P1443: CHECK THE VOLTAGE ON THE PURGE FLOW SENSOR WITH THE ENGINE RUNNING Continuous Diagnostic Trouble Code (DTC) P1443 indicates an Evaporative Emission Control System Purge Flow Sensor malfunction. Possible causes: — Damaged CANP solenoid. — Damaged PFS. • Key on, engine running. • Access PF PID with Scan Tool. • Does the PF PID voltage fluctuate around 2.50 volts or 1.00 volt in one minute?	Yes No	▶ ▶	For PF PID voltage from 2.30 to 2.60 volts: GO to HW11. For PF PID voltage from 0.90 to 1.10 volts: GO to HW10. GO to HW6.

Fig. 197   Test HW: EVAP Purge Flow System (Part 25 of 25). 1995

Note

You should enter this pinpoint test only when you have been directed here.

Remember

This Pinpoint Test is intended to diagnose only the following:

- Crankshaft Position Sensor (CKP)
- CKP Harness
- CKP Connector
- Ignition Control Module (ICM)
- Power ground circuit to ICM
- Vehicle Power circuit to ICM
- Spark plug wires

FM0159401197010X

Fig. 198 Test JA: Ignition No Spark (Part 1 of 17). 1994-95

3.8L Mustang

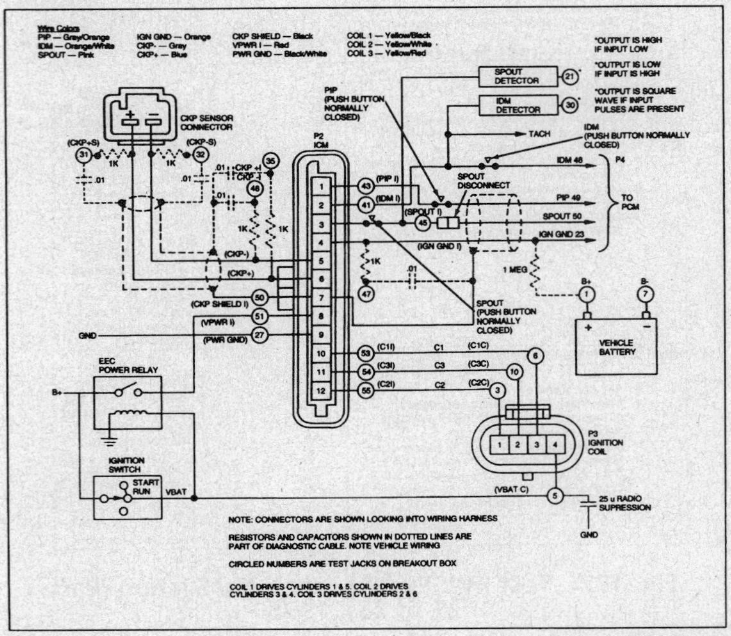

FM0159401197020X

Fig. 198 Test JA: Ignition No Spark (Part 2 of 17). 1994-95

4.6L Thunderbird/Cougar

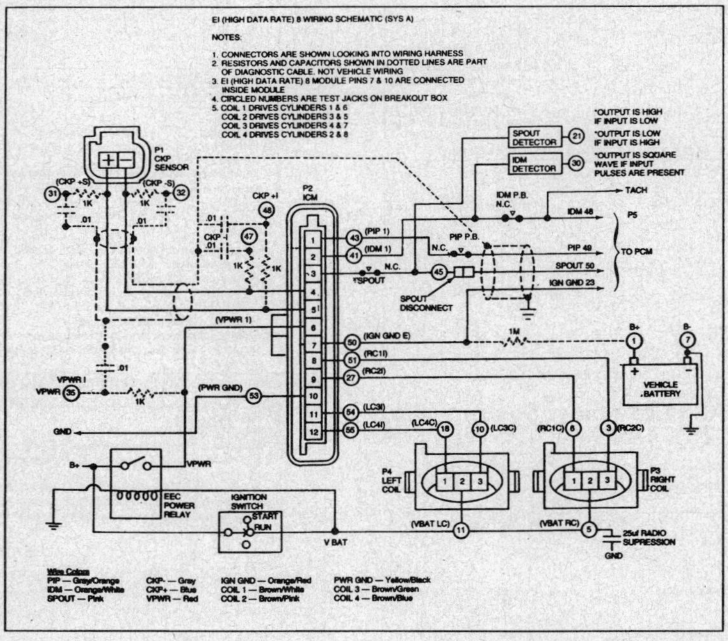

FM0159401197030X

Fig. 198 Test JA: Ignition No Spark (Part 3 of 17). 1994-95

TEST STEP	RESULT	▶	ACTION TO TAKE
JA1 CHECK PLUGS AND WIRES—KEY OFF			
NOTE: 3.8L MUSTANG JA1 THROUGH JA22. 4.6L THUNDERBIRD/COUGAR JA30 THROUGH JA51. • Check spark plug wires for insulation damage, looseness, shorting or other damage. • Remove and check spark plugs for damage, wear, carbon deposits and proper plug gap. • Examine all wiring harnesses and connectors for damaged, burned or overheated insulation, damaged pins and loose or broken conditions. • **Check sensor shield connector.** • **Are spark plugs and wires OK?**	Yes No	▶ ▶	REINSTALL plugs and wires. GO to JA2. SERVICE or REPLACE damaged component. REMOVE all test equipment. RECONNECT all components. CLEAR Continuous Memory. RERUN Quick Test.
JA2 CHECK FOR VEHICLE START WITH DIAGNOSTIC HARNESS INSTALLED			
WARNING: NEVER CONNECT THE PCM TO THE EEC BREAKOUT BOX WHEN PERFORMING EI DIAGNOSTICS. • Key off. • Install EI diagnostic harness to breakout box and ICM (Rotunda 007-00059). **Do not connect CKP sensor tee or coil tee.** • Use EI (High Data Rate) 6 overlay. • Connect EI diagnostic harness negative lead to battery, leave positive lead disconnected. • Set EI diagnostic harness box type switch to "4/6" cylinder position. • **Will vehicle start and run?**	Yes No	▶ ▶	GO to JA22. GO to JA3.
JA3 CHECK PWR GND TO ICM—KEY OFF			
• Key off. • DVOM on 200 ohm scale. • When making measurements on a wiring harness, both a visual inspection and continuity test must be performed. • Measure resistance between J27 (PWR GND) and J7 (B-) at breakout box. • **Is resistance less than 5.0 ohms?**	Yes No	▶ ▶	GO to JA4. CHECK connectors, SERVICE or REPLACE harness. PWR GND to ICM is open. REMOVE all test equipment. RECONNECT all components. CLEAR Continuous Memory. RERUN Quick Test.

FM0159401197040X

Fig. 198   Test JA: Ignition No Spark (Part 4 of 17). 1994-95

TEST STEP	RESULT	▶	ACTION TO TAKE
JA4 CHECK FOR VPWR TO ICM—KEY OFF			
• Key off. • DVOM on 40 volt DC scale. • Key on, engine off. • When making voltage checks and a reference to ground is made, use either the negative battery lead or cast iron on the engine. B+ means the positive battery cable at the battery. • When making voltage checks, a ground reading means any value within a range of zero to 1 volt. Also VPWR readings mean any value that falls within a range of B+ to 2 volts less than B+. • Measure voltage between (+)J51 (VPWR I) and (-)J7 (B-) at breakout box. • **Is DC voltage greater than 10.5 volts?**	Yes No	▶ ▶	GO to JA5. CHECK connectors, SERVICE or REPLACE harness. VPWR to ICM is open. REMOVE all test equipment. RECONNECT all components. CLEAR Continuous Memory. RERUN Quick Test.
JA5 CHECK CKP+ BIAS AT ICM—KOEO			
• Key off. • DVOM on 40 volt DC scale. • Key on, engine off. • Do not use an incandescent lamp to check CRP+ or CKP-. The lamp will prevent the circuit from operating. • Measure voltage between (+)J35 (CKP+ I) and (-)J7 (B-) at breakout box. • **Is DC voltage between 1.0 and 2.0 volts?**	Yes No	▶ ▶	GO to JA11. Bias fault. GO to JA6.
JA6 CHECK CKP+ —BIAS FAULT—CKP SENSOR DISCONNECTED—KOEO			
• Key off. • Disconnect CKP sensor from vehicle harness connector. • DVOM on 40 volt DC scale. • Key on, engine off. • Measure voltage between (+)J35 (CKP+ I) and (-)J7 (B-) at breakout box. • **Is DC voltage greater than 1.0 volt but less than 2.0 volts?**	Yes No	▶ ▶	GO to JA7. Bias fault. GO to JA19.
JA7 CHECK CKP- —BIAS FAULT—CKP SENSOR DISCONNECTED —KOEO			
• Key off. • DVOM on 40 volt DC scale. • Key on, engine off. • Measure voltage between (+)J48 (CKP- I) and (-)J7 (B-) at breakout box. • **Is DC voltage between 1.0 and 2.0 volts?**	Yes No	▶ ▶	REPLACE CKP sensor. Short to ground. REMOVE all test equipment. RECONNECT all components. CLEAR Continuous Memory. RERUN Quick Test. GO to JA8.

FM0159401197050X

Fig. 198   Test JA: Ignition No Spark (Part 5 of 17). 1994-95

TEST STEP	RESULT	▶	ACTION TO TAKE
JA8 CHECK FOR BIAS HIGH OR BIAS LOW FAULT—BIAS FAULT			
• Was bias voltage reading in JA7 less than 1.0 volt?	Yes No	▶ ▶	GO to JA9. Bias fault. GO to JA10. Bias fault.
JA9 CHECK CKP- CIRCUIT— FOR SHORT TO GROUND—BIAS LOW FAULT—CKP SENSOR AND ICM DISCONNECTED			
• Key off. • Disconnect ICM from ICM tee, leave EI diagnostic harness connected to vehicle harness connector. • DVOM on 20K ohm scale. • Measure resistance between J48 (CKP- I) and J7 (B-) at breakout box. • **Is resistance greater than 10K ohms?**	Yes No	▶ ▶	REPLACE ICM. CKP- shorted low. REMOVE all test equipment. RECONNECT all components. CLEAR Continuous Memory. RERUN Quick Test. CHECK connectors, SERVICE or REPLACE harness. CKP- is shorted low. REMOVE all test equipment. RECONNECT all components. CLEAR Continuous Memory. RERUN Quick Test.
JA10 CHECK CKP- —FOR SHORT HIGH—BIAS HIGH FAULT —CKP SENSOR AND ICM DISCONNECTED—KOEO			
• Key off. • Disconnect ICM from ICM tee. Leave EI diagnostic harness connected to vehicle harness connector. • DVOM on 40 volt DC scale. • Key on, engine off. • Measure voltage between (+)J48 (CKP- I) and (-)J7 (B-) at breakout box. • **Is DC voltage less than 0.5 volts?**	Yes No	▶ ▶	REPLACE ICM. CKP- shorted high. REMOVE all test equipment. RECONNECT all components. CLEAR Continuous Memory. RERUN Quick Test. CHECK connectors, SERVICE or REPLACE harness. CKP- is shorted high. REMOVE all test equipment. RECONNECT all components. CLEAR Continuous Memory. RERUN Quick Test.

FM0159401197060X

Fig. 198   Test JA: Ignition No Spark (Part 6 of 17). 1994-95

TEST STEP	RESULT	▶	ACTION TO TAKE
JA11 CHECK CKP AMPLITUDE AT ICM			
• Key off. • DVOM on 40 volt AC scale. • Crank engine and measure voltage between J35 (CKP+ I) and J48 (CKP- I) at breakout box. • **Is settled AC voltage reading greater than 0.4 volts?**	Yes No	▶ ▶	GO to Pinpoint Test Step JC1. Amplitude fault. GO to JA12.
JA12 CHECK CKP AMPLITUDE AT ICM—AMPLITUDE FAULT—ICM DISCONNECTED—KOEC			
• Key off. • Disconnect ICM from ICM tee, leave EI diagnostic harness connected to vehicle harness connector. • DVOM on 40 volt AC scale. • Crank engine and measure voltage between J35 (CKP+ I) and J48 (CKP- I) at breakout box. • **Is settled AC voltage reading greater than 0.4 volts?**	Yes No	▶ ▶	REPLACE ICM. CKP is shorted in ICM. REMOVE all test equipment. RECONNECT all components. CLEAR Continuous Memory. RERUN Quick Test. GO to JA13.
JA13 CHECK CKP CIRCUIT RESISTANCE—ICM DISCONNECTED—AMPLITUDE FAULT—KEY OFF			
• Key off. • DVOM on 20K ohm scale. • Measure resistance between J48 (CKP- I) and J35 (CKP+ I) at breakout box. • **Is resistance between 2580 and 2700 ohms?**	Yes No	▶ ▶	GO to JA17. Resistance fault. GO to JA14.
JA14 CHECK FOR RESISTANCE HIGH OR RESISTANCE LOW FAULT			
• Was the resistance from JA13 or JA22 less than 2580 ohms?	Yes No	▶ ▶	Resistance low fault. GO to JA18. Resistance high fault. GO to JA15.
JA15 CHECK CKP+ OPEN—RESISTANCE HIGH FAULT—KEY OFF			
• Key off. • Connect CKP sensor tee to CKP sensor and vehicle harness connector. • DVOM on 20K ohm scale • Measure resistance between J31 (CKP+ S) and J35 (CKP+ I) at breakout box. • **Is resistance less than 2050 ohms?**	Yes No	▶ ▶	GO to JA16. CHECK connectors, SERVICE or REPLACE harness. CKP + open. REMOVE all test equipment. RECONNECT all components. CLEAR Continuous Memory. RERUN Quick Test.

FM0159401197070X

Fig. 198   Test JA: Ignition No Spark (Part 7 of 17). 1994-95

TEST STEP		RESULT	▶	ACTION TO TAKE
JA16	CHECK CKP CIRCUIT FOR OPEN—RESISTANCE HIGH FAULT—KEY OFF			
	• Key off. • DVOM on 20K ohm scale. • Measure resistance between J32 (CKP- S) and J48 (CKP- I) at breakout box. • **Is resistance less than 2050 ohms?**	Yes	▶	REPLACE CKP sensor. High resistance. REMOVE all test equipment. RECONNECT all components. CLEAR Continuous Memory. RERUN Quick Test.
		No	▶	CHECK connectors. SERVICE or REPLACE harness. CKP- open. REMOVE all test equipment. RECONNECT all components. CLEAR Continuous Memory. RERUN Quick Test.
JA17	CHECK CKPS AIR GAP AND TRIGGER WHEEL			
	• Key off. • Check trigger wheel and CKP sensor for damage. • **Is CKP sensor and trigger data wheel OK?**	Yes	▶	REPLACE CKP sensor. No output from sensor. REMOVE all test equipment. RECONNECT all components. CLEAR Continuous Memory. RERUN Quick Test.
		No	▶	SERVICE or REPLACE bad parts. REMOVE all test equipment. RECONNECT all components. CLEAR Continuous Memory. RERUN Quick Test.

FM0159401197080X

Fig. 198   Test JA: Ignition No Spark (Part 8 of 17). 1994-95

TEST STEP		RESULT	▶	ACTION TO TAKE
JA18	CHECK FOR CKP+ SHORTED TO CKP-—RESISTANCE LOW FAULT—CKP SENSOR AND ICM DISCONNECTED—KEY OFF			
	• Key off. • Disconnect CKP sensor from vehicle harness connector. • DVOM on 20K ohm scale. • Measure resistance between J35 (CKP+ I) and J48 (CKP- I) at breakout box. • **Is resistance greater than 3K ohms?**	Yes	▶	REPLACE CKP sensor. Shorted sensor windings. REMOVE all test equipment. RECONNECT all components. CLEAR Continuous Memory. RERUN Quick Test.
		No	▶	CHECK connectors. SERVICE or REPLACE harness. CKP+ shorted to CKP- in harness. REMOVE all test equipment. RECONNECT all components. CLEAR Continuous Memory. RERUN Quick Test.
JA19	CHECK FOR BIAS VOLTAGE HIGH OR BIAS VOLTAGE LOW FAULT			
	• **Was bias voltage reading in JA6 less than 1.0 volt?**	Yes	▶	Bias voltage low fault. GO to JA20.
		No	▶	Bias voltage high fault. GO to JA21.
JA20	CHECK CKPS+ CIRCUIT FOR SHORT TO GROUND—CKP SENSOR AND ICM DISCONNECTED—BIAS LOW FAULT—KEY OFF			
	• Key off. • Disconnect ICM from ICM tee, leave EI diagnostic harness connected to vehicle harness connector. • DVOM on 20K ohm scale. • Measure resistance between J35 (CKP+ I) and J7 (B-) at breakout box. • **Is resistance greater than 10K ohms?**	Yes	▶	REPLACE ICM. REMOVE all test equipment. RECONNECT all components. CLEAR Continuous Memory. RERUN Quick Test.
		No	▶	CHECK connectors. SERVICE or REPLACE harness. CKP+ is shorted low. REMOVE all test equipment. RECONNECT all components. CLEAR Continuous Memory. RERUN Quick Test.

FM0159401197090X

Fig. 198   Test JA: Ignition No Spark (Part 9 of 17). 1994-95

TEST STEP		RESULT	▶	ACTION TO TAKE
JA21	CHECK CKPS+ CIRCUIT FOR SHORT HIGH—BIAS HIGH FAULT—CKP SENSOR AND ICM DISCONNECTED—KOEO			
	• Key off. • Disconnect ICM from ICM tee, leave EI diagnostic harness connected to vehicle harness connector. • DVOM on 40 volt DC scale. • Key on, engine off. • Measure voltage between +J35 (CKP+ I) and -J7 (B-) at breakout box. • **Is DC voltage less than 0.5 volts?**	Yes	▶	REPLACE ICM. REMOVE all test equipment. RECONNECT all components. CLEAR Continuous Memory. RERUN Quick Test.
		No	▶	CHECK connectors, SERVICE or REPLACE harness. CKP+ is shorted high. REMOVE all test equipment. RECONNECT all components. CLEAR Continuous Memory. RERUN Quick Test.
JA22	CHECK CKP CIRCUIT RESISTANCE—ICM DISCONNECTED			
	• Key off. • Disconnect ICM from ICM tee, leave EI diagnostic harness connected to vehicle harness connector. • DVOM on 20K ohm scale. • Measure resistance between J48 (CKP- I) and J35 (CKP+ I) at breakout box. • **Is resistance between 2580 and 2700 ohms?**	Yes	▶	REPLACE ICM. REMOVE all test equipment. RECONNECT all components. CLEAR Continuous Memory. RERUN Quick Test.
		No	▶	Resistance fault. GO to JA14.
JA30	CHECK PLUGS AND WIRES—KEY OFF			
	NOTE: 3.8L MUSTANG JA1 THROUGH JA22. 4.6L THUNDERBIRD / COUGAR JA30 THROUGH JA51. • Check spark plug wires for insulation damage, looseness, shorting or other damage. • Remove and check spark plugs for damage, wear, carbon deposits and proper plug gap. • Examine all wiring harnesses and connectors for damaged, burned or overheated insulation, damaged pins and loose or broken conditions. • Check sensor shield connector. • **Are spark plugs and wires OK?**	Yes	▶	REINSTALL plugs and wires. GO to JA31.
		No	▶	SERVICE or REPLACE damaged component. REMOVE all test equipment. RECONNECT all components. CLEAR Continuous Memory. RERUN Quick Test.

FM0159401197100X

Fig. 198   Test JA: Ignition No Spark (Part 10 of 17). 1994-95

TEST STEP		RESULT	▶	ACTION TO TAKE
JA31	CHECK FOR VEHICLE START WITH DIAGNOSTIC HARNESS INSTALLED			
	WARNING: NEVER CONNECT THE PCM TO THE EEC BREAKOUT BOX WHEN PERFORMING EI DIAGNOSTICS.	Yes	▶	GO to JA51.
		No	▶	GO to JA32.
	• Key off. • Install EI diagnostic harness to breakout box and the ICM and vehicle harness (Rotunda 007-00059 or equivalent). **Do not connect CKP sensor tee or coil tee.** • Use EI (High Data Rate) 8 overlay. • Connect EI diagnostic harness negative lead to battery, leave positive lead disconnected. • Set EI diagnostic harness box type switch to "8" cylinder position. • **Will vehicle start and run?**			
JA32	CHECK PWR GND TO ICM—KEY OFF			
	• Key off. • DVOM on 200 ohm scale. • When making measurements on a wiring harness, both a visual inspection and continuity test must be performed. • Measure resistance between J53 (PWR GND) and J7 (B-) at breakout box. • **Is the resistance less than 5.0 ohms?**	Yes	▶	GO to JA33.
		No	▶	CHECK connectors. SERVICE or REPLACE harness. Power ground is open. REMOVE all test equipment. RECONNECT all components. CLEAR Continuous Memory. RERUN Quick Test.
JA33	CHECK FOR VPWR TO ICM—KOEO			
	• Key off. • DVOM on 40 volt DC scale. • Key on, engine off. • When making a voltage check, a ground reading means any value within a range of zero to 1 volt. Also, VPWR readings mean any value that falls within a range of B+ to 2 volts less than B+. • When making voltage checks and a reference to ground is made, use either the negative battery lead or cast iron on the engine. B+ means the positive battery cable at the battery. • Measure voltage between (+)J35 (VPWR I) and (-)J7 (B-) at breakout box. • **Is DC voltage greater than 10.5 volts?**	Yes	▶	GO to JA34.
		No	▶	CHECK connectors. SERVICE or REPLACE harness. VPWR to ICM is open. REMOVE all test equipment. RECONNECT all components. CLEAR Continuous Memory. RERUN Quick Test.

FM0159401197110X

Fig. 198   Test JA: Ignition No Spark (Part 11 of 17). 1994-95

TEST STEP		RESULT	▶	ACTION TO TAKE
JA34	CHECK CKP+ BIAS AT ICM—KOEO			
	• Key off. • DVOM on 40 volt DC scale. • Key on, engine off. • Do not use an incandescent lamp to check CKP+ or CKP-. The lamp will prevent the circuit from operating. • Measure voltage between (+)J48 (CKP+ I) and (-)J7 (B-) at breakout box. • **Is DC voltage between 1.0 and 2.0 volts?**	Yes No	▶ ▶	GO to JA40. Bias fault. GO to JA35.
JA35	CHECK CKP+ BIAS SENSOR DISCONNECTED—BIAS FAULT—KOEO			
	• Key off. • Disconnect CKP sensor from vehicle harness connector. • DVOM on 40 volt DC scale. • Key on, engine off. • Measure voltage between (+)J48 (CKP+ I) and (-)J7 (B-) at breakout box. • **Is DC voltage greater than 1.0 volt but less than 2.0 volts?**	Yes No	▶ ▶	GO to JA36. Bias fault. GO to JA48.
JA36	CHECK CKP- SENSOR—BIAS FAULT—CKP SENSOR DISCONNECTED—KOEO			
	• Key off. • DVOM on 40 volt DC scale. • Key on, engine off. • Measure voltage between (+)J47 (CKP-I) and (-)J7 (B-) at breakout box. • **Is DC voltage between 1.0 and 2.0 volts?**	Yes No	▶ ▶	REPLACE CKP sensor. Short to ground. REMOVE all test equipment. RECONNECT all components. CLEAR Continuous Memory. RERUN Quick Test. Bias fault. GO to JA37.
JA37	DETERMINE IF BIAS HIGH OR BIAS LOW FAULT—KEY OFF			
	• **Was bias voltage reading in JA36 less than 1.0 volt?**	Yes No	▶ ▶	Bias low fault. GO to JA38. Bias high fault. GO to JA39.

FM0159401197120X

Fig. 198 Test JA: Ignition No Spark (Part 12 of 17). 1994-95

TEST STEP		RESULT	▶	ACTION TO TAKE
JA38	CHECK CKP SENSOR— FOR SHORT TO GROUND—BIAS LOW FAULT—CKP SENSOR AND ICM DISCONNECTED—KEY OFF			
	• Key off. • Disconnect ICM from ICM tee, leave EI diagnostic harness connected to vehicle harness connector. • DVOM on 20K ohm scale. • Measure resistance between J47 (CKP-I) and J7 (B-) at breakout box. • **Is the resistance greater than 10K ohms?**	Yes No	▶ ▶	REPLACE ICM. CKP- is shorted low. REMOVE all test equipment. RECONNECT all components. CLEAR Continuous Memory. RERUN Quick Test. CHECK connectors, SERVICE or REPLACE harness. CKP- is shorted low. REMOVE all test equipment. RECONNECT all components. CLEAR Continuous Memory. RERUN Quick Test.
JA39	CHECK CKP- SENSOR FOR SHORT HIGH—BIAS HIGH FAULT—CKP SENSOR AND ICM DISCONNECTED—KOEO			
	• Key off. • Disconnect ICM from ICM tee. Leave EI diagnostic harness connected to vehicle harness connector. • DVOM on 40 volt DC scale. • Key on, engine off. • Measure voltage between (+)J47 (CKP- I) and (-)J7 (B-) at the breakout box. • **Is DC voltage less than 0.5 volts?**	Yes No	▶ ▶	REPLACE ICM. CKP- shorted high. REMOVE all test equipment. RECONNECT all components. CLEAR Continuous Memory. RERUN Quick Test. CHECK connectors. SERVICE or REPLACE harness. CKP- is shorted high. REMOVE all test equipment. RECONNECT all components. CLEAR Continuous Memory. RERUN Quick Test.
JA40	CHECK CKP SENSOR AMPLITUDE AT ICM—KOEC			
	• Key off. • DVOM on 40 volt AC scale. • Crank engine and measure voltage between J48 (CKP+ I) and J47 (CKP- I) at breakout box. • **Is settled AC voltage reading greater than 0.4 volts?**	Yes No	▶ ▶	GO to Pinpoint Test Step JC1. Amplitude fault. GO to JA41.

FM0159401197130X

Fig. 198 Test JA: Ignition No Spark (Part 13 of 17). 1994-95

TEST STEP		RESULT	▶	ACTION TO TAKE
JA41	CHECK CKP AMPLITUDE AT ICM—AMPLITUDE FAULT—ICM DISCONNECTED—KOEC			
	• Key off. • Disconnect ICM from ICM tee, leave EI diagnostic harness connected to vehicle harness connector. • DVOM on 40 volt AC scale. • Crank engine and measure voltage between J48 (CKP+ I) and J47 (CKP- I) at breakout box. • **Is settled AC voltage reading greater than 0.4 volts?**	Yes No	▶ ▶	REPLACE ICM. CKP is shorted in ICM. REMOVE all test equipment. RECONNECT all components. CLEAR Continuous Memory. RERUN Quick Test. GO to JA42.
JA42	CHECK CIRCUIT RESISTANCE—AMPLITUDE FAULT—KEY OFF			
	• Key off. • DVOM on 20K ohm scale. • Measure resistance between J47 (CKP- I) and J48 (CKP+ I) at the breakout box. • **Is resistance between 2300 and 2500 ohms?**	Yes No	▶ ▶	GO to JA46. CKP- circuit resistance fault. GO to JA43.
JA43	DETERMINE IF RESISTANCE HIGH OR RESISTANCE LOW FAULT			
	• **Was the resistance reading from JA42 less than 2300 ohms?**	Yes No	▶ ▶	Low resistance fault. GO to JA47. High resistance fault. GO to JA44.
JA44	CHECK CKP+ SENSOR OPEN—RESISTANCE HIGH FAULT—KEY OFF			
	• Key off. • Connect CKP sensor tee to CKP sensor and vehicle harness connector. • DVOM on 20K ohm scale. • Measure resistance between J31 (CKP+ S) and J48 (CKP+ I) at the breakout box. • **Is resistance less than 2050 ohms?**	Yes No	▶ ▶	GO to JA45. CHECK connectors, SERVICE or REPLACE harness. CKP+ open. REMOVE all test equipment. RECONNECT all components. CLEAR Continuous Memory. RERUN Quick Test.

FM0159401197140X

Fig. 198 Test JA: Ignition No Spark (Part 14 of 17). 1994-95

TEST STEP		RESULT	▶	ACTION TO TAKE
JA45	CHECK FOR CKP OPEN—RESISTANCE HIGH FAULT—KEY OFF			
	• Key off. • DVOM on 20K ohm scale. • Measure resistance between J32 (CKP- S) and J47 (CKP- I) at the breakout box. • **Is resistance less than 2050 ohms?**	Yes No	▶ ▶	REPLACE CKP sensor. High resistance. REMOVE all test equipment. RECONNECT all components. CLEAR Continuous Memory. RERUN Quick Test. CHECK connectors. SERVICE or REPLACE harness. CKP- open. REMOVE all test equipment. RECONNECT all components. CLEAR Continuous Memory. RERUN Quick Test.
JA46	CHECK CKP SENSOR AND TRIGGER WHEEL			
	• Key off. • Check trigger wheel and CKP sensor for damage. • **Is CKP sensor and trigger data wheel OK?**	Yes No	▶ ▶	REPLACE CKP sensor. No output from sensor. REMOVE all test equipment. RECONNECT all components. CLEAR Continuous Memory. RERUN Quick Test. SERVICE or REPLACE damaged parts. REMOVE all test equipment. RECONNECT all components. CLEAR Continuous Memory. RERUN Quick Test.

FM0159401197150X

Fig. 198 Test JA: Ignition No Spark (Part 15 of 17). 1994-95

TEST STEP	RESULT	▶	ACTION TO TAKE
JA47 CHECK FOR CKP+ SHORTED TO CKP- —RESISTANCE LOW FAULT—CKP SENSOR DISCONNECTED—KEY OFF			
• Key off. • Disconnect CKP sensor from the vehicle harness connector. • DVOM on 20K ohm scale. • Measure resistance between J48 (CKP+ I) and J47 (CKP- I) at the breakout box. • Is resistance greater than 3K ohms?	Yes	▶	REPLACE CKP sensor. Shorted sensor windings. REMOVE all test equipment. RECONNECT all components. CLEAR Continuous Memory. RERUN Quick Test.
	No	▶	CHECK connectors, SERVICE or REPLACE harness. CKP+ shorted to CKP- in harness. REMOVE all test equipment. RECONNECT all components. CLEAR Continuous Memory. RERUN Quick Test.
JA48 DETERMINE IF BIAS VOLTAGE HIGH OR BIAS VOLTAGE LOW FAULT			
• **Was bias voltage reading in JA35 less than 1.0 volt?**	Yes	▶	Low bias voltage fault. GO to JA49
	No	▶	High bias voltage fault. GO to JA50
JA49 CHECK CKP+ SENSOR FOR SHORT TO GROUND—CKP SENSOR AND ICM DISCONNECTED—LOW BIAS VOLTAGE FAULT—KEY OFF			
• Key off. • Disconnect the ICM from ICM tee, leave EI diagnostic harness connected to vehicle harness connector. • DVOM on 20K ohm scale. • Measure resistance between J48 (CKP+ I) and J7 (B-) at breakout box. • Is resistance greater than 10K ohms?	Yes	▶	REPLACE ICM. CKP+ shorted low. REMOVE all test equipment. RECONNECT all components. CLEAR Continuous Memory. RERUN Quick Test
	No	▶	CHECK connectors, SERVICE or REPLACE harness. CKP+ is shorted low. REMOVE all test equipment. RECONNECT all components. CLEAR Continuous Memory. RERUN Quick Test

FM0159401197160X

Fig. 198 Test JA: Ignition No Spark (Part 16 of 17). 1994-95

TEST STEP	RESULT	▶	ACTION TO TAKE
JA50 CHECK CKP+ SENSOR FOR SHORT HIGH—BIAS VOLTAGE HIGH FAULT—CKP SENSOR AND ICM DISCONNECTED—KOEO			
• Key off. • Disconnect ICM from ICM tee, leave EI diagnostic harness connected to vehicle harness connector. • DVOM on 40 volt DC scale. • Key on, engine off. • Measure voltage between +J48 (CKP+ I) and -J7 (B-) at breakout box. • Is DC voltage less than 0.5 volts?	Yes	▶	REPLACE ICM. CKPs+ shorted high. REMOVE all test equipment. RECONNECT all components. CLEAR Continuous Memory. RERUN Quick Test.
	No	▶	CHECK connectors, SERVICE or REPLACE harness. CKP+ is shorted high. REMOVE all test equipment. RECONNECT all components. CLEAR Continuous Memory. RERUN Quick Test.
JA51 CHECK CKP SENSOR RESISTANCE—CKP CIRCUIT FAULT—KEY OFF			
• Key off. • Disconnect ICM from ICM tee, leave EI diagnostic harness connected to vehicle harness connector. • DVOM on 20K ohm scale. • Measure resistance between J47 (CKP- I) and J48 (CKP+ I) at breakout box. • Is resistance between 2300 and 2500 ohms?	Yes	▶	REPLACE ICM. REMOVE all test equipment. RECONNECT all components. CLEAR Continuous Memory. RERUN Quick Test.
	No	▶	GO to JA43 Resistance fault.

FM0159401197170X

Fig. 198 Test JA: Ignition No Spark (Part 17 of 17). 1994-95

Note

You should enter this pinpoint test only when you have been directed here.

Remember

This pinpoint test is designed to diagnose only the following:

• Spark Plugs
• Spark Plug Wires

FM0159401198010X

Fig. 199 Test JB: Ignition Misfire Under Load (Part 1 of 10). 1994-95

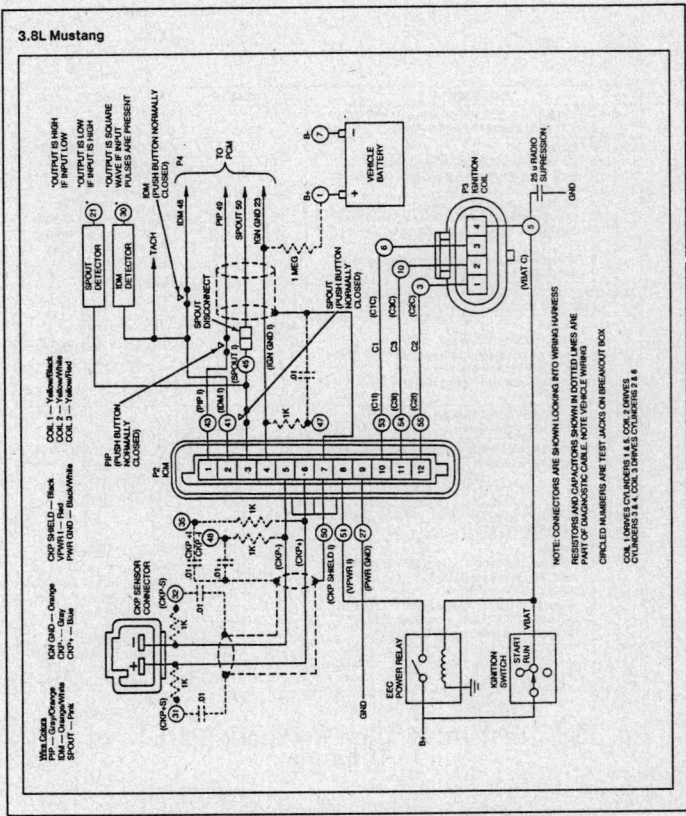

Fig. 199 Test JB: Ignition Misfire Under Load (Part 2 of 10). 1994-95

4.6L Thunderbird/Cougar

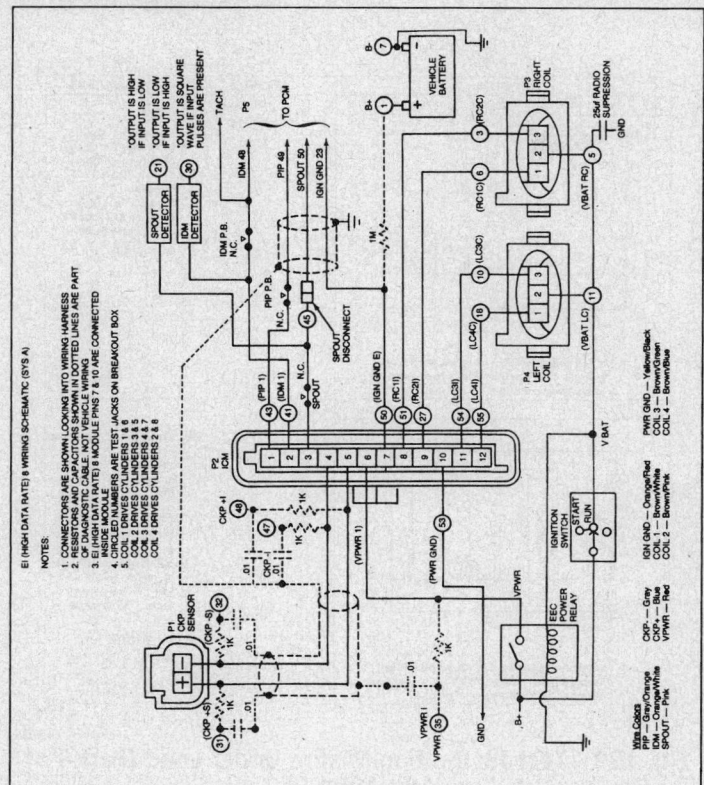

Fig. 199 Test JB: Ignition Misfire Under Load (Part 3 of 10).
1994-95

Preliminary Notes

The engine analyzer is used to diagnose problems in the secondary side of the ignition system.

Checkout

- Visually inspect the engine compartment to ensure all vacuum hoses and spark plug wires are properly routed and securely connected.
- Examine all wiring harnesses and connectors for damaged, burned or overheated insulation and loose or broken conditions.
- Be certain the battery is fully charged.
- All accessories should be off during diagnosis.

Equipment

Obtain the following test equipment or an equivalent:

- Engine Analyzer (Rotunda 010-00594).

NOTE: In order for the diagnostic procedures to provide accurate results, it is essential that the calibration of the engine analyzer be maintained. Refer to the equipment manual for the procedure to calibrate engine analyzer.

Fig. 199 Test JB: Ignition Misfire Under Load (Part 4 of 10). 1994-95

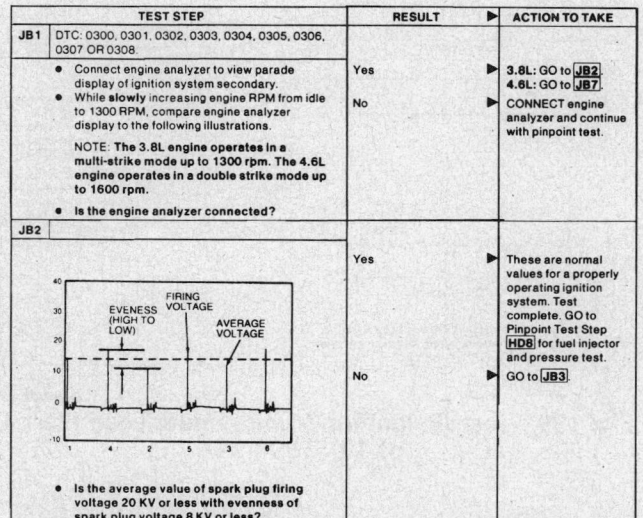

Fig. 199 Test JB: Ignition Misfire Under Load (Part 5 of 10). 1994-95

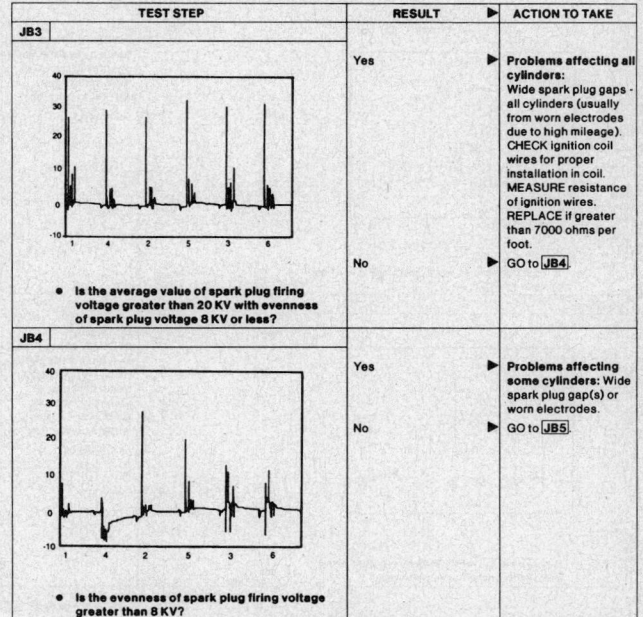

Fig. 199 Test JB: Ignition Misfire Under Load (Part 6 of 10). 1994-95

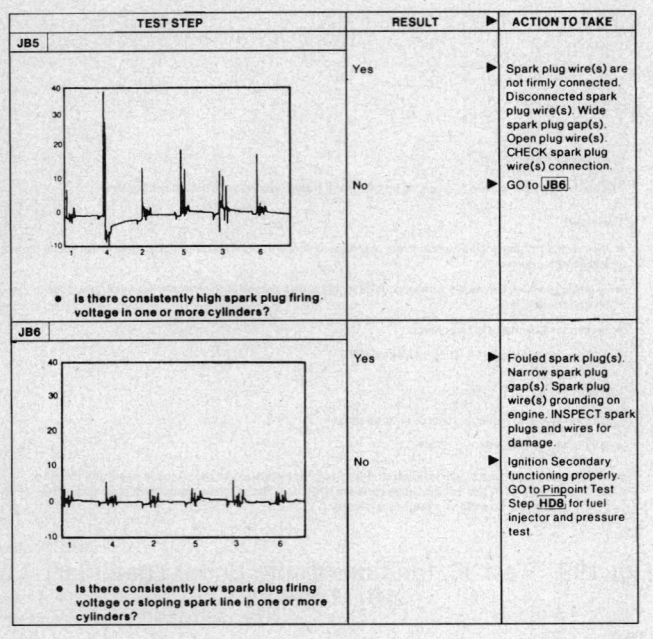

TEST STEP	RESULT	▶	ACTION TO TAKE
JB5	Yes	▶	Spark plug wire(s) are not firmly connected. Disconnected spark plug wire(s). Wide spark plug gap(s). Open plug wire(s). CHECK spark plug wire(s) connection.
● Is there consistently high spark plug firing voltage in one or more cylinders?	No	▶	GO to JB6.
JB6	Yes	▶	Fouled spark plug(s). Narrow spark plug gap(s). Spark plug wire(s) grounding on engine. INSPECT spark plugs and wires for damage.
● Is there consistently low spark plug firing voltage or sloping spark line in one or more cylinders?	No	▶	Ignition Secondary functioning properly. GO to Pinpoint Test Step HD8 for fuel injector and pressure test.

FM0159401198070X

Fig. 199 Test JB: Ignition Misfire Under Load (Part 7 of 10). 1994-95

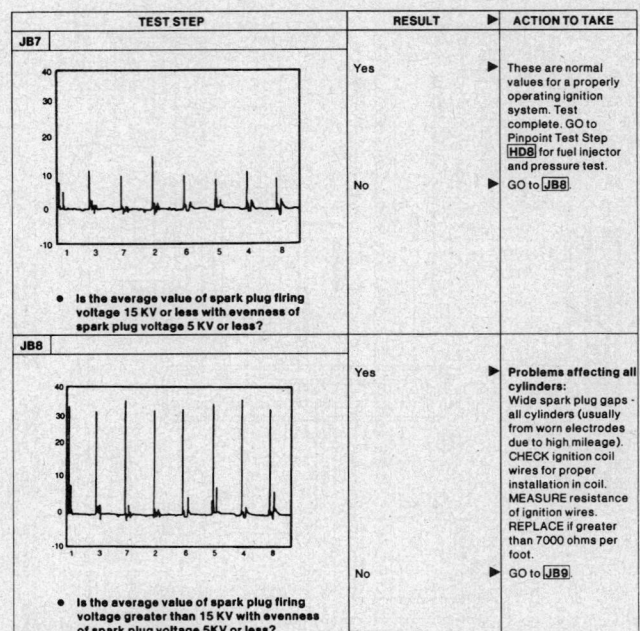

TEST STEP	RESULT	▶	ACTION TO TAKE
JB7	Yes	▶	These are normal values for a properly operating ignition system. Test complete. GO to Pinpoint Test Step HD8 for fuel injector and pressure test.
● Is the average value of spark plug firing voltage 15 KV or less with evenness of spark plug voltage 5 KV or less?	No	▶	GO to JB8.
JB8	Yes	▶	Problems affecting all cylinders: Wide spark plug gaps - all cylinders (usually from worn electrodes due to high mileage). CHECK ignition coil wires for proper installation in coil. MEASURE resistance of ignition wires. REPLACE if greater than 7000 ohms per foot.
● Is the average value of spark plug firing voltage greater than 15 KV with evenness of spark plug voltage 5KV or less?	No	▶	GO to JB9.

FM0159401198080X

Fig. 199 Test JB: Ignition Misfire Under Load (Part 8 of 10). 1994-95

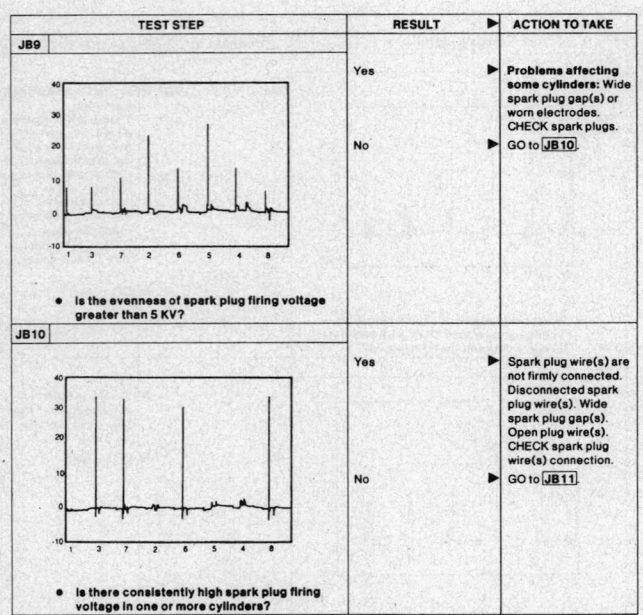

TEST STEP	RESULT	▶	ACTION TO TAKE
JB9	Yes	▶	Problems affecting some cylinders: Wide spark plug gap(s) or worn electrodes. CHECK spark plugs.
● Is the evenness of spark plug firing voltage greater than 5 KV?	No	▶	GO to JB10.
JB10	Yes	▶	Spark plug wire(s) are not firmly connected. Disconnected spark plug wire(s). Wide spark plug gap(s). Open plug wire(s). CHECK spark plug wire(s) connection.
● Is there consistently high spark plug firing voltage in one or more cylinders?	No	▶	GO to JB11.

FM0159401198090X

Fig. 199 Test JB: Ignition Misfire Under Load (Part 9 of 10). 1994-95

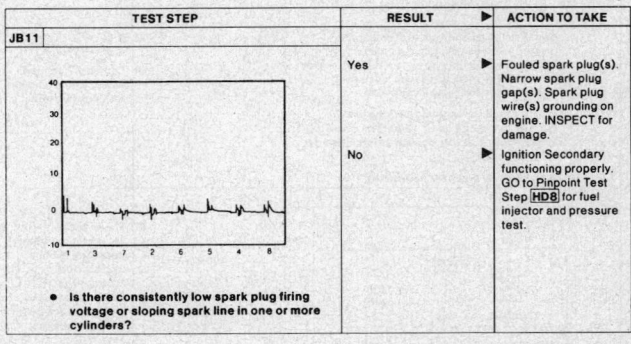

TEST STEP	RESULT	▶	ACTION TO TAKE
JB11	Yes	▶	Fouled spark plug(s). Narrow spark plug gap(s). Spark plug wire(s) grounding on engine. INSPECT for damage.
● Is there consistently low spark plug firing voltage or sloping spark line in one or more cylinders?	No	▶	Ignition Secondary functioning properly. GO to Pinpoint Test Step HD8 for fuel injector and pressure test.

FM0159401198100X

Fig. 199 Test JB: Ignition Misfire Under Load (Part 10 of 10). 1994-95

Note

You should enter this pinpoint test only when you have been directed here.

Remember

This pinpoint test is designed to diagnose only the following:

- Ignition Coil Packs
- Ignition Coil Harness
- ICM
- Vehicle Power circuit to Coil Packs.

FM0159401199010X

Fig. 200   Test JC: Ignition Coil 1, 2, 3, 4 Failure (Part 1 of 21). 1994-95

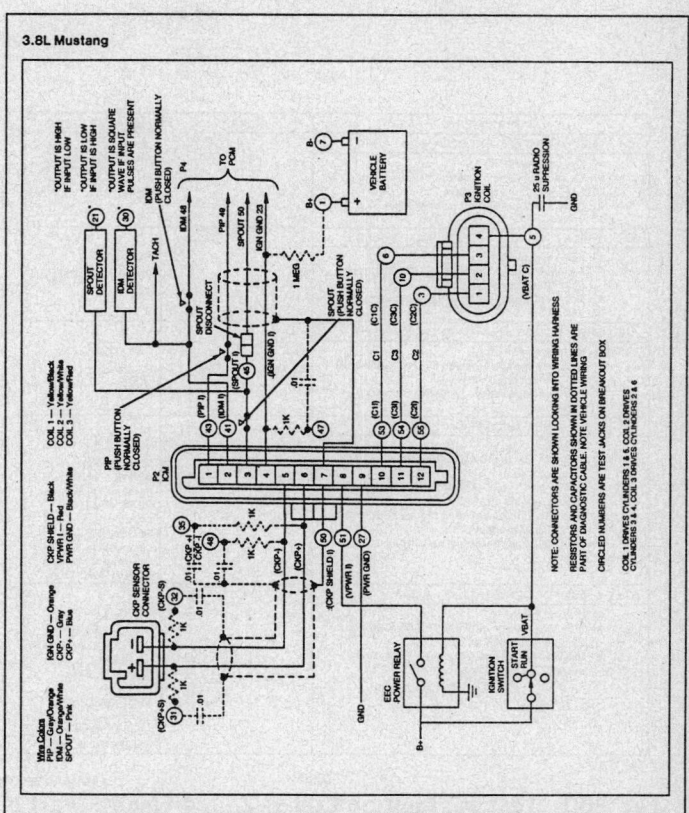

3.8L Mustang

Fig. 200   Test JC: Ignition Coil 1, 2, 3, 4 Failure (Part 2 of 21). 1994-95

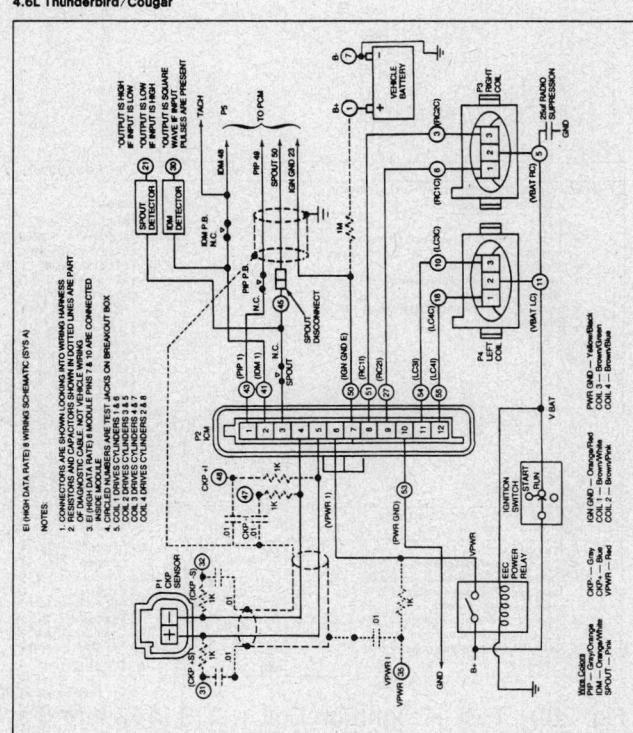

4.6L Thunderbird/Cougar

FM0159401199030X

Fig. 200   Test JC: Ignition Coil 1, 2, 3, 4 Failure (Part 3 of 21). 1994-95

TEST STEP	RESULT	▶	ACTION TO TAKE
JC1 CHECK FOR SPARK DURING CRANK			
• DTC: 1364, 1352, 1353 or 1354.	Yes	▶	Ignition System OK.
• Using a Neon Bulb Spark Tester (OTC D89P-6666-A) or Air Gap Spark Tester (D81P-6666-A), check for spark at all spark plug wires while cranking.	No	▶	GO to **JC2**. Spark fault.
• When using the spark plug firing indicator, place the grooved end as close as possible to the plug boot. Very weak or no flashing may be caused by a fouled plug.			
• **Was spark consistent on all spark plug wires (one spark per crankshaft revolution)?**			
JC2 CHECK PLUGS AND WIRES			
• Check spark plug wires for insulation damage, looseness, shorting or other damage.	Yes	▶	REINSTALL plugs and wires. GO to **JC3**.
• Remove and check spark plugs for damage, wear, carbon deposits and proper plug gap.	No	▶	SERVICE or REPLACE damaged component. REMOVE all test equipment. RECONNECT all components. CLEAR Continuous Memory. RERUN Quick Test.
• Examine all wiring harnesses and connectors for damaged, burned or overheated insulation, damaged pins, and loose or broken conditions.			
• Check sensor shield connector.			
• Are spark plugs and wires OK?			
JC3 CHECK FOR COIL PWR AT COIL			
WARNING: NEVER CONNECT PCM TO THE EEC BREAKOUT BOX WHEN PERFORMING EI DIAGNOSTICS.	Yes	▶	GO to **JC4**.
• Key off.	No	▶	CHECK connectors, SERVICE or REPLACE harness. COIL PWR is open. REMOVE all test equipment. RECONNECT all components. CLEAR Continuous Memory. RERUN Quick Test.
• Install EI diagnostic harness to breakout box.			
• Connect negative lead to battery.			
• Set EI diagnostic harness type switch to "4/6 cylinder" position.			
• Install the coil tee (the tee is blue with 4 pins).			
• Use EI (High Data Rate) 6 overlay.			
• DVOM on 20 volt DC scale.			
• Key on, engine off.			
• When making voltage checks, a ground reading means any value within a range of zero to 1 volt. Also, VPWR or COIL PWR readings mean any value that falls within a range of B+ to 2 volts less than B+.			
• Measure voltage between (+)J5 (COIL PWR) and (-)J7 (B-) at breakout box.			
• Is DC voltage greater than 10.0 volts?			

FM0159401199040X

Fig. 200   Test JC: Ignition Coil 1, 2, 3, 4 Failure (Part 4 of 21). 1994-95

TEST STEP	RESULT	▶	ACTION TO TAKE
JC4 CHECK FOR C1 HIGH AT COIL PACK—KOEO			
• Key on, engine off. • Measure voltage between (+)J6 (C1C) and (-)J7 (B-) at breakout box. • **Is DC voltage reading greater than 10.0 volts?**	Yes No	▶ ▶	GO to **JC5**. C1 low fault. GO to **JC16**.
JC5 CHECK FOR C2 HIGH AT COIL PACK—KOEO			
• Key on, engine off. • Measure voltage between (+)J3 (C2C) and (-)J7 (B-) at breakout box. • **Is DC voltage reading greater than 10.0 volts?**	Yes No	▶ ▶	GO to **JC6**. C2 low fault. GO to **JC18**.
JC6 CHECK FOR C3 HIGH AT COIL PACK—KOEO			
• Key on, engine off. • Measure voltage between (+)J10 (C3C) and (-)J7 (B-) at breakout box. • **Is DC voltage reading greater than 10.0 volts?**	Yes No	▶ ▶	GO to **JC7**. C3 low fault. GO to **JC20**.
JC7 CHECK FOR C1 HIGH AT ICM—KOEO			
• Key off. • Connect ICM tee to ICM and vehicle harness connector. • DVOM on 40 volt DC scale. • Key on, engine off. • Measure voltage between (+)J53 (C1I) and (-)J7 (B-) at breakout box. • **Is DC voltage reading greater than 10.0 volts?**	Yes No	▶ ▶	GO to **JC8**. CHECK connectors, SERVICE or REPLACE harness. C1 is open. REMOVE all test equipment. RECONNECT all components. CLEAR Continuous Memory. RERUN Quick Test.
JC8 CHECK FOR C2 HIGH AT ICM—KOEO			
• Key on, engine off. • Measure voltage between (+)J55 (C2I) and (-)J7 (B-) at breakout box. • **Is DC voltage reading greater than 10.0 volts?**	Yes No	▶ ▶	GO to **JC9**. CHECK connectors, SERVICE or REPLACE harness. C2 is open. REMOVE all test equipment. RECONNECT all components. CLEAR Continuous Memory. RERUN Quick Test.

FM0159401199050X

Fig. 200   Test JC: Ignition Coil 1, 2, 3, 4 Failure (Part 5 of 21). 1994-95

TEST STEP	RESULT	▶	ACTION TO TAKE
JC9 CHECK FOR C3 HIGH AT ICM—KOEO			
• Key on, engine off. • Measure voltage between (+)J54 (C3I) and -J7 (B-) at breakout box. • **Is DC voltage reading greater than 10.0 volts?**	Yes No	▶ ▶	GO to **JC10**. CHECK connectors, SERVICE or REPLACE harness. C3 is open. REMOVE all test equipment. RECONNECT all components. CLEAR Continuous Memory. RERUN Quick Test.
JC10 CHECK FOR C1 LOW AT COIL CONNECTOR—COIL DISCONNECTED—KOEO			
• Key off. • Disconnect the coil from the coil tee. Leave EI diagnostic harness coil connected to vehicle harness coil connector. • DVOM on 40 volt DC scale. • Key on, engine off. • Measure voltage between (+)J6 (C1C) and (-)J7 (B-) at breakout box. • **Is DC voltage reading less than 0.5 volts?**	Yes No	▶ ▶	GO to **JC11**. C1 high fault. GO to **JC22**.
JC11 CHECK FOR C2 LOW AT COIL CONNECTOR—COIL DISCONNECTED—KOEO			
• Key on, engine off. • Measure voltage between (+)J3 (C2C) and (-)J7 (B-) at breakout box. • **Is DC voltage reading less than 0.5 volts?**	Yes No	▶ ▶	GO to **JC12**. C2 high fault. GO to **JC23**.
JC12 CHECK FOR C3 LOW AT COIL CONNECTOR—COIL DISCONNECTED			
• Key on, engine off. • Measure voltage between (+)J10 (C3C) and (-)J7 (B-) at breakout box. • **Is DC voltage reading less than 0.5 volts?**	Yes No	▶ ▶	GO to **JC13**. C3 high fault. GO to **JC24**.
JC13 CHECK C1 AT COIL CONNECTOR WHILE CRANKING ENGINE—COIL DISCONNECTED—KOEC			
• Connect EI diagnostic harness positive lead to battery. • Connect incandescent test lamp between J1 (B+) and J6 (C1C). • Crank engine. • **Does lamp blink consistently and brightly (one blink per engine revolution)?**	Yes No	▶ ▶	GO to **JC14**. REPLACE ICM. C1 open in ICM. REMOVE all test equipment. RECONNECT all components. CLEAR Continuous Memory. RERUN Quick Test.

FM0159401199060X

Fig. 200   Test JC: Ignition Coil 1, 2, 3, 4 Failure (Part 6 of 21). 1994-95

TEST STEP	RESULT	▶	ACTION TO TAKE
JC14 CHECK C2 AT COIL CONNECTOR WHILE CRANKING ENGINE—COIL DISCONNECTED—KOEC			
• Connect incandescent test lamp between J1 (B+) and J3 (C2C). • Crank engine. • **Does lamp blink consistently and brightly (one blink per engine revolution)?**	Yes No	▶ ▶	GO to **JC15**. REPLACE ICM. C3 open in ICM. REMOVE all test equipment. RECONNECT all components. CLEAR Continuous Memory. RERUN Quick Test.
JC15 CHECK C3 AT COIL CONNECTOR WHILE CRANKING ENGINE—COIL DISCONNECTED—KOEC			
• Connect test lamp between J1 (B+) and J10 (C3C). • Crank engine. • **Does lamp blink consistently and brightly (one blink per engine revolution)?**	Yes No	▶ ▶	REPLACE coil pack. Input to coil pack is OK, but no high voltage output. REMOVE all test equipment. RECONNECT all components. CLEAR Continuous Memory. RERUN Quick Test. REPLACE ICM. C3 open in ICM. REMOVE all test equipment. RECONNECT all components. CLEAR Continuous Memory. RERUN Quick Test.
JC16 CHECK FOR C1 SHORT LOW—COIL DISCONNECTED—KEY OFF			
• Key off. • DVOM on 20K ohm scale. • Disconnect coil from coil tee, leave EI diagnostic harness connected to vehicle harness coil connector. • Measure resistance between J7 (B-) and J6 (C1C) at breakout box. • **Is resistance reading greater than 2K ohms?**	Yes No	▶ ▶	REPLACE coil pack. C1 open in coil. REMOVE all test equipment. RECONNECT all components. CLEAR Continuous Memory. RERUN Quick Test. GO to **JC17**.

FM0159401199070X

Fig. 200   Test JC: Ignition Coil 1, 2, 3, 4 Failure (Part 7 of 21). 1994-95

TEST STEP	RESULT	▶	ACTION TO TAKE
JC17 CHECK FOR C1 SHORT LOW—ICM AND COIL DISCONNECTED—KEY OFF			
• Key off. • Disconnect ICM from vehicle harness connector. • DVOM on 20K ohm scale. • Measure resistance between J7 (B-) and J6 (C1C) at breakout box. • **Is resistance reading greater than 10K ohms?**	Yes No	▶ ▶	REPLACE ICM. C1 is shorted low. REMOVE all test equipment. RECONNECT all components. CLEAR Continuous Memory. RERUN Quick Test. CHECK connectors, SERVICE or REPLACE harness. C1 is shorted low. REMOVE all test equipment. RECONNECT all components. CLEAR Continuous Memory. RERUN Quick Test. NOTE: A C1 short to ground may have damaged the coil.
JC18 CHECK FOR C2 SHORT LOW—COIL DISCONNECTED—KEY OFF			
• Key off. • DVOM on 20K ohm scale. • Disconnect coil from coil tee, leave EI diagnostic harness connected to vehicle harness coil connector. • Measure resistance between J7 (B-) and J3 (C2C) at breakout box. • **Is resistance reading greater than 2K ohms?**	Yes No	▶ ▶	REPLACE coil pack. C2 open in coil. REMOVE all test equipment. RECONNECT all components. CLEAR Continuous Memory. RERUN Quick Test. GO to **JC19**.

FM0159401199080X

Fig. 200   Test JC: Ignition Coil 1, 2, 3, 4 Failure (Part 8 of 21). 1994-95

TEST STEP	RESULT	▶	ACTION TO TAKE
JC19 CHECK FOR C2 LOW—ICM AND COIL DISCONNECTED—KEY OFF • Key off. • Disconnect ICM from vehicle harness connector. • DVOM on 20K ohm scale. • Measure between J3 (C2C) and J7 (B-) at breakout box. • **Is resistance reading greater than 10K ohms?**	Yes No	▶ ▶	REPLACE ICM. C2 shorted low. REMOVE all test equipment. RECONNECT all components. CLEAR Continuous Memory. RERUN Quick Test. CHECK connectors, SERVICE or REPLACE harness. C2 is shorted low. REMOVE all test equipment. RECONNECT all components. CLEAR Continuous Memory. RERUN Quick Test. NOTE: A C2 short to ground may have damaged the coil.
JC20 CHECK FOR C3 SHORT LOW—COIL DISCONNECTED—KEY OFF • Key off. • DVOM on 20K ohm scale. • Disconnect coil from coil tee, leave EI diagnostic harness connected to vehicle harness coil connector. • Measure resistance between J7 (B-) and J10 (C3C) at breakout box. • **Is resistance reading greater than 2K ohms?**	Yes No	▶ ▶	REPLACE coil pack. C3 open in coil. REMOVE all test equipment. RECONNECT all components. CLEAR Continuous Memory. RERUN Quick Test. GO to JC21

FM0159401199090X

Fig. 200   Test JC: Ignition Coil 1, 2, 3, 4 Failure (Part 9 of 21). 1994-95

TEST STEP	RESULT	▶	ACTION TO TAKE
JC21 CHECK FOR C3 SHORT LOW—ICM AND COIL DISCONNECTED—KEY OFF • Key off. • Disconnect ICM from vehicle harness connector. • DVOM on 20K ohm scale. • Measure resistance between J7 (B-) and J10 (C3C) at breakout box. • **Is resistance greater than 10K ohms?**	Yes No	▶ ▶	REPLACE ICM. C3 is shorted low. REMOVE all test equipment. RECONNECT all components. CLEAR Continuous Memory. RERUN Quick Test. CHECK connectors, SERVICE or REPLACE harness. C3 is shorted low. REMOVE all test equipment. RECONNECT all components. CLEAR Continuous Memory. RERUN Quick Test. NOTE: A C3 short to ground may have damaged the coil.
JC22 CHECK FOR C1 LOW—ICM AND COIL DISCONNECTED—KOEO • Key off. • Disconnect ICM from the ICM tee, leave EI diagnostic harness connected to vehicle harness connector. • DVOM on 40 volt DC scale. • Key on, engine off. • Measure voltage between (+)J6 (C1C) and (-)J7 (B-) at breakout box. • **Is DC voltage reading less than 0.5 volts?**	Yes No	▶ ▶	REPLACE ICM. C1 is shorted high. REMOVE all test equipment. RECONNECT all components. CLEAR Continuous Memory. RERUN Quick Test. CHECK connectors, SERVICE or REPLACE harness. C1 is shorted high. REMOVE all test equipment. RECONNECT all components. CLEAR Continuous Memory. RERUN Quick Test.

FM0159401199100X

Fig. 200   Test JC: Ignition Coil 1, 2, 3, 4 Failure (Part 10 of 21). 1994-95

TEST STEP	RESULT	▶	ACTION TO TAKE
JC23 CHECK FOR C2 LOW—ICM AND COIL DISCONNECTED • Key off. • Disconnect ICM from the ICM tee, leave EI diagnostic harness connected to vehicle harness connector. • DVOM on 40 volt DC scale. • Key on, engine off. • Measure voltage between (+)J3 (C2C) and (-)J7 (B-) at breakout box. • **Is DC voltage reading less than 0.5 volts?**	Yes No	▶ ▶	REPLACE ICM. C2 is shorted high. REMOVE all test equipment. RECONNECT all components. CLEAR Continuous Memory. RERUN Quick Test. CHECK connectors, SERVICE or REPLACE harness. C2 is shorted high. REMOVE all test equipment. RECONNECT all components. CLEAR Continuous Memory. RERUN Quick Test.
JC24 CHECK FOR C3 LOW—ICM AND COIL DISCONNECTED • Key off. • Disconnect ICM from the ICM tee, leave EI diagnostic harness connected to vehicle harness connector. • DVOM on 40 volt DC scale. • Key on, engine off. • Measure voltage between (+)J10 (C3C) and (-)J7 (B-) at breakout box. • **Is DC voltage reading less than 0.5 volts?**	Yes No	▶ ▶	REPLACE ICM. C3 is shorted high. REMOVE all test equipment. RECONNECT all components. CLEAR Continuous Memory. RERUN Quick Test. CHECK connectors, SERVICE or REPLACE harness. C3 is shorted high. REMOVE all test equipment. RECONNECT all components. CLEAR Continuous Memory. RERUN Quick Test.
JC30 CHECK FOR SPARK DURING CRANK—KOEC • DTCs 1364, 1352, 1353, 1354, or 1355 • Using a Neon Bulb Spark Tester (Special Service Tool D89P-6666-A) or Air Gap Spark Tester (D81P-6666-A). Check for spark at all spark plug wires while cranking. • When using the spark plug firing indicator, place the grooved end as close as possible to the plug boot. Very weak or no flashing may be caused by a fouled plug. • Was spark consistent on all spark plug wires (one spark per crankshaft revolution)?	Yes No	▶ ▶	The ignition system is OK. GO to JC31 Spark fault.

FM0159401199110X

Fig. 200   Test JC: Ignition Coil 1, 2, 3, 4 Failure (Part 11 of 21). 1994-95

TEST STEP	RESULT	▶	ACTION TO TAKE
JC31 CHECK FOR SPARK AT ALL RIGHT SPARK PLUG WIRES DURING CRANK—KOEC • Was spark consistent on all right spark plug wires (one spark per crankshaft revolution)? NOTE: Check spark at spark plugs.	Yes No	▶ ▶	GO to JC32. GO to JC48.
JC32 CHECK LEFT SPARK PLUGS AND WIRES—KEY OFF • Check left side coil pack spark plug wires for insulation damage, looseness, shorting or other damage. • Remove and check left side spark plugs for damage, wear, carbon deposits and proper plug gap. • Left coil plugs and wires are attached to the left coil pack. • Examine all wiring harnesses and connectors for damaged, burned or overheated insulation, damaged pins and loose or broken condition. • **Check sensor shield connector.** • **Are spark plugs and wires OK?**	Yes No	▶ ▶	REINSTALL plugs and wires. GO to JC33 SERVICE or REPLACE damaged component. REMOVE all test equipment. RECONNECT all components. CLEAR Continuous Memory. RERUN Quick Test.
JC33 CHECK FOR COIL PWR TO LEFT COIL FAULT—KOEO **WARNING: NEVER CONNECT PCM TO THE EEC BREAKOUT BOX WHEN PERFORMING EI DIAGNOSTICS.** • Key off. • Install EI (High Data Rate) diagnostic harness to breakout box. • Install the left coil tee. The tee is yellow (left coil). • Connect EI diagnostic harness negative lead to battery. • Use 4.6L EI (High Data Rate) 8 overlay. • Set EI harness type switch to "8 cylinder" position. • DVOM on 40 volt DC scale. • Key on, engine off. • When making voltage checks, a ground reading means any value within a range of zero to 1 volt. Also VPWR or COIL PWR readings mean any value that falls within a range of B+ to 2 volts less than B+. • Measure voltage between (+)J11 (COIL PWR L) and (-)J7 (B-) at breakout box. • **Is DC voltage greater than 10.0 volts?**	Yes No	▶ ▶	GO to JC34. CHECK connectors, SERVICE or REPLACE harness. COIL PWR is open to left coil. REMOVE all test equipment. RECONNECT all components. CLEAR Continuous Memory. RERUN Quick Test.

FM0159401199120X

Fig. 200   Test JC: Ignition Coil 1, 2, 3, 4 Failure (Part 12 of 21). 1994-95

TEST STEP	RESULT	▶	ACTION TO TAKE
JC34 CHECK FOR C3 HIGH AT COIL PACK—KOEO • Key on, engine off. • Measure voltage between (+)J10 (LC3C) and (-)J7 (B-) at breakout box. • **Is DC voltage reading greater than 10.0 volts?**	Yes No	▶ ▶	GO to **JC35**. C3 low fault. GO to **JC42**.
JC35 CHECK FOR C4 HIGH AT COIL PACK—KOEO • Key on, engine off. • Measure voltage between (+)J18 (LC4C) and (-)J7 (B-) at the breakout box. • **Is DC voltage reading greater than 10.0 volts?**	Yes No	▶ ▶	GO to **JC36**. C4 low fault. GO to **JC44**.
JC36 CHECK FOR C3 HIGH AT ICM—KOEO • Key off. • Connect ICM tee to the ICM and vehicle harness connector. • DVOM on 40 volt DC scale. • Key on, engine off. • Measure voltage between (+)J54 (LC3I) and (-)J7 (B-) at the breakout box. • **Is DC voltage reading greater than 10.0 volts?**	Yes No	▶ ▶	GO to **JC37**. CHECK connectors, SERVICE or REPLACE harness. C3 is open. REMOVE all test equipment. RECONNECT all components. CLEAR Continuous Memory. RERUN Quick Test.
JC37 CHECK FOR C4 HIGH AT ICM—KOEO • Key on, engine off. • Measure voltage between (+)J55 (LC4I) and (-)J7 (B-) at breakout box. • **Is DC voltage reading greater than 10.0 volts?**	Yes No	▶ ▶	GO to **JC38**. CHECK connectors, SERVICE or REPLACE harness. C4 is open. REMOVE all test equipment. RECONNECT all components. CLEAR Continuous Memory. RERUN Quick Test.
JC38 CHECK FOR C3 LOW AT COIL CONNECTOR—COIL DISCONNECTED—KOEO • Key off. • Disconnect left coil pack from coil tee, leave EI diagnostic harness connected to vehicle harness left coil connector. • DVOM on 40 volt DC scale. • Key on, engine off. • Measure voltage between (+)J10 (LC3C) and (-)J7 (B-) at breakout box. • **Is DC voltage reading less than 0.5 volts?**	Yes No	▶ ▶	GO to **JC39**. C3 high fault. GO to **JC46**.

FM0159401199130X

Fig. 200   Test JC: Ignition Coil 1, 2, 3, 4 Failure (Part 13 of 21). 1994-95

TEST STEP	RESULT	▶	ACTION TO TAKE
JC39 CHECK FOR C4 LOW AT COIL CONNECTOR—COIL DISCONNECTED—KOEO • Key on, engine off. • Measure voltage between (+)J18 (LC4C) and (-)J7 (B-) at breakout box. • **Is DC voltage reading less than 0.5 volts?**	Yes No	▶ ▶	GO to **JC40**. C4 high fault. GO to **JC47**.
JC40 CHECK FOR C3 AT COIL CONNECTOR WHILE CRANKING—COIL DISCONNECTED—KOEC • Connect EI diagnostic harness positive lead to battery. • Connect an incandescent test lamp between J1 (B+) and J10 (LC3C). • Crank engine. • **Does lamp blink consistently and brightly (one blink per engine revolution?**	Yes No	▶ ▶	GO to **JC41**. REPLACE ICM. C3 open. REMOVE all test equipment. RECONNECT all components. CLEAR Continuous Memory. RERUN Quick Test.
JC41 CHECK C4 AT COIL CONNECTOR WHILE CRANKING—COIL DISCONNECTED—KOEC • Connect an incandescent test lamp between J1 (B+) and J18 (LC4C). • Crank engine. • **Does lamp blink consistently and brightly (one blink per engine revolution)?**	Yes No	▶ ▶	REPLACE left coil pack. Input to coil pack is OK, but no high voltage output. REMOVE all test equipment. RECONNECT all components. CLEAR Continuous Memory. RERUN Quick Test. REPLACE ICM. C4 open in ICM. REMOVE all test equipment. RECONNECT all components. CLEAR Continuous Memory. RERUN Quick Test.
JC42 CHECK FOR C3 SHORT LOW—COIL DISCONNECTED—KEY OFF • Key off. • DVOM on 20K ohm scale. • Disconnect coil from coil tee, leave EI diagnostic harness connected to vehicle harness coil connector. • Measure resistance between J7 (B-) and J10 (C3C) at breakout box. • **Is resistance reading less than 2K ohms?**	Yes No	▶ ▶	GO to **JC43**. REPLACE Left Coil Pack. C3 open in coil. REMOVE all test equipment. RECONNECT all components. CLEAR Continuous Memory. RERUN Quick Test.

FM0159401199140X

Fig. 200   Test JC: Ignition Coil 1, 2, 3, 4 Failure (Part 14 of 21). 1994-95

TEST STEP	RESULT	▶	ACTION TO TAKE
JC43 CHECK FOR C3 SHORT LOW—ICM AND COIL DISCONNECTED—KEY OFF • Key off. • Disconnect ICM from vehicle harness. • DVOM on 20K ohm scale. • Measure resistance between J7 (B-) and J10 (C3C) at breakout box. • **Is resistance greater than 10K ohms?**	Yes No	▶ ▶	REPLACE ICM. C3 is shorted low. REMOVE all test equipment. RECONNECT all components. CLEAR Continuous Memory. RERUN Quick Test. CHECK connectors, SERVICE or REPLACE harness. C3 is shorted low. REMOVE all test equipment. RECONNECT all components. CLEAR Continuous Memory. RERUN Quick Test.
JC44 CHECK FOR C4 SHORT LOW—COIL DISCONNECTED—KEY OFF • Key off. • DVOM on 20K ohm scale. • Disconnect coil from coil tee, leave EI diagnostic harness connected to vehicle harness coil connector. • Measure resistance between J7 (B-) and J18 (LC4C) at breakout box. • **Is resistance reading less than 2K ohms?**	Yes No	▶ ▶	GO to **JC45**. REPLACE left coil pack. C4 open in coil. REMOVE all test equipment. RECONNECT all components. CLEAR Continuous Memory. RERUN Quick Test.
JC45 CHECK FOR C4 SHORT LOW—ICM AND COIL DISCONNECTED—KEY OFF • Key off. • Disconnect ICM from vehicle harness connector. • DVOM on 20K ohm scale. • Measure resistance between J7 (B-) and J18 (LC4C) at breakout box. • **Is resistance reading greater than 10K ohms?**	Yes No	▶ ▶	REPLACE ICM. C4 is shorted low. REMOVE all test equipment. RECONNECT all components. CLEAR Continuous Memory. RERUN Quick Test. CHECK connectors, SERVICE or REPLACE harness. C4 is shorted low. REMOVE all test equipment. RECONNECT all components. CLEAR Continuous Memory. RERUN Quick Test.

FM0159401199150X

Fig. 200   Test JC: Ignition Coil 1, 2, 3, 4 Failure (Part 15 of 21). 1994-95

TEST STEP	RESULT	▶	ACTION TO TAKE
JC46 CHECK FOR C3 LOW—ICM AND COIL DISCONNECTED—KOEO • Key off. • Disconnect ICM from the ICM tee, leave EI diagnostic harness connected to vehicle harness connector. • DVOM on 40 volt DC scale. • Key on, engine off. • Measure voltage between (+)J10 (LC3C) and (-)J7 (B-) at breakout box. • **Is DC voltage reading less than 0.5 volts?**	Yes No	▶ ▶	REPLACE ICM. C3 is shorted high. REMOVE all test equipment. RECONNECT all components. CLEAR Continuous Memory. RERUN Quick Test. CHECK connectors, SERVICE or REPLACE harness. C3 is shorted high. REMOVE all test equipment. RECONNECT all components. CLEAR Continuous Memory. RERUN Quick Test.
JC47 CHECK FOR C4 LOW—ICM AND COIL DISCONNECTED—KOEO • Key off. • Disconnect ICM from ICM tee, leave EI diagnostic harness connected to vehicle harness connector. • DVOM on 40 volt DC scale. • Key on, engine off. • Measure voltage between (+)J18 (LC4C) and (-)J7 (B-) at breakout box. • **Is DC voltage reading less than 0.5 volts?**	Yes No	▶ ▶	REPLACE ICM. C4 is shorted high. REMOVE all test equipment. RECONNECT all components. CLEAR Continuous Memory. RERUN Quick Test. CHECK connectors, SERVICE or REPLACE harness. C4 is shorted high. REMOVE all test equipment. RECONNECT all components. CLEAR Continuous Memory. RERUN Quick Test.
JC48 CHECK RIGHT PLUGS AND WIRES—KEY OFF • Check right side coil pack spark plug wires for insulation damage, looseness, shorting or other damage. • Remove and check right spark plugs for damage, wear, carbon deposits and proper plug gap. NOTE: Right coil plugs and wires are attached to the right coil. • **Are spark plugs and wires OK?**	Yes No	▶ ▶	REINSTALL plugs and wires. GO to **JC49**. SERVICE or REPLACE damaged component. REMOVE all test equipment. RECONNECT all components. CLEAR Continuous Memory. RERUN Quick Test.

Fig. 200   Test JC: Ignition Coil 1, 2, 3, 4 Failure (Part 16 of 21). 1994-95

TEST STEP	RESULT	▶	ACTION TO TAKE
JC49 CHECK FOR RIGHT COIL PWR—KOEO WARNING: NEVER CONNECT PCM TO THE EEC BREAKOUT BOX WHEN PERFORMING EI DIAGNOSTICS. • Key off. • Install EI diagnostic harness to the breakout box. • Connect EI diagnostic harness negative lead to battery. • Install the right coil tee. • Use 4.6L EI (High Data Rate) 8 overlay. • Set EI harness box type switch to 8 cylinder position. • Key on, engine off. • Measure voltage between (+)J5 (COIL PWR R) and (-)J7 (B-) at breakout box. • **Is DC voltage greater than 10.0 volts?**	Yes No	▶ ▶	GO to **JC50**. CHECK connectors, SERVICE or REPLACE harness. COIL PWR is open to right coil. REMOVE all test equipment. RECONNECT all components. CLEAR Continuous Memory. RERUN Quick Test.
JC50 CHECK FOR C1 HIGH AT RIGHT COIL PACK—KOEO • DVOM on 40 volt DC scale. • Key on, engine off. • Measure voltage between (+)J3 (RC1C) and (-)J7 (B-) at breakout box. • **Is DC voltage reading greater than 10.0 volts?**	Yes No	▶ ▶	GO to **JC51**. C1 low fault. GO to **JC58**.
JC51 CHECK FOR C2 HIGH AT RIGHT COIL PACK • Key on, engine off. • Measure voltage between (+)J6 (RC2C) and (-)J7 (B-) at breakout box. • **Is DC voltage reading greater than 10.0 volts?**	Yes No	▶ ▶	GO to **JC52**. C2 low fault. GO to **JC60**.
JC52 CHECK FOR C1 HIGH AT ICM—KOEO • Key off. • Connect ICM tee to the ICM and vehicle harness connector. • DVOM on 40 volt DC scale. • Key on, engine off. • Measure voltage between (+)J51 (RC1I) and (-)J7 (B-) at breakout box. • **Is DC voltage reading greater than 10.0 volts?**	Yes No	▶ ▶	GO to **JC53**. CHECK connectors, SERVICE or REPLACE harness. C1 is open. REMOVE all test equipment. RECONNECT all components. CLEAR Continuous Memory. RERUN Quick Test.

FM0159401199170X

Fig. 200 Test JC: Ignition Coil 1, 2, 3, 4 Failure (Part 17 of 21). 1994-95

TEST STEP	RESULT	▶	ACTION TO TAKE
JC57 CHECK C2 AT COIL CONNECTOR WHILE CRANKING ENGINE—COIL DISCONNECTED • Connect an incandescent test lamp between J1 (B+) and J6 (RC2C). • Crank engine. • **Does lamp blink consistently and brightly (one blink per engine revolution)?**	Yes No	▶ ▶	REPLACE Right Coil Pack. Input to coil pack is OK, but no high voltage output. REMOVE all test equipment. RECONNECT all components. CLEAR Continuous Memory. RERUN Quick Test. REPLACE ICM. C2 is open in ICM. REMOVE all test equipment. RECONNECT all components. CLEAR Continuous Memory. RERUN Quick Test.
JC58 CHECK FOR C1 SHORT LOW—COIL DISCONNECTED • Key off. • DVOM on 20K ohm scale. • Disconnect coil from coil tee, leave EI diagnostic harness connected to vehicle harness coil connector. • Measure resistance between J7 (B-) and J3 (RC1C) at breakout box. • **Is resistance reading less than 2K ohms?**	Yes No	▶ ▶	GO to **JC59**. REPLACE Right Coil Pack. C1 is open in coil. REMOVE all test equipment. RECONNECT all components. CLEAR Continuous Memory. RERUN Quick Test.
JC59 CHECK FOR C1 SHORT LOW—ICM AND COIL DISCONNECTED • Key off. • Disconnect ICM from vehicle harness. • DVOM on 20K ohm scale. • Measure resistance between J7 (B-) and J3 (RC1C) at breakout box. • **Is resistance reading greater than 10K ohms?**	Yes No	▶ ▶	REPLACE ICM. C1 is shorted low. REMOVE all test equipment. RECONNECT all components. CLEAR Continuous Memory. RERUN Quick Test. CHECK connectors, SERVICE or REPLACE harness. C1 is shorted to low. REMOVE all test equipment. RECONNECT all components. CLEAR Continuous Memory. RERUN Quick Test.

FM0159401199190X

Fig. 200 Test JC: Ignition Coil 1, 2, 3, 4 Failure (Part 19 of 21). 1994-95

TEST STEP	RESULT	▶	ACTION TO TAKE
JC53 CHECK FOR C2 HIGH AT ICM • Key on, engine off. • Measure voltage between (+)J27 (RC2I) and (-)J7 (B-) at breakout box. • **Is DC voltage reading greater than 10.0 volts?**	Yes No	▶ ▶	GO to **JC54**. CHECK connectors, SERVICE or REPLACE harness. C2 is open. REMOVE all test equipment. RECONNECT all components. CLEAR Continuous Memory. RERUN Quick Test.
JC54 CHECK C1 LOW AT COIL CONNECTOR—COIL DISCONNECTED • Key off. • Disconnect right coil from coil tee, leave EI diagnostic harness connected to vehicle harness right coil connector. • DVOM on 40 volt DC scale. • Key on, engine off. • Measure voltage between (+)J3 (RC1C) and (-)J7 (B-) at breakout box. • **Is DC voltage reading less than 0.5 volts?**	Yes No	▶ ▶	GO to **JC55**. C1 high fault. GO to **JC62**.
JC55 CHECK FOR C2 LOW AT COIL CONNECTOR—COIL DISCONNECTED • Key on, engine off. • Measure voltage between (+)J6 (RC2C) and (-)J7 (B-) at breakout box. • **Is DC voltage reading less than 0.5 volts?**	Yes No	▶ ▶	GO to **JC56**. C2 high fault. GO to **JC63**.
JC56 CHECK C1 AT COIL CONNECTOR WHILE CRANKING ENGINE—COIL DISCONNECTED • Connect EI diagnostic harness positive lead to battery. • Connect an incandescent test lamp between J1 (B+) and J3 (RC1C). • Crank engine. • **Does lamp blink consistently and brightly (one blink per engine revolution)?**	Yes No	▶ ▶	GO to **JC57**. REPLACE ICM. C1 is open. REMOVE all test equipment. RECONNECT all components. CLEAR Continuous Memory. RERUN Quick Test.

FM0159401199180X

Fig. 200 Test JC: Ignition Coil 1, 2, 3, 4 Failure (Part 18 of 21). 1994-95

TEST STEP	RESULT	▶	ACTION TO TAKE
JC60 CHECK FOR C2 SHORT LOW—COIL DISCONNECTED • Key off. • DVOM on 20K ohm scale. • Disconnect coil from coil tee, leave EI diagnostic harness connected to vehicle harness coil connector. • Measure resistance between J7 (B-) and J6 (RC2C) at breakout box. • **Is resistance reading less than 2K ohms?**	Yes No	▶ ▶	GO to **JC61**. REPLACE Right Coil Pack. C2 open in coil. REMOVE all test equipment. RECONNECT all components. CLEAR Continuous Memory. RERUN Quick Test.
JC61 CHECK FOR C2 SHORT LOW—ICM AND COIL DISCONNECTED • Key off. • Disconnect ICM from vehicle harness. • DVOM on 20K ohm scale. • Measure resistance between J6 (RC2C) and J7 (B-) at breakout box. • **Is resistance reading greater than 10K ohms?**	Yes No	▶ ▶	REPLACE ICM. C2 is shorted low. REMOVE all test equipment. RECONNECT all components. CLEAR Continuous Memory. RERUN Quick Test. CHECK connectors, SERVICE or REPLACE harness. C2 is shorted low. REMOVE all test equipment. RECONNECT all components. CLEAR Continuous Memory. RERUN Quick Test.
JC62 CHECK FOR C1 HIGH—ICM AND COIL DISCONNECTED • Key off. • Disconnect ICM from ICM tee, leave EI diagnostic harness connected to vehicle harness connector. • DVOM on 40 volt DC scale. • Key on, engine off. • Measure voltage between (+)J3 (RC1C) and (-)J7 (B-) at breakout box. • **Is DC voltage reading less than 0.5 volts?**	Yes No	▶ ▶	REPLACE ICM. REMOVE all test equipment. RECONNECT all components. CLEAR Continuous Memory. RERUN Quick Test. CHECK connectors, SERVICE or REPLACE harness. C1 is shorted high. REMOVE all test equipment. RECONNECT all components. CLEAR Continuous Memory. RERUN Quick Test.

Fig. 200 Test JC: Ignition Coil 1, 2, 3, 4 Failure (Part 20 of 21). 1994-95

TEST STEP	RESULT	▶	ACTION TO TAKE
JC63 CHECK FOR C2 LOW—ICM AND COIL DISCONNECTED—KOEO • Key off. • Disconnect ICM from ICM tee, leave EI diagnostic harness connected to vehicle harness connector. • DVOM on 40 volt DC scale. • Key on, engine off. • Measure voltage between (+)J6 (RC2C) and (-)J7 (B-) at breakout box. • **Is DC voltage reading less than 0.5 volts?**	Yes No	▶ ▶	REPLACE ICM. REMOVE all test equipment. RECONNECT all components. CLEAR Continuous Memory. RERUN Quick Test. CHECK connectors, SERVICE or REPLACE harness. C2 is shorted high. REMOVE all test equipment. RECONNECT all components. CLEAR Continuous Memory. RERUN Quick Test.

FM0159401199210X

Fig. 200 Test JC: Ignition Coil 1, 2, 3, 4 Failure (Part 21 of 21). 1994-95

Note

You should enter this Pinpoint Test only when directed here.

Remember

This Pinpoint Test is intended to diagnose the following:

- Crankshaft Position (CKP) Sensor
- CKP Harness
- CKP Connector
- Spark Plug Wires
- Powertrain Control Module (PCM)

TEST STEP	RESULT	▶	ACTION TO TAKE
JD1 CHECK PLUGS AND WIRES—KEY OFF			
• Check spark plug wires for insulation damage, looseness, shorting or other damage. • Remove and check spark plugs for damage, wear, carbon deposits and proper plug gap. • Examine all wiring harnesses and connectors for damaged, burned or overheated insulation, damaged pins and loose or broken conditions. • Check sensor shield connector. • **Are spark plugs and wires OK?**	Yes No	▶ ▶	REINSTALL plugs and wires. GO to JD2. SERVICE or REPLACE damaged component. REMOVE all test equipment. RECONNECT all components. CLEAR Continuous Memory. RERUN Quick Test.
JD2 CHECK PWR GND TO PCM—KEY OFF			
• Key off. • Disconnect Scan Tool from DLC. • Disconnect PCM. Inspect for damaged or pushed out pins, corrosion, loose wires, etc. Service as necessary. • Install breakout box and connect PCM. • DVOM on 200 ohm scale. • When making measurements on a wiring harness, both a visual inspection and continuity test must be performed. • Measure resistance between Pin 103 (PWR GND) at the breakout box and -(B-). • **Is resistance less than 5.0 ohms?**	Yes No	▶ ▶	GO to JD3. CHECK connectors, SERVICE or REPLACE harness. PWR GND to ICM is open. REMOVE all test equipment. RECONNECT all components. CLEAR Continuous Memory. RERUN Quick Test.

Fig. 201   Test JD: No Spark-Integrated Ignition (Part 1 of 7). 1995

TEST STEP	RESULT	▶	ACTION TO TAKE
JD3 CHECK FOR VPWR TO PCM—KEY OFF			
• Key off. • DVOM on 40 volt DC scale. • Key on, engine off. • When making voltage check, a ground reading means any value within a range of zero to 1 volt. Also, VPWR readings mean any value that falls within a range of B+ to 2 volts less than B+. • When making voltage checks and a reference to ground is made, use either the negative battery lead or cast iron on the engine. B+ means the positive battery cable at the battery. • Measure voltage between (+) Pin 97 (VPWR I) at the breakout box and (-) (B-). • **Is DC voltage greater than 10.5 volts?**	Yes No	▶ ▶	GO to JD4. CHECK connectors, SERVICE or REPLACE harness. VPWR to PCM is open. REMOVE all test equipment. RECONNECT all components. CLEAR Continuous Memory. RERUN Quick Test.
JD4 CHECK CKP+ BIAS AT PCM—KOEO			
• Key off. • DVOM on 40 volt DC scale. • Key on, engine off. • Do not use an incandescent lamp to check CKP+ or CKP-. The lamp will prevent the circuit from operating. • Measure voltage between Pin 21 (CKP+ I) at the breakout box and (-) (B-). • **Is DC voltage between 1.0 and 2.0 volts?**	Yes No	▶ ▶	GO to JD10. Bias fault. GO to JD5.
JD5 CHECK CKP+BIAS SENSOR DISCONNECTED—BIAS FAULT—KOEO			
• Key off. • Disconnect CKP sensor from vehicle harness connector. • DVOM on 40 volt DC scale. • Key on, engine off. • Measure voltage between Pin 21 (CKP+ I) at the breakout box and (-) (B-). • **Is DC voltage greater than 1.0 volt but less than 2.0 volts?**	Yes No	▶ ▶	GO to JD6. Bias fault. GO to JD18.
JD6 CHECK CKP- SENSOR—BIAS FAULT—CKP SENSOR DISCONNECTED—KOEO			
• Key off. • DVOM on 40 volt DC scale. • Key on, engine off. • Measure voltage between Pin 22 (CKP- I) at the breakout box and (-) (B-). • **Is DC voltage between 1.0 and 2.0 volts?**	Yes No	▶ ▶	REPLACE CKP sensor. Short to ground. REMOVE all test equipment. RECONNECT all components. CLEAR Continuous Memory. RERUN Quick Test. Bias fault. GO to JD7.

Fig. 201   Test JD: No Spark-Integrated Ignition (Part 2 of 7). 1995

TEST STEP	RESULT	▶	ACTION TO TAKE
JD7 DETERMINE IF BIAS HIGH OR BIAS LOW FAULT—KEY OFF			
• Was bias voltage reading in JD6 less than 1.0 volt?	Yes No	▶ ▶	Bias low fault. GO to JD8. Bias high fault. GO to JD9.
JD8 CHECK CKP SENSOR—FOR SHORT TO GROUND—BIAS LOW FAULT—CKP SENSOR AND PCM DISCONNECTED—KEY OFF			
• Key off. • Disconnect PCM from breakout box. • DVOM on 20K ohm scale. • Measure resistance between Pin 22 (CKP- I) at the breakout box and -(B-). • **Is the resistance greater than 10K ohms?**	Yes No	▶ ▶	REPLACE PCM. CKP- is shorted low. REMOVE all test equipment. RECONNECT all components. CLEAR Continuous Memory. RERUN Quick Test. CHECK connectors, SERVICE or REPLACE harness. CKP- is shorted low. REMOVE all test equipment. RECONNECT all components. CLEAR Continuous Memory. RERUN Quick Test.
JD9 CHECK CKP- SENSOR FOR SHORT HIGH—BIAS HIGH FAULT—CKP SENSOR AND PCM DISCONNECTED—KOEO			
• Key off. • Disconnect PCM from breakout box. • DVOM on 40 volt DC scale. • Key on, engine off. • Measure voltage between Pin 22 (CKP- I) at the breakout box and -(B-). • **Is DC voltage less than 0.5 volts?**	Yes No	▶ ▶	REPLACE PCM. CKP- shorted high. REMOVE all test equipment. RECONNECT all components. CLEAR Continuous Memory. RERUN Quick Test. CHECK connectors, SERVICE or REPLACE harness. CKP- is shorted high. REMOVE all test equipment. RECONNECT all components. CLEAR Continuous Memory. RERUN Quick Test.

Fig. 201   Test JD: No Spark-Integrated Ignition (Part 3 of 7). 1995

TEST STEP	RESULT	▶	ACTION TO TAKE
JD10 CHECK CKP SENSOR AMPLITUDE AT PCM—KOEC			
• Key off. • DVOM on 40 volt AC scale. • Crank engine and measure voltage between Pin 21 (CKP+ I) and Pin 22 (CKP- I) at breakout box. • **Is settled AC voltage reading greater than 0.4 volt?**	Yes No	▶ ▶	GO to Pinpoint Test Step JE1. Amplitude fault. GO to JD11.
JD11 CHECK CKP AMPLITUDE AT PCM—AMPLITUDE FAULT—PCM DISCONNECTED—KOEC			
• Key off. • Disconnect PCM from breakout box. • DVOM on 40 volt AC scale. • Crank engine and measure voltage between Pin 21 (CKP+ I) and Pin 22 (CKP- I) at breakout box. • **Is settled AC voltage reading greater than 0.4 volt?**	Yes No	▶ ▶	REPLACE PCM. CKP is shorted in PCM. REMOVE all test equipment. RECONNECT all components. CLEAR Continuous Memory. RERUN Quick Test. GO to JD12.
JD12 CHECK CIRCUIT RESISTANCE—AMPLITUDE FAULT—KEY OFF			
• Key off. • DVOM on 20K ohm scale. • Measure resistance between Pin 22 (CKP- I) and Pin 21 (CKP+ I) at breakout box. • **Is resistance between 300 and 800 ohms?**	Yes No	▶ ▶	GO to JD16. CKP- circuit resistance fault. GO to JD13.
JD13 DETERMINE IF RESISTANCE HIGH OR RESISTANCE LOW FAULT			
• Was the resistance from JD12 less than 300 ohms?	Yes No	▶ ▶	Low resistance fault. GO to JD17. High resistance fault. GO to JD14.

Fig. 201   Test JD: No Spark-Integrated Ignition (Part 4 of 7). 1995

TEST STEP	RESULT	▶	ACTION TO TAKE
JD14 CHECK CKP+ SENSOR OPEN—RESISTANCE HIGH FAULT—KEY OFF • Key off. • Install EI diagnostic harness to breakout box and the CKP Sensor and vehicle harness (Rotunda 007-00059 or equivalent). • Connect EI diagnostic harness negative lead to battery, leave positive lead disconnected. • For 8 Cylinder Applications: Use EI (High Data Rate) 8 Overlay. Set EI diagnostic harness box type switch to "8" cylinder position. • For 6 Cylinder Applications: Use EI (High Data Rate) 6 Overlay. Set EI diagnostic harness box type switch to "4/6" cylinder position. • For 2.3L Dual Plug Applications: Use EI (High Data Rate) 2.3L Dual Plug Overlay. Set EI diagnostic harness box type switch to "4/6" cylinder position. • DVOM on 20K ohm scale. • Measure resistance between J31 (CKP+ S) at the EI breakout box and Pin 21 (CKP+ I) at the PCM breakout box. • Is resistance less than 1050 ohms?	Yes No	▶ ▶	GO to JD15. CHECK connectors, SERVICE or REPLACE harness. CKP+ open. REMOVE all test equipment. RECONNECT all components. CLEAR Continuous Memory. RERUN Quick Test.
JD15 CHECK FOR CKP OPEN—RESISTANCE HIGH FAULT—KEY OFF • Key off. • DVOM on 20K ohm scale. • Measure resistance between J32 (CKP- S) and Pin 22 (CKP- I) at breakout box. • Is resistance less than 1050 ohms?	Yes No	▶ ▶	REPLACE CKP sensor. High resistance. REMOVE all test equipment. RECONNECT all components. CLEAR Continuous Memory. RERUN Quick Test. CHECK connectors. SERVICE or REPLACE harness. CKP- open. REMOVE all test equipment. RECONNECT all components. CLEAR Continuous Memory. RERUN Quick Test.

Fig. 201 Test JD: No Spark-Integrated Ignition (Part 5 of 7). 1995

TEST STEP	RESULT	▶	ACTION TO TAKE
JD16 CHECK CKP SENSOR AND TRIGGER WHEEL • Key off. • Check trigger wheel and CKP sensor for damage. • Is CKP sensor and trigger data wheel OK?	Yes No	▶ ▶	REPLACE CKP sensor. No output from sensor. REMOVE all test equipment. RECONNECT all components. CLEAR Continuous Memory. RERUN Quick Test. SERVICE or REPLACE damaged parts. REMOVE all test equipment. RECONNECT all components. CLEAR Continuous Memory. RERUN Quick Test.
JD17 CHECK FOR CKP+ SHORTED TO CKP-—RESISTANCE LOW FAULT—CKP SENSOR DISCONNECTED—KEY OFF • Key off. • Disconnect CKP sensor from vehicle harness connector. • DVOM on 20K ohm scale. • Measure resistance between Pin 21 (CKP+ I) and Pin 22 (CKP- I) at breakout box. • Is resistance greater than 1000 ohms?	Yes No	▶ ▶	REPLACE CKP sensor. Shorted windings. REMOVE all test equipment. RECONNECT all components. CLEAR Continuous Memory. RERUN Quick Test. CHECK connectors. SERVICE or REPLACE harness. CKP+ shorted to CKP- in harness. REMOVE all test equipment. RECONNECT all components. CLEAR Continuous Memory. RERUN Quick Test.
JD18 DETERMINE IF BIAS VOLTAGE HIGH OR BIAS VOLTAGE LOW FAULT • Was bias voltage reading in JD5 less than 1.0 volt?	Yes No	▶ ▶	Low bias voltage fault. GO to JD19. High bias voltage fault. GO to JD20.

Fig. 201 Test JD: No Spark-Integrated Ignition (Part 6 of 7). 1995

TEST STEP	RESULT	▶	ACTION TO TAKE
JD19 CHECK CKP+ SENSOR FOR SHORT TO GROUND—CKP SENSOR AND PCM DISCONNECTED—LOW BIAS FAULT—KEY OFF • Key off. • Disconnect PCM from PCM tee, leave EI diagnostic harness connected to vehicle harness connector. • DVOM on 20K ohm scale. • Measure resistance between Pin 21 (CKP+ I) at the breakout box and (B-). • Is resistance greater than 10K ohms?	Yes No	▶ ▶	REPLACE PCM. CKP+ shorted low. REMOVE all test equipment. RECONNECT all components. CLEAR Continuous Memory. RERUN Quick Test. CHECK connectors, SERVICE or REPLACE harness. CKP+ is shorted low. REMOVE all test equipment. RECONNECT all components. CLEAR Continuous Memory. RERUN Quick Test.
JD20 CHECK CKP+ SENSOR FOR SHORT HIGH—BIAS VOLTAGE HIGH FAULT—CKP SENSOR AND PCM DISCONNECTED—KOEO • Key off. • Disconnect PCM from breakout box. • DVOM on 40 volt DC scale. • Key on, engine off. • Measure voltage between Pin 21 (CKP+ I) at the breakout box and -(B-). • Is DC voltage less than 0.5 volt?	Yes No	▶ ▶	REPLACE PCM. CKPS+ shorted high. REMOVE all test equipment. RECONNECT all components. CLEAR Continuous Memory. RERUN Quick Test. CHECK connectors. SERVICE or REPLACE harness. CKP+ is shorted high. REMOVE all test equipment. RECONNECT all components. CLEAR Continuous Memory. RERUN Quick Test.

Fig. 201 Test JD: No Spark-Integrated Ignition (Part 7 of 7). 1995

Remember

This Pinpoint Test is intended to diagnose the following:

• Ignition Coil Packs
• Ignition Coil Harness
• Vehicle Power Circuit to Coil Packs
• Powertrain Control Module (PCM)

TEST STEP	RESULT	▶	ACTION TO TAKE
JE1 CHECK FOR SPARK DURING CRANK NOTE: 3.0L and 4.0L Trucks: JE1 through JE24 2.3L Truck: JE70 through JE103 4.6L Car: JE30 through JE63. • DTC: P0351, P0352, P0353 or P0350. • Using a Neon Bulb Spark Tester (OTC D89P-6666-A) or Air Gap Spark Tester (D81P-6666-A), check for spark at all spark plug wires while cranking. • When using the spark plug firing indicator, place the grooved end as close as possible to the plug boot. Very weak or no flashing may be caused by a fouled plug. • Was spark consistent on all spark plug wires (one spark per crankshaft revolution)?	Yes No	▶ ▶	Ignition System OK. GO to JE2. Spark fault.
JE2 CHECK PLUGS AND WIRES • Check spark plug wires for insulation damage, looseness, shorting or other damage. • Remove and check spark plugs for damage, wear, carbon deposits and proper plug gap. • Examine all wiring harnesses and connectors for damaged, burned or overheated insulation, damaged pins, and loose or broken conditions. • Check sensor shield connector. • Are spark plugs and wires OK?	Yes No	▶ ▶	REINSTALL plugs and wires. GO to JE3. SERVICE or REPLACE damaged component. REMOVE all test equipment. RECONNECT all components. CLEAR Continuous Memory. RERUN Quick Test.

Fig. 202 Test JE: Integrated Ignition-Coil 1, 2, 3 or 4 Failure (Part 1 of 19). 1995

TEST STEP	RESULT	▶	ACTION TO TAKE
JE3 CHECK FOR COIL PWR AT COIL **WARNING: NEVER CONNECT PCM TO THE EEC BREAKOUT BOX WHEN PERFORMING EI DIAGNOSTICS.** • Key off. • Install EI diagnostic harness to breakout box. • Connect negative lead to battery. • Set EI diagnostic harness type switch to "4/6 cylinder" position. • Install the coil tee (the tee is blue with 4 pins). • Use EI (High Data Rate) 6 overlay. • DVOM on 40 volt DC scale. • Key on, engine off. • When making voltage checks, a ground reading means any value within a range of zero to 1 volt. Also, VPWR or COIL PWR readings mean any value that falls within a range of B+ to 2 volts less than B+. • Measure voltage between (+)J5 (COIL PWR) and (-)J7 (B-) at breakout box. • **Is DC voltage greater than 10.0 volts?**	Yes No	▶ ▶	GO to JE4. CHECK connectors, SERVICE or REPLACE harness. COIL PWR is open. REMOVE all test equipment. RECONNECT all components. CLEAR Continuous Memory. RERUN Quick Test.
JE4 CHECK FOR C1 HIGH AT COIL PACK—KOEO • Key on, engine off. • Measure voltage between (+)J3 (C1C) and (-)J7 (B-) at the EI breakout box. • **Is DC voltage reading greater than 10.0 volts?**	Yes No	▶ ▶	GO to JE5. C1 low fault. GO to JE16.
JE5 CHECK FOR C2 HIGH AT COIL PACK—KOEO • Key on, engine off. • Measure voltage between (+)J6 (C2C) and (-)J7 (B-) at the EI breakout box. • **Is DC voltage reading greater than 10.0 volts?**	Yes No	▶ ▶	GO to JE6. C2 low fault. GO to JE18.
JE6 CHECK FOR C3 HIGH AT COIL PACK—KOEO • Key on, engine off. • Measure voltage between (+)J10 (C3C) and (-)J7 (B-) at the EI breakout box. • **Is DC voltage reading greater than 10.0 volts?**	Yes No	▶ ▶	GO to JE7. C3 low fault. GO to JE20.

Fig. 202   Test JE: Integrated Ignition-Coil 1, 2, 3 or 4 Failure (Part 2 of 19). 1995

TEST STEP	RESULT	▶	ACTION TO TAKE
JE7 CHECK FOR C1 HIGH AT PCM—KOEO • Key off. • DVOM on 40 volt DC scale. • Key on, engine off. • Measure voltage between Pin 26 (C1I) at the PCM breakout box and (-)J7 (B-) at the EI breakout box. • **Is DC voltage reading greater than 10.0 volts?**	Yes No	▶ ▶	GO to JE8. CHECK connectors, SERVICE or REPLACE harness. C1 is open. REMOVE all test equipment. RECONNECT all components. CLEAR Continuous Memory. RERUN Quick Test.
JE8 CHECK FOR C2 HIGH AT PCM—KOEO • Key on, engine off. • Measure voltage between Pin 52 (C2I) at the PCM breakout box and (-)J7 (B-) at the EI breakout box. • **Is DC voltage reading greater than 10.0 volts?**	Yes No	▶ ▶	GO to JE9. CHECK connectors, SERVICE or REPLACE harness. C2 is open. REMOVE all test equipment. RECONNECT all components. CLEAR Continuous Memory. RERUN Quick Test.
JE9 CHECK FOR C3 HIGH AT PCM—KOEO • Key on, engine off. • Measure voltage between Pin 78 (C3I) at the PCM breakout box and (-)J7 (B-) at the EI breakout box. • **Is DC voltage reading greater than 10.0 volts?**	Yes No	▶ ▶	GO to JE10. CHECK connectors, SERVICE or REPLACE harness. C3 is open. REMOVE all test equipment. RECONNECT all components. CLEAR Continuous Memory. RERUN Quick Test.
JE10 CHECK FOR C1 LOW AT COIL CONNECTOR—COIL DISCONNECTED—KOEO • Key off. • Disconnect the coil from the coil tee. Leave EI diagnostic harness coil tee connected to vehicle harness coil connector. • DVOM on 40 volt DC scale. • Key on, engine off. • Measure voltage between (+)J3 (C1C) and (-)J7 (B-) at the EI breakout box. • **Is DC voltage reading less than 0.5 volt?**	Yes No	▶ ▶	GO to JE11. C1 high fault. GO to JE22.

Fig. 202   Test JE: Integrated Ignition-Coil 1, 2, 3 or 4 Failure (Part 3 of 19). 1995

TEST STEP	RESULT	▶	ACTION TO TAKE
JE11 CHECK FOR C2 LOW AT COIL CONNECTOR—COIL DISCONNECTED—KOEO • Key on, engine off. • Measure voltage between (+)J6 (C2C) and (-)J7 (B-) at the EI breakout box. • **Is DC voltage reading less than 0.5 volt?**	Yes No	▶ ▶	GO to JE12. C2 high fault. GO to JE23.
JE12 CHECK FOR C3 LOW AT COIL CONNECTOR—COIL DISCONNECTED • Key on, engine off. • Measure voltage between (+)J10 (C3C) and (-)J7 (B-) at the EI breakout box. • **Is DC voltage reading less than 0.5 volt?**	Yes No	▶ ▶	GO to JE13. C3 high fault. GO to JE24.
JE13 CHECK C1 AT COIL CONNECTOR WHILE CRANKING ENGINE—COIL DISCONNECTED—KOEC • Connect EI diagnostic harness positive lead to battery. • Connect incandescent test lamp between J1 (B+) and J3 (C1C). • Crank engine. • **Does lamp blink consistently and brightly (one blink per engine revolution)?**	Yes No	▶ ▶	GO to JE14. REPLACE PCM. C1 open in PCM. REMOVE all test equipment. RECONNECT all components. CLEAR Continuous Memory. RERUN Quick Test.
JE14 CHECK C2 AT COIL CONNECTOR WHILE CRANKING ENGINE—COIL DISCONNECTED—KOEC • Connect incandescent test lamp between J1 (B+) and J6 (C2C). • Crank engine. • **Does lamp blink consistently and brightly (one blink per engine revolution)?**	Yes No	▶ ▶	GO to JE15. REPLACE PCM. C3 open in PCM. REMOVE all test equipment. RECONNECT all components. CLEAR Continuous Memory. RERUN Quick Test.

Fig. 202   Test JE: Integrated Ignition-Coil 1, 2, 3 or 4 Failure (Part 4 of 19). 1995

TEST STEP	RESULT	▶	ACTION TO TAKE
JE15 CHECK C3 AT COIL CONNECTOR WHILE CRANKING ENGINE—COIL DISCONNECTED—KOEC • Connect test lamp between J1 (B+) and J10 (C3C). • Crank engine. • **Does lamp blink consistently and brightly (one blink per engine revolution)?**	Yes No	▶ ▶	REPLACE coil pack. Input to coil pack is OK, but no high voltage output. REMOVE all test equipment. RECONNECT all components. CLEAR Continuous Memory. RERUN Quick Test. REPLACE PCM. C3 open in PCM. REMOVE all test equipment. RECONNECT all components. CLEAR Continuous Memory. RERUN Quick Test.
JE16 CHECK FOR C1 SHORT LOW—COIL DISCONNECTED—KEY OFF • Key off. • DVOM on 20K ohm scale. • Disconnect coil from coil tee, leave EI diagnostic harness connected to vehicle harness coil connector. • Measure resistance between J7 (B-) and J3 (C1C) at breakout box. • **Is resistance reading greater than 2K ohms?**	Yes No	▶ ▶	REPLACE coil pack. C1 open in coil. REMOVE all test equipment. RECONNECT all components. CLEAR Continuous Memory. RERUN Quick Test. GO to JE17.

Fig. 202   Test JE: Integrated Ignition-Coil 1, 2, 3 or 4 Failure (Part 5 of 19). 1995

TEST STEP	RESULT	▶	ACTION TO TAKE
JE 17 CHECK FOR C1 SHORT LOW—PCM AND COIL DISCONNECTED—KEY OFF			
• Key off. • Disconnect PCM from vehicle harness connector. • DVOM on 20K ohm scale. • Measure resistance between J7 (B-) and J3 (C1C) at breakout box. • Is resistance reading greater than 10K ohms?	Yes	▶	REPLACE PCM. C1 is shorted low. REMOVE all test equipment. RECONNECT all components. CLEAR Continuous Memory. RERUN Quick Test.
	No	▶	CHECK connectors, SERVICE or REPLACE harness. C1 is shorted low. REMOVE all test equipment. RECONNECT all components. CLEAR Continuous Memory. RERUN Quick Test. NOTE: A C1 short to ground may have damaged the coil.
JE 18 CHECK FOR C2 SHORT LOW—COIL DISCONNECTED—KEY OFF			
• Key off. • DVOM on 20K ohm scale. • Disconnect coil from coil tee, leave EI diagnostic harness connected to vehicle harness coil connector. • Measure resistance between J7 (B-) and J6 (C2C) at breakout box. • Is resistance reading greater than 2K ohms?	Yes	▶	REPLACE coil pack. C2 open in coil. REMOVE all test equipment. RECONNECT all components. CLEAR Continuous Memory. RERUN Quick Test.
	No	▶	GO to JE19.

Fig. 202 Test JE: Integrated Ignition-Coil 1, 2, 3 or 4 Failure (Part 6 of 19). 1995

TEST STEP	RESULT	▶	ACTION TO TAKE
JE 19 CHECK FOR C2 LOW—PCM AND COIL DISCONNECTED—KEY OFF			
• Key off. • Disconnect PCM from vehicle harness connector. • DVOM on 20K ohm scale. • Measure resistance between J6 (C2C) and J7 (B-) at breakout box. • Is resistance reading greater than 10K ohms?	Yes	▶	REPLACE PCM. C2 shorted low. REMOVE all test equipment. RECONNECT all components. CLEAR Continuous Memory. RERUN Quick Test.
	No	▶	CHECK connectors, SERVICE or REPLACE harness. C2 is shorted low. REMOVE all test equipment. RECONNECT all components. CLEAR Continuous Memory. RERUN Quick Test. NOTE: A C2 short to ground may have damaged the coil.
JE20 CHECK FOR C3 SHORT LOW—COIL DISCONNECTED—KEY OFF			
• Key off. • DVOM on 20K ohm scale. • Disconnect coil from coil tee, leave EI diagnostic harness connected to vehicle harness coil connector. • Measure resistance between J7 (B-) and J10 (C3C) at breakout box. • Is resistance reading greater than 2K ohms?	Yes	▶	REPLACE coil pack. C3 open in coil. REMOVE all test equipment. RECONNECT all components. CLEAR Continuous Memory. RERUN Quick Test.
	No	▶	GO to JE21.

Fig. 202 Test JE: Integrated Ignition-Coil 1, 2, 3 or 4 Failure (Part 7 of 19). 1995

TEST STEP	RESULT	▶	ACTION TO TAKE
JE21 CHECK FOR C3 SHORT LOW—PCM AND COIL DISCONNECTED—KEY OFF			
• Key off. • Disconnect PCM from vehicle harness connector. • DVOM on 20K ohm scale. • Measure resistance between J7 (B-) and J10 (C3C) at breakout box. • Is resistance greater than 10K ohms?	Yes	▶	REPLACE PCM. C3 is shorted low. REMOVE all test equipment. RECONNECT all components. CLEAR Continuous Memory. RERUN Quick Test.
	No	▶	CHECK connectors, SERVICE or REPLACE harness. C3 is shorted low. REMOVE all test equipment. RECONNECT all components. CLEAR Continuous Memory. RERUN Quick Test. NOTE: A C3 short to ground may have damaged the coil.
JE22 CHECK FOR C1 LOW—PCM AND COIL DISCONNECTED—KOEO			
• Key off. • Disconnect PCM from the vehicle harness connector. • DVOM on 40 volt DC scale. • Key on, engine off. • Measure voltage between (+)J3 (C1C) and (-)J7 (B-) at breakout box. • Is DC voltage reading less than 0.5 volt?	Yes	▶	REPLACE PCM. C1 is shorted high. REMOVE all test equipment. RECONNECT all components. CLEAR Continuous Memory. RERUN Quick Test.
	No	▶	CHECK connectors, SERVICE or REPLACE harness. C1 is shorted high. REMOVE all test equipment. RECONNECT all components. CLEAR Continuous Memory. RERUN Quick Test.

Fig. 202 Test JE: Integrated Ignition-Coil 1, 2, 3 or 4 Failure (Part 8 of 19). 1995

TEST STEP	RESULT	▶	ACTION TO TAKE
JE23 CHECK FOR C2 LOW—PCM AND COIL DISCONNECTED			
• Key off. • Disconnect PCM from the vehicle harness connector. • DVOM on 40 volt DC scale. • Key on, engine off. • Measure voltage between (+)J6 (C2C) and (-)J7 (B-) at breakout box. • Is DC voltage reading less than 0.5 volt?	Yes	▶	REPLACE PCM. C2 is shorted high. REMOVE all test equipment. RECONNECT all components. CLEAR Continuous Memory. RERUN Quick Test.
	No	▶	CHECK connectors, SERVICE or REPLACE harness. C2 is shorted high. REMOVE all test equipment. RECONNECT all components. CLEAR Continuous Memory. RERUN Quick Test.
JE24 CHECK FOR C3 LOW—PCM AND COIL DISCONNECTED			
• Key off. • Disconnect PCM from the vehicle harness connector. • DVOM on 40 volt DC scale. • Key on, engine off. • Measure voltage between (+)J10 (C3C) and (-)J7 (B-) at breakout box. • Is DC voltage reading less than 0.5 volt?	Yes	▶	REPLACE PCM. C3 is shorted high. REMOVE all test equipment. RECONNECT all components. CLEAR Continuous Memory. RERUN Quick Test.
	No	▶	CHECK connectors, SERVICE or REPLACE harness. C3 is shorted high. REMOVE all test equipment. RECONNECT all components. CLEAR Continuous Memory. RERUN Quick Test.

Fig. 202 Test JE: Integrated Ignition-Coil 1, 2, 3 or 4 Failure (Part 9 of 19). 1995

TEST STEP	RESULT	▶	ACTION TO TAKE
JE30 CHECK FOR SPARK DURING CRANK—KOEC • DTCs P0350, P0351, P0352, P0353, or P0354 • Using a Neon Bulb Spark Tester (Special Service Tool D89P-6666-A) or Air Gap Spark Tester (D81P-6666-A). Check for spark at all spark plug wires while cranking. • When using the spark plug firing indicator, place the grooved end as close as possible to the plug boot. Very weak or no flashing may be caused by a fouled plug. • Was spark consistent on all spark plug wires (one spark per crankshaft revolution?)	Yes No	▶ ▶	The ignition system is OK. GO to JE31. Spark fault.
JE31 CHECK FOR SPARK AT ALL RIGHT SPARK PLUG WIRES DURING CRANK—KOEC • Was spark consistent on all right spark plug wires (one spark per crankshaft revolution)? NOTE: Check spark at spark plugs.	Yes No	▶ ▶	GO to JE32. GO to JE48.
JE32 CHECK LEFT SPARK PLUGS AND WIRES—KEY OFF • Check left side coil pack spark plug wires for insulation damage, looseness, shorting or other damage. • Remove and check left side spark plugs for damage, wear, carbon deposits and proper plug gap. • Left coil plugs and wires are attached to the left coil pack. • Examine all wiring harnesses and connectors for damaged, burned or overheated insulation, damaged pins and loose or broken condition. • Check sensor shield connector. • Are spark plugs and wires OK?	Yes No	▶ ▶	REINSTALL plugs and wires. GO to JE33. SERVICE or REPLACE damaged component. REMOVE all test equipment. RECONNECT all components. CLEAR Continuous Memory. RERUN Quick Test.

Fig. 202 Test JE: Integrated Ignition-Coil 1, 2, 3 or 4 Failure (Part 10 of 19). 1995

TEST STEP	RESULT	▶	ACTION TO TAKE
JE33 CHECK FOR COIL PWR TO LEFT COIL FAULT—KOEO **WARNING: NEVER CONNECT PCM TO THE EEC BREAKOUT BOX WHEN PERFORMING EI DIAGNOSTICS.** • Key off. • Install EI (High Data Rate) diagnostic harness to breakout box. • Install the left coil tee. The tee is yellow (left coil). • Connect EI diagnostic harness negative lead to battery. • Use 4.6L EI (High Data Rate) 8 overlay. • Set EI harness type switch to "8 cylinder" position. • DVOM on 40 volt DC scale. • Key on, engine off. • When making voltage checks, a ground reading means any value within a range of zero to 1 volt. Also VPWR or COIL PWR readings mean any value that falls within a range of B+ to 2 volts less than B+. • Measure voltage between (+)J11 (COIL PWR L) and (-)J7 (B-) at breakout box. • Is DC voltage greater than 10.0 volts?	Yes No	▶ ▶	GO to JE34. CHECK connectors, SERVICE or REPLACE harness. COIL PWR is open to left coil. REMOVE all test equipment. RECONNECT all components. CLEAR Continuous Memory. RERUN Quick Test.
JE34 CHECK FOR C3 HIGH AT COIL PACK—KOEO • Key on, engine off. • Measure voltage between (+)J10 (LC3C) and (-)J7 (B-) at breakout box. • Is DC voltage reading greater than 10.0 volts?	Yes No	▶ ▶	GO to JE35. C3 low fault. GO to JE42.
JE35 CHECK FOR C4 HIGH AT COIL PACK—KOEO • Key on, engine off. • Measure voltage between (+)J18 (LC4C) and (-)J7 (B-) at the breakout box. • Is DC voltage reading greater than 10.0 volts?	Yes No	▶ ▶	GO to JE36. C4 low fault. GO to JE44.
JE36 CHECK FOR C3 HIGH AT PCM—KOEO • Key off. • DVOM on 40 volt DC scale. • Key on, engine off. • Measure voltage between Pin 78 (LC3I) at the PCM breakout box and (-)J7 (B-) at the EI breakout box. • Is DC voltage reading greater than 10.0 volts?	Yes No	▶ ▶	GO to JE37. CHECK connectors, SERVICE or REPLACE harness. C3 is open. REMOVE all test equipment. RECONNECT all components. CLEAR Continuous Memory. RERUN Quick Test.

Fig. 202 Test JE: Integrated Ignition-Coil 1, 2, 3 or 4 Failure (Part 11 of 19). 1995

TEST STEP	RESULT	▶	ACTION TO TAKE
JE37 CHECK FOR C4 HIGH AT PCM—KOEO • Key on, engine off. • Measure voltage between Pin 104 (LC4I) at the PCM breakout box and (-)J7 (B-) at the EI breakout box. • Is DC voltage reading greater than 10.0 volts?	Yes No	▶ ▶	GO to JE38. CHECK connectors, SERVICE or REPLACE harness. C4 is open. REMOVE all test equipment. RECONNECT all components. CLEAR Continuous Memory. RERUN Quick Test.
JE38 CHECK FOR C3 LOW AT COIL CONNECTOR—COIL DISCONNECTED—KOEO • Key off. • Disconnect left coil pack from coil tee, leave EI diagnostic harness connected to vehicle harness left coil connector. • DVOM on 40 volt DC scale. • Key on, engine off. • Measure voltage between (+)J10 (LC3C) and (-)J7 (B-) at the EI breakout box. • Is DC voltage reading less than 0.5 volt?	Yes No	▶ ▶	GO to JE39. C3 high fault. GO to JE46.
JE39 CHECK FOR C4 LOW AT COIL CONNECTOR—COIL DISCONNECTED—KOEO • Key on, engine off. • Measure voltage between (+)J18 (LC4C) and (-)J7 (B-) at the EI breakout box. • Is DC voltage reading less than 0.5 volt?	Yes No	▶ ▶	GO to JE40. C4 high fault. GO to JE47.
JE40 CHECK C3 AT COIL CONNECTOR WHILE CRANKING—COIL DISCONNECTED—KOEC • Connect EI diagnostic harness positive lead to battery. • Connect an incandescent test lamp between J1 (B+) and J10 (LC3C). • Crank engine. • Does lamp blink consistently and brightly (one blink per engine revolution?	Yes No	▶ ▶	GO to JE41. REPLACE PCM. C3 open. REMOVE all test equipment. RECONNECT all components. CLEAR Continuous Memory. RERUN Quick Test.

Fig. 202 Test JE: Integrated Ignition-Coil 1, 2, 3 or 4 Failure (Part 12 of 19). 1995

TEST STEP	RESULT	▶	ACTION TO TAKE
JE41 CHECK C4 AT COIL CONNECTOR WHILE CRANKING—COIL DISCONNECTED—KOEC • Connect an incandescent test lamp between J1 (B+) and J18 (LC4C). • Crank engine. • Does lamp blink consistently and brightly (one blink per engine revolution)?	Yes No	▶ ▶	REPLACE left coil pack. Input to coil pack is OK, but no high voltage output. REMOVE all test equipment. RECONNECT all components. CLEAR Continuous Memory. RERUN Quick Test. REPLACE PCM. C4 open in PCM. REMOVE all test equipment. RECONNECT all components. CLEAR Continuous Memory. RERUN Quick Test.
JE42 CHECK FOR C3 SHORT LOW—COIL DISCONNECTED—KEY OFF • Key off. • DVOM on 20K ohm scale. • Disconnect coil from coil tee, leave EI diagnostic harness connected to vehicle harness coil connector. • Measure resistance between J7 (B-) and J10 (C3C) at breakout box. • Is resistance reading less than 2K ohms?	Yes No	▶ ▶	GO to JE43. REPLACE Left Coil Pack. C3 open in coil. REMOVE all test equipment. RECONNECT all components. CLEAR Continuous Memory. RERUN Quick Test.
JE43 CHECK FOR C3 SHORT LOW—PCM AND COIL DISCONNECTED—KEY OFF • Key off. • Disconnect PCM from vehicle harness. • DVOM on 20K ohm scale. • Measure resistance between J7 (B-) and J10 (C3C) at breakout box. • Is resistance greater than 10K ohms?	Yes No	▶ ▶	REPLACE PCM. C3 is shorted low. REMOVE all test equipment. RECONNECT all components. CLEAR Continuous Memory. RERUN Quick Test. CHECK connectors, SERVICE or REPLACE harness. C3 is shorted low. REMOVE all test equipment. RECONNECT all components. CLEAR Continuous Memory. RERUN Quick Test.

Fig. 202 Test JE: Integrated Ignition-Coil 1, 2, 3 or 4 Failure (Part 13 of 19). 1995

TEST STEP	RESULT ▶	ACTION TO TAKE
JE44 CHECK FOR C4 SHORT LOW—COIL DISCONNECTED—KEY OFF • Key off. • DVOM on 20K ohm scale. • Disconnect coil from coil tee, leave EI diagnostic harness connected to vehicle harness coil connector. • Measure resistance between J7 (B-) and J18 (LC4C) at breakout box. • **Is resistance reading less than 2K ohms?**	Yes ▶ No ▶	GO to JE45. REPLACE left coil pack. C4 open in coil. REMOVE all test equipment. RECONNECT all components. CLEAR Continuous Memory. RERUN Quick Test.
JE45 CHECK FOR C4 SHORT LOW—PCM AND COIL DISCONNECTED—KEY OFF • Key off. • Disconnect PCM from vehicle harness connector. • DVOM on 20K ohm scale. • Measure resistance between J7 (B-) and J18 (LC4C) at breakout box. • **Is resistance reading greater than 10K ohms?**	Yes ▶ No ▶	REPLACE PCM. C4 is shorted low. REMOVE all test equipment. RECONNECT all components. CLEAR Continuous Memory. RERUN Quick Test. CHECK connectors, SERVICE or REPLACE harness. C4 is shorted low. REMOVE all test equipment. RECONNECT all components. CLEAR Continuous Memory. RERUN Quick Test.
JE46 CHECK FOR C3 LOW—PCM AND COIL DISCONNECTED—KOEO • Key off. • Disconnect PCM from the vehicle harness connector. • DVOM on 40 volt DC scale. • Key on, engine off. • Measure voltage between (+)J10 (LC3C) and (-)J7 (B-) at breakout box. • **Is DC voltage reading less than 0.5 volt?**	Yes ▶ No ▶	REPLACE PCM. C3 is shorted high. REMOVE all test equipment. RECONNECT all components. CLEAR Continuous Memory. RERUN Quick Test. CHECK connectors, SERVICE or REPLACE harness. C3 is shorted high. REMOVE all test equipment. RECONNECT all components. CLEAR Continuous Memory. RERUN Quick Test.

Fig. 202 Test JE: Integrated Ignition-Coil 1, 2, 3 or 4 Failure (Part 14 of 19). 1995

TEST STEP	RESULT ▶	ACTION TO TAKE
JE47 CHECK FOR C4 LOW—PCM AND COIL DISCONNECTED—KOEO • Key off. • Disconnect PCM from the vehicle harness connector. • DVOM on 40 volt DC scale. • Key on, engine off. • Measure voltage between (+)J18 (LC4C) and (-)J7 (B-) at breakout box. • **Is DC voltage reading less than 0.5 volt?**	Yes ▶ No ▶	REPLACE PCM. C4 is shorted high. REMOVE all test equipment. RECONNECT all components. CLEAR Continuous Memory. RERUN Quick Test. CHECK connectors, SERVICE or REPLACE harness. C4 is shorted high. REMOVE all test equipment. RECONNECT all components. CLEAR Continuous Memory. RERUN Quick Test.
JE48 CHECK RIGHT PLUGS AND WIRES—KEY OFF • Check right side coil pack spark plug wires for insulation damage, looseness, shorting or other damage. • Remove and check right spark plugs for damage, wear, carbon deposits and proper plug gap. NOTE: Right coil plugs and wires are attached to the right coil. • **Are spark plugs and wires OK?**	Yes ▶ No ▶	REINSTALL plugs and wires. GO to JE49. SERVICE or REPLACE damaged component. REMOVE all test equipment. RECONNECT all components. CLEAR Continuous Memory. RERUN Quick Test.
JE49 CHECK FOR RIGHT COIL PWR—KOEO WARNING: NEVER CONNECT PCM TO THE EEC BREAKOUT BOX WHEN PERFORMING EI DIAGNOSTICS. • Key off. • Connect EI diagnostic harness negative lead to battery. • Install the right coil tee. • DVOM on 40 volt DC scale. • Set EI harness box type switch to 8 cylinder position. • Key on, engine off. • Measure voltage between (+)J5 (COIL PWR R) and (-)J7 (B-) at breakout box. • **Is DC voltage greater than 10.0 volts?**	Yes ▶ No ▶	GO to JE50. CHECK connectors, SERVICE or REPLACE harness. COIL PWR is open to right coil. REMOVE all test equipment. RECONNECT all components. CLEAR Continuous Memory. RERUN Quick Test.

Fig. 202 Test JE: Integrated Ignition-Coil 1, 2, 3 or 4 Failure (Part 15 of 19). 1995

TEST STEP	RESULT ▶	ACTION TO TAKE
JE50 CHECK FOR C1 HIGH AT RIGHT COIL PACK—KOEO • DVOM on 40 volt DC scale. • Key on, engine off. • Measure voltage between (+)J3 (RC1C) and (-)J7 (B-) at breakout box. • **Is DC voltage reading greater than 10.0 volts?**	Yes ▶ No ▶	GO to JE51. C1 low fault. GO to JE58.
JE51 CHECK FOR C2 HIGH AT RIGHT COIL PACK • Key on, engine off. • Measure voltage between (+)J6 (RC2C) and (-)J7 (B-) at breakout box. • **Is DC voltage reading greater than 10.0 volts?**	Yes ▶ No ▶	GO to JE52. C2 low fault. GO to JE60.
JE52 CHECK FOR C1 HIGH AT PCM—KOEO • Key off. • DVOM on 40 volt DC scale. • Key on, engine off. • Measure voltage between Pin 26 (RC1I) at the PCM breakout box and (-)J7 (B-) at the EI breakout box. • **Is DC voltage reading greater than 10.0 volts?**	Yes ▶ No ▶	GO to JE53. CHECK connectors, SERVICE or REPLACE harness. C1 is open. REMOVE all test equipment. RECONNECT all components. CLEAR Continuous Memory. RERUN Quick Test.
JE53 CHECK FOR C2 HIGH AT PCM • Key on, engine off. • Measure voltage between Pin 52 (RC2I) at the PCM breakout box and (-)J7 (B-) at the EI breakout box. • **Is DC voltage reading greater than 10.0 volts?**	Yes ▶ No ▶	GO to JE54. CHECK connectors, SERVICE or REPLACE harness. C2 is open. REMOVE all test equipment. RECONNECT all components. CLEAR Continuous Memory. RERUN Quick Test.
JE54 CHECK C1 LOW AT COIL CONNECTOR—COIL DISCONNECTED • Key off. • Disconnect right coil from coil tee, leave EI diagnostic harness connected to vehicle harness right coil connector. • DVOM on 40 volt DC scale. • Key on, engine off. • Measure voltage between (+)J3 (RC1C) and (-)J7 (B-) at breakout box. • **Is DC voltage reading less than 0.5 volt?**	Yes ▶ No ▶	GO to JE55. C1 high fault. GO to JE62.

Fig. 202 Test JE: Integrated Ignition-Coil 1, 2, 3 or 4 Failure (Part 16 of 19). 1995

TEST STEP	RESULT ▶	ACTION TO TAKE
JE55 CHECK FOR C2 LOW AT COIL CONNECTOR—COIL DISCONNECTED • Key on, engine off. • Measure voltage between (+)J6 (RC2C) and (-)J7 (B-) at breakout box. • **Is DC voltage reading less than 0.5 volt?**	Yes ▶ No ▶	GO to JE56. C2 high fault. GO to JE63.
JE56 CHECK C1 AT COIL CONNECTOR WHILE CRANKING ENGINE—COIL DISCONNECTED • Connect EI diagnostic harness positive lead to battery. • Connect an incandescent test lamp between J1 (B+) and J3 (RC1C). • Crank engine. • **Does lamp blink consistently and brightly (one blink per engine revolution)?**	Yes ▶ No ▶	GO to JE57. REPLACE PCM. C1 is open. REMOVE all test equipment. RECONNECT all components. CLEAR Continuous Memory. RERUN Quick Test.
JE57 CHECK C2 AT COIL CONNECTOR WHILE CRANKING ENGINE—COIL DISCONNECTED • Connect an incandescent test lamp between J1 (B+) and J6 (RC2C). • Crank engine. • **Does lamp blink consistently and brightly (one blink per engine revolution)?**	Yes ▶ No ▶	REPLACE Right Coil Pack. Input to coil pack is OK, but no high voltage output. REMOVE all test equipment. RECONNECT all components. CLEAR Continuous Memory. RERUN Quick Test. REPLACE PCM. C2 is open in PCM. REMOVE all test equipment. RECONNECT all components. CLEAR Continuous Memory. RERUN Quick Test.
JE58 CHECK FOR C1 SHORT LOW—COIL DISCONNECTED • Key off. • DVOM on 20K ohm scale. • Disconnect coil from coil tee, leave EI diagnostic harness connected to vehicle harness coil connector. • Measure resistance between J7 (B-) and J3 (RC1C) at breakout box. • **is resistance reading less than 2K ohms?**	Yes ▶ No ▶	GO to JE59. REPLACE Right Coil Pack. C1 is open in coil. REMOVE all test equipment. RECONNECT all components. CLEAR Continuous Memory. RERUN Quick Test.

Fig. 202 Test JE: Integrated Ignition-Coil 1, 2, 3 or 4 Failure (Part 17 of 19). 1995

TEST STEP	RESULT	▶	ACTION TO TAKE
JE59 CHECK FOR C1 SHORT LOW—PCM AND COIL DISCONNECTED • Key off. • Disconnect PCM from vehicle harness. • DVOM on 20K ohm scale. • Measure resistance between J7 (B-) and J3 (RC1C) at breakout box. • Is resistance reading greater than 10K ohms?	Yes	▶	REPLACE PCM. C1 is shorted low. REMOVE all test equipment. RECONNECT all components. CLEAR Continuous Memory. RERUN Quick Test.
	No	▶	CHECK connectors, SERVICE or REPLACE harness. C1 is shorted to low. REMOVE all test equipment. RECONNECT all components. CLEAR Continuous Memory. RERUN Quick Test.
JE60 CHECK FOR C2 SHORT LOW—COIL DISCONNECTED • Key off. • DVOM on 20K ohm scale. • Disconnect coil from coil tee, leave EI diagnostic harness connected to vehicle harness coil connector. • Measure resistance between J7 (B-) and J6 (RC2C) at breakout box. • Is resistance reading less than 2K ohms?	Yes No	▶ ▶	GO to **JE61**. REPLACE Right Coil Pack. C2 open in coil. REMOVE all test equipment. RECONNECT all components. CLEAR Continuous Memory. RERUN Quick Test.
JE61 CHECK FOR C2 SHORT LOW—PCM AND COIL DISCONNECTED • Key off. • Disconnect PCM from vehicle harness. • DVOM on 20K ohm scale. • Measure resistance between J6 (RC2C) and J7 (B-) at breakout box. • Is resistance reading greater than 10K ohms?	Yes	▶	REPLACE PCM. C2 is shorted low. REMOVE all test equipment. RECONNECT all components. CLEAR Continuous Memory. RERUN Quick Test.
	No	▶	CHECK connectors, SERVICE or REPLACE harness. C2 is shorted low. REMOVE all test equipment. RECONNECT all components. CLEAR Continuous Memory. RERUN Quick Test.

Fig. 202   Test JE: Integrated Ignition-Coil 1, 2, 3 or 4 Failure (Part 18 of 19). 1995

TEST STEP	RESULT	▶	ACTION TO TAKE
JE62 CHECK FOR C1 HIGH—PCM AND COIL DISCONNECTED • Key off. • Disconnect PCM from the vehicle harness connector. • DVOM on 40 volt DC scale. • Key on, engine off. • Measure voltage between (+)J3 (RC1C) and (-)J7 (B-) at breakout box. • Is DC voltage reading less than 0.5 volt?	Yes	▶	REPLACE PCM. REMOVE all test equipment. RECONNECT all components. CLEAR Continuous Memory. RERUN Quick Test.
	No	▶	CHECK connectors, SERVICE or REPLACE harness. C1 is shorted high. REMOVE all test equipment. RECONNECT all components. CLEAR Continuous Memory. RERUN Quick Test.
JE63 CHECK FOR C2 LOW—PCM AND COIL DISCONNECTED—KOEO • Key off. • Disconnect PCM from the vehicle harness connector. • DVOM on 40 volt DC scale. • Key on, engine off. • Measure voltage between (+)J6 (RC2C) and (-)J7 (B-) at breakout box. • Is DC voltage reading less than 0.5 volt?	Yes	▶	REPLACE PCM. REMOVE all test equipment. RECONNECT all components. CLEAR Continuous Memory. RERUN Quick Test.
	No	▶	CHECK connectors, SERVICE or REPLACE harness. C2 is shorted high. REMOVE all test equipment. RECONNECT all components. CLEAR Continuous Memory. RERUN Quick Test.

Fig. 202   Test JE: Integrated Ignition-Coil 1, 2, 3 or 4 Failure (Part 19 of 19). 1995

Pinpoint Test Schematics

Crown Victoria/Grand Marquis, Town Car

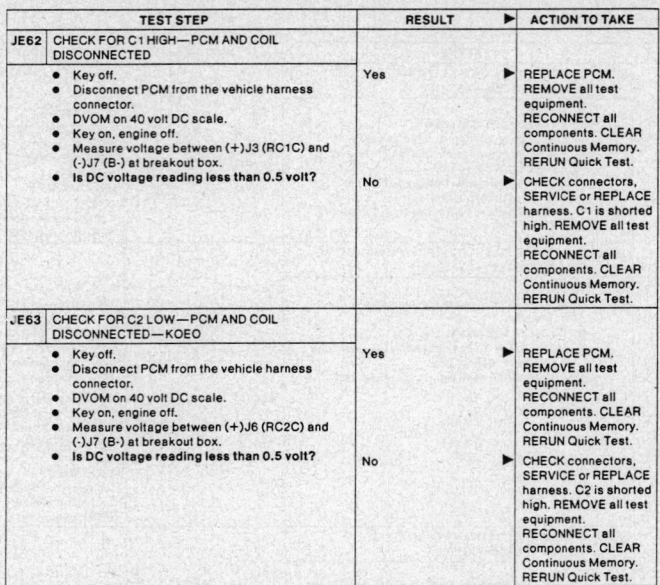

Fig. 203   Test KA: Fuel Pump Relay (Part 2 of 10). 1995

Remember

This Pinpoint Test is intended to diagnose the following:
* Fuel Pump Relay (9345)
* Inertia Fuel Shutoff (IFS) switch (9341)
* Harness circuits: B(+), VPWR, FP, GND, FPM and Power-To-Pump(s)
* Powertrain Control Module (PCM) (12A650)

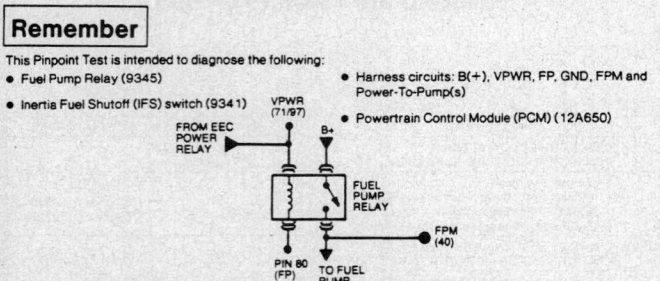

Fig. 203   Test KA: Fuel Pump Relay (Part 1 of 10). 1995

TEST STEP	RESULT	▶	ACTION TO TAKE
KA1 DIAGNOSTIC TROUBLE CODE (DTC) P0230: CHECK FOR VPWR TO FUEL PUMP RELAY DTC P0230 indicates a fuel pump primary circuit failure. Possible causes: — Open or shorted circuit. — Damaged fuel pump relay. — Damaged PCM. • Disconnect fuel pump relay. • Key on, engine off. • Measure voltage between VPWR circuit at the fuel pump relay vehicle harness connector and chassis ground. • Is voltage greater than 10.5 volts?	Yes No	▶ ▶	GO to **KA2**. SERVICE open in VPWR circuit between the EEC power relay and the fuel pump relay. RECONNECT fuel pump relay. RERUN Quick Test.
KA2 CHECK FUEL PUMP RELAY • Key off. • Fuel pump relay disconnected. • Check fuel pump relay coil resistance: — Measure resistance between Pins 85 and 86 at the fuel pump relay (pin numbers molded on relay). — Resistance should be between 40 and 85 ohms. • Check fuel pump relay for internal shorts. — Measure resistance between Pin 85 and both Pins 30 and 87 at the fuel pump relay. — Both resistances should be greater than 10,000 ohms. • Are all resistance checks OK?	Yes No	▶ ▶	GO to **KA3**. REPLACE fuel pump relay. RERUN Quick Test.

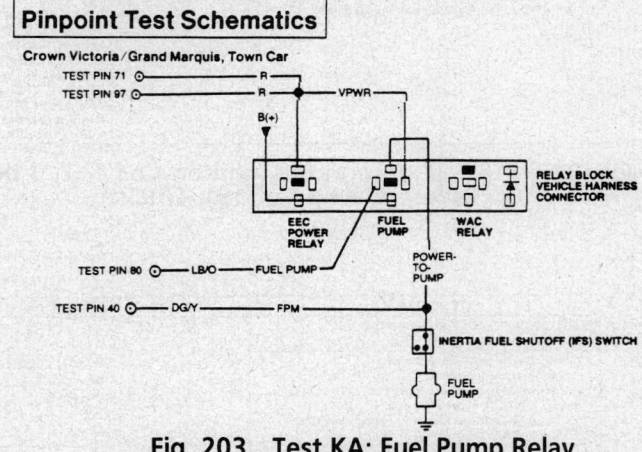

Fig. 203   Test KA: Fuel Pump Relay (Part 3 of 10). 1995

TEST STEP	RESULT	▶	ACTION TO TAKE
KA3 CHECK FUEL PUMP CIRCUIT FOR SHORT TO POWER • Key off. • Fuel pump relay disconnected. • Disconnect Powertrain Control Module (PCM). Inspect for damaged or pushed out pins, corrosion, loose wires, etc. Service as necessary. • Install breakout box, leave PCM disconnected. • Key on, engine off. • Measure voltage between Test Pin 80 (FP) at the breakout box and chassis ground. • **Is voltage less than 1.0 volt?**	Yes No	▶ ▶	GO to **KA4**. SERVICE short to power. REMOVE breakout box. RECONNECT all components. RERUN Quick Test.
KA4 CHECK FUEL PUMP CIRCUIT FOR SHORT TO GROUND • Key off. • Disconnect Scan Tool from DLC. • Breakout box installed, PCM disconnected. • Fuel pump relay disconnected. • Measure resistance between Test Pin 80 and Test Pins 51 or 103 (PWR GND) and 91 (SIG RTN) at the breakout box. • **Is resistance greater than 10,000 ohms?**	Yes No	▶ ▶	GO to **KA5**. SERVICE short circuit. REMOVE breakout box. RECONNECT all components. RERUN Quick Test.
KA5 CHECK FUEL PUMP CIRCUIT CONTINUITY • Key off. • Breakout box installed, PCM disconnected. • Fuel pump relay disconnected. • Measure resistance between Fuel Pump circuit at the fuel pump relay vehicle harness connector and Test Pin 80 at the breakout box. • **Is resistance less than 5.0 ohms?**	Yes No	▶ ▶	REPLACE PCM. RECONNECT all components. RERUN Quick Test. SERVICE open circuit. REMOVE breakout box. RECONNECT all components. RERUN Quick Test.

**Fig. 203   Test KA: Fuel Pump Relay
(Part 4 of 10). 1995**

TEST STEP	RESULT	▶	ACTION TO TAKE
KA15 CHECK INERTIA FUEL SHUTOFF (IFS) SWITCH • Key off. • Locate and disconnect Inertia Fuel Shutoff (IFS) switch (verify that switch is reset). • Measure resistance between the C and NC pins of the IFS switch. • **Is resistance less than 5.0 ohms?**	Yes No	▶ ▶	GO to **KA16**. REPLACE or RESET IFS switch. RERUN Quick Test.
KA16 CHECK POWER-TO-PUMP CIRCUIT CONTINUITY BETWEEN IFS SWITCH AND FUEL PUMP RELAY • Key off. • IFS switch disconnected. • Disconnect fuel pump relay. • Measure resistance of the Power-to-Pump circuit between the fuel pump relay and IFS switch vehicle harness connectors. • **Is resistance less than 5.0 ohms?**	Yes No	▶ ▶	RECONNECT IFS switch and fuel pump relay. check for open in Power-to-Pump circuit (IFS switch to pump), poor fuel pump ground, open in fuel pump, etc. After any service, RECONNECT all components and RERUN Quick Test. SERVICE open in Power-to-Pump circuit between IFS switch and FPM connection to circuit.
KA20 DIAGNOSTIC TROUBLE CODE (DTC) P0231: DOES ENGINE START? DTC P0231 indicates a fuel pump secondary circuit failure between the B(+) supply and the FPM connection to the power-to-pump circuit. Possible causes: No Start: — Open circuit between the B(+) supply and the FPM connection to the power-to-pump circuit. — Fuel pump relay contacts always open. Engine Starts: — Damaged PCM. • **Does the engine start?**	Yes No	▶ ▶	REPLACE PCM. RERUN Quick Test. GO to **KA21**.

**Fig. 203   Test KA: Fuel Pump Relay
(Part 6 of 10). 1995**

TEST STEP	RESULT	▶	ACTION TO TAKE
KA21 CHECK FOR B(+) TO FUEL PUMP RELAY • Key off. • Disconnect fuel pump relay. • Measure voltage between B(+) circuit at the fuel pump relay vehicle harness connector and chassis ground. • **Is voltage greater than 10.5 volts?**	Yes No	▶ ▶	GO to **KA22**. VERIFY integrity of fuse/fuse link for B(+) supply to fuel pump relay. If OK, SERVICE open in B(+) circuit. RECONNECT fuel pump relay. RERUN Quick Test.
KA22 CHECK POWER-TO-PUMP CIRCUIT CONTINUITY • Key off. • Fuel pump relay disconnected. • Measure resistance between power-to-pump circuit at the fuel pump relay vehicle harness connector and the battery negative post. • **Is resistance less than 10.0 ohms?**	Yes No	▶ ▶	REPLACE fuel pump relay. RERUN Quick Test. SERVICE open in power-to-pump circuit between FPM splice and fuel pump relay. RECONNECT fuel pump relay. RERUN Quick Test.

**Fig. 203   Test KA: Fuel Pump Relay
(Part 7 of 10). 1995**

TEST STEP	RESULT	▶	ACTION TO TAKE
KA10 DIAGNOSTIC TROUBLE CODE (DTC) P0232: DOES ENGINE START? DTC P0232 indicates that one of the following has occurred: No Start: — Inertia Fuel Shutoff (IFS) switch not reset or electrically open. — Open circuit between the fuel pump and FPM circuit connection to the power-to-pump circuit. — Poor fuel pump ground. — Fuel pump electrically open. Engine Starts: — Fuel pump secondary circuit short to power. — Fuel pump relay contacts always closed. — Open in FPM circuit between PCM and connection to the power-to-pump circuit. — Damaged PCM. • **Does the engine start?**	Yes No	▶ ▶	GO to **KA11**. GO to **KA15**.
KA11 VERIFY THAT FUEL PUMP IS OFF • Key on, wait five seconds. • Listen for motor noise from fuel pump (it may be necessary to listen by fuel tank). • **Is fuel pump off?**	Yes No	▶ ▶	GO to **KA13**. GO to **KA12**.
KA12 CHECK FOR FUEL PUMP RELAY ALWAYS CLOSED • Key off. • Locate and disconnect fuel pump relay. • Key on. • **Is fuel pump off with relay disconnected?**	Yes No	▶ ▶	REPLACE fuel pump relay. RERUN Quick Test. SERVICE short to power in power-to-pump/FPM circuit. RECONNECT fuel pump relay. RERUN Quick Test.
KA13 CHECK FPM CIRCUIT CONTINUITY • Key off. • Disconnect PCM. Inspect for damaged or pushed out pins, corrosion, loose wires, etc. Service as necessary. • Install breakout box, leave PCM disconnected. • Disconnect fuel pump relay. • Measure resistance between Test Pin 40 (FPM) at the breakout box and power-to-pump circuit at the fuel pump relay vehicle harness connector. • **Is resistance less than 5.0 ohms?**	Yes No	▶ ▶	REPLACE PCM. REMOVE breakout box. RECONNECT fuel pump relay. RERUN Quick Test. SERVICE open circuit. REMOVE breakout box. RECONNECT all components. RERUN Quick Test.

**Fig. 203   Test KA: Fuel Pump Relay
(Part 5 of 10). 1995**

TEST STEP	RESULT	▶	ACTION TO TAKE
KA30 CONTINUOUS MEMORY DIAGNOSTIC TROUBLE CODE (DTC) P0232: CHECK EEC-V HARNESS A Continuous Memory DTC P0232 indicates that one of the following intermittent conditions has occurred: — Fuel pump circuit activated when PCM expected circuit to be off (i.e., fuel system test or prime procedure). — Inertia fuel shutoff switch was tripped, then reset. — Open circuit in or between the fuel pump and FPM circuit at the PCM (refer to schematic). — Poor fuel pump ground. — FPM or power-to-pump circuit short to power. — Fuel pump relay contacts stuck closed. — Engine stall due to excessive load. • Key on, engine off. • Access FPM PID on Scan Tool. • Observe the FPM PID for an indication of a fault while performing the following (the FPM PID will turn ON when an open or short to power is detected): — Shake, wiggle, bend the Power-to-Pump circuit between the power-to-pump pin at the fuel pump relay and the fuel pump. — Shake, wiggle, bend the fuel pump ground circuit from the fuel pump to ground. — Lightly tap the fuel pump to simulate road shock. — Shake, wiggle, bend the FPM circuit between the PCM and the splice to the Power-to-Pump circuit. — Lightly tap Inertia Fuel Shutoff switch to simulate road shock. — Lightly tap the fuel pump relay to simulate road shock. • Key off. • Inspect the fuel pump vehicle harness connector and the fuel pump ground for corrosion, damaged pins, etc. • **Is fault indicated/found?**	Yes No	▶ ▶	ISOLATE fault and SERVICE as necessary. COMPLETE PCM reset to clear DTCs Powertrain Control Module (PCM) Reset.) RERUN Quick Test. Unable to duplicate and/or identify fault at this time. GO to Pinpoint Test Step **Z1** with the following data: FPM PID and list of possible causes.

**Fig. 203   Test KA: Fuel Pump Relay
(Part 8 of 10). 1995**

TEST STEP		RESULT	▶	ACTION TO TAKE
KA35	**CONTINUOUS MEMORY DIAGNOSTIC TROUBLE CODE (DTC) P0231: CHECK EEC-V HARNESS**			
	A Continuous Memory DTC P0231 indicates that sometime during vehicle operation when the fuel pump was commanded on the FPM circuit voltage went low. (Since there is no FP primary circuit DTC P0230, the primary circuit is assumed to be OK.)	Yes	▶	ISOLATE fault and SERVICE as necessary. COMPLETE PCM reset to clear DTCs
	Possible causes: — Open in B(+) circuit to the fuel pump relay. — Fuel pump relay contacts open. — Open in Power-to-Pump circuit between the fuel pump relay and FPM slice.			Powertrain Control Module (PCM) Reset.) RERUN Quick Test.
	• Scan Tool connected. • Key on, engine off. • Access Output Test Mode on Scan Tool.	No	▶	Unable to duplicate and/or identify fault at this time. GO to Pinpoint Test Step **Z1** with the following data: FPM PID and list of possible causes.
	• While in Output Test Mode, access the FPM PID (if the Scan Tool being used will not allow you to view PIDs while in Output Test Mode, disconnect PCM, install a breakout box, reconnect PCM and connect a DVOM between Test Pin 40 (FPM) and Test Pin 51 (GND). • Command the outputs on. The FPM PID will be on (or the DVOM voltage will be greater than 10.0 volts). • Observe FPM PID (or DVOM voltage) for an indication of a fault while performing the following (the FPM PID or DVOM voltage will change suddenly when a fault is detected, indicating an open): — Shake, wiggle, bend the B(+) circuit to the fuel pump relay. — Lightly tap the fuel pump relay to simulate road shock. — Shake, wiggle, bend the Power-to-Pump circuit between the fuel pump relay and the FPM splice. • Key off. • Inspect the fuel pump relay connector for corrosion, damaged pins, etc. • **Is a fault indicated?**			

Fig. 203 Test KA: Fuel Pump Relay (Part 9 of 10). 1995

TEST STEP		RESULT	▶	ACTION TO TAKE
KA40	**CONTINUOUS MEMORY DIAGNOSTIC TROUBLE CODE (DTC) P0230: CHECK EEC-V HARNESS**			
	A Continuous Memory DTC P0230 indicates a fuel pump primary circuit failure has occurred during vehicle operation.	Yes	▶	ISOLATE fault and SERVICE as necessary. COMPLETE PCM reset to clear DTCs
	Possible causes: — Open in VPWR to fuel pump relay. — Open coil in pump relay. — Open in Fuel Pump circuit (PCM Pin 80).			Powertrain Control Module (PCM) Reset.) RERUN Quick Test.
	• Scan Tool connected. • Key on, engine off. Wait 5 seconds. • Access FPF PID (Ranger) or FPA PID (all others). The FPA or FPF PID will be off, indicating that the PCM detects VPWR voltage through the fuel pump relay coil and FP circuit (Pin 80) to the PCM.	No	▶	Unable to duplicate and/or identify fault at this time. GO to Pinpoint Test Step **Z1** with the following data: FPA or FPF PID and list of possible causes. For testing the FP circuit with the engine running, also monitor the FPM PID. This is because all FP circuit failures may be detected using only the FPA or FPF PID.
	• Observe the FPA or FPF PID for an indication of a fault while performing the following (the FPA or FPF PID will turn on, when an open is detected (this is because the PCM will not detect VPWR voltage on Pin 80 (FP))): — Shake, wiggle, bend the fuel pump circuit between the PCM (Pin 80) and the fuel pump relay. — Shake, wiggle bend the VPWR circuit between the EEC-V Power Relay and the Fuel Pump Relay. — Lightly tap the fuel pump relay (to simulate road shock). • Key off. • Inspect the PCM and fuel pump relay connectors for corrosion, damaged pins, etc. • **Is a fault indicated?**			

Fig. 203 Test KA: Fuel Pump Relay (Part 10 of 10). 1995

Remember

This Pinpoint Test is intended to diagnose the following:

• Harness circuits: VPWR, GND and B(+) to FPDM Power Supply Relay in CCRM; B(+) and GND to FPDM; FPM; FP; Power-To-Pump; Fuel Pump Ground

• Inertia Fuel Shutoff (IFS) Switch (9341)

• Fuel Pump Driver Module (FPDM) (9D370)

• Constant Control Relay Module (CCRM) (FPDM Power Supply Relay / Circuits) (12B577 / 12B581)

• Powertrain Control Module (PCM) (12A650)

Fig. 204 Test KB: Fuel Pump Driver Module (Part 1 of 15). 1995

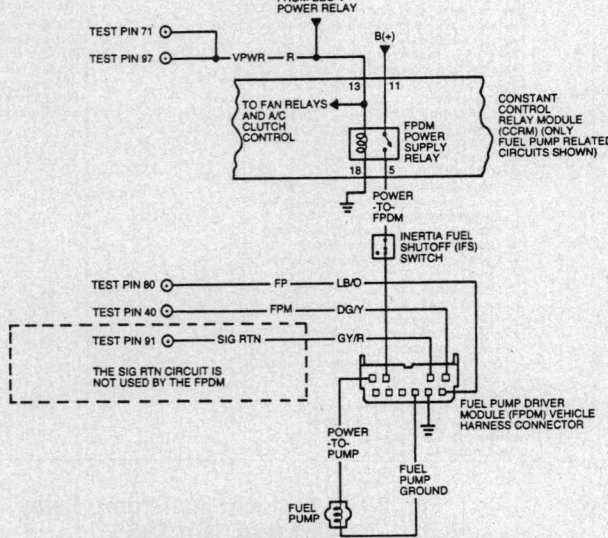

Fig. 204 Test KB: Fuel Pump Driver Module (Part 2 of 15). 1995

TEST STEP		RESULT	▶	ACTION TO TAKE
KB1	**DTC P1233 OR P1234: CHECK IF PCM IS NOW RECEIVING AN FPM SIGNAL**			
	Diagnostic Trouble Code (DTC) P1233 or P1234 indicates that the Powertrain Control Module (PCM) has stopped receiving diagnostic information from the Fuel Pump Driver Module (FPDM). The FPDM diagnostic information is sent to the PCM as a duty cycle on the Fuel Pump Monitor (FPM) circuit. This could be due to an intermittent or hard fault concern. The only difference between the DTC P1233 and P1234 is that the P1233 is a MIL DTC.	Yes	▶	The PCM is now receiving a signal from the FPDM. One possible cause of the DTC P1233 or P1234 may be that the IFS switch was tripped, then reset. **If engine is now a no start:** Disregard the DTC P1233 or P1234 at this time. RETURN to Section 5 and continue the Diagnostic Subroutine as directed. After servicing the no start, to diagnose intermittent causes of the DTC P1233 or P1234, RETURN to **KB25**. **If engine will start:** An intermittent fault may exist. GO to **KB25**.
	Possible causes: — Inertia Fuel Shutoff (IFS) switch needs to be reset. — Open Power-To-FPDM circuit (from Constant Control Relay Module (CCRM)). — Open FPDM ground circuit. — Open B(+) to CCRM (pin 11). — Open ground to CCRM (pin 18). — Open VPWR to CCRM (pin 13). — Open or shorted FPM circuit. — Damaged IFS. — Damaged CCRM. — Damaged FPDM. — Damaged PCM. • Scan tool connected. • Key on, engine off. • Access FPM PID. • **Is the FPM PID between 20% and 80%?**	No	▶	A hard fault is present. GO to **KB2**.
KE2	**DOES THE ENGINE START?**			
	• **Does the engine start?**	Yes	▶	GO to **KB15** (to check the FPM circuit).
		No	▶	VERIFY IFS switch is set (button depressed). If OK, GO to **KB3**.

Fig. 204 Test KB: Fuel Pump Driver Module (Part 3 of 15). 1995

TEST STEP	RESULT	▶	ACTION TO TAKE
KB3 CHECK POWER AND GROUND CIRCUITS TO FPDM			
• Key off.	Yes	▶	Key off. REPLACE FPDM. RECONNECT all components. RERUN Quick Test.
• Disconnect FPDM.			
• Key on, engine off.			
• Measure voltage between the Power-To-FPDM pin and ground pin at the FPDM vehicle harness connector.	No	▶	GO to KB7.
• Is voltage greater than 10.5 volts?			

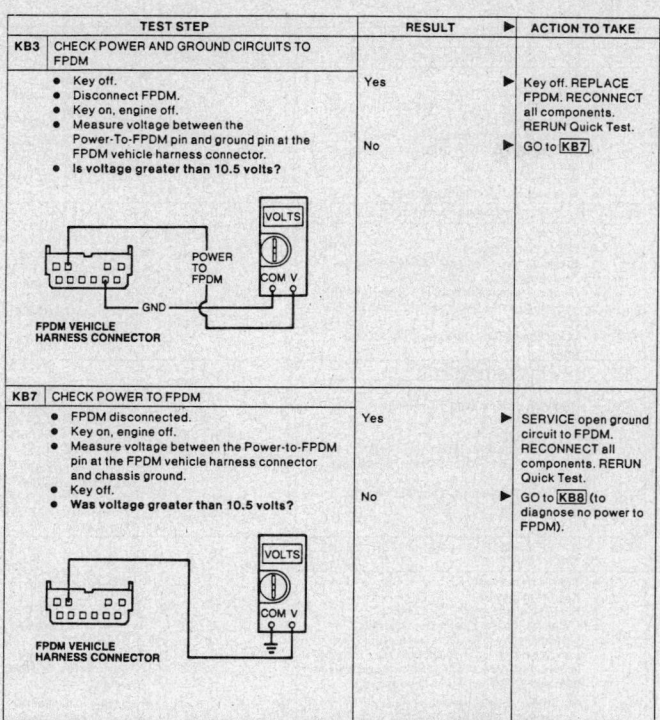

FPDM VEHICLE HARNESS CONNECTOR — POWER TO FPDM — GND — VOLTS — COM V

TEST STEP	RESULT	▶	ACTION TO TAKE
KB7 CHECK POWER TO FPDM			
• FPDM disconnected.	Yes	▶	SERVICE open ground circuit to FPDM. RECONNECT all components. RERUN Quick Test.
• Key on, engine off.			
• Measure voltage between the Power-to-FPDM pin at the FPDM vehicle harness connector and chassis ground.			
• Key off.	No	▶	GO to KB8 (to diagnose no power to FPDM).
• Was voltage greater than 10.5 volts?			

FPDM VEHICLE HARNESS CONNECTOR — VOLTS — COM V

Fig. 204   Test KB: Fuel Pump Driver Module (Part 4 of 15). 1995

TEST STEP	RESULT	▶	ACTION TO TAKE
KB8 CHECK FOR B(+) TO CCRM (FPDM POWER SUPPLY RELAY)			
• Key off.	Yes	▶	GO to KB9.
• FPDM disconnected.			
• Disconnect CCRM.			
• Measure voltage between pin 11 (B+) of the CCRM vehicle harness connector and chassis ground.	No	▶	SERVICE open B(+) to CCRM. RECONNECT all components. RERUN Quick Test.
• Is voltage greater than 10.5 volts?			
KB9 CHECK FOR GROUND TO CCRM (FPDM POWER SUPPLY RELAY)			
• Key off.	Yes	▶	GO to KB10.
• FPDM disconnected.			
• CCRM disconnected.			
• Disconnect Scan Tool from DLC.	No	▶	SERVICE open ground circuit to CCRM. RECONNECT all components. RERUN Quick Test.
• Measure resistance between pin 18 (GND) of the CCRM vehicle harness connector and the battery negative post.			
• Is resistance less than 5.0 ohms?			
KB10 CHECK POWER-TO-FPDM CIRCUIT CONTINUITY			
• Key off.	Yes	▶	RECONNECT FPDM. GO to KB11.
• FPDM disconnected.			
• CCRM disconnected.			
• Measure resistance between pin 5 of the CCRM vehicle harness and the Power-To-FPDM pin of the FPDM vehicle harness connector.	No	▶	The Power-To-FPDM circuit is open. GO to KB13 to help isolate fault.
• Is resistance less than 5.0 ohms?			
KB11 CHECK VPWR CONTINUITY BETWEEN EEC-V POWER RELAY AND CCRM			
• Key off.	Yes	▶	REPLACE CCRM. RECONNECT all components. RERUN Quick Test.
• CCRM disconnected.			
• Disconnect EEC-V Power Relay.			
• Measure resistance between the VPWR pin at the EEC-V Power Relay vehicle harness connector and pin 13 (VPWR) of the CCRM vehicle harness connector.	No	▶	SERVICE open VPWR circuit between EEC-V Power Relay and CCRM. RECONNECT all components. RERUN Quick Test.
• Is resistance less than 5.0 ohms?			

VPWR — EEC-V POWER RELAY VEHICLE HARNESS CONNECTOR

Fig. 204   Test KB: Fuel Pump Driver Module (Part 5 of 15). 1995

TEST STEP	RESULT	▶	ACTION TO TAKE
KB13 ISOLATE OPEN IN POWER-TO-FPDM CIRCUIT			
• Key off.	Yes	▶	VERIFY that the IFS switch is set (button depressed). If OK, REPLACE IFS switch. RECONNECT all components. RERUN Quick Test.
• CCRM disconnected.			
• FPDM disconnected.			
• Disconnect IFS switch.			
• Measure resistance of the Power-To-FPDM circuit between pin 5 of the CCRM vehicle harness connector and the IFS switch vehicle harness connector.	No	▶	SERVICE open in the appropriate area of the Power-To-FPDM circuit. RECONNECT all components. RERUN Quick Test.
• Measure resistance of the Power-To-FPDM circuit between the FPDM vehicle harness connector and the IFS switch vehicle harness connector.			
• Are both resistances less than 5.0 ohms?			
KB15 CHECK FPM CIRCUIT CONTINUITY			
• Key off.	Yes	▶	GO to KB16.
• Disconnect FPDM.			
• Disconnect PCM. Inspect for damaged or pushed out pins, corrosion, loose wires, etc. Service as necessary.	No	▶	SERVICE open FPM circuit. REMOVE breakout box. RECONNECT all components. RERUN Quick Test.
• Install breakout box, leave PCM disconnected.			
• Measure resistance between Test Pin 40 (FPM) at the breakout box and the FPM circuit at the FPDM vehicle harness connector.			
• Is resistance less than 5.0 ohms?			

FPM (40) — FPDM VEHICLE HARNESS CONNECTOR

TEST STEP	RESULT	▶	ACTION TO TAKE
KB16 CHECK FPM CIRCUIT FOR SHORT TO POWER			
• Key off.	Yes	▶	GO to KB17.
• FPDM disconnected.			
• Breakout box installed, PCM disconnected.	No	▶	SERVICE FPM circuit short to power. REMOVE breakout box. RECONNECT all components. RERUN Quick Test.
• Key on, engine off.			
• Measure voltage between Test Pin 40 (FPM) and Test Pin 51 (PWR GND) at the breakout box.			
• Key off.			
• Was voltage less than 1.0 volt?			

Fig. 204   Test KB: Fuel Pump Driver Module (Part 6 of 15). 1995

TEST STEP	RESULT	▶	ACTION TO TAKE
KB17 CHECK FPM FOR SHORT TO GROUND			
• Key off.	Yes	▶	GO to KB18.
• FPDM disconnected.			
• Breakout box installed, PCM disconnected.	No	▶	SERVICE FPM short to ground. REMOVE breakout box. RECONNECT all components. RERUN Quick Test.
• Disconnect Scan Tool from DLC.			
• Measure resistance between Test Pin 40 (FPM) and Test Pins 51, 76 (PWR GND) and 91 (SIG RTN).			
• Is each resistance greater than 10,000 ohms?			
KB18 CHECK FOR FPM OUTPUT FROM FPDM			
• Key off.	Yes	▶	Key off. REPLACE PCM. REMOVE breakout box. RECONNECT all components. RERUN Quick Test.
• Breakout box installed, PCM disconnected.			
• Scan Tool disconnected.			
• Reconnect FPDM.			
• Key on, engine off.	No	▶	Key off. REPLACE FPDM. REMOVE breakout box. RECONNECT all components. RERUN Quick Test.
• Measure DC voltage between Test Pin 40 (FPM) and Test Pin 76 (PWR GND) at the breakout box.			
• Is voltage between .02 and 1.0 volt DC? (It is OK for the voltage to cycle below this range and then come back in it.)			

Fig. 204   Test KB: Fuel Pump Driver Module (Part 7 of 15). 1995

TEST STEP	RESULT	▶	ACTION TO TAKE
KB25 CHECK CIRCUITS THAT MAY CAUSE AN INTERMITTENT LOSS OF POWER SUPPLY TO THE FPDM. ALSO CHECK FOR INTERMITTENT OPENS OR SHORTS ON THE FPM CIRCUIT.			
• Scan Tool connected.	Yes	▶	ISOLATE fault and SERVICE as necessary. PERFORM PCM Reset to clear DTCs (Powertrain Control Module (PCM) Reset). RERUN Quick Test.
• Key on, engine off.			
• FPM PID displayed on Scan Tool.			
• Observe FPM PID for an indication of a fault while performing the following (If the FPM PID goes less than 20%, an open in the power supply to the FPDM, or an open or short to ground on the FPM circuit may exist. If the FPMDC PID goes greater than 80%, an open or short to power on the FPM circuit may exist.):			
— Shake, wiggle, bend the following circuits:			
• FPDM ground.	No	▶	Unable to duplicate and/or identify fault at this time. GO to Pinpoint Test Step Z1 with the following data: FPM PID and list of possible causes.
• Power-To-FPDM circuit between the FPDM and the CCRM.			
• CCRM ground circuit from pin 18 (CCRM).			
• B(+) to CCRM pin 11.			
• VPWR circuit between the EEC-V power relay and Pin 13 of the CCRM.			
• FPM circuit between the FPDM and the PCM.			
— Lightly tap on the CCRM, IFS Switch and FPDM to simulate road shock.			
• Key off.			
• Is a fault indicated?			

Fig. 204   Test KB: Fuel Pump Driver Module (Part 8 of 15). 1995

TEST STEP	RESULT	▶	ACTION TO TAKE
KB30 DTCs P0230, P1235 OR P1236: CHECK FPM PID TO SEE IF FAULT IS PRESENT NOW			
Diagnostic Trouble Codes (DTCs) P0230, P1235 or P1236 indicate that an FP circuit (PCM pin 80) fault has been detected. This could be due to an intermittent or hard fault concern. The only difference between the DTC P1235 and P1236 is that the P1235 is a MIL DTC. Possible causes: — FP circuit open or short. — Damaged Fuel Pump Driver Module (FPDM). — Damaged PCM. NOTE: If the FPDM does not receive a valid fuel pump command signal from the PCM on the FP circuit, the FPDM will go into FMEM and run the fuel pump at 100%. When this happens, the FPDM will also send a 25% duty cycle signal to the PCM on the Fuel Pump Monitor (FPM) circuit. • Scan Tool connected. • Key on, engine off. • Access FPM PID. • **Is the FPM PID between 20% and 30%?**	Yes No	▶ ▶	A hard fault is present. GO to **KB31** (to check the FP circuit). DTC P0230, P1235 or P1236 is intermittent. GO to **KB40**.
KB31 FPM PID IS BETWEEN 20% AND 30%: CHECK FP CIRCUIT CONTINUITY			
• Key off. • Disconnect FPDM. • Disconnect PCM. Inspect for damaged or pushed out pins, corrosion, loose wires, etc. Service as necessary. • Install breakout box, leave PCM disconnected. • Measure resistance between test pin 80 (FP) at the breakout box and the FP circuit at the FPDM vehicle harness connector. • **Is resistance less than 5.0 ohms?**	Yes No	▶ ▶	GO to **KB32**. SERVICE open FP circuit. REMOVE breakout box. RECONNECT all components. RERUN Quick Test.

FPDM VEHICLE HARNESS CONNECTOR — FP (80)

Fig. 204 Test KB: Fuel Pump Driver
Module (Part 9 of 15). 1995

TEST STEP	RESULT	▶	ACTION TO TAKE
K332 CHECK FP CIRCUIT FOR SHORT TO POWER			
• Key off. • FPDM disconnected. • Breakout box installed, PCM disconnected. • Key on, engine off. • Measure voltage between Test Pin 80 (FP) and Test Pin 51 (PWR GND) at the breakout box. • Key off. • **Was voltage less than 1.0 volt?**	Yes No	▶ ▶	GO to **KB33**. SERVICE FP circuit short to power. REMOVE breakout box. RECONNECT all components. RERUN Quick Test.
KB33 CHECK FP CIRCUIT FOR SHORT TO GROUND			
• Key off. • FPDM disconnected. • Breakout box installed, PCM disconnected. • Disconnect Scan Tool from DLC. • Measure resistance between Test Pin 80 (FP) and Test Pins 51, 76 (PWR GND) and 91 (SIG RTN). • **Is each resistance greater than 10,000 ohms?**	Yes No	▶ ▶	GO to **KB34**. SERVICE FP circuit short to ground. REMOVE breakout box. RECONNECT all components. RERUN Quick Test.
KE34 CHECK FP CIRCUIT IN FPDM			
• Key off. • Breakout box installed, PCM disconnected. • Reconnect FPDM. • Key on, engine off. • Measure voltage between Test Pin 80 (FP) and Test Pin 51 (PWR GND) at the breakout box. • **Is voltage between 4.5 and 5.5 volts?**	Yes No	▶ ▶	REPLACE PCM. REMOVE breakout box. RECONNECT all components. RERUN Quick Test. REPLACE FPDM. REMOVE breakout box. RECONNECT all components. RERUN Quick Test.
KB40 CHECK FP CIRCUIT FOR INTERMITTENT OPENS OR SHORTS			
• Scan Tool connected. • Key on, engine off. • FPM PID displayed on Scan Tool. • Listen for the fuel pump to turn on while performing the following: (The fuel pump will turn on when an open or short on the FP circuit is detected. Also, the FPM PID will be between 20% and 30% when a fault is detected.) — Shake, wiggle, bend the FP circuit between FPDM and the PCM. — Lightly tap on the FPDM (to simulate road shock). • Key off. • **Is a fault indicated?**	Yes No	▶ ▶	ISOLATE fault and SERVICE as necessary. PERFORM PCM Reset to clear DTCs Powertrain Control Module (PCM) Reset). Unable to duplicate and/or identify fault at this time. GO to Pinpoint Test Step **Z1** with the following data: FPM PID and list of possible causes.

Fig. 204 Test KB: Fuel Pump Driver
Module (Part 10 of 15). 1995

TEST STEP	RESULT	▶	ACTION TO TAKE
KB45 NO FUEL PRESSURE WITH NO DTCs: CHECK IF FUEL PUMP RUNS			
• Key off. • While listening for the fuel pump to run, turn the key on. The fuel pump should run for about one second, then turn off. Repeat if necessary. • If the fuel pump cannot be heard, perform the following: — Key on, engine off. — Scan Tool connected. — Enter Output Test Mode. — Command outputs on. — Listen by the fuel tank to check if the fuel pump is running. — Exit Output Test Mode. • **Does the fuel pump run?**	Yes No	▶ ▶	The fuel pump electrical circuits are OK. GO to Pinpoint Test Step **HC1** to check the mechanical operation of the fuel pump, etc. GO to **KB46**.
KB46 FUEL PUMP DOES NOT RUN: CHECK FPM PID			
• Scan Tool connected. • Key on, engine off. • Access FPM PID. • **Is the FPM PID between 70% and 80%?**	Yes No	▶ ▶	The FPDM detects a fault in the fuel pump secondary circuits (Power-To-Pump, Fuel Pump Ground, internal fuel pump). GO to **KB49**. GO to the Pinpoint Test Step **HC1** (to check the mechanical operation of the fuel pump). Be aware that the following things are known at this point of diagnosis: — The FPDM does NOT detect a fault in the fuel pump secondary circuits. — A fault in the primary circuit (FP, PCM pin 80) would result in the FPDM taking FMEM action and running the pump all the time. — A fault in the FPDM power supply or ground circuits would result in an EEC-V Self-Test DTC.

Fig. 204 Test KB: Fuel Pump Driver
Module (Part 11 of 15). 1995

TEST STEP	RESULT	▶	ACTION TO TAKE
KB47 DTCS P1237 OR P1238: CHECK FPM PID TO SEE IF FAULT IS PRESENT NOW			
Diagnostic Trouble Codes (DTCs) P1237 or P1238 indicate that the Fuel Pump Driver Module (FPDM) has detected a fuel pump secondary circuit fault. This could be due to an intermittent or hard fault concern. The only difference between the DTC P1237 and P1238 is that the P1237 is a MIL DTC. Possible causes: — Open or shorted Power-To-Pump circuit. — Open fuel pump ground circuit to FPDM. — Open or shorted circuit in fuel pump. — Locked fuel pump rotor. — Damaged FPDM. • Scan Tool connected. • Key on, engine off. • Access FPM PID. • **Is the FPM PID between 70% and 80%?**	Yes No	▶ ▶	A hard fault is present. GO to **KB48**. DTC P1237 or P1238 is intermittent. GO to **KB57**.
KB48 DOES THE ENGINE START?			
• **Does the engine start?**	Yes No	▶ ▶	DISCONNECT FPDM. GO to **KB62**. GO TO **KB49** (to check fuel pump secondary circuits).
KB49 FPM PID IS BETWEEN 70% AND 80%: CHECK POWER-TO-PUMP, FUEL PUMP GROUND AND INTERNAL FUEL PUMP CIRCUIT CONTINUITY			
• Key off. • Disconnect Scan Tool from DLC. • Disconnect FPDM. • Measure resistance between the Power-To-Pump circuit and the fuel pump ground circuit at the FPDM vehicle harness connector. • **Is resistance less than 10.0 ohms?**	Yes No	▶ ▶	GO to **KB50**. An open secondary circuit exists. GO to **KB54** to isolate fault.

POWER-TO-PUMP — FUEL PUMP GROUND — FPDM VEHICLE HARNESS CONNECTOR

Fig. 204 Test KB: Fuel Pump Driver
Module (Part 12 of 15). 1995

TEST STEP		RESULT	▶	ACTION TO TAKE
KB50	**CHECK FUEL PUMP GROUND CIRCUIT FOR SHORT TO POWER**			
	• FPDM disconnected. • Key on, engine off. • Measure voltage between the fuel pump ground circuit at the FPDM vehicle harness connector and chassis ground. • Key off. • **Was voltage less than 1.0 volt?**	Yes No	▶ ▶	GO to KB51. SERVICE short to power. RECONNECT all components. RERUN Quick Test.
KB51	**CHECK POWER-TO-PUMP CIRCUIT FOR SHORT TO GROUND**			
	• Key off. • Scan Tool disconnected. • Disconnect fuel pump. • Measure resistance between the Power-To-Pump circuit at the FPDM vehicle harness connector and the battery negative post. • **Is resistance greater than 10,000 ohms?**	Yes No	▶ ▶	GO to KB52. SERVICE short to ground. RECONNECT all components. RERUN Quick Test.
KB52	**CHECK FOR VOLTAGE TO FUEL PUMP**			
	• Key off. • Fuel pump disconnected. • Reconnect FPDM. • Reconnect Scan Tool. • Key on, engine off. • Enter Output Test Mode (refer to Section 2). (To perform this test step without a Scan Tool, the fuel pump can be commanded on for one second by cycling the key from off to on. Repeat as needed.) • Command outputs on (this commands the fuel pump on). • Measure voltage between the Power-To-Pump circuit and the fuel pump ground circuit at the fuel pump vehicle harness connector. • Key off. • **With the pump commanded on, is the voltage greater than 10.0 volts?**	Yes No	▶ ▶	REPLACE fuel pump. RECONNECT all components. RERUN Quick Test. VERIFY vehicle battery was at proper charge during test. If OK, REPLACE FPDM. RECONNECT all components. RERUN Quick Test.
KB54	**ISOLATE OPEN CIRCUIT**			
	• Key off. • FPDM disconnected. • Disconnect fuel pump. • Measure resistance of the Power-To-Pump circuit between the FPDM and the fuel pump. • Measure resistance of the fuel pump ground circuit between the FPDM and the fuel pump. • Measure internal resistance of the fuel pump. • **Is each resistance less than 10.0 ohms?**	Yes No	▶ ▶	No fault is detected. Verify results of previous test steps. SERVICE open in appropriate circuit (if open was internal to fuel pump, REPLACE pump). RECONNECT all components. RERUN Quick Test.

Fig. 204   Test KB: Fuel Pump Driver Module (Part 13 of 15). 1995

TEST STEP		RESULT	▶	ACTION TO TAKE
KB57	**CHECK FUEL PUMP SECONDARY CIRCUITS FOR INTERMITTENT OPENS OR SHORTS**			
	• Scan Tool connected. • Key on, engine off. • Enter Output Test Mode. • Command outputs on (this will turn the fuel pump on). • Listen for the fuel pump to turn off while performing the following (if the fuel pump cannot be heard, it may be necessary to disconnect the pump and insert a test lamp in the vehicle harness connector): — Shake, wiggle, bend the Power-To-Pump circuit and fuel pump ground circuit between the FPDM and the fuel pump. — Lightly tap the fuel pump and the FPDM to simulate road shock. • Key off. • **Is a fault indicated?**	Yes No	▶ ▶	ISOLATE fault and SERVICE as necessary. PERFORM PCM Reset to clear any DTC(s) . Powertrain Control Module (PCM) Reset). Unable to duplicate and/or identify fault at this time. GO to Pinpoint Test Step Z1 with the following data: FPM PID and list of possible causes for DTC P1237 or P1238.
KB60	**FUEL PUMP ALWAYS RUNS; CHECK FPM PID**			
	• Scan Tool connected. • Key on, engine off. • Access FPM PID. • **Is the FPM PID between 20% and 30%?**	Yes No	▶ ▶	The Fuel Pump Driver Module (FPDM) detects a fault in the FP circuit input from the PCM. When this occurs, the FPDM will always run the fuel pump when the key is on. GO to KB31 to diagnose the FP circuit. Key off. GO to KB61 (to check if FPDM is always powered).

Fig. 204   Test KB: Fuel Pump Driver Module (Part 14 of 15). 1995

TEST STEP		RESULT	▶	ACTION TO TAKE
KB61	**CHECK POWER-TO-FPDM CIRCUIT VOLTAGE TO FPDM WITH THE KEY OFF**			
	• Key off. • Disconnect the Fuel Pump Driver Module (FPDM). • Measure voltage between the Power-To-FPDM circuit and chassis ground. • **Is voltage greater than 2.0 volts with the key off?** POWER-TO-FPDM (FROM CCRM) FPDM VEHICLE HARNESS CONNECTOR	Yes No	▶ ▶	Power is always being supplied to the FPDM, which will result in the fuel pump always running. GO to KB65. GO to KB62.
KB62	**CHECK FPDM**			
	• FPDM disconnected. • Key on, engine off. • **Is the fuel pump off?**	Yes No	▶ ▶	REPLACE FPDM. RECONNECT all components. RE-EVALUATE symptom. SERVICE Power-To-Pump circuit short to power. RECONNECT all components. RE-EVALUATE symptom.
KB65	**CHECK POWER-TO-FPDM CIRCUIT VOLTAGE WITH CCRM DISCONNECTED**			
	• Key off. • FPDM disconnected. • Disconnect CCRM. • Again measure voltage between the Power-To-FPDM circuit at the FPDM vehicle harness connector and chassis ground. • **Is the voltage still greater than 2.0 volts?**	Yes No	▶ ▶	SERVICE Power-to-FPDM circuit short to power. RECONNECT all components. RE-EVALUATE symptom. REPLACE CCRM. RECONNECT all components. RE-EVALUATE symptom.

Fig. 204   Test KB: Fuel Pump Driver Module (Part 15 of 15). 1995

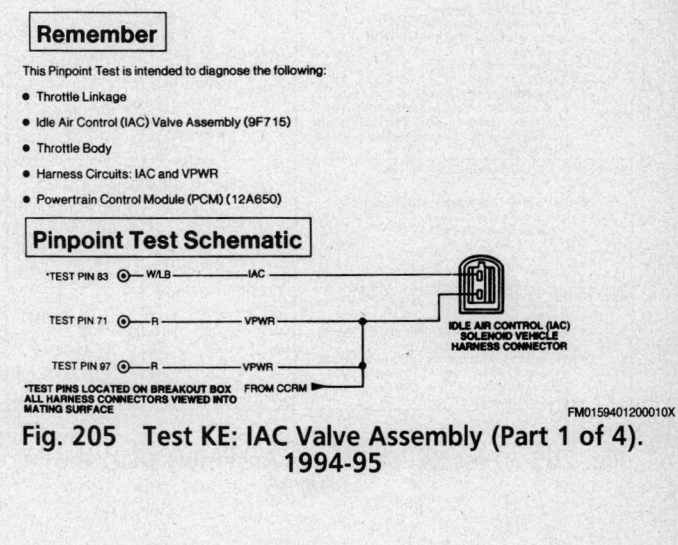

Remember

This Pinpoint Test is intended to diagnose the following:

- Throttle Linkage
- Idle Air Control (IAC) Valve Assembly (9F715)
- Throttle Body
- Harness Circuits: IAC and VPWR
- Powertrain Control Module (PCM) (12A650)

Pinpoint Test Schematic

*TEST PIN 83 ⊙— W/LB ——— IAC

TEST PIN 71 ⊙— R ——— VPWR

TEST PIN 97 ⊙— R ——— VPWR

IDLE AIR CONTROL (IAC) SOLENOID VEHICLE HARNESS CONNECTOR

FROM CCRM

*TEST PINS LOCATED ON BREAKOUT BOX ALL HARNESS CONNECTORS VIEWED INTO MATING SURFACE

FM0159401200010X

Fig. 205   Test KE: IAC Valve Assembly (Part 1 of 4). 1994-95

TEST STEP	RESULT	▶	ACTION TO TAKE
KE1 IDLE CONCERNS OR STALLS: RUN KOER SELF-TEST			
The symptom flow charts have indicated that there was no change in idle quality when the IAC was disconnected. • Run Key On Engine Running (KOER) Self-Test and look for a DTC 0505 indicating an IAC malfunction. • Is DTC 0505 output?	Yes No	▶ ▶	KOER DTC 0505 has indicated a malfunction in the IAC. GO to **KE2**. The IAC system is OK. RETURN to Symptom Flow Charts.
KE2 DTC 0505 OR STARTS ONLY AT PART THROTTLE: CHECK VPWR TO IAC			
Diagnostic Trouble Code (DTC) 0505 indicates that Self-Test has detected an IAC system malfunction. The DTC is output in KOER Self-Test when a minimum rpm cannot be reached as demanded by the PCM during the test. Possible Causes: — IAC circuit open. — IAC circuit shorted to PWR. — VPWR circuit open. — Contaminated IAC valve assembly. — Damaged throttle body. — Damaged PCM. • Key off. • Disconnect IAC solenoid vehicle harness connector. • Key on. • Measure voltage between VPWR circuit at the IAC solenoid vehicle harness connector and battery ground. • Is voltage greater than 10.5 volts?	Yes No	▶ ▶	GO to **KE3**. SERVICE open in VPWR to IAC solenoid. RECONNECT all components. RERUN Quick Test.
KE3 CHECK IAC SOLENOID RESISTANCE			
• Key off. • IAC solenoid vehicle harness connector disconnected. • Measure solenoid resistance. NOTE: Due to diode in solenoid, place DVOM (+) lead on VPWR pin and (-) lead on IAC pin. • Is resistance between 6.0 and 13.0 ohms?	Yes No	▶ ▶	GO to **KE4**. REPLACE IAC valve assembly. RECONNECT all components. RERUN Quick Test.
KE4 CHECK IAC SOLENOID FOR AN INTERNAL SHORT TO IAC CASE			
• Key off. • IAC solenoid vehicle harness connector disconnected. • Measure resistance from either IAC solenoid pin to IAC valve assembly case. • Is resistance greater than 10,000 ohms?	Yes No	▶ ▶	GO to **KE5**. REPLACE IAC valve assembly. RECONNECT all components. RERUN Quick Test.

FM0159401200020X

Fig. 205   Test KE: IAC Valve Assembly (Part 2 of 4). 1994-95

TEST STEP	RESULT	▶	ACTION TO TAKE
KE15 DTC 1505: CHECK INLET AIR CONNECTION			
Diagnostic Trouble Code (DTC) 1505 indicates the IAC system has reached the adaptive clip. Possible Causes: — Air leaks. — Plugged air filter element. — Throttle body / linkage binding. — Contaminated or damaged IAC valve assembly. — Damaged throttle body. • Key off. • Inspect the entire inlet air system for leaks such as loose connection at throttle body or air cleaner, cracked or punctured ducting, etc. • Is there a leak or loose connection in the air inlet system?	Yes No	▶ ▶	SERVICE as necessary. RESET KAM (REFER to Powertrain Control Module (PCM) Reset). RERUN Quick Test. GO to **KE16**.
KE16 CHECK FOR A PLUGGED AIR FILTER			
• Key off. • Remove air filter element and check for excessive dirt or moisture. • Is the air filter plugged?	Yes No	▶ ▶	SERVICE as necessary. RESET KAM (REFER to Powertrain Control Module (PCM) Reset). RERUN Quick Test. GO to **KE17**.
KE17 INSPECT THROTTLE BODY AND LINKAGE			
• Key off. • Disconnect accelerator cable and air cleaner tube from throttle body. • Exercise both cable and throttle body linkage separately while checking for binding, interference and full freedom of travel. • Is a fault indicated?	Yes No	▶ ▶	GO to Pinpoint Test Step **HU3**. GO to Pinpoint Test Step **HU8**.

FM0159401200040X

Fig. 205   Test KE: IAC Valve Assembly (Part 4 of 4). 1994-95

TEST STEP	RESULT	▶	ACTION TO TAKE
KE5 CHECK IAC CIRCUIT CONTINUITY			
• Key off. • IAC solenoid disconnected. • Disconnect PCM. Inspect for damaged or pushed out pins, corrosion, loose wires, etc. Service as necessary. • Install breakout box, leave PCM disconnected. • Measure resistance between Test Pin 83 (IAC) at the breakout box and IAC circuit at IAC solenoid vehicle harness connector. • Is resistance less than 5.0 ohms?	Yes No	▶ ▶	GO to **KE6**. SERVICE open circuit. REMOVE breakout box. RECONNECT all components. RERUN Quick Test.
KE6 CHECK IAC CIRCUIT FOR SHORT TO PWR			
• Key off. • Breakout box installed. PCM disconnected. • IAC solenoid disconnected. • Key on, engine off. • Measure voltage between Test Pin 83 (IAC) at the breakout box and chassis ground. • Is voltage less than 1.0 volt?	Yes No	▶ ▶	GO to **KE7**. SERVICE short circuit. REMOVE breakout box. RECONNECT all components. RERUN Quick Test.
KE7 CHECK IAC CIRCUIT FOR SHORT TO GROUND			
• Key off. • Breakout box installed, PCM disconnected. • IAC solenoid disconnected. • Measure resistance between Test Pin 83 (IAC) and Test Pins 51 and 103 (PWR GND) at the breakout box. • Is each resistance greater than 10,000 ohms?	Yes No	▶ ▶	GO to **KE8**. SERVICE short circuit. RECONNECT all components. RERUN Quick Test.
KE8 CHECK IAC SIGNAL FROM PCM			
• Key off. • Breakout box installed. • Reconnect PCM to breakout box. • Reconnect IAC solenoid. • Connect DVOM between Test Pin 83 (IAC) and Test Pin 51 (PWR GND) at the breakout box. • Start engine. • Slowly increase rpm to 3000 rpm. • Is voltage between 3.0 and 11.5 volts?	Yes No	▶ ▶	REMOVE IAC and check throttle body. If OK, REPLACE IAC valve assembly. REMOVE breakout box. RECONNECT all components. RERUN Quick Test. REPLACE PCM. REMOVE breakout box. RECONNECT all components. RERUN Quick Test.

FM0159401200030X

Fig. 205   Test KE: IAC Valve Assembly (Part 3 of 4). 1994-95

> **Remember**

This Pinpoint Test is intended to diagnose the following:

• Harness circuits: VPWR, A/C Demand (or EATC) to WAC relay, ACCS, WAC, Power-to-A/C Clutch
• WOT A/C Cutout (WAC) Relay
• Powertrain Control Module (PCM) (12A650)

Fig. 206   Test KM: WOT A/C Cut-Off Relay, A/C Circuits (Part 1 of 11). 1995

Pinpoint Test Schematics

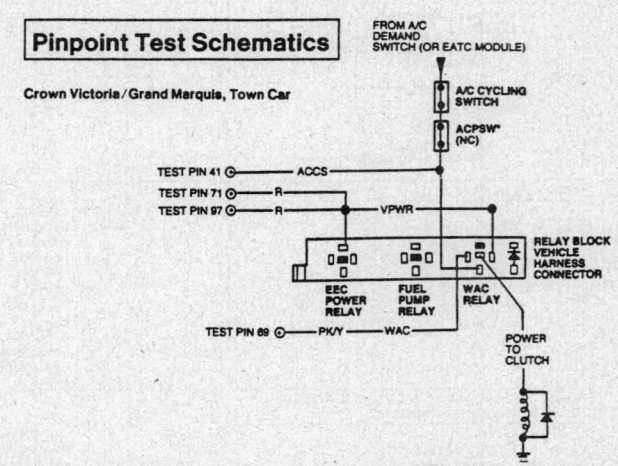

*High pressure contacts of the A/C Pressure Switch (ACPSW) (also known as Refrigerant Containment Switch).

Test Pin 41—ACCS	
Application	**Wire Color**
Crown Victoria / Grand Marquis	DG/O
Town Car	P

Test Pin 69—WAC	
Application	**Wire Color**
Crown Victoria / Grand Marquis	O/LB
Town Car	PK/Y

Fig. 206   Test KM: WOT A/C Cut-Off Relay, A/C Circuits (Part 2 of 11). 1995

TEST STEP		RESULT	▶	ACTION TO TAKE
KM1	KOEO/KOER DTC P1460: VERIFY ACCS PID IS OFF			
	Key On Engine Off (KOEO) and Key On Engine Running (KOER) Diagnostic Trouble Code (DTC) P1460 indicates the A/C was on during Self-Test or a WAC circuit fault.	Yes	▶	Key off. GO to KM2.
		No	▶	Key off. GO to KM20 (to check A/C circuits for short to power).
	NOTE: Verify A/C and defrost was off during KOEO/KOER Self-Tests. If the vehicle is not equipped with A/C, the WAC circuit is not used and the DTC P1460 can be ignored.			
	Possible causes:			
	— A/C on during Self Test.			
	— Open or shorted circuit.			
	— Damaged WAC relay.			
	— Damaged PCM.			
	● Scan Tool connected to DLC.			
	● Start engine.			
	● A/C and defroster off.			
	● Access ACCS PID.			
	● Is the ACCS PID off?			
KM2	CHECK FOR VPWR TO WAC RELAY			
	● Disconnect WAC relay.	Yes	▶	GO to KM3.
	● Key on, engine off.	No	▶	SERVICE open in VPWR circuit between the EEC power relay and the WAC relay. RECONNECT WAC relay. RERUN Quick Test.
	● Measure voltage between VPWR circuit at the WAC relay vehicle harness connector and chassis ground.			
	● Is voltage greater than 10.5 volts?			

Fig. 206   Test KM: WOT A/C Cut-Off Relay, A/C Circuits (Part 3 of 11). 1995

TEST STEP		RESULT	▶	ACTION TO TAKE
KM6	CHECK WAC CIRCUIT CONTINUITY			
	● Key off.	Yes	▶	REPLACE PCM. RECONNECT all components. RERUN Quick Test.
	● Breakout box installed, PCM disconnected.	No	▶	SERVICE open circuit. REMOVE breakout box. RECONNECT all components. RERUN Quick Test.
	● WAC relay disconnected.			
	● Measure resistance between WAC circuit at the WAC relay vehicle harness connector and Test Pin 69 at the breakout box.			
	● Is resistance less than 5.0 ohms?			
KM10	ACCS PID OFF WITH A/C ON: CHECK FOR VOLTAGE TO A/C CYCLING SWITCH			
	● Key on, engine off.	Yes	▶	GO to KM11.
	● Disconnect A/C Cycling Switch.	No	▶	
	● A/C demand switch to A/C on.			check A/C demand switch or EATC module operation, applicable fuses, wiring to A/C Cycling Switch, etc.
	● Measure voltage between the A/C demand switch (or EATC module) side of the A/C Cycling Switch vehicle harness connector and chassis ground.			
	● Key off.			
	● Was voltage greater than 10.5 volts?			

Fig. 206   Test KM: WOT A/C Cut-Off Relay, A/C Circuits (Part 5 of 11). 1995

TEST STEP		RESULT	▶	ACTION TO TAKE
KM11	CHECK FOR VOLTAGE TO A/C PRESSURE SWITCH (ACPSW)			
	● Key off.	Yes	▶	GO to KM12.
	● Reconnect A/C Cycling Switch.	No	▶	VERIFY operation of A/C Cycling Switch.
	● Disconnect ACPSW (also known as Refrigerant Containment Switch).			
	● Key on, engine off.			If OK,
	● A/C on.			SERVICE open between A/C Cycling Switch and ACPSW. RECONNECT all components. RE-EVALUATE symptom.
	● Measure voltage between the A/C Demand Switch (or EATC module) pin at the ACPSW vehicle harness connector and chassis ground.			
	● Key off.			
	● Was voltage greater than 10.5 volts?			
KM12	CHECK CONTINUITY OF ACPSW HIGH PRESSURE CONTACTS			
	● Key off.	Yes	▶	GO to KM13.
	● ACPSW disconnected.	No	▶	
	● Measure resistance of the ACPSW high pressure contacts (these are the normally closed contacts).			check for overpressurized A/C system, etc. If OK, REPLACE ACPSW. RE-EVALUATE symptom.
	● Is resistance less than 5.0 ohms?			

Fig. 206   Test KM: WOT A/C Cut-Off Relay, A/C Circuits (Part 6 of 11). 1995

TEST STEP		RESULT	▶	ACTION TO TAKE
KM3	CHECK WAC RELAY			
	● Key off.	Yes	▶	GO to KM4.
	● WAC relay disconnected.	No	▶	REPLACE WAC relay. RERUN Quick Test.
	● Check WAC relay coil resistance.			
	— Measure resistance between Pin 85 and 86 at the WAC relay (pin numbers molded on relay).			
	— Resistance should be between 40 and 85 ohms.			
	● Check WAC relay for internal shorts.			
	— Measure resistance between Pin 85 and Pin 30, 87 and 87A at the WAC relay.			
	— All three resistances should be greater than 10,000 ohms.			
	● Are all resistance checks OK?			
	WAC RELAY: 87, 87A, 86, 85, 30. COIL - 85 AND 86. COMMON - 30. NO - 87. NC - 87A			
KM4	CHECK WAC CIRCUIT FOR SHORT TO POWER			
	● Key off.	Yes	▶	GO to KM5.
	● WAC relay disconnected.	No	▶	SERVICE short to power. REMOVE breakout box. RECONNECT all components. RERUN Quick Test.
	● Disconnect PCM. Inspect for damaged or pushed out pins, corrosion, loose wires, etc. Service as necessary.			
	● Install breakout box, leave PCM disconnected.			
	● Key on, engine off.			
	● Measure voltage between Test Pin 69 (WAC) at the breakout box and chassis ground.			
	● Is voltage less than 1.0 volt?			
KM5	CHECK WAC CIRCUIT FOR SHORT TO GROUND			
	● Key off.	Yes	▶	GO to KM6.
	● Disconnect Scan Tool from DLC.	No	▶	SERVICE short circuit. REMOVE breakout box. RECONNECT all components. RERUN Quick Test.
	● Breakout box installed, PCM disconnected.			
	● WAC relay disconnected.			
	● Measure resistance between Test Pin 69 and Test Pins 51, 103 (PWR GND) and 91 (SIG RTN) at the breakout box.			
	● Is each resistance greater than 10,000 ohms?			

Fig. 206   Test KM: WOT A/C Cut-Off Relay, A/C Circuits (Part 4 of 11). 1995

TEST STEP		RESULT	▶	ACTION TO TAKE
KM13	CHECK FOR VOLTAGE TO PCM ON ACCS CIRCUIT			
	● Key off.	Yes	▶	REPLACE PCM. REMOVE breakout box. RECONNECT all components. RE-EVALUATE symptom.
	● Reconnect ACPSW.	No	▶	SERVICE open circuit between the ACPSW and PCM. REMOVE breakout box. RECONNECT all components. RE-EVALUATE symptom.
	● Disconnect PCM. Inspect for damaged or pushed out pins, loose wires, corrosion, etc. Service as necessary.			
	● Install breakout box, leave PCM disconnected.			
	● Key on.			
	● A/C ON.			
	● Measure voltage between Test Pin 41 (ACCS) and Test Pin 77 (PWR GND) at the breakout box.			
	● Is voltage greater than 10.5 volts?			
KM15	NO/LOW VOLTAGE TO A/C CLUTCH (ACCS PID ON WITH A/C ON, NO DTCS): CHECK A/C DEMAND SWITCH VOLTAGE TO WAC RELAY			
	● Key off.	Yes	▶	GO to KM16.
	● Disconnect WAC relay.	No	▶	SERVICE open in A/C demand circuit between WAC relay and ACCS splice to PCM. RECONNECT all components. RE-EVALUATE symptom.
	● Key on.			
	● A/C demand switch to A/C on.			
	● Measure voltage between the A/C Demand Switch (or EATC module) pin at the WAC relay vehicle harness connector and chassis ground.			
	● Key off, A/C off.			
	● Was voltage greater than 10.5 volts?			
KM16	CHECK CONTINUITY OF POWER-TO-A/C CLUTCH AND A/C CLUTCH GROUND CIRCUITS			
	● Key off.	Yes	▶	REPLACE WAC relay. RECONNECT all components. RE-EVALUATE symptom.
	● WAC relay disconnected.	No	▶	SERVICE open circuit. RECONNECT all components. RE-EVALUATE symptom.
	● Disconnect A/C clutch.			
	● Disconnect Scan Tool from DLC.			
	● Measure resistance between the Power-to-Clutch circuit at the WAC relay vehicle harness connector and the power side of the A/C clutch vehicle harness connector.			
	● Measure resistance between the ground side of the A/C clutch vehicle harness connector and the battery negative post.			
	● Is each resistance less than 5.0 ohms?			

Fig. 206   Test KM: WOT A/C Cut-Off Relay, A/C Circuits (Part 7 of 11). 1995

TEST STEP	RESULT	▶	ACTION TO TAKE
KM20 ACCS PID ON: DISCONNECT ACPSW AND CHECK IF ACCS PID TURNS OFF			
• Key off. • Disconnect A/C Pressure Switch (ACPSW) (also known as the Refrigerant Containment/Switch). • Key on, engine off. • Access ACCS PID. • **Is ACCS PID off?**	Yes	▶	Key off. VERIFY operation of A/C Demand Switch or EATC module. **If OK,** SERVICE short to power in A/C Demand circuit to ACPSW. RECONNECT all components. RE-EVALUATE symptom.
	No	▶	Key off. GO to **KM21**
KM21 CHECK POWER-TO-A/C CLUTCH CIRCUIT FOR SHORT TO POWER			
• Key off. • Disconnect WAC relay. • Key on. • Measure voltage between Power-to-Clutch of the WAC relay vehicle harness connector and the chassis ground. • Key off. • **Was voltage less than 1.0 volt?**	Yes	▶	GO to **KM22**.
	No	▶	SERVICE short to power. RECONNECT all components. RE-EVALUATE symptom.
KM22 CHECK ACCS CIRCUIT FOR SHORT TO POWER			
• Key off. • ACPSW and WAC relay disconnected. • Disconnect PCM. Inspect for damaged or pushed out pins, corrosion, loose wires, etc. Service as necessary. • Install breakout box, leave PCM disconnected. • Key on. • Measure voltage between Test Pin 41 (ACCS) and Test Pins 51 and 103 (PWR GND). • Key off. • **Was voltage less than 1.0 volt?**	Yes	▶	GO to **KM23**.
	No	▶	SERVICE ACCS circuit short to power. REMOVE breakout box. RECONNECT all components. RE-EVALUATE symptom.

Fig. 206   Test KM: WOT A/C Cut-Off Relay, A/C Circuits (Part 8 of 11). 1995

TEST STEP	RESULT	▶	ACTION TO TAKE
KM23 CHECK ACCS CIRCUIT VOLTAGE TO PCM WITH WAC RELAY CONNECTED			
• Key off. • Reconnect WAC relay. • ACPSW disconnected. • Breakout box installed, PCM disconnected. • Key on. • Again, measure voltage between Test Pin 41 (ACCS) and Test Pins 51 and 103 (PWR GND). • Key off. • **Was voltage less than 1.0 volt?**	Yes	▶	REPLACE PCM. REMOVE breakout box. RECONNECT all components. RE-EVALUATE symptom.
	No	▶	REPLACE WAC relay. REMOVE breakout box. RECONNECT all components. RE-EVALUATE symptom.
KM25 NO WAC W/NO DTCs: CHECK WAC RELAY			
• Scan Tool connected. • A/C clutch and WAC relay connected. • Key on, engine off. • Access Output Test Mode on Scan Tool • A/C on. • While listening to the A/C clutch, command the outputs off and on a couple times. • **Does the A/C clutch engage and disengage when the outputs are cycled off and on?**	Yes	▶	Key off. EEC system is operating properly. If symptom is intermittent, GO to Pinpoint Test Step **Z1** with the following data: WACA PID Otherwise, testing is complete. Key off.
	No	▶	VERIFY that the A/C clutch was engaged during testing. If not, REPEAT test with clutch engaged. If clutch was engaged, REPLACE WAC relay. RECONNECT all components. RE-EVALUATE symptom.

Fig. 206   Test KM: WOT A/C Cut-Off Relay, A/C Circuits (Part 9 of 11). 1995

TEST STEP	RESULT	▶	ACTION TO TAKE
KM30 CONTINUOUS MEMORY DIAGNOSTIC TROUBLE CODE (DTC) P1460: CHECK WAC CIRCUIT FOR INTERMITTENT OPEN OR SHORT TO GROUND			
A Continuous Memory DTC P1460 indicates a WAC circuit failure has occurred during vehicle operation. Possible causes: — Open VPWR to WAC relay. — Open coil in WAC relay. — Open or short in WAC circuit (PCM Pin 69). • Scan Tool connected. • Key on, engine off. • Access Output Test Mode on Scan Tool • While in Output Test Mode, access the WAC PID and WACA PID NOTE: If the Scan Tool will not allow access to PIDs while in Output Test Mode, disconnect PCM, install a breakout box, reconnect PCM and connect a DVOM between Test Pin 71 (VPWR) and Test Pin 69 (WAC). • Command the outputs so the WAC PID is off (or DVOM voltage will be greater than 10.0 volts). The WACA PID is off, WACF PID = off, or DVOM voltage is greater than 10.0 volts because the PCM detects VPWR voltage through the WAC relay coil and WAC circuit (Pin 69) to the PCM. • Observe the WACA PID, WACF PID, or DVOM voltage for an indication of a fault while performing the following (the WACA PID will turn on (WACF PID will = on) when an open or short to ground is detected this is because the PCM will not detect VPWR voltage on Pin 69 (WAC): — Shake, wiggle, bend the WAC circuit between the PCM (Pin 69) and the WAC relay. — Shake, wiggle, bend the VPWR circuit between the EEC-V Power Relay and the WAC relay. — Lightly tap the WAC relay (to simulate road shock). • **Is a fault indicated?**	Yes	▶	Key off. ISOLATE fault and SERVICE as necessary. COMPLETE PCM Reset to Clear DTCs Powertrain Control Module (PCM) Reset). RERUN Quick Test.
	No	▶	LEAVE key on. GO to **KM31**.

Fig. 206   Test KM: WOT A/C Cut-Off Relay, A/C Circuits (Part 10 of 11). 1995

TEST STEP	RESULT	▶	ACTION TO TAKE
KM31 CHECK WAC CIRCUIT FOR INTERMITTENT SHORT TO POWER			
• Key on, engine off. • Scan Tool connected. • Exit Output Test Mode. • Access WACA PID • Disconnect WAC relay. • WACA PID should be on, or WACF PID should = off. • Observe WACA or WACF PID for an indication of a fault while performing the following (the WACA PID will turn off, or the WACF PID will = on, if a short to power is detected): — Shake, wiggle, bend the WAC circuit between the PCM (Pin 69) and the WAC relay. • Key off. • Inspect the PCM and WAC relay connectors for corrosion, damaged pins, etc. • **Is a fault indicated?**	Yes	▶	ISOLATE fault and SERVICE as necessary. COMPLETE PCM Reset to clear DTCs Powertrain Control Module (PCM) Reset). RERUN Quick Test.
	No	▶	Unable to duplicate and/or identify fault at this time. GO to Pinpoint Test Step **Z1** with the following data: WACA or WACF PID and list of Possible Causes.

Fig. 206   Test KM: WOT A/C Cut-Off Relay, A/C Circuits (Part 11 of 11). 1995

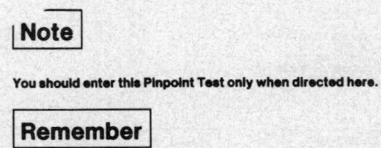

Note

You should enter this Pinpoint Test only when directed here.

Remember

This Pinpoint Test is intended to diagnose only the following:
• Connection between the Scan Tool and the Powertrain Control Module (PCM).
• Connection between the Scan Tool and the battery power supply.
• Proper key sequence executed for output(s).

FM015940120101010X

Fig. 207   Test MB: DCM/OTM Not Functioning (Part 1 of 2). 1994-95

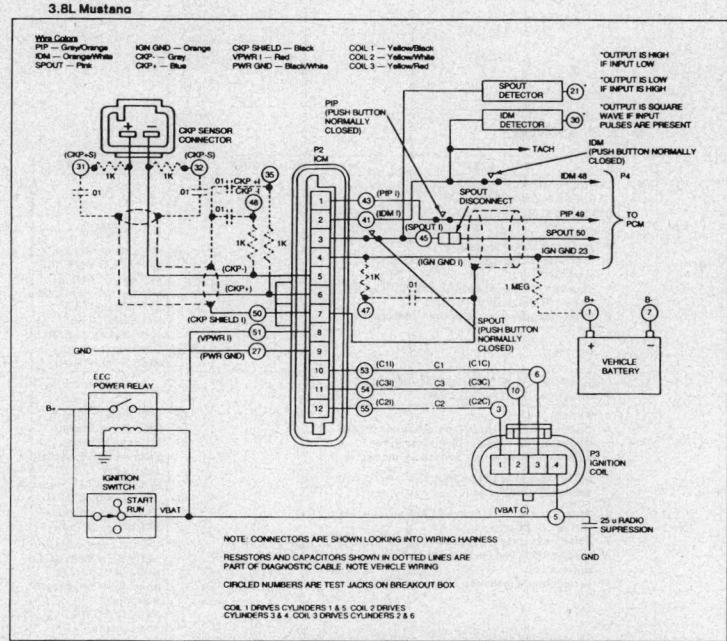

Fig. 207 Test MB: DCM/OTM Not Functioning (Part 2 of 2). 1994-95

TEST STEP	RESULT	▶	ACTION TO TAKE
MB1 CHECK VEHICLE DLC TO SCAN TOOL CONNECTION AND WIRING			
• Key off. • Inspect the connection between the Scan Tool and vehicle Data Link Connector (DLC) for damaged or pushed out pins, etc. • Inspect the Scan Tool wiring cable for obvious damage. • Are the DLC and Scan Tool properly connected and is the Scan Tool wiring cable OK?	Yes No	▶ ▶	GO to MB2. SERVICE as necessary. RUN the Scan Tool "System Readiness" test to verify communication between the Scan Tool and PCM.
MB2 CHECK SCAN TOOL POWER SUPPLY CONNECTOR AND WIRING CABLE			
• Key off. • Inspect the connector and wiring cable between the Scan Tool and the vehicle battery power supply (or at the cigarette lighter) for obvious damage. • Are the power supply connector and wiring cable OK?	Yes No	▶ ▶	There are no installation problems between the Scan Tool and the vehicle. GO to Output Test Mode. VERIFY that the proper key sequence was used for output(s) in the Output Test Mode. SERVICE as necessary. RUN the Scan Tool "System Readiness" test to verify communication between the Scan Tool and PCM

FM0159401202020X

Fig. 208 Test MC: Spark Output Check-EI (Part 2 of 7). 1994-95

Note

You should enter this Pinpoint Test only when directed here.

Reminder

This Pinpoint Test is intended to diagnose the following:

• Ignition Control Module (ICM) (12K072)

• Harness Circuit: SPOUT, Vehicle Power (VPWR) to PCM

• Powertrain Control Module (PCM) (12A650)

FM0159401202010X

Fig. 208 Test MC: Spark Output Check-EI (Part 1 of 7). 1994-95

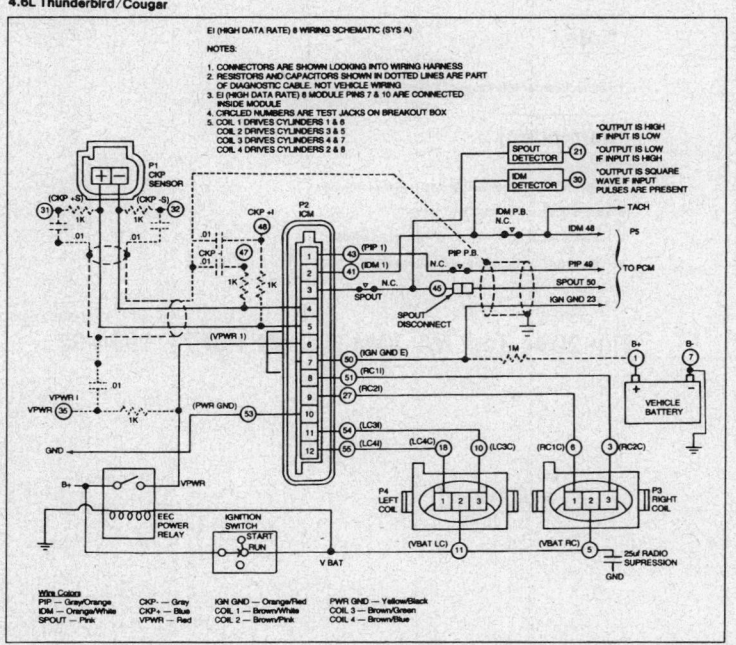

FM0159401202030X

Fig. 208 Test MC: Spark Output Check-EI (Part 3 of 7). 1994-95

TEST STEP	RESULT	▶	ACTION TO TAKE
MC1 CHECK FOR POWER TO PCM: VREF CIRCUIT VOLTAGE AT TP SENSOR			
• Key off. • TP sensor disconnected. • Key on, engine off. • Measure voltage between VREF circuit at SIG RTN circuit at the TP sensor vehicle harness connector. • Is the voltage between 4.0 and 6.0 volts?	Yes No	▶ ▶	GO to MC2. Key off. RECONNECT all components. GO to Pinpoint Test Step C1.
MC2 CHECK BASE TIMING—KOER			
WARNING: NEVER CONNECT PCM TO EEC BREAKOUT BOX WHEN PERFORMING EI DIAGNOSTICS. • Key off. • Install EI diagnostic harness to breakout box and to both the ICM and vehicle harness. **Do not connect the CKP sensor tee or coil tees.** • Connect EI diagnostic harness negative and positive leads to battery. For 4.6L: • Use EI 8 overlay. • Set EI diagnostic harness type switch to "8" position. For 3.8L: • Use EI 6 overlay. • Set EI diagnostic harness type switch to "4/6" position. • Connect timing light (must be EI compatible). • Do not use an incandescent test lamp to check SPOUT. The lamp will prevent the circuit from operating. • Start engine and allow it to warm up. • Is timing 10 ± 2 degrees BTDC when the diagnostic harness SPOUT button is pushed?	Yes No	▶ ▶	GO to MC3. Base timing fault. GO to MC9.
MC3 CHECK FOR SPARK ANGLE ADVANCE—KOER			
• Is engine timing greater than 15 degrees BTDC when the diagnostic harness SPOUT button is released?	Yes No	▶	Ignition System is OK. REFER to further symptom diagnosis. Advance spark fault. GO to MC4.

FM0159401202040X

Fig. 208 Test MC: Spark Output Check-EI (Part 4 of 7). 1994-95

TEST STEP	RESULT	▶	ACTION TO TAKE
MC4 CHECK SPOUT AT ICM—KOER • Key off. • DVOM on 40 volt AC scale. • Start engine and measure voltage between J21 (EI diagnostic harness SPOUT detector) and (-)J7 (B-) at breakout box. • Is AC voltage reading greater than 5.0 volts?	Yes No	▶ ▶	REPLACE ICM. SPOUT input to ICM is OK, but no spark advance is present. REMOVE all test equipment. RECONNECT all components. CLEAR Continuous Memory. RERUN Quick Test. SPOUT fault. GO to **MC5**.
MC5 CHECK FOR SPOUT SHORT IN ICM—SPOUT FAULT—SPOUT CIRCUIT OPEN—KOER • Key off. • DVOM on 40 volt AC scale. • Push and hold EI diagnostic harness SPOUT button down (opens SPOUT circuit to ICM). • Start engine and measure voltage between (+)J21 (EI diagnostic harness SPOUT detector) and (-)J7 (B-) at breakout box. • Is AC voltage reading greater than 5.0 volts?	Yes No	▶ ▶	REPLACE ICM. SPOUT is shorted in ICM. REMOVE all test equipment. RECONNECT all components. CLEAR Continuous Memory. RERUN Quick Test. GO to **MC6**.
MC6 CHECK FOR SPOUT SHORT HIGH IN HARNESS—ICM AND PCM DISCONNECTED—KOEO • Key off. • Disconnect PCM. NOTE: This erases continuous memory, and sets the P1000 code. • Disconnect the ICM tee from the ICM, but leave the vehicle harness connected to module tee. • DVOM on 40 volt DC scale. • Key on, engine off. • Measure voltage between J45 (SPOUT I) and J7 (B-) at the breakout box. • Is DC voltage reading less than 0.5 volts?	Yes No	▶ ▶	GO to **MC7**. CHECK connectors, SERVICE or REPLACE harness. SPOUT is shorted high. REMOVE all test equipment. RECONNECT all components. CLEAR Continuous Memory. RERUN Quick Test.

Fig. 208 Test MC: Spark Output Check-EI (Part 5 of 7). 1994-95

TEST STEP	RESULT	▶	ACTION TO TAKE
MC7 CHECK FOR SPOUT SHORT TO GROUND IN HARNESS—ICM AND PCM DISCONNECTED—KEY OFF • Key off. • DVOM on 20K ohm scale. • Disconnect EI diagnostic harness positive lead to battery. • Measure resistance between J45 (SPOUT I) and J7 (B-) at breakout box. • Is the resistance greater than 10K ohms?	Yes No	▶ ▶	GO to **MC8**. CHECK connectors, SERVICE or REPLACE harness. SPOUT is shorted low. REMOVE all test equipment. RECONNECT all components. CLEAR Continuous Memory. RERUN Quick Test.
MC8 CHECK FOR SPOUT OPEN TO ICM—ICM AND PCM DISCONNECTED—KEY OFF • Key off. • Disconnect Powertrain Control Module (PCM). Inspect for damaged or pushed out pins, corrosion, loose wires. Service as necessary. NOTE: This erases continuous memory, and sets the P1000 code. • Install breakout box, leave PCM disconnected. • DVOM on 200 ohm scale. • Measure resistance between J45 (SPOUT I) at breakout box and Pin 50 at the second breakout box. • Is resistance less than 5.0 ohms?	Yes No	▶ ▶	REPLACE PCM. SPOUT is not being transmitted by the PCM. REMOVE all test equipment. RECONNECT all components. CLEAR Continuous Memory. RERUN Quick Test. CHECK connectors, SERVICE or REPLACE harness. SPOUT is open. REMOVE all test equipment. RECONNECT all components. CLEAR Continuous Memory. RERUN Quick Test.

Fig. 208 Test MC: Spark Output Check-EI (Part 6 of 7). 1994-95

TEST STEP	RESULT	▶	ACTION TO TAKE
MC9 INSPECT CKP SENSOR AND TRIGGER WHEEL—TIMING FAULT • Is the CKP sensor or Trigger Wheel damaged, i.e., loose or misaligned?	Yes No	▶ ▶	REPLACE or SERVICE as required. REMOVE all test equipment. RECONNECT all components. CLEAR Continuous Memory. RERUN Quick Test. REPLACE ICM. Incorrect output. REMOVE all test equipment. RECONNECT all components. CLEAR Continuous Memory. RERUN Quick Test.

Fig. 208 Test MC: Spark Output Check-EI (Part 7 of 7). 1994-95

Note

You should enter this Pinpoint Test only when directed here.

Reminder

This Pinpoint Test is intended to diagnose the following:
• Ignition Control Module (ICM) (12K072)
• Harness Circuit: IDM, Verify PWR GND and VPWR
• Powertrain Control Module (PCM) (12A850)

Fig. 209 Test NA: IDM-EI (Part 1 of 7). 1994-95

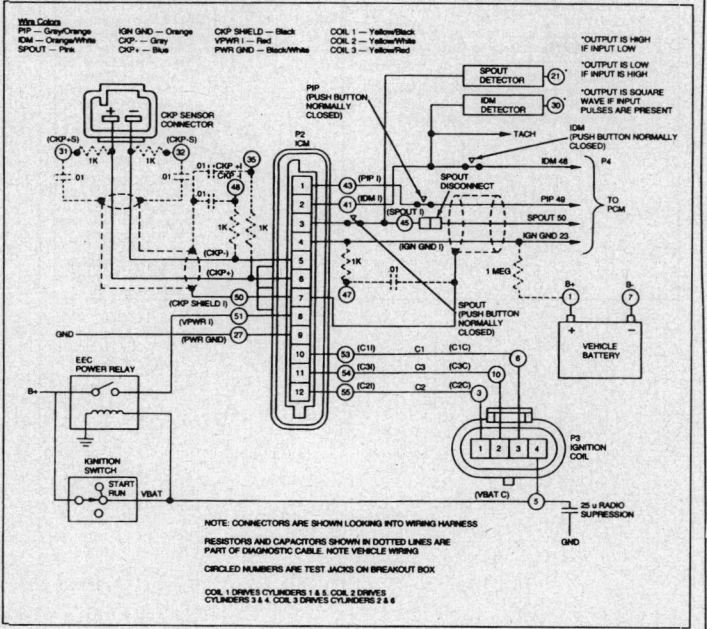

Fig. 209   Test NA: IDM-EI (Part 2 of 7). 1994-95

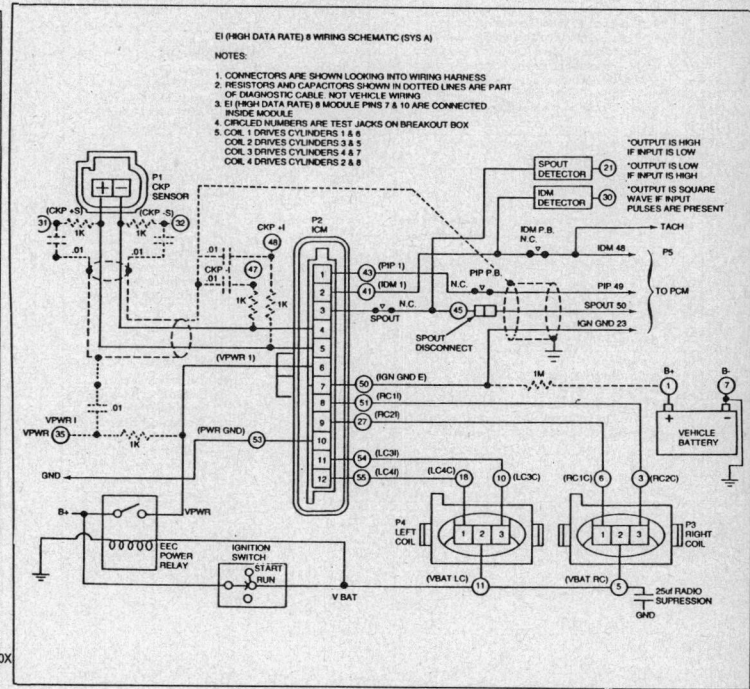

Fig. 209   Test NA: IDM-EI (Part 3 of 7). 1994-95

TEST STEP	RESULT	▶	ACTION TO TAKE
NA1 CONTINUOUS MEMORY DTC 0320: ERRATIC IGNITION			
Continuous Memory DTC 0320 indicates two successive erratic Profile Ignition Pickup (PIP) pulses occurred, resulting in a possible engine miss or stall. Possible causes: — Loose wires / connectors. — Arcing secondary ignition components (coil, cap, rotor, wires, plugs, etc.). — On-board transmitter (2-way radio). ● **Are any of the above present?** *Verify all 2-way radio installations. Carefully follow manufacturer's installation instructions regarding the routing of antenna and power leads.	Yes No	▶ ▶	SERVICE as necessary. CLEAR Continuous Memory DTC 0320. For No Starts: GO to A1. All others: GO to NA3.
NA2 CONTINUOUS MEMORY DTC 1351: CHECK FOR OTHER EEC DTCS			
Continuous Memory DTC 1351 indicates a loss of IDM input to the PCM. Possible causes: — Open circuit. — Shorted circuit. — Damaged ICM. — Damaged PCM. ● Is vehicle a No Start or is Continuous Memory DTC 1352, 1353, 1354, 1355, or 1364 present?	Yes No	▶ ▶	For 3.8L: GO to Pinpoint Test Step JC1. For 4.6L: GO to Pinpoint Test Step JC30. GO to NA3.

Fig. 209   Test NA: IDM-EI (Part 4 of 7). 1994-95

TEST STEP	RESULT	▶	ACTION TO TAKE
NA3 CHECK FOR IDM AT ICM—KOER	Yes	▶	GO to NA4.
WARNING: NEVER CONNECT THE PCM TO EEC BREAKOUT BOX WHEN PERFORMING EI DIAGNOSTICS. ● Key off. ● Install EI diagnostic harness to breakout box, and to both the ICM and vehicle harness. **Do not connect CKP sensor tee or coil tees.** ● Connect EI diagnostic harness negative and positive leads to battery. For 4.6L: ● Use EI 8 overlay. ● Set EI diagnostic harness type switch to "8" position. For 3.8L: ● Use EI 6 overlay. ● Set EI diagnostic harness type switch to "4/6" position. ● DVOM on 40 volt AC scale. ● Do not use an incandescent test lamp to check IDM. The lamp will prevent the circuit from operating. ● Start engine and measure voltage between (+)J30 (EI diagnostic harness IDM detector) and (-)J7 (B-) at breakout box. NOTE: If pulses are present, the IDM detector output will be between 5.0 and 7.0 volts AC. ● Is AC voltage between 5.0 and 7.0 volts?	No	▶	GO to NA5. IDM fault.
NA4 CHECK FOR IDM OPEN TO PCM—IDM FAULT—ICM AND PCM DISCONNECTED—KEY OFF			
● Key off. ● Disconnect PCM. Inspect for damaged or pushed out pins, corrosion, loose wires. Service as necessary. ● Disconnect ICM from tee, leave EI diagnostic harness connected to vehicle harness connector. ● DVOM on 200 ohm scale. NOTE: This erases continuous memory, and sets the code P1000. ● Install a second breakout box to PCM vehicle harness connector. ● Measure resistance between J41 (IDM I) at breakout box and Pin 48 at second breakout box. ● Is resistance less than 5.0 ohms?	Yes No	▶ ▶	REPLACE PCM. PCM does not respond to IDM input. REMOVE all test equipment. RECONNECT all components. CLEAR Continuous Memory. RERUN Quick Test. CHECK connectors, SERVICE or REPLACE harness. IDM is open. REMOVE all test equipment. RECONNECT all components. CLEAR Continuous Memory. RERUN Quick Test.

Fig. 209   Test NA: IDM-EI (Part 5 of 7). 1994-95

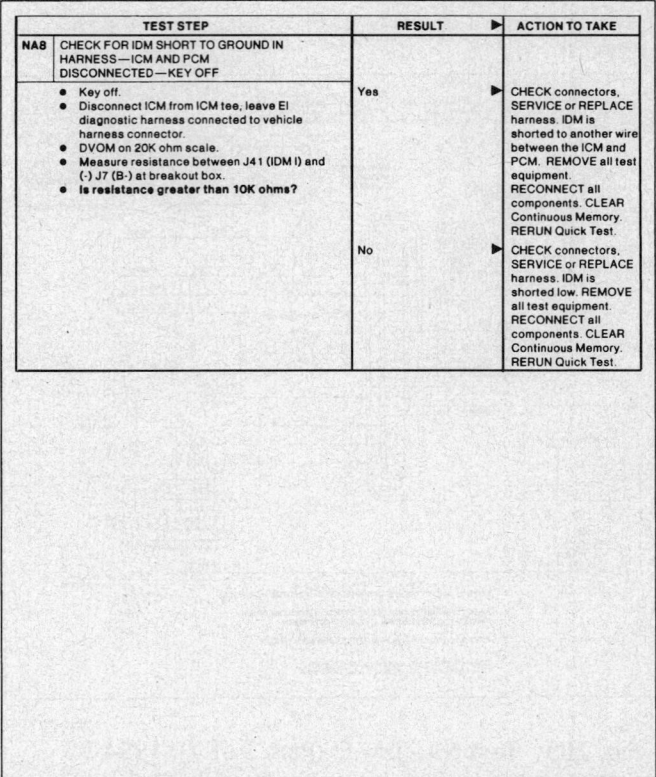

TEST STEP	RESULT	▶	ACTION TO TAKE
NA5 CHECK IDM OUTPUT FROM ICM—IDM FAULT—IDM CIRCUIT OPEN—KOER • Key off. • DVOM on 40 volt AC scale. • Push and hold EI diagnostic harness IDM button down (opens IDM circuit to PCM). • Start engine and measure voltage between J30 (EI diagnostic harness IDM detector) and J7 (B-) at breakout box. • **Is AC voltage greater than 5.0 volts?**	Yes No	▶ ▶	GO to **NA6**. REPLACE ICM. No IDM output from module. REMOVE all test equipment. RECONNECT all components. CLEAR Continuous Memory. RERUN Quick Test.
NA6 CHECK FOR IDM SHORT IN PCM—PCM DISCONNECTED—KOEC • Key off. • Disconnect PCM. • DVOM on 40 volt AC scale. • Crank engine and measure voltage between J30 (EI diagnostic harness IDM detector) and (-)J7 (B-) at breakout box. • **Is AC voltage less than 5.0 volts?**	Yes No	▶ ▶	GO to **NA7**. REPLACE PCM. PCM is loading IDM signal. REMOVE all test equipment. RECONNECT all components. CLEAR Continuous Memory. RERUN Quick Test.
NA7 CHECK FOR IDM SHORT HIGH IN HARNESS —ICM AND PCM DISCONNECTED—KOEO • Key off. • DVOM on 40 volt DC scale. • Key on, engine off. • Measure voltage between (+)J41 (IDM I) and (-)J7 (B-) at breakout box. • **Is DC voltage less than 0.5 volts?**	Yes No	▶ ▶	GO to **NA8**. CHECK connectors, SERVICE or REPLACE harness. IDM is shorted high. REMOVE all test equipment. RECONNECT all components. CLEAR Continuous Memory. RERUN Quick Test.

FM0159401203060X

Fig. 209 Test NA: IDM-EI (Part 6 of 7). 1994-95

TEST STEP	RESULT	▶	ACTION TO TAKE
NA8 CHECK FOR IDM SHORT TO GROUND IN HARNESS—ICM AND PCM DISCONNECTED—KEY OFF • Key off. • Disconnect ICM from ICM tee, leave EI diagnostic harness connected to vehicle harness connector. • DVOM on 20K ohm scale. • Measure resistance between J41 (IDM I) and (-) J7 (B-) at breakout box. • **Is resistance greater than 10K ohms?**	Yes No	▶ ▶	CHECK connectors, SERVICE or REPLACE harness. IDM is shorted to another wire between the ICM and PCM. REMOVE all test equipment. RECONNECT all components. CLEAR Continuous Memory. RERUN Quick Test. CHECK connectors, SERVICE or REPLACE harness. IDM is shorted low. REMOVE all test equipment. RECONNECT all components. CLEAR Continuous Memory. RERUN Quick Test.

FM0159401203070X

Fig. 209 Test NA: IDM-EI (Part 7 of 7). 1994-95

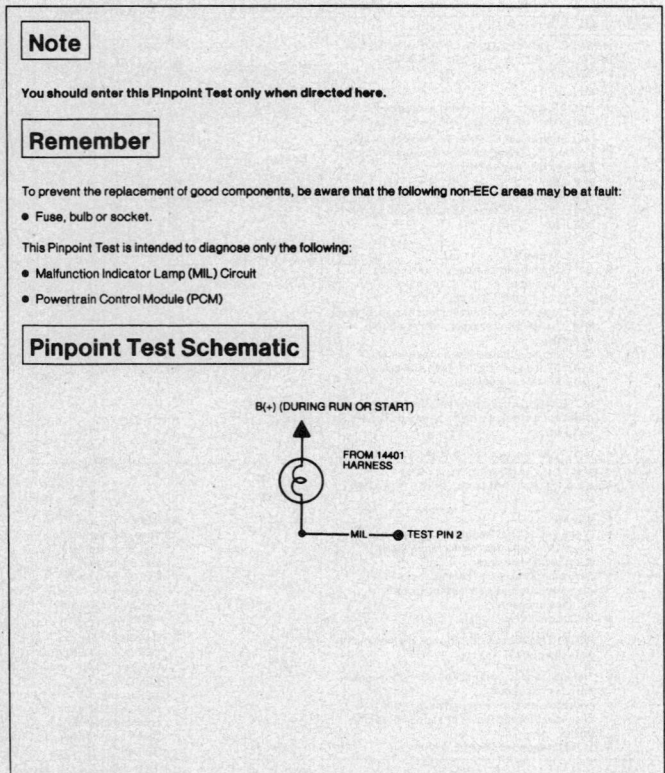

Note

You should enter this Pinpoint Test only when directed here.

Remember

To prevent the replacement of good components, be aware that the following non-EEC areas may be at fault:
• Fuse, bulb or socket.

This Pinpoint Test is intended to diagnose only the following:
• Malfunction Indicator Lamp (MIL) Circuit
• Powertrain Control Module (PCM)

Pinpoint Test Schematic

FM0159401204010X

Fig. 210 Test NB: MIL (Part 1 of 3). 1994-95

TEST STEP	RESULT	▶	ACTION TO TAKE
NB1 MALFUNCTION INDICATOR LAMP (MIL) ALWAYS ON: CHECK MIL CIRCUIT FOR SHORTS TO GROUND NOTE: If vehicle will not start, perform Pinpoint Test Step **A1** High Data Rate Electronic Ignition. • If any Key On Engine Off Continuous Memory Diagnostic Trouble Codes are present, service before proceeding. • Key off. • Disconnect PCM. Inspect for damaged or pushed out pins, corrosion, loose wires, etc. Service as necessary. • Install breakout box, leave PCM disconnected. • Measure resistance between Test Pin 2 and Test Pin 51 or 103 at the breakout box. • **Is resistance less than 5.0 ohms?**	Yes No	▶ ▶	SERVICE short circuit between Test Pin 2 and Malfunction Indicator Lamp (MIL). REMOVE breakout box. RECONNECT PCM. RERUN Quick Test. REPLACE PCM. REMOVE breakout box. RERUN Quick Test.
NB4 MALFUNCTION INDICATOR LAMP (MIL) NEVER ON: CHECK FOR B(+) AT MIL FUSE (GROUND SIDE) NOTE: If vehicle will not start, go to Pinpoint Test Step **A1** High Data Rate Electronic Ignition. • Key on, engine off. • Measure voltage from battery negative post to ''Ground'' side of the MIL fuse. • **Is voltage greater than 10.5 volts?**	Yes No	▶ ▶	GO to **NB6**. GO to **NB5**.
NB5 CHECK FOR B+ AT FUSE • Key on, engine off. • Measure voltage from battery negative post to B+ side of the fuse. • **Is voltage greater than 10.5 volts?**	Yes No	▶ ▶	REPLACE the fuse. VERIFY service by turning ignition key to the on position. SERVICE open in the MIL or B+ circuit. VERIFY service by turning ignition key to the on position.

FM0159401204020X

Fig. 210 Test NB: MIL (Part 2 of 3). 1994-95

TEST STEP	RESULT	▶	ACTION TO TAKE
NB6 CHECK FOR 12 VOLTS TO THE BULB			
• Key on, engine off. • Measure voltage from Instrument Cluster connector (Circuit 251) Pin 11 to battery negative post. • Is voltage greater than 10.5 volts?	Yes No	▶ ▶	GO to **NB7** GO to EVTM to service open in the fuse, MIL bulb or B+ circuit.
NB7 CHECK CONTINUITY MIL CIRCUIT			
• Key off. • Disconnect PCM. Inspect for damaged or pushed out pins, corrosion, loose wires, etc. Service as necessary. • Install breakout box, leave PCM disconnected. • Measure resistance between Test Pin 2 at the breakout box and Pin 2 at the Instrument Cluster connector (Circuit 251). • Is resistance less than 5.0 ohms?	Yes No	▶ ▶	REPLACE PCM. REMOVE breakout box. VERIFY the service by turning the ignition key to the ON position. SERVICE open in the MIL circuit. REMOVE breakout box. RECONNECT PCM. VERIFY service by turning key to the ON position.

Fig. 210 Test NB: MIL (Part 3 of 3). 1994-95

FM0159401204030X

Note

You should enter this Pinpoint Test only when directed here.

Remember

This Pinpoint Test is intended to diagnose only the following:

• Standard Corporate Protocol (SCP) communication bus harness circuits: BUS (+), BUS (-)

• Harness Circuits: Chassis ground, Power Ground (PWR GND), Battery Voltage (VBAT)

• Powertrain Control Module (PCM)

Pinpoint Test Schematic

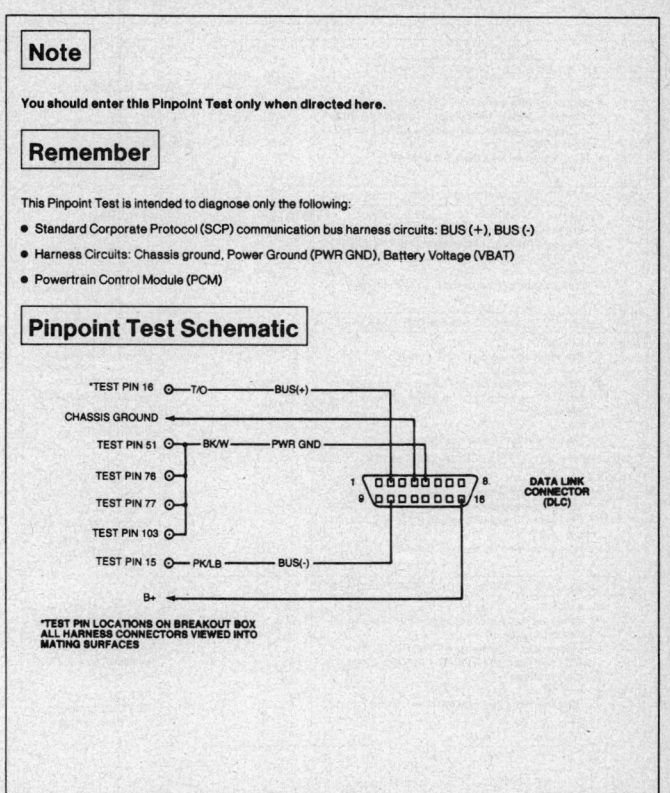

*TEST PIN LOCATIONS ON BREAKOUT BOX
ALL HARNESS CONNECTORS VIEWED INTO
MATING SURFACES

Fig. 211 Test QA: Unable To Activate Self-Test (Part 1 of 4). 1994-95

FM0159401205010X

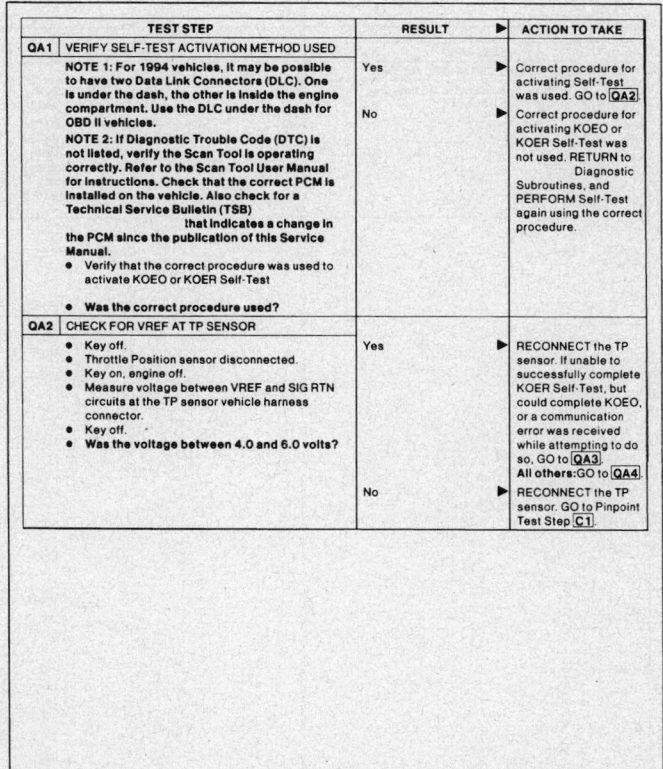

TEST STEP	RESULT	▶	ACTION TO TAKE
QA1 VERIFY SELF-TEST ACTIVATION METHOD USED			
NOTE 1: For 1994 vehicles, it may be possible to have two Data Link Connectors (DLC). One is under the dash, the other is inside the engine compartment. Use the DLC under the dash for OBD II vehicles. NOTE 2: If Diagnostic Trouble Code (DTC) is not listed, verify the Scan Tool is operating correctly. Refer to the Scan Tool User Manual for instructions. Check that the correct PCM is installed on the vehicle. Also check for a Technical Service Bulletin (TSB) that indicates a change in the PCM since the publication of this Service Manual. • Verify that the correct procedure was used to activate KOEO or KOER Self-Test • **Was the correct procedure used?**	Yes No	▶ ▶	Correct procedure for activating Self-Test was used. GO to **QA2**. Correct procedure for activating KOEO or KOER Self-Test was not used. RETURN to Diagnostic Subroutines, and PERFORM Self-Test again using the correct procedure.
QA2 CHECK FOR VREF AT TP SENSOR			
• Key off. • Throttle Position sensor disconnected. • Key on, engine off. • Measure voltage between VREF and SIG RTN circuits at the TP sensor vehicle harness connector. • Key off. • Was the voltage between 4.0 and 6.0 volts?	Yes No	▶ ▶	RECONNECT the TP sensor. If unable to successfully complete KOER Self-Test, but could complete KOEO, or a communication error was received while attempting to do so, GO to **QA3**. All others: GO to **QA4**. RECONNECT the TP sensor. GO to Pinpoint Test Step **C1**.

Fig. 211 Test QA: Unable To Activate Self-Test (Part 2 of 4). 1994-95

FM0159401205020X

TEST STEP	RESULT	▶	ACTION TO TAKE
QA3 RETRIEVE ANY CONTINUOUS MEMORY DTCS			
NOTE: If a failure is present in the VS sensor, MAF sensor, MLP sensor or their harness circuits, this could cause the EEC strategy NOT to complete KOER Self-Test and/or cause the PCM to generate a communication error message. • Scan Tool connected. • Key on, engine off. • Retrieve and record all Continuous Memory DTCs (MIL and non-MIL). • Key off. • **Are any Continuous Memory DTCs present?**	Yes No	▶ ▶	GO to DTC Charts in Diagnostic Subroutines, for pinpoint test direction. Unable to retrieve ANY Self-Test DTCs. Can not use DTC charts. GO to **QA4**.
QA4 CHECK B+ AT DATA LINK CONNECTOR (DLC)			
• Key on, engine off. • Inspect the DLC for damage. Service as necessary. • Measure voltage between B+ circuit cavity at the DLC and engine block ground. • Key off. • Was voltage greater than 10.5 volts?	Yes No	▶ ▶	GO to **QA5**. SERVICE open in DLC B+ circuit. RERUN Quick Test.
QA5 CHECK DLC CHASSIS GROUND CONTINUITY			
• Key off. • Measure resistance between chassis ground circuit cavity at the DLC and engine block ground. • Is resistance less than 5.0 ohms?	Yes No	▶ ▶	GO to **QA6**. SERVICE open in DLC chassis ground circuit. RERUN Quick Test.
QA6 CHECK DLC PWR GND CIRCUIT CONTINUITY			
• Key off. • Disconnect PCM. Inspect for damaged or pushed out pins, loose wires, corrosion, etc. Service as necessary. • Install breakout box, leave PCM disconnected. • Measure resistance between Test Pin 51 or 103 (PWR GND) at the breakout box and the PWR GND circuit cavity at the DLC. • Is resistance less than 5.0 ohms?	Yes No	▶ ▶	GO to **QA7**. SERVICE open in DLC PWR GND circuit. RECONNECT the PCM. REMOVE breakout box. RERUN Quick Test.

Fig. 211 Test QA: Unable To Activate Self-Test (Part 3 of 4). 1994-95

FM0159401205030X

TEST STEP	RESULT	▶	ACTION TO TAKE
QA7 CHECK DLC BUS(-) CIRCUIT CONTINUITY • Key off. • Breakout box installed, PCM disconnected. • Measure resistance between Test Pin 15 [BUS (-)] at the breakout box and the BUS (-) circuit at the DLC. • Is resistance less than 5.0 ohms?	Yes No	▶ ▶	GO to **QA8**. SERVICE open in the DLC BUS(-) circuit. RECONNECT the PCM. REMOVE breakout box. RERUN Quick Test.
QA8 CHECK BUS(-) CIRCUIT FOR SHORT TO GROUND • Key off. • Breakout box installed, PCM disconnected. • Measure resistance between Test Pin 15 [BUS (-)] at the breakout box and engine block ground. • Is resistance greater than 10,000 ohms?	Yes No	▶ ▶	GO to **QA9**. SERVICE short to ground in the BUS(-) circuit. RECONNECT the PCM. REMOVE breakout box. RERUN Quick Test.
QA9 CHECK BUS(-) CIRCUIT FOR SHORT TO POWER • Key off. • Breakout box installed, PCM disconnected. • Key on, engine off. • Measure voltage between Test Pin 15 [BUS (-)] and Test Pin 51 or 103 (PWR GND) at the breakout box. • Key off. • Was the voltage greater than 1.0 volt?	Yes No	▶ ▶	SERVICE short to power in the BUS(-) circuit. RECONNECT the PCM. REMOVE breakout box. RERUN Quick Test. GO to **QA10**.
QA10 CHECK DLC BUS(+) CIRCUIT CONTINUITY • Key off. • Breakout box installed, PCM disconnected. • Measure resistance between Test Pin 16 [BUS (+)] at the breakout box and BUS(+) circuit at the DLC. • Is resistance less than 5.0 ohms?	Yes No	▶ ▶	GO to **QA11**. SERVICE open in DLC BUS(+) circuit. RECONNECT the PCM. REMOVE breakout box. RERUN Quick Test.
QA11 CHECK BUS(+) CIRCUIT FOR SHORT TO POWER • Key off. • Breakout box installed, PCM disconnected. • Key on, engine off. • Measure voltage between Test Pin 15 [BUS (+)] and Test Pins 51 or 103 (PWR GND) at the breakout box. • Key off. • Was the voltage greater than 1.0 volt?	Yes No	▶ ▶	SERVICE short to power in the BUS(+) circuit. RECONNECT the PCM. REMOVE breakout box. RERUN Quick Test. REPLACE the PCM. REMOVE breakout box. RERUN Quick Test.

FM0159401205040X

Fig. 211   Test QA: Unable To Activate Self-Test (Part 4 of 4). 1994-95

Note

You should enter this Pinpoint Test only when directed here.

Remember

This Pinpoint Test is intended to diagnose only the following:
• Battery terminal condition.
• Keep Alive Power (KAPWR) wire routing.
• Harness circuit: KAPWR.
• Powertrain Control Module (PCM).

Pinpoint Test Schematic

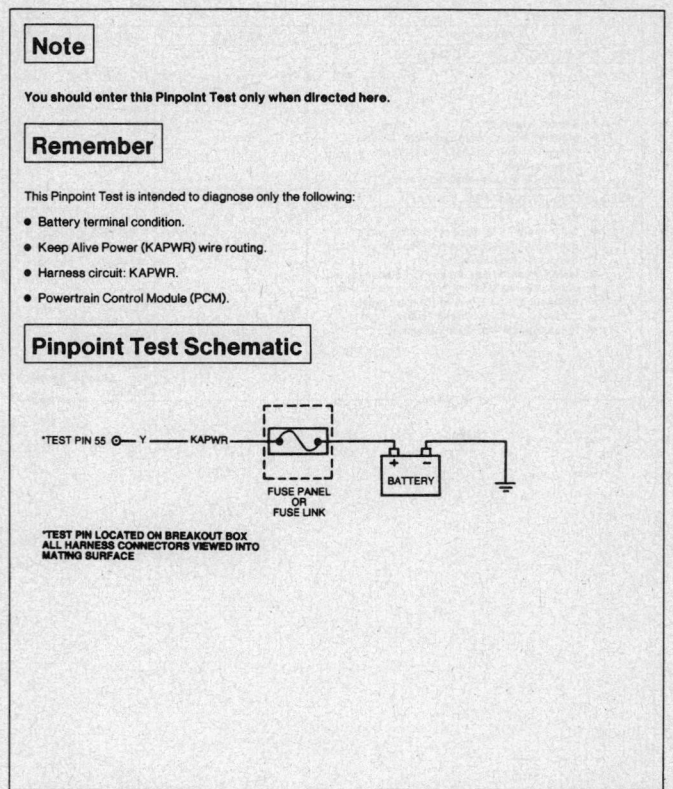

FM0159401206010X

Fig. 212   Test QB: DTC 1605 (Part 1 of 3). 1994-95

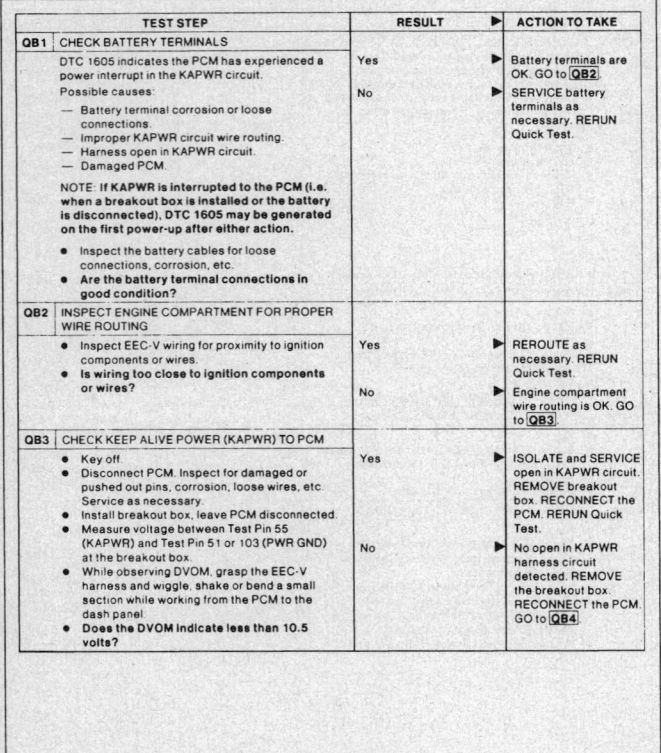

TEST STEP	RESULT	▶	ACTION TO TAKE
QB1 CHECK BATTERY TERMINALS DTC 1605 indicates the PCM has experienced a power interrupt in the KAPWR circuit. Possible causes: — Battery terminal corrosion or loose connections. — Improper KAPWR circuit wire routing. — Harness open in KAPWR circuit. — Damaged PCM. NOTE: If KAPWR is interrupted to the PCM (i.e. when a breakout box is installed or the battery is disconnected), DTC 1605 may be generated on the first power-up after either action. • Inspect the battery cables for loose connections, corrosion, etc. • Are the battery terminal connections in good condition?	Yes No	▶ ▶	Battery terminals are OK. GO to **QB2**. SERVICE battery terminals as necessary. RERUN Quick Test.
QB2 INSPECT ENGINE COMPARTMENT FOR PROPER WIRE ROUTING • Inspect EEC-V wiring for proximity to ignition components or wires. • Is wiring too close to ignition components or wires?	Yes No	▶ ▶	REROUTE as necessary. RERUN Quick Test. Engine compartment wire routing is OK. GO to **QB3**.
QB3 CHECK KEEP ALIVE POWER (KAPWR) TO PCM • Key off. • Disconnect PCM. Inspect for damaged or pushed out pins, corrosion, loose wires, etc. Service as necessary. • Install breakout box, leave PCM disconnected. • Measure voltage between Test Pin 55 (KAPWR) and Test Pin 51 or 103 (PWR GND) at the breakout box. • While observing DVOM, grasp the EEC-V harness and wiggle, shake or bend a small section while working from the PCM to the dash panel. • Does the DVOM indicate less than 10.5 volts?	Yes No	▶ ▶	ISOLATE and SERVICE open in KAPWR circuit. REMOVE breakout box. RECONNECT the PCM. RERUN Quick Test. No open in KAPWR harness circuit detected. REMOVE the breakout box. RECONNECT the PCM. GO to **QB4**.

FM0159401206020X

Fig. 212   Test QB: DTC 1605 (Part 2 of 3). 1994-95

TEST STEP	RESULT	▶	ACTION TO TAKE
QB4 CHECK FOR REPEAT OF DTC 1605 • Activate Key On Engine Off Self-Test. • Is DTC 1605 present?	Yes No	▶ ▶	REPLACE the PCM. RERUN Quick Test. SERVICE other DTCs as necessary. If none, testing is complete. DTC 1605 was due to previous service action mentioned in the NOTE in QB1.

FM0159401206030X

Fig. 212   Test QB: DTC 1605 (Part 3 of 3). 1994-95

Diagnostic Trouble Code (DTC) P1000 indicates that not all of the On Board Diagnostic II (OBD II) monitors have completed. In some states, this code must be cleared to pass an inspection/maintenance test. The customer should be informed that the law specifies additional city and highway driving must be done to complete the check of the On Board Diagnostic system. This additional driving must occur before the vehicle is tested at the inspection/maintenance station. The amount of driving required varies with individual driving patterns.

DTC P1000 is set by the PCM with any of the following conditions:
- The vehicle is new from the factory and has not yet been through a complete OBD II Drive Cycle.
- The battery or PCM has been disconnected.
- An OBD II monitor failure had occurred before completion of an OBD II Drive Cycle.
- The PCM DTCs have been erased with a Scan Tool as part of the normal repair process.

The only way a DTC P1000 can be removed from memory is when all the OBD II monitors have successfully completed during normal vehicle operation.

| Remember |

It is not necessary to remove the P1000 from the PCM by driving the vehicle unless it is requested by the customer to pass an inspection/maintenance test.

Inform the customer of the need for additional driving when required to pass an inspection/maintenance test.

Fig. 213   Test QC: OBD II Monitor Testing Not Complete-DTC P1000 (Part 1 of 2). 1994-95

	TEST STEP	RESULT	▶	ACTION TO TAKE
QC1	DTC P1000: CHECK FOR OTHER DTCS			
	This pinpoint test should be used only if a Diagnostic Trouble Code (DTC) P1000 was received in Continuous Memory. Ignore any DTC P1000s in KOEO or KOER. DTC P1000 indicates that all of the OBD II monitors have not yet been successfully tested. • Were any other DTCs received with the P1000?	Yes No	▶	GO to Powertrain Diagnostic Trouble Code (DTC) Charts, for Pinpoint Test direction and SERVICE other DTCs. No EEC-V system faults have been detected. GO to QC2.
QC2	REQUEST TO REMOVE P1000			
	A complete OBD II Drive Cycle has not yet been performed to remove the DTC P1000 from the PCM. • Has the customer requested the DTC P1000 be removed from the PCM memory?	Yes No	▶	PERFORM the OBD II Drive Cycle. (REFER to , Drive Cycles.) If DTC P1000 is still present, GO to QC3. No faults in the EEC-V system have been detected. INFORM the customer that if the law in this state requires additional driving in order to remove the DTC P1000 from the PCM memory, it must be performed before an inspection/maintenance test.
QC3	CHECK VSS PID			
	Perform a short road test and look for a change in the VSS PID. • Was the VSS PID greater than zero MPH/KPH?	Yes No	▶	GO to QC4. SERVICE open VSS circuit. RERUN the OBD II Drive Cycle. RERUN Quick Test.
QC4	CHECK ECT TEMPERATURE			
	Drive the vehicle long enough to obtain the highest engine operating temperature and record the ECT temperature PID. • Was the ECT PID reading greater than 180°F/82°C?	Yes No	▶	ADDITIONAL driving is required. PERFORM the OBD II Drive Cycle. RERUN Quick Test. REPLACE the cooling system thermostat. PERFORM the OBD II Drive Cycle. RERUN Quick Test.

Fig. 213   Test QC: OBD II Monitor Testing Not Complete-DTC P1000 (Part 2 of 2). 1994-95

| Note |

You should enter this Pinpoint Test only when directed here.

| Remember |

This Pinpoint Test is intended to diagnose the following:
- Harness circuits: Transmission Control Indicator Lamp (TCIL) and Transmission Control Switch (TCS).
- Powertrain Control Module (PCM)

Pinpoint Test Schematic

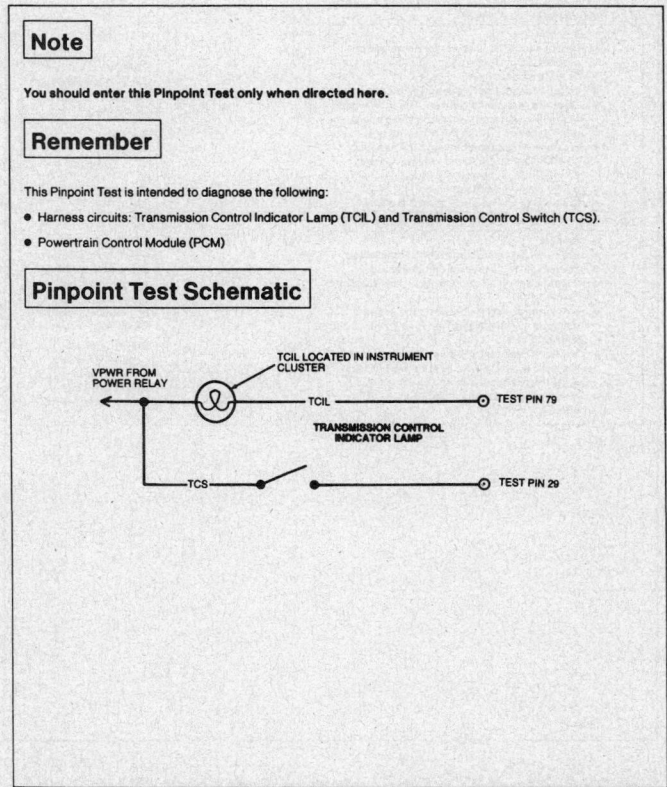

Fig. 214   Test TB: TCS/TCIL (Part 1 of 3). 1994-95

FM015940120801OX

	TEST STEP	RESULT	▶	ACTION TO TAKE
TB1	DTC 1780			
	Diagnostic Trouble Code (DTC) 1780 indicates the Transmission Control Switch (TCS) was not cycled during Key On Engine Running (KOER) Self-Test. Possible Causes: — TCS damaged or switch not cycled during Self-Test. — Shorted or open harness. — Damaged Powertrain Control Module (PCM). • Did TCS cycle during Self-Test?	Yes No	▶	GO to TB2. RERUN KOER Self-Test to cycle TCS.
TB2	CHECK TRANSMISSION CONTROL SWITCH (TCS) CIRCUIT FOR VOLTAGE			
	• Key off. • Disconnect PCM. Inspect for damaged or pushed out pins, corrosion, loose wires, etc. Service as necessary. • Install breakout box, leave PCM disconnected. • Key on, engine off. Measure the voltage between Test Pin 29 and Test Pins 24 and 77 at the breakout box while cycling the TCS several times. • Does the voltage cycle?	Yes No	▶	REPLACE PCM. REMOVE breakout box. RERUN Quick Test. GO to TB3.
TB3	CHECK HARNESS CIRCUIT(S) FOR SHORT TO GROUND			
	• Key off. • Breakout box installed, leave PCM disconnected. • Disconnect TCS. Inspect both ends for damaged or pushed out pins, moisture, corrosion, loose wires, etc. Service as necessary. • Measure the resistance between Test Pin 29 and Test Pins 24 and 77 at the breakout box. • Is the resistance greater than 10,000 ohms?	Yes No	▶	GO to TB4. SERVICE short circuit. RERUN Self-Test.
TB4	CHECK CONTINUITY OF THE TCS HARNESS			
	• Key off. • Breakout box installed, leave PCM disconnected. • Measure the resistance between TCS keypower at the fuse panel (ohmmeter positive probe) and power side of the TCS vehicle harness connector (ohmmeter negative probe). • Is the resistance less than 5.0 ohms?	Yes No	▶	GO to TB5. SERVICE open circuit. REMOVE breakout box. RECONNECT all components. RERUN Quick Test.

Fig. 214   Test TB: TCS/TCIL (Part 2 of 3). 1994-95

FM015940120802OX

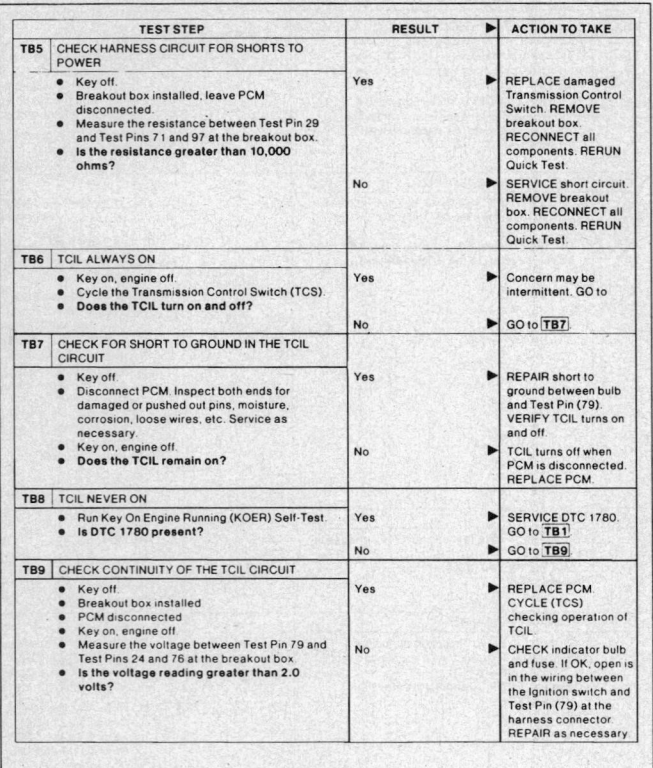

TEST STEP	RESULT	▶	ACTION TO TAKE
TB5 CHECK HARNESS CIRCUIT FOR SHORTS TO POWER • Key off. • Breakout box installed, leave PCM disconnected. • Measure the resistance between Test Pin 29 and Test Pins 71 and 97 at the breakout box. • **Is the resistance greater than 10,000 ohms?**	Yes	▶	REPLACE damaged Transmission Control Switch. REMOVE breakout box. RECONNECT all components. RERUN Quick Test.
	No	▶	SERVICE short circuit. REMOVE breakout box. RECONNECT all components. RERUN Quick Test.
TB6 TCIL ALWAYS ON • Key on, engine off. • Cycle the Transmission Control Switch (TCS). • **Does the TCIL turn on and off?**	Yes	▶	Concern may be intermittent. GO to
	No	▶	GO to TB7
TB7 CHECK FOR SHORT TO GROUND IN THE TCIL CIRCUIT • Key off. • Disconnect PCM. Inspect both ends for damaged or pushed out pins, moisture, corrosion, loose wires, etc. Service as necessary. • Key on, engine off. • **Does the TCIL remain on?**	Yes	▶	REPAIR short to ground between bulb and Test Pin (79). VERIFY TCIL turns on and off.
	No	▶	TCIL turns off when PCM is disconnected. REPLACE PCM.
TB8 TCIL NEVER ON • Run Key On Engine Running (KOER) Self-Test. • **Is DTC 1780 present?**	Yes	▶	SERVICE DTC 1780. GO to TB1
	No	▶	GO to TB9
TB9 CHECK CONTINUITY OF THE TCIL CIRCUIT • Key off. • Breakout box installed. • PCM disconnected. • Key on, engine off. • Measure the voltage between Test Pin 79 and Test Pins 24 and 76 at the breakout box. • **Is the voltage reading greater than 2.0 volts?**	Yes	▶	REPLACE PCM. CYCLE (TCS) checking operation of TCIL.
	No	▶	CHECK indicator bulb and fuse. If OK, open is in the wiring between the Ignition switch and Test Pin (79) at the harness connector. REPAIR as necessary.

FM0159401208030X

Fig. 214   Test TB: TCS/TCIL (Part 3 of 3). 1994-95

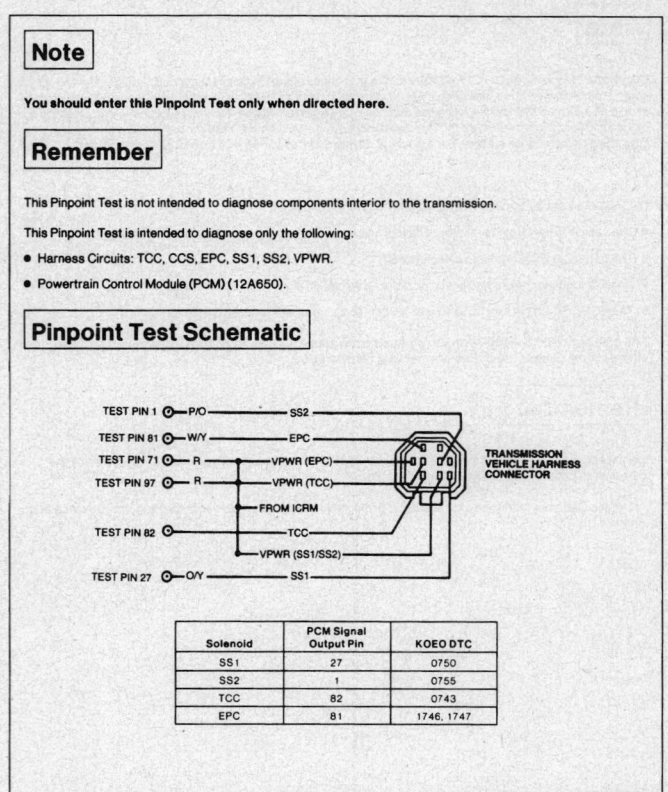

Note

You should enter this Pinpoint Test only when directed here.

Remember

This Pinpoint Test is not intended to diagnose components interior to the transmission.

This Pinpoint Test is intended to diagnose only the following:
• Harness Circuits: TCC, CCS, EPC, SS1, SS2, VPWR.
• Powertrain Control Module (PCM) (12A650).

Pinpoint Test Schematic

Solenoid	PCM Signal Output Pin	KOEO DTC
SS1	27	0750
SS2	1	0755
TCC	82	0743
EPC	81	1746, 1747

FM0159401209010X

Fig. 215   Test TC: Transmission Solenoids (Part 1 of 5). 1994-95

TEST STEP	RESULT	▶	ACTION TO TAKE
TC1 ENTER OUTPUT STATE DIAGNOSTIC TEST MODE: CHECK TRANSMISSION ELECTRICAL OPERATION DTC 0743 indicates TCC electrical malfunction. DTC 0750 indicates SS1 electrical malfunction. DTC 0755 indicates SS2 electrical malfunction. DTC 1746 indicates EPC circuit open. DTC 1747 indicates EPC circuit shorted. Possible Causes: — Solenoid assembly damaged. — PCM damaged. — VPWR circuit open or shorted to GND. — Solenoid circuit open or, shorted to VPWR or GND. • Key off. • Disconnect transmission connector. • Using a mirror, inspect both ends of the connector for damaged or pushed out pins, corrosion, loose wires, etc. Service as necessary. • Disconnect electrical connector on the speed control servo, if equipped. • Connect DVOM positive test lead to the VPWR circuit and negative test lead to the transmission solenoid circuit at the transmission vehicle harness connector. • Key on, engine off. • Turn on Scan Tool outputs with the trigger button. • Observe transmission solenoid voltage reading on the DVOM and record. • Cycle the Scan Tool trigger button on and off several times. • **Does the transmission solenoid circuit cycle 0.5 volts or greater on the DVOM?**	Yes	▶	Transmission Diagnosis for internal harness and solenoids. GO to TC2
	No	▶	
TC2 CHECK VPWR TO SOLENOID • Key off. • Disconnect transmission connector. • Using a mirror, inspect both ends of the connector for damaged or pushed out pins, corrosion, loose wires, etc. Service as necessary. • Key on, engine off. • Measure voltage between the VPWR pins at the transmission vehicle harness connector and chassis/battery ground. • **Is voltage greater than 10.5 volts?**	Yes	▶	GO to TC3
	No	▶	SERVICE open in VPWR circuit. RECONNECT all components. COMPLETE PCM reset to clear DTC. RERUN Quick Test.

FM0159401209020X

Fig. 215   Test TC: Transmission Solenoids (Part 2 of 5). 1994-95

TEST STEP	RESULT	▶	ACTION TO TAKE
TC3 CHECK CONTINUITY OF SOLENOID SIGNAL AND VPWR HARNESS CIRCUIT • Key off. • Disconnect PCM. Inspect for damaged or pushed out pins, corrosion, loose wires, etc. Service as necessary. • Install breakout box, leave PCM disconnected. • Measure resistance between the VPWR pins at the transmission vehicle harness connector and Test Pin 71/97 at the breakout box. • Measure resistance between the suspect solenoid signal pin at the vehicle harness connector and the same suspect solenoid signal pin at the breakout box. • **Is each resistance less than 5.0 ohms?**	Yes	▶	GO to TC4
	No	▶	SERVICE open circuit. REMOVE breakout box. RECONNECT all components. RERUN Quick Test.
TC4 CHECK SOLENOID CIRCUIT FOR SHORT • Key off. • Breakout box installed, PCM disconnected. • Transmission connector disconnected. • Refer to schematic and table in this Pinpoint Test. • Measure resistance between the suspect solenoid signal pin and Test Pins 71/97 at the breakout box. • Measure resistance between the suspect solenoid signal pin and Test Pins 51/76 and 91 at the breakout box and chassis ground. • **Is each resistance greater than 10,000 ohms?**	Yes	▶	REPLACE PCM. REMOVE breakout box. RECONNECT all components. COMPLETE PCM reset to clear DTC. RERUN Quick Test.
	No	▶	SERVICE short circuits. REMOVE breakout box. RECONNECT all components. RERUN Quick Test.

FM0159401209030X

Fig. 215   Test TC: Transmission Solenoids (Part 3 of 5). 1994-95

ELECTRONIC ENGINE CONTROL SYSTEM (EEC-V)

	TEST STEP	RESULT	▶	ACTION TO TAKE
TC5	CHECK TRANSMISSION ELECTRICAL OPERATION			
	Diagnostic Trouble Code (DTC) P0741, P0743 indicates TCC electrical malfunction. DTC P1754 indicates CCS electrical malfunction. DTC P0746 indicates EPC solenoid malfunction. DTC P1746 indicates EPC circuit open. DTC P1747 indicates EPC circuit shorted. DTC P1749 indicates EPC solenoid failed low. Possible causes: — Internal Transmission. — Damaged Solenoid. — Solenoid circuit open or shorted to VPWR or GND. VPWR circuit open or shorted. — Damaged PCM. ● Key off. ● Disconnect transmission vehicle harness connector. Inspect for damaged or pushed out pins, corrosion, loose wires, etc. Service as necessary. ● Connect DVOM between the VPWR pins and the suspect solenoid pin. ● Scan Tool connected. ● Key on, engine off. ● Enter Output Test Mode. ● Cycle the suspect solenoid on and off. ● **Does the voltmeter reading cycle?**	No	▶	GO to TC6.
TC6	CHECK VPWR TO SOLENOID			
	● Key off. ● Transmission vehicle harness connector disconnected. ● Disconnect PCM. Inspect for damaged or pushed out pins, corrosion, loose wires, ect. Service as necessary. ● Install breakout box, leave PCM disconnected. ● Disconnect Scan Tool. ● Key on, engine off. ● Measure voltage between Test Pin 71/97 at the breakout box and chassis ground. ● **Is the voltage greater than 10.5 volts?**	Yes No	▶ ▶	GO to TC7. SERVICE VPWR circuit. REMOVE breakout box. RECONNECT all components. RERUN Quick Test.

Fig. 215   Test TC: Transmission Solenoids (Part 4 of 5). 1995

	TEST STEP	RESULT	▶	ACTION TO TAKE
TC7	CHECK CONTINUITY OF SOLENOID VPWR AND SIGNAL HARNESS CIRCUIT			
	● Key off. ● Disconnect PCM and Scan Tool. ● Breakout box installed, leave PCM disconnected. ● Disconnect transmission vehicle harness connector. Inspect both ends for damaged or pushed out pins, corrosion, loose wires, etc. Service as necessary. ● Measure resistance between the VPWR pins at the transmission vehicle harness connector and Test Pin 71/97 at the breakout box. ● Measure resistance between the suspect transmission solenoid pin at the vehicle harness connector and the same suspect Test Pin at the breakout box. ● **Is each resistance less than 5.0 ohms?**	Yes No	▶ ▶	GO to TC8. SERVICE open circuit. REMOVE breakout box. RECONNECT all components. RERUN Quick Test.
TC8	CHECK SOLENOID CIRCUIT FOR SHORT TO POWER OR GROUND			
	● Key off. ● Transmission vehicle harness connector disconnected. ● Breakout box installed, PCM disconnected. ● Refer to table and schematic of this Pinpoint Test. ● Measure resistance between the suspect solenoid signal Test Pin and Test Pin 71/97 at the breakout box. ● Measure resistance between the suspect solenoid signal Test Pin and Test Pins 51/76 and 91 at the breakout box and chassis ground. ● **Is each resistance greater than 10,000 ohms?**	Yes No	▶ ▶	REFER to Transmission Diagnosis. SERVICE short circuit. REMOVE breakout box. RECONNECT all components. RERUN Quick Test.

Fig. 215   Test TC: Transmission Solenoids (Part 5 of 5). 1995

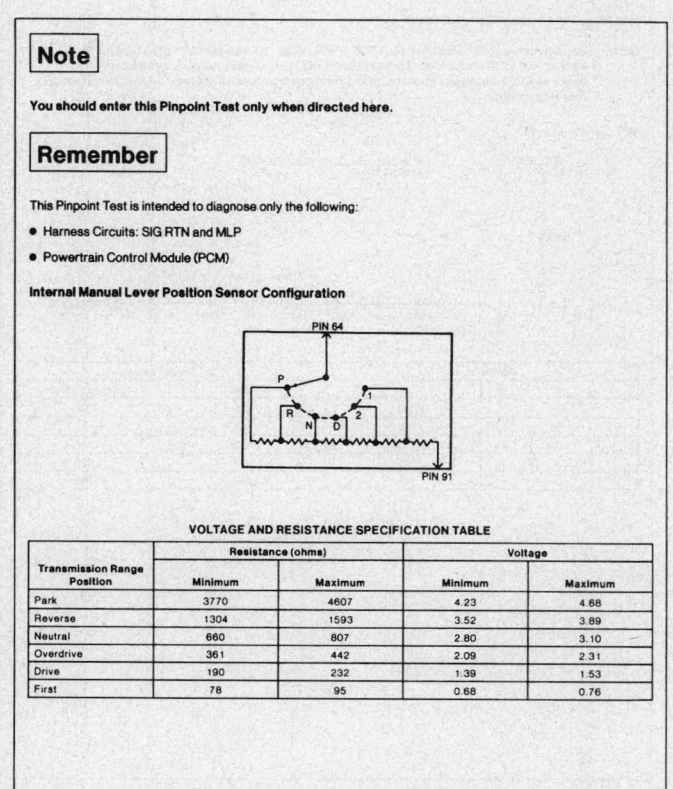

Note

You should enter this Pinpoint Test only when directed here.

Remember

This Pinpoint Test is intended to diagnose only the following:

● Harness Circuits: SIG RTN and MLP
● Powertrain Control Module (PCM)

Internal Manual Lever Position Sensor Configuration

VOLTAGE AND RESISTANCE SPECIFICATION TABLE

Transmission Range Position	Resistance (ohms)		Voltage	
	Minimum	Maximum	Minimum	Maximum
Park	3770	4607	4.23	4.68
Reverse	1304	1593	3.52	3.89
Neutral	660	807	2.80	3.10
Overdrive	361	442	2.09	2.31
Drive	190	232	1.39	1.53
First	78	95	0.68	0.76

FM015940121010X

Fig. 216   Test TD: MLP Sensor (Part 1 of 4). 1994-95

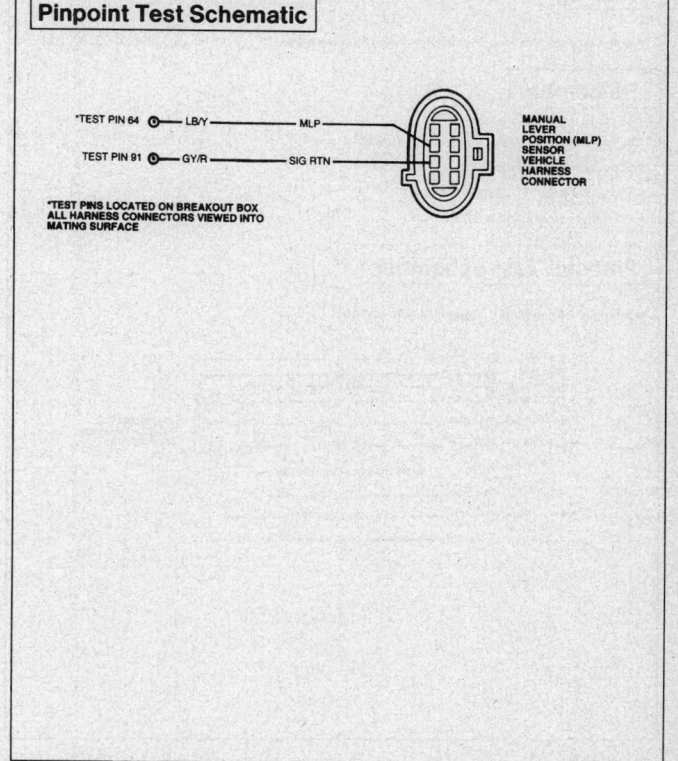

Pinpoint Test Schematic

*TEST PINS LOCATED ON BREAKOUT BOX
ALL HARNESS CONNECTORS VIEWED INTO MATING SURFACE

FM015940121020X

Fig. 216   Test TD: MLP Sensor (Part 2 of 4). 1994-95

TEST STEP		RESULT	▶	ACTION TO TAKE
TD1	**CHECK MLP SENSOR ALIGNMENT**			
	Diagnostic Trouble Code (DTC) 0707 MLP sensor shorted to ground. DTC 0708 MLP circuit high, open circuit. DTC 1705 MLP not in Park during Key On Engine Off (KOEO) Self-Test. Possible Causes: — Misadjusted linkage. — Misaligned MLP sensor. — SIG RTN circuit open or shorted to GND. — MLP signal circuit open or shorted to VPWR or GND. — PCM damaged. • Key off. • Apply parking brake. • Place MLP lever in Neutral. • Verify MLP Sensor Tool (Rotunda T92P-7010-AH) or equivalent fits in the appropriate slot. • **Does the tool fit properly?**	Yes No	▶ ▶	REMOVE tool. GO to [TD2]. LOOSEN the two MLP sensor mounting screws. MOVE the sensor about to allow insertion of the MLP sensor tool in the appropriate slots. TIGHTEN the screws to specification. VERIFY shift linkage adjustment. RERUN Quick Test.
TD2	**CHECK MLP SENSOR RESPONSE**			
	• Key off. • Brake applied. • Scan Tool connected. • Access MLP and MLPV PID. • Key on, engine off. • Move the shift lever through all gear ranges. • **Is each voltage reading within specifications?**	Yes. No	▶ ▶	GO to [TD5]. GO to [TD3].
TD3	**CHECK CONTINUITY OF MLP SENSOR HARNESS CIRCUITS**			
	• Key off. • Disconnect PCM. • Inspect for damaged or pushed out pins, corrosion, loose wires, etc. Service as necessary. • Disconnect MLP sensor. • Inspect both ends of the connector for damaged or pushed out pins, corrosion, loose wires, etc. Service as necessary. • Install breakout box, leave PCM disconnected. • Measure resistance between Test Pin 64 at the breakout box and MLP signal pin at the vehicle harness connector. • Measure resistance between Test Pin 91 at the breakout box and the SIG RTN pin at the vehicle harness connector. • **Is each resistance less than 5.0 ohms?**	Yes No	▶ ▶	GO to [TD4]. SERVICE open circuit(s). REMOVE breakout box. RECONNECT all components. RERUN Quick Test.

FM0159401210030X

Fig. 216   Test TD: MLP Sensor (Part 3 of 4). 1994-95

TEST STEP		RESULT	▶	ACTION TO TAKE
TD4	**CHECK MLP SENSOR CIRCUIT FOR SHORT TO POWER AND GROUND**			
	• Key off. • MLP sensor disconnected. • Breakout box installed, PCM disconnected. • Measure resistance between Test Pin 64 and Test Pins 71 or 97, 76 or 77, and 91 at the breakout box. • Measure resistance between Test Pin 64 at the breakout box and chassis ground. • **Is each resistance greater than 10,000 ohms?**	Yes No	▶ ▶	GO to [TD5]. SERVICE short in harness. REMOVE breakout box. RECONNECT all components. RERUN Quick Test.
TD5	**CHECK MLP SENSOR RESISTANCE**			
	• Key off. • Connect MLP sensor. • Breakout box installed, PCM disconnected. • Unlock steering column. • Measure resistance between Test Pin 64 and Test Pin 91 at the breakout box in each gear range position. • **Is each resistance reading within specification?**	Yes No	▶ ▶	REPLACE PCM. REMOVE breakout box. RERUN Quick Test. REPLACE MLP sensor. ADJUST MLP sensor per procedure in [TD1]. REMOVE breakout box. RERUN Quick Test.

FM0159401210040X

Fig. 216   Test TD: MLP Sensor (Part 4 of 4). 1994-95

Notes

You should enter this Pinpoint Test only when directed here.

Remember

This Pinpoint Test is intended to diagnose the following:

• Transmission Fluid Temperature (TFT) sensor
• Harness circuits: TFT SIG and SIG RTN
• Powertrain Control Module (PCM)

Pinpoint Test Schematic

Mustang and Thunderbird/Cougar (AODE/4R70W)

TEST PIN 37	O/BK	TFT
TEST PIN 1	P/O	SS2
TEST PIN 91	GY/R	SIG RTN
TEST PIN 81	W/Y	EPC
TEST PIN 71/97	R	TCC VPWR
TEST PIN 71/97	R	EPC VPWR
		FROM EEC POWER RELAY
TEST PIN 82		TCC
TEST PIN 71/97	R	SS1 AND SS2 VPWR
TEST PIN 27	O/Y	SS1

TRANSMISSION VEHICLE HARNESS CONNECTOR

FM0159401211010X

Fig. 217   Test TE: TFT Sensor (Part 1 of 12). 1994

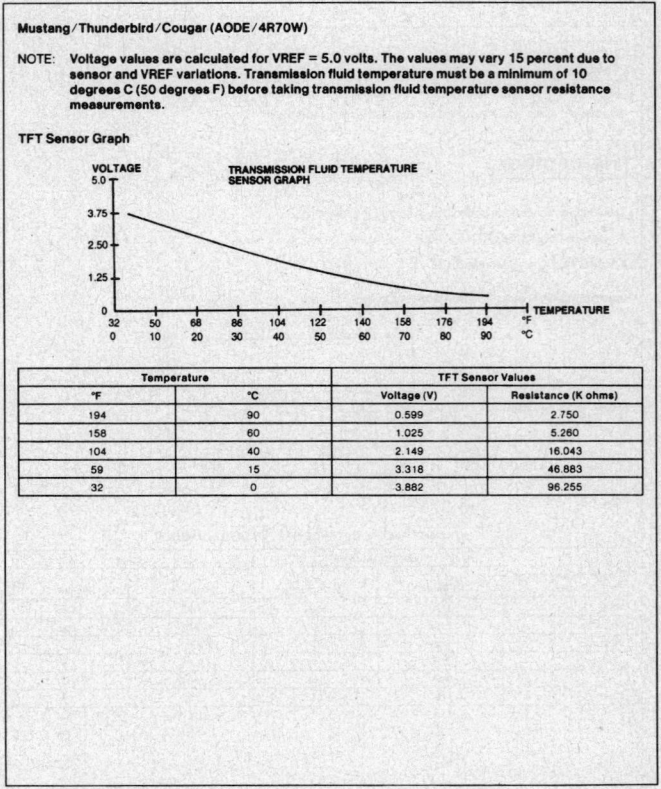

Mustang/Thunderbird/Cougar (AODE/4R70W)

NOTE: Voltage values are calculated for VREF = 5.0 volts. The values may vary 15 percent due to sensor and VREF variations. Transmission fluid temperature must be a minimum of 10 degrees C (50 degrees F) before taking transmission fluid temperature sensor resistance measurements.

TFT Sensor Graph

Temperature		TFT Sensor Values	
°F	°C	Voltage (V)	Resistance (K ohms)
194	90	0.599	2.750
158	60	1.025	5.260
104	40	2.149	16.043
59	15	3.318	46.883
32	0	3.882	96.255

FM0159401211020X

Fig. 217   Test TE: TFT Sensor (Part 2 of 12). 1994

Pinpoint Test Schematics

Mustang, Thunderbird/Cougar, Crown Victoria/Grand Marquis, Town Car (AODE/4R70W)

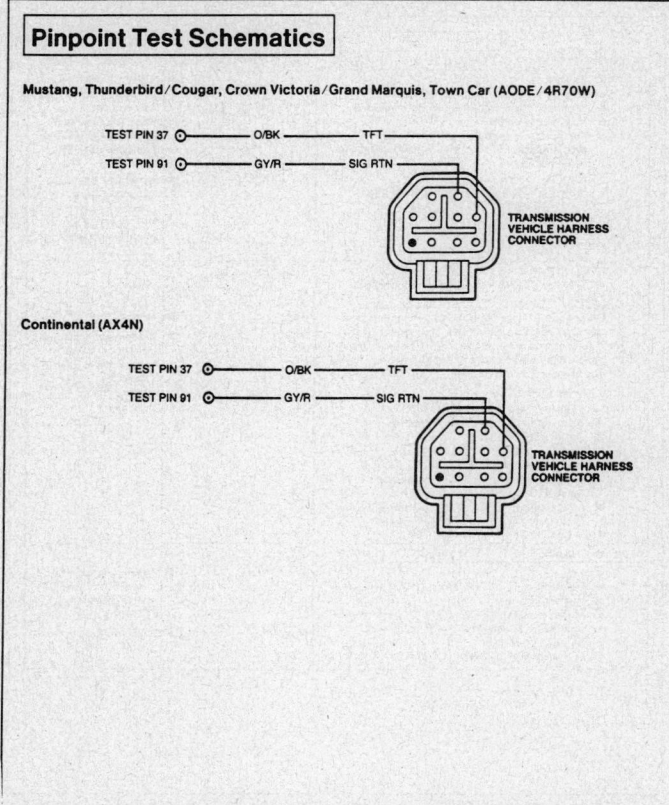

Tables and Charts

NOTE: Voltage values are calculated for VREF = 5.0 volts. The values may vary 15 percent due to sensor and VREF variations. Transmission fluid temperature must be a minimum of 10 degrees C (50 degrees F) before taking transmission fluid temperature sensor resistance measurements.

TFT Sensor Graph

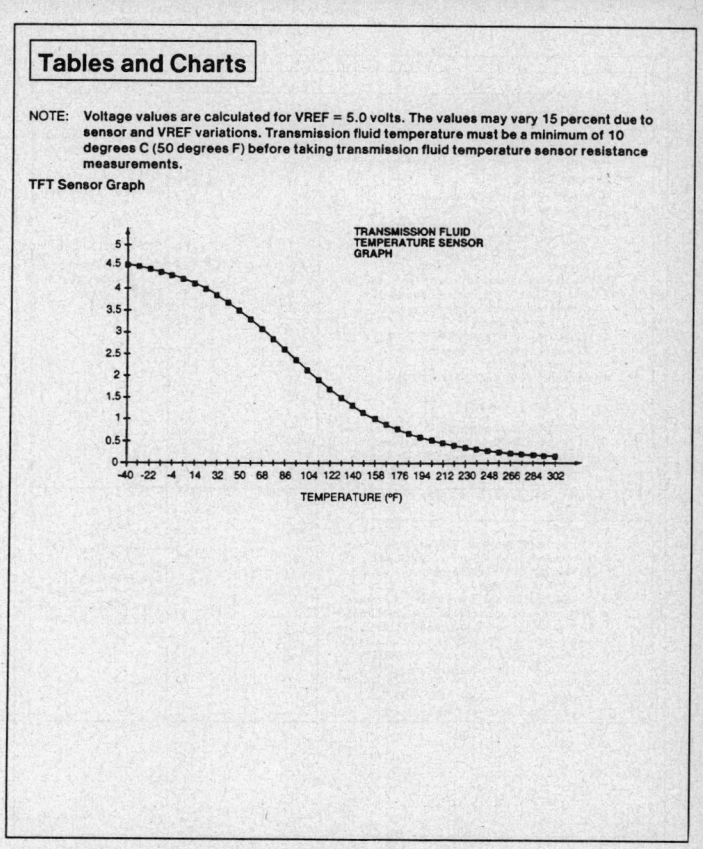

Fig. 217   Test TE: TFT Sensor (Part 3 of 12). 1995

Fig. 217   Test TE: TFT Sensor (Part 4 of 12). 1995

Temperature		TFT Sensor Values	
°C	°F	Volts (V)	Resistance (K ohms)
-40	-40	4.541	965.808
-35	-31	4.509	700.178
-30	-22	4.467	513.019
-25	-13	4.413	379.674
-20	-4	4.345	283.664
-15	5	4.259	213.842
-10	14	4.155	162.584
-5	23	4.03	124.614
0	32	3.882	96.255
5	41	3.714	75.201
10	50	3.525	59.175
15	59	3.318	46.883
20	68	3.095	37.387
25	77	2.862	30
30	86	2.623	24.215
35	95	2.383	19.657
40	104	2.149	16.043
45	113	1.923	13.161
50	122	1.71	10.85
55	131	1.513	8.99
60	140	1.333	7.487
65	149	1.17	6.265
70	158	1.025	5.268
75	167	0.897	4.45
80	176	0.784	3.775
85	185	0.685	3.215
90	194	0.599	2.75
95	203	0.523	2.361
100	212	0.458	2.034
105	221	0.401	1.758
110	230	0.352	1.523
115	239	0.309	1.324
120	248	0.272	1.155
125	257	0.239	1.01
130	266	0.212	0.8866
135	275	0.187	0.7805
140	284	0.166	0.6891
145	293	0.148	0.6101
150	302	0.132	0.5417

Fig. 217   Test TE: TFT Sensor (Part 5 of 12). 1995

	TEST STEP	RESULT	▶	ACTION TO TAKE
TE1	KOEO AND KOER DTC 07 12: ATTEMPT TO INDUCE OPPOSITE CONDITION			
	Diagnostic Trouble Code (DTC) 07 12 indicates that Self-Test has detected a TFT sensor circuit input below the minimum acceptable voltage. Possible Causes: — Fluid level not to specification. — Damaged TFT sensor. — Short to GND or SIG RTN in TFT SIG harness circuit. — Damaged PCM. ● Key off. ● Disconnect transmission connector. Inspect for damaged or pushed out pins, corrosion, loose wires, etc. Service as necessary. ● Activate Key On Engine Off (KOEO) and Key On Engine Running (KOER) Self-Tests, (transmission connector remains disconnected). ● Is DTC 07 13 present? NOTE: Disregard any other DTCs generated at this time.	Yes No	▶ ▶	The fault that produced DTC 07 12 is not within the TFT harness circuits or the PCM. TFT sensor service. The opposite condition could not be induced. GO to TE2.
TE2	CHECK VREF AT THE THROTTLE POSITION SENSOR			
	● Key off. ● Transmission connector disconnected. ● Disconnect Throttle Position (TP) sensor. ● Key on, engine off. ● Measure voltage between the TP sensor VREF and SIG RTN circuits at the TP sensor vehicle harness connector. ● Is voltage between 4.0 and 6.0 volts?	Yes No	▶ ▶	VREF voltage is in range. RECONNECT TP sensor. GO to TE3. VREF voltage is out of range. RECONNECT transmission connector.
TE3	CHECK TFT SIG CIRCUIT FOR SHORTS TO GROUND AND SIG RTN			
	● Key off. ● Transmission connector disconnected. ● Disconnect PCM. Inspect for damaged or pushed out pins, corrosion, loose wires, etc. Service as necessary. ● Install breakout box, leave PCM disconnected. ● Measure resistance between Test Pin 37 (TFT SIG) and Test Pins 51 or 103 (PWR GND) and 91 (SIG RTN) at the breakout box. ● Is each resistance greater than 10,000 ohms?	Yes No	▶ ▶	REPLACE damaged PCM. REMOVE breakout box. RECONNECT all components. RERUN Quick Test. SERVICE short circuit between TFT SIG and PWR GND or SIG RTN. RECONNECT all components. REMOVE breakout box. RERUN Quick Test.

FM0159401211030X

Fig. 217   Test TE: TFT Sensor (Part 6 of 12). 1994-95

TEST STEP	RESULT	▶	ACTION TO TAKE
TE10 KOEO AND KOER DTC 07 13: ATTEMPT TO INDUCE OPPOSITE CONDITION Diagnostic Trouble Code (DTC) 07 13 indicates that self-test has detected a TFT sensor circuit input above the maximum acceptable voltage. Possible Causes: — Fluid level not to specifications. — Damaged TFT sensor. — Short to VPWR in TFT SIG harness circuit. — Open in TFT SIG or SIG RTN harness circuit. — Damaged PCM. • Key off. • Disconnect transmission bulkhead connector at the TFT sensor. Inspect for damaged or pushed out pins, corrosion, loose wires, etc. Service as necessary. • Insert a jumper wire from TFT SIG circuit to SIG RTN circuit at the transmission vehicle harness connector. • Activate Key On Engine Off (KOEO) and (KOER) Self-Tests. • **Is DTC 0712 present?** NOTE: Disregard any other DTCs generated at this time. If NO DTCs are generated (module not responding), then immediately GO to step **TE12**.	Yes No	▶ ▶	The fault that produced DTC 07 13 is not within the TFT harness circuits or the PCM. REMOVE jumper wire. TFT sensor service. The opposite condition could not be induced. REMOVE jumper wire. GO to **TE11**.
TE11 CHECK CONTINUITY OF TFT SIG AND SIG RTN CIRCUITS • Key off. • Transmission connector disconnected. • Disconnect PCM. Inspect for damaged or pushed out pins, corrosion, loose wires, etc. Service as necessary. • Install breakout box, leave PCM disconnected. • Measure resistance between TFT SIG circuit at the transmission vehicle harness connector and Test Pin 37 (TFT SIG) at the breakout box. • Measure resistance between TFT SIG circuit at the transmission vehicle harness connector and Test Pin 91 (SIG RTN) at the breakout box. • **Is each resistance less than 5.0 ohms?**	Yes No	▶ ▶	GO to **TE12**. SERVICE open in TFT SIG or SIG RTN harness circuit. REMOVE breakout box. RECONNECT all components. RERUN Quick Test.

Fig. 217 Test TE: TFT Sensor (Part 7 of 12). 1994-95

FM015940121104OX

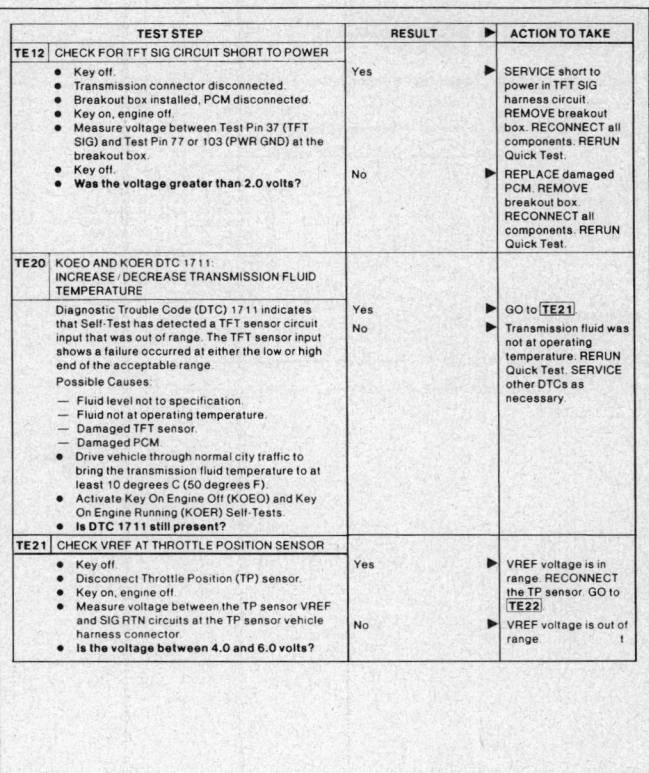

TEST STEP	RESULT	▶	ACTION TO TAKE
TE12 CHECK FOR TFT SIG CIRCUIT SHORT TO POWER • Key off. • Transmission connector disconnected. • Breakout box installed, PCM disconnected. • Key on, engine off. • Measure voltage between Test Pin 37 (TFT SIG) and Test Pin 77 or 103 (PWR GND) at the breakout box. • Key off. • **Was the voltage greater than 2.0 volts?**	Yes No	▶ ▶	SERVICE short to power in TFT SIG harness circuit. REMOVE breakout box. RECONNECT all components. RERUN Quick Test. REPLACE damaged PCM. REMOVE breakout box. RECONNECT all components. RERUN Quick Test.
TE20 KOEO AND KOER DTC 1711: INCREASE / DECREASE TRANSMISSION FLUID TEMPERATURE Diagnostic Trouble Code (DTC) 1711 indicates that Self-Test has detected a TFT sensor circuit input that was out of range. The TFT sensor input shows a failure occurred at either the low or high end of the acceptable range. Possible Causes: — Fluid level not to specification. — Fluid not at operating temperature. — Damaged TFT sensor. — Damaged PCM. • Drive vehicle through normal city traffic to bring the transmission fluid temperature to at least 10 degrees C (50 degrees F). • Activate Key On Engine Off (KOEO) and Key On Engine Running (KOER) Self-Tests. • **Is DTC 1711 still present?**	Yes No	▶ ▶	GO to **TE21**. Transmission fluid was not at operating temperature. RERUN Quick Test. SERVICE other DTCs as necessary.
TE21 CHECK VREF AT THROTTLE POSITION SENSOR • Key off. • Disconnect Throttle Position (TP) sensor. • Key on, engine off. • Measure voltage between the TP sensor VREF and SIG RTN circuits at the TP sensor vehicle harness connector. • **Is the voltage between 4.0 and 6.0 volts?**	Yes No	▶ ▶	VREF voltage is in range. RECONNECT the TP sensor. GO to **TE22**. VREF voltage is out of range.

Fig. 217 Test TE: TFT Sensor (Part 8 of 12). 1994-95

FM015940121105OX

TEST STEP	RESULT	▶	ACTION TO TAKE
TE22 CHECK TFT SENSOR RESISTANCE AS TRANSMISSION FLUID TEMPERATURE IS VARIED • Key off. • Disconnect PCM. Inspect for damaged or pushed out pins, corrosion, loose wires, etc. Service as necessary. • Install breakout box, connect PCM to breakout box. • Key on, engine off. • Verify that transmission oil pan is warm to the touch. **IF IT IS HOT:** — Measure and record TFT sensor resistance between Test Pin 37 (TFT SIG) and Test Pin 91 (SIG RTN) at the breakout box. — Let transmission cool down and repeat the measurement. (The last measurement should be greater than the first.) **IF IT IS COLD:** — Measure and record TFT sensor resistance between Test Pin 37 (TFT SIG) and Test Pin 91 (SIG RTN) at the breakout box. — Reconnect the PCM and drive vehicle for short time to elevate temperature. — Disconnect the PCM and repeat the measurement at the breakout box. (The last measurement should be less than the first.) • **Did resistance measurements differ as expected and was last measurement within specifications?**	Yes No	▶ ▶	REPLACE damaged PCM. REMOVE breakout box. RERUN Quick Test. REMOVE breakout box. RECONNECT PCM. TFT sensor service.

Fig. 217 Test TE: TFT Sensor (Part 9 of 12). 1994-95

FM015940121106OX

TEST STEP	RESULT	▶	ACTION TO TAKE
TE90 CONTINUOUS MEMORY DTC 07 12: VERIFY TFT SIG VOLTAGE Diagnostic Trouble Code (DTC) 07 12 indicates that Self-Test has detected a TFT sensor circuit input that was below the minimum acceptable voltage (sometime during normal vehicle operation). Possible Causes: — Fluid level not to specification. — Short to GND or SIG RTN in TFT SIG harness circuit. — Damaged TFT sensor. — Damaged PCM. • Key on, engine off. • Access TFT PID with a Scan Tool. • **Is TFT PID voltage less than 0.5 volts?**	Yes No	▶ ▶	The TFT SIG voltage is less than the acceptable minimum, but is not intermittent. GO to **TE1**. The fault that produced Continuous Memory DTC 07 12 is intermittent. GO to **TE91**.
TE91 WIGGLE TEST TFT SENSOR HARNESS CIRCUITS • Key on, engine off. • Access TFT PID with a Scan Tool. • Observe TFT PID for an indication of a fault while performing the following: — Shake, wiggle and bend TFT SIG and SIG RTN circuits between transmission and PCM. A fault is indicated by a sudden change in TFT PID voltage. • **Is a fault indicated?**	Yes No	▶ ▶	ISOLATE fault and SERVICE as necessary. RECONNECT all components. COMPLETE PCM reset to clear DTCs (REFER to Powertrain Control Module (PCM) Reset). RERUN Quick Test. Unable to duplicate and / or identify fault at this time. with the following data: TFT PID and the list of Possible Causes found in **TE90**.

Fig. 217 Test TE: TFT Sensor (Part 10 of 12). 1994-95

FM015940121107OX

TEST STEP	RESULT	▶	ACTION TO TAKE
TE100 CONTINUOUS MEMORY DTC 0713: VERIFY TFT SIG VOLTAGE			
Continuous Memory Diagnostic Trouble Code (DTC) 0713 indicates that Self-Test has detected a TFT sensor circuit input that was above the maximum acceptable voltage (sometime during normal vehicle operation in the past). Possible Causes: — Fluid level not to specification. — Open in TFT SIG or SIG RTN harness circuit. — Short to VPWR in TFT SIG harness circuit. — Damaged TFT sensor. — Damaged PCM. ● Key on, engine off. ● Access TFT PID with a Scan Tool. ● **Is TFT PID voltage greater than 4.8 volts?**	Yes	▶	The TFT SIG voltage is greater than the acceptable maximum, but is not intermittent. GO TO **TE10**.
	No	▶	The fault that produced Continuous Memory DTC 0713 is intermittent. GO to **TE101**.
TE101 WIGGLE TEST TFT SENSOR HARNESS CIRCUITS			
● Key on, engine off. ● Access TFT PID with a Scan Tool. ● Observe TFT PID for an indication of a fault while performing the following: — Shake, wiggle and bend TFT SIG and SIG RTN circuits between transmission and PCM. A fault is indicated by a sudden change in TFT PID voltage. ● **Is a fault indicated?**	Yes	▶	ISOLATE fault and SERVICE as necessary. RECONNECT all components. COMPLETE PCM reset to clear DTCs (REFER to Powertrain Control Module (PCM) Reset). RERUN Quick Test.
	No	▶	Unable to duplicate and / or identify fault at this time. with the following data: TFT PID and the list of Possible Causes found in **TE100**.

FM0159401211080X

Fig. 217 Test TE: TFT Sensor (Part 11 of 12). 1994-95

TEST STEP	RESULT	▶	ACTION TO TAKE
TE110 CONTINUOUS MEMORY DTC 1783: RERUN KOEO SELF-TEST			
Continuous Memory Diagnostic Trouble Code (DTC) 1783 indicates a transmission over temperature condition occurred. Possible Causes: — Damaged transmission cooling system. — Excessive loading, e.g. trailer towing. — Damaged clutch. — Improper transmission fluid level. — Damaged transmission connector. ● Key off. ● Disconnect transmission connector. Inspect for damaged or pushed out pins, corrosion, loose wires, etc. Service as necessary and reconnect. ● Rerun Key On Engine Off (KOEO) Self-Test and record all DTCs. ● **Any transmission related DTCs generated?** NOTE: If DTC 1783 repeats and no other DTC is generated, transmission over temperature condition.	Yes	▶	ADDRESS any transmission related DTCs by referring to Diagnostic Trouble Code Charts
	No	▶	Transmission Service temperature condition (check clutch, transmission fluid level etc.).

FM0159401211090X

Fig. 217 Test TE: TFT Sensor (Part 12 of 12). 1994-95

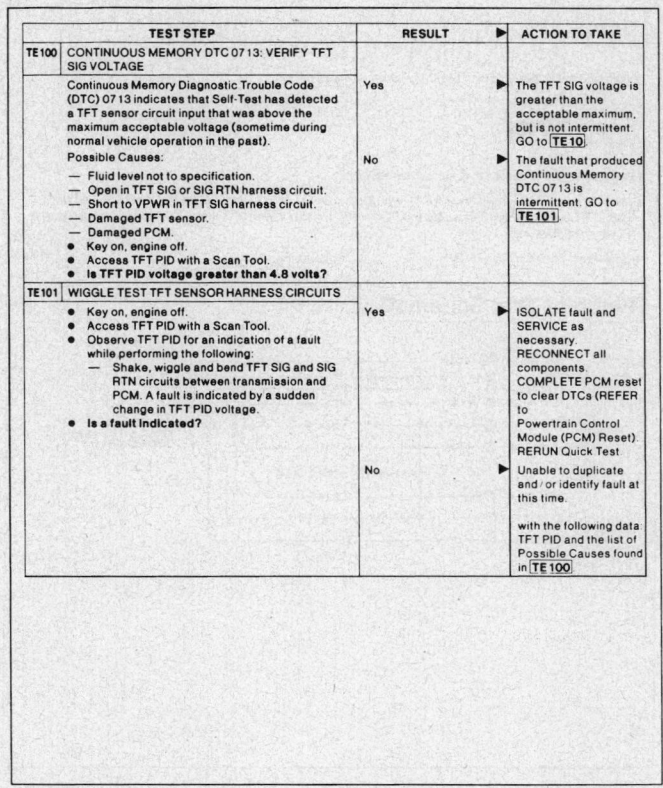

Note

You should enter this Pinpoint Test only when directed here.

Remember

This Pinpoint Test is intended to diagnose only the following:

● Output Shaft Speed (OSS) Sensor
● Harness circuits
● Powertrain Control Module (PCM)

Pinpoint Test Schematics

*TEST PIN 84 OSS+
*TEST PIN 91 SIG RTN

OUTPUT SHAFT SPEED SENSOR OSS VEHICLE HARNESS CONNECTOR

NOTE: A 4.7 OHM RESISTOR IS LOCATED IN THE OSS SENSOR FOR NOISE SUPRESSION

*TEST PINS LOCATED ON BREAKOUT BOX ALL HARNESS CONNECTORS VIEWED INTO MATING SURFACE

FM0159401212010X

Fig. 218 Test TF: OSS Sensor (Part 1 of 3). 1994-95

TEST STEP	RESULT	▶	ACTION TO TAKE
TF1 CONTINUOUS MEMORY DTC 0720: PERFORM TRANSMISSION DRIVE CYCLE			
Continuous Memory Diagnostic Trouble Code (DTC) 0720 indicates an intermittent fault or a hard fault is present. Perform a transmission drive cycle to identify which condition exists. If the DTC repeats, a hard fault is present. Possible Causes: — Transmission (internal components). — Damaged OSS. — Damaged harness circuits. — Damaged PCM. Transmission Drive Cycle — Record and clear Continuous DTCs. — Warm engine to operating temperature. — Place gear selector in DRIVE. — Accelerate heavily to 35 mph. (Obey all local laws.) — Return to idle. — Shut the engine off. — After drive cycle is completed, run Key On Engine Off (KOEO) Self-Test. ● **Did Continuous DTC 0720 repeat?**	Yes	▶	GO to **TF2**.
	No	▶	The fault that produced DTC 0720 is intermittent. For further diagnosis, go to Pinpoint Test Step **Z1** with the following data: OSS PID, 11B5 = actual OSS output, and the list of Possible Causes.
TF2 CHECK OSS CIRCUIT CONTINUITY			
● Key off. ● Disconnect PCM. Inspect for damaged or pushed out pins, corrosion, loose wires, etc. Service as necessary. ● Install breakout box, PCM disconnected. ● Disconnect OSS. ● Measure resistance between Test Pin 84 at the breakout box and OSS circuit at the sensor harness connector. ● **Is resistance less than 5.0 ohms?**	Yes	▶	GO to **TF3**.
	No	▶	SERVICE open circuit. REMOVE breakout box. RECONNECT all components. REPEAT Transmission Drive Cycle. REFER to TFI.
TF3 CHECK OSS CIRCUIT FOR SHORT TO GROUND			
● Key off. ● OSS disconnected. ● Breakout box installed, PCM disconnected. ● Measure resistance between Test Pin 84 and Test Pin 51 (GND) at the breakout box. ● **Is the resistance less than 5.0 ohms?**	Yes	▶	SERVICE short circuit including resistor integrity, if applicable. REMOVE breakout box. RECONNECT all components. REPEAT transmission Drive Cycle. REFER to TFI.
	No	▶	GO to **TF4**.

Fig. 218 Test TF: OSS Sensor (Part 2 of 3). 1994-95

TEST STEP	RESULT	▶	ACTION TO TAKE
TF4 CHECK OSS CIRCUIT FOR SHORT TO POWER • Key off. • OSS disconnected. • Breakout box installed, PCM disconnected. • Measure resistance between Test Pin 84 and Test Pin 71 (VPRW) at the breakout box. • **Is the resistance less than 5.0?**	Yes	▶	SERVICE short circuit. REMOVE breakout box. RECONNECT all components. REPEAT Transmission Drive Cycle. REFER to TFI.
	No	▶	GO to **TF5**.
TF5 CHECK OSS RESISTANCE • Key off. • OSS disconnected. • Measure resistance of OSS. • **Is resistance between 450 and 650 ohms?**	Yes	▶	GO to Transmission Group in Service Manual to verify internal components. If OK, then replace PCM. REMOVE breakout box. RECONNECT OSS. REPEAT Transmission Drive Cycle. REFER to TFI.
	No	▶	REPLACE OSS. REMOVE breakout box. REPEAT Transmission Drive Cycle. REFER TO TFI.

FM0159401212030X

Fig. 218 Test TF: OSS Sensor (Part 3 of 3). 1994-95

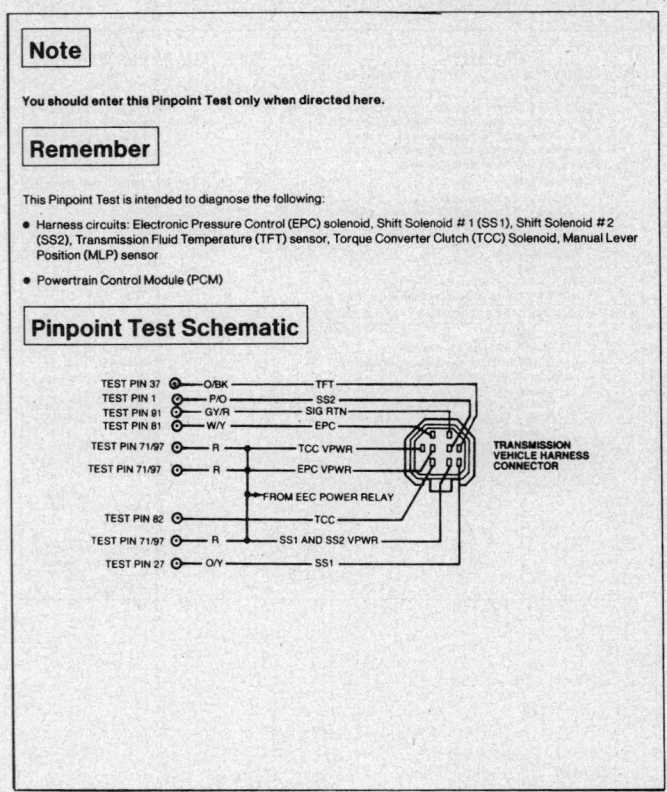

Note

You should enter this Pinpoint Test only when directed here.

Remember

This Pinpoint Test is intended to diagnose the following:

• Harness circuits: Electronic Pressure Control (EPC) solenoid, Shift Solenoid # 1 (SS1), Shift Solenoid #2 (SS2), Transmission Fluid Temperature (TFT) sensor, Torque Converter Clutch (TCC) Solenoid, Manual Lever Position (MLP) sensor

• Powertrain Control Module (PCM)

Pinpoint Test Schematic

FM0159401213010X

Fig. 219 Test TG: Electronic Transmission-Continuous Memory DTC (Part 1 of 12). 1994

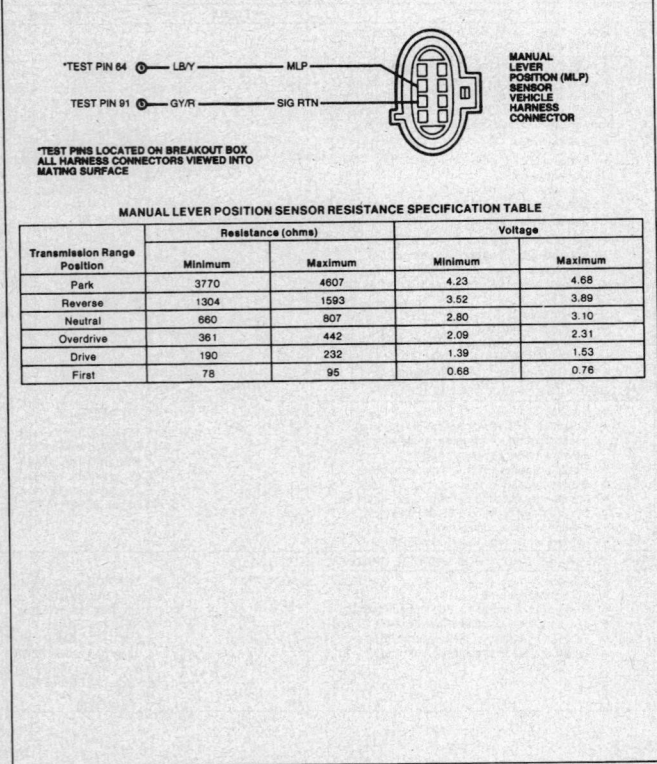

MANUAL LEVER POSITION SENSOR RESISTANCE SPECIFICATION TABLE

Transmission Range Position	Resistance (ohms)		Voltage	
	Minimum	Maximum	Minimum	Maximum
Park	3770	4607	4.23	4.68
Reverse	1304	1593	3.52	3.89
Neutral	660	807	2.80	3.10
Overdrive	361	442	2.09	2.31
Drive	190	232	1.39	1.53
First	78	95	0.68	0.76

FM0159401213020X

Fig. 219 Test TG: Electronic Transmission-Continuous Memory DTC (Part 2 of 12). 1994

TEST STEP	RESULT	▶	ACTION TO TAKE
TG90 PERFORM DRIVE CYCLE • Retrieve and record any Continuous Memory Diagnostic Trouble Codes (DTCs), MIL and non-MIL. • Complete PCM reset to clear DTCs (refer to Powertrain Control Module (PCM) Reset). • Check transmission fluid level. NOTE: Obey all traffic laws. • Drive Cycle. — Gear position in OVERDRIVE range, press the Transmission Control Switch (TCS) (the Transmission Control Indicator Lamp (TCIL) should illuminate) and moderately accelerate from stop to 40 mph. This will allow the transmission to shift into third gear. Hold speed and throttle opening steady for a minimum of 30 seconds. — Press the TCS (the TCIL should turn off) and accelerate from 40 mph to 60 mph. This will allow the transmission to shift into fourth gear. Hold speed and throttle steady for a minimum of 15 seconds. — With transmission in fourth gear and maintaining steady speed and throttle opening, lightly apply and release brake (to operate brake lamps). Then hold speed and throttle steady for at least an additional 5 seconds. — Brake to a stop and remain stopped for a minimum of twenty seconds with transmission in OVERDRIVE. — Repeat this drive cycle at least five times. • Retrieve Continuous Memory DTCs again and record all DTCs. • **Is a system pass present?**	Yes No	▶ ▶	Unable to duplicate fault at this time. COMPLETE PCM reset to clear DTCs (REFER to Powertrain Control Module (PCM) Reset) and internal transmission damage and intermittent fault diagnosis. For DTCs 0705, 0707, 0708 and 1706: GO to **TG91**. For DTCs 0741, 0743, 1741 and 1744: GO to **TG110**. For DTCs 0750 and 0755: GO to **TG120**. For DTCs 1746 and 1747: GO to **TG130**. For all other DTCs: GO to **TG140**.
TG91 CHECK FOR DTC 1706 DTC 1706 indicates high vehicle speed detected while vehicle was in PARK. Possible Causes: — Damaged harness. — Damaged MLP sensor. — Damaged PCM. • **Did DTC 1706 repeat during the drive cycle?**	Yes No	▶ ▶	GO to **TG101**. GO to **TG92**.

FM0159401213030X

Fig. 219 Test TG: Electronic Transmission-Continuous Memory DTC (Part 3 of 12). 1994

TEST STEP	RESULT	▶	ACTION TO TAKE
TG92 CHECK FOR DTC 0705 DTC 0705 indicates the MLP sensor circuit voltage was out of the expected range. Possible Causes: — Damaged MLP sensor. — Open in MLP harness SIG circuit. — Open in MLP harness SIG RTN circuit. — Short to GRND in MLP harness SIG circuit. — Short to PWR in MLP harness SIG circuit. — Damaged PCM. ● **Did DTC 0705 repeat during the drive cycle test?**	Yes No	▶ ▶	GO to **TG93**. GO to **TG96**.
TG93 CHECK FOR DTC 0705 WITH DTC 0707 DTC 0707 indicates the MLP circuit voltage was below the allowed minimum voltage. Possible Causes: — Damaged MLP sensor. — Short to GRND in MLP harness SIG circuit. — Open in MLP harness SIG circuit. — Damaged PCM. ● **Did DTC 0705 repeat with DTC 0707 during the drive cycle test?**	Yes No	▶ ▶	GO to **TG97**. GO to **TG94**.
TG94 CHECK FOR DTC 0705 GENERATED WITH DTC 0708 DTC 0708 indicates the MLP sensor circuit voltage was above the allowed maximum value. Possible causes: — Damaged MLP sensor. — Open in MLP harness SIG RTN circuit. — Short to PWR in MLP harness SIG circuit. — Damaged PCM. ● **Did DTC 0705 repeat with DTC 0708 during the drive cycle test?**	Yes No	▶ ▶	GO to **TG99**. GO to **TG95**.

FM0159401213040X

Fig. 219 Test TG: Electronic Transmission-Continuous Memory DTC (Part 4 of 12). 1994

TEST STEP	RESULT	▶	ACTION TO TAKE
TG95 CHECK MLP SENSOR ALIGNMENT ● Key off. ● Apply parking brake. ● Place transmission in NEUTRAL. ● Verify the MLP tool (Rotunda T92P-7010-AH) or equivalent fits in the appropriate slot. ● **Does the tool fit properly?**	Yes No	▶ ▶	REMOVE tool. GO to **TG101**. PLACE the transmission in NEUTRAL, loosen the two MLP sensor mounting bolts. MOVE the sensor about to allow insertion of the MLP sensor tool in the appropriate slots. TIGHTEN the two mounting bolts to specification. REMOVE the tool. VERIFY shift linkage adjustment. COMPLETE PCM reset to clear DTCs (REFER to Powertrain Control Module (PCM) Reset). RERUN drive cycle test step **TG90** to verify repair.
TG96 CHECK FOR DTC 0707 DTC 0707 indicates the MLP circuit voltage was below the allowed minimum voltage. Possible Causes: — Damaged MLP sensor. — Short to GND in MLP harness SIG circuit. — Open in MLP harness SIG circuit. — Damaged PCM. ● **Did DTC 0707 repeat during the drive cycle test?**	Yes No	▶ ▶	GO to **TG97**. GO to **TG99**.

FM0159401213050X

Fig. 219 Test TG: Electronic Transmission-Continuous Memory DTC (Part 5 of 12). 1994

TEST STEP	RESULT	▶	ACTION TO TAKE
TG97 CHECK CONTINUITY OF THE MLP HARNESS SIG CIRCUIT ● Key off. ● Disconnect PCM. Inspect for damaged or pushed out pins, corrosion or loose wires, etc. Service as necessary. ● Disconnect MLP sensor. ● Using a mirror, inspect both ends of transmission harness connector at MLP sensor for damaged or pushed out pins, corrosion, loose wires, etc. Service as necessary. ● Install breakout box, leave PCM disconnected. ● Measure resistance between Test Pin 64 (MLP SIG) at the breakout box and MLP SIG circuit at the MLP sensor vehicle harness connector. ● **Is resistance less than 5.0 ohms?**	Yes No	▶ ▶	GO to **TG98**. SERVICE open circuit. REMOVE breakout box. RECONNECT all components. RERUN drive cycle test step **TG90** to verify repair
TG98 CHECK FOR SHORT TO GND IN MLP HARNESS SIG CIRCUIT ● Key off. ● MLP sensor disconnected. ● Breakout box installed, PCM disconnected. ● Measure resistance between Test Pin 64 (MLP SIG) at the breakout box and chassis ground. ● **Is resistance greater than 10,000 ohms?**	Yes No	▶ ▶	GO to **TG101**. SERVICE short circuit. REMOVE breakout box. RECONNECT all components. RERUN drive cycle test step **TG90** to verify the repair.

FM0159401213060X

Fig. 219 Test TG: Electronic Transmission-Continuous Memory DTC (Part 6 of 12). 1994

TEST STEP	RESULT	▶	ACTION TO TAKE
TG99 DTC 0708 WAS GENERATED DURING THE DRIVE CYCLE TEST. CHECK MLP SIG RTN HARNESS CIRCUIT CONTINUITY DTC 0708 indicates the MLP circuit voltage was above the allowed maximum. Possible Causes: — Open in MLP harness SIG RTN circuit. — Short to PWR in MLP harness SIG circuit. — Damaged MLP sensor. — Damaged PCM. ● Key off. ● Disconnect PCM. Inspect for damaged or pushed out pins, corrosion or loose wires, etc. Service as necessary. ● Disconnect MLP sensor. ● Using a mirror, inspect both ends of transmission harness connector at MLP sensor for damaged or pushed out pins, corrosion, loose wires, etc. Service as necessary. ● Install breakout box, leave PCM disconnected. ● Measure resistance between Test Pin 91 (SIG RTN) at the breakout box and SIG RTN circuit at the MLP sensor vehicle harness connector. ● **Is resistance less than 5.0 ohms?**	Yes No	▶ ▶	GO to **TG100**. SERVICE open circuit. REMOVE breakout box. RECONNECT all components. RERUN drive cycle test step **TG90** to verify repair.
TG100 CHECK FOR SHORT TO PWR IN MLP SIG HARNESS CIRCUIT ● Key off. ● MLP sensor disconnected. ● Breakout box installed, PCM disconnected. ● Measure resistance between Test Pin 64 (MLP SIG) and Test Pins 97 (VPWR), 24 (PWR GND), 91 (SIG RTN) at the breakout box. ● **Is each resistance greater than 10,000 ohms?**	Yes No	▶ ▶	GO to **TG101**. SERVICE short circuit. REMOVE breakout box. RECONNECT all components. RERUN drive cycle test step **TG90** to verify the repair.
TG101 CHECK MLP SENSOR RESISTANCE ● Key off. ● Connect MLP sensor. ● Breakout box installed, PCM disconnected. ● Unlock steering column. ● Measure resistance between Test Pin 64 (MLP SIG) and Test Pin 91 (SIG RTN) at the breakout box in each gear selector position. REFER to the MLP sensor resistance specification table in the front of this pinpoint test. ● **Is each resistance within specification?**	Yes No	▶ ▶	REPLACE the PCM. REMOVE the breakout box. RERUN the drive cycle test step **TG90** to verify the repair. REPLACE MLP sensor. REMOVE breakout box. RERUN the drive cycle test step **TG90** to verify the repair.

FM0159401213070X

Fig. 219 Test TG: Electronic Transmission-Continuous Memory DTC (Part 7 of 12). 1994

TEST STEP	RESULT	▶	ACTION TO TAKE
TG110 CONTINUOUS MEMORY DTCS 0741, 0743, 1741 AND 1744: CHECK TCC HARNESS CIRCUITS AND CONNECTOR FOR INTERMITTENT FAULT			
Diagnostic Trouble Code (DTC) 0741 indicates a TCC solenoid performance error. DTC 0743 indicates a TCC solenoid electrical fault present. DTC 1741 indicates a TCC solenoid control error. DTC 1744 indicates a TCC system performance error. Possible Causes: — Damaged harness connector. — Intermittent harness continuity. — Damaged TCC solenoid. — Worn friction elements. ● Key off. ● Disconnect PCM. Inspect for damaged or pushed out pins, corrosion, loose wires, etc. Service as necessary. ● Install breakout box, connect PCM. ● Connect one DVOM test lead to Test Pin 82 (TCC SIG) and the other test lead to Test Pin 71 (VPWR). ● Key on, engine off. ● Observe DVOM display for indication of a fault while performing the following: — Shake, wiggle and bend the harness of the TCC. — Lightly tap on the TCC connector to simulate a road shock. NOTE: A fault is indicated by a sudden voltage change. ● Is a fault indicated?	Yes No	▶ ▶	ISOLATE fault and SERVICE as necessary. COMPLETE PCM reset to clear DTCs (REFER to Powertrain Control Module (PCM) Reset). RERUN drive cycle test step **TG90** to verify the repair. If the concern still exists, possible internal transmission damage. COMPLETE PCM reset to clear DTCs (REFER to Powertrain Control Module (PCM) Reset). possible internal transmission damage.

FM0159401213080X

Fig. 219   Test TG: Electronic Transmission-Continuous Memory DTC (Part 8 of 12). 1994

TEST STEP	RESULT	▶	ACTION TO TAKE
TG120 CONTINUOUS MEMORY DTCS 0750 AND 0755: CHECK SHIFT SOLENOID HARNESS CIRCUITS AND CONNECTOR FOR INTERMITTENT FAULT			
Diagnostic Trouble Code (DTC) 0750 indicates a SS1 malfunction. DTC 0755 indicates a SS2 malfunction. Possible Causes: — Intermittent harness continuity. — Damaged shift solenoid. — Damaged harness connector. — Damaged Powertrain Control Module (PCM) connector pins. ● Key off. ● Inspect shift solenoid wires between transmission and PCM. Service as necessary. ● Disconnect PCM. Inspect for damaged or pushed out pins, corrosion, loose wires, etc. Service as necessary. ● Install breakout box, connect PCM. ● Connect DVOM to Test Pins as indicated below: — **For DTC 0750:** Connect one DVOM test lead to Test Pin 27 (SS1 SIG) and the other to Test Pin 71 (VPWR). — **For DTC 0755:** Connect one DVOM test lead to Test Pin 1 (SS2 SIG) and the other to Test Pin 71 (VPWR). ● Key on, engine off. ● Observe DVOM display for indication of a fault while performing the following: — Shake, wiggle and bend the harness of the shift solenoid. Lightly tap on the shift solenoid connector to simulate a road shock. NOTE: A fault is indicated by a sudden voltage change. ● Is a fault indicated?	Yes No	▶ ▶	ISOLATE fault and SERVICE as necessary. COMPLETE PCM reset to clear DTCs (REFER to Powertrain Control Module (PCM) Reset). RERUN drive cycle test step **TG90** to verify the repair. If the concern still exists, possible internal transmission damage. COMPLETE PCM reset to clear DTCs (REFER to Powertrain Control Module (PCM) Reset). possible internal transmission damage.

FM0159401213090X

Fig. 219   Test TG: Electronic Transmission-Continuous Memory DTC (Part 9 of 12). 1994

TEST STEP	RESULT	▶	ACTION TO TAKE
TG130 CONTINUOUS MEMORY DTCs 1746 AND 1747: CHECK EPC SOLENOID HARNESS CIRCUITS AND CONNECTOR FOR INTERMITTENT FAULT			
Continuous Memory Diagnostic Trouble Code (DTC) 1746 indicates an open in the EPC solenoid circuit. Continuous Memory DTC 1747 indicates a short in the EPC solenoid circuit. Possible Causes: — Damaged harness connector. — Damaged EPC solenoid. — Intermittent harness continuity. — Damaged Powertrain Control Module (PCM) connector pins. ● Key off. ● Inspect EPC solenoid wires between transmission and PCM. Service as necessary. ● Disconnect PCM. Inspect for damaged or pushed out pins, corrosion, loose wires, etc. Service as necessary. ● Install breakout box, connect PCM to breakout box. ● Connect one DVOM test lead to Test Pin 81 (EPC SIG) and the other to Test Pin 97 (EPC VPWR). ● Key on, engine off. ● Observe DVOM display for indication of a fault while performing the following: — Shake, wiggle and bend the harness of the EPC solenoid. — Lightly tap on the EPC solenoid connector to simulate a road shock. NOTE: A fault is indicated by a sudden voltage change. ● Is a fault indicated?	Yes No	▶ ▶	ISOLATE fault and SERVICE as necessary. RECONNECT all components. COMPLETE PCM reset to clear DTCs (REFER to Powertrain Control Module (PCM) Reset). RERUN drive cycle test step **TG90** to verify the repair. If concern still exists, possible internal transmission damage. COMPLETE PCM reset to clear DTCs (REFER to Powertrain Control Module (PCM) Reset). possible internal transmission damage.

FM0159401213100X

Fig. 219   Test TG: Electronic Transmission-Continuous Memory DTC (Part 10 of 12). 1994

TEST STEP	RESULT	▶	ACTION TO TAKE
TG140 REMAINING DTCS FOR ELECTRONIC TRANSMISSIONS: CHECK HARNESS CIRCUITS			
Continuous Memory DTC 0731 indicates an incorrect gear ratio after first gear was commanded. Continuous Memory DTC 0732 indicates an incorrect gear ratio after second gear was commanded. Continuous Memory DTC 0733 indicates an incorrect gear ratio after third gear was commanded. Continuous Memory DTC 0734 indicates an incorrect gear ratio after fourth gear was commanded. Continuous Memory DTC 0735 indicates an incorrect gear ratio after fifth gear was commanded. Continuous Memory DTC 0751 indicates shift solenoid # 1 not performing mechanically as expected. Continuous Memory DTC 0756 indicates shift solenoid # 2 not performing mechanically as expected. Continuous Memory DTC 1731 indicates an improper 1 - 2 shift. Continuous Memory DTC 1732 indicates an improper 2 - 3 shift. Continuous Memory DTC 1733 indicates an improper 3 - 4 shift. Continuous Memory DTC 1734 indicates an improper 4 - 5 shift. Continuous Memory DTC 1786 indicates a 3 - 2 downshift error. Continuous Memory DTC 1787 indicates a 2 - 1 downshift error.			

FM0159401213110X

Fig. 219   Test TG: Electronic Transmission-Continuous Memory DTC (Part 11 of 12). 1994

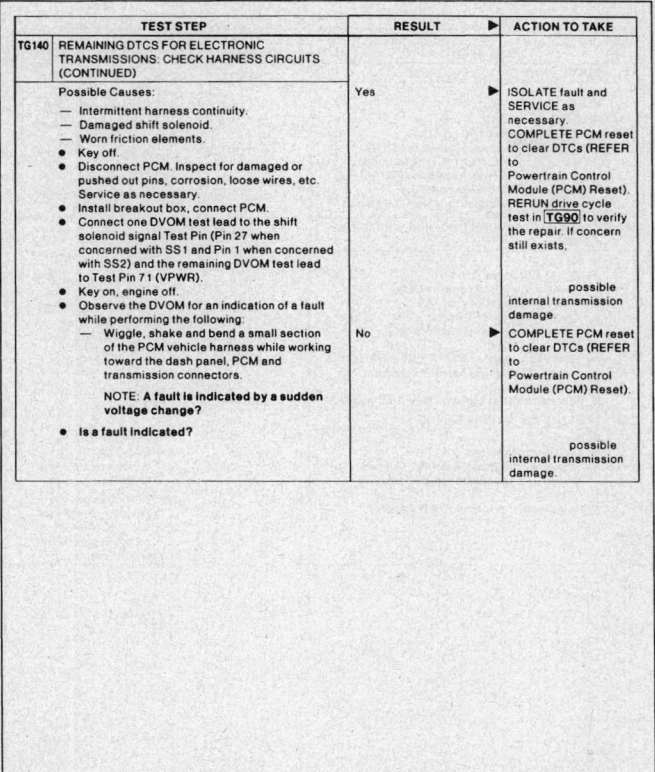

TEST STEP	RESULT	▶	ACTION TO TAKE
TG140 REMAINING DTCS FOR ELECTRONIC TRANSMISSIONS: CHECK HARNESS CIRCUITS (CONTINUED)			
Possible Causes: — Intermittent harness continuity. — Damaged shift solenoid. — Worn friction elements. ● Key off. ● Disconnect PCM. Inspect for damaged or pushed out pins, corrosion, loose wires, etc. Service as necessary. ● Install breakout box, connect PCM. ● Connect one DVOM test lead to the shift solenoid signal Test Pin (Pin 27 when concerned with SS1 and Pin 1 when concerned with SS2) and the remaining DVOM test lead to Test Pin 71 (VPWR). ● Key on, engine off. ● Observe the DVOM for an indication of a fault while performing the following: — Wiggle, shake and bend a small section of the PCM vehicle harness while working toward the dash panel, PCM and transmission connectors. NOTE: A fault is indicated by a sudden voltage change. ● Is a fault indicated?	Yes No	▶ ▶	ISOLATE fault and SERVICE as necessary. COMPLETE PCM reset to clear DTCs (REFER to Powertrain Control Module (PCM) Reset). RERUN drive cycle test in **TG90** to verify the repair. If concern still exists, possible internal transmission damage. COMPLETE PCM reset to clear DTCs (REFER to Powertrain Control Module (PCM) Reset). possible internal transmission damage.

FM0159401213120X

Fig. 219   Test TG: Electronic Transmission-Continuous Memory DTC (Part 12 of 12). 1994

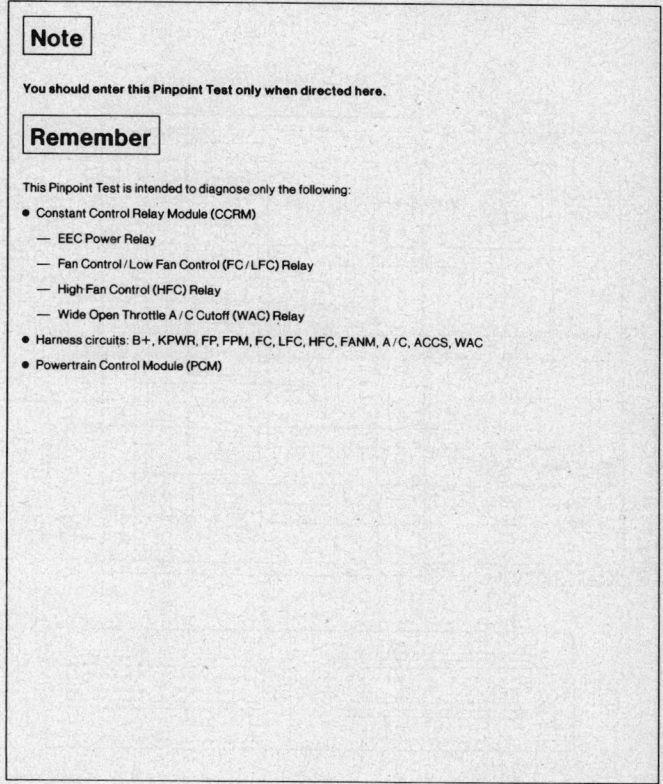

Note

You should enter this Pinpoint Test only when directed here.

Remember

This Pinpoint Test is intended to diagnose only the following:

● Constant Control Relay Module (CCRM)
  — EEC Power Relay
  — Fan Control / Low Fan Control (FC / LFC) Relay
  — High Fan Control (HFC) Relay
  — Wide Open Throttle A / C Cutoff (WAC) Relay
● Harness circuits: B+, KPWR, FP, FPM, FC, LFC, HFC, FANM, A / C, ACCS, WAC
● Powertrain Control Module (PCM)

FM0159401214010X

Fig. 220   Test X: CCRM (Part 1 of 51). 1994-95

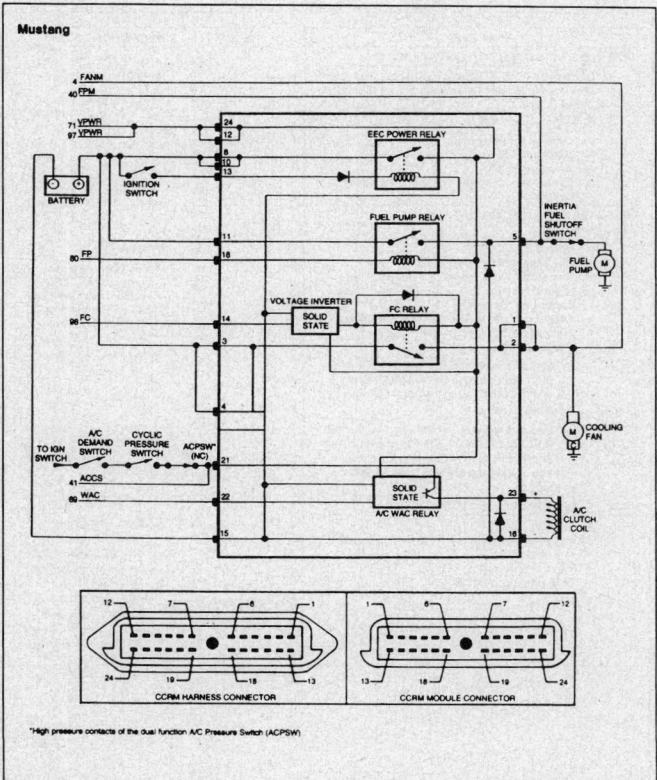

FM0159401214020X

Fig. 220   Test X: CCRM (Part 2 of 51). 1994-95

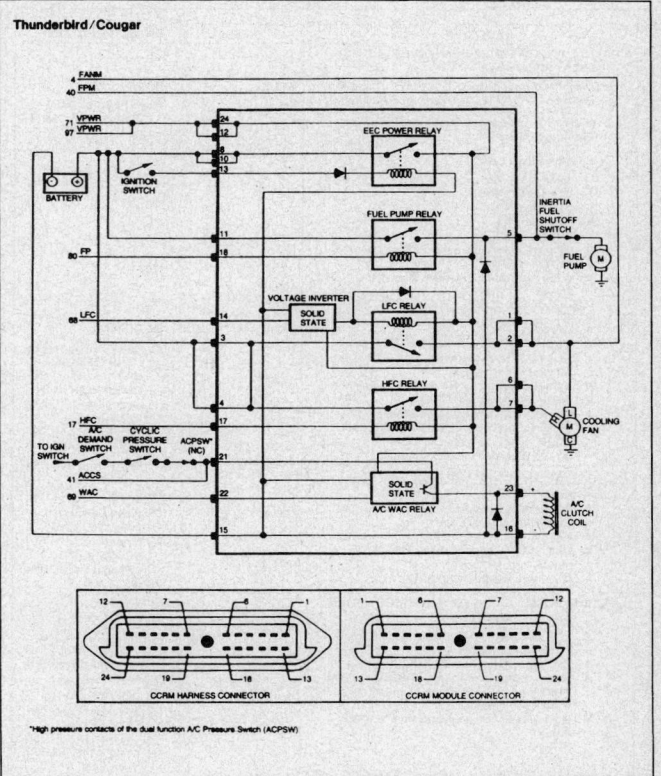

FM0159401214030X

Fig. 220   Test X: CCRM (Part 3 of 51). 1994-95

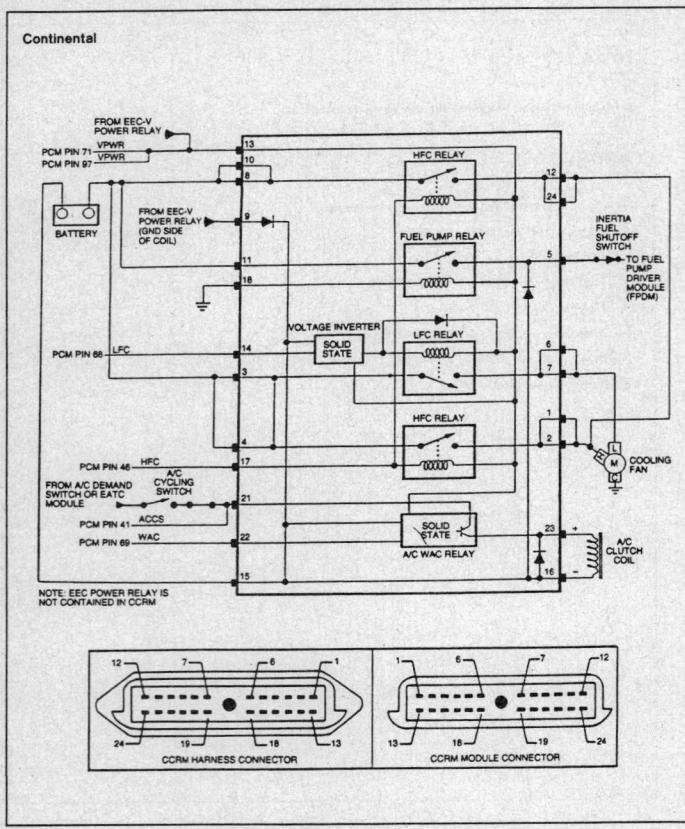

Continental

Fig. 220 Test X: CCRM (Part 4 of 51). 1995

	TEST STEP		RESULT	▶	ACTION TO TAKE
X1	CHECK VPWR CIRCUIT CONTINUITY				
	• Key off. • IAC disconnected. • Disconnect CCRM. • Disconnect Scan Tool from DLC. • Measure resistance between the VPWR circuit at the IAC solenoid vehicle harness connector and Pins 12 and 24 (VPWR) of the CCRM vehicle harness connector. • **Are both resistances less than 5.0 ohms?**		Yes No	▶ ▶	RECONNECT IAC solenoid. GO to X2. SERVICE open VPWR circuit between the CCRM and the splice to the IAC solenoid. RECONNECT all components. RERUN Quick Test.
X2	CHECK B(+) AND IGN START/RUN VOLTAGE TO CCRM				
	• Key off. • CCRM disconnected. • Connect the DVOM negative (-) test lead to the battery negative post. • Check for voltage on Pin 8 and Pin 10 (B+) of the CCRM vehicle harness connector. • Key on, engine off. • Check for voltage on Pin 13 (IGN START/RUN) of the CCRM vehicle harness connector. • Key off. • **Were all voltages greater than 10.5 volts?**		Yes No	▶ ▶	GO to X3. SERVICE open in B (+) or IGN START/RUN circuit. RECONNECT all components. RERUN Quick Test.
X3	CHECK CCRM GROUND CIRCUIT				
	• Key off. • CCRM disconnected. • Measure voltage between Pin 8 (B+) and Pin 15 (GND) at the CCRM vehicle harness connector. • **Is voltage greater than 10.5 volts?**		Yes No	▶ ▶	REPLACE CCRM. RECONNECT all components. RERUN Quick Test. SERVICE open ground circuit to CCRM (Pin 15). RECONNECT all components. RERUN Quick Test.

FM0159401214040X

Fig. 220 Test X: CCRM (Part 5 of 51). 1994-95

	TEST STEP		RESULT	▶	ACTION TO TAKE
X15	DTC 1479: CHECK HIGH FAN CONTROL (HFC) RELAY RESISTANCE				
	Diagnostic Trouble Code (DTC) 1479 indicates a High Fan Control (HFC) primary circuit failure. NOTE: For one speed fan applications, disregard DTC 1479. Possible causes are: — Open or shorted circuit. — Damaged CCRM. — Damaged PCM. • Key off. • Disconnect CCRM. • Measure resistance between Pin 17 and Pin 24 at the CCRM. • **Is the resistance between 50 and 100 ohms?**		Yes No	▶ ▶	GO to X16. REPLACE CCRM. RERUN Quick Test.
X16	CHECK HFC CIRCUIT CONTINUITY				
	• Key off. • Disconnect PCM. Inspect for damaged or pushed out pins, corrosion, loose wires, etc. Service as necessary. • Install breakout box, leave PCM disconnected. • CCRM disconnected. • Measure resistance between Test Pin 17 (HFC) at breakout box and Pin 17 (HFC) of CCRM vehicle harness connector. • **Is resistance less than 5.0 ohms?**		Yes No	▶ ▶	GO to X17. SERVICE open in HFC circuit. REMOVE breakout box. RECONNECT all components. RERUN Quick Test.
X17	CHECK HFC CIRCUIT FOR SHORT TO POWER				
	• Key off. • Breakout box installed, PCM disconnected. • CCRM disconnected. • Key on. • Measure voltage between Test Pin 17 and battery negative post. • **Is voltage less than 1.0 volt?**		Yes No	▶ ▶	Key off. GO to X18. SERVICE short to power. REMOVE breakout box. RECONNECT all components. RERUN Quick Test.
X18	CHECK HFC CIRCUIT FOR SHORTS TO GROUND				
	• Key off. • Breakout box installed, PCM disconnected. • CCRM disconnected. • Disconnect Scan Tool from DLC. • Measure resistance between Test Pin 17 and Test Pins 51, 103 (PWR GND) and 91 (SIG RTN) at the breakout box. • **Is each resistance greater than 10,000 ohms?**		Yes No	▶ ▶	REPLACE PCM. REMOVE breakout box. RECONNECT all components. RERUN Quick Test. SERVICE short to ground in HFC circuit. REMOVE breakout box. RECONNECT all components. RERUN Quick Test.

FM0159401214050X

Fig. 220 Test X: CCRM (Part 6 of 51). 1994-95

	TEST STEP		RESULT	▶	ACTION TO TAKE
X20	DTC 1474: DOES FAN RUN WITH KEY ON?				
	Diagnostic Trouble Code (DTC) 1474 indicates an LFC (FC for one speed fan applications) primary circuit failure. Possible causes are: — Open or shorted circuit, — Damaged CCRM. — Damaged PCM. • **Does the cooling fan always run with the key on?**		Yes No	▶ ▶	GO to X23. GO to X21.
X21	CHECK FC/LFC CIRCUIT FOR SHORT TO GROUND				
	• Key off. • Disconnect Scan Tool from DLC. • Disconnect PCM. Inspect for damaged or pushed out pins, corrosion, loose wires, etc. Service as necessary. • Install breakout box, leave PCM disconnected. • Disconnect CCRM. • For Mustang: — Measure resistance between Test Pin 98 (FC) and Test Pins 51, 103 (PWR GND) and 91 (SIG RTN) at the breakout box. For Thunderbird: — Measure resistance between Test Pin 68 (LFC) and Test Pins 51, 103 (PWR GND) and 91 (SIG RTN) at the breakout box. • **Is each resistance greater than 10,000 ohms?**		Yes No	▶ ▶	GO to X22. SERVICE short to ground in FC/LFC circuit. RECONNECT all components. RERUN Quick Test.
X22	CHECK FAN RUNNING MODE				
	• Key off. • Breakout box installed, PCM disconnected. • Connect CCRM. • Key on, engine off. • **Is the fan running?**		Yes No	▶ ▶	REPLACE PCM. REMOVE breakout box. RECONNECT all components. RERUN Quick Test. REPLACE CCRM. REMOVE breakout box. RECONNECT all components. RERUN Quick Test.

FM0159401214060X

Fig. 220 Test X: CCRM (Part 7 of 51). 1994-95

TEST STEP		RESULT	▶	ACTION TO TAKE
X23	**CHECK FC/LFC CIRCUIT CONTINUITY**			

	• Key off.
	• Disconnect PCM. Inspect for damaged or pushed out pins, corrosion, and loose wires, etc. Service as necessary.
	• Install breakout box, leave PCM disconnected.
	• Disconnect CCRM.
	• **For Mustang:**
	  • Measure resistance between Test Pin 98 (FC) at the breakout box and Pin 14 (FC) at the CCRM vehicle harness connector.
	  For Thunderbird:
	  — Measure resistance between Test Pin 68 (LFC) at the breakout box and Pin 14 (LFC) at the CCRM vehicle harness connector.
	• **Is resistance less than 5.0 ohms?**
		Yes
		
		No
			▶
			
			▶
				GO TO X24.
				
				SERVICE open in FC/LFC circuit. REMOVE breakout box. RECONNECT all components. RERUN Quick Test.

X24	**CHECK FC/LFC CIRCUIT FOR SHORT TO POWER**			

	• Key off.
	• Breakout box installed, PCM disconnected.
	• CCRM disconnected.
	• Key on, engine off.
	• **For Mustang:**
	  — Measure voltage between Test Pin 98 and battery negative post.
	  For Thunderbird:
	  — Measure voltage between Test Pin 68 and battery negative post.
	• **Is voltage less than 1.0 volt?**
		Yes
		
		No
			▶
			
			▶
				GO TO X25.
				
				SERVICE short to power in FC/LFC circuit. REMOVE breakout box. RECONNECT all components. RERUN Quick Test.

X25	**FC/LFC CIRCUIT FAULT ISOLATION CHECK**			

	• Key off.
	• Breakout box installed, PCM disconnected.
	• Reconnect CCRM.
	• Key on, engine off.
	• **For Mustang:**
	  — Jumper Test Pin 98 to Test Pin 77 (PWR GND) at the breakout box.
	  For Thunderbird:
	  — Jumper Test Pin 68 to Test Pin 77 (PWR GND) at the breakout box.
	• **Does fan continue to run?**
		Yes
		
		No
			▶
			
			▶
				REPLACE CCRM. REMOVE breakout box. RECONNECT all components. RERUN Quick Test.
				
				REPLACE PCM. REMOVE breakout box. RECONNECT all components. RERUN Quick Test.

FM0159401214070X

Fig. 220   Test X: CCRM (Part 8 of 51). 1994-95

TEST STEP		RESULT	▶	ACTION TO TAKE
X30	**DTC 1473: IS DTC 1474 OR 1479 ALSO PRESENT?**			
	Diagnostic Trouble Code (DTC) 1473 indicates that when (the cooling fan was off, the Fan Monitor (FANM) circuit was high (due to the internal circuitry of the PCM, the Fan Monitor circuit will go high when its path to ground is open or if there is a short to power on a Power-to-Fan circuit). This could be due to an intermittent or hard fault concern. Possible Causes (without DTC 1474/1479): — Power-to-Low/High Speed Fan circuit short to power. — Open FANM circuit. — Open in Power-To-Fan circuit (low speed for two speed fan applications) between cooling fan and FANM splice. — Open cooling fan ground circuit. — Damaged cooling fan. — Damaged CCRM. — Damaged PCM. • **Is DTC 1474 or 1479 also present with the 1473?**	Yes No	▶ ▶	GO to Powertrain DTC Charts, for direction to service DTCs 1474 and 1479. GO to X31.
X31	**DOES FAN ALWAYS RUN?**			
	• Engine cooled so fan would not normally come on. • A/C and defroster off. • Key on, engine off. • **Is the fan running?**	Yes No	▶ ▶	Key off. GO to X32 (to check for short to power). Key off. GO to X35 (to determine if a hard fault is present).
X32	**CHECK FOR SHORT IN CCRM**			
	• Key off. • Disconnect CCRM. • Key on, engine off. • **Is the fan running?**	Yes No	▶ ▶	Key off. GO to X33. Key off. REPLACE CCRM. RERUN Quick Test.

FM0159401214080X

Fig. 220   Test X: CCRM (Part 9 of 51). 1994-95

TEST STEP		RESULT	▶	ACTION TO TAKE
X33	**CHECK FOR SHORT IN PCM**			
	• Key off. • CCRM disconnected. • Disconnect PCM. • Key on, engine off. • **Is the fan running?**	Yes No	▶ ▶	For two speed fan applications: Key off. GO to X34. For one speed fan applications: SERVICE short to power in the Power-to-Fan circuit. RECONNECT all components. RERUN Quick Test. Key off. REPLACE PCM. RECONNECT CCRM. RERUN Quick Test.
X34	**CHECK POWER-TO-LOW SPEED FAN CIRCUIT FOR SHORT TO POWER**			
	• Key off. • CCRM disconnected. • PCM disconnected. • Disconnect cooling fan. • Key on, engine off. • Measure voltage between Pin 1 of the CCRM vehicle harness connector and the battery negative post. • Key off. • **Is the voltage less than 1.0 volt?**	Yes No	▶ ▶	SERVICE short to power in the Power-to-High Speed Fan circuit. RECONNECT all components. RERUN Quick Test. SERVICE short to power in the Power-to-Low Speed Fan circuit. RECONNECT all components. RERUN Quick Test.
X35	**CHECK FANM INPUT TO DETERMINE IF AN INTERMITTENT OR HARD FAULT CONCERN IS PRESENT**			
	• Access the FANM PID. • Verify the cooling fan is off. • **Is the FANM PID off?**	Yes No	▶ ▶	An intermittent fault may exist. GO to X85. A hard fault is present. GO to X36.
X36	**CHECK IF FAN WILL RUN (LOW SPEED FOR TWO SPEED FAN APPLICATIONS)**			
	• Scan Tool connected. • Key on, engine off. • Access Output Test Mode on Scan Tool. • Turn Low Speed Fan on. • **Is the fan running?**	Yes No	▶ ▶	Key off. GO to X37. REMAIN in Output Test Mode. GO to X40.

FM0159401214090X

Fig. 220   Test X: CCRM (Part 10 of 51). 1994-95

TEST STEP		RESULT	▶	ACTION TO TAKE
X37	**CHECK FAN MONITOR (FANM) CIRCUIT**			
	• Key off. • Disconnect PCM. Inspect for damaged or pushed out pins, corrosion, loose wires, etc. Service as necessary. • Install breakout box, leave PCM disconnected. • Measure resistance between Test Pin 4 (FANM) and Test Pins 76 or 77 (PWR GND) at the breakout box. • **Is resistance less than 20.0 ohms?**	Yes No	▶ ▶	REPLACE PCM. REMOVE breakout box. RECONNECT all components. RERUN Quick Test. SERVICE open in FANM circuit between PCM and splice to Power-to-(Low Speed) Fan circuit. REMOVE breakout box. RECONNECT all components. RERUN Quick Test.
X40	**CHECK FOR VOLTAGE TO COOLING FAN**			
	• Still in Output Test Mode. • Disconnect cooling fan. • Again, turn Low Speed Fan on. • Measure voltage between the Power-to-(Low Speed) Fan circuit pin at the cooling fan vehicle harness connector and the battery negative post. • Key off. • **Was voltage greater than 10.5 volts?**	Yes No	▶ ▶	GO to X41. SERVICE open in the Power-to-(Low Speed) Fan circuit between the cooling fan and the Fan Monitor (FANM) splice to circuit. RECONNECT cooling fan. RERUN Quick Test.
X41	**CHECK GROUND CIRCUIT TO COOLING FAN**			
	• Key off. • Cooling fan disconnected. • Disconnect Scan Tool from DLC. • Measure resistance between the ground circuit pin at the cooling fan vehicle harness connector and the battery negative post. • **is resistance less than 5.0 ohms?**	Yes No	▶ ▶	REPLACE cooling fan. RERUN Quick Test. SERVICE open ground circuit to cooling fan. RECONNECT cooling fan. RERUN Quick Test.

FM0159401214100X

Fig. 220   Test X: CCRM (Part 11 of 51). 1994-95

TEST STEP	RESULT	▶	ACTION TO TAKE
X45 DTC 1480: CHECK FOR B(+) TO CCRM (FC/LFC RELAY)			
Diagnostic Trouble Code (DTC) 1480 indicates that when the Fan (low speed for two speed fan applications) was commanded on, the Fan Monitor (FANM) circuit did not go high.	Yes	▶	GO to **X46**.
	No	▶	SERVICE open in B(+) circuit. RECONNECT circuit. RERUN Quick Test.
Possible Causes:			
— B(+) circuit open to CCRM (FC/LFC relay).			
— Power-to-(Low Speed) Fan circuit open between CCRM and FANM splice to circuit.			
— Damaged CCRM.			
— Damaged PCM.			
● Key off.			
● Disconnect CCRM.			
● Connect negative (-) test lead of DVOM to the battery negative post.			
● Check for voltage on Pins 3 and 4 (B+) of the CCRM vehicle harness connector.			
● **Are both voltages greater than 10.5 volts?**			
X46 CHECK POWER-TO-(LOW SPEED) FAN CIRCUIT CONTINUITY			
● Key off.	Yes	▶	GO to **X47**.
● CCRM disconnected.	No	▶	SERVICE open in Power-to-(Low Speed) Fan circuit between the CCRM and the FANM splice into the circuit. RECONNECT all components. RERUN Quick Test.
● Disconnected cooling fan.			
● Measure resistance between the Power-to-(Low Speed) Fan circuit pin at the cooling fan vehicle harness connector and Pins 1 and 2 at the CCRM vehicle harness connector.			
● **Are both resistances less than 5.0 ohms?**			
X47 CHECK CCRM			
● Key off.	Yes	▶	REPLACE PCM. RECONNECT all components. RERUN Quick Test.
● Cooling fan disconnected.	No	▶	Key off. REPLACE CCRM. RECONNECT all components. RERUN Quick Test.
● Reconnect CCRM.			
● Scan Tool connected.			
● Key on, engine off.			
● Access Output Test Mode on Scan Tool (refer to Section 2).			
● Turn Low Speed Fan on.			
● Measure voltage between the Power-to-(Low Speed) Fan circuit pin at the cooling fan vehicle harness connector and the battery negative post.			
● **Is voltage greater than 10.5 volts?**			

FM0159401214110X

Fig. 220   Test X: CCRM (Part 12 of 51). 1994-95

TEST STEP	RESULT	▶	ACTION TO TAKE
X50 DTC 1481: CHECK IF HIGH SPEED FAN OPERATES			
Diagnostic Trouble Code (DTC) 1481 indicates that when the High Speed Fan was commanded on, the Fan Monitor (FANM) circuit did not go high. This could be due to an intermittent or hard fault concern.	Yes	▶	An intermittent fault may exist. GO to **X80**.
	No	▶	A hard fault is present. GO to **X51**.
NOTE: For one speed fan applications, disregard DTC 1481.			
Possible Causes:			
— B(+) circuit open to CCRM (HFC relay).			
— Power-to-High Speed Fan circuit open.			
— Faulty cooling fan.			
— Faulty CCRM.			
● Scan Tool connected.			
● Key on, engine off.			
● Access Output Test Mode on Scan Tool (refer to Section 2).			
● Command high speed fan on.			
● **Does the high speed fan operate?**			
X51 CHECK FOR B(+) TO CCRM			
● Key off.	Yes	▶	GO to **X52**.
● Disconnect CCRM.	No	▶	SERVICE open in B(+) circuit. RECONNECT CCRM. RERUN Quick Test.
● Connect negative (-) test lead of DVOM to the battery negative post.			
● Check for voltage on Pins 3 and 4 (B+) of the CCRM vehicle harness connector.			
● **Are both voltages greater than 10.5 volts?**			
X52 CHECK IF HIGH SPEED FAN WILL RUN - BYPASSING CCRM			
● Key off.	Yes	▶	REPLACE CCRM. RERUN Quick Test.
● CCRM disconnected.	No	▶	GO to **X53**.
● Connect a jumper wire between Pin 4 and Pin 6 of the CCRM vehicle harness connector.			
● Check if high speed fan is running.			
● Remove jumper wire.			
● **Did high speed fan run with jumper wire installed?**			

FM0159401214120X

Fig. 220   Test X: CCRM (Part 13 of 51). 1994-95

TEST STEP	RESULT	▶	ACTION TO TAKE
X53 CHECK CONTINUITY OF POWER-TO-HIGH SPEED FAN CIRCUIT			
● Key off.	Yes	▶	REPLACE cooling fan. RECONNECT all components. RERUN Quick Test.
● CCRM disconnected.	No	▶	SERVICE open in Power-to-High Speed Fan circuit. RECONNECT all components. RERUN Quick Test.
● Disconnect cooling fan.			
● Measure resistance between the Power-to-High Speed Fan circuit pin at the cooling fan vehicle harness connector and Pins 6 and 7 at the CCRM vehicle harness connector.			
● **Are both resistances less than 5.0 ohms?**			
X55 ACPSW PID "CLOSED" WITH ACPSW DISCONNECTED: CHECK ACPSW CIRCUIT FOR SHORT TO GROUND			
● Key off.	Yes	▶	REPLACE PCM. REMOVE breakout box. RECONNECT all components. RE-EVALUATE symptom.
● ACPSW disconnected.	No	▶	SERVICE ACPSW circuit short to ground. REMOVE breakout box. RECONNECT all components. RE-EVALUATE symptom.
● Disconnect Scan Tool from DLC.			
● Disconnect Powertrain Control Module (PCM). Inspect for damaged or pushed out pins, corrosion, loose wires, etc. Service as necessary.			
● Install breakout box, leave PCM disconnected.			
● Measure resistance between Test Pin 86 (ACPSW) and Test Pins 77 and 103 (PWR GND).			
● **Are both resistances greater than 10,000 ohms?**			

FM0159401214130X

Fig. 220   Test X: CCRM (Part 14 of 51). 1994-95

TEST STEP	RESULT	▶	ACTION TO TAKE
X60 CONTINUOUS MEMORY DTC 1474: CHECK FAN CONTROL (FC) OR LOW FAN CONTROL (LFC) CIRCUIT FOR OPEN OR SHORT TO POWER			
Continuous Memory Diagnostic Trouble Code (DTC) 1474 indicates that an LFC (FC for one speed fan applications) circuit failure has occurred during vehicle operation.	Yes	▶	Key off. ISOLATE fault and SERVICE as necessary. COMPLETE PCM Reset to clear DTCs (REFER to Powertrain Control Module (PCM) Reset). RERUN Quick Test.
Possible causes:			
— Open or shorted FC/LFC circuit.	No	▶	GO to **X61**.
● Key off.			
● Disconnect cooling fan connector. Inspect connectors for damaged or pushed out pins, corrosion, loose wires, etc. Service as necessary.			
● Connect a non-powered test lamp between the Power-to-(Low Speed) Fan circuit and ground circuit at the cooling fan vehicle harness connector.			
● Key on, engine off.			
● Observe test lamp for an indication of a fault while performing the following (the lamp will come on when a fault is detected, indicating an open or short to power):			
— Shake, wiggle, bend the FC/LFC circuit between the PCM and CCRM.			
— Lightly tap on the CCRM to simulate road shock.			
● **Is a fault indicated?**			
X61 CHECK FC/LFC CIRCUIT FOR SHORT TO GROUND			
● Key on, engine off.	Yes	▶	ISOLATE fault and SERVICE as necessary. COMPLETE PCM Reset to clear DTCs (REFER to Powertrain Control Module (PCM) Reset). RERUN Quick Test.
● Cooling fan disconnected, test lamp installed.			
● Scan Tool connected.			
● Access Output Test Mode on Scan Tool			
● Command Low Speed Fan on.	No	▶	GO to Pinpoint Test Step **Z1** with the following data: LFCA PID and list of Possible Causes.
● Observe test lamp for an indication of a fault while performing the following (the lamp will turn off when a fault is detected, indicating a short to ground):			
— Shake, wiggle, bend the FC/LFC circuit between the PCM and CCRM.			
— Lightly tap on the CCRM to simulate road shock.			
● Key off.			
● **Is a fault indicated?**			

FM0159401214140X

Fig. 220   Test X: CCRM (Part 15 of 51). 1994-95

	TEST STEP	RESULT	▶	ACTION TO TAKE
X65	DTC 1479: CHECK HIGH FAN CONTROL (HFC) CIRCUIT FOR OPEN OR SHORT TO POWER			
	Continuous Memory Diagnostic Trouble Code (DTC) 1479 indicates that an HFC circuit failure has occurred during vehicle operation. NOTE: For one speed fan applications disregard DTC 1479. Possible Causes: — Open or shorted HFC circuit. ● Key off. ● Scan Tool connected. ● Disconnect cooling fan connector. Inspect connectors for damaged or pushed out pins, corrosion, loose wires, etc. Service as necessary. ● Connect a non-powered test lamp between the Power-to-High Speed Fan circuit and ground circuit at the cooling fan vehicle harness connector. ● Key on, engine off. ● Access Output Test Mode on Scan Tool (refer to Section 2). ● Command High Speed Fan on. ● Observe test lamp for an indication of a fault while performing the following (the lamp will turn off when a fault is detected, indicated an open or short to power): — Shake, wiggle, bend the HFC circuit between the PCM and CCRM. — Lightly tap on the CCRM to simulate road shock. ● Is a fault indicated?	Yes No	▶ ▶	Key off. ISOLATE fault and SERVICE as necessary. COMPLETE PCM Reset to clear DTCs (REFER to Powertrain Control Module (PCM) Reset). RERUN Quick Test. GO to X66.
X66	CHECK HFC CIRCUIT FOR SHORT TO GROUND			
	● Key on, engine off. ● Cooling fan disconnected, test lamp installed. ● Scan Tool connected. ● Command High Speed Fan off. ● Observe test lamp for an indication of a fault while performing the following (the lamp will turn on when a fault is detected, indicating a short to ground): — Shake, wiggle, bend the HFC circuit between the PCM and CCRM. — Lightly tap on the CCRM to simulate road shock. ● Key off. ● Is a fault indicated?	Yes No	▶ ▶	ISOLATE fault and SERVICE as necessary. COMPLETE PCM Reset to clear DTCs (REFER to Powertrain Control Module (PCM) Reset). RERUN Quick Test. GO to Pinpoint Test Step Z1 with the following data: HFCA PID and list of Possible Causes.

FM0159401214150X

Fig. 220   Test X: CCRM (Part 16 of 51). 1994-95

	TEST STEP	RESULT	▶	ACTION TO TAKE
X75	DTC 1480: CHECK POWER-TO-FAN (LOW SPEED FOR TWO SPEED FAN APPLICATIONS) AND B(+) TO FC/LFC RELAY CIRCUITS FOR OPENS			
	Continuous Memory Diagnostic Trouble Code (DTC) 1480 indicates that sometime while the (low speed) fan was on, the Fan Monitor (FANM) circuit went low. Possible Causes: — Open in Power-to-(Low Speed) Fan circuit between the B(+) supply to the CCRM and the FANM splice into circuit. — Open in B(+) circuit to CCRM (FC/LFC relay). ● Key off. ● Scan Tool connected. ● Disconnect cooling fan connector. ● Connect a non-powered test lamp between the Power-to-(Low Speed) Fan circuit and ground circuit at the cooling fan vehicle harness connector. ● Key on, engine off. ● Access Output Test Mode on Scan Tool ● Command Low Speed Fan on. ● Observe test lamp for an indication of a fault while performing the following (the lamp will turn off when a fault is detected, indicating an open): — Shake, wiggle, bend the Power-to-(Low Speed) Fan circuit between the CCRM and the FANM splice to circuit. — Shake, wiggle, bend the B(+) circuit between the B(+) supply and the CCRM (Pins 3 and 4). — Lightly tap on the CCRM to simulate road shock. ● Key off. ● Is a fault indicated?	Yes No	▶ ▶	ISOLATE fault and SERVICE as necessary. COMPLETE PCM Reset to clear DTCs (REFER to Powertrain Control Module (PCM) Reset). RERUN Quick Test. GO to Pinpoint Test Step Z1 with the following data: FANM and FCA/LFCA PIDs (to verify when (low speed) fan is commanded on) and list of Possible Causes.

FM0159401214160X

Fig. 220   Test X: CCRM (Part 17 of 51). 1994-95

	TEST STEP	RESULT	▶	ACTION TO TAKE
X80	DTC 1481: CHECK POWER-TO-HIGH SPEED FAN AND B(+) TO HFC RELAY CIRCUITS FOR OPENS			
	Continuous Memory Diagnostic Trouble Code (DTC) 1481 indicates that sometime while the high speed fan was on, the Fan Monitor (FANM) circuit went low. NOTE: For one speed fan applications, disregard DTC 1481. Possible Causes: — Open in Power-to-High Speed Fan circuit between the B(+) supply to the CCRM and the splice in the cooling fan. — Open in B(+) circuit to CCRM (HFC relay). ● Key off. ● Scan Tool connected. ● Disconnect cooling fan connector. ● Connect a non-powered test lamp between the Power-to-High Speed Fan circuit and ground circuit at the cooling fan vehicle harness connector. ● Key on, engine off. ● Access Output Test Mode on Scan Tool. ● Command High Speed Fan on. ● Observe test lamp for an indication of a fault while performing the following (the lamp will turn off when a fault is detected, indicating an open): — Shake, wiggle, bend the Power-to-High Speed Fan circuit between the CCRM and the cooling fan. — Shake, wiggle, bend the B(+) circuit between the B(+) supply and the CCRM (Pins 3 and 4) — Lightly tap on the CCRM to simulate road shock. ● Connect DVOM between the Power-to-High Speed Fan pin and ground pin at the fan connector. ● DVOM set to measure resistance. ● Observe DVOM for an indication of an open circuit while performing the following: — Shake, wiggle, bend the fan harness (if applicable) — Lightly tap on the cooling fan to simulate road shock. ● Is a fault indicated?	Yes No	▶ ▶	ISOLATE fault and SERVICE as necessary. COMPLETE PCM Reset to clear DTCs (REFER to Powertrain Control Module (PCM) Reset). RERUN Quick Test. GO to Pinpoint Test Step Z1 with the following data: FANM and HFCA PIDs (to verify when high speed fan is commanded on) and list of Possible Causes.

FM0159401214170X

Fig. 220   Test X: CCRM (Part 18 of 51). 1994-95

	TEST STEP	RESULT	▶	ACTION TO TAKE
X85	CHECK FOR INTERMITTENT OPEN OR SHORT TO POWER IN POWER-TO-(LOW SPEED) FAN, FAN MONITOR (FANM) AND FAN GROUND CIRCUITS			
	● Scan Tool connected. ● Key on, engine off. ● A/C off. ● Cooling fan must be off. ● Access FANM PID. WARNING: STAY AWAY FROM THE COOLING FAN BLADES WHILE PERFORMING THIS TEST STEP. THE COOLING FAN MAY COME ON. ● Observe Scan Tool for an indication of a fault while performing the following (a fault will be indicated by the FANM PID turning ON): — Shake, wiggle, bend the Power-to-(Low Speed) Fan circuit between the CCRM and the cooling fan. — Shake, wiggle, bend the cooling fan ground circuit. — Lightly tap on the cooling fan and CCRM to simulate road shock. — Shake, wiggle, bend the FANM circuit between the PCM and splice. ● Disconnect the cooling fan and CCRM. Inspect the connectors for corrosion, damaged pins, etc. ● Key off. ● Was a fault indicated?	Yes No	▶ ▶	If the cooling fan turned on when the fault was detected, a short to power exists. If the fan did not come on, check for an open circuit. ISOLATE fault and SERVICE as necessary. RECONNECT all components. COMPLETE PCM Reset to clear DTCs (REFER to Powertrain Control Module (PCM) Reset). RERUN Quick Test. GO to Pinpoint Test Step Z1 with the following data: FANM, FCA/LFCA and HFCA PIDs (to verify that the fan is commanded off during testing) and list of Possible Causes.
X100	ACCS PID OFF WITH A/C ON: CHECK FOR VOLTAGE TO CYCLIC PRESSURE SWITCH			
	● Key on, engine off. ● Disconnect Cyclic Pressure Switch. ● A/C demand switch to A/C on. ● Measure voltage between the A/C demand switch side of the Cyclic Pressure Switch vehicle harness connector and battery negative post. ● Key off. ● Was voltage greater than 10.5 volts?	Yes No	▶	GO to X101. check A/C demand switch operation, applicable fuses, wiring to Cyclic Pressure Switch, etc.

FM0159401214180X

Fig. 220   Test X: CCRM (Part 19 of 51). 1994-95

TEST STEP	RESULT	▶	ACTION TO TAKE
X101 CHECK FOR VOLTAGE TO DUAL FUNCTION A/C PRESSURE SWITCH (ACPSW) • Key off. • Reconnect Cyclic Pressure Switch. • Disconnect ACPSW (also known as Refrigerant Containment / Fan Function Switch). • Key on, engine off. • A/C on. • Measure voltage between the A/C Demand Switch pin at the ACPSW vehicle harness connector and the battery negative post. • Key off. • **Was voltage greater than 10.5 volts?**	Yes No	▶ ▶	GO to **X102**. VERIFY operation of Cyclic Pressure Switch. If OK, SERVICE open between Cyclic Pressure Switch and ACPSW. RECONNECT all components. RE-EVALUATE symptom.
X102 CHECK CONTINUITY OF ACPSW HIGH PRESSURE CONTACTS • Key off. • ACPSW disconnected. • Measure resistance of the ACPSW high pressure contacts. • **Is resistance less than 5.0 ohms?**	Yes No	▶ ▶	GO to **X103**. check for overpressurized A/C system, etc. If OK, REPLACE ACPSW. RE-EVALUATE symptom.

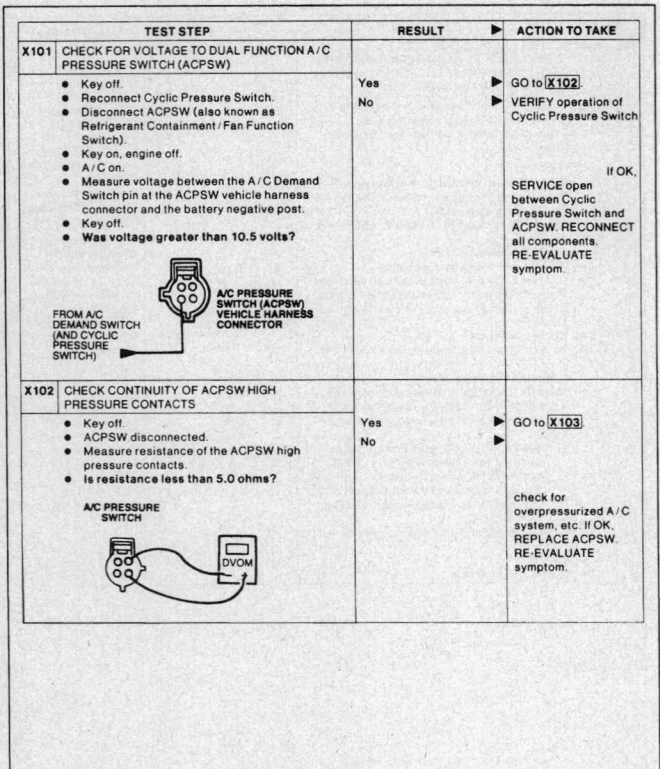

FM0159401214190X

Fig. 220 Test X: CCRM (Part 20 of 51). 1994-95

TEST STEP	RESULT	▶	ACTION TO TAKE
X103 CHECK FOR VOLTAGE TO PCM ON ACCS CIRCUIT • Key off. • Reconnect ACPSW. • Disconnect PCM. Inspect for damaged or pushed out pins, loose wires, corrosion, etc. Service as necessary. • Install breakout box, leave PCM disconnected. • Key on. • A/C ON. • Measure voltage between Test Pin 41 (ACCS) and Test Pin 77 (PWR GND) at the breakout box. • **Is voltage greater than 10.5 volts?**	Yes No	▶ ▶	REPLACE PCM. REMOVE breakout box. RECONNECT all components. RE-EVALUATE symptom. SERVICE open circuit between the ACPSW an PCM. REMOVE breakout box. RECONNECT all components. RE-EVALUATE symptom.
X105 KOEO/KOER DTC 1460: CHECK WAC CIRCUIT FOR SHORT TO POWER Key On Engine Off (KOEO) and Key On Engine Running (KOER) Diagnostic Trouble Code (DTC) 1460 indicates a WAC circuit fault. **NOTE: Verify A/C and Defrost were off during KOEO/KOER Self-Test. If vehicle is not equipped with A/C, the WAC circuit is not used and the DTC 1460 can be ignored.** Possible Causes: — A/C on during Self-Test. — Open or shorted circuit. — Damaged CCRM. — Damaged PCM. • Key off. • Disconnect CCRM. • Disconnect PCM. Inspect for damaged or pushed out pins, corrosion, loose wires, etc. Service as necessary. • Install breakout box, leave PCM disconnected. • Key on. • Measure voltage between Test Pin 69 (WAC) and Test Pins 51 and 103 (PWR GND) at the breakout box. • Key off. • **Was voltage less than 1.0 volt?**	Yes No	▶ ▶	GO to **X106**. SERVICE WAC circuit short to power. REMOVE breakout box. RECONNECT all components. RERUN Quick Test.

FM0159401214200X

Fig. 220 Test X: CCRM (Part 21 of 51). 1994-95

TEST STEP	RESULT	▶	ACTION TO TAKE
X106 CHECK WAC CIRCUIT FOR SHORT TO GND • Key off. • CCRM disconnected. • Breakout box installed, PCM disconnected. • Disconnect Scan Tool from DLC. • Measure resistance between Test Pin 69 (WAC) and Test Pins 51, 103 (PWR GND) and 91 (SIG RTN). • **Is each resistance greater than 10,000 ohms?**	Yes No	▶ ▶	GO to **X107**. SERVICE WAC circuit short to ground. REMOVE breakout box. RECONNECT all components. RERUN Quick Test.
X107 CHECK WAC CIRCUIT CONTINUITY • Key off. • CCRM disconnected. • Breakout box installed, PCM disconnected. • Measure resistance between Test Pin 69 (WAC) at the breakout box and Pin 22 at the CCRM vehicle harness connector. • **Is resistance less than 5.0 ohms?**	Yes No	▶ ▶	GO to **X108**. SERVICE open WAC circuit. REMOVE breakout box. RECONNECT all components. RERUN Quick Test.
X108 CHECK OPERATION OF WAC IN CCRM • Key off. • Breakout box installed, PCM disconnected. • Reconnect CCRM. • A/C clutch connected. • Key on. • A/C demand switch to A/C on. • Connect a jumper wire between Test Pin 69 (WAC) and Test Pin 77 (PWR GND) at the breakout box. • Disconnect and reconnect the jumper several times while listening to the A/C clutch. • **Does the A/C clutch engage and disengage as the jumper is disconnected and reconnected?**	Yes No	▶ ▶	Key off. REPLACE PCM. REMOVE breakout box. RECONNECT all components. RERUN Quick Test. Key off. REPLACE CCRM. INSPECT Power-to-A/C Clutch circuit for short to ground. SERVICE as necessary. REMOVE breakout box. RECONNECT all components. RERUN Quick Test.
X110 NO A/C (ACCS PID ON WITH A/C ON, NO DTCS): CHECK A/C DEMAND SWITCH VOLTAGE TO CCRM • Key off. • Disconnect CCRM. • Key on. • A/C demand switch to A/C on. • Measure voltage between Pin 21 and Pin 15 at the CCRM vehicle harness connector. • Key off, A/C off. • **Was voltage greater than 10.5 volts?**	Yes No	▶ ▶	GO to **X111**. SERVICE open in A/C demand circuit between CCRM and ACCS splice to PCM. RECONNECT all components. RE-EVALUATE symptom.

FM0159401214210X

Fig. 220 Test X: CCRM (Part 22 of 51). 1994-95

TEST STEP	RESULT	▶	ACTION TO TAKE
X111 CHECK CONTINUITY OF POWER-TO-A/C CLUTCH AND A/C CLUTCH GROUND CIRCUITS • Key off. • CCRM disconnected. • Disconnect A/C clutch. • Disconnect Scan Tool from DLC. • Measure resistance between Pin 23 of the CCRM vehicle harness connector and the power side of the A/C clutch vehicle harness connector. • Measure resistance between Pin 16 of the CCRM vehicle harness connector and the ground side of the A/C clutch vehicle harness connector. • **Is each resistance less than 5.0 ohms?**	Yes No	▶ ▶	REPLACE CCRM. RECONNECT all components. RE-EVALUATE symptom. SERVICE open circuit. RECONNECT all components. RE-EVALUATE symptom.

FM0159401214220X

Fig. 220 Test X: CCRM (Part 23 of 51). 1994-95

TEST STEP	RESULT	▶	ACTION TO TAKE
X120 DTC 1460: CHECK FOR INTERMITTENT OPEN OR SHORT IN WAC CIRCUIT			
Continuous Memory Diagnostic Trouble Code (DTC) 1460 indicates that a WAC circuit failure has occurred during vehicle operation. NOTE: If vehicle is not equipped with A/C, the WAC circuit is not used and the DTC 1460 can be ignored. Possible Causes: — Open or shorted WAC circuit. ● Key off. ● Scan Tool connected. ● Disconnect A/C Cyclic Pressure Switch. ● Install a jumper wire in the Cyclic Pressure Switch vehicle harness connector (to complete the circuit). ● Key on, engine off. ● A/C demand switch on. ● Check WAC circuit for open or short to power while performing the following (the A/C clutch will click on when a fault is detected): — Shake, wiggle, bend the WAC circuit from the CCRM to the PCM. — Lightly tap the CCRM to simulate road shock. ● Access Output Test Mode on the Scan Tool ● Turn outputs off (this will prevent the WAC circuit from turning off the A/C clutch). ● Check WAC circuit for short to ground while performing the following (the A/C clutch will click off when a fault is detected): — Shake, wiggle, bend the WAC circuit from the CCRM to the PCM. — Lightly tap the CCRM to simulate road shock. ● Key off, A/C off. ● **Is a fault indicated?**	Yes No	▶ ▶	ISOLATE fault and SERVICE as necessary. REMOVE jumper wire. RECONNECT all components. COMPLETE PCM Reset to clear DTCs (REFER to Powertrain Control Module (PCM) Reset). RERUN Quick Test. GO to Pinpoint Test Step **Z1** with the following data: WACA PID and list of Possible Causes.

Fig. 220   Test X: CCRM (Part 24 of 51). 1994-95

TEST STEP	RESULT	▶	ACTION TO TAKE
X125 ACCS PID ON. DISCONNECT ACPSW AND CHECK IF ACCS PID TURNS OFF			
● Key off. ● Disconnect A/C Pressure Switch (ACPSW) (also known as the Refrigerant Containment / Fan Function Switch). ● Key on, engine off. ● Access ACCS PID. ● **Is ACCS PID off?**	Yes No	▶ ▶	Key off. VERIFY operation of A/C Demand Switch If OK, SERVICE short to power in A/C Demand circuit to ACPSW. RECONNECT all components. RE-EVALUATE symptom. Key off. GO to **X126**.
X126 CHECK POWER-TO-A/C CLUTCH CIRCUIT FOR SHORT TO POWER			
● Key off. ● Disconnect CCRM. ● Key on. ● Measure voltage between Pin 23 of the CCRM vehicle harness connector and the battery negative post. ● Key off. ● **Was voltage less than 1.0 volt?**	Yes No	▶ ▶	GO to **X127**. SERVICE short to power. RECONNECT all components. RE-EVALUATE symptom.
X127 CHECK ACCS CIRCUIT FOR SHORT TO POWER			
● Key off. ● ACPSW and CCRM disconnected. ● Disconnect PCM. Inspect for damaged or pushed out pins, corrosion, loose wires, etc. Service as necessary. ● Install breakout box, leave PCM disconnected. ● Key on. ● Measure voltage between Test Pin 41 (ACCS) and Test Pins 51 and 103 (PWR GND). ● Key off. ● **Was voltage less than 1.0 volt?**	Yes No	▶ ▶	GO to **X128**. SERVICE short to power. REMOVE breakout box. RECONNECT all components. RE-EVALUATE symptom.

Fig. 220   Test X: CCRM (Part 25 of 51). 1994-95

TEST STEP	RESULT	▶	ACTION TO TAKE
X128 CHECK ACCS CIRCUIT VOLTAGE TO PCM WITH CCRM CONNECTED			
● Key off. ● Reconnect CCRM. ● ACPSW disconnected. ● Breakout box installed. PCM disconnected. ● Key on. ● Again, measure voltage between Test Pin 41 (ACCS) and Test Pins 51 and 103 (PWR GND). ● Key off. ● **Was voltage less than 1.0 volt?**	Yes No	▶ ▶	REPLACE PCM. REMOVE breakout box. RECONNECT all components. RE-EVALUATE symptom. REPLACE CCRM. REMOVE breakout box. RECONNECT all components. RE-EVALUATE symptom.
X130 NO WAC W/ NO DTCS: CHECK CCRM			
● Key off. ● Disconnect PCM. ● Install breakout box, leave PCM disconnected. ● A/C clutch and CCRM connected. ● Key on. ● A/C demand switch on. ● Connect jumper between Test Pin 69 (WAC) and Test Pin 76 (PWR GND) at the breakout box. ● Disconnect and reconnect jumper several times while listening to the A/C clutch. ● **Does the A/C clutch engage and disengage as the jumper is disconnected and reconnected?**	Yes No	▶ ▶	Key off. EEC system is operating properly. If symptom is intermittent, GO to Pinpoint Test Step **Z1** with the following data: WACA PID. Otherwise, testing is complete. REMOVE breakout box. RECONNECT all components. Key off. REPLACE CCRM. REMOVE breakout box. RECONNECT all components. RE-EVALUATE symptom.

Fig. 220   Test X: CCRM (Part 26 of 51). 1994-95

TEST STEP	RESULT	▶	ACTION TO TAKE
X150 NO FUEL PRESSURE: CHECK IF FUEL PUMP RUNS			
● Key off. ● While listening for fuel pump to run, turn the key on. The fuel pump should run for about one second, then turn off. ● If the fuel pump cannot be heard, perform the following: — Key on, engine off. — Scan Tool connected. — Enter Output Test Mode — Turn outputs on. — Listen by the fuel tank to check if the fuel pump is running. ● Key off. ● **Does the fuel pump run?**	Yes No	▶ ▶	The fuel pump electrical circuits are OK. GO to Pinpoint Test Step **HC1** to check the mechanical operation of the fuel pump. GO to **X151**.
X151 CHECK IF FPA PID IS OFF WITH KEY ON ENGINE OFF			
NOTE: For 1994 OBD II vehicles, there are no DTCs for the electric fuel pump circuits. The next few pinpoint tests will isolate the cause of a fuel pump that will not run. ● Key on. ● View FPA PID. ● **Is FPA PID off?**	Yes No	▶ ▶	GO to **X152**. Key off. GO to **X157**.
X152 CHECK IF FPA PID IS ON DURING CRANK			
NOTE: The Scan Tool must be connected to a reliable power source that is powered with the ignition key in the START position (e.g. directly to the vehicle battery). Also verify that the vehicle battery is fully charged. ● Key on. ● While viewing FPA PID, crank engine. ● **Is the FPA PID on during crank?**	Yes No	▶ ▶	GO to **X153**. Key off. GO to **X160**.

Fig. 220   Test X: CCRM (Part 27 of 51). 1994-95

TEST STEP	RESULT	▶ ACTION TO TAKE
X153 CHECK IF FPM PID IS OFF WITH KEY ON ENGINE OFF		
• Key on. • View FPM PID. • **Is FPM PID off?**	Yes	▶ GO to **X154**.
	No	▶ Key off. VERIFY Inertia Fuel Shutoff Switch (IFS) is reset. If OK, open in Power-to-Pump circuit (between FPM splice and pump), poor fuel pump ground, open in pump or IFS switch etc. During testing, DISCONNECT Scan Tool from DLC.
X154 CHECK IF FPM PID IS ON DURING CRANK		
• Key on. • While viewing FPM PID, crank engine. • **Is the FPM PID on during crank?**	Yes	▶ The fuel pump electrical circuits checkout OK. GO to Pinpoint Test Step **HC1** to check for mechanical fuel system concerns.
	No	▶ Key off. GO to **X165**.
X157 CHECK FUEL PUMP RELAY COIL RESISTANCE		
• Key off. • Disconnect CCRM. • Measure resistance of CCRM between Pin 18 and Pin 24. • **Is resistance between 65 and 120 ohms?**	Yes	▶ GO to **X158**.
	No	▶ REPLACE CCRM. RE-EVALUATE symptom.
X158 CHECK FP CIRCUIT CONTINUITY		
• Key off. • CCRM disconnected. • Disconnect PCM. Inspect for damaged or pushed out pins, corrosion, loose wires, etc. Service as necessary. • Install breakout box, leave PCM disconnected. • Measure resistance between Test Pin 80 (FP) at the breakout box and Pin 18 at the CCRM vehicle harness connector. • **Is resistance less than 5.0 ohms?**	Yes	▶ REPLACE PCM. REMOVE breakout box. RECONNECT all components. RE-EVALUATE symptom.
	No	▶ SERVICE open in FP circuit. REMOVE breakout box. RECONNECT all components. RE-EVALUATE symptom.

FM0159401214270X

Fig. 220 Test X: CCRM (Part 28 of 51). 1994-95

TEST STEP	RESULT	▶ ACTION TO TAKE
X160 CHECK FP CIRCUIT FOR SHORT TO POWER IN CCRM		
• Key off. • Disconnect CCRM. • Measure resistance of fuel pump relay coil in CCRM between Pin 18 and Pin 24. Resistance should be between 65 and 120 ohms. • Measure resistance of CCRM between Pin 18 and the following Pins: 1 through 11 and 13. Each resistance should be greater than 10,000 ohms. • **Are the CCRM checks OK?**	Yes	▶ GO to **X161**.
	No	▶ REPLACE CCRM. RE-EVALUATE symptom.
X161 CHECK FP CIRCUIT FOR SHORT TO POWER		
• Key off. • CCRM disconnected. • Disconnect PCM. Inspect for damaged or pushed out pins, corrosion, loose wires, etc. Service as necessary. • Key on. • Measure voltage between Pin 18 of the CCRM vehicle harness connector and the battery negative post. • **Is voltage less than 1.0 volt?**	Yes	▶ REPLACE PCM. RECONNECT all components. RE-EVALUATE symptom.
	No	▶ SERVICE FP circuit short to power. RECONNECT all components. RE-EVALUATE symptom.
X165 CHECK FOR B+ TO FUEL PUMP RELAY		
• Key off. • Disconnect CCRM. • Measure voltage between Pin 11 of the CCRM vehicle harness connector and the battery negative post. • **Is voltage greater than 10.5 volts?**	Yes	▶ GO to **X166**.
	No	▶ VERIFY integrity of fuse / fuse link for B(+) supply to CCRM (fuel pump relay). If OK, SERVICE open in B(+) supply to CCRM. RECONNECT all components. RE-EVALUATE symptom.
X166 CHECK POWER-TO-PUMP CIRCUIT CONTINUITY		
• Key off. • CCRM disconnected. • Disconnect Scan Tool from DLC. • Measure resistance between Pin 5 of the CCRM vehicle harness connector and the battery negative post. • **Is resistance less than 10.0 ohms?**	Yes	▶ REPLACE CCRM. RE-EVALUATE symptom.
	No	▶ SERVICE open in Power-to-Pump circuit between CCRM and FPM splice. RECONNECT all components. RE-EVALUATE symptom.

FM0159401214280X

Fig. 220 Test X: CCRM (Part 29 of 51). 1994-95

TEST STEP	RESULT	▶ ACTION TO TAKE
X175 FUEL PUMP ALWAYS RUNS: CHECK IF FPA PID IS OFF		
• Scan Tool connected. • Key on, engine off. Wait 5 seconds. • Access FPA PID. • **Is the FPA PID off?**	Yes	▶ GO to **X176**.
	No	▶ Key off. GO to **X180**.
X176 CHECK IF FPM PID IS OFF		
• Scan Tool connected. • Key on, engine off. • Access FPM PID. • **Is the FPM PID off?**	Yes	▶ EEC system does not indicate a fault. If symptom is intermittent, GO to Pinpoint Test Step **Z1** with the following data: FPA and FPM PIDs. Otherwise, testing is complete.
	No	▶ Key off. GO to **X177**.
X177 CHECK CCRM		
• Key off. • Disconnect CCRM. • Key on, engine off. • **Is fuel pump off with CCRM disconnected?**	Yes	▶ Key off. REPLACE CCRM. RE-EVALUATE symptom.
	No	▶ Key off. SERVICE Power-to-Pump / FPM circuit short to power. RECONNECT CCRM. RE-EVALUATE symptom.
X180 CHECK PCM		
• Key off. • Disconnect PCM. • Key on, engine off. • **Is fuel pump off with PCM disconnected?**	Yes	▶ Key off. REPLACE PCM. RE-EVALUATE symptom.
	No	▶ Key off. GO to **X181**.

FM0159401214290X

Fig. 220 Test X: CCRM (Part 30 of 51). 1994-95

TEST STEP	RESULT	▶ ACTION TO TAKE
X181 CHECK FUEL PUMP (FP) CIRCUIT FOR SHORT TO GROUND		
• Key off. • PCM disconnected. • Disconnect Scan Tool from DLC. • Disconnect CCRM. • Inspect PCM and CCRM connectors for damaged or pushed out pins, corrosion, loose wires, etc. Service as necessary. • Install breakout box, leave PCM disconnected. • Measure resistance between Test Pin 80 (FP) and Test Pins 51, 103 (PWR GND) and 91 (SIG RTN). • **Are resistances greater than 10,000 ohms?**	Yes	▶ REPLACE CCRM. REMOVE breakout box. RECONNECT all components. RE-EVALUATE symptom.
	No	▶ SERVICE FP circuit short to ground. REMOVE breakout box. RECONNECT all components. RE-EVALUATE symptom.

FM0159401214300X

Fig. 220 Test X: CCRM (Part 31 of 51). 1994

Fig. 220 Test X: CCRM (Part 32 of 51). 1995

TEST STEP	RESULT	▶	ACTION TO TAKE
X181 CHECK FUEL PUMP (FP) CIRCUIT FOR SHORT TO GROUND • Key off. • PCM disconnected. • Disconnect Scan Tool from DLC. • Disconnect CCRM. • Inspect PCM and CCRM connectors for damaged or pushed out pins, corrosion, loose wires, etc. Service as necessary. • Install breakout box, leave PCM disconnected. • Measure resistance between Test Pin 80 (FP) and Test Pins 103 (PWR GND) and 91 (SIG RTN). • **Are resistances greater than 10,000 ohms?**	Yes No	▶ ▶	REPLACE CCRM. REMOVE breakout box. RECONNECT all components. RE-EVALUATE symptom. SERVICE FP circuit short to ground. REMOVE breakout box. RECONNECT all components. RE-EVALUATE symptom.
X190 DIAGNOSTIC TROUBLE CODE (DTC) P0230: CHECK VPWR CIRCUIT TO CCRM DTC P0230 indicates a fuel pump primary circuit failure. Possible causes: — Open or shorted Fuel Pump (FP) circuit. — Open VPWR circuit to CCRM. — Damaged CCRM. — Damaged PCM. • Key off. • Disconnect CCRM. • Disconnect EEC-V Power Relay. • Measure resistance between Pin 13 of the CCRM vehicle harness connector and the VPWR circuit at the EEC-V Power Relay vehicle harness connector. • **Is resistance less than 5.0 ohms?** VPWR **EEC-V POWER RELAY VEHICLE HARNESS CONNECTOR**	Yes No	▶ ▶	RECONNECT EEC-V Power Relay. GO to X191. SERVICE open in VPWR circuit between EEC-V Power Relay and CCRM. RECONNECT all components. RERUN Quick Test.

Fig. 220 Test X: CCRM (Part 33 of 51). 1995

TEST STEP	RESULT	▶	ACTION TO TAKE
X191 CHECK FUEL PUMP RELAY AND FP CIRCUIT IN CCRM • Key off. • CCRM disconnected. • Check fuel pump relay coil resistance: — Measure resistance between Pin 13 and Pin 18 of the CCRM. — Resistance should be between 65 and 120 ohms. • Check CCRM for internal short to power: — Measure resistance of CCRM between Pin 18 and the following Pins: 1 through 8, 10, 11, 12 and 24. — Each resistance should be greater than 10,000 ohms. • Check CCRM for internal short to ground: — Measure resistance of CCRM between Pin 18 and both Pin 15 and the CCRM case. — Both resistances should be greater than 1000 ohms. • **Are the CCRM checks OK?**	Yes No	▶ ▶	GO to X192. REPLACE CCRM. RECONNECT all components. RERUN Quick Test.
X192 CHECK FUEL PUMP CIRCUIT FOR SHORT TO POWER • Key off. • CCRM disconnected. • Disconnect PCM. Inspect for damaged or pushed out pins, corrosion, loose wires, etc. Service as necessary. • Key on, engine off. • Measure voltage between Pin 18 at the CCRM vehicle harness connector and the battery negative post. • **Is voltage less than 1.0 volt?**	Yes No	▶ ▶	GO to X193. SERVICE short to power. RECONNECT all components. RERUN Quick Test.
X193 CHECK FUEL PUMP CIRCUIT FOR SHORT TO GROUND • Key off. • PCM disconnected. • CCRM disconnected. • Disconnect Scan Tool from DLC. • Measure resistance between Pin 18 at the CCRM vehicle harness connector and the battery negative post. • **Is resistance greater than 10,000 ohms?**	Yes No	▶ ▶	GO to X194. SERVICE short to ground. RECONNECT all components. RERUN Quick Test.

Fig. 220 Test X: CCRM (Part 34 of 51). 1995

TEST STEP	RESULT	▶	ACTION TO TAKE
X194 CHECK FUEL PUMP CIRCUIT CONTINUITY • Key off. • PCM disconnected. • CCRM disconnected. • Install breakout box. • Measure resistance between Pin 18 at the CCRM vehicle harness connector and Test pin 80 (FP) at the breakout box. • **Is resistance less than 5.0 ohms?**	Yes No	▶ ▶	If P0231 or P0232 is also present with the P0230: GO to X195. All others: REPLACE PCM. RECONNECT all components. RERUN Quick Test. SERVICE open circuit. REMOVE breakout box. RECONNECT all components. RERUN Quick Test.
X195 CHECK THE FUEL PUMP PRIMARY CIRCUIT INSIDE THE PCM • Key off. • Remove breakout box. • Reconnect PCM. • Reconnect CCRM. • Reconnect Scan Tool to DLC. • Key on, engine off. • Access FPA PID on Scan Tool. • **Is the FPA PID off?**	Yes No	▶ ▶	GO to X196. KEY off. REPLACE PCM. RECONNECT all components. RERUN Quick Test.
X196 CHECK THE FUEL PUMP PRIMARY CIRCUIT INSIDE THE PCM NOTE: The Scan Tool must be connected to a reliable power source that is powered with the ignition key in the START position (e.g. directly to the vehicle battery). Also verify that the vehicle battery is fully charged. • Key on, engine off. • While viewing the FPA PID, crank engine. • **Is the FPA PID on during crank?**	Yes No	▶ ▶	Key off. The fuel pump primary circuit is OK in the harness and PCM. If P0231 is present: GO to X210. If P0232 is present: GO to X200. Key off. REPLACE PCM. RECONNECT all components. RERUN Quick Test.

Fig. 220 Test X: CCRM (Part 35 of 51). 1995

TEST STEP	RESULT	▶	ACTION TO TAKE
X200 DIAGNOSTIC TROUBLE CODE DTC P0232: DOES ENGINE START? Diagnostic Trouble Code (DTC) P0232 indicates that one of the following has occurred: No Start: — Inertia Fuel Shutoff (IFS) switch not reset or electrically open. — Open circuit between the fuel pump and FPM circuit connection to power-to-pump circuit. — Poor fuel pump ground. — Fuel pump electrically open. Engine Starts: — Fuel pump secondary circuit short to power. — Fuel pump relay contacts always closed. — Open in FPM circuit between PCM and connection to power-to-pump circuit. — Damaged PCM. • **Does the engine start?**	Yes No	▶ ▶	GO to X201. GO to X205.
X201 VERIFY THAT FUEL PUMP IS OFF • Key on, wait 5 seconds. • Listen for motor noise from fuel pump (it may be necessary to listen by fuel tank). • **Is fuel pump off?**	Yes No	▶ ▶	GO to X204. GO to X203.
X203 CHECK FOR FUEL PUMP RELAY ALWAYS CLOSED • Key off. • Disconnect CCRM. • Key on. • **Does fuel pump shut off when CCRM is disconnected?**	Yes No	▶ ▶	REPLACE CCRM. RERUN Quick Test. SERVICE short to power in power-to-pump / FPM circuit. RECONNECT CCRM. RERUN Quick Test.
X204 CHECK FPM CIRCUIT CONTINUITY • Key off. • Disconnect PCM. Inspect for damaged or pushed out pins, corrosion, loose wires, etc. Service as necessary. • Install breakout box, leave PCM disconnected. • Disconnect CCRM. • Measure resistance between Test Pin 40 (FPM) at the breakout box and Pin 5 at the CCRM vehicle harness connector. • **Is resistance less than 5.0 ohms?**	Yes No	▶ ▶	REPLACE PCM. RECONNECT CCRM. RERUN Quick Test. SERVICE open circuit. REMOVE breakout box. RECONNECT all components. RERUN Quick Test.

FORD–Electronic Engine Controls

TEST STEP	RESULT	▶	ACTION TO TAKE
X205 CHECK INERTIA FUEL SHUTOFF SWITCH • Key off. • Locate and disconnect Inertia Fuel Shutoff (IFS) switch (verify that switch is reset). • Measure resistance between the ''C'' and ''NC'' pins of the IFS switch. • **Is resistance less than 5.0 ohms?**	Yes No	▶ ▶	GO to X206. REPLACE or RESET IFS switch. RERUN Quick Test.
X206 CHECK POWER-TO-PUMP CIRCUIT CONTINUITY BETWEEN IFS SWITCH AND CCRM • Key off. • IFS switch disconnected. • Disconnect CCRM. • Measure resistance of the Power-To-Pump circuit between the IFS switch vehicle harness connector and pin 5 of the CCRM vehicle harness connector. • **Is resistance less than 5.0 ohms?**	Yes No	▶ ▶	RECONNECT IFS switch and CCRM. check for open in Power-To-Pump circuit (IFS switch to pump), poor fuel pump ground, open in fuel pump, etc. After any service, RECONNECT all components and RERUN Quick Test. SERVICE open in Power-To-Pump circuit between IFS switch and FPM connection to circuit.
X210 DIAGNOSTIC TROUBLE CODE DTC P0231: DOES ENGINE START? Diagnostic Trouble Code (DTC) P0231 indicates a fuel pump secondary circuit failure between the B(+) supply and the FPM connection to the power-to-pump circuit. Possible causes: No Starts: — Open circuit between the B(+) supply and the FPM connection to the power-to-pump circuit. — Fuel pump relay contacts always open. Engine Starts: — Damaged PCM. • **Does the engine start?**	Yes No	▶ ▶	REPLACE PCM. RERUN Quick Test. GO to X211.

Fig. 220   Test X: CCRM (Part 36 of 51). 1995

TEST STEP	RESULT	▶	ACTION TO TAKE
X211 CHECK FOR B(+) TO FUEL PUMP RELAY • Key off. • Disconnect CCRM. • Measure voltage between Pin 11 at the CCRM vehicle harness connector and the battery negative post. • **Is voltage greater than 10.5 volts?**	Yes No	▶ ▶	GO to X212. VERIFY integrity of fuse/fuse link for B(+) supply to CCRM (fuel pump relay). If OK, SERVICE open in B(+) supply to CCRM. RECONNECT CCRM. RERUN Quick Test.
X212 CHECK POWER-TO-PUMP CIRCUIT CONTINUITY • Key off. • CCRM disconnected. • Measure resistance between Pin 5 at the CCRM vehicle harness connector and the battery negative post. • **Is resistance less than 10.0 ohms?**	Yes No	▶ ▶	REPLACE CCRM. RERUN Quick Test. SERVICE open in power-to-pump circuit between FPM splice and CCRM. RECONNECT CCRM. RERUN Quick Test.

Fig. 220   Test X: CCRM (Part 37 of 51). 1995

TEST STEP	RESULT	▶	ACTION TO TAKE
X220 CONTINUOUS MEMORY DTC P0232: CHECK EEC-V HARNESS Continuous Memory Diagnostic Trouble Code (DTC) P0232 indicates that one of the following intermittent conditions has occurred: — Fuel pump circuit activated when PCM expected circuit to be off (i.e. fuel system test or prime procedure). — Inertia Fuel Shutoff switch was tripped, then reset. — Open circuit in or between the fuel pump and FPM circuit at the PCM (refer to schematic). — Poor fuel pump ground. — FPM or power-to-pump circuit short to power. — Fuel pump relay contacts stuck closed. — Engine stall due to excessive load. • Key on, engine off. • Access FPM PID on Scan Tool. • Observe the FPM PID for an indication of a fault while performing the following (the FPM PID will turn ON when an open or short to power is detected): — Shake, wiggle, bend the Power-To-Pump circuit between the CCRM Pin 5 and the fuel pump. — Shake, wiggle, bend the fuel pump ground circuit from the fuel pump to ground. — Lightly tap the fuel pump to simulate road shock. — Lightly tap Inertia Fuel Shutoff switch to simulate road shock. — Lightly tap the CCRM to simulate road shock. — Shake, wiggle, bend the FPM circuit between the PCM and the splice to the Power-To-Pump circuit. • Key off. • Inspect the fuel pump vehicle harness connector and the fuel pump ground for corrosion, damaged pins, etc. • **Is a fault indicated/found?**	Yes No	▶ ▶	ISOLATE fault and SERVICE as necessary. COMPLETE PCM. RESET to clear DTC(s) Powertrain Control Module (PCM) Reset). RERUN Quick Test. GO to Pinpoint Test Step Z1 with the following data: FPM PID and list of possible causes.

Fig. 220   Test X: CCRM (Part 38 of 51). 1995

TEST STEP	RESULT	▶	ACTION TO TAKE
X225 CONTINUOUS MEMORY DTC P0231: CHECK EEC-V HARNESS Continuous Memory Diagnostic Trouble Code (DTC) P0231 indicates that sometime during vehicle operation when the fuel pump was commanded on, the FPM circuit voltage went low. Possible causes: — Open in B(+) circuit to the fuel pump relay. — Fuel pump relay contacts open. — Open in Power-to-Pump circuit between the CCRM and FPM splice. • Scan Tool connected. • Key on, engine off. • Access Output Test Mode on Scan Tool (refer to Section 2). • While in Output Test Mode, access the FPM PID (if the Scan Tool will not allow access to PIDs while in Output Test Mode, disconnect PCM, install a breakout box, reconnect PCM and connect a DVOM between Test Pin 40 (FPM) and Test Pin 51 (GND). • Command the outputs on. The FPM PID will be on (or the DVOM voltage will be greater than 10.0 volts). • Observe FPM PID (or DVOM voltage) for an indication of a fault while performing the following (the FPM PID or DVOM voltage will change suddenly when a fault is detected, indicating an open): — Shake, wiggle, bend the fuel pump relay B(+) circuit to the CCRM (Pin 11). — Lightly tap the CCRM (to simulate road shock). — Shake, wiggle, bend the Power-to-Pump circuit between the CCRM and the FPM splice. • Key off. • Inspect the CCRM connector for corrosion, damaged pins, etc. • **Is a fault indicated?**	Yes No	▶ ▶	ISOLATE fault and SERVICE as necessary. COMPLETE PCM Reset to clear DTCs Powertrain Control Module (PCM) Reset). RERUN Quick Test. GO to Pinpoint Test Step Z1 with the following data: FPM PID and list of possible causes.

Fig. 220   Test X: CCRM (Part 39 ot 51). 1995

TEST STEP		RESULT	▶	ACTION TO TAKE
X230	**CONTINUOUS MEMORY DTC P0230: CHECK EEC-V HARNESS**			

	Continuous Memory Diagnostic Trouble Code (DTC) P0230 indicates a fuel pump primary circuit failure has occurred during vehicle operation. Possible causes:
	— Open VPWR to CCRM.
	— Open coil in fuel pump relay.
	— Open in Fuel Pump Circuit (PCM Pin 80).
	● Scan Tool connected.
	● Key on, engine off. Wait 5 seconds.
	● Access FPA PID. The FPA PID will be off, indicating that the PCM detects VPWR voltage through the fuel pump relay coil and FP circuit (Pin 80) to the PCM.
	● Observe the FPA PID for an indication of a fault while performing the following (the FPA PID will turn on when an open is detected (this is because the PCM will not detect VPWR voltage on Pin 80 (FP)):
	  ● Shake, wiggle, bend the Fuel Pump circuit between the PCM (Pin 80) and CCRM (Pin 18).
	  ● Shake, wiggle, bend the VPWR circuit between the EEC-V Power Relay and the CCRM (Pin 13).
	  ● Lightly tap the CCRM (to simulate road shock).
	● Key off.
	● Inspect the PCM and CCRM connectors for corrosion, damaged pins, etc.
	● **Is a fault indicated?**
		Yes
		
		No
			▶
			
			▶
				ISOLATE fault and SERVICE as necessary. COMPLETE PCM Reset to clear DTCs
				
				Powertrain Control Module (PCM) Reset). RERUN Quick Test.
				
				If P0231 or P0232 is also present with P0230:
				An intermittent fuel pump secondary circuit fault may exist.
				For P0231:
				GO to X225.
				For P0232:
				GO to X220.
				All others:
				GO to Pinpoint Test Step Z1 with the following data: FPA PID and list of possible causes. For testing the FP circuit with the engine running, also monitor the FPM PID. This is because the FPA PID will always read ON when the PCM is turning on the fuel pump, so an open harness circuit using the FPA PID could not be detected.

X240	**ELECTRIC COOLING FAN CONCERN: DID THE FAN OPERATE AT ANY SPEED?**			
	NOTE: For the proper results of these pinpoint tests, no fault DTCs must have been present during EEC-V Quick Test. ● For one speed fan applications (Mustang), GO directly to X241. ● **During the operational check of both fan speeds, did the fan operate at any speed?**	Yes No	▶ ▶	Only one fan speed is operational. GO to X250. Cooling fan will not operate at any speed. GO to X241.

Fig. 220   Test X: CCRM (Part 40 of 51). 1995

TEST STEP		RESULT	▶	ACTION TO TAKE
X241	**COOLING FAN WILL NOT OPERATE AT ANY SPEED: COMMAND FAN ON (HIGH SPEED FOR TWO SPEED APPLICATIONS) AND CHECK FOR VOLTAGE AT FAN**			
	● Scan Tool connected. ● Key on, engine off. ● Still in Output Test Mode, with fan commanded off. ● Disconnect cooling fan (either one for Windstar). ● Command fan on (high speed for two speed fan applications). ● Measure voltage between the Power-To-(High Speed) Fan circuit at the cooling fan vehicle harness connector and chassis ground. ● Key off. ● **Was voltage greater than 10.0 volts?**	Yes No	▶ ▶	Power is being supplied to fan. GO to X245. GO to X242.

Fig. 220   Test X: CCRM (Part 41 of 51). 1995

TEST STEP		RESULT	▶	ACTION TO TAKE
X242	**CHECK FOR B(+) TO FAN RELAYS IN CCRM**			

	● Key off.
	● Cooling fan disconnected.
	● Disconnect CCRM.
	● Connect negative probe of DVOM to the battery negative post.
	● For Mustang, Thunderbird/Cougar:
	  — Check voltage at pins 3 and 4 of the CCRM vehicle harness connector.
	● For Continental:
	  — Check voltage at pins 3, 4, 8 and 10 of the CCRM vehicle harness connector.
		Yes
		No
			▶
			▶
				GO to X243.
				B(+) fault. CHECK condition of related fuses/fuse links. If OK, SERVICE open circuit. If fuse/fuse link is damaged, CHECK B(+) circuit for short to ground before replacing.
				For Continental:
				If open was to only CCRM pins 3 and 4, after service, GO to X272 (to check both HFC relays in CCRM and Power-To-Fan circuit). Otherwise, RECONNECT all components. RE-EVALUATE symptom.
				
				All others: RECONNECT all components. RE-EVALUATE symptom.

Fig. 220   Test X: CCRM (Part 42 of 51). 1995

TEST STEP		RESULT	▶	ACTION TO TAKE
X243	**CHECK POWER-TO-FAN(S) CIRCUIT CONTINUITY BETWEEN CCRM AND COOLING FAN(S)**			

	● Key off.
	● CCRM disconnected.
	● Cooling fan disconnected.
	● For Mustang:
	  — Measure resistance between pin 2 of the CCRM vehicle harness connector and the Power-To-Fan circuit at the fan vehicle harness connector.
	● For Thunderbird/Cougar:
	  — Measure resistance between pin 6 of the CCRM vehicle harness connector and the Power-To-High Fan circuit at the fan vehicle harness connector.
	  — Measure resistance between Pin 2 of the CCRM vehicle harness connector and the Power-To-Low circuit at the fan vehicle harness connector.
	● For Continental:
	  — Measure resistance between the Power-To-High Fan circuit at the fan vehicle harness connector and Pins 2 and 12 of the CCRM vehicle harness connector.
	  — Measure resistance between Pin 6 of the CCRM vehicle harness connector and the Power-To-Low Fan circuit at the fan vehicle harness connector.
		Yes
		
		No
			▶
			
			▶
				REPLACE CCRM. RECONNECT all components. RE-EVALUATE symptom.
				SERVICE open Power-To-Fan circuits(s).
				For Continental:
				After service, GO to X273 (to check both HFC relays in CCRM).
				
				All others:
				RECONNECT all components and RE-EVALUATE symptom.

X245	**CHECK COOLING FAN GROUND CIRCUIT**			
	● Key off. ● Cooling fan disconnected. ● Disconnect Scan Tool from DLC. ● Measure resistance between the ground circuit at the cooling fan vehicle harness connector and chassis ground. ● **Is resistance less than 5.0 ohms?**	Yes No	▶ ▶	REPLACE fan motor. RECONNECT all components. RE-EVALUATE symptom. SERVICE open ground circuit. RECONNECT all components. RE-EVALUATE symptom.

Fig. 220   Test X: CCRM (Part 43 of 51). 1995

TEST STEP		RESULT	▶	ACTION TO TAKE
X246	CHECK FOR VOLTAGE TO OTHER COOLING FAN			
	• Key off.	Yes	▶	REPLACE both fan motors. RECONNECT all components. RE-EVALUATE symptom.
	• One cooling fan disconnected.			
	• Reconnect Scan Tool.			
	• Key on, engine off.			
	• Again, access Output Test Mode.	No	▶	SERVICE open power or ground circuit to the fan that was just tested. RECONNECT all components. RE-EVALUATE symptom. If the other fan does not operate, REPLACE it and again RE-EVALUATE symptom.
	• Disconnect the other cooling fan.			
	• Command the high speed fan on.			
	• Measure voltage between the Power-To-Fan circuit and ground circuit at the vehicle harness connector of the fan that was just disconnected.			
	• Key off.			
	• Was voltage greater than 10.0 volts?			
X250	DETERMINE WHICH FAN SPEED IS OPERATIONAL			
	• Was the low speed fan operational?	Yes	▶	High speed fan inoperative. For Thunderbird/Cougar: GO to X265. For Continental: GO to X260.
		No	▶	Low speed fan inoperative. For Thunderbird/Cougar, Continental: GO to X251.

Fig. 220   Test X: CCRM (Part 44 of 51). 1995

TEST STEP		RESULT	▶	ACTION TO TAKE
X251	LOW SPEED FAN INOPERATIVE (THUNDERBIRD/COUGAR, CONTINENTAL): COMMAND LOW SPEED FAN ON AND CHECK FOR VOLTAGE TO COOLING FAN			
	• Scan Tool connected.	Yes	▶	REPLACE fan motor. RECONNECT all components. RE-EVALUATE symptom.
	• Key on, engine off.			
	• Still in Output Test Mode with fan commanded off.			
	• Disconnect cooling fan.	No	▶	For Thunderbird/Cougar: GO to X253. For Continental: GO to X252.
	• Command low speed fan on.			
	• Measure voltage between the Power-To-Low fan circuit and ground circuit at the cooling fan vehicle harness connector.			
	• Key off.			
	• Was voltage greater than 10.0 volts?			
X252	CHECK FOR B(+) TO LFC RELAY IN CCRM			
	• Key off.	Yes	▶	GO to X253.
	• Cooling fan disconnected.	No	▶	B(+) fault. CHECK condition of related fuses/fuse links. If OK, SERVICE open circuit. If fuse/fuse link is damaged, CHECK B(+) circuit for short to ground before replacing. After service, RECONNECT all components. RE-EVALUATE symptom.
	• Disconnect CCRM.			
	• Connect negative probe of DVOM to chassis ground.			
	• Check for voltage at Pins 3 and 4 of the CCRM vehicle harness connector.			
	• Are both voltages greater than 10.0 volts?			
X253	CHECK POWER-TO-LOW FAN CIRCUIT CONTINUITY BETWEEN CCRM AND FAN			
	• Key off.	Yes	▶	REPLACE CCRM. RECONNECT all components. RE-EVALUATE symptom.
	• For Thunderbird/Cougar, disconnect CCRM.			
	• CCRM disconnected.			
	• Cooling fan disconnected.	No	▶	SERVICE open circuit. RECONNECT all components. RE-EVALUATE symptom.
	• Measure resistance between the Power-To-Low Fan circuit at the cooling fan vehicle harness connector and Pins 1 and 2 (6 and 7 for Continental) of the CCRM vehicle harness connector.			
	• Are both resistances less than 5.0 ohms?			

Fig. 220   Test X: CCRM (Part 45 of 51). 1995

TEST STEP		RESULT	▶	ACTION TO TAKE
X255	LOW SPEED FAN INOPERATIVE (WINDSTAR): CHECK FOR B(+) TO LFC RELAY IN CCRM			
	• Key off.	Yes	▶	GO to X256.
	• Disconnect CCRM.	No	▶	B(+) fault. CHECK condition of related fuses and Fan Dropping Resistor. If OK, SERVICE open circuit. If fuse is damaged, CHECK B(+) circuit for short to ground before replacing. After service, RECONNECT all components. RE-EVALUATE symptom.
	• Connect negative probe of DVOM to chassis ground.			
	• Check for voltage at Pins 6 and 7 of the CCRM vehicle harness connector.			
	• Are both voltages greater than 9.0 volts?			
X256	CHECK POWER-TO-FAN CIRCUIT CONTINUITY			
	• Key off.	Yes	▶	REPLACE CCRM. RECONNECT all components. RE-EVALUATE symptom.
	• CCRM disconnected.			
	• Disconnect one of the cooling fans (either one).	No	▶	SERVICE open Power-To-Fan circuit. RECONNECT all components. RE-EVALUATE symptom.
	• Measure resistance between Pin 3 of the CCRM vehicle harness connector and the Power-To-Fan circuit at the cooling fan vehicle harness connector.			
	• Is resistance less than 5.0 ohms?			
X260	HIGH SPEED FAN INOPERATIVE (CONTINENTAL): COMMAND HIGH SPEED FAN ON AND CHECK FOR VOLTAGE TO COOLING FAN			
	• Scan Tool connected.	Yes	▶	REPLACE fan motor. RECONNECT all components. RE-EVALUATE symptom.
	• Key on, engine off.			
	• Still in Output Test Mode with fan commanded off.			
	• Disconnect cooling fan.	No	▶	GO to X261.
	• Command high speed fan on.			
	• Measure voltage between the Power-To-High Fan circuit at the cooling fan vehicle harness connector and chassis ground.			
	• Key off.			
	• Was voltage greater than 10.5 volts?			

Fig. 220   Test X: CCRM (Part 46 of 51). 1995

TEST STEP		RESULT	▶	ACTION TO TAKE
X261	CHECK FOR B(+) TO CCRM PINS 8 AND 10			
	• Key off.	Yes	▶	GO to X262.
	• Cooling fan disconnected.	No	▶	B(+) fault. CHECK condition of related fuses/fuse links. If OK, SERVICE open circuit. If fuse/fuse link is damaged, CHECK B(+) circuit for short to ground before replacing. After service, GO to X263 to CHECK the Power-To-High Fan circuits and CCRM.
	• Disconnect CCRM.			
	• Connect negative probe of DVOM to chassis ground.			
	• Check for voltage at Pins 8 and 10 of the CCRM vehicle harness connector.			
	• Is voltage greater than 10.5 volts?			
X262	CHECK CONTINUITY OF POWER-TO-HIGH FAN CIRCUITS			
	• Key off.	Yes	▶	REPLACE CCRM. RECONNECT all components. RE-EVALUATE symptom.
	• Cooling fan disconnected.			
	• CCRM disconnected.	No	▶	If both resistance measurements were greater than 5.0 ohms: SERVICE open circuit. RECONNECT all components. RE-EVALUATE symptom. If one resistance measurement was greater than 5.0 ohms and one was less than 5.0 ohms: SERVICE open circuit. After service, GO to X273 (to check both HFC relays in CCRM).
	• Measure resistance between the Power-To-High Fan circuit at the cooling fan vehicle harness connector and both Pins 1 and 12 of the CCRM vehicle harness connector.			
	• Are both resistances less than 5.0 ohms?			

Fig. 220   Test X: CCRM (Part 47 of 51). 1995

TEST STEP		RESULT	▶	ACTION TO TAKE
X263	VERIFY POWER-TO-HIGH FAN CIRCUIT CONTINUITY BETWEEN CCRM PIN 1 AND THE COOLING FAN			
	• Key off. • Cooling fan disconnected. • CCRM disconnected. • Measure resistance between Pin 1 and Pin 12 of the CCRM vehicle harness connector. • **Is resistance less than 5.0 ohms?**	Yes	▶	GO to X273 (to check both HFC relays in CCRM).
		No	▶	SERVICE open between CCRM Pin 1 and the Pin 12 splice to the Power-To-High Fan circuit. After also servicing the B(+) circuit, RECONNECT all components. RE-EVALUATE symptom.
X265	HIGH SPEED FAN INOPERATIVE (THUNDERBIRD / COUGAR): COMMAND HIGH SPEED FAN ON AND CHECK FOR VOLTAGE TO COOLING FAN			
	• Scan Tool connected. • Key on, engine off. • Still in Output Test Mode with fan commanded off. • Disconnect cooling fan. • Command high speed fan on. • Measure voltage between the Power-To-High Fan circuit at the cooling fan vehicle harness connector and chassis ground. • Key off. • **Was voltage greater than 10.5 volts?**	Yes	▶	REPLACE fan motor. RECONNECT all components. RE-EVALUATE symptom.
		No	▶	GO to X266.
X266	CHECK CONTINUITY OF POWER-TO-HIGH FAN CIRCUIT			
	• Key off. • Cooling fan disconnected. • Disconnect CCRM. • Measure resistance between Pin 6 of the CCRM vehicle harness connector and the Power-To-High Fan circuit at the cooling fan vehicle harness connector. • **Is resistance less than 5.0 ohms?**	Yes	▶	REPLACE CCRM. RECONNECT all components. RE-EVALUATE symptom.
		No	▶	SERVICE open in Power-To-High Fan circuit. RECONNECT all components. RE-EVALUATE symptom.

Fig. 220   Test X: CCRM (Part 48 of 51). 1995

TEST STEP		RESULT	▶	ACTION TO TAKE
X268	HIGH SPEED FAN INOPERATIVE (WINDSTAR): CHECK FOR B(+) TO HFC RELAYS IN CCRM			
	• Key off. • Disconnect CCRM. • Connect negative probe of DVOM to chassis ground. • Check for voltage at Pins 1, 2, 12 and 24 of the CCRM vehicle harness connector. • **Is each voltage greater than 10.5 volts?**	Yes	▶	GO to X269.
		No	▶	B(+) fault. CHECK condition of related fuses / fuse links. If OK, SERVICE open circuit. If fuse / fuse link is damaged, CHECK B(+) circuit for short to ground before replacing. If open was only to two pins (either 1 and 2, or 12 and 24), after service GO to X272 (to CHECK the Power-To-Fan circuit and CCRM). Otherwise, RECONNECT all components. RE-EVALUATE symptom.
X269	CHECK POWER-TO-FAN CIRCUIT CONTINUITY BETWEEN CCRM VEHICLE HARNESS CONNECTOR PINS 4 AND 8			
	• Key off. • CCRM disconnected. • Measure resistance between Pins 4 and 8 at the CCRM vehicle harness connector. • **Is resistance less than 5.0 ohms?**	Yes	▶	REPLACE CCRM. RECONNECT all components. RE-EVALUATE symptom.
		No	▶	SERVICE open circuit between CCRM Pin 8 and the Pin 4 splice to the Power-To-Fan circuit. After service, GO to X273 (to check both HFC relays in the CCRM).

Fig. 220   Test X: CCRM (Part 49 of 51). 1995

TEST STEP		RESULT	▶	ACTION TO TAKE
X272	CHECK POWER-TO-FAN HARNESS CONTINUITY BETWEEN HFC RELAYS			
	• Key off. • CCRM disconnected. • **For Continental:** — Measure resistance between Pins 1 and 12 of the CCRM vehicle harness connector.	Yes	▶	GO to X273 (to check both HFC relays in CCRM).
		No	▶	SERVICE open circuit. After also servicing the B(+) circuit, RECONNECT all components. RE-EVALUATE symptom.
X273	VERIFY OPERATION OF BOTH HFC RELAYS IN CCRM			
	• Key off. • CCRM disconnected. • Connect a jumper wire between Pin 13 of the CCRM and the battery positive (+) post. • Connect another jumper wire between Pin 17 of the CCRM and the battery negative (-) post. • Measure resistance between Pin 1 and Pins 2, 3 and 4 of the CCRM. • Measure resistance between Pin 12 and Pins 8, 10, and 24 of the CCRM. • **Are all resistances less than 5.0 ohms?**	Yes	▶	Both HFC relays are OK. REMOVE jumper wires. After original service, RECONNECT all components. RE-EVALUATE symptom.
		No	▶	REPLACE CCRM. After also performing original service, RECONNECT all components. RE-EVALUATE symptom.
X275	COOLING FAN ALWAYS RUNS: DISCONNECT CCRM AND CHECK IF FAN STILL RUNS			
	NOTE: For proper results of these pinpoint tests, no fault DTCs must have been present during EEC-V Quick Test. For two-speed fan applications, the ACP or ACPSW PID check in Section 4 must also have been performed. • Accessories off (A / C, etc.). • Key on, verify "cooling fan always on" symptom. • Key off. • Disconnect CCRM. • Key on, engine off. • Is cooling fan still on?	Yes	▶	Key off. For Mustang: SERVICE Power-To-Fan circuit short to power. RECONNECT CCRM. RE-EVALUATE symptom. For applications with FANM circuit wired to PCM (Thunderbird / Cougar, GO to X276. For Continental: GO to X277.
		No	▶	Key off. REPLACE CCRM. RE-EVALUATE symptom.

Fig. 220   Test X: CCRM (Part 50 of 51). 1995

TEST STEP		RESULT	▶	ACTION TO TAKE
X276	VERIFY FANM IS NOT SHORT TO POWER IN PCM (DISCONNECT PCM AND CHECK IF FAN STILL RUNS)			
	• Key off. • CCRM disconnected. • Disconnect PCM. • Key on, engine off. • Does fan still run?	Yes	▶	Key off.
		No	▶	For Thunderbird / Cougar: GO to X277. Key off. REPLACE PCM. RECONNECT all components. RE-EVALUATE symptom.
X277	CHECK "POWER-TO-LOW FAN" AND "POWER-TO-HIGH FAN" CIRCUITS FOR SHORT TO POWER			
	• Key off. • CCRM disconnected. • PCM disconnected (Thunderbird / Cougar). • Disconnect cooling fan. • Key on, engine off. • Connect negative probe of DVOM to chassis ground. • Check for voltage at both the Power-To-Low Fan and Power-To-High Fan circuits at the cooling fan vehicle harness connector. • **Are both voltages less than 1.0 volt?**	Yes	▶	No fault is indicated at this time. VERIFY results of previous test steps. If OK, RECONNECT all components
		No	▶	SERVICE short to power. RECONNECT all components. RE-EVALUATE symptom.

Fig. 220   Test X: CCRM (Part 51 of 51). 1995

Note

You should enter this Pinpoint Test only when directed here.

Remember

Preliminary checks must be performed before continuing with this Pinpoint Test.

Check:

- Electrical connections
- Vacuum leaks
- Fuel level and quality
- Ignition wiring connections
- Air intake filters, tubes and gaskets
- Aftermarket alterations
- Basic engine (valves, timing, etc.)

Description

Pinpoint Test Z is a set of instructions for isolating an intermittent fault. It combines the use of a scan tool with a Breakout Box (BOB), a fuel psi gauge, vacuum gauge, DVOM, Transmission Tester and Ignition Tester. Actual values can be compared to typical values in the Diagnostic Reference Value Charts at the end of this section to aid in finding the fault.

FM0159401215010X

Fig. 221   Test Z: Intermittents (Part 1 of 23). 1994-95

TEST STEP	RESULT	▶	ACTION TO TAKE
Z1 INTERMITTENT TEST PROCEDURE			
Choose an Intermittent Diagnostic Procedure:		▶	GO to Test Step **Z10**
• Intermittent Input Wiggle Procedure		▶	GO to Test Step **Z20**
• Intermittent Output Actuator Switch Procedure		▶	GO to Test Step **Z30**
• Intermittent Water Soak Procedure		▶	GO to Test Step **Z40**
• Intermittent Road Test Procedure		▶	GO to Test Step **Z50**
• Intermittent Ignition Procedure			
Z10 INTERMITTENT KOEO INPUT WIGGLE PROCEDURE			
WARNING: USE CAUTION WHEN PERFORMING ANY OF THE TEST STEPS. ALWAYS BE AWARE OF HANDS, CLOTHING OR TOOLS NEAR COOLING FANS, ENGINE DRIVE BELTS OR HOT SURFACES.	Yes	▶	Possible wiring or component problem. CHECK each wire for corrosion, bent or loose terminals and wire terminal crimps. SERVICE as necessary. Otherwise, REPLACE component. VERIFY repair. If unable to verify, REINSTALL original part and GO to **Z11**.
• Key off.			
• Connect Scan tool to DLC.			
• Access PIDs based on information from the pinpoint test or intermittent symptom charts at the end of this pinpoint test.			
• Go to the area of the suspected wiring or component fault.			
• Key on, engine off.	No	▶	GO to **Z11** for PCM wiring check.
• Lightly tap on component while viewing PID values. Wiggle and pull each component wire (Signal, Signal Return and VREF, if applicable) at the component.			
• Look for abrupt changes in PID values. Compare the actual values to the Diagnostic Reference Values at the end of this pinpoint test.			
• **Are any PID values out of range or drop out and back into range?**			

FM0159401215020X

Fig. 221   Test Z: Intermittents (Part 2 of 23). 1994-95

TEST STEP	RESULT	▶	ACTION TO TAKE
Z11 INTERMITTENT KOEO INPUT WIGGLE PROCEDURE			
• Continue to monitor the information from the previous step.	Yes	▶	Possible wiring or component problem. CHECK each wire for corrosion, bent or loose terminals and wire terminal crimps. SERVICE as necessary. Otherwise, if the value dropped out while checking the PCM harness connector and there is no evidence of a fault, REPLACE PCM. If unable to verify, REINSTALL original PCM. Return to **Z1** and choose another procedure.
• Go to the area of the suspected wiring or component fault.			
• Turn ignition key to the on position.			
• Wiggle and pull each sensor wire (Signal, Signal Return and VREF, if applicable) from the component back to the PCM connector.			
• Look for abrupt changes in PID values. Compare the actual values to the Diagnostic Reference Values.			
• **Are any PID values out of range or drop out and back into range?**			
	No	▶	Unable to verify fault. GO to **Z12** KOER Wiggle Test.
Z12 INTERMITTENT KOER INPUT WIGGLE PROCEDURE			
WARNING: USE CAUTION WHEN PERFORMING ANY OF THE TEST STEPS. ALWAYS BE AWARE OF HANDS, CLOTHING OR TOOLS NEAR COOLING FANS, ENGINE DRIVE BELTS OR HOT SURFACES.	Yes	▶	Possible wiring or component problem. CHECK each wire for corrosion, bent or loose terminals and wire terminal crimps. SERVICE as necessary. Otherwise, REPLACE component. VERIFY repair. If unable to verify, REINSTALL original part, and GO to **Z13**.
• Key off.			
• Access PIDs based on information from the pinpoint test or from the Intermittent Symptom Chart.			
• Go to the area of the suspected wiring or component fault.			
• Key on, engine running.			
• Lightly tap on component while viewing PID values. Also wiggle and pull each component wire (Signal, Signal Return and VREF, if applicable) at the component.	No	▶	GO to **Z13** for PCM wiring check.
• Look for abrupt changes in PID values. Compare the actual values to the Diagnostic Reference Values.			
• Are any PID values out of range or drop out and back into range?			

FM0159401215030X

Fig. 221   Test Z: Intermittents (Part 3 of 23). 1994-95

TEST STEP	RESULT	▶	ACTION TO TAKE
Z13 INTERMITTENT KOER INPUT WIGGLE PROCEDURE			
• Continue to monitor the information from the previous step.	Yes	▶	Possible wiring or component problem. CHECK each wire for corrosion, bent or loose terminals and wire terminal crimps. SERVICE as necessary. Otherwise if the value dropped out while checking the PCM harness connector and there is no evidence of a wiring fault, REPLACE PCM. If unable to verify repair, REINSTALL original PCM and RETURN to **Z1** and choose another procedure.
• Go to the area of the suspected wiring or component fault.			
• Key on, engine running.			
• Wiggle and pull each component wire (Signal, Signal Return and VREF, if applicable) from the component back to the PCM connector.			
• Look for abrupt changes in PID values. Compare the actual values to the Diagnostic Reference Values.			
• **Are any PID values out of range or drop out and back into range?**			
	No	▶	Unable to verify fault. RETURN to **Z1** and choose another procedure.

FM0159401215040X

Fig. 221   Test Z: Intermittents (Part 4 of 23). 1994-95

TEST STEP		RESULT	▶	ACTION TO TAKE
Z20	**INTERMITTENT KOEO OUTPUT PROCEDURE**			

Some outputs / switches may need to be driven in order to be checked (i.e. fuel injectors and idle air controllers). GO to **Z40** for the Intermittent Road Test Procedure to check outputs that are not controlled in the Output Test Mode.
• Key off.
• Connect Scan tool to DLC.
• Select the PIDs / circuits to monitor based on the information sent from the pinpoint test or Intermittent Symptom Charts at the end of this pinpoint test.
• Go to the area of the suspected wiring or component fault.
• Record any continuous codes before proceeding to the next step. A DTC P 1000 will be generated when the PCM is disconnected. **Caution must be used for the next steps. Cooling fans or fuel pump may turn on.**
• Disconnect PCM and install a breakout box.
• Connect a voltmeter:
  – Red lead to output control circuit.
  – Black lead to battery ground.
  If using the NGS, go to the voltmeter and link up to the PID display. Select the PIDs from the previous steps and record as necessary.
• Key on, engine off.
• Enter Output Test Mode
 	
• Turn the output on. Observe the volt reading and PID display.
• While outputs are on, lightly tap on component and look for the voltage change.
• **Did the voltage remain steady and less than 1 volt?**
	Yes
	
	No
		▶
		
		▶
			Unable to verify fault. GO to **Z21**
			
			Fault area is identified. If fault occurred while tapping on component, REPLACE part and VERIFY repair. If unable to verify, REINSTALL original part and GO to **Z21**.

Z21	**INTERMITTENT OUTPUT WIRING TEST**			
• Key on. • Scan tool, voltmeter and breakout box connected. • Continue to monitor PIDs / circuits • Turn output on. • Wiggle, push and pull on the component wire (VPWR and signal) from the component back to the PCM connector. • **Was the voltage steady and less than 1 volt?**	Yes No	▶ ▶	Unable to verify fault. RETURN to **Z1** and choose another procedure. Possible wiring problem. CHECK each wire for corrosion, bent or loose terminals. SERVICE as necessary. VERIFY repair.

FM0159401215050X

Fig. 221   Test Z: Intermittents (Part 5 of 23). 1994-95

TEST STEP		RESULT	▶	ACTION TO TAKE
Z30	**INTERMITTENT WATER SOAK PROCEDURE**			
• Key off. • Connect Scan tool to DLC. • Access PIDs based on information from the pinpoint test or from the Intermittent Symptom Chart at the end of this pinpoint test. • Go to the area of the suspected wiring, vacuum or component fault (based off the PIDs selected and ignition component attached to the Symptom Chart). • Key on, engine running. • Accurately spray water on each component circuit wire, component or vacuum line related to the possible fault area. • Look for abrupt changes in PID values or engine running conditions. • Compare the actual values to the Diagnostic Reference Values at the end of this pinpoint test. • **Are any PID values out of range or drop out and back into range or was there a noticeable engine misfire / stumble?**	Yes No	▶ ▶	Fault area is identified. If fault occurred while spraying on component, REPLACE part and VERIFY repair. If unable to verify, REINSTALL original part. If fault occurred while spraying the circuit wiring, CHECK each wire for corrosion, bent or loose terminals and wire terminal crimps. SERVICE as necessary. If fault occurred while spraying the vacuum line, SERVICE as necessary. VERIFY repair. If unable to verify repair, PERFORM test over. Unable to verify fault. CONTINUE to **Z31**

FM0159401215060X

Fig. 221   Test Z: Intermittents (Part 6 of 23). 1994-95

TEST STEP		RESULT	▶	ACTION TO TAKE
Z31	**INTERMITTENT WATER SOAK PROCEDURE**			
• With the engine still running, continue to individually water soak the ignition control module, plugs, wires, CKP and CMP sensors. • Continue to individually water soak any relays (CCRM) associated with fault. • Look for abrupt changes in PID values or engine running conditions. • Compare the actual values to the Diagnostic Reference Values. • **Are any PID values out of range or drop out and back into range or was there a noticeable engine misfire / stumble?**	Yes No	▶ ▶	Fault area is identified. If fault occurred while spraying on component, REPLACE part and VERIFY repair. If unable to verify, REINSTALL original part. If fault occurred while spraying the circuit wire for corrosion, bent or loose terminals and wire terminal crimps. SERVICE as necessary. If fault occurred while spraying the vacuum line, SERVICE as necessary, VERIFY repair. If unable to verify any repair, REPEAT test step. Unable to verify fault. RETURN to **Z1** and choose another procedure.

FM0159401215070X

Fig. 221   Test Z: Intermittents (Part 7 of 23). 1994-95

TEST STEP		RESULT	▶	ACTION TO TAKE
Z40	**INTERMITTENT ROAD TEST PROCEDURE**			
The Intermittent Road Test Procedure is a set of instructions for monitoring the PIDs and / or components with a Scan tool during a road test. This is done under four different conditions - KOEO, HOT IDLE, 30 mph and 55 mph. The Diagnostic Reference Value Charts at the end of this pinpoint test should be used to compare the data from the vehicle to typical data on the charts. For 30 and 55 mph procedures, a passenger is required and a route is also recommended. To perform an OBD II Drive Cycle Drive Cycles to help plan a route. • Copy the list of PIDs in the order given by the Intermittent Symptom Charts at the end of this pinpoint test. These PIDs will be monitored during the Road Test Procedure. If sent from a pinpoint test, recommended PIDs should also be sent. • Key off. • Connect Scan Tool to DLC. • Connect other diagnostic aids if available to help find fault (i.e. fuel PSI gauge, vacuum gauge or Intermittent Ignition Analyzer). • Key on, engine off. • Access the PIDs based on the information from the pinpoint test or Intermittent Symptom Charts at the end of this pinpoint test. • Compare the actual values from the vehicle to the KOEO values from the Diagnostic Reference Value Chart at the end of this pinpoint test. • **Are any values out of range?**	Yes No	▶ ▶	Fault identified. **For Input fault:** GO to **Z10**. **For output fault:** GO to **Z20** Unable to verify fault. GO to **Z41**.
Z41	**INTERMITTENT ROAD TEST PROCEDURE**			
• Continue to monitor the PIDs listed in the previous step. • Key on, engine running. • Scan Tool connected • Warm engine to operating temperature (approximately 195°F). • Continue to view the PIDs based on the information from the pinpoint test or from the Intermittent Symptom Charts at the end of this pinpoint test. • Compare the actual values from the vehicle to the HOT IDLE values in the Diagnostic Reference Value Chart. • **Are any PID values out of range or suddenly drop out and back into range?**	Yes No	▶ ▶	Fault identified. **For input fault:** GO to **Z10** **For output fault:** GO to **Z20** Unable to verify fault. GO to **Z42**.

FM0159401215080X

Fig. 221   Test Z: Intermittents (Part 8 of 23). 1994-95

TEST STEP	RESULT	▶	ACTION TO TAKE
Z42 INTERMITTENT ROAD TEST PROCEDURE			
NOTE: Look for certain conditions that cause an intermittent fault to occur.	Yes	▶	Fault identified. For input fault: GO to **Z10**. For output fault: GO to **Z20**.
• Continue to monitor the PIDs listed in **Z40**. • Instrument the vehicle as in the previous steps. • Select a person to assist in performing the 30 mph road test. • Make sure engine is at operating temperature before comparing or recording diagnostic values. • Drive the vehicle in a steady 30 mph range with accessories off. • Access the PIDs based on the information from the pinpoint test or from the Intermittent Symptom Charts. • Compare the actual values from the vehicle to the 30 mph values in the Diagnostic Reference Value Chart. • **Are any PID values out of range or drop out and back into the range?**	No	▶	Unable to verify fault. GO to **Z43**.
Z43 INTERMITTENT ROAD TEST PROCEDURE			
NOTE: Look for certain conditions that cause the intermittent fault to occur.	Yes	▶	Fault identified. For input fault: GO to **Z10**. For output fault: GO to **Z20**.
• Continue to monitor the PIDs listed in **Z40**. • Instrument the vehicle as in the previous steps. • Select another person to assist in performing the 55 mph test. • Make sure engine is at operating temperature before comparing or recording diagnostic values. • Drive the vehicle in a steady 55 mph range with accessories off. • Access the PIDs based on information from the pinpoint test or from the Intermittent Symptom Charts at the end of this pinpoint test. • Compare the actual values from the vehicle to the 55 mph values from the Diagnostic Reference Value Chart. • **Are any values out of range or drop out and back into range?**	No	▶	Unable to verify fault. RETURN to **Z1** and choose another procedure.

FM0159401215090X

Fig. 221   Test Z: Intermittents (Part 9 of 23). 1994-95

TEST STEP	RESULT	▶	ACTION TO TAKE
Z50 INTERMITTENT IGNITION PROCEDURE			
PRELIMINARY CHECKS	Yes	▶	GO to **Z51**.
NOTE: This pinpoint test is intended to be used only with Rotunda's Intermittent Ignition Analyzer Part No. (Rotunda 007-00075). If this analyzer is not available, return to Z1 and choose another procedure. Quick Test must be performed and instructions in the EEC-V Pinpoint Test steps completed before starting the intermittent ignition procedure.	No	▶	REPEAT **Z50**.
NOTE: Spark timing adjustments are not possible.			
When making voltage checks, a GROUND or LOW reading means any value within a range of 0 to 1 volt. Also, VPWR or COIL PWR or HIGH readings mean any value that falls within a range of B+ to 2 volts less than B+.			
When making resistance checks, make sure the ignition is in the key off position and the Scan Tool is disconnected from the DLC.			
For ICM Pin-Outs and System and Component Descriptions.			
Equipment Required for this Pinpoint: • Volt-Ohmmeter (Rotunda 105-00050). • Ignition Intermittent Analyzer (Rotunda 007-00075). • Check sensor shield connector. • Be certain the battery is fully charged. • All accessories should be off during diagnosis. • **Is vehicle prepared for equipment set-up?**			

FM0159401215100X

Fig. 221   Test Z: Intermittents (Part 10 of 23). 1994-95

TEST STEP	RESULT	▶	ACTION TO TAKE
Z51 INTERMITTENT IGNITION PROCEDURE			
• Key off. All accessories should be off during testing. • Select proper Overlay and Program Cartridge to match the ignition system to be tested. • Install overlay on tester's front panel. • Insert Program Cartridge into the cartridge slot (marked on the right hand side of the front panel). Make sure the cartridge is fully inserted. • Select and install the EI High Data Rate harness adapter to the DIST tester. • Verify that the Tester switches, CKP SIMULATION and WIGGLE TEST are in the OFF position. • Disconnect the vehicle wiring harness from ICM. — Depress tab on connector clip to remove the ignition harness. — Inspect connectors for dirt, corrosion, moisture, and bent or broken pins. — Clean or repair as required. • Hook Tester to ICM: — Plug male connector of tester into engine harness connector. — Plug female connector of tester into ICM. • Key On Engine Off (KOEO), Press Tester's RESET button. The tester performs Self-Test when it is reset or powered up. During the Self-Test, all LEDs will light and a beep will be heard. • **Did the tester perform Self-Test and is the VPWR LED on?**	Yes No	▶ ▶	GO to **Z53**. GO to tester check in Z52.
Z52 TESTER CHECK			
• Key off. • Disconnect tester from vehicle. • Connect a jumper wire from VPWR jack to vehicle battery POS (+) terminal. • Connect a jumper wire from PWR GND jack to vehicle battery NEG (-) terminal. • If tester performs Self-Test, reconnect tester to vehicles and go to **Z190**. • If tester does not perform Self-Test, refer to tester manual. • If LEDs do not light or a beep is not heard during Self-Test, refer to tester manual. • **Did tester pass Self-Test?**	Yes No	▶ ▶	GO to **Z53**. DIST does not pass Self-Test. REFER to Warranty supplied with DIST.

FM0159401215110X

Fig. 221   Test Z: Intermittents (Part 11 of 23). 1994-95

TEST STEP	RESULT	▶	ACTION TO TAKE
Z53 RECREATE THE FAULT			
• Turn the ignition to Key On Engine Off (KOEO). Observe the Fault Memory and System Status LEDs. • **Are any Fault Memory or System Status LEDs on?**	Yes No	▶ ▶	GO to **Z55**. GO to **Z54**.
Z54 RECREATE THE FAULT			
• With the DIST connected to the vehicle, try to recreate the fault by test driving the vehicle. If the vehicle is a No Start, perform a Key On Engine Cranking (KOEC) test in the service bay. • **Are any Fault Memory or System Status LEDs on?**	Yes No	▶ ▶	GO to **Z55**. Fault NOT related to Ignition System. RETURN to **Z1** and choose another procedure.
Z55 COIL FAULT			
• Are any COIL LEDs on?	Yes No	▶ ▶	GO to **Z80**. GO to **Z56**.
Z56 IGN GND FAULT			
• Is the IGN GND LED on?	Yes No	▶ ▶	GO to **Z200**. GO to **Z57**.
NOTE: If IGN GND or CKP SHD FAULT MEMORY LEDs turn on during any testing operations, GO to **Z210** for CKP SHD FAULT. GO to **Z200** for IGN GND FAULT.			
Z57 CKP SHD FAULT			
• Is the CKP SHD FAULT LED on?	Yes No	▶ ▶	GO to **Z210**. GO to **Z58**.
Z58 ICM FAULT			
• Is the ICM OK LED blinking?	Yes No	▶ ▶	GO to **Z59**. GO to **Z95**.
Z59 CKP BIAS FAULT			
• Is the CKP BIAS LED on?	Yes No	▶ ▶	GO to **Z120**. GO to **Z60**.
Z60 CKP SIGNAL FAULT			
• Is the CKP SIGNAL LED on during cranking?	Yes No	▶ ▶	GO to **Z130**. GO to **Z61**.
Z61 IDM FAULT			
• Is the IDM LED on?	Yes No	▶ ▶	GO to **Z95**. GO to **Z62**.
Z62 IDM TACH FAULT			
• Is the IDM TACH LED on?	Yes No	▶ ▶	GO to **Z95**. GO to **Z63**.

FM0159401215120X

Fig. 221   Test Z: Intermittents (Part 12 of 23). 1994-95

TEST STEP		RESULT	▶	ACTION TO TAKE
Z63	CKP FAULT			
	• Is the CKP LED on?	Yes	▶	GO to Z130.
		No	▶	GO to Z64.
Z64	SPOUT FAULT			
	• Is the SPOUT LED on?	Yes	▶	GO to Z170.
		No	▶	GO to Z65.
Z65	PIP FAULT			
	• Is the PIP LED on?	Yes	▶	GO to Z150.
		No	▶	GO to Z66.
Z66	BASE TIMING FAULT			
	NOTE: If the engine is cold, the engine may stay at base timing for a long period of time. To check if the ignition timing is working, increase the engine RPM slightly and observe the BASE TIMING LED.	Yes	▶	GO to Z170.
		No	▶	REPEAT Step Z67.
	• Is the BASE TIMING LED on continuously?			
Z67	SECONDARY FAULT			
	• Are all COIL LEDs double flashing?	Yes	▶	GO to Intermittent Ignition Analyzer service manual for CKP SIMULATION TEST.
		No	▶	RETURN to Z1 and choose another procedure.
Z80	VBATC CHECK			
	• Key off.	Yes	▶	GO to Z81.
	• Disconnect ignition coil pack(s).	No	▶	SERVICE VBATC open circuit(s) to coil pack(s).
	• Key on, engine off.			
	• Measure the voltage from VBATC pin in the coil pack harness connector COIL jack.			
	• Is the voltage between 10 and 14 volts?			
Z81	CHECK FOR SHORTS			
	• Key off.	Yes	▶	GO to Z86.
	• Measure the resistance from COIL jacks to IGN GND jack.	No	▶	GO to Z82.
	• Measure the resistance from COIL jacks to VBAT jack.			
	• Is each resistance less than 6K ohms?			
Z82	COIL LINE CONTINUITY			
	• Measure the resistance from each COIL JACK to its pin in the coil pack harness connector.	Yes	▶	GO to Z83.
	• Is each resistance less than 5 ohms?	No	▶	SERVICE open in coil circuit.

FM0159401215130X

Fig. 221   Test Z: Intermittents (Part 13 of 23). 1994-95

TEST STEP		RESULT	▶	ACTION TO TAKE
Z83	COIL CHECK			
	• Reconnect coil pack(s).	Yes	▶	GO to Z88.
	• Key on, engine off.	No	▶	GO to Z84.
	• Press the tester reset button.			
	• Are any COIL LEDs on?			
Z84	WIGGLE TEST			
	• Place wiggle test switch to ON.	Yes	▶	PRESS RESET button. CONTINUE to test until intermittent is isolated.
	• Place MODE switch to B.	No	▶	GO to Z85.
	• Press RESET button and wait 5 seconds for initialization.			
	• Wiggle Test.			
	• Are any fault memory LEDs on?			
Z85	WIGGLE TEST			
	• Key off.	Yes	▶	PRESS RESET button. CONTINUE to test until intermittent is isolated.
	• Disconnect coil pack(s).	No	▶	REPLACE ICM.
	• Key on, engine off.			
	• Press RESET button and wait 5 seconds for initialization.			
	• Wiggle Test.			
	• Are any fault memory LEDs on?			
Z86	DISCONNECT ICM · RECHECK FOR SHORTS			
	• Disconnect ICM.	Yes	▶	SERVICE short in coil circuit(s).
	• Measure the resistance from COIL jacks to IGN GND jack.	No	▶	GO to Z87.
	• Measure the resistance from COIL jacks to VBAT jack.			
	• Is any resistance less than 10K ohms?			
Z87	CHECK COIL LINES SHORTED TO EACH OTHER			
	• Measure the resistance from each COIL jack to all other COIL jacks.	Yes	▶	SERVICE short in coil circuit(s).
	• Is any resistance less than 10K ohms?	No	▶	REPLACE ICM.
Z88	KEY OFF			
	• Check the ignition system connectors for corrosion.	Yes	▶	SERVICE corroded connectors as needed.
	• Is there any corrosion?	No	▶	REPLACE ignition coil pack(s).
Z95	IDM TACH FAULT			
	• Was the IDM TACH LED on when the fault was recreated?	Yes	▶	REPLACE ICM.
		No	▶	GO to Z96.

FM0159401215140X

Fig. 221   Test Z: Intermittents (Part 14 of 23). 1994-95

TEST STEP		RESULT	▶	ACTION TO TAKE
Z96	CHECK FOR SHORTS			
	• Key off.	Yes	▶	GO to Z97.
	• Disconnect ICM from the tester.	No	▶	GO to Z102.
	• Measure resistance from IDM jack to VPWR jack.			
	• Measure resistance from IDM jack to PWR GND jack.			
	• Is each resistance greater than 10K ohms?			
Z97	VEHICLE TESTING ON			
	• Is the vehicle being tested an EI - High Data Rate 4 cylinder?	Yes	▶	GO to Z104.
		No	▶	GO to Z98.
Z98	ICM CHECK			
	• Reconnect the ICM.	Yes	▶	GO to Z99.
	• Key on, engine off.	No	▶	REPLACE the ICM.
	• Press the RESET button.			
	• Is the ICM OK LED blinking?			
Z99	WIGGLE TEST			
	• Key off.	Yes	▶	PRESS RESET button. CONTINUE to test until intermittent is isolated.
	• Disconnect ICM from tester.	No	▶	GO to Z100.
	• EI - High Data Rate 4			
	— Connect IDM to IDM TACH jacks using a jumper wire.			
	• Key on, engine off.			
	• Set wiggle test switch to ON position.			
	• EI - High Data Rate 4 & 6			
	— Set MODE switch to B.			
	• EI - High Data Rate 8			
	— Set MODE switch to C.			
	• Press RESET button and wait 5 seconds for initialization.			
	• Wiggle Test.			
	• Are any fault memory LEDs on?			
Z100	WIGGLE TEST			
	• Key off.	Yes	▶	PRESS RESET button. CONTINUE to test until intermittent is isolated.
	• Disconnect PCM from vehicle harness.	No	▶	EI - High Data Rate 4: REMOVE jumper wire between IDM and IDM TACH. GO to Z101.
	NOTE: This erases continuous memory, and sets the P1000 code.			
	• Key on, engine off.			
	• Press RESET button and wait 5 seconds for initialization.			
	• Wiggle Test.			
	• Are any fault memory LEDs on?			
Z101	SELF-TEST CODES			
	• Were any IDM Self-Test codes found during Self-Test?	Yes	▶	GO to Z105.
		No	▶	REPLACE ICM.

FM0159401215150X

Fig. 221   Test Z: Intermittents (Part 15 of 23). 1994-95

TEST STEP		RESULT	▶	ACTION TO TAKE
Z102	DISCONNECT PCM - RETEST FOR SHORTS TO PWR			
	• Disconnect PCM from vehicle harness.	Yes	▶	GO to Z103.
	NOTE: This erases continuous memory, and sets the P1000 code.	No	▶	SERVICE IDM short circuit in harness
	• Measure the resistance from IDM jack to VPWR jack.			
	• Is each resistance greater than 10K ohms?			
Z103	DISCONNECT PCM - RETEST FOR SHORTS TO GND			
	• Measure the resistance from IDM jack to PWR GND jack.	Yes	▶	REPLACE PCM.
	• Is each resistance greater than 10K ohms?	No	▶	SERVICE IDM short circuit in harness.
Z104	CHECK IDM TACH FOR SHORTS			
	• Measure the resistance from IDM TACH to PWR GND jacks.	Yes	▶	GO to Z98.
	• Measure the resistance from IDM TACH to VPWR jacks.	No	▶	SERVICE tachometer short circuit in harness.
	• Is each resistance greater than 10K ohms?			
Z105	IDM PCM CHECK			
	• Key off.	Yes	▶	REPLACE PCM.
	• Measure the resistance from IDM jack to Pin 4 of PCM breakout box.	No	▶	SERVICE open circuit in harness between ICM and PCM.
	• Is resistance less than 5 ohms?			
Z120	CHECK CKP BIAS			
	• Key off.	Yes	▶	GO to Z122.
	• Disconnect CKP sensor from vehicle harness.	No	▶	GO to Z121.
	• Key on, engine off.			
	• Is the CKP BIAS LED on?			
Z121	CHECK CKP+ FOR SHORTS			
	• Key off.	Yes	▶	REPLACE ICM.
	• Disconnect ICM.	No	▶	SERVICE CKP+ short circuit(s) in harness.
	• Measure the resistance from CKP+ jack to VPWR jack.			
	• Measure the resistance from CKP+ jack to PWR GND jack.			
	• Is each resistance greater than 10K ohms?			
Z122	CHECK CKP- FOR SHORTS			
	• Key off.	Yes	▶	REPLACE shorted CKP sensor.
	• Measure the resistance from CKP- jack to PWR GND jack.	No	▶	GO to Z123.
	• Measure the resistance from CKP- jack to VPWR jack.			
	• Is each resistance greater than 10K ohms?			

FM0159401215160X

Fig. 221   Test Z: Intermittents (Part 16 of 23). 1994-95

TEST STEP	RESULT	▶	ACTION TO TAKE
Z123 DISCONNECT ICM - RETEST FOR SHORTS			
• Disconnect ICM from tester. • Measure the resistance from CKP- jack to PWR GND jack. • Measure the resistance from CKP- jack to VPWR jack. • **Is each resistance greater than 10K ohms?**	Yes No	▶ ▶	REPLACE ICM. SERVICE CKP- short circuit(s) in harness.
Z130 CKP SIGNAL CHECK			
• Crank or start the engine. • Observe the CKP SIGNAL LED • **Is the LED on during engine cranking or running?**	Yes No	▶ ▶	GO to **Z131**. GO to **Z132**.
Z131 WIGGLE TEST			
• Key on, engine off. • Place WIGGLE TEST switch to ON position. • Set mode switch to B. • Press RESET button and wait 5 seconds for initialization. • Wiggle Test. • **Are any fault memory LEDs on?**	Yes No	▶ ▶	PRESS RESET button. CONTINUE to test until intermittent is isolated. Intermittent not recreated during testing. RETURN to **Z1** and choose another procedure.
Z132 CHECK CKP+ HARNESS CONTINUITY			
• Key off. • Disconnect CKP sensor. • Measure the resistance from CKP+ jack to CKP+ pin in the harness connectors. • **Is resistance less than 5 ohms?**	Yes No	▶ ▶	GO to **Z133**. SERVICE CKP+ open circuit(s) in harness.
Z133 CHECK CKP - HARNESS CONTINUITY			
• Measure the resistance from CKP- jack to CKP- pin in the harness connectors. • **Is resistance less than 5 ohms?**	Yes No	▶ ▶	GO to **Z134**. SERVICE CKP- open circuit(s) in harness.
Z134 CHECK CKP SIGNAL LINES SHORTED TOGETHER			
• Measure the resistance from CKP+ jack to CKP- jack. • **Is resistance greater than 10K ohms?**	Yes No	▶ ▶	GO to **Z135**. GO to **Z136**.
Z135 SENSOR DAMAGE CHECK			
• Inspect the CKP sensor and the DATA WHEEL for proper alignment, correct air gap and physical damage. • **Is the CKP sensor or trigger wheel damaged, i.e. loose or misaligned?**	Yes No	▶ ▶	REPLACE CKP sensor. SERVICE as needed.

FM0159401215170X

Fig. 221   Test Z: Intermittents (Part 17 of 23). 1994-95

TEST STEP	RESULT	▶	ACTION TO TAKE
Z136 DISCONNECT ICM - RECHECK FOR SHORTED CKP LINES			
• Disconnect ICM from tester. • Measure the resistance from CKP+ jack to CKP- jack. • **Is resistance greater than 10K ohms?**	Yes No	▶ ▶	REPLACE ICM. CKP+ and CKP- are shorted together. SERVICE as needed.
Z150 CAPTURE FAULT			
• Crank, start engine. • Recreate vehicle fault. • **Is the PIP LED on or blinking?**	Blinking On	▶ ▶	GO to **Z151**. GO to **Z157**.
Z151 CHECK FOR SHORTS			
• Key off. • Disconnect ICM from tester. • Measure the resistance from PIP jack to PWR GND jack. • Measure the resistance from PIP jack to VPWR jack. • **Is each resistance greater than 10K ohms?**	Yes No	▶ ▶	GO to **Z152**. GO to **Z158**.
Z152 CHECK PIP			
• Key on, engine off. • Measure voltage from PIP jack to PWR GND jack. • **Is the voltage greater than 8 volts?**	Yes No	▶ ▶	SERVICE PIP circuit shorted to VPWR. GO to **Z153**.
Z153 CHECK ICM PIP CIRCUIT			
• Key off. • Reconnect ICM to tester. • Key on, engine off. • Measure the voltage from PIP jack to PWR GND jack. • **Is the voltage less than 10.5?**	Yes No	▶ ▶	REPLACE ICM. GO to **Z154**.
Z154 WIGGLE TEST			
• Place wiggle test switch to ON position. • Set MODE switch to B. • Press RESET button and wait 5 seconds for initialization. • Wiggle Test. • **Are any fault memory LEDs on?**	Yes No	▶ ▶	PRESS RESET button. CONTINUE to test until intermittent is isolated. GO to **Z155**.
Z155 WIGGLE TEST			
• Key off. • Disconnect ICM from tester. • Key on, engine off. • Place wiggle test switch to ON. • Place the MODE switch to ON. • Press RESET button and wait 5 seconds for initialization. • Wiggle Test. • **Are any fault memory LEDs on?**	Yes No	▶ ▶	PRESS RESET button. CONTINUE to test until intermittent is isolated. GO to **Z156**.

FM0159401215180X

Fig. 221   Test Z: Intermittents (Part 18 of 23). 1994-95

TEST STEP	RESULT	▶	ACTION TO TAKE
Z156 WIGGLE TEST			
• Key off. • Place wiggle test switch to ON. • Place the MODE switch to B. • Press RESET button and wait 5 seconds for initialization. • Wiggle Test. • **Are any fault memory LEDs on?**	Yes No	▶ ▶	PRESS RESET button. CONTINUE to test until intermittent is isolated. REPLACE ICM.
Z157 WIGGLE TEST			
• Key on, engine off. • Place wiggle test switch to ON position. • Set the MODE switch to B. • Press RESET button and wait 5 seconds for initialization. • Wiggle Test. • **Are any fault memory LEDs on?**	Yes No	▶ ▶	PRESS RESET button. CONTINUE to test until intermittent is isolated. REPLACE ICM.
Z158 DISCONNECT PCM AND RECHECK FOR SHORTS			
• Disconnect the PCM from the vehicle harness. NOTE: This erases continuous memory and sets the P1000 DTC. • Measure the resistance from PIP jack to PWR GND jack. • Measure the resistance from PIP jack to VPWR jack. • **Is each resistance greater than 10K ohms?**	Yes No	▶ ▶	SERVICE short in PIP circuit harness. PCM system failure. REFER to the vehicle Service Manual for engine control testing.
Z170 START AND RUN VEHICLE			
• Does the vehicle start and run?	Yes No	▶ ▶	GO to **Z171**. GO to **Z178**.
Z171 BASE TIMING CHECK			
• Start and run engine. • Observe the BASE TIMING LED. • **Is the BASE TIMING LED on continuously without any fault memory LEDs on?**	Yes No	▶ ▶	REPLACE ICM. GO to **Z172**.
Z172 SPOUT STATUS			
• Check the SPOUT LED. • **Is the SPOUT LED on or blinking?**	Blinking On	▶ ▶	GO to **Z173**. GO to **Z180**.

FM0159401215190X

Fig. 221   Test Z: Intermittents (Part 19 of 23). 1994-95

TEST STEP	RESULT	▶	ACTION TO TAKE
Z173 CHECK FOR SHORTS			
• Key off. • Disconnect PCM from vehicle harness. NOTE: This erases continuous memory, and sets the P1000 code. • Measure the resistance from SPOUT jack to PWR GND jack. • Measure the resistance from SPOUT jack to VPWR jack. • **Is each resistance greater than 10K ohms?**	Yes No	▶ ▶	GO to **Z174**. GO to **Z183**.
Z174 CHECK FOR SHORTS			
• Reconnect PCM to vehicle harness. • Disconnect ICM. • Measure the resistance from SPOUT jack to PWR GND jack. • **Is resistance greater than 10K ohms?**	Yes No	▶ ▶	GO to **Z175**. REPLACE the PCM.
Z175 CHECK FOR SHORTS			
• Measure the resistance from SPOUT jack to VPWR jack. • **Is resistance greater than 10K ohms?**	Yes No	▶ ▶	GO to **Z176**. REPLACE the PCM.
Z176 WIGGLE TEST			
• Key on, engine off. • Place wiggle test switch in the ON position. • Set the MODE switch to B. • Press RESET button and wait 5 seconds for initialization. • Wiggle Test. • **Are any fault memory LEDs on?**	Yes No	▶ ▶	PRESS RESET button. CONTINUE to test until intermittent is isolated. GO to **Z177**.
Z177 WIGGLE TEST			
• Wiggle test switch to ON position. • Set the MODE switch to A. • Press RESET button and wait 5 seconds for initialization. • Wiggle Test. • **Are any fault memory LEDs on?**	Yes No	▶ ▶	PRESS RESET button. CONTINUE to test until intermittent is isolated. Intermittent not recreated during testing. RETURN to **Z1** and choose another procedure.
Z178 CHECK PIP TO PCM HARNESS CONTINUITY			
• Key off. • Disconnect the PCM from the vehicle harness. NOTE: This erases continuous memory, and sets the P1000 code. • Measure the resistance from PIP jack to Pin 56 at the PCM breakout box. • **Is resistance less than 5 ohms?**	Yes No	▶ ▶	GO to **Z179**. SERVICE open in PIP circuit harness.

FM0159401215200X

Fig. 221   Test Z: Intermittents (Part 20 of 23). 1994-95

ELECTRONIC ENGINE CONTROL SYSTEM (EEC-V)

TEST STEP	RESULT	▶	ACTION TO TAKE
Z179 CHECK IGN GND TO PCM HARNESS CONTINUITY • Measure the resistance from IGN GND jack to Pin 16 at the PCM breakout box. • **Is resistance less 5 ohms?**	Yes No	▶ ▶	REPLACE the PCM. SERVICE open in IGN GND circuit harness.
Z180 CHECK SPOUT TO PCM HARNESS CONTINUITY • Key off. • Disconnect PCM from vehicle harness. NOTE: This erases continuous memory, and **sets the P1000 code.** • Measure the resistance from SPOUT jack to Pin 36 at the PCM breakout box. • **Is resistance less than 5 ohms?**	Yes No	▶ ▶	GO to **Z181** SERVICE open SPOUT circuit in harness between PCM and ICM.
Z181 WIGGLE TEST • Reconnect PCM. • Disconnect ICM. • Key on, engine off. • Place the wiggle test switch to the ON position. • Set the MODE switch to B. • Press RESET button and wait 5 seconds for initialization. • Wiggle Test. • **Are any fault memory LEDs on?**	Yes No	▶ ▶	PRESS RESET button. CONTINUE to test until intermittent is isolated. GO to **Z182**
Z182 WIGGLE TEST • Set MODE switch to A. • Press the tester RESET button and wait 5 seconds for initialization. • Wiggle Test. • **Are any fault memory LEDs on?**	Yes No	▶ ▶	PRESS RESET button. CONTINUE to test until intermittent is isolated. REPLACE PCM.
Z183 DISCONNECT ICM AND RECHECK FOR SHORTS • Disconnect ICM from the tester. • Measure the resistance from SPOUT jack to PWR GND jack. • Measure the resistance from SPOUT jack to VPWR jack. • **Is each resistance greater than 10K ohms?**	Yes No	▶ ▶	REPLACE ICM. SERVICE short in SPOUT circuit harness.
Z190 CHECK FOR VPWR • Key on, engine off. • Measure the voltage from VPWR jack to the battery NEG(-) terminal. • **Is the reading greater than 6 volts?**	Yes No	▶ ▶	GO to **Z191** SERVICE open in VPWR circuit harness to ICM.

FM0159401215210X

Fig. 221   Test Z: Intermittents (Part 21 of 23). 1994-95

TEST STEP	RESULT	▶	ACTION TO TAKE
Z191 CHECK PWR GND HARNESS • Key off. • Measure the resistance from PWR GND jack to the battery's NEG(-) terminal. • **Is resistance less than 5 ohms?**	Yes No	▶ ▶	GO to **Z192** SERVICE open in PWR GND circuit harness to ICM.
Z192 WIGGLE TEST • Connect a jumper wire from PWR GND jack to the battery NEG(-) terminal. • Wiggle Test. • **Did the tester reset?**	Yes No	▶ ▶	SERVICE open in VPWR circuit to ICM harness. SERVICE open in PWR GND circuit to ICM harness.
Z200 CHECK IGN GND • Key on, engine off. • Measure the voltage from PWR GND jack to IGN GND jack. • **Is the voltage reading between 0.5 and -0.5 volts?**	Yes No	▶ ▶	GO to **Z201** GO to **Z202**.
Z201 WIGGLE TEST • Place the wiggle test switch to the ON position. • Set the MODE switch to B. • Press RESET button and wait 5 seconds for initialization. • Wiggle Test. • **Are any fault memory LEDs on?**	Yes No	▶ ▶	PRESS RESET button. CONTINUE to test until intermittent is isolated. Intermittent not recreated during testing. RETURN to **Z1** and choose another procedure.
Z202 CHECK FOR SHORTS • Key off. • Disconnect the PCM from vehicle's harness. NOTE: This erases continuous memory, and sets the P1000 code. • Measure the resistance from IGN GND jack to VPWR jack. • **Is resistance greater than 10K ohms?**	Yes No	▶ ▶	REPLACE ICM. SERVICE short in IGN GND circuit harness.
Z210 CHECK FOR SHORTS • Key off. • Measure the resistance from CKP SHD jack to VPWR jack. • **Is resistance greater than 10K ohms?**	Yes No	▶ ▶	GO to **Z211** GO to **Z212**

FM0159401215220X

Fig. 221   Test Z: Intermittents (Part 22 of 23). 1994-95

TEST STEP	RESULT	▶	ACTION TO TAKE
Z211 WIGGLE TEST • Key on, engine off. • Place wiggle test switch to the ON position. • Set the MODE switch to B. • Press RESET button and wait 5 seconds for initialization. • Wiggle Test. • **Are any fault memory LEDs on?**	Yes No	▶ ▶	PRESS RESET button. CONTINUE to test until intermittent is isolated. REPLACE ICM.
Z212 CHECK FOR SHORTS • Disconnect ICM from the tester. • Measure the resistance from CKP SHD jack to VPWR jack. • **Is resistance greater than 10K ohms?**	Yes No	▶ ▶	REPLACE ICM. SERVICE short in CKP SHD circuit harness.

FM0159401215230X

Fig. 221   Test Z: Intermittents (Part 23 of 23). 1994-95

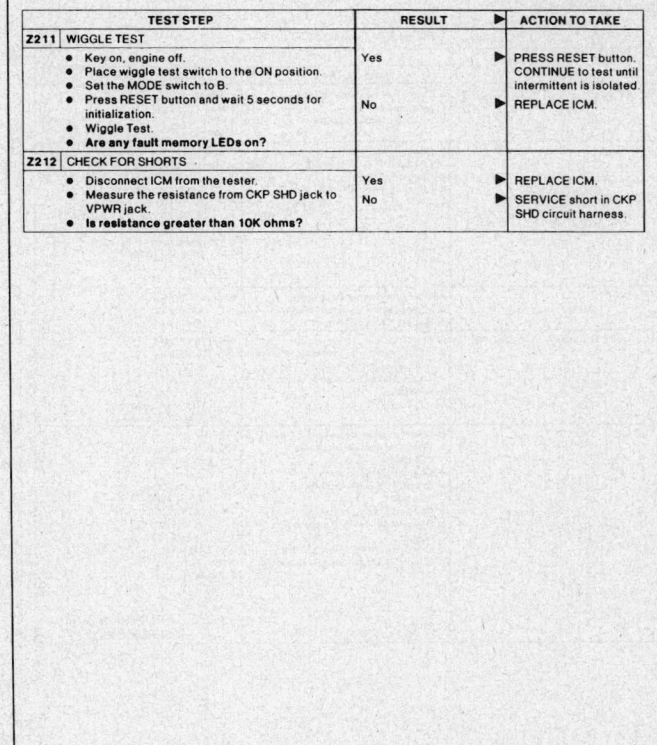

FM0159401216010X

Fig. 222   Pinpoint test, intermittent symptom index (Part 1 of 15). 1994-95

Driveability

EEC Related Shift Symptoms	Chart Number
A/T Upshift Concern	10
A/T Downshift Concern	10
Engagement Concern	10
Hard or Soft Shifts	11
Erratic, Hunting Shifts	12
No Overdrive	13

Fig. 222   Pinpoint test, intermittent symptom index (Part 2 of 15). 1994-95

Starting Concerns

NO START/NORMAL CRANK

System	Checks	
	Visual/Mechanical	EEC-V PIDS/Components/CKTS
Fuel	• Check fuel pump and Inertia Fuel Shutoff (IFS) switch. • Check for fuel contamination/quality. • Check fuel filter. • Check fuel level/gauge operation. • Check for restricted fuel lines. • Check for correct fuel pressure.	• Fuel Pump System: FP PID/FUELB1/FUELB2 FPM PID/ SFT11/12/21/22/1/2 FP relay LFT 1 & 2/O2S 11, 12, 21 & 22 • Fuel Injection: INJs 1, 2 (MFI) INJs 1, 2, ... (SFI) FPW 1, 2, PID
Ignition	• Inspect spark plugs and plug wires. • Check ignition switch. • Check ignition coil for voltage. • Inspect ICM for damage. • Check for presence of anti-theft devices.	• Ignition System: SPARK PID MISF PID IGN GND circuit IGN coils
Power and Grounds	• Check for low battery voltage. • Check starter and starter circuit for voltage. • Inspect electrical connections, wires, and harnesses.	• EEC-V power: VREF PID VPWR PID EEC-V power relay • EEC-V grounds: SIG RTN circuit PWR GND circuit CSE GND circuit
Air/Vacuum	• Check vacuum lines for leaks, blockage or wear. • Check air intake system.	• TP PID • MAF PID • IAC PID
Other	• Check engine coolant level. • Check thermostat for proper operation. • Check EGR valve stuck open. • Check for moisture entry into PCM. • Check camshaft timing and cylinder compression. • Check for restricted exhaust.	• ECT PID • DPFE PID NOTE: BOLD PIDS EQUAL GENERIC PIDS

Fig. 222   Pinpoint test, intermittent symptom chart 1 (Part 3 of 15). 1994-95

Starting Concerns

STALL AFTER START HARD START/LONG CRANK

System	Checks	
	Visual/Mechanical	EEC-V PIDS/Components/CKTS
Ignition	• Inspect spark plugs and plug wires. • Check ignition switch. • Check ignition coil for voltage. • Inspect ICM for damage. • Check for presence of anti-theft devices.	• Ignition System: MISF PID SPARK PID IGN GND circuit
Fuel	• Check fuel pump and Inertia Fuel Shutoff (IFS) switch. • Check for fuel contamination/quality. • Check fuel filter. • Check fuel level/gauge operation. • Check for restricted fuel lines. • Check for correct fuel pressure.	• Fuel Pump System: FP PID/FUELB1/FUELB2 FPM PID/ SFT11/12/21/22/1/2 FP relay LFT 1 & 2/O2S 11, 12, 21 & 22 • Fuel Injection: INJs 1, 2 (MFI) INJs 1, 2, ... (SFI) FPW 1, 2 PID
Power and Grounds	• Check for low battery voltage. • Inspect electrical connections, wires, and harnesses. • Check starter and starter circuit for voltage.	• EEC-V Power: VREF PID VPWR PID • EEC-V Grounds: SIG RTN circuit PWR GND circuit CSE GND circuit
Air/Vacuum	• Check vacuum lines for leaks, blockage or wear. • Check air intake system.	• TP PID • MAF PID • IAC PID • IAT PID
Other	• Check engine coolant level. • Check thermostat for proper operation. • Check EGR valve stuck open. • Check for moisture entry in PCM. • Check throttle body for binding. • Check for proper idle speed control. • Check camshaft timing and cylinder compression. • Check for restricted exhaust. • Check IAC Solenoid connection.	• ECT PID • EPC PID • EGR Systems DPFE PID EVR PID • A/C Systems ACCS PID ACPSW PID WAC PID WACA PID • IAC PID NOTE: BOLD PIDS EQUAL GENERIC PIDS

Fig. 222   Pinpoint test, intermittent symptom chart 2 (Part 4 of 15). 1994-95

Unique Idle Concerns

SLOW RTN/SLOW/FAST IDLE

System	Checks	
	Visual/Mechanical	EEC-V PIDS/Components/CKTS
Air/Vacuum	• Check vacuum lines for leaks, blockage or wear. • Check air intake system.	• TP PID • MAF PID • IAC PID • IAT PID
Fuel	• Check for correct fuel pressure. • Check for fuel contamination/quality. • Check fuel filter. • Check for restricted fuel lines.	• HO2S(s) PID • Fuel Pump System: FPA PID/FUELB1/FUELB2 FPM PID/ SFT11/12/21/22/1/2 FP relay LFT 1 & 2/O2S 11, 12, 21 & 22 • Fuel Injection: INJs 1, 2 (MFI) INJs 1, 2, ... (SFI) FPW 1, 2 PID
Ignition	• Check for correct base timing. • Inspect spark plugs and plug wires. • Inspect ICM for damage.	• Ignition System: MISF PID SPARK PID
Power and Grounds	• Check for low battery voltage. • Inspect electrical connections, wires, and harnesses. • Check starter and starter circuit for voltage.	• EEC-V Power: VREF PID VPWR PID • EEC-V Grounds: SIG RTN circuit PWR GND circuit CSE GND circuit
Other	• Check engine coolant and oil levels. • Check thermostat for proper operation. • Check EGR valve stuck open. • Check PCV valve for correct operation. • Check for restricted exhaust. • Check for sticking or binding throttle linkage. • Check throttle body for binding. • Check for proper idle speed control.	• ECT PID • EGR Systems: DPFE PID EVR PID • A/C Systems: ACCS PID ACPSW PID WAC PID WACA PID • LFC PID • HFC PID • FANM PID • OCT PID NOTE: BOLD PIDS EQUAL GENERIC PIDS

Fig. 222   Pinpoint test, intermittent symptom chart 3 (Part 5 of 15). 1994-95

Unique Idle Concerns

ROLLING IDLE

System	Checks	
	Visual/Mechanical	EEC-V PIDS/Components/CKTS
Air/Vacuum	• Check vacuum lines for leaks, blockage or wear. • Check air intake system.	• TP PID • MAF PID • IAC PID • IAT PID

Fuel	• Check for correct fuel pressure.
	• Check for fuel contamination/quality.
	• Check fuel filter.
	• Check for restricted fuel lines.
		• HO2S(s) PID
		• Fuel Pump System:
		  FP PID/FUELB1/FUELB2
		  FPM PID/
		  SFT11/12/21/22/1/2
		  FP relay LFT 1 & 2/O2S 11, 12, 21 & 22
		• Fuel Injection:
		  INJs 1, 2 (MFI)
		  INJs 1, 2...(SFI)
		  FPW 1, 2 PID

Ignition	• Check for correct base timing.
	• Inspect spark plugs and plug wires.
	• Inspect ICM for damage.
		• Ignition System:
		  MISF PID
		  SPARK PID
		  IGNITION COILS

Power and Grounds	• Check for low battery voltage.
	• Inspect electrical connections, wires, and harnesses.
		• EEC-V Power:
		  VREF PID
		  VPWR PID
		• EEC-V Grounds:
		  SIG RTN/CASE GND
		• CIRCUIT

Other	• Check engine coolant and oil levels.
	• Check thermostat for proper operation.
	• Check EGR valve stuck open.
	• Check PCV valve for correct operation.
	• Check for restricted exhaust.
	• Check for worn camshaft lobes.
	• Check camshaft timing and cylinder compression.
		• ECT PID
		• EGR Systems:
		  DPFE PID
		  EVR PID
		• A/C Systems:
		  ACCS PID
		  ACPSW PID
		  WAC PID
		  WACA PID
		• LFC PID
		• HFC PID
		• FANM PID
		
		NOTE: **BOLD PIDS EQUAL GENERIC PIDS**

FM0159401216060X

Fig. 222   Pinpoint test, intermittent symptom chart 4 (Part 6 of 15). 1994-95

Surge

ACCELERATION/CRUISE

System	Checks	
	Visual/Mechanical	EEC-V PIDS/Components/CKTS
Air/Vacuum	• Check vacuum lines for leaks, blockage or wear. • Check air intake system.	• TP PID • MAF PID • IAC PID • IAT PID

Fuel	• Check for correct fuel pressure.
	• Check for fuel contamination/quality.
	• Check for restricted fuel lines.
	• Check fuel filter.
		• HO2S(s) PID
		• Fuel Pump System:
		  FP PID/FUELB1/FUELB2
		  FPM PID
		  SFT11/12/21/22/1/2
		  FP relay LFT 1 & 2/O2S 11, 12, 21 & 22
		• Fuel Injection:
		  INJs 1, 2 (MFI)
		  INJs 1, 2...(SFI)
		  FPW 1, 2 PID

Ignition	• Check for correct base timing. • Inspect spark plugs and plug wires. • Inspect ICM for damage.	• Ignition System: **MISF PID**

Other	• Check EGR valve sticking.
	• Check PCV valve for correct operation.
	• Check for restricted exhaust.
	• Check for low A/C refrigerant charge.
	• Inspect engine and transmission electrical wiring and connections.
		• EGR Systems:
		  DPFE PID
		  EVR PID
		• A/C Systems:
		  ACCS PID
		  ACPSW PID
		  WAC PID
		• Transmission Systems:
		  TCC PID
		  GEAR/PNP/MLP PID
		• LFC PID
		• HFC PID
		• FANM PID
		
		NOTE: **BOLD PIDS EQUAL GENERIC PIDS**

FM0159401216070X

Fig. 222   Pinpoint test, intermittent symptom chart 5 (Part 7 of 15). 1994-95

Lack/Loss of Power

ACCELERATION/CRUISE

System	Checks	
	Visual/Mechanical	EEC-V PIDS/Components/CKTS
Air/Vacuum	• Check vacuum lines for leaks, blockage or wear. • Check air intake system.	• TP PID • **MAF PID** • IAC PID • IAT PID

Fuel	• Check for correct fuel pressure.
	• Check for fuel contamination/quality.
	• Check fuel filter.
	• Check for restricted fuel lines.
		• HO2S(S) PID
		• Fuel Pump System:
		  FP PID/FUELB1/FUELB2
		  FPM PID/
		  SFT11/12/21/22/1/2
		  FP relay LFT 1 & 2/O2S 11, 12, 21 & 22
		• Fuel Injection:
		  INJs 1, 2 (MFI)
		  INJs 1, 2...(SFI)
		  FPW 1, 2 PID

Ignition	• Check for correct base timing.
	• Inspect spark plugs and plug wires.
	• Inspect ICM for damage.
		• Ignition System:
		  MISF PIP
		  SPARK PID

Other	• Check EGR valve sticking.
	• Check PCV valve for correct operation.
	• Check for restricted exhaust.
	• Check for low A/C refrigerant charge.
	• Inspect engine and transmission electrical wiring and connections.
		• EGR Systems:
		  DPFE PID
		  EVR PID
		• A/C Systems:
		  ACCS PID
		  ACPSW PID
		  WAC PID
		  WACA PID
		• Transmission Systems:
		  TCC PID
		  GEAR/PNP/MLP PID
		
		NOTE: **BOLD PIDS EQUAL GENERIC PIDS**

FM0159401216080X

Fig. 222   Pinpoint test, intermittent symptom chart 6 (Part 8 of 15). 1994-95

Spark Knock/Cooling System

ACCELERATION/CRUISE

System	Checks	
	Visual/Mechanical	EEC-V PIDS/Components/CKTS
Air/Vacuum	• Check vacuum lines for leaks, blockage or wear. • Check air intake system. • Check for exhaust leak.	• TP PID • **MAF PID** • IAC PID • IAT PID

Ignition	• Check for correct base timing.
	• Inspect spark plugs and plug wires.
	• Inspect ICM for damage.
		• Ignition System:
		  MISF PIP
		  CKP Sensor
		  IGN COILS

Fuel	• Check for correct fuel pressure.
	• Check for fuel contamination/quality.
	• Check fuel filter.
	• Check for restricted fuel lines.
		• Fuel Pump System:
		  FP PID/FUELB1/FUELB2
		  FPM PID
		  SFT11/12/21/22/1/2
		  FP relay LFT 1 & 2/O2S 11, 12, 21 & 22
		• Fuel Injection:
		  INJs 1, 2 (MFI)
		  INJs 1, 2...(SFI)
		  FPW 1, 2 PID

Other	• Check EGR valve sticking.
	• Check PCV valve for correct operation.
	• Check engine coolant level.
	• Check thermostat operation.
	• Inspect electrical connections, wires and harnesses.
	• Check for restricted exhaust.
	• Check for partially binding brakes.
	• Check camshaft timing and cylinder compression.
	• Check the transmission for proper shifting sequence.
	• Check for cooling system restrictions, bent, kinked lines.
	• Check transmission cooling system for restrictions.
		• EGR Systems:
		  DPFE PID
		  EVR PID
		• A/C Systems:
		  ACCS PID
		  ACPSW PID
		  WAC PID
		  WACA PID
		• LFC PID
		• HFC PID
		• FANM PID
		• ECT PID
		• Transmission System:
		  TCC PID
		  EPC PID
		  GEAR/PNP/MLP PID
		
		NOTE: **BOLD PIDS EQUAL GENERIC PIDS**

FM0159401216090X

Fig. 222   Pinpoint test, intermittent symptom chart 7 (Part 9 of 15). 1994-95

Stalls/Quits/MIL/Poor Fuel Economy/Emissions Compliance

IDLE/ACCELERATION/CRUISE/DECELERATION

System	Checks	
	Visual/Mechanical	EEC-V PIDS/Components/CKTS
Air/Vacuum	• Check vacuum lines for leaks, blockage or wear. • Check air intake system.	• **TP** PID • **MAF** PID • IAC PID

Ignition	• Inspect spark plugs and plug wires.
	• Check ignition switch.
	• Check ignition coil for voltage.
	• Inspect ICM for damage.
	• Check for presence of anti-theft devices.
		• Ignition System:
		  MISF PID
		  IGN GND circuit
		  CKP sensor
		  IGN coils

Fuel	• Check for correct fuel pressure.
	• Check fuel pump and Inertia Fuel Shutoff (IFS) switch.
	• Check for fuel contamination/quality.
	• Check fuel filter.
	• Check for fuel level/gauge operation.
	• Check for restricted fuel lines.
		• Fuel Pump System:
		  FP PID/**FUELB1**/**FUELB2**
		  FPM PID/**SFT**11/12/21/22
		  FP relay LFT 1 & 2/O2S 11, 12, 21 & 22
		• Fuel Injection:
		  INJs 1, 2 (MFI)
		  INJs 1, 2.. (SFI)
		  FPW 1, 2 PID

Power and Grounds	• Check for low battery voltage.
	• Inspect electrical connections, wires, and harnesses.
		• EEC-V Power:
		  VREF PID
		  VPWR PID
		  EEC-V power relay
		• EEC-V Grounds:
		  SIG RTN circuit
		  PWR GND circuit
		  CSE GND circuit

Other	• Check engine coolant level.
	• Check thermostat for proper operation.
	• Check EGR valve stuck open.
	• Check for moisture entry in PCM.
	• Check throttle body for binding.
	• Check for proper idle speed control.
	• Check camshaft timing and cylinder compression.
	• Check for restricted exhaust.
	• Check torque converter operation.
		• **ECT** PID
		• **EPC** PID
		• EGR Systems:
		  DPFE PID
		  EVR PID
		• A/C Systems:
		  ACCS PID
		  ACPSW PID
		  WAC PID
		  WACA PID
		• Transmission Systems
		  TCC PID
		  PNP/GEAR PID
		  SS1
		  SS2
		  EPC
		  OSS
		• IAC PID
		
		NOTE: **BOLD PIDS EQUAL GENERIC PIDS**

FM0159401216100X

Fig. 222 Pinpoint test, intermittent symptom chart 8 (Part 10 of 15). 1994-95

Runs Rough/Misses/Buck/Jerk/Surge/Backfires/Hesitation

IDLE/ACCELERATION/CRUISE/DECELERATION

System	Checks	
	Visual/Mechanical	EEC-V PIDS/Components/CKTS
Air/Vacuum	• Check vacuum lines for leaks, blockage or wear. • Check air intake system.	• **TP** PID • **MAF** PID • IAC PID • IAT PID

Fuel	• Check for correct fuel pressure.
	• Check for fuel contamination/quality.
	• Check fuel filter.
	• Check for restricted fuel lines.
		• **HO2S(s)** PID
		• Fuel Pump System:
		  FP PID/**FUELB1**/**FUELB2**
		  FPM PID/**SFT**11/12/21/22
		  FP relay LFT 1 & 2/O2S 11, 12, 21 & 22
		• Fuel Injection:
		  INJs 1, 2 (MFI)
		  INJs 1, 2.. (SFI)
		  FPW 1, 2 PID

Ignition	• Check for correct base timing.
	• Inspect spark plugs and plug wires.
	• Inspect ICM for damage.
		• Ignition System:
		  MISF PID
		  CKP sensor
		  IGN coils
		  SPARK PID

Power and Grounds	• Check for generator/regulator noise interference.
	• Inspect electrical connections, wires, and harnesses.
		• EEC-V Power:
		  VREF PID
		• EEC-V Grounds:
		  SIG RTN

Other	• Check engine coolant level.
	• Check thermostat operation.
	• Check EGR valve sticking.
	• Check PCV valve for correct operation.
	• Check for restricted exhaust.
	• Check for partially binding brakes.
	• Check camshaft timing and cylinder compression.
	• Check for weak or broken valve springs.
		• EGR Systems:
		  DPFE PID
		  EVR PID
		• Transmission Systems
		  TCC PID
		  EPC PID
		  LFC PID
		  HFC PID
		  FANM PID
		• **ECT** PID
		
		NOTE: **BOLD PIDS EQUAL GENERIC PIDS**

FM0159401216110X

Fig. 222 Pinpoint test, intermittent symptom chart 9 (Part 11 of 15). 1994-95

A/T Upshift - Downshift/Engagement Concerns

System	Checks	
	Visual/Mechanical	EEC-V PIDS/Components/CKTS

AODE, 4R70W Transmission	• Check transmission fluid level.
	• Check transmission fluid for contamination.
	• Check for transmission fluid leaks.
	• Check transmission fluid pressures.
	• Check transmission electrical connections for corrosion, bent pins, or damage.
		• Transmission components
		  SS1 solenoid
		  SS2 solenoid
		  EPC PID
		  TFT PID
		  OSS PID
		  TCS PID
		  MLP/PNP/GEAR PID
		  TCIL CKT

Checks for All Transmissions	• Inspect associated electrical connections, wires, and harnesses. • Check shift linkage and adjustment. • Check tire size and axle ratio. • Check for driveline modifications or aftermarket accessories. • Check internal transmission components.	• **TP** PID • **ECT** PID • **MAF** PID • **VSS/TSS** PID • **RPM** PID • IAT PID • **MISF** PID NOTE: **BOLD PIDS EQUAL GENERIC PIDS**

FM0159401216120X

Fig. 222 Pinpoint test, intermittent symptom chart 10 (Part 12 of 15). 1994-95

Hard/Soft Transmission Shift

System	Checks	
	Visual/Mechanical	EEC-V PIDS/Components/CKTS

AODE, 4R70W Transmission	• Check transmission fluid level.
	• Check transmission fluid for contamination.
	• Check for transmission fluid leaks.
	• Check transmission fluid pressures.
		• Transmission components
		  EPC PID
		  TFT PID
		  OSS PID
		  MLP/PNP/GEAR PID

Checks for All Transmissions	• Inspect associated electrical connections, wires, and harnesses. • Check for damaged U-joints. • Check for driveline modifications or aftermarket accessories. • Check internal transmission components.	• **TP** PID • **MAF** PID • **RPM** PID NOTE: **BOLD PIDS EQUAL GENERIC PIDS**

FM0159401216130X

Fig. 222 Pinpoint test, intermittent symptom chart 11 (Part 13 of 15). 1994-95

Erratic, Hunting Shifts

System	Checks	
	Visual/Mechanical	EEC-V PIDS/Components/CKTS
AODE, 4R70W Transmission	• Check transmission fluid level. • Check transmission fluid for contamination. • Check for transmission fluid leaks. • Check transmission fluid pressures. • Check transmission electrical connections for corrosion, bent pins, or damage.	• Transmission components SS1 solenoid SS2 solenoid TCC PID MLP/PNP/GEAR PID OSS PID TCS PID
Checks for All Transmissions	• Inspect ICM for damage. • Inspect associated electrical connections, wires, and harnesses. • Check shift linkage and adjustment. • Check for driveline modifications or aftermarket accessories. • Check internal transmission components.	• **TP** PID • **MAF** PID • **VSS** • **RPM** PID NOTE: **BOLD PIDS EQUAL GENERIC PIDS**

FM0159401216140X

Fig. 222   Pinpoint test, intermittent symptom chart 12 (Part 14 of 15). 1994-95

No Overdrive

System	Checks	
	Visual/Mechanical	EEC-V PIDS/Components/CKTS
AODE, 4R70W Transmission	• Check transmission fluid level. • Check transmission fluid for contamination. • Check for transmission fluid leaks. • Check transmission fluid pressures. • Check transmission electrical connections for corrosion, bent pins, or damage.	• Transmission components SS1 solenoid SS2 solenoid TSS PID MLP/PNP/GEAR PID
Checks for All Transmissions	• Inspect associated electrical connections, wires and harnesses. • Check shift linkage and adjustment. • Check internal transmission components.	• **TP** PID • **MAF** PID • **VSS/TSS** PID • **RPM** PID NOTE: **BOLD PIDS EQUAL GENERIC PIDS**

FM0159401216150X

Fig. 222   Pinpoint test, intermittent symptom chart 13 (Part 15 of 15). 1994-95

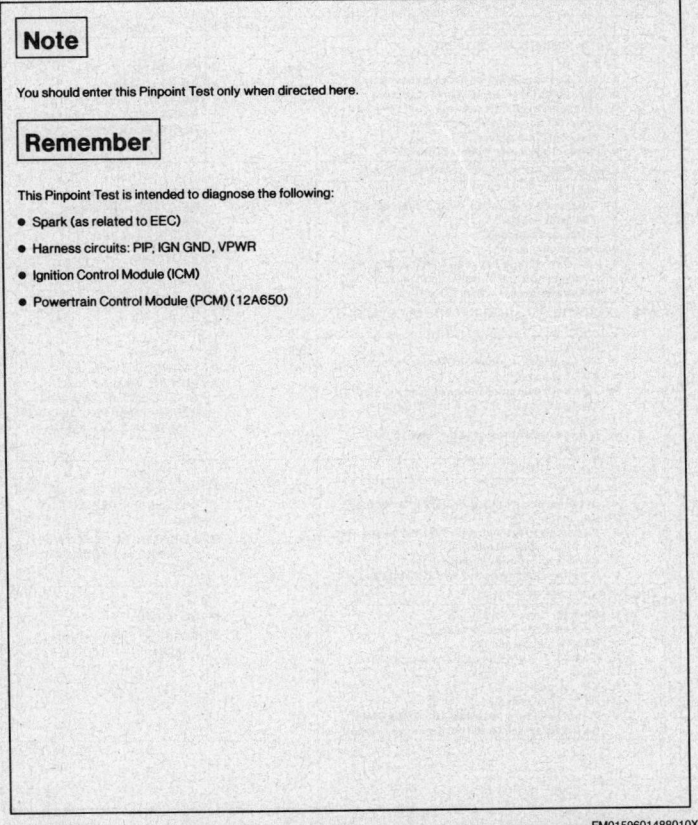

Note

You should enter this Pinpoint Test only when directed here.

Remember

This Pinpoint Test is intended to diagnose the following:

• Spark (as related to EEC)

• Harness circuits: PIP, IGN GND, VPWR

• Ignition Control Module (ICM)

• Powertrain Control Module (PCM) (12A650)

FM0159601488010X

Fig. 223   Test A: No Start (Part 1 of 11). 1996

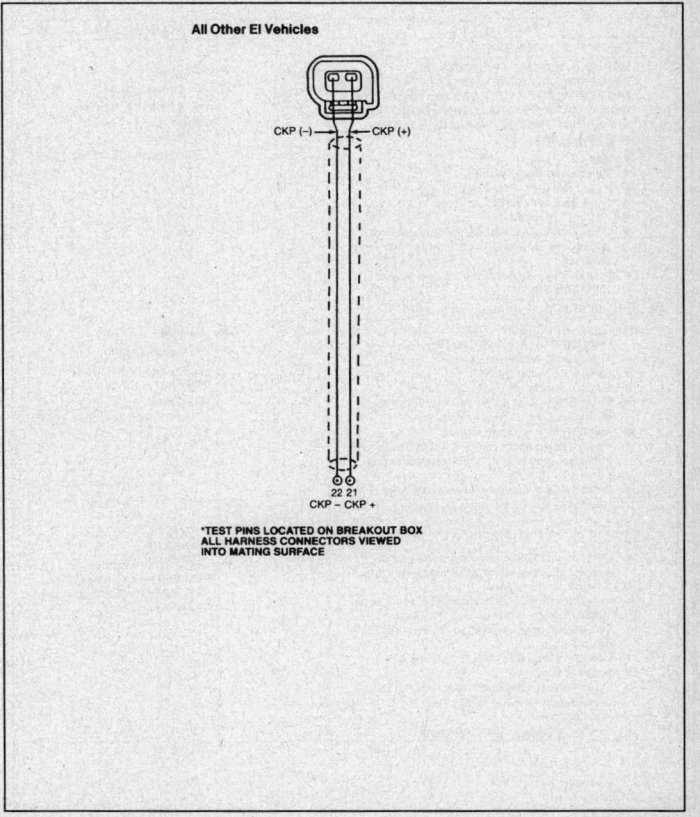

All Other EI Vehicles

CKP (−)   CKP (+)

22 21
CKP − CKP +

*TEST PINS LOCATED ON BREAKOUT BOX
ALL HARNESS CONNECTORS VIEWED
INTO MATING SURFACE

FM0159601488030X

Fig. 223   Test A: No Start (Part 2 of 11). 1996

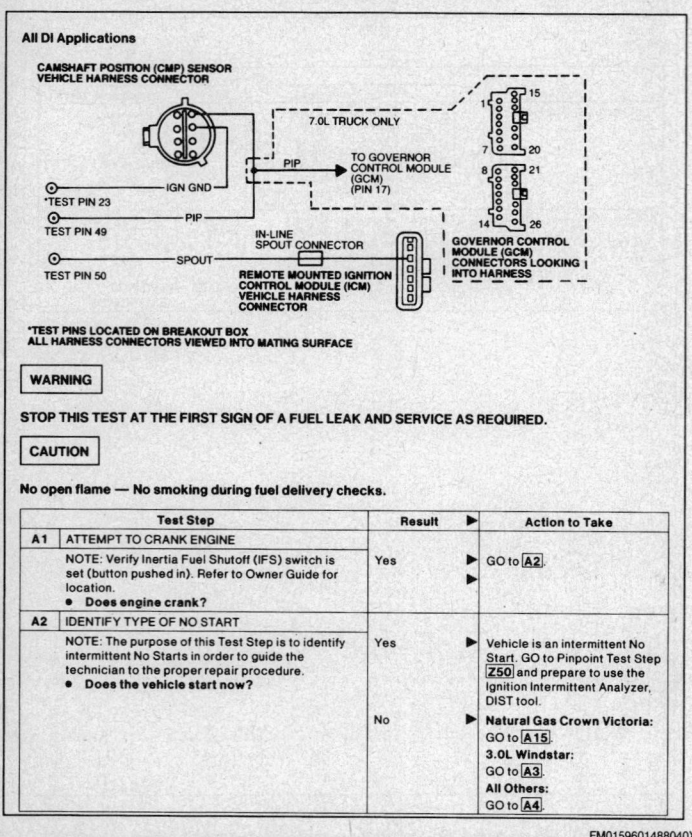

All DI Applications

CAMSHAFT POSITION (CMP) SENSOR
VEHICLE HARNESS CONNECTOR

7.0L TRUCK ONLY

PIP → TO GOVERNOR CONTROL MODULE (GCM) (PIN 17)

*TEST PIN 23
IGN GND
*TEST PIN 49
PIP
IN-LINE SPOUT CONNECTOR
TEST PIN 50
SPOUT
REMOTE MOUNTED IGNITION CONTROL MODULE (ICM) VEHICLE HARNESS CONNECTOR

GOVERNOR CONTROL MODULE (GCM) CONNECTORS LOOKING INTO HARNESS

*TEST PINS LOCATED ON BREAKOUT BOX
ALL HARNESS CONNECTORS VIEWED INTO MATING SURFACE

| WARNING |

STOP THIS TEST AT THE FIRST SIGN OF A FUEL LEAK AND SERVICE AS REQUIRED.

| CAUTION |

No open flame — No smoking during fuel delivery checks.

Test Step		Result	▶	Action to Take
A1	ATTEMPT TO CRANK ENGINE			
	NOTE: Verify Inertia Fuel Shutoff (IFS) switch is set (button pushed in). Refer to Owner Guide for location. ● Does engine crank?	Yes	▶	GO to A2.
A2	IDENTIFY TYPE OF NO START			
	NOTE: The purpose of this Test Step is to identify intermittent No Starts in order to guide the technician to the proper repair procedure. ● Does the vehicle start now?	Yes	▶	Vehicle is an intermittent No Start. GO to Pinpoint Test Step Z50 and prepare to use the Ignition Intermittent Analyzer, DIST tool.
		No	▶	Natural Gas Crown Victoria: GO to A15. 3.0L Windstar: GO to A3. All Others: GO to A4.

FM0159601488040X

Fig. 223 Test A: No Start (Part 3 of 11). 1996

Test Step		Result	▶	Action to Take
A3	CHECK MIL DURING CRANK			
	● Key off. ● Key on, observe Malfunction Indicator Lamp (MIL). MIL should be on, if not, go to Pinpoint Test Step NB1. ● Turn the key to start position and observe MIL while cranking the engine. ● Did the MIL turn off during crank?	Yes	▶	MIL turning off during crank indicates PIP circuit is OK. GO to A4.
		No	▶	GO to A6.
A4	CHECK FOR VREF AT THROTTLE POSITION (TP) SENSOR			
	● Key off. ● Disconnect TP sensor. ● Key on, engine off. ● Measure voltage between VREF circuit and SIG RTN circuit at the TP sensor vehicle harness connector. Refer to the illustration. ● Is voltage between 4.0 and 6.0 volts?	Yes	▶	RECONNECT TP sensor. GO to A5.
		No	▶	GO to Pinpoint Test Step C1.
A5	CHECK FEPS CIRCUIT FOR SHORT TO POWER			
	● Key off. ● Key on, engine off. ● Measure voltage between Pin 13 at the data link connector and battery negative post. ● Is voltage greater than 9.0 volts?	Yes	▶	SERVICE short to power. REMOVE breakout box. RECONNECT all components. RERUN Quick Test.
		No	▶	For 3.4L Taurus SHO: GO to A17. All Others: GO to A6.
A6	CHECK FOR SPARK AT THE PLUGS			
	● Disconnect the spark plug wire to any accessible cylinder. ● Connect spark tester between spark plug wire and engine ground. ● Connect Spark Plug Firing Indicator D81P-6666-A or D89P-6666-A or equivalent. ● Crank engine and check for spark. ● Reconnect the spark plug wire to the spark plug. ● Was spark present and consistent?	Yes	▶	GO to A7.
		No	▶	For 3.0L Windstar: GO to Pinpoint Test Step JA1. For 2.0L Probe: GO to Pinpoint Test Step JK1. All Others: GO to Pinpoint Test Step JD1.

FM0159601488050X

Fig. 223 Test A: No Start (Part 4 of 11). 1996

Test Step		Result	▶	Action to Take
A7	CHECK FUEL PRESSURE			
	WARNING: BEFORE SERVICING OR REPLACING ANY COMPONENTS IN THE FUEL SYSTEM, REDUCE THE POSSIBILITY OF INJURY OR FIRE BY FOLLOWING DIRECTIONS IN PINPOINT TEST HC. WARNING, CAUTION, AND HANDLING. ● Key off. ● Release the fuel pressure. ● Install fuel pressure tester. ● Scan Tool connected. ● Key on, engine off. ● Enter Output Test Mode (refer to Section 2A) and run the fuel pump to obtain maximum fuel pressure. ● Is fuel pressure between 35 and 40 psi (240-280 kPa)?	Yes	▶	GO to A8.
		No	▶	For Continental: GO to Pinpoint Test Step KB45. All Others: GO to Pinpoint Test Step HC1.
A8	CHECK FUEL PRESSURE LEAKDOWN			
	● Observe "WARNING, CAUTION AND HANDLING" in Pinpoint Test HC. ● Fuel pressure tester installed. ● Scan Tool connected. ● Key on, engine off. ● Enter Output Test Mode and run fuel pump to obtain maximum fuel pressure. ● Exit Output Test Mode, key off. ● Verify fuel pressure remains within 5 psi of the maximum pressure for 1 minute after turning pump off. ● Does fuel pressure remain within 5 psi?	Yes	▶	GO to A9.
		No	▶	For Continental: GO to Pinpoint Test Step KB45. All Others: GO to Pinpoint Test Step HC1.
A9	CHECK CONTINUITY OF IGNITION GROUND CIRCUIT			
	● Key off. ● Disconnect PCM. Inspect for damaged or pushed out pins, corrosion, loose wires, etc. Service as necessary. ● Install breakout box, leave PCM disconnected. ● Install EI diagnostic harness (Rotunda 007-00059 or equivalent) to ignition breakout box. ● Connect ICM tee to vehicle harness. ● Install ICM overlay. ● Measure resistance between Test Pin 23 at breakout box and IGN GND circuit pin at the EI diagnostic harness. ● Is resistance less than 5.0 ohms?	Yes	▶	GO to A10.
		No	▶	SERVICE open circuit. REMOVE breakout box. RECONNECT all components. RERUN Quick Test.

FM015960148806OX

Fig. 223 Test A: No Start (Part 5 of 11). 1996

Test Step		Result	▶	Action to Take
A10	CHECK PIP CIRCUIT CONTINUITY			
	● Key off. ● Breakout box installed, PCM disconnected. ● EI harness installed, ICM disconnected. ● Measure resistance between Test Pin 49 at breakout box and PIP circuit at the EI diagnostic harness. ● Is resistance less than 5.0 ohms?	Yes	▶	GO to A11.
		No	▶	SERVICE open circuit. REMOVE breakout box. RECONNECT all components. RERUN Quick Test.
A11	CHECK PIP CIRCUIT FOR SHORT TO POWER			
	● Key off. ● Breakout box installed, PCM disconnected. ● ICM disconnected. ● EI harness installed. ● Key on, engine off. ● Measure voltage between Test Pin 49 at breakout box and battery negative post. ● Is voltage greater than 1.0 volts?	Yes	▶	SERVICE short to power. REMOVE breakout box. RECONNECT all components. RERUN Quick Test.
		No	▶	GO to A12.
A12	CHECK PIP SIGNAL CIRCUIT FOR SHORTS TO GROUND			
	● Key off. ● Breakout box installed, PCM disconnected. ● ICM disconnected. ● Measure resistance between Test Pin 49 (PIP) and Test Pins 23, 51, 91 and 103 (short to ground). ● Is each resistance greater than 10,000 ohms?	Yes	▶	GO to A13.
		No	▶	SERVICE short circuit. REMOVE breakout box. RECONNECT all components. RERUN Quick Test. If vehicle does not start, GO to A13.
A13	CHECK PIP SIGNAL			
	● Key off. ● Breakout box installed, PCM disconnected. ● Reconnect ICM. ● Measure voltage between Test Pin 49 and Test Pin 23 at breakout box. ● Crank engine, record reading. ● Is voltage between 3.0 and 7.0 volts?	Yes	▶	REPLACE PCM. REMOVE breakout box. RERUN Quick Test.
		No	▶	REPLACE ICM. REMOVE breakout box. RERUN Quick Test.
A15	CHECK FUEL PRESSURE			
	● Connect Scan Tool to DLC. ● Access IPS PID (fuel pressure). ● Record fuel pressure. ● Connect fuel pressure gauge to schrader valve. ● Key on, engine off. ● Record fuel pressure. ● Is fuel pressure between 105 and 130 psi on the Scan Tool and fuel pressure gauge?	Yes	▶	GO to A16.
		No	▶	GO to Fuel Systems Pinpoint Test Step HB1.

FM0159601488070X

Fig. 223 Test A: No Start (Part 6 of 11). 1996

Fig. 223 Test A: No Start (Part 7 of 11). 1996

Test Step	Result	▶	Action to Take
A16 CHECK INJECTOR SIGNAL FROM NGV MODULE			
NOTE: Requires standard 12 volt test lamp. • Key off. • Install 60 pin breakout box to NGV module, keep NGV module connected. • Connect test lamp between Test Pin 75 and ground. • Crank engine. NOTE: A properly operating system will show a dim glow. • **Does test lamp have a dim glow while cranking?**	Yes No	▶ ▶	GO to **A6**. RECONNECT all components. No light or continuously bright light. GO to Fuel System Pinpoint Test Step **HA47**.
A17 CHECK PCM DRIVER TO COILS			
• Key off. • Connect PCM breakout box. • Connect incandescent test lamp between B+ and to each coil driver circuit. • Crank engine. • **Does lamp blink consistently and brightly (one blink per engine revolution)?**	Yes No	▶ ▶	REPLACE PCM. REMOVE breakout box. RECONNECT all components. RERUN Quick Test. GO to Pinpoint Test Step **JD4**.
A20 IDENTIFY TYPE OF NO START			
NOTE: The purpose of this Test Step is to identify intermittent No Starts in order to guide the technician to the proper repair procedure. • **Does the vehicle start now?**	Yes No	▶ ▶	Vehicle is an intermittent No Start. GO to Pinpoint Test Step **Z50**. GO to **A21**.
A21 ATTEMPT TO CRANK ENGINE			
NOTE: Verify Inertia Fuel Shutoff (IFS) switch is set (button pushed in). Refer to Owner Guide for location. • **Does engine crank?**	Yes No	▶ ▶	GO to **A22**. REFER to Starting / Engine
A22 CHECK FOR VREF AT THROTTLE POSITION (TP) SENSOR			
• Key off. • Disconnect TP sensor. • Key on, engine off. • Measure voltage between VREF circuit and SIG RTN circuit at the TP sensor vehicle harness connector. • **Is voltage between 4.0 and 6.0 volts?**	Yes No	▶ ▶	RECONNECT TP sensor. GO to **A23**. GO to Pinpoint Test Step **C1**.

FM015960148080X

Fig. 223 Test A: No Start (Part 8 of 11). 1996

Test Step	Result	▶	Action to Take
A23 CHECK FOR SPARK AT PLUGS			
• Disconnect the spark plug wire to any accessible cylinder. • Connect spark tester between spark plug wire and engine ground. • Crank engine and check for spark. • Reconnect the spark plug wire to the spark plug. • **Was spark present and consistent?**	Yes No	▶ ▶	GO to **A33**. GO to **A24**.
A24 CHECK FOR SPARK AT COIL			
• Remove high tension coil wire from distributor and install spark tester. • Check for spark while cranking. • Reconnect high tension coil wire to distributor. • **Was spark present during crank?**	Yes No	▶ ▶	GO to Pinpoint Test Step **JB12** for ICM, cap, rotor and wire diagnosis. GO to **A25**.
A25 CHECK CONTINUITY OF IGN GND CIRCUIT			
• Key off. • Disconnect Camshaft Position (CMP) sensor. • Disconnect Powertrain Control Module (PCM) 104 pin connector. Inspect for damaged or pushed out pins, corrosion, loose wires, etc. Service as necessary. • Install breakout box, leave PCM disconnected. • Connect DI diagnostic harness to EEC breakout box, connect B- lead to negative post of battery, connect ICM tee to ICM and vehicle harness, and connect CMP tee to CMP vehicle harness. • Do not connect B+ lead of DI diagnostic harness to battery. **CAUTION: Do not connect PCM to EEC breakout box when it is used with DI diagnostic harness.** • Make sure PIP OPEN / NORMAL / SPOUT OPEN switch on DI diagnostic harness is in the NORMAL position. • Use DI overlay on breakout box. • Measure resistance between Test Pin 23 at breakout box and Pin 35 at the DI diagnostic harness (IGN GND circuit). • **Is resistance less than 5.0 ohms?**	Yes No	▶ ▶	GO to **A26**. SERVICE open circuit. REMOVE breakout box. RECONNECT all components. RERUN Quick Test.
A26 ISOLATION OF PROBLEM TO SPOUT CIRCUIT			
• Reconnect CMP sensor to vehicle harness. • Breakout box installed. • Connect PCM to breakout box. • Timing switch to "DIST" position on breakout box. • Attempt to start vehicle. • **Does the vehicle start?**	Yes No	▶ ▶	Timing switch to "Computed" position on breakout box. GO to **A31**. GO to **A27**.

FM015960148090X

Fig. 223 Test A: No Start (Part 9 of 11). 1996

Test Step	Result	▶	Action to Take
A27 CHECK SPOUT SIGNAL			
• Key on, engine off. • Breakout box installed, PCM connected. • Timing switch to "DIST" position on breakout box. • Crank engine. • Measure AC voltage between Test Pin 50 (SPOUT) at breakout box and battery negative post during crank. • **Is voltage between 3.0 and 6.0 volts?**	Yes No	▶ ▶	EEC system OK. REMOVE breakout box. RECONNECT all components. GO to Pinpoint Test Step **JG1** for DI system diagnosis. PLACE timing switch to "Computed" position and GO to **A28**.
A28 CHECK SPOUT AND PIP CIRCUITS FOR SHORT TO POWER			
• Key off. • Breakout box installed. • Disconnect PCM. • Disconnect ICM and CMP sensor. • Key on. • Measure voltage between Test Pin 50 (SPOUT) at breakout box and battery negative post. • Measure voltage between Test Pin 49 (PIP) at breakout box and battery negative post. • **Is voltage greater than 10.5 volts?**	Yes No	▶ ▶	SERVICE short circuit to the START circuit or to the VPWR circuit in the harness. REMOVE breakout box. RECONNECT all components. RERUN Quick Test. GO to **A29**.
A29 CHECK SPOUT AND PIP CIRCUITS FOR SHORTS TO GROUND			
• Key off. • Breakout box installed. • PCM, ICM and CMP sensor disconnected. • Measure resistance between Test Pin 50 (SPOUT) and Test Pins 23, 51, 103 and 91 (short to GROUND) and 49 (short to PIP) at breakout box. • Measure resistance between Test Pin 49 (PIP) and Test Pins 23, 51, 103 and 91 (short to GROUND) at breakout box. • **Is each resistance greater than 10,000 ohms?**	Yes No	▶ ▶	GO to **A30**. SERVICE short circuit. REMOVE breakout box. RECONNECT all components. RERUN Quick Test. If vehicle does not start, GO to **A30**

FM015960148100X

Fig. 223 Test A: No Start (Part 10 of 11). 1996

Test Step	Result	▶	Action to Take
A30 ISOLATE SHORT(S) IN PCM TO POWER AND GROUND			
• Key off. • Breakout box installed. • Reconnect PCM to breakout box. • ICM and CMP sensor disconnected. • Measure resistance between Test Pin 50 (SPOUT) and Test Pins 71 and 97 (short to POWER) and Test Pins 51 and 103 (short to GROUND) at breakout box. • Measure resistance between Test Pin 49 (PIP) and Test Pins 71 and 97 (short to POWER) and Test Pins 51 and 103 (short to GROUND) at breakout box. • **Is each resistance greater than 500 ohms?**	Yes No	▶ ▶	RECONNECT all components. GO to **A31**. REPLACE PCM. REMOVE breakout box. RECONNECT all components. RERUN Quick Test.
A31 CHECK PIP SIGNAL			
• Key off. • Breakout box installed, PCM connected. • Measure voltage between Test Pin 49 and Test Pin 51 or 103 at breakout box. • Crank engine, record reading. • **Is voltage between 3.0 and 7.0 volts?**	Yes No	▶ ▶	REPLACE PCM. REMOVE breakout box. RECONNECT all components. RERUN Quick Test. GO to **A32**.
A32 CHECK CONTINUITY OF PIP CIRCUIT			
• Key off. • Breakout box installed. • Disconnect PCM. • ICM and CMP sensor disconnected. • Measure resistance between Test Pin 49 at breakout box and PIP circuit at Pin 15 and Pin 34 at the DI diagnostic harness. • **Is each resistance less than 5.0 ohms?**	Yes No	▶ ▶	REMOVE PCM breakout box. RECONNECT all components. GO to Pinpoint Test Step **JG1** for DI system diagnosis. SERVICE open circuit. REMOVE breakout box. RECONNECT all components. RERUN Quick Test.
A33 SPOUT SIGNAL VERIFICATION			
• Key off. • Disconnect PCM. Inspect for damaged or pushed out pins, corrosion, loose wires, etc. Service as necessary. • Install breakout box and connect PCM to breakout box. • Ensure timing switch is in "Computed" position on breakout box. • Measure voltage between Test Pin 50 (SPOUT) and Test Pins 51 and 103 at the breakout box during crank. • **Is voltage between 3.0 and 6.0 volts?**	Yes No	▶ ▶	GO to **A34**. GO to **A28**.

FM015960148110X

	Test Step		Result	▶	Action to Take
A34	CHECK FUEL PRESSURE				
	WARNING: BEFORE SERVICING OR REPLACING ANY COMPONENTS IN THE FUEL SYSTEM, REDUCE THE POSSIBILITY OF INJURY OR FIRE BY FOLLOWING DIRECTIONS IN PINPOINT TEST HC "WARNING, CAUTION AND HANDLING."		Yes	▶	GO to A35.
			No	▶	GO to Pinpoint Test Step HC1
	• Key off. • Release the fuel pressure. • Install fuel pressure tester. • Scan Tool connected. • Key on, engine off. • Enter Output Test Mode and run the fuel pump to obtain maximum fuel pressure. • **Is fuel pressure between 35 and 40 psi (240-280 kPa)?**				
A35	CHECK FUEL PRESSURE LEAKDOWN				
	• Observe "WARNING, CAUTION and HANDLING" in Pinpoint Test HC. • Fuel pressure tester installed. • Scan Tool connected. • Key on, engine off. • Enter Output Test Mode and run fuel pump to obtain maximum fuel pressure. • Exit Output Test Mode, key off. • Verify fuel pressure remains within 5 psi of the maximum pressure for 1 minute after turning pump off. • **Does fuel pressure remain within 5 psi?**		Yes	▶	RETURN to Symptom Index.
			No	▶	GO to Pinpoint Test Step HC1

FM0159601488120X

Fig. 223   Test A: No Start (Part 11 of 11). 1996

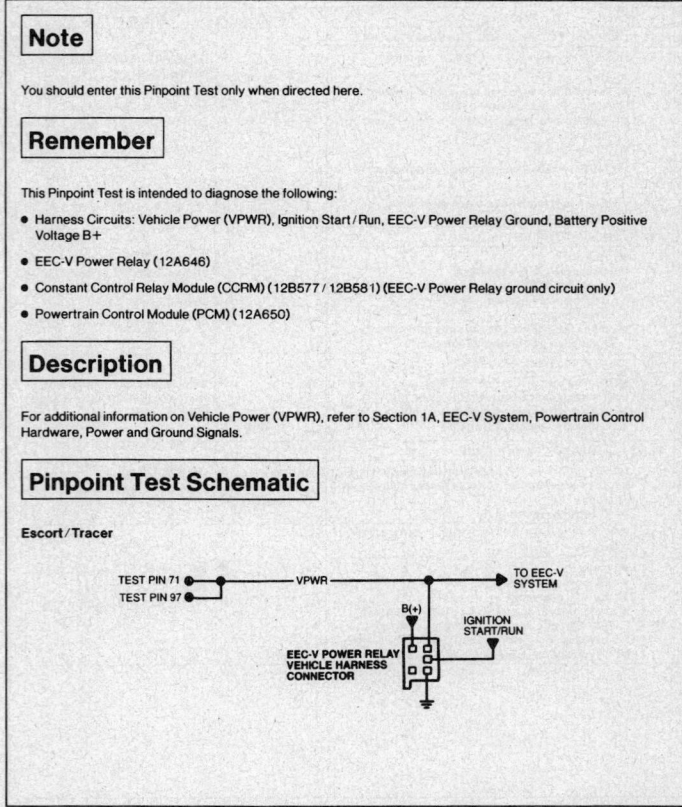

Note

You should enter this Pinpoint Test only when directed here.

Remember

This Pinpoint Test is intended to diagnose the following:

• Harness Circuits: Vehicle Power (VPWR), Ignition Start / Run, EEC-V Power Relay Ground, Battery Positive Voltage B+
• EEC-V Power Relay (12A646)
• Constant Control Relay Module (CCRM) (12B577 / 12B581) (EEC-V Power Relay ground circuit only)
• Powertrain Control Module (PCM) (12A650)

Description

For additional information on Vehicle Power (VPWR), refer to Section 1A, EEC-V System, Powertrain Control Hardware, Power and Ground Signals.

Pinpoint Test Schematic

Escort / Tracer

FM0159601489010X

Fig. 224   Test B: EEC-V Power Relay (Part 1 of 5). 1996

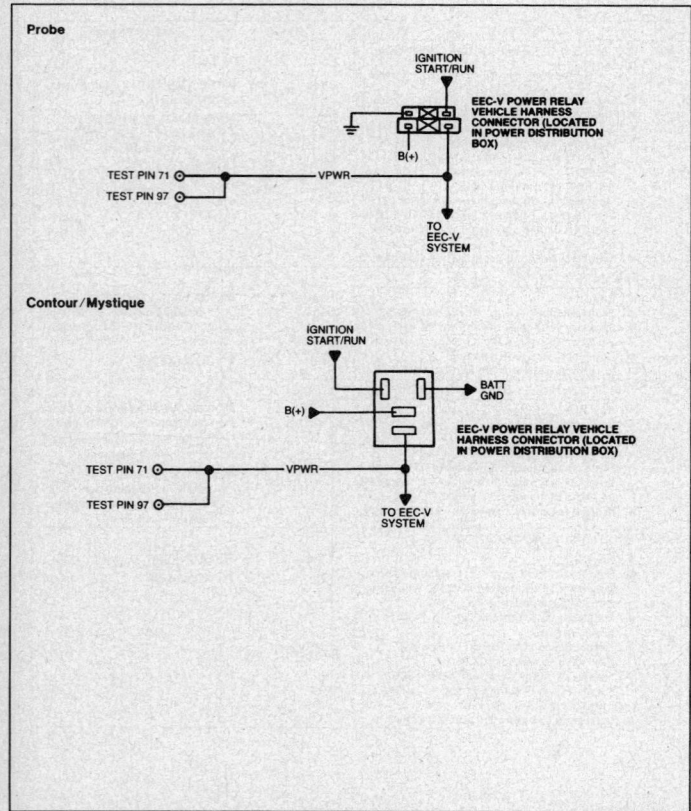

FM0159601489020X

Fig. 224   Test B: EEC-V Power Relay (Part 2 of 5). 1996

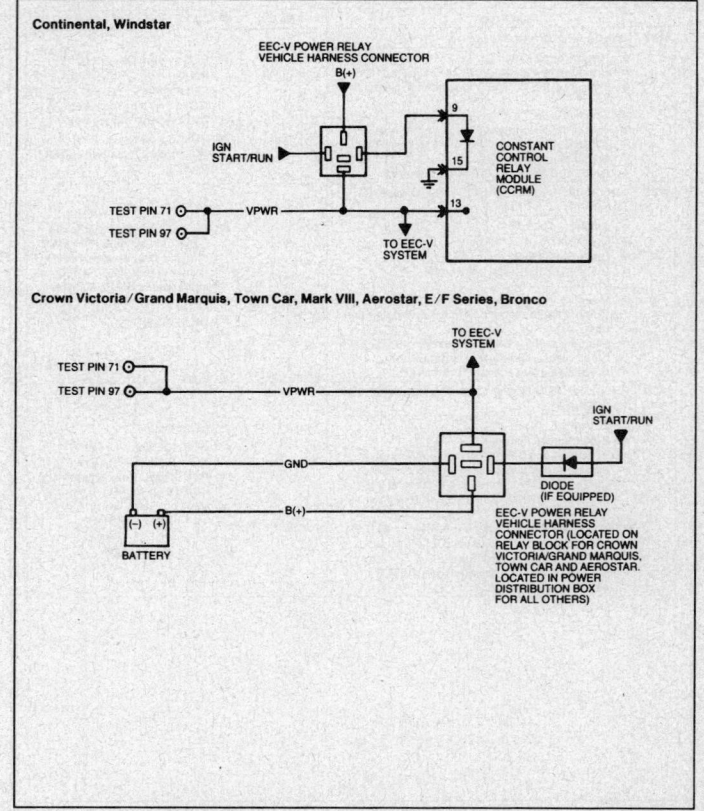

FM0159601489030X

Fig. 224   Test B: EEC-V Power Relay (Part 3 of 5). 1996

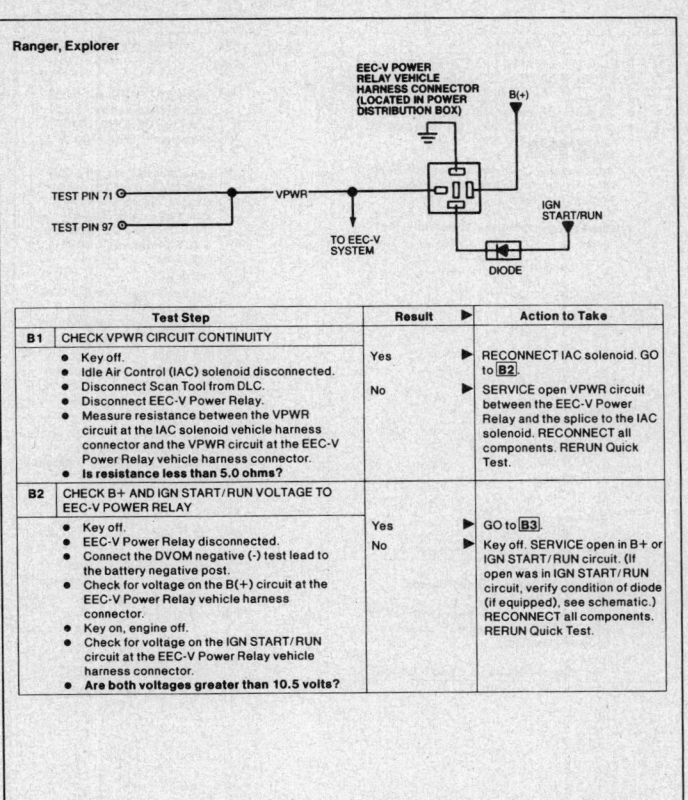

Ranger, Explorer

Test Step	Result	▶	Action to Take
B1 CHECK VPWR CIRCUIT CONTINUITY • Key off. • Idle Air Control (IAC) solenoid disconnected. • Disconnect Scan Tool from DLC. • Disconnect EEC-V Power Relay. • Measure resistance between the VPWR circuit at the IAC solenoid vehicle harness connector and the VPWR circuit at the EEC-V Power Relay vehicle harness connector. • **Is resistance less than 5.0 ohms?**	Yes No	▶ ▶	RECONNECT IAC solenoid. GO to **B2**. SERVICE open VPWR circuit between the EEC-V Power Relay and the splice to the IAC solenoid. RECONNECT all components. RERUN Quick Test.
B2 CHECK B+ AND IGN START/RUN VOLTAGE TO EEC-V POWER RELAY • Key off. • EEC-V Power Relay disconnected. • Connect the DVOM negative (–) test lead to the battery negative post. • Check for voltage on the B(+) circuit at the EEC-V Power Relay vehicle harness connector. • Key on, engine off. • Check for voltage on the IGN START/RUN circuit at the EEC-V Power Relay vehicle harness connector. • **Are both voltages greater than 10.5 volts?**	Yes No	▶ ▶	GO to **B3**. SERVICE open in B+ or IGN START/RUN circuit. (If open was in IGN START/RUN circuit, verify condition of diode (if equipped), see schematic.) RECONNECT all components. RERUN Quick Test.

FM0159601489040X

Fig. 224 Test B: EEC-V Power Relay (Part 4 of 5). 1996

Test Step	Result	▶	Action to Take
B3 CHECK GROUND CIRCUIT TO EEC-V POWER RELAY • EEC-V Power Relay disconnected. • Measure voltage between the B(+) circuit and the ground circuit at the EEC-V Power Relay vehicle harness connector. • Key off. • **Was voltage greater than 10.5 volts?**	Yes No	▶ ▶	REPLACE EEC-V Power Relay. RECONNECT all components. RERUN Quick Test. Ground circuit fault to EEC-V Power Relay. **For applications with CCRM (Continental, Windstar):** GO to **B5**. **All others:** SERVICE open ground circuit. RECONNECT all components. RERUN Quick Test.
B5 CHECK GROUND CIRCUIT FROM CCRM • Key off. • EEC-V Power Relay disconnected. • Disconnect CCRM. • Measure resistance between pin 15 (GND) of the CCRM vehicle harness connector and the battery negative post. • **Is resistance less than 5.0 ohms?**	Yes No	▶	GO to **B6**. SERVICE open ground circuit. RECONNECT all components. RERUN Quick Test.
B6 CHECK GROUND CIRCUIT CONTINUITY BETWEEN EEC-V POWER RELAY AND CCRM • Key off. • EEC-V Power Relay disconnected. • CCRM disconnected. • Measure resistance between pin 9 of the CCRM vehicle harness connector and the ground circuit at the EEC-V Power Relay vehicle harness connector. • **Is resistance less than 5.0 ohms?**	Yes No	▶	GO to **B7**. SERVICE open circuit. RECONNECT all components. RERUN Quick Test.
B7 CHECK GROUND CIRCUIT IN CCRM • Key off. • EEC-V Power Relay disconnected. • CCRM disconnected. • Measure resistance of CCRM ground circuit by placing the DVOM (+) lead on pin 9 and the DVOM (–) lead on pin 15 (specific DVOM +/– placement is due to diode in circuit). • **Is resistance less than 5.0 ohms?**	Yes No	▶ ▶	Ground circuits check OK. VERIFY test results. If OK, continue diagnosis. Ground circuit is open in the CCRM. VERIFY that harness circuits to pin 9 and pin 15 of the CCRM are not short to power. SERVICE as necessary. REPLACE CCRM. RECONNECT all components. RERUN Quick Test.

FM0159601489050X

Fig. 224 Test B: EEC-V Power Relay (Part 5 of 5). 1996

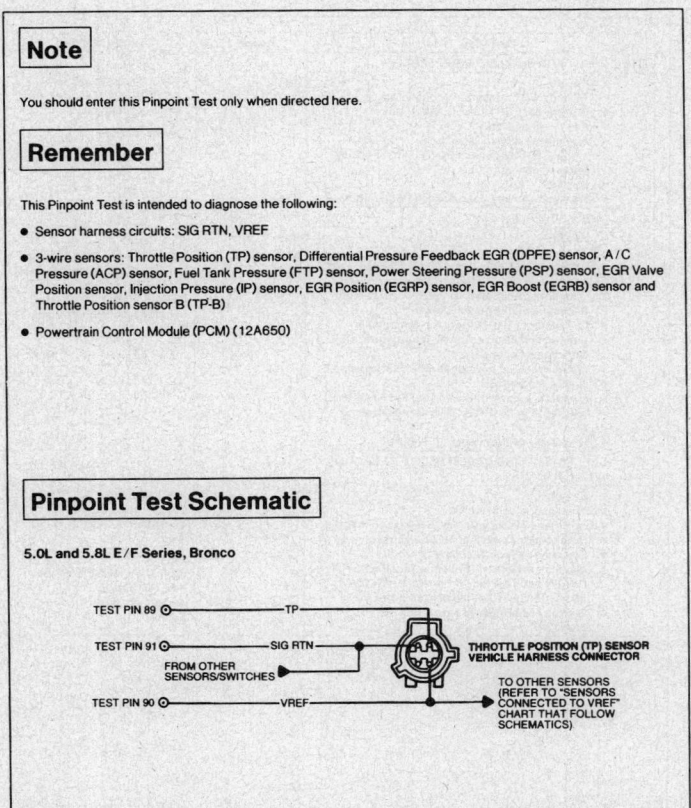

Note

You should enter this Pinpoint Test only when directed here.

Remember

This Pinpoint Test is intended to diagnose the following:

• Sensor harness circuits: SIG RTN, VREF
• 3-wire sensors: Throttle Position (TP) sensor, Differential Pressure Feedback EGR (DPFE) sensor, A/C Pressure (ACP) sensor, Fuel Tank Pressure (FTP) sensor, Power Steering Pressure (PSP) sensor, EGR Valve Position sensor, Injection Pressure (IP) sensor, EGR Position (EGRP) sensor, EGR Boost (EGRB) sensor and Throttle Position sensor B (TP-B)
• Powertrain Control Module (PCM) (12A650)

Pinpoint Test Schematic

5.0L and 5.8L E/F Series, Bronco

FM0159601490010X

Fig. 225 Test C: Reference Voltage (Part 1 of 8). 1996

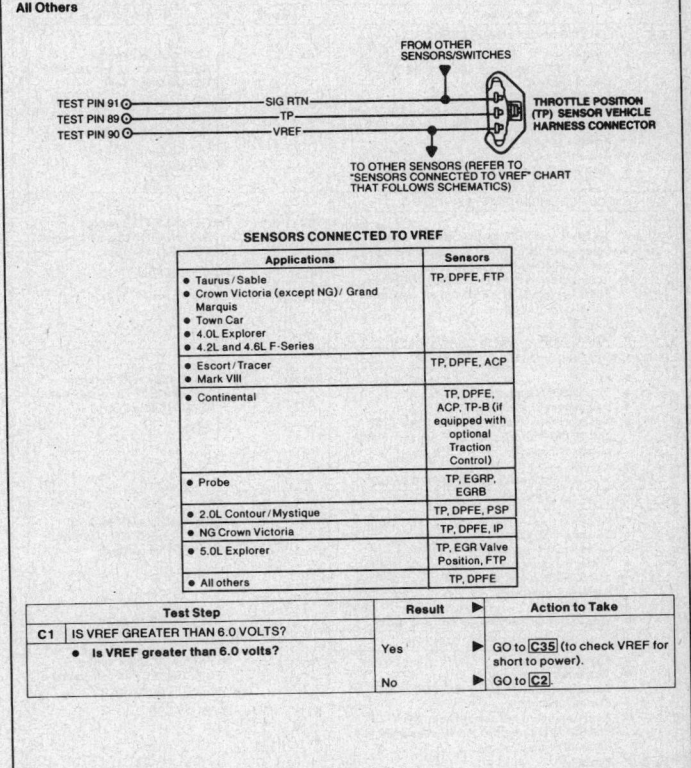

All Others

SENSORS CONNECTED TO VREF

Applications	Sensors
• Taurus / Sable • Crown Victoria (except NG) / Grand Marquis • Town Car • 4.0L Explorer • 4.2L and 4.6L F-Series	TP, DPFE, FTP
• Escort / Tracer • Mark VIII	TP, DPFE, ACP
• Continental	TP, DPFE, ACP, TP-B (if equipped with optional Traction Control)
• Probe	TP, EGRP, EGRB
• 2.0L Contour / Mystique	TP, DPFE, PSP
• NG Crown Victoria	TP, DPFE, IP
• 5.0L Explorer	TP, EGR Valve Position, FTP
• All others	TP, DPFE

Test Step	Result	▶	Action to Take
C1 IS VREF GREATER THAN 6.0 VOLTS? • Is VREF greater than 6.0 volts?	Yes No	▶ ▶	GO to **C35** (to check VREF for short to power). GO to **C2**.

FM0159601490020X

Fig. 225 Test C: Reference Voltage (Part 2 of 8). 1996

FORD—Electronic Engine Controls

Test Step	Result	▶	Action to Take
C2 CHECK BATTERY VOLTAGE • Key on, engine off. • Measure voltage across battery terminals. • **Is voltage greater than 10.5 volts?**	Yes No	▶ ▶	GO to **C3**. Key off. service discharged battery.
C3 CHECK SIG RTN CIRCUIT TO SENSOR WHERE VREF CHECK FAILED • Key on, engine off. • Sensor where VREF check failed disconnected. • Measure voltage between battery positive post and SIG RTN circuit at the appropriate sensor vehicle harness connector. • **Is voltage greater than 10.5 volts and within 1.0 volt of battery voltage?**	Yes No	▶ ▶	GO to **C4**. SIG RTN/PWR GND fault present. GO to **C25**.
C4 CAN THE ECT PID BE ACCESSED? NOTE: The purpose of this test step is to determine if the Scan Tool is able to communicate with the PCM. • Key on, engine off. • Attempt to access the ECT PID. • **Can the ECT PID be accessed?**	Yes No	▶ ▶	GO to **C20** (to check VREF for opens). GO to **C5** (to check for VPWR, and VREF for shorts).
C5 CHECK FOR VPWR TO IAC SOLENOID • Key off. • TP sensor disconnected. • Disconnect Idle Air Control (IAC) solenoid. • Key on, engine off. • Measure voltage between the VPWR circuit at the IAC vehicle harness connector and the battery negative post. • Key off. • **Was voltage greater than 10.5 volts?** **IDLE AIR CONTROL (IAC) VEHICLE HARNESS CONNECTOR**	Yes No	▶ ▶	RECONNECT IAC solenoid. **For Probe:** GO to **C13**. **All Others:** GO to **C6**. VPWR is not present. RECONNECT TP sensor. **For applications with EEC-V Power Relay inside CCRM (Mustang, Taurus/Sable and Thunderbird/Cougar):** GO to Pinpoint Test Step **X1**. **All others:** GO to Pinpoint Test Step **B1**.

FM0159601490030X

Fig. 225   Test C: Reference Voltage (Part 3 of 8). 1996

Test Step	Result	▶	Action to Take
C6 CHECK FOR SHORTED DPFE OR EGR VALVE POSITION SENSOR • Key off. • TP sensor disconnected. • Disconnect DPFE sensor (EGR valve position sensor for 5.0L Explorer). • Key on, engine off. • Again measure voltage between VREF and SIG RTN circuits at the TP sensor vehicle harness connector. • Key off. • **Was voltage between 4.0 and 6.0 volts?**	Yes No	▶ ▶	REPLACE DPFE sensor (EGR valve position sensor for 5.0L Explorer). RECONNECT all components. RERUN Quick Test. **For applications with a Fuel Tank Pressure (FTP) sensor (Taurus/Sable, Crown Victoria (ex. NG)/Grand Marquis, Town Car, Explorer, 4.2L F-Series and 4.6L F-Series):** GO to **C7**. **For applications with an A/C Pressure (ACP) sensor (Escort/Tracer, Continental and Mark VIII):** GO to **C8**. **For applications with Power Steering Pressure (PSP) sensor (2.0L Contour/Mystique):** GO to **C10**. **For applications with Injection Pressure (IP) sensor (NG Crown Victoria):** GO to **C11**. **All others:** GO to **C15**.
C7 CHECK FOR SHORTED FTP SENSOR • Key off. • TP and DPFE sensors disconnected. • Disconnect FTP sensor. • Again, measure voltage between the VREF and SIG RTN circuits at the TP sensor vehicle harness connector. • Key off. • **Was voltage between 4.0 and 6.0 volts?**	Yes No	▶ ▶	REPLACE the FTP sensor. RECONNECT all components. RERUN Quick Test. GO to **C15**.

FM0159601490040X

Fig. 225   Test C: Reference Voltage (Part 4 of 8). 1996

Test Step	Result	▶	Action to Take
C8 CHECK FOR SHORTED ACP SENSOR • Key off. • TP and DPFE sensors disconnected. • Disconnect ACP sensor. • Key on, engine off. • Again measure voltage between the VREF and SIG RTN circuits at the TP sensor vehicle harness connector. • Key off. • **Was voltage between 4.0 and 6.0 volts?**	Yes No	▶ ▶	REPLACE ACP sensor. RECONNECT all components. RERUN Quick Test. **For Continental equipped with optional Traction Control (with TP-B sensor):** GO to **C9**. **All others:** GO to **C15**.
C9 CHECK FOR SHORTED TP-B SENSOR • Key off. • TP, DPFE and ACP sensors disconnected. • Disconnect Throttle Position sensor B (TP-B). • Key on, engine off. • Again measure voltage between VREF and SIG RTN circuits at the TP sensor vehicle harness connector. • Key off. • **Was voltage between 4.0 and 6.0 volts?**	Yes No	▶ ▶	REPLACE TP-B sensor. RECONNECT all components. RERUN Quick Test. GO to **C15**.
C10 CHECK FOR SHORTED PSP SENSOR • Key off. • TP and DPFE sensors disconnected. • Disconnect PSP sensor. • Again, measure voltage between the VREF and SIG RTN circuits at the TP sensor vehicle harness connector. • Key off. • **Was voltage between 4.0 and 6.0 volts?**	Yes No	▶ ▶	REPLACE the PSP sensor. RECONNECT all components. RERUN Quick Test. GO to **C15**.
C11 CHECK FOR SHORTED IP SENSOR • Key off. • TP and DPFE sensors disconnected. • Disconnect IP sensor. • Again, measure voltage between the VREF and SIG RTN circuits at the TP sensor vehicle harness connector. • Key off. • **Was voltage between 4.0 and 6.0 volts?**	Yes No	▶ ▶	REPLACE the IP sensor. RECONNECT all components. RERUN Quick Test. GO to **C15**.
C13 CHECK FOR SHORTED EGRP SENSOR • Key off. • TP sensor disconnected. • Disconnect EGR Position (EGRP) sensor. • Key on, engine off. • Again, measure voltage between VREF and SIG RTN circuits at the TP sensor vehicle harness connector. • Key off. • **Was voltage between 4.0 and 6.0 volts?**	Yes No	▶ ▶	REPLACE EGRP sensor. RECONNECT all components. RERUN Quick Test. GO to **C14**.

FM0159601490050X

Fig. 225   Test C: Reference Voltage (Part 5 of 8). 1996

Test Step	Result	▶	Action to Take
C14 CHECK FOR SHORTED EGRB SENSOR • Key off. • TP and EGRP sensors disconnected. • Disconnect EGR Boost (EGRB) sensor. • Key on, engine off. • Again, measure voltage between the VREF and SIG RTN circuits at the TP sensor vehicle harness connector. • Key off. • **Was voltage between 4.0 amd 6.0 volts?**	Yes No	▶ ▶	REPLACE EGRB sensor. RECONNECT all components. RERUN Quick Test. GO to **C15**.
C15 CHECK VPWR TO PCM • Key off. • TP sensor disconnected. • All other sensors wired to VREF disconnected from previous test steps (if necessary, refer to "Sensors Connected To VREF" chart at the beginning of this pinpoint test). • Disconnect PCM. Inspect for damaged or pushed out pins, corrosion, loose wires, etc. Service as necessary. • Install breakout box, leave PCM disconnected. • Key on, engine off. • Measure voltage between Test Pin 71 (VPWR) and Test Pin 77 (PWR GND) at the breakout box. • **Is voltage greater than 10.5 volts?**	Yes No	▶ ▶	GO to **C16**. SERVICE open VPWR circuit between PCM and splice to IAC solenoid. REMOVE breakout box. RECONNECT all components. RERUN Quick Test.
C16 CHECK VREF CIRCUIT FOR SHORT TO GROUND OR SIG RTN • Key off. • TP sensor disconnected. • All other sensors wired to VREF disconnected. • Breakout box installed, PCM disconnected. • Disconnect Scan Tool from DLC. • Measure resistance between Test Pin 90 (VREF) and Test Pins 51 or 103 (PWR GND) and 91 (SIG RTN) at the breakout box. • **Is each resistance greater than 10,000 ohms?**	Yes No	▶ ▶	REPLACE PCM. REMOVE breakout box. RECONNECT all components. RERUN Quick Test. SERVICE VREF short to ground. REMOVE breakout box. RECONNECT all components. RERUN Quick Test.

FM0159601490060X

Fig. 225   Test C: Reference Voltage (Part 6 of 8). 1996

9-244

ELECTRONIC ENGINE CONTROL SYSTEM (EEC-V)

Test Step	Result	▶	Action to Take
C20 CHECK VREF CONTINUITY TO PCM			
• Key off. • Sensor where VREF check failed disconnected. • Disconnect PCM. Inspect for damaged or pushed out pins, corrosion, loose wires, etc. Service as necessary. • Install breakout box, leave PCM disconnected. • Measure resistance between Test Pin 90 (VREF) at the breakout box and the VREF circuit at the appropriate sensor vehicle harness connector. • **Is resistance less than 5.0 ohms?**	Yes	▶	REPLACE PCM. REMOVE breakout box. RECONNECT all components. RERUN Quick Test.
	No	▶	SERVICE open VREF circuit. REFER to the EVTM schematic (if available) etc. and DTCs received to help pinpoint the location of the open. REMOVE breakout box. RECONNECT all components. RERUN Quick Test.
C25 CAN THE ECT PID BE ACCESSED?			
NOTE: The purpose of this test step is to determine if the Scan Tool is able to communicate with the PCM. • Key on, engine off. • Attempt to access the ECT PID. • **Can the ECT PID be accessed?**	Yes	▶	GO to C26.
	No	▶	GO to C28.
C26 ARE KOEO DTCs PRESENT FOR TWO OR MORE SENSORS / SWITCHES CONNECTED TO THE SIG RTN CIRCUIT?			
• **Are KOEO DTCs present for two or more sensors / switches connected to the SIG RTN circuit (refer to the EEC-V schematic in Section 1A)?**	Yes	▶	GO to C27.
	No	▶	SERVICE open SIG RTN circuit to the sensor where the VREF check failed. RECONNECT all components. RERUN Quick Test.
C27 CHECK SIG RTN CIRCUIT CONTINUITY TO PCM			
• Key off. • Scan Tool disconnected. • Sensor where VREF check failed disconnected. • Disconnect PCM. Inspect for damaged or pushed out pins, corrosion, loose wires, etc. Service as necessary. • Install breakout box, leave PCM disconnected. • Measure resistance between the SIG RTN circuit at the appropriate sensor vehicle harness connector and Test Pin 91 (SIG RTN) at the breakout box. • **Is resistance less than 5.0 ohms?**	Yes	▶	RECONNECT sensor. GO to C28.
	No	▶	SERVICE open SIG RTN circuit. REFER to the EVTM schematic (if available), etc. and DTCs received to help pinpoint the location of the open. REMOVE breakout box. RECONNECT all components. RERUN Quick Test.

FM0159601490070X

Fig. 225 Test C: Reference Voltage (Part 7 of 8). 1996

Test Step	Result	▶	Action to Take
C28 CHECK PCM PWR GND CIRCUITS			
• Key off. • Disconnect Scan Tool from DLC. • Breakout box installed, processor disconnected. • Measure resistance between the battery negative post and Test Pins 51, 77 and 103 (PWR GND) at the breakout box. • **Is each resistance less than 5.0 ohms?**	Yes	▶	GO to C29.
	No	▶	SERVICE open circuit. REMOVE breakout box. RECONNECT all components. RERUN Quick Test.
C29 CHECK GROUND CIRCUITS IN PCM			
• Key off. • Scan Tool disconnected. • Breakout box installed. • Connect PCM to breakout box. • Measure resistance between Test Pin 91 (SIG RTN) and Test Pins 51, 77 and 103 (PWR GND) at the breakout box. • **Is each resistance less than 5.0 ohms?**	Yes	▶	SIG RTN / PWR GND circuits are OK in the harness and PCM. VERIFY results of previous test steps. RERUN Quick Test to verify DTC / symptom.
	No	▶	REPLACE PCM. REMOVE breakout box. RECONNECT all components. RERUN Quick Test.
C35 CHECK VREF FOR SHORT TO POWER			
• Key off. • Sensor where VREF check failed disconnected. • Disconnect all other sensors connected to VREF (refer to "Sensors Connected to VREF" chart at beginning of this pinpoint test). • Disconnect PCM. Inspect for damaged or pushed out pins, corrosion, loose wires, etc. Service as necessary. • Leave PCM disconnected. • Key on, engine off. • Measure voltage between the VREF circuit at the TP sensor vehicle harness connector and the battery negative post. • **Is voltage less than 0.5 volts?**	Yes	▶	REPLACE PCM. RECONNECT all components. RERUN Quick Test.
	No	▶	SERVICE VREF short to power in harness. RECONNECT all components. RERUN Quick Test.

FM0159601490080X

Fig. 225 Test C: Reference Voltage (Part 8 of 8). 1996

Note

You should enter this Pinpoint Test only when directed here.

Remember

This Pinpoint Test is intended to diagnose the following:

• Intake Air Temperature (IAT) Sensor (12A697)
• Engine Coolant Temperature (ECT) Sensor (12A648)
• Harness Circuits: IAT, ECT and SIG RTN
• Powertrain Control Module (PCM) (12A650)

Tables and Charts

Engine coolant temperature must be greater than 10°C (50°F) to pass the KOEO Self-Test and greater than 82°C (180°F) to pass the KOER Self-Test. To accomplish this, the engine should be at normal operating temperature.

Ambient temperature should be above 10°C (50°F) to receive acceptable input from the Intake Air Temperature (IAT) sensor.

FM0159601491010X

Fig. 226 Test DA: Intake Air Temperature / Engine Coolant Temperature Sensors (Part 1 of 9). 1996

Voltage values were calculated for VREF = 5.0 volts. These values may vary 15 percent due to sensor and VREF variations.

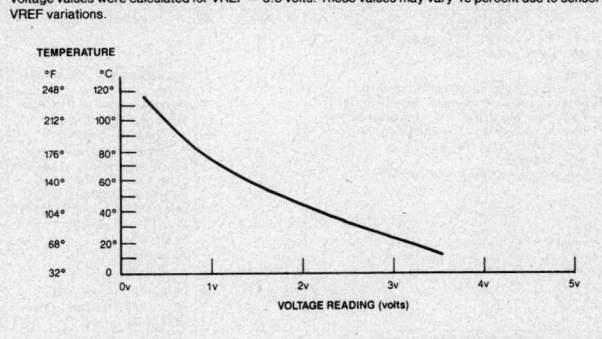

Temperature		Engine Coolant / Intake Air Temperature Sensor Values	
°F	°C	Voltage (volts)	Resistance (K ohms)
248	120	.27	1.18
230	110	.35	1.55
212	100	.46	2.07
194	90	.60	2.80
176	80	.78	3.84
158	70	1.02	5.37
140	60	1.33	7.70
122	50	1.70	10.97
104	40	2.13	16.15
86	30	2.60	24.27
68	20	3.07	37.30
50	10	3.51	58.75

FM0159601491020X

Fig. 226 Test DA: Intake Air Temperature / Engine Coolant Temperature Sensors (Part 2 of 9). 1996

Pinpoint Test Schematics

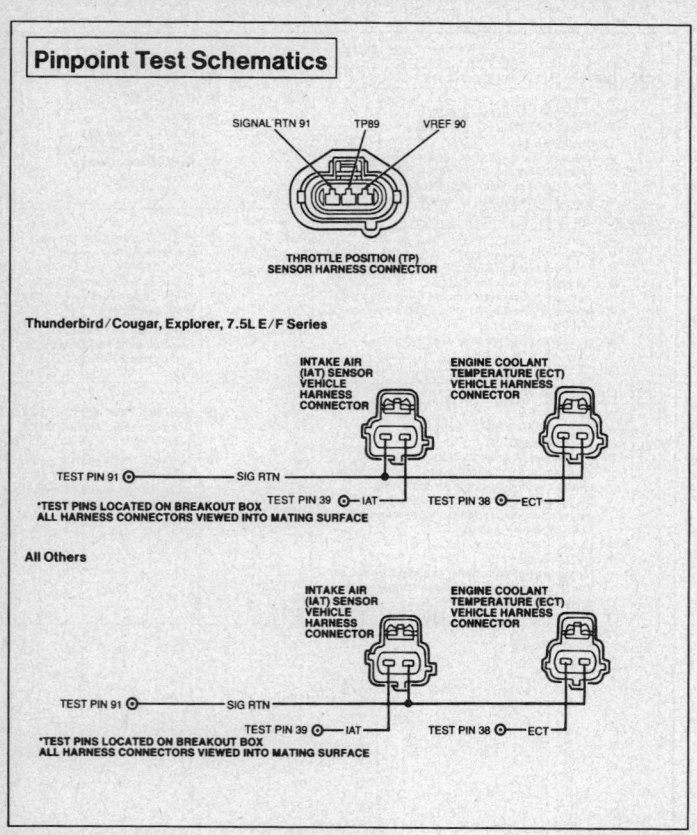

FM0159601491030X

Fig. 226   Test DA: Intake Air Temperature/Engine Coolant Temperature Sensors (Part 3 of 9). 1996

Test Step	Result	▶	Action to Take
DA1 CHECK OPERATION AND INSTALLATION OF TEMPERATURE SENSOR			
Diagnostic Trouble Code (DTC) P1116 (ECT) indicates the temperature sensor is out of Self-Test range. Correct range is 0.3 to 3.7 volts. Possible causes: — Check for overheating condition. — Low coolant level (ECT). — Damaged harness connector. — Damaged sensor. — Poor thermostat operation. ● Run engine at 2000 rpm until engine temperature becomes stabilized. **No Starts:** — Go to DA3. **Vehicles that stall:** — Return to , Symptom Flowcharts. ● Check that upper radiator hose is hot and pressurized. ● Rerun Key On Engine Running (KOER) Self-Test. ● **Is DTC P1116 present?**	Yes No	▶ ▶	GO to DA2. Engine was not at closed loop operating conditions. SERVICE any other DTCs as necessary.
DA2 CHECK VREF CIRCUIT VOLTAGE AT TP SENSOR			
● Refer to schematic at the beginning of the pinpoint test. ● Key off. ● Disconnect Throttle Position (TP) sensor. ● Key on, engine off. ● Measure the voltage between VREF circuit and SIG RTN circuit at the TP sensor vehicle harness connector. ● **Is voltage between 4.0 volts and 6.0 volts?**	Yes No	▶ ▶	There is sufficient VREF voltage. RECONNECT TP sensor. GO to DA3. GO to Pinpoint Test Step C1.

FM0159601491040X

Fig. 226   Test DA: Intake Air Temperature/Engine Coolant Temperature Sensors (Part 4 of 9). 1996

Test Step	Result	▶	Action to Take
DA3 CHECK RESISTANCE OF TEMPERATURE SENSOR WITH ENGINE OFF			
● Key off. ● Disconnect suspect temperature sensor. ● Measure resistance between sensor Signal Circuit and SIG RTN circuit at the temperature sensor. Refer to the chart at the beginning of this Pinpoint Test for resistance specifications. ● **Is resistance within specification?**	Yes No	▶ ▶	**For ECT sensor with a No Start:** Do not service DTC P1116 at this time. RETURN to Symptom Flowcharts. For symptoms of cooling fan concerns, overheating and lack of heat, do not service DTC P1116. SERVICE next DTC. If no other DTC exists, RETURN to Symptom Flowcharts. **All others:** GO to DA4. REPLACE suspect sensor. RECONNECT vehicle harness. RERUN Quick Test.
DA4 CHECK RESISTANCE OF TEMPERATURE SENSOR WITH ENGINE RUNNING			
NOTE: Verify that engine is at operating temperature before taking ECT readings. ● Key off. ● Suspect temperature sensor disconnected. ● Run engine for two minutes at 2000 rpm. ● Measure resistance between sensor signal circuit and SIG RTN circuit at the temperature sensor. Refer to the chart at the beginning of this Pinpoint Test for resistance specifications. ● **Is resistance within specification?**	Yes No	▶ ▶	REPLACE PCM. RECONNECT vehicle harness. RERUN Quick Test. REPLACE suspect sensor. RECONNECT vehicle harness. RERUN Quick Test.

FM0159601491050X

Fig. 226   Test DA: Intake Air Temperature/Engine Coolant Temperature Sensors (Part 5 of 9). 1996

Test Step	Result	▶	Action to Take
DA10 DTC P0118 OR P0113: SIMULATE OPPOSITE SIGNAL TO PCM			
Diagnostic Trouble Code (DTC) P0118 (ECT) or P0113 (IAT) indicates the sensor signal is greater than the Self-Test maximum. The maximum for ECT and IAT sensors is 4.6 volts or -46°F (-50°C). Possible causes: — Open in harness (IAT or ECT). — Improper harness connection. — Damaged sensor. — Damaged PCM. ● Key off. ● Disconnect suspect temperature sensor. ● Connect a jumper wire between the sensor signal circuit and SIG RTN circuit at the temperature sensor vehicle harness connector. ● Scan Tool installed. ● Key on. NOTE: If a Scan Tool communication problem exists, remove jumper wire immediately and go to DA12. ● Access ECT or IAT PID. ● **Is the ECT or IAT PID less than 0.2 volts (greater than 248°F/120°C)?**	Yes No	▶ ▶	REPLACE suspect sensor. REMOVE jumper wire. RECONNECT vehicle harness. RERUN Quick Test. REMOVE jumper wire. GO to DA11.
DA11 CHECK CONTINUITY OF SENSOR SIGNAL AND SIG RTN CIRCUITS			
● Key off. ● Suspect temperature sensor disconnected. ● Disconnect PCM. Inspect for damaged or pushed out pins, corrosion, loose wires, etc. Service as necessary. ● Install breakout box, leave PCM disconnected. ● Measure resistance between sensor signal circuit at the temperature sensor vehicle harness connector and Test Pin 38 (ECT) or 39 (IAT) at the breakout box. ● Measure resistance between SIG RTN circuit at the temperature sensor vehicle harness connector and Test Pin 91 (SIG RTN) at the breakout box. ● **Is each resistance less than 5.0 ohms?**	Yes No	▶ ▶	REPLACE PCM. REMOVE breakout box. RECONNECT components. RERUN Quick Test. SERVICE open circuits. REMOVE breakout box. RECONNECT all components. RERUN Quick Test.

FM0159601491060X

Fig. 226   Test DA: Intake Air Temperature/Engine Coolant Temperature Sensors (Part 6 of 9). 1996

ELECTRONIC ENGINE CONTROL SYSTEM (EEC-V)

Test Step	Result	▶	Action to Take
DA12 CHECK FOR SENSOR SIGNAL SHORTED TO VREF			
• Key off. • Suspect temperature sensor disconnected. • Disconnect PCM. Inspect for damaged or pushed out pins, corrosion, loose wires, etc. Service as necessary. • Install breakout box, leave PCM disconnected. • Measure resistance between sensor signal circuit Test Pin 38 (ECT) or 39 (IAT) and VREF at the breakout box. • **Is each resistance greater than 10,000 ohms?**	Yes No	▶ ▶	REPLACE PCM. RERUN Quick Test. LOCATE and SERVICE short to VREF. RERUN Quick Test.
DA20 DTC P0112 OR P0117: SIMULATE OPPOSITE SIGNAL TO PCM			
Diagnostic Trouble Code (DTC) P0117 (ECT) or DTC P0112 (IAT) indicates the sensor signal is less than Self-Test minimum. The IAT and ECT sensor minimum is 0.2 volt 250°F (121°C). Possible causes: — Grounded circuit in harness. — Damaged sensor. — Improper harness connection. — Damaged PCM. • Key off. • Disconnect vehicle harness from suspect sensor. Inspect for damaged or pushed out pins, corrosion, loose wires, etc. Service as necessary. • Scan Tool installed. • Key on. • Access ECT or IAT PID. • **Is the ECT or IAT PID greater than 4.2 volts (less than -40°F/C)?**	Yes No	▶ ▶	REPLACE sensor. RECONNECT harness. RERUN Quick Test. GO to **DA21**.
DA21 CHECK VREF CIRCUIT VOLTAGE AT TP SENSOR			
• Refer to schematic at the beginning of the pinpoint test. • Key off. • Disconnect TP sensor. • Key on, engine off. • Measure the voltage between VREF circuit and SIG RTN circuit at the TP sensor vehicle harness connector. • **Is voltage between 4.0 and 6.0 volts?**	Yes No	▶ ▶	There is sufficient VREF voltage. RECONNECT TP sensor. GO to **DA22**. GO to Pinpoint Test Step **C1**.

FM015960149107OX

Fig. 226 Test DA: Intake Air Temperature/Engine Coolant Temperature Sensors (Part 7 of 9). 1996

Test Step	Result	▶	Action to Take
DA22 CHECK SIGNAL CIRCUIT FOR SHORT TO GROUND			
• Key off. • Suspect temperature sensor disconnected. • Disconnect PCM. Inspect for damaged or pushed out pins, corrosion, loose wires, etc. Service as necessary. • Install breakout box, PCM disconnected. • Measure resistance between Test Pin 38 (ECT) or 39 (IAT) and Test Pins 24 or 51 (PWR GND) and 91 (SIG RTN) at the breakout box. • **Is each resistance greater than 10,000 ohms?**	Yes No	▶ ▶	REPLACE PCM. REMOVE breakout box. RECONNECT all components. RERUN Quick Test. SERVICE short circuit. REMOVE breakout box. RECONNECT all components. RERUN Quick Test.
DA90 DTCS P0112, P1112, P0113, P0117, P1117 OR P0118: INTERMITTENT CHECK			
Diagnostic Trouble Codes (DTCs) P0112, P1112 or P0113 (IAT DTCs) and P0117, P1117 or P0118 (ECT DTCs) are not received during KOEO and KOER Self-Tests, but are output during Continuous Memory Self-Test and may be intermittent. Possible causes: — Damaged harness. — Damaged harness connector. — Damaged IAT or ECT sensor. — Low coolant (ECT). — Damaged PCM. • Key off. • Scan Tool connected. • Key on. • Monitor the ECT or IAT PID. • While observing the PID, perform the following: — Tap on the sensor to simulate road shock. — Wiggle the sensor connector. • **Is there any large change in the temperature reading?**	Yes No	▶ ▶	DISCONNECT and INSPECT connectors. If OK, REPLACE the sensor. COMPLETE PCM Reset to clear DTCs (REFER to Powertrain Control Module (PCM) Reset). RERUN Quick Test. For Continuous DTCs P1112 and P1117, COMPLETE Comprehensive Component Monitor Drive Cycle (REFER to Drive Cycles). GO to **DA91**.
DA91 CHECK EEC-V WIRING HARNESS			
• Still monitoring PID. • While observing the appropriate PID, perform the following: — Hold the vehicle harness close to the sensor connector. Wiggle, shake and bend small sections of wiring harness while working toward the PCM. • **Is there any change in the temperature reading?**	Yes No	▶ ▶	ISOLATE fault. SERVICE as necessary. COMPLETE PCM Reset to clear DTCs (REFER to Powertrain Control Module (PCM) Reset). RERUN Quick Test. For Continuous DTCs P1112 and P1117, COMPLETE Comprehensive Component Monitor Drive Cycle (REFER to Drive Cycles). GO to **DA92**.

FM015960149108OX

Fig. 226 Test DA: Intake Air Temperature/Engine Coolant Temperature Sensors (Part 8 of 9). 1996

Test Step	Result	▶	Action to Take
DA92 CHECK PCM AND VEHICLE HARNESS CONNECTOR			
• Key off. • Disconnect PCM. • Disconnect sensor connector. Inspect for spread terminals, pushed out pins and loose or crimped wires. • **Are connectors and terminals OK?**	Yes No	▶ ▶	Fault is not present at this time. COMPLETE PCM Reset to clear DTCs (REFER to Powertrain Control Module (PCM) Reset). RERUN Quick Test. For Continuous Memory DTCs P1112 and P1117, COMPLETE Comprehensive Component Monitor Drive Cycle (REFER to Drive Cycles). SERVICE as necessary. COMPLETE PCM Reset to clear DTCs (REFER to Powertrain Control Module (PCM) Reset). RERUN Quick Test. For Continuous Memory DTCs P1112 or P1117, COMPLETE Comprehensive Component Monitor Drive Cycle (REFER to Drive Cycles).
DA100 DTC P0125 INDICATES EXCESSIVE TIME TO ENTER CLOSED LOOP FUEL CONTROL			
Diagnostic Trouble Code (DTC) P0125 indicates the ECT sensor has not achieved the required temperature level to enter closed loop operating conditions within a specified amount of time after starting engine. This DTC will light the MIL. Possible causes: — Insufficient warm up time. — Leaky or stuck open thermostat. — Low coolant. • Check coolant level. • **Is the coolant level fill correct?**	Yes No	▶ ▶	GO to Thermostat Diagnostics located in the Cooling System Group in the Service Manual for further diagnostics. FILL to proper level. COMPLETE PCM reset to clear DTCs (REFER to Powertrain Control Module (PCM) Reset). COMPLETE Comprehensive Component Monitor Drive Cycle (REFER to Drive Cycles). RERUN Quick Test.

FM015960149109OX

Fig. 226 Test DA: Intake Air Temperature/Engine Coolant Temperature Sensors (Part 9 of 9). 1996

Note

You should enter this Pinpoint Test only when directed here.

Remember

This Pinpoint Test is intended to diagnose the following:

• Engine Fuel Temperature (EFT) Sensor (9F951)
• Harness Circuits: EFT and SIG RTN
• Powertrain Control Module (PCM) (12A650)

Tables and Charts

The Engine Fuel Temperature (EFT) sensor will operate within the range of -40°C to 120°C or -40°F to 248°F.

FM015960149201OX

Fig. 227 Test DB: Engine Fuel Temperature Sensor (Part 1 of 7). 1996

Pinpoint Test Schematics

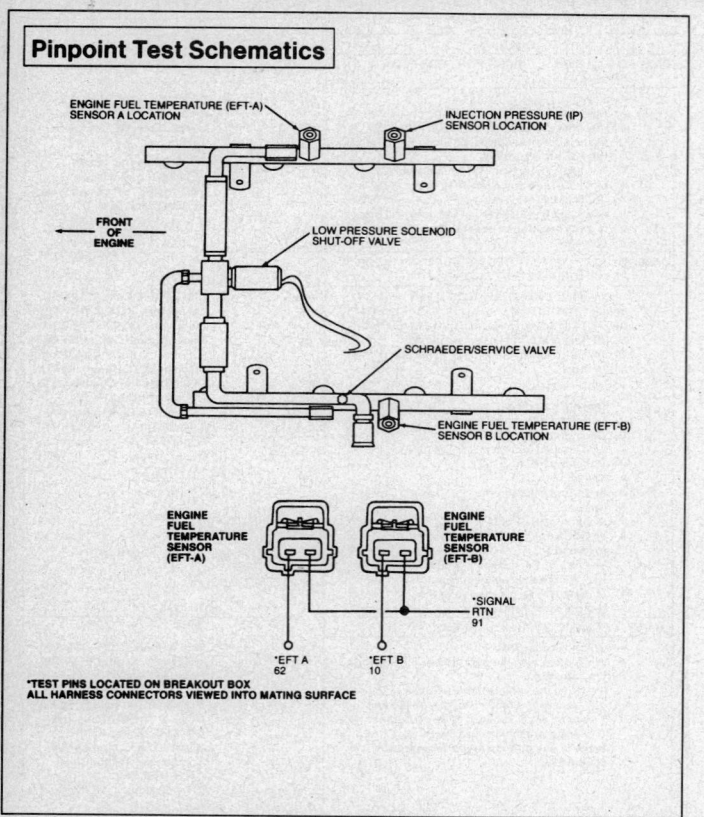

Fig. 227   Test DB: Engine Fuel Temperature Sensor (Part 2 of 7). 1996

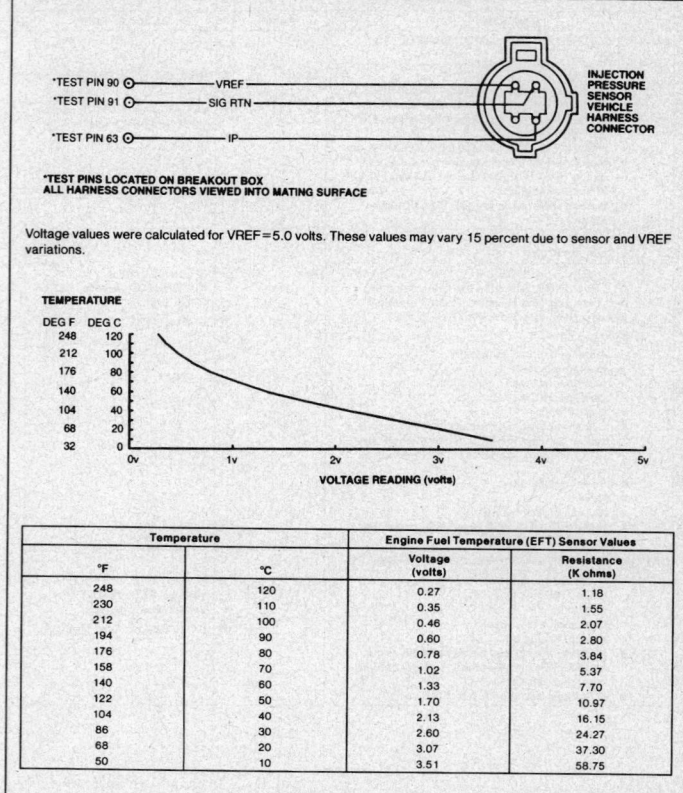

Voltage values were calculated for VREF=5.0 volts. These values may vary 15 percent due to sensor and VREF variations.

Temperature		Engine Fuel Temperature (EFT) Sensor Values	
°F	°C	Voltage (volts)	Resistance (K ohms)
248	120	0.27	1.18
230	110	0.35	1.55
212	100	0.46	2.07
194	90	0.60	2.80
176	80	0.78	3.84
158	70	1.02	5.37
140	60	1.33	7.70
122	50	1.70	10.97
104	40	2.13	16.15
86	30	2.60	24.27
68	20	3.07	37.30
50	10	3.51	58.75

Fig. 227   Test DB: Engine Fuel Temperature Sensor (Part 3 of 7). 1996

Test Step	Result	►	Action to Take
DB1 DTC P0183 OR P0188: SIMULATE OPPOSITE SIGNAL TO PCM			
Diagnostic Trouble Code (DTC) P0183 (EFT A) or P0188 (EFT B) indicates the sensor signal is greater than the Self-Test maximum. The maximum for EFT A and EFT B sensors is 4.6 volts or -46°F (-50°C). Possible causes: — Open in harness (EFT A or EFT B). — Improper harness connection. — Damaged sensor. — Damaged PCM. • Key off. • Disconnect suspect temperature sensor (refer to Pinpoint Test Schematic for location). • Connect a jumper wire between the sensor signal circuit and SIG RTN circuit at the temperature sensor vehicle harness connector. • Scan Tool installed. • Key on. NOTE: If a Scan Tool communication problem exists, remove jumper wire immediately and go to **DB3**. • Access EFT A or EFT B PID. • **Is the EFT less than 0.2 volt (greater than 248°F/120°C)?**	Yes No	► ►	REPLACE suspect sensor following service manual procedure. REMOVE jumper wire. RECONNECT vehicle harness. RERUN Quick Test. REMOVE jumper wire. GO to **DB2**.
DB2 CHECK CONTINUITY OF SENSOR SIGNAL AND SIG RTN CIRCUITS			
• Key off. • Suspect temperature sensor disconnected. • Disconnect PCM. Inspect for damaged or pushed out pins, corrosion, loose wires, etc. Service as necessary. • Install breakout box, leave PCM disconnected. • Measure resistance between sensor signal circuit at the temperature sensor vehicle harness connector and Test Pin 62 (EFT A) or 10 (EFT B) at the breakout box. • Measure resistance between SIG RTN circuit at the temperature sensor vehicle harness connector and Test Pin 91 (SIG RTN) at the breakout box. • **Is each resistance less than 5.0 ohms?**	Yes No	► ►	REPLACE PCM. REMOVE breakout box. RECONNECT components. RERUN Quick Test. SERVICE open circuits. REMOVE breakout box. RECONNECT all components. RERUN Quick Test.

Fig. 227   Test DB: Engine Fuel Temperature Sensor (Part 4 of 7). 1996

Test Step	Result	►	Action to Take
DB3 CHECK FOR SENSOR SIGNAL SHORTED TO VREF			
• Key off. • Suspect temperature sensor disconnected. • Disconnect PCM. Inspect for damaged or pushed out pins, corrosion, loose wires, etc. Service as necessary. • Install breakout box, leave PCM disconnected. • Measure resistance between sensor signal circuit Test Pin 62 (EFT A) or 10 (EFT B) and VREF at the breakout box. • **Is each resistance greater than 10,000 ohms?**	Yes No	► ►	REPLACE PCM. RERUN Quick Test. LOCATE and SERVICE short to VREF. RERUN Quick Test.
DB4 DTC P0182 OR P0187: SIMULATE OPPOSITE SIGNAL TO PCM			
Diagnostic Trouble Code (DTC) P0182 (EFT A) or DTC P0187 (EFT B) indicates the sensor signal is less than Self-Test minimum. The EFT A and EFT B sensor minimum is 0.2 volt 250°F (121°C). Possible causes: — Grounded circuit in harness. — Damaged sensor. — Improper harness connection. — Damaged PCM. • Key off. • Disconnect vehicle harness from suspect sensor (refer to Pinpoint Test Schematic for location). Inspect for damaged or pushed out pins, corrosion, loose wires, etc. Service as necessary. • Scan Tool installed. • Key on. • Access EFT A or EFT B PID. • **Is the EFT A or EFT B PID more than 4.2 volts (less than -40°F/C)?**	Yes No	► ►	REPLACE sensor following service manual procedure. RECONNECT harness. RERUN Quick Test. GO to **DB5**.
DB5 CHECK VREF CIRCUIT VOLTAGE AT IP SENSOR			
• Refer to schematic at the beginning of the pinpoint test. • Key off. • Disconnect Injection Pressure (IP) sensor. • Key on, engine off. • Measure the voltage between VREF circuit and SIG RTN circuit at the IP sensor vehicle harness connector. • **Is voltage between 4.0 and 6.0 volts?**	Yes No	► ►	There is sufficient VREF voltage. RECONNECT IP sensor. GO to **DB6**. RECONNECT IP sensor. GO to Pinpoint Test Step **C1**.

Fig. 227   Test DB: Engine Fuel Temperature Sensor (Part 5 of 7). 1996

Test Step		Result	▶	Action to Take
DB6	CHECK SIGNAL CIRCUIT FOR SHORT TO GROUND			
	• Key off. • Suspect temperature sensor disconnected. • Disconnect PCM. Inspect for damaged or pushed out pins, corrosion, loose wires, etc. Service as necessary. • Install breakout box, PCM disconnected. • Measure resistance between Test Pin 62 (EFT A) or 10 (EFT B) and Test Pins 24 or 51 (PWR GND) and 91 (SIG RTN) at the breakout box. • **Is each resistance greater than 10,000 ohms?**	Yes	▶	REPLACE PCM. REMOVE breakout box. RECONNECT all components. RERUN Quick Test.
		No	▶	SERVICE short circuit. REMOVE breakout box. RECONNECT all components. RERUN Quick Test.
DB7	DTCS P0182, P0183, P0187 and P0188: INTERMITTENT CHECK			
	Diagnostic Trouble Codes (DTCs) P0182, P0183 (EFT A DTCs) and P0187, P0188 (EFT B DTCs) are not received during KOEO and KOER Self-Tests, but are output during Continuous Memory Self-Test and may be intermittent. Possible causes: — Damaged harness. — Damaged harness connector. — Damaged EFT A or EFT B sensor. — Damaged PCM. • Key off. • Scan Tool connected. • Key on. • Monitor the EFT-A or EFT-B PID. • While observing the PID, perform the following: — Tap on the sensor to simulate road shock. — Wiggle the sensor connector. • **Is there any large change in the temperature reading?**	Yes	▶	DISCONNECT and INSPECT connectors. If OK, REPLACE the sensor. COMPLETE PCM Reset to clear DTCs (REFER to Powertrain Control Module (PCM) Reset). RERUN Quick Test.
		No	▶	GO to DB8.
DB8	CHECK EEC-V WIRING HARNESS			
	• Still monitoring PID. • While observing the appropriate PID, perform the following: — Hold the vehicle harness close to the sensor connector. Wiggle, shake and bend small sections of wiring harness while working toward the PCM. • **Is there any change in the temperature reading?**	Yes	▶	ISOLATE fault. SERVICE as necessary. COMPLETE PCM Reset to clear DTCs (REFER to Powertrain Control Module (PCM) Reset). RERUN Quick Test.
		No	▶	GO to DB9.

FM0159601492060X

Fig. 227   Test DB: Engine Fuel Temperature Sensor (Part 6 of 7). 1996

Test Step		Result	▶	Action to Take
DB9	CHECK PCM AND VEHICLE HARNESS CONNECTOR			
	• Key off. • Disconnect PCM. • Disconnect sensor connector. Inspect for spread terminals, pushed out pins and loose or crimped wires. • **Are connectors and terminals OK?**	Yes	▶	Fault is not present at this time. COMPLETE PCM Reset to clear DTCs (REFER to Powertrain Control Module (PCM) Reset). RERUN Quick Test.
		No	▶	SERVICE as necessary. COMPLETE PCM Reset to clear DTCs (REFER to Powertrain Control Module (PCM) Reset). RERUN Quick Test.

FM0159601492070X

Fig. 227   Test DB: Engine Fuel Temperature Sensor (Part 7 of 7). 1996

Note

You should enter this Pinpoint Test only when directed here.

Remember

This Pinpoint Test is intended to diagnose the following:

- Mass Air Flow (MAF) Sensor (12B579)
- Harness Circuits:

  MAF SIG, MAF RTN (signal return to MAF sensor), Vehicle Power (VPWR), and Power Ground (PWR GND)

- Powertrain Control Module (PCM) (12A650)

Tables and Charts

VOLTAGE TO MASS AIR FLOW CONVERSION TABLE

Applications	Voltage Signal					
	0.34V	0.39V	0.60V	1.00V	1.96V	3.90V
2.0L Contour / Mystique	0.39 gm/sec	0.45 gm/sec	0.72 gm/sec	2.10 gm/sec	7.64 gm/sec	40.59 gm/sec
2.5L Contour / Mystique	0.33 gm/sec	0.95 gm/sec	1.69 gm/sec	5.53 gm/sec	22.92 gm/sec	137.98 gm/sec
3.4L Taurus SHO 4.6L Mustang 4.6L Continental 4.6L Mark VIII	1.39 gm/sec	1.60 gm/sec	2.69 gm/sec	8.36 gm/sec	32.99 gm/sec	193.69 gm/sec
4.6L F-Series 7.5L F-Series	1.35 gm/sec	1.56 gm/sec	2.66 gm/sec	8.31 gm/sec	32.99 gm/sec	190.18 gm/sec
3.8L Mustang 4.0L Aerostar 4.0L Explorer 4.0L Ranger	1.46 gm/sec	1.68 gm/sec	2.52 gm/sec	7.64 gm/sec	27.09 gm/sec	151.79 gm/sec
(Continued)						

FM0159601493010X

Fig. 228   Test DC: Mass Air Flow Sensor (Part 1 of 14). 1996

VOLTAGE TO MASS AIR FLOW CONVERSION TABLE (Cont'd)

Applications	Voltage Signal					
	0.34V	0.39V	0.60V	1.00V	1.96V	3.90V
4.9L F-Series 5.0L F-Series / Bronco 5.8L F-Series / Bronco	1.68 gm/sec	1.93 gm/sec	3.32 gm/sec	8.43 gm/sec	28.97 gm/sec	151.44 gm/sec
4.9L E-Series 5.0L E-Series 5.8L E-Series	1.24 gm/sec	1.42 gm/sec	2.98 gm/sec	8.38 gm/sec	29.88 gm/sec	151.25 gm/sec
2.0L Probe 3.0L Windstar	0.82 gm/sec	0.88 gm/sec	1.25 gm/sec	3.44 gm/sec	14.48 gm/sec	135.95 gm/sec
3.0L 4V Taurus / Sable 3.8L Windstar 4.2L F-Series	1.43 gm/sec	1.64 gm/sec	2.58 gm/sec	7.53 gm/sec	26.57 gm/sec	154.40 gm/sec
3.8L Thunderbird / Cougar 4.6L Thunderbird / Cougar	1.44 gm/sec	1.66 gm/sec	2.73 gm/sec	8.06 gm/sec	29.33 gm/sec	153.31 gm/sec
3.0L 2V Taurus / Sable 3.0L Taurus FF	1.31 gm/sec	1.11 gm/sec	1.72 gm/sec	4.82 gm/sec	17.00 gm/sec	146.84 gm/sec
2.3L Ranger 3.0L Ranger	0.93 gm/sec	1.07 gm/sec	1.71 gm/sec	4.58 gm/sec	16.23 gm/sec	135.17 gm/sec
1.9L Escort / Tracer 3.0L Aerostar	0.94 gm/sec	1.07 gm/sec	1.68 gm/sec	4.77 gm/sec	16.87 gm/sec	88.91 gm/sec
4.6L Crown Victoria / Grand Marquis 4.6L NG Crown Victoria / 4.6L Town Car	1.28 gm/sec	1.48 gm/sec	2.37 gm/sec	6.97 gm/sec	26.16 gm/sec	148.18 gm/sec

Pinpoint Test Schematics

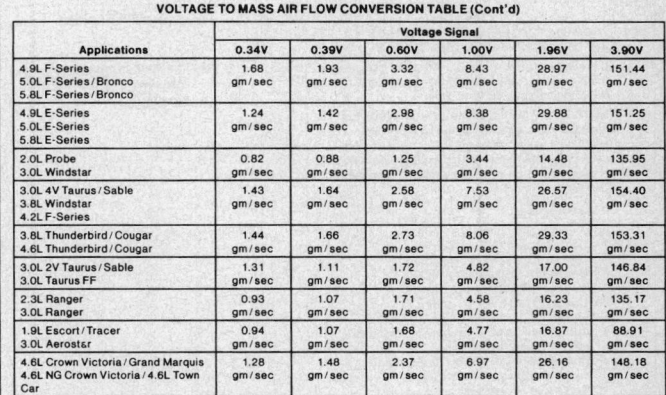

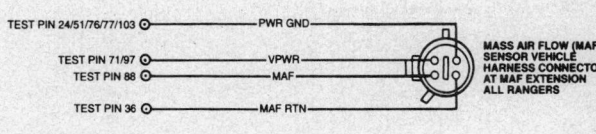

*TEST PINS LOCATED ON BREAKOUT BOX
ALL HARNESS CONNECTORS VIEWED INTO MATING SURFACE

FM0159601493020X

Fig. 228   Test DC: Mass Air Flow Sensor (Part 2 of 14). 1996

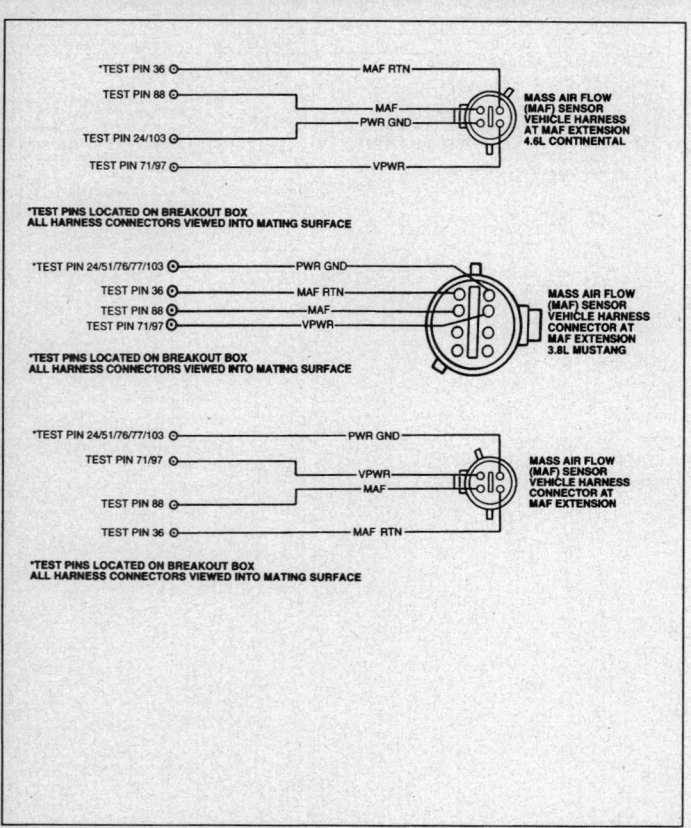

Fig. 228   Test DC: Mass Air Flow Sensor (Part 3 of 14). 1996

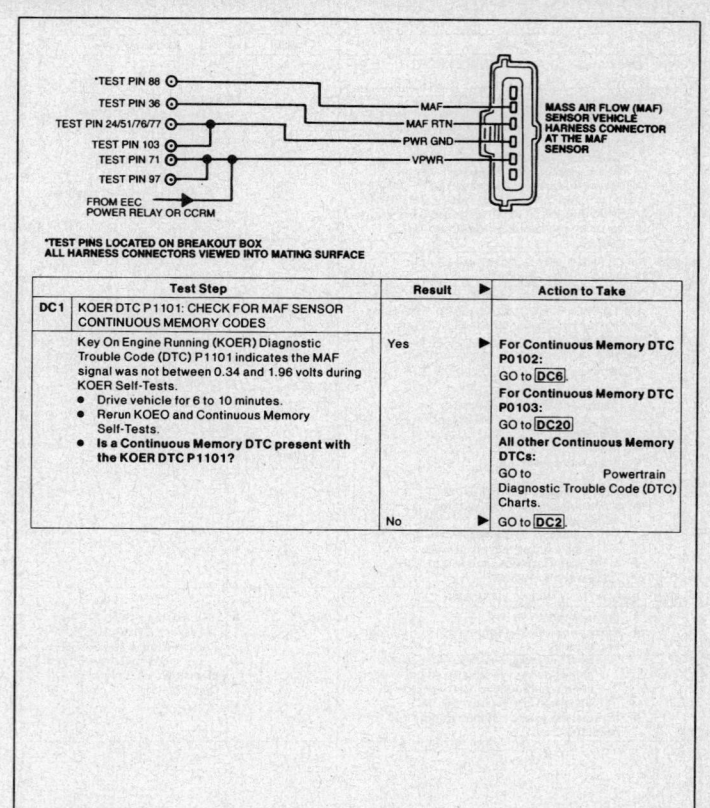

Fig. 228   Test DC: Mass Air Flow Sensor (Part 4 of 14). 1996

Test Step	Result	►	Action to Take
DC2 KOEO DTC P1101 AND KOER DTC P1101: CHECK MAF SENSOR OUTPUT VOLTAGE Diagnostic Trouble Code (DTC) P1101 indicates the Mass Air Flow (MAF) signal was greater than 0.20 volt during KOEO Self-Test. NOTE: DTC P1101 could be generated by a low charged vehicle battery or the garage exhaust ventilation system. Service the battery as necessary. Then remove ventilation system and properly vent to outside atmosphere. Rerun KOEO Self-Test. Possible causes: — Damaged MAF sensor. — Contaminated MAF sensor. — MAF sensor partially connected. — Open PWR GND harness circuit. — Open MAF RTN harness circuit. — Damaged PCM. • Key off. • Check that the MAF sensor is connected. If not, service as necessary. • Disconnect PCM. Inspect for damaged or pushed out pins, corrosion, loose wires, etc. Service as necessary. • Scan Tool connected. • Install breakout box, connect PCM to breakout box. • Key on, engine off. • Measure between Test Pin 88 (MAF SIG) and Test Pins 24 or 103 (PWR GND) at the breakout box. • **Is the voltage greater than 0.20 volts?**	Yes No	► ►	The MAF SIG voltage is greater than expected. Go to DC12. GO to DC8.

Fig. 228   Test DC: Mass Air Flow Sensor (Part 5 of 14). 1996

Test Step	Result	►	Action to Take
DC3 CONTINUOUS MEMORY DTC P1100: CHECK FOR MAF CIRCUIT INTERMITTENT VOLTAGE INPUT Continuous Memory Diagnostic Trouble Code (DTC) P1100 indicates the MAF sensor signal went below 0.39 volt or above 3.90 volts (refer to Voltage to Mass Air Flow Conversion Table at beginning of this Pinpoint Test) sometime during the last 40 warm-up cycles. Possible causes: — MAF sensor connector with poor continuity. — MAF harness with poor continuity. — MAF harness intermittent short. — MAF sensor internal intermittent open or short. • Start engine and bring to idle. NOTE: If a stabilized idle is not at least 700 rpm, go to Symptom Flowcharts. • Scan Tool connected. • Run throttle up to 1500 rpm for 5 seconds, and bring back to idle. • Access MAF V PID (MAF PID) for a fault indication while performing the following: — Lightly tap on MAF sensor and wiggle harness connector to simulate road shock. • **Is the MAF V PID (MAF PID) changing below the minimum 0.39 volt or above a maximum 3.90 volts (refer to Voltage to Mass Air Flow Conversion Table at beginning of this Pinpoint Test)?**	Yes No	► ►	DISCONNECT and INSPECT the MAF sensor connector. If OK, REPLACE the MAF sensor. RESET KAM (REFER to Powertrain Control Module (PCM) Reset). RERUN Quick Test. GO to DC4.

Fig. 228   Test DC: Mass Air Flow Sensor (Part 6 of 14). 1996

Test Step	Result	►	Action to Take
DC4 CHECK MAF HARNESS TO PCM FOR INTERMITTENT OPENS OR SHORTS			
• Key off. • Disconnect PCM. Inspect for damaged or pushed out pins, corrosion, loose wires, etc. Service as necessary. • Install breakout box, reconnect PCM. • Key on, engine off. • Connect DVOM between Test Pin 88 (MAF SIG) and Test Pin 36 (MAF RTN) at the breakout box. • While viewing DVOM, do the following: — Grasp the vehicle harness closest to the MAF sensor connector. — Shake and bend a small section of the harness all the way to the dash panel. — Wiggle, shake and bend the harness from the dash panel to the PCM. • **Is the voltage changing below the minimum 0.39 volt or above the maximum 3.90 volts?**	Yes	►	ISOLATE fault and SERVICE as necessary. RECONNECT all components. RESET KAM (REFER to Powertrain Control Module (PCM) Reset). RERUN Quick Test.
	No	►	Unable to duplicate and/or identify fault at this time. GO to Pinpoint Test Step **Z1** with the following data: MAF V PID (MAF PID) and list of Possible Causes.

FM015960149307OX

Fig. 228   Test DC: Mass Air Flow Sensor (Part 7 of 14). 1996

Test Step	Result	►	Action to Take
DC6 CONTINUOUS MEMORY AND KOER DTC P0102: CHECK MAF SIGNAL LOW INPUT TO PCM			
Diagnostic Trouble Code (DTC) P0102 indicates the MAF signal went below 0.39 volts (refer to Voltage to Mass Air Flow Conversion Table at beginning of this Pinpoint Test) sometime during normal engine operation (Continuous) or during Key On Engine Running (KOER) Self-Test. Possible causes: — Damaged MAF sensor. — MAF sensor disconnected. — MAF circuit open. — VPWR circuit open. — PWR GND circuit open. — MAF RTN circuit open. — MAF circuit shorted to ground. — Air Intake Leak (near MAF sensor). — Throttle Position (TP) system (possible closed throttle indication). — Damaged PCM. • Check broken/loose air outlet tube clamps (throttle body and air cleaner assembly ends), cracks/holes in air outlet tube, worn gaskets between MAF sensor and air cleaner assembly. Service as necessary. • Start engine and bring to idle. NOTE: If a KOER DTC P0505 is present, go to Powertrain Diagnostic Trouble Code (DTC) Charts. For A/T vehicles, if the engine stalls and cannot maintain an idle, go to **DC9**. • Run engine up 1500 rpm for 5 seconds, then bring it back to idle. • Access MAF V PID (MAF PID) with a Scan Tool. • **Is the MAF V PID (MAF PID) less than 0.39 volts (refer to Voltage to Mass Air Flow Conversion Table at beginning of this Pinpoint Test)?**	Yes	►	The MAF SIG voltage is lower than acceptable minimum. GO to **DC7**.
	No	►	For KOER reading between 0.60 and 1.00 volt (refer to Voltage to Mass Air Flow Conversion Table at beginning of this Pinpoint Test): GO to **DC15**. All others: GO to **DC2**.
DC7 CHECK VPWR CIRCUIT VOLTAGE			
• Key off. • Disconnect MAF sensor. • Key on, engine off. • Measure the voltage between VPWR circuit at the MAF sensor vehicle harness connector and the battery negative post. • **Is the voltage greater than 10.5 volts?**	Yes	►	VPWR harness circuit from EEC power relay or CCRM to MAF sensor is OK. GO to **DC8**.
	No	►	SERVICE open VPWR circuit. RESET KAM (REFER to Powertrain Control Module (PCM) Reset). RERUN Quick Test.

FM015960149308OX

Fig. 228   Test DC: Mass Air Flow Sensor (Part 8 of 14). 1996

Test Step	Result	►	Action to Take
DC8 CHECK CONTINUITY OF VPWR CIRCUIT			
• Key off. • MAF sensor disconnected. • Disconnect PCM. Inspect for damaged or pushed out pins, corrosion, loose wires, etc. SERVICE as necessary. • Install breakout box, leave PCM disconnected. • Measure resistance between VPWR circuit at the MAF sensor vehicle harness connector and Test Pin 71 or 97 (VPWR) at the breakout box. • **Is resistance less than 5.0 ohms?**	Yes	►	VPWR harness circuit to PCM is OK. GO to **DC9**.
	No	►	SERVICE open in VPWR harness circuit. REMOVE breakout box. RECONNECT all components. RESET KAM (REFER to Powertrain Control Module (PCM) Reset). RERUN Quick Test.
DC9 CHECK MAF CIRCUIT FOR SHORTS TO GROUND AND MAF RTN CIRCUIT			
• Key off. • MAF sensor disconnected. • Breakout box installed, PCM disconnected. • Disconnect Scan Tool from DLC. • Measure the resistance between Test Pin 88 (MAF SIG) and Test Pin 36 (MAF RTN) at the breakout box. • Measure the resistance between Test Pin 88 (MAF SIG) and Test Pins 51 and 103 (PWR GND) at the breakout box. • **Is each resistance greater than 10,000 ohms?**	Yes	►	MAF SIG harness circuits to PCM are OK. GO to **DC10**.
	No	►	SERVICE short circuit between MAF SIG and GROUND or MAF RTN. REMOVE breakout box. RECONNECT all components. RESET KAM (REFER to Powertrain Control Module (PCM) Reset). RERUN Quick Test.
DC10 CHECK MAF RTN CIRCUIT SHORT TO PWR GND CIRCUITS			
• Key off. • MAF sensor disconnected. • Breakout box installed, PCM disconnected. • Scan Tool disconnected from DLC. • Measure the resistance between Test Pin 36 (MAF RTN) and Test Pins 51 and 103 (PWR GND) at the breakout box. • **Is each resistance greater than 10,000 ohms?**	Yes	►	MAF RTN and GROUND harness circuits to PCM are OK. RECONNECT Scan Tool. GO to **DC11**.
	No	►	SERVICE short circuit between MAF RTN and PWR GND. REMOVE breakout box. RECONNECT all components. RESET KAM (REFER Powertrain Control Module (PCM) Reset). RERUN Quick Test.

FM015960149309OX

Fig. 228   Test DC: Mass Air Flow Sensor (Part 9 of 14). 1996

Test Step	Result	►	Action to Take
DC11 CHECK CONTINUITY OF MAF SIG CIRCUIT			
• Key off. • MAF sensor disconnected. • Breakout box installed, PCM disconnected. • Measure resistance between MAF SIG circuit at the MAF sensor vehicle harness connector and Test Pin 88 (MAF SIG) at the breakout box. • **Is resistance less than 5.0 ohms?**	Yes	►	MAF SIG harness circuit to PCM is OK. GO to **DC12**.
	No	►	SERVICE open in MAF SIG harness circuit. REMOVE breakout box. RECONNECT all components. RESET KAM (REFER to Powertrain Control Module (PCM) Reset). RERUN Quick Test.
DC12 CHECK PWR GND CIRCUIT TO MAF SENSOR			
• Key off. • MAF sensor disconnected. • Breakout box installed. • PCM connected to breakout box. • Key on, engine off. • Measure the voltage between VPWR circuit and PWR GND circuit at the MAF sensor vehicle harness connector. • **Is the voltage greater than 10.5 volts?**	Yes	►	PWR GND harness circuit from battery negative post to MAF sensor is OK. GO to **DC14**.
	No	►	GO to **DC13**.
DC13 CHECK PWR GND CIRCUIT CONTINUITY			
• Key off. • MAF sensor disconnected. • Breakout box installed. • Disconnect PCM. • Disconnect Scan Tool from DLC. • Measure the resistance between PWR GND circuit at the MAF sensor vehicle harness connector and battery negative post. • **Is the resistance less than 10 ohms?**	Yes	►	PWR GND harness circuit to MAF sensor is OK. RECONNECT Scan Tool. GO to **DC14**.
	No	►	SERVICE open in PWR GND harness circuit. REMOVE breakout box. RECONNECT all components. RESET KAM (REFER to Powertrain Control Module (PCM) Reset). RERUN Quick Test.
DC14 CHECK MAF RTN CIRCUIT CONTINUITY			
• Key off. • MAF sensor disconnected. • Breakout box installed, PCM disconnected. • Measure the resistance between MAF RTN circuit at the MAF sensor vehicle harness connector and Test Pin 36 (MAF RTN) at the breakout box. • **Is the resistance less than 5.0 ohms?**	Yes	►	MAF RTN harness circuit to PCM is OK. GO to **DC15**.
	No	►	SERVICE open in MAF RTN harness circuit. REMOVE breakout box. RECONNECT all components. RESET KAM (REFER to Powertrain Control Module (PCM) Reset). RERUN Quick Test.

FM015960149310OX

Fig. 228   Test DC: Mass Air Flow Sensor (Part 10 of 14). 1996

Test Step	Result	►	Action to Take
DC15 CHECK MAF CIRCUIT FOR SHORT TO GROUND IN PCM			
• Key off.	Yes	►	GO to **DC16**.
• MAF sensor disconnected.	No	►	MAF SIG shorted to PWR GND
• Breakout box installed.			or MAF RTN in the PCM.
• Reconnect PCM to breakout box.			REPLACE the PCM. REMOVE
• Disconnect Scan Tool from DLC.			breakout box. RECONNECT
• Measure the resistance between Test Pin 88 (MAF SIG) and Test Pin 36 (MAF RTN) at the breakout box.			MAF sensor.
• Measure the resistance between Test Pin 88 (MAF SIG) and Test Pins 51 and 103 (PWR GND) at the breakout box.			
• **Is each resistance greater than 10,000 ohms?**			
DC16 CHECK MAF RTN CIRCUIT FOR SHORT TO PWR GND IN PCM			
• Key off.	Yes	►	RECONNECT Scan Tool. GO to
• MAF sensor disconnected.			**DC17**.
• Breakout box installed.	No	►	MAF RTN shorted to PWR GND
• PCM connected to breakout box.			in PCM. REPLACE PCM.
• Scan Tool disconnected from DLC.			REMOVE breakout box.
• Measure the resistance between Test Pin 36 (MAF RTN) and Test Pins 51 and 103 (PWR GND) at the breakout box.			RECONNECT all components. RERUN Quick Test.
• **Is each resistance greater than 10,000 ohms?**			
DC17 CHECK MAF CIRCUIT OUTPUT			
• Key off.	Yes	►	MAF SIG to the PCM is OK. GO
• MAF sensor connected.			to **DC18**.
• Breakout box installed, PCM connected.	No	►	MAF SIG or PWR GND is open
• Key on, engine running.			or shorted in the MAF sensor.
NOTE: If a stabilized idle is not at least 700 rpm, go to Symptom Flowcharts.			REPLACE MAF sensor. REMOVE breakout box. RECONNECT PCM. RESET
• Measure the voltage between Test Pin 88 (MAF SIG) at the breakout box and battery negative post.			KAM (REFER to Powertrain Control Module (PCM) Reset). RERUN Quick
• **Is the voltage at idle between 0.34 and 1.96 volts?**			Test.

FM0159601493110X

Fig. 228   Test DC: Mass Air Flow Sensor (Part 11 of 14). 1996

Test Step	Result	►	Action to Take
DC18 VERIFY MAF CIRCUIT INPUT AND OUTPUT			
• Key off.	Yes	►	MAF RTN in MAF sensor is OK,
• MAF sensor connected.			GO to **DC19**.
• Breakout box installed, PCM connected.	No	►	MAF RTN open in the MAF
• Key on, engine running.			sensor. REPLACE MAF sensor.
• Measure the voltage between Test Pin 88 (MAF SIG) and Test Pin 36 (MAF RTN) at the breakout box.			REMOVE breakout box. RECONNECT PCM. RESET KAM (REFER to
• **Is the voltage between 0.34 and 1.96 volts?**			Powertrain Control Module (PCM) Reset). RERUN Quick Test.
DC19 CHECK MAF CIRCUIT OUTPUT WITH SCAN TOOL			
• Key off.	Yes	►	Unable to identify fault at this
• MAF sensor connected.			time. CHECK possible
• Breakout box installed, PCM connected.			intermittent. GO to Pinpoint
• Key on, engine running.			Test Step **Z1**.
• Access MAF V PID (MAF PID) with a Scan Tool at idle.	No	►	**If an idle concern is not present:**
• **Is the MAF V PID (MAF PID) between 0.34 and 1.96 volts (refer to Voltage to Mass Air Flow Conversion Table at the beginning of this Pinpoint Test)?**			MAF SIG or MAF RTN is open or shorted in the PCM. REPLACE PCM. REMOVE breakout box. RECONNECT PCM. RERUN Quick Test.
			If a fault was not detected and an idle concern is still present:
			REMOVE breakout box. RECONNECT all components. Disregard DTC P0102 at this time. RETURN to Diagnostic Subroutines.

FM0159601493120X

Fig. 228   Test DC: Mass Air Flow Sensor (Part 12 of 14). 1996

Test Step	Result	►	Action to Take
DC20 DTC P0103: CHECK MAF SIGNAL HIGH INPUT TO PCM			
Diagnostic Trouble Code (DTC) P0103 indicates the MAF Signal went above 3.90 volts (refer to Voltage to Mass Air Flow Conversion Table at the beginning of this Pinpoint Test) sometime during normal engine operation (Continuous), during Key On Engine Off Self-Test, or during Key On Engine Running Self-Test.	Yes	►	MAF SIG shorted to VPWR in MAF sensor. REMOVE jumper between PWR GND and SIG RTN at the MAF sensor vehicle harness connector. REPLACE MAF sensor. RESET KAM (REFER to Powertrain Control Module (PCM) Reset). RERUN Quick Test.
NOTE: DTC P0103 could be generated by foreign material blocking the MAF sensor screen causing an air flow restriction. If contaminants are found on the screen, check air filter installation in air cleaner tray and proper sealing of air cleaner and air tubes before proceeding. Rerun Quick Test after repair.	No	►	Power short in circuit but not in MAF sensor. REMOVE jumper between PWR GND and SIG RTN at the MAF sensor vehicle harness connector. GO to **DC21**.
Possible causes:			
— Blocked MAF sensor screen.			
— Damaged MAF sensor.			
— MAF SIG harness short to VPWR.			
— Damaged PCM.			
• Start engine and bring to idle.			
NOTE: If a KOER DTC P0505 is present, go to Section 5A, Powertrain Diagnostic Trouble Code (DTC) Charts. For 2.3L A/T Ranger that stalls and cannot maintain an idle, replace PCM.			
• Run throttle up to 1500 rpm for 5 seconds, and bring it back to idle.			
• Access MAF V PID (MAF PID) with a Scan Tool.			
NOTE: MAF V PID (MAF PID) should be greater than 3.90 volts (refer to Voltage to Mass Air Flow Conversion Table at the beginning of this Pinpoint Test).			
• Key off.			
• Disconnect MAF sensor.			
• Jumper PWR GND and MAF RTN pins at the MAF sensor vehicle harness connector.			
• Key on, engine running.			
• Again access MAF V PID (MAF PID) with a Scan Tool.			
• **Did the MAF V PID (MAF PID) drop from the previous reading to below 0.39 volts (refer to Voltage to Mass Air Flow Conversion Table at the beginning of this Pinpoint Test)?**			

FM0159601493130X

Fig. 228   Test DC: Mass Air Flow Sensor (Part 13 of 14). 1996

Test Step	Result	►	Action to Take
DC21 CHECK MAF SIG FOR SHORT TO POWER (EXCLUDING VREF) IN HARNESS			
• Key off.	Yes	►	SERVICE short between MAF
• MAF sensor disconnected.			SIG and Power (excluding
• Disconnect PCM. Inspect for damaged or pushed out pins, corrosion, loose wires, etc. SERVICE as necessary.			VREF) in harness circuit. REMOVE breakout box. RECONNECT all components. RERUN Quick Test.
• Install breakout box, leave PCM disconnected.	No	►	GO to **DC22**.
• Key on, engine off.			
• Measure the voltage between Test Pin 88 (MAF SIG) and Test Pin 24 or 103 (PWR GND) at the breakout box.			
• **Is the voltage greater than 10.5 volts?**			
DC22 CHECK MAF SIG FOR SHORT TO POWER IN PCM			
• Key off.	Yes	►	**If an idle concern is not present:**
• MAF sensor disconnected.			MAF SIG or MAF RTN is open or shorted in the PCM. REPLACE PCM. REMOVE breakout box. RECONNECT PCM. RERUN Quick Test.
• PCM disconnected.			
• Measure the resistance between Test Pin 88 (MAF SIG) and Test Pins 71 or 97 (VPWR) at the breakout box.			
• **Is the resistance greater than 10,000 ohms?**			**If a fault was not detected and an idle concern is still present:**
			REMOVE breakout box. RECONNECT all components. Disregard DTC P0102 at this time. RETURN to Diagnostic Subroutines.
	No	►	SERVICE short between MAF SIG and VREF in harness circuit. REMOVE breakout box. RECONNECT all components. RESET KAM (REFER to Section 2A, Powertrain Control Module (PCM) Reset). RERUN Quick Test.

FM0159601493140X

Fig. 228   Test DC: Mass Air Flow Sensor (Part 14 of 14). 1996

Note

You should enter this Pinpoint Test only when directed here.

Remember

This Pinpoint Test is intended to diagnose the following:

- Injector Pressure (IP) Sensor (9F972)
- Harness Circuits: IP and SIG RTN
- Powertrain Control Module (PCM) (12A650)

Tables and Charts

Normal operating range is from 0 to 150 psi and values may vary by +/- 2.5%.

The Injection Pressure (IP) sensor operates within the range of -40°C to 125°C.

FM0159601494010X

Fig. 229   Test DD: Injection Pressure Sensor (Part 1 of 8). 1996

Pinpoint Test Schematics

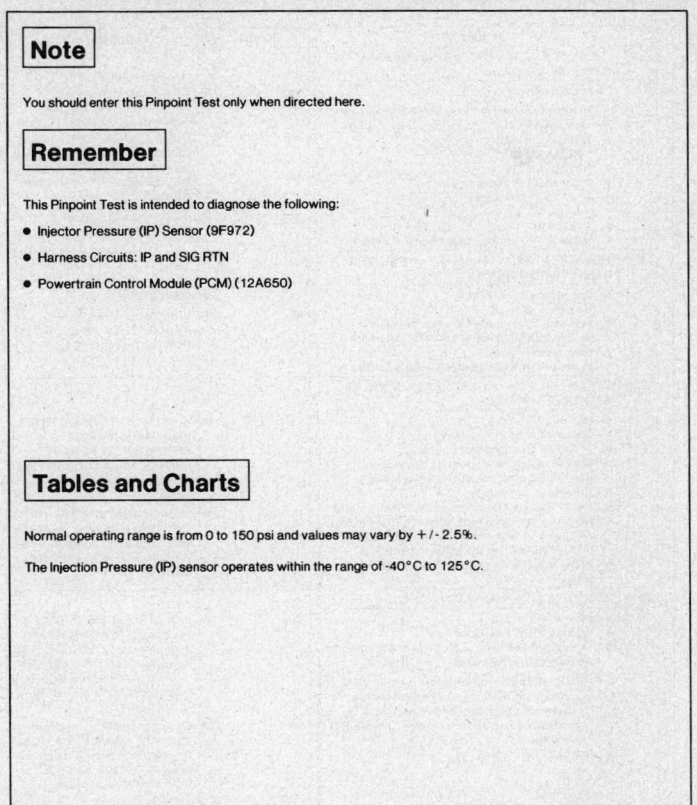

*TEST PINS LOCATED ON BREAKOUT BOX
ALL HARNESS CONNECTORS VIEWED INTO MATING SURFACE

FM0159601494020

Fig. 229   Test DD: Injection Pressure Sensor (Part 2 of 8). 1996

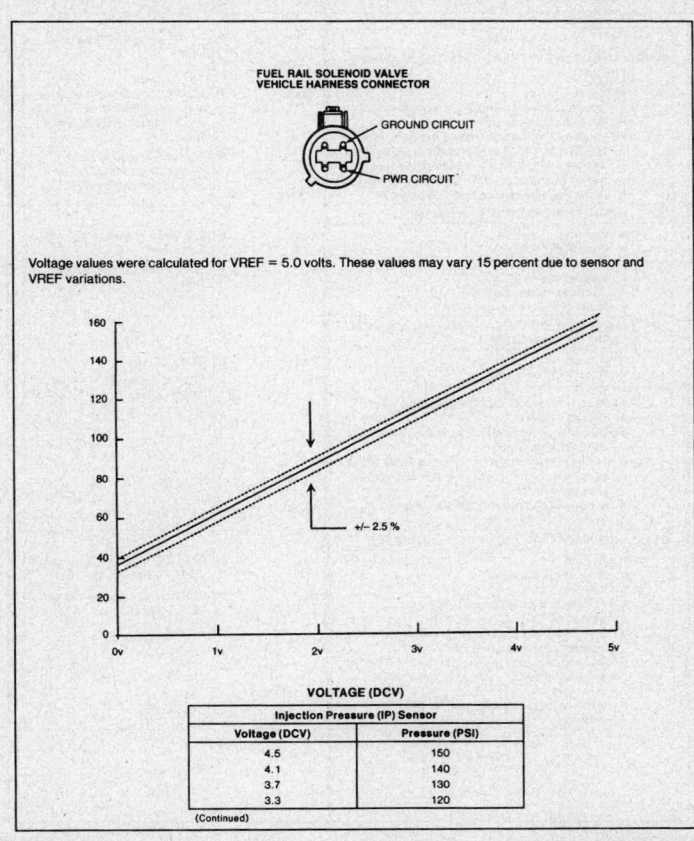

Voltage values were calculated for VREF = 5.0 volts. These values may vary 15 percent due to sensor and VREF variations.

Injection Pressure (IP) Sensor	
Voltage (DCV)	Pressure (PSI)
4.5	150
4.1	140
3.7	130
3.3	120
(Continued)	

VOLTAGE (DCV)

FM0159601494030X

Fig. 229   Test DD: Injection Pressure Sensor (Part 3 of 8). 1996

VOLTAGE (DCV) (Cont'd)

Injection Pressure (IP) Sensor	
Voltage (DCV)	Pressure (PSI)
2.9	110
2.5	100
2.1	90
1.7	80
1.3	70
0.9	60
0.5	50
0.1	40
0	37.6

	Test Step	Result	▶	Action to Take
DD1	DTC P0192: VERIFY DTC WITH IP PID			
	Diagnostic Trouble Code (DTC) P0192 indicates the IP sensor signal is less than Self-Test minimum. The IP sensor minimum is 0.5 volts at 50 psig. Possible causes: — IP signal shorted to Signal RTN or PWR GND. — IP signal open. — Low fuel pressure. — Damaged IP sensor. — Damaged PCM. • Key off. • Scan Tool connected. • Key on. • Verify there is sufficient fuel. • Access IP PID. • Is the IP PID voltage less than 0.2 volt?	Yes No	▶ ▶	Fault is present, GO to **DD2**. Fault may be intermittent. GO to **DD10**.
DD2	GENERATE OPPOSITE SIGNAL			
	• Key off. • Scan Tool connected. • Disconnect IP vehicle harness connector from IP sensor. • Jumper IP SIG test pin to VREF test pin at the IP VEHICLE harness connector. NOTE: If any Scan Tool communication problem exists, remove jumper and go to **DD8**. • Access IP PID. • Is the IP PID voltage greater than 4.6 volts?	Yes No	▶ ▶	IP sensor is damaged. REPLACE IP sensor REMOVE jumper. RERUN Quick Test. VREF or IP SIG open in the harness or PCM, IP SIG shorted to SIG RTN or GND in the harness or PCM. REMOVE jumper. GO to **DD3**

FM0159601494040X

Fig. 229   Test DD: Injection Pressure Sensor (Part 4 of 8). 1996

Part 5 of 8

Test Step	Result	▶	Action to Take
DD3 MEASURE VREF VOLTAGE AT THE IP SENSOR HARNESS CONNECTOR			
• IP sensor disconnected. • Key on, engine off. • Measure the voltage between the sensor VREF circuit and the SIG RTN circuit at the IP harness connector. • **Is the voltage between 4.0 and 6.0 volts?**	Yes No	▶ ▶	GO to **DD4**. VREF is out of range. RECONNECT IP sensor. GO to Pinpoint Test Step **C1**.
DD4 CHECK IP CIRCUIT CONTINUITY			
• Key off. • IP sensor disconnected. • Disconnect PCM. Inspect for damaged or pushed out pins, corrosion, loose wires, etc. Service as necessary. • Install breakout box, leave PCM disconnected. • Measure the resistance between IP circuit at the IP vehicle harness connector and Test Pin 63 (IP SIG) at the breakout box. • **Is the resistance less than 5.0 ohms?**	Yes No	▶ ▶	GO to **DD5**. SERVICE open in the IP SIG wire. REMOVE breakout box. RECONNECT all components. RERUN Quick Test.
DD5 CHECK IP CIRCUIT FOR SHORTS TO SIG RTN AND PWR GND			
• Key off. • IP disconnected. • Breakout box installed. • PCM disconnected. • Measure the resistance between Test Pin 63 (IP SIG) and Test Pin 91 (SIG RTN) and Test Pin 24 or 103 (PWR GND) at the breakout box. • **Is the resistance greater than 10,000 ohms?**	No	▶	SERVICE short in IP SIG shorted to SIG RTN or PWR GND in the harness. REMOVE breakout box. RECONNECT all components. RERUN Quick Test.
DD6 DTC P0193: CHECK FUEL PRESSURE			
Diagnostic Trouble Code (DTC) P0193 indicates the IP sensor signal is greater than Self-Test maximum. The IP sensor maximum is 4.5 volts at 150 psi. Possible causes: — IP signal shorted to VREF or PWR in harness. — Damaged PCM. — Damaged IP sensor. — VREF shorted to PWR. — High fuel pressure. • Key off. • Scan Tool connected. • Fuel pressure gauge connected. • Key on. • Access and monitor IP sensor pressure PID. • **Are both readings greater than 140 psi and within 10 psi of each other?**	Yes No	▶ ▶	GO to Pinpoint Test Step **HB1**. GO to **DD7**.

Fig. 229 Test DD: Injection Pressure Sensor (Part 5 of 8). 1996

Part 6 of 8

Test Step	Result	▶	Action to Take
DD7 DTC P0193: VERIFY DTC WITH IP PID: GENERATE OPPOSITE SIGNAL			
Possible causes: — IP signal shorted to VREF or PWR in harness. — Damaged PCM. — Damaged IP sensor. — VREF shorted to PWR. • Key off. • Disconnect IP sensor. • Scan Tool connected. • Key on. • Access IP PID. • **Is the IP PID voltage less than 0.2 volts?**	Yes No	▶ ▶	Continuous Memory DTC P0193 only: Fault may be intermittent. GO to **DD10**. KOEO and KOER DTC, REPLACE (IP) sensor following service manual procedures. RECONNECT all components. RERUN Quick Test. IP SIG shorted to VREF or PWR. GO to **DD8**.
DD8 MEASURE VREF VOLTAGE AT THE IP SENSOR HARNESS CONNECTOR			
• IP sensor disconnected. • Key on, engine off. • Measure the voltage between the sensor VREF circuit and the SIG RTN circuit at the IP harness connector. • **Is the voltage between 4.0 and 6.0 volts?**	Yes No	▶ ▶	GO to **DD9**. VREF is out of range. RECONNECT IP sensor. GO to Pinpoint Test Step **C1**.
DD9 CHECK FOR IP SIGNAL CIRCUIT SHORTED TO SIG RTN OR PWR GND			
• Key off. • Disconnect Scan Tool from DLC. • IP sensor disconnected. • Disconnect PCM. Inspect for damaged or pushed out pins, corrosion, loose wires, etc. Service as necessary. • Install breakout box, leave PCM disconnected. • Measure the resistance between Test Pin 63 (IP SIG) and Test Pin 91 (SIG RTN) and 24 or 103 (PWR GND) at the breakout box. • **Is the resistance greater than 10,000 ohms?**	Yes No	▶ ▶	IP SIG is shorted to SIG RTN or PWR GND in the PCM. REPLACE PCM. REMOVE breakout box. RECONNECT all components. RERUN Quick Test. IP SIG shorted to SIG RTN or PWR GND in the harness. SERVICE short. REMOVE breakout box. RECONNECT all components. RERUN Quick Test.
DD10 WIGGLE TEST SENSOR AND HARNESS			
• Key on, engine off. • Access IP PID with Scan Tool. • Observe IP PID for an indication of a fault while performing the following: — Lightly tap on the IP sensor, wiggle the IP sensor connector and vehicle harness between the sensor and PCM. A fault is indicated by a sudden change in the IP PID voltage. • **Is a fault indicated?**	Yes No	▶ ▶	ISOLATE fault and SERVICE as necessary. RECONNECT all components. COMPLETE PCM Reset to clear DTCs (REFER to Powertrain Control Module (PCM) Reset). RERUN Quick Test. Unable to duplicate and / or identify fault at this time. GO to Pinpoint Test Step **Z1** with the following data: IP and VREF PIDs and list of possible causes.

Fig. 229 Test DD: Injection Pressure Sensor (Part 6 of 8). 1996

Part 7 of 8

Test Step	Result	▶	Action to Take
DD11 DTC P0191: CHECK FUEL PRESSURE			
Diagnostic Trouble Code (DTC) P0191 indicates the IP sensor signal has exceeded the Self-Test Calibration limits and can only be retrieved during KOEO and KOER Self-Test. DTC P0191 (IP) circuit malfunction low limit is 1.7 volts at 80 psig and 3.8 volts at 135 psig. for the high limit. Possible causes: — High pressure. — Low fuel pressure. — Damaged IP sensor. — Excessive resistance. — Low or no fuel. • Key on. • Verify there is sufficient fuel. • Key off. • Fuel pressure gauge connected to schrader valve. • Key on. • **Is the pressure reading between 80 psig and 135 psig?**	Yes No	▶ ▶	GO to **DD12**. REMOVE pressure gauge. GO to Pinpoint Test Step **HB1**.
DD12 CHECK FUEL PRESSURE WITH IP PID			
• Key off. • Scan Tool connected. • Fuel pressure gauge connected. • Key on. • Access and monitor IP PID. • **Is the IP pressure reading within 10 psig of the fuel pressure gauge reading?**	Yes No	▶ ▶	RERUN Quick Test. GO to **DD13**.
DD13 VERIFY FUEL RAIL SOLENOID VALVE OPENS			
• Key off. • Scan Tool connected. • Key on. • Access and enter the Output Test Mode. • Cycle output ON and then OFF several times. • **Is a click felt or heard?**	Yes No	▶ ▶	EXIT Output Test Mode. RECONNECT solenoid valve. GO to **DD14**. GO to **DD17**.
DD14 VERIFY VREF AT IP SENSOR			
• Key off. • IP sensor disconnected. • Key on, engine off. • Measure the voltage between the VREF circuit and the SIG RTN circuit at the IP sensor vehicle harness connector. • **Is the voltage reading between 4.0 and 6.0 volts?**	Yes No	▶ ▶	GO to **DD15**. RECONNECT IP sensor. GO to Pinpoint Test Step **C1**.

Fig. 229 Test DD: Injection Pressure Sensor (Part 7 of 8). 1996

Part 8 of 8

Test Step	Result	▶	Action to Take
DD15 CHECK FOR EXCESSIVE RESISTANCE IN THE IP CIRCUIT			
• Key off. • Breakout box installed. PCM disconnected. • IP sensor disconnected. • Measure the resistance between Test Pins 91 SIG RTN and 63 IP sensor at the breakout box and the IP sensor vehicle harness connector (refer to schematic at the beginning of test). • **Is the resistance less than 5.0 ohms?**	Yes No	▶ ▶	SERVICE cause of excessive resistance. RECONNECT PCM and IP sensor. RERUN Quick Test. REMOVE breakout box. RECONNECT PCM and IP sensor. GO to **DD16**.
DD16 MONITOR IP CIRCUIT WITH SCAN TOOL			
• Key off. • Scan Tool connected. • IP sensor disconnected. • Key on, engine off. • Access and monitor IP PID. • **Is the IP PID value less than 0.2 volt?**	Yes No	▶ ▶	REPLACE IP sensor. RERUN Quick Test. REPLACE PCM. RERUN Quick Test.
DD17 CHECK FOR VOLTAGE AT FUEL RAIL SOLENOID HARNESS CONNECTOR			
• Key off. • Scan Tool connected. • Key on. • Access and enter Output Test Mode. • Select: All On. • Disconnect the Fuel Rail Solenoid valve at the vehicle harness connector. • Measure the voltage between the PWR circuit at the vehicle harness connector and battery ground. • **Is the voltage reading greater than 10.5 volts?**	Yes No	▶ ▶	GO to **DD18**. SERVICE open PWR circuit. RERUN Quick Test.
DD18 CHECK GROUND CIRCUIT FOR CONTINUITY			
• Key off. • Scan Tool connected. • Key on. • Access and enter Output Test Mode. • Select: All On. • Disconnect the Fuel Rail Solenoid valve at the vehicle harness connector. • Measure the voltage between the PWR circuit and ground circuit at the vehicle harness connector. • **Is the voltage reading greater than 10.5 volts?**	Yes No	▶ ▶	REPLACE Fuel Rail Solenoid Valve. RERUN Quick Test. SERVICE open ground circuit. RERUN Quick Test.

Fig. 229 Test DD: Injection Pressure Sensor (Part 8 of 8). 1996

Note

You should enter this Pinpoint Test only when directed here.

Remember

This Pinpoint Test is intended to diagnose the following:

- Flexible Fuel (FF) sensor (9C044).
- Harness circuits: FF SIG, Vehicle Power (VPWR) and Power Ground (PWR GND).
- Powertrain Control Module (PCM) (12A650).

Warning

- HANDLE METHANOL-GASOLINE FUEL BLENDS WITH EXTREME CAUTION. BE SURE TO WEAR CHEMICAL GOGGLES AND IMPERVIOUS GLOVES.
- DO NOT EAT, SMOKE OR DRINK WHEN FUEL BLENDS ARE BEING HANDLED.
- FLAMES FROM METHANOL OR METHANOL-GASOLINE BLENDS MAY BE INVISIBLE.
- INHALING VAPORS FROM FUEL BLENDS IS HARMFUL TO YOUR HEALTH. HANDLE ONLY IN WELL VENTILATED AREAS.

FM015960149501OX

Fig. 230   Test DE: Flexible Fuel Sensor (Part 1 of 11). 1996

Safe Fuel Handling

Gasoline, methanol and methanol blends

FIRE

- REPORT ALL FIRES to the appropriate authorities.
- FLAMES from methanol or methanol-gasoline blends MAY BE INVISIBLE.
- Know the locations of PORTABLE EXTINGUISHER, FIRE BLANKETS, FIRE ALARMS and EYE WASH, SHOWER FACILITIES. Learn how to use them.
- Use a B or AFFF (light water) type FIRE EXTINGUISHER to fight flammable liquid fires.

FIRST AID

- IF SWALLOWED

  — If GASOLINE has been swallowed, DO NOT induce vomiting, SEEK MEDICAL ATTENTION IMMEDIATELY!

  — If METHANOL OR A METHANOL/GASOLINE BLEND has been swallowed, induce vomiting under the direction of a physician or Poison Control Center. SEEK MEDICAL ATTENTION IMMEDIATELY!

- When overcome by vapors, MOVE VICTIM TO FRESH AIR if safe. If not breathing, give artificial respiration or Cardiopulmonary Resuscitation (CPR) as appropriate. SEEK MEDICAL ATTENTION IMMEDIATELY!
- IF SPLASHED IN EYES, FLUSH with large amounts of water for 15 minutes. Remove contact lenses, if worn. SEEK MEDICAL ATTENTION.

HEALTH

- ALL FUELS may be HARMFUL OR FATAL IF SWALLOWED.
- IF FUEL IS SWALLOWED, onset of serious health effects may be delayed 12 to 24 hours.
- FUELS AND PRODUCTS CONTAINING METHANOL (e.g: windshield washer fluid) may cause blindness if swallowed.
- ALL FUEL VAPORS may be HARMFUL IF INHALED.
- ALL FUELS are IRRITATING to the EYES and RESPIRATORY SYSTEM.
- FUELS made with GASOLINE may contain benzene which is a cancer causing agent.

HANDLING

- Use FLAMMABLE LIQUID HANDLING PRECAUTIONS.
- Wear CHEMICAL GOGGLES and NITRIDE GLOVES (additional protective clothing and equipment may be necessary in some instances).
- Keep flammable liquids in APPROVED LABELED CLOSED CONTAINERS.

FM015960149502OX

Fig. 230   Test DE: Flexible Fuel Sensor (Part 2 of 11). 1996

- Use in WELL VENTILATED AREAS and CONTROL VAPORS. Be aware that vapors ARE NOT VISIBLE, are heavier than air, can travel along the floor and will settle in lower areas.
- When transferring flammable liquids, BOND the RECEIVING CONTAINER to the SOURCE and GROUND the SOURCE to the EARTH.
- DO NOT SMOKE or use HEAT/SPARK PRODUCING EQUIPMENT near vapors.
- DO NOT eat, smoke or drink where these products are handled, processed or stored.
- NEVER SIPHON BY MOUTH.
- WASH HANDS thoroughly after HANDLING any FUEL.

SPILLS

- Notify the proper authorities in the EVENT of any spill you have NOT been trained to clean up.
- STOP, CONTAIN AND CLEAN UP small spills with an absorbent material.

Pinpoint Test Schematic

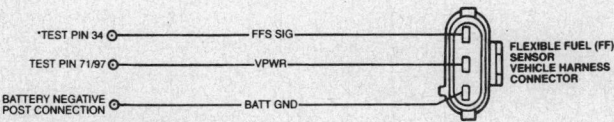

*TEST PIN 34 ○——— FFS SIG

TEST PIN 71/97 ○——— VPWR

BATTERY NEGATIVE POST CONNECTION ○——— BATT GND

FLEXIBLE FUEL (FF) SENSOR VEHICLE HARNESS CONNECTOR

*TEST PINS LOCATED ON BREAKOUT BOX
ALL HARNESS CONNECTORS VIEWED INTO MATING SURFACE

FM015960149503OX

Fig. 230   Test DE: Flexible Fuel Sensor (Part 3 of 11). 1996

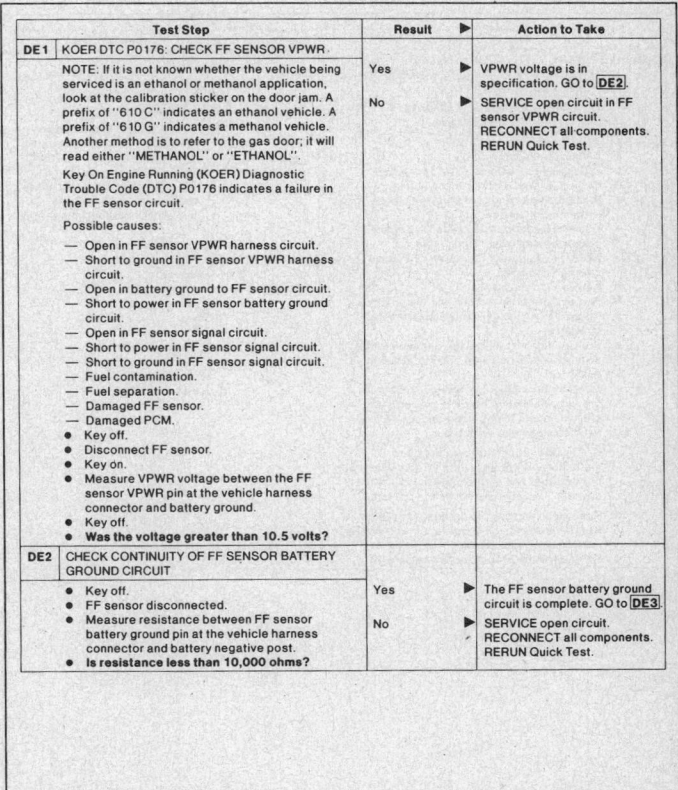

Test Step		Result	▶	Action to Take
DE1	KOER DTC P0176: CHECK FF SENSOR VPWR			
	NOTE: If it is not known whether the vehicle being serviced is an ethanol or methanol application, look at the calibration sticker on the door jam. A prefix of "610 C" indicates an ethanol vehicle. A prefix of "610 G" indicates a methanol vehicle. Another method is to refer to the gas door; it will read either "METHANOL" or "ETHANOL".	Yes	▶	VPWR voltage is in specification. GO to **DE2**.
	Key On Engine Running (KOER) Diagnostic Trouble Code (DTC) P0176 indicates a failure in the FF sensor circuit.	No	▶	SERVICE open circuit in FF sensor VPWR circuit. RECONNECT all components. RERUN Quick Test.
	Possible causes:			
	— Open in FF sensor VPWR harness circuit. — Short to ground in FF sensor VPWR harness circuit. — Open in battery ground to FF sensor circuit. — Short to power in FF sensor battery ground circuit. — Open in FF sensor signal circuit. — Short to power in FF sensor signal circuit. — Short to ground in FF sensor signal circuit. — Fuel contamination. — Fuel separation. — Damaged FF sensor. — Damaged PCM.			
	• Key off. • Disconnect FF sensor. • Key on. • Measure VPWR voltage between the FF sensor VPWR pin at the vehicle harness connector and battery ground. • Key off. • **Was the voltage greater than 10.5 volts?**			
DE2	CHECK CONTINUITY OF FF SENSOR BATTERY GROUND CIRCUIT			
	• Key off. • FF sensor disconnected. • Measure resistance between FF sensor battery ground pin at the vehicle harness connector and battery negative post. • **Is resistance less than 10,000 ohms?**	Yes	▶	The FF sensor battery ground circuit is complete. GO to **DE3**.
		No	▶	SERVICE open circuit. RECONNECT all components. RERUN Quick Test.

FM015960149504OX

Fig. 230   Test DE: Flexible Fuel Sensor (Part 4 of 11). 1996

Test Step	Result	▶	Action to Take
DE3 CHECK CONTINUITY OF FF SENSOR SIGNAL CIRCUIT • Key off. • FF sensor disconnected. • Disconnect PCM. Inspect for damaged or pushed out pins, corrosion, loose wires, etc. Service as necessary. • Install breakout box, leave PCM disconnected. • Measure resistance between FF sensor signal circuit pin at the FF sensor vehicle harness connector and Test Pin 34 (FF SIG) at the breakout box. • **Is resistance less than 5 ohms?**	Yes No	▶ ▶	The FF sensor signal circuit is complete. GO TO DE4. SERVICE open circuit. REMOVE breakout box. RECONNECT all components. RERUN Quick Test.
DE4 CHECK FOR SHORT TO POWER IN FF SENSOR SIGNAL CIRCUIT • Key off. • FF sensor disconnected. • Breakout box installed, PCM disconnected. • Measure resistance between Test Pin 34 (FF SIG) and Test Pins 90 (VREF), 71 (VPWR) and 97 (VPWR) at the breakout box. • **Is each resistance greater than 10,000 ohms?**	Yes No	▶ ▶	There is no short to power in the FF sensor SIG circuit. GO to DE5. SERVICE short circuit. REMOVE breakout box. RECONNECT all components. RERUN Quick Test.
DE5 CHECK FOR SHORT TO GROUND IN FF SENSOR SIGNAL CIRCUIT • Key off. • Disconnect Scan Tool from DLC. • FF sensor disconnected. • Breakout box installed, PCM disconnected. • Measure resistance between Test Pin 34 (FF SIG) and Test Pins 51 (PWR GRND), 91 (SIG RTN) and 103 (PWR GRND) at the breakout box. • **Is resistance greater tha 10,000 ohms?**	Yes No	▶ ▶	There is no short to ground in the FF sensor SIG circuit. GO to DE6. SERVICE short circuit. REMOVE breakout box. RECONNECT all components. RERUN Quick Test.

FM0159601495050X

Fig. 230   Test DE: Flexible Fuel Sensor (Part 5 of 11). 1996

Test Step	Result	▶	Action to Take
DE6 CHECK FF SENSOR DEDICATED FAILURE MODE PID • Key on, engine running. • With the engine at idle, access the FFFM PID with a Scan Tool and note the PID status. • **Is the FFFM PID indicating an "ON" condition?**	Yes No	▶ ▶	The FF sensor may be damaged. GO to DE7. The FF sensor output frequency does not indicate an above maximum FF sensor failure mode. **For Ethanol Vehicles:**If you know the percentage of ethanol in the fuel of the vehicle under service, GO to DE10. **For Methanol Vehicles:**If you know the percentage of methanol in the fuel of the vehicle under service, GO to DE11. If you do not know the percentage of ethanol or methanol in the fuel of the vehicle under service, GO to DE8.
DE7 CHECK FF SENSOR FREQUENCY • Key on, engine running. • Access the FF PID with a Scan Tool and record the PID frequency value. • **Is the FF PID indicating a value between 42 and 145 Hz?**	Yes No	▶ ▶	The FF sensor output does not indicate a failure. **For Ethanol Vehicles:**If you know the percentage of ethanol in the fuel of the vehicle under service, GO to DE10. **For Methanol Vehicles:**If you know the percentage of methanol in the fuel of the vehicle under service, GO to DE11. If the percentage of ethanol or methanol in the fuel of the vehicle under service is unknown, GO to DE8. The FF sensor is damaged. REPLACE the FF sensor. REMOVE breakout box. RECONNECT all components. RERUN Quick Test.

FM0159601495060X

Fig. 230   Test DE: Flexible Fuel Sensor (Part 6 of 11). 1996

Test Step	Result	▶	Action to Take
DE8 DETERMINE SEPARATION POINT OF WATER / METHANOL (OR WATER / ETHANOL) AND GASOLINE IN THE FUEL NOTE: This step requires the Rotunda FFV Fuel Test Kit 014-00770 or equivalent. • Key off. • FF sensor disconnected. • Breakout box installed, PCM connected. • Fill beaker with 5 ml of clean water. • Place the hose end of the fuel drain hose assembly in gas can. • Connect fuel drain hose assembly to fuel pressure relief valve. Turn connector clockwise to tighten. Turn ON / OFF valve clockwise to open. • Key on. • Allow 22 ml of fuel to drain into the cas gan. • Pour 20 ml of the fuel into 25 ml graduated cylinder. • Pour enough water from the beaker into the 25 ml graduated cylinder to bring total volume to 24 ml. • Insert stopper plug in opening of 25 ml graduated cylinder. Hold it in place as you shake cylinder to mix water and fuel. Allow liquid to stand and separate. NOTE: After about three minutes, the methanol and water (or ethanol and water) will mix together and settle to the bottom of the cylinder. The gasoline will rise to the top. • Record the level on the graduated cylinder where the methanol / water (or ethanol / water) mixture and gasoline meet. • **Have all of the steps been completed?**	Yes No	▶ ▶	GO to DE9. COMPLETE all steps before continuing. Gasoline and water will separate. However, if the fuel does not appear to separate, then the fuel is either 100 percent methanol or a mixture of methanol and water.

FM0159601495070X

Fig. 230   Test DE: Flexible Fuel Sensor (Part 7 of 11). 1996

Test Step	Result	▶	Action to Take
DE9 CALCULATE PERCENTAGE OF METHANOL (OR ETHANOL) IN THE FUEL • Use the following equation to calculate and record the percentage of methanol (or ethanol) in the fuel sample collected in step DE8: Percent methanol (or ethanol) = (A - 4) x 5 NOTE: The letter "A" in the above equation equals the level on the graduated cylinder recorded from step DE8 where the methanol / water (or ethanol / water) mixture and gasoline meet; see illustration below. EXAMPLE: If the reading from step DE8 is 14 ml then the percentage of methanol (or ethanol) in the fuel mixture is (14 - 4) x 5, which equals 50. Therefore, the percentage of methanol (or ethanol) in the fuel mixture is 50. • **Has the percentage of methanol (or ethanol) in the fuel mixture been determined?**	Yes No	▶ ▶	The results are accurate to + /- 10%. POUR any remaining fuel back into the vehicle via the fuel filler. **For ethanol vehicles:** GO to DE10. **For methanol vehicles:** GO to DE11. COMPLETE the determination of the methanol (or ethanol) percentage before continuing.

STOPPER

25 ml
23
21
19
17
15
GASOLINE
13   14ml
11
9
METHANOL/WATER MIXTURE
7
5
3

25ml GRADUATED CYLINDER

FM0159601495080X

Fig. 230   Test DE: Flexible Fuel Sensor (Part 8 of 11). 1996

ELECTRONIC ENGINE CONTROL SYSTEM (EEC-V)

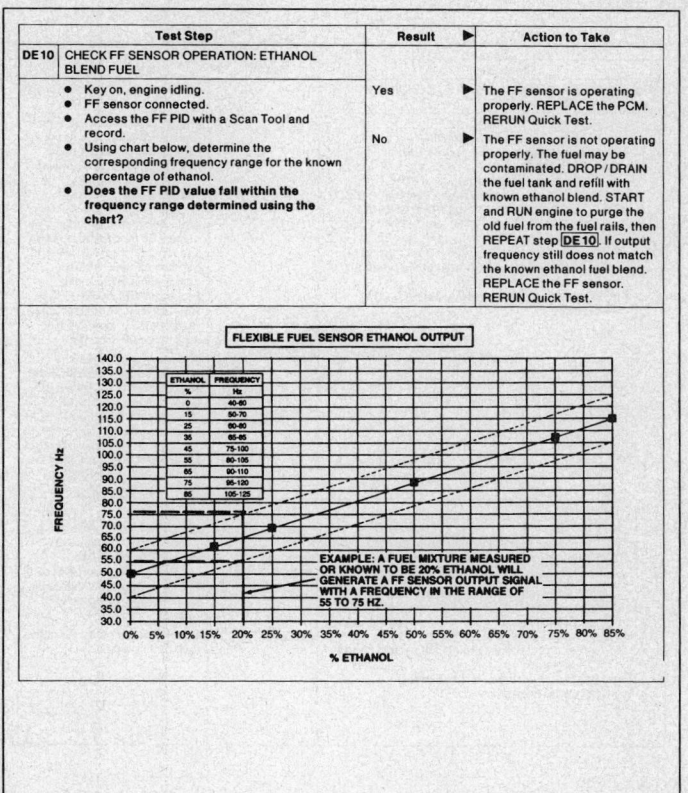

Test Step		Result	▶	Action to Take
DE 10	**CHECK FF SENSOR OPERATION: ETHANOL BLEND FUEL**			
• Key on, engine idling. • FF sensor connected. • Access the FF PID with a Scan Tool and record. • Using chart below, determine the corresponding frequency range for the known percentage of ethanol. • **Does the FF PID value fall within the frequency range determined using the chart?**		Yes	▶	The FF sensor is operating properly. REPLACE the PCM. RERUN Quick Test.
		No	▶	The FF sensor is not operating properly. The fuel may be contaminated. DROP/DRAIN the fuel tank and refill with known ethanol blend. START and RUN engine to purge the old fuel from the fuel rails, then REPEAT step DE10. If output frequency still does not match the known ethanol fuel blend. REPLACE the FF sensor. RERUN Quick Test.

Fig. 230 Test DE: Flexible Fuel Sensor (Part 9 of 11). 1996

FM0159601495090X

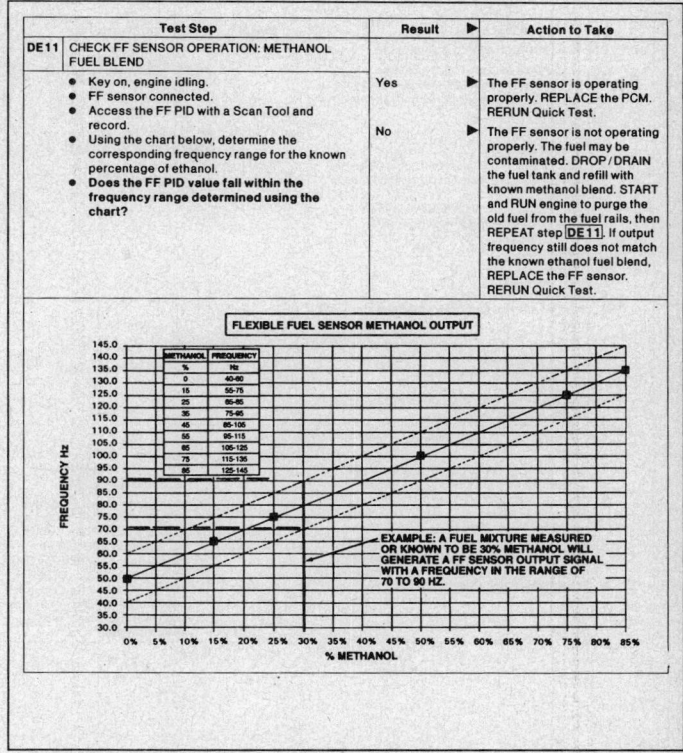

Test Step		Result	▶	Action to Take
DE 11	**CHECK FF SENSOR OPERATION: METHANOL FUEL BLEND**			
• Key on, engine idling. • FF sensor connected. • Access the FF PID with a Scan Tool and record. • Using the chart below, determine the corresponding frequency range for the known percentage of methanol. • **Does the FF PID value fall within the frequency range determined using the chart?**		Yes	▶	The FF sensor is operating properly. REPLACE the PCM. RERUN Quick Test.
		No	▶	The FF sensor is not operating properly. The fuel may be contaminated. DROP/DRAIN the fuel tank and refill with known methanol blend. START and RUN engine to purge the old fuel from the fuel rails, then REPEAT step DE11. If output frequency still does not match the known ethanol fuel blend, REPLACE the FF sensor. RERUN Quick Test.

FM0159601495100X

Fig. 230 Test DE: Flexible Fuel Sensor (Part 10 of 11). 1996

Test Step		Result	▶	Action to Take
DE20	**CONTINUOUS MEMORY DTC P0176: COMPLETE KOER SELF-TEST**			
Continuous Memory Diagnostic Trouble Code (DTC) P0176 indicates a FF sensor circuit failure has occurred. Possible causes: — Damaged FF sensor harness circuits. — Damaged FF sensor. — Damaged PCM. • Output all KOER self-test DTCs. • **Is P0176 output in KOER?** NOTE: Ignore all other DTCs output at this time.		Yes	▶	The FF sensor circuit failure is currently present. GO to Test Step DE1 and ADDRESS the KOER DTC.
		No	▶	The FF sensor circuit failure is not currently present. GO to DE21.
DE21	**CHECK FF SENSOR CIRCUIT FOR INTERMITTENT FAULT**			
• Key off. • Disconnect PCM. Inspect for damaged or pushed out pins, corrosion, loose wires, etc. Service as necessary. • Install breakout box, connect PCM. • Connect one DVOM test lead to Test Pin 34 (FFS SIG) and the other lead to Test Pin 51 (PWR GRND) or the battery negative post. • Key on, engine off. • Observe the DVOM voltage display for an indication of a fault while performing the following: NOTE: The voltage should remain steady within the 4 to 6 volts range. A voltage below 4 volts or greater than 6 volts is an indication of a fault. — Shake, wiggle and bend the FF sensor harness. — Shake and lightly tap the FF sensor to simulate road shock. • Key off. • **Was a fault indicated?**		Yes	▶	The FF sensor circuit fault is intermittent. ISOLATE and SERVICE fault as necessary. REMOVE breakout box and DVOM. RECONNECT all components. COMPLETE PCM. RESET to clear DTCs. (REFER to Powertrain Control Module (PCM) Reset). RERUN Quick Test
		No	▶	FF sensor circuit fault is intermittent and cannot be identified or duplicated at this time. REMOVE breakout box and DVOM. RECONNECT all components. COMPLETE PCM. RESET to clear DTCs. (REFER to Powertrain Control Module (PCM) Reset.)

FM0159601495110X

Fig. 230 Test DE: Flexible Fuel Sensor (Part 11 of 11). 1996

Note

You should enter this Pinpoint Test only when directed here.

Remember

This Pinpoint Test is intended to diagnose the following:

• Harness circuits: Vehicle speed circuit signal (VSC SIG), vehicle speed circuit ground (VSC GRND)
• Powertrain Control Module (PCM) (12A650)

Pinpoint Test Schematic

TEST PIN 58 ⊙————— VSC SIG —————

TEST PIN 33 ⊙————— VSC GND—————

ANTI-LOCK BRAKE SYSTEM (ABS) MODULE CONNECTOR

FM0159601496010X

Fig. 231 Test DF: Vehicle Speed Circuit check (Part 1 of 4). 1996

Test Step	Result	▶	Action to Take
DF1 DTC P0500: CHECK VEHICLE SPEED PID			
Diagnostic Trouble Code (DTC) indicates the Powertrain Control Module (PCM) detected an error in the vehicle speed information received from the ABS module. Possible causes: — Damaged ABS module. — Damaged ABS module speed sensors. — Damaged ABS module speed sensor harness circuits. — Open in ABS module to PCM harness circuits. — Short to ground in ABS module to PCM harness circuits. — Damaged PCM. • Key on. • Scan Tool installed. • Access VSS PID. • Obeying all local traffic laws, perform the following: — Take the vehicle to a suitable location and gradually increase the vehicle speed to 50 MPH, while observing the VSS PID MPH values. • **Does the VSS PID value match the speed at which you were traveling?**	Yes	▶	The VSS PID value was as expected. The fault that produced DTC P0500 is intermittent. GO to **DF4**.
	No	▶	The VSS PID value was not as expected. GO to **DF2**.
DF2 CHECK CONTINUITY OF HARNESS CIRCUITS			
• Key off. • Breakout box installed, PCM disconnected. • Disconnect the ABS module from the PCM. • Measure resistance between Test Pin 58 VSC SIG at the breakout and the VSC SIG circuit at the ABS module connector. • Measure resistance between Test Pin 33 VSC GRND at the breakout and the VSC GRND circuit at the ABS module connector. • **Is each resistance less than 5.0 ohms?**	Yes	▶	The harness circuits from the ABS module to the PCM are complete. GO to **DF3**.
	No	▶	The harness circuit from the ABS module to the PCM are not complete. SERVICE the open circuit(s). RECONNECT all components. COMPLETE PCM Reset to clear DTCs (REFER to Powertrain Control Module (PCM) Reset). RUN the VSC Drive Cycle in **DF5** to verify the repair.

FM0159601496020X

Fig. 231 Test DF: Vehicle Speed Circuit check (Part 2 of 4). 1996

Test Step	Result	▶	Action to Take
DF3 CHECK HARNESS CIRCUITS FOR SHORTS TO GROUND AND POWER			
• Key off. • Disconnect Scan Tool from DLC. • Breakout box installed, leave PCM disconnected. • ABS module disconnected from PCM. • Measure resistance between Test Pin 58 (VSC SIG) and Test Pin's 51, 103 (PWR GND), 33 (VSC GRND) 91 (SIG RTN) and 71 (VPWR) at the breakout box. • Measure resistance between Test Pins 33 (VSC GRND) and 71 (VPWR) at the breakout box. • **Is each resistance greater than 10,000 ohms?**	Yes	▶	There are no shorts to power or ground in the harness circuits. REMOVE the breakout box. RECONNECT all components. REFER to the 1996 Taurus / Sable _____ ; Brake System, Anti-Lock for further diagnosis of the ABS module, its speed sensors and its speed sensor harness circuits. If those components are working properly, REPLACE the PCM. RECONNECT all components. RUN the VSC Drive Cycle in **DF5** to verify the repair.
	No	▶	There is a short within the harness circuits. SERVICE the short circuit(s). REMOVE the breakout box. RECONNECT all components. COMPLETE PCM Reset to clear DTCs (REFER to Powertrain Control Module (PCM) Reset). RUN the VSC Drive Cycle in **DF5** to verify the repair.
DF4 VISUAL INSPECTION			
• Key off. • Visually inspect the vehicle speed circuit harness circuits for any potential failures. Use the following check list for reference: — Loose harness connection of vehicle speed circuits at the ABS module. — Loose harness connection of vehicle speed circuits at the PCM. — Incorrect harness routing of vehicle speed circuits. • **Did the visual inspection reveal any potential failure?**	Yes	▶	SERVICE fault as necessary. COMPLETE PCM Reset to clear DTCs (REFER to Powertrain Control Module (PCM) Reset). RUN VSC Drive Cycle in **DF5** to verify the repair.
	No	▶	Unable to duplicate or identify fault at this time.

FM0159601496030X

Fig. 231 Test DF: Vehicle Speed Circuit check (Part 3 of 4). 1996

Test Step	Result	▶	Action to Take
DF5 VSC DRIVE CYCLE TEST			
Warm engine to operating temperature. Perform the VSC Drive Cycle at least three times as outlined below: **AUTOMATIC TRANSMISSIONS:** — Place gear selector in DRIVE range. — Obey all local traffic laws. — Accelerate heavily to 35 MPH. — Coast down to an idle and stop the vehicle. — Shut the engine off. — After the drive cycle is completed, retrieve any Continuous Memory DTCs. **MANUAL TRANSMISSIONS:** — Shift to second from first gear. — Obey all local traffic laws. — Accelerate moderately to 40 mph. — Coast down to an idle and stop the vehicle. — After the drive cycle is completed, retrieve any Continuous Memory DTCs. • **Were any Continuous Memory DTCs generated during the drive cycle?**	Yes	▶	Testing is not complete. The repair has not been verified. Address DTC(s) generated in Powertrain Diagnostic Trouble Code (DTC) Charts.
	No	▶	Testing is complete. The repair has been verified.

FM0159601496040X

Fig. 231 Test DF: Vehicle Speed Circuit check (Part 4 of 4). 1996

Note

You should enter this Pinpoint Test only when directed here.

Remember

This Pinpoint Test is intended to diagnose the following:
• Knock sensor (12A699)
• Harness circuits: KS and SIG RTN
• Powertrain Control Module (PCM) (12A650)

Pinpoint Test Schematic

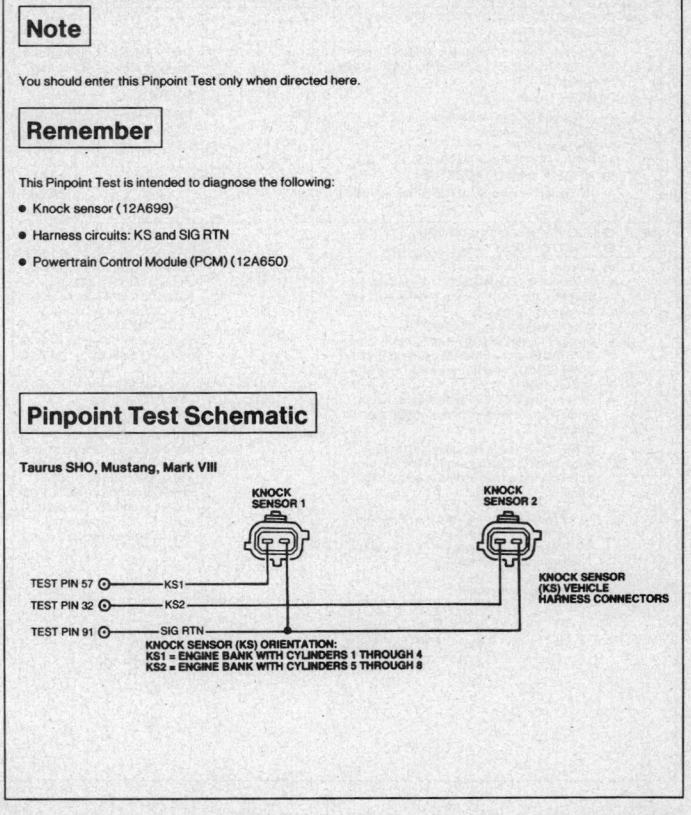

Taurus SHO, Mustang, Mark VIII

FM0159601497010X

Fig. 232 Test DG: Knock Sensor (Part 1 of 3). 1996

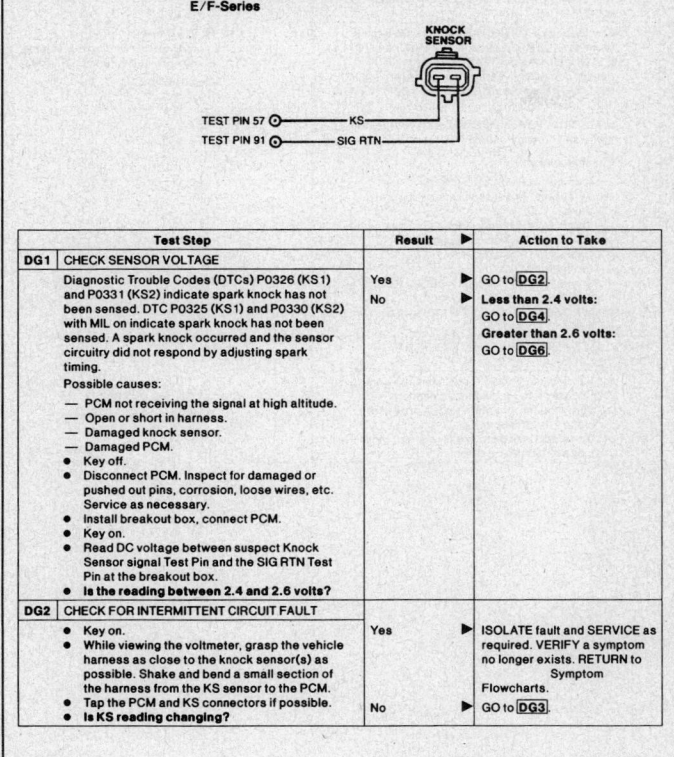

Contour/Mystique, Taurus 3.0L-4V,
E/F-Series

KNOCK
SENSOR

TEST PIN 57 — KS
TEST PIN 91 — SIG RTN

	Test Step	Result	▶	Action to Take
DG1	CHECK SENSOR VOLTAGE			
	Diagnostic Trouble Codes (DTCs) P0326 (KS1) and P0331 (KS2) indicate spark knock has not been sensed. DTC P0325 (KS1) and P0330 (KS2) with MIL on indicate spark knock has not been sensed. A spark knock occurred and the sensor circuitry did not respond by adjusting spark timing. Possible causes: — PCM not receiving the signal at high altitude. — Open or short in harness. — Damaged knock sensor. — Damaged PCM. • Key off. • Disconnect PCM. Inspect for damaged or pushed out pins, corrosion, loose wires, etc. Service as necessary. • Install breakout box, connect PCM. • Key on. • Read DC voltage between suspect Knock Sensor signal Test Pin and the SIG RTN Test Pin at the breakout box. • **Is the reading between 2.4 and 2.6 volts?**	Yes No	▶ ▶	GO to DG2. **Less than 2.4 volts:** GO to DG4. **Greater than 2.6 volts:** GO to DG6.
DG2	CHECK FOR INTERMITTENT CIRCUIT FAULT			
	• Key on. • While viewing the voltmeter, grasp the vehicle harness as close to the knock sensor(s) as possible. Shake and bend a small section of the harness from the KS sensor to the PCM. • Tap the PCM and KS connectors if possible. • **Is KS reading changing?**	Yes No	▶ ▶	ISOLATE fault and SERVICE as required. VERIFY a symptom no longer exists. RETURN to Symptom Flowcharts. GO to DG3.

FM0159601497020X

Fig. 232   Test DG: Knock Sensor (Part 2 of 3). 1936

	Test Step	Result	▶	Action to Take
DG3	CHECK FOR VOLTAGE INCREASE			
	• Key off. • Disconnect PCM. • Inspect for damaged or pushed out pins, corrosion, loose wires, etc. Service as necessary. • Install breakout box, connect PCM. • Disconnect Scan Tool. • Start and run engine. • Monitor voltage on the AC setting at idle and at 3,000 rpm between the suspect Knock Sensor Test Pin and SIG RTN Test Pin at the breakout box. • **Does the AC voltage reading increase?**	No	▶	All others with DTC: REPLACE PCM. RECONNECT all components. RERUN Quick Test. GO to DG4.
DG4	CHECK CONTINUITY OF KS AND SIG RTN CIRCUITS			
	• Key off. • Breakout box installed, PCM disconnected. • Disconnect suspect KS. • Measure resistance of the KS signal circuit between the KS signal Test Pin at the breakout box and the same signal pin at the vehicle harness connector. • Measure resistance of the SIG RTN between Test Pin at the breakout box and the same SIG RTN pin at the vehicle harness connector. • **Is each resistance less than 5.0 ohms?**	Yes No	▶ ▶	GO to DG5. SERVICE open circuit. REMOVE breakout box. RECONNECT all components. RERUN Quick Test.
DG5	CHECK KS CIRCUIT FOR SHORT TO GROUND			
	• Key off. • Breakout box installed, PCM disconnected. KS disconnected. • Measure resistance between KS signal Test Pins and SIG RTN, PWR GND at the breakout box and chassis GND. • **Is each resistance greater than 10,000 ohms?**	Yes No	▶ ▶	REPLACE suspect KS. REMOVE breakout box. RECONNECT all components. RERUN Quick Test. SERVICE short circuit. REMOVE breakout box. RECONNECT all components. RERUN Quick Test.
DG6	CHECK KS CIRCUITS FOR SHORT TO POWER			
	• Key off. • Breakout box installed, PCM disconnected. • KS disconnected. • Key on, engine off. • Measure voltage between the KS signal Test Pins and PWR GND Test Pins at the breakout box. • **Is voltage less than 0.5 volts?**	Yes No	▶ ▶	REPLACE PCM. REMOVE breakout box. RECONNECT all components. RERUN Quick Test. SERVICE short circuit. REMOVE breakout box. RECONNECT all components. RERUN Quick Test.

FM0159601497030X

Fig. 232   Test DG: Knock Sensor (Part 3 of 3). 1996

Note

You should enter this Pinpoint Test only when directed here.

Remember

This Pinpoint Test is intended to diagnose the following:

• Throttle Position (TP) Sensor (9B989)
• Binding and Sticking Throttle Linkage
• Harness Circuits:

  TP SIG, SIG RTN, VREF, Vehicle Power (VPWR), Power Ground (PWR GND)

• Powertrain Control Module (PCM) (12A650)

Tables and Charts

NOTE: The normal range of the throttle angle measurement for the Throttle Position (TP) sensor is 0 to 85 degrees.

FM0159601498010X

Fig. 233   Test DH: Throttle Position Sensor (Part 1 of 11). 1996

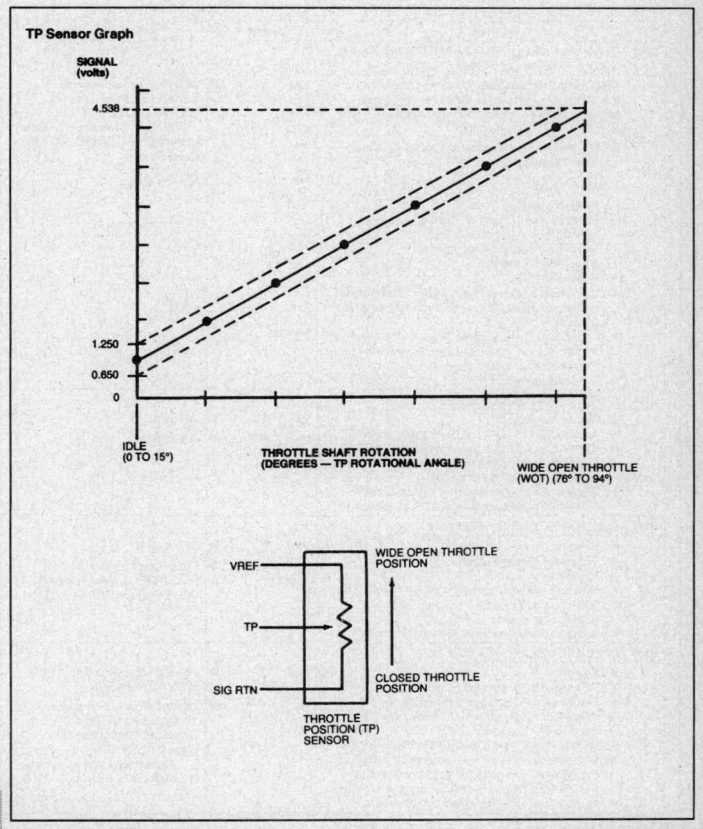

FM0159601498020X

Fig. 233   Test DH: Throttle Position Sensor (Part 2 of 11). 1996

Pinpoint Test Schematic

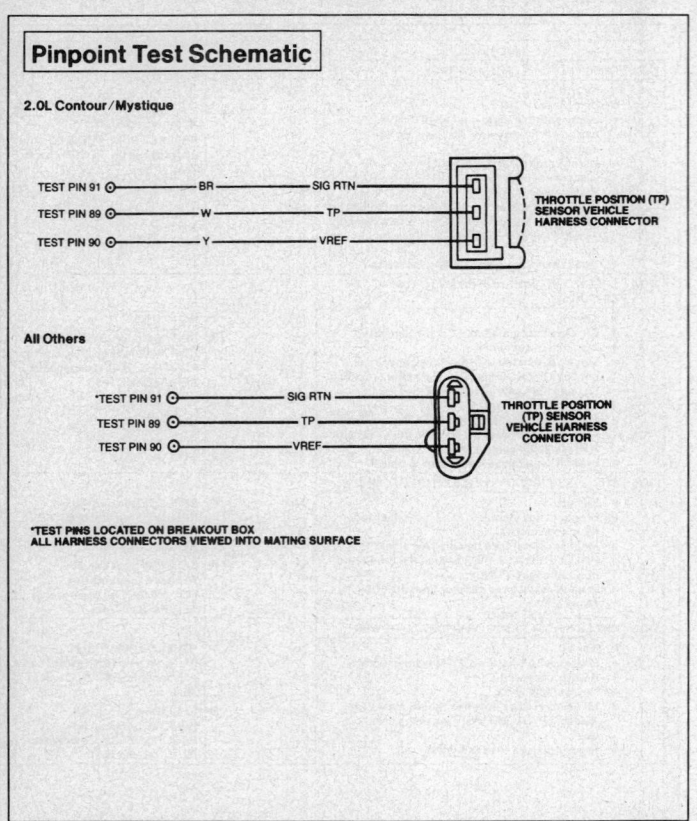

2.0L Contour/Mystique

TEST PIN 91 — BR — SIG RTN
TEST PIN 89 — W — TP
TEST PIN 90 — Y — VREF

THROTTLE POSITION (TP) SENSOR VEHICLE HARNESS CONNECTOR

All Others

*TEST PIN 91 — SIG RTN
TEST PIN 89 — TP
TEST PIN 90 — VREF

THROTTLE POSITION (TP) SENSOR VEHICLE HARNESS CONNECTOR

*TEST PINS LOCATED ON BREAKOUT BOX
ALL HARNESS CONNECTORS VIEWED INTO MATING SURFACE

FM0159601498030X

Fig. 233   Test DH: Throttle Position Sensor (Part 3 of 11). 1996

	Test Step	Result	▶	Action to Take
DH1	**KOEO AND KOER DTC P1124: CHECK FOR OTHER DTCS**			
	Key On Engine Off (KOEO) and Key On Engine Running (KOER) Diagnostic Trouble Codes (DTC) P1124 indicates the Throttle Position (TP) sensor's rotational setting and signal are not in the Self-Test range of 13.23% to 24.02% (0.66 to 1.20 volts). NOTE: Throttle Position Sensor A (TP-A) is the same as Throttle Position (TP) Sensor. Possible causes: — Binding or bent throttle linkage. — TP sensor not seated properly (tightened down). — Throttle plate below closed throttle position. — Throttle plate / screw misadjusted. — Damaged TP sensor. — Damaged PCM. • Check for DTC P1400 in KOEO or KOER Self-Test. • **Is KOEO or KOER DTC P1400 present with KOEO DTC P1124?**	Yes No	▶ ▶	RETURN to Powertrain Diagnostic Trouble Code Charts, for DTC P1400. GO to **DH2**.
DH2	**CHECK FOR STUCK THROTTLE PLATE OR LINKAGE**			
	• Visually inspect the throttle linkage and throttle plate for binding or sticking. • Verify the throttle plate and linkage is at closed throttle position. • **Does the throttle move freely and return to closed throttle position?**	Yes No	▶ ▶	Throttle plate and linkage are OK. GO to **DH8**. SERVICE as necessary. RERUN Quick Test.

FM0159601498040X

Fig. 233   Test DH: Throttle Position Sensor (Part 4 of 11). 1996

	Test Step	Result	▶	Action to Take
DH3	**DTC P1120: CHECK FRAYED TP CIRCUIT WIRES OR CORROSION ON CONNECTORS**			
	Diagnostic Trouble Code (DTC) P1120 indicates the TP signal is within the Self-Test range but below the closed throttle position range of 3.43% to 9.80% (0.17 to 0.49 volt). NOTE: Throttle Position Sensor A (TP-A) is the same as Throttle Position (TP) Sensor. Possible causes: — Frayed wires. — Corrosion on TP sensor, PCM or harness connectors. — VREF harness opens or shorts. — Damaged TP sensor. — Damaged PCM. • Do a complete visual inspection of the harness connector at the TP sensor (including pins) for corrosion. • Do a complete visual inspection of the harness wires between the TP sensor and the PCM for insulation fraying and corrosion. • **Is a fault present?**	Yes No	▶ ▶	SERVICE as necessary. COMPLETE PCM Reset to clear all DTCs (REFER to Powertrain Control Module (PCM) Reset). RERUN Quick Test. GO to **DH4**.
DH4	**CHECK FOR STUCK TP SENSOR**			
	• Key on, engine off. • Access TP PID (TPV PID) with the Scan Tool. • Slowly move throttle from closed throttle position to wide open throttle position and observe the TP PID (TPV PID). • **While opening the throttle, is the TP PID (TPV PID) reading below 9.80% (0.49 volt)?**	Yes No	▶ ▶	GO to **DH5**. GO to **DH20**.
DH5	**CHECK VREF CIRCUIT VOLTAGE**			
	• Key off. • TP sensor disconnected. • Key on, engine off. • Measure voltage between VREF circuit and SIG RTN circuit at the TP sensor vehicle harness connector. • **Is the voltage between 4.0 and 6.0 volts?**	Yes No	▶ ▶	GO to **DH6**. TURN ignition key off. RECONNECT all components. GO to Pinpoint Test Step **C1**.
DH6	**CHECK TP CIRCUIT CONTINUITY**			
	• Key off. • TP sensor disconnected. • Disconnect PCM. Inspect for damaged or pushed out pins, corrosion, loose wires, etc. Service as necessary. • Install breakout box, leave PCM disconnected. • Measure the resistance between TP circuit at the TP sensor vehicle harness connector and Test Pin 89 (TP SIG) at the breakout box. • **Is the resistance less than 5.0 ohms?**	Yes No	▶ ▶	TP SIG harness circuit to PCM is OK. GO to **DH7**. SERVICE corrosion or open in TP SIG harness circuit. COMPLETE PCM Reset to clear DTCs (REFER to Powertrain Control Module (PCM) Reset). RERUN Quick Test.

FM0159601498050X

Fig. 233   Test DH: Throttle Position Sensor (Part 5 of 11). 1996

	Test Step	Result	▶	Action to Take
DH7	**CHECK TP SENSOR SIGNAL TO PCM**			
	• Key off. • Connect PCM to breakout box. • Connect TP sensor. • Start engine and idle for 2 minutes. • Slowly open the throttle from closed position, while doing next step. • Measure the voltage between Test Pin 89 (TP SIG) and Test Pin 91 (SIG RTN) at the breakout box. • **Is the voltage at any time between 0.17 to 0.49 volt?**	Yes No	▶ ▶	TP sensor is damaged. REPLACE TP sensor. REMOVE breakout box. RERUN Quick Test. RERUN Quick Test. If DTC 1120 is still present, GO to **DH20**.
DH8	**DTC P0123: GENERATE OPPOSITE DTC P0122**			
	Diagnostic Trouble Code (DTC) P0123 indicates the TP sensor signal is greater than the Self-Test maximum value of 92.27% (4.60 volts). NOTE: An intermittent fault can cause a Continuous Memory DTC P0123. If Continuous Memory DTC P0123 is still present after DH8 through DH10, go to **DH20**. NOTE: Throttle Position Sensor A (TP-A) is the same as Throttle Position (TP) Sensor. Possible causes: — Damaged TP sensor. — TP not seated properly (tightened down). — TP SIG harness short to VREF or VPWR. — VREF harness short to VPWR. — Open SIG RTN harness circuit. — Damaged PCM. • Key off. • Disconnect TP sensor. Inspect for damaged or pushed out pins, corrosion, loose wires, etc. Service as necessary. • Leave TP sensor disconnected. • Key on, engine off. • Access TP PID (TPV PID) with the Scan Tool. • **Is the TP PID (TPV PID) less than 3.43% (0.17 volt)?**	Yes No	▶ ▶	TP SIG is either shorted to VREF in TP sensor or SIG RTN is open in the TP sensor or harness. GO to **DH9**. TP SIG circuit is shorted to VPWR or VREF. GO to **DH10**.
DH9	**CHECK VREF CIRCUIT VOLTAGE**			
	• Key off. • TP sensor disconnected. • Key on, engine off. • Measure voltage between VREF circuit and SIG RTN circuit at the TP sensor vehicle harness connector. • **Is the voltage between 4.0 and 6.0 volts?**	Yes No	▶ ▶	TP SIG shorted to VREF or SIG RTN open in the TP sensor. REPLACE TP sensor. RERUN Quick Test. Key off. RECONNECT all components. GO to Pinpoint Test Step **C1**.

FM0159601498060X

Fig. 233   Test DH: Throttle Position Sensor (Part 6 of 11). 1996

ELECTRONIC ENGINE CONTROL SYSTEM (EEC-V)

Test Step	Result	▶	Action to Take
DH10 CHECK TP CIRCUIT FOR SHORTS TO VREF OR VPWR • Key off. • TP sensor disconnected. • Disconnect PCM. Inspect for damaged or pushed out pins, corrosion, loose wires, etc. Service as necessary. • Install breakout box, leave PCM disconnected. • Measure the resistance between Test Pin 89 (TP SIG) and Test Pins 90 (VREF) and 71 or 97 (VPWR) at the breakout box. • **Is each resistance greater than 10,000 ohms?**	Yes No	▶ ▶	TP SIG is shorted to VREF or VPWR in PCM. REPLACE PCM. REMOVE breakout box. RECONNECT TP sensor. RERUN Quick Test. TP SIG is shorted to VREF in the harness. SERVICE short in harness circuit between TP SIG and VREF. REMOVE breakout box. RECONNECT all components. RERUN Quick Test.
DH11 DTC P0122: GENERATE OPPOSITE DTC P0123 Diagnostic Trouble Code (DTC) P0122 indicates the TP sensor signal is less than the Self-Test minimum value of 3.43% (0.17 volts). NOTE: Throttle Position Sensor A (TP-A) is the same as Throttle Position (TP) Sensor. NOTE: An intermittent fault can cause a Continuous Memory DTC P0122. If a Continuous Memory DTC P0122 is still present after DH11 through DH14, go to **DH20**. Possible causes: — Damaged TP sensor. — TP not seated properly (tightened down). — Open TP SIG or VREF harness. — TP SIG harness short to SIG RTN or PWR GND. — Damaged PCM. • Key off. • Disconnect TP sensor. Inspect for damaged or pushed out pins, corrosion, loose wires, etc. Service as necessary. • Leave TP sensor disconnected. • Jumper VREF circuit to TP circuit at the TP sensor vehicle harness connector. • Key on, engine off. NOTE: If any Scan Tool communication problem exists, remove jumper and go to **DH14**. • Access TP PID (TPV PID) with the Scan Tool. • **Is the TP PID (TPV PID) greater than 92.27% (4.60 volts)?**	Yes No	▶ ▶	TP SIG shorted to SIG RTN in TP sensor, or TP SIG or VREF open in TP sensor. REPLACE TP sensor. REMOVE jumper. RERUN Quick Test. VREF or TP SIG open in harness or PCM, or TP SIG shorted to SIG RTN (or PWR GND) in harness or PCM. REMOVE jumper. GO to **DH12**.

FM0159601498070X

Fig. 233   Test DH: Throttle Position Sensor (Part 7 of 11). 1996

Test Step	Result	▶	Action to Take
DH12 CHECK VREF CIRCUIT VOLTAGE • Key off. • TP sensor disconnected. • Key on, engine off. • Measure voltage between VREF circuit and SIG RTN circuit at the TP sensor vehicle harness connector. • **Is the voltage between 4.0 and 6.0 volts?**	Yes No	▶ ▶	TP SIG open or shorted to SIG RTN (or PWR GND) in the harness or PCM. GO to **DH13**. Key off. RECONNECT all components. GO to Pinpoint Test Step **C1**.
DH13 CHECK TP CIRCUIT CONTINUITY • Key off. • TP sensor disconnected. • Disconnect PCM. Inspect for damaged or pushed out pins, corrosion, loose wires, etc. Service as necessary. • Install breakout, leave PCM disconnected. • Measure the resistance between TP circuit at the TP sensor vehicle harness connector and Test Pin 89 (TP SIG) at the breakout box. • **Is the resistance less than 5.0 ohms?**	Yes No	▶ ▶	TP SIG harness circuit to PCM is OK. GO to **DH14**. SERVICE open in TP SIG harness circuit. REMOVE breakout box. RECONNECT all components. RERUN Quick Test.
DH14 CHECK TP CIRCUIT FOR SHORTS TO SIG RTN OR PWR GND • Key off. • TP sensor disconnected. • Breakout box installed. • PCM disconnected. • Disconnect Scan Tool from DLC. • Measure the resistance between Test Pin 89 (TP SIG) and Test Pins 91 (SIG RTN) and 24 or 103 (PWR GND) at the breakout box. • **Is each resistance greater than 10,000 ohms?**	Yes No	▶ ▶	TP SIG open or shorted to SIG RTN (or PWR GND) in the PCM. REPLACE PCM. REMOVE breakout box. RECONNECT all components. RERUN Quick Test. SERVICE TP SIG shorted to SIG RTN (or PWR GND) in the harness. REMOVE breakout box. RECONNECT all components. RERUN Quick Test.
DH15 CONTINUOUS MEMORY DTC P1121: TP SENSOR AND MAF SENSOR RATIONALITY CHECK Continuous Memory DTC P1121 indicates the TP sensor is inconsistent with the MAF sensor. NOTE: Throttle Position Sensor A (TP-A) is the same as Throttle Position (TP) Sensor. Possible causes: — Damaged TP sensor. — TP sensor not seated properly (almost completely detached from throttle body). — Air leak between MAF sensor and throttle body. • Attempt to start engine. • **Does the engine run?**	Yes No	▶ ▶	GO to **DH16**. CHECK for major leaks, cracks, and openings between MAF sensor and throttle body. If OK, GO to Pinpoint Test Step **A1**.

FM0159601498080X

Fig. 233   Test DH: Throttle Position Sensor (Part 8 of 11). 1996

Test Step	Result	▶	Action to Take
DH16 CHECK MECHANICAL OPERATION OF TP SENSOR • Key on, engine off. • Access TP PID (TPV PID) with the Scan Tool. • Slowly move throttle from closed throttle position to wide open throttle position and observe the TP PID (TPV PID). • **While opening and closing the throttle, is there a change in the TP PID (TPV PID) between 13.23% (0.66 volts) and 24.02% (1.20 volts)?**	Yes No	▶ ▶	GO to **DH17**. REPLACE TP sensor. COMPLETE PCM Reset to clear DTCs (REFER to , Powertrain Control Module (PCM) Reset). VERIFY a symptom no longer exists. RERUN Quick Test.
DH17 CHECK TP SENSOR SIGNAL HIGH VERSUS THE ENGINE LOAD WHILE DRIVING VEHICLE • Key on, engine running. • Do normal drive, exercising the throttle and TP sensor while accessing PIDS. • Access TP PID (TPV PID) and LOAD PID with the Scan Tool and record readings. • **Is the TP PID (TPV PID) greater than 49.02% (2.44 volts) and the LOAD PID reading less than 25%?**	Yes No	▶ ▶	CHECK for air leaks between the MAF and the throttle body, including air noise sounds while engine is running. SERVICE as necessary. If OK, REPLACE the TP sensor. RERUN Quick Test. GO to **DH18**.
DH18 CHECK TP SENSOR SIGNAL LOW VERSUS THE ENGINE LOAD WHILE DRIVING VEHICLE • Key on, engine running. NOTE: If the vehicle is a no start, go to Pinpoint Test Step **A1**. • Do normal drive, exercising the throttle and TP sensor near higher gears (preferably overdrive) while accessing PIDS. • Access TP PID (TPV PID) and LOAD PID with the Scan Tool and record readings. • **Is the TP PID (TPV PID) reading less than 4.90% (0.24 volts) and the LOAD PID reading greater than 60%?**	Yes No	▶ ▶	CHECK if the TP sensor is loosely connected to the throttle body (screws not securely tightened down). SERVICE as necessary. COMPLETE PCM Reset to clear DTCs (REFER to , Powertrain Control Module (PCM) Reset). DRIVE vehicle exercising the throttle. RERUN Quick Test. If Continuous Memory P1121 is now present, REPLACE MAF sensor. Unable to identify the fault at this time. If vehicle is still a No Start, GO to Pinpoint Test Step **A1**.

FM0159601498090X

Fig. 233   Test DH: Throttle Position Sensor (Part 9 of 11). 1996

Test Step	Result	▶	Action to Take
DH20 CONTINUOUS MEMORY DTCS P1120 OR P1125: CHECK FOR TP CIRCUIT INTERMITTENT VOLTAGE INPUT Continuous Memory Diagnostic Trouble Code (DTC) P1125 indicates the TP sensor signal went below 9.80% (0.49 volts) or above 92.27% (4.60 volts) sometime during the last 80 warm-up cycles. NOTE: Throttle Position Sensor A (TP-A) is the same as Throttle Position (TP) Sensor. Possible causes: — TP sensor connector with poor continuity. — TP harness with poor continuity. — TP harness intermittent short. — TP sensor internal electrical or substrate open or electrical short. • Start engine and bring to idle. • Run throttle up to 1500 rpm for 5 seconds. • Key on, engine running. • Access TP PID (TPV PID) for a fault indication with a Scan Tool while performing the following: — Lightly tap on TP sensor and wiggle harness connector to simulate road shock. • **Is the TP PID (TPV PID) changing below the minimum 9.80% (0.49 volt) or above the maximum 92.27% (4.60 volts)?**	Yes No	▶ ▶	DISCONNECT and INSPECT the TP sensor connector. If OK, REPLACE the TP sensor. COMPLETE PCM Reset to clear DTCs (REFER to , Powertrain Control Module (PCM) Reset). RERUN Quick Test. GO to **DH21**.
DH21 CHECK TP HARNESS TO PCM FOR INTERMITTENT OPENS OR SHORTS • Key off. • Disconnect PCM. Inspect for damaged or pushed out pins, corrosion, loose wires, etc. Service as necessary. • Install breakout box, reconnect PCM. • Key on, engine off. • Connect DVOM between Test Pin 89 (TP SIG) and Test Pin 91 (SIG RTN) at the breakout box. • While viewing DVOM, do the following: — Grasp the vehicle harness closest to the TP sensor connector. — Shake and bend a small section of the harness all the way to the dash panel. — Wiggle, shake and bend the harness from the dash panel to the PCM. • **Is the voltage changing below the minimum 0.49 volt or above the maximum 4.60 volts?**	Yes No	▶ ▶	ISOLATE fault and SERVICE as necessary. RECONNECT all components. COMPLETE PCM Reset to clear DTCs (REFER to , Powertrain Control Module (PCM) Reset). RERUN Quick Test. Unable to duplicate and/or identify fault at this time. GO to Pinpoint Test Step **Z1** with the following data: TP and (TP V PIDs) and list of possible causes.

FM0159601498100X

Fig. 233   Test DH: Throttle Position Sensor (Part 10 of 11). 1996

Test Step	Result	▶	Action to Take
DH22 DTC P0121: VERIFY THAT KOER SELF-TEST COMPLETES			
• Diagnostic Trouble Code (DTC) P0121 indicates an in-range operating TP sensor circuit failure.	Yes	▶	KEEP engine running at idle. GO to **DH23**.
NOTE: Throttle Position Sensor A (TP-A) is the same as Throttle Position (TP) Sensor.	No	▶	VERIFY a symptom no longer exists. RERUN Quick Test.
• Key off.			
• Start engine, bring to idle (closed throttle position).			
• Activate Key On Engine Running (KOER) Self-Test with the Scan Tool.			
• **Is DTC P0121 present or does KOER Self-Test fail to terminate?**			
DH23 ATTEMPT TO RECREATE DTC P0121 OR DRIVEABILITY SYMPTOM			
• Key on, engine running.	Yes	▶	GO to **DH24**.
• Attempt to take vehicle for a drive, while still in Key On Engine Running Self-Test on Scan Tool.	No	▶	VERIFY a symptom no longer exists. RERUN Quick Test.
NOTE: If KOER Self-Test terminates when placing the selector in gear (drive or reverse). GO to **DH24** directly.			
• Turn ignition to the key off position, wait 15 seconds.			
• Again, start engine.			
• Activate KOER Self-Test with the Scan Tool.			
• **Is DTC P0121 still present or does KOER Self-Test again fail to terminate?**			
DH24 CHECK TP CIRCUIT			
• Check for opens in the TP SIG and SIG RTN harness wires between both the TP sensor and the PCM vehicle harness connectors.	Yes	▶	SERVICE open in TP SIG or SIG RTN harness circuit. VERIFY a symptom no longer exists. RERUN Quick Test.
• **Is an open indicated?**	No	▶	REPLACE TP sensor. RERUN Quick Test. VERIFY a symptom no longer exists.

FM0159601498110X

Fig. 233   Test DH: Throttle Position Sensor (Part 11 of 11). 1996

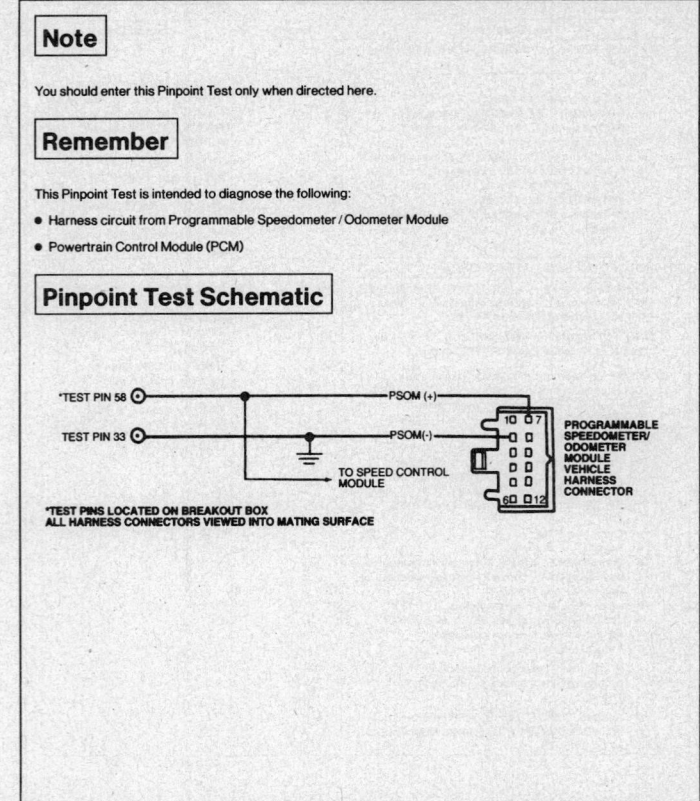

Note

You should enter this Pinpoint Test only when directed here.

Remember

This Pinpoint Test is intended to diagnose the following:

• Harness circuit from Programmable Speedometer / Odometer Module
• Powertrain Control Module (PCM)

Pinpoint Test Schematic

*TEST PINS LOCATED ON BREAKOUT BOX
ALL HARNESS CONNECTORS VIEWED INTO MATING SURFACE

FM0159601499010X

Fig. 234   Test DJ: Programmable Speedometer/Odometer Module (Part 1 of 3). 1996

Test Step	Result	▶	Action to Take
DJ1 CHECK SENSOR AND HARNESS			
Diagnostic Trouble Code (DTC) P0500 indicates vehicle speed sensor malfunction. DTC P0503 indicates electrical noise problems. DTC P1500 indicates intermittent sensor circuit failure. DTC P1501 indicates sensor out-of self test range. Possible causes:	Yes	▶	SERVICE as necessary. COMPLETE PCM reset to clear DTCs (REFER to Powertrain Control Module (PCM) Reset). VERIFY a symptom no longer exists.
— Damaged Programmable Speedometer/Odometer Module.	No	▶	GO to **DJ2**.
— Damaged Rear Anti-Lock Brake System, Sensor.			
— Damaged Speed Control Module.			
— Damaged Powertrain Control Module (PCM).			
— Harness open or shorted.			
• Key off.			
• Inspect Rear Anti-Lock Brake sensor and electrical connector for being properly seated and installed.			
• Inspect connector for damage, corrosion, etc.			
• Inspect wire harness from sensor to the Modules for damage due to chaffing, burnt, corrosion, etc.			
• **Has any problem been found?**			
DJ2 CHECK FOR INTERMITTENT CIRCUIT FAULT			
• Key off.	Yes	▶	ISOLATE fault and SERVICE as necessary. COMPLETE PCM reset to clear DTCs (REFER to Powertrain Control Module (PCM) Reset). RERUN Quick Test.
• Scan Tool connected.			
• Access VSS PID.			
• Record VSS data while driving vehicle simulating road shock.			
• If possible, drive vehicle through a pool of water.	No	▶	GO to **DJ3**.
• Return to Service Bay and review recorded PID.			
• **Is a blip shown on the recorded graph?**			
DJ3 CHECK SIGNAL TO MODULE			
• Key off.	Yes	▶	REPLACE PCM. REMOVE breakout box. RECONNECT all components. RERUN Quick Test.
• Disconnect PCM. Inspect for damaged or pushed out pins, corrosion, loose wires, etc. Service as necessary.			
• Install breakout box, reconnect PCM.	No	▶	GO to **DJ4**.
• DVOM on the 20 volt AC scale.			
• Observe voltage between Test Pin 58 and Test Pin 33 at the breakout box while gradually increasing vehicle speed to 50 mph.			
• **Is maximum voltage received greater than 4.0 volts?**			

FM0159601499020X

Fig. 234   Test DJ: Programmable Speedometer/Odometer Module (Part 2 of 3). 1996

Test Step	Result	▶	Action to Take
DJ4 CHECK CONTINUITY HARNESS			
• Key off.	Yes	▶	GO to **DJ5**.
• Breakout box installed, PCM disconnected.	No	▶	SERVICE open circuit. REMOVE breakout box. RECONNECT all components. RERUN Quick Test.
• Disconnect Programmable Speedometer/Odometer Module vehicle harness connector.			
• Disconnect Speed Control Module. Inspect for damaged or pushed out pins, corrosion, loose wires, etc. Service as necessary.			
• Measure resistance between Test Pin 58 at the breakout box and the same pin at the Module vehicle harness connector.			
• Measure resistance between Test Pin 33 at the breakout box and the same pin at the Module vehicle harness connector, and chassis GND.			
• **Is each resistance less than 5.0 ohms?**			
DJ5 CHECK FOR SHORT TO POWER AND GROUND			
• Key off.	Yes	▶	REFER to the Instrument Cluster, Speed Control or Brake Group in the Service Manual.
• Breakout box installed, PCM disconnected.			
• Programmable Speedometer/Odometer Module disconnected.			
• Measure resistance between Test Pin 58 and Test Pins 33, 24 and 71 at the breakout box.	No	▶	SERVICE short circuit. REMOVE breakout box. RECONNECT all components. RERUN Quick Test.
• **Is each resistance greater than 10,000 ohms?**			

FM0159601499030X

Fig. 234   Test DJ: Programmable Speedometer/Odometer Module (Part 3 of 3). 1996

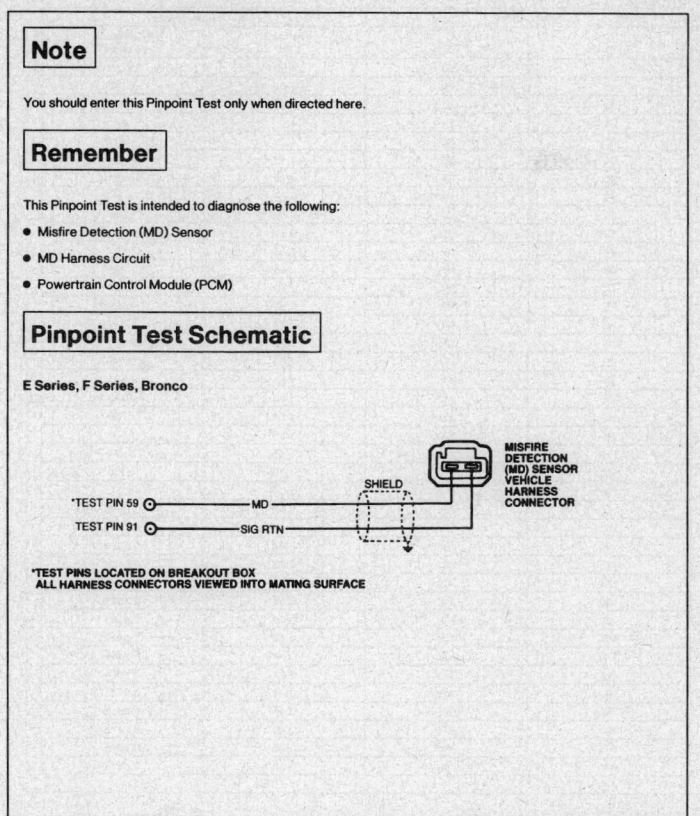

Note

You should enter this Pinpoint Test only when directed here.

Remember

This Pinpoint Test is intended to diagnose the following:

● Misfire Detection (MD) Sensor
● MD Harness Circuit
● Powertrain Control Module (PCM)

Pinpoint Test Schematic

E Series, F Series, Bronco

*TEST PINS LOCATED ON BREAKOUT BOX
ALL HARNESS CONNECTORS VIEWED INTO MATING SURFACE

FM0159601500010X

Fig. 235   Test DK: Misfire Detection Sensor (Part 1 of 3). 1996

Test Step	Result	►	Action to Take
DK1 DTC P0385: START ENGINE			
Diagnostic Trouble Code (DTC) P0385 indicates that Self-Test has detected a Misfire Detection (MD) Sensor circuit failure. Possible causes: — MD circuit open. — MD circuit shorted to GND. — MD circuit shorted to PWR. — SIG RTN open. — Damaged MD Sensor. — Damaged PCM. ● Start engine. ● **Will the engine start?**	Yes No	► ►	GO to DK2. DTC P0385 is not the cause of the No Start. GO to Symptom Flowcharts.
DK2 CLEAR AND ATTEMPT TO RE-GENERATE DTC P0385			
● Complete PCM Reset to clear DTCs (refer to Powertrain Control Module (PCM) Reset). ● Start engine. ● Increase rpm to greater than 1500 rpm for 10 seconds. Repeat two times. ● Key off. ● Retrieve all Continuous Memory DTCs. ● **Is DTC P0385 present?**	Yes No	► ►	GO to DK5. The fault that produced DTC P0385 is intermittent. GO to Pinpoint Test Step Z50.
DK5 CHECK CONTINUITY TO PCM			
● Key off. ● MD sensor vehicle harness connector disconnected. ● Disconnect PCM. Inspect for damaged or pushed out pins, corrosion, loose wires, etc. Service as necessary. ● Install breakout box, leave PCM disconnected. ● Measure resistance between MD circuit at the MD vehicle harness connector and Test Pin 59 (MD) at the breakout box. ● Measure resistance between SIG RTN circuit at the MD vehicle harness connector and Test Pin 91 (SIG RTN) at the breakout box. ● **Are resistance measurements less than 5.0 ohms?**	Yes No	► ►	GO to DK6. SERVICE open circuit. REMOVE breakout box. RECONNECT all components. RERUN Quick Test.
DK6 CHECK MD FOR SHORT TO POWER			
● Key off. ● MD sensor disconnected. ● Breakout box installed, PCM disconnected. ● Key on, engine off. ● Measure voltage between Test Pin 59 (MD) and Test Pins 51 and 103 (PWR GND) at the breakout box. ● **Is voltage less than 1.0 volt?**	Yes No	► ►	GO to DK7. SERVICE MD circuit for short to power. REMOVE breakout box. RECONNECT all components. RERUN Quick Test.

FM0159601500020X

Fig. 235   Test DK: Misfire Detection Sensor (Part 2 of 3). 1996

Test Step	Result	►	Action to Take
DK7 CHECK MD FOR SHORT TO GND			
● Key off. ● Breakout box installed, PCM disconnected. ● MD sensor disconnected. ● Measure resistance between Test Pin 59 (MD) and Test Pins 51, 103 (PWR GND) and 91 (SIG RTN). ● **Is each resistance greater than 10,000 ohms?**	Yes No	► ►	GO to DK8. SERVICE MD circuit for short to GND or SIG RTN. REMOVE breakout box. RECONNECT all components. RERUN Quick Test.
DK8 CHECK FOR SHORTS IN PCM			
● Key off. ● MD sensor disconnected. ● Breakout box installed. ● Connect PCM to breakout box. ● Measure resistance between Test Pin 59 (MD) and Test Pins 51, 103 (PWR GND), 71, 97 (VPWR), 91 (SIG RTN), and 23 (IGN GND) at the breakout box. ● **Is each resistance greater than 500 ohms?**	Yes No	► ►	GO to DK9. REPLACE PCM. REMOVE breakout box. RECONNECT all components. RERUN Quick Test.
DK9 CHECK MD SENSOR OUTPUT			
● Key off. ● Breakout box installed, PCM connected. ● Reconnect MD sensor. ● DVOM on AC scale (to monitor less than 5.0 volts). ● Measure voltage between Test Pin 59 (MD) and Test Pins 51 and 103 (PWR GND) at the breakout box while running engine at varying rpm. ● **Does AC voltage vary greater than 0.1 volt AC?**	Yes No	► ►	REPLACE PCM. REMOVE breakout box. RECONNECT all components. RERUN Quick Test. GO to DK10.
DK10 INSPECT MD SENSOR TRIGGER WHEEL			
● Is the MD sensor trigger wheel damaged, i.e., loose or misaligned?	Yes No	► ►	REPLACE or SERVICE as required. REMOVE all test equipment. RECONNECT all components. RERUN Quick Test. REPLACE sensor. REMOVE breakout box. RECONNECT all components. RERUN Quick Test.

FM0159601500030X

Fig. 235   Test DK: Misfire Detection Sensor (Part 3 of 3). 1996

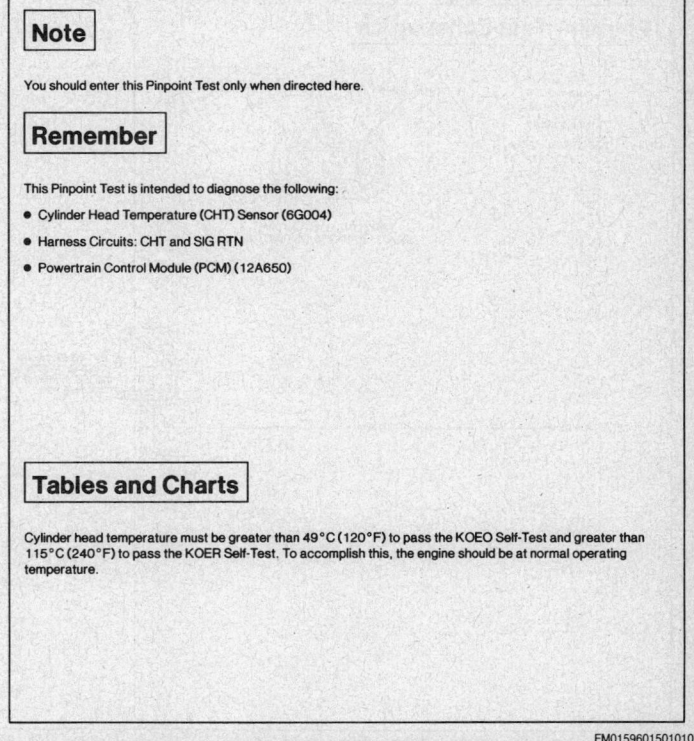

Note

You should enter this Pinpoint Test only when directed here.

Remember

This Pinpoint Test is intended to diagnose the following:

● Cylinder Head Temperature (CHT) Sensor (6G004)
● Harness Circuits: CHT and SIG RTN
● Powertrain Control Module (PCM) (12A650)

Tables and Charts

Cylinder head temperature must be greater than 49°C (120°F) to pass the KOEO Self-Test and greater than 115°C (240°F) to pass the KOER Self-Test. To accomplish this, the engine should be at normal operating temperature.

FM0159601501010X

Fig. 236   Test DL: Cylinder Head Temperature Sensor (Part 1 of 9). 1996

Voltage values were calculated for VREF = 5.0 volts. These values may vary 15 percent due to sensor and VREF variations.

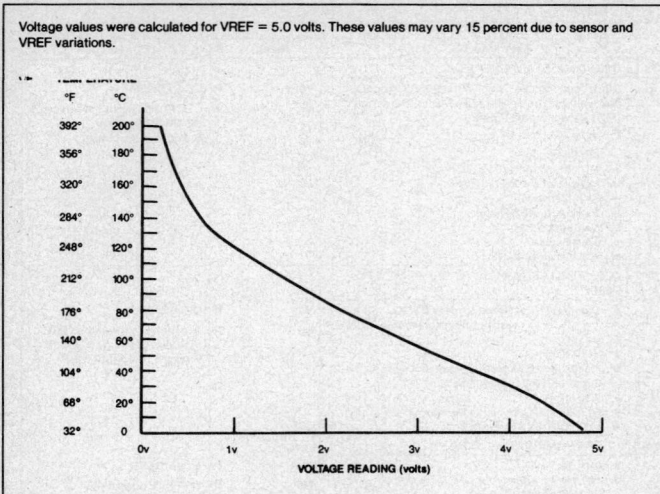

Temperature		CHT Sensor Values	
°C	°F	Voltage (V)	Resistance (K ohms)
-40	-40	4.98	965.808
-35	-31	4.97	700.178
-30	-22	4.96	513.019
-25	-13	4.95	379.674
-20	-4	4.93	283.664
-15	5	4.91	213.842
-10	14	4.88	162.584
-5	23	4.85	124.614
0	32	4.80	96.255
5	41	4.75	75.201

(Continued)

Temperature		CHT Sensor Values	
°C	°F	Voltage (V)	Resistance (K ohms)
10	50	4.69	59.175
15	59	4.61	46.883
20	68	4.52	37.387
25	77	4.41	30
30	86	4.29	24.215
35	95	4.16	19.657
40	104	4.0	16.043
45	113	3.83	13.161
50	122	3.65	10.85
55	131	3.45	8.99
60	140	3.25	7.487
65	149	3.04	6.265
70	158	2.83	5.268
75	167	2.62	4.45
80	176	2.42	3.775
85	185	2.22	3.215
90	194	2.03	2.75
95	203	1.85	2.361
100	212	1.68	2.034
105	221	1.53	1.758
110	230	1.38	1.523
115	239	1.17	1.324
120	248	1.12	1.155
125	257	1.01	1.01
130	266	0.91	0.8866
135	275	0.82	0.7805
140	284	0.74	0.6891
145	293	0.66	0.6101
150	302	0.60	0.5417
155	311	0.54	0.4821
160	320	0.46	0.4301
165	329	0.42	0.3847
170	338	0.38	0.3449
175	347	0.34	0.3099
180	356	0.31	0.2791
185	365	0.28	0.2519
190	374	0.26	0.2278
195	383	0.25	0.2065
200	392	0.23	0.1875

FM0159601501020X

Fig. 236   Test DL: Cylinder Head Temperature Sensor (Part 2 of 9). 1996

FM0159601501030X

Fig. 236   Test DL: Cylinder Head Temperature Sensor (Part 3 of 9). 1996

Pinpoint Test Schematics

SIGNAL RTN 91   TP89   VREF 90

THROTTLE POSITION (TP) SENSOR HARNESS CONNECTOR

CHT

CYLINDER HEAD TEMPERATURE SENSOR HARNESS CONNECTOR

TEST PIN 91 ○——— SIG RTN

66 CHT

FM0159601501040X

Fig. 236   Test DL: Cylinder Head Temperature Sensor (Part 4 of 9). 1996

Test Step	Result	▶	Action to Take
DL1 DTC P1288: CHECK OPERATION AND INSTALLATION OF TEMPERATURE SENSOR			
Diagnostic Trouble Code (DTC) P1228 indicates the Cylinder Head Temperature (CHT) sensor is out of Self-Test range. Correct range is 1.2 to 3.7 volts. Possible causes: — Engine overheating — Low coolant level (ECT). — Damaged harness connector. — Damaged sensor. — Poor thermostat operation. • Run engine at 2000 rpm until engine temperature becomes stabilized. • Check that upper radiator hose is hot and pressurized. • Rerun Key On Engine Running (KOER) Self-Test. • Is DTC P1288 present?	Yes No	▶ ▶	GO to DL2. Engine temperature was not stabilized. SERVICE any other DTCs as necessary.
DL2 CHECK VREF CIRCUIT VOLTAGE AT TP SENSOR			
• Refer to schematic at the beginning of the pinpoint test. • Key off. • Disconnect Throttle Position (TP) sensor. • Key on, engine off. • Measure the voltage between VREF circuit and SIG RTN circuit at the TP sensor vehicle harness connector. • Is voltage between 4.0 volts and 6.0 volts?	Yes No	▶ ▶	There is sufficient VREF voltage. RECONNECT TP sensor. GO to DL3. GO to Pinpoint Test Step C1.
DL3 CHECK RESISTANCE OF TEMPERATURE SENSOR WITH ENGINE OFF			
• Key off. • Disconnect temperature sensor. • Measure resistance between sensor Signal Circuit and SIG RTN circuit at the temperature sensor. Refer to the chart at the beginning of this Pinpoint Test for resistance specifications. • Is resistance within specification?	Yes No	▶ ▶	GO to DL4. REPLACE sensor. RECONNECT vehicle harness. RERUN Quick Test.

FM0159601501050X

Fig. 236   Test DL: Cylinder Head Temperature Sensor (Part 5 of 9). 1996

ELECTRONIC ENGINE CONTROL SYSTEM (EEC-V)

Test Step	Result	▶	Action to Take
DL4 CHECK RESISTANCE OF TEMPERATURE SENSOR WITH ENGINE RUNNING			
NOTE: Verify that engine is at operating temperature before taking CHT readings. • Key off. • Temperature sensor disconnected. • Run engine for two minutes at 2000 rpm. • Measure resistance between sensor signal circuit and SIG RTN circuit at the temperature sensor. Refer to the chart at the beginning of this Pinpoint Test for resistance specifications. • **Is resistance within specification?**	Yes No	▶ ▶	REPLACE PCM. RECONNECT vehicle harness. RERUN Quick Test. REPLACE sensor. RECONNECT vehicle harness. RERUN Quick Test.
DL10 DTC P1289: SIMULATE OPPOSITE SIGNAL TO PCM			
Diagnostic Trouble Code (DTC) P1289 indicates the sensor signal is greater than the Self-Test maximum. Possible causes: — Open in harness. — Improper harness connection. — Damaged sensor. — Damaged PCM. • Key off. • Disconnect temperature sensor. • Connect a jumper wire between the sensor signal circuit and SIG RTN circuit at the temperature sensor vehicle harness connector. • Scan Tool installed. • Key on. NOTE: If a Scan Tool communication problem exists, remove jumper wire immediately and go to DL12. • Access CHT PID. • **Is the CHT PID less than 0.2 volts (greater than 375°F / 190°C)?**	Yes No	▶ ▶	REPLACE sensor. REMOVE jumper wire. RECONNECT vehicle harness. RERUN Quick Test. REMOVE jumper wire. GO to DL11.

Fig. 236   Test DL: Cylinder Head Temperature Sensor (Part 6 of 9). 1996

FM0159601501060X

Test Step	Result	▶	Action to Take
DL11 CHECK CONTINUITY OF SENSOR SIGNAL AND SIG RTN CIRCUITS			
• Key off. • Temperature sensor disconnected. • Disconnect PCM. Inspect for damaged or pushed out pins, corrosion, loose wires, etc. Service as necessary. • Install breakout box, leave PCM disconnected. • Measure resistance between sensor signal circuit at the temperature sensor vehicle harness connector and Test Pin 66 (CHT) at the breakout box. • Measure resistance between SIG RTN circuit at the temperature sensor vehicle harness connector and Test Pin 91 (SIG RTN) at the breakout box. • **Is each resistance less than 5.0 ohms?**	Yes No	▶ ▶	REPLACE PCM. REMOVE breakout box. RECONNECT components. RERUN Quick Test. SERVICE open circuits. REMOVE breakout box. RECONNECT all components. RERUN Quick Test.
DL12 CHECK FOR SENSOR SIGNAL SHORTED TO VREF			
• Key off. • Temperature sensor disconnected. • Disconnect PCM. Inspect for damaged or pushed out pins, corrosion, loose wires, etc. Service as necessary. • Install breakout box, leave PCM disconnected. • Measure resistance between sensor signal circuit Test Pin 66 (CHT) and VREF at the breakout box. • **Is each resistance greater than 10,000 ohms?**	Yes No	▶ ▶	REPLACE PCM. RERUN Quick Test. LOCATE and SERVICE short to VREF. RERUN Quick Test.
DL20 DTC P1290: SIMULATE OPPOSITE SIGNAL TO PCM			
Diagnostic Trouble Code (DTC) P1290 indicates the sensor signal is less than Self-Test minimum. Possible causes: — Grounded circuit in harness. — Damaged sensor. — Improper harness connection. — Damaged PCM. • Key off. • Disconnect vehicle harness from suspect sensor. Inspect for damaged or pushed out pins, corrosion, loose wires, etc. Service as necessary. • Scan Tool installed. • Key on. • Access CHT PID. • **Is the CHT PID more than 4.6 volts (less than -40°F / C)?**	Yes No	▶ ▶	REPLACE sensor. RECONNECT harness. RERUN Quick Test. GO to DL21.

FM0159601501070X

Fig. 236   Test DL: Cylinder Head Temperature Sensor (Part 7 of 9). 1996

Test Step	Result	▶	Action to Take
DL21 CHECK VREF CIRCUIT VOLTAGE AT TP SENSOR			
• Refer to schematic at the beginning of the pinpoint test. • Key off. • Disconnect TP sensor. • Key on, engine off. • Measure the voltage between VREF circuit and SIG RTN circuit at the TP sensor vehicle harness connector. • **Is voltage between 4.0 and 6.0 volts?**	Yes No	▶ ▶	There is sufficient VREF voltage. RECONNECT TP sensor. GO to DL22. GO to Pinpoint Test Step C1.
DL22 CHECK SIGNAL CIRCUIT FOR SHORT TO GROUND			
• Key off. • Temperature sensor disconnected. • Disconnect PCM. Inspect for damaged or pushed out pins, corrosion, loose wires, etc. Service as necessary. • Install breakout box, PCM disconnected. • Measure resistance between Test Pin 66 (CHT) and Test Pins 24 or 51 (PWR GND) and 91 (SIG RTN) at the breakout box. • **Is each resistance greater than 10,000 ohms?**	Yes No	▶ ▶	REPLACE PCM. REMOVE breakout box. RECONNECT all components. RERUN Quick Test. SERVICE short circuit. REMOVE breakout box. RECONNECT all components. RERUN Quick Test.
DL90 DTCS P1289 OR P1290: INTERMITTENT CHECK			
Diagnostic Trouble Codes (DTCs) P1289 or P1290 were not received during KOEO and KOER Self-Tests, but are output during Continuous Memory Self-Test and may be intermittent. Possible causes: — Damaged harness. — Damaged harness connector. — Damaged IAT or ECT sensor. — Low coolant (ECT). — Damaged PCM. • Key off. • Scan Tool connected. • Key on. • Monitor the CHT PID. • While observing the PID, perform the following: — Tap on the sensor to simulate road shock. — Wiggle the sensor connector. • **Is there any large change in the temperature reading?**	Yes No	▶ ▶	DISCONNECT and INSPECT connectors. If OK, REPLACE the sensor. COMPLETE PCM Reset to clear DTCs (REFER to , Powertrain Control Module (PCM) Reset). COMPLETE Comprehensive Component Monitor Drive Cycle (REFER to Drive Cycles). RERUN Quick Test. GO to DL91.

FM0159601501080X

Fig. 236   Test DL: Cylinder Head Temperature Sensor (Part 8 of 9). 1996

Test Step	Result	▶	Action to Take
DL91 CHECK EEC-V WIRING HARNESS			
• Still monitoring PID. • While observing the appropriate PID, perform the following: — Hold the vehicle harness close to the sensor connector. Wiggle, shake and bend small sections of wiring harness while working toward the PCM. • **Is there any change in the temperature reading?**	Yes No	▶ ▶	ISOLATE fault. SERVICE as necessary. COMPLETE PCM Reset to clear DTCs (REFER to Powertrain Control Module (PCM) Reset). COMPLETE Comprehensive Component Monitor Drive Cycle (REFER to Drive Cycles). RERUN Quick Test. GO to DL92.
DL92 CHECK PCM AND VEHICLE HARNESS CONNECTOR			
• Key off. • Disconnect PCM. • Disconnect sensor connector. Inspect for spread terminals, pushed out pins and loose or crimped wires. • **Are connectors and terminals OK?**	Yes No	▶ ▶	Fault is not present at this time. COMPLETE PCM Reset to clear DTCs (REFER to Powertrain Control Module (PCM) Reset). COMPLETE Comprehensive Component Monitor Drive Cycle (REFER to Drive Cycles). RERUN Quick Test. SERVICE as necessary. COMPLETE PCM Reset to clear DTCs (REFER to Section 2A, Powertrain Control Module (PCM) Reset). COMPLETE Comprehensive Component Monitor Drive Cycle (REFER to Drive Cycles). RERUN Quick Test.
DL100 DTC P1299 INDICATES AN ENGINE OVERHEAT CONDITION OCCURRED			
Diagnostic Trouble Code (DTC) P1299 indicates an engine overheat condition was detected by the Cylinder Head Temperature (CHT) sensor. An FMEM Strategy called Failsafe Cooling was activated to cool the engine. (Refer to Section 1A, EEC-V System, for more information on Failsafe Cooling Strategy and the Cylinder Head Temperature Sensor.) Possible causes: — Engine cooling system problems. — Base engine problems. — Low coolant or loss of coolant. • Check coolant level. • **Is the coolant level fill correct?**	Yes No	▶ ▶	GO to Engine Cooling Group of the Service Manual for SYMPTOM Engine Overheats. GO to Engine Cooling Group of the Service Manual for SYMPTOM Loss of Engine coolant.

FM0159601501090X

Fig. 236   Test DL: Cylinder Head Temperature Sensor (Part 9 of 9). 1996

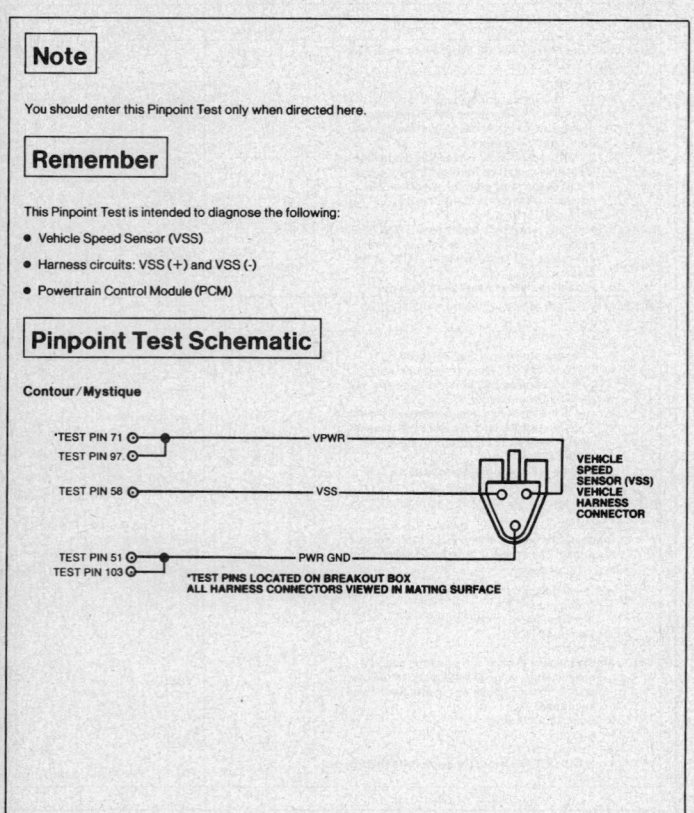

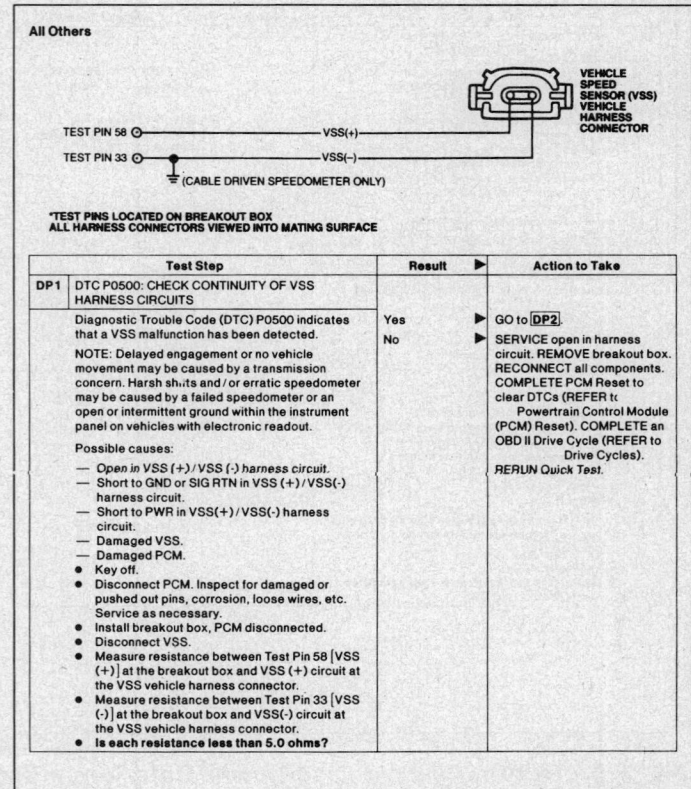

Fig. 237   Test DP: Vehicle Speed Sensor (Part 1 of 8). 1996

Fig. 237   Test DP: Vehicle Speed Sensor (Part 2 of 8). 1996

Test Step	Result	▶	Action to Take
DP2 CHECK VSS HARNESS CIRCUITS FOR SHORTS TO GROUND, SIG RTN AND POWER			
• Key off. • VSS disconnected. • Breakout box installed, PCM disconnected. • Measure resistance between Test Pin 58 [VSS (+)] and Test Pins 24, 61, 76 and 103 (PWR GND). • Measure resistance between Test Pin 58 [VSS (+)] and Test Pin 33 [VSS (-)]. • Measure resistance between Test Pin 58 [VSS (+)] and Test Pin 91 (SIG RTN). • Measure resistance between Test Pin 58 [VSS (+)] and Test Pin 71 (VPWR). • Measure resistance between Test Pins 33 [VSS (-)] and 71 (VPWR) at the breakout box. • **Is each resistance greater than 500 ohms?**	Yes No	▶ ▶	GO to DP3. SERVICE short circuit. REMOVE the breakout box. RECONNECT all components. COMPLETE PCM Reset to clear DTCs (REFER to Powertrain Control Module (PCM) Reset). COMPLETE an OBD II Drive Cycle (REFER to Drive Cycles). RERUN Quick Test.
DP3 CHECK VSS RESISTANCE			
• Key off. • VSS disconnected. • Measure the resistance of the VSS. • **Is resistance between 190 and 250 ohms?**	Yes No	▶ ▶	REMOVE breakout box. REPLACE the PCM. RECONNECT the VSS. COMPLETE PCM Reset to clear DTCs (REFER to Powertrain Control Module (PCM) Reset). COMPLETE an OBD II Drive Cycle (REFER to Drive Cycles). RERUN Quick Test. REPLACE the VSS. REMOVE breakout box. RECONNECT the PCM. COMPLETE PCM Reset to clear DTCs (REFER to Powertrain Control Module (PCM) Reset). COMPLETE an OBD II Drive Cycle (REFER to Drive Cycles). RERUN Quick Test.

Fig. 237   Test DP: Vehicle Speed Sensor (Part 3 of 8). 1996

Test Step	Result	▶	Action to Take
DP5 DTC P0500: CHECK VSS SIGNAL OUTPUT TO POWERTRAIN CONTROL MODULE (PCM)			
Diagnostic Trouble Code (DTC) P0500 indicates that a VSS malfunction has been detected. NOTE: Delayed engagement or no vehicle movement may be caused by a transmission concern. Harsh shifts and/or erratic speedometer may be caused by a failed speedometer or an open or intermittent ground within the instrument panel on vehicles with electronic readout. Possible causes: — Open in VSS, VPWR, PWR GND harness circuit. — Short to GND in VSS harness circuit. — Short to PWR in VSS harness circuit. — Damaged VSS. — Damaged PCM. • Key off. • Disconnect Powertrain Control Module (PCM). Inspect for damaged or pushed out pins, corrosion, loose wires, etc. Service as necessary. • Install breakout box, PCM disconnected. • Key on. • Observe voltage reading between Test Pin 58 and Test Pin 103 at breakout box while slowly rotating the drive wheel(s). • The voltage should rise above 5.0 volts and fall below 1.0 volt in a regular cycle. Observe several cycles. • **Does the VSS output voltage rise and fall as specified while slowly rotating the drive wheel(s)?**	Yes No	▶ ▶	REMOVE breakout box. REPLACE PCM. RECONNECT VSS. COMPLETE PCM Reset to clear DTCs (REFER to Powertrain Control Module (PCM) Reset.) COMPLETE an OBDII Drive Cycle (REFER to Drive Cycles). RERUN Quick Test. GO to DP6.
DP6 CHECK FOR BATTERY VOLTAGE TO VSS			
• Key off. • Disconnect VSS. • Key on. • Measure voltage at VPWR pin to GND pin at the VSS vehicle harness connector. • **Is the voltage greater than 10.5 volts?**	Yes No	▶ ▶	GO to DP7. GO to DP10.

Fig. 237   Test DP: Vehicle Speed Sensor (Part 4 of 8). 1996

Test Step	Result	▶	Action to Take
DP7 CHECK VSS CIRCUIT SHORT TO POWER			
• VSS disconnected. • Key on, PCM disconnected. • Measure voltage between Test Pin 58 and Test Pin 103 at the breakout box. • **Is voltage less than 1.0 volt?**	Yes	▶	GO to **DP8**.
	No	▶	SERVICE short to power. REMOVE breakout box. RECONNECT all components. COMPLETE PCM Reset to clear DTCs (REFER to Powertrain Control Module (PCM) Reset). COMPLETE an OBD II Drive Cycle (REFER to Drive Cycles). RERUN Quick Test.
DP8 CHECK VSS CIRCUIT SHORT TO GROUND			
• Key off. • VSS disconnected. • Measure resistance between Test Pin 58 and Test Pin 103 at the breakout box. • **Is resistance greater than 3,000 ohms?**	Yes	▶	GO to **DP9**.
	No	▶	SERVICE short to ground. REMOVE breakout box. RECONNECT all components. COMPLETE PCM Reset to clear DTCs (REFER to Powertrain Control Module (PCM) Reset). COMPLETE an OBD II Drive Cycle (REFER to Drive Cycles). RERUN Quick Test.
DP9 CHECK CONTINUITY OF VSS HARNESS CIRCUIT			
• Key off, VSS disconnected. • PCM disconnected. • Measure resistance between Test Pin 58 at the breakout box and the VSS circuit at the VSS vehicle harness connector. • **Is resistance less than 5.0 ohms?**	Yes	▶	REPLACE VSS. REMOVE the breakout box. RECONNECT all components. COMPLETE PCM Reset to clear DTCs (REFER to Powertrain Control Module (PCM) Reset). COMPLETE an OBD II Drive Cycle (REFER to Drive Cycles). RERUN Quick Test.
	No	▶	SERVICE open circuit. REMOVE breakout box. RECONNECT all components. COMPLETE PCM Reset to clear DTCs (REFER to Powertrain Control Module (PCM) Reset). COMPLETE an OBD II Drive Cycle (REFER to Drive Cycles). RERUN Quick Test.

FM0159601502050X

Fig. 237   Test DP: Vehicle Speed Sensor (Part 5 of 8). 1996

Test Step	Result	▶	Action to Take
DP10 CHECK CONTINUITY OF VSS GROUND HARNESS CIRCUIT			
• Key off, VSS disconnected. • PCM disconnected. • Measure resistance between GND Pin at the VSS vehicle harness connector and chassis ground. • **Is resistance less than 5.0 ohms?**	Yes	▶	SERVICE open VPWR to VSS. REMOVE breakout box. RECONNECT all components. COMPLETE PCM Reset to clear DTCs (REFER to Powertrain Control Module (PCM) Reset). COMPLETE an OBD II Drive Cycle (REFER to , Drive Cycles). RERUN Quick Test.
	No	▶	SERVICE open VSS GND circuit. REMOVE breakout box. RECONNECT all components. COMPLETE PCM Reset to clear DTCs (REFER to Powertrain Control Module (PCM) Reset). COMPLETE an OBD II Drive Cycle (REFER to Drive Cycles). RERUN Quick Test.
DP15 KOER DTC P1501: CHECK PCM VSS PID FOR INPUT SIGNAL			
Diagnostic Trouble Code (DTC) P1501 indicates the VSS input signal is out of Self Test range. NOTE: When the PCM detects a VSS input signal any time during KOER testing, a DTC P1501 will be set and the testing will abort. Possible causes: — Noisy VSS input signal from RFI/EMI external sources such as ignition wires or charging circuit as examples. • Start the engine and idle in neutral. • Access the VSS PID with a scan tool and observe for vehicle speed input to the PCM. • Increase the engine speed, not greater than 2000 rpm, several times while observing the VSS PID. • **Is the reading on the VSS PID less than 3 mph (5kPh)?**	Yes	▶	Unable to duplicate or identify a fault at this time. COMPLETE PCM Reset to clear DTCs (REFER to Powertrain Control Module (PCM) Reset. COMPLETE an OBDII Drive Cycle (REFER to Drive Cycles). RERUN Quick Test. If DTC P1501 still exists. GO to Pinpoint Test Step **Z1** with the following data: the VSS PID and list of possible causes.
	No	▶	GO to **DP22**

FM0159601502060X

Fig. 237   Test DP: Vehicle Speed Sensor (Part 6 of 8). 1996

Test Step	Result	▶	Action to Take
DP20 DTC P0503: INSPECT VSS AND CIRCUIT FOR AN INTERMITTENT			
Continuous Memory DTC P0503 indicates poor VSS performance. Possible causes: — Noisy VSS input signal from RFI/EMI external sources such as ignition wires or charging circuit as examples. — Damaged VSS or driven gears. — Damaged wiring harness or connectors. • Check for harness intermittents: — Pins properly seated in connector shell; wiring properly crimped; no corrosion; sensor securely mounted. • **Are there any indications of harness intermittents?**	Yes	▶	SERVICE as necessary. COMPLETE PCM Reset to clear DTCs (REFER to Powertrain Control Module (PCM) Reset. COMPLETE an OBDII Drive Cycle (REFER to , Drive Cycles). RERUN Quick Test.
	No	▶	GO to **DP21**.
DP21 CHECK PCM VSS PID FOR INPUT SIGNAL			
• Access the VSS PID with a scan tool. • Drive the vehicle at several steady state speeds above and below 30 mph (50 kph). • During each steady state speed observe the VSS PID for variations of (+) or (-) 5 mph (8 kph) for greater than 10 seconds. NOTE: For Scan Tools which have Data Record feature, recording data for playback may help in identifying variations easier. • **Were there any indications of a noisy or intermittent signal with the VSS PID?**	Yes	▶	GO to **DP22**.
	No	▶	Unable to duplicate or identify a fault at this time. DTC P0503 may have been set from sources external to the vehicle. SERVICE any other DTCs.
DP22 CHECK VSS HARNESS ROUTING			
• Check VSS harness routing — Verify that the harness is not routed adjacent to high current wires i.e. ignition wires or alternator wiring. — Verify VSS harness is shielded and grounded, if applicable. — Check continuity of the VSS harness; refer to step **DP1**. • **Are any problems evident?**	Yes	▶	SERVICE as necessary. COMPLETE PCM Reset to clear DTCs (REFER to Powertrain Control Module (PCM) Reset. COMPLETE an OBDII Drive Cycle (REFER to Drive Cycles). RERUN Quick Test.
	No	▶	Unable to duplicate or identify a fault at this time. GO to Pinpoint Test Step **Z1** with the following data: the VSS PID and list of possible causes.

FM0159601502070X

Fig. 237   Test DP: Vehicle Speed Sensor (Part 7 of 8). 1996

Test Step	Result	▶	Action to Take
DP25 DTC P1500: VISUAL INSPECTION			
Diagnostic Trouble Code (DTC) P1500 indicates the VSS input signal was intermittent. Possible causes: — Intermittent VSS connections. — Intermittent open in VSS harness circuit(s). — Intermittent short in VSS harness circuit(s). — Damaged VSS. — Damaged PCM. • Key off. • Visually inspect the VSS and VSS harness circuits for any potential failures. Use the following check list for reference: — Loose VSS connector. — Pushed out VSS connector pins. — Damaged VSS wiring harness insulation. — Incorrect harness routing. — Incorrect VSS mounting. • **Did the visual inspection reveal a potential failure?**	Yes	▶	SERVICE fault as necessary. COMPLETE PCM Reset to clear DTCs (REFER to Powertrain Control Module (PCM) Reset). COMPLETE an OBD II Drive Cycle (REFER to Drive Cycles). RERUN Quick Test.
	No	▶	RECONNECT all components. Unable to duplicate or identify fault at this time. GO to Pinpoint Test Step **Z1** with the following data: the VSS PID, the VSS check list and list of Possible Causes.

FM0159601502080X

Fig. 237   Test DP: Vehicle Speed Sensor (Part 8 of 8). 1996

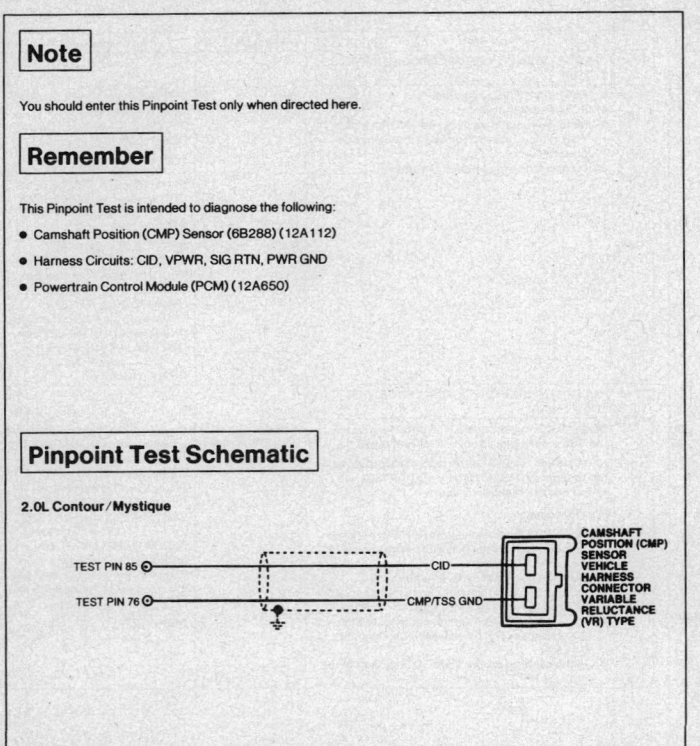

Note

You should enter this Pinpoint Test only when directed here.

Remember

This Pinpoint Test is intended to diagnose the following:

- Camshaft Position (CMP) Sensor (6B288) (12A112)
- Harness Circuits: CID, VPWR, SIG RTN, PWR GND
- Powertrain Control Module (PCM) (12A650)

Pinpoint Test Schematic

2.0L Contour/Mystique

FM0159601503010X

Fig. 238   Test DR: Cylinder Identification Circuit (Part 1 of 6). 1996

2.5L Contour/Mystique

3.0L Windstar

3.0L 2V Taurus/Sable, 3.0L Taurus/Sable FF, 3.8L Mustang, 3.8L Thunderbird/Cougar, 3.0L Ranger, 4.0L Ranger, 3.0L Aerostar, 4.0L Aerostar, 3.8L Windstar, 4.0L Explorer, 5.0L Explorer, 4.2L F-Series

FM0159601503020X

Fig. 238   Test DR: Cylinder Identification Circuit (Part 2 of 6). 1996

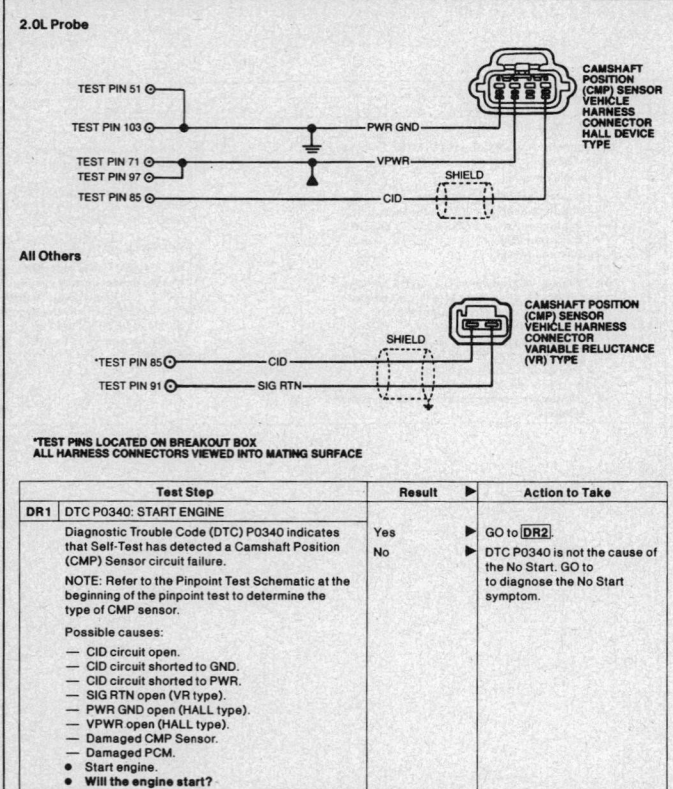

2.0L Probe

All Others

*TEST PINS LOCATED ON BREAKOUT BOX
ALL HARNESS CONNECTORS VIEWED INTO MATING SURFACE

Test Step	Result ▶	Action to Take
DR1 DTC P0340: START ENGINE		
Diagnostic Trouble Code (DTC) P0340 indicates that Self-Test has detected a Camshaft Position (CMP) Sensor circuit failure. NOTE: Refer to the Pinpoint Test Schematic at the beginning of the pinpoint test to determine the type of CMP sensor. Possible causes: — CID circuit open. — CID circuit shorted to GND. — CID circuit shorted to PWR. — SIG RTN open (VR type). — PWR GND open (HALL type). — VPWR open (HALL type). — Damaged CMP Sensor. — Damaged PCM. ● Start engine. ● **Will the engine start?**	Yes ▶ No ▶	GO to **DR2**. DTC P0340 is not the cause of the No Start. GO to to diagnose the No Start symptom.

FM0159601503030X

Fig. 238   Test DR: Cylinder Identification Circuit (Part 3 of 6). 1996

Test Step	Result ▶	Action to Take
DR2 CLEAR AND ATTEMPT TO RE-GENERATE DTC P0340		
● Complete PCM Reset to clear DTCs (refer to Section 2, Powertrain Control Module (PCM) Reset). ● Start engine. ● Increase rpm to greater than 1500 rpm for 10 seconds. Repeat two times. ● Key off. ● Retrieve all Continuous Memory DTCs. ● **Is DTC P0340 present?**	Yes ▶ No ▶	For VR type CMP: GO to **DR5**. For Hall Device type CMP: GO to **DR3**. The fault that produced DTC P0340 is intermittent. GO to Pinpoint Test Step **Z1** with the following data: List of Possible Causes.
DR3 CHECK VPWR TO CMP SENSOR		
● Key off. ● Disconnect CMP sensor vehicle harness connector. ● Key on, engine off. ● Measure voltage between VPWR circuit at the CMP vehicle harness connector and battery negative post. ● **Is voltage greater than 10.5 volts?**	Yes ▶ No ▶	GO to **DR4**. SERVICE open in VPWR circuit. RECONNECT all components. COMPLETE PCM Reset to clear DTCs (REFER to Powertrain Control Module (PCM) Reset). RERUN Quick Test.
DR4 CHECK PWR GND TO CMP SENSOR		
● Key off. ● CMP sensor disconnected. ● Measure resistance between PWR GND circuit at the CMP vehicle harness connector and battery negative post. ● **Is resistance less than 5.0 ohms?**	Yes ▶ No ▶	GO to **DR5**. SERVICE open in PWR GND circuit. COMPLETE PCM Reset to clear DTCs (REFER to Powertrain Control Module (PCM) Reset). RERUN Quick Test.

FM0159601503040X

Fig. 238   Test DR: Cylinder Identification Circuit (Part 4 of 6). 1996

Test Step		Result	▶	Action to Take
DR5	CHECK CONTINUITY TO PCM			
	• Key off. • CMP sensor vehicle harness connector disconnected. • Disconnect PCM. Inspect for damaged or pushed out pins, corrosion, loose wires, etc. Service as necessary. • Install breakout box, leave PCM disconnected. • Measure resistance between CID circuit at the CMP vehicle harness connector and Test Pin 85 (CID) at the breakout box. **For VR type CMP: (Contour/Mystique)** — Also measure resistance between CMP/TSS GND circuit at the CMP vehicle harness connector and Test Pin 76 (CMP/TSS GND) at the breakout box. **For VR type CMP: (All others:)** — Also measure resistance between SIG RTN circuit at the CMP vehicle harness connector and Test Pin 91 (SIG RTN) at the breakout box. • **Are resistance measurements less than 5.0 ohms?**	Yes No	▶ ▶	GO to DR6. SERVICE open circuit. REMOVE breakout box. RECONNECT all components. RERUN Quick Test.
DR6	CHECK CID FOR SHORT TO POWER			
	• Key off. • CMP sensor disconnected. • Breakout box installed, PCM disconnected. • Key on, engine off. • Measure voltage between Test Pin 85 (CID) and Test Pins 51 and 103 (PWR GND) at the breakout box. • **Is voltage less than 1.0 volt?**	Yes No	▶ ▶	GO to DR7. SERVICE CID circuit for short to power. REMOVE breakout box. RECONNECT all components. RERUN Quick Test.
DR7	CHECK CID FOR SHORT TO GND			
	• Key off. • Breakout box installed, PCM disconnected. • CMP sensor disconnected. • Disconnect Scan Tool from DLC. • Measure resistance between Test Pin 85 (CID) and Test Pins 51, 103 (PWR GND) and 91 (SIG RTN). • **Is each resistance greater than 10,000 ohms?**	Yes No	▶ ▶	GO to DR8. SERVICE CID circuit for short to GND or SIG RTN. REMOVE breakout box. RECONNECT all components. RERUN Quick Test.

FM0159601503050X

Fig. 238   Test DR: Cylinder Identification Circuit (Part 5 of 6). 1996

Test Step		Result	▶	Action to Take
DR8	CHECK FOR SHORTS IN PCM			
	• Key off. • CMP sensor disconnected. • Breakout box installed. • Connect PCM to breakout box. • Measure resistance between Test Pin 85 (CID) and Test Pins 51, 103 (PWR GND), 71, 97 (VPWR), 91 (SIG RTN), and 23 (IGN GND) at the breakout box. • **Is each resistance greater than 500 ohms?**	Yes No	▶ ▶	For VR type CMP: GO to DR9. For Hall Device type CMP: GO to DR10. REPLACE PCM. REMOVE breakout box. RECONNECT all components. RERUN Quick Test.
DR9	CHECK CMP SENSOR OUTPUT			
	• Key off. • Breakout box installed, PCM connected. • Reconnect CMP sensor. • DVOM on AC scale (to monitor less than 5.0 volts). • Measure voltage between Test Pin 85 (CID) and Test Pins 51, 103 (PWR GND) at the breakout box while running engine at varying rpm. • **Does AC voltage vary greater than 0.1 volt AC?**	Yes No	▶ ▶	REPLACE PCM. REMOVE breakout box. RECONNECT all components. RERUN Quick Test. REPLACE CMP sensor. REMOVE breakout box. RECONNECT all components. RERUN Quick Test.
DR10	CHECK CMP SENSOR OUTPUT			
	• Key off. • Breakout box installed, PCM disconnected. • Reconnect CMP sensor. • Connect DVOM between Test Pin 85 (CID) and Test Pins 51 or 103 (PWR GND) at the breakout box. • Bump engine in short bursts with the starter without starting engine for at least 10 engine revolutions. • **Does DVOM reading switch between "low" (less than 2.0 volts DC) and "high" (greater than 8.0 volts DC)?**	Yes No	▶ ▶	REPLACE PCM. REMOVE breakout box. RECONNECT all components. RERUN Quick Test. REPLACE CMP sensor. REMOVE breakout box. RECONNECT all components. RERUN Quick Test.

FM0159601503060X

Fig. 238   Test DR: Cylinder Identification Circuit (Part 6 of 6). 1996

Note

You should enter this Pinpoint Test only when directed here.

Remember

This Pinpoint Test is intended to diagnose the following:
• Harness circuits: ACP, VREF, SIG RTN
• Air Conditioning Pressure (ACP) Sensor (19D594)
• Powertrain Control Module (PCM) (12A650)

Pinpoint Test Schematic

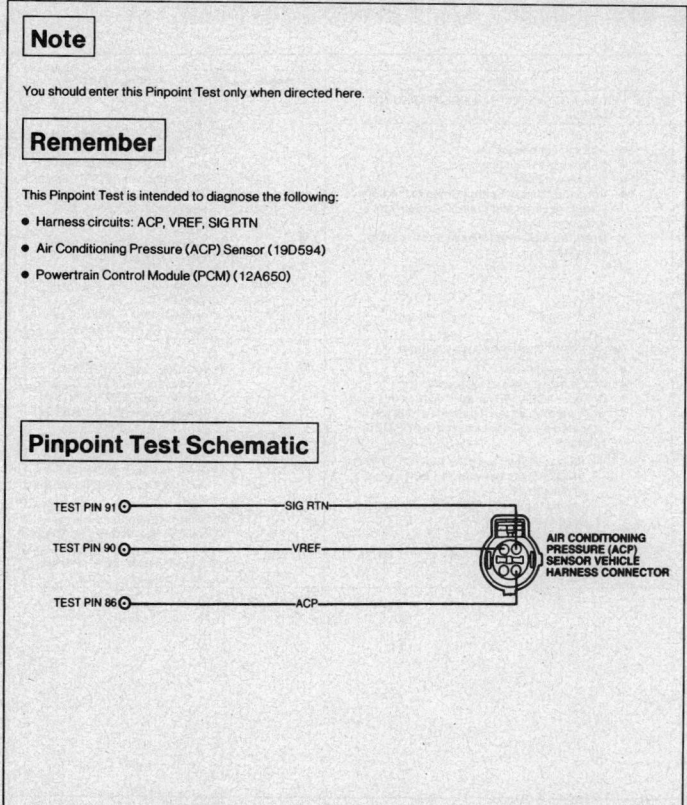

FM015960150401 0X

Fig. 239   Test DS: A/C Pressure Sensor (Part 1 of 9). 1996

Test Step		Result	▶	Action to Take
DS1	DTC P1461: CHECK ACP V PID			
	Diagnostic Trouble Code (DTC) P1461 indicates that Self-Test has detected the ACP circuit above the maximum allowed voltage. Possible causes: — Open SIG RTN circuit to ACP sensor. — Open ACP circuit (Escort/Tracer). — ACP circuit short to VREF or power. — VREF short to power. — Damaged ACP sensor. — Damaged PCM. • Scan Tool connected. • Key on, engine off. • Access ACP V PID. • **Is ACP V PID less than 4.9 volts?**	Yes No	▶ ▶	The ACP circuit voltage is now below the maximum. An intermittent fault may exist. GO to DS18. A hard fault is present. GO to DS2.
DS2	CHECK VREF AND SIG RTN CIRCUITS			
	• Key off. • Disconnect ACP sensor. • Key on, engine off. • Measure voltage between the VREF and SIG RTN circuits at the ACP sensor vehicle harness connector. • **Is voltage between 4.0 and 6.0 volts?**	Yes No	▶ ▶	GO to DS3. VREF is out of range, or SIG RTN circuit to ACP sensor is open. GO to Pinpoint Test Step C1.
DS3	INDUCE OPPOSITE ACP SIGNAL			
	• Key on, engine off. • ACP sensor disconnected. • Scan Tool connected. • Again access ACP V PID. • **Is ACP V PID now less than 4.9 volts?**	Yes No	▶ ▶	Key off. REPLACE ACP sensor following the instructions in the Group 12 of the Service Manual. RECONNECT all components. START engine. TURN A/C on, WAIT 15 seconds then TURN A/C off. Key off. RERUN Quick Test. GO to DS4.

FM0159601504020X

Fig. 239   Test DS: A/C Pressure Sensor (Part 2 of 9). 1996

Test Step		Result	▶	Action to Take
DS4	**CHECK ACP CIRCUIT FOR SHORT TO VREF**	Yes	▶	GO to **DS5**.
	• Key off. • ACP sensor disconnected. • Disconnect Scan Tool from DLC. • Disconnect PCM. Inspect for damaged or pushed out pins, corrosion, loose wires, etc. Service as necessary. • Measure resistance between the ACP circuit and VREF circuit at the ACP sensor vehicle harness connector. • **Is resistance greater than 10,000 ohms?**	No	▶	SERVICE ACP circuit short to VREF. RECONNECT all components. START engine. TURN A/C on, WAIT 15 seconds then TURN A/C off. Key off. RERUN Quick Test.
DS5	**CHECK ACP CIRCUIT FOR SHORT TO POWER**	Yes	▶	For Escort/Tracer: GO to **DS6**. **All others:** REPLACE PCM. RECONNECT all components. START engine. TURN A/C on, WAIT 15 seconds then TURN A/C off. Key off. RERUN Quick Test.
	• Key off. • ACP sensor disconnected. • PCM disconnected. • Key on, engine off. • Measure voltage between the ACP circuit at the ACP sensor vehicle harness connector and chassis ground. • Key off. • **Was voltage less than 1.0 volt?**	No	▶	SERVICE ACP circuit short to power. RECONNECT all components. START engine. TURN A/C on, WAIT 15 seconds then TURN A/C off. Key off. RERUN Quick Test.
DS6	**CHECK ACP CIRCUIT CONTINUITY**	Yes	▶	GO to **DS7**.
	• Key off. • ACP sensor disconnected. • PCM disconnected. • Install breakout box, leave PCM disconnected. • Measure resistance between Test Pin 86 (ACP) at the breakout box and the ACP circuit at the ACP sensor vehicle harness connector. • **Is resistance less than 5.0 ohms?**	No	▶	SERVICE open circuit. REMOVE breakout box. RECONNECT all components. START engine. TURN A/C on, WAIT 15 seconds then TURN A/C off. Key off. RERUN Quick Test.

FM015960150 4030X

Fig. 239   Test DS: A/C Pressure Sensor (Part 3 of 9). 1996

Test Step		Result	▶	Action to Take
DS7	**CHECK PCM**	Yes	▶	REPLACE ACP sensor. REMOVE breakout box. RECONNECT all components. TURN A/C on, WAIT 15 seconds then TURN A/C off. Key off. RERUN Quick Test.
	• Key off. • ACP sensor disconnected. • Breakout box installed. • Reconnect PCM to breakout box. • Connect a jumper wire between Test Pin 86 (ACP) and Test Pin 91 (SIG RTN) at the breakout box. • Key on, engine off. • Again access ACP V PID. NOTE: If the Scan Tool is now unable to communicate, follow "YES" Action to Take. • **Is ACP V PID now less than 4.9 volts?**	No	▶	REPLACE PCM. REMOVE breakout box. RECONNECT all components. START engine. TURN A/C on, WAIT 15 seconds then TURN A/C off. Key off. RERUN Quick Test.
DS10	**DTC P1462: CHECK ACP V PID**	Yes	▶	The ACP circuit voltage is now above the minimum. An intermittent fault may exist. GO to **DS18**.
	Diagnostic Trouble Code (DTC) P1462 indicates that Self-Test has detected the ACP circuit below the minimum allowed voltage. Possible causes: — Open ACP circuit. — ACP circuit short to SIG RTN or ground. — Open VREF to ACP sensor. — Damaged ACP sensor. — Damaged PCM. • Scan Tool connected. • Key on, engine off. • Access ACP V PID. • **Is ACP V PID greater than 0.15 volts?**	No	▶	A hard fault is present. GO to **DS11**.
DS11	**CHECK VREF AT ACP SENSOR**	Yes	▶	GO to **DS12**.
	• Key off. • Disconnect ACP sensor. • Key on, engine off. • Measure voltage between the VREF and SIG RTN circuits at the ACP sensor vehicle harness connector. • **Is voltage between 4.0 and 6.0 volts?**	No	▶	VREF is out of range. GO to Pinpoint Test Step **C1**.

VREF (90)   SIG RTN (91)   ACP (86)

**ACP SENSOR
VEHICLE HARNESS CONNECTOR**

FM015960150 4040X

Fig. 239   Test DS: A/C Pressure Sensor (Part 4 of 9). 1996

Test Step		Result	▶	Action to Take
DS12	**INDUCE OPPOSITE ACP SIGNAL**	Yes	▶	Key off. REPLACE ACP sensor. RECONNECT all components. START engine. TURN A/C on, WAIT 15 seconds then TURN A/C off. Key off. RERUN Quick Test.
	• Key off. • ACP sensor disconnected. • Scan Tool connected. • Connect a jumper wire between the ACP circuit and the VREF circuit at the ACP sensor vehicle harness connector. • Key on, engine off. • Access ACP V PID. NOTE: If any Scan Tool communication problem occurs, remove jumper immediately and go directly to **DS13**. • **Is the ACP V PID greater than 4.0 volts?**	No	▶	Key off. GO to **DS13**.
DS13	**CHECK ACP CIRCUIT FOR SHORT TO GROUND OR SIG RTN**	Yes	▶	GO to **DS14**.
	• Key off. • ACP sensor disconnected. • Disconnect Scan Tool from DLC. • Disconnect PCM. Inspect for damaged or pushed out pins, corrosion, loose wires, etc. Service as necessary. • Measure resistance between the ACP circuit and the SIG RTN circuit at the ACP sensor vehicle harness connector. • Measure resistance between the ACP circuit at the ACP sensor vehicle harness connector and the battery negative post. • **Are both resistances greater than 10,000 ohms?**	No	▶	SERVICE short circuit. RECONNECT all components. START engine. TURN A/C on, WAIT 15 seconds then TURN A/C off. Key off. RERUN Quick Test.
DS14	**CHECK ACP CIRCUIT CONTINUITY**	Yes	▶	GO to **DS15**.
	• Key off. • PCM disconnected. • ACP sensor disconnected. • Install breakout box, leave PCM disconnected. • Measure resistance between Test Pin 86 (ACP) at the breakout box and the ACP circuit at the ACP sensor vehicle harness connector. • **Is resistance less than 5.0 ohms?**	No	▶	SERVICE open ACP circuit. RECONNECT all components. START engine. TURN A/C on, WAIT 15 seconds then TURN A/C off. Key off. RERUN Quick Test.
DS15	**WILL THE A/C CLUTCH ENGAGE?**	Yes	▶	REPLACE PCM. REMOVE breakout box. RECONNECT all components. TURN A/C on, WAIT 15 seconds then TURN A/C off. Key off. RERUN Quick Test.
	• PCM disconnected. • Reconnect ACP sensor. • Key on, engine off. • While listening for the A/C clutch to engage, turn the A/C on. Repeat if necessary. • Key off. • **Did the A/C clutch engage when the A/C was turned on?**	No	▶	GO to **DS16**.

FM015960150 4050X

Fig. 239   Test DS: A/C Pressure Sensor (Part 5 of 9). 1996

Test Step		Result	▶	Action to Take
DS16	**VERIFY A/C SYSTEM HAS A REFRIGERANT CHARGE**	Yes	▶	REPLACE PCM. REMOVE A/C System Manifold Gauge Set, etc. as required. RECONNECT all components. START engine. TURN A/C on, WAIT 15 seconds then TURN A/C off. Key off. RERUN Quick Test.
	• Key off. • ACP sensor connected. • Remove breakout box. • Reconnect PCM. • Go to the Climate Control Group of the Service Manual to verify that the A/C system has a refrigerant charge. • **Does the A/C system have a refrigerant charge?**	No	▶	SERVICE A/C system as directed by the Service Manual. RECONNECT all components. START engine. TURN A/C on, WAIT 15 seconds then TURN A/C off. Key off. RERUN Quick Test.
DS18	**WIGGLE TEST HARNESS AND SENSOR**	Yes	▶	ISOLATE fault and SERVICE as necessary. RECONNECT all components. PERFORM PCM Reset to clear DTC(s) (REFER Powertrain Control Module (PCM) Reset). START engine. TURN A/C on, WAIT 15 seconds then TURN A/C off. Key off. RERUN Quick Test.
	• Key on, engine off. • ACP V PID accessed on Scan Tool. • Observe ACP V PID for an indication of a fault while performing the following (a fault will be indicated by a sudden change in ACP V PID voltage): — Shake, wiggle, bend the ACP, SIG RTN and VREF circuits between the ACP sensor and the PCM. — Lightly tap on the ACP sensor (to simulate road shock). • **Is a fault indicated?**	No	▶	Unable to duplicate and/or identify fault at this time. GO to Pinpoint Test Step **Z1** with the following data: ACP V PID and list of possible causes.

FM015960150 4060X

Fig. 239   Test DS: A/C Pressure Sensor (Part 6 of 9). 1996

ELECTRONIC ENGINE CONTROL SYSTEM (EEC-V)

Test Step	Result	▶	Action to Take
DS20 **DTC P1463: VERIFY A/C CLUTCH CAN DISENGAGE**			
Diagnostic Trouble Code (DTC) P1463 indicates that the A/C Pressure (ACP) Sensor did not detect a sufficient change in A/C system pressure when the A/C was turned on. Possible causes: — A/C system inoperative due to a mechanical concern. — A/C system inoperative due to an electrical concern (although ACCS circuit voltage is getting to PCM Pin 41). — A/C clutch always engaged. — Open ACP or VREF circuit. — Damaged ACP sensor. ● A/C and defroster off. ● Start engine. ● Verify that the A/C clutch can disengage. ● **Is the A/C clutch disengaged?**	Yes No	▶ ▶	GO to **DS21**. (A/C Compressor Runs Continuously, A/C Always On) diagnose the always engaged A/C clutch.
DS21 **CHECK FOR VOLTAGE AND GROUND TO A/C CLUTCH (USING NON POWERED TEST LAMP)**			
NOTE: If voltage and ground to A/C clutch has already been checked in the Flow Charts, or the A/C clutch can be heard "clicking" when the A/C is turned on, GO to the question at the end of this test step. ● Key off. ● Disconnect A/C Cycling Switch. Install a jumper wire in the A/C Cycling Switch vehicle harness connector (to complete the circuit). ● Disconnect the A/C clutch. ● Connect a non-powered test lamp between the power pin and ground pin at the A/C clutch vehicle harness connector. ● Start engine. ● Turn A/C on, wait 15 seconds. ● Monitor test lamp. ● After testing turn key off, remove jumper and reconnect A/C clutch and A/C cycling switch. ● For Mark VIII, be aware that this test may set DTC P1530. If P1530 was not present until after this test step, disregard DTC and clear before returning vehicle to customer. ● **Does test lamp light (or can A/C clutch be heard clicking on)?**	Yes No	▶ ▶	GO to **DS22**. For Escort/Tracer: GO to **KM15**. For Continental: GO to **X110**. For Mark VIII: VERIFY test results. If OK, disregard P1463. RETURN to Diagnostic Subroutine, to service any other DTC or to continue vehicle diagnosis.

Test Step	Result	▶	Action to Take
DS22 **CHECK IF A SUFFICIENT A/C PRESSURE CHANGE CAN BE DETECTED BY THE ACP PID**			
● Scan Tool connected. ● Start engine. ● A/C off. ● Access ACP V PID. ● Note ACP V PID voltage. ● While monitoring ACP V PID voltage, turn A/C on. Five seconds after A/C clutch engagement, note voltage (if clutch does not engage, follow NO Action To Take). ● **Did the ACP V PID voltage change more than 0.3 volts within five seconds of clutch engagement?**	Yes No	▶ ▶	The ACP Sensor and PCM can detect a sufficient change in A/C system pressure. check for proper operation of the A/C system. After any service, RECONNECT all components. PERFORM PCM Reset to clear DTC(s) (REFER to Powertrain Control Module (PCM) Reset). START engine. TURN A/C on, WAIT 15 seconds then TURN A/C off. Key off. RERUN Quick Test. Key off, A/C off. GO to **DS23**.
DS23 **CHECK A/C SYSTEM PRESSURE AND PRESSURE CHANGE**			
● Key off. ● Refer to the Climate Control Group of the Service Manual for proper procedures to install the A/C System Manifold Gauge Set and to check the A/C system high pressure readings. ● Start engine. ● A/C off. ● Note the A/C high pressure reading. ● While monitoring the A/C system high pressure reading, turn the A/C on. Five seconds after clutch engagement, note the pressure (the pressure should increase). ● A/C off. ● **Did the A/C high pressure reading change more than 30 psi within five seconds of clutch engagement?**	Yes No	▶ ▶	GO to **DS24**. A/C system pressure did not change as expected. to check for proper mechanical operation of the A/C system. After any service, RECONNECT all components. PERFORM PCM Reset to clear DTC(s) (REFER to Powertrain Control Module (PCM) Reset). START engine. TURN A/C on, WAIT 15 seconds then TURN A/C off. Key off. RERUN Quick Test.

Test Step	Result	▶	Action to Take
DS24 **CHECK VREF AT ACP SENSOR**			
● Key off. ● Disconnect ACP sensor. ● Key on, engine off. ● Measure voltage between the VREF and SIG RTN circuits at the ACP sensor vehicle harness connector. ● Key off. ● **Was voltage between 4.0 and 6.0 volts?**	Yes No	▶ ▶	GO to **DS25**. VREF is out of range. GO to Pinpoint Test Step **C1**.
DS25 **CHECK ACP CIRCUIT CONTINUITY**			
● Key off. ● ACP sensor disconnected. ● Disconnect PCM. Inspect for damaged or pushed out pins, corrosion, loose wires, etc. Service as necessary. ● Install breakout box. Leave PCM disconnected. ● Measure resistance between Test Pin 86 (ACP) and the ACP circuit at the ACP sensor vehicle harness connector. ● **Is resistance less than 5.0 ohms?**	Yes No	▶ ▶	REPLACE ACP sensor REMOVE breakout box. RECONNECT all components. PERFORM PCM Reset to clear DTC(s) (if applicable) (REFER to , Powertrain Control Module (PCM) Reset). START engine. TURN A/C on, WAIT 15 seconds then TURN A/C off. Key off. RERUN Quick Test. SERVICE open ACP circuit. REMOVE breakout box. RECONNECT all components. PERFORM PCM Reset to clear DTC(s) (if applicable) (REFER to Powertrain Control Module (PCM) Reset). START engine. TURN A/C on, WAIT 15 seconds then TURN A/C off. Key off. RERUN Quick Test.

Note

You should enter this Pinpoint Test only when directed here.

Remember

This Pinpoint Test is intended to diagnose the following:

● PSP sensor (3N824)
● Harness circuits: PSP signal, SIG RTN, VREF
● Powertrain Control Module (PCM) (12A650)

Pinpoint Test Schematic

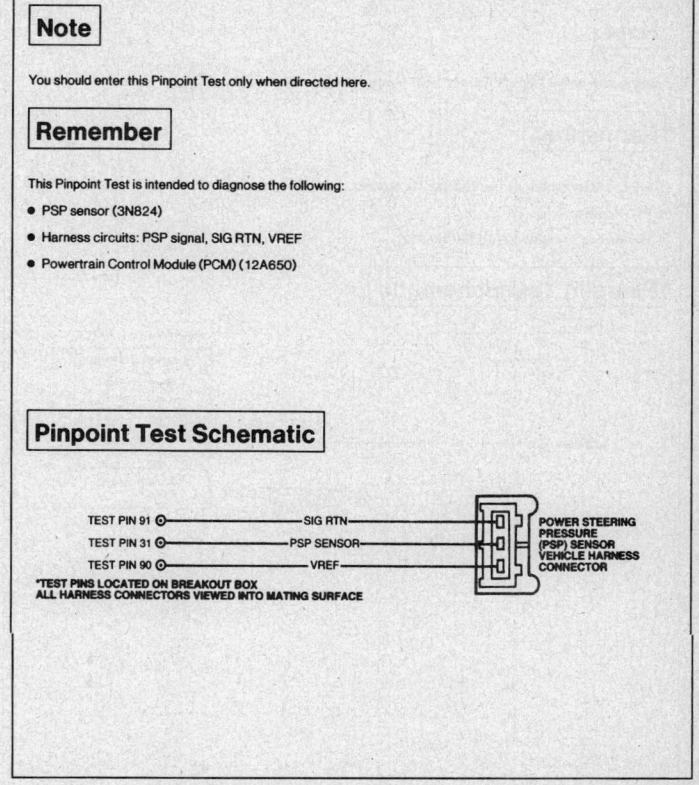

TEST PIN 91 ⊙———— SIG RTN
TEST PIN 31 ⊙———— PSP SENSOR
TEST PIN 90 ⊙———— VREF

POWER STEERING PRESSURE (PSP) SENSOR VEHICLE HARNESS CONNECTOR

*TEST PINS LOCATED ON BREAKOUT BOX
ALL HARNESS CONNECTORS VIEWED INTO MATING SURFACE

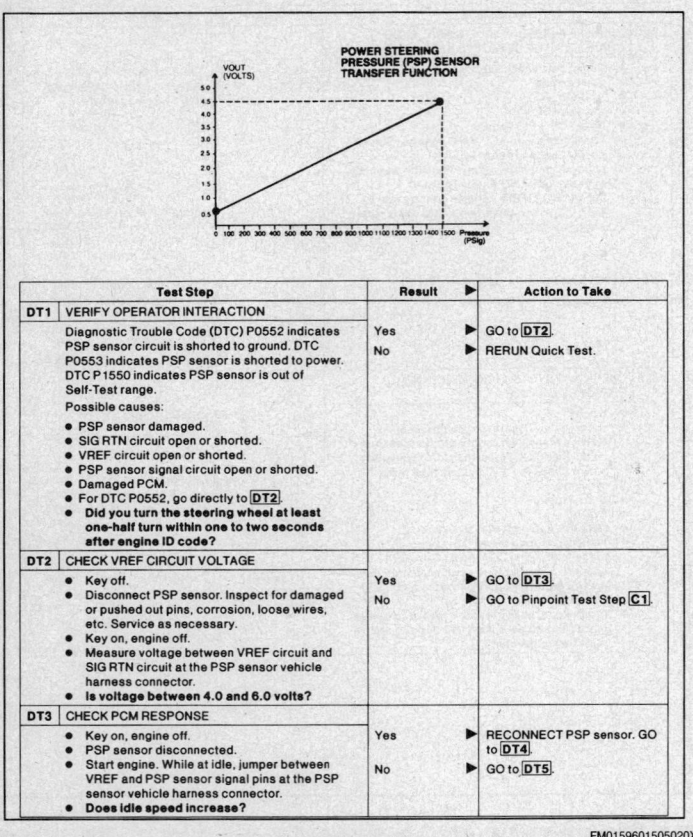

POWER STEERING PRESSURE (PSP) SENSOR TRANSFER FUNCTION

Test Step	Result	▶	Action to Take
DT1 VERIFY OPERATOR INTERACTION			
Diagnostic Trouble Code (DTC) P0552 indicates PSP sensor circuit is shorted to ground. DTC P0553 indicates PSP sensor is shorted to power. DTC P1550 indicates PSP sensor is out of Self-Test range. Possible causes: ● PSP sensor damaged. ● SIG RTN circuit open or shorted. ● VREF circuit open or shorted. ● PSP sensor signal circuit open or shorted. ● Damaged PCM. ● For DTC P0552, go directly to ☐DT2☐. ● **Did you turn the steering wheel at least one-half turn within one to two seconds after engine ID code?**	Yes No	▶ ▶	GO to ☐DT2☐. RERUN Quick Test.
DT2 CHECK VREF CIRCUIT VOLTAGE			
● Key off. ● Disconnect PSP sensor. Inspect for damaged or pushed out pins, corrosion, loose wires, etc. Service as necessary. ● Key on, engine off. ● Measure voltage between VREF circuit and SIG RTN circuit at the PSP sensor vehicle harness connector. ● **Is voltage between 4.0 and 6.0 volts?**	Yes No	▶ ▶	GO to ☐DT3☐. GO to Pinpoint Test Step ☐C1☐.
DT3 CHECK PCM RESPONSE			
● Key on, engine off. ● PSP sensor disconnected. ● Start engine. While at idle, jumper between VREF and PSP sensor signal pins at the PSP sensor vehicle harness connector. ● **Does idle speed increase?**	Yes No	▶ ▶	RECONNECT PSP sensor. GO to ☐DT4☐. GO to ☐DT5☐.

FM0159601505020X

Fig. 240   Test DT: Power Steering Pressure Sensor (Part 2 of 3). 1996

Test Step	Result	▶	Action to Take
DT4 CHECK PSP SENSOR OPERATION			
● Key off. ● Disconnect PCM. Inspect for damaged or pushed out pins, corrosion, loose wires, etc. Service as necessary. ● Install breakout box, connect PCM to breakout box. ● Key on, engine at idle. ● Measure the voltage between the PSP sensor signal Test Pin and SIG RTN Test Pin at the breakout box. ● While turning the steering wheel end-to-end, observe voltage change. ● **Is voltage reading changing between 0.5 and 4.5 volts?**	Yes No	▶ ▶	GO to Pinpoint Test Step ☐Z1☐ for Intermittent Fault Diagnosis. REPLACE PSP sensor. REMOVE breakout box. RECONNECT all components. RERUN Quick Test.
DT5 CHECK CONTINUITY OF PSP SIGNAL CIRCUIT			
● Key off. ● Disconnect PCM. Inspect for damaged or pushed out pins, corrosion, loose wires, etc. Service as necessary. ● Install breakout box, leave PCM disconnected. ● PSP sensor disconnected. ● Measure resistance between the PSP signal Test Pin at the breakout box and the same PSP signal pin at the sensor vehicle harness connector. ● Measure resistance between the VREF Test Pin at the breakout box and the same VREF pin at the sensor vehicle harness connector. ● Measure resistance between SIG RTN Test Pin at the breakout box and the same SIG RTN pin at the vehicle harness connector. ● **Is each resistance less than 5.0 ohms?**	Yes No	▶ ▶	GO to ☐DT6☐. SERVICE open circuit. REMOVE breakout box. RECONNECT all components. RERUN Quick Test.
DT6 CHECK PSP SIGNAL FOR SHORT TO POWER OR GROUND			
● Key off. ● Breakout box installed, PCM disconnected. ● PSP sensor disconnected. ● Measure resistance between the PSP sensor signal Test Pin and VREF, SIG RTN and Chassis Ground Test Pins at the breakout box. ● **Is each resistance greater than 10,000 ohms?**	Yes No	▶ ▶	REPLACE PCM. REMOVE breakout box. RECONNECT all components. RERUN Quick Test. SERVICE short circuit. REMOVE breakout box. RECONNECT all components. RERUN Quick Test.

FM0159601505030X

Fig. 240   Test DT: Power Steering Pressure Sensor (Part 3 of 3). 1996

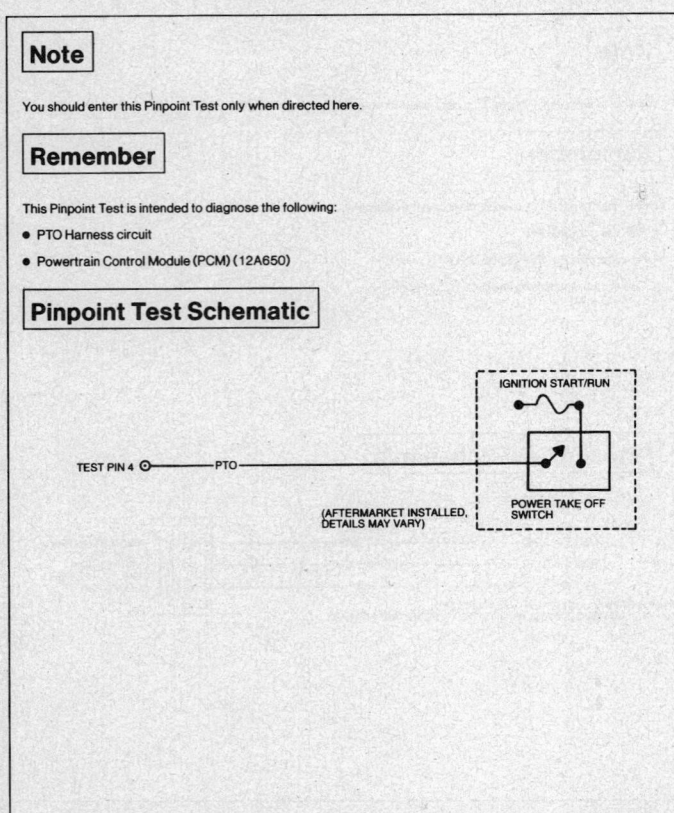

☐ **Note** ☐

You should enter this Pinpoint Test only when directed here.

☐ **Remember** ☐

This Pinpoint Test is intended to diagnose the following:

● PTO Harness circuit
● Powertrain Control Module (PCM) (12A650)

Pinpoint Test Schematic

IGNITION START/RUN

TEST PIN 4 ⊙ — PTO

(AFTERMARKET INSTALLED, DETAILS MAY VARY)

POWER TAKE OFF SWITCH

FM0159601506010X

Fig. 241   Test FB: Power Take Off (Part 1 of 4). 1996

Test Step	Result	▶	Action to Take
FB1 PTO STAT PID DOES NOT CYCLE: CHECK PTO SWITCH FOR SHORT TO POWER			
The PCM uses the PTO circuit to indicate an additional load is being applied to the engine. If a vehicle is experiencing a problem with the PTO circuit or does not have a PTO circuit, the OBD II Monitors may set a false DTC. Possible causes: — PTO circuit short to power in aftermarket switch / input to the PTO harness connector. — PTO circuit short to VPWR. — Damaged PCM. ● Key off. ● Disconnect PTO switch vehicle harness connector. ● Key on, engine off. ● Connect Scan Tool to DLC. ● Access PTO STAT PID. ● **Is PTO STAT PID on?**	Yes No	▶ ▶	PTO switch is OK. GO to ☐FB2☐. PTO switch from aftermarket installation is always on. REFER to aftermarket component manufacturer for service information. After service, RECONNECT all components and PERFORM Drive Cycle (REFER to Drive Cycles) and RERUN Quick Test.
FB2 CHECK PTO CIRCUIT FOR SHORT TO POWER			
● Key off. ● PTO switch disconnected. ● Disconnect PCM. Inspect for damaged or pushed out pins, corrosion, loose wires, etc. Service as necessary. ● Install breakout box, leave PCM disconnected. ● Key on. ● Measure voltage between Test Pin 4 (PTO) and Test Pins 51 / 103 (PWR GND) at the breakout box. ● **Is voltage less than 1.0 volt?**	Yes No	▶ ▶	REPLACE PCM. REMOVE breakout box. RECONNECT all components. RERUN Quick Test. SERVICE short to power. REMOVE breakout box. RECONNECT all components. RERUN Quick Test.
FB3 MIL ON: CHECK PTO PID			
The PCM uses the PTO circuit to indicate an additional load is being applied to the engine. If a vehicle is experiencing a problem with the PTO circuit or does not have a PTO circuit, the OBD II Monitors may set a false DTC. Possible causes: — Open in PTO circuit. — Short to chassis ground in PTO circuit. ● Key on, engine off. ● Connect Scan Tool to DLC. ● Access the PTO STAT PID. NOTE: Some vehicles may not support a PTO STAT PID. ● **Is the PTO STAT PID available and displaying on or off?**	Yes No	▶ ▶	GO to ☐FB4☐. GO to ☐FB9☐.

FM0159601506020X

Fig. 241   Test FB: Power Take Off (Part 2 of 4). 1996

Test Step	Result	►	Action to Take
FB4 CHECK PTO CIRCUIT WITH SCAN TOOL			
NOTE: This step requires operating the PTO component. Refer to aftermarket manufacturer for PTO operating instructions. Follow all safety precautions. • Scan Tool connected, PTO STAT PID accessed. • Key on (may need to start engine to engage PTO). • Cycle PTO switch / handle while viewing PTO STAT PID. • **Did PTO STAT PID cycle ON, delay, then turn OFF?**	Yes No	► ►	PTO input is OK. RETURN to Symptom Flowcharts. Faulty PTO circuit. GO to FB5.
FB5 CHECK PTO CIRCUIT FOR SHORT TO GROUND			
• Key off. • Disconnect Scan Tool from DLC. • Disconnect PTO switch vehicle harness connector. • Measure resistance between PTO circuit at the PTO switch vehicle harness connector and chassis ground. • **Is resistance greater than 10,000 ohms?**	Yes No	► ►	GO to FB7. GO to FB6.
FB6 ISOLATE SHORT TO CHASSIS GROUND			
• Key off. • PTO switch disconnected. • Scan Tool disconnected. • Disconnect PCM. Inspect for damaged or pushed out pins, corrosion, loose wires, etc. Service as necessary. • Install breakout box, leave PCM disconnected. • Measure resistance between Test Pin 4 (PTO) and Test Pin 77 / 103 (PWR GND). • **Is resistance greater than 10,000 ohms?**	Yes No	► ►	REPLACE PCM. REMOVE breakout box. RECONNECT all components. RERUN Quick Test. SERVICE PTO circuit short to chassis ground. RECONNECT all components. RERUN Quick Test.
FB7 CHECK PTO CIRCUIT FROM PTO SWITCH HARNESS CONNECTOR TO PCM			
• Key off. • Scan Tool disconnected. • PTO switch disconnected. • Connect Jumper wire between B+ post and PTO circuit at the PTO switch vehicle harness connector. • Key on, engine off. • Access PTO STAT PID. • **Is PTO STAT PID on?**	Yes No	► ►	PTO circuit from switch vehicle harness connector to PCM is OK. REFER to aftermarket component manufacturer for service information on PTO switch, etc. After service, PERFORM PCM Reset to clear DTC(s) (REFER to Powertrain Control Module (PCM) Reset). RERUN Quick Test. GO to FB8.

FM0159601506030X

Fig. 241　Test FB: Power Take Off (Part 3 of 4). 1996

Test Step	Result	►	Action to Take
FB8 CHECK CIRCUIT CONTINUITY			
• Key off. • PTO switch disconnected. • Disconnect PCM. Inspect for damaged or pushed out pins, corrosion, loose wires, etc. Service as necessary. • Install breakout box, leave PCM disconnected. • Measure resistance from Test Pin 4 (PTO) at the breakout box to PTO circuit at the PTO switch vehicle harness connector. • **Is resistance less than 5.0 ohms?**	Yes No	► ►	REPLACE PCM. REMOVE breakout box. RECONNECT all components. RERUN Quick Test. SERVICE open PTO circuit. REMOVE breakout box. RECONNECT all components. RERUN Quick Test.
FB9 PERFORM KOEO AND KOER QUICK TESTS			
The following steps are used for PTO diagnostics when the vehicle does not support the PTO circuit or PTO STAT PID. • Perform KOEO Self-Test. Refer to Diagnostic Subroutine DSR3 for procedure. • Perform KOER Self-Test. Refer to Diagnostic Subroutine DSR5 for procedure. • Perform base timing check. Refer to , Diagnostic Subroutine DSR4 for procedure. • **Are any KOEO or KOER DTCs present or is base timing incorrect?**	Yes No	► ►	FOLLOW direction in DSR3 or DSR5 to SERVICE the KOEO or KOER DTCs. Follow DSR4 for base timing check. GO to FB10.
FB10 PERFORM OBD II DRIVE CYCLE WITH PTO DISENGAGED			
• Perform PCM Reset (refer to Powertrain Control Module (PCM) Reset). NOTE: Make sure the PTO is disengaged. • Perform OBD II Drive Cycle (refer to , Drive Cycles). • Retrieve all Continuous Memory DTCs (refer to Accessing All Continuous Memory DTCs). • **Are any Continuous Memory DTCs stored?** NOTE: The purpose of this test step is to determine if the PTO operation resulted in any Continuous Memory DTCs stored due to the extra load of the PTO component on the engine.	Yes No	► ►	GO to Powertrain Diagnostic Trouble Code (DTC) Chart, to ADDRESS the first Continuous Memory DTC. MIL may have been caused by engaging the PTO, creating a load on the engine, while the OBD II Monitors were running. If the symptom persists, GO to Pinpoint Test Step Z1 with the following data: PTO STAT, LOAD PIDs and list of possible causes.

FM0159601506040X

Fig. 241　Test FB: Power Take Off (Part 4 of 4). 1996

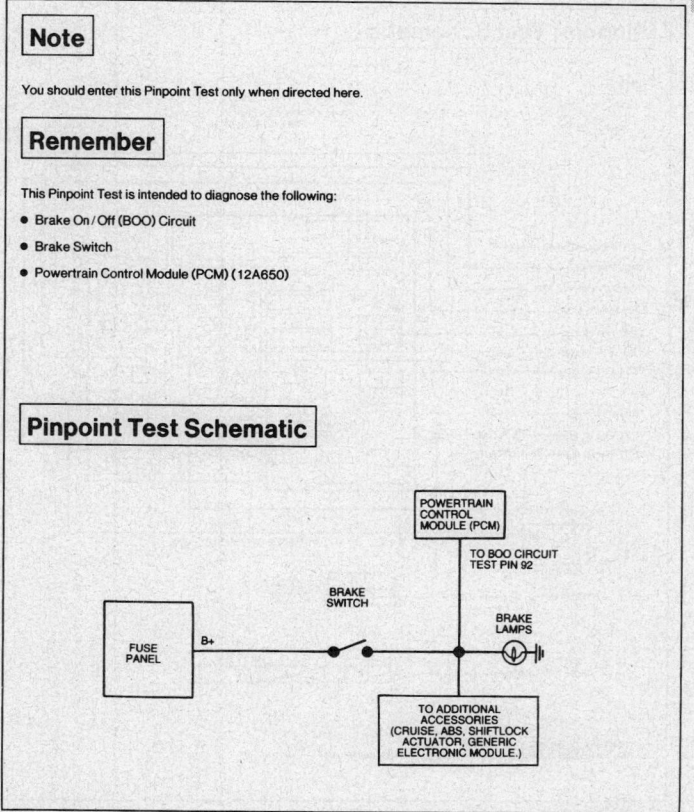

Note

You should enter this Pinpoint Test only when directed here.

Remember

This Pinpoint Test is intended to diagnose the following:

● Brake On / Off (BOO) Circuit

● Brake Switch

● Powertrain Control Module (PCM) (12A650)

Pinpoint Test Schematic

FUSE PANEL — B+ — BRAKE SWITCH — BRAKE LAMPS

POWERTRAIN CONTROL MODULE (PCM) — TO BOO CIRCUIT TEST PIN 92

TO ADDITIONAL ACCESSORIES (CRUISE, ABS, SHIFTLOCK ACTUATOR, GENERIC ELECTRONIC MODULE.)

FM0159601507010X

Fig. 242　Test FD: Brake On/Off Switch (Part 1 of 4). 1996

Test Step	Result	►	Action to Take
FD1 KOER DTC P 1703: VERIFY BRAKE PEDAL WAS PRESSED			
Diagnostic Trouble Code (DTC) P 1703 indicates that when the brake pedal was pressed and released during the Key On Engine Running (KOER) Self-Test, the BOO signal did not cycle high and low. Possible causes: — Brake pedal not pressed and released during the KOER Self-Test. — Brake pedal pressed during entire KOER Self-Test. — Open to ground or power. — Damaged brake switch. — Damaged PCM. • **Was the brake pedal pressed and released during KOER Self-Test?**	Yes No	► ►	GO to FD3. RERUN KOER Self-Test. PRESS and RELEASE brake pedal.
FD2 KOEO DTC P 1703			
Diagnostic Trouble Code (DTC) P 1703 indicates that during Key On Engine Off (KOEO) Self-Test, voltage was seen on the BOO Test Pin at the PCM. Possible causes: — Brake pedal pressed during KOEO Self-Test. — BOO Test Pin shorted to B+. — Defective brake switch. • **Was brake pedal pressed during KOEO Self-Test?**	Yes No	► ►	RERUN KOEO Self-Test. Avoid pressing brake pedal during test. GO to FD3.
FD3 DTCS P0703 AND P 1703: CHECK OPERATION OF STOP LAMPS			
Continuous Memory DTC P0703 indicates a Brake ON / OFF (BOO) switch input malfunction. Possible causes: — Open to ground or power. — Damaged brake switch. — Damaged PCM. • Depress and release the brake pedal several times and observe stoplamp operation. • **Do the stoplamps operate normally?**	Yes No	► ►	GO to FD4. GO to FD5 for stoplamps never on. GO to FD7 for stoplamps always on.
FD4 CHECK FOR PCM BOO PID CYCLING			
• Key on, engine off. • Access BOO PID with Scan Tool. • Depress and release the brake pedal several times while viewing the BOO PID. NOTE: If BOO PID is not accessible, GO to FD10. • **Does the BOO PID cycle ON/OFF?**	Yes No	► ►	GO to Pinpoint Test Step Z10 for intermittent input WIGGLE procedure. GO to FD10.

FM0159601507020X

Fig. 242　Test FD: Brake On/Off Switch (Part 2 of 4). 1996

Test Step	Result	▶	Action to Take
FD5 CHECK FOR POWER TO BRAKE SWITCH			
NOTE: Using a 12v test lamp, verify the integrity of related fuses in the fuse panel and check the condition of the stoplamp bulbs before starting this test. • Key off. • Disconnect brake switch. • Measure B+ input voltage between switch and chassis ground. • **Is voltage greater than 10 volts?**	Yes No	▶ ▶	GO to **FD6**. SERVICE open B+ circuit to brake switch. RECONNECT switch. RERUN Quick Test.
FD6 VERIFY INTEGRITY OF BRAKE SWITCH			
• Brake switch disconnected. • Connect DVOM test probes to brake switch terminals at the brake switch. • DVOM on ohms scale. • Press brake pedal while monitoring reading. • **Is the resistance less than 5.0 ohms?**	Yes No	▶ ▶	SERVICE open circuit between brake switch and stoplamp ground. RECONNECT brake switch. RERUN Quick Test. REPLACE brake switch. RECONNECT brake switch. RERUN Quick Test.
FD7 VERIFY BRAKE SWITCH IS NOT ALWAYS CLOSED			
• Key off. • Brake switch disconnected. • Key on, engine off. • **Are stoplamps still on?**	Yes No	▶ ▶	GO to **FD8**. VERIFY proper installation of brake switch. If OK, REPLACE switch. RECONNECT switch. RERUN Quick Test.
FD8 CHECK FOR SHORT TO POWER IN PCM			
• Key off. • Brake switch disconnected. • Disconnect PCM. • Key on. • **Are stoplamps still on?**	Yes No	▶ ▶	GO to **FD9**. REPLACE PCM. RECONNECT brake switch. RERUN Quick Test.
FD9 CHECK FOR SHORT TO POWER IN SHIFTLOCK ACTUATOR			
• Key off. • PCM disconnected. • Disconnect shiftlock actuator, cruise control module, ABS module and Generic Electronic module (if equipped) to isolate brake switch wiring. • Key on, engine off. • **Are stoplamps still on?**	Yes No	▶ ▶	SERVICE short to power in BOO / Stoplamp circuit. RECONNECT PCM, brake switch and other accessories. RERUN Quick Test. SERVICE short in accessories (i.e., shiftlock actuator, ABS module, etc.). RECONNECT all components. RERUN Quick Test.

Fig. 242 Test FD: Brake On/Off Switch (Part 3 of 4). 1996

Test Step	Result	▶	Action to Take
FD10 CHECK FOR BOO CIRCUIT CYCLING			
• Key off. • Disconnect PCM. Inspect for damaged or pushed out pins, corrosion, loose wires, etc. Service as necessary. • Install breakout box, leave PCM disconnected. • DVOM on 20 volt scale. • Measure the voltage between BOO Test Pin 92 and Test Pins 51 and 77 at the breakout box while pressing and releasing the brake. • **Does the voltage cycle?**	Yes No	▶ ▶	REPLACE PCM. REMOVE breakout box. RERUN Self-Test. SERVICE open in BOO circuit between PCM and BOO connection to stoplamp circuit. RERUN Self-Test.

Fig. 242 Test FD: Brake On/Off Switch (Part 4 of 4). 1996

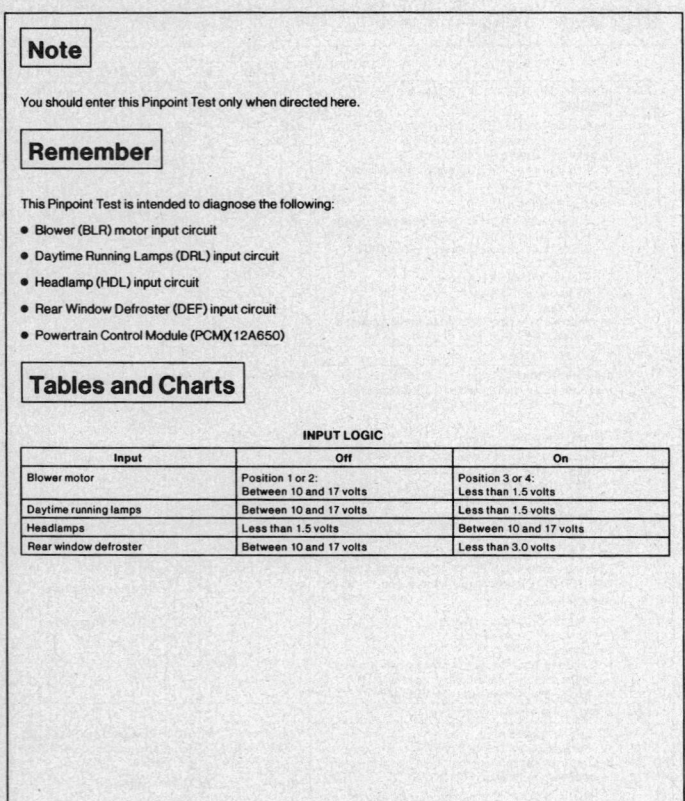

Note

You should enter this Pinpoint Test only when directed here.

Remember

This Pinpoint Test is intended to diagnose the following:

• Blower (BLR) motor input circuit
• Daytime Running Lamps (DRL) input circuit
• Headlamp (HDL) input circuit
• Rear Window Defroster (DEF) input circuit
• Powertrain Control Module (PCM)(12A650)

Tables and Charts

INPUT LOGIC

Input	Off	On
Blower motor	Position 1 or 2: Between 10 and 17 volts	Position 3 or 4: Less than 1.5 volts
Daytime running lamps	Between 10 and 17 volts	Less than 1.5 volts
Headlamps	Less than 1.5 volts	Between 10 and 17 volts
Rear window defroster	Between 10 and 17 volts	Less than 3.0 volts

Fig. 243 Test FE: Electrical Load Inputs (Part 1 of 8). 1996

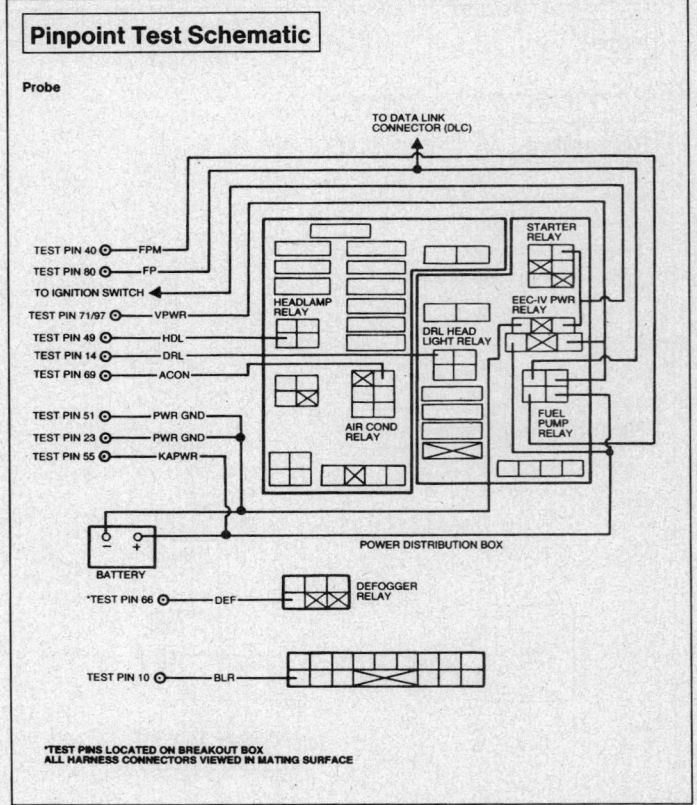

Fig. 243 Test FE: Electrical Load Inputs (Part 2 of 8). 1996

Test Step	Result	▶	Action to Take
FE1 CHECK FOR BLOWER MOTOR CIRCUIT CONCERN			
• Was an idle speed symptom observed only when the blower (BLR) motor was ON?	Yes	▶	The idle speed concern is related to the BLR circuit, GO to **FE10**.
	No	▶	The idle speed concern is not related to the BLR circuit, GO to **FE2**.
FE2 CHECK FOR DAYTIME RUNNING LAMP CIRCUIT CONCERN			
• Was an idle speed symptom observed only when the daytime running lamps (DRL) were ON?	Yes	▶	The idle speed concern is related to the DRL circuit, CO to **FE20**.
	No	▶	The idle speed concern is not related to the DRL circuit, GO to **FE3**.
FE3 CHECK FOR HEADLAMP CIRCUIT CONCERN			
• Was an idle speed symptom observed only when the headlamp (HDL) switch is turned ON?	Yes	▶	The idle speed concern is related to the HDL circuit, GO to **FE30**.
	No	▶	The idle speed concern is not related to the HDL circuit, GO to **FE4**.
FE4 CHECK FOR REAR WINDOW DEFROSTER CIRCUIT CONCERN			
• Was an idle speed symptom observed only when the rear window defroster (DEF) switch is turned ON?	Yes	▶	The idle speed is related to the DEF circuit, GO to **FE40**.
	No	▶	The idle speed is not related to the DEF circuit. RETURN to Symptom Flowcharts
FE10 CHECK VOLTAGE OF BLR CIRCUIT, SWITCH IN LOW SPEED POSITION			
• Key off. • Disconnect PCM. Inspect for damaged or pushed out pins, corrosion, loose wires, etc. Service as necessary. • Install breakout box, leave PCM disconnected. • Key on, engine off. • Push the climate control blower motor switch to low speed position 1 or 2. • Turn all other accessories off. • Measure the voltage between Test Pin 10 (BLR) at the breakout box and chassis ground. • **Is the voltage between 10 and 17 volts?**	Yes	▶	Blower motor input voltage is correct with the switch in the low speed position. GO to **FE11**.
	No	▶	Blower motor input voltage is not correct when the switch is in the low speed position. GO to **FE13**.

FM015960150B030X

Fig. 243 Test FE: Electrical Load Inputs (Part 3 of 8). 1996

Test Step	Result	▶	Action to Take
FE11 CHECK VOLTAGE OF BLR CIRCUIT, SWITCH IN HIGH SPEED POSITION			
• Key off. • Breakout box installed, PCM disconnected. • Push the climate control blower motor switch to high speed position 3 or 4. • Turn all other accessories off. • Key on, engine off. • Measure the voltage between Test Pin 10 (BLR) at the breakout box and chassis ground. • **Is voltage less than 1.5 volts?**	Yes	▶	The blower motor input circuit is operating properly. REPLACE the PCM. REMOVE breakout box. VERIFY a symptom no longer exists.
	No	▶	The blower motor input voltage is not correct when the switch is in the high speed position. GO to **FE12**.
FE12 CHECK BLR CIRCUIT FOR SHORT TO POWER			
• Key off. • Disconnect blower motor relay (refer to Pinpoint Test schematic). • Breakout box installed, PCM disconnected. • Measure resistance between Test Pin 10 (BLR) and Test Pins 71/97 (VPWR) at the breakout box. • **Is resistance greater than 10,000 ohms?**	Yes	▶	There is no short to power in the blower motor input circuit. REMOVE breakout box. RECONNECT all components. check for damaged blower motor switch or relay.
	No	▶	SERVICE short circuit. REMOVE breakout box. RECONNECT all components. VERIFY a symptom no longer exists.
FE13 CHECK BLR CIRCUIT CONTINUITY			
• Key off. • Disconnect blower motor relay (refer to Pinpoint Test schematic). • Breakout box installed, PCM disconnected. • Measure resistance between Test Pin 10 (BLR) at breakout box and BLR circuit at Power Distribution box (refer to the Pinpoint Test schematic). • **Is resistance less than 5.0 ohms?**	Yes	▶	The blower motor input circuit is complete. GO to **FE14**.
	No	▶	SERVICE open circuit. REMOVE breakout box. RECONNECT all components. VERIFY a symptom no longer exists.
FE14 CHECK BLR CIRCUIT FOR SHORT TO GROUND			
• Key off. • Disconnect Scan Tool from DLC. • Blower motor relay disconnected. • Breakout box installed, PCM disconnected. • Measure resistance between Test Pin 10 (BLR) and Test Pins 23, 76 (PWR GND) and Test Pin 91 (SIG RTN) at breakout box. • **Is resistance greater than 10,000 ohms?**	Yes	▶	The blower motor input circuit does not contain any shorts to ground. REMOVE breakout box. RECONNECT all components. check for damaged blower motor switch or relay.
		▶	SERVICE short circuit. REMOVE breakout box. RECONNECT all components. VERIFY a symptom no longer exists.

FM015960150B040X

Fig. 243 Test FE: Electrical Load Inputs (Part 4 of 8). 1996

Test Step	Result	▶	Action to Take
FE20 CHECK VOLTAGE OF DRL CIRCUIT PARKING BRAKE AND HEADLAMPS ON			
• Key off. • Disconnect PCM. Inspect for damaged or pushed out pins, corrosion, loose wires, etc. Service as necessary. • Install breakout box, leave PCM disconnected. • Apply parking brake. • Key on, engine off. • Turn headlamps on. • Turn all other accessories off. • Measure voltage between Test Pin 14 (DRL) at breakout box and chassis ground. • **Is voltage between 10 and 17 volts?**	Yes	▶	Daytime running lamp input voltage is correct with the headlamp switch in the on position. GO to **FE21**.
	No	▶	Daytime running lamp input voltage is not correct with the headlamp switch in the on position. GO to **FE23**.
FE21 CHECK VOLTAGE OF DRL CIRCUIT PARKING BRAKE AND HEADLAMPS OFF			
• Key off. • Breakout box installed, PCM disconnected. • Release parking brake. • Key on, engine off. • Turn headlamps off. • Measure voltage between Test Pin 14 (DRL) at breakout box and chassis ground. • **Is voltage less than 1.5 volts?**	Yes	▶	Daytime running lamp input voltage is correct with the headlamp switch in the off position. REPLACE PCM. REMOVE breakout box. VERIFY a symptom no longer exists.
	No	▶	Daytime running lamp input voltage is not correct with the headlamp switch in the off position. GO to **FE22**.
FE22 CHECK DRL CIRCUIT FOR SHORT TO POWER			
• Key off. • Breakout box installed, PCM disconnected. • Disconnect Daytime Running Lamps relay (refer to Pinpoint Test schematic). • Measure resistance between Test Pin 14 (DRL) and Test Pins 71/97 (VPWR) at breakout box. • **Is resistance greater than 10,000 ohms?**	Yes	▶	There is no short to power in the daytime running lamp input circuit. REMOVE breakout box. RECONNECT all components. REFER to Group 13 in the Service Manual to check DRL module.
	No	▶	SERVICE short circuit. REMOVE breakout box. RECONNECT all components. VERIFY a symptom no longer exists.

FM015960150B050X

Fig. 243 Test FE: Electrical Load Inputs (Part 5 of 8). 1996

Test Step	Result	▶	Action to Take
FE23 CHECK DRL CIRCUIT CONTINUITY			
• Key off. • Breakout box installed, PCM disconnected. • Disconnect Daytime Running Lamps relay (refer to Pinpoint Test schematic). • Measure resistance between Test Pin 14 (DRL) at breakout box and Daytime Running Lamps relay signal pin cavity at DRL relay female connector. • **Is resistance less than 5.0 ohms?**	Yes	▶	The daytime running lamp input circuit is complete. GO to **FE24**.
	No	▶	SERVICE open circuit. REMOVE breakout box. RECONNECT all components. VERIFY a symptom no longer exists.
FE24 CHECK DRL CIRCUIT FOR SHORT TO GROUND			
• Key off. • Disconnect Scan Tool from DLC. • Daytime Running Lamps relay disconnected. • Breakout box installed, PCM disconnected. • Measure resistance between Test Pin 14 (DRL) and Test Pins 23, 76 (PWR GND) and Test Pin 91 (SIG RTN) at breakout box. • **Is resistance greater than 10,000 ohms?**	Yes	▶	There is no short to ground in the DRL input circuit. REMOVE breakout box. RECONNECT all components. check for damaged DRL module.
	No	▶	SERVICE short circuit. REMOVE breakout box. RECONNECT all components. VERIFY a symptom no longer exists.
FE30 CHECK VOLTAGE OF HDL CIRCUIT HEADLAMPS OFF			
• Key off. • Disconnect PCM. Inspect for damaged or pushed out pins, corrosion, loose wires, etc. Service as necessary. • Install breakout box, leave PCM disconnected. • Key on, engine off. • Turn headlamps and all other accessories off. • Measure voltage between Test Pin 49 (HDL) at breakout box and chassis ground. • **Is voltage less than 1.5 volts?**	Yes	▶	Headlamp input voltage is correct with the headlamp switch in the off position. GO to **FE31**.
	No	▶	Headlamp input voltage is not correct with the headlamp switch in the off position. GO to **FE34**.
FE31 CHECK VOLTAGE OF HDL CIRCUIT HEADLAMPS ON			
• Key off. • Breakout box installed, PCM disconnected. • Key on, engine off. • All accessories off. • Turn headlamps on. • Measure voltage between Test Pin 49 (HDL) at breakout box and chassis ground. • **Is voltage between 10 and 17 volts?**	Yes	▶	REPLACE PCM. REMOVE breakout box. VERIFY a symptom no longer exists.
	No	▶	Headlamp input voltage is not correct with the headlamp switch in the off position. GO to **FE32**.

FM015960150B060X

Fig. 243 Test FE: Electrical Load Inputs (Part 6 of 8). 1996

Test Step	Result	▶	Action to Take
FE32 CHECK HDL CIRCUIT CONTINUITY • Key off. • Disconnect headlamp relay (refer to Pinpoint Test schematic). • Breakout box installed, PCM disconnected. • Measure resistance between Test Pin 49 (HDL) at breakout box and HDL circuit at Power Distribution box (refer to Pinpoint Test schematic). • **Is resistance less than 5.0 ohms?**	Yes No	▶ ▶	The headlamp input circuit is complete. GO TO **FE33**. SERVICE open circuit. REMOVE breakout box. RECONNECT all components. VERIFY a symptom no longer exists.
FE33 CHECK HDL CIRCUIT FOR SHORT TO GROUND • Key off. • Disconnect Scan Tool from DLC. • Headlamp relay disconnected. • Breakout box installed, PCM disconnected. • Measure resistance between Test Pin 49 (HDL) and Test Pins 23, 76 (PWR GND) and Test Pin 91 (SIG RTN) at breakout box. • **Is each resistance greater than 10,000 ohms?**	Yes No	▶ ▶	There is no short to ground in the HDL input circuit. REMOVE breakout box. RECONNECT all components. check for damaged HDL switch. SERVICE short circuit. REMOVE breakout box. RECONNECT all components. VERIFY a symptom no longer exixts.
FE34 CHECK HDL CIRCUIT FOR SHORT TO POWER • Key off. • Disconnect headlamp relay (refer to Pinpoint Test schematic). • Breakout box installed, PCM disconnected. • Measure resistance between Test Pin 49 (HDL) and Test Pins 71/97 (VPWR) at breakout box. • **Is each resistance greater than 10,000 ohms?**	Yes No	▶ ▶	There is no short to power in the headlamp input circuit. REMOVE breakout box. RECONNECT all components. check for damaged HDL switch. SERVICE short circuit. REMOVE breakout box. RECONNECT all components. VERIFY a symptom no longer exists.
FE40 CHECK VOLTAGE OF DEF CIRCUIT DEFROSTER OFF • Key off. • Disconnect PCM. Inspect for damaged or pushed out pins, corrosion, loose wires, etc. Service as necessary. • Install breakout box, leave PCM disconnected. • Key on, engine off. • Turn rear window defroster and all other accessories off. • Measure voltage between Test Pin 66 (DEF) at breakout box and chassis ground. • **Is voltage between 10 and 17 volts?**	Yes No	▶ ▶	Defroster input voltage is correct with the switch in the off position. GO TO **FE41**. Defroster input voltage is not correct with the switch in the off position. GO TO **FE43**.

Fig. 243   Test FE: Electrical Load Inputs (Part 7 of 8). 1996

FM0159601508070X

Test Step	Result	▶	Action to Take
FE41 CHECK VOLTAGE OF DEF CIRCUIT DEFROSTER ON • Key off. • Breakout box installed, PCM disconnected. • Key on, engine off. • Turn all accessories off. • Turn rear window defroster on. • Measure voltage between Test Pin 66 (DEF) at breakout box and chassis ground. • **Is voltage less than 3.0 volts?**	Yes No	▶ ▶	REPLACE PCM. REMOVE breakout box. VERIFY a symptom no longer exists. Defroster input voltage is not correct with the switch in the on position. GO TO **FE42**.
FE42 CHECK DEF CIRCUIT FOR SHORT TO POWER • Key off. • Disconnect rear window defroster relay (refer to Pinpoint Test schematic). • Breakout box installed, PCM disconnected. • Measure resistance between Test Pin 66 (DEF) and Test Pins 71/97 (VPWR) at breakout box. • **Is each resistance greater than 10,000 ohms?**	Yes No	▶ ▶	There is no short to ground in the DEF input circuit. REMOVE breakout box. RECONNECT all components. check for fault in DEF switch and relay circuit. SERVICE short circuit. REMOVE breakout box. RECONNECT all components. VERIFY a symptom no longer exists.
FE43 CHECK DEF CIRCUIT CONTINUITY • Key off. • Disconnect rear window defroster switch (refer to Pinpoint Test schematic). • Breakout box installed, PCM disconnected. • Measure resistance between Test Pin 66 (DEF) at breakout box and DEF circuit at Power Distribution box (refer to Pinpoint Test schematic). • **Is resistance less than 5.0 ohms?**	Yes No	▶ ▶	The defroster input circuit is complete. GO TO **FE44**. SERVICE open circuit. REMOVE breakout box. RECONNECT all components. VERIFY a symptom no longer exists.
FE44 CHECK DEF CIRCUIT FOR SHORT TO GROUND • Key off. • Disconnect Scan Tool from DLC. • Rear window defroster relay disconnected. • Breakout box installed, PCM disconnected. • Measure resistance between Test Pin 66 (DEF) and Test Pin 23, 76 (PWR GND) and Test Pin 91 (SIG RTN) at breakout box. • **Is resistance greater than 10,000 ohms?**	Yes No	▶ ▶	There is no short to ground in the DEF input circuit. REMOVE breakout box. RECONNECT all components. check for fault in DEF switch and relay circuit. SERVICE short circuit. REMOVE breakout box. RECONNECT all components. VERIFY a symptom no longer exists.

FM0159601508080X

Fig. 243   Test FE: Electrical Load Inputs (Part 8 of 8). 1996

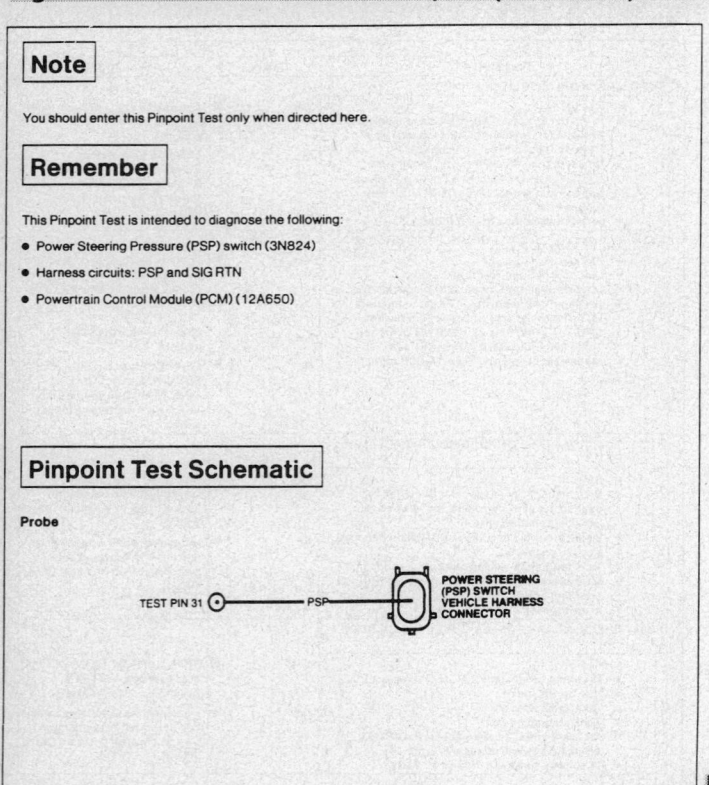

Note

You should enter this Pinpoint Test only when directed here.

Remember

This Pinpoint Test is intended to diagnose the following:
• Power Steering Pressure (PSP) switch (3N824)
• Harness circuits: PSP and SIG RTN
• Powertrain Control Module (PCM) (12A650)

Pinpoint Test Schematic

Probe

FM0159601509010X

Fig. 244   Test FF: Power Steering Pressure Switch (Part 1 of 4). 1996

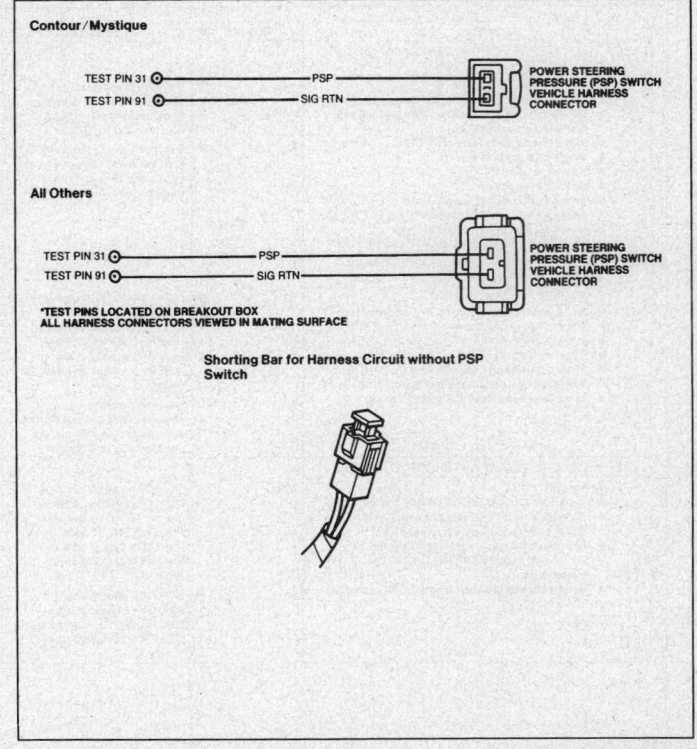

FM0159601509020X

Fig. 244   Test FF: Power Steering Pressure Switch (Part 2 of 4). 1996

	Test Step	Result	►	Action to Take
FF1	**VERIFY ELECTRICAL FUNCTION**			
	Diagnostic Trouble Code (DTC) P1650 indicates PSP signal out of Self-Test range. DTC P1651 indicates PSP signal malfunction.	Yes	►	GO to Pinpoint Test Step [Z1] for intermittent input wiggle procedure.
	NOTE: Vehicle may have been built without PSP switch. Check and verify vehicle has PSP switch. Disregard servicing DTC P1650 or P1651 if there is not a PSP switch.	No	►	**For Probe:** GO to [FF2] **All others:** GO to [FF3]
	Possible causes:			
	— PSP switch / shorting bar damaged.			
	— SIG RTN circuit open or shorted to GND.			
	— PSP signal circuit open or shorted to SIG RTN.			
	— PCM damaged.			
	• Key on, engine running.			
	• View PSP PID with Scan Tool while turning the steering wheel back and forth.			
	• **Does the Scan Tool indicate voltage Low/High or High/Low?**			
FF2	**CHECK PROBE PSP SWITCH OPERATION**			
	• Key off.	Yes	►	REPLACE PSP switch. RERUN Quick Test.
	• Install tachometer.	No	►	GO to [FF4].
	• Start engine and let it idle in Park/Neutral.			
	• Disconnect PSP switch vehicle harness connector and inspect both ends for damage. Service as necessary.			
	• Jumper the PSP signal circuit to SIG RTN or GND at the PSP vehicle harness connector.			
	• **Does engine rpm increase?**			
FF3	**CHECK PSP SWITCH OPERATION**			
	• Key off.	Yes	►	REPLACE PSP switch or shorting bar. RERUN Quick Test.
	• Install tachometer.	No	►	GO to [FF4].
	• Start engine and let it idle in Park/Neutral.			
	• Disconnect PSP switch vehicle harness connector or shorting bar and inspect both ends for damage. Service as necessary.			
	• **Does engine rpm increase?**			

FM0159601509030X

Fig. 244   Test FF: Power Steering Pressure Switch (Part 3 of 4). 1996

	Test Step	Result	►	Action to Take
FF4	**CHECK CONTINUITY OF PSP CIRCUITS**			
	• Key off.	Yes	►	GO to [FF5].
	• PSP disconnected.	No	►	SERVICE open circuit. REMOVE breakout box. RECONNECT all components. RERUN Quick Test.
	• Disconnect PCM. Inspect for damaged or pushed out pins, corrosion, loose wires, etc. Service as necessary.			
	• Install breakout box, leave PCM disconnected.			
	• Measure resistance between Test Pin 31 at the breakout box and PSP circuit at the PSP switch vehicle harness connector.			
	• On vehicles with dual pins, measure resistance between Test Pin 91 at the breakout box and SIG RTN circuit at the PSP switch vehicle harness connector.			
	• **Is each resistance less than 5.0 ohms?**			
FF5	**CHECK PSP CIRCUIT FOR SHORT**			
	• Key off.	Yes	►	SERVICE short in harness. REMOVE breakout box. RECONNECT all components. RERUN Quick Test.
	• PSP switch disconnected.	No	►	**For Probe:** GO to [FF6] **All others:** GO to [FF7]
	• Breakout box installed, leave PCM disconnected.			
	• Measure resistance between Test Pin 31 and Test Pin 91 at the breakout box.			
	• Measure resistance between Test Pin 31 at the breakout box and chassis ground.			
	• **Is either resistance less than 10,000 ohms?**			
FF6	**CHECK PROBE PSP SWITCH RESISTANCE**			
	• Key off.	Yes	►	REPLACE PCM. REMOVE breakout box. RECONNECT all components. RERUN Quick Test.
	• PSP switch vehicle harness disconnected.	No	►	REPLACE PSP switch. REMOVE breakout box. RECONNECT all components. RERUN Quick Test.
	• Start engine and let it idle in Park/Neutral.			
	• Measure resistance between PSP switch signal and chassis GND while turning the steering wheel.			
	• **Is the resistance less than 5.0 ohms?**			
FF7	**CHECK PSP SWITCH RESISTANCE**			
	• Key off.	Yes	►	REPLACE PCM. REMOVE breakout box. RECONNECT all components. RERUN Quick Test.
	• PSP switch vehicle harness disconnected.	No	►	REPLACE PSP switch. REMOVE breakout box. RECONNECT all components. RERUN Quick Test.
	• Measure resistance between PSP switch terminals.			
	• **Is the resistance less than 5.0 ohms?**			

FM0159601509040X

Fig. 244   Test FF: Power Steering Pressure Switch (Part 4 of 4). 1996

Note

You should enter this Pinpoint Test only when directed here.

Remember

This Pinpoint Test is intended to diagnose the following:

• Harness circuits: SIG RTN, Octane Adjust (OCT ADJ)

• Octane shorting bar connector

Pinpoint Test Schematic

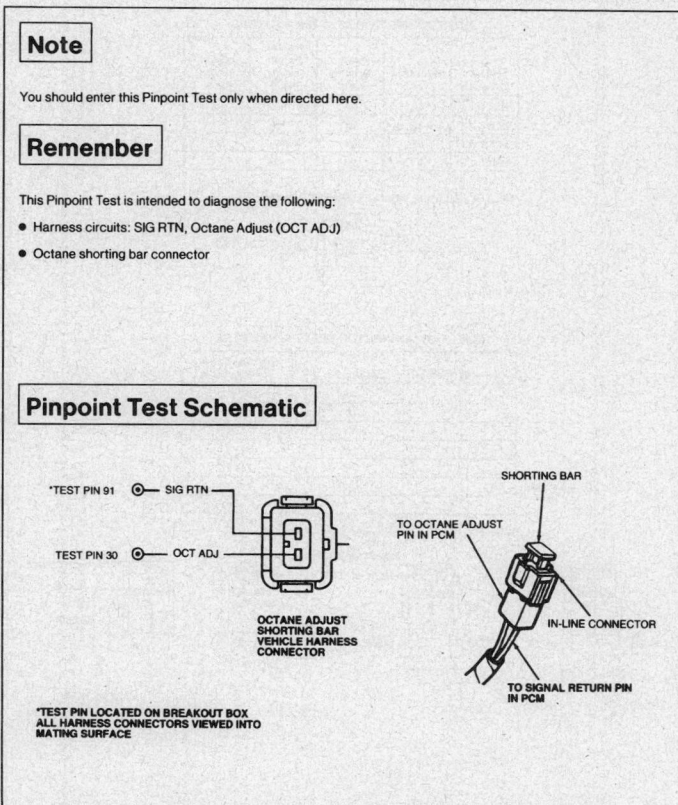

*TEST PIN 91 — SIG RTN

TEST PIN 30 — OCT ADJ

OCTANE ADJUST SHORTING BAR VEHICLE HARNESS CONNECTOR

SHORTING BAR

TO OCTANE ADJUST PIN IN PCM

IN-LINE CONNECTOR

TO SIGNAL RETURN PIN IN PCM

*TEST PIN LOCATED ON BREAKOUT BOX ALL HARNESS CONNECTORS VIEWED INTO MATING SURFACE

FM0159601510010X

Fig. 245   Test FG: Octane Adjust (Part 1 of 3). 1996

	Test Step	Result	►	Action to Take
FG1	**DTC P1390: VISUALLY INSPECT OCTANE ADJUST IN-LINE CONNECTOR**			
	Diagnostic Trouble Code (DTC) P1390 indicates OCT ADJ shorting bar is not in or the OCT ADJ circuit is open.	Yes	►	GO to [FG2].
		No	►	GO to [FG4].
	• Key off.			
	• Visually inspect in-line connector.			
	• **Is shorting bar removed?**			
FG2	**CHECK FOR MODIFICATION DECAL**			
	• **Is there a modification decal attached to the vehicle indicating that OCT ADJ shorting bar was removed?**	Yes	►	Testing complete. If vehicle has spark knock concern.
		No	►	GO to [FG3].
FG3	**CHECK FOR DTC P1390**			
	• Replace OCT ADJ shorting bar.	Yes	►	GO to [FG4].
	• Key off.	No	►	Testing complete. EEC system OK.
	• Connect Scan Tool.			
	• Activate Key On Engine Off Self-Test.			
	• **Is DTC P1390 present?**			
FG4	**CHECK CONTINUITY OF OCTANE ADJUST CIRCUIT**			
	NOTE: There should be continuity from OCT ADJ circuit through the in-line connector and shorting bar to SIG RTN circuit.	Yes	►	REPLACE PCM. REMOVE breakout box. RERUN Quick Test.
	• Key off.	No	►	SERVICE open OCT ADJ circuit or shorting bar or SIG RTN circuit. REMOVE breakout box. RERUN Quick Test.
	• Disconnect Powertrain Control Module (PCM). Inspect for damaged or pushed out pins, corrosion, loose wires, etc. Service as necessary.			
	• Install breakout box, leave PCM disconnected.			
	• Measure resistance between Test Pin 91 and OCT ADJ Test Pin 30 at the breakout box.			
	• **Is the resistance less than 5.0 ohms?**			
FG5	**CHECK FOR DTC P1390**			
	• Start engine and idle vehicle at operating temperature.	Yes	►	GO to [FG1].
	• Key off.	No	►	GO to [FG6].
	• Connect Scan Tool.			
	• Activate Key On Engine Off Self-Test.			
	• **Is DTC P1390 present?**			
FG6	**VERIFY IN-LINE CONNECTOR SHORTING BAR IS INSTALLED**			
	• Key off.	Yes	►	GO to [FG8].
	• Visually inspect OCT ADJ in-line connector.	No	►	GO to [FG7].
	• **Is shorting bar installed?**			

FM0159601510020X

Fig. 245   Test FG: Octane Adjust (Part 2 of 3). 1996

Test Step		Result	►	Action to Take
FG7	**CHECK FOR MODIFICATION DECAL**			
	• Is there a modification decal attached to vehicle indicating that OCT ADJ shorting bar was removed?	Yes	►	GO to **FG10**.
		No	►	REPLACE shorting bar. address spark knock concern.
FG8	**CHECK FOR TSB**			
	• Is there a Technical Service Bulletin (TSB) authorizing removal of the shorting OCT ADJ bar?	Yes	►	GO to **FG9**.
		No	►	address spark knock concern.
FG9	**REMOVE OCT ADJ SHORTING BAR**			
	• Remove OCT ADJ shorting bar only if there is a TSB authorization.	Yes	►	GO to **FG10**.
	• Drive vehicle to verify spark knock.	No	►	Testing complete. EEC system OK.
	• Is spark knock present?			
FG10	**CHECK OCTANE ADJUST CIRCUIT FOR A SHORT TO GROUND**			
	• Key off.	Yes	►	GO to **FG11**.
	• Disconnect Powertrain Control Module (PCM). Inspect for damaged or pushed out pins, corrosion, loose wires, etc. Service as necessary.	No	►	SERVICE short circuit. REMOVE breakout box. If spark knock is still present,
	• Install breakout box, leave PCM disconnected.			
	• Measure resistance between OCT ADJ circuit at the in-line connector and Test Pins 51, 91 and 103 at the breakout box.			
	• Is each resistance greater than 10,000 ohms?			
FG11	**CHECK PCM INTEGRITY**			
	• Key off.	Yes	►	REMOVE breakout box. If spark knock is still present,
	• OCT ADJ shorting bar removed because of TSB authorization.	No	►	REPLACE PCM. REMOVE breakout box. If spark knock is still present,
	• Breakout box installed, PCM connected.			
	• Key on.			
	• Measure voltage between OCT ADJ circuit and Test Pins 51 and 103 at the breakout box.			
	• Is voltage greater than 4.0 volts?			

FM0159601510030X

Fig. 245   Test FG: Octane Adjust (Part 3 of 3). 1996

Note

You should enter this Pinpoint Test only when directed here.

Remember

This Pinpoint Test is intended to diagnose the following:

● HO2S / Heater (9F472)
● HO2S Connections
● Vacuum Systems
● Fuel Injector(s) (9F593)
● Harness Circuits: HO2S GND, HO2S, INJ 1-8, VPWR and SIG RTN
● Powertrain Control Module (PCM) (12A650)

WARNING

PROBING OR PIERCING WIRING INSULATION IS NOT PERMITTED AND MAY ALLOW WATER ENTRY, CAUSING CORROSION AND SHORTING WHICH MAY RESULT IN HO2S FAILURE.

FM0159601511010X

Fig. 246   Test H: Fuel Control (Part 1 of 29). 1996

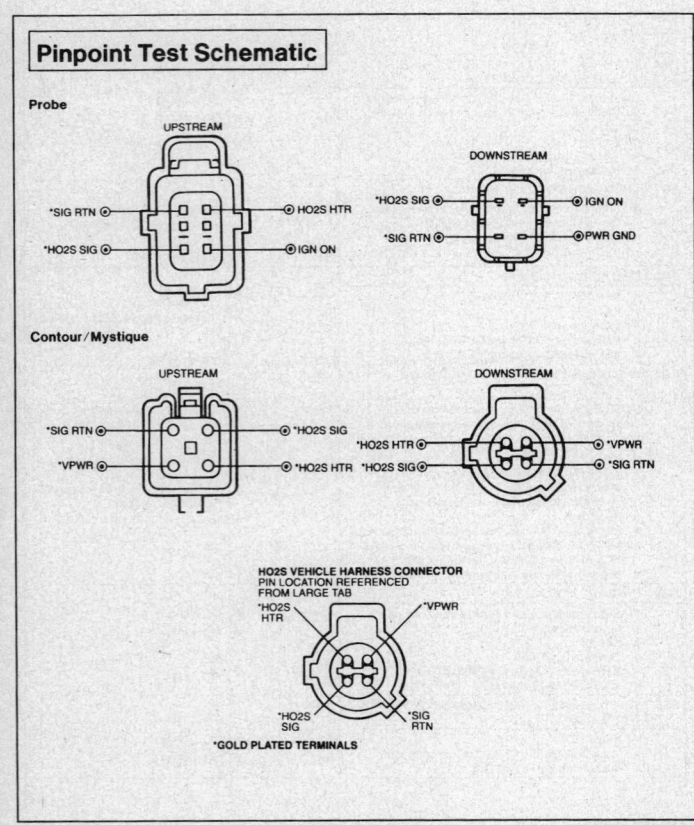

Fig. 246   Test H: Fuel Control (Part 2 of 29). 1996

FM0159601511020X

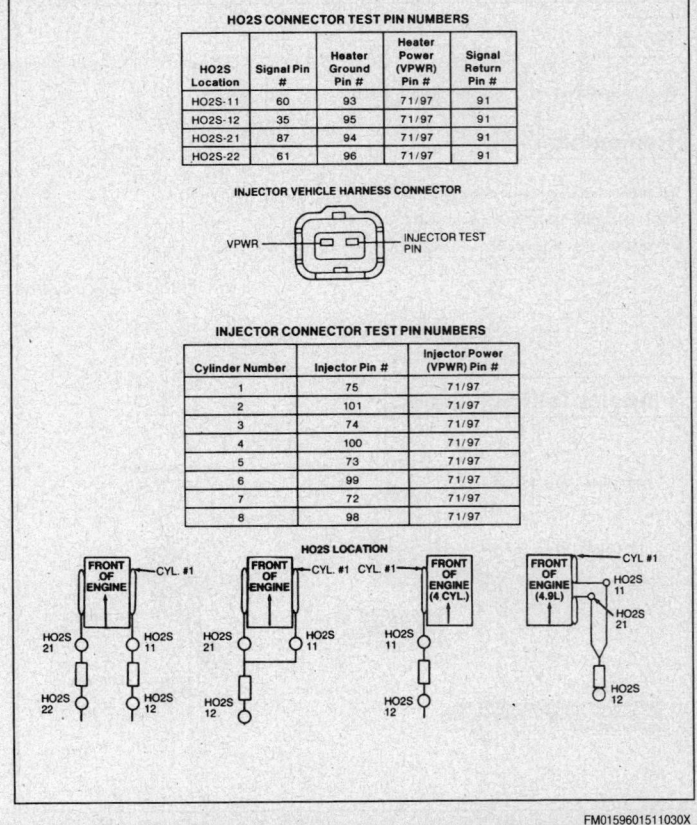

Fig. 246   Test H: Fuel Control (Part 3 of 29). 1996

FM0159601511030X

ELECTRONIC ENGINE CONTROL SYSTEM (EEC-V)

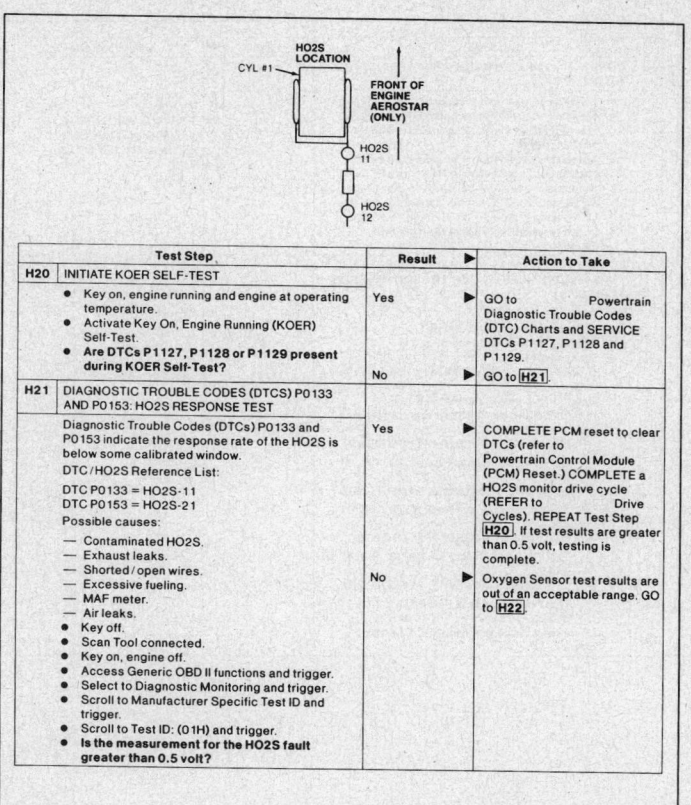

HO2S LOCATION

CYL #1

FRONT OF ENGINE AEROSTAR (ONLY)

HO2S 11

HO2S 12

Test Step	Result	▶	Action to Take
H20 INITIATE KOER SELF-TEST			
• Key on, engine running and engine at operating temperature. • Activate Key On, Engine Running (KOER) Self-Test. • **Are DTCs P1127, P1128 or P1129 present during KOER Self-Test?**	Yes	▶	GO to Powertrain Diagnostic Trouble Codes (DTC) Charts and SERVICE DTCs P1127, P1128 and P1129.
	No	▶	GO to H21.
H21 DIAGNOSTIC TROUBLE CODES (DTCS) P0133 AND P0153: HO2S RESPONSE TEST			
Diagnostic Trouble Codes (DTCs) P0133 and P0153 indicate the response rate of the HO2S is below some calibrated window. DTC/HO2S Reference List: DTC P0133 = HO2S-11 DTC P0153 = HO2S-21 Possible causes: — Contaminated HO2S. — Exhaust leaks. — Shorted/open wires. — Excessive fueling. — MAF meter. — Air leaks. • Key off. • Scan Tool connected. • Key on, engine off. • Access Generic OBD II functions and trigger. • Select to Diagnostic Monitoring and trigger. • Scroll to Manufacturer Specific Test ID and trigger. • Scroll to Test ID: (01H) and trigger. • **Is the measurement for the HO2S fault greater than 0.5 volt?**	Yes	▶	COMPLETE PCM reset to clear DTCs (refer to Powertrain Control Module (PCM) Reset.) COMPLETE a HO2S monitor drive cycle (REFER to Drive Cycles). REPEAT Test Step H20. If test results are greater than 0.5 volt, testing is complete.
	No	▶	Oxygen Sensor test results are out of an acceptable range. GO to H22.

FM015960151104OX

Fig. 246   Test H: Fuel Control (Part 4 of 29). 1996

Test Step	Result	▶	Action to Take
H22 CHECK FOR SOURCE OF POTENTIAL HO2S CONTAMINATION			
• Investigate the following items as a potential source of HO2S contamination. — Use of unapproved silicon sealers. — Fuel contaminated by silicon additives. — Excessive oil burning (i.e. rings, valve seals and oil overfill). — Glycol (antifreeze) leaking internally in the engine. — Lead contaminated fuel. — Use of unapproved cleaning agents. • **Are any of the above conditions present?**	Yes	▶	REPAIR source of contamination. REPLACE HO2S and oil/filter. COMPLETE PCM reset to clear DTCs (REFER to Powertrain Control Module (PCM) Reset). COMPLETE a HO2S monitor drive cycle (REFER to Drive Cycles).
	No	▶	GO to H23.
H23 CHECK FOR UNMETERED AIR LEAKS			
Fuel calculations can be affected by unmetered air leaks. • Carefully inspect the following areas for potential air leaks. — Hoses connecting to MAF. — Hoses connecting to throttle body. — Intake manifold gasket leaks. — PCV disconnected. — Vacuum lines disconnected. — Improperly seated dip stick and tube. — Exhaust leaks at flanges and gaskets. • **Are there any air leaks?**	Yes	▶	Air leaks located. REPAIR source of air leak. COMPLETE PCM reset to clear DTCs (REFER to Powertrain Control Module (PCM) Reset.) COMPLETE a HO2S monitor drive cycle (REFER to Drive Cycles).
	No	▶	GO to H24.
H24 CHECK OF HO2S CIRCUIT WIRING WITH PCM CONNECTED			
• Key off. • PCM connected. • Suspect HO2S disconnected. • Jumper HO2S Signal to VPWR at the HO2S harness connector. • Scan Tool connected. • Key on, engine off. • Access the correct HO2S PID. NOTE: HO2S displayed as O2S on Scan Tool. • **Is the voltage greater than 1.50 volts?**	Yes	▶	HO2S signal circuit is not faulty. REPLACE HO2S. CHANGE oil/filter. COMPLETE PCM reset to clear DTCs (REFER to Powertrain Control Module (PCM) Reset). COMPLETE a HO2S monitor drive cycle (REFER to Drive Cycles).
	No	▶	GO to H25.

FM015960151105OX

Fig. 246   Test H: Fuel Control (Part 5 of 29). 1996

Test Step	Result	▶	Action to Take
H25 CHECK RESISTANCE OF HO2S SIGNAL CIRCUIT			
• Key off. • PCM disconnected, breakout box installed. • Measure the resistance between HO2S Signal Test Pin at the breakout box and the HO2S harness connector. • Measure the resistance between Signal RTN test pin at the breakout box and the HO2S harness connector. — HO2S-11 = Sig. Pin 60 — HO2S-21 = Sig. Pin 87 — HO2S-11 = Sig. RTN Pin 91 — HO2S-21 = Sig. RTN Pin 91 • **Is the resistance less than 5.0 ohms?**	Yes	▶	GO to H26.
	No	▶	Resistance is high. SERVICE open circuit. REMOVE breakout box. RECONNECT all components. COMPLETE a HO2S monitor drive cycle (REFER to Drive Cycles).
H26 CHECK FOR SHORT IN HO2S CIRCUIT			
• Key off. • Disconnect Scan Tool from DLC. • Breakout box installed. PCM disconnected. • Measure the resistance between the HO2S Signal Test Pin at the breakout box and VPWR circuit and HO2S Signal Test Pin and Signal return at the breakout box. — HO2S-11 = Sig. Pin 60 — HO2S-21 = Sig. Pin 87 — VPWR = 71/97 — Signal RTN = 91 • **Is the resistance greater than 10,000 ohms?**	Yes	▶	REPLACE PCM. COMPLETE a HO2S monitor drive cycle (REFER to Drive Cycles).
	No	▶	SERVICE short circuit. REMOVE breakout box. RECONNECT all components. COMPLETE a HO2S monitor drive cycle (REFER to Drive Cycles).
H27 DTCS P0131 AND P0151: CONTAMINATED HO2S / VOLTAGE SHIFT			
Diagnostic Trouble Codes (DTCs) P0131 and P0151 are set when the HO2S generates a negative voltage. — DTC P0131 = HO2S-11 — DTC P0151 = HO2S-21 Possible causes: — Contaminated HO2S (water, fuel, etc.). — Crossed HO2S signal/signal return wiring. • Check for water in HO2S connector. • **Is there water in the HO2S connector?**	Yes	▶	REPAIR source of water entry. Dry out connector. REPLACE HO2S. RERUN Quick Test.
	No	▶	GO to H28.

FM015960151106OX

Fig. 246   Test H: Fuel Control (Part 6 of 29). 1996

Test Step	Result	▶	Action to Take
H28 VERIFY WIRING IS IN PROPER PIN LOCATION			
• Key off. • Suspect sensor disconnected. • Install breakout box, leave PCM disconnected. • Use the following list to measure the resistance between the appropriate test pins at the breakout box and the HO2S Signal and Signal RTN at the harness connector(s). — HO2S-11 = P0131 — HO2S Signal Test Pin 60 — HO2S-21 = P0151 — HO2S Signal Test Pin 87 — HO2S Signal RTN Test Pin 91 • **Is the resistance less than 5.0 ohms?**	Yes	▶	REPLACE HO2S. REMOVE breakout box. RECONNECT all components. RERUN Quick Test.
	No	▶	REPAIR wiring as necessary. REMOVE breakout box. RECONNECT all components. RERUN Quick Test.
H30 DTCS P0135, P0141, P0155 AND P0161: HO2S HEATER SIGNAL CIRCUIT IS OPEN, SHORTED TO GROUND, SHORTED TO B+ OR EXCESSIVE CURRENT DRAW			
Diagnostic Trouble Codes (DTCs) P0135, P0141, P0155 and P0161 indicate a short to ground, open, or short to VPWR in the HO2S heater circuit. DTC/HO2S Reference List: DTC P0135 = HO2S HTR-11 DTC P0141 = HO2S HTR-12 DTC P0155 = HO2S HTR-21 DTC P0161 = HO2S HTR-22 Possible causes: — Shorts to B+ in harness or HO2S. — Water in connectors. — Cut or pulled wires. — Disconnected wiring. — Open VPWR circuit. — Open GND circuit. — Low battery voltage. — Corrosion or poor mating terminals. — Damaged PCM. • Visually inspect the HO2S circuit for exposed wiring, contamination, corrosion and proper assembly. NOTE: On some applications, a vehicle hoist may be required to access the HO2S harness. • **Were any concerns found during the visual inspection?**	Yes	▶	REPAIR any concerns found in the visual inspection. RERUN Quick Test.
	No	▶	GO to H31.

FM015960151107OX

Fig. 246   Test H: Fuel Control (Part 7 of 29). 1996

Test Step	Result	▶	Action to Take
H31 PERFORM KEY ON ENGINE OFF (KOEO) SELF-TEST			
• Key off. • Scan Tool connected. • Key on. • Engine at 2000 rpm for 5 minutes. • Key off. • Key on, engine off. • Activate KOEO Self-Test. • **Are DTCs P0135, P0141, P0155 and/or P0161 present?**	Yes No	▶ ▶	GO to **H32**. No DTCs present. FAULT may be intermittent. GO to Pinpoint Test Step **Z1** with the following data: HO2S PIDs and a list of possible causes.
H32 CHECK FOR VPWR AT THE VEHICLE HARNESS CONNECTOR			
NOTE: If DTCs P0135 and P0155 or P0141 and P0161 are displayed, both heater circuits will require testing. DTCs displayed separately are tested individually. • Key off. • Disconnect the appropriate HO2S(s). • Inspect both ends of the connectors for damaged or pushed out pins, moisture, corrosion, contamination, etc. Service as necessary. • Key on, engine off. • Measure the voltage between VPWR and SIG RTN circuit at the HO2S vehicle harness connector(s) (refer to schematic at the beginning of this Pinpoint Test). • **Is the voltage greater than 10.5 volts?**	Yes No	▶ ▶	GO to **H34**. GO to **H33**.
H33 CHECK FOR OPEN VPWR CIRCUIT			
• Key off. • Install breakout box, PCM disconnected. • Suspect sensor disconnected. • Measure the resistance between the VPWR Test Pin at the breakout box and VPWR at the HO2S vehicle harness connector. • **Is the resistance less than 4.0 ohms?**	Yes No	▶ ▶	GO to **H34**. CHECK fuse in circuit. If fuse is OK, REPAIR open circuit. REMOVE breakout box. RECONNECT all components. RERUN Quick Test.
H34 CHECK HO2S HEATER RESISTANCE			
• Key off. • HO2S disconnected. • Connect DVOM to HO2S HTR GND and VPWR Test Pins at the HO2S sensor connector, and measure the resistance. • **Is the resistance between 3 and 30 ohms?**	Yes No	▶ ▶	GO to **H35**. REPLACE HO2S. REMOVE breakout box. RECONNECT all components. RERUN Quick Test.

FM0159601511080X

Fig. 246 Test H: Fuel Control (Part 8 of 29). 1996

Test Step	Result	▶	Action to Take
H35 CHECK FOR HEATER GND AND VPWR SHORTED TO HO2S CASE			
• Suspect sensor disconnected. • Measure the resistance between the HO2S Heater GND at the HO2S connector and the HO2S case. • Measure the resistance between the HO2S Heater GND connector and the Signal RTN Pin. • Measure the resistance between the HO2S VPWR at the HO2S sensor connector and the HO2S sensor case. • **Is the resistance greater than 10,000 ohms?**	Yes No	▶ ▶	GO to **H36**. REPLACE HO2S. REMOVE breakout box. RECONNECT all components. RERUN Quick Test.
H36 CHECK FOR SHORTS TO OTHER GROUNDS AND VPWR IN THE HO2S HEATER GROUND HARNESS CIRCUITS			

• Key off.
 • Disconnect Scan Tool from DLC.
 • Suspect sensor disconnected.
 • Disconnect PCM.
 • Breakout box installed, leave PCM disconnected.
 • Use the following list to measure the resistance between the appropriate test pins at the breakout box.
   — DTC P0135 = HO2S HTR-11 (HTR GND) Test Pin 93 and Test Pins 24, 76, 103, 91 and 97.
   — DTC P0141 = HO2S HTR-12 (HTR GND) Test Pin 95 and Test Pins 24, 76, 103, 91 and 97.
   — DTC P0155 = HO2S HTR-21 (HTR GND) Test Pin 94 and Test Pins 24, 76, 103, 91 and 97.
   — DTC P0161 = HO2S HTR-22 (HTR GND) Test Pin 96 and Test Pins 24, 76, 103, 91 and 97.
 • **Is the resistance greater than 10,000 ohms?**
	Yes
	 No
		▶
		 ▶
			GO to **H37**.
			 REPAIR shorted circuit. REMOVE breakout box. RECONNECT all components. RERUN Quick Test.

FM0159601511090X

Fig. 246 Test H: Fuel Control (Part 9 of 29). 1996

Test Step	Result	▶	Action to Take
H37 CHECK FOR OPEN HO2S HEATER GROUND HARNESS CIRCUIT			

• Key off.
 • Suspect sensor disconnected.
 • Breakout box installed, PCM disconnected.
 • Use the following list to measure the resistance between the appropriate test pins at the breakout box and the HO2S HTR GND at the vehicle harness connector.
   — HO2S HTR-11 Test Pin 93 (HTR GND)
   — HO2S HTR-12 Test Pin 95 (HTR GND)
   — HO2S HTR-21 Test Pin 94 (HTR GND)
   — HO2S HTR-22 Test Pin 96 (HTR GND)
 • **Is the resistance less than 4.0 ohms?**
	Yes
	
	 No
		▶
		
		 ▶
			Open or shorted or excessive resistance in the heater circuit in the PCM. REPLACE PCM. REMOVE breakout box. RECONNECT all components. RERUN Quick Test.
			 REPAIR open or excessive resistance in the heater circuit in harness. REMOVE breakout box. RECONNECT all components. RERUN Quick Test.

FM0159601511100X

Fig. 246 Test H: Fuel Control (Part 10 of 29). 1996

Test Step	Result	▶	Action to Take
H40 DTCs P1131, P1151, P1132 AND P1152: UPSTREAM HO2S(S) NOT SWITCHING. DTCs P1130 AND P1150: FUEL SYSTEM NOT SWITCHING AT THE ADAPTIVE LIMITS (RICH OR LEAN)			

Diagnostic Trouble Codes (DTCs) P1131 bank (1) (Cylinder # 1) and P1151 bank (2) indicate the fuel/air ratio is correcting rich for an overly lean condition. The HO2S voltage is less than 0.45 volt. DTCs P1132 bank (1) (Cylinder # 1) and P1152 bank (2) indicate the fuel/air ratio is correcting lean for an overly rich condition. The HO2S voltage is greater than 0.45 volt.
 DTCs P1130 and P1150 indicate the fuel control system has reached maximum compensation for a lean or rich condition and the HO2S is not switching.
 DTC/HO2S Reference List
   — HO2S-11 = DTCs P1131, P1132 and P1130
   — HO2S-21 = DTCs P1151, P1152 and P1150
 Possible causes:
 Fuel system
   — Excessive fuel pressure.
   — Leaking fuel injector(s).
   — Leaking fuel pressure regulator.
   — Low fuel pressure.
   — Contaminated injector(s)
 Induction system
   — Air leaks after the MAF.
   — Vacuum leaks.
   — Restricted air inlet.
   — PCV system.
   — Fuel purge system.
   — Improperly seated dip stick.
 EGR
   — Leaking gasket.
   — Stuck open EGR valve.
   — Leaking diaphragm.
 Base engine
   — Oil overfill.
   — Cam timing.
   — Cylinder compression.
   — Exhaust leaks before or near the HO2Ss.
 • Check air intake for leaks, obstructions and damage.
 • Check air filter, air filter housing for blockage.
 • Verify integrity of the PCV system.
 • Check for vacuum leaks.
 • **Are there any of the above concerns?**
	Yes
	
	 No
		▶
		
		 ▶
			SERVICE as necessary. RERUN Quick Test.
			 GO to **H42**.

FM0159601511110X

Fig. 246 Test H: Fuel Control (Part 11 of 29). 1996

Test Step	Result	▶	Action to Take
H41 DTCs P0172, P0174, P0171 AND P0175: FUEL SYSTEM AT THE CORRECTED ADAPTIVE LIMITS			
Diagnostic Trouble Codes (DTCs) P0171 bank (1) (cylinder # 1) and DTC P0174 bank (2) indicate the fuel/air ratio is too lean. The fuel adaptive system is at the rich correction limit.	Yes	▶	SERVICE as necessary. RERUN Quick Test.
DTC P0172 bank (1) and DTC P0175 bank (2) indicate the fuel/air ratio is too rich. The fuel adaptive syste is at the lean correction limit.	No	▶	GO to **H42**.
DTCs HO2S Reference list: — HO2S-11 = DTCs P0171 and P0172 — HO2S-21 = DTCs P0174 and P0175 Possible causes: Fuel system — Excessive fuel pressure. — Leaking fuel injector(s). — Leaking fuel pressure regulator. — Low fuel pressure. — Contaminated injector(s) Induction system — Air leaks after the MAF. — Vacuum leaks. — Restricted air inlet. — PCV system. — Fuel purge system. — Improperly seated dip stick. EGR — leaking gasket. — Stuck open EGR valve. — Leaking diaphragm. Base engine — Oil overfill. — Cam timing. — Cylinder compression. — Exhaust leaks before or near the HO2S's. • Check air intake for leaks, obstructions and damage. • Check air filter, air filter housing for blockage. • Verify integrity of the PCV system. • Check for vacuum leaks. • **Are there any of the above concerns?**			

FM0159601511120X

Fig. 246   Test H: Fuel Control (Part 12 of 29). 1996

Test Step	Result	▶	Action to Take
H42 INITIATE KOER SELF-TEST			
• Key off. • Scan Tool connected. • Disconnect fuel vapor hose from intake manifold and plug fitting at intake manifold. • Start engine and run at 2000 rpm for 1 minute and return to idle. • Enter Key On Engine Running (KOER) Self-Test. • **Are HO2S DTCs P1127, P1128 P1129, P1131, P1132, P1151 or P1152 present?**	Yes	▶	If DTC(s) P1127, P1128, or P1129 are present, GO to Powertrain Diagnostic Trouble Code (DTC) Charts and SERVICE those DTCs first. If DTC(s) P0131 and/or P0151 are present in Continuous Memory, SERVICE DTC P0131 or P0151 in the order they are displayed. GO to **H27**. All others, GO to **H43**.
	No	▶	For DTCs P1130, P1150, P0171, P0174, P0172 and P0175: GO to **H43**. If DTC(s) P1132 and/or P1152 are no longer present, RECONNECT fuel vapor line. GO to **HW10**. **All others:** The fault that produced the DTC is an intermittent. GO to Pinpoint Test Step **Z1** with the following list: HO2S-11, 21 PIDs and list of Possible Causes.
H43 CHECK FUEL PRESSURE			
WARNING: THE FUEL SYSTEM IS PRESSURIZED WHEN THE ENGINE IS NOT RUNNING. TO PREVENT INJURY OR FIRE, USE CAUTION WHEN WORKING ON THE FUEL SYSTEM. • Key off. • Install fuel pressure gauge. • Verify vacuum source to fuel pressure regulator. **If engine will start:** • Start engine and idle. Record fuel pressure. • Increase engine speed to 2500 rpm and maintain for one minute. Record fuel pressure. **No Start:** • Cycle key on and off several times. Record fuel pressure. • **Is the fuel pressure between 30-45 psi (210-310 kPa)?**	Yes	▶	Fuel system is capable of required fuel pressure. GO to **H44**.
	No	▶	Fuel pressure out of specification. GO to Pinpoint Test **HC**.

FM0159601511130X

Fig. 246   Test H: Fuel Control (Part 13 of 29). 1996

Test Step	Result	▶	Action to Take
H44 CHECK SYSTEM ABILITY TO HOLD FUEL PRESSURE			
• Fuel pressure gauge installed. • Cycle key on and off several times. • Verify there are no external leaks (repair as necessary). • **Does the fuel pressure remain within 5 psi of the highest reading after one minute?**	Yes	▶	For DTCs P1130, P1150, P0171, P0172, P0174 and P0175: GO to **H45**. For No Starts: GO to **H46**. For fuel control DTCs displayed with misfire DTCs: GO to **H47**. All other DTCs: GO to **H51**.
	No	▶	Excessive pressure loss. GO to Pinpoint Test Step **HC3**.
H45 CHECK SYSTEM ABILITY TO HOLD FUEL PRESSURE WITH KEY ON			
• Fuel pressure gauge installed. • Cycle key on then off several times. • Turn key on and engine off, monitor fuel pressure gauge. • **Does the fuel pressure remain within 5 psi of the highest reading after 10 seconds?**	Yes	▶	For DTCs P1130, P1150, P0171 and P0174: GO to **H47**.
	No	▶	For DTCs P0172 and P0175: GO to **H49**.
H46 CHECK ABILITY OF INJECTOR(S) TO DELIVER FUEL			
• Pressure gauge installed. • Cycle key several times. • Locate and disconnect the Inertia Fuel Shutoff (IFS) Switch. • Monitor pressure gauge while cranking the engine for at least five seconds. • **Was there a pressure drop greater than 5 psi (34 kPa) while cranking the engine?**	Yes	▶	The EEC-V System is not the cause of the no start. REMOVE the fuel pressure gauge. RECONNECT the IFS switch. REFER to Symptom Flowcharts, for further diagnosis.
	No	▶	REMOVE fuel pressure gauge. RECONNECT IFS switch. GO to **H47**.

FM0159601511140X

Fig. 246   Test H: Fuel Control (Part 14 of 29). 1996

Test Step	Result	▶	Action to Take
H47 CHECK RESISTANCE OF INJECTOR(S) AND HARNESS			
• Key off. • Disconnect PCM. Inspect for damaged or pushed out pins, corrosion, loose wires, etc. Service as necessary. NOTE: This erases Continuous Memory DTCs. • Install breakout box, leave PCM disconnected. NOTE: If misfire DTCs are displayed with the Fuel Control DTCs, use the misfire DTCs to determine the injector circuits requiring testing. • Measure resistance between suspect injector Test Pin(s) and Test Pin 71 or 97 at the breakout box using the chart below.	Yes	▶	Fuel injector and harness resistance is OK. GO to **H50**.
	No	▶	GO to **H48**.

Cyl. No.	Test Pin	Cyl. No.	Test Pin
1	75	5	73
2	101	6	99
3	74	7	72
4	100	8	98

Test Step	Result	▶	Action to Take
• **Is the resistance between 11.0-18.0 ohms?**			
H48 CHECK CONTINUITY OF FUEL INJECTOR HARNESS			
• Key off. • Breakout box installed, PCM disconnected. • Disconnect injector harness connector at the suspect injector. • Measure the resistance between Test Pin 71 or 97 at the breakout box and the VPWR pin at the injector harness connector. • Measure resistance between the Injector Test Pin(s) at the breakout box and the Injector Signal Pin at the injector connector. (Refer to chart in **H47** for Injector Pin location.) • **Is each resistance less than 5.0 ohms?**	Yes	▶	GO to **H49**.
	No	▶	SERVICE open harness circuit. REMOVE breakout box. RECONNECT PCM and fuel injectors. RERUN Quick Test.

FM0159601511150X

Fig. 246   Test H: Fuel Control (Part 15 of 29). 1996

Test Step	Result	▶	Action to Take
H49 CHECK INJECTOR HARNESS CIRCUIT FOR SHORT TO POWER OR GROUND			
• Key off. • Breakout box installed, PCM disconnected. • Suspect injector harness disconnected. • Measure resistance between the injector Test Pin(s) and Test Pin 71 or 97, 24, 76 and 103 at the breakout box (refer to chart in **H47**). • Measure the resistance between the Injector Test Pin(s) at the breakout box and chassis ground. • **Is each resistance greater than 10,000 ohms?**	Yes No	▶ ▶	GO to **H50**. SERVICE short circuit. REMOVE breakout box. RECONNECT PCM and all fuel injector(s). RERUN Quick Test.
H50 CHECK INJECTOR DRIVER SIGNAL			
Requires standard 12 volt test lamp. • Key off. • Breakout box installed. • Connect PCM to breakout box. • Connect test lamp between Test Pin 71 or 97 and each injector Test Pin (refer to chart in **H47**). • Crank or start engine. NOTE: Properly operating system will show a dim glow at idle on the test lamp. • **Does test lamp have a dim glow while cranking or running engine?**	Yes No	▶ ▶	REMOVE breakout box. RECONNECT PCM. GO to **H51**. No light / Continuous bright light. REPLACE PCM. REMOVE breakout box. RERUN Quick Test.
H51 FLOW TEST FUEL INJECTOR(S)			
• Flow test fuel injector(s). • Use the Rotunda Injector Tester 113-00001, SBDS Injector Tester or equivalent to flow test the injectors according to the instructions for the injector tester. • **Is the leakage and flow within specification?**	Yes No	▶ ▶	DTCs P0171, P0172, P0174 and P0175: The fault that produced the DTC is an intermittent. GO to Pinpoint Test Step **Z1** with the following data: SF1, SF2, LFT1, LFT2 PIDs and list of possible causes. **For DTCs P1130 and P1150:** GO to **H57**. **For DTCs P1131 and P1151:** GO to **H52**. **For DTCs P1132 and P1152:** GO to **H53**. REPLACE injector. RERUN Quick Test.

FM0159601511160X

Fig. 246   Test H: Fuel Control (Part 16 of 29). 1996

Test Step	Result	▶	Action to Take
H52 CHECK FOR SECONDARY AIR INTRUSION			
NOTE: If the vehicle is not equipped with Secondary Air Injection, GO to **H53**. HO2S always lean could be caused by: — Leak in hoses from thermactor pump to engine. — Secondary Air diverted upstream of HO2S. • Key off. • Disconnect Secondary Air Injection hose(s) from engine and plug engine side of secondary air system. • Key on, engine on and at operating temperature. • Activate Engine Running Self-Test. • **Are DTC(s) P1131 or P1151 present?**	Yes No	▶ ▶	RECONNECT secondary air injection hose and GO to **H53**. Cause of DTC(s) is in the Secondary Air Injection. GO to **HM7** for secondary air injection diagnostics.
H53 CHECK CYLINDER COMPRESSION			
NOTE: Use the Misfire DTC(s) displayed on prior DTC retrieval to determine which cylinder(s) to check compression on. • Check cylinder compression. Refer to Group 03 (Engine) of the Service Manual. • **Are cylinder compression readings within specification?**	Yes No	▶ ▶	For DTCs P1131, P1130, P1151 and P1150: GO to **H54**. For DTCs P1132 and P1152: GO to **H59**. Misfire DTCs displayed with fuel control DTCs: GO to **HD20**. REPAIR as necessary. COMPLETE PCM Reset to clear DTCs (REFER to Powertrain Control Module (PCM) Reset). RERUN Quick Test.

FM0159601511170X

Fig. 246   Test H: Fuel Control (Part 17 of 29). 1996

Test Step	Result	▶	Action to Take
H54 CHECK HO2S INTEGRITY			
Diagnostic Trouble Codes (DTCs) P1131 and P1151 and / or P1130 and P1150 indicate HO2S always lean, slow to switch, lack of switching or fuel at adaptive limit. Possible causes: — Moisture inside the HO2S harness connector resulting in a short to ground. — HO2S coated with contaminants. — HO2S circuit open. — HO2S circuit shorted to ground. • Key off. • Inspect HO2S harness for chafing, burned out wires or other damage and service. • Inspect HO2S and connector for indications of submersions in water, oil, coolant, etc., and service. • Run engine at 2000 rpm for two minutes. • Key off. • Activate Key On Engine Running (KOER) Self-Test. • **Are DTCs P1131 and / or P1151 present?**	Yes No	▶ ▶	GO to **H55**. HO2S system is OK. Fuel delivery system is OK. Faults may have been repaired while doing inspection. Testing is complete at this time.
H55 CHECK HO2S ABILITY TO GENERATE A VOLTAGE GREATER THAN 0.5 VOLT			
Any vacuum or air leaks in non-EEC areas could cause DTCs P1131, P1151, P1130 and P1150. Possible causes: — Leaking vacuum actuators. — Engine sealing (Intake and IAC). — EGR system (valve). — PCV system (hose and valve). — Unmetered air leaks between throttle body and Mass Air Flow (MAF) sensor assembly. — Silicone contaminated HO2S. • Key off. • Disconnect the suspect HO2S from vehicle harness. • Connect DVOM to the HO2S Signal and HO2S SIG RTN or HO2S GND at the HO2S sensor connector. • DVOM on 20 volt scale. • Run engine at 2000 rpm for two minutes. • Rerun KOER Self-Test and monitor HO2S voltage. • **Does DVOM indicate greater than 0.5 volt during or at the end of Self-Test?**	Yes No	▶ ▶	GO to **H56**. REPLACE HO2S. RERUN Quick Test.

FM0159601511180X

Fig. 246   Test H: Fuel Control (Part 18 of 29). 1996

Test Step	Result	▶	Action to Take
H56 CHECK CONTINUITY OF HO2S AND HO2S GROUND CIRCUITS			
• Key off. • Breakout box installed, PCM disconnected. • Disconnect suspect HO2S from harness. Inspect both ends of connector for damaged or pushed out pins, moisture, corrosion, loose pins, etc., and service. • Measure the resistance between HO2S Signal Test Pin at the breakout box and the HO2S vehicle harness connector. Use the Pin assignment below and record the reading. • Measure resistance between SIG RTN test pin at the breakout box and HO2S SIG RTN vehicle harness connector. Record readings. — HO2S-11 SIG = Test Pin 60 — HO2S-21 SIG = Test Pin 87 — HO2S SIG RTN = Test Pin 91 • **Is the resistance reading less than 5.0 ohms?**	Yes No	▶ ▶	GO to **H57**. SERVICE open circuit. REMOVE breakout box. RECONNECT PCM and HO2S. RERUN Quick Test.
H57 CHECK HO2S CIRCUIT WIRING HARNESS FOR SHORT TO GROUND			
• Key off. • Breakout box installed, PCM disconnected. • HO2S disconnected. • Measure resistance between the HO2S Signal Test Pin and Test Pins 24, 51, 76, 77 and 103 at the breakout box. • **Is each resistance greater than 10,000 ohms?**	Yes No	▶ ▶	GO to **H58**. SERVICE short circuit. REMOVE breakout box. RECONNECT PCM and HO2S. RERUN Quick Test.
H58 CHECK HO2S FOR SHORT TO GROUND			
• Key off. • Breakout box installed, PCM disconnected. • HO2S connected. • Measure resistance between PWR GND / SIG RTN Test Pin and HO2S Signal Test Pin at the breakout box. HO2S-11 SIG = Test Pin 60 HO2S-21 SIG = Test Pin 87 HO2S PWR GND = Test Pin 24, 76 and 103 HO2S SIG RTN = Test Pin 91 • **Is resistance greater than 10,000 ohms?**	Yes No	▶ ▶	For DTCs P1130 and P1150: GO to **H59**. For Continuous Memory DTCs P1131 and P1151: GO to **H64**. For KOER DTCs P1131 and P1151: REMOVE breakout box. RECONNECT HO2S. REPLACE PCM. REPLACE HO2S. REMOVE breakout box. RECONNECT PCM. RERUN Quick Test.

FM0159601511190X

Fig. 246   Test H: Fuel Control (Part 19 of 29). 1996

Test Step	Result	▶	Action to Take
H59 CHECK FOR DTCS P1132 AND P1152 WITH P1130 AND P1150			
• Key off. • Scan Tool connected. • Activate Key On Engine Running (KOER) Self-Test. • **Are DTCs P1132 or P1152 present?**	Yes	▶	GO to **H60**.
	No	▶	The fault that produced the DTC is an intermittent. GO to Pinpoint Test Step **Z1** with the following data: HO2S-11, 21 PIDs and list of possible causes.
H60 CHECK FOR HO2S SIGNAL SHORTED TO POWER			
Diagnostic Trouble Codes (DTCs) P1132 and P1152 and / or P1130 and P1150 indicate HO2S always rich. Possible causes: — Moisture inside the HO2S harness connector resulting in a short to power. — HO2S circuit shorted to power. DTC P1130, P1132=HO2S-11 DTC P1150, P1152=HO2S-21 • Key on, engine off. • Scan Tool connected. • Access the Parameter Identification (PID) for the DTC generated. NOTE: HO2S displayed as O2S on Scan Tool. • **Is the voltage greater than 1.0 volt and less than 4.0 volts?**	Yes	▶	An over voltage condition exists in the HO2S circuit. GO to **H61**.
	No	▶	GO to **H63**.
H61 CHECK FOR SHORTS TO VOLTAGE SOURCE IN THE HARNESS CIRCUIT			

• Key off.
 • Disconnect Scan Tool from DLC.
 • Suspect sensor disconnected.
 • Disconnect PCM. Inspect for damaged or pushed out pins, corrosion, loose wires, etc. Service as necessary.
 • Install breakout box, leave PCM disconnected.
 • Use the following list to measure the resistance between the appropriate test pins at the breakout box.
 — DTC P1130, P1132=HO2S-11
     Test Pin 60 and Test Pins 71, 93 and 97.
 — DTC P1150, P1152=HO2S-21
     Test Pin 87 and Test Pins 71, 93 and 97.
 • **Is the resistance greater than 10,000 ohms?**
	Yes	▶	REMOVE breakout box. RECONNECT PCM. GO to **H62**.

	No	▶	REPAIR short to power. REMOVE breakout box. RECONNECT all components. RERUN Quick Test.

FM0159601511200X

Fig. 246   Test H: Fuel Control (Part 20 of 29). 1996

Test Step	Result	▶	Action to Take
H62 CHECK FOR HO2S SIGNAL SHORTED TO HO2S HEATER CIRCUIT IN THE SENSOR			
• Key off. • Suspect HO2S sensor disconnected. • Scan Tool connected. • Key on, engine off. • Access HO2S PID corresponding to DTCs received. NOTE: HO2S displayed as O2S on Scan Tool. • **Is the HO2S voltage less than 0.2 volt?**	Yes	▶	REPLACE HO2S. RECONNECT all components. RERUN Quick Test.
	No	▶	REPLACE PCM. RECONNECT all components. RERUN Quick Test.
H63 ATTEMPT TO GENERATE DTCS P1131 AND P1151			
• Key off. • HO2S disconnected. • Jumper HO2S Signal at the HO2S harness vehicle connector to the battery negative post. • Activate Key On Engine Running (KOER) Self-Test. • **Are DTCs P1131 or P1151 present?**	Yes	▶	REMOVE jumper. GO to **H64**.
	No	▶	REMOVE jumper. RECONNECT HO2S. DISCONNECT PCM. INSPECT both ends of connector for damaged or pushed out pins, moisture, corrosion, loose pins, etc. and service as necessary. If OK, REPLACE PCM. RERUN KOER Self-Test.
H64 HO2S CHECK			
• Key off. • Suspect HO2S disconnected. • Connect DVOM to HO2S Signal circuit and HO2S SIG RTN at the HO2S sensor connector. • DVOM on 20 volt scale. • Disconnect vacuum hose from vacuum tree. • Start engine and run at 2000 rpm. • **Does the DVOM indicate less than 0.4 volt within 30 seconds?**	Yes	▶	RECONNECT vacuum hose and HO2S. GO to **H70**.
	No	▶	REPLACE HO2S. RECONNECT vacuum hose. RERUN Quick Test.
H70 MONITOR HO2S (PID) FOR NORMAL SWITCHING			
• Key on, engine running. • Engine at operating temperature. • Access suspect HO2S PID using Scan Tool. NOTE: HO2S displayed as O2S on Scan Tool. • Access HO2S PID while wiggling, bending, and shaking small sections of the EEC harness from the PCM to the HO2S. • **Did the HO2S voltage stay high (greater than 0.45 volt) or low (less than 0.45 volt)?**	Yes	▶	ISOLATE cause of lack of HO2S switches and service. COMPLETE PCM Reset to clear DTCs (REFER to Powertrain Control Module (PCM) Reset). RERUN Quick Test.
	No	▶	GO to **H71**.

FM0159601511210X

Fig. 246   Test H: Fuel Control (Part 21 of 29). 1996

Test Step	Result	▶	Action to Take
H71 TEST DRIVE WHILE MONITORING HO2S PID FOR NORMAL SWITCHING			
NOTE: This test step requires an observer to monitor PID for proper operation. • Scan Tool still attached. • Access HO2S PID. • While observer views PID, test drive vehicle under different road conditions in an attempt to simulate the original fault. • **Does HO2S appear to switch properly?**	Yes	▶	UNABLE to duplicate fault. CLEAR any DTCs. Testing complete at this time.
	No	▶	REPLACE HO2S. COMPLETE PCM reset to clear DTCs (REFER to Powertrain Control Module (PCM) Reset). RERUN Quick Test.
H80 DTCS P0136 AND P0156 MONITOR DOWNSTREAM HO2S OUTPUT VOLTAGE FOR ACTIVITY. DTCS P1137, P1138, P1157 AND / OR P1158 INDICATE LACK OF HO2S SWITCHING.			
DTC P0136 and P0156 indicate the output voltage of the downstream HO2S is less than some calibratable functional window. KOER DTCs P1137, P1138, P1157 and P1158 can only be retrieved when the KOER Self-Test when the fuel control is ramped rich and lean and monitored for a voltage change on the downstream HO2S. Possible causes: • Wiring Concerns — Pinched, shorted, and corroded wiring and pins — Crossed sensor wires • Other Concerns — Exhaust leaks — Contaminated or damaged sensor • **Are any of the above concerns present?**	Yes	▶	SERVICE as necessary. COMPLETE PCM reset to clear DTCs (REFER to Powertrain Control Module (PCM) Reset). RERUN Quick Test.
	No	▶	Continuous Memory DTCs P0136 and P0156. GO to **H81**. All others GO to **H82**.
H81 CHECK FOR KOER DTCS P1137, P1138, P1157 AND P1158			
• Key off. • Scan Tool connected. • Key on. • Engine at 2000 rpm for 5 minutes. • Activate KOER Self-Test. • Check for DTCs. • **Are DTCs P1137, P1138, P1157 and P1158 present?**	Yes	▶	GO to **H82**.
	No	▶	**For DTCs P0136 and P0156:** The fault that produced the DTC is an intermittent. GO to Pinpoint Test Step **Z1** with the following data: HO2S-12,22 PIDs and list of possible causes.

FM0159601511220X

Fig. 246   Test H: Fuel Control (Part 22 of 29). 1996

Test Step	Result	▶	Action to Take
H82 CHECK EXHAUST SYSTEM FOR LEAKS			
NOTE: Any exhaust leaks between the engine and the end of the catalyst may cause DTCs P0136 and P0156. • Key off. • Place vehicle on a hoist, transmission in park, emergency brake applied, raise vehicle. • Inspect the following: — Exhaust flanges for leaks. — HO2S torque. — Check for punctures and cracks in catalyst and pipes leading to them. • **Are there any exhaust leaks?**	Yes	▶	REPLACE or REPAIR as required. COMPLETE PCM reset to clear DTCs (REFER to , Powertrain Control Module (PCM) Reset). RERUN Quick Test.
	No	▶	GO to **H83**.
H83 CHECK HO2S HARNESS CIRCUIT FOR SHORT TO VPWR AND GROUND			
• Key off. • Disconnect Scan Tool from DLC. • Breakout box installed, PCM disconnected. Inspect both ends of connector for damaged or pushed out pins, moisture, corrosion, loose pins, etc. and service as necessary. • HO2S disconnected. • Measure the resistance between HO2S Signal Test Pin and SIG RTN Test Pin at the breakout box. • Measure the resistance between HO2S Signal Test Pin and VPWR and VREF Test Pin at the breakout box. • Measure the resistance between HO2S Signal Test Pin and PWR GND Test Pin at the breakout box. HO2S-12 SIG = Test Pin 35 HO2S-22 SIG = Test Pin 61 HO2S SIG RTN = Test Pin 91 PWR GND = Test Pins 24 and 103 VPWR = Test Pins 71 and 97 VREF = Test Pin 90 • **Is resistance greater than 10,000 ohms?**	Yes	▶	GO to **H84**.
	No	▶	SERVICE short in harness. COMPLETE PCM reset to clear DTCs (REFER to Powertrain Control Module (PCM) Reset). RERUN Quick Test.

FM0159601511230X

Fig. 246   Test H: Fuel Control (Part 23 of 29). 1996

ELECTRONIC ENGINE CONTROL SYSTEM (EEC-V)

FORD–Electronic Engine Controls

Test Step	Result	▶	Action to Take
H84 CHECK CONTINUITY OF HO2S AND HO2S GROUND CIRCUITS • Key off. • Breakout box installed, PCM disconnected. • Disconnect suspect HO2S from harness. • Measure the resistance between HO2S Signal Test Pin at the breakout box and the HO2S vehicle harness connector. Record readings. • Measure resistance between SIG RTN Test Pin at the breakout box and HO2S SIG RTN vehicle harness connector. Record readings. — HO2S-12 SIG = Test Pin 35 — HO2S-22 SIG = Test Pin 61 — HO2S SIG RTN = Test Pin 91 • **Is the resistance reading less than 5.0 ohms?**	Yes No	▶ ▶	GO to **H85**. REPAIR open circuit in harness. REMOVE breakout box. RECONNECT all components. RERUN Quick Test.
H85 CHECK HO2S CIRCUIT CONTINUITY • Key off. • PCM connected to vehicle harness. • Suspect HO2S connected to vehicle harness. • Scan Tool connected. • Key on, engine off. • Access the correct HO2S PID. NOTE: HO2S displayed as O2S on Scan Tool.	Yes No	▶ ▶	GO to **H88**. GO to **H86**.

DTC	HO2S	PINS
P0136	HO2S-12	35 and 97
P0156	HO2S-22	61 and 97

Test Step	Result	▶	Action to Take
• **Is the voltage greater than 1.5 volts?**			
H86 CHECK CONTINUITY OF HO2S GROUND CIRCUIT IN THE PCM • Key off. • PCM connected to breakout box. Vehicle harness disconnected from breakout box. • Measure the resistance between SIG RTN Test Pin and PWR GND Test Pin at the breakout box. • **Is the resistance reading less than 5.0 ohms?**	Yes No	▶ ▶	REMOVE breakout box. RECONNECT PCM. GO to **H87**. REPLACE PCM. REMOVE breakout box. RECONNECT all components.

FM0159601511240X
Fig. 246   Test H: Fuel Control (Part 24 of 29). 1996

Test Step	Result	▶	Action to Take
H87 APPLY 12 VOLTS TO SUSPECT HO2S CIRCUIT • Key off. • Suspect HO2S disconnected. • Jumper VPWR to HO2S signal circuit at the vehicle harness connector. • Key on. • Accesss HO2S PID and monitor. • **Is the PID value greater than 1.5 volts?**	Yes No	▶ ▶	REPLACE HO2S. RECONNECT all components. COMPLETE an HO2S Monitor Drive Cycle (REFER to Drive Cycles). RERUN Quick Test. REPLACE PCM. RECONNECT all components. COMPLETE an HO2S Monitor Drive Cycle (REFER to Drive Cycles). RERUN Quick Test.
H88 CHECK FOR OVER VOLTAGE ON THE HO2S CIRCUIT IN THE PCM • Key on. • PCM connected to vehicle harness. • HO2S disconnected. • Inspect both ends of connector for damaged or pushed out pins, moisture, corrosion, loose pins, etc. and service as necessary. • Measure the voltage between SIG RTN Test Pin at the HO2S vehicle harness connector and battery negative post. • Measure the voltage between HO2S Signal Test Pin at the HO2S vehicle harness connector and battery negative post. • **Are the voltage readings greater than 1.5 volts?**	Yes No	▶ ▶	REPLACE PCM. RECONNECT all components. RERUN Quick Test. REPLACE HO2S. RECONNECT all components. RERUN Quick Test.
H90 DTCS P0136 AND P0156: MONITOR DOWNSTREAM HO2S OUTPUT VOLTAGE FOR ACTIVITY DTCs P0136 and P0156 indicate the output voltage of the downstream HO2S is less than some calibratable functional window. Possible causes: • Wiring Concerns — Pinched, shorted, and corroded wiring and pins — Crossed sensor wires • Other Concerns — Exhaust leaks — Contaminated or damaged sensor • **Are any of the concerns present?**	Yes No	▶ ▶	SERVICE as necessary. COMPLETE PCM reset to clear DTCs (REFER to Powertrain Control Module (PCM) Reset). COMPLETE a HO2S monitor drive cycle (REFER to Drive Cycle) RERUN Continuous Memory Self-Test. GO to **H91**.

FM0159601511250X
Fig. 246   Test H: Fuel Control (Part 25 of 29). 1996

Test Step	Result	▶	Action to Take
H91 CHECK FOR CROSSED HO2S HARNESS CONNECTOR • Key off. • Disconnect the HO2S that corresponds to the DTCs.	Yes No	▶ ▶	DTCs correspond to correct HO2S location indicating HO2S are not crossed. GO to **H92**. CHECK for crossed HO2S and wiring. REFER to schematic for correct HO2S pin location. COMPLETE an HO2S Monitor Drive Cycle (REFER to Drive Cycles). RERUN Continuous Memory Self-Test.

HO2S	Original DTC	Heater DTC
HO2S-12	P0136	P0141
HO2S-22	P0156	P0161

Test Step	Result	▶	Action to Take
• Activate KOEO Self-Test. • **Is a corresponding HO2S HTR DTC generated?** NOTE: Disregard any DTCs other than HO2S HTR codes.			
H92 CHECK EXHAUST SYSTEM FOR LEAKS NOTE: Any exhaust leaks between the engine and the end of the catalyst may cause DTCs P0136 and P0156. • Key off. • Place vehicle on a hoist, transmission in park, emergency brake applied, raise vehicle. • Inspect the following: — Exhaust flanges for leaks. — HO2S torque. — Check for punctures and cracks in catalyst and pipes leading to them. • **Are there any exhaust leaks?**	Yes No	▶ ▶	REPLACE or REPAIR as required. COMPLETE PCM reset to clear DTCs (REFER to , Powertrain Control Module (PCM) Reset). COMPLETE a HO2S Monitor Drive Cycle (REFER to Drive Cycles). RERUN Continuous Memory Self-Test. GO to **H93**.

FM0159601511260X
Fig. 246   Test H: Fuel Control (Part 26 of 29). 1996

Test Step	Result	▶	Action to Take
H93 CHECK HO2S HARNESS CIRCUIT FOR SHORT TO VPWR AND GROUND • Key off. • Disconnect Scan Tool from DLC. • Breakout box installed, PCM disconnected. Inspect both ends of connector for damaged or pushed out pins, moisture, corrosion, loose pins, etc. and service as necessary. • HO2S disconnected. • Measure the resistance between HO2S Signal Test Pin and SIG RTN Test Pin at the breakout box. • Measure the resistance between HO2S Signal Test Pin and VPWR and VREF Test Pin at the breakout box. • Measure the resistance between HO2S Signal Test Pin and PWR GND Test Pin at the breakout box. HO2S-12 SIG = Test Pin 35 HO2S-22 SIG = Test Pin 61 HO2S SIG RTN = Test Pin 91 PWR GND = Test Pins 24 and 103 VPWR = Test Pins 71 and 97 VREF = Test Pin 90 • **Is resistance greater than 10,000 ohms?**	Yes No	▶ ▶	GO to **H94**. SERVICE short in harness. COMPLETE PCM reset to clear DTCs (REFER to Powertrain Control Module (PCM) Reset). COMPLETE a HO2S Monitor Drive Cycle (REFER to Drive Cycles). RERUN Continuous Memory Self-Test.
H94 CHECK CONTINUITY OF HO2S AND HO2S GROUND CIRCUITS • Key off. • Breakout box installed, PCM disconnected. • Disconnect suspect HO2S from harness. • Measure the resistance between HO2S Signal Test Pin at the breakout box and the HO2S vehicle harness connector. Record readings. • Measure resistance between SIG RTN Test Pin at the breakout box and HO2S SIG RTN vehicle harness connector. Record readings. — HO2S-12 SIG = Test Pin 35 — HO2S-22 SIG = Test Pin 61 — HO2S SIG RTN = Test Pin 91 • **Is the resistance reading less than 5.0 ohms?**	Yes No	▶ ▶	GO to **H95**. REPAIR open circuit in harness. REMOVE breakout box. RECONNECT all components. RERUN Quick Test. COMPLETE a HO2S Monitor Drive Cycle (REFER to Drive Cycles). RERUN Continuous Memory Self-Test.

FM0159601511270X
Fig. 246   Test H: Fuel Control (Part 27 of 29). 1996

9-284

ELECTRONIC ENGINE CONTROL SYSTEM (EEC-V)

Test Step	Result	▶	Action to Take
H95 CHECK HO2S CIRCUIT CONTINUITY			
• Key off. • PCM connected to vehicle harness. • Suspect HO2S connected to vehicle harness. • Scan Tool connected. • Key on, engine off. • Access the correct HO2S PID. NOTE: HO2S displayed as O2S on Scan Tool.	Yes No	▶ ▶	GO to H97. GO to H96.

DTC	HO2S	PINS
P0136	HO2S-12	35 and 97
P0156	HO2S-22	61 and 97

• **Is the voltage greater than 1.5 volts?**

Test Step	Result	▶	Action to Take
H96 CHECK CONTINUITY OF HO2S GROUND CIRCUIT IN THE PCM			
• Key off. • PCM connected to breakout box. Vehicle harness disconnected from breakout box. • Measure the resistance between SIG RTN Test Pin and PWR GND Test Pin at the breakout box. • **Is the resistance reading less than 5.0 ohms?**	Yes No	▶ ▶	REPLACE HO2S. REMOVE breakout box. RECONNECT all components. COMPLETE a HO2S Monitor Drive Cycle (REFER to Drive Cycles). RERUN Continuous Memory Self-Test. REPLACE PCM. REMOVE breakout box. RECONNECT all components. COMPLETE a HO2S Monitor Drive Cycle (REFER to Drive Cycles). RERUN Continuous Memory Self-Test.
H97 CHECK FOR OVER VOLTAGE ON THE HO2S CIRCUIT IN THE PCM			
• Key on. • PCM connected to vehicle harness. • HO2S disconnected. • Inspect both ends of connector for damaged or pushed out pins, moisture, corrosion, loose pins, etc. and service as necessary. • Measure the voltage between SIG RTN Test Pin at the HO2S vehicle harness connector and battery negative post. • Measure the voltage between HO2S Signal Test Pin at the HO2S vehicle harness connector and battery negative post. • **Are the voltage readings greater than 1.5 volts?**	Yes No	▶ ▶	REPLACE PCM. RECONNECT all components. RERUN Quick Test. COMPLETE a HO2S Monitor Drive Cycle (REFER to Drive Cycles). RERUN Continuous Memory Self-Test. REPLACE HO2S. RECONNECT all components. RERUN Quick Test. COMPLETE a HO2S Monitor Drive Cycle (REFER to Drive Cycles). RERUN Continuous Memory Self-Test.

FM015960151128OX

Fig. 246   Test H: Fuel Control (Part 28 of 29). 1996

Test Step	Result	▶	Action to Take
H100 KOER P1127			
DTC P1127 indicates the HO2S heater(s) were not on during KOER Self-Test and testing of the HO2S did not occur. The HO2S heaters are turned on and off when certain temperatures are reached. The HO2S heaters are activated during exhaust temperature modeling, which allows for upstream heates being energized independent of the downstream heaters. Possible causes: — Exhaust system to cool. • Key off. • Scan tool connected. • Key on, engine on. • Access all HO2S heaters and HO2S heater monitor PIDs. • **Do all PIDs indicate on?**	Yes No	▶ ▶	RERUN Quick Test. RUN engine until all PIDs indicate on. RERUN Quick Test.
H110 KOER DTCS P1128 AND P1129			
DTC P1128 and P1129 indicate that during KOER testing either the upstream or downstream or both HO2S signal(s) are swapped from bank to bank. — P1128 references to the upstram HO2S. — P1129 references to the downstream HO2S. Possible causes: — Crossed HO2S harness connectors. — Crossed wiring at HO2S harness connectors. — Crossed HO2S wiring at 104-Pin harness connector. • Key off. • Visually inspect vehicle HO2S harness connector(s) for any indication of being crossed (stretched wires, wire harnesses not mounted properly). • **Are there crossed connections or wires?**	Yes No	▶ ▶	SERVICE as necessary. RERUN Quick Test. GO to H111.

FM015960151129OX

Fig. 246   Test H: Fuel Control (Part 29 of 29). 1996

Note

You should enter this Pinpoint Test only when directed here.

Remember

This Pinpoint Test is intended to diagnose the following:

• HO2S / Heater (9F472)
• HO2S Connections
• Vacuum Systems
• Fuel Injector(s) (9F593)
• Harness Circuits: HO2S GND, HO2S, INJ 1-8, VPWR and SIG RTN
• Powertrain Control Module (PCM) (12A650)
• Natural Gas Module (NG) (9F954)

FM015960151201O

Fig. 247   Test HA: Natural Gas Fuel Control (Part 1 of 24). 1996

Pinpoint Test Schematic

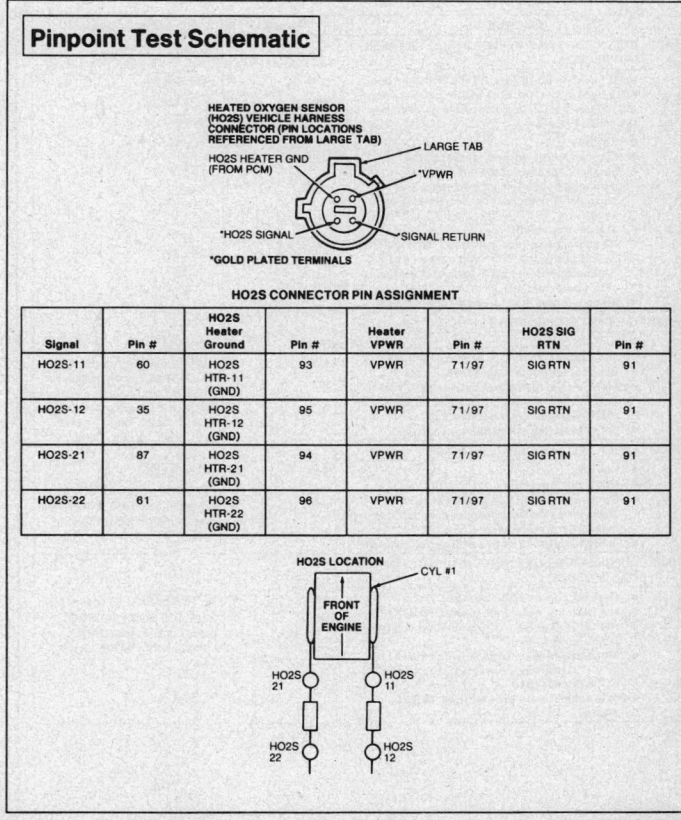

HEATED OXYGEN SENSOR (HO2S) VEHICLE HARNESS CONNECTOR (PIN LOCATIONS REFERENCED FROM LARGE TAB)

LARGE TAB

HO2S HEATER GND (FROM PCM)

*VPWR

*HO2S SIGNAL

SIGNAL RETURN

*GOLD PLATED TERMINALS

HO2S CONNECTOR PIN ASSIGNMENT

Signal	Pin #	HO2S Heater Ground	Pin #	Heater VPWR	Pin #	HO2S SIG RTN	Pin #
HO2S-11	60	HO2S HTR-11 (GND)	93	VPWR	71/97	SIG RTN	91
HO2S-12	35	HO2S HTR-12 (GND)	95	VPWR	71/97	SIG RTN	91
HO2S-21	87	HO2S HTR-21 (GND)	94	VPWR	71/97	SIG RTN	91
HO2S-22	61	HO2S HTR-22 (GND)	96	VPWR	71/97	SIG RTN	91

HO2S LOCATION

CYL #1

FRONT OF ENGINE

HO2S 21   HO2S 11

HO2S 22   HO2S 12

FM015960151202OX

Fig. 247   Test HA: Natural Gas Fuel Control (Part 2 of 24). 1996

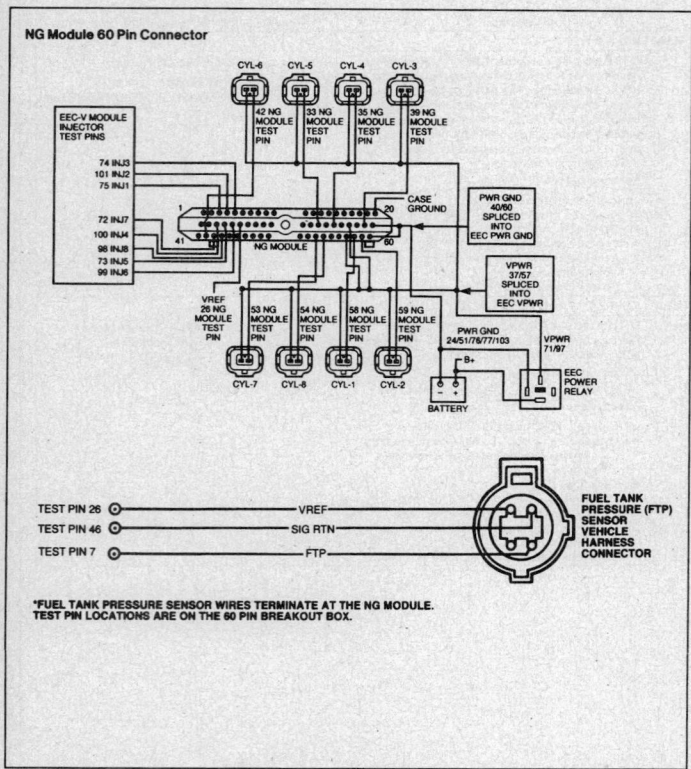

NG Module 60 Pin Connector

TEST PIN 26 ⊙ —————— VREF
TEST PIN 46 ⊙ —————— SIG RTN
TEST PIN 7 ⊙ —————— FTP

FUEL TANK PRESSURE (FTP) SENSOR VEHICLE HARNESS CONNECTOR

*FUEL TANK PRESSURE SENSOR WIRES TERMINATE AT THE NG MODULE.
TEST PIN LOCATIONS ARE ON THE 60 PIN BREAKOUT BOX.

FM0159601512030X

**Fig. 247   Test HA: Natural Gas Fuel Control (Part 3 of 24).
1996**

Test Step		Result	▶	Action to Take
HA30	DTCS P0135, P0141, P0155 AND P0161: HO2S HEATER SIGNAL CIRCUIT IS OPEN, SHORTED TO GROUND, SHORTED TO B+ OR EXCESSIVE CURRENT DRAW			
	Diagnostic Trouble Codes (DTCs) P0135, P0141, P0155 and P0161 indicate a short to ground, or open, or short to VPWR in the HO2S heater circuit. DTC/HO2S Reference List DTC P0135 = HO2S HTR-11 DTC P0141 = HO2S HTR-12 DTC P0155 = HO2S HTR-21 DTC P0161 = HO2S HTR-22 Possible causes: — Shorts to B+ in harness or HO2S. — Water in connectors. — Cut or pulled wires. — Disconnected wiring. — Open VPWR circuit. — Open GND circuit. — Low battery voltage. — Corrosion or poor mating terminals. — Damaged PCM. • Visually inspect the HO2S circuit for exposed wiring, contamination, corrosion and proper assembly. NOTE: On some applications, a vehicle hoist may be required to access the HO2S harness. • Were any concerns found during the visual inspection?	Yes No	▶ ▶	SERVICE any concerns found in the visual inspection. RERUN Quick Test. GO to **HA31**.
HA31	PERFORM KOEO SELF-TEST • Key off. • Scan Tool connected. • Key on. • Engine at 2000 rpm for 5 minutes. • Key off. • Key on, engine off. • Activate key on, engine off (KOEO) Self-Test. • Are DTCs P0135, P0141, P0155 and/or P0161 present?	Yes No	▶ ▶	GO to **HA32**. No DTCs present. Fault may be intermittent. GO to Pinpoint Test Step **Z1** with the following data: HO2S PIDs and a list of possible causes.

FM0159601512040X

**Fig. 247   Test HA: Natural Gas Fuel Control (Part 4 of 24).
1996**

Test Step		Result	▶	Action to Take
HA32	CHECK FOR VPWR AT THE VEHICLE HARNESS CONNECTOR			
	NOTE: If DTCs P0135 or P0155 or P0141 and P0161 are displayed, both heater circuits will require testing. DTCs displayed separately are tested individually. • Key off. • Disconnect the appropriate HO2S(s). • Inspect both ends of the connectors for damaged or pushed out pins, moisture, corrosion, contamination, etc. Service as necessary. • Key on, engine off. • Measure the voltage between VPWR and SIG RTN circuit at the HO2S vehicle harness connector (refer to schematic at the beginning of this pinpoint test). • Is the voltage greater than 10.5 volts?	Yes No	▶ ▶	GO to **HA34**. GO to **HA33**.
HA33	CHECK FOR OPEN VPWR CIRCUIT • Key off. • Install breakout box, PCM disconnected. • Suspect sensor disconnected. • Measure the resistance between the VPWR Test Pin at the breakout box and VPWR at the HO2S vehicle harness connector. • Is the resistance less than 4.0 ohms?	Yes No	▶ ▶	GO to **HA34**. CHECK fuse in circuit. If fuse is OK, SERVICE open circuit. REMOVE breakout box. RECONNECT all components. RERUN Quick Test.
HA34	CHECK HO2S HEATER RESISTANCE • Key off. • HO2S disconnected. • Connect DVOM to HO2S HTR GND and VPWR Test Pins at the HO2S sensor connector, and measure the resistance. • Is the resistance between 3 and 30 ohms?	Yes No	▶ ▶	GO to **HA35**. REPLACE HO2S. REMOVE breakout box. RECONNECT all components. RERUN Quick Test.
HA35	CHECK FOR HEATER GND AND VPWR SHORTED TO HO2S CASE • Suspect sensor disconnected. • Measure the resistance between the HO2S Heater GND at the HO2S connector and the HO2S case. • Measure the resistance between the HO2S VPWR at the HO2S sensor connector and the HO2S sensor case. • Is the resistance greater than 10,000 ohms?	Yes No	▶ ▶	GO to **HA36**. REPLACE HO2S. REMOVE breakout box. RECONNECT all components. RERUN Quick Test.

FM0159601512050X

**Fig. 247   Test HA: Natural Gas Fuel Control (Part 5 of 24).
1996**

Test Step		Result	▶	Action to Take
HA36	CHECK FOR SHORTS TO OTHER GROUNDS AND VPWR IN THE HO2S HEATER GROUND HARNESS CIRCUITS			

	• Key off.
	• Disconnect Scan Tool from DLC.
	• Suspect sensor disconnected.
	• Disconnect PCM.
	• Breakout box installed, leave PCM disconnected.
	• Use the following list to measure the resistance between the appropriate test pins at the breakout box.
	— DTC P0135 = HO2S HTR-11 (HTR GND)
	  Test Pin 93 and Test Pins 24, 76, 103, 91 and 97.
	— DTC P0141 = HO2S HTR-12 (HTR GND)
	  Test Pin 95 and Test Pins 24, 76, 103, 91 and 97.
	— DTC P0155 = HO2S HTR-21 (HTR GND)
	  Test Pin 94 and Test Pins 24, 76, 103, 91 and 97.
	— DTC P0161 = HO2S HTR-22 (HTR GND)
	  Test Pin 96 and Test Pins 24, 76, 103, 91 and 97.
	• Is the resistance greater than 10,000 ohms?
		Yes
		No
			▶
			▶
				GO to **HA37**.
				REPAIR shorted circuit. REMOVE breakout box. RECONNECT all components. RERUN Quick Test.

HA37	CHECK FOR OPEN HO2S HEATER GROUND HARNESS CIRCUIT • Key off. • Suspect sensor disconnected. • Breakout box installed, PCM disconnected. • Use the following list to measure the resistance between the appropriate test pins at the breakout box and the HO2S HTR GND at the vehicle harness connector. — HO2S HTR-11 Test Pin 93 (HTR GND) — HO2S HTR-12 Test Pin 95 (HTR GND) — HO2S HTR-21 Test Pin 94 (HTR GND) — HO2S HTR-22 Test Pin 96 (HTR GND) • Is the resistance less than 4.0 ohms?	Yes No	▶ ▶	Open or shorted or excessive resistance in the heater circuit in the PCM. REPLACE PCM. REMOVE breakout box. RECONNECT all components. RERUN Quick Test. REPAIR open or excessive resistance in the heater circuit in harness. REMOVE breakout box. RECONNECT all components. RERUN Quick Test.

FM0159601512060X

**Fig. 247   Test HA: Natural Gas Fuel Control (Part 6 of 24).
1996**

Test Step	Result	▶	Action to Take
HA40 DTC P1131, P1151, P1132 AND P1152: UPSTREAM HO2S(S) NOT SWITCHING. DTCs P1130 AND P1150: FUEL SYSTEM NOT SWITCHING AT THE ADAPTIVE LIMITS (RICH OR LEAN)			
Diagnostic Trouble Codes (DTCs) P1131 bank (1) (Cylinder # 1) and P1151 bank (2) indicate the fuel/air ratio is correcting rich for an overly lean condition. The HO2S voltage is less than 0.45 volt. DTCs P1132 bank (1) (Cylinder # 1) and P1152 bank (2) indicate the fuel/air ratio is correcting lean for an overly rich condition. The HO2S voltage is greater than 0.45 volt. DTCs P1130 and P1150 indicate the fuel control system has reached its maximum compensation for lean or rich condition and the HO2S is not switching. — HO2S-11 = DTCs P1131, P1132 and P1130 — HO2S-21 = DTCs P1151, P1152 and P1150 Possible cause: Fuel system — Excessive fuel pressure. — Leaking fuel injector(s). — Leaking fuel pressure regulator. — Low fuel pressure. — Contaminated injector(s). Ignition — Spark plugs. — Plug wires. — Coil(s). Induction system — Air leaks after the MAF. — Vacuum leaks. — Restricted air inlet. — PCV system. — Fuel purge system. — Improperly seated dip stick. Base engine — Oil overfill. — Cam timing. — Cylinder compression. — Exhaust leaks before or near the HO2Ss. ● Check air intake for leaks, obstructions and damage. ● Check air filter, air filter housing for blockage. ● Verify integrity of the PCV system. ● Check for disconnected plug wires. ● Check for vacuum leaks. ● **Are there any of the above concerns?**	Yes No	▶ ▶	SERVICE as necessary. RERUN Quick Test. GO to **HA42**.

Fig. 247   Test HA: Natural Gas Fuel Control (Part 7 of 24). 1996

FM015960I512070X

Test Step	Result	▶	Action to Take
HA41 DTCs P0172, P0174, P0171 AND P0175: FUEL SYSTEM AT THE CORRECTED ADAPTIVE LIMITS			
Diagnostic Trouble Codes (DTCs) P0171 bank (1) (cylinder # 1) and DTC P0174 bank (2) indicate the fuel/air ratio is too lean. The fuel adaptive system is at the rich correction limit. DTC P0172 bank (1) and DTC P0175 bank (2) indicate the fuel/air ratio is too rich. The fuel adaptive system is at the lean correction limit. DTCs HO2S Reference list: — HO2S-11 = DTCs P0171 and P0172 — HO2S-21 = DTCs P0174 and P0175 Possible causes: Fuel system — Excessive fuel pressure. — Leaking fuel injector(s). — High fuel pressure. — Low fuel pressure. — Contaminated injector(s) Ignition — Spark plugs. — Plug wires. — Coils. Induction system — Air leaks after the MAF. — Vacuum leaks. — Restricted air inlet. — PCV system. — Improperly seated dip stick. Base engine — Oil overfill. — Cam timing. — Cylinder compression. — Exhaust leaks before or near the HO2S's. ● Check air intake for leaks, obstructions and damage. ● Check air filter, air filter housing for blockage. ● Verify fuel level. ● Verify integrity of the PCV system. ● Check for disconnected plug wires. ● Check for vacuum leaks. ● Verify customer did not run out of fuel. ● **Are there any of the above concerns?**	Yes No	▶ ▶	SERVICE as necessary. RERUN Quick Test. GO to **HA42**.

FM015960I512080X

Fig. 247   Test HA: Natural Gas Fuel Control (Part 8 of 24). 1996

Test Step	Result	▶	Action to Take
HA42 INITIATE KOER SELF-TEST			
● Key off. ● Scan Tool connected. ● Enter Key On Engine Running (KOER) Self-Test. ● **Are HO2S DTCs P1131, P1132, P1151 or P1152 present?**	Yes No	▶ ▶	GO to **HA43**. For DTCs P1130, P1150 P0171, P0174, P0172 and P0175: GO to **HA43**. All others: The fault that produced the DTC is intermittent. GO to Pinpoint Test Step **Z1** with the following data: HO2S-11, 21, 12, 22 PIDs and list of possible causes.
HA43 CHECK FUEL PRESSURE			
WARNING: THE FUEL SYSTEM IS PRESSURIZED WHEN THE ENGINE IS NOT RUNNING. TO PREVENT INJURY OR FIRE, USE CAUTION WHEN WORKING ON THE FUEL SYSTEM. BECOME FAMILIAR WITH THE WARNING, CAUTION AND NOTE IN PINPOINT TEST HB BEFORE SERVICING. ● Key off. ● Scan Tool connected. ● NG fuel pressure gauge connected at the fuel rail schrader valve. NOTE: Fuel rail pressure gauge is part of the NG Special Rotunda Tool Kit 134-00114. ● Access IP PID and monitor both gauge and PID. ● Key on, engine off. Record pressure readings. ● Key on, engine on. Record pressure readings. ● Increase engine speed to 2500 rpms and maintain for one minute. Record pressure reading. ● **Are the fuel pressure readings between 105-130 psi (725-930 kPa)?**	Yes No	▶ ▶	Fuel system is capable of required pressure. GO to **HA44**. Fuel pressure out of specification. GO to Pinpoint Test **HB1**.

FM015960I512090X

Fig. 247   Test HA: Natural Gas Fuel Control (Part 9 of 24). 1996

Test Step	Result	▶	Action to Take
HA44 CHECK SYSTEM ABILITY TO HOLD FUEL PRESSURE			
● Fuel pressure gauge installed. ● Cycle key on and off several times. ● Verify there are no external leaks (repair as necessary). ● **Does the fuel pressure remain within 10 psi of the highest reading after two minutes?**	Yes No	▶ ▶	For DTCs P1130, P1150, P0171, P0172, P0174 and P0175: GO to **HA45**. For No Starts: GO to **HA45**. All other DTCs: GO to **HA62**. Excessive pressure loss. GO to Pinpoint Test Step **HB1**.
HA45 CHECK SYSTEM ABILITY TO HOLD FUEL PRESSURE WITH KEY ON			
● Key off. ● Scan Tool connected. ● Access and monitor IP sensor PID. ● Key On, Engine Off. Monitor fuel pressure gauge. ● **Does the fuel pressure remain within 10 psi of the highest reading after 10 seconds?**	Yes No	▶ ▶	For No Starts: GO to **HA46**. For DTCs P1130, P1150, P0171 and P0174: GO to **HA55**. For DTCs P0172 and P0175: GO to **HA57**.
HA46 CHECK ABILITY OF INJECTOR(S) TO DELIVER FUEL			
● Key off. ● Scan Tool connected. ● Access and monitor IP sensor PID. ● Cycle key several times. ● Locate and disconnect the Inertia Fuel Shutoff (IFS) Switch. ● Crank the engine for ten seconds and monitor PID reading. ● **Was there a pressure drop greater than 20 psi (34 kPa)?**	Yes No	▶ ▶	The EEC-V System is not the cause of the no start. REMOVE the fuel pressure gauge. RECONNECT the IFS switch. REFER to Symptom Flowcharts for further diagnosis. REMOVE fuel pressure gauge. RECONNECT IFS switch. GO to **H47**.
HA47 CHECK FOR VREF AT NATURAL GAS MODULE			
● Key off. ● Disconnect Natural Gas (NG) module from harness. Inspect for damaged or pushed out pins, corrosion, loose wires, etc. Service as necessary. ● Install 60-pin breakout box. NG module connected. ● Key on, engine off. ● Measure the voltage between Test Pin 26 (VREF) and Test Pin 46 (SIG RTN) at the breakout box. ● **Is the voltage reading between 4.0 and 6.0 volts?**	Yes No	▶ ▶	GO to **HA55**. VREF out of range. REMOVE breakout box. RECONNECT NG module. GO to **HA48**.

FM015960I512100X

Fig. 247   Test HA: Natural Gas Fuel Control (Part 10 of 24). 1996

Part 11 (HA48–HA53)

Test Step	Result	►	Action to Take
HA48 WAS VREF GREATER THAN 6.0 VOLTS			
• Was the VREF reading greater than 6.0 volts on the previous test step?	Yes	►	VREF shorted to power. GO to **HA53**.
	No	►	VREF less than 4.0 volts. GO to **HA49**.
HA49 CHECK BATTERY VOLTAGE			
• Key on, engine off.	Yes	►	GO to **HA50**.
• Measure the voltage across the battery terminals.	No	►	Key off. service discharged battery.
• Is the voltage reading greater than 10.5 volts?			
HA50 CHECK FOR POWER AT NG MODULE			
• Key off.	Yes	►	GO to **HA52**.
• Install 60-Pin breakout box. NG module connected.	No	►	GO to **HA51**.
• Measure the voltage between Test Pin 37 or 57 and Test Pin 40 or 60 at the breakout box.			
• Is the voltage reading greater than 10.5 volts?			
HA51 CHECK POWER BETWEEN 37/57 AND BATTERY GROUND			
• Key off.	Yes	►	REMOVE breakout box. SERVICE open ground circuit.
• Breakout box installed. NG module connected.	No	►	REMOVE breakout box. SERVICE open power circuit.
• Key on.			
• Measure the voltage between Test Pin 37 or 57 at the breakout box and battery ground.			
• Is the voltage reading greater than 10.5 volts?			
HA52 DISCONNECT FUEL TANK PRESSURE SENSOR			
• Key off.	Yes	►	FOLLOW Service Manual instructions. REPLACE Fuel Tank Pressure sensor.
• Locate Fuel Tank Pressure Sensor at the rear of the vehicle and disconnect.	No	►	GO to **HA54**.
• Key on, engine off.			
• Measure the voltage between the VREF circuit and SIG RTN circuit at the fuel tank pressure sensor vehicle harness connector (refer to schematic for pin location).			
• Is the voltage reading between 4.0 and 6.0 volts?			
HA53 CHECK FOR VREF SHORT TO POWER IN THE HARNESS			
• Fuel Tank Pressure sensor disconnected.	Yes	►	REMOVE breakout box. REPLACE NG module.
• Install 60-pin breakout box to NG module harness connector. NG module disconnected.	No	►	REMOVE breakout box. SERVICE short to power.
• Key on.			
• Measure between the Test Pin 26 (VREF) and Test Pin 40 (PWR GND) at the breakout box.			
• Is the voltage reading less than 1.0 volt?			

FM0159601512110X

Fig. 247   Test HA: Natural Gas Fuel Control (Part 11 of 24). 1996

Part 12 (HA54–HA55)

Test Step	Result	►	Action to Take
HA54 CHECK FOR VREF SHORTED TO GROUND CIRCUITS			
• Key off.	Yes	►	REMOVE breakout box. REPLACE NG module.
• Install 60-Pin breakout box to NG module harness connector. NG module disconnected.	No	►	REMOVE breakout box. SERVICE short to ground.
• Fuel Tank Pressure sensor disconnected.			
• Measure resistance between the Test Pin 26 (VREF) and Test Pin 20, 40, 46 and 60 at the breakout box.			
• Is the resistance greater than 10,000 ohms?			
HA55 CHECK RESISTANCE OF INJECTOR(S) AND HARNESS FROM THE NATURAL GAS VEHICLE (NG) MODULE TO THE INJECTOR(S)			
• Key off.	Yes	►	Fuel injector(s) and harness resistance is OK from the NG module harness connector to the injector.
• 60-Pin breakout box installed. NG module disconnected.			**For No Start and DTCs:**
• Measure the resistance between suspect injector Test Pin(s) and Test Pin 37 or 57 (VPWR) at the breakout box (use chart for injector pin location).			GO to **HA58**.
	No	►	GO to **HA56**.

Cyl. No.	Test Pin	Cyl. No.	Test Pin
1	58	5	33
2	59	6	42
3	39	7	53
4	35	8	54

• Is the resistance between 3.0 and 6.0 ohms?

FM0159601512120X

Fig. 247   Test HA: Natural Gas Fuel Control (Part 12 of 24). 1996

Part 13 (HA56–HA57)

Test Step	Result	►	Action to Take
HA56 CHECK CONTINUITY OF HARNESS FROM NG MODULE TO THE INJECTOR			
• Key off.	Yes	►	GO to **HA57**.
• 60-Pin breakout box installed, NG module disconnected.	No	►	SERVICE open harness circuit. REMOVE breakout box. RECONNECT all components. RERUN Quick Test.
• Measure resistance between the NG module harness connector Test Pins at the 60-Pin breakout box and the Injector(s) harness connector(s) at the injector(s).			
• Measure the resistance between the NG module harness connector Test Pin 37/57 at the breakout box and the injector harness connector(s) (use chart for injector pin location).			

Cyl. No.	Test Pin	Cyl. No.	Test Pin
1	58	5	33
2	59	6	42
3	39	7	53
4	35	8	54

• is each resistance less than 5.0 ohms?

Test Step	Result	►	Action to Take
HA57 CHECK INJECTOR HARNESS CIRCUIT FOR SHORTS TO POWER OR GROUND			
• Key off.	Yes	►	For DTCs P0172 and P0175, GO to **HA60**. REPLACE only damaged injector(s). REMOVE breakout box. RECONNECT all components. RERUN Quick Test.
• Disconnect Scan Tool from DLC.			
• Breakout box installed, NG module disconnected.			
• Disconnect injector(s) harness connector.	No	►	SERVICE short circuit. REMOVE breakout box. RECONNECT all components. RERUN Quick Test.
• Measure the resistance between the injector Test Pin(s) and Test Pin(s) 37 or 57 (VPWR) and 40 or 60 (PWR GND) at the breakout box.			
• Measure the resistance between the injector Test Pin(s) at the breakout box and Test Pin (20) Chassis ground.			

Cyl. No.	Test Pin	Cyl. No.	Test Pin
1	58	5	33
2	59	6	42
3	39	7	53
4	35	8	54

• is each resistance greater than 10,000 ohms?

FM0159601512130X

Fig. 247   Test HA: Natural Gas Fuel Control (Part 13 of 24). 1996

Part 14 (HA58–HA59)

Test Step	Result	►	Action to Take
HA58 CHECK INJECTOR DRIVER SIGNAL AT 60 PIN BREAKOUT BOX			
Requires standard 12 volt test lamp.	Yes	►	PCM and NG circuits are OK. REMOVE breakout box. For no starts, RETURN to Symptom Flowcharts.
• 60-Pin breakout box installed at NG module harness connector.			**All others:**
• Connect NG module to breakout box.			GO to **HA62**.
• Connect test lamp between Test Pin 37 or 57 and injector Test Pin 58, 59, 39, 35, 33, 42, 53 and 54 at the breakout box while cranking or starting the engine.	No	►	No light/continuous bright light, GO to **HA59**.
NOTE: A properly operating system will show a dim glow at idle on the test lamp.			
• Does the test lamp have a dim glow while cranking or running the engine?			
HA59 CHECK PCM INJECTOR HARNESS CIRCUIT FOR CONTINUITY			
• Key off.	Yes	►	GO to **HA60**.
• Both 104 and 60-Pin breakout boxes installed, PCM and NG module disconnected.	No	►	SERVICE open harness circuit. REMOVE breakout box. RECONNECT all components. RERUN Quick Test.
• Measure the resistance between VPWR Test Pin 71 or 97 at the 104-Pin breakout box and Test Pin 37 or 57 at the 60-Pin breakout box.			
• Measure the resistance between the Injector Test Pin(s) at the breakout boxes (refer to chart for test pin location).			

	PCM Output to 60-Pin NG Input	
Cyl. No.	PCM Test Pin	NG Test Pin
1	75	3
2	101	4
3	74	5
4	100	23
5	73	24
6	99	25
7	72	43
8	98	44

• Is each resistance less than 5.0 ohms?

FM0159601512140X

Fig. 247   Test HA: Natural Gas Fuel Control (Part 14 of 24). 1996

Test Step	Result	▶	Action to Take
HA60 CHECK PCM INJECTOR HARNESS CIRCUIT FOR SHORT TO POWER OR GROUND			
• Key off.	Yes	▶	For DTCs P0172 and P0175: GO to **HA62**. REMOVE 60-Pin breakout box. RECONNECT NG module. GO to **HA61**.
• Breakout boxes installed, PCM and NG module disconnected.			
• measure the resistance between the Injector Test Pin(s) 71 or 97 and Test Pins 24, 25, 76 and 103 at the 104-Pin breakout box (refer to chart in **HA48**).	No	▶	SERVICE short circuit. REMOVE breakout boxes. RECONNECT all components. RERUN Quick Test.
• Measure the resistance between the Injector Test Pin(s) 3, 4, 5, 23, 24, 25, 43 and 44 and Test Pin(s) 37 or 57 and 40 and 60 at the 60-Pin breakout box (refer to chart in **HA48**).			
• Measure the resistance between the Injector Test Pin(s) 3, 4, 5, 23, 24, 25, 43 and 44 and Test Pin(s) 20 Chassis ground at the 60-Pin breakout box.			
• **Is each resistance greater than 10,000 ohms?**			
HA61 CHECK INJECTOR DRIVER SIGNAL FROM PCM			
Requires standard 12 volt test lamp.	Yes	▶	For no starts: REPLACE NG module. REMOVE breakout box. RECONNECT all components. RERUN Quick Test. For DTCs: REMOVE breakout box. RECONNECT all components. GO to **HA62**.
• 104-Pin breakout box installed, PCM connected to breakout box.			
• Connect test lamp between Test Pin 71 or 97 and Injector Test Pin(s) 75, 101, 74, 100, 73, 99, 72 and 98 at the breakout box while cranking or starting the engine.			
NOTE: A properly operating system will show a dim glow at idle on the test lamp.	No	▶	No light / continuous bright light. REPLACE PCM. REMOVE breakout box. RECONNECT all components. RERUN Quick Test.
• **Does the test lamp have a dim glow while cranking or starting the engine?**			

Fig. 247 Test HA: Natural Gas Fuel Control (Part 15 of 24). 1996

Test Step	Result	▶	Action to Take
HA62 FLOW TEST FUEL INJECTOR(S)			
• Flow test fuel injector(s).	Yes	▶	DTCs P0171, P0172, P0174 and P0175:
• Use the Rotunda NG Injector Tester found in the Special NG Tool Kit 113-00114 or equivalent to flow test NG injectors according to the instructions for the injector tester or test steps located in Pinpoint Test Step **HB15**.			The fault that produced the DTC is an intermittent. GO to Pinpoint Test Step **Z1** with the following data: SF1, SF2, LFT1, LFT2 PIDs and list of possible causes.
• **Is the leakage and flow within specification?**			DTCs P1130 and P1150: GO to **H54**. For DTCs P1131 and P1151: GO to **H64**. For DTCs P1132 and P1152: GO to **H63**.
	No	▶	REPLACE injector. RERUN Quick Test.
HA63 CHECK CYLINDER COMPRESSION			
• Check cylinder compression.	Yes	▶	For DTCs P1131, P1130, P1151 and P1150: GO to **H64**. For DTCs P1132 and P1152: GO to **H69**.
• **Are cylinder compression readings within specification?**			
	No	▶	REPAIR as necessary. COMPLETE PCM Reset to clear DTCs (REFER to Powertrain Control Module (PCM) Reset). RERUN Quick Test.

Fig. 247 Test HA: Natural Gas Fuel Control (Part 16 of 24). 1996

Test Step	Result	▶	Action to Take
HA64 CHECK HO2S INTEGRITY			
Diagnostic Trouble Codes (DTCs) P1131 and P1151 and / or P1130 and P1150 indicate HO2S always lean, slow to switch, lack of switching or fuel at adaptive limit.	Yes	▶	GO to **HA65**.
Possible causes:	No	▶	HO2S system is OK. Fuel delivery system is OK. Faults may have been repaired while doing inspection. Testing is complete at this time.
— Moisture inside the HO2S harness connector resulting in a short to ground.			
— HO2S coated with contaminants.			
— HO2S circuit open.			
— HO2S circuit shorted to ground.			
• Key off.			
• Inspect HO2S harness for chafing, burned out wires or other damage and service.			
• Inspect HO2S and connector for indications of submersions in water, oil, coolant, etc., and service.			
• Run engine at 2000 rpm for two minutes.			
• Key off.			
• Activate Key On Engine Running (KOER) Self-Test.			
• **Are DTCs P1131 and / or P1151 present?**			
HA65 CHECK HO2S ABILITY TO GENERATE A VOLTAGE GREATER THAN 0.5 VOLT			
Any vacuum or air leaks in non-EEC areas could cause DTCs P1131, P1151, P1130 and P1150.	Yes	▶	GO to **HA66**.
Possible causes:	No	▶	REPLACE HO2S. RERUN Quick Test.
— Leaking vacuum actuators.			
— Engine sealing (Intake and IAC).			
— EGR system (valve).			
— PCV system (hose and valve).			
— Unmetered air leaks between throttle body and Mass Air Flow (MAF) sensor assembly.			
— Silicone contaminated HO2S.			
• Key off.			
• Disconnect the suspect HO2S from vehicle harness.			
• Connect DVOM to the HO2S Signal and HO2S SIG RTN or HO2S GND at the HO2S sensor connector.			
• DVOM on 20 volt scale.			
• Run engine at 2000 rpm for two minutes.			
• Rerun KOER Self-Test and monitor HO2S voltage.			
• **Does DVOM indicate greater than 0.5 volt during or at the end of Self-Test?**			

Fig. 247 Test HA: Natural Gas Fuel Control (Part 17 of 24). 1996

Test Step	Result	▶	Action to Take
HA66 CHECK CONTINUITY OF HO2S AND HO2S GROUND CIRCUITS			
• Key off.	Yes	▶	GO to **HA67**.
• Breakout box installed, PCM disconnected.	No	▶	SERVICE open circuit. REMOVE breakout box. RECONNECT PCM and HO2S. RERUN Quick Test.
• Disconnect suspect HO2S from harness. Inspect both ends of connector for damaged or pushed out pins, moisture, corrosion, loose pins, etc., and service.			
• Measure the resistance between HO2S Signal Test Pin at the breakout box and the HO2S vehicle harness connector. Use the Pin assignment below and record the reading.			
• Measure resistance between SIG RTN test pin at the breakout box and HO2S SIG RTN vehicle harness connector. Record readings.			
— HO2S-11 SIG = Test Pin 60			
— HO2S-21 SIG = Test Pin 87			
— HO2S SIG RTN = Test Pin 91			
• **Is the resistance reading less than 5.0 ohms?**			
HA67 CHECK HO2S CIRCUIT WIRING HARNESS FOR SHORT TO GROUND			
• Key off.	Yes	▶	GO to **HA68**.
• Breakout box installed, PCM disconnected.	No	▶	SERVICE short circuit. REMOVE breakout box. RECONNECT PCM and HO2S. RERUN Quick Test.
• HO2S disconnected.			
• Measure resistance between the HO2S Signal Test Pin and Test Pins 24, 51, 76, 77 and 103 at the breakout box.			
• **Is each resistance greater than 10,000 ohms?**			
HA68 CHECK HO2S FOR SHORT TO GROUND			
• Key off.	Yes	▶	For DTCs P1130 and P1150: GO to **HA69**. For DTCs P1131C and P1151C: GO to **HA74**. For KOER DTCs P1131 and P1151: REMOVE breakout box. RECONNECT HO2S. REPLACE PCM.
• Breakout box installed, PCM disconnected.			
• HO2S connected.			
• Measure resistance between PWR GND / SIG RTN Test Pin and HO2S Signal Test Pin at the breakout box.			
HO2S-11 SIG = Test Pin 60			
HO2S-21 SIG = Test Pin 87			
HO2S PWR GND = Test Pin 24, 76 and 103	No	▶	REPLACE HO2S. REMOVE breakout box. RECONNECT PCM. RERUN Quick Test.
HO2S SIG RTN = Test Pin 91			
• **Is resistance greater than 10,000 ohms?**			

Fig. 247 Test HA: Natural Gas Fuel Control (Part 18 of 24). 1996

Test Step	Result	►	Action to Take
HA69 CHECK FOR DTCS P1132 AND P1152 WITH P1130 AND P1150 • Key off. • Scan Tool connected. • Activate Key On Engine Running (KOER) Self-Test. • **Are DTCs P1132 or P1152 present?**	Yes No	► ►	GO to **HA70**. The fault that produced the DTC is an intermittent. GO to Pinpoint Test Step **Z1** with the following data: HO2S-11, 21 PIDs and list of possible causes.
HA70 CHECK FOR HO2S SIGNAL SHORTED TO POWER Diagnostic Trouble Codes (DTCs) P1132 and P1152 and/or P1130 and P1150 indicate HO2S always rich. Possible causes: — Moisture inside the HO2S harness connector resulting in a short to power. — HO2S circuit shorted to power. DTC P1130, P1132 = HO2S-11 DTC P1150, P1152 = HO2S-21 • Key on, engine off. • Scan Tool connected. • Access the Parameter Identification (PID) for the DTC generated. NOTE: HO2S displayed as O2S on Scan Tool. • **Is the voltage greater than 1.0 volt and less than 4.0 volts?**	Yes No	► ►	An over voltage condition exists in the HO2S circuit. GO to **HA71**. GO to **HA73**.

HA71 CHECK FOR SHORTS TO VOLTAGE SOURCE IN THE HARNESS CIRCUIT
 • Key off.
 • Disconnect Scan Tool from DLC.
 • Suspect sensor disconnected.
 • Disconnect PCM. Inspect for damaged or pushed out pins, corrosion, loose wires, etc. Service as necessary.
 • Install breakout box, leave PCM disconnected.
 • Use the following list to measure the resistance between the appropriate test pins at the breakout box.
   — DTC P1130, P1132 = HO2S-11
     Test Pin 60 and Test Pins 71, 93 and 97.
   — DTC P1150, P1152 = HO2S-21
     Test Pin 87 and Test Pins 71, 93 and 97.
 • **Is the resistance greater than 10,000 ohms?**
	Yes
	
	 No
		►
		
		 ►
			REMOVE breakout box. RECONNECT PCM. GO to **HA72**.
			 REPAIR short to power. REMOVE breakout box. RECONNECT all components. RERUN Quick Test.

FM0159601512190X

Fig. 247   Test HA: Natural Gas Fuel Control (Part 19 of 24). 1996

Test Step	Result	►	Action to Take
HA72 CHECK FOR HO2S SIGNAL SHORTED TO HO2S HEATER CIRCUIT IN THE SENSOR • Key off. • Suspect HO2S sensor disconnected. • Scan Tool connected. • Key on, engine off. • Access HO2S PID corresponding to DTCs received. NOTE: HO2S displayed as O2S on Scan Tool. • **Is the HO2S voltage less than 0.2 volt?**	Yes No	► ►	REPLACE HO2S. RECONNECT all components. RERUN Quick Test. REPLACE PCM. RECONNECT all components. RERUN Quick Test.
HA73 ATTEMPT TO GENERATE DTCS P1131 AND P1151 • Key off. • HO2S disconnected. • Jumper HO2S Signal at the HO2S harness vehicle connector to the battery negative post. • Activate Key On Engine Running (KOER) Self-Test. • **Are DTCs P1131 or P1151 present?**	Yes No	► ►	REMOVE jumper. GO to **HA74**. REMOVE jumper. RECONNECT HO2S. DISCONNECT PCM. INSPECT both ends of connector for damaged or pushed out pins, moisture, corrosion, loose pins, etc. and service as necessary. If OK, REPLACE PCM. RERUN KOER Self-Test.
HA74 HO2S CHECK • Key off. • Suspect HO2S disconnected. • Connect DVOM to HO2S Signal circuit and HO2S SIG RTN at the HO2S sensor connector. • DVOM on 20 volt scale. • Disconnect vacuum hose from vacuum tree. • Start engine and run at 2000 rpm. • **Does the DVOM indicate less than 0.4 volt within 30 seconds?**	Yes No	► ►	RECONNECT vacuum hose and HO2S. GO to **HA75**. REPLACE HO2S. RECONNECT vacuum hose. RERUN Quick Test.
HA75 MONITOR HO2S (PID) FOR NORMAL SWITCHING • Key on, engine running. • Engine at operating temperature. • Access HO2S PID for suspect HO2S using Scan Tool. NOTE: HO2S displayed as O2S on Scan Tool. • Access HO2S PID while wiggling, bending, and shaking small sections of the EEC harness from the PCM to the HO2S. • **Did the HO2S voltage stay high (greater than 0.45 volt) or low (less than 0.45 volt)?**	Yes No	► ►	ISOLATE cause of lack of HO2S switches and service. COMPLETE PCM Reset to clear DTCs (REFER to Powertrain Control Module (PCM) Reset). RERUN Quick Test. GO to **HA76**.

FM0159601512200X

Fig. 247   Test HA: Natural Gas Fuel Control (Part 20 of 24). 1996

Test Step	Result	►	Action to Take
HA76 TEST DRIVE WHILE MONITORING HO2S PID FOR NORMAL SWITCHING NOTE: This test step requires an observer to monitor PID for proper operation. • Scan Tool still attached. • Access HO2S PID. • While observer views PID, test drive vehicle under different road conditions in an attempt to simulate the original fault. • **Does HO2S appear to switch properly?**	Yes No	► ►	UNABLE to duplicate fault. CLEAR any DTCs. Testing complete at this time. REPLACE HO2S. COMPLETE PCM reset to clear DTCs (REFER to Powertrain Control Module (PCM) Reset). RERUN Quick Test.

HA80 DTCS P1137, P1138, P1157 AND/OR P1158 LACK OF DOWNSTREAM HO2S SWITCHING
 Key On, Engine Running (KOER) Diagnostic Trouble Codes (DTCs) P1137, P1138, P1157 and P1158 can only be retrieved during KOER Self-Test when the fuel control is ramped rich and lean and monitored for a voltage change on the downstream HO2S.
 Possible causes:
 • Wiring Concerns
   — Pinched, shorted, and corroded wiring and pins
 • Other Concerns
   — Exhaust leaks
   — Defective PCM
   — Contaminated or damaged sensor
 • **Are any of the above concerns present?**
	Yes
	
	 No
		►
		
		 ►
			SERVICE as necessary. RERUN Quick Test.
			 GO to **HA81**.

HA81 CHECK EXHAUST SYSTEM FOR LEAKS
 NOTE: Any exhaust leaks between the engine and the end of the catalyst may have caused these DTCs.
 • Key off.
 • Place vehicle on a hoist, transmission in park, emergency brake applied, raise vehicle.
 • Inspect the following:
   — Exhaust flanges for leaks.
   — HO2S torque.
   — Check for punctures and cracks in catalyst and pipes leading to them.
 • **Are there any exhaust leaks?**
	Yes
	
	 No
		►
		
		 ►
			REPLACE or REPAIR as required. RERUN Quick Test.
			 GO to **HA82**.

FM0159601512210X

Fig. 247   Test HA: Natural Gas Fuel Control (Part 21 of 24). 1996

Test Step	Result	►	Action to Take
HA82 CHECK HO2S CIRCUIT CONTINUITY • Key off. • PCM connected to vehicle harness. • Suspect HO2S connected to vehicle harness. • Scan Tool connected. • Key on, engine off. • Access the correct HO2S PID. NOTE: HO2S displayed as O2S on Scan Tool.	Yes No	► ►	REPLACE HO2S. RERUN Quick Test. GO to **HA83**.

DTC	HO2S	PINS
P1137, P1138	HO2S-12	35 and 97
P1157, P1158	HO2S-22	61 and 97

• **Is the voltage greater than 1.60 volts?**			
HA83 CHECK HO2S HARNESS CIRCUIT FOR SHORT TO VPWR AND GROUND • Key off. • Disconnect Scan Tool from DLC. • Breakout box installed, PCM disconnected. Inspect both ends of connector for damaged or pushed out pins, moisture, corrosion, loose pins, etc. and service as necessary. • HO2S disconnected. • Measure the resistance between HO2S Signal Test Pin and SIG RTN Test Pin at the breakout box. • Measure the resistance between HO2S Signal Test Pin and VPWR and VREF Test Pin at the breakout box. • Measure the resistance between HO2S Signal Test Pin and PWR GND Test Pin at the breakout box. HO2S-12 SIG = Test Pin 35 HO2S-22 SIG = Test Pin 61 HO2S SIG RTN = Test Pin 91 PWR GND = Test Pins 24 and 103 VPWR = Test Pins 71 and 97 VREF = Test Pin 90 • **Is resistance greater than 10,000 ohms?**	Yes No	► ►	GO to **HA84**. SERVICE short in harness. RERUN Quick Test.

FM0159601512220X

Fig. 247   Test HA: Natural Gas Fuel Control (Part 22 of 24). 1996

Test Step	Result	▶	Action to Take
HA84 CHECK CONTINUITY OF HO2S AND HO2S GROUND CIRCUITS			
• Key off. • Breakout box installed, PCM disconnected. • Disconnect suspect HO2S from harness. • Measure the resistance between HO2S Signal Test Pin at the breakout box and the HO2S vehicle harness connector. Record readings. • Measure resistance between SIG RTN Test Pin at the breakout box and HO2S SIG RTN vehicle harness connector. Record readings. — HO2S-12 SIG = Test Pin 35 — HO2S-22 SIG = Test Pin 61 — HO2S SIG RTN = Test Pin 91 • **Is the resistance reading less than 5.0 ohms?**	Yes No	▶ ▶	REPLACE PCM. REMOVE breakout box. RECONNECT all components. RERUN Quick Test. REPAIR open circuit in harness. REMOVE breakout box. RECONNECT all components. RERUN Quick Test.
HA90 KOER DTC P1127			
Key On, Engine Running (KOER) Diagnostic Trouble Code (DTC) P1127 indicates the HO2S heater(s) were not on during KOER self-test and testing of the HO2S did not occur. The HO2S heaters are energized when certain temperatures are met. The HO2S heaters are energized based on exhaust temperature modeling, which allows upstream heaters to be energized independently of the downstream heaters. Possible causes: — Exhaust system to cool. • Key off. • Scan Tool connected. • Key on, engine off. • Access HRT11, 12, 21, 22 and monitor PIDs. • **Do all PIDs indicate on?**	Yes No	▶ ▶	RERUN Quick Test. RUN engine until all PIDs indicate on. RERUN Quick Test.

FM015960151223OX

Fig. 247   Test HA: Natural Gas Fuel Control (Part 23 of 24). 1996

Test Step	Result	▶	Action to Take
HA100 KOER DTC P1128 AND P1129			
Key On, Engine Running (KOER) Diagnostic Trouble Codes (DTCs) P1128 and P1129 indicate that during KOER testing, either the upstream or the downstream or both HO2S signals are swapped from bank to bank. — P1128 references to the upstream HO2S. — P1129 references to the downstream HO2S. Possible causes: — Crossed HO2S harness connectors. — Crossed wiring at HO2S harness connectors. — Crossed HO2S wiring at 104-Pin harness connector. • Key off. • Visual inspect vehicle HO2S harness connector(s) for any crossed or stretched wires or wire harnesses not mounted properly. • **Are there any indications of crossed connectors or wires?**	Yes No	▶ ▶	SERVICE as necessary. RERUN Quick Test. GO to **HA101**.
HA101 VERIFY PROPER HO2S SIGNAL PIN LOCATION			
• Key off. • PCM disconnected, breakout box installed. • Disconnect both of the suspect HO2S sensors from the vehicle harness connector. P1128 = HO2S 11/21 Upstream P1129 = HO2S 12/22 Downstream • Use the DTC adn the chart to measure the resistance between the breakout box and the HO2S harness vehicle connectors. HO2S-11 Test Pin 60 HO2S-21 Test Pin 87 HO2S-12 Test Pin 35 HO2S-22 Test Pin 61 • **Is the resistance less than 5.0 ohms?**	Yes No	▶ ▶	HO2S SIG circuit is OK. REMOVE breakout box. RECONNECT PCM. RERUN Quick Test. CONNECT HO2S connector to proper HO2S or RELOCATE HO2S signal pins in the 104 harness connector or HO2S harness connector. RERUN Quick Test.

TA24267A

Fig. 247   Test HA: Natural Gas Fuel Control (Part 24 of 24). 1996

FM015960151224OX

Note

You should enter this Pinpoint Test only when directed here.

Remember

This Pinpoint Test is intended to diagnose the following:

• Fuel Pressure
• Fuel Supply Lines
• Fuel Filter
• Fuel Injectors
• Fuel Pressure Regulator
• Fuel Injection Supply Manifold (Fuel Rail)
• Solenoid Shut-Off Valves

Tables and Charts

TOOLS AND FUEL INJECTOR APPLICATION CHART

Engine Application	Part Number 9F593	Electrical Connector Color	Resistance Ohms	Pressure Drop PISG	Fuel Delivery System Special Tool Kit		
					Tool Kit PT. NO. 134-00114 Contains		
4.6L NG Crown Victoria	F5TE-BA	GREEN	4-6	40 +/- 10 (275 +/- 70 kpa) and within 3 psi of each other	Fuel Pressure Gauge	Filler Connector Venting Tool	Injector Flow Tester

FM015960151301OX

Fig. 248   Test HB: Natural Gas Fuel Delivery System (Part 1 of 11). 1996

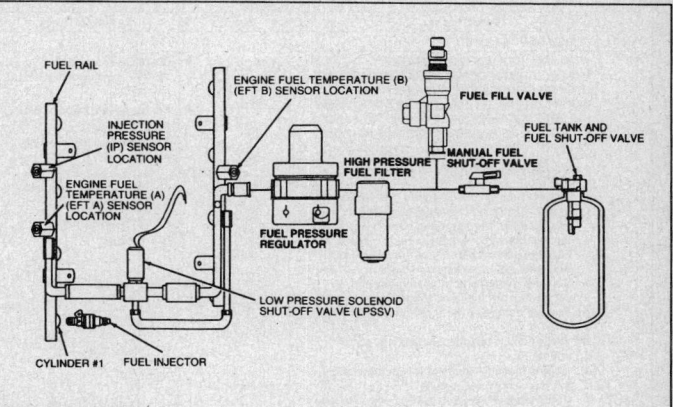

WARNING

NATURAL GAS IN THE FUEL SYSTEM IS AT HIGH PRESSURE AT ALL TIMES. TO AVOID INJURY OR FIRE, RELEASE THE FUEL PRESSURE FROM THE FUEL SYSTEM BEFORE DISASSEMBLING ANY FUEL SYSTEM COMPONENT. TO RELEASE THE PRESSURE FROM THE SYSTEM FOLLOW THE PRESSURE RELIEF PROCEDURE:

PRESSURE RELIEF PROCEDURE

• CLOSE THE 1/4 TURN MANUAL FUEL SHUT-OFF VALVE, OR, THUMP INERTIA FUEL SHUTOFF (IFS) SWITCH AND VERIFY THE BUTTON HAS BEEN UPSET (DO NOT RESET).
• CONNECT NATURAL GAS FUEL PRESSURE TESTING KIT 134-00114 AT THE SCHRADER VALVE LOCATED ON THE INJECTION SUPPLY MANIFOLD. TESTING KIT VALVE SHOULD BE CLOSED.
• POSITION THE TESTING KIT VENTING HOSE TO A WELL VENTILATED LOCATION, PREFERABLY OUTSIDE OR INTO VENT STACK.
• GRADUALLY OPEN THE TESTING KIT VALVE TO RELIEVE THE FUEL PRESSURE IN THE VEHICLE FUEL SYSTEM AND ALLOW IT TO ESCAPE.

FM015960151302OX

Fig. 248   Test HB: Natural Gas Fuel Delivery System (Part 2 of 11). 1996

Caution

Use care to prevent combustion from escaping fuel. No smoking, open flames or any kind of arcing.

Safe Fuel Handling Practices: Natural Gas—Fire

- REPORT ALL FIRES to the appropriate authorities.
- FLAMES from natural gas have a yellow and/or blue color.
- Know the locations of PORTABLE FIRE EXTINGUISHER, FIRE BLANKETS, and FIRE ALARMS. Learn how to use them.
- Use a FIRE BLANKET to fight flammable gas fires.

First Aid

- When overcome by vapors, if safe, MOVE VICTIM TO FRESH AIR. If not breathing, give artificial respiration or CPR (Cardiopulmonary Resuscitation) as appropriate. **SEEK MEDICAL ATTENTION IMMEDIATELY.**
- If IRRITATES EYES, FLUSH with large amounts of water for 15 minutes. Remove contact lenses, if worn. **SEEK MEDICAL ATTENTION.**

Health

- NATURAL GAS (and all other fuel vapors) may be HARMFUL BY INHALATION.
- ALL FUELS may be HARMFUL OR FATAL IF SWALLOWED.
- FUELS AND PRODUCTS containing methanol (e.g. windshield washer fluid) may cause blindness if swallowed.
- ALL FUELS are IRRITATING to the EYES and RESPIRATORY SYSTEM.

Handling

- Be aware of the MERCUROUS MERCAPTAN "ROTTEN EGG" smell of natural gas.
- Use FLAMMABLE GAS HANDLING PRECAUTIONS.
- Keep flammable gases in APPROVED, LABELED CONTAINERS.
- Use in WELL-VENTILATED AREAS and CONTROL VAPORS. Be aware that natural gas IS NOT VISIBLE, is lighter than air, can travel along the ceiling, and may collect in high hollows.
- When transferring flammable gases, CONNECT THE VENT STACK to the SOURCE and GROUND the SOURCE to the EARTH.

FM0159601513030X

Fig. 248   Test HB: Natural Gas Fuel Delivery System (Part 3 of 11). 1996

- DO NOT SMOKE, or use HEAT/SPARK PRODUCING EQUIPMENT near natural gas.
- DO NOT eat, drink or smoke where fuels are handled, processed or stored.
- WASH HANDS thoroughly after HANDLING any FUEL.

Leakage

- Notify the proper authorities in the EVENT of any leakage you have NOT been trained to address.
- STOP, and allow fuel to VENTILATE TO OUTSIDE ATMOSPHERE after any fuel escape.

NOTE

A small amount of pressure (3 psig) will remain in the fuel rail.

High pressure still exists in the fuel tanks and upstream of the 1/4 turn manual fuel shut off valve is closed.

When pressurizing the fuel system, if 1/4 turn manual fuel shut-off valve is open, leave open. If the valve is closed, slowly open the valve.

FM0159601513040X

Fig. 248   Test HB: Natural Gas Fuel Delivery System (Part 4 of 11). 1996

Test Step		Result	▶	Action to Take
HB1	CHECK SYSTEM INTEGRITY			
	WARNING: BEFORE SERVICING OR REPLACING ANY COMPONENTS IN THE FUEL SYSTEM, REDUCE THE POSSIBILITY OF INJURY OR FIRE BY FOLLOWING DIRECTIONS IN FUEL SYSTEM "WARNING, CAUTION AND NOTE" AT THE BEGINNING OF THIS PINPOINT TEST. ● Key on, engine off for 5 seconds. ● Key off. ● Visually inspect the complete fuel delivery system, including fuel lines, connections, fuel rail, pressure regulator and injector areas for leaks (hissing noise), looseness, cracks, kinks, pinching, or abrasion caused by an accident, collision, mishandling, etc. ● Visually inspect electrical harness and connectors for loose pins, corrosion, abrasion or other damage from accident, mishandling, etc. ● Verify vehicle has followed maintenance schedule. ● Inspect fuel filter element for contamination and service as necessary. ● Verify Inertia Fuel Shutoff (IFS) switch is set. ● Verify vehicle battery is fully charged. ● Verify electrical/fuse integrity. ● Verify 1/4 turn manual shut off valve is open. ● **Have any concerns been identified?**	Yes ▶ No ▶		SERVICE as necessary. VERIFY a symptom no longer exists. **For symptom of poor fuel range:** GO to NG fuel tank venting procedures **For symptom of fuel smell:** GO to HB20. All other symptoms: GO to HB2.
HB2	CHECK FUEL TANK PRESSURE			
	● Key off. ● Install fuel tank venting tool (supplied in Tool Kit 134-00114) to vehicle fueling connector. ● Open bypass on fill valve ● Key on. ● Record fuel tank pressure reading and fuel gauge reading. ● Key off. ● **Is the fuel pressure reading greater than 500 psig?**	Yes No	▶ ▶	GO to HB5. VERIFY fuel level, if OK, CHECK for power at tank solenoid valve. GO to HB3.

FM0159601513050X

Fig. 248   Test HB: Natural Gas Fuel Delivery System (Part 5 of 11). 1996

Test Step		Result	▶	Action to Take
HB3	CHECK FOR VOLTAGE AT THE FUEL TANK SOLENOID VALVE HARNESS VEHICLE CONNECTOR			
	● Key off. ● Scan Tool connected. ● Key on. ● Enter Output Test mode. ● Select "ALL ON." ● Measure the voltage between the VPWR and the GND circuit at the fuel tank solenoid valve vehicle harness connector (refer to EVTM for location). ● **Is the voltage reading greater than 10.5 volts?**	Yes ▶ No ▶		GO to NG fuel tank venting procedures solenoid valve diagnostics. GO to HB4.
HB4	CHECK VPWR BETWEEN FUEL TANK SOLENOID VEHICLE HARNESS CONNECTOR AND BATTERY GROUND			
	● Key off. ● Scan Tool connected. ● Key on. ● Enter Output Test mode. ● Select "ALL ON." ● Measure the voltage between the VPWR circuit at the fuel tank solenoid valve vehicle harness connector and battery ground. ● **Is the voltage reading greater than 10.5 volts?**	Yes ▶ No ▶		SERVICE the open ground circuit at the vehicle harness connector. VERIFY a symptom no longer exists. SERIVE open in VPWR circuit at the vehicle harness connector. VERIFY a symptom no longer exists.
HB5	CHECK FUEL PRESSURE			
	● Observe "Warning, Caution and Note." ● Key off. ● Connect Fuel Pressure Tester to schrader valve. ● Release fuel pressure from injection supply manifold (Fuel Rail) back to fuel tanks. ● Key on, engine on (if possible, start engine). ● Key off. ● After two minutes, obtain pressure reading from pressure tester. ● **Is fuel pressure between 100 psig (680 KPa) and 130 psig (930 KPa)?**	Yes ▶ No ▶		**For no starts:** RETURN to Section 4A, Symptom Flowcharts. All others: GO to HB6. REPLACE fuel pressure regulator. VERIFY a symptom no longer exists.

FM0159601513060X

Fig. 248   Test HB: Natural Gas Fuel Delivery System (Part 6 of 11). 1996

Test Step	Result	▶	Action to Take
HB6 VERIFY INJECTION PRESSURE SENSOR ACCURACY			
• Observe "WARNING, CAUTION and NOTE." • Key off. • Fuel Pressure Tester connected. • Install Scan Tool. • Key on, engine off. • Note pressure of IP sensor with Scan Tool. • Note pressure at schrader valve with fuel pressure tester. • Key off. • Close the 1/4 turn manual shut off valve and vent fuel pressure to 50-70 psig (345-485 kPa). • Key on, engine off. • Note pressure of IP sensor with Scan Tool. • Note pressure at schrader valve with pressure tester. • Key off. • Slowly open the 1/4 turn shut off valve. • **Is the IP sensor pressure constant and within 10 psi (70 kPa) of the pressure at the schrader valve?**	Yes No	▶ ▶	For NO starts: RETURN to Symptom Flowcharts. All others: GO to **HB10** GO to **HB7**.
HB7 VERIFY FUEL RAIL SOLENOID VALVE OPENS			
• Observe "WARNING, CAUTION and NOTE." • Key off. • Fuel Pressure Tester connected. • Scan Tool installed. • Close 1/4 turn manual shut off valve. • Release the fuel pressure back to the 1/4 turn manual shut off valve. • Slowly open the 1/4 turn manual valve. • Key on, engine off. • Access and enter the Output Test Mode. • Select "ALL ON" and then "ALL OFF" serveral times by toggling the trigger button on the Scan Tool and listening or feeling for a click at the fuel rail solenoid. • Key off. • **Was a click of the solenoid valve felt or heard?**	Yes No	▶ ▶	REPLACE Injection Pressure sensor. VERIFY a symptom no longer exists. GO to **HB8**.

Fig. 248   Test HB: Natural Gas Fuel Delivery System (Part 7 of 11). 1996

Test Step	Result	▶	Action to Take
HB8 CHECK FOR VOLTAGE AT THE FUEL RAIL SOLENOID VALVE VEHICLE HARNESS CONNECTOR			
• Key off. • Scan Tool connected. • Key on. • Enter Output Test Mode. • Select "All On." • Measure the voltage between the VPWR and the GND circuit at the fuel rail solenoid valve vehicle harness connector. • **Is the voltage reading greater than 10.5 volts?**	Yes No	▶ ▶	REPLACE fuel rail solenoid valve. VERIFY a symptom no longer exists. GO to **HB9**.
HB9 CHECK VPWR BETWEEN FUEL TANK SOLENOID VEHICLE HARNESS CONNECTOR AND BATTERY GROUND			
• Key off. • Scan Tool connected. • Key on. • Enter Output Test mode. • Select "All On." • Measure the voltage between the VPWR circuit at the fuel rail solenoid valve vehicle harness connector and battery ground. • **Is the voltage reading greater than 10.5 volts?**	Yes No	▶ ▶	SERVICE the open ground circuit at the vehicle harness connector. VERIFY a symptom no longer exists. SERVICE open VPWR circuit at the vehicle harness connector. VERIFY a symptom no longer exists.
HB10 VERIFY FUEL RAIL SOLENOID VALVE SEALS			
• Observe "WARNING, CAUTION and NOTE". • Key off. • Fuel Pressure Tester connected. • Scan Tool installed. • Close the 1/4 turn manual shut off valve. • Release the fuel pressure back to the 1/4 turn manual shut off valve. • Slowly open the 1/4 turn manual shut off valve. • After two minutes, note pressure of IP sensor with Scan Tool. • **Is pressure at IP sensor less than 10 psig (70 KPa)?**	Yes No	▶ ▶	GO to **HB11**. REPLACE solenoid valve. VERIFY a symptom no longer exists.

Fig. 248   Test HB: Natural Gas Fuel Delivery System (Part 8 of 11). 1996

Test Step	Result	▶	Action to Take
HB11 VERIFY FUEL RAIL SOLENOID VALVE PARTIALLY OPENS			
• Observe "WARNING, CAUTION and NOTE". • Key off. • Fuel Pressure Tester connected. • Scan Tool installed. • Close the 1/4 turn manual shut off valve. • Relieve pressure from injection supply manifold (fuel rail) back to the 1/4 turn manual valve. • Slowly open the 1/4 turn manual valve. • Key on, engine off. • Note pressure of IP sensor with Scan Tool. • Note pressure at schrader valve with pressure tester. • Key off. • **Is the IP sensor pressure within 10 psi (70 kPa) of the schrader valve pressure after keying on with the engine off?**	Yes No	▶ ▶	GO to **HB12** REPLACE solenoid valve. VERIFY a symptom no longer exists.
HB12 VERIFY FUEL RAIL SOLENOID VALVE FULLY OPENS			
• Observe "WARNING, CAUTION and NOTE". • Key off. • Fuel Pressure Tester connected. • Scan Tool installed. • Close the 1/4 turn manual shut off valve. • Relieve pressure from injection supply manifold (fuel rail) back to the 1/4 turn manual valve. • Slowly open the 1/4 turn manual valve. • Snap start engine (Key on and immediately start engine). • Immediately increase engine speed to approximately 2,500 rpm. • Note fuel pressure at schrader valve with fuel pressure tester. • Note IP sensor pressure with Scan Tool. • Key off. • **Is the IP sensor pressure within 10 psi (70 kPa) of the pressure at the schrader valve?**	Yes No	▶ ▶	GO to **HB13**. REPLACE solenoid valve. VERIFY a symptom no longer exists.

Fig. 248   Test HB: Natural Gas Fuel Delivery System (Part 9 of 11). 1996

Test Step	Result	▶	Action to Take
HB13 VEIRFY FUEL PRESSURE WITH ENGINE ON			
• Observe "WARNING, CAUTION and NOTE". • Key off. • Scan Tool installed. • Key on, engine running. • Note IP sensor pressure at idle with Scan Tool. • Increase engine speed to approximately 2,500 rpm. • Note IP sensor pressure at 2,500 rpm with Scan Tool. • Key off. • **Is idle pressure between 100 psig (690 KPa) and 125 psig (863 KPa) and is pressure at 2,500 rpm greater than 90 psig (620 KPa)?**	Yes No	▶ ▶	GO to **HB14** VERIFY a blockage does not exist in fuel lines. REPLACE fuel pressure regulator. VERIFY a symptom no longer exists.
HB14 VERIFY REGULATOR THERMOSTAT			
• Observe "WARNING, CAUTION and NOTE". • Key off. • Key on, engine on. • Allow engine coolant to reach normal operating temperature. • CAREFULLY measure the temperature of fuel pressure regulator coolant bowl or coolant outlet with a thermometer or temperature probe. • Key off. • **Is the regulator temperature between 15°C (59°F) and 60°C (140°F)?**	Yes No	▶ ▶	GO to **HB15**. If fuel regulator coolant bowl is less than 60°C (140°F): CHECK coolant lines and coolant system for proper operation. If OK, REPLACE fuel regulator coolant bowl. If fuel regulator coolant bowl is greater than 60°C (140°F): REPLACE regulator thermostat bowl. VERIFY a symptom no longer exists.
HB15 VERIFY FUEL INJECTOR FLOW			
NOTE: SBDS may be used for Injector Flow Testing when available. • Observe "WARNING, CAUTION and NOTE". • Key off. • Scan Tool installed. • Key on, engine off. • Note initial IP sensor pressure using the Scan Tool. • Electronic Fuel Injector Tester installed to suspect injector. • Select pulse width of 200 m sec. • Activate the injector tester. • Note final IP sensor pressure using Scan Tool. • Subtract final pressure from initial pressure. • Repeat above test procedures for all remaining injectors. • Key off. • **Is the pressure drop between 35 psig (207 kPa) and 50 psig) (345 kPa) and all injectors within 3 psi of each other?**	Yes No	▶ ▶	RETURN to Symptom Flowcharts, for additional symptom diagnostics. REPLACE injector(s) that does not meet pressure specification. VERIFY a symptom no longer exists.

Fig. 248   Test HB: Natural Gas Fuel Delivery System (Part 10 of 11). 1996

Test Step	Result	▶	Action to Take
HB20 FUEL LEAK CHECK			
NOTE: After the vehicle has soaked for several hours (hasn't run), a slight natural gas smell may emanate from within the intake manifold and air intake system. This is normal, as the injectors leak down from the fuel rail to the intake manifold over several hours. Possible causes: — Loose fitting connectors. — Damaged or worn seals or fittings. — Damaged fuel lines or fuel system components. ● Key off. ● Install fuel rail pressure gauge. ● Key on, engine off (verify pressure is greater than 90 psi). If the fuel system does have a fuel leak, it will be necessary to repeat this step to maintain pressure. ● Check for leaks with a soapy water solution such as Snoop, by covering the complete joint with this solution. Examine the components or joints for 60 seconds for signs of bubbles. ● Do any bubbles develop?	Yes No	▶ ▶	VERIFY proper torque. RECHECK for leaks. If leaks still exist, SERVICE or REPLACE as necessary. No leaks detected. NO further diagnostics required.

FM0159601513110X

Fig. 248   Test HB: Natural Gas Fuel Delivery System (Part 11 of 11). 1996

DEPOSIT RESISTANT INJECTOR APPLICATION AND TEST INFORMATION (Cont'd)

Engine Application	Part Number 9F593	Electrical Connector Color	Resistance Ohms	Flow # / Hr.	Rotunda Injector Tester Information	
					Flow Tube	Color Scale
Truck:						
2.3L	F57E-BB	Dk. Red	11-18	16	2A	White
3.0L	F47E-AD	Gray	11-18	14	1A	Gray
3.8L	F65E-AD	Dk. Gray	11-18	21	1A	Yellow
4.0L	92TF-AA	Red	11-18	19	2A	White
4.2L	F65E-AA	Dk. Gray	11-18	21	1A	Yellow
4.6L	F0TE-DA	Gold	11-18	19	1A	Yellow
4.9L	F0SE-BA	Gray	11-18	14	1A	Gray
5.0L	F2TE-AA	Gold	11-18	19	1A	Yellow
5.8L	F2TE-AA	Gold	11-18	19	1A	Yellow
7.0L	F0TE-DA	Gold	11-18	19	1A	Yellow
7.5L	F1TE-DA	Lt.Blue	11-18	24	2B	Lt. Blue

N / A = Not Applicable

WARNING

FUEL IN THE FUEL SYSTEM REMAINS UNDER HIGH PRESSURE EVEN WHEN THE ENGINE IS NOT RUNNING. TO AVOID INJURY OR FIRE, RELEASE THE FUEL PRESSURE FROM THE FUEL SYSTEM BEFORE DISCONNECTING ANY FUEL LINE. TO RELEASE THE PRESSURE FROM THE SYSTEM PERFORM THE FOLLOWING:

— CONNECT THE ROTUNDA FUEL PRESSURE TESTING KIT T80L-9974-B OR EQUIVALENT AT THE SCHRADER VALVE LOCATED ON THE FUEL RAIL. TESTING KIT VALVE SHOULD BE CLOSED.

— GRADUALLY OPEN THE TESTING KIT VALVE TO RELIEVE FUEL PRESSURE IN THE VEHICLE FUEL SYSTEM AND DRAIN THE FUEL INTO A SUITABLE CONTAINER OR RETURN IT TO THE FUEL TANK.

— TO AVOID UNNECESSARY FUEL SPILLAGE AND FIRE HAZARD ANY TIME FUEL LINES ARE DISCONNECTED, THE IGNITION SWITCH SHOULD BE IN THE OFF POSITION UNLESS FUEL PUMP OPERATION IS REQUIRED FOR TEST PURPOSES.

FM0159601514020X

Fig. 249   Test HC: Fuel Delivery System (Part 2 of 8). 1996

Note

You should enter this Pinpoint Test only when directed here.

Remember

This Pinpoint Test is intended to diagnose the following:

● Chassis Components
● Engine Vacuum
● Fuel Pressure
● Fuel Filter
● Fuel Return
● Fuel Supply
● Fuel Injector

Tables and Charts

DEPOSIT RESISTANT INJECTOR APPLICATION AND TEST INFORMATION

Engine Application	Part Number 9F593	Electrical Connector Color	Resistance Ohms	Flow # / Hr.	Rotunda Injector Tester Information	
					Flow Tube	Color Scale
Car:						
1.9L	F0SE-BA	Gray	11-18	14	1A	Gray
2.0L Contour / Mystique	968F-AB	Dk. Gray	11-18	21	2A	White
2.0L	F6CE-A5A	Tan	11-18	17	1A	Yellow
2.5L	F43E-AC	Gold	11-18	19	1A	Yellow
3.0L 2V	F47E-AE	Gray	11-18	14	1A	Gray
3.0L FFV	F6DE-AA	Green	11-18	25	2A	Green
3.0L 4V	F5DE-BA	Lt. Blue	11-18	24	2B	Lt. Blue
3.4L Taurus	F6DE-BA	Gold	11-18	19	1A	Yellow
3.8L	F1ZE-BC	Gray	11-18	14	1A	Gray
4.6L 2V	F4SE-AB	Gold	11-18	19	1A	Yellow
4.6L 2V	F0TE-DA	Gold	11-18	19	1A	Yellow
4.6L NG	F5TE-BA	Aqua	4-6	160	N/A	N/A
4.6L 4V	F55E-AE	Lt. Blue	11-18	24	2B	Lt. Blue

(Continued)

FM0159601514010X

Fig. 249   Test HC: Fuel Delivery System (Part 1 of 8). 1996

CAUTION

Use care to prevent combustion from fuel spillage. No smoking, open flames or any kind of arcing.

SAFE FUEL HANDLING PRACTICES

GASOLINE, METHANOL AND METHANOL BLENDS

FIRE
● REPORT ALL FIRES to the appropriate authorities.
● FLAMES from methanol or methanol-gasoline blends MAY BE INVISIBLE.
● Know the locations of PORTABLE FIRE EXTINGUISHERS, FIRE BLANKETS, FIRE ALARMS and EYE / WASH SHOWER FACILITIES. Learn how to use them.
● Use a B or AFFF (light water) type FIRE EXTINGUISHER to fight flammable liquid fires.

FIRST AID
● IF SWALLOWED:
— If GASOLINE has been swallowed, DO NOT induce vomiting. SEEK MEDICAL ATTENTION IMMEDIATELY!
— If METHANOL OR A METHANOL / GASOLINE BLEND has been swallowed, induce vomiting under the direction of a physician or Poison Control Center. SEEK MEDICAL ATTENTION IMMEDIATELY!
● When overcome by vapors, if safe, MOVE VICTIM TO FRESH AIR. If not breathing, give artificial respiration or CPR (Cardiopulmonary Resuscitation) as appropriate. SEEK MEDICAL ATTENTION IMMEDIATELY!
● If SPLASHED IN EYES, FLUSH with large amounts of water for 15 minutes. Remove contact lenses, if worn. SEEK MEDICAL ATTENTION.
● If SPLASHED ON SKIN, REMOVE CONTAMINATED CLOTHING. WASH SKIN thoroughly with soap and water.

HEALTH
● ALL FUELS may be HARMFUL OR FATAL IF SWALLOWED.
● BE AWARE, IF SWALLOWED, onset of serious health effects may be delayed 12 to 24 hours.
● FUELS AND PRODUCTS containing methanol (e.g. windshield washer fluid) may cause blindness if swallowed.
● ALL FUEL VAPORS may be HARMFUL BY INHALATION.

FM0159601514030X

Fig. 249   Test HC: Fuel Delivery System (Part 3 of 8). 1996

- ALL FUELS may be HARMFUL BY SKIN ABSORPTION.

- ALL FUELS are IRRITATING to the EYES and RESPIRATORY SYSTEM.

- FUELS made with GASOLINE may contain benzene which is a cancer-causing agent.

HANDLING

- Use FLAMMABLE LIQUID HANDLING PRECAUTIONS.

- Wear CHEMICAL GOGGLES and NITRILE GLOVES (additional protective clothing and equipment may be necessary in some instances).

- Keep flammable liquids in APPROVED, LABELED, CLOSED CONTAINERS.

- Use in WELL-VENTILATED AREAS and CONTROL VAPORS. Be aware that vapors ARE NOT VISIBLE, are heavier than air, can travel along the floor, and will settle in lower areas.

- When transferring flammable liquids, BOND the RECEIVING CONTAINER to the SOURCE and GROUND the SOURCE to the EARTH.

- DO NOT SMOKE or use HEAT/SPARK PRODUCING EQUIPMENT near vapors.

- DO NOT eat, smoke or drink where these products are handled, processed or stored.

- **NEVER** SIPHON BY MOUTH.

- WASH HANDS thoroughly after HANDLING any FUEL.

SPILLS

- Notify the proper authorities in the EVENT of any spill you have NOT been trained to clean up.

- STOP, CONTAIN, AND CLEAN UP small spills with an absorbent material.

Test Step	Result	▶	Action to Take
HC1 CHECK SYSTEM INTEGRITY • Key off. • Visually inspect the complete fuel delivery system, including fuel lines, connections, pump, pressure regulator and injector areas for leaks, looseness, cracks, kinks, pinching, or abrasion caused by an accident, collision, mishandling, etc. • Visually inspect electrical harness and connectors for loose pins, corrosion, abrasion, or other damage from accident, mishandling, etc. • Verify vehicle has followed maintenance schedule. • Verify Inertia Fuel Shutoff (IFS) switch set. • Verify vehicle battery is fully charged. • Verify electrical / fuse integrity. • Verify sufficient fuel in the tank. • **Has any problem been found?**	Yes No	▶ ▶	SERVICE as necessary. RERUN Quick Test. GO to HC2.

Fig. 249   Test HC: Fuel Delivery System (Part 4 of 8). 1996

Test Step	Result	▶	Action to Take
HC2 CHECK FUEL PRESSURE **WARNING: BEFORE SERVICING OR REPLACING ANY COMPONENTS IN THE FUEL SYSTEM, REDUCE THE POSSIBILITY OF INJURY OR FIRE BY FOLLOWING DIRECTIONS IN FUEL SYSTEM "CAUTION, HANDLING AND WARNING" AT THE BEGINNING OF THIS PINPOINT TEST.** • Key off. • Release the fuel pressure. • Install fuel pressure tester. • Scan Tool connected. • Key on, engine off. • Enter Output Test Mode (refer to Section 2A) and run the fuel pump to obtain maximum fuel pressure. • **Is fuel pressure between 35 and 40 psi (240-280 kPa)?**	Yes No	▶ ▶	GO to HC3. GO to HC9.
HC3 CHECK FUEL PRESSURE LEAKDOWN • Observe "Warning, Caution and Notes." • Fuel pressure tester installed. • Scan Tool connected. • Key on, engine off. • Enter Output Test Mode and run fuel pump to obtain maximum fuel pressure. • Exit Output Test Mode, key off. • Verify fuel pressure remains within 5 psi of the maximum pressure for 1 minute after turning pump off. • **Does fuel pressure remain within 5 psi?**	Yes No	▶ ▶	GO to HC5. GO to HC4.
HC4 CHECK PRESSURE REGULATOR DIAPHRAGM • Key off. • Fuel pressure tester installed. • Start and run engine for 10 seconds. • Key off, wait 10 seconds. • Start and run engine for 10 seconds. • Key off, remove vacuum hose from fuel pressure regulator. • Inspect for fuel in the vacuum hose or regulator port. • **Is vacuum hose and regulator port free of fuel?**	Yes No	▶ ▶	GO to HC11. REPLACE fuel pressure regulator. RERUN Quick Test.

Fig. 249   Test HC: Fuel Delivery System (Part 5 of 8). 1996

Test Step	Result	▶	Action to Take
HC5 CHECK FUEL PRESSURE, ENGINE RUNNING • Key off. • Fuel pressure tester installed. • Disconnect vacuum hose at the fuel pressure regulator and plug it. • Drive vehicle with heavy accelerations while observing fuel pressure gauge reading. • **Does fuel pressure reading hold steady within 3 psi during test?**	Yes No	▶ ▶	UNPLUG vacuum hose and RECONNECT to the regulator. GO to HC6. GO to HC8.
HC6 CHECK FUEL PRESSURE REGULATOR RESPONSE TO VACUUM • Key off. • Fuel pressure tester installed. • Install vacuum gauge to intake manifold. • Start engine and observe both gauges. • Accelerate and decelerate engine speed to vary the vacuum gauge reading. • **Does fuel pressure gauge reading increase as vacuum gauge reading decreases, or decrease as vacuum gauge reading increases?**	Yes No	▶ ▶	REMOVE vacuum gauge and fuel pressure tester. Problem is elsewhere. RETURN to Symptom Flow Charts, for further direction. GO to HC7.
HC7 CHECK VACUUM SUPPLY • Key off. • Fuel pressure tester installed. • Vacuum hose disconnected and plugged at the regulator. • Install hand held vacuum pump to the fuel pressure regulator. • Start engine, run at idle. • Observe fuel pressure while applying vacuum. • **Does the fuel pressure change as the vacuum changes?**	Yes No	▶ ▶	SERVICE vacuum system. UNPLUG vacuum hose and RECONNECT to the pressure regulator. RERUN Quick Test. REPLACE fuel pressure regulator. RERUN Quick Test.
HC8 CHECK FUEL FILTER • Observe "Warning, Caution and Handling" at the beginning of this pinpoint test. • Key off. • Scan Tool connected. • Replace in-line fuel filter, if not replaced recently (check maintenance log). • Key on, engine off. • Enter Output Test Mode (OTM) to run the fuel pump. • Check fuel pressure. • **Is fuel pressure within specification?**	Yes No	▶ ▶	GO to HC11. GO to HC12.

Fig. 249   Test HC: Fuel Delivery System (Part 6 of 8). 1996

Test Step	Result	▶	Action to Take
HC9 CHECK REGULATOR FOR CAUSE OF HIGH PRESSURE CAUSE • Key off. • Scan Tool connected. • Remove fuel return line at the fuel rail and connect a short hose from rail to a measured container of at least one quart capacity. • Key on, engine off. • Enter Output Test Mode (OTM) (refer to Section 2A) and run the fuel pump. • Record fuel pressure reading and note whether fuel is being returned to the measured container. • Exit OTM to shut off the fuel pump, key off. • **Is fuel pressure between 35 and 40 psi (240-280 kPa) and is fuel returning to the container?**	Yes No	▶ ▶	GO to HC10. Fuel Pressure greater than 45 psi (290 kPa), REPLACE Fuel Pressure Regulator. No fuel pressure, GO to HC12.
HC10 CHECK FUEL RETURN SYSTEM • Key off. • Observe "Warning, Caution and Handling" at the beginning of this pinpoint test. • Fuel line disconnected at the fuel pressure regulator. • Check the fuel return system for restriction due to blockage, kinking, or pinching. • Disconnect the fuel return line near the fuel tank. • Apply 3-5 psi regulated shop air to the return line at the pressure regulator side. • **Does air flow freely through the line?**	Yes No	▶ ▶	REPLACE the fuel pump assembly. RERUN Quick Test. SERVICE the fuel return line. RERUN Quick Test.
HC11 CHECK FUEL INJECTOR LEAKAGE AND FLOW • Key off. • Observe "Warning, Caution and Handling" at the beginning of this Pinpoint Test. • Check injectors for leakage and flow rate, using Rotunda Injector Tester 113-00001 and Rotunda Fuel Pump Check Valve-Pressure Regulator and Injector Leakage Tool 113-00010, SBDS Injector Tester or equivalent. • **Is the flow rate for each injector within specification?**	Yes No	▶ ▶	VERIFY no other leaks. If none are found, REPLACE fuel pump assembly. RERUN Quick Test. REPLACE the defective injector. RECONNECT all components. RERUN Quick Test.

Fig. 249   Test HC: Fuel Delivery System (Part 7 of 8). 1996

Test Step	Result	▶	Action to Take
HC12 CHECK FUEL PUMP VOLTAGE			
• Key off. • Scan tool connected. • Disconnect the electrical fuel pump vehicle harness connector. Inspect for damaged or pushed out pins, corrosion, loose wires, etc. Service as necessary. • Key on, engine off. • Enter Output Test Mode and turn on the fuel pump circuit. • Use DVOM to check voltage to the fuel pump, at the fuel pump connector, fuel pump relay, VCRM or CCRM. (Refer to the EVTM for the specified vehicle.) • **Is the voltage greater than 10.5 volts?**	Yes	▶	CHECK for fuel pump ground connection, SERVICE as required. If OK, REPLACE fuel pump. RECONNECT all components. GO to **HC2** for verification.
	No	▶	LOCATE cause of low voltage in fuel pump circuit. SERVICE as required. GO to **HC2** for verification.

FM0159601514080X

Fig. 249   Test HC: Fuel Delivery System (Part 8 of 8). 1996

Crankshaft Position (CKP) Sensor (Variable Reluctance)

CKP SENSOR

CRANKSHAFT WHEEL

Powertrain Control Module (PCM)

ICM

Ignition Control Module (ICM)

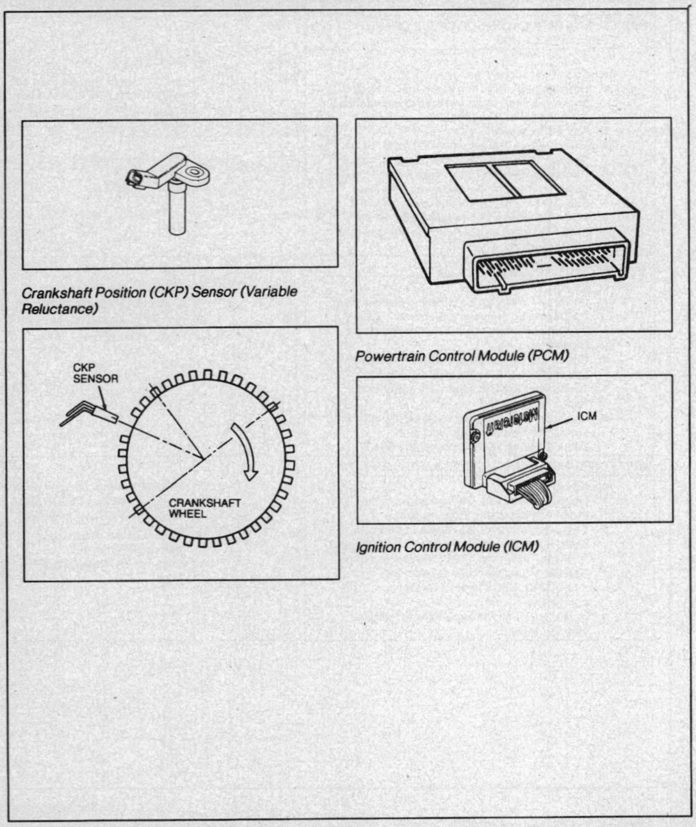

FM0159601515020X

Fig. 250   Test HD: Misfire Detection Monitor (Part 2 of 8). 1996

Note

You should enter this Pinpoint Test only when directed here.

Remember

This Pinpoint Test is intended to diagnose the following:

• Ignition System
• Fuel Injectors
• Fuel Pressure
• Vacuum System
• Evaporative System
• EVAP Canister Purge Solenoid
• Base Engine

FM0159601515010X

Fig. 250   Test HD: Misfire Detection Monitor (Part 1 of 8). 1996

Test Step	Result	▶	Action to Take
HD1 CHECK POSSIBLE CAUSES TO MISFIRE			
Misfire Continuous Memory Diagnostic Trouble Codes (DTCs): P0301 - Cyl # 1, Inj Test Pin 75 P0302 - Cyl # 2, Inj Test Pin 101 P0303 - Cyl # 3, Inj Test Pin 74 P0304 - Cyl # 4, Inj Test Pin 100 P0305 - Cyl # 5, Inj Test Pin 73 P0306 - Cyl # 6, Inj Test Pin 99 P0307 - Cyl # 7, Inj Test Pin 72 P0308 - Cyl # 8, Inj Test Pin 98 P0300 - multiple cylinders misfiring, or cannot identify cylinder due to Camshaft Position sensor failure. Possible causes: — Ignition System. — Fuel Injectors. — Fuel Pressure. — Evaporative System. — Canister Purge. — Base Engine. — Running out of fuel. NOTE: Running out of fuel may turn on the MIL and possibly store a Continuous Misfire DTC. • **Has the vehicle recently run out of fuel?**	Yes	▶	OBD II system OK. COMPLETE PCM RESET to clear DTCs (REFER to Powertrain Control Module (PCM) Reset). RETURN vehicle to customer.
	No	▶	GO to **HD2**.
HD2 CHECK FOR OTHER CONTINUOUS MEMORY DTCS			
NOTE: Check for other Continuous Memory DTCs which could cause the misfire DTC. Possible causes: — Camshaft Position Sensor (CID). — Octane Adjust (Oct Adj). — Ignition Coil Primary Circuit. — Knock Sensor (KS). • **Are there any other Continuous Memory DTCs present?**	Yes	▶	ADDRESS the next Continuous Memory DTC. DISREGARD Misfire DTC at this time. GO to for Powertrain DTC Charts.
	No	▶	GO to **HD3**.
HD3 CHECK FOR ON-DEMAND SELF-TEST DTCS			
NOTE: Check for any key on, engine off DTCs which could cause the Misfire DTC. • **Are any Key On Engine Off or DTCs displayed on the Scan Tool?**	Yes	▶	GO to , Powertrain DTC Charts, and PROCEED as required.
	No	▶	GO to Pinpoint Test Step **JB1** to evaluate spark plugs and secondary wires. If OK, GO to **HD4**.

FM0159601515030X

Fig. 250   Test HD: Misfire Detection Monitor (Part 3 of 8). 1996

Test Step	Result	▶	Action to Take
HD4 CHECK FOR OTHER KEY ON ENGINE RUNNING DTCS			
NOTE: Check for any other key on, engine running DTCs which could cause the Misfire DTC. • **Are any additional key on, engine running DTCs displayed on the Scan Tool?**	Yes No	▶ ▶	If DTCs P1131 or P1151 are present, GO to HD8. All others: GO to Section 5A, Powertrain DTC Charts, and proceed as required. GO to HD5 for misfire DTC.
HD5 CHECK / COMPARE PID VALUES			
• Key off. • Connect Scan Tool. • Accessories off (A/C, heater, etc.). • Start engine and warm to normal operating temperature. • Access (DPFEGR) PID with the Scan Tool. • Key on, engine off. • Record DPFEGR PID value. • Start engine, let idle. • Compare key on, engine off and engine running DPFEGR values. • **Was engine running DPFEGR value within 0.15 volt of key on, engine off value?**	Yes No	▶ ▶	Disconnect Scan Tool. GO to HD8. GO to Pinpoint Test Step HE100.
HD8 CHECK RESISTANCE OF INJECTOR(S) AND HARNESS			
• Key off. • Disconnect PCM. Inspect for damaged or pushed out pins, corrosion, loose wires etc. Service as necessary. NOTE: This erases Continuous Memory DTCs. • Install breakout box, leave PCM disconnected. • Measure resistance between suspect injector test pin and Test Pin 71 or 97 at the breakout box. Refer to the list in HD1. • **Is the resistance between 11.0-18.0 ohms?**	Yes No	▶ ▶	Injector and harness resistance is OK, GO to HD9. GO to Pinpoint Test Step H48 to evaluate fuel injectors.
HD9 CHECK INJECTOR DRIVER SIGNAL			
NOTE: Requires a standard 12 volt test lamp. • Key off. • Breakout box installed. • Connect PCM to breakout box. • Connect Test Lamp between Test Pin 71 or 97 and suspect injector test pin. • Start engine. • **Does test lamp have a dim glow while running engine?** NOTE: Properly operating system will show a dim glow on the Test Lamp.	Yes No	▶ ▶	GO to HD10. No light or bright light. REPLACE PCM. REMOVE breakout box. RERUN Quick Test.

FM0159601515040X

Fig. 250   Test HD: Misfire Detection Monitor (Part 4 of 8). 1996

Test Step	Result	▶	Action to Take
HD10 CHECK FUEL PRESSURE			
WARNING: THE FUEL SYSTEM WILL REMAIN PRESSURIZED WHEN ENGINE IS NOT RUNNING. TO PREVENT INJURY OR FIRE, USE CAUTION WHILE WORKING ON THE FUEL SYSTEM. • Key off. • Install fuel pressure gauge. • Start and run engine at idle. Record fuel pressure. • Increase engine speed to 2500 rpms and maintain for one minute. Note and compare fuel pressure. • **Is fuel pressure between 30-45 psi (210-310 kPa)?**	Yes No	▶ ▶	GO to HD11.
HD11 CHECK ABILITY OF FUEL SYSTEM TO HOLD FUEL PRESSURE			
• Start and run engine at idle. Note fuel pressure. • Increase engine speed to 2500 rpms and maintain for one minute. • Visually look for fuel leaking at the injector O-ring, fuel pressure regulator and the fuel lines to the fuel charging assembly. Service as necessary. • Turn engine off. • Key on, engine off. • **Does fuel pressure remain at specification within 5 psi for 60 seconds?**	Yes No	▶ ▶	GO to HD12. determine which area within the Fuel Delivery System is at fault.
HD12 CHECK FUEL INJECTOR FOR FLOW AND LEAKAGE			
• Refer to "Warning, Caution and Handling" at the beginning of Pinpoint Test HC to avoid fuel spillage and injury. • Verify that the flow rate for each fuel injector is within specification using Rotunda Injector Tester 113-00001, SBDS Injector Flow Tester or equivalent. • **Is flow rate for each injector within specification?**	Yes No	▶ ▶	Fuel Delivery System is not considered the likely area to have caused the Misfire DTC. GO to HD20 to evaluate the Vacuum System. REPLACE or CLEAN the defective injector(s) as required. RERUN Quick Test.

FM0159601515050X

Fig. 250   Test HD: Misfire Detection Monitor (Part 5 of 8). 1996

Test Step	Result	▶	Action to Take
HD20 CHECK VACUUM SYSTEM			
• Visually inspect all vacuum lines for damage, such as pinched lines, cracks, proper routing and assembly. • Refer to the Electrical and Vacuum Troubleshooting Manual (EVTM) for vacuum service information and repair. NOTE: Some vacuum leaks can be found audibly. • **Is the vehicle vacuum system OK?**	Yes No	▶ ▶	GO to HD21. SERVICE the vacuum system. REFER to the EVTM. RERUN Quick Test.
HD21 CHECK EVAPORATIVE EMISSION SYSTEM			
The Misfire Monitor can be influenced by Evaporative Emission System. The next four pinpoint test steps will evaluate the Evaporative Emission System. • Check the carbon canister for fuel saturation. • **Is there an excess amount of liquid fuel present in the canister?**	Yes No	▶ ▶	REPLACE carbon canister. RERUN Quick Test. GO to HD22. CHECK fuel tank vent system.
HD22 PRESSURE TEST EVAPORATIVE SYSTEM			
• Remove vapor line at canister. • Install a TEE in the line. • Install a pressure gauge to one side of TEE. • Supply air to the other side of TEE, up to a maximum of .75 psi. • **Is evaporative emission system holding pressure?**	Yes No	▶ ▶	RECONNECT canister line, GO to HD23. SERVICE as necessary. RERUN Quick Test.
HD23 CHECK VACUUM IN EVAPORATIVE SYSTEM			
• Check for blockage/restrictions or cut hoses between engine vacuum port and carbon canister. • Check for blockage in fuel tank vent system. • **Is there a fault indicated?**	Yes No	▶ ▶	REPLACE damaged vacuum hoses, or REMOVE blockage/restrictions. RERUN Quick Test. For vehicles with EVAP canister purge solenoid: GO to HD24. For vehicles with VMV: GO to HD26.

FM0159601515060X

Fig. 250   Test HD: Misfire Detection Monitor (Part 6 of 8). 1996

Test Step	Result	▶	Action to Take
HD24 CHECK EVAP CANISTER PURGE SOLENOID			
This pinpoint test step will verify the mechanical integrity of EVAP canister purge solenoid. The solenoid and circuit have been checked electrically and reported during KOEO Self-Test. • Key off. • Disconnect EVAP canister purge solenoid. • Connect 12 volt DC power source to solenoid. **CAUTION must be observed for proper pin orientation. Refer to the vehicle electrical schematic in** • Connect positive power source to VPWR circuit and negative lead to EVAP canister purge circuit at the EVAP canister purge solenoid harness connector. • Apply 53 kPa (16 in-Hg) of vacuum to the manifold side of the EVAP canister purge solenoid. Apply power source. • **Does the solenoid open and pass air freely?**	Yes No	▶ ▶	Evaporative System is functioning properly. GO to HD25 for Base Engine concerns. REPLACE EVAP Canister Purge solenoid. RERUN Quick Test.
HD25 CHECK FOR BASE ENGINE CONCERNS			
The purpose of this pinpoint test step is to determine if there are any base engine concerns that may have caused the Misfire DTC or drive concern. Perform the following tests in order to evaluate base engine integrity. • Perform an Engine Compression test. • Perform Dynamic Valve Train analysis. • Check Positive Crankcase Ventilation System. • Check possible leakage points. Refer to the Diagnosis and Testing pages in the Engine Group Service Manual for all of the above repair procedures. • **Is any service required?**	Yes No	▶ ▶	RERUN Quick Test. The cause of the Misfire DTC is intermittent and diagnosis will be in the Ignition System. GO to the Ignition Intermittent procedure in Pinpoint Test Step Z50. FOLLOW instructions for using the Ignition Intermittent Analyzer, also known as the DIST tool.
HD26 CHECKF OR VMV HOUSING LEAKS			
• Key off. • VMV electrically connected. • Install a hand vacuum pump to the fuel vapor port to carbon canister on the VMV.k vacuum at line. • Apply 16 in-Hg (53 kPa) of vacuum with the vacuum pump. • **Does the VMV hold vacuum at room temperature?**	Yes No	▶ ▶	GO to HD27. REMOVE vacuum pump. REPLACE damaged VMV. RECONNECT all components. COMPLETE PCM Reset to clear DTCs (REFER to Powertrain Control Module (PCM) Reset). RERUN Quick Test.

FM0159601515070X

Fig. 250   Test HD: Misfire Detection Monitor (Part 7 of 8). 1996

Test Step	Result	▶	Action to Take
HD27 CHECK FOR FILTER CONTAMINATION OR DAMAGE ON VMV			
• Key off. • Vacuum line from input vacuum port to intake manifold on the VMV (control vacuum solenoid part of valve) is removed. • Install a hand held vacuum pump to the open input vacuum port on the VMV. • Apply 10-15 in-Hg (48-52 kPa) of vacuum to the VMV. • **Does the VMV hold vacuum or very slow to release vacuum to atmosphere?**	Yes	▶	SERVICE VMV filter. If unable to clean filter or REMOVE blockage to filter, REPLACE VMV. RECONNECT all components. COMPLETE PCM Reset to clear DTCs (REFER to Powertrain Control Module (PCM) Reset). RERUN Quick Test.
	No	▶	REMOVE vacuum pump. RECONNECT all components. GO to **HD25**.

FM0159601515080X

Fig. 250   Test HD: Misfire Detection Monitor (Part 8 of 8). 1996

Note

You should enter this Pinpoint Test only when directed here.

Remember

This Pinpoint Test is intended to diagnose the following:

• Differential Pressure Feedback EGR (D.P.F. EGR) Sensor (9J460)
• Exhaust Gas Recirculation (EGR) Valve (9D460) (9D475)
• EGR Vacuum Regulator (EGR V.R.) Solenoid (9J459)
• Orifice Tube Assembly (9D477)
• D.P.F. EGR Sensor Pressure Hoses
• Vacuum Lines
• Harness Circuits: VREF, DPFE, SIG, SIG RTN, EVR, EVR PWR
• Powertrain Control Module (PCM) (12A650)

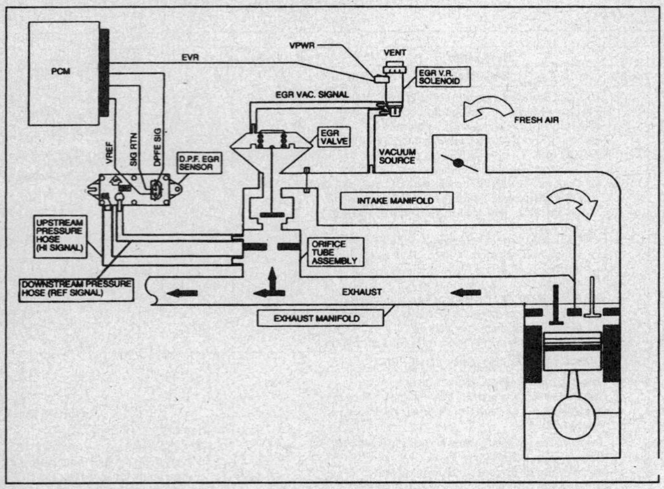

FM0159601516010X

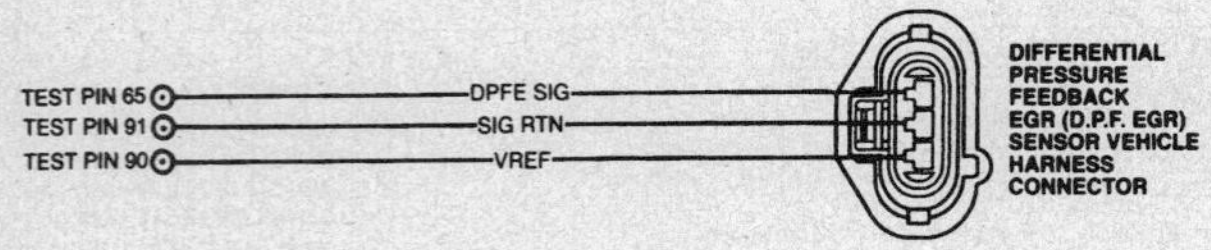

Fig. 251   Test HE: Exhaust Gas Recirculation Systems (Part 1 of 37). 1996

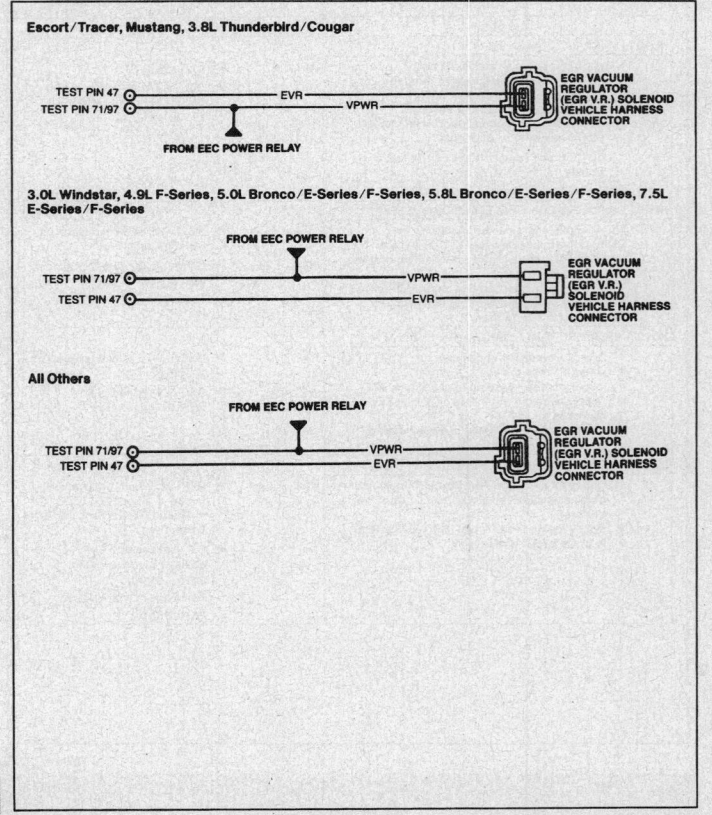

Fig. 251   Test HE: Exhaust Gas Recirculation Systems (Part 2 of 37). 1996

FM0159601516020X

FM0159601516030X

Fig. 251   Test HE: Exhaust Gas Recirculation Systems (Part 3 of 37). 1996

ELECTRONIC ENGINE CONTROL SYSTEM (EEC-V)

Test Step	Result	▶	Action to Take
HE1 DTC P1400: VERIFY DIFFERENTIAL PRESSURE FEEDBACK EGR (D.P.F. EGR) VOLTAGE			
Diagnostic Trouble Code (DTC) P1400 indicates that Self-Test has detected DPFE SIG circuit input below the minimum. Possible causes: — Leaking upstream pressure hose. — DPFE SIG shorted to GND or SIG RTN. — VREF shorted to GND or SIG RTN. — Damaged D.P.F. EGR sensor. — Damaged PCM. ● Key off, engine off. ● Access DPFEGR PID (formerly DPFE) with a Scan Tool. NOTE: D.P.F. EGR sensor input with no EGR flow is 0.45 volts ± 0.25 volts. ● **Is DPFEGR PID voltage less than 0.2 volts?**	Yes No	▶ ▶	The D.P.F. EGR sensor voltage is less than the acceptable minimum. GO to **HE2**. INSPECT pressure signal hoses for leaks. SERVICE as necessary. If OK, fault that produced DTC P1400 is intermittent. GO to **HE6**.
HE2 INDUCE OPPOSITE D.P.F. EGR SIGNAL			
● Key off. ● Disconnect D.P.F. EGR sensor vehicle harness connector. ● Connect a jumper wire between the sensor VREF circuit and DPFE SIG circuit at the D.P.F. EGR sensor vehicle harness connector. ● Key on, engine off. NOTE: If a Scan Tool communication problem exists, remove jumper immediately and go directly to **HE3**. ● Access DPFEGR PID with a Scan Tool. ● **Is DPFEGR PID value between 4.0 and 6.0 volts?**	Yes No	▶ ▶	REPLACE damaged D.P.F. EGR sensor. RECONNECT all components. COMPLETE PCM Reset to clear DTCs (REFER to , Powertrain Control Module (PCM) Reset). RERUN Quick Test. REMOVE jumper. GO to **HE3**.
HE3 MEASURE VREF VOLTAGE AT D.P.F. EGR SENSOR VEHICLE HARNESS CONNECTOR			
● D.P.F. EGR sensor disconnected. ● Key on, engine off. ● Measure voltage between the sensor VREF circuit and SIG RTN circuit at the D.P.F. EGR sensor vehicle harness connector. ● **Is VREF voltage between 4.0 and 6.0 volts?**	Yes No	▶ ▶	GO to **HE4**. VREF voltage is out of range. GO to Pinpoint Test Step **C1**.

FM0159601516040X

Fig. 251   Test HE: Exhaust Gas Recirculation Systems (Part 4 of 37). 1996

Test Step	Result	▶	Action to Take
HE4 CHECK DPFE SIG CIRCUIT FOR SHORTS TO GROUND AND SIG RTN			
● Key off. ● D.P.F. EGR sensor disconnected. ● Disconnect Scan Tool from DLC. ● Disconnect PCM. Inspect for damaged or pushed out pins, corrosion, loose wires, etc. Service as necessary. ● Install breakout box, leave PCM disconnected. ● Measure resistance between Test Pin 65 (DPFE SIG) and Test Pins 91 (SIG RTN), 51 (PWR GND) and 103 (PWR GND) at the breakout box. ● **Is each resistance greater than 10,000 ohms?**	Yes No	▶ ▶	REPLACE damaged PCM. REMOVE breakout box. RECONNECT all components. RERUN Quick Test. SERVICE short circuit between DPFE SIG and GROUND or SIG RTN. REMOVE breakout box. RECONNECT all components. RERUN Quick Test.
HE6 WIGGLE TEST SENSOR AND HARNESS			
● Key on, engine off. ● Access DPFEGR PID with a Scan Tool. ● Observe DPFEGR PID for an indication of a fault while performing the following: — Lightly tap on D.P.F. EGR sensor. Wiggle the D.P.F. EGR sensor connector and vehicle harness between sensor and PCM. A fault is indicated by a sudden change in DPFEGR PID voltage. ● **Is a fault indicated?**	Yes No	▶ ▶	ISOLATE fault and SERVICE as necessary. RECONNECT all components. COMPLETE PCM Reset to clear DTCs (REFER to , Powertrain Control Module (PCM) Reset). RERUN Quick Test. Unable to duplicate and/or identify fault at this time. GO to Pinpoint Test Step **Z1** with the following data: DPFEGR and EGRVR (formerly EVR) PIDs and list of possible causes.
HE10 DTC P1401: VERIFY DIFFERENTIAL PRESSURE FEEDBACK EGR (D.P.F. EGR) SENSOR VOLTAGE			
Diagnostic Trouble Code (DTC) P1401 indicates that Self-Test has detected DPFE SIG circuit input above the maximum. Possible causes: — DPFE SIG open. — DPFE SIG shorted to VREF or PWR. — VREF shorted to PWR. — SIG RTN open. — Damaged D.P.F. EGR sensor. — Damaged PCM. ● Key on, engine off. ● Access D.P.F. EGR sensor (formerly DPFE) with a Scan Tool. NOTE: D.P.F. EGR sensor input with no EGR flow is 0.45 volts ± 0.25 volts. ● **Is DPFEGR PID voltage greater than 4.0 volts?**	Yes No	▶ ▶	The D.P.F. EGR sensor voltage is greater than the acceptable maximum. GO to **HE11**. The fault that produced DTC P1401 is intermittent. GO to **HE19**.

FM0159601516050X

Fig. 251   Test HE: Exhaust Gas Recirculation Systems (Part 5 of 37). 1996

Test Step	Result	▶	Action to Take
HE11 CHECK DPFE SIG FOR SHORT TO PWR			
● Key off. ● Disconnect D.P.F. EGR sensor vehicle harness connector. ● Key on, engine off. ● Measure voltage between DPFE SIG circuit at the D.P.F. EGR sensor vehicle harness connector and battery ground. ● **Is voltage greater than 10.5 volts?**	Yes No	▶ ▶	The D.P.F. EGR sensor voltage input is indicating a short to PWR. GO to **HE12**. GO to **HE13**.
HE12 CHECK DPFE SIG FOR SHORT TO PWR IN HARNESS			
● Key off. ● D.P.F. EGR sensor disconnected. ● Disconnect PCM. Inspect for damaged or pushed out pins, corrosion, loose wires, etc. Service as necessary. ● Install breakout box, leave PCM disconnected. ● Key on, engine off. ● Measure voltage between Test Pin 65 (DPFE SIG) and Test Pins 51 and 103 (PWR GND) at the breakout box. ● **Is voltage greater than 10.5 volts?**	Yes No	▶ ▶	SERVICE short between DPFE SIG and PWR circuit. REMOVE breakout box. RECONNECT all components. RERUN Quick Test. REPLACE damaged PCM. REMOVE breakout box. RECONNECT all components. RERUN Quick Test.
HE13 INDUCE OPPOSITE D.P.F. EGR SENSOR SIGNAL			
● Key off. ● Disconnect D.P.F. EGR sensor vehicle harness connector. ● Connect a jumper wire between the sensor DPFE SIG circuit and SIG RTN circuit at the D.P.F. EGR sensor vehicle harness connector. ● Key on, engine off. NOTE: If a Scan Tool communication problem exists, remove jumper immediately and go directly to **HE18**. ● Access DPFEGR PID with a Scan Tool. ● **Is DPFEGR PID voltage less than 0.05 volts?**	Yes No	▶ ▶	REMOVE jumper. GO to **HE14**. Unable to induce opposite signal. GO to **HE16**.
HE14 VERIFY THAT VREF IS IN RANGE			
● D.P.F. EGR sensor disconnected. ● Key on, engine off. ● Measure voltage between the sensor VREF circuit and SIG RTN circuit at the D.P.F. EGR sensor vehicle harness connector. ● **Is VREF voltage between 4.0 and 6.0 volts?**	Yes No	▶ ▶	GO to **HE15**. VREF voltage is out of range. GO to Pinpoint Test Step **C1**.

FM0159601516060X

Fig. 251   Test HE: Exhaust Gas Recirculation Systems (Part 6 of 37). 1996

Test Step	Result	▶	Action to Take
HE15 CHECK DPFE SIG FOR SHORT TO VREF IN HARNESS			
● Key off. ● D.P.F. EGR sensor disconnected. ● Disconnect PCM. Inspect for damaged or pushed out pins, corrosion, loose wires, etc. Service as necessary. ● Install breakout box, leave PCM disconnected. ● Measure resistance between Test Pin 65 (DPFE SIG) and Test Pin 90 (VREF) at the breakout box. ● **Is resistance greater than 10,000 ohms?**	Yes No	▶ ▶	REPLACE damaged D.P.F. EGR sensor. REMOVE breakout box. RECONNECT all components. RERUN Quick Test. SERVICE short between DPFE SIG and VREF circuit. REMOVE breakout box. RECONNECT all components. RERUN Quick Test.
HE16 CHECK DPFE SIG FOR OPEN IN HARNESS			
● Key off. ● D.P.F. EGR sensor disconnected. ● Disconnect PCM. Inspect for damaged or pushed out pins, corrosion, loose wires, etc. Service as necessary. ● Install breakout box, leave PCM disconnected. ● Measure resistance between Test Pin 65 (DPFE SIG) and DPFE SIG circuit at the D.P.F. EGR sensor vehicle harness connector. ● **Is resistance less than 5.0 ohms?**	Yes No	▶ ▶	GO to **HE17**. SERVICE open in DPFE SIG circuit. REMOVE breakout box. RECONNECT all components. RERUN Quick Test.
HE17 CHECK SIG RTN FOR OPEN IN HARNESS			
● Key off. ● D.P.F. EGR sensor disconnected. ● Breakout box installed, PCM disconnected. ● Measure resistance between Test Pin 91 (SIG RTN) and SIG RTN circuit at the D.P.F. EGR sensor vehicle harness connector. ● **Is resistance less than 5.0 ohms?**	Yes No	▶ ▶	REPLACE damaged PCM. REMOVE breakout box. RECONNECT all components. RERUN Quick Test. SERVICE open in SIG RTN circuit. REMOVE breakout box. RECONNECT all components. RERUN Quick Test.
HE18 CHECK DPFE SIG FOR SHORT TO VREF IN HARNESS			
● Key off. ● D.P.F. EGR sensor disconnected. ● Disconnect PCM. Inspect for damaged or pushed out pins, corrosion, loose wires, etc. Service as necessary. ● Install breakout box, leave PCM disconnected. ● Measure resistance between Test Pin 65 (DPFE SIG) and Test Pin 90 (VREF) at the breakout box. ● **Is resistance greater than 10,000 ohms?**	Yes No	▶ ▶	REPLACE damaged PCM. REMOVE breakout box. RECONNECT all components. RERUN Quick Test. SERVICE short between DPFE SIG and VREF circuit. REMOVE breakout box. RECONNECT all components. RERUN Quick Test.

FM0159601516070X

Fig. 251   Test HE: Exhaust Gas Recirculation Systems (Part 7 of 37). 1996

FORD—Electronic Engine Controls

Test Step	Result	▶	Action to Take
HE19 WIGGLE TEST SENSOR AND HARNESS • Key on, engine off. • Access DPFEGR PID with a Scan Tool. • Observe DPFEGR PID for an indication of a fault while performing the following: — Lightly tap on D.P.F. EGR sensor; wiggle the D.P.F. EGR sensor connector and vehicle harness between sensor and PCM. A fault is indicated by a sudden change in DPFEGR PID voltage. • Is a fault indicated?	Yes No	▶ ▶	ISOLATE fault and SERVICE as necessary. RECONNECT all components. COMPLETE PCM Reset to clear DTCs (REFER to Powertrain Control Module (PCM) Reset). RERUN Quick Test. Unable to duplicate and/or identify fault at this time. GO to Pinpoint Test Step **Z1** with the following data: DPFEGR and EGRVR (formerly EVR) PIDS and list of Possible Causes.
HE20 DTC P0402: CHECK FOR EGR FLOW AT IDLE WITH EGR VACUUM HOSE DISCONNECTED Diagnostic Trouble Code (DTC) P0402 indicates that Self-Test has detected EGR flow at idle. NOTE: If DTC P1405 is in Continuous Memory, diagnose that first starting with HE50. Possible causes: — EGR valve stuck open. — EGR vacuum regulator (EGR V.R.) solenoid vent plugged or iced. — EVR circuit shorted to GND. — EVR circuit shorted to VREF. — Pinched/iced pressure hoses. — Improper vacuum hose connection. — Plugged/pinched EGR V.R. vacuum hose. — Plugged EGR tube. — Damaged EGR V.R. solenoid. — Damaged Differential Pressure Feedback EGR (D.P.F. EGR) sensor. — Damaged PCM. • Key off. • Disconnect vacuum hose at EGR valve and plug hose. • Run Key On Engine Running (KOER) Self-Test. • Is KOER DTC P0402 output or unable to run KOER Self-Test due to engine stall or no start?	Yes No	▶ ▶	There is possible EGR flow at idle. INSPECT pressure hoses first for pinching and icing. If OK, REMOVE and INSPECT the EGR valve and EGR tube for signs of contamination, unusual wear, carbon deposits, binding and other damage. SERVICE as necessary (use Rotunda EGR Valve Cleaner 021-00056, if needed). RECONNECT all components. COMPLETE PCM Reset to clear DTCs (REFER to Powertrain Control Module (PCM) Reset). RERUN Quick Test. RECONNECT vacuum hose to EGR valve. GO to **HE21**.

FM0159601516080X

Fig. 251   Test HE: Exhaust Gas Recirculation Systems (Part 8 of 37). 1996

Test Step	Result	▶	Action to Take
HE21 CHECK FOR EGR FLOW AT IDLE WITH EGR VACUUM HOSE CONNECTED • Key off. • EGR vacuum hose connected. • Run KOER Self-Test. • Is KOER DTC P0402 output or unable to run KOER Self-Test due to engine stall or no start?	Yes No	▶ ▶	There is possible EGR flow at idle. GO to **HE22**. The fault that produced DTC P0402 is intermittent. INSPECT pressure hoses for pinching and icing. SERVICE as necessary If OK, GO to **HE30**.
HE22 CHECK EGR SYSTEM VACUUM HOSES FOR INTEGRITY AND CONNECTION NOTE: A pinched or plugged EGR vacuum hose can trap vacuum between the EGR V.R. solenoid and EGR valve not allowing the EGR valve to close. • Key off. • Trace each vacuum hose from EGR V.R. solenoid and verify that each hose is connected correctly. (Refer to vehicle vacuum diagram label.) • Verify that the EGR valve vacuum hose is not pinched or plugged and routed properly. • Are vacuum hoses OK?	Yes No	▶ ▶	RECONNECT vacuum hoses. GO to **HE23**. SERVICE vacuum hoses as necessary. RECONNECT all components. COMPLETE PCM Reset to clear DTCs (REFER to Powertrain Control Module (PCM) Reset). RERUN Quick Test.
HE23 CHECK D.P.F. EGR SENSOR OUTPUT BY APPLYING VACUUM WITH HAND PUMP • Key off. • Disconnect pressure hoses at D.P.F. EGR sensor. • Connect a hand vacuum pump to the downstream pickup marked "REF" on the sensor. • Key on, engine off. • Access DPFEGR PID (formerly DPFE) with a Scan Tool. PID voltage should be 0.45 ± 0.25 volts. • Apply 8-9 in-Hg vacuum to the D.P.F. EGR sensor. The PID voltage should be above 4.0 volts. Quickly release vacuum from sensor. PID voltage should drop to less than 1 volt in less than 3 seconds. • Does the DPFEGR PID voltage indicate a fault in the D.P.F. EGR sensor?	Yes No	▶ ▶	REPLACE damaged D.P.F. EGR sensor. RECONNECT all components. COMPLETE PCM Reset to clear DTCs (REFER to Powertrain Control Module (PCM) Reset). RERUN Quick Test. RECONNECT D.P.F. EGR sensor. GO to **HE24**.

FM0159601516090X

Fig. 251   Test HE: Exhaust Gas Recirculation Systems (Part 9 of 37). 1996

Test Step	Result	▶	Action to Take
HE24 CHECK FOR EGR FLOW AT IDLE WITH EGR V.R. SOLENOID CONNECTOR OFF • Key off. • Disconnect vacuum hose at EGR valve and connect hose to vacuum gauge. • Start engine and bring to an idle. • While monitoring vacuum gauge, disconnect the EGR V.R. solenoid vehicle harness connector. — The EGR valve requires vacuum greater than 1.6 in-Hg to begin to open. If the vacuum reading remains greater than 1.6 in-Hg after the EGR V.R. solenoid is electrically disconnected, this would indicate a mechanical fault in the EGR V.R. solenoid. • Does the EGR vacuum remain greater than 1.6 in-Hg at idle even after EGR V.R. solenoid is electrically disconnected?	Yes No	▶ ▶	This indicates a fault in the EGR V.R. solenoid. GO to **HE25**. GO to **HE26**.
HE25 INSPECT EGR V.R. SOLENOID VENT FOR PLUGGING • Key off. • Disconnect EGR V.R. solenoid vacuum hoses. • Remove EGR V.R. solenoid vent cap (if removable). • Remove filter and inspect for blockage or icing in some cases. • With the EGR vacuum supply port plugged, apply 10 to 15 in-Hg of vacuum directly to EGR V.R. solenoid vacuum source port with a hand vacuum pump. If the vacuum holds or is slow to release to atmosphere, the EGR V.R. solenoid vent could be plugged or restricted. NOTE: A plugged EGR V.R. solenoid vent will not allow EGR vacuum to vent to atmosphere.	Yes No	▶ ▶	SERVICE EGR V.R. solenoid as necessary. If unable to service, REPLACE EGR V.R. solenoid. RECONNECT all components. COMPLETE PCM Reset to clear DTCs (REFER to Powertrain Control Module (PCM) Reset). RERUN Quick Test. REPLACE damaged EGR V.R. solenoid. RECONNECT all components. COMPLETE PCM Reset to clear DTCs (REFER to Powertrain Control Module (PCM) Reset). RERUN Quick Test.

EGR V.R. SOLENOID VENT
VACUUM SUPPLY PORT PLUGGED
APPLY VACUUM TO SOURCE PORT

• Is the EGR V.R. solenoid vent or vent filter plugged or restricted?

FM0159601516100X

Fig. 251   Test HE: Exhaust Gas Recirculation Systems (Part 10 of 37). 1996

Test Step	Result	▶	Action to Take
HE26 MEASURE EGR V.R. SOLENOID COIL RESISTANCE • Key off. • EGR V.R. solenoid disconnected. • Measure resistance across EGR V.R. solenoid. • Is resistance between 26 and 40 ohms?	Yes No	▶ ▶	GO to **HE27**. REPLACE damaged EGR V.R. solenoid. RECONNECT all components. COMPLETE PCM Reset to clear DTCs (REFER to Powertrain Control Module (PCM) Reset). RERUN Quick Test.
HE27 CHECK EVR CIRCUIT FOR SHORT TO GROUND IN HARNESS • Key off. • Disconnect Scan Tool from DLC. • EGR V.R. solenoid disconnected. • Disconnect PCM. Inspect for damaged or pushed out pins, corrosion, loose wires, etc. Service as necessary. • Install breakout box, leave PCM disconnected. • Measure resistance between Test Pin 47 (EVR) and Test Pins 51 and 103 (PWR GND) at the breakout box. • Is resistance greater than 10,000 ohms?	Yes No	▶ ▶	GO to **HE28**. SERVICE short between EVR circuit and ground. REMOVE breakout box. RECONNECT all components. RERUN Quick Test.
HE28 CHECK EVR CIRCUIT FOR SHORT TO VREF • Key off. • Breakout box installed, PCM disconnected. • Measure resistance between Test Pin 47 (EVR) and Test Pin 90 (VREF) at the breakout box. • Is resistance greater than 10,000 ohms?	Yes No	▶ ▶	REPLACE damaged PCM. REMOVE breakout box. RECONNECT all components. RERUN Quick Test. SERVICE short between EVR circuit and VREF. REMOVE breakout box. RECONNECT all components. RERUN Quick Test.

FM0159601516110X

Fig. 251   Test HE: Exhaust Gas Recirculation System (Part 11 of 37). 1996

Test Step	Result	▶	Action to Take
HE30 CHECK D.P.F. EGR SENSOR OUTPUT BY APPLYING VACUUM WITH HAND PUMP			
• Key off. • Disconnect pressure hoses at D.P.F. EGR sensor. • Connect a hand vacuum pump to the downstream pickup marked "REF" on the sensor. • Key on, engine off. • Access DPFEGR PID (formerly DPFE) with a Scan Tool. PID voltage should be 0.45 ± 0.25 volts. • Apply 8-9 in-Hg vacuum to the D.P.F. EGR sensor. The PID voltage should be above 4.0 volts. Quickly release vacuum from sensor. PID voltage should drop to less than 1 volt in less than 3 seconds. • **Does the DPFEGR PID voltage indicate a fault in the D.P.F. EGR sensor?**	Yes ▶ No ▶		REPLACE damaged D.P.F. EGR sensor. RECONNECT all components. COMPLETE PCM Reset to clear DTCs (REFER to Powertrain Control Module (PCM) Reset). RERUN Quick Test. RECONNECT D.P.F. EGR sensor. GO to **HE31**.
HE31 CHECK D.P.F. EGR SENSOR VOLTAGE WHILE EXERCISING EGR VALVE			
• Key on, engine off. • View DPFEGR PID with a Scan Tool and make note of voltage. NOTE: Typical D.P.F. EGR sensor voltage with no EGR flow is 0.45 volts ± 0.25 volts. • Disconnect vacuum hose at EGR valve and plug hose. • Connect a hand vacuum pump to EGR valve. • Start engine and bring to idle. • Observe DPFEGR PID at idle and compare to the key on engine off voltage. (A higher voltage at idle could be due to a non-seating EGR valve.) • Apply just enough vacuum to EGR valve to open it (2 to 3 in-Hg) without stalling engine and release vacuum. Repeat several times while observing DPFEGR PID on Scan Tool. (DPFEGR PID voltage should increase as valve begins to open and return to initial value as vacuum is released. A slow to return voltage could be an indication of a binding or a slow closing EGR valve.) • **Does the DPFEGR PID voltage indicate an open, binding or slow closing EGR valve?**	Yes ▶ No ▶		REMOVE and INSPECT the EGR valve for signs of contamination, unusual wear, carbon deposits, binding and other damage. SERVICE as necessary (use Rotunda EGR Valve Cleaner 021-00056, if needed). RECONNECT all components. COMPLETE PCM Reset to clear DTCs (REFER to Powertrain Control Module (PCM) Reset). RERUN Quick Test. RECONNECT EGR vacuum hose. GO to **HE32**.

FM0159601516120X

Fig. 251   Test HE: Exhaust Gas Recirculation System (Part 12 of 37). 1996

Test Step	Result	▶	Action to Take
HE32 MONITOR EGR VALVE VACUUM WHILE WIGGLING EVR CIRCUIT			
NOTE: An intermittent short to GND in the EVR circuit will cause the vacuum applied to the EGR valve to be higher than normal while the short is present. The vacuum available at the EGR valve at idle is normally below 1.0 in-Hg and it takes about 1.6 in-Hg for the valve to begin to open. • Key off. • Disconnect vacuum hose at EGR valve and connect hose to a vacuum gauge. • Key on, engine running. • Observe vacuum gauge for an indication of a fault while performing the following: — Lightly tap on the EGR V.R. solenoid; wiggle the EGR V.R. solenoid connector and vehicle harness between solenoid and PCM. A fault is indicated by a sudden jump in vacuum reading. • **Is a fault indicated?**	Yes ▶ No ▶		ISOLATE fault and SERVICE as necessary. RECONNECT all components. COMPLETE PCM Reset to clear DTCs (REFER to Powertrain Control Module (PCM) Reset). RERUN Quick Test. RECONNECT vacuum hose. GO to **HE33**.
HE33 INSPECT EGR V.R. SOLENOID AND VACUUM HOSES FOR POTENTIAL PLUGGING			
• Key off. • Remove EGR V.R. solenoid vent filter and inspect for contamination and excessive water absorption. (In cold climate, excessive water in filter could freeze and plug the EGR V.R. solenoid vent.) • Inspect EGR vacuum hose for possible blockage or pinching. • **Is EGR V.R. solenoid vent or filter contaminated or vacuum line plugged?**	Yes ▶ No ▶		SERVICE EGR V.R. solenoid or EGR vacuum hose as necessary. RECONNECT all components. COMPLETE PCM Reset to clear DTCs (REFER to Powertrain Control Module (PCM) Reset). RERUN Quick Test. Unable to duplicate and/or identify fault at this time. GO to Pinpoint Test Step **Z1** with the following data: DPFEGR and EGRVR (formerly EVR) PIDs and list of Possible Causes.

FM0159601516130X

Fig. 251   Test HE: Exhaust Gas Recirculation System (Part 13 of 37). 1996

Test Step	Result	▶	Action to Take
HE50 DTC P1405: INSPECT UPSTREAM PRESSURE HOSE CONNECTIONS			
Diagnostic Trouble Code (DTC) P1405 indicates that Continuous Memory Self-Test has detected the exhaust manifold side (upstream) differential pressure feedback EGR (D.P.F. EGR) sensor pressure hose is off or plugged. Possible causes: — Upstream pressure hose off. — Upstream pressure hose plugged. — Plugged or damaged pressure pickup tubes. • Key off. • Inspect upstream hose at D.P.F. EGR sensor and orifice tube assembly for disconnect or poor connection. • **Is hose off or poorly connected?**	Yes ▶ No ▶		RECONNECT upstream hose or SERVICE as necessary. COMPLETE PCM Reset to clear DTCs (REFER to Powertrain Control Module (PCM) Reset). COMPLETE EGR Monitor Drive Cycle (Refer to Drive Cycles). RERUN Quick Test. GO to **HE51**.
HE51 INSPECT UPSTREAM PRESSURE HOSE FOR PLUGGING			
NOTE: It is essential that the D.P.F. EGR pressure hose used is the correct service part and not a substitute. • Visually inspect upstream pressure hose routing. Hose should not be pinched or have dips in it where water could settle or freeze. • Carefully remove upstream pressure hose and inspect for plugging, water or leaks. • **Is there a fault detected in the hose?**	Yes ▶ No ▶		SERVICE or REPLACE upstream pressure hose as necessary. COMPLETE PCM Reset to clear DTCs (REFER to Powertrain Control Module (PCM) Reset). COMPLETE EGR Monitor Drive Cycle. RERUN Quick Test. GO to **HE52**.

FM0159601516140X

Fig. 251   Test HE: Exhaust Gas Recirculation System (Part 14 of 37). 1996

Test Step	Result	▶	Action to Take
HE52 CHECK ORIFICE TUBE ASSEMBLY AND D.P.F. EGR SENSOR			
• Inspect the connection marked "HI" on the D.P.F. EGR sensor for plugging or damage at the sensor. • Inspect the exhaust manifold side pressure pickup tube at the orifice tube assembly for plugging or damage. • **Is the D.P.F. EGR sensor or orifice tube assembly plugged or damaged?**	Yes ▶ No ▶		SERVICE or REPLACE D.P.F. EGR sensor or orifice tube assembly as necessary. COMPLETE PCM Reset to clear DTCs (REFER to Powertrain Control Module (PCM) Reset). COMPLETE EGR Monitor Drive Cycle (Refer to Drive Cycles). RERUN Quick Test. GO to **HE53**.
HE53 CHECK D.P.F. EGR SENSOR OUTPUT BY APPLYING VACUUM WITH HAND PUMP			
• Key off. • Disconnect pressure hoses at D.P.F. EGR sensor. • Connect a hand vacuum pump to the downstream pickup marked "REF" on the sensor. • Key on, engine off. • Access DPFEGR PID (formerly DPFE) with a Scan Tool. PID voltage should be 0.45 ± 0.25 volts. • Apply 8-9 in-Hg vacuum to the D.P.F. EGR sensor. The PID voltage should be above 4.0 volts. Quickly release vacuum from sensor. PID voltage should drop to less than 1 volt in less than 3 seconds. • **Does the DPFEGR PID voltage indicate a fault in the D.P.F. EGR sensor?**	Yes ▶ No ▶		REPLACE damaged D.P.F. EGR sensor. RECONNECT all components. COMPLETE PCM Reset to clear DTCs (REFER to Powertrain Control Module (PCM) Reset). COMPLETE EGR Monitor Drive Cycle (Refer to Drive Cycles). RERUN Quick Test. Fault may have been recently serviced without clearing DTCs. RECONNECT all components. COMPLETE PCM Reset to clear DTCs (REFER to Powertrain Control Module (PCM) Reset). RERUN Quick Test.

FM0159601516150X

Fig. 251   Test HE: Exhaust Gas Recirculation System (Part 15 of 37). 1996

Test Step	Result	▶	Action to Take
HE60 DTC P1406: INSPECT DOWNSTREAM PRESSURE HOSE CONNECTIONS			
Diagnostic Trouble Code (DTC) P1406 indicates that Continuous Memory Self-Test has detected the intake manifold side (downstream) differential pressure feedback EGR (D.P.F. EGR) sensor pressure hose is off or plugged. NOTE: If the fault is currently present, DTC P 1408 will be output in Key On Engine Running (KOER) Self-Test. Possible causes: — Downstream pressure hose off. — Downstream pressure hose plugged. — Orifice tube assembly loose. — Orifice tube assembly broken. — Plugged or damaged pressure pickup tubes. — Slow responding D.P.F. EGR sensor. • Key off. • Inspect downstream hose at D.P.F. EGR sensor and orifice tube assembly for disconnect or poor connection. • **Is hose OFF or poorly connected?**	Yes No	▶ ▶	RECONNECT downstream hose or SERVICE as necessary. COMPLETE PCM Reset to clear DTCs (REFER to Powertrain Control Module (PCM) Reset). RERUN Quick Test. GO to **HE61**.
HE61 INSPECT DOWNSTREAM PRESSURE HOSE FOR PLUGGING			
NOTE: It is essential that the D.P.F. EGR sensor pressure hose is the correct service part and not a substitute. • Visually inspect downstream pressure hose routing. Hose should not be pinched or have dips in it where water could settle or freeze. • Carefully remove downstream pressure hose and inspect for plugging, water or leaks. • **Is there a fault detected in the hose?**	Yes No	▶ ▶	SERVICE or REPLACE downstream pressure hose as necessary. COMPLETE PCM Reset to clear DTCs (REFER to Powertrain Control Module (PCM) Reset). RERUN Quick Test. GO to **HE62**.

FM0159601516160X

Fig. 251   Test HE: Exhaust Gas Recirculation System (Part 16 of 37). 1996

Test Step	Result	▶	Action to Take
HE62 CHECK ORIFICE TUBE ASSEMBLY AND D.P.F. EGR SENSOR			
• Inspect the connection marked "REF" on the D.P.F. EGR sensor for plugging or damage at the sensor. • Inspect the intake manifold side pressure pickup tube and orifice tube assembly for plugging, loose connection or damage. • **Is the D.P.F. EGR sensor or orifice tube assembly plugged, loose or damaged?**	Yes No	▶ ▶	SERVICE or REPLACE D.P.F. EGR sensor or orifice tube assembly as necessary. COMPLETE PCM Reset to clear DTCs (REFER to Powertrain Control Module (PCM) Reset). RERUN Quick Test. RECONNECT all components. GO to **HE63**.
HE63 CHECK D.P.F. EGR SENSOR OUTPUT BY APPLYING VACUUM WITH HAND PUMP			
• Key off. • Disconnect pressure hoses at D.P.F. EGR sensor. • Connect a hand vacuum pump to the downstream pickup marked "REF" on the D.P.F. EGR sensor. • Key on, engine off. • Access DPFEGR PID (formerly DPFE) with a Scan Tool. PID voltage should be 0.45 volt ± 0.25 volt. • Apply 8-9 in-Hg vacuum to the D.P.F. EGR sensor. The PID voltage should be above 4.0 volts. Quickly release vacuum from sensor. PID voltage should drop to less than 1 volt in less than 3 seconds. • **Does the DPFEGR PID voltage indicate a fault in the D.P.F. EGR sensor?**	Yes No	▶ ▶	REPLACE damaged D.P.F. EGR sensor. RECONNECT all components. COMPLETE PCM Reset to clear DTCs (REFER to Powertrain Control Module (PCM) Reset). RERUN Quick Test. Fault may have been recently serviced without clearing DTCs. RECONNECT all components. COMPLETE PCM Reset to clear DTCs (REFER to Powertrain Control Module (PCM) Reset). RERUN Quick Test.

FM0159601516170X

Fig. 251   Test HE: Exhaust Gas Recirculation System (Part 17 of 37). 1996

Test Step	Result	▶	Action to Take
HE70 DTC P0401: RUN KOER SELF-TEST			
Diagnostic Trouble Code (DTC) P0401 indicates that Continuous Memory Self-Test has detected insufficient EGR flow. Possible causes: — EGR valve stuck closed or iced. — EGR valve diaphragm leaks. — EGR valve or flow path restricted. — EGR vacuum hose off, plugged or leaks. — VPWR circuit open to EGR Vacuum Regulator (EGR V.R.) solenoid. — EVR circuit to PCM open. — EVR circuit to PCM shorted to PWR. — Differential Pressure Feedback EGR (D.P.F. EGR) sensor pressure hoses both off. — D.P.F. EGR sensor pressure hoses reversed. — D.P.F. EGR sensor VREF circuit open. — Downstream pressure hose off. — Downstream pressure hose plugged. — Damaged orifice tube assembly. — Damaged EGR V.R. solenoid. — Damaged D.P.F. EGR sensor. — Damaged PCM. • Run KOER Self-Test. • **Is KOER DTC P1408 output?**	Yes No	▶ ▶	The KOER Self-Test has detected an EGR fault that is currently present. GO to **HE71**. REMOVE and INSPECT the EGR Valve and intake manifold EGR port for restriction. If OK, the fault that produced DTC P0401 is intermittent. GO to **HE90**.

FM0159601516180X

Fig. 251   Test HE: Exhaust Gas Recirculation System (Part 18 of 37). 1996

Test Step	Result	▶	Action to Take
HE71 DTC P1408: OUTPUT CONTINUOUS MEMORY DTCS			
Diagnostic Trouble Code (DTC) P1408 indicates that Key On Engine Running (KOER) Self-Test has detected EGR flow out of range. Possible causes: — EGR valve stuck closed or iced. — EGR valve diaphragm leaks. — EGR valve or flow path restricted. — EGR vacuum hose off, plugged or leaks. — VPWR circuit open to EGR vacuum regulator (EGR V.R.) solenoid. — EVR circuit to PCM open. — EVR circuit to PCM shorted to PWR. — Differential Pressure Feedback EGR (D.P.F. EGR) sensor pressure hoses both off. — D.P.F. EGR sensor pressure hoses reversed. — D.P.F. EGR sensor VREF circuit open. — Downstream pressure hose off. — Downstream pressure hose plugged. — Damaged orifice tube assembly. — Damaged EGR V.R. solenoid. — Damaged D.P.F. EGR sensor. — Damaged PCM. • Output all Continuous Memory DTCs. NOTE: If DTCs other than DTC P1403 or P1406 are output, record codes and refer to Diagnostic Trouble Code Charts in Section 5A after completing this Pinpoint Test. • **Is DTC P1406 output?**	Yes No	▶ ▶	GO to **HE60**. GO to **HE72**.
HE72 RUN KOER SELF-TEST WHILE MONITORING EGR VACUUM			
• Key off. • Disconnect vacuum hose at EGR valve and connect hose to a vacuum gauge. • Run Key On Engine Running (KOER) Self-Test while monitoring gauge. Approximately 30 seconds into test, EGR flow will be requested for a few seconds. The vacuum at this time should increase above 1.6 in-Hg to open the EGR valve. NOTE: Since the EGR vacuum hose is disconnected, ignore DTCs during this KOER Self-Test. • **Does the vacuum increase to 3.0 in-Hg or greater at any time during KOER Self-Test?**	Yes No	▶ ▶	The vacuum indicated is sufficient to open the EGR valve. Fault is unlikely to be in EGR vacuum control. GO to **HE73**. The vacuum indicated is insufficient to open the EGR valve. GO to **HE80**.

FM0159601516190X

Fig. 251   Test HE: Exhaust Gas Recirculation Systems (Part 19 of 37). 1996

Test Step	Result	▶	Action to Take
HE73 INSPECT D.P.F. EGR SENSOR PRESSURE HOSES			
• Key off. • Visually inspect both pressure hoses for reversed connection at D.P.F. EGR sensor or at orifice tube assembly. • Inspect hoses for improper routing. Hoses should not be pinched or have dips where water could settle or freeze. • Inspect both hoses for leaks and blockage. • Inspect D.P.F. EGR sensor and orifice tube assembly for blockage or damage at the pick up tubes. • **Is there a fault detected?**	Yes	▶	SERVICE pressure hoses as necessary. RECONNECT all components. COMPLETE PCM Reset to clear DTCs (REFER to Powertrain Control Module (PCM) Reset). RERUN Quick Test.
	No	▶	RECONNECT all components. GO to HE74.

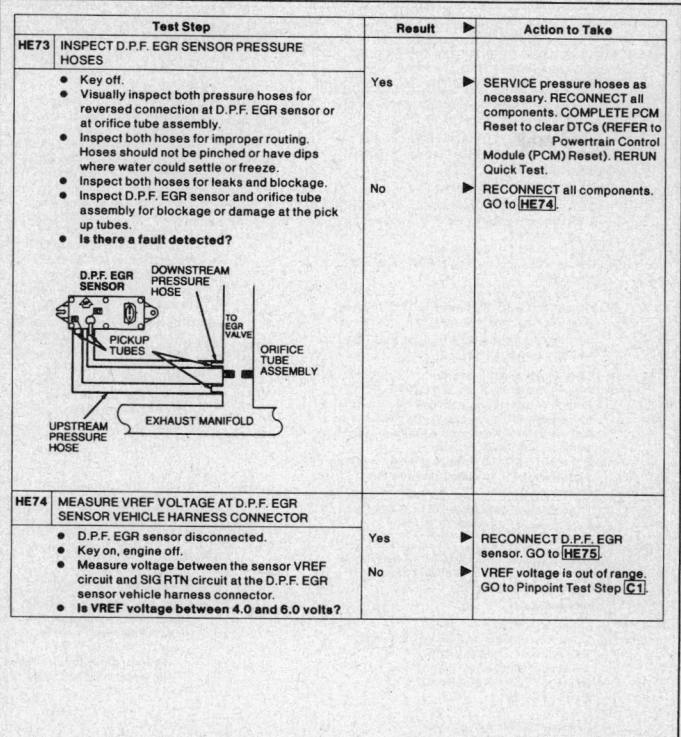

Test Step	Result	▶	Action to Take
HE74 MEASURE VREF VOLTAGE AT D.P.F. EGR SENSOR VEHICLE HARNESS CONNECTOR			
• D.P.F. EGR sensor disconnected. • Key on, engine off. • Measure voltage between the sensor VREF circuit and SIG RTN circuit at the D.P.F. EGR sensor vehicle harness connector. • **Is VREF voltage between 4.0 and 6.0 volts?**	Yes	▶	RECONNECT D.P.F. EGR sensor. GO to HE75.
	No	▶	VREF voltage is out of range. GO to Pinpoint Test Step C1.

FM0159601516200X

Fig. 251   Test HE: Exhaust Gas Recirculation Systems (Part 20 of 37). 1996

Test Step	Result	▶	Action to Take
HE75 CHECK D.P.F. EGR SENSOR OUTPUT BY APPLYING VACUUM WITH HAND PUMP			
• Key off. • Disconnect pressure hoses at D.P.F. EGR sensor. • Connect a hand vacuum pump to the downstream pickup marked "REF" on the sensor. • Key on, engine off. • Access DPFEGR PID (formerly DPFE) with a Scan Tool. PID voltage should be 0.45 volt ± 0.25 volt. • Apply 8-9 in-Hg vacuum to the D.P.F. EGR sensor. The PID voltage should be above 4.0 volts. Quickly release vacuum from sensor. PID voltage should drop to less than 1.0 volt in less than 3 seconds. • **Does the DPFEGR PID voltage indicate a fault in the D.P.F. EGR sensor?**	Yes	▶	REPLACE damaged D.P.F. EGR sensor. RECONNECT all components. COMPLETE PCM Reset to clear DTCs (REFER to Powertrain Control Module (PCM) Reset). RERUN Quick Test.
	No	▶	RECONNECT pressure hoses. GO to HE76.
HE76 CHECK EGR VALVE FUNCTION BY APPLYING VACUUM WITH HAND PUMP			
• Key off. • Disconnect vacuum hose at EGR valve and plug hose. • Connect a hand vacuum pump to EGR valve. • Start engine and bring to idle. • Access DPFEGR and RPM PIDs with a Scan Tool. • Slowly apply 5-10 in-Hg of vacuum to the EGR valve and hold it for 10 seconds. If engine wants to stall, increase rpm with throttle to maintain a minimum of 800 rpm. • Look for the following: — EGR valve starts opening at about 1.6 in-Hg vacuum indicated by increasing DPFEGR PID voltage. — DPFEGR PID voltage increasing until EGR valve is fully open. DPFEGR PID should read 2.5 volts minimum with full vacuum applied. — DPFEGR PID voltage steady when vacuum is held. If voltage drops within a few seconds, the EGR valve or vacuum source could be leaking. • **Does the DPFEGR PID voltage indicate that the EGR valve is functioning as described in this test?**	Yes	▶	RECONNECT all components. GO to HE85.
	No	▶	REMOVE and INSPECT the EGR valve for signs of contamination, unusual wear, carbon deposits, binding, leaking diaphragm and other damage. If EGR valve is OK, look for an obstructed EGR port in the intake manifold. SERVICE as necessary (use Rotunda EGR Valve Cleaner 021-00056, if needed). RECONNECT all components. COMPLETE PCM Reset to clear DTCs (REFER to Powertrain Control Module (PCM) Reset). RERUN Quick Test.

FM0159601516210X

Fig. 251   Test HE: Exhaust Gas Recirculation Systems (Part 21 of 37). 1996

Test Step	Result	▶	Action to Take
HE80 CHECK VACUUM SOURCE AND VACUUM HOSES TO AND FROM EGR V.R. SOLENOID			
• Key off. • Disconnect vacuum hoses at EGR V.R. solenoid. • Connect EGR V.R. vacuum supply hose to a vacuum gauge. • With engine warm and at idle, take vacuum gauge reading. • Inspect vacuum lines between vacuum source and EGR V.R. solenoid and between EGR V.R. solenoid and EGR valve for leaks, kinks, disconnects, blockage, routing or any damage. • **Is the vacuum gauge reading a minimum of 15 in-Hg at idle and vacuum lines OK?**	Yes	▶	RECONNECT all components. GO to HE81.
	No	▶	ISOLATE fault and SERVICE as necessary. RECONNECT all components. COMPLETE PCM Reset to clear DTCs (REFER to Powertrain Control Module (PCM) Reset). RERUN Quick Test.
HE81 CHECK VPWR TO EGR V.R. SOLENOID			
• Key off. • EGR V.R. solenoid disconnected. • Key on, engine off. • Measure voltage between VPWR circuit and chassis ground at the EGR V.R. solenoid vehicle harness connector. • **Is EGR V.R. solenoid VPWR voltage greater than 10.5 volts?**	Yes	▶	GO to HE82.
	No	▶	SERVICE open in EGR V.R. solenoid VPWR circuit. RECONNECT all components. COMPLETE PCM Reset to clear DTCs (REFER to Powertrain Control Module (PCM) Reset). RERUN Quick Test.
HE82 MEASURE RESISTANCE ACROSS EGR V.R. SOLENOID			
• Key off. • EGR V.R. solenoid disconnected. • Measure resistance across EGR V.R. solenoid. • **Is solenoid resistance between 26 and 40 ohms?**	Yes	▶	GO to HE83.
	No	▶	REPLACE damaged EGR V.R. solenoid. RECONNECT all components. COMPLETE PCM Reset to clear DTCs (REFER to Powertrain Control Module (PCM) Reset). RERUN Quick Test.
HE83 CHECK EVR CIRCUIT FOR SHORT TO PWR			
• Key off. • EGR V.R. solenoid disconnected. • Disconnect PCM. Inspect for damaged or pushed out pins, corrosion, loose wires, etc. Service as necessary. • Install breakout box, leave PCM disconnected. • Key on, engine off. • Measure voltage between Test Pin 47 (EVR) and chassis ground. • **Is voltage greater than 1.0 volt?**	Yes	▶	SERVICE EVR circuit for short to PWR. RECONNECT all components. COMPLETE PCM Reset to clear DTCs (REFER to Powertrain Control Module (PCM) Reset). RERUN Quick Test.
	No	▶	GO to HE84.

FM0159601516220X

Fig. 251   Test HE: Exhaust Gas Recirculation Systems (Part 22 of 37). 1996

Test Step	Result	▶	Action to Take
HE84 CHECK EVR CIRCUIT FOR OPEN IN HARNESS			
• Key off. • EGR V.R. solenoid disconnected. • Breakout box installed, PCM disconnected. • Measure resistance between Test Pin 47 (EVR) and EVR circuit at the EGR V.R. solenoid vehicle harness connector. • **Is resistance less than 5.0 ohms?**	Yes	▶	RECONNECT EGR V.R. solenoid. GO to HE85.
	No	▶	SERVICE open in EVR circuit. RECONNECT all components. COMPLETE PCM Reset to clear DTCs (REFER to Section Powertrain Control Module (PCM) Reset). RERUN Quick Test.
HE85 CHECK EGR V.R. SOLENOID VACUUM OUTPUT CAPABILITY BY GROUNDING EVR CIRCUIT			
• Key off. • Breakout box installed, PCM connected. • EGR V.R. solenoid connected. • Disconnect vacuum hose at the EGR valve and connect to a vacuum gauge. • Key on, engine running. • With engine at idle, jumper Test Pin 47 (EVR) to chassis ground. • **Is vacuum gauge reading 4.0 in-Hg or greater?**	Yes	▶	REPLACE damaged PCM. RECONNECT all components. RERUN Quick Test.
	No	▶	REPLACE damaged EGR V.R. solenoid. RECONNECT all components. COMPLETE PCM Reset to clear DTCs (REFER to Section Powertrain Control Module (PCM) Reset). RERUN Quick Test.
HE90 INSPECT EGR SYSTEM FOR AN INTERMITTENT FAILURE			
• Key off. • Visually inspect the EGR system for signs of intermittent failure. • **Is a fault found?**	Yes	▶	SERVICE fault as necessary. RECONNECT all components. COMPLETE PCM Reset to clear DTCs (REFER to Section 2A, Powertrain Control Module (PCM) Reset). RERUN Quick Test.
	No	▶	GO to HE91.

FM0159601516230X

Fig. 251   Test HE: Exhaust Gas Recirculation Systems (Part 23 of 37). 1996

Test Step	Result	▶	Action to Take
HE91 CHECK EGR VALVE FUNCTION BY APPLYING VACUUM WITH HAND PUMP • Key off. • Disconnect hose at EGR valve and plug hose. • Connect a hand vacuum pump to EGR valve. • Start engine and bring to idle. • Access DPFEGR and RPM PIDs with a Scan Tool. • Slowly apply 5-10 in-Hg of vacuum to the EGR valve and hold it for 10 seconds. If engine wants to stall, increase rpm with throttle to maintain a minimum of 800 rpm. • Look for the following: — EGR valve starts opening at about 1.6 in-Hg vacuum indicated by increasing DPFEGR PID voltage. — DPFEGR PID voltage increasing until EGR valve is fully open. DPFEGR PID should read 2.5 volts minimum with full vacuum applied. — DPFEGR PID voltage steady when vacuum is held. If voltage drops within a few seconds, the EGR valve or vacuum source could be leaking. • **Does the DPFEGR PID voltage indicate that the EGR valve is functioning as described in this test?**	Yes No	▶ ▶	GO to **HE92**. REMOVE and INSPECT the EGR valve for signs of contamination, unusual wear, carbon deposits, binding, leaking diaphragm and other damage. If EGR valve is OK, look for an obstructed EGR port in the intake manifold. SERVICE as necessary (use Rotunda EGR Valve Cleaner 021-00056, if needed). RECONNECT all components. COMPLETE PCM Reset to clear DTCs (REFER to Powertrain Control Module (PCM) Reset). RERUN Quick Test.
HE92 INSPECT EGR VACUUM SIGNAL SUPPLY FOR INTERMITTENT FAILURE • Key off. • Disconnect PCM. Inspect for damaged or pushed out pins, corrosion, loose wires, etc. Service as necessary. • Install breakout box and connect PCM to breakout box. • Disconnect hose at EGR valve and connect to a vacuum gauge. • Key on, engine running. • Jumper Test Pin 47 (EVR) to chassis ground to activate the EVR to full ON. At idle, the vacuum gauge should read above 4.0 in-Hg. • Observe vacuum gauge for an indication of a fault while performing the following: — Lightly tap on the EGR V.R. solenoid and wiggle the EGR V.R. solenoid connector, vacuum lines and vehicle harness between the solenoid and PCM. A fault is indicated by a sudden drop in vacuum reading. • **Is a fault indicated?**	Yes No	▶ ▶	ISOLATE fault and SERVICE as necessary. RECONNECT all components. COMPLETE PCM Reset to clear DTCs (REFER to Powertrain Control Module (PCM) Reset). RERUN Quick Test. Unable to duplicate and/or identify fault at this time. (In cold climates, the EGR valve may temporarily freeze shut and thaw when the engine warms up causing the intermittent DTC.) GO to Pinpoint Test Step **Z1** with the following data: DPFEGR and EGRVR (formerly EVR) PIDs and list of Possible Causes.

FM0159601516240X

Fig. 251   Test HE: Exhaust Gas Recirculation Systems (Part 24 of 37). 1996

Test Step	Result	▶	Action to Take
HE100 EGR DIAGNOSIS BY SYMPTOM: CHECK FOR EGR FLOW WITH EGR VACUUM HOSE DISCONNECTED AND PLUGGED NOTE: Perform KOER Self-Test and service any DTCs before proceeding with this test. The symptom flowcharts have indicated possible EGR flow at idle with no EGR Diagnostic Trouble Codes output. Possible causes: — EGR valve not fully seating. — EGR vacuum regulator (E.V.R.) solenoid vent restricted. — Damaged EGR V.R. solenoid. • Disconnect vacuum hose at EGR valve and plug hose. • Key on, engine off. • Access DPFEGR PID (formerly DPFE) with a Scan Tool and note voltage. NOTE: D.P.F. sensor input with no EGR flow is 0.45 volt ± 0.25 volt. • Start engine and bring to idle. • With engine at idle, look at the DPFEGR PID voltage and compare to the engine off reading. An increase in the voltage at idle indicates that the differential pressure feedback EGR sensor is sensing EGR flow. • **Is the DPFEGR PID voltage greater at idle by a minimum of 0.15 volts than with the engine off?**	Yes No	▶ ▶	The DPFEGR PID voltage is indicating EGR flow at idle. Since the EGR vacuum hose is disconnected and plugged, the fault is most likely in the EGR valve. REMOVE and INSPECT the EGR valve for signs of contamination, unusual wear, carbon deposits, binding and other damage. SERVICE as necessary (use Rotunda EGR Valve Cleaner 021-00056, if needed). RECONNECT all components. VERIFY a symptom no longer exists. This indicates a fault in the EGR valve vacuum supply. INSPECT the EGR V.R. solenoid vent and vent filter for restrictions. SERVICE as necessary. If OK, REPLACE EGR V.R. solenoid. VERIFY a symptom no longer exists.
HE110 DTC P1409: MEASURE RESISTANCE ACROSS EGR VACUUM REGULATOR (EGR V.R.) SOLENOID Diagnostic Trouble Code (DTC) P1409 indicates that Self-Test has detected an electrical malfunction in the EVR circuit. Possible causes: — Open EVR circuit. — Open VPWR circuit to EGR V.R. solenoid. — EVR circuit shorted to VPWR. — EVR circuit shorted to GND. — Damaged EGR V.R. solenoid. — Damaged PCM. • Key off. • Disconnect EGR V.R. solenoid. • Measure EGR V.R. solenoid resistance. • **Is solenoid resistance between 26 and 40 ohms?**	Yes No	▶ ▶	The EGR V.R. solenoid resistance is within specification. Go to **HE111**. REPLACE EGR V.R. solenoid. RECONNECT all components. COMPLETE PCM Reset to clear DTCs (Refer Powertrain Control Module (PCM) Reset). RERUN Quick Test.

FM0159601516250X

Fig. 251   Test HE: Exhaust Gas Recirculation Systems (Part 25 of 37). 1996

Test Step	Result	▶	Action to Take
HE111 CHECK VPWR CIRCUIT VOLTAGE AT EGR V.R. SOLENOID • Key on, engine off. • EGR V.R. solenoid disconnected. • Measure voltage between VPWR circuit at the EGR V.R. solenoid vehicle harness connector and chassis GND. • **Is voltage greater than 10.5 volts?**	Yes No	▶ ▶	GO to **HE112**. SERVICE open in VPWR circuit to EGR V.R. solenoid. RECONNECT all components. COMPLETE PCM Reset to clear DTCs (Refer to Powertrain Control Module (PCM) Reset). RERUN Quick Test.
HE112 CHECK EVR CIRCUIT CONTINUITY • Key off. • EGR V.R. solenoid disconnected. • Disconnect PCM. Inspect for damaged or pushed out pins, corrosion, loose wires, etc. Service as necessary. • Install breakout box and leave PCM disconnected. • Measure resistance between Test Pin 47 (EVR) and EVR circuit at the EGR V.R. solenoid vehicle harness connector. • **Is resistance less than 5.0 ohms?**	Yes No	▶ ▶	GO to **HE113**. SERVICE open in EVR circuit. RECONNECT all components. RERUN Quick Test.
HE113 CHECK EVR CIRCUIT FOR SHORTS TO POWER OR GROUND • Key off. • EGR V.R. solenoid disconnected. • Breakout box installed, leave PCM disconnected. • Measure resistance between Test Pin 47 (EVR) and Test Pins 71 and 97 (VPWR) at the breakout box. • Measure resistance between Test Pin 47 (EVR) and Test Pins 24 and 103 (PWR GND) at the breakout box. • **Is each resistance greater than 10,000 ohms?**	Yes No	▶ ▶	REPLACE damaged PCM. RECONNECT all components. RERUN Quick Test. SERVICE EVR circuit for short to PWR or PWR GND. RECONNECT all components. RERUN Quick Test.

FM0159601516260X

Fig. 251   Test HE: Exhaust Gas Recirculation Systems (Part 26 of 37). 1996

Test Step	Result	▶	Action to Take
HE120 CONTINUOUS MEMORY DTC P1409: WIGGLE EGR VACUUM REGULATOR (EGR V.R.) SOLENOID WHILE MONITORING VPWR Continuous Memory DTC P1409 indicates that Continuous Memory Self-Test has detected an electrical malfunction in the EGR V.R. solenoid sometime during vehicle operation. NOTE: If DTC P1409 was output in Key On Engine Off (KOEO) or Key On Engine Running (KOER) Self-Test, go to **HE110** to diagnose present fault. Possible causes: — Open EVR circuit. — Open VPWR circuit to EGR V.R. solenoid. — EVR circuit shorted to VPWR. — EVR circuit shorted to GND. — Damaged EGR V.R. solenoid. — Damaged PCM. • Disconnect PCM. Inspect for damaged or pushed out pins, corrosion, loose wires, etc. • Install breakout box, leave PCM disconnected. • Measure voltage between Test Pin 47 (EVR) and Test Pins 24 (PWR GND) at the breakout box. • Key on. • Voltage should read greater than 10.5 volts. For an indication of a fault, look for this voltage to drop while performing the following: — Lightly tap on the EGR V.R. solenoid. — Wiggle the EGR V.R. solenoid connector. — Grasp the EGR V.R. solenoid vehicle harness connector and wiggle wires between solenoid and PCM. • **Is a fault indicated?**	Yes No	▶ ▶	ISOLATE fault and SERVICE as necessary. RECONNECT all components. RERUN Quick Test. Unable to duplicate and/or identify fault at this time. GO to Pinpoint Test Step **Z1** with the following data: DPFEGR (formerly DPFE) and EGRVR (formerly EVR) PIDs and list of possible causes.
HE130 DTC P0400: ACCESS DPFEGR PID WITH SCAN TOOL Diagnostic Trouble Code (DTC) P0400 indicates that Self-Test has detected an EGR system malfunction. Possible causes: — Any EGR system failure. • Key on, engine off. • Access DPFEGR PID (formerly DPFE) with a Scan Tool. NOTE: Differential pressure feedback EGR (D.P.F. EGR) sensor input with no EGR flow is 0.45 volts ± 0.25 volts. • **Is DPFEGR PID voltage less than 0.2 volts?**	Yes No	▶ ▶	The D.P.F. EGR sensor voltage is less than the acceptable minimum. GO to **HE134**. GO to **HE131**.

FM0159601516270X

Fig. 251   Test HE: Exhaust Gas Recirculation Systems (Part 27 of 37). 1996

Test Step	Result	▶	Action to Take
HE131 CHECK FOR HIGH D.P.F. EGR SENSOR VOLTAGE • Key on, engine off. • **Is DPFEGR PID voltage greater than 4.0 volts?**	Yes	▶	The D.P.F. EGR sensor voltage is greater than the acceptable maximum. GO TO **HE137**.
	No	▶	GO to **HE132**.
HE132 COMPARE DPFEGR PID VOLTAGE WITH THE ENGINE OFF AND ENGINE AT IDLE • Key on, engine off. • Note the DPFEGR PID voltage with the key on and engine off. • Start engine and bring to idle. NOTE: If engine will not start or stalls, go directly to **HE133**. • With the engine at idle, look at DPFEGR PID voltage and compare it to the engine off reading. An increase in the voltage at idle indicates that the D.P.F. EGR sensor is sensing EGR flow. • **Is the DPFEGR PID voltage greater at idle by a minimum of 0.15 volts than with the engine off?**	Yes	▶	The DPFEGR PID voltage is indicating EGR flow at idle. GO to **HE133**.
	No	▶	GO to **HE160**.
HE133 CHECK DPFEGR PID VOLTAGE WITH EGR VACUUM HOSE DISCONNECTED • Key off. • Disconnect vacuum hose at EGR valve and plug hose. • Compare DPFEGR PID voltage with engine off and engine at idle as described in **HE132** but with the EGR vacuum hose disconnected this time. • **Is the DPFEGR PID voltage greater at idle by a minimum of 0.15 volts than with the engine off or is engine a no start or stall?**	Yes	▶	The DPFEGR PID voltage or symptom is indicating EGR flow at idle. REMOVE and INSPECT the EGR valve for signs of contamination, unusual wear, carbon deposits, binding and other damage. SERVICE as necessary (use Rotunda EGR Valve Cleaner 021-00056, if needed). RECONNECT all components. RERUN Quick Test.
	No	▶	GO to **HE150**.

FM0159601516280X

Test Step	Result	▶	Action to Take
HE134 INDUCE OPPOSITE D.P.F. EGR SENSOR SIGNAL • Key off. • Disconnect D.P.F. EGR sensor vehicle harness connector. • Connect a jumper wire between the sensor VREF circuit and DPFE SIG circuit at the D.P.F. EGR sensor vehicle harness connector. • Key on, engine off. NOTE: If a Scan Tool communication problem exists, remove jumper immediately and go directly to **HE135**. • Access DPFEGR PID with a Scan Tool. • **Is DPFEGR PID value between 4.0 and 6.0 volts?**	Yes	▶	REPLACE damaged D.P.F. EGR sensor. RECONNECT all components. COMPLETE PCM Reset to clear DTCs (REFER to Powertrain Control Module (PCM) Reset). RERUN Quick Test.
	No	▶	REMOVE jumper. GO to **HE135**.
HE135 MEASURE VREF VOLTAGE AT D.P.F. EGR SENSOR VEHICLE HARNESS CONNECTOR • D.P.F. EGR sensor disconnected. • Key on, engine off. • Measure voltage between the sensor VREF circuit and SIG RTN circuit at the D.P.F. EGR sensor vehicle harness connector. • **Is VREF voltage between 4.0 and 6.0 volts?**	Yes	▶	GO to **HE136**.
	No	▶	VREF voltage is out of range. GO to Pinpoint Test Step **C1**.
HE136 CHECK DPFE SIG CIRCUIT FOR SHORTS TO GROUND AND SIG RTN • Key off. • D.P.F. EGR sensor disconnected. • Disconnect PCM. Inspect for damaged or pushed out pins, corrosion, loose wires, etc. Service as necessary. • Install breakout box, leave PCM disconnected. • Measure resistance between Test Pin 65 (DPFE SIG) and Test Pin 91 (SIG RTN) and Test Pins 51 and 103 (PWR GND) at the breakout box. • **Is each resistance greater than 10,000 ohms?**	Yes	▶	REPLACE damaged PCM. REMOVE breakout box. RECONNECT all components. RERUN Quick Test.
	No	▶	SERVICE short circuit between DPFE SIG and GROUND or SIG RTN. REMOVE breakout box. RECONNECT all components. RERUN Quick Test.
HE137 CHECK DPFE SIG CIRCUIT FOR SHORT TO PWR • Key off. • Disconnect D.P.F. EGR sensor vehicle harness connector. • Key on, engine off. • Measure voltage between DPFE SIG circuit at the D.P.F. EGR sensor vehicle harness connector and battery ground. • **Is voltage greater than 10.5 volts?**	Yes	▶	The D.P.F. EGR sensor voltage is indicating a short to PWR. GO to **HE138**.
	No	▶	GO to **HE139**.

Test Step	Result	▶	Action to Take
HE138 CHECK DPFE SIG CIRCUIT FOR SHORT TO PWR IN HARNESS • Key off. • D.P.F. EGR sensor disconnected. • Disconnect PCM. Inspect for damaged or pushed out pins, corrosion, loose wires, etc. Service as necessary. • Install breakout box, leave PCM disconnected. • Key on, engine off. • Measure voltage between Test Pin 65 (DPFE SIG) and Test Pins 51 and 103 (PWR GND) at the breakout box. • **Is voltage greater than 10.5 volts?**	Yes	▶	SERVICE short between DPFE SIG and PWR circuit. REMOVE breakout box. RECONNECT all components. RERUN Quick Test.
	No	▶	REPLACE damaged PCM. REMOVE breakout box. RECONNECT all components. RERUN Quick Test.
HE139 INDUCE OPPOSITE D.P.F. EGR SENSOR SIGNAL • Key off. • Disconnect D.P.F. EGR sensor vehicle harness connector. • Connect a jumper wire between the sensor DPFE SIG circuit and SIG RTN circuit at the D.P.F. EGR sensor vehicle harness connector. • Key on, engine off. NOTE: If a Scan Tool communication problem exists, remove jumper immediately and go directly to **HE144**. • Access DPFEGR PID with a Scan Tool. • **Is DPFEGR PID voltage less than 0.05 volts?**	Yes	▶	REMOVE jumper. GO to **HE140**.
	No	▶	Unable to induce opposite signal. GO to **HE142**.
HE140 VERIFY THAT VREF IS IN RANGE • D.P.F. EGR sensor disconnected. • Key on, engine off. • Measure voltage between the sensor VREF circuit and SIG RTN circuit at the D.P.F. EGR sensor vehicle harness connector. • **Is VREF voltage between 4.0 and 6.0 volts?**	Yes	▶	GO to **HE141**.
	No	▶	VREF voltage is out of range. GO to Pinpoint Test Step **C1**.
HE141 CHECK DPFE SIG CIRCUIT FOR SHORT TO VREF IN HARNESS • Key off. • D.P.F. EGR sensor disconnected. • Disconnect PCM. Inspect for damaged or pushed out pins, corrosion, loose wires, etc. Service as necessary. • Install breakout box, leave PCM disconnected. • Measure resistance between Test Pin 65 (DPFE SIG) and Test Pin 90 (VREF) at the breakout box. • **Is resistance greater than 10,000 ohms?**	Yes	▶	REPLACE damaged D.P.F. EGR sensor. REMOVE breakout box. RECONNECT all components. RERUN Quick Test.
	No	▶	SERVICE short between DPFE SIG and VREF circuit. REMOVE breakout box. RECONNECT all components. RERUN Quick Test.

FM0159601516300X

Test Step	Result	▶	Action to Take
HE142 CHECK DPFE SIG CIRCUIT FOR OPEN IN HARNESS • Key off. • D.P.F. EGR sensor disconnected. • Disconnect PCM. Inspect for damaged or pushed out pins, corrosion, loose wires, etc. Service as necessary. • Install breakout box, leave PCM disconnected. • Measure resistance between Test Pin 65 (DPFE SIG) and DPFE SIG circuit at the D.P.F. EGR sensor vehicle harness connector. • **Is resistance less than 5.0 ohms?**	Yes	▶	GO to **HE143**.
	No	▶	SERVICE open in DPFE SIG circuit. REMOVE breakout box. RECONNECT all components. RERUN Quick Test.
HE143 CHECK SIG RTN FOR OPEN IN HARNESS • Key off. • D.P.F. EGR sensor disconnected. • Breakout box installed, PCM disconnected. • Measure resistance between Test Pin 91 (SIG RTN) and SIG RTN circuit at the D.P.F. EGR sensor vehicle harness connector. • **Is resistance less than 5.0 ohms?**	Yes	▶	REPLACE damaged PCM. REMOVE breakout box. RECONNECT all components. RERUN Quick Test.
	No	▶	SERVICE open in SIG RTN circuit. REMOVE breakout box. RECONNECT all components. RERUN Quick Test.
HE144 CHECK DPFE SIG CIRCUIT FOR SHORT TO VREF IN HARNESS • Key off. • D.P.F. EGR sensor disconnected. • Disconnect PCM. Inspect for damaged or pushed out pins, corrosion, loose wires, etc. Service as necessary. • Install breakout box, leave PCM disconnected. • Measure resistance between Test Pin 65 (DPFE SIG) and Test Pin 90 (VREF) at the breakout box. • **Is resistance greater than 10,000 ohms?**	Yes	▶	REPLACE damaged PCM. REMOVE breakout box. RECONNECT all components. RERUN Quick Test.
	No	▶	SERVICE short between DPFE SIG and VREF circuit. REMOVE breakout box. RECONNECT all components. RERUN Quick Test.
HE150 CHECK EGR SYSTEM VACUUM HOSES FOR INTEGRITY AND CONNECTION NOTE: A pinched or plugged EGR vacuum hose can trap vacuum between the EGR vacuum regulator (EGR V.R.) solenoid and EGR valve not allowing the EGR valve to close. • Key off. • Trace each vacuum hose from EGR V.R. solenoid and verify that each hose is connected correctly. (Refer to vehicle vacuum diagram label.) • Verify that the EGR valve vacuum hose is not pinched or plugged and routed properly. • **Are vacuum hoses OK?**	Yes	▶	RECONNECT vacuum hoses. GO to **HE151**.
	No	▶	SERVICE vacuum hoses as necessary. RECONNECT all components. COMPLETE PCM Reset to clear DTCs (REFER to Powertrain Control Module (PCM) Reset). RERUN Quick Test.

FM0159601516310X

Test Step	Result	▶	Action to Take
HE151 CHECK FOR EGR FLOW AT IDLE WITH EGR V.R. SOLENOID CONNECTOR OFF			
• Key on, engine off. • Note the DPFEGR PID voltage with the key on and engine off. • Disconnect EGR V.R. solenoid vehicle harness connector. • Start engine and bring to idle. • Compare DPFEGR PID voltage at idle to the engine off voltage. • **Is the DPFEGR PID voltage greater at idle by a minimum of 0.15 volts than with the engine off or is engine a no start or stall?**	Yes No	▶ ▶	This indicates an EGR V.R. solenoid mechanical fault. GO to HE152. GO to HE153.
HE152 INSPECT EGR V.R. SOLENOID VENT FOR PLUGGING			
• Key off. • Disconnect EGR V.R. solenoid vacuum hoses. • Remove EGR V.R. solenoid vent cap (if removable). • Remove filter and inspect for blockage or icing in some cases. • With the EGR V.R. vacuum supply port plugged, apply 10 to 15 in-Hg of vacuum directly to vacuum source port with a hand vacuum pump. If the vacuum holds or is slow to release to atmosphere, the EGR V.R. solenoid vent could be plugged or restricted. NOTE: A plugged EGR V.R. solenoid vent will not allow EGR vacuum to vent to atmosphere.	Yes No	▶ ▶	SERVICE EGR V.R. solenoid as necessary. If unable to service, REPLACE EGR V.R. solenoid. RECONNECT all components. COMPLETE PCM Reset to clear DTCs (REFER to Powertrain Control Module (PCM) Reset). RERUN Quick Test. REPLACE damaged EGR V.R. solenoid. RECONNECT all components. COMPLETE PCM Reset to clear DTCs (REFER to Powertrain Control Module (PCM) Reset). RERUN Quick Test.

EGR V.R. SOLENOID VENT

VACUUM SUPPLY PORT PLUGGED

APPLY VACUUM TO SOURCE PORT

• **Is the EGR V.R. solenoid vent or vent filter plugged or restricted?**

FM0159601516320X

Fig. 251   Test HE: Exhaust Gas Recirculation Systems (Part 32 of 37). 1996

Test Step	Result	▶	Action to Take
HE153 MEASURE EGR V.R. SOLENOID COIL RESISTANCE			
• Key off. • EGR V.R. solenoid disconnected. • Measure resistance across EGR V.R. solenoid. • **Is resistance between 26 and 40 ohms?**	Yes No	▶ ▶	GO to HE154. REPLACE damaged EGR V.R. solenoid. RECONNECT all components. COMPLETE PCM Reset to clear DTCs (REFER to Powertrain Control Module (PCM) Reset). RERUN Quick Test.
HE154 CHECK D.P.F. EGR SENSOR OUTPUT BY APPLYING VACUUM WITH HAND PUMP			
• Key off. • Disconnect pressure hoses at D.P.F. EGR sensor. • Connect a hand vacuum pump to the downstream pickup marked "REF" on the sensor. • Key on, engine off. • Access DPFEGR PID with a Scan Tool. PID voltage should be 0.45 ± 0.25 volts. • Apply 8-9 in-Hg vacuum to the D.P.F. EGR sensor. The PID voltage should be above 4.0 volts. Quickly release vacuum from sensor. PID voltage should drop to less than 1 volt in less than 3 seconds. • **Does the DPFEGR PID voltage indicate a fault in the D.P.F. EGR sensor?**	Yes No	▶ ▶	REPLACE damaged D.P.F. EGR sensor. RECONNECT all components. COMPLETE PCM Reset to clear DTCs (REFER to Powertrain Control Module (PCM) Reset). RERUN Quick Test. RECONNECT D.P.F. EGR sensor. GO to HE155.
HE155 CHECK EVR CIRCUIT FOR SHORT TO GROUND IN HARNESS			
• Key off. • EGR V.R. solenoid disconnected. • Disconnect PCM. Inspect for damaged or pushed out pins, corrosion, loose wires, etc. Service as necessary. • Install breakout box, leave PCM disconnected. • Measure resistance between Test Pin 47 (EVR) and Test Pins 51 and 103 (PWR GND) at the breakout box. • **Is resistance greater than 10,000 ohms?**	Yes No	▶ ▶	REPLACE damaged PCM. REMOVE breakout box. RECONNECT all components. RERUN Quick Test. SERVICE short between EVR circuit and GROUND. REMOVE breakout box. RECONNECT all components. RERUN Quick Test.

FM0159601516330X

Fig. 251   Test HE: Exhaust Gas Recirculation Systems (Part 33 of 37). 1996

Test Step	Result	▶	Action to Take
HE160 CHECK FOR REVERSED PRESSURE HOSES			
• Key off. • Visually inspect hoses for proper connection between D.P.F. EGR sensor and EGR orifice tube assembly. — The hose connection marked "HI" on the D.P.F. EGR sensor should connect to the exhaust side of the orifice tube and the connection marked "REF" connects to the intake manifold side of the orifice tube. The HI side hose has a larger inside diameter than the REF side hose. • **Are the D.P.F. EGR sensor pressure hoses connected properly?**	Yes No	▶ ▶	GO to HE161. SERVICE hoses as necessary (if hoses are replaced, USE only the service part and not a substitute). COMPLETE PCM Reset to clear DTCs (REFER to Powertrain Control Module (PCM) Reset). RERUN Quick Test.

D.P.F. EGR SENSOR

DOWNSTREAM PRESSURE HOSE   TO EGR VALVE   ORIFICE TUBE ASSEMBLY

EXHAUST MANIFOLD

UPSTREAM PRESSURE HOSE

Test Step	Result	▶	Action to Take
HE161 CHECK UPSTREAM AND DOWNSTREAM PRESSURE SIGNAL HOSES			
• Key off. • Remove and inspect both pressure signal hoses between D.P.F. EGR sensor and EGR orifice tube. • Look for disconnects, leaks, pinching, plugging, poor routing, incorrect hose substitution, and possible freezing in cold weather. • Check both the D.P.F. EGR sensor and orifice tube connections for plugging or damage. • **Is a fault found?**	Yes No	▶ ▶	SERVICE as necessary. Use only the service replacement hoses if new hoses are needed. COMPLETE PCM Reset (REFER to Powertrain Control Module (PCM) Reset). RERUN Quick Test. RECONNECT all components. GO to HE162.

FM0159601516340X

Fig. 251   Test HE: Exhaust Gas Recirculation Systems (Part 34 of 37). 1996

Test Step	Result	▶	Action to Take
HE162 CHECK D.P.F. EGR SENSOR OUTPUT BY APPLYING VACUUM WITH HAND PUMP			
• Key off. • Disconnect pressure hoses at D.P.F. EGR sensor. • Connect a hand vacuum pump to the downstream pickup marked "REF" on the sensor. • Key on, engine off. • Access DPFEGR PID with a Scan Tool. PID voltage should be 0.45 volt ± 0.25 volt. • Apply 8-9 in-Hg vacuum to the D.P.F. EGR sensor. The PID voltage should be above 4.0 volts. Quickly release vacuum from sensor. PID voltage should drop to less than 1.0 volt in less than 3 seconds. • **Does the DPFEGR PID voltage indicate a fault in the D.P.F. EGR sensor?**	Yes No	▶ ▶	REPLACE damaged D.P.F. EGR sensor. RECONNECT all components. COMPLETE PCM Reset to clear DTCs (REFER to Powertrain Control Module (PCM) Reset). RERUN Quick Test. RECONNECT pressure hoses. GO to HE163.
HE163 CHECK EGR VALVE FUNCTION BY APPLYING VACUUM WITH HAND PUMP			
• Key off. • Disconnect vacuum hose at EGR valve and plug hose. • Connect a hand vacuum pump to EGR valve. • Start engine and bring to idle. • Access DPFEGR and RPM PIDs with a Scan Tool. • Slowly apply 5-10 in-Hg of vacuum to the EGR valve and hold it for 10 seconds. If engine wants to stall, increase rpm with throttle to maintain a minimum of 800 rpm. • Look for the following: — EGR valve starts opening at about 1.6 in-Hg vacuum indicated by increasing DPFEGR PID voltage. — DPFEGR PID voltage increasing until EGR valve is fully open. DPFEGR PID should read 2.5 volts minimum with full vacuum applied. — DPFEGR PID voltage steady when vacuum is held. If voltage drops within a few seconds, the EGR valve or vacuum source could be leaking. • **Does the DPFEGR PID voltage indicate that the EGR valve is functioning as described in this test?**	Yes No	▶ ▶	RECONNECT all components. GO to HE164. REMOVE and INSPECT the EGR valve for signs of contamination, unusual wear, carbon deposits, binding, leaking diaphragm and other damage. If EGR valve is OK, look for an obstructed EGR port in the intake manifold. SERVICE as necessary (use Rotunda EGR Valve Cleaner 021-00056, if needed). RECONNECT all components. COMPLETE PCM Reset to clear DTCs (REFER to Powertrain Control Module (PCM) Reset). RERUN Quick Test.

FM0159601516350X

Fig. 251   Test HE: Exhaust Gas Recirculation Systems (Part 35 of 37). 1996

ELECTRONIC ENGINE CONTROL SYSTEM (EEC-V)

Test Step	Result	▶	Action to Take
HE164 CHECK VACUUM SOURCE AND VACUUM HOSES TO AND FROM EGR V.R. SOLENOID • Key off. • Disconnect vacuum hoses at EGR V.R. solenoid. • Connect EGR V.R. solenoid vacuum supply hose to a vacuum gauge. • With engine warm and at idle, take vacuum gauge reading. • Inspect vacuum lines between vacuum source and EGR V.R. solenoid EVR and between EGR V.R. solenoid and EGR valve for leaks, kinks, disconnects, blockage, routing or any damage. • **Is the vacuum gauge reading a minimum of 15 in-Hg at idle and vacuum lines OK?**	Yes No	▶ ▶	RECONNECT all components. GO to HE165. ISOLATE fault and SERVICE as necessary. RECONNECT all components. COMPLETE PCM Reset to clear DTCs (REFER to Powertrain Control Module (PCM) Reset). RERUN Quick Test.
HE165 CHECK VPWR TO EGR V.R. SOLENOID • Key off. • EGR V.R. solenoid disconnected. • Key on, engine off. • Measure voltage between VPWR circuit and chassis ground at the EGR V.R. solenoid vehicle harness connector. • **Is EGR V.R. solenoid VPWR voltage greater than 10.5 volts?**	Yes No	▶ ▶	GO to HE166. SERVICE open in EGR V.R. solenoid VPWR circuit. RECONNECT all components. COMPLETE PCM Reset to clear DTCs (REFER to Powertrain Control Module (PCM) Reset). RERUN Quick Test.
HE166 MEASURE RESISTANCE ACROSS EGR V.R. SOLENOID • Key off. • EGR V.R. solenoid disconnected. • Measure resistance across EGR V.R. solenoid. • **Is solenoid resistance between 26 and 40 ohms?**	Yes No	▶ ▶	GO to HE167. REPLACE damaged EGR V.R. solenoid. RECONNECT all components. COMPLETE PCM Reset to clear DTCs (REFER to Powertrain Control Module (PCM) Reset). RERUN Quick Test.
HE167 CHECK EVR CIRCUIT FOR SHORT TO PWR • Key off. • EGR V.R. solenoid disconnected. • Disconnect PCM. Inspect for damaged or pushed out pins, corrosion, loose wires, etc. Service as necessary. • Install breakout box, leave PCM disconnected. • Key on, engine off. • Measure voltage between Test Pin 47 (EVR) and chassis ground. • **Is voltage greater than 1.0 volt?**	Yes No	▶ ▶	SERVICE EVR circuit for short to PWR. RECONNECT all components. COMPLETE PCM Reset to clear DTCs (REFER to Powertrain Control Module (PCM) Reset). RERUN Quick Test. GO to HE168.

FM0159601516360X

Fig. 251   Test HE: Exhaust Gas Recirculation Systems (Part 36 of 37). 1996

Test Step	Result	▶	Action to Take
HE168 CHECK EVR CIRCUIT FOR OPEN IN HARNESS • Key off. • EGR V.R. solenoid disconnected. • Breakout box installed, PCM disconnected. • Measure resistance between Test Pin 47 (EVR) and EVR circuit at the EGR V.R. solenoid vehicle harness connector. • **Is resistance less than 5.0 ohms?**	Yes No	▶ ▶	RECONNECT EGR V.R. solenoid. GO to HE169. SERVICE open in EVR circuit. RECONNECT all components. COMPLETE PCM Reset to clear DTCs (REFER to Powertrain Control Module (PCM) Reset). RERUN Quick Test.
HE169 CHECK EGR V.R. SOLENOID VACUUM OUTPUT CAPABILITY BY GROUNDING EVR CIRCUIT • Key off. • Breakout box installed, PCM connected. • EGR V.R. solenoid connected. • Disconnect vacuum hose at the EGR valve and connect to a vacuum gauge. • Key on, engine running. • With engine at idle, jumper Test Pin 47 (EVR) to chassis ground. • **Is vacuum gauge reading 4.0 in-Hg or greater?**	Yes No	▶ ▶	REPLACE damaged PCM. RECONNECT all components. RERUN Quick Test. REPLACE damaged EGR V.R. solenoid. RECONNECT all components. COMPLETE PCM Reset to clear DTCs (REFER to Powertrain Control Module (PCM) Reset). RERUN Quick Test.
HE180 CONTINUOUS MEMORY DTC P0400: PERFORM EGR DRIVE CYCLE Continuous Memory Diagnostic Trouble Code (DTC) P0400 indicates that Self-Test has detected an EGR system malfunction sometime during vehicle operation. NOTE: If DTC P0400 is output in either Key On Engine Off (KOEO) or Key On Engine Running (KOER) Self-Test, go directly to step HE130. Possible causes: — Restricted EGR valve or EGR port. — Any EGR system failure occurring intermittently. • Record all DTCs received for reference. Complete a PCM reset to clear DTCs (refer to Powertrain Control Module (PCM) Reset). • Complete the EGR monitor drive cycle (refer to Drive Cycles). • Output all DTCs and perform both KOEO and KOER Self-Tests (refer to Section 5A, Diagnostic Subroutines). • **Is DTC P0400 output?**	Yes No	▶ ▶	If DTC P0400 is output in either KOEO or KOER Self-Test: GO to HE130. If DTC P0400 is only output from Continuous Memory: REMOVE and INSPECT the EGR valve and intake manifold for contamination and restriction. SERVICE as necessary (Use Rotunda EGR Valve Cleaner 021-00056, if needed). If no restriction is found, GO to Pinpoint Test Step Z1 with the following data: DPFEGR and EGRVR (formerly EVR) PIDs and list of Possible Causes. DTC P0400 is intermittent. GO to Pinpoint Test Step Z1 with the following data: DPFEGR and EGRVR (formerly EVR) PIDs and list of possible causes.

FM0159601516370X

Fig. 251   Test HE: Exhaust Gas Recirculation Systems (Part 37 of 37). 1996

Note

You should enter this Pinpoint Test only when directed here.

Remember

This Pinpoint Test is intended to diagnose the following:

• Exhaust system pipes (front and rear)
• Exhaust system muffler and tail-pipe assembly
• Catalytic converter
• Exhaust manifold
• Harness circuits: Downstream Heated Oxygen Sensors (HO2S)

FM0159601517010X

Fig. 252   Test HF: Catalyst Efficiency Monitor & Exhaust Systems (Part 1 of 8). 1996

Test Step	Result	▶	Action to Take
HF1 DTCs P0420, P0421, P0430 or P0431: CHECK FOR MISFIRE MONITOR DTCS Diagnostic Trouble Codes (DTC) P0420 and P0421 indicate that bank 1 catalyst system efficiency is below the acceptable threshold. Diagnostic Trouble Codes (DTC) P0430 and P0431 indicate that bank 2 catalyst system efficiency is below the acceptable threshold. NOTE 1: Complete the spark timing check in Quick Test before proceeding with this test step. Spark timing retarded below specification may increase exhaust gas temperature and decrease catalyst efficiency over time. NOTE 2: Be sure customer has not: (1) Refueled vehicle with leaded gasoline. (2) Experienced high vehicle oil consumption. NOTE 3: If entering this Pinpoint Test for symptoms only, go immediately to HF5. NOTE 4: Internal deterioration of a catalytic converter is usually caused by abnormal engine operation upstream of the catalyst. Events that may produce higher than normal temperatures in the catalyst are particularly suspect. For example, misfiring can cause higher than normal catalyst operating temperatures. Possible causes: — Use of leaded fuel. — Oil contamination. — Cylinder misfiring. — Damaged HO2S. — Damaged ECT sensor. — Downstream HO2S wires improperly connected. — Fuel pressure too high. — Damaged exhaust system pipe. — Damaged exhaust manifold. — Damaged muffler / tail-pipe assembly. — Damaged catalytic converter. • Key on, engine off. • Retrieve and record all Continuous Memory DTCs (MIL and non-MIL). • **Were any of the following misfire monitor DTCs recorded: P0300, P0301, P0302, P0303, P0304, P0305, P0306, P0307 and P0308?**	Yes No	▶ ▶	GO to Powertrain Diagnostic Trouble Code (DTC) Charts, to address the misfire monitor DTCs. GO to HF2.

FM0159601517020X

Fig. 252   Test HF: Catalyst Efficiency Monitor & Exhaust Systems (Part 2 of 8). 1996

Test Step	Result	▶	Action to Take
HF2 CHECK FOR HO2S MONITOR DTCS			
NOTE 1: Incorrect HO2S signal input (e.g. rich/lean input signal when the engine is operating under lean/rich conditions) may cause an abnormal temperature increase in the catalyst.	Yes	▶	GO to Powertrain Diagnostic Trouble Code (DTC) Charts, to address the HO2S Monitor DTCs.
NOTE 2: Non-California applications will not have an active HO2S monitor. As a result, a Catalyst Efficiency Monitor DTC can be generated for a rear HO2S concern on these applications, go to the HO2S monitor Pinpoint Test Step **H81**. If any repair actions are necessary in Pinpoint Test H, run KOER Self-Test, to verify the repair. If repair actions are not necessary, go to **HF3**.	No	▶	GO to **HF3**.
● Were any of the following HO2S monitor DTCs recorded in HF1: P0136, P0138, P0140 and P0141 (Bank 1, rear HO2S) or P0156, P0158, P0160 and P0161 (Bank 2, rear HO2S)?			
HF3 CHECK FOR ECT SENSOR DTCS			
NOTE: ECT sensor DTCs can be an indication that the thermostat is not operating correctly or that the coolant level is not filled to specifications, producing above normal operating temperatures.	Yes	▶	GO to Powertrain Diagnostic Trouble Code (DTC) Charts, to address the ECT sensor DTCs.
● Were any of the following ECT sensor DTCs recorded in HF1: P0117, P0118, P0125 and P1117?	No	▶	GO to **HF4**.
HF4 CHECK FOR ANY OTHER DTCS			
● Were any other DTCs recorded in HF1 (not including the initial P0420/P0421 or P0430/P0431 DTCs)?	Yes	▶	GO to Powertrain Diagnostic Trouble Code (DTC) Charts, to address the DTCs.
	No	▶	GO to **HF5**.
HF5 CHECK REAR HO2S WIRING			
NOTE: If the electrical connections of the rear HO2S are interchanged/crossed, the Catalyst Efficiency Monitor Test will be failed.	Yes	▶	Correctly route/connect the rear HO2S harness circuit(s). COMPLETE the PCM Reset to clear all DTCs (REFER to Powertrain Control Module (PCM) Reset). RERUN Quick Test.
● Inspect the wiring of each rear HO2S for proper routing and connection. ● Are the HO2S wires improperly routed?	No	▶	No EEC-V root causes related to the DTCs or symptoms. GO to **HF6**.

FM0159601517030X

Fig. 252   Test HF: Catalyst Efficiency Monitor & Exhaust Systems (Part 3 of 8). 1996

Test Step	Result	▶	Action to Take
HF6 CHECK FUEL PRESSURE			
WARNING: THE FUEL SYSTEM WILL REMAIN PRESSURIZED WHEN THE ENGINE IS NOT RUNNING. TO PREVENT INJURY OR FIRE, USE CAUTION WHEN WORKING ON THE FUEL SYSTEM.	Yes	▶	Fuel pressure is OK. REMOVE the fuel pressure gauge. GO to **HF7**.
NOTE: Fuel pressures above specification may produce an abnormally rich air/fuel mixture. The rich air/fuel mixture may cause higher than normal catalyst operating temperatures.	No	▶	Fuel pressure is out of specification. **For Probe:** REFER to Probe Fuel Delivery System
● Key off. ● Inspect the vacuum hose going to the fuel pressure regulator for proper installation, cracks, etc. Service as necessary. ● Install fuel pressure gauge. ● Verify vacuum source to fuel pressure regulator. ● Start and run the engine at idle. Record the fuel pressure. ● Increase engine speed to 2500 rpm and maintain for one minute. Record the fuel pressure. ● **Is the fuel pressure between 30 and 40 psi (210-310 kPa)?**			**All others:** REFER to Pinpoint Test Step **HC1**, Fuel Delivery Systems, for diagnosis. COMPLETE PCM Reset to clear DTCs (REFER to Powertrain Control Module (PCM) Reset). RERUN Quick Test.
HF7 CHECK FOR OBVIOUS LEAK SOURCES IN THE EXHAUST SYSTEM			
NOTE: If a catalyst is in series with a leaking exhaust system, it can fail the Catalyst Efficiency Monitor test.	Yes	▶	CHECK that the exhaust manifold to catalyst inlet pipe joint is tight. GO to **HF8**.
● Key off. ● Inspect the following for leaks, cracks, loose connections or punctures: — Exhaust manifold. — Front exhaust pipe. — Rear exhaust pipe. — Muffler/tail-pipe assembly. ● **Are the above components free of cracks and punctures, etc.?**	No	▶	REPLACE/REPAIR the leak source(s). COMPLETE PCM Reset to clear DTCs (REFER to Powertrain Control Module (PCM) Reset). RERUN Quick Test.
HF8 CHECK FOR OBVIOUS RESTRICTIONS IN THE EXHAUST SYSTEM			
● Inspect the following for dents, areas of collapsed material and unusual bending: — Front exhaust pipe. — Rear exhaust pipe. — Muffler/tail-pipe assembly. ● **Are the components free of dents and areas of collapsed material or unusual bending, etc.?**	Yes	▶	GO to **HF9**.
	No	▶	REPLACE/REPAIR the restricted component(s) as necessary. COMPLETE PCM Reset to clear DTCs (REFER to Powertrain Control Module (PCM) Reset). RERUN Quick Test.

FM0159601517040X

Fig. 252   Test HF: Catalyst Efficiency Monitor & Exhaust Systems (Part 4 of 8). 1996

Test Step	Result	▶	Action to Take
HF9 CHECK MANIFOLD VACUUM FOR INDICATION OF EXCESSIVE EXHAUST SYSTEM RESTRICTION			
● Attach a vacuum gauge to the intake manifold vacuum source. ● Install a tachometer. ● Observe the vacuum gauge needle while performing the following: NOTE: The vacuum gauge reading may be normal when the engine is first started and idled. However, excessive restriction in the exhaust system will cause the vacuum gauge needle to drop to a low point even while the engine is idled. — Start the engine and gradually increase the rpm to 2000 with the transmission in NEUTRAL. ● Decrease engine speed to base idle rpm. ● Key off. ● **Did manifold vacuum rise above 16 inches Hg with the engine rpm at 2000?**	Yes	▶	GO to **HF10**.
	No	▶	Manifold vacuum did not reach an acceptable level. An excessive restriction may be present. GO to **HF11**.

FM0159601517050X

Fig. 252   Test HF: Catalyst Efficiency Monitor & Exhaust Systems (Part 5 of 8). 1996

Test Step	Result	▶	Action to Take
HF10 CHECK MANIFOLD VACUUM FOR INDICATION OF MODERATE EXHAUST SYSTEM RESTRICTION			
● Vacuum gauge installed. ● Tachometer installed. ● Key on, engine idling. ● Increase the engine speed gradually from base idle rpm to 2000 rpm with the transmission in NEUTRAL. ● Observe the speed the vacuum gauge needle rises, while maintaining the increased engine rpm.	Yes	▶	A moderate restriction may be present. GO to **HF11**.
NOTE: 1 On a non-restricted exhaust system, the vacuum gauge needle will rise quickly to the normal range as the increased rpm is maintained. NOTE: 2 On a restricted exhaust system, the vacuum gauge needle will rise slowly to the normal range as the increased rpm is maintained. NOTE: 3 The rate of speed the vacuum gauge needle rises to the normal range is slower on a restricted system than on a non-restricted system as the increased rpm is maintained. ● Decrease engine speed to base idle rpm. ● Key off. ● **Is the rate of speed that the vacuum gauge needle rises back to the normal range (above 16 inches Hg) much slower than that of a non-restricted system?**	No	▶	No indications of restrictions or leaks have been detected in the exhaust system. If here because of DTCs P0420/P0421 or P0430/P0431, the catalytic converter is chemically inactive. REPLACE the catalytic converter, being careful to avoid improper routing of the rear HO2S. COMPLETE PCM Reset to clear DTCs (REFER to Powertrain Control Module (PCM) Reset). RERUN Quick Test. REMOVE the vacuum gauge and tachometer. For further diagnosis of symptom (e.g. Lack of Power, Loss of Power, or No Start) REFER to Symptom Flowcharts

FM0159601517060X

Fig. 252   Test HF: Catalyst Efficiency Monitor & Exhaust Systems (Part 6 of 8). 1996

ELECTRONIC ENGINE CONTROL SYSTEM (EEC-V)

Test Step	Result	▶	Action to Take
HF 11 CHECK MANIFOLD VACUUM WITH EXHAUST MANIFOLD DISCONNECTED FOR INDICATION OF A RESTRICTION			
• Key off.	Yes	▶	The exhaust system restriction is downstream of the exhaust manifold. RECONNECT exhaust system at exhaust manifold. GO to **HF 12**.
• Disconnect exhaust system immediately after the exhaust manifold.			
• Repeat the vacuum measurement found in test step H10.	No	▶	A restriction is present in the exhaust manifold. REMOVE the vacuum gauge and tachometer. INSPECT each exhaust port for casting flash/restrictions by dropping a length of chain into it (NOTE: Do not use a wire or lamp to check the ports. The restriction may be large enough for both to pass through, but small enough to cause excessive back pressure at high engine rpm.). REPLACE the exhaust manifold if unable to remove the casting flash/restriction. COMPLETE PCM Reset to clear DTCs (REFER to Powertrain Control Module (PCM) Reset). RERUN Quick Test.
• **Did the vacuum needle QUICKLY rise above 16 inches Hg with the engine rpm at 2000?**			
NOTE: An intake manifold gasket leak can also cause the vacuum gauge needle to remain well below the normal range.			

FM0159601517070X

Fig. 252   Test HF: Catalyst Efficiency Monitor & Exhaust Systems (Part 7 of 8). 1996

Test Step	Result	▶	Action to Take
HF 12 CHECK MANIFOLD VACUUM WITH MUFFLER/TAIL-PIPE ASSEMBLY DISCONNECTED FOR INDICATION OF A RESTRICTION			
• Key off.	Yes	▶	There is a restriction in the muffler/tail-pipe assembly. REPLACE the muffler/tail-pipe assembly. REMOVE the vacuum gauge and tachometer. COMPLETE PCM Reset to clear DTCs (REFER to Powertrain Control Module (PCM) Reset). RERUN Quick Test.
• Disconnect muffler/tail-pipe assembly located after the catalytic converter.			
• Repeat the vacuum measurement found in test step **HF10**.	No	▶	There is a restriction in the catalytic converter. REMOVE the vacuum gauge and tachometer. REPLACE the catalytic converter, being careful to avoid improper routing of the rear HO2S and INSPECT the muffler to be certain converter debris has not entered. RECONNECT muffler/tail-pipe assembly. COMPLETE PCM Reset to clear DTCs (REFER to Powertrain Control Module (PCM) Reset). RERUN Quick Test.
• **Did the vacuum needle QUICKLY rise above 16 inches Hg with the engine rpm at 2000?**			

FM0159601517080X

Fig. 252   Test HF: Catalyst Efficiency Monitor & Exhaust Systems (Part 8 of 8). 1996

Note

You should enter this Pinpoint Test only when directed here.

Remember

This Pinpoint Test is intended to diagnose only the following.

• Positive Crankcase Ventilation (PCV) valve (6A666) and related vacuum lines.

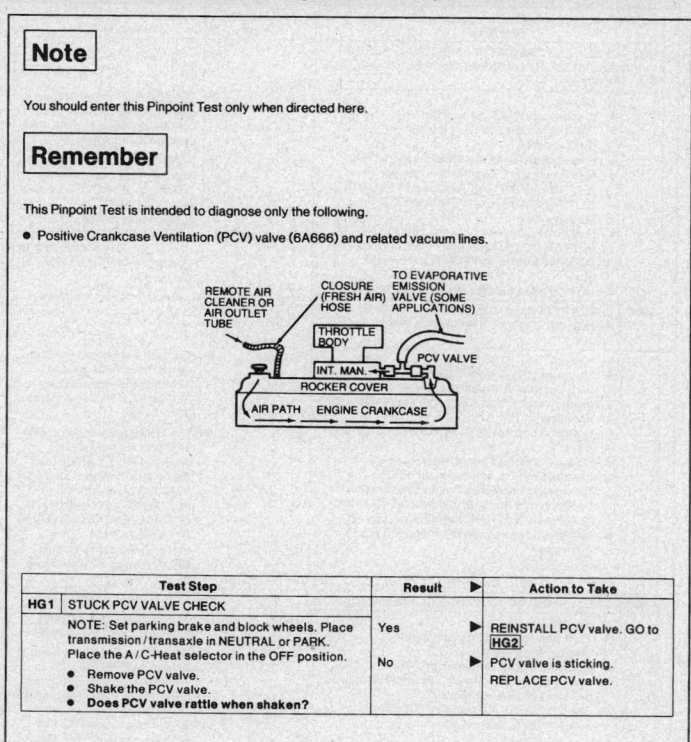

Test Step	Result	▶	Action to Take
HG1 STUCK PCV VALVE CHECK			
NOTE: Set parking brake and block wheels. Place transmission/transaxle in NEUTRAL or PARK. Place the A/C-Heat selector in the OFF position.	Yes	▶	REINSTALL PCV valve. GO to **HG2**.
• Remove PCV valve.	No	▶	PCV valve is sticking. REPLACE PCV valve.
• Shake the PCV valve.			
• **Does PCV valve rattle when shaken?**			

FM0159601518010X

Fig. 253   Test HG: Positive Crankcase Ventilation System (Part 1 of 2). 1996

Test Step	Result	▶	Action to Take
HG2 PCV SYSTEM CHECK			
• Start engine and bring to normal operating temperature.	Yes	▶	PCV System is OK. RECONNECT hose. RETURN to for other possible causes of vehicle symptoms.
• Disconnect closure (fresh air) hose from remote air cleaner or air outlet tube (tube connecting mass air meter and throttle body).	No	▶	System is leaking/plugged or Evaporative Emission System is leaking (if equipped). GO to **HG3**.
• Place a stiff piece of paper over the hose end. Wait one minute.			
• **Does vacuum hold the paper in place?**			
HG3 EVAPORATIVE EMISSION SYSTEM CHECK			
NOTE: If the evaporative emission hose is not connected to the PCV hose, follow the "No" Action to take in this test step (Refer to VECI decal).	Yes	▶	PCV system is OK. GO to Evaporative Emission System Testing. **For applications with Fuel Tank Pressure (FTP) sensor:** GO to Pinpoint Test Step **HX47**. **All others:** GO to Pinpoint Test Step **HW10**.
• Disconnect evaporative emission hose at connection to PCV hose (if equipped). Cap the connector.			
• Again place a stiff piece of paper over the closure (fresh air) hose, as in **HG2**. Wait one minute.	No	▶	CHECK for vacuum leaks/obstruction in the PCV system (e.g. oil cap, PCV valve, hoses, cut grommets, rocker cover bolt torque/gasket leak, etc). SERVICE as necessary.
• **Does vacuum now hold the paper in place?**			

FM0159601518020X

Fig. 253   Test HG: Positive Crankcase Ventilation System (Part 2 of 2). 1996

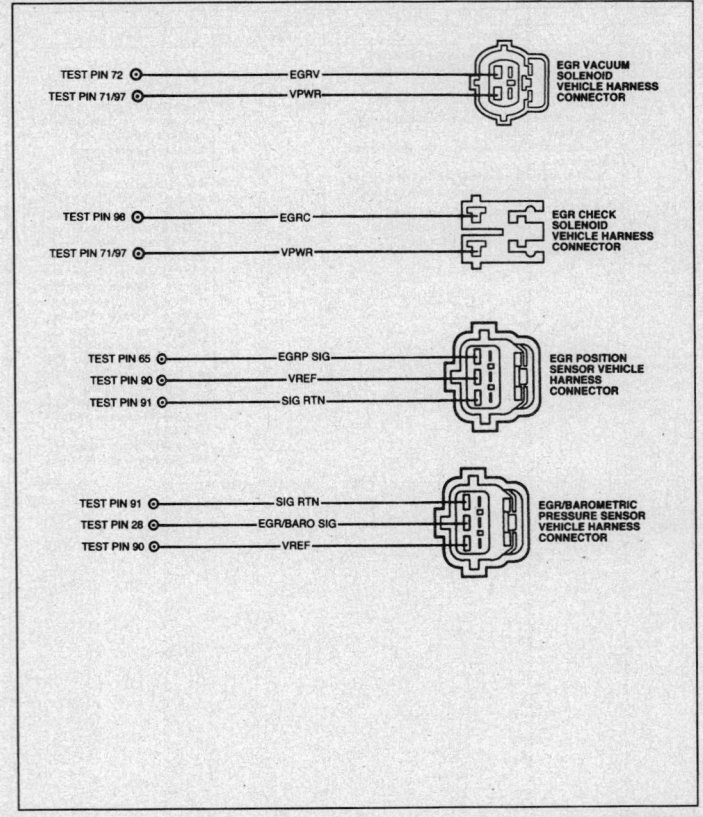

Note

You should enter this pinpoint test only when directed here.

Remember

This pinpoint test is intended to diagnose the following:

- Exhaust Gas Recirculation (EGR) Vacuum solenoid
- Exhaust Gas Recirculation (EGR) Atmospheric solenoid
- Exhaust Gas Recirculation (EGR) Valve Position sensor
- Exhaust Gas Recirculation (EGR) valve
- Exhaust Gas Recirculation (EGR) / Barometric (BARO) pressure sensor
- Vacuum lines
- Harness circuits: VREF, EGRV, EGRV VPWR, EGRA, EGRA VPWR, EGRP SIG, EGRP SIG RTN, EGRC VPWR, EGR / BARO SIG, EGR / BARO SIG RTN
- Powertrain Control Module (PCM)(12A650)

Pinpoint Test Schematic

FM0159601519010X
Fig. 254   Test HH: EGR Monitor & System (Part 1 of 25). 1996 Probe

FM0159601519020X
Fig. 254   Test HH: EGR Monitor & System (Part 2 of 25). 1996 Probe

Test Step		Result	▶	Action to Take
HH1	CONTINUOUS MEMORY DTC P0106: CHECK EGR BAROMETRIC PRESSURE SENSOR VREF VOLTAGE			
	Continuous Memory Diagnostic Trouble Code (DTC) P0106 indicates that the EGR Barometric Pressure sensor input signal is out of self-test range. Possible causes: — Damaged EGR Barometric Pressure sensor VREF harness circuit. — Open in EGR Barometric Pressure sensor SIG or SIG RTN harness circuits. — Short to power or ground in EGR Barometric Pressure sensor SIG harness circuit. — Damaged EGR Barometric Pressure sensor. — Damaged EGR Control solenoid-valve to EGR / BARO sensor hose. — Damage in EGR Control solenoid-valve circuits. — Damaged EGR Control solenoid-valve. — Damaged PCM. • Key on, engine off. • EGR Barometric Pressure sensor disconnected. • Measure voltage between VREF and SIG RTN circuits at the EGR Barometric Pressure sensor vehicle harness connector. • Key off. • **Is voltage between 4.0 and 6.0 volts?**	Yes No	▶ ▶	VREF voltage is in specification. GO to **HH2**. VREF voltage is not in specification. GO to Pinpoint Test Step **C1**.
HH2	CHECK CONTINUITY OF EGR BAROMETRIC PRESSURE SENSOR HARNESS CIRCUITS			
	• Key off. • EGR Barometric Pressure sensor disconnected. • Disconnect the PCM. Inspect for damaged or push out pins, corrosion, loose wires, etc. Service as necessary. • Install breakout box, leave PCM disconnected. • Measure the resistance between EGR / BARO SIG circuit at the EGR Barometric Pressure sensor vehicle harness connector and Test Pin 34 at the breakout box. • Measure the resistance between EGR / BARO SIG RTN circuit at the EGR Barometric Pressure sensor vehicle harness connector Test Pin 91 (SIG RTN) at the breakout box. • **Is each resistance less than 5 ohms?**	Yes No	▶ ▶	EGR Barometric Pressure sensor harness circuits are complete. GO to **HH3**. SERVICE open in appropriate EGR Barometric Pressure sensor harness circuit. COMPLETE PCM reset to clear DTCs (REFER to Powertrain Control Module (PCM) Reset). RERUN Quick Test.

FM0159601519030X
Fig. 254   Test HH: EGR Monitor & System (Part 3 of 25). 1996 Probe

Test Step		Result	▶	Action to Take
HH3	CHECK EGR BAROMETRIC PRESSURE SENSOR SIG CIRCUITS FOR SHORT TO GROUND AND POWER			
	• Key off. • Disconnect Scan Tool from DLC. • EGR Barometric Pressure sensor disconnected. • Breakout box installed, PCM disconnected. • Measure resistance between Test Pin 34 (EGR / BARO SIG) and Test Pins 91 (SIG RTN), 51 (PWR GND) and 103 (PWR GND) at the breakout box. • Measure resistance between Test Pin 34 (EGR / BARO SIG) and Test Pins 71 (VPWR), 90 (VREF) and 97 (VPWR) at the breakout box. • **Is resistance greater than 10,000 ohms?**	Yes No	▶ ▶	The EGR Barometric Pressure sensor SIG circuit does not contain any short circuits in the harness. GO to **HH4**. SERVICE short in EGR Barometric Pressure sensor SIG circuit. REMOVE breakout box. RECONNECT all components. COMPLETE PCM reset to clear DTCs (REFER to Powertrain Control Module (PCM) Reset). RERUN Quick Test.
HH4	CHECK RESPONSE OF EGR BAROMETRIC PRESSURE SENSOR TO MANUALLY APPLIED SIGNAL			
	• Key off. • Disconnect hose from EGR check solenoid to EGR Barometric Pressure sensor. • Inspect for damage, blockage, etc. Service as necessary. • Breakout box installed, PCM connected. • Key on. • Using a hand-held pump, slowly apply and maintain 21''-Hg, while measuring EGR Barometric Pressure sensor voltage response between Test Pin 34 (EGR / BARO SIG) and Test Pin 51 (PWR GND) of breakout box. • **Is the voltage response between 0.8 and 1.5 volts?**	Yes No	▶ ▶	The EGR Barometric Pressure sensor functions normally. REMOVE the vacuum pump. RECONNECT all components. GO to **HH5**. The EGR Barometric Pressure sensor is not functioning properly. REPLACE the EGR Barometric Pressure sensor. REMOVE breakout box. RECONNECT all components. COMPLETE PCM reset to clear DTCs (REFER to Powertrain Control Module (PCM) Reset). RERUN Quick Test.
HH5	CHECK VPWR AT EGR CONTROL SOLENOID			
	• Key off. • EGR Control solenoid disconnected. • Key on, engine idling. • Measure voltage between VPWR circuit and chassis ground at the EGR Control solenoid vehicle harness connector. • **Is EGR Control solenoid VPWR voltage greater than 10.5 volts?**	Yes No	▶ ▶	EGR Control solenoid has VPWR applied. GO to **HH6**. SERVICE open in EGR Control solenoid VPWR circuit. RECONNECT all components. COMPLETE PCM reset to clear DTCs (REFER to Powertrain Control Module (PCM) Reset). RERUN Quick Test.

FM0159601519040X
Fig. 254   Test HH: EGR Monitor & System (Part 4 of 25). 1996 Probe

Test Step	Result	►	Action to Take
HH6 CHECK RESISTANCE OF EGR CONTROL SOLENOID • Key off. • EGR Control solenoid disconnected. • Measure solenoid resistance. • **Is resistance between 30 and 70 ohms?**	Yes No	► ►	EGR Control solenoid resistance OK. GO to **HH7**. EGR Control solenoid resistance is out of specification. REPLACE the EGR Control solenoid. COMPLETE PCM reset to clear DTCs (REFER to Powertrain Control Module (PCM) Reset). RERUN Quick Test.
HH7 CHECK EGR CONTROL SOLENOID CIRCUIT CONTINUITY • Key off. • EGR Control solenoid disconnected. • Disconnect PCM. Inspect for damaged pushed out pins, corrosion, loose wires, etc. Service as necessary. • Install breakout box, leave PCM disconnected. • Measure resistance between Test Pin 98 (EGRC) at the breakout box and the EGRC circuit at the solenoid vehicle harness connector. • **Is the resistance less than 5.0 ohms?**	Yes No	► ►	EGR Control harness circuit is complete. GO to **HH8**. SERVICE open in EGR Control harness circuit. REMOVE the breakout box. RECONNECT all components. COMPLETE PCM Reset to clear DTCs (REFER to Powertrain Control Module (PCM) Reset). RERUN Quick Test.
HH8 CHECK EGR CONTROL SOLENOID CIRCUIT FOR SHORT TO POWER AND GROUND • Key off. • Disconnect Scan Tool from DLC. • EGR Control solenoid disconnected. • Breakout box installed, PCM disconnected. • Measure resistance between Test Pin 98 (EGRC) and Test Pins 71,97 (VPWR) and 90 (VREF) at the breakout box. • Measure resistance between Test Pin 98 (EGRC) and Test Pins 51,103 (PWR GND) and 91 (SIG RTN) at the breakout box. • **Is each resistance greater than 10,000 ohms?**	Yes No	► ►	The EGR Control solenoid harness circuits are free of shorts. REMOVE breakout box. RECONNECT all components. GO to **HH9**. SERVICE short in EGR Control solenoid harness circuit. REMOVE breakout box. RECONNECT all components. COMPLETE PCM reset to clear DTCs (REFER to Powertrain Control Module (PCM) Reset). RERUN Quick Test.

Fig. 254 Test HH: EGR Monitor & System (Part 5 of 25). 1996 Probe

Test Step	Result	►	Action to Take
HH9 CHECK EGR CONTROL SOLENOID VALVE OPERATION • Key off. • Breakout box installed, PCM connected. • Disconnect the vacuum line from the intake manifold vacuum reservoir to the EGR Control solenoid at the EGR Control solenoid. • Install vacuum pump at the input port of the EGR Control solenoid, apply 8 to 10"-Hg of the vacuum to the EGR Control solenoid. • Disconnect the vacuum line from the EGR Control solenoid to the EGR Barometric Pressure sensor at the EGR Control solenoid, install a vacuum gauge at the unattached end of the vacuum line. • Key on. • Momentarily jumper to ground Test Pin 98 (EGRC) at the breakout box and observe the vacuum gauge. • Key off. • **Was vacuum signal indicated by the vacuum gauge?**	Yes No	► ►	The EGR Control solenoid valve is functioning properly. REPLACE the damaged PCM. REMOVE the breakout box. REMOVE the vacuum gauge and vacuum pump. RECONNECT all components. COMPLETE PCM reset to clear DTCs (REFER to Powertrain Control Module (PCM) Reset). RERUN Quick Test. The EGR Control solenoid valve is not functioning properly. REPLACE the damaged EGR Control solenoid. REMOVE the breakout box. REMOVE the vacuum gauge and vacuum pump. RECONNECT all components. COMPLETE PCM reset to clear DTCs (REFER to Powertrain Control Module (PCM) Reset). RERUN Quick Test.
HH10 CONTINUOUS MEMORY DTC P0107: CHECK EGR BAROMETRIC PRESSURE SENSOR VREF VOLTAGE Continuous Memory Diagnostic Trouble Code (DTC) P0107 indicates that the EGR/BARO SIG circuit input is less than the self-test minimum. Possible causes: — Damaged EGR Barometric Pressure sensor VREF harness circuit. — Open in EGR Barometric Pressure sensor SIG circuit. — Short to GND in EGR/BARO circuit. — Damaged EGR Barometric Pressure sensor. — Damaged EGR Control solenoid to EGR Barometric Pressure sensor hose. — Damaged EGR Control solenoid-valve. — Damaged PCM. • Key on, engine off. • EGR Barometric Pressure sensor disconnected. • Measure voltage between VREF circuit and SIG RTN circuit at the EGR Barometric Pressure sensor vehicle harness connector. • **Is voltage between 4.0 and 6.0 volts?**	Yes No	► ►	VREF voltage is in specification. GO to **HH11**. VREF voltage is not in specification. GO to Pinpoint Test Step **C1**.

Fig. 254 Test HH: EGR Monitor & System (Part 6 of 25). 1996 Probe

Test Step	Result	►	Action to Take
HH11 CHECK CONTINUITY OF EGR BAROMETRIC PRESSURE SENSOR SIG CIRCUIT • Key off. • EGR Barometric Pressure sensor disconnected. • Disconnect the PCM. Inspect for damaged or pushed out pins, corrosion, loose wires, etc. Service as necessary. • Install breakout box, leave PCM disconnected. • Measure the resistance between EGR/BARO SIG circuit at the EGR Barometric Pressure sensor vehicle harness connector and Test Pin 34 at the breakout box. • **Is each resistance less than 5 ohms?**	Yes No	► ►	EGR Barometric Pressure sensor SIG circuit is complete. GO to **HH12**. SERVICE open in EGR Barometric Pressure sensor SIG circuit. COMPLETE PCM reset to clear DTCs (REFER to Powertrain Control Module (PCM) Reset). RERUN Quick Test.
HH12 CHECK EGR BAROMETRIC PRESSURE SIG CIRCUIT FOR SHORT TO GROUND • Key off. • Disconnect Scan Tool from DLC. • EGR Barometric Pressure sensor disconnected. • Breakout box installed, PCM disconnected. • Measure resistance between Test Pin 34 (EGR/BARO SIG) and Test Pins 91 (SIG RTN), 51 (PWR GND) and 103 (PWR GND) at the breakout box. • **Is resistance greater than 10,000 ohms?**	Yes No	► ►	EGR Barometric Pressure sensor SIG is not shorted to GND. GO to **HH13**. SERVICE short in EGR Barometric Pressure sensor SIG circuit. REMOVE breakout box. RECONNECT all components. COMPLETE PCM reset to clear DTCs (REFER to Powertrain Control Module (PCM) Reset). RERUN Quick Test.
HH13 CHECK RESPONSE OF EGR BAROMETRIC PRESSURE SENSOR TO MANUALLY APPLIED SIGNAL • Key off. • Disconnect hose from EGR check solenoid to EGR Barometric Pressure sensor. • Inspect for damage, blockage, etc. Service as necessary. • Breakout box installed, PCM connected. • Key on. • Using a hand-held pump, slowly apply and maintain 21"-Hg, while measuring EGR Barometric Pressure sensor voltage response between Test Pin 34 (EGR/BARO SIG) and Test Pin 51 (PWR GND) at the breakout box. • **Is the voltage response between 0.8 and 1.5 volts?**	Yes No	► ►	The EGR Barometric Pressure sensor functions normally. REMOVE the vacuum pump. RECONNECT all components. GO to **HH5**. The EGR Barometric Pressure sensor is not functioning properly. REPLACE the EGR Barometric Pressure sensor. REMOVE breakout box. RECONNECT all components. COMPLETE PCM reset to clear DTCs (REFER to Powertrain Control Module (PCM) Reset). RERUN Quick Test.

Fig. 254 Test HH: EGR Monitor & System (Part 7 of 25). 1996 Probe

Test Step	Result	►	Action to Take
HH20 CONTINUOUS MEMORY DTC P0108: CHECK EGR BAROMETRIC PRESSURE SENSOR VREF VOLTAGE Continuous Memory Diagnostic Trouble Code (DTC) P0108 indicates that the EGR Barometric Pressure sensor input signal is out of self-test range. Possible causes: — Damaged EGR Barometric Pressure sensor VREF circuit. — Open in EGR Barometric Pressure sensor SIG RTN circuit. — Short to PWR in EGR Barometric Pressure sensor SIG circuit. — Damaged EGR Barometric Pressure sensor. — Damaged EGR Control solenoid to EGR Barometric Pressure sensor hose. — Damage in EGR Control solenoid-valve. — Damaged PCM. • Key on, engine off. • EGR Barometric Pressure sensor disconnected. • Measure voltage between VREF circuit and SIG RTN circuit at the EGR Barometric Pressure sensor vehicle harness connector. • **Is voltage between 4.0 and 6.0 volts?**	Yes No	► ►	VREF voltage is in specification. GO to **HH21**. VREF voltage is not in specification. GO to Pinpoint Test Step **C1**.
HH21 CHECK CONTINUITY OF EGR BAROMETRIC PRESSURE SENSOR SIG RTN CIRCUIT • Key off. • EGR Barometric Pressure sensor disconnected. • Disconnect the PCM. Inspect for damaged or push out pins, corrosion, loose wires, etc. Service as necessary. • Install breakout box, leave PCM disconnected. • Measure the resistance between EGR Barometric Pressure SIG RTN circuit at the EGR Barometric Pressure sensor vehicle harness connector Test Pin 91 at the breakout box. • **Is each resistance less than 5 ohms?**	Yes No	► ►	EGR Barometric Pressure sensor SIG RTN circuit is complete. GO to **HH22**. SERVICE open in EGR Barometric Pressure sensor SIG RTN circuit. COMPLETE PCM reset to clear DTCs (REFER to Powertrain Control Module (PCM) Reset). RERUN Quick Test.

Fig. 254 Test HH: EGR Monitor & System (Part 8 of 25). 1996 Probe

Test Step	Result	▶	Action to Take
HH22 CHECK EGR BAROMETRIC PRESSURE SENSOR SIG CIRCUIT FOR SHORT TO POWER • Key off. • EGR Barometric Pressure sensor disconnected. • Breakout box installed, PCM disconnected. • Measure resistance between Test Pin 34 (EGR/BARO SIG) and Test Pins 71, 97 (VPWR) and 90 (VREF) at the breakout box. • **Is resistance greater than 10,000 ohms?**	Yes No	▶ ▶	The EGR Barometric Pressure sensor SIG is not shorted to POWER. GO to **HH23**. SERVICE short in EGR Barometric Pressure sensor SIG circuit. REMOVE breakout box. RECONNECT all components. COMPLETE PCM reset to clear DTCs (REFER to Powertrain Control Module (PCM) Reset). RERUN Quick Test.
HH23 CHECK RESPONSE OF EGR BAROMETRIC PRESSURE SENSOR TO MANUALLY APPLIED SIGNAL • Key off. • Disconnect hose from EGR check solenoid to EGR Barometric Pressure sensor. • Inspect for damage, blockage, etc. Service as necessary. • Breakout box installed, PCM connected. • Key on. • Using a hand-held pump, slowly apply and maintain 21"-Hg, while measuring EGR Barometric Pressure sensor voltage response between Test Pin 34 (EGR/BARO SIG) and Test Pin 51 (PWR GND) at the breakout box. • **Is the voltage response between 0.8 and 1.5 volts?**	Yes No	▶ ▶	The EGR Barometric Pressure sensor functions normally. REMOVE the vacuum pump. RECONNECT all components. GO to **HH5**. The EGR Barometric Pressure sensor is not functioning properly. REPLACE the EGR Barometric Pressure sensor. REMOVE breakout box. RECONNECT all components. COMPLETE PCM reset to clear DTCs (REFER to Powertrain Control Module (PCM) Reset). RERUN Quick Test.

FM0159601519090X

Fig. 254 Test HH: EGR Monitor & System (Part 9 of 25). 1996 Probe

Test Step	Result	▶	Action to Take
HH30 DTC P1400: VERIFY EGR POSITION SIGNAL VOLTAGE Diagnostic Trouble Code (DTC) P1400 indicates that the EGRP SIG circuit input is less than the self-test minimum. Possible Causes: — Damaged EGR Position sensor/EGR valve assembly. — Open in EGR Position sensor VREF circuit. — Open in EGR Position sensor SIG RTN circuit. — Short to GND in EGR Position sensor SIG circuit. — Damaged PCM. • Key on, engine off. • Access EGRVP (EGR Valve position sensor input) PID with a Scan Tool. • **Is EGRVP PID less than 0.2 volt?**	Yes No	▶ ▶	The EGR Position sensor voltage is less than the acceptable minimum. GO to **HH31**. The fault that produced DTC P1400 is intermittent. GO to **HH35**.
HH31 ATTEMPT TO GENERATE OPPOSITE CODE • Key off. • Disconnect EGR Position sensor. • Jumper the VREF circuit to the EGR Position sensor SIG circuit at the sensor vehicle harness connector. • Rerun KOEO and KOER self-test, if the vehicle will not start, immediately remove the jumper wire and go to step **HH34**. • **Is DTC P1401 present (ignore all other DTCs)?**	Yes No	▶ ▶	The EGR Position sensor harness circuits and the PCM are in proper working condition. REPLACE the EGR Position sensor/EGR valve assembly. COMPLETE PCM reset to clear DTCs (REFER to Powertrain Control Module (PCM) Reset). RERUN Quick Test. The EGR Position sensor harness circuits and the PCM are suspect. REMOVE the jumper wire. GO to **HH32**.
HH32 CHECK EGR POSITION SENSOR VREF VOLTAGE • Key on, engine off. • EGR Position sensor disconnected. • Measure voltage between VREF circuit and SIG RTN circuit at the EGR Position sensor vehicle harness connector. • **Is voltage between 4.0 and 6.0 volts?**	Yes No	▶ ▶	VREF voltage is in specification. GO to **HH33**. VREF voltage is not in specification. GO to Pinpoint Test Step **C1**.

FM0159601519100X

Fig. 254 Test HH: EGR Monitor & System (Part 10 of 25). 1996 Probe

Test Step	Result	▶	Action to Take
HH33 CHECK CONTINUITY OF EGR POSITION SENSOR SIG RTN CIRCUIT • Key off. • EGR Position sensor disconnected. • Disconnect the PCM. Inspect for damaged pushed out pins, corrosion, loose wires, etc. Service as necessary. • Install breakout box, leave PCM disconnected. • Measure resistance between EGRP SIG RTN circuit at the EGR Position sensor vehicle harness connector and Test Pin 91 at the breakout box. • **Is resistance less than 5 ohms?**	Yes No	▶ ▶	EGRP SIG RTN circuit is complete. GO to **HH34**. SERVICE open in EGRP SIG RTN circuit. COMPLETE PCM reset to clear DTCs (REFER to Powertrain Control Module (PCM) Reset). RERUN Quick Test.
HH34 CHECK EGR POSITION SENSOR SIG CIRCUIT FOR SHORT TO GROUND • Key off. • Disconnect Scan Tool from DLC. • EGR Position sensor disconnected. • Breakout box installed, PCM disconnected. • Measure resistance between Test Pin 65 (EGRP SIG) and Test Pins 91 (SIG RTN), 51 and 103 (PWR GND) at the breakout box. • **Is resistance greater than 10,000 ohms?**	Yes No	▶ ▶	REPLACE damaged PCM. REMOVE breakout box. RECONNECT all components. COMPLETE PCM reset to clear DTCs (REFER to Powertrain Control Module (PCM) Reset). RERUN Quick Test. SERVICE short in EGRP SIG circuit. REMOVE breakout box. RECONNECT all components. COMPLETE PCM reset to clear DTCs (REFER to Powertrain Control Module (PCM) Reset). RERUN Quick Test.
HH35 WIGGLE TEST SENSOR AND HARNESS • Key on, engine off. • Access EGRVP PID with a Scan Tool. • Observe EGRVP PID for an indication of a fault while performing the following: — Lightly tap on EGR Position sensor. — Wiggle the EGR Position sensor connector and vehicle harness between sensor and PCM. A fault is indicated by a sudden change in EGRVP PID voltage. • **Is a fault indicated?**	Yes No	▶ ▶	ISOLATE fault and SERVICE as necessary. RECONNECT all components. COMPLETE PCM reset to clear DTCs (REFER to Powertrain Control Module (PCM) Reset). RERUN Quick Test. Unable to duplicate and/or identify fault at this time. GO to Pinpoint Test Step **Z1** with the following data: EGRV PID and list of Possible Causes.

FM0159601519110X

Fig. 254 Test HH: EGR Monitor & System (Part 11 of 25). 1996 Probe

Test Step	Result	▶	Action to Take
HH40 DTC P1401: VERIFY EGR POSITION SENSOR SIGNAL VOLTAGE Diagnostic Trouble Code (DTC) P1401 indicates that the EGRP SIG circuit input is greater than the self-test maximum. Possible Causes: — Damaged EGR Position sensor/EGR valve assembly. — Open in EGR Position sensor harness circuit. — Short to EGR Position sensor harness circuit. — Damaged EGR Vacuum solenoid. — Damaged EGR Vacuum solenoid harness circuits. — Damaged EGR Vacuum solenoid-valve. — Damaged PCM. • Key on, engine off. • Access EGRVP (EGR Valve position sensor input) PID with a Scan Tool. • **Is EGRVP PID greater than 4.0?**	Yes No	▶ ▶	The EGRP SIG circuit input voltage is greater than the acceptable maximum. GO to **HH41**. The fault that produced DTC P1401 is intermittent. GO to **HH49**.
HH41 ATTEMPT TO GENERATE OPPOSITE DTC • Key off. • Disconnect EGR Position sensor. • Connect a jumper wire between the EGR Position sensor SIG and SIG RTN circuits at the EGR Position sensor vehicle harness connector. • Rerun KOEO and KOER self-test (if the vehicle will not start, immediately remove the jumper wire and go to step **HH44**). • **Is DTC P1400 present (ignore all other DTCs)?**	Yes No	▶ ▶	The EGR Position sensor harness circuits are OK. REMOVE jumper wire. GO to **HH45**. REMOVE the jumper wire. GO to **HH42**.
HH42 CHECK CONTINUITY OF EGR POSITION SENSOR SIG CIRCUIT • Key off. • EGR Position sensor disconnected. • Disconnect the PCM. Inspect for damaged or pushed out pins, corrosion, loose wires, etc. Service as necessary. • Install breakout box, leave the PCM disconnected. • Measure the resistance between EGR Position sensor SIG circuit at the EGR Position sensor vehicle harness connector and Test Pin 65 (EGRP SIG) at the breakout box. • **Is resistance less than 5 ohms?**	Yes No	▶ ▶	The EGR Position sensor SIG circuit is complete. GO to **HH43**. SERVICE open in EGR Position sensor SIG circuit. REMOVE breakout box. RECONNECT all components. COMPLETE PCM reset to clear DTCs (REFER to Powertrain Control Module (PCM) Reset). RERUN Quick Test.

FM0159601519120X

Fig. 254 Test HH: EGR Monitor & System (Part 12 of 25). 1996 Probe

ELECTRONIC ENGINE CONTROL SYSTEM (EEC-V)

Test Step	Result	▶	Action to Take
HH43 CHECK CONTINUITY OF EGR POSITION SENSOR SIG RTN CIRCUIT			
• Key off. • EGR Position sensor disconnected. • PCM disconnected. • Measure the resistance between EGR Position sensor SIG RTN circuit at the EGR Position sensor vehicle harness connector and Test Pin 91 (SIG RTN) at the breakout box. • **Is resistance less than 5 ohms?**	Yes	▶	The EGR Position sensor SIG RTN circuit is complete. GO to **HH44**.
	No	▶	SERVICE open in EGR Position sensor SIG RTN circuit. REMOVE breakout box. RECONNECT all components. COMPLETE PCM reset to clear DTCs (REFER to Powertrain Control Module (PCM) Reset). RERUN Quick Test.
HH44 CHECK EGR POSITION SENSOR SIG CIRCUIT FOR SHORT TO POWER			
• Key off. • EGR Position sensor disconnected. • Breakout box installed, PCM disconnected. • Measure resistance between Test Pin 65 (EGRP SIG) and Test Pins 71 (VPWR), 90 (VREF) and 97 (VPWR) at the breakout box. • **Is resistance greater than 10,000 ohms?**	Yes	▶	REPLACE the damaged PCM. REMOVE breakout box. RECONNECT all components.
	No	▶	SERVICE short to power in EGR Position sensor SIG circuit. REMOVE breakout box. RECONNECT all components. COMPLETE PCM reset to clear DTCs (REFER to Powertrain Control Module (PCM) Reset). RERUN Quick Test.
HH45 CHECK EGR VACUUM SOLENOID CIRCUIT FOR SHORT TO GROUND			
• Key off. • Disconnect Scan Tool from DLC. • EGR Vacuum solenoid disconnected. • Breakout box installed, PCM disconnected. • Measure resistance between Test Pin 71 (EGRV) and Test Pins 23, 77 and 103 (PWR GND) at the breakout box. • **Is each resistance greater than 10,000 ohms?**	Yes	▶	The EGR Vacuum solenoid harness circuits do not contain any shorts to ground. REMOVE breakout box. RECONNECT all components. GO to **HH46**.
	No	▶	SERVICE short in EGR Vacuum solenoid harness circuit. REMOVE breakout box. RECONNECT all components. COMPLETE PCM reset to clear DTCs (REFER to Powertrain Control Module (PCM) Reset). RERUN Quick Test.

FM0159601519130X

Fig. 254   Test HH: EGR Monitor & System (Part 13 of 25). 1996 Probe

Test Step	Result	▶	Action to Take
HH46 CHECK EGR VACUUM SOLENOID-VALVE			
• Key off. • Breakout box installed, PCM disconnected. • Disconnect the vacuum line from the EGR Vacuum solenoid to the EGR Atmospheric solenoid. Install a vacuum gauge at the unattached end of the vacuum line. • Disconnect the vacuum line from the intake manifold vacuum reservoir to the EGR Vacuum solenoid. • Install a vacuum pump at the input port of the EGR Vacuum solenoid and apply 8 to 10"-Hg of vacuum to the EGR Vacuum solenoid while observing the vacuum gauge. • **Is a vacuum signal indicated by the vacuum gauge?**	Yes	▶	The EGR Vacuum solenoid-valve is stuck open. REPLACE the damaged EGR Vacuum solenoid. REMOVE the breakout box. REMOVE vacuum gauge and pump. RECONNECT all components. COMPLETE PCM reset to clear DTCs (REFER to Powertrain Control Module (PCM) Reset). RERUN Quick Test.
	No	▶	The EGR Vacuum solenoid-valve is OK. GO to **HH47**.
HH47 CHECK PCM CONTROL OF EGR VACUUM SOLENOID			
• Key off. • Breakout box installed, PCM connected. • Vacuum gauge installed between the EGR Vacuum and EGR Atmospheric solenoids. • Vacuum pump installed at input port of the EGR Atmospheric solenoid and apply 8 to 10"-Hg of vacuum is applied to the EGR Vacuum solenoid. • Key on and observe the vacuum gauge. • **Is a vacuum signal indicated by the vacuum gauge once the key is on?**	Yes	▶	The PCM is improperly energizing the EGR Vacuum solenoid-valve. REPLACE the damaged PCM. REMOVE the breakout box. REMOVE the vacuum gauge and pump. RECONNECT all components. RERUN Quick Test.
	No	▶	The PCM is not properly energizing the EGR Vacuum solenoid-valve. GO to **HH48**.

FM0159601519140X

Fig. 254   Test HH: EGR Monitor & System (Part 14 of 25). 1996 Probe

Test Step	Result	▶	Action to Take
HH48 CHECK EGR VACUUM SOLENOID ELECTRO-MECHANICAL OPERATION			
• Key off. • Breakout box installed, PCM connected. • Vacuum gauge installed between the EGR Vacuum and EGR Atmospheric solenoids. • Vacuum pump installed at input port of the EGR Vacuum solenoid and apply 8 to 10"-Hg of vacuum is applied to the EGR Vacuum solenoid. • Key on. • Momentarily jumper Test Pin 72 (EGRV) to Test Pin 103 (PWR GND) at the breakout box and observe the vacuum gauge. • Key off. • **Was a vacuum signal indicated by the vacuum gauge?**	Yes	▶	THe electro-mechanical operation of the EGR Vacuum solenoid-valve is OK. REPLACE the EGR Position sensor / EGR valve assembly. REMOVE the breakout box. REMOVE the vacuum gauge and pump. RECONNECT all components. COMPLETE PCM reset to clear DTCs (REFER to Powertrain Control Module (PCM) Reset). RERUN Quick Test.
	No	▶	The electro-mechanical operation of the EGR Vacuum solenoid-valve is damaged. REPLACE the EGR Vacuum solenoid-valve. REMOVE the breakout box. REMOVE the vacuum gauge and pump. RECONNECT all components. COMPLETE PCM reset to clear DTCs (REFER to Powertrain Control Module (PCM) Reset). RERUN Quick Test.
HH49 WIGGLE TEST SENSOR AND HARNESS			
• Key on, engine off. • Access EGRVP PID with a Scan Tool. • Observe EGRVP PID for an indication of a fault while performing the following: — Lightly tap on EGR Position sensor. — Wiggle the EGRP sensor connector and vehicle harness between sensor and PCM. A fault is indicated by a sudden change in EGRVP PID voltage. • **Is a fault indicated?**	Yes	▶	ISOLATE fault and SERVICE as necessary. RECONNECT all components. COMPLETE PCM reset to clear DTCs (REFER to Powertrain Control Module (PCM) Reset). RERUN Quick Test.
	No	▶	Unable to duplicate and / or identify fault at this time. GO to Pinpoint Test Step **Z1** with the following data: EGRV PID and list of Possible Causes.

FM0159601519150X

Fig. 254   Test HH: EGR Monitor & System (Part 15 of 25). 1996 Probe

Test Step	Result	▶	Action to Take
HH50 KOER DTC P1408: CHECK FOR VACUUM SIGNAL TO EGR VALVE			
Diagnostic Trouble Code (DTC) P1408 indicates a lack of EGR valve movement was detected by the EGR Position sensor circuit during KOER self-test. NOTE: If DTCs P1400 (Continuous Memory or KOER), P1401 (Continuous Memory or KOER) of P1407 (Continuous Memory) are present, GO to Powertrain Control Module (PCM) Charts and address them before continuing. DTC P1400 should be addresses first if it is still present. Possible causes: — Damaged vacuum lines. — Damaged EGR Atmospheric solenoid. — Damaged EGR Atmospheric solenoid harness circuits. — Damaged EGR Atmospheric solenoid-valve. — Damaged EGR valve. — Damaged EGR Vacuum solenoid. — Damaged EGR Vacuum solenoid harness circuits. — Damaged EGR Vacuum solenoid-valve. — Damaged PCM. • Key off. • Disconnect vacuum line from the EGR Atmospheric solenoid to the EGR valve at the EGR valve. • Install vacuum gauge at unattached end of the disconnected vacuum line. • Rerun KOER self-test while observing the vacuum gauge (ignore any DTCs output during KOER). • Key off. • **Did the vacuum gauge indicate a vacuum signal was present during part of KOER self-test?**	Yes	▶	The EGR valve has vacuum applied to it under normal KOER conditions. Disconnect the vacuum gauge. GO to **HH51**.
	No	▶	The EGR valve does not have a vacuum applied to it under normal KOER conditions. Disconnect the vacuum gauge. REMOVE and INSPECT the vacuum line. If OK, RECONNECT the vacuum line and GO to **HH52**, otherwise SERVICE the vacuum line as necessary and RECONNECT all components. COMPLETE PCM reset to clear DTCs (REFER to Powertrain Control Module (PCM) Reset). RERUN Quick Test.

FM0159601519160X

Fig. 254   Test HH: EGR Monitor & System (Part 16 of 25). 1996 Probe

Test Step	Result	▶	Action to Take
HH51 CHECK RESPONSE OF EGR VALVE TO MANUALLY APPLIED VACUUM SIGNAL ● Key off. ● Vacuum line from the EGR Atmospheric solenoid to the EGR valve disconnected at the EGR valve. ● Install the breakout box, PCM connected. ● Key on. ● Using a hand-held vacuum pump, slowly apply and remove 7"-Hg of vacuum repeatedly, while measuring the EGR Position sensor voltage response between Test Pin 65 (EGRP SIG) and Test Pin 91 (SIG RTN) at the breakout box. ● **Based on EGR Position sensor voltage, does the EGR valve open and close in as the vacuum signal is applied and removed?**	Yes	▶	The EGR valve functions normally; the PCM is not properly receiving/utilizing information from the EGR Position sensor. REMOVE the vacuum pump. REMOVE the breakout box. REPLACE the damaged PCM. RECONNECT all components. COMPLETE PCM reset to clear DTCs (REFER to Powertrain Control Module (PCM) Reset). RERUN Quick Test.
	No	▶	The EGR valve does not open and close properly. REMOVE the vacuum pump. REMOVE the breakout box. REPLACE the damaged EGR Position sensor/EGR valve assembly. RECONNECT all components, COMPLETE PCM reset to clear DTCs (REFER to Powertrain Control Module (PCM) Reset). RERUN Quick Test.

FM0159601519170X

Fig. 254 Test HH: EGR Monitor & System (Part 17 of 25). 1996 Probe

Test Step	Result	▶	Action to Take
HH52 CHECK FOR VACUUM SIGNAL TO EGR ATMOSPHERIC SOLENOID ● Key off. ● Disconnect vacuum line from the EGR Vacuum solenoid to the EGR Atmospheric solenoid at the EGR Atmospheric solenoid input port. ● Install vacuum gauge at unattached end of the disconnected vacuum line. ● Rerun KOER self-test while observing the vacuum gauge (ignore any DTCs output during KOER). ● Key off. ● **Did the vacuum gauge indicate a vacuum signal was present during part of KOER self-test?**	Yes	▶	The EGR Vacuum solenoid electrical and vacuum circuits are operating properly. REMOVE the vacuum gauge. RECONNECT the vacuum line. GO to HH53.
	No	▶	The EGR Atmospheric solenoid does not have vacuum applied to it under normal KOER conditions. Disconnect the vacuum gauge. REMOVE and INSPECT the vacuum line. If O.K., RECONNECT the vacuum line and GO to HH58, otherwise service the vacuum line as necessary and RECONNECT all components. COMPLETE PCM reset to clear DTCs (REFER to Powertrain Control Module (PCM) Reset). RERUN Quick Test.
HH53 CHECK VPWR TO EGR ATMOSPHERIC SOLENOID ● Key off. ● EGR Atmospheric solenoid disconnected. ● Key on, engine off. ● Measure voltage between VPWR circuit and chassis ground at the EGR Atmospheric solenoid vehicle harness connector. ● **Is EGR Atmospheric solenoid VPWR voltage greater than 10.5 volts?**	Yes	▶	EGR Atmospheric solenoid normally has VPWR applied to it. GO to HH54.
	No	▶	SERVICE open in EGR Atmospheric solenoid VPWR circuit. RECONNECT all components. COMPLETE PCM reset to clear DTCs (REFER to Powertrain Control Module (PCM) Reset). RERUN Quick Test.

FM0159601519180X

Fig. 254 Test HH: EGR Monitor & System (Part 18 of 25). 1996 Probe

Test Step	Result	▶	Action to Take
HH54 CHECK RESISTANCE OF EGR ATMOSPHERIC SOLENOID ● Key off. ● EGR Atmospheric solenoid disconnected. ● Measure solenoid resistance. ● **Is resistance between 30 and 70 ohms?**	Yes	▶	EGR Atmospheric solenoid resistance is OK. Go to HH55.
	No	▶	EGR Atmospheric solenoid resistance is out of specification. REPLACE the EGR Atmospheric solenoid. COMPLETE PCM reset to clear DTCs (REFER to Powertrain Control Module (PCM) Reset). RERUN Quick Test.
HH55 CHECK EGR ATMOSPHERIC SOLENOID CIRCUIT CONTINUITY ● Key off. ● EGR Atmospheric solenoid disconnected. ● Disconnect PCM. Inspect for damaged pushed out pins, corrosion, loose wires, etc. Service as necessary. ● Install breakout box, leave PCM disconnected. ● Measure resistance between Test Pin 68 (EGRA) at the breakout box and the EGR Atmospheric circuit at the solenoid vehicle harness connector. ● **Is the resistance less than 5.0 ohms?**	Yes	▶	EGR Atmospheric harness circuit is complete. GO to HH56.
	No	▶	SERVICE open in EGR Atmospheric harness circuit. REMOVE the breakout box. RECONNECT all components. COMPLETE PCM Reset to clear DTCs (REFER to Powertrain Control Module (PCM) Reset). RERUN Quick Test.
HH56 CHECK EGR ATMOSPHERIC SOLENOID CIRCUIT FOR SHORT TO POWER AND SHORT TO GROUND ● Key off. ● Disconnect Scan Tool from DLC. ● EGR Atmoshperic solenoid disconnected. ● Breakout box installed, PCM disconnected. ● Measure resistance between Test Pin 68 (EGRA) and Test Pins 71, 97 (VPWR) and 90 (VREF) at the breakout box. ● Measure resistance between Test Pin 68 (EGRA) and Test Pins 51, 103 (PWR GND) and 91 (SIG RTN) at the breakout box. ● **Is each resistance greater than 10,000 ohms?**	Yes	▶	The EGR Atmospheric solenoid harness circuits are free of shorts. REMOVE breakout box. RECONNECT all components. GO to HH57.
	No	▶	SERVICE short in EGR Atmospheric solenoid harness circuit. REMOVE breakout box. RECONNECT all components. COMPLETE PCM reset to clear DTCs (REFER to Powertrain Control Module (PCM) Reset). RERUN Quick Test.

FM0159601519190X

Fig. 254 Test HH: EGR Monitor & System (Part 19 of 25). 1996 Probe

Test Step	Result	▶	Action to Take
HH57 CHECK EGR ATMOSPHERIC SOLENOID VALVE FUNCTION ● Key off. ● Breakout box installed, PCM connected. ● Disconnect the vacuum line from the EGR Vacuum solenoid to the EGR Atmospheric solenoid at the EGR Atmospheric solenoid. ● Install vacuum pump at the input port of the EGR Atmospheric solenoid. ● Disconnect the vacuum line from the EGR Atmospheric solenoid to the EGR valve at the EGR valve, install a vacuum gauge at the unattached end of the vacuum line. ● Disconnect the vacuum line from the EGR Atmospheric solenoid to the air cleaner at the cleaner, plug the vacuum line at the unattached end. ● Key on. ● Apply 8 to 10"-Hg of the vacuum to the EGR Atmospheric solenoid. ● Momentarily jumper Test Pin 68 (EGRA) to ground at the breakout box and observe the vacuum gauge. ● Key off. ● **Was vacuum signal indicated by the vacuum gauge?**	Yes	▶	The EGR Atmospheric solenoid valve is functioning properly. REPLACE the damaged PCM. REMOVE the breakout box. REMOVE the vacuum gauge and vacuum pump. RECONNECT all components. RERUN Quick Test.
	No	▶	The EGR Atmospheric solenoid valve is not functioning properly. REPLACE the damaged PCM. REMOVE the breakout box. REMOVE the vacuum gauge and vacuum pump. RECONNECT all components. RERUN Quick Test.
HH58 CHECK VPWR AT EGR VACUUM SOLENOID ● Key off. ● EGR Vacuum solenoid disconnected. ● Key on, engine off. ● Measure voltage between VPWR circuit and chassis ground at the EGR Vacuum solenoid vehicle harness connector. ● **Is EGR Vacuum solenoid VPWR voltage greater than 10.5 volts?**	Yes	▶	EGR Vacuum solenoid normally has VPWR applied. GO to HH59.
	No	▶	SERVICE open in EGR Vacuum solenoid VPWR circuit. RECONNECT all components. COMPLETE PCM reset to clear DTCs (REFER to Powertrain Control Module (PCM) Reset). RERUN Quick Test.

FM0159601519200X

Fig. 254 Test HH: EGR Monitor & System (Part 20 of 25). 1996 Probe

ELECTRONIC ENGINE CONTROL SYSTEM (EEC-V)

Test Step		Result	▶	Action to Take
HH59	CHECK RESISTANCE OF EGR VACUUM SOLENOID			
	• Key off. • EGR Vacuum solenoid disconnected. • Measure solenoid resistance. • **Is resistance between 30 and 70 ohms?**	Yes	▶	EGR Vacuum solenoid resistance is OK. GO to HH60.
		No	▶	EGR Vacuum solenoid resistance is out os specification. REPLACE the EGR Vacuum solenoid. COMPLETE PCM reset to clear DTCs (REFER to Powertrain Control Module (PCM) Reset). RERUN Quick Test.
HH60	CHECK EGR VACUUM SOLENOID CIRCUIT CONTINUITY			
	• Key off. • EGR Vacuum solenoid disconnected. • Disconnect PCM. Inspect for damaged pushed out pins, corrosion, loose wires, etc. Service as necessary. • Install breakout box, leave PCM disconnected. • Measure resistance between Test Pin 72 (EGRV) at the breakout box and the EGRV circuit at the solenoid vehicle harness connector. • **Is the resistance less than 5.0 ohms?**	Yes	▶	EGR Vacuum harness circuit is complete. GO to HH61.
		No	▶	SERVICE open in EGR Vacuum harness circuit. REMOVE the breakout box. RECONNECT all components. COMPLETE PCM Reset to clear DTCs (REFER to Powertrain Control Module (PCM) Reset). RERUN Quick Test.
HH61	CHECK EGR VACUUM SOLENOID CIRCUIT FOR SHORT TO POWER			
	• Key off. • EGR Vacuum solenoid disconnected. • Breakout box installed, PCM disconnected. • Measure resistance between Test Pin 72 (EGRV) and Test Pins 71, 97 (VPWR) and 90 (VREF) at the breakout box. • **Is each resistance greater than 10,000 ohms?**	Yes	▶	The EGR Vacuum solenoid harness circuits are free of shorts. REMOVE breakout box. RECONNECT all components. GO to HH62.
		No	▶	SERVICE short in EGR Vacuum solenoid harness circuit. REMOVE breakout box. RECONNECT all components. COMPLETE PCM reset to clear DTCs (REFER to Powertrain Control Module (PCM) Reset). RERUN Quick Test.

FM0159601519210X

Fig. 254 Test HH: EGR Monitor & System (Part 21 of 25). 1996 Probe

Test Step		Result	▶	Action to Take
HH62	CHECK EGR CONTROL SOLENOID VALVE FUNCTION			
	• Key off. • Breakout box installed, PCM connected. • Disconnect the vacuum line from the intake manifold vacuum reservoir to the EGR Vacuum solenoid at the EGR Vacuum solenoid. • Install vacuum pump at the input port of the EGR Vacuum solenoid. • Disconnect the vacuum line from the EGR Vacuum solenoid to the EGR Atmospheric solenoid, install a vacuum gauge at the unattached end of the vacuum line. • Key on. • Apply 8 to 10''-Hg of the vacuum to the EGR Vacuum solenoid. • Momentarily jumper Test Pin 72 (EGRV) at the breakout box and observe the vacuum gauge. • Key off. • **Was vacuum signal indicated by the vacuum gauge?**	Yes	▶	The EGR Vacuum solenoid valve is functioning properly. REPLACE the damaged PCM. REMOVE the breakout box. REMOVE the vacuum gauge and vacuum pump. RECONNECT all components. RERUN Quick Test.
		No	▶	The EGR Vacuum solenoid valve is not functioning properly. REPLACE the damaged EGR Vacuum solenoid. REMOVE the breakout box. REMOVE the vacuum gauge and vacuum pump. RECONNECT all components. COMPLETE PCM reset to clear DTCs (REFER to Powertrain Control Module (PCM) Reset). RERUN Quick Test.

FM0159601519220X

Fig. 254 Test HH: EGR Monitor & System (Part 22 of 25). 1996 Probe

Test Step		Result	▶	Action to Take
HH70	CONTINUOUS MEMORY DTCS P0400 AND P1407: OUTPUT ALL DTCS			
	Diagnostic Trouble Code (DTC) P0400 indicates an EGR valve / flow failure. Diagnostic Trouble Code (DTC) P1407 indicates the EGR valve did not move. Possible causes: — Damaged EGR Vacuum solenoid. — Damaged EGR Vacuum solenoid harness circuits. — Damaged EGR Atmospheric solenoid. — Damaged EGR Atmospheric solenoid harness circuits. — Damaged EGR valve. — Damaged EGR Position sensor. — Damaged EGR Position sensor harness circuits. — Damaged EGR Control solenoid. — Damaged EGR Control solenoid harness circuits. — Restriction in exhaust system. — Damaged PCM. • Output all Continuous Memory, KOEO and KOER self-test DTCs. • **Is P0106, P0107, P0108, P1400, P1401 or P1408 output?** NOTE: If any other DTCs are output, record them and address them after completing this Pinpoint Test.	Yes	▶	Self-test indicates that the EGR system has been damaged. GO to Powertrain Diagnostic Trouble Codes (DTCs) Charts, to address the DTCs.
		No	▶	GO to HH71.
HH71	CHECK VPWR TO EGR CONTROL SOLENOID			
	• Key off. • EGR Control solenoid disconnected. • Key on, engine off. • Measure voltage between VPWR circuit and chassis ground at the EGR Control solenoid vehicle harness connector. • **Is EGR Control solenoid VPWR voltage greater than 10.5 volts?**	Yes	▶	EGR Control solenoid normally has VPWR applied to it. GO to HH72.
		No	▶	SERVICE open in EGR Control solenoid VPWR circuit. RECONNECT all components. COMPLETE PCM reset to clear DTCs (REFER to Powertrain Control Module (PCM) Reset). RERUN Quick Test.

FM0159601519230X

Fig. 254 Test HH: EGR Monitor & System (Part 23 of 25). 1996 Probe

Test Step		Result	▶	Action to Take
HH72	CHECK RESISTANCE OF EGR CONTROL SOLENOID			
	• Key off. • EGR Control solenoid disconnected. • Measure solenoid resistance. • **Is resistance between 30 and 70 ohms?**	Yes	▶	EGR Control solenoid resistance is OK. Go to HH73.
		No	▶	EGR Control solenoid resistance is out of specification. REPLACE the EGR Control solenoid. COMPLETE PCM reset to clear DTCs (REFER to Powertrain Control Module (PCM) Reset). RERUN Quick Test.
HH73	CHECK EGR CONTROL SOLENOID CIRCUIT CONTINUITY			
	• Key off. • EGR Control solenoid disconnected. • Disconnect PCM. Inspect for damaged pushed out pins, corrosion, loose wires, etc. Service as necessary. • Install breakout box, leave PCM disconnected. • Measure resistance between Test Pin 98 (EGRC) at the breakout box and the EGR Control solenoid circuit at the solenoid vehicle harness connector. • **Is the resistance less than 5.0 ohms?**	Yes	▶	EGR Control harness circuit is complete. GO to HH74.
		No	▶	SERVICE open in EGR Control harness circuit. REMOVE the breakout box. RECONNECT all components. COMPLETE PCM Reset to clear DTCs (REFER to Powertrain Control Module (PCM) Reset). RERUN Quick Test.
HH74	CHECK EGR CONTROL SOLENOID CIRCUIT FOR SHORT TO POWER AND SHORT TO GROUND			
	• Key off. • EGR Control solenoid disconnected. • Breakout box installed, PCM disconnected. • Measure resistance between Test Pin 98 (EGRC) and Test Pins 71, 97 (VPWR) and 90 (VREF) at the breakout box. • Measure resistance between Test Pin 98 (EGRC) and Test Pins 51, 103 (PWR GND) and 91 (SIG RTN) at the breakout box. • **Is each resistance greater than 10,000 ohms?**	Yes	▶	The EGR Control solenoid harness circuits are free of shorts. REMOVE breakout box. RECONNECT all components. GO to HH75.
		No	▶	SERVICE short in EGR Control solenoid harness circuit. REMOVE breakout box. RECONNECT all components. COMPLETE PCM reset to clear DTCs (REFER to Powertrain Control Module (PCM) Reset). RERUN Quick Test.

FM0159601519240X

Fig. 254 Test HH: EGR Monitor & System (Part 24 of 25). 1996 Probe

Test Step	Result	▶	Action to Take
HH75 CHECK OPERATION OF EGR CONTROL SOLENOID VALVE • Key off. • Breakout box installed, PCM connected. • Disconnect the vacuum line from the EGR Control solenoid to the intake manifold vacuum reservoir at the EGR Control solenoid. Inspect vacuum line for damage, service as necessary. • Install vacuum pump at the input port of the EGR Control solenoid, apply 8 to 10''-Hg of vacuum. • Disconnect the vacuum line from the EGR Control solenoid to the EGR Barometric Pressure sensor at the EGR Barometric Pressure sensor. Inspect vacuum line for damage, service as necessary. • Install a vacuum gauge at the unattached end of the vacuum line. • Key on. • Jumper Test Pin 98 (EGRC) to ground at the breakout box and observe the vacuum gauge. Remove jumper. • Apply 8 to 10''-Hg of vacuum to the EGR Control solenoid once again. • Again, jumper Test Pin 98 (EGRC) to ground at the breakout box and observe the vacuum gauge. Remove jumper. • Key off. • **Was a vacuum signal indicated at any time by the vacuum gauge?**	Yes	▶	The EGR Control solenoid valve is functioning properly. REPLACE the damaged PCM. REMOVE the breakout box. REMOVE the vacuum pump and gauge. RECONNECT all vacuum lines. The fault that produced DTC 0400 is intermittent and can not be identified at this time. GO to Pinpoint Test Step **Z1** with the list of Possible Causes for DTC 0400.
	No	▶	The EGR Control solenoid valve is not functioning properly. REPLACE the damaged EGR Control solenoid. REMOVE the breakout box. REMOVE the vacuum gauge and vacuum pump. RECONNECT all components. COMPLETE PCM reset to clear DTCs (REFER to Powertrain Control Module (PCM) Reset). RERUN Quick Test.

FM015960151925OX

Fig. 254 Test HH: EGR Monitor & System (Part 25 of 25). 1996 Probe

---

Note

You should enter this Pinpoint Test only when directed here.

Remember

This Pinpoint Test is intended to diagnose the following:

- Harness circuits: Batt+, EAIR, EAIR Monitor, Ground
- Solid State Relay (SSR)
- Electric Air Pump (EAP)
- Air Injection Bypass Solenoid (AIRB)
- Powertrain Control Module (PCM)
- Air Injection Diverter Solenoid (AIRD)

- Air Diverter (AIRD) Valve
- Vacuum Supply
- Mechanical Air Pump
- Air Silencer
- Air Resonator
- Air Check Valve
- Vacuum Reservoir

FM015960152101OX

Fig. 255 Test HM: Secondary Air Injection System (Part 1 of 21). 1996

Pinpoint Test Schematic

Electric Secondary Air Injection System

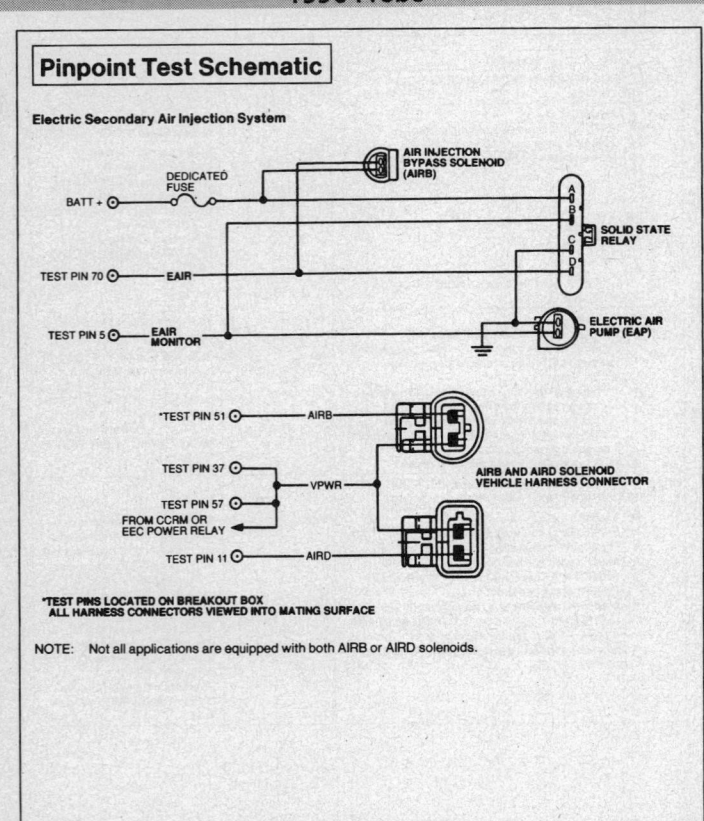

*TEST PINS LOCATED ON BREAKOUT BOX
ALL HARNESS CONNECTORS VIEWED INTO MATING SURFACE

NOTE: Not all applications are equipped with both AIRB or AIRD solenoids.

FM015960152102OX

Fig. 255 Test HM: Secondary Air Injection System (Part 2 of 21). 1996

Test Step	Result	▶	Action to Take
HM1 CHECK B+ AT SOLID STATE RELAY Diagnostic Trouble Code (DTC) P0412 indicates EAIR primary circuit malfunction. Possible causes: — EAIR circuit open. — EAIR circuit short to power. — AIR bypass solenoid malfunction. — Solid State Relay malfunction. — Damaged PCM. • Key off. • Disconnect SSR. • Key on, engine off. • Measure voltage between B+ circuit at SSR vehicle harness connector and battery negative post. • **Is voltage greater than 10.5 volts?**	Yes	▶	Supplied voltage is OK, GO to **HM2**.
	No	▶	GO to **HM6**.
HM2 CHECK CONTINUITY OF EAIR CIRCUIT • Key off. • Solid State Relay disconnected. • Disconnect AIR bypass solenoid. • Remove Secondary Air dedicated fuse temporarily. • Disconnect PCM. Inspect for damaged or pushed out pins, corrosion, loose wires, etc. Service as necessary. • Install breakout box, leave PCM disconnected. • Measure resistance between EAIR circuit at SSR vehicle harness connector and Test Pin 70 at the breakout box. • Measure resistance between EAIR circuit at the AIR bypass vehicle harness connector and Test Pin 70 at the breakout box. • **Is resistance less than 5.0 ohms?**	Yes	▶	GO to **HM3**.
	No	▶	SERVICE open EAIR circuit. REMOVE breakout box. RECONNECT all components. COMPLETE PCM Reset to clear DTCs (REFER to Powertrain Control Module (PCM) Reset). RERUN Quick Test.
HM3 CHECK EAIR CIRCUIT FOR SHORT TO POWER AND GROUND • Key off. • AIR bypass solenoid disconnected. • Solid State Relay disconnected. • PCM disconnected, breakout box installed. • Measure resistance between Test Pins 70 and Test Pin 51, 71, 90, 97 and 105 at the breakout box. • **Is each resistance greater than 10,000 ohms?**	Yes	▶	The EAIR harness is OK. GO to **HM4**.
	No	▶	SERVICE EAIR circuit for short. REMOVE breakout box. RECONNECT all components. COMPLETE PCM Reset to clear DTCs (REFER to Powertrain Control Module (PCM) Reset). RERUN Quick Test.

FM015960152103OX

Fig. 255 Test HM: Secondary Air Injection System (Part 3 of 21). 1996

Test Step	Result	▶	Action to Take
HM4 CHECK EAIR CIRCUIT FOR SHORT TO POWER AND GROUND			
• Key off. • Reconnect AIR bypass solenoid. • Solid State Relay and PCM disconnected, breakout box installed. • Measure resistance between Test Pin 70 and Test Pins 51, 71, 90, 97 and 103 at the breakout box. • **Is each resistance greater than 10,000 ohms?**	Yes	▶	EAIR circuit with AIR bypass solenoid OK. GO to HM5.
	No	▶	REPLACE AIR bypass solenoid. REMOVE breakout box. RECONNECT components. COMPLETE PCM Reset to clear DTCs (REFER to Powertrain Control Module (PCM) Reset). RERUN Quick Test.
HM5 CHECK EAIR CIRCUIT FOR SHORT TO POWER AND GROUND			
• Key off. • AIR bypass solenoid disconnected. • Reconnect Solid State Relay. • PCM disconnected, breakout box installed. • Measure resistance between Test Pin 70 and Test Pins 51, 71, 90, 97 and 103 at the breakout box. • **Is each resistance greater than 10,000 ohms?**	Yes	▶	If P0411 or P1411 are also present: GO to HM9. All others: REPLACE PCM. RECONNECT all components. COMPLETE PCM Reset to clear DTCs (REFER to Powertrain Control Module (PCM) Reset). RERUN Quick Test.
	No	▶	REPLACE Solid State Relay. REMOVE breakout box. RECONNECT components. COMPLETE PCM Reset to clear DTCs (REFER to Powertrain Control Module (PCM) Reset). RERUN Quick Test.
HM6 CHECK CONTINUITY OF B+ CIRCUIT			
• Key off. • Disconnect Solid State Relay. • Measure resistance between Solid State Relay vehicle harness connector and Secondary Air dedicated fuse. • **Is resistance less than 5.0 ohms?**	Yes	▶	SERVICE Secondary Air dedicated fuse. RECONNECT Solid State Relay. RERUN Quick Test.
	No	▶	SERVICE open in B+ circuit. RECONNECT Solid State Relay. COMPLETE PCM Reset to clear DTCs (REFER to Powertrain Control Module (PCM) Reset.) RERUN Quick Test.

FM015960152 1040X

Fig. 255 Test HM: Secondary Air Injection System (Part 4 of 21). 1996

Test Step	Result	▶	Action to Take
HM7 VISUALLY INSPECT EAP HOSES			
DTC P0411/P1411 indicates Secondary Air not detected. In order to test the pump, it must be capable of driving the HO2S lean. NOTE: Some applications have one or two Air Diverter (AIRD) valves. • Key off. • Visually inspect EAP hoses from the EAP to the AIRD valves. • Inspect air hose for cracks, binding and obstructions. • **Are EAP hoses OK?**	Yes	▶	GO to HM8.
	No	▶	SERVICE or REPLACE damaged parts. COMPLETE PCM Reset to clear DTCs (REFER to Powertrain Control Module (PCM) Reset). RERUN Quick Test.
HM8 CHECK ELECTRIC AIR PUMP OPERATION			
• Key off. • Disconnect air hose from either AIRD valve(s). • Check air flow at the open hose by placing a hand over the outlet of the hose. Caution must be observed while performing this test. Beware of moving vehicle components and heat. • Key on, engine running. • After a 5 second delay, air will be present between 30-90 seconds. • **Is air flow present?**	Yes	▶	GO to HM9.
	No	▶	SERVICE air hose to AIRD valves for leaks or blockage. If OK, GO to HM11.
HM9 CHECK FOR VACUUM AT AIRD VALVES			
• Key off. • Reconnect PCM. • Disconnect vacuum control line from the AIRD valve(s). • Key on, engine running. • After a 5 second delay, vacuum will be present between 30-90 seconds. • **Is vacuum present at the AIRD valve(s)?**	Yes	▶	GO to HM10.
	No	▶	GO to HM30.

FM015960152 1050X

Fig. 255 Test HM: Secondary Air Injection System (Part 5 of 21). 1996

Test Step	Result	▶	Action to Take
HM10 CHECK AIRD VALVE(S) INTEGRITY			
• Key off. • Reconnect vacuum control line. • Disconnect air tube from AIRD valve(s) outlet side. • Cork off the air tube to prevent exhaust gases from escaping. • Inspect AIRD valve(s) outlets for damage from hot exhaust gases. Service as necessary. Caution must be observed while performing this test. • Key on, engine running. • After a 5 second delay, air will be present between 30-90 seconds. • **Is air present from the AIRD valve(s)?**	Yes	▶	GO to Shop Manuals to service the exhaust tubes from the AIRD Valve to the exhaust manifold(s). COMPLETE PCM Reset to clear DTCs (REFER to Powertrain Control Module (PCM) Reset). RERUN Quick Test.
	No	▶	SERVICE hose from EAP to AIRD Valve. If OK, REPLACE the appropriate AIRD Valve(s). RECONNECT all components. COMPLETE PCM Reset to clear DTCs (REFER to Powertrain Control Module (PCM) Reset). RERUN Quick Test.
HM11 CHECK ELECTRIC AIR PUMP OPERATION			
• Key off. • Disconnect EAP. • Measure voltage between EAIR monitor circuit and ground at the EAP vehicle harness connector. • Key on, engine running. • **Is voltage greater than 10.5 volts for 20-30 seconds after a 5 to 10 second delay?**	Yes	▶	GO to HM13.
	No	▶	GO to HM12.
HM12 CHECK EAP GROUND INTEGRITY			
• Key off. • EAP disconnected. • Measure resistance between EAP ground circuit at the vehicle harness connector and chassis ground. • **Is resistance less than 5 ohms?**	Yes	▶	GO to HM19.
	No	▶	SERVICE open ground circuit. RECONNECT all components. COMPLETE PCM Reset to clear DTCs (REFER to Powertrain Control Module (PCM) Reset). RERUN Quick Test.

FM015960152 1060X

Fig. 255 Test HM: Secondary Air Injection System (Part 6 of 21). 1996

Test Step	Result	▶	Action to Take
HM13 CHECK AIR HOSE TO EAP			
• Key off. • Disconnect inlet air hose. • Visually inspect inlet air hose for binding and obstructions to the EAP. • **Is the hose integrity OK?**	Yes	▶	REPLACE EAP. RECONNECT all components. COMPLETE PCM Reset to clear DTCs (REFER to Powertrain Control Module (PCM) Reset). RERUN Quick Test.
	No	▶	SERVICE air hose. COMPLETE PCM Reset to clear DTCs (REFER to Powertrain Control Module (PCM) Reset). RERUN Quick Test.
HM18 CHECK FOR VOLTAGE AT SOLID STATE RELAY			
DTC P1413 indicates EAIR monitor circuit is low while the EAP was commanded ON. • Key off. • Disconnect Solid State Relay. • Key on. • Measure voltage between B+ circuit at Solid State Relay vehicle harness connector and chassis ground. • **Is voltage greater than 10.5 volts?**	Yes	▶	GO to HM19.
	No	▶	GO to HM24.
HM19 CHECK EAIR MONITOR CIRCUIT FOR VOLTAGE			
• Key off. • Reconnect Solid State Relay. • Disconnect EAP. • Measure voltage between EAIR monitor circuit at the EAP vehicle harness connector and chassis ground. • Key on. • **Is voltage greater than 10.5 volts?**	Yes	▶	If DTC P0411 is present, REPLACE EAP. If not, GO to HM23.
	No	▶	GO to HM20.
HM20 CHECK EAIR MONITOR CIRCUIT FOR VOLTAGE, SSR CONNECTED			
• Key off. • SSR connected. • EAP disconnected. Disconnect PCM, install breakout box. • Measure voltage between Test Pin 5 and chassis ground. • Key on. • **Is voltage greater than 10.5 volts?**	Yes	▶	REPLACE PCM. RECONNECT all components. COMPLETE PCM Reset to clear DTCs (REFER to Powertrain Control Module (PCM) Reset). RERUN Quick Test.
	No	▶	GO to 21.

FM015960152 1070X

Fig. 255 Test HM: Secondary Air Injection System (Part 7 of 21). 1996

Test Step		Result	▶	Action to Take
HM21	CHECK CONTINUITY OF EAIR MONITOR CIRCUIT			
	• Key off. • Disconnect Solid State Relay. • Disconnect PCM. Install breakout box. • EAP disconnected. • Measure resistance between Test Pin 5 at the breakout box and EAIR monitor circuit at the Solid State Relay vehicle harness connector. • Measure resistance between EAIR monitor circuit at the Solid State Relay vehicle harness connector and EAIR monitor circuit at the EAP vehicle harness connector. • **Is each resistance less than 5.0 ohms?**	Yes No	▶ ▶	GO to **HM22**. SERVICE open EAIR monitor circuit. RECONNECT all components. COMPLETE PCM Reset to clear DTCs (REFER to Powertrain Control Module (PCM) Reset). RERUN Quick Test.
HM22	CHECK EAIR MONITOR CIRCUIT FOR SHORT TO GROUND			
	• Key off. • Solid State Relay disconnected. • EAP disconnected. • Breakout box installed, PCM disconnected. • Measure resistance between Test Pin 5 and Test Pin 51, 76 and 91 at the breakout box. • **Is each resistance greater than 10,000 ohms?**	Yes No	▶ ▶	REPLACE Solid State Relay. RECONNECT all components. COMPLETE PCM Reset to clear DTCs (REFER to Powertrain Control Module (PCM) Reset). RERUN Quick Test. SERVICE EAIR monitor circuit for short to ground. RECONNECT all components. COMPLETE PCM Reset to clear DTCs (REFER to Powertrain Control Module (PCM) Reset). RERUN Quick Test.
HM23	CHECK EAIR MONITOR CIRCUIT FOR VOLTAGE, EAP CONNECTED			
	• Key off. • Reconnect EAP. • Install breakout box. PCM connected. • Key on, engine running. • Measure voltage between Test Pin 5 at the breakout box and chassis ground. • **Is voltage greater than 10.5 after the 5 second delay?**	Yes No	▶ ▶	REPLACE PCM. REMOVE breakout box. COMPLETE PCM Reset to clear DTCs (REFER to Powertrain Control Module (PCM) Reset). RERUN Quick Test. SERVICE open EAIR monitor circuit. REMOVE breakout box. COMPLETE PCM Reset to clear DTCs (REFER to Powertrain Control Module (PCM) Reset). RERUN Quick Test.

FM015960152108OX

Fig. 255   Test HM: Secondary Air Injection System (Part 8 of 21). 1996

Test Step		Result	▶	Action to Take
HM24	CHECK CONTINUITY OF B+ CIRCUIT			
	• Key off. • Solid State Relay disconnected. • Measure resistance between Solid State Relay vehicle harness connector B+ circuit and Solid State Relay dedicated fuse B+ circuit. • **Is resistance less than 5 ohms?**	Yes No	▶ ▶	SERVICE Solid State Relay dedicated fuse. RECONNECT all components. COMPLETE PCM Reset to clear DTCs (REFER to Powertrain Control Module (PCM) Reset). RERUN Quick Test. SERVICE open B+ circuit. RECONNECT all components. COMPLETE PCM Reset to clear DTCs (REFER to Powertrain Control Module (PCM) Reset). RERUN Quick Test.
HM25	CHECK EAIR MONITOR CIRCUIT FOR CONTINUITY			
	DTC P1414 indicates EAP commanded off, but PCM indicates EAP is on. • Key off. • Disconnect Solid State Relay. • Disconnect PCM, install breakout box. • Disconnect Electric Air Pump (EAP). • Measure resistance between Test Pin 5 at the breakout box and EAP harness connector. • **Is resistance less than 5 ohms?**	Yes No	▶ ▶	GO to **HM26**. SERVICE EAIR monitor circuit for open. RECONNECT all components. COMPLETE PCM Reset to clear DTCs (REFER to Powertrain Control Module (PCM) Reset). RERUN Quick Test.
HM26	CHECK EAP FOR OPEN			
	• Key off. • EAP disconnected. • SSR disconnected. • PCM disconnected. • Measure resistance across EAP terminals at EAP. • **Is resistance between 0.5-5.0 ohms?**	Yes No	▶ ▶	GO to **HM27**. REPLACE EAP. RECONNECT all components. COMPLETE PCM Reset to clear DTCs (REFER to Powertrain Control Module (PCM) Reset). RERUN Quick Test.
HM27	CHECK EAIR MONITOR CIRCUIT FOR SHORT TO POWER, COMPONENTS DISCONNECTED			
	• Key off. • EAP disconnected. • Solid State Relay (SSR) disconnected. • Powertrain Control Module (PCM) disconnected. • Install breakout box. • Key on. • Measure voltage between Test Pin 5 at the breakout box and chassis ground. • **Is voltage greater than 10.5 volts?**	Yes No	▶ ▶	SERVICE EAIR monitor for short to power. RECONNECT all components. COMPLETE PCM Reset to clear DTCs (REFER to Powertrain Control Module (PCM) Reset). RERUN Quick Test. EAMM circuit is OK. GO to **HM28**.

FM015960152109OX

Fig. 255   Test HM: Secondary Air Injection System (Part 9 of 21). 1996

Test Step		Result	▶	Action to Take
HM28	CHECK EAIR MONITOR CIRCUIT FOR SHORT TO POWER, COMPONENTS CONNECTED			
	• Key off. • Reconnect PCM. • Reconnect Solid State Relay. • Breakout box installed. • EAP connected. • Key on. • Measure voltage between Test Pin 5 at the breakout box and chassis ground. • **Is voltage greater than 5.0 volts?**	Yes No	▶ ▶	GO to **HM29**. EAP is not grounded, SERVICE open ground to EAP. RECONNECT all components. COMPLETE PCM Reset to clear DTCs (REFER to Powertrain Control Module (PCM) Reset). RERUN Quick Test.
HM29	CHECK EAIR MONITOR AND EAIR CIRCUIT FOR SHORT TO POWER			
	• Key off. • Reconnect Solid State Relay and EAP. • Breakout box installed, PCM connected. • Key on. • Measure voltage between Test Pin 5 at the breakout box and chassis ground. • Measure voltage between Test Pin 70 at the breakout box and chassis ground. • **Are both greater than 10.5 volts?**	Yes No	▶ ▶	REPLACE Solid State Relay. REMOVE breakout box. RECONNECT all components. COMPLETE PCM Reset to clear DTCs (REFER to Powertrain Control Module (PCM) Reset). RERUN Quick Test. REPLACE PCM. REMOVE breakout box. RECONNECT all components. COMPLETE PCM Reset to clear DTCs (REFER to Powertrain Control Module (PCM) Reset). RERUN Quick Test.
HM30	CHECK VACUUM HOSE INTEGRITY			
	• Key off. • Check vacuum hose between AIRB solenoid and AIRD valve. • Check for blockage and restrictions. • Check for leaks and cracks. • Check for kinks or disconnects. • **Are the above checks OK?**	Yes No	▶ ▶	GO to **HM31**. REPLACE the vacuum line connecting the AIR bypass solenoid to AIRD valve(s). COMPLETE PCM Reset to clear DTCs (REFER to Powertrain Control Module (PCM) Reset). RERUN Quick Test.

FM015960152110OX

Fig. 255   Test HM: Secondary Air Injection System (Part 10 of 21). 1996

Test Step		Result	▶	Action to Take
HM31	CHECK AIR BYPASS SOLENOID ELECTRICAL OPERATION			
	• Key on, engine off. • Connect Scan Tool. • Enter Output Test Mode (OTM). Refer to Diagnostic Methods. • Disconnect AIR bypass solenoid. • Connect DVOM to AIR bypass solenoid vehicle harness connecfor. • Turn the outputs on, then turn outputs off while observing DVOM. • **Does EAIR circuit voltage cycle greater than .5 volt?**	Yes No	▶ ▶	REMAIN in Output Test Mode. GO to **HM32**. GO to **HM33**.
HM32	CHECK AIR BYPASS SOLENOID FOR MECHANICAL OPERATION			
	• While remaining in Output Test Mode, reconnect AIR bypass solenoid. • Disconnect source vacuum hose from AIR bypass solenoid. • Apply 16 in-Hg. (53 kPa) of vacuum to source side of AIR bypass solenoid. • Turn the outputs on, then turn outputs off. • **Was vacuum released?**	Yes No	▶ ▶	SERVICE vacuum hose from manifold vacuum tree to AIR bypass solenoid. RECONNECT all components. COMPLETE PCM Reset to clear DTCs (REFER to Powertrain Control Module (PCM) Reset). RERUN Quick Test. REPLACE AIR bypass solenoid. RECONNECT all components. COMPLETE PCM Reset to clear DTCs (REFER to Powertrain Control Module (PCM) Reset). RERUN Quick Test.
HM33	CHECK AIR BYPASS SOLENOID RESISTANCE			
	• Key off. • Disconnect AIR bypass solenoid vehicle harness connector. • Measure AIR bypass solenoid resistance. • **Is resistance between 50-100 ohms?**	Yes No	▶ ▶	GO to **HM34**. REPLACE AIR bypass solenoid. RECONNECT all components. COMPLETE PCM Reset to clear DTCs (REFER to Powertrain Control Module (PCM) Reset). RERUN Quick Test.
HM34	CHECK VPWR CIRCUIT VOLTAGE			
	• Key on, engine off. • AIR bypass solenoid disconnected. • Measure voltage between VPWR at the AIR bypass solenoid vehicle harness connector and battery ground. • **Is voltage greater than 10.5 volts?**	Yes No	▶ ▶	GO to **HM35**. SERVICE open VPWR circuit. RECONNECT AIR bypass. COMPLETE PCM Reset to clear DTCs (REFER to Powertrain Control Module (PCM) Reset). RERUN Quick Test.

FM015960152111OX

Fig. 255   Test HM: Secondary Air Injection System (Part 11 of 21). 1996

Test Step		Result	►	Action to Take
HM35	CHECK CONTINUITY OF EAIR CIRCUIT			
	• Key off. • AIR bypass solenoid disconnected. • Disconnect Solid State Relay. • Install breakout box, leave PCM disconnected. • Measure resistance between Test Pin 70 at the breakout box and EAIR circuit at the AIR solenoid bypass vehicle harness connector and at the Solid State Relay vehicle harness connector. • **Is resistance less than 5.0 ohms?**	Yes No	► ►	GO to HM36. SERVICE open EAIR circuit. RECONNECT components. COMPLETE PCM Reset to clear DTCs (REFER to Powertrain Control Module (PCM) Reset). RERUN Quick Test.
HM36	CHECK EAIR CIRCUIT FOR SHORT TO GROUND			
	• Key off. • AIR bypass solenoid disconnected. • Solid State Relay disconnected. • Breakout box installed, PCM disconnected. • Disconnect Scan Tool. • Measure resistance between Test Pin 70 and Test Pins 51, 76 and 91 at the breakout box. • **Is each resistance greater than 10,000 ohms?**	Yes No	► ►	GO to HM37. SERVICE short to ground. RECONNECT components. COMPLETE PCM Reset to clear DTCs (REFER to Powertrain Control Module (PCM) Reset). RERUN Quick Test.
HM37	CHECK EAIR CIRCUIT FOR SHORT TO POWER			
	• Key off. • AIR bypass solenoid disconnected. • Solid State Relay disconnected. • Breakout box installed, PCM disconnected. • Measure resistance between Test Pin 70 and Test Pins 71 and 97 at the breakout box. • **Is each resistance greater than 10,000 ohms?**	Yes No	► ►	REPLACE PCM. RECONNECT components. COMPLETE PCM Reset to clear DTCs (REFER to Powertrain Control Module (PCM) Reset). RERUN Quick Test. SERVICE short to power. RECONNECT components. COMPLETE PCM Reset to clear DTCs (REFER to Powertrain Control Module (PCM) Reset). RERUN Quick Test.

FM015960152112OX

Fig. 255 Test HM: Secondary Air Injection System (Part 12 of 21). 1996

Test Step		Result	►	Action to Take
HM40	DIAGNOSTIC TROUBLE CODE (DTC) P0411			
	DTC P0411 indicates that Secondary Air is not being diverted when requested. Possible causes: — Vacuum hoses damaged. — AIRB / AIRD valve inoperative. — Air Pump inoperative. — AIRB / AIRD solenoids damaged. • Visually inspect vacuum lines for disconnects in the AIR system. • Visually inspect for proper vacuum line routing. Refer to VECI decal. • Visually inspect Air Pump for broken or loose Air Pump Belt. Refer to HM81 for adjustment / replacement. • **Were any problems found?**	Yes No	► ►	SERVICE as necessary. RERUN Quick Test. GO to HM41.
HM41	CHECK AIR VACUUM LINES			
	• Carefully check AIR vacuum lines; — From AIRB solenoid to AIRB valve. — From AIRD solenoid to AIRD valve. — From Manifold Vacuum TREE to AIRB / AIRD solenoids. • Check for obstructions, cracks, kinks, and leaks, etc. • **Are vacuum lines in good condition?**	Yes No	► ►	For vehicles with a single AIRB valve: GO to HM42. For vehicles with a single AIRD valve or both valves: GO to HM47. For vehicles with a single combination AIRD / AIRB valve: GO to HM55. SERVICE as necessary. RERUN Quick Test.
HM42	CHECK FOR VACUUM AT THE AIRB VALVE			
	• Key off. • Remove control vacuum line from AIRB valve. • Key on, engine running at normal operating temperature. • Check for vacuum at control vacuum line. • **Is vacuum present?**	Yes No	► ►	GO to HM43. GO to HM63.
HM43	INSPECT AIRB VALVE			
	• Key off. • Disconnect air hose at AIRB valve outlet. • Inspect AIRB valve outlet for damage from hot exhaust gas. • **Is AIRB valve damaged?**	Yes No	► ►	REPLACE AIRB valve, then GO to HM60 to inspect air check valve. GO to HM44.
HM44	CHECK AIRB VALVE DIAPHRAGM			
	• Connect auxiliary vacuum source to AIRB valve. • Apply 34 kPa (10 in-Hg) vacuum and trap. • **Does valve hold vacuum?**	Yes No	► ►	LEAVE vacuum applied. GO to HM45. REPLACE AIRB valve. VERIFY a symptom no longer exists.

FM015960152113OX

Fig. 255 Test HM: Secondary Air Injection System (Part 13 of 21). 1996

Test Step		Result	►	Action to Take
HM45	CHECK AIRB OPERATION / FLOW			
	• Key on, engine running. • Increase engine speed to 1500 rpm. • Check for air flow at valve outlet (audibly or by feel). • **Is air flow present?**	Yes No	► ►	GO to HM46. GO to HM71 to check air pump operation and belt.
HM46	CHECK AIRB OPERATION / DUMP			
	• Vent auxiliary vacuum source to zero. • Check that air flow switches from the valve outlet to the dump port or silencer ports (audibly or by feel). • **Does the air flow switch?**	Yes No	► ►	GO to HM47. REPLACE AIRB valve.
HM47	VISUALLY INSPECT AIRD VALVE			
	• Key off. • Remove hoses from AIRD valve outlets. • Inspect outlets for damage from hot exhaust gases. • **Is AIRD valve damaged?**	Yes No	► ►	REPLACE AIRD valve, then GO to HM60 for air check valve. GO to HM48.
HM48	CHECK FOR VACUUM AT AIRD VALVE			
	NOTE: The next two test steps will require your attention to time. • Key off. • Remove vacuum supply line from vacuum nipple on valve. • Key on, engine running at normal operating temperature. • After engine has started, check for vacuum. • **Was vacuum present after a 10 second delay?**	Yes No	► ►	GO to HM49. GO to HM63 to VERIFY solenoid AIRD vacuum function.
HM49	CHECK AIRD VALVE DIAPHRAGM			
	• Connect an auxiliary vacuum source to the AIRD valve. • Apply 34 kPa (10 in-Hg) vacuum and hold. • **Does valve hold vacuum?**	Yes No	► ►	GO to HM50. REPLACE AIRD valve. VERIFY a symptom no longer exists.
HM50	CHECK FOR AIR SUPPLY AT AIRD VALVE			
	• Key on, engine running to normal operating temperature. • Verify that air is being supplied to the AIRD valve. • **Is air present?**	Yes No	► ►	GO to HM51. GO to HM71 for AIR pump operation.
HM51	CHECK AIR AT AIRD OUTLET(S)			
	• Key on engine running. • Apply 34 kPa (10 in-Hg) of vacuum to AIRD valve. • Increase engine speed to 1500 rpm. • **Does air flow come out of valve outlet?**	Yes No	► ►	GO to HM52. REPLACE AIRD valve. VERIFY a symptom no longer exists.

FM015960152114OX

Fig. 255 Test HM: Secondary Air Injection System (Part 14 of 21). 1996

Test Step		Result	►	Action to Take
HM52	CHECK FOR AIR AT OTHER AIRD OUTLET			
	• Key on engine running. • Vent the auxiliary vacuum source to zero. • **Does air flow switch from one outlet to the other outlet?**	Yes No	► ►	GO to HM63. REPLACE AIRD valve. VERIFY a symptom no longer exists.
HM55	VISUALLY INSPECT COMBINATION AIRB / AIRD VALVE			
	• Key off. • Remove hoses from combination Air Control Valve outlets. • Inspect outlets for damage from hot exhaust gases. • **Does valve appear to be damaged?**	Yes No	► ►	REPLACE combination AIRB / AIRD valve, then GO to HM60 to VERIFY check valve function. GO to HM56.
HM56	CHECK COMBINATION AIRB / AIRD VALVE			
	• Key off. • Outlet hoses disconnected. • Disconnect and plug the air bypass vacuum supply line. • Start engine. • Maintain engine speed at 1500 rpm. • **Is air flow present at combination air control vents?**	Yes No	► ►	GO to HM57. GO to HM71 to verify AIR Pump function. If OK, REPLACE combination AIRB / AIRD valve.
HM57	CHECK FOR MANIFOLD VACUUM			
	• Key on engine running. • Disconnect both the air bypass and air diverter vacuum supply lines. • Measure manifold vacuum at both supply lines. • Start engine. • Measure vacuum at air diverter supply line for 5-30 seconds after starting. • Measure vacuum at air bypass line (timing not critical). • **Is appropriate manifold vacuum present?**	Yes No	► ►	GO to HM58. GO to HM63.
HM58	CHECK COMBINATION AIRB / AIRD VALVE OPERATION			
	• Key off. • Reconnect the air bypass vacuum supply line. • Air diverter vacuum supply line disconnected and plugged. • Start engine and idle at 1500 rpm. • **Is air flow present at one outlet and no air flow present at the other outlet?**	Yes No	► ►	GO to HM59. REPLACE combination AIRB / AIRD valve. RECONNECT all hoses. VERIFY a symptom no longer exists.

FM015960152115OX

Fig. 255 Test HM: Secondary Air Injection System (Part 15 of 21). 1996

Test Step	Result	▶	Action to Take
HM59 CHECK COMBINATION AIRB / AIRD VALVE OPERATION WITH VACUUM APPLIED		▶	GO to **HM63**
NOTE: If the combination valve is a bleed type valve, the amount of air flow will be affected. • Key off. • Air diverter vacuum supply line disconnected and unplugged. • Apply 27-34 kPa (8-10 in-Hg) vacuum to air diverter nipple on the combination valve. • Start engine and idle at 1500 rpm. • **Is air flow present at valve outlet?**	Yes No	▶	REPLACE combination AIRB / AIRD valve. VERIFY a symptom no longer exists.
HM60 VISUALLY INSPECT CHECK VALVE SYSTEM—(EXTERNALLY)		▶	GO to **HM61**
• Key off. • Visually inspect secondary air hoses, tubes, control valves and check valves for leaks or external signs of damage (from back flow of hot exhaust gases). • **Are hoses and valves intact?**	Yes No	▶	SERVICE or REPLACE damaged parts including check valve. VERIFY a symptom no longer exists.
HM61 VISUALLY INSPECT HOSES AT VALVES—(INTERNALLY)		▶	GO to **HM62**
• Remove hose from check valve inlet. • Inspect inside the hose for damage from hot exhaust gas. • **Is the hose clean and undamaged?**	Yes No	▶	REPLACE hose and check valve. VERIFY a symptom no longer exists.
HM62 INSPECT CHECK VALVE FUNCTION		▶	REPLACE check valve. VERIFY a symptom no longer exists.
NOTE: Check valve may "burble" as air is drawn in. • Key on engine running. • Listen for escaping exhaust gas or feel for gas (only if engine temperature is at an acceptable level). • **Is any exhaust gas escaping?**	Yes No	▶	address other possible causes.
HM63 CHECK AIRB AND AIRD SOLENOIDS ELECTRICAL OPERATION		▶	GO to **HM64**
• Connect Scan Tool. • DVOM on 20 volt scale. • Enter Output Test Mode (DTM) (refer to Section 2A, Diagnostic Methods). • Disconnect suspect solenoid. • Connect DVOM positive test lead to VPWR circuit and negative test lead to signal circuit of suspect vehicle harness connector. • While observing DVOM, turn outputs on, then turn outputs off. • **Does solenoid circuit cycle voltage?**	Yes No	▶	REMOVE jumper. GO to **HM76**.

Fig. 255   Test HM: Secondary Air Injection System (Part 16 of 21). 1996

Test Step	Result	▶	Action to Take
HM64 CHECK VACUUM SUPPLY TO AIRD / AIRB SOLENOID		▶	REPLACE AIRB or AIRD solenoid. RECONNECT all components. COMPLETE PCM Reset to clear DTCs (REFER to Powertrain Control Module (PCM) Reset). RERUN Quick Test.
• Key off. • Remove vacuum inlet line at suspect (AIRD / AIRB) solenoid. • Start engine and let idle. • Check vacuum at line. • **Is vacuum present?**	Yes No	▶	GO to **HM66**.
HM66 CHECK VACUUM SUPPLY TO RESERVOIR		▶	Cars: GO to **HM67**. Trucks: GO to **HM68**.
• Key off. • Remove vacuum inlet line at reservoir (For single piece connector, this port is marked man or vac.). • Start engine. • Check for vacuum on line. • **Is vacuum present?**	Yes No	▶	If vehicle has a check valve: GO to **HM69**. If NO check valve: SERVICE vacuum line for leaks, blockage, etc. Verify a symptom no longer exists.
HM67 CHECK RESERVOIR TO HOLD VACUUM		▶	REPLACE vacuum reservoir. VERIFY a symptom no longer exists.
• Key off. • Connect a hand vacuum pump to reservoir port. • Apply 15-20 in-Hg (51-67 KPa). • **Is vacuum loss greater than 0.5 in-Hg (1.7 kPa) after 60 seconds?**	Yes No	▶	GO to Symptom Flowcharts, to address other possible causes.
HM68 CHECK RESERVOIR TO HOLD VACUUM		▶	REPLACE reservoir outlet hose. If problem is still present, GO to Symptom Flowchart, for other possible causes.
• Key off. • Connect vacuum gauge to outlet port (not marked man or vac), keep inlet line connected to vacuum port. • Start engine and run for 30 seconds. • **Does gauge increase approximately 15 to 20 in-Hg?**	Yes No	▶	REPLACE vacuum reservoir. VERIFY a symptom no longer exists.
HM69 CHECK AIR FLOW AT CHECK VALVE		▶	GO to **HM70**
• Key off. • Remove check valve from vacuum lines (note which direction check valve is installed). • Connect auxiliary vacuum source to black side of check valve. • Connect vacuum gauge to opposite side of check valve. • Apply 54 kPa (16 in-Hg) vacuum to black side. • **Does gauge indicate 54 kPa (16 in-Hg)?**	Yes No	▶	REPLACE Check Valve. VERIFY a symptom no longer exists.

Fig. 255   Test HM: Secondary Air Injection System (Part 17 of 21). 1996

Test Step	Result	▶	Action to Take
HM70 VERIFY CHECK VALVE'S ABILITY TO HOLD VACUUM		▶	GO to Symptom Flowcharts, to address other possible causes.
• Key off. • Remove auxiliary vacuum source from the check valve. • **Does vacuum gauge reading remain above 50 kPa (15 in-Hg) for 10 seconds?**	Yes No	▶	REPLACE Check Valve. VERIFY a symptom no longer exists.
HM71 CHECK BELT TENSION		▶	GO to **HM72**
CAUTION: Do not pry on pump to adjust belt. The aluminum housing is likely to collapse. Refer to AIR Pump drive belt adjustment. • Key off. • Check belt tension and adjust to specification. • **Is belt tension adjusted properly?**	Yes No	▶	ADJUST to specification. GO to **HM81** to adjust belt tension.
HM72 CHECK AIR PUMP OPERATION		▶	RETURN to Symptom Flowchart, for other possible causes.
• Key off. • Disconnect air supply hose from AIRB valve. • Check air flow at the pump outlet. • **Does air flow increase as the engine speed increases?**	Yes No	▶	If equipped with Silencer/Filter: GO to **HM73**. If not: REPLACE AIR Pump.
HM73 CHECK SILENCER / FILTER FOR OBSTRUCTION		▶	REPLACE AIR Pump and VERIFY a symptom no longer exists.
• Remove inlet hose (if so equipped). • Inspect inlet of silencer / filter for blockage (bugs, leaves, debris, etc.). • **Is inlet open?**	Yes No	▶	REMOVE all debris and VERIFY a symptom no longer exists.
HM75 DIAGNOSTIC TROUBLE CODES (DTCS) P0413, 0414, 0416 AND 0417: CHECK VOLTAGE OF VPWR CIRCUIT		▶	GO to **HM76**.
DTCs P0413, 0414, 0416 and 0417 indicate that voltage output for Secondary Air Injection solenoid(s) did not change when activated. Possible causes: — AIRB / AIRD circuits shorted to power. — AIRB / AIRD circuits open or shorted to ground. — AIRB / AIRD resistance out of range. — Damaged Powertrain Control Module (PCM). • Disconnect AIRB / AIRD solenoid connector. • Key on, engine off. • Measure voltage between VPWR circuit and battery ground of one solenoid, then repeat for the other solenoid. • **Is each voltage greater than 10.5 volts?**	Yes No	▶	SERVICE open harness circuit. RECONNECT both solenoids. RERUN Quick Test.

Fig. 255   Test HM: Secondary Air Injection System (Part 18 of 21). 1996

Test Step	Result	▶	Action to Take
HM76 MEASURE AIRB / AIRD SOLENOID RESISTANCE		▶	GO to **HM77**.
• Key off. • Disconnect both AIRB / AIRD solenoid connectors and measure both solenoid resistances. • **Is each resistance between 50 and 100 ohms?**	Yes No	▶	REPLACE AIRB / AIRD solenoid assembly. RECONNECT both solenoids. RERUN Quick Test.
HM77 CHECK CIRCUIT CONTINUITY		▶	GO to **HM78**.
• Key off. • Disconnect Powertrain Control Module (PCM). Inspect for damaged or pushed out pins, corrosion, loose wires, etc. Service as necessary. • Install breakout box, leave PCM disconnected. • Measure resistance between AIRB circuit at breakout box and AIRB circuit at vehicle harness connector. • Measure resistance between AIRD circuit at the breakout box and AIRD circuit at vehicle harness connector. • **Is each resistance less than 5.0 ohms?**	Yes No	▶	SERVICE open harness circuit. REMOVE breakout box. RECONNECT PCM and both solenoids. RERUN Quick Test.
HM78 CHECK FOR SHORT TO GROUND		▶	GO to **HM79**.
• Key off. • Breakout box installed, PCM disconnected. • Disconnect Scan Tool. • Disconnect both AIRB / AIRD solenoids. • Measure resistance between AIRB circuit at the breakout box and Test Pins 51, 91 and 103. Measure resistance between AIRD circuit at the breakout box and Test Pins 51, 91 and 103 at the breakout box. • **Is each resistance greater than 10,000 ohms?**	Yes No	▶	SERVICE short to ground. REMOVE breakout box. RECONNECT PCM and AIRB / AIRD solenoids. RERUN Quick Test.
HM79 CHECK FOR SHORT TO POWER		▶	REPLACE PCM. REMOVE breakout box. RECONNECT both solenoids. RERUN Quick Test.
• Key off. • Breakout box installed, PCM disconnected. • Both AIRB / AIRD solenoids disconnected. • Measure resistance between AIRB circuit at the breakout box and Test Pins 71 and 97. Measure resistance between AIRD circuit at the breakout box and Test Pins 71 and 97 at the breakout box. • **Is each resistance greater than 10,000 ohms?**	Yes No	▶	SERVICE short to power. REMOVE breakout box. RECONNECT PCM and AIRB / AIRD solenoids. RERUN Quick Test. If DTC is present, REPLACE PCM.

Fig. 255   Test HM: Secondary Air Injection System (Part 19 of 21). 1996

ELECTRONIC ENGINE CONTROL SYSTEM (EEC-V)

Test Step		Result	▶	Action to Take
HM80	CHECK AIR SOLENOID			
	NOTE: A rolling idle could be the result of a leaking AIR solenoid. Quick Test may also indicate Diagnostic Trouble Codes (DTCs) P0411, P0413, P1414, P0416, P0417.	Yes	▶	REPLACE Secondary Air solenoid assembly.
	• Start engine and run until temperature is fully stabilized.	No	▶	For Rolling idle: RETURN to Symptom Flowcharts For DTC P0411: GO to HM66
	• Turn the engine off.			
	• Disconnect the vacuum hose at the AIR solenoid.			
	• Plug the vacuum hose.			
	• Restart engine.			
	• After a few minutes of engine running, the ''rolling'' idle should stop.			
	• If no rolling idle is present.			
	• Unplug the vacuum hose.			
	• Verify vacuum is present.			
	• **Does rolling idle stop or is vacuum present?**			
HM81	EXCESSIVE BELT NOISE			
	Possible causes:	Yes	▶	TIGHTEN to specification using Tool T75L-9480-A. VERIFY a symptom no longer exists.
	• Loose belt.	No	▶	GO to HM82
	• Seized pump.			
	• Loose pulley.			
	• Loose or broken mounting brackets or bolts.			
	CAUTION: Do not use pry bar to move the air pump for belt adjustment.			
	• Inspect for loose belt.			
	• Use Belt Tension Gauge T63L-8620-A to measure belt tension.			
	• **Is belt loose?**			
HM82	CHECK LOOSE PULLEY, MOUNTING BRACKETS			
	• Check for loose pulley and mounting brackets.	Yes	▶	RETURN
	• Check for seized air pump.	No	▶	For seized pump: REPLACE pump.
	• Check for broken bolts.			For loose or broken bolts or brackets:
	• **Are the above components OK?**			REPLACE parts as required and TIGHTEN bolts to 13.6-17.0 N·m (120-150 lb-in).

FM0159601521200X

Fig. 255   Test HM: Secondary Air Injection System (Part 20 of 21). 1996

Test Step		Result	▶	Action to Take
HM83	CHECK FOR EXCESSIVE AIR NOISE			
	• NOTE: The Secondary Air System is not completely noiseless. To determine if the Air System is the root cause, proceed with the following.	Yes	▶	REPLACE any cracked or worn hoses. TIGHTEN mounting bolts to 34 N·m (25 lb-ft). DO NOT OVERTIGHTEN. CHECK air pump fittings. SERVICE as required. RECONNECT belt tension to specification. VERIFY a symptom no longer exists.
	CONDITIONS: Chirps, Squeaks, Ticks, Putt-Putt, Hiss, Rap or Roar.	No	▶	RECONNECT belt tension to specification.
	• Disconnect the belt drive only after verifying that the belt tension is correct. (Refer to HM81 of Pinpoint Test).			
	• Start and run engine.			
	• **Do the above conditions disappear?**			

FM0159601521210X

Fig. 255   Test HM: Secondary Air Injection System (Part 21 of 21). 1996

Note

You should enter this Pinpoint Test only when directed here.

Remember

This Pinpoint Test is intended to diagnose the following:

• Throttle Position Sensor B (TP-B) (9F953)
• Traction Control (TC) Series Throttle (9F937)
• Series Throttle Stepper Motor (9N825)
• Series Throttle Controller (STC) (9F952)
• Harness Circuits: TP-B, VREF, SIG RTN, VPWR, PWR GND, TAPW, TA-B1, TA-B2, BCOMM, TA-A1, TA-A2, ACOMM
• Powertrain Control Module (PCM) (12A650)

FM0159601522010X

Fig. 256   Test HT: Traction Control System (Part 1 of 14). 1996

Tables and Charts

TP-B Sensor Graph

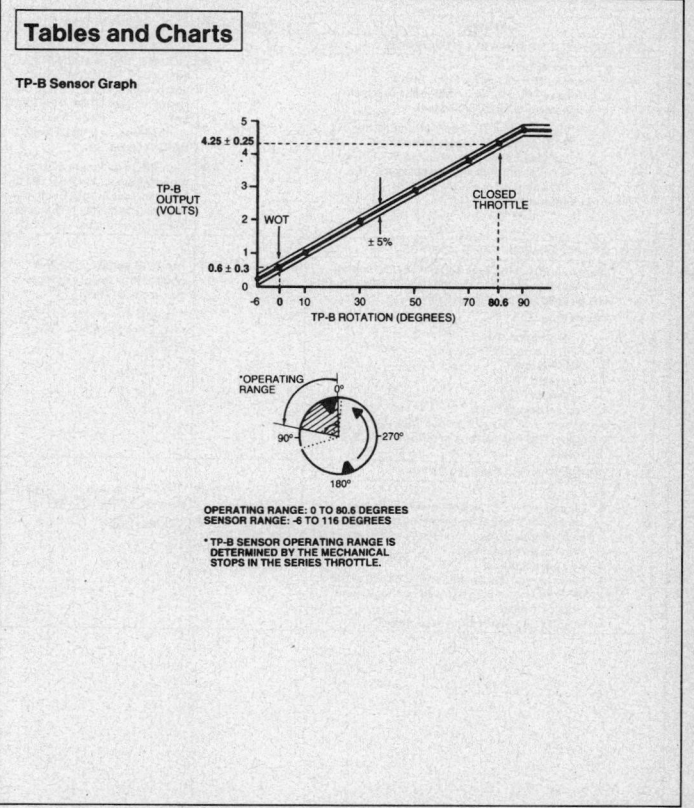

OPERATING RANGE: 0 TO 80.6 DEGREES
SENSOR RANGE: -6 TO 116 DEGREES

* TP-B SENSOR OPERATING RANGE IS DETERMINED BY THE MECHANICAL STOPS IN THE SERIES THROTTLE.

FM0159601522020X

Fig. 256   Test HT: Traction Control System (Part 2 of 14). 1996

Pinpoint Test Schematic

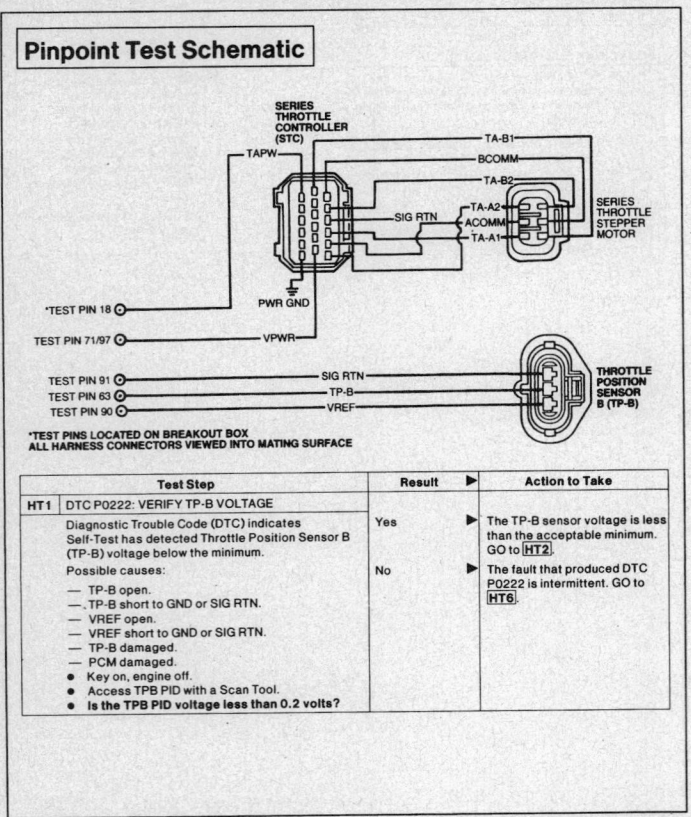

*TEST PINS LOCATED ON BREAKOUT BOX
ALL HARNESS CONNECTORS VIEWED INTO MATING SURFACE

Test Step	Result	▶	Action to Take
HT1 DTC P0222: VERIFY TP-B VOLTAGE			
Diagnostic Trouble Code (DTC) indicates Self-Test has detected Throttle Position Sensor B (TP-B) voltage below the minimum. Possible causes: — TP-B open. — TP-B short to GND or SIG RTN. — VREF open. — VREF short to GND or SIG RTN. — TP-B damaged. — PCM damaged. • Key on, engine off. • Access TPB PID with a Scan Tool. • **Is the TPB PID voltage less than 0.2 volts?**	Yes	▶	The TP-B sensor voltage is less than the acceptable minimum. GO to **HT2**.
	No	▶	The fault that produced DTC P0222 is intermittent. GO to **HT6**.

Test Step	Result	▶	Action to Take
HT2 INDUCE OPPOSITE TP-B SIGNAL			
• Key off. • Disconnect TP-B sensor vehicle harness connector. Inspect for damaged or pushed out pins, corrosion, moisture, loose wires, etc. Service as necessary. • Connect a jumper wire between the sensor VREF circuit and TP-B circuit at the TP-B sensor vehicle harness connector. • Key on, engine off. NOTE: If a Scan Tool communication problem exists, remove jumper immediately and go directly to step HT5. • Access TPB PID with a Scan Tool. • **Is TPB PID between 4.0 and 6.0 volts?**	Yes	▶	REPLACE damaged TP-B sensor. RECONNECT all components. COMPLETE PCM Reset to clear DTCs. (REFER to Powertrain Control Module (PCM) Reset.) RERUN Quick Test.
	No	▶	GO to **HT3**.
HT3 MEASURE VREF VOLTAGE AT TP-B SENSOR VEHICLE HARNESS CONNECTOR			
• TP-B sensor disconnected. • Key on, engine off. • Measure voltage between the sensor VREF circuit and SIG RTN circuit at the TP-B sensor vehicle harness connector. • **Is VREF voltage between 4.0 and 6.0 volts?**	Yes	▶	GO to **HT4**.
	No	▶	VREF voltage is out of range. GO to Pinpoint Test Step **C1**.
HT4 CHECK TP-B CIRCUIT FOR OPEN IN HARNESS			
• Key off. • TP-B sensor disconnected. • Disconnect PCM. Inspect for damaged or pushed out pins, corrosion, loose wires, etc. Service as necessary. • Install breakout box, leave PCM disconnected. • Measure resistance between Test Pin 63 (TP-B) and TP-B circuit at the TP-B sensor vehicle harness connector. • **Is resistance less than 5.0 ohms?**	Yes	▶	GO to **HT5**.
	No	▶	SERVICE open in TP-B circuit. REMOVE breakout box. RECONNECT all components. RERUN Quick Test.
HT5 CHECK TP-B CIRCUIT FOR SHORTS TO GROUND AND SIG RTN			
• Key off. • TP-B sensor disconnected. • Breakout box installed, leave PCM disconnected. • Disconnect Scan Tool from DLC. • Measure resistance between Test Pin 63 (TP-B) and Test Pin 91 (SIG RTN) and Test Pins 51 / 103 (PWR GND) at the breakout box. • **Is each resistance greater than 10,000 ohms?**	Yes	▶	REPLACE damaged PCM. REMOVE breakout box. RECONNECT all components. RERUN Quick Test.
	No	▶	SERVICE short circuit between TP-B and GROUND or SIG RTN. REMOVE breakout box. RECONNECT all components. RERUN Quick Test.

FM0159601522030X

Fig. 256 Test HT: Traction Control System (Part 3 of 14). 1996

FM0159601522040X

Fig. 256 Test HT: Traction Control System (Part 4 of 14). 1996

Test Step	Result	▶	Action to Take
HT6 WIGGLE TEST SENSOR AND HARNESS			
• Key on, engine off. • Access TPB PID with a Scan Tool. • Observe TPB PID for an indication of a fault while performing the following: — Lightly tap on TP-B sensor, wiggle the TP-B sensor connector and vehicle harness between sensor and PCM. A fault is indicated by a sudden change in TPB PID voltage. • **Is a fault indicated?**	Yes	▶	ISOLATE fault and SERVICE as necessary. RECONNECT all components. COMPLETE PCM Reset to clear DTCs. (REFER to Powertrain Control Module (PCM) Reset.) RERUN Quick Test.
	No	▶	UNABLE to duplicate and / or identify fault at this time. GO to Pinpoint Test Step **Z1** with the following data: PID TPB and list of possible causes.
HT10 DTC P0223: VERIFY TP-B VOLTAGE			
Diagnostic Trouble Code (DTC) indicates Self-Test has detected Throttle Position Sensor B (TP-B) voltage above the maximum. Possible causes: — TP-B short to VREF. — TP-B short to PWR. — SIG RTN open. — Damaged TP-B. — Damaged PCM. • Key on, engine off. • Access TPB PID with a Scan Tool. • **Is the TPB PID voltage greater than 4.0 volts?**	Yes	▶	The TP-B sensor voltage is greater than the acceptable maximum. GO to **HT11**.
	No	▶	The fault that produced DTC P0222 is intermittent. GO to **HT16**.
HT11 CHECK TP-B FOR SHORT TO PWR			
• Key off. • Disconnect TP-B sensor vehicle harness connector. Inspect for damaged or pushed out pins, corrosion, moisture, loose wires, etc. Service as necessary. • Key on, engine off. • Measure voltage between TP-B circuit at the TP-B sensor vehicle harness connector and battery ground. • **Is voltage greater than 10.5 volts?**	Yes	▶	The TP-B voltage is indicating a short to PWR. GO to **HT12**.
	No	▶	GO to **HT13**.

Test Step	Result	▶	Action to Take
HT12 CHECK TP-B FOR SHORT TO PWR IN HARNESS			
• Key off. • TP-B sensor disconnected. • Disconnect PCM. Inspect for damaged or pushed out pins, corrosion, loose wires, etc. Service as necessary. • Install breakout box, leave PCM disconnected. • Key on, engine off. • Measure voltage between Test Pin 63 (TP-B) and Test Pins 51 and 103 (PWR GND) at the breakout box. • **Is voltage greater than 10.5 volts?**	Yes	▶	SERVICE short between TP-B and PWR circuit. REMOVE breakout box. RECONNECT all components. RERUN Quick Test.
	No	▶	REPLACE damaged PCM. REMOVE breakout box. RECONNECT all components. RERUN Quick Test.
HT13 INDUCE OPPOSITE TP-B SIGNAL			
• Key off. • Disconnect TP-B sensor vehicle harness connector. • Key on, engine off. • Access TPB PID with a Scan Tool. • **Is the TPB PID voltage less than 0.1 volt?**	Yes	▶	GO to **HT14**.
	No	▶	UNABLE to induce opposite signal. GO to **HT15**.
HT14 VERIFY THAT VREF IS IN RANGE			
• TP-B sensor disconnected. • Key on, engine off. • Measure voltage between the sensor VREF circuit and SIG RTN circuit at the TP-B sensor vehicle harness connector. • **Is VREF voltage between 4.0 and 6.0 volts?**	Yes	▶	REPLACE damaged TP-B sensor. RECONNECT all components. COMPLETE PCM Reset to clear DTCs. (REFER to Powertrain Control Module (PCM) Reset.) RERUN Quick Test.
	No	▶	VREF voltage is out of range. GO to Pinpoint Test Step **C1**.
HT15 CHECK TP-B FOR SHORT TO VREF			
• Key off. • TP-B sensor disconnected. • Disconnect PCM. Inspect for damaged or pushed out pins, corrosion, loose wires, etc. Service as necessary. • Install breakout box, leave PCM disconnected. • Measure resistance between Test Pin 63 (TP-B) and Test Pin 90 (VREF) at the breakout box. • **Is resistance greater than 10,000 ohms?**	Yes	▶	REPLACE damaged PCM. REMOVE breakout box. RECONNECT all components. RERUN Quick Test.
	No	▶	SERVICE short between TP-B and VREF circuit. REMOVE breakout box. RECONNECT all components. RERUN Quick Test.

FM0159601522050X

Fig. 256 Test HT: Traction Control System (Part 5 of 14). 1996

FM0159601522060X

Fig. 256 Test HT: Traction Control System (Part 6 of 14). 1996

Test Step	Result	▶	Action to Take
HT16 WIGGLE TEST SENSOR AND HARNESS			
• Key on, engine off. • Access TPB PID with a Scan Tool. • Observe TPB PID for an indication of a fault while performing the following: — Lightly tap on TP-B sensor, wiggle the TP-B sensor connector and vehicle harness between sensor and PCM. A fault is indicated by a sudden change in TPB PID voltage. • **Is a fault indicated?**	Yes	▶	ISOLATE fault and SERVICE as necessary. RECONNECT all components. COMPLETE PCM Reset to clear DTCS. (REFER to Powertrain Control Module (PCM) Reset.) RERUN Quick Test.
	No	▶	UNABLE to duplicate and / or identify fault at this time. GO to Pinpoint Test **Z1** with the following data: TPB PID and list of possible causes.
HT20 DTC P1220: INSPECT SERIES THROTTLE (ST) SYSTEM			
Diagnostic Trouble Code (DTC) P1220 indicates Self-Test has detected a Series Throttle Control system malfunction. Possible Causes: — Any ST Stepper Motor circuit fault. — VPWR open to STC module. — SIG RTN open to STC module. — SIG RTN open to TP-B sensor. — PWR GND open to STC module. — TAPW circuit open. — TAPW circuit short to PWR. — TAPW circuit short to GND or SIG RTN. — Damaged Series Throttle (ST). — Damaged STC module. — Damaged ST Stepper Motor. — Damaged TP-B sensor. — Damaged PCM. • Key off. • Remove air tube from Series Throttle (ST) Body. • Visually inspect the Series Throttle Assembly for obstruction, loose motor or electrical connector, loose TP-B sensor, or any other damage. Service as necessary. • Determine if the Series Throttle plate is binding or stuck. The plate is normally wide open and should spring back open when closed by hand and released. Push throttle plate closed several times and look for a smooth transition. • **Is a fault found?**	Yes	▶	If throttle appears to bind or if stuck, GO to **HT21**. SERVICE all other faults as necessary. RECONNECT all components. COMPLETE ST PCM Reset to clear DTCs. (REFER to Powertrain Control Module (PCM) Reset.) RERUN Quick Test.
	No	▶	GO to **HT22**.

Fig. 256   Test HT: Traction Control System (Part 7 of 14). 1996

Test Step	Result	▶	Action to Take
HT21 INSPECT SERIES THROTTLE (ST) ASSEMBLY AND ST STEPPER MOTOR			
This test step is also the entry for No Traction Control, Poor or Erratic Traction Control and Lack / Loss of Power symptoms. • Key off. • Remove Traction Control Throttle Assembly (do not separate Series Throttle from main throttle body). • Remove ST Stepper Motor. • Push the series throttle plate through its full range of travel and release. Verify that the throttle travels freely and that the throttle gear contacts the stop screws in both directions. The throttle should return freely when released. • Rotate the motor shaft at the motor in both directions and verify that it does not bind in either direction. • **Does the stepper motor bind or the series throttle plate not bind with stepper motor removed?**	Yes	▶	REPLACE ST Stepper Motor. RECONNECT all components. COMPLETE PCM Reset to clear DTCs. (REFER to Powertrain Control Module (PCM) Reset.) RERUN Quick Test.
	No	▶	REPLACE Series Throttle. RECONNECT all components. COMPLETE PCM Reset to clear DTCs. (REFER to Powertrain Control Module (PCM) Reset.) RERUN Quick Test.
HT22 CHECK TP-B SENSOR VOLTAGE			
This step is to check for an open in the SIG RTN circuit of the TP-B sensor. • Key on, engine off. • Access TPB PID with a Scan Tool. • **Is TPB PID voltage greater than 4.5 volts with Series Throttle wide open?**	Yes	▶	GO to **HT33**.
	No	▶	GO to **HT23**.

Fig. 256   Test HT: Traction Control System (Part 8 of 14). 1996

Test Step	Result	▶	Action to Take
HT23 MEASURE SERIES THROTTLE (ST) STEPPER MOTOR COIL RESISTANCE			
This test step is also the entry for No Traction Control and Poor or Erratic Traction Control symptoms. • Key off. • Disconnect Series Throttle Stepper Motor vehicle harness connector. • Measure resistance of all four coils between the pins indicated below at the motor.	Yes	▶	GO to **HT24**.
	No	▶	REPLACE ST Stepper Motor. RECONNECT all components. COMPLETE PCM Reset to clear DTCs. (REFER to Powertrain Control Module (PCM) Reset.) RERUN Quick Test.

Pins	Resistance
TA-B1 and BCOMM	1 - 5 OHMS
TA-B2 and BCOMM	1 - 5 OHMS
TA-A1 and ACOMM	1 - 5 OHMS
TA-A2 and ACOMM	1 - 5 OHMS

• **Is each coil resistance within specification?**

Fig. 256   Test HT: Traction Control System (Part 9 of 14). 1996

Test Step	Result	▶	Action to Take
HT24 CHECK ST STEPPER MOTOR COILS FOR SHORTS			
• Key off. • ST Stepper Motor vehicle harness connector disconnected. • Measure resistance between Pins ACOMM and BCOMM at the ST Stepper Motor (reference motor pinout in Step **HT23**). • Measure resistance between pins ACOMM and motor housing and BCOMM and motor housing. • **Are all resistance checks greater than 10,000 ohms?**	Yes	▶	For DTC P1220: GO to **HT25**.
	No	▶	REPLACE ST Stepper Motor. RECONNECT all components. COMPLETE PCM Reset to clear DTCs. (REFER to Powertrain Control Module (PCM) Reset.) RERUN Quick Test.
HT25 INSPECT ST STEPPER MOTOR CIRCUIT CONTINUITY			
• Key off. • ST Stepper Motor vehicle harness connector disconnected. • Disconnect Series Throttle Controller (STC) vehicle harness connector. • Measure the circuit resistance of each of the wires between the ST Stepper Motor and STC vehicle harness connectors (refer to the beginning of the Pinpoint Test for connector pinout). • **Are all resistance checks less than 5.0 ohms?**	Yes	▶	GO to **HT26**.
	No	▶	SERVICE open in circuit with greater than 5.0 ohms resistance. RECONNECT all components. RERUN Quick Test.
HT26 INSPECT ST STEPPER MOTOR CIRCUITS FOR SHORTS			
• Key off. • ST Stepper Motor vehicle harness connector disconnected. • Series Throttle Controller vehicle harness connector disconnected. • Disconnect Scan Tool from DLC. • Measure resistance between each pin and all other pins within the ST Stepper Motor vehicle harness connector. • Measure resistance between each pin at the ST Stepper Motor vehicle harness connector and battery ground. • **Are all resistance checks greater than 10,000 ohms?**	Yes	▶	GO to **HT27**.
	No	▶	SERVICE shorted circuit. RECONNECT all components. COMPLETE PCM Reset to clear DTCs. (REFER to Powertrain Control Module (PCM) Reset.) RERUN Quick Test.

Fig. 256   Test HT: Traction Control System (Part 10 of 14). 1996

Part 11 (HT27–HT30)

Test Step	Result	▶	Action to Take
HT27 CHECK VPWR VOLTAGE TO SERIES THROTTLE CONTROLLER (STC) • Series Throttle Controller (STC) disconnected. • Key on, engine off. • Measure voltage between VPWR at the STC vehicle harness connector and chassis ground (refer to the beginning of the Pinpoint Test for connector pinout). • **Is voltage greater than 10.5 volts?**	Yes No	▶ ▶	GO to **HT28**. SERVICE open circuit in VPWR to Series Throttle Controller. RECONNECT all components. COMPLETE PCM Reset to clear DTCs. (REFER to Powertrain Control Module (PCM) Reset.) RERUN Quick Test.
HT28 CHECK SIG RTN AND PWR GND TO SERIES THROTTLE CONTROLLER (STC) • Key off. • Series Throttle Controller (STC) disconnected. • Measure continuity between SIG RTN at the STC vehicle harness connector and chassis ground. • Measure continuity between PWR GND at the STC vehicle harness connector and chassis ground. • **Are all resistance readings less than 5.0 ohms?**	Yes No	▶ ▶	GO to **HT29**. SERVICE open circuit in either SIG RTN or PWR GND to STC vehicle harness connector. RECONNECT all components. COMPLETE PCM Reset to clear DTCs. (REFER to Powertrain Control Module (PCM) Reset.) RERUN Quick Test.
HT29 CHECK TAPW FOR OPEN CIRCUIT IN HARNESS • Key off. • Series Throttle Controller disconnected. • Disconnect PCM. Inspect for damaged or pushed out pins, corrosion, loose wires, etc. Service as necessary. • Install breakout box, leave PCM disconnected. • Measure resistance between Test Pin 18 (TAPW) at the breakout box and TAPW circuit at the Series Throttle Controller vehicle harness connector. • **Is resistance less than 5.0 ohms?**	Yes No	▶ ▶	GO to **HT30**. SERVICE open in TAPW circuit. REMOVE breakout box. RECONNECT all components. RERUN Quick Test.
HT30 CHECK TAPW FOR SHORT TO PWR IN HARNESS • Key off. • Series Throttle Controller disconnected. • Breakout box installed, PCM disconnected. • Key on, engine off. • Measure voltage between Test Pin 18 (TAPW) and battery ground. • **Is voltage greater than .05 volts?**	Yes No	▶ ▶	SERVICE TAPW circuit for short to PWR. REMOVE breakout box. RECONNECT all components. RERUN Quick Test. GO to **HT31**.

FM0159601522110X

Fig. 256   Test HT: Traction Control System (Part 11 of 14). 1996

Part 12 (HT31–HT33)

Test Step	Result	▶	Action to Take
HT31 CHECK TAPW FOR SHORT TO GND OR SIG RTN IN HARNESS • Key off. • Series Throttle Controller disconnected. • Breakout box installed, PCM disconnected. • Measure resistance between Test Pin 18 (TAPW) and Test Pin 91 (SIG RTN) and Test Pins 51 and 103 (PWR GND) at the breakout box. • **Is each resistance greater than 10,000 ohms?**	Yes No	▶ ▶	If DTC P1220 is output during either KOEO or KOER Self-Test: GO to **HT32**. All others: UNABLE to duplicate and/or identify fault at this time, GO to Pinpoint Test Step **Z1** with the following data: TATC, TPB PIDs and list of possible causes. SERVICE short circuit. REMOVE breakout box. RECONNECT all components. RERUN Quick Test.
HT32 MONITOR SIGNAL FROM PCM TO SERIES THROTTLE CONTROLLER • Key off. • Series Throttle Controller (STC) disconnected. • Breakout box installed, PCM connected. • Connect DVOM between Test Pin 18 (TAPW) and Test Pin 91 (SIG RTN). NOTE: On every power-up, the Series Throttle is momentarily commanded shut from its normal wide open rest position. The PCM will output a signal to the STC module on the TAPW circuit to close the Series Throttle. This signal can be verified by a change in voltage on the DVOM. • Key on, engine off. • Immediately monitor DVOM for a brief change in voltage. • **Does the DVOM indicate a brief change in voltage by a minimum of 2 volts?**	Yes No	▶ ▶	REPLACE damaged Series Throttle Controller. RECONNECT all components. RERUN Quick Test. REPLACE damaged PCM. RECONNECT all components. RERUN Quick Test.
HT33 CHECK VREF CIRCUIT VOLTAGE AT TP-B SENSOR • Key off. • Disconnect TP-B sensor vehicle harness connector. • Key on, engine off. • Measure the voltage between VREF circuit and SIG RTN circuit at the TP-B sensor vehicle harness connector. • **Is voltage between 4.0 and 6.0 volts?**	Yes No	▶ ▶	REPLACE damaged TP-B sensor. RECONNECT all components. COMPLETE PCM Reset to clear DTCs (REFER to Powertrain Control Module (PCM) Reset). RERUN Quick Test. GO to Pinpoint Test Step **C1**.

FM0159601522120X

Fig. 256   Test HT: Traction Control System (Part 12 of 14). 1996

Part 13 (HT40)

Test Step	Result	▶	Action to Take
HT40 DTC P1224: CHECK SERIES THROTTLE ASSEMBLY Diagnostic Trouble Code (DTC) P1224 indicates that Key On Engine Off (KOEO) or Key On Engine Running (KOER) Self-Test has detected the TP-B Sensor voltage out of range. NOTE: Diagnose all other Traction Control DTCs first if received. Possible causes: — TP-B sensor binding or sticking. — Throttle Stop Screws misadjusted. — VREF out of range. — Damaged TP-B sensor. — Damaged Series Throttle. • Key off. • Disconnect air tube at Series Throttle assembly. • Key on, engine off. — The Series Throttle is commanded shut for a brief moment on every power-up. When the throttle returns to its wide open rest position, the TP-B sensor voltage should also return to wide open voltage. • Access TPB PID with a Scan Tool. • Push the series throttle plate shut and release while monitoring the TPB PID on the Scan Tool. Look for binding, sticking and TP-B sensor voltage returning to its wide open voltage. • **Is there binding or sticking in the Series Throttle or the TP-B sensor voltage not returning to its wide open voltage?**	Yes No	▶ ▶	ISOLATE fault and SERVICE as necessary. RECONNECT all components. RERUN Quick Test. GO to **HT41**.

FM0159601522130X

Fig. 256   Test HT: Traction Control System (Part 13 of 14). 1996

Part 14 (HT41–HT50)

Test Step	Result	▶	Action to Take
HT41 CHECK TP-B VOLTAGE AT WIDE OPEN THROTTLE • Access TPB PID with a Scan Tool. • Key on, engine off. — The TP-B sensor voltage should increase for a moment while the Series Throttle is initialized and should return to specification when the throttle springs back open. The TP-B sensor voltage at wide open throttle is between 0.3 and 0.9 volt. • **Is the TPB PID voltage between 0.3 and 0.9 volt at wide open throttle?**	Yes No	▶ ▶	GO to **HT42**. REMOVE TP-B sensor and ST Stepper Motor from Series Throttle. ROTATE each part manually while looking for binding in each direction. INSPECT series throttle stop screws for tampering or wear. ISOLATE fault and SERVICE as necessary. If fault is not found, REPLACE TP-B sensor. RECONNECT all components. COMPLETE PCM Reset to clear DTCs. (REFER to Powertrain Control Module (PCM) Reset.) RERUN Quick Test.
HT42 MEASURE VREF VOLTAGE AT TP-B SENSOR • Key off. • Disconnect the TP-B sensor vehicle harness connector. • Key on. • Measure voltage between VREF and SIG RTN circuit at the TP-B vehicle harness connector. • **Is VREF voltage between 4.0 and 6.0 volts?**	Yes No	▶ ▶	REPLACE damaged TP-B Sensor. RECONNECT all components. RERUN Quick Test. VREF voltage is out of range. GO to Pinpoint Test Step **C1**.
HT50 CLOSE SERIES THROTTLE MANUALLY AND CHECK ENGINE FOR STALLING This step is the entry for Stalls/Quits symptom. • Key off. • Remove air tube at Series Throttle. • Inspect the Series Throttle Assembly for obstruction, loose fasteners, loose electrical connections, or any other damage. Service as necessary. • Start the engine and bring to a steady speed between 2000 and 3000 rpm. • With rpm held constant, manually close the Series Throttle plate completely shut (may require two people to perform this step). • **Does the engine stall when Series Throttle plate is completely shut?**	Yes No	▶ ▶	INSPECT series throttle for binding, sticking and contamination. REMOVE and INSPECT TP-B sensor and stepper motor to isolate fault if necessary. SERVICE as necessary. RECONNECT all components. COMPLETE PCM Reset to clear DTCs. (REFER to Powertrain Control Module (PCM) Reset.) RERUN Quick Test. Series Throttle is OK. RECONNECT air tube. RETURN to Symptom Flowcharts.

FM0159601522140X

Fig. 256   Test HT: Traction Control System (Part 14 of 14). 1996

Note

You should enter this Pinpoint Test only when directed here.

Remember

This Pinpoint Test is intended to diagnose the following:

- Throttle Body Assembly (9E926)
- Speed Control Cable
- Accelerator Cable - Linkage to Throttle Body (9C799)
- Air Cleaner Assembly (including air filter)
- Air Inlet Tube
- Clean Air Tube (Hose) and Resonator (9R504)
- Intake Manifold Runner Control Housing Assembly (IMRC) (9U531) and (9J447)
- IMRC Actuator Assembly (9J559)
- Harness Circuits: IMRC, IMRC Monitor, SIG RTN, PWR GND, VPWR
- Powertrain Control Module (PCM) (12A650)

FM0159601523010X

**Fig. 257   Test HU: Air Intake Systems (Part 1 of 31).
1996**

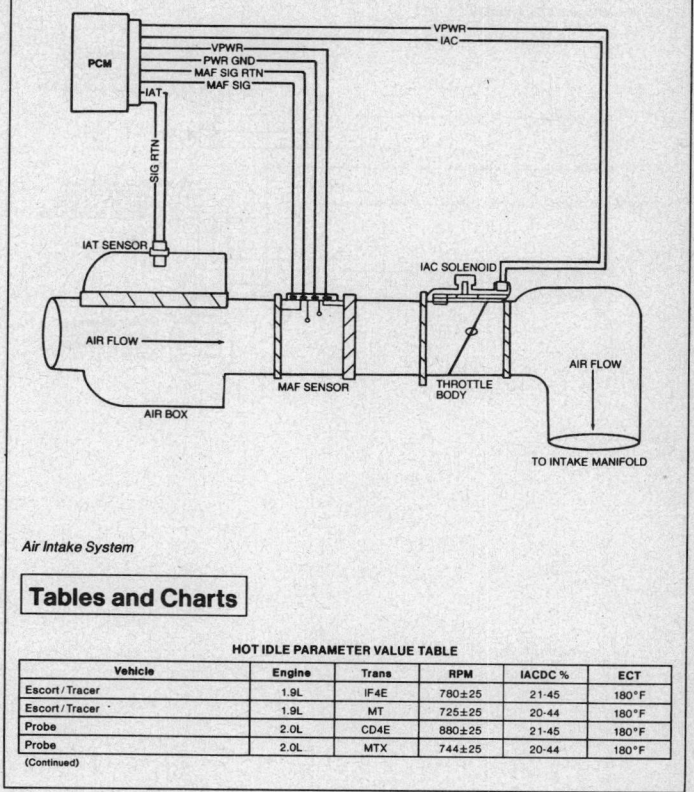

Air Intake System

Tables and Charts

HOT IDLE PARAMETER VALUE TABLE

Vehicle	Engine	Trans	RPM	IACDC %	ECT
Escort / Tracer	1.9L	IF4E	780±25	21-45	180°F
Escort / Tracer	1.9L	MT	725±25	20-44	180°F
Probe	2.0L	CD4E	880±25	21-45	180°F
Probe	2.0L	MTX	744±25	20-44	180°F
(Continued)					

FM0159601523020X

**Fig. 257   Test HU: Air Intake Systems (Part 2 of 31).
1996**

HOT IDLE PARAMETER VALUE TABLE (Cont'd)

Vehicle	Engine	Trans	RPM	IACDC %	ECT
Contour / Mystique	2.0L	CD4E	800±25	19-43	180°F
Contour / Mystique	2.0L	MTX	880±25	21-45	180°F
Contour / Mystique	2.5L	CD4E	744±25	20-44	180°F
Contour / Mystique	2.5L	MTX	725±25	19-43	180°F
Taurus / Sable	3.0L	AX4N	900±25	19-43	180°F
Taurus / Sable	3.0L FF	AX4N	900±25	19-43	180°F
Taurus / Sable	3.0L 4V	AX4N	900±26	19-43	180°F
Taurus SHO	3.4L	AX4N	900±27	19-43	180°F
Mustang	3.8L	AODE	700±25	21-45	180°F
Mustang	3.8L	T5OD	720±25	20-44	180°F
Mustang	4.6L	AODE	656±25	21-45	180°F
Mustang	4.6L	T5OD	656±25	20-44	180°F
Mustang	4.6L 4V	T5OD	656±25	20-44	180°F
Thunderbird / Cougar	3.8L	4R70W	704±25	20-44	180°F
Thunderbird / Cougar	4.6L	4R70W	768±25	20-44	180°F
Crown Victoria / Grand Marquis	4.6L	AODE	800±25	19-43	180°F
Crown Victoria	4.6L NG	AODE	800±25	19-43	180°F
Continental	4.6L	AX4N	800±25	19-43	180°F
Town Car	4.6L	4R70W	800±25	20-44	180°F
Mark VIII	4.6L	4R70W	900±28	20-45	180°F
Ranger	2.3L	A4LD	768±25	20-44	180°F
Ranger	2.3L	M5	720±25	20-45	180°F
Ranger	3.0L	A4LD	900±25	20-44	180°F
Ranger	3.0L	M5	850±25	20-44	180°F
Ranger	4.0L	A4LD	824±25	20-44	180°F
Ranger	4.0L	M5	750±25	20-45	180°F
Aerostar	3.0L	4R44E	750±25	20-45	180°F
Aerostar	4.0L	4R55E	750±25	20-45	180°F
Windstar	3.0L	AXODE	700±25	20-45	180°F
Windstar	3.8L	AXODE	700±25	20-45	180°F
Explorer	4.0L	4R55E	750±26	20-46	180°F
Explorer	4.0L	M5	750±27	20-47	180°F
Explorer	5.0L	4R70W	750±27	20-47	180°F
Explorer	5.0L	MT	750±27	20-47	180°F
F Series	4.2L	4R70W	824±25	20-44	180°F
F Series	4.2L	M5	750±25	20-44	180°F
F Series	4.6L	4R70W	824±25	20-44	180°F
F Series	4.6L	M5	750±25	20-44	180°F
E/F/B	4.9L	M5	750±25	20-45	180°F
(Continued)					

FM0159601523030X

**Fig. 257   Test HU: Air Intake Systems (Part 3 of 31).
1996**

HOT IDLE PARAMETER VALUE TABLE (Cont'd)

Vehicle	Engine	Trans	RPM	IACDC %	ECT
E/F/B	4.9L	C6	824±25	20-44	180°F
E/F/B	4.9L	M5	750±25	20-45	180°F
E/F/B	5.0L	C6	824±25	20-44	180°F
E/F/B	5.0L	M5	750±25	20-45	180°F
E/F/B	5.8L	C6	824±25	20-44	180°F
E/F/B	5.8L	M5	750±25	20-45	180°F
E/F	7.5L	C6	824±25	20-44	180°F
E/F	7.5L	M5	750±25	20-45	180°F

During some Intake Manifold Runner Control repair procedures, it may be necessary to perform a drive cycle for verification of the IMRC and PCM operation. The table lists RPM, IMRCM and IMRC PID values during acceleration and de-acceleration.

INTAKE MANIFOLD DRIVE CYCLE PID TABLE

RPM	IMRCM VDC	IMRC ON/OFF
KOEO	5.0 ± .2	OFF
Idle to 3000	5.0 ± .2	OFF
Above 3500	0.7 ± .2	ON
3000 to Idle	5.0 ± .2	OFF

Pinpoint Test Schematics

2.5L Contour / Mystique, 3.0L 4V Taurus / Sable, 3.4L Taurus SHO, 4.6L 4V Mustang, Continental

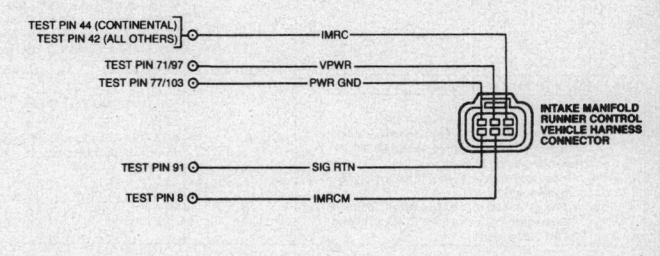

FM0159601523040X

**Fig. 257   Test HU: Air Intake Systems (Part 4 of 31).
1996**

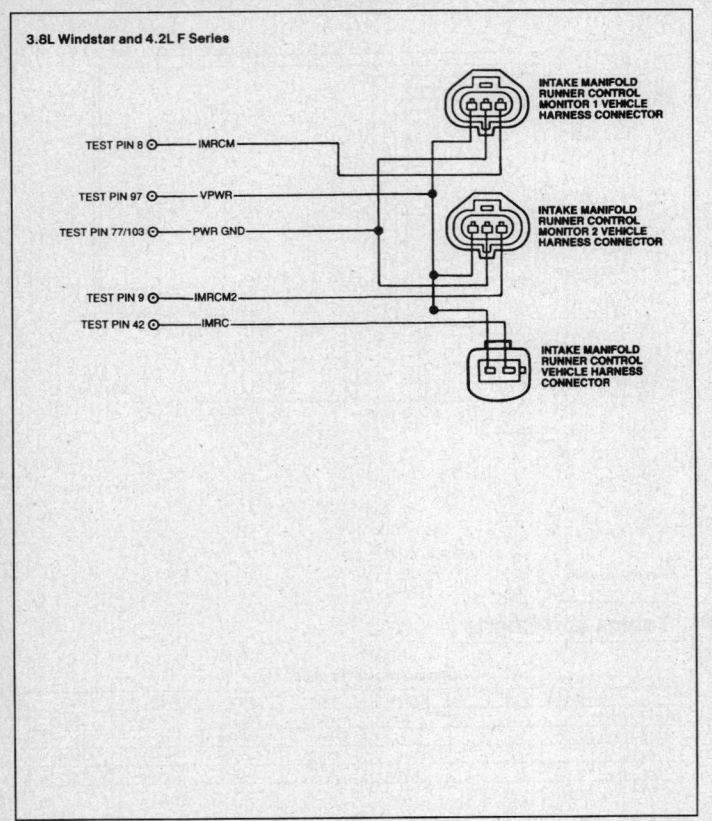

Fig. 257   Test HU: Air Intake Systems (Part 5 of 31). 1996

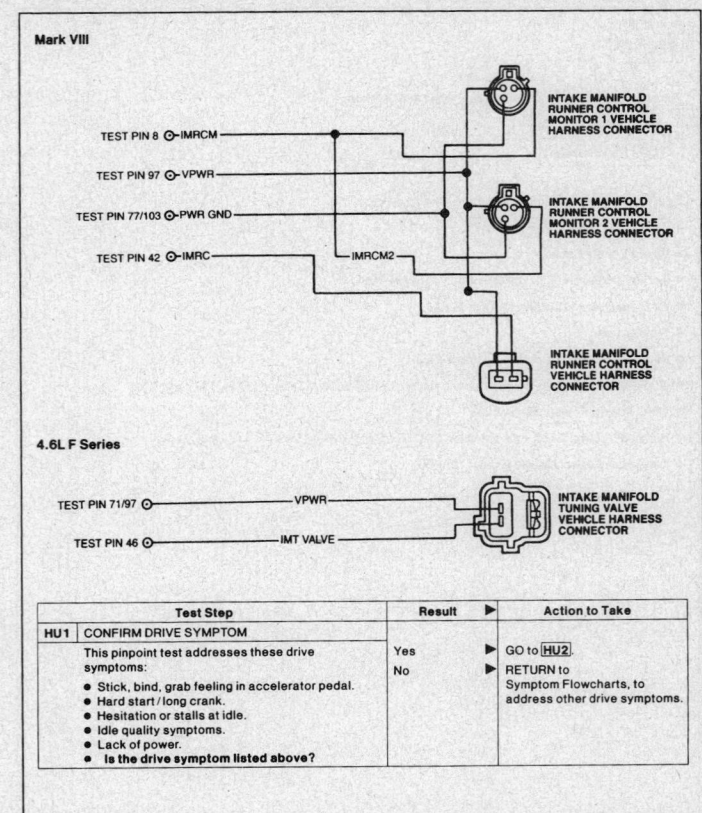

4.6L F Series

Test Step		Result	▶	Action to Take
HU1	CONFIRM DRIVE SYMPTOM			
	This pinpoint test addresses these drive symptoms: • Stick, bind, grab feeling in accelerator pedal. • Hard start/long crank. • Hesitation or stalls at idle. • Idle quality symptoms. • Lack of power. • **Is the drive symptom listed above?**	Yes No	▶ ▶	GO to HU2. RETURN to Symptom Flowcharts, to address other drive symptoms.

Fig. 257   Test HU: Air Intake Systems (Part 6 of 31). 1996

Test Step		Result	▶	Action to Take
HU2	SELECT DIAGNOSTIC TEST STEP			
	• Does the air intake system symptom relate to stick, bind, grab conditions on the throttle body?	Yes No	▶ ▶	GO to HU3. GO to HU7.
HU3	CHECK ACCELERATOR AND SPEED CONTROL CABLES FOR FREEDOM OF TRAVEL			
	• Key off. • Disconnect accelerator cable and speed control cable from throttle body linkage. • Inspect cables for freedom of travel from accelerator pedal / speed control device to throttle body linkage cable connector. • **Do cables travel freely?**	Yes No	▶ ▶	GO to HU4. SERVICE cable as necessary.
HU4	CHECK THROTTLE RETURN SCREW SETTING			
	• Key off. • Cables removed from throttle body linkage. • Remove the clean air tube from the throttle body and verify that there is no foreign material or debris preventing the throttle plate from rotating to the fully closed position. • Verify that the Throttle Return Screw (TRC) is in contact with the throttle linkage lever arm when the throttle is in the closed plate (idle) position. Refer to the Air Intake and Throttle Body Systems in Section 1A for TRC screw description. • **Does the TRC screw contact lever arm?**	Yes No	▶ ▶	GO to HU6. The following adjustment should be made only in the event the TRC screw does not contact the throttle lever arm. **Do not adjust TRC screw to try to correct idle quality concerns.** NOTE: TRC adjust procedure cannot be performed on the 1.9L engine, throttle body assembly must be replaced if TRC screw does not contact lever arm. 1.) PLACE a 0.002 inch feeler gauge between the TRC screw and lever arm. ADJUST TRC screw until it just contacts the feeler gauge. 2.) REMOVE the feeler gauge and turn the screw clockwise a half turn. 3.) GO to HU5.
HU5	VERIFY TP SENSOR IN RANGE			
	• Key on, engine off. • Access TP PID with the Scan Tool. • Slowly move throttle from closed to wide open throttle position and observe the TP PID for smooth reading change. • Release throttle and allow to return to fully closed position. • **While at closed throttle position, is the TP PID reading between 13% (0.66 volt) and 24% (1.20 volts)?**	Yes No	▶ ▶	REMOVE Scan Tool. GO to HU6. REMOVE Scan Tool. REPLACE throttle body assembly.

Fig. 257   Test HU: Air Intake Systems (Part 7 of 31). 1996

Test Step		Result	▶	Action to Take
HU6	CHECK FOR THROTTLE BODY STICKING, BINDING, GRABBING			
	• Key off. • Cables removed from throttle body linkage. • Clean air tube removed from throttle body. • Snap throttle from open to closed position several times. • Gently cycle throttle by hand from closed to wide open position. Inspect for freedom of travel particularly during the initial throttle opening. • Check for foreign material or debris in the throttle bore and plate area that can cause sticking or binding. NOTE: Throttle bodies use a special coating / sealant on the throttle bore and plate area to make them tolerant to engine sludge accumulation. Sludge or oil film deposits in this area do not cause a sticking or binding condition and do not require servicing. DO NOT CLEAN THE THROTTLE BORE AND PLATE AREA. CLEANING WILL DAMAGE THE THROTTLE BODY ASSEMBLY. • **Does the throttle rotate freely without sticking, binding or grabbing condition?**	Yes No	▶ ▶	RECONNECT accelerator cable and clean air tube to the throttle body assembly. RETURN to Symptom Flowcharts, if the drive symptom persists. REPLACE throttle body assembly. RECONNECT all components.
HU7	CHECK AIR FILTER ELEMENT			
	• Inspect air filter element. • **Is the air filter excessively dirty?**	Yes No	▶ ▶	REPLACE air filter. RETURN to Symptom Flowcharts if drive symptom persists. GO to HU8.
HU8	CHECK FOR PROPER OPERATION OF RELATED ENGINE SYSTEMS			
	NOTE: If here from Pinpoint Test QA, go directly to HU9. • Verify that the following engine systems have been properly diagnosed and corrected before proceeding with the Air Intake system diagnostics: — Positive Crankcase Ventilation (PCV) System. — Ignition System. — Exhaust System. — Engine Cooling System (engine coolant temperature is above 180 degrees F.). — Incorrect fuel pressure, plugged fuel filter, fuel quality (contamination). • **Have the systems been properly checked and are they functioning correctly?**	Yes No	▶ ▶	GO to HU9. GO to Symptom Flowcharts, with the symptom, for direction.

Fig. 257   Test HU: Air Intake Systems (Part 8 of 31). 1996

Test Step	Result	▶	Action to Take
HU9 CHECK FOR VACUUM LEAKS • Key on, engine running. • With engine at idle, listen for vacuum leaks. • Inspect the entire inlet air system from the Mass Air Flow (MAF) sensor to the intake manifold for leaks such as: — Cracked or punctured inlet air tube. — Loose connections on the inlet air tube at the air cleaner housing or throttle body. — Idle Air Control (IAC) valve assembly or gasket seal. — EGR valve gasket seal leak to intake manifold. — Intake manifold assembly or gasket seal. — EGR valve diaphragm or control solenoid. — Vacuum supply connectors and hose. — PCV connectors and hose. • **Are any leaks detected in the areas listed above?**	Yes No	▶ ▶	SERVICE as necessary. GO to **HU10**.
HU10 CHECK IDLE • Key off. • Transmission in Park (wheels blocked and parking brake engaged). • A/C, heater and all accessories are off. • Key on, engine running. • Engine at normal operating temperature and cooling fan off. **WARNING: DO NOT UNPLUG COOLING FAN. IT MAY CAUSE ENGINE OVERHEATING.** • Connect Scan Tool (refer to Scan Tool Hookup). • Access engine RPM PID. NOTE: Engine idle RPM is controlled by the PCM and cannot be adjusted. The PCM is calibrated to control idle at the speeds listed in the Hot Idle PID Value Table at the beginning of the pinpoint test. When performing this test, verify the RPM is within the specification. If the engine is allowed to idle for an extended period of time, or if the engine temperature is hot enough to require cooling fan on, it may be necessary to turn the engine off and repeat this test procedure. • Access IAC PID, idle air percent duty cycle. • **Do the RPM and IAC PID readings match the values in the Hot Idle PID Value Table at the beginning of the pinpoint test?**	Yes No	▶ ▶	GO to **HU11**. GO to **HU12**.

FM0159601523090X

Fig. 257 Test HU: Air Intake Systems (Part 9 of 31). 1996

Test Step	Result	▶	Action to Take
HU11 CHECK IDLE CONTROL RESPONSE • Transmission still in Park. • A/C, heater and all accessories off. • Engine at normal operating temperature and cooling fan off, but not unplugged. **WARNING: DO NOT UNPLUG COOLING FAN. IT MAY CAUSE ENGINE OVERHEATING.** • Key on, engine running. • Goose throttle and let it return to the idle position. • **Does the engine stall or does the RPM fluctuate excessively before returning to the idle speed specified in HU10?**	Yes No	▶ ▶	GO to **HU12**. Air Intake system is OK. DISCONNECT Scan Tool. RETURN to Symptom Flowcharts to check other possible causes of the drive symptoms.
HU12 CHECK IAC SOLENOID FOR PROPER FUNCTION • Transmission still in Park. • A/C, heater and all accessories off. • Engine at normal operating temperature and cooling fan off, but not unplugged. **WARNING: DO NOT UNPLUG COOLING FAN. IT MAY CAUSE ENGINE OVERHEATING.** • Key on, engine running. • Disconnect IAC solenoid vehicle harness connector. • **Does the RPM drop or engine stall?**	Yes No	▶ ▶	Fast Idle Symptom: GO to **HU14**. Other Symptoms: GO to **HU13**. IAC solenoid is defective, REPLACE IAC solenoid only. RESET KAM (REFER to Powertrain Control Module (PCM) Reset). NOTE: Do not attempt to clean the IAC solenoid.
HU13 THROTTLE BODY VISUAL / FUNCTIONAL CHECK • Key off. • Remove throttle body assembly (see Vehicle Shop Manual). • Hold throttle body up to a light source. With the throttle plate closed, no light should be visible between the plate and bore (sludge tolerant coating intact). The hole in the throttle plate (in some applications only) should be visible and unobstructed. • Rotate the throttle lever and allow it to return. It should not stick or bind and should return to the closed plate position (TRC screw contacting lever) freely when released. • **Does the throttle body pass these visual/functional checks?**	Yes No	▶ ▶	Throttle body is functioning properly. REINSTALL throttle body assembly. RETURN to Symptom Flowcharts to check other possible causes of symptom. Throttle body is defective. REPLACE entire throttle body assembly. RESET KAM (REFER to Powertrain Control Module (PCM) Reset).

FM0159601523100X

Fig. 257 Test HU: Air Intake Systems (Part 10 of 31). 1996

Test Step	Result	▶	Action to Take
HU14 CHECK IAC CIRCUIT FOR SHORT TO GROUND • Key off. • IAC solenoid disconnected. • Disconnect PCM. Inspect for damaged or pushed out pins, corrosion, loose wires, etc. Service as necessary. • Install breakout box, leave PCM disconnected. • Measure resistance between Test Pin 83 (IAC) and Test Pins 51 or 103 (PWR GND) at the breakout box. • **Is each resistance greater than 10,000 ohms?**	Yes No	▶ ▶	REPLACE damaged PCM. REMOVE breakout box. RECONNECT all components. RERUN Quick Test. SERVICE short circuit. REMOVE breakout box. RECONNECT all components. RERUN Quick Test.
HU15 PERFORM VISUAL INSPECTION DTCs P1518, P1537 and P1538 indicate IMRC may be stuck open. DTCs P1512, P1513 and P1519 indicate IMRC may be stuck closed. DTCs P1516 and P1517 indicate IMRC input error. DTC P1520 indicates IMRC control circuit malfunction. Possible causes: — Cables improperly routed (binding) or seized. — Damaged/disconnected IMRC housing return springs. — Lever/shaft return stop obstructed/bent. — Lever/shaft wide open stop obstructed/bent. — IMRC lever/shaft stick/bind or disconnected. — IMRC actuator cable/gears seized. • View cable routing. Make sure cables are not binding or improperly routed. For vacuum operated IMRC systems, make sure sensor linkage is attached and secure. With engine off or at idle, cable core wire at IMRC housing attachment should have slack and lever should contact Closed Plate Stop Screw. Refer to the IMRC System Description in Section 1A, Air Intake and Throttle Body, for illustrations. • Manually open and close IMRC plates at intake manifold, feel for sticking/binding. NOTE: IMRC return spring is strong. Make sure return springs operate properly and plates open and close fully. • **Is fault indicated?**	Yes No	▶ ▶	SERVICE as necessary. REFER to Vehicle Service Manual for hardware removal procedures. VERIFY service. Passed visual inspection, GO to **HU16**.

FM0159601523110X

Fig. 257 Test HU: Air Intake Systems (Part 11 of 31). 1996

Test Step	Result	▶	Action to Take
HU16 PERFORM IMRC FUNCTIONAL TEST For vacuum operated IMRC systems, start engine for 20 seconds to build vacuum reservoir. • Key off. • Connect Scan Tool to Data Link Connector (DLC). • Key on, engine off. • Access Output Test Mode (OTM - refer to OTM). **CAUTION: Keep fingers clear of IMRC lever/cable mechanism.** • Turn all outputs on (IMRC included). • When IMRC is commanded on, both levers should rotate to full open position. At least one of the levers should contact the wide open stop, the other may be slightly off the wide open stop. This is normal. • **Did the IMRC levers cycle from fully close to fully open?**	Yes No	▶ ▶	Passed check. Exit OTM. NOTE: Always service DTC P1520 first. **For DTC P1512 and P1513:** GO to **HU41**. **For DTC P1516 and P1517:** GO to **HU64**. **For DTC P1518:** GO to **HU26**. **For DTC P1519:** GO to **HU29**. **For DTC P1520:** GO to **HU19**. **For DTC P1537 and P1538:** GO to **HU52**. Exit OTM. GO to **HU17**.
HU17 PERFORM IMRC OPERATIONAL TEST • Perform the necessary safety precautions to start engine. • Apply parking brake and block wheels. • Key on, engine running. • Rev engine to above 3500 RPM. **CAUTION: Keep fingers clear of IMRC lever/cable mechanism.** • When engine speed is above approximately 3500 RPM, both levers should rotate to full open position. At least one lever should contact the wide open stop, the other may be slightly off the wide open stop. This is normal. When engine returns to idle (or below 3000 RPM), both levers must contact Closed Plate Stop Screw. • **Did the IMRC levers cycle from fully closed to fully open when the RPM was above 3500?**	Yes No	▶ ▶	Passed operational test. NOTE: Always service DTC P1520 first. **For DTC P1512 and P1513:** GO to **HU41**. **For DTC P1516 and P1517:** GO to **HU64**. **For DTC P1518:** GO to **HU26**. **For DTC P1519:** GO to **HU29**. **For DTC P1520:** GO to **HU19**. **For DTC P1537 and P1538:** GO to **HU52**. Failed operational test. GO to **HU18**.

Fig. 257 Test HU: Air Intake Systems (Part 12 of 31). 1996

HU18–HU19

Test Step	Result	▶	Action to Take
HU18 PERFORM IMRC PHYSICAL TEST			
• Disconnect IMRC cables from both left and right intake runners.	Yes	▶	Passed physical check, RECONNECT IMRC cables. NOTE: Always service DTC P1520 first.
• Rotate by hand both the left and right bank IMRC housing lever assembly fully open and then closed.			For DTC P1512 and P1513: GO TO **HU41**.
NOTE: IMRC return springs are strong.			For DTC P1516 and P1517: GO TO **HU64**.
• Feel for sticking or binding plate rotation.			For DTC P1518: GO TO **HU26**.
• Feel for return spring tension (3-4 inch lbs).			For DTC P1519: GO TO **HU29**.
• Do the IMRC plates open and close completely (lever contacting Closed Plate Stop Screw) without obstruction?			For DTC P1520: GO TO **HU19**.
			For DTC P1537 and P1538: GO TO **HU52**.
	No	▶	Failed physical test.
			clean and inspect IMRC runner plates for sludge contaminants, warping, misaligned, etc.
HU19 VERIFY IMRC CIRCUIT VOLTAGE			
Intake Manifold Runner Control circuit malfunction.	Yes	▶	Fault is present. GO to **HU20**.
Possible causes:	No	▶	Fault is intermittent. GO to **HU36**.
— IMRC control circuit open.			
— IMRC VPWR circuit open.			
— IMRC control circuit shorted to PWR GND or SIG RTN.			
— IMRC control circuit shorted to VPWR.			
— Damaged IMRC actuator.			
— Damaged PCM.			
• Key off.			
• Connect Scan Tool to DLC.			
• Key on, engine off.			
• Access IMRCF PID.			
• Does IMRCF PID display ON?			

FM0159601523130X

Fig. 257 Test HU: Air Intake Systems (Part 13 of 31). 1996

HU20–HU23

Test Step	Result	▶	Action to Take
HU20 IMRC VOLTAGE CHECK			
• Key off.	Yes	▶	VPWR OK. GO TO **HU21**.
• Disconnect IMRC module connector from vehicle harness.	No	▶	SERVICE open in IMRC VPWR circuit. RECONNECT all components. RERUN Quick Test.
• Key on, engine off.			
• Measure voltage between VPWR circuit at the IMRC actuator vehicle harness connector and BATT(-).			
• Is IMRC VPWR voltage greater than 10.5 volts?			
HU21 CHECK IMRC PWR GND CIRCUIT			
• Key off.	Yes	▶	Passed PWR GND check. GO to **HU22**.
• IMRC actuator disconnected.	No	▶	SERVICE open in IMRC PWR GND circuit. RECONNECT all components. RERUN Quick Test.
• Key on, engine off.			
• Measure voltage between PWR GND circuit and VPWR circuit at the IMRC actuator vehicle harness connector.			
• Is voltage greater than 10.5 volts?			
HU22 CHECK IMRC CIRCUIT DRIVER FOR SHORT TO GROUND			
• Key off.	Yes	▶	Passed check. GO to **HU23**.
• Disconnect Scan Tool from DLC.	No	▶	GO to **HU39**.
• IMRC actuator disconnected.			
• Measure resistance from IMRC control circuit at the vehicle harness connector to BATT(-).			
• Is resistance greater than 10,000 ohms?			
HU23 CHECK IMRC CIRCUIT DRIVER FOR SHORT TO VPWR / VREF			
• Key off.	Yes	▶	GO to **HU24**.
• IMRC actuator disconnected.	No	▶	SERVICE IMRC control circuit short to VPWR / VREF. REMOVE breakout box. RECONNECT all components. RERUN Quick Test.
• Disconnect PCM. Inspect for damaged or pushed out pins, corrosion, loose wires, etc. Service as necessary.			
• Install breakout box, leave PCM disconnected.			
• Measure voltage between IMRC Test Pin and Test Pins 51 or 103 (PWR GND) at the breakout box.			

Application	IMRC Test Pin
Continental	44
All Others	42

• Is voltage less than 1.0 volt?			

FM0159601523140X

Fig. 257 Test HU: Air Intake Systems (Part 14 of 31). 1996

HU24–HU27

Test Step	Result	▶	Action to Take
HU24 CHECK IMRC CIRCUIT DRIVER FOR OPEN			
• Key off.	Yes	▶	GO to **HU25**.
• IMRC actuator and PCM disconnected, breakout box connected.	No	▶	SERVICE open IMRC control circuit. REMOVE breakout box. RECONNECT all components. RERUN Quick Test.
• Measure resistance from IMRC Test Pin and IMRC control circuit at IMRC actuator vehicle harness connector.			
• Is resistance less than 5.0 ohms?			
HU25 VERIFY PCM IMRC DRIVER			
• Key off.	Yes	▶	REPLACE PCM. REMOVE breakout box. RECONNECT all components. RERUN Quick Test.
• Reconnect IMRC actuator.	No	▶	REPLACE IMRC actuator. REMOVE breakout box. RECONNECT all components. RERUN Quick Test.
• Breakout box installed, PCM disconnected.			
• Key on, engine off.			
• Jumper IMRC Test Pin to Test Pins 51 or 103 (PWR GND) at the breakout box.			
• Do the IMRC plates open?			
HU26 DTC P1518: VERIFY IMRC MONITOR CIRCUIT VOLTAGE			
Diagnostic Trouble Code (DTC) P1518 indicates the IMRC monitor circuit voltage is less than expected.	Yes	▶	Fault is intermittent. GO to **HU34**.
Possible causes:	No	▶	Failed IMRC monitor circuit check. GO to **HU27**.
— IMRC monitor signal circuit shorted to PWR GND or SIG RTN.			
— Damaged IMRC actuator.			
— Damaged PCM.			
NOTE: If the IMRC plates are physically open, go to **HU20**.			
• Key off.			
• Connect Scan Tool to Data Link Connector (DLC).			
• Key on, engine off.			
• Access IMRCM PID.			
• Is IMRCM PID reading with the plates closed greater than 1.6 volts?			
HU27 CHECK IMRC MONITOR CIRCUIT			
• Key off.	Yes	▶	Make sure IMRC plates are closed and DTC P1520 is not present. Then REPLACE IMRC actuator. COMPLETE PCM Reset to clear DTCs (REFER to Powertrain Control Module (PCM) Reset). RECONNECT all components. RERUN Quick Test.
• Disconnect IMRC actuator connector from vehicle harness.			
• Key on, engine off.			
• Access IMRCM PID.			
• Did IMRCM PID reading increase to more than 1.6 volts when the IMRC actuator was disconnected?	No	▶	GO to **HU28**.

FM0159601523150X

Fig. 257 Test HU: Air Intake Systems (Part 15 of 31). 1996

HU28–HU29

Test Step	Result	▶	Action to Take
HU28 RESISTANCE CHECK ON IMRC MONITOR CIRCUIT			
• Key off.	Yes	▶	REPLACE damaged PCM. REMOVE breakout box. RECONNECT all components. COMPLETE PCM Reset to clear DTCs (REFER to Powertrain Control Module (PCM) Reset). RERUN Quick Test.
• IMRC actuator disconnected.			
• Disconnect PCM. Inspect for damaged or pushed out pins, corrosion, loose wires, etc. Service as necessary.			
• Measure resistance from IMRC monitor circuit at the vehicle harness connector to BATT(-).	No	▶	SERVICE short in IMRC monitor circuit to BATT(-). RECONNECT all components. COMPLETE PCM Reset to clear DTCs (REFER to Powertrain Control Module (PCM) Reset). RERUN Quick Test.
• Is resistance greater than 10,000 ohms?			
HU29 DTC P1519: IMRC MONITOR CIRCUIT INPUT GREATER THAN EXPECTED			
NOTE: If DTC P1520 is present, service DTC before entering this pinpoint test step.	Yes	▶	Expected reading. REMOVE jumper wire. GO to **HU40**.
Diagnostic Trouble Code (DTC) P1519 indicates the IMRC monitor circuit signal is greater than expected.	No	▶	REMOVE jumper wire. GO to **HU30**.
Possible causes:			
— IMRC monitor circuit open.			
— IMRC control circuit open.			
— IMRC monitor circuit short to VREF.			
— IMRC monitor return circuit open.			
— IMRC control circuit shorted to ground.			
— Damaged IMRC actuator.			
— IMRC VPWR circuit open.			
— Damaged PCM.			
• Connect Scan Tool to Data Link Connector (DLC).			
• Key on, engine off.			
• Disconnect IMRC actuator connector from vehicle harness.			
• Connect a wire jumper from IMRC monitor circuit pin to SIG RTN pin at IMRC vehicle harness connector.			
NOTE: If any Scan Tool communication problem exists, remove jumper and go to **HU38**.			
• Access IMRCM PID.			
• Is IMRCM PID reading less than 0.2 volt?			

FM0159601523160X

Fig. 257 Test HU: Air Intake Systems (Part 16 of 31). 1996

Fig. 257 Test HU: Air Intake Systems (Part 17 of 31). 1996

Test Step	Result	▶	Action to Take
HU30 SIG RTN CIRCUIT CONTINUITY CHECK • Key off. • Disconnect Scan Tool from DLC. • IMRC actuator disconnected. • Measure resistance between BATT(-) and SIG RTN circuit at the IMRC vehicle harness connector. • **Is reading less than 55.0 ohms?**	Yes No	▶ ▶	Expected reading. GO to **HU31**. SERVICE open SIG RTN circuit RECONNECT all components. PERFORM IMRC Drive Cycle Test Step **HU33** to verify repair.
HU31 IMRC MONITOR CIRCUIT CONTINUITY CHECK • Key off. • Disconnect PCM. Inspect for damaged or pushed out pins, corrosion, loose wires, etc. Service as necessary. • Install breakout box, leave PCM disconnected. • Measure resistance between Test Pin 8 (IMRC monitor) and IMRC monitor circuit at the IMRC actuator vehicle harness connector. • **Is resistance less than 5.0 ohms?**	Yes No	▶ ▶	REPLACE damaged PCM. RECONNECT all components. PERFORM IMRC Drive Cycle Test Step **HU33** to verify repair. SERVICE open in IMRC monitor circuit. RECONNECT all components. PERFORM IMRC Drive Cycle Test Step **HU33** to verify repair.
HU32 ENTER OTM TO CHECK CIRCUIT OPERATION • Key off. • Reconnect all components. • Connect Scan Tool to DLC. • Key on, engine off. • Access Output Test Mode (OTM) (refer to Section 2A). • While in Output Test Mode, access the IMRC and IMRCM PIDs. If the Scan Tool will not allow access to PIDs while in Output Test Mode, disconnect PCM, install a breakout box, reconnect PCM and connect a DVOM between Test Pin 8 (IMRC monitor circuit) and Test Pins 51 or 103 (PWR GND). • Command the outputs on. The IMRCM PID value should be less than 1.6 volts (the DVOM voltage should have the same reading). Also, the IMRC PID should be in the ON state. • **Is the IMRCM PID / DVOM reading less than 1.6 volts?**	Yes No	▶ ▶	Fault is intermittent. GO to **HU34**. REPLACE damaged IMRC actuator. REMOVE breakout box. RECONNECT all components. PERFORM IMRC Drive Cycle Test Step **HU33** to verify service.

FM0159601523170X

Fig. 257 Test HU: Air Intake Systems (Part 18 of 31). 1996

Test Step	Result	▶	Action to Take
HU33 IMRC DRIVE CYCLE • Key on, engine off. • Connect Scan Tool to Data Link Connector (DLC). • Complete PCM Reset to clear DTCs (refer to Powertrain Control Module (PCM) Reset). • Access IMRC, IMRCM and RPM PIDs. • Vehicle at operating temperature (minimum 10 minute warm up). • Drive vehicle, obey all traffic and safety laws. • Transmission in OVERDRIVE range. • SAFELY perform three (3) accelerations from stop to more than 3500 rpms (IMRC, IMRCM and RPM PIDs should change. Refer to IMRC Drive Cycle PID Table at the beginning of the Pinpoint Test). • Perform Quick Test (refer to Diagnostic Subroutines). • **Are any DTCs received?**	Yes No	▶ ▶	GO to Powertrain DTC chart. PASSED IMRC Drive Cycle. NO IMRC fault is present at this time.
HU34 IMRC MONITOR CIRCUIT LOW WIGGLE TEST • Key on, engine off. • Connect Scan Tool to Data Link Connector (DLC). • IMRC actuator disconnected. • Connect a wire jumper from IMRC monitor circuit pin to SIG RTN pin at IMRC connector. • Access IMRCM PID (with jumper connected, reading should be less than 0.2 volt). • While viewing the IMRCM PID, wiggle wiring from IMRC connector to PCM connector. • **Did IMRCM PID reading jump from less than 0.2 volt to greater than 1.6 volts?**	Yes No	▶ ▶	Intermittent fault area has been identified. ISOLATE and SERVICE as necessary. REMOVE jumper wire. RECONNECT all components. COMPLETE PCM Reset to DTCs (REFER to Powertrain Control Module (PCM) Reset). RERUN Quick Test. GO to **HU35**.
HU35 IMRC MONITOR CIRCUIT HIGH WIGGLE TEST • Key off. • Scan Tool connected. • Key on, engine off. • IMRC actuator disconnected. • Access IMRCM PID. • While viewing the IMRCM PID, wiggle wiring from IMRC connector to PCM connector. • **Did IMRCM PID reading jump to less than 1.6 volts?**	Yes No	▶ ▶	Intermittent fault area has been identified. ISOLATE and SERVICE as necessary. PERFORM this test step again to verify repair. Unable to duplicate and/or identify fault at this time. GO to Pinpoint Test Step **Z1** with the following data: IMRCM and IMRC PIDs and list of possible causes.

FM0159601523180X

Fig. 257 Test HU: Air Intake Systems (Part 19 of 31). 1996

Test Step	Result	▶	Action to Take
HU36 INTERMITTENT CIRCUIT HIGH MALFUNCTION TEST • Key off. • Reconnect all components. • Connect Scan Tool to DLC. • Key on, engine off. • Access Output Test Mode • While in Output Test Mode, access the IMRC and IMRCM PIDs. If the Scan Tool will not allow access to PIDs while in Output Test Mode, disconnect PCM, install a breakout box, reconnect PCM and connect a DVOM between IMRC Test Pin and Test Pins 51 or 103 (PWR GND). • Command the outputs on. The IMRC PID value should be ON (the DVOM voltage should be less than 1.0 volt) and the IMRCM PID value should be less than 1.6 volts. — Shake, wiggle and bend the IMRC Control Circuit wiring from the IMRC actuator back to the PCM while viewing the IMRC DVOM reading or IMRCM PID reading. — Look for a sudden change in the IMRCM PID reading or in the DVOM reading to indicate when a fault is detected. Application | IMRC Test Pin Continental | 44 All Others | 42 • **Is a fault indicated?**	Yes No	▶ ▶	Possible open in IMRC control circuit or PWR circuit to the IMRC actuator. ISOLATE fault and SERVICE as necessary. PERFORM this test step over to verify service. GO to **HU37**.
HU37 INTERMITTENT CIRCUIT LOW MALFUNCTION TEST This step checks if the IMRC Control Circuit is intermittently shorting to ground and causing the IMRC plates to open. • Key off. • All components connected. • While viewing IMRC plates, wiggle wiring and connectors from IMRC actuator to PCM. • **Did the IMRC plates open while wiggling / pulling on the wiring?**	Yes No	▶ ▶	Possible short to ground in the IMRC Control Circuit. ISOLATE fault and SERVICE as necessary. PERFORM this test step over to verify service. Unable to duplicate and/or identify fault at this time. GO to Pinpoint Test Step **Z1** with the following data: IMRCM and IMRC PIDs and list of possible causes.

FM0159601523190X

Fig. 257 Test HU: Air Intake Systems (Part 20 of 31). 1996

Test Step	Result	▶	Action to Take
HU38 CHECK IMRC MONITOR CIRCUIT FOR SHORT TO VREF IN HARNESS • Key off. • IMRC actuator disconnected. • Disconnect PCM. Inspect for damaged or pushed out pins, corrosion, loose wires etc. Service as necessary. • Install breakout box, leave PCM disconnected. • Measure resistance between Test Pin 8 (IMRC monitor circuit) and Test Pin 90 (VREF) at the breakout box. • **Is resistance greater than 10,000 ohms?**	Yes No	▶ ▶	REPLACE PCM. REMOVE breakout box. RECONNECT all components. RERUN Quick Test. SERVICE short between IMRC monitor circuit and VREF circuit. RERUN Quick Test.
HU39 RESISTANCE CHECK ON IMRC CONTROL CIRCUIT • Key off. • IMRC actuator disconnected. • Disconnect PCM. Inspect for damaged or pushed out pins, corrosion, loose wires etc. Service as necessary. • Install breakout box, leave PCM disconnected. • Measure resistance between IMRC Test Pin and Test Pins 51 or 103 (PWR GND) at the breakout box. Application | IMRC Test Pin Continental | 44 All Others | 42 • **Is resistance greater than 10,000 ohms?**	Yes No	▶ ▶	REPLACE PCM. REMOVE breakout box. RECONNECT all components. COMPLETE PCM Reset to clear DTCs (REFER to Powertrain Control Module (PCM) Reset). RERUN Quick Test. SERVICE short to PWR GND in IMRC control circuit. REMOVE breakout box. RECONNECT all components. COMPLETE PCM Reset to clear DTCs (REFER to Powertrain Control Module (PCM) Reset). RERUN Quick Test.
HU40 ENTER OTM TO CHECK IMRC CIRCUIT • Key off. • Reconnect all components. • Connect Scan Tool to DLC. • Key on, engine off. • Access Output Test Mode (OTM) • While in OTM, turn all outputs on. Observe the IMRC levers. • **Did the IMRC levers cycle open during the OTM command?**	Yes No	▶ ▶	GO to **HU32**. GO to **HU20**.

FM0159601523200X

Test Step	Result	▶	Action to Take
HU41 PHYSICAL CHECK OF IMRC ACTUATOR			
Diagnostic Trouble Codes (DTCs) P1512, P1513, P1516 and P1517 indicate the IMRC plates may be stuck open. Bank 1 on a "V" type engine is on the right side when sitting in the drivers seat or near the dash panel on a transverse mounted engine. Possible causes: — IMRC monitor circuit open. — IMRC monitor circuit short to power. — IMRC VPWR circuit open. — IMRC vacuum solenoid control circuit short to ground. — Damaged IMRC sensor. — Damaged IMRC vacuum solenoid. — Leaky, kinked, disconnected or blocked vacuum lines. — Damaged PCM. • For vacuum operated IMRC systems, start engine for 20 seconds to build vacuum reservoir for KOEO testing. • Key on, engine off. • Connect Scan Tool to Data Link Connector (DLC). • Access IMRCM and IMRC2M (if applicable) PIDs. • Physically rotate IMRC plates while viewing the IMRCM PID and the IMRC2M PID (except Mark VIII). • **Did the IMRC monitor PIDs read greater than 3 volts when rotating the IMRC levers open?**	Yes No	▶ ▶	Passed physical test. GO to **HU47**. Failed physical test. GO to **HU42**.
HU42 CHECK IMRC MONITOR SIGNAL			
• For vacuum operated IMRC system, start engine for 20 seconds to build a vacuum reservoir for KOEO testing. • Key on, engine off. • Access IMRCM and IMRC2M PIDs. • Disconnect both Bank 1 and 2 IMRC sensors. • Jumper both IMRC sensor monitor signals at the harness connector to chassis ground. • **Did the IMRCM and IMRC2M (if applicable) PIDs change to less than 1 volt?**	Yes No	▶ ▶	Passed test. GO to **HU43**. Failed test. GO to **HU44**.

FM0159601523210X

Fig. 257 Test HU: Air Intake Systems (Part 21 of 31). 1996

Test Step	Result	▶	Action to Take
HU43 CHECK IMRC2 MONITOR SIGNAL			
• Key off. • Both IMRC sensors disconnected. • Measure internal resistance in the IMRC sensors. — Bank 1 IMRC sensor signal to sensor PWR GND. — Bank 2 IMRC signal to sensor PWR GND. • Also — Bank 1 IMRC sensor signal to sensor VPWR — Bank 2 IMRC sensor signal to sensor VPWR • **Is each resistance between 100 and 10,000 ohms?**	Yes No	▶ ▶	UNABLE to duplicate and/or identify fault at this time. GO to Pinpoint Test Step **Z1** with the following data: IMRCM, IMRC2M and IMRC PIDs and list of possible causes. REPLACE the IMRC sensor that failed the resistance check. RECONNECT all components. GO to **HU33**.
HU44 CHECK IMRC1 MONITOR POWER GROUND			
• Key off. • Both IMRC sensors disconnected. • Disconnect Scan Tool from DLC. • Measure resistance between PWR GND at Bank 1 IMRC vehicle harness connector and chassis ground. • Measure resistance between PWR GND at Bank 2 IMRC vehicle harness connector and chassis ground. • **Are both resistance readings less than 100 ohms?**	Yes No	▶ ▶	Passed check. GO to **HU45**. SERVICE open IMRC monitor signal return circuit. RECONNECT all components. GO to **HU33**.
HU45 CHECK IMRC1 MONITOR SIGNAL SHORT TO PWR			
• Key off. • Both IMRC sensors disconnected. • Disconnect PCM. Inspect for damaged or pushed out pins, corrosion, loose wires, etc. Service as necessary. • Install breakout box, leave PCM disconnected. • Key on. • Connect negative (-) test lead of DVOM to Test Pin 77/103 (PWR GND). • For Mark VIII: — Check for voltage on Test Pin 8. • All other vehicles: — Check for voltage on Test Pins 8 and 9. • **Are voltage readings less than 1 volt?**	Yes No	▶ ▶	Passed check. GO to **HU46**. SERVICE circuit short to VPWR. RECONNECT all components. GO to **HU33**.

FM0159601523220X

Fig. 257 Test HU: Air Intake Systems (Part 22 of 31). 1996

Test Step	Result	▶	Action to Take
HU46 CHECK IMRC1 MONITOR SIGNAL RETURN			
• Key off. • Both IMRC sensors disconnected. • Breakout box installed, PCM disconnected. • For Mark VIII: — Measure resistance between Bank 1 IMRC monitor signal circuit at vehicle harness connector and Test Pin 8 (IMRCM). — Measure resistance between Bank 2 IMRC monitor signal circuit at vehicle harness connector and Test Pin 8 (IMRCM). • All other vehicles: — Measure resistance between Bank 1 IMRC monitor signal circuit at vehicle harness connector and Test Pin 8 (IMRCM). — Measure resistance between Bank 2 IMRC monitor signal circuit at vehicle harness connector and Test Pin 9 (IMRCM). • **Are the resistance readings less than 5.0 ohms?**	Yes No	▶ ▶	REPLACE PCM. RECONNECT all components. GO to **HU33**. SERVICE open bank 1 or bank 2 IMRC monitor signal circuit. RECONNECT all components. GO to **HU33**.
HU47 IMRC OUTPUT TEST MODE CHECK			
• Key on, engine off. • Scan Tool connected. • Access the IMRCM and IMRC2M PIDs and note values. • Start engine and note the IMRCM and IMRC2M PID values again. • **Did the IMRCM and IMRC2M PIDs change values?**	Yes No	▶ ▶	UNABLE to duplicate and/or identify fault at this time. GO to Pinpoint Test Step **Z1** with the following data: IMRCM, IMRC2M and IMRC PIDs and list of possible causes. GO to **HU48**.
HU48 BANK 1 IMRC VACUUM CHECK			
• Key off. • Disconnect vacuum hose at Bank 1 IMRC sensor. • Connect IMRC sensor vacuum supply hose to a vacuum gauge. • Start engine and idle, take vacuum gauge reading. • Inspect vacuum lines between vacuum source and IMRC sensor for leaks, kinks, disconnects, blockage, routing or any damage. Service as necessary. • **Is the vacuum gauge reading a minimum of 10 in-Hg?**	Yes No	▶ ▶	REPLACE Bank 1 IMRC sensor. RECONNECT all components. GO to **HU33**. GO to **HU49**.

FM0159601523230X

Fig. 257 Test HU: Air Intake Systems (Part 23 of 31). 1996

Test Step	Result	▶	Action to Take
HU49 BANK 2 IMRC VACUUM CHECK			
• Key off. • Disconnect vacuum hose at Bank 2 IMRC sensor. • Connect IMRC vacuum supply hose to a vacuum gauge. • Start engine and idle, take vacuum gauge reading. Inspect vacuum lines between vacuum source and IMRC sensor for leaks, kinks, disconnects, blockage, routing or any damage. Service as necessary. • Inspect vacuum lines between vacuum. • **Is the vacuum gauge reading a minimum of 10 in-Hg?**	Yes No	▶ ▶	REPLACE Bank 2 IMRC sensor. RECONNECT all components. GO to **HU33**. REMOVE vacuum gauge, REINSTALL hose to sensor. GO to **HU50**.
HU50 CHECK IMRC CIRCUIT TO PCM			
• Key off. • Disconnect Scan Tool from DLC. • Disconnect PCM. Inspect for damaged or pushed out pins, corrosion, loose wires, etc. Service as necessary. • Install breakout box, leave PCM disconnected. • Measure resistance between Test Pin 42 (IMRC) and Test Pin 77/103 (PWR GND). • **Is the resistance reading greater than 10K ohms?**	Yes No	▶ ▶	GO to **HU51**. SERVICE IMRC control circuit short to PWR GND. RECONNECT all components. GO to **HU33**.
HU51 CHECK IMRC CIRCUIT FOR SHORT			
• Key off. • Disconnect supply vacuum hose at IMRC vacuum solenoid from engine manifold. • Connect vacuum gauge to IMRC vacuum solenoid supply hose. • Reconnect PCM, breakout box installed. • Jumper Test Pin 42 (IMRC) to Test Pin 77/104 (PWR GND). • Start engine and idle. • Read vacuum gauge reading. • Inspect vacuum lines between vacuum source and IMRC vacuum solenoid for leaks, kinks, disconnects, blockage, routing or any damage. Service as necessary. • **Is the vacuum gauge reading a minimum of 10 in-Hg?**	Yes No	▶ ▶	REPLACE IMRC vacuum solenoid. RECONNECT all components. GO to **HU33**. REPLACE PCM. RECONNECT all components. REMOVE breakout box. GO to **HU33**.

FM0159601523240X

Fig. 257 Test HU: Air Intake Systems (Part 24 of 31). 1996

Test Step		Result	▶	Action to Take
HU52	**CHECK IMRC ACTUATOR CONNECTION**			
• Diagnostic Trouble Codes (DTCs) P1516, P1517, P1537 and P1538 indicate the IMRC plates are stuck open.		Yes	▶	Fault is intermittent. GO to **HU54**.
• Bank 1 on a V engine is on the right side when sitting in the drivers seat or near the dash panel on a transverse mounted engine.		No	▶	GO to **HU53**.
Possible causes:				
— IMRC monitor circuit shorted to ground.				
— IMRC monitor VPWR circuit open.				
— IMRC control circuit open.				
— IMRC control circuit shorted to VPWR/VREF.				
— IMRC vacuum supply open.				
— Damaged IMRC sensor.				
— Leaky, kinked, disconnected or blocked vacuum lines.				
— Damaged PCM.				
• For vacuum operated IMRC systems, start engine for 20 seconds to build vacuum reservoir.				
• Key on, engine off.				
• Connect Scan Tool to DLC.				
• Access IMRCM and IMRC2M PID (for Mark VIII, do not access IMRC2M PID).				
• **Are the IMRC monitor PID readings greater than 1 volt?**				
HU53	**CHECK IMRC MONITOR PID READING**			
• For vacuum operated IMRC systems, start engine for 20 seconds to build vacuum reservoir.		Yes	▶	ISOLATE damaged IMRC sensor and REPLACE. RECONNECT all components. GO to **HU33**.
• Key on, engine off.		No	▶	Fault is present. GO to **HU55**.
• Scan Tool connected.				
• Access IMRCM and IMRC2M PID (for Mark VIII, do not access IMRC2M PID).				
• Disconnect Bank 1 IMRC sensor and note PID value.				
• Disconnect Bank 2 IMRC sensor and note PID value.				
• Reconnect Bank 2 IMRC sensor and note PID value.				
• Reconnect Bank 1 IMRC sensor and note PID value.				
• **Did the IMRC monitor PID values increase to greater than 1 volt?**				

FM0159601523250X

Fig. 257   Test HU: Air Intake Systems (Part 25 of 31). 1996

Test Step		Result	▶	Action to Take
HU54	**INTERMITTENT IMRC CHECK**			
• For vacuum operated IMRC systems, start engine for 20 seconds to build vacuum reservoir.		Yes	▶	ISOLATE fault and SERVICE as necessary. RECONNECT all components. GO to **HU33**.
• Key on, engine off.		No	▶	Unable to duplicate and/or identify fault at this time. GO to Pinpoint Test Step **Z1** with the following data: IMRCM, IMRC2M, IMRCF and IMRC PIDs and a list of possible causes.
• Scan Tool connected.				
• Access the IMRCF, IMRCM and IMRC2M (for Mark VIII, do not access IMRC2M PID).				
• While viewing the PIDs, wiggle the IMRC wiring from the component to the PCM.				
• Look for a sudden drop or change in the PID values.				
NOTE: Vacuum holding the IMRC levers will bleed off and cause a sudden PID value change after 30 seconds. This is normal. Restart engine for 20 seconds, again.				
• **Was a fault indicated in the PID(s) while wiggling the wiring?**				
HU55	**CHECK IMRC VACUUM SUPPLY**			
• Key off.		Yes	▶	Passed check. RECONNECT vacuum hoses. GO to **HU56**.
• Disconnect vacuum hose from IMRC vacuum solenoid.		No	▶	SERVICE open in vacuum source. RECONNECT all components. GO to **HU33**.
• Install vacuum gauge on supply hose from engine manifold.				
• Inspect vacuum lines for leaks, kinks, disconnects, blockage, routing or any damage.				
• Start engine and idle.				
• **Is vacuum gauge reading greater than 10 in-Hg at idle and the vacuum lines are OK?**				

FM0159601523260X

Fig. 257   Test HU: Air Intake Systems (Part 26 of 31). 1996

Test Step		Result	▶	Action to Take
HU56	**CHECK VACUUM SUPPLY TO IMRC SENSORS**			
• Key off.		Yes	▶	Passed check. GO to **HU60**.
• Disconnect vacuum supply to bank 1 IMRC sensor.		No	▶	Failed vacuum check. RECONNECT all components. GO to **HU57**.
• Install vacuum gauge to IMRC sensor vacuum hose.				
• Inspect vacuum lines for leaks, kinks, disconnects, blockage, routing or any damage.				
• Start engine and idle.				
• Take vacuum reading and reinstall hose to Bank 1 IMRC sensor.				
• Disconnect vacuum supply to Bank 2 IMRC sensor.				
• Install vacuum gauge to IMRC sensor vacuum hose.				
• Inspect vacuum lines for leaks, kinks, disconnects, blockage, routing or any damage. Service as necessary.				
• Take vacuum reading with engine idling.				
• **Are both vacuum gauge readings greater than 10 in-Hg?**				
HU57	**CHECK IMRC VPWR CIRCUIT**			
• Key off.		Yes	▶	Passed check. GO to **HU58**.
• Disconnect IMRC vacuum solenoid connector.		No	▶	SERVICE open VPWR circuit. RECONNECT all components. GO to **HU33**.
• Key on, engine off.				
• Measure voltage between the VPWR circuit at the connector and chassis ground.				
• **Is the voltage greater than 10.5 volts?**				
HU58	**CHECK IMRC CIRCUIT FOR OPEN**			
• Key off.		Yes	▶	GO to **HU59**.
• Disconnect PCM. Inspect for damaged or pushed out pins, corrosion, loose wires, etc. Service as necessary.		No	▶	SERVICE open IMRC circuit. REMOVE breakout box. RECONNECT all components. GO to **HU33**.
• Install breakout box, leave PCM disconnected.				
• Measure resistance between Test Pin 42 (IMRC) and IMRC circuit at the IMRC vacuum solenoid vehicle harness connector.				
• **Is the resistance less than 5.0 ohms?**				
HU59	**CHECK IMRC CIRCUIT FOR SHORT**			
• Key on, engine off.		Yes	▶	SERVICE IMRC circuit short to VPWR/VREF circuit. REMOVE breakout box. RECONNECT all components. GO to **HU33**.
• Breakout box installed, PCM and IMRC vacuum solenoid disconnected.		No	▶	REPLACE IMRC vacuum solenoid. RECONNECT all components. GO to **HU33**.
• Measure voltage between Test Pin 42 (IMRC) and Test Pin 77/103 (PWR GND).				
• **Is reading greater than 10.5 volts?**				

FM0159601523270X

Fig. 257   Test HU: Air Intake Systems (Part 27 of 31). 1996

Test Step		Result	▶	Action to Take
HU60	**IMRC MONITOR VPWR CHECK**			
• Key off.		Yes	▶	GO to **HU61**.
• Disconnect Bank 1 and Bank 2 IMRC sensors.		No	▶	SERVICE open VPWR circuit. RECONNECT all components. GO to **HU33**.
• Key on, engine off.				
• Measure voltage between VPWR at Bank 1 IMRC sensor vehicle harness connector and chassis ground.				
• Measure voltage between VPWR at Bank 2 IMRC sensor vehicle harness connector and chassis ground.				
• **Are both voltage readings greater than 10.5 volts?**				
HU61	**IMRC MONITOR CHECK FOR SHORT**			
• Key off.		Yes	▶	Test passed. GO to **HU62**.
• Disconnect Scan Tool from DLC.		No	▶	Test failed. GO to **HU63**.
• Both IMRC sensors disconnected.				
• Measure resistance from Bank 1 IMRC monitor signal circuit to chassis ground.				
• Measure resistance from Bank 2 IMRC monitor signal circuit to chassis ground.				
• **Are both resistance readings greater than 10,000 ohms?**				
HU62	**IMRC SENSOR RESISTANCE CHECK**			
• Key off.		Yes	▶	Unable to duplicate and/or identify fault at this time. GO to Pinpoint Test Step **Z1** with the following data: IMRCM, IMRC2M, IMRCF and IMRC PIDs and a list of possible causes.
• Both IMRC sensors disconnected.		No	▶	REPLACE the IMRC sensor that failed the measurement. RECONNECT all components. GO to **HU33**.
• Measure resistance between Bank 1 IMRC sensor signal pin and PWR GND sensor pin.				
• Measure resistance between Bank 2 IMRC sensor signal pin and PWR GND sensor pin.				
• **Are both resistance readings between 1K and 20K ohms?**				

FM0159601523280X

Fig. 257   Test HU: Air Intake Systems (Part 28 of 31). 1996

Test Step	Result	►	Action to Take
HU63 CHECK PCM FOR INTERNAL SHORT • Key off. • Both IMRC sensors disconnected. • Disconnect PCM. Inspect for damaged or pushed out pins, corrosion, loose wires, etc. Service as necessary. • Install breakout box, leave PCM disconnected. • For Mark VIII: — Measure resistance between Test Pin 8 (IMRC monitor) and Test Pin 77 / 103 (PWR GND). • All other vehicles: — Measure resistance between Test Pin 8 (IMRC monitor) and Test Pin 77 / 103 (PWR GND). — Measure resistance between Test Pin 9 (IMRC monitor) and Test Pin 77 / 103 (PWR GND). • **Is resistance greater than 10,000 ohms?**	Yes No	► ►	REPLACE PCM. RECONNECT all components. GO to HU33. SERVICE the IMRC monitor circuit short to PWR GND. RECONNECT all components. GO to HU33.
HU64 DETERMINE IMRC FAULT PATH Diagnostic Trouble Codes (DTCs) P1516 or P1517 indicate the IMRC plates were open or closed longer than expected. This step determines the diagnostic path for DTCs P1516 or P1517. • For vacuum operated IMRC systems, start engine for 20 seconds to build vacuum reservoir. • Connect Scan Tool to DLC. • Key on, engine off. • Access IMRCM, and IMRC2M (for Mark VIII, do not access IMRC2M PID). • **Are the PID values greater than 3 volts?**	Yes No	► ►	For vacuum actuated IMRC systems: GO to HU41. For electrically actuated IMRC systems: GO to HU29. For vacuum actuated IMRC systems: GO to HU55. For electrically actuated IMRC systems: GO to HU26.
HU65 CHECK IMT VALVE ACTUATOR CONNECTION Lack or loss of power may be caused by a damaged Intake Manifold Tuning (IMT) valve. Possible causes: — Open IMT valve circuit. — Open VPWR circuit. — Shorted IMT valve circuit. — Damaged IMT valve. — Damaged PCM. • Key off. • Disconnect IMT valve. Inspect for damaged or pushed out pins, corrosion, loose wires, etc. • **Was a fault indicated?**	Yes No	► ►	SERVICE as necessary. Passed visual inspection. GO to HU66.

FM0159601523290X

Fig. 257 Test HU: Air Intake Systems (Part 29 of 31). 1996

Test Step	Result	►	Action to Take
HU66 CHECK IMT VALVE VPWR CIRCUIT • IMT valve actuator disconnected from vehicle harness. • Key on, engine off. • Measure voltage between VPWR circuit at the IMT valve vehicle harness connector and chassis ground. • **Is the reading greater than 10.5 volts?**	Yes No	► ►	Passed check. GO to HU67. SERVICE open IMT valve VPWR circuit. RECONNECT all components. VERIFY a symptom no longer exists.
HU67 CHECK IMT VALVE CIRCUIT FOR OPEN • Key off. • IMT valve actuator disconnected from vehicle harness. • Disconnect PCM. Inspect for damaged or pushed out pins, corrosion, loose wires, etc. Service as necessary. • Install breakout box, leave PCM disconnected. • Measure resistance between Test 46 (IMT valve) and IMT valve circuit at the IMT valve vehicle harness connector. • **Is resistance less than 5.0 ohms?**	Yes No	► ►	Passed check. GO to HU68. SERVICE open in IMT valve circuit. RECONNECT all components. VERIFY a symptom no longer exists.
HU68 CHECK IMT VALVE CIRCUIT FOR SHORT TO PWR GND • Key off. • Disconnect Scan Tool from DLC. • IMT valve actuator and PCM disconnected, breakout box connected. • Measure resistance from Test Pin 46 (IMT valve) and Test Pin 77 / 103 (PWR GND) at the breakout box. • **Is the resistance greater than 10,000 ohms?**	Yes No	► ►	Passed check. GO to HU69. SERVICE short in IMT valve circuit to PWR GND in harness circuit. REMOVE breakout box. RECONNECT all components. VERIFY a symptom no longer exists.
HU69 CHECK IMT VALVE CIRCUIT FOR SHORT TO VREF / VPWR • Key off. • IMT valve actuator and PCM disconnected, breakout box connected. • Measure volts from Test Pin 46 (IMT valve) and Test Pins 77 / 103 (PWR GND) at the breakout box. • **Is the reading greater than 10.5 volts?**	Yes No	► ►	SERVICE short in IMT valve circuit to VPWR in harness circuit. REMOVE breakout box. RECONNECT all components. VERIFY a symptom no longer exists. Passed check. GO to HU70.

FM0159601523300X

Fig. 257 Test HU: Air Intake Systems (Part 30 of 31). 1996

Test Step	Result	►	Action to Take
HU70 CHECK IMT VALVE ACTUATOR INTERNAL RESISTANCE • Key off. • Reconnect IMT valve. • PCM disconnected, breakout box connected. • Measure resistance from Test Pin 46 (IMT valve) and Test Pin 97 (VPWR) at the breakout box. • **Is the resistance between 5 and 300 ohms?**	Yes No	► ►	REPLACE PCM. REMOVE breakout box. RECONNECT all components. VERIFY a symptom no longer exists. REPLACE IMT valve actuator. REMOVE breakout box. RECONNECT all components. VERIFY a symptom no longer exists.

FM0159601523310X

Fig. 257 Test HU: Air Intake Systems (Part 31 of 31). 1996

ELECTRONIC ENGINE CONTROL SYSTEM (EEC-V)

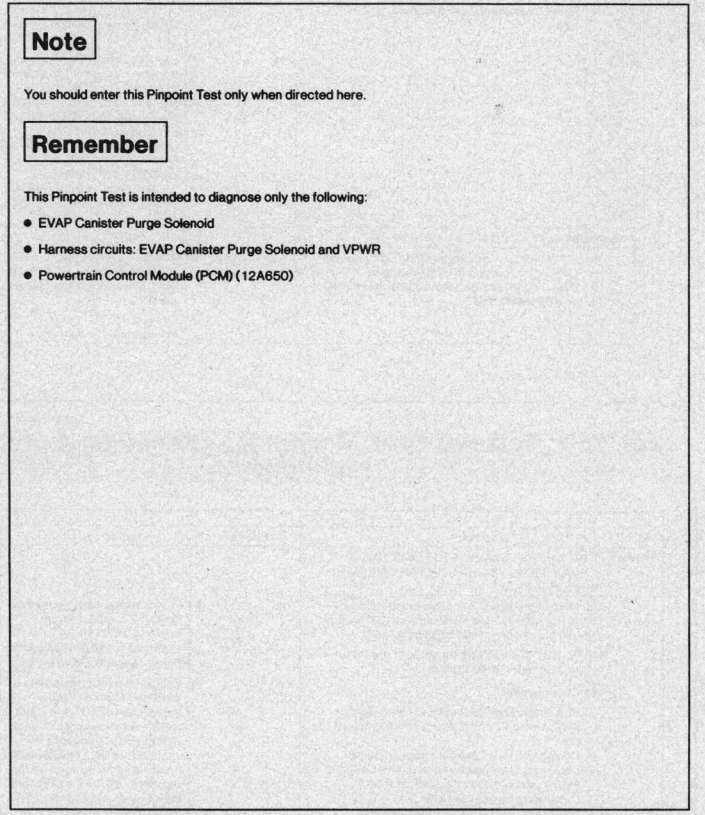

Note

You should enter this Pinpoint Test only when directed here.

Remember

This Pinpoint Test is intended to diagnose only the following:

- EVAP Canister Purge Solenoid
- Harness circuits: EVAP Canister Purge Solenoid and VPWR
- Powertrain Control Module (PCM) (12A650)

FM0159601524010X

Fig. 258   Test HV: EVAP Monitor & System (Part 1 of 9). 1996 Probe

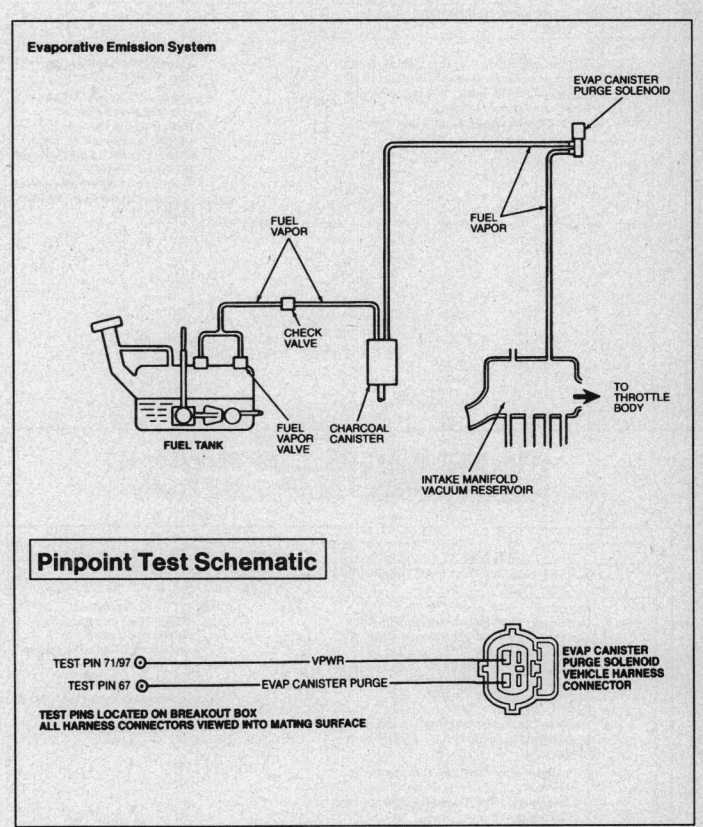

Evaporative Emission System

EVAP CANISTER PURGE SOLENOID

FUEL VAPOR

FUEL VAPOR

CHECK VALVE

TO THROTTLE BODY

FUEL VAPOR VALVE

CHARCOAL CANISTER

INTAKE MANIFOLD VACUUM RESERVOIR

FUEL TANK

Pinpoint Test Schematic

TEST PIN 71/97 ⊙——————— VPWR

TEST PIN 67 ⊙——————— EVAP CANISTER PURGE

EVAP CANISTER PURGE SOLENOID VEHICLE HARNESS CONNECTOR

TEST PINS LOCATED ON BREAKOUT BOX
ALL HARNESS CONNECTORS VIEWED INTO MATING SURFACE

FM0159601524020X

Fig. 258   Test HV: EVAP Monitor & System (Part 2 of 9). 1996 Probe

Test Step	Result	►	Action to Take
HV1 DTC 0443: CHECK EVAP CANISTER PURGE SOLENOID VPWR			
Diagnostic Trouble Code (DTC) P0433 indicates a failure in the EVAP Canister Purge solenoid circuit.	Yes	►	The EVAP Canister Purge solenoid VPWR is OK. GO to **HV2**.
NOTE: If the DTC P0433 was generated in Continuous Memory only, GO to **HV5**.	No	►	The EVAP Canister Purge solenoid VPWR circuit is open. SERVICE open in VPWR harness circuit. RECONNECT all components. VERIFY a symptom no longer exists. COMPLETE PCM Reset to clear DTCs (REFER to Powertrain Control Module (PCM) Reset). RERUN Quick Test.
Possible causes: — VPWR circuit open. — EVAP Canister Purge solenoid SIG open in harness. — EVAP Canister Purge solenoid SIG circuit short to PWR GND or SIG RTN. — Damaged EVAP Canister Purge solenoid. — Damaged PCM. ● Key off. ● Disconnect EVAP Canister Purge solenoid. ● Key on, engine off. ● Measure voltage between VPWR at the EVAP Canister Purge solenoid vehicle harness connector and battery ground. ● **Is voltage greater than 10.5 volts?**			
HV2 CHECK EVAP CANISTER PURGE SOLENOID RESISTANCE			
● Key off. ● EVAP Canister Purge solenoid disconnected. ● Measure resistance between EVAP Canister Purge solenoid SIG and VPWR circuits at the vehicle harness connector. ● **Is resistance between 27 and 35 ohms?**	Yes	►	The EVAP Canister Purge solenoid resistance is in specification. GO to **HV3**.
	No	►	The EVAP Canister Purge solenoid is damaged. REPLACE the solenoid. VERIFY a symptom no longer exists. COMPLETE PCM Reset to clear DTCs (REFER to Powertrain Control Module (PCM) Reset). RERUN Quick Test.

Fig. 258   Test HV: EVAP Monitor & System (Part 3 of 9). 1996 Probe

Test Step	Result	►	Action to Take
HV3 CHECK CONTINUITY OF EVAP CANISTER PURGE SOLENOID SIG CIRCUIT			
● Key off. ● EVAP Canister Purge solenoid disconnected. ● Disconnect PCM. Inspect for damaged or pushed out pins, corrosion, loose wires, etc. Service as necessary. ● Install breakout box, leave PCM disconnected. ● Measure resistance between Test Pin 67 (EVAP Canister Purge solenoid SIG) at the breakout box and the EVAP Canister Purge solenoid SIG circuit at the solenoid vehicle harness connector. ● **Is the resistance less than 5.0 ohms?**	Yes	►	EVAP Canister Purge solenoid SIG circuit is OK. GO to **HV4**.
	No	►	EVAP Canister Purge solenoid SIG circuit is open. SERVICE open in harness circuit. REMOVE breakout box. RECONNECT all components. VERIFY a symptom no longer exists. COMPLETE PCM Reset to clear DTCs (REFER to Powertrain Control Module (PCM) Reset). RERUN Quick Test.
HV4 CHECK EVAP CANISTER PURGE SOLENOID SIG CIRCUIT FOR SHORT TO PWR GND			
● Key off. ● EVAP Canister Purge solenoid disconnected. ● Breakout box installed. ● Disconnect Scan Tool from DLC. ● Measure the resistance between Test Pin 67 (EVAP Canister Purge solenoid SIG) and Test Pins 24 and 103 (PWR GND). ● **Is each resistance greater than 10,000 ohms?**	Yes	►	EVAP Canister Purge solenoid harness circuits are OK. REPLACE the damaged PCM. REMOVE the breakout box. RECONNECT all components. COMPLETE PCM Reset to clear DTCs (REFER to Powertrain Control Module (PCM) Reset). RERUN Quick Test.
	No	►	EVAP Canister Purge solenoid harness circuit contains a short to power ground. SERVICE harness short circuit. REMOVE breakout box. RECONNECT all components. VERIFY a symptom no longer exists. COMPLETE PCM Reset to clear DTCs (REFER to Powertrain Control Module (PCM) Reset). RERUN Quick Test.
HV5 COMPLETE KOEO AND KOER SELF-TEST			
● Complete Key On, Engine Off (KOEO) and Key On, Engine Running (KOER) self-test. ● **Was DTC P0443 generated in either KOEO or KOER self-test?**	Yes	►	The failure generating the DTC is not intermittent . RETURN to **HV1** and address the cause of the DTC.
	No	►	The cause DTC P0443 is intermittent. GO to **HV6**.

FM0159601524040X

Fig. 258   Test HV: EVAP Monitor & System (Part 4 of 9). 1996 Probe

Test Step	Result	►	Action to Take
HV6 CHECK FOR INTERMITTENT FAULT IN HARNESS AND CONNECTOR			
● Key off. ● Disconnect PCM. Inspect for damaged or pushed out pins, corrosion, loose wires, etc. ● Install breakout box. ● Connect DVOM to Test Pin 67 (EVAP Canister Purge solenoid SIG) and Test Pin 71 (VPWR) at the breakout box. ● Key on, engine off. ● Observe DVOM display for an indication of a fault (changing voltage) while performing the following: — Lightly tap on the EVAP Canister Purge solenoid. — Wiggle the EVAP Canister Purge solenoid connector. — Grasp the EVAP Canister Purge solenoid vehicle harness connector and wiggle the wires between the solenoid and PCM. ● **Is a fault detected?**	Yes	►	ISOLATE the fault and SERVICE as necessary. REMOVE breakout box. RECONNECT all components. RERUN Quick Test.
	No	►	Unable to duplicate and / or identify fault at this time. GO to Pinpoint Test Step **Z1** with a list of possible causes.

FM0159601524050X

Fig. 258   Test HV: EVAP Monitor & System (Part 5 of 9). 1996 Probe

Test Step	Result	►	Action to Take
HV10 CONTINUOUS MEMORY DTC P0440: CHECK FOR MANIFOLD VACUUM AT EVAP CANISTER PURGE SOLENOID			
Continuous Memory Diagnostic Trouble Code (DTC) P0440 indicates the Evaporative Emission System purge control has been damaged.	Yes	►	Vacuum is normally applied to the EVAP Canister Purge solenoid. RECONNECT the vapor line to the EVAP Canister Purge solenoid. GO to **HV11**.
NOTE: If DTC P0443 was received, it should be addressed before DTC P0440.	No	►	Vacuum is not being applied to the EVAP Canister Purge solenoid. INSPECT the vapor line for damage or disconnect. SERVICE as necessary. If vapor line is OK, CHECK intake manifold vacuum reservoir for blockage. VERIFY a symptom no longer exists. COMPLETE PCM Reset to clear DTCs (REFER to Powertrain Control Module (PCM) Reset). RERUN Quick Test.
Possible causes: — Damaged vapor line between EVAP Canister Purge solenoid and intake manifold vacuum reservoir. — Damaged EVAP Canister Purge solenoid. — Damaged vapor line between EVAP Canister Purge solenoid and charcoal canister. — Damaged charcoal canister. — Damaged vapor line between charcoal canister and check valve. — Damaged vapor line between check valve and fual vapor valves. — Damaged PCM. ● Key off. ● Disconnect vapor line between EVAP Canister Purge solenoid and intake manifold vacuum reservoir at the EVAP Canister Purge solenoid valve. ● Key on, engine idling. ● Place a finger over the opening of the unattached vapor line end. ● Remove finger from the vapor line. ● Key off. ● **Was a vacuum signal present?**			

FM0159601524060X

Fig. 258   Test HV: EVAP Monitor & System (Part 6 of 9). 1996 Probe

ELECTRONIC ENGINE CONTROL SYSTEM (EEC-V)

Test Step	Result	▶	Action to Take
HV11 CHECK EVAP CANISTER PURGE SOLENOID MECHANICAL OPERATION: SOLENOID DE-ENERGIZED			
• Key off. • Disconnect the vapor line between the EVAP Canister Purge solenoid and the intake manifold vacuum reservoir at the EVAP Canister Purge solenoid. • Install vacuum pump at intake manifold side of the EVAP canister purge solenoid. • Disconnect the vapor line between the EVAP Canister Purge solenoid and the charcoal canister at the EVAP Canister Purge solenoid. • Install vacuum gauge at the charcoal canister side of the EVAP canister purge solenoid. • Apply 8 in-Hg of vacuum to the EVAP Canister Purge solenoid while observing the vacuum gauge. • **Does the vacuum gauge indicate a vacuum signal is passing through the EVAP Canister Purge solenoid?**	Yes No	▶ ▶	The EVAP Canister Purge solenoid is damaged. REMOVE vacuum gauge and replace and REPLACE the solenoid. RECONNECT all vapor lines. VERIFY a symptom no longer exists. COMPLETE PCM Reset to clear DTCs (REFER to Powertrain Control Module (PCM) Reset). RERUN Quick Test. The EVAP Canister Purge solenoid is operating properly. GO to **HV12**.
HV12 CHECK EVAP CANISTER PURGE SOLENOID MECHANICAL OPERATION: SOLENOID ENERGIZED			
• Key off. • Install breakout box, leave PCM connected. • Vacuum pump installed at intake manifold side of the EVAP canister purge solenoid with 8 in-Hg applied to the EVAP Canister Purge solenoid. • Vacuum gauge installed at charcoal canister side of EVAP canister purge solenoid. • Key on. • Momentarily jumper to ground Test Pin 67 (EVAP Canister Purge solenoid SIG) at the breakout box and observe the vacuum gauge. • Key off. • **Was a vacuum signal indicated by the vacuum gauge?**	Yes No	▶ ▶	The EVAP Canister Purge solenoid is operating properly under energized and de-energized conditions. REMOVE the vacuum gauge and pump from the EVAP Canister Purge solenoid. RECONNECT vapor line between EVAP canister purge solenoid and intake manifold vacuum reservoir. GO to **HV13**. The EVAP Canister Purge solenoid is not operating properly. REPLACE the EVAP Canister Purge solenoid. REMOVE the vacuum gauge and pump from the EVAP Canister Purge solenoid. RECONNECT all vapor lines. VERIFY a symptom no longer exists. COMPLETE PCM Reset to clear DTCs (REFER to Powertrain Control Module (PCM) Reset). RERUN Quick Test.

FM0159601524070X

Fig. 258   Test HV: EVAP Monitor & System (Part 7 of 9). 1996 Probe

Test Step	Result	▶	Action to Take
HV13 CHECK VAPOR LINE: CHARCOAL CANISTER TO EVAP CANISTER PURGE SOLENOID			
• Key off. • Disconnect vapor line between charcoal canister and EVAP canister purge solenoid at both ends. • Inspect vapor line for blockage or obstructions. Service as necessary. • Plug one end of the vapor line and install a vacuum pump at the remaining end. • Apply 16 in-Hg of vacuum with the vacuum pump. • Observe the vacuum display for at least 15 seconds. • Release the vacuum applied by the vacuum pump. • **Did the vapor line hold the vacuum?**	Yes No	▶ ▶	The vapor line is not damaged. REMOVE the vacuum pump. REMOVE the plug from the remaining end. RECONNECT the vapor line. GO to **HV14**. The vapor line is damaged. REPLACE the vapor line. REMOVE the vacuum pump. RECONNECT all components. VERIFY a symptom no longer exists. COMPLETE PCM Reset to clear DTCs (REFER to Powertrain Control Module (PCM) Reset). RERUN Quick Test.
HV14 CHECK CHARCOAL CANISTER			
• Check for cracks or other damage to the charcoal canister. • **Is the charcoal canister cracked or damaged?**	Yes No	▶ ▶	REPLACE the damaged charcoal canister. RECONNECT all components. VERIFY a symptom no longer exists. COMPLETE PCM Reset to clear DTCs (REFER to Powertrain Control Module (PCM) Reset). RERUN Quick Test. The charcoal canister is not damaged. GO to **HV15**.
HV15 CHECK VAPOR LINE: CHECK VALVE TO CHARCOAL CANISTER			
• Key off. • Disconnect vapor line between charcoal canister and check valve at both ends. • Inspect vapor line for blockage or obstruction. Service as necessary. • Plug one end of the vapor line and install a hand held pressure pump at the remaining end. • Apply 1.0 in-Hg of pressure to the vapor line with the pressure pump. • Observe the pressure gauge on the pump for at least 15 seconds. • **Did the vapor line hold a constant pressure?**	Yes No	▶ ▶	The vapor line is not damaged. REMOVE the pressure pump. REMOVE the plug from the remaining end. RECONNECT the vapor line. GO to **HV16**. The vapor line is damaged. REPLACE the vapor line. VERIFY a symptom no longer exists. COMPLETE PCM Reset to clear DTCs (REFER to Powertrain Control Module (PCM) Reset). RERUN Quick Test.

FM0159601524080X

Fig. 258   Test HV: EVAP Monitor & System (Part 8 of 9). 1996 Probe

Test Step	Result	▶	Action to Take
HV16 VERIFY OPERATION OF CHECK VALVE			
NOTE: A properly functioning check valve will allow the passage of fuel vapor in only one direction. • Key off. • Disconnect both vapor lines from the check valve. • Apply 1.0 in-Hg of pressure to the charcoal canister side of the check valve while placing a finger near the opening at other end of check valve. • **Was air flow detected from the check valve?**	Yes No	▶ ▶	The check valve is damaged. REPLACE the check valve. REMOVE the pressure pump. RECONNECT all components. VERIFY a symptom no longer exists. COMPLETE PCM Reset to clear DTCs (REFER to Powertrain Control Module (PCM) Reset). RERUN Quick Test. The check valve is functioning properly. RECONNECT all components. GO to **HV17**.
HV17 CHECK VAPOR LINE: CHECK VALVE TO FUEL TANK VALVES			
• Key off. • Disconnect vapor line between check valve and fuel tank at both ends. • Inspect vapor line for blockage or obstruction. Service as necessary. • Plug both ends of the vapor line at the fuel tank and install a hand held pressure pump with gauge at the check valve end. • Apply 1.0 in-Hg of pressure to the vapor line with the pressure pump. • Observe the pressure gauge on the pump for at least 15 seconds. • **Did the vapor line hold a constant pressure?**	Yes No	▶ ▶	The vapor line is not damaged. REMOVE the pressure pump. REMOVE the plugs from the remaining ends. RECONNECT the vapor line. GO to the Probe Fuel Delivery section of the service manual and CHECK the fuel vapor valve for sticking. The vapor line is damaged. REPLACE the vapor line. REMOVE the vacuum pump. VERIFY a symptom no longer exists. COMPLETE PCM Reset to clear DTCs (REFER to Powertrain Control Module (PCM) Reset). RERUN Quick Test.

FM0159601524090X

Fig. 258   Test HV: EVAP Monitor & System (Part 9 of 9). 1996 Probe

Note

You should enter this Pinpoint Test only when directed here.

Remember

This Pinpoint Test is intended to diagnose the following:

• EVAP Canister Purge (CANP) Solenoid (9C915)
• Purge Flow (PF) Sensor (14A606)
• Vapor Management Valve (VMV) (9C915)
• Carbon Canister (9D653)
• Fuel Vapor Hoses
• Vapor Orifice Roll-Over Valve (9B593)
• Vacuum or vapor leaks caused by loose fuel fill cap
• Fuel Tank air / vapor leaks
• Harness circuits: EVAP CANISTER PURGE SIG, PFS SIG, VMV SIG, Vehicle Power (VPWR), and Power Ground (PWR GND)
• Powertrain Control Module (PCM) (12A650)

FM0159601525010X

Fig. 259   Test HW: EVAP Purge System (Part 1 of 27). 1996

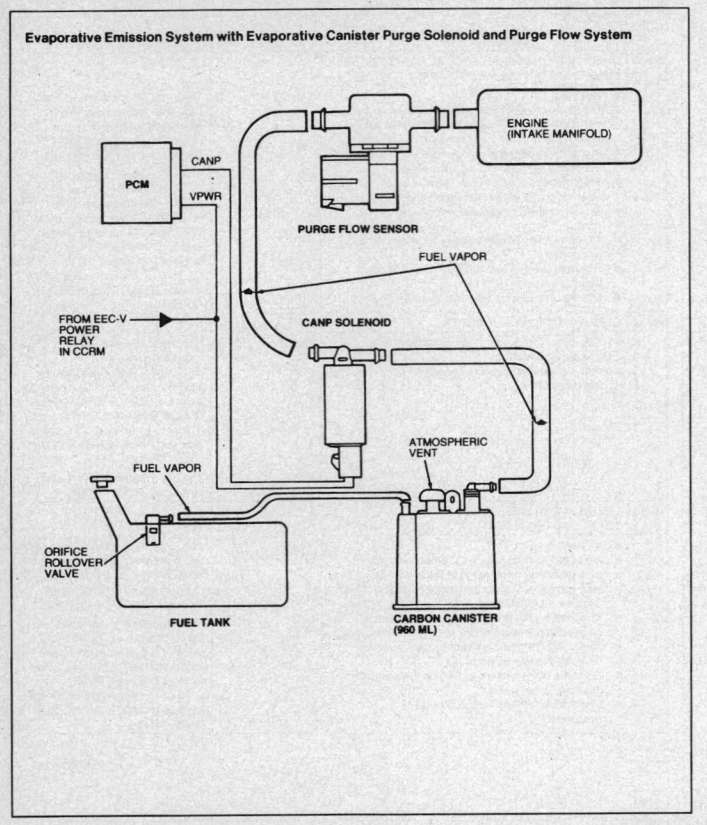

Fig. 259   Test HW: EVAP Purge System (Part 2 of 27). 1996

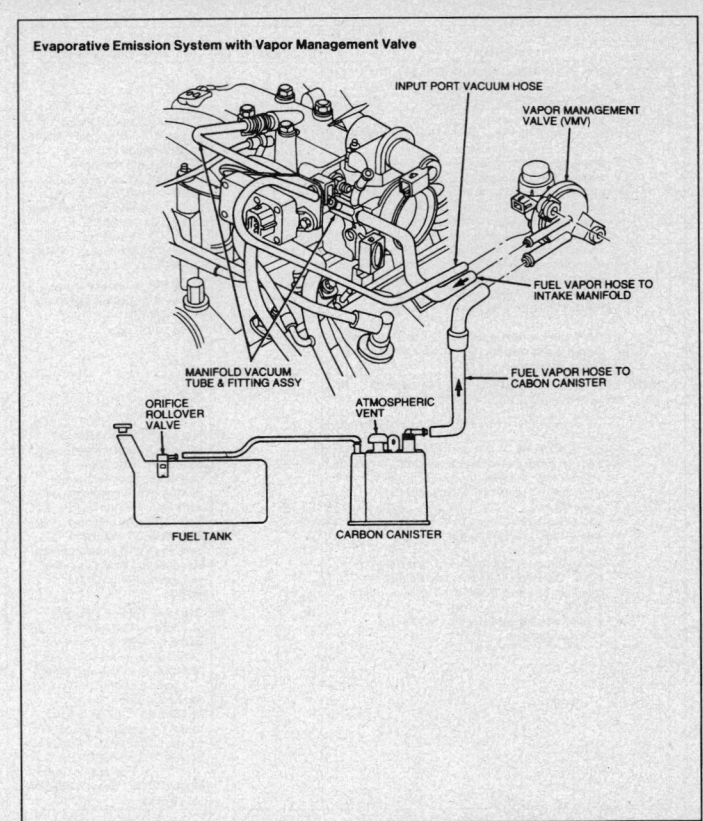

Fig. 259   Test HW: EVAP Purge System (Part 3 of 27). 1996

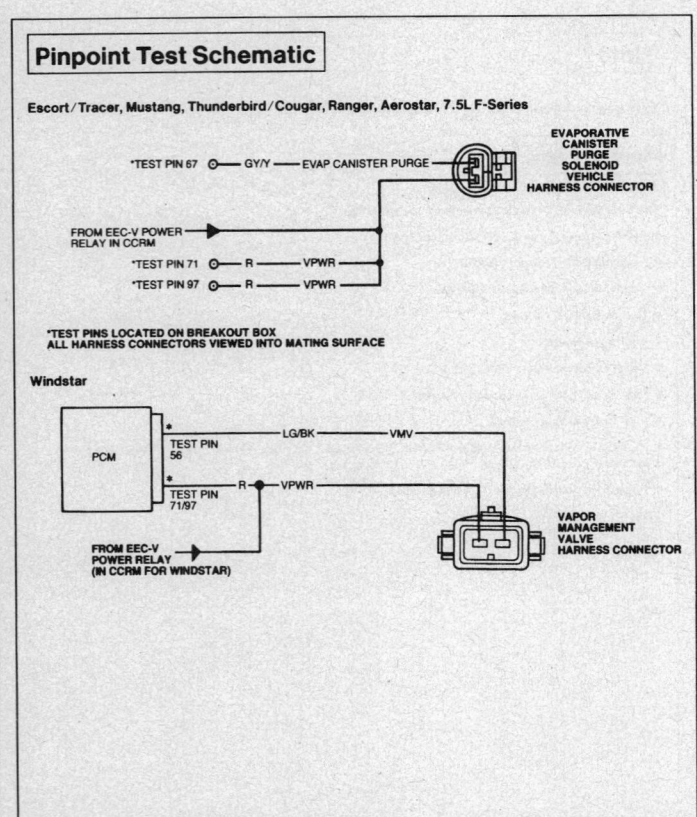

Fig. 259   Test HW: EVAP Purge System (Part 4 of 27). 1996

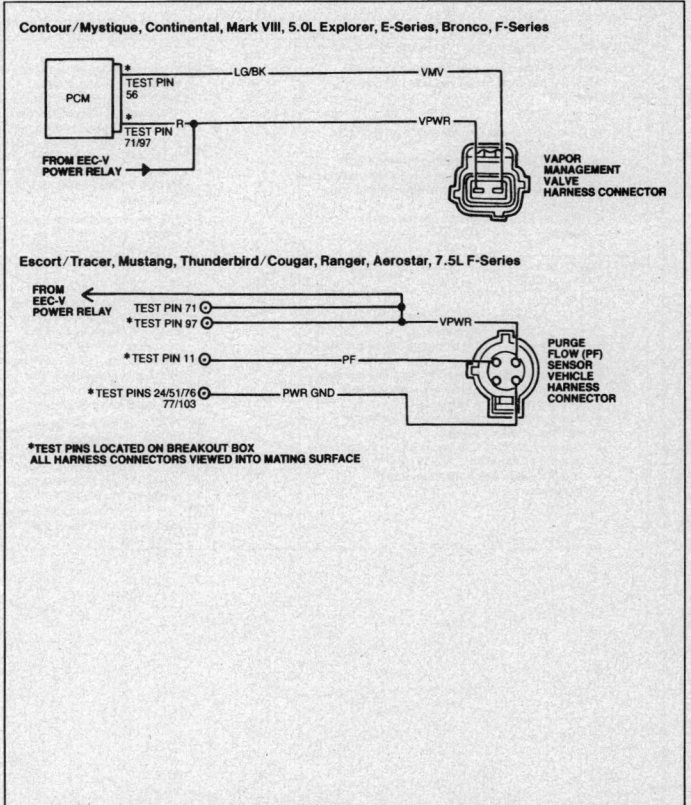

Fig. 259   Test HW: EVAP Purge System (Part 5 of 27). 1996

Test Step	Result	▶	Action to Take
HW1 DTC P0443: CHECK VPWR TO EVAP CANISTER PURGE SOLENOID OR VAPOR MANAGEMENT (VMV) VALVE			
Diagnostic Trouble Code (DTC) P0443 indicates a failure in the EVAP Canister Purge solenoid (or VMV) circuit. Possible causes: — VPWR circuit open. — EVAP CANISTER PURGE SIG (or VMV SIG) open. — EVAP CANISTER PURGE SIG (or VMV SIG)) shorted to PWR GND or SIG RTN. — Damaged EVAP Canister Purge solenoid or Vapor Management Valve (VMV). — Damaged PCM. ● Key off. ● Disconnect EVAP Canister Purge solenoid (or VMV). ● Key on, engine off. ● Measure the voltage between VPWR at the EVAP Canister Purge solenoid (or VMV) vehicle harness connector and battery ground. ● **Is the voltage greater than 10.5 volts?**	Yes No	▶ ▶	GO to HW2. SERVICE open in VPWR harness. RECONNECT all components. COMPLETE PCM Reset to clear DTCs (REFER to Powertrain Control Module (PCM) Reset). RERUN Quick Test.
HW2 CHECK EVAP CANISTER PURGE SOLENOID (OR VMV) RESISTANCE			
● Key off. ● EVAP Canister Purge solenoid (or VMV) disconnected. ● Measure the resistance between EVAP CANISTER PURGE SIG (or VMV SIG) and VPWR on the EVAP Canister Purge solenoid (or VMV). ● **Is resistance between 30 and 90 ohms (or VMV resistance between 30 and 36 ohms)?**	Yes No	▶ ▶	**For EVAP Canister Purge solenoid applications:** GO to HW3. **For VMV applications:** GO to HW4. REPLACE damaged EVAP Canister Purge solenoid (or VMV). RECONNECT all components. COMPLETE PCM Reset to clear DTCs (REFER to Powertrain Control Module (PCM) Reset). RERUN Quick Test.

FM0159601525060X

Fig. 259   Test HW: EVAP Purge System (Part 6 of 27). 1996

Test Step	Result	▶	Action to Take
HW3 CHECK EVAP CANISTER PURGE SOLENOID SHORT TO CASE GROUND			
● Key off. ● EVAP Canister Purge solenoid disconnected. ● Measure the resistance between the EVAP CANISTER PURGE SIG pin on the solenoid and the EVAP Canister Purge solenoid casing. ● Measure the resistance between the VPWR pin on the solenoid and the EVAP Canister Purge solenoid casing. ● **Are both resistance readings greater than 90 ohms?**	Yes No	▶ ▶	EVAP Canister Purge solenoid is OK. GO to HW4. REPLACE damaged EVAP Canister Purge solenoid. RECONNECT all components. COMPLETE PCM Reset to clear DTCs (REFER to Powertrain Control Module (PCM) Reset). RERUN Quick Test.
HW4 CHECK EVAP CANISTER PURGE SIG OR VMV SIG FOR OPEN IN HARNESS			
● Key off. ● EVAP Canister Purge solenoid (or VMV) disconnected. ● Disconnect PCM. Inspect for damaged or pushed out pins, corrosion, loose wires, etc. Service as necessary. ● Install breakout box, leave PCM disconnected. ● Measure the resistance between Test Pin 67 (EVAP CANISTER PURGE SIG) or Test Pin 56 (VMV SIG) at the breakout box and CANP SIG (or VMV SIG) circuit at the EVAP Canister Purge solenoid (or VMV) vehicle harness connector. ● **Is the resistance less than 5.0 ohms?**	Yes No	▶ ▶	GO to HW5. SERVICE open in EVAP SIG (or VMV SIG) harness. REMOVE breakout box. RECONNECT all components. COMPLETE PCM Reset to clear DTCs (REFER to Powertrain Control Module (PCM) Reset. RERUN Quick Test.

FM0159601525070X

Fig. 259   Test HW: EVAP Purge System (Part 7 of 27). 1996

Test Step	Result	▶	Action to Take
HW5 CHECK EVAP CANISTER PURGE SIG (OR VMV SIG) CIRCUIT FOR SHORT TO PWR GND			
● Key off. ● EVAP Canister Purge solenoid (or VMV) disconnected. ● Breakout box installed, PCM disconnected. ● Disconnect Scan Tool from DLC. ● Measure the resistance between Test Pin 67 (EVAP CANISTER PURGE SIG) or Test Pin 56 (VMV SIG) and Test Pins 24 and 103 (PWR GND) at the breakout box. ● **Is each resistance greater than 10,000 ohms?**	Yes No	▶ ▶	EVAP CANISTER PURGE SIG (or VMV SIG) is open or shorted to PWR GND in the PCM. REPLACE damaged PCM. REMOVE breakout box. RECONNECT all components. COMPLETE PCM Reset to clear DTCs (REFER to Powertrain Control Module (PCM) Reset). RERUN Quick Test. SERVICE harness short between EVAP CANISTER PURGE SIG (or VMV SIG) and PWR GND. REMOVE breakout box. RECONNECT all components. COMPLETE PCM Reset to clear DTCs (REFER to Powertrain Control Module (PCM) Reset). RERUN Quick Test.

FM0159601525080X

Fig. 259   Test HW: EVAP Purge System (Part 8 of 27). 1996

Test Step	Result	▶	Action to Take
HW6 CONTINUOUS MEMORY DTC P1443: MONITOR IDLE AIR CONTROL DUTY CYCLE (IAC AT IDLE) - VMV PURGE SYSTEMS			

Continuous Memory Diagnostic Trouble Code (DTC) P1443 can be initiated by an IAC valve speed error sometime during vehicle operation. If a Continuous Memory DTC P1507 is received with the DTC P1443 in Self-Test, GO directly to Pinpoint Test Step KE30.
NOTE: The following overspeed check is to be done on Windstar, Continental, Contour/Mystique, Mark VIII, 5.0L Explorer, Bronco, F-Series, E-Series.
● Key on, engine off.
● Access IAC, TP, and RPM PIDs with a Scan Tool.
● With engine at normal operating temperature, accessories off and at idle, the IAC duty cycle should be between 20% to 45%.
● Observe the IAC and RPM PIDs for an indication of a fault while performing the following:
  — While at idle, wiggle the IAC connector and vehicle harness between the IAC and PCM. A fault is indicated by a sudden increase in rpm and decrease in duty cycle.
  — Goose the engine several times while looking for slow return to idle (observing the TP PID). This may indicate a sticking IAC valve.
● **Is a fault indicated?**
	Yes
	
	No
		▶
		
		▶
			ISOLATE fault and SERVICE as necessary. RECONNECT all components. VERIFY a symptom no longer exists. COMPLETE PCM Reset to clear DTCs (REFER to Powertrain Control Module (PCM) Reset). RERUN Quick Test.
			GO to HW10.

FM0159601525090X

Fig. 259   Test HW: EVAP Purge System (Part 9 of 27). 1996

Test Step	Result	►	Action to Take
HW7 CONTINUOUS MEMORY DTC P1443: CHECK THE VOLTAGE ON THE PURGE FLOW (PF) SENSOR WITH THE ENGINE RUNNING			
Continuous Memory Diagnostic Trouble Codes (DTC) P1443 indicates an incorrect Evaporative System Purge Control Valve Flow. Possible causes: — Pushed out pins in Purge Flow (PF) sensor connector or matching harness connector. — Damaged EVAP Canister Purge solenoid. — Damaged PF sensor. • Key on, engine running. • Disconnect PF sensor vehicle harness connector. • Check for pushed out pins in both mating connectors. Service as necessary. • If pins are OK, reconnect the PF sensor vehicle harness connector. • Key on, engine running. • Access PF PID with Scan Tool. • **Does the PF PID fluctuate around 2.50 volts or 1.00 volts in one minute?**	Yes No	► ►	For voltage from 2.30 to 2.60 volts: GO to **HW15**. For voltage from 0.90 to 1.10 volts: GO to **HW14**. GO to **HW8**.
HW8 MEASURE PURGE FLOW (PF) SENSOR RESISTANCE (VPWR CIRCUIT)			
• Key off. • PF sensor disconnected. NOTE: Allow the vehicle and PF sensor to cool down or warm up to a room temperature (55°F to 80°F) before taking a resistance measurement on the PF sensor. This may take 15 to 20 minutes. • Measure the resistance between PFS SIG (Pin 2) and VPWR (Pin 1) on the Purge Flow (PF) sensor. • Measure the resistance between PWR GND (Pin 3) and VPWR (Pin 1) on the Purge Flow (PF) sensor. (Refer to schematic in Pinpoint Test Step **HW28**.) • **Is the resistance greater than 160 ohms between Pin 1 and Pin 2 or greater than 190 ohms between Pin 1 and Pin 3?**	Yes No	► ►	VPWR is open in the PF sensor. REPLACE damaged PF sensor. RECONNECT all components. VERIFY a symptom no longer exists. COMPLETE PCM Reset to clear DTCs (REFER to Powertrain Control Module (PCM) Reset). RERUN Quick Test. GO to **HW9**.

FM0159601525100X

Fig. 259 Test HW: EVAP Purge System (Part 10 of 27). 1996

Test Step	Result	►	Action to Take
HW9 CHECK VPWR FOR OPEN IN HARNESS			
• Key off. • PFS disconnected. • Disconnect PCM. Inspect for damaged or pushed out pins, corrosion, loose wires, etc. Service as necessary. • Install breakout box, leave PCM disconnected. • Measure the resistance between Test Pins 71 and 97 at the breakout box and VPWR circuit at the PF sensor vehicle harness connector. • **Is the resistance less than 5.0 ohms?**	Yes No	► ►	LEAVE breakout box installed. GO to **HW10**. SERVICE open in VPWR harness. REMOVE breakout box. RECONNECT all components. VERIFY a symptom no longer exists. COMPLETE PCM Reset to clear DTCs (REFER to Powertrain Control Module (PCM) Reset). RERUN Quick Test.

FM0159601525110X

Fig. 259 Test HW: EVAP Purge System (Part 11 of 27). 1996

Test Step	Result	►	Action to Take
HW10 CONTINUOUS MEMORY DTC P1443: VISUAL INSPECTION OF EVAPORATIVE SYSTEM			
Continuous Memory Diagnostic Trouble Code (DTC) P1443 indicates an Evaporative Emission Control System - vacuum system, evaporative canister purge solenoid (mechanical) or vapor management valve (mechanical) malfunction. NOTE: On the 5.0L Explorer, the Fuel Tank Pressure (FTP) sensor and the Canister Vent (CV) solenoid are not used for the Evaporative Emission system testing. These components are not part of the diagnostic check for the DTC P1443. Possible causes: — Fuel fill cap missing or damaged. — Damaged carbon canister. — Pinched, plugged, blocked, cracked, cut or disconnected fuel vapor tubes / hoses between the fuel tank, carbon canister, EVAP Canister Purge solenoid, Purge Flow (PF) sensor, Vapor Management Valve (VMV) and the engine intake manifold. — Damaged EVAP Canister Purge solenoid. — Damaged PF sensor. — Damaged VMV. — EVAP CANISTER PURGE SIG, VMV SIG or PF SIG circuit shorted to VPWR. NOTE: Fuel saturation of carbon canister cannot be effectively checked by the canister weight or intensity of odor (smell). Vehicle must run over an extended period of time to purge fuel (vapor) build-up in carbon canister. • Key off. • Check for missing fuel fill cap. • Check for a damaged carbon canister. • Check for disconnected fuel vapor tubes / hoses. • Check for kinked or pinched fuel vapor tubes / hoses. • Check for fuel tank and fill pipe leaks. • **Is a fault indicated?**	Yes No	► ►	ATTACH fuel fill cap or REPLACE damaged carbon canister if necessary. SERVICE all fuel vapor tubes / hoses as necessary. VERIFY a symptom no longer exists. COMPLETE PCM Reset to clear DTCs (REFER to Powertrain Control Module (PCM) Reset). RERUN Quick Test. GO to **HW11**.

FM0159601525120X

Fig. 259 Test HW: EVAP Purge System (Part 12 of 27). 1996

Test Step	Result	►	Action to Take
HW11 EVAPORATIVE LEAK DETECTION USING ROTUNDA EVAPORATIVE EMISSION SYSTEM TESTER			
• Key off. • Remove the fuel fill cap at fuel tank. • Install the Rotunda Evaporative Emission System Tester (Rotunda catalog number: 134-00056), including the compressed gas (nitrogen or argon) and pressure regulator. NOTE: Tester kit contains all required adapters (schrader valve, fuel cap per vehicle application, etc.). • Disconnect and plug (cap) the fuel vapor hose from the Purge Flow (PF) sensor to the EVAP Canister Purge solenoid at the PF sensor or the fuel vapor hose from the VMV at the engine intake manifold port (or vacuum tree). • Remove Atmospheric Vent cap (blue or black) on the carbon canister(s). • Plug open vent on carbon canister(s) with a rubber plug or strong adhesive tape. • On the 5.0L Explorer, also disconnect the hose from the CV solenoid to atmosphere and plug the open port at the CV solenoid. • For vehicles with an Evaporative Canister Purge solenoid (not VMV) cycle the solenoid open through output test mode with the scan tool (or disconnect solenoid harness connection and energize solenoid using a voltage source). • Key on, engine off. • Pressurize the vehicle evaportive system at 14 in. -H2O using the Evaporative Emission System Tester and following the instructions that come with the tester. • Observe the tester installation leak self-test for 2 minutes and then the vehicle evaporative system leak test. • **Is a system leak indicated by the tester red light on?**	Yes No	► ►	ALLOW the two position control valve on the tester to provide a continuing flow of the gas to the closed evaporative system. MAINTAIN 14 in. -H2O pressure on the system (monitor tester pressure gauges). GO to **HW12**. GO to **HW13**.

FM0159601525130X

Fig. 259 Test HW: EVAP Purge System (Part 13 of 27). 1996

Test Step	Result	▶	Action to Take
HW12 CHECK FOR EVAPORATIVE LEAKS WITH THE ULTRA-SONIC LEAK DETECTOR • Key on, engine off. • The fuel vapor hose from the PF sensor (or VMV) at the engine intake manifold (or vacuum tree) is still plugged (capped). • The fuel vapor tube/hose at carbon canister(s) from EVAP Canister Purge solenoid (or VMV) is still-plugged (capped). • Evaporative Emission System Tester still pressurizing the vehicle evaporative system. • Remove the ultra-sonic detector provided with the Rotunda Evaporative Emission Tester. • Place the earphones from the detector over your ears and adjust the audio dial on the detector. • Closely pass the probe of the ultra-sonic detector over the fule vapor hoses and connections in the entire evaporative system (fuel tank, carbon canister(s), EVAP Canister Purge solenoid or VMV, PF sensor and to engine intake manifold). • Check for audible sound changes (noticeable quiet to louder pitch). • **Is a sudden audible change indicated?**	Yes No	▶ ▶	ISOLATE the pressure leak in the evaporative emission system. REPLACE damaged tubes/hoses with cracks, splits or holes. RECONNECT loose tubes/hoses. REMOVE all rubber plugs or tape blocking the atmospheric vent on the carbon canister(s). REINSTALL the blue or black dust cap on the carbon canister atmospheric vent. **For EVAP Canister Purge solenoid leaks:** GO to **HW14**. **For VMV housing leaks:** GO to **HW21**. For fuel tank or fuel vapor valve leaks, REMOVE the tester, gas source and the plug (cap) in fuel vapor tubes/hoses. ATTACH fuel full cap. REMOVE all rubber plugs or tape blocking the atmospheric vent on the carbon canister(s). REINSTALL the blue or black dust cap on the carbon canister atmospheric vent. RECONNECT all components. VERIFY a symptom no longer exists. COMPLETE PCM Reset to clear DTCs (REFER to Powertrain Control Module (PCM) Reset. RERUN Quick Test. KEEP the Evaporative Emission System Tester hooked up. RELEASE pressure on evaporative system by closing the regulator valve at the gas source. GO to **HW13**.

FM015960152514OX

Fig. 259 Test HW: EVAP Purge System (Part 14 of 27). 1996

Test Step	Result	▶	Action to Take
HW13 CHECK FOR FUEL VAPOR HOSE RESTRICTIONS BETWEEN EVAP CANISTER PURGE SOLENOID OR VMV, FUEL TANK AND CARBON CANISTER • Key on, engine off. • The fuel vapor hose from the PF sensor (or VMV) at the engine intake manifold (or vacuum tree) is still plugged (capped). • The fuel vapor tube/hose at the carbon canister(s) from the EVAP Canister Purge solenoid (or VMV) is still plugged (capped). • Remove and plug the fuel vapor hose to carbon canister(s) at the EVAP Canister Purge solenoid (or VMV). • Reinitiate pressurizing of the vehicle evaporative system using the Rotunda Evaporative Emission System Tester. Refer to Pinpoint Test Step **HW11** for pressurizing instructions. • When the pressure on the evaporative system is stabilized close to 14 in. -H2O, record the reading. • Remvoe the plug at the fuel vapor hose to carbon canister at the EVAP Canister Purge solenoid (or VMV). • Observe the pressure gauges on the tester. • **Does the pressure immediately drop?**	Yes No	▶ ▶	REMOVE tester, gas source and all plugs (caps) in fuel vapor hoses. RECONNECT fuel vapor hose from VMV or fuel vapor/vacuum hose from PF sensor to the engine intake manifold port (or vacuum tree). ATTACH fuel fill cap. REMOVE all rubber plugs or tape blocking the atmospheric vent on the carbon canister(s). REINSTALL the blue or black dust cap on the carbon canister atmospheric vent. **For EVAP Canister Purge solenoid systems:** GO to **HW14**. **For VMV systems:** GO to **HW21**. ISOLATE blockage, bends or kinks in fuel vapor tubes/hoses betwen the fuel tank, the EVAP Canister Purge solenoid (or VMV) and the carbon canister(s). STRAIGHTEN kinks or bends in fuel vapor tubes/hoses. for bolckages, REMOVE tester, gas source and all plugs (caps) in fuel vapor hoses. ATTACH fuel fill cap. RECONNECT all fuel vapor hoses. REMOVE all rubber plugs or tape blocking the atmospheric vent on the carbon canister(s). REINSTALL the blue or black dust cap on the carbon canister atmospheric vent. VERIFY a symptom no longer exists. COMPLETE PCM Reset to clear DTCs (REFER to Powertrain Control Module (PCM) Reset. RERUN Quick Test.

FM015960152515OX

Fig. 259 Test HW: EVAP Purge System (Part 15 of 27). 1996

Test Step	Result	▶	Action to Take
HW14 CHECK EVAP CANISTER PURGE SOLENOID FOR VACUUM LEAKS - CLOSED VACUUM POSITION • Key off. • Disconnect the vacuum hose at both ends of the EVAP Canister Purge solenoid. • Install a hand held vacuum pump to the intake manifold vacuum side of the EVAP Canister Purge solenoid. • Disconnect the EVAP Canister Purge solenoid electrically. • Apply 16 in-Hg (53 kPa) of vacuum to the EVAP Canister Purge solenoid. • **Does the EVAP Canister Purge solenoid hold vacuum for 20 seconds?**	Yes No	▶ ▶	LEAVE the vacuum pump connected. GO to **HW15**. REMOVE vacuum pump. REPLACE EVAP Canister Purge solenoid. RECONNECT all components. VERIFY a symptom no longer exists. COMPLETE PCM Reset to clear DTCs (REFER to Powertrain Control Module (PCM) Reset). RERUN Quick Test.
HW15 CHECK EVAP CANISTER PURGE SOLENOID MECHANICAL OPERATION - OPEN VACUUM POSITION • Key off. • Reconnect EVAP Canister Purge solenoid electrically. • Vacuum hose at both ends of the EVAP Canister Purge solenoid disconnected. • Connect Scan Tool. • Apply 16 in-Hg (53 kPa) of vacuum to the EVAP Canister Purge solenoid on the intake manifold side with a vacuum pump. • Access Output Test Mode on Scan Tool. • Key on, engine off. • **Does the EVAP Canister Purge solenoid open and vacuum reading on the pump drop (air passes freely) when commanding the output on?**	Yes No	▶ ▶	CHECK fuel vapor hose between carbon canister and EVAP Canister Purge solenoid for blockage or kinks. SERVICE as necessary. If no fault is indicated, REMOVE vacuum pump. GO to **HW16**. REPLACE EVAP Canister Purge solenoid. VERIFY a symptom no longer exists. COMPLETE PCM Reset to clear DTCs (REFER to Powertrain Control Module (PCM) Reset). RERUN Quick Test.

FM015960152516OX

Fig. 259 Test HW: EVAP Purge System (Part 16 of 27). 1996

Test Step	Result	▶	Action to Take
HW16 CHECK FOR INTAKE MANIFOLD VACUUM AT THE EVAP CANISTER PURGE SOLENOID • Key off. • EVAP Canister Purge solenoid and PF sensor connected electrically. • Intake manifold vacuum side of EVAP Canister Purge solenoid disconnected. • Start engine. • Place thumb on open end of vacuum hose at EVAP Canister Purge solenoid. • **Is vacuum present at the vacuum hose opening?**	Yes No	▶ ▶	LEAVE intake manifold vacuum hose to EVAP Canister Purge solenoid disconnected. GO to **HW17**. RECONNECT intake manifold hose to EVAP Canister Purge solenoid. CHECK vacuum hoses between EVAP Canister Purge solenoid, PF sensor and intake manifold for proper routing, leaks, cracks, blockage and kinks. CHECK for PF sensor cracked housing. REPLACE vacuum hoses or damaged PF sensor as necessary. VERIFY a symptom no longer exists. COMPLETE PCM Reset to clear DTCs (REFER to Powertrain Control Module (PCM) Reset). RERUN Quick Test.
HW17 CHECK PF SENSOR SEAL LEAK DOWN • Key off. • Purge Flow (PF) sensor connected electrically. • Plug open end of intake manifold vacuum hose to EVAP Canister Purge solenoid or PF sensor vacuum port to EVAP Canister Purge solenoid. • Disconnect vacuum hose at the intake manifold port on the PF sensor. • Install hand held vacuum pump at the intake manifold port on the PF sensor. • Apply 4.1 in-Hg (13.6 kPa) vacuum to the PF sensor. • **Does the PF sensor bleed off all the vacuum in less than 2.5 seconds?**	Yes No	▶ ▶	Excessive leak on PF sensor is detected. REPLACE PF sensor. REMOVE vacuum pump. RECONNECT all vacuum hoses. VERIFY a symptom no longer exists. COMPLETE PCM Reset to clear DTCs (REFER to Powertrain Control Module (PCM) Reset). RERUN Quick Test. REMOVE vacuum pump. RECONNECT vacuum hose to EVAP Canister Purge solenoid. LEAVE vacuum hose to intake manifold port on PF sensor disconnected. GO to **HW18**.

FM015960152517OX

Fig. 259 Test HW: EVAP Purge System (Part 17 of 27). 1996

Test Step	Result	▶	Action to Take
HW18 CHECK FOR INTAKE MANIFOLD VACUUM AT PF SENSOR			
• Key off. • EVAP Canister Purge solenoid and PF sensor connected electrically. • Intake manifold vacuum side of PF sensor disconnected. • Start engine. • Place thumb on open end of vacuum hose at PF sensor. • **Is vacuum present at the vacuum hose opening?**	Yes	▶	CHECK for large vacuum leak or open in vacuum line between PF sensor and engine intake manifold. SERVICE as necessary. RECONNECT all components. RECONNECT all vacuum/fuel vapor hoses. **For DTC P1443:** GO to **HW19**. **All others:** RETURN to Symptom Flowcharts.
	No	▶	CHECK for small vacuum leak between PF sensor and the engine intake manifold. SERVICE as necessary. If OK, VERIFY a symptom no longer exists. COMPLETE PCM Reset to clear DTCs (REFER to Powertrain Control Module (PCM) Reset). RERUN Quick Test.
HW19 CHECK EVAP CANISTER PURGE SOLENOID (OR VMV) RESISTANCE			
• Key off. • Disconnect EVAP Canister Purge solenoid (or VMV). • Measure the resistance between EVAP CANISTER PURGE SIG (or VMV SIG) and VPWR on the EVAP Canister Purge solenoid (or VMV). • **Is the resistance between 30 and 90 ohms (or VMV resistance between 30 and 36 ohms)?**	Yes	▶	EVAP Canister Purge solenoid (or VMV) is OK electrically. GO to **HW20**.
	No	▶	REPLACE damaged EVAP Canister Purge solenoid (or VMV). VERIFY a symptom no longer exists. COMPLETE PCM Reset to clear DTCs (REFER to Powertrain Control Module (PCM) Reset). RERUN Quick Test.

FM0159601525180X

Fig. 259 Test HW: EVAP Purge System (Part 18 of 27). 1996

Test Step	Result	▶	Action to Take
HW20 CHECK EVAP CANISTER PURGE SIG CIRCUIT (OR VMV SIG) FOR SHORT TO VPWR			
• Key off. • Disconnect EVAP Canister Purge solenoid (or VMV). • Disconnect PCM. Inspect for damaged or pushed out pins, corrosion, loose wires, etc. Service as necessary. • Install breakout box, leave PCM disconnected. • Measure the resistance between Test Pin 67 (EVAP CANISTER PURGE SIG) or Test Pin 56 (VMV SIG) and Test Pins 71 and 97 (VPWR) at the breakout box. • **Is each resistance greater than 10,000 ohms?**	Yes	▶	EVAP CANISTER PURGE SIG (or VMV SIG) is shorted to VPWR in the PCM. REPLACE PCM. REMOVE breakout box and Scan Tool. RECONNECT all components. VERIFY a symptom no longer exists. RERUN Quick Test.
	No	▶	SERVICE harness short between EVAP CANISTER PURGE SIG (or VMV SIG) and VPWR. REMOVE breakout box and Scan Tool. RECONNECT all components. VERIFY a symptom no longer exists. COMPLETE PCM Reset to clear DTCs. (REFER to Powertrain Control Module (PCM) Reset). RERUN Quick Test.
HW21 CHECK FOR VMV HOUSING LEAKS			
• Key off. • VMV electrically connected. • Disconnect fuel vapor hose to the engine intake manifold on the VMV. • Fuel vapor tube/hose to carbon canister(s) at VMV disconnected. • Install a hand vacuum pump to the fuel vapor port to carbon canister(s) on the VMV. • Apply 16 in-Hg (53 kPa) of vacuum with the vacuum pump. • **Does the VMV hold vacuum?**	Yes	▶	LEAVE fuel vapor hose at VMV disconnected. GO to **HW22**.
	No	▶	REMOVE vacuum pump. REPLACE damaged VMV. RECONNECT all components. VERIFY a symptom no longer exists. COMPLETE PCM Reset to clear DTCs (REFER to Powertrain Control Module (PCM) Reset). RERUN Quick Test.

FUEL VAPOR TO INTAKE MANIFOLD
FUEL VAPOR TO CARBON CANISTER
INPUT PORT VACUUM (TO INTAKE MANIFOLD)

FM0159601525190X

Fig. 259 Test HW: EVAP Purge System (Part 19 of 27). 1996

Test Step	Result	▶	Action to Take
HW22 CHECK FOR FILTER CONTAMINATION OR DAMAGE ON THE VMV			
• Key off. • Disconnect the vacuum line from the input vacuum port to engine intake manifold on the VMV. • Install a hand vacuum pump to the input vacuum port on the VMV. • Apply 10-15 in-Hg (48-52 kPa) of vacuum to the VMV. • **Does the VMV hold vacuum or show a very slow release of vacuum to atmosphere?**	Yes	▶	SERVICE VMV filter. If unable to remove filter or blockage to filter, REPLACE VMV. RECONNECT all components. VERIFY a symptom no longer exists. COMPLETE PCM Reset to clear DTCs (REFER to Powertrain Control Module (PCM) Reset). RERUN Quick Test.
	No	▶	REMOVE vacuum pump. GO to **HW23**.
HW23 CHECK FOR VPWR TO VMV			
• Key off. • Disconnect PCM. Inspect for damaged or pushed out pins, corrosion, loose wires, etc. Service as necessary. • Install breakout box, PCM connected to breakout box. • Disconnect VMV vehicle harness connector. • Key on, engine off. • Measure the voltage between VPWR at the VMV vehicle harness connector and battery ground. • **is the voltage greater than 10.5 volts?**	Yes	▶	VPWR circuit is OK. GO to **HW24**.
	No	▶	SERVICE open in VPWR circuit. VERIFY that breakout box is properly connected to PCM and harness. RECONNECT VMV. VERIFY a symptom no longer exists. COMPLETE PCM Reset to clear DTCs (REFER to Powertrain Control Module (PCM) Reset). RERUN Quick Test.

FM0159601525200X

Fig. 259 Test HW: EVAP Purge System (Part 20 of 27). 1996

Test Step	Result	▶	Action to Take
HW24 CHECK FOR MECHANICALLY STUCK CLOSED VMV			
• Key off. • Input port vacuum and fuel vapor hoses from the Vapor Management Valve (VMV) to the engine intake manifold connected. • Fuel vapor tube/hose to the carbon canister(s) at the VMV disconnected. • Install a vacuum gauge to the fuel vapor port to carbon canister(s) at the VMV. Refer to the schematic in Pinpoint Test Step **HW21**. • Breakout box installed, PCM connected to breakout box. • Start engine. • Idle engine for 5 minutes. • Observe vacuum gauge. Reading should be near zero in-Hg. • Connect a jumper between Test Pin 56 (VMV SIG) and Test Pins 51 or 103 (PWR GND) at the breakout box, while engine is still running. • Idle the engine for 5 more minutes. • Observe the vacuum gauge. • **Does the vacuum reading on the vacuum gauge change from zero to approximately engine manifold vacuum?**	Yes	▶	REMOVE vacuum gauge and jumper from breakout box. LEAVE breakout box installed. RECONNECT all vacuum and fuel vapor hoses. GO to **HW25**.
	No	▶	VMV is mechanically stuck closed. REPLACE damaged VMV. REMOVE vacuum gauge and breakout box. RECONNECT all components. VERIFY a symptom no longer exists. COMPLETE PCM Reset to clear DTCs (REFER to Powertrain Control Module (PCM) Reset). RERUN Quick Test.
HW25 CHECK FOR INTAKE MANIFOLD VACUUM TO VMV: BOTH INPUT PORT VACUUM HOSE AND FUEL VAPOR HOSE			
• Key off. • Vapor Management Valve (VMV) electrically connected. • Disconnected both the input port vacuum and fuel vapor hoses from the VMV at the VMV. Refer to the schematic in Pinpoint Test Step **HW21**. • Start engine. • Place thumb at the end of the input port vacuum hose and then the end of the fuel vapor hose. • **is vacuum present at both open hose ends?**	Yes	▶	RECONNECT all fuel vapor tubes/hoses and vacuum hoses. LEAVE breakout box installed. GO to **HW26**.
	No	▶	ISOLATE causes of missing intake manifold vacuum. CHECK vacuum/fuel vapor hose routing for holes in hoses and for kinked or blocked hoses to engine intake manifold. GO to Engine Group Service Manual for engine vacuum loss. If OK, VERIFY a symptom no longer exists. COMPLETE PCM Reset to clear DTCs (REFER to Powertrain Control Module (PCM) Reset). RERUN Quick Test.

FM0159601525210X

Fig. 259 Test HW: EVAP Purge System (Part 21 of 27). 1996

Test Step	Result	▶	Action to Take
HW26 CHECK FOR INPUT PORT VACUUM HOSE AND FUEL VAPOR HOSE RESTRICTIONS BETWEEN VAPOR MANAGEMENT VALVE AND ENGINE INTAKE MANIFOLD • Key off. • Fuel vapor hose from VMV to the carbon canister at the VMV disconnected. • Disconnect inport vacuum hose and fuel vapor hose to the engine intake manifold at the VMV (other end of hoses already disconnected). • Breakout box installed. • Install a hand vacuum pump to one end of each disconnected hose from the VMV to the engine intake manifold. • Apply 16 in-Hg (53 kPa) of vacuum with the vacuum pump. • Observe the vacuum reading for 30 seconds. • **Does the vacuum bleed off immediately?**	Yes ▶ No ▶		REMOVE vacuum pump. RECONNECT all vacuum / fuel vapor hoses. LEAVE breakout box installed. **For DTC P1443:** GO to **HW19**. **All others:** RETURN to Symptom Flowcharts. REMOVE vacuum pump. CHECK the suspect vacuum or fuel vapor hose for kinks or blockages. SERVICE as necessary. REMOVE breakout box. RECONNECT all components. VERIFY a symptom no longer exists. COMPLETE PCM Reset to clear DTCs (REFER to Section 2A, Powertrain Control Module (PCM) Reset). RERUN Quick Test.
HW27 CONTINUOUS MEMORY DTC P1444: VERIFY PFS SIG VOLTAGE Continous Memory Diagnostic Trouble Code (DTC) P1444 indicates that Self-Test has detected a PFS SIG circuit input below the minimum. Possible causes: — PGS SIG shorted to PWR GND. — Damaged Purge Flow (PF) Sensor. — Damaged PCM. • Key on, engine off. • Access PF PID with a Scan Tool. NOTE: PF sensor input to the PCM is 0.14 to 4.80 volts. • **Is PF PID voltage less than 0.14 volt?**	Yes ▶ No ▶		The PFS SIG voltage is less than the acceptable minimum. GO to **HW28**. Fault may have been an intermittent DTC P1444. GO to **HW30**.

Test Step	Result	▶	Action to Take
HW28 MEASURE PURGE FLOW (PF) SENSOR RESISTANCE • Key off. • Disconnect PF sensor vehicle harness connector. • NOTE: Allow the vehicle and PF sensor to cool down or warm up to a room temperature (55°F to 80°F) before taking a resistance measurement on the PF sensor. This may take 15 to 20 minutes. • Measure the resistance between PFS SIG (Pin 2) and PWR GND (Pin 3) on the Purge Flow (PF) Sensor.	Yes ▶ No ▶		PFS SIG is shorted to PWR GND in PF sensor. REPLACE damaged PF sensor. RECONNECT all components. COMPLETE PCM Reset to clear DTCs (REFER to Powertrain Control Module (PCM) Reset). RERUN Quick Test. GO to **HW29**.

Test Step	Result	▶	Action to Take
• **Is the resistance less than 25.50 ohms?**			
HW29 CHECK PFS SIG CIRCUIT FOR SHORTS TO PWR GND • Key off. • PF sensor disconnected. • Disconnect PCM. Inspect for damaged or pushed out pins, corrosion, loose wires, etc. Service as necessary. • Install breakout box, leave PCM disconnected. • Disconnect Scan Tool from DLC. • Measure the resistance between Test Pin 11 (PFS SIG) and Test Pins 24 and 103 (PWR GND) at the breakout box. • **Is each resistance greater than 10,000 ohms?**	Yes ▶ No ▶		PF SIG is shorted to PWR GND in the PCM. REPLACE damaged PCM. REMOVE breakout box. RECONNECT all components. RERUN Quick Test. SERVICE harness short between PFS SIG and PWR GND. REMOVE breakout box. RECONNECT all components. COMPLETE PCM Reset to clear DTCs (REFER to Powertrain Control Module (PCM) Reset). RERUN Quick Test.

Test Step	Result	▶	Action to Take
HW30 WIGGLE TEST PURGE FLOW SENSOR AND HARNESS • Key on, engine off. • Access PF PID with a Scan Tool. • Observe PF PID for an indication of a fault while performing the following: — Lightly tap on PF sensor; wiggle the PF sensor connector and vehicle harness between the sensor and the PCM. A fault is indicated by a sudden change in PF PID voltage (less than 0.14 volts). • **Is a fault indicated?**	Yes ▶ No ▶		ISOLATE fault and SERVICE as necessary. RECONNECT all components. COMPLETE PCM Reset to clear DTCs (REFER to Powertrain Control Module (PCM) Reset). RERUN Quick Test. Unable to duplicate and / or identify fault at this time. GO to Pinpoint Test Step **Z1** with the following data: PF PID and a list of possible causes.
HW31 CONTINUOUS MEMORY DTC P1445: VERIFY PFS SIG VOLTAGE Continuous Memory Diagnostic Trouble Code (DTC) P1445 indicates that Self-Test has detected a PFS SIG circuit input above the maximum. Possible causes: — PFS SIG shorted to VPWR. — PFS SIG open circuit. — VPWR open circuit. — Damaged Purge Flow (PF) Sensor. — Damagedd PCM. • Key on, engine off. • Access PF PID with a Scan Tool. NOTE: PF sensor input to the PCM is 0.14 to 4.80 volts. • **Is PF PID voltage greater than 4.80 volts?**	Yes ▶ No ▶		The PFS SIG voltage is greater than the acceptable maximum. GO to **HW32**. Fault may have been an intermittent DTC P1445. GO to **HW37**.

Test Step	Result	▶	Action to Take
HW32 MEASURE PURGE FLOW (PF) SENSOR RESISTANCE • Key off. • Disconnect PF sensor vehicle harness connector. • NOTE: Allow the vehicle and PF sensor to cool down or warm up to a room temperature (55°F to 80°F) before taking a resistance measurement on the PF sensor. This may take 15 to 20 minutes. • Measure the resistance between PFS SIG (Pin 2) and VPWR (Pin 1) on the Purge Flow (PF) sensor. (Refer to schematic in Pinpoint Test Step **HW28**.) • **Is the resistance between 40 and 230 ohms?**	Yes ▶ No ▶		GO to **HW33**. REPLACE damaged PF sensor. RECONNECT all components. COMPLETE PCM Reset to clear DTCs (REFER to Powertrain Control Module (PCM) Reset). RERUN Quick Test.
HW33 CHECK PF SENSOR SHORT TO VPWR • Key off. • PF sensor disconnected. • Key on, engine off. • Measure the voltage between PFS SIG circuit at the PF sensor vehicle harness connector and battery ground. • **Is the voltage greater than 10.5 volts?**	Yes ▶ No ▶		The PFS SIG input is indicating a short to VPWR. GO to **HW34**. GO to **HW35**.
HW34 CHECK PFS SIG CIRCUIT FOR SHORT TO VPWR • Key off. • PF sensor disconnected. • Disconnect PCM. Inspect for damaged or pushed out pins, corrosion, loose wires, etc. Service as necessary. • Install breakout box, leave PCM disconnected. • Key on, engine off. • Measure the resistance between Test Pin 11 (PFS SIG) and Test Pins 24 and 103 (PWR GND) at the breakout box. • **Is the voltage greater than 10.5 volts?**	Yes ▶ No ▶		SERVICE harness short between PFS SIG and VPWR. REMOVE breakout box. RECONNECT all components. COMPLETE PCM Reset to clear DTCs (REFER to Powertrain Control Module (PCM) Reset). RERUN Quick Test. REPLACE damaged PCM. REMOVE breakout box. RECONNECT all components. RERUN Quick Test.

Test Step	Result	▶	Action to Take
HW35 CHECK PF SENSOR SIG FOR OPEN IN HARNESS			
• Key off. • PF sensor disconnected. • Disconnect PCM. Inspect for damaged or pushed out pins, corrosion, loose wires, etc. Service as necessary. • Install breakout box, leave PCM disconnected. • Measure the resistance between Test Pin 11 (PFS SIG) at the breakout box and PFS SIG circuit at the PF sensor vehicle harness connector. • **Is the resistance less than 5.0 ohms?**	Yes No	▶ ▶	GO to HW36. SERVICE open in PFS SIG harness. RECONNECT all components. COMPLETE PCM Reset to clear DTCs (REFER to Powertrain Control Module (PCM) Reset). RERUN Quick Test.
HW36 CHECK PWR GND FOR OPEN IN HARNESS			
• Key off. • PF sensor disconnected. • PCM disconnected. • Measure the resistance between Test Pins 24 and 103 (PWR GND) at the breakout box and PWR GND circuit at the PF sensor vehicle harness connector. • **Is the resistance less than 5.0 ohms?**	Yes No	▶ ▶	REPLACE damaged PCM. REMOVE breakout box. RECONNECT all components. RERUN Quick Test. SERVICE open in PWR GND harness. REMOVE breakout box. RECONNECT all components. COMPLETE PCM Reset to clear DTCs (REFER to Powertrain Control Module (PCM) Reset). RERUN Quick Test.
HW37 WIGGLE TEST PURGE FLOW SENSOR AND HARNESS			
• Key on, engine off. • Access PF PID with a Scan Tool. • Observe PF PID for an indication of a fault while performing the following: — Lightly tap on PFS; wiggle the PF sensor connector and vehicle harness between the sensor and the PCM. A fault is indicated by a sudden change in PF PID voltage (greater than 4.80 volts). • **Is a fault indicated?**	Yes No	▶ ▶	ISOLATE fault and SERVICE as necessary. RECONNECT all components. COMPLETE PCM Reset to clear DTCs (REFER to Powertrain Control Module (PCM) Reset). RERUN Quick Test. UNABLE to duplicate and/or identify fault at this time. GO to Pinpoint Test Step Z1 with the following data: PF PID and a list of Possible Causes.

FM0159601525260X

Fig. 259   Test HW: EVAP Purge System (Part 26 of 27). 1996

Test Step	Result	▶	Action to Take
HW38 CONTINUOUS MEMORY DTC P0443: INSPECT EVAP CANISTER PURGE SOLENOID (OR VMV) CIRCUIT FOR INTERMITTENT FAILURE			
Continuous Memory Diagnostic Trouble Code (DTC) P0443 may indicate a EVAP Canister Purge solenoid (or VMV) circuit failure. Possible causes: — Damaged EVAP Canister Purge solenoid. — Damaged VMV. — EVAP CANISTER PURGE SIG, VMV SIG or VPWR harness circuit open. • Rerun KOEO, KOER and Continuous Memory Self-Tests. • **Is DTC P0443 present in Continuous Memory Self-Test only?**	Yes No	▶ ▶	GO to HW39. GO to HW1.
HW39 WIGGLE TEST SOLENOID AND HARNESS			
• Key off. • Disconnect PCM. Inspect for damaged or pushed out pins, corrosion, loose wires, etc. Service as necessary. • Install breakout box, leave PCM disconnected. • Measure the resistance between Test Pin 67 (EVAP CANISTER PURGE SIG) or Test Pin 56 (VMV SIG) and Test Pins 71 and 97 (VPWR), while performing the following: — Lightly tap on the EVAP Canister Purge solenoid or VMV, and observe a resistance change. — Wiggle the EVAP Canister Purge solenoid or VMV connector and vehicle harness between the solenoid (or valve) and the PCM, observe a resistance change. • **Does the resistance reading change to below 30 ohms or above 90 ohms (36 ohms for VMV)?**	Yes No	▶ ▶	ISOLATE fault and SERVICE as necessary. RECONNECT all components. COMPLETE PCM Reset to clear DTCs (REFER to Powertrain Control Module (PCM) Reset). RERUN Quick Test. UNABLE to duplicate and/or identify fault at this time. GO to Pinpoint Test Step Z1 with the resistance readings and list of Possible Causes.

FM0159601525270X

Fig. 259   Test HW: EVAP Purge System (Part 27 of 27). 1996

Note

You should enter this Pinpoint Test only when directed here.

Remember

This Pinpoint Test is intended to diagnose the following:

• Canister Vent (CV) Solenoid (9F945)
• Carbon Canister (9D653)
• Fuel Fill Cap (9030)
• Fuel Tank Pressure (FTP) Sensor (9C052)
• Fuel Vapor Valve (9B593)
• Fuel Vapor Control Valve (9B190)
• Vapor Management Valve (VMV) (9C915)
• Fuel Fill Cap valve leaks
• Vacuum Lines
• Fuel Tank
• Fuel Vapor Hoses
• Harness circuits: CV SIG, FTP SIG, VMV SIG, SIG RTN, Vehicle Power (VPWR), Reference Voltage (VREF), and Power Ground (PWR GND)
• Powertrain Control Module (PCM) (12A650)

FM0159601526010X

Fig. 260   Test HX: EVAP Monitor & System (Part 1 of 33). 1996 Except Probe

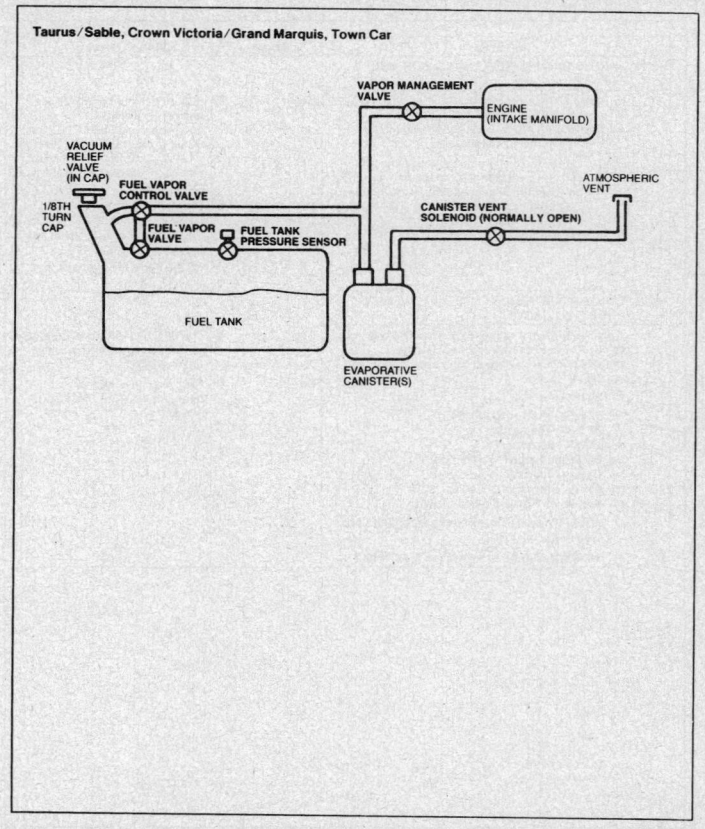

Taurus/Sable, Crown Victoria/Grand Marquis, Town Car

FM0159601526020X

Fig. 260   Test HX: EVAP Monitor & System (Part 2 of 33). 1996 Except Probe

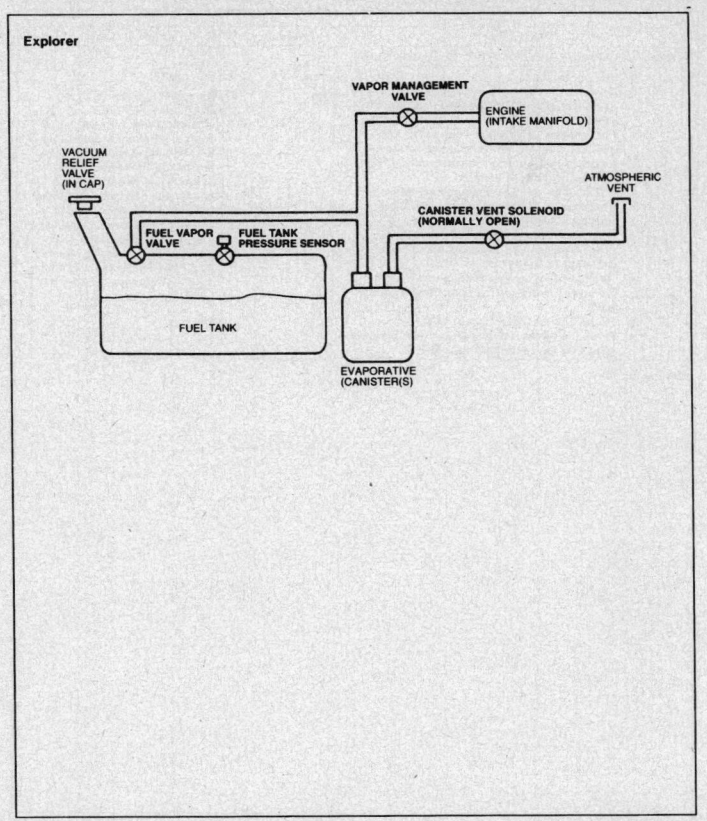

**Fig. 260   Test HX: EVAP Monitor & System (Part 3 of 33).
1996 Except Probe**

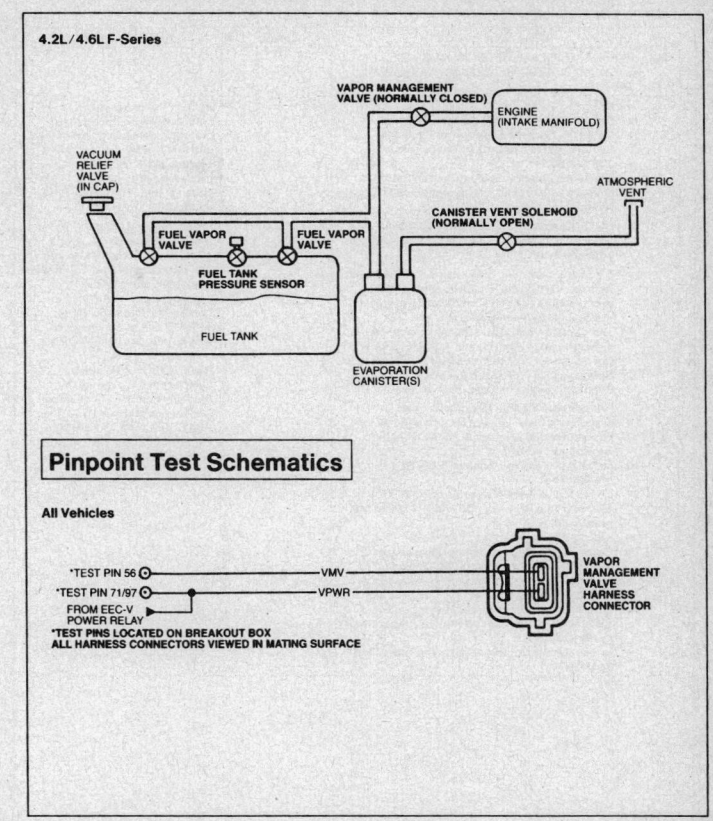

**Fig. 260   Test HX: EVAP Monitor & System (Part 4 of 33).
1996 Except Probe**

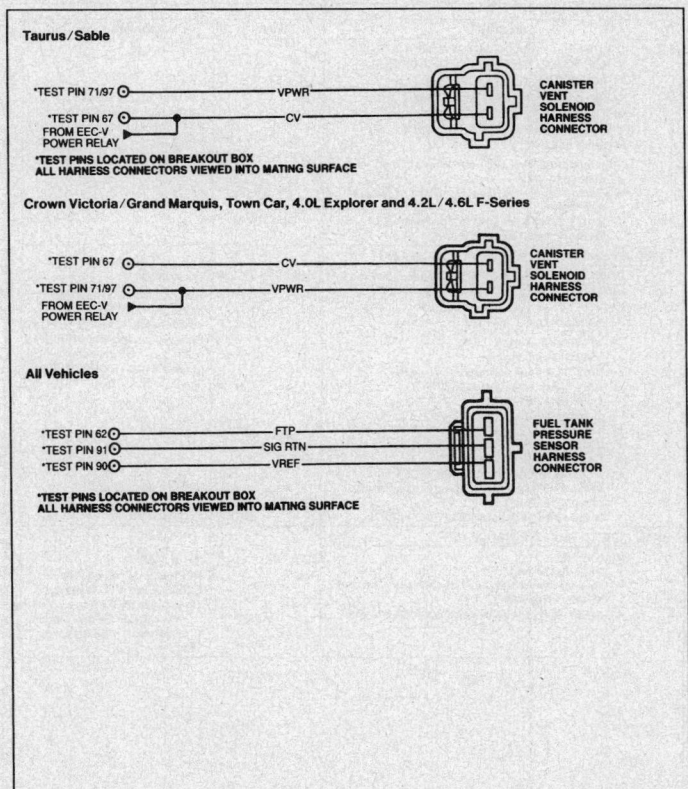

**Fig. 260   Test HX: EVAP Monitor & System (Part 5 of 33).
1996 Except Probe**

	Test Step	Result	►	Action to Take
HX1	CONTINUOUS MEMORY DTC P0442 OR P1442: CHECK FOR LOOSE GAS FILLER CAP			
	Continuous Memory Diagnostic Trouble Code (DTC) P0442 or P1442 indicates that a leak has been detected (as small as 0.40 inch). The only difference between the DTC P0442 and P1442 is that the P0442 is a MIL DTC. Possible causes: — Loose fuel fill cap. — Small vapor leaks at the plastic vacuum line connection to the Vapor Management Valve (VMV). — Small vpor leaks at the fuel vapor hose connections to the VMV, the Fuel Tank Pressure (FTP) sensor and carbon canister. — Small cuts or holes in the vacuum lines or vapor hoses in the evaporative emission system. ● Key off. ● Check if the fuel fill cap is on securely (inspect for a possible cap thread wear). ● **Was the fuel fill cap very loose?**	Yes	►	REMOVE fuel fill cap and REINSTALL fuel fillcap only 1/8 turn so that cap initially clicks by sound or touch. If entering this Pinpoint Test Step because of Continuous Memory DTC P0442 or P1442, GO to **HX61**. Otherwise, VERIFY a symptom no longer exists.
		No	►	GO to **HX2**.
HX2	VISUAL INSPECTION OF VACUUM/FUEL VAPOR CONNECTIONS, FUEL VAPOR TUBES/HOSES			
	● Pull slightly on the vacuum hose at the VMV. ● Check for loose connections. ● Pull slightly on the fuel vapor tubes/hoses at the VMV, the FTP sensor and the carbon canister. ● Check again for loose connections. ● Visually inspect for cuts or small holes in the fuel vapor tubes/hoses in the evaporative emission system. ● **Is a fault detected?**	Yes	►	SERVICE as necessary. If entering this Pinpoint Test Step because of Continuous Memory DTC P0442 or P1442, GO to **HX61**. Otherwise, VERIFY a symptom no longer exists.
		No	►	GO to **HX3**.

**Fig. 260   Test HX: EVAP Monitor & System (Part 6 of 33).
1996 Except Probe**

Test Step	Result	▶	Action to Take
HX3 EVAPORATIVE LEAK DETECTION USING ROTUNDA EVAPORATIVE EMISSION SYSTEM TESTER • Key off. • Remove the fuel fill cap from the vehicle. • Install the Rotunda Evaporative Emission System Tester (Rotunda catalog number 134-00056). • Connect a compressed gas source (nitrogen or argon with pressure regulator closed) to the tester. NOTE: Tester kit contains all required adapters (schrader valve, fuel cap per vehicle application etc.). • Disconnect and plug (cap) the fuel vapor hose from the VMV at the engine intake manifold port (vacuum tree) on all vehicles (except on the Taurus/Sable or Explorer). • The Canister Vent (CV) solenoid should be closed by accessing Output Test Mode with the Scan Tool or at the breakout box. • Select ALL OFF mode on the Scan Tool. • Push start button on Scan Tool. **For Crown Victoria/Grand Marquis:** • Disconnect PCM. Inspect for damaged or pushed out pins, corrosion, loose wires, etc. Service as necessary. • Install breakout box, connect PCM to the breakout box. • Connect a jumper between Test Pin 67 (CV SIG) and Test Pin 51 or 103 (PWR GND) at the breakout box. • Key on, engine off. • Pressurize the vehicle evaporative system at 14 in-H2O using the Evaporative Emission System Tester and following the instructions that come with the tester. • Observe the tester installation leak self-test for 2 minutes and then the vehicle evaporative system leak test. • **Is a system leak indicated by the tester red light on?**	Yes No	▶ ▶	ALLOW the two position control valve on the tester to provide a continuing flow of the gas to the closed evaporative system. MAINTAIN 14 in-H2O pressure on the system (monitor tester pressure gauges). GO to **HX4**. Pressure in the evaporative system will discharge after a green (passed) light is on and the test is completed. REMOVE the tester, gas source, breakout box and the plug (cap) in the fuel vapor hose. ATTACH fuel fill cap only 1/8 turn so that cap initially clicks by sound or touch. RECONNECT PCM and all components. If entering this Pinpoint Test Step because of Continuous Memory DTC P0442 or P1442, GO to **HX61**. Otherwise, VERIFY a symptom no longer exists.

FM0159601526070X

Fig. 260   Test HX: EVAP Monitor & System (Part 7 of 33). 1996 Except Probe

Test Step	Result	▶	Action to Take
HX4 MECHANICAL CHECK OF THE CV SOLENOID • Key on, engine off. • Continue to pressurize the vehicle evaporative system at 14 in-H2O using the Evaporative Emission System Tester. • For vehicles with a filtered cap on the CV solenoid, remove the CV solenoid where it is attached to the carbon canister and plug open port on the carbon canister. • For all other vehicles, clamp (pinched closed) the purge air inlet tube/hose to atmosphere from the CV solenoid port. • If the tube/hose is not flexible enough to prevent damage by clamping, discontinue pressurizing the system. • Remove tube/hose to atmosphere from the CV solenoid and cap the open port on the CV solenoid. • Re-pressurize the system at 14 in-H2O. • **Does the evaporative system again indicate a leak by the tester red light on?**	Yes No	▶ ▶	GO to **HX5**. CV solenoid is mechanically stuck open. REPLACE CV solenoid. REMOVE tester, gas source, breakout box and plug (cap) from fuel vapor hose at the engine intake manifold. ATTACH fuel fill cap only 1/8 turn so that cap clicks by sound or touch. RECONNECT PCM and all components. If entering this Pinpoint Test Step because of Continuous Memory DTC P0442 or P1442, GO to **HX61**. Otherwise, VERIFY a symptom no longer exists.

FM0159601526080X

Fig. 260   Test HX: EVAP Monitor & System (Part 8 of 33). 1996 Except Probe

Test Step	Result	▶	Action to Take
HX5 CHECK FOR 0.40 INCH EVAPORATIVE LEAKS WITH THE ULTRA-SONIC LEAK DETECTOR • Key on, engine off. • The fuel vapor hose from the VMV at the engine intake manifold (vacuum tree) is still plugged (capped) on all vehicles (except on the Taurus/Sable or Explorer). • CV solenoid still closed. • Evaporative Emission System Tester still pressurizing the vehicle evaporative system. • Remove the ultra-sonic detector provided with the Rotunda Evaporative Emission Tester. • Place the earphones from the detector over your ears and adjust the audio dial on the detector. • Closely pass the probe of the ultra-sonic detector over the vacuum/fuel vapor hoses and connections from the fuel tank to the carbon canister and the VMV, from the carbon canister to the CV solenoid, and from the VMV to the engine intake manifold. • Check for audible sound changes (noticeably quiet to louder pitch). • **Is a sudden audible change indicated?**	Yes No	▶ ▶	ISOLATE the pressure leak in the evaporative emission system. REPLACE damaged tubes/hoses with cracks, splits or holes. RECONNECT loose tubes/hoses. For fuel tank leaks or fuel vapor control valve and fuel vapor valve concerns. REMOVE the tester, gas source, breakout box and plug (cap) in fuel vapor hose at he engine intake manifold. ATTACH fuel fill cap only 1/8 turn so that cap initially clicks by sound or touch. RECONNECT PCM and fuel vapor hose at engine intake manifold. If entering this Pinpoint Test Step because of Continuous Memory DTC P0442 or P1442, GO to **HX61**. Otherwise, VERIFY a symptom no longer exists. The evaporative emission system is OK or small leak undetectable at this time. REMOVE the tester, gas source, breakout box and the plug (cap) in the fuel vapor hose at the engine intake manifold. ATTACH fuel fill cap only 1/8 turn to that cap initially clicks by sound or touch. RECONNECT PCM and fuel vapor hose at engine intake manifold. If entering this Pinpoint Test Step because of Continuous Memory DTC P0442 or P1442, GO to **HX61**. Otherwise, VERIFY a symptom no longer exists.

FM0159601526090X

Fig. 260   Test HX: EVAP Monitor & System (Part 9 of 33). 1996 Except Probe

Test Step	Result	▶	Action to Take
HX6 CONTINUOUS MEMORY DTC P0443: INSPECT VAPOR MANAGEMENT VALVE CIRCUIT FOR INTERMITTENT FAILURE Continuous Memory Diagnostic Trouble Code (DTC) P0443 may indicate an intermittent Vapor Management Valve (VMV) circuit failure. Possible causes: — Intermittent VMV SIG or VPWR circuit open. — Damaged VMV. • Rerun KOEO, KOER and Continuous Memory Self-Tests. • **Is DTC P0443 present in Continuous Memory Self-Test only?**	Yes No	▶ ▶	The fault that produced Continuous Memory DTC P0443 may be intermittent. GO to **HX12**. GO to **HX7**.
HX7 DTC P0443: CHECK FOR VPWR TO VMV Diagnostic Trouble Code (DTC) P0443 indicates a failure in the Vapor Management Valve (VMV) circuit. Possible causes: — VPWR circuit open. — VMV SIG circuit open. — VMV SIG circuit shorted to PWR GND. — VMV SIG circuit shorted to VPWR. — Damaged VMV. — Damaged PCM. • Key off. • Disconnect VMV. • Key on, engine off. • Measure the voltage between VPWR at the VMV vehicle harness connector and battery ground. • **Is the voltage greater than 10.5 volts?**	Yes No	▶ ▶	GO to **HX8**. SERVICE open in the VPWR harness. RECONNECT all components. COMPLETE PCM Reset to clear DTCs (REFER to Powertrain Control Module (PCM) Reset). RERUN Quick Test.
HX8 CHECK VMV RESISTANCE • Key off. • VMV disconnected. • Measure the resistance between VMV SIG and VPWR on the VMV. • **Is the resistance between 30 and 36 ohms?**	Yes No	▶ ▶	GO to **HX9**. REPLACE damaged VMV. COMPLETE PCM Reset to clear DTCs (REFER to Powertrain Control Module (PCM) Reset). RERUN Quick Test.

FM0159601526100X

Fig. 260   Test HX: EVAP Monitor & System (Part 10 of 33). 1996 Except Probe

Test Step	Result	▶	Action to Take
HX9 CHECK CONTINUITY OF VMV SIG CIRCUIT • Key off. • VMV disconnected. • Disconnect PCM. Inspect for damaged or pushed out pins, corrosion loose wires, etc. Service as necessary. • Install breakout box, leave PCM disconnected. • Measure the resistance between Test Pin 56 (VMV SIG) at the breakout box and VMV SIG circuit at the vehicle harness connector. • **Is the resistance less than 5.0 ohms?**	Yes No	▶ ▶	GO to HX10. SERVICE open in the VMV SIG harness. REMOVE breakout box. RECONNECT all components. COMPLETE PCM Reset to clear DTCs (REFER to Powertrain Control Module (PCM) Reset). RERUN Quick Test.
HX10 CHECK VMV SIG CIRCUIT FOR SHORT TO PWR GND • Key off. • VMV disconnected. • Breakout box installed, PCM disconnected. • Disconnect Scan Tool from DLC. • Measure the resistance between Test Pin 56 (VMV SIG) and Test Pins 24 and 103 (PWR GND) at the breakout box. • **Is each resistance greater than 10,000 ohms?**	Yes No	▶ ▶	GO to HX11. SERVICE harness short between VMV SIG and PWR GND. REMOVE breakout box. RECONNECT all components. COMPLETE PCM Reset to clear DTCs (REFER to Powertrain Control Module (PCM) Reset). RERUN Quick Test.
HX11 CHECK VMV SIG CIRCUIT FOR SHORT TO VPWR • Key off. • VMV disconnected. • Breakout box installed, leave PCM disconnected. • Key on, engine off. • Measure the voltage between Test Pin 56 (VMV SIG) and Test Pins 51 and 103 (PWR GND) at the breakout box. • **Is the voltage greater than 10.5 volts?**	Yes No	▶ ▶	SERVICE harness short between VMV SIG and VPWR. REMOVE breakout box. RECONNECT all components. COMPLETE PCM Reset to clear DTCs (REFER to Powertrain Control Module (PCM) Reset). RERUN Quick Test. VMV SIG is open, shorted to PWR GND or shorted VPWR in the PCM. REPLACE damaged PCM. REMOVE breakout box. RECONNECT all components. RERUN Quick Test.

FM0159601526110X

Fig. 260   Test HX: EVAP Monitor & System (Part 11 of 33). 1996 Except Probe

Test Step	Result	▶	Action to Take

HX12 WIGGLE TEST VMV AND HARNESS
• Key off.
• Disconnect PCM. Inspect for damaged or pushed out pins, corrosion, loose wires, etc. Service as necessary.
• Install breakout box, leave PCM disconnected.
• Measure the resistance between Test Pin 56 (VMV SIG) and Test Pins 71 and 97 (VPWR) while performing the following:
  — Lightly tap on the VMV and observe a resistance change.
  — Wiggle the VMV connector and vehicle harness between the valve and the PCM, observe a resistance change.
• **Does the resistance reading change to below 30 ohms or above 36 ohms?**
	Yes
	
	 No
		▶
		
		 ▶
			ISOLATE fault and SERVICE as necessary. RECONNECT all components. COMPLETE PCM Reset to clear DTCs (REFER to Powertrain Control Module (PCM) Reset). RERUN Quick Test.
			
			 UNABLE to duplicate and/or identify fault at this time. GO to Pinpoint Test Step Z1 with the following data: resistance readings from this test and a list of possible causes.

HX13 CONTINUOUS MEMORY DTC P0446: CHECK VREF CIRCUIT BETWEEN FUEL TANK PRESSURE SENSOR AND PCM
Continuous Memory Diagnostic Trouble Code (DTC) P0446 indicates an Evaporative Emission Control System vent control malfunction.
Possible causes:
  — VREF circuit to FTP sensor open.
  — Damaged FTP sensor.
  — Carbon canister vent restriction.
  — Damaged Canister Vent (CV) solenoid filter.
  — Kinks or blockage in the fuel vapor hose/tube between CV solenoid and atmosphere.
  — CV SIG circuit short to PWR GND.
  — Damaged CV solenoid.
  — Damaged PCM.
• Key off.
• Loosen fuel fill cap on passenger cars.
• Remove fuel fill cap.
• Key on, engine off.
• Access FTP V PID with a Scan Tool.
• **Is the FTP V PID voltage between 2.37 and 2.87 volts?**
	Yes
	
	 No
		▶
		
		 ▶
			ATTACH fuel fill cap only 1/8 turn so that cap initially clicks by sound or touch. GO to HX15.
			
			 ATTACH fuel fill cap only 1/8 turn so that cap initially clicks by sound or touch. GO to HX14.

FM0159601526120X

Fig. 260   Test HX: EVAP Monitor & System (Part 12 of 33). 1996 Except Probe

Test Step	Result	▶	Action to Take
HX14 CHECK VREF AT THE FTP SENSOR VEHICLE HARNESS CONNECTOR • Key off. • Disconnect FTP sensor vehicle harness connector. • Key on, engine off. • Measure the voltage between the VREF circuit and SIG RTN circuit at the FTP sensor vehicle harness connector. • **Is the VREF voltage between 4.0 and 6.0 volts?**	Yes No	▶ ▶	VREF is open in the FTP sensor. REPLACE FTP sensor. REMOVE breakout box. RECONNECT all components. COMPLETE PCM Reset to clear DTCs (REFER to Powertrain Control Module (PCM) Reset). RERUN Quick Test. VREF voltage is out of range. GO to Pinpoint Test Step C1.
HX15 CHECK FOR RESTRICTION AT CARBON CANISTER AND CANISTER VENT SOLENOID • Check for excessive debris in the carbon canister or restrictions at the carbon canister atmosphere venting port to CV solenoid (most applications have CV solenoid directly attached to carbon canister). • Check for kinks or bends in the purge air inlet tube (larger diameter hose) between the CV solenoid and atmosphere. • **Is an obstruction indicated?**	Yes No	▶ ▶	SERVICE as necessary. RECONNECT all components. COMPLETE PCM Reset to clear DTCs (REFER to Powertrain Control Module (PCM) Reset). RERUN Quick Test. GO to HX16.
HX16 CHECK TUBE FROM CANISTER VENT SOLENOID FILTER PORT TO ATMOSPHERE • Disconnect purge air inlet tube (larger diameter hose) to atmosphere at the CV solenoid port. If vehicle is not equipped with a tube to atmosphere from the CV solenoid, go to Pinpoint Test Step HX17. • Locate other end of tube to atmosphere (opening usually found in the fuel filler housing). • Drop a 3/8 inch steel ball bearing (marble, etc.) down end of tube near the fuel filler housing. • **Does the ball bearing roll out of the end of tube at the CV solenoid?**	Yes No	▶ ▶	RECONNECT all components. GO to HX17. LOCATE obstruction in the tube. SERVICE as necessary. COMPLETE PCM Reset to clear DTCs (REFER to Powertrain Control Module (PCM) Reset). RERUN Quick Test.

FM0159601526130X

Fig. 260   Test HX: EVAP Monitor & System (Part 13 of 33). 1996 Except Probe

Test Step	Result	▶	Action to Take
HX17 CHECK CANISTER VENT SOLENOID MECHANICAL OPERATION - OPEN VACUUM POSITION • Key off. • Disconnect the vacuum hose at both ends of the Canister Vent (CV) solenoid. • If the CV solenoid is directly attached to the carbon canister, disconnect the fuel vapor hose from the VMV to the carbon canister at the carbon canister. • Install a hand held vacuum pump to the vent to atmosphere side of the CV solenoid. • CV solenoid electrically connected. • Apply 16 in-Hg (53 kPa) of vacuum to the CV solenoid. • **Does the CV solenoid hold vacuum for one minute?**	Yes No	▶ ▶	REMOVE vacuum pump. REPLACE CV solenoid or carbon canister-CV solenoid assembly. RECONNECT all components. COMPLETE PCM Reset to clear DTCs (REFER to Powertrain Control Module (PCM) Reset). RERUN Quick Test. RECONNECT all components. GO to HX18.
HX18 DTC P0446: CHECK FOR INTERMITTENT CANISTER VENT SOLENOID MALFUNCTION • Key on, engine off. • Access EVAPCVF PID with a Scan Tool. NOTE: A Scan Tool display of YES indicates a Canister Vent fault is present. • **Does the EVAPCVF PID display a YES?**	Yes No	▶ ▶	GO to HX19. GO to HX21.
HX19 CHECK CANISTER VENT SOLENOID RESISTANCE • Key off. • Disconnect Canister Vent (CV) solenoid vehicle harness connector. • Measure the resistance between the CV SIG and VPWR and the CV solenoid. • **Is the resistance less than 45 ohms?**	Yes No	▶ ▶	CV SIG is shorted to ground in the CV solenoid. REPLACE CV solenoid. RECONNECT all components. COMPLETE PCM Reset to clear DTCs (REFER to Powertrain Control Module (PCM) Reset). RERUN Quick Test. GO to HX20.

FM0159601526140X

Fig. 260   Test HX: EVAP Monitor & System (Part 14 of 33). 1996 Except Probe

Test Step	Result	▶	Action to Take
HX20 CHECK CV SIG CIRCUIT FOR SHORT TO PWR GND			
• Key off. • CV solenoid disconnected. • Disconnect PCM. Inspect for damaged or pushed out pins, corrosion, loose wires, etc. Service as necessary. • Install breakout box, leave PCM disconnected. • Disconnect Scan Tool from DLC. • Measure the resistance between Test Pin 67 (CV SIG) and Test Pins 51 and 103 (PWR GND) at the breakout box. • **Is each resistance greater than 10,000 ohms?**	Yes	▶	CV SIG is shorted to PWR GND in the PCM. REPLACE PCM. REMOVE breakout box. RECONNECT all components. RERUN Quick Test.
	No	▶	SERVICE harness short between CV SIG and PWR GND. REMOVE breakout box. RECONNECT all components. COMPLETE PCM Reset to clear DTCs (REFER to Powertrain Control Module (PCM) Reset). RERUN Quick Test.
HX21 WIGGLE TEST CANISTER VENT SOLENOID AND HARNESS			
• Key on, engine off. • Access EVAPCVF PID with the Scan Tool. • Observe the EVAPCVF PID while performing the following: — Lightly tap on the CV solenoid. — Wiggle the CV solenoid connector and the vehicle harness between the solenoid and the PCM. — A fault is indicated by an EVAPCVF PID change in state. • **Does the EVAPCVF PID display change between YES and NO while performing the wiggle test?**	Yes	▶	ISOLATE fault and SERVICE as necessary. COMPLETE PCM Reset to clear DTCs (REFER to Powertrain Control Module (PCM) Reset). RERUN Quick Test.
	No	▶	UNABLE to duplicate and/or identify fault at the time. GO to Pinpoint Test Step **Z1** with the following data: EVAPCVF PID and a list possible causes.

Fig. 260 Test HX: EVAP Monitor & System (Part 15 of 33). 1996 Except Probe

Test Step	Result	▶	Action to Take
HX22 DTC P0452: CHECK FOR FUEL SATURATION OF THE FTP SENSOR			
Diagnostic Trouble Code (DTC) P0452 indicates that Self-Test has detected an FTP SIG circuit input below minimum. Possible causes: — Fuel Tank Pressure (FTP) sensor completely submerged in liquid fuel. — Inside contamination of the electrical connector on the FTP sensor. — FTP SIG shorted to SIG RTN or PWR GND. — Damaged FTP sensor. — Damaged PCM. • Key off. • Visually check for liquid fuel contamination of the FTP sensor electrical connector. • Check for completely submerged FTP sensor in liquid fuel (may affect correct FTP voltage reading). • **Does FTP sensor and its electrical connector show signs of fuel contamination?**	Yes	▶	SERVICE FTP sensor electrical connector as necessary. If FTP sensor is completely submerged in fuel, DRAIN fuel tank and REFILL to proper fuel level. COMPLETE PCM Reset to clear DTCs (REFER to Powertrain Control Module (PCM) Reset). RERUN Quick Test.
	No	▶	INSTALL original FTP sensor in the fuel tank. GO to **HX23**.
HX23 VERIFY FTP SIG VOLTAGE			
• Key on, engine off. • Access FTP V PID with a Scan Tool. NOTE: FTP sensor input with no pressure/vacuum on the fuel tank (filler cap open or not open to atmosphere) is 2.62 volts ± 0.25 volts. • **Is the FTP V PID voltage less than 0.22 volt?**	Yes	▶	The FTP SIG voltage is less than the acceptable minimum. GO to **HX24**.
	No	▶	The fault that produced the DTC P0452 is intermittent. GO to **HX27**.
HX24 INDUCE OPPOSITE FTP SIGNAL			
• Key off. • Disconnect FTP sensor vehicle harness connector. • Connect a jumper wire between the sensor VREF circuit and the FTP SIG circuit at the FTP sensor vehicle harness connector. • Key on, engine off. NOTE: If a Scan Tool communication problem exists, remove jumper immediately and go directly to **HX25**. • Access FTP V PID with a Scan Tool. • **Is the FTP V PID value between 4.0 and 6.0 volts?**	Yes	▶	REPLACE damaged FTP sensor. RECONNECT all components. COMPLETE PCM Reset to clear DTCs (REFER to Powertrain Control Module (PCM) Reset). RERUN Quick Test.
	No	▶	REMOVE jumper. GO to **HX25**.

Fig. 260 Test HX: EVAP Monitor & System (Part 16 of 33). 1996 Except Probe

Test Step	Result	▶	Action to Take
HX25 CHECK VREF AT FTP SENSOR VEHICLE HARNESS CONNECTOR			
• FTP sensor disconnected. • Key on, engine off. • Measure the voltage between the VREF circuit and SIG RTN circuit at the FTP sensor vehicle harness connector. • **Is the VREF voltage between 4.0 and 6.0 volts?**	Yes	▶	GO to **HX26**.
	No	▶	VREF voltage is out of range. GO to Pinpoint Test Step **C1**.
HX26 CHECK FTP SIG CIRCUIT FOR SHORTS TO SIG RTN AND PWR GND			
• Key off. • FTP sensor disconnected. • Disconnect PCM. Inspect for damaged or pushed out pins, corrosion, loose wires, etc. Service as necessary. • Install breakout box, leave PCM disconnected. • Disconnect Scan Tool from DLC. • Measure the resistance between Test Pin 62 (FTP SIG) and Test Pin 91 (SIG RTN) at the breakout box. • Measure the resistance between Test Pin 62 (FTP SIG) and Test Pins 51 and 103 (PWR GND) at the breakout box. • **Is each resistance greater than 10,000 ohms?**	Yes	▶	FTP SIG is shorted to SIG RTN or PWR GND in the PCM. REPLACE PCM. REMOVE breakout box. RECONNECT all components. RERUN Quick Test.
	No	▶	SERVICE harness short between FTP SIG and SIG RTN or PWR GND. REMOVE breakout box. RECONNECT all components. COMPLETE PCM Reset to clear DTCs (REFER to Powertrain Control Module (PCM) Reset). RERUN Quick Test.
HX27 WIGGLE TEST FTP SENSOR AND HARNESS			
• Key on, engine off. • Access FTP V PID with the Scan Tool. • Observe the FTP V PID while performing the following: — Lightly tap on the sides of the FTP sensor. Do not tap on top of the sensor cover because that may result in an incorrect reading or damage the sensor. This action requires two technicians to lower the fuel tank to access the sensor location. — Wiggle the FTP sensor connector and the vehicle harness between the sensor and the PCM. — A fault is indicated by a sudden change in the FTP V PID voltage. • **Is a fault indicated?**	Yes	▶	ISOLATE fault and SERVICE as necessary. COMPLETE PCM Reset to clear DTCs (REFER to Powertrain Control Module (PCM) Reset). RERUN Quick Test.
	No	▶	UNABLE to duplicate and/or identify fault at this time. GO to Pinpoint Test Step **Z1** with the following data: FTP V PID and a list of possible causes.

Fig. 260 Test HX: EVAP Monitor & System (Part 17 of 33). 1996 Except Probe

Test Step	Result	▶	Action to Take
HX28 DTC P0453: VERIFY FTP SIG VOLTAGE			
Diagnostic Trouble Code (DTC) P0453 indicates that Self-Test has detected a FTP SIG circuit input above the maximum. Possible causes: — FTP SIG open. — FTP SIG shorted the VREF or VPWR. — VREF shorted to VPWR. — SIG RTN open. — Damaged FTP sensor. — Damaged PCM. • Key on, engine off. • Access FTP V PID with a Scan Tool. NOTE: FTP sensor input with no pressure/vacuum on the fuel tank (filler cap open or not open to atmosphere) is 2.62 volts ± 0.25 volts. • **Is the FTP V PID voltage greater than 4.50 volts?**	Yes	▶	The FTP SIG voltage is greater than acceptable maximum. GO to **HX29**.
	No	▶	The fault that produced DTC P0453 is intermittent. GO to **HX37**.
HX29 CHECK FTP SIG AT THE FTP SENSOR FOR SHORT TO POWER			
• Key off. • Disconnect FTP sensor vehicle harness connector. • Key on, engine off. • Measure voltage between FTP SIG circuit at the FTP sensor vehicle harness connector and battery ground. • **Is the voltage greater than 10.5 volts?**	Yes	▶	The FTP SIG is indicating a short to VPWR. GO to **HX30**.
	No	▶	GO to **HX31**.
HX30 CHECK FTP SIG CIRCUIT FOR SHORT TO VPWR			
• Key off. • FTP sensor disconnected. • Disconnect PCM. Inspect for damaged or pushed out pins, corrosion, loose wires, etc. Service as necessary. • Install breakout box, leave PCM disconnected. • Key on, engine off. • Measure the voltage between Test Pin 62 (FTP SIG) and Test Pins 51 and 103 (PWR GND) at the breakout box. • **Is the voltage greater than 10.5 volts?**	Yes	▶	SERVICE harness short between FTP SIG and VPWR. REMOVE breakout box. RECONNECT all components. COMPLETE PCM Reset to clear DTCs (REFER to Powertrain Control Module (PCM) Reset). RERUN Quick Test.
	No	▶	FTP SIG is shorted to VPWR in the PCM. REPLACE damaged PCM. REMOVE breakout box. RECONNECT all components. RERUN Quick Test.

Fig. 260 Test HX: EVAP Monitor & System (Part 18 of 33). 1996 Except Probe

Test Step	Result	▶	Action to Take
HX31 INDUCE OPPOSITE FTP SIGNAL • Key off. • FTP sensor disconnected. • Connect a jumper wire between the sensor SIG RTN circuit and the FTP SIG circuit at the FTP sensor vehicle harness connector. • Key on, engine off. NOTE: If a Scan Tool communication problem exists, remvoe jumper immediately and go directly to **HX36**. • Access FTP V PID with a Scan Tool. • **Is the FTP V PID voltage less than 0.10 volt?**	Yes No	▶ ▶	REMOVE jumper. GO to **HX32**. Unable to induce opposite signal. GO to **HX34**.
HX32 VERIFY THAT VREF IS IN RANGE • FTP sensor disconnected. • Key on, engine off. • Measure the voltage between the VREF circuit and the SIG RTN circuit at the FTP sensor vehicle harness connector. • **Is the VREF voltage between 4.0 and 6.0 volts?**	Yes No	▶ ▶	GO to **HX33**. VREF voltage is out of range. GO to Pinpoint Test Step **C1**.
HX33 CHECK FTP SIG FOR SHORT TO VREF IN SENSOR OR HARNESS • Key off. • FTP sensor disconnected. • Disconnect PCM. Inspect for damaged or pushed out pins, corrosion, loose wires, etc. Service as necessary. • Install breakout box, leave PCM disconnected. • Measure the resistance between Test Pin 62 (FTP SIG) and Test Pin 90 (VREF) at the breakout box. • **Is the resistance greater than 10,000 ohms?**	Yes No	▶ ▶	SIG RTN in the FTP sensor or FTP SIG is shorted to VREF in the FTP sensor. REPLACE damaged FTP sensor. REMOVE breakout box. RECONNECT all components. COMPLETE PCM Reset to clear DTCs (REFER to Powertrain Control Module (PCM) Reset). RERUN Quick Test. SERVICE harness short between FTP SIG and VREF. REMOVE breakout box. RECONNECT all components. COMPLETE PCM Reset to clear DTCs (REFER to Powertrain Control Module (PCM) Reset). RERUN Quick Test.

FM0159601526190X

Fig. 260   Test HX: EVAP Monitor & System (Part 19 of 33). 1996 Except Probe

Test Step	Result	▶	Action to Take
HX34 CHECK CONTINUITY OF THE FTP SIG CIRCUIT • Key off. • FTP sensor disconnected. • Disconnect PCM. Inspect for damaged or pushed out pins, corrosion, loose wires, etc. Service as necessary. • Install breakout box, leave PCM disconnected. • Measure the resistance between Test Pin 62 (FTP SIG) and FTP SIG circuit at the FTP sensor vehicle harness connector. • **Is the resistance less than 5.0 ohms?**	Yes No	▶ ▶	GO to **HX35**. SERVICE open in FTP SIG harness. REMOVE breakout box. RECONNECT all components. COMPLETE PCM Reset to clear DTCs (REFER to , Powertrain Control Module (PCM) Reset). RERUN Quick Test.
HX35 CHECK CONTINUITY OF THE SIG RTN CIRCUIT • Key off. • FTP sensor disconnected. • Disconnect PCM. Inspect for damaged or pushed out pins, corrosion, loose wires, etc. Service as necessary. • Install breakout box, leave PCM disconnected. • Measure the resistance between Test Pin 91 (SIG RTN) and SIG RTN circuit at the FTP sensor vehicle harness connector. • **Is the resistance less than 5.0 ohms?**	Yes No	▶ ▶	FTP SIG or SIG RTN is open in the PCM. REPLACE damaged PCM. REMOVE breakout box. RECONNECT all components. RERUN Quick Test. SERVICE open in the SIG RTN harness. REMOVE breakout box. RECONNECT all components. COMPLETE PCM Reset to clear DTCs (REFER to Powertrain Control Module (PCM) Reset). RERUN Quick Test.
HX36 CHECK FTP SIG FOR SHORT TO VREF IN PCM OR HARNESS • Key off. • FTP sensor disconnected. • Disconnect PCM. Inspect for damaged or pushed out pins, corrosion, loose wires, etc. Service as necessary. • Install breakout box, leave PCM disconnected. • Measure the resistance between Test Pin 62 (FTP SIG) and Test Pin 90 (VREF) at the breakout box. • **Is the resistance greater than 10,000?**	Yes No	▶ ▶	FTP SIG is shorted to VREF in the PCM. REMOVE breakout box. RECONNECT all components. RERUN Quick Test. SERVICE harness short to between FTP SIG and VREF. REMOVE breakout box. RECONNECT all components. COMPLETE PCM Reset to clear DTCs (REFER to Powertrain Control Module (PCM) Reset). RERUN Quick Test.

FM0159601526200X

Fig. 260   Test HX: EVAP Monitor & System (Part 20 of 33). 1996 Except Probe

Test Step	Result	▶	Action to Take

HX37 WIGGLE TEST FTP SENSOR AND HARNESS
• Key on, engine off.
• Access FTP V PID with a Scan Tool.
• Observe the FTP V PID while performing the following:
  — Lightly tap on the sides of the FTP sensor. Do not tap on top of the sensor cover because that may result in an incorrect reading or damage the sensor. This action requires two technicians to lower the fuel tank to access the sensor location.
  — Wiggle the FTP sensor connector and the vehicle harness between the sensor and the PCM.
  — A fault is indicated by a sudden change in the FTP V PID voltage.
• **Is a fault indicated?**
	Yes
	
	No
		▶
		
		▶
			ISOLATE fault and SERVICE as necessary. COMPLETE PCM Reset to clear DTCs (REFER to Powertrain Control Module (PCM) Reset). RERUN Quick Test.
			UNABLE to duplicate and/or identify fault at this time. GO to Pinpoint Test Step **Z1** with the following data: FTP V PID and a list of possible causes.

FM0159601526210X

Fig. 260   Test HX: EVAP Monitor & System (Part 21 of 33). 1996 Except Probe

Test Step	Result	▶	Action to Take

HX40 CONTINUOUS MEMORY DTC P0455 or P1455: VISUAL INSPECTION OF EVAPORATIVE SYSTEM
Continuous Memory Diagnostic Trouble Code (DTC) P0455 or P1455 indicates that a substantial leak or blockage has been detected in the Evaporative Emission System. The only difference between the DTC P0455 and P1455 is that the P0455 is a MIL DTC.
Possible causes:
  — Fuel fill cap missing or defective.
  — Fuel vapor control valve or fuel vapor valve stuck closed.
  — Loose, cracked or cut vacuum/fuel vapor hoses between the engine intake manifold and the fuel tank.
  — Pinched or blocked vacuum/fuel vapor hoses between the engine intakew manifold, the fuel tank and the carbon canister.
  — Fuel Tank Pressure (FTP) sensor mechanical malfunction.
  — Mechanically open CV solenoid.
  — Mechanically closed Vapor Management Valve (VMV).
  — CV SIG circuit open.
  — CV SIG circuit short to VPWR.
• Key off.
• Check for missing fuel fill cap.
• Check for defective valve in fuel fill cap.
• Check for a damaged carbon canister.
• Check for disconnected fuel vapor tubes/hoses.
• Check for kinked or pinched fuel vapor tubes/hoses.
• Check for fuel tank and fill pipe leaks.
• **Is a fault indicated?**
	Yes
	
	No
		▶
		
		▶
			ATTACH fuel fill cap only 1/8 turn so that cap initially clicks by sound or touch. REPLACE damaged carbon canister when necessary. For fuel tank concerns,
			
			   RECONNECT all components. If entering this Pinpoint Test Step because of Continuous Memory DTC P0455 or P 1455, GO to **HX61**. Otherwise, VERIFY a symptom no longer exists.
			GO to **HX41**.

FM0159601526220X

Fig. 260   Test HX: EVAP Monitor & System (Part 22 of 33). 1996 Except Probe

Test Step	Result	▶	Action to Take
HX41 EVAPORATIVE LEAK DETECTION USING ROTUNDA EVAPORATIVE EMISSION SYSTEM TESTER • Key off. • Remove the fuel fill cap at fuel tank. • Install the Rotunda Evaporative Emission System Tester (Rotunda catalog number 134 00056), including the compressed gas (nitrogen or argon) and the pressure regulator. NOTE: Tester kit contains all required adapters (schrader valve, fuel cap per vehicle application, etc.) • Disconnect and plug (cap) the fuel vapor hose from the Vapor Management Valve (VMV) at the engine intake manifold port (vacuum tree) on all vehicles (except on Taurus/Sable or Explorer). • The Canister Vent (CV) solenoid should be closed by accessing Output Test Mode with the Scan Tool or at the breakout box. • Select ALL OFF mode on Scan Tool. • Push start button on Scan Tool. **For Crown Victoria/Grand Marquis:** • Disconnect PCM. Inspect for damaged or pushed out pins, corrosion, loose wires, etc. Service as necessary. • Install breakout box, connect PCM to breakout box. • Connect a jumper between Test Pin 67 (CV SIG) and Test Pin 51 or 103 (PWR GND) at the breakout box. • Key on, engine off. • Pressurize the vehicle evaporative system at 14 in-H2O using the Evaporative Emission System Tester and following the instruction that come with the tester. • Observe the tester installation leak self-test for 2 minutes and then the vehicle evaporative system leak test. • **Is a system leak indicated by the tester red light on?**	Yes No	▶ ▶	ALL CW the two position control valve on the tester to provide a continuing flow of the gas to the closed evaporative system. MAINTAIN 14 in-H2O pressure on the system (monitor tester pressure gauges). GO to **HX43**. GO to **HX42**.

Fig. 260   Test HX: EVAP Monitor & System (Part 23 of 33). 1996 Except Probe

Test Step	Result	▶	Action to Take
HX42 MECHANICAL CHECK OF THE FUEL TANK PRESSURE SENSOR • Key on, engine off. • Continue to pressurize the vehicle evaporative system at 14 in-H2O using the Evaporative Emission System Tester. • Access FTP V (FTP) PID with the Scan Tool. NOTE: FTP sensor input with 14 in-H2O pressure on a closed evaporative system is 4.60 volts. • Observe the FTP V (FTP) PID at 14 in-H2O pressure on the system. • **Is the FTP V (FTP) PID reading 4.60 volts ± 0.18 volts (14 in-H2O ± 0.50 in-H2O)?**	Yes No	▶ ▶	Pressure in the evaporative system will discharge after a green (passed) light is on and the test is completed. GO to **HX46**. FTP sensor is mechanically damaged. REPLACE FTP sensor. REMOVE tester, inert gas source, breakout box with jumper and plug (cap) in the fuel vapor hose. ATTACH fuel fill cap only 1/8 turn so that cap initially clicks by sound or touch. RECONNECT PCM and all components. If entering this Pinpoint Test Step because of Continuous Memory DTC P0455 or P1455, GO to **HX61**. Otherwise, VERIFY a symptom no longer exists.
HX43 MECHANICAL CHECK OF THE CANISTER VENT SOLENOID • Key on, engine off. • Continue to pressurize the vehicle evaporative system 14 in-H2O using the Evaporative Emission System Tester. • Clamp (pinched closed) the purge air inlet tube/hose to atmosphere from the CV solenoid port. • If the tube/hose is not flexible enough to prevent damage by clamping, discontinue pressurizing the system. • Remove tube/hose to atmosphere from the CV solenoid and cap the open port on the CV solenoid. • Re-pressurize the system at 14 in-H2O. • **Does the evaporative system again indicate a leak by the tester red light on?**	Yes No	▶ ▶	GO to **HX45**. GO to **HX44**.

Fig. 260   Test HX: EVAP Monitor & System (Part 24 of 33). 1996 Except Probe

Test Step	Result	▶	Action to Take
HX44 CHECK FOR VPWR TO CV SOLENOID • Key off. • Breakout box installed. NOTE: If Output Test Mode commanded the CV solenoid closed, disconnect PCM. Inspect for damaged or pushed out pins, corrosion, loose wires, etc. Service as necessary. • PCM connected to breakout box. • Disconnect CV solenoid vehicle harness connector. • Key on, engine off. • Measure the voltage between VPWR at the CV solenoid vehicle harness connector and battery ground. • **Is the voltage greater than 10.5 volts?**	Yes No	▶ ▶	CV solenoid is mechanically stuck open. REPLACE CV solenoid. REMOVE tester, gas source, breakout box and plug (cap) from fuel vapor hose. ATTACH fuel fill cap only 1/8 turn so that cap initially clicks by sound or touch. RECONNECT PCM and all components. If entering this Pinpoint Test Step because of Continuous Memory DTC P0455 or P1455, GO to **HX61**. Otherwise, VERIFY a symptom no longer exists. SERVICE open in VPWR circuit. REMOVE breakout box. RECONNECT all components. If entering this Pinpoint Test Step because of Continuous Memory DTC P0455 or P1455, GO to **HX61**. Otherwise, VERIFY a symptom no longer exists.

Fig. 260   Test HX: EVAP Monitor & System (Part 25 of 33). 1996 Except Probe

Test Step	Result	▶	Action to Take
HX45 CHECK FOR EVAPORATIVE LEAKS WITH THE ULTRA-SONIC LEAK DETECTOR • Key on, engine off. • The fuel vapor hose from the VMV at the engine intake manifold (vacuum tree) is still plugged (capped) on all vehicles (except on the Taurus/Sable or Explorer). • CV solenoid still closed. • Evaporative Emission System Tester still pressurizing the vehicle evaporative system. • Remove the ultra-sonic detector provided with the Rotunda Evaporative Emission System Tester. • Place the earphones from the detector over your ears and adjust the audio dial on the detector. • Closely pass the probe of the ultra-sonic detector over the fuel vapor hoses and connections from the fuel tank to the carbon canister and the VMV, from the carbon canister to the CV solenoid and from the VMV to the engine intake manifold. • Check for audible sound changes (noticeably quiet to louder pitch). • **Is a sudden audible change indicated?**	Yes No	▶ ▶	ISOLATE the pressure leak in the evaporative emission system. REPLACE damaged tubes/hoses with cracks, splits or holes. RECONNECT loose tubes/hoses. **For VMV housing leaks:** GO to **HX49**. For fuel tank, fuel vapor control valve and fuel vapor valve leaks, REMOVE the tester, gas source, breakout box and the plug (cap) in fuel vapor hose at the engine intake manifold. ATTACH fuel fill cap only 1/8 turn so that cap initially clicks by sound or touch. RECONNECT PCM and fuel vapor hose at the engine intake manifold. If entering this Pinpoint Test Step because of Continuous Memory DTC P0455 or P1455, GO to **HX61**. Otherwise, VERIFY a symptom no longer exists. KEEP the Evaporative Emission System Tester hooked up. RELEASE pressure on evaporative system by closing the regulator valve at the gas source. GO to **HX46**.

Fig. 260   Test HX: EVAP Monitor & System (Part 26 of 33). 1996 Except Probe

Test Step	Result	▶	Action to Take
HX46 CHECK FOR FUEL VAPOR HOSE RESTRICTIONS BETWEEN VAPOR MANAGEMENT VALVE, FUEL TANK AND CARBON CANISTER			
• Key on, engine off. • The fuel vapor hose from the VMV at the engine intake manifold (vacuum tree) is still plugged (capped) on all vehicles (except Taurus / Sable or Explorer). • CV solenoid still closed. • Remove and plug the fuel vapor hose to carbon canister at the VMV. • Reinitiate pressurizing the vehicle evaporative system using the Rotunda Evaporative Emission System Tester. Refer to Pinpoint Test Step **HX41** for pressurizing instructions. • When the pressure on the evaporative system is stabilized at 14 in-H2O, record the reading. • Remove the plug at the fuel vapor hose to carbon canister at the VMV. • Observe teh pressure gauges on the tester. • **Does the pressure immediately drop?**	Yes	▶	REMOVE tester, gas source, jumper at the breakout box and all plugs / caps in fuel vapor / vacuum hoses. ATTACH fuel fill cap only 1 / 8 turn so that cap initially clicks by sound or touch. GO to **HX47**.
	No	▶	ISOLATE blockages, bends or kinks in fuel vapor tubes / hoses between the fuel tank, the VMV and the carbon canister. Straighten kinks or bends in fuel vapor tubes / hoses. For blockages, REMOVE tester, gas source, breakout box and all plugs / caps in fuel vapor / vacuum hoses. ATTACH fuel fill cap only 1 / 8 turn so that cap initially clicks by sound or touch. RECONNECT PCM and all fuel vapor / vacuum hoses. If entering this Pinpoint Test Step because of Continuous Memory DTC P0455 or P 1455, GO to **HX61**. Otherwise, VERIFY a symptom no longer exists.

FM015960152627OX

Fig. 260   Test HX: EVAP Monitor & System (Part 27 of 33). 1996 Except Probe

Test Step	Result	▶	Action to Take
HX47 CHECK FOR INTAKE MANIFOLD VACUUM TO VMV: BOTH INPUT PORT VACUUM HOSE AND FUEL VAPOR HOSE			
• Key off. • Vapor Management Valve (VMV) electrically connected. • Disconnect both the input port vacuum and fuel vapor hoses from the VMV at the engine intake manifold ports (all vehicles). • Cut two small pieces of known vacuum hose and attach one end of each hose to an open vacuum port at the engine intake manifold. • Start engine. • Place thumb at end of hose and then the other attached known section of hose. • **Is vacuum present at both open hose ends?**	Yes	▶	REMOVE both small pieces of vacuum hose at the engine intake manifold vacuum ports. LEAVE the input port vacuum and fuel vapor hoses to engine intake manifold disconnected. GO to **HX48**.
	No	▶	REMOVE both small pieces of vacuum hose at the engine intake manifold vacuum and all plugs / caps in fuel vapor / vacuum hoses. RECONNECT all components. ISOLATE causes of missing intake manifold vacuum. If entering this Pinpoint Test Step because of Continuous Memory DTC P0455 or P 1455, GO to **HX61**. Otherwise, VERIFY a symptom no longer exists.

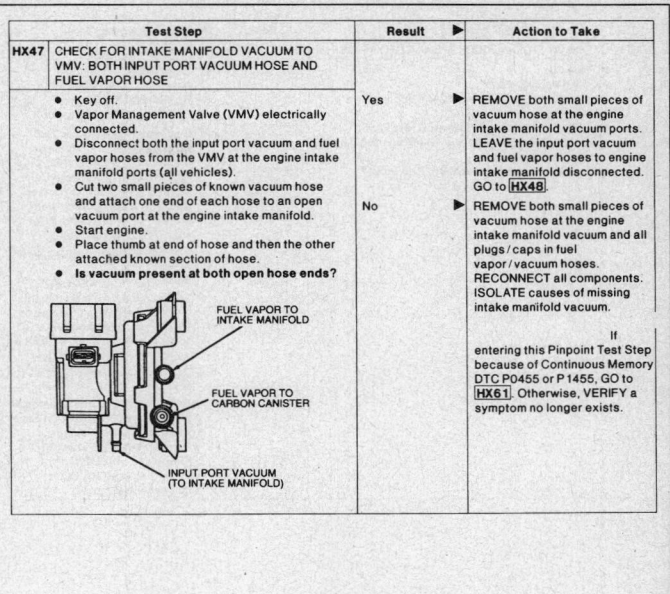

FUEL VAPOR TO INTAKE MANIFOLD

FUEL VAPOR TO CARBON CANISTER

INPUT PORT VACUUM (TO INTAKE MANIFOLD)

FM015960152628OX

Fig. 260   Test HX: EVAP Monitor & System (Part 28 of 33). 1996 Except Probe

Test Step	Result	▶	Action to Take
HX48 CHECK FOR INPUT PORT VACUUM HOSE AND FUEL VAPOR HOSE RESTRICTIONS BETEEN VAPOR MANAGEMENT VALVE AND ENGINE INTAKE MANIFOLD			
• Key off. • Fuel vapor hose form VMV to the carbon canister at the VMV disconnected. • Disconnect input port vacuum hose and fuel vapor hose to the engine intake manifold at the VMV (other all of hoses already disconnected). • Breakout box installed. • Install a hand vacuum pump to one end of each disconnected hose from the VMV to the engine intake manifold. • Apply 16 in-Hg (53 kPa) of vacuum with the vacuum pump. • Observe the vacuum reading for 30 seconds. • **Does the vacuum bleed off immediately?**	Yes	▶	REMOVE vacuum pump. RECONNECT all hoses between VMV and engine intake manifold. LEAVE breakout installed and fuel vapor hose from the VMV to the carbon canister at VMV disconnected. GO to **HX49**.
	No	▶	REMOVE vacuum pump. CHECK the suspect vacuum or fue vapor hose for kinks or blockages. SERVICE as necessary. REMOVE breakout box. RECONNECT all components. If entering this Pinpoint Test Step because of Continuous Memory DTC P0455 or P 1455, GO to **HX61**. Otherwise, VERIFY a symptom no longer exists.
HX49 CHECK FOR VMV HOUSING LEAKS			
• Key off. • Breakout box installed. • Make sure no jumper is attached between any pins on the breakout box. • VMV electrically connected. • Install a hand vacuum pump to the fuel vapor port to carbon canister on the VMV. • Apply 16 in-Hg (53 kPa) of vacuum with the vacuum pump. • **Does the VMV hold vacuum?**	Yes	▶	GO to **HX50**.
	No	▶	REMOVE vacuum pump and breakout box. REPLACE damaged VMV. RECONNECT all components. If entering this Pinpoint Test Step because of Continuous Memory DTC P0455 or P 1455, GO to **HX61**. Otherwise, VERIFY a symptom no longer exists.
HX50 CHECK FOR VPWR TO VMV			
• Key off. • Breakout box installed, PCM connected to breakout box. • Disconnect VMV vehicle harness connector. • Key on, engine off. • Measure the voltage between VPWR and VMV vehicle harness connector and battery ground. • **Is the voltage greater than 10.5 volts?**	Yes	▶	VPWR circuit is OK. GO to **HX51**.
	No	▶	SERVICE open in VPWR circuit. VERIFY that breakout box is properly connected to PCM and harness. RECONNECT VMV. If entering this Pinpoint Test Step because of Continuous Memory DTC P0455 or P 1455, GO to **HX61**. Otherwise, VERIFY a symptom no longer exists.

FM015960152629OX

Fig. 260   Test HX: EVAP Monitor & System (Part 29 of 33). 1996 Except Probe

Test Step	Result	▶	Action to Take
HX51 CHECK FOR MECHANICALLY STUCK CLOSED VMV			
• Key off. • Input port vacuum and fuel vapor hoses from the Vapor Management Valve (VMV) to the engine intake manifold connected. • Fuel vapor hose to the carbon canister at the VMV disconnected. • Install a vacuum gauge to the fuel vapor port to carbon canister at the VMV. Refer to the schematic in Pinpoint Test Step **HX47**. • Disconnect PCM. Inspect for damaged or pushed out pins, corrosion, loose wires, etc. Service as necessary. • Breakout box installed, PCM connected to breakout box. • Start engine. • Idle engine for 5 minutes. • Observe vacuum gauge. Reading should be near zero in-Hg. • Connect a jumper between Test Pin 56 (VMV SIG) and Test Pins 51 or 103 (PWR GND) at the breakout box while engine is still running. • Idle the engine for 5 more minutes. • Observe vacuum gauge. • **Does the vacuum reading on the vacuum gauge change from zero to engine manifold vacuum?**	Yes	▶	REMOVE vacuum gauge and jumper from breakout box. LEAVE breakout box installed. RECONNECT all vacuum and fuel vapor hoses. GO to **HX52**.
	No	▶	VMV is mechanically stuck closed. REPLACE damaged VMV. REMOVE vacuum gauge and breakout box. RECONNECT all components. If entering this Pinpoint Test Step because of Continuous Memory DTC P0455 or P 1455, GO to **HX61**. Otherwise, VERIFY a symptom no longer exists.
HX52 CHECK CONTINUITY OF CV SIG CIRCUIT			
• Key off. • Disconnect Canister Vent (CV) solenoid vehicle harness connector. • Breakout box installed. • Disconnected PCM. • Measure the resistance between Test Pin 67 (CV SIG) at the breakout box and CV SIG circuit at the CV solenoid vehicle harness connector. • **Is the resistance less than 5.0 ohms?**	Yes	▶	GO to **HX53**.
	No	▶	SERVICE open in the CV SIG harness. REMOVE breakout box. RECONNECT all components. If entering this Pinpoint Test Step because of Continuous Memory DTC P0455 or P 1455, GO to **HX61**. Otherwise, VERIFY a symptom no longer exists.

FM015960152630OX

Fig. 260   Test HX: EVAP Monitor & System (Part 30 of 33). 1996 Except Probe

Test Step	Result	▶	Action to Take
HX53 CHECK CV SIG CIRCUIT FOR SHORT TO POWER ● Key off. ● CV disconnected. ● Breakout box installed, PCM disconnected. ● Key on, engine off. ● Measure the voltage between Test Pin 67 (CV SIG) and Test Pins 51 and 103 (PWR GND) at the breakout box. ● **Is the voltage greater than 10.5 volts?**	Yes No	▶ ▶	SERVICE harness short between CV SIG and VPWR. REMOVE breakout box. RECONNECT all components. If entering this Pinpoint Test Step because of Continuous Memory DTC P0455 or P1455, GO to **HX61**. Otherwise, VERIFY a symptom no longer exists. CV SIG may be open or shorted to VPWR in the PCM. REMOVE breakout box. **For Continuous Memory DTC P0455:** REPLACE PCM. RECONNECT all components. If entering this Pinpoint Test Step because of a Continuous Memory DTC, GO to **HX61**. Otherwise, VERIFY a symptom no longer exists. **For Continuous Memory DTC P1455:** RECONNECT all components. If entering this Pinpoint Test Step because of a Continuous Memory DTC, GO to **HX61**. Otherwise, RETURN to to diagnose any other driveability symptom.

FM0159601526310X

Fig. 260   Test HX: EVAP Monitor & System (Part 31 of 33). 1996 Except Probe

Test Step	Result	▶	Action to Take
HX56 CONTINUOUS MEMORY DTC P1450 OR P1452: CHECK FOR FILTER CONTAMINATION OR DAMAGE IN THE VMV Continuous Memory Diagnostic Trouble Code (DTC) P1450 or P1452 indicates that Self-Test has detected the inability of the Evaporative Emission Control System to bleed up fuel tank vacuum. The only difference between the DTC P1450 and P1452 is that the P1450 is a MIL DTC. Possible causes: — Contaminated control vacuum solenoid filter on the Vapor Management Valve (VMV). — Damaged control vacuum solenoid on the VMV. — VREF circuit open between Fuel Tank Pressure (FTP) sensor and PCM. — Damaged FTP sensor. ● Key off. ● Remove vacuum line from the input vacuum port to intake manifold on the control vacuum solenoid part of the VMV. ● Apply 10 in-Hg of vacuum with a hand held vacuum pump to the open port on the solenoid part of the VMV. ● **Does the solenoid on the VMV hold vacuum or slowly release vacuum to atmosphere?**	Yes No	▶ ▶	SERVICE VMV. If unable to SERVICE filter, REPLACE damaged VMV. REMOVE vacuum pump. RECONNECT all components. If entering this Pinpoint Test Step because of Continuous Memory DTC P1450 or P1452, GO to **HX61**. Otherwise, VERIFY a symptom no longer exists. REMOVE vacuum pump. RECONNECT all components. GO to **HX57**.
HX57 VISUAL CHECK OF VREF CONNECTIONS AT FUEL TANK PRESSURE SENSOR AND PCM ● Key off. ● Observe the VREF wire at both the Fuel Tank Pressure (FTP) sensor and PCM connectors. ● **Does the VREF wire appear to be connected at both the FTP sensor and the PCM?**	Yes No	▶ ▶	GO to **HX58**. SERVICE as necessary. If entering this Pinpoint Test Step because of Continuous Memory DTC P1450 or P1452, GO to **HX61**. Otherwise, VERIFY a symptom no longer exists.

FM0159601526320X

Fig. 260   Test HX: EVAP Monitor & System (Part 32 of 33). 1996 Except Probe

Test Step	Result	▶	Action to Take
HX58 CHECK CONTINUITY OF VREF CIRCUIT AT THE FTP SENSOR ● Key off. ● Disconnect FTP sensor vehicle harness connector. ● Disconnect PCM. Inspect for damaged or pushed out wires, corrosion, loose wires, etc. Service as necessary. ● Install breakout box, leave PCM disconnected. ● Measure the resistance between Test Pin 90 (VREF) at the breakout box and VREF circuit at the FTP sensor vehicle harness connector. ● **Is the resistance less than 5.0 ohms?**	Yes No	▶ ▶	VREF is open in the FTP sensor. REPLACE damaged FTP sensor REMOVE breakout box. RECONNECT all components. If entering this Pinpoint Test Step because of Continuous Memory DTC P1450 or P1452, GO to **HX61**. Otherwise, VERIFY a symptom no longer exists. SERVICE open in the VREF harness to the FTP sensor. REMOVE breakout box. RECONNECT all components. If entering this Pinpoint Test Step because of Continuous Memory DTC P1450 or P1452, GO to **HX61**. Otherwise, VERIFY a symptom no longer exists.
HX61 VERIFY AN EVAPORATIVE EMISSION SYSTEM REPAIR ● Key off. ● Connect Scan Tool to DLC. ● Complete a PCM Reset to clear DTCs (refer to Powertrain Control Module (PCM) Reset). After completing the PCM Reset, leave the ignition key on. NOTE: If the ignition key is turned off after the PCM Reset, an Evaporative Emission System soak (none operating vehicle) time of several hours will be required before the Evaporative Emission Monitor test will be complete. If the key is left on after the PCM Reset, this soak time will not be required to complete the Evaporative Emission Monitor test. ● Without turning the ignition key off, start the engine. ● Do the OBD II Drive Cycle (refer to Drive Cycles). ● **Does the OBD II Drive Cycle complete?**	Yes No	▶ ▶	GO to Section 5A, Diagnostic Subroutine Step **DSR1** to RERUN Quick Test. RERUN this Pinpoint Test Step. For additional information on Evaporative Emission Monitor entry conditions, etc., REFER to Drive Cycles.

TA24266A

FM0159601526330X

Fig. 260   Test HX: EVAP Monitor & System (Part 33 of 33). 1996 Except Probe

Note

You should enter this Pinpoint Test only when directed here.

Remember

This Pinpoint Test is intended to diagnose the following:
● Crankshaft Position (CKP) Sensor
● CKP Harness
● CKP Connector
● Spark Plug Wires
● Powertrain Control Module (PCM)

Pinpoint Test Schematics

Escort/Tracer, 2.5L Contour/Mystique, Taurus/Sable, Taurus SHO, Mustang, Thunderbird/Cougar, Crown Victoria/Grand Marquis, Town Car, Mark VIII, 2.3L Ranger, 3.0L Ranger, 3.0L Aerostar, 3.8L Windstar, F Series

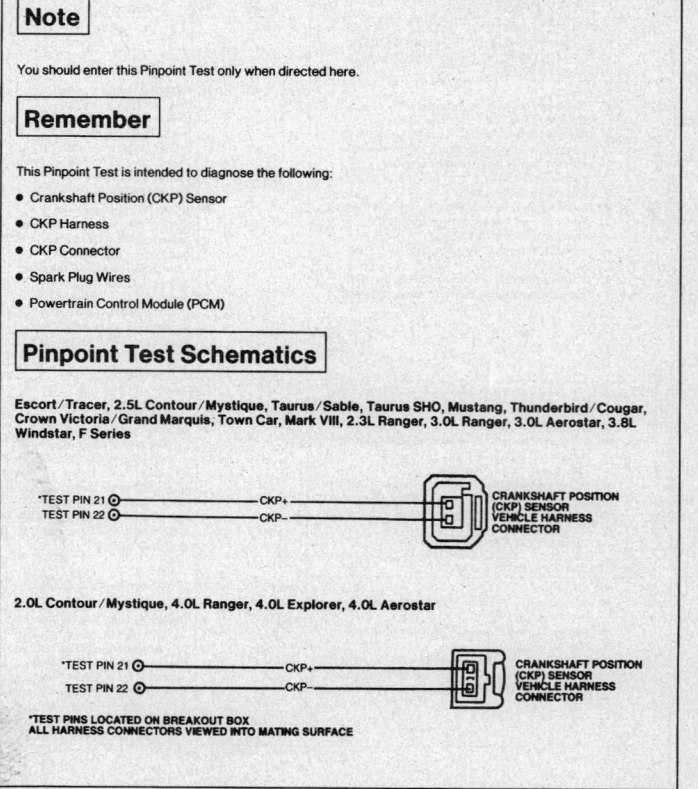

2.0L Contour/Mystique, 4.0L Ranger, 4.0L Explorer, 4.0L Aerostar

*TEST PINS LOCATED ON BREAKOUT BOX
ALL HARNESS CONNECTORS VIEWED INTO MATING SURFACE

FM0159601530010X

Fig. 261   Test JD: Integrated Ignition/No Spark (Part 1 of 8). 1996

Test Step	Result	▶	Action to Take
JD1 CHECK PLUGS AND WIRES • Perform this check on all vehicles except coil on plug applications (3.4L Taurus SHO). • Check spark plug wires for insulation damage, looseness, shorting or other damage. • Remove and check spark plugs for damage, wear, carbon deposits and proper plug gap. • Examine all wiring harnesses and connectors for damaged, burned or overheated insulation, damaged pins and loose or broken conditions. • Check sensor shield connector. • **Are spark plugs and wires OK?**	Yes No	▶ ▶	REINSTALL plugs and wires. GO to **JD4**. SERVICE or REPLACE damaged component. REMOVE all test equipment. RECONNECT all components. Complete PCM reset to clear DTCs Powertrain Control Module (PCM) Reset. RERUN Quick Test.
JD4 CHECK CKP+ BIAS AT PCM • Key off. • Disconnect Scan Tool from DLC. • Disconnect PCM. Inspect for damaged or pushed out pins, corrosion, loose wires, etc. Service as necessary. • Install breakout box and connect PCM. • DVOM on 40 volt DC scale. • Key on, engine off. • When making a voltage check, a ground reading means any value within a range of zero to 1 volt. Also, VPWR readings mean any value within a range of B+ to 2 volts less than B+. • When making a voltage check and a reference to ground is made, use the negative battery lead. B+ means the battery positive cable at the battery. • Do not use an incandescent lamp to check CKP+ or CKP-. The lamp will prevent the circuit from operating. • Measure voltage between test Pin 21 (CKP+) at the breakout box and (B-). • **Is DC voltage between 1.0 and 2.0 volts?**	Yes No	▶ ▶	GO to **JD10**. Bias fault. GO to **JD5**.
JD5 CHECK CKP+BIAS FAULT • Key off. • Disconnect CKP sensor from vehicle harness connector. • DVOM on 40 volt DC scale. • Key on, engine off. • Measure voltage between test Pin 21 (CKP+) at the breakout box and (B-). • **Is DC voltage greater than 1.0 volt but less than 2.0 volts?**	Yes No	▶ ▶	GO to **JD6**. Bias fault. GO to **JD18**.

FM015960153020X

Fig. 261   Test JD: Integrated Ignition/No Spark (Part 2 of 8). 1996

Test Step	Result	▶	Action to Take
JD6 CHECK CKP- SENSOR FOR BIAS FAULT • Key off. • Disconnect CKP sensor from vehicle harness connector. • DVOM on 40 volt DC scale. • Key on, engine off. • Measure voltage between test Pin 22 (CKP-) at the breakout box and (B-). • **Is DC voltage between -1.0 and 2.0 volts?**	Yes No	▶ ▶	Short to ground. REPLACE CKP sensor. REMOVE all test equipment. RECONNECT all components. Complete PCM reset to clear DTCs (REFER to Powertrain Control Module (PCM) Reset). RERUN Quick Test. Bias fault. GO to **JD7**.
JD7 DETERMINE IF BIAS HIGH OR BIAS LOW FAULT • Key off. • **Was bias voltage reading in JD6 less than 1.0 volt?**	Yes No	▶ ▶	Bias low fault. GO to **JD8**. Bias high fault. GO to **JD9**.
JD8 CHECK CKP SENSOR FOR SHORT TO GROUND FOR BIAS LOW FAULT • Key off. • Disconnect CKP sensor from vehicle harness connector. • Disconnect PCM from breakout box. • DVOM on 20K ohm scale. • When making measurements on a wiring harness, both a visual inspection and continuity test must be peformed. • Measure resistance between test Pin 22 (CKP-) at the breakout box and (B-). • **Is the resistance greater than 10K ohms?**	Yes No	▶ ▶	CKP- is shorted low. REPLACE PCM. REMOVE all test equipment. Complete PCM reset to clear DTCs (REFER to Powertrain Control Module (PCM) Reset). RERUN Quick Test. CKP- is shorted low. CHECK connectors, SERVICE or REPLACE harness. REMOVE all test equipment. RECONNECT all components. Complete PCM reset to clear DTCs (REFER to Powertrain Control Module (PCM) Reset). RERUN Quick Test.

FM015960153030X

Fig. 261   Test JD: Integrated Ignition/No Spark (Part 3 of 8). 1996

Test Step	Result	▶	Action to Take
JD9 CHECK CKP- SENSOR FOR SHORTED HIGH FOR BIAS HIGH FAULT • Key off. • Disconnect CKP sensor from vehicle harness connector. • Disconnect PCM from breakout box. • DVOM on 40 volt DC scale. • Key on, engine off. • Measure voltage between test Pin 22 (CKP-) at the breakout box and (B-). • **Is DC voltage less than 0.5 volts?**	Yes No	▶ ▶	CKP- shorted high. REPLACE PCM. REMOVE all test equipment. RECONNECT all components. Complete PCM reset to clear DTCs (REFER to Powertrain Control Module (PCM) Reset). RERUN Quick Test. CKP- is shorted high. CHECK connectors. SERVICE or REPLACE harness. REMOVE all test equipment. RECONNECT all components. Complete PCM reset to clear DTCs (REFER to Powertrain Control Module (PCM) Reset). RERUN Quick Test.
JD10 CHECK CKP SENSOR AMPLITUDE AT PCM • Key off. • DVOM on 40 volt AC scale. • Crank engine and measure voltage between test Pin 21 (CKP+) and test Pin 22 (CKP-) at breakout box. • **Is settled AC voltage reading greater than 0.4 volt?**	Yes No	▶ ▶	For 4 cylinder applications (except 2.3L Ranger): GO to **JE1** For 2.3L Ranger: GO to **JE20** For 6 cylinder applications: GO to **JE60** For 8 cylinder applications (except 3.4L Taurus SHO): GO to **JE90** For 3.4L Taurus SHO: GO to **JF1** Amplitude fault. GO to **JD11**.
JD11 CHECK CKP AMPLITUDE AT PCM FOR AMPLITUDE FAULT • Key off. • Disconnect PCM from breakout box. • DVOM on 40 volt AC scale. • Crank engine and measure voltage between test Pin 21 (CKP+) and test Pin 22 (CKP-) at breakout box. • **Is settled AC voltage reading greater than 0.4 volt?**	Yes No	▶ ▶	CKP is shorted in PCM. REPLACE PCM. REMOVE all test equipment. RECONNECT all components. Complete PCM reset to clear DTCs (REFER to Powertrain Control Module (PCM) Reset). RERUN Quick Test. GO to **JD12**.

FM015960153040X

Fig. 261   Test JD: Integrated Ignition/No Spark (Part 4 of 8). 1996

Test Step	Result	▶	Action to Take
JD12 CHECK CIRCUIT RESISTANCE FOR AMPLITUDE FAULT • Key off. • DVOM on 20K ohm scale. • When making measurements on a wiring harness, both a visual inspection and continuity test must be peformed. • Measure resistance between test Pin 22 (CKP-) and test Pin 21 (CKP+) at breakout box. • **Is resistance between 300 and 800 ohms?**	Yes No	▶ ▶	GO to **JD16**. CKP- circuit resistance fault. GO to **JD13**.
JD13 DETERMINE IF RESISTANCE HIGH OR RESISTANCE LOW FAULT • **Was the resistance from JD12 less than 300 ohms?**	Yes No	▶ ▶	Low resistance fault. GO to **JD17**. High resistance fault. GO to **JD14**.

JD14 CHECK FOR CKP+ HARNESS OPEN—RESISTANCE HIGH FAULT
• Key off.
• Install EI diagnostic harness to breakout box and the CKP Sensor and vehicle harness (Rotunda 007-00059 or equivalent).
• Connect EI diagnostic harness negative lead to battery, leave positive lead disconnected.
• **For 8 Cylinder Applications:**
  Use EI (High Data Rate) 8 Overlay.
  Set EI diagnostic harness box type switch to "8" cylinder position.
• **For 6 Cylinder Applications:**
  Use EI (High Data Rate) 6 Overlay.
  Set EI diagnostic harness box type switch to "4/6" cylinder position.
• **For 2.3L Ranger:**
  Use EI (High Data Rate) 2.3L Dual Plug Overlay.
  Set EI diagnostic harness box type switch to "4/6" cylinder position.
• **For 4 Cylinder Applications:**
  Use EI (High Data Rate) 4 Overlay. Set EI diagnostic harness box type switch to "4/6" cylinder position.
• DVOM on 20K ohm scale.
• Measure resistance between J31 (CKP+ S) at the EI breakout box and test Pin 21 (CKP+) at the PCM breakout box.
• **Is resistance less than 1050 ohms?**
	Yes
	No
		▶
		▶
			GO to **JD15**.
			CKP+ open. CHECK connectors, SERVICE or REPLACE harness. REMOVE all test equipment. RECONNECT all components. Complete PCM reset to clear DTCs (REFER to Powertrain Control Module (PCM) Reset). RERUN Quick Test.

FM015960153050X

Fig. 261   Test JD: Integrated Ignition/No Spark (Part 5 of 8). 1996

Test Step	Result	▶	Action to Take
JD15 CHECK FOR CKP HARNESS OPEN FOR RESISTANCE HIGH FAULT			
• Key off. • DVOM on 20K ohm scale. • Measure resistance between J32 (CKP- S) at the EI breakout box and test Pin 22 (CKP-) at PCM breakout box. • Is resistance less than 1050 ohms?	Yes	▶	High resistance. REPLACE CKP sensor. REMOVE all test equipment. RECONNECT all components. Complete PCM reset to clear DTCs (REFER to Powertrain Control Module (PCM) Reset). RERUN Quick Test.
	No	▶	CKP- open. CHECK connectors. SERVICE or REPLACE harness. REMOVE all test equipment. RECONNECT all components. Complete PCM reset to clear DTCs (REFER to Powertrain Control Module (PCM) Reset). RERUN Quick Test.
JD16 CHECK CKP SENSOR AND TRIGGER WHEEL			
• Key off. • Check trigger wheel and CKP sensor for damage. • Is CKP sensor and trigger data wheel OK?	Yes	▶	No output from sensor. REPLACE CKP sensor. REMOVE all test equipment. RECONNECT all components. Complete PCM reset to clear DTCs (REFER to Powertrain Control Module (PCM) Reset). RERUN Quick Test.
	No	▶	SERVICE or REPLACE damaged parts. REMOVE all test equipment. RECONNECT all components. Complete PCM reset to clear DTCs (REFER to Powertrain Control Module (PCM) Reset). RERUN Quick Test.

FM0159601530060X

Fig. 261 Test JD: Integrated Ignition/No Spark (Part 6 of 8). 1996

Test Step	Result	▶	Action to Take
JD17 CHECK FOR CKP+ SHORTED TO CKP- FOR RESISTANCE LOW FAULT			
• Key off. • Disconnect CKP sensor from vehicle harness connector. • DVOM on 20K ohm scale. • Measure resistance between test Pin 21 (CKP+) and test Pin 22 (CKP-) at breakout box. • Is resistance greater than 1000 ohms?	Yes	▶	Shorted sensor windings. REPLACE CKP sensor. REMOVE all test equipment. RECONNECT all components. Complete PCM reset to clear DTCs (REFER to Powertrain Control Module (PCM) Reset). RERUN Quick Test.
	No	▶	CKP+ shorted to CKP- in harness. CHECK connectors. SERVICE or REPLACE harness. REMOVE all test equipment. RECONNECT all components. Complete PCM reset to clear DTCs (REFER to Powertrain Control Module (PCM) Reset). RERUN Quick Test.
JD18 DETERMINE IF BIAS VOLTAGE HIGH OR BIAS VOLTAGE LOW FAULT			
• **Was bias voltage reading in JD5 less than 1.0 volt?**	Yes	▶	Low bias voltage fault. GO to JD19.
	No	▶	High bias voltage fault. GO to JD20.
JD19 CHECK CKP+ HARNESS FOR SHORT TO GROUND FOR LOW BIAS FAULT			
• Key off. • Disconnect CKP sensor from vehicle harness connector. • Disconnect PCM from breakout box. • DVOM on 20K ohm scale. • When making measurements on a wiring harness, both a visual inspection and continuity test must be performed. • Measure resistance between test Pin 21 (CKP+) at the PCM breakout box and (B-). • Is resistance greater than 10K ohms?	Yes	▶	CKP+ is shorted low. REPLACE PCM. REMOVE all test equipment. RECONNECT all components. Complete PCM reset to clear DTCs (REFER to Powertrain Control Module (PCM) Reset). RERUN Quick Test.
	No	▶	CKP+ is shorted low. CHECK connectors, SERVICE or REPLACE harness. REMOVE all test equipment. RECONNECT all components. Complete PCM reset to clear DTCs (REFER to Powertrain Control Module (PCM) Reset). RERUN Quick Test.

FM0159601530070X

Fig. 261 Test JD: Integrated Ignition/No Spark (Part 7 of 8). 1996

Test Step	Result	▶	Action to Take
JD20 CHECK CKP+ HARNESS FOR SHORTED HIGH FOR BIAS VOLTAGE HIGH FAULT			
• Key off. • Disconnect CKP sensor from vehicle harness connector. • Disconnect PCM from breakout box. • DVOM on 40 volt DC scale. • Key on, engine off. • Measure voltage between test Pin 21 (CKP+) at the PCM breakout box and (B-). • Is DC voltage less than 0.5 volt?	Yes	▶	CKP+ shorted high. REPLACE PCM. REMOVE all test equipment. RECONNECT all components. Complete PCM reset to clear DTCs (REFER to Powertrain Control Module (PCM) Reset). RERUN Quick Test.
	No	▶	CKP+ is shorted high. CHECK connectors, SERVICE or REPLACE harness. REMOVE all test equipment. RECONNECT all components. Complete PCM reset to clear DTCs (REFER to Powertrain Control Module (PCM) Reset). RERUN Quick Test.

FM0159601530080X

Fig. 261 Test JD: Integrated Ignition/No Spark (Part 8 of 8). 1996

Note

You should enter this Pinpoint Test only when directed here.

Remember

This Pinpoint Test is intended to diagnose the following:

• Ignition Coil Packs
• Ignition Coil Harness
• Vehicle Power Circuit to Coil Packs
• Powertrain Control Module (PCM)

Caution

Fouled plugs or a damaged ignition may cause high catalyst temperatures. Check components next to the catalyst and muffler for heat damage.

Test Step	Result	▶	Action to Take
JE1 CHECK FOR SPARK DURING CRANK			
Diagnostic Trouble Code (DTC) P0350 is an ignition coil primary circuit malfunction. DTCs P0351 and P0352 are ignition coil 1 and 2 primary circuit malfunctions. • Using a Neon Bulb Spark Tester (Special Service Tool D89P-6666-A) or Air Gap Spark Tester (D81P-6666-A), check for spark at all spark plug wires while cranking. • When using the spark plug firing indicator, place the grooved end as close as possible to the plug boot. Very weak or no flashing may be caused by a fouled plug. • Was spark consistent on ALL spark plug wires (one spark per crankshaft revolution)?	Yes	▶	Ignition system is OK. REFER to Symptom Flowcharts.
	No	▶	Spark fault. GO to JE2.

FM0159601531010X

Fig. 262 Test JE: Integrated Ignition Coil 1, 2, 3 or 4 Failure (Part 1 of 37). 1996

Test Step		Result	▶	Action to Take
JE2	CHECK SPARK PLUGS AND WIRES			
	• Key off.	Yes	▶	REINSTALL plugs and wires. GO TO JE3.
	• Check spark plug wires for insulation damage, looseness, shorting or other damage.	No	▶	SERVICE or REPLACE damaged component. REMOVE all test equipment. RECONNECT all components. Complete PCM reset to clear DTCs (REFER to Powertrain Control Module (PCM) Reset). RERUN Quick Test.
	• Remove and check right spark plugs for damage, wear, carbon deposits and proper plug gap.			
	• Examine all wiring harnesses and connectors for damaged, burned or overheated insulation, damaged pins, and loose or broken conditions.			
	• **Are spark plugs and wires OK?**			
JE3	CHECK FOR COIL PWR AT COIL			
	WARNING: NEVER CONNECT PCM TO EEC BREAKOUT BOX WHEN PERFORMING EI DIAGNOSTICS.	Yes	▶	GO to JE4.
	• Key off.	No	▶	COIL PWR is open. CHECK connectors, SERVICE or REPLACE harness. REMOVE all test equipment. RECONNECT all components. Complete PCM reset to clear DTCs (REFER to Powertrain Control Module (PCM) Reset). RERUN Quick Test.
	• Install EI (High Data Rate) diagnostic harness to breakout box.			
	• Connect negative lead to battery.			
	• Set EI diagnostic harness box type switch to "4/6 cylinder" position.			
	• Install right (blue) coil tee.			
	• Use EI (High Data Rate) 4 overlay.			
	• DVOM on 40 volt DC scale.			
	• Key on, engine off.			
	• When making voltage checks, a ground reading means any value within a range of zero to 1 volt. Also, VPWP or coil PWR readings mean any value within a range of B+ to 2 volts less than B+.			
	• Measure voltage between (+)J5 (COIL PWR) and (-)JJ7 (B-) at the EI breakout box.			
	• **Is DC voltage greater than 10.0 volts?**			
JE4	CHECK FOR C1 HIGH AT COIL PACK			
	• Key on, engine off.	Yes	▶	GO to JE5.
	• Measure voltage between (+)J3 (C1C) and (-)JJ7 (B-) at breakout box.	No	▶	C1 low fault. GO to JE12.
	• **Is DC voltage reading greater than 10.0 volts?**			
JE5	CHECK FOR C2 HIGH AT COIL PACK			
	• DVOM on 40 volt DC scale.	Yes	▶	GO to JE6.
	• Key on, engine off.	No	▶	C2 low fault. GO to JE14.
	• Measure voltage between (+)J6 (C2C) and (-)J7 (B-) at the EI breakout box.			
	• **Is DC voltage reading greater than 10.0 volts?**			

FM0159601531020X

Fig. 262 Test JE: Integrated Ignition Coil 1, 2, 3 or 4 Failure (Part 2 of 37). 1996

Test Step		Result	▶	Action to Take
JE6	FOR C1 HIGH AT PCM			
	• Key off.	Yes	▶	GO to JE7.
	• Disconnect PCM. Inspect for damaged or pushed out pins, corrosion, loose wires, etc. Service as necessary.	No	▶	C1 is open. CHECK connectors, SERVICE or REPLACE harness. REMOVE all test equipment. RECONNECT all components. Complete PCM reset to clear DTCs (REFER to Powertrain Control Module (PCM) Reset). RERUN Quick Test.
	• Install breakout box and connect PCM.			
	• DVOM on 40 volt DC scale.			
	• Key on, engine off.			
	• Measure voltage between Pin 26 (C1I) at the PCM breakout box and (-)J7 (B-) at the EI breakout box.			
	• **Is DC voltage reading greater than 10.0 volts?**			
JE7	CHECK FOR C2 HIGH AT ICM			
	• Key on, engine off.	Yes	▶	GO to JE8.
	• Measure voltage between Pin 52 at the PCM breakout box (C2I) and (-)J7 (B-) at the EI breakout box.	No	▶	C2 is open. CHECK connectors, SERVICE or REPLACE harness. REMOVE all test equipment. RECONNECT all components. Complete PCM reset to clear DTCs (REFER to Powertrain Control Module (PCM) Reset). RERUN Quick Test.
	• **Is DC voltage reading greater than 10.0 volts?**			
JE8	CHECK FOR C1 LOW AT COIL CONNECTOR			
	• Key off.	Yes	▶	GO to JE9.
	• Disconnect the coil from the coil tee, leave EI diagnostic harness coil tee connected to the vehicle harness coil connector.	No	▶	C1 high fault. GO to JE16.
	• DVOM on 40 volt DC scale.			
	• Key on, engine off.			
	• Measure voltage between (+)J3 (C1C) and (-)J7 (B-) at the EI breakout box.			
	• **Is DC voltage reading less than 0.5 volts?**			
JE9	FOR C2 LOW AT COIL CONNECTOR			
	• Key on, engine off.	Yes	▶	GO to JE10.
	• DVOM on 40 volt DC scale.	No	▶	C2 high fault. GO to JE17.
	• Measure voltage between (+)J6 (C2C) and (-)J7 (B-) at the EI breakout box.			
	• **Is DC voltage reading less than 0.5 volts?**			

FM0159601531030X

Fig. 262 Test JE: Integrated Ignition Coil 1, 2, 3 or 4 Failure (Part 3 of 37). 1996

Test Step		Result	▶	Action to Take
JE10	CHECK C1 AT COIL CONNECTOR WHILE CRANKING ENGINE			
	• Connect an incandescent test lamp between J1 (B+) and J3 (C1C).	Yes	▶	GO to JE11.
	• Connect positive lead of EI diagnostic harness to battery.	No	▶	C1 open. REPLACE PCM. REMOVE all test equipment. RECONNECT all components. Complete PCM reset to clear DTCs (REFER to Powertrain Control Module (PCM) Reset). RERUN Quick Test.
	• Crank engine.			
	• **Does lamp blink consistently and brightly (one blink per engine revolution)?**			
JE11	C2 AT COIL CONNECTOR WHILE CRANKING ENGINE			
	• Connect an incandescent test lamp between J1 (B+) and J6 (C2C).	Yes	▶	Input to coil pack is OK, but no high voltage output. REPLACE coil pack. REMOVE all test equipment. RECONNECT all components. Complete PCM reset to clear DTCs (REFER to Powertrain Control Module (PCM) Reset). RERUN Quick Test.
	• Crank engine.			
	• **Does lamp blink consistently and brightly (one blink per engine revolution)?**	No	▶	C2 open in PCM. REPLACE PCM. REMOVE all test equipment. RECONNECT all components. Complete PCM reset to clear DTCs (REFER to Powertrain Control Module (PCM) Reset). RERUN Quick Test.
JE12	CHECK FOR C1 SHORT LOW			
	• Key off.	Yes	▶	C1 open in coil. REPLACE right coil pack. REMOVE all test equipment. RECONNECT all components. Complete PCM reset to clear DTCs (REFER to Powertrain Control Module (PCM) Reset). RERUN Quick Test.
	• DVOM on 20K ohm scale.			
	• Disconnect coil from coil tee, leave EI diagnostic harness connected to vehicle harness coil connector.			
	• Measure resistance between J7 (B-) and J3 (RC1C) at the EI breakout box.			
	• **Is resistance reading greater than 2K ohms?**	No	▶	GO to JE13.

FM0159601531040X

Fig. 262 Test JE: Integrated Ignition Coil 1, 2, 3 or 4 Failure (Part 4 of 37). 1996

Test Step		Result	▶	Action to Take
JE13	CHECK FOR C1 SHORT LOW			
	• Key off.	Yes	▶	C1 is shorted low in PCM. REPLACE PCM. REMOVE all test equipment. RECONNECT all components. Complete PCM reset to clear DTCs (REFER to Powertrain Control Module (PCM) Reset). RERUN Quick Test.
	• Disconnect PCM from vehicle harness connector.			
	• DVOM on 20K ohm scale.			
	• Measure resistance between J7 (B-) and J3 (C1C) at the EI breakout box.			
	• **Is resistance reading greater than 10K ohms?**	No	▶	C1 is shorted low. CHECK connectors, SERVICE or REPLACE harness.
				NOTE: A C1 short to ground may have damaged the coil.
				REMOVE all test equipment. RECONNECT all components. Complete PCM reset to clear DTCs (REFER to Powertrain Control Module (PCM) Reset). RERUN Quick Test.
JE14	CHECK FOR C2 SHORT LOW			
	• Key off.	Yes	▶	C2 open in coil. REPLACE coil pack. REMOVE all test equipment. RECONNECT all components. Complete PCM reset to clear DTCs (REFER to Powertrain Control Module (PCM) Reset). RERUN Quick Test.
	• DVOM on 20K ohm scale.			
	• Disconnect coil from coil tee, leave EI diagnostic harness connected to vehicle harness coil connector.			
	• Measure resistance between J7 (B-) and J6 (C2C) at the EI breakout box.			
	• **Is resistance reading greater than 2K ohms?**	No	▶	GO to JE15.

FM0159601531050X

Fig. 262 Test JE: Integrated Ignition Coil 1, 2, 3 or 4 Failure (Part 5 of 37). 1996

Test Step	Result	▶	Action to Take
JE15 CHECK FOR C2 LOW			
• Key off. • Disconnect PCM from vehicle harness. • DVOM on 20K ohm scale. • Measure resistance between J6 (C2C) and J7 (B-) at the EI breakout box. • **Is resistance reading greater than 10K ohms?**	Yes	▶	C2 shorted low in PCM. REPLACE PCM. REMOVE all test equipment. RECONNECT all components. Complete PCM reset to clear DTCs (REFER to Powertrain Control Module (PCM) Reset). RERUN Quick Test.
	No	▶	C2 is shorted low. CHECK connector, SERVICE or REPLACE harness. NOTE: A C2 short to ground may have damaged the coil. REMOVE all test equipment. RECONNECT all components. Complete PCM reset to clear DTCs (REFER to Powertrain Control Module (PCM) Reset). RERUN Quick Test.
JE16 CHECK FOR C1 HIGH			
• Key off. • Disconnect PCM from vehicle harness connector. • DVOM on 40 volt DC scale. • Key on, engine off. • Measure voltage between (+)J3 (C1C) and (-)J7 (B-) at the EI breakout box. • **Is DC voltage reading less than 0.5 volts?**	Yes	▶	C1 is shorted high. REPLACE PCM. REMOVE all test equipment. RECONNECT all components. Complete PCM reset to clear DTCs (REFER to Powertrain Control Module (PCM) Reset). . RERUN Quick Test.
	No	▶	C1 shorted high. CHECK connector, SERVICE or REPLACE harness. REMOVE all test equipment. RECONNECT all components. Complete PCM reset to clear DTCs (REFER to Powertrain Control Module (PCM) Reset). RERUN Quick Test.

FM015960153106OX

Fig. 262   Test JE: Integrated Ignition Coil 1, 2, 3 or 4 Failure (Part 6 of 37). 1996

Test Step	Result	▶	Action to Take
JE17 CHECK FOR C2 HIGH			
• Key off. • Disconnect PCM from vehicle harness. • DVOM on 40 volt DC scale. • Key on, engine off. • Measure voltage between (+)J6 (C2C) and (-)J7 (B-) at the EI breakout box. • **Is DC voltage reading less than 0.5 volts?**	Yes	▶	C2 is shorted high. REPLACE PCM. REMOVE all test equipment. RECONNECT all components. Complete PCM reset to clear DTCs (REFER to Powertrain Control Module (PCM) Reset). RERUN Quick Test.
	No	▶	C2 is shorted high. CHECK connectors, SERVICE or REPLACE harness. REMOVE all test equipment. RECONNECT all components. Complete PCM reset to clear DTCs (REFER to Powertrain Control Module (PCM) Reset). RERUN Quick Test.
JE20 CHECK FOR SPARK DURING CRANK			
Diagnostic Trouble Code (DTC) P0350 is an ignition coil primary circuit malfunction. DTCs P0351, P0352, P0353 and P0354 are ignition coil 1, 2, 3 and 4 primary circuit malfunctions. • Using a Neon Bulb Spark Tester (Special Service Tool D89P-6666-A) or Air Gap Spark Tester (D81P-6666-A), check for spark at all spark plug wires while cranking. • When using the spark plug firing indicator, place the grooved end as close as possible to the plug boot. Very weak or no flashing may be caused by a fouled plug. • **Was spark consistent on all spark plug wires (one spark per crankshaft revolution?)**	Yes	▶	The ignition system is OK. REFER to Symptom Flowcharts.
	No	▶	Spark fault. GO to **JE21**.
JE21 CHECK FOR SPARK AT ALL RIGHT SPARK PLUG WIRES DURING CRANK			
• **Was spark consistent on all right spark plug wires (one spark per crankshaft revolution)?** NOTE: Check spark at spark plugs.	Yes	▶	GO to **JE22**.
	No	▶	GO to **JE38**.

FM015960153107OX

Fig. 262   Test JE: Integrated Ignition Coil 1, 2, 3 or 4 Failure (Part 7 of 37). 1996

Test Step	Result	▶	Action to Take
JE22 CHECK LEFT SPARK PLUGS AND WIRES			
• Key off. • Check left side spark plug wires for insulation damage, looseness, shorting or other damage. • Remove and check left side spark plugs for damage, wear, carbon deposits and proper plug gap. • Left plugs and wires are attached to the front coil pack. • Examine all wiring harnesses and connectors for damaged, burned or overheated insulation, damaged pins and loose or broken condition. • **Are spark plugs and wires OK?**	Yes	▶	REINSTALL plugs and wires. GO to **JE23**.
	No	▶	SERVICE or REPLACE damaged component. REMOVE all test equipment. RECONNECT all components. Complete PCM reset to clear DTCs (REFER to Powertrain Control Module (PCM) Reset). RERUN Quick Test.
JE23 CHECK FOR COIL PWR TO LEFT COIL FAULT			
WARNING: NEVER CONNECT PCM TO THE EEC BREAKOUT BOX WHEN PERFORMING EI DIAGNOSTICS. • Key off. • Install EI (High Data Rate) diagnostic harness to breakout box. • Install the left coil tee. The tee is yellow (left coil). • Connect EI diagnostic harness negative lead to battery. • Use 2.3L DP EI (High Data Rate) overlay. • Set EI harness type switch to "8 cylinder" position. • DVOM on 40 volt DC scale. • Key on, engine off. • When making voltage checks, a ground reading means any value within a range of zero to 1 volt. Also VPWR or COIL PWR readings mean any value that falls within a range of B+ to 2 volts less than B+. • Measure voltage between (+)J15 (COIL PWR L) and (-) J60 (B-) at the EI breakout box. • **Is DC voltage greater than 10.0 volts?**	Yes	▶	GO to **JE24**.
	No	▶	COIL PWR is open to left coil. CHECK connectors, SERVICE or REPLACE harness. REMOVE all test equipment. RECONNECT all components. Complete PCM reset to clear DTCs (REFER to Powertrain Control Module (PCM) Reset). RERUN Quick Test.
JE24 CHECK FOR C3 HIGH AT COIL PACK			
• Key on, engine off. • Measure voltage between (+)J30 (LC3C) and (-)J60 (B-) at the EI breakout box. • **Is DC voltage reading greater than 10.0 volts?**	Yes	▶	GO to **JE25**.
	No	▶	C3 low fault. GO to **JE32**.

FM015960153108OX

Fig. 262   Test JE: Integrated Ignition Coil 1, 2, 3 or 4 Failure (Part 8 of 37). 1996

Test Step	Result	▶	Action to Take
JE25 CHECK FOR C4 HIGH AT COIL PACK			
• Key on, engine off. • Measure voltage between (+)J28 (LC4C) and (-)J60 (B-) at the EI breakout box. • **Is DC voltage reading greater than 10.0 volts?**	Yes	▶	GO to **JE26**.
	No	▶	C4 low fault. GO to **JE34**.
JE26 CHECK FOR C3 HIGH AT PCM			
• Key off. • Disconnect PCM. Inspect for damaged or pushed out pins, corrosion, loose wires, etc. Service as necessary. • Install breakout box and connect PCM. • DVOM on 40 volt DC scale. • Key on, engine off. • Measure voltage between Pin 78 (LC3I) at the PCM breakout box and (-)J60 (B-) at the EI breakout box. • **Is DC voltage reading greater than 10.0 volts?**	Yes	▶	GO to **JE27**.
	No	▶	C3 is open. CHECK connectors, SERVICE or REPLACE harness. REMOVE all test equipment. RECONNECT all components. Complete PCM reset to clear DTCs (REFER to Powertrain Control Module (PCM) Reset). RERUN Quick Test.
JE27 CHECK FOR C4 HIGH AT PCM			
• Key on, engine off. • Measure voltage between Pin 104 (LC4I) at the PCM breakout box and (-)J60 (B-) at the EI breakout box. • **Is DC voltage reading greater than 10.0 volts?**	Yes	▶	GO to **JE28**.
	No	▶	C4 is open. CHECK connectors, SERVICE or REPLACE harness. REMOVE all test equipment. RECONNECT all components. Complete PCM reset to clear DTCs (REFER to Powertrain Control Module (PCM) Reset). RERUN Quick Test.
JE28 CHECK FOR C3 LOW AT COIL CONNECTOR			
• Key off. • Disconnect left coil pack from coil tee, leave EI diagnostic harness connected to vehicle harness left coil connector. • DVOM on 40 volt DC scale. • Key on, engine off. • Measure voltage between (+)J30 (LC3C) and (-)J60 (B-) at the EI breakout box. • **Is DC voltage reading less than 0.5 volt?**	Yes	▶	GO to **JE29**.
	No	▶	C3 high fault. GO to **JE36**.
JE29 CHECK FOR C4 LOW AT COIL CONNECTOR			
• Key on, engine off. • Measure voltage between (+)J28 (LC4C) and (-)J60 (B-) at the EI breakout box. • **Is DC voltage reading less than 0.5 volt?**	Yes	▶	GO to **JE30**.
	No	▶	C4 high fault. GO to **JE37**.

FM015960153109OX

Fig. 262   Test JE: Integrated Ignition Coil 1, 2, 3 or 4 Failure (Part 9 of 37). 1996

ELECTRONIC ENGINE CONTROL SYSTEM (EEC-V)

Test Step	Result	►	Action to Take
JE30 CHECK C3 AT COIL CONNECTOR WHILE CRANKING • Connect EI diagnostic harness positive lead to battery. • Connect an incandescent test lamp between J57 (B+) and J30 (LC3C). • Crank engine. • **Does lamp blink consistently and brightly (one blink per engine revolution?**	Yes No	► ►	GO to JE31. C3 open. REPLACE PCM. REMOVE all test equipment. RECONNECT all components. Complete PCM reset to clear DTCs (REFER to Powertrain Control Module (PCM) Reset). RERUN Quick Test.
JE31 CHECK C4 AT COIL CONNECTOR WHILE CRANKING • Connect an incandescent test lamp between J57 (B+) and J28 (LC4C). • Crank engine. • **Does lamp blink consistently and brightly (one blink per engine revolution)?**	Yes No	► ►	Input to coil pack is OK, but no high voltage output. REPLACE left coil pack. REMOVE all test equipment. RECONNECT all components. Complete PCM reset to clear DTCs (REFER to Powertrain Control Module (PCM) Reset). RERUN Quick Test. C4 open in PCM. REPLACE PCM. REMOVE all test equipment. RECONNECT all components. Complete PCM reset to clear DTCs (REFER to Powertrain Control Module (PCM) Reset). RERUN Quick Test.
JE32 CHECK FOR C3 SHORT LOW • Key off. • DVOM on 20K ohm scale. • Disconnect coil from coil tee, leave EI diagnostic harness connected to vehicle harness coil connector. • Measure resistance between J60 (B-) and J30 (C3C) at the EI breakout box. • **Is resistance reading less than 2K ohms?**	Yes No	► ►	GO to JE33. C3 open in coil. REPLACE Left Coil Pack. REMOVE all test equipment. RECONNECT all components. Complete PCM reset to clear DTCs (REFER to Powertrain Control Module (PCM) Reset). RERUN Quick Test.

Fig. 262 Test JE: Integrated Ignition Coil 1, 2, 3 or 4 Failure (Part 10 of 37). 1996

Test Step	Result	►	Action to Take
JE33 CHECK FOR C3 SHORT LOW • Key off. • Disconnect PCM from vehicle harness. • DVOM on 20K ohm scale. • Measure resistance between J60 (B-) and J30 (C3C) at the EI breakout box. • **Is resistance greater than 10K ohms?**	Yes No	► ►	C3 is shorted low in PCM. REPLACE PCM. REMOVE all test equipment. RECONNECT all components. Complete PCM reset to clear DTCs (REFER to Powertrain Control Module (PCM) Reset). RERUN Quick Test. C3 is shorted low. CHECK connectors, SERVICE or REPLACE harness. REMOVE all test equipment. RECONNECT all components. Complete PCM reset to clear DTCs (REFER to Powertrain Control Module (PCM) Reset). RERUN Quick Test. NOTE: A C3 short to ground may have damaged the coil.
JE34 CHECK FOR C4 SHORT LOW • Key off. • DVOM on 20K ohm scale. • Disconnect coil from coil tee, leave EI diagnostic harness connected to vehicle harness coil connector. • Measure resistance between J60 (B-) and J28 (LC4C) at the EI breakout box. • **Is resistance reading less than 2K ohms?**	Yes No	► ►	GO to JE35. C4 open in coil. REPLACE left coil pack. REMOVE all test equipment. RECONNECT all components. Complete PCM reset to clear DTCs (REFER to Powertrain Control Module (PCM) Reset). RERUN Quick Test.

Fig. 262 Test JE: Integrated Ignition Coil 1, 2, 3 or 4 Failure (Part 11 of 37). 1996

Test Step	Result	►	Action to Take
JE35 CHECK FOR C4 SHORT LOW • Key off. • Disconnect PCM from vehicle harness connector. • DVOM on 20K ohm scale. • Measure resistance between J60 (B-) and J28 (LC4C) at the EI breakout box. • **Is resistance reading greater than 10K ohms?**	Yes No	► ►	C4 is shorted low in PCM. REPLACE PCM. REMOVE all test equipment. RECONNECT all components. Complete PCM reset to clear DTCs (REFER to Powertrain Control Module (PCM) Reset). RERUN Quick Test. C4 is shorted low. CHECK connectors, SERVICE or REPLACE harness. REMOVE all test equipment. RECONNECT all components. Complete PCM reset to clear DTCs (REFER to Powertrain Control Module (PCM) Reset). RERUN Quick Test. NOTE: A C4 short to ground may have damaged the coil.
JE36 CHECK FOR C3 LOW • Key off. • Disconnect PCM from the vehicle harness connector. • DVOM on 40 volt DC scale. • Key on, engine off. • Measure voltage between (+)J30 (LC3C) and (-)J60 (B-) at the EI breakout box. • **Is DC voltage reading less than 0.5 volt?**	Yes No	► ►	C3 is shorted high in PCM. REPLACE PCM. REMOVE all test equipment. RECONNECT all components. Complete PCM reset to clear DTCs (REFER to Powertrain Control Module (PCM) Reset). RERUN Quick Test. C3 is shorted high. CHECK connectors, SERVICE or REPLACE harness. REMOVE all test equipment. RECONNECT all components. Complete PCM reset to clear DTCs (REFER to Powertrain Control Module (PCM) Reset). RERUN Quick Test.

Fig. 262 Test JE: Integrated Ignition Coil 1, 2, 3 or 4 Failure (Part 12 of 37). 1996

Test Step	Result	►	Action to Take
JE37 CHECK FOR C4 LOW • Key off. • Disconnect PCM from the vehicle harness connector. • DVOM on 40 volt DC scale. • Key on, engine off. • Measure voltage between (+)J28 (LC4C) and (-)J60 (B-) at the EI breakout box. • **Is DC voltage reading less than 0.5 volt?**	Yes No	► ►	C4 is shorted high in PCM. REPLACE PCM. REMOVE all test equipment. RECONNECT all components. Complete PCM reset to clear DTCs (REFER to Powertrain Control Module (PCM) Reset). RERUN Quick Test. C4 is shorted high. CHECK connectors, SERVICE or REPLACE harness. REMOVE all test equipment. RECONNECT all components. Complete PCM reset to clear DTCs (REFER to Powertrain Control Module (PCM) Reset). RERUN Quick Test.
JE38 CHECK RIGHT SPARK PLUGS AND WIRES • Key off. • Check right side spark plug wires for insulation damage, looseness, shorting or other damage. • Remove and check right spark plugs for damage, wear, carbon deposits and proper plug gap. • Right plugs and wires are attached to the rear coil pack. • Examine all wiring harnesses and connectors for damaged, burned or overheated insulation, damaged pins, and loose or broken conditions. • **Are spark plugs and wires OK?**	Yes No	► ►	REINSTALL plugs and wires. GO to JE39. SERVICE or REPLACE damaged component. REMOVE all test equipment. RECONNECT all components. Complete PCM reset to clear DTCs (REFER to Powertrain Control Module (PCM) Reset). RERUN Quick Test.

Fig. 262 Test JE: Integrated Ignition Coil 1, 2, 3 or 4 Failure (Part 13 of 37). 1996

Test Step		Result	►	Action to Take
JE39	CHECK FOR RIGHT COIL PWR			
	WARNING: NEVER CONNECT PCM TO THE EEC BREAKOUT BOX WHEN PERFORMING EI DIAGNOSTICS. • Key off. • Install EI diagnostic harness to breakout box (Rotunda 007-00059 or equivalent). • Connect EI diagnostic harness negative lead to battery. • Install coil tee to right side spark plug wires coil. • DVOM on 40 volt DC scale. • Set EI harness box type switch to 8 cylinder position. • Key on, engine off. • Measure voltage between (+)J26 (COIL PWR R) and (-)J60 (B-) at the EI breakout box. • **Is DC voltage greater than 10.0 volts?**	Yes No	► ►	GO to JE40. COIL PWR is open to right coil. CHECK connectors, SERVICE or REPLACE harness. REMOVE all test equipment. RECONNECT all components. Complete PCM reset to clear DTCs (REFER to Powertrain Control Module (PCM) Reset). RERUN Quick Test.
JE40	CHECK FOR C1 HIGH AT RIGHT COIL PACK			
	• DVOM on 40 volt DC scale. • Key on, engine off. • Measure voltage between (+)J23 (RC1C) and (-)J60 (B-) at the EI breakout box. • **Is DC voltage reading greater than 10.0 volts?**	Yes No	► ►	GO to JE41. C1 low fault. GO to JE48.
JE41	CHECK FOR C2 HIGH AT RIGHT COIL PACK			
	• Key on, engine off. • Measure voltage between (+)J24 (RC2C) and (-)J60 (B-) at the EI breakout box. • **Is DC voltage reading greater than 10.0 volts?**	Yes No	► ►	GO to JE42. C2 low fault. GO to JE50.
JE42	CHECK FOR C1 HIGH AT PCM			
	• Key off. • Disconnect PCM. Inspect for damaged or pushed out pins, corrosion, loose wires, etc. Service as necessary. • Install breakout box and connect PCM. • DVOM on 40 volt DC scale. • Key on, engine off. • Measure voltage between Pin 26 (RC1I) at the PCM breakout box and (-)J60 (B-) at the EI breakout box. • **Is DC voltage reading greater than 10.0 volts?**	Yes No	► ►	GO to JE43. C1 is open. CHECK connectors, SERVICE or REPLACE harness. REMOVE all test equipment. RECONNECT all components. Complete PCM reset to clear DTCs (REFER to Powertrain Control Module (PCM) Reset). RERUN Quick Test.

Fig. 262 Test JE: Integrated Ignition Coil 1, 2, 3 or 4 Failure (Part 14 of 37). 1996

Test Step		Result	►	Action to Take
JE43	CHECK FOR C2 HIGH AT PCM			
	• Key on, engine off. • Measure voltage between Pin 52 (RC2I) at the PCM breakout box and (-)J60 (B-) at the EI breakout box. • **Is DC voltage reading greater than 10.0 volts?**	Yes No	► ►	GO to JE44. C2 is open. CHECK connectors, SERVICE or REPLACE harness. REMOVE all test equipment. RECONNECT all components. Complete PCM reset to clear DTCs (REFER to Powertrain Control Module (PCM) Reset). RERUN Quick Test.
JE44	CHECK C1 LOW AT COIL CONNECTOR			
	• Key off. • Disconnect right coil from coil tee, leave EI diagnostic harness connected to vehicle harness right coil connector. • DVOM on 40 volt DC scale. • Key on, engine off. • Measure voltage between (+)J23 (RC1C) and (-)J60 (B-) at the EI breakout box. • **Is DC voltage reading less than 0.5 volt?**	Yes No	► ►	GO to JE45. C1 high fault. GO to JE52.
JE45	CHECK FOR C2 LOW AT COIL CONNECTOR			
	• Key on, engine off. • Measure voltage between (+)J24 (RC2C) and (-)J60 (B-) at the EI breakout box. • **Is DC voltage reading less than 0.5 volt?**	Yes No	► ►	GO to JE46. C2 high fault. GO to JE53.
JE46	CHECK C1 AT COIL CONNECTOR WHILE CRANKING ENGINE			
	• Connect EI diagnostic harness positive lead to battery. • Connect an incandescent test lamp between J57 (B+) and J23 (RC1C). • Crank engine. • **Does lamp blink consistently and brightly (one blink per engine revolution)?**	Yes No	► ►	GO to JE47. C1 is open. REPLACE PCM. REMOVE all test equipment. RECONNECT all components. Complete PCM reset to clear DTCs (REFER to Powertrain Control Module (PCM) Reset). RERUN Quick Test.

Fig. 262 Test JE: Integrated Ignition Coil 1, 2, 3 or 4 Failure (Part 15 of 37). 1996

Test Step		Result	►	Action to Take
JE47	CHECK C2 AT COIL CONNECTOR WHILE CRANKING ENGINE			
	• Connect an incandescent test lamp between J57 (B+) and J24 (RC2C). • Crank engine. • **Does lamp blink consistently and brightly (one blink per engine revolution)?**	Yes No	► ►	Input to coil pack is OK, but no high voltage output. REPLACE Right Coil Pack. REMOVE all test equipment. RECONNECT all components. Complete PCM reset to clear DTCs (REFER to Powertrain Control Module (PCM) Reset). RERUN Quick Test. C2 is open in PCM. REPLACE PCM. REMOVE all test equipment. RECONNECT all components. Complete PCM reset to clear DTCs (REFER to Powertrain Control Module (PCM) Reset). RERUN Quick Test.
JE48	CHECK FOR C1 SHORT LOW			
	• Key off. • DVOM on 20K ohm scale. • Disconnect coil from coil tee, leave EI diagnostic harness connected to vehicle harness coil connector. • Measure resistance between J60 (B-) and J23 (RC1C) at the EI breakout box. • **Is resistance reading less than 2K ohms?**	Yes No	► ►	GO to JE49. C1 is open in coil. REPLACE Right Coil Pack. REMOVE all test equipment. RECONNECT all components. Complete PCM reset to clear DTCs (REFER to Powertrain Control Module (PCM) Reset). RERUN Quick Test.

Fig. 262 Test JE: Integrated Ignition Coil 1, 2, 3 or 4 Failure (Part 16 of 37). 1996

Test Step		Result	►	Action to Take
JE49	CHECK FOR C1 SHORT LOW			
	• Key off. • Disconnect PCM from vehicle harness. • DVOM on 20K ohm scale. • Measure resistance between J60 (B-) and J23 (RC1C) at the EI breakout box. • **Is resistance reading greater than 10K ohms?**	Yes No	► ►	C1 is shorted low in PCM. REPLACE PCM. REMOVE all test equipment. RECONNECT all components. Complete PCM reset to clear DTCs (REFER to Powertrain Control Module (PCM) Reset). RERUN Quick Test. C1 is shorted to low. CHECK connectors, SERVICE or REPLACE harness. REMOVE all test equipment. RECONNECT all components. Complete PCM reset to clear DTCs (REFER to Powertrain Control Module (PCM) Reset). RERUN Quick Test. NOTE: A C1 short to ground may have damaged the coil.
JE50	CHECK FOR C2 SHORT LOW			
	• Key off. • DVOM on 20K ohm scale. • Disconnect coil from coil tee, leave EI diagnostic harness connected to vehicle harness coil connector. • Measure resistance between J60 (B-) and J24 (RC2C) at the EI breakout box. • **Is resistance reading less than 2K ohms?**	Yes No	► ►	GO to JE51. C2 open in coil. REPLACE Right Coil Pack. REMOVE all test equipment. RECONNECT all components. Complete PCM reset to clear DTCs (REFER to Powertrain Control Module (PCM) Reset). RERUN Quick Test.

Fig. 262 Test JE: Integrated Ignition Coil 1, 2, 3 or 4 Failure (Part 17 of 37). 1996

ELECTRONIC ENGINE CONTROL SYSTEM (EEC-V)

Fig. 262 Test JE: Integrated Ignition Coil 1, 2, 3 or 4 Failure (Part 18 of 37). 1996

Test Step	Result	▶	Action to Take
JE51 CHECK FOR C2 SHORT LOW • Key off. • Disconnect PCM from vehicle harness. • DVOM on 20K ohm scale. • Measure resistance between J24 (RC2C) and J60 (B-) at the EI breakout box. • **Is resistance reading greater than 10K ohms?**	Yes	▶	C2 is shorted low in PCM. REPLACE PCM. REMOVE all test equipment. RECONNECT all components. Complete PCM reset to clear DTCs (REFER to Powertrain Control Module (PCM) Reset). RERUN Quick Test.
	No	▶	C2 is shorted low. CHECK connectors, SERVICE or REPLACE harness. REMOVE all test equipment. RECONNECT all components. Complete PCM reset to clear DTCs (REFER to Powertrain Control Module (PCM) Reset). RERUN Quick Test. NOTE: A C2 short to ground may have damaged the coil.
JE52 CHECK FOR C1 HIGH • Key off. • Disconnect PCM from the vehicle harness connector. • DVOM on 40 volt DC scale. • Key on, engine off. • Measure voltage between (+)J23 (RC1C) and (-)J60 (B-) at the EI breakout box. • **Is DC voltage reading less than 0.5 volt?**	Yes	▶	C1 is shorted high in PCM. REPLACE PCM. REMOVE all test equipment. RECONNECT all components. Complete PCM reset to clear DTCs (REFER to Powertrain Control Module (PCM) Reset). RERUN Quick Test.
	No	▶	C1 is shorted high. CHECK connectors, SERVICE or REPLACE harness. REMOVE all test equipment. RECONNECT all components. Complete PCM reset to clear DTCs (REFER to Powertrain Control Module (PCM) Reset). RERUN Quick Test.

FM0159601531180X

Fig. 262 Test JE: Integrated Ignition Coil 1, 2, 3 or 4 Failure (Part 19 of 37). 1996

Test Step	Result	▶	Action to Take
JE53 CHECK FOR C2 LOW • Key off. • Disconnect PCM from the vehicle harness connector. • DVOM on 40 volt DC scale. • Key on, engine off. • Measure voltage between (+)J24 (RC2C) and (-)J60 (B-) at the EI breakout box. • **Is DC voltage reading less than 0.5 volt?**	Yes	▶	C2 is shorted high in PCM. REPLACE PCM. REMOVE all test equipment. RECONNECT all components. Complete PCM reset to clear DTCs (REFER to Powertrain Control Module (PCM) Reset). RERUN Quick Test.
	No	▶	C2 is shorted high. CHECK connectors, SERVICE or REPLACE harness. REMOVE all test equipment. RECONNECT all components. Complete PCM reset to clear DTCs (REFER to Powertrain Control Module (PCM) Reset). RERUN Quick Test.
JE60 CHECK FOR SPARK DURING CRANK DTC P0350 is an ignition coil primary circuit malfunction. DTCs P0351, P0352 and P0353 are ignition coil 1, 2 and 3 primary circuit malfunctions. • Using a Neon Bulb Spark Tester (OTC D89P-6666-A) or Air Gap Spark Tester (D81P-6666-A), check for spark at all spark plug wires while cranking. • When using the spark plug firing indicator, place the grooved end as close as possible to the plug boot. Very weak or no flashing may be caused by a fouled plug. • **Was spark consistent on all spark plug wires (one spark per crankshaft revolution)?**	Yes	▶	Ignition System OK. REFER to Symptom Flowcharts.
	No	▶	GO to **JE61**. Spark fault.
JE61 CHECK PLUGS AND WIRES • Check spark plug wires for insulation damage, looseness, shorting or other damage. • Remove and check spark plugs for damage, wear, carbon deposits and proper plug gap. • Examine all wiring harnesses and connectors for damaged, burned or overheated insulation, damaged pins, and loose or broken conditions. • Check sensor shield connector. • **Are spark plugs and wires OK?**	Yes	▶	REINSTALL plugs and wires. GO to **JE62**.
	No	▶	SERVICE or REPLACE damaged component. REMOVE all test equipment. RECONNECT all components. Complete PCM reset to clear DTCs (REFER to Powertrain Control Module (PCM) Reset). RERUN Quick Test.

FM0159601531190X

Fig. 262 Test JE: Integrated Ignition Coil 1, 2, 3 or 4 Failure (Part 20 of 37). 1996

Test Step	Result	▶	Action to Take
JE62 CHECK FOR COIL PWR AT COIL **WARNING: NEVER CONNECT PCM TO THE EEC BREAKOUT BOX WHEN PERFORMING EI DIAGNOSTICS.** • Key off. • Install EI diagnostic harness to breakout box. • Connect negative lead to battery. • Set EI diagnostic harness type switch to "4/6 cylinder" position. • Install the coil tee (the tee is blue with 4 pins). • Two different coil packs are used on six cylinder vehicles. The orientation of the coil pack connector and the arrangement of the coil pinouts are different (refer to Section 1A, Ignition System Overview, Figures 18 and 19). • Be sure to use the correct EI (High Data Rate) 6 overlay. The overlay for the vertical connector coil pack is labeled VERTICAL. The overlay for the horizontal connector coil pack is labeled HORIZONTAL. • DVOM on 40 volt DC scale. • Key on, engine off. • When making voltage checks, a ground reading means any value within a range of zero to 1 volt. Also, VPWR or COIL PWR readings mean any value that falls within a range of B+ to 2 volts less than B+. • Measure voltage between (+)J5 (COIL PWR) and (-)J7 (B-) at the EI breakout box. • **Is DC voltage greater than 10.0 volts?**	Yes	▶	GO to **JE63**.
	No	▶	COIL PWR is open. CHECK connectors, SERVICE or REPLACE harness. REMOVE all test equipment. RECONNECT all components. Complete PCM reset to clear DTCs (REFER to Powertrain Control Module (PCM) Reset). RERUN Quick Test.
JE63 CHECK FOR C1 HIGH AT COIL PACK • Key on, engine off. • **For Vertical Connector Coil Pack Applications:** Measure voltage between (+)J6 (C1C and (-)J7 (B-) at the EI breakout box. • **For Horizontal Connector Coil Pack Applications:** Measure voltage between (+)J3 (C1C) and (-)J7 (B-) at the EI breakout box. • **Is DC voltage reading greater than 10.0 volts?**	Yes	▶	GO to **JE64**.
	No	▶	C1 low fault. GO to **JE75**.

FM0159601531200X

Fig. 262 Test JE: Integrated Ignition Coil 1, 2, 3 or 4 Failure (Part 21 of 37). 1996

Test Step	Result	▶	Action to Take
JE64 CHECK FOR C2 HIGH AT COIL PACK • Key on, engine off. • **For Vertical Connector Coil Pack Applications:** Measure voltage between (+)J3 (C2C) and (-)J7 (B-) at the EI breakout box. • **For Horizontal Connector Coil Pack Applications:** Measure voltage between (+)J6 (C2C) and (-)J7 (B-) at the EI breakout box. • **Is DC voltage reading greater than 10.0 volts?**	Yes	▶	GO to **JE65**.
	No	▶	C2 low fault. GO to **JE77**.
JE65 CHECK FOR C3 HIGH AT COIL PACK • Key on, engine off. • Measure voltage between (+)J10 (C3C) and (-)J7 (B-) at the EI breakout box. • **Is DC voltage reading greater than 10.0 volts?**	Yes	▶	GO to **JE66**.
	No	▶	C3 low fault. GO to **JE79**.
JE66 CHECK FOR C1 HIGH AT PCM • Key off. • Disconnect PCM. Inspect for damaged or pushed out pins, corrosion, loose wires, etc. Service as necessary. • Install breakout box and connect PCM. • DVOM on 40 volt DC scale. • Key on, engine off. • Measure voltage between Pin 26 (C1I) at the PCM breakout box and (-)J7 (B-) at the EI breakout box. • **Is DC voltage reading greater than 10.0 volts?**	Yes	▶	GO to **JE67**.
	No	▶	C1 is open. CHECK connectors, SERVICE or REPLACE harness. REMOVE all test equipment. RECONNECT all components. Complete PCM reset to clear DTCs (REFER to Powertrain Control Module (PCM) Reset). RERUN Quick Test.
JE67 CHECK FOR C2 HIGH AT PCM • Key on, engine off. • Measure voltage between Pin 52 (C2I) at the PCM breakout box and (-)J7 (B-) at the EI breakout box. • **Is DC voltage reading greater than 10.0 volts?**	Yes	▶	GO to **JE68**.
	No	▶	C2 is open. CHECK connectors, SERVICE or REPLACE harness. REMOVE all test equipment. RECONNECT all components. Complete PCM reset to clear DTCs (REFER to Powertrain Control Module (PCM) Reset). RERUN Quick Test.

FM0159601531210X

Test Step	Result	▶	Action to Take
JE68 CHECK FOR C3 HIGH AT PCM • Key on, engine off. • Measure voltage between Pin 78 (C3I) at the PCM breakout box and (-)J7 (B-) at the EI breakout box. • Is DC voltage reading greater than 10.0 volts?	Yes No	▶ ▶	GO to **JE69**. C3 is open. CHECK connectors, SERVICE or REPLACE harness. REMOVE all test equipment. RECONNECT all components. Complete PCM reset to clear DTCs (REFER to Powertrain Control Module (PCM) Reset). RERUN Quick Test.
JE69 CHECK FOR C1 LOW AT COIL CONNECTOR • Key off. • Disconnect the coil from the coil tee. Leave EI diagnostic harness coil tee connected to vehicle harness coil connector. • DVOM on 40 volt DC scale. • Key on, engine off. • **For Vertical Connector Coil Pack Applications:** Measure voltage between (+)J6 (C1C and (-)J7 (B-) at the EI breakout box. • **For Horizontal Connector Coil Pack Applications:** Measure voltage between (+)J3 (C1C) and (-)J7 (B-) at the EI breakout box. • Is DC voltage reading less than 0.5 volt?	Yes No	▶ ▶	GO to **JE70**. C1 high fault. GO to **JE81**.
JE70 CHECK FOR C2 LOW AT COIL CONNECTOR • Key on, engine off. • **For Vertical Connector Coil Pack Applications:** Measure voltage between (+)J3 (C2C) and (-)J7 (B-) at the EI breakout box. • **For Horizontal Connector Coil Pack Applications:** Measure voltage between (+)J6 (C2C) and (-)J7 (B-) at the EI breakout box. • Is DC voltage reading less than 0.5 volt?	Yes No	▶ ▶	GO to **JE71**. GO to **JE82**. C2 high fault. GO to **JE82**.
JE71 CHECK FOR C3 LOW AT COIL CONNECTOR • Key on, engine off. • Measure voltage between (+)J10 (C3C) and (-)J7 (B-) at the EI breakout box. • Is DC voltage reading less than 0.5 volt?	Yes No	▶ ▶	GO to **JE72**. C3 high fault. GO to **JE83**.

FM0159601531220X

Fig. 262 Test JE: Integrated Ignition Coil 1, 2, 3 or 4 Failure (Part 22 of 37). 1996

Test Step	Result	▶	Action to Take
JE72 CHECK C1 AT COIL CONNECTOR WHILE CRANKING ENGINE • Connect EI diagnostic harness positive lead to battery. • **For Vertical Connector Coil Pack Applications:** Connect incandescent test lamp between J1 (B+) and J6 (C1C). • **For Horizontal Connector Coil Pack Applications:** Connect incandescent test lamp between J1 (B+) and J3 (C1C). • Crank engine. • **Does lamp blink consistently and brightly (one blink per engine revolution)?**	Yes No	▶ ▶	GO to **JE73**. C1 open in PCM. REPLACE PCM. REMOVE all test equipment. RECONNECT all components. Complete PCM reset to clear DTCs (REFER to Powertrain Control Module (PCM) Reset). RERUN Quick Test.
JE73 CHECK C2 AT COIL CONNECTOR WHILE CRANKING ENGINE • **For Vertical Connector Coil Pack Applications:** Connect incandescent test lamp between J1 (B+) and J3 (C2C). • **For Horizontal Connector Coil Pack Applications:** Connect incandescent test lamp between J1 (B+) and J6 (C2C). • Crank engine. • **Does lamp blink consistently and brightly (one blink per engine revolution)?**	Yes No	▶ ▶	GO to **JE74**. C2 open in PCM. REPLACE PCM. REMOVE all test equipment. RECONNECT all components. Complete PCM reset to clear DTCs (REFER to Powertrain Control Module (PCM) Reset). RERUN Quick Test.
JE74 CHECK C3 AT COIL CONNECTOR WHILE CRANKING ENGINE • Connect test lamp between J1 (B+) and J10 (C3C). • Crank engine. • **Does lamp blink consistently and brightly (one blink per engine revolution)?**	Yes No	▶ ▶	Input to coil pack is OK, but no high voltage output. REPLACE coil pack. REMOVE all test equipment. RECONNECT all components. Complete PCM reset to clear DTCs (REFER to Powertrain Control Module (PCM) Reset). RERUN Quick Test. C3 open in PCM. REPLACE PCM. REMOVE all test equipment. RECONNECT all components. Complete PCM reset to clear DTCs (REFER to Powertrain Control Module (PCM) Reset). RERUN Quick Test.

FM0159601531230X

Fig. 262 Test JE: Integrated Ignition Coil 1, 2, 3 or 4 Failure (Part 23 of 37). 1996

Test Step	Result	▶	Action to Take
JE75 CHECK FOR C1 SHORT LOW • Key off. • DVOM on 20K ohm scale. • Disconnect coil from coil tee, leave EI diagnostic harness connected to vehicle harness coil connector. • **For Vertical Connector Coil Pack Applications:** Measure resistance between (+)J6 (C1C) and (-)J7 (B-) at the EI breakout box. • **For Horizontal Connector Coil Pack Applications:** Measure resistance between (+)J3 (C1C) and (-)J7 (B-) at the EI breakout box. • Is resistance reading greater than 2K ohms?	Yes No	▶ ▶	C1 open in coil. REPLACE coil pack. REMOVE all test equipment. RECONNECT all components. Complete PCM reset to clear DTCs (REFER to Powertrain Control Module (PCM) Reset). RERUN Quick Test. GO to **JE76**.
JE76 CHECK FOR C1 SHORT LOW • Key off. • Disconnect PCM from vehicle harness connector. • DVOM on 20K ohm scale. • **For Vertical Connector Coil Pack Applications:** Measure resistance between (+)J6 (C1C) and (-)J7 (B-) at the EI breakout box. • **For Horizontal Connector Coil Pack Applications:** Measure resistance between (+)J3 (C1C) and (-)J7 (B-) at the EI breakout box. • Is resistance reading greater than 10K ohms?	Yes No	▶ ▶	C1 is shorted low in PCM. REPLACE PCM. REMOVE all test equipment. RECONNECT all components. Complete PCM reset to clear DTCs (REFER to Powertrain Control Module (PCM) Reset). RERUN Quick Test. C1 is shorted low. CHECK connectors, SERVICE or REPLACE harness. REMOVE all test equipment. RECONNECT all components. Complete PCM reset to clear DTCs (REFER to Powertrain Control Module (PCM) Reset). RERUN Quick Test. NOTE: A C1 short to ground may have damaged the coil.

FM0159601531240X

Fig. 262 Test JE: Integrated Ignition Coil 1, 2, 3 or 4 Failure (Part 24 of 37). 1996

Test Step	Result	▶	Action to Take
JE77 CHECK FOR C2 SHORT LOW • Key off. • DVOM on 20K ohm scale. • Disconnect coil from coil tee, leave EI diagnostic harness connected to vehicle harness coil connector. • **For Vertical Connector Coil Pack Applications:** Measure resistance between (+)J3 (C2C) and (-)J7 (B-) at the EI breakout box. • **For Horizontal Connector Coil Pack Applications:** Measure resistance between (+)J6 (C2C) and (-)J7 (B-) at the EI breakout box. • Is resistance reading greater than 2K ohms?	Yes No	▶ ▶	C2 open in coil. REPLACE coil pack. REMOVE all test equipment. RECONNECT all components. Complete PCM reset to clear DTCs (REFER to Powertrain Control Module (PCM) Reset). RERUN Quick Test. GO to **JE78**.
JE78 CHECK FOR C2 SHORT LOW • Key off. • Disconnect PCM from vehicle harness connector. • DVOM on 20K ohm scale. • **For Vertical Connector Coil Pack Applications:** Measure resistance between (+)J3 (C2C) and (-)J7 (B-) at the EI breakout box. • **For Horizontal Connector Coil Pack Applications:** Measure resistance between (+)J6 (C2C) and (-)J7 (B-) at the EI breakout box. • Is resistance reading greater than 10K ohms?	Yes No	▶ ▶	C2 is shorted low in PCM. REPLACE PCM. REMOVE all test equipment. RECONNECT all components. Complete PCM reset to clear DTCs (REFER to Powertrain Control Module (PCM) Reset). RERUN Quick Test. C2 is shorted low. CHECK connectors, SERVICE or REPLACE harness. REMOVE all test equipment. RECONNECT all components. Complete PCM reset to clear DTCs (REFER to Powertrain Control Module (PCM) Reset). RERUN Quick Test. NOTE: A C2 short to ground may have damaged the coil.
JE79 CHECK FOR C3 SHORT LOW • Key off. • DVOM on 20K ohm scale. • Disconnect coil from coil tee, leave EI diagnostic harness connected to vehicle harness coil connector. • Measure resistance between J7 (B-) and J10 (C3C) at the EI breakout box. • Is resistance reading greater than 2K ohms?	Yes No	▶ ▶	C3 open in coil. REPLACE coil pack. REMOVE all test equipment. RECONNECT all components. Complete PCM reset to clear DTCs (REFER to Powertrain Control Module (PCM) Reset). RERUN Quick Test. GO to **JE80**.

FM0159601531250X

Fig. 262 Test JE: Integrated Ignition Coil 1, 2, 3 or 4 Failure (Part 25 of 37). 1996

Test Step	Result	▶	Action to Take
JE80 CHECK FOR C3 SHORT LOW			
• Key off. • Disconnect PCM from vehicle harness connector. • DVOM on 20K ohm scale. • Measure resistance between J7 (B-) and J10 (C3C) at the EI breakout box. • **Is resistance greater than 10K ohms?**	Yes	▶	C3 is shorted low in PCM. REPLACE PCM. REMOVE all test equipment. RECONNECT all components. Complete PCM reset to clear DTCs (REFER to Powertrain Control Module (PCM) Reset). RERUN Quick Test.
	No	▶	C3 is shorted low. CHECK connectors, SERVICE or REPLACE harness. REMOVE all test equipment. RECONNECT all components. Complete PCM reset to clear DTCs (REFER to Powertrain Control Module (PCM) Reset). RERUN Quick Test. NOTE: A C3 short to ground may have damaged the coil.
JE81 CHECK FOR C1 HIGH			
• Key off. • Disconnect PCM from the vehicle harness connector. • DVOM on 40 volt DC scale. • Key on, engine off. • **For Vertical Connector Coil Pack Applications:** Measure voltage between (+)J6 (C1C) and (-)J7 (B-) at the EI breakout box. • **For Horizontal Connector Coil Pack Applications:** Measure voltage between (+)J3 (C1C) and (-)J7 (B-) at the EI breakout box. • **Is DC voltage reading less than 0.5 volt?**	Yes	▶	C1 is shorted high in PCM. REPLACE PCM. REMOVE all test equipment. RECONNECT all components. Complete PCM reset to clear DTCs (REFER to Powertrain Control Module (PCM) Reset). RERUN Quick Test.
	No	▶	C1 is shorted high. CHECK connectors, SERVICE or REPLACE harness. REMOVE all test equipment. RECONNECT all components. Complete PCM reset to clear DTCs (REFER to Powertrain Control Module (PCM) Reset). RERUN Quick Test.

FM015960153126OX

Fig. 262   Test JE: Integrated Ignition Coil 1, 2, 3 or 4 Failure (Part 26 of 37). 1996

Test Step	Result	▶	Action to Take
JE82 CHECK FOR C2 HIGH			
• Key off. • Disconnect PCM from the vehicle harness connector. • DVOM on 40 volt DC scale. • Key on, engine off. • **For Vertical connector coil pack applications:** Measure voltage between (+)J3 (C2C) and (-)J7 (B-) at the EI breakout box. • **For Horizontal connector coil pack applications:** Measure voltage between (+)J6 (C2C) and (-)J7 (B-) at the EI breakout box. • **Is DC voltage reading less than 0.5 volt?**	Yes	▶	C2 is shorted high in PCM. REPLACE PCM. REMOVE all test equipment. RECONNECT all components. Complete PCM reset to clear DTCs (REFER to Powertrain Control Module (PCM) Reset). RERUN Quick Test.
	No	▶	C2 is shorted high. CHECK connectors, SERVICE or REPLACE harness. REMOVE all test equipment. RECONNECT all components. Complete PCM reset to clear DTCs (REFER to Powertrain Control Module (PCM) Reset). RERUN Quick Test.
JE83 CHECK FOR C3 HIGH			
• Key off. • Disconnect PCM from the vehicle harness connector. • DVOM on 40 volt DC scale. • Key on, engine off. • Measure voltage between (+)J10 (C3C) and (-)J7 (B-) at the EI breakout box. • **Is DC voltage reading less than 0.5 volt?**	Yes	▶	C3 is shorted high in PCM. REPLACE PCM. REMOVE all test equipment. RECONNECT all components. Complete PCM reset to clear DTCs (REFER to Powertrain Control Module (PCM) Reset). RERUN Quick Test.
	No	▶	C3 is shorted high. CHECK connectors, SERVICE or REPLACE harness. REMOVE all test equipment. RECONNECT all components. CLEAR Continuous Memory. RERUN Quick Test.

FM015960153127OX

Fig. 262   Test JE: Integrated Ignition Coil 1, 2, 3 or 4 Failure (Part 27 of 37). 1996

Test Step	Result	▶	Action to Take
JE90 CHECK FOR SPARK DURING CRANK			
Diagnostic Trouble Code (DTC) P0350 is an ignition coil primary circuit malfunction. DTCs P0351, P0352, P0353 and P0354 are ignition coil A, B, C and D primary circuit malfunctions. • Using a Neon Bulb Spark Tester (Special Service Tool D89P-6666-A) or Air Gap Spark Tester (D81P-6666-A), check for spark at all spark plug wires while cranking. • When using the spark plug firing indicator, place the grooved end as close as possible to the plug boot. Very weak or no flashing may be caused by a fouled plug. • **Was spark consistent on all spark plug wires (one spark per crankshaft revolution?)**	Yes	▶	The ignition system is OK. GO to _____ Symptom Flow Charts.
	No	▶	Spark fault. GO to JE91.
JE91 CHECK FOR SPARK AT ALL RIGHT CYLINDER BANK COIL PACK SPARK PLUG WIRES			
• Check for spark at all right cylinder bank coil pack spark plug wires while cranking. NOTE: For Continental, check for spark at all rear coil pack spark plug wires while cranking. NOTE: Check spark at coil pack. • **Was spark consistent on all right cylinder bank coil pack spark plug wires (one spark per crankshaft revolution)?**	Yes	▶	GO to JE92.
	No	▶	GO to JE108.
JE92 CHECK LEFT SPARK PLUGS AND WIRES			
• Key off. • Check left side coil pack spark plug wires for insulation damage, looseness, shorting or other damage. • Remove and check left side spark plugs for damage, wear, carbon deposits and proper plug gap. • Left coil plugs and wires are attached to the left coil pack. • Examine all wiring harnesses and connectors for damaged, burned or overheated insulation, damaged pins and loose or broken condition. • Check sensor shield connector. • **Are spark plugs and wires OK?**	Yes	▶	REINSTALL plugs and wires. GO to JE93.
	No	▶	SERVICE or REPLACE damaged component. REMOVE all test equipment. RECONNECT all components. Complete PCM reset to clear DTCs (REFER to Powertrain Control Module (PCM) Reset). RERUN Quick Test.

FM015960153128OX

Fig. 262   Test JE: Integrated Ignition Coil 1, 2, 3 or 4 Failure (Part 28 of 37). 1996

Test Step	Result	▶	Action to Take
JE93 CHECK FOR COIL PWR TO LEFT COIL FAULT			
WARNING: NEVER CONNECT PCM TO THE EEC BREAKOUT BOX WHEN PERFORMING EI DIAGNOSTICS. • Key off. • Install EI (High Data Rate) diagnostic harness to breakout box. • Install the left coil tee. The tee is yellow (left coil). • Connect EI diagnostic harness negative lead to battery. • Use 4.6L EI (High Data Rate) 8 overlay. • Set EI harness type switch to ''8 cylinder'' position. • DVOM on 40 volt DC scale. • Key on, engine off. • When making voltage checks, a ground reading means any value within a range of zero to 1 volt. Also VPWR or COIL PWR readings mean any value that falls within a range of B+ to 2 volts less than B+. • Measure voltage between (+)J11 (COIL PWR L) and (-)J7 (B-) at the EI breakout box. • **Is DC voltage greater than 10.0 volts?**	Yes	▶	GO to JE94.
	No	▶	COIL PWR is open to left coil. CHECK connectors, SERVICE or REPLACE harness. REMOVE all test equipment. RECONNECT all components. Complete PCM reset to clear DTCs (REFER to Powertrain Control Module (PCM) Reset). RERUN Quick Test.
JE94 CHECK FOR C3 HIGH AT COIL PACK			
• Key on, engine off. • Measure voltage between (+)J10 (LC3C) and (-)J7 (B-) at the EI breakout box. • **Is DC voltage reading greater than 10.0 volts?**	Yes	▶	GO to JE95.
	No	▶	C3 low fault. GO to JE102.
JE95 CHECK FOR C4 HIGH AT COIL PACK			
• Key on, engine off. • Measure voltage between (+)J18 (LC4C) and (-)J7 (B-) at the EI breakout box. • **Is DC voltage reading greater than 10.0 volts?**	Yes	▶	GO to JE96.
	No	▶	C4 low fault. GO to JE104.
JE96 CHECK FOR C3 HIGH AT PCM			
• Key off. • Disconnect PCM. Inspect for damaged or pushed out pins, corrosion, loose wires, etc. Service as necessary. • Install breakout box and connect PCM. • DVOM on 40 volt DC scale. • Key on, engine off. • Measure voltage between Pin 78 (LC3I) at the PCM breakout box and (-)J7 (B-) at the EI breakout box. • **Is DC voltage reading greater than 10.0 volts?**	Yes	▶	GO to JE97.
	No	▶	C3 is open. CHECK connectors, SERVICE or REPLACE harness. REMOVE all test equipment. RECONNECT all components. Complete PCM reset to clear DTCs (REFER to Powertrain Control Module (PCM) Reset). RERUN Quick Test.

FM015960153129OX

Fig. 262   Test JE: Integrated Ignition Coil 1, 2, 3 or 4 Failure (Part 29 of 37). 1996

Test Step	Result	►	Action to Take
JE97 CHECK FOR C4 HIGH AT PCM • Key on, engine off. • Measure voltage between Pin 104 (LC4I) at the PCM breakout box and (-)J7 (B-) at the EI breakout box. • **Is DC voltage reading greater than 10.0 volts?**	Yes	►	GO to JE98.
	No	►	C4 is open. CHECK connectors, SERVICE or REPLACE harness. REMOVE all test equipment. RECONNECT all components. Complete PCM reset to clear DTCs (REFER to Powertrain Control Module (PCM) Reset). RERUN Quick Test.
JE98 CHECK FOR C3 LOW AT COIL CONNECTOR • Key off. • Disconnect left coil pack from coil tee, leave EI diagnostic harness connected to vehicle harness left coil connector. • DVOM on 40 volt DC scale. • Key on, engine off. • Measure voltage between (+)J10 (LC3C) and (-)J7 (B-) at the EI breakout box. • **Is DC voltage reading less than 0.5 volt?**	Yes	►	GO to JE99.
	No	►	C3 high fault. GO to JE106.
JE99 CHECK FOR C4 LOW AT COIL CONNECTOR • Key on, engine off. • Measure voltage between (+)J18 (LC4C) and (-)J7 (B-) at the EI breakout box. • **Is DC voltage reading less than 0.5 volt?**	Yes	►	GO to JE100.
	No	►	C4 high fault. GO to JE107.
JE100 CHECK FOR C3 AT COIL CONNECTOR WHILE CRANKING • Connect EI diagnostic harness positive lead to battery. • Connect an incandescent test lamp between J1 (B+) and J10 (LC3C). • Crank engine. • **Does lamp blink consistently and brightly (one blink per engine revolution?**	Yes	►	GO to JE101.
	No	►	C3 open. REPLACE PCM. REMOVE all test equipment. RECONNECT all components. Complete PCM reset to clear DTCs (REFER to Powertrain Control Module (PCM) Reset). RERUN Quick Test.

FM0159601531300X

Fig. 262   Test JE: Integrated Ignition Coil 1, 2, 3 or 4 Failure (Part 30 of 37). 1996

Test Step	Result	►	Action to Take
JE101 CHECK C4 AT COIL CONNECTOR WHILE CRANKING • Connect an incandescent test lamp between J1 (B+) and J18 (LC4C). • Crank engine. • **Does lamp blink consistently and brightly (one blink per engine revolution)?**	Yes	►	Input to coil pack is OK, but no high voltage output. REPLACE left coil pack. REMOVE all test equipment. RECONNECT all components. Complete PCM reset to clear DTCs (REFER to Powertrain Control Module (PCM) Reset). RERUN Quick Test.
	No	►	C4 open in PCM. REPLACE PCM. REMOVE all test equipment. RECONNECT all components. Complete PCM reset to clear DTCs (REFER to Powertrain Control Module (PCM) Reset). RERUN Quick Test.
JE102 CHECK FOR C3 SHORT LOW • Key off. • DVOM on 20K ohm scale. • Disconnect coil from coil tee, leave EI diagnostic harness connected to vehicle harness coil connector. • Measure resistance between J7 (B-) and J10 (C3C) at the EI breakout box. • **Is resistance reading less than 2K ohms?**	Yes	►	GO to JE103.
	No	►	C3 open in coil. REPLACE Left Coil Pack. REMOVE all test equipment. RECONNECT all components. Complete PCM reset to clear DTCs (REFER to Powertrain Control Module (PCM) Reset). RERUN Quick Test.

FM0159601531310X

Fig. 262   Test JE: Integrated Ignition Coil 1, 2, 3 or 4 Failure (Part 31 of 37). 1996

Test Step	Result	►	Action to Take
JE103 CHECK FOR C3 SHORT LOW • Key off. • Disconnect PCM from vehicle harness. • DVOM on 20K ohm scale. • Measure resistance between J7 (B-) and J10 (C3C) at the EI breakout box. • **is resistance greater than 10K ohms?**	Yes	►	C3 is shorted low in PCM. REPLACE PCM. REMOVE all test equipment. RECONNECT all components. Complete PCM reset to clear DTCs (REFER to Powertrain Control Module (PCM) Reset). RERUN Quick Test.
	No	►	C3 is shorted low. CHECK connectors, SERVICE or REPLACE harness. REMOVE all test equipment. RECONNECT all components. Complete PCM reset to clear DTCs (REFER to Powertrain Control Module (PCM) Reset). RERUN Quick Test. NOTE: A C3 short to ground may have damaged the coil.
JE104 CHECK FOR C4 SHORT LOW • Key off. • DVOM on 20K ohm scale. • Disconnect coil from coil tee, leave EI diagnostic harness connected to vehicle harness coil connector. • Measure resistance between J7 (B-) and J18 (LC4C) at the EI breakout box. • **Is resistance reading less than 2K ohms?**	Yes	►	GO to JE105.
	No	►	C4 open in coil. REPLACE left coil pack. REMOVE all test equipment. RECONNECT all components. Complete PCM reset to clear DTCs (REFER to Powertrain Control Module (PCM) Reset). RERUN Quick Test.

FM0159601531320X

Fig. 262   Test JE: Integrated Ignition Coil 1, 2, 3 or 4 Failure (Part 32 of 37). 1996

Test Step	Result	►	Action to Take
JE105 CHECK FOR C4 SHORT LOW • Key off. • Disconnect PCM from vehicle harness connector. • DVOM on 20K ohm scale. • Measure resistance between J7 (B-) and J18 (LC4C) at the EI breakout box. • **Is resistance reading greater than 10K ohms?**	Yes	►	C4 is shorted low in PCM. REPLACE PCM. REMOVE all test equipment. RECONNECT all components. Complete PCM reset to clear DTCs (REFER to Powertrain Control Module (PCM) Reset). RERUN Quick Test.
	No	►	C4 is shorted low. CHECK connectors, SERVICE or REPLACE harness. REMOVE all test equipment. RECONNECT all components. Complete PCM reset to clear DTCs (REFER to Powertrain Control Module (PCM) Reset). RERUN Quick Test. NOTE: A C4 short to ground may have damaged the coil.
JE106 CHECK FOR C3 LOW • Key off. • Disconnect PCM from the vehicle harness connector. • DVOM on 40 volt DC scale. • Key on, engine off. • Measure voltage between (+)J10 (LC3C) and (-)J7 (B-) at the EI breakout box. • **Is DC voltage reading less than 0.5 volt?**	Yes	►	C3 is shorted high in PCM. REPLACE PCM. REMOVE all test equipment. RECONNECT all components. Complete PCM reset to clear DTCs (REFER to Powertrain Control Module (PCM) Reset). RERUN Quick Test.
	No	►	C3 is shorted high. CHECK connectors, SERVICE or REPLACE harness. REMOVE all test equipment. RECONNECT all components. Complete PCM reset to clear DTCs (REFER to Powertrain Control Module (PCM) Reset). RERUN Quick Test.

FM0159601531330X

Fig. 262   Test JE: Integrated Ignition Coil 1, 2, 3 or 4 Failure (Part 33 of 37). 1996

Test Step	Result	▶	Action to Take
JE107 CHECK FOR C4 LOW • Key off. • Disconnect PCM from the vehicle harness connector. • DVOM on 40 volt DC scale. • Key on, engine off. • Measure voltage between (+)J18 (LC4C) and (-)J7 (B-) at the EI breakout box. • **Is DC voltage reading less than 0.5 volt?**	Yes	▶	C4 is shorted high in PCM. REPLACE PCM. REMOVE all components. RECONNECT all components. Complete PCM reset to clear DTCs (REFER to Powertrain Control Module (PCM) Reset). RERUN Quick Test.
	No	▶	C4 is shorted high. CHECK connectors, SERVICE or REPLACE harness. REMOVE all test equipment. RECONNECT all components. Complete PCM reset to clear DTCs (REFER to Powertrain Control Module (PCM) Reset). RERUN Quick Test.
JE108 CHECK RIGHT PLUGS AND WIRES • Check right side coil pack spark plug wires for insulation damage, looseness, shorting or other damage. • Remove and check right spark plugs for damage, wear, carbon deposits and proper plug gap. • **Are spark plugs and wires OK?**	Yes	▶	REINSTALL plugs and wires. GO to JE109.
	No	▶	SERVICE or REPLACE damaged component. REMOVE all test equipment. RECONNECT all components. Complete PCM reset to clear DTCs (REFER to Powertrain Control Module (PCM) Reset). RERUN Quick Test.
JE109 CHECK FOR RIGHT COIL PWR **WARNING: NEVER CONNECT PCM TO THE EEC BREAKOUT BOX WHEN PERFORMING EI DIAGNOSTICS.** • Key off. • Connect EI diagnostic harness negative lead to battery. • Install the right coil tee. • DVOM on 40 volt DC scale. • Set EI harness box type switch to 8 cylinder position. • Key on, engine off. • Measure voltage between (+)J5 (COIL PWR R) and (-)J7 (B-) at the EI breakout box. • **Is DC voltage greater than 10.0 volts?**	Yes	▶	GO to JE110.
	No	▶	COIL PWR is open to right coil. CHECK connectors, SERVICE or REPLACE harness. REMOVE all test equipment. RECONNECT all components. Complete PCM reset to clear DTCs (REFER to Powertrain Control Module (PCM) Reset). RERUN Quick Test.

Fig. 262   Test JE: Integrated Ignition Coil 1, 2, 3 or 4 Failure (Part 34 of 37). 1996

Test Step	Result	▶	Action to Take
JE110 CHECK FOR C1 HIGH AT RIGHT COIL PACK • DVOM on 40 volt DC scale. • Key on, engine off. • Measure voltage between (+)J3 (RC1C) and (-)J7 (B-) at the EI breakout box. • **Is DC voltage reading greater than 10.0 volts?**	Yes	▶	GO to JE111.
	No	▶	C1 low fault. GO to JE118.
JE111 CHECK FOR C2 HIGH AT RIGHT COIL PACK • Key on, engine off. • Measure voltage between (+)J6 (RC2C) and (-)J7 (B-) at the EI breakout box. • **Is DC voltage reading greater than 10.0 volts?**	Yes	▶	GO to JE112.
	No	▶	C2 low fault. GO to JE120.
JE112 CHECK FOR C1 HIGH AT PCM • Key off. • Disconnect PCM. Inspect for damaged or pushed out pins, corrosion, loose wires, etc. Service as necessary. • Install breakout box and connect PCM. • DVOM on 40 volt DC scale. • Key on, engine off. • Measure voltage between Pin 26 (RC1I) at the PCM breakout box and (-)J7 (B-) at the EI breakout box. • **Is DC voltage reading greater than 10.0 volts?**	Yes	▶	GO to JE113.
	No	▶	C1 is open. CHECK connectors, SERVICE or REPLACE harness. REMOVE all test equipment. RECONNECT all components. Complete PCM reset to clear DTCs (REFER to Powertrain Control Module (PCM) Reset). RERUN Quick Test.
JE113 CHECK FOR C2 HIGH AT PCM • Key on, engine off. • Measure voltage between Pin 52 (RC2I) at the PCM breakout box and (-)J7 (B-) at the EI breakout box. • **Is DC voltage reading greater than 10.0 volts?**	Yes	▶	GO to JE114.
	No	▶	C2 is open. CHECK connectors, SERVICE or REPLACE harness. REMOVE all test equipment. RECONNECT all components. Complete PCM reset to clear DTCs (REFER to Powertrain Control Module (PCM) Reset). RERUN Quick Test.
JE114 CHECK C1 LOW AT COIL CONNECTOR • Key off. • Disconnect right coil from coil tee, leave EI diagnostic harness connected to vehicle harness right coil connector. • DVOM on 40 volt DC scale. • Key on, engine off. • Measure voltage between (+)J3 (RC1C) and (-)J7 (B-) at the EI breakout box. • **Is DC voltage reading less than 0.5 volt?**	Yes	▶	GO to JE115.
	No	▶	C1 high fault. GO to JE122.

Fig. 262   Test JE: Integrated Ignition Coil 1, 2, 3 or 4 Failure (Part 35 of 37). 1996

Test Step	Result	▶	Action to Take
JE115 CHECK FOR C2 LOW AT COIL CONNECTOR • Key on, engine off. • Measure voltage between (+)J6 (RC2C) and (-)J7 (B-) at the EI breakout box. • **Is DC voltage reading less than 0.5 volt?**	Yes	▶	GO to JE116.
	No	▶	C2 high fault. GO to JE123.
JE116 CHECK C1 AT COIL CONNECTOR WHILE CRANKING ENGINE • Connect EI diagnostic harness positive lead to battery. • Connect coil. • Connect an incandescent test lamp between J1 (B+) and J3 (RC1C). • Crank engine. • **Does lamp blink consistently and brightly (one blink per engine revolution)?**	Yes	▶	GO to JE117.
	No	▶	C1 is open. REPLACE PCM. REMOVE all test equipment. RECONNECT all components. Complete PCM reset to clear DTCs (REFER to Powertrain Control Module (PCM) Reset). RERUN Quick Test.
JE117 CHECK C2 AT COIL CONNECTOR WHILE CRANKING ENGINE • Connect an incandescent test lamp between J1 (B+) and J6 (RC2C). • Crank engine. • **Does lamp blink consistently and brightly (one blink per engine revolution)?**	Yes	▶	Input to coil pack is OK, but no high voltage output. REPLACE Right Coil Pack. REMOVE all test equipment. RECONNECT all components. Complete PCM reset to clear DTCs (REFER to Powertrain Control Module (PCM) Reset). RERUN Quick Test.
	No	▶	C2 is open in PCM. REPLACE PCM. REMOVE all test equipment. RECONNECT all components. RERUN Quick Test.
JE118 CHECK FOR C1 SHORT LOW • Key off. • DVOM on 20K ohm scale. • Disconnect coil from coil tee, leave EI diagnostic harness connected to vehicle harness coil connector. • Measure resistance between J7 (B-) and J3 (RC1C) at the EI breakout box. • **Is resistance reading less than 2K ohms?**	Yes	▶	GO to JE119.
	No	▶	C1 is open in coil. REPLACE Right Coil Pack. REMOVE all test equipment. RECONNECT all components. Complete PCM reset to clear DTCs (REFER to Powertrain Control Module (PCM) Reset). RERUN Quick Test.

Fig. 262   Test JE: Integrated Ignition Coil 1, 2, 3 or 4 Failure (Part 36 of 37). 1996

Test Step	Result	▶	Action to Take
JE119 CHECK FOR C1 SHORT LOW • Key off. • Disconnect PCM from vehicle harness. • DVOM on 20K ohm scale. • Measure resistance between J7 (B-) and J3 (RC1C) at the EI breakout box. • **Is resistance reading greater than 10K ohms?**	Yes	▶	C1 is shorted low in PCM. REPLACE PCM. REMOVE all test equipment. RECONNECT all components. Complete PCM reset to clear DTCs (REFER to Powertrain Control Module (PCM) Reset). RERUN Quick Test.
	No	▶	C1 is shorted low. CHECK connectors, SERVICE or REPLACE harness. REMOVE all test equipment. RECONNECT all components. Complete PCM reset to clear DTCs (REFER to Powertrain Control Module (PCM) Reset). RERUN Quick Test. NOTE: A C1 short to ground may have damaged the coil.
JE120 CHECK FOR C2 SHORT LOW • Key off. • DVOM on 20K ohm scale. • Disconnect coil from coil tee, leave EI diagnostic harness connected to vehicle harness coil connector. • Measure resistance between J7 (B-) and J6 (RC2C) at the EI breakout box. • **Is resistance reading less than 2K ohms?**	Yes	▶	GO to JE121.
	No	▶	C2 open in coil. REPLACE Right Coil Pack. REMOVE all test equipment. RECONNECT all components. Complete PCM reset to clear DTCs (REFER to Powertrain Control Module (PCM) Reset). RERUN Quick Test.

Fig. 262   Test JE: Integrated Ignition Coil 1, 2, 3 or 4 Failure (Part 37 of 37). 1996

Note

You should enter this Pinpoint Test only when directed here.

Remember

This Pinpoint Test is intended to diagnose the following:

- Ignition Coils
- Ignition Coil Harness
- Cylinder Identification (CID) Sensor
- Powertrain Control Module (PCM)

Test Step	Result	▶	Action to Take
JF1 PRELIMINARY CHECKS ON CYLINDERS 5, 6, 7, 8			
• Continuous Memory Diagnostic Trouble Code (DTC) P0350 indicates an ignition coil primary circuit malfunction. Continuous Memory DTCs P0351, P0352, P0353, P0354, P0355, P0356, P0357 and P0358 indicate an ignition coil primary circuit malfunction has occured in coils one through eight. • Check coils on cylinders 5, 6, 7 and 8 for insulation damage, looseness, shorting or other damage. • Remove and check spark plugs from cylinders 5, 6, 7 and 8 for damage, wear, carbon deposits and proper plug gap. • Examine all wiring harnesses and connectors for damaged, burned or overheated insulation, damaged pins and loose or broken conditions. • **Are coils, spark plugs and harnesses OK?**	Yes No	▶ ▶	REINSTALL plugs and coils. SERVICE or REPLACE damaged component. REMOVE all test equipment. RECONNECT all components. COMPLETE PCM reset to clear DTCs (REFER to Powertrain Control Module (PCM) Reset). RERUN Quick Test.
JF2 CHECK CYLINDER 1 FOR COIL DTC P0351			
• **Is DTC P0351 present in Continuous Memory?**	Yes No	▶ ▶	Cylinder 1 Coil Fault. GO to **JF11**. GO to **JF3**.
JF3 CHECK CYLINDER 2 FOR COIL DTC P0352			
• **Is DTC P0352 present in Continuous Memory?**	Yes No	▶ ▶	Cylinder 2 Coil Fault. GO to **JF19**. GO to **JF4**.

FM0159601532010X

Fig. 263   Test JF: Integrated Ignition Coil On Plug Coil 1 Through 8 Failure (Part 1 of 26). 1996

Test Step	Result	▶	Action to Take
JF4 CHECK CYLINDER 3 FOR COIL DTC P0353			
• **Is DTC P0353 present in Continuous Memory?**	Yes No	▶ ▶	Cylinder 3 Coil Fault. GO to **JF27**. GO to **JF5**.
JF5 CHECK CYLINDER 4 FOR COIL DTC P0354			
• **Is DTC P0354 in Continuous Memory?**	Yes No	▶ ▶	Cylinder 4 Coil Fault. GO to **JF35**. GO to **JF6**.
JF6 CHECK CYLINDER 5 FOR COIL DTC P0355			
• **Is DTC P0355 in Continuous Memory?**	Yes No	▶ ▶	Cylinder 5 Coil Fault. GO to **JF43**. GO to **JF7**.
JF7 CHECK CYLINDER 6 FOR COIL DTC P0356			
• **Is DTC P0356 in Continuous Memory?**	Yes No	▶ ▶	Cylinder 6 Coil Fault. GO to **JF51**. GO to **JF8**.
JF8 CHECK CYLINDER 7 FOR COIL DTC P0357			
• **Is DTC P0357 in Continuous Memory?**	Yes No	▶ ▶	Cylinder 7 Coil Fault. GO to **JF59**. GO to **JF9**.
JF9 CHECK CYLINDER 8 FOR COIL DTC P0358			
• **Is DTC P0358 in Continuous Memory?**	Yes No	▶ ▶	Cylinder 8 Coil Fault. GO to **JF67**. GO to **JF10**.
JF10 CHECK ALL CYLINDERS FOR COIL DTC P0340 AND P0350			
• **Is DTC P0340 present along with DTC P0350 in Continuous Memory?**	Yes No	▶ ▶	Cylinder identification fault. GO to **DR1**. GO to Symptom Flowcharts.

FM0159601532020X

Fig. 263   Test JF: Integrated Ignition Coil On Plug Coil 1 Through 8 Failure (Part 2 of 26). 1996

Test Step	Result	▶	Action to Take
JF11 CYLINDER 1 COIL FAULT. CHECK FOR POWER TO THE COIL			
WARNING: NEVER CONNECT PCM TO THE EEC BREAKOUT BOX WHEN PERFORMING INTEGRATED EI DIAGNOSTICS. • Key off. • Install EI (High Data Rate) diagnostic harness to breakout box. • Install Coil / CKP (black) connector to coil 1 and harness. • Connect EI diagnostic negative lead to battery. • Use 3.4L EI (High Data Rate) 8 overlay. • Set EI harness type switch to "8 cylinder" position. • DVOM on 40 volt scale. • Key on, engine off. • When making voltage checks, a ground reading means any value within a range of zero to 1 volt. Also VPWR or COIL PWR readings mean any value that falls within a range of B+ to 2 volts less than B+. • Measure voltage between (+) J31 (COIL PWR) and (-) J7 (B-) at the EI breakout box. • **Is DC voltage reading greater than 10.0 volts?**	Yes No	▶ ▶	GO to **JF12**. COIL PWR is open to coil. CHECK connectors, SERVICE or REPLACE harness. REMOVE all test equipment. RECONNECT all components. COMPLETE PCM reset to clear DTCs (REFER to Powertrain Control Module (PCM) Reset). RERUN Quick Test.
JF12 CHECK FOR COIL 1 HIGH AT COIL			
• Key on, engine off. • Measure voltage between (+) J32 (COIL 1) and (-) J7 (B-) at the EI breakout box. • **Is DC voltage reading greater than 10.0 volts?**	Yes No	▶ ▶	GO to **JF13**. COIL 1 low fault. GO to **JF16**.
JF13 CHECK FOR COIL 1 HIGH AT PCM			
• Key on, engine off. • Measure voltage between Pin 26 (COIL 1) at the PCM breakout box and (-) J7 (B-) at the EI breakout box. • **Is DC voltage reading greater than 10.0 volts?**	Yes No	▶ ▶	GO to **JF14**. COIL 1 is open. CHECK connectors. SERVICE or REPLACE harness. REMOVE all test equipment. RECONNECT all components. COMPLETE PCM reset to clear DTCs (REFER to Powertrain Control Module (PCM) Reset). RERUN Quick Test.

FM0159601532030X

Fig. 263   Test JF: Integrated Ignition Coil On Plug Coil 1 Through 8 Failure (Part 3 of 26). 1996

Test Step	Result	▶	Action to Take
JF14 CHECK FOR COIL 1 LOW AT COIL CONNECTOR			
• Key off. • Disconnect coil 1 from Coil / CKP connector, leave EI diagnostic harness connected to vehicle harness. • DVOM on 40 volt scale. • Key on, engine off. • Measure voltage between (+) J32 (COIL 1) and (-) J7 (B-) at the EI breakout box. • **Is DC voltage reading less than 0.5 volt?**	Yes No	▶ ▶	GO to **JF15**. COIL 1 high fault. GO to **JF18**.
JF15 CHECK COIL 1 AT COIL CONNECTOR WHILE CRANKING			
• Connect EI diagnostic harness positive lead to battery. • Connect an incandescent test lamp between J1 (B+) and J32 (COIL 1) at the EI breakout box. • Crank engine. • **Does lamp blink consistently and brightly, one blink per engine revolution?**	Yes No	▶ ▶	GO to **JF16**. COIL 1 open. REPLACE PCM. REMOVE all test equipment. RECONNECT all components. COMPLETE PCM reset to clear DTCs (REFER to Powertrain Control Module (PCM) Reset). RERUN Quick Test.
JF16 CHECK FOR COIL 1 SHORT LOW			
• Key off. • DVOM on 20K ohm scale. • Disconnect coil 1 from COIL / CKP connector, leave EI diagnostic harness connected to vehicle harness coil connector. • Measure resistance between J7 (B-) and J32 (COIL 1) at the EI breakout box. • **Is the resistance reading less than 2K ohms?**	Yes No	▶ ▶	GO to **JF17**. COIL 1 is open in coil. REPLACE coil. REMOVE all test equipment. RECONNECT all components. COMPLETE PCM reset to clear DTCs (REFER to Powertrain Control Module (PCM) Reset). RERUN Quick Test.

FM0159601532040X

Fig. 263   Test JF: Integrated Ignition Coil On Plug Coil 1 Through 8 Failure (Part 4 of 26). 1996

Test Step	Result	►	Action to Take
JF17 CHECK FOR COIL 1 SHORT LOW			
• Key off. • Disconnect PCM from vehicle harness. • DVOM on 20K ohm scale. • Measure resistance between J7 (B-) and J32 (COIL 1) at the EI breakout box. • Is the resistance reading greater than 10K ohms?	Yes	►	COIL 1 is shorted low. REPLACE PCM. REMOVE all test equipment. RECONNECT all components. COMPLETE PCM reset to clear DTCs (REFER to Powertrain Control Module (PCM) Reset). RERUN Quick Test.
	No	►	COIL 1 is shorted low. CHECK connectors. SERVICE or REPLACE harness. REMOVE all test equipment. RECONNECT all components. COMPLETE PCM reset to clear DTCs (REFER to Powertrain Control Module (PCM) Reset). RERUN Quick Test.
JF18 CHECK FOR COIL 1 SHORT LOW			
• Key off. • Disconnect PCM from vehicle harness. • DVOM on 40 volt scale. • Measure voltage (+) J32 (COIL 1) and (-) J7 (B-) at the EI breakout box. • Is the voltage reading less than 0.5 volt?	Yes	►	COIL 1 is shorted high. REPLACE PCM. REMOVE all test equipment. RECONNECT all components. COMPLETE PCM reset to clear DTCs (REFER to Powertrain Control Module (PCM) Reset). RERUN Quick Test.
	No	►	COIL 1 is shorted high. CHECK connectors. SERVICE or REPLACE harness. REMOVE all test equipment. RECONNECT all components. COMPLETE PCM reset to clear DTCs (REFER to Powertrain Control Module (PCM) Reset). RERUN Quick Test.

FM0159601532050X

Fig. 263   Test JF: Integrated Ignition Coil On Plug Coil 1 Through 8 Failure (Part 5 of 26). 1996

Test Step	Result	►	Action to Take
JF19 CYLINDER 2 COIL FAULT. CHECK FOR POWER TO THE COIL			
• **WARNING: NEVER CONNECT PCM TO THE EEC BREAKOUT BOX WHEN PERFORMING INTEGRATED EI DIAGNOSTICS.** Key off. • Install EI (High Data Rate) diagnostic harness to breakout box. • Install Coil/CKP (black) connector to coil 2 and harness. • Connect EI diagnostic negative lead to battery. • Use 3.4L EI (High Data Rate) 8 overlay. • Set EI harness type switch to "8 cylinder" position. • DVOM on 40 volt scale. • Key on, engine off. • When making voltage checks, a ground reading means any value within a range of zero to 1 volt. Also VPWR or COIL PWR readings mean any value that falls within a range of B+ to 2 volts less than B+. • Measure voltage between (+) J31 (COIL PWR) and (-) J7 (B-) at the EI breakout box. • Is DC voltage reading greater than 10.0 volts?	Yes	►	GO to JF20.
	No	►	COIL PWR is open to coil. CHECK connectors. SERVICE or REPLACE harness. REMOVE all test equipment. RECONNECT all components. COMPLETE PCM reset to clear DTCs (REFER to Powertrain Control Module (PCM) Reset). RERUN Quick Test.
JF20 CHECK FOR COIL 2 HIGH AT COIL			
• Key on, engine off. • Measure voltage between (+) J32 (COIL 2) and (-) J7 (B-) at the EI breakout box. • Is DC voltage reading greater than 10.0 volts?	Yes	►	GO to JF21.
	No	►	COIL 2 low fault. GO to JF24.
JF21 CHECK FOR COIL 2 HIGH AT PCM			
• Key on, engine off. • Measure voltage between Pin 104 (COIL 2) at the PCM breakout box and (-) J7 (B-) at the EI breakout box. • Is DC voltage reading greater than 10.0 volts?	Yes	►	GO to JF22.
	No	►	COIL 2 is open. CHECK connectors. SERVICE or REPLACE harness. REMOVE all test equipment. RECONNECT all components. COMPLETE PCM reset to clear DTCs (REFER to Powertrain Control Module (PCM) Reset). RERUN Quick Test.

FM0159601532060X

Fig. 263   Test JF: Integrated Ignition Coil On Plug Coil 1 Through 8 Failure (Part 6 of 26). 1996

Test Step	Result	►	Action to Take
JF22 CHECK FOR COIL 2 LOW AT COIL CONNECTOR			
• Key off. • Disconnect coil 2 from Coil/CKP connector, leave EI diagnostic harness connected to vehicle harness. • DVOM on 40 volt scale. • Key on, engine off. • measure voltage between (+) J32 (COIL 2) and (-) J7 (B-) at the EI breakout box. • Is DC voltage reading less than 0.5 volt?	Yes	►	GO to JF23.
	No	►	COIL 2 high fault. GO to JF26.
JF23 CHECK COIL 2 AT COIL CONNECTOR WHILE CRANKING			
• Connect EI diagnostic harness positive lead to battery. • Connect an incandescent test lamp between J1 (B+) and J32 (COIL 2) at the EI breakout box. • Crank engine. • **Does lamp blink consistently and brightly, one blink per engine revolution?**	Yes	►	GO to JF24.
	No	►	COIL 2 open. REPLACE PCM. REMOVE all test equipment. RECONNECT all components. COMPLETE PCM reset to clear DTCs (REFER to Powertrain Control Module (PCM) Reset). RERUN Quick Test.
JF24 CHECK FOR COIL 2 SHORT LOW			
• Key off. • DVOM on 20K ohm scale. • Disconnect coil from COIL/CKP connector, leave EI diagnostic harness connected to vehicle harness coil connector. • Measure resistance between J7 (B-) and J32 (COIL 2) at the EI breakout box. • Is the resistance reading less than 2K ohms?	Yes	►	GO to JF25.
	No	►	COIL 2 is open in coil. REPLACE coil. REMOVE all test equipment. RECONNECT all components. COMPLETE PCM reset to clear DTCs (REFER to Powertrain Control Module (PCM) Reset). RERUN Quick Test.

FM0159601532070X

Fig. 263   Test JF: Integrated Ignition Coil On Plug Coil 1 Through 8 Failure (Part 7 of 26). 1996

Test Step	Result	►	Action to Take
JF25 CHECK FOR COIL 2 SHORT LOW			
• Key off. • Disconnect PCM from vehicle harness. • DVOM on 20K scale. • Measure resistance between J7 (B-) and J32 (COIL 2) at the EI breakout box. • Is the resistance reading greater than 10K ohms?	Yes	►	COIL 2 is shorted low. REPLACE PCM. REMOVE all test equipment. RECONNECT all components. COMPLETE PCM reset to clear DTCs (REFER to Powertrain Control Module (PCM) Reset). RERUN Quick Test.
	No	►	COIL 2 is shorted low. SERVICE or REPLACE harness. REMOVE all test equipment. RECONNECT all components. COMPLETE PCM reset to clear DTCs (REFER to Powertrain Control Module (PCM) Reset). RERUN Quick Test.
JF26 CHECK FOR COIL 2 SHORT LOW			
• Key off. • Disconnect PCM from vehicle harness. • DVOM on 40 volt scale. • Measure voltage (+) J32 (COIL 2) and (-) J7 (B-) at the EI breakout box. • Is the voltage reading less than 0.5 volt?	Yes	►	COIL 2 is shorted high. REMVOE all test equipment. RECONNECT all components. COMPLETE PCM reset to clear DTCs (REFER to Powertrain Control Module (PCM) Reset). RERUN Quick Test.
	No	►	COIL 2 is shorted high. CHECK connectors. SERVICE or REPLACE harness. REMOVE all test equipment. RECONNECT all components. COMPLETE PCM reset to clear DTCs (REFER tc Powertrain Control Module (PCM) Reset). RERUN Quick Test.

FM0159601532080X

Fig. 263   Test JF: Integrated Ignition Coil On Plug Coil 1 Through 8 Failure (Part 8 of 26). 1996

Test Step	Result	▶	Action to Take
JF27 CYLINDER 3 COIL FAULT. CHECK FOR POWER TO THE COIL			
• **WARNING: NEVER CONNECT PCM TO THE EEC BREAKOUT BOX WHEN PERFORMING INTEGRATED EI DIAGNOSTICS.** • Key off. • Install EI (High Data Rate) diagnostic harness to breakout box. • Install Coil/CKP (black) connector to coil 3 and harness. • Connect EI diagnostic negative lead to battery. • Use 3.4L EI (High Data Rate) 8 overlay. • Set EI harness type switch to "8 cylinder" position. • DVOM on 40 volt scale. • Key on, engine off. • When making voltage checks, a ground reading means any value within a range of zero to 1 volt. Also VPWR or COIL PWR readings mean any value that falls within a range of B+ to 2 volts less than B+. • Measure voltage between (+) J31 (COIL PWR) and (-) J7 (B-) at the EI breakout box. • **Is DC voltage reading greater than 10.0 volts?**	Yes No	▶ ▶	GO to JF28. COIL PWR is open to coil. SERVICE or REPLACE harness. REMOVE all test equipment. RECONNECT all components. COMPLETE PCM reset to clear DTCs (REFER to Powertrain Control Module (PCM) Reset). RERUN Quick Test.
JF28 CHECK FOR COIL 3 HIGH AT COIL			
• Key on, engine off. • Measure voltage between (+) J32 (COIL 3) and (-) J7 (B-) at the EI breakout box. • **Is DC voltage reading greater than 10.0 volts?**	Yes No	▶ ▶	GO to JF29. COIL 3 low fault. GO to JF32.
JF29 CHECK FOR COIL 3 HIGH AT PCM			
• Key on, engine off. • Measure voltage between Pin 78 (COIL 3) at the PCM breakout box and (-) J7 (B-) at the EI breakout box. • **Is DC voltage reading greater than 10.0 volts?**	Yes No	▶ ▶	GO to JF30. COIL 3 is open. CHECK connectors. SERVICE or REPLACE harness. REMOVE all test equipment. RECONNECT all components. COMPLETE PCM reset to clear DTCs (REFER to Powertrain Control Module (PCM) Reset). RERUN Quick Test.

FM0159601532090X

Fig. 263   Test JF: Integrated Ignition Coil On Plug Coil 1 Through 8 Failure (Part 9 of 26). 1996

Test Step	Result	▶	Action to Take
JF30 CHECK FOR COIL 3 LOW AT COIL CONNECTOR			
• Key off. • Disconnect coil 3 from Coil/CKP connector, leave EI diagnostic harness connected to vehicle harness. • DVOM on 40 volt scale. • Key on, engine off. • Measure voltage between (+) J32 (COIL 3) and (-) J7 (B-) at the EI breakout box. • **Is DC voltage reading less than 0.5 volt?**	Yes No	▶ ▶	GO to JF31. COIL 3 high fault. GO to JF34.
JF31 CHECK COIL 3 AT COIL CONNECTOR WHILE CRANKING			
• Connect EI diagnostic harness positive lead to battery. • Connect an incandescent test lamp between J1 (B+) and J32 (COIL 3) at the EI breakout box. • Crank engine. • **Does lamp blink consistently and brightly, one blink per engine revolution?**	Yes No	▶ ▶	GO to JF32. COIL 3 open. REPLACE PCM. REMOVE all test equipment. RECONNECT all components. COMPLETE PCM reset to clear DTCs (REFER to Powertrain Control Module (PCM) Reset). RERUN Quick Test.
JF32 CHECK FOR COIL 3 SHORT LOW			
• Key off. • DVOM on 20K ohm scale. • Disconnect coil from COIL/CKP connector, leave EI diagnostic harness connected to vehicle harness coil connector. • Measure resistance between J7 (B-) and J32 (COIL 3) at the EI breakout box. • **Is the resistance reading less than 2K ohms?**	Yes No	▶ ▶	GO to JF33. COIL 3 is open in coil. REPLACE coil. REMOVE all test equipment. RECONNECT all components. COMPLETE PCM reset to clear DTCs (REFER to Powertrain Control Module (PCM) Reset). RERUN Quick Test.

FM0159601532100X

Fig. 263   Test JF: Integrated Ignition Coil On Plug Coil 1 Through 8 Failure (Part 10 of 26). 1996

Test Step	Result	▶	Action to Take
JF33 CHECK FOR COIL 3 SHORT LOW			
• Key off. • Disconnect PCM from vehicle harness. • DVOM on 20K scale. • Measure resistance between J7 (B-) and J32 (COIL 3) at the EI breakout box. • **Is the resistance reading greater than 10K ohms?**	Yes No	▶ ▶	COIL 3 is shorted low. REMOVE all test equipment. RECONNECT all components. COMPLETE PCM reset to clear DTCs (REFER to Powertrain Control Module (PCM) Reset). RERUN Quick Test. COIL 3 is shorted low. CHECK connectors. SERVICE or REPLACE harness. REMOVE all test equipment. RECONNECT all components. COMPLETE PCM reset to clear DTCs (REFER to Powertrain Control Module (PCM) Reset). RERUN Quick Test.
JF34 CHECK FOR COIL 3 SHORT LOW			
• Key off. • Disconnect PCM from vehicle harness. • DVOM on 40 volt scale. • Measure voltage (+) J32 (COIL 3) and (-) J7 (B-) at the EI breakout box. • **Is the voltage reading less than 0.5 volt?**	Yes No	▶ ▶	COIL 3 is shorted high. REPLACE PCM. REMOVE all test equipment. RECONNECT all components. COMPLETE PCM reset to clear DTCs (REFER to Powertrain Control Module (PCM) Reset). RERUN Quick Test. COIL 3 is shorted high. CHECK connectors. SERVICE or REPLACE harness. REMOVE all test equipment. RECONNECT all components. COMPLETE PCM reset to clear DTCs (REFER to Powertrain Control Module (PCM) Reset). RERUN Quick Test.

FM015960153211OX

Fig. 263   Test JF: Integrated Ignition Coil On Plug Coil 1 Through 8 Failure (Part 11 of 26). 1996

Test Step	Result	▶	Action to Take
JF35 CYLINDER 4 COIL FAULT. CHECK FOR POWER TO THE COIL			
• **WARNING: NEVER CONNECT PCM TO THE EEC BREAKOUT BOX WHEN PERFORMING INTEGRATED EI DIAGNOSTICS.** • Key off. • Install EI (High Data Rate) diagnostic harness to breakout box. • Install Coil/CKP (black) connector to coil 4 and harness. • Connect EI diagnostic negative lead to battery. • Use 3.4L EI (High Data Rate) 8 overlay. • Set EI harness type switch to "8 cylinder" position. • DVOM on 40 volt scale. • Key on, engine off. • When making voltage checks, a ground reading means any value within a range of zero to 1 volt. Also VPWR or COIL PWR readings mean any value that falls within a range of B+ to 2 volts less than B+. • Measure voltage between (+) J31 (COIL PWR) and (-) J7 (B-) at the EI breakout box. • **Is DC voltage reading greater tha 10.0 volts?**	Yes No	▶ ▶	GO to JF36. COIL PWR is open to coil. CHECK connectors. SERVICE or REPLACE harness. REMOVE all test equipment. RECONNECT all components. COMPLETE PCM reset to clear DTCs (REFER to Powertrain Control Module (PCM) Reset). RERUN Quick Test.
JF36 CHECK FOR COIL 4 HIGH AT COIL			
• Key on, engine off. • Measure voltage between (+) J32 (COIL 4) and (-) J7 (B-) at the EI breakout box. • **Is DC voltage reading greater than 10.0 volts?**	Yes No	▶ ▶	GO to JF37. COIL 4 low fault. GO to JF40.
JF37 CHECK FOR COIL 4 HIGH AT PCM			
• Key on, engine off. • Measure voltage between Pin 78 (COIL 4) at the PCM breakout box and (-) J7 (B-) at the EI breakout box. • **Is DC voltage reading greater than 10.0 volts?**	Yes No	▶ ▶	GO to JF38. COIL 4 is open. CHECK connectors. SERVICE or REPLACE harness. REMOVE all test equipment. RECONNECT all components. COMPLETE PCM reset to clear DTCs (REFER to Powertrain Control Module (PCM) Reset). RERUN Quick Test.

FM015960153212OX

Fig. 263   Test JF: Integrated Ignition Coil On Plug Coil 1 Through 8 Failure (Part 12 of 26). 1996

Test Step	Result	▶	Action to Take
JF38 CHECK FOR COIL 4 LOW AT COIL CONNECTOR			
• Key off. • Disconnect coil 4 from Coil / CKP connector, leave EI diagnostic harness connected to vehicle harness. • DVOM on 40 volt scale. • Key on, engine off. • Measure voltage between (+) J32 (COIL 4) and (-) J7 (B-) at the EI breakout box. • **Is DC voltage reading less than 0.5 volt?**	Yes No	▶ ▶	GO to **JF39**. COIL 4 high fault. GO to **JF42**.
JF39 CHECK COIL 4 AT COIL CONNECTOR WHILE CRANKING			
• Connect EI diagnostic harness positive lead to battery. • Connect an incandescent test lamp between J1 (B+) and J32 (COIL 4) at the EI breakout box. • Crank engine. • **Does lamp blink consistently and brightly, one blink per engine revolution?**	Yes No	▶ ▶	GO to **JF40**. COIL 4 open. REPLACE PCM. REMOVE all test equipment. RECONNECT all components. COMPLETE PCM reset to clear DTCs (REFER to Powertrain Control Module (PCM) Reset). RERUN Quick Test.
JF40 CHECK FOR COIL 4 SHORT LOW			
• Key off. • DVOM on 20K ohm scale. • Disconnect coil from COIL / CKP connector, leave EI diagnostic harness connected to vehicle harness coil connector. • measure resistance between J7 (B-) and J32 (COIL 4) at the EI breakout box. • **Is the resistance reading less than 2K ohms?**	Yes No	▶ ▶	GO to **JF41**. COIL 4 is open in coil. REPLACE coil. REMOVE all test equipment. RECONNECT all components. COMPLETE PCM reset to clear DTCs (REFER to Powertrain Control Module (PCM) Reset). RERUN Quick Test.

FM0159601532130X

Fig. 263 Test JF: Integrated Ignition Coil On Plug Coil 1 Through 8 Failure (Part 13 of 26). 1996

Test Step	Result	▶	Action to Take
JF41 CHECK FOR COIL 4 SHORT LOW			
• Key off. • Disconnect PCM from vehicle harness. • DVOM on 20K ohm scale. • Measure resistance between J7 (B-) and J32 (COIL 4) at the EI breakout box. • **Is the resistance reading greater than 10K ohms?**	Yes No	▶ ▶	COIL 4 is shorted low. REPLACE PCM. REMOVE all test equipment. RECONNECT all components. COMPLETE PCM reset to clear DTCs (REFER to Powertrain Control Module (PCM) Reset). RERUN Quick Test. COIL 4 is shorted low. CHECK connectors. SERVICE or REPLACE harness. REMOVE all test equipment. RECONNECT all components. COMPLETE PCM reset to clear DTCs (REFER to Powertrain Control Module (PCM) Reset). RERUN Quick Test.
JF42 CHECK FOR COIL 4 SHORT LOW			
• Key off. • Disconnect PCM from vehicle harness. • DVOM on 40 volt scale. • Measure voltage (+) J32 (COIL 4) and (-) J7 (B-) at the EI breakout box. • **Is the voltage reading less tha 0.5 volt?**	Yes No	▶ ▶	COIL 4 is shorted high. REPLACE PCM. REMOVE all test equipment. RECONNECT all components. COMPLETE PCM reset to clear DTCs (REFER to Powertrain Control Module (PCM) Reset). RERUN Quick Test. COIL 4 is shorted high. CHECK connectors. SERVICE or REPLACE harness. REMOVE all test equipment. RECONNECT all components. COMPLETE PCM reset to clear DTCs (REFER to Powertrain Control Module (PCM) Reset). RERUN Quick Test.

FM0159601532140X

Fig. 263 Test JF: Integrated Ignition Coil On Plug Coil 1 Through 8 Failure (Part 14 of 26). 1996

Test Step	Result	▶	Action to Take
JF43 CYLINDER 5 COIL FAULT. CHECK FOR POWER TO THE COIL			
• **WARNING: NEVER CONNECT PCM TO THE EEC BREAKOUT BOX WHEN PERFORMING INTEGRATED EI DIAGNOSTICS.** • Key off. • Install EI (High Data Rate) diagnostic harness to breakout box. • Install Coil / CKP (black) connector to coil 5 and harness. • Connect EI diagnostic negative lead to battery. • Use 3.4L EI (High Data Rate) 8 overlay. • Set EI harness type switch to "8 cylinder" position. • DVOM on 40 volt scale. • Key on, engine off. • When making voltage checks, a ground reading means any value within a range of zero to 1 volt. Also VPWR or COIL PWR readings mean any value that falls within a range of B+ to 2 volts less than B+. • Measure voltage between (+) J31 (COIL PWR) and (-) J7 (B-) at the EI breakout box. • **Is DC voltage reading greater than 10.0 volts?**	Yes No	▶ ▶	GO to **JF44**. COIL PWR is open to coil. CHECK connectors. SERVICE or REPLACE harness. REMOVE all test equipment. RECONNECT all components. COMPLETE PCM reset to clear DTCs (REFER to Powertrain Control Module (PCM) Reset). RERUN Quick Test.
JF44 CHECK FOR COIL 5 HIGH AT COIL			
• Key on, engine off. • Measure voltage between (+) J32 (COIL 5) and (-) J7 (B-) at the EI breakout box. • **Is DC voltage reading greater than 10.0 volts?**	Yes No	▶ ▶	GO to **JF45**. COIL 5 low fault. GO to **JF48**.
JF45 CHECK FOR COIL 5 HIGH AT PCM			
• Key on, engine off. • Measure voltage between Pin 52 (COIL 5) at the PCM breakout box and (-) J7 (B-) at the EI breakout box. • **Is DC voltage reading greater than 10.0 volts?**	Yes No	▶ ▶	GO to **JF46**. COIL 5 is open. CHECK connectors. SERVICE or REPLACE harness. REMOVE all test equipment. RECONNECT all components. COMPLETE PCM reset to clear DTCs (REFER to Powertrain Control Module (PCM) Reset). RERUN Quick Test.

FM0159601532150X

Fig. 263 Test JF: Integrated Ignition Coil On Plug Coil 1 Through 8 Failure (Part 15 of 26). 1996

Test Step	Result	▶	Action to Take
JF46 CHECK FOR COIL 5 AT COIL CONNECTOR			
• Key off. • Disconnect coil 5 from Coil / CKP connector, leave EI diagnostic harness connected to vehicle harness. • DVOM on 40 volt scale. • Key on, engine off. • Measure voltage between (+) J32 (COIL 5) and (-) J7 (B-) at the EI breakout box. • **Is DC voltage reading less than 0.5 volt?**	Yes No	▶ ▶	GO to **JF47**. COIL 5 high fault. GO to **JF50**.
JF47 CHECK COIL 5 AT COIL CONNECTOR WHILE CRANKING			
• Connect EI diagnostic harness positive lead to battery. • Connect an incandescent test lamp between J1 (B+) and J32 (COIL 5) at the EI breakout box. • Crank engine. • **Does lamp blink consistently and brightly, one blink per engine revolution?**	Yes No	▶ ▶	GO to **JF48**. COIL 5 open. REPLACE PCM. REMOVE all test equipment. RECONNECT all components. COMPLETE PCM reset to clear DTCs (REFER to Powertrain Control Module (PCM) Reset). RERUN Quick Test.
JF48 CHECK FOR COIL 5 SHORT LOW			
• Key off. • DVOM on 20K ohm scale. • Disconnect coil from COIL / CKP connector, leave EI diagnostic harness connected to vehicle harness coil connector. • Measure resistance between J7 (B-) and J32 (COIL 5) at the EI breakout box. • **Is the resistance reading less than 2K ohms?**	Yes No	▶ ▶	GO to **JF49**. COIL 5 is open in coil. REPLACE coil. REMOVE all test equipment. RECONNECT all components. COMPLETE PCM reset to clear DTCs (REFER to Powertrain Control Module (PCM) Reset). RERUN Quick Test.

FM0159601532160X

Fig. 263 Test JF: Integrated Ignition Coil On Plug Coil 1 Through 8 Failure (Part 16 of 26). 1996

FORD—Electronic Engine Controls

Test Step	Result	▶	Action to Take
JF49 CHECK FOR COIL 5 SHORT LOW • Key off. • Disconnect PCM from vehicle harness. • DVOM on 20K scale. • Measure resistance between J7 (B-) and J32 (COIL 5) at the EI breakout box. • **Is the resistance reading greater than 10K ohms?**	Yes	▶	COIL 5 is shorted low. REPLACE PCM. REMOVE all test equipment. RECONNECT all components. COMPLETE PCM reset to clear DTCs (REFER to Powertrain Control Module (PCM) Reset). RERUN Quick Test.
	No	▶	COIL 5 is shorted low. CHECK connectors. SERVICE or REPLACE harness. REMOVE all test equipment. RECONNECT all components. COMPLETE PCM reset to clear DTCs (REFER to Powertrain Control Module (PCM) Reset). RERUN Quick Test.
JF50 CHECK FOR COIL 5 SHORT LOW • Key off. • Disconnect PCM from vehicle harness. • DVOM on 40 volt scale. • Measure voltage (+) J32 (COIL 5) and (-) J7 (B-) at the EI breakout box. • **Is the voltage reading less than 0.5 volt?**	Yes	▶	COIL 5 is shorted high. REPLACE PCM. REMOVE all test equipment. RECONNECT all components. COMPLETE PCM reset to clear DTCs (REFER to Powertrain Control Module (PCM) Reset). RERUN Quick Test.
	No	▶	COIL 5 is shorted high. CHECK connectors. SERVICE or REPLACE harness. REMOVE all test equipment. RECONNECT all components. COMPLETE PCM reset to clear DTCs (REFER to Powertrain Control Module (PCM) Reset). RERUN Quick Test.

FM0159601532170X

Fig. 263   Test JF: Integrated Ignition Coil On Plug Coil 1 Through 8 Failure (Part 17 of 26). 1996

Test Step	Result	▶	Action to Take
JF51 CYLINDER 6 COIL FAULT. CHECK FOR POWER TO THE COIL • **WARNING: NEVER CONNECT PCM TO THE EEC BREAKOUT BOX WHEN PERFORMING INTEGRATED EI DIAGNOSTICS.** • Key off. • Install EI (High Data Rate) diagnostic harness to breakout box. • Install Coil/CKP (black) connector to coil 6 and harness. • Connect EI diagnostic negative lead to battery. • Use 3.4L EI (High Data Rate) 8 overlay. • Set EI harness type switch to "8 cylinder" position. • DVOM on 40 volt scale. • Key on, engine off. • When making voltage checks, a ground reading means any value within a range of zero to 1 volt. Also VPWR or COIL PWR readings mean any value that falls within a range of B+ to 2 volts less than B+. • Measure voltage between (+) J31 (COIL PWR) and (-) J7 (B-) at the EI breakout box. • **Is DC voltage reading greater than 10.0 volts?**	Yes	▶	GO to JF52.
	No	▶	COIL PWR is open to coil. CHECK connectors. SERVICE or REPLACE harness. REMOVE all test equipment. RECONNECT all components. COMPLETE PCM reset to clear DTCs (REFER to Powertrain Control Module (PCM) Reset). RERUN Quick Test.
JF52 CHECK FOR COIL 6 HIGH AT COIL • Key on, engine off. • Measure voltage between (+) J32 (COIL 6) and (-) J7 (B-) at the EI breakout box. • **Is DC voltage reading greater than 10.0 volts?**	Yes	▶	GO to JF53.
	No	▶	COIL 6 low fault. GO to JF56.
JF53 CHECK OR COIL 6 HIGH AT PCM • Key on, engine off. • Measure voltage between Pin 1 (COIL 6) at the PCM breakout box and (-) J7 (B-) at the EI breakout box. • **Is DC voltage reading greater than 10.0 volts?**	Yes	▶	GO to JF54.
	No	▶	COIL 6 is open. CHECK connectors. SERVICE OR REPLACE harness. REMOVE all test equipment. RECONNECT all components. COMPLETE PCM reset to clear DTCs (REFER to Powertrain Control Module (PCM) Reset). RERUN Quick Test.

FM0159601532180X

Fig. 263   Test JF: Integrated Ignition Coil On Plug Coil 1 Through 8 Failure (Part 18 of 26). 1996

Test Step	Result	▶	Action to Take
JF54 CHECK FOR COIL 6 LOW AT COIL CONNECTOR • Key off. • Disconnect coil 6 from Coil/CKP connector, leave EI diagnostic harness connected to vehicle harness. • DVOM on 40 volt scale. • Key on, engine off. • Measure voltage between (+) J32 (COIL 6) and (-) J7 (B-) at the EI breakout box. • **Is DC voltage reading less than 0.5 volt?**	Yes	▶	GO to JF55.
	No	▶	COIL 6 high fault. GO to JF58.
JF55 CHECK COIL 6 AT COIL CONNECTOR WHILE CRANKING • Connect EI diagnostic harness positive lead to battery. • Connect an incandescent test lamp between J1 (B+) and J32 (COIL 6) at the EI breakout box. • Crank engine. • **Does lamp blink consistently and brightly, one blink per engine revolution?**	Yes	▶	GO to JF56.
	No	▶	COIL 6 open. REPLACE PCM. REMOVE all test equipment. RECONNECT all components. COMPLETE PCM reset to clear DTCs (REFER to Powertrain Control Module (PCM) Reset). RERUN Quick Test.
JF56 CHECK FOR COIL 6 SHORT LOW • Key off. • DVOM on 20K ohm scale. • Disconnect coil from COIL/CKP connector, leave EI diagnostic harness connected to vehicle harness coil connector. • Measure resistance between J7 (B-) and J32 (COIL 6) at the EI breakout box. • **Is the resistance reading less than 2K ohms?**	Yes	▶	GO to JF57.
	No	▶	COIL 6 is open in coil. REPLACE coil. REMOVE all test equipment. RECONNECT all components. COMPLETE PCM reset to clear DTCs (REFER to Powertrain Control Module (PCM) Reset). RERUN Quick Test.

FM0159601532190X

Fig. 263   Test JF: Integrated Ignition Coil On Plug Coil 1 Through 8 Failure (Part 19 of 26). 1996

Test Step	Result	▶	Action to Take
JF57 CHECK FOR COIL 6 SHORT LOW • Key off. • Disconnect PCM from vehicle harness. • DVOM on 20K ohm scale. • Measure resistance between J7 (B-) and J32 (COIL 6) at the EI breakout box. • **Is the resistance reading greater than 10K ohms?**	Yes	▶	COIL 6 is shorted low. REPLACE PCM. REMOVE all test equipment. RECONNECT all components. COMPLETE PCM reset to clear DTCs (REFER to Powertrain Control Module (PCM) Reset). RERUN Quick Test.
	No	▶	COIL 6 is shorted low. CHECK connectors. SERVICE or REPLACE harness. REMOVE all test equipment. RECONNECT all components. COMPLETE PCM reset to clear DTCs (REFER to Powertrain Control Module (PCM) Reset). RERUN Quick Test.
JF58 CHECK FOR COIL 6 SHORT LOW • Key off. • Disconnect PCM from vehicle harness. • DVOM on 40 volt scale. • Measure voltage (+) J32 (COIL 6) and (-) J7 (B-) at the EI breakout box. • **Is the voltage reading less than 0.5 volt?**	Yes	▶	COIL 6 is shorted high. REPLACE PCM. REMOVE all test equipment. RECONNECT all components. COMPLETE PCM reset to clear DTCs (REFER to Powertrain Control Module (PCM) Reset). RERUN Quick Test.
	No	▶	COIL 6 is shorted high. CHECK connectors. SERVICE or REPLACE harness. REMOVE all test equipment. RECONNECT all components. COMPLETE PCM reset to clear DTCs (REFER to Powertrain Control Module (PCM) Reset). RERUN Quick Test.

FM0159601532200X

Fig. 263   Test JF: Integrated Ignition Coil On Plug Coil 1 Through 8 Failure (Part 20 of 26). 1996

Test Step	Result	▶	Action to Take
JF59 CYLINDER 7 COIL FAULT. CHECK FOR POWER TO THE COIL			
• **WARNING: NEVER CONNECT PCM TO THE EEC BREAKOUT BOX WHEN PERFORMING INTEGRATED EI DIAGNOSTICS.** • Key off. • Install EI (High Data Rate) diagnostic harness to breakout box. • Install Coil / CKP (black) connector to coil 7 and harness. • Connect EI diagnostic negative lead to battery. • Use 3.4L EI (High Data Rate) 8 overlay. • Set EI harness type switch to "8 cylinder" position. • DVOM on 40 volt scale. • Key on, engine off. • When making voltage checks, a ground reading means any value within a range of zero to 1 volt. Also VPWR or COIL PWR readings mean any value that falls within a range of B+ to 2 volts less than B+. • Measure voltage between (+) J31 (COIL PWR) and (-) J7 (B-) at the EI breakout box. • **Is DC voltage reading greater than 10.0 volts?**	Yes No	▶ ▶	GO to **JF60**. COIL PWR is open to coil. CHECK connectors. SERVICE or REPLACE harness. REMOVE all test equipment. RECONNECT all components. COMPLETE PCM reset to clear DTCs (REFER to Powertrain Control Module (PCM) Reset). RERUN Quick Test.
JF60 CHECK FOR COIL 7 HIGH AT COIL			
• Key on, engine off. • Measure voltage between (+) J32 (COIL 7) and (-) J7 (B-) at the EI breakout box. • **Is DC voltage reading greater than 10.0 volts?**	Yes No	▶ ▶	GO to **JF61**. COIL 7 low fault. GO to **JF64**.
JF61 CHECK FOR COIL 7 HIGH AT PCM			
• Key on, engine off. • Measure voltage between Pin 53 (COIL 7) at the PCM breakout box and (-) J7 (B-) at the EI breakout box. • **Is DC voltage reading greater than 10.0 volts?**	Yes No	▶ ▶	GO to **JF62**. COIL 7 is open. CHECK connectors. SERVICE or REPLACE harness. REMOVE all test equipment. RECONNECT all components. COMPLETE PCM reset to clear DTCs (REFER to Powertrain Control Module (PCM) Reset). RERUN Quick Test.

FM0159601532210X

Fig. 263   Test JF: Integrated Ignition Coil On Plug Coil 1 Through 8 Failure (Part 21 of 26). 1996

Test Step	Result	▶	Action to Take
JF62 CHECK FOR COIL 7 LOW AT COIL CONNECTOR			
• Key off. • Disconnect coil 7 from Coil / CKP connector, leave EI diagnostic harness connected to vehicle harness. • DVOM on 40 volt scale. • Key on, engine off. • Measure voltage between (+) J32 (COIL 7) and (-) J7 (B-) at the EI breakout box. • **Is DC voltage reading less than 0.5 volt?**	Yes No	▶ ▶	GO to **JF63**. COIL 7 high fault. GO to **JF66**.
JF63 CHECK FOR COIL 7 AT COIL CONNECTOR WHILE CRANKING			
• Connect EI diagnostic harness positive lead to battery. • Connect an incandescent test lamp between J1 (B+) and J32 (COIL 7) at the EI breakout box. • Crank engine. • **Does lamp blink consistently and brightly, one blink per engine revolution?**	Yes No	▶ ▶	GO to **JF64**. COIL 7 open. REPLACE PCM. REMOVE all test equipment. RECONNECT all components. COMPLETE PCM reset to clear DTCs (REFER to Powertrain Control Module (PCM) Reset). RERUN Quick Test.
JF64 CHECK FOR COIL 7 SHORT LOW			
• Key off. • DVOM on 20K ohm scale. • Disconnect coil from COIL / CKP connector, leave EI diagnostic harness connected to vehicle harness coil connector. • Measure resistance between J7 (B-) and J32 (COIL 7) at the EI breakout box. • **Is the resistance reading less than 2K ohms?**	Yes No	▶ ▶	GO to **JF65**. COIL 7 is open in coil. REPLACE coil. REMOVE all test equipment. RECONNECT all components. COMPLETE PCM reset to clear DTCs (REFER to Powertrain Control Module (PCM) Reset). RERUN Quick Test.

FM0159601532220X

Fig. 263   Test JF: Integrated Ignition Coil On Plug Coil 1 Through 8 Failure (Part 22 of 26). 1996

Test Step	Result	▶	Action to Take
JF65 CHECK FOR COIL 7 SHORT LOW			
• Key off. • Disconnect PCM from vehicle harness. • DVOM on 20K ohm scale. • Measure resistance between J7 (B-) and J32 (COIL 7) at the EI breakout box. • **Is the resistance greater than 10K ohms?**	Yes No	▶ ▶	COIL 7 is shorted low. REPLACE PCM. REMOVE all test equipment. RECONNECT all components. COMPLETE PCM reset to clear DTCs (REFER to Powertrain Control Module (PCM) Reset). RERUN Quick Test. COIL 7 is shorted low. CHECK connectors. SERVICE or REPLACE harness. REMOVE all test equipment. RECONNECT all components. COMPLETE PCM reset to clear DTCs (REFER to Powertrain Control Module (PCM) Reset). RERUN Quick Test.
JF66 CHECK FOR COIL 7 SHORT LOW			
• Key off. • Disconnect PCM from vehicle harness. • DVOM on 40 volt scale. • Measure voltage (+) J32 (COIL 7) and (-) J7 (B-) at the EI breakout box. • **Is the voltage reading less than 0.5 volt?**	Yes No	▶ ▶	COIL 7 is shorted high. REPLACE PCM. REMOVE all test equipment. RECONNECT all components. COMPLETE PCM reset to clear DTCs (REFER to Powertrain Control Module (PCM) Reset). RERUN Quick Test. COIL 7 is shorted high. CHECK connectors. SERVICE or REPLACE harness. REMOVE all test equipment. RECONNECT all components. COMPLETE PCM reset to clear DTCs (REFER to Powertrain Control Module (PCM) Reset). RERUN Quick Test.

FM0159601532230X

Fig. 263   Test JF: Integrated Ignition Coil On Plug Coil 1 Through 8 Failure (Part 23 of 26). 1996

Test Step	Result	▶	Action to Take
JF67 CYLINDER 8 COIL FAULT. CHECK FOR POWER TO THE COIL			
• **WARNING: NEVER CONNECT PCM TO THE EEC BREAKOUT BOX WHEN PERFORMING INTEGRATED EI DIAGNOSTICS.** • Key off. • Install EI (High Data Rate) diagnostic harness to breakout box. • Install Coil / CKP (black) connector to coil 8 and harness. • Connect EI diagnostic negative lead to battery. • Use 3.4L EI (High Data Rate) 8 overlay. • Set EI harness type switch to "8 cylinder" position. • DVOM on 40 volt scale. • Key on, engine off. • When making voltage checks, a ground reading means any value within a range of zero to 1 volt. Also VPWR or COIL PWR readings mean any value that falls within a range of B+ to 2 volts less than B+. • Measure voltage between (+) J31 (COIL PWR) and (-) J7 (B-) at the EI breakout box. • **Is DC voltage reading greater than 10.0 volts?**	Yes No	▶ ▶	GO to **JF68**. COIL PWR is open to coil. CHECK connectors. SERVICE or REPLACE harness. REMOVE all test equipment. RECONNECT all components. COMPLETE PCM reset to clear DTCs (REFER to Powertrain Control Module (PCM) Reset). RERUN Quick Test.
JF68 CHECK FOR COIL 8 HIGH AT PCM			
• Key on, engine off. • Measure voltage between (+) J32 (COIL 8) and (-) J7 (B-) at the EI breakout box. • **Is DC voltage reading greater than 10.0 volts?**	Yes No	▶ ▶	GO to **JF69**. COIL 8 low fault. GO to **JF72**.
JF69 CHECK FOR COIL 8 HIGH AT PCM			
• Key on, engine off. • Measure voltage between Pin 53 (COIL 8) at the PCM breakout box and (-) J7 (B-) at the EI breakout box. • **Is DC voltage reading greater than 10.0 volts?**	Yes No	▶ ▶	GO to **JF70**. COIL 8 is open. CHECK connectors. SERVICE or REPLACE harness. REMOVE all test equipment. RECONNECT all components. COMPLETE PCM reset to clear DTCs (REFER to Powertrain Control Module (PCM) Reset). RERUN Quick Test.

FM0159601532240X

Fig. 263   Test JF: Integrated Ignition Coil On Plug Coil 1 Through 8 Failure (Part 24 of 26). 1996

Test Step		Result	▶	Action to Take
JF70	CHECK FOR COIL 8 LOW AT COIL CONNECTOR			
	• Key off. • Disconnect coil 8 from COIL / CKP connector, leave EI diagnostic harness connected to vehicle harness. • DVOM on 40 volt scale. • Measure voltage between (+) J32 (COIL 8) and (-) J7 (B-) at the EI breakout box. • **Is DC voltage reading less than 0.5 volt?**	Yes No	▶ ▶	GO to JF71. COIL 8 high fault. GO to JF74.
JF71	CHECK COIL 8 AT COIL CONNECTOR WHILE CRANKING			
	• Connect EI diagnostic harness positive lead to battery. • Connect an incandescent test lamp between J1 (B+) and J32 (COIL 8) at the EI breakout box. • Crank engine. • **Does lamp blink consistently and brightly, one blink per engine revolution?**	Yes No	▶ ▶	GO to JF72. COIL 8 open. REPLACE PCM. REMOVE all test equipment. RECONNECT all components. COMPLETE PCM reset to clear DTCs (REFER to Powertrain Control Module (PCM) Reset). RERUN Quick Test.
JF72	CHECK FOR COIL 8 SHORT LOW			
	• Key off. • DVOM on 20K ohm scale. • Disconnect coil from COIL / CKP connector, leave EI diagnostic harness connected to vehicle harness coil connector. • Measure resistance between J7 (B-) and J32 (COIL 8) at the EI breakout box. • **Is the resistance reading less than 2K ohms?**	Yes No	▶ ▶	GO to JF73. COIL 8 is open in coil. REPLACE coil. REMOVE all test equipment. RECONNECT all components. COMPLETE PCM reset to clear DTCs (REFER to Powertrain Control Module (PCM) Reset). RERUN Quick Test.

Fig. 263   Test JF: Integrated Ignition Coil On Plug Coil 1 Through 8 Failure (Part 25 of 26). 1996

Test Step		Result	▶	Action to Take
JF73	CHECK FOR COIL 8 SHORT LOW			
	• Key off. • Disconnect PCM from vehicle harness. • DVOM on 20K ohm scale. • Measure resistance between J7 (B-) and J32 (COIL 8) at the EI breakout box. • **Is the resistance reading greater than 10K ohms?**	Yes No	▶ ▶	COIL 8 is shorted low. REPLACE PCM. REMOVE all test equipment. RECONNECT all components. COMPLETE PCM reset to clear DTCs (REFER to Powertrain Control Module (PCM) Reset). RERUN Quick Test. COIL 8 is shorted low. CHECK connectors. SERVICE or REPLACE harness. REMOVE all test equipment. RECONNECT all components. COMPLETE PCM reset to clear DTCs (REFER to Powertrain Control Module (PCM) Reset). RERUN Quick Test.
JF74	CHECK FOR COIL 8 SHORT LOW			
	• Key off. • Disconnect PCM from vehicle harness. • DVOM on 40 volt scale. • Measure voltage (+) J32 (COIL 8) and (-) J7 (B-) at the EI breakout box. • **Is the voltage reading less than 0.5 volt?**	Yes No	▶ ▶	COIL 8 is shorted high. REPLACE PCM. REMOVE all test equipment. RECONNECT all components. COMPLETE PCM reset to clear DTCs (REFER to Powertrain Control Module (PCM) Reset). RERUN Quick Test. COIL 8 is shorted high. CHECK connectors. SERVICE or REPLACE harness. REMOVE all test equipment. RECONNECT all components. COMPLETE PCM reset to clear DTCs (REFER to Powertrain Control Module (PCM) Reset). RERUN Quick Test.

Fig. 263   Test JF: Integrated Ignition Coil On Plug Coil 1 Through 8 Failure (Part 26 of 26). 1996

Note

You should enter this Pinpoint Test only when directed here.

Remember

This Pinpoint Test is intended to diagnose the following:

- Camshaft Sensor (CMP)
- CMP Harness
- CKP Connector
- Ignition Control Module (ICM)
- Power ground circuit to ICM
- Vehicle Power circuit to ICM
- Spark plug wires

Pinpoint Test Schematic

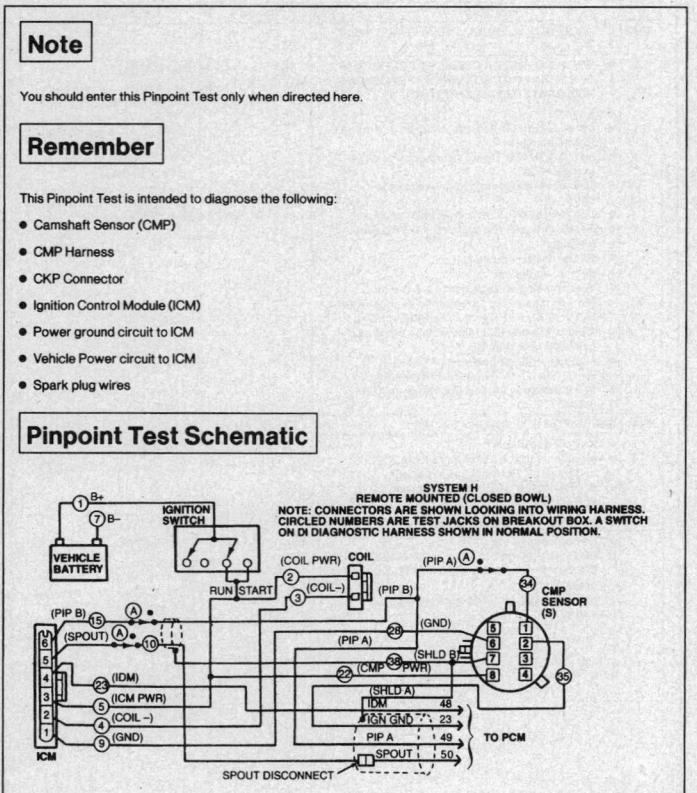

Fig. 264   Test JG: Distributor Ignition (Part 1 of 12). 1996

Test Step		Result	▶	Action to Take
JG1	WAS QUICK TEST COMPLETED?			
	• Were all tests in Section 5A, Diagnostic Subroutines, followed correctly?	Yes No	▶ ▶	GO to JG2. REFER to Diagnostic Subroutines.
JG2	CHECK FOR GOOD BATTERY			
	• Is battery voltage greater than 12 volts DC with the key on?	Yes No	▶ ▶	GO to JG3. SERVICE battery.
JG3	CHECK FOR SPARK AT COIL DURING CRANK			
	• Using an Air Gap Spark Tester (D81P-6666-A) or a Neon Bulb Spark Tester (D89P-6666-A) or equivalent, check for spark during crank at coil wire. • Was spark present during crank?	Yes No	▶ ▶	GO to JG9. GO to JG4.
JG4	CHECK FOR ICM POWER			
	• Key off. • Connect DI diagnostic harness to EEC breakout box, connect B- lead to negative post of battery, and connect ICM tee to ICM and vehicle harness. • Do not connect B+ lead of DI diagnostic harness to battery. **CAUTION: Do not connect PCM to EEC breakout box when it is used with DI diagnostic harness.** • Make sure PIP OPEN / NORMAL / SPOUT OPEN switch on DI diagnostic harness is in the NORMAL position. • Use DI overlay on breakout box. • DVOM on 40 volt DC scale. • Key on. • Measure voltage between J5 (ICM PWR) and J7 (B-) at breakout box. • **Is voltage greater than 10 volts DC?**	Yes No	▶ ▶	GO to JG5. SERVICE power open to ICM in harness or connector. REMOVE all test equipment. RECONNECT all components. COMPLETE PCM Reset to clear DTCs (REFER to Powertrain Control Module (PCM) Reset). RERUN Quick Test.
JG5	CHECK FOR PIP SIGNAL			
	• DVOM on 40 volt AC scale. • Crank engine and measure voltage between J15 (PIP) and J7 (B-). • **Is voltage between 3.0 and 8.5 volts AC?**	Yes No	▶ ▶	GO to JG6. GO to JG11.
JG6	CHECK FOR SPOUT SIGNAL			
	• Crank engine and measure voltage between J10 (SPOUT) and J7 (B-). • **Is voltage between 3.0 and 8.5 volts AC?**	Yes No	▶ ▶	GO to JG7. GO to JG18.

Fig. 264   Test JG: Distributor Ignition (Part 2 of 12). 1996

Test Step	Result	▶	Action to Take
JG7 CHECK COIL PWR AT COIL			
• Key off. • Connect diagnostic harness coil tee to vehicle harness; do not connect diagnostic harness to coil. • Key on. • DVOM on 40 volt DC scale. • Measure voltage between J2 (COIL PWR) and J7 (B-). • **Is voltage greater than 10 volts DC?**	Yes	▶	GO to JG8.
	No	▶	SERVICE power open to coil in harness or connector. REMOVE all test equipment. RECONNECT all components. COMPLETE PCM Reset to clear DTCs (REFER to Powertrain Control Module (PCM) Reset). RERUN Quick Test.
JG8 CHECK FOR COIL- SIGNAL			
• Key off. • Connect B+ lead of DI diagnostic harness to positive post of battery. • Connect 12 volt incandescent test lamp between J1 (B+) and J3 (COIL-). • Key on. • Crank engine. • **Did test lamp flash brightly?**	Yes	▶	REPLACE coil. REMOVE all test equipment. RECONNECT all components. COMPLETE PCM Reset to clear DTCs (REFER to Powertrain Control Module (PCM) Reset). RERUN Quick Test.
	No	▶	GO to JG27.
JG9 CHECK FOR SPARK AT ALL WIRES			
• Using an Air Gap Spark Tester (D81P-6666-A) or Neon Bulb Spark Tester (D89P-6666-A) or equivalent, check for spark at all wires. • **Was spark present at all plugs during crank?**	Yes	▶	GO to JG10.
	No	▶	SERVICE distributor cap, rotor, plugs or plug wires. REMOVE all test equipment. RECONNECT all components. COMPLETE PCM Reset to clear DTCs (REFER to Powertrain Control Module (PCM) Reset). RERUN Quick Test.
JG10 CHECK PLUGS			
• Remove and check plugs for damage, wear, carbon deposits and proper plug gap. • **Are plugs OK?**	Yes	▶	Not an Ignition problem. REFER to Symptom Flowcharts.
	No	▶	SERVICE plugs. REMOVE all test equipment. RECONNECT all components. COMPLETE PCM Reset to clear DTCs (REFER to Powertrain Control Module (PCM) Reset). RERUN Quick Test.

FM0159601533030X

Test Step	Result	▶	Action to Take
JG11 CHECK FOR CMP POWER AT CMP SENSOR			
• Connect diagnostic harness CMP sensor tee to CMP sensor and vehicle harness. • DVOM on 40 volt DC scale. • Key on. • Measure voltage between-J22 (CMP PWR) and J7 (B-). • **Is voltage greater than 10 volts DC?**	Yes	▶	GO to JG12.
	No	▶	SERVICE power to CMP sensor in harness or connector. REMOVE all test equipment. RECONNECT all components. COMPLETE PCM Reset to clear DTCs (REFER to Powertrain Control Module (PCM) Reset). RERUN Quick Test.
JG12 CHECK FOR PIP FROM CMP SENSOR			
• Turn switch on diagnostic cable to PIP OPEN. • DVOM on 40 volt AC scale. • Crank engine and measure voltage between: -J34 (PIP A) and J7 (B-). • **Is voltage between 3.0 and 8.5 volts AC?**	Yes	▶	GO to JG13.
	No	▶	CHECK CMP sensor wiring, if OK, REPLACE CMP sensor. REMOVE all test equipment. RECONNECT all components. COMPLETE PCM Reset to clear DTCs (REFER to Powertrain Control Module (PCM) Reset). RERUN Quick Test.
JG13 CHECK PIP WITH ICM DISCONNECTED			
• Key off. • Turn switch on diagnostic cable to NORMAL. • Disconnect diagnostic harness ICM tee from ICM only; leave ICM tee connected to vehicle harness. • Crank engine and measure voltage between -J34 (PIP A) and J7 (B-). • **Is voltage between 3.0 and 8.5 volts AC?**	Yes	▶	REPLACE ICM. REMOVE all test equipment. RECONNECT all components. COMPLETE PCM Reset to clear DTCs (REFER to Powertrain Control Module (PCM) Reset). RERUN Quick Test.
	No	▶	GO to JG14.
JG14 CHECK PIP WITH PCM DISCONNECTED			
• Disconnect PCM. • Crank engine and measure voltage between -J34 (PIP A) and J7 (B-). • **Is voltage between 3.0 and 8.5 volts AC?**	Yes	▶	REPLACE PCM. REMOVE all test equipment. RECONNECT all components. COMPLETE PCM Reset to clear DTCs (REFER to Powertrain Control Module (PCM) Reset). RERUN Quick Test.
	No	▶	GO to JG15.

FM0159601533040X

Fig. 264   Test JG: Distributor Ignition (Part 3 of 12). 1996   Fig. 264   Test JG: Distributor Ignition (Part 4 of 12). 1996

Test Step	Result	▶	Action to Take
JG15 CHECK PIP A TO PCM FOR SHORT HIGH			
• Key off. • Disconnect diagnostic harness CMP sensor tee from CMP sensor only; leave CMP sensor tee connected to vehicle harness. • DVOM on 40 volt DC scale. • Key on. • Measure voltage between -J34 (PIP A) and J7 (B-). • **Is voltage less than 0.5 volt DC?**	Yes	▶	SERVICE PIP between CMP sensor tee from CMP sensor and PCM or ICM in harness for short low. REMOVE all test equipment. RECONNECT all components. COMPLETE PCM Reset to clear DTCs (REFER to Powertrain Control Module (PCM) Reset). RERUN Quick Test.
	No	▶	SERVICE PIP between CMP sensor and PCM or ICM in harness for short high. REMOVE all test equipment. RECONNECT all components. COMPLETE PCM Reset to clear DTCs (REFER to Powertrain Control Module (PCM) Reset). RERUN Quick Test.
JG18 CHECK FOR SPOUT IN HARNESS			
• Turn switch to SPOUT OPEN position on diagnostic harness. • Crank engine and measure voltage between J10 (SPOUT) and J7 (B-). • **Is voltage between 3.0 and 8.5 volts AC?** NOTE: If engine starts, continue diagnostics.	Yes	▶	REPLACE ICM. REMOVE all test equipment. RECONNECT all components. COMPLETE PCM Reset to clear DTCs (REFER to Powertrain Control Module (PCM) Reset). RERUN Quick Test.
	No	▶	GO to JG19.
JG19 CHECK FOR SPOUT HIGH			
• Key off. • Disconnect diagnostic harness ICM tee from ICM only; leave ICM tee connected to vehicle harness. • Turn switch to NORMAL on diagnostic harness. • DVOM on 40 volt DC scale. • Measure voltage between J10 (SPOUT) and J7 (B-) with key on. • **Is voltage less than 0.5 volt DC?**	Yes	▶	GO to JG21.
	No	▶	GO to JG20.

FM0159601533050X

Test Step	Result	▶	Action to Take
JG20 CHECK FOR SPOUT SHORT HIGH IN HARNESS			
• Key off. • Disconnect PCM. • Measure voltage between J10 (SPOUT) and J7 (B-) with key on. • **Is voltage less than 0.5 volt DC?**	Yes	▶	GO to JG23.
	No	▶	SERVICE SPOUT between PCM and ICM in harness for short high. REMOVE all test equipment. RECONNECT all components. COMPLETE PCM Reset to clear DTCs (REFER to Powertrain Control Module (PCM) Reset). RERUN Quick Test.
JG21 CHECK FOR SPOUT SHORT LOW			
• Key off. • DVOM on 20K ohm scale. • Measure resistance between J10 (SPOUT) and J7 (B-). • **Is resistance greater than 10K ohms?**	Yes	▶	GO to JG23.
	No	▶	GO to JG22.
JG22 CHECK FOR SPOUT SHORT LOW IN HARNESS			
• Disconnect PCM. • Measure resistance between J10 (SPOUT) and J7 (B-). • **Is resistance greater than 10K ohms?**	Yes	▶	GO to JG23.
	No	▶	SERVICE SPOUT between PCM and ICM in harness for short low. REMOVE all test equipment. RECONNECT all components. COMPLETE PCM Reset to clear DTCs (REFER to Powertrain Control Module (PCM) Reset). RERUN Quick Test.
JG23 CHECK FOR PIP OPEN IN HARNESS			
• Key off. • DVOM on 40 volt AC scale. • Disconnect PCM. • Crank engine and measure voltage between Pin 49 (PIP) of PCM harness connector and J7 (B-). • **Is voltage between 3.0 and 8.5 volts AC?**	Yes	▶	GO to JG24.
	No	▶	GO to JG26.
JG24 CHECK IGN GND AT PCM			
• Key off. • Reconnect diagnostic harness ICM tee to ICM. • DVOM on 200 ohm scale. • Measure resistance between Pin 23 (IGN GND) of PCM harness connector and J7 (B-) at the breakout box. • **Is resistance less than 5.0 ohms?**	Yes	▶	REPLACE PCM. REMOVE all test equipment. RECONNECT all components. COMPLETE PCM Reset to clear DTCs (REFER to Powertrain Control Module (PCM) Reset). RERUN Quick Test.
	No	▶	GO to JG25.

FM0159601533060X

Fig. 264   Test JG: Distributor Ignition (Part 5 of 12). 1996   Fig. 264   Test JG: Distributor Ignition (Part 6 of 12). 1996

Test Step	Result	▶	Action to Take
JG25 CHECK FOR IGN GND AT CMP SENSOR			
• Connect diagnostic harness CMP sensor tee to CMP sensor and vehicle harness. • Measure resistance between -J35 (IGN GND) and J7 (B-). • **Is resistance less than 5.0 ohms?**	Yes	▶	SERVICE IGN GND between PCM and CMP sensor in harness for open. REMOVE all test equipment. RECONNECT all components. COMPLETE PCM Reset to clear DTCs (REFER to Powertrain Control Module (PCM) Reset). RERUN Quick Test.
	No	▶	IGN GND open in CMP sensor. SERVICE IGN GND wire or REPLACE CMP sensor. REMOVE all test equipment. RECONNECT all components. COMPLETE PCM Reset to clear DTCs (REFER to Powertrain Control Module (PCM) Reset). RERUN Quick Test.
JG26 CHECK PIP A AT CMP SENSOR			
• Turn switch from NORMAL to PIP OPEN position. • Connect diagnostic harness CMP sensor tee to CMP sensor and vehicle harness. • Crank engine and measure voltage between -J34 (PIP A) and J7 (B-). • **Is voltage between 3.0 and 8.5 volts AC?**	Yes	▶	SERVICE PIP open in harness between PCM and CMP sensor. REMOVE all test equipment. RECONNECT all components. COMPLETE PCM Reset to clear DTCs (REFER to Powertrain Control Module (PCM) Reset). RERUN Quick Test.
	No	▶	SERVICE PIP wire or REPLACE CMP sensor. PIP open in CMP sensor. REMOVE all test equipment. RECONNECT all components. COMPLETE PCM Reset to clear DTCs (REFER to Powertrain Control Module (PCM) Reset). RERUN Quick Test.

FM0159601533070X

Fig. 264   Test JG: Distributor Ignition (Part 7 of 12). 1996

Test Step	Result	▶	Action to Take
JG27 CHECK FOR COIL- OPEN IN HARNESS			
• Key off. • Disconnect diagnostic harness ICM tee from ICM only; leave ICM tee connected to vehicle harness. • Disconnect B+ lead of DI diagnostic harness from battery. • DVOM on 200 ohm scale. • Measure the resistance between J3 (COIL-) and J4 (ICM COIL-). • **Is resistance less than 5.0 ohms?**	Yes	▶	GO to JG28.
	No	▶	SERVICE open coil- between ICM and coil in harness. REMOVE all test equipment. RECONNECT all components. COMPLETE PCM Reset to clear DTCs (REFER to Powertrain Control Module (PCM) Reset). RERUN Quick Test.
JG28 CHECK FOR COIL- SHORT HIGH IN HARNESS			
• DVOM on 40 volt DC scale. • Key on. • Measure voltage between J3 (COIL-) and J7 (B-). • **Is voltage less than 5.5 volts DC?**	Yes	▶	GO to JG29.
	No	▶	SERVICE coil - short high in harness between coil and ICM. Coil may be damaged. REMOVE all test equipment. RECONNECT all components. COMPLETE PCM Reset to clear DTCs (REFER to Powertrain Control Module (PCM) Reset). RERUN Quick Test.
JG29 CHECK FOR COIL- SHORT LOW IN HARNESS			
• Key off. • DVOM on 20K ohm scale. • Measure resistance between J3 (COIL-) and J7 (B-). • **Is resistance greater than 10K ohms?**	Yes	▶	GO to JG30.
	No	▶	SERVICE coil - short low in harness between coil and ICM. REMOVE all test equipment. RECONNECT all components. COMPLETE PCM Reset to clear DTCs (REFER to Powertrain Control Module (PCM) Reset). RERUN Quick Test.
JG30 CHECK GND AT ICM			
• Key off. • DVOM on 200 ohm scale. • Measure resistance between J9 (GND) and J7 (B-). • **Is resistance less than 5.0 ohms?**	Yes	▶	REPLACE ICM. REMOVE all test equipment. RECONNECT all components. COMPLETE PCM Reset to clear DTCs (REFER to Powertrain Control Module (PCM) Reset). RERUN Quick Test.
	No	▶	GO to JG31.

FM0159601533080X

Fig. 264   Test JG: Distributor Ignition (Part 8 of 12). 1996

Test Step	Result	▶	Action to Take
JG31 CHECK GND AT CMP SENSOR			
• Connect diagnostic harness CMP sensor tee to the CMP sensor and vehicle harness. • Measure resistance between -J28 (GND) and J7 (B-). • **Is resistance less than 5.0 ohms?**	Yes	▶	SERVICE open GND in harness between CMP sensor and ICM. REMOVE all test equipment. RECONNECT all components. COMPLETE PCM Reset to clear DTCs (REFER to Powertrain Control Module (PCM) Reset). RERUN Quick Test. RERUN Quick Test.
	No	▶	GND open in CMP sensor or connector. SERVICE GND wire or REPLACE sensor. REMOVE all test equipment. RECONNECT all components. COMPLETE PCM Reset to clear DTCs (REFER to Powertrain Control Module (PCM) Reset). RERUN Quick Test.
JG40 WAS QUICK TEST COMPLETED?			
• **Were all tests in Section 5A, Diagnostic Subroutines, followed correctly?**	Yes	▶	GO to JG41.
	No	▶	REFER to Diagnostic Subroutines.
JG41 CHECK FOR GOOD BATTERY			
• **Is battery voltage greater than 12 volts DC with the key on?**	Yes	▶	GO to JG42.
	No	▶	SERVICE battery.
JG42 CHECK FOR PIP SIGNAL			
• Key off. • Connect DI diagnostic harness to EEC breakout box, connect B- lead to negative post of battery, and connect ICM tee to ICM and vehicle harness. • Do not connect B+ lead of DI diagnostic harness to battery. **CAUTION: Do not connect PCM to EEC breakout box when it is used with DI diagnostic harness.** • Make sure PIP OPEN / NORMAL / SPOUT OPEN switch on DI diagnostic harness is in the NORMAL position. • Use DI overlay on breakout box. • Make sure SPOUT in-line connector is disconnected. • DVOM on 40 volt AC scale. • Crank engine and measure voltage between J15 (PIP) and J7 (B-). • **Is voltage between 3.0 and 8.5 volts AC?**	Yes	▶	REPLACE ICM. REMOVE all test equipment. RECONNECT all components. COMPLETE PCM Reset to clear DTCs (REFER to Powertrain Control Module (PCM) Reset). RERUN Quick Test.
	No	▶	GO to JG43.

FM0159601533090X

Fig. 264   Test JG: Distributor Ignition (Part 9 of 12). 1996

Test Step	Result	▶	Action to Take
JG43 CHECK FOR PIP FROM PIP SENSOR			
• Connect diagnostic harness CMP sensor tee to CMP sensor and vehicle harness. • Turn switch on diagnostic cable to PIP OPEN. • DVOM on 40 volt AC scale. • Crank engine and measure voltage between -J34 (PIP) and J7 (B-). • **Is voltage between 3.0 and 8.5 volts AC?**	Yes	▶	SERVICE PIP between ICM and PIP splice in harness for open. COMPLETE PCM Reset to clear DTCs (REFER to Powertrain Control Module (PCM) Reset). RERUN Quick Test.
	No	▶	CHECK CMP sensor wiring and connector, if OK REPLACE CMP sensor. REMOVE all test equipment. RECONNECT all components. COMPLETE PCM Reset to clear DTCs (REFER to Powertrain Control Module (PCM) Reset). RERUN Quick Test.
JG50 CHECK IDM SIGNAL AT PCM CONNECTOR			
• Key off. • Connect DI diagnostic harness to EEC breakout box, connet B- lead to negative post of battery, and connect ICM tee to ICM and vehicle harness. • Make sure PIP OPEN / NORMAL / SPOUT OPEN switch on DI diagnostic harness is in NORMAL position. • Use DI diagnostic overlay on breakout box. • Disconnect PCM. • DVOM on 40 volt AC scale. • Crank engine and measure voltage between Pin 48 (IDM) of the PCM connector and J7 (B-). • **Is voltage greater than 1.0 volt AC?**	Yes	▶	REPLACE PCM. REMOVE all test equipment. RECONNECT all components. COMPLETE PCM Reset to clear DTCs (REFER to Powertrain Control Module (PCM) Reset). RERUN Quick Test.
	No	▶	GO to JG51.
JG51 CHECK FOR IDM SHORT HIGH IN HARNESS			
• Key off. • Disconnect diagnostic harness ICM tee from ICM only; leave ICM tee connected to vehicle harness. • DVOM on 40 volt DC scale. • Key on. • Measure voltage between J23 (IDM) and J7 (B-). • **Is voltage less than 0.5 volt DC?**	Yes	▶	GO to JG52.
	No	▶	SERVICE IDM short high in harness between PCM connector and ICM connector. REMOVE all test equipment. RECONNECT all components. COMPLETE PCM Reset to clear DTCs (REFER to Powertrain Control Module (PCM) Reset). RERUN Quick Test.

FM0159601533100X

Fig. 264   Test JG: Distributor Ignition (Part 10 of 12). 1996

Test Step	Result	▶	Action to Take
JG52 CHECK FOR IDM SHORT LOW IN HARNESS • Key off. • DVOM on 20K ohm scale. • Measure resistance between J23 (IDM) and J7 (B-). • **Is resistance greater than 10K ohms?**	Yes No	▶ ▶	GO to **JG53**. SERVICE IDM short low in harness between PCM connector and ICM connector. REMOVE all test equipment. RECONNECT all components. COMPLETE PCM Reset to clear DTCs (REFER to Powertrain Control Module (PCM) Reset). RERUN Quick Test.
JG53 CHECK FOR IDM OPEN IN HARNESS • Measure resistance between J23 (IDM) and Pin 48 of the PCM connector. • **Is resistance less than 5.0 ohms?**	Yes No	▶ ▶	REPLACE ICM. REMOVE all test equipment. RECONNECT all components. COMPLETE PCM Reset to clear DTCs (REFER to Powertrain Control Module (PCM) Reset). RERUN Quick Test. SERVICE IDM open in harness between ICM and PCM connector. REMOVE all test equipment. RECONNECT all components. COMPLETE PCM Reset to clear DTCs (REFER to Powertrain Control Module (PCM) Reset). RERUN Quick Test.
JG60 CHECK BASE TIMING **CAUTION: Do not use a remote starter while doing timing check.** • Key off. • Install timing light. • Remove SPOUT in line connector. • Run engine at normal operating condition. • **Is base timing within ±3 degrees of specified base timing?**	Yes No	▶ ▶	GO to **JG62**. GO to **JG61**.
JG61 SET BASE TIMING • With engine at idle, or timing rpm if specified, adjust base timing to 10 degrees BTDC. Reference Service Manual, Distributor Removal and Installation. • Reconnect SPOUT in line connector. • Run engine at normal operating condition. • **Is base timing 10 ± 3 degrees?**	Yes No	▶ ▶	GO to **JG62**. SET base timing correctly.

FM0159601533110X

Fig. 264 Test JG: Distributor Ignition (Part 11 of 12). 1996

Test Step	Result	▶	Action to Take
JG62 CHECK FOR SPARK ADVANCE • Key off. • Reconnect SPOUT in line connector. • Run engine at normal operating condition, varying engine speed. • **Is timing greater than 18 degrees and/or does timing advance?**	Yes No	▶ ▶	Not an ignition problem, REFER to Symptom Flowcharts. GO to **JG63**.
JG63 CHECK FOR GOOD SPOUT TO ICM • Connect DI diagnostic harness to EEC breakout box, connect B- lead to negative post of battery, and connect ICM and vehicle harness. • Turn switch on diagnostic cable to SPOUT OPEN. • Use DI overlay on breakout box. • DVOM on 40 volt AC scale. • Run engine and measure voltage between J10 (SPOUT) and J7 (B-). • **Is voltage between 3.0 and 8.5 volts AC?**	Yes No	▶ ▶	REPLACE ICM. REMOVE all test equipment. RECONNECT all components. COMPLETE PCM Reset to clear DTCs (REFER to Powertrain Control Module (PCM) Reset). RERUN Quick Test. GO to **JG64**.
JG64 CHECK FOR SPOUT OPEN IN HARNESS • Key off. • Disconnect PCM. • Disconnect diagnostic harness ICM tee from ICM only; leave ICM tee connected to vehicle harness. • DVOM on 200 ohm scale. • Measure resistance between Pin 50 (SPOUT) of the EEC vehicle harness connector and J10 (SPOUT) at the breakout box. • **Is resistance less than 5.0 ohms?**	Yes No	▶ ▶	REPLACE PCM. REMOVE all test equipment. RECONNECT all components. COMPLETE PCM Reset to clear DTCs (REFER to Powertrain Control Module (PCM) Reset). RERUN Quick Test. SERVICE SPOUT open in harness between PCM and ICM. REMOVE all test equipment. RECONNECT all components. COMPLETE PCM Reset to clear DTCs (REFER to Powertrain Control Module (PCM) Reset). RERUN Quick Test.

FM0159601533120X

Fig. 264 Test JG: Distributor Ignition (Part 12 of 12). 1996

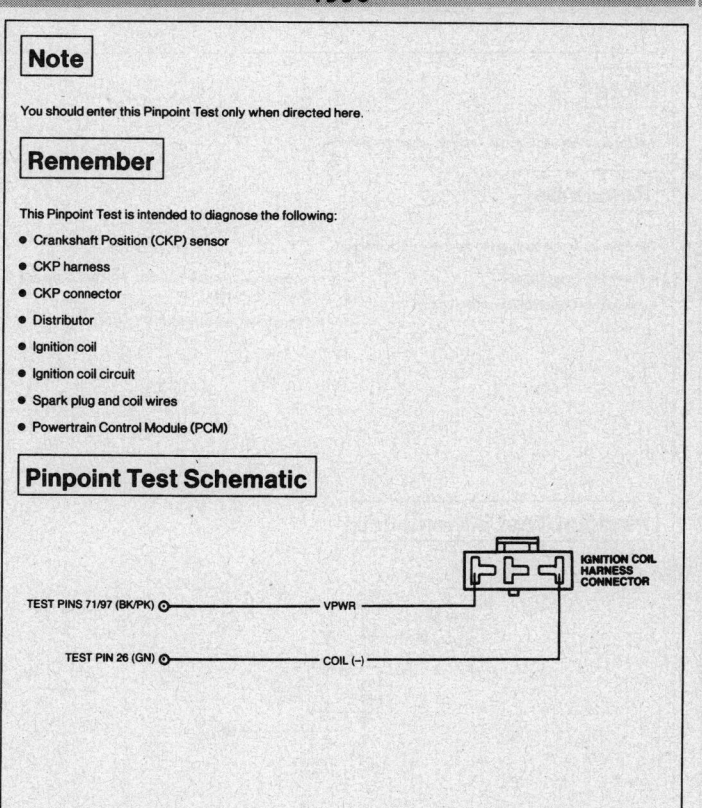

Note

You should enter this Pinpoint Test only when directed here.

Remember

This Pinpoint Test is intended to diagnose the following:

• Crankshaft Position (CKP) sensor
• CKP harness
• CKP connector
• Distributor
• Ignition coil
• Ignition coil circuit
• Spark plug and coil wires
• Powertrain Control Module (PCM)

Pinpoint Test Schematic

FM0159601534010X

Fig. 265 Test JK: Distributor Ignition No Spark (Part 1 of 5). 1996 Probe

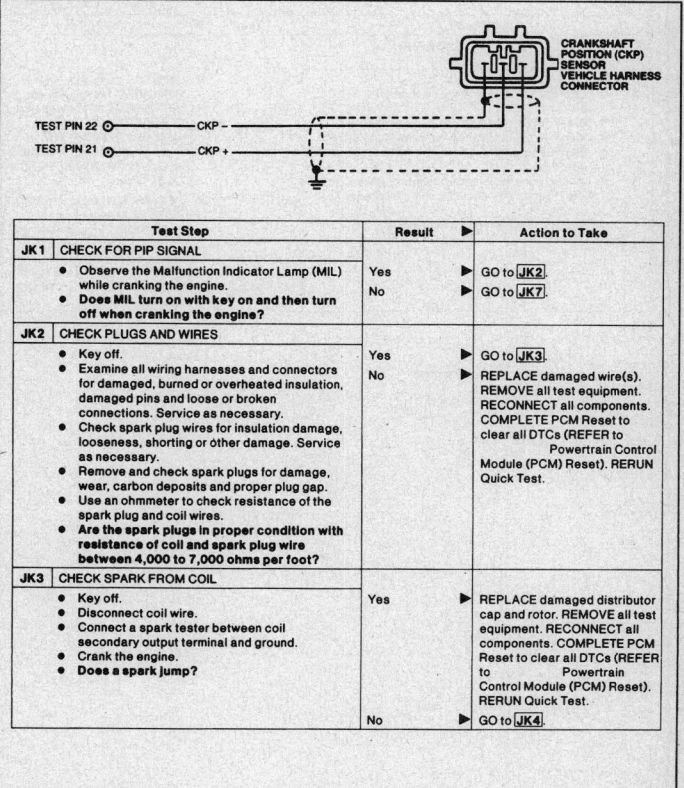

Test Step	Result	▶	Action to Take
JK1 CHECK FOR PIP SIGNAL • Observe the Malfunction Indicator Lamp (MIL) while cranking the engine. • **Does MIL turn on with key on and then turn off when cranking the engine?**	Yes No	▶ ▶	GO to **JK2**. GO to **JK7**.
JK2 CHECK PLUGS AND WIRES • Key off. • Examine all wiring harnesses and connectors for damaged, burned or overheated insulation, damaged pins and loose or broken connections. Service as necessary. • Check spark plug wires for insulation damage, looseness, shorting or other damage. Service as necessary. • Remove and check spark plugs for damage, wear, carbon deposits and proper plug gap. • Use an ohmmeter to check resistance of the spark plug and coil wires. • **Are the spark plugs in proper condition with resistance of coil and spark plug wire between 4,000 to 7,000 ohms per foot?**	Yes No	▶ ▶	GO to **JK3**. REPLACE damaged wire(s). REMOVE all test equipment. RECONNECT all components. COMPLETE PCM Reset to clear all DTCs (REFER to Powertrain Control Module (PCM) Reset). RERUN Quick Test.
JK3 CHECK SPARK FROM COIL • Key off. • Disconnect coil wire. • Connect a spark tester between coil secondary output terminal and ground. • Crank the engine. • **Does a spark jump?**	Yes No	▶ ▶	REPLACE damaged distributor cap and rotor. REMOVE all test equipment. RECONNECT all components. COMPLETE PCM Reset to clear all DTCs (REFER to Powertrain Control Module (PCM) Reset). RERUN Quick Test. GO to **JK4**.

FM0159601534020X

Fig. 265 Test JK: Distributor Ignition No Spark (Part 2 of 5). 1996 Probe

Test Step	Result	▶	Action to Take
JK4 CHECK FOR COIL (-) SIGNAL • Key off. • Ignition coil vehicle harness connector disconnected. • Connect a 12 volt incandescent test lamp between BK/PK wire and GN wire at ignition coil vehicle harness connector. • Key on. • Observe the test lamp while cranking the engine. • **Does test lamp flash brightly?**	Yes No	▶ ▶	REPLACE damaged ignition coil. REMOVE all test equipment. RECONNECT all components. COMPLETE PCM Reset to clear all DTCs (REFER to Powertrain Control Module (PCM) Reset). RERUN Quick Test. REMOVE test lamp. GO to JK5.
JK5 CHECK FOR OPEN IN COIL (-) SIGNAL • Key off. • Ignition coil vehicle harness connector disconnected. • Disconnect PCM. Inspect for damaged or pushed out pins, corrosion, loose wires, etc. Service as necessary. • Install breakout box, leave PCM disconnected. • Measure resistance between GN wire at ignition coil vehicle harness connector and Test Pin 26 (coil (-)). • **Is resistance less than 10,000 ohms?**	Yes No	▶ ▶	GO to JK6. SERVICE open in coil (-) circuit. REMOVE all test equipment. RECONNECT all components. COMPLETE PCM Reset to clear all DTCs (REFER to Powertrain Control Module (PCM) Reset). RERUN Quick Test.
JK6 CHECK FOR COIL (-) SHORT • Key off. • Ignition coil vehicle harness connector disconnected. • Breakout box installed, PCM disconnected. • Measure the resistance between Test Pin 26 (coil (-)) and Test Pins 24 and 103 (PWR GND). • Measure the resistance between Test Pin 26 (coil (-)) and Test Pins 71 and 97 (VPWR). • **Are both resistances greater than 10,000 ohms?**	Yes No	▶ ▶	REPLACE damaged PCM. REMOVE all test equipment. RECONNECT all components. COMPLETE PCM Reset to clear all DTCs (REFER to Powertrain Control Module (PCM) Reset). RERUN Quick Test. SERVICE short(s) in coil (-) circuit. REMOVE all test equipment. RECONNECT all components. COMPLETE PCM Reset to clear all DTCs (REFER to Powertrain Control Module (PCM) Reset). RERUN Quick Test.

FM0159601534030X

Fig. 265   Test JK: Distributor Ignition No Spark (Part 3 of 5). 1996 Probe

Test Step	Result	▶	Action to Take
JK7 CHECK RESISTANCE OF CKP • Key off. • Examine toothed crankshaft wheel behind drive belts for missing teeth or other damage. Service as necessary. • Disconnect Crankshaft Position (CKP) sensor vehicle harness connector. • Measure the resistance of the CKP sensor between CKP+ (21) and CKP- (22) at the sensor connector. • **Is resistance between 520 and 580 ohms?**	Yes No	▶ ▶	GO to JK8. REPLACE damaged CKP sensor. REMOVE all test equipment. RECONNECT all components. COMPLETE PCM Reset to clear all DTCs (REFER to Powertrain Control Module (PCM) Reset). RERUN Quick Test.

CKP+ (21)   CKP- (22)   SHIELD

CRANKSHAFT POSITION (CKP) SENSOR CONNECTOR

Test Step	Result	▶	Action to Take
JK8 CHECK OUTPUT OF CKP SENSOR • Key off. • CKP sensor vehicle harness connector disconnected. • DVOM set to 20V AC. • Key on. • Measure the voltage at the CKP sensor while cranking the engine. • **Is AC voltage approximately 1 volt while cranking the engine?**	Yes No	▶ ▶	GO to JK9. REPLACE damaged CKP sensor. REMOVE all test equipment. RECONNECT all components. COMPLETE PCM Reset to clear all DTCs (REFER to Powertrain Control Module (PCM) Reset). RERUN Quick Test.
JK9 CHECK FOR SHORT • Key off. • CKP sensor vehicle harness connector disconnected. • Disconnect PCM. Inspect for damaged or pushed out pins, corrosion, loose wires, etc. Service as necessary. • Install breakout box, leave PCM disconnected. • Measure the resistance between Test Pins 21 (CKP+), 22 (CKP-) and Test Pins 76, 77 or 103 (PWR GND). • Measure the resistance between Test Pins 21 (CKP+), 22 (CKP-) and Test Pins 76, 77 or 103 (PWR GND). • **Is resistance less than 5 ohms?**	Yes No	▶ ▶	SERVICE short. REMOVE all test equipment. RECONNECT all components. COMPLETE PCM Reset to clear all DTCs (REFER to Powertrain Control Module (PCM) Reset). RERUN Quick Test. GO to JK10.

FM0159601534040X

Fig. 265   Test JK: Distributor Ignition No Spark (Part 4 of 5). 1996 Probe

Test Step	Result	▶	Action to Take
JK10 CHECK CONTINUITY OF CKP+ AND CKP- SIGNALS • Key off. • CKP sensor vehicle harness connector disconnected. • Breakout box installed, PCM disconnected. • Measure the resistance between Test Pin 21 (CKP+) and CKP+ circuit at vehicle harness connector. • Measure the resistance between Test Pin 22 (CKP-) and CKP- circuit at vehicle harness connector. • **Are both resistances less than 10,000 ohms?**	Yes No	▶ ▶	REPLACE damaged PCM. REMOVE all test equipment. RECONNECT all components. COMPLETE PCM Reset to clear all DTCs (REFER to Powertrain Control Module (PCM) Reset). RERUN Quick Test. SERVICE open(s) in circuit(s). REMOVE all test equipment. RECONNECT all components. COMPLETE PCM Reset to clear all DTCs (REFER to Powertrain Control Module (PCM) Reset). RERUN Quick Test.

FM0159601534050X

Fig. 265   Test JK: Distributor Ignition No Spark (Part 5 of 5). 1996 Probe

Note

You should enter this Pinpoint Test only when directed here.

Remember

This Pinpoint Test is intended to diagnose the following:

• Fuel Pump Relay (9345)
• Inertia Fuel Shutoff (IFS) switch (9341)
• Harness circuits: B(+), VPWR, FP, GND, FPM and Power-To-Pump(s)
• Powertrain Control Module (PCM) (12A650)

Pinpoint Test Schematics

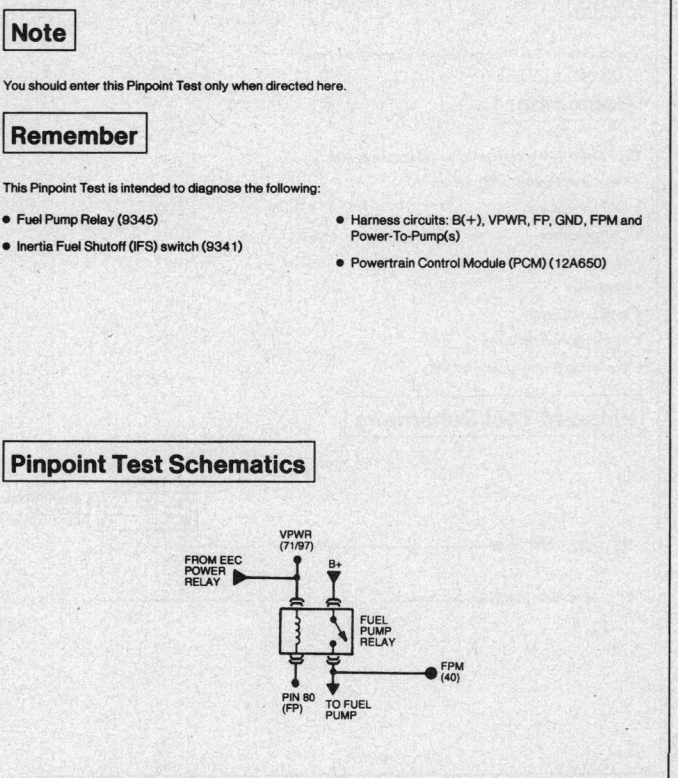

FM0159601535010X

Fig. 266   Test KA: Fuel Pump Relay (Part 1 of 15). 1996

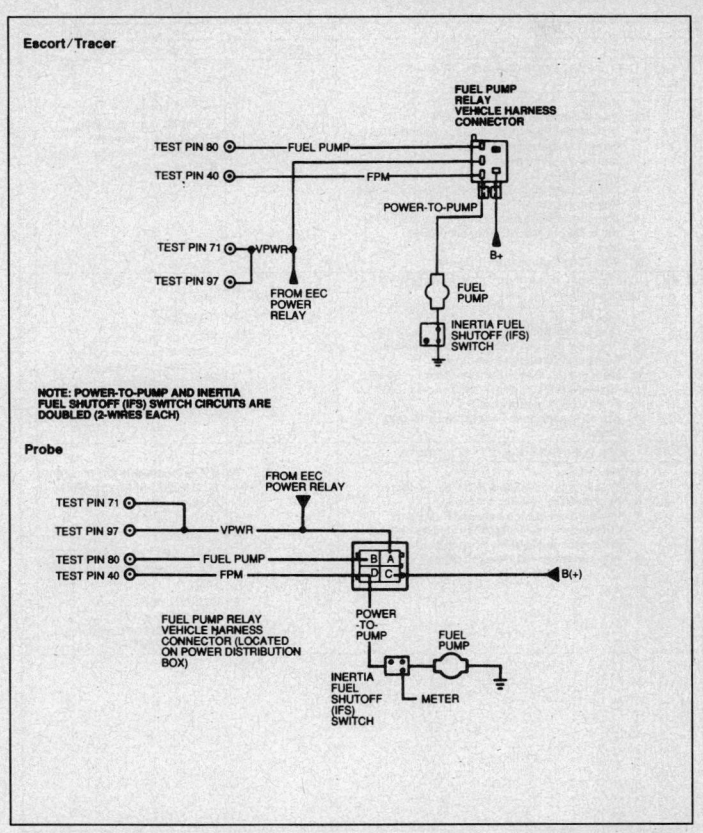

Fig. 266   Test KA: Fuel Pump Relay (Part 2 of 15). 1996

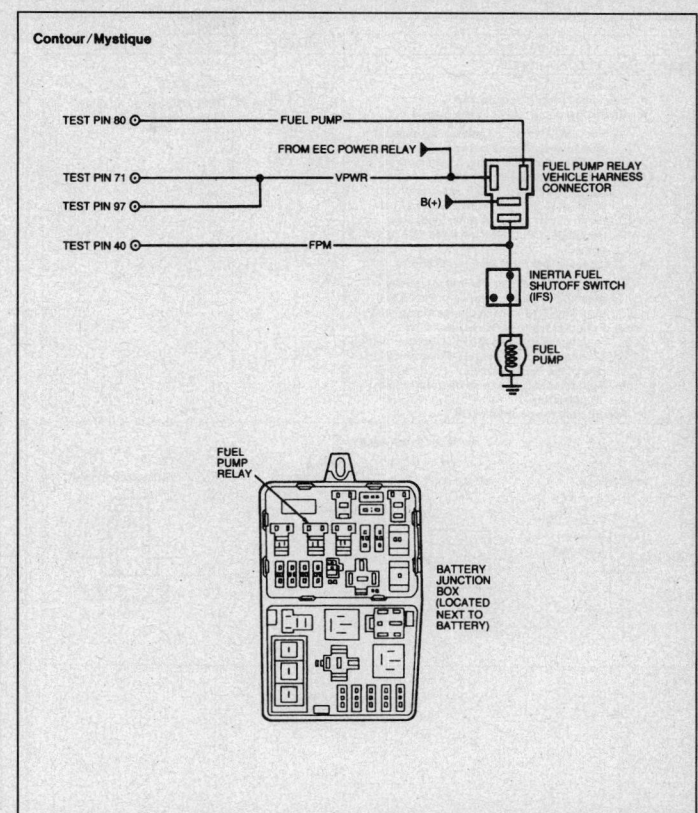

Fig. 266   Test KA: Fuel Pump Relay (Part 3 of 15). 1996

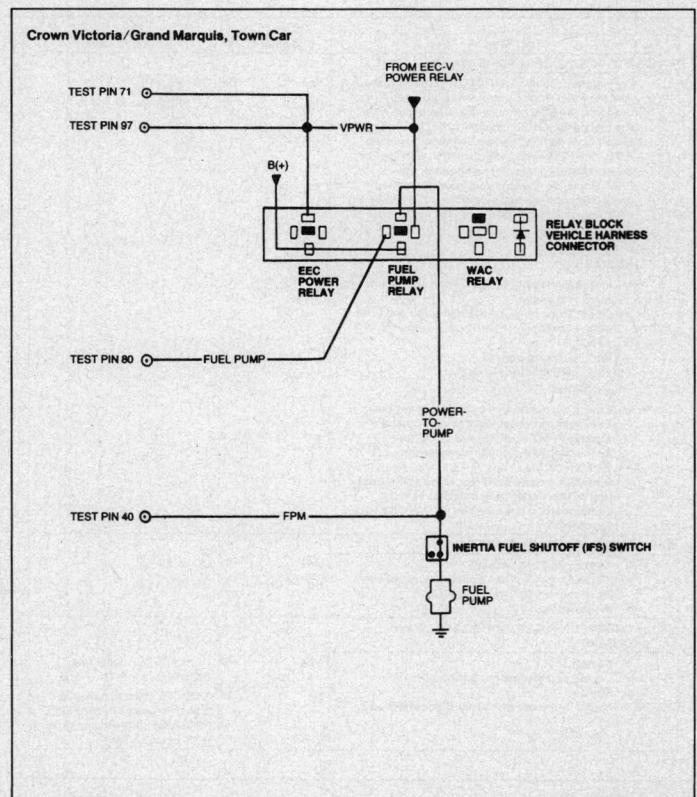

Fig. 266   Test KA: Fuel Pump Relay (Part 4 of 15). 1996

	Test Step	Result	▶	Action to Take
KA1	**DTC P0230: CHECK FOR VPWR TO FUEL PUMP RELAY**			
	Diagnostic Trouble Code (DTC) P0230 indicates a fuel pump primary circuit failure.	Yes	▶	GO to **KA2**.
	Possible causes:	No	▶	SERVICE open in VPWR circuit between the EEC power relay and the fuel pump relay. RECONNECT fuel pump relay. RERUN Quick Test.
	— Open or shorted circuit. — Damaged fuel pump relay. — Damaged PCM. ● Disconnect fuel pump relay. ● Key on, engine off. ● Measure voltage between VPWR circuit at the fuel pump relay vehicle harness connector and chassis ground. ● Key off. ● **Was voltage greater than 10.5 volts?**			

Fig. 266   Test KA: Fuel Pump Relay (Part 5 of 15). 1996

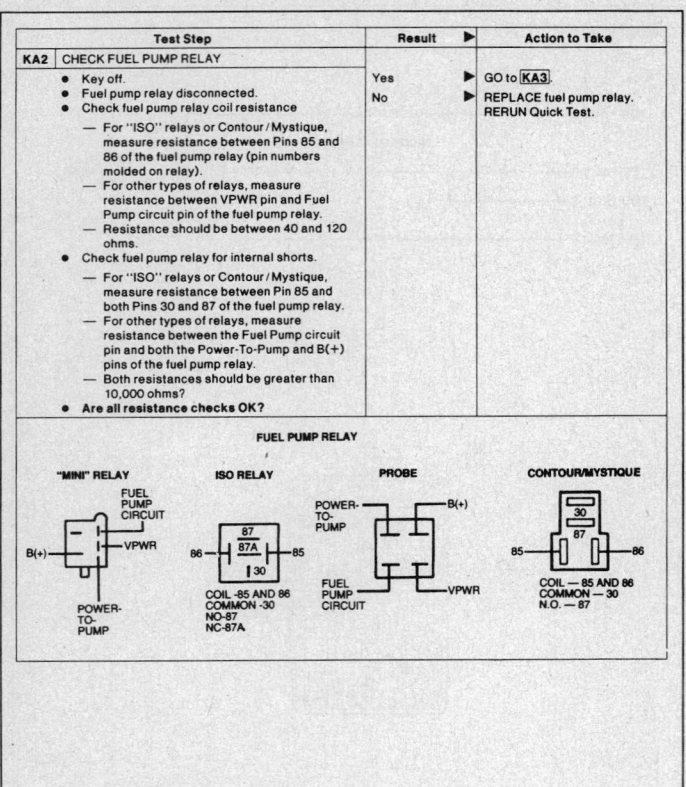

Test Step	Result	▶	Action to Take
KA2 CHECK FUEL PUMP RELAY			
• Key off.			
• Fuel pump relay disconnected.	Yes	▶	GO to **KA3**.
• Check fuel pump relay coil resistance	No	▶	REPLACE fuel pump relay. RERUN Quick Test.
— For "ISO" relays or Contour/Mystique, measure resistance between Pins 85 and 86 of the fuel pump relay (pin numbers molded on relay).			
— For other types of relays, measure resistance between VPWR pin and Fuel Pump circuit pin of the fuel pump relay.			
— Resistance should be between 40 and 120 ohms.			
• Check fuel pump relay for internal shorts.			
— For "ISO" relays or Contour/Mystique, measure resistance between Pin 85 and both Pins 30 and 87 of the fuel pump relay.			
— For other types of relays, measure resistance between the Fuel Pump circuit pin and both the Power-To-Pump and B(+) pins of the fuel pump relay.			
— Both resistances should be greater than 10,000 ohms?			
• **Are all resistance checks OK?**			

FM0159601535110X

Fig. 266   Test KA: Fuel Pump Relay (Part 6 of 15). 1996

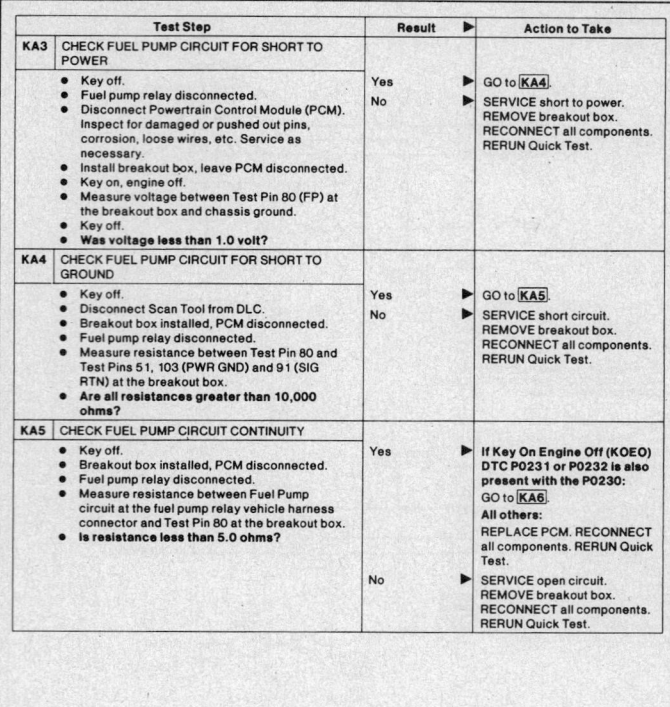

Test Step	Result	▶	Action to Take
KA3 CHECK FUEL PUMP CIRCUIT FOR SHORT TO POWER			
• Key off.			
• Fuel pump relay disconnected.	Yes	▶	GO to **KA4**.
• Disconnect Powertrain Control Module (PCM). Inspect for damaged or pushed out pins, corrosion, loose wires, etc. Service as necessary.	No	▶	SERVICE short to power. REMOVE breakout box. RECONNECT all components. RERUN Quick Test.
• Install breakout box, leave PCM disconnected.			
• Key on, engine off.			
• Measure voltage between Test Pin 80 (FP) at the breakout box and chassis ground.			
• Key off.			
• **Was voltage less than 1.0 volt?**			
KA4 CHECK FUEL PUMP CIRCUIT FOR SHORT TO GROUND			
• Key off.			
• Disconnect Scan Tool from DLC.	Yes	▶	GO to **KA5**.
• Breakout box installed, PCM disconnected.	No	▶	SERVICE short circuit. REMOVE breakout box. RECONNECT all components. RERUN Quick Test.
• Fuel pump relay disconnected.			
• Measure resistance between Test Pin 80 and Test Pins 51, 103 (PWR GND) and 91 (SIG RTN) at the breakout box.			
• **Are all resistances greater than 10,000 ohms?**			
KA5 CHECK FUEL PUMP CIRCUIT CONTINUITY			
• Key off.			
• Breakout box installed, PCM disconnected.	Yes	▶	If Key On Engine Off (KOEO) DTC P0231 or P0232 is also present with the P0230: GO to **KA6**. **All others:** REPLACE PCM. RECONNECT all components. RERUN Quick Test.
• Fuel pump relay disconnected.			
• Measure resistance between Fuel Pump circuit at the fuel pump relay vehicle harness connector and Test Pin 80 at the breakout box.			
• **Is resistance less than 5.0 ohms?**	No	▶	SERVICE open circuit. REMOVE breakout box. RECONNECT all components. RERUN Quick Test.

FM0159601535120X

Fig. 266   Test KA: Fuel Pump Relay (Part 7 of 15). 1996

Test Step	Result	▶	Action to Take
KA6 CHECK THE FUEL PUMP PRIMARY CIRCUIT INSIDE THE PCM			
NOTE: The next two test steps will check the FP circuit in the PCM. To do this either the FPA or FPF PID will be monitored, whichever is available. The FPA PID detects the actual voltage on the FP circuit, and will indicate "ON" when the circuit is grounded and "OFF" when it is not. The FPF PID is able to detect for faults on the FP circuit, and will indicate "NO" when no fault is detected and "YES" when a fault is detected.	Yes	▶	Key off. REPLACE PCM. RECONNECT all components. RERUN Quick Test.
	No	▶	GO to **KA7**.
• Key off.			
• Remove breakout box.			
• Reconnect PCM.			
• Reconnect fuel pump relay.			
• Reconnect Scan Tool to DLC.			
• Key on, engine off.			
• Access FPA or FPF PID (whichever is available) on Scan Tool.			
• **Is the FPF PID "Yes" (or FPA PID on)?**			
KA7 CHECK THE FUEL PUMP PRIMARY CIRCUIT INSIDE THE PCM WHILE CRANKING ENGINE			
NOTE: The Scan Tool must be connected to a reliable power source that is powered with the ignition key in the START position (e.g. directly to the vehicle battery). Also verify that the vehicle battery is fully charged.	Yes	▶	Key off. REPLACE PCM. RECONNECT all components. RERUN Quick Test.
• Key on, engine off.	No	▶	Key off. The fuel pump primary circuit is OK in the harness and PCM.
• While viewing the PFA or FPF PID, crank engine.			If KOEO P0231 is present: GO to **KA20**.
• **Is the FPF PID "Yes" (or FPA PID off) during crank?**			If KOEO P0232 is present: GO to **KA10**.

FM0159601535130X

Fig. 266   Test KA: Fuel Pump Relay (Part 8 of 15). 1996

Test Step	Result	▶	Action to Take
KA10 DTC P0232: DOES ENGINE START?			
Diagnostic Trouble Code (DTC) P0232 indicates that the Powertrain Control Module (PCM) detected the FPM circuit voltage was high when the fuel pump was commanded off. The FPM circuit is wired to a "pull-up" voltage inside the PCM. The FPM circuit will go high if, with the key on and the fuel pump commanded off, the FPM/Power-To-Pump circuit loses its path to ground through the fuel pump. The FPM circuit will also be high if the FPM/Power-To-Pump circuit is shorted to power.	Yes	▶	GO to **KA11**.
	No	▶	GO to **KA15**.
Possible causes:			
No Start:			
— Inertia Fuel Shutoff (IFS) switch not reset or electrically open.			
— Open circuit between the fuel pump and FPM circuit connection to the power-to-pump circuit.			
— Poor fuel pump ground.			
— Fuel pump electrically open.			
Engine Starts:			
— Fuel pump secondary circuit short to power.			
— Fuel pump relay contacts always closed.			
— Open in FPM circuit between PCM and connection to the power-to-pump circuit.			
— Damaged PCM.			
• **Does the engine start (for trucks with dual fuel tanks, verify tank selector is in the same position it was when DTC P0232 was received)?**			
KA11 VERIFY THAT FUEL PUMP IS OFF			
• Key on, wait five seconds.	Yes	▶	GO to **KA13**.
• Listen for motor noise from fuel pump (it may be necessary to listen by fuel tank).	No	▶	GO to **KA12**.
• **Is fuel pump off?**			
KA12 CHECK FOR FUEL PUMP RELAY ALWAYS CLOSED			
• Key off.	Yes	▶	REPLACE fuel pump relay. RERUN Quick Test.
• Locate and disconnect fuel pump relay.	No	▶	SERVICE short to power in power-to-pump/FPM circuit. RECONNECT fuel pump relay. RERUN Quick Test.
• Key on.			
• **Is fuel pump off with relay disconnected?**			

FM0159601535140X

Fig. 266   Test KA: Fuel Pump Relay (Part 9 of 15). 1996

Test Step	Result	▶	Action to Take
KA13 CHECK FPM CIRCUIT CONTINUITY			
• Key off. • Disconnect PCM. Inspect for damaged or pushed out pins, corrosion, loose wires, etc. Service as necessary. • Install breakout box, leave PCM disconnected. • Disconnect fuel pump relay. • Measure resistance between Test Pin 40 (FPM) at the breakout box and power-to-pump circuit at the fuel pump relay vehicle harness connector. • **Is resistance less than 5.0 ohms?**	Yes No	▶ ▶	GO to **KA14**. SERVICE open circuit. REMOVE breakout box. RECONNECT all components. RERUN Quick Test.
KA14 CHECK FPM CIRCUIT IN PCM			
• Key off. • Remove breakout box. • Reconnect PCM. • Reconnect fuel pump relay. • Scan Tool connected to DLC. • Key on, engine off. • Access FPM PID on Scan Tool. • **Is the FPM PID off?**	Yes No	▶ ▶	No fault is detected. The FPM circuit is OK in the harness and PCM. DISREGARD the P0232 at this time. RETURN to the Diagnostic Subroutine that the P0232 was received and continue diagnosis as directed. REPLACE PCM. RERUN Quick Test.
KA15 CHECK INERTIA FUEL SHUTOFF (IFS) SWITCH			
• Key off. • Locate and disconnect Inertia Fuel Shutoff (IFS) switch (verify that switch is reset). • Measure resistance between the C and NC pins of the IFS switch. • **Is resistance less than 5.0 ohms?**	Yes No	▶ ▶	GO to **KA16**. REPLACE or RESET IFS switch. RERUN Quick Test.
KA16 CHECK POWER-TO-PUMP CIRCUIT CONTINUITY BETWEEN IFS SWITCH AND FUEL PUMP RELAY			
• Key off. • IFS switch disconnected. • Disconnect fuel pump relay. • Measure resistance of the Power-to-Pump circuit between the fuel pump relay and IFS switch vehicle harness connectors. • **Is resistance less than 7.0 ohms?**	Yes No	▶ ▶	RECONNECT fuel pump relay. GO to **KA17**. SERVICE open in Power-to-Pump circuit between IFS switch and FPM connection to circuit. (REFER to vehicle schematics to determine IFS location in circuit.) RECONNECT all components. RERUN Quick Test.

FM0159601535150X

Fig. 266   Test KA: Fuel Pump Relay (Part 10 of 15). 1996

Test Step	Result	▶	Action to Take
KA17 CHECK FUEL PUMP GROUND CIRCUIT			
• Key off. • IFS switch disconnected. • Disconnect fuel pump (for trucks with dual tanks, disconnect pump that was selected in **KA10**). • Measure resistance between the fuel pump motor ground circuit at the fuel pump vehicle harness connector and chassis ground. • **Is resistance less than 5.0 ohms?**	Yes No	▶ ▶	GO to **KA18**. SERVICE open fuel pump ground circuit. RECONNECT all components. RERUN Quick Test.
KA18 CHECK CONTINUITY OF POWER-TO-PUMP CIRCUIT BETWEEN THE IFS AND FUEL PUMP			
• Key off. • Fuel pump disconnected. • IFS disconnected. • Measure resistance of the Power-To-Pump circuit between the IFS and fuel pump vehicle harness connectors. • **Is resistance less than 5.0 ohms?**	Yes No	▶ ▶	GO to **KA19**. SERVICE open circuit. RECONNECT all components. RERUN Quick Test.
KA19 CHECK INTERNAL RESISTANCE OF FUEL PUMP			
• Key off. • Fuel pump disconnected. • IFS disconnected. • Measure internal resistance of the fuel pump motor between the Power-To-Pump pin and ground pin of the fuel pump. • **Is resistance less than 10.0 ohms?**	Yes No	▶ ▶	All fuel pump circuit checks are OK. VERIFY test step results. If all test steps are OK, RECONNECT all components. Disregard the P0232 at this time. RETURN to Diagnostic Subroutine in where DTC was received and FOLLOW directions to CONTINUE diagnosis. REPLACE fuel pump. RECONNECT all components. RERUN Quick Test.

FM0159601535160X

Fig. 266   Test KA: Fuel Pump Relay (Part 11 of 15). 1996

Test Step	Result	▶	Action to Take
KA20 DTC P0231: DOES ENGINE START?			
NOTE: If key on, engine off DTC P0230 is also present, go to **KA1** (to check the primary fuel pump circuits first). Diagnostic Trouble Code (DTC) P0231 indicates a fuel pump secondary circuit failure between the B(+) supply and the FPM connection to the power-to-pump circuit. Possible causes: No Start: — Open circuit between the B(+) supply and the FPM connection to the Power-To-Pump circuit. — Fuel pump relay contacts always open. Engine Starts: — Damaged PCM. • **Does the engine start?**	Yes No	▶ ▶	REPLACE PCM. RERUN Quick Test. GO to **KA21**.
KA21 CHECK FOR B(+) TO FUEL PUMP RELAY			
• Key off. • Disconnect fuel pump relay. • Measure voltage between B(+) circuit at the fuel pump relay vehicle harness connector and chassis ground. • **Is voltage greater than 10.5 volts?**	Yes No	▶ ▶	GO to **KA22**. VERIFY integrity of fuse/fuse link for B(+) supply to fuel pump relay. If OK, SERVICE open in B(+) circuit. If fuse/fuse link is damaged, check B(+) and power-to-pump circuits for short to ground before replacing. RECONNECT fuel pump relay. RERUN Quick Test.
KA22 CHECK POWER-TO-PUMP CIRCUIT CONTINUITY			
• Key off. • Fuel pump relay disconnected. • Measure resistance between power-to-pump circuit at the fuel pump relay vehicle harness connector and the battery negative post. • **Is resistance less than 10.0 ohms?**	Yes No	▶ ▶	REPLACE fuel pump relay. RERUN Quick Test. SERVICE open in power-to-pump circuit between FPM splice and fuel pump relay. RECONNECT fuel pump relay. RERUN Quick Test.

FM0159601535170X

Fig. 266   Test KA: Fuel Pump Relay (Part 12 of 15). 1996

Test Step	Result	▶	Action to Take
KA30 CONTINUOUS MEMORY DTC P0232: CHECK EEC-V HARNESS			
NOTE: If Continuous Memory (DTC) P0230 is also present, GO to **KA40**. A Continuous Memory Diagnostic Trouble Code (DTC) P0232 indicates that one of the following intermittent conditions has occurred: — Fuel pump circuit activated when PCM expected circuit to be off (i.e., fuel system test or prime procedure). — Inertia fuel shutoff switch was tripped, then reset. — Open circuit in or between the fuel pump and FPM circuit at the PCM (refer to schematic). — Poor fuel pump ground. — FPM or power-to-pump circuit short to power. — Fuel pump relay contacts stuck closed. — Engine stall due to excessive load. NOTE: For trucks with dual fuel tanks, perform Key On, Engine Off (KOEO) Self-Test twice, once with the front tank selected and once with the rear tank selected. If no KOEO DTCs are present both times, continue with this test (intermittent concern). If KOEO DTC P0232 is present in only one test, refer to the Fuel/Engine Group of the Service Manual to check for open circuit between Fuel Tank selector switch and suspect pump circuit ground. • Key on, engine off. • Access FPM PID on Scan Tool. • Observe the FPM PID for an indication of a fault while performing the following (the FPM PID will turn ON when an open or short to power is detected): — Shake, wiggle, bend the Power-to-Pump circuit between the power-to-pump pin at the fuel pump relay and the fuel pump. — Shake, wiggle, bend the fuel pump ground circuit from the fuel pump to ground. — Lightly tap the fuel pump to simulate road shock. — Shake, wiggle, bend the FPM circuit between the PCM and the splice to the Power-to-Pump circuit. — Lightly tap Inertia Fuel Shutoff switch to simulate road shock. — Lightly tap the fuel pump relay to simulate road shock. • **Is a fault indicated/found?**	Yes No	▶ ▶	Key off. ISOLATE fault and SERVICE as necessary. COMPLETE PCM reset to clear DTCs (REFER to Powertrain Control Module (PCM) Reset.) RERUN Quick Test. Key off. Unable to duplicate and/or identify fault at this time. GO to Pinpoint Test Step **Z1** with the following data: FPM PID and list of possible causes.

FM0159601535180X

Fig. 266   Test KA: Fuel Pump Relay (Part 13 of 15). 1996

Test Step	Result	▶	Action to Take
KA35 CONTINUOUS MEMORY DTC P0231: CHECK EEC-V HARNESS A Continuous Memory Diagnostic Trouble Code (DTC) P0231 indicates that sometime during vehicle operation when the fuel pump was commanded on the FPM circuit voltage went low. (Since there is no FP primary circuit DTC P0230, the primary circuit is assumed to be OK.) Possible causes: — Open in B(+) circuit to the fuel pump relay. — Fuel pump relay contacts open. — Open in Power-to-Pump circuit between the fuel pump relay and FPM slice. ● Key off. ● Disconnect PCM. Inspect for damaged or pushed out pins, corrosion, loose wires, etc. Service as necessary. ● Install breakout box. Leave PCM disconnected. ● Install a jumper wire between Test Pin 80 (FP) and Test Pin 77 (PWR GND). ● Connect a DVOM between Test Pin 40 (FPM) and Test Pin 51 (PWR GND). ● Key on. The fuel pump will turn on and DVOM voltage will be greater than 10.0 volts. ● Observe DVOM voltage for an indication of a fault while performing the following (DVOM voltage will change suddenly when a fault is detected, indicating an open): — Shake, wiggle, bend the B(+) circuit to the fuel pump relay. — Lightly tap the fuel pump relay to simulate road shock. — Shake, wiggle, bend the Power-to-Pump circuit between the fuel pump relay and the FPM splice. ● Key off. ● Inspect the fuel pump relay connector for corrosion, damaged pins, etc. ● **Is a fault indicated?**	Yes No	▶ ▶	ISOLATE fault and SERVICE as necessary. REMOVE breakout box. RECONNECT all components. RERUN Quick Test. Unable to duplicate and/or identify fault at this time. GO to Pinpoint Test Step [Z1] with the following data: FPM PID and list of possible causes.

FM0159601535190X

Fig. 266 Test KA: Fuel Pump Relay (Part 14 of 15). 1996

Test Step	Result	▶	Action to Take
KA40 CONTINUOUS MEMORY DTC P0230: CHECK EEC-V HARNESS A Continuous Memory Diagnostic Trouble Code (DTC) P0230 indicates a fuel pump primary circuit failure has occurred during vehicle operation. Possible causes: — Open in VPWR circuit to fuel pump relay. — Open coil in fuel pump relay. — Open in fuel pump circuit (PCM Pin 80). ● Scan Tool connected. ● Key on, engine off. Wait 5 seconds. ● Access FPF PID or FPA PID (whichever is available). The FPF PID will be no (the FPA PID will be off), indicating that the PCM detects VPWR voltage through the fuel pump relay coil and FP circuit (Pin 80) to the PCM. ● Observe the FPA or FPF PID for an indication of a fault while performing the following (the FPF PID will read yes (the FPA PID will turn on), when an open is detected (this is because the PCM will not detect VPWR voltage on Pin 80 (FP))): — Shake, wiggle, bend the fuel pump circuit between the PCM (Pin 80) and the fuel pump relay. — Shake, wiggle bend the VPWR circuit between the EEC-V Power Relay and the Fuel Pump Relay. — Lightly tap the fuel pump relay (to simulate road shock). ● Key off. ● Inspect the PCM and fuel pump relay connectors for corrosion, damaged pins, etc. ● **Is a fault indicated?**	Yes No	▶ ▶	ISOLATE fault and SERVICE as necessary. COMPLETE PCM reset to clear DTCs (REFER to Powertrain Control Module (PCM) Reset.) RERUN Quick Test. Unable to duplicate and/or identify fault at this time. GO to Pinpoint Test Step [Z1] with the following data: FPA or FPF PID and list of possible causes. For testing the FP circuit with the engine running, also monitor the FPM PID. This is because not all FP circuit failures may be detected using only the FPA or FPF PID.

FM0159601535200X

Fig. 266 Test KA: Fuel Pump Relay (Part 15 of 15). 1996

Note

You should enter this Pinpoint Test only when directed here.

Remember

This Pinpoint Test is intended to diagnose the following:

- Harness circuits: VPWR, GND and B(+) to FPDM Power Supply Relay in CCRM; B(+) and GND to FPDM; FPM; FP; Power-To-Pump; Fuel Pump Ground
- Inertia Fuel Shutoff (IFS) Switch (9341)
- Fuel Pump Driver Module (FPDM) (9D370)
- Constant Control Relay Module (CCRM) (FPDM Power Supply Relay / Circuits) (12B577 / 12B581)
- Powertrain Control Module (PCM) (12A650)

FM0159601536010X

Fig. 267   Test KB: Fuel Pump Driver Module (Part 1 of 15). 1996

Pinpoint Test Schematic

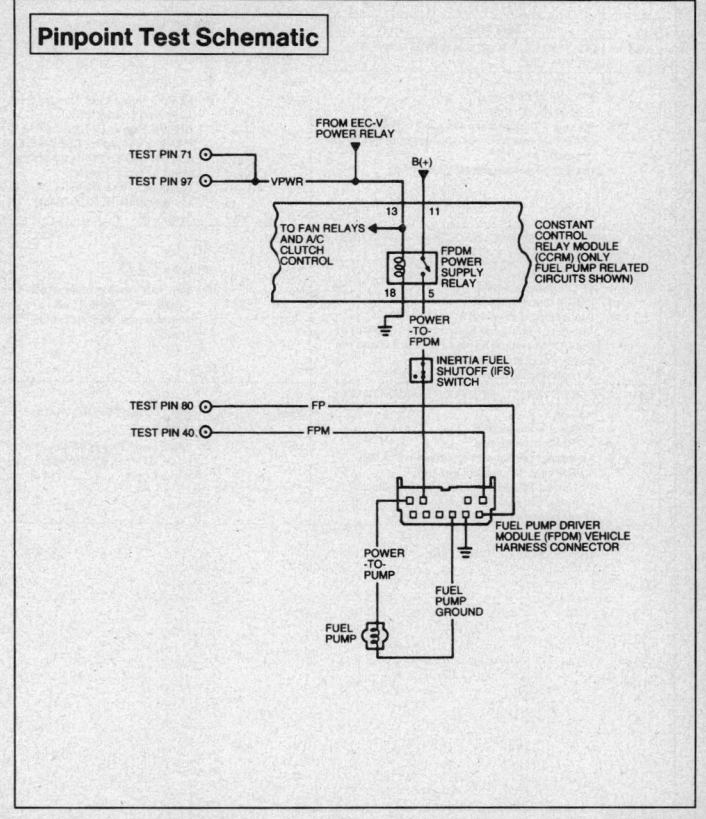

FM0159601536020X

Fig. 267   Test KB: Fuel Pump Driver Module (Part 2 of 15). 1996

Test Step	Result	▶	Action to Take
KB1 DTC P1233 OR P1234: CHECK IF PCM IS NOW RECEIVING AN FPM SIGNAL			
Diagnostic Trouble Code (DTC) P1233 or P1234 indicates that the Powertrain Control Module (PCM) has stopped receiving diagnostic information from the Fuel Pump Driver Module (FPDM). The FPDM diagnostic information is sent to the PCM as a duty cycle on the Fuel Pump Monitor (FPM) circuit. This could be due to an intermittent or hard fault concern. The only difference between the DTC P1233 and P1234 is that the P1233 is a MIL DTC. Possible causes:	Yes	▶	The PCM is now receiving a signal from the FPDM. One possible cause of the DTC P1233 or P1234 may be that the IFS switch was tripped, then reset. **If engine is now a no start:** Disregard the DTC P1233 or P1234 at this time continue the Diagnostic Subroutine as directed. After servicing the no start, to diagnose intermittent causes of the DTC P1233 or P1234, RETURN to KB25. **If engine will start:** An intermittent fault may exist. GO to KB25.
— Inertia Fuel Shutoff (IFS) switch needs to be reset. — Open Power-To-FPDM circuit (from Constant Control Relay Module (CCRM)). — Open FPDM ground circuit. — Open B(+) to CCRM (pin 11). — Open ground to CCRM (pin 18). — Open VPWR to CCRM (pin 13). — Open or shorted FPM circuit. — Damaged IFS. — Damaged CCRM. — Damaged FPDM. — Damaged PCM. • Scan tool connected. • Key on, engine off. • Access FPM PID. • Is the FPM PID between 20% and 80%?	No	▶	A hard fault is present. GO to KB2.
KB2 DOES THE ENGINE START?			
• Does the engine start?	Yes	▶	GO to KB15 (to check the FPM circuit).
	No	▶	VERIFY IFS switch is set (button depressed). If OK, GO to KB3.

FM0159601536030X

Fig. 267   Test KB: Fuel Pump Driver Module (Part 3 of 15). 1996

Test Step	Result	▶	Action to Take
KB3 CHECK POWER AND GROUND CIRCUITS TO FPDM			
• Key off. • Disconnect FPDM. • Key on, engine off. • Measure voltage between the Power-To-FPDM pin and ground pin at the FPDM vehicle harness connector. • Is voltage greater than 10.5 volts?	Yes	▶	Key off. REPLACE FPDM. RECONNECT all components. RERUN Quick Test.
	No	▶	GO to KB7.
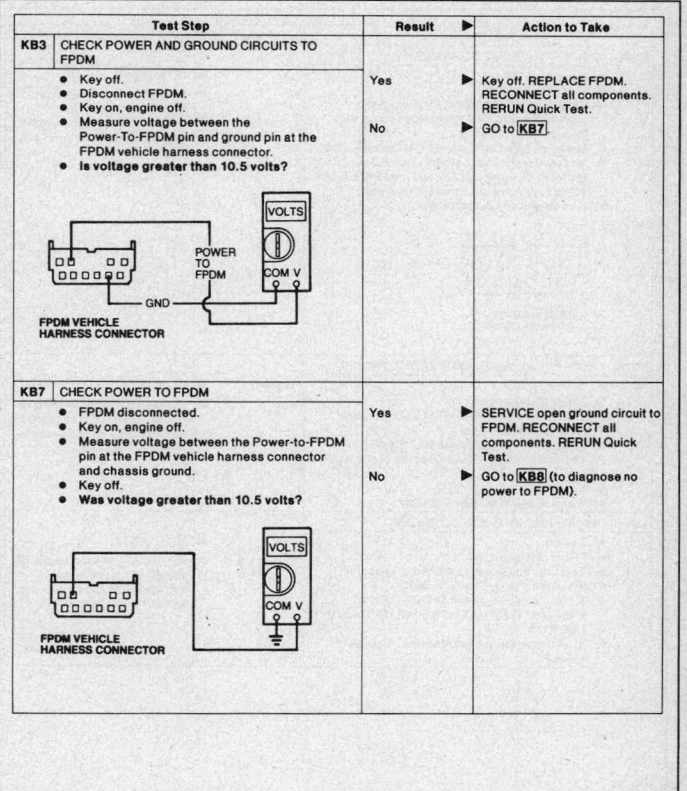			
KB7 CHECK POWER TO FPDM			
• FPDM disconnected. • Key on, engine off. • Measure voltage between the Power-to-FPDM pin at the FPDM vehicle harness connector and chassis ground. • Key off. • Was voltage greater than 10.5 volts?	Yes	▶	SERVICE open ground circuit to FPDM. RECONNECT all components. RERUN Quick Test.
	No	▶	GO to KB8 (to diagnose no power to FPDM).

FM0159601536040X

Fig. 267   Test KB: Fuel Pump Driver Module (Part 4 of 15). 1996

Test Step	Result	▶	Action to Take
KB8 CHECK FOR B(+) TO CCRM (FPDM POWER SUPPLY RELAY) • Key off. • FPDM disconnected. • Disconnect CCRM. • Measure voltage between pin 11 (B+) of the CCRM vehicle harness connector and chassis ground. • **Is voltage greater than 10.5 volts?**	Yes No	▶ ▶	GO to **KB9**. VERIFY integrity of fuse for B+ supply to CCRM. If OK, SERVICE open B(+) to CCRM. If fuse is damaged, CHECK B+ and power-to-FPDM circuits for short to ground before replacing. RECONNECT all components. RERUN Quick Test.
KB9 CHECK FOR GROUND TO CCRM (FPDM POWER SUPPLY RELAY) • Key off. • FPDM disconnected. • CCRM disconnected. • Disconnect Scan Tool from DLC. • Measure resistance between pin 18 (GND) of the CCRM vehicle harness connector and the battery negative post. • **Is resistance less than 5.0 ohms?**	Yes No	▶ ▶	GO to **KB10**. SERVICE open ground circuit to CCRM. RECONNECT all components. RERUN Quick Test.
KB10 CHECK POWER-TO-FPDM CIRCUIT CONTINUITY • Key off. • FPDM disconnected. • CCRM disconnected. • Measure resistance between pin 5 of the CCRM vehicle harness and the Power-To-FPDM pin of the FPDM vehicle harness connector. • **Is resistance less than 5.0 ohms?**	Yes No	▶ ▶	RECONNECT FPDM. GO to **KB11**. The Power-To-FPDM circuit is open. GO to **KB13** to help isolate fault.

FM0159601536050X

Fig. 267 Test KB: Fuel Pump Driver Module (Part 5 of 15). 1996

Test Step	Result	▶	Action to Take
KB11 CHECK VPWR CONTINUITY BETWEEN EEC-V POWER RELAY AND CCRM • Key off. • CCRM disconnected. • Disconnect EEC-V Power Relay. • Measure resistance between the VPWR pin at the EEC-V Power Relay vehicle harness connector and pin 13 (VPWR) of the CCRM vehicle harness connector. • **Is resistance less than 5.0 ohms?** **EEC-V POWER RELAY VEHICLE HARNESS CONNECTOR**	Yes No	▶ ▶	REPLACE CCRM. RECONNECT all components. RERUN Quick Test. SERVICE open VPWR circuit between EEC-V Power Relay and CCRM. RECONNECT all components. RERUN Quick Test.
KB13 ISOLATE OPEN IN POWER-TO-FPDM CIRCUIT • Key off. • CCRM disconnected. • FPDM disconnected. • Disconnect IFS switch. • Measure resistance of the Power-To-FPDM circuit between pin 5 of the CCRM vehicle harness connector and the IFS switch vehicle harness connector. • Measure resistance of the Power-To-FPDM circuit between the FPDM vehicle harness connector and the IFS switch vehicle harness connector. • **Are both resistances less than 5.0 ohms?**	Yes No	▶ ▶	VERIFY that the IFS switch is set (button depressed). If OK, REPLACE IFS switch. RECONNECT all components. RERUN Quick Test. SERVICE open in the appropriate area of the Power-To-FPDM circuit. RECONNECT all components. RERUN Quick Test.

FM0159601536060X

Fig. 267 Test KB: Fuel Pump Driver Module (Part 6 of 15). 1996

Test Step	Result	▶	Action to Take
KB15 CHECK FPM CIRCUIT CONTINUITY • Key off. • Disconnect FPDM. • Disconnect PCM. Inspect for damaged or pushed out pins, corrosion, loose wires, etc. Service as necessary. • Install breakout box, leave PCM disconnected. • Measure resistance between Test Pin 40 (FPM) at the breakout box and the FPM circuit at the FPDM vehicle harness connector. • **Is resistance less than 5.0 ohms?** FPM (40) **FPDM VEHICLE HARNESS CONNECTOR**	Yes No	▶ ▶	GO to **KB16**. SERVICE open FPM circuit. REMOVE breakout box. RECONNECT all components. RERUN Quick Test.
KB16 CHECK FPM CIRCUIT FOR SHORT TO POWER • Key off. • FPDM disconnected. • Breakout box installed, PCM disconnected. • Key on, engine off. • Measure voltage between Test Pin 40 (FPM) and Test Pin 51 (PWR GND) at the breakout box. • Key off. • **Was voltage less than 1.0 volt?**	Yes No	▶ ▶	GO to **KB17**. SERVICE FPM circuit short to power. REMOVE breakout box. RECONNECT all components. RERUN Quick Test.
KB17 CHECK FPM FOR SHORT TO GROUND • Key off. • FPDM disconnected. • Breakout box installed, PCM disconnected. • Disconnect Scan Tool from DLC. • Measure resistance between Test Pin 40 (FPM) and Test Pins 51, 76 (PWR GND) and 91 (SIG RTN). • **Is each resistance greater than 10,000 ohms?**	Yes No	▶ ▶	GO to **KB18**. SERVICE FPM short to ground. REMOVE breakout box. RECONNECT all components. RERUN Quick Test.

FM0159601536070X

Fig. 267 Test KB: Fuel Pump Driver Module (Part 7 of 15). 1996

Test Step	Result	▶	Action to Take
KB18 CHECK FOR FPM OUTPUT FROM FPDM • Key off. • Breakout box installed, PCM disconnected. • Scan Tool disconnected. • Reconnect FPDM. • Key on, engine off. • Measure DC voltage between Test Pin 40 (FPM) and Test Pin 51 (PWR GND) at the breakout box. • **Is voltage between .02 and 1.0 volt DC? (It is OK for the voltage to cycle below this range and then come back in it.)**	Yes No	▶ ▶	Key off. REPLACE PCM. REMOVE breakout box. RECONNECT all components. RERUN Quick Test. Key off. REPLACE FPDM. REMOVE breakout box. RECONNECT all components. RERUN Quick Test.

KB25 CHECK CIRCUITS THAT MAY CAUSE AN INTERMITTENT LOSS OF POWER SUPPLY TO THE FPDM. ALSO CHECK FOR INTERMITTENT OPENS OR SHORTS ON THE FPM CIRCUIT.
• Scan Tool connected.
• Key on, engine off.
• FPM PID displayed on Scan Tool.
• Observe FPM PID for an indication of a fault while performing the following (If the FPM PID goes less than 20%, an open in the power supply to the FPDM, or an open or short to ground on the FPM circuit may exist. If the FPM PID goes greater than 80%, an open or short to power on the FPM circuit may exist.):
— Shake, wiggle, bend the following circuits:
  • FPDM ground.
  • Power-To-FPDM circuit between the FPDM and the CCRM.
  • CCRM ground circuit from pin 18 (CCRM).
  • B(+) to CCRM pin 11.
  • VPWR circuit between the EEC-V power relay and Pin 13 of the CCRM.
  • FPM circuit between the FPDM and the PCM.
— Lightly tap on the CCRM, IFS Switch and FPDM to simulate road shock.
• Key off.
• **Is a fault indicated?**
	Yes
	
	No
		▶
		
		▶
			ISOLATE fault and SERVICE as necessary. PERFORM PCM Reset to clear DTCs (REFER to Powertrain Control Module (PCM) Reset). RERUN Quick Test.
			Unable to duplicate and/or identify fault at this time. GO to Pinpoint Test Step **Z1** with the following data: FPM PID and list of possible causes.

FM0159601536080X

Fig. 267 Test KB: Fuel Pump Driver Module (Part 8 of 15). 1996

Test Step	Result	▶	Action to Take
KB30 DTCs P0230, P1235 OR P1236: CHECK FPM PID TO SEE IF FAULT IS PRESENT NOW			
Diagnostic Trouble Codes (DTCs) P0230, P1235 or P1236 indicate than an FP circuit (PCM pin 80) fault has been detected. This could be due to an intermittent or hard fault concern. The only difference between the DTC P1235 and P1236 is that the P1235 is a MIL DTC.	Yes	▶	A hard fault is present. GO to **KB31** (to check the FP circuit).
Possible causes: — FP circuit open or short. — Damaged Fuel Pump Driver Module (FPDM). — Damaged PCM.	No	▶	DTC P0230, P1235 or P1236 is intermittent. GO to **KB40**.
NOTE: If the FPDM does not receive a valid fuel pump command signal from the PCM on the FP circuit, the FPDM will go into FMEM and run the fuel pump at 100%. When this happens, the FPDM will also send a 25% duty cycle signal to the PCM on the Fuel Pump Monitor (FPM) circuit. • Scan Tool connected. • Key on, engine off. • Access FPM PID. • **Is the FPM PID between 20% and 30%?**			
KB31 FPM PID IS BETWEEN 20% AND 30%: CHECK FP CIRCUIT CONTINUITY			
• Key off. • Disconnect FPDM. • Disconnect PCM. Inspect for damaged or pushed out pins, corrosion, loose wires, etc. Service as necessary. • Install breakout box, leave PCM disconnected. • Measure resistance between test pin 80 (FP) at the breakout box and the FP circuit at the FPDM vehicle harness connector. • **Is resistance less than 5.0 ohms?**	Yes	▶	GO to **KB32**.
	No	▶	SERVICE open FP circuit. REMOVE breakout box. RECONNECT all components. RERUN Quick Test.

FP (80)

FPDM VEHICLE HARNESS CONNECTOR

FM0159601536090X

Fig. 267   Test KB: Fuel Pump Driver Module (Part 9 of 15). 1996

Test Step	Result	▶	Action to Take
KB32 CHECK FP CIRCUIT FOR SHORT TO POWER			
• Key off. • FPDM disconnected. • Breakout box installed, PCM disconnected. • Key on, engine off. • Measure voltage between Test Pin 80 (FP) and Test Pin 51 (PWR GND) at the breakout box. • Key off. • **Was voltage less than 1.0 volt?**	Yes No	▶ ▶	GO to **KB33**. SERVICE FP circuit short to power. REMOVE breakout box. RECONNECT all components. RERUN Quick Test.
KB33 CHECK FP CIRCUIT FOR SHORT TO GROUND			
• Key off. • FPDM disconnected. • Breakout box installed, PCM disconnected. • Disconnect Scan Tool from DLC. • Measure resistance between Test Pin 80 (FP) and Test Pins 51, 76 (PWR GND) and 91 (SIG RTN). • **Is each resistance greater than 10,000 ohms?**	Yes No	▶ ▶	GO to **KB34**. SERVICE FP circuit short to ground. REMOVE breakout box. RECONNECT all components. RERUN Quick Test.
KB34 CHECK FP CIRCUIT IN FPDM			
• Key off. • Breakout box installed, PCM disconnected. • Reconnect FPDM. • Key on, engine off. • Measure voltage between Test Pin 80 (FP) and Test Pin 51 (PWR GND) at the breakout box. • **Is voltage between 4.5 and 5.5 volts?**	Yes No	▶ ▶	REPLACE PCM. REMOVE breakout box. RECONNECT all components. RERUN Quick Test. REPLACE FPDM. REMOVE breakout box. RECONNECT all components. RERUN Quick Test.
KB40 CHECK FP CIRCUIT FOR INTERMITTENT OPENS OR SHORTS			
• Scan Tool connected. • Key on, engine off. • FPM PID displayed on Scan Tool. • Listen for the fuel pump to turn on while performing the following: (The fuel pump will turn on when an open or short on the FP circuit is detected. Also, the FPM PID will be between 20% and 30% when a fault is detected.) — Shake, wiggle, bend the FP circuit between FPDM and the PCM. — Lightly tap on the FPDM (to simulate road shock). • Key off. • **Is a fault indicated?**	Yes No	▶ ▶	ISOLATE fault and SERVICE as necessary. PERFORM PCM Reset to clear DTCs (REFER to Powertrain Control Module (PCM) Reset). Unable to duplicate and/or identify fault at this time. GO to Pinpoint Test Step **Z1** with the following data: FPM PID and list of possible causes.

FM0159601536100X

Fig. 267   Test KB: Fuel Pump Driver Module (Part 10 of 15). 1996

Test Step	Result	▶	Action to Take
KB45 NO FUEL PRESSURE WITH NO DTCs: CHECK IF FUEL PUMP RUNS			
• Key off. • While listening for the fuel pump to run, turn the key on. The fuel pump should run for about one second, then turn off. Repeat if necessary. • If the fuel pump cannot be heard, perform the following: — Key on, engine off. — Scan Tool connected. — Enter Output Test Mode on Scan Tool — Command outputs on. — Listen by the fuel tank to check if the fuel pump is running. When the outputs are commanded on, the PCM may turn the fuel pump off within 5 seconds. REPEAT test if necessary. — Exit Output Test Mode. • **Does the fuel pump run?**	Yes No	▶ ▶	The fuel pump electrical circuits are OK. GO to Pinpoint Test Step **HC1** to check the mechanical operation of the fuel pump, etc. GO to **KB46**.
KB46 FUEL PUMP DOES NOT RUN: CHECK FPM PID			
• Scan Tool connected. • Key on, engine off. • Access FPM PID. • **Is the FPM PID between 70% and 80%?**	Yes No	▶ ▶	The FPDM detects a fault in the fuel pump secondary circuits (Power-To-Pump, Fuel Pump Ground, internal fuel pump). GO to **KB49**. GO to Pinpoint Test Step **HC1** (to check the mechanical operation of the fuel pump). Be aware that the following things are known at this point of diagnosis: — The FPDM does NOT detect a fault in the fuel pump secondary circuits. — A fault in the primary circuit (FP, PCM pin 80) would result in the FPDM taking FMEM action and running the pump all the time. — A fault in the FPDM power supply or ground circuits would result in an EEC-V Self-Test DTC.

FM0159601536110X

Fig. 267   Test KB: Fuel Pump Driver Module (Part 11 of 15). 1996

Test Step	Result	▶	Action to Take
KB47 DTCS P1237 OR P1238: CHECK FPM PID TO SEE IF FAULT IS PRESENT NOW			
Diagnostic Trouble Codes (DTCs) P1237 or P1238 indicate that the Fuel Pump Driver Module (FPDM) has detected a fuel pump secondary circuit fault. This could be due to an intermittent or hard fault concern. The only difference between the DTC P1237 and P1238 is that the P1237 is a MIL DTC.	Yes No	▶ ▶	A hard fault is present. GO to **KB48**. DTC P1237 or P1238 is intermittent. GO to **KB57**.
Possible causes: — Open or shorted Power-To-Pump circuit. — Open fuel pump ground circuit to FPDM. — Open or shorted circuit in fuel pump. — Locked fuel pump rotor. — Damaged FPDM. • Scan Tool connected. • Key on, engine off. • Access FPM PID. • **Is the FPM PID between 70% and 80%?**			
KB48 DOES THE ENGINE START?			
• **Does the engine start?**	Yes No	▶ ▶	DISCONNECT FPDM. GO to **KB62**. GO TO **KB49** (to check fuel pump secondary circuits).
KB49 FPM PID IS BETWEEN 70% AND 80%: CHECK POWER-TO-PUMP, FUEL PUMP GROUND AND INTERNAL FUEL PUMP CIRCUIT CONTINUITY			
• Key off. • Disconnect Scan Tool from DLC. • Disconnect FPDM. • Measure resistance between the Power-To-Pump circuit and the fuel pump ground circuit at the FPDM vehicle harness connector. • **Is resistance less than 10.0 ohms?**	Yes No	▶ ▶	GO to **KB50**. An open secondary circuit exists. GO to **KB54** to isolate fault.

POWER-TO-PUMP

FUEL PUMP GROUND

FPDM VEHICLE HARNESS CONNECTOR

FM0159601536120X

Fig. 267   Test KB: Fuel Pump Driver Module (Part 12 of 15). 1996

Test Step	Result	▶	Action to Take
KB50 CHECK FUEL PUMP GROUND CIRCUIT FOR SHORT TO POWER • FPDM disconnected. • Key on, engine off. • Measure voltage between the fuel pump ground circuit at the FPDM vehicle harness connector and chassis ground. • Key off. • **Was voltage less than 1.0 volt?**	Yes No	▶ ▶	GO to KB51. SERVICE short to power. RECONNECT all components. RERUN Quick Test.
KB51 CHECK POWER-TO-PUMP CIRCUIT FOR SHORT TO GROUND • Key off. • Scan Tool disconnected. • Disconnect fuel pump. • Measure resistance between the Power-To-Pump circuit at the FPDM vehicle harness connector and the battery negative post. • **Is resistance greater than 10,000 ohms?**	Yes No	▶ ▶	GO to KB52. SERVICE short to ground. RECONNECT all components. RERUN Quick Test.
KB52 CHECK FOR VOLTAGE TO FUEL PUMP • Key off. • Fuel pump disconnected. • Reconnect FPDM. • Reconnect Scan Tool. • Key on, engine off. • Enter Output Test Mode on Scan Tool (refer to Section 2A). (To perform this test step without a Scan Tool, the fuel pump can be commanded on for one second by cycling the key from off to on. Repeat as needed.) • Command outputs on (this commands the fuel pump on for about 5 seconds). • Measure voltage between the Power-To-Pump circuit and the fuel pump ground circuit at the fuel pump vehicle harness connector. • Key off. • **With the pump commanded on, is the voltage greater than 10.0 volts?**	Yes No	▶ ▶	REPLACE fuel pump. RECONNECT all components. RERUN Quick Test. VERIFY vehicle battery was at proper charge during test. VERIFY pump on command did not "time-out" before voltage check was made. If OK, REPLACE FPDM. RECONNECT all components. RERUN Quick Test.
KB54 ISOLATE OPEN CIRCUIT • Key off. • FPDM disconnected. • Disconnect fuel pump. • Measure resistance of the Power-To-Pump circuit between the FPDM and the fuel pump. • Measure resistance of the fuel pump ground circuit between the FPDM and the fuel pump. • Measure internal resistance of the fuel pump. • **Is each resistance less than 10.0 ohms?**	Yes No	▶ ▶	No fault is detected. Verify results of previous test steps. SERVICE open in appropriate circuit (if open was internal to fuel pump, REPLACE pump). RECONNECT all components. RERUN Quick Test.

FM0159601536130

Fig. 267 Test KB: Fuel Pump Driver Module (Part 13 of 15). 1996

Test Step	Result	▶	Action to Take
KB57 CHECK FUEL PUMP SECONDARY CIRCUITS FOR INTERMITTENT OPENS OR SHORTS • Disconnect PCM. • Key on, engine off. The fuel pump will turn on (this is because the FPDM will turn the pump on if a valid FP signal is not received from the PCM.) • Command outputs on (this will turn the fuel pump on). • Listen for the fuel pump to turn on while performing the following (if the fuel pump cannot be heard, it may be necessary to disconnect the pump and insert a test lamp in the vehicle harness connector): — Shake, wiggle, bend the Power-To-Pump circuit and fuel pump ground circuit between the FPDM and the fuel pump. — Lightly tap the fuel pump and the FPDM to simulate road shock. • Key off. • **Is a fault indicated?**	Yes No	▶ ▶	ISOLATE fault and SERVICE as necessary. RECONNECT PCM. RERUN Quick Test. Unable to duplicate and/or identify fault at this time. RECONNECT PCM. GO to Pinpoint Test Step Z1 with the following data: FPM PID and list of possible causes for DTC P1237 or P1238.
KB60 FUEL PUMP ALWAYS RUNS: CHECK FPM PID • Scan Tool connected. • Key on, engine off. • Access FPM PID. • **Is the FPM PID between 20% and 30%?**	Yes No	▶ ▶	The Fuel Pump Driver Module (FPDM) detects a fault in the FP circuit input from the PCM. When this occurs, the FPDM will always run the fuel pump when the key is on. GO to KB31 to diagnose the FP circuit. Key off. GO to KB61 (to check if FPDM is always powered).

FM0159601536140X

Fig. 267 Test KB: Fuel Pump Driver Module (Part 14 of 15). 1996

Test Step	Result	▶	Action to Take
KB61 CHECK POWER-TO-FPDM CIRCUIT VOLTAGE TO FPDM WITH THE KEY OFF • Key off. • Disconnect the Fuel Pump Driver Module (FPDM). • Measure voltage between the Power-To-FPDM circuit and chassis ground. • **Is voltage greater than 2.0 volts with the key off?**	Yes No	▶ ▶	Power is always being supplied to the FPDM, which will result in the fuel pump always running. GO to KB65. GO to KB62.

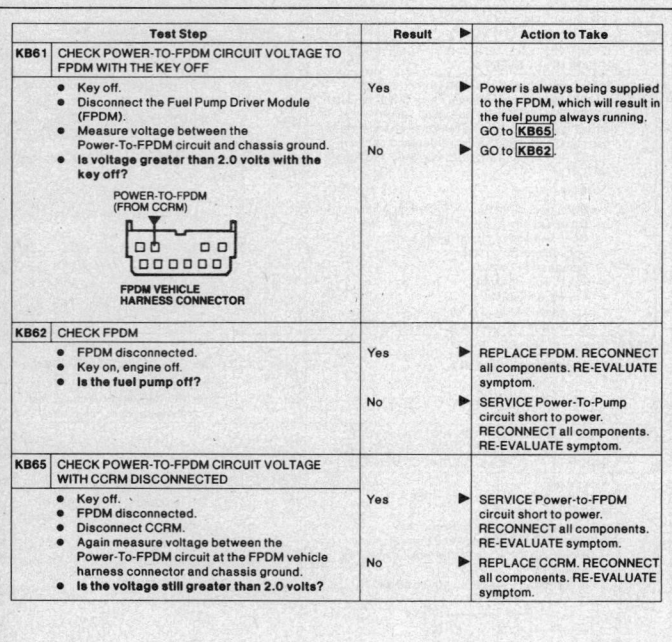

POWER-TO-FPDM (FROM CCRM)

FPDM VEHICLE HARNESS CONNECTOR

Test Step	Result	▶	Action to Take
KB62 CHECK FPDM • FPDM disconnected. • Key on, engine off. • **Is the fuel pump off?**	Yes No	▶ ▶	REPLACE FPDM. RECONNECT all components. RE-EVALUATE symptom. SERVICE Power-To-Pump circuit short to power. RECONNECT all components. RE-EVALUATE symptom.
KB65 CHECK POWER-TO-FPDM CIRCUIT VOLTAGE WITH CCRM DISCONNECTED • Key off. • FPDM disconnected. • Disconnect CCRM. • Again measure voltage between the Power-To-FPDM circuit at the FPDM vehicle harness connector and chassis ground. • **Is the voltage still greater than 2.0 volts?**	Yes No	▶ ▶	SERVICE Power-to-FPDM circuit short to power. RECONNECT all components. RE-EVALUATE symptom. REPLACE CCRM. RECONNECT all components. RE-EVALUATE symptom.

FM0159601536150X

Fig. 267 Test KB: Fuel Pump Driver Module (Part 15 of 15). 1996

Note

You should enter this Pinpoint Test only when directed here.

Remember

This Pinpoint Test is intended to diagnose the following:

• Fuel Shutoff Valve Relay
• Inertia Fuel Shutoff (IFS) switch (9341)

• Harness circuits: B(+), VPWR, FSV, GND, FSVM and Power-To-Fuel Shutoff Valves
• Powertrain Control Module (PCM) (12A650)

Pinpoint Test Schematics

VPWR (71/97)   B+

FROM EEC POWER RELAY

FUEL SHUTOFF VALVE RELAY

PIN 80 (FSV)   TO FUEL SHUTOFF VALVES   PIN 40 (FSVM)

FM0159601537010X

Fig. 268 Test KC: Fuel Shutoff Valve Relay (Part 1 of 12). 1996

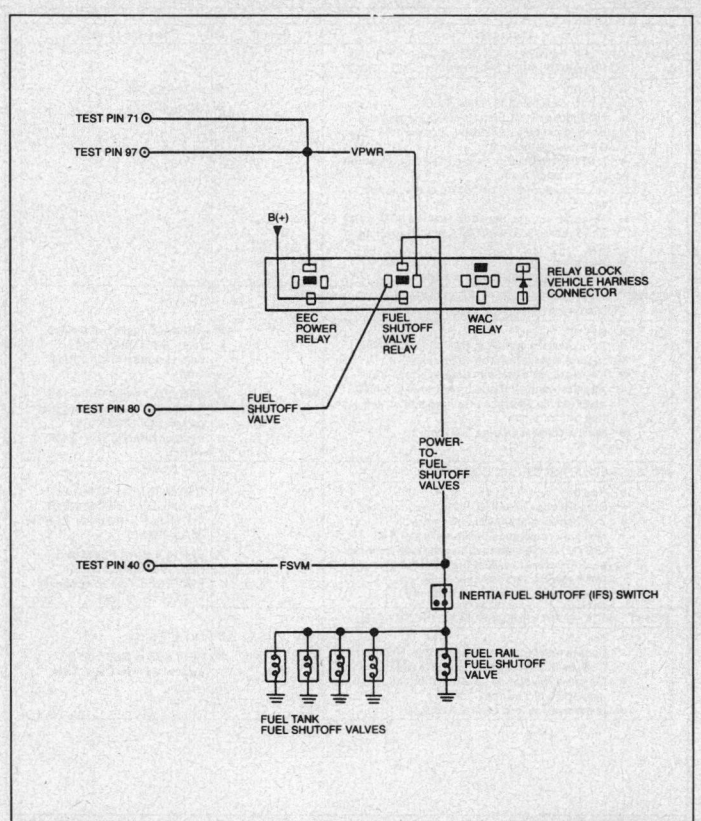

FM0159601537020X

Fig. 268   Test KC: Fuel Shutoff Valve Relay (Part 2 of 12). 1996

	Test Step	Result	▶	Action to Take
KC1	DTC P0230: CHECK FOR VPWR TO FUEL SHUTOFF VALVE RELAY			
	Diagnostic Trouble Code (DTC) P0230 indicates a Fuel Shutoff Valve primary circuit failure. Possible causes: — Open or shorted circuit. — Damaged fuel shutoff valve relay. — Damaged PCM. ● Disconnect fuel shutoff valve relay. ● Key on, engine off. ● Measure voltage between VPWR circuit at the fuel shutoff valve relay vehicle harness connector and chassis ground. ● Is voltage greater than 10.5 volts?	Yes No	▶ ▶	GO to **KC2**. SERVICE open in VPWR circuit between the EEC power relay and the fuel shutoff valve relay. RECONNECT fuel shutoff valve relay. RERUN Quick Test.
KC2	CHECK FUEL SHUTOFF VALVE RELAY			
	● Key off. ● Fuel shutoff valve relay disconnected. ● Check fuel shutoff valve relay coil resistance: — Measure resistance between Pins 85 and 86 at the fuel shutoff valve relay (pin numbers molded on relay). — Resistance should be between 40 and 85 ohms. ● Check fuel shutoff valve relay for internal shorts. — Measure resistance between Pin 85 and both Pins 30 and 87 at the fuel shutoff valve relay. — Both resistances should be greater than 10,000 ohms. ● Are all resistance checks OK?	Yes No	▶ ▶	GO to **KC3**. REPLACE fuel shutoff valve relay. RERUN Quick Test.

FUEL SHUTOFF VALVE RELAY

COIL - 85 AND 86
COMMON - 30
NO - 87
NC - 87A

FM0159601537030X

Fig. 268   Test KC: Fuel Shutoff Valve Relay (Part 3 of 12). 1996

	Test Step	Result	▶	Action to Take
KC3	CHECK FUEL SHUTOFF VALVE CIRCUIT FOR SHORT TO POWER			
	● Key off. ● Fuel shutoff valve relay disconnected. ● Disconnect Powertrain Control Module (PCM). Inspect for damaged or pushed out pins, corrosion, loose wires, etc. Service as necessary. ● Install breakout box, leave PCM disconnected. ● Key on, engine off. ● Measure voltage between Test Pin 80 (FSV) at the breakout box and chassis ground. ● Key off. ● Was voltage less than 1.0 volt?	Yes No	▶ ▶	GO to **KC4**. SERVICE short to power. REMOVE breakout box. RECONNECT all components. RERUN Quick Test.
KC4	CHECK FUEL SHUTOFF VALVE CIRCUIT FOR SHORT TO GROUND			
	● Key off. ● Disconnect Scan Tool from DLC. ● Breakout box installed, PCM disconnected. ● Fuel shutoff valve relay disconnected. ● Measure resistance between Test Pin 80 and Test Pins 51, 103 (PWR GND) and 91 (SIG RTN) at the breakout box. ● Are all resistances greater than 10,000 ohms?	Yes No	▶ ▶	GO to **KC5**. SERVICE short circuit. REMOVE breakout box. RECONNECT all components. RERUN Quick Test.
KC5	CHECK FUEL SHUTOFF VALVE CIRCUIT CONTINUITY			
	● Key off. ● Breakout box installed, PCM disconnected. ● Fuel shutoff valve relay disconnected. ● Measure resistance between Fuel Shutoff Valve circuit at the fuel shutoff valve relay vehicle harness connector and Test Pin 80 at the breakout box. ● Is resistance less than 5.0 ohms?	Yes No	▶ ▶	If Key On Engine Off (KOEO) DTC P0231 or P0232 is also present with the P0230: GO to **KC6**. All others: REPLACE PCM. RECONNECT all components. RERUN Quick Test. SERVICE open circuit. REMOVE breakout box. RECONNECT all components. RERUN Quick Test.

FM0159601537040X

Fig. 268   Test KC: Fuel Shutoff Valve Relay (Part 4 of 12). 1996

	Test Step	Result	▶	Action to Take
KC6	CHECK THE FUEL SHUTOFF VALVE PRIMARY CIRCUIT INSIDE THE PCM			
	NOTE: The next two test steps will check the FSV circuit in the PCM. To do this the FSVF PID will be monitored. The FSVF PID is able to detect for faults on the FP circuit, and will indicate "NO" when no fault is detected and "YES" when a fault is detected. ● Key off. ● Remove breakout box. ● Reconnect PCM. ● Reconnect fuel shutoff valve relay. ● Reconnect Scan Tool to DLC. ● Key on, engine off. ● Access FSV PID on Scan Tool. ● Is the FSVF PID "YES"?	Yes No	▶ ▶	Key off. REPLACE PCM. RECONNECT all components. RERUN Quick Test. GO to **KC7**.
KC7	CHECK FUEL SHUTOFF VALVE PRIMARY CIRCUIT INSIDE PCM WHILE CRANKING ENGINE			
	NOTE: The Scan Tool must be connected to a reliable power source that is powered with the ignition key in the START position (e.g. directly to the vehicle battery). Also verify that the vehicle battery is fully charged. ● Key on, engine off. ● While viewing the FSVF PID, crank the engine. ● Is the FSVF PID "YES" during crank?	Yes No	▶ ▶	Key off. REPLACE PCM. RECONNECT all components. RERUN Quick Test. Key off. The fuel pump primary circuit is OK in the harness and PCM. If P0231 is present: GO to **KC20**. If P0232 is present: GO to **KC10**.

FM0159601537050X

Fig. 268   Test KC: Fuel Shutoff Valve Relay (Part 5 of 12). 1996

Test Step	Result	▶	Action to Take
KC10 DTC P0232: DOES ENGINE START?			
Diagnostic Trouble Code (DTC) P0232 indicates that the Powertrain Control Module (PCM) detected the FSVM circuit voltage was high when the fuel shutoff valves were commanded off. The FSVM circuit is wired to a "pull-up" voltage inside the PCM. The FSVM circuit will go high if, with the key on and the fuel shutoff valves commanded off, the FSVM/Power-To-Fuel Shutoff Valves circuit loses its path to ground through the fuel shutoff valves. It is important to note that continuity to ground through only one fuel shutoff valve will result in FSVM voltage being low. Continuity to ground through ALL the fuel shutoff valves, or the common portion of the circuit must be lost. The FSVM circuit will also be high if the FSVM/Power-To-Fuel Shutoff Valves circuit is short to power. Possible causes: No Start: — Inertia Fuel Shutoff (IFS) switch not reset or electrically open. — Open circuit between the fuel shutoff valves and FSVM circuit connection to the Power-To-Fuel Shutoff Valves circuit. — All fuel shutoff valves, or their ground circuits electrically open. Engine Starts: — Power-To-Fuel Shutoff Valve circuit short to power. — Fuel shutoff valve relay contacts stuck closed. — Open in FSVM circuit between PCM and connection to Power-To-Fuel Shutoff Valves circuit. — Damaged PCM. • **Does the engine start?**	Yes No	▶ ▶	GO to **KC11**. GO to **KC15**.

FM0159601537060X

Fig. 268   Test KC: Fuel Shutoff Valve Relay (Part 6 of 12). 1996

Test Step	Result	▶	Action to Take
KC11 CHECK IF POWER IS ALWAYS BEING SUPPLIED TO POWER-TO-FUEL SHUTOFF VALVES CIRCUIT			
• Key off. • Disconnect Scan Tool from DLC. • Disconnect PCM. Inspect for damaged or pushed out pins, corrosion, loose wires, etc. Service as necessary. • Install breakout box, leave PCM disconnected. • Key on, engine off. • All accessories off (including dome lights, etc.). • Measure voltage between Test Pin 40 (FSVM) and Test Pin 51 (PWR GND) at the breakout box. • Key off. • **Was voltage less than 1.5 volts?**	Yes No	▶ ▶	GO to **KC13**. GO to **KC12**.
KC12 CHECK FOR FUEL SHUTOFF VALVE RELAY CONTACTS ALWAYS CLOSED			
• Key off. • Breakout box installed, PCM disconnected. • Disconnect fuel shutoff valve relay. • Key on, engine off (with accessories off). • Again measure voltage between Test Pin 40 and Test Pin 51 at the breakout box. • Key off. • **Was voltage less than 1.5 volts?**	Yes No	▶ ▶	REPLACE fuel shutoff valve relay. RECONNECT all components. RERUN Quick Test. SERVICE Power-To-Shutoff Valves/FSVM circuit short to power. RECONNECT all components. RERUN Quick Test.
KC13 CHECK FSVM CIRCUIT CONTINUITY			
• Key off. • Breakout box installed, PCM disconnected. • Disconnect fuel shutoff valve relay. • Measure resistance between Test Pin 40 (FSVM) at the breakout box and power-to-fuel shutoff valves circuit at the fuel shutoff valve relay vehicle harness connector. • **Is resistance less than 5.0 ohms?**	Yes No	▶ ▶	REPLACE PCM. REMOVE breakout box. RECONNECT fuel shutoff valve relay. RERUN Quick Test. SERVICE open FSVM circuit. REMOVE breakout box. RECONNECT all components. RERUN Quick Test.
KC15 CHECK INERTIA FUEL SHUTOFF (IFS) SWITCH			
• Key off. • Locate and disconnect Inertia Fuel Shutoff (IFS) switch (verify that switch is reset). • Measure resistance between the C and NC pins of the IFS switch. • **Is resistance less than 5.0 ohms?**	Yes No	▶ ▶	GO to **KC16**. REPLACE or RESET IFS switch. RERUN Quick Test.

FM0159601537070X

Fig. 268   Test KC: Fuel Shutoff Valve Relay (Part 7 of 12). 1996

Test Step	Result	▶	Action to Take
KC16 CHECK POWER-TO-FUEL SHUTOFF VALVES CIRCUIT CONTINUITY BETWEEN IFS SWITCH AND FUEL SHUTOFF VALVE RELAY			
• Key off. • IFS switch disconnected. • Disconnect fuel shutoff valve relay. • Measure resistance of the Power-to-Fuel Shutoff Valves circuit between the fuel shutoff valve relay and IFS switch vehicle harness connectors. • **Is resistance less than 5.0 ohms?**	Yes No	▶ ▶	RECONNECT fuel shutoff valve relay. GO to **KC17**. SERVICE open in Power-to-Fuel Shutoff Valves circuit between IFS switch and FSVM connection to circuit.
KC17 CHECK POWER-TO-FUEL SHUTOFF VALVES CIRCUIT CONTINUITY TO GROUND THROUGH THE FUEL SHUTOFF VALVES			
• Key off. • IFS switch disconnected. • Measure resistance between the Power-to-Fuel Shutoff Valves circuit to the fuel shutoff valves at the IFS switch vehicle harness connector and chassis ground. • **Is resistance less than 10.0 ohms?**	Yes No	▶ ▶	No fault is indicated. VERIFY previous test step results. If OK, disregard the P0232 at this time. RETURN to Diagnostic Subroutines that the P0232 was received and continue diagnosis as directed. SERVICE open circuit. Open is either in the "common" power-to-fuel shutoff valves circuit before any splice to the individual fuel shutoff valves, or in each of the "individual" fuel shutoff valve circuits path to ground. After service, RECONNECT all components. RERUN Quick Test.

FM0159601537080X

Fig. 268   Test KC: Fuel Shutoff Valve Relay (Part 8 of 12). 1996

Test Step	Result	▶	Action to Take
KC20 DTC P0231: DOES ENGINE START?			
NOTE: If Key On, Engine Off (KOEO) DTC P0230 is also present, go to **KC1** (to check primary fuel shutoff valve circuit first). Diagnostic Trouble Code (DTC) P0231 indicates a fuel shutoff valve secondary circuit failure between the B(+) supply and the FSVM connection to the Power-To-Fuel Shutoff Valve circuit. Possible causes: No Start: — Open circuit between the B(+) supply and the FSVM connection to the Power-To-Fuel Shutoff Valve circuit. — Fuel shutoff valve relay contacts always open. Engine Starts: — Damaged PCM. • **Does the engine start?**	Yes No	▶ ▶	REPLACE PCM. RERUN Quick Test. GO to **KC21**.
KC21 CHECK FOR B(+) TO FUEL SHUTOFF VALVE RELAY			
• Key off. • Disconnect fuel shutoff valve relay. • Measure voltage between B(+) circuit at the fuel shutoff valve relay vehicle harness connector and the battery negative post. • **Is voltage greater than 10.5 volts?**	Yes No	▶ ▶	GO to **KC22**. VERIFY integrity of fuse for B(+) supply to fuel shutoff valve relay. If OK, SERVICE open in B(+) circuit. If fuse is damaged, check B(+) and power-to-fuel shutoff valves circuit for short to ground before replacing. RECONNECT fuel shutoff valve relay. RERUN Quick Test.
KC22 CHECK POWER-TO-FUEL SHUTOFF VALVES CIRCUIT CONTINUITY			
• Key off. • Fuel shutoff valve relay disconnected. • Measure resistance between power-to-fuel shutoff valves circuit at the fuel shutoff valve relay vehicle harness connector and the battery negative post. • **Is resistance less than 10.0 ohms?**	Yes No	▶ ▶	REPLACE fuel shutoff valve relay. RERUN Quick Test. SERVICE open in power-to-fuel shutoff valves circuit between FSVM splice and fuel shutoff valve relay. RECONNECT fuel shutoff valve relay. RERUN Quick Test.

FM0159601537090X

Fig. 268   Test KC: Fuel Shutoff Valve Relay (Part 9 of 12). 1996

Test Step	Result	►	Action to Take
KC30 CONTINUOUS MEMORY DTC P0232: CHECK EEC-V HARNESS			
NOTE: If Continuous Memory Diagnostic Trouble Code (DTC) P0230 is also present, go to **KC40**.	Yes	►	ISOLATE fault and SERVICE as necessary. COMPLETE PCM reset to clear DTCs (REFER to Powertrain Control Module (PCM) Reset.) RERUN Quick Test.
A Continuous Memory DTC P0232 indicates that one of the following intermittent conditions has occurred:			
— Fuel shutoff valve circuit activated when PCM expected circuit to be off (i.e., fuel system test or prime procedure).	No	►	Unable to duplicate and / or identify fault at this time. GO to Pinpoint Test Step **Z1** with the following data: FSVM PID and list of possible causes.
— Inertia fuel shutoff switch was tripped, then reset.			
— An open in the FSVM/Power-To-Fuel Shutoff Valves circuit which would cause the FSVM to lose its path to ground (refer to schematic).			
— FSVM or power-to-fuel shutoff valves circuit short to power.			
— Fuel shutoff valve relay contacts stuck closed.			
— Engine stall due to excessive load.			
• Key on, engine off.			
• Access FSVM PID on Scan Tool.			
• Observe the FSVM PID for an indication of a fault while performing the following (the FSVM PID will turn ON when an open or short to power is detected):			
— Shake, wiggle, bend the Power-to-Fuel Shutoff Valves circuit between the power-to-fuel shutoff valves pin at the fuel shutoff valve relay and the fuel shutoff valves.			
— Shake, wiggle, bend the fuel shutoff valves ground circuits from each fuel shutoff valve to ground.			
— Shake, wiggle, bend the FSVM circuit between the PCM and the splice to the Power-to-Fuel Shutoff Valves circuit.			
— Lightly tap Inertia Fuel Shutoff switch to simulate road shock.			
— Lightly tap the fuel shutoff valve relay to simulate road shock.			
• Key off.			
• **Is fault indicated/found?**			

FM0159601537100X

Fig. 268   Test KC: Fuel Shutoff Valve Relay (Part 10 of 12). 1996

Test Step	Result	►	Action to Take
KC35 CONTINUOUS MEMORY DTC P0231: CHECK EEC-V HARNESS			
A Continuous Memory Diagnostic Trouble Code (DTC) P0231 indicates that sometime during vehicle operation when the fuel shutoff valves were commanded on the FSVM circuit voltage went low. (Since there is no FSV primary circuit DTC P0230, the primary circuit is assumed to be OK.)	Yes	►	ISOLATE fault and SERVICE as necessary. REMOVE breakout box. RECONNECT all components. RERUN Quick Test.
Possible causes:	No	►	Unable to duplicate and / or identify fault at this time. GO to Pinpoint Test Step **Z1** with the following data: FSVM PID and list of possible causes.
— Open in B(+) circuit to the fuel shutoff valve relay.			
— Fuel shutoff valve relay contacts open.			
— Open in Power-to-Fuel Shutoff Valves circuit between the fuel shutoff valve relay and FSVM slice.			
• Key off.			
• Disconnect PCM. Inspect for damaged or pushed out pins, corrosion, loose wires, etc. Service as necessary.			
• Install breakout box. Leave PCM disconnected.			
• Install a jumper wire between Test Pin 80 (FSV) and Test Pin 77 (PWR GND).			
• Connect a DVOM between Test Pin 40 (FSVM) and Test Pin 51 (PWR GND).			
• Key on. The fuel shutoff valves will turn on and DVOM voltage will be greater than 10.0 volts.			
• Observe DVOM voltage for an indication of a fault while performing the following (the DVOM voltage will change suddenly when a fault is detected, indicating an open):			
— Shake, wiggle, bend the B(+) circuit to the fuel shutoff valve relay.			
— Lightly tap the fuel shutoff valve relay to simulate road shock.			
— Shake, wiggle, bend the Power-to-Fuel Shutoff Valves circuit between the fuel shutoff valve relay and the FSVM splice.			
• Key off.			
• Inspect the fuel shutoff valve relay connector for corrosion, damaged pins, etc.			
• **Is fault indicated?**			

FM0159601537110X

Fig. 268   Test KC: Fuel Shutoff Valve Relay (Part 11 of 12). 1996

Test Step	Result	►	Action to Take
KC40 CONTINUOUS MEMORY DTC P0230: CHECK EEC-V HARNESS			
A Continuous Memory Diagnostic Trouble Code (DTC) P0230 indicates a fuel shutoff valve primary circuit failure has occurred during vehicle operation.	Yes	►	ISOLATE fault and SERVICE as necessary. COMPLETE PCM reset to clear DTCs (REFER to Powertrain Control Module (PCM) Reset.) RERUN Quick Test.
Possible causes:			
— Open in VPWR to fuel shutoff valve relay.	No	►	Unable to duplicate and / or identify fault at this time. GO to Pinpoint Test Step **Z1** with the following data: FSVM PID and list of possible causes. For testing the FSV circuit with the engine running, also monitor the FSVM PID. This is because not all FSV circuit failures may be detected using only the FSVF PID.
— Open coil in fuel shutoff valve relay.			
— Open in Fuel Shutoff Valve circuit (PCM Pin 80).			
• Scan Tool connected.			
• Key on, engine off. Wait 5 seconds.			
• Access FSVF PID. The FSVF PID will be no, indicating that the PCM detects VPWR voltage through the fuel shutoff valve relay coil and FSV circuit (Pin 80) to the PCM.			
• Observe the FSVF PID for an indication of a fault while performing the following (the FSVF PID will be yes when an open is detected (this is because the PCM will not detect VPWR voltage on Pin 80 (FSV))):			
— Shake, wiggle, bend the fuel shutoff valve circuit between the PCM (Pin 80) and the fuel shutoff valve relay.			
— Shake, wiggle, bend the VPWR circuit between the EEC-V Power Relay and the Fuel Shutoff Valve Relay.			
— Lightly tap the fuel shutoff valve relay (to simulate road shock).			
• Key off.			
• Inspect the PCM and fuel shutoff valve relay connectors for corrosion, damaged pins, etc.			
• **Is a fault indicated?**			

FM0159601537120X

Fig. 268   Test KC: Fuel Shutoff Valve Relay (Part 12 of 12). 1996

Note

You should enter this Pinpoint Test only when directed here.

Remember

This Pinpoint Test is intended to diagnose the following:

- Throttle Linkage
- Idle Air Control (IAC) Valve Assembly (9F715)
- Throttle Body
- Harness Circuits: IAC and VPWR
- Powertrain Control Module (PCM) (12A650)

Pinpoint Test Schematic

3.0L Windstar, 4.9L F-Series, 5.0L and 5.8L Bronco/E-Series/F-Series, 7.5L E-Series/F-Series

*TEST PIN 83 —— IAC
TEST PIN 71 —— VPWR
TEST PIN 97 —— VPWR

IDLE AIR CONTROL (IAC) SOLENOID VEHICLE HARNESS CONNECTOR

*TEST PINS LOCATED ON BREAKOUT BOX
ALL HARNESS CONNECTORS VIEWED INTO MATING SURFACE

FROM POWER RELAY

FM0159601538010X

Fig. 269   Test KE: IAC Valve Assembly (Part 1 of 9). 1996

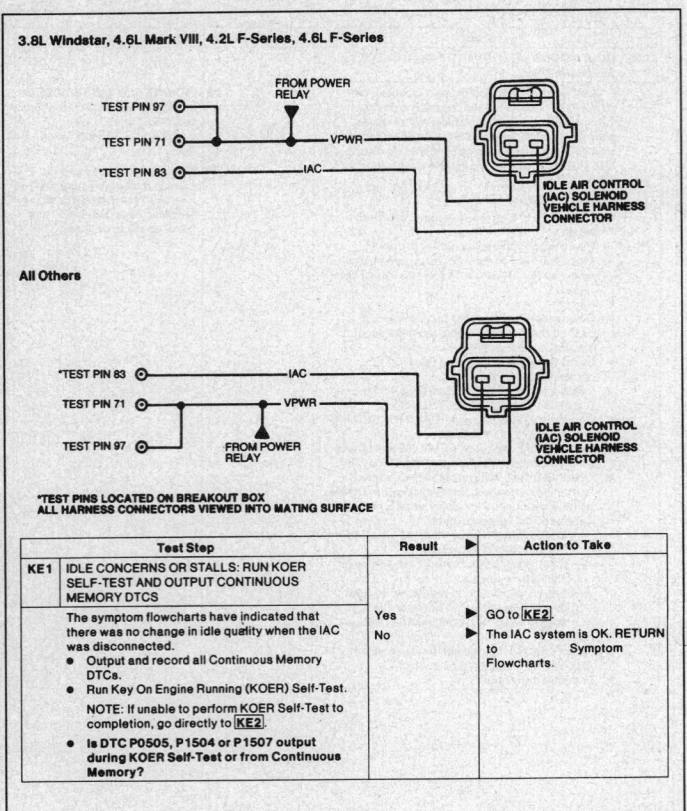

3.8L Windstar, 4.6L Mark VIII, 4.2L F-Series, 4.6L F-Series

All Others

*TEST PINS LOCATED ON BREAKOUT BOX
ALL HARNESS CONNECTORS VIEWED INTO MATING SURFACE

Test Step	Result	▶	Action to Take
KE1 IDLE CONCERNS OR STALLS: RUN KOER SELF-TEST AND OUTPUT CONTINUOUS MEMORY DTCS			
The symptom flowcharts have indicated that there was no change in idle quality when the IAC was disconnected. • Output and record all Continuous Memory DTCs. • Run Key On Engine Running (KOER) Self-Test. NOTE: If unable to perform KOER Self-Test to completion, go directly to KE2. • Is DTC P0505, P1504 or P1507 output during KOER Self-Test or from Continuous Memory?	Yes	▶	GO to KE2.
	No	▶	The IAC system is OK. RETURN to Symptom Flowcharts.

Fig. 269   Test KE: IAC Valve Assembly (Part 2 of 9). 1996

FM0159601538020X

Test Step	Result	▶	Action to Take
KE2 DTC P0505, DTC P1504, DTC P1507 OR STARTS ONLY AT PART THROTTLE: CHECK VPWR TO IAC SOLENOID			
DTC P0505 indicates that Self-Test has detected an IAC system malfunction. DTC P1504 indicates that Self-Test has detected an IAC circuit malfunction. DTC P1507 indicates that Self-Test has detected an IAC underspeed error. Possible causes: — IAC circuit open. — IAC circuit shorted to PWR. — IAC short to GND (P1504). — VPWR circuit open. — Air inlet plugged (P0505, P1507). — Air inlet leakage (P1507). — Damaged IAC valve assembly. — Damaged throttle body (P0505, P1507). — Damaged PCM. • Key off. • Disconnect IAC solenoid vehicle harness connector. • Key on. • Measure voltage between VPWR circuit at the IAC solenoid vehicle harness connector and battery ground. • Is voltage greater than 10.5 volts?	Yes	▶	GO to KE3.
	No	▶	SERVICE open in VPWR to IAC solenoid. RECONNECT all components. RERUN Quick Test.
KE3 CHECK IAC SOLENOID RESISTANCE			
• Key off. • IAC solenoid vehicle harness connector disconnected. • Measure solenoid resistance. NOTE: Due to diode in solenoid, place DVOM (+) lead on VPWR pin and (-) lead on IAC pin. • Is resistance between 6.0 and 13.0 ohms?	Yes	▶	GO to KE4.
	No	▶	REPLACE IAC valve assembly. RECONNECT all components. RERUN Quick Test.
KE4 CHECK IAC SOLENOID FOR AN INTERNAL SHORT TO IAC CASE			
• Key off. • IAC solenoid vehicle harness connector disconnected. • Measure resistance from either IAC solenoid pin to IAC valve assembly case. • Is resistance greater than 10,000 ohms?	Yes	▶	For DTC P1504: GO to KE7. All others: GO to KE5.
	No	▶	REPLACE IAC valve assembly. RECONNECT all components. RERUN Quick Test.

Fig. 269   Test KE: IAC Valve Assembly (Part 3 of 9). 1996

FM0159601538030X

Test Step	Result	▶	Action to Take
KE5 CHECK AIR INLET FOR PLUGGING			
• Key off. • Inspect the entire inlet air system for debris blockage and other damage. • Remove and inspect the air filter element for excessive dirt. • Is the air inlet system OK?	Yes	▶	GO to KE6.
	No	▶	SERVICE as necessary. RECONNECT all components. RERUN Quick Test.
KE6 CHECK FOR VACUUM LEAKS			
• Key on, engine running. • With engine running at idle, listen for vacuum leaks. • Inspect the entire inlet air system from the Mass Airflow (MAF) sensor to the intake manifold for leaks such as: — Cracked or punctured inlet air tube. — Loose inlet air tube at air cleaner housing or throttle body. — IAC valve assembly or gasket seal. — EGR valve gasket seal. — Vacuum supply connector and hose. — PCV connectors and hose. • Are any leaks detected in the above areas?	Yes	▶	SERVICE as necessary. RECONNECT all components. RERUN Quick Test.
	No	▶	GO to KE7.
KE7 CHECK IAC CIRCUIT CONTINUITY			
• Key off. • IAC solenoid disconnected. • Disconnect PCM. Inspect for damaged or pushed out pins, corrosion, loose wires, etc. Service as necessary. • Install breakout box, leave PCM disconnected. • Measure resistance between Test Pin 83 (IAC) at the breakout box and IAC circuit at IAC solenoid vehicle harness connector. • Is resistance less than 5.0 ohms?	Yes	▶	GO to KE8.
	No	▶	SERVICE open circuit. REMOVE breakout box. RECONNECT all components. RERUN Quick Test.
KE8 CHECK IAC CIRCUIT FOR SHORT TO PWR			
• Key off. • Breakout box installed. PCM disconnected. • IAC solenoid disconnected. • Key on, engine off. • Measure voltage between Test Pin 83 (IAC) at the breakout box and chassis ground. • Is voltage less than 1.0 volt?	Yes	▶	GO to KE9.
	No	▶	SERVICE short circuit. REMOVE breakout box. RECONNECT all components. RERUN Quick Test.

Fig. 269   Test KE: IAC Valve Assembly (Part 4 of 9). 1996

FM0159601538040X

Test Step	Result	▶	Action to Take
KE9 CHECK IAC CIRCUIT FOR SHORT TO GROUND			
• Key off. • Breakout box installed, PCM disconnected. • IAC solenoid disconnected. • Disconnect Scan Tool from DLC. • Measure resistance between Test Pin 83 (IAC) and Test Pins 51 and 103 (PWR GND) at the breakout box. • Is each resistance greater than 10,000 ohms?	Yes	▶	GO to KE10.
	No	▶	SERVICE short circuit. RECONNECT all components. RERUN Quick Test.
KE10 CHECK IAC SIGNAL FROM PCM			
• Key off. • Breakout box installed. • Reconnect PCM to breakout box. • Reconnect IAC solenoid. • Connect DVOM between Test Pin 83 (IAC) and Test Pin 51 (PWR GND) at the breakout box. • Start engine. • Slowly increase rpm to 3000 rpm. • Is voltage between 3.0 and 11.5 volts?	Yes	▶	For Continuous Memory DTCs P1504 and P1507: GO to KE30. All others: INSPECT throttle body for damage. SERVICE as necessary. If OK, REPLACE IAC valve assembly. RESET Keep Alive Memory (KAM) (REFER to Powertrain Control Module (PCM) Reset). RERUN Quick Test.
	No	▶	REPLACE PCM. REMOVE breakout box. RECONNECT all components. RERUN Quick Test.

Fig. 269   Test KE: IAC Valve Assembly (Part 5 of 9). 1996

FM0159601538050X

Test Step	Result	▶	Action to Take
KE20 DTC P1506: CHECK FOR VACUUM LEAKS	Yes	▶	SERVICE as necessary. RECONNECT all components. COMPLETE PCM Reset to clear DTCs. (REFER to Powertrain Control Module (PCM) Reset). RERUN Quick Test.
Diagnostic Trouble Code (DTC) P1506 indicates Self-Test has detected an IAC overspeed error. Possible causes: — IAC circuit short to GND. — IAC assembly stuck open. — Vacuum leak. — Damaged IAC assembly. — Damaged throttle body. — Damaged PCM. • Key on, engine running. • With the engine at idle, listen for vacuum leaks. • Inspect the entire inlet air system from the Mass Air Flow (MAF) sensor to the intake manifold for damage or leaks such as: • Cracked or punctured inlet air tube. • Loose inlet air tube at the air cleaner housing or throttle body. • IAC valve assembly or gasket seal. • Intake manifold assembly or gasket seal. • EGR valve gasket seal. • Vacuum supply connectors and hose. • PCV valve, connectors and hose. • **Are any leaks detected in the above areas?**	No	▶	GO to **KE21**.

Fig. 269 Test KE: IAC Valve Assembly (Part 6 of 9). 1996

Test Step	Result	▶	Action to Take
KE21 CHECK EVAP SYSTEM FOR A STUCK OPEN VALVE OR SOLENOID	Yes	▶	RECONNECT all components. GO to **KE22**.
• Key off. • Disconnect hoses at EVAP Canister Purge Valve or Solenoid. • Connect a hand vacuum pump to the fuel vapor port to carbon canister at the EVAP Canister Purge Valve or to either port if equipped with a EVAP Canister Purge Solenoid. • Apply 16 in-Hg (53 kPa) of vacuum to EVAP Canister Purge Valve or Solenoid. EVAP CANISTER PURGE VALVE FUEL VAPOR TO INTAKE MANIFOLD FUEL VAPOR TO CARBON CANISTER (CONNECT HAND VACUUM PUMP HERE) INPUT PORT VACUUM (TO INTAKE MANIFOLD) • **Does the EVAP Canister Purge Valve or Solenoid hold vacuum for 20 seconds?**	No	▶	REPLACE EVAP Valve or solenoid. RECONNECT all components. COMPLETE PCM Reset to clear DTCs (REFER to Powertrain Control Module (PCM) Reset). RERUN Quick Test.
KE22 CHECK IAC SOLENOID FOR PROPER FUNCTION	Yes	▶	GO to **KE23**.
• Key on, engine running. • Bring engine to normal operating temperature. • Transmission in Park or Neutral. • Disconnect IAC solenoid vehicle harness connector. • **Does the RPM drop or engine stall?**	No	▶	INSPECT throttle body for damage or defect. SERVICE as necessary. If OK, REPLACE IAC valve assembly. CLEAR Keep Alive Memory (REFER to Powertrain Control Module (PCM) Reset). RERUN Quick Test.

Fig. 269 Test KE: IAC Valve Assembly (Part 7 of 9). 1996

Test Step	Result	▶	Action to Take
KE23 CHECK IAC CIRCUIT FOR SHORT TO GND	Yes	▶	For fast idle symptom currently present: REPLACE PCM. REMOVE breakout box. RECONNECT all components. RERUN Quick Test. All others: RECONNECT all components. GO to **KE30**.
• Key off. • Disconnect Scan Tool from DLC. • IAC solenoid disconnected. • Disconnect PCM. Inspect for damaged or pushed out pins, corrosion, loose wires, etc. Service as necessary. • Measure resistance between Test Pin 83 (IAC) and Test Pins 51 and 103 (PWR GND) at the breakout box. • **Is each resistance greater than 10,000 ohms?**	No	▶	SERVICE short circuit. RECONNECT all components. RERUN Quick Test.
KE25 DTC P1505: CHECK INLET AIR CONNECTION	Yes	▶	SERVICE as necessary. RESET KAM (REFER to Powertrain Control Module (PCM) Reset). RERUN Quick Test.
Diagnostic Trouble Code (DTC) P1505 indicates the IAC system has reached the adaptive clip. NOTE: For a brief description of the Adaptive IAC Strategy Possible causes: — Air leaks. — Plugged air filter element. — Throttle body/linkage binding. — Contaminated or damaged IAC valve assembly. — Damaged throttle body. • Key off. • Inspect the entire inlet air system for leaks such as loose connection at throttle body or air cleaner, cracked or punctured ducting, etc. • **Is there a leak or loose connection in the air inlet system?**	No	▶	GO to **KE26**.
KE26 CHECK FOR A PLUGGED AIR FILTER	Yes	▶	SERVICE as necessary. RESET KAM (REFER to Powertrain Control Module (PCM) Reset). RERUN Quick Test.
• Key off. • Remove air filter element and check for excessive dirt or moisture. • **Is the air filter plugged?**	No	▶	GO to **KE27**.
KE27 INSPECT THROTTLE BODY AND LINKAGE	Yes	▶	GO to Pinpoint Test Step **HU3**.
• Key off. • Disconnect accelerator cable and air cleaner tube from throttle body. • Exercise both cable and throttle body linkage separately while checking for binding, interference and full freedom of travel. • **Is a fault indicated?**	No	▶	GO to Pinpoint Test Step **HU8**.

Fig. 269 Test KE: IAC Valve Assembly (Part 8 of 9). 1996

Test Step	Result	▶	Action to Take
KE30 CHECK IAC SYSTEM FOR INTERMITTENT OPEN OR SHORT	Yes	▶	ISOLATE fault and SERVICE as necessary. RECONNECT all components. COMPLETE PCM Reset to clear DTCs (REFER to Powertrain Control Module (PCM) Reset).
• Scan Tool connected. • Key on, engine running. • Access IAC and RPM PIDs with a Scan Tool. • With engine at normal operating temperature, accessories off and at idle, the IAC duty cycle should be between 20% and 45%. • Observe the IAC and RPM PIDs for an indication of a fault while performing the following at idle. — Lightly tap on IAC valve assembly and wiggle harness connector to simulate road shock. — Grasp the vehicle harness closest to the IAC valve assembly. Shake and bend a small section of the harness from the IAC to the dash panel and from the dash panel to the PCM. • **Do the IAC or RPM PIDs suddenly change in value indicating a fault?**	No	▶	For idle quality, starting or stalling symptoms currently present: REPLACE IAC valve assembly. RECONNECT all components. COMPLETE PCM Reset to clear DTCs (REFER to Powertrain Control Module (PCM) Reset). All others: Unable to duplicate and/or identify fault at this time. GO to Pinpoint Test Step **Z1** with the following data: IAC, RPM PIDs and list of possible causes.

Fig. 269 Test KE: IAC Valve Assembly (Part 9 of 9). 1996

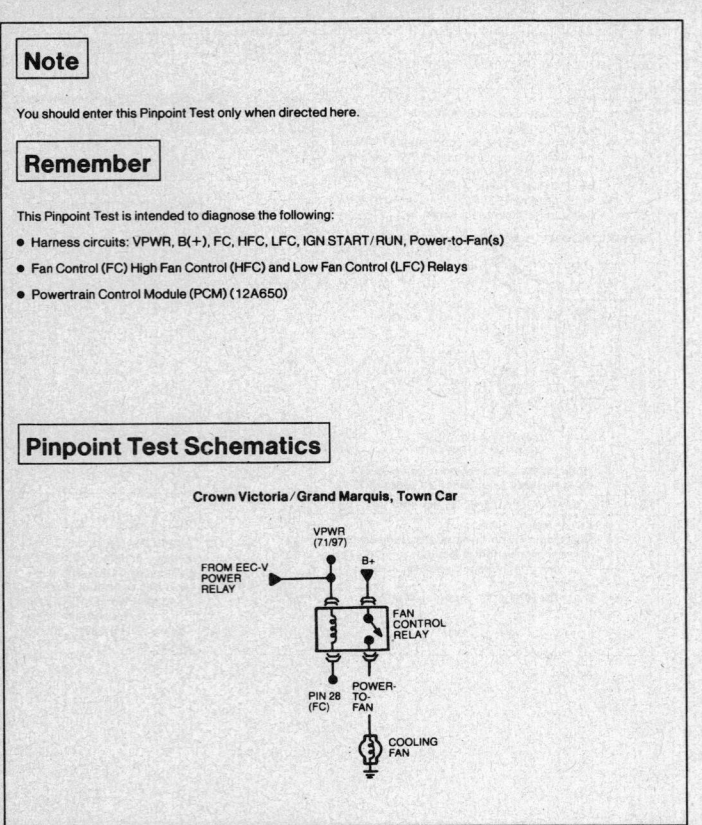

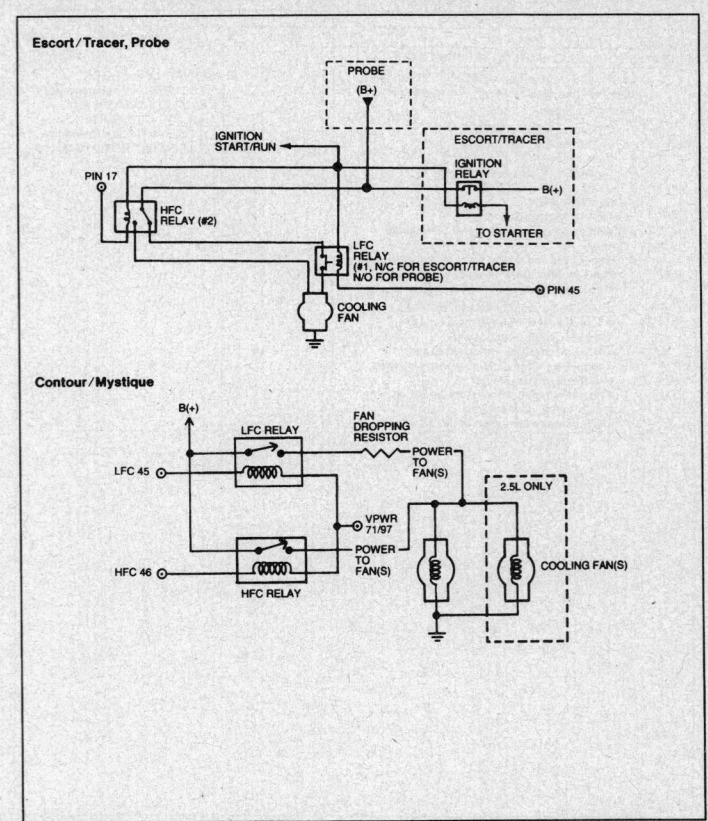

Note

You should enter this Pinpoint Test only when directed here.

Remember

This Pinpoint Test is intended to diagnose the following:

- Harness circuits: VPWR, B(+), FC, HFC, LFC, IGN START/RUN, Power-to-Fan(s)
- Fan Control (FC) High Fan Control (HFC) and Low Fan Control (LFC) Relays
- Powertrain Control Module (PCM) (12A650)

Pinpoint Test Schematics

FM0159601539010X

Fig. 270   Test KF: Fan Control Relay (Part 1 of 22). 1996

FM0159601539020X

Fig. 270   Test KF: Fan Control Relay (Part 2 of 22). 1996

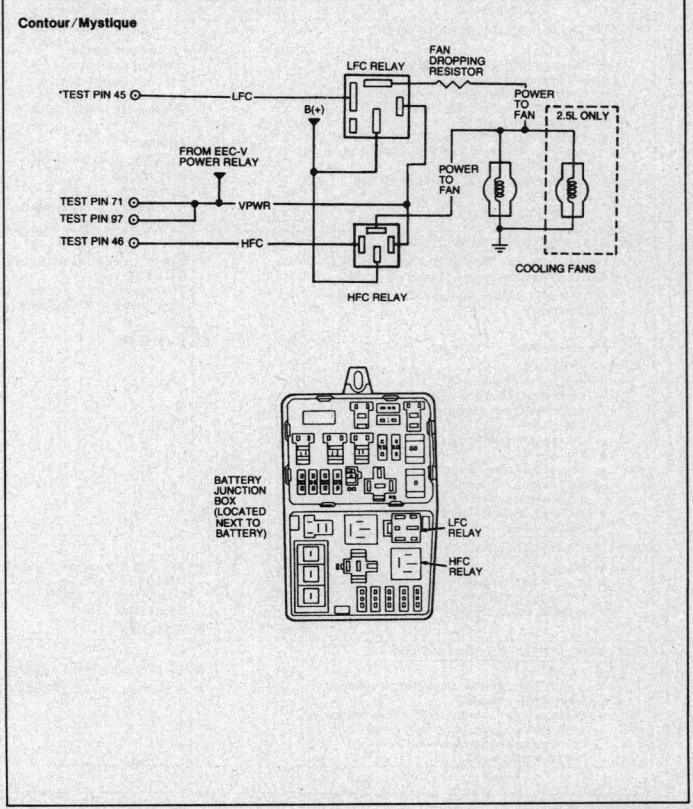

FM0159601539030X

FM0159601539040X

Fig. 270   Test KF: Fan Control Relay (Part 3 of 22). 1996   Fig. 270   Test KF: Fan Control Relay (Part 4 of 22). 1996

Crown Victoria/Grand Marquis, Town Car

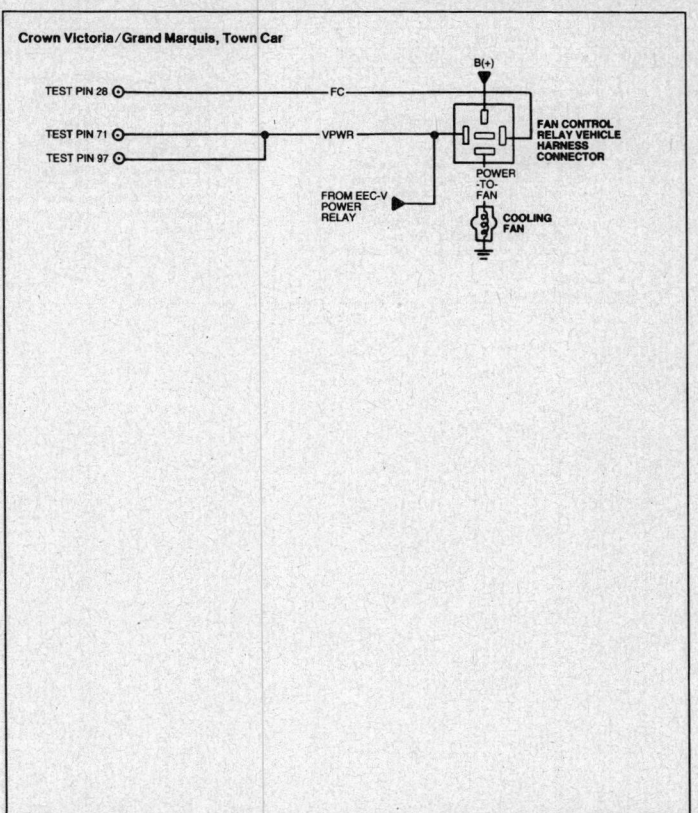

Fig. 270 Test KF: Fan Control Relay (Part 5 of 22). 1996

Test Step	Result	▶	Action to Take
KF1 DTC P1474/P1479: CHECK FOR VPWR (IGN START/RUN FOR ESCORT/TRACER, PROBE) TO APPLICABLE FAN CONTROL RELAY			
Diagnostic Trouble Code (DTC) P1474 indicates a Low Fan Control (LFC) (Fan Control (FC) for single speed fan applications) primary circuit failure. DTC P1479 indicates a High Fan Control (HFC) primary circuit failure. Possible causes: — Open or shorted FC, LFC or HFC circuit. — Open VPWR (IGN Start/Run for Escort/Tracer and Probe) circuit to fan control relay. — Damaged fan control relay (FC, LFC or HFC). — Damaged PCM. ● NOTE: During diagnosis, use the chart below to determine the correct pin number, circuit and relay being tested.	Yes No	▶ ▶	GO to **KF2**. SERVICE open VPWR or IGN Start/Run circuit to the applicable fan control relay. RECONNECT fan control relay. RERUN Quick Test.

		Test Pin Number		
DTC	**Circuit/ Relay**	**Escort/ Tracer, Probe**	**Contour/ Mystique**	**Crown Victoria/ Grand Marquis, Town Car**
P1474	LFC	45	45	—
P1474	FC	—	—	45
P1479	HFC	17	46	—

● Key off.
● Disconnect appropriate fan control relay.
● Key on.
● Measure voltage between the VPWR (IGN Start/Run for Escort/Tracer and Probe) circuit at the applicable fan control relay vehicle harness connector and the battery negative post.
● **Is voltage greater than 10.5 volts?**

Fig. 270 Test KF: Fan Control Relay (Part 6 of 22). 1996

Test Step	Result	▶	Action to Take
KF2 CHECK FOR FC, LFC or HFC CIRCUIT CYCLING			
● Key on, engine off. ● Applicable fan control relay disconnected. ● Scan Tool connected. ● Access Output Test Mode on Scan Tool ● Connect DVOM positive lead to the VPWR (or IGN Start/Run) circuit and the negative lead to the FC, LFC or HFC cicuit at the applicable fan control relay vehicle harness connector. ● While observing DVOM, command the appropriate cooling fan speed on and off a couple times. ● **Does voltage change more than 0.5 volts when the cooling fan output is commanded on and off?**	Yes No	▶ ▶	Key off. REPLACE appropriate fan control relay. RERUN Quick Test. Key off. GO to **KF3**.
KF3 CHECK FC, LFC or HFC CIRCUIT FOR SHORT TO POWER			
● Key off. ● Applicable fan control relay disconnected. ● Disconnect PCM. Inspect for damaged or pushed out pins, corrosion, loose wires, etc. Service as necessary. ● Key on, engine off. ● Measure voltage between the FC, LFC or HFC circuit at the applicable fan control relay vehicle harness connector and the battery negative post. ● Key off. ● **Was voltage less than 1.0 volt?**	Yes No	▶ ▶	GO to **KF4**. SERVICE FC, LFC or HFC circuit short to power. RECONNECT all components. RERUN Quick Test.
KF4 CHECK FC, LFC or HFC CIRCUIT FOR SHORT TO GROUND			
● Key off. ● Disconnect Scan Tool from DLC. ● Appropriate fan control relay disconnected. ● PCM disconnected. ● Install breakout box, leave PCM disconnected. ● Measure resistance between the appropriate fan control circuit Test Pin (FC, LFC or HFC) and Test Pins 51, 103 (PWR GND) and 91 (SIG RTN) at the breakout box. ● **Is each resistance greater than 10,000 ohms?**	Yes No	▶ ▶	GO to **KF5**. SERVICE appropriate fan control circuit short to ground. REMOVE breakout box. RECONNECT all components. RERUN Quick Test.

Fig. 270 Test KF: Fan Control Relay (Part 7 of 22). 1996

Test Step	Result	▶	Action to Take
KF5 CHECK FC, LFC or HFC CIRCUIT CONTINUITY			
● Key off. ● Appropriate fan control relay disconnected. ● Breakout box installed, PCM disconnected. ● Measure resistance between the appropriate fan control circuit Test Pin (FC, LFC or HFC) at the breakout box and the FC, LFC or HFC circuit at the appropriate fan control relay vehicle harness connector. ● **Is resistance less than 5.0 ohms?**	Yes No	▶ ▶	REPLACE PCM. REMOVE breakout box. RECONNECT all components. RERUN Quick Test. SERVICE open FC, LFC or HFC circuit. REMOVE breakout box. RECONNECT all components. RERUN Quick Test.
KF10 CONTINUOUS MEMORY DTC P1474: CHECK FAN CONTROL (FC) (LOW FAN CONTROL (LFC) FOR TWO SPEED FAN APPLICATIONS) CIRCUIT FOR OPEN OR SHORT TO POWER			
Continuous Memory Diagnostic Trouble Code (DTC) P1474 indicates that an FC (LFC for two speed fan applications) circuit failure has occurred during vehicle operation. Possible causes: — Open or shorted FC or LFC circuit. — Open VPWR (IGN Start/Run for Probe) circuit to FC or LFC relay. ● Key off. ● A/C and defrost off. ● Scan Tool connected. ● Disconnect cooling fan connector (both for 2.5L Contour/Mystique). Inspect connectors for damaged or pushed out pins, corrosion, loose wires, etc. Service as necessary. ● Connect a non-powered test lamp between the Power-to-(Low Speed) Fan circuit and ground circuit at the cooling fan vehicle harness connector (either one for 2.5L Contour/Mystique). ● Key on, engine off. ● Access Output Test Mode on Scan Tool ● Command Low Speed Fan on. ● Observe test lamp for an indication of a fault while performing the following (the lamp will turn off when a fault is detected, indicating an open or short to power: — Shake, wiggle, bend the FC or LFC circuit between the PCM and FC or LFC relay. — Shake, wiggle, bend the VPWR or IGN Start/Run circuit to the FC or LFC relay. — Lightly tap on the FC or LFC relay to simulate road shock. ● **Is a fault indicated?**	Yes No	▶ ▶	Key off. ISOLATE fault and SERVICE as necessary. COMPLETE PCM Reset to clear DTCs (REFER to Powertrain Control Module (PCM) Reset). RERUN Quick Test. GO to **KF11**.

Fig. 270 Test KF: Fan Control Relay (Part 8 of 22). 1996

Test Step		Result	►	Action to Take
KF11	CHECK FC OR LFC CIRCUIT FOR SHORT TO GROUND			
	• Key on, engine off. • Cooling fan disconnected, test lamp installed. • Scan Tool connected. • Command Low Speed Fan off. • Observe test lamp for an indication of a fault while performing the following (the lamp will turn on when a fault is detected, indicating an FC or LFC circuit short to ground): — Shake, wiggle, bend the FC or LFC circuit between the PCM and FC or LFC relay. — Lightly tap on the FC or LFC relay to simulate road shock. • Key off. • **Is a fault indicated?**	Yes	►	ISOLATE fault and SERVICE as necessary. COMPLETE PCM Reset to clear DTCs (REFER to Powertrain Control Module (PCM) Reset). RERUN Quick Test.
		No	►	GO to Pinpoint Test Step **Z1** with the following data: LFCF PID or LFCA PID (whichever is available) and list of Possible Causes.
KF15	CONTINUOUS MEMORY DTC P1474: CHECK LOW FAN CONTROL (LFC) CIRCUIT FOR OPEN OR SHORT TO POWER			
	Continuous Memory Diagnostic Trouble Code (DTC) P1474 indicates that an LFC circuit failure has occurred during vehicle operation. Possible causes: — Open or shorted LFC circuit. — Open VPWR (IGN Start/Run for Escort/Tracer) circuit to LFC relay. • Key off. • A/C and defrost off. • Disconnect cooling fan connector. Inspect connectors for damaged or pushed out pins, corrosion, loose wires, etc. Service as necessary. • Connect a non-powered test lamp between the Power-to-Low Speed Fan circuit and ground circuit at the cooling fan vehicle harness connector. • Key on, engine off. • Observe test lamp for an indication of a fault while performing the following (since the LFC circuit is grounded to turn the fan OFF, the lamp will come on when an open or short to power is detected): — Shake, wiggle, bend the LFC circuit between the PCM and the LFC relay. — Shake, wiggle, bend the VPWR or IGN Start/Run circuit to the LFC relay. — Lightly tap on the LFC relay to simulate road shock. • **Is a fault indicated?**	Yes	►	Key off. ISOLATE fault and SERVICE as necessary. COMPLETE PCM Reset to clear DTCs (REFER to Powertrain Control Module (PCM) Reset). RERUN Quick Test.
		No	►	GO to **KF16**.

Fig. 270   Test KF: Fan Control Relay (Part 9 of 22). 1996

Test Step		Result	►	Action to Take
KF16	CHECK LFC CIRCUIT FOR SHORT TO GROUND			
	• Key on, engine off. • Cooling fan disconnected, test lamp installed. • Scan Tool connected. • Access Output Test Mode on Scan Tool • Command Low Speed Fan on. • Observe test lamp for an indication of a fault while performing the following (the lamp will turn off when a fault is detected, indicating a short to ground): — Shake, wiggle, bend the LFC circuit between the PCM and the LFC relay. — Lightly tap on the LFC relay to simulate road shock. • Key off. • **Is a fault indicated?**	Yes	►	ISOLATE fault and SERVICE as necessary. COMPLETE PCM Reset to clear DTCs (REFER to Powertrain Control Module (PCM) Reset). RERUN Quick Test.
		No	►	GO to Pinpoint Test Step **Z1** with the following data: LFCF PID or LFCA PID (whichever is available) and list of possible causes.

Fig. 270   Test KF: Fan Control Relay (Part 10 of 22). 1996

Test Step		Result	►	Action to Take
KF20	CONTINUOUS MEMORY DTC P1479: CHECK HIGH FAN CONTROL (HFC) CIRCUIT FOR OPEN OR SHORT TO POWER			
	Continuous Memory Diagnostic Trouble Code (DTC) P1479 indicates that an HFC circuit failure has occurred during vehicle operation. NOTE: For one speed fan applications, disregard DTC P1479. Possible causes: — Open or shorted HFC circuit. — Open VPWR (IGN Start/Run for Escort/Tracer and Probe) circuit to HFC relay. • Key off. • A/C and defrost off. • Scan Tool connected. • Disconnect cooling fan connector(s) (both for 2.5L Contour/Mystique). Inspect connectors for damaged or pushed out pins, corrosion, loose wires, etc. Service as necessary. • Connect a non-powered test lamp between the Power-to-High Speed Fan circuit and ground circuit at the cooling fan vehicle harness connector (either one for 2.5L). • Key on, engine off. • Access Output Test Mode on Scan Tool • Command High Speed Fan on. • Observe test lamp for an indication of a fault while performing the following (the lamp will turn off when a fault is detected, indicating an open or short to power): — Shake, wiggle, bend the HFC circuit between the PCM and HFC relay. — Shake, wiggle, bend the VPWR or IGN Start/Run circuit to the HFC relay. — Lightly tap on the HFC relay to simulate road shock. • **Is a fault indicated?**	Yes	►	Key off. ISOLATE fault and SERVICE as necessary. COMPLETE PCM Reset to clear DTCs (REFER to Powertrain Control Module (PCM) Reset). RERUN Quick Test.
		No	►	GO to **KF21**.

Fig. 270   Test KF: Fan Control Relay (Part 11 of 22). 1996

Test Step		Result	►	Action to Take
KF21	CHECK HFC CIRCUIT FOR SHORT TO GROUND			
	• Key on, engine off. • Cooling fan(s) disconnected, test lamp installed. • Scan Tool connected. • Command High Speed Fan off. • Observe test lamp for an indication of a fault while performing the following (the lamp will turn on when a fault is detected, indicating an HFC circuit short to ground): — Shake, wiggle, bend the HFC circuit between the PCM and HFC relay. — Lightly tap on the HFC relay to simulate road shock. • Key off. • **Is a fault indicated?**	Yes	►	ISOLATE fault and SERVICE as necessary. COMPLETE PCM Reset to clear DTCs (REFER to Powertrain Control Module (PCM) Reset). RERUN Quick Test.
		No	►	GO to Pinpoint Test Step **Z1** with the following data: HFCF PID or HFCA PID (whichever is available) and list of possible causes.
KF25	ELECTRIC COOLING FAN DOES NOT OPERATE: CHECK FOR POWER AND GROUND TO FAN			
	• No DTCs received in EEC-V Quick Test. • Key on, engine off. • Output Test Mode accessed on Scan Tool. • Disconnect cooling fan. • Command cooling fan on. • Measure voltage between the Power-to-Fan circuit and ground circuit at the cooling fan vehicle harness connector. • **Was voltage greater than 10.5 volts?**	Yes	►	Key off. REPLACE cooling fan. VERIFY a symptom no longer exists.
		No	►	Remain in Output Test Mode. GO to **KF26**
KF26	CHECK GROUND CIRCUIT TO COOLING FAN			
	• Still in Output Test Mode with cooling fan commanded on. • Cooling fan disconnected. • Measure voltage between the Power-to-Fan circuit at the cooling fan vehicle harness connector and the battery negative post. • **Is voltage now greater than 10.5 volts?**	Yes	►	Key off. SERVICE open ground circuit to cooling fan. RECONNECT cooling fan. VERIFY a symptom no longer exists.
		No	►	Key off. GO to **KF27**.
KF27	CHECK FOR B(+) TO FAN CONTROL (FC) RELAY			
	• Key off. • Disconnect Fan Control (FC) relay. • Measure voltage between the B(+) circuit at the FC relay vehicle harness connector and the battery negative post. • **Is voltage greater than 10.5 volts?**	Yes	►	GO to **KF28**.
		No	►	RETEST with key on. If voltage is still less than 10.5 volts, turn key off and SERVICE open B(+) circuit to FC relay. RECONNECT all components. VERIFY a symptom no longer exists.

Fig. 270   Test KF: Fan Control Relay (Part 12 of 22). 1996

Test Step	Result	▶	Action to Take
KF28 CHECK POWER-TO FAN CIRCUIT CONTINUITY			
• Key off. • Cooling fan disconnected. • FC relay disconnected. • Measure resistance between the Power-to-Fan circuit at the FC relay vehicle harness connector and the Power-to-Fan circuit at the cooling fan vehicle harness connector. • **Is resistance less than 5.0 ohms?**	Yes	▶	REPLACE cooling fan relay. RECONNECT all components. VERIFY a symptom no longer exists.
	No	▶	SERVICE open Power-to-Fan circuit. RECONNECT all components. VERIFY a symptom no longer exists.
KF30 ELECTRIC COOLING FAN CONCERN (WITH NO DTCs): DID THE FAN OPERATE AT ANY SPEED?			
• **During the operational check of both fan speeds, did the fan operate at any speed?**	Yes	▶	Only one fan speed is operational. GO to **KF40**.
	No	▶	Cooling fan will not operate at any speed. GO to **KF31**.
KF31 COOLING FAN WILL NOT OPERATE AT ANY SPEED: COMMAND HIGH SPEED FAN ON AND CHECK FOR VOLTAGE TO COOLING FAN			
• Scan Tool connected. • Key on, engine off. • Still in Output Test Mode, with fan commanded off. • Disconnect cooling fan. • Command high speed fan on. • Measure voltage between the Power-To-High Speed Fan circuit at the cooling fan vehicle harness connector and chassis ground. • Key off. • **Was voltage greater than 10.0 volts?**	Yes	▶	Power is being supplied to fan. GO to **KF35** (to check cooling fan ground circuit).
	No	▶	Power is not being supplied to fan. GO to **KF32**.

FM015960153130X

Fig. 270 Test KF: Fan Control Relay (Part 13 of 22). 1996

Test Step	Result	▶	Action to Take
KF32 CHECK FOR B(+) TO HFC RELAY			
• Key off. • Cooling fan disconnected. • Disconnect HFC relay. • For Escort / Tracer, turn key on. • Measure voltage between the B(+) circuit (from IGN relay for Escort / Tracer) and chassis ground. • For Escort / Tracer, turn key off. • **Is voltage greater than 10.0 volts?**	Yes	▶	GO to **KF33**.
	No	▶	B(+) fault. CHECK condition of related fuses / fuse links. For Escort / Tracer, also verify operation of Ignition Relay. If OK, SERVICE open circuit. If fuse / fuse link is damaged, CHECK B(+) and Power-To-Fan circuits for short to ground before replacing. RECONNECT all components. VERIFY a symptom no longer exists.

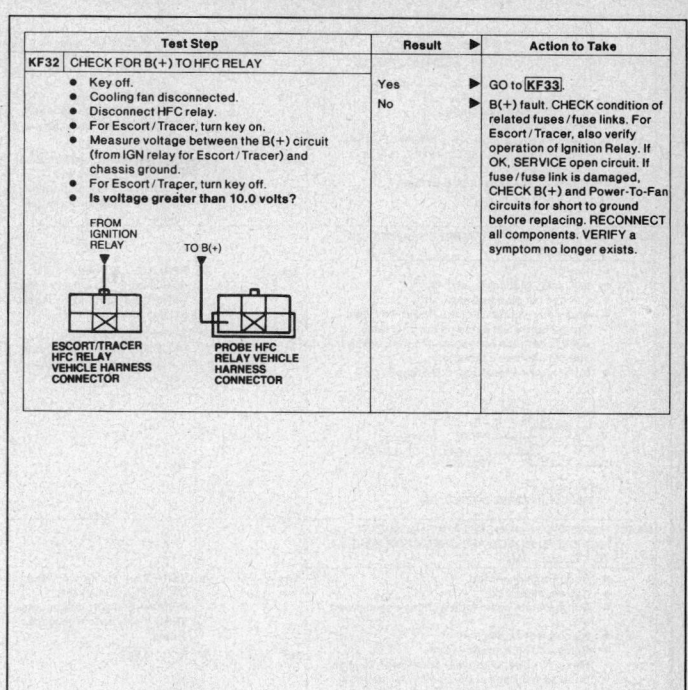

FM015960153140X

Fig. 270 Test KF: Fan Control Relay (Part 14 of 22). 1996

Test Step	Result	▶	Action to Take
KF33 CHECK CONTINUITY OF POWER-TO-FAN CIRCUITS			
• Key off. • HFC relay disconnected. • Cooling fan disconnected. • Disconnect LFC relay. • Measure resistance of the Power-To-High Speed Fan circuit between the HFC relay vehicle harness connector and the cooling fan vehicle harness connector. • Measure resistance of the Power-To-Low Speed Fan circuit between the LFC relay vehicle harness connector and the cooling fan vehicle harness connector. • **Are both resistances less than 5.0 ohms?**	Yes	▶	REPLACE HFC relay. RECONNECT all components. VERIFY a symptom no longer exists.
	No	▶	SERVICE open Power-To-Fan (s) circuit. RECONNECT all components. VERIFY a symptom no longer exists.
KF35 CHECK COOLING FAN GROUND CIRCUIT			
• Key off. • Cooling fan disconnected. • Disconnect Scan Tool from DLC. • Measure resistance between the ground circuit at the cooling fan vehicle harness connector and chassis ground. • **Is resistance less than 5.0 ohms?**	Yes	▶	REPLACE fan motor. RECONNECT all components. VERIFY a symptom no longer exists.
	No	▶	SERVICE open ground circuit. RECONNECT all components. VERIFY a symptom no longer exists.
KF40 DETERMINE WHICH FAN SPEED IS OPERATIONAL			
• **Was the low speed fan operational?**	Yes	▶	High speed fan inoperative. GO to **KF46**.
	No	▶	Low speed fan inoperative. GO to **KF41**.

FM015960153150X

Fig. 270 Test KF: Fan Control Relay (Part 15 of 22). 1996

Test Step	Result	▶	Action to Take
KF41 LOW SPEED FAN INOPERATIVE: COMMAND LOW SPEED FAN ON AND CHECK FOR VOLTAGE TO COOLING FAN			
• Scan Tool connected. • Key on, engine off. • Still in Output Test Mode with fan commanded off. • Disconnect cooling fan. • Command low speed fan on. • Measure voltage between the Power-To-Low Speed Fan circuit at the cooling fan vehicle harness connector and chassis ground. • Key off. • **Was voltage greater than 10.0 volts?**	Yes	▶	VERIFY ground circuit to fan. If OK, REPLACE fan motor. RECONNECT all components. VERIFY a symptom no longer exists.
	No	▶	GO to **KF42**.
KF42 CHECK FOR VOLTAGE FROM HFC RELAY TO LFC RELAY			
• Disconnect LFC relay. • Key on, engine off. • Measure voltage between the FROM HFC Relay circuit at the LFC relay vehicle harness connector and chassis ground. • Key off. • **Was voltage greater than 10.0 volts**	Yes	▶	GO to **KF44**.
	No	▶	GO to **KF43**.

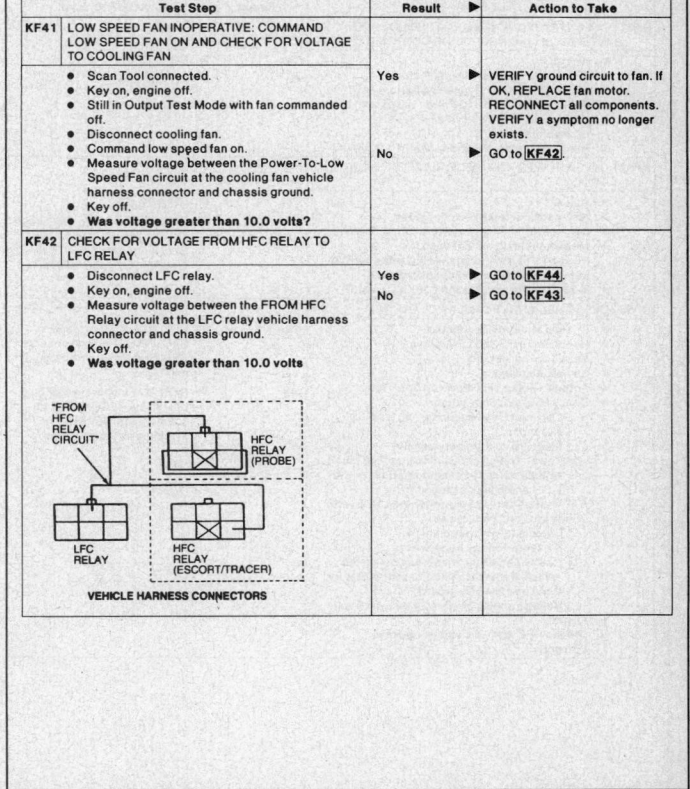

FM015960153160X

Fig. 270 Test KF: Fan Control Relay (Part 16 of 22). 1996

Test Step	Result	▶	Action to Take
KF43 CHECK CONTINUITY BETWEEN HFC AND LFC RELAY			
• Key off. • LFC relay disconnected. • Disconnect HFC relay. • Measure resistance of the FROM HFC Relay circuit between the LFC and HFC relays vehicle harness connectors. • **Is resistance less than 5.0 ohms?**	Yes	▶	REPLACE HFC relay. RECONNECT all components. VERIFY a symptom no longer exists.
	No	▶	SERVICE open circuit between the LFC and HFC relays. RECONNECT all components. VERIFY a symptom no longer exists.
KF44 CHECK POWER-TO-LOW SPEED FAN CIRCUIT CONTINUITY			
• Key off. • LFC relay disconnected. • Cooling fan disconnected. • Measure resistance of the Power-To-Low Speed fan circuit between the LFC relay vehicle harness connector and the cooling fan vehicle harness connector. • **Is resistance less than 5.0 ohms?**	Yes	▶	REPLACE LFC relay. RECONNECT all components. VERIFY a symptom no longer exists.
	No	▶	SERVICE open circuit. RECONNECT all components. VERIFY a symptom no longer exists.
KF46 HIGH SPEED FAN INOPERATIVE: COMMAND HIGH SPEED FAN ON AND CHECK FOR VOLTAGE TO COOLING FAN			
• Scan Tool connected. • Key on, engine off. • Still in Output Test Mode with fan commanded off. • Disconnect cooling fan. • Command high speed fan on. • Measure voltage between the Power-To-High Speed Fan circuit at the cooling fan vehicle harness connector and chassis ground. • Key off. • **Was voltage greater than 10.0 volts?**	Yes	▶	VERIFY ground circuit to fan. If OK, REPLACE fan motor. RECONNECT all components. VERIFY a symptom no longer exists.
	No	▶	GO to KF47.

Fig. 270   Test KF: Fan Control Relay (Part 17 of 22). 1996

Test Step	Result	▶	Action to Take
KF47 CHECK POWER-TO-HIGH SPEED FAN CIRCUIT CONTINUITY			
• Key off. • Cooling fan disconnected. • Disconnect HFC relay. • Measure resistance of the Power-To-High Speed fan circuit between the HFC relay vehicle harness connector and the cooling fan vehicle harness connector. • **Is resistance less than 5.0 ohms?**	Yes	▶	REPLACE HFC relay. RECONNECT all components. VERIFY a symptom no longer exists.
	No	▶	SERVICE open circuit. RECONNECT all components. VERIFY a symptom no longer exists.
KF50 LOW SPEED AND/OR HIGH SPEED COOLING FAN DOES NOT OPERATE: CHECK FOR B(+) TO HFC AND LFC RELAYS			
NOTE: For 2.5L Contour/Mystique, if one cooling fan does not operate, but the other operates normally, GO to KF70. • Key off. • Disconnect HFC and LFC relays. • Check for voltage on the B(+) circuit at both HFC and LFC relay vehicle harness connectors. • **Are both voltages greater than 10.5 volts?**	Yes	▶	GO to KF51.
	No	▶	VERIFY condition of related fuses/fuse links. If OK, SERVICE open B(+) circuit. If fuse/fuse link was damaged, CHECK B(+) and Power-to-Fan(s) circuits for short to ground before replacing. RECONNECT all components. VERIFY a symptom no longer exists.

Fig. 270   Test KF: Fan Control Relay (Part 18 of 22). 1996

Test Step	Result	▶	Action to Take
KF51 CHECK POWER-TO-FAN, FAN GROUND AND INTERNAL FAN CIRCUITS FOR CONTINUITY			
• Key off. • HFC and LFC relays disconnected. • Measure resistance between battery negative post and the Power-To-Fan circuit at both the HFC and LFC relay vehicle harness connectors. • **Are both resistances less than 15.0 ohms?**	Yes	▶	GO to KF52.
	No	▶	GO to KF56.
KF52 CHECK POWER-TO-FAN CIRCUIT FOR SHORT TO GROUND			
• Key off. • HFC and LFC relays disconnected. • Disconnect cooling fan(s)(both for 2.5L). • Measure resistance between the Power-To-Fan circuit at the HFC relay vehicle harness connector and chassis ground. • **Is resistance greater than 10,000 ohms?**	Yes	▶	GO to KF53.
	No	▶	SERVICE Power-To-Fan circuit short to ground. RECONNECT all components. VERIFY a symptom no longer exists.
KF53 CHECK HFC AND LFC RELAY OPERATION			

• Cooling fan(s) disconnected.
• Reconnect HFC and LFC relays.
• Scan Tool connected.
• Key on, engine off.
• Access Output Test Mode on Scan Tool.
• Check HFC relay operation:
  — Command high speed fan on, wait 10 seconds.
  — Measure voltage between the Power-To-Fan circuit at the cooling fan vehicle harness connector (either one for 2.5L) and chassis ground.
  — Voltage should be greater than 10.5 volts.
• Check LFC relay operation:
  — Command low speed fan on.
  — Measure voltage between the Power-To-Fan circuit at the cooling fan vehicle harness connector (either one for 2.5L) and chassis ground.
  — Voltage should be greater than 10.0 volts.
• Key off.
• **Did the HFC and LFC relays operate correctly?**
	Yes	▶	REPLACE cooling fan(s). RECONNECT all components. VERIFY a symptom no longer exists.

	No	▶	REPLACE inoperative HFC or LFC relay. RECONNECT all components. VERIFY a symptom no longer exists.

Fig. 270   Test KF: Fan Control Relay (Part 19 of 22). 1996

Test Step	Result	▶	Action to Take
KF56 CHECK POWER-TO-FAN CIRCUIT CONTINUITY BETWEEN THE COOLING FAN AND THE HFC AND LFC RELAYS			
• Key off. • HFC and LFC relays disconnected. • Disconnect cooling fan (either one for 2.5L). • Measure resistance of the Power-To-Fan circuit between the cooling fan vehicle harness connector and both the HFC and LFC vehicle harness connectors. • **Are both resistances less than 15.0 ohms?**	Yes	▶	GO to KF57.
	No	▶	SERVICE open in Power-To-Fan circuit (if open is only between LFC relay and fan, first verify dropping resistor connection). RECONNECT all components. VERIFY a symptom no longer exists.
KF57 CHECK COOLING FAN GROUND CIRCUIT			
• Key off. • Cooling fan disconnected. • Measure resistance between the ground circuit at the cooling fan vehicle harness connector and chassis ground. • **Is resistance less than 5.0 ohms?**	Yes	▶	REPLACE inoperative cooling fan(s). RECONNECT all components. VERIFY a symptom no longer exists.
	No	▶	SERVICE open ground circuit. RECONNECT all components. VERIFY a symptom no longer exists.
KF60 ELECTRIC COOLING FAN ALWAYS RUNS: DISCONNECT FAN CONTROL (FC) RELAY AND CHECK IF FAN IS STILL RUNNING			
• No DTCs received in EEC-V KOEO Self-Test. • Key off. • Disconnect Fan Control (FC) relay. • Key on, engine off. • **Is cooling fan still on?**	Yes	▶	Key off. SERVICE short to power on Power-to-Fan circuit. RECONNECT FC relay. VERIFY a symptom no longer exists.
	No	▶	Key off. REPLACE FC relay. VERIFY a symptom no longer exists.
KF65 LOW AND/OR HIGH SPEED COOLING FAN ALWAYS RUNS (NO DTCs, ACP(SW) PID OK): VERIFY IGNITION RELAY IS OPENING			
NOTE: Verify A/C and defrost are off. • For Probe and Contour/Mystique, GO directly to KF66. • **Is the cooling fan always on with the key off, but operating normally with the key on?**	Yes	▶	VERIFY that ignition relay contacts are not always closed. If OK, CHECK circuit from ignition relay to fan relays for short to B(+). After service, VERIFY a symptom no longer exists.
	No	▶	GO to KF66.
KF66 CHECK FOR LFC RELAY ALWAYS CLOSED			
• Key off. • Disconnect LFC relay. • Key on. • **Does fan continue to run?**	Yes	▶	GO to KF67.
	No	▶	Key off. REPLACE LFC relay. VERIFY a symptom no longer exists.

Fig. 270   Test KF: Fan Control Relay (Part 20 of 22). 1996

Test Step	Result	►	Action to Take
KF67 CHECK HFC RELAY			
• Key off. • LFC relay disconnected. • Disconnect HFC relay. • Key on. • **Does fan continue to run?**	Yes	►	**For Contour/Mystique:** Key off. SERVICE Power-To-Fan circuit for short to power. RECONNECT all components. VERIFY a symptom no longer exists. **All others:** GO to KF68.
	No	►	REPLACE HFC relay. RECONNECT all components. VERIFY a symptom no longer exists.
KF68 CHECK POWER-TO-LOW SPEED FAN CIRCUIT FOR SHORT TO POWER			
• Key off. • LFC and HFC relays disconnected. • Disconnect cooling fan. • Key on. • Measure voltage between the Power-To Low Speed fan circuit at the cooling fan vehicle harness connector and chassis ground. • **Is voltage less than 1.0 volt?**	Yes	►	SERVICE Power-To High Speed fan circuit for short to power. RECONNECT all components. VERIFY a symptom no longer exists.
	No	►	SERVICE Power-To Low Speed fan circuit for short to power. RECONNECT all components. VERIFY a symptom no longer exists.
KF70 ONE COOLING FAN INOPERATIVE WITH NO DTCs (THE OTHER COOLING FAN OPERATES NORMALLY): CHECK FOR POWER AND GROUND TO INOPERATIVE FAN			
• Key off. • Disconnect both cooling fans. • Access Output Test Mode on Scan Tool • Command high speed fan on. • Measure voltage between the Power-To-Fan circuit and ground circuit at the inoperative cooling fan vehicle harness connector. • **Is voltage greater than 10.0 volts?**	Yes	►	Key off. REPLACE inoperative cooling fan. RECONNECT all components. VERIFY a symptom no longer exists.
	No	►	REMAIN in Output Test Mode. GO to KF71.

FM0159601539210X

Fig. 270   Test KF: Fan Control Relay (Part 21 of 22). 1996

Test Step	Result	►	Action to Take
KF71 CHECK POWER-TO-FAN CIRCUIT			
• Still in Output Test Mode. • Cooling fans disconnected. • High speed fan commanded on. • Measure voltage between the Power-To Fan circuit at the inoperative cooling fan vehicle harness connector and chassis ground. • Key off. • **Was voltage greater than 10.0 volts?**	Yes	►	SERVICE open ground circuit to inoperative cooling fan. RECONNECT all components. VERIFY a symptom no longer exists.
	No	►	SERVICE open in Power-To-Fan circuit between inoperative cooling fan and splice to other fan. RECONNECT all components. VERIFY a symptom no longer exists.

FM0159601539220X

Fig. 270   Test KF: Fan Control Relay (Part 22 of 22). 1996

Note

You should enter this Pinpoint Test only when directed here.

Remember

This Pinpoint Test is intended to diagnose the following:

• Harness circuit: SIL
• Top gear switch
• SIL dimmer relay
• SIL bulb and SIL circuit fuse
• Powertrain Control Module (PCM) (12A650)

Pinpoint Test Schematics

Escort/Tracer

*TEST PIN 72 ──── SIL ──── I/P SHIFT INDICATOR LAMP ──── TOP GEAR SWITCH ──── TO IGNITION RUN CIRCUIT

*TEST PINS LOCATED ON BREAKOUT BOX
ALL HARNESS CONNECTORS VIEWED INTO MATING SURFACE

Test Step	Result	►	Action to Take
KL1 CHECK SIL OPERATION			
NOTE: To verify Shift Indicator Light (SIL) operation, observe the SIL while driving the vehicle. The SIL should turn on when optimum shift speed is reached in each gear and remain off while in the highest gear. If the SIL is always on, look for a short to ground in the SIL circuit. If the SIL is always off, look for an open in the SIL circuit. • **Is SIL on all the time?**	Yes	►	GO to KL4.
	No	►	GO to KL2.

FM0159601540010X

Fig. 271   Test KL: Shift Indicator Lamp (Part 1 of 3). 1996

Test Step	Result	►	Action to Take
KL2 CHECK SIL CIRCUIT FUSE			
• Key off. • Remove SIL circuit fuse and inspect. • **Is fuse OK?**	Yes	►	RECONNECT SIL circuit fuse. GO to KL3.
	No	►	SERVICE short to ground between SIL circuit fuse and SIL bulb. REPLACE SIL circuit fuse. VERIFY SIL operation.
KL3 CHECK SIL BULB			
• Key off. • Remove SIL bulb and inspect. • **Is SIL bulb OK?**	Yes	►	GO to KL5.
	No	►	REPLACE SIL bulb. VERIFY SIL operation.
KL4 CHECK SIL CIRCUIT FOR SHORT TO GROUND			
• Key off. • Reconnect top gear switch. • Shift transmission to highest gear. • Breakout box installed, PCM disconnected. • Measure resistance between Test Pin 53 and Test Pin 60 at the breakout box. • **Is resistance greater than 10,000 ohms?**	Yes	►	REPLACE PCM. REMOVE breakout box. RERUN Quick Test.
	No	►	SERVICE short to ground between top gear switch and PCM. REMOVE breakout box. RECONNECT PCM. VERIFY SIL operation.
KL5 CHECK FOR VOLTAGE TO SIL SOCKET			
• Key off. • SIL bulb removed. • Transmission in any gear except top gear. • Key on, engine off. • Measure voltage between power contact SIL socket and chassis ground. • **Is voltage greater than 10.5 volts?**	Yes	►	GO to KL7.
	No	►	RECONNECT SIL bulb. GO to KL6.
KL6 CHECK OPERATION OF TOP GEAR SWITCH			
NOTE: The top gear switch is a normally closed switch and is in the ignition RUN circuit to the SIL bulb. The top gear switch should be open only when the vehicle is shifted to top gear. • Key off. • Transmission in any gear except top gear. • Disconnect top gear switch. • Measure resistance of the top gear switch. • **Is resistance less than 5.0 ohms?**	Yes	►	SERVICE open in ignition run circuit to the SIL bulb socket.
	No	►	REPLACE top gear switch. VERIFY SIL operation.

FM0159601540020X

Fig. 271   Test KL: Shift Indicator Lamp (Part 2 of 3). 1996

Test Step	Result	▶	Action to Take
KL7 CHECK CONTINUITY OF SIL CIRCUIT			
• Key off. • SIL bulb removed. • Disconnect Powertrain Control Module (PCM). Inspect for damaged or pushed out pins, corrosion, loose wires, etc. Service as necessary. • Install breakout box, leave PCM disconnected. • Measure resistance between Test Pin 72 at the breakout box and SIL circuit contact at the SIL bulb socket. • **Is resistance less than 5.0 ohms?**	Yes	▶	REPLACE PCM. REMOVE breakout box. RECONNECT SIL bulb. VERIFY SIL operation.
	No	▶	SERVICE open circuit. REMOVE breakout box. RECONNECT all components. VERIFY SIL operation.

FM0159601540030

Fig. 271   Test KL: Shift Indicator Lamp (Part 3 of 3). 1996

Note

You should enter this Pinpoint Test only when directed here.

Remember

This Pinpoint Test is intended to diagnose the following:

• Harness circuits: VPWR, A/C Demand (or EATC) to WAC relay, ACCS, WAC, Power-to-A/C Clutch, ACON

• WOT A/C Cutout (WAC) Relay

• A/C Relay (Escort/Tracer, Probe)

• Powertrain Control Module (PCM) (12A650)

FM0159601541010X

Fig. 272   Test KM: WOT A/C Cut-Off (WAC) Relay, A/C Circuits (Part 1 of 29). 1996

Pinpoint Test Schematics

Escort/Tracer

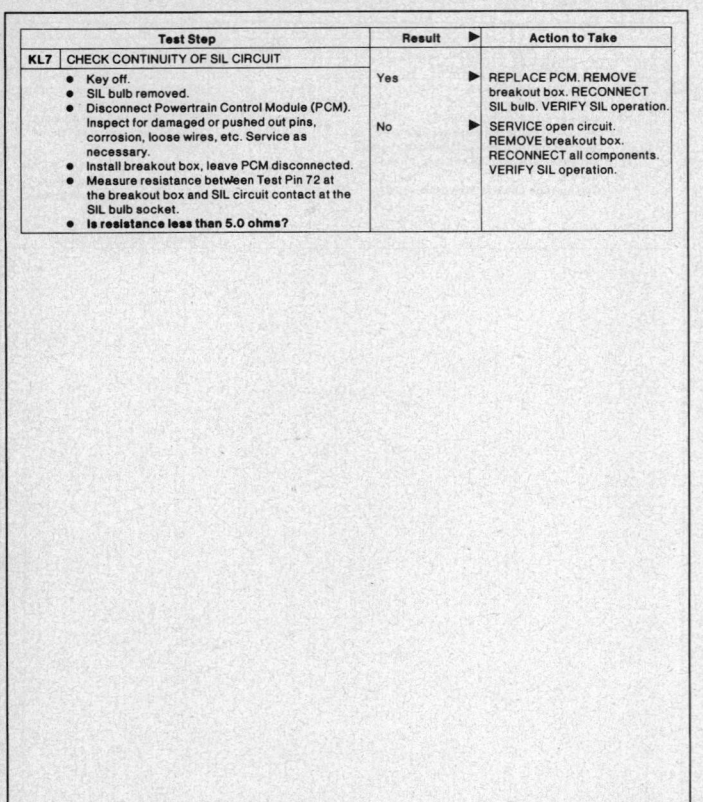

FM0159601541020X

Fig. 272   Test KM: WOT A/C Cut-Off (WAC) Relay, A/C Circuits (Part 2 of 29). 1996

Probe

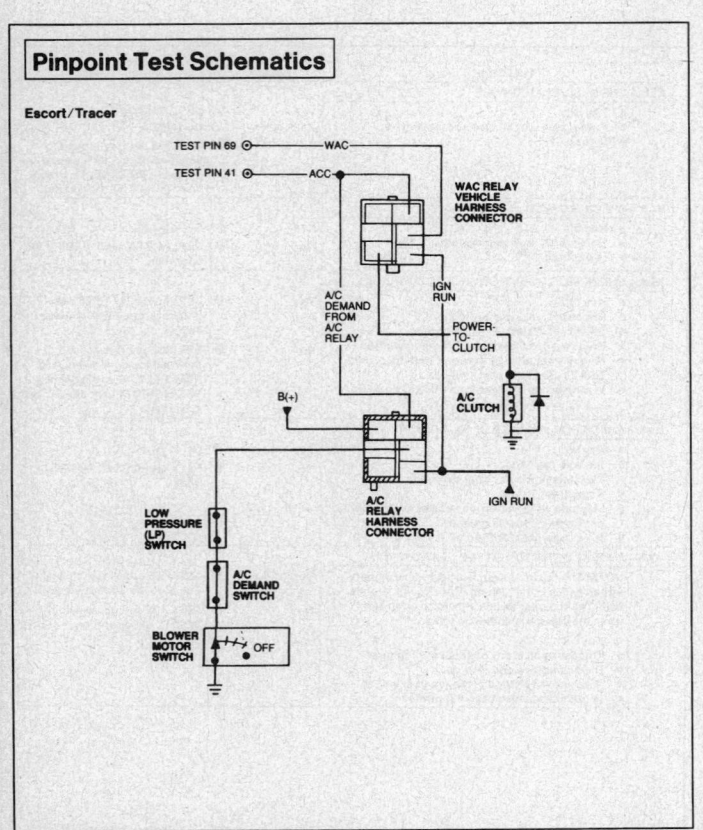

FM0159601541030X

Fig. 272   Test KM: WOT A/C Cut-Off (WAC) Relay, A/C Circuits (Part 3 of 29). 1996

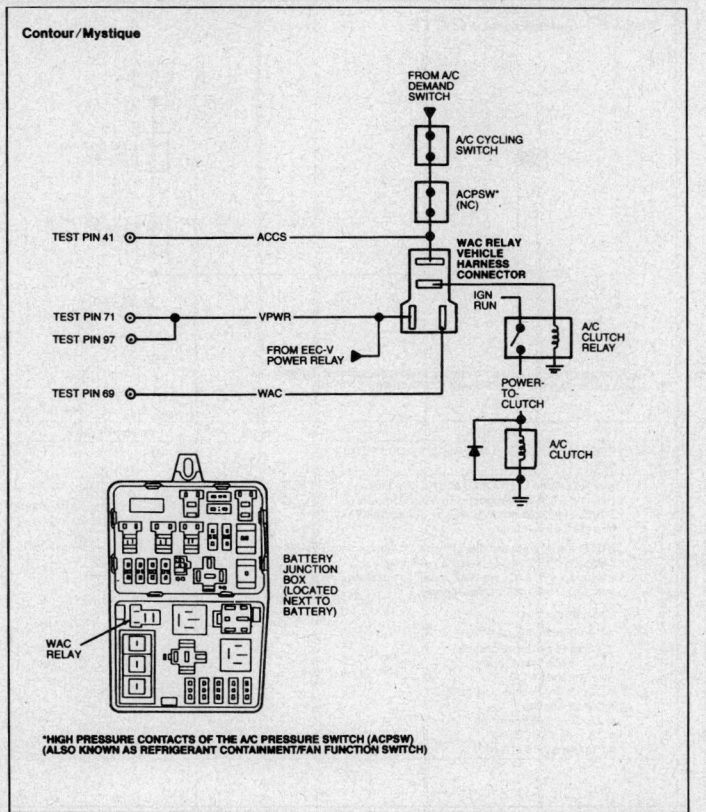

Fig. 272 Test KM: WOT A/C Cut-Off (WAC) Relay, A/C Circuits (Part 4 of 29). 1996

FM0159601541040X

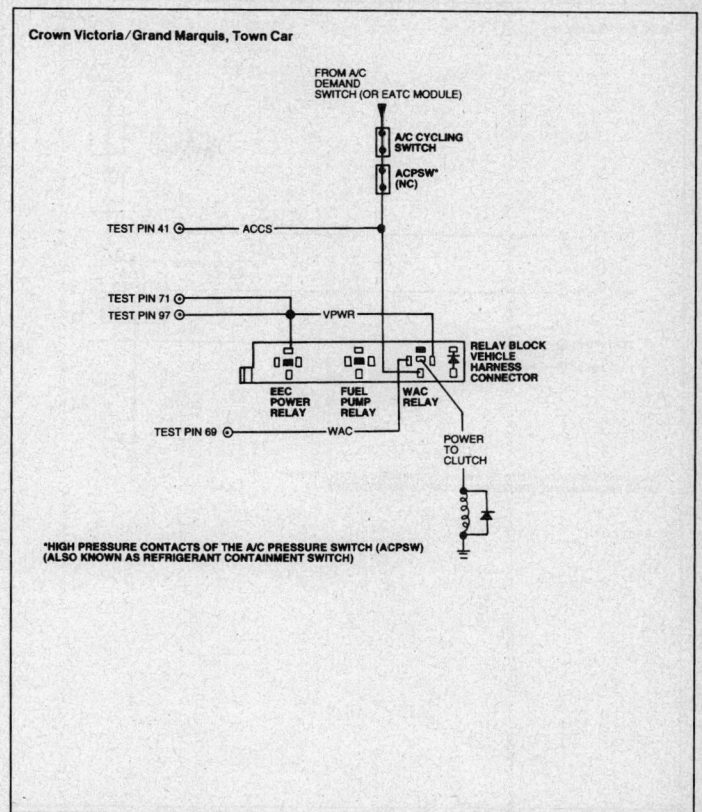

Fig. 272 Test KM: WOT A/C Cut-Off (WAC) Relay, A/C Circuits (Part 5 of 29). 1996

FM0159601541050X

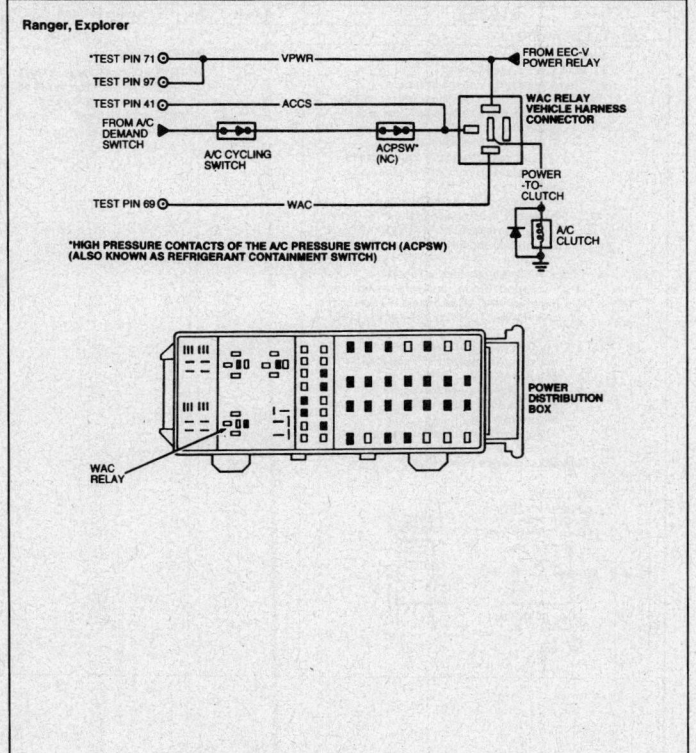

Fig. 272 Test KM: WOT A/C Cut-Off (WAC) Relay, A/C Circuits (Part 6 of 29). 1996

FM0159601541060X

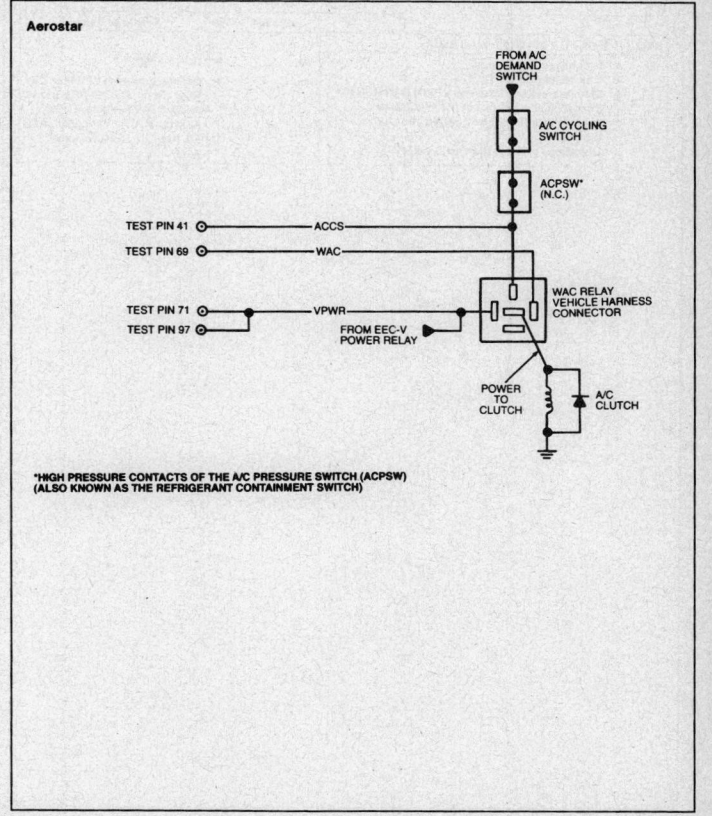

Fig. 272 Test KM: WOT A/C Cut-Off (WAC) Relay, A/C Circuits (Part 7 of 29). 1996

FM0159601541070X

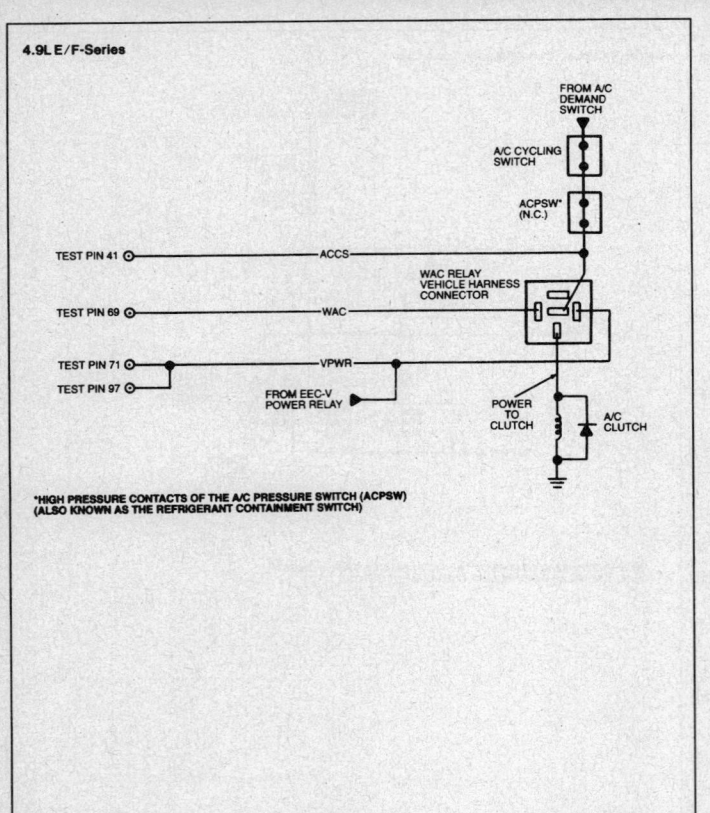

4.9L E/F-Series

FROM A/C DEMAND SWITCH

A/C CYCLING SWITCH

ACPSW* (N.C.)

TEST PIN 41 — ACCS

WAC RELAY VEHICLE HARNESS CONNECTOR

TEST PIN 69 — WAC

TEST PIN 71 — VPWR
TEST PIN 97

FROM EEC-V POWER RELAY

POWER TO CLUTCH

A/C CLUTCH

*HIGH PRESSURE CONTACTS OF THE A/C PRESSURE SWITCH (ACPSW) (ALSO KNOWN AS THE REFRIGERANT CONTAINMENT SWITCH)

FM015960154108OX

Fig. 272 Test KM: WOT A/C Cut-Off (WAC) Relay, A/C Circuits (Part 8 of 29). 1996

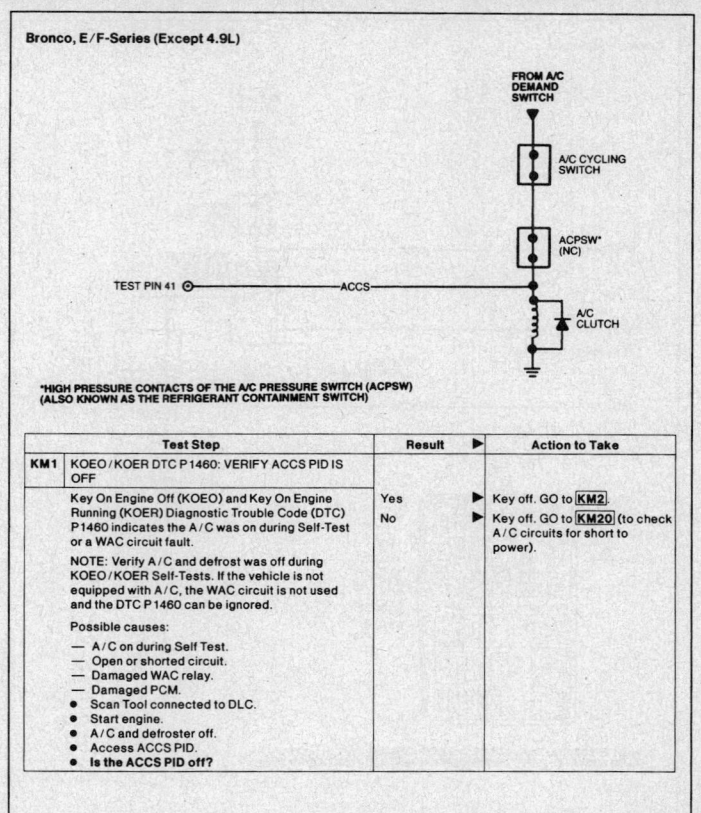

Bronco, E/F-Series (Except 4.9L)

FROM A/C DEMAND SWITCH

A/C CYCLING SWITCH

ACPSW* (NC)

TEST PIN 41 — ACCS

A/C CLUTCH

*HIGH PRESSURE CONTACTS OF THE A/C PRESSURE SWITCH (ACPSW) (ALSO KNOWN AS THE REFRIGERANT CONTAINMENT SWITCH)

	Test Step	Result	▶	Action to Take
KM1	KOEO/KOER DTC P 1460: VERIFY ACCS PID IS OFF			
	Key On Engine Off (KOEO) and Key On Engine Running (KOER) Diagnostic Trouble Code (DTC) P 1460 indicates the A/C was on during Self-Test or a WAC circuit fault. NOTE: Verify A/C and defrost was off during KOEO/KOER Self-Tests. If the vehicle is not equipped with A/C, the WAC circuit is not used and the DTC P 1460 can be ignored. Possible causes: — A/C on during Self Test. — Open or shorted circuit. — Damaged WAC relay. — Damaged PCM. ● Scan Tool connected to DLC. ● Start engine. ● A/C and defroster off. ● Access ACCS PID. ● **Is the ACCS PID off?**	Yes No	▶ ▶	Key off. GO to **KM2**. Key off. GO to **KM20** (to check A/C circuits for short to power).

FM015960154109OX

Fig. 272 Test KM: WOT A/C Cut-Off (WAC) Relay, A/C Circuits (Part 9 of 29). 1996

	Test Step	Result	▶	Action to Take
KM2	CHECK FOR VPWR TO WAC RELAY			
	● Disconnect WAC relay. ● Key on, engine off. ● Measure voltage between VPWR (IGN RUN for Escort/Tracer) circuit at the WAC relay vehicle harness connector and chassis ground. ● **Is voltage greater than 10.5 volts?**	Yes No	▶ ▶	GO to **KM3**. SERVICE open in VPWR or IGN RUN circuit. RECONNECT WAC relay. START engine. TURN A/C on, WAIT 15 seconds. A/C off. Key Off. RERUN Quick Test.

FM015960154110OX

Fig. 272 Test KM: WOT A/C Cut-Off (WAC) Relay, A/C Circuits (Part 10 of 29). 1996

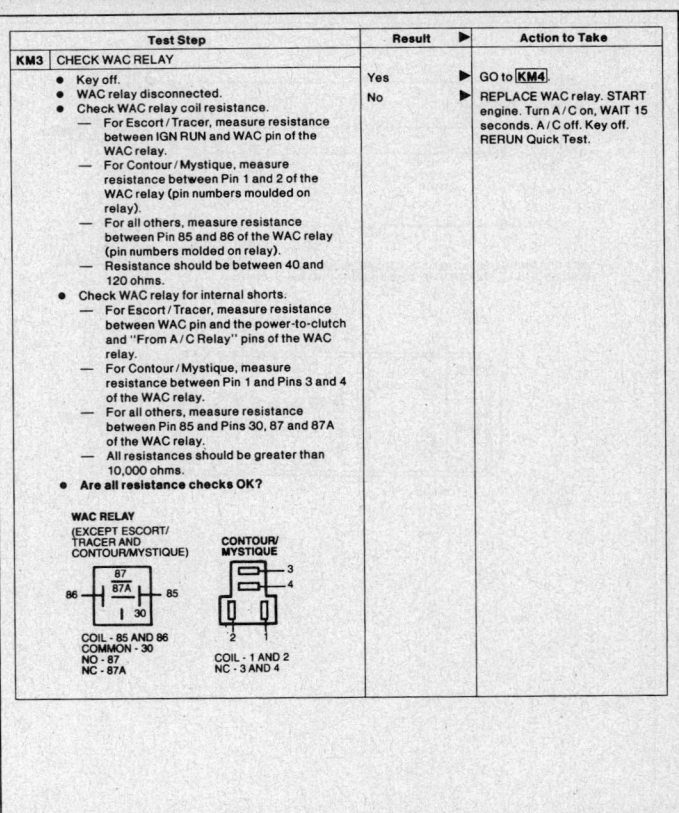

	Test Step	Result	▶	Action to Take
KM3	CHECK WAC RELAY			
	● Key off. ● WAC relay disconnected. ● Check WAC relay coil resistance. — For Escort/Tracer, measure resistance between IGN RUN and WAC pin of the WAC relay. — For Contour/Mystique, measure resistance between Pin 1 and 2 of the WAC relay (pin numbers moulded on relay). — For all others, measure resistance between Pin 85 and 86 of the WAC relay (pin numbers molded on relay). — Resistance should be between 40 and 120 ohms. ● Check WAC relay for internal shorts. — For Escort/Tracer, measure resistance between WAC pin and the power-to-clutch and "From A/C Relay" pins of the WAC relay. — For Contour/Mystique, measure resistance between Pin 1 and Pins 3 and 4 of the WAC relay. — For all others, measure resistance between Pin 85 and Pins 30, 87 and 87A of the WAC relay. — All resistances should be greater than 10,000 ohms. ● **Are all resistance checks OK?**	Yes No	▶ ▶	GO to **KM4**. REPLACE WAC relay. START engine. Turn A/C on, WAIT 15 seconds. A/C off. Key off. RERUN Quick Test.

WAC RELAY
(EXCEPT ESCORT/TRACER AND CONTOUR/MYSTIQUE)

CONTOUR/MYSTIQUE

COIL - 85 AND 86
COMMON - 30
NO - 87
NC - 87A

COIL - 1 AND 2
NC - 3 AND 4

FM015960154111OX

Fig. 272 Test KM: WOT A/C Cut-Off (WAC) Relay, A/C Circuits (Part 11 of 29). 1996

Test Step	Result	▶	Action to Take
KM4 CHECK WAC CIRCUIT FOR SHORT TO POWER • Key off. • WAC relay disconnected. • Disconnect PCM. Inspect for damaged or pushed out pins, corrosion, loose wires, etc. Service as necessary. • Install breakout box, leave PCM disconnected. • Key on, engine off. • Measure voltage between Test Pin 69 (WAC) at the breakout box and chassis ground. • **Is voltage less than 1.0 volt?**	Yes No	▶ ▶	GO to KM5. SERVICE short to power. REMOVE breakout box. RECONNECT all components. START engine. Turn A/C on, WAIT 15 seconds. A/C off. Key off. RERUN Quick Test.
KM5 CHECK WAC CIRCUIT FOR SHORT TO GROUND • Key off. • Disconnect Scan Tool from DLC. • Breakout box installed, PCM disconnected. • WAC relay disconnected. • Measure resistance between Test Pin 69 and Test Pins 51, 103 (PWR GND) and 91 (SIG RTN) at the breakout box. • **Is each resistance greater than 10,000 ohms?**	Yes No	▶ ▶	GO to KM6. SERVICE short circuit. REMOVE breakout box. RECONNECT all components. START engine. Turn A/C on, WAIT 15 seconds. A/C off. Key off. RERUN Quick Test.
KM6 CHECK WAC CIRCUIT CONTINUITY • Key off. • Breakout box installed, PCM disconnected. • WAC relay disconnected. • Measure resistance between WAC circuit at the WAC relay vehicle harness connector and Test Pin 69 at the breakout box. • **Is resistance less than 5.0 ohms?**	Yes No	▶ ▶	REPLACE PCM. RECONNECT all components. START engine. Turn A/C on, WAIT 15 seconds. A/C off. Key off. RERUN Quick Test. SERVICE open circuit. REMOVE breakout box. RECONNECT all components. START engine. Turn A/C on, WAIT 15 seconds. A/C off. Key off. RERUN Quick Test.
KM10 ACCS PID OFF WITH A/C ON: CHECK FOR VOLTAGE TO A/C CYCLING SWITCH • Key on, engine off. • Disconnect A/C Cycling Switch. • A/C demand switch to A/C on. • Measure voltage between the A/C demand switch (or EATC module) side of the A/C Cycling Switch vehicle harness connector and chassis ground. • Key off. • **Was voltage greater than 10.5 volts?**	Yes No	▶ ▶	GO to KM11. check A/C demand switch or EATC module operation, applicable fuses, wiring to A/C Cycling Switch, etc.

FM0159601541120X

Fig. 272 Test KM: WOT A/C Cut-Off (WAC) Relay, A/C Circuits (Part 12 of 29). 1996

Test Step	Result	▶	Action to Take
KM11 CHECK FOR VOLTAGE TO A/C PRESSURE SWITCH (ACPSW) • Key off. • Reconnect A/C Cycling Switch. • Disconnect ACPSW (also known as Refrigerant Containment Switch). • Key on, engine off. • A/C on. • Measure voltage between the A/C Demand Switch (or EATC module) pin at the ACPSW vehicle harness connector and chassis ground. • Key off. • **Was voltage greater than 10.5 volts?**	Yes No	▶ ▶	GO to KM12. VERIFY operation of A/C Cycling Switch If OK, SERVICE open between A/C Cycling Switch and ACPSW. RECONNECT all components. VERIFY a symptom no longer exists.

"DUAL FUNCTION" A/C PRESSURE SWITCH (ACPSW) VEHICLE HARNESS CONNECTOR

FROM A/C DEMAND SWITCH OR EATC MODULE (AND A/C CYCLING SWITCH)

"SINGLE FUNCTION" A/C PRESSURE SWITCH (ACPSW) VEHICLE HARNESS CONNECTOR

Test Step	Result	▶	Action to Take
KM12 CHECK CONTINUITY OF ACPSW HIGH PRESSURE CONTACTS • Key off. • ACPSW disconnected. • Measure resistance of the ACPSW high pressure contacts (these are the normally closed contacts). • **Is resistance less than 5.0 ohms?**	Yes No	▶ 	RECONNECT ACPSW. GO to KM13. check for overpressurized A/C system, etc. If OK, REPLACE ACPSW. VERIFY a symptom no longer exists.

FM0159601541130X

Fig. 272 Test KM: WOT A/C Cut-Off (WAC) Relay, A/C Circuits (Part 13 of 29). 1996

Test Step	Result	▶	Action to Take
KM13 CHECK FOR VOLTAGE TO PCM ON ACCS CIRCUIT • Key off. • Disconnect PCM. Inspect for damaged or pushed out pins, loose wires, corrosion, etc. Service as necessary. • Install breakout box, leave PCM disconnected. • Key on. • A/C ON. • Measure voltage between Test Pin 41 (ACCS) and Test Pin 77 (PWR GND) at the breakout box. • **Is voltage greater than 10.5 volts?**	Yes No	▶ ▶	REPLACE PCM. REMOVE breakout box. RECONNECT all components. VERIFY a symptom no longer exists. SERVICE open circuit between the ACPSW and PCM. REMOVE breakout box. RECONNECT all components. VERIFY a symptom no longer exists.
KM15 NO/LOW VOLTAGE TO A/C CLUTCH (ACCS PID ON WITH A/C ON): CHECK A/C DEMAND SWITCH VOLTAGE TO WAC RELAY • Key off. • Disconnect WAC relay. • Key on. • A/C demand switch to A/C on. • For Escort/Tracer, also turn on blower motor (any speed). — For Escort/Tracer, measure voltage between the "A/C Demand from A/C Relay" circuit at the WAC relay vehicle harness connector. — For all except Escort/Tracer, measure voltage between the A/C Demand Switch (or EATC module) input pin at the WAC relay vehicle harness connector and chassis ground. • Key off, A/C off. • **Was voltage greater than 10.5 volts?**	Yes No	▶ ▶	For Contour/Mystique: GO to KM100. All others: GO to KM16. SERVICE open in A/C demand circuit between WAC relay and ACCS splice to PCM. RECONNECT all components. VERIFY a symptom no longer exists.
KM16 CHECK CONTINUITY OF POWER-TO-A/C CLUTCH AND A/C CLUTCH GROUND CIRCUITS • Key off. • WAC relay disconnected. • Disconnect A/C clutch. • Disconnect Scan Tool from DLC. • Measure resistance between the Power-to-Clutch circuit at the WAC relay vehicle harness connector and the power side of the A/C clutch vehicle harness connector. • Measure resistance between the ground side of the A/C clutch vehicle harness connector and the battery negative post. • **Is each resistance less than 5.0 ohms?**	Yes No	▶ ▶	REPLACE WAC relay. RECONNECT all components. VERIFY a symptom no longer exists. SERVICE open circuit. RECONNECT all components. VERIFY a symptom no longer exists.

FM0159601541140X

Fig. 272 Test KM: WOT A/C Cut-Off (WAC) Relay, A/C Circuits (Part 14 of 29). 1996

Test Step	Result	▶	Action to Take
KM19 DTC P1464: CHECK ACCS PID Diagnostic Trouble Code (DTC) P1464 indicates the ACCS input to the Powertrain Control Module (PCM) was high during Self-Test. NOTE: Verify A/C and defrost were off during Self-Test. If A/C or defrost were on, turn off and rerun Self-Test. • Key on, engine off. • Scan Tool connected. • A/C and defrost off. • Access ACCS PID. • **Is ACCS PID on?**	Yes No	▶ ▶	GO to KM20. The ACCS PID indicates that the ACCS input to the PCM is low. VERIFY test results. With A/C and defrost off, RERUN Self-Test where P1464 was received.
KM20 ACCS PID ON: DISCONNECT ACPSW AND CHECK IF ACCS PID TURNS OFF • Key off. • Disconnect A/C Pressure Switch (ACPSW) (also known as the Refrigerant Containment Switch). • Key on, engine off. • Access ACCS PID. • **Is ACCS PID off?**	Yes No	▶ ▶	Key off. VERIFY operation of A/C Demand Switch or EATC module If OK, SERVICE short to power in A/C Demand circuit in ACPSW. RECONNECT all components. VERIFY a symptom no longer exists. Key off. **For applications without WAC relay (E/F Series, Bronco):** GO to KM22. **For Contour/Mystique:** GO to KM110. **All Others:** GO to KM21.
KM21 CHECK POWER-TO-A/C CLUTCH CIRCUIT FOR SHORT TO POWER • Key off. • Disconnect WAC relay. • Key on. • Measure voltage between Power-to-Clutch of the WAC relay vehicle harness connector and the chassis ground. • Key off. • **Was voltage less than 1.0 volt?**	Yes No	▶ ▶	GO to KM22. SERVICE short to power. RECONNECT all components. VERIFY a symptom no longer exists.

FM0159601541150X

Fig. 272 Test KM: WOT A/C Cut-Off (WAC) Relay, A/C Circuits (Part 15 of 29). 1996

Part 16 of 29 — KM22, KM23, KM25

Test Step	Result	▶	Action to Take
KM22 CHECK ACCS CIRCUIT FOR SHORT TO POWER • Key off. • ACPSW and WAC relay (if equipped) disconnected. • Disconnect PCM. Inspect for damaged or pushed out pins, corrosion, loose wires, etc. Service as necessary. • Install breakout box, leave PCM disconnected. • Key on. • Measure voltage between Test Pin 41 (ACCS) and Test Pins 51 and 103 (PWR GND). • Key off. • **Was voltage less than 1.0 volt?**	Yes	▶	**For applications without WAC relay:** REPLACE PCM. REMOVE breakout box. RECONNECT all components. RERUN Quick Test. **All others:** GO to **KM23**.
	No	▶	SERVICE ACCS circuit short to power. REMOVE breakout box. RECONNECT all components. VERIFY a symptom no longer exists.
KM23 CHECK ACCS CIRCUIT VOLTAGE TO PCM WITH WAC RELAY CONNECTED • Key off. • Reconnect WAC relay. • ACPSW disconnected. • Breakout box installed, PCM disconnected. • Key on. • Again, measure voltage between Test Pin 41 (ACCS) and Test Pins 51 and 103 (PWR GND). • Key off. • **Was voltage less than 1.0 volt?**	Yes	▶	REPLACE PCM. REMOVE breakout box. RECONNECT all components. VERIFY a symptom no longer exists.
	No	▶	REPLACE WAC relay. REMOVE breakout box. RECONNECT all components. VERIFY a symptom no longer exists.
KM25 NO WAC W/NO DTCs: CHECK WAC RELAY • Scan Tool connected. • A/C clutch and WAC relay connected. • Key on, engine off. • Access Output Test Mode or Scan Tool. • A/C on. • While listening to the A/C clutch, command the outputs off and on a couple times. • **Does the A/C clutch engage and disengage when the outputs are cycled off and on?**	Yes	▶	Key off. EEC system is operating properly. If symptom is intermittent, GO to Pinpoint Test Step **Z1** with the following data: WACF PID or WACA PID. Otherwise, testing is complete. Key off. service any other symptoms.
	No	▶	VERIFY that the A/C clutch was engaged during testing. If not, REPEAT test with clutch engaged. If clutch was engaged, REPLACE WAC relay. RECONNECT all components. VERIFY a symptom no longer exists.

Fig. 272   Test KM: WOT A/C Cut-Off (WAC) Relay, A/C Circuits (Part 16 of 29). 1996

Part 17 of 29 — KM30

Test Step	Result	▶	Action to Take
KM30 CONTINUOUS MEMORY DTC P1460: CHECK WAC (ACON FOR PROBE) CIRCUIT FOR INTERMITTENT CONCERNS A Continuous Memory Diagnostic Trouble Code (DTC) P1460 indicates a WAC (ACON for Probe) circuit failure has occurred during vehicle operation. NOTE: If the vehicle is not equipped with A/C, the WAC circuit is not used and the P1460 can be ignored. Possible causes: — Open or short in WAC/ACON circuit (PCM Pin 69). — For Escort/Tracer, open IGN RUN to WAC relay. — For Probe, open IGN RUN to A/C relay. — For all others, open VPWR to WAC relay. • Key off. • Scan Tool connected. • Disconnect A/C Cycling Switch (Low Pressure (LP) Switch for Escort/Tracer and Probe). • Install a jumper wire in the A/C Cycling/LP Switch vehicle harness connector (to complete the circuit). • Key on, engine off. • A/C demand switch on. • For Escort/Tracer, also turn blower motor on (any speed). • Check WAC circuit for open or short to power (for Probe, this test will check ACON for short to ground) while performing the following (the A/C clutch will click on when a fault is detected): — Shake, wiggle, bend the WAC/ACON circuit between the WAC (Pin 69) and the WAC relay (A/C relay for Probe). — Lightly tap on the WAC or A/C relay (to simulate road shock). • **Is a fault indicated?**	Yes	▶	ISOLATE fault and SERVICE as necessary. REMOVE jumper wire. RECONNECT all components. COMPLETE PCM RESET to clear DTCs (REFER to Powertrain Control Module (PCM) Reset). START engine. Turn A/C on, WAIT 15 seconds. A/C off. Key off. RERUN Quick Test.
	No	▶	GO to **KM31**.

Fig. 272   Test KM: WOT A/C Cut-Off (WAC) Relay, A/C Circuits (Part 17 of 29). 1996

Part 18 of 29 — KM31, KM50, KM51

Test Step	Result	▶	Action to Take
KM31 CHECK WAC/ACON CIRCUIT FOR INTERMITTENT CONCERNS • Key on, engine off. • Jumper wire installed in A/C Cycling or LP Switch. • A/C demand on. • For Escort/Tracer, blower motor on. • Scan Tool connected. • Access Output Test Mode on Scan Tool. • For Probe: — Turn outputs on (to turn on the A/C clutch). All others: — Turn outputs off (this will prevent the WAC circuit from turning off the A/C clutch). • Check WAC circuit for short to ground (ACON circuit for open in VPWR or IGN RUN circuit while performing the following (the A/C clutch will click off when a fault is detected): — Shake, wiggle, bend the WAC/ACON circuit between the PCM (Pin 69) and the WAC or A/C relay. — Shake, wiggle, bend the VPWR or IGN RUN circuit to the WAC or A/C relay. — Lightly tap on the WAC or A/C relay (to simulate road shock). • Key off, A/C off. • **Is a fault indicated?**	Yes	▶	ISOLATE fault and SERVICE as necessary. REMOVE jumper wire. RECONNECT all components. COMPLETE PCM RESET to clear DTCs (REFER to Powertrain Control Module (PCM) Reset). START engine. Turn A/C on, WAIT 15 seconds. A/C off. Key off. RERUN Quick Test.
	No	▶	Unable to duplicate and/or identify fault at this time. GO to Pinpoint Test Step **Z1** with the following data: WACF or WACA PID (whichever is available) and list of possible causes.
KM50 LOW/NO VOLTAGE TO A/C CLUTCH (ACCS PID ON WITH A/C ON, NO DTCS): COMMAND "ACON: OUTPUT ON AND AGAIN CHECK FOR VOLTAGE AT A/C CLUTCH • Scan Tool connected. • Key on, engine off. • A/C clutch disconnected. • Enter Output Test Mode on Scan Tool. • Command outputs on (to ground ACON circuit). • Again measure voltage between the power pin and ground pin at the A/C clutch vehicle harness connector. • **Is voltage greater than 10.5 volts?**	Yes	▶	Key off. EEC system OK. check for mechanical concerns, open circuit in A/C clutch, etc. After service, RECONNECT all components and VERIFY a symptom no longer exists.
	No	▶	Key off. GO to **KM51**.
KM51 CHECK FOR B+ VOLTAGE TO A/C RELAY • Key off. • Disconnect A/C relay. • Key on. • Measure voltage between B+ circuit at A/C relay vehicle harness connector and chassis ground. • **Is voltage greater than 10.5 volts?**	Yes	▶	Key off. GO to **KM52**.
	No	▶	Key off. VERIFY condition of related fuses. If OK, SERVICE open circuit. RECONNECT all components. VERIFY a symptom no longer exists.

Fig. 272   Test KM: WOT A/C Cut-Off (WAC) Relay, A/C Circuits (Part 18 of 29). 1996

Part 19 of 29 — KM52, KM55, KM56, KM57

Test Step	Result	▶	Action to Take
KM52 CHECK CONTINUITY OF POWER TO CLUTCH CIRCUIT AND A/C CLUTCH GROUND CIRCUIT • Key off. • A/C relay disconnected. • A/C clutch disconnected. • Measure resistance between power side of the A/C clutch vehicle harness connector and Power-to-Clutch circuit at A/C relay vehicle harness connector. • Measure resistance between the ground side of the A/C clutch vehicle harness connector and the battery negative post. • **Are both resistances less than 5.0 ohms?**	Yes	▶	REPLACE A/C relay. RECONNECT all components. VERIFY a symptom no longer exists.
	No	▶	SERVICE open circuit. RECONNECT all components. VERIFY a symptom no longer exists.
KM55 ACCS PID OFF WITH A/C ON: CHECK A/C DEMAND (ACD) SWITCH CIRCUIT CONTINUITY TO LOW PRESSURE (LP) SWITCH • Key off. • A/C demand switch to A/C on. • Disconnect LP switch. • Measure resistance between A/C demand switch side of LP switch vehicle harness connector and chassis ground. • **Is resistance less than 5.0 ohms?**	Yes	▶	GO to **KM56**.
	No	▶	VERIFY operation of A/C demand switch . If OK, SERVICE open circuit. RECONNECT all components. VERIFY a symptom no longer exists.
KM56 MEASURE RESISTANCE OF LP SWITCH • Key off. • LP switch disconnected. • Measure resistance of LP switch. • **Is resistance less than 5.0 ohms?**	Yes	▶	GO to **KM57**.
	No	▶	RECONNECT all components. VERIFY a symptom no longer exists.
KM57 CHECK ACD CIRCUIT CONTINUITY FROM LP SWITCH TO POWERTRAIN CONTROL MODULE (PCM) • Key off. • LP switch disconnected. • Disconnect Powertrain Control Module (PCM). Inspect for damaged or pushed out pins, corrosion, loose wires, etc. Service as necessary. • Install breakout box, leave PCM disconnected. • Measure resistance between Test Pin 41 at the breakout box and PCM side of LP switch vehicle harness connector. • **Is resistance less than 5.0 ohms?**	Yes	▶	REPLACE PCM. REMOVE breakout box. RECONNECT all components. VERIFY a symptom no longer exists.
	No	▶	SERVICE open circuit. RECONNECT all components. VERIFY a symptom no longer exists.

Fig. 272   Test KM: WOT A/C Cut-Off (WAC) Relay, A/C Circuits (Part 19 of 29). 1996

Part 20 of 29

Test Step	Result	▶	Action to Take
KM60 KOEO/KOER DTC P1460: CHECK FOR IGN RUN VOLTAGE TO A/C RELAY			
Key On, Engine Off (KOEO) or Key On, Engine Running (KOER). Diagnostic Trouble Code (DTC) P1460 indicates an A/C relay primary circuit fault. NOTE: Verify A/C and defrost were off during KOEO/KOER Self-Test. Possible causes: — Open or shorted circuit. — Damaged A/C relay. — Damaged Powertrain Control Module (PCM). ● Key off. ● Disconnect A/C relay. ● Key on. ● Measure voltage between IGN RUN circuit at A/C relay vehicle harness connector and chassis ground. ● **Is voltage greater than 10.5 volts?**	Yes No	▶ ▶	GO to **KM61**. VERIFY condition of related fuses. If OK, SERVICE open circuit. RECONNECT all components. START engine. TURN A/C on, WAIT 15 seconds. A/C off. Key off. RERUN Quick Test.
IGN RUN / ACON (PIN 69) / POWER-TO-CLUTCH / B(+) **A/C RELAY VEHICLE HARNESS CONNECTOR**			
KM61 CHECK ACON CIRCUIT FOR SHORT TO POWER			
● Key off. ● A/C relay disconnected. ● Disconnect Powertrain Control Module (PCM). Inspect for damaged or pushed out pins, corrosion, loose wire, etc. Service as necessary. ● Install breakout box, leave PCM disconnected. ● Key on, engine off. ● Measure voltage between Test Pin 69 (ACON) at the breakout box and chassis ground. ● **Is voltage less than 1.0 volt?**	Yes No	▶ ▶	GO to **KM62**. SERVICE short to power. REMOVE breakout box. RECONNECT all components. START engine. TURN A/C on, WAIT 15 seconds. A/C off. Key off. RERUN Quick Test.

FM0159601541200X

Fig. 272   Test KM: WOT A/C Cut-Off (WAC) Relay, A/C Circuits (Part 20 of 29). 1996

Part 21 of 29

Test Step	Result	▶	Action to Take
KM62 CHECK ACON CIRCUIT FOR SHORT TO GROUND			
● Key off. ● A/C relay disconnected. ● Disconnect Scan Tool from DLC. ● Breakout box installed, PCM disconnected. ● Measure resistance between Test Pin 69 at the breakout box and chassis ground. ● **Is resistance greater than 10,000 ohms?**	Yes No	▶ ▶	GO to **KM63**. SERVICE short to ground. REMOVE breakout box. RECONNECT all components. START engine. TURN A/C on, WAIT 15 seconds. A/C off. Key off. RERUN Quick Test.
KM63 CHECK ACON CIRCUIT CONTINUITY			
● Key off. ● A/C relay disconnected. ● Breakout box installed, PCM disconnected. ● Measure resistance between Test Pin 69 at breakout box and ACON circuit at A/C relay vehicle harness connector. ● **Is resistance less than 5.0 ohms?**	Yes No	▶ ▶	GO to **KM64**. SERVICE open circuit. REMOVE breakout box. RECONNECT all components. START engine. TURN A/C on, WAIT 15 seconds. A/C off. Key off. RERUN Quick Test.
KM64 CHECK A/C RELAY			
● Key off. ● Breakout box installed, PCM disconnected. ● Reconnect A/C relay. ● Disconnect A/C clutch. ● Connect DVOM between the Power-To-A/C Clutch pin and ground pin at the A/C clutch vehicle harness connector. ● Key on, engine off. ● DVOM voltage should be less than 1.0 volt. ● Connect a jumper wire between Test Pin 69 (ACON) at the breakout box and ground. This should activate the A/C relay. ● DVOM voltage should now be greater than 10.5 volts. ● Key off. ● **Is the DVOM voltage as expected?**	Yes No	▶ ▶	REMOVE jumper wire and breakout box. RECONNECT all components. START engine. TURN A/C on, WAIT 15 seconds. A/C off. Key off. RERUN KOEO/KOER Self-Test to verify P1460 is still present. If KOEO/KOER P1460 is still present, REPLACE PCM and RERUN Quick Test. If P1460 is not present, the concern may have been intermittent. continue this, or any other symptom diagnosis. REPLACE A/C relay. REMOVE jumper wire and breakout box. RECONNECT all components. START engine. TURN A/C on, WAIT 15 seconds. A/C off. Key off. RERUN Quick Test.

FM0159601541210X

Fig. 272   Test KM: WOT A/C Cut-Off (WAC) Relay, A/C Circuits (Part 21 of 29). 1996

Part 22 of 29

Test Step	Result	▶	Action to Take
KM70 DTC P1464 OR ACCS PID ALWAYS ON WITH A/C OFF: CHECK ACCS PID WITH LP SWITCH DISCONNECTED			
Diagnostic Trouble Code (DTC) P1464 indicates that the A/C demand input to the Powertrain Control Module (PCM) was low (indicating A/C was on) during Self-Test. NOTE: Before entering this test, verify A/C and defrost are off. If A/C or defrost were on, rerun Self-Test (or recheck ACCS PID). ● A/C and defrost off. ● Disconnect Low Pressure (LP) switch. ● Key on, engine off. ● Access ACCS PID on Scan Tool. ● **Is ACCS PID on?**	Yes No	▶ ▶	For Escort/Tracer: GO to **KM74**. All others: GO to **KM72**. GO to **KM71**.
KM71 CHECK LOW PRESSURE (LP) SWITCH			
● Key off. ● LP switch disconnected. ● Measure resistance between chassis ground and both pins of LP switch. ● **Are both resistances greater than 10,000 ohms?**	Yes No	▶ ▶	VERIFY operation of A/C demand switch. If OK, SERVICE short to ground between LP switch and A/C demand switch. RECONNECT all components. VERIFY a symptom no longer exists. REPLACE LP switch RECONNECT all components. VERIFY a symptom no longer exists.
KM72 CHECK ACD CIRCUIT TO PCM FOR SHORT TO GROUND			
● Key off. ● LP switch disconnected. ● Disconnect Powertrain Control Module (PCM). Inspect for damaged or pushed out pins, corrosion, loose wires, etc. Service as necessary. ● Measure resistance between PCM side of the LP switch vehicle harness connector and chassis ground. ● **Is resistance greater than 10,000 ohms?**	Yes No	▶ ▶	REPLACE PCM. RECONNECT all components. VERIFY a symptom no longer exists. SERVICE short to ground. RECONNECT all components. VERIFY a symptom no longer exists.
KM74 CHECK ACCS PID WITH A/C RELAY DISCONNECTED			
● LP switch disconnected. ● Disconnect A/C relay. ● Key on, engine off. ● Access ACCS PID. ● **Is the ACCS PID still on?**	Yes No	▶ ▶	GO to **KM75**. Key off. GO to **KM78**.

FM0159601541220X

Fig. 272   Test KM: WOT A/C Cut-Off (WAC) Relay, A/C Circuits (Part 22 of 29). 1996

Part 23 of 29

Test Step	Result	▶	Action to Take
KM75 CHECK ACCS PID WITH WAC RELAY DISCONNECTED			
● LP switch and A/C relay disconnected. ● Disconnect WAC relay. ● Key on, engine off. ● Access ACCS PID. ● **Is the ACCS PID still on?**	Yes No	▶ ▶	Key off. GO to **KM76**. Key off. SERVICE Power-To-Clutch circuit for short to power. RECONNECT all components. VERIFY a symptom no longer exists.
KM76 CHECK A/C DEMAND AND ACC CIRCUIT FOR SHORT TO POWER			
● Key off. ● LP switch, A/C relay and WAC relay disconnected. ● Disconnect Powertrain Control Module (PCM). ● Install breakout box, leave PCM disconnected. ● Key on, engine off. ● Measure voltage between Test Pin 41 (ACC) and chassis ground. ● Key off. ● **Was voltage less than 1.0 volt?**	Yes No	▶ ▶	REPLACE PCM. REMOVE breakout box. RECONNECT all components. VERIFY a symptom no longer exists. SERVICE A/C demand/ACC circuit short to power. REMOVE breakout box. RECONNECT all components. VERIFY a symptom no longer exists.
KM78 CHECK A/C DEMAND CIRCUIT TO A/C RELAY FOR SHORT TO GROUND			
● Key off. ● LP switch and A/C relay disconnected. ● Disconnect Scan Tool from DLC. ● Measure resistance between the A/C Demand to A/C relay circuit at the LP switch vehicle harness connector and chassis ground. ● **Is resistance greater than 10,000 ohms?**	Yes No	▶ ▶	REPLACE A/C relay. RECONNECT all components. VERIFY a symptom no longer exists. SERVICE short to ground. RECONNECT all components. VERIFY a symptom no longer exists.
KM80 A/C ALWAYS ON (ACCS PID OFF WITH A/C OFF, NO DTCS): CHECK POWER TO CLUTCH CIRCUIT FOR SHORT TO POWER			
● Key off. ● Disconnect A/C relay. ● Disconnect A/C clutch. ● Key on. ● Measure voltage between power side of A/C Clutch vehicle harness connector and battery negative post. ● **Is voltage less than 1.0 volt?**	Yes No	▶ ▶	GO to **KM81**. SERVICE Power-to-Clutch circuit short to power. RECONNECT all components. VERIFY a symptom no longer exists.

FM0159601541230X

Fig. 272   Test KM: WOT A/C Cut-Off (WAC) Relay, A/C Circuits (Part 23 of 29). 1996

Test Step	Result	▶	Action to Take
KM81 CHECK A/C RELAY • Key off. • A/C relay disconnected. • Measure resistance between power-to-clutch pin and both the IGN RUN and B+ pins at the A/C relay. • **Are both resistances greater than 10,000 ohms?**	Yes No	▶ ▶	EEC system OK. After service, RECONNECT all components. VERIFY a symptom no longer exists. REPLACE A/C relay. RECONNECT all components. VERIFY a symptom no longer exists.
KM90 ACCS PID OFF WITH A/C AND BLOWER ON: CHECK A/C DEMAND VOLTAGE TO WAC RELAY FROM A/C RELAY • Key off. • Disconnect WAC relay. • Key on, engine off. • Turn A/C on. • Turn blower motor on (any speed). • Measure voltage between the "A/C Demand from A/C Relay" circuit at the WAC relay vehicle harness connector and chassis ground. • Key off. • **Was voltage greater than 10.5 volts?**	Yes No	▶ ▶	A/C demand voltage is getting to WAC relay. GO to **KM97** to check ACC circuit to PCM. A/C demand voltage is not getting to WAC relay. GO to **KM91**.

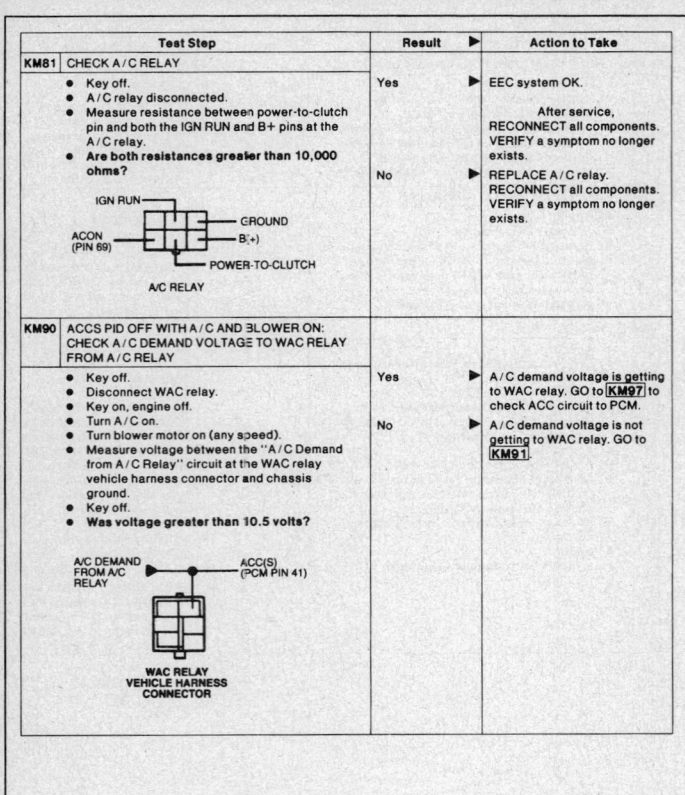

Fig. 272   Test KM: WOT A/C Cut-Off (WAC) Relay, A/C Circuits (Part 24 of 29). 1996

FM0159601541240X

Test Step	Result	▶	Action to Take
KM91 CHECK CONTINUITY OF "FROM A/C RELAY" CIRCUIT BETWEEN WAC RELAY AND A/C RELAY • Key off. • WAC relay disconnected. • Disconnect A/C relay. • Measure resistance of the "From A/C" circuit between the vehicle harness connectors of the WAC relay and A/C relay. • **Is resistance less than 5.0 ohms?**	Yes No	▶ ▶	RECONNECT WAC relay. GO to **KM92**. SERVICE open circuit betwen WAC and A/C relays. RECONNECT all components. VERIFY a symptom no longer exists.
KM92 CHECK B(+) AND IGN RUN CIRCUITS TO A/C RELAY • Key off. • A/C relay disconnected. • Measure voltage between the B(+) circuit at the A/C relay vehicle harness connector and chassis ground. • Key on, engine off. • Measure voltage between the IGN RUN circuit at the A/C relay vehicle harness connector and chassis ground. • Key off. • **Were both voltages greater than 10.5 volts?**	Yes No	▶ ▶	GO to **KM93**. SERVICE open B(+) or IGN RUN circuit to A/C relay. RECONNECT all components. VERIFY a symptom no longer exists.

Fig. 272   Test KM: WOT A/C Cut-Off (WAC) Relay, A/C Circuits (Part 25 of 29). 1996

FM0159601541250X

Test Step	Result	▶	Action to Take
KM93 CHECK A/C DEMAND CIRCUIT TO A/C RELAY • A/C relay disconnected. • Key on, engine off. • A/C demand switch on. • Blower motor switch on (any speed). • Measure voltage between the IGN RUN circuit and the A/C demand circuit (from the Low Pressure Switch) at the A/C relay vehicle harness connector. • **Was voltage greater than 10.5 volts?**	Yes No	▶ ▶	REPLACE A/C relay. RECONNECT all components. VERIFY a symptom no longer exists. A/C demand circuit fault to A/C relay. GO to **KM94**.
KM94 CHECK A/C DEMAND CIRCUIT TO LOW PRESSURE (LP) SWITCH • A/C relay disconnected. • Disconnect Low Pressure (LP) Switch. • Key on, engine off. • A/C demand and blower motor on. • Measure voltage between the IGN RUN circuit at the A/C relay vehicle harness connector and the A/C demand switch side of the LP switch vehicle harness connector. • Key off. • **Was voltage greater than 10.5 volts?**	Yes No	▶ ▶	A/C demand circuit is OK to LP switch. GO to **KM95**. A/C demand circuit fault to LP switch. check operation of A/C demand switch and blower motor switch, circuit continuity between A/C demand switch and blower motor switch, ground circuit to blower motor switch, etc.
KM95 MEASURE RESISTANCE OF LP SWITCH • Key off. • LP switch disconnected. • Measure resistance of LP switch. • **Is resistance less than 5.0 ohms?**	Yes No	▶ ▶	SERVICE open A/C demand circuit between LP switch and A/C relay. RECONNECT all components. VERIFY a symptom no longer exists. check for proper refrigerant charge, proper operation of the LP switch, etc.
KM97 CHECK ACC CIRCUIT CONTINUITY BETWEEN WAC RELAY AND PCM • Key off. • WAC relay disconnected. • Disconnect Powertrain Control Module (PCM). Inspect for damaged or pushed out pins, corrosion, loose wires, etc. Service as necessary. • Install breakout box, leave PCM disconnected. • Measure resistance between Test Pin 41 (ACC) at the breakout box and the "A/C Demand from A/C Relay (ACC)" circuit at the WAC relay vehicle harness connector. • **Is resistance less than 5.0 ohms?**	Yes No	▶ ▶	REPLACE PCM. REMOVE breakout box. RECONNECT all components. VERIFY a symptom no longer exists. SERVICE open ACC circuit between PCM and splice to "A/C Demand from A/C Relay" circuit. REMOVE breakout box. RECONNECT all components. VERIFY a symptom no longer exists.

Fig. 272   Test KM: WOT A/C Cut-Off (WAC) Relay, A/C Circuits (Part 26 of 29). 1996

FM0159601541260X

Test Step	Result	▶	Action to Take
KM100 CHECK NORMALLY CLOSED CONTACTS OF THE WAC RELAY • Key off. • WAC relay disconnected. • Measure resistance of the normally closed contacts of the WAC relay (Pins 3 and 4 of relay). • **Is resistance less than 5.0 ohms?**	Yes No	▶ ▶	GO to **KM101**. REPLACE WAC relay. RECONNECT all components. VERIFY a symptom no longer exists.
KM101 CHECK IGNITION RUN VOLTAGE TO A/C CLUTCH RELAY • Key off. • Disconnect A/C clutch relay (refer to pinpoint test cover page schematic and, if available, the EVTM). • Key on, engine off. • Measure voltage between the ignition run circuit at the A/C Clutch relay vehicle harness connector and the battery negative post. • Key off. • **Was voltage greater than 10.5 volts?**	Yes No	▶ ▶	GO to **KM102**. CHECK condition of related fuse. If fuse is damaged, verify ignition run circuit is not short to ground. If OK, SERVICE open circuit. RECONNECT all components. VERIFY a symptom no longer exists.
KM102 CHECK GROUND CIRCUIT TO A/C CLUTCH RELAY • Key off. • A/C Clutch relay disconnected. • Measure resistance between the ground circuit at the A/C Clutch relay vehicle harness connector and the battery negative post. • **Is resistance less than 5.0 ohms?**	Yes No	▶ ▶	GO to **KM103**. SERVICE open circuit. RECONNECT all components. VERIFY a symptom no longer exists.
KM103 CHECK A/C DEMAND CIRCUIT CONTINUITY BETWEEN WAC RELAY AND A/C CLUTCH RELAY • Key off. • WAC relay and A/C clutch relay disconnected. • Measure resistance of the A/C demand circuit between the WAC relay and A/C clutch relay vehicle harness connectors. • **Is resistance less than 5.0 ohms?**	Yes No	▶ ▶	GO to **KM104**. SERVICE open circuit. RECONNECT all components. VERIFY a symptom no longer exists.

Fig. 272   Test KM: WOT A/C Cut-Off (WAC) Relay, A/C Circuits (Part 27 of 29). 1996

FM0159601541270X

ELECTRONIC ENGINE CONTROL SYSTEM (EEC-V)

Test Step	Result	▶	Action to Take
KM104 CHECK CONTINUITY OF POWER-TO-CLUTCH AND A/C CLUTCH GROUND CIRCUITS			
• Key off. • A/C clutch relay disconnected. • Disconnect A/C clutch. • Disconnect Scan Tool from DLC. • Measure resistance of Power-To-Clutch circuit between the A/C Clutch relay and the A/C clutch vehicle harness-connectors. • Measure resistance of the A/C clutch ground circuit between the A/C clutch vehicle harness connector and the battery negative post. • **Is each resistance less than 5.0 ohms?**	Yes	▶	REPLACE A/C Clutch relay. RECONNECT all components. VERIFY a symptom no longer exists.
	No	▶	SERVICE open circuit. RECONNECT all components. VERIFY a symptom no longer exists.
KM110 DISCONNECT A/C CLUTCH RELAY AND CHECK IF ACCS PID TURNS OFF			
• Key off. • ACPSW disconnected. • Disconnect A/C Clutch relay (refer to pinpoint test cover page schematic and, if available, the EVTM). • Key on, engine off. • Again, access ACCS PID. • **Is ACCS PID now off?**	Yes	▶	REPLACE A/C Clutch relay. RECONNECT all components. VERIFY a symptom no longer exists.
	No	▶	GO to **KM111**.
KM111 CHECK A/C DEMAND CIRCUIT BETWEEN WAC RELAY AND A/C CLUTCH RELAY FOR SHORT TO POWER			
• Key off. • A/C Clutch relay and ACPSW disconnected. • Disconnect WAC relay. • Key on, engine off. • Measure voltage between the "A/C demand circuit to A/C Clutch relay" at the WAC relay vehicle harness connector and the battery negative post. • Key off. • **Was voltage less than 1.0 volt?**	Yes	▶	GO to **KM112**.
	No	▶	SERVICE short to power. RECONNECT all components. VERIFY a symptom no longer exists.
KM112 CHECK ACCS PID WITH WAC RELAY DISCONNECTED			
• Key on, engine off. • WAC relay disconnected. • ACPSW and A/C relay disconnected. • Again, access ACCS PID. • **Is ACCS PID off?**	Yes	▶	Key off. REPLACE WAC relay. RECONNECT all components. VERIFY a symptom no longer exists.
	No	▶	Key off. GO to **KM113**.

FM0159601541280X

Fig. 272   Test KM: WOT A/C Cut-Off (WAC) Relay, A/C Circuits (Part 28 of 29). 1996

Test Step	Result	▶	Action to Take
KM113 CHECK ACCS CIRCUIT TO PCM FOR SHORT TO POWER			
• Key off. • ACPSW, WAC relay and A/C relay disconnected. • Disconnect PCM. Inspect connector for damaged or pushed out pins, corrosion, loose wires, etc. Service as necessary. • Install breakout box, leave PCM disconnected. • Key on. • Measure voltage between Test Pin 41 (ACCS) and Test Pins 51 and 103 (PWR GND) at the breakout box. • Key off. • **Was voltage less than 1.0 volt?**	Yes	▶	REPLACE PCM. REMOVE breakout box. RECONNECT all components. VERIFY a symptom no longer exists.
	No	▶	SERVICE short to power. REMOVE breakout box. RECONNECT all components. VERIFY a symptom no longer exists.
KM115 VOLTAGE ALWAYS AT A/C CLUTCH (ACCS PID OFF): CHECK FOR A/C CLUTCH RELAY CONTACTS STUCK CLOSED			
• Disconnect A/C clutch. • Disconnect A/C Clutch relay (refer to pinpoint test cover page schematic and if available the EVTM). • Key on, engine off. • Again measure voltage between the power pin and ground pin at the A/C clutch vehicle harness connector. • Key off. • **Was voltage less than 2.0 volts?**	Yes	▶	REPLACE A/C Clutch relay. RECONNECT all components. VERIFY a symptom no longer exists.
	No	▶	SERVICE Power-To-Clutch circuit short to power. RECONNECT all components. VERIFY a symptom no longer exists.

FM0159601541290X

Fig. 272   Test KM: WOT A/C Cut-Off (WAC) Relay, A/C Circuits (Part 29 of 29). 1996

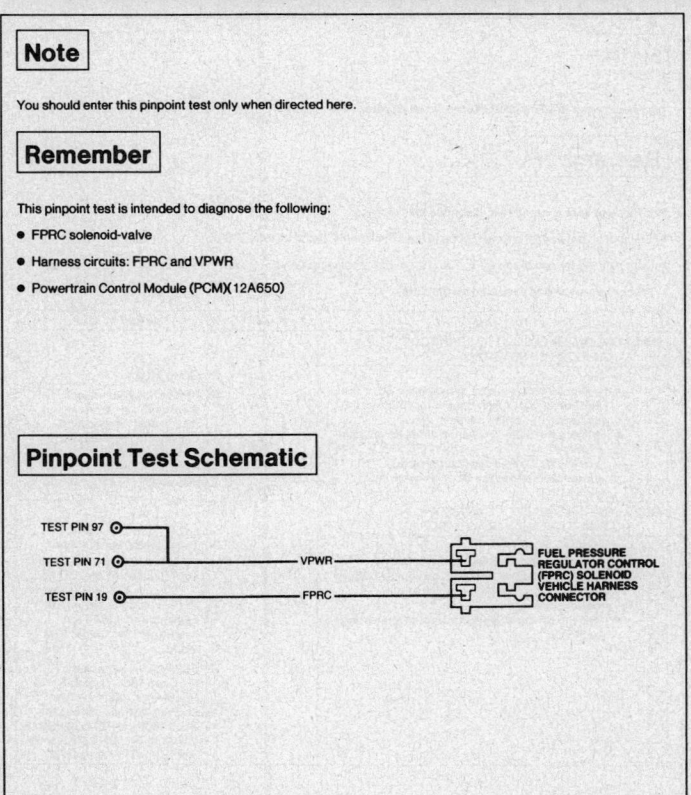

Note

You should enter this pinpoint test only when directed here.

Remember

This pinpoint test is intended to diagnose the following:

• FPRC solenoid-valve
• Harness circuits: FPRC and VPWR
• Powertrain Control Module (PCM)(12A650)

Pinpoint Test Schematic

TEST PIN 97
TEST PIN 71 —— VPWR —— FUEL PRESSURE REGULATOR CONTROL (FPRC) SOLENOID VEHICLE HARNESS CONNECTOR
TEST PIN 19 —— FPRC ——

FM0159601542010X

Fig. 273   Test KN: Fuel Pressure Regulator Control Solenoid (Part 1 of 5). 1996 Probe

Test Step	Result	▶	Action to Take
KN1 CHECK FPRC SOLENOID VPWR			
The Symptom Flowcharts have indicated a lack of power was observed during acceleration and/or cruise drive modes. Possible causes: — Damaged FPRC solenoid. — Damaged FPRC solenoid valve. — Damaged input port or output port vacuum lines. — Damaged FPRC solenoid valve harness circuits. — Damaged PCM. • Key off. • FPRC solenoid disconnected. • Key on, engine off. • Measure solenoid VPWR at FPRC solenoid vehicle harness connector and ground. • **Is voltage greater than 10.5 volts?**	Yes	▶	FPRC solenoid-valve VPWR circuit is complete. GO to **KN2**.
	No	▶	FPRC solenoid-valve VPWR circuit is not complete. SERVICE open in VPWR harness circuit. RECONNECT FPRC solenoid-valve. VERIFY a symptom no longer exists.
KN2 CHECK FPRC SOLENOID HARNESS CIRCUIT CONTINUITY			
• Key off. • FPRC solenoid disconnected. • Disconnect PCM. Inspect for damaged or pushed out pins, corrosion, loose wires, etc. Service as necessary. • Install breakout box, leave PCM disconnected. • Measure resistance between test Pin 19 (FPRC) at the breakout box and the FPRC circuit at the solenoid vehicle harness connector. • **Is resistance less than 5.0 ohms?**	Yes	▶	FPRC solenoid circuit is complete. GO to **KN3**.
	No	▶	FPRC solenoid circuit lacks continuity. SERVICE open circuit. REMOVE breakout box. RECONNECT all components. VERIFY a symptom no longer exists.
KN3 CHECK FPRC SOLENOID CIRCUIT FOR SHORTS TO POWER AND GROUND			
• Key off. • FPRC solenoid disconnected. • Breakout box installed, PCM disconnected. • Disconnect Scan Tool from DLC. • Measure resistance between Test Pin 19 (FPRC) and Test Pins 71 and 97 (VPWR) at the breakout box. • Measure resistance between Test Pin 19 (FPRC) and Test Pins 24, 77 (PWR GND) and 91 (SIG RTN) at the breakout box. • **Is resistance greater than 10,000 ohms?**	Yes	▶	There are no power or ground short circuits to the FPRC solenoid. GO to **KN4**.
	No	▶	A power or ground short circuit exists in the FRPC solenoid harness circuit. SERVICE short circuit. REMOVE breakout box. RECONNECT all components. VERIFY a symptom no longer exists.

FM0159601542020X

Fig. 273   Test KN: Fuel Pressure Regulator Control Solenoid (Part 2 of 5). 1996 Probe

Test Step	Result	▶	Action to Take
KN4 CHECK VACUUM LINE: MANIFOLD VACUUM SOURCE TO FPRC SOLENOID INPUT PORT • Key off. • Disconnect and inspect vacuum line between the manifold vacuum source and the FPRC solenoid input vacuum port for blockage, kinks, cracks, etc. • **Is vacuum line free of damage?**	Yes No	▶ ▶	Vacuum line is OK. RECONNECT vacuum line to manifold vacuum tee, leaving one end of the line unattached. GO to **KN5**. Vacuum line is damaged. SERVICE or REPLACE damaged vacuum line. VERIFY a symptom no longer exists.
KN5 CHECK VACUUM SIGNAL: MANIFOLD VACUUM SOURCE TO FPRC SOLENOID INPUT • Key off. • Tee in a vacuum gauge at the unattached end of the vacuum line. • Start engine while observing the vacuum gauge display. • Key off. • **Was a vacuum signal present?**	Yes No	▶ ▶	FPRC solenoid valve normally receives manifold vacuum signal. REMOVE vacuum gauge. RECONNECT all components. GO to **KN6**. REMOVE vacuum gauge. RECONNECT all components. REFER to Probe Service Manual to address base engine manifold vacuum concern.
KN6 CHECK VACUUM LINE: FUEL PRESSURE REGULATOR TO FPRC SOLENOID OUTPUT PORT • Key off. • Disconnect and inspect vacuum line between the fuel pressure regulator and the FPRC solenoid output vacuum port for blockage, kinks, cracks, etc. • **Is vacuum line free of damage?**	Yes No	▶ ▶	Vacuum line is OK. RECONNECT vacuum line. GO to **KN7**. Vacuum line is damaged. SERVICE or REPLACE damaged vacuum line. VERIFY a symptom no longer exists.

Fig. 273 Test KN: Fuel Pressure Regulator Control Solenoid (Part 3 of 5). 1996 Probe

Test Step	Result	▶	Action to Take
KN7 CHECK FOR FPRC SOLENOID - VALVE STUCK CLOSED • Key off. • Breakout box installed, PCM connected. • Disconnect the vacuum line from the FPRC solenoid to the fuel pressure regulator at the fuel pressure regulator. Install a vacuum gauge at the unattached end of the vacuum line. • Disconnect the vacuum line from intake manifold vacuum to the FPRC solenoid at the manifold vacuum source. • Install vacuum pump at the input port of the FPRC solenoid and apply 8 to 10 -Hg of vacuum to the FPRC solenoid while observing the vacuum gauge. • NOTE: The FPRC solenoid-valve contains a normally open valve. If the solenoid is not energized while the vacuum is applied at the input port, the vacuum signal will normally be allowed to pass. • **Is a vacuum signal indicated by the vacuum gauge?**	Yes No	▶ ▶	The FPRC solenoid-valve is not stuck closed. GO to **KN8**. The FPRC solenoid-valve is stuck closed. REPLACE the damaged FPRC solenoid. REMOVE vacuum gauge and pump. RECONNECT all components. VERIFY a symptom no longer exists.
KN8 CHECK FOR FPRC SOLENOID - VALVE STUCK OPEN • Key off. • Breakout box installed, PCM connected. • Vacuum gauge installed at output port of the FPRC solenoid-valve. • Vacuum pump installed at input port of the FPRC solenoid-valve and apply 8 to 10 -Hg of vacuum is applied to the FPRC solenoid valve input port. • Key on. • Momentarily jumper Test Pin 19 (FPRC) to Test Pin 103 (PWR GND) at the breakout box and observe the vacuum gauge. • NOTE: The FPRC solenoid-valve contains a normally open valve. If the solenoid is energized while the vacuum is applied at the input port, the vacuum signal will normally not be allowed to pass because the solenoid-valve will be closed. • Key off. • **Was a vacuum signal indicated by the vacuum gauge?**	Yes No	▶ ▶	The FPRC solenoid-valve is not stuck open. REMOVE vacuum pump and gauge. RECONNECT all components. GO to **KN9**. The FPRC solenoid-valve is stuck open. REPLACE the damaged FPRC solenoid. REMOVE vacuum gauge and pump. RECONNECT all components. VERIFY a symptom no longer exists.

Fig. 273 Test KN: Fuel Pressure Regulator Control Solenoid (Part 4 of 5). 1996 Probe

Test Step	Result	▶	Action to Take
KN9 CHECK PCM CONTROL OF FPRC SOLENOID-VALVE • Key off. • Tee in a vacuum gauge between the FPRC solenoid-valve output port and the fuel pressure regulator so that the gauge display may be seen while driving. • Perform the following road test as outlined below: — Warm engine to operating temperature. — Obey all traffic laws. — Observe the vacuum gauge display while accelerating heavily to 40 MPH, then decelerate to a steady cruise below 20 MPH. • NOTE: The vacuum gauge display should indicate a low vacuum (FPRC solenoid-valve closed) during the heavy acceleration and a higher vacuum (FPRC solenoid-valve open) during the steady cruise if the FPRC solenoid is being properly controlled by the PCM. Repeat the road test as necessary to confirm the status of the FPRC solenoid-valve operation. • **Did vacuum signal to fuel pressure regulator fall and rise as expected?**	Yes No	▶ ▶	The PCM is properly controlling the FPRC solenoid-valve. REMOVE the vacuum gauge. REFER to Probe fuel pressure regulator diagnostics. The PCM is not properly controlling the FPRC solenoid-valve. REMOVE the vacuum gauge. REPLACE the PCM. VERIFY a symptom no longer exists.

Fig. 273 Test KN: Fuel Pressure Regulator Control Solenoid (Part 5 of 5). 1996 Probe

> **Note**
>
> You should enter this Pinpoint Test only when directed here.

> **Remember**
>
> This Pinpoint Test is intended to diagnose the following:
> • Connection between the Scan Tool and the Powertrain Control Module (PCM).
> • Connection between the Scan Tool and the battery power supply.
> • Proper key sequence executed for output(s).

Test Step	Result	▶	Action to Take
MB1 CHECK VEHICLE DLC TO SCAN TOOL CONNECTION AND WIRING • Key off. • Inspect the connection between the Scan Tool and vehicle Data Link Connector (DLC) for damaged or pushed out pins, etc. • Inspect the Scan Tool wiring cable for obvious damage. • **Are the DLC and Scan Tool properly connected and is the Scan Tool wiring cable OK?**	Yes No	▶ ▶	GO to **MB2**. SERVICE as necessary. RUN the Scan Tool "System Readiness" test to verify communication between the Scan Tool and PCM (REFER to the Scan Tool User Manual for instructions, if necessary).
MB2 CHECK SCAN TOOL POWER SUPPLY CONNECTOR AND WIRING CABLE • Key off. • Inspect the connector and wiring cable between the Scan Tool and the vehicle battery power supply (or at the cigarette lighter) for obvious damage. • **Are the power supply connector and wiring cable OK?**	Yes No	▶ ▶	There are no installation problems between the Scan Tool and the vehicle. GO to Output Test Mode. VERIFY that the proper key sequence was used for output(s) in the Output Test Mode. SERVICE as necessary. RUN the Scan Tool "System Readiness" test to verify communication between the Scan Tool and PCM (REFER to the Scan Tool User Manual for instructions, if necessary).

Fig. 274 Test MB: Output Test Mode Not Functioning. 1996

ELECTRONIC ENGINE CONTROL SYSTEM (EEC-V)

Note

You should enter this Pinpoint Test only when directed here.

Remember

This Pinpoint Test is intended to diagnose the following:

- Powertrain Control Module (PCM)

Test Step		Result	▶	Action to Take
MD1	CHECK FOR POWER TO PCM: VREF CIRCUIT VOLTAGE AT TP SENSOR			
	Continuous Memory Diagnostic Trouble Code (DTC) P1359 indicates a loss of SPOUT output from PCM. • Key off. • TP sensor disconnected. • Key on, engine off. • Measure voltage between VREF circuit and SIG RTN circuit at the TP sensor vehicle harness connector. • **Is the voltage between 4.0 and 6.0 volts?**	Yes	▶	KEY off. RECONNECT all components. GO to **MD2**.
		No	▶	Key off. RECONNECT all components. GO to Pinpoint Test Step **C1**.
MD2	INSPECT CKP SENSOR AND TRIGGER WHEEL—TIMING FAULT			
	• Is the CKP sensor or Trigger Wheel damaged, i.e., loose or misaligned?	Yes	▶	REPLACE or SERVICE as required. REMOVE all test equipment. RECONNECT all components. Complete PCM Reset to clear DTCs (REFER to Powertrain Control Module (PCM) Reset). RERUN Quick Test.
		No	▶	Incorrect output. REPLACE PCM. REMOVE all test equipment. RECONNECT all components. Complete PCM Reset to clear DTCs (REFER to Powertrain Control Module (PCM) Reset). RERUN Quick Test.

FM0159601545000X

Fig. 275   Test MD: Spark Output Check/Integrated Electronic Ignition. 1996

Note

You should enter this Pinpoint Test only when directed here.

Remember

To prevent the replacement of good components, be aware that the following non-EEC areas may be at fault:

- Fuse, bulb or socket.

This Pinpoint Test is intended to diagnose only the following:

- Malfunction Indicator Lamp (MIL) Circuit
- Powertrain Control Module (PCM)

Pinpoint Test Schematic

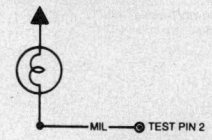

B(+) (DURING RUN OR START)

MIL ———○ TEST PIN 2

FM0159601547010X

Fig. 276   Test NB: Malfunction Indicator Lamp (Part 1 of 3). 1996

Test Step		Result	▶	Action to Take
NB1	MALFUNCTION INDICATOR LAMP (MIL) ALWAYS ON: CHECK MIL CIRCUIT FOR SHORTS TO GROUND			
	NOTE: If vehicle will not start, go to Pinpoint Test Step **A1**. • If any Key On Engine Off or Continuous Memory Diagnostic Trouble Codes are present, service before proceeding. • Key off. • Disconnect PCM. Inspect for damaged or pushed out pins, corrosion, loose wires, etc. Service as necessary. • Install breakout box, leave PCM disconnected. • Measure resistance between Test Pin 2 and Test Pin 51 or 103 at the breakout box. • **Is resistance less than 5.0 ohms?**	Yes	▶	SERVICE short circuit between Test Pin 2 and Malfunction Indicator Lamp (MIL). REMOVE breakout box. RECONNECT PCM. RERUN Quick Test.
		No	▶	REPLACE PCM. REMOVE breakout box. RERUN Quick Test.
NB2	MALFUNCTION INDICATOR LAMP (MIL) NEVER ON			
	NOTE: If vehicle will not start, go to Pinpoint Test Step **A1**. • Key on, engine off. • Measure voltage from battery negative post to "Ground" side of the MIL fuse. Refer to the EVTM for the specific location of the MIL fuse. • **Is voltage greater than 10.5 volts?**	Yes	▶	GO to **NB4**.
		No	▶	GO to **NB3**.
NB3	CHECK FOR B+ AT FUSE			
	• Key on, engine off. • Measure voltage from battery negative post to B+ side of the fuse. • **Is voltage greater than 10.5 volts?**	Yes	▶	REPLACE the fuse. VERIFY service by turning ignition key to the on position.
		No	▶	GO to EVTM to service power distribution (to the fuse) from the Primary Junction Box.
NB4	CHECK FOR VOLTAGE ON THE MIL B+ CIRCUIT			
	NOTE: Refer to the Electrical and Vacuum Troubleshooting Manual (EVTM) for connector shape and location. • Disconnect Instrument Cluster connector. • Key on, engine off. • Measure voltage between (MIL) B+ circuit at the Instrument Cluster connector and Battery Negative Post. • **Is voltage greater than 10.5 volts?**	Yes	▶	GO to **NB5**.
		No	▶	Service open B+ circuit.

FM0159601547020X

Fig. 276   Test NB: Malfunction Indicator Lamp (Part 2 of 3). 1996

Test Step		Result	▶	Action to Take
NB5	CHECK CONTINUITY MIL CIRCUIT			
	• Key off. • Disconnect PCM. Inspect for damaged or pushed out pins, corrosion, loose wires, etc. Service as necessary. • Install breakout box, leave PCM disconnected. • Measure resistance between Test Pin 2 at the breakout box and MIL circuit at the Instrument Cluster connector. • **Is resistance less than 5.0 ohms?**	Yes	▶	diagnose Instrument Cluster and Bulb. If OK, REPLACE PCM. REMOVE breakout box. VERIFY the service by turning the ignition key to the ON position.
		No	▶	SERVICE open in the MIL circuit. REMOVE breakout box. RECONNECT PCM. VERIFY service by turning key to the ON position.

FM0159601547030X

Fig. 276   Test NB: Malfunction Indicator Lamp (Part 3 of 3). 1996

Note

You should enter this Pinpoint Test only when directed here.

Remember

This Pinpoint Test is intended to diagnose the following:

● Powertrain Control Module (PCM)

Test Step		Result	▶	Action to Take
NC1	CONTINUOUS MEMORY DTC P0320: ERRATIC IGNITION			
	Continuous Memory Diagnostic Trouble Code (DTC) P0320 indicates two successive erratic Profile Ignition Pickup (PIP) pulses occurred resulting in a possible engine miss or stall. Possible causes: — Loose wires / connectors. — Arcing secondary ignition components (coil, wires, plugs, etc.). — On-board transmitter (2-way radio). * ● Are any of the above present? *Verify all 2-way radio installations. Carefully follow manufacturer's installation instructions regarding the routing of antenna and power leads.	Yes No	▶ ▶	SERVICE as necessary. Complete PCM Reset to clear DTCs (REFER to Powertrain Control Module (PCM) Reset). RERUN Quick Test. For No Starts: GO to Pinpoint Test Step A1. For Intermittent Faults: GO to Pinpoint Test Step Z50. All others: Loss of PIP. REPLACE PCM.
NC2	CONTINUOUS MEMORY DTC P1351 OR P1358: CHECK FOR OTHER EEC DTCS			
	Continuous Memory Diagnostic Trouble Code (DTC) P1351 or P1358 indicates a loss of IDM input to the PCM. Possible causes: — Open circuit. — Shorted circuit. — Intermittent faults. — Damaged PCM. ● Are Continuous Memory DTCs P0350, P0351, P0352, P0353 or P0354 present?	Yes No	▶ ▶	For 4 cylinder (except 2.3L Ranger): GO to Pinpoint Test Step JE1. For 2.3L Ranger: GO to Pinpoint Test Step JE20. For 6 cylinder: GO to Pinpoint Test Step JE60. For 8 cylinder: GO to Pinpoint Test Step JE90. Loss of IDM. REPLACE PCM.

FM0159601548000X

Fig. 277   Test NC: Ignition Diagnostic Monitor/Integrated Electronic Ignition. 1996

Note

You should enter this Pinpoint Test only when directed here.

Test Step		Result	▶	Action to Take
ND1	DTC P1270: EXCESSIVE ENGINE RPM / VEHICLE SPEED			
	Continuous Memory Diagnostic Trouble Code (DTC) P1270 indicates the vehicle has been operated in a manner which caused the engine or vehicle speed to exceed a calibrated limit. Possible causes: — Wheel slippage (water, ice, mud, snow, etc.). — Engine over revved in neutral. — Vehicle driven at high rate of speed. ● Has the vehicle been operated in any of the above conditions?	Yes No	▶ ▶	OBD II system is OK. COMPLETE PCM Reset to clear DTCs (REFER to Powertrain Control Module (PCM) Reset). RETURN vehicle to customer with information about DTC P1270. COMPLETE PCM Reset to clear DTCs (REFER to Powertrain Control Module (PCM) Reset). GO to Symptom Flowcharts, if there are other driveability concerns. If there are no other symptoms, RETURN vehicle to customer.

FM0159601549000X

Fig. 278   Test ND: Engine RPM/Vehicle Speed Limiter. 1996

Note

You should enter this Pinpoint Test only when directed here.

Remember

This Pinpoint Test is intended to diagnose the following:

● Standard Corporate Protocol (SCP) communication bus harness circuits: BUS (+), BUS (-)
● Harness Circuits: Chassis ground, Power Ground (PWR GND), Battery Voltage (VBAT)
● Powertrain Control Module (PCM) (12A650)

Pinpoint Test Schematic

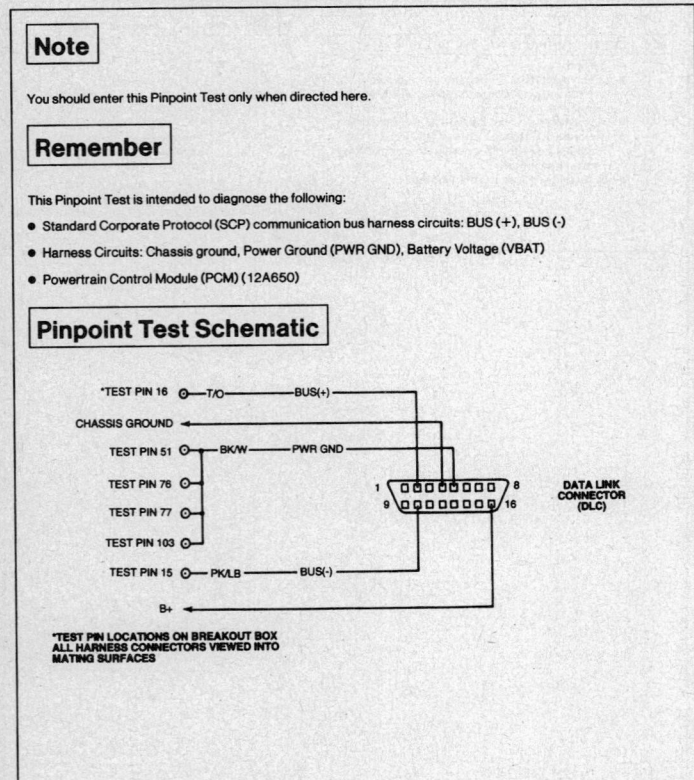

*TEST PIN LOCATIONS ON BREAKOUT BOX
ALL HARNESS CONNECTORS VIEWED INTO
MATING SURFACES

FM0159601550010X

Fig. 279   Test QA: Unable To Activate Self-Test/SCP Communication Error/DTC Not Listed (Part 1 of 5). 1996

Test Step		Result	▶	Action to Take
QA1	VERIFY SELF-TEST ACTIVATION METHOD			
	Diagnostic Trouble Code (DTC) P1001 indicates that Key On Engine Running (KOER) self-test cannot be completed. This Pinpoint Test addresses the following concerns: — Unable to access Continuous Memory DTCs. — Unable to activate KOEO Self-Test. — Unable to activate KOER Self-Test. — Scan Tool communication problem. — DTC displayed by Scan Tool not listed. Possible causes: — Damaged DLC. — Incorrect Self-Test activation method. — VREF is not in specification. — Idle RPM out of specification. — Open in DLC harness circuit. — Short in DLC harness circuit. — Damaged EEC-V power relay circuit. — Damaged PCM. ● Key off. ● Disconnect Scan Tool from DLC. Inspect DLC for damage. Service as necessary. ● Verify that the correct procedure was used to activate CONT, KOEO or KOER Self-Test for the Scan Tool. ● Was the correct Self-Test activation method used?	Yes No	▶ ▶	Correct procedure was used for activating Self-Test. GO to QA2. Correct procedure was not used for activating Self-Test. RETURN to Diagnostic Subroutines, and COMPLETE Self-Test using the correct procedure.
QA2	CHECK FOR VREF AT TP SENSOR			
	● Key off. ● Throttle Position sensor disconnected. ● Key on, engine off. ● Measure voltage between VREF and SIG RTN circuits at the TP sensor vehicle harness connector. ● Key off. ● Was the voltage between 4.0 and 6.0 volts?	Yes No	▶ ▶	Voltage is in specification. RECONNECT the TP sensor. GO to QA3. Voltage is not in specification. RECONNECT the TP sensor. GO to Pinpoint Test Step C1.
QA3	ABILITY TO ACCESS CONTINUOUS MEMORY DTCs			
	● Could Continuous Memory DTCs be accessed before this pinpoint test was entered?	Yes No	▶ ▶	GO to QA4. UNABLE to access Continuous Memory DTCs. GO to QA7.
QA4	ABILITY TO ACTIVATE KOEO SELF-TEST			
	● Could KOEO Self-Test be activated/completed before this pinpoint test was entered?	Yes No	▶ ▶	GO to QA5. UNABLE to activate KOEO Self-Test. GO to QA6.

FM0159601550020X

Fig. 279   Test QA: Unable To Activate Self-Test/SCP Communication Error/DTC Not Listed (Part 2 of 5). 1996

Test Step		Result	►	Action to Take
QA5	**ABILITY TO ACTIVATE KOER SELF-TEST**			
• Could KOER Self-Test be activated / completed before this pinpoint test was entered?		Yes	►	The DTC is not listed in the Powertrain Diagnostic Trouble Code (DTC) Charts. CHECK that the correct PCM is installed on the vehicle. Also CHECK for a Technical Service Bulletin (TSB) that indicates a PCM change
		No	►	UNABLE to activate or complete KOER Self-Test. GO to [QA6].
QA6	**RETRIEVE ANY CONTINUOUS MEMORY DTCs**			
NOTE 1: If failures are present in the following components or systems, this could cause the EEC strategy NOT to complete KOER self-test and / or cause the PCM to generate a Scan Tool communication error message: idle speed control; EGR system; fuel control system; electronic secondary air system; vehicle speed sensor circuits; mass air flow sensor circuits; transmission range sensor circuits. NOTE 2: For information on retrieving MIL and non-MIL DTCs, refer to Continuous Memory Self-Test. • Scan Tool connected. • Key on, engine off. • Retrieve and record all Continuous Memory DTCs (MIL and non-MIL). • Key off. • **Were any Continuous Memory DTCs present?**		Yes	►	Continuous Memory DTCs are present. GO to Powertrain Diagnostic Trouble Code (DTC) Charts, for Pinpoint Test direction.
		No	►	UNABLE to retrieve any Self-Test DTCs. GO to [QA7].
QA7	**CHECK B+ AT DATA LINK CONNECTOR (DLC)**			
• Key off. • Inspect the DLC for damage. Service as necessary. • Measure voltage between B+ circuit cavity at the DLC and engine block ground. • **Was voltage greater than 10.5 volts?**		Yes	►	GO to [QA8].
		No	►	SERVICE open in DLC B+ circuit. RERUN Quick Test.
QA8	**CHECK DLC CHASSIS GROUND CONTINUITY**			
• Key off. • Measure resistance between chassis ground circuit cavity at the DLC and chassis ground. • **Is resistance less than 5.0 ohms?**		Yes	►	GO to [QA9].
		No	►	SERVICE open in DLC chassis ground circuit. RERUN Quick Test.

FM0159601550030X

Fig. 279 Test QA: Unable To Activate Self-Test/SCP Communication Error/DTC Not Listed (Part 3 of 5). 1996

Test Step		Result	►	Action to Take
QA9	**CHECK DLC PWR GND CIRCUIT CONTINUITY**			
• Key off. • Disconnect PCM. Inspect for damaged or pushed out pins, loose wires, corrosion, etc. Service as necessary. • Install breakout box, leave PCM disconnected. • Disconnect Scan Tool from DLC. • Measure resistance between Test Pin 51 or 103 (PWR GND) at the breakout box and the PWR GND circuit cavity at the DLC. • **Is resistance less than 5.0 ohms?**		Yes No	► ►	GO to [QA10]. SERVICE open in DLC PWR GND circuit. RECONNECT the PCM. REMOVE breakout box. RERUN Quick Test.
QA10	**CHECK DLC BUS(-) CIRCUIT CONTINUITY**			
• Key off. • Breakout box installed, PCM disconnected. • Measure resistance between Test Pin 15 (BUS (-)) at the breakout box and the BUS (-) circuit at the DLC. • **Is resistance less than 5.0 ohms?**		Yes No	► ►	GO to [QA11]. SERVICE open in the DLC BUS(-) circuit. RECONNECT the PCM. REMOVE breakout box. RERUN Quick Test.
QA11	**CHECK BUS(-) CIRCUIT FOR SHORT TO GROUND**			
• Key off. • Breakout box installed, PCM disconnected. • Scan Tool disconnected from DLC. • Measure resistance between Test Pin 15 (BUS (-)) at the breakout box and chassis ground. • **Is resistance greater than 10,000 ohms?**		Yes No	► ►	GO to [QA12]. SERVICE short to ground in the BUS(-) circuit. RECONNECT the PCM. REMOVE breakout box. RERUN Quick Test.
QA12	**CHECK BUS(-) CIRCUIT FOR SHORT TO POWER**			
• Key off. • Breakout box installed, PCM disconnected. • Scan Tool disconnected from DLC. • Key on, engine off. • Measure voltage between Test Pin 15 (BUS(-)) and Test Pins 51 or 103 (PWR GND) at the breakout box. • **Was the voltage greater than 6.0 volts?**		Yes No	► ►	SERVICE short to power in the BUS(-) circuit. RECONNECT the PCM. REMOVE the breakout box. RERUN Quick Test. GO to [QA13].
QA13	**CHECK DLC BUS(+) CIRCUIT CONTINUITY**			
• Key off. • Breakout box installed, PCM disconnected. • Measure resistance between Test Pin 16 (BUS (+)) at the breakout box and BUS(+) circuit at the DLC. • **Is resistance less than 5.0 ohms?**		Yes No	► ►	GO to [QA14]. SERVICE open in DLC BUS(+) circuit. RECONNECT the PCM. REMOVE breakout box. RERUN Quick Test.

FM0159601550040X

Fig. 279 Test QA: Unable To Activate Self-Test/SCP Communication Error/DTC Not Listed (Part 4 of 5). 1996

Test Step		Result	►	Action to Take
QA14	**CHECK BUS (+) CIRCUIT FOR SHORT TO GROUND**			
• Key off. • Scan Tool disconnected from DLC. • Measure resistance between Test Pin 16 (BUS (+)) at the breakout box and chassis ground. • **Is resistance greater than 10,000 ohms?**		Yes No	► ►	There is no short to ground in the BUS (+) circuit. GO to [QA15]. SERVICE short to ground in the BUS (+) circuit. RECONNECT the PCM. REMOVE breakout box. RERUN Quick Test.
QA15	**CHECK BUS(+) CIRCUIT FOR SHORT TO POWER**			
• Key off. • Breakout box installed, PCM disconnected. • Scan Tool disconnected from DLC. • Key on, engine off. • Measure voltage between Test Pin 16 (BUS (+)] and Test Pins 51 or 103 (PWR GND) at the breakout box. • Key off. • **Was the voltage greater than 1.0 volt?**		Yes No	► ►	SERVICE short to power in the BUS(+) circuit. RECONNECT the PCM. REMOVE breakout box. RERUN Quick Test. GO to [QA16].
QA16	**POWER TAKE OFF (PTO) APPLICATIONS**			
• Is the vehicle equipped with a Power Take Off?		Yes No	► ►	GO to [QA17]. Vehicle is not equipped with PTO. REPLACE the PCM. REMOVE breakout box. RERUN Quick Test.
QA17	**CHECK PTO ON/OFF PID**			
• Scan Tool connected. • Key on, engine running. • View PTO STAT PID. • Cycle PTO switch / actuator ON and OFF (follow PTO aftermarket instructions). • **Did PTO STAT PID cycle ON, delay, then OFF?**		Yes No	► ►	PTO circuit is OK. REPLACE the PCM. REMOVE breakout box. RERUN Quick Test. PTO circuit is not OK. GO to Pinpoint Test Step [FB1] for further investigation.

FM0159601550050X

Fig. 279 Test QA: Unable To Activate Self-Test/SCP Communication Error/DTC Not Listed (Part 5 of 5). 1996

Note

You should enter this Pinpoint Test only when directed here.

Remember

This Pinpoint Test is intended to diagnose the following:
- Battery terminal condition
- Keep Alive Power (KAPWR) wire routing
- Harness circuit: KAPWR
- Powertrain Control Module (PCM) (12A650)

Pinpoint Test Schematic

*TEST PIN 55 —— Y —— KAPWR

FUSE PANEL OR FUSE LINK

BATTERY

*TEST PIN LOCATED ON BREAKOUT BOX
ALL HARNESS CONNECTORS VIEWED INTO MATING SURFACE

FM0159601551010X

Fig. 280 Test QB: DTC P0603/P1605 (Part 1 of 2). 1996

	Test Step	Result	▶	Action to Take
QB1	**CHECK BATTERY TERMINALS**			
	Diagnostic Trouble Code (DTC) P0603/P1605 indicates the PCM has experienced a power interrupt in the KAPWR circuit. Possible causes:	Yes	▶	Battery terminals are OK. GO to **QB2**.
	— Battery terminal corrosion or loose connections. — Improper KAPWR circuit wire routing. — Harness open in KAPWR circuit. — Damaged PCM. NOTE: If KAPWR is interrupted to the PCM (i.e. when a breakout box is installed or the battery is disconnected), DTC P0603/P1605 may be generated on the first power-up. • Inspect the battery cables for loose connections, corrosion, etc. • **Are the battery terminal connections in good condition?**	No	▶	SERVICE battery terminals as necessary. RERUN Quick Test.
QB2	**INSPECT ENGINE COMPARTMENT FOR PROPER WIRE ROUTING**			
	• Inspect EEC-V wiring for proximity to ignition components or wires.	Yes	▶	REROUTE as necessary. RERUN Quick Test.
	• **Is wiring too close to ignition components or wires?**	No	▶	Engine compartment wire routing is OK. GO to **QB3**
QB3	**CHECK KEEP ALIVE POWER (KAPWR) TO PCM**			
	• Key off. • Disconnect PCM. Inspect for damaged or pushed out pins, corrosion, loose wires, etc. Service as necessary. • Install breakout box, leave PCM disconnected. • Measure voltage between Test Pin 55 (KAPWR) and Test Pin 51 or 103 (PWR GND) at the breakout box. • While observing DVOM, grasp the EEC-V harness and wiggle, shake or bend a small section while working from the PCM to the dash panel. • **Does the DVOM indicate less than 10.5 volts?**	Yes No	▶ ▶	ISOLATE and SERVICE open in KAPWR circuit. REMOVE breakout box. RECONNECT the PCM. RERUN Quick Test. No open in KAPWR harness circuit detected. REMOVE the breakout box. RECONNECT the PCM. GO to **QB4**.
QB4	**CHECK FOR REPEAT OF DTC P0603/P1605**			
	• Activate Key On Engine Off Self-Test. • **Is DTC P0603/P1605 present?**	Yes No	▶ ▶	REPLACE the PCM. RERUN Quick Test. SERVICE other DTCs as necessary. If none, testing is complete. DTC P0603/P1605 was due to previous service action mentioned in the NOTE in QB1.

FM015960155 1020X

Fig. 280 Test QB: DTC P0603/P1605 (Part 2 of 2). 1996

Note

You should enter this Pinpoint Test only when directed here.

Remember

It is not necessary to remove the DTC P1000 from the PCM by driving the vehicle unless it is requested by the customer to pass an inspection/maintenance test.

Inform the customer of the need for additional driving when required to pass an inspection/maintenance test.

Description

Diagnostic Trouble Code (DTC) P1000 indicates that not all of the On Board Diagnostic II (OBD II) monitors have completed. In some states, this DTC must be cleared to pass an inspection/maintenance test. The customer should be informed that the law specifies additional city and highway driving must be done to complete the check of the On Board Diagnostic system. This additional driving must occur before the vehicle is tested at the inspection/maintenance station. The amount of driving required varies with individual driving patterns.

DTC P1000 is set by the PCM with any of the following conditions:
• The vehicle is new from the factory and has not yet been through a complete OBD II Drive Cycle.
• The battery or PCM has been disconnected.
• An OBD II monitor failure had occurred before completion of an OBD II Drive Cycle.
• The PCM DTCs have been erased with a Scan Tool as part of the normal repair process.

DTC P1000 may not be removed from the PCM because:
• There is a thermostat stuck open and a DTC is not output.
• There is an open VSS circuit and a DTC is not output.
• If the vehicle has a PTO, the circuit is shorted to VPWP or VBAT or the PTO is on during testing.

The only way a DTC P1000 can be removed from memory is when all the OBD II monitors have successfully completed during normal vehicle operation.

FM015960155 2010X

Fig. 281 Test QC: OBD II Monitor Testing Not Complete/DTC P1000 (Part 1 of 2). 1996

	Test Step	Result	▶	Action to Take
QC1	**DTC P1000: CHECK FOR OTHER DTCS**			
	This pinpoint test should be used only if a Diagnostic Trouble Code (DTC) P1000 was received in Continuous Memory. Ignore any DTC P1000s in KOEO or KOER. DTC P1000 indicates that all of the OBD II monitors have not yet been successfully tested. • **Were any other DTCs received with the P1000?**	Yes No	▶ ▶	GO to Powertrain Diagnostic Trouble Code (DTC) Charts, for Pinpoint Test direction and SERVICE other DTCs. GO to **QC4**. If the vehicle is equipped with a Power Take Off (PTO) GO to **QC2**.
QC2	**PTO APPLICATIONS**			
	• **Is the vehicle equipped with a Power Take Off?**	Yes No	▶ ▶	GO to **QC3**. GO to **QC4**.
QC3	**CHECK PTO ON-OFF PID**			
	• Scan Tool connected. • Key on, engine running. • View PTO STAT PID. • Cycle PTO switch/actuator ON and OFF (follow PTO aftermarket instructions). • **Did PTO STAT PID cycle ON, delay, then OFF?**	Yes No	▶ ▶	PTO circuit is OK. GO to **QC4**. GO to Pinpoint Test Step **FB1**.
QC4	**REQUEST TO REMOVE P1000**			
	A complete OBD II Drive Cycle has not yet been performed to remove the DTC P1000 from the PCM. • **Has the customer requested the DTC P1000 be removed from the PCM memory?**	Yes No	▶ ▶	PERFORM the OBD II Drive Cycle. (REFER to Drive Cycles.) If DTC P1000 is still present, GO to **QC5**. INFORM the customer that if the law in this state requires additional driving in order to remove the DTC P1000 from the PCM memory, it must be performed before an inspection/maintenance test.
QC5	**CHECK VSS PID**			
	Perform a short road test and look for a change in the VSS PID. • **Was the VSS PID greater than zero MPH/KPH?**	Yes No	▶ ▶	GO to **QC6**. SERVICE open VSS circuit. RERUN the OBD II Drive Cycle. RERUN Quick Test.
QC6	**CHECK ECT TEMPERATURE**			
	Drive the vehicle long enough to obtain the highest engine operating temperature and record the ECT temperature PID. • **Was the ECT PID reading greater than 180°F/82°C?**	Yes No	▶ ▶	ADDITIONAL driving is required. PERFORM the OBD II Drive Cycle. RERUN Quick Test. REPLACE the cooling system thermostat. PERFORM the OBD II Drive Cycle. RERUN Quick Test.

FM015960155 2020X

Fig. 281 Test QC: OBD II Monitor Testing Not Complete/DTC P1000 (Part 2 of 2). 1996

Note

You should enter this Pinpoint Test only when directed here.

Description

Continuous Memory Diagnostic Trouble Code (DTC) P1260 indicates the Anti-Theft System has detected a break in the on-board security test due to an attempted theft or system hardware failure. When the PCM receives the message that a theft condition exists, fuel delivery to the engine is disabled on start-up. As a fail safe, fuel delivery is not disabled if the vehicle is operating and a system failure occurs. Use of the proper key or remote or keyless entry to unlock the door, disarms the Anti-Theft System and enables fuel delivery to start the vehicle.

	Test Step	Result	▶	Action to Take
QD1	**DTC P1260**			
	NOTE: All other DTCs should be diagnosed before DTC P1260. Diagnostic Trouble Code (DTC) P1260 indicates the Lighting Control Module (LCM) determined a theft condition existed at some time. • **Have all other DTCs been diagnosed?**	Yes No	▶ ▶	GO to **QD2**. GO to Powertrain Diagnostic Trouble Code (DTC) Charts, for Pinpoint Test direction and SERVICE other DTCs.
QD2	**START ENGINE**			
	• Disarm the Anti-Theft system. • Complete PCM Reset to clear DTC P1260 (refer to Powertrain Control Module (PCM) Reset). • Attempt to start the engine. • **Will the engine start?**	Yes No	▶ ▶	NO system faults exist at present. RETURN vehicle to customer and advise that a theft condition existed some time in the past. GO to **QD3**.
QD3	**CHECK TO SEE IF DTC P1260 IS PRESENT**			
	• Retrieve Continuous Memory DTCs. • **Is DTC P1260 present?**	Yes No	▶ ▶	COMPLETE PCM reset to clear DTC. diagnose DTC P1260. DTC P1260 is not the cause of the No Start. GO to Symptom Flowcharts to diagnose the No Start symptom.

FM015960155 3000X

Fig. 282 Test QD: DTC P1260. 1996

ELECTRONIC ENGINE CONTROL SYSTEM (EEC-V)

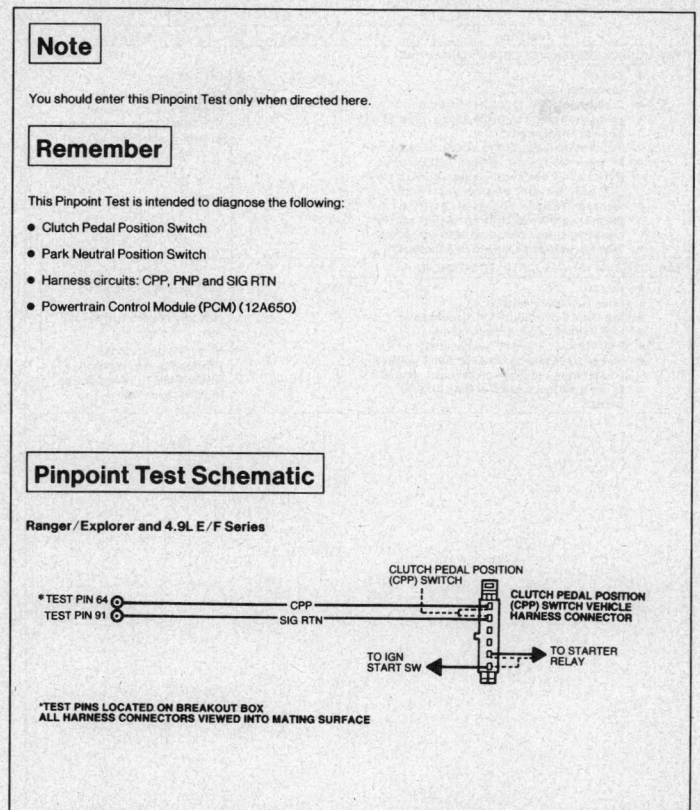

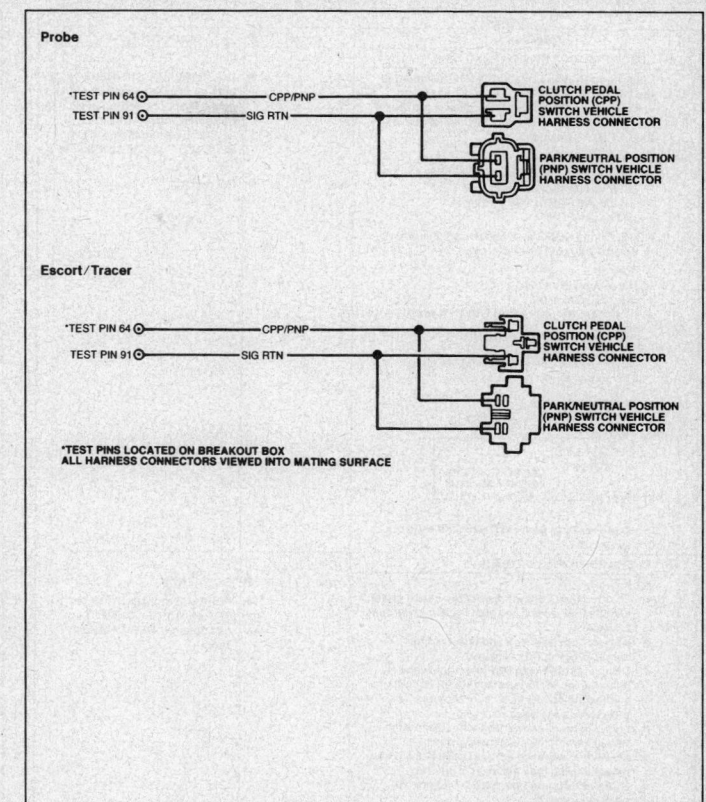

Fig. 283 Test TA: Park/Neutral Position Switch & Clutch Pedal Position Switch (Part 1 of 6). 1996

Fig. 283 Test TA: Park/Neutral Position Switch & Clutch Pedal Position Switch (Part 2 of 6). 1996

Test Step	Result	▶	Action to Take
TA1 CHECK CPP OR PNP SWITCH FUNCTION			
Diagnostic Trouble Code (DTC) P1709 indicates the voltage is high or the switch is open when the voltage should be low or the switch should be closed grounding the circuit. DTC P0704 indicates a malfunction of the Clutch Pedal Position (CPP) or Park/Neutral Position (PNP) switch. Possible causes: — Starter Relay disconnected during Quick Test. — CPP circuit shorted to power. — Open in the SIG RTN circuit. — Damaged CPP or PNP switch. — Damaged PCM. NOTE: During KOEO Self-Test, clutch pedal must be down or gearshift lever in neutral. • Key off. • Scan Tool connected. • Key on, engine off. • Access PNP PID and observe PID cycling ON/OFF with clutch pedal up, then down. • **Does reading go from ON to OFF?**	Yes No	▶ ▶	DISCONNECT PCM. INSPECT both ends of the connector for damaged or pushed out pins, corrosion, loose wires, etc. SERVICE as necessary. If OK, REPLACE PCM. RERUN Quick Test. GO to **TA2**.
TA2 CHECK CPP OR PNP SWITCH			
• Key off. • Locate the CPP switch or the PNP switch near the transmission shift linkage. • Inspect switch and bracket for damage, bent, broken, etc. Service as required. • Disconnect CPP or PNP vehicle harness connector and inspect for damage, pushed out or broken pins, or broken wires, etc. Service as required. • Measure resistance across the CPP or PNP switch terminals with the clutch pedal down. • **Is the resistance less than 5.0 ohms?**	Yes No	▶ ▶	GO to **TA3**. REPLACE the CPP or PNP switch. RECONNECT all components. RERUN Quick Test.

Test Step	Result	▶	Action to Take
TA3 CHECK CONTINUITY OF CPP/PNP CIRCUIT			
• Key off. • Disconnect Scan Tool. • Disconnect PCM. Inspect for damaged or pushed out pins, corrosion, loose wires, etc. Service as required. • Install breakout box, leave PCM disconnected. • Measure resistance between Test Pin 64 at the breakout box and the same CPP or PNP signal pin at the vehicle harness connector. • Where applicable, measure resistance between Test Pin 91 at the breakout box and the same SIG RTN pin at CPP or PNP vehicle harness connector. • **Is each resistance less than 5.0 ohms?**	Yes No	▶ ▶	GO to **TA4**. SERVICE open circuit. REMOVE breakout box. RECONNECT all components. RERUN Quick Test.
TA4 CHECK CPP OR PNP CIRCUIT FOR SHORT			
• Key off. • Scan Tool disconnected. • Breakout box installed, PCM disconnected. • CPP, PNP vehicle harness disconnected. • Measure resistance between Test Pins 64 and 91 at the breakout box and chassis ground. • **Is the resistance greater than 10,000 ohms?**	Yes No	▶ ▶	REPLACE PCM. REMOVE breakout box. RECONNECT all components. RERUN Quick Test. SERVICE short circuit. REMOVE breakout box. RECONNECT all components. RERUN Quick Test.

Fig. 283 Test TA: Park/Neutral Position Switch & Clutch Pedal Position Switch (Part 3 of 6). 1996

Fig. 283 Test TA: Park/Neutral Position Switch & Clutch Pedal Position Switch (Part 4 of 6). 1996

Test Step	Result	▶	Action to Take
TA5 CHECK PNP / CPP SWITCH FUNCTION			
Diagnostic Trouble Code (DTC) P1709 indicates the voltage is high or the switch is open when voltage should be low or switch closed grounding the circuit. DTC P0704 indicates malfunction of the CPP or PNP switch. Possible causes: — Starter Relay disconnected during Quick Test. — CPP circuit shorted to power. — Damaged CPP or PNP switch. — Damaged PCM. NOTE: During KOEO test, clutch pedal must be down and gearshift lever in neutral. • Key off. • Scan tool connected. • Key on, engine off. • Look for PNP PID cycling ON / OFF with: (1) Transmission in NEUTRAL and the clutch pedal up. (2) Transmission in GEAR and the clutch pedal down. • **Does reading go from ON to OFF for both switches?**	Yes No	▶ ▶	DISCONNECT PCM. INSPECT both ends of the connector for damaged or pushed out pins, corrosion, loose wires, etc. SERVICE as necessary. If OK, REPLACE PCM. RERUN Quick Test. GO to **TA6**.
TA6 CHECK PNP / CPP SWITCHES			
• Key off. • Located the CPP switch near the clutch pedal and the PNP switch near the transmission shift linkage. • Inspect both switches and brackets for damage. Service as required. • Disconnect CPP and PNP electrical vehicle harness connector and inspect for damage, pushed out or broken pins, or broken wires, etc. Service as required. • Measure resistance across the CPP switch terminals with the clutch pedal down. • Measure resistance across the PNP switch terminals with the shift lever in neutral. • **Is the resistance less than 5.0 ohms for both switches?**	Yes No	▶ ▶	GO to **TA7**. REPLACE damaged CPP or PNP switch. RECONNECT components. RERUN Quick Test.

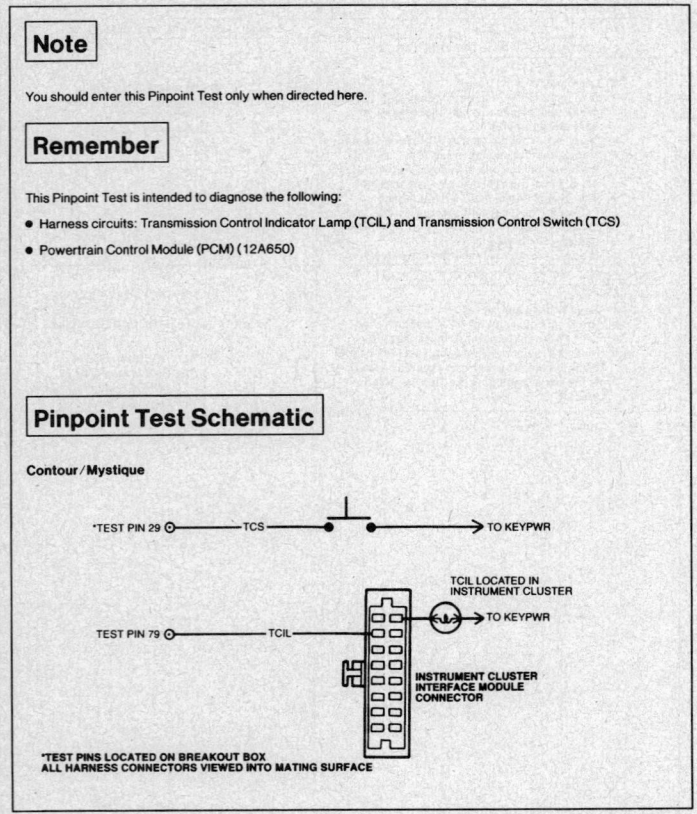

Fig. 283   Test TA: Park/Neutral Position Switch & Clutch Pedal Position Switch (Part 5 of 6). 1996

Test Step	Result	▶	Action to Take
TA7 CHECK CONTINUITY OF PNP / CPP CIRCUIT			
• Key off. • Disconnect Scan Tool. • Disconnect PCM. Inspect for damaged or pushed out pins, corrosion, loose wires, etc. Service as required. * • Install breakout box, leave PCM disconnected. • Measure resistance between Test Pin 91 at the breakout box and the same SIG RTN pin at CPP and PNP vehicle harness connector. • Measure resistance between Test Pin 64 at the breakout box and the same CPP and PNP signal pin at the vehicle harness connector. • **Is each resistance less than 5.0 ohms?**	Yes No	▶ ▶	GO to **TA8**. SERVICE open circuit. REMOVE breakout box. RECONNECT all components. RERUN Quick Test.
TA8 CHECK PNP / CPP CIRCUIT FOR SHORT			
• Key off. • Scan Tool disconnected. • Breakout box install, PCM disconnected. • CPP vehicle harness disconnected. • PNP vehicle harness disconnected. • Measure resistance between Test Pins 64 and 91 at the breakout box and chassis ground. • **Is the resistance greater than 10,000 ohms?**	Yes No	▶ ▶	REPLACE PCM. REMOVE breakout box. RECONNECT all components. RERUN Quick Test. SERVICE short circuit. REMOVE breakout box. RECONNECT all components. RERUN Quick Test.

Fig. 283   Test TA: Park/Neutral Position Switch & Clutch Pedal Position Switch (Part 6 of 6). 1996

Note

You should enter this Pinpoint Test only when directed here.

Remember

This Pinpoint Test is intended to diagnose the following:
• Harness circuits: Transmission Control Indicator Lamp (TCIL) and Transmission Control Switch (TCS)
• Powertrain Control Module (PCM) (12A650)

Pinpoint Test Schematic

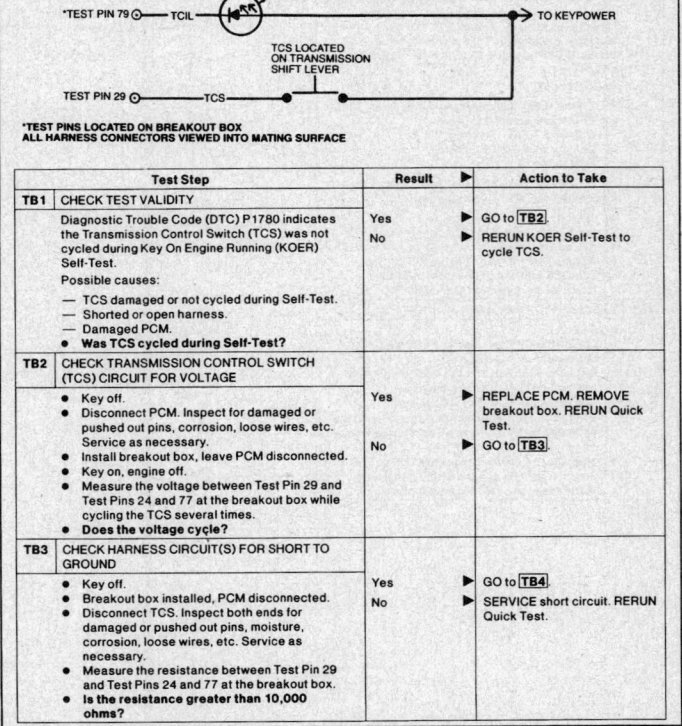

Test Step	Result	▶	Action to Take
TB1 CHECK TEST VALIDITY			
Diagnostic Trouble Code (DTC) P1780 indicates the Transmission Control Switch (TCS) was not cycled during Key On Engine Running (KOER) Self-Test. Possible causes: — TCS damaged or not cycled during Self-Test. — Shorted or open harness. — Damaged PCM. • **Was TCS cycled during Self-Test?**	Yes No	▶ ▶	GO to **TB2**. RERUN KOER Self-Test to cycle TCS.
TB2 CHECK TRANSMISSION CONTROL SWITCH (TCS) CIRCUIT FOR VOLTAGE			
• Key off. • Disconnect PCM. Inspect for damaged or pushed out pins, corrosion, loose wires, etc. Service as necessary. • Install breakout box, leave PCM disconnected. • Key on, engine off. • Measure the voltage between Test Pin 29 and Test Pins 24 and 77 at the breakout box while cycling the TCS several times. • **Does the voltage cycle?**	Yes No	▶ ▶	REPLACE PCM. REMOVE breakout box. RERUN Quick Test. GO to **TB3**.
TB3 CHECK HARNESS CIRCUIT(S) FOR SHORT TO GROUND			
• Key off. • Breakout box installed, PCM disconnected. • Disconnect TCS. Inspect both ends for damaged or pushed out pins, moisture, corrosion, loose wires, etc. Service as necessary. • Measure the resistance between Test Pin 29 and Test Pins 24 and 77 at the breakout box. • **Is the resistance greater than 10,000 ohms?**	Yes No	▶ ▶	GO to **TB4**. SERVICE short circuit. RERUN Quick Test.

Fig. 284   Test TB: Transmission Control Switch & Indicator Lamp (Part 1 of 4). 1996

Fig. 284   Test TB: Transmission Control Switch & Indicator Lamp (Part 2 of 4). 1996

Test Step		Result	▶	Action to Take
TB4	CHECK CONTINUITY OF THE TCS HARNESS			
	• Key off. • Breakout box installed, leave PCM disconnected. • Measure the resistance between TCS keypower at the fuse panel (ohmmeter positive probe) and power side of the TCS vehicle harness connector (ohmmeter negative probe). • Measure resistance between Test Pin 29 at the breakout box and signal side of the transmission control switch vehicle harness connector. • **Are both resistances less than 5.0 ohms?**	Yes No	▶ ▶	GO to TB5. SERVICE open circuit. REMOVE breakout box. RECONNECT all components. RERUN Quick Test.
TB5	CHECK HARNESS CIRCUIT FOR SHORTS TO POWER			
	• Key off. • Breakout box installed, leave PCM disconnected. • Measure the resistance between Test Pin 29 and Test Pins 71 and 97 at the breakout box. • **Is the resistance greater than 10,000 ohms?**	Yes No	▶ ▶	REPLACE damaged Transmission Control Switch. REMOVE breakout box. RECONNECT all components. RERUN Quick Test. SERVICE short circuit. REMOVE breakout box. RECONNECT all components. RERUN Quick Test.
TB6	CYCLE TCIL			
	• Key on, engine off. • Cycle the Transmission Control Switch (TCS). • **Does the TCIL turn on and off?**	Yes No	▶ ▶	Concern may be intermittent. GO to Pinpoint Test Step Z1. GO to TB7.
TB7	CHECK FOR SHORT TO GROUND IN THE TCIL CIRCUIT			
	• Key off. • Disconnect PCM. Inspect both ends for damaged or pushed out pins, moisture, corrosion, loose wires, etc. Service as necessary. • Key on, engine off. • **Does the TCIL remain on?**	Yes No	▶ ▶	SERVICE short to ground between bulb and Test Pin (79). VERIFY a symptom no longer exists. TCIL turns off when PCM is disconnected. REPLACE PCM. RERUN Quick Test.
TB8	CHECK FOR DTC P1780			
	• Run Key On Engine Running (KOER) Self-Test. • **Is DTC P1780 present?**	Yes No	▶ ▶	SERVICE DTC 1780. GO to TB1. GO to TB9.

FM0159601555030X

Fig. 284   Test TB: Transmission Control Switch & Indicator Lamp (Part 3 of 4). 1996

Test Step		Result	▶	Action to Take
TB9	CHECK CONTINUITY OF THE TCIL CIRCUIT			
	• Key off. • Breakout box installed. • PCM disconnected. • Key on, engine off. • Measure the voltage between Test Pin 79 and Test Pins 24 and 76 at the breakout box. • **Is the voltage reading greater than 2.0 volts?**	Yes No	▶ ▶	REPLACE PCM. CYCLE (TCS) to check operation of TCIL. CHECK indicator bulb and fuse. If OK, open is in the wiring between the Ignition switch and Test Pin 79 at the harness connector. SERVICE as necessary.

FM0159601555040X

Fig. 284   Test TB: Transmission Control Switch & Indicator Lamp (Part 4 of 4). 1996

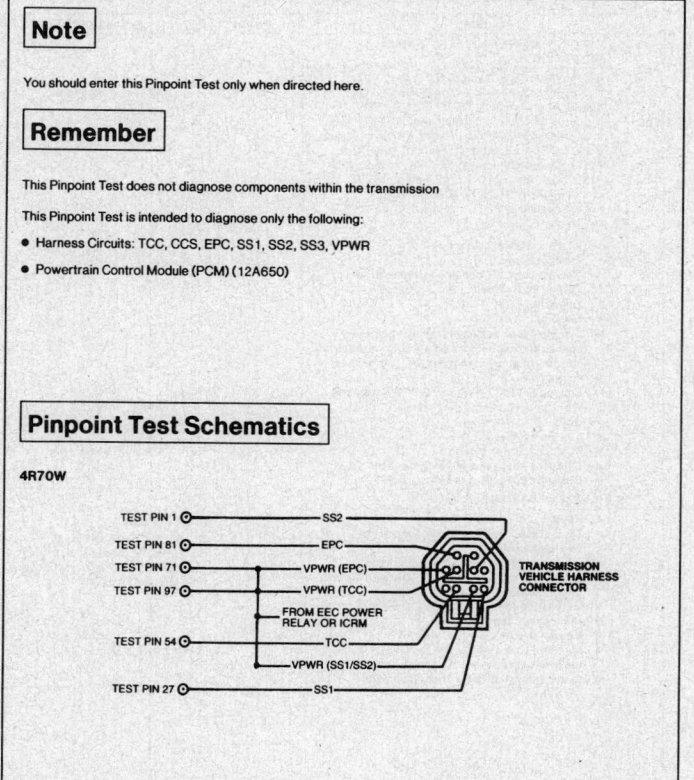

FM0159601556010X

Fig. 285   Test TC: Transmission Solenoids (Part 1 of 9). 1996

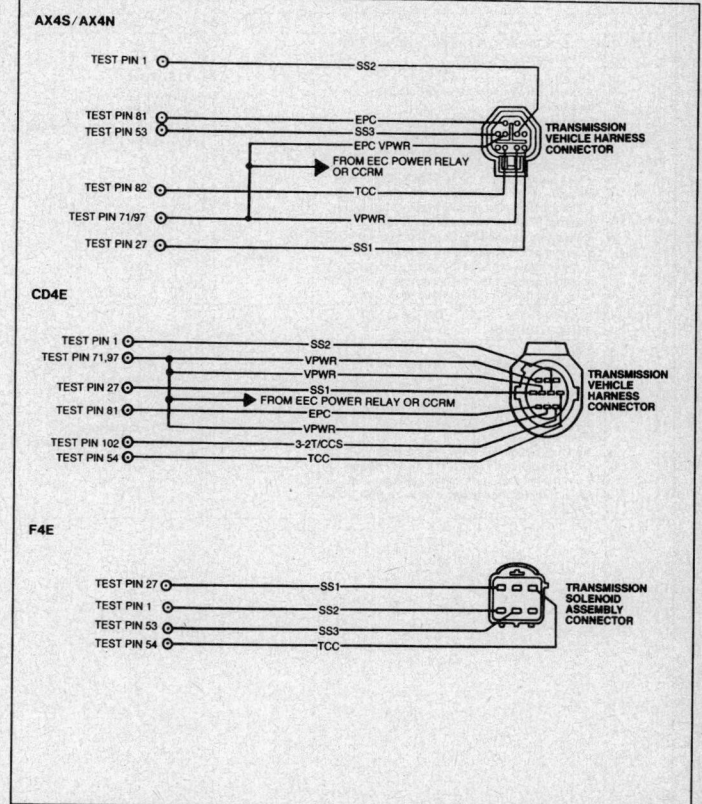

FM0159601556020X

Fig. 285   Test TC: Transmission Solenoids (Part 2 of 9). 1996

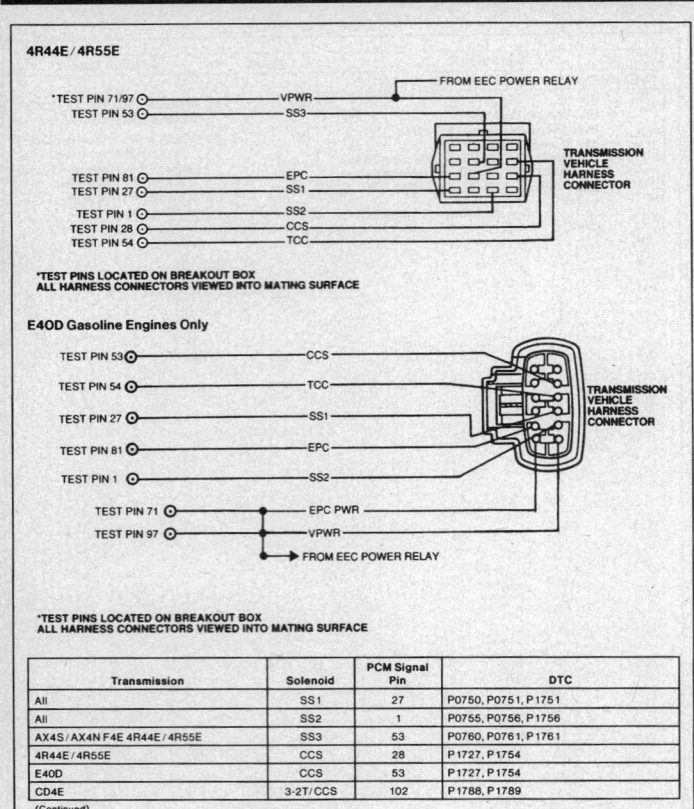

4R44E / 4R55E

```
*TEST PIN 71/97 ○─────── VPWR ──────── FROM EEC POWER RELAY
 TEST PIN 53 ○─────── SS3

 TEST PIN 81 ○─────── EPC
 TEST PIN 27 ○─────── SS1
 TEST PIN 1 ○─────── SS2
 TEST PIN 28 ○─────── CCS
 TEST PIN 54 ○─────── TCC
```
TRANSMISSION VEHICLE HARNESS CONNECTOR

*TEST PINS LOCATED ON BREAKOUT BOX
ALL HARNESS CONNECTORS VIEWED INTO MATING SURFACE

E40D Gasoline Engines Only

```
 TEST PIN 53 ○─────── CCS
 TEST PIN 54 ○─────── TCC
 TEST PIN 27 ○─────── SS1
 TEST PIN 81 ○─────── EPC
 TEST PIN 1 ○─────── SS2

 TEST PIN 71 ○─────── EPC PWR
 TEST PIN 97 ○─────── VPWR
                └────── FROM EEC POWER RELAY
```
TRANSMISSION VEHICLE HARNESS CONNECTOR

*TEST PINS LOCATED ON BREAKOUT BOX
ALL HARNESS CONNECTORS VIEWED INTO MATING SURFACE

Transmission	Solenoid	PCM Signal Pin	DTC
All	SS1	27	P0750, P0751, P1751
All	SS2	1	P0755, P0756, P1756
AX4S / AX4N F4E 4R44E / 4R55E	SS3	53	P0760, P0761, P1761
4R44E / 4R55E	CCS	28	P1727, P1754
E40D	CCS	53	P1727, P1754
CD4E	3-2T / CCS	102	P1788, P1789
(Continued)			

FM0159601556030X

Fig. 285 Test TC: Transmission Solenoids (Part 3 of 9). 1996

Transmission	Solenoid	PCM Signal Pin	DTC
All Except F4E	EPC	81	P0746, P1746, P1747, P1749
AX4N / AX4S	TCC	82	P0741, P0743, P1741, P1742, P1743, P1744
4R70W, CD4E, 4R44E / 4R55E F4E, E40D	TCC	54	P0741, P0743, P1741, P1742, P1743, P1744

	Test Step	Result	►	Action to Take
TC1	CHECK TRANSMISSION ELECTRICAL OPERATION			
	Diagnostic Trouble Code (DTC) P0731/P0781 indicates gear # 1 incorrect ratio. DTC P0732/P0782 indicates gear # 2 incorrect ratio. DTC P0733/P0783 indicates gear # 3 incorrect ratio. DTC P0734/P0784 indicates gear # 4 incorrect ratio. DTC P0750/P0751, P1751 indicates SS1 electrical malfunction. DTC P0755/P0756/P1756 indicates SS2 electrical malfunction. DTC P0760/P0761/P1761 indicates SS3 electrical malfunction. Possible causes: — Internal Transmission. — Damaged solenoid. — Solenoid circuit open or shorted to VPWR or GND. — VPWR circuit open or shorted. — PCM damaged. ● Key off. ● Disconnect transmission vehicle harness connector. Inspect for damaged or pushed out pins, corrosion, loose wires, etc. Service as necessary. ● Connect DVOM between the VPWR pin and the suspect solenoid pin at the transmission vehicle harness connector. ● Perform KOEO Self-Test. ● **Does voltmeter reading cycle?**	Yes No	► ►	Transmission Diagnosis. GO to [TC2].
TC2	CHECK VPWR TO SOLENOID			
	● Key off. ● Transmission vehicle harness connector disconnected. ● Disconnect PCM. Inspect for damaged or pushed out pins, corrosion, loose wires, etc. Service as necessary. ● Install breakout box, leave PCM disconnected. ● Key on, engine off. ● Measure voltage between Test Pin 71/97 at the breakout box and chassis ground. ● **Is voltage greater than 10.5 volts?**	Yes No	► ►	GO to [TC3]. SERVICE VPWR circuit. REMOVE breakout box. RECONNECT all components. RERUN Quick Test.

FM0159601556040X

Fig. 285 Test TC: Transmission Solenoids (Part 4 of 9). 1996

	Test Step	Result	►	Action to Take
TC3	CHECK CONTINUITY OF SOLENOID VPWR AND VPWR HARNESS CIRCUIT			
	● Key off. ● Transmission vehicle harness connector disconnected. ● Disconnect PCM. Inspect both ends of the connector for damaged or pushed out pins, corrosion, loose wires, etc. Service as necessary. ● Install breakout box, leave PCM disconnected. ● Measure resistance between the VPWR pins at the transmission vehicle harness connector and Test Pin 71/97 at the breakout box. ● Measure resistance between the suspect solenoid signal pin at the transmission vehicle harness connector and the same suspect solenoid signal pin at the breakout box. ● **Is each resistance less than 5.0 ohms?**	Yes No	► ►	GO to [TC4]. SERVICE open circuit. REMOVE breakout box. RECONNECT all components. RERUN Quick Test.
TC4	CHECK SOLENOID CIRCUIT FOR SHORT TO POWER OR GROUND			
	● Key off. ● Transmission vehicle harness connector disconnected. ● PCM disconnected. ● Measure resistance between the suspect solenoid signal pin and Test Pin 71/97 at the breakout box. ● Measure resistance between the suspect solenoid signal pin and Test Pins 51/76 and 91 at the breakout box and chassis ground. ● **Is each resistance greater than 10,000 ohms?**	Yes No	► ►	Transmission Diagnosis for internal harness and/or solenoid. SERVICE short circuit. REMOVE breakout box. RECONNECT all components. RERUN Quick Test.

FM0159601556050X

Fig. 285 Test TC: Transmission Solenoids (Part 5 of 9). 1996

	Test Step	Result	►	Action to Take
TC5	CHECK TRANSMISSION ELECTRICAL OPERATION			
	Diagnostic Trouble Code (DTC) P0741, P0743, P1741, P1742, P1743, P1744 indicates TCC electrical malfunction. DTC P1727, P1754 indicates CCS electrical malfunction. DTC P1788 indicates 3-2T/CCS circuit open. DTC P1789 indicates 3-2 T/CCS circuit shorted. DTC P0746 indicates EPC solenoid malfuction. DTC P1746 indicates EPC circuit open. DTC P1747 indicates EPC circuit shorted. DTC P1749 indicates EPC solenoid failed low. Possible causes: — Internal Transmission. — Damaged Solenoid. — Solenoid circuit open or shorted to VPWR or GND. VPWR circuit open or shorted. — Damaged PCM. ● Key off. ● Disconnect transmission vehicle harness connector. Inspect for damaged or pushed out pins, corrosion, loose wires, etc. Service as necessary. ● Connect DVOM between the VPWR pins and the suspect solenoid pin. ● Scan Tool connected. ● Key on, engine off. ● Enter Output Test Mode. ● Cycle the suspect solenoid on and off. ● **Does the voltmeter reading cycle?**	Yes No	► ►	Transmission Diagnosis. GO to [TC6].
TC6	CHECK VPWR TO SOLENOID			
	● Key off. ● Transmission vehicle harness connector disconnected. ● Disconnect PCM. Inspect for damaged or pushed out pins, corrosion, loose wires, ect. Service as necessary. ● Install breakout box, leave PCM disconnected. ● Disconnect Scan Tool. ● Key on, engine off. ● Measure voltage between Test Pin 71/97 at the breakout box and chassis ground. ● **Is the voltage greater than 10.5 volts?**	Yes No	► ►	GO to [TC7]. SERVICE VPWR circuit. REMOVE breakout box. RECONNECT all components. RERUN Quick Test.

FM0159601556060X

Fig. 285 Test TC: Transmission Solenoids (Part 6 of 9). 1996

ELECTRONIC ENGINE CONTROL SYSTEM (EEC-V)

Test Step	Result	▶	Action to Take
TC7 CHECK CONTINUITY OF SOLENOID VPWR AND SIGNAL HARNESS CIRCUIT			
• Key off. • Disconnect PCM and Scan Tool. • Breakout box installed, leave PCM disconnected. • Disconnect transmission vehicle harness connector. Inspect both ends for damaged or pushed out pins, corrosion, loose wires, etc. Service as necessary. • Measure resistance between the VPWR pins at the transmission vehicle harness connector and Test Pin 71/97 at the breakout box. • Measure resistance between the suspect transmission solenoid pin at the vehicle harness connector and the same suspect Test Pin at the breakout box. • **Is each resistance less than 5.0 ohms?**	Yes No	▶ ▶	GO to TC8. SERVICE open circuit. REMOVE breakout box. RECONNECT all components. RERUN Quick Test.
TC8 CHECK SOLENOID CIRCUIT FOR SHORT TO POWER OR GROUND			
• Key off. • Transmission vehicle harness connector disconnected. • Breakout box installed, PCM disconnected. • Refer to table and schematic of this Pinpoint Test. • Measure resistance between the suspect solenoid signal Test Pin and Test Pin 71/97 at the breakout box. • Measure resistance between the suspect solenoid signal Test Pin and Test Pins 51/76 and 91 at the breakout box and chassis ground. • **Is each resistance greater than 10,000 ohms?**	Yes No	▶ ▶	Transmission Diagnosis. SERVICE short circuit. REMOVE breakout box. RECONNECT all components. RERUN Quick Test.

FM0159601556070X

**Fig. 285   Test TC: Transmission Solenoids (Part 7 of 9).
1996**

Test Step	Result	▶	Action to Take
TC9 CHECK TRANSMISSION ELECTRICAL OPERATION			
Diagnostic Trouble Code (DTC) 0731/0781 indicate gear # 1 incorrect ratio. DTC 0732/0782 indicate gear # 2 incorrect ratio. DTC 0733/0783 indicate gear # 3 incorrect ratio. DTC 0734/0784 indicate gear # 4 incorrect ratio. DTC 0750/0751 indicates SS1 electrical malfunction. DTC 0755/0756/1756 indicates SS2 electrical malfunction. DTC 0760/0761/1761 indicates SS3 electrical malfunction. DTC P0741, P0743 indicates TCC electrical malfunction. Possible causes: — Internal transmission. — Damaged solenoid. — Solenoid circuit open or shorted to PWR or GND. — GND, VPWR circuit open or shorted. — Damaged PCM. • Key off. • Disconnect transmission vehicle harness connector. Inspect for damaged or pushed out pins, corrosion, loose wires, etc. Service as necessary. • Connect DVOM between the suspect solenoid signal pin and chassis GND. • Perform KOEO Self-Test. • **Does voltmeter reading cycle?**	Yes No	▶ ▶	Transmission Diagnosis. GO to TC10.
TC10 CHECK CONTINUITY OF GND PATH			
• Key off. • Measure resistance between transmission case, engine block, chassis and the battery negative post. • **Is each resistance less than 5.0 ohms?**	Yes No	▶ ▶	GO to TC11. SERVICE GND path. RECONNECT all components. RERUN Quick Test.
TC11 CHECK CONTINUITY OF SOLENOID HARNESS			
• Key off. • Transmission vehicle harness connector disconnected. • Disconnect PCM. Inspect both ends of the connector for damaged or pushed out pins, corrosion, loose wires, etc. Service as necessary. • Install breakout box, leave PCM disconnected. • Measure resistance between the suspect solenoid pins at the transmission vehicle harness connector and the same signal test pin at the breakout box. • **Is each resistance less than 5.0 ohms?**	Yes No	▶ ▶	GO to TC12. SERVICE open circuit. REMOVE breakout box. RECONNECT all components. RERUN Quick Test.

FM0159601556080X

**Fig. 285   Test TC: Transmission Solenoids (Part 8 of 9).
1996**

Test Step	Result	▶	Action to Take
TC12 CHECK SOLENOID CIRCUIT FOR SHORT TO POWER OR GROUND			
• Key off. • Transmission vehicle harness connector disconnected. • Breakout box installed, PCM disconnected. • Key on, engine off. • Measure voltage between the suspect solenoid signal pin and Test Pins 51/77 at the breakout box and chassis ground. • **Is voltage less than 5.0 volt?**	Yes No	▶ ▶	REPLACE PCM. REMOVE breakout box. RECONNECT all components. RERUN Quick Test. SERVICE short circuit. REMOVE breakout box. RECONNECT all components. RERUN Quick Test.

FM0159601556090X

**Fig. 285   Test TC: Transmission Solenoids (Part 9 of 9).
1996**

Note

You should enter this Pinpoint Test only when directed here.

Remember

This Pinpoint Test is intended to diagnose the following:

• Harness Circuits: SIG RTN and TR
• Powertrain Control Module (PCM)

Tables and Charts

Escort/Tracer: Internal Transmission Range Sensor Configuration

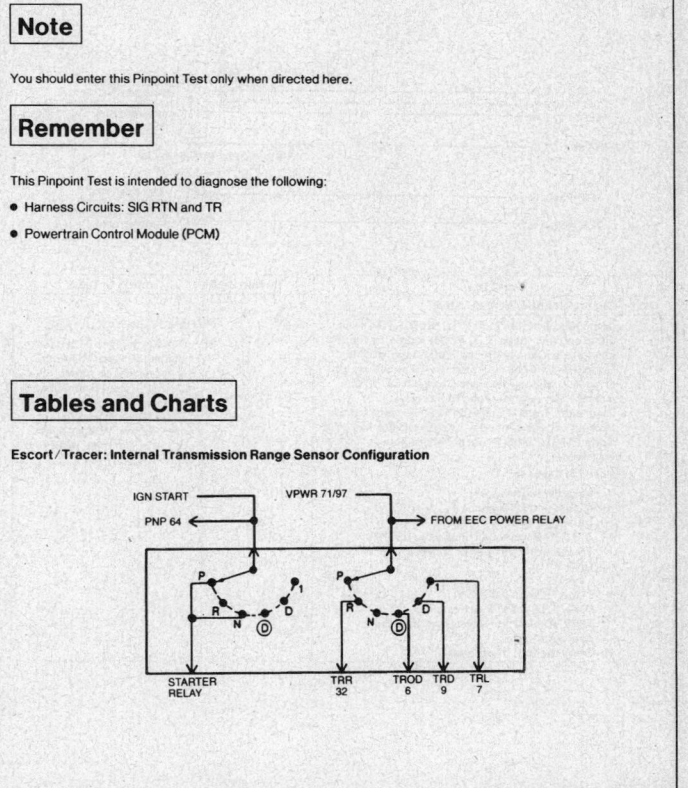

FM0159601557010X

**Fig. 286   Test TD: Transmission Range Sensor (Part 1 of 8).
1996**

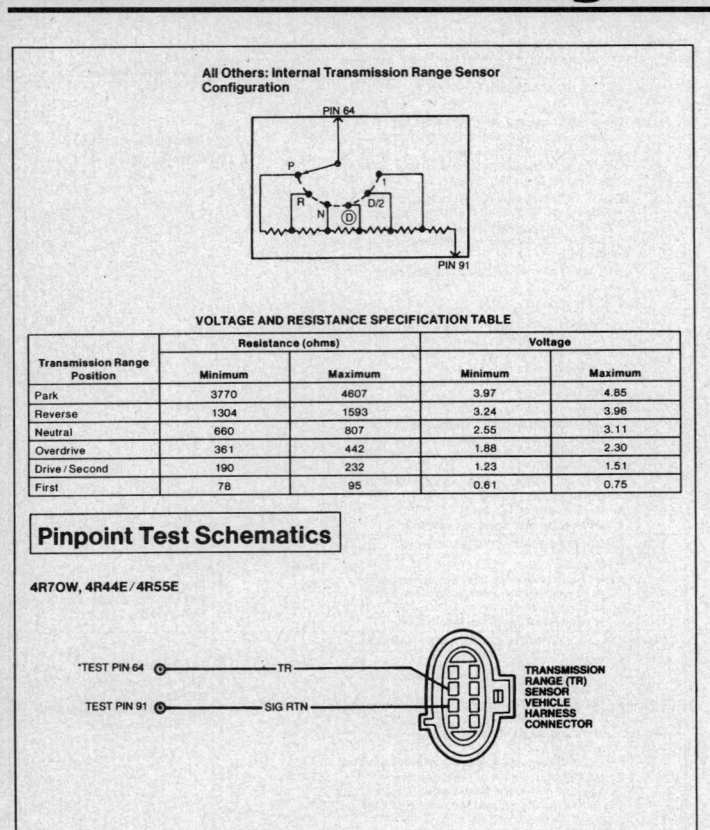

All Others: Internal Transmission Range Sensor Configuration

VOLTAGE AND RESISTANCE SPECIFICATION TABLE

Transmission Range Position	Resistance (ohms)		Voltage	
	Minimum	Maximum	Minimum	Maximum
Park	3770	4607	3.97	4.85
Reverse	1304	1593	3.24	3.96
Neutral	660	807	2.55	3.11
Overdrive	361	442	1.88	2.30
Drive / Second	190	232	1.23	1.51
First	78	95	0.61	0.75

Pinpoint Test Schematics

4R7OW, 4R44E / 4R55E

FM015960155700X

Fig. 286   Test TD: Transmission Range Sensor (Part 2 of 8). 1996

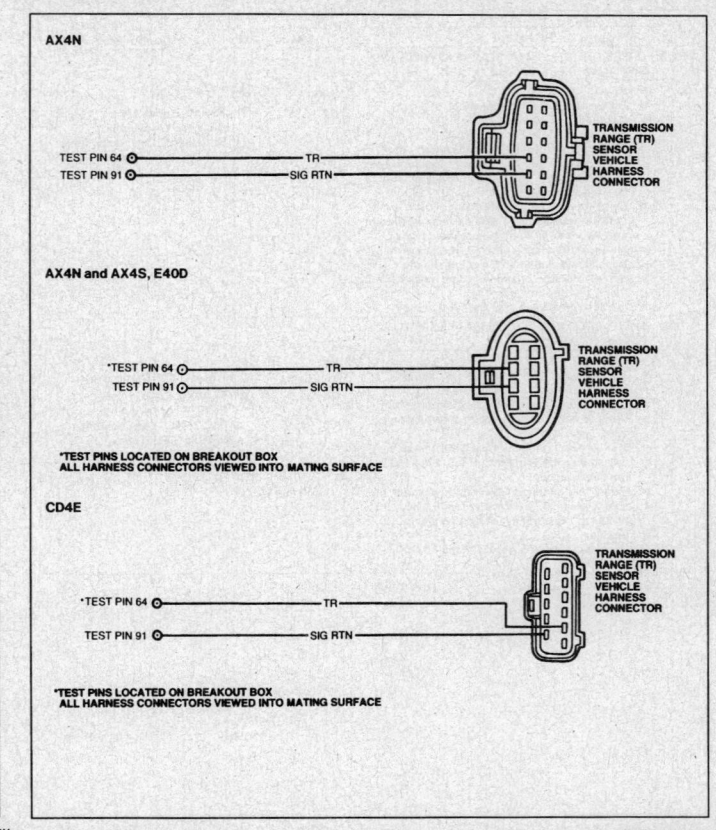

AX4N

AX4N and AX4S, E40D

*TEST PINS LOCATED ON BREAKOUT BOX
ALL HARNESS CONNECTORS VIEWED INTO MATING SURFACE

CD4E

*TEST PINS LOCATED ON BREAKOUT BOX
ALL HARNESS CONNECTORS VIEWED INTO MATING SURFACE

FM0159601557030X

Fig. 286   Test TD: Transmission Range Sensor (Part 3 of 8). 1996

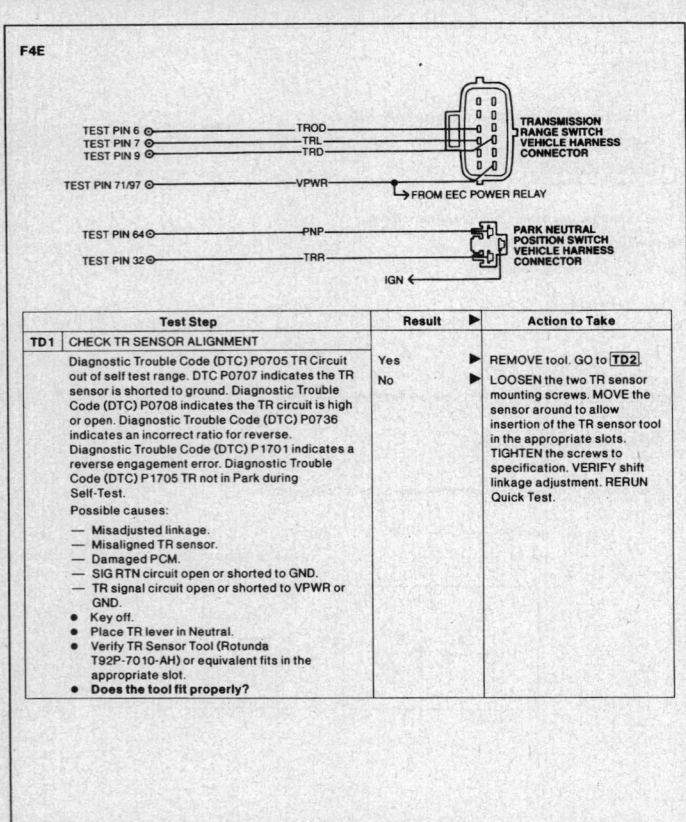

F4E

Test Step		Result	▶	Action to Take
TD1	CHECK TR SENSOR ALIGNMENT			
	Diagnostic Trouble Code (DTC) P0705 TR Circuit out of self test range. DTC P0707 indicates the TR sensor is shorted to ground. Diagnostic Trouble Code (DTC) P0708 indicates the TR circuit is high or open. Diagnostic Trouble Code (DTC) P0736 indicates an incorrect ratio for reverse. Diagnostic Trouble Code (DTC) P1701 indicates a reverse engagement error. Diagnostic Trouble Code (DTC) P1705 TR not in Park during Self-Test. Possible causes: — Misadjusted linkage. — Misaligned TR sensor. — Damaged PCM. — SIG RTN circuit open or shorted to GND. — TR signal circuit open or shorted to VPWR or GND. • Key off. • Place TR lever in Neutral. • Verify TR Sensor Tool (Rotunda T92P-7010-AH) or equivalent fits in the appropriate slot. • Does the tool fit properly?		Yes	▶	REMOVE tool. GO to TD2.
			No	▶	LOOSEN the two TR sensor mounting screws. MOVE the sensor around to allow insertion of the TR sensor tool in the appropriate slots. TIGHTEN the screws to specification. VERIFY shift linkage adjustment. RERUN Quick Test.

FM0159601557040X

Fig. 286   Test TD: Transmission Range Sensor (Part 4 of 8). 1996

Test Step		Result	▶	Action to Take
TD2	CHECK FOR INTERMITTENT CIRCUIT FAULT (WIGGLE TEST)			
	• Key on, engine off. • Scan Tool connected. • Access TR and TR-V PIDs. • Shift lever into Park position. • Grasp the vehicle harness starting at the TR sensor connector. • Shake and bend a small section of the harness all the way to the PCM. • Tap the TRS and connector and look for a fluctuation of the TR display. • Are TR and TR-V readings changing?	Yes	▶	GO to TD4.
		No	▶	GO to TD3.
TD3	CHECK TR SENSOR SYSTEM VOLTAGE			
	• Key on, engine off. • Scan Tool connected. • Access TR and TR-V PIDs. • Verify that the readings are between 4.0 and 5.0 volts in Park position. • Move the shift lever through all the gear ranges. Refer to the Voltage and Resistance Specification Table at the beginning of the Pinpoint Test. • Is each voltage reading within specification?	Yes	▶	Transmission Diagnosis.
		No	▶	GO to TD4.
TD4	CHECK CONTINUITY OF TR SENSOR HARNESS CIRCUITS			
	• Key off. • Disconnect PCM, disconnect Scan Tool. • Inspect for damaged or pushed out pins, corrosion, loose wires, etc. Service as necessary. • Disconnect TR sensor. • Inspect both ends of the connector for damaged or pushed out pins, corrosion, loose wires, etc. Service as necessary. • Install breakout box, leave PCM disconnected. • Measure resistance between Test Pin 64 at the breakout box and TR signal pin at the vehicle harness connector. • Measure resistance between Test Pin 91 at the breakout box and the SIG RTN pin at the vehicle harness connector. • Is each resistance less than 5.0 ohms?	Yes	▶	GO to TD5.
		No	▶	SERVICE open circuit. REMOVE breakout box. RECONNECT all components. RERUN Quick Test.

FM0159601557050X

Fig. 286   Test TD: Transmission Range Sensor (Part 5 of 8). 1996

Test Step	Result	▶	Action to Take
TD5 CHECK TR CIRCUIT FOR SHORT TO POWER OR GROUND • Key off. • TR sensor disconnected, Scan Tool disconnected. • Breakout box installed, PCM disconnected. • Measure resistance between Test Pin 64 and Test Pins 71/97, 76/77, and 91 at the breakout box. • Measure resistance between Test Pin 64 at the breakout box and chassis ground. • **Is each resistance greater than 10,000 ohms?**	Yes No	▶ ▶	GO to **TD6** SERVICE short in harness. REMOVE breakout box. RECONNECT all components. RERUN Quick Test.
TD6 CHECK TR SENSOR RESISTANCE • Key off. • Connect TR sensor, Scan Tool disconnected. • Breakout box installed, PCM disconnected. • Unlock steering column. • Measure resistance between Test Pin 64 and Test Pin 91 at the breakout box in each gear range position. REFER to Voltage and Resistance Specification Table at the beginning of the Pinpoint Test. • **Is each resistance reading within specification?**	Yes No	▶ ▶	REFER to Transmission Diagnosis. REPLACE TR sensor. REMOVE breakout box. RERUN Quick Test.
TD7 CHECK TR SWITCH ALIGNMENT DTC P0705 TR circuit out of self test range. DTC P0707 TR circuit shorted to ground. DTC P0708 TR circuit high, open circuit. DTC P1705 TR not in Park during Self Test. DTC P1709 Park-Neutral (PNP) circuit out of self test range. Possible causes: — TR lever not in PARK. — Misadjusted linkage. — Misaligned TR switch. — Damaged PCM. — TR signal circuit open or shorted to VPWR or GND. • Key off. • Place TR lever in NEUTRAL. • Verify TR switch alignment per Section 07-14A of the Service Manual. • **Is switch alignment correct?**	Yes No	▶ ▶	GO to **TD8** INSPECT TR Linkage and Switch assembly for damage, SERVICE as necessary. RERUN Quick Test.

FM0159601557060X

Fig. 286   Test TD: Transmission Range Sensor (Part 6 of 8). 1996

Test Step	Result	▶	Action to Take
TD8 CHECK FOR INTERMITTENT CIRCUIT FAULT • Key on, engine off. • Scan Tool connected. • Access PNP, TR and TRS PIDs. • While observing the PID modes, shake and bend a small section of the harness from the TRS to the PNP and PCM. • Tap the TR sensor and connectors and look for a fluctuation of the TR and PNP display. • Repeat the steps with the shift lever in the various positions. • **Do the PID readings change?**	Yes No	▶ ▶	GO to **TD12** GO to **TD9**.
TD9 CHECK VOLTAGE OF THE PNP CIRCUIT • Key off. • Scan Tool connected. • Disconnect the PNP lead at the starter relay. • Key on, engine off. • Verify voltage at the lead, while in PARK or NEUTRAL, is less than 0.5 volt or, greater than 4.5 volts in any other transmission range. • **Are voltage readings as specified?**	Yes No	▶ ▶	Transmission Range Position Switch Diagnosis and Testing. GO to **TD10**.
TD10 CHECK VOLTAGE OF THE TR CIRCUIT • Key off. • Disconnect Scan Tool, disconnect PCM. • Inspect for damage or pushed out pins, corrosion, loose wires, etc. Service as necessary. • Install breakout box, leave PCM disconnected. • Key on, engine off. • Verify greater than 10.5 volts on Test Pin 71/97. • Refer to the schematic at beginning of this pinpoint test and verify greater than 10.5 volts at Test Pins 32, 6, 9 and 7 for the transmission range. • **Are the voltage readings as specified?**	Yes No	▶ ▶	Transmission Range Position Switch Diagnosis and Testing. GO to **TD11**.
TD11 CHECK CONTINUITY OF THE PNP HARNESS • Key off. • PCM disconnected, Scan Tool disconnected. • Breakout box installed. • Disconnect PNP switch vehicle harness connector. • Inspect both ends of the connectors for damage or pushed out pins, corrosion, loose wires, etc. Service as necessary. • Measure resistance between Test Pin 64 at the breakout box and PNP Test Pin at the vehicle harness connector. • **Is resistance less than 5.0 ohms?**	Yes No	▶ ▶	GO to **TD13**. SERVICE open circuit. REMOVE breakout box. RECONNECT all components. RERUN Quick Test.

FM0159601557070X

Fig. 286   Test TD: Transmission Range Sensor (Part 7 of 8). 1996

Test Step	Result	▶	Action to Take
TD12 CHECK CONTINUITY OF THE TR SWITCH HARNESS • Key off. • PCM disconnected, Scan Tool disconnected. • Breakout box installed. • Disconnect TR switch vehicle harness connector. • Inspect both ends of connectors for damaged or pushed out pins, corrosion, loose wires, etc. Service as necessary. • Measure resistance between Test Pins 32, 6, 9 and 7 at the breakout box and TRR, TROD, TRD and TRL signal pin at the vehicle harness connector. • **Is each resistance greater than 5.0 ohms?**	Yes No	▶ ▶	GO to **TD13**. SERVICE open circuits. REMOVE breakout box. RECONNECT all components. RERUN Quick Test.
TD13 CHECK TR CIRCUIT FOR SHORT TO POWER OR GROUND • Key off. • TR switch and PNP switch disconnected. • Scan Tool disconnected. • Breakout box installed, PCM disconnected. • Measure resistance between Test Pin 64 and Test Pins 91 and 71 at the breakout box. • Measure resistance between Test Pins 32, 6, 9 and 7 and Test Pins 91 and 71 at the breakout box. • **Is each resistance greater than 10,000 ohms?**	Yes No	▶ ▶	REPLACE PCM. REMOVE breakout box. RECONNECT all components. RERUN Quick Test. SERVICE short in harness. REMOVE breakout box. RERUN Quick Test.

FM0159601557080X

Fig. 286   Test TD: Transmission Range Sensor (Part 8 of 8). 1996

Note

You should enter this Pinpoint Test only when directed here.

Remember

This Pinpoint Test is intended to diagnose the following:

• Transmission Fluid Temperature (TFT) sensor
• Harness circuits: TFT SIG and SIG RTN
• Powertrain Control Module (PCM)

Tables and Charts

NOTE: Voltage values are calculated for VREF = 5.0 volts. The values may vary 15 percent due to sensor and VREF variations. Transmission fluid temperature must be a minimum of 10 degrees C (50 degrees F) before taking transmission fluid temperature sensor resistance measurements.

FM0159601558010X

Fig. 287   Test TE: Transmission Fluid Temperature Sensor (Part 1 of 11). 1996

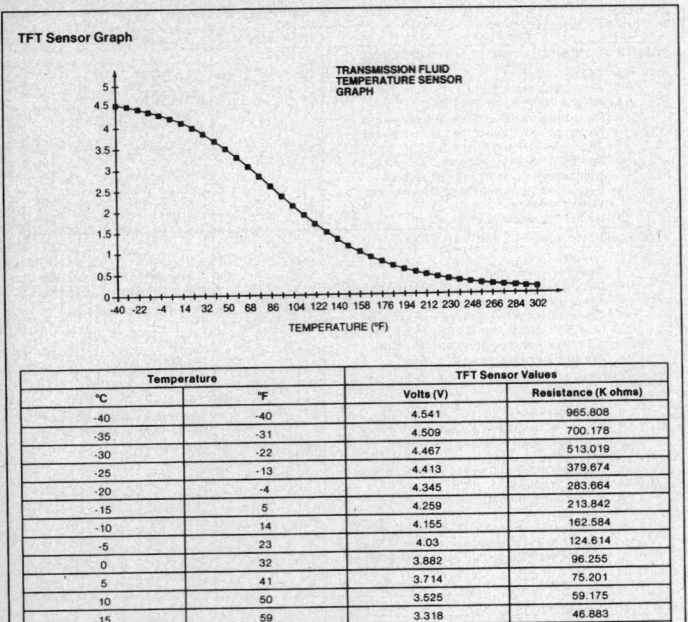

TFT Sensor Graph

TRANSMISSION FLUID TEMPERATURE SENSOR GRAPH

Temperature		TFT Sensor Values	
°C	°F	Volts (V)	Resistance (K ohms)
-40	-40	4.541	965.808
-35	-31	4.509	700.178
-30	-22	4.467	513.019
-25	-13	4.413	379.674
-20	-4	4.345	283.664
-15	5	4.259	213.842
-10	14	4.155	162.584
-5	23	4.03	124.614
0	32	3.882	96.255
5	41	3.714	75.201
10	50	3.525	59.175
15	59	3.318	46.883
20	68	3.095	37.387
25	77	2.862	30
30	86	2.623	24.215
35	95	2.383	19.657
40	104	2.149	16.043
45	113	1.923	13.161
50	122	1.71	10.85
55	131	1.513	8.99
60	140	1.333	7.487

(Continued)

FM0159601558020X

Fig. 287   Test TE: Transmission Fluid Temperature Sensor (Part 2 of 11). 1996

Temperature		TFT Sensor Values	
°C	°F	Volts (V)	Resistance (K ohms)
65	149	1.17	6.265
70	158	1.025	5.268
75	167	0.897	4.45
80	176	0.784	3.775
85	185	0.685	3.215
90	194	0.599	2.75
95	203	0.523	2.361
100	212	0.458	2.034
105	221	0.401	1.758
110	230	0.352	1.523
115	239	0.309	1.324
120	248	0.272	1.155
125	257	0.239	1.01
130	266	0.212	0.8866
135	275	0.187	0.7805
140	284	0.166	0.6891
145	293	0.148	0.6101
150	302	0.132	0.5417

Pinpoint Test Schematics

Mustang, Thunderbird/Cougar, Crown Victoria/Grand Marquis, Town Car, Mark VIII (4R70W), 4.2L F-Series/Bronco, 4.6L F-Series/Bronco, 5.0L E/F-Series, Bronco (4R70W)

TEST PIN 37 — TFT
TEST PIN 91 — SIG RTN

TRANSMISSION VEHICLE HARNESS CONNECTOR

FM0159601558030X

Fig. 287   Test TE: Transmission Fluid Temperature Sensor (Part 3 of 11). 1996

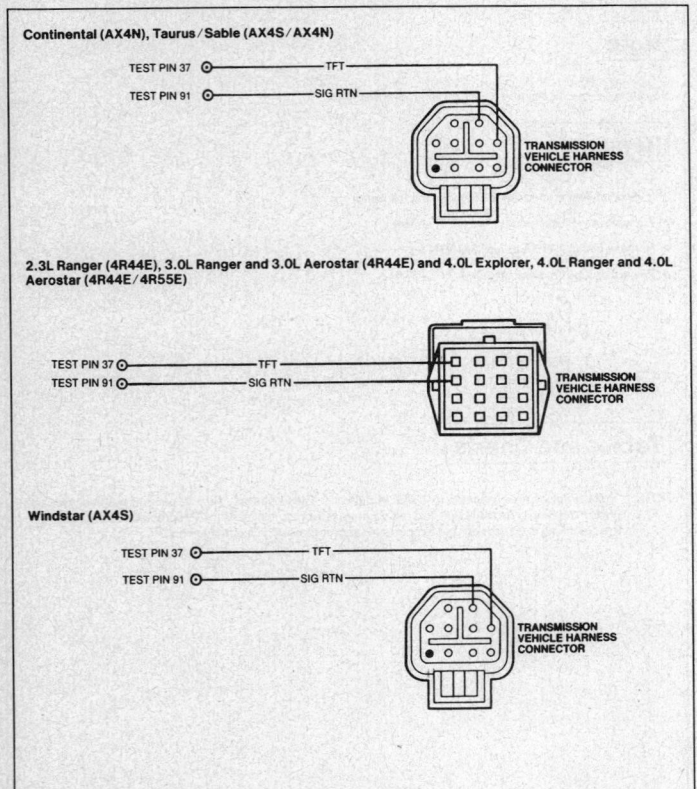

Continental (AX4N), Taurus/Sable (AX4S/AX4N)

TEST PIN 37 — TFT
TEST PIN 91 — SIG RTN

TRANSMISSION VEHICLE HARNESS CONNECTOR

2.3L Ranger (4R44E), 3.0L Ranger and 3.0L Aerostar (4R44E) and 4.0L Explorer, 4.0L Ranger and 4.0L Aerostar (4R44E/4R55E)

TEST PIN 37 — TFT
TEST PIN 91 — SIG RTN

TRANSMISSION VEHICLE HARNESS CONNECTOR

Windstar (AX4S)

TEST PIN 37 — TFT
TEST PIN 91 — SIG RTN

TRANSMISSION VEHICLE HARNESS CONNECTOR

FM0159601558040X

Fig. 287   Test TE: Transmission Fluid Temperature Sensor (Part 4 of 11). 1996

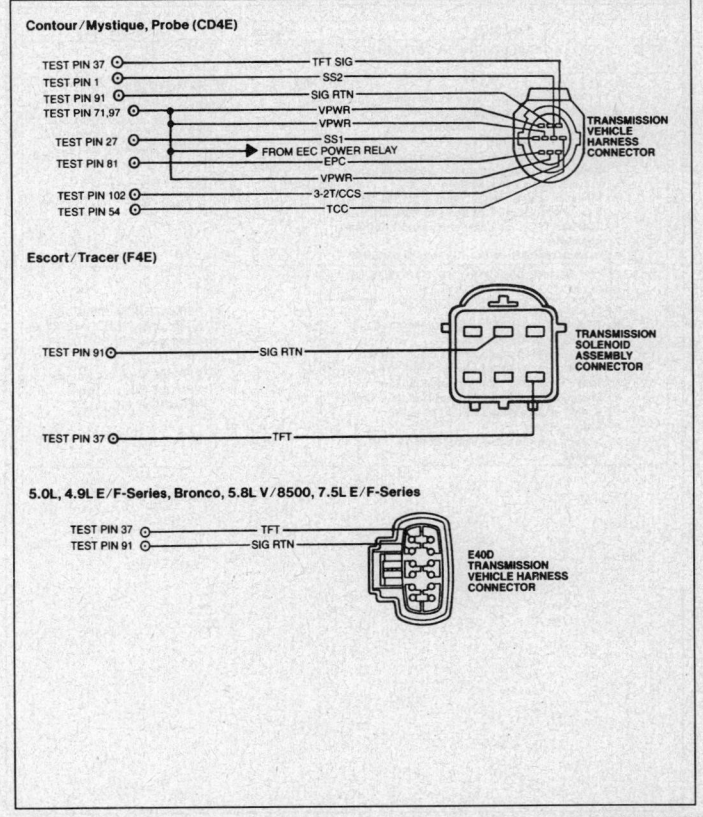

Contour/Mystique, Probe (CD4E)

TEST PIN 37 — TFT SIG
TEST PIN 1 — SS2
TEST PIN 91 — SIG RTN
TEST PIN 71,97 — VPWR
VPWR
SS1
TEST PIN 27 — FROM EEC POWER RELAY
TEST PIN 81 — EPC
VPWR
TEST PIN 102 — 3-2T/CCS
TEST PIN 54 — TCC

TRANSMISSION VEHICLE HARNESS CONNECTOR

Escort/Tracer (F4E)

TEST PIN 91 — SIG RTN

TRANSMISSION SOLENOID ASSEMBLY CONNECTOR

TEST PIN 37 — TFT

5.0L, 4.9L E/F-Series, Bronco, 5.8L V/8500, 7.5L E/F-Series

TEST PIN 37 — TFT
TEST PIN 91 — SIG RTN

E40D TRANSMISSION VEHICLE HARNESS CONNECTOR

FM0159601558050X

Fig. 287   Test TE: Transmission Fluid Temperature Sensor (Part 5 of 11). 1996

ELECTRONIC ENGINE CONTROL SYSTEM (EEC-V)

Test Step	Result	▶	Action to Take
TE1 KOEO AND KOER DTC P0712: ATTEMPT TO INDUCE OPPOSITE CONDITION			
Diagnostic Trouble Code (DTC) P0712 indicates that Self-Test has detected a TFT sensor circuit input below the minimum acceptable voltage. Possible causes: — Fluid level not to specification. — Damaged TFT sensor. — Short to GND or SIG RTN in TFT SIG harness circuit. — Damaged PCM. ● Key off. ● Disconnect transmission connector. Inspect for damaged or pushed out pins, corrosion, loose wires, etc. Service as necessary. ● Activate Key On Engine Off (KOEO) and Key On Engine Running (KOER) Self-Tests, (transmission connector remains disconnected). ● **Is DTC P0713 present?** NOTE: Disregard any other DTCs generated at this time.	Yes	▶	The fault that produced DTC P0712 is not within the TFT harness circuits or the PCM.
	No	▶	The opposite condition could not be induced. GO to **TE2**.
TE2 CHECK VREF AT THE THROTTLE POSITION SENSOR			
● Key off. ● Transmission connector disconnected. ● Disconnect Throttle Position (TP) sensor. ● Key on, engine off. ● Measure voltage between the TP sensor VREF and SIG RTN circuits at the TP sensor vehicle harness connector. ● **Is voltage between 4.0 and 6.0 volts?**	Yes	▶	VREF voltage is in range. RECONNECT TP sensor. GO to **TE3**.
	No	▶	VREF voltage is out of range. RECONNECT transmission connector. GO to Pinpoint Test Step **C1**.
TE3 CHECK TFT SIG CIRCUIT FOR SHORTS TO GROUND AND SIG RTN			
● Key off. ● Transmission connector disconnected. ● Disconnect PCM. Inspect for damaged or pushed out pins, corrosion, loose wires, etc. Service as necessary. ● Install breakout box, leave PCM disconnected. ● Measure resistance between Test Pin 37 (TFT SIG) and Test Pins 51 or 103 (PWR GND) and 91 (SIG RTN) at the breakout box. ● **Is each resistance greater than 10,000 ohms?**	Yes	▶	REPLACE damaged PCM. REMOVE breakout box. RECONNECT all components. RERUN Quick Test.
	No	▶	SERVICE short circuit between TFT SIG and PWR GND or SIG RTN. RECONNECT all components. REMOVE breakout box. RERUN Quick Test.

FM0159601558060X

Fig. 287   Test TE: Transmission Fluid Temperature Sensor (Part 6 of 11). 1996

Test Step	Result	▶	Action to Take
TE10 KOEO AND KOER DTC P0713: ATTEMPT TO INDUCE OPPOSITE CONDITION			
Diagnostic Trouble Code (DTC) P0713 indicates that Self-test has detected a TFT sensor circuit input above the maximum acceptable voltage. Possible causes: — Fluid level not to specifications. — Damaged TFT sensor. — Short to VPWR in TFT SIG harness circuit. — Open in TFT SIG or SIG RTN harness circuit. — Damaged PCM. ● Key off. ● Disconnect transmission bulkhead connector. Inspect for damaged or pushed out pins, corrosion, loose wires, etc. Service as necessary. ● Insert a jumper wire from TFT SIG circuit to SIG RTN circuit at the transmission vehicle harness connector. ● Activate Key On Engine Off (KOEO) and (KOER) Self-Tests. ● **Is DTC P0712 present?** NOTE: Disregard any other DTCs generated at this time. If no DTCs are generated (module not responding), then immediately GO to step **TE12**.	Yes	▶	The fault that produced DTC P0713 is not within the TFT harness circuits or the PCM. REMOVE jumper wire.
	No	▶	The opposite condition could not be induced. REMOVE jumper wire. GO to **TE11**.
TE11 CHECK CONTINUITY OF TFT SIG AND SIG RTN CIRCUITS			
● Key off. ● Transmission connector disconnected. ● Disconnect PCM. Inspect for damaged or pushed out pins, corrosion, loose wires, etc. Service as necessary. ● Install breakout box, leave PCM disconnected. ● Measure resistance between TFT SIG circuit at the transmission vehicle harness connector and Test Pin 37 (TFT SIG) at the breakout box. ● Measure resistance between TFT SIG RTN circuit at the transmission vehicle harness connector and Test Pin 91 (SIG RTN) at the breakout box. ● **Is each resistance less than 5.0 ohms?**	Yes	▶	GO to **TE12**.
	No	▶	SERVICE open in TFT SIG or SIG RTN harness circuit. REMOVE breakout box. RECONNECT all components. RERUN Quick Test.

FM0159601558070X

Fig. 287   Test TE: Transmission Fluid Temperature Sensor (Part 7 of 11). 1996

Test Step	Result	▶	Action to Take
TE12 CHECK FOR TFT SIG CIRCUIT SHORT TO POWER			
● Key off. ● Transmission connector disconnected. ● Breakout box installed, PCM disconnected. ● Key on, engine off. ● Measure voltage between Test Pin 37 (TFT SIG) and Test Pin 77 or 103 (PWR GND) at the breakout box. ● Key off. ● **Was the voltage greater than 2.0 volts?**	Yes	▶	SERVICE short to power in TFT SIG harness circuit. REMOVE breakout box. RECONNECT all components. RERUN Quick Test.
	No	▶	REPLACE damaged PCM. REMOVE breakout box. RECONNECT all components. RERUN Quick Test.
TE20 KOEO AND KOER DTC P1711: INCREASE / DECREASE TRANSMISSION FLUID TEMPERATURE			
Diagnostic Trouble Code (DTC) P1711 indicates that Self-Test has detected a TFT sensor circuit input that was out of range. The TFT sensor input shows a failure occurred at either the low or high end of the acceptable range. Possible causes: — Fluid level not to specification. — Fluid not at operating temperature. — Damaged TFT sensor. — Damaged PCM. ● Drive vehicle through normal city traffic to bring the transmission fluid temperature to at least 10 degrees C (50 degrees F). ● Activate Key On Engine Off (KOEO) and Key On Engine Running (KOER) Self-Tests. ● **Is DTC P1711 still present?**	Yes	▶	GO to **TE21**.
	No	▶	Transmission fluid was not at operating temperature. RERUN Quick Test. SERVICE other DTCs as necessary.
TE21 CHECK VREF AT THROTTLE POSITION SENSOR			
● Key off. ● Disconnect Throttle Position (TP) sensor. ● Key on, engine off. ● Measure voltage between the TP sensor VREF and SIG RTN circuits at the TP sensor vehicle harness connector. ● **Is the voltage between 4.0 and 6.0 volts?**	Yes	▶	VREF voltage is in range. RECONNECT the TP sensor. GO to **TE22**.
	No	▶	VREF voltage is out of range. GO to Pinpoint Test Step **C1**.

FM0159601558080X

Fig. 287   Test TE: Transmission Fluid Temperature Sensor (Part 8 of 11). 1996

Test Step	Result	▶	Action to Take
TE22 CHECK TFT SENSOR RESISTANCE AS TRANSMISSION FLUID TEMPERATURE IS VARIED			
● Key off. ● Disconnect PCM. Inspect for damaged or pushed out pins, corrosion, loose wires, etc. Service as necessary. ● Install breakout box, leave PCM disconnected. ● Verify that transmission oil pan is warm to the touch. IF IT IS HOT: — Measure and record TFT sensor resistance between Test Pin 37 (TFT SIG) and Test Pin 91 (SIG RTN) at the breakout box. — Let transmission cool down and repeat the measurement. (The last measurement should be greater than the first.) IF IT IS COLD: — Measure and record TFT sensor resistance between Test Pin 37 (TFT SIG) and Test Pin 91 (SIG RTN) at the breakout box. — Reconnect the PCM and drive vehicle for short time to elevate temperature. — Disconnect the PCM and repeat the measurement at the breakout box. (The last measurement should be less than the first.) NOTE: Refer to Tables and Charts at the beginning of this pinpoint test. ● **Did resistance measurements differ as expected and was last measurement within specifications?**	Yes	▶	REPLACE damaged PCM. REMOVE breakout box. RERUN Quick Test.
	No	▶	REMOVE breakout box. RECONNECT PCM.

FM0159601558090X

Fig. 287   Test TE: Transmission Fluid Temperature Sensor (Part 9 of 11). 1996

Test Step	Result	▶	Action to Take
TE90 CONTINUOUS MEMORY DTC P0712: VERIFY TFT SIG VOLTAGE			
Diagnostic Trouble Code (DTC) P0712 indicates that Self-Test has detected a TFT sensor circuit input that was below the minimum acceptable voltage (sometime during normal vehicle operation). Possible causes: — Fluid level not to specification. — Short to GND or SIG RTN in TFT SIG harness circuit. — Damaged TFT sensor. — Damaged PCM. ● Key on, engine off. ● Access TFT PID with a Scan Tool. ● Is TFT PID voltage less than 0.5 volts?	Yes	▶	The TFT SIG voltage is less than the acceptable minimum, but is not intermittent. GO to **TE1**.
	No	▶	The fault that produced Continuous Memory DTC P0712 is intermittent. GO to **TE91**.
TE91 WIGGLE TEST TFT SENSOR HARNESS CIRCUITS			
● Key on, engine off. ● Access TFT PID with a Scan Tool. ● Observe TFT PID for an indication of a fault while performing the following: — Shake, wiggle and bend TFT SIG and SIG RTN circuits between transmission and PCM. A fault is indicated by a sudden change in TFT PID voltage. ● Is a fault indicated?	Yes	▶	ISOLATE fault and SERVICE as necessary. RECONNECT all components. COMPLETE PCM Reset to clear DTCs (REFER to Powertrain Control Module (PCM) Reset). RERUN Quick Test.
	No	▶	Unable to duplicate and/or identify fault at this time. GO to Pinpoint Test Step **Z1** with the following data: TFT PID and the list of Possible Causes found in **TE90**.
TE100 CONTINUOUS MEMORY DTC P0713: VERIFY TFT SIG VOLTAGE			
Continuous Memory Diagnostic Trouble Code (DTC) P0713 indicates that Self-Test has detected a TFT sensor circuit input that was above the maximum acceptable voltage (sometime during normal vehicle operation in the past). Possible causes: — Fluid level not to specification. — Open in TFT SIG or SIG RTN harness circuit. — Short to VPWR in TFT SIG harness circuit. — Damaged TFT sensor. — Damaged PCM. ● Key on, engine off. ● Access TFT PID with a Scan Tool. ● Is TFT PID voltage greater than 4.8 volts?	Yes	▶	The TFT SIG voltage is greater than the acceptable maximum, but is not in termittent. GO to **TE10**.
	No	▶	The fault that produced Continuous Memory DTC P0713 is intermittent. GO to **TE101**.

FM0159601558100X

Fig. 287   Test TE: Transmission Fluid Temperature Sensor (Part 10 of 11). 1996

Test Step	Result	▶	Action to Take
TE101 WIGGLE TEST TFT SENSOR HARNESS CIRCUITS			
● Key on, engine off. ● Access TFT PID with a Scan Tool. ● Observe TFT PID for an indication of a fault while performing the following: — Shake, wiggle and bend TFT SIG and SIG RTN circuits between transmission and PCM. A fault is indicated by a sudden change in TFT PID voltage. ● Is a fault indicated?	Yes	▶	ISOLATE fault and SERVICE as necessary. RECONNECT all components. COMPLETE PCM Reset to clear DTCs (REFER to Powertrain Control Module (PCM) Reset). RERUN Quick Test.
	No	▶	Unable to duplicate and/or identify fault at this time. GO to Pinpoint Test Step **Z1** with the following data: TFT PID and the list of Possible Causes found in **TE100**.
TE110 CONTINUOUS MEMORY DTC P1783: RERUN KOEO SELF-TEST			
Continuous Memory Diagnostic Trouble Code (DTC) P1783 indicates a transmission over temperature condition occurred. Possible causes: — Damaged transmission cooling system. — Excessive loading, e.g. trailer towing. — Damaged clutch. — Improper transmission fluid level. — Damaged transmission connector. ● Key off. ● Disconnect transmission connector. Inspect for damaged or pushed out pins, corrosion, loose wires, etc. Service as necessary and reconnect. ● Rerun Key On Engine Off (KOEO) Self-Test and record all DTCs. ● Any transmission related DTCs generated? NOTE: If DTC P1783 repeats and no other DTC is generated, refer to Transmission Service Manual for transmission over temperature condition.	Yes	▶	ADDRESS any transmission related DTCs by referring to Diagnostic Trouble Code Charts
	No	▶	over temperature condition (check clutch, transmission fluid level etc.).

FM0159601558110X

Fig. 287   Test TE: Transmission Fluid Temperature Sensor (Part 11 of 11). 1996

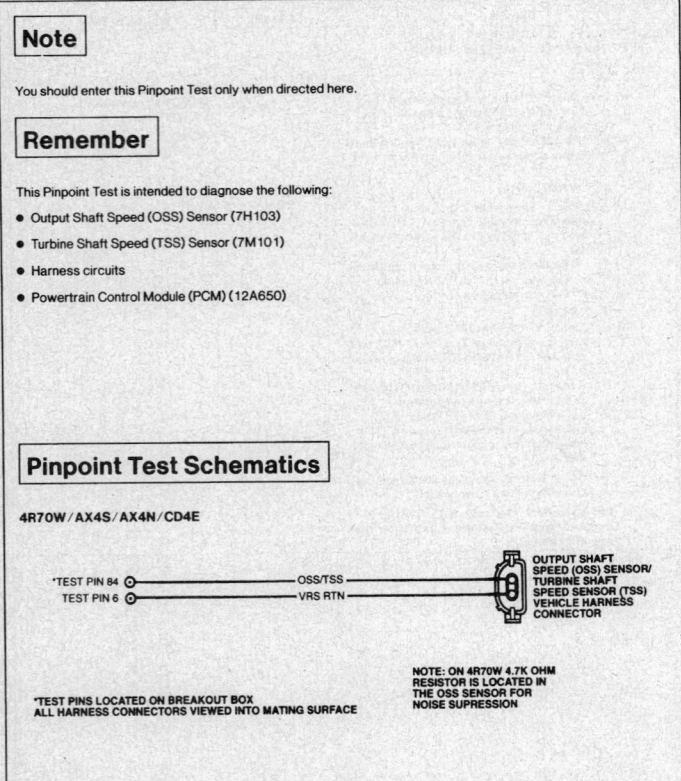

FM0159601559010X

Fig. 288   Test TF: Output Shaft/Turbine Shaft Speed Sensor (Part 1 of 7). 1996

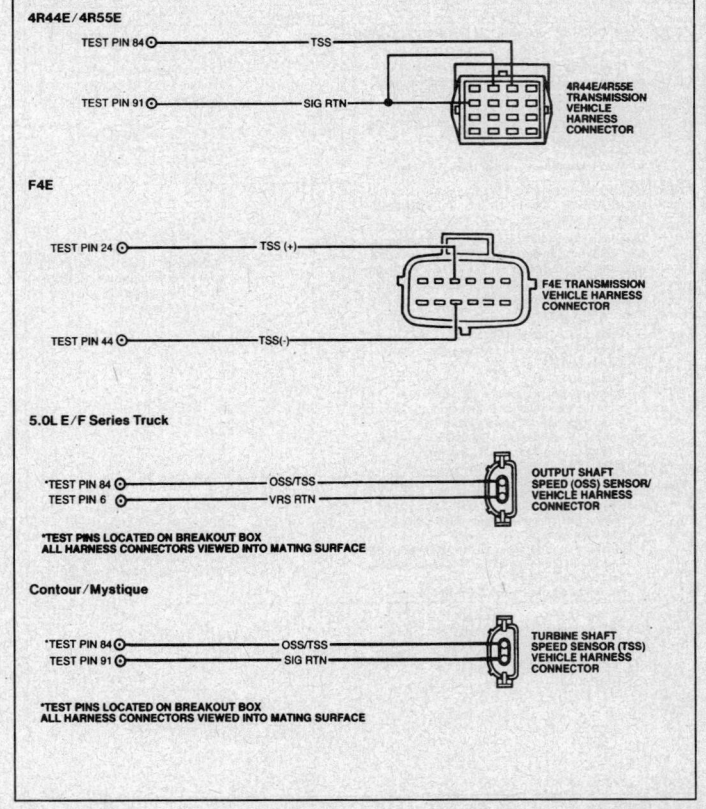

FM0159601559020X

Fig. 288   Test TF: Output Shaft/Turbine Shaft Speed Sensor (Part 2 of 7). 1996

Test Step	Result	►	Action to Take
TF1 CONTINUOUS MEMORY DTC P0715/P0720: PERFORM TRANSMISSION DRIVE CYCLE			
Continuous Memory Diagnostic Trouble Codes (DTCs) P0715/P0720 indicates an intermittent fault or a hard fault is present. Perform a transmission drive cycle to identify which condition exists. If the DTC repeats, a hard fault is present. Possible causes: — Transmission (internal components). — Damaged OSS/TSS. — Damaged harness circuits. — Damaged PCM. Transmission Drive Cycle — Record and clear Continuous Memory DTCs. — Warm engine to operating temperature. — Place gear selector in DRIVE. — Accelerate heavily to 35 mph. (Obey all local laws.) — Return to idle. — Shut the engine off. — After drive cycle is completed, output Continuous DTCs. • **Did Continuous Memory DTC P0715/P0720 repeat?**	Yes No	► ►	GO to **TF3**. GO to **TF2**.
TF2 CHECK FOR INTERMITTENT CIRCUIT FAULT (WIGGLE TEST)			
• Key on, engine off. • Scan Tool connected. • Access OSS PiD 11B5 or TSS PID 11B4 (actual output). • Grasp the vehicle harness starting at the transmission bulk head. • Shake and bend a small section of the harness all the way to the PCM. • Look for fluctuations of the display. • **Are the readings changing?**	Yes No	► ►	GO to **TF3**. The fault that produced the DTCs is intermittent. GO to Pinpoint Test Step **Z1** with the following data: OSS PID 11B5, or TSS PID 11B4 and the list of possible causes.

FM0159601559030X

Fig. 288   Test TF: Output Shaft/Turbine Shaft Speed Sensor (Part 3 of 7). 1996

Test Step	Result	►	Action to Take
TF3 CHECK OSS/TSS CIRCUIT CONTINUITY			
• Key off. • Disconnect PCM. Inspect for damaged or pushed out pins, corrosion, loose wires, etc. Service as necessary. • Install breakout box, PCM disconnected. • Disconnect OSS/TSS. • Measure resistance between Test Pin 84 at the breakout box and OSS/TSS circuit at the sensor harness connector. • Measure resistance between Test Pin 91 at the breakout box and SIG RTN circuit at the TSS vehicle harness connector. • **Is each resistance less than 5.0 ohms?**	Yes No	► ►	GO to **TF4**. SERVICE open circuit. REMOVE breakout box. RECONNECT all components. REPEAT Transmission Drive Cycle in TF1.
TF4 CHECK OSS/TSS CIRCUIT FOR SHORT TO GROUND			
• Key off. • Disconnect Scan Tool. • OSS/TSS disconnected. • Breakout box installed, PCM disconnected. • Measure resistance between Test Pin 84 and Test Pin 51, 76, 103 (GND) and 91 (SIG RTN) at the breakout box. • **Is the resistance less than 5.0 ohms?**	Yes No	► ►	SERVICE short circuit including resistor integrity, if applicable. REMOVE breakout box. RECONNECT all components. REPEAT transmission Drive Cycle in TF1. GO to **TF5**.
TF5 CHECK OSS/TSS CIRCUIT FOR SHORT TO POWER			
• Key off. • OSS/TSS disconnected. • Breakout box installed, PCM disconnected. • Measure resistance between Test Pin 84 and Test Pin 71 (VPWR) at the breakout box. • **Is the resistance less than 5.0?**	Yes No	► ►	SERVICE short circuit. REMOVE breakout box. RECONNECT all components. REPEAT Transmission Drive Cycle in TF1. GO to **TF6**.
TF6 CHECK OSS/TSS RESISTANCE			
• Key off. • OSS/TSS disconnected. • Measure resistance of OSS/TSS. • Use the chart to measure the resistance of the OSS/TSS. 	Transmission	Sensor	Resistance
CD4E	TSS	149 to 290 ohms
AX4S/AX4N	TSS	100 to 200 ohms
4R70W	OSS	450 to 750 ohms
4R44E/4R55E	TSS	64 to 120 ohms | • **Is the resistance within specification?**	Yes No	► ►	GO to Transmission to verify internal components. If OK, then replace PCM. REMOVE breakout box. RECONNECT OSS/TSS. REPEAT Transmission Drive Cycle in TF1. REPLACE OSS/TSS. REMOVE breakout box. REPEAT Transmission Drive Cycle in TF1.

FM0159601559040X

Fig. 288   Test TF: Output Shaft/Turbine Shaft Speed Sensor (Part 4 of 7). 1996

Test Step	Result	►	Action to Take
TF7 CONTINUOUS MEMORY DTC P0721			
Continuous Memory DTC P0721 indicates a noisy circuit from RFI/EMI external sources or an intermittent condition. Vehicle may also have shift concerns. • Check for intermittents: — Sensor securely mounted. — Both circuits are properly crimped. — Pins seated in connector shell. — No corrosion on pins. • **Are all of the above acceptable?**	Yes No	► ►	GO to **TF8**. SERVICE as required. RERUN Quick Test.
TF8 CHECK TSS/OSS HARNESS ROUTING			
• Check TSS/OSS routing. — Verify TSS/OSS harness is not adjacent to high current wires i.e. Ignition Wires. — Verify TSS/OSS harness is shielded and grounded, if applicable. • **Are the above concerns OK?**	Yes No	► ►	GO to Transmission. If OK, GO to Pinpoint Test Step **Z1** with OSS PID 11B5 or TSS PID 11B4 (sensor output). SERVICE as required. RERUN Quick Test.
TF10 KOER DTC P0715: CHECK TSS RESISTANCE			
Key On, Engine Running Diagnostic Trouble Code (DTC) P0715 indicates an error has been detected in the Turbine Shaft Speed (TSS) Sensor input signal. Possible causes: — Open or shorted harness. — Damaged TSS. — Damaged PCM. • Key off. • Disconnect transmission connector (12 pin at transmission). • Measure resistance between TSS(+) and TSS(-) pins at transmission 12 pin connector. • **Is resistance between 200 and 600 ohms?** TSS (+) (24) TRANSMISSION CONNECTOR TSS(-) (44)	Yes No	► ►	GO to **TF11**. INSPECT transmission wiring for opens/shorts. If OK, REPLACE transmission speed sensor. RERUN Quick Test.

FM0159601559050X

Fig. 288   Test TF: Output Shaft/Turbine Shaft Speed Sensor (Part 5 of 7). 1996

Test Step	Result	►	Action to Take
TF11 CHECK TSS CIRCUITS FOR SHORT TO POWER			
• Key off. • Transmission 12 pin connector disconnected. • Disconnect Powertrain Control Module (PCM). Inspect for damaged or pushed out pins, corrosion, loose wires, etc. Service as necessary. • Key on. • Measure voltage between TSS (+) circuit at the transmission 12 pin vehicle harness connector and chassis ground. • Measure voltage between TSS(-) circuit at the transmission 12 pin vehicle harness connector and chassis ground. • **Are both voltages less than 0.5 volt?**	Yes No	► ►	Key off. GO to **TF12**. SERVICE short circuit. RECONNECT all components. RERUN Quick Test.
TF12 CHECK TSS CIRCUITS FOR SHORT TO GROUND OR EACH OTHER			
• Key off. • Transmission 12 pin connector disconnected. • PCM disconnected. • Disconnect Scan Tool. • Measure resistance between TSS (+) circuit at transmission 12 pin vehicle harness connector and chassis ground. • Measure resistance between TSS(-) circuit at transmission 12 pin vehicle harness connector and chassis ground. • Measure resistance between TSS (+) and TSS(-) circuits at transmission 12 pin vehicle harness connector. • **Are all resistances greater than 10,000 ohms?**	Yes No	► ►	GO to **TF13**. SERVICE short circuit. RECONNECT all components. RERUN Quick Test.
TF13 CHECK TSS CIRCUIT CONTINUITY			
• Key off. • Transmission 12 pin connector disconnected. • Install breakout box or F4E tester. Leave PCM disconnected. • Measure resistance between Test Pin 24 and TSS (+) circuit at transmission 12 pin vehicle harness connector. • Measure resistance between Test Pin 44 and TSS(-) circuit at transmission 12 pin vehicle harness connector. • **Are both resistances less than 5.0 ohms?**	Yes No	► ►	GO to **TF14**. SERVICE open circuit. REMOVE breakout box. RECONNECT all components. RERUN Quick Test.

FM0159601559060X

Fig. 288   Test TF: Output Shaft/Turbine Shaft Speed Sensor (Part 6 of 7). 1996

Test Step		Result	►	Action to Take
TF14	**CHECK PCM FOR INTERNAL SHORTS**			
	• Key off. • Breakout box installed. • Connect PCM to breakout box. • Transmission 12 pin connector disconnected. • Measure resistance between Test Pin 24 and Test Pins 44, 37, 57, 40 and 60. • **Is each resistance greater than 500 ohms?**	Yes No	► ►	GO to **TF15**. REPLACE PCM. REMOVE breakout box. RECONNECT all components. RERUN Quick Test.
TF15	**CHECK TSS OUTPUT**			
	• Key off. • PCM connected to breakout box. • Reconnect transmission 12 pin connector. • DVOM on AC scale (to monitor less than 5.0 volts AC). • Start engine. • Measure voltage between Test Pins 24 and 44 at breakout box while varying engine rpm. • **Does AC voltage vary more than 0.5 volt?**	Yes No	► ►	REPLACE PCM. REMOVE breakout box. RERUN Quick Test. REPLACE TSS. REMOVE breakout box. RERUN Quick Test.

FM0159601559070X

Fig. 288   Test TF: Output Shaft/Turbine Shaft Speed Sensor (Part 7 of 7). 1996

Note

You should enter this Pinpoint Test only when directed here.

Remember

This Pinpoint Test is intended to diagnose the following:

- Constant Control Relay Module (CCRM)
  - EEC Power Relay (if contained in CCRM)
  - Fuel Pump Relay
  - Fan Control / Low Fan Control (FC/LFC) Relay
  - High Fan Control (HFC) Relay
  - Wide Open Throttle A/C Cutoff (WAC) Relay
- Harness circuits: B+, FP, LFP, FPM, FC, LFC, HFC, ACCS, WAC, VPWR (TO CCRM), Power-to-A/C Clutch, Power-to-(Fuel) Pump, Power-to-(Low/High Speed) Fan
- Low Speed Fuel Pump Relay (4.6L 4V Mustang)
- Powertrain Control Module (PCM) (12A650)

FM0159601561010X

Fig. 289   Test X: Constant Control Relay Module (Part 1 of 51). 1996

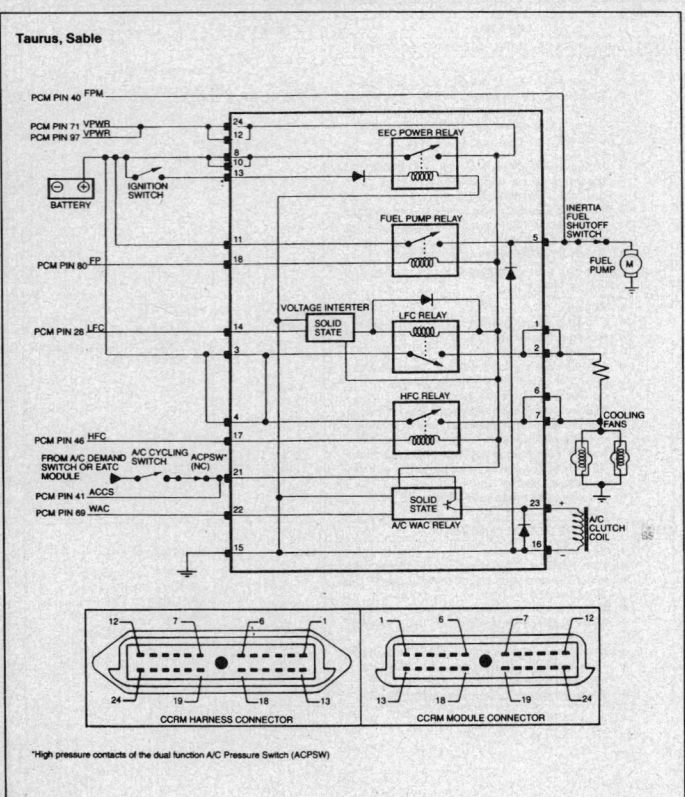

FM0159601561020X

Fig. 289   Test X: Constant Control Relay Module (Part 2 of 51). 1996

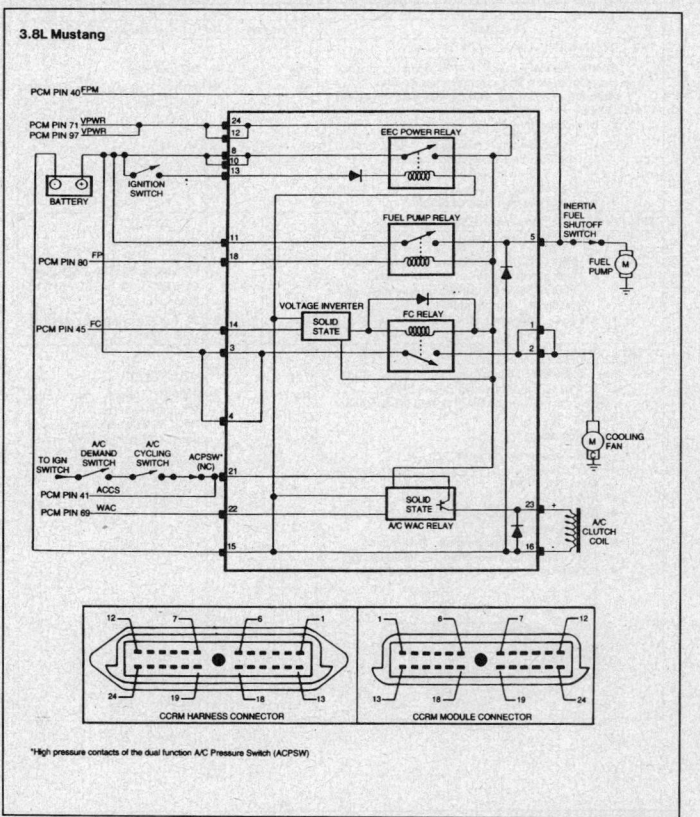

FM0159601561030X

Fig. 289   Test X: Constant Control Relay Module (Part 3 of 51). 1996

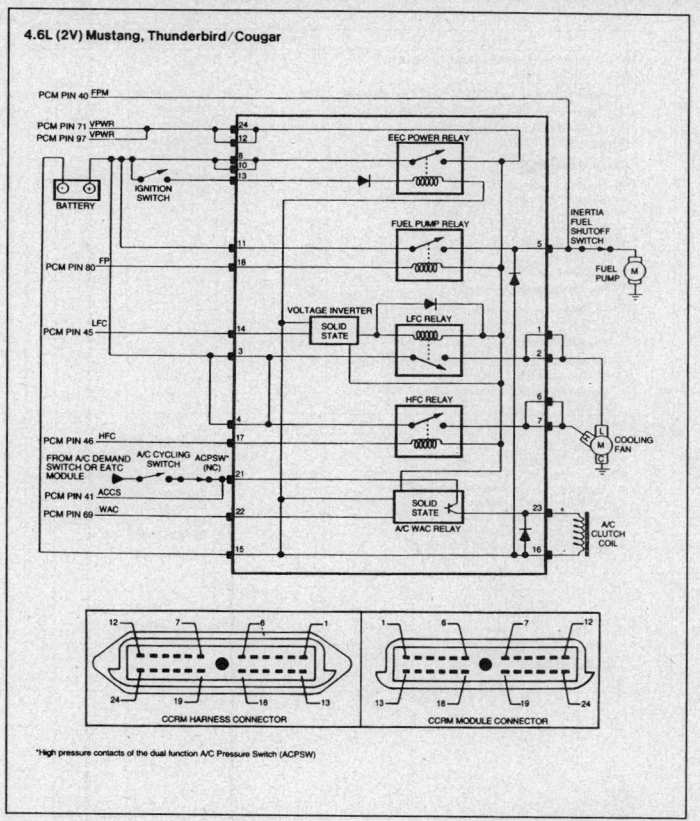

Fig. 289   Test X: Constant Control Relay Module (Part 4 of 51). 1996

FM0159601561040X

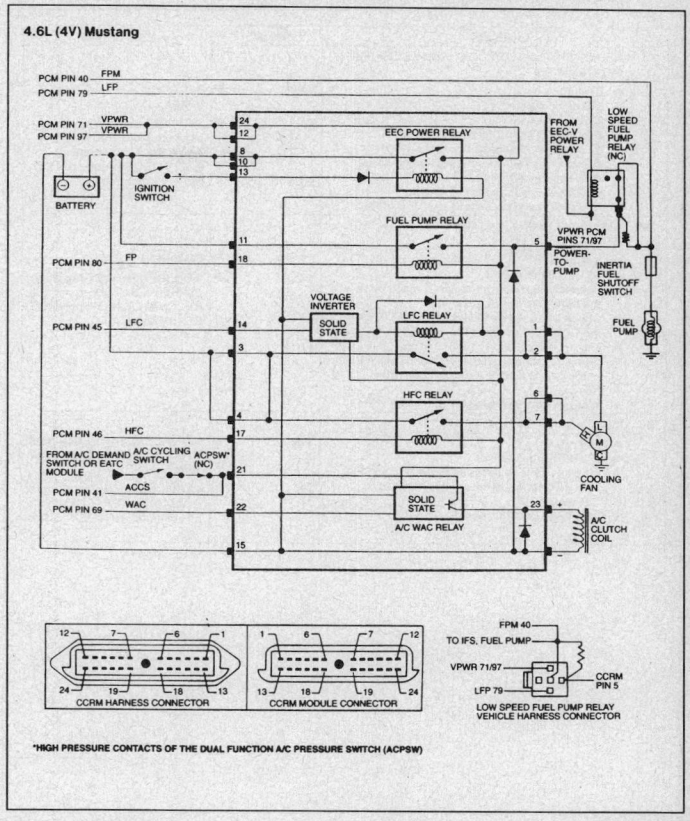

Fig. 289   Test X: Constant Control Relay Module (Part 5 of 51). 1996

FM0159601561050X

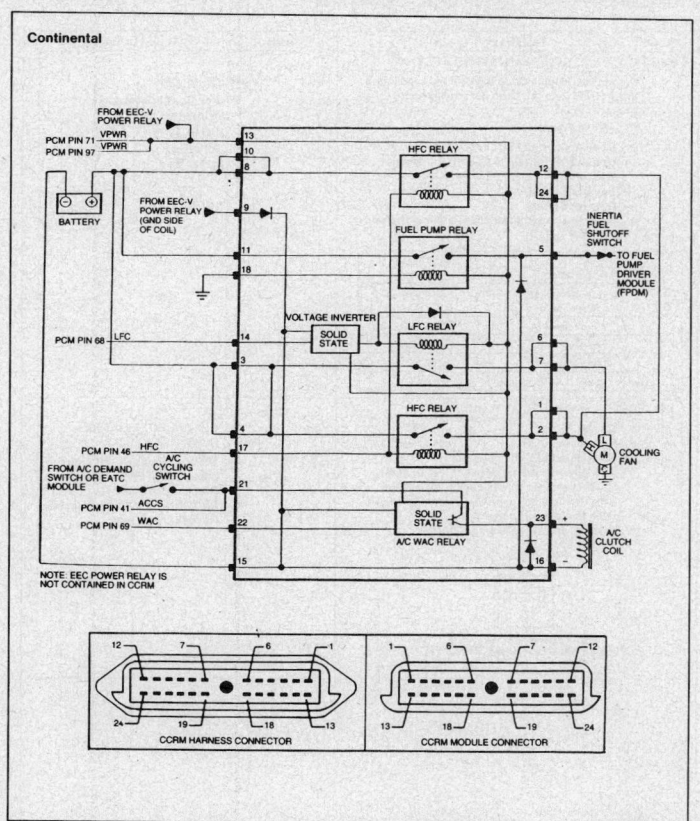

Fig. 289   Test X: Constant Control Relay Module (Part 6 of 51). 1996

FM0159601561060X

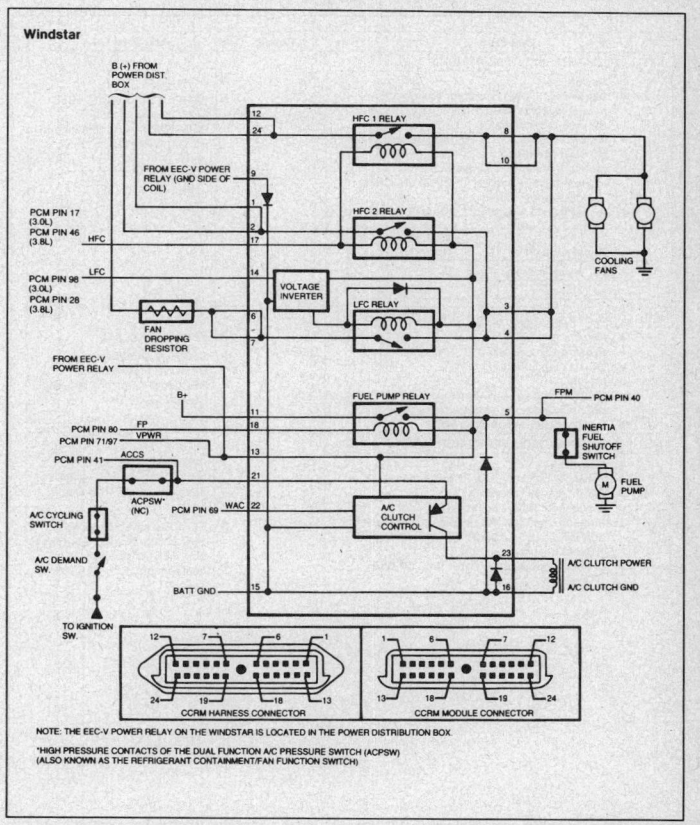

Fig. 289   Test X: Constant Control Relay Module (Part 7 of 51). 1996

FM0159601561070X

Test Step	Result	▶	Action to Take
X1 CHECK VPWR CIRCUIT CONTINUITY BETWEEN IAC AND CCRM • Key off. • IAC disconnected. • Disconnect CCRM. • Disconnect Scan Tool from DLC. • Measure resistance between the VPWR circuit at the IAC solenoid vehicle harness connector and Pins 12 and 24 (VPWR) of the CCRM vehicle harness connector. • **Are both resistances less than 5.0 ohms?**	Yes No	▶ ▶	RECONNECT IAC solenoid. GO to X2 . SERVICE open VPWR circuit between the CCRM and the splice to the IAC solenoid. RECONNECT all components. RERUN Quick Test.
X2 CHECK B(+) AND IGN START/RUN VOLTAGE TO CCRM • Key off. • CCRM disconnected. • Connect the DVOM negative (-) test lead to the battery negative post. • Check for voltage on Pin 8 and Pin 10 (B+) of the CCRM vehicle harness connector. • Key on, engine off. • Check for voltage on Pin 13 (IGN START/RUN) of the CCRM vehicle harness connector. • Key off. • **Were all voltages greater than 10.5 volts?**	Yes No	▶ ▶	GO to X3 . SERVICE open in B (+) or IGN START/RUN circuit. RECONNECT all components. RERUN Quick Test.
X3 CHECK CCRM GROUND CIRCUIT • Key off. • CCRM disconnected. • Measure voltage between Pin 8 (B+) and Pin 15 (GND) at the CCRM vehicle harness connector. • **Is voltage greater than 10.5 volts?**	Yes No	▶ ▶	REPLACE CCRM. RECONNECT all components. RERUN Quick Test. SERVICE open ground circuit to CCRM (Pin 15). RECONNECT all components. RERUN Quick Test.

FM0159601561080X

Fig. 289   Test X: Constant Control Relay Module (Part 8 of 51). 1996

Test Step	Result	▶	Action to Take
X15 DTC P 1479: CHECK HIGH FAN CONTROL (HFC) RELAY RESISTANCE Diagnostic Trouble Code (DTC) P1479 indicates a High Fan Control (HFC) primary circuit failure. NOTE: For one speed fan applications, disregard DTC P1479. Possible causes: — Open or shorted HFC circuit. — Open VPWR circuit to CCRM (Continental, Windstar). — Damaged CCRM. — Damaged PCM. • Key off. • Disconnect CCRM. **For Continental, Windstar:** — Measure resistance between Pin 17 and Pin 13 at the CCRM. **For All Others:** — Measure resistance between Pin 17 and Pin 24 at the CCRM. • **Is the resistance between 30 and 100 ohms?**	Yes No	▶ ▶	**For Continental and Windstar:** GO to X16 **All others:** GO to X17 REPLACE CCRM. RERUN Quick Test.
X16 CHECK VPWR CIRCUIT TO CCRM • Key off. • CCRM disconnected. • Disconnect EEC-V Power Relay. • Measure resistance between Pin 13 at the CCRM vehicle harness connector and the VPWR circuit at the EEC-V Power Relay vehicle harness connector. • **Is resistance less than 5.0 ohms?**	Yes No	▶ ▶	RECONNECT EEC-V Power Relay. GO to X17 . SERVICE open VPWR circuit between the EEC-V Power Relay and the CCRM. RECONNECT all components. RERUN Quick Test.

VPWR

EEC-V POWER RELAY
VEHICLE HARNESS CONNECTOR

FM0159601561090X

Fig. 289   Test X: Constant Control Relay Module (Part 9 of 51). 1996

Test Step	Result	▶	Action to Take
X17 CHECK HFC CIRCUIT CONTINUITY • Key off. • Disconnect PCM. Inspect for damaged or pushed out pins, corrosion, loose wires, etc. Service as necessary. • Install breakout box, leave PCM disconnected. • CCRM disconnected. • Measure resistance between the HFC Test Pin at breakout box and Pig 17 (HFC) of CCRM vehicle harness connector. • **Is resistance less than 5.0 ohms?**	Yes No	▶ ▶	GO to X18 . SERVICE open in HFC circuit. REMOVE breakout box. RECONNECT all components. RERUN Quick Test.

Application	HFC Test Pin (at PCM)
3.0L Windstar	17
All others	46

Test Step	Result	▶	Action to Take
X18 CHECK HFC CIRCUIT FOR SHORT TO POWER • Key off. • Breakout box installed, PCM disconnected. • CCRM disconnected. • Key on. • Measure voltage between the HFC Test Pin at the breakout box and battery negative post. • **Is voltage less than 1.0 volt?**	Yes No	▶ ▶	Key off. GO to X19 . SERVICE short to power. REMOVE breakout box. RECONNECT all components. RERUN Quick Test.
X19 CHECK HFC CIRCUIT FOR SHORTS TO GROUND • Key off. • Breakout box installed, PCM disconnected. • CCRM disconnected. • Disconnect Scan Tool from DLC. • Measure resistance between the HFC Test Pin and Test Pins 51, 103 (PWR GND) and 91 (SIG RTN) at the breakout box. • **Is each resistance greater than 10,000 ohms?**	Yes No	▶ ▶	REPLACE PCM. REMOVE breakout box. RECONNECT all components. RERUN Quick Test. SERVICE short to ground in HFC circuit. REMOVE breakout box. RECONNECT all components. RERUN Quick Test.

FM0159601561100X

Fig. 289   Test X: Constant Control Relay Module (Part 10 of 51). 1996

Test Step	Result	▶	Action to Take
X20 DTC P 1474: DOES FAN RUN WITH KEY ON? Diagnostic Trouble Code (DTC) P1474 indicates an LFC (FC for one speed fan applications) primary circuit failure. Possible causes: — Open or shorted FC/LFC circuit. — Open VPWR circuit to CCRM (Continental, Windstar). — Damaged CCRM. — Damaged PCM. • **Does the cooling fan always run with the key on?**	Yes No	▶ ▶	GO to X24 . **For Continental and Windstar:** GO to X21 **All others:** GO to X22 .

Application	FC/LFC Test Pin (At PCM)
Thunderbird/Cougar, 4.6L Mustang	45 (LFC)
Continental	68 (LFC)
3.8L Mustang	45 (FC)
3.0L Windstar	98 (LFC)
Taurus/Sable, 3.8L Windstar	28 (LFC)

Test Step	Result	▶	Action to Take
X21 CHECK VPWR CIRCUIT TO CCRM • Key off. • Disconnect CCRM. • Disconnect EEC-V Power Relay. • Measure resistance between Pin 13 at the CCRM vehicle harness connector and the VPWR circuit at the EEC-V Power Relay vehicle harness connector. • **Is resistance less than 5.0 ohms?**	Yes No	▶ ▶	RECONNECT EEC-V Power Relay. GO to X22 . SERVICE open VPWR circuit between the EEC-V Power Relay and the CCRM. RECONNECT all components. RERUN Quick Test.

VPWR

EEC-V POWER RELAY
VEHICLE HARNESS CONNECTOR

FM0159601561110X

Fig. 289   Test X: Constant Control Relay Module (Part 11 of 51). 1996

Test Step	Result	▶	Action to Take
X22 CHECK FC/LFC CIRCUIT FOR SHORT TO GROUND • Key off. • Disconnect Scan Tool from DLC. • Disconnect PCM. Inspect for damaged or pushed out pins, corrosion, loose wires, etc. Service as necessary. • Install breakout box, leave PCM disconnected. • Disconnect CCRM. • Measure resistance between the FC/LFC Test Pin and Test Pins 51, 103 (PWR GND) and 91 (SIG RTN) at the breakout box. • **Is each resistance greater than 10,000 ohms?**	Yes No	▶ ▶	GO to X23. SERVICE short to ground in FC/LFC circuit. RECONNECT all components. RERUN Quick Test.
X23 CHECK FAN RUNNING MODE • Key off. • Breakout box installed, PCM disconnected. • Connect CCRM. • Key on, engine off. • **Is the fan running?**	Yes No	▶ ▶	REPLACE PCM. REMOVE breakout box. RECONNECT all components. RERUN Quick Test. REPLACE CCRM. REMOVE breakout box. RECONNECT all components. RERUN Quick Test.
X24 CHECK FC/LFC CIRCUIT CONTINUITY • Key off. • Disconnect PCM. Inspect for damaged or pushed out pins, corrosion, loose wires, etc. Service as necessary. • Install breakout box, leave PCM disconnected. • Disconnect CCRM. • Measure resistance between the FC/LFC Test Pin at the breakout box and Pin 14 at the CCRM vehicle harness connector. • **Is resistance less than 5.0 ohms?**	Yes No	▶ ▶	GO to X25. SERVICE open in FC/LFC circuit. REMOVE breakout box. RECONNECT all components. RERUN Quick Test.
X25 CHECK FC/LFC CIRCUIT FOR SHORT TO POWER • Key off. • Breakout box installed, PCM disconnected. • CCRM disconnected. • Key on, engine off. • Measure voltage between the FC/LFC Test Pin at the breakout box and battery negative post. • **Is voltage less than 1.0 volt?**	Yes No	▶ ▶	GO to X26. SERVICE short to power in FC/LFC circuit. REMOVE breakout box. RECONNECT all components. RERUN Quick Test.

FM0159601561120X

Fig. 289 Test X: Constant Control Relay Module (Part 12 of 51). 1996

Test Step	Result	▶	Action to Take
X26 FC/LFC CIRCUIT FAULT ISOLATION CHECK • Key off. • Breakout box installed, PCM disconnected. • Reconnect CCRM. • Key on, engine off. • For Mustang, Thunderbird/Cougar: — Jumper Test Pin 45 (FC/LFC) to Test Pin 77 (PWR GND) at the breakout box. For Continental: — Jumper Test Pin 68 (LFC) to Test Pin 77 (PWR GND) at the breakout box. For Taurus/Sable, 3.8L Windstar: — Jumper Test Pin 28 (LFC) to Test Pin 77 (PWR GND) at the breakout box. For 3.0L Windstar: — Jumper Test Pin 98 (LFC) to Test Pin 77 (PWR GND) at the breakout box. • **Does fan continue to run?**	Yes No	▶ ▶	REPLACE CCRM. REMOVE breakout box. RECONNECT all components. RERUN Quick Test. REPLACE PCM. REMOVE breakout box. RECONNECT all components. RERUN Quick Test.

FM0159601561130X

Fig. 289 Test X: Constant Control Relay Module (Part 13 of 51). 1996

Test Step	Result	▶	Action to Take
X30 CONTINUOUS MEMORY DTC P1474: CHECK FAN CONTROL (FC) OR LOW FAN CONTROL (LFC) CIRCUIT FOR OPEN OR SHORT TO POWER Continuous Memory Diagnostic Trouble Code (DTC) P1474 indicates that an LFC (FC for one speed fan applications) circuit failure has occurred during vehicle operation. Possible causes: — Open or shorted FC/LFC circuit. — Open VPWR circuit to CCRM (Continental, Windstar). • Key off. • Disconnect cooling fan connector(s) (both for Taurus/Sable and Windstar). Inspect connectors for damaged or pushed out pins, corrosion, loose wires, etc. Service as necessary. • Connect a non-powered test lamp between the Power-to-(Low Speed) Fan circuit and ground circuit at the cooling fan vehicle harness connector (either one for Taurus/Sable and Windstar). • Key on, engine off. • Observe test lamp for an indication of a fault while performing the following (since the FC/LFC circuit is grounded to turn the fan OFF, the lamp will come on when an open or short to power is detected): — Shake, wiggle, bend the FC/LFC circuit between the PCM and CCRM. — Lightly tap on the CCRM to simulate road shock. • **Is a fault indicated?**	Yes No	▶ ▶	Key off. ISOLATE fault and SERVICE as necessary. COMPLETE PCM Reset to clear DTCs (REFER to Powertrain Control Module (PCM) Reset). RERUN Quick Test. GO to X31.

FM0159601561140X

Fig. 289 Test X: Constant Control Relay Module (Part 14 of 51). 1996

Test Step	Result	▶	Action to Take
X31 CHECK FC/LFC CIRCUIT FOR SHORT TO GROUND (FOR CONTINENTAL AND WINDSTAR, ALSO CHECK FOR OPEN VPWR TO CCRM) • Key on, engine off. • Cooling fan(s) disconnected, test lamp installed. • Scan Tool connected. • Access Output Test Mode on Scan Tool. • Command Low Speed Fan on. • Observe test lamp for an indication of a fault while performing the following (the lamp will turn off when a fault is detected, indicating a short to ground or an open in VPWR): — Shake, wiggle, bend the FC/LFC circuit between the PCM and CCRM. — Lightly tap on the CCRM to simulate road shock. — For Continental and Windstar, also shake, wiggle, bend the VPWR circuit between the EEC-V Power Relay and CCRM. • Key off. • **Is a fault indicated?**	Yes No	▶ ▶	ISOLATE fault and SERVICE as necessary. COMPLETE PCM Reset to clear DTCs (REFER to Powertrain Control Module (PCM) Reset). RERUN Quick Test. GO to Pinpoint Test Step Z1 with the following data: LFCF PID or LFCA PID (whichever is available) and list of Possible Causes.

FM0159601561150X

Fig. 289 Test X: Constant Control Relay Module (Part 15 of 51). 1996

Test Step	Result	►	Action to Take
X35 CHECK HIGH FAN CONTROL (HFC) CIRCUIT FOR OPEN OR SHORT TO POWER			
Continuous Memory Diagnostic Trouble Code (DTC) P1479 indicates that an HFC circuit failure has occurred during vehicle operation. NOTE: For one speed fan applications, disregard DTC P1479. Possible causes: — Open or shorted HFC circuit. — Open VPWR circuit to CCRM (Continental and Windstar) • Key off. • Scan Tool connected. • Disconnect cooling fan connector(s) (both for Taurus/Sable and Windstar). Inspect connectors for damaged or pushed out pins, corrosion, loose wires, etc. Service as necessary. • Connect a non-powered test lamp between the Power-to-High Speed Fan circuit and ground circuit at the cooling fan vehicle harness connector (either one for Taurus/Sable and Windstar). • Key on, engine off. • Access Output Test Mode on Scan Tool • Command High Speed Fan on. • Observe test lamp for an indication of a fault while performing the following (the lamp will turn off when a fault is detected, indicating an open or short to power): — Shake, wiggle, bend the HFC circuit between the PCM and CCRM. — Lightly tap on the CCRM to simulate road shock. — For Continental and Windstar; also shake, wiggle, bend the VPWR circuit between the EEC-V Power Relay and CCRM. • **Is a fault indicated?**	Yes ► No ►		Key off. ISOLATE fault and SERVICE as necessary. COMPLETE PCM Reset to clear DTCs (REFER to Powertrain Control Module (PCM) Reset). RERUN Quick Test. GO to **X36**.

FM015960156116OX

Fig. 289 Test X: Constant Control Relay Module (Part 16 of 51). 1996

Test Step	Result	►	Action to Take
X36 CHECK HFC CIRCUIT FOR SHORT TO GROUND			
• Key on, engine off. • Cooling fan(s) disconnected, test lamp installed. • Scan Tool connected. • Command High Speed Fan off. • Observe test lamp for an indication of a fault while performing the following (the lamp will turn on when a fault is detected, indicating a short to ground): — Shake, wiggle, bend the HFC circuit between the PCM and CCRM. — Lightly tap on the CCRM to simulate road shock. • Key off. • **Is a fault indicated?**	Yes ► No ►		ISOLATE fault and SERVICE as necessary. COMPLETE PCM Reset to clear DTCs (REFER to Powertrain Control Module (PCM) Reset). RERUN Quick Test. GO to Pinpoint Test Step **Z1** with the following data: HFCF PID or HFCA PID (whichever is available) and list of Possible Causes.
X40 ELECTRIC COOLING FAN CONCERN: DID THE FAN OPERATE AT ANY SPEED?			
NOTE: For the proper results of these pinpoint tests, no fault DTCs must have been present during EEC-V Quick Test. • For one speed fan applications (3.8L Mustang), GO directly to **X41**. • **During the operational check of both fan speeds, did the fan operate at any speed?**	Yes ► No ►		Only one fan speed is operational. For Taurus/Sable: GO to **X41**. All others: GO to **X50**. Cooling fan will not operate at any speed. GO to **X41**.
X41 COOLING FAN WILL NOT OPERATE AT ANY SPEED: COMMAND FAN ON (HIGH SPEED FOR TWO SPEED APPLICATIONS) AND CHECK FOR VOLTAGE AT FAN			
• Scan Tool connected. • Key on, engine off. • Still in Output Test Mode, with fan commanded off. • Disconnect cooling fan (either one for Taurus/Sable and Windstar). • Command fan on (high speed for two speed fan applications). • Measure voltage between the Power-To-(High Speed) Fan circuit at the cooling fan vehicle harness connector and chassis ground. • Key off. • **Was voltage greater than 10.0 volts?**	Yes ► No ►		Power is being supplied to fan. GO to **X45**. GO to **X42**.

FM015960156117OX

Fig. 289 Test X: Constant Control Relay Module (Part 17 of 51). 1996

Test Step	Result	►	Action to Take
X42 CHECK FOR B(+) TO FAN RELAYS IN CCRM			
• Key off. • Cooling fan disconnected. • Disconnect CCRM. • Connect negative probe of DVOM to the battery negative post. • **For Taurus/Sable, Mustang, Thunderbird/Cougar:** — Check voltage at pins 3 and 4 of the CCRM vehicle harness connector. **For Continental:** — Check voltage at pins 3, 4, 8 and 10 of the CCRM vehicle harness connector. **For Windstar:** — Check voltage at pins 1, 2, 6, 7, 12 and 24 of the CCRM vehicle harness connector. • **Is each voltage greater than 10.0 volts?**	Yes ► No ►		GO to **X43**. B(+) fault. CHECK condition of related fuses/fuse links. If OK, SERVICE open circuit. If fuse/fuse link is damaged, CHECK B(+) circuit for short to ground before replacing. **For Continental:** If open was to only CCRM pins 3 and 4, after service, GO to **X72** (to check both HFC relays in CCRM and Power-To-Fan circuit). Otherwise, RECONNECT all components. RE-EVALUATE symptom. **For Windstar:** If open was only to CCRM pins 1, 2, 6 and 7, after service, GO to **X72** (to check both HFC relays in CCRM and Power-To-Fan circuit). Otherwise, RECONNECT all components. RE-EVALUATE symptom. **All others:** RECONNECT all components. RE-EVALUATE symptom.

FM015960156118OX

Fig. 289 Test X: Constant Control Relay Module (Part 18 of 51). 1996

Test Step	Result	►	Action to Take
X43 CHECK POWER-TO-FAN(S) CIRCUIT CONTINUITY BETWEEN CCRM AND COOLING FAN(S)			
• Key off. • CCRM disconnected. • Cooling fan disconnected. • **For 3.8L Mustang:** — Measure resistance between pin 2 of the CCRM vehicle harness connector and the Power-To-Fan circuit at the fan vehicle harness connector. **For Taurus/Sable, 4.6L Mustang and Thunderbird/Cougar:** — Measure resistance between pin 6 of the CCRM vehicle harness connector and the Power-To-High Fan circuit at the fan vehicle harness connector. — Measure resistance between Pin 2 of the CCRM vehicle harness connector and the Power-To-Low circuit at the fan vehicle harness connector. **For Continental:** — Measure resistance between the Power-To-High Fan circuit at the fan vehicle harness connector and Pins 2 and 12 of the CCRM vehicle harness connector. — Measure resistance between Pin 6 of the CCRM vehicle harness connector and the Power-To-Low Fan circuit at the fan vehicle harness connector. **For Windstar:** — Measure resistance between the Power-To-Fan circuit at the fan vehicle harness connector and Pins 4 and 8 of the CCRM vehicle harness connector. • **Is each resistance less than 7.0 ohms?**	Yes ► No ►		REPLACE CCRM. RECONNECT all components. RE-EVALUATE symptom. SERVICE open Power-To-Fan circuit(s). **For Continental:** After service, GO to **X73** (to check both HFC relays in CCRM). **For Windstar:** If open was just between CCRM Pin 4 and the fan, after service GO to **X73** (to check both HFC relays in CCRM). Otherwise, RECONNECT all components and RE-EVALUATE symptom. **All others:** RECONNECT all components and RE-EVALUATE symptom.
X45 CHECK COOLING FAN GROUND CIRCUIT			
• Key off. • Cooling fan disconnected. • Disconnect Scan Tool from DLC. • Measure resistance between the ground circuit at the cooling fan vehicle harness connector and chassis ground. • **Is resistance less than 5.0 ohms?**	Yes ► No ►		**For Taurus/Sable and Windstar:** GO to **X46**. **All others:** REPLACE fan motor. RECONNECT all components. RE-EVALUATE symptom. SERVICE open ground circuit. RECONNECT all components. RE-EVALUATE symptom.

FM015960156119OX

Fig. 289 Test X: Constant Control Relay Module (Part 19 of 51). 1996

ELECTRONIC ENGINE CONTROL SYSTEM (EEC-V)

Test Step		Result	▶	Action to Take
X46	CHECK FOR VOLTAGE TO OTHER COOLING FAN			
	• Key off. • One cooling fan disconnected. • Reconnect Scan Tool. • Disconnect the other cooling fan. • Key on, engine off. • Again, access Output Test Mode. • Command the high speed fan on. • Measure voltage between the Power-To-Fan circuit and ground circuit at the vehicle harness connector of the fan that was just disconnected. • Key off. • **Was voltage greater than 10.0 volts?**	Yes	▶	REPLACE both fan motors. RECONNECT all components. RE-EVALUATE symptom.
		No	▶	SERVICE open power or ground circuit to the fan that was just tested. RECONNECT all components. RE-EVALUATE symptom. If the other fan does not operate, REPLACE it and again RE-EVALUATE symptom.
X48	ONE FAN SPEED INOPERATIVE (TAURUS/SABLE): CHECK CONTINUITY OF POWER-TO-LOW FAN OR POWER-TO-HIGH FAN CIRCUIT			
	• Key off. • Disconnect CCRM. • Disconnect cooling fan (either one). • **For low speed fan inoperative:** — Measure resistance between Pin 2 of the CCRM vehicle harness connector and the Power-To-Fan circuit at the fan vehicle harness connector. • **For high speed fan inoperative:** — Measure resistance between Pin 6 of the CCRM vehicle harness connector and the Power-To-Fan circuit at the fan vehicle harness connector. • **Is resistance less than 7.0 ohms?**	Yes	▶	REPLACE CCRM. RECONNECT all components. RE-EVALUATE symptom.
		No	▶	SERVICE open circuit. RECONNECT all components. RE-EVALUATE SYMPTOM.

FM015960156120OX

Fig. 289 Test X: Constant Control Relay Module (Part 20 of 51). 1996

Test Step		Result	▶	Action to Take
X50	DETERMINE WHICH FAN SPEED IS OPERATIONAL			
	• **Was the low speed fan operational?**	Yes	▶	High speed fan inoperative. **For Mustang, Thunderbird/Cougar:** GO TO X65. **For Continental:** GO TO X60. **For Windstar:** Key off. GO to X68.
		No	▶	Low speed fan inoperative. **For Mustang, Thunderbird/Cougar, Continental:** GO to X51. **For Windstar:** Key off. GO to X55.
X51	LOW SPEED FAN INOPERATIVE (MUSTANG THUNDERBIRD/COUGAR, CONTINENTAL): COMMAND LOW SPEED FAN ON AND CHECK FOR VOLTAGE TO COOLING FAN			
	• Scan Tool connected. • Key on, engine off. • Still in Output Test Mode with fan commanded off. • Disconnect cooling fan. • Command low speed fan on. • Measure voltage between the Power-To-Low fan circuit and ground circuit at the cooling fan vehicle harness connector. • Key off. • **Was voltage greater than 10.0 volts?**	Yes	▶	REPLACE fan motor. RECONNECT all components. RE-EVALUATE symptom.
		No	▶	**For Mustang, Thunderbird/Cougar:** GO to X53. **For Continental:** GO to X52.
X52	CHECK FOR B(+) TO LFC RELAY IN CCRM			
	• Key off. • Cooling fan disconnected. • Disconnect CCRM. • Connect negative probe of DVOM to chassis ground. • Check for voltage at Pins 3 and 4 of the CCRM vehicle harness connector. • **Are both voltages greater than 10.0 volts?**	Yes	▶	GO to X53.
		No	▶	B(+) fault. CHECK condition of related fuses/fuse links. If OK, SERVICE open circuit. If fuse/fuse link is damaged, CHECK B(+) circuit for short to ground before replacing. After service, RECONNECT all components. RE-EVALUATE symptom.

FM015960156121OX

Fig. 289 Test X: Constant Control Relay Module (Part 21 of 51). 1996

Test Step		Result	▶	Action to Take
X53	CHECK POWER-TO-LOW FAN CIRCUIT CONTINUITY BETWEEN CCRM AND FAN			
	• Key off. • For Mustang and Thunderbird/Cougar, disconnect CCRM. • CCRM disconnected. • Cooling fan disconnected. • Measure resistance between the Power-To-Low Fan circuit at the cooling fan vehicle harness connector and Pins 1 and 2 (6 and 7 for Continental) of the CCRM vehicle harness connector. • **Are both resistances less than 5.0 ohms?**	Yes	▶	REPLACE CCRM. RECONNECT all components. RE-EVALUATE symptom.
		No	▶	SERVICE open circuit. RECONNECT all components. RE-EVALUATE symptom.
X55	LOW SPEED FAN INOPERATIVE (WINDSTAR): CHECK FOR B(+) TO LFC RELAY IN CCRM			
	• Key off. • Disconnect CCRM. • Connect negative probe of DVOM to chassis ground. • Check for voltage at Pins 6 and 7 of the CCRM vehicle harness connector. • **Are both voltages greater than 9.0 volts?**	Yes	▶	GO to X56.
		No	▶	B(+) fault. CHECK condition of related fuses and Fan Dropping Resistor. If OK, SERVICE open circuit. If fuse is damaged, CHECK B(+) circuit for short to ground before replacing. After service, RECONNECT all components. RE-EVALUATE symptom.
X56	CHECK POWER-TO-FAN CIRCUIT CONTINUITY			
	• Key off. • CCRM disconnected. • Disconnect one of the cooling fans (either one). • Measure resistance between Pin 3 of the CCRM vehicle harness connector and the Power-To-Fan circuit at the cooling fan vehicle harness connector. • **Is resistance less than 5.0 ohms?**	Yes	▶	REPLACE CCRM. RECONNECT all components. RE-EVALUATE symptom.
		No	▶	SERVICE open Power-To-Fan circuit. RECONNECT all components. RE-EVALUATE symptom.
X60	HIGH SPEED FAN INOPERATIVE (CONTINENTAL): COMMAND HIGH SPEED FAN ON AND CHECK FOR VOLTAGE TO COOLING FAN			
	• Scan Tool connected. • Key on, engine off. • Still in Output Test Mode with fan commanded off. • Disconnect cooling fan. • Command high speed fan on. • Measure voltage between the Power-To-High Fan circuit at the cooling fan vehicle harness connector and chassis ground. • Key off. • **Was voltage greater than 10.5 volts?**	Yes	▶	REPLACE fan motor. RECONNECT all components. RE-EVALUATE symptom.
		No	▶	GO to X61.

FM015960156122OX

Fig. 289 Test X: Constant Control Relay Module (Part 22 of 51). 1996

Test Step		Result	▶	Action to Take
X61	CHECK FOR B(+) TO CCRM PINS 8 AND 10			
	• Key off. • Cooling fan disconnected. • Disconnect CCRM. • Connect negative probe of DVOM to chassis ground. • Check for voltage at Pins 8 and 10 of the CCRM vehicle harness connector. • **Is voltage greater than 10.5 volts?**	Yes	▶	GO to X62.
		No	▶	B(+) fault. CHECK condition of related fuses/fuse links. If OK, SERVICE open circuit. If fuse/fuse link is damaged, CHECK B(+) circuit for short to ground before replacing. After service, GO to X63 to CHECK the Power-To-High Fan circuits and CCRM.
X62	CHECK CONTINUITY OF POWER-TO-HIGH FAN CIRCUITS			
	• Key off. • Cooling fan disconnected. • CCRM disconnected. • Measure resistance between the Power-To-High Fan circuit at the cooling fan vehicle harness connector and both Pins 1 and 12 of the CCRM vehicle harness connector. • **Are both resistances less than 5.0 ohms?**	Yes	▶	REPLACE CCRM. RECONNECT all components. RE-EVALUATE symptom.
		No	▶	**If both resistance measurements were greater than 5.0 ohms:** SERVICE open circuit. RECONNECT all components. RE-EVALUATE symptom. **If one resistance measurement was greater than 5.0 ohms and one was less than 5.0 ohms:** SERVICE open circuit. After service, GO to X73 (to check both HFC relays in CCRM).
X63	VERIFY POWER-TO-HIGH FAN CIRCUIT CONTINUITY BETWEEN CCRM PIN 1 AND THE COOLING FAN			
	• Key off. • Cooling fan disconnected. • CCRM disconnected. • Measure resistance between Pin 1 and Pin 12 of the CCRM vehicle harness connector. • **Is resistance less than 5.0 ohms?**	Yes	▶	GO to X73 (to check both HFC relays in CCRM).
		No	▶	SERVICE open between CCRM Pin 1 and the Pin 12 splice to the Power-To-High Fan circuit. After also servicing the B(+) circuit, RECONNECT all components. RE-EVALUATE symptom.

FM015960156123OX

Fig. 289 Test X: Constant Control Relay Module (Part 23 of 51). 1996

Test Step	Result	▶	Action to Take
X65 HIGH SPEED FAN INOPERATIVE (MUSTANG, THUNDERBIRD / COUGAR): COMMAND HIGH SPEED FAN ON AND CHECK FOR VOLTAGE TO COOLING FAN			
• Scan Tool connected. • Key on, engine off. • Still in Output Test Mode with fan commanded off. • Disconnect cooling fan. • Command high speed fan on. • Measure voltage between the Power-To-High Fan circuit at the cooling fan vehicle harness connector and chassis ground. • Key off. • **Was voltage greater than 10.5 volts?**	Yes No	▶ ▶	REPLACE fan motor. RECONNECT all components. RE-EVALUATE symptom. GO to X66.
X66 CHECK CONTINUITY OF POWER-TO-HIGH FAN CIRCUIT			
• Key off. • Cooling fan disconnected. • Disconnect CCRM. • Measure resistance between Pin 6 of the CCRM vehicle harness connector and the Power-To-High Fan circuit at the cooling fan vehicle harness connector. • **Is resistance less than 5.0 ohms?**	Yes No	▶ ▶	REPLACE CCRM. RECONNECT all components. RE-EVALUATE symptom. SERVICE open in Power-To-High Fan circuit. RECONNECT all components. RE-EVALUATE symptom.
X68 HIGH SPEED FAN INOPERATIVE (WINDSTAR): CHECK FOR B(+) TO HFC RELAYS IN CCRM			
• Key off. • Disconnect CCRM. • Connect negative probe of DVOM to chassis ground. • Check for voltage at Pins 1, 2, 12 and 24 of the CCRM vehicle harness connector. • **Is each voltage greater than 10.5 volts?**	Yes No	▶ ▶	GO to X69. B(+) fault. CHECK condition of related fuses / fuse links. If OK, SERVICE open circuit. If fuse / fuse link is damaged, CHECK B(+) circuit for short to ground before replacing. If open was only to two pins (either 1 and 2, or 12 and 24), after service GO to X72 (to CHECK the Power-To-Fan circuit and CCRM). Otherwise, RECONNECT all components. RE-EVALUATE symptom.

FM0159601561240X

Fig. 289 Test X: Constant Control Relay Module (Part 24 of 51). 1996

Test Step	Result	▶	Action to Take
X69 CHECK POWER-TO-FAN CIRCUIT CONTINUITY BETWEEN CCRM VEHICLE HARNESS CONNECTOR PINS 4 AND 8			
• Key off. • CCRM disconnected. • Measure resistance between Pins 4 and 8 at the CCRM vehicle harness connector. • **Is resistance less than 5.0 ohms?**	Yes No	▶ ▶	REPLACE CCRM. RECONNECT all components. RE-EVALUATE symptom. SERVICE open circuit between CCRM Pin 8 and the Pin 4 splice to the Power-To-Fan circuit. After service, GO to X73 (to check both HFC relays in the CCRM).
X72 CHECK POWER-TO-FAN HARNESS CONTINUITY BETWEEN HFC RELAYS			
• Key off. • CCRM disconnected. • For **Continental:** — Measure resistance between Pins 1 and 12 of the CCRM vehicle harness connector. For **Windstar:** — Measure resistance between Pins 4 and 8 at the CCRM vehicle harness connector. • **Is resistance less than 5.0 ohms?**	Yes No	▶ ▶	GO to X73 (to check both HFC relays in the CCRM). SERVICE open circuit. After also servicing the B(+) circuit, RECONNECT all components. RE-EVALUATE symptom.
X73 VERIFY OPERATION OF BOTH HFC RELAYS IN CCRM			
• Key off. • CCRM disconnected. • Connect a jumper wire between Pin 13 of the CCRM and the battery positive (+) post. • Connect another jumper wire between Pin 17 of the CCRM and the battery negative (-) post. • Measure resistance between Pin 1 and Pins 2, 3 and 4 of the CCRM. • Measure resistance between Pin 12 and Pins 8, 10, and 24 of the CCRM. • **Are all resistances less than 5.0 ohms?**	Yes No	▶ ▶	Both HFC relays are OK. REMOVE jumper wires. After original service, RECONNECT all components. RE-EVALUATE symptom. REPLACE CCRM. After also performing original service, RECONNECT all components. RE-EVALUATE symptom.

FM0159601561250X

Fig. 289 Test X: Constant Control Relay Module (Part 25 of 51). 1996

Test Step	Result	▶	Action to Take
X80 COOLING FAN ALWAYS RUNS: DISCONNECT CCRM AND CHECK IF FAN STILL RUNS			
NOTE: For proper results of these pinpoint tests, no fault DTCs must have been present during EEC-V Quick Test. For two-speed fan applications, the ACP or ACPSW PID check must also have been performed. • Accessories off (A / C, etc.). • Key on, verify "cooling fan always on" symptom. • Key off. • Disconnect CCRM. • Key on, engine off. • **Is cooling fan still on?**	Yes No	▶ ▶	Key off. For **Taurus / Sable, 3.8L Mustang, Windstar :** SERVICE Power-To-Fan circuit short to power. RECONNECT CCRM. RE-EVALUATE symptom. **For all others:** GO to X81. Key off. REPLACE CCRM. RE-EVALUATE symptom.
X81 CHECK "POWER-TO-LOW FAN" AND "POWER-TO-HIGH FAN" CIRCUITS FOR SHORT TO POWER			
• Key off. • CCRM disconnected. • Disconnect cooling fan. • Key on, engine off. • Connect negative probe of DVOM to chassis ground. • Check for voltage at both the Power-To-Low Fan and Power-To-High Fan circuits at the cooling fan vehicle harness connector. • **Are both voltages less than 1.0 volt?**	Yes No	▶ ▶	No fault is indicated at this time. VERIFY results of previous test steps. If OK, RECONNECT all components SERVICE short to power. RECONNECT all components. RE-EVALUATE symptom.
X85 ONE COOLING FAN INOPERATIVE WITH NO DTCS (THE OTHER COOLING FAN OPERATES NORMALLY): CHECK POWER AND GROUND CIRCUITS TO INOPERATIVE FAN			
• Key off. • Disconnect both cooling fans. • Access Output Test Mode on Scan Tool • Command High Speed Fan on. • Measure voltage between the Power-to-Fan pin and ground pin at the inoperative fan vehicle harness connector. • **Is voltage greater than 10.5 volts?**	Yes No	▶ ▶	Key off. REPLACE inoperative cooling fan. RECONNECT all components. RE-EVALUATE symptom. REMAIN in Output Test Mode. GO to X86.

FM0159601561260X

Fig. 289 Test X: Constant Control Relay Module (Part 26 of 51). 1996

Test Step	Result	▶	Action to Take
X86 CHECK POWER-TO-FAN CIRCUIT			
• Still in Output Test Mode. • Cooling fans disconnected. • High speed fan commanded on. • Measure voltage between the Power-to-Fan pin at the inoperative fan vehicle harness connector and the battery negative post. • Key off. • **Was voltage greater than 10.5 volts?**	Yes No	▶ ▶	SERVICE open ground to inoperative fan. RECONNECT all components. RE-EVALUATE symptom. SERVICE open in Power-to-Fan circuit between inoperative fan and splice to other fan. RECONNECT all components. RE-EVALUATE symptom.
X100 ACCS PID OFF WITH A / C ON: CHECK FOR VOLTAGE TO A / C CYCLING SWITCH			
• Key off. • Key on, engine off. • Disconnect A / C cycling switch. • A / C demand switch to A / C on. • Measure voltage between the A / C demand switch (or EATC module) side of the A / C Cycling Switch vehicle harness connector and the battery negative post. • Key off. • **Was voltage greater than 10.5 volts?**	Yes No	▶ ▶	GO to X101. check A / C demand switch operation, applicable fuses, wiring to A / C cycling switch, etc.
X101 CHECK IF A / C CYCLING SWITCH CONTACTS ARE CLOSED			
• Key off. • A / C Cycling Switch disconnected. • Measure resistance of the A / C Cycling Switch contacts at the A / C Cycling Switch connector. • **Is resistance less than 5.0 ohms?**	Yes No	▶ ▶	**For Continental:** RECONNECT A / C cycling switch. GO to X104. **All others:** GO to X102. check the operation of the A / C Cycling Switch, proper refrigerant charge, etc. SERVICE as necessary. RECONNECT all components. RE-EVALUATE symptom.

FM0159601561270X

Fig. 289 Test X: Constant Control Relay Module (Part 27 of 51). 1996

Test Step	Result	►	Action to Take
X102 CHECK FOR VOLTAGE TO DUAL FUNCTION A/C PRESSURE SWITCH (ACPSW)			
• Key off. • Reconnect A/C Cycling Switch. • Disconnect ACPSW (also known as Refrigerant Containment/Fan Function Switch). • Key on, engine off. • A/C on. • Measure voltage between the A/C Demand Switch pin at the ACPSW vehicle harness connector and the battery negative post. • Key off. • **Was voltage greater than 10.5 volts?**	Yes No	► ►	GO to X103. SERVICE open between A/C Cycling Switch and ACPSW. RECONNECT all components. RE-EVALUATE symptom.
X103 CHECK CONTINUITY OF ACPSW HIGH PRESSURE CONTACTS			
• Key off. • ACPSW disconnected. • Measure resistance of the ACPSW high pressure contacts. • **Is resistance less than 5.0 ohms?**	Yes No	►	GO to X104. check for overpressurized A/C system, etc. If OK, REPLACE ACPSW, RE-EVALUATE symptom.

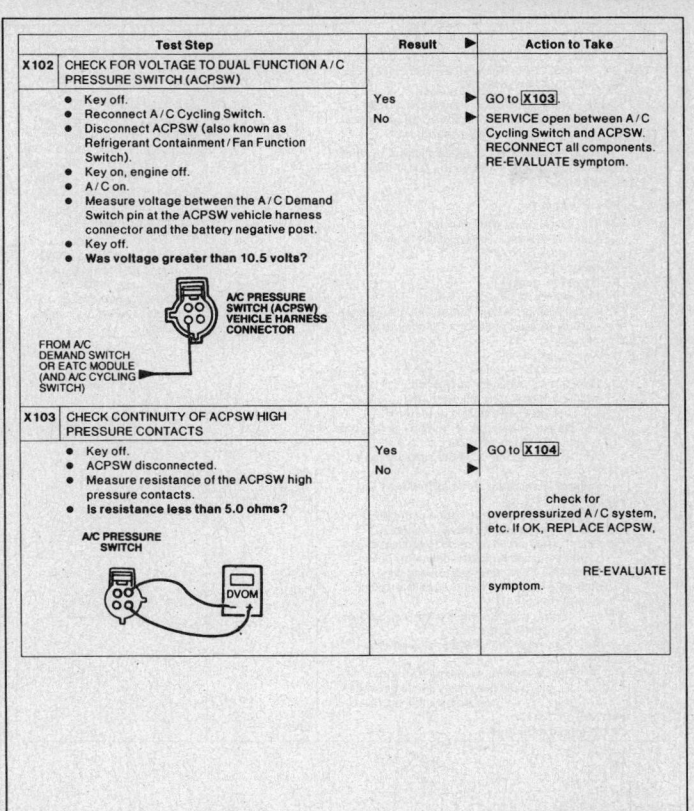

FM015960 1561280X

Fig. 289 Test X: Constant Control Relay Module (Part 28 of 51). 1996

Test Step	Result	►	Action to Take
X104 CHECK FOR VOLTAGE TO PCM ON ACCS CIRCUIT			
• Key off. • Reconnect ACPSW (if applicable). • Disconnect PCM. Inspect for damaged or pushed out pins, loose wires, corrosion, etc. Service as necessary. • Install breakout box, leave PCM disconnected. • Key on. • A/C ON. • Measure voltage between Test Pin 41 (ACCS) and Test Pin 77 (PWR GND) at the breakout box. • **Is voltage greater than 10.5 volts?**	Yes No	► ►	REPLACE PCM. REMOVE breakout box. RECONNECT all components. RE-EVALUATE symptom. SERVICE open circuit between the ACPSW A/C cycling switch for Continental and PCM. REMOVE breakout box. RECONNECT all components. RE-EVALUATE symptom.
X105 KOEO/KOER DTC P1460: VERIFY ACCS PID IS OFF			
Key On Engine Off (KOEO) and Key On Engine Running (KOER) Diagnostic Trouble Code (DTC) P1460 indicates a WAC circuit fault or that the A/C was on during Self-Test. NOTE: Verify A/C and Defrost were off during KOEO/KOER Self-Test. If vehicle is not equipped with A/C, the WAC circuit is not used and the DTC P1460 can be ignored. Possible causes: — A/C on during Self-Test. — Open or shorted circuit. — Damaged CCRM. — Damaged PCM. • Scan Tool connected to DLC. • Start engine. • A/C and defroster off. • Access ACCS PID. • **Is the ACCS PID off?**	Yes No	► ►	Key off. GO to X106. Key off. GO to X125 (to check A/C circuits for short to power).
X106 CHECK WAC CIRCUIT FOR SHORT TO POWER			
• Key off. • Disconnect CCRM. • Disconnect PCM. Inspect for damaged or pushed out pins, corrosion, loose wires, etc. Service as necessary. • Install breakout box, leave PCM disconnected. • Key on. • Measure voltage between Test Pin 69 (WAC) and Test Pins 51 and 103 (PWR GND) at the breakout box. • Key off. • **Was voltage less than 1.0 volt?**	Yes No	► ►	GO to X107. SERVICE WAC circuit short to power. REMOVE breakout box. RECONNECT all components. START engine. TURN AC on, WAIT 15 seconds. A/C off. Key off. RERUN Quick Test.

FM015960 1561290X

Fig. 289 Test X: Constant Control Relay Module (Part 29 of 51). 1996

Test Step	Result	►	Action to Take
X107 CHECK WAC CIRCUIT FOR SHORT TO GROUND			
• Key off. • CCRM disconnected. • Breakout box installed, PCM disconnected. • Disconnect Scan Tool from DLC. • Measure resistance between Test Pin 69 (WAC) and Test Pins 51, 103 (PWR GND) and 91 (SIG RTN). • **Is each resistance greater than 10,000 ohms?**	Yes No	► ►	GO to X108. SERVICE WAC circuit short to ground. REMOVE breakout box. RECONNECT all components. START engine. TURN AC on, WAIT 15 seconds. A/C off. Key off. RERUN Quick Test.
X108 CHECK WAC CIRCUIT CONTINUITY			
• Key off. • CCRM disconnected. • Breakout box installed, PCM disconnected. • Measure resistance between Test Pin 69 (WAC) at the breakout box and Pin 22 at the CCRM vehicle harness connector. • **Is resistance less than 5.0 ohms?**	Yes No	► ►	GO to X109. SERVICE open WAC circuit. REMOVE breakout box. RECONNECT all components. START engine. TURN AC on, WAIT 15 seconds. A/C off. Key off. RERUN Quick Test.
X109 CHECK OPERATION OF WAC IN CCRM			
• Key off. • Breakout box installed, PCM disconnected. • Reconnect CCRM. • A/C clutch connected. • Key on. • A/C demand switch to A/C on. • Connect a jumper wire between Test Pin 69 (WAC) and Test Pin 77 (PWR GND) at the breakout box. • Disconnect and reconnect the jumper several times while listening to the A/C clutch. • **Does the A/C clutch engage and disengage as the jumper is disconnected and reconnected?**	Yes No	► ►	Key off. REPLACE PCM. REMOVE breakout box. RECONNECT all components. START engine. TURN AC on, WAIT 15 seconds. A/C off. Key off. RERUN Quick Test. Key off. REPLACE CCRM. INSPECT Power-to-A/C Clutch circuit for short to ground. Service as necessary. REMOVE breakout box. RECONNECT all components. START engine. TURN AC on, WAIT 15 seconds. A/C off. Key off. RERUN Quick Test.
X110 NO/LOW VOLTAGE TO A/C CLUTCH (ACCS PID IS ON WITH A/C ON AND NO DTCS, OR DIRECTED HERE FROM PINPOINT TEST DS): CHECK A/C DEMAND SWITCH VOLTAGE TO CCRM			
• Key off. • Disconnect CCRM. • Key on. • A/C demand switch to A/C on. • Measure voltage between Pin 21 and Pin 15 at the CCRM vehicle harness connector. • Key off, A/C off. • **Was voltage greater than 10.5 volts?**	Yes No	► ►	GO to X111. SERVICE open in A/C demand circuit between CCRM and ACCS splice to PCM. RECONNECT all components. RE-EVALUATE symptom.

FM015960 1561300X

Fig. 289 Test X: Constant Control Relay Module (Part 30 of 51). 1996

Test Step	Result	►	Action to Take
X111 CHECK CONTINUITY OF POWER-TO-A/C CLUTCH AND A/C CLUTCH GROUND CIRCUITS			
• Key off. • CCRM disconnected. • Disconnect A/C clutch. • Disconnect Scan Tool from DLC. • Measure resistance between Pin 23 of the CCRM vehicle harness connector and the power side of the A/C clutch vehicle harness connector. • Measure resistance between Pin 16 of the CCRM vehicle harness connector and the ground side of the A/C clutch vehicle harness connector. • **Is each resistance less than 5.0 ohms?**	Yes No	► ►	REPLACE CCRM. RECONNECT all components. RE-EVALUATE symptom. SERVICE open circuit. RECONNECT all components. RE-EVALUATE symptom.
X115 DTC P1469: CHECK FOR CAUSES OF FAST A/C COMPRESSOR CLUTCH CYCLING			
Continuous Memory Diagnostic Trouble Code (DTC) P1469 indicates frequent A/C compressor clutch cycling. To set DTC P1469, the ACCS input to the Powertrain Control Module (PCM) (Pin 41) must be changing states in less than 8.5 second intervals for a calibratable amount of time. Possible causes: — Mechanical A/C system concern (ex. low refrigerant charge, damaged A/C cycling switch, etc.). — Intermittent open between the Electronic Automatic Temperature Control (EATC) module and the Pin 41 input (ACCS) to the PCM. • Refer to the Climate Control System to test A/C compressor clutch cycle times, and to check causes of fast clutch cycling. • **Is a fault indicated?**	Yes No	► ►	SERVICE as required according to Service Manual direction. PERFORM PCM Reset to clear DTC(s) (REFER to Powertrain Control Module (PCM) Reset). START engine and turn A/C on for about 2 minutes. Engine off, A/C off. RERUN Quick Test. GO to X116 (to CHECK for intermittent electrical concern).

FM015960 1561310X

Fig. 289 Test X: Constant Control Relay Module (Part 31 of 51). 1996

Test Step	Result	▶	Action to Take
X116 CHECK FOR INTERMITTENT OPEN BETWEEN EATC MODULE AND PCM • Scan Tool connected. • Key on. • Access ACCS PID. • A/C on. • Observe ACCS PID for an indication of a fault while performing the following (the ACCS PID will turn off and on quickly when a fault is detected, indicating an intermittent open): — Shake, wiggle, bend the A/C demand/ACCS circuit between the EATC module and PCM. The drawing below shows the portion of circuit to be checked. — Lightly tap the A/C cycling switch to simulate road shock. • Disconnect and inspect the A/C cycling switch connector and the EATC module connector. • Is a fault indicated?	Yes No	▶ ▶	Key off. ISOLATE fault and SERVICE as necessary. RECONNECT all components. PERFORM PCM Reset to clear DTC(s) (REFER to Powertrain Control Module (PCM) Reset). START engine and TURN A/C on for about 2 minutes. Engine off, A/C off. RERUN Quick Test. UNABLE to duplicate fault at this time. RECONNECT all components. PERFORM PCM Reset to clear DTC(s) (REFER tc Powertrain Control Module (PCM) Reset). service any additional symptoms.

CIRCUIT TO BE TESTED — PCM PIN 41 — FROM EATC MODULE — A/C CYCLING SWITCH — TO CONSTANT CONTROL RELAY MODULE (CCRM)

FM0159601561320X

Fig. 289   Test X: Constant Control Relay Module (Part 32 of 51). 1996

Test Step	Result	▶	Action to Take
X120 DTC P1460: CHECK FOR INTERMITTENT OPEN OR SHORT IN WAC CIRCUIT Continuous Memory Diagnostic Trouble Code (DTC) P1460 indicates that a WAC circuit failure has occurred during vehicle operation. NOTE: If vehicle is not equipped with A/C, the WAC circuit is not used and the DTC P1460 can be ignored. Possible causes: — Open or shorted WAC circuit. — Open VPWR to CCRM (Continental and Windstar only). • Key off. • Scan Tool connected. • Disconnect A/C Cycling Switch. • Install a jumper wire in the A/C Cycling Switch vehicle harness connector (to complete the circuit). • Key on, engine off. • A/C demand switch on. • Check WAC circuit for open or short to power while performing the following (the A/C clutch will click on when a fault is detected): — Shake, wiggle, bend the WAC circuit from the CCRM to the PCM. — Lightly tap the CCRM to simulate road shock. • Access Output Test Mode on the Scan Tool • Turn outputs off (this will prevent the WAC circuit from turning off the A/C clutch). • Check WAC circuit for short to ground, and for Continental and Windstar, check for open VPWR to CCRM, while performing the following (the A/C clutch will click off when a fault is detected): — Shake, wiggle, bend the WAC circuit from the CCRM to the PCM. — Lightly tap the CCRM to simulate road shock. — For Continental and Windstar, shake, wiggle, bend the VPWR circuit between the EEC-V Power Relay and the CCRM. • Key off, A/C off. • Is a fault indicated?	Yes No	▶ ▶	ISOLATE fault and SERVICE as necessary. REMOVE jumper wire. RECONNECT all components. COMPLETE PCM Reset to clear DTCs (REFER to Powertrain Control Module (PCM) Reset). START engine. TURN AC on, WAIT 15 seconds. A/C off. Key off. RERUN Quick Test. REMOVE jumper wire. GO to Pinpoint Test Step **Z1** with the following data: WACF PID or WACA PID (whichever is available) and list of Possible Causes.

FM0159601561330X

Fig. 289   Test X: Constant Control Relay Module (Part 33 of 51). 1996

Test Step	Result	▶	Action to Take
X124 DTC P1464: CHECK ACCS PID Diagnostic Trouble Code (DTC) P1464 indicates the ACCS input to the Powertrain Control Module (PCM) was high during Self-Test. NOTE: Verify A/C and defrost were off during Self-Test. If A/C or defrost were on, turn off and rerun Self-Test. • Key on, engine off. • Scan Tool connected. • A/C and defrost off. • Access ACCS PID. • Is ACCS PID on?	Yes No	▶ ▶	GO to **X125.** The ACCS PID indicates that the ACCS input to the PCM is low. VERIFY test results. With A/C and defrost off, RERUN Self-Test where P1464 was received.
X125 ACCS PID ON: DISCONNECT A/C CYCLING SWITCH AND CHECK IF ACCS PID TURNS OFF • Key off. • Disconnect A/C Cycling Switch. • Key on, engine off. • Access ACCS PID. • Is ACCS PID off?	Yes No	▶ ▶	Key off. VERIFY operation of A/C Demand Switch. If OK, SERVICE short to power in A/C Demand Switch. RECONNECT all components. RE-EVALUATE symptom. Key off. GO to **X126.**
X126 CHECK POWER-TO-A/C CLUTCH CIRCUIT FOR SHORT TO POWER • Key off. • Disconnect CCRM. • Key on. • Measure voltage between Pin 23 of the CCRM vehicle harness connector and the battery negative post. • Key off. • Was voltage less than 1.0 volt?	Yes No	▶ ▶	GO to **X127.** SERVICE short to power. RECONNECT all components. RE-EVALUATE symptom.
X127 CHECK ACCS CIRCUIT FOR SHORT TO POWER • Key off. • A/C Cycling Switch and CCRM disconnected. • Disconnect PCM. Inspect for damaged or pushed out pins, corrosion, loose wires, etc. Service as necessary. • Install breakout box, leave PCM disconnected. • Key on. • Measure voltage between Test Pin 41 (ACCS) and Test Pins 51 and 103 (PWR GND). • Key off. • Was voltage less than 1.0 volt?	Yes No	▶ ▶	GO to **X128.** SERVICE short to power. REMOVE breakout box. RECONNECT all components. RE-EVALUATE symptom.

FM0159601561340X

Fig. 289   Test X: Constant Control Relay Module (Part 34 of 51). 1996

Test Step	Result	▶	Action to Take
X128 CHECK ACCS CIRCUIT VOLTAGE TO PCM WITH CCRM CONNECTED • Key off. • Reconnect CCRM. • A/C Cycling Switch disconnected. • Breakout box installed, PCM disconnected. • Key on. • Again, measure voltage between Test Pin 41 (ACCS) and Test Pins 51 and 103 (PWR GND). • Key off. • Was voltage less than 1.0 volt?	Yes No	▶ ▶	REPLACE PCM. REMOVE breakout box. RECONNECT all components. RE-EVALUATE symptom. REPLACE CCRM. REMOVE breakout box. RECONNECT all components. RE-EVALUATE symptom.
X130 NO WAC W/NO DTCS: CHECK CCRM • Scan Tool connected. • A/C clutch and CCRM connected. • Key on, engine off. • Access Output Test Mode on Scan Tool • A/C demand switch on. • While listening for the A/C clutch, command the outputs off and on a couple of times. • Does the A/C clutch engage and disengage when the outputs are cycled off and on?	Yes No	▶ ▶	Key off. EEC system is operating properly. If symptom is intermittent, GO to Pinpoint Test Step **Z1** with the following data: WACF PID or WACA PID (whichever is available). Otherwise, testing is complete. REMOVE breakout box. RECONNECT all components. service any other symptoms. VERIFY that the A/C clutch was engaged during testing. If not, REPEAT test with clutch engaged. If clutch was engaged, REPLACE CCRM. RECONNECT all components. RE-EVALUATE symptom.
X135 ACPSW PID "CLOSED" WITH ACPSW DISCONNECTED: CHECK ACPSW CIRCUIT FOR SHORT TO GROUND • Key off. • ACPSW disconnected. • Disconnect Scan Tool from DLC. • Disconnect PCM. Inspect for damaged or pushed out pins, corrosion, loose wires, etc. Service as necessary. • Install breakout box, leave PCM disconnected. • Measure resistance between Test Pin 86 (ACPSW) and Test Pins 77 and 103 (PWR GND) at the breakout box. • Are both resistances greater than 10,000 ohms?	Yes No	▶ ▶	REPLACE PCM. REMOVE breakout box. RECONNECT all components. RE-EVALUATE symptom. SERVICE ACPSW circuit short to ground. REMOVE breakout box. RECONNECT all components. RE-EVALUATE symptom.

FM0159601561350X

Fig. 289   Test X: Constant Control Relay Module (Part 35 of 51). 1996

Part 36 of 51

Test Step	Result	▶	Action to Take
X150 DIAGNOSTIC TROUBLE CODE (DTC) P0230: CHECK FUEL PUMP RELAY AND FP CIRCUIT IN CCRM			
DTC P0230 indicates a fuel pump primary circuit failure. Possible causes: — Open or shorted Fuel Pump (FP) circuit. — Open VPWR circuit to CCRM (Windstar). — Damaged CCRM. — Damaged PCM. • Key off. • CCRM disconnected. • Check fuel pump relay coil resistance: — For Windstar, measure resistance between Pin 13 and Pin 18 of CCRM. — For all others, measure resistance between Pin 18 and Pin 24 of the CCRM. — Resistance should be between 65 and 120 ohms. • Check CCRM for internal short circuit: — For Windstar, measure resistance of CCRM between Pin 18 and the following pins: 1 through 8, 10, 11, 12, 15 and 24. — For all others, measure resistance of CCRM between Pin 18 and the following pins: 1 through 11, 13 and 15. — For all applications, measure resistance between Pin 18 and the CCRM case. — Each resistance should be greater than 1000 ohms. • Are the CCRM checks OK?	Yes No	▶ ▶	For Windstar: GO to X151. For all others: GO to X152. REPLACE CCRM. RECONNECT all components. RERUN Quick Test.
X151 CHECK VPWR CIRCUIT TO CCRM			
• Key off. • CCRM disconnected. • Disconnect EEC-V Power Relay. • Measure resistance between Pin 13 of the CCRM vehicle harness connector and the VPWR circuit at the EEC-V Power Relay vehicle harness connector. • Is resistance less than 5.0 ohms?	Yes No	▶ ▶	RECONNECT EEC-V Power Relay. GO to X152. SERVICE open in VPWR circuit between EEC-V Power Relay and CCRM. RECONNECT all components. RERUN Quick Test.

VPWR

EEC-V POWER RELAY VEHICLE HARNESS CONNECTOR

FM015960156136OX

Fig. 289   Test X: Constant Control Relay Module (Part 36 of 51). 1996

Part 37 of 51

Test Step	Result	▶	Action to Take
X152 CHECK FUEL PUMP CIRCUIT FOR SHORT TO POWER			
• Key off. • CCRM disconnected. • Disconnect PCM. Inspect for damaged or pushed out pins, corrosion, loose wires, etc. Service as necessary. • Key on, engine off. • Measure voltage between Pin 18 at the CCRM vehicle harness connector and the battery negative post. • Is voltage less than 1.0 volt?	Yes No	▶ ▶	GO to X153. SERVICE short to power. RECONNECT all components. RERUN Quick Test.
X153 CHECK FUEL PUMP CIRCUIT FOR SHORT TO GROUND			
• Key off. • PCM disconnected. • CCRM disconnected. • Disconnect Scan Tool from DLC. • Measure resistance between Pin 18 at the CCRM vehicle harness connector and the battery negative post. • Is resistance greater than 10,000 ohms?	Yes No	▶ ▶	GO to X154. SERVICE short to ground. RECONNECT all components. RERUN Quick Test.
X154 CHECK FUEL PUMP CIRCUIT CONTINUITY			
• Key off. • PCM disconnected. • CCRM disconnected. • Install breakout box. • Measure resistance between Pin 18 at the CCRM vehicle harness connector and Test pin 80 (FP) at the breakout box. • Is resistance less than 5.0 ohms?	Yes No	▶ ▶	If Key On, Engine Off (KOEO) DTC P0231 or P0232 is also present with the P0230: GO to X155. All others: REPLACE PCM. RECONNECT all components. RERUN Quick Test. SERVICE open circuit. REMOVE breakout box. RECONNECT all components. RERUN Quick Test.

FM015960156137OX

Fig. 289   Test X: Constant Control Relay Module (Part 37 of 51). 1996

Part 38 of 51

Test Step	Result	▶	Action to Take
X155 CHECK THE FUEL PUMP PRIMARY CIRCUIT INSIDE THE PCM			
NOTE: The next two test steps will check the FP circuit in the PCM. To do this either the FPA or FPF PID will be monitored, whichever is available. The FPA PID detects the actual voltage on the FP circuit, and will indicate "ON" when the circuit is grounded and "OFF" when it is not. The FPF PID is able to detect for faults on the FP circuit, and will indicate "NO" when no fault is detected and "YES" when a fault is detected. • Key off. • Remove breakout box. • Reconnect PCM. • Reconnect CCRM. • Reconnect Scan Tool to DLC. • Key on, engine off. • Access FPA or FPF PID (whichever is available) on Scan Tool. • Is the FPF PID "YES" (or FPA PID on)?	Yes No	▶ ▶	KEY off. REPLACE PCM. RECONNECT all components. RERUN Quick Test. GO to X156.
X156 CHECK THE FUEL PUMP PRIMARY CIRCUIT INSIDE THE PCM			
NOTE: The Scan Tool must be connected to a reliable power source that is powered with the ignition key in the START position (e.g. directly to the vehicle battery). Also verify that the vehicle battery is fully charged. • Key on, engine off. • While viewing the FPA or FPF PID, crank engine. • Is the FPF PID "YES" (or the FPA PID off) during crank?	Yes No	▶ ▶	Key off. REPLACE PCM. RECONNECT all components. RERUN Quick Test. Key off. The fuel pump primary circuit is OK in the harness and PCM. If KOEO P0231 is present: GO to X180. If KOEO P0232 is present: GO to X170.
X160 DIAGNOSTIC TROUBLE CODE (DTC) P1232 CHECK FOR VPWR TO FUEL PUMP RELAY			
DTC P1232 indicates a low speed fuel pump primary circuit failure. Possible causes: — Open or shorted circuit. — Damaged low speed fuel pump relay. — Damaged PCM. • Disconnect low speed fuel pump relay. • Key on, engine off. • Measure voltage between VPWR circuit at the low speed fuel pump relay vehicle harness connector and chassis ground. • Is voltage greater than 10.5 volts?	Yes No	▶ ▶	GO to X161. SERVICE open in VPWR circuit between the EEC power relay and the low speed fuel pump relay. RECONNECT low speed fuel pump relay. RERUN Quick Test.

FM015960156138OX

Fig. 289   Test X: Constant Control Relay Module (Part 38 of 51). 1996

Part 39 of 51

Test Step	Result	▶	Action to Take
X161 CHECK LOW SPEED FUEL PUMP RELAY			
• Key off. • Low speed fuel pump relay disconnected. • Check low speed fuel pump relay coil resistance: — Measure resistance between Pins 85 and 86 of the low speed fuel pump relay (pin numbers molded on relay). — Resistance should be between 40 and 85 ohms. • Check low speed fuel pump relay for internal shorts. — Measure resistance between Pin 85 and both Pins 30 and 87 of the low speed fuel pump relay. — Both resistances should be greater than 10,000 ohms. • Are all resistance checks OK?	Yes No	▶ ▶	GO to X162. REPLACE low speed fuel pump relay. RERUN Quick Test.

LOW SPEED
FUEL PUMP RELAY

| 87 |
| 87A |
| 30 |

86 — 85

COIL - 85 AND 86
COMMON - 30
NO-87
NC -87A

Test Step	Result	▶	Action to Take
X162 CHECK LOW FUEL PUMP CIRCUIT FOR SHORT TO POWER			
• Key off. • Low speed fuel pump relay disconnected. • Disconnect Powertrain Control Module (PCM). Inspect for damaged or pushed out pins, corrosion, loose wires, etc. Service as necessary. • Install breakout box, leave PCM disconnected. • Key on, engine off. • Measure voltage between Test Pin 79 (LFP) at the breakout box and chassis ground. • Is voltage less than 1.0 volt?	Yes No	▶ ▶	GO to X163. SERVICE short to power. REMOVE breakout box. RECONNECT all components. RERUN Quick Test.

FM015960156139OX

Fig. 289   Test X: Constant Control Relay Module (Part 39 of 51). 1996

Test Step	Result	▶	Action to Take
X163 CHECK LOW FUEL PUMP CIRCUIT FOR SHORT TO GROUND • Key off. • Disconnect Scan Tool from DLC. • Breakout box installed, PCM disconnected. • Low speed fuel pump relay disconnected. • Measure resistance between Test Pin 79 and Test Pins 51 or 103 (PWR GND) and 91 (SIG RTN) at the breakout box. • **Is resistance greater than 10,000 ohms?**	Yes No	▶ ▶	GO to X164. SERVICE short circuit. REMOVE breakout box. RECONNECT all components. RERUN Quick Test.
X164 CHECK LOW FUEL PUMP CIRCUIT CONTINUITY • Key off. • Breakout box installed, PCM disconnected. • Low speed fuel pump relay disconnected. • Measure resistance between the Low Fuel Pump circuit at the fuel pump relay vehicle harness connector and Test Pin 79 at the breakout box. • **Is resistance less than 5.0 ohms?**	Yes No	▶ ▶	REPLACE PCM. RECONNECT all components. RERUN Quick Test. SERVICE open circuit. REMOVE breakout box. RECONNECT all components. RERUN Quick Test.
X170 DIAGNOSTIC TROUBLE CODE DTC P0232: DOES ENGINE START? DTC P0232 indicates that the Powertrain Control Module (PCM) detected the FPM circuit voltage was high when the fuel pump was commanded off. The FPM circuit is wired to a "pull-up" voltage inside the PCM. The FPM circuit will go high if, with the key on and the fuel pump commanded off, the FPM/Power-to-Pump circuit loses its path to ground through the fuel pump. The FPM circuit will also be high if the FPM/Power-to-Pump circuit is shorted to power. Possible causes: No Start: — Inertia Fuel Shutoff (IFS) switch not reset or electrically open. — Open circuit between the fuel pump and FPM circuit connection to power-to-pump circuit. — Poor fuel pump ground. — Fuel pump electrically open. Engine Starts: — Fuel pump secondary circuit short to power. — Fuel pump relay contacts always closed. — Open in FPM circuit between PCM and connection to power-to-pump circuit. — Damaged PCM. • **Does the engine start?**	Yes No	▶ ▶	GO to X171. GO to X175.

Fig. 289 Test X: Constant Control Relay Module (Part 40 of 51). 1996

Test Step	Result	▶	Action to Take
X171 VERIFY THAT FUEL PUMP IS OFF • Key on, wait 5 seconds. • Listen for motor noise from fuel pump (it may be necessary to listen by fuel tank). • **Is fuel pump off?**	Yes No	▶ ▶	GO to X173. GO to X172.
X172 CHECK FOR FUEL PUMP RELAY ALWAYS CLOSED • Key off. • Disconnect CCRM. • Key on. • **Does fuel pump shut off when CCRM is disconnected?**	Yes No	▶ ▶	REPLACE CCRM. RERUN Quick Test. SERVICE short to power in power-to-pump/FPM circuit. RECONNECT CCRM. RERUN Quick Test.
X173 CHECK FPM CIRCUIT CONTINUITY • Key off. • Disconnect PCM. Inspect for damaged or pushed out pins, corrosion, loose wires, etc. Service as necessary. • Install breakout box, leave PCM disconnected. • Disconnect CCRM. • Measure resistance between Test Pin 40 (FPM) at the breakout box and Pin 5 at the CCRM vehicle harness connector. • **Is resistance less than 7.0 ohms?**	Yes No	▶ ▶	GO to X174. SERVICE open circuit. REMOVE breakout box. RECONNECT all components. RERUN Quick Test.
X174 CHECK FPM CIRCUIT IN PCM • Key off. • Remove breakout box. • Reconnect PCM. • Reconnect CCRM. • Scan Tool connected to DLC. • Key on, engine off. • Access FPM PID on Scan Tool. • **Is the FPM PID off?**	Yes No	▶ ▶	No fault is detected. The FPM circuit is OK in the harness and the PCM. DISREGARD the P0232 at this time. RETURN to the Diagnostic Subroutine that the P0232 was received and continue diagnosis as directed. REPLACE PCM. RERUN Quick Test.
X175 CHECK INERTIA FUEL SHUTOFF SWITCH • Key off. • Locate and disconnect Inertia Fuel Shutoff (IFS) switch (verify that switch is reset). • Measure resistance between the "C" and "NC" pins of the IFS switch. • **Is resistance less than 5.0 ohms?**	Yes No	▶ ▶	GO to X176. REPLACE or RESET IFS switch. RERUN Quick Test.

Fig. 289 Test X: Constant Control Relay Module (Part 41 of 51). 1996

Test Step	Result	▶	Action to Take
X176 CHECK POWER-TO-PUMP CIRCUIT CONTINUITY BETWEEN IFS SWITCH AND CCRM • Key off. • IFS switch disconnected. • Disconnect CCRM. • Measure resistance of the Power-To-Pump circuit between the IFS switch vehicle harness connector and pin 5 of the CCRM vehicle harness connector. • **Is resistance less than 7.0 ohms?**	Yes No	▶ ▶	RECONNECT CCRM. GO to X177. SERVICE open in Power-To-Pump circuit between IFS switch and FPM connection to circuit.
X177 CHECK FUEL PUMP GROUND CIRCUIT • Key off. • IFS switch disconnected. • Disconnect fuel pump. • Measure resistance between the fuel pump motor ground circuit at the fuel pump vehicle harness connector and chassis ground. • **Is resistance less than 5.0 ohms?**	Yes No	▶ ▶	GO to X178. SERVICE open fuel pump ground circuit. RECONNECT all components. RERUN Quick Test.
X178 CHECK CONTINUITY OF POWER-TO-PUMP CIRCUIT BETWEEN THE IFS SWITCH AND FUEL PUMP • Key off. • Fuel pump disconnected. • IFS disconnected. • Measure resistance of the Power-To-Pump circuit between the IFS switch and fuel pump vehicle harness connectors. • **Is resistance less than 5.0 ohms?**	Yes No	▶ ▶	GO to X179. SERVICE open circuit. RECONNECT all components. RERUN Quick Test.
X179 CHECK INTERNAL RESISTANCE OF FUEL PUMP • Key off. • Fuel pump disconnected. • IFS disconnected. • Measure internal resistance of the fuel pump motor between the Power-To-Pump pin and ground pin of the fuel pump connector. • **Is resistance less than 10.0 ohms?**	Yes No	▶ ▶	All fuel pump circuit checks are OK. VERIFY test step results. If all test steps are OK, RECONNECT all components and RETURN to Diagnostic Subroutine where DTC was received and FOLLOW directions to continue diagnosis. REPLACE fuel pump. RECONNECT all components. RERUN Quick Test.

Fig. 289 Test X: Constant Control Relay Module (Part 42 of 51). 1996

Test Step	Result	▶	Action to Take
X180 DIAGNOSTIC TROUBLE CODE DTC P0231: DOES ENGINE START? NOTE: If Key On, Engine Off DTC P0230 is also present and has not been diagnosed, go to X150 (to check the primary fuel pump circuits first). Diagnostic Trouble Code (DTC) P0231 indicates a fuel pump secondary circuit failure between the B(+) supply and the FPM connection to the power-to-pump circuit. Possible causes: No Starts: — Open circuit between the B(+) supply and the FPM connection to the power-to-pump circuit. — Fuel pump relay contacts always open. Engine Starts: — For 4.6L 4V Mustang, open power-to-pump circuit between low speed fuel pump relay and FPM splice. — Damaged PCM. • **Does the engine start?**	Yes No	▶ ▶	For 4.6L 4V Mustang: GO to X185. For all others: REPLACE PCM. RERUN Quick Test. GO to X181.
X181 CHECK FOR B(+) TO FUEL PUMP RELAY IN CCRM • Key off. • Disconnect CCRM. • Measure voltage between Pin 11 at the CCRM vehicle harness connector and the battery negative post. • **Is voltage greater than 10.5 volts?**	Yes No	▶ ▶	GO to X182. VERIFY integrity of fuse/fuse link for B(+) supply to CCRM (fuel pump relay). If OK, SERVICE open in B(+) supply to CCRM. If fuse/fuse link is damaged, check B(+) circuit for short to ground before replacing. RECONNECT CCRM. RERUN Quick Test.
X182 CHECK POWER-TO-PUMP CIRCUIT CONTINUITY • Key off. • CCRM disconnected. • Measure resistance between Pin 5 at the CCRM vehicle harness connector and the battery negative post. • **Is resistance less than 12.0 ohms?**	Yes No	▶ ▶	REPLACE CCRM. RERUN Quick Test. **For 4.6L 4V Mustang:** GO to X183. **All others:** SERVICE open in power-to-pump circuit between FPM splice and CCRM. RECONNECT CCRM. RERUN Quick Test.

Fig. 289 Test X: Constant Control Relay Module (Part 43 of 51). 1996

Test Step	Result	▶	Action to Take
X183 ISOLATE OPEN IN POWER-TO-PUMP CIRCUIT • Key off. • CCRM disconnected. • Disconnect low speed fuel pump relay. • Measure resistance of the Power-To-Pump circuit between the low speed fuel pump relay vehicle harness connector and Pin 5 of the CCRM vehicle harness connector. • **Is resistance less than 5.0 ohms?**	Yes	▶	SERVICE open in Power-To-Pump circuit between the low speed fuel pump relay and the FPM splice to the circuit. Also VERIFY continuity of the normally closed contacts of the low speed fuel pump relay (Pins 30 and 87A of the relay). RECONNECT all components. RERUN Quick Test.
	No	▶	SERVICE open Power-To-Pump circuit between the CCRM and the low speed fuel pump relay. RECONNECT all components. RERUN Quick Test.

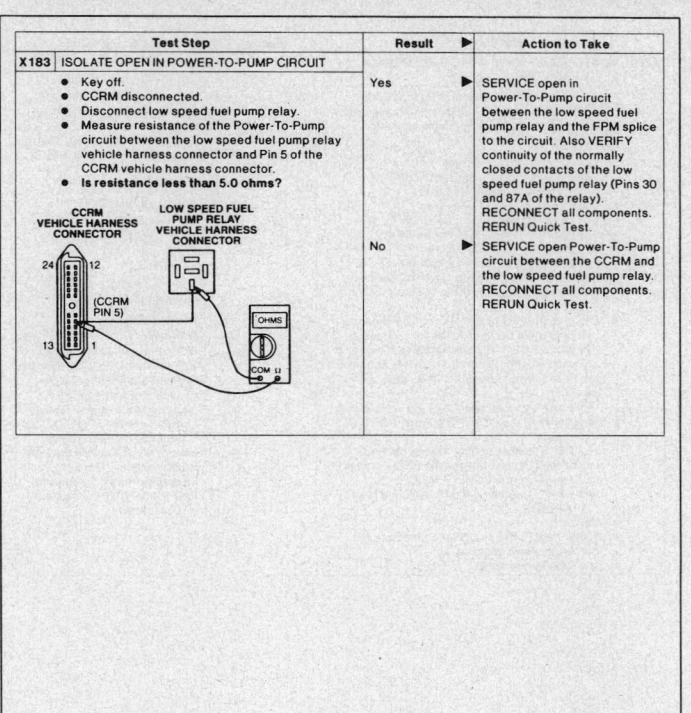

FM015960156144OX

Fig. 289   Test X: Constant Control Relay Module (Part 44 of 51). 1996

Test Step	Result	▶	Action to Take
X185 CHECK POWER-TO-PUMP CIRCUIT CONTINUITY BETWEEN LOW SPEED FUEL PUMP RELAY AND FPM CIRCUIT SPLICE • Key off. • Disconnect Scan Tool from DLC. • Disconnect low speed fuel pump relay. • Measure resistance of the Power-to-Pump circuit through the resistor from the Power-To-Pump pin shown below at the low speed fuel pump relay vehicle harness connector and chassis ground. • **Is resistance less than 12.0 ohms?**	Yes	▶	REPLACE PCM. RECONNECT all components. RERUN Quick Test.
	No	▶	VERIFY condition of resistor in Power-To-Pump circuit. If OK, SERVICE open Power-To-Pump circuit between the low speed fuel pump relay and the FPM splice to the circuit. RECONNECT all components. RERUN Quick Test.

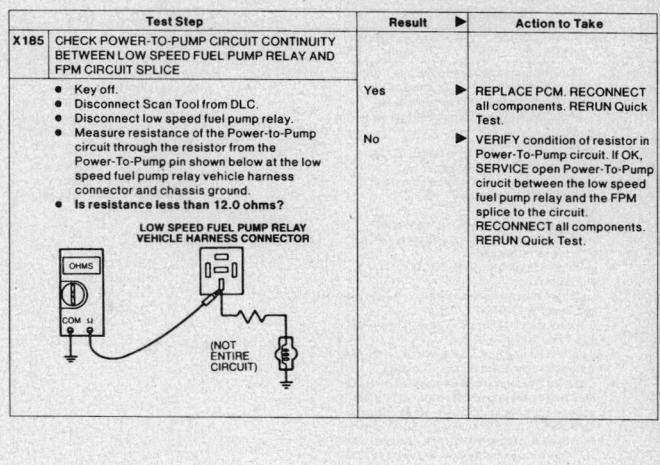

FM015960156145OX

Fig. 289   Test X: Constant Control Relay Module (Part 45 of 51). 1996

Test Step	Result	▶	Action to Take
X190 CONTINUOUS MEMORY DTC P0232: CHECK EEC-V HARNESS NOTE: If Continuous Memory DTC P0230 is also present and has not been diagnosed, GO to **X200** (to check primary circuit first). Continuous Memory Diagnostic Trouble Code (DTC) P0232 indicates that one of the following intermittent conditions has occurred: — Fuel pump circuit activated when PCM expected circuit to be off (i.e. fuel system test or prime procedure). — Inertia Fuel Shutoff switch was tripped, then reset. — Open circuit in or between the fuel pump and FPM circuit at the PCM (refer to schematic). — Poor fuel pump ground. — FPM or power-to-pump circuit short to power. — Fuel pump relay contacts stuck closed. — Engine stall due to excessive load. • Key on, engine off. • Access FPM PID on Scan Tool. • Observe the FPM PID for an indication of a fault while performing the following (the FPM PID will turn ON when an open or short to power is detected): — For 4.6L 4V Mustang: shake, wiggle, bend the Power-To-Pump circuit between the CCRM Pin 5 and the low speed fuel pump relay and from the relay to the fuel pump. — For all except the 4.6L 4V Mustang: shake, wiggle, bend the Power-To-Pump circuit between the CCRM Pin 5 and the fuel pump. — Shake, wiggle, bend the fuel pump ground circuit from the fuel pump to ground. — Lightly tap the fuel pump to simulate road shock. — Lightly tap Inertia Fuel Shutoff switch to simulate road shock. — Lightly tap the low speed fuel pump relay (4.6L 4V Mustang). — Lightly tap the CCRM to simulate road shock. — Shake, wiggle, bend the FPM circuit between the PCM and the splice to the Power-To-Pump circuit. • Key off. • Inspect the fuel pump vehicle harness connector and the fuel pump ground for corrosion, damaged pins, etc. • **Is a fault indicated/found?**	Yes	▶	ISOLATE fault and SERVICE as necessary. COMPLETE PCM RESET to clear DTC(s) (REFER to Powertrain Control Module (PCM) Reset). RERUN Quick Test.
	No	▶	GO to Pinpoint Test Step **Z1** with the following data: FPM PID and list of possible causes.

FM015960156146OX

Fig. 289   Test X: Constant Control Relay Module (Part 46 of 51). 1996

Test Step	Result	▶	Action to Take
X194 CONTINUOUS MEMORY DIAGNOSTIC TROUBLE CODE (DTC) P0231: CHECK POWER-TO-PUMP CIRCUIT CONTINUITY BETWEEN LOW SPEED FUEL PUMP RELAY AND FPM CIRCUIT SPLICE DTC P0231 indicates that sometime while the fuel pump was commanded on, the FPM circuit went low. For the two speed fuel pump system on the 4.6L 4V Mustang, an open in the Power-To-Pump circuit that goes through the resistor could be a possible cause of this DTC, and would only be detected when the normally closed contacts of the low speed fuel pump relay are commanded open. • Key off. • Disconnect Scan Tool from DLC. • Disconnect low speed fuel pump relay. • Measure resistance of the Power-To-Pump circuit through the resistor from the Power-To-Pump pin shown below at the low speed fuel pump relay vehicle harness connector and chassis ground. • **Is resistance less than 12.0 ohms?**	Yes	▶	RECONNECT low speed fuel pump relay. RECONNECT Scan Tool to DLC. GO to **X195**.
	No	▶	VERIFY condition of resistor in Power-To-Pump circuit. If OK, SERVICE open Power-To-Pump circuit between the low speed fuel pump relay and the FPM splice to the circuit. RECONNECT all components. COMPLETE PCM reset to clear DTCs (REFER to Powertrain Control Module (PCM) Reset). RERUN Quick Test.

FM015960156147OX

Fig. 289   Test X: Constant Control Relay Module (Part 47 of 51). 1996

Test Step	Result	▶	Action to Take
X195 CONTINUOUS MEMORY DTC P0231: CHECK EEC-V HARNESS			
Continuous Memory Diagnostic Trouble Code (DTC) P0231 indicates that sometime during vehicle operation when the fuel pump was commanded on, the FPM circuit voltage went low. Possible causes: — Open in B(+) circuit to the fuel pump relay. — Fuel pump relay contacts open. — Open in Power-to-Pump circuit between the CCRM and FPM splice. • Key off. • Disconnect PCM. Inspect for damaged or pushed out pins, corrosion, loose wires, etc. Service as necessary. • Install breakout box. Leave PCM disconnected. • Install a jumper wire between Test Pin 80 (FP) and Test Pin 77 (PWR GND). • Connect a DVOM between Test Pin 40 (FPM) and Test Pin 51 (PWR GND). • Key on. The fuel pump will turn on and DVOM voltage will be greater than 10.0 volts. • Observe DVOM voltage for an indication of a fault while performing the following (DVOM voltage will change suddenly when a fault is detected, indicating an open): — Shake, wiggle, bend the fuel pump relay B(+) circuit to the CCRM (Pin 11). — For 4.6L 4V Mustang: shake, wiggle, bend the Power-To-Pump circuit between the CCRM Pin 5 and the low speed fuel pump relay, and from the relay to the FPM splice. — For all except the 4.6L 4V Mustang: shake, wiggle, bend the Power-to-Pump circuit between the CCRM and the FPM splice. — Lightly tap the low speed fuel pump relay (4.6L 4V Mustang). • Key off. • Inspect the CCRM connector for corrosion, damaged pins, etc. • **Is a fault indicated?**	Yes No	▶ ▶	ISOLATE fault and SERVICE as necessary. COMPLETE PCM Reset to clear DTCs (REFER to Powertrain Control Module (PCM) Reset). RERUN Quick Test. GO to Pinpoint Test Step **Z1** with the following data: FPM PID and list of possible causes.

FM0159601561480X

Fig. 289 Test X: Constant Control Relay Module (Part 48 of 51). 1996

Test Step	Result	▶	Action to Take
X200 CONTINUOUS MEMORY DTC P0230: CHECK EEC-V HARNESS			
Continuous Memory Diagnostic Trouble Code (DTC) P0230 indicates a fuel pump primary circuit failure has occurred during vehicle operation. Possible causes: — Open coil in fuel pump relay. — Open in Fuel Pump Circuit (PCM Pin 80). — Open VPWR to CCRM (Windstar). • Scan Tool connected. • Key on, engine off. Wait 5 seconds. • Access FPA or FPF PID (whichever is available). The FPF PID will be "NO" or the FPA PID will be off, indicating that the PCM detects VPWR voltage through the fuel pump relay coil and FP circuit (Pin 80) to the PCM. • Observe the FPA or FPF PID for an indication of a fault while performing the following (the FPF PID will be "YES", or the FPA PID will turn on, when an open is detected (this is because the PCM will not detect VPWR voltage on Pin 80 (FP)): — Shake, wiggle, bend the Fuel Pump circuit between the PCM (Pin 80) and CCRM (Pin 18). — For Windstar, shake, wiggle, bend the VPWR circuit between the EEC-V Power Relay and the CCRM (Pin 13). — Lightly tap the CCRM (to simulate road shock). • Key off. • Inspect the PCM and CCRM connectors for corrosion, damaged pins, etc. • **Is a fault indicated?**	Yes No	▶ ▶	ISOLATE fault and SERVICE as necessary. COMPLETE PCM Reset to clear DTCs (REFER to Powertrain Control Module (PCM) Reset). RERUN Quick Test. **If P0231 or P0232 is also present with P0230:** An intermittent fuel pump secondary circuit fault may exist. For P0231: GO to **X195**. For P0232: GO to **X190**. **All others:** GO to Pinpoint Test Step **Z1** with the following data: FPA or FPF PID and list of possible causes. For testing the FP circuit with the engine running, also monitor the FPM PID. This is because the FPA PID will always read ON when the PCM is turning on the fuel pump, so an open harness circuit using the FPA or FPF PID could not be detected.

FM0159601561490X

Fig. 289 Test X: Constant Control Relay Module (Part 49 of 51). 1996

Test Step	Result	▶	Action to Take
X205 CONTINUOUS MEMORY DIAGNOSTIC TROUBLE CODE (DTC) P1232: CHECK EEC-V HARNESS			
A Continuous Memory DTC P1232 indicates a low speed fuel pump primary circuit failure has occurred during vehicle operation. Possible causes: — Open in VPWR to low speed fuel pump relay. — Open coil in low speed fuel pump relay. — Open in Low Fuel Pump (LFP) circuit (PCM Pin 79). • Scan Tool connected. • Key on, engine off. Wait 5 seconds. • Access LFPF PID. The LFPF PID will be "NO", indicating that the PCM detects VPWR voltage through the low speed fuel pump relay coil and LFP circuit (Pin 79) to the PCM. • Observe the LFPF PID for an indication of a fault while performing the following (the LFPF PID will be "YES" if a fault is detected. — Shake, wiggle, bend the LFP circuit between the PCM (Pin 79) and the low speed fuel pump relay. — Shake, wiggle, bend the VPWR circuit between the EEC-V Power Relay and the low speed fuel pump relay. — Lightly tap the low speed fuel pump relay (to simulate road shock). • Key off. • Inspect the PCM and low speed fuel pump relay connector for corrosion, damaged pins, etc. • **Is a fault indicated?**	Yes No	▶ ▶	ISOLATE fault and SERVICE as necessary. COMPLETE PCM reset to clear DTCs (REFER to Powertrain Control Module (PCM) Reset). RERUN Quick Test. Unable to duplicate and/or identify fault at this time. GO to Pinpoint Test Step **Z1** with the following data: LFPF PID and list of possible causes.

FM0159601561500X

Fig. 289 Test X: Constant Control Relay Module (Part 50 of 51). 1996

Test Step	Result	▶	Action to Take
X210 HARD START/LACK OF POWER: CHECK LOW SPEED FUEL PUMP RELAY NORMALLY CLOSED CONTACTS			
The purpose of the next two test steps is to verify that the secondary circuits used for high speed fuel pump operation are OK. • Key off. • Disconnect low speed fuel pump relay. • Measure resistance between Pin 30 and Pin 87A of the relay (pin numbers molded on relay). • **Is resistance less than 5.0 ohms?** 	Yes No	▶ ▶	Normally closed contacts of the relay are OK. GO to **X211**. REPLACE low speed fuel pump relay. RE-EVALUATE symptom.
X211 CHECK POWER-TO-PUMP CIRCUIT (HIGH SPEED PORTION) FROM LOW SPEED FUEL PUMP RELAY			
• Key off. • Low speed fuel pump relay disconnected. • Measure resistance between the Power-To-Pump circuit pin of the low speed fuel pump relay vehicle harness connector shown below and chassis ground. • **Is resistance less than 10.0 ohms?** 	Yes No	▶ ▶	The secondary circuits for high speed fuel pump operation are OK. SERVICE open in Power-To-Pump circuit between the low speed fuel pump relay and the splice where the circuit through the resistor connects (REFER to Pinpoint Test X cover page schematic). RECONNECT all components. RE-EVALUATE symptom.

FM0159601561510X

Fig. 289 Test X: Constant Control Relay Module (Part 51 of 51). 1996

Note

You should enter this Pinpoint Test only when directed here.

Remember

This Pinpoint Test is intended to diagnose the following:

- Harness circuits: All associated with VLCM
- Variable Load Control Module (VLCM) (14B239 (Module), 14B205 (Assembly))
- Powertrain Control Module (PCM) (12A650)

FM015960156 2010X

Fig. 290   Test XB: Variable Load Control Module (Part 1 of 37). 1996

Pinpoint Test Schematic

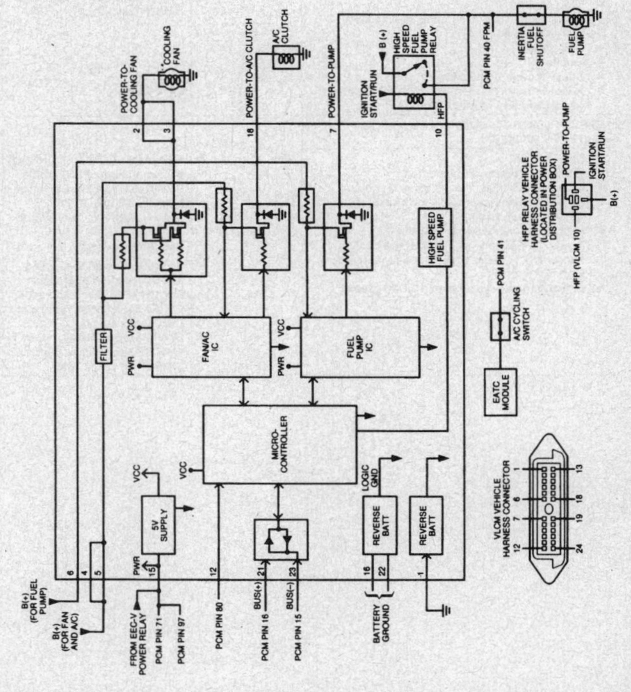

FM015960156 2020X

Fig. 290   Test XB: Variable Load Control Module (Part 2 of 37). 1996

Test Step		Result	▶	Action to Take
XB1	DTC P1484: CLEAR AND ATTEMPT TO REGENERATE DTC			
	Diagnostic Trouble Code (DTC) P1484 indicates the VLCM PWR GND (Pin 1) is open. This could be due to a hard fault or an intermittent condition. Possible causes: — Open VLCM PWR GND circuit. — Damaged VLCM. NOTE: If DTC P1484 is present in Key On Engine Off (KOEO) or Key On Engine Running (KOER) Self-Test, GO to **XB2**. ● Perform PCM Reset to clear DTC(s) Powertrain Control Module (PCM) Reset). ● Start engine. ● Turn A/C on, wait 15 seconds. ● A/C off. ● Engine off. ● Access Continuous Memory DTCs. ● **Is Continuous Memory DTC P1484 present?**	Yes No	▶ ▶	DTC P1484 is a hard fault. GO to **XB2**. DTC P1484 is intermittent. GO to **XB4**.
XB2	CHECK VLCM PWR GND CIRCUIT CONTINUITY			
	● Key off. ● Disconnect VLCM. Inspect for damaged or pushed out pins, corrosion, loose wires, etc. Service as necessary. ● Measure resistance between Pin 1 of the VLCM vehicle harness connector and the battery negative post. ● **Is resistance less than 5.0 ohms?**	Yes No	▶ ▶	REPLACE VLCM. RECONNECT all components. PERFORM PCM Reset to clear Continuous Memory DTC(s). START engine. A/C on, WAIT 15 seconds. Key off, A/C off. RERUN Quick Test. SERVICE open in VLCM PWR GND circuit. RECONNECT all components. PERFORM PCM Reset to clear Continuous Memory DTC(s). START engine. A/C on, WAIT 15 seconds. Key off, A/C off. RERUN Quick Test.

FM015960156 2030X

Fig. 290   Test XB: Variable Load Control Module (Part 3 of 37). 1996

Test Step		Result	▶	Action to Take
XB4	CHECK VLCM PWR GND CIRCUIT FOR INTERMITTENT OPENS			
	● Key off. ● Visually check the VLCM PWR GND circuit (VLCM Pin 1) from the VLCM to the circuit's ground point. The VLCM PWR GND circuit is grounded to sheetmetal at the LH side radiator support near the battery ground. ● Disconnect VLCM. Inspect for damaged or pushed out pins, corrosion, loose wires, etc. Service as necessary. ● Connect a test lamp between Pin 15 and Pin 1 of the VLCM vehicle harness connector. ● Observe test lamp for an indication of a fault while performing the following (the lamp will go out when a fault is found, indicating an open): — Shake, wiggle, bend the VLCM PWR GND circuit between the VLCM vehicle harness connector and the circuit's ground point. ● **Is a fault indicated?**	Yes No	▶ ▶	ISOLATE fault and SERVICE as necessary. RECONNECT all components. START engine. A/C on, WAIT 15 seconds. A/C off, key off. RERUN Quick Test. Unable to duplicate and/or identify fault at this time. RECONNECT all components. GO to Pinpoint Test Step **Z1** with the list of possible causes.
XB10	DTC P1483: CLEAR AND ATTEMPT TO REGENERATE DTC			
	Diagnostic Trouble Code (DTC) P1483 indicates that when the cooling fan was activated, the Power-to-Cooling Fan circuit exceeded the normal current draw. This could be due to a hard fault or an intermittent condition. Possible causes: — Power-to-Cooling Fan circuit short to ground. — Damaged cooling fan motor. — Damaged VLCM. NOTE: If DTC P1483 was present in Key On Engine Off (KOEO) or Key On Engine Running (KOER) Self-Test, GO to **XB11**. ● Perform PCM Reset to clear DTC(s) Powertrain Control Module (PCM) Reset). ● Start engine. ● Turn A/C on, wait 15 seconds. ● A/C off. ● Engine off. ● Access Continuous Memory DTCs. ● **Is Continuous Memory DTC P1483 present?**	Yes No	▶ ▶	DTC P1483 is a hard fault. GO to **XB11**. DTC P1483 is intermittent. GO to **XB14**.

FM015960156 2040X

Fig. 290   Test XB: Variable Load Control Module (Part 4 of 37). 1996

Test Step	Result	▶	Action to Take
XB11 CHECK COOLING FAN MOTOR • Perform PCM Reset to clear Continuous Memory DTCs. • Disconnect cooling fan motor. • Start engine. • Turn A/C off, wait 15 seconds (but no more than 20 seconds). • A/C off. • Engine off. • Again access Continuous Memory DTCs. • **Is Continuous Memory DTC P1483 present (disregard any other codes)?**	Yes No	▶ ▶	GO to XB12. REPLACE cooling fan motor. RECONNECT all components. RERUN Quick Test.
XB12 CHECK POWER-TO-COOLING FAN CIRCUIT FOR SHORT TO GROUND • Key off. • Cooling fan motor disconnected. • Disconnect VLCM. Inspect for damaged or pushed out pins, corrosion, loose wires, etc. Service as necessary. • Measure resistance between the Power-To-Cooling Fan circuit at the cooling fan vehicle harness connector and the battery negative post. • **Is resistance greater than 10,000 ohms?**	Yes No	▶ ▶	REPLACE VLCM. RECONNECT all components. PERFORM PCM Reset to clear Continuous Memory DTC(s). START engine. TURN A/C on, wait 15 seconds. A/C off, key off. RERUN Quick Test. SERVICE Power-To-Cooling Fan circuit short to ground. RECONNECT all components. PERFORM PCM Reset to clear Continuous Memory DTC(s). START engine. TURN A/C on, WAIT 15 seconds. A/C off, key off. RERUN Quick Test.

Fig. 290   Test XB: Variable Load Control Module (Part 5 of 37). 1996

FM0159601562050X

Test Step	Result	▶	Action to Take
XB14 CHECK VLCM CONNECTOR AND POWER-TO-COOLING FAN CIRCUIT FOR INTERMITTENT SHORT TO GROUND • Key off. • Visually check the Power-To-Cooling Fan circuit from the VLCM to the cooling fan. • Disconnect VLCM. Inspect for damaged or pushed out pins, corrosion, loose wires, etc. Service as necessary. • Connect a test lamp between Pin 2 and Pin 4 of the VLCM vehicle harness connector. • Observe test lamp for an indication of a fault while performing the following: (The lamp will be on, but not to full brightness. A short to ground will be indicated by the lamp getting brighter.) — Shake, wiggle, bend the Power-To-Cooling Fan circuit near the cooling fan. • Disconnect cooling fan. Inspect for damaged or pushed out pins, corrosion, loose wires, etc. Service as necessary. • Test lamp still connected between Pin 2 and Pin 4 of the VLCM vehicle harness connector. • Observe test lamp for an indication of a fault while performing the following (the lamp will turn on, indicating a short to ground): — Again, shake, wiggle, bend the Power-To-Cooling Fan circuit from the VLCM vehicle harness connector to the cooling fan vehicle harness connector. • **Is a fault indicated?**	Yes No	▶ ▶	ISOLATE fault and SERVICE as necessary. RECONNECT all components. START engine. A/C on, WAIT 5 seconds. A/C off, key off. RERUN Quick Test. Unable to duplicate and/or identify fault at this time. RECONNECT all components. GO to Pinpoint Test Step Z1 with the list of possible causes.

Fig. 290   Test XB: Variable Load Control Module (Part 6 of 37). 1996

FM0159601562060X

Test Step	Result	▶	Action to Take
XB20 KEY ON ENGINE OFF DTC P1473: VERIFY COOLING FAN IS NOT ALWAYS ON Key On Engine Off (KOEO) Diagnostic Trouble Code (DTC) P1473 indicates an open or short to power in the Power-To-Cooling Fan circuit. Possible causes: — Open or short to power in the Power-To-Cooling Fan circuit (harness). — Open cooling fan motor ground circuit. — Open circuit in cooling fan. — Damaged VLCM. NOTE: Verify that the cooling fan was not turning during KOEO Self-Test. If the fan was turning, back voltage could be sent to the VLCM through the Power-To-Cooling Fan circuit resulting in an invalid P1473 DTC. • Engine cooled down (so cooling fan would normally be off). • A/C and defroster off. • Key on, engine off. • **Is cooling fan on?**	Yes No	▶ ▶	Key off. GO to XB25 (to check for short to power). Key off. GO to XB21 (to check for opens).
XB21 CHECK COOLING FAN GROUND CIRCUIT • Key off. • Disconnect cooling fan. • Measure resistance between the cooling fan ground circuit at the cooling fan vehicle harness connector and chassis ground. • **Is resistance less than 5.0 ohms?**	Yes No	▶	GO to XB22. SERVICE open cooling fan ground circuit. RECONNECT all components. RERUN Quick Test.
XB22 CHECK POWER-TO-COOLING FAN CIRCUIT CONTINUITY • Key off. • Cooling fan disconnected. • Disconnect VLCM. Inspect for damaged or pushed out pins, corrosion, loose wires, etc. Service as necessary. • Measure resistance between the Power-To-Cooling Fan circuit at the cooling fan vehicle harness connector and Pins 2 and 3 of the VLCM vehicle harness connector. • **Is resistance less than 5.0 ohms?**	Yes No	▶	GO to XB23. SERVICE open in Power-To-Cooling Fan circuit. RECONNECT all components. RERUN Quick Test.
XB23 CHECK COOLING FAN • Key off. • Cooling fan disconnected. • Measure resistance of the cooling fan between the Power-To-Cooling Fan pin and ground pin of the cooling fan connector. • **Is resistance less than 10.0 ohms?**	Yes No	▶ ▶	REPLACE VLCM. RECONNECT all components. RERUN Quick Test. REPLACE cooling fan. RECONNECT all components. RERUN Quick Test.

Fig. 290   Test XB: Variable Load Control Module (Part 7 of 37). 1996

FM0159601562070X

Test Step	Result	▶	Action to Take
XB25 CHECK POWER-TO-COOLING FAN CIRCUIT FOR SHORT TO POWER • Key off. • Disconnect cooling fan. • Disconnect VLCM. Inspect for damaged or pushed out pins, corrosion, loose wires, etc. Service as necessary. • Key on, engine off. • Measure voltage between the Power-To-Cooling fan circuit at the cooling fan vehicle harness connector and chassis ground. • **Is voltage less than 1.0 volt?**	Yes No	▶ ▶	REPLACE VLCM. RECONNECT all components. RERUN Quick Test. SERVICE short to power in the Power-To-Cooling Fan circuit. RECONNECT all components.
XB40 DTC P1539: CLEAR AND ATTEMPT TO REGENERATE DTC Diagnostic Trouble Code (DTC) P1539 indicates that when the A/C was turned on, the Power-To-A/C Clutch circuit exceeded the normal current draw. This could be due to a hard fault or an intermittent condition. Possible causes: — Power-to-A/C Clutch circuit short to ground. — Damaged A/C clutch. — Damaged VLCM. NOTE: If DTC P1539 was present in Key On Engine Off (KOEO) or Key On Engine Running (KOER) Self-Test, GO to XB41. • Perform PCM Reset to clear DTC(s) • Start engine. • Turn A/C on, wait 15 seconds. • A/C off. • Engine off. • Access Continuous Memory DTC(s). • **Is DTC P1539 present?**	Yes No	▶ ▶	DTC P1539 is a hard fault. GO to XB41. DTC P1539 is intermittent. GO to XB44.
XB41 CHECK A/C CLUTCH • Perform PCM Reset to clear Continuous Memory DTC(s). • Disconnect A/C clutch. • Start engine. • Turn A/C on, wait 15 seconds. • A/C off. • Engine off. • Access Continuous Memory DTC(s) again. • **Is DTC P1539 present (ignore DTC P1530 if received)?**	Yes No	▶ ▶	GO to XB42. CHECK any A/C clutch external wiring for shorts to ground. If OK, REPLACE A/C clutch. RECONNECT all components. PERFORM PCM Reset to clear Continuous Memory DTC(s) (if necessary). RERUN Quick Test.

Fig. 290   Test XB: Variable Load Control Module (Part 8 of 37). 1996

FM0159601562080X

Test Step	Result	▶	Action to Take
XB42 CHECK POWER-TO-A/C CLUTCH CIRCUIT FOR SHORT TO GROUND • Key off. • A/C clutch disconnected. • Disconnect VLCM. Inspect for damaged or pushed out pins, corrosion, loose wires, etc. Service as necessary. • Measure resistance between the Power-To-A/C Clutch circuit at the A/C clutch vehicle harness connector and the battery negative post. • **Is resistance greater than 10,000 ohms?**	Yes No	▶ ▶	REPLACE VLCM. RECONNECT all components. PERFORM PCM Reset to clear Continuous Memory DTC(s). START engine. TURN A/C on, WAIT 15 seconds. A/C off. Key off. RERUN Quick Test. SERVICE Power-To-A/C Clutch circuit short to ground. RECONNECT all components. PERFORM PCM Reset to clear Continuous Memory DTC(s). START engine. TURN A/C on, WAIT 15 seconds. A/C off. Key off. RERUN Quick Test.
XB44 CHECK POWER-TO-A/C CLUTCH CIRCUIT FOR INTERMITTENT SHORT TO GROUND • Key off. • Visually check the Power-To-A/C Clutch circuit from the VLCM to the A/C clutch. • Disconnect VLCM. Inspect for damaged or pushed out pins, corrosion, loose wires, etc. Service as necessary. • Disconnect A/C clutch. Inspect for damaged or pushed out pins, corrosion, loose wires, etc. Service as necessary. • Connect a test lamp between Pin 4 and Pin 18 of the VLCM vehicle harness connector. • Observe test lamp for an indication of a fault while performing the following (the lamp will turn on when a fault is detected, indicating a short to ground): — Shake, wiggle, bend the Power-To-A/C Clutch circuit from the A/C clutch vehicle harness connector to the VLCM vehicle harness connector. • **Is a fault indicated?**	Yes No	▶ ▶	ISOLATE fault and SERVICE as necessary. RECONNECT all components. START engine. A/C on, WAIT 15 seconds. A/C off, key off. RERUN Quick Test. Unable to duplicate and/or identify fault at this time. RECONNECT all components. GO to Pinpoint Test Step **Z1** with the list of possible causes.

FM015960156209OX

Fig. 290   Test XB: Variable Load Control Module (Part 9 of 37). 1996

Test Step	Result	▶	Action to Take
XB50 DTC P1530:CLEAR AND ATTEMPT TO REGENERATE DTC Diagnostic Trouble Code (DTC) P1530 indicates an open or short to power in the Power-To-A/C Clutch circuit. This could be due to a hard fault or an intermittent condition. Possible causes: — Open or short to power in the Power-To-A/C Clutch circuit (harness). — Open A/C clutch ground circuit. — Open circuit in A/C clutch. — Damaged VLCM. NOTE: If DTC P1530 was present in Key On Engine Off (KOEO) or Key On Engine Running (KOER) Self-Test, GO to **XB51**. • Perform PCM Reset to clear DTC(s) (refer to Section 2A, Powertrain Control Module (PCM) Reset). • A/C off, defroster off (testing for DTC P1530 is done only with the A/C off). • Start engine, wait 15 seconds. • Engine off. • Access Continuous Memory DTC(s). • **Is DTC P1530 present?**	Yes No	▶ ▶	DTC P1530 is a hard fault. GO to **XB51**. DTC P1530 is intermittent. GO to **XB55**.
XB51 CHECK POWER-TO-A/C CLUTCH CIRCUIT FOR SHORT TO POWER • Key off. • Disconnect A/C clutch. • Disconnect VLCM. Inspect for damaged or pushed out pins, corrosion, loose wires, etc. Service as necessary. • Key on. • Measure voltage between the Power-To-A/C Clutch circuit at the A/C clutch vehicle harness connector and chassis ground. • Key off. • **Was the voltage less than 1.0 volt?**	Yes No	▶ ▶	GO to **XB52**. SERVICE Power-To-A/C Clutch circuit for short to power. RECONNECT all components. PERFORM PCM Reset to clear Continuous Memory DTC(s). A/C off, defroster off. START engine. WAIT 15 seconds. Key off. RERUN Quick Test.

FM01596015621OOX

Fig. 290   Test XB: Variable Load Control Module (Part 10 of 37). 1996

Test Step	Result	▶	Action to Take
XB52 CHECK CONTINUITY OF POWER-TO-A/C CLUTCH AND A/C CLUTCH GROUND CIRCUITS • Key off. • A/C clutch disconnected. • VLCM disconnected. • Measure resistance between Pin 18 of the VLCM vehicle harness connector and the Power-To-A/C Clutch circuit at the A/C clutch vehicle harness connector. • Measure resistance between the A/C clutch ground circuit at the A/C clutch vehicle harness connector and chassis ground. • **Are both resistances less than 5.0 ohms?**	Yes No	▶ ▶	GO to **XB53**. SERVICE open in applicable circuit. RECONNECT all components. PERFORM PCM Reset to clear Continuous Memory DTC(s). A/C off, defroster off. START engine, WAIT 15 seconds. Key off. RERUN Quick Test.
XB53 CHECK CONTINUITY OF A/C CLUTCH • Key off. • A/C clutch disconnected. • VLCM disconnected. • Measure resistance of the A/C clutch coil (between the Power-To-A/C Clutch and A/C clutch ground pins of the A/C clutch connector). • **Is resistance less than 10.0 ohms?**	Yes No	▶ ▶	REPLACE VLCM. RECONNECT all components. PERFORM PCM Reset to clear Continuous Memory DTC(s). A/C off, defroster off. START engine, WAIT 15 seconds. Key off. RERUN Quick Test. REPLACE A/C clutch (refer to Group 12 of the Service Manual). RECONNECT all components. PERFORM PCM Reset to clear Continuous Memory DTC(s). A/C off, defroster off. START engine, WAIT 15 seconds. Key off. RERUN Quick Test.
XB55 CHECK POWER-TO-A/C CLUTCH CIRCUIT FOR INTERMITTENT SHORT TO POWER NOTE: Be aware that P1530 could have been set during previous testing if the A/C clutch was disconnected and the engine was started. • Key off. • Visually check the Power-To-A/C Clutch circuit from the VLCM to the A/C clutch. Also check the A/C clutch ground circuit from the A/C clutch to its ground point (RH side radiator support). • A/C off. • Key on, engine off. • Shake, wiggle, bend the Power-To-A/C Clutch circuit between the VLCM and A/C clutch (especially in the vicinity of power circuits). A short to power will be indicated by the A/C clutch engaging. • Key off. • **Is a fault indicated?**	Yes No	▶ ▶	ISOLATE fault and SERVICE as necessary. RERUN Quick Test. GO to **XB56**.

FM015960156211OX

Fig. 290   Test XB: Variable Load Control Module (Part 11 of 37). 1996

Test Step	Result	▶	Action to Take
XB56 CHECK POWER-TO-A/C CLUTCH AND A/C CLUTCH GROUND CIRCUITS FOR INTERMITTENT OPENS • Key off. • Disconnect A/C clutch. Inspect for damaged or pushed out pins, corrosion, loose wires, etc. Service as necessary. • Connect a test lamp between the Power-To-A/C Clutch and A/C clutch ground circuits at the A/C clutch vehicle harness connector. • Disconnect VLCM. Inspect for damaged or pushed out pins, corrosion, loose wires, etc. Service as necessary. • Connect a jumper wire between the battery positive (B+) post and Pin 18 (power-to-A/C clutch) of the VLCM vehicle harness connector (be careful not to short jumper to any other pins). • Observe test lamp for an indication of a fault while performing the following (the lamp will go out when a fault is detected, indicating an open circuit): — Shake, wiggle, bend the power-to-A/C clutch and A/C clutch ground circuits. • **Is a fault indicated?**	Yes No	▶ ▶	ISOLATE fault and SERVICE as necessary. REMOVE jumper wire and test lamp. RECONNECT all components. RERUN Quick Test. REMOVE jumper wire and test lamp. Unable to duplicate and/or identify fault at this time. RECONNECT all components. GO to Pinpoint Test Step **Z1** with the list of possible causes.
XB60 KOEO/KOER DTC P1625 AND/OR P1626: CHECK FOR B(+) TO VLCM PINS 4 AND 5 Diagnostic Trouble Code (DTC) P1625 indicates that the B(+) supply to the VLCM fan circuit is not detected. Diagnostic Trouble Code (DTC) P1626 indicates that the B(+) supply to the VLCM A/C circuit is not detected. NOTE: Since B(+) to the VLCM fan and A/C circuits is supplied on the same VLCM pins (4 and 5), the diagnostics for P1625 and P1626 are the same. Possible causes: — Open B(+) circuit to VLCM pins 4 and 5. — Damaged VLCM. • Key off. • Disconnect VLCM. Inspect for damaged or pushed out pins, corrosion, loose wires, etc. Service as necessary. • Connect negative lead of the DVOM to the battery negative (-) post. • Measure voltage at pin 4 and pin 5 of the VLCM vehicle harness connector. • **Are both voltages greater than 10.5 volts?**	Yes No	▶ ▶	REPLACE VLCM. RERUN Quick Test. VERIFY condition of related fuses. If fuse is damaged, verify B(+) circuit is not short to ground. If fuse is OK, SERVICE open B(+) circuit to VLCM. RECONNECT all components. RERUN Quick Test.

FM015960156212OX

Fig. 290   Test XB: Variable Load Control Module (Part 12 of 37). 1996

	Test Step	Result	▶	Action to Take
XB65	CONTINUOUS MEMORY DTC P1625 AND/OR P1626: CHECK FOR INTERMITTENT OPEN IN B(+) CIRCUIT TO VLCM PINS 4 AND 5			
	Continuous Memory Diagnostic Trouble Code (DTC) P1625 indicates that an open B(+) supply to the VLCM fan circuit has been detected.	Yes	▶	ISOLATE fault and SERVICE as necessary. RECONNECT all components. RERUN Quick Test.
	Continuous Memory Diagnostic Trouble Code (DTC) P1626 indicates that an open B(+) supply to the VLCM A/C circuit has been detected.	No	▶	Unable to duplicate and/or identify fault at this time. GO to Pinpoint Test Step [Z1] with list of possible causes.
	NOTE: Since B(+) to the VLCM fan and A/C circuits is supplied on the same VLCM pins (4 and 5), the diagnostics for P1625 and P1626 are the same.			
	Possible causes:			
	— Intermittent open in B(+) circuit to VLCM (pins 4 and 5).			
	• Key off.			
	• Disconnect VLCM. Inspect for damaged or pushed out pins, corrosion, loose wires, etc. Service as necessary.			
	• Connect a test lamp between Pin 5 (B(+)) of the VLCM vehicle harness connector and chassis ground.			
	• Observe test lamp for an indication of a fault while performing the following (the lamp will go out when a fault is detected, indicating an open circuit):			
	— Shake, wiggle, bend the B(+) circuit to VLCM Pins 4 and 5.			
	— Lightly tap related fuses. Remove related fuse(s). Inspect for corrosion, damaged pins, etc. Reconnect fuse(s) after checking.			
	• Is a fault indicated?			
XB70	NO A/C (WITH NO DTCs): CHECK ACCS INPUT TO PCM WITH A/C ON			
	• Scan Tool connected to DLC.	Yes	▶	EEC-V system OK. check for A/C system mechanical problems, etc.
	• Start engine.			
	• Access ACCS PID on Scan Tool.	No	▶	The PCM is not receiving or recognizing the ACCS input. GO to [XB71].
	• Turn A/C on.			
	• Is the ACCS PID on?			

FM015960156213OX

Fig. 290 Test XB: Variable Load Control Module (Part 13 of 37). 1996

	Test Step	Result	▶	Action to Take
XB71	VERIFY A/C CYCLING SWITCH WAS NOT OPEN IN XB70 TESTING			
	• Key off.	Yes	▶	Key off. EEC-V system OK. REMOVE jumper wire and RECONNECT A/C Cycling switch. check for A/C system mechanical problems, etc. Be aware that during the XB70 testing the A/C Cycling switch was open, although this could be due to normal cycling switch and the improper refrigerant charge.
	• Disconnect A/C Cycling switch.			
	• Connect a jumper wire in the A/C Cycling switch vehicle harness connector (to complete the circuit).			
	• Again start engine, access ACCS PID on Scan Tool then turn A/C on.			
	• Is the ACCS PID now on?	No	▶	Key off. GO to [XB72].
XB72	CHECK FOR A/C DEMAND VOLTAGE FROM ELECTRONIC AUTOMATIC TEMPERATURE CONTROL (EATC) MODULE AT A/C CYCLING SWITCH			
	• Key off.	Yes	▶	GO to [XB73].
	• A/C Cycling switch disconnected.	No	▶	VERIFY power supply to, and operation of, the EATC module. If OK, SERVICE open between EATC module and A/C Cyciling switch. RECONNECT all components. VERIFY a symptom no longer exists.
	• A/C on.			
	• Key on.			
	• Measure voltage between the circuit from the EATC module at the A/C cycling switch vehicle harness connector and chassis ground.			
	• Key off.			
	• A/C off.			
	• Was voltage greater than 10.5 volts?			
XB73	CHECK ACCS CIRCUIT CONTINUITY BETWEEN A/C CYCLING SWITCH AND PCM (PIN 41)			
	• Key off.	Yes	▶	REPLACE PCM. REMOVE breakout box. RECONNECT all components. VERIFY a symptom no longer exists.
	• A/C Cycling switch disconnected.			
	• Disconnect PCM. Inspect for damaged or pushed out pins, corrosion, loose wires, etc. Service as necessary.	No	▶	SERVICE open circuit between the A/C cycling switch and the PCM. REMOVE breakout box. RECONNECT all components. VERIFY a symptom no longer exists.
	• Install breakout box, leave PCM disconnected.			
	• Measure continuity between test pin 41 (ACCS) at the breakout box and the ACCS circuit to the PCM at the A/C Cycling Switch vehicle harness connector.			
	• Is resistance less than 5.0 ohms?			

FM015960156214OX

Fig. 290 Test XB: Variable Load Control Module (Part 14 of 37). 1996

	Test Step	Result	▶	Action to Take
XB75	DTC P1464: CHECK ACCS PID			
	Diagnostic Trouble Code (DTC) P1464 indicates the ACCS input to the Powertrain Control Module (PCM) was high during Self-Test.	Yes	▶	GO to [XB76].
		No	▶	The ACCS PID indicates that the ACCS input to the PCM is low. VERIFY test results. With A/C and defrost off, RERUN Self-Test where P1464 was received.
	NOTE: Verify A/C and defrost were off during Self-Test. If A/C or defrost were on, turn off and rerun Self-Test.			
	• Key on, engine off.			
	• Scan Tool connected to DLC.			
	• A/C and defrost off.			
	• Access ACCS PID.			
	• Is ACCS PID on?			
XB76	ACCS PID ON: DISCONNECT A/C CYCLING SWITCH AND CHECK IF ACCS PID TURNS OFF			
	• Key off.	Yes	▶	Key off. VERIFY operation of EATC module. If OK, SERVICE short to power in the A/C demand circuit to the A/C Cycling switch. RECONNECT all components. VERIFY a symptom no longer exists.
	• Disconnect A/C Cycling Switch.			
	• Key on, engine off.			
	• Access ACCS PID.			
	• Is ACCS PID now off?	No	▶	Key off. GO to [XB77].
XB77	CHECK ACCS CIRCUIT FOR SHORT TO POWER			
	• Key off.	Yes	▶	REPLACE PCM. REMOVE breakout box. RECONNECT all components. RERUN Quick Test.
	• A/C Cycling switch disconnected.			
	• Disconnect PCM. Inspect for damaged or pushed out pins, corrosion, loose wires, etc. Service as necessary.	No	▶	SERVICE ACCS circuit short to power. REMOVE breakout box. RECONNECT all components. VERIFY a symptom no longer exists.
	• Install breakout box, leave PCM disconnected.			
	• Key on.			
	• Measure voltage between Test Pin 41 (ACCS) and Test Pins 51 and 103 (PWR GND) at the breakout box.			
	• Key off.			
	• Was voltage less than 1.0 volt?			

FM015960156215OX

Fig. 290 Test XB: Variable Load Control Module (Part 15 of 37). 1996

	Test Step	Result	▶	Action to Take
XB90	DTC P0230: DOES ENGINE START?			
	Diagnostic Trouble Code (DTC) P0230 indicates a fuel pump primary circuit failure.	Yes	▶	GO to [XB95] (to check for short to ground).
	Possible causes:	No	▶	GO to [XB91] (to check for opens and short to power).
	No Start:			
	— Open or short to power in FP circuit.			
	— Open VPWR to VLCM Pin 15.			
	— Damaged VLCM.			
	— Damaged PCM.			
	Engine Starts:			
	— Short to ground in FP circuit.			
	— Damaged VLCM.			
	— Damaged PCM.			
	• Does the engine start?			
XB91	CHECK FOR VPWR TO VLCM PIN 15			
	• Key off.	Yes	▶	GO to [XB92].
	• Disconnect VLCM. Inspect for damaged or pushed out pins, corrosion, loose wires, etc. Service as necessary.	No	▶	SERVICE open VPWR circuit between VLCM and EEC-V power relay. Be aware that, since DTC(s) were received, VPWR is not open to the PCM. RECONNECT VLCM. RERUN Quick Test.
	• Key on.			
	• Measure voltage between Pin 15 (VPWR) of the VLCM vehicle harness connector and the battery negative post.			
	• Key off.			
	• Was voltage greater than 10.5 volts?			
XB92	CHECK FUEL PUMP (FP) CIRCUIT CONTINUITY			
	• Key off.	Yes	▶	GO to [XB93].
	• VLCM disconnected.	No	▶	SERVICE open in FP circuit. REMOVE breakout box. RECONNECT all components. RERUN Quick Test.
	• Disconnect PCM. Inspect for damaged or pushed out pins, corrosion, loose wires, etc. Service as necessary.			
	• Install breakout box, leave PCM disconnected.			
	• Measure continuity between Test Pin 80 (FP) at the breakout box and Pin 12 of the VLCM vehicle harness connector.			
	• Is resistance less than 5.0 ohms?			
XB93	CHECK FP CIRCUIT FOR SHORT TO POWER			
	• Key off.	Yes	▶	GO to [XB94].
	• Breakout box installed, PCM disconnected.	No	▶	SERVICE FP circuit short to power. REMOVE breakout box. RECONNECT all components. RERUN Quick Test.
	• VLCM disconnected.			
	• Key on.			
	• Measure voltage between Test Pin 80 and Test Pin 77 (PWR GND) at the breakout box.			
	• Key off.			
	• Was voltage less than 1.0 volt?			

FM015960156216OX

Fig. 290 Test XB: Variable Load Control Module (Part 16 of 37). 1996

Test Step	Result	▶	Action to Take
XB94 CHECK VLCM FP CIRCUIT • Key off. • Breakout box installed, PCM disconnected. • Reconnect VLCM. • Jumper Test Pin 80 to Test Pin 77 at the breakout box. • Key on. • **Does the fuel pump run?**	Yes No	▶ ▶	Key off. REMOVE jumper. REPLACE PCM. REMOVE breakout box. RECONNECT all components. RERUN Quick Test. Key off. REMOVE jumper. REPLACE VLCM. REMOVE breakout box. RECONNECT all components. RERUN Quick Test.
XB95 CHECK PCM FOR SHORT TO GND • Key off. • Disconnect PCM. Inspect for damaged or pushed out pins, corrosion, loose wires, etc. Service as necessary. • Key on. • **Does the fuel pump run?**	Yes No	▶ ▶	Key off. GO to **XB96**. Key off. REPLACE PCM. RECONNECT all components. RERUN Quick Test.
XB96 CHECK FUEL PUMP (FP) CIRCUIT FOR SHORT TO GROUND • Key off. • Install breakout box, leave PCM disconnected. • Disconnect VLCM. Inspect for damaged or pushed out pins, corrosion, loose wires, etc. Service as necessary. • Measure resistance between Test Pin 80 (FP) and Test Pins 51, 77 (PWR GND) and 91 (SIG RTN) at the breakout box. • **Is each resistance greater than 10,000 ohms?**	Yes No	▶ ▶	REPLACE VLCM. REMOVE breakout box. RECONNECT all components. RERUN Quick Test. SERVICE FP circuit short to ground. REMOVE breakout box. RECONNECT all components. RERUN Quick Test.

FM0159601562170X

Fig. 290 Test XB: Variable Load Control Module (Part 17 of 37). 1996

Test Step	Result	▶	Action to Take
XB100 DTC P0232: WILL ENGINE START Diagnostic Trouble Code (DTC) P0232 indicates that one of the following has occurred: No Start: — Inertia Fuel Shutoff (IFS) switch not reset or electrically open. — Open in Power-To-Pump circuit between the FPM splice and the fuel pump. — Poor fuel pump ground. — Open circuit in fuel pump. Engine Starts: — Power-To-Pump / FPM circuit short to power. — High Speed Fuel Pump (HFP) relay contacts stuck closed. — HFP circuit (VLCM Pin 10) short to ground (DTC P1236 also present). — Open FPM circuit between PCM and Power-To-Pump splice. — Damaged VLCM (DTC P1236 present if damage is to HFP circuit). — Damaged PCM. NOTE: If DTC P1236 (HFP primary circuit failure) is also present with the P0232, continue with this test procedure. • **Will the engine start?**	Yes No	▶ ▶	GO to **XB101**. VERIFY IFS switch is set (button depressed). If OK, GO to **XB109** (to check for open in Power-To-Pump circuit between FPM splice and fuel pump ground).
XB101 VERIFY THAT FUEL PUMP IS OFF • Key on, wait 5 seconds. • Listen for motor noise from fuel pump. • **Is fuel pump off?**	Yes No	▶ ▶	Key off. GO to **XB106** (to check FPM circuit continuity). Key off. GO to **XB102** (to check Power-To-Pump / FPM circuit short to power, HFP circuit short to ground or HFP relay contacts always closed).
XB102 CHECK VLCM • Key off. • Disconnect VLCM. Inspect for damaged or pushed out pins, corrosion, loose wires, etc. Service as necessary. • Key on. • **Is fuel pump off?**	Yes No	▶ ▶	Key off. REPLACE VLCM. RECONNECT all components. RERUN Quick Test. Key off. GO to **XB103**.

FM0159601562180X

Fig. 290 Test XB: Variable Load Control Module (Part 18 of 37). 1996

Test Step	Result	▶	Action to Take
XB103 CHECK HFP RELAY AND CIRCUITS • Key off. • VLCM disconnected. • Disconnect HFP relay. • Key on. • **Is fuel pump off?**	Yes No	▶ ▶	Key off. GO to **XB104** (to check HFP circuit). Key off. SERVICE short to power in Power-To-Pump / FPM circuit. RECONNECT all components. RERUN Quick Test.
XB104 CHECK HFP CIRCUIT FOR SHORT TO GND • Key off. • VLCM disconnected. • HFP relay disconnected. • Measure resistance between Pin 10 (HFP) at the VLCM vehicle harness connector and the battery negative post. • **Is resistance greater than 10,000 ohms?**	Yes No	▶ ▶	REPLACE HFP relay. RECONNECT all components. RERUN Quick Test. SERVICE HFP circuit short to ground. RECONNECT all components. RERUN Quick Test.
XB106 CHECK FPM CIRCUIT CONTINUITY • Key off. • Disconnect PCM. Inspect for damaged or pushed out pins, corrosion, loose wires, etc. Service as necessary. • Install breakout box, leave PCM disconnected. • Disconnect High Speed Fuel Pump (HFP) relay. • Measure resistance between Test Pin 40 (FPM) at the breakout box and the Power-To-Pump circuit at the HFP relay vehicle harness connector. • **Is resistance less than 5.0 ohms?**	Yes No	▶ ▶	REPLACE PCM. REMOVE breakout box. RECONNECT all components. RERUN Quick Test. SERVICE open in FPM circuit between PCM and splice to Power-To-Pump circuit. REMOVE breakout box. RECONNECT all components. RERUN Quick Test.

HFP RELAY VEHICLE
HARNESS CONNECTOR
(LOCATED IN POWER
DISTRIBUTION BOX)

POWER-TO-PUMP

HFP (VLCM 10) — IGN START/RUN

B+

FM0159601562190X

Fig. 290 Test XB: Variable Load Control Module (Part 19 of 37). 1996

Test Step	Result	▶	Action to Take
XB109 CHECK POWER-TO-PUMP CIRCUIT BETWEEN FPM SPLICE AND INERTIA FUEL SHUTOFF (IFS) SWITCH • Key off. • Disconnect IFS switch. • Disconnect High Speed Fuel Pump (HFP) relay. • Measure resistance between the Power-To-Pump circuit (from VLCM) at the IFS switch vehicle harness connector and the Power-To-Pump circuit at the HFP relay vehicle harness connector. • **Is resistance less than 5.0 ohms?**	Yes No	▶ ▶	GO to **XB110**. SERVICE open in Power-To-Pump circuit between the IFS switch and the FPM splice to the circuit. RECONNECT all components. RERUN Quick Test.
XB110 CHECK INERTIA FUEL SHUTOFF (IFS) SWITCH • Key off. • IFS switch disconnected. • Measure resistance between the C (common) and NC (normally closed) pins of the IFS switch. • **Is resistance less than 5.0 ohms?**	Yes No	▶ ▶	GO to **XB111**. VERIFY IFS switch was reset. If OK, REPLACE IFS switch. RECONNECT all components. RERUN Quick Test.
XB111 CHECK POWER-TO-PUMP CIRCUIT FROM IFS SWITCH TO FUEL PUMP AND CHECK FUEL PUMP GROUND CIRCUIT • Key off. • IFS switch disconnected. • Disconnect fuel pump. • Measure resistance of the Power-To-Pump circuit between the IFS switch and fuel pump vehicle harness connectors. • Measure resistance between the fuel pump ground circuit at the fuel pump vehicle harness connector and chassis ground. • **Are both resistances less than 5.0 ohms?**	Yes No	▶ ▶	RECONNECT IFS switch. GO to **XB112**. SERVICE open circuit. RECONNECT all components. RERUN Quick Test.
XB112 CHECK FUEL PUMP • Key off. • Fuel pump disconnected. • Measure resistance of the fuel pump between the Power-To-Pump pin and fuel pump ground pin of the fuel pump connector. • **Is resistance less than 10.0 ohms?**	Yes No	▶ ▶	Fuel pump circuits test OK. VERIFY results of previous test steps. If OK, disregard the P0232 at this time. RETURN to the Diagnostic Subroutine that the P0232 was received and continue diagnosis as directed. REPLACE fuel pump. RECONNECT all components. RERUN Quick Test.

FM0159601562200X

Fig. 290 Test XB: Variable Load Control Module (Part 20 of 37). 1996

Test Step	Result	▶	Action to Take
XB115 KOEO DTC P0231: IS KOEO DTC P0230 OR P0232 ALSO PRESENT?			
Key On Engine Off (KOEO) Diagnostic Trouble Code (DTC) P0231 indicates that the FPM circuit did not detect voltage when the fuel pump was commanded on. This could be because; B(+) voltage was not detected to VLCM pin 6; or when the fuel pump was activated, the Power-To-Pump circuit exceeded the normal current draw (which would result in the VLCM FMEM turning off the fuel pump). DTC P0231 will not be set if an open Power-To-Pump circuit is detected.	Yes	▶	For KOEO DTC P0230: GO to **XB90** For KOEO DTC P0232: GO to **XB100**
Possible causes are: — Open in B(+) supply to VLCM (Pin 6). — Power-To-Pump / FPM circuit short to ground, or B(+) supply to High Speed Fuel Pump (HFP) relay short to ground. These conditions may also result in the fuse for the B(+) supply to the HFP relay being damaged, and DTC P1231 being set. — Fuel Pump primary circuit fault (P0230 also present). — Fuel pump motor seized. — Damaged VLCM. • **Is KOEO DTC P0230 or P0232 also present?**	No	▶	GO to **XB116**
XB116 CHECK THE VLCMFPF PID TO DETERMINE IF THE P0231 WAS SET DUE TO AN OVERCURRENT CONDITION			
• Scan Tool connected. • Key on, engine off. • Access the VLCMFPF PID. • **Does the VLCMFPF PID = Yes?**	Yes	▶	DTC P0231 was set due to an overcurrent condition. Key off. GO to **XB120**
	No	▶	Key off. GO to **XB117**
XB117 CHECK FOR B(+) TO VLCM PIN 6			
• Key off. • Disconnect VLCM. Inspect for damaged or pushed out pins, corrosion, loose wires, etc. Service as necessary. • Measure voltage between Pin 6 (B(+)) of the VLCM vehicle harness connector and the battery negative post. • **Is voltage greater than 10.5 volts?**	Yes	▶	REPLACE VLCM. RECONNECT all components. RERUN Quick Test.
	No	▶	VERIFY condition of related fuse. If fuse is damaged, verify B(+) circuit is not short to ground. If fuse is OK, SERVICE open B(+) circuit to VLCM. RECONNECT all components. RERUN Quick Test.
XB120 CHECK IF FUSE FOR B(+) SUPPLY TO HFP RELAY IS DAMAGED			
• **Is the fuse for the B(+) supply to the HFP relay damaged?**	Yes	▶	GO to **XB121**
	No	▶	GO to **XB122**

FM015960156210X

Fig. 290   Test XB: Variable Load Control Module (Part 21 of 37). 1996

Test Step	Result	▶	Action to Take
XB121 CHECK B(+) CIRCUIT TO HFP RELAY FOR SHORT TO GROUND			
• Key off. • Remove damaged fuse for HFP relay B(+). • Disconnect HFP relay. • Disconnect Scan Tool from DLC. • Disconnect any other components connected to the B(+) supply circuit for the HFP relay. • Measure resistance between the B(+) circuit at the HFP relay vehicle harness connector and the battery negative post. • **Is resistance greater than 10,000 ohms?**	Yes	▶	REPLACE fuse. RECONNECT any other components connected to the B(+) circuit one at a time and VERIFY fuse is not damaged. If OK, RECONNECT HFP relay and GO to **XB122**
	No	▶	SERVICE short circuit. REPLACE damaged fuse. RECONNECT all components. RERUN Quick Test.
XB122 CHECK POWER-TO-PUMP / FPM CIRCUIT TO INERTIA FUEL SHUTOFF (IFS) SWITCH FOR SHORT TO GROUND			
• Key off. • Disconnect Scan Tool from DLC (if not already disconnected). • Disconnect PCM, VLCM and IFS switch. Inspect for damaged or pushed out pins, corrosion, loose wires, etc. Service as necessary. • Measure resistance between Pin 7 (Power-To-Pump) of the VLCM vehicle harness connector and the battery negative post. • **Is resistance greater than 10,000 ohms?**	Yes	▶	GO to **XB123**
	No	▶	SERVICE Power-To-Pump or FPM circuit short to ground. RECONNECT all components. RERUN Quick Test.
XB123 CHECK POWER-TO-PUMP CIRCUIT BETWEEN IFS SWITCH AND FUEL PUMP FOR SHORT TO GROUND			
• Key off. • PCM, VLCM and IFS switch disconnected. • Disconnect fuel pump. • Measure resistance between the Power-To-Pump circuit to the fuel pump at the IFS switch vehicle harness connector and the battery negative post. • **Is resistance greater than 10,000 ohms?**	Yes	▶	GO to **XB124**
	No	▶	SERVICE Power-To-Pump circuit short to ground. RECONNECT all components. RERUN Quick Test.

FM015960156220X

Fig. 290   Test XB: Variable Load Control Module (Part 22 of 37). 1996

Test Step	Result	▶	Action to Take
XB124 CHECK VLCM			
• Key off. • IFS switch and fuel pump disconnected. • Reconnect VLCM. • Install breakout box to PCM connector. Leave PCM disconnected. • Jumper Test Pin 80 (FP) to Test Pin 77 (PWR GND) at the breakout box. • While measuring voltage between Test Pin 40 (FPM) and Test Pin 51 (PWR GND) at the breakout box, turn key on for at least 2 seconds. • Key off. • **Was voltage greater than 8.5 volts for at least two seconds?**	Yes	▶	VERIFY the IFS switch is not internally short to ground. If OK, REPLACE fuel pump. REMOVE breakout box. RECONNECT all components. RERUN Quick Test.
	No	▶	REPLACE VLCM. REMOVE breakout box. RECONNECT all components. RERUN Quick Test.
XB130 KOEO DTC P1230: CHECK POWER-TO-PUMP CIRCUIT CONTINUITY BETWEEN VLCM AND FPM SPLICE			
Key On Engine Off (KOEO) Diagnostic Trouble Code (DTC) P1230 indicates that when the fuel pump was commanded off, an open was detected in the Power-To-Pump circuit between the VLCM and the FPM splice to the circuit.	Yes	▶	REPLACE VLCM. RECONNECT all components. RERUN Quick Test.
Possible causes: — Open Power-To-Pump circuit between VLCM and FPM splice. — Damaged VLCM. • Key off. • Disconnect VLCM. Inspect for damaged or pushed out pins, corrosion, loose wires, etc. Service as necessary. • Disconnect Inertia Fuel Shutoff (IFS) switch. • Measure resistance between Pin 7 (Power-To-Pump) at the VLCM vehicle harness connector and the Power-To-Pump circuit from the VLCM at the IFS switch vehicle harness connector. • **Is resistance less than 5.0 ohms?**	No	▶	SERVICE open in Power-To-Pump circuit between the VLCM and the FPM splice to the circuit. RECONNECT all components. RERUN Quick Test.

FM015960156230X

Fig. 290   Test XB: Variable Load Control Module (Part 23 of 37). 1996

Test Step	Result	▶	Action to Take
XB135 KOEO DTC P1231: CHECK FOR B(+) TO HFP RELAY			
Key On Engine Off (KOEO) Diagnostic Trouble Code (DTC) P1231 indicates that when the High Speed Fuel Pump (HFP) relay was activated, and the fuel pump driver in the VLCM (to VLCM Pin 7) was off, voltage was not detected on the FPM circuit.	Yes	▶	GO to **XB136**
Possible causes: — Open B(+) circuit to HFP relay. — Open in Power-To-Pump circuit between HFP relay and splice. — Damaged HFP relay. NOTE: If KOEO DTC P1235 or P1236 is also present, go to **XB140**. • Key off. • Disconnect HFP relay (located in Power Distribution Box). • Measure voltage between the B(+) circuit at the HFP relay vehicle harness connector and the battery negative post. • **Is voltage greater than 10.5 volts?**	No	▶	VERIFY condition of related fuse. If fuse is damaged, check B(+) and Power-To-Pump circuits for short to ground. If OK, SERVICE open B(+) circuit. RECONNECT all components. RERUN Quick Test.

HFP RELAY VEHICLE HARNESS CONNECTOR (LOCATED IN POWER DISTRIBUTION BOX)

POWER-TO-PUMP

HFP (VLCM 10) — IGN START/RUN

B+

Test Step	Result	▶	Action to Take
XB136 CHECK POWER-TO-PUMP CIRCUIT CONTINUITY BETWEEN HFP RELAY AND THE IFS SWITCH			
• Key off. • HFP relay disconnected. • Disconnect Inertia Fuel Shutoff (IFS) switch. • Measure resistance of the Power-To-Pump circuit between the HFP relay and the IFS switch vehicle harness connectors. • **Is resistance less than 5.0 ohms?**	Yes	▶	REPLACE HFP relay. RECONNECT all components. RERUN Quick Test.
	No	▶	SERVICE open in Power-To-Pump circuit between the HFP relay and the splice. RECONNECT all components. RERUN Quick Test.

FM015960156240X

Fig. 290   Test XB: Variable Load Control Module (Part 24 of 37). 1996

Test Step	Result	►	Action to Take
XB140 KOEO DTC P1235 OR P1236			
Key On Engine Off (KOEO) Diagnostic Trouble Code (DTC) P1235 or P1236 indicate a High Speed Fuel Pump (HFP) primary circuit failure (the circuit that is connected to Pin 10 of the VLCM). The only difference between the P1235 and the P1236 is that the P1235 is a MIL DTC. Possible causes: — Open or shorted HFP circuit (VLCM Pin 10). — Open Ignition Start/Run circuit to HFP relay. — Damaged HFP relay. — Damaged VLCM. • Key off. • Disconnect HFP relay (located in Power Distribution Box). • Key on, engine off. • Measure voltage between the Ignition Start/Run circuit at the HFP relay vehicle harness connector and the battery negative post. • Key off. • **Was voltage greater than 10.5 volts?**	Yes No	► ►	GO to **XB141**. SERVICE open in Ignition Start/Run circuit to the HFP relay. RECONNECT all components. RERUN Quick Test.

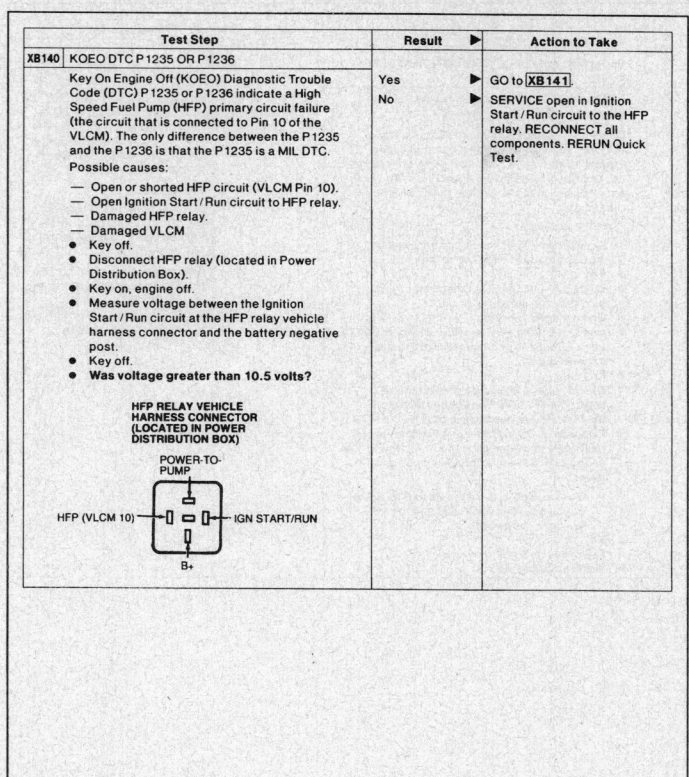

Test Step	Result	►	Action to Take
XB141 CHECK HFP RELAY			
• Key off. • HFP relay disconnected. • Check HFP relay coil resistance: — Measure resistance between Pins 85 and 86 of the HFP relay. — Resistance should be between 40 and 85 ohms. • Check HFP relay for internal shorts: — Measure resistance between Pin 85 and both Pins 30 and 87 of the fuel pump relay. — Both resistances should be greater than 10,000 ohms. • **Are all resistance checks OK?** HFP RELAY COIL - 85 AND 86 COMMON - 30 NO - 87 NC - 87A	Yes No	► ►	GO to **XB142**. REPLACE HFP relay. RECONNECT all component. RERUN Quick Test.
XB142 CHECK HFP CIRCUIT FOR SHORT TO POWER			
• Key off. • HFP relay disconnected. • Disconnect VLCM. Inspect for damaged or pushed out Pins, corrosion, loose wires, etc. Service as necessary. • Key on, engine off. • Measure voltage between the HFP circuit at the HFP relay vehicle harness connector and the battery negative post. • Key off. • **Was voltage less than 1.0 volt?**	Yes No	► ►	GO to **XB143**. SERVICE HFP circuit short to power. RECONNECT all component. RERUN Quick Test.
XB143 CHECK HFP CIRCUIT FOR SHORT TO GROUND			
• Key off. • Disconnect Scan Tool from DLC. • VLCM disconnected. • HFP relay disconnected. • Measure resistance between the HFP circuit at the HFP relay vehicle harness connector and the battery negative post. • **Is resistance greater than 10,000 ohms?**	Yes No	► ►	GO to **XB144**. SERVICE HFP circuit short to ground. RECONNECT all component. RERUN Quick Test.

Fig. 290   Test XB: Variable Load Control Module (Part 25 of 37). 1996

FM015960156225OX

Fig. 290   Test XB: Variable Load Control Module (Part 26 of 37). 1996

FM015960156226OX

Test Step	Result	►	Action to Take
XB144 CHECK HFP CIRCUIT CONTINUITY			
• Key off. • VLCM disconnected. • HFP relay disconnected. • Measure resistance between Pin 10 (HFP) of the VLCM vehicle harness connector and the HFP circuit at the HFP relay vehicle harness connector. • **Is resistance less than 5.0 ohms?**	Yes No	► ►	REPLACE VLCM. RECONNECT all components. RERUN Quick Test. SERVICE open HFP circuit. RECONNECT all component. RERUN Quick Test.
XB150 CONTINUOUS MEMORY DTC P0230: CHECK FUEL PUMP (FP) CIRCUIT AND VPWR CIRCUIT TO VLCM FOR INTERMITTENT CONCERN			
Continuous Memory Diagnostic Trouble Code (DTC) P0230 indicates that a fuel pump primary circuit failure has occurred during vehicle operation. Possible Causes: — Open or short in Fuel Pump (FP) circuit. — Open in VPWR circuit to VLCM Pin 15. • Scan Tool connected to DLC. • Key on, engine off. • Access FPF PID on Scan Tool. • Observe FPF PID for an indication of a fault while performing the following (the FPF PID will be "YES" if a fault is detected): — Shake, wiggle, bend the FP circuit from the VLCM (Pin 12) to PCM (Pin 80). — Shake, wiggle, bend the VPWR circuit between the VLCM (Pin 15) and the EEC-V power relay. • Inspect the PCM and VLCM connectors for corrision, damaged Pins, etc. • **Is a fault indicated?**	Yes No	► ►	Key off. ISOLATE fault and SERVICE as necessary. RECONNECT all components. COMPLETE PCM Reset to clear DTC(s) (REFER to Powertrain Control Module (PCM) Reset). RERUN Quick Test. Unable to duplicate and/or identify fault at this time. GO to Pinpoint Test Step **Z1** with the following data: FPF PID and list of possible causes.

Test Step	Result	►	Action to Take
XB155 CONTINUOUS MEMORY DTC P0232: CHECK POWER-TO-PUMP AND FPM CIRCUIT FOR INTERMITTENT CONCERNS			
NOTE: If Continuous Memory DTC P0230 is present, go to **XB150**. If Continuous Memory DTC P1235 or P1236 is present, go to **XB170**. Continuous Memory Diagnostic Trouble Code (DTC) P0232 indicates that sometime during vehicle operation, with the fuel pump commanded off, FPM voltage was high. Possible causes: — Fuel pump circuit activated when the PCM expected the circuit to be off (i.e. fuel system test or prime procedure). — Inertia Fuel Shutoff (IFS) switch was tripped, then reset. — Open in the FPM, Power-To-Pump (FPM splice to fuel pump), fuel pump or fuel pump ground circuit. — FPM or Power-To-Pump circuit short to power. — VLCM output driver or HFP relay contacts stuck closed. • Scan Tool connected • Key on, engine off. • Access FPM PID on Scan Tool. • Observe the FPM PID for an indication of a fault while performing the following (the FPM PID will turn ON when an open or short to power is detected): — Shake, wiggle, bend the Power-To-Pump circuit between the fuel pump and the VLCM Pin 7. Also check the portion of the Power-To-Pump circuit that goes to the HFP relay. — Shake, wiggle, bend the fuel pump ground circuit. — Shake, wiggle, bend the FPM circuit between the PCM Pin 40 and the splice to the Power-To-Pump circuit. — Lightly tap the HFP relay and the IFS switch (to simulate road shock). • Inspect the connectors of the following components: VLCM, PCM, HFP relay and IFS switch. • **Is a fault indicated?**	Yes No	► ►	ISOLATE fault and SERVICE as necessary. COMPLETE PCM Reset to clear DTC(s) (REFER to Powertrain Control Module (PCM) Reset). RERUN Quick Test. GO to Pinpoint Test Step **Z1** with the following data: FPM PID and list of possible causes.

Fig. 290   Test XB: Variable Load Control Module (Part 27 of 37). 1996

FM015960156227OX

Fig. 290   Test XB: Variable Load Control Module (Part 28 of 37). 1996

FM015960156228OX

Test Step	Result	▶	Action to Take
XB160 CONTINUOUS MEMORY DTC P0231: CHECK THE VLCMFPF PID TO DETERMINE IF P0231 WAS SET DUE TO AN OVERCURRENT CONDITION			
NOTE: If Continuous Memory DTC P0230 is present, go to **XB150**.	Yes	▶	GO to **XB165**.
	No	▶	Key Off. GO to **XB161**.
Continuous Memory Diagnostic Trouble Code (DTC) P0231 indicates that sometime during vehicle operation, while the fuel pump was commanded on, FPM voltage was low. Possible causes: If VLCMFPF PID = NO: — Open in B(+) supply to VLCM Pin 6. — Open Power-To-Pump circuit between the VLCM and the FPM splice to the circuit. If VLCMFPF PID = YES: — Power-To-Pump / FPM circuit short to ground, or B(+) supply to the High Speed Fuel Pump (HPF) relay short to ground. If these conditions resulted in the fuse for the B(+) supply to the HFP relay being damaged, KOEO DTC P1231 would be set. — Fuel pump rotor locked. ● Scan Tool connected. ● Key on, engine off. ● Access VLCMFPF PID. ● **Does the VLCMFPF PID = YES?**			
XB161 CHECK B(+) CIRCUIT TO VLCM PIN 6 FOR INTERMITTENT OPEN			
● Key off. ● Disconnect VLCM. Inspect for damaged or pushed out Pins, corrosion, loose wires, etc. Service as necessary. ● Connect a test lamp between Pin 6 (B+) of the VLCM vehicle harness connector and the battery negative post. ● Observe test lamp for an indication of a fault while performing the following (the test lamp will go out when a fault is detected, indicating an open): — Shake, wiggle, bend the B(+) circuit to Pin 6 of the VLCM. — Lightly tap on the related fuse (to simulate road shock). ● Visually check related fuse. ● **Is a fault indicated?**	Yes	▶	ISOLATE fault and SERVICE as necessary. COMPLETE PCM Reset to clear DTC(s) (REFER to Powertrain Control Module (PCM) Reset). RERUN Quick Test.
	No	▶	GO to **XB162**.

FM015960156 2290X

Fig. 290   Test XB: Variable Load Control Module (Part 29 of 37). 1996

Test Step	Result	▶	Action to Take
XB162 CHECK POWER-TO-PUMP CIRCUIT BETWEEN VLCM AND FPM SPLICE FOR INTERMITTENT OPEN			
NOTE: For DTC P0231, continue with this test step.	Yes	▶	ISOLATE fault and SERVICE as necessary. COMPLETE PCM Reset to clear DTC(s) (REFER to Powertrain Control Module (PCM) Reset). RERUN Quick Test.
Continuous Memory Diagnostic Trouble Code (DTC) P1230 indicates that sometime during vehicle operation, with the fuel pump commanded off, an open was detected in the Power-To-Pump circuit between the VLCM and the FPM splice to the circuit. Possible causes: — Open Power-To-Pump circuit between the VLCM and the FPM splice to the circuit. ● Key off. ● Disconnect VLCM (if not disconnected in previous test step). ● Disconnect IFS switch. ● Connect DVOM between Pin 7 of the VLCM vehicle harness connector and the battery negative post. ● Key on. ● DVOM voltage should be greater than 7.0 volts. This is the pull-up voltage supplied to the FPM / Power-To-Pump circuit by the PCM. ● Observe DVOM voltage for an indication of a fault while performing the following (the DVOM voltage will suddenly drop if an open is detected): — Shake, wiggle, bend the Power-To-Pump circuit between the VLCM and the FPM splice to the circuit. ● Key off. ● Reconnect IFS switch. ● **Is a fault detected?**	No	▶	**For P1230:** Go to Pinpoint Test Step **Z1** with the following data: FPM PID and list of possible causes. **For P0231 only:** In some cases, a P0231 could have been caused by a primary FP circuit concern, without a P0230 being set. GO TO **XB150** to CHECK the FP circuit.

FM015960156 2300X

Fig. 290   Test XB: Variable Load Control Module (Part 30 of 37). 1996

Test Step	Result	▶	Action to Take
XB165 CHECK POWER-TO-PUMP CIRCUIT FOR INTERMITTENT SHORT TO GROUND			
● Disconnect IFS switch. ● Scan Tool connected to DLC. ● Key on, engine off. ● Access FPM PID. ● Observe FPM PID for an indication of a fault while performing the following (the FPM PID will turn OFF when a fault is detected, indicating the PCM pull-up voltage on the FPM circuit has a path to ground): — Shake, wiggle, bend the following circuits: The Power-To-Pump circuit between the VLCM and the IFS switch; the portion of the Power-To-Pump circuit that goes to the HFP relay; the FPM circuit between the PCM and splice. ● Key off. ● **Is a fault indicated?**	Yes	▶	ISOLATE fault and SERVICE as necessary. RECONNNECT IFS switch. COMPLETE PCM Reset to clear DTC(s) (REFER to Powertrain Control Module (PCM) Reset). RERUN Quick Test.
	No	▶	RECONNECT IFS switch, DISCONNECT fuel pump connector and REPEAT test, CHECKING the Power-To-Pump circuit between the IFS switch and the fuel pump. If a fault is still not detected, GO to Pinpoint Test Step **Z1** with the following data: FPM PID and list of possible causes.
XB170 CONTINUOUS MEMORY DTC P1235 OR P1236: CHECK HFP CIRCUIT FOR SHORT TO GROUND			
Continuous Memory Diagnostic Trouble Code (DTC) P1235 and P1236 indicate that, sometime during vehicle operation, a HFP primary circuit (VLCM Pin 10) fault was detected. The only difference between P1235 and P1236 is that P1235 is a MIL DTC. Possible causes: — HFP circuit open. — HFP circuit short to ground or power. — Open Ignition Start / Run circuit to HFP relay. ● Key on, engine off. ● Listen for HFP relay clicking on while performing the following (the relay clicking on would indicate a HFP circuit short to ground): — Shake, wiggle, bend the HFP circuit between Pin 10 of the VLCM and the HFP relay. ● Key off. ● **Is a fault indicated?**	Yes	▶	ISOLATE fault and SERVICE as necessary. COMPLETE PCM Reset to clear DTC(s) (REFER to Powertrain Control Module (PCM) Reset). RERUN Quick Test.
	No	▶	GO to **XB171**.

FM015960156 2310X

Fig. 290   Test XB: Variable Load Control Module (Part 31 of 37). 1996

Test Step	Result	▶	Action to Take
XB171 CHECK HFP CIRCUIT AND IGNITION START / RUN CIRCUIT TO HFP RELAY FOR INTERMITTENT OPEN			
● Key off. ● Disconnect VLCM. Inspect for damaged or pushed out Pins, corrosion, loose wires, etc. Service as necessary. ● Connect DVOM between Pin 10 of the VLCM vehicle harness connector and the battery negative post. ● Key on, engine off. ● Check for open in HFP or Ignition Start / Run circuits by performing the following (DVOM voltage will suddenly drop if an open is detected): — Shake, wiggle, bend the HFP circuit between Pin 10 of the VLCM and the HFP relay. — Shake, wiggle, bend the Ignition Start / Run circuit to the HFP relay. — Lightly tap on the HFP relay (to simulate road shock). ● Key off. ● **Is a fault indicated?**	Yes	▶	ISOLATE fault and SERVICE as necessary. RECONNECT IFS switch. COMPLETE PCM Reset to clear DTC(s) (REFER to Powertrain Control Module (PCM) Reset). RERUN Quick Test.
	No	▶	GO to **XB172**.
XB172 CHECK HFP CIRCUIT FOR INTERMITTENT SHORT TO POWER			
● Key off. ● VLCM disconnected. ● DVOM connected between Pin 10 of the VLCM vehicle harness connector and the battery negative post. ● Disconnect HFP relay. ● Key on, engine off. ● Check HFP circuit for a short to power by performing the following (DVOM voltage will increase if a short to power is detected): — Again shake, wiggle, bend the HFP circuit between the VLCM and the HFP relay. ● Key off. ● **Is a fault indicated?**	Yes	▶	ISOLATE fault and SERVICE as necessary. RECONNECT VLCM and HFP relay. COMPLETE PCM Reset to clear DTC(s) (REFER to Powertrain Control Module (PCM) Reset). RERUN Quick Test.
	No	▶	RECONNECT VLCM and HFP relay. GO to Pinpoint Test Step **Z1** with the following data: list of possible causes.

FM015960156 2320X

Fig. 290   Test XB: Variable Load Control Module (Part 32 of 37). 1996

Test Step	Result	▶	Action to Take
XB180 DTC U1021, U1073, U1131: ARE ANY POWERTRAIN (P) DTC(S) PRESENT IN KOEO, KOER OR CONTINUOUS MEMORY SELF-TEST?			
The following "U" Diagnostic Trouble Codes (DTCs) indicate a failure in the two way communication between the Powertrain Control Module (PCM) and the VLCM. For the two way communication, the PCM and VLCM use the BUS (+) and BUS (-) circuits.	Yes	▶	ADDRESS the first DTC output in the following Self-Test order: 1) KOEO 2) KOER 3) Continuous Memory
DTC U1021 indicates a lack of A/C status response. DTC U1073 indicates a lack of engine coolant fan status response. DTC U1131 indicates a lack of fuel pump status response.	No	▶	No "P" DTC(s) present. GO to **XB181**.
Possible causes without any "P" DTCs: — Vehicle operated, or attempted to be started, with low or dead battery. — Open or shorted BUS(+) or BUS(-) circuit. — BUS(+)/BUS(-) circuit(s) too close to high current/voltage circuits (ex. secondary ignition wires, cellular phone or C.B. antennas, etc.). — Damaged VLCM (possible only if "U" DTC(s) is present in KOEO or KOER Self-Test). **Are any Powertrain DTC(s) ("P" prefix) present in Key On Engine Off (KOEO), Key On Engine Running (KOER) or Continuous Memory Self-Test?**			
XB181 IS THE "U" DTC(S) PRESENT IN KOEO OR KOER SELF-TEST?			
Is the "U" DTC(s) present in KOEO or KOER Self-Test?	Yes	▶	A fault is now present. However, the PCM is able to communicate with the Scan Tool, and the BUS(+) and BUS(-) circuits are OK to the DLC. GO to **XB182**.
	No	▶	An intermittent fault may exist. GO to **XB187**.

FM0159601562330X

Fig. 290   Test XB: Variable Load Control Module (Part 33 of 37). 1996

Test Step	Result	▶	Action to Take
XB182 CHECK BUS(+) AND BUS(-) CIRCUITS FOR SHORT TO POWER			
• Key off. • Disconnect Scan Tool from DLC. • Disconnect VLCM. Inspect connector for damaged or pushed out Pins, corrosion, loose wires, etc. Service as necessary. • Disconnect PCM. Inspect connector for damaged or pushed out Pins, corrosion, loose wires, etc. Service as necessary. • Install breakout box, leave PCM disconnected. • Key on, engine off. • Measure voltage between Test Pin 15 (BUS(-)) at the breakout box and the battery negative post. • Measure voltage between Test Pin 16 (BUS(+)) at the breakout box and the battery negative post. • Key off. • **Were both voltages less than 1.0 volt?**	Yes	▶	GO to **XB183**.
	No	▶	SERVICE short to power. REMOVE breakout box. RECONNECT all components. RERUN Quick Test.
XB183 CHECK BUS(+) AND BUS(-) CIRCUITS FOR SHORT TO GROUND OR EACH OTHER			
• Key off. • VLCM and Scan Tool disconnected. • Breakout box installed, PCM disconnected. • Measure resistance between Test Pin 15 and Test Pins 51, 77 (PWR GND) and 91 (SIG RTN) at the breakout box. • Measure resistance between Test Pin 16 and Test Pins 51, 77 (PWR GND) and 91 (SIG RTN) at the breakout box. • Measure resistance between Test Pin 15 and Test Pin 16 at the breakout box. • **Are all resistances greater than 10,000 ohms?**	Yes	▶	GO to **XB184**.
	No	▶	SERVICE short circuit. REMOVE breakout box. RECONNECT all components. RERUN Quick Test.

FM0159601562340X

Fig. 290   Test XB: Variable Load Control Module (Part 34 of 37). 1996

Test Step	Result	▶	Action to Take
XB184 CHECK BUS(+) AND BUS(-) CIRCUIT CONTINUITY			
• Key off. • VLCM disconnected. • Breakout box installed, PCM disconnected. • Measure resistance between Test Pin 15 at the breakout box and Pin 23 (BUS(-)) of the VLCM vehicle harness connector. • Measure resistance between Test Pin 16 at the breakout box and Pin 21 (BUS(+)) of the VLCM vehicle harness connector. • **Are both resistances less than 5.0 ohms?**	Yes	▶	INSPECT BUS(+) and BUS(-) for proper routing. VERIFY that the circuits are not mis-routed by any high current/voltage circuits (ex. secondary ignition wiring, cellular phone or C.B. radio antennas, etc.). Also VERIFY that the battery is properly charged. SERVICE as necessary. RERUN KOEO/KOER Self-Test to VERIFY that the "U" DTC will repeat. If all other checks are OK and the KOEO/KOER DTC will repeat, REPLACE VLCM. REMOVE breakout box. RECONNECT all components. RERUN Quick Test.
	No	▶	SERVICE open circuit. REMOVE breakout box. RECONNECT all components. RERUN Quick Test.
XB187 PRELIMINARY CHECKS			
• Inspect BUS(+) and BUS(-) circuits for proper routing. Verify that the circuits are not mis-routed by any high current/voltage circuits (ex. secondary ignition wiring, cellular phone or C.B. radio antennas, etc.). • If the vehicle has been operated, or was attempted to be started, with a low or dead battery, "U" DTC(s) could be set. If possible, check to see if this situation has occured. • **Are the preliminary checks OK?**	Yes	▶	GO to **XB188**.
	No	▶	SERVICE as necessary. PERFORM PCM Reset to clear DTC(s) (REFER to Powertrain Control Module (PCM) Reset). RERUN Quick Test.

FM0159601562350X

Fig. 290   Test XB: Variable Load Control Module (Part 35 of 37). 1996

Test Step	Result	▶	Action to Take
XB188 CHECK BUS(+) AND BUS(-) CIRCUITS FOR INTERMITTENT SHORT TO POWER			
• Key off. • Disconnect Scan Tool from DLC. • Disconnect VLCM. Inspect connector for damaged or pushed out Pins, corrosion, loose wires, etc. Service as necessary. • Disconnect PCM. Inspect connector for damaged or pushed out Pins, corrosion, loose wires, etc. Service as necessary. • Install breakout box, leave PCM disconnected. • Connect a jumper wire between Pin 21 (BUS(+)) and Pin 23 (BUS(-)) of the VLCM vehicle harness connector. This will connect the two circuits so they can be tested together. • Check the BUS(+) and BUS(-) circuits for intermittent short to power by performing the following: — Connect DVOM to measure voltage between Test Pin 15 (BUS(-)) and Test Pin 77 (PWR GND) at the breakout box. — Key on. — Observe DVOM for an indication of a fault while performing the following (DVOM voltage will increase to greater than 1.0 volt when a short to power is detected): — Shake, wiggle, bend the BUS(+) and BUS(-) circuits from the PCM to the VLCM and the portion of the circuits that go to the DLC. — Key off. • **Is a fault indicated?**	Yes	▶	ISOLATE fault and SERVICE as necessary. REMOVE breakout box and jumper wire. RECONNECT VLCM and PCM. RERUN Quick Test.
	No	▶	GO to **XB189**.

FM0159601562360X

Fig. 290   Test XB: Variable Load Control Module (Part 36 of 37). 1996

Test Step	Result	▶	Action to Take

XB189 CHECK BUS(+) AND BUS(-) CIRCUITS FOR INTERMITTENT OPEN, SHORT TO GROUND OR SHORT TO EACH OTHER
● Key off.
● Breakout box installed, PCM disconnected.
● VLCM disconnected.
● Jumper wire installed between Pin 21 and Pin 23 of the VLCM vehicle harness connector.
● Check the BUS(+) and BUS(-) circuits for intermittent short to ground by performing the following:
  — Connect DVOM to measure resistance between Test Pin 15 BUS(-) and Test Pin 77 (PWR GND) at the breakout box.
  — Observe DVOM for an indication of a fault while performing the following (DVOM resistance will drop below 10,000 ohms if a short to ground is detected):
  — Again shake, wiggle, bend the BUS(+) and BUS(-) circuits from the PCM to the VLCM, and the portion of the circuits that go to the DLC.
● Check for intermittent opens by performing the following:
  — Connect DVOM to measure resistance between Test Pin 15 and Test Pin 16 at the breakout box.
  — Observe DVOM for an indication of a fault while performing the following (DVOM resistance will increase to greater than 5.0 ohms when an open is detected).
  — Again shake, wiggle, bend the BUS(+) and BUS(-) circuits from the PCM to the VLCM.
● Check the BUS(+) and BUS(-) circuits for intermittent short to each other by performing the following:
  — Remove jumper wire at VLCM vehicle harness connector.
  — Connect DVOM to measure resistance between Test Pin 15 and Test Pin 16 at the breakout box.
  — Observe DVOM for an indication of a fault while performing the following (DVOM resistance will drop below 10,000 ohms if a short is detected).
  — Again shake, wiggle, bend the BUS(+) and BUS(-) circuits from the PCM to the VLCM, and the portion of the circuits that go to the DLC.
● **Is a fault detected?**
	Yes
	
	No
		▶
		
		▶
			ISOLATE fault and SERVICE as necessary. REMOVE breakout box. RECONNECT VLCM and PCM. RERUN Quick Test.
			
			No fault is identified at this time. REMOVE breakout box. RECONNECT PCM and VLCM.
			
			continue diagnosis of vehicle symptoms.

FM0159601562370X

Fig. 290   Test XB: Variable Load Control Module (Part 37 of 37). 1996

Note

You should enter this Pinpoint Test only when directed here.

Remember

Preliminary checks must be performed before continuing this Pinpoint Test.

Check:

● Electrical connections
● Vacuum leaks
● Fuel level and quality
● Ignition wiring connections
● Air intake filters, tubes and gaskets
● Aftermarket alterations
● Basic engine (valves, timing, etc.)

Description

This pinpoint test contains instructions for isolating an intermittent fault. It combines the use of a Scan Tool with a Breakout Box (BOB), a fuel psi gauge, vacuum gauge, DVOM, Transmission Tester and Ignition Tester. Actual values can be compared to typical values listed in the Diagnostic Reference Values to aid in finding the fault.

If available, the Service Bay Diagnostic System (SBDS) can be used for Intermittent Diagnostics.

FM0159601563010X

Fig. 291   Test Z: Intermittent (Part 1 of 37). 1996

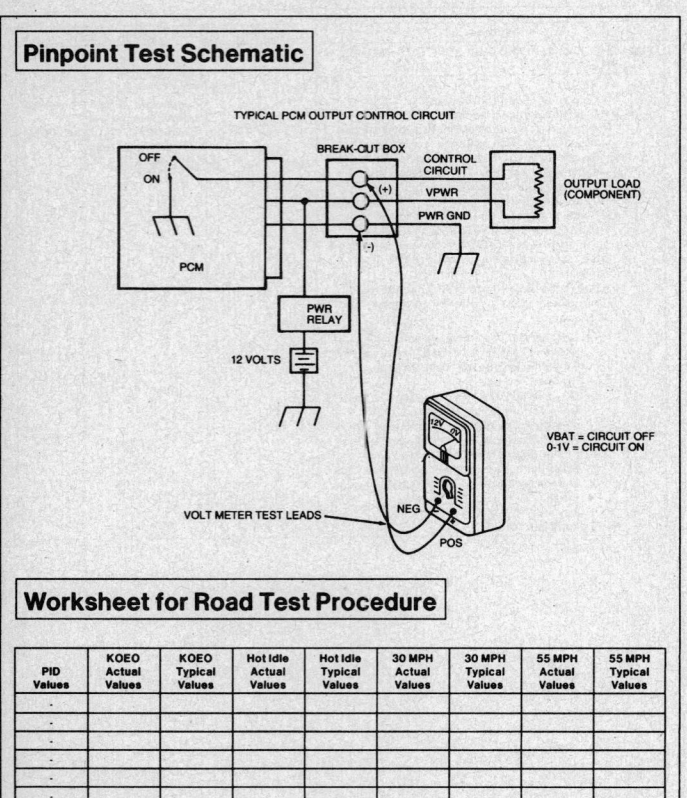

Worksheet for Road Test Procedure

PID Values	KOEO Actual Values	KOEO Typical Values	Hot Idle Actual Values	Hot Idle Typical Values	30 MPH Actual Values	30 MPH Typical Values	55 MPH Actual Values	55 MPH Typical Values
·								
·								
·								
·								
(Continued)								

FM0159601563020X

Fig. 291   Test Z: Intermittent (Part 2 of 37). 1996

PID Values	KOEO Actual Values	KOEO Typical Values	Hot Idle Actual Values	Hot Idle Typical Values	30 MPH Actual Values	30 MPH Typical Values	55 MPH Actual Values	55 MPH Typical Values
MEASURED VALUES								
·								
·								
·								
·								
OTHER VALUES								
·								
·								
·								
WEATHER CONDITIONS:				DRIVING ROUTE:				
·								
·								

NOTE: Use the Worksheet for Road Test Procedure to list the typical values from the Diagnostic Reference Values at the end of this pinpoint test. The typical values can be compared to the actual values obtained during the road test procedure.

Use this chart to choose which Intermittent test to run for the circuit or component. If the vehicle is a no-start, the ignition test should be run first.

INTERMITTENT TEST PRIORITIZATION CHART

	Priority Is From 1 (High) to 4 (Low)				
	Input Test	Output Test	Water Soak	Road Test	Ignition Test*
4X4L	N/A	1	3	2	N/A*
ACCS	1	N/A	3	2	N/A*
ACP	N/A	1	3	2	N/A*
BOO	1	N/A	3	2	N/A*
EVAPCVA	N/A	1	3	2	N/A*
(Continued)					

FM0159601563030X

Fig. 291   Test Z: Intermittent (Part 3 of 37). 1996

INTERMITTENT TEST PRIORITIZATION CHART (Cont'd)

	Input Test	Output Test	Water Soak	Road Test	Ignition Test[a]
				Priority is From 1 (High) to 4 (Low)	
TATC	N/A	1	3	4	2
CMP	1	N/A	3	4	2
DPFEGR	1	N/A	2	3	N/A*
AIR	N/A	1	3	2	N/A*
EOT	1	N/A	2	3	N/A*
EPC	N/A	1	3	2	N/A*
EVRVR	N/A	1	3	2	N/A*
FP	1	N/A	3	2	N/A*
HFC	N/A	1	3	2	N/A*
O2S	1	N/A	3	2	N/A*
HTR11A	N/A	1	3	2	N/A*
HTR12A	N/A	1	3	2	N/A*
HTR21A	N/A	1	3	2	N/A*
HTR22A	N/A	1	3	2	N/A*
IAC	N/A	1	3	2	N/A*
IAT	1	N/A	2	3	N/A*
IMRC	N/A	1	3	2	N/A*
IMRCM	1	N/A	2	3	N/A*
INJ	N/A	1	3	2	N/A*
TP	1	N/A	3	2	N/A*
LFC	N/A	1	3	2	N/A*
MAF	1	N/A	2	3	N/A*
FPM	N/A	1	3	2	N/A*
MIL	N/A	1	N/A	2	N/A*
OCTADJ	1	N/A	3	2	N/A*
PF	1	N/A	2	3	N/A*
PSP	1	N/A	3	2	N/A*
SS1	N/A	1	3	2	N/A*
SS2	N/A	1	3	2	N/A*
SS3	N/A	1	3	2	N/A*
TCC	N/A	1	3	2	N/A*
TCIL	N/A	1	N/A	2	N/A*
TCS	1	N/A	N/A	2	N/A*
TFT	1	N/A	3	2	N/A*
TPB	1	N/A	3	2	N/A*
TR	1	N/A	3	2	N/A*
TSS	1	N/A	3	2	N/A*

(Continued)

FM0159601563040X

Fig. 291   Test Z: Intermittent (Part 4 of 37). 1996

INTERMITTENT TEST PRIORITIZATION CHART (Cont'd)

	Input Test	Output Test	Water Soak	Road Test	Ignition Test[a]
				Priority is From 1 (High) to 4 (Low)	
EVAPCP	N/A	1	3	2	N/A*
VSS	1	N/A	3	2	N/A*
WAC	N/A	1	3	2	N/A*

a   N/A = Not Applicable

Test Step	Result ▶	Action to Take

Z1   INTERMITTENT TEST PROCEDURE
 	
 NOTE: All Intermittent Procedures are used in conjunction with the Intermittent Symptom Charts and the Typical Diagnostic Reference Values at the end of the pinpoint.
 	
 • If directed here from another pinpoint test, refer to PIDs, circuits or components that were recommended or else refer to the Symptom Chart at the end of the pinpoint for the proper selection.
 • Based on the Intermittent Prioritization Chart, choose an Intermittent Diagnostic Procedure below:
  • Input Test - This test is used on sensing devices such as temperature, position, oxygen, etc.
  • Output Test - This test is used on output devices such as relays, coils, solenoids, etc.
  • Water Soak Test - This test is used on both input and output devices. Especially useful on spark plug wires, relays and hall effect sensors.
  • Road Test - This test is used on both input and output devices. Four modes of engine operation are monitored for intermittent.
  • Ignition Test - This test is used to diagnose the ignition system using the Electronic Ignition (EI) System Tester.
 • Have you chosen an Intermittent Diagnostic Test procedure?
	Yes ▶
	
	 No ▶
		For the Input Test: GO Z10.
		 For Output Test: GO to Z20.
		 For Water Soak Test: GO to Z30.
		 For Road Test: GO to Z40.
		 For Ignition Test: GO to Z50.
		
		 To diagnose other driveability symptoms, GO to Symptom Flowcharts.

FM0159601563050X

Fig. 291   Test Z: Intermittent (Part 5 of 37). 1996

Test Step	Result ▶	Action to Take
Z10 INTERMITTENT KOEO INPUT WIGGLE PROCEDURE **WARNING: USE CAUTION WHEN PERFORMING ANY OF THE TEST STEPS. ALWAYS BE AWARE OF HANDS, CLOTHING OR TOOLS NEAR COOLING FANS, ENGINE DRIVE BELTS OR HOT SURFACES.** • Key off. • Connect Scan Tool to DLC. • Access PIDs based on information from the pinpoint test or Intermittent Symptom Charts at the end of this pinpoint test. • Go to the area of the suspected wiring or component fault. • Key on, engine off. • If input is a switch-type component, turn on manually. • Lightly tap on component while viewing PID values. Wiggle and pull each component wire (Signal, Signal Return and VREF, if applicable) at the component. • Look for abrupt changes in PID values. Compare the actual PID values to the KOEO Diagnostic Reference PID Values at the end of this pinpoint test. • Are any PID values out of range or suddenly drop out and back into range?	Yes ▶ No ▶	Possible wiring or component problem. CHECK each wire for corrosion, bent or loose terminals and poor wire terminal crimps. SERVICE as necessary. Otherwise, REPLACE component. VERIFY repair. If unable to verify, REINSTALL original part and GO to Z11. GO to Z11 for PCM wiring check.
Z11 INTERMITTENT KOEO INPUT WIGGLE PROCEDURE • Continue to monitor the information from the previous step. • Go to the area of the suspected wiring or component fault. • Turn ignition key to the ON position. • Wiggle and pull each sensor wire (Signal, Signal Return and VREF, if applicable) from the component back to the PCM connector. • Look for abrupt changes in PID values. Compare the actual values to the KOEO Diagnostic Reference PID Values. • Are any PID values out of range or suddenly drop out and back into range?	Yes ▶ No ▶	Possible wiring or component problem. CHECK each wire for corrosion, bent or loose terminals and poor wire terminal crimps. SERVICE as necessary. Otherwise, if the value dropped out while checking the PCM harness connector and there is no evidence of a fault, REPLACE PCM. If unable to verify, REINSTALL original PCM. Return to Z1 and choose another procedure to follow. Unable to verify fault. GO to Z12 KOER Wiggle Test.

FM0159601563060X

Fig. 291   Test Z: Intermittent (Part 6 of 37). 1996

Test Step	Result ▶	Action to Take
Z12 INTERMITTENT KOER INPUT WIGGLE PROCEDURE **WARNING: USE CAUTION WHEN PERFORMING ANY OF THE TEST STEPS. ALWAYS BE AWARE OF HANDS, CLOTHING OR TOOLS NEAR COOLING FANS, ENGINE DRIVE BELTS OR HOT SURFACES.** • Key off. • Access PIDs based on information from the pinpoint test or from the Intermittent Symptom Chart. • Go to the area of the suspected wiring or component fault. • Key on, engine running. • Lightly tap on component while viewing PID values. Also wiggle and pull each component wire (Signal, Signal Return and VREF, if applicable) at the component. • Look for abrupt changes in PID values. Compare the actual values to the HOT IDLE Diagnostic Reference PID Values. • Are any PID values out of range or suddenly drop out and back into range?	Yes ▶ No ▶	Possible wiring or component problem. CHECK each wire for corrosion, bent or loose terminals and poor wire terminal crimps. SERVICE as necessary. Otherwise, REPLACE component. VERIFY repair. If unable to verify, REINSTALL original part, and GO to Z13. GO to Z13 for PCM wiring check.
Z13 INTERMITTENT KOER INPUT WIGGLE PROCEDURE • Continue to monitor the information from the previous step. • Go to the area of the suspected wiring or component fault. • Key on, engine running. • Wiggle and pull each component wire (Signal, Signal Return and VREF, if applicable) from the component back to the PCM connector. • Look for abrupt changes in PID values. Compare the actual values to the HOT IDLE Diagnostic Reference PID Values. • Are any PID values out of range or suddenly drop out and back into range?	Yes ▶ No ▶	Possible wiring or component problem. CHECK each wire for corrosion, bent or loose terminals and poor wire terminal crimps. SERVICE as necessary. Otherwise if the value dropped out while checking the PCM harness connector and there is no evidence of a wiring fault, REPLACE PCM. If unable to verify repair, REINSTALL original PCM and RETURN to Z1 and choose another procedure to follow. Unable to verify fault. RETURN to Z1 and choose another procedure to follow.

FM0159601563070X

Fig. 291   Test Z: Intermittent (Part 7 of 37). 1996

Z20	INTERMITTENT KOEO OUTPUT PROCEDURE	Result	▶	Action to Take
	Some outputs/switches may need to be driven in order to be checked (i.e. fuel injectors and idle air controllers). GO to **Z40** for the Intermittent Road Test Procedure for outputs that are not controlled in the Output Test Mode. • Key off. • Connect Scan Tool to DLC. • Select the PIDs/circuits to monitor based on the information from the pinpoint test or Intermittent Symptom Charts at the end of this pinpoint test. • Go to the area of the suspected wiring or component fault. • Record any Continuous DTCs before proceeding to the next step. A DTC P1000 will be generated when the PCM is disconnected. **Caution must be used for the next steps. Cooling fans or fuel pump may turn on.** • Disconnect PCM. Inspect for damaged or pushed out pins, corrosion, loose wires, etc. Service as necessary. • Install breakout box and connect PCM to breakout box. • Connect a voltmeter (refer to beginning of Pinpoint Test for illustration): — Red lead to output control circuit. — Black lead to battery ground. If using the NGS, go to the voltmeter and link up to the PID display. Select the PIDs from the previous steps and record as necessary. • Key on, engine off. • Enter Output Test Mode • Turn the output on. Observe the volt reading and PID display. • While outputs are on, lightly tap on component and look for the voltage change. • **Did the voltage remain steady and less than 1 volt?**	Yes No	▶ ▶	Unable to verify fault, GO to **Z21**. Fault area is identified. If fault occurred while tapping on component, REPLACE part. REMOVE breakout box. RECONNECT all components. VERIFY repair. If unable to verify, REINSTALL original part and GO to **Z21**.

Fig. 291 Test Z: Intermittent (Part 8 of 37). 1996

Z21	INTERMITTENT OUTPUT WIRING TEST	Result	▶	Action to Take
	• Key on. • Scan tool, voltmeter and breakout box connected. • Continue to monitor PIDs/circuits. • Turn outputs on. • Wiggle, push and pull on the component wire (VPWR and control circuit) from the component back to the PCM connector. • **Was the voltage steady and less than 1 volt?**	Yes No	▶ ▶	Unable to verify fault. REMOVE breakout box. RECONNECT all components. RETURN to **Z1** and choose another procedure. Possible wiring problem. CHECK each wire for corrosion, bent or loose terminals. SERVICE as necessary. VERIFY repair.
Z30	INTERMITTENT WATER SOAK PROCEDURE			
	• Key off. • Connect Scan Tool to DLC. • Access PIDs based on information from the pinpoint test or from the Intermittent Symptom Chart at the end of this pinpoint test. • Go to the area of the suspected wiring, vacuum or component fault (based on the PIDs selected and ignition component attached to the Symptom Chart). • Key on, engine running. • Accurately spray water on each component circuit wire, component or vacuum line related to the possible fault area. • Look for abrupt changes in PID values or engine running conditions. • Compare the actual values to the HOT IDLE Diagnostic Reference PID Values at the end of this pinpoint test. • **Are any PID values out of range or suddenly drop out and back into range or was there a noticeable engine misfire/stumble?**	Yes No	▶ ▶	Fault area is identified. If fault occurred while spraying on component, REPLACE part and VERIFY repair. If unable to verify, REINSTALL original part. If fault occurred while spraying the circuit wiring, CHECK each wire for corrosion, bent or loose terminals and poor wire terminal crimps. SERVICE as necessary. If fault occurred while spraying the vacuum line, SERVICE as necessary. VERIFY repair. Unable to verify fault. CONTINUE to **Z31**.

Fig. 291 Test Z: Intermittent (Part 9 of 37). 1996

Z31	INTERMITTENT WATER SOAK PROCEDURE	Result	▶	Action to Take
	• With the engine still running, continue to individually water soak the ignition control module, spark plugs, wires, CKP and CMP sensors. • Continue to water soak any relays (e.g., CCRM) associated with fault. • Look for abrupt changes in PID values or engine running conditions. • Compare the actual values to the HOT IDLE Diagnostic Reference PID Values. • **Are any PID values out of range or suddenly drop out and back into range or was there a noticeable engine misfire/stumble?**	Yes No	▶ ▶	Fault area is identified. If fault occurred while spraying on component, REPLACE part and VERIFY repair. If unable to verify, REINSTALL original part. If fault occurred while spraying, CHECK each circuit wire for corrosion, bent or loose terminals and poor wire terminal crimps. SERVICE as necessary. If fault occurred while spraying the vacuum line, SERVICE as necessary, VERIFY repair. If unable to verify any repair, REPEAT test. Unable to verify fault. RETURN to **Z1** and choose another procedure.

Fig. 291 Test Z: Intermittent (Part 10 of 37). 1996

Z40	INTERMITTENT ROAD TEST PROCEDURE	Result	▶	Action to Take
	The Intermittent Road Test Procedure is a set of instructions for monitoring the PIDs and/or components with a Scan Tool during a road test. This is done under four different conditions - KOEO, HOT IDLE, 30 mph and 55 mph. The Typical Diagnostic Reference Value Charts at the end of this pinpoint test should be used to compare the data from the vehicle to data on the charts. Use worksheet at the beginning of the Pinpoint Test. • Copy the list of PIDs in the order given in the Intermittent Symptom Charts at the end of this pinpoint test. These PIDs will be monitored during the Road Test Procedure. If sent from a pinpoint test, the recommended PIDs should also be selected. • Key off. • Connect Scan Tool to DLC. • Connect other diagnostic aids if available to help find fault (i.e. breakout box, fuel psi gauge, vacuum gauge or Intermittent Ignition Analyzer). • Key on, engine off. • Access the PIDs. • Compare the actual values from the vehicle to the KOEO values from the Typical Diagnostic Reference Value Chart at the end of this pinpoint test. • **Are any values out of range?**	Yes No	▶ ▶	Fault identified. **For input type fault:** GO to **Z10**. **For output type fault:** GO to **Z20**. Unable to verify fault. GO to **Z41**.
Z41	INTERMITTENT ROAD TEST PROCEDURE			
	• Continue to monitor the PIDs listed in the previous step. • Key on, engine running. • Scan Tool connected. • Warm engine to operating temperature (approximately 195°F). • Continue to view the PIDs based on the information from the pinpoint test or from the Intermittent Symptom Charts at the end of this pinpoint test. • Compare the actual values from the vehicle to the HOT IDLE values in the Typical Diagnostic Reference Value Chart. • **Are any PID values out of range or suddenly drop out and back into range?**	Yes No	▶ ▶	Fault identified. **For input type fault:** GO to **Z10**. **For output type fault:** GO to **Z20**. Unable to verify fault. GO to **Z42**.

Fig. 291 Test Z: Intermittent (Part 11 of 37). 1996

Test Step	Result	▶	Action to Take
Z42 INTERMITTENT ROAD TEST PROCEDURE			
NOTE: Look for certain conditions that cause an intermittent fault to occur. (Refer to Section 2, Recreating the Fault.) • Continue to monitor the PIDs listed in Z40. • Instrument the vehicle as in the previous steps. • Select a person to assist in performing the 30 mph road test. • Make sure engine is at operating temperature before comparing or recording diagnostic values. • Drive the vehicle in a steady 30 mph range with accessories off. • Access the PIDs based on the information from the pinpoint test or from the Intermittent Symptom Charts at the end of this pinpoint test. • Compare the actual values from the vehicle to the 30 mph values in the Diagnostic Reference Value Chart. • **Are any PID values out of range or suddenly drop out and back into range?**	Yes No	▶ ▶	Fault identified. **For input type fault:** GO to Z10. **For output type fault:** GO to Z20. Unable to verify fault. GO to Z43.
Z43 INTERMITTENT ROAD TEST PROCEDURE			
NOTE: Look for certain conditions that cause the intermittent fault to occur. (Refer to Section 2, Recreating the Fault.) • Continue to monitor the PIDs listed in Z40. • Instrument the vehicle as in the previous steps. • Select another person to assist in performing the 55 mph test. • Make sure engine is at operating temperature before comparing or recording diagnostic values. • Drive the vehicle in a steady 55 mph range with accessories off. • Access the PIDs based on information from the pinpoint test or from the Intermittent Symptom Charts at the end of this pinpoint test. • Compare the actual values from the vehicle to the 55 mph values from the Typical Diagnostic Reference Value Chart. • **Are any values out of range or suddenly drop out and back into range?**	Yes No	▶ ▶	Fault identified. **For input type fault:** GO to Z10. **For output type fault:** GO to Z20. Unable to verify fault. RETURN to Z1 and choose another procedure.

FM0159601563120X

Fig. 291 Test Z: Intermittent (Part 12 of 37). 1996

Test Step	Result	▶	Action to Take
Z50 INTERMITTENT IGNITION PROCEDURE			
PRELIMINARY CHECKS NOTE: This pinpoint test should be used with the Intermittent Ignition Analyzer (Part No. Rotunda 007-00075). If this analyzer is not available, return to Z1 and choose another procedure. Quick Test must be performed and instructions in the EEC-V Pinpoint Test steps completed before starting the intermittent ignition procedure. When making voltage checks, a GROUND or LOW reading means any value within a range of 0 to 1 volt. Also, VPWR or COIL PWR or HIGH readings mean any value that falls within a range of B+ to 2 volts less than B+. When making resistance checks, make sure the ignition is in the key off position and the Scan Tool is disconnected from the DLC. For ICM and PCM Pin-Outs and System and Component Descriptions, refer to Ignition System Equipment Required for this Pinpoint Test: • Volt-Ohmmeter (Rotunda 105-00050 or equivalent). • Ignition Intermittent Analyzer (Rotunda 007-00075). • Check sensor shield connector. • Be certain the battery is fully charged. • All accessories should be off during diagnosis. • **Is vehicle prepared for equipment set-up?**	Yes No	▶ ▶	GO to Z51. REPEAT Z50.

FM0159601563130X

Fig. 291 Test Z: Intermittent (Part 13 of 37). 1996

Test Step	Result	▶	Action to Take
Z51 INTERMITTENT IGNITION PROCEDURE			

• Key off. All accessories should be off during testing.
• Select proper Overlay and Program Cartridge to match the ignition system to be tested.
• Install overlay on front panel of tester.
• Insert Program Cartridge into the cartridge slot (marked on the right hand side of the front panel). Make sure the cartridge is fully inserted.
• Select and install the proper harness adapter to the DIST tester (distributor ignition, EI High Data Rate or 104-Pin PCM Adapters).
• Verify that the Tester switches, CKP SIMULATION (EI High Data Rate only) and WIGGLE TEST are in the OFF position.
• Disconnect the vehicle wiring harness from ICM or PCM.
  — Depress tab on connector clip to remove the ignition harness (ICM only).
  — Inspect connectors for dirt, corrosion, moisture, and bent or broken pins.
  — Clean or repair as required.
• Hook Tester to ICM or PCM:
  — Plug male connector of tester into engine harness connector.
  — Plug female connector of tester into ICM or PCM.
• Key on, engine off. Press Tester RESET button. The tester performs Self-Test when it is Reset or powered up. During the Self-Test, all LEDs will light and a beep will be heard.
• **Did the tester perform Self-Test and is the VPWR LED (ICM PWR LED for Distributor Ignition) on?**
	Yes
	
	 No
		▶
		
		 ▶
			For EI High Data Rate (3.0L Windstar):
			GO to Z53.
			For Integrated EI High Data Rate:
			GO to Z220.
			For Distributor Ignition:
			GO to Z53.
			
			GO to tester check in Z52.

FM0159601563140X

Fig. 291 Test Z: Intermittent (Part 14 of 37). 1996

Test Step	Result	▶	Action to Take
Z52 TESTER CHECK			
• Key off. • Disconnect tester from vehicle. • Connect a jumper wire from VPWR jack to vehicle battery POS (+) terminal. • Connect a jumper wire from PWR GND jack to vehicle battery NEG (-) terminal. • If tester performs Self-Test, reconnect tester to vehicle and : For EI High Data Rate (3.0L Windstar): Go to Z190. For Integrated EI High Data Rate: Go to Z190. For Distributor Ignition: Go to Z312. • If tester does not perform Self-Test, refer to tester manual. • If LEDs do not light or a beep is not heard during Self-Test, refer to tester manual. • **Did tester pass Self-Test?**	Yes No	▶ ▶	**For EI High Data Rate (3.0L Windstar):** **For Integrated EI High Data Rate:** GO to Z220. **For Distributor Ignition:** GO to Z53. DIST does not pass Self-Test. REFER to Warranty supplied with DIST.
Z53 RECREATE THE FAULT			
• Key on, engine off. Observe the FAULT MEMORY and SYSTEM STATUS LEDs. • **Are any FAULT MEMORY or SYSTEM STATUS LEDs on?**	Yes No	▶ ▶	**For EI High Data Rate (3.0L Windstar):** GO to Z54. **For Distributor Ignition:** GO to Z270. GO to Z59.
Z54 COIL FAULT			
• **Are any COIL FAULT MEMORY LEDs on?**	Yes No	▶ ▶	GO to Z80. GO to Z55.
Z55 IGN GND FAULT			
• **Is the IGN GND FAULT MEMORY LED on?** NOTE: If IGN GND or CKP SHD FAULT MEMORY LEDs turn on during any testing operations, GO to Z210 for CKP SHD FAULT. GO to Z200 for IGN GND FAULT.	Yes No	▶ ▶	GO to Z200. GO to Z56.
Z56 CKP SHD FAULT			
• **Is the CKP SHD FAULT MEMORY LED on?**	Yes No	▶ ▶	GO to Z210. GO to Z57.
Z57 ICM STATUS			
• **Is the ICM OK SYSTEM STATUS LED blinking?**	Yes No	▶ ▶	GO to Z58. GO to Z96.

FM0159601563150X

Fig. 291 Test Z: Intermittent (Part 15 of 37). 1996

	Test Step	Result	►	Action to Take
Z58	CKP BIAS STATUS			
	• Is the CKP BIAS SYSTEM STATUS LED on?	Yes	►	GO to Z59.
		No	►	GO to Z120.
Z59	RECREATE THE FAULT			
	• With the DIST connected to the vehicle, try to recreate the fault by test driving the vehicle. If the vehicle is a No Start, crank engine for 5 to 10 seconds.	Yes	►	For EI High Data Rate: GO to Z60. For Distributor Ignition: GO to Z270.
	• Are any FAULT MEMORY or SYSTEM STATUS LEDs on?	No	►	Fault NOT related to Ignition System. RETURN to Z1 and choose another procedure.
Z60	CKP SIGNAL FAULT			
	• Is the CKP SIGNAL SYSTEM STATUS LED on during cranking?	Yes	►	GO to Z61.
		No	►	GO to Z130.
Z61	IDM FAULT			
	• Is the IDM FAULT MEMORY LED on?	Yes	►	GO to Z96.
		No	►	GO to Z63.
Z63	CKP FAULT			
	• Is the CKP FAULT MEMORY LED on?	Yes	►	GO to Z130.
		No	►	GO to Z64.
Z64	SPOUT FAULT			
	• Is the SPOUT FAULT MEMORY LED on?	Yes	►	GO to Z170.
		No	►	GO to Z65.
Z65	PIP FAULT			
	• Is the PIP FAULT MEMORY LED on?	Yes	►	GO to Z150.
		No	►	GO to Z66.
Z66	BASE TIMING FAULT			
	NOTE: If the engine is cold, the engine may stay at base timing for a long period of time. To check if the ignition timing is working, increase the engine rpm slightly and observe the BASE TIMING LED.	Yes	►	GO to Z170.
		No	►	GO to Z67.
	• Is the BASE TIMING SYSTEM STATUS LED on continuously?			
Z67	COIL FAULT			
	• Are any COIL FAULT MEMORY LEDS on?	Yes	►	GO to Z80.
		No	►	GO to Z68.
Z68	SECONDARY FAULT			
	• Are all COIL FAULT MEMORY LEDs double flashing?	Yes	►	GO to Intermittent Ignition Analyzer service manual for CKP SIMULATION TEST.
		No	►	GO to Z69.

FM0159601563160X

Fig. 291   Test Z: Intermittent (Part 16 of 37). 1996

	Test Step	Result	►	Action to Take
Z69	IGN GND FAULT			
	• Is the IGN GND FAULT MEMORY LED on?	Yes	►	Z200.
		No	►	Z70.
Z70	CKP SHD FAULT			
	• Is the CKP SHD FAULT MEMORY LED on?	Yes	►	GO to Z210.
		No	►	RETURN to Z1 and choose another procedure.
Z80	B+ CHECK			
	• Key off.	Yes	►	GO to Z81.
	• Disconnect ignition coil pack.	No	►	SERVICE B+ open circuit(s) to coil pack(s). RETEST.
	• Key on, engine off.			
	• Measure the voltage from B+ pin in the coil pack harness connectors to IGN GND jack.			
	• Is the voltage between 10 and 14 volts?			
Z81	CHECK FOR SHORTS			
	• Key off.	Yes	►	GO to Z86.
	• Measure the resistance from COIL jacks to IGN GND jack.	No	►	GO to Z82.
	• Measure the resistance from COIL jacks to VPWR jack.			
	• Is any resistance less than 6K ohms?			
Z82	COIL LINE CONTINUITY			
	• Measure the resistance from each COIL JACK to its pin in the coil pack harness connector.	Yes	►	GO to Z83.
	• Is each resistance less than 5 ohms?	No	►	SERVICE open in coil circuit. RETEST.
Z83	COIL CHECK			
	• Reconnect coil pack.	Yes	►	GO to Z88.
	• Key on, engine off.	No	►	GO to Z84.
	• Press the tester Reset button.			
	• Are any COIL LEDs on?			
Z84	WIGGLE TEST			
	• Place wiggle test switch to ON.	Yes	►	PRESS RESET button. CONTINUE to test until intermittent is isolated.
	• Place MODE switch to B.	No	►	GO to Z85.
	• Press RESET button and wait 5 seconds for initialization.			
	• Wiggle Test.			
	• Are any FAULT MEMORY LEDs on?			
Z85	COIL DISCONNECTED. WIGGLE TEST			
	• Key off.	Yes	►	PRESS RESET button. CONTINUE to test until intermittent is isolated.
	• Disconnect coil pack.	No	►	REPLACE ICM. RETEST.
	• Key on, engine off.			
	• Press RESET button and wait 5 seconds for initialization.			
	• Wiggle Test.			
	• Are any FAULT MEMORY LEDs on?			

FM0159601563170X

Fig. 291   Test Z: Intermittent (Part 17 of 37). 1996

	Test Step	Result	►	Action to Take
Z86	DISCONNECT ICM. RECHECK FOR SHORTS			
	• Disconnect ICM.	Yes	►	SERVICE short in coil circuit(s). RETEST.
	• Measure the resistance from COIL jacks to IGN GND jack.	No	►	GO to Z87.
	• Measure the resistance from COIL jacks to VPWR jack.			
	• Is any resistance less than 10K ohms?			
Z87	CHECK COIL LINES SHORTED TO EACH OTHER			
	• Measure the resistance from each COIL jack to all other COIL jacks.	Yes	►	SERVICE short in coil circuit(s). RETEST.
	• Is any resistance less than 10K ohms?	No	►	REPLACE ICM. RETEST.
Z88	CHECK FOR CORROSION			
	• Key off.	Yes	►	SERVICE corroded connectors as needed. RETEST.
	• Check the ignition system connectors for corrosion.	No	►	REPLACE ignition coil pack. RETEST.
	• Is there any corrosion?			
Z96	CHECK FOR SHORTS			
	• Key off.	Yes	►	GO to Z98.
	• Disconnect ICM from the tester.	No	►	GO to Z102.
	• Measure resistance from IDM jack to VPWR jack.			
	• Measure resistance from IDM jack to PWR GND jack.			
	• Is each resistance greater than 10K ohms?			
Z98	ICM CHECK			
	• Reconnect the ICM.	Yes	►	GO to Z99.
	• Key on, engine off.	No	►	REPLACE the ICM. RETEST.
	• Press the RESET button.			
	• Is the ICM OK LED blinking?			
Z99	WIGGLE TEST			
	• Key off.	Yes	►	PRESS RESET button. CONTINUE to test until intermittent is isolated.
	• Disconnect ICM from tester.	No	►	GO to Z100.
	• Key on, engine off.			
	• Set MODE switch to B.			
	• Set wiggle test switch to ON position.			
	• Press RESET button and wait 5 seconds for initialization.			
	• Wiggle test.			
	• Are any fault memory LEDs on?			

FM0159601563180X

Fig. 291   Test Z: Intermittent (Part 18 of 37). 1996

	Test Step	Result	►	Action to Take
Z100	PCM DISCONNECTED. WIGGLE TEST			
	• Key off.	Yes	►	PRESS RESET button. CONTINUE to test until intermittent is isolated.
	• Disconnect PCM from vehicle harness.	No	►	GO to Z101.
	NOTE: This erases Continuous Memory and sets the DTC P1000.			
	• Key on, engine off.			
	• Press RESET button and wait 5 seconds for initialization.			
	• Wiggle Test.			
	• Are any FAULT MEMORY LEDs on?			
Z101	QUICK TEST DTCS			
	• Were any IDM DTCs found during Self-Test?	Yes	►	GO to Z105.
		No	►	REPLACE ICM. RETEST.
Z102	DISCONNECT PCM. RETEST FOR SHORTS TO PWR			
	• Disconnect PCM from vehicle harness.	Yes	►	GO to Z103.
	NOTE: This erases Continuous Memory and sets the DTC P1000.	No	►	SERVICE IDM short circuit in harness. RETEST.
	• Measure the resistance from IDM jack to VPWR jack.			
	• Is each resistance greater than 10K ohms?			
Z103	DISCONNECT PCM. RETEST FOR SHORTS TO GND			
	• Measure the resistance from IDM jack to PWR GND jack.	Yes	►	REPLACE PCM. RETEST.
	• Is each resistance greater than 10K ohms?	No	►	SERVICE IDM short circuit in harness. RETEST.
Z105	IDM PCM CHECK			
	• Key off.	Yes	►	REPLACE PCM. RETEST.
	• Measure the resistance from IDM jack to Pin 4 of PCM breakout box.	No	►	SERVICE open circuit in harness between ICM and PCM. RETEST.
	• Is resistance less than 5 ohms?			
Z120	CHECK CKP BIAS			
	• Key off.	Yes	►	GO to Z122.
	• Disconnect CKP sensor from vehicle harness.	No	►	GO to Z121.
	• Key on, engine off.			
	• Is the CKP BIAS SYSTEM STATUS LED on?			
Z121	CHECK CKP+ FOR SHORTS			
	• Key off.	Yes	►	REPLACE ICM. RETEST.
	• Disconnect ICM.	No	►	SERVICE CKP+ short circuit(s) in harness. RETEST.
	• Measure the resistance from CKP+ jack to VPWR jack.			
	• Measure the resistance from CKP+ jack to PWR GND jack.			
	• Is each resistance greater than 10K ohms?			

FM0159601563190X

Fig. 291   Test Z: Intermittent (Part 19 of 37). 1996

ELECTRONIC ENGINE CONTROL SYSTEM (EEC-V)

Test Step	Result	►	Action to Take
Z122 CHECK CKP- FOR SHORTS • Key off. • Measure the resistance from CKP- jack to PWR GND jack. • Measure the resistance from CKP- jack to VPWR jack. • **Is each resistance greater than 10K ohms?**	Yes No	► ►	REPLACE shorted CKP sensor. RETEST. GO to Z123.
Z123 DISCONNECT ICM - RETEST FOR SHORTS • Disconnect ICM from tester. • Measure the resistance from CKP- jack to PWR GND jack. • Measure the resistance from CKP- jack to VPWR jack. • **Is each resistance greater than 10K ohms?**	Yes No	► ►	REPLACE ICM. RETEST. SERVICE CKP- short circuit(s) in harness. RETEST.
Z130 CKP SIGNAL CHECK • Crank or start the engine. • Observe the CKP SIGNAL LED. • **Is the CKP SIGNAL SYSTEM STATUS LED on during engine cranking or running?**	Yes No	► ►	GO to Z131. GO to Z132.
Z131 WIGGLE TEST • Key on, engine off. • Place WIGGLE TEST switch to ON position. • Set mode switch to B. • Press RESET button and wait 5 seconds for initialization. • Wiggle Test. • **Are any FAULT MEMORY LEDs on?**	Yes No	► ►	PRESS RESET button. CONTINUE to test until intermittent is isolated. Intermittent not recreated during testing. RETURN to Z1 and choose another procedure.
Z132 CHECK CKP+ HARNESS CONTINUITY • Key off. • Disconnect CKP sensor. • Measure the resistance from CKP+ jack to CKP+ pin in the harness connectors. • **Is resistance less than 5 ohms?**	Yes No	► ►	GO to Z133. SERVICE CKP+ open circuit(s) in harness. RETEST.
Z133 CHECK CKP - HARNESS CONTINUITY • Measure the resistance from CKP- jack to CKP- pin in the harness connectors. • **Is resistance less than 5 ohms?**	Yes No	► ►	GO to Z134. SERVICE CKP- open circuit(s) in harness. RETEST.
Z134 CHECK CKP SIGNAL LINES SHORTED TOGETHER • Measure the resistance from CKP+ jack to CKP- jack. • **Is resistance greater than 10K ohms?**	Yes No	► ►	GO to Z135. GO to Z136.

Fig. 291 Test Z: Intermittent (Part 20 of 37). 1996

Test Step	Result	►	Action to Take
Z135 SENSOR DAMAGE CHECK • Inspect the CKP sensor and the data wheel for proper alignment, correct air gap and physical damage. • **Is the CKP sensor or trigger wheel damaged, i.e. loose or misaligned?**	Yes No	► ►	SERVICE as needed. RETEST. REPLACE CKP sensor. RETEST.
Z136 DISCONNECT ICM - RECHECK FOR SHORTED CKP LINES • Disconnect ICM from tester. • Measure the resistance from CKP+ jack to CKP- jack. • **Is resistance greater than 10K ohms?**	Yes No	► ►	REPLACE ICM. RETEST. CKP+ and CKP- are shorted together. SERVICE as needed. RETEST.
Z150 CAPTURE FAULT • Crank, start engine. • Recreate vehicle fault. • **Is the PIP FAULT MEMORY LED blinking?**	Yes No	► ►	PIP FAULT MEMORY LED blinking. GO to Z151. PIP FAULT MEMORY LED on. GO to Z157.
Z151 CHECK FOR SHORTS • Key off. • Disconnect ICM from tester. • Measure the resistance from PIP jack to PWR GND jack. • Measure the resistance from PIP jack to VPWR jack. • **Is each resistance greater than 10K ohms?**	Yes No	► ►	GO to Z152. GO to Z158.
Z152 CHECK PIP • Key on, engine off. • Measure voltage from PIP jack to PWR GND jack. • **Is the voltage greater than 8 volts?**	Yes No	► ►	SERVICE PIP circuit shorted to VPWR. RETEST. GO to Z153.
Z153 CHECK ICM PIP CIRCUIT • Key off. • Reconnect ICM to tester. • Key on, engine off. • Measure the voltage from PIP jack to PWR GND jack. • **Is the voltage less than 10.5 volts?**	Yes No	► ►	REPLACE ICM. RETEST. GO to Z154.
Z154 WIGGLE TEST • Place wiggle test switch to ON position. • Set MODE switch to B. • Press RESET button and wait 5 seconds for initialization. • Wiggle Test. • **Are any FAULT MEMORY LEDs on?**	Yes No	► ►	PRESS RESET button. CONTINUE to test until intermittent is isolated. GO to Z155.

Fig. 291 Test Z: Intermittent (Part 21 of 37). 1996

Test Step	Result	►	Action to Take
Z155 ICM DISCONNECTED FROM TESTER. WIGGLE TEST • Key off. • Disconnect ICM from tester. • Key on, engine off. • Place wiggle test switch to ON. • Place the MODE switch to ON. • Press RESET button and wait 5 seconds for initialization. • Wiggle Test. • **Are any FAULT MEMORY LEDs on?**	Yes No	► ►	PRESS RESET button. CONTINUE to test until intermittent is isolated. GO to Z156.
Z156 WIGGLE TEST • Key off. • Place wiggle test switch to ON. • Place the MODE switch to B. • Press RESET button and wait 5 seconds for initialization. • Wiggle Test. • **Are any FAULT MEMORY LEDs on?**	Yes No	► ►	PRESS RESET button. CONTINUE to test until intermittent is isolated. REPLACE ICM. RETEST.
Z157 WIGGLE TEST • Key on, engine off. • Place wiggle test switch to ON position. • Set the MODE switch to B. • Press RESET button and wait 5 seconds for initialization. • Wiggle Test. • **Are any FAULT MEMORY LEDs on?**	Yes No	► ►	PRESS RESET button. CONTINUE to test until intermittent is isolated. REPLACE ICM. RETEST.
Z158 DISCONNECT PCM AND RECHECK FOR SHORTS • Disconnect the PCM from the vehicle harness. NOTE: This erases Continuous Memory and sets the DTC P 1000. • Measure the resistance from PIP jack to PWR GND jack. • Measure the resistance from PIP jack to VPWR jack. • **Is each resistance greater than 10K ohms?**	Yes No	► ►	REPLACE PCM. RETEST. SERVICE short in PIP circuit harness. RETEST.
Z170 START AND RUN VEHICLE • **Does the vehicle start and run?**	Yes No	► ►	GO to Z171. GO to Z178.
Z171 BASE TIMING CHECK • Start and run engine. • Observe the BASE TIMING LED. • **Is the BASE TIMING SYSTEM STATUS LED on continuously without any FAULT MEMORY LEDs on?**	Yes No	► ►	REPLACE ICM. RETEST. GO to Z172.

Fig. 291 Test Z: Intermittent (Part 22 of 37). 1996

Test Step	Result	►	Action to Take
Z172 SPOUT STATUS • Check the SPOUT LED. • **Is the SPOUT FAULT MEMORY LED on or blinking?**	Yes No	► ►	SPOUT FAULT MEMORY LED blinking. GO to Z173. SPOUT FAULT MEMORY LED on. GO to Z180.
Z173 PCM DISCONNECTED. CHECK FOR SHORTS • Key off. • Disconnect PCM from vehicle harness. NOTE: This erases Continuous Memory and sets the DTC P 1000. • Measure the resistance from SPOUT jack to PWR GND jack. • Measure the resistance from SPOUT jack to VPWR jack. • **Is each resistance greater than 10K ohms?**	Yes No	► ►	GO to Z174. GO to Z183.
Z174 ICM DISCONNECTED. CHECK FOR SHORTS • Reconnect PCM to vehicle harness. • Disconnect ICM. • Measure the resistance from SPOUT jack to PWR GND jack. • **Is resistance greater than 10K ohms?**	Yes No	► ►	GO to Z175. REPLACE the PCM. RETEST.
Z175 CHECK FOR SHORTS • Measure the resistance from SPOUT jack to VPWR jack. • **Is resistance greater than 10K ohms?**	Yes No	► ►	GO to Z176. REPLACE the PCM. RETEST.
Z176 WIGGLE TEST MODE B • Key on, engine off. • Place wiggle test switch in the ON position. • Set the MODE switch to B. • Press RESET button and wait 5 seconds for initialization. • Wiggle Test. • **Are any FAULT MEMORY LEDs on?**	Yes No	► ►	PRESS RESET button. CONTINUE to test until intermittent is isolated. GO to Z177.
Z177 WIGGLE TEST MODE A • Wiggle test switch to ON position. • Set the MODE switch to A. • Press RESET button and wait 5 seconds for initialization. • Wiggle Test. • **Are any FAULT MEMORY LEDs on?**	Yes No	► ►	PRESS RESET button. CONTINUE to test until intermittent is isolated. Intermittent not recreated during testing. RETURN to Z1 and choose another procedure.

Fig. 291 Test Z: Intermittent (Part 23 of 37). 1996

Test Step	Result	▶	Action to Take
Z178 CHECK PIP TO PCM HARNESS CONTINUITY • Key off. • Disconnect the PCM from the vehicle harness. NOTE: This erases Continuous Memory, and sets the DTC P1000. • Measure the resistance from PIP jack to Pin 56 at the PCM breakout box. • **Is resistance less than 5 ohms?**	Yes No	▶ ▶	GO to Z179. SERVICE open in PIP circuit harness. RETEST.
Z179 CHECK IGN GND TO PCM HARNESS CONTINUITY • Measure the resistance from IGN GND jack to Pin 16 at the PCM breakout box. • **Is resistance less 5 ohms?**	Yes No	▶ ▶	REPLACE the PCM. RETEST. SERVICE open in IGN GND circuit harness. RETEST.
Z180 CHECK SPOUT TO PCM HARNESS CONTINUITY • Key off. • Disconnect PCM from vehicle harness. NOTE: This erases Continuous Memory, and sets the DTC P1000. • Measure the resistance from SPOUT jack to Pin 36 at the PCM breakout box. • **Is resistance less than 5 ohms?**	Yes No	▶ ▶	GO to Z181. SERVICE open SPOUT circuit in harness between PCM and ICM. RETEST.
Z181 WIGGLE TEST MODE B • Reconnect PCM. • Disconnect ICM. • Key on, engine off. • Place the wiggle test switch to the ON position. • Set the MODE switch to B. • Press RESET button and wait 5 seconds for initialization. • Wiggle Test. • **Are any FAULT MEMORY LEDs on?**	Yes No	▶ ▶	PRESS RESET button. CONTINUE to test until intermittent is isolated. GO to Z182.
Z182 WIGGLE TEST MODE A • Set MODE switch to A. • Press the tester RESET button and wait 5 seconds for initialization. • Wiggle Test. • **Are any FAULT MEMORY LEDs on?**	Yes No	▶ ▶	PRESS RESET button. CONTINUE to test until intermittent is isolated. REPLACE PCM. RETEST.
Z183 DISCONNECT ICM AND RECHECK FOR SHORTS • Disconnect ICM from the tester. • Measure the resistance from SPOUT jack to PWR GND jack. • Measure the resistance from SPOUT jack to VPWR jack. • **Is each resistance greater than 10K ohms?**	Yes No	▶ ▶	REPLACE ICM. RETEST. SERVICE short in SPOUT circuit harness. RETEST.

FM0159601563240X

Fig. 291   Test Z: Intermittent (Part 24 of 37). 1996

Test Step	Result	▶	Action to Take
Z190 CHECK FOR VPWR • Key on, engine off. • Measure the voltage from VPWR jack to the battery NEG(-) terminal. • **Is the reading greater than 6 volts?**	Yes No	▶ ▶	GO to Z191. **For Integrated EI:** SERVICE open in VPWR circuit harness to PCM. RETURN to Z51. **For EI:** SERVICE open in VPWR circuit harness to ICM. RETURN to Z51.
Z191 CHECK PWR GND HARNESS • Key off. • Measure the resistance from PWR GND jack to the battery's NEG(-) terminal. • **Is resistance less than 5 ohms?**	Yes No	▶ ▶	GO to Z192. **For Integrated EI:** SERVICE open in PWR GND circuit harness to PCM. RETURN to Z51. **For EI:** SERVICE open in PWR GND circuit harness to ICM. RETURN to Z51.
Z192 WIGGLE TEST • Connect a jumper wire from PWR GND jack to the battery NEG(-) terminal. • Wiggle Test. • **Did the tester Reset?**	Yes No	▶ ▶	**For Integrated EI:** SERVICE open in VPWR circuit harness to PCM. RETURN to Z51. **For EI:** SERVICE open in VPWR circuit harness to ICM. RETURN to Z51. **For Integrated EI:** SERVICE open in PWR GND circuit harness to PCM. RETURN to Z51. **For EI:** SERVICE open in PWR GND circuit harness to ICM. RETURN to Z51.
Z200 CHECK IGN GND • Key on, engine off. • Measure the voltage from PWR GND jack to IGN GND jack. • **Is the voltage reading between 0.5 and -0.5 volt?**	Yes No	▶ ▶	GO to Z201. GO to Z202.

FM0159601563250X

Fig. 291   Test Z: Intermittent (Part 25 of 37). 1996

Test Step	Result	▶	Action to Take
Z201 WIGGLE TEST • Place the wiggle test switch to the ON position. • Set the MODE switch to B. • Press RESET button and wait 5 seconds for initialization. • Wiggle Test. • **Are any FAULT MEMORY LEDs on?**	Yes No	▶ ▶	PRESS RESET button. CONTINUE to test until intermittent is isolated. Intermittent not recreated during testing. RETURN to Z1 and choose another procedure.
Z202 CHECK FOR SHORTS • Key off. • Disconnect the PCM from vehicle's harness. NOTE: This erases Continuous Memory, and sets the DTC P1000. • Measure the resistance from IGN GND jack to VPWR jack. • **Is resistance greater than 10K ohms?**	Yes No	▶ ▶	REPLACE ICM. RETEST. SERVICE short in IGN GND circuit harness. RETEST.
Z210 CHECK FOR SHORTS • Key off. • Measure the resistance from CKP SHD jack to VPWR jack. • **Is resistance greater than 10K ohms?**	Yes No	▶ ▶	GO to Z211. GO to Z212.
Z211 WIGGLE TEST • Key on, engine off. • Place wiggle test switch to the ON position. • Set the MODE switch to B. • Press RESET button and wait 5 seconds for initialization. • Wiggle Test. • **Are any FAULT MEMORY LEDs on?**	Yes No	▶ ▶	PRESS RESET button. CONTINUE to test until intermittent is isolated. REPLACE ICM. RETEST.
Z212 CHECK FOR SHORTS • Disconnect ICM from the tester. • Measure the resistance from CKP SHD jack to VPWR jack. • **Is resistance greater than 10K ohms?**	Yes No	▶ ▶	REPLACE ICM. RETEST. SERVICE short in CKP SHD circuit harness.
Z220 CHECK FOR COIL FAULTS • Key on, engine off. • Press RESET button and wait for tester to initialize. • **Are any COIL FAULT MEMORY LEDs on or flashing?**	Yes No	▶ ▶	GO to Z229. GO to Z221.
Z221 CHECK CASE GND / CKP SHIELD • Key on, engine off. • **Is the CASE GND./ CKP SHD FAULT MEMORY LED on or flashing?**	Yes No	▶ ▶	GO to Z253. GO to Z222.

FM0159601563260X

Fig. 291   Test Z: Intermittent (Part 26 of 37). 1996

Test Step	Result	▶	Action to Take
Z222 CKP BIAS CHECK • Key on, engine off. • **Is the CKP BIAS SYSTEM STATUS LED on?**	Yes No	▶ ▶	GO to Z223. GO to Z243.
Z223 CHECK FOR CKP SIGNAL • With the DIST connected to the vehicle, try to recreate the fault by test driving the vehicle. If the vehicle is a No Start, crank engine for 5 to 10 seconds. • **Is the CKP SIGNAL SYSTEM STATUS LED on during crank or start?**	Yes No	▶ ▶	GO to Z224. GO to Z247.
Z224 COIL FAULT • Key on, engine running or key on, engine cranking. • **Are any COIL FAULT MEMORY LEDs on?**	Yes No	▶ ▶	GO to Z229. GO to Z225.
Z225 CASE GND / CKP SHIELD FAULT • Key on, engine running or key on, engine cranking. • **Is the CASE GND / CKP SHIELD FAULT MEMORY LED on?**	Yes No	▶ ▶	GO to Z253. GO to Z226.
Z226 CKP FAULT • Key on, engine running or key on, engine cranking. • **Is the CKP FAULT MEMORY LED on?**	Yes No	▶ ▶	GO to Z247. GO to Z227.
Z227 CTO FAULT • Key on, engine running or key on, engine cranking. • **Is the CTO FAULT MEMORY LED on?**	Yes No	▶ ▶	GO to Z239. Fault not related to Ignition System. RETURN to Z1 and choose another procedure.
Z229 B+ CHECK • Key off. • Disconnect Coil Pack(s). • Key on, engine off. • Measure voltage from B(+) at coil pack connector(s) to PWR GND jack. • **Is the voltage between 10 and 14 volts?**	Yes No	▶ ▶	GO to Z230. SERVICE B(+) harness(es) to coil pack(s). RETEST.
Z230 CHECK FOR SHORTS • Key off. • Measure resistance from COIL jacks to PWR GND jack. • Measure resistance from COIL jacks to VPWR jack. • **Is any resistance less than 6K ohms?**	Yes No	▶ ▶	GO to Z236. GO to Z231.

FM0159601563270X

Fig. 291   Test Z: Intermittent (Part 27 of 37). 1996

Fig. 291 Test Z: Intermittent (Part 28 of 37). 1996

Test Step	Result	▶	Action to Take
Z231 CHECK COIL LINE CONTINUITY • Measure resistance from each COIL jack to its pin in the coil harness connector. • **Is each resistance less than 5K ohms?**	Yes No	▶ ▶	GO to **Z232**. SERVICE coil harness. RETEST.
Z232 CHECK COIL LINES SHORT TOGETHER • Measure resistance from every COIL jack to all other COIL jacks. • **Is any resistance less than 10K ohms?**	Yes No	▶ ▶	GO to **Z237**. GO to **Z233**.
Z233 CHECK FOR HARD FAULT • Reconnect coil pack(s). • Key on, engine off. • Press RESET button. • Wait for tester initialization. • Wait for coil test to run. • **Are any COIL FAULT MEMORY LEDs on or flashing?**	Yes No	▶ ▶	GO to **Z238**. GO to **Z234**.
Z234 COILS DISCONNECTED. WIGGLE TEST • Place WIGGLE TEST switch to ON. • Place MODE switch to B. • Press RESET button. • Wait for WIGGLE TEST ACTIVE LED to light. • Wiggle Test. • **Are any FAULT MEMORY LEDs on?**	Yes No	▶ ▶	PRESS RESET and WAIT for WIGGLE TEST ACTIVE LED light. CONTINUE to test until intermittent is isolated. SERVICE as needed. RETEST. GO to **Z235**.
Z235 WIGGLE TEST • Key off. • Disconnect coil pack(s). • Key on, engine off. • Wait for WIGGLE TEST ACTIVE LED to light. • Wiggle test. • **Are any FAULT MEMORY LEDs on?**	Yes No	▶ ▶	PRESS RESET and WAIT for WIGGLE TEST ACTIVE LED light. CONTINUE to test until intermittent is isolated. SERVICE as needed. RETEST. REPLACE PCM. RETEST.
Z236 ISOLATE COIL LINE SHORTS • Disconnect PCM. • Reconnect coil to vehicle harness. • Measure resistance from each COIL jack to PWR GND jack. • Measure resistance from each COIL jack to VPWR jack. • **Is any resistance less than 10K ohms?**	Yes No	▶ ▶	SERVICE coil harness. RETEST. REPLACE PCM. RETEST.
Z237 ISOLATE COIL LINE SHORTS • Disconnect PCM. • Reconnect DIST to vehicle harness. • Measure resistance from every COIL jack to all other COIL jacks. • **Is any resistance less than 10K ohms?**	Yes No	▶ ▶	SERVICE coil harness. RETEST. REPLACE PCM. RETEST.

FM0159601563280X

Fig. 291 Test Z: Intermittent (Part 29 of 37). 1996

Test Step	Result	▶	Action to Take
Z238 CHECK FOR CORROSION • Key off. • Check ignition system connectors for corrosion. • **Is any corrosion present?**	Yes No	▶ ▶	SERVICE connectors. RETEST. REPLACE damaged coil pack(s). RETEST.
Z239 CHECK FOR SHORTS • Key off. • Measure resistance from CTO to VPWR jack. • Measure resistance from CTO to PWR GND jack. • **Is any resistance less than 1K ohm?**	Yes No	▶ ▶	GO to **Z240** GO to **Z241**
Z240 ISOLATE SHORTS • Disconnect PCM. • Reconnect DIST to vehicle harness. • Measure resistance from CTO to VPWR jack. • Measure resistance from CTO to PWR GND jack. • **Is any resistance less than 1K ohm?**	Yes No	▶ ▶	SERVICE CTO harness/tachometer. RETEST. REPLACE PCM. RETEST.
Z241 WIGGLE TEST MODE B • Key on, engine off. • Place WIGGLE TEST switch to ON. • Place MODE switch to B. • Press RESET button. • Wait for WIGGLE TEST ACTIVE LED to light. • **Are any FAULT MEMORY LEDs on?**	Yes No	▶ ▶	PRESS RESET and WAIT for WIGGLE TEST ACTIVE LED light. CONTINUE to test until intermittent is isolated. SERVICE as needed. RETEST. GO to **Z242**.
Z242 WIGGLE TEST • 6 or 4 cylinder: Set MODE switch to A. • 8 cylinder: Set MODE switch to C. • Press RESET button. • Wait for WIGGLE TEST ACTIVE LED to light. • Wiggle Test. • **Are any FAULT MEMORY LEDs on?**	Yes No	▶ ▶	PRESS RESET and WAIT for WIGGLE TEST ACTIVE LED light. CONTINUE to test until intermittent is isolated. SERVICE as needed. RETEST. REPLACE PCM. RETEST.
Z243 CHECK CKP BIAS • Key off. • Disconnect vehicle harness from CKP sensor. • Key on, engine off. • **Is the CKP BIAS SYSTEM STATUS LED on?**	Yes No	▶ ▶	GO to **Z245**. GO to **Z244**.
Z244 ISOLATE CKP SHORT • Key off. • Disconnect PCM. • Reconnect DIST to vehicle harness. • Measure resistance from CKP+ jack to VPWR jack. • **Is resistance greater than 10K ohms?**	Yes No	▶ ▶	REPLACE PCM. RETEST. SERVICE CKP harness. RETEST.

FM0159601563290X

Fig. 291 Test Z: Intermittent (Part 30 of 37). 1996

Test Step	Result	▶	Action to Take
Z245 CHECK FOR SHORTS • Key off. • Measure resistance from CKP- jack to PWR GND jack. • Measure resistance from CKP- jack to VPWR jack. • **Are both resistances greater than 10K ohms?**	Yes No	▶ ▶	REPLACE CKP sensor. RETEST. GO to **Z246**.
Z246 ISOLATE SHORTS • Disconnect PCM. • Reconnect DIST to vehicle harness. • Measure resistance from CKP-jack to PWR GND jack. • Measure resistance from CKP-jack to VPWR jack. • **Are both resistances greater than 10K ohms?**	Yes No	▶ ▶	REPLACE PCM. RETEST. SERVICE CKP harness. RETEST.
Z247 CHECK CKP SIGNAL • Crank or start engine. • **Is the CKP SIGNAL SYSTEM STATUS LED on during crank or engine run?**	Yes No	▶ ▶	GO to **Z252**. GO to **Z248**.
Z248 CHECK FOR CKP LINE CONTINUITY • Key off. • Disconnect CKP sensor. • Measure resistance from CKP+ jack to CKP+ pin in harness sensor connector. • Measure resistance from CKP- jack to CKP- pin in harness sensor connector. • **Are both resistances less than 5K ohms?**	Yes No	▶ ▶	GO to **Z249**. SERVICE CKP harness. RETEST.
Z249 CHECK CKPS SHORTED TOGETHER • Measure resistance from CKP+ jack to CKP- jack. • **Is the resistance greater than 10K ohms?**	Yes No	▶ ▶	GO to **Z251**. GO to **Z250**.
Z250 ISOLATE SHORT • Disconnect PCM. • Reconnect DIST to vehicle harness. • Measure resistance from CKP+ jack to CKP- jack. • **Is the resistance greater than 10K ohms?**	Yes No	▶ ▶	REPLACE PCM. RETEST. SERVICE CKP harness. RETEST.
Z251 CHECK FOR PHYSICAL DAMAGE • Inspect CKP sensor and data wheel for misalignment, incorrect air gap and physical damage. • **Are the sensor and data wheel OK?**	Yes No	▶ ▶	REPLACE CKP sensor. RETEST. SERVICE as needed. RETEST.

FM0159601563300X

Fig. 291 Test Z: Intermittent (Part 31 of 37). 1996

Test Step	Result	▶	Action to Take
Z252 WIGGLE TEST • Key on, engine off. • Place WIGGLE TEST switch to ON. • Place MODE switch to B. • Press RESET button. • Wait for WIGGLE TEST ACTIVE LED to light. • Wiggle Test. • **Are any FAULT MEMORY LEDs on?**	Yes No	▶ ▶	PRESS RESET and WAIT for WIGGLE TEST ACTIVE LED light. CONTINUE to test until intermittent is isolated. SERVICE as needed. RETEST. REPLACE PCM. RETEST.
Z253 CHECK CKP SHD FOR SHORT TO PWR • Measure resistance from CASE GND/CKP SHD jack to VPWR jack. • **Is the resistance greater than 10K ohms?**	Yes No	▶ ▶	GO to **Z255**. GO to **Z254**.
Z254 ISOLATE SHORT • Disconnect PCM. • Reconnect DIST to vehicle harness. • Measure resistance from CASE GND/CKP SHD jack to VPWR jack. • **Is the resistance greater than 10K ohms?**	Yes No	▶ ▶	REPLACE PCM. RETEST. SERVICE CASE GND/CKP SHD SHIELD harness. RETEST.
Z255 WIGGLE TEST • Key on, engine off. • Place WIGGLE TEST switch to ON. • Place MODE switch to B. • Press RESET button. • Wait for WIGGLE TEST ACTIVE LED to light. • Wiggle Test. • **Are any FAULT MEMORY LEDs on?**	Yes No	▶ ▶	PRESS RESET and WAIT for WIGGLE TEST ACTIVE LED light. CONTINUE to test until intermittent is isolated. SERVICE as needed. RETEST. SERVICE CASE GND/CKP shield harness. RETEST.
Z270 CHECK FOR COIL FAULT • **Is the COIL FAULT MEMORY LED on?**	Yes No	▶ ▶	GO to **Z277**. GO to **Z271**.
Z271 CHECK FOR IDM FAULT • **Is the IDM FAULT MEMORY LED on?**	Yes No	▶ ▶	GO to **Z287**. GO to **Z272**.
Z272 CHECK FOR PIP ACTIVE FAULT • **Is the PIP ACTIVE SYSTEM STATUS LED on?**	Yes No	▶ ▶	GO to **Z273**. GO to **Z291**.
Z273 CHECK FOR PIP FAULT • **Is the PIP FAULT MEMORY LED ON?**	Yes No	▶ ▶	GO to **Z291**. GO to **Z274**.
Z274 CHECK FOR PIP DUTY FAULT • **Is the PID DUTY FAULT MEMORY LED on?**	Yes No	▶ ▶	GO to **Z291**. GO to **Z275**.

FM0159601563310X

Test Step	Result	▶	Action to Take
Z275 CHECK FOR BASE TIMING FAULT			
• Is the BASE TIMING SYSTEM STATUS LED on continuously?	Yes	▶	GO to Z302.
	No	▶	GO to Z276.
Z276 CHECK FOR SPOUT FAULT			
• Is the SPOUT FAULT MEMORY LED on?	Yes	▶	GO to Z310.
	No	▶	GO to Z59.
Z277 CHECK COIL VOLTAGE			
• Key on, engine off.	Yes	▶	GO to Z278.
• Measure the voltage from COIL jack to IGN GND jack.	No	▶	GO to Z280.
• Is voltage between 10 and 14 volts?			
Z278 CHECK FOR SHORTS TO PWR			
• Key off.	Yes	▶	GO to Z279.
• Disconnect Coil.	No	▶	GO to Z284.
• Measure the resistance from COIL jack to ICM PWR jack.			
• Is resistance less than 2K ohms?			
Z279 CHECK HARNESS FOR SHORTS TO PWR			
• Disconnect ICM.	Yes	▶	SERVICE harness. RETEST.
• Measure resistance from COIL to ICM PWR jacks.	No	▶	REPLACE ICM. RETEST.
• Is resistance less than 10K ohms?			
Z280 CHECK COIL PACK PWR			
• Key off.	Yes	▶	GO to Z281.
• Disconnect Coil.	No	▶	SERVICE Coil PWR line. RETEST.
• Key on, engine off.			
• Measure the voltage from COIL jack to IGN GND jack.			
• Is voltage between 10 and 14 volts?			
Z281 CHECK FOR SHORTS TO GND			
• Key off.	Yes	▶	GO to Z282.
• Measure the resistance from COIL jack to IGN GND jack.	No	▶	GO to Z283.
• Is resistance greater than 10K ohms?			
Z282 CHECK HARNESS CONTINUITY			
• Measure the resistance from COIL jack to COIL signal pin in the Coil harness connector.	Yes	▶	REPLACE Coil. RETEST.
• Is resistance less than 5 ohms?	No	▶	SERVICE harness. RETEST.
Z283 CHECK HARNESS FOR SHORTS TO GND			
• Disconnect ICM.	Yes	▶	REPLACE ICM. RETEST.
• Measure the resistance from COIL jack to IGN GND jack.	No	▶	SERVICE harness. RETEST.
• Is resistance greater than 10K ohms?			

FM0159601563320X

Fig. 291 Test Z: Intermittent (Part 32 of 37). 1996

Test Step	Result	▶	Action to Take
Z284 COIL TEST			
• Reconnect Coil.	Yes	▶	REPLACE Coil. RETEST.
• Key on, engine off.	No	▶	GO to Z285.
• Press RESET button.			
The tester will perform a coil test after it resets.			
• Is the COIL FAULT MEMORY LED on?			
Z285 WIGGLE TEST - MODE B			
• WIGGLE TEST switch to ON.	Yes	▶	PRESS RESET button. CONTINUE to test until intermittent is isolated. SERVICE fault. RETEST.
• MODE switch to B.			
• Press RESET button.			
• Wait for initialization.	No	▶	GO to Z286.
• Wiggle Test.			
• Are any FAULT MEMORY LEDs on?			
Z286 WIGGLE TEST. COIL DISCONNECTED			
• Key off.	Yes	▶	PRESS RESET button. CONTINUE to test until intermittent is isolated. SERVICE fault. RETEST.
• Disconnect Coil.			
• Key on, engine off.			
• Press RESET button.	No	▶	REPLACE ICM. RETEST.
• Wait for initialization.			
• Wiggle Test.			
• Are any FAULT MEMORY LEDs on?			
Z287 QUICK TEST DTCS			
• Was this pinpoint test entered because of an IDM Self-Test code?	Yes	▶	GO to Z289.
	No	▶	GO to Z288.
Z288 WIGGLE TEST - MODE B			
• Key on, engine off.	Yes	▶	PRESS RESET button. CONTINUE to test until intermittent is isolated. SERVICE fault. RETEST.
• WIGGLE TEST switch to ON.			
• MODE switch to B.			
• Press RESET button.	No	▶	Intermittent not recreated during testing. RETURN to Z1 and choose another procedure.
• Wait for initialization.			
• Wiggle Test.			
• Are any FAULT MEMORY LEDs on?			
Z289 CHECK HARNESS CONTINUITY			
• Disconnect PCM.	Yes	▶	GO to Z290.
• Measure the resistance from IDM / START jack to IDM Pin 4 at PCM breakout box.	No	▶	SERVICE harness. RETEST.
• Is resistance less than 5 ohms?			

FM0159601563330X

Fig. 291 Test Z: Intermittent (Part 33 of 37). 1996

Test Step	Result	▶	Action to Take
Z290 WIGGLE TEST			
• Connect a BOB (Break Out Box) to the PCM harness connector.	Yes	▶	PRESS RESET button. CONTINUE to test until intermittent is isolated. SERVICE fault. RETEST.
• Connect the PCM to BOB.			
• Connect ROVING jack and IDM Pin 4 at PCM BOB with a jumper wire.	No	▶	Intermittent not recreated during testing. RETURN to Z1 and choose another procedure.
• WIGGLE TEST switch to ON.			
• MODE switch to B.			
• Press RESET button.			
• Wait for initialization.			
• Wiggle Test.			
• Are any FAULT MEMORY LEDs on?			
Z291 CHECK FOR SHORTS			
• Key off.	Yes	▶	GO to Z292.
• Measure the resistance from PIP jack to IGN GND jack.	No	▶	GO to Z294.
• Measure the resistance from PIP jack to ICM PWR jack.			
• Is each resistance greater than 10K ohms?			
Z292 CHECK HARNESS CONTINUITY			
• Disconnect the distributor connector.	Yes	▶	GO to Z293.
• Measure resistance from PIP jack to PIP pin in the distributor harness connector.	No	▶	SERVICE harness. RETEST.
• Is resistance less than 5 ohms?			
Z293 WIGGLE TEST - MODE B			
• Reconnect the distributor connector.	Yes	▶	PRESS RESET button. CONTINUE to test until intermittent is isolated. SERVICE fault. RETEST.
• Key on, engine off.			
• WIGGLE TEST switch to ON.			
• MODE switch to B.	No	▶	GO to Z294.
• Press RESET button.			
• Wait for initialization.			
• Wiggle Test.			
• Are any FAULT MEMORY LEDs on?			
Z294 WIGGLE TEST - MODE A			
• MODE switch to A.	Yes	▶	PRESS RESET button. CONTINUE to test until intermittent is isolated. SERVICE fault. RETEST.
• Press RESET button.			
• Wait for initialization.			
• Wiggle Test.	No	▶	GO to Z295.
• Are any FAULT MEMORY LEDs on?			
Z295 WIGGLE TEST - MODE C			
• MODE switch to C.	Yes	▶	PRESS RESET button. CONTINUE to test until intermittent is isolated. SERVICE fault. RETEST.
• Press RESET button.			
• Wait for initialization.			
• Wiggle Test.	No	▶	GO to Z296.
• Are any FAULT MEMORY LEDs on?			

FM0159601563340X

Fig. 291 Test Z: Intermittent (Part 34 of 37). 1996

Test Step	Result	▶	Action to Take
Z296 WIGGLE TEST - ROVING			
• Connect ROVING and PIP jacks.	Yes	▶	PRESS RESET button. CONTINUE to test until intermittent is isolated. SERVICE fault. RETEST.
• MODE switch to B.			
• Press RESET button.			
• Wait for initialization.	No	▶	GO to Z298.
• Wiggle Test.			
• Are any FAULT MEMORY LEDs on?			
Z297 WIGGLE TEST - ROVING AT PCM			
• Insert a BOB (Break Out Box) at the PCM.	Yes	▶	PRESS RESET button. CONTINUE to test until intermittent is isolated. SERVICE fault. RETEST.
• Connect ROVING jack and PIP Pin 56 at the PCM BOB.			
• Press RESET button.			
• Wait for initialization.	No	▶	GO to Z298.
• Wiggle Test.			
• Are any FAULT MEMORY LEDs on?			
Z298 CHECK PIP SENSOR			
• Remove the distributor cap.	Yes	▶	REPLACE SENSOR. RETEST.
• Inspect the PIP sensor and data wheel for damage, proper mounting and proper alignment.	No	▶	SERVICE as needed. RETEST.
• Is the sensor OK?			
Z299 CHECK HARNESS, SENSOR AND ICM FOR SHORTS			
• Disconnect PCM.	Yes	▶	REPLACE PCM. RETEST.
• Measure the resistance from PIP jack to IGN GND jack.	No	▶	GO to Z300.
• Measure the resistance from PIP jack to ICM PWR jack.			
• Is each resistance greater than 10K ohms?			
Z300 CHECK HARNESS AND SENSOR FOR SHORTS			
• Disconnect ICM.	Yes	▶	REPLACE ICM. RETEST.
• Measure the resistance from PIP jack to IGN GND jack.	No	▶	GO to Z301.
• Measure the resistance from PIP jack to ICM PWR jack.			
• Is each resistance greater than 10K ohms?			
Z301 CHECK HARNESS FOR SHORTS			
• Disconnect the distributor connector.	Yes	▶	SERVICE or REPLACE PIP sensor harness. RETEST.
• Measure the resistance from PIP jack to IGN GND jack.	No	▶	SERVICE harness. RETEST.
• Measure the resistance from PIP jack to ICM PWR jack.			
• Is each resistance greater than 10K ohms?			
Z302 BASE TIME STATUS			
• Is the BASE TIMING LED on continuously during run with no FAULT MEMORY LEDs?	Yes	▶	REPLACE ICM. RETEST.
	No	▶	GO to Z303.

FM0159601563350X

Fig. 291 Test Z: Intermittent (Part 35 of 37). 1996

Test Step		Result	▶	Action to Take
Z303	CHECK FOR SHORTS			
	• Key off. • Measure resistance from SPOUT jack to ICM PWR jack. • Measure resistance from SPOUT jack to IGN GND jack. • **Is each resistance greater than 10K ohms?**	Yes No	▶ ▶	GO TO **Z304**. GO to **Z310**
Z304	CHECK SPOUT HARNESS CONTINUITY			
	• Disconnect PCM. • Measure resistance from SPOUT jack to SPOUT Pin 36 at PCM breakout box. • **Is resistance less than 5 ohms?**	Yes No	▶ ▶	GO to **Z305**. SERVICE harness. RETEST.
Z305	CHECK PIP HARNESS CONTINUITY			
	• Measure the resistance from PIP jack to PIP Pin 56 at the PCM breakout box. • **Is resistance less than 5 ohms?**	Yes No	▶ ▶	GO to **Z306**. SERVICE harness between CMP sensor and PCM and between CMP sensor and ICM. RETEST.
Z306	CHECK IGN GND HARNESS CONTINUITY			
	• Measure the resistance from IGN GND jack to IGN GND Pin 16 at PCM breakout box. • **Is resistance less than 5 ohms?**	Yes No	▶ ▶	GO to **Z307**. SERVICE harness. RETEST.
Z307	WIGGLE TEST - MODE B			
	• Reconnect PCM. • Key on, engine off. • WIGGLE TEST switch to ON. • MODE switch to B. • Press RESET button. • Wait for initialization. • Wiggle Test. • **Are any FAULT MEMORY LEDs on?**	Yes No	▶ ▶	PRESS RESET button. CONTINUE to test until intermittent is isolated. SERVICE fault. RETEST. GO to **Z308**.
Z308	WIGGLE TEST - MODE C			
	• MODE switch to C. • Press RESET button. • Wait for initialization. • Wiggle Test. • **Are any FAULT MEMORY LEDs on?**	Yes No	▶ ▶	PRESS RESET button. CONTINUE to test until intermittent is isolated. SERVICE fault. RETEST. GO to **Z309**.
Z309	WIGGLE TEST - ROVING			
	• Insert a BOB (Break Out Box) at PCM. • Connect ROVING jack to SPOUT Pin 36 at PCM BOB using a jumper wire. • **Are any FAULT MEMORY LEDs on?**	Yes No	▶ ▶	PRESS RESET button. CONTINUE to test until intermittent is isolated. SERVICE fault. RETEST. REPLACE PCM. RETEST.

FM0159601563360X

Fig. 291   Test Z: Intermittent (Part 36 of 37). 1996

Test Step		Result	▶	Action to Take
Z310	CHECK HARNESS AND PCM FOR SHORTS			
	• Disconnect ICM. • Measure resistance from SPOUT jack to ICM PWR jacks. • Measure resistance from SPOUT jack to IGN GND jacks. • **Is each resistance greater than 10K ohms?**	Yes No	▶ ▶	REPLACE ICM. RETEST. GO to **Z311**.
Z311	CHECK HARNESS FOR SHORTS			
	• Disconnect PCM. • Measure resistance from SPOUT jack to IGN PWR jacks. • Measure resistance from SPOUT jack to IGN GND jacks. • **Is each resistance greater than 10K ohms?**	Yes No	▶ ▶	REPLACE ICM. RETEST. SERVICE harness. RETEST.
Z312	CHECK ICM GND			
	• Key off. • Measure the resistance from IGN GND jack to battery NEG(-) terminal. • **Is resistance less than 5 ohms?**	Yes No	▶ ▶	GO to **Z313**. GO to **Z315**.
Z313	CHECK ICM PWR			
	• Key on, engine off. • Measure the voltage from ICM PWR jack to the battery NEG(-) terminal. • **Is voltage greater than 6 volts?**	Yes No	▶ ▶	GO to **Z314**. SERVICE ICM PWR line. RETEST.
Z314	WIGGLE TEST			
	• Connect a jumper wire from IGN GND jack to the battery NEG(-) terminal. • Wiggle Test. • **Did the tester reset?**	Yes No	▶ ▶	SERVICE intermittent ICM PWR line. RETEST. SERVICE intermittent IGN GND line. RETEST.
Z315	CHECK HARNESS CONTINUITY			
	• Disconnect the distributor connector. • Measure resistance from IGN GND jack to IGN GND pin in the distributor's harness connector. • **Is resistance less than 5 ohms?**	Yes No	▶ ▶	GO to **Z316**. SERVICE harness. RETEST.
Z316	CHECK DISTRIBUTOR GND			
	• Measure the resistance from the distributor metal surface to the battery NEG(-) terminal. • **Is resistance less than 5 ohms?**	Yes No	▶ ▶	SERVICE or REPLACE PIP sensor and sensor harness. RETEST. SERVICE the distributor GND. CHECK mounting of the distributor to the engine block and the engine block to the battery NEG(-) terminal connection. RETEST.

FM0159601563370X

Fig. 291   Test Z: Intermittent (Part 37 of 37). 1996

Select a symptom from the chart below. For multiple symptoms, select the symptom that is most evident. Go to the chart selected and perform the visual / mechanical and EEC checks in the order that is suggested.

Contents

System / Symptom		Chart Number
Driveability		
Starting Concerns	No Start / Normal Crank	1
	Hard Start / Long Crank	2
	Stall After Start	2
Unique Idle Concerns	Slow Return to Idle	3
	Rolling Idle	4
	Fast Idle	3
	Low / Slow Idle	3
Driveability — Performance While Driving Concerns		
Stalls / Quits (607000)	Idle	8
	Acceleration	8
	Cruise	8
	Deceleration	8
Runs Rough (608000)	Idle	9
	Acceleration	9
	Cruise	9
Misses (609000)	Idle	9
	Acceleration	9
	Cruise	9
Buck / Jerk (610000)	Acceleration	9
	Cruise	9
	Deceleration	9
Hesitation / Stumble (611000)	Acceleration	9
Surge (61200)	Acceleration	5
	Cruise	5
Backfires (613000)	Idle	9
	Acceleration	9
	Deceleration	9

FM0159601564010X

Fig. 292   Pinpoint test, intermittent symptom index (Part 1 of 2). 1996

System / Symptom		Chart Number
Driveability — Performance While Driving Concerns (continued)		
Lack / Loss of Power (614000)	Acceleration	6
	Cruise	6
Spark Knock (615000)	Acceleration	7
	Cruise	7
Additional Driveability Concerns		
Diesels / Runs On		7
Poor Fuel Economy		8
Emissions Compliance		8
Cooling System Concerns Overheating		7
Electrical	MIL On (warning indicators)	8
EEC Related Shift Symptoms		
A / T Upshift Concern		10
A / T Downshift Concern		10
Engagement Concern		10
Hard or Soft Shifts		11
Erratic, Hunting Shifts		12
No Overdrive		13

FM0159601564020X

Fig. 292   Pinpoint test, intermittent symptom index (Part 2 of 2). 1996

Starting Concerns

NO START/NORMAL CRANK

System	Checks — Visual/Mechanical	Checks — EEC-V PIDS/Components/CKTS
Fuel	• Check fuel pump and Inertia Fuel Shutoff (IFS) switch. • Check for fuel contamination/quality. • Check fuel filter. • Check fuel level/gauge operation. • Check for restricted fuel lines. • Check for correct fuel pressure.	• Fuel System PIDs: FP, FPM, **FUELSYS1/2**, HTR11A/12A/21A/22A, HTRX1/2, LONGFT1/21/22, O2S11/12/21/22, SHRTFT11/2/11/12/21/22, FUELPW1/2 • Fuel System Components/Circuits: Injectors1/2...., Fuel Pump Relay
Ignition	• Inspect spark plugs and plug wires. • Check ignition switch. • Check ignition coil for voltage. • Inspect ICM for damage. • Check for presence of anti-theft devices.	• Ignition System: **SPARKADJ PID**, MISF PID, IGN GND circuit, IGN coils
Power and Grounds	• Check for low battery voltage. • Check starter and starter circuit for voltage. • Inspect electrical connections, wires, and harnesses.	• EEC-V power: VREF PID, VPWR PID, EEC-V power relay • EEC-V grounds: SIG RTN circuit, PWR GND circuit, CSE GND circuit
Air/Vacuum	• Check vacuum lines for leaks, blockage or wear. • Check air intake system.	• TP PID • MAF PID • IAC PID
Other	• Check engine coolant level. • Check thermostat for proper operation. • Check EGR valve stuck open. • Check for moisture entry into PCM. • Check camshaft timing and cylinder compression. • Check for restricted exhaust.	• ECT PID • DPFEGR PID • TR PID

NOTE: Generic PIDS are in bold.

FM0159601565000X

Fig. 293 Pinpoint test, intermittent symptom chart 1. 1996

Starting Concerns

STALL AFTER START HARD START/LONG CRANK

System	Checks — Visual/Mechanical	Checks — EEC-V PIDS/Components/CKTS
Ignition	• Inspect spark plugs and plug wires. • Check ignition switch. • Check ignition coil for voltage. • Inspect EI system for damage. • Check for presence of anti-theft devices.	• Ignition System: MISF PID, **SPARKADV PID**, IGN GND circuit
Fuel	• Check fuel pump and Inertia Fuel Shutoff (IFS) switch. • Check for fuel contamination/quality. • Check fuel filter. • Check fuel level/gauge operation. • Check for restricted fuel lines. • Check for correct fuel pressure.	• Fuel System PIDs: FP, FPM, **FUELSYS1/2**, HTR11A/12A/21A/22A, HTRX1/2, LONGFT1/2, O2S11/12/21/22, SHRTFT11/2/11/12/21/22, FPW1/2 • Fuel System Components/Circuits: Injectors1/2..., Fuel Pump Relay
Power and Grounds	• Check for low battery voltage. • Inspect electrical connections, wires, and harnesses. • Check starter and starter circuit for voltage.	• EEC-V Power: FP, VPWR PID, EEC-V power relay • EEC-V Grounds: SIG RTN circuit, PWR GND circuit, CSE GND circuit
Air/Vacuum	• Check vacuum lines for leaks, blockage or wear. • Check air intake system.	• TP PID • MAF PID • IAC PID • IAT PID
Other	• Check engine coolant level. • Check thermostat for proper operation. • Check EGR valve stuck open. • Check for moisture entry in PCM. • Check throttle body for binding. • Check for proper idle speed control. • Check camshaft timing and cylinder compression. • Check for restricted exhaust. • Check IAC Solenoid connection.	• ECT PID • EPC PID • EGR Systems: DPFEGR PID, EGRVR PID • A/C Systems: ACCS PID, ACP PID, WAC PID, WACA PID • IAC PID

NOTE: Generic PIDS are in bold.

FM0159601566000X

Fig. 294 Pinpoint test, intermittent symptom chart 2. 1996

Unique Idle Concerns

SLOW RTN/SLOW/FAST IDLE

System	Checks — Visual/Mechanical	Checks — EEC-V PIDS/Components/CKTS
Air/Vacuum	• Check vacuum lines for leaks, blockage or wear. • Check air intake system.	• TP PID • MAF PID • IAC PID • IAT PID
Fuel	• Check for correct fuel pressure. • Check for fuel contamination/quality. • Check fuel filter. • Check for restricted fuel lines.	• Fuel System PIDs: FP, FPM, **FUELB1/2**, HTR11A/12A/21A/22A, HTRX1/2, LONGFT1/2, O2S11/12/21/22, SHRTFT1/2/11/12/21/22, FPW1/2 • Fuel System Components/Circuits: Injectors1/2...
Ignition	• Check for correct base timing. • Inspect spark plugs and plug wires. • Inspect EI system for damage.	• Ignition System: MISF PID, **SPARKADJ PID**
Power and Grounds	• Check for low battery voltage. • Inspect electrical connections, wires, and harnesses. • Check starter and starter circuit for voltage.	• EEC-V Power: VREF PID, VPWR PID • EEC-V Grounds: SIG RTN circuit, PWR GND circuit, CSE GND circuit
Other	• Check engine coolant and oil levels. • Check thermostat for proper operation. • Check EGR valve stuck open. • Check PCV valve for correct operation. • Check for restricted exhaust. • Check for sticking or binding throttle linkage. • Check throttle body for binding. • Check for proper idle speed control.	• ECT PID • EGR Systems: EGRVR PID, DPFEGR PID • A/C Systems: ACCS PID, ACP PID, WAC PID, WACA PID • LFC PID • HFC PID • OCT ADJ PID

NOTE: Generic PIDS are in bold.

FM0159601567000X

Fig. 295 Pinpoint test, intermittent symptom chart 3. 1996

Unique Idle Concerns

ROLLING IDLE

System	Checks — Visual/Mechanical	Checks — EEC-V PIDS/Components/CKTS
Air/Vacuum	• Check vacuum lines for leaks, blockage or wear. • Check air intake system.	• TP PID • MAF PID • IAC PID • IAT PID
Fuel	• Check for correct fuel pressure. • Check for fuel contamination/quality. • Check fuel filter. • Check for restricted fuel lines.	• Fuel System PIDs: FP, FPM, **FUELB1/2**, HTR11A/12A/21A/22A, HTRX1/2, LONGFT1/2, O2S11/12/21/22, SHRTFT1/2/11/12/21/22, FPW1/2 • Fuel System Components/Circuits: Injectors1/2...
Ignition	• Check for correct base timing. • Inspect spark plugs and plug wires. • Inspect ICM for damage.	• Ignition System: MISF PID, **SPARKADJ PID**, IGNITION COILS
Power and Grounds	• Check for low battery voltage. • Inspect electrical connections, wires, and harnesses.	• EEC-V Power: VREF PID, VPWR PID • EEC-V Grounds: SIG RTN/CASE GND • CIRCUIT
Other	• Check engine coolant and oil levels. • Check thermostat for proper operation. • Check EGR valve stuck open. • Check PCV valve for correct operation. • Check for restricted exhaust. • Check for worn camshaft lobes. • Check camshaft timing and cylinder compression.	• ECT PID • EGR Systems: EGRVR PID, DPFEGR PID • A/C Systems: ACCS PID, ACP PID, WAC PID, WACA PID • LFC PID • HFC PID

NOTE: Generic PIDS are in bold.

FM0159601568000X

Fig. 296 Pinpoint test, intermittent symptom chart 4. 1996

Surge

ACCELERATION/CRUISE

System	Checks	
	Visual/Mechanical	EEC-V PIDS/Components/CKTS
Air/Vacuum	• Check vacuum lines for leaks, blockage or wear. • Check air intake system.	• TP PID • MAF PID • IAC PID • IAT PID

Fuel	• Check for correct fuel pressure.
	• Check for fuel contamination/quality.
	• Check for restricted fuel lines.
	• Check fuel filter.
		• Fuel System PIDs:
		  FP
		  FPM
		  FUELB1/2
		  HTR11A/12A/21A/22A
		  HTRX1/2
		  LONGFT1/2
		  O2S1/12/21/22
		  SHRTFT1/2/11/12/21/22
		  FPW1/2
		• Fuel System Components/Circuits:
		  Injectors 1/2...
		  Fuel Pump Relay

Ignition	• Check for correct base timing. • Inspect spark plugs and plug wires. • Inspect ICM for damage.	• Ignition System: MISF PID

Other	• Check EGR valve sticking.
	• Check PCV valve for correct operation.
	• Check for restricted exhaust.
	• Check for low A/C refrigerant charge.
	• Inspect engine and transmission electrical wiring and connections.
		• EGR Systems:
		  EGRVR PID
		  DPFEGR PID
		• A/C Systems:
		  ACCS PID
		  ACP PID
		  WAC PID
		  WACA PID
		• Transmission Systems
		  TCC PID
		  GEAR/PNP/TR PID
		• LFC PID
		• HFC PID

NOTE: Generic PIDS are in bold.

FM015960157000X

Fig. 297 Pinpoint test, intermittent symptom chart 5. 1996

Lack/Loss of Power

ACCELERATION/CRUISE

System	Checks	
	Visual/Mechanical	EEC-V PIDS/Components/CKTS
Air/Vacuum	• Check vacuum lines for leaks, blockage or wear. • Check air intake system.	• TP PID • MAF PID • IAC PID • IAT PID

Fuel	• Check for correct fuel pressure.
	• Check for fuel contamination/quality.
	• Check fuel filter.
	• Check for restricted fuel lines.
		• Fuel System PIDs:
		  FP
		  FPM
		  FUELSYS1/2
		  HTR11A/12A/21A/22A
		  HTRX1/2
		  LONGFT1/2
		  O2S11/12/21/22
		  SHRTFT1/2/11/12/21/22
		  FPW1/2
		• Fuel System Components/Circuits:
		  Injectors 1/2...
		  Fuel Pump Relay

Ignition	• Check for correct base timing.
	• Inspect spark plugs and plug wires.
	• Inspect ICM for damage.
		• Ignition System:
		  MISF PID
		  SPARKADJ PID

Other	• Check EGR valve sticking.
	• Check PCV valve for correct operation.
	• Check for restricted exhaust.
	• Check for low A/C refrigerant charge.
	• Inspect engine and transmission electrical wiring and connections.
		• EGR Systems:
		  EGRVR PID
		  DPFEGR PID
		• A/C Systems:
		  ACCS PID
		  ACP PID
		  WAC PID
		  WACA PID
		• Transmission Systems
		  TCC PID
		  GEAR/PNP/TR PID

NOTE: Generic PIDS are in bold.

FM015960157000X

Fig. 298 Pinpoint test, intermittent symptom chart 6. 1996

Spark Knock/Cooling System/Diesels/Runs On

ACCELERATION/CRUISE

System	Checks	
	Visual/Mechanical	EEC-V PIDS/Components/CKTS
Air/Vacuum	• Check vacuum lines for leaks, blockage or wear. • Check air intake system. • Check for exhaust leak.	• TP PID • MAF PID • IAC PID • IAT PID

Ignition	• Check for correct base timing.
	• Inspect spark plugs and plug wires.
	• Inspect ICM for damage.
		• Ignition System:
		  MISF PID
		  CKP Sensor
		  IGN COILS

Fuel	• Check for correct fuel pressure.
	• Check for fuel contamination/quality.
	• Check fuel filter.
	• Check for restricted fuel lines.
		• Fuel System PIDs:
		  FP
		  FPM
		  FUELB1/2
		  HTR11A/12A/21A/22A
		  HTRX1/2
		  LONGFT1/2
		  O2S11/12/21/22
		  SHRTFT1/2/11/12/21/22
		  FPW1/2
		• Fuel System Components/Circuits:
		  Injectors 1/2....

Other	• Check EGR valve sticking.
	• Check PCV valve for correct operation.
	• Check engine coolant level.
	• Check thermostat operation.
	• Inspect electrical connections, wires and harnesses.
	• Check for restricted exhaust.
	• Check for partially binding brakes.
	• Check camshaft timing and cylinder compression.
	• Check the transmission for proper torque converter clutch scheduling.
	• Check for cooling system restrictions, bent, kinked lines.
		• EGR Systems:
		  EGRVR PID
		  DPFEGR PID
		• A/C Systems
		  ACCS PID
		  ACP PID
		  WAC PID
		  WACA PID
		• LFC PID
		• HFC PID
		• ECT PID
		• Transmission System
		  TCC PID

NOTE: Generic PIDS are in bold.

FM015960157100X

Fig. 299 Pinpoint test, intermittent symptom chart 7. 1996

Stalls/Quits/MIL/Poor Fuel Economy/Emissions Compliance

IDLE/ACCELERATION/CRUISE/DECELERATION

System	Checks	
	Visual/Mechanical	EEC-V PIDS/Components/CKTS
Air/Vacuum	• Check vacuum lines for leaks, blockage or wear. • Check air intake system.	• TP PID • MAF PID • IAC PID

Ignition	• Inspect spark plugs and plug wires.
	• Check ignition switch.
	• Check ignition coil for voltage.
	• Inspect EI system for damage.
	• Check for presence of anti-theft devices.
		• Ignition System:
		  MISF PID
		  IGN GND circuit
		  CKP sensor
		  IGN coils

Fuel	• Check for correct fuel pressure.
	• Check fuel pump and Inertia Fuel Shutoff (IFS) switch.
	• Check for fuel contamination/quality.
	• Check fuel filter.
	• Check for fuel level/gauge operation.
	• Check for restricted fuel lines.
		• Fuel System PIDs:
		  FP
		  FPM
		  FUELB1/2
		  HTR11A/12A/21A/22A
		  HTRX1/2
		  LONGFT1/2
		  O2S11/12/21/22
		  SHRTFT1/2/11/12/21/22
		  FPW1/2
		• Fuel System Components/Circuits:
		  Injectors 1/2....
		  Fuel Pump Relay

Power and Grounds	• Check for low battery voltage.
	• Inspect electrical connections, wires and harnesses.
		• EEC-V Power:
		  VREF PID
		  VPWR PID
		  EEC-V power relay
		• EEC-V Grounds:
		  SIG RTN circuit
		  PWR GND circuit
		  CSE GND circuit

Other	• Check engine coolant level.
	• Check thermostat for proper operation.
	• Check EGR valve stuck open.
	• Check for moisture entry in PCM.
	• Check throttle body for binding.
	• Check for proper idle speed control.
	• Check camshaft timing and cylinder compression.
	• Check for restricted exhaust.
	• Check torque converter operation.
		• ECT PID
		• EPC PID
		• EGR Systems:
		  EGRVR PID
		  DPFEGR PID
		• A/C Systems:
		  ACCS PID
		  ACP PID
		  WAC PID
		  WACA PID
		• Transmission Systems
		  TCC PID
		  SS1 solenoid
		  SS2 solenoid
		  SS3 solenoid, CCS solenoid
		• IAC PID

NOTE: Generic PIDS are in bold.

FM015960157200X

Fig. 300 Pinpoint test, intermittent symptom chart 8. 1996

Runs Rough/Misses/Buck/Jerk/Backfires/Hesitation

IDLE/ACCELERATION/CRUISE/DECELERATION

System	Checks	
	Visual/Mechanical	EEC-V PIDS/Components/CKTS
Air/Vacuum	• Check vacuum lines for leaks, blockage or wear. • Check air intake system.	• TP PID • MAF PID • IAC PID • IAT PID

Fuel	• Check for correct fuel pressure.
	• Check for fuel contamination/quality.
	• Check fuel filter.
	• Check for restricted fuel lines.
		• Fuel System PIDs:
		  FP
		  FPM
		  FUELB1/2
		  HTR11A/12A/21A/22A
		  HTRX1/2
		  LONGFT1/2
		  O2S11/12/21/22
		  SHRTFT1/2/11/12/21/22
		  FPW1/2
		• Fuel System Components/Circuits:
		  Injectors 1/2.....
		  Fuel Pump Relay

Ignition	• Check for correct base timing.
	• Inspect spark plugs and plug wires.
	• Inspect EI system for damage.
		• Ignition System:
		  MISF PID
		  CKP sensor
		  IGN coils
		  SPARKADJ PID

Power and Grounds	• Check for generator/regulator noise interference.
	• Inspect electrical connections, wires, and harnesses.
		• EEC-V Power:
		  VREF PID
		• EEC-V Grounds:
		  SIG RTN

Other	• Check engine coolant level.
	• Check thermostat operation.
	• Check EGR valve sticking.
	• Check PCV valve for correct operation.
	• Check for restricted exhaust.
	• Check for partially binding brakes.
	• Check camshaft timing and cylinder compression.
	• Check for weak or broken valve springs.
		• EGR Systems:
		  EGRVR PID
		  DPFEGR PID
		• Transmission Systems
		  TCC PID
		• **LFC PID**
		• **HFC PID**
		• **ECT PID**

NOTE: Generic PIDS are in bold.

FM0159601573000X

Fig. 301 Pinpoint test, intermittent symptom chart 9. 1996

A/T Upshift - Downshift/Engagement Concerns

System	Checks	
	Visual/Mechanical	EEC-V PIDS/Components/CKTS

Automatic Transmission	• Check transmission fluid level.
	• Check transmission fluid for contamination.
	• Check for transmission fluid leaks.
	• Check transmission fluid pressures.
	• Check transmission electrical connections for corrosion, bent pins, or damage.
	• Inspect associated electrical connections, wires, and harnesses.
	
	• Check shift linkage and adjustment.
	• Check tire size and axle ratio.
	• Check for driveline modifications or aftermarket accessories.
	• Check internal transmission components.
		• Transmission components
		  SS1 solenoid
		  SS2 solenoid
		  SS3 solenoid
		  EPC PID
		  TFT PID
		  TSS PID
		  TCS PID
		  TR/PNP/GEAR PID
		  TCIL CKT
		  OSS PID
		• **TP** PID
		• **ECT** PID
		• **MAF** PID
		• **VSS/TSS/OSS** PID
		• **RPM** PID
		• **IAT** PID
		• **MISF** PID

NOTE: Generic PIDS are in bold.

FM0159601574000X

Fig. 302 Pinpoint test, intermittent symptom chart 10. 1996

Hard/Soft Transmission Shift

System	Checks	
	Visual/Mechanical	EEC-V PIDS/Components/CKTS

Automatic Transmission	• Check transmission fluid level.
	• Check transmission fluid for contamination.
	• Check for transmission fluid leaks.
	• Check transmission fluid pressures.
	• Inspect associated electrical connections, wires, and harnesses.
	• Check for damaged U-joints.
	• Check for driveline modifications or aftermarket accessories.
	• Check internal transmission components.
		• Transmission components
		  EPC PID
		  TFT PID
		  TSS PID
		  TR/PNP/GEAR PID
		  OSS PID
		• **TP** PID
		• **MAF** PID
		• **RPM** PID

NOTE: Generic PIDS are in bold.

FM0159601575000X

Fig. 303   Pinpoint test, intermittent symptom chart 11. 1996

Erratic Shifts

System	Checks	
	Visual/Mechanical	EEC-V PIDS/Components/CKTS

Automatic Transmission	• Check transmission fluid level.
	• Check transmission fluid for contamination.
	• Check for transmission fluid leaks.
	• Check transmission fluid pressures.
	• Check transmission electrical connections for corrosion, bent pins, or damage.
	• Inspect EI system for damage.
	• Inspect associated electrical connections, wires, and harnesses.
	• Check shift linkage and adjustment.
	• Check for driveline modifications or aftermarket accessories.
	• Check internal transmission components.
		• Transmission components
		  SS1 solenoid
		  SS2 solenoid
		  SS3 solenoid
		  TCC PID
		  TR/PNP/GEAR PID
		  TSS PID
		  TCS PID
		  OSS PID

NOTE: Generic PIDS are in bold.

FM0159601576000X

Fig. 304   Pinpoint test, intermittent symptom chart 12. 1996

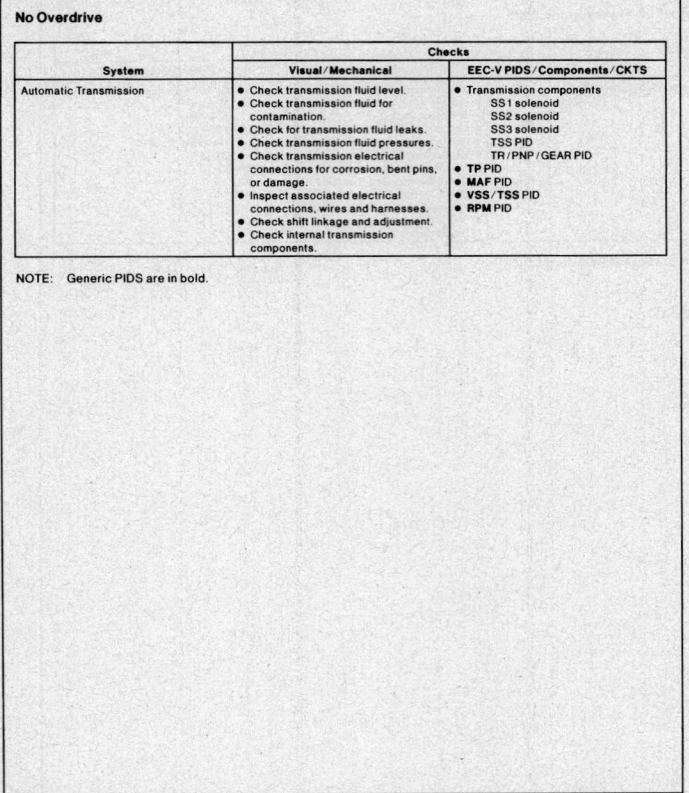

No Overdrive

System	Checks	
	Visual/Mechanical	EEC-V PIDS/Components/CKTS
Automatic Transmission	• Check transmission fluid level. • Check transmission fluid for contamination. • Check for transmission fluid leaks. • Check transmission fluid pressures. • Check transmission electrical connections for corrosion, bent pins, or damage. • Inspect associated electrical connections, wires and harnesses. • Check shift linkage and adjustment. • Check internal transmission components.	• Transmission components SS1 solenoid SS2 solenoid SS3 solenoid TSS PID TR/PNP/GEAR PID • **TP** PID • **MAF** PID • **VSS**/TSS PID • **RPM** PID

NOTE: Generic PIDS are in bold.

FM0159601577000X

Fig. 305   Pinpoint test, intermittent symptom chart 13. 1996

Aspire, Capri, Escort & Tracer (1.8L/4-112), Festiva & Probe (2.0L/4-121 w/4EAT & 2.5L/V6-152) Electronic Engine Control (EEC) System

NOTE: On Air Bag Equipped Models, Refer To "Air Bag System Precautions" Located In The Front Of This Manual For System Disarming & Arming Procedures.

NOTE: If Unsure Of The System Used On The Vehicle Being Serviced, Refer To The "Engine Systems Identification Chart."

NOTE: If Uncertain About The Proper Use Of Information Contained In This Section, Please Refer To "How To Use This Manual" Located In The Front Of This Manual.

NOTE: Prior To Performing Any Service Operations Listed In This Section, Consult The "Technical Service Bulletins" Section For Related Information.

NOTE: Electrical Symbol & Wire Color Code Identification Located In The Front Of This Manual May Be Used As An Aid When Using Wiring Circuits Found In This Section.

INDEX

Page No.

Component Description: 10-4
 Barometric Pressure (BP) Sensor. 10-4
 Boost Pressure Switch 10-4
 Brake On/Off Switch. 10-4
 Bypass Air (BPA) Valve. 10-5
 Canister Purge (CANP) Solenoid . 10-5
 Carbon Canister 10-5
 Clutch Pedal Position (CPR)
  Switch. 10-5
 Cooling Fan Engine Coolant
  Temperature (ECTF) Sensor . . . 10-5
 Crankshaft Position (CKP) Sensor 10-5
 Crankshaft Position Sensor No. 1
  (CKP1) 10-6
 Crankshaft Position Sensor No. 2
  (CKP2) 10-6
 Cylinder Identification (CID)
  Sensor 10-6
 Dashpot 10-7
 Data Link Connector (DLC) 10-7
 Engine Coolant Temperature
  Sensor 10-7
 Fuel Pressure Regulator Control
  (FPRC) Solenoid 10-7
 Heated Oxygen Sensor (HO2S) . . 10-7
 High Speed Inlet Air Control
  Solenoid 10-7

Page No.

Idle Air Control (IAC) (Idle Speed
  Control) (ISC)) Solenoid 10-7
Idle Speed Control Bypass Air
  Valve. 10-8
Idle Switch 10-8
Intake Air Temperature (IAT)
  Sensor 10-8
Knock Control Module (KCM) 10-8
Knock Sensor (KS). 10-8
Malfunction Indication Light 10-8
Manual Lever Position Switch 10-8
Mass Air Flow (MAF) Sensor. 10-8
Oxygen Sensor (O2S). 10-8
Park/Neutral Position (PNP)
  Switch. 10-8
Power Steering Pressure Switch. . 10-8
Powertrain Control Module (PCM)
  (Electronic Control Assembly)
  (ECA)). 10-8
Self-Test Output/Self Test Input
  Connectors 10-8
Shutter Valve. 10-9
Throttle Position (TP) Sensor 10-9
Vane Air Temperature 10-9
Volume Air Flow (VAF) Meter 10-9
Description 10-4
Diagnosis & Testing: 10-9

Page No.

Accessing Diagnostic Trouble Codes 10-9
Check Engine & Manual Light
  Operations. 10-10
Malfunction Indicator Light. 10-10
With Analog Voltmeter 10-10
With New Generation Star (NGS)
  Tester. 10-10
With Super Star II Tester. 10-9
Clearing Diagnostic Trouble Codes 10-11
Pinpoint Tests. 10-11
Quick Tests. 10-11
System Testing. 10-11
1993-95. 10-11
Description 10-9
Engine Running Self-Test. 10-9
Key-On Engine Off Self-Test 10-9
Self-Test. 10-9
Switch Monitor Test. 10-9
Diagnostic Trouble Code
  Interpretation. 10-10
Diagnostic Chart Index: 10-35
Sensor Specifications 10-2

SENSOR SPECIFICATIONS

Sensor	Temperature°F	Vacuum, Inch Hg.	Voltage	Resistance	Throttle Position	Air Vane Position	EGR, % Open
1993—95							
Barometric Pressure ①	—	0	3.26—4.42	—	—	—	—
	—	5	2.86—3.86	—	—	—	—
	—	10	2.26—3.06	—	—	—	—
	—	15	1.64—2.22	—	—	—	—
	—	20	1.07—1.45	—	—	—	—
	—	25	.049—.067	—	—	—	—
Barometric Pressure ⑧	—	0	3.9				
	—	3.94	3.6	—	—	—	—
	—	7.87	3.1	—	—	—	—
	—	11.81	2.5	—	—	—	—
	—	15.75	2.0	—	—	—	—
	—	19.69	1.5	—	—	—	—
	—	23.62	.9	—	—	—	—
	—	27.56	.4	—	—	—	—
Coolant Temperature	-4	—	4.7	14,600—17,800	—	—	—
	32	—	3.4	—	—	—	—
	68	—	2.5	2200—2700	—	—	—
	104	—	2.0	—	—	—	—
	140	—	1.2	—	—	—	—
	176	—	.7	250—350	—	—	—
	194	—	.45	—	—	—	—
	203	—	.33	—	—	—	—
	212	—	.2	—	—	—	—
Cooling Fan Engine Coolant Temperature	196	—	—	1700—1840	—	—	—
	207	—	—	1420—1530	—	—	—
	226	—	—	1030—1110	—	—	—
EGR Temperature	68	—	—	182,000—336,000	—	—	—
	85	—	—	112,000—165,000	—	—	—
	105	—	—	41,300—47,600	—	—	—
	125	—	—	7500—10,500	—	—	—
EGR Valve Position	—	—	.4—.8	—	—	—	0
	—	—	.7—1.1	—	—	—	10
	—	—	1.1—1.5	—	—	—	20
	—	—	1.4—1.8	—	—	—	30
	—	—	1.8—2.2	—	—	—	40
	—	—	2.1—2.5	—	—	—	50
	—	—	2.5—2.9	—	—	—	60
	—	—	2.8—3.2	—	—	—	70
	—	—	3.2—3.6	—	—	—	80
	—	—	3.5—3.9	—	—	—	90
	—	—	3.9—4.3	—	—	—	100
	—	0	.8	—	—	—	—
	—	5.9	5.0	—	—	—	—

Continued

SENSOR SPECIFICATIONS–Continued

Sensor	Temperature °F	Vacuum, Inch Hg.	Voltage	Resistance	Throttle Position	Air Vane Position	EGR, % Open
1993—95 -CONTINUED							
Intake Air Temperature ②	-4	—	4.7	10,000—20,000	—	—	—
	32	—	3.4	4000—7000	—	—	—
	68	—	2.5	2000—3000	—	—	—
	104	—	2.0	900—1300	—	—	—
	140	—	1.2	400—700	—	—	—
	176	—	.7	—	—	—	—
Intake Air Temperature ⑧	32	—	—	17,100—79,400	—	—	—
	55	—	—	54,300—58,600	—	—	—
	77	—	—	29,700—36,300	—	—	—
	110	—	—	17,900—19,300	—	—	—
	185	—	—	3300—3700	—	—	—
Throttle Position ⑦	—	—	.5	400	0	—	—
	—	—	1.3	600	1/4	—	—
	—	—	2.2	1278	1/2	—	—
	—	—	2.9	1462	3/4	—	—
	—	—	3.7	1480	Full	—	—
Throttle Position ⑨	—	—	.998	989	1/8	—	—
	—	—	1.6	1104	2/8	—	—
	—	—	2.37	1278	3/8	—	—
	—	—	2.74	1462	4/8	—	—
	—	—	3.15	1480	5/8	—	—
	—	—	3.43	1459	6/8	—	—
	—	—	3.6	1144	7/8	—	—
	—	—	4.02	1072	8/8	—	—
Transmission Oil Temperature ⑥	-8	—	—	325,500	—	—	—
	32	—	—	52,000	—	—	—
	68	—	—	23,000	—	—	—
	104	—	—	11,000	—	—	—
	140	—	—	5600	—	—	—
	212	—	—	1710	—	—	—
	266	—	—	860	—	—	—
Transmission Oil Temperature ⑦	-4	—	—	13,470—17,170	—	—	—
	32	—	—	5450—6680	—	—	—
	68	—	—	2440—2890	—	—	—
	104	—	—	1190—1370	—	—	—
	140	—	—	628—705	—	—	—
	176	—	—	354—387	—	—	—
	212	—	—	209—225	—	—	—
	248	—	—	130—137	—	—	—
	266	—	—	104—109	—	—	—
Volume Air Flow Meter ③ ④ ⑤	—	—	3.24	—	—	1/8	—
	—	—	5.6	—	—	2/8	—
	—	—	5.62	—	—	3/8	—
	—	—	5.83	—	—	4/8	—

Continued

COMPUTERIZED ENGINE CONTROLS (ASPIRE, CAPRI, ESCORT & TRACER (1.8L/4-112), FESTIVA & PROBE (2.0L/4-121 w/4EAT & 2.5L/V6-152) ELECTRONIC ENGINE CONTROL (EEC) SYSTEM

10-3

SENSOR SPECIFICATIONS–Continued

Sensor	Temperature°F	Vacuum, Inch Hg.	Voltage	Resistance	Throttle Position	Air Vane Position	EGR, % Open
1993—95-CONTINUED							
Volume Air Flow Meter ③ ④ ⑤ -Cont'd	—	—	6.02	—	—	5/8	—
	—	—	6.57	—	—	6/8	—
	—	—	7.46	—	—	7/8	—
	—	—	7.87	—	—	8/8	—

① —1.6L/4-98 engine.
② —Except 2.0L/4-121 w/4EAT transmission.
③ —1.6L/4-98 engines.

④ —1.3L/4-81 & 1.8L/4-112 w/vane door fully open, .5—1.5 volts, w/vane door fully closed, 4.5—5 volts.
⑤ —Voltage values may vary ±15%.

⑥ —1.8L/4-112 w/4EAT transmission.
⑦ —2.0L/4-121 & 2.5L/V6-152 w/4EAT transmission.
⑧ —2.0L/4-121 w/4EAT transmission.
⑨ —1.6L/4-98 & 1.8L/4-112 engines.

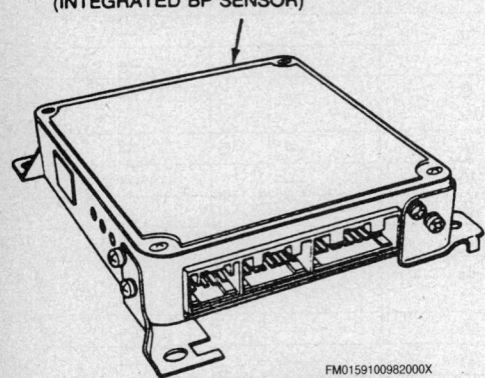

ELECTRONIC CONTROL ASSEMBLY (ECA) (INTEGRATED BP SENSOR)

FM0159100982000X

Fig. 1 Barometric pressure sensor. Except 1.6L/4-98 & 2.0L/4-121

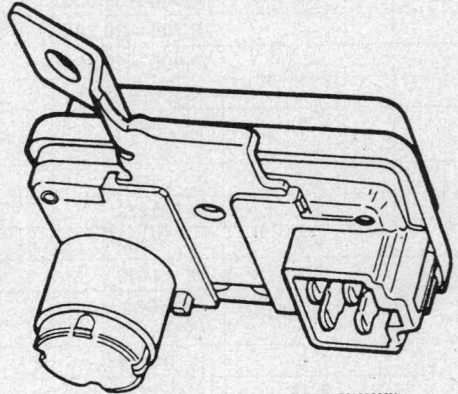

FM0159100983000X

Fig. 2 Barometric pressure sensor. 1.6L/4-98

FM0159100984000X

Fig. 3 Barometric pressure sensor. 2.0L/4-121

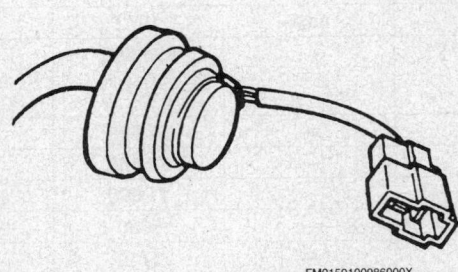

FM0159100986000X

Fig. 4 Boost pressure switch. 1.6L/4-98 turbo

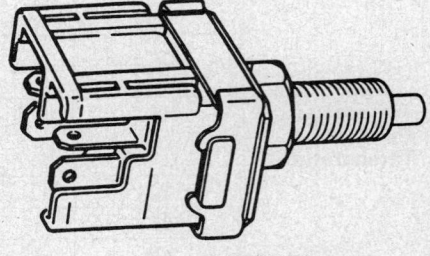

FM0159100987000X

Fig. 5 Brake on-off switch. 1.3L/4-81, 1.6L/4-98 & 1.8L/4-112

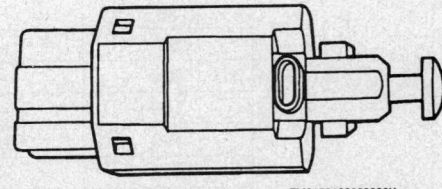

FM0159100988000X

Fig. 6 Brake on-off switch. 2.0L/4-121 & 2.5L/V6-152

DESCRIPTION

The EEC system provides accurate, instantaneous fuel metering control of fuel injection timing and duration. The system is composed of several sensors that monitor engine performance and efficiency. The Powertrain Control Module (PCM) processes the input data from these sensors and produces output control signals to the fuel injectors, regulating precise fuel discharge through the injector nozzles. The PCM also produces output signals that adjust ignition spark timing to provide a best balance between driveability and fuel economy.

The EEC system also controls exhaust gas recirculation (EGR) and knock control to eliminate detonation under adverse driving conditions.

COMPONENT DESCRIPTION

BAROMETRIC PRESSURE (BP) SENSOR

The BP sensor, **Figs. 1 through 3,** is used to sense changes in barometric pressure, allowing the powertrain control module (PCM) (electronic control assembly)

(ECA)) to sense the altitude at which the vehicle is operating. On models except 1.6L/4-98, the sensor is integrated with the electronic control assembly (ECA). On 1.6L/4-98 models, the sensor is located behind the righthand side cowl panel. On 2.0L/4-121 w/4EAT models, behind RH kick panel on center console.

BOOST PRESSURE SWITCH

On 1.6L/4-98 turbocharged models, the boost pressure switch sends a signal to the PCM (ECA) when the boost pressure reaches 10.4–11.6 psi. This is used for over-boost protection, **Fig. 4.**

BRAKE ON/OFF SWITCH

The brake on-off switch detects braking operation (deceleration) and sends an input signal to the electronic control assembly. The brake on/off switch is located on the brake pedal, **Figs. 5 and 6.**

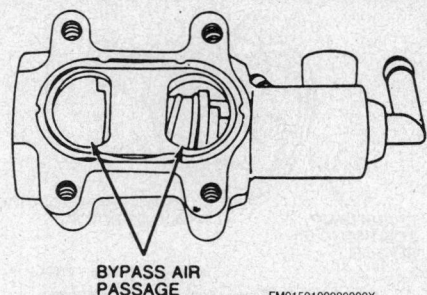

BYPASS AIR
PASSAGE

FM0159100989000X

Fig. 7   Bypass air valve.
1.8L/4-112

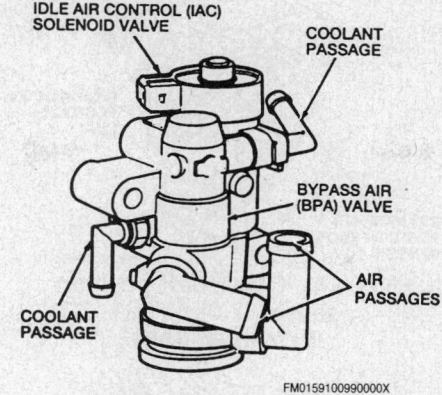

IDLE AIR CONTROL (IAC)
SOLENOID VALVE

COOLANT
PASSAGE

BYPASS AIR
(BPA) VALVE

COOLANT
PASSAGE

AIR
PASSAGES

FM0159100990000X

Fig. 8   Bypass air valve.
1.3L/4-81 & 1.6L/4-98

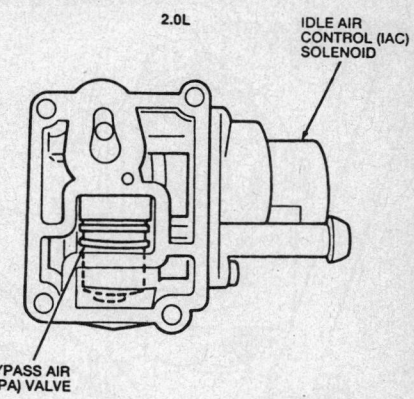

2.0L

IDLE AIR
CONTROL (IAC)
SOLENOID

BYPASS AIR
(BPA) VALVE

FM0159100991000X

Fig. 9   Bypass air valve.
2.0L/4-121

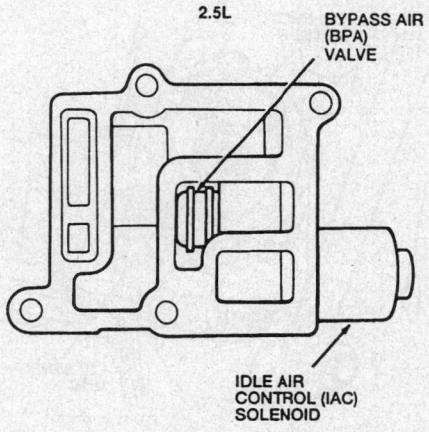

2.5L

BYPASS AIR
(BPA)
VALVE

IDLE AIR
CONTROL (IAC)
SOLENOID

FM0159100992000X

Fig. 10   Bypass air valve.
2.5L/V6-152

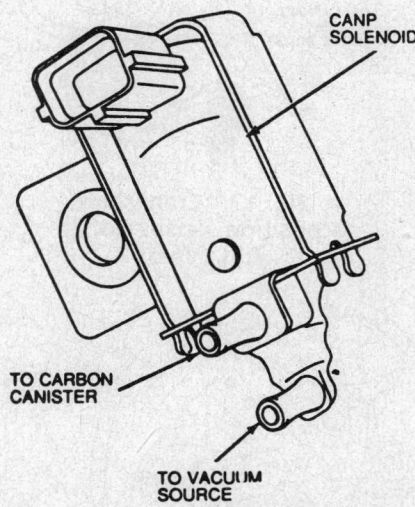

CANP
SOLENOID

TO CARBON
CANISTER

TO VACUUM
SOURCE

FM0159100993000X

Fig. 11   Canister purge
regulator solenoid valve

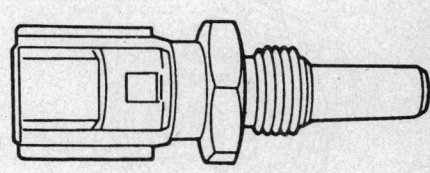

FM0159100994000X

Fig. 12   Cooling fan engine
coolant temperature sensor

BYPASS AIR (BPA) VALVE

This BPA valve consists of a thermowax material that expands or contracts depending on engine coolant temperature. The valve opens below 104°F to allow bypass air to flow into the intake plenum and closes above 104°F. The BPA valve increases idle speed during cold engine conditions to speed engine warm up and to prevent cold engine stalling, **Figs. 7 through 10.** On 1.3L/4-81 models, mounted the LH side of intake manifold. On 1.6L/4-98 models, the bypass air valve is mounted on the RH side of the intake manifold. On 1.8L/4-112 models, the valve is mounted on the intake manifold. On 2.0L/4-121 models, the valve is located on top of the throttle body. On 2.5L/V6-152 models, the valve is mounted on the bottom of the throttle body.

CANISTER PURGE (CANP) SOLENOID

The CANP solenoid regulates the amount of evaporative vapors drawn from the carbon canister into the engine. The electronic control assembly PCM (ECA) signals the CANP solenoid to open vacuum passage between the carbon canister and intake plenum when certain conditions for evaporative vapor purge are met. Inputs to the computer provide all necessary engine conditions and driving modes, **Fig. 11.** On 1.3L/4-81, 1.6L/4-98 and 1.8L/4-112, the CANP solenoid is located near the center of the cowl panel. On

2.0L/4-121 models, the solenoid is on the RH side of the intake manifold. On 2.5L/V6-152 models, it is located on the back of the intake manifold.

CARBON CANISTER

The fuel vapors from the fuel tank are stored in the carbon canister until the vehicle is operated, at which time, the vapors will purge from the canister into the engine for consumption. Purging of the fuel vapors to the engine occurs only when certain engine conditions are met and is regulated by the canister purge solenoid as controlled by the PCM (ECA). On models with 1.3L/4-81 engine, the carbon canister is mounted on left side under brake booster. On 1.6L/4-98 and 1.8L/4-112 engines, it is located on right corner near cowl panel. On 2.0L/4-121 and 2.5L/V6-152 engines, it is located behind the LH strut.

CLUTCH PEDAL POSITION (CPR) SWITCH

The clutch engage switch detects when the clutch is engaged and sends an input signal to the PCM (ECA). The clutch engage switch is mounted at the clutch pedal.

COOLING FAN ENGINE COOLANT TEMPERATURE (ECTF) SENSOR

The ECTF sensor detects the coolant temperature and inputs the information to the PCM. Once the coolant reaches a certain level, the PCM sends an output signal for operating the cooling fans to maintain coolant temperature at a normal level, **Fig. 12.** On 2.0L/4-121 w/4EAT engines, the sensor is threaded into the coolant temperature sensor housing on the LH side of the engine. On 2.5L/V6-152 engines, it is threaded into the cooling elbow on the RH side of the engine.

CRANKSHAFT POSITION (CKP) SENSOR

The CKP sensor, located within the distributor, **Figs. 13 through 15** provides crankshaft position input to the electronic control assembly which the PCM (ECA) converts to engine speed (RPM) information. On 1.8L/4-112 and 1.3L/4-81 engines, a disc with four equally spaced slots cut into it rotates with the distributor shaft. As the disc rotates, each slot passes through a fixed photo sensor which senses the slots and sends a signal to the PCM (ECA) reflecting crankshaft rotation speed.

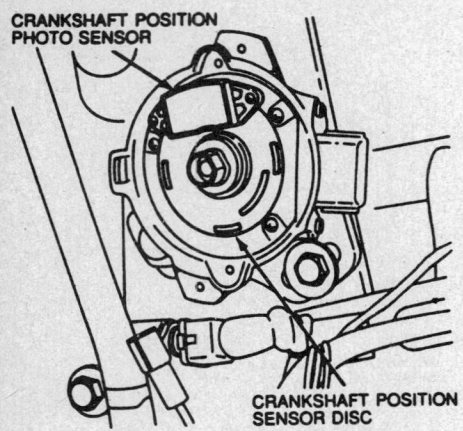

Fig. 13 Crankshaft position sensor. 1.3L/4-81 & 1.8L/4-112

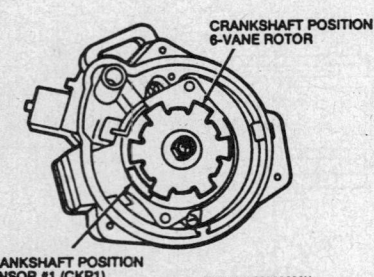

Fig. 16 Crankshaft position sensor No. 1. 2.5L/V6-152

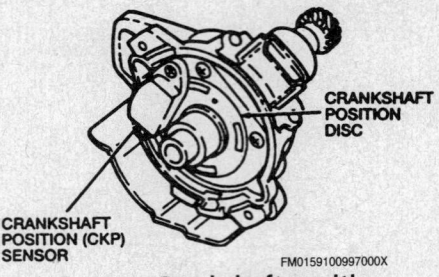

Fig. 14 Crankshaft position sensor. 2.0L/4-121 w/manual trans.

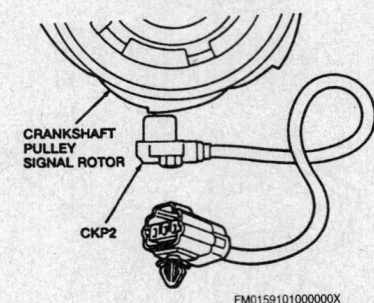

Fig. 17 Crankshaft position sensor No. 2. 2.5L/V6-152

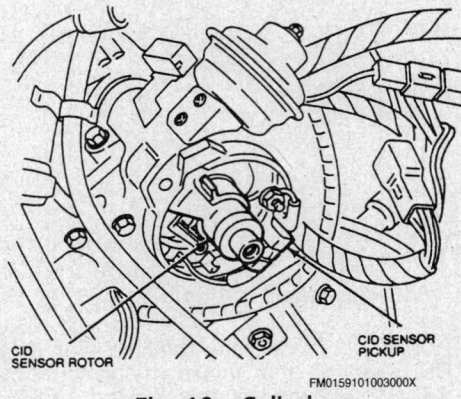

Fig. 19 Cylinder identification sensors. 1.6L/4-98 non-turbo

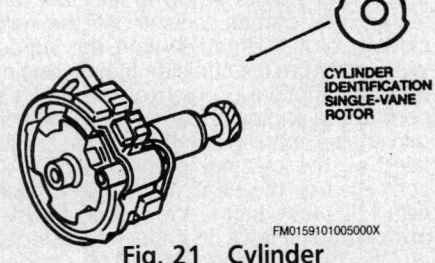

Fig. 21 Cylinder identification sensors. 2.0L/4-121 w/4EAT trans.

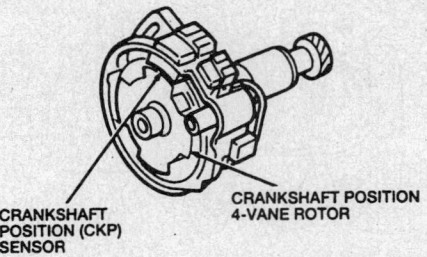

Fig. 15 Crankshaft position sensor. 2.0L/4-121 w/auto. trans.

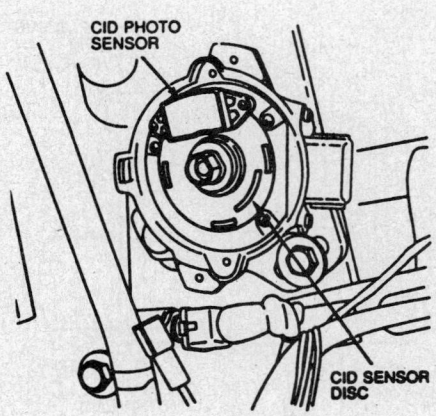

Fig. 18 Cylinder identification sensors. 1.8L/4-112

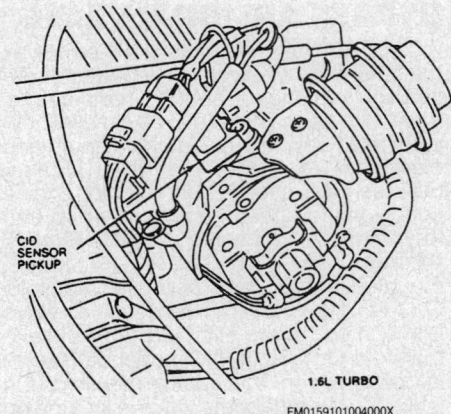

Fig. 20 Cylinder identification sensors. 1.6L/4-98 turbo

CRANKSHAFT POSITION SENSOR NO. 1 (CKP1)

The CKP1, **Fig. 16**, is mounted inside the distributor housing. A six vane rotor is mounted to the distributor shaft and spins at the speed of the camshaft. As the rotor passes through a magnetic Hall effect pickup switch, the six vanes are detected and sent to the PCM in a pulse wave form. The crankshaft position can be determined to 60 degree intervals for fuel injection timing, ignition timing and emission control.

CRANKSHAFT POSITION SENSOR NO. 2 (CKP2)

The CKP2, **Fig. 17**, also detects the crankshaft position. This signal is generated directly at the crankshaft pulley. It is used at higher vehicle speed when the timing belt does not accurately represent the crankshaft position. The input signal is sent to the PCM and used for adjusting fuel injection timing, ignition timing and engine control.

CYLINDER IDENTIFICATION (CID) SENSOR

The CID sensor, **Figs. 18 through 23**, provides accurate crankshaft position input to the electronic control assembly. On models with 1.8L/4-112 engine, a disc with two slots cut into it rotates with the distributor shaft. As the disc rotates, the slot passes through a fixed photo sensor which indicates to the PCM (ECA) the No. 1 cylinder TDC position. The cylinder identification sensors are mounted in the distributor housing. On models with 1.6L/4-98 non-turbo engine, a fixed magnetic sensor is attached to the distributor housing. A rotor is mounted onto the distributor shaft inside the housing. As the distributor

rotates the magnetic sensor detects No. 1 cylinder top dead center. On models with 1.6L/4-98 turbo engine, a rotor is mounted onto the distributor shaft which rotates past a fixed magnetic pickup which detects No. 1 cylinder top dead center. On 2.0L/4-121 w/4EAT-152 and 2.5L/V6-152 engines, a single vane rotor cap is mounted on the distributor shaft, below the crankshaft position rotor cap and spins based on camshaft speed. As it rotates through the magnetic Hall effect pickup switch, the sensor detects the opening on the rotor cap and sends an input signal to the PCM.

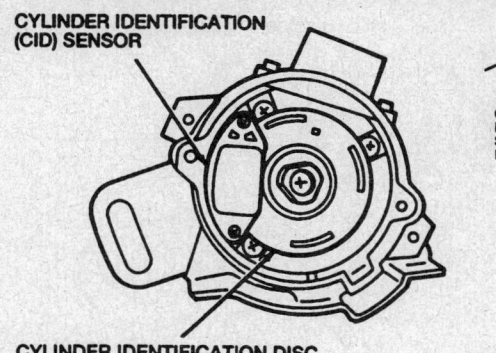

Fig. 22 Cylinder
identification sensors.
2.0L/4-121 w/manual
trans.

FM0159101006000X

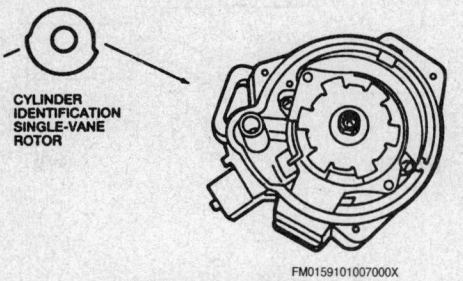

Fig. 23 Cylinder
identification sensors.
2.5L/V6-152

FM0159101007000X

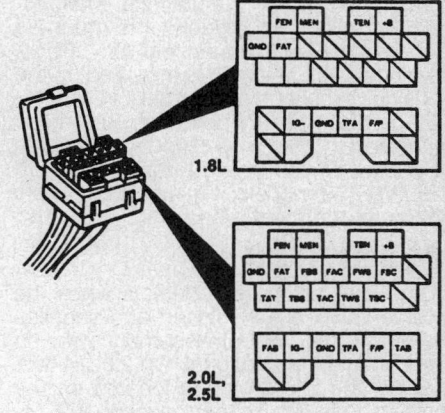

Fig. 24 Data link
connector

FM0159101008000X

DASHPOT

The dashpot allows the throttle plate to gradually close during deceleration. This action prevents hesitation during the transition from deceleration to sudden acceleration and prevents engine stalling on sudden deceleration.

DATA LINK CONNECTOR (DLC)

The DLC, **Fig. 24,** accesses several systems in the vehicle for diagnostic procedures. The EEC, electronic transaxle control, initial set, fuel pump, engine speed, ABS, horn/air bag, battery voltage and switch monitor systems can be diagnosed through the DLC. On 1.8L/4-112 engine, the DLC is located behind the battery, next to the LH strut tower. On 2.0L/4-121 and 2.5L/V6-152 engines, the DLC is behind the battery, next to the main fuse panel.

ENGINE COOLANT TEMPERATURE SENSOR

The engine coolant temperature sensor constantly supplies the electronic control assembly with a signal reflecting engine coolant temperature. On 1.3L/4-81 models, the engine coolant temperature sensor is threaded into the top of the lower intake manifold. On 1.6L/4-98 models, the engine coolant temperature sensor is threaded into the top of the lower intake manifold. On 1.8L/4-112 models, it is threaded into the engine near the thermostat housing. On 2.0L/4-121 models, it is threaded into the coolant temperature sensor housing on the LH side of the engine. On 2.5L/V6-152 models, it is threaded into the coolant elbow on the RH side of the engine.

FUEL PRESSURE REGULATOR CONTROL (FPRC) SOLENOID

On all models except 1.3L/4-81, the pressure regulator control solenoid controls vacuum applied to the fuel pressure regulator. On a hot start, the electronic

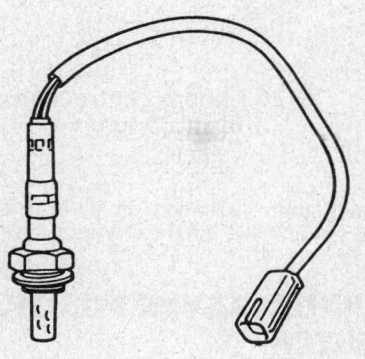

Fig. 25 Heated
oxygen sensor

FM0159101009000X

control assembly activates the pressure regulator control solenoid and vacuum to the fuel pressure regulator is cut. This action increases fuel pressure which prevents fuel percolation that may cause hard starts during hot conditions. On 1.6L/4-98 engine, it is mounted on the cowl panel next to the CANP solenoid. On 1.8L/4-112 engine, it is mounted on the engine below the fuel pressure regulator. On 2.0L/4-121 engine, it is mounted on the lower RH side of the intake manifold. On 2.5L/V6-152 engines, it is mounted to the MC-VAF meter housing.

HEATED OXYGEN SENSOR (HO2S)

The HO2S, **Fig. 25,** reads the oxygen level in the exhaust and sends an input to the PCM, reflecting whether the mixture is too lean or too rich. If the exhaust has a high concentration of oxygen, a voltage signal of less then .4 volts is sent to the PCM. If there is a low concentration of oxygen in the exhaust, a voltage signal of .6 volts or more is sent to the PCM. The 2.0L/4-121 engine uses a single sensor and the 2.5L/V6-152 engine uses a right and lefthand oxygen sensor.

HIGH SPEED INLET AIR CONTROL SOLENOID

The high speed inlet air control (HSIA) solenoid controls the vacuum applied to the inlet air shutter valve actuator. The IAC solenoid applies vacuum to shutter valve at low (RPM) which holds the shutter valve closed, and vents the shutter valve actuator vacuum to atmosphere above 5000 RPM to allow the shutter valve to open. The IAC solenoid is controlled by an output signal from the electronic control assembly.

IDLE SPEED CONTROL BYPASS AIR VALVE

On all models except 1.8L/4-112, the idle speed control bypass air valve (ISC/BPA) controls idle speed by regulating the throttle plate bypass air. The ISC/BPA valve consists of the bypass air valve which functions only during cold engine condition below 140°F and the idle speed control solenoid which works throughout the entire engine speed and temperature range. The bypass air valve functions by sensing engine coolant temperature supplied to the valve while the ISC solenoid is controlled by an PCM (ECA) output duty signal determined by various input sensors. On 1.3L/4-81 models, the idle speed control bypass air valve is located on the lefthand side of the intake manifold. On 1.6L/4-98 models, the valve is located on the righthand side of the intake manifold.

IDLE AIR CONTROL (IAC) (IDLE SPEED CONTROL (ISC)) SOLENOID

On 1.8L/4-112 models, the IAC(ISC) solenoid controls idle speed during all modes of engine operation. The solenoid receives duty cycle signals from the electronic control assembly that controls a rotary valve which opens or closes the air bypass passage depending on the signal received. The valve will rotate to a half opened position as the signal from the PCM (ECA) stops. This assures bypass air to the engine is maintained as a fail safe measure in the event of an ISC electrical malfunction. On 1.3L/4-81 models, it is mounted the LH side of intake manifold. On 1.6L/4-98 models, the solenoid is mounted on the RH side of the intake manifold. On 1.8L/4-121 models, it is mounted on the intake manifold. On 2.0L/4-121 models, the valve is located on top of the throttle body. On 2.5L/V6-152 models, it is mounted on the bottom of the throttle body.

IDLE SWITCH

The idle switch (IDL) detects when the throttle valve is fully closed and supplies the electronic control assembly with an idle condition input signal. On 2.0L/4-121 models, the idle switch is located on the throttle body. On models except 2.0L/4-121, the idle switch is integrated with the throttle position sensor and operates in a similar manner.

INTAKE AIR TEMPERATURE (IAT) SENSOR

The IAT sensor detects the incoming airflow temperature. As the air temperature decreases, the sensor resistance increases. The resistance, sent to the PCM as an input signal, is used a for temperature to density calculations. The PCM determines the air density and cold enrichment fuel flow. On 2.5L/V6-152 engine, it is mounted on the Measuring Core-Volume Air Flow (MC-VAF) meter. On 1.3L/4-81, 1.6L/4-98 and 1.8L/4-112 engines, it is integrated in the Volume Air Flow (VAF) meter. On 2.0L/4-121 engine, it is mounted to the air filter housing.

KNOCK CONTROL MODULE (KCM)

When vibration in the engine occurs, voltage is generated by the knock sensor and signal is sent through the KCM, **Fig. 26**, and to the electronic control assembly. The KCM acts as a signal filter which only allows the knocking signals considered to be above normal engine vibrations to reach the PCM (ECA). The computer will then retard ignition timing and reduce turbocharger boost pressure accordingly.

KNOCK SENSOR (KS)

The KS is an electronic device capable of measuring vibration and converting the vibration signal to an electrical output that measures the engine knock. The voltage signal generated by the knock sensor is sent to the knock control unit for filtering and then to the electronic control assembly for control of ignition timing. The sensor is threaded in the engine block near the oil pressure switch.

MALFUNCTION INDICATION LIGHT

The malfunction indication light provides a visual signal to the driver when an electronic engine control (EEC) circuit failure. The MIL light is also used when performing the EEC diagnostics by flashing service codes during EEC quick test. The

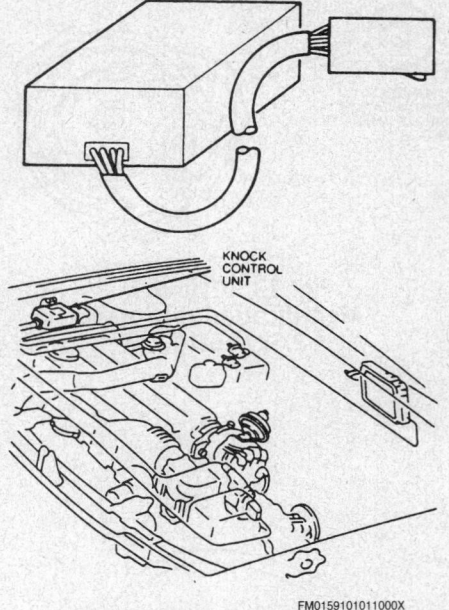

Fig. 26 Knock control unit. 1.6L/4-98 turbo

malfunction indication light is marked CHECK ENGINE on the drivers instrument panel.

MANUAL LEVER POSITION SWITCH

On all models except 1.3L/4-81 engine, the manual lever position switch, detects shift lever position and sends a signal to the electronic control assembly, w/4EAT control module and incorporates a neutral drive switch which enables the starting system. The manual lever position switch is located on transaxle with shift linkage.

MASS AIR FLOW (MAF) SENSOR

The MAF sensor measures the amount of air flowing into the throttle body. This information is sent to the PCM to determine injector pulse width timing.

PARK/NEUTRAL POSITION (PNP) SWITCH

The PNP switch detects when the manual transaxle is in the in gear or neutral position and sends an input signal to the electronic control assembly. The neutral gear switch is threaded into transaxle.

OXYGEN SENSOR (O2S)

The O2S supplies the electronic control assembly with a signal which indicates a rich or lean condition during engine operation. The sensor threads into the engine exhaust manifold.

POWER STEERING PRESSURE SWITCH

The power steering pressure switch detects power steering operation and sends

Fig. 27 Self-test output/self-test input connector locations. 1.3L/4-81, 1.6L/4-98, 2.0L/4-121 & 2.5L/V6-152

a signal to the electronic control assembly. The power steering pressure switch is threaded into power steering pump.

POWERTRAIN CONTROL MODULE (PCM) (ELECTRONIC CONTROL ASSEMBLY) (ECA))

The microprocessor called the PCM (ECA), receives data from a number of sensors and other electronic components (switches and relays). The computer contains a specific calibration for optimum emissions, fuel economy and driveability. Based on information received and programmed into its memory, the PCM (ECA) generates output signals to control various relays, solenoids and other actuators. On 1.3L/4-81 models, the PCM (ECA) module is located under left side of instrument panel. On all other models is mounted on the floor panel behind the center console.

SELF-TEST OUTPUT/SELF TEST INPUT CONNECTORS

The self-test output and self-test input connectors are both used while performing the electronic engine control Quick Test diagnostic procedure with either a Super Star II tester or analog voltmeter. When the self-test input connector is jumped to ground, a signal is sent to the electronic control assembly activating the PCM (ECA) self-test mode. The self-test output connector is used for retrieving output signals from the PCM (ECA) which appear as numbered codes on the Super Star II tester or needle sweeps on the analog voltmeter. Codes retrieved from the memory represent a malfunction within the EEC system, **Figs. 27 and 28**.

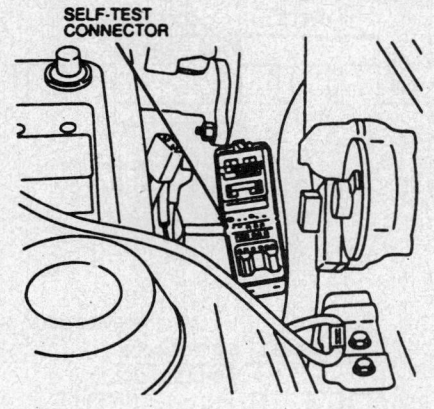

Fig. 28 Self-test output/self-test input connector locations. 1.8L/4-112

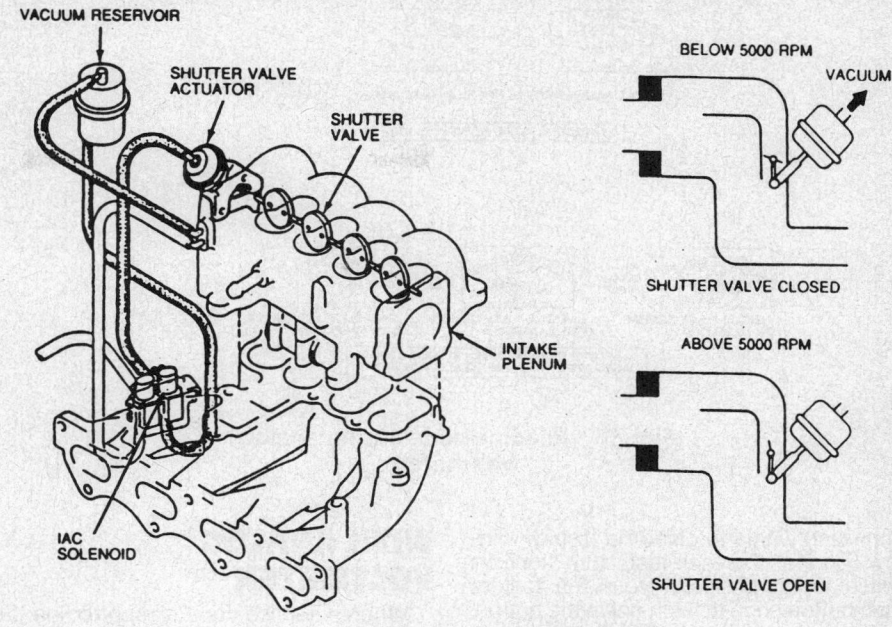

Fig. 29 Shutter valve. 1.8L/4-112

SHUTTER VALVE

On 1.8L/4-112 models, the shutter valve located in the intake plenum, **Fig. 29**, opens and closes an intake path in the intake plenum which increases the length of the intake runner when opened and shortens the runner when closed. This action improves torque characteristics at low and high engine (RPM). A high speed inlet air control solenoid is used to control the vacuum to the shutter valve actuator as signaled by the PCM (ECA). A vacuum reservoir is used to store needed vacuum which otherwise would not be available during wide open throttle and other low vacuum engine operating modes.

THROTTLE POSITION (TP) SENSOR

The TP sensor detects throttle plate opening angle. It supplies the electronic control assembly with an input indicating throttle position. On 1.8L/4-112 automatic transmission models, the sensor consists of a combination potentiometer and idle switch. On models with 1.3L/4-81, 1.6L/4-98 and 1.8L/4-112 manual transmission models, the sensor consists of two switches sensing only closed or wide open throttle positions. These switches are referred to as the idle switch and wide open throttle switch. The throttle position sensor is mounted on throttle body. On 2.0L/4-121 models, the TP sensor detects the throttle plate opening angle with a potentiometer and sends inputs to the PCM. The sensor also determines the air intake if the MAF sensor fails. On the 2.5L/V6-152 engine, the sensor operates the same as the 2.0L/4-121 engine, but also integrates the idle switch in the housing. The idle switch detects when the throttle plate is closed and an idle condition occurs and notifies the PCM.

VOLUME AIR FLOW (VAF) METER

The VAF meter measures air flowing into the engine and is mounted between the air cleaner and throttle body assembly. The meter contains a movable vane which connects to a potentiometer. As air flow through the meter, the movable vane and potentiometer change position and provide an input to the electronic control assembly with vane position information. The PCM (ECA) can then translate vane position information into the volume of air flowing into the engine.

VANE AIR TEMPERATURE

The vane air temperature sensor is an integral part of the vane air flow meter. The sensor measures inlet air temperature and provides an input signal to the electronic control assembly.

DIAGNOSIS & TESTING

Description

SELF-TEST

The self-test is divided into three specialized tests, Key On/Engine Off, Engine Running, and Switch Monitor test. The self-test in not a conclusive test by itself, but it used as part of the functional Quick Test diagnostic procedure. The processor stores the self-test program in its permanent memory. When activated, it checks the electronic engine control or w/4EAT system by testing its memory integrity and processing capability, and verifies that various sensors and actuators are connected and operating properly.

Unlike EEC-IV, no sensors or switches are exercised during the self-test. Also, intermittent codes are not erased if the fault is removed after 40 vehicle cycles. Therefore, any intermittent code will be stored in permanent memory until erased.

KEY-ON ENGINE OFF SELF-TEST

This conducts a test of the electronic engine control or 4EAT system with power applied and engine off.

ENGINE RUNNING SELF-TEST

This is a test of electronic engine control or 4EAT system with the engine running. The sensors are checked under actual operating conditions and at normal operating temperatures.

SWITCH MONITOR TEST

This is a test of EEC input switches with the engine off and cool.

Accessing Diagnostic Trouble Codes

WITH SUPER STAR II TESTER

After attaching the Super STAR II test and turning on its power switch, the tester will run a display check and the numerals 888 will begin to flash in the display window. A steady 00 will then appear when center button is unlatched to signify that the Super STAR tester II is ready to start the self-test and receive the tests service codes. **The EEC system does not transmit a Pass code. A blank screen will appear continuously.**

To receive input or output codes, latch the center button in the test position at the front of the Super STAR tester II, turn ignition key to ON position, turn the Super STAR tester II ON, unlatch then re-latch the center button. If for any reason the

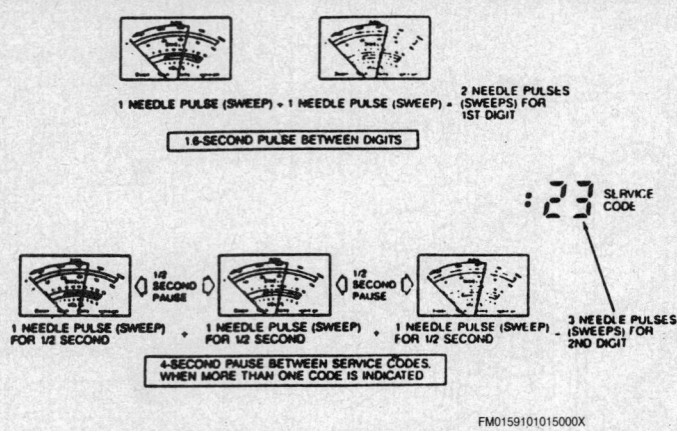

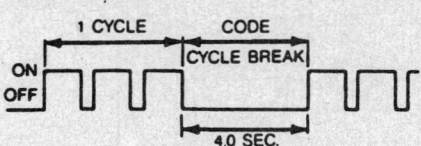

Fig. 31 Reading service
code cycle break

Fig. 30 Reading codes using analog
voltmeter

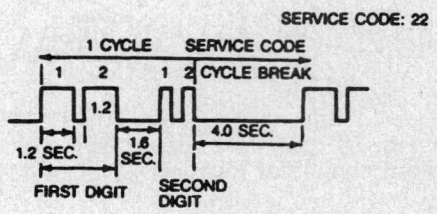

Fig. 32 Reading first digit
of service code

technician wants to clear the display window during the self-test, turn ignition switch to off position, press the testers push button once to latch down the button. Every time the Super STAR tester II is turned off, the low battery indicator (LO BAT) should show briefly at the upper left corner of the tester display window. If the LO BAT indicator shows steadily at any other time during the operation of the Super STAR II tester with any service code, turn its power switch to OFF and replace the 9 volt battery in the tester.

The Super STAR II tester will display the last service code received, even after disconnecting it from the vehicle. It will hold the service code on the display until the power is turned off or the push button is unlatched and re-latched. **Anyone who departs from the instructions provided, must first establish that he compromises neither his personal safety nor the vehicle integrity by his choice of methods, tool or parts.**

WITH NEW GENERATION STAR (NGS) TESTER

1. Turn ignition switch to Off position.
2. Connect appropriate EEC adapter cable to NGS scan tool.
3. Connect adapter leads to the Data Link Connector (DLC) and Self-Test Input (STI) connector.
4. Connect timing light if required.
5. Select diagnostic test mode from main menu.
6. Select self-test, then slow or fast code format.
7. Depress START key, this will short STI to ground and start self-test.
8. Screen will display all fast DTCs, then all slow DTCs.
9. After all DTCs have been output, depress STOP key.
10. Depress CANCEL to exit self-test to diagnostic test mode menu. **Depressing the STOP or CANCEL key before all slow DTCs have been output, will erase any Continuous DTCs from PCM memory.**
11. Press CANCEL to return to main menu.

WITH ANALOG VOLTMETER

When a service code is reported on the analog voltmeter for a function test, it will represent itself as a pulsing or sweeping movement of the voltmeter needle across the dial face of the voltmeter. A single digit number of three will be reported by three needle pulses (sweeps), **Fig. 30**.

As previously described a service code is sometimes represented by a two digit number, such as 23. As a result, the self-test service code of 23 will appear on the voltmeter as two needle pulses (sweeps), then after a 1.6 second pause the needle will pulse (sweep) three times. The continuous memory codes are not separated from the Key-On/Engine Off codes. They are produced on the voltmeter in the same manner as the Key-On/Engine Off codes.

MALFUNCTION INDICATOR LIGHT

Then malfunction indicator light or check engine light is intended to alert the driver of certain malfunctions in the engine control system.

If such a fault occurs, the processor will substitute a value or values and continue operating. This process is Limited Operating Strategy (LOS). In some cases this action may result in a slight change in driveability.

CHECK ENGINE & MANUAL LIGHT OPERATIONS

The check engine will remain on while the key in the Run position, and go off once the vehicle has started. The manual shift light will remain on while in the manual shift mode and off in all other modes. If the check engine light should remain on after the vehicle has started, run Key-On/Engine Off self-test to completion. If the light continues to remain On, proceed to Pinpoint test PGC. If the check engine

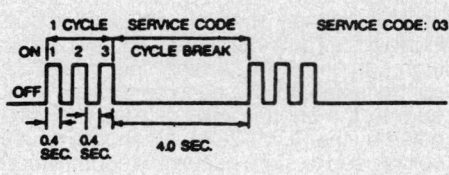

Fig. 33 Reading second
digit of service code

light never comes On, proceed to Pinpoint test.

If the light comes on for a period then goes off, and a service code is present, the fault is intermittent. If the light never comes on, proceed to Pinpoint test. **When EEC is in self-test, then check engine light will also flash service codes.**

Diagnostic Trouble Code Interpretation

The EEC and 4EAT system transmits its information by the use of the self-test service codes. These service codes are two digit numbers representing the results of the self-test. The service codes are transmitted on the self-test output line found in the vehicle self-test connector. They are in the form of timed pulses, and read by the use of a voltmeter or a Super Star Tester II.

1. Code cycle break. The time between service code cycles is 4.0 seconds, **Fig. 31**.
2. First digit of service code (tens position) during one cycle, **Fig. 32**.
3. Second digit of service code (ones position) during one cycle, **Fig. 33**.

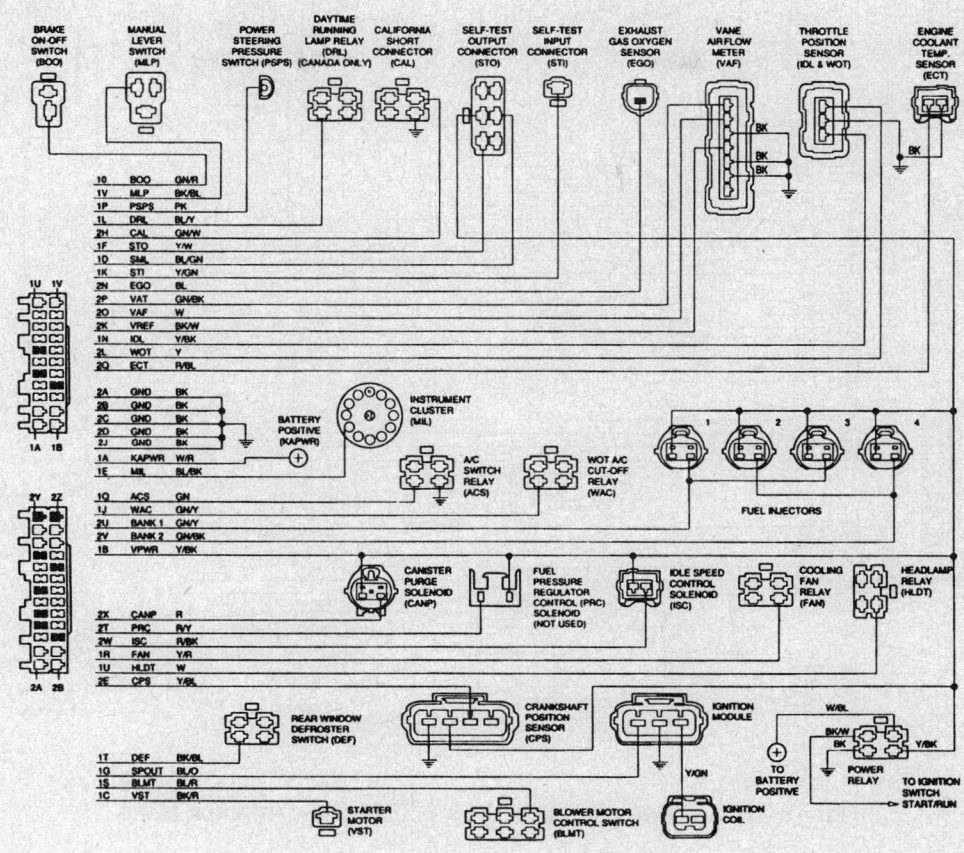

Fig. 34   EEC wiring diagram. 1993 1.3L/4-81 w/auto. trans.

Clearing Diagnostic Trouble Codes

1. Disconnect battery ground cable, then depress brake pedal for 5-10 seconds.
2. Rerun quick test to verify service code(s) have been erased.

Quick Tests

To test and service this system correctly first perform all three phases of the Quick Tests; Key On Engine-Off, Engine Running and Switch Monitor. If vehicle passes all three phases of the Quick Tests, it is likely that vehicle problem is mechanical not electronic.

Pinpoint Tests

Do not perform any of the following pinpoint test unless you are instructed to do so by the Quick Test. Each pinpoint test assumes that a fault has been detected in the system with direction to enter a specif-

ic repair routine. Service codes retrieved in Quick Test steps, implies that a hard fault is present and the associated pinpoint test should be performed to isolate the cause.

If more than one service code is received, always start service with the first code received. Probable components listed in routines should be diagnosed only when Quick Test steps 1-11 have resulted in a pass code. With the knowledge of the symptom, a close observation can be made of each specified component, by performing the associated pinpoint test. Before performing pinpoint test check wiring circuits, components and wiring to the control module. Loose connections, corrosion, overheating and physical damage are often cause of failure.

Do not replace any components unless the test result indicates that components should be replaced. Do not measure voltage or resistance at the control module or connect any test lights to it, unless specified to do so by the pinpoint test charts.

Disconnect solenoids and switches from the harness before measuring for

continuity, resistance, or energizing with a power source.

When using the Pinpoint test procedure, follow each step in order, starting from the first step in the appropriate test. Follow each step until the fault is located. Erase codes and perform Quick Test to insure any repairs made are effective.

An open circuit is defined as any resistance reading obtained greater than 10,000 ohms, unless otherwise specified. A short circuit is defined as any resistance reading obtained of less than 5 ohms, unless otherwise specified.

System Testing 1993–95

Refer to **Figs. 34 through 57,** for wiring diagrams and ECA connector pin usage. Refer to **Figs. 58 through 65,** for quick test codes and code definitions. Refer to **Figs. 66 through 79,** for quick test procedures. Refer to **Figs. 80 through 124,** for pinpoint test procedures.

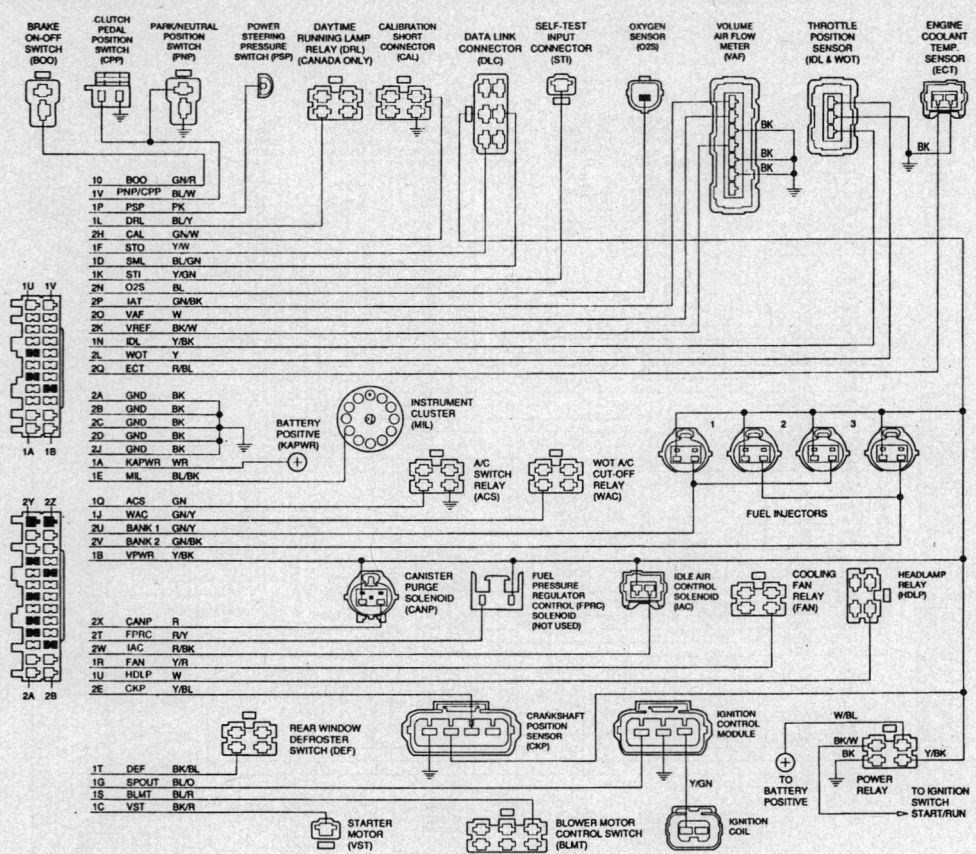

Fig. 35 EEC wiring diagram. 1993 1.3L/4-81 w/manual trans

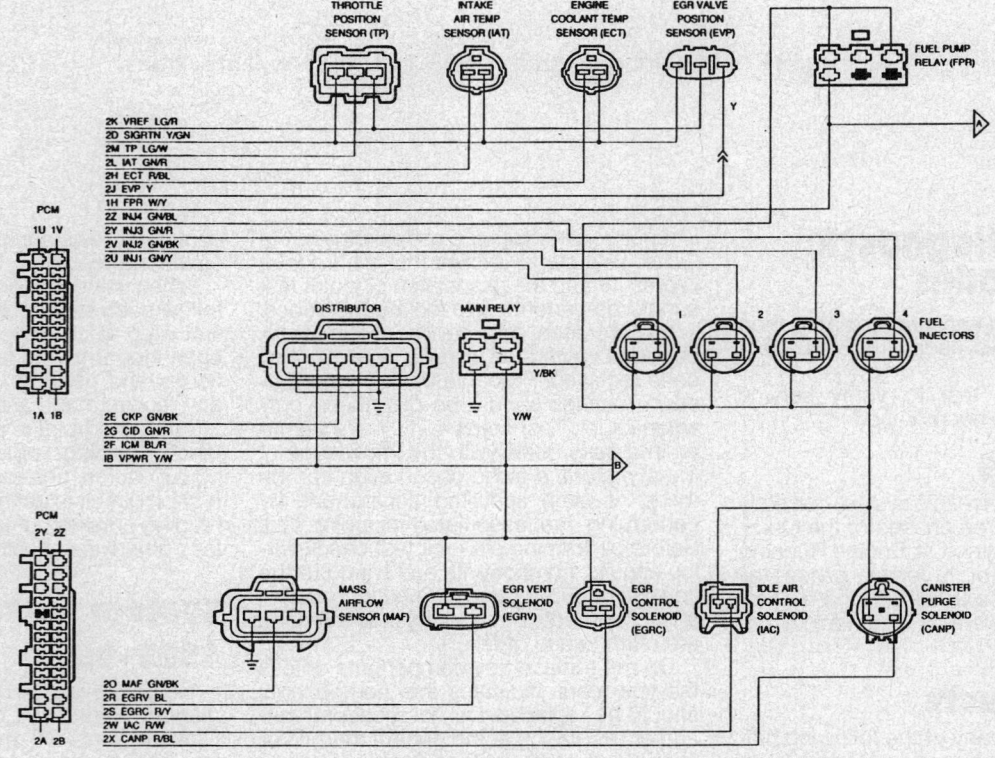

Fig. 36 EEC wiring diagram (Part 1 of 2). 1994–95 1.3L/4-81

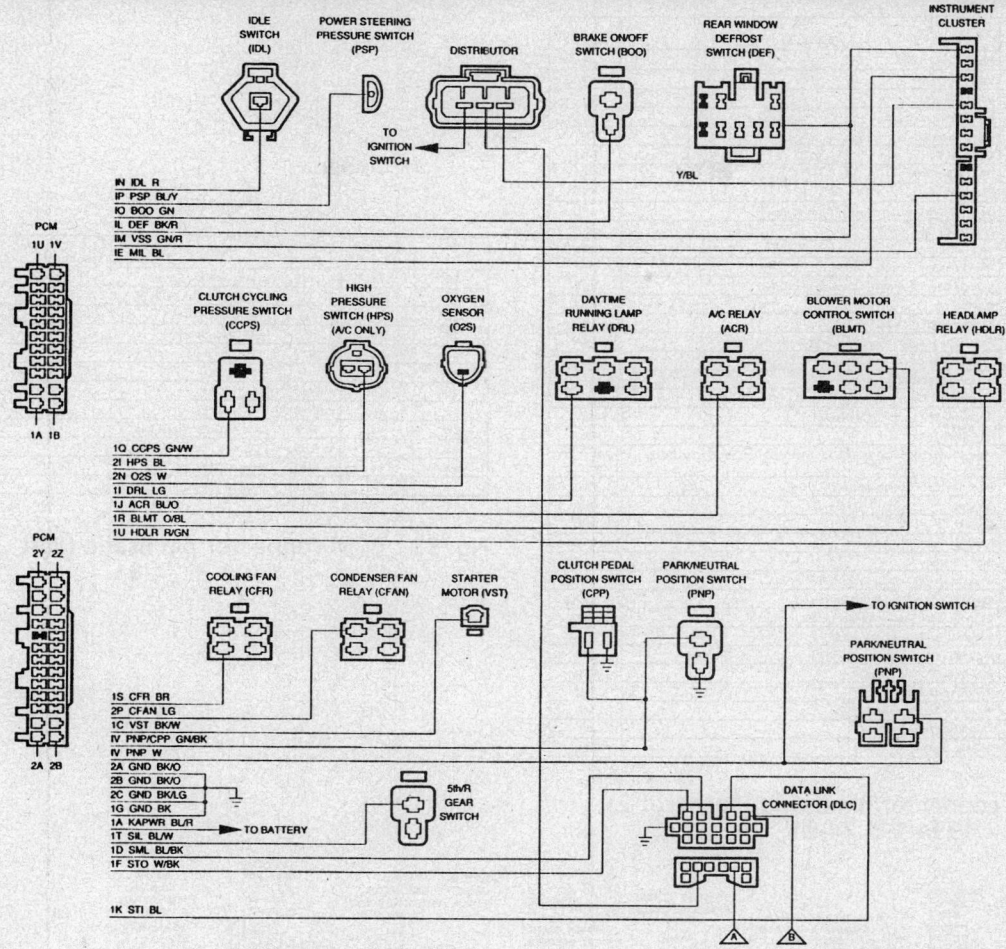

Fig. 36 EEC wiring diagram (Part 2 of 2). 1994–95 1.3L/4-81

FM015940104902OX

PCM Pin	Breakout Box Pin	Wire Color	Application	Abbrev.
1A	1	W/R	Keep Alive Power	KAPWR
1B	37,57	Y/BK	Vehicle Power	VPWR
1C	5	BK/R	Vehicle Start	VST
1D	38	BL/GN	Switch Monitor Lamp	SML
1E	15	BL/BK	Malfunction Indicator Lamp	MIL
1F	17	Y/W	Self Test Output	STO
1G	36	BL/O	Spark Output	SPOUT
1J	54	GN/Y	WOT A/C Cut-Off Relay	WAC
1K	48	Y/GN	Self Test Input	STI
1L	42	BL/Y	Daytime Running Lamp Relay (Canada Only)	DRL
1N	18	Y/BK	Idle Switch	IDL
1O	2	GN/R	Brake On/Off Switch	BOO
1P	19	PK	Power Steering Pressure Switch	PSP
1Q	10	GN	A/C Switch Relay	ACS
1R	22	Y/R	Engine Cooling Fan Relay	FAN
1S	23	BL/R	Blower Motor Control Switch	BLMT
1T	30	BK/BL	Rear Window Defroster Switch	DEF
1U	28	W	Headlamp Relay	HDLP
1V	43	BL/W	Park/Neutral Position Switch/Clutch Pedal Position Switch (MTX)	PNP/CPP
1V	43	BK/BL	Manual Lever Position Switch (ATX)	MLP
2A	39,40,44,60	BK	Ground	GND
2B	20	BK	Ground	GND
2C	16	BK	Ground	GND
2D	46,49	BK	Ground	GND
2E	56	Y/BL	Crankshaft Position Sensor	CKP
2H	51	GN/W	Calibration Short Connector	CAL
2J	6	BK	Ground	GND
2K	26	BK/W	Reference Voltage	VREF
2L	27	Y	Wide Open Throttle Switch	WOT
2N	29	BL	Oxygen Sensor	O2S
2O	25	W	Volume Air Flow Meter	VAF
2P	45	GN/BK	Intake Air Temperature Sensor	IAT
2Q	7	R/BL	Engine Coolant Temperature Sensor	ECT
2T	11	R/Y	Fuel Pressure Regulator Control Solenoid (Not Used)	FPRC
2U	58	GN/Y	Fuel Injectors 1 and 3	BANK 1
2V	59	GN/BK	Fuel Injectors 2 and 4	BANK 2
2W	41	R/BK	Idle Air Control Solenoid	IAC
2X	31	R	Canister Purge Solenoid	CANP

Fig. 37 PCM connector pin usage.
1993 1.3L/4-81

PCM Pin	Breakout Box Pin	Wire Color	Application	Abbrev.
1A	1	BL/R	Keep Alive Power	KAPWR
1B	37,57	Y/W	Vehicle Power	VPWR
1C	5	BK/W	Vehicle Start	VST
1D	38	BL/BK	Switch Monitor Lamp	SML
1E	15	BL	Malfunction Indicator Lamp	MIL
1F	17	W/BK	Self Test Output	STO
1G	36	BK	Ground (MTX Only)	GND
1H	55	W/Y	Fuel Pump Relay	FPR
1I	35	LG	Daytime Running Lamp Relay (Canada Only)	DRL
1J	54	BL/O	A/C Relay (A/C Only)	ACR
1K	48	BL	Self Test Input	STI
1L	42	BK/R	Rear Window Defroster Switch	DEF
1M	21	GN/R	Vehicle Speed Sensor (In Instrument Cluster)	VSS
1N	18	R	Idle Switch	IDL
1O	2	GN	Brake ON/OFF Switch	BOO
1P	19	BL/Y	Power Steering Pressure Switch (5-Door ATX Only)	PSP
1Q	10	GN/W	Clutch Cycling Pressure Switch (A/C Only)	CCPS
1R	22	O/BL	Blower Motor Switch	BLMT
1S	23	BR	Cooling Fan Relay	CFR
1T	30	BL/W	Shift Indicator Lamp (MTX Only)	SIL
1U	28	R/GN	Headlamp Relay	HDLR
1V	43	GN/BK	Park/Neutral Position Switch/Clutch Pedal Position Switch (MTX Only)	PNP/CPP
1V	43	W	Park/Neutral Position Switch (ATX Only)	PNP
2A	39,40,44,60	BK/O	Ground	GND
2B	20	BK/O	Ground	GND
2C	16	BK/LG	Ground	GND
2D	46,49	Y/GN	Signal Return	SIGRTN
2E	56	GN/BK	Crankshaft Position Sensor (In Distributor)	CKP
2F	3	BL/R	Ignition Control Module (In Distributor)	ICM
2G	24	GN/R	Cylinder Identification Sensor (In Distributor)	CID
2H	51	R/BL	Engine Coolant Temperature Senor	ECT
2I	50	BL	High Pressure Switch (A/C Only)	HPS
2J	6	Y	EGR Valve Position Sensor	EVP
2K	26	LG/R	Reference Voltage	VREF
2L	27	GN/R	Intake Air Temperature Sensor	IAT
2M	47	LG/W	Throttle Position Sensor	TP
2N	29	W	Oxygen Sensor	O2S

FM015940105101 0X

Fig. 38 PCM connector pin usage (Part 1 of 2). 1994 1.3L/4-81

PCM Pin	Breakout Box Pin	Wire Color	Application	Abbrev.
2O	25	GN/BK	Mass Air Flow Sensor	MAF
2P	45	LG	Condenser Fan Relay (A/C Only)	CFAN
2Q	7	—	NOT USED	—
2R	13	BL	EGR Vent Solenoid	EGRV
2S	53	R/Y	EGR Control Solenoid	EGRC
2T	11	—	NOT USED	—
2U	58	GN/Y	Injector #1	INJ1
2V	59	GN/BK	Injector #2	INJ2
2W	41	R/W	Idle Air Control Solenoid	IAC
2X	31	R/BL	Canister Purge Solenoid	CANP
2Y	33	GN/R	Injector #3	INJ3
2Z	8	GN/BL	Injector #4	INJ4

FM0159401051020X

Fig. 38 PCM connector pin usage (Part 2 of 2). 1994 1.3L/4-81

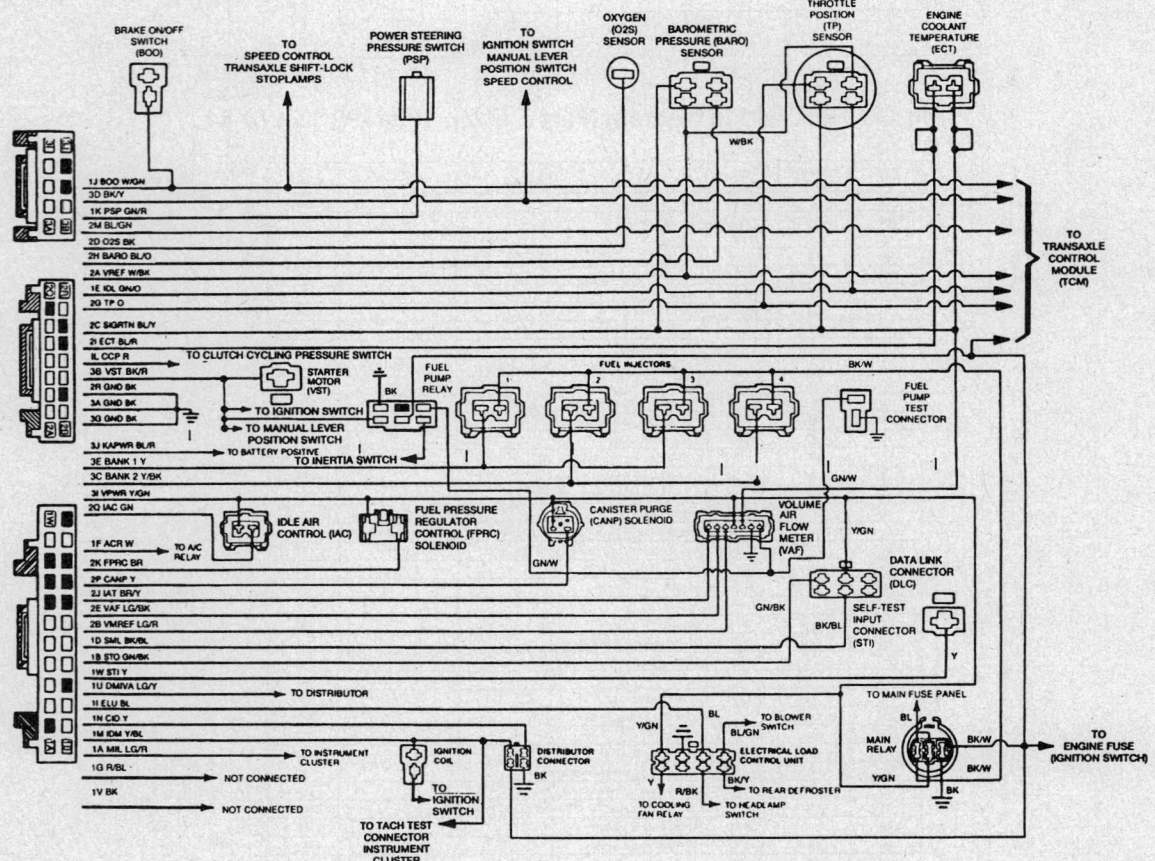

Fig. 39 EEC wiring diagram. 1993–94 1.6L/4-98 non-turbo w/auto. trans.

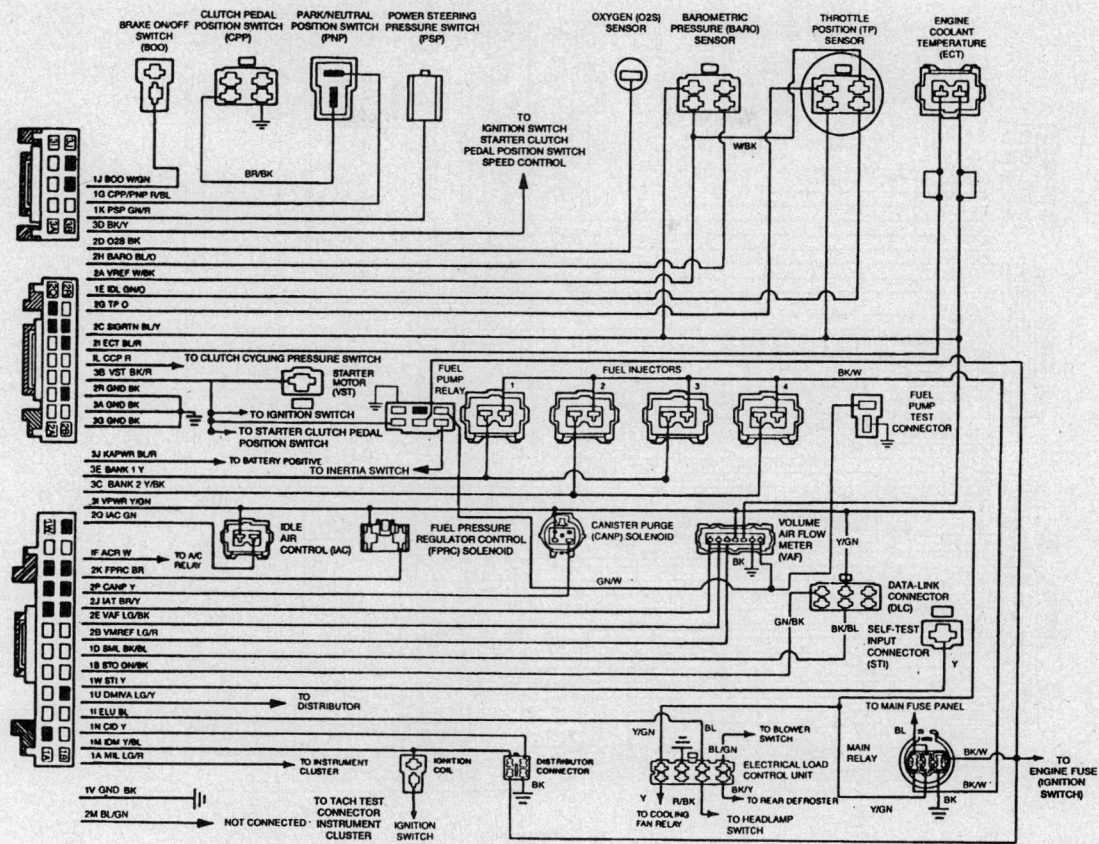

Fig. 40   EEC wiring diagram. 1993–94 1.6L/4-98 non-turbo w/manual trans.

PCM Pin	Breakout Box Pin	Wire Color	Application	Abbrev.
1A	51	LG/R	MIL Lamp	MIL
1B	17	GN/BK	Self Test Output	STO
1D	38	BK/BL	Switch Monitor Lamp	SML
1E	28	GN/O	Idle Switch	IDL
1F	30	W	A/C Relay	ACR
1G	8	R/BL	Park/Neutral Position Switch (MTX)	PNP
1I	24	BL	Electrical Load Control Unit	ELU
1J	3	W/GN	Brake On/Off Switch	BOO
1K	19	GN/R	Power Steering Pressure Switch	PSP
1L	14	R	Clutch Cycling Pressure Switch	CCP
1M	6	Y/BL	Ignition Diagnostic Monitor	IDM
1N	34	Y	Cylinder Identification Sensor	CID
1U	36	LG/Y	Distributor Mounted Ignition Module With Vacuum Advance	DMIVA
1V	44	BK	Ground (MTX)	GND
1W	48	Y	Self Test Input	STI
2A	26	W/BK	Reference Voltage	VREF
2B	18	LG/R	Volume Air Flow Reference	VMREF
2C	46	BL/Y	Signal Return	SIGRTN
2D	29	BK	Oxygen Sensor	O2S
2E	43	LG/BK	Volume Air Flow Signal	VAF
2G	47	O	Throttle Position Sensor	TP
2H	45	BL/O	Barometric Pressure Sensor	BARO
2I	7	BL/R	Engine Coolant Temperature Sensor	ECT
2J	25	BR/Y	Intake Air Temperature Sensor	IAT
2K	31	BR	Fuel Pressure Regulator Control Solenoid	FPRC
2M	52	BL/GN	Water Temperature Switch (ATX)	WTS
2P	32	Y	Canister Purge Solenoid	CANP
2Q	41	GN	Idle Air Control	IAC
2R	49	BK	Ground	GND
3A	20	BK	Ground	GND
3B	5	BK/R	Vehicle Start	VST
3C	59	Y/BK	Fuel Injectors 2 and 4	BANK 2
3D	2	BK/Y	Manual Lever Position Switch (4EAT) / Starter Clutch Pedal Position Switch (MTX)	MLP/SCPP
3E	58	Y	Fuel Injectors 1 and 3	BANK 1
3G	40	BK	Ground	GND
3I	37	Y/GN	Vehicle Power	VPWR
3J	1	BL/R	Keep Alive Power	KAPWR

FM0159301054000X

**Fig. 41   PCM connector pin usage. 1993–94
1.6L/4-98 non-turbo**

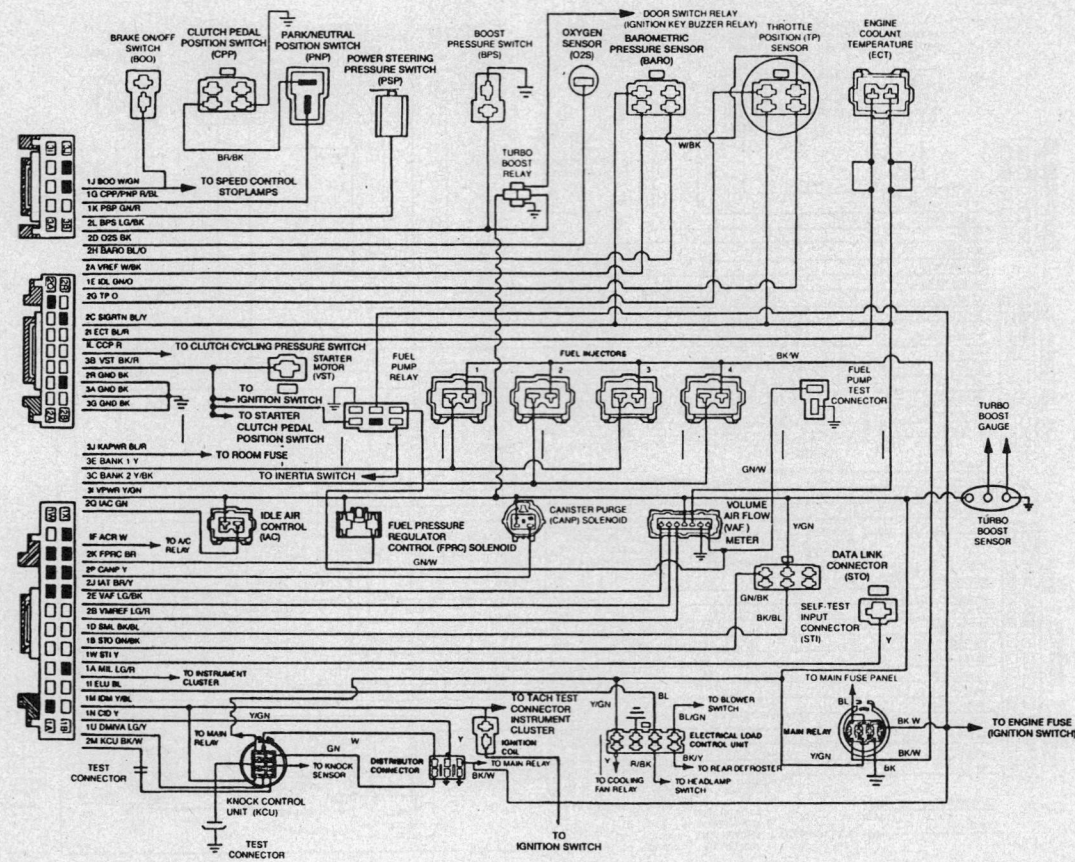

Fig. 42 EEC wiring diagram. 1993–94 1.6L/4-98 turbo

FM0159301055000X

PCM Pin	Breakout Box Pin	Wire Color	Application	Abbrev.
1A	51	LG/R	MIL Lamp	MIL
1B	17	GN/BK	Self Test Output	STO
1D	38	BK/BL	Switch Monitor Lamp	SML
1E	28	GN/O	Idle Switch	IDL
1F	30	W	A/C Relay	ACR
1G	8	R/BL	Park/Neutral Position Switch/Starter Clutch Pedal Position Switch	PNP/SCPP
1I	24	BL	Electrical Load Control Unit	ELU
1J	3	W/GN	Brake On/Off Switch	BOO
1K	19	GN/R	Power Steering Pressure Switch	PSP
1L	14	R	Clutch Cycling Pressure Switch	CCP
1M	6	Y/BL	Ignition Diagnostic Monitor	IDM
1N	34	Y	Cylinder Identification Sensor	CID
1U	36	LG/Y	Distributor Mounted Ignition Module With Vacuum Advance	DMIVA
1W	48	Y	Self Test Input	STI
2A	26	W/BK	Reference Voltage	VREF
2B	18	LG/R	Volume Air Flow Reference	VMREF
2C	46	BL/Y	Signal Return	SIGRTN
2D	29	BK	Oxygen Sensor	O2S
2E	43	LG/BK	Volume Air Flow Signal	VAF
2G	47	O	Throttle Position Sensor	TP
2H	45	BL/O	Barometric Pressure Sensor	BARO
2I	7	BL/R	Engine Coolant Temperature Sensor	ECT
2J	25	BR/Y	Intake Air Temperature Sensor	IAT
2K	31	BR	Fuel Pressure Regulator Control Solenoid	FPRC
2L	12	LG/BK	Boost Pressure Switch	BPS
2M	52	BK/W	Knock Control Unit	KCU
2P	32	Y	Canister Purge Solenoid	CANP
2Q	41	GN	Idle Air Control	IAC
2R	49	BK	Ground	GND
3A	20	BK	Ground	GND
3B	5	BK/R	Vehicle Start	VST
3C	59	Y/BK	Fuel Injectors 2 and 4	BANK 2
3E	58	Y	Fuel Injectors 1 and 3	BANK 1
3G	40	BK	Ground	GND
3I	37	Y/GN	Vehicle Power	VPWR
3J	1	BL/R	Keep Alive Power	KAPWR

FM0159301056000X

Fig. 43 PCM connector pin usage. 1993–94
1.6L/4-98 turbo

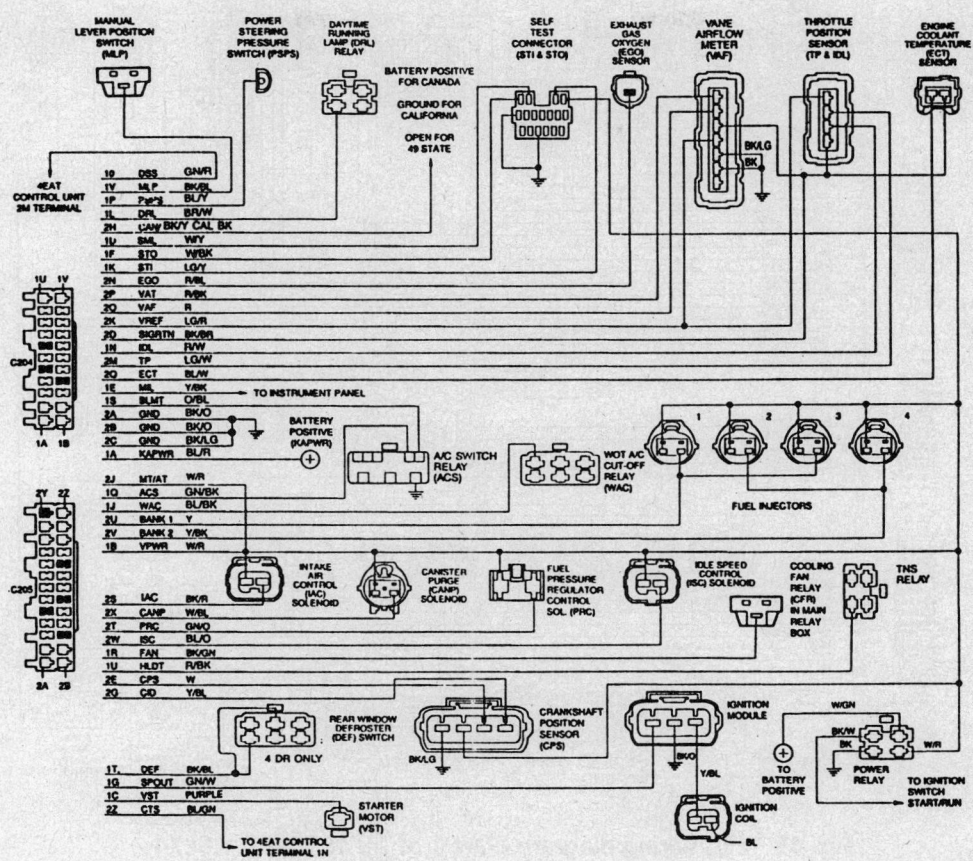

Fig. 44   EEC wiring diagram (Part 1 of 2). 1993 1.8L/4-112
w/auto. trans.

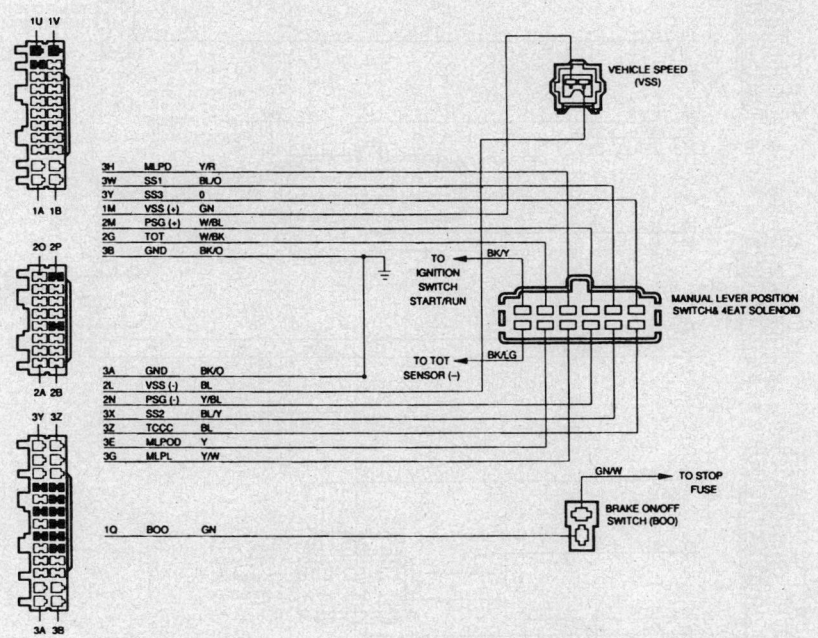

Fig. 44   EEC wiring diagram (Part 2 of 2). 1993 1.8L/4-112 w/auto.
trans.

COMPUTERIZED ENGINE CONTROLS (ASPIRE, CAPRI, ESCORT & TRACER (1.8L/4-112), FESTIVA & PROBE (2.0L/4-121 w/4EAT & 2.5L/V6-152) ELECTRONIC ENGINE CONTROL (EEC) SYSTEM

10-17

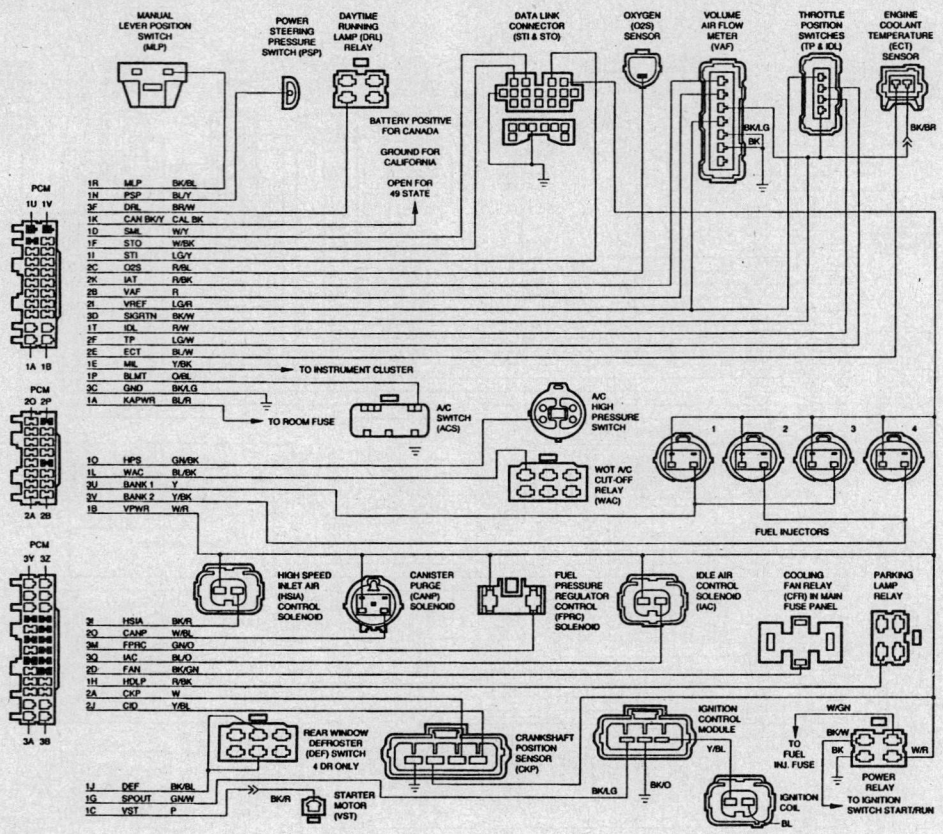

Fig. 45   EEC wiring diagram (Part 1 of 2). 1994–95 1.8L/4-112 w/auto. trans.

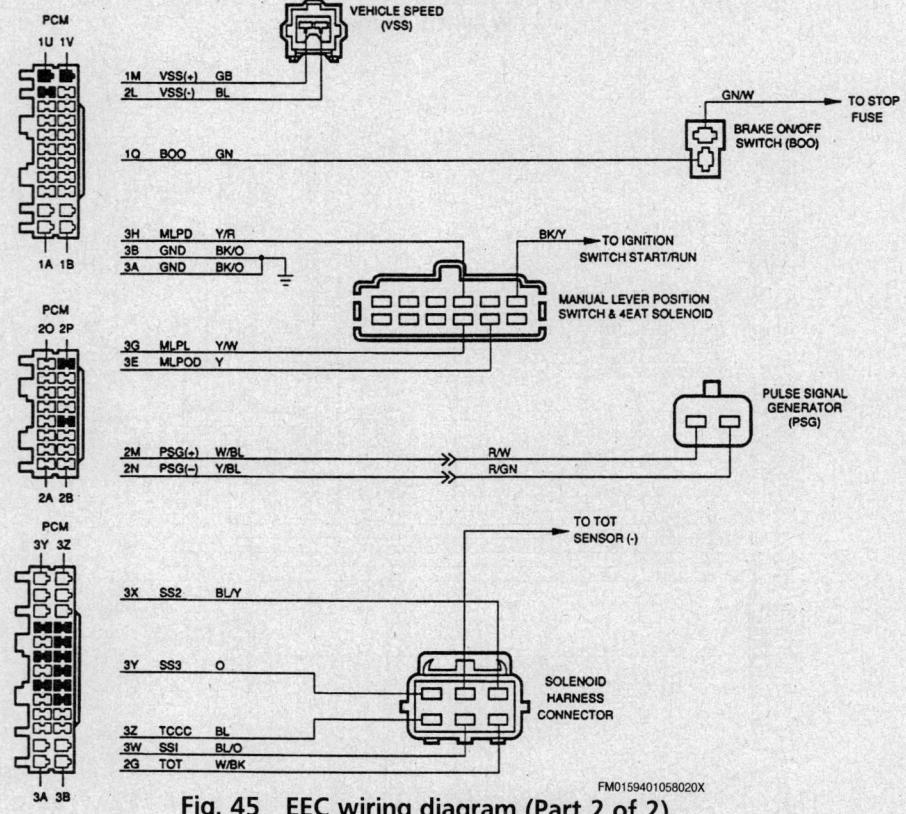

Fig. 45   EEC wiring diagram (Part 2 of 2). 1994–95 1.8L/4-112 w/auto. trans.

PCM Pin	Breakout Box Pin	Wire Color	Application	Abbrev.
1A	1	BL/R	Keep Alive Power	KAPWR
1B	37, 57	W/R	Vehicle Power	VPWR
1C	5	P	Vehicle Start	VST
1D	38	W/Y	Switch Monitor Lamp	SML
1E	51	Y/BK	Malfunction Indicator Lamp	MIL
1F	17	W/BK	Self Test Output	STO
1G	36	GN/W	Ignition Control Module	ICM
1H	32	R/BK	Headlamp Switch	HDLP
1I	48	LG/Y	Self Test Input	STI
1J	34	BK/BL	Rear Window Defroster Switch	DEF
1K	19	BK, BK/Y	Ground (Calif), Vehicle Power (Can)	GND (CAL), VPWR (CAN)
1L	10	BL/BK	A/C Relay	ACR
1M	3	GN	Vehicle Speed Sensor (+)	VSS+
1N	24	BL/Y	Power Steering Pressure Switch	PSP
1O	41	GN/BK	A/C Switch	ACS
1P	22	O/BL	Blower Motor Control Switch	BLMT
1Q	2	GN	Brake ON/OFF Switch	BOO
1R	30	BK/BL	Manual Lever Position Switch	MLP
1T	18	R/W	Idle Switch	IDL
2A	45	W	Crankshaft Position Sensor	CKP
2B	44	R	Volume Air Flow Sensor	VAF
2C	29	R/BL	Oxygen Sensor	O2S
2D	43	BK/GN	Cooling Fan Switch	CFS
2E	7	BL/W	Engine Coolant Temperature Sensor	ECT
2F	47	LG/W	Throttle Position Sensor	TP
2G	50	W/BK	Transaxle Oil Temperature Sensor	TOT
2I	26	LG/R	Reference Voltage	VREF
2J	27	Y/BL	Cylinder Identification Sensor	CID
2K	25	R/BK	Intake Air Temperature Sensor	IAT
2L	28	BL	Vehicle Speed Sensor (-)	VSS-
2M	23	W/BL	Pulse Signal Generator (+)	PSG+
2N	—	Y/BL	Pulse Signal Generator (-)	PSG-
2O	31	W/BL	Canister Purge Solenoid	CANP
3A	40, 60	BK/O	Ground	GND
3B	20	BK/O	Ground	GND

FM0159301059010X

PCM Pin	Breakout Box Pin	Wire Color	Application	Abbrev.
3C	49	BK/LG	Ground	GND
3D	—	BK/W	Signal Return	SIGRTN
3E	46	Y	Overdrive Range (Selector Lever)	MLPOD
3F	16	BR/W	Daytime Running Lamp Relay (Canada Only)	DRL
3G	6	Y/W	Low Range (Selector Lever)	MLPL
3H	4	Y/R	Drive Range (Selector Lever)	MLPD
3I	42	BK/R	High Speed Inlet Air Control Solenoid	HSIA
3M	21A	GN/O	Fuel Pressure Regulator Control Solenoid	FPRC
3Q	21B	BL/O	Intake Air Control Solenoid	IAC
3U	58	Y	Fuel Injectors 1 and 3	BANK1
3V	59	Y/BK	Fuel Injectors 2 and 4	BANK2
3W	12	BL/O	1-2 Shift Solenoid (Shift Solenoid #1)	SS1
3X	13	BL/Y	2-3 Shift Solenoid (Shift Solenoid #2)	SS2
3Y	14	O	3-4 Shift Solenoid (Shift Solenoid #3)	SS3
3Z	15	BL	Torque Converter Clutch Control Solenoid	TCCC

FM0159301059020X

Fig. 46 PCM connector pin usage (Part 2 of 2). 1993–95 1.8L/4-112 w/auto. trans.

Fig. 46 PCM connector pin usage (Part 1 of 2). 1993–95 1.8L/4-112 w/auto. trans.

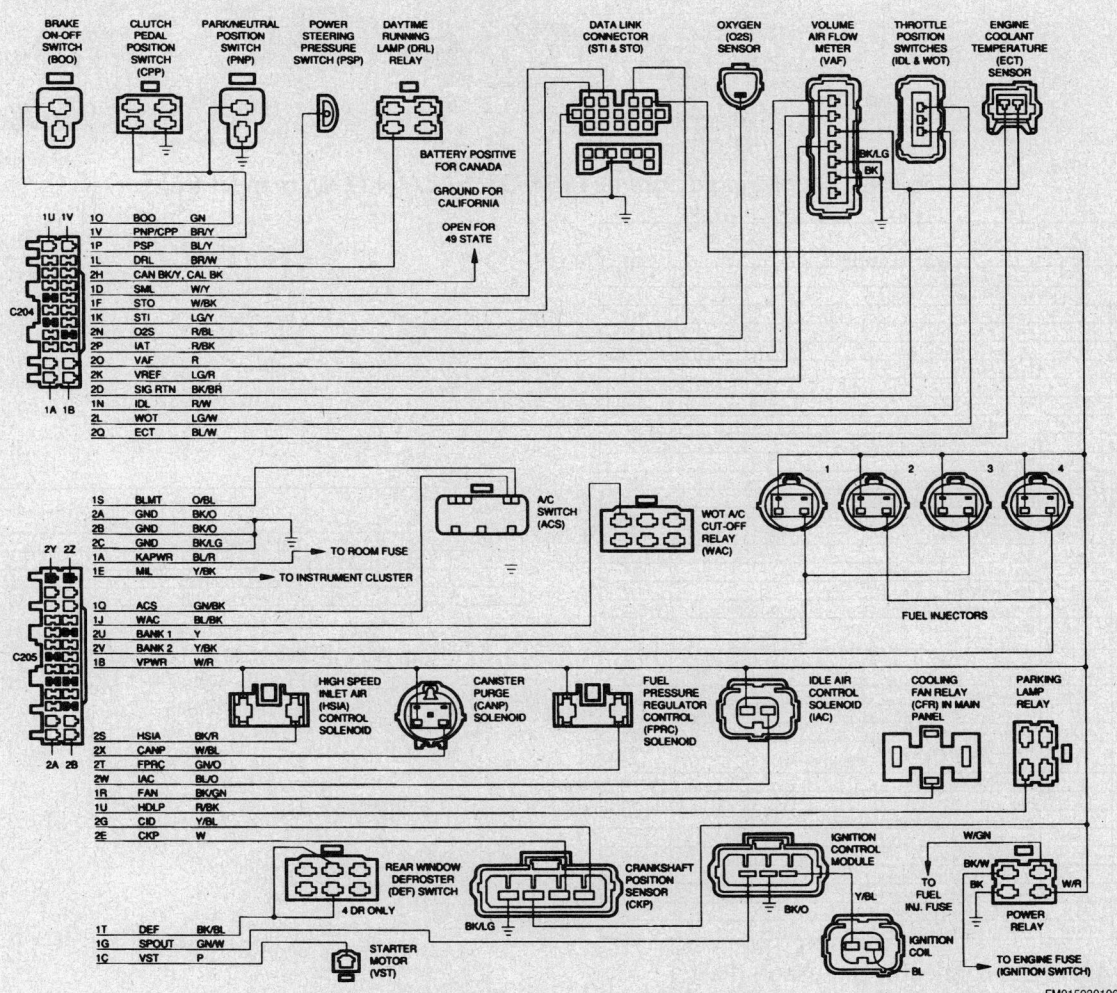

FM0159301061000X

Fig. 47 EEC wiring diagram. 1993 1.8L/4-112 w/manual trans.

COMPUTERIZED ENGINE CONTROLS (ASPIRE, CAPRI, ESCORT & TRACER (1.8L/4-112), FESTIVA & PROBE (2.0L/4-121 w/4EAT & 2.5L/V6-152) ELECTRONIC ENGINE CONTROL (EEC) SYSTEM

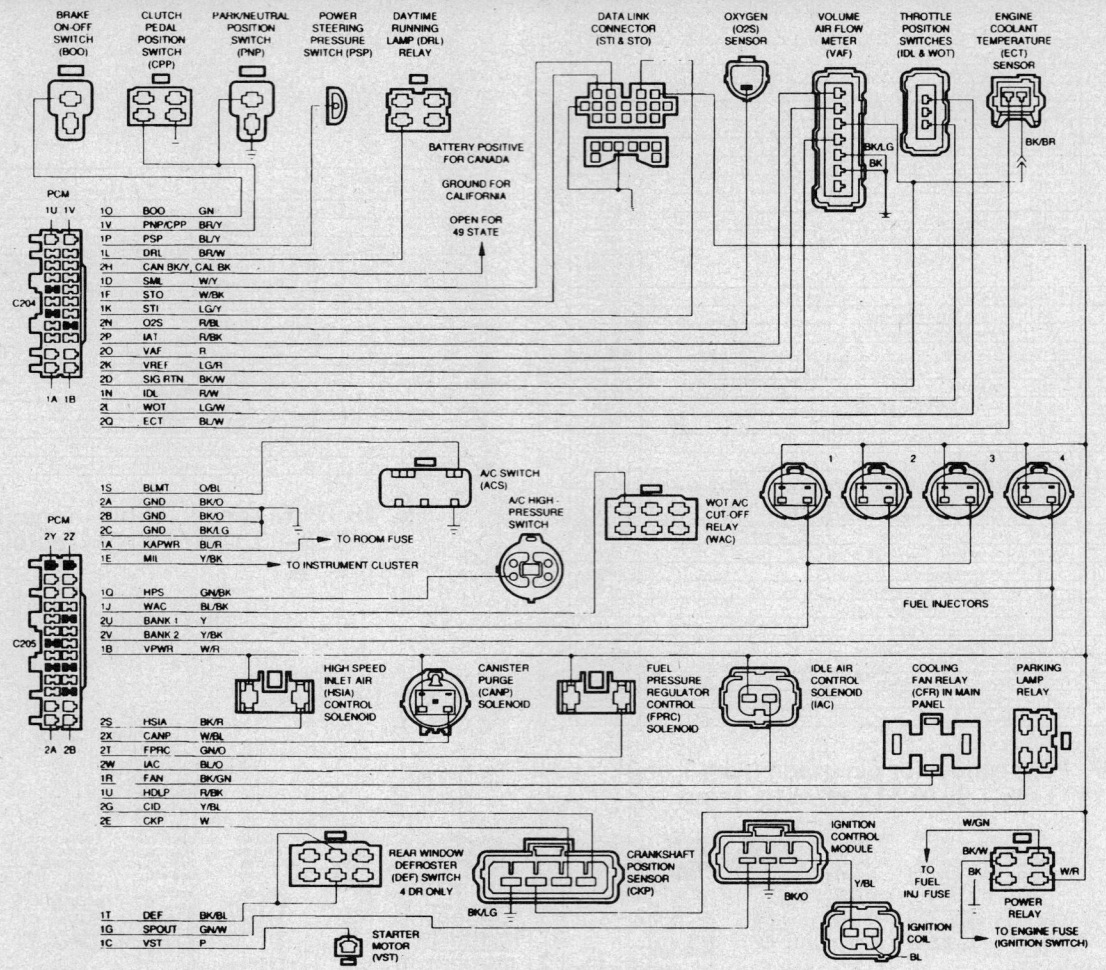

Fig. 48   EEC wiring diagram. 1994–95 1.8L/4-112 w/manual trans.

PCM Pin	Breakout Box Pin	Wire Color	Application	Abbrev.
1A	1	BL/R	Keep Alive Power	KAPWR
1B	37, 57	W/R	Vehicle Power	VPWR
1C	5	P	Vehicle Start	VST
1D	38	W/Y	Switch Monitor Lamp	SML
1E	15	Y/BK	Malfunction Indicator Lamp	MIL
1F	17	W/BK	Self Test Output	STO
1G	36	GN/W	Spark Output	SPOUT
1J	54	BL/BK	WOT A/C Cut-Off Relay	WAC
1K	48	LG/Y	Self Test Input	STI
1L	42	BR/W	Daytime Running Lamp Relay (Canada Only)	DRL
1N	18	R/W	Idle Switch	IDL
1O	2	GN	Brake On/Off Switch	BOO
1P	19	BL/Y	Power Steering Pressure Switch	PSP
1Q	10	GN/BK	A/C Switch	ACS
1R	22	BK/GN	Engine Cooling Fan	FAN
1S	23	O/BL	Blower Motor Control Switch	BLMT
1T	30	BK/BL	Rear Window Defroster Switch	DEF
1U	28	R/BK	Headlamp Switch	HDLP
1V	43	BR/Y	Park/Neutral Position Switch/Clutch Pedal Position Switch	PNP/CPP
2A	39, 40, 44, 60	BK/O	Ground	GND
2B	20	BK/O	Ground	GND
2C	16	BK/LG	Ground	GND
2D	46, 49	BK/BR	Signal Return	SIGRTN
2E	56	W	Crankshaft Position Sensor	CKP
2G	24	Y/BL	Cylinder Identification Sensor	CID
2H	51	BK/Y	Vehicle Power (Canada Only)	VPWR (CAN)
2H	51	BK	Ground (California Only)	GND (CAL)
2K	26	LG/R	Reference Voltage	VREF
2L	27	LG/W	Wide Open Throttle Switch	WOT
2N	29	R/BL	Oxygen Sensor	O2S
2O	25	R	Volume Air Flow Meter	VAF
2P	45	R/BK	Intake Air Temperature Sensor	IAT
2Q	7	BL/W	Engine Coolant Temperature Sensor	ECT
2S	53	BK/R	High Speed Inlet Air Control Solenoid	HSIA
2T	11	GN/O	Fuel Pressure Regulator Control Solenoid	FPRC

FM0159301062010X

Fig. 49   PCM connector pin usage (Part 1 of 2). 1993–95 1.8L/4-112 w/manual trans.

PCM Pin	Breakout Box Pin	Wire Color	Application	Abbrev.
2U	58	Y	Fuel Injectors 1 and 3	BANK1
2V	59	Y/BK	Fuel Injectors 2 and 4	BANK2
2W	41	BL/O	Idle Air Control Solenoid	IAC
2X	31	W/BL	Canister Purge Solenoid	CANP

FM0159301062020X

Fig. 49   PCM connector pin usage (Part 2 of 2). 1993–95 1.8L/4-112 w/manual trans.

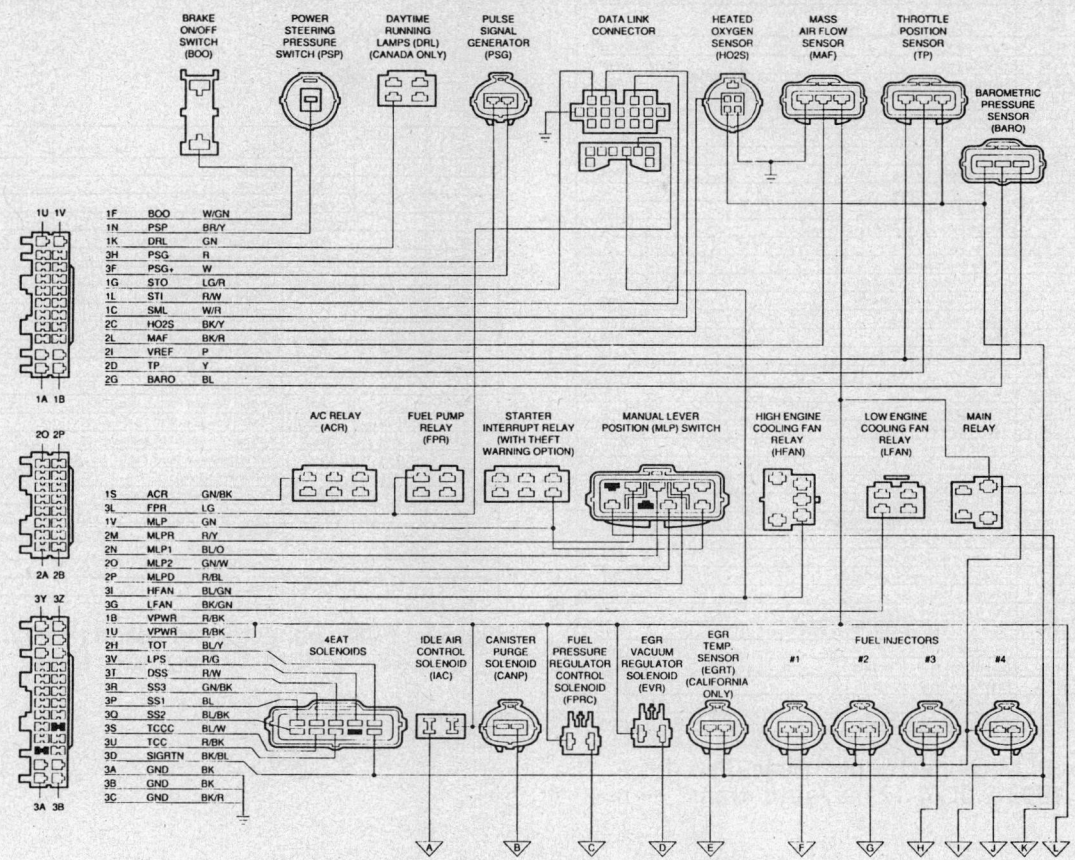

Fig. 50   EEC wiring diagram (Part 1 of 2). 1993 2.0L/4-121 w/auto. trans.

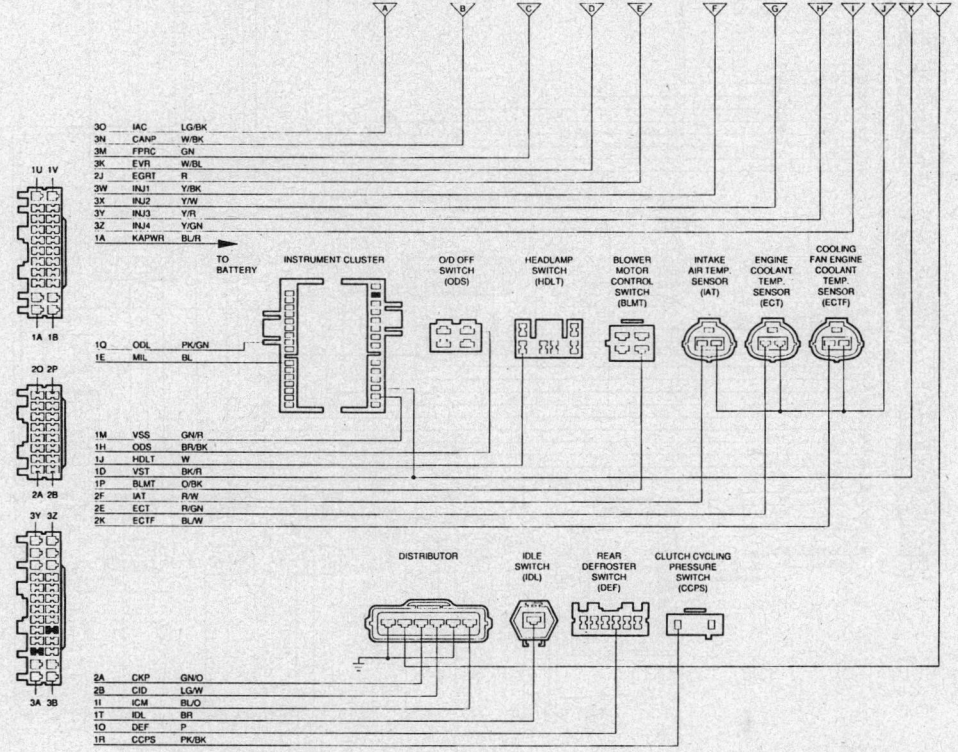

Fig. 50   EEC wiring diagram (Part 2 of 2). 1993 2.0L/4-121 w/auto. trans.

COMPUTERIZED ENGINE CONTROLS (ASPIRE, CAPRI, ESCORT & TRACER (1.8L/4-112), FESTIVA & PROBE (2.0L/4-121
w/4EAT & 2.5L/V6-152) ELECTRONIC ENGINE CONTROL (EEC) SYSTEM

10-21

PCM Pin	Breakout Box Pin	Wire Color	Application	Abbrev.
1A	1	BL/R	Keep Alive Power	KAPWR
1B	37	R/BK	Vehicle Power	VPWR
1C	38	W/R	Switch Monitor Lamp	SML
1D	5	BK/R	Vehicle Start	VST
1E	51	BL	Malfunction Indicator Lamp	MIL
1F	2	W/GN	Brake ON/OFF Switch	BOO
1G	17	LG/R	Self Test Output	STO
1H	23	BR/BK	Overdrive OFF Switch	ODS
1I	36	BL/O	Ignition Control Module	ICM
1J	32	W	Headlamp Switch	HDLT
1K	28	GN	Daytime Running Lamp Relay (Canada Only)	DRL
1L	48	R/W	Self Test Input	STI
1M	3	GN/R	Vehicle Speed Sensor	VSS
1N	10	BR/Y	Power Steering Pressure Switch	PSP
1O	34	P	Rear Window Defroster Switch	DEF
1P	22	O/BK	Blower Motor Control Switch	BLMT
1Q	15	PK/GN	Overdrive OFF Lamp	ODL
1R	41	PK/BK	Clutch Cycling Pressure Switch	CCPS
1S	14	GN/BK	A/C Relay	ACR
1T	18	BR	Idle Switch	IDL
1U	57	R/BK	Vehicle Power	VPWR
1V	30	GN	Manual Lever Position Switch	MLP
2A	56	GN/O	Crankshaft Position Sensor	CKP
2B	4	LG/W	Cylinder Identification Sensor	CID
2C	29	BK/Y	Heated Oxygen Sensor	HO2S
2D	47	Y	Throttle Position Sensor	TP
2E	7	R/GN	Engine Coolant Temperature Sensor	ECT
2F	25	R/W	Intake Air Temperature Sensor	IAT
2G	45	BL	Barometric Pressure Sensor	BARO
2H	44	BL/Y	Transaxle Oil Temperature Sensor	TOT
2I	26	P	Reference Voltage	VREF
2J	9	R	EGR Temperature Sensor (California Only)	EGRT
2K	50	BL/W	Cooling Fan Engine Coolant Temperature Sensor	ECTF
2L	27	BK/R	Mass Air Flow Sensor	MAF
2M	35	R/Y	Reverse Range (Selector Lever)	MLPR
2N	49	BL/O	First Range (Selector Lever)	MLP1
2O	43	GN/W	Second Range (Selector Lever)	MLP2
2P	19	R/BL	Drive Range (Selector Lever)	MLPD

FM0159301064010X

Fig. 51   PCM connector pin usage (Part 1 of 2). 1993 2.0L/4-121 w/auto. trans.

PCM Pin	Breakout Box Pin	Wire Color	Application	Abbrev.
3A	40, 60	BK	Ground	GND
3B	20	BK	Ground	GND
3C	16	BK/R	Ground	GND
3D	46	BK/BL	Signal Return	SIGRTN
3F	24	W	Pulse Signal Generator (+)	PSG+
3G	55	BK/GN	High Cooling Fan Relay	HFAN
3H	52	R	Pulse Signal Generator (-)	PSG-
3I	54	BL/GN	Low Cooling Fan Relay	LFAN
3K	33	W/BL	EGR Vacuum Regulator Solenoid	EVR
3L	8	LG	Fuel Pump Relay	FPR
3M	53A	GN	Fuel Pressure Regulator Control Solenoid	FPRC
3N	31A	W/BK	Canister Purge Solenoid	CANP
3O	21A	LG/BR	Idle Air Control Solenoid	IAC
3P	6A	BL	1-2 Shift Solenoid (Shift Solenoid # 1)	SS1
3Q	53B	BL/BK	2-3 Shift Solenoid (Shift Solenoid # 2)	SS2
3R	31B	GN/BK	3-4 Shift Solenoid (Shift Solenoid # 3)	SS3
3S	21B	BL/W	Torque Converter Clutch Control Solenoid	TCCC
3T	6B	R/W	Downshift Solenoid	DSS
3U	11	R/BK	Torque Converter Clutch Solenoid	TCC
3V	42	R/GN	Line Pressure Solenoid	LPS
3W	58	Y/BK	Injector #1	INJ1
3X	59	Y/W	Injector #2	INJ2
3Y	12	Y/R	Injector #3	INJ3
3Z	13	Y/GN	Injector #4	INJ4

FM0159301064020X

Fig. 51   PCM connector pin usage (Part 2 of 2). 1993 2.0L/4-121 w/auto. trans.

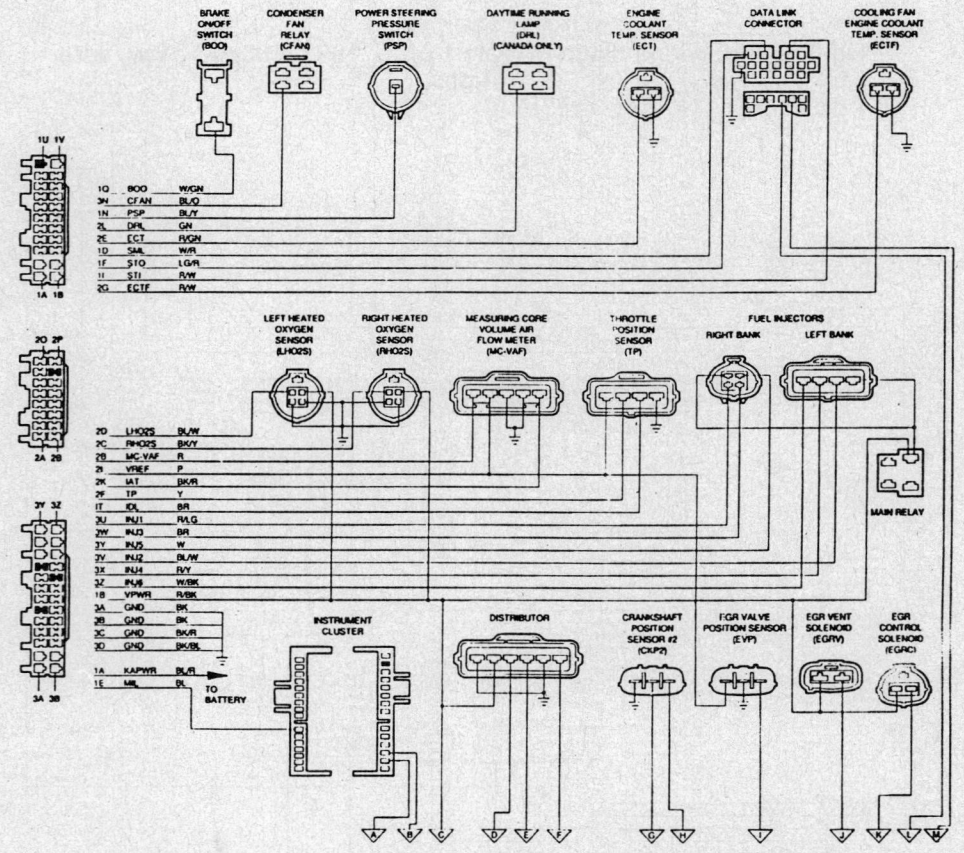

FM0159301065010X

Fig. 52   EEC wiring diagram (Part 1 of 2). 1993 2.5L/V6-152 w/auto. trans.

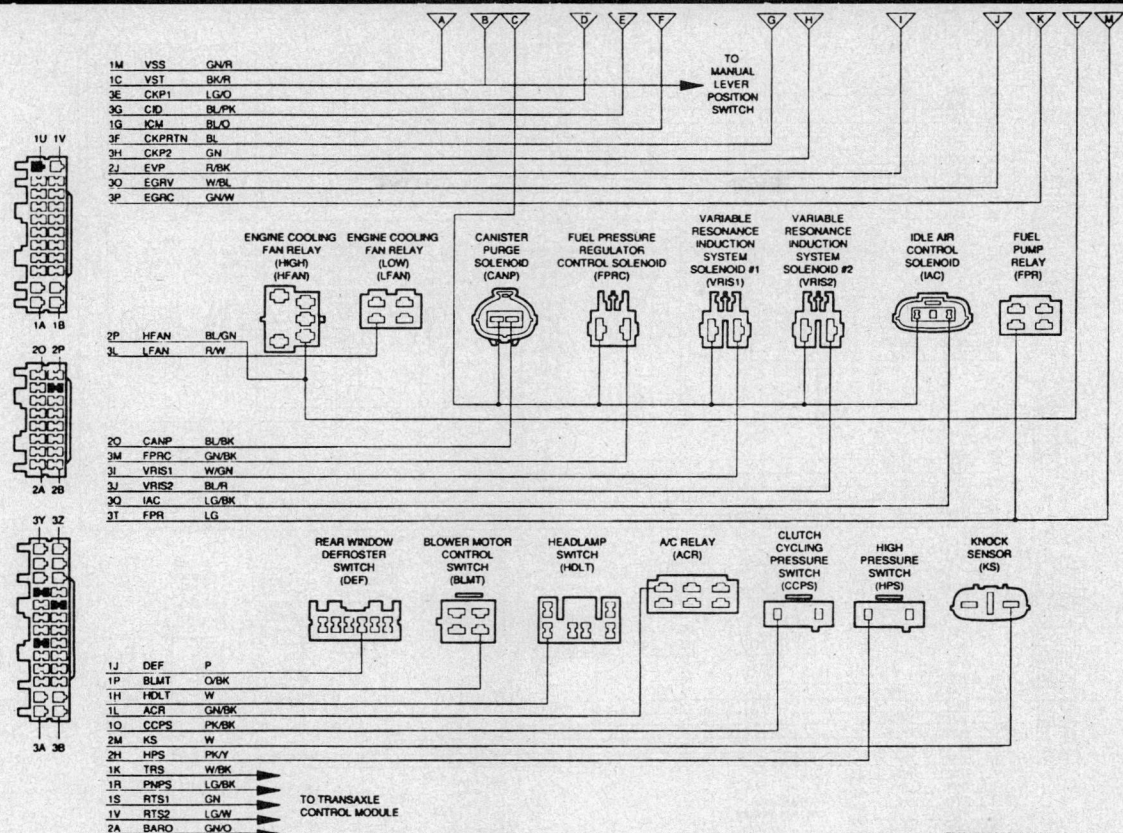

Fig. 52   EEC wiring diagram (Part 2 of 2). 1993 2.5L/V6-152 w/auto. trans.

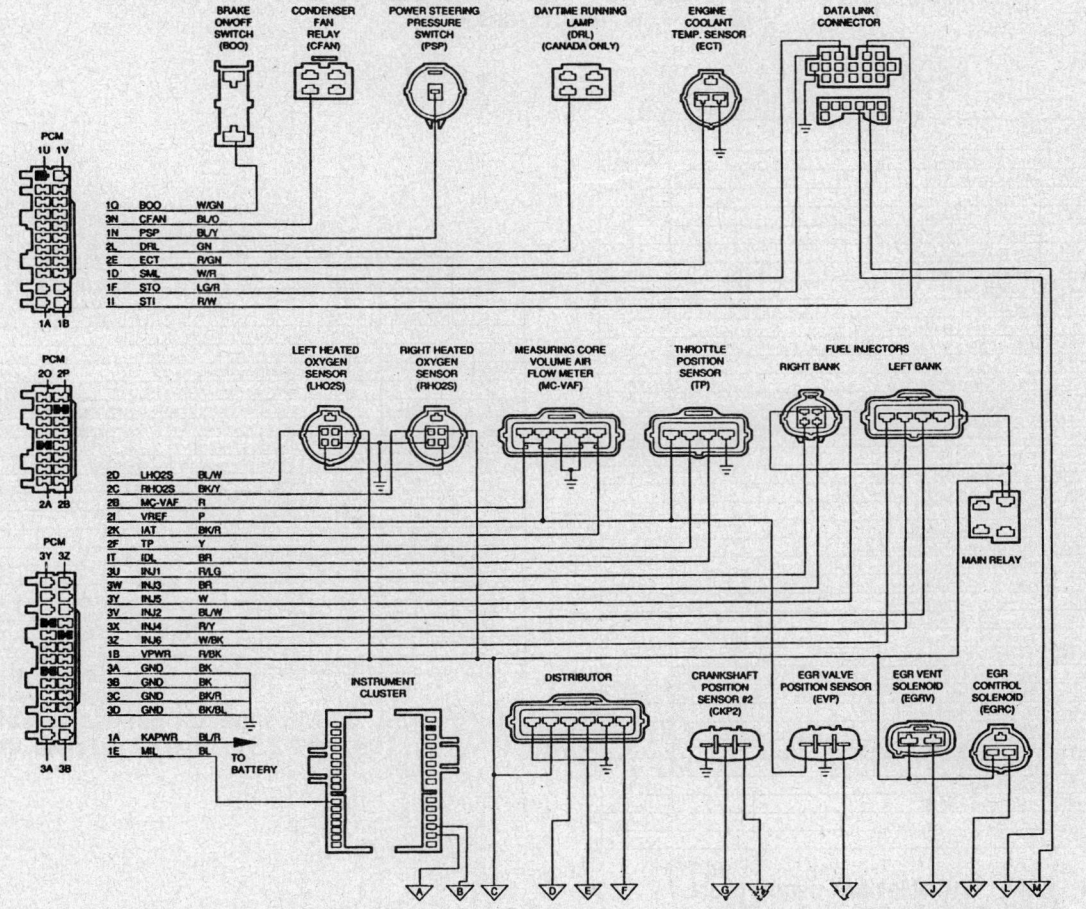

Fig. 53   EEC wiring diagram (Part 1 of 2). 1994–95 2.5L/V6-152 w/auto. trans.

COMPUTERIZED ENGINE CONTROLS (ASPIRE, CAPRI, ESCORT & TRACER (1.8L/4-112), FESTIVA & PROBE (2.0L/4-121 w/4EAT & 2.5L/V6-152) ELECTRONIC ENGINE CONTROL (EEC) SYSTEM

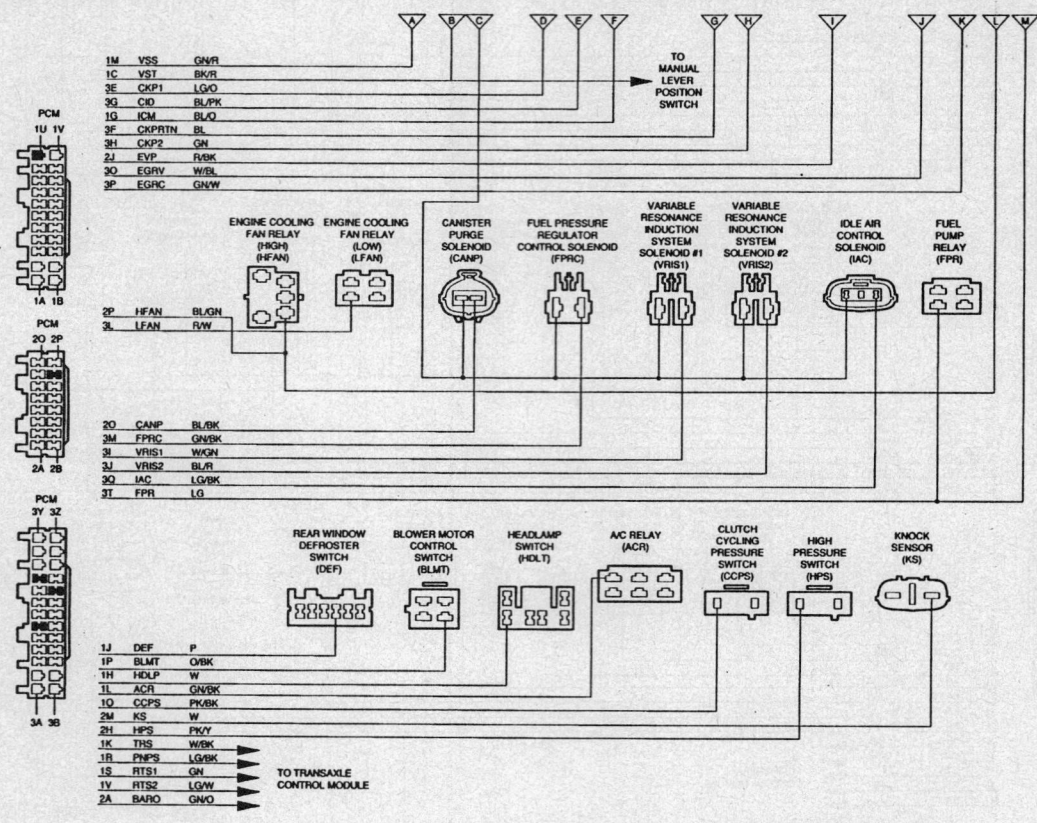

Fig. 53   EEC wiring diagram (Part 2 of 2). 1994–95 2.5L/V6-152 w/auto. trans.

PCM Pin	Breakout Box Pin	Wire Color	Application	Abbrev.
1A	1	BL/R	Keep Alive Power	KAPWR
1B	37, 57	R/BK	Vehicle Power	VPWR
1C	5	BK/R	Vehicle Start	VST
1D	38	W/R	Switch Monitor Lamp	SML
1E	51	BL	Malfunction Indicator Lamp	MIL
1F	17	LG/R	Self Test Output	STO
1G	36	BL/O	Ignition Control Module	ICM
1H	32	W	Headlamp Switch	HDLT
1I	48	R/W	Self Test Input	STI
1J	34	P	Rear Window Defroster Switch	DEF
1K	19	W/BK	Torque Reduce/Engine Coolant Temperature Signal (To TCM)	TRS
1L	10	GN/BK	A/C Relay	ACR
1M	3	GN/R	Vehicle Speed Sensor	VSS
1N	24	BL/Y	Power Steering Pressure Switch	PSP
1O	41	PK/BK	Clutch Cycling Pressure Switch	CCPS
1P	22	O/BK	Blower Motor Control Switch	BLMT
1Q	2	W/GN	Brake ON/OFF Switch	BOO
1R	30	LG/BK	Park/Neutral Position Signal	PNPS
1S	8	GN	Reduce Torque Signal #1 (From TCM)	RTS1
1T	18	BR	Idle Switch	IDL
1V	11	LG/W	Reduce Torque Signal #2 (From TCM)	RTS2
2A	45	GN/O	Barometric Pressure Sensor Signal	BARO
2B	44	R	Measuring Core Volume Air Flow Sensor	MC-VAF
2C	29	BK/Y	Right Heated Oxygen Sensor	RHO2S
2D	43	BL/W	Left Heated Oxygen Sensor	LHO2S
2E	7	R/GN	Engine Coolant Temperature Sensor	ECT
2F	47	Y	Throttle Position Sensor	TP
2G	50	R/W	Cooling Fan Engine Coolant Temperature Sensor	ECTF
2H	9	PK/Y	High Pressure Switch	HPS
2I	26	P	Reference Voltage	VREF
2J	27	R/BK	EGR Valve Position Sensor	EVP
2K	25	BK/R	Intake Air Temperature Sensor	IAT
2L	28	GN	Daytime Running Lamp (Canada Only)	DRL
2M	23	W	Knock Sensor	KS
2O	31	BL/BK	Canister Purge Solenoid	CANP
2P	54	BL/GN	High Cooling Fan Relay	HFAN
3A	40, 60	BK	Ground	GND
3B	20	BK	Ground	GND

FM0159301067010X

Fig. 54   PCM connector pin usage (Part 1 of 2). 1993–95 2.5L/V6-152 w/auto. trans.

PCM Pin	Breakout Box Pin	Wire Color	Application	Abbrev.
3C	49	BK/R	Ground	GND
3D	46	BK/BL	Ground	GND
3E	56	LG/O	Crankshaft Position Sensor #1	CKP1
3F	16	BL	Crankshaft Position Signal Return	CKPRTN
3G	6	BL/PK	Cylinder Identification Sensor	CID
3H	4	GN	Crankshaft Position Sensor #2	CKP2
3I	42	W/GN	Variable Resonance Induction System Solenoid #1	VRIS1
3J	35	BL/R	Variable Resonance Induction System Solenoid #2	VRIS2
3L	55	R/W	Low Cooling Fan Relay	LFAN
3M	21A	GN/BK	Fuel Pressure Regulator Control Solenoid	FPRC
3N	53A	BL/O	Condenser Fan Relay	CFAN
3O	33A	W/BL	EGR Vent Solenoid	EGRV
3P	52A	GN/W	EGR Control Solenoid	EGRC
3Q	21B	LG/BK	Idle Air Control Solenoid	IAC
3T	52B	LG	Fuel Pump Relay	FPR
3U	58	R/LG	Injector #1	INJ1
3V	59	BL/W	Injector #2	INJ2
3W	12	BR	Injector #3	INJ3
3X	13	R/Y	Injector #4	INJ4
3Y	14	W	Injector #5	INJ5
3Z	15	W/BK	Injector #6	INJ6

FM0159301067020X

Fig. 54   PCM connector pin usage (Part 2 of 2). 1993–95 2.5L/V6-152 w/auto. trans.

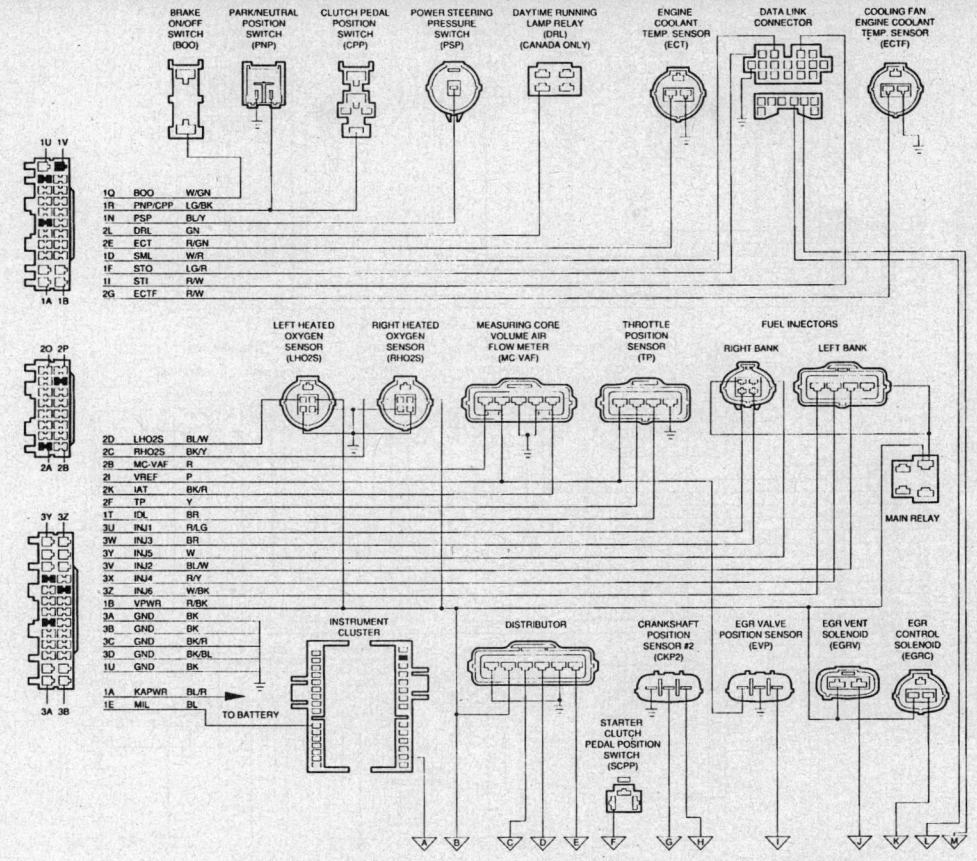

Fig. 55 EEC wiring diagram (Part 1 of 2). 1993 2.5L/V6-152 w/manual trans.

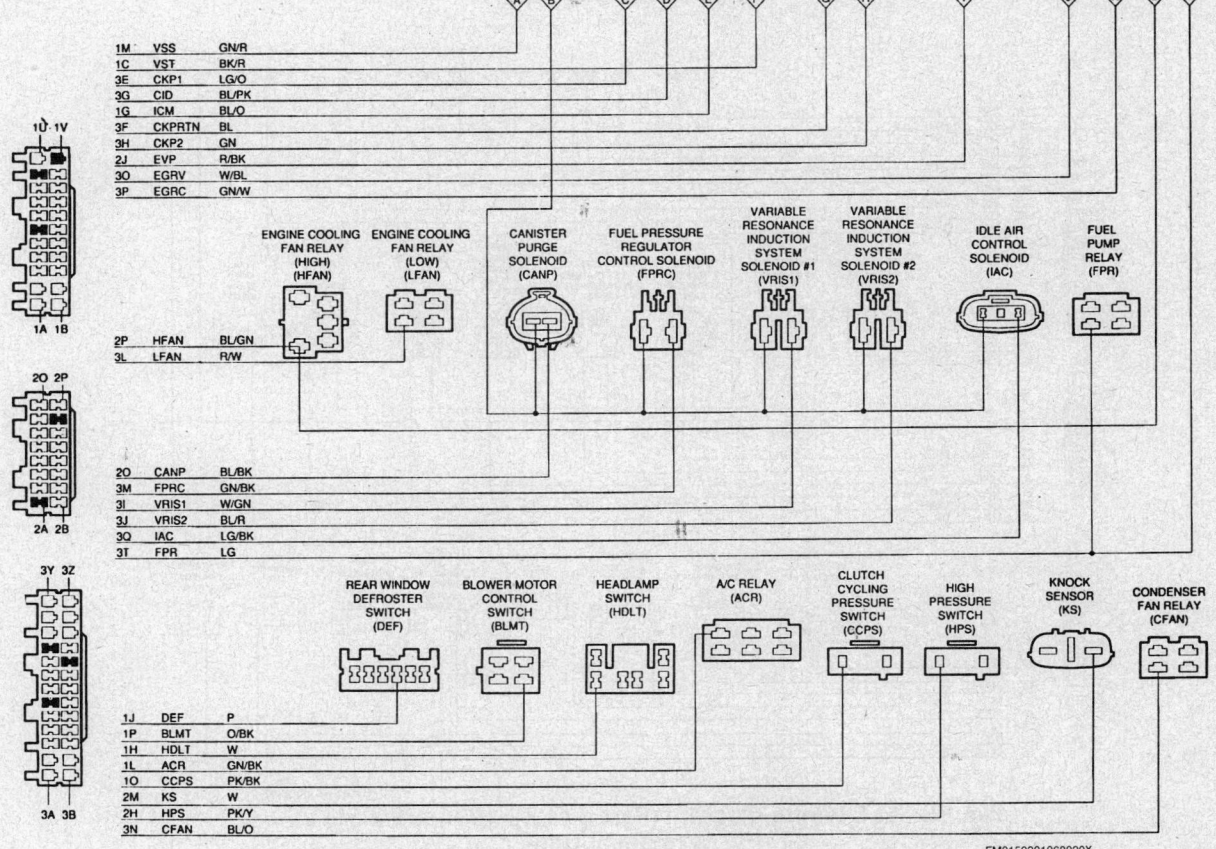

Fig. 55 EEC wiring diagram (Part 2 of 2). 1993 2.5L/V6-152 w/manual trans.

COMPUTERIZED ENGINE CONTROLS (ASPIRE, CAPRI, ESCORT & TRACER (1.8L/4-112), FESTIVA & PROBE (2.0L/4-121
w/4EAT & 2.5L/V6-152) ELECTRONIC ENGINE CONTROL (EEC) SYSTEM

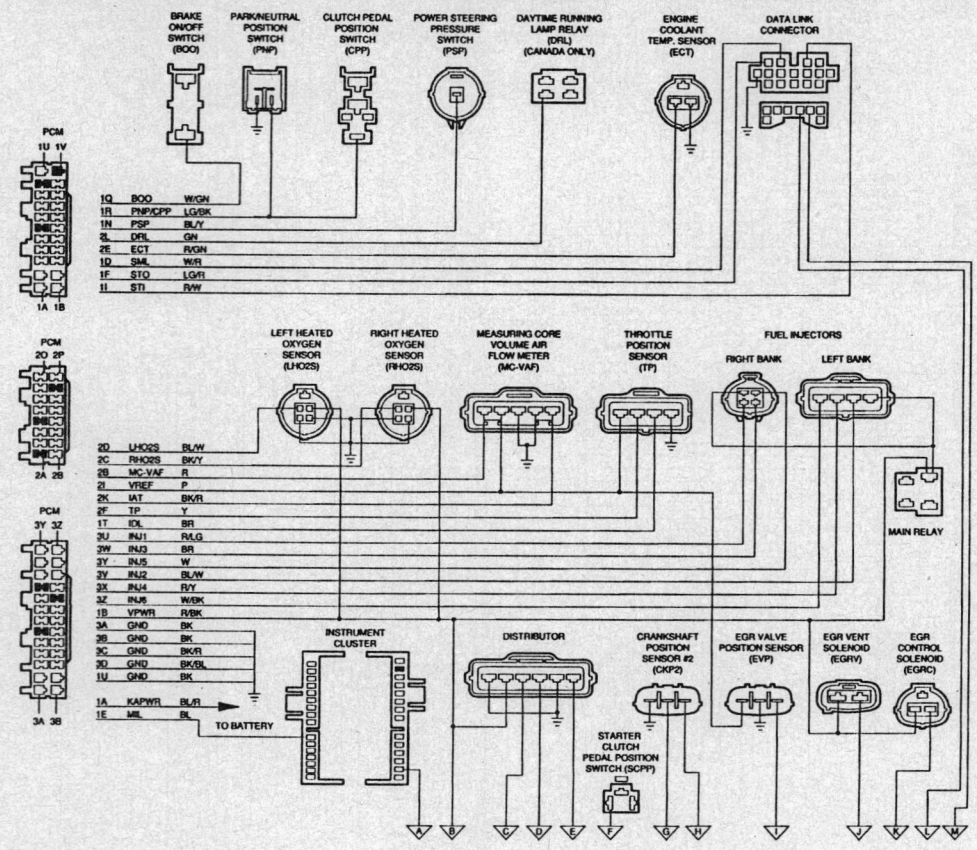

Fig. 56 EEC wiring diagram (Part 1 of 2). 1994–95 2.5L/V6-152 w/ manual trans.

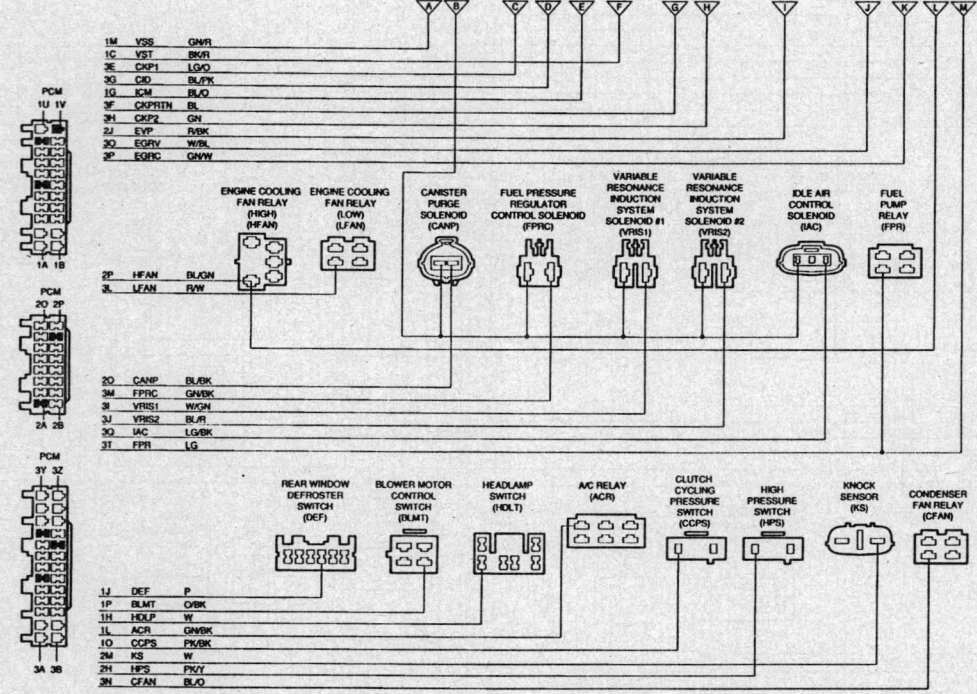

Fig. 56 EEC wiring diagram (Part 2 of 2). 1994–95 2.5L/V6-152 w/manual trans.

PCM Pin	Breakout Box Pin	Wire Color	Application	Abbrev.
1A	1	BL/R	Keep Alive Power	KAPWR
1B	37, 57	R/BK	Vehicle Power	VPWR
1C	5	BK/R	Vehicle Start	VST
1D	38	W/R	Switch Monitor Lamp	SML
1E	51	BL	Malfunction Indicator Lamp	MIL
1F	17	LG/R	Self Test Output	STO
1G	36	BL/O	Ignition Control Module	ICM
1H	32	W	Headlamp Switch	HDLT
1I	48	R/W	Self Test Input	STI
1J	34	P	Rear Window Defroster Switch	DEF
1L	10	GN/BK	A/C Relay	ACR
1M	3	GN/R	Vehicle Speed Sensor	VSS
1N	24	BL/Y	Power Steering Pressure Switch	PSP
1O	41	PK/BK	Clutch Cycling Pressure Switch	CCPS
1P	22	O/BK	Blower Motor Control Switch	BLMT
1Q	2	W/GN	Brake ON/OFF Switch	BOO
1R	30	LG/BK	Park Neutral Position Switch/Clutch Pedal Position Switch	PNP/CPP
1T	18	BR	Idle Switch	IDL
1U	39	BK	Ground (MTX)	GND
2B	44	R	Measuring Core Volume Air Flow Sensor	MC-VAF
2C	29	BK/Y	Right Heated Oxygen Sensor	RHO2S
2D	43	BL/W	Left Heated Oxygen Sensor	LHO2S
2E	7	R/GN	Engine Coolant Temperature Sensor	ECT
2F	47	Y	Throttle Position Sensor	TP
2G	50	R/W	Cooling Fan Engine Coolant Temperature Sensor	ECTF
2H	9	PK/Y	High Pressure Switch	HPS
2I	26	P	Reference Voltage	VREF
2J	27	R/BK	EGR Valve Position Sensor	EVP
2K	25	BK/R	Intake Air Temperature Sensor	IAT
2L	28	GN	Daytime Running Lamp (Canada Only)	DRL
2M	23	W	Knock Sensor	KS
2O	31	BL/BK	Canister Purge Solenoid	CANP
2P	54	BL/GN	High Cooling Fan Relay	HFAN
3A	40, 60	BK	Ground	GND
3B	20	BK	Ground	GND
3C	49	BK/R	Ground	GND
3D	46	BK/BL	Ground	GND
3E	56	LG/O	Crankshaft Position Sensor #1	CKP1

FM0159301070010X

Fig. 57 PCM connector pin usage (Part 1 of 2). 1993–94 2.5L/V6-152 w/manual trans.

PCM Pin	Breakout Box Pin	Wire Color	Application	Abbrev.
3F	16	BL	Crankshaft Position Signal Return	CKPRTN
3G	6	BL/PK	Cylinder Identification Sensor	CID
3H	4	GN	Crankshaft Position Sensor #2	CKP2
3I	42	W/GN	Variable Resonance Induction System Solenoid #1	VRIS1
3J	35	BL/R	Variable Resonance Induction System Solenoid #2	VRIS2
3L	55	R/W	Low Cooling Fan Relay	LFAN
3M	21A	GN/BK	Fuel Pressure Regulator Control Solenoid	FPRC
3N	53A	BL/O	Condenser Fan Relay	CFAN
3O	33A	W/BL	EGR Vent Solenoid	EGRV
3P	52A	GN/W	EGR Control Solenoid	EGRC
3Q	21B	LG/BK	Idle Air Control Solenoid	IAC
3T	52B	LG	Fuel Pump Relay	FPR
3U	58	R/LG	Injector #1	INJ1
3V	59	BL/W	Injector #2	INJ2
3W	12	BR	Injector #3	INJ3
3X	13	R/Y	Injector #4	INJ4
3Y	14	W	Injector #5	INJ5
3Z	15	W/BK	Injector #6	INJ6

FM0159301070020X

Fig. 57 PCM connector pin usage (Part 2 of 2). 1993–94 2.5L/V6-152 w/manual trans.

Diagnostic Trouble Code	Diagnostic Trouble Code Definition
02	Crankshaft Position Sensor (CKP)
08	Volume Air Flow (VAF) Signal
09	Engine Coolant Temperature (ECT) Sensor
10	Intake Air Temperature (IAT) Sensor
14	Barometric Pressure (BARO) Sensor
15	Oxygen Sensor (O2S) - voltage always below 0.55V
17	Oxygen Sensor (O2S) - voltage does not change
26	Canister Purge (CANP) Solenoid
34	Idle Air Control (IAC) Solenoid
"STO LO" always ON	Not able to initiate diagnostic test mode
"STI LO" always ON and no codes (Blank SUPER STAR II screen)	Pass Code

FM0159301071000X

Fig. 58 Quick test codes & code definition. 1993 1.3L/4-81

PCM Diagnostic Trouble Code	Diagnostic Trouble Code Definition
03	Cylinder Identification (CID) Sensor
04	Crankshaft Position Sensor (CKP)
06	Vehicle Speed Sensor (VSS)
08	Mass Air Flow (MAF) Sensor
09	Engine Coolant Temperature (ECT) Sensor
10	Intake Air Temperature (IAT) Sensor
12	Throttle Position (TP) Sensor
14	Barometric Pressure (BARO) Sensor
15	Oxygen Sensor (O2S) Voltage Below 0.55V
16	EGR Valve Position (EVP) Sensor
17	Oxygen Sensor (O2S) Voltage Does Not Change
"STO LO" always ON	Not able to initiate diagnostic test mode
"STI LO" always ON and no codes (Blank Super STAR II screen)	Pass Code

FM0159301072000X

Fig. 59 Quick test codes & code definition. 1994 1.3L/4-81

PCM Diagnostic Trouble Code	Diagnostic Trouble Code Definition
03	Camshaft Position (CMP) Sensor
04	Crankshaft Position (CKP) Sensor
06	Vehicle Speed Sensor (VSS)
08	Mass Air Flow (MAF) Sensor
09	Engine Coolant Temperature (ECT) Sensor
10	Intake Air Temperature (IAT) Sensor
12	Throttle Position (TP) Sensor
14	Barometric Pressure (BARO) Sensor
15	Oxygen Sensor (O2S) Voltage Below 0.55V
16	EGR Valve Position Sensor
17	Oxygen Sensor (O2S) Voltage Does Not Change
25	EVAP Canister Purge Solenoid
26	EGR Control (EGRC) Solenoid
28	EGR Vent (EGRV) Solenoid
29	Idle Air Control (IAC) Solenoid
"STO LO" always ON	Not Able to Initiate Diagnostic Test Mode
"STI LO" always ON and no codes (Blank Super Star II screen)	Pass Code

FM0159301222000X

Fig. 60 Quick test codes & code definition. 1995 1.3L/4-81

PCM Diagnostic Trouble Code	Diagnostic Trouble Code Definition
01	Ignition Diagnostic Monitor (IDM)
03	Cylinder Identification (CID) Sensor
08	Volume Air Flow (VAF) Meter
09	Engine Coolant Temperature (ECT) Sensor
10	Intake Air Temperature (IAT) Sensor
12	Throttle Position (TP) Sensor
14	Barometric Pressure (BARO) Sensor
15	Oxygen Sensor (O2S) - voltage always below 0.55V (Lean)
17	Oxygen Sensor (O2S) - voltage has not changed 30 sec. after the engine exceeds 1,500 RPM
25	Fuel Pressure Regulator Control (FPRC) Solenoid
26	Canister Purge (CANP) Solenoid
34	Idle Air Control (IAC) Solenoid
"STO LO" always ON	Not able to initiate diagnostic test mode
"STI LO" always ON and no codes (Blank SUPER STAR II screen)	Pass Code

FM0159301073000X

Fig. 61 Quick test codes & code definition. 1993–94 1.6L/4-98

PCM Diagnostic Trouble Code	Diagnostic Trouble Code Definition
02	Crankshaft Position Sensor # 2 (CKP2)
03	Cylinder Identification (CID) Sensor
04	Crankshaft Position Sensor # 1 (CKP1)
05	Knock Sensor (KS)
08	Measuring Core Volume Air Flow (MC-VAF) Sensor
09	Engine Coolant Temperature (ECT) Sensor
10	Intake Air Temperature (IAT) Sensor
12	Throttle Position (TP) Sensor
14	Barometric Pressure (BARO) Sensor
15	Left Heated Oxygen Sensor (LHO2S) Voltage Always Below 0.55V
16	EGR Valve Position (EVP) Sensor
17	Left Heated Oxygen Sensor (LHO2S) Voltage Does Not Change
23	Right Heated Oxygen Sensor (RHO2S) Voltage Always Below 0.55V
24	Right Heated Oxygen Sensor (RHO2S) Voltage Does Not Change
25	Fuel Pressure Regulator Control (FPRC) Solenoid
26	Canister Purge (CANP) Solenoid
28	EGR Control (EGRC) Solenoid
29	EGR Vent (EGRV) Solenoid
34	Idle Air Control (IAC) Solenoid
41	Variable Resonance Induction System (VRIS) Solenoid # 1
46	Variable Resonance Induction System (VRIS) Solenoid # 2
67	Low Cooling Fan (LFAN) Relay
69	Cooling Fan Engine Coolant Temperature (ECTF) Sensor
"STO LO" always ON	Not able to initiate diagnostic test mode
"STO LO" always ON and no codes (Blank SUPER STAR II screen)	Pass Code

FM0159301074000X

Fig. 62 Quick test codes & code definition. 1993–95 1.8L/4-112

Diagnostic Trouble Code	Diagnostic Trouble Code Definition
02	Crankshaft Position (CKP) Sensor
03	Cylinder Identification (CID) Sensor
06	Vehicle Speed (VSS) Sensor
08	Mass Air Flow (MAF) Sensor
09	Engine Coolant Temperature (ECT) Sensor
11	Intake Air Temperature (IAT) Sensor
12	Throttle Position (TP) Sensor
14	Barometric Pressure (BARO) Sensor
15	Heated Oxygen Sensor (HO2S) Voltage Always Below 0.55V
16	EGR Temperature (EGRT) Sensor
17	Heated Oxygen Sensor (HO2S) Voltage Does Not Change
25	Fuel Pressure Regulator Control (FPRC) Solenoid
26	Canister Purge (CANP) Solenoid
28	EGR Vacuum Regulator (EVR) Solenoid
34	Idle Air Control (IAC) Solenoid
55	Pulse Signal Generator (PSG)
56	Transaxle Oil Temperature (TOT) Sensor
60	1-2 Shift Solenoid (SS1)
61	2-3 Shift Solenoid (SS2)
62	3-4 Shift Solenoid (SS3)
63	Torque Converter Clutch Control (TCCC) Solenoid
64	Downshift Solenoid (DSS)
65	Torque Converter Clutch (TCC) Solenoid
66	Line Pressure Solenoid (LPS)
67	Low Cooling Fan (LFAN) Relay
68	High Cooling Fan (HFAN) Relay
69	Cooling Fan Engine Coolant Temperature (ECTF) Sensor
"STO LO" always ON	Not able to initiate diagnostic test mode
"STO LO" always ON and no codes (Blank SUPER STAR II screen)	Pass Code

FM0159301075000X

Fig. 63 Quick test codes & code definition. 1993 2.0L/4-121 w/auto. trans.

PCM Diagnostic Trouble Code	Diagnostic Trouble Code Definition
02	Crankshaft Position Sensor # 2 (CKP2)
03	Cylinder Identification (CID) Sensor
04	Crankshaft Position Sensor # 1 (CKP1)
05	Knock Sensor (KS)
08	Measuring Core Volume Air Flow (MC-VAF) Sensor
09	Engine Coolant Temperature (ECT) Sensor
10	Intake Air Temperature (IAT) Sensor
12	Throttle Position (TP) Sensor
14	Barometric Pressure (BARO) Sensor
15	Left Heated Oxygen Sensor (LHO2S) Voltage Always Below 0.55V
16	EGR Valve Position (EVP) Sensor
17	Left Heated Oxygen Sensor (LHO2S) Voltage Does Not Change
23	Right Heated Oxygen Sensor (RHO2S) Voltage Always Below 0.55V
24	Right Heated Oxygen Sensor (RHO2S) Voltage Does Not Change
25	Fuel Pressure Regulator Control (FPRC) Solenoid
26	Canister Purge (CANP) Solenoid
28	EGR Control (EGRC) Solenoid
29	EGR Vent (EGRV) Solenoid
34	Idle Air Control (IAC) Solenoid
41	Variable Resonance Induction System (VRIS) Solenoid # 1
46	Variable Resonance Induction System (VRIS) Solenoid # 2
67	Low Cooling Fan (LFAN) Relay
69	Cooling Fan Engine Coolant Temperature (ECTF) Sensor
"STO LO" always ON	Not able to initiate diagnostic test mode
"STO LO" always ON and no codes (Blank Super STAR II screen)	Pass Code

FM0159301076000X

Fig. 64 Quick test codes & code definition. 1993–94 2.5L/V6-152

PCM Diagnostic Trouble Code	Diagnostic Trouble Code Definition
02	Crankshaft Position Sensor # 2 (CKP2)
03	Camshaft Position (CMP) Sensor
04	Crankshaft Position Sensor # 1 (CKP1)
05	Knock Sensor (KS)
08	Measuring Core Volume Air Flow (MC-VAF) Sensor
09	Engine Coolant Temperature (ECT) Sensor
10	Intake Air Temperature (IAT) Sensor
12	Throttle Position (TP) Sensor
14	Barometric Pressure (BARO) Sensor
15	Left Heated Oxygen Sensor (LHO2S) - voltage always below 0.55V
16	EGR Valve Position Sensor
17	Left Heated Oxygen Sensor (LHO2S) Voltage does not change
23	Right Heated Oxygen Sensor (RHO2S) - voltage always below 0.55V
24	Right Heated Oxygen Sensor (RHO2S) - voltage does not change
25	Fuel Pressure Regulator Control (FPRC) Solenoid
26	EVAP Canister Purge (CANP) Solenoid
28	EGR Control (EGRC) Solenoid
29	EGR Vent (EGRV) Solenoid
34	Idle Air Control (IAC) Solenoid
41	Variable Resonance Induction System (VRIS) Solenoid # 1
46	Variable Resonance Induction System (VRIS) Solenoid # 2
67	Low Fan Control (FC) Relay
"STO LO" always ON	Not able to initiate diagnostic test mode
"STO LO" always ON and no codes (Blank Super STAR II screen)	Pass Code

FM0159501223000X

Fig. 65 Quick test codes & code definition. 1995 2.5L/V6-152

TEST STEP		RESULT	▶	ACTION TO TAKE
QT1	PERFORM VISUAL INSPECTION			
	• Inspect the air cleaner and inlet ducting, tubes, and clamps. • Check all engine vacuum hoses for damage, leaks, cracks, blockage, improper routing, etc. • Check the PCM wiring harness for improper connections, bent or broken pins, corrosion, loose wires, improper routing, blown fuses, etc. • Check the processor, sensors and actuators for physical damage. • Check the engine coolant for proper level. • Check the engine oil level and quality. • Check the battery voltage. Refer to Service Manual Section 14-01 for checking and charging procedures. • Do all components and fluids appear OK?	Yes No	▶ ▶	GO to QT2, Vehicle Preparation. SERVICE the fault(s) in the system as required and REEVALUATE the symptom(s).
QT2	PERFORM VEHICLE PREPARATION			
	• Perform all the following safety steps required to start and run vehicle tests: — Apply the parking brake. — Place the selector lever firmly into the PARK position (NEUTRAL on manual transaxle). — Block the drive wheels. • Turn off all electrical loads: — Radios — Lights — A/C — Rear window defroster — Heater, blower fans, etc. • Have all the safety steps been performed and all electrical loads been turned off?	Yes No	▶ ▶	GO to QT3, Equipment Hookup. Personal safety and correct diagnostic results are dependent on test step QT2. MAKE all the necessary repairs to perform vehicle preparation.

FM0159301077000X

Fig. 66 Quick test QT1 & QT2, visual inspection & vehicle preparation. 1993–94

TEST STEP	RESULT	▶	ACTION TO TAKE
QT3 | PERFORM EQUIPMENT HOOKUP			
• If using New Generation Star (NGS) Scan Tool	Yes	▶	GO to QT4, Key ON, Engine Off Test.
— Key OFF.	No	▶	SERVICE the fault(s) as necessary and REPEAT QT3
— Connect the DLC Adapter to the Diagnostic Data Link (DDL) connector on the NGS Scan Tool.			
— Connect Rotunda Super MECS Adapter 007-00052 to the DLC Adapter. Refer to the art on the following pages.			
— Connect the adapter cable leads to the STO and STI connectors on 1.3L and 1.6L engines or to the Data Link Connector (DLC) on the 1.8L, 2.0L 4EAT and 2.5L engines.			
— Connect the adapter cable ground clip to the negative (-) battery terminal for the 1.3L and 1.6L engines.			
— Slide the adapter switch on the Super MECS Adapter to the PCM position for the 1.8L, 2.0L 4EAT and 2.5L engines.			
— Connect the NGS Power Cable to the battery with the battery adapter.			
• If using SUPER STAR II Tester			
— Key OFF.			
— Connect Rotunda Super MECS Adapter 007-00052 to the SUPER STAR II Tester. Refer to the art on the following pages. The previously issued Rotunda Adapter 007-00036 may still be used on the 1.3L and 1.6L engines while Rotunda Adapter 007-00049 may be used on the 1.8L, 2.0L 4EAT and 2.5L engines.			
— Connect the adapter cable leads to the STO and STI connectors on 1.3L and 1.6L engines or to the Data Link Connector (DLC) on the 1.8L, 2.0L 4EAT and 2.5L engines.			
— Connect the adapter cable ground clip to the negative (-) battery terminal for the 1.3L and 1.6L engines.			
— Slide the adapter switch on the Super MECS adapter to the PCM position for the 1.8L, 2.0L 4EAT and 2.5L engines.			
— Slide the SUPER STAR II Tester switch to the MECS position.			
• Is equipment hooked up properly?			

FM0159301078010X

Fig. 67   Quick test QT3, equipment hook-up (Part 1 of 4). 1993–94

TEST STEP	RESULT	▶	ACTION TO TAKE
QT3 | PERFORM EQUIPMENT HOOKUP (CONTINUED)			
• If using Analog VOM	Yes	▶	GO to QT4, Key ON, Engine Off Test.
— Key OFF.	No	▶	SERVICE the fault(s) as necessary and REPEAT QT3.
— Connect the VOM positive (+) lead to the PCM STO line and the negative (-) lead to engine ground.			
— Jumper the PCM STI to engine ground.			
— Set the VOM on a DC voltage range to read from 0 to 20 volts.			
• If using Malfunction Indicator Lamp (MIL)			
NOTE: If the MIL flashes continuously prior to equipment hookup, go to EEC Pinpoint Test STI.			
— To use the MIL, jumper the PCM STI line to engine ground.			
• Is equipment hooked up properly?			

FM0159301078020X

Fig. 67   Quick test QT3, equipment hook-up (Part 2 of 4). 1993–94

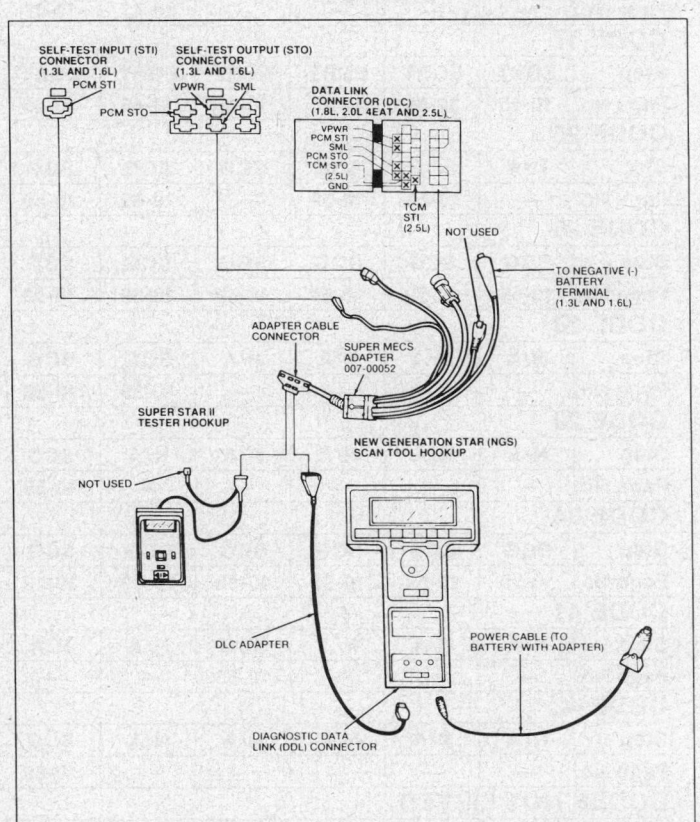

FM0159301078030X

Fig. 67   Quick test QT3, equipment hook-up (Part 3 of 4). 1993–94

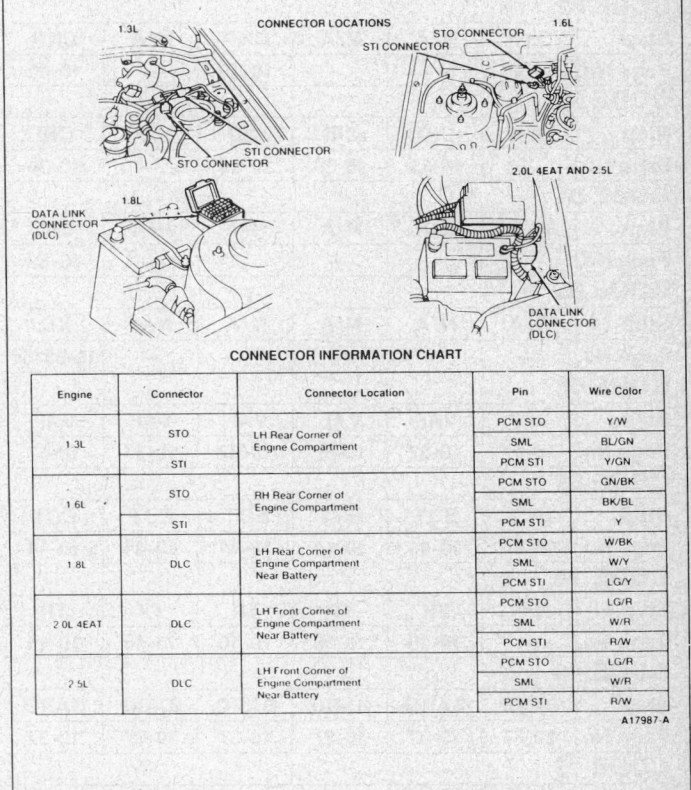

FM0159301078040X

Fig. 67   Quick test QT3, equipment hook-up (Part 4 of 4). 1993–94

COMPUTERIZED ENGINE CONTROLS (ASPIRE, CAPRI, ESCORT & TRACER (1.8L/4-112), FESTIVA & PROBE (2.0L/4-121 w/4EAT & 2.5L/V6-152) ELECTRONIC ENGINE CONTROL (EEC) SYSTEM

10-29

TEST STEP		RESULT	▶	ACTION TO TAKE
QT4	PERFORM KEY ON ENGINE OFF TEST			
• Follow one of the test procedures based on the type of equipment used:		Code(s)	▶	GO to QT5.
NOTE: When performing the Diagnostic Test Mode on the 1.8L 4EAT or 2.0L 4EAT, either engine or transaxle codes can be received. Refer to the 4EAT Quick Test in this section for a list of transaxle related codes.		STAR Tester always displays STO LO, or VOM always displays 0 volts		GO to EEC Pinpoint Test STI.
• If using New Generation Star (NGS) Scan Tool		No codes and engine starts	▶	GO to QT6, Key ON Engine Running Test.
— Follow the procedure in the appendix to activate and deactivate the Diagnostic Test Mode.		No codes and no start	▶	GO to QT10.
• If using SUPER STAR II Tester				
— Latch the center button to the TEST position.				
— Turn the SUPER STAR II Tester ON. (The tester will sound and "888" will be displayed for two seconds.)				
— Key ON.				
— Unlatch and relatch the center test button.				
— After all codes are received, unlatch the center button to review all codes retained in tester memory.				
— Record the diagnostic trouble codes.				
• If using Analog VOM				
— Key ON.				
— Turn the VCM ON.				
— Observe the VOM needle for any code indications				
— Record the diagnostic trouble codes.				
• If using Malfunction Indicator Lamp (MIL)				
— Key ON.				
— Observe the MIL				
— Record the diagnostic trouble codes.				

FM015930107900X

Fig. 68   Quick test QT4, key On/engine Off test. 1993–94

TEST STEP		RESULT	▶	ACTION TO TAKE
QT5	ERASE AND RETEST			
NOTE: Erasing diagnostic trouble codes and retesting will give an indication whether diagnostic trouble codes received in test step QT4 represent hard or intermittent faults. Hard faults will repeat immediately and codes will be displayed during retest.		Code(s)	▶	GO to QT7 and REFER to the Diagnostic Trouble Code Chart for Pinpoint Test direction.
• Confirm code(s) were received in test step QT4.		No Code(s)	▶	GO to QT6, Key ON Engine Running Test.
• Turn the SUPER STAR II Tester or VOM OFF, or disconnect the NGS Scan Tool.		No codes and no start	▶	GO to QT10.
• Disconnect the negative battery cable and depress the brake pedal for 5-10 seconds to erase codes in memory.				
• Perform the Key ON Engine Off Test as instructed in test step QT4.				
NOTE: If codes retrieved the first time cannot be re-created, it may be necessary to tap suspect sensors, shake and wiggle harness, or drive the vehicle in order to induce a failure. Repeat step QT4 each time.				
• Record the diagnostic trouble codes.				
QT6	PERFORM KEY ON ENGINE RUNNING TEST			
NOTE: If using the New Generation Star (NGS) Scan Tool, activate and deactivate the Diagnostic Test Mode.		Code(s)	▶	GO to QT7 and REFER to the Diagnostic Trouble Code Chart for Pinpoint Test direction.
• Deactivate the Diagnostic Test Mode by unlatching the center button on the SUPER STAR II Tester and turning the tester OFF or disconnect the jumper connecting PCM STI to ground.		No Codes and sent here by QT4	▶	GO to QT8, Switch Monitor Test.
• Run the engine at 2000 rpm for three minutes.		No Codes and sent here by QT5	▶	EEC Intermittent Fault
• If using Super Star II Tester, turn the SUPER STAR II Tester ON.				
• Latch the center button on the SUPER STAR II Tester or jumper the PCM STI to ground if using VOM or MIL.				
• Turn the engine off.				
• Start the engine and run the engine at idle.				
• Activate the Diagnostic Test Mode by unlatching and relatching the SUPER STAR II Tester.				
• Record the diagnostic trouble codes.				

FM015930108000X

Fig. 69   Quick test QT5 & QT6, erase & retest & key On/engine running test. 1993–94

Service Code/Step/Page No.	1.3L/4-81 EFI	1.6L/4-98 Non-Turbo	1.6L/4-98 Turbo	1.8L/4-112 EFI	2.2L Non-Turbo	2.2L Turbo
CODE 01						
Step	N/A	IDM	IDM	N/A	IDM	IDM
Page No.	—	10-52	10-52	—	10-52	10-52
CODE 02						
Step	CKP	N/A	N/A	CKP	N/A	CKP
Page No.	10-40	—	—	10-40	—	10-40
CODE 03						
Step	N/A	CID	CID	CID	N/A	CID
Page No.	—	10-39	10-39	10-39	—	10-39
CODE 04						
Step	N/A	N/A	N/A	N/A	N/A	CID
Page No.	—	—	—	—	—	10-39
CODE 05						
Step	N/A	N/A	N/A	N/A	N/A	KC
Page No.	—	—	—	—	—	10-53/54
CODE 08						
Step	VAF	VAF	VAF	VAF	VAF	VAF
Page No.	10-67	10-67	10-67	10-67	10-67	10-67
CODE 09						
Step	ECT	ECT	ECT	ECT	ECT	ECT
Page No.	10-44	10-44	10-44	10-44	10-44	10-44
CODE 12						
Step	N/A	TP	TP	TP	TP	TP
Page No.	—	10-46	10-46	10-46	10-46	10-46
CODE 14						
Step	BARO	BARO	BARO	BARO	BARO	BARO
Page No.	10-37	10-37	10-37	10-37	10-37	10-37
CODE 15						
Step	EGR	EGRT	EGRT	EGRT	EGRT	EGRT
Page No.	10-45	10-45	10-45	10-45	10-45	10-45

Service Code/Step/Page No.	1.3L/4-81 EFI	1.6L/4-98 Non-Turbo	1.6L/4-98 Turbo	1.8L/4-112 EFI	2.2L Non-Turbo	2.2L Turbo
CODE 16						
Step	N/A	N/A	N/A	N/A	EVP	EVP
Page No.	—	—	—	—	10-47	10-47
CODE 17						
Step	EGRT	EGRT	EGRT	EGRT	EGRT	EGRT
Page No.	10-45	10-45	10-45	10-45	10-45	10-45
CODE 25						
Step	N/A	SCG	SCG	SCG	SCG	SCG
Page No.	—	10-59	10-59	10-59	10-59	10-59
CODE 26						
Step	SCG	SCG	SCG	SCG	SCG	SCG
Page No.	10-59	10-59	10-59	10-59	10-59	10-59
CODE 28						
Step	N/A	N/A	N/A	N/A	SCG	SCG
Page No.	—	—	—	—	10-59	10-59
CODE 29						
Step	N/A	N/A	N/A	N/A	N/A	SCG
Page No.	—	—	—	—	—	10-59
CODE 34						
Step	SCG	SCG	SCG	SCG	SCG	SCG
Page No.	10-59	10-59	10-59	10-59	10-59	10-59
CODE 41						
Step	N/A	N/A	N/A	SCG	N/A	N/A
Page No.	—	—	—	10-59	—	—
CODE 42						
Step	N/A	N/A	N/A	N/A	N/A	SCG
Page No.	—	—	—	—	—	10-59
CODES NOT LISTED						
Step	PGC	PGC	PGC	PGC	PGC	PGC
Page No.	10-57	10-57	10-57	10-57	10-57	10-57

Fig. 69   Quick test QT7, diagnostic trouble code service chart. 1993–94

TEST STEP		RESULT	▶	ACTION TO TAKE
QT8	PERFORM SWITCH MONITOR TEST	All switches OK	▶	GO to QT11, Component Verification Test.
	NOTE: If using the New Generation Star (NGS) Scan Tool, activate and deactivate the Switch Monitor Test. • The Switch Monitor Test checks input signals from the individual input switches to the PCM. • Test all switches individually - leaving a switch ON while testing another will lead to a false test result. • Turn engine off, and allow to cool before starting Switch Monitor Test. • If using Super Star II Tester, deactivate Diagnostic Test Mode by unlatching the center button of the SUPER STAR II Tester and turning the tester OFF. • Turn all accessories off. • Apply the parking brake. • Place transaxle in NEUTRAL or PARK. • Key ON. • If using SUPER STAR II Tester, leave tester connected, turn tester ON, latch center button, and watch the output of the LED on the adapter cable as each switch is exercised. • If using VOM, jumper PCM STI to ground, connect VOM(+) lead to SML line and (-) lead to engine ground. (See illustration in QT3). • Exercise all switches listed in QT9 and record results.	All switches fail	▶	GO to EEC Pinpoint Test SML
		One or more switches fail	▶	GO to EEC Pinpoint Test(s) for all switches that fail. REFER to Test Step QT9 for the list of Pinpoint Tests.

FM0159301081000X

Fig. 70 Quick test QT8, switch monitor test. 1993–94

TEST STEP	RESULT	▶	ACTION TO TAKE
QT9 SWITCH MONITOR TEST CHART			

Switch/Relay	1.3L	1.6L Non-Turbo	1.6L Turbo	1.8L	2.0L 4EAT	2.5L	Condition	Super Star II Tester / NGS Scan Tool LED, or Analog VOM Indication	EEC Pinpoint Test
A/C Selector (ACS) Switch	X	X	X	X	X	X	A/C selector switch on (and blower on for 1.3L, 1.6L and 1.8L)	LED on, or less than 1.5 volts	STG
Blower Motor (BLMT) Switch	X	X	X	X	X	X	Blower switch on 2nd or above position for 1.3L, 1.6L, 1.8L and 3rd or Hi position with mode switch on for 2.0L and 2.5L	LED on, or less than 1.5 volts	STG (ELU for 1.6L)
Brake ON/OFF (BOO) Switch	X	X	X	X MTX	X	X	Brake pedal depressed	LED on, or less than 1.5 volts	STP
Coolant Temperature Switch (CTS)	X	X	X		X		Cooling fan on low speed (ground fan if necessary)	LED on, or less than 1.5 volts	STP (ELU for 1.6L)
Daytime Running Lamp (DRL) Relay (Canada Only)						X	Parking brake released	LED on, or less than 1.5 volts	DRL
Headlamp (HDLP) Switch	X	X	X	X	X	X	Headlamp switch on	LED on, or less than 1.5 volts	STP (ELU for 1.6L)
High Cooling Fan (HFAN) Relay				X	X		Accelerator pedal depressed (fan should operate at high speed)	LED on, or less than 1.5 volts	ROC
Idle (IDL) Switch	X	X	X	X	X		Accelerator pedal depressed	LED on, or less than 1.5 volts	STG
Knock Control (KC)			X				Tap on engine lift bracket while engine running	LED on, or less than 1.5 volts	KC
Low Cooling Fan (LFAN) Relay				X			A C selector switch on (fan should operate at low speed)	LED on, or less than 1.5 volts	ROC

FM0159301082010X

Fig. 71 Quick test QT9 & QT10, switch monitor test chart & check no start symptom (Part 1 of 2). 1993–94

TEST STEP	RESULT	▶	ACTION TO TAKE
QT9 SWITCH MONITOR TEST CHART (CONTINUED)			

Switch/Relay	1.3L	1.6L Non-Turbo	1.6L Turbo	1.8L	2.0L 4EAT	2.5L	Condition	Super Star II Tester / NGS Scan Tool LED, or Analog VOM Indication	EEC Pinpoint Test
Manual Lever Position (MLP) Switch (ATX)	X	X		X	X	X	Selector lever in R, Ⓝ, D, L for 1.3L, 1.6L, 1.8L or R, D, 2, 1 for 2.0L, 2.5L	LED on, or less than 1.5 volts	STP
Overdrive OFF Switch (ODS)					X		Overdrive OFF switch depressed	LED on, or less than 1.5 volts	STG
Park/Neutral Position (PNP) Switch / Clutch Pedal Position (CPP) Switch (MTX)	X	X	X	X		X	Transaxle in gear and clutch pedal released	LED on, or less than 1.5 volts	STG
Rear Defroster (DEF) Switch	X	X	X	X	X	X	Rear defroster switch on	LED on, or less than 1.5 volts	STP (ELU for 1.6L)
Wide Open Throttle (WOT) Switch	X		X	X MTX			Accelerator pedal fully depressed	LED off, or 12 volts	STG

QT10	CHECK NO START SYMPTOM			
	• Key OFF. • Remove spark plug wire from # 1 spark plug. • Crank engine using ignition switch. • Repeat for all spark plug wires. • Were sparks present at all wires?	Yes	▶	GO to Section 9B, Fuel Delivery Systems.
		No	▶	GO to Section 8B, Ignition System Diagnostic Procedures.

FM0159301082020X

Fig. 71 Quick test QT9 & QT10, switch monitor test chart & check no start symptom (Part 2 of 2). 1993–94

TEST STEP		RESULT	▶	ACTION TO TAKE
QT11	COMPONENT VERIFICATION TEST	Yes	▶	REPEAT Test Step QT11 until all possible components have been checked. If all components check out OK, RETURN to the Diagnostic Routines.
	NOTE: Refer to EEC Engine Supplement — Car and Section 17B, Emission Related Components to aid in determining possible causes of the symptom. • Refer to EEC Pinpoint Test Procedures, and perform the EEC Pinpoint Test for each component that could cause the symptom. • Does each Pinpoint Test check out OK?	No	▶	SERVICE the fault(s) as indicated in Pinpoint Test and RECHECK the symptom(s).

FM0159301063000X

Fig. 72 Quick test QT11, component verification test. 1993–94

TEST STEP		RESULT	▶	ACTION TO TAKE
QT1	PERFORM VISUAL INSPECTION			
	• Inspect the air cleaner and inlet ducting, tubes, and clamps.	Yes	▶	GO to QT2, Vehicle Preparation.
	• Check all engine vacuum hoses for damage, leaks, cracks, blockage, improper routing, etc.	No	▶	SERVICE the fault(s) in the system as required and REEVALUATE the symptom(s).
	• Check the Powertrain Control Module (PCM) wiring harness for improper connections, bent or broken pins, corrosion, loose wires, improper routing, blown fuses, etc.			
	• Check the processor, sensors, and actuators for physical damage.			
	• Check the engine coolant for proper level.			
	• Check the engine oil level and quality.			
	• Check the battery voltage.			
	• Do all components and fluids appear OK?			
QT2	PERFORM VEHICLE PREPARATION			
	• Perform all the following safety steps required to start and run vehicle tests:	Yes (Using Rotunda New Generation Star [NGS] Tester)	▶	GO to QT3, Equipment Hookup.
	— Apply the parking brake.			
	— Place the selector lever firmly into the PARK (P) position (NEUTRAL [N] on manual transaxle).	Yes (Using Rotunda Super STAR II Tester)	▶	GO to QT4, Equipment Hookup.
	— Block the drive wheels.			
	• Turn off all electrical loads:	Yes (Using Analog VOM or Malfunction Indicator Lamp [MIL])	▶	GO to QT5, Equipment Hookup.
	— Radios			
	— Lights			
	— A/C			
	— Rear window defroster			
	— Heater, blower fans, etc.			
	• Have all the safety steps been performed and all electrical loads been turned off?		▶	Personal safety and correct diagnostic results are dependent on test step QT2. MAKE all the necessary repairs to perform vehicle preparation.

FM015950122400X

Fig. 73   Quick test QT1 & QT2, visual inspection & vehicle preparation. 1995

TEST STEP		RESULT	▶	ACTION TO TAKE
QT3	PERFORM EQUIPMENT HOOKUP (NGS TESTER ONLY)			
		Yes	▶	GO to QT6, Key ON, Engine Off Test.
	• Key OFF.	No	▶	SERVICE the fault(s) as necessary and REPEAT QT3.
	• Connect the Data Link Connector (DLC) Adapter to the Diagnostic Data Link (DDL) connector on the Rotunda NGS Tester 007-00500 or equivalent.			
	• Connect Rotunda Super MECS Adapter 007-00052 or equivalent to the DLC Adapter.			
	• Connect the adapter cable lead to the DLC.			
	• Slide the adapter switch on the Super MECS Adapter to the PCM position.			
	• Connect the NGS Power Cable to the battery with the battery adapter.			
	• Is the equipment hooked up properly?			
QT4	PERFORM EQUIPMENT HOOKUP (SUPER STAR II TESTER ONLY)			
		Yes	▶	GO to QT6, Key ON, Engine Off Test.
	• Key OFF.	No	▶	SERVICE the fault(s) as necessary and REPEAT QT4.
	• Connect Rotunda Super MECS Adapter 007-00052 or equivalent to the Rotunda Super STAR II Tester 007-0041B or equivalent. The previously issued Rotunda Adapter 007-00049 may be used.			
	• Connect the adapter cable lead to the DLC.			
	• Slide the adapter switch on the Super MECS adapter to the PCM position.			
	• Slide the Super STAR II Tester switch to the MECS position.			
	• Is the equipment hooked up properly?			

FM0159501225000X

Fig. 74   Quick test QT3 & QT4, Super Star & NGS tester hookup, 1995

TEST STEP		RESULT	▶	ACTION TO TAKE
QT5	PERFORM EQUIPMENT HOOKUP (ANALOG VOM OR MALFUNCTION INDICATOR LAMP ONLY)			
		Yes	▶	GO to QT6, Key ON, Engine Off Test.
	• If using Analog VOM:	No	▶	SERVICE the fault(s) as necessary and REPEAT QT5.
	— Key OFF.			
	— Connect the VOM positive (+) lead to the PCM STO line and the negative (-) lead to engine ground.			
	— Jumper the PCM STI to engine ground.			
	— Set the VOM on a DC voltage range to read from 0 to 20 volts.			
	• If using MIL:			
	— To use the MIL, jumper the PCM STI line to engine ground.			
	• Is the equipment hooked up properly?			

FM0159501226000X

Fig. 75   Quick test QT5, analog VOM or MIL equipment hookup. 1995

TEST STEP		RESULT	▶	ACTION TO TAKE
QT6	PERFORM KEY ON ENGINE OFF TEST			
	• Follow one of the test procedures based on the type of equipment used:	Yes code(s)	▶	GO to QT7, Erase and Retest.
	NOTE: When performing the Diagnostic Test Mode on the 1.8L 4EAT either engine or transaxle codes can be received.	No codes present and STAR Tester always displays STO LO, or VOM always displays 0 volts	▶	GO to EEC Pinpoint Test STI.
		No codes and engine starts	▶	GO to QT8, Key ON Engine Running Test.
	• Are any diagnostic codes present?	No codes and no start	▶	GO to QT10, Check for Spark.
	• If using Super STAR II Tester:			
	— Latch the center button to the TEST position.			
	— Turn the Super STAR II Tester ON (the tester will sound and "888" will be displayed for two seconds).			
	— Key ON.			
	— Unlatch and relatch the center test button.			
	— After all codes are received, unlatch the center button to review all codes retained in tester memory.			
	NOTE: The "STI LO" indicator will flash as the codes are received by the Super STAR II Tester. If the "STI LO" indicator goes out and does not come back on, no codes exist.			
	• Are any diagnostic trouble codes present?			
	• If using Analog VOM:			
	— Key ON.			
	— Turn the VOM ON.			
	— Observe the VOM needle for any code indications.			
	• Are any diagnostic trouble codes present?			
	• If using MIL:			
	— Key ON.			
	— Observe the MIL.			
	• Are any diagnostic trouble codes present?			

FM0159501227000X

Fig. 76   Quick test QT6, key on engine off (KOEO) test. 1995

TEST STEP	RESULT	▶	ACTION TO TAKE
QT9 PERFORM SWITCH MONITOR TEST	Yes All switches OK	▶	GO to **QT11**, Component Verification Test.
NOTE: A list of switches to be tested is found in the Switch Monitor Test Charts located after EEC Quick Test. • The Switch Monitor Test checks input signals from the individual input switches to the PCM. • Test all switches individually - leaving a switch ON while testing another will lead to a false test result. • Turn engine off and allow to cool before starting Switch Monitor Test. • If using Super STAR II Tester, deactivate the Diagnostic Test Mode by unlatching the center button of the Super STAR II Tester and turning the tester OFF. • Turn all accessories off. • Apply the parking brake. • Place transaxle in NEUTRAL (N) or PARK (P). • Key ON. • If using Super STAR II Tester, leave tester connected, turn tester ON, latch center button, and watch the output of the LED on the adapter cable as each switch is exercised. • If using VOM, jumper PCM STI to ground, connect VOM(+) lead to SML line and (-) lead to engine ground. • **Do all the switches listed in the Switch Monitor Test Charts test OK?**	No All switches fail One or more switches fail	▶ ▶	GO to EEC Pinpoint Test **SML** GO to EEC Pinpoint Test(s), for all switches that fail. REFER to the Switch Monitor Test Charts found after Quick Test for the list of Pinpoint Tests.
QT10 CHECK FOR SPARK • Key OFF. • Connect a Rotunda Spark Tester D81P-6666-A, or equivalent, between the # 1 spark plug wire (plug end) and ground. • Crank engine using ignition switch. • Repeat for all spark plug wires. • **Were sparks present at all wires?**	Yes No	▶ ▶	GO to Fuel Delivery Systems. GO to Ignition Systems.

FM0159501229000X

Fig. 78   Quick test QT9 & QT10, switch monitor test & spark check. 1995

TEST STEP	RESULT	▶	ACTION TO TAKE
QT7 ERASE AND RETEST NOTE: Erasing diagnostic trouble codes and retesting will give an indication whether diagnostic trouble codes received in test step QT6 represent hard or intermittent faults. Hard fault codes will repeat immediately and will be displayed during retest. • Confirm code(s) were received in test step QT6. • Turn the Super STAR II Tester or VOM OFF, or disconnect the NGS Tester. • Disconnect the negative battery cable and depress the brake pedal for 5-10 seconds to erase codes in memory. • Reconnect the negative battery cable. • Perform the Key ON Engine Off Test as instructed in test step QT6. NOTE: If codes retrieved the first time cannot be recreated, it may be necessary to tap suspect sensors, shake and wiggle harness, or drive the vehicle in order to induce a failure. Repeat step QT6 each time. • **Are any diagnostic trouble codes present?**	Yes code(s) No codes No codes and no start	▶ ▶ ▶	REFER to the EEC Diagnostic Trouble Code Chart after Quick Test for Pinpoint Test direction. GO to **QT8**, Key ON Engine Running Test. GO to **QT10**, Check for Spark.
QT8 PERFORM KEY ON ENGINE RUNNING TEST • Deactivate the Diagnostic Test Mode by unlatching the center button on the Super STAR II Tester and turning the tester OFF, or disconnect the jumper connecting PCM STI to ground if using VOM or MIL. • Connect a Rotunda 88 Digital Multimeter 105-00053, or equivalent as a tachometer. • Run the engine at 2000 rpm for three minutes. • If using Super STAR II Tester, turn the Super STAR II Tester ON. • Latch the center button on the Super STAR II Tester, or jumper the PCM STI to ground if using VOM or MIL. • Turn the engine off. • Start the engine and run the engine at idle. • Activate the Diagnostic Test Mode by unlatching then relatching the Super STAR II Tester. • **Are any diagnostic trouble codes present?**	Yes code(s) No codes and sent here by QT6	▶ ▶	REFER to the EEC Diagnostic Trouble Code Chart after Quick Test for Pinpoint Test direction. GO to **QT9**, Switch Monitor Test.

FM0159501228000X

Fig. 77   Quick test QT7 & QT8, erase/reset & key on engine running (KOER) test. 1995

TEST STEP	RESULT	▶	ACTION TO TAKE
QT11 COMPONENT VERIFICATION TEST • Refer to EEC Pinpoint Tests, and perform the EEC Pinpoint Test for each component that could cause the symptom. • **Does each Pinpoint Test check out OK?**	Yes No	▶ ▶	REPEAT Test Step **QT11** until all possible components have been checked. If all components check out OK, RETURN to Diagnostic Routines. SERVICE the fault(s) as indicated in Pinpoint Test and RECHECK the symptom(s).

FM0159501230000X

Fig. 79   Quick test QT11, component verification test. 1995

Diagnostic Trouble Code/ Step/ Page No.	1.3L	1.6L	1.8L/4-112	2.0L/4-121 w/ 4EAT	2.5L/V6-152
CODE 01					
Step	N/A	IDM	N/A	N/A	N/A
Page No.	—	10-52	—	—	—
CODE 02					
Step	CKP	N/A	CKP	CKP1	CKP2
Page No.	10-40	—	10-40	10-42	10-42
CODE 04					
Step	N/A	N/A	N/A	N/A	CKP1
Page No.	—	—	—	—	10-42
CODE 05					
Step	N/A	N/A	N/A	N/A	KS
Page No.	—	—	—	—	10-54
CODE 08					
Step	VAF	VAF	VAF	VAF	MC-VAF
Page No.	10-67	10-67	10-67	10-67	10-55
CODE 09					
Step	ECT	ECT	ECT	ECT	ECT
Page No.	10-44	10-44	10-44	10-44	10-44
CODE 10					
Step	IAT	IAT	IAT	N/A	IAT
Page No.	10-50	10-50	10-50	—	10-50
CODE 11					
Step	N/A	N/A	N/A	IAT	N/A
Page No.	—	—	—	10-50	—
CODE 12					
Step	N/A	TP	TP	TP	TP
Page No.	—	10-66	10-66	10-66	10-66
CODE 14					
Step	BARO	BARO	BARO	BARO	BARO
Page No.	10-38	10-38	10-38	10-38	10-38
CODE 15					
Step	O2S	O2S	O2S	HO2S	HO2S
Page No.	10-57	10-57	10-57	10-49	10-49
CODE 17					
Step	O2S	O2S	O2S	HO2S	HO2S
Page No.	10-57	10-57	10-57	10-49	10-49
CODE 23					
Step	N/A	N/A	N/A	N/A	HO2S
Page No.	—	—	—	—	10-49

Diagnostic Trouble Code/ Step/ Page No.	1.3L	1.6L	1.8L/4-112	2.0L/4-121 w/ 4EAT	2.5L/V6-152
CODE 24					
Step	N/A	N/A	N/A	N/A	HO2S
Page No.	—	—	—	—	10-49
CODE 25					
Step	N/A	SCG	SCG	SCG	SCG
Page No.	—	10-59	10-59	10-59	10-59
CODE 26					
Step	SCG	SCG	SCG	SCG	SCG
Page No.	10-59	10-59	10-59	10-59	10-59
CODE 28					
Step	N/A	N/A	N/A	SCG	SCG
Page No.	—	—	—	10-59	10-59
CODE 29					
Step	N/A	N/A	N/A	N/A	SCG
Page No.	—	—	—	—	10-59
CODE 34					
Step	SCG	SCG	SCG	SCG	SCG
Page No.	10-59	10-59	10-59	10-59	10-59
CODE 41					
Step	N/A	N/A	SCG	N/A	SCG
Page No.	—	—	10-59	—	10-59
CODE 46					
Step	N/A	N/A	N/A	N/A	SCG
Page No.	—	—	—	—	10-59
CODE 67					
Step	N/A	N/A	N/A	ROC	ROC
Page No.	—	—	—	10-58	10-58
CODE 68					
Step	N/A	N/A	N/A	ROC	N/A
Page No.	—	—	—	10-58	—
CODE 69					
Step	N/A	N/A	N/A	ECTF	ECTF
Page No.	—	—	—	10-44	10-44
CODES NOT LISTED					
Step	PGC	PGC	PGC	PGC	PGC
Page No.	10-57	10-57	10-57	10-57	10-57

Fig. 79 Quick test, diagnostic trouble code service chart. 1995

DIAGNOSTIC CHART INDEX

Pinpoint Test Letter	Pinpoint Test Title	Page No. 10-	Fig. No.
1993			
BARO	Barometric Pressure	37	80
CID	Cylinder Identification (1.6L)	39	83
CID	Cylinder Identification (1.8L/4-112, 2.0L/4-121 & 2.5L/V6-152)	39	84
CKP	Crankshaft Position Sensor (1.3L/4-81 & 1.8L/4-112)	40	85
CKP1	Crankshaft Position Sensor (2.0L/4-121 & 2.5L/V6-152)	42	88
CKP2	Crankshaft Position Sensor (2.5L/V6-152)	42	89
ECT	Engine Coolant Temperature	44	91
ECTF	Cooling Fan Engine Coolant Temperature	45	92
EGRT	Exhaust Gas Recirculation Temperature	45	93
ELU	Electrical Load Control Unit	46	94
EVP	EGR Valve Position	47	95
HO2S	Heated Oxygen Sensor	48	97
IAT	Intake Air Temperature	50	99
ICM	Ignition Control Module	51	100
IDM	Ignition Diagnostic Monitor	52	101
KC	Knock Control (1.6L/4-98 Turbo)	53	102
KS	Knock Sensor (2.5L/V6-152)	54	103
MAF	Mass Airflow Sensor	54	104
MC-VAF	Measuring Core Volume Airflow	55	106
MIL	Malfunction Indicator Lamp	56	107
O2S	Oxygen Sensor	57	108
PGC	Power & Ground Connection	57	109
ROC	Relay Output Check	58	110
SCG	Solenoid Controlled By Ground	59	111
SML	Switch Monitor Lamp	60	112
STG	Switch To Ground	61	113
STI	Self Test Input	62	114
STO	Self Test Output	63	115
STP	Switch To Power	63	116
TP	Throttle Position	64	117
VAF	Vane Air Flow	67	119
VPWR	Vehicle Power	69	120
VREF	Reference Voltage	70	121
VSS	Vehicle Speed Sensor	72	122
1994			
BARO	Barometric Pressure	37	80
CID	Cylinder Identification (1.6L)	39	83
CID	Cylinder Identification (1.8L/4-112, 2.0L/4-121 & 2.5L/V6-152)	39	84
CKP	Crankshaft Position Sensor (1.3L/4-81 & 1.8L/4-112)	40	85
CKP1	Crankshaft Position Sensor (2.0L/4-121 & 2.5L/V6-152)	42	89
CKP2	Crankshaft Position Sensor (2.5L/V6-152)	42	88
ECT	Engine Coolant Temperature	44	91
ECTF	Cooling Fan Engine Coolant Temperature	45	92
ELU	Electrical Load Control Unit	46	94
EVP	EGR Valve Position	47	95
HO2S	Heated Oxygen Sensor	48	97
IAT	Intake Air Temperature	50	99
ICM	Ignition Control Module	51	100
IDM	Ignition Diagnostic Monitor	52	101
KC	Knock Control (1.6L/4-98 Turbo)	53	102

Continued

COMPUTERIZED ENGINE CONTROLS (ASPIRE, CAPRI, ESCORT & TRACER (1.8L/4-112), FESTIVA & PROBE (2.0L/4-121 w/4EAT & 2.5L/V6-152) ELECTRONIC ENGINE CONTROL (EEC) SYSTEM

DIAGNOSTIC CHART INDEX—Continued

Pinpoint Test Letter	Pinpoint Test Title	Page No. 10-	Fig. No.
1993 -CONTINUED			
KS	Knock Sensor (2.5L/V6-152)	54	103
MC-VAF	Measuring Core Volume Airflow	55	106
MIL	Malfunction Indicator Lamp	56	107
O2S	Oxygen Sensor	57	108
PGC	Power & Ground Connection	57	109
ROC	Relay Output Check	58	110
SCG	Solenoid Controlled By Ground	59	111
SML	Switch Monitor Lamp	60	112
STG	Switch To Ground	61	113
STI	Self Test Input	62	114
STO	Self Test Output	63	115
STP	Switch To Power	63	116
TP	Throttle Position	64	117
VAF	Vane Air Flow	67	119
VPWR	Vehicle Power	69	120
VREF	Reference Voltage	70	121
VSS	Vehicle Speed Sensor	72	122
1995			
BARO	Barometric Pressure (Except 2.5L/V6-152 w/4EAT)	38	81
BARO	Barometric Pressure (2.5L/V6-152 w/4EAT)	38	82
CKP	Crankshaft Position Sensor (1.3L)	40	86
CKP	Crankshaft Position Sensor (1.8L/4-112)	41	87
CKP1	Crankshaft Position Sensor (2.0L/4-121 & 2.5L/V6-152)	42	88
CKP2	Crankshaft Position Sensor (2.5L/V6-152)	42	89
CMP	Camshaft Position Sensor	43	90
ECT	Engine Coolant Temperature	44	91
EVP	EGR Valve Position	47	96
HO2S	Heated Oxygen Sensor (1.8L/4-112 & 2.5L/V6-152)	49	98
IAT	Intake Air Temperature	50	99
ICM	Ignition Control Module	51	100
IDM	Ignition Diagnostic Monitor	52	101
KS	Knock Sensor (2.5L/V6-152)	54	103
MAF	Mass Airflow Sensor (1.3L)	54	104
MC-VAF	Measuring Core Volume Airflow	55	106
MIL	Malfunction Indicator Lamp	56	107
O2S	Oxygen Sensor	57	108
PGC	Power & Ground Connection	57	109
ROC	Relay Output Check	58	110
SCG	Solenoid Controlled By Ground	59	111
SML	Switch Monitor Lamp	60	112
STG	Switch To Ground	61	113
STI	Self Test Input	62	114
STO	Self Test Output	63	115
STP	Switch To Power	63	116
TP	Throttle Position	66	118
VAF	Vane Air Flow	67	119
VPWR	Vehicle Power	69	120
VREF	Reference Voltage	70	121
VSS	Vehicle Speed Sensor	72	123

Barometric Pressure (BP) Sensor

Note

You should enter this Pinpoint Test only when a service code 14 is received in Quick Test Steps 5 or 6, or when Quick Test Step 11 directs you here.

Remember

This Pinpoint Test is intended to diagnose only the following:

● Circuits: BP

Special Note

1.3L, 1.8L and 2.2L all

The barometric pressure sensor is located within the ECA and cannot be replaced as a separate item. If a service code 14 exists and cannot be erased, then the ECA must be replaced.

Fig. 80   Pinpoint test BARO,
barometric pressure (Part 1 of 4).
1993–94

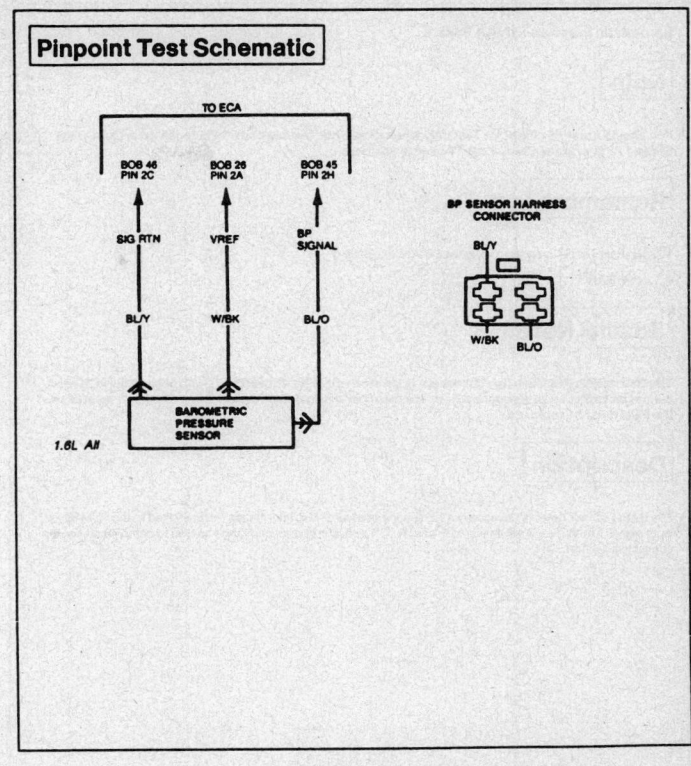

Pinpoint Test Schematic

Fig. 80   Pinpoint test BARO,
barometric pressure (Part 2 of 4).
1993–94

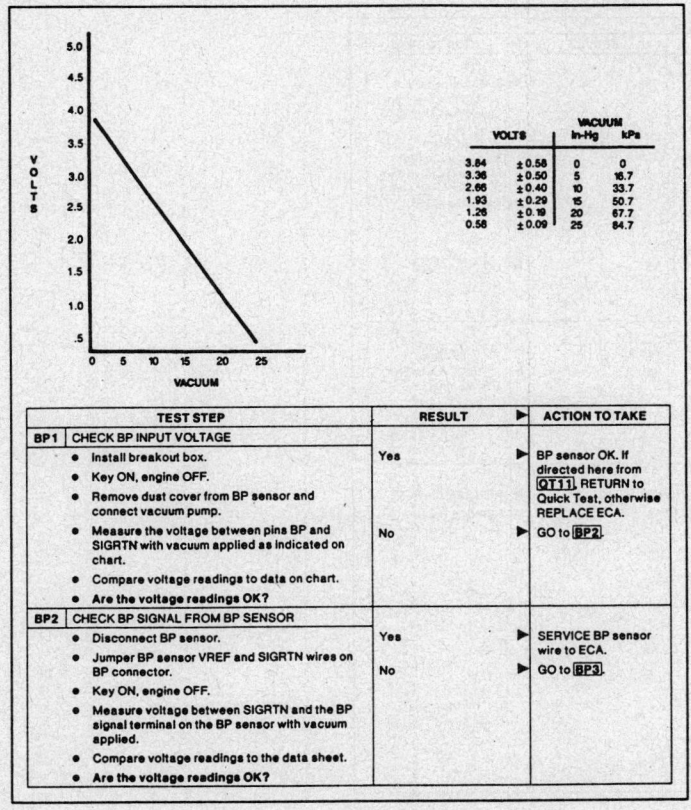

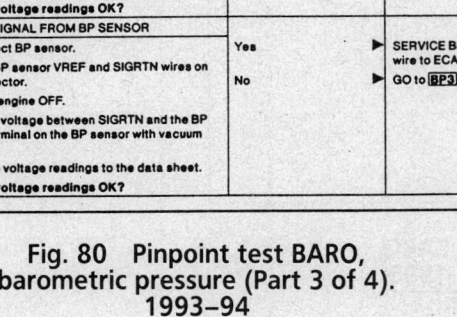

TEST STEP	RESULT	▶	ACTION TO TAKE
BP1 **CHECK BP INPUT VOLTAGE**			
● Install breakout box.	Yes		BP sensor OK. If directed here from QT11, RETURN to Quick Test, otherwise REPLACE ECA.
● Key ON, engine OFF.			
● Remove dust cover from BP sensor and connect vacuum pump.	No	▶	GO to BP2.
● Measure the voltage between pins BP and SIGRTN with vacuum applied as indicated on chart.			
● Compare voltage readings to data on chart.			
● Are the voltage readings OK?			
BP2 **CHECK BP SIGNAL FROM BP SENSOR**			
● Disconnect BP sensor.	Yes		SERVICE BP sensor wire to ECA.
● Jumper BP sensor VREF and SIGRTN wires on BP connector.	No	▶	GO to BP3.
● Key ON, engine OFF.			
● Measure voltage between SIGRTN and the BP signal terminal on the BP sensor with vacuum applied.			
● Compare voltage readings to the data sheet.			
● Are the voltage readings OK?			

Fig. 80   Pinpoint test BARO,
barometric pressure (Part 3 of 4).
1993–94

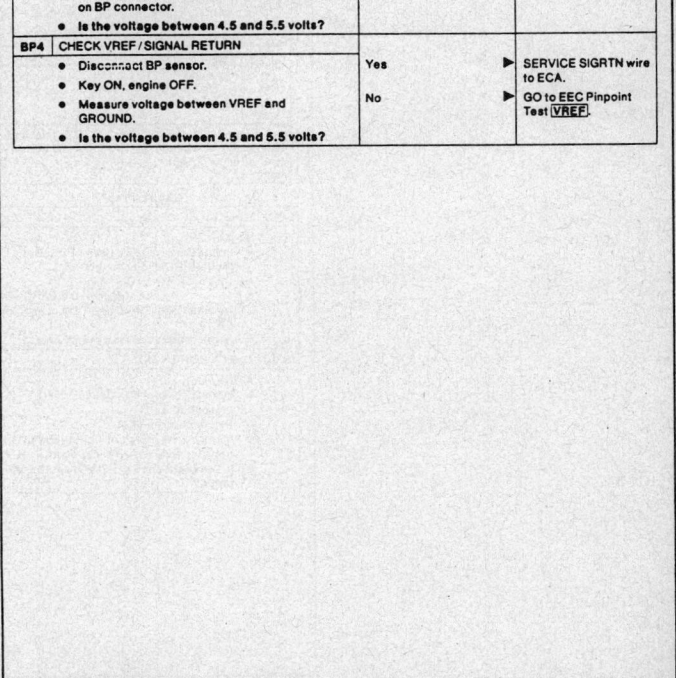

TEST STEP	RESULT	▶	ACTION TO TAKE
BP3 **CHECK BP VOLTAGE REFERENCE**			
● Disconnect BP sensor.	Yes	▶	REPLACE BP sensor.
● Key ON, engine OFF.	No	▶	GO to BP4.
● Measure voltage between VREF and SIGRTN on BP connector.			
● Is the voltage between 4.5 and 5.5 volts?			
BP4 **CHECK VREF / SIGNAL RETURN**			
● Disconnect BP sensor.	Yes	▶	SERVICE SIGRTN wire to ECA.
● Key ON, engine OFF.	No	▶	GO to EEC Pinpoint Test VREF.
● Measure voltage between VREF and GROUND.			
● Is the voltage between 4.5 and 5.5 volts?			

Fig. 80   Pinpoint test BARO,
barometric pressure (Part 4 of 4).
1993–94

FORD–Computerized Engine Controls

Barometric Pressure (BARO) Sensor

Note

You should enter this Pinpoint Test only when diagnostic trouble code 14 is received in Quick Test Steps 7 or 8, or when Quick Test 11 directs you here.

Remember

This Pinpoint Test is intended to diagnose only the following:

● Circuit: BARO

Special Note

The Barometric Pressure (BARO) sensor is located within the Powertrain Control Module (PCM) and cannot be replaced as a separate item. If a diagnostic trouble code 14 exists and cannot be erased, the PCM must be replaced.

Description

The BARO sensor detects changes in atmospheric pressure. This information is transferred to the PCM by an input signal. The PCM will adjust air/fuel ratio, A/C cutoff, idle speed, and purge control to compensate for the changing pressure.

1.3L, 1.8L, 2.5L (Sensor Integrated into PCM)

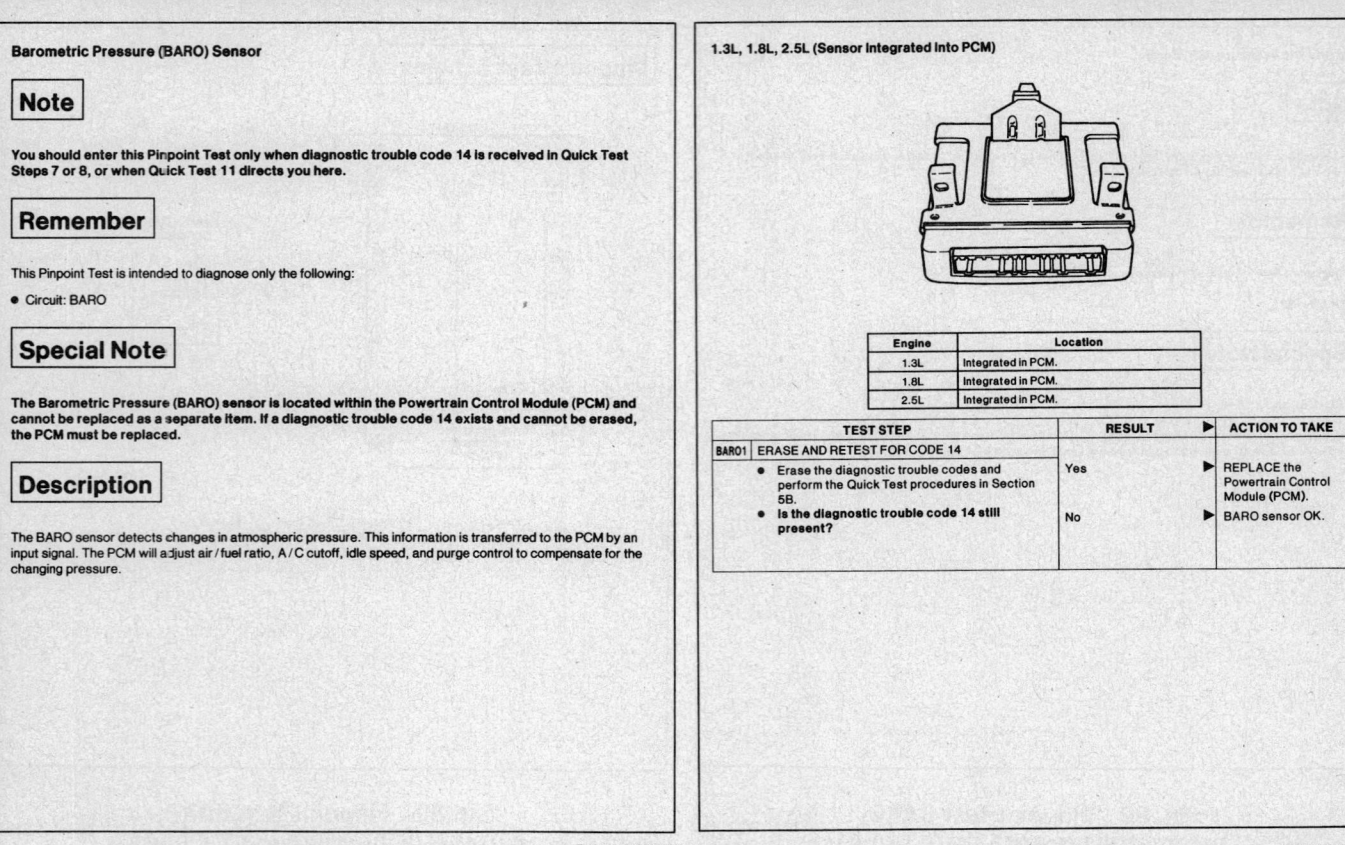

Engine	Location
1.3L	Integrated in PCM.
1.8L	Integrated in PCM.
2.5L	Integrated in PCM.

TEST STEP	RESULT	▶	ACTION TO TAKE
BARO1 ERASE AND RETEST FOR CODE 14 ● Erase the diagnostic trouble codes and perform the Quick Test procedures in Section 5B. ● Is the diagnostic trouble code 14 still present?	Yes	▶	REPLACE the Powertrain Control Module (PCM).
	No	▶	BARO sensor OK.

FM0159501231010X

Fig. 81 Pinpoint test BARO, barometric pressure (Part 1 of 2). 1995 except 2.5L/V6–152 w/4EAT

FM0159501231020X

Fig. 81 Pinpoint test BARO, barometric pressure (Part 2 of 2). 1995 except 2.5L/V6–152 w/4EAT

TEST STEP	RESULT	▶	ACTION TO TAKE
BAR01 CHECK BARO SIGNAL ● Key OFF. ● Install Breakout Box (BOB). ● Key ON. ● Measure the voltage between BOB Pin 45 and ground. **Barometric Pressure / Voltage** Less than 89.6 kPa (672 mm-Hg [26.5 in-Hg]) (above approx. 1,500 m [4,921 ft]) / Less than 3.5 volts Greater than 89.6 kPa (672 mm-Hg [26.5 in-Hg]) (below approx. 1,500 m [4,921 ft]) / Greater than 3.5 volts ● Is the voltage correct?	Yes	▶	BARO circuit OK. If sent to this test from Quick Test Step QT7 or QT8 REPLACE the Transaxle Control Module (TCM). If sent to the test from Quick Test Step QT9
	No	▶	GO to BARO2.
BARO2 CHECK FOR OPEN ● Key OFF. ● Install Breakout Box (leave Powertrain Control Module [PCM] disconnected). ● Disconnect the TCM. ● Measure the resistance of the BARO wire between BOB Pin 45 and TCM connector Pin 2R. ● Is the resistance less than 5 ohms?	Yes	▶	GO to BARO3.
	No	▶	SERVICE the BARO wire for open.
BARO3 CHECK FOR SHORT ● Key OFF. ● Install Breakout Box (leave PCM disconnected). ● Disconnect the TCM. ● Measure the resistance of the BARO wire between BOB Pin 45 and ground. ● Is the resistance greater than 10,000 ohms?	Yes	▶	REPLACE the PCM.
	No	▶	SERVICE the BARO wire for short.

Fig. 82 Pinpoint test BARO, barometric pressure. 1995 2.5L/V6–152 w/4EAT

Cylinder Identification (CID) Sensor — 1.6L

Note

You should enter this Pinpoint Test only when diagnostic trouble code 03 is received in Quick Test Steps 5 or 6, or when Quick Test Step 11 directs you here.

Remember

This Pinpoint Test is intended to diagnose only the following:

- Circuit: CID

Pinpoint Test Schematic

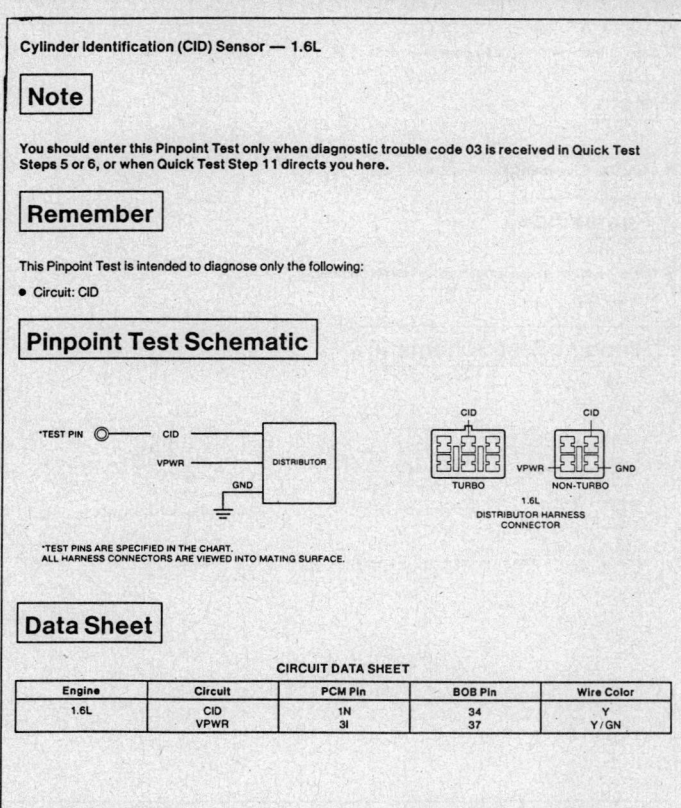

*TEST PINS ARE SPECIFIED IN THE CHART.
ALL HARNESS CONNECTORS ARE VIEWED INTO MATING SURFACE.

Data Sheet

CIRCUIT DATA SHEET

Engine	Circuit	PCM Pin	BOB Pin	Wire Color
1.6L	CID	1N	34	Y
	VPWR	3I	37	Y/GN

FM0159301085010X

Fig. 83 Pinpoint test CID, cylinder identification (Part 1 of 2). 1993–94 1.6L/4-98

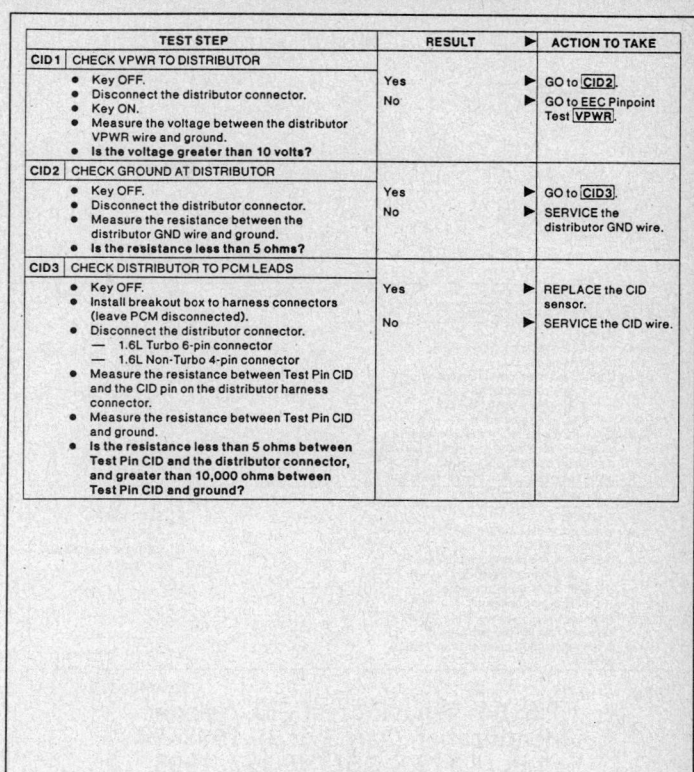

	TEST STEP	RESULT	▶	ACTION TO TAKE
CID 1	CHECK VPWR TO DISTRIBUTOR			
	• Key OFF. • Disconnect the distributor connector. • Key ON. • Measure the voltage between the distributor VPWR wire and ground. • Is the voltage greater than 10 volts?	Yes ▶ No ▶		GO to CID2. GO to EEC Pinpoint Test VPWR.
CID 2	CHECK GROUND AT DISTRIBUTOR			
	• Key OFF. • Disconnect the distributor connector. • Measure the resistance between the distributor GND wire and ground. • Is the resistance less than 5 ohms?	Yes ▶ No ▶		GO to CID3. SERVICE the distributor GND wire.
CID 3	CHECK DISTRIBUTOR TO PCM LEADS			
	• Key OFF. • Install breakout box to harness connectors (leave PCM disconnected). • Disconnect the distributor connector. — 1.6L Turbo 6-pin connector — 1.6L Non-Turbo 4-pin connector • Measure the resistance between Test Pin CID and the CID pin on the distributor harness connector. • Measure the resistance between Test Pin CID and ground. • Is the resistance less than 5 ohms between Test Pin CID and the distributor connector, and greater than 10,000 ohms between Test Pin CID and ground?	Yes ▶ No ▶		REPLACE the CID sensor. SERVICE the CID wire.

FM0159301085020X

Fig. 83 Pinpoint test CID, cylinder identification (Part 2 of 2). 1993–94 1.6L/4-98

Cylinder Identification (CID) Sensor — 1.8L, 2.0L 4EAT, 2.5L

Note

You should enter this Pinpoint Test only when diagnostic trouble code 03 is received in Quick Test Steps 5 or 6, or when Quick Test 11 directs you here.

Remember

This Pinpoint Test is intended to diagnose only the following:

- Circuit: CID

Pinpoint Test Schematic

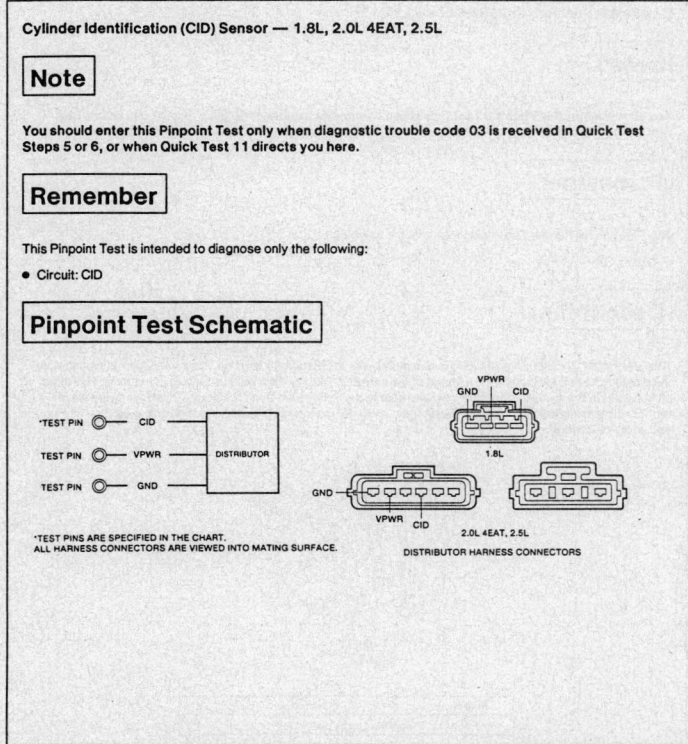

*TEST PINS ARE SPECIFIED IN THE CHART.
ALL HARNESS CONNECTORS ARE VIEWED INTO MATING SURFACE.

FM0159301086010X

Fig. 84 Pinpoint test CID, cylinder identification (Part 1 of 3). 1993–94 1.8L/4-112 & 2.5L/V6-152, 1993 2.0L/4-121 w/4EAT

Data Sheet

CIRCUIT DATA SHEET

Engine	Circuit	PCM Pin	BOB Pin	Wire Color
1.8L MTX	CID	2G	24	Y/BL
	VPWR	1B	37, 57	W/R
	GND	2C	16	BK/LG
1.8L 4EAT	CID	2J	27	Y/BL
	VPWR	1B	37, 57	W/R
	GND	3C	49	BK/LG
2.0L 4EAT	CID	2B	4	LG/W
	VPWR	1B, 1U	37, 57	R/BK
	GND	3C	16	BK/R
2.5L	CID	3G	6	BL/P
	VPWR	1B	37, 57	R/BK
	GND	3C	49	BK/R

	TEST STEP	RESULT	▶	ACTION TO TAKE
CID 1	CHECK CID SIGNAL			
	• Key OFF. • Install breakout box (connect PCM). • Measure the voltage at Test Pin CID while bumping starter. • Does the voltage alternate between approximately 0 volts and 5 volts?	Yes ▶ No ▶		CID circuit OK. If sent to this test by Quick Test Step QT11, RETURN . Otherwise, REPLACE the PCM. GO to CID2.
CID 2	CHECK VPWR TO DISTRIBUTOR			
	• Key OFF. • Disconnect the distributor connector. — 1.8L 4-pin connector — 2.0L 4EAT 6-pin connector — 2.5L 6-pin connector • Key ON. • Measure the voltage at the VPWR wire on the distributor harness connector. • Is the voltage greater than 10 volts?	Yes ▶ No ▶		GO to CID3. GO to EEC Pinpoint Test VPWR. If VPWR is OK, SERVICE VPWR wire to distributor.
CID 3	CHECK GROUND AT DISTRIBUTOR			
	• Key OFF. • Disconnect the distributor connector. — 1.8L 4-pin connector — 2.0L 4EAT 6-pin connector — 2.5L 6-pin connector • Measure the resistance of the GND wire between the distributor harness connector and ground. • Is the resistance less than 5 ohms?	Yes ▶ No ▶		GO to CID4. SERVICE the distributor GND wire.

FM0159301086020X

Fig. 84 Pinpoint test CID, cylinder identification (Part 2 of 3). 1993–94 1.8L/4-112 & 2.5L/V6-152, 1993 2.0L/4-121 w/4EAT

TEST STEP		RESULT	▶	ACTION TO TAKE
CID4	**CHECK CID WIRE FOR OPEN**			
• Key OFF. • Install breakout box (leave PCM disconnected). • Disconnect the distributor connector. — 1.8L 4-pin connector — 2.0L 4EAT 6-pin connector — 2.5L 6-pin connector • Measure the resistance of the CID wire between Test Pin CID and the CID wire at the distributor harness connector. • **Is the resistance less than 5 ohms?**		Yes No	▶ ▶	GO to CID5. SERVICE the CID wire for open.
CID5	**CHECK CID WIRE FOR SHORT**			
• Key OFF. • Install breakout box (leave PCM disconnected). • Disconnect the distributor connector. — 1.8L 4-pin connector — 2.0L 4EAT 6-pin connector — 2.5L 6-pin connector • Measure the resistance of the CID wire between Test Pin CID and ground. • **Is the resistance greater than 10,000 ohms?**		Yes No	▶ ▶	REPLACE the distributor. SERVICE the CID wire for short.

FM0159301086030X

Fig. 84   Pinpoint test CID, cylinder identification (Part 3 of 3). 1993–94 1.8L/4-112 & 2.5L/V6-152, 1993 2.0L/4-121 w/4EAT

Crankshaft Position (CKP) Sensor — 1.3L, 1.8L

Note

You should enter this Pinpoint Test only when diagnostic trouble code 02 is received in Quick Test Steps 5 or 6, or when Quick Test Step 11 directs you here.

Remember

This Pinpoint Test is intended to diagnose only the following:

• Circuit: CKP

Pinpoint Test Schematic

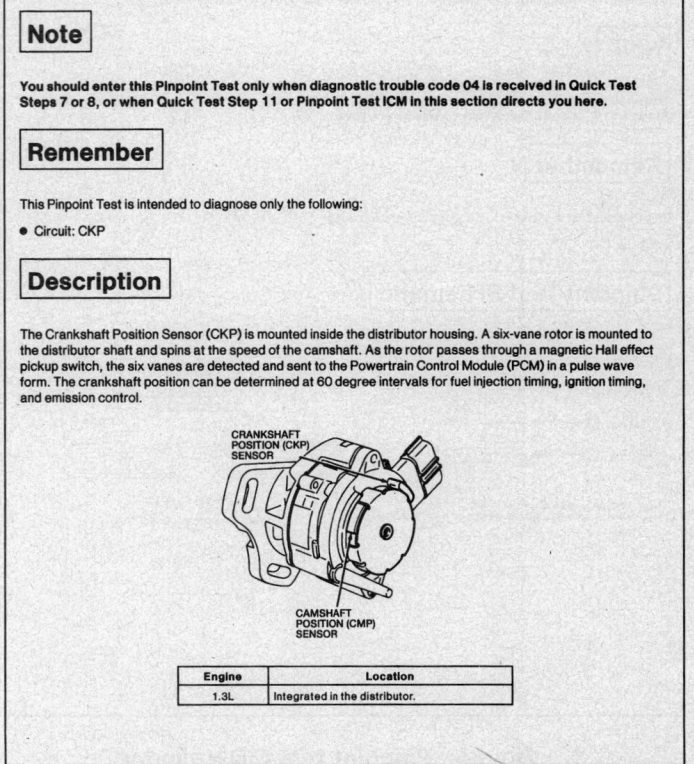

*TEST PINS ARE SPECIFIED IN THE CHART.
ALL HARNESS CONNECTORS ARE VIEWED INTO MATING SURFACE.

FM0159301087010X

Fig. 85   Pinpoint test CKP, crankshaft position sensor (Part 1 of 2). 1993–94 1.3L/4-81 & 1.8L/4-112

Data Sheet

CIRCUIT DATA SHEET

Engine	Circuit	PCM Pin	BOB Pin	Wire Color
1.3L	CKP VPWR GND	2E 1B 2C	56 37, 57 16	Y / BL Y / BK BK
1.8L MTX	CKP VPWR GND	2E 1B 2C	56 37, 57 16	W W / R BK / LG
1.8L 4EAT	CKP VPWR GND	2A 1B 3C	45 37, 57 49	W W / R BK / LG

TEST STEP		RESULT	▶	ACTION TO TAKE
CKP1	**CHECK VPWR TO DISTRIBUTOR**			
• Key OFF. • Disconnect the distributor connector. • Key ON. • Measure the voltage between the distributor VPWR wire and ground. • **Is the voltage greater than 10 volts?**		Yes No	▶ ▶	GO to CKP2. GO to EEC Pinpoint Test VPWR.
CKP2	**CHECK GROUND AT DISTRIBUTOR**			
• Key OFF. • Disconnect the distributor connector. • Measure the resistance between the distributor GND wire and ground. • **Is the resistance less than 5 ohms?**		Yes No	▶ ▶	GO to CKP3. SERVICE the distributor GND wire.
CKP3	**CHECK DISTRIBUTOR TO PCM LEADS**			
• Key OFF. • Install breakout box (leave PCM disconnected) • Disconnect the distributor connector • Measure the resistance between the Test Pin CKP and the CKP pin on the distributor harness connector. • Measure the resistance between the Test Pin CKP and ground. • **Is the resistance less than 5 ohms between the Test Pin and the distributor harness connector, and greater than 10,000 ohms between the Test Pin and ground?**		Yes No	▶ ▶	REPLACE the CKP sensor. SERVICE the CKP wire.

FM0159301087020X

Fig. 85   Pinpoint test CKP, crankshaft position sensor (Part 2 of 2). 1993–94 1.3L/4-81 & 1.8L/4-112

Crankshaft Position (CKP) Sensor — 1.3L

Note

You should enter this Pinpoint Test only when diagnostic trouble code 04 is received in Quick Test Steps 7 or 8, or when Quick Test Step 11 or Pinpoint Test ICM in this section directs you here.

Remember

This Pinpoint Test is intended to diagnose only the following:

• Circuit: CKP

Description

The Crankshaft Position Sensor (CKP) is mounted inside the distributor housing. A six-vane rotor is mounted to the distributor shaft and spins at the speed of the camshaft. As the rotor passes through a magnetic Hall effect pickup switch, the six vanes are detected and sent to the Powertrain Control Module (PCM) in a pulse wave form. The crankshaft position can be determined at 60 degree intervals for fuel injection timing, ignition timing, and emission control.

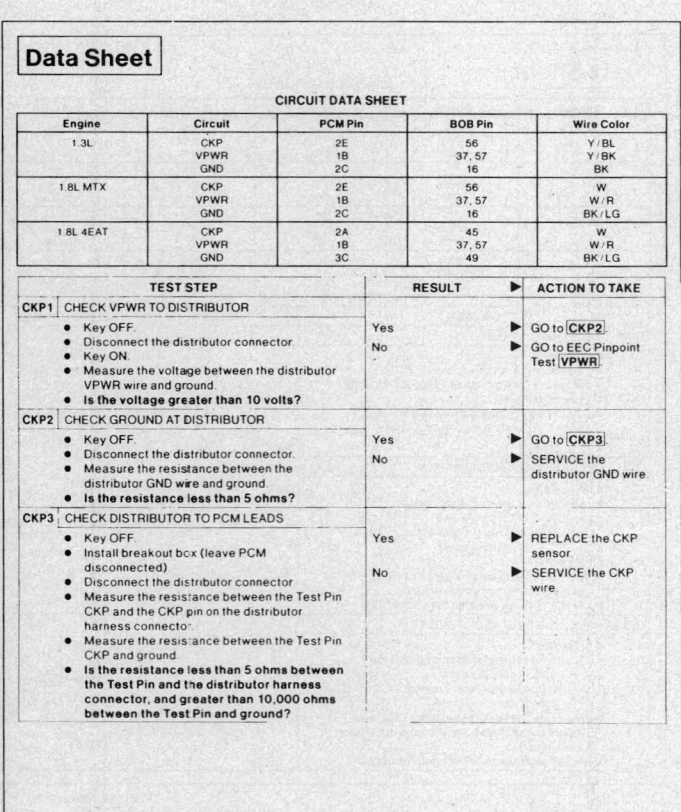

Engine	Location
1.3L	Integrated in the distributor.

FM0159501233010X

Fig. 86   Pinpoint test CKP, crankshaft position sensor (Part 1 of 3). 1995 1.3L/4-81

Pinpoint Test Schematic

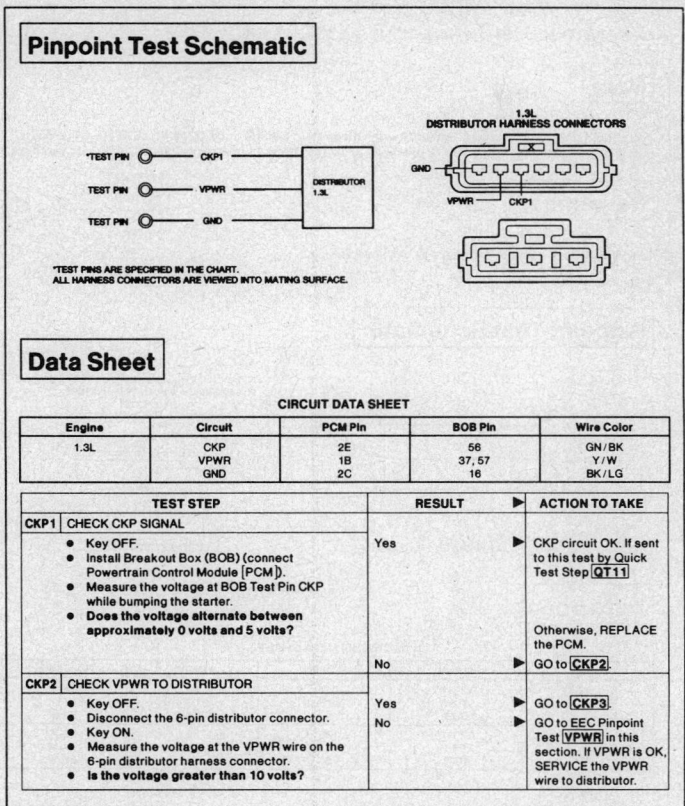

*TEST PINS ARE SPECIFIED IN THE CHART.
ALL HARNESS CONNECTORS ARE VIEWED INTO MATING SURFACE.

Data Sheet

CIRCUIT DATA SHEET

Engine	Circuit	PCM Pin	BOB Pin	Wire Color
1.3L	CKP	2E	56	GN/BK
	VPWR	1B	37, 57	Y/W
	GND	2C	16	BK/LG

TEST STEP		RESULT	▶	ACTION TO TAKE
CKP1	CHECK CKP SIGNAL			
<ul><li>Key OFF.</li><li>Install Breakout Box (BOB) (connect Powertrain Control Module [PCM]).</li><li>Measure the voltage at BOB Test Pin CKP while bumping the starter.</li><li>**Does the voltage alternate between approximately 0 volts and 5 volts?**</li></ul>		Yes	▶	CKP circuit OK. If sent to this test by Quick Test Step QT11.
				Otherwise, REPLACE the PCM.
		No	▶	GO to CKP2.
CKP2	CHECK VPWR TO DISTRIBUTOR			
<ul><li>Key OFF.</li><li>Disconnect the 6-pin distributor connector.</li><li>Key ON.</li><li>Measure the voltage at the VPWR wire on the 6-pin distributor harness connector.</li><li>**Is the voltage greater than 10 volts?**</li></ul>		Yes	▶	GO to CKP3.
		No	▶	GO to EEC Pinpoint Test VPWR in this section. If VPWR is OK, SERVICE the VPWR wire to distributor.

FM0159501233020X

Fig. 86 Pinpoint test CKP, crankshaft position sensor (Part 2 of 3). 1995 1.3L/4–81

TEST STEP		RESULT	▶	ACTION TO TAKE
CKP3	CHECK GROUND AT DISTRIBUTOR			
<ul><li>Key OFF.</li><li>Disconnect the 6-pin distributor connector.</li><li>Measure the resistance of the GND wire between the 6-pin distributor harness connector and ground.</li><li>**Is the resistance less than 5 ohms?**</li></ul>		Yes	▶	GO to CKP4.
		No	▶	SERVICE the distributor GND wire.
CKP4	CHECK CKP WIRE FOR OPEN			
<ul><li>Key OFF.</li><li>Install Breakout Box (leave PCM disconnected).</li><li>Disconnect the 6-pin distributor connector.</li><li>Measure the resistance of the CKP wire between BOB Test Pin CKP and the CKP wire at the 6-pin distributor harness connector.</li><li>**Is the resistance less than 5 ohms?**</li></ul>		Yes	▶	GO to CKP5.
		No	▶	SERVICE the CKP wire for open.
CKP5	CHECK CKP WIRE FOR SHORT			
<ul><li>Key OFF.</li><li>Install Breakout Box (leave PCM disconnected).</li><li>Disconnect the 6-pin distributor connector.</li><li>Measure the resistance of the CKP wire between BOB Test Pin CKP and ground.</li><li>Measure the resistance between the CKP wire and all the other wire terminals on the 6-pin distributor connector.</li><li>**Are the resistances greater than 10,000 ohms?**</li></ul>		Yes	▶	REPLACE the distributor.
		No	▶	SERVICE the CKP wire for short.

FM0159501233030X

Fig. 86 Pinpoint test CKP, crankshaft position sensor (Part 3 of 3). 1995 1.3L/4–81

Crankshaft Position (CKP) Sensor — 1.8L

Note

You should enter this Pinpoint Test only when diagnostic trouble code 02 is received in Quick Test Steps 7 or 8, or when Quick Test Step 11 directs you here.

Remember

This Pinpoint Test is intended to diagnose only the following:

- Circuit: CKP

Description

The Crankshaft Position (CKP) sensor provides crankshaft position input to the Powertrain Control Module (PCM) which uses this information to control fuel injection, ignition timing, and emissions.

On the 1.8L, a slotted disc is mounted to the distributor shaft. As the four slots on the disc pass through a photo sensor, an input signal is sent to the PCM. This signal notifies the PCM of the crankshaft position at 90 degree intervals.

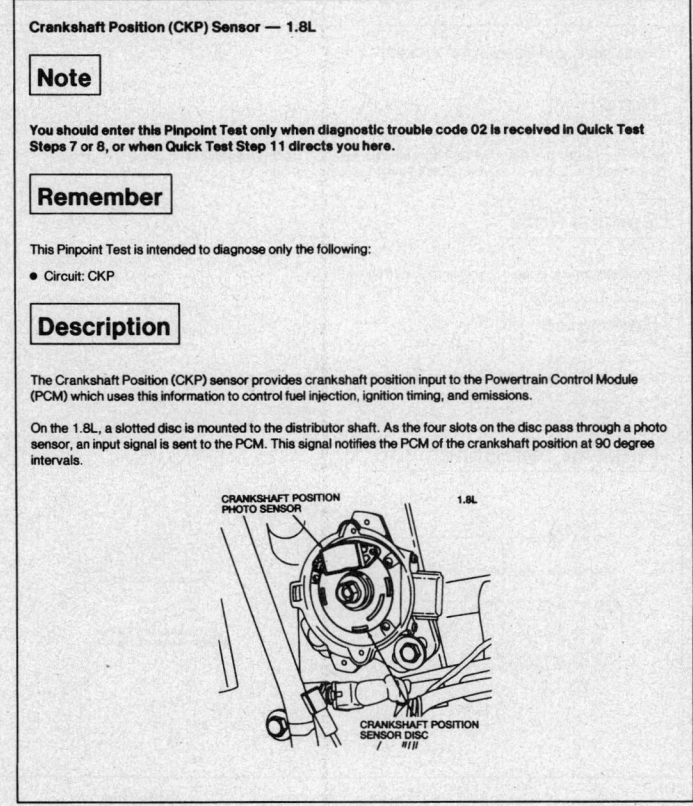

FM0159501234010X

Fig. 87 Pinpoint test CKP, crankshaft position sensor (Part 1 of 3). 1995 1.8L/4-112

Engine	Location
1.8L	Integrated in the distributor.

Pinpoint Test Schematic

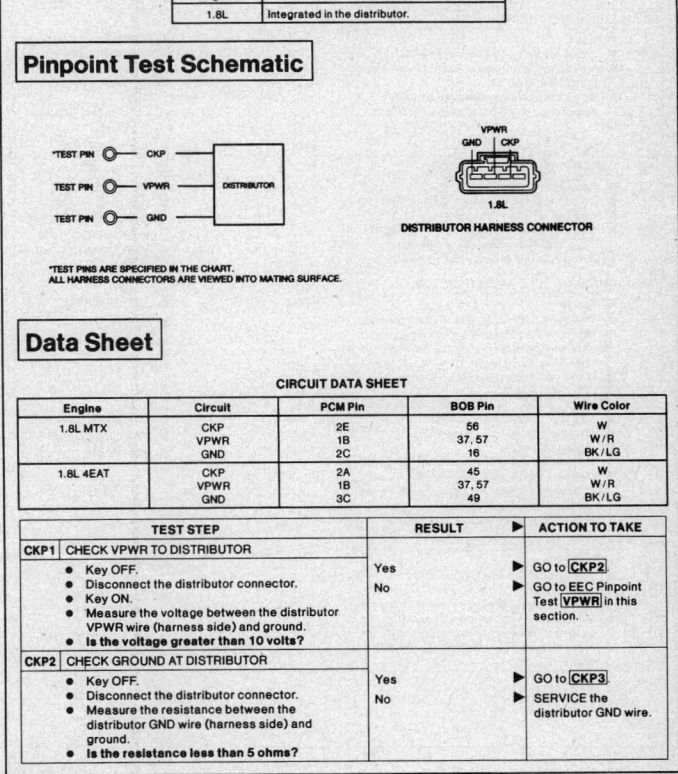

*TEST PINS ARE SPECIFIED IN THE CHART.
ALL HARNESS CONNECTORS ARE VIEWED INTO MATING SURFACE.

Data Sheet

CIRCUIT DATA SHEET

Engine	Circuit	PCM Pin	BOB Pin	Wire Color
1.8L MTX	CKP	2E	56	W
	VPWR	1B	37, 57	W/R
	GND	2C	16	BK/LG
1.8L 4EAT	CKP	2A	45	W
	VPWR	1B	37, 57	W/R
	GND	3C	49	BK/LG

TEST STEP		RESULT	▶	ACTION TO TAKE
CKP1	CHECK VPWR TO DISTRIBUTOR			
<ul><li>Key OFF.</li><li>Disconnect the distributor connector.</li><li>Key ON.</li><li>Measure the voltage between the distributor VPWR wire (harness side) and ground.</li><li>**Is the voltage greater than 10 volts?**</li></ul>		Yes	▶	GO to CKP2.
		No	▶	GO to EEC Pinpoint Test VPWR in this section.
CKP2	CHECK GROUND AT DISTRIBUTOR			
<ul><li>Key OFF.</li><li>Disconnect the distributor connector.</li><li>Measure the resistance between the distributor GND wire (harness side) and ground.</li><li>**Is the resistance less than 5 ohms?**</li></ul>		Yes	▶	GO to CKP3.
		No	▶	SERVICE the distributor GND wire.

FM0159501234020X

Fig. 87 Pinpoint test CKP, crankshaft position sensor (Part 2 of 3). 1995 1.8L/4-112

COMPUTERIZED ENGINE CONTROLS (ASPIRE, CAPRI, ESCORT & TRACER (1.8L/4-112), FESTIVA & PROBE (2.0L/4-121 w/4EAT & 2.5L/V6-152) ELECTRONIC ENGINE CONTROL (EEC) SYSTEM

10-41

TEST STEP		RESULT	▶	ACTION TO TAKE
CKP3	**CHECK DISTRIBUTOR TO PCM LEADS**			
	• Key OFF. • Install Breakout Box (BOB) (leave Powertrain Control Module [PCM] disconnected). • Disconnect the distributor connector. • Measure the resistance between the BOB Test Pin CKP and the CKP pin on the distributor harness connector. • Measure the resistance between the BOB Test Pin CKP and ground. • **Is the resistance less than 5 ohms between the BOB Test Pin and the distributor harness connector, and greater than 10,000 ohms between the Test Pin and ground?**	Yes No	▶ ▶	REPLACE the CKP sensor. SERVICE the CKP wire.

FM0159501234030X

Fig. 87   Pinpoint test CKP, crankshaft position sensor (Part 3 of 3). 1995 1.8L/4-112

Crankshaft Position Sensor No. 1 (CKP1) — 2.0L 4EAT, 2.5L

Note

You should enter this Pinpoint Test only when diagnostic trouble code 02 (2.0L 4EAT) or 04 (2.5L) is received in Quick Test Steps 5 or 6, or when Quick Test Step 11 or Pinpoint Test ICM directs you here.

Remember

This Pinpoint Test is intended to diagnose only the following:
• Circuit: CKP1

Pinpoint Test Schematic

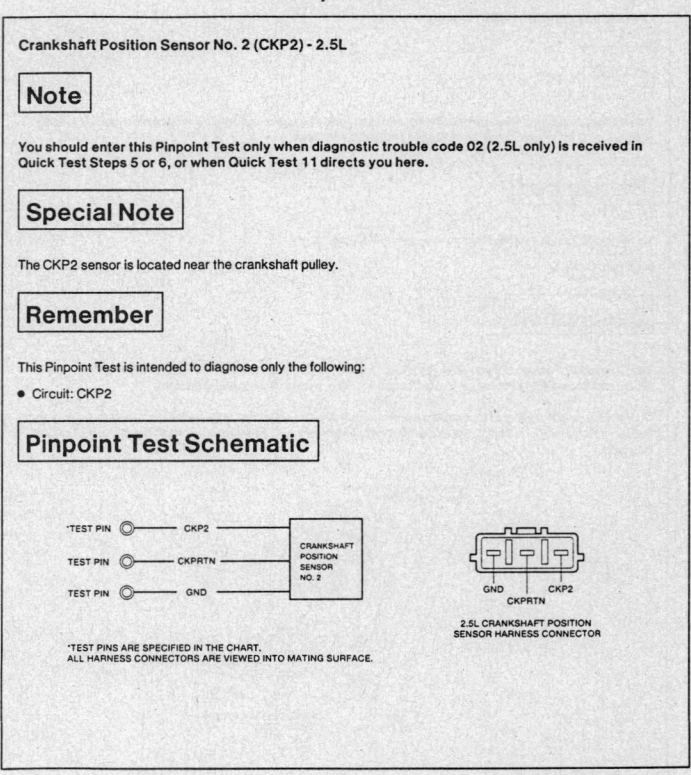

Data Sheet

	CIRCUIT DATA SHEET			
Engine	Circuit	PCM Pin	BOB Pin	Wire Color
2.0L 4EAT	CKP1 VPWR GND	2A 1B, 1U 3C	56 37, 57 16	GN/O R/BK BK/R
2.5L	CKP1 VPWR GND	3E 1B 3C	56 37, 57 49	LG/O R/BK BK/R

FM0159301088010X

Fig. 88   Pinpoint test CKP1, crankshaft position sensor No. 1 (Part 1 of 2). 1993 2.0L/4-121 w/4EAT & 1993–95 2.5L/V6-152

TEST STEP		RESULT	▶	ACTION TO TAKE
CKP1-1	**CHECK CKP 1 SIGNAL**			
	• Key OFF. • Install breakout box (connect PCM). • Measure the voltage at Test Pin CKP 1 while bumping starter. • **Does the voltage alternate between approximately 0 volts and 5 volts?**	Yes No	▶ ▶	CKP1 circuit OK. If sent to this test by Quick Test Step [QT 11], RETURN. Otherwise, REPLACE the PCM. GO to [CKP1-2].
CKP1-2	**CHECK VPWR TO DISTRIBUTOR**			
	• Key OFF. • Disconnect the 6-pin distributor connector. • Key ON. • Measure the voltage at the VPWR wire on the 6-pin distributor harness connector. • **Is the voltage greater than 10 volts?**	Yes No	▶ ▶	GO to [CKP1-3]. GO to EEC Pinpoint Test [VPWR]. If VPWR is OK, SERVICE the VPWR wire to distributor.
CKP1-3	**CHECK GROUND AT DISTRIBUTOR**			
	• Key OFF. • Disconnect the 6-pin distributor connector. • Measure the resistance of the GND wire between the 6-pin distributor harness connector and ground. • **Is the resistance less than 5 ohms?**	Yes No	▶ ▶	GO to [CKP1-4]. SERVICE the distributor GND wire.
CKP1-4	**CHECK CKP 1 WIRE FOR OPEN**			
	• Key OFF. • Install breakout box (leave PCM disconnected). • Disconnect the 6-pin distributor connector. • Measure the resistance of the CKP 1 wire between Test Pin CKP 1 and the CKP 1 wire at the 6-pin distributor harness connector. • **Is the resistance less than 5 ohms?**	Yes No	▶ ▶	GO to [CKP1-5]. SERVICE the CKP 1 wire for open.
CKP1-5	**CHECK CKP 1 WIRE FOR SHORT**			
	• Key OFF. • Install breakout box (leave PCM disconnected). • Disconnect the 6-pin distributor connector. • Measure the resistance of the CKP 1 wire between Test Pin CKP 1 and ground. • **Is the resistance greater than 10,000 ohms?**	Yes No	▶ ▶	REPLACE the distributor. SERVICE the CKP 1 wire for short.

FM0159301088020X

Fig. 88   Pinpoint test CKP1, crankshaft position sensor No. 1 (Part 2 of 2). 1993 2.0L/4-121 w/4EAT & 1993–95 2.5L/V6-152

Crankshaft Position Sensor No. 2 (CKP2) - 2.5L

Note

You should enter this Pinpoint Test only when diagnostic trouble code 02 (2.5L only) is received in Quick Test Steps 5 or 6, or when Quick Test 11 directs you here.

Special Note

The CKP2 sensor is located near the crankshaft pulley.

Remember

This Pinpoint Test is intended to diagnose only the following:
• Circuit: CKP2

Pinpoint Test Schematic

FM0159301089010X

Fig. 89   Pinpoint test CKP2, crankshaft position sensor No. 2 (Part 1 of 2). 1993–95 2.5L/V6-152

Data Sheet

CIRCUIT DATA SHEET

Engine	Circuit	PCM Pin	BOB Pin	Wire Color
2.5L	CKP2	3H	4	GN
	CKPRTN	3F	16	BL
	GND	3C	49	BK/R

TEST STEP	RESULT	►	ACTION TO TAKE
CKP2-1 CHECK CKP2 SENSOR • Key OFF. • Install breakout box (leave PCM disconnected). • Measure the resistance between Test Pin CKP2 and Test Pin CKPRTN. • Is the resistance 520-580 ohms at 20°C (68°F)?	Yes	►	CKP2 circuit OK. If sent to this test by Quick Test Step QT11, RETURN Otherwise, REPLACE the PCM.
	No	►	GO to CKP2-2.
CKP2-2 CHECK CKP2 SENSOR WIRES TO PCM FOR OPEN • Key OFF. • Install breakout box (leave PCM disconnected). • Disconnect the CKP2 sensor connector. • Measure the resistance of the CKP2 and CKPRTN wires between the Test Pins and the corresponding terminals on the CKP2 sensor harness connector. • Are the resistances less than 5 ohms?	Yes	►	GO to CKP2-3.
	No	►	SERVICE the wire(s) in question for opens.
CKP2-3 CHECK CKP2 SENSOR WIRES TO PCM FOR SHORTS • Key OFF. • Install breakout box (leave PCM disconnected). • Disconnect the CKP2 sensor connector. • Measure the resistance of the CKP2 and CKPRTN wires between the Test Pins and ground. • Are the resistances greater than 10,000 ohms?	Yes	►	GO to CKP2-4.
	No	►	SERVICE the wire(s) in question for shorts.
CKP2-4 CHECK GROUND CIRCUIT CONTINUITY • Key OFF. • Disconnect the CKP2 sensor connector. • Measure the resistance between sensor harness connector GND terminal and ground. • Is the resistance less than 5 ohms?	Yes	►	REPLACE the CKP2 sensor.
	No	►	SERVICE the GND circuit for opens.

FM0159301089020X

Fig. 89 Pinpoint test CKP2, crankshaft position sensor No. 2 (Part 2 of 2). 1993–95 2.5L/V6-152

Camshaft Position (CMP) Sensor

Note

You should enter this Pinpoint Test only when diagnostic trouble code 03 is received in Quick Test Steps 7 or 8, or when Quick Test 11 directs you here.

Remember

This Pinpoint Test is intended to diagnose only the following:

• Circuit: CMP

Description

The Camshaft Position (CMP) sensor detects the Number 1 cylinder when it reaches Top Dead Center (TDC) and signals the Powertrain Control Module (PCM) to control fuel injection.

On 1.3L and 2.5L engines, a single vane rotor cap is mounted to the distributor shaft, below the crankshaft position rotor cap, where it spins according to the camshaft speed. As it rotates through a magnetic Hall effect pickup switch, the sensor detects the opening on the rotor cap and sends an input signal to the PCM.

On 1.8L engines, a slotted disc is mounted to the distributor shaft. As the distributor shaft spins, the slotted disc passes a single opening through a phototransistor. The phototransistor transmits an input signal to the PCM.

FM0159501232010X

Fig. 90 Pinpoint test CMP, camshaft position sensor (Part 1 of 5). 1995

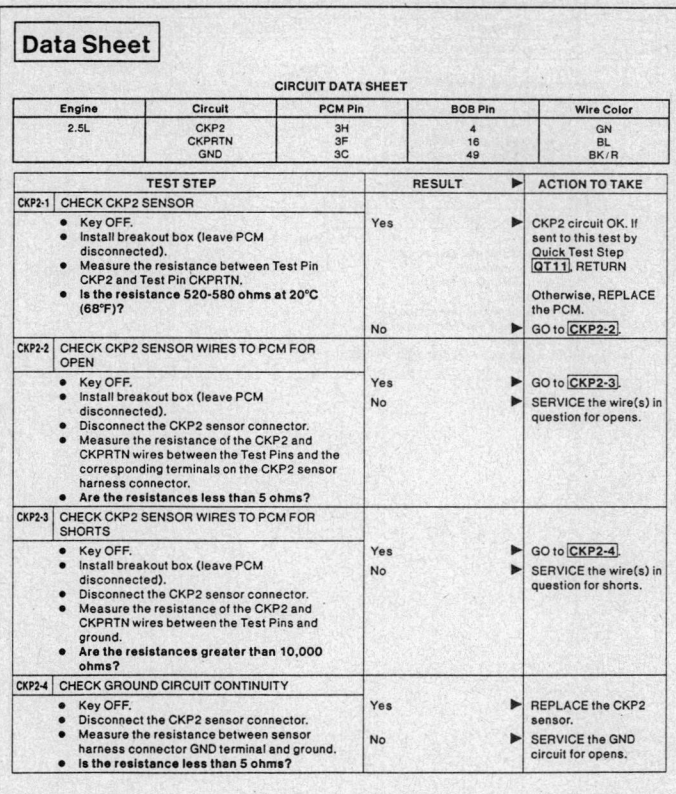

Engine	Location
1.3L, 1.8L, 2.5L	Integrated in the distributor.

FM0159501232020X

Fig. 90 Pinpoint test CMP, camshaft position sensor (Part 2 of 5). 1995

Pinpoint Test Schematic

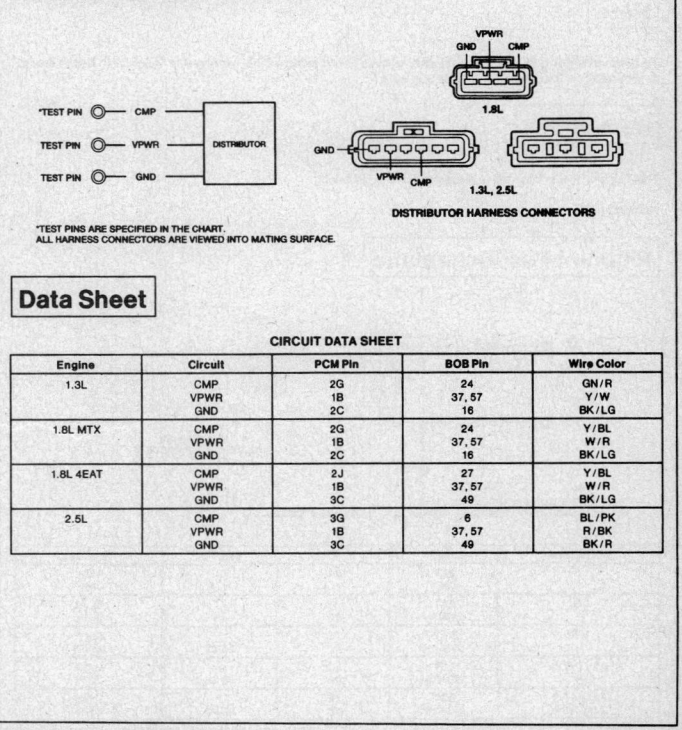

*TEST PINS ARE SPECIFIED IN THE CHART.
ALL HARNESS CONNECTORS ARE VIEWED INTO MATING SURFACE.

Data Sheet

CIRCUIT DATA SHEET

Engine	Circuit	PCM Pin	BOB Pin	Wire Color
1.3L	CMP	2G	24	GN/R
	VPWR	1B	37, 57	Y/W
	GND	2C	16	BK/LG
1.8L MTX	CMP	2G	24	Y/BL
	VPWR	1B	37, 57	W/R
	GND	2C	16	BK/LG
1.8L 4EAT	CMP	2J	27	Y/BL
	VPWR	1B	37, 57	W/R
	GND	3C	49	BK/LG
2.5L	CMP	3G	6	BL/PK
	VPWR	1B	37, 57	R/BK
	GND	3C	49	BK/R

FM0159501232030X

Fig. 90 Pinpoint test CMP, camshaft position sensor (Part 3 of 5). 1995

	TEST STEP	RESULT	▶	ACTION TO TAKE
CMP1	**CHECK CMP SIGNAL**			
	• Key OFF. • Install Breakout Box (BOB) (connect Powertrain Control Module [PCM]). • Measure the voltage at Test Pin CMP while bumping the starter. • **Does the voltage alternate between approximately 0 volts and 5 volts?**	Yes No	▶ ▶	CMP circuit OK. If sent to this test by Quick Test Step **QT11** Otherwise, REPLACE the PCM. GO to **CMP2**.
CMP2	**CHECK VPWR TO DISTRIBUTOR**			
	• Key OFF. • Disconnect the distributor connectors. — 1.8L 4-pin connector — 1.3L and 2.5L 6-pin connector • Key ON. • Measure the voltage at the VPWR wire on the distributor harness connector. • **Is the voltage greater than 10 volts?**	Yes No	▶ ▶	GO to **CMP3**. GO to EEC Pinpoint Test **VPWR** in this section. If VPWR is OK, SERVICE VPWR wire to distributor.
CMP3	**CHECK GROUND AT DISTRIBUTOR**			
	• Key OFF. • Disconnect the distributor connectors. — 1.8L 4-pin connector — 1.3L and 2.5L 6-pin connector • Measure the resistance of the GND wire between the distributor harness connector and ground. • **Is the resistance less than 5 ohms?**	Yes No	▶ ▶	GO to **CMP4**. SERVICE the distributor GND wire.
CMP4	**CHECK CMP WIRE FOR OPEN**			
	• Key OFF. • Install Breakout Box (leave PCM disconnected). • Disconnect the distributor connectors. — 1.8L 4-pin connector — 1.3L and 2.5L 6-pin connector • Measure the resistance of the CMP wire between BOB Test Pin CMP and the CMP wire at the distributor harness connector. • **Is the resistance less than 5 ohms?**	Yes No	▶ ▶	GO to **CMP5**. SERVICE the CMP wire for open.

FM0159501232040X

Fig. 90 Pinpoint test CMP, camshaft position sensor (Part 4 of 5). 1995

	TEST STEP	RESULT	▶	ACTION TO TAKE
CMP5	**CHECK CMP WIRE FOR SHORT TO GROUND**			
	• Key OFF. • Install Breakout Box (leave PCM disconnected). • Disconnect the distributor connectors. — 1.8L 4-pin connector — 1.3L and 2.5L 6-pin connector • Measure the resistance of the CMP wire between BOB Test Pin CMP and ground. • **Is the resistance greater than 10,000 ohms?**	Yes No	▶ ▶	GO to **CMP6**. SERVICE the CMP wire for short to ground.
CMP6	**CHECK FOR SHORTS IN HARNESS**			
	• Key OFF. • Disconnect the distributor connectors. — 1.8L 4-pin connector — 1.3L and 2.5L 6-pin connector • PCM disconnected. • Measure the resistance between the CMP wire and all the other wire terminals on the distributor connector. • **Are all the resistances greater than 10,000 ohms?**	Yes No	▶ ▶	REPLACE the distributor. SERVICE the wire(s) in question.

FM0159501232050X

Fig. 90 Pinpoint test CMP, camshaft position sensor (Part 5 of 5). 1995

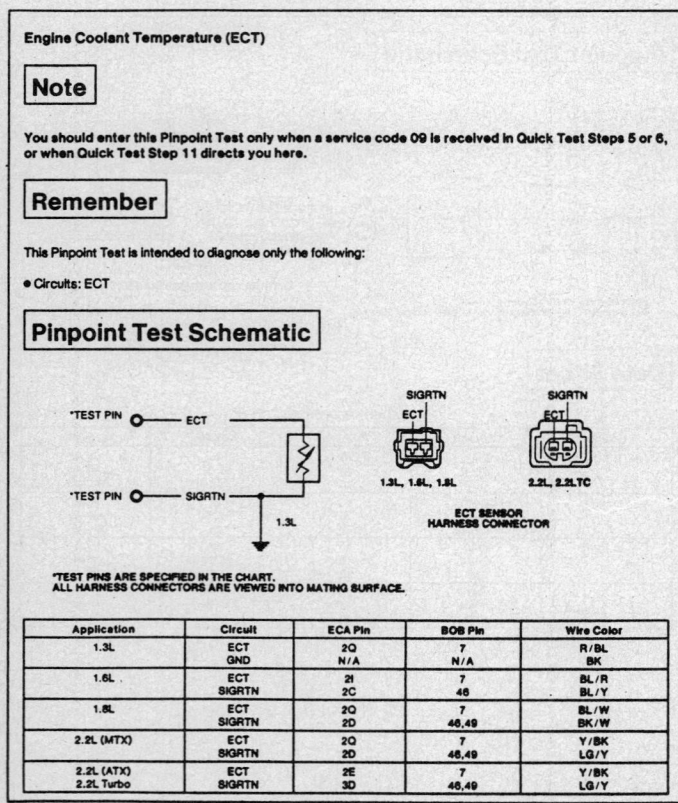

Engine Coolant Temperature (ECT)

Note

You should enter this Pinpoint Test only when a service code 09 is received in Quick Test Steps 5 or 6, or when Quick Test Step 11 directs you here.

Remember

This Pinpoint Test is intended to diagnose only the following:
• Circuits: ECT

Pinpoint Test Schematic

*TEST PINS ARE SPECIFIED IN THE CHART.
ALL HARNESS CONNECTORS ARE VIEWED INTO MATING SURFACE.

Application	Circuit	ECA Pin	BOB Pin	Wire Color
1.3L	ECT GND	2Q N/A	7 N/A	R/BL BK
1.6L	ECT SIGRTN	2I 2C	7 46	BL/R BL/Y
1.8L	ECT SIGRTN	2Q 2D	7 46,49	BL/W BK/W
2.2L (MTX)	ECT SIGRTN	2Q 2D	7 46,49	Y/BK LG/Y
2.2L (ATX) 2.2L Turbo	ECT SIGRTN	2E 3D	7 46,49	Y/BK LG/Y

DUMMY00000000000

Fig. 91 Pinpoint test ECT, engine coolant temperature (Part 1 of 3)

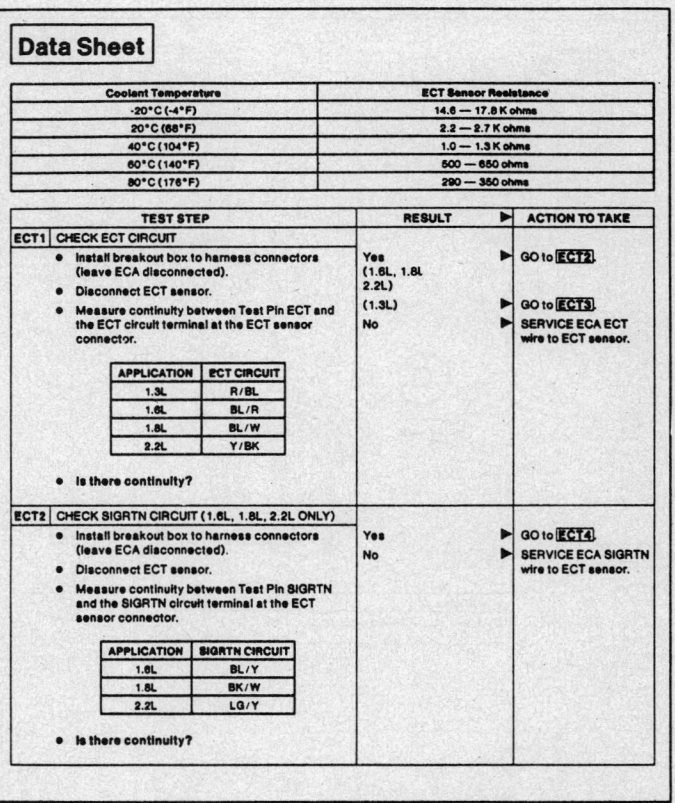

Data Sheet

Coolant Temperature	ECT Sensor Resistance
-20°C (-4°F)	14.6 — 17.8 K ohms
20°C (68°F)	2.2 — 2.7 K ohms
40°C (104°F)	1.0 — 1.3 K ohms
60°C (140°F)	500 — 650 ohms
80°C (176°F)	290 — 350 ohms

	TEST STEP	RESULT	▶	ACTION TO TAKE
ECT1	**CHECK ECT CIRCUIT**			
	• Install breakout box to harness connectors (leave ECA disconnected). • Disconnect ECT sensor. • Measure continuity between Test Pin ECT and the ECT circuit terminal at the ECT sensor connector.	Yes (1.6L, 1.8L 2.2L) (1.3L) No	▶ ▶ ▶	GO to **ECT2**. GO to **ECT3**. SERVICE ECA ECT wire to ECT sensor.
	APPLICATION / ECT CIRCUIT 1.3L — R/BL 1.6L — BL/R 1.8L — BL/W 2.2L — Y/BK • **Is there continuity?**			
ECT2	**CHECK SIGRTN CIRCUIT (1.6L, 1.8L, 2.2L ONLY)**			
	• Install breakout box to harness connectors (leave ECA disconnected). • Disconnect ECT sensor. • Measure continuity between Test Pin SIGRTN and the SIGRTN circuit terminal at the ECT sensor connector.	Yes No	▶ ▶	GO to **ECT4**. SERVICE ECA SIGRTN wire to ECT sensor.
	APPLICATION / SIGRTN CIRCUIT 1.6L — BL/Y 1.8L — BK/W 2.2L — LG/Y • **Is there continuity?**			

DUMMY000000000000

Fig. 91 Pinpoint test ECT, engine coolant temperature (Part 2 of 3)

TEST STEP		RESULT	▶	ACTION TO TAKE
ECT3	CHECK GROUND CIRCUIT (1.3L ONLY)			
	• Disconnect ECT sensor.	Yes	▶	GO to ECT4.
	• Measure continuity between "BK" wire at ECT sensor and ground.	No	▶	SERVICE ECT sensor "BK" wire to ground.
	• Is there continuity?			
ECT4	CHECK ECT SENSOR RESISTANCE			
	• Install breakout box (ECA connected).	Yes	▶	REPLACE ECA.
	• Engine at normal operating temperature.	No	▶	REPLACE ECT sensor.
	• Measure resistance between Test Pins ECT and SIGRTN for 1.6L, 1.8L, 2.2L.			
	• Measure resistance between Test Pin ECT and a ground pin for 1.3L.			
	• Is the resistance between 500-1000 ohms?			

Fig. 91   Pinpoint test ECT, engine coolant temperature (Part 3 of 3)

Cooling Fan Engine Coolant Temperature (ECTF) Sensor — 2.0L 4EAT, 2.5L

Note

You should enter this Pinpoint Test only when diagnostic trouble code 69 is received in Quick Test Steps 5 or 6, or when Quick Test Step 11 directs you here.

Remember

This Pinpoint Test is intended to diagnose only the following:

• Circuit: ECTF

Pinpoint Test Schematic

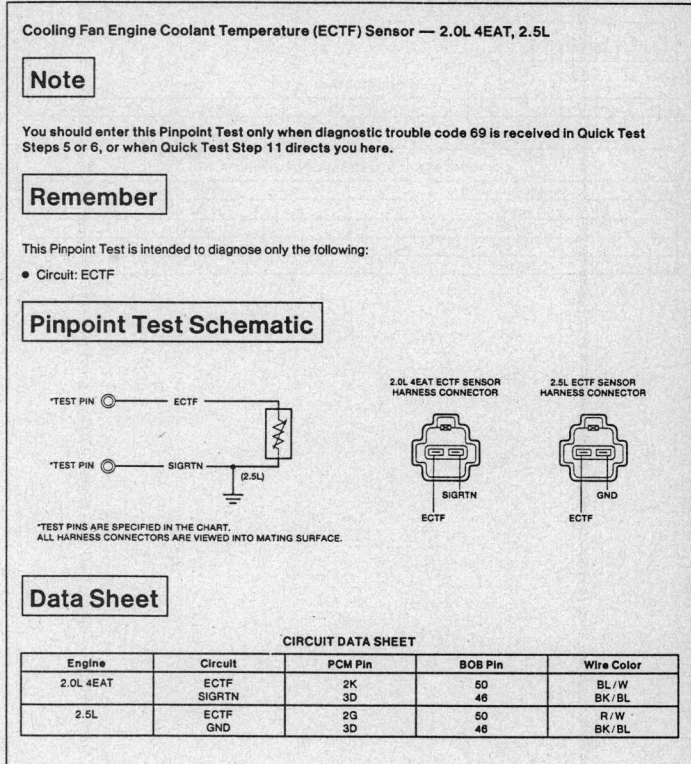

*TEST PINS ARE SPECIFIED IN THE CHART.
ALL HARNESS CONNECTORS ARE VIEWED INTO MATING SURFACE.

Data Sheet

CIRCUIT DATA SHEET

Engine	Circuit	PCM Pin	BOB Pin	Wire Color
2.0L 4EAT	ECTF	2K	50	BL/W
	SIGRTN	3D	46	BK/BL
2.5L	ECTF	2G	50	R/W
	GND	3D	46	BK/BL

FM0159301091010X

Fig. 92   Pinpoint test ECTF, cooling fan engine coolant temperature (Part 1 of 2). 1993 2.0L/4-121 w/4EAT & 1993–94 2.5L/V6-152

ECTF RESISTANCE DATA SHEET

Coolant Temperature °C (°F)	ECTF Sensor Resistance (kohms)
91 (196)	1.70 - 1.84
97 (207)	1.42 - 1.53
108 (226)	1.03 - 1.11

TEST STEP		RESULT	▶	ACTION TO TAKE
ECTF1	CHECK ECTF SENSOR RESISTANCE			
	• Run engine until coolant reaches temperatures specified in Data Sheet. Monitor temperature at ECTF sensor using Rotunda Digital Thermometer 055-00100 or equivalent.	Yes	▶	ECTF circuit OK. If directed here from Quick Test Step QT11, then RETURN
	• Key OFF.			Otherwise, REPLACE the PCM.
	• Install breakout box (leave PCM disconnected).	No	▶	GO to ECTF2.
	• Measure the resistance between Test Pins ECTF and SIGRTN (2.0L 4EAT), or GND (2.5L).			
	• Are the resistance values within specified range shown on Data Sheet?			
ECTF2	CHECK ECTF CIRCUIT			
	• Key OFF.	Yes (2.0L 4EAT)	▶	GO to ECTF3.
	• Install breakout box (leave PCM disconnected).	Yes (2.5L)	▶	GO to ECTF4.
	• Disconnect the ECTF sensor connector.	No	▶	SERVICE the ECTF wire between the PCM and the ECTF sensor.
	• Measure the resistance between ECTF Test Pin and ECTF terminal at the ECTF sensor harness connector (resistance should be less than 5 ohms).			
	• Measure the resistance between ECTF Test Pin and ground (resistance should be greater than 10,000 ohms).			
	• Are the resistance values OK?			
ECTF3	CHECK SIGRTN CIRCUIT (2.0L 4EAT ONLY)			
	• Key OFF.	Yes	▶	REPLACE the ECTF sensor.
	• Install breakout box (leave PCM disconnected).	No	▶	SERVICE the SIGRTN wire between the PCM and the ECTF sensor connector.
	• Disconnect the ECTF sensor connector.			
	• Measure the resistance between SIGRTN Test Pin and SIGRTN terminal at the ECTF sensor harness connector.			
	• Is the resistance less than 5 ohms?			
ECTF4	CHECK GROUND CIRCUIT (2.5L ONLY)			
	• Key OFF.	Yes	▶	REPLACE the ECTF sensor.
	• Disconnect the ECTF sensor connector.	No	▶	SERVICE the GND wire between the PCM and the ECTF sensor.
	• Measure the resistance between GND terminal on the ECTF sensor harness connector and ground.			
	• Is the resistance less than 5 ohms?			

FM0159301091020X

Fig. 92   Pinpoint test ECTF, cooling fan engine coolant temperature (Part 2 of 2). 1993 2.0L/4-121 w/4EAT & 1993–94 2.5L/V6-152

Exhaust Gas Recirculation Temperature (EGRT) Sensor — 2.0L 4EAT

Note

You should enter this Pinpoint Test only when diagnostic trouble code 16 is received in Quick Test Steps 5 and 6, or when Quick Test Step 11 directs you here.

Remember

This Pinpoint Test is intended to diagnose only the following:

• Circuit: EGRT

Special Note

The EGRT is only available on 2.0L 4EAT vehicles equipped with California emissions.

Pinpoint Test Schematic

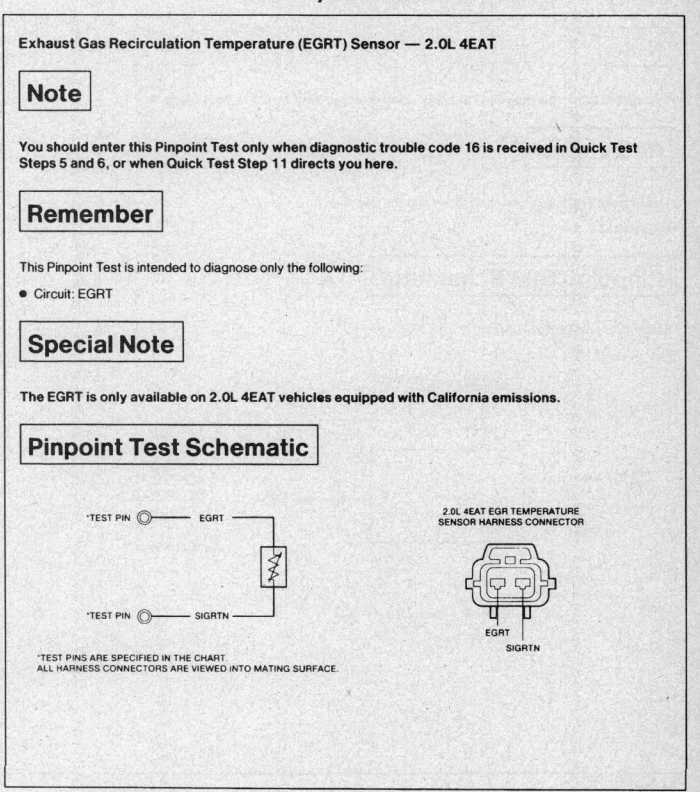

*TEST PINS ARE SPECIFIED IN THE CHART.
ALL HARNESS CONNECTORS ARE VIEWED INTO MATING SURFACE.

FM0159301092010X

Fig. 93   Pinpoint test EGRT, exhaust gas recirculation temperature (Part 1 of 3). 1993 2.0L/4-121 w/4EAT

Data Sheet

CIRCUIT DATA SHEET

Engine	Circuit	PCM Pin	BOB Pin	Wire Color
2.0L 4EAT	EGRT	2J	9	R
	SIGRTN	3D	46	BK/BL

EGRT SENSOR RESISTANCE DATA SHEET

Temperature °C (°F)	Resistance (kohms)
20 (68)	182 - 336
30 (85)	112 - 165
41 (105)	41.3 - 47.6
52 (125)	7.5 - 10.5

TEST STEP	RESULT	▶	ACTION TO TAKE
EGRT1 CHECK EGRT SENSOR RESISTANCE • Monitor the temperature at the EGRT sensor using Rotunda Digital Thermometer 055-00100 or equivalent. • Run engine until the EGRT sensor is at temperature specified in Data Sheet. • Key OFF. • Install breakout box (leave PCM disconnected). • Measure the resistance between Test Pins EGRT and SIGRTN. • **Are the resistances within specified range?**	Yes No	▶	EGRT circuit OK. If directed here from Quick Test Step QT11, then RETURN Otherwise, REPLACE the PCM. GO to EGRT2.
EGRT2 CHECK EGRT WIRE • Key OFF. • Install breakout box (leave PCM disconnected). • Disconnect the EGRT sensor connector. • Measure the resistance between the EGRT Test Pin and the EGRT terminal on the EGRT sensor harness connector, (resistance should be less than 5 ohms). • Measure the resistance between EGRT Test Pin and ground, (resistance should be greater than 10,000 ohms). • **Are the resistances OK?**	Yes No	▶ ▶	GO to EGRT3. SERVICE the EGRT wire between the PCM and the EGRT sensor.
EGRT3 CHECK SIGRTN WIRE • Key OFF. • Install breakout box (leave PCM disconnected). • Measure the resistance between the SIGRTN Test Pin and the SIGRTN terminal on the EGRT sensor connector. • **Is the resistance less than 5 ohms?**	Yes No	▶ ▶	REPLACE the EGRT sensor. SERVICE the SIGRTN wire between the PCM and the EGRT sensor.

FM0159301092020X

Fig. 93 Pinpoint test EGRT, exhaust gas recirculation temperature (Part 2 of 3). 1993 2.0L/4-121 w/4EAT

FM0159301092030X

Fig. 93 Pinpoint test EGRT, exhaust gas recirculation temperature (Part 3 of 3). 1993 2.0L/4-121 w/4EAT

Electrical Load Control Unit (ELU) — 1.6L

Note

You should enter this Pinpoint Test only when directed here by Quick Test Steps 9 or 11.

Remember

This Pinpoint Test is intended to diagnose only the following:
• Circuit: ELU

Pinpoint Test Schematic

Electrical Load Control Unit

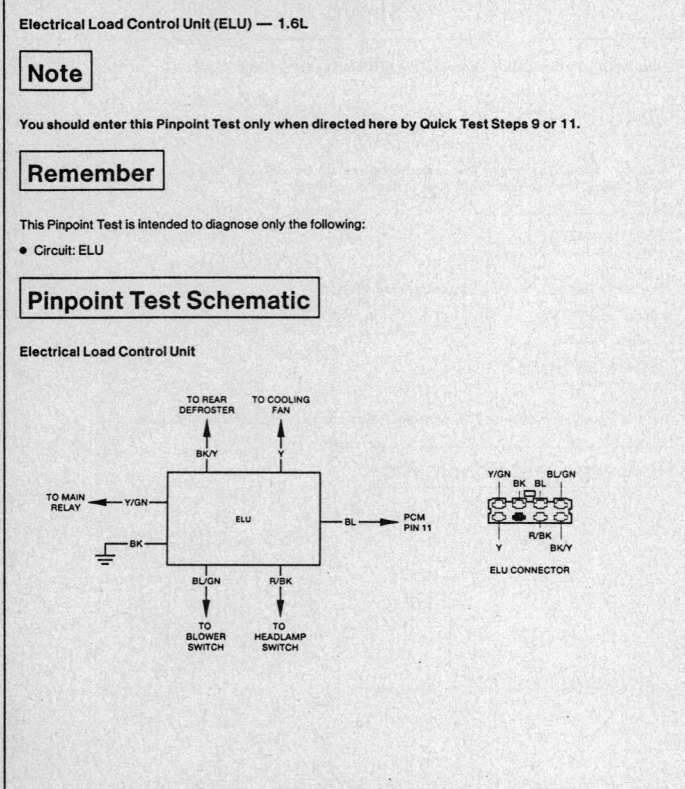

FM0159301093010X

Fig. 94 Pinpoint test ELU, electrical load control unit (Part 1 of 3). 1993–94 1.6L/4-98

Data Sheet

CIRCUIT DATA SHEET

Engine	Circuit	PCM Pin	BOB Pin	Wire Color
1.6L	ELU	1I	11	BL

TEST STEP	RESULT	▶	ACTION TO TAKE
ELU1 CHECK ELU SIGNAL VOLTAGE • Key OFF. • Install breakout box (leave PCM connected). • Key ON. • Measure the voltage between the ELU Test Pin 11 and ground while exercising the inputs below. • Compare readings to the table:	Yes No	▶ ▶	ELU is functional. If sent here from Quick Test Step QT11, RETURN otherwise REPLACE the PCM. GO to ELU2.

Switch Position	Voltage
All accessories off	Greater than 10 volts
Rear defroster on	Less than 1.5 volts
Headlamps on	Less than 1.5 volts
Blower speed 2 to 4	Less than 1.5 volts
Cooling fan on	Less than 1.5 volts

• **Are the voltages OK?**

TEST STEP	RESULT	▶	ACTION TO TAKE
ELU2 CHECK ELU SIGNAL TO PCM • Key OFF. • Install breakout box (leave PCM disconnected). • Key ON. • Measure the resistance between the ELU Test Pin 11 and ground while exercising the below inputs. • Compare readings to the table:	Yes No	▶ ▶	REPLACE the PCM. GO to ELU3.

Switch Position	Resistance
All accessories off	Greater than 10,000 ohms
Rear defroster on	Less than 5 ohms
Headlamps on	Less than 5 ohms
Blower speed 2 to 4	Less than 5 ohms
Cooling fan on	Less than 5 ohms

• **Are the resistances OK?**

FM0159301093020X

Fig. 94 Pinpoint test ELU, electrical load control unit (Part 2 of 3). 1993–94 1.6L/4-98

TEST STEP		RESULT	▶	ACTION TO TAKE
ELU3	**CHECK ELU POWER**			
• Key OFF.		Yes	▶	GO to ELU4.
• Disconnect the ELU connector.		No	▶	SERVICE the "Y/GN"
• Key ON.				wire between the ELU
• Measure the voltage on the "Y/GN" wire at the ELU connector.				and the main relay.
• **Is the voltage greater than 10 volts?**				
ELU4	**CHECK ELU GROUND**			
• Key OFF.		Yes	▶	GO to ELU5.
• Disconnect the ELU connector.		No	▶	SERVICE the "BK"
• Measure the resistance of the "BK" wire between the ELU connector and ground.				wire.
• **Is the resistance less than 5 ohms?**				
ELU5	**CHECK ELU INPUTS SIGNALS**			
• Key OFF.		Yes	▶	REPLACE the ELU.
• Disconnect the ELU connector.		No	▶	REFER to the Service
• Take the following measurements on the ELU inputs.				
• All measurements are from the input wire on the ELU connector to ground.				the rear defroster.
NOTE: Voltage measurements are made with the key ON. Resistance measurements are made with the key OFF.				the headlamps.
				the cooling fan.
				the blower speed.

Switch and Position	Measurements
Rear defroster on	Greater than 10 volts
Rear defroster off	Less than 5 volts
Headlamps on	Greater than 10 volts
Headlamps off	Less than 5 volts
Cooling fan on	Less than 1.5 volts
Cooling fan off	Greater than 10 volts
Blower speed 2 to 4	Less than 5 ohms
Blower speed 1 or off	Greater than 10,000 ohms

• **Are the measurements OK?**

FM0159301093030X

Fig. 94 Pinpoint test ELU, electrical load control unit (Part 3 of 3). 1993–94 1.6L/4-98

Exhaust Gas Recirculation Valve Position (EVP) Sensor — 2.5L

Note

You should enter this Pinpoint Test only when diagnostic trouble code 16 is received in Quick Test Steps 5 or 6, or when Quick Test Step 11 directs you here.

Remember

This Pinpoint Test is intended to diagnose only the following:

• Circuit: EVP

Pinpoint Test Schematic

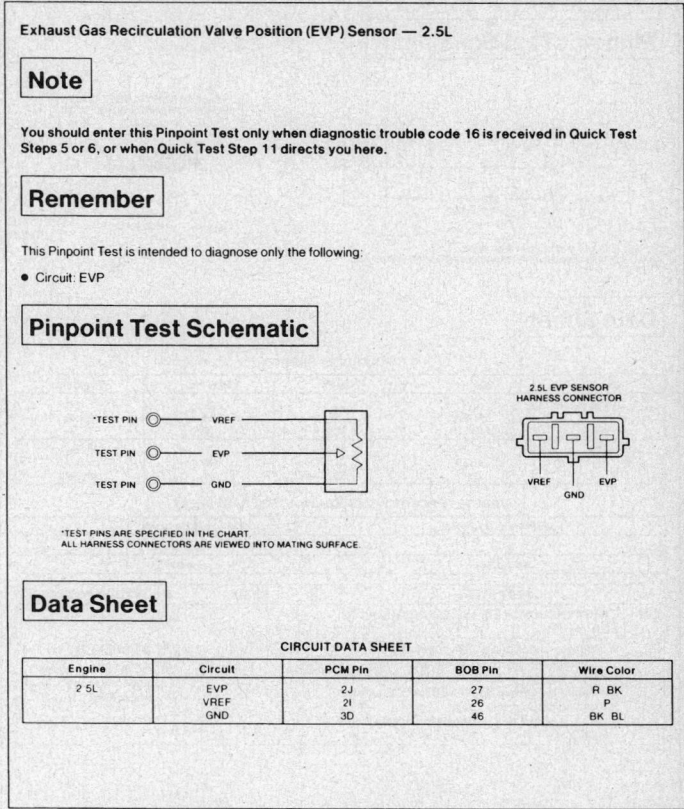

*TEST PINS ARE SPECIFIED IN THE CHART.
ALL HARNESS CONNECTORS ARE VIEWED INTO MATING SURFACE.

Data Sheet

CIRCUIT DATA SHEET				
Engine	Circuit	PCM Pin	BOB Pin	Wire Color
2.5L	EVP	2J	27	R BK
	VREF	2I	26	P
	GND	3D	46	BK BL

FM0159301094010X

Fig. 95 Pinpoint test EVP, EGR valve position (Part 1 of 2). 1993–94 2.5L/V6-152

EVP VACUUM/VOLTAGE DATA SHEET	
Vacuum mm-Hg (in-Hg)	**Voltage (volts)**
0 (0)	Approx. 0.8
150 (5.90)	Approx. 5.0

TEST STEP		RESULT	▶	ACTION TO TAKE
EVP1	**CHECK EVP SIGNAL TO PCM**			
• Key OFF.		Yes	▶	EVP circuit OK. If
• Install breakout box (connect PCM).				directed here from
• Connect Rotunda Vacuum Tester 021-00014 or equivalent to the EGR valve vacuum port.				Quick Test Step QT11, then RETURN.
• Key ON.				Otherwise,
• Measure the voltage between Test Pins EVP and GND.				REPLACE the PCM.
• Compare the voltage readings to the Data Sheet as vacuum is increased.		No	▶	GO to EVP2.
• **Are the voltages OK?**				
EVP2	**CHECK VREF AT EVP SENSOR**			
• Key OFF.		Yes	▶	GO to EVP3.
• Disconnect the EVP sensor connector.		No	▶	GO to EEC Pinpoint
• Key ON.				Test VREF.
• Measure the voltage at VREF terminal on EVP sensor harness connector.				
• **Is the voltage between 4.5 and 5.5 volts?**				
EVP3	**CHECK GROUND AT EVP SENSOR**			
• Key OFF.		Yes	▶	GO to EVP4.
• Disconnect the EVP sensor connector.		No	▶	SERVICE the EVP
• Measure the resistance between GND terminal at EVP sensor harness connector and ground.				sensor GND wire.
• **Is the resistance less than 5 ohms?**				
EVP4	**CHECK EVP WIRE FOR OPEN**			
• Key OFF.		Yes	▶	GO to EVP5.
• Install breakout box (leave PCM disconnected).		No	▶	SERVICE the EVP wire
• Disconnect the EVP sensor connector.				for open(s).
• Measure the resistance of the EVP wire between Test Pin EVP and EVP terminal on the EVP sensor harness connector.				
• **Is the resistance less than 5 ohms?**				
EVP5	**CHECK EVP WIRE FOR SHORT**			
• Key OFF.		Yes	▶	REPLACE the EVP
• Install breakout box (leave PCM disconnected).				sensor.
• Disconnect the EVP sensor connector.		No	▶	SERVICE the EVP wire
• Measure the resistance between Test Pin EVP and ground.				for short(s).
• **Is the resistance greater than 10,000 ohms?**				

FM0159301094020X

Fig. 95 Pinpoint test EVP, EGR valve position (Part 2 of 2). 1993–94 2.5L/V6-152

Exhaust Gas Recirculation (EGR) Valve Position Sensor — 1.3L, 2.5L

Note

You should enter this Pinpoint Test only when diagnostic trouble code 16 is received in Quick Test Steps 7 or 8, or when Quick Test Step 11 directs you here.

Remember

This Pinpoint Test is intended to diagnose only the following:

• Circuit: EVP

Description

The Exhaust Gas Recirculation (EGR) valve position sensor provides information to the Powertrain Control Module (PCM) reflecting the EGR valve position. There are two purposes for the EGR valve position sensor. The sensor indicates the amount of exhaust gas flowing into the engine by monitoring the EGR valve movement, and also notifies the PCM of electrical failure in the EGR valve.

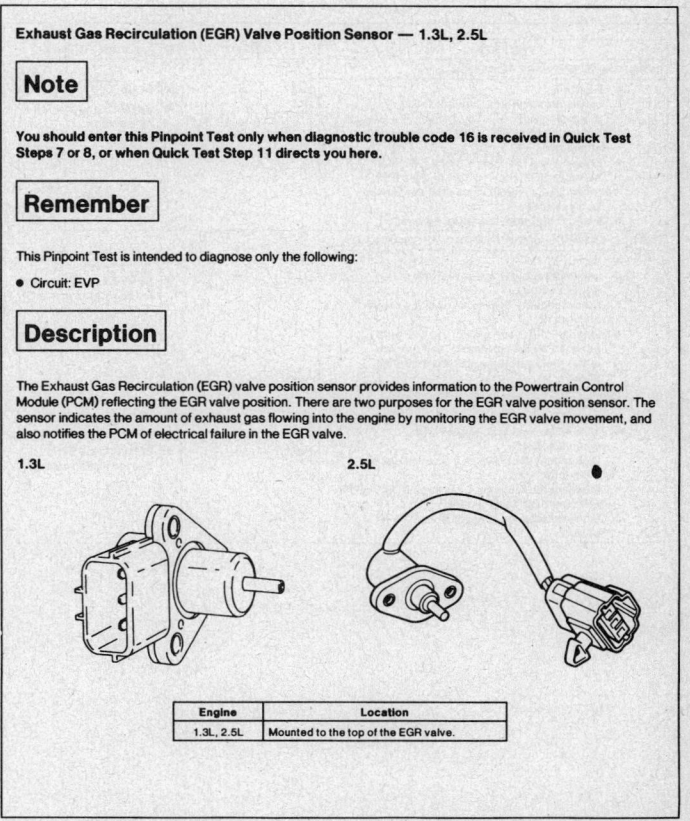

Engine	Location
1.3L, 2.5L	Mounted to the top of the EGR valve.

FM0159501235010X

Fig. 96 Pinpoint test EVP, EGR valve position (Part 1 of 4). 1995 1.3L/4-81 & 2.5L/V6-152

Pinpoint Test Schematic

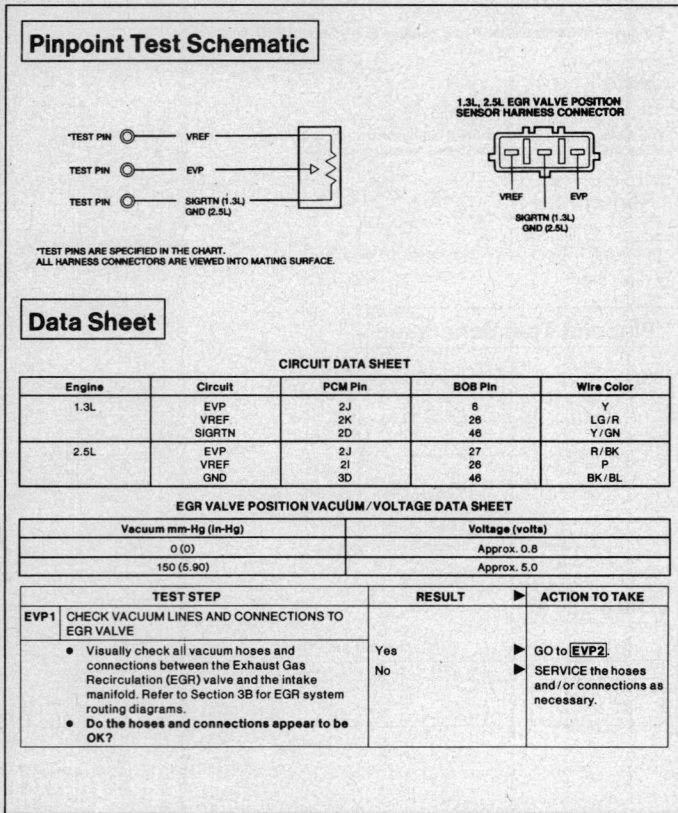

*TEST PIN ── VREF
TEST PIN ── EVP
TEST PIN ── SIGRTN (1.3L)
GND (2.5L)

1.3L, 2.5L EGR VALVE POSITION
SENSOR HARNESS CONNECTOR

VREF   EVP

SIGRTN (1.3L)
GND (2.5L)

*TEST PINS ARE SPECIFIED IN THE CHART.
ALL HARNESS CONNECTORS ARE VIEWED INTO MATING SURFACE.

Data Sheet

CIRCUIT DATA SHEET

Engine	Circuit	PCM Pin	BOB Pin	Wire Color
1.3L	EVP	2J	8	Y
	VREF	2K	26	LG/R
	SIGRTN	2D	46	Y/GN
2.5L	EVP	2J	27	R/BK
	VREF	2I	26	P
	GND	3D	46	BK/BL

EGR VALVE POSITION VACUUM/VOLTAGE DATA SHEET

Vacuum mm-Hg (in-Hg)	Voltage (volts)
0 (0)	Approx. 0.8
150 (5.90)	Approx. 5.0

	TEST STEP	RESULT	►	ACTION TO TAKE
EVP1	CHECK VACUUM LINES AND CONNECTIONS TO EGR VALVE			
	• Visually check all vacuum hoses and connections between the Exhaust Gas Recirculation (EGR) valve and the intake manifold. Refer to Section 3B for EGR system routing diagrams. • Do the hoses and connections appear to be OK?	Yes No	► ►	GO to EVP2. SERVICE the hoses and/or connections as necessary.

FM0159501235020X

Fig. 96   Pinpoint test EVP, EGR valve position (Part 2 of 4). 1995 1.3L/4-81 & 2.5L/V6-152

	TEST STEP	RESULT	►	ACTION TO TAKE
EVP2	CHECK VACUUM AT EGR VALVE			
	• Key OFF. • Connect a Rotunda Vacuum/Pressure Tester 059-00008, or equivalent, between the EGR valve and the vacuum hose leading to the EGR valve. • Key ON, engine running. • Warm the engine until it is at normal operating temperature. • Drive the vehicle while observing the vacuum gauge.	Yes No	► ►	GO to EVP3. CHECK the vacuum hoses and connections for splits, blockage, leaks, or damage. If OK, REFER to Exhaust Gas Recirculation (EGR) Systems.

Condition	1.3L Vacuum mm-Hg (in-Hg)	2.5L Vacuum mm-Hg (in-Hg)
Normal cruising	126 (5)	254 (10)
Idle, deceleration, or high speed	0 (0)	0 (0)

	TEST STEP	RESULT	►	ACTION TO TAKE
	• Are the vacuum readings OK?			
EVP3	CHECK EVP SIGNAL TO PCM			
	• Key OFF. • Install Breakout Box (BOB) (connect Powertrain Control Module [PCM]). • Connect Rotunda Vacuum Tester 021-00014 or equivalent to the EGR valve vacuum port. • Key ON. • Measure the voltage between Test Pins EVP and SIGRTN (1.3L) or GND (2.5L). • Compare the voltage readings to the Data Sheet as vacuum is increased. • Are the voltages OK?	Yes No	► ►	EVP circuit OK. If directed here from Quick Test Step QT11. Otherwise, REPLACE the PCM. GO to EVP4.
EVP4	CHECK VREF AT EGR VALVE POSITION SENSOR			
	• Key OFF. • Disconnect the EGR valve position sensor connector. • Key ON. • Measure the voltage at the VREF terminal on the EGR valve position sensor harness connector. • Is the voltage between 4.5 and 5.5 volts?	Yes No	► ►	GO to EVP5. GO to EEC Pinpoint Test VREF in this section.
EVP5	CHECK GROUND AT EGR VALVE POSITION SENSOR			
	• Key OFF. • Disconnect the EGR valve position sensor connector. • Measure the resistance between the SIGRTN (1.3L) or the GND (2.5L) terminal at the EGR valve position sensor harness connector and ground. • Is the resistance less than 5 ohms?	Yes No	► ►	GO to EVP6. SERVICE the EGR valve position sensor SIGRTN (1.3L) or GND (2.5L) wire.

FM0159501235030X

Fig. 96   Pinpoint test EVP, EGR valve position (Part 3 of 4). 1995 1.3L/4-81 & 2.5L/V6-152

	TEST STEP	RESULT	►	ACTION TO TAKE
EVP6	CHECK EVP WIRE FOR OPEN			
	• Key OFF. • Install Breakout Box (leave PCM disconnected). • Disconnect the EGR valve position sensor connector. • Measure the resistance of the EVP wire between BOB Test Pin EVP and the EVP terminal on the EGR valve position sensor harness connector. • Is the resistance less than 5 ohms?	Yes No	► ►	GO to EVP7. SERVICE the EVP wire for open(s).
EVP7	CHECK EVP WIRE FOR SHORT TO GROUND			
	• Key OFF. • Install Breakout Box (leave PCM disconnected). • Disconnect the EGR valve position sensor connector. • Measure the resistance of the EVP wire between BOB Test Pin EVP and ground. • Is the resistance greater than 10,000 ohms?	Yes No	► ►	GO to EVP8. SERVICE the EVP wire for short(s) to ground.
EVP8	CHECK EVP WIRE FOR SHORT TO VREF			
	• Key OFF. • Install Breakout Box (leave PCM disconnected). • Disconnect the EGR valve position sensor connector. • Measure the resistance between BOB Test Pin EVP and BOB Test Pin VREF. • Is the resistance greater than 10,000 ohms?	Yes No	► ►	REPLACE the EGR valve position sensor. SERVICE the EVP and/or VREF wire(s).

FM0159501235040X

Fig. 96   Pinpoint test EVP, EGR valve position (Part 4 of 4). 1995 1.3L/4-81 & 2.5L/V6-152

Heated Oxygen Sensor (HO2S) — 2.0L 4EAT, 2.5L

Note

You should enter this Pinpoint Test only when diagnostic trouble code 15 or 17 (2.0L 4EAT and 2.5L), 23 or 24 (2.5L only) is received in Quick Test Steps 5 or 6, or when Quick Test Step 11 directs you here.

Remember

This Pinpoint Test is intended to diagnose only the following:

• Circuit: HO2S

Special Note

For 2.5L, a code 15 or 17 indicates a LHO2S (left sensor) malfunction, and a code 23 or 24 indicates a RHO2S (right sensor) malfunction. A code 15 or 23 indicates a continuous HO2S output voltage of less than 0.55 volts. A code 17 or 24 indicates that the HO2S feedback system output does not change. A code 17 or 24 may indicate a condition other than a HO2S circuit malfunction.

Pinpoint Test Schematic

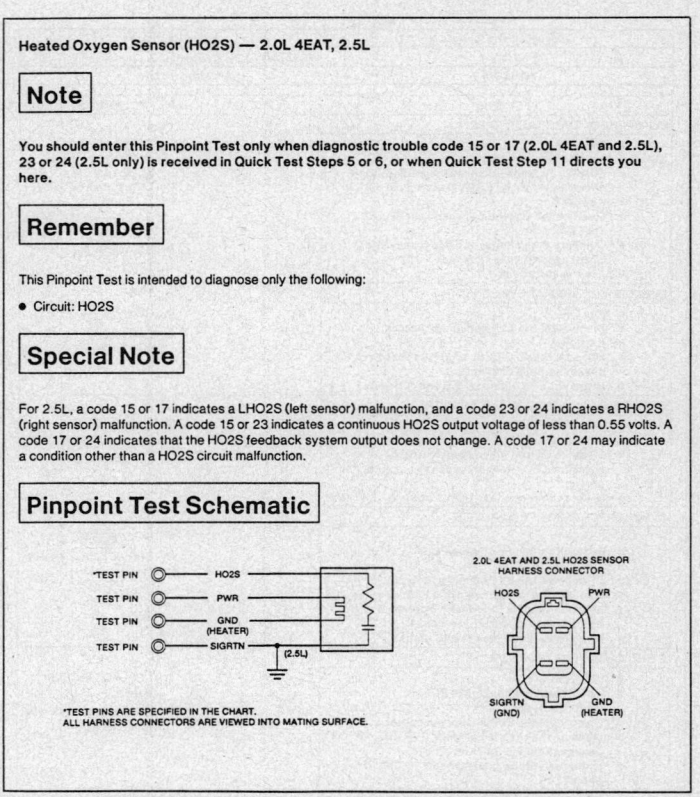

*TEST PIN ── HO2S
TEST PIN ── PWR
TEST PIN ── GND (HEATER)
TEST PIN ── SIGRTN (2.5L)

2.0L 4EAT AND 2.5L HO2S SENSOR
HARNESS CONNECTOR

HO2S   PWR

SIGRTN (GND)   GND (HEATER)

*TEST PINS ARE SPECIFIED IN THE CHART.
ALL HARNESS CONNECTORS ARE VIEWED INTO MATING SURFACE.

FM0159301095010X

Fig. 97   Pinpoint test HO2S, heated oxygen sensor (Part 1 of 4). 1993 2.0L/4-121 w/4EAT & 1993–94 2.5L/V6-152

Data Sheet

CIRCUIT DATA SHEET

Engine	Circuit	PCM Pin	BOB Pin	Wire Color
2.0L 4EAT	HO2S	2C	29	BK/Y
	SIGRTN	3D	46	BK/BL
2.5L	RHO2S	2C	29	BK/Y
	LHO2S	2D	43	BL/W
	GND	3D	46	BK/BL

HO2S VOLTAGE DATA SHEET

Condition	Voltage
Key ON, engine off	0 volts
Idle (cold)	0 volts
Idle (warm)	0 - 1.0 volts (not constant)
Acceleration	0.5 - 1.0 volts
Deceleration	0 - 0.5 volts

TEST STEP	RESULT	▶	ACTION TO TAKE
HO2S1 CHECK HO2S SENSOR VOLTAGE • Key OFF. • Install breakout box (connect PCM). • Run engine at 2,000-3,000 rpm for 2 minutes or until engine reaches normal operating temperature. • Measure the voltage at Test Pin HO2S. Compare the voltage readings to Data Sheet. • **Are the voltages OK?**	Yes No (2.5L) No (2.0L 4EAT)	▶ ▶ ▶	GO to HO2S6. GO to HO2S2. GO to HO2S3.
HO2S2 CHECK HO2S SENSOR GROUND (2.5L) • Key OFF. • Disconnect the HO2S sensor connector. • Measure the resistance of the GND wire between the GND terminal at the HO2S sensor connector and ground. • **Is the resistance less than 5 ohms?**	Yes No	▶ ▶	GO to HO2S4. SERVICE the HO2S sensor GND wire.
HO2S3 CHECK HO2S SENSOR SIGRTN (2.0L 4EAT) • Key OFF. • Install breakout box (leave PCM disconnected). • Disconnect the HO2S sensor connector. • Measure the resistance of the SIGRTN wire between Test Pin SIGRTN and the SIGRTN terminal at the HO2S sensor harness connector. • **Is the resistance less than 5 ohms?**	Yes No	▶ ▶	GO to HO2S4. SERVICE the HO2S sensor SIGRTN wire.

FM0159301095020X

Fig. 97   Pinpoint test HO2S, heated oxygen sensor (Part 2 of 4). 1993 2.0L/4-121 w/4EAT & 1993–94 2.5L/V6-152

TEST STEP	RESULT	▶	ACTION TO TAKE
HO2S4 CHECK HO2S WIRE TO PCM FOR OPEN • Key OFF. • Install breakout box (leave PCM disconnected). • Disconnect the HO2S sensor connector. • Measure the resistance of the HO2S wire between Test Pin HO2S and the HO2S terminal at the HO2S sensor harness connector. • **Is the resistance less than 5 ohms?**	Yes No	▶ ▶	GO to HO2S5. SERVICE the HO2S wire for open(s).
HO2S5 CHECK HO2S WIRE TO PCM FOR SHORT • Key OFF. • Install breakout box (leave PCM disconnected). • Disconnect the HO2S sensor connector. • Measure the resistance of the HO2S wire between Test Pin HO2S and ground. • **Is the resistance greater than 10,000 ohms?**	Yes No	▶ ▶	REPLACE the HO2S sensor. SERVICE the HO2S wire for short(s).
HO2S6 CHECK HO2S HEATER RESISTANCE • Key OFF. • Disconnect the HO2S sensor connector. • Measure the resistance between the HO2S sensor PWR terminal and "heater" GND terminal on the sensor. • **Is the resistance approximately 6 ohms (at 20°C, 68°F)?**	Yes No	▶ ▶	GO to HO2S7. REPLACE the HO2S sensor.
HO2S7 CHECK POWER TO HO2S SENSOR HEATER • Key OFF. • Disconnect the HO2S sensor connector. • Key ON. • Measure the voltage at the PWR terminal on the HO2S sensor harness connector. • **Is the voltage greater than 10 volts?**	Yes No (2.0L 4EAT) No (2.5L)	▶ ▶ ▶	GO to HO2S9. GO to HO2S8. GO to EEC Pinpoint Test VPWR. If VPWR is OK, SERVICE VPWR wire to HO2S sensor.
HO2S8 CHECK PWR WIRE TO HO2S SENSOR (2.0L 4EAT) • Key OFF. • Remove the 15A AIR COND fuse located in the interior fuse panel. • Disconnect the HO2S sensor connector. • Measure the resistance of the "BL/BK" wire between the HO2S sensor harness connector and the 15A AIR COND fuse terminal. • **Is the resistance less than 5 ohms?**	Yes No	▶ ▶	REPLACE the 15A AIR COND fuse. If fuse fails again, SERVICE short. SERVICE the "BL/BK" wire.

FM0159301095030A

Fig. 97   Pinpoint test HO2S, heated oxygen sensor (Part 3 of 4). 1993 2.0L/4-121 w/4EAT & 1993–94 2.5L/V6-152

TEST STEP	RESULT	▶	ACTION TO TAKE
HO2S9 CHECK HO2S SENSOR HEATER GROUND • Key OFF. • Disconnect the HO2S sensor connector. • Measure the resistance of the HO2S sensor heater GND wire between the HO2S sensor harness connector and ground. • **Is the resistance less than 5 ohms?**	Yes No	▶ ▶	HO2S circuit OK. If directed here from Quick Test step QT11, then RETURN Otherwise, REPLACE the PCM. SERVICE the HO2S sensor heater GND wire.

FM0159301095040X

Fig. 97   Pinpoint test HO2S, heated oxygen sensor (Part 4 of 4). 1993 2.0L/4-121 w/4EAT & 1993–94 2.5L/V6-152

Pinpoint Test Schematic

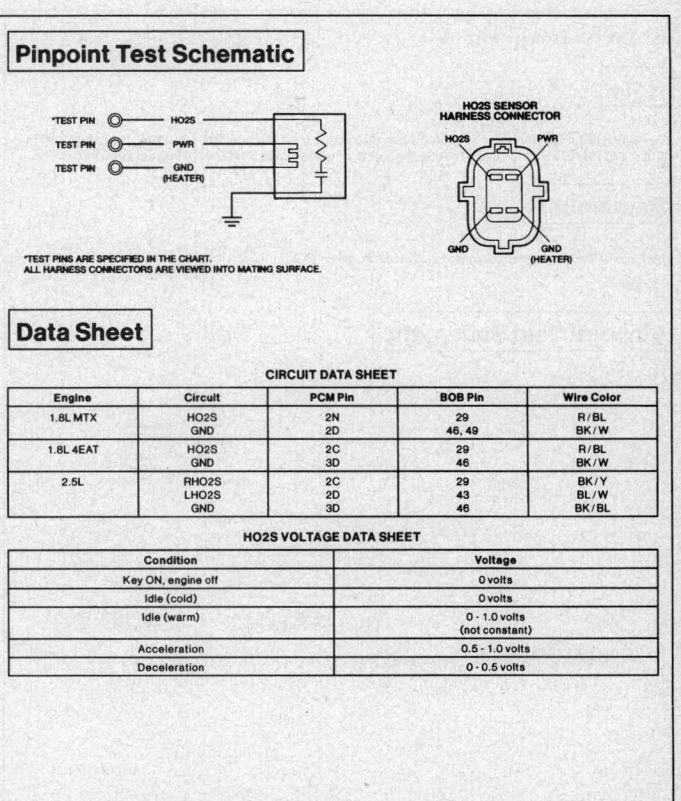

*TEST PINS ARE SPECIFIED IN THE CHART.
ALL HARNESS CONNECTORS ARE VIEWED INTO MATING SURFACE.

Data Sheet

CIRCUIT DATA SHEET

Engine	Circuit	PCM Pin	BOB Pin	Wire Color
1.8L MTX	HO2S	2N	29	R/BL
	GND	2D	46, 49	BK/W
1.8L 4EAT	HO2S	2C	29	R/BL
	GND	3D	46	BK/W
2.5L	RHO2S	2C	29	BK/Y
	LHO2S	2D	43	BL/W
	GND	3D	46	BK/BL

HO2S VOLTAGE DATA SHEET

Condition	Voltage
Key ON, engine off	0 volts
Idle (cold)	0 volts
Idle (warm)	0 - 1.0 volts (not constant)
Acceleration	0.5 - 1.0 volts
Deceleration	0 - 0.5 volts

FM0159501236010X

Fig. 98   Pinpoint test HO2S, heated oxygen sensor (Part 1 of 3). 1995 1.8L/4-112 & 2.5L/V6-152

	TEST STEP	RESULT	▶	ACTION TO TAKE
HO2S1	CHECK HO2S SENSOR VOLTAGE			
	• Key OFF. • Install Breakout Box (BOB) (connect Powertrain Control Module [PCM]). • Run engine at 2,000-3,000 rpm for 2 minutes or until engine reaches normal operating temperature. • Measure the voltage at BOB Test Pin HO2S. Compare the voltage readings to Data Sheet. • **Are the voltages OK?**	Yes No	▶ ▶	GO to HO2S5. GO to HO2S2.
HO2S2	CHECK HO2S SENSOR GROUND			
	• Key OFF. • Disconnect the HO2S connector. • Measure the resistance of the GND wire between the GND terminal at the HO2S sensor harness connector and ground. • **Is the resistance less than 5 ohms?**	Yes No	▶ ▶	GO to HO2S3. SERVICE the HO2S GND wire.
HO2S3	CHECK HO2S WIRE TO PCM FOR OPEN			
	• Key OFF. • Install Breakout Box (leave PCM disconnected). • Disconnect the HO2S sensor connector. • Measure the resistance of the HO2S wire between BOB Test Pin HO2S and the HO2S terminal at the HO2S sensor harness connector. • **Is the resistance less than 5 ohms?**	Yes No	▶ ▶	GO to HO2S4. SERVICE the HO2S wire for open(s).
HO2S4	CHECK HO2S WIRE TO PCM FOR SHORT			
	• Key OFF. • Install Breakout Box (leave PCM disconnected). • Disconnect the HO2S connector. • Measure the resistance of the HO2S wire between BOB Test Pin HO2S and ground. • **Is the resistance greater than 10,000 ohms?**	Yes No	▶ ▶	REPLACE the HO2S sensor. SERVICE the HO2S wire for short(s).
HO2S5	CHECK HO2S HEATER RESISTANCE			
	• Key OFF. • Disconnect the HO2S connector. • Measure the resistance between the HO2S PWR terminal and "heater" GND terminal on the sensor. • **Is the resistance approximately 6 ohms at 20°C (68°F)?**	Yes No	▶ ▶	GO to HO2S6. REPLACE the HO2S.

FM0159501236020X

Fig. 98 Pinpoint test HO2S, heated oxygen sensor (Part 2 of 3). 1995 1.8L/4-112 & 2.5L/V6-152

	TEST STEP	RESULT	▶	ACTION TO TAKE
HO2S6	CHECK POWER TO HO2S SENSOR HEATER			
	• Key OFF. • Disconnect the HO2S connector. • Key ON. • Measure the voltage at the PWR terminal on the HO2S harness connector. • **Is the voltage greater than 10 volts?**	Yes No (1.8L) No (2.5L)	▶ ▶ ▶	GO to HO2S7. CHECK the 15A ENGINE fuse. If fuse is blown, REPLACE fuse. If fuse is OK or fuse fails again, SERVICE the PWR wire between the interior fuse panel and the HO2S. GO to EEC Pinpoint Test VPWR in this section. If VPWR is OK, SERVICE VPWR wire to HO2S sensor.
HO2S7	CHECK HO2S SENSOR HEATER GROUND			
	• Key OFF. • Disconnect the HO2S connector. • Measure the resistance of the HO2S heater GND wire between the HO2S harness connector and ground. • **Is the resistance less than 5 ohms?**	Yes No	▶ ▶	HO2S circuit OK. If directed here from Quick Test Step QT11. Otherwise, REPLACE the PCM. SERVICE the HO2S heater GND wire.

FM0159501236030X

Fig. 98 Pinpoint test HO2S, heated oxygen sensor (Part 3 of 3). 1995 1.8L/4-112 & 2.5L/V6-152

Intake Air Temperature (IAT) Sensor

Note

You should enter this Pinpoint Test only when diagnostic trouble code 10 (1.3L, 1.6L, 1.8L, 2.5L) or 11 (2.0L 4EAT) is received in Quick Test Steps 5 or 6, or when Quick Test Step 11 directs you here.

Remember

This Pinpoint Test is intended to diagnose only the following:
• Circuit: IAT

Pinpoint Test Schematic

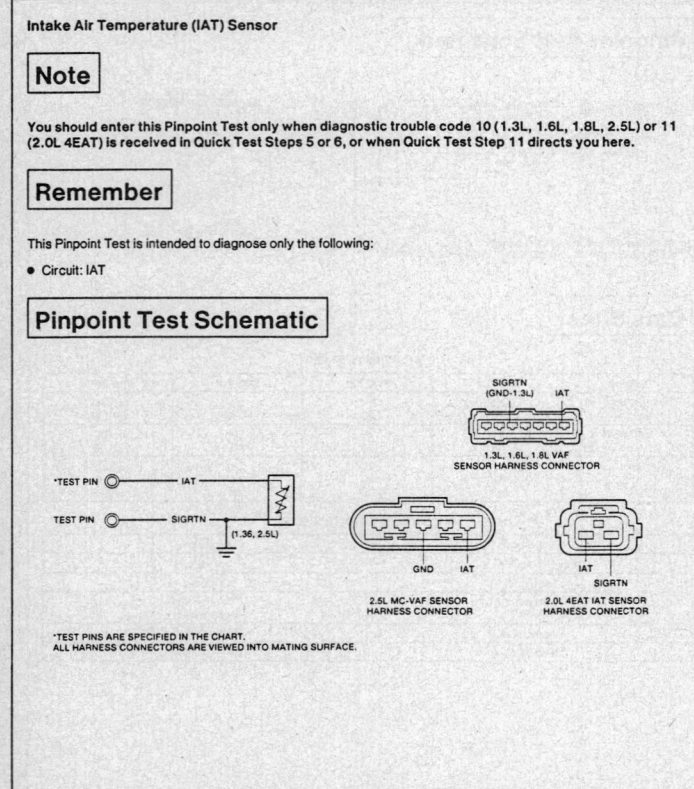

*TEST PINS ARE SPECIFIED IN THE CHART.
ALL HARNESS CONNECTORS ARE VIEWED INTO MATING SURFACE.

Fig. 99 Pinpoint test IAT, intake air temperature (Part 1 of 3)

Data Sheet

CIRCUIT DATA SHEET				
Engine	Circuit	PCM Pin	BOB Pin	Wire Color
1.3L	IAT GND	2P 2D	45 46, 49	GN/BK BK
1.6L	IAT SIGRTN	2J 2C	25 46, 49	BR/Y BL/Y
1.8L MTX	IAT SIGRTN	2P 2D	45 46, 49	R/BK BK/W
1.8L 4EAT	IAT SIGRTN	2K 3D	25 46	R/BK BK/W
2.0L 4EAT	IAT SIGRTN	2F 3D	25 46	R/W BK/BL
2.5L	IAT GND	2K 3D	25 46	BK/R BK/BL

2.0L 4EAT RESISTANCE DATA SHEET		1.3L, 1.6L, 1.8L, 2.5L RESISTANCE DATA SHEET	
Temperature °C (°F)	Resistance (kohms)	Temperature °C (°F)	Resistance (kohms)
0 (32)	72.1 - 79.4	-20 (-4)	10.0 - 20.0
13 (55)	54.3 - 58.6	0 (32)	4.0 - 7.0
25 (77)	29.7 - 36.3	20 (68)	2.0 - 3.0
43 (110)	17.9 - 19.3	40 (104)	0.9 - 1.3
85 (185)	3.3 - 3.7	60 (140)	0.4 - 0.7

	TEST STEP	RESULT	▶	ACTION TO TAKE
IAT1	CHECK IAT RESISTANCE			
	• Key OFF. • Install breakout box (leave PCM disconnected). • Access the IAT sensor. — in VAF sensor on 1.3L, 1.6L, 1.8L — in air cleaner assembly on 2.0L 4EAT — in MC-VAF sensor on 2.5L • Monitor the temperature at the IAT sensor using Rotunda Digital Thermometer 055-00100 or equivalent. • Measure the resistance between Test Pin IAT and Test Pin SIGRTN (GND on 1.3L, 2.5L). • Compare the resistance readings to the Data Sheet as IAT sensor is heated using a blow dryer or Rotunda Heat Gun 107-00300 or equivalent. • **Are the resistances OK?**	Yes No	▶ ▶	IAT circuit OK. If directed here from Quick Test Step QT11, RETURN. Otherwise, REPLACE the PCM. GO to IAT2.

Fig. 99 Pinpoint test IAT, intake air temperature (Part 2 of 3)

TEST STEP		RESULT	▶	ACTION TO TAKE
IAT2	CHECK IAT WIRE FOR OPEN			
	• Key OFF. • Install breakout box (leave PCM disconnected). • Disconnect the following connector: — VAF sensor connector on 1.3L, 1.6L, 1.8L — IAT sensor connector on 2.0L 4EAT — MC-VAF sensor connector on 2.5L • Measure the resistance of the IAT wire between Test Pin IAT and the IAT terminal at the IAT sensor harness connector. • **Is the resistance less than 5 ohms?**	Yes No	▶ ▶	GO to IAT3. SERVICE the IAT wire for open(s).
IAT3	CHECK IAT WIRE FOR SHORT			
	• Key OFF. • Install breakout box (leave PCM disconnected). • Disconnect the following connector: — VAF sensor connector on 1.3L, 1.6L, 1.8L — IAT sensor connector on 2.0L 4EAT — MC-VAF sensor connector on 2.5L • Measure the resistance of the IAT wire between Test Pin IAT and ground. • **Is the resistance greater than 10,000 ohms?**	Yes (1.3L, 2.5L) Yes (1.6L, 1.8L, 2.0L 4EAT) No	▶ ▶ ▶	GO to IAT4. GO to IAT5. SERVICE the IAT wire for short(s).
IAT4	CHECK IAT SENSOR GROUND (1.3L, 2.5L)			
	• Key OFF. • Disconnect the following connector: — VAF sensor connector on 1.3L — MC-VAF sensor connector on 2.5L • Measure the resistance of the GND wire between the IAT sensor harness connector and ground. • **Is the resistance less than 5 ohms?**	Yes No	▶ ▶	REPLACE the VAF sensor 1.3L or the MC-VAF sensor on 2.5L. SERVICE the IAT GND wire.
IAT5	CHECK IAT SENSOR SIGRTN (1.6L, 1.8L, 2.0L 4EAT)			
	• Key OFF. • Install breakout box (leave PCM disconnected). • Disconnect the following connector: — VAF sensor connector on 1.6L, 1.8L — IAT sensor connector 2.0L 4EAT • Measure the resistance of the SIGRTN wire between Test Pin SIGRTN and the SIGRTN terminal on the IAT sensor harness connector. • **Is the resistance less than 5 ohms?**	Yes No	▶ ▶	REPLACE the IAT sensor 2.0L or the VAF sensor 1.6L, 1.8L. SERVICE the IAT SIGRTN wire.

Fig. 99   Pinpoint test IAT, intake air temperature (Part 3 of 3)

Ignition Control Module (ICM) — 2.0L 4EAT, 2.5L

Note

You should enter this Pinpoint Test only when Quick Test Step 11, or Test Step IGN 13 Ignition System Diagnostic Procedures directs you here.

Remember

This Pinpoint Test is intended to diagnose only the following:

• Circuit: ICM

Special Note

The ignition control module is located in the distributor assembly.

Pinpoint Test Schematic

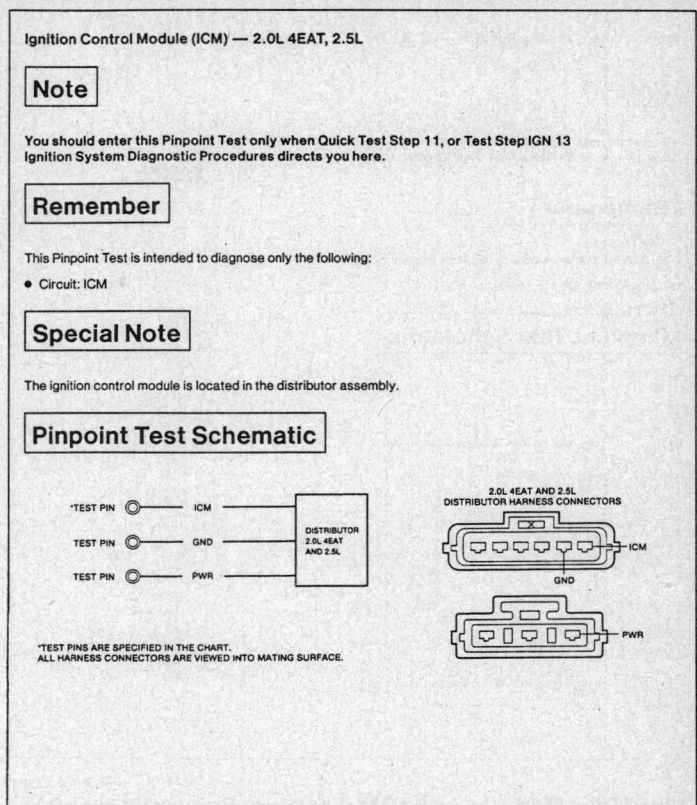

Fig. 100   Pinpoint test ICM, ignition control module (Part 1 of 3). 1993 2.0L/4-121 w/4EAT & 1993–95 1.3L/4-81 & 2.5L/V6-152

Data Sheet

CIRCUIT DATA SHEET

Engine	Circuit	PCM Pin	BOB Pin	Wire Color
2.0L 4EAT	ICM	1I	36	BL/O
	GND	NA	NA	BK
	PWR	NA	NA	BK/P
2.5L	ICM	1G	36	BL/O
	GND	NA	NA	BK/W
	PWR	NA	NA	BK/P

TEST STEP		RESULT	▶	ACTION TO TAKE
ICM1	CHECK FOR CONTINUOUS SPARK			
	• Key OFF. • Disconnect a spark plug wire. • Connect Rotunda Air Gap Spark Tester D81P-6666-A to the disconnected spark plug wire. • Crank the engine. • **Is a continuous strong blue spark produced while cranking the engine?**	Yes No	▶ ▶	ICM circuit OK. GO to ICM2.
ICM2	CHECK ICM SIGNAL FROM PCM			
	• Key OFF. • Install breakout box (connect PCM). • Disconnect the 3-pin distributor connector. • Crank the engine. • Measure the voltage between Test Pin ICM and ground. • **Is voltage greater than 0.7 volts?**	Yes No	▶ ▶	GO to ICM3. GO to EEC Pinpoint Tests CID and CKP1. If OK, REPLACE the PCM.
ICM3	CHECK ICM WIRE FOR OPEN			
	• Key OFF. • Install breakout box (leave PCM disconnected). • Disconnect the 6-pin distributor connector. • Measure the resistance between Test Pin ICM and the ICM terminal at the 6-pin distributor connector. • **Is the resistance less than 5 ohms?**	Yes No	▶ ▶	GO to ICM4. SERVICE the ICM wire for open(s).
ICM4	CHECK ICM WIRE FOR SHORT			
	• Key OFF. • Install breakout box (leave PCM disconnected). • Disconnect the 6-pin distributor connector. • Measure the resistance between Test Pin ICM and ground. • **Is the resistance greater than 10,000 ohms?**	Yes No	▶ ▶	GO to ICM5. SERVICE the ICM wire for short(s).

Fig. 100   Pinpoint test ICM, ignition control module (Part 2 of 3). 1993 2.0L/4-121 w/4EAT & 1993–95 1.3L/4-81 & 2.5L/V6-152

TEST STEP		RESULT	▶	ACTION TO TAKE
ICM5	CHECK GROUND AT DISTRIBUTOR			
	• Key OFF. • Disconnect the 6-pin distributor connector. • Measure the resistance between the GND terminal at the harness connector and ground. • **Is the resistance less than 5 ohms?**	Yes No	▶ ▶	GO to ICM6. SERVICE the distributor GND wire for opens.
ICM6	CHECK PWR TO DISTRIBUTOR			
	• Key OFF. • Disconnect the 3-pin distributor connector. • Key ON. • Measure the voltage on the PWR terminal at the harness connector. • **Is the voltage greater than 10 volts?**	Yes No	▶ ▶	REPLACE the distributor. SERVICE the PWR wire between the distributor and the ignition switch.

FM0159301097030X

Fig. 100   Pinpoint test ICM, ignition control module (Part 3 of 3). 1993 2.0L/4-121 w/4EAT & 1993–95 1.3L/4-81 & 2.5L/V6-152

FM0159301097020X

Ignition Diagnostic Monitor (IDM) — 1.3L, 1.6L, 1.8L

Note

You should enter this Pinpoint Test only when diagnostic trouble code 01 is received in Quick Test Steps 5 or 6, when Quick Test Step 11 directs you here, or when Test Step IGN14 directs you here.

Remember

This Pinpoint Test is intended to diagnose only the following:
- Circuits: IDM, SPOUT, VPWR to ignition

Pinpoint Test Schematic

1.6L

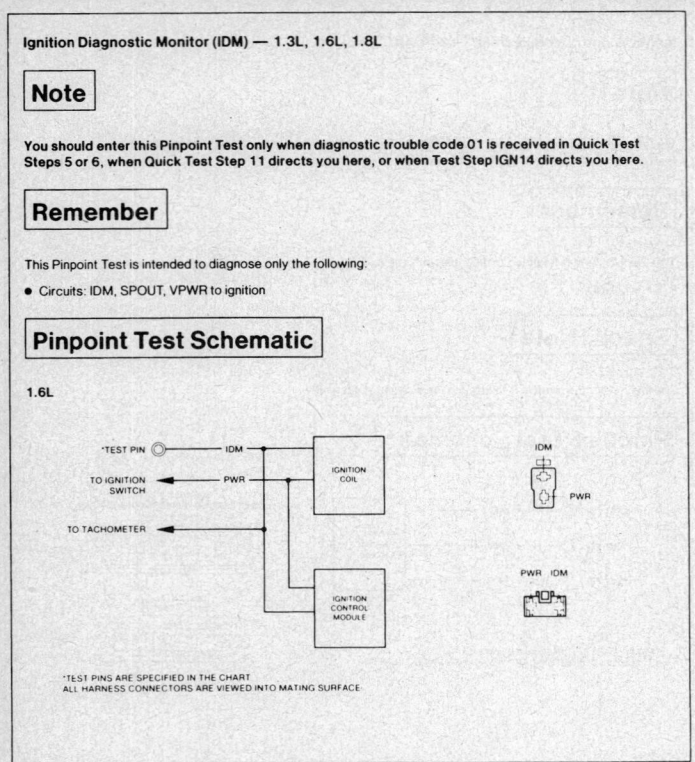

*TEST PINS ARE SPECIFIED IN THE CHART
ALL HARNESS CONNECTORS ARE VIEWED INTO MATING SURFACE.

FM015930109801OX

Fig. 101 Pinpoint test IDM, ignition diagnostic monitor (Part 1 of 5). 1993–94 1.3L/4-81, 1.6L/4-98 & 1993–95 1.8L/4-112

1.3L and 1.8L

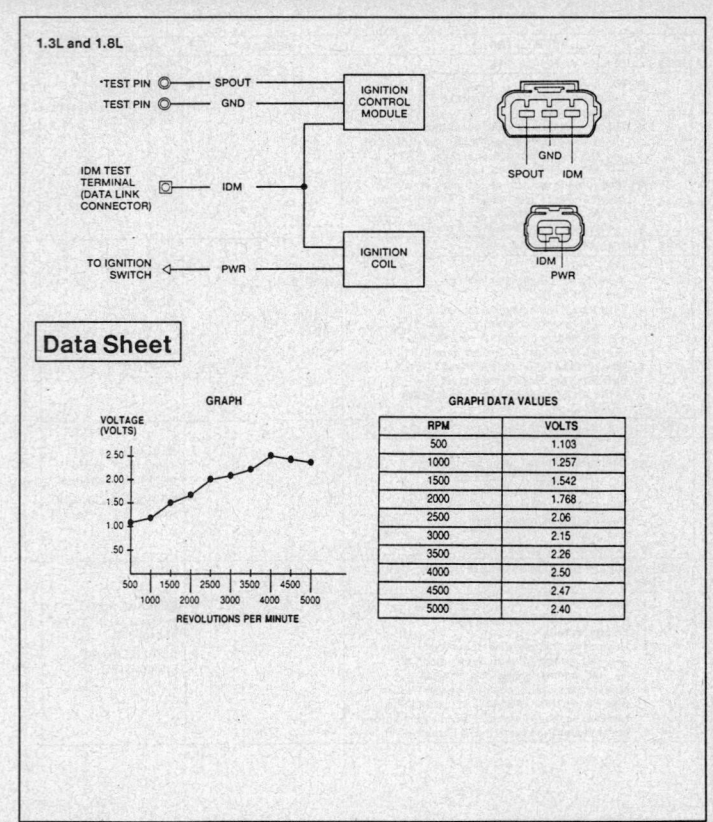

Data Sheet

GRAPH DATA VALUES	
RPM	VOLTS
500	1.103
1000	1.257
1500	1.542
2000	1.768
2500	2.06
3000	2.15
3500	2.26
4000	2.50
4500	2.47
5000	2.40

FM015930109802OX

Fig. 101 Pinpoint test IDM, ignition diagnostic monitor (Part 2 of 5). 1993–94 1.3L/4-81, 1.6L/4-98 & 1993–95 1.8L/4-112

CIRCUIT DATA SHEET

Engine	Circuit	PCM Pin	BOB Pin	Wire Color
1.3L	IDM	NA	NA	Y/GN
	PWR	NA	NA	BK/W
	SPOUT	1G	36	BL/O
	GND	2A	39, 40, 44, 60	BK
1.6L	IDM	1M	6	Y/BL
	PWR	NA	NA	BK/W
1.8L MTX	IDM	NA	NA	Y/BL
	PWR	NA	NA	BL
	SPOUT	1G	36	GN/W
	GND	2A	39, 40, 44, 60	BK/O
1.8L 4EAT	IDM	NA	NA	Y/BL
	PWR	NA	NA	BL
	SPOUT	1G	36	GN/W
	GND	3A	40, 60	BK/O

	TEST STEP	RESULT	▶	ACTION TO TAKE
IDM1	**CHECK FOR CONTINUOUS SPARK AT COIL** • Key OFF. • Connect Rotunda Air Gap Spark Tester D81P-6666-A between coil secondary wire and ground. • Crank the engine. • Does the spark jump the tester air gap continuously, each time the engine is cranked?	Yes (1.6L)	▶	GO to **IDM2**.
		Yes (1.3L, 1.8L)	▶	IDM circuit OK. If directed here from Quick Test Step **QT11**, RETURN Otherwise, REPLACE the PCM.
		No	▶	GO to **IDM3**.
IDM2	**CHECK IDM TO PCM** • Key OFF. • Install breakout box (leave PCM disconnected). • Connect test light between Test Pin VPWR and Test Pin IDM. • Crank the engine. • Does the test light flash while cranking the engine?	Yes	▶	IDM circuit OK. If directed here from Quick Test Step **QT11**, RETURN Otherwise, REPLACE the PCM.
		No	▶	SERVICE the IDM wire to coil.
IDM3	**CHECK FOR CONTINUOUS IDM AT COIL** • Key OFF. • Disconnect the coil connector. • Connect test light between coil IDM wire and PWR wire. • Crank the engine. • Does the test light flash continuously, each time the engine is cranked?	Yes	▶	GO to **IDM4**.
		No	▶	GO to **IDM5**.

FM015930109803OX

Fig. 101 Pinpoint test IDM, ignition diagnostic monitor (Part 3 of 5). 1993–94 1.3L/4-81, 1.6L/4-98 & 1993–95 1.8L/4-112

	TEST STEP	RESULT	▶	ACTION TO TAKE
IDM8	**CHECK SPOUT AT IGNITION CONTROL MODULE (ICM)** • Key OFF. • Disconnect the ignition control module connector. • Connect test light between ignition coil PWR wire and ignition control module SPOUT wire. • Crank the engine. • Does the test light flash?	Yes	▶	CHECK the ignition control module SPOUT wire for shorts to ground. If OK, then REPLACE the ignition control module.
		No	▶	GO to **IDM9**.
IDM9	**CHECK SPOUT CIRCUIT FROM PCM** • Key OFF. • Disconnect the ignition control module connector. • Install breakout box (leave PCM disconnected). • Measure the resistance of the SPOUT wire between BOB Test Pin and the ignition control module. • Is the resistance less than 5 ohms?	Yes	▶	CHECK the ignition control module SPOUT wire for shorts to any other circuit. If OK, then REPLACE the PCM.
		No	▶	SERVICE the ignition control module SPOUT wire to PCM.

FM015930109804OX

Fig. 101 Pinpoint test IDM, ignition diagnostic monitor (Part 4 of 5). 1993–94 1.3L/4-81, 1.6L/4-98 & 1993–95 1.8L/4-112

TEST STEP	RESULT	▶	ACTION TO TAKE
IDM4 CHECK POWER TO COIL			
• Key OFF. • Disconnect the coil connector. • Measure the voltage on the coil PWR wire. • Key ON. • **Is the voltage greater than 10 volts?**	Yes No	▶ ▶	REPLACE the coil. SERVICE the coil PWR wire to ignition switch.
IDM5 CHECK FOR CONTINUOUS IDM FROM IGNITION CONTROL MODULE (ICM)			
• Key OFF. • Disconnect the ignition control module connector. • (1.3L, 1.8L): jumper ignition control module SPOUT and GND wires back into the mating connector. • (1.6L): jumper PWR wire back into mating connector. NOTE: Leave IDM wire disconnected. • Connect test light between IDM terminal (on ignition control module) and PWR (1.6L), or PWR from ignition coil (1.3L, 1.8L). • Crank the engine. • **Does the test light flash continuously each time the engine is cranked?**	Yes No (1.3L, 1.8L) No (1.6L)	▶ ▶ ▶	SERVICE the ignition control module IDM wire to coil. GO to IDM7. GO to IDM6.
IDM6 CHECK POWER TO IGNITION CONTROL MODULE (ICM)			
• Key OFF. • Disconnect the ignition control module connector. • Measure the voltage on the ignition control module PWR wire. • Key ON. • **Is the voltage greater than 10 volts?**	Yes No	▶ ▶	GO to IDM7. SERVICE the ignition control module PWR wire to ignition switch.
IDM7 CHECK GROUND AT IGNITION CONTROL MODULE (ICM)			
• Key OFF. • Disconnect the ignition control module connector. • (1.3L, 1.8L): connect test light between ignition coil PWR wire and ignition control module GND wire. • (1.6L): connect test light between ignition control module PWR wire and ignition control module GND wire. • Key ON. • **Is the test light on?**	Yes (1.3L, 1.8L) Yes (1.6L) No	▶ ▶ ▶	GO to IDM8. REPLACE the ignition control module. SERVICE the ignition control module ground wire.

FM0159301098050X

Fig. 101 Pinpoint test IDM, ignition diagnostic monitor (Part 5 of 5). 1993–94 1.3L/4-81, 1.6L/4-98 & 1993–95 1.8L/4-112

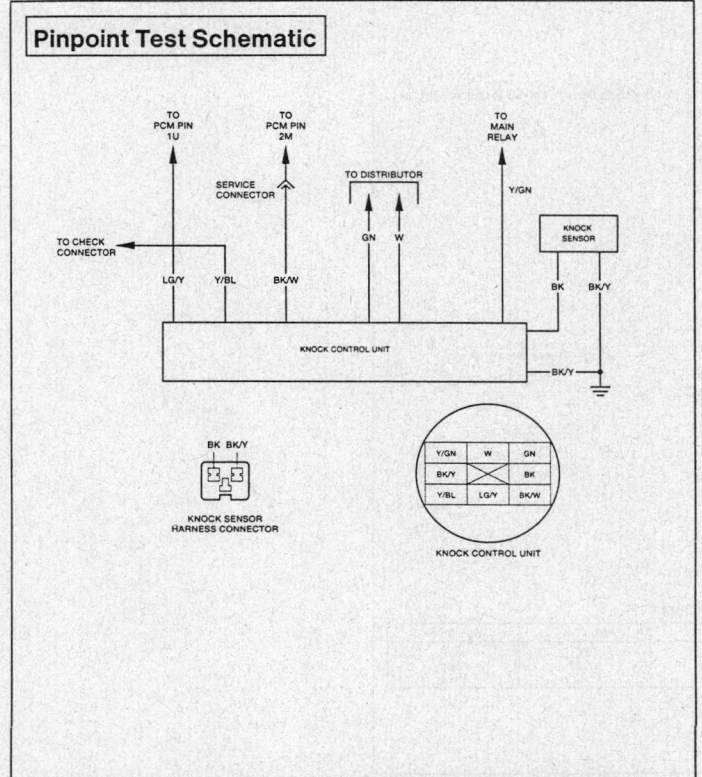

FM0159301099020X

Fig. 102 Pinpoint test KC, knock control (Part 2 of 3). 1993–94 1.6L/4-98 Turbo

Knock Control (KC) — 1.6L Turbo

Note

You should enter this Pinpoint Test only when Quick Test Step 11 directs you here.

Remember

This Pinpoint Test is intended to diagnose only the following:

• Circuit: KC

FM0159301099010X

Fig. 102 Pinpoint test KC, knock control (Part 1 of 3). 1993–94 1.6L/4-98 Turbo

TEST STEP	RESULT	▶	ACTION TO TAKE
KC1 CHECK KNOCK CONTROL FAIL-SAFE			
• Key OFF. • Disconnect and plug distributor vacuum hose. • Key ON, engine running. • Connect Rotunda Timing Analyzer 059-00006, or equivalent and record the timing measurement. • Disconnect the knock control service connector (near PCM). • **Did the ignition timing retard?**	Yes No	▶ ▶	SERVICE the open knock sensor and/or knock sensor wires. GO to KC2.
KC2 CHECK KNOCK CONTROL FUNCTION			
• Key OFF. • Disconnect the distributor vacuum hose. • Key ON, engine running. • Disconnect the knock control service connector (near PCM). • Connect timing lamp and record the timing measurement. • Tap the intake plenum with a plastic hammer. • **Did the ignition timing retard?**	Yes No	▶ ▶	GO to KC3. GO to KC4.
KC3 RETEST KNOCK CONTROL			
• Key OFF. • Reconnect the knock control service connector (near PCM). • Key ON, engine running. • Connect timing lamp and record the timing measurement. • Tap the intake plenum with a plastic hammer. • **Did the ignition timing retard?**	Yes No	▶ ▶	REPLACE the knock control unit. Knock control unit OK.
KC4 TEST KNOCK SENSOR			
• Key OFF. • Disconnect and plug distributor vacuum hose. • Key ON, engine running. • Disconnect the knock control service connector (near PCM). • Connect a good knock sensor to the vehicle. • Connect timing lamp and record the timing measurement. • Tap the intake plenum with a plastic hammer. • **Did the ignition timing retard?**	Yes No	▶ ▶	REPLACE the knock sensor. GO to KC5.
KC5 CHECK KNOCK CONTROL WIRING			
• Key OFF. • Verify VPWR ("Y/GN" wire) and GND ("BK/Y" wire) to the knock control unit. • Check all knock control unit wiring for opens and shorts. • **Are all knock control unit wires OK?**	Yes No	▶ ▶	REPLACE the knock control unit. SERVICE the wire(s) in question.

FM0159301099030X

Fig. 102 Pinpoint test KC, knock control (Part 3 of 3). 1993–94 1.6L/4-98 Turbo

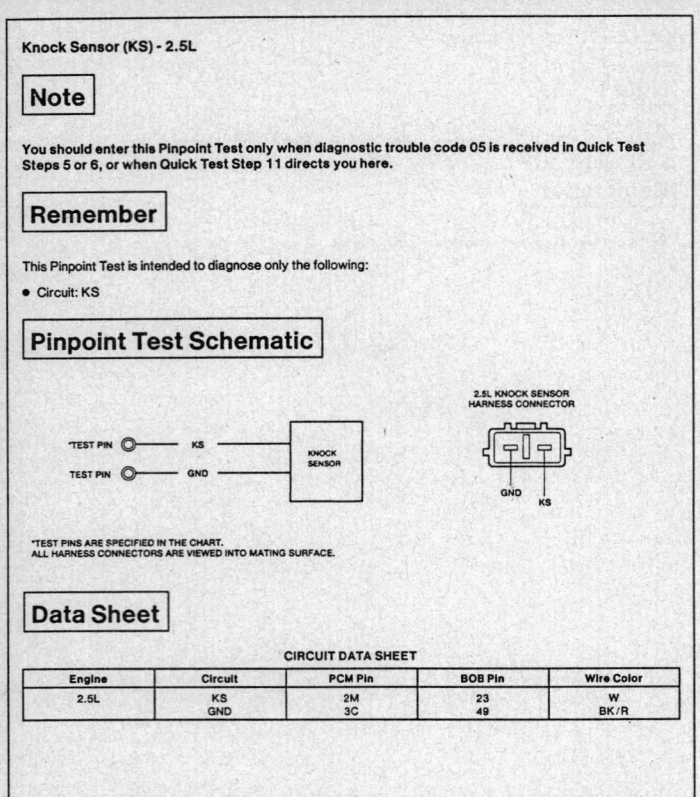

Knock Sensor (KS) - 2.5L

Note

You should enter this Pinpoint Test only when diagnostic trouble code 05 is received in Quick Test Steps 5 or 6, or when Quick Test Step 11 directs you here.

Remember

This Pinpoint Test is intended to diagnose only the following:

• Circuit: KS

Pinpoint Test Schematic

*TEST PIN — KS
TEST PIN — GND

KNOCK SENSOR

2.5L KNOCK SENSOR HARNESS CONNECTOR

GND   KS

*TEST PINS ARE SPECIFIED IN THE CHART.
ALL HARNESS CONNECTORS ARE VIEWED INTO MATING SURFACE.

Data Sheet

CIRCUIT DATA SHEET

Engine	Circuit	PCM Pin	BOB Pin	Wire Color
2.5L	KS	2M	23	W
	GND	3C	49	BK/R

FM0159301100010X

Fig. 103   Pinpoint test KS, knock sensor (Part 1 of 2). 1993–95 2.5L/V6-152

TEST STEP		RESULT	▶	ACTION TO TAKE
KS1	**CHECK SIGNAL FROM PCM** • Key OFF. • Install breakout box (connect PCM). • Key ON. • Measure the voltage between Test Pin KS and ground using a digital voltmeter. • **Is the voltage approximately 2.4 volts?**	Yes No	▶ ▶	GO to **KS2**. GO to EEC Pinpoint Test **VPWR**. If VPWR is OK, REPLACE the PCM.
KS2	**CHECK KS WIRE FOR OPEN** • Key OFF. • Install breakout box (leave PCM disconnected). • Disconnect the knock sensor connector. • Measure the resistance between Test Pin KS and KS terminal at knock sensor harness connector. • **Is the resistance less than 5 ohms?**	Yes No	▶ ▶	GO to **KS3**. SERVICE the KS wire for open(s).
KS3	**CHECK KS WIRE FOR SHORT** • Key OFF. • Install breakout box (leave PCM disconnected). • Disconnect the knock sensor connector. • Measure the resistance between Test Pin KS and ground. • **Is the resistance greater than 10,000 ohms?**	Yes No	▶ ▶	GO to **KS4**. SERVICE the KS wire for short(s).
KS4	**CHECK KNOCK SENSOR GROUND** • Key OFF. • Disconnect the knock sensor connector. • Measure the resistance of the GND wire between the knock sensor harness connector and ground. • **Is the resistance less than 5 ohms?**	Yes No	▶ ▶	If directed here from Quick Test Step **QT11**, then RETURN Otherwise, REPLACE the knock sensor. SERVICE the GND wire for open(s).

FM0159301100020X

Fig. 103   Pinpoint test KS, knock sensor (Part 2 of 2). 1993–95 2.5L/V6-152

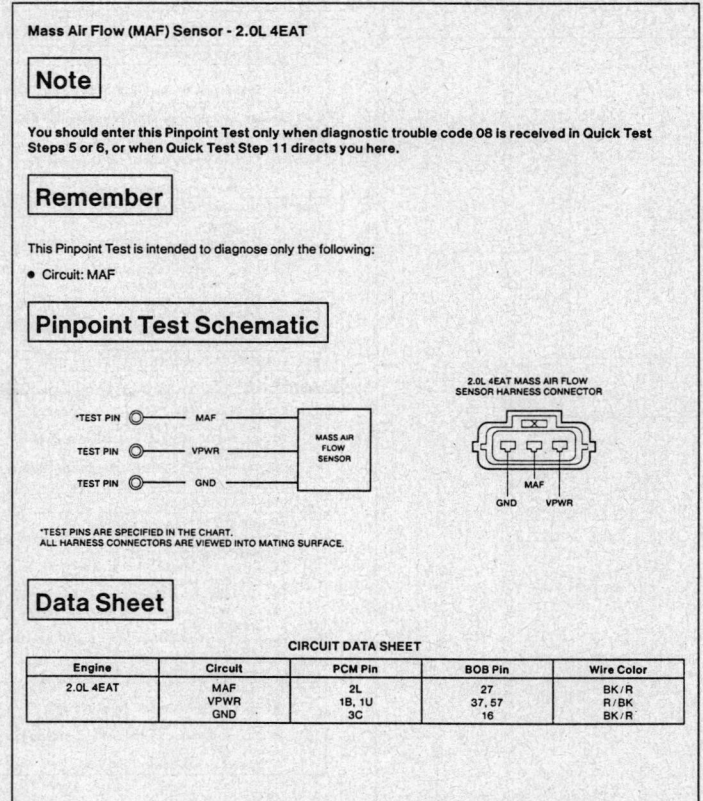

Mass Air Flow (MAF) Sensor - 2.0L 4EAT

Note

You should enter this Pinpoint Test only when diagnostic trouble code 08 is received in Quick Test Steps 5 or 6, or when Quick Test Step 11 directs you here.

Remember

This Pinpoint Test is intended to diagnose only the following:

• Circuit: MAF

Pinpoint Test Schematic

*TEST PIN — MAF
TEST PIN — VPWR
TEST PIN — GND

MASS AIR FLOW SENSOR

2.0L 4EAT MASS AIR FLOW SENSOR HARNESS CONNECTOR

MAF
GND   VPWR

*TEST PINS ARE SPECIFIED IN THE CHART.
ALL HARNESS CONNECTORS ARE VIEWED INTO MATING SURFACE.

Data Sheet

CIRCUIT DATA SHEET

Engine	Circuit	PCM Pin	BOB Pin	Wire Color
2.0L 4EAT	MAF	2L	27	BK/R
	VPWR	1B, 1U	37, 57	R/BK
	GND	3C	16	BK/R

Fig. 104   Pinpoint test MAF, mass airflow sensor (Part 1 of 2). 1993 2.0L/4-121 w/4EAT

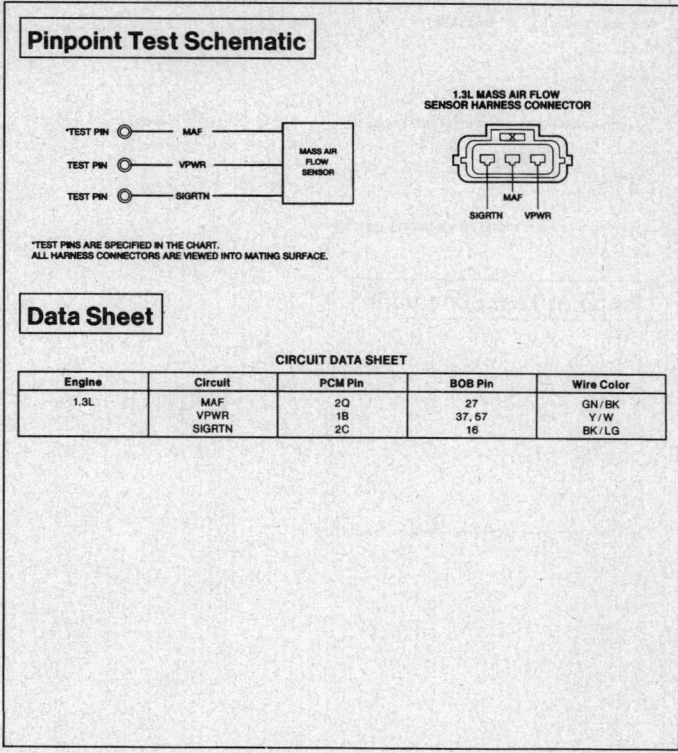

Fig. 105 Pinpoint test MAF, mass airflow sensor (Part 1 of 2). 1995 1.3L/4-81

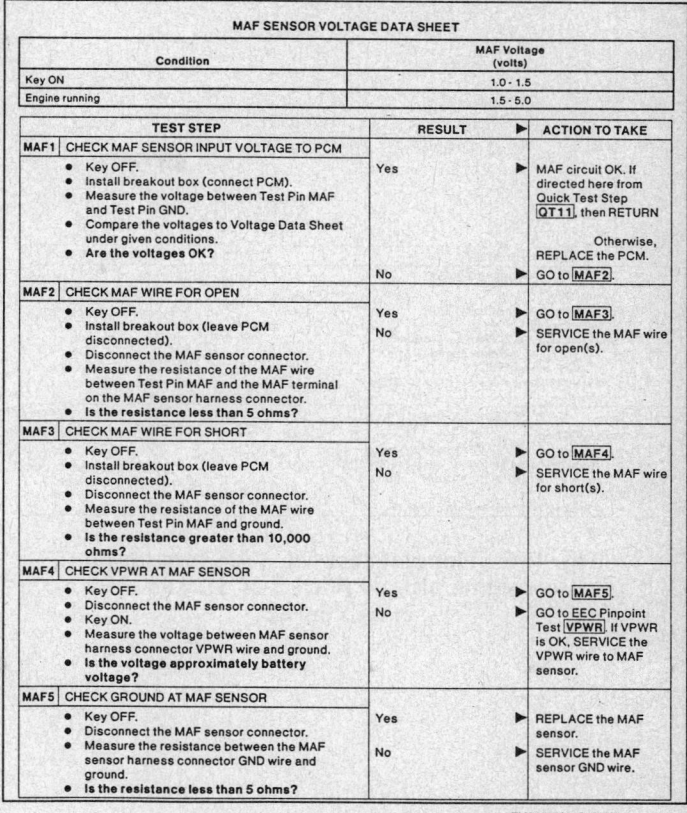

Fig. 105 Pinpoint test MAF, mass airflow sensor (Part 2 of 2). 1993 2.0L/4-121 w/4EAT & 1995 1.3L/4-81

Measuring Core-Volume Air Flow (MC-VAF) Sensor - 2.5L

Note

You should enter this Pinpoint Test only when diagnostic trouble code 08 is received in Quick Test Steps 5 or 6, or when Quick Test Step 11 directs you here.

Remember

This Pinpoint Test is intended to diagnose only the following:
● Circuit: MC-VAF

Pinpoint Test Schematic

*TEST PINS ARE SPECIFIED IN THE CHART.
ALL HARNESS CONNECTORS ARE VIEWED INTO MATING SURFACE.

Data Sheet

CIRCUIT DATA SHEET

Engine	Circuit	PCM Pin	BOB Pin	Wire Color
2.5L	MC-VAF	2B	44	R
	VREF	2I	26	P
	GND	3D	46	BK BL

FM0159301102010X

Fig. 106 Pinpoint test MC-VAF, measuring core volume airflow (Part 1 of 3). 1993–95 2.5L/V6-152

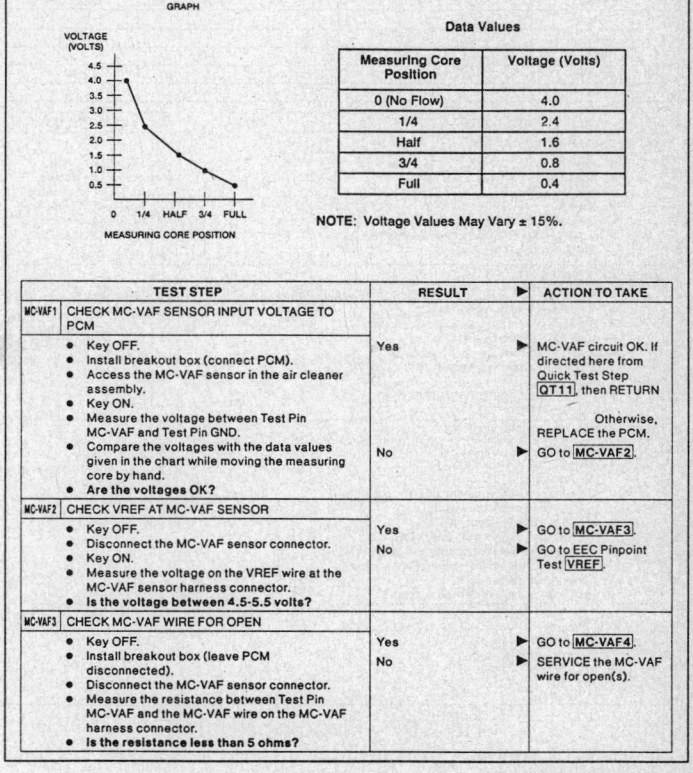

Fig. 106 Pinpoint test MC-VAF, measuring core volume airflow (Part 2 of 3). 1993–95 2.5L/V6-152

COMPUTERIZED ENGINE CONTROLS (ASPIRE, CAPRI, ESCORT & TRACER (1.8L/4-112), FESTIVA & PROBE (2.0L/4-121 w/4EAT & 2.5L/V6-152) ELECTRONIC ENGINE CONTROL (EEC) SYSTEM

10-55

	TEST STEP	RESULT	▶	ACTION TO TAKE
MC-VAF4	CHECK MC-VAF WIRE FOR SHORT			
	• Key OFF. • Install breakout box (leave PCM disconnected). • Disconnect the MC-VAF sensor connector. • Measure the resistance between Test Pin MC-VAF and ground. • **Is the resistance greater than 10,000 ohms?**	Yes No	▶ ▶	GO to MC-VAF5. SERVICE the MC-VAF wire for short(s).
MC-VAF5	CHECK MC-VAF SENSOR GROUND			
	• Key OFF. • Disconnect the MC-VAF sensor connector. • Measure the resistance between Test Pin GND and the GND wire at the MC-VAF harness connector. • **Is the resistance less than 5 ohms?**	Yes No	▶ ▶	REPLACE the MC-VAF sensor. SERVICE the MC-VAF sensor GND wire.

FM0159301102030X

Fig. 106 Pinpoint test MC-VAF, measuring core volume airflow (Part 3 of 3). 1993–95 2.5L/V6-152

Malfunction Indicator Lamp (MIL)

Note

You should enter this Pinpoint Test only when the   Quick Test directs you here.

Remember

This Pinpoint Test is intended to diagnose only the following:

• Circuit: MIL

Pinpoint Test Schematic

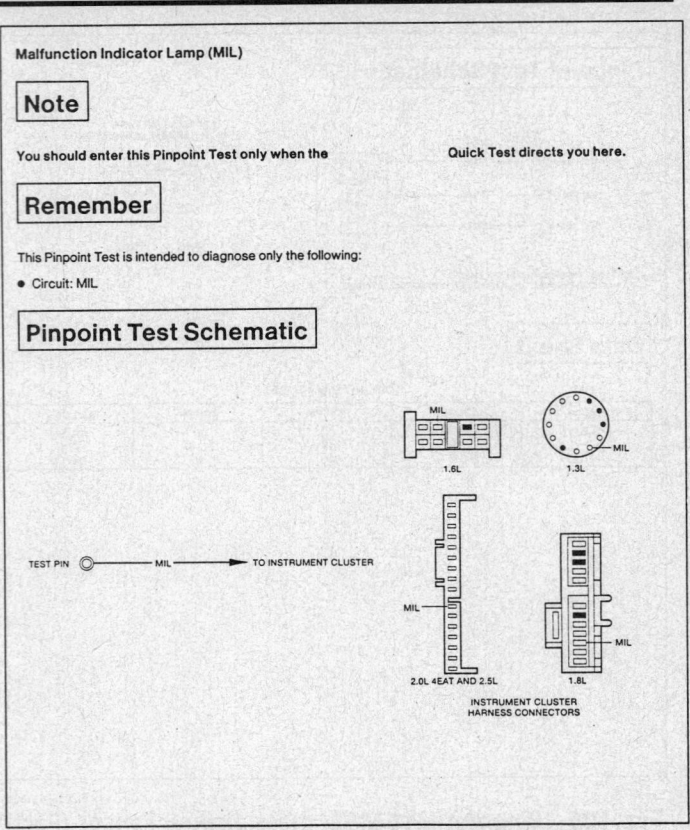

Fig. 107 Pinpoint test MIL, malfunction indicator lamp (Part 1 of 3)

Data Sheet

CIRCUIT DATA SHEET

Engine	Circuit	PCM Pin	BOB Pin	Wire Color
1.3L	MIL	1E	51	BL/BK
1.6L	MIL	1A	51	Y/BK
1.8L	MIL	1E	51	Y/BK
2.0L 4EAT	MIL	1E	51	BL
2.5L	MIL	1E	51	BL

	TEST STEP	RESULT	▶	ACTION TO TAKE
MIL1	CHECK MIL OPERATION			
	• Key OFF. • Install breakout box (leave PCM disconnected). • Key ON. • Ground Test Pin MIL. • **Does Malfunction Indicator Lamp (CHECK ENGINE lamp) illuminate?**	Yes No	▶ ▶	MIL circuit OK. If diagnostic trouble codes do not flash on MIL during Quick Test or MIL never comes on, REPLACE the PCM. GO to MIL2.
MIL2	CHECK MIL BULB			
	• Key OFF. • Remove the instrument cluster. • Remove the malfunction indicator lamp (CHECK ENGINE lamp) bulb. • Apply 12 volts between the terminals of the malfunction indicator lamp (CHECK ENGINE lamp) bulb. • **Does the MIL (CHECK ENGINE lamp) illuminate?**	Yes No	▶ ▶	GO to MIL3. REPLACE the malfunction indicator lamp (CHECK ENGINE lamp) bulb.
MIL3	CHECK MIL WIRE FOR OPEN			
	• Key OFF. • Install breakout box (leave PCM disconnected). • Disconnect the instrument cluster connector. — 12-pin connector on 1.3L, 1.8L — 8-pin connector on 1.6L — 16-pin connector on 2.0L 4EAT, 2.5L • Measure the resistance between Test Pin MIL and the MIL terminal at the instrument cluster harness connector. • **Is the resistance less than 5 ohms?**	Yes No	▶ ▶	GO to MIL4. SERVICE the MIL wire for open.

Fig. 107 Pinpoint test MIL, malfunction indicator lamp (Part 2 of 3)

	TEST STEP	RESULT	▶	ACTION TO TAKE
MIL4	CHECK MIL WIRE FOR SHORT			
	• Key OFF. • Install breakout box (leave PCM disconnected). • Disconnect the instrument cluster connector. — 12-pin connector on 1.3L — 8-pin connector on 1.6L — 16-pin connector on 2.0L 4EAT, 2.5L • Measure the resistance between Test Pin MIL and ground. • **Is the resistance greater than 10,000 ohms?**	Yes No	▶ ▶	REPLACE the instrument cluster printed circuit board. SERVICE the MIL wire for short.

Fig. 107 Pinpoint test MIL, malfunction indicator lamp (Part 3 of 3)

Oxygen Sensor (O2S) — 1.3L, 1.6L, 1.8L

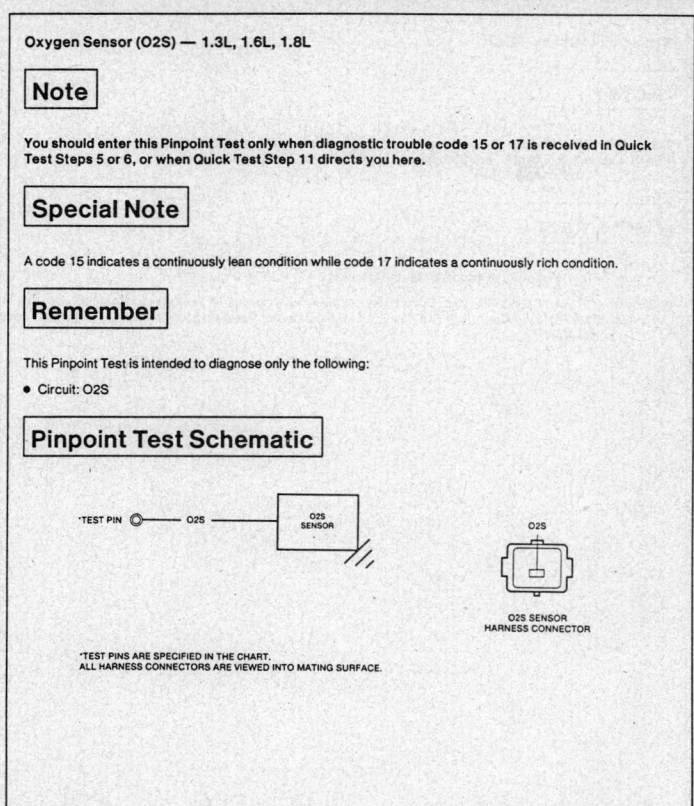

Note

You should enter this Pinpoint Test only when diagnostic trouble code 15 or 17 is received in Quick Test Steps 5 or 6, or when Quick Test Step 11 directs you here.

Special Note

A code 15 indicates a continuously lean condition while code 17 indicates a continuously rich condition.

Remember

This Pinpoint Test is intended to diagnose only the following:

- Circuit: O2S

Pinpoint Test Schematic

*TEST PIN — O2S — O2S SENSOR

O2S

O2S SENSOR HARNESS CONNECTOR

*TEST PINS ARE SPECIFIED IN THE CHART.
ALL HARNESS CONNECTORS ARE VIEWED INTO MATING SURFACE.

FM0159301104010X

Fig. 108 Pinpoint test O2S, oxygen sensor (Part 1 of 2). 1993–95 1.3L/4-81, 1.6L/4-98 & 1.8L/4-112

Data Sheet

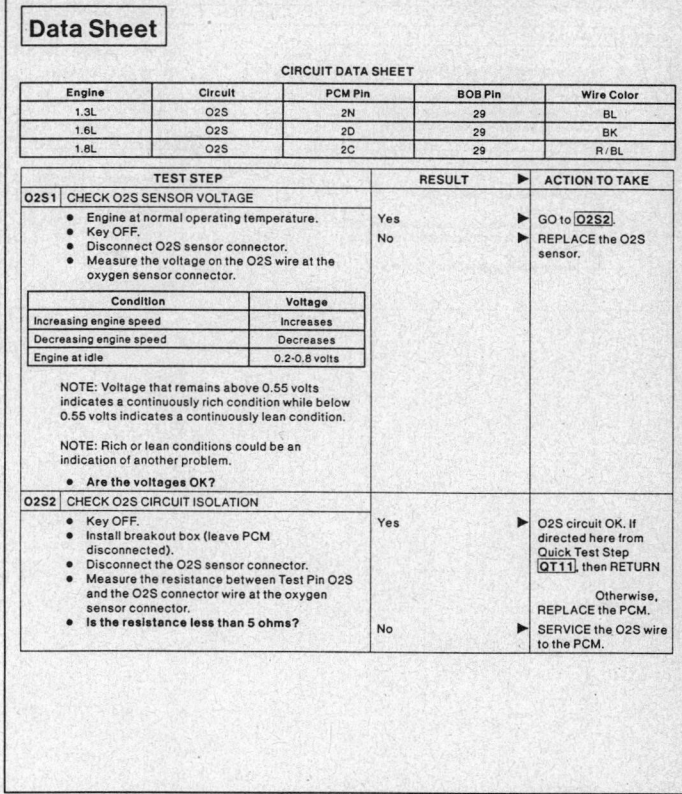

CIRCUIT DATA SHEET

Engine	Circuit	PCM Pin	BOB Pin	Wire Color
1.3L	O2S	2N	29	BL
1.6L	O2S	2D	29	BK
1.8L	O2S	2C	29	R/BL

TEST STEP		RESULT	▶	ACTION TO TAKE
O2S1 CHECK O2S SENSOR VOLTAGE				
• Engine at normal operating temperature. • Key OFF. • Disconnect O2S sensor connector. • Measure the voltage on the O2S wire at the oxygen sensor connector.		Yes	▶	GO to O2S2.
		No	▶	REPLACE the O2S sensor.

Condition	Voltage
Increasing engine speed	Increases
Decreasing engine speed	Decreases
Engine at idle	0.2-0.8 volts

NOTE: Voltage that remains above 0.55 volts indicates a continuously rich condition while below 0.55 volts indicates a continuously lean condition.

NOTE: Rich or lean conditions could be an indication of another problem.

• Are the voltages OK?

TEST STEP		RESULT	▶	ACTION TO TAKE
O2S2 CHECK O2S CIRCUIT ISOLATION				
• Key OFF. • Install breakout box (leave PCM disconnected). • Disconnect the O2S sensor connector. • Measure the resistance between Test Pin O2S and the O2S connector wire at the oxygen sensor connector. • Is the resistance less than 5 ohms?		Yes	▶	O2S circuit OK. If directed here from Quick Test Step QT11, then RETURN Otherwise, REPLACE the PCM.
		No	▶	SERVICE the O2S wire to the PCM.

FM0159301104020X

Fig. 108 Pinpoint test O2S, oxygen sensor (Part 2 of 2). 1993–95 1.3L/4-81, 1.6L/4-98 & 1.8L/4-112

Power and Ground Connections (PGC)

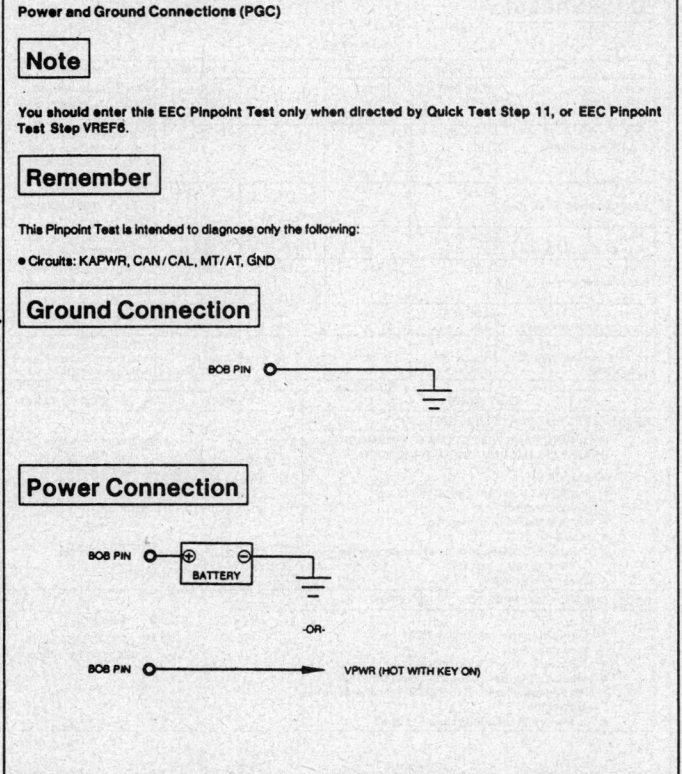

Note

You should enter this EEC Pinpoint Test only when directed by Quick Test Step 11, or EEC Pinpoint Test Step VREF6.

Remember

This Pinpoint Test is intended to diagnose only the following:

- Circuits: KAPWR, CAN/CAL, MT/AT, GND

Ground Connection

BOB PIN

Power Connection

BOB PIN — BATTERY

-OR-

BOB PIN — VPWR (HOT WITH KEY ON)

Fig. 109 Pinpoint test PGC, power & ground connection (Part 1 of 3)

Connection Data Sheet

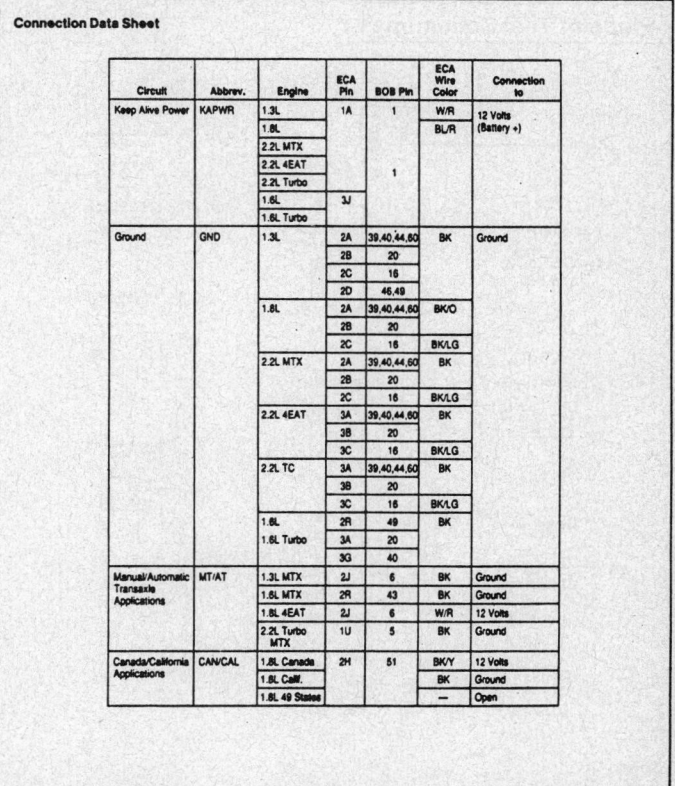

Circuit	Abbrev.	Engine	ECA Pin	BOB Pin	ECA Wire Color	Connection to
Keep Alive Power	KAPWR	1.3L	1A	1	W/R	12 Volts (Battery +)
		1.8L			BL/R	
		2.2L MTX				
		2.2L 4EAT		1		
		2.2L Turbo				
		1.6L	1J			
		1.6L Turbo				
Ground	GND	1.3L	2A	39,40,44,60	BK	Ground
			2B	20		
			2C	16		
			2D	46,49		
		1.8L	2A	39,40,44,60	BK/O	
			2B	20		
			2C	16	BK/LG	
		2.2L MTX	2A	39,40,44,60	BK	
			2B	20		
			2C	16	BK/LG	
		2.2L 4EAT	3A	39,40,44,60	BK	
			3B	20		
			3C	16	BK/LG	
		2.2L TC	3A	39,40,44,60	BK	
			3B	20		
			3C	16	BK/LG	
		1.6L	2R	49	BK	
		1.6L Turbo	3A	20		
			3G	40		
Manual/Automatic Transaxle Applications	MT/AT	1.3L MTX	2J	6	BK	Ground
		1.6L MTX	2R	43	BK	Ground
		1.8L 4EAT	2J	6	W/R	12 Volts
		2.2L Turbo MTX	1U	5	BK	Ground
Canada/California Applications	CAN/CAL	1.8L Canada	2H	51	BK/Y	12 Volts
		1.8L Calif.			BK	Ground
		1.8L 49 States		—		Open

Fig. 109 Pinpoint test PGC, power & ground connection (Part 2 of 3)

TEST STEP		RESULT	▶	ACTION TO TAKE
PGC1	CHECK VOLTAGE • Key OFF. • Install breakout box (leave PCM disconnected). • Key ON, if checking power other than KAPWR. • Measure the voltage on Test Pin KAPWR. • Is the voltage approximately battery voltage?	Yes No	▶ ▶	GO to PGC2. SERVICE the wire in question.
PGC2	CHECK GROUNDS • Key OFF. • Install breakout box (leave PCM disconnected). • Measure the resistance between GND Test Pin and ground. Repeat for each GND Test Pin to ground. • Are the resistances less than 5 ohms?	Yes No	▶ ▶	If sent here from EEC Pinpoint Test VREF or STO or 4EAT Pinpoint Test VREF, REPLACE the PCM. SERVICE the wire in question.

Fig. 109 Pinpoint test PGC, power & ground connection (Part 3 of 3)

Relay Output Check (ROC)

Note

You should enter this Pinpoint Test only when diagnostic trouble code 67 (LFAN) or 68 (2.0L 4EAT HFAN) is received in Quick Test Step 5 or 6, or when Quick Test Step 11 directs you here.

Remember

This Pinpoint Test is intended to diagnose only the following:

• Circuits: ACR (A/C Relay), FPR (Fuel Pump Relay), HCFAN (High Condenser Fan Relay), HFAN (High Cooling Fan Relay), LCFAN (Low Condenser Fan Relay), LFAN (Low Cooling Fan Relay), WAC (Wide-Open Throttle A/C Cutoff Relay)

Fig. 110 Pinpoint test ROC, relay output check (Part 1 of 4)

Pinpoint Test Schematic

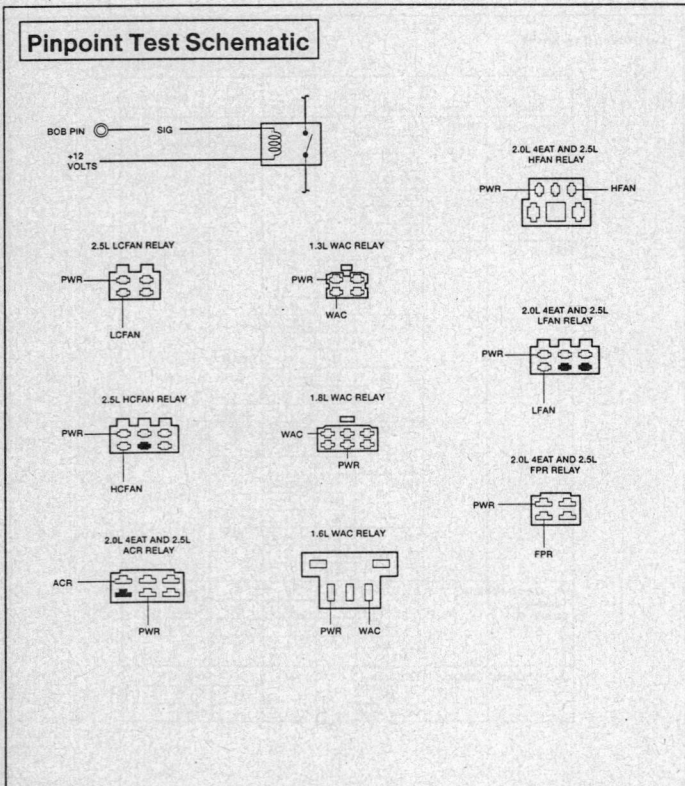

Fig. 110 Pinpoint test ROC, relay output check (Part 2 of 4)

Data Sheet

CIRCUIT DATA SHEET

Relay (SIG)	Engine	PCM Pin	BOB Pin	Wire Color	Function
ACR (A/C Relay)	2.0L 4EAT 2.5L	1S 1L	14 10	GN/BK GN/BK	PCM grounds ACR wire to turn on A/C system, when A/C is selected.
FPR (Fuel Pump Relay)	2.0L 4EAT 2.5L	3L 3T	8 52B	LG LG	PCM grounds FPR wire to turn on Fuel Pump while cranking engine or while engine is running.
HCFAN (High Condenser Fan Relay)	2.5L	2P	54	BL/GN	PCM grounds HCFAN wire to turn on High Condenser Fan.
HFAN (High Cooling Fan Relay)	2.0L 4EAT 2.5L	3I 2P	54 54	BL/GN BL/GN	PCM grounds HFAN wire to turn on High Cooling Fan.
LCFAN (Low Condenser Fan Relay)	2.5L	3N	53A	BL/O	PCM grounds LCFAN wire to turn on Low Condenser Fan.
LFAN (Low Cooling Fan Relay)	2.0L 4EAT 2.5L	3G 3L	55 55	BK/GN R/W	PCM grounds LFAN wire to turn on Low Cooling Fan.
WAC (Wide-Open Throttle A/C Cutoff Relay)	1.3L 1.8L MTX 1.8L 4EAT	1J 1J 1L	54 54 10	GN/Y BL/BK BL/BK	PCM opens ground to cutoff A/C clutch during start and wide open throttle driving.

TEST STEP		RESULT	▶	ACTION TO TAKE
ROC1	PERFORM RELAY CLICK TEST **WARNING: FANS WILL OPERATE WHEN HCFAN, HFAN, LCFAN, OR LFAN ARE GROUNDED.** • Key OFF. • Install breakout box (leave PCM disconnected). • Locate the relay in question. • Key ON. • Feel and/or listen to relay in question while grounding relay Test Pin. • Does relay click?	Yes No	▶ ▶	If sent here from Quick Test Step QT5 or QT6, REPLACE the PCM. GO to ROC2.
ROC2	CHECK RELAY WIRE TO PCM FOR OPEN • Key OFF. • Install breakout box (leave PCM disconnected). • Disconnect the relay in question. • Measure the resistance between relay Test Pin and relay terminal to PCM at relay harness connector. • Is the resistance less than 5 ohms?	Yes No	▶ ▶	GO to ROC3. SERVICE the wire in question for opens.

Fig. 110 Pinpoint test ROC, relay output check (Part 3 of 4)

TEST STEP		RESULT	▶	ACTION TO TAKE
ROC3	CHECK RELAY WIRE TO PCM FOR SHORT			
	NOTE: When checking HFAN or HCFAN relays you must disconnect both the HFAN relay and the HCFAN relay. • Key OFF. • Install breakout box (leave PCM disconnected). • Disconnect the relay in question. • Measure the resistance between relay Test Pin and ground. • **Is the resistance greater than 10,000 ohms?**	Yes No	▶ ▶	GO to ROC4. SERVICE the wire in question for shorts.
ROC4	CHECK POWER TO RELAY IN QUESTION			
	• Key OFF. • Disconnect the relay in question. • Key ON. • Measure the voltage on PWR wire at relay harness connector. • **Is the voltage greater than 10 volts?**	Yes No	▶ ▶	REPLACE the relay in question. SERVICE the PWR wire in question.

Fig. 110   Pinpoint test ROC, relay output check (Part 4 of 4)

Solenoid Controlled By Ground (SCG)

Note

You should enter this Pinpoint Test only when a diagnostic trouble code 25, 26, 28, 29, 34, 41 or 46 is received in Quick Test Steps 5 or 6, or when Quick Test Step 11 directs you here.

Remember

This Pinpoint Test is intended to diagnose only the following:

● Circuits: CANP (Canister Purge), EGRC (EGR Control), EGRV (EGR Vent), EVR (EGR Vacuum Regulator), FPRC (Fuel Pressure Regulator Control), HSIA (High Speed Inlet Air Control), IAC (Idle Air Control), INJ (Injectors), VRIS1 (Variable Resonance Induction System Solenoid #1), VRIS2 (Variable Resonance Induction System Solenoid #2).

Fig. 111   Pinpoint test SCG, solenoid controlled by ground (Part 1 of 6)

Pinpoint Test Schematic

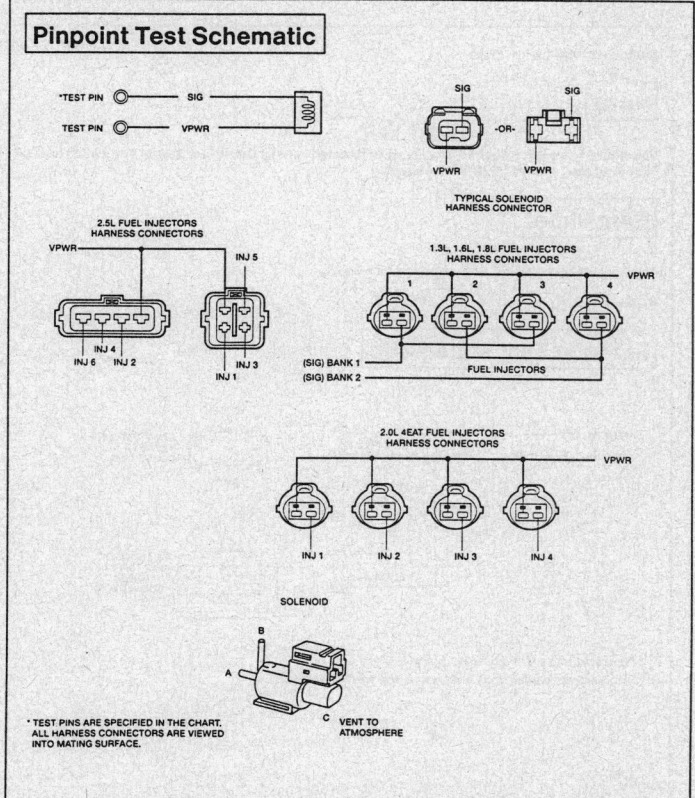

* TEST PINS ARE SPECIFIED IN THE CHART. ALL HARNESS CONNECTORS ARE VIEWED INTO MATING SURFACE.

Fig. 111   Pinpoint test SCG, solenoid controlled by ground (Part 2 of 6)

Data Sheet

CIRCUIT DATA SHEET

Engine	SIG	PCM Pin	BOB Pin	Wire Color	Diagnostic Trouble Code
1.3L	CANP	2X	31	R	26
	IAC	2W	41	R/BK	34
	BANK1	2U	58	GN/Y	—
	BANK2	2V	59	GN/BK	—
1.6L	CANP	2P	32	Y	26
	IAC	2Q	41	GN	34
	FPRC	2K	31	BR	25
	BANK1	3E	58	Y	—
	BANK2	3C	59	Y/BK	—
1.8L MTX	CANP	2X	31	W/BL	26
	IAC	2W	41	BL/O	34
	HSIA	2S	53	BK/R	41
	FPRC	2T	11	GN/O	25
	BANK1	2U	58	Y	—
	BANK2	2V	59	Y/BK	—
1.8L 4EAT	CANP	2O	31	W/BL	26
	IAC	3Q	21B	BL/O	34
	HSIA	3I	42	BK/R	41
	FPRC	3M	21A	GN/O	25
	BANK1	3U	58	Y	—
	BANK2	3V	59	Y/BK	—
2.0L 4EAT	FPRC	3M	53A	GN	25
	CANP	3N	31A	W/BK	26
	EVR	3K	33	W/BL	28
	INJ1	3W	58	Y/BK	NA
	INJ2	3X	59	Y/W	NA
	INJ3	3Y	12	Y/R	NA
	INJ4	3Z	13	Y/GN	NA
	IAC	3O	21B	LG/BK	34
	VPWR¹	1B, 1U	37, 57	R/BK	NA
2.5L	FPRC	3M	21A	GN/BK	25
	CANP	2O	31	BL/BK	26
	EGRC	3P	52A	GN/W	28
	EGRV	3O	33A	W/BL	29
	INJ1	3U	58	R/LG	NA
	INJ2	3V	59	BL/W	NA
	INJ3	3W	12	BR	NA
	INJ4	3X	13	R/Y	NA
	INJ5	3Y	14	W	NA
	INJ6	3Z	15	W/BK	NA
	IAC	3Q	21B	LG/BK	34
	VRIS1	3I	42	W/GN	41
	VRIS2	3J	35	BL/R	46
	VPWR¹	1B	37, 57	R/BK	NA

¹VPWR is a "W/R" wire to the fuel injectors.

Fig. 111   Pinpoint test SCG, solenoid controlled by ground (Part 3 of 6)

SOLENOID DATA SHEET

Solenoid	Activated by: (PCM ground solenoid under these conditions)	*Click Test Method
INJ (Fuel Injectors)	Cranking or running engine.	• Connect PCM. Key ON, crank engine. Listen to injector (clicking sound) with stethoscope.
CANP (Canister Purge)	Vehicle in gear, operating temperature above 60°C (140°F) during cruise and acceleration.	• Key ON, apply vacuum from intake manifold, vacuum should hold. • Ground Test Pin with jumper, vacuum should release.
EGRC (EGR Control)	Engine coolant temperature above 40°C (104°F). EGRC: normal driving (cruising)	• Key ON, apply vacuum from intake manifold. Vacuum should hold. • Ground Test Pin, vacuum should release.
EGRV (EGR Vent)	Engine coolant temperature above 40°C (104°F). EGRV: during idle, deceleration, or wide open throttle conditions	• Key ON, apply vacuum from EGR valve. Vacuum should not hold. • Ground Test Pin, vacuum should hold.
EVR (EGR Vacuum Regulator)	Engine coolant temperature below 70°C (158°F) or engine speed below 1500 rpm.	• Disconnect hoses at solenoid. Verify air flow between ports on the solenoid. Refer to diagram of ports shown in the electrical schematic. Ports / Air flow A-B / No A-C / No B-C / Yes • Key ON. Ground Test Pin. Verify air flow between ports on the solenoid. Ports / Air flow A-B / Yes A-C / No B-C / No
VRIS (Variable Resonance Induction System)	Engine at low speed, low vacuum condition.	• Disconnect hoses at solenoid. Verify air flow between ports on the solenoid. Refer to diagram of ports shown in the electrical schematic. Ports / Air flow A-B / No A-C / No B-C / Yes • Key ON. Ground Test Pin. Verify air flow between ports on the solenoid. Ports / Air flow A-B / Yes A-C / No B-C / No
FPRC (Fuel Pressure Regulator Control)	Engine running, coolant temperature above 90°C (190°F) for 1.6L and 1.8L or 70°C (158°F) for 2.0L 4EAT and 2.5L, intake air temperature above 20°C (68°F), engine speed less than 1,500 rpm (for approx. 2 minutes after start).	• Key ON, apply vacuum to nipple from intake manifold. Vacuum should hold. • Ground Test Pin, vacuum should slowly release as ground is applied intermittently.

(Continued)

Fig. 111 Pinpoint test SCG, solenoid controlled by ground (Part 4 of 6)

SOLENOID DATA SHEET (Cont'd)

Solenoid	Activated by: (PCM ground solenoid under these conditions)	*Click Test Method
IAC (Idle Air Control)	Cranking and running engine.	• Disconnect the PCM. • Key ON. • Ground Test Pin intermittently. • Listen for IAC solenoid (clicking sound).
HSIA (High Speed Inlet Air Control)	Engine speed below 5000 rpm.	• Key ON, apply vacuum to nipple from reservoir. Vacuum should hold. • Ground Test Pin. Vacuum should release.

* Install breakout box, leave PCM disconnected for all Click Tests (except the injector click test).

Fig. 111 Pinpoint test SCG, solenoid controlled by ground (Part 5 of 6)

TEST STEP	RESULT	▶	ACTION TO TAKE
SCG1 CHECK SOLENOID FUNCTION • Key OFF. • Install breakout box (leave PCM disconnected). • Check for proper function of solenoid in question as described in the Data Sheet "Click Test Method" column. • Does the solenoid in question function properly?	Yes	▶	Solenoids OK. If directed here by Quick Test Step QT5 or QT6, REPLACE the PCM.
	No	▶	GO to SCG2.
SCG2 CHECK POWER TO SOLENOID • Key OFF. • Disconnect the connector of the solenoid in question. • Key ON. • Measure the voltage on the VPWR wire at the solenoid harness connector. • Is the voltage approximately battery voltage?	Yes	▶	GO to SCG3.
	No	▶	GO to EEC Pinpoint Test VPWR. If VPWR is OK, SERVICE the VPWR wire to solenoid.
SCG3 CHECK SOLENOID WIRE TO PCM FOR OPEN • Key OFF. • Install breakout box (leave PCM disconnected). • Disconnect the connector of the solenoid in question. • Measure the resistance between the solenoid Test Pin and the terminal at the solenoid harness connector. • Is the resistance less than 5 ohms?	Yes	▶	GO to SCG4.
	No	▶	SERVICE the solenoid wire to PCM for opens.
SCG4 CHECK SOLENOID WIRE TO PCM FOR SHORT • Key OFF. • Install breakout box (leave PCM disconnected). • Disconnect the connector of the solenoid in question. • Measure the resistance between the solenoid Test Pin and ground. • Is the resistance greater than 10,000 ohms?	Yes	▶	REPLACE the solenoid.
	No	▶	SERVICE the solenoid wire to PCM for shorts.

Fig. 111 Pinpoint test SCG, solenoid controlled by ground (Part 6 of 6)

Switch Monitor Lamp (SML)

Note

You should enter this Pinpoint Test only when directed here by Quick Test Step 8. The switch monitor lamp is located on the SUPER STAR II adapter.

Remember

This Pinpoint Test is intended to diagnose only the following:

• Circuits: SML

Pinpoint Test Schematic

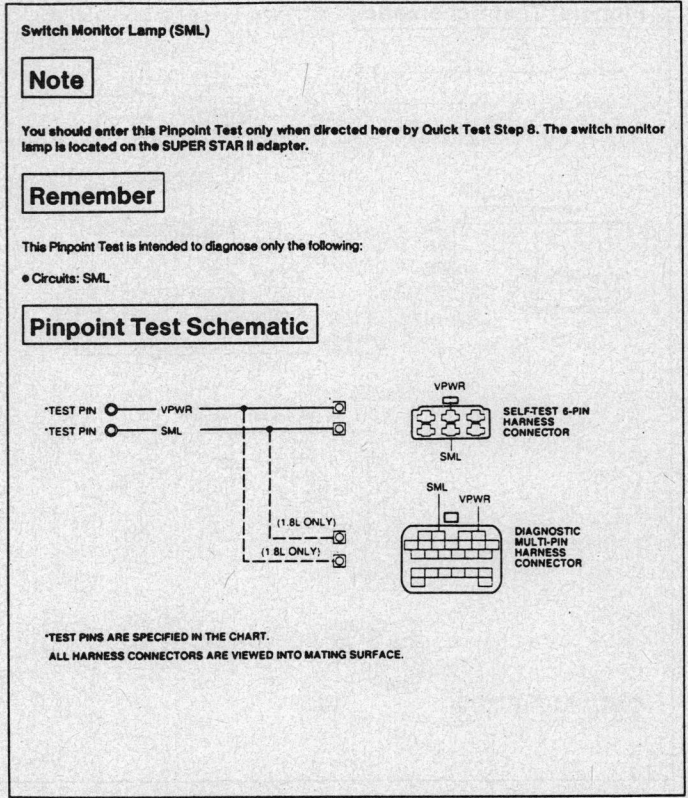

*TEST PINS ARE SPECIFIED IN THE CHART.
ALL HARNESS CONNECTORS ARE VIEWED INTO MATING SURFACE.

Fig. 112 Pinpoint test SML, switch monitor lamp (Part 1 of 2)

Application	Circuit	ECA Pin	BOB Pin	Wire Color
1.3L	SML	1D	38	BL/GN
	VPWR	1B	37,57	Y/BK
1.6L, 1.6L Turbo	SML	1D	38	BK/BL
	VPWR	3I	37	Y/GN
1.8L	SML	1D	38	W/Y
	VPWR	1B	37,57	W/R
2.2L, 2.2L Turbo	SML	1D	38	W/Y
	VPWR	1B	37,57	R/BK

TEST STEP		RESULT	▶	ACTION TO TAKE
SML1	**CHECK SWITCH MONITOR LINE CONTINUITY**			
• Install breakout box to harness connectors (leave ECA disconnected).		Yes	▶	GO to **SML2**.
• Measure resistance between Test Pin SML and diagnostic connector SML wire.		No	▶	SERVICE diagnostic connector SML wire to ECA.
• Is the resistance less than 5 ohms?				
SML2	**CHECK SWITCH MONITOR LAMP ISOLATION**			
• Install breakout box to harness connectors (leave ECA disconnected).		Yes	▶	SERVICE ECA SML wire to diagnostic connector for shorts.
• Measure resistance between Test Pin SML and all other Test Pins.		No	▶	GO to **SML3**.
• Is the resistance between Test Pin SML and any other Test Pin less than 5 ohms?				
SML3	**CHECK VPWR TO DIAGNOSTIC CONNECTOR**			
• Measure voltage between VPWR wire at the diagnostic connector and ground.		Yes	▶	REPLACE ECA.
• Key ON.		No	▶	GO to EEC Pinpoint Test **VPWR**.
• Is voltage above 10 volts?				

Fig. 112 Pinpoint test SML, switch monitor lamp (Part 2 of 2)

Switch To Ground (STG)

Note

You should enter this Pinpoint Test only when directed by Quick Test Steps 9 or 11.

Remember

This Pinpoint Test is intended to diagnose only the following:

• Circuits and Switches: PSPS, ACS, BLMT, WOT, NGS/CES, BPS, IDL

Switch Type A

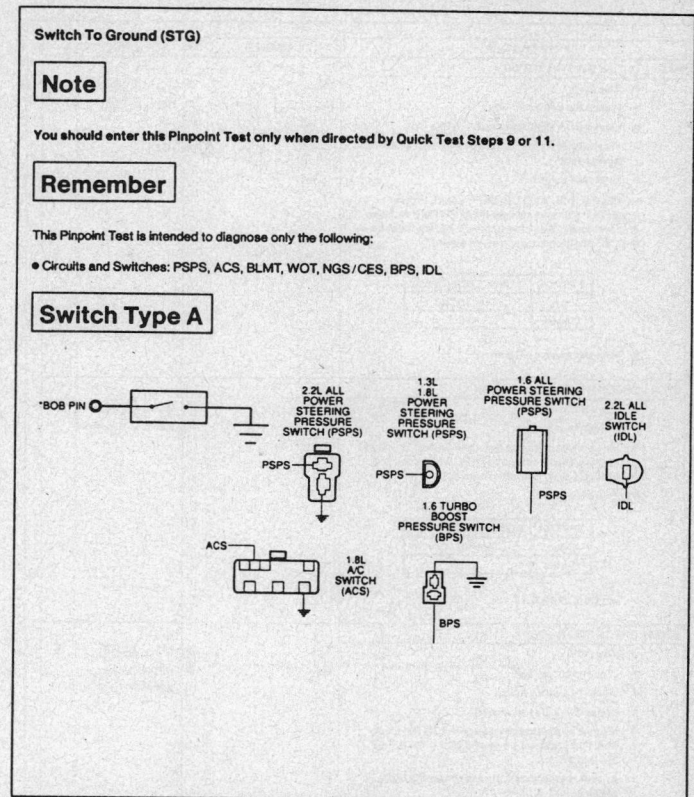

Fig. 113 Pinpoint test STG, switch to ground (Part 1 of 6). 1993–94

Switch Type B

Switch Type C

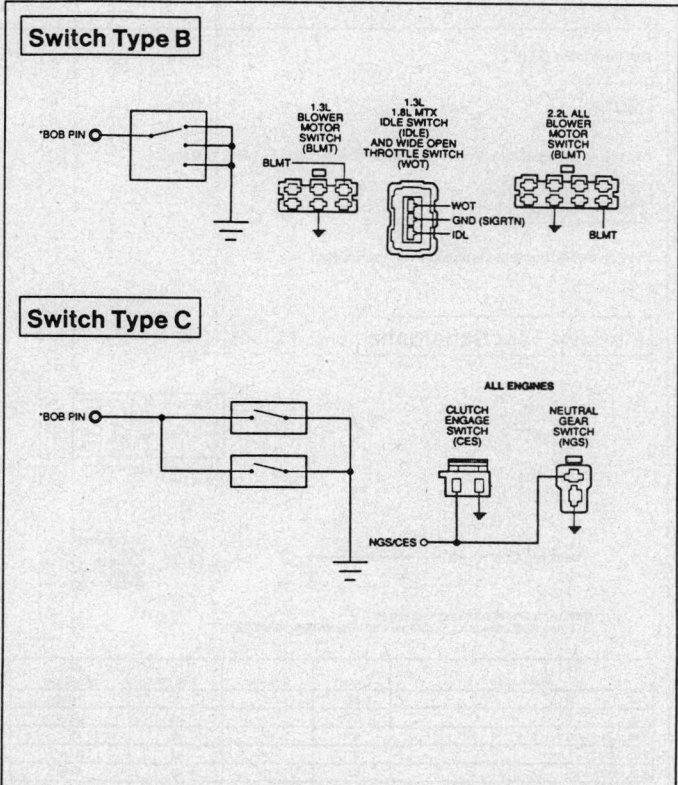

Fig. 113 Pinpoint test STG, switch to ground (Part 2 of 6). 1993–94

Switch	Abbrev.	Engine	ECA Pin	BOB Pin	Wire Color	Switch Exercise	Switch to
Idle	IDL	1.3L	1N	18	Y/BK	Open switch — depress throttle	SIGRTN
		1.8L			R/W		
		2.2L (MTX)					
		2.2L 4EAT	1T	18	LG/W		Ground
		2.2L Turbo					
		1.6L	1E	28	GN/O		
Wide Open Throttle	WOT 1.3L Type B 1.8L MTX Type A	1.3L	2L	27	Y		Ground
		1.8L			LG/W	Close switch — open throttle	SIGRTN
Power Steering Pressure	PSPS Type A	1.3L	1P	19	PK	Open — P/S pressure below 1690 – 1740 kPa (245 – 252 psi)	Ground
		1.8L	1P		BL/Y		
		2.2L MTX	1P		BR/R	Close — P/S pressure above 2000 – 2600 kPa (290 – 377 psi)	
		2.2L 4EAT 2.2L Turbo	1N				
		1.6L 1.6L Turbo	1K		GN/R		
Blower Motor	BLMT Type A	1.3L	1S	23	BL/R	Close switch — Blower ON (above "1" for 1.3L and 1.8L, above "2" for 2.2L)	Ground
		1.8L MTX			O/BL		
		2.2L MTX					
		2.2L 4EAT 2.2L Turbo	1P	22	BL/BK		
A/C On-Off	ACS Type A	1.3L	1Q	10	GN	Close switch — A/C button pushed (blower ON)	Ground
		1.8L			GN/BK		
Neutral Gear Switch and Clutch Engage Switch	NGS/CES (MTX Only) Type C	1.3L	1V	43	BL/W	Close CES — Clutch pedal up	Ground (either switch closed)
		1.8L			BR/Y		
		2.2L			R/BL		
		2.2L Turbo	1R			Close NGS — Trans. in Neutral	
		1.6L	1G	8	R/BL		
Boost Pressure Switch	BPS Type A	1.6L Turbo	2L	12	LG/BK	Open — Boost pressure under 72 kPa (10 psi) Close — Boost pressure above 72 – 80 kPa (10 – 12 psi)	Ground

Fig. 113 Pinpoint test STG, switch to ground (Part 3 of 6). 1993–94

COMPUTERIZED ENGINE CONTROLS (ASPIRE, CAPRI, ESCORT & TRACER (1.8L/4-112), FESTIVA & PROBE (2.0L/4-121 w/4EAT & 2.5L/V6-152) ELECTRONIC ENGINE CONTROL (EEC) SYSTEM

10-61

TEST STEP		RESULT	▶	ACTION TO TAKE
STG1	CHECK SWITCH SIGNAL			
	• Key OFF.	Yes	▶	GO to **STG4**.
	• Install the breakout box.	No	▶	GO to **STG2**.
	• Leave ECA disconnected.			
	• Measure resistance between switch BOB Pin and ground.			
	• Exercise switch.			
	NOTE: For 1.3L A/C ON-OFF switch, blower motor resistor and 15 amp HEATER fuse must be disconnected, and blower motor switch must be in the "1" position to test switch signal.			

SWITCH	RESISTANCE (OHMS)
Open	Over 10,000
Closed	0-5

	• Is resistance switching?			
STG2	CHECK SWITCH OPERATION			
	• Key OFF.	Yes	▶	GO to **STG3**
	• Disconnect switch.	No	▶	REPLACE switch.
	• Measure resistance between switch terminals (2-pin switch) or switch to ECA terminal and ground (1-pin or multi-pin switches).			
	• Exercise switch.			

SWITCH	RESISTANCE (OHMS)
Open	Over 10,000
Closed	0-5

	• Is resistance OK?			
STG3	CHECK FOR SHORTS			
	• Key OFF.	Yes	▶	GO to **STG4**.
	• Disconnect switch.	No	▶	SERVICE wire in question for shorts.
	• Install breakout box.			
	• Leave ECA disconnected.			
	• Measure resistance between BOB Pin from chart on previous page and test pins, 37, 57, 60, and 26.			
	• Are all resistances greater than 10,000 ohms?			

Fig. 113   Pinpoint test STG, switch to ground (Part 4 of 6). 1993–94

TEST STEP		RESULT	▶	ACTION TO TAKE
STG4	CHECK CONTINUITY			
	• Key OFF.	Yes (Sent to this test by Quick Test Step QT9.)	▶	REPLACE ECA.
	• Disconnect switch.			
	• Install breakout box.			
	• Leave ECA disconnected.	Yes (Sent to this test by Quick Test Step QT 11.)	▶	RETURN to **QT11**.
	• Measure resistance between BOB Pin and switch connector.			
	• Is resistance less than 5 ohms?	No	▶	SERVICE wire in question for opens.

Fig. 113   Pinpoint test STG, switch to ground (Part 5 of 6). 1993–94

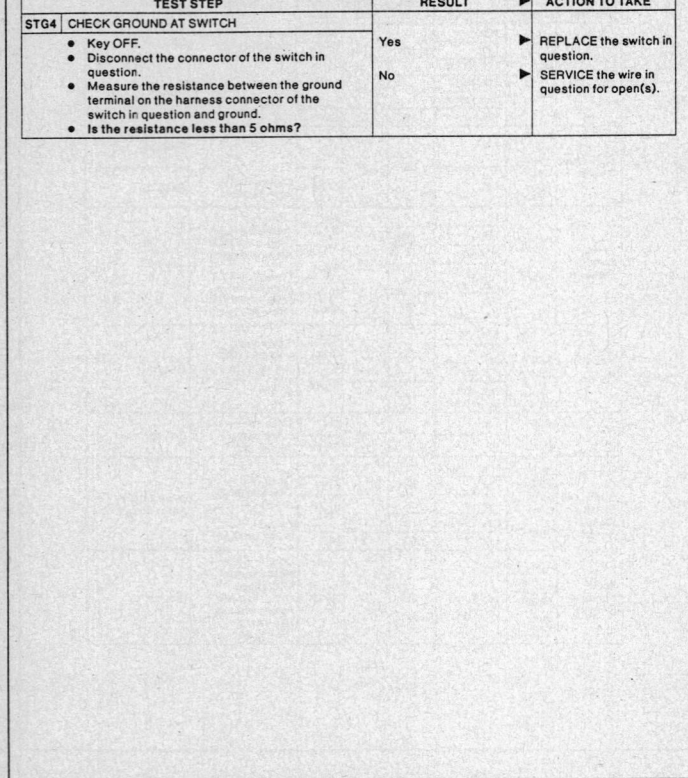

TEST STEP		RESULT	▶	ACTION TO TAKE
STG4	CHECK GROUND AT SWITCH			
	• Key OFF.	Yes	▶	REPLACE the switch in question.
	• Disconnect the connector of the switch in question.	No	▶	SERVICE the wire in question for open(s).
	• Measure the resistance between the ground terminal on the harness connector of the switch in question and ground.			
	• Is the resistance less than 5 ohms?			

Fig. 113   Pinpoint test STG, switch to ground (Part 6 of 6). 1993–94

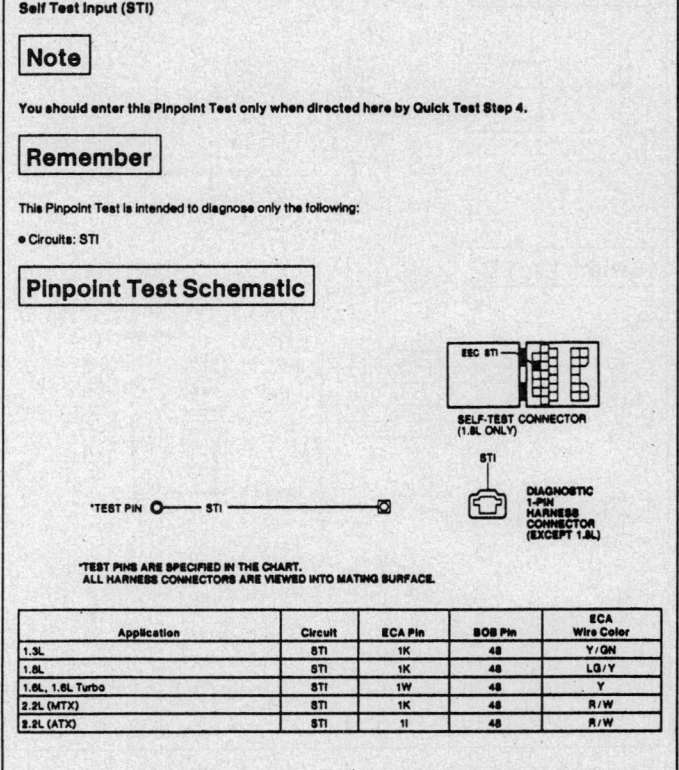

Self Test Input (STI)

Note

You should enter this Pinpoint Test only when directed here by Quick Test Step 4.

Remember

This Pinpoint Test is intended to diagnose only the following:

• Circuits: STI

Pinpoint Test Schematic

EEC STI

SELF-TEST CONNECTOR (1.8L ONLY)

STI

DIAGNOSTIC 1-PIN HARNESS CONNECTOR (EXCEPT 1.8L)

*TEST PIN ○── STI ──◻

*TEST PINS ARE SPECIFIED IN THE CHART. ALL HARNESS CONNECTORS ARE VIEWED INTO MATING SURFACE.

Application	Circuit	ECA Pin	BOB Pin	ECA Wire Color
1.3L	STI	1K	48	Y/GN
1.8L	STI	1K	48	LG/Y
1.6L, 1.6L Turbo	STI	1W	48	Y
2.2L (MTX)	STI	1K	48	R/W
2.2L (ATX)	STI	1I	48	R/W

Fig. 114   Pinpoint test STI, self test input (Part 1 of 2)

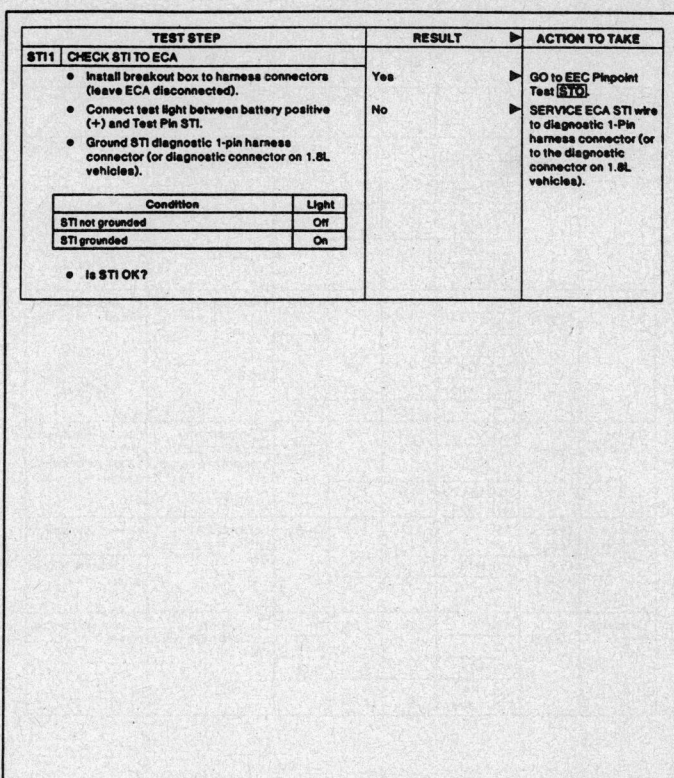

TEST STEP	RESULT	▶	ACTION TO TAKE
STI1 CHECK STI TO ECA ● Install breakout box to harness connectors (leave ECA disconnected). ● Connect test light between battery positive (+) and Test Pin STI. ● Ground STI diagnostic 1-pin harness connector (or diagnostic connector on 1.8L vehicles).	Yes No	▶ ▶	GO to EEC Pinpoint Test **STO**. SERVICE ECA STI wire to diagnostic 1-Pin harness connector (or to the diagnostic connector on 1.8L vehicles).

Condition	Light
STI not grounded	Off
STI grounded	On

● Is STI OK?

Fig. 114   Pinpoint test STI, self test input (Part 2 of 2)

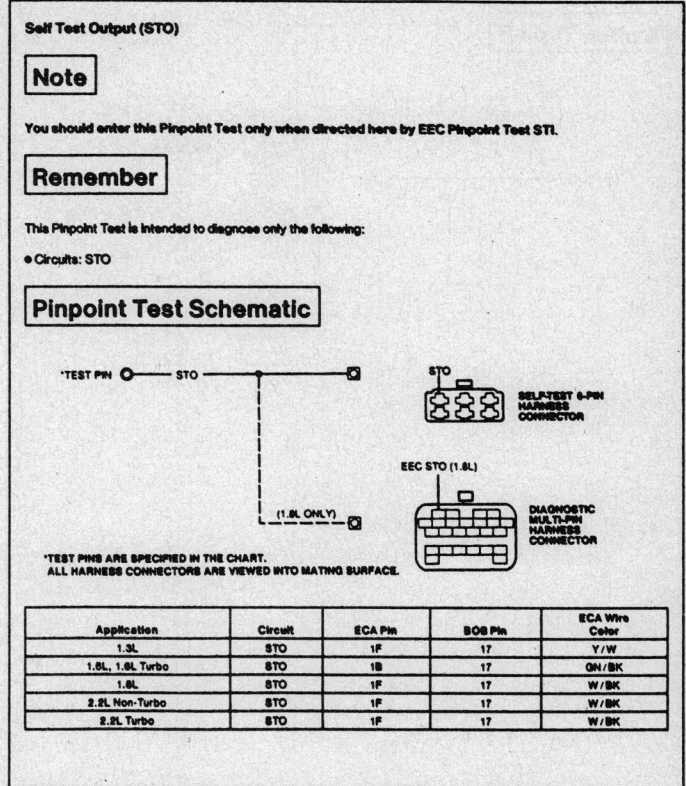

Self Test Output (STO)

Note

You should enter this Pinpoint Test only when directed here by EEC Pinpoint Test STI.

Remember

This Pinpoint Test is intended to diagnose only the following:

● Circuits: STO

Pinpoint Test Schematic

*TEST PINS ARE SPECIFIED IN THE CHART.
ALL HARNESS CONNECTORS ARE VIEWED INTO MATING SURFACE.

Application	Circuit	ECA Pin	BOB Pin	ECA Wire Color
1.3L	STO	1F	17	Y/W
1.6L, 1.6L Turbo	STO	1B	17	GN/BK
1.8L	STO	1F	17	W/BK
2.2L Non-Turbo	STO	1F	17	W/BK
2.2L Turbo	STO	1F	17	W/BK

Fig. 115   Pinpoint test STO, self test output (Part 1 of 2)

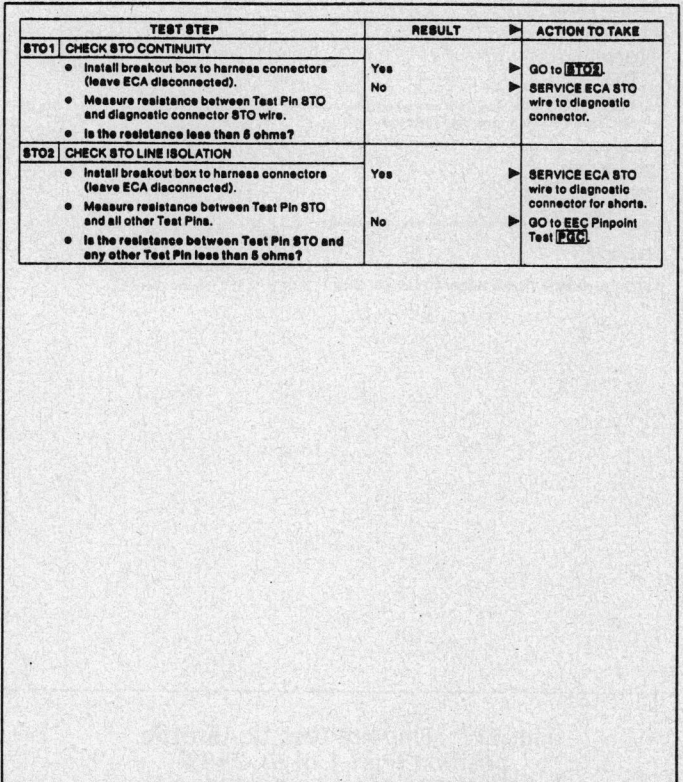

TEST STEP	RESULT	▶	ACTION TO TAKE
STO1 CHECK STO CONTINUITY ● Install breakout box to harness connectors (leave ECA disconnected). ● Measure resistance between Test Pin STO and diagnostic connector STO wire. ● Is the resistance less than 5 ohms?	Yes No	▶ ▶	GO to **STO2**. SERVICE ECA STO wire to diagnostic connector.
STO2 CHECK STO LINE ISOLATION ● Install breakout box to harness connectors (leave ECA disconnected). ● Measure resistance between Test Pin STO and all other Test Pins. ● Is the resistance between Test Pin STO and any other Test Pin less than 5 ohms?	Yes No	▶ ▶	SERVICE ECA STO wire to diagnostic connector for shorts. GO to EEC Pinpoint Test **FGC**.

Fig. 115   Pinpoint test STO, self test output (Part 2 of 2)

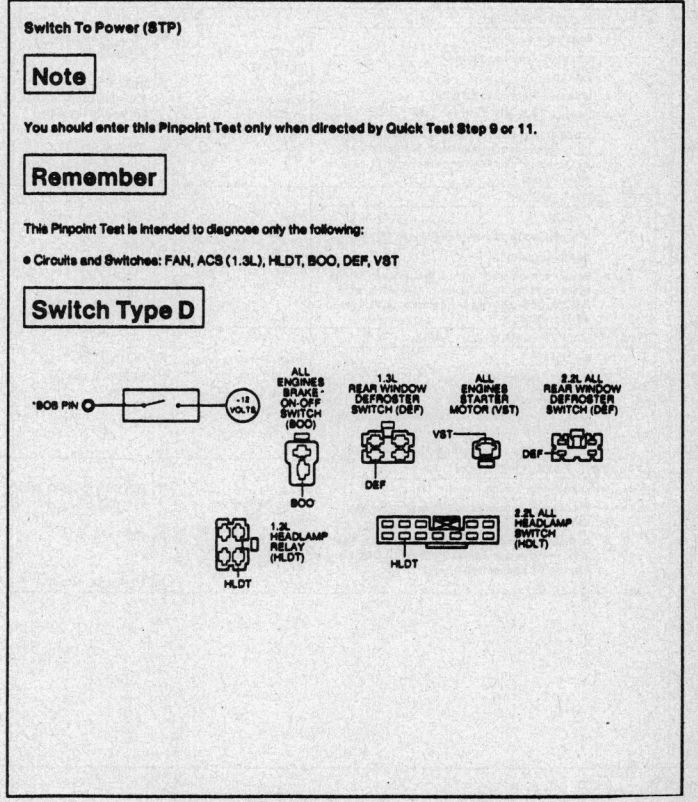

Switch To Power (STP)

Note

You should enter this Pinpoint Test only when directed by Quick Test Step 9 or 11.

Remember

This Pinpoint Test is intended to diagnose only the following:

● Circuits and Switches: FAN, ACS (1.3L), HLDT, BOO, DEF, VST

Switch Type D

Fig. 116   Pinpoint test STP, switch to power (Part 1 of 4)

Switch Type F

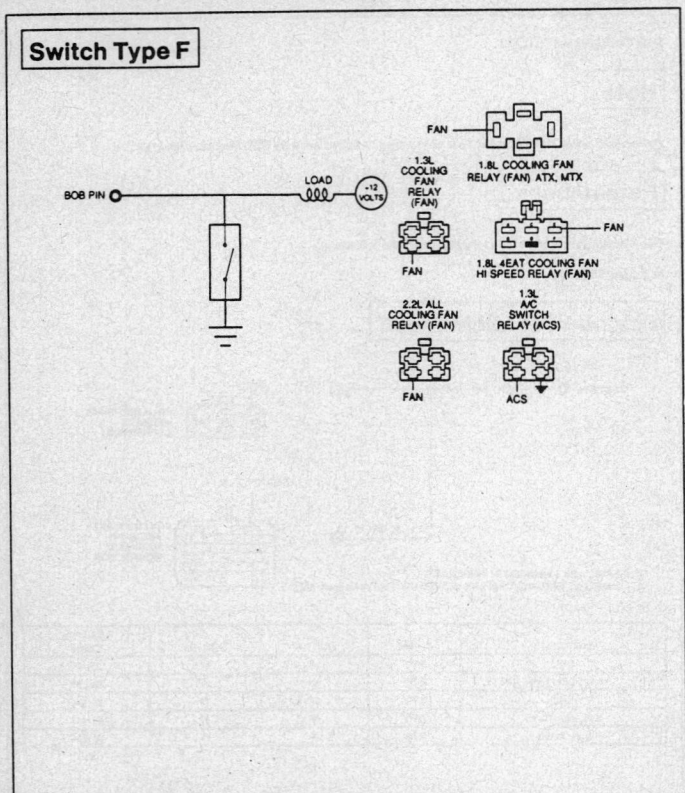

Fig. 116   Pinpoint test STP, switch to power (Part 2 of 4)

Switch	Abbrev.	Engine	ECA Pin	BOB Pin	Wire Color	Switch Exercise	Switch to
A/C Switch	ACS Type F	1.3L	1Q	1O	GN	Close switch by turning A/C ON and blower ON	12 volts with key ON and switch open
Brake On/ Off Switch	BOO Type D	1.3L	1O	2	GN/R	Close switch by pushing brake pedal	12 volts with switch closed
		1.8L MTX			GN		
		2.2L MTX			W/GN		
		1.6L 1.6L Turbo	1J	3			
		2.2L 4EAT 2.2L Turbo MTX	1Q	2			
Vehicle Start	VST Type D	1.3L	1C	5	BK/R	Crank engine	12 volts with switch closed
		1.8L			P		
		2.2L MTX			BK/PK		
		2.2L 4EAT		23			
		2.2L Turbo					
		1.6L	3B	5	BK/R		
Cooling Fan Relay	Fan Type F	1.3L	1R	22	Y/R	Close switch by grounding coolant temperature switch	Ground with switch closed
		1.8L, 2.2L MTX			BK/GN		12 volts with switch open
		2.2L 4EAT 2.2L Turbo	2D	51			
Rear Window Def.	DEF Type D	1.3L 1.8L	1T	30	BK/BL	Close switch by turning rear defrost ON	12 volts with switch closed
	DEF Type F	2.2L MTX					12 volts with switch open
		2.2L 4EAT 2.2L Turbo	1J	34			
Headlamp Switch	HLDT Type D	1.3L	1U	28	W	Close switch by turning headlamps ON	12 volts with switch closed
		1.8L			R/BK		
		2.2L MTX			W/BL		
		2.2L 4EAT 2.2L Turbo	1H	32			

Fig. 116   Pinpoint test STP, switch to power (Part 3 of 4)

TEST STEP	RESULT	►	ACTION TO TAKE
STP1 TEST SWITCH SIGNAL • Install breakout box. • Leave ECA disconnected. • Key ON. • Measure voltage at BOB Pin. • Exercise switch. • Does voltage switch from 0-4 volts to 10-14 volts (or from 10-14 volts to 0-4 volts for A/C switch, cooling fan relay, or 2.2L rear window def.)?	Yes (sent to this test by QT11) Yes (sent to this test by QT9) No	► ► ►	RETURN to Quick Test Step QT11. REPLACE ECA. (Confirm SML circuit is OK before replacing ECA.) GO to STP2.
STP2 TEST AT SWITCH • Key ON. • Measure voltage at switch (wire to ECA). • Exercise switch. • Does voltage switch from 0-4 volts to 10-14 volts (or from 10-14 volts to 0-4 volts for A/C switch, cooling fan relay, or 2.2L rear window def.)?	Yes No	► ►	SERVICE wire from switch to ECA for opens. GO to STP3.
STP3 CHECK FOR SHORTS TO POWER • Key OFF. • Install breakout box. • Leave ECA disconnected. • Measure resistance between switch BOB Pin and BOB Pins 37, 57 and 1. • Is resistance greater than 10,000 ohms?	Yes No	► ►	GO to STP4. SERVICE wire for shorts.
STP4 TEST SWITCH OPERATION • Disconnect switch. • Measure the resistance between the switch terminals. • Is the resistance less than 5 ohms with the switch closed and greater than 10,000 ohms with the switch open?	Yes (sent to this test by QT11) Yes (sent to this test by QT9) No	► ► ►	RETURN to Quick Test Step QT11. REPLACE ECA. REPLACE switch.

Fig. 116   Pinpoint test STP, switch to power (Part 4 of 4)

Throttle Position (TP)

Note

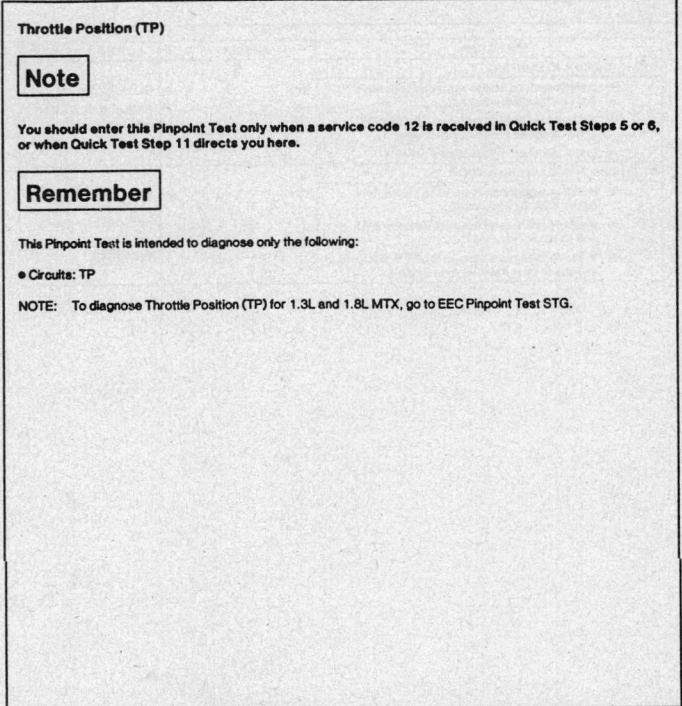

You should enter this Pinpoint Test only when a service code 12 is received in Quick Test Steps 5 or 6, or when Quick Test Step 11 directs you here.

Remember

This Pinpoint Test is intended to diagnose only the following:

● Circuits: TP

NOTE: To diagnose Throttle Position (TP) for 1.3L and 1.8L MTX, go to EEC Pinpoint Test STG.

Fig. 117   Pinpoint test TP, throttle position (Part 1 of 5). 1993 2.0L/4-121 w/4EAT & 1993–94 1.6L/4-98, 1.8L/4-112 w/4EAT & 2.5L/V6-152

Pinpoint Test Schematic

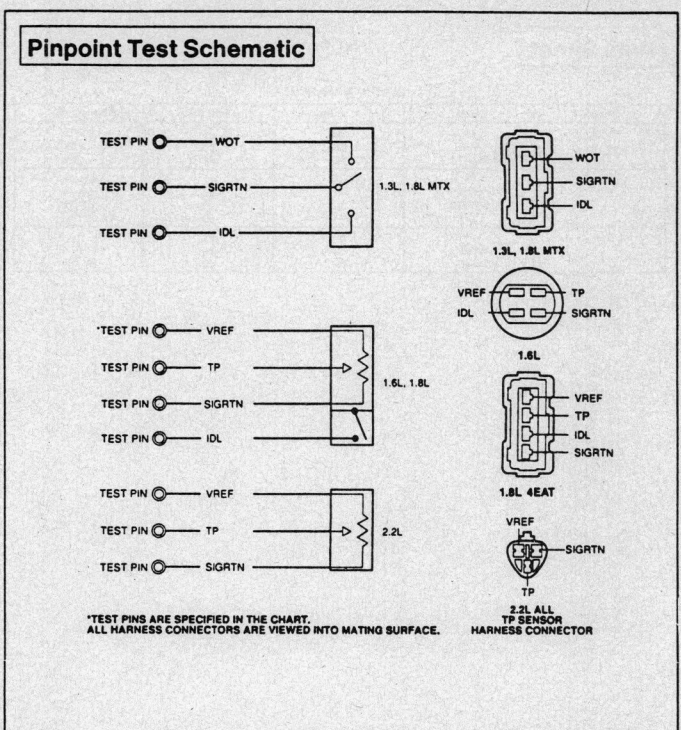

Application	Circuit	ECA Pin	BOB Pin	Wire Color
1.6L, 1.6L Turbo	TP	2G	47	O
	VREF	2A	26	W/BK
	SIGRTN	2C	46,49	BL/Y
	IDL	1E	28	GN/O
1.8L 4EAT	TP	2M	47	LG/W
	VREF	2K	26	LG/R
	SIGRTN	2D	46,49	BK/W
	IDL	1N	18	R/W
2.2L 4EAT (MTX)	TP	2F (2M)	47	LG/BK
	VREF	2I (2K)	26	LG/R
	SIGRTN	3D (2D)	46,49	LG/Y
2.2L Turbo	TP	2F	47	LG/BK
	VREF	2I	26	LG/R
	SIGRTN	3D	46,49	LG/Y

Fig. 117   Pinpoint test TP, throttle position (Part 2 of 5). 1993 2.0L/4-121 w/4EAT & 1993–94 1.6L/4-98, 1.8L/4-112 w/4EAT & 2.5L/V6-152

Fig. 117   Pinpoint test TP, throttle position (Part 3 of 5). 1993 2.0L/4-121 w/4EAT & 1993–94 1.6L/4-98, 1.8L/4-112 w/4EAT & 2.5L/V6-152

Data Sheet

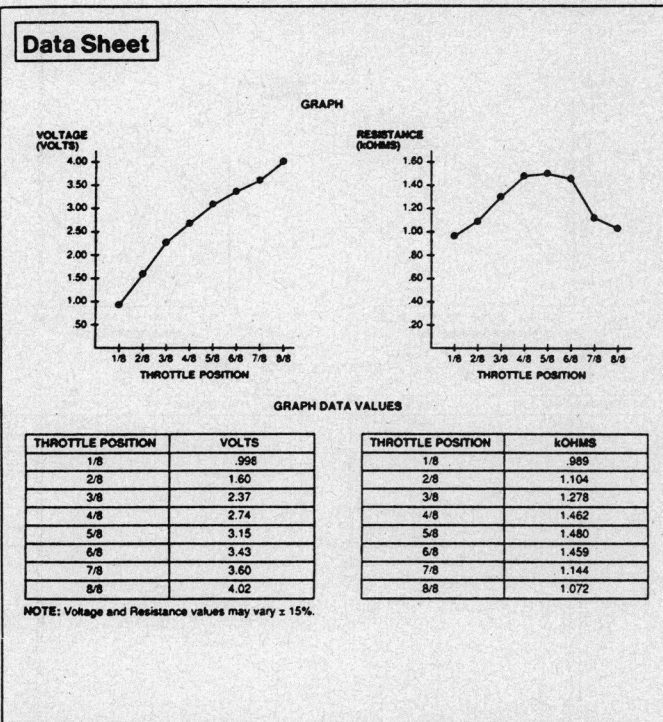

GRAPH DATA VALUES

THROTTLE POSITION	VOLTS
1/8	.998
2/8	1.60
3/8	2.37
4/8	2.74
5/8	3.15
6/8	3.43
7/8	3.60
8/8	4.02

THROTTLE POSITION	kOHMS
1/8	.989
2/8	1.104
3/8	1.278
4/8	1.462
5/8	1.480
6/8	1.459
7/8	1.144
8/8	1.072

NOTE: Voltage and Resistance values may vary ± 15%.

	TEST STEP	RESULT	ACTION TO TAKE
TP1	CHECK TP INPUT VOLTAGE TO PCM • Key OFF. • Install breakout box (connect PCM). • Key ON. • Measure the voltage at Test Pin TP. • Compare the voltage readings to the graph and chart as the accelerator pedal is depressed. • Are the voltages OK?	Yes	TP circuit OK. If directed here from Quick Test Step QT11, RETURN Otherwise, REPLACE the PCM.
		No	GO to TP2.
TP2	CHECK VREF • Key OFF. • Disconnect the throttle position sensor connector. • Key ON. • Measure the voltage on the VREF wire at the throttle position sensor harness connector. • Is the voltage between 4.5 and 5.5 volts?	Yes (1.6L, 1.8L 4EAT, 2.0L 4EAT)	GO to TP3.
		Yes (2.5L)	GO to TP4.
		No	GO to EEC Pinpoint Test VREF.
TP3	CHECK WIRES TO PCM (1.6L, 1.8L 4EAT, 2.0L 4EAT) • Key OFF. • Install breakout box (leave PCM disconnected). • Disconnect the throttle position sensor connector. • Measure the resistances of the TP wire and SIGRTN wire between Test Pins and the throttle position sensor harness connector. • Measure the resistance of the TP wire between Test Pin TP and ground. • Are the resistances less than 5 ohms between Test Pins and the throttle position sensor harness connector, and greater than 10,000 ohms between Test Pin TP and ground?	Yes	REPLACE the throttle position sensor.
		No	SERVICE the TP wire.
TP4	CHECK TP GROUND (2.5L) • Key OFF. • Disconnect the throttle position sensor connector. • Measure the resistance of the GND wire between the throttle position sensor harness connector and ground. • Is the resistance less than 5 ohms?	Yes	REPLACE the throttle position sensor.
		No	SERVICE the GND wire.

Fig. 117   Pinpoint test TP, throttle position (Part 4 of 5). 1993 2.0L/4-121 w/4EAT & 1993–94 1.6L/4-98, 1.8L/4-112 w/4EAT & 2.5L/V6-152

Fig. 117   Pinpoint test TP, throttle position (Part 5 of 5). 1993 2.0L/4-121 w/4EAT & 1993–94 1.6L/4-98, 1.8L/4-112 w/4EAT & 2.5L/V6-152

Pinpoint Test Schematic

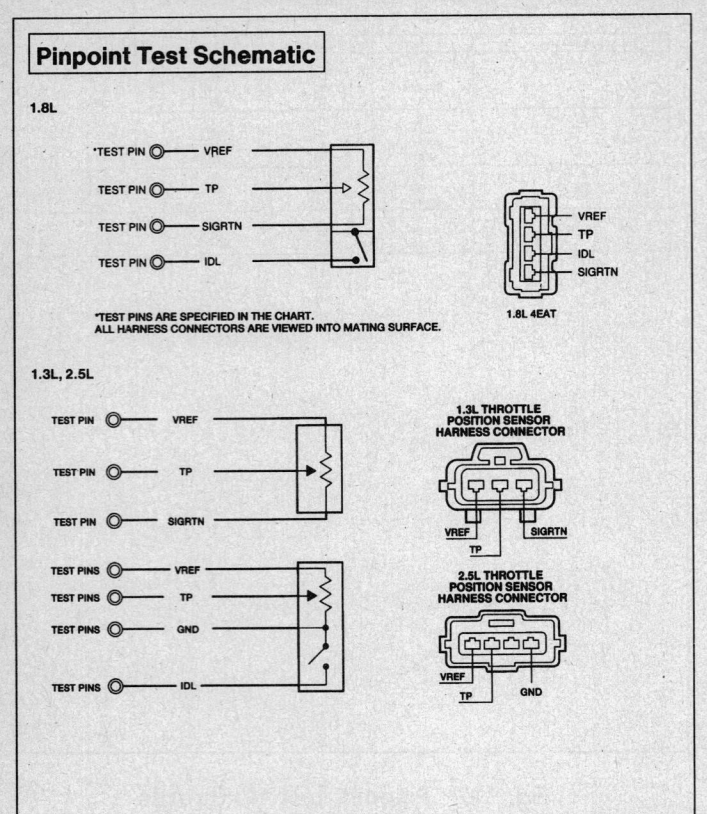

Fig. 118   Pinpoint test TP, throttle position (Part 1 of 6). 1995

Data Sheet

CIRCUIT DATA SHEET

Engine	Circuit	PCM Pin	BOB Pin	Wire Color
1.3L	TP	2M	47	LG/W
	VREF	2K	26	LG/R
	SIGRTN	2D	46	Y/GN
1.8L	TP	2F	47	LG/W
	VREF	2I	26	LG/R
	SIGRTN	3D	46	BK/W
	IDL	1T	18	R/W
2.5L	TP	2F	47	Y
	VREF	2I	26	P
	GND	3D	46	BK/BL

Fig. 118   Pinpoint test TP, throttle position (Part 2 of 6). 1995

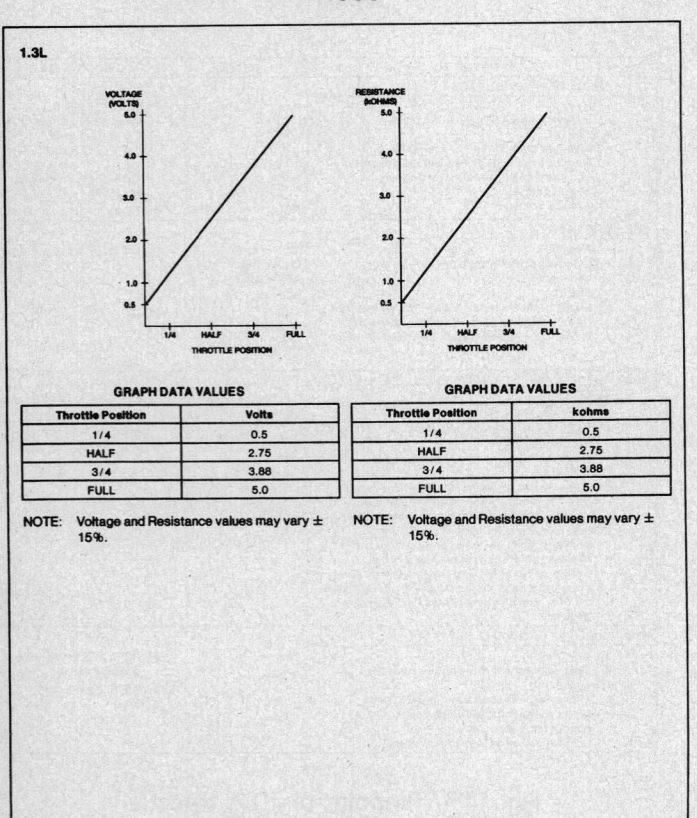

1.3L

GRAPH DATA VALUES

Throttle Position	Volts
1/4	0.5
HALF	2.75
3/4	3.88
FULL	5.0

NOTE: Voltage and Resistance values may vary ± 15%.

Throttle Position	kohms
1/4	0.5
HALF	2.75
3/4	3.88
FULL	5.0

NOTE: Voltage and Resistance values may vary ± 15%.

Fig. 118   Pinpoint test TP, throttle position (Part 3 of 6). 1995

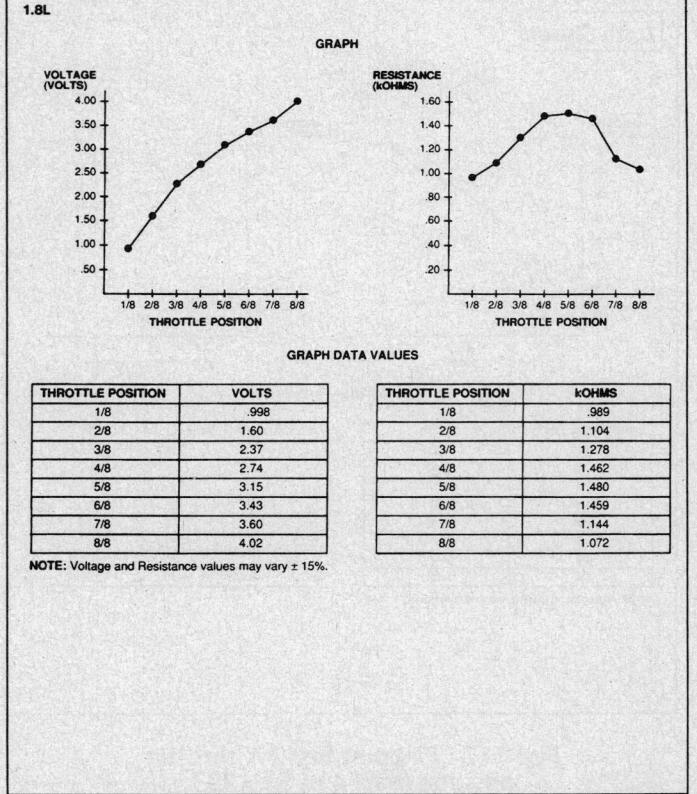

1.8L

GRAPH DATA VALUES

THROTTLE POSITION	VOLTS
1/8	.998
2/8	1.60
3/8	2.37
4/8	2.74
5/8	3.15
6/8	3.43
7/8	3.60
8/8	4.02

THROTTLE POSITION	kOHMS
1/8	.989
2/8	1.104
3/8	1.278
4/8	1.462
5/8	1.480
6/8	1.459
7/8	1.144
8/8	1.072

NOTE: Voltage and Resistance values may vary ± 15%.

Fig. 118   Pinpoint test TP, throttle position (Part 4 of 6). 1995

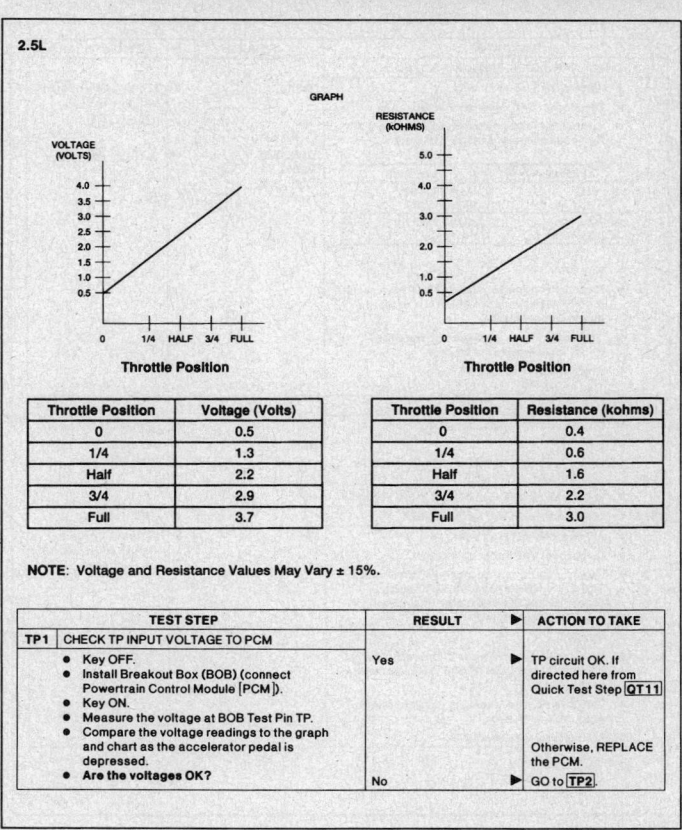

NOTE: Voltage and Resistance Values May Vary ± 15%.

Throttle Position	Voltage (Volts)
0	0.5
1/4	1.3
Half	2.2
3/4	2.9
Full	3.7

Throttle Position	Resistance (kohms)
0	0.4
1/4	0.6
Half	1.6
3/4	2.2
Full	3.0

	TEST STEP	RESULT	▶	ACTION TO TAKE
TP1	CHECK TP INPUT VOLTAGE TO PCM			
	• Key OFF. • Install Breakout Box (BOB) (connect Powertrain Control Module [PCM]). • Key ON. • Measure the voltage at BOB Test Pin TP. • Compare the voltage readings to the graph and chart as the accelerator pedal is depressed. • **Are the voltages OK?**	Yes	▶	TP circuit OK. If directed here from Quick Test Step **QT11**. Otherwise, REPLACE the PCM.
		No	▶	GO to **TP2**.

FM0159501237050X

Fig. 118   Pinpoint test TP, throttle position (Part 5 of 6).
1995

	TEST STEP	RESULT	▶	ACTION TO TAKE
TP2	CHECK VREF			
	• Key OFF. • Disconnect the TP sensor connector. • Key ON. • Measure the voltage on the VREF wire at the throttle position sensor harness connector. • **Is the voltage between 4.5 and 5.5 volts?**	Yes	▶	GO to **TP3**.
		No	▶	GO to EEC Pinpoint Test **VREF**.
TP3	CHECK WIRES TO PCM			
	• Key OFF. • Install Breakout Box (leave PCM disconnected). • Disconnect the TP sensor connector. • Measure the resistances of the TP wire and SIGRTN (1.3L, 1.8L) wire between BOB Test Pins and the TP sensor harness connector. • Measure the resistance of the TP wire between BOB Test Pin TP and ground. • **Are the resistances less than 5 ohms between BOB Test Pins and the TP sensor harness connector, and greater than 10,000 ohms between BOB Test Pin TP and ground?**	Yes (2.5L) Yes (All Others) No	▶ ▶ ▶	GO to **TP4**. REPLACE the throttle position sensor. SERVICE the wire(s) in question.
TP4	CHECK TP GROUND (2.5L)			
	• Key OFF. • Disconnect the TP sensor connector. • Measure the resistance of the GND wire between the TP sensor harness connector and ground. • **Is the resistance less than 5 ohms?**	Yes No	▶ ▶	REPLACE the throttle position sensor. SERVICE the GND wire.

FM0159501237060X

Fig. 118   Pinpoint test TP, throttle position (Part 6 of 6).
1995

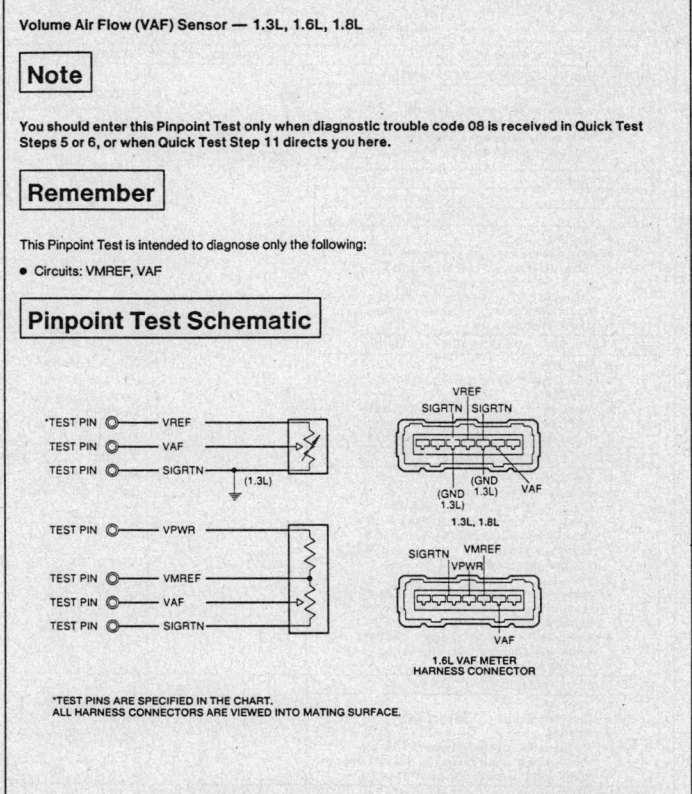

FM0159301114010X

Fig. 119   Pinpoint test VAF, vane air flow
(Part 1 of 5). 1993–95 1.3L/4-81,
1.6L/4-98 & 1.8L/4-112

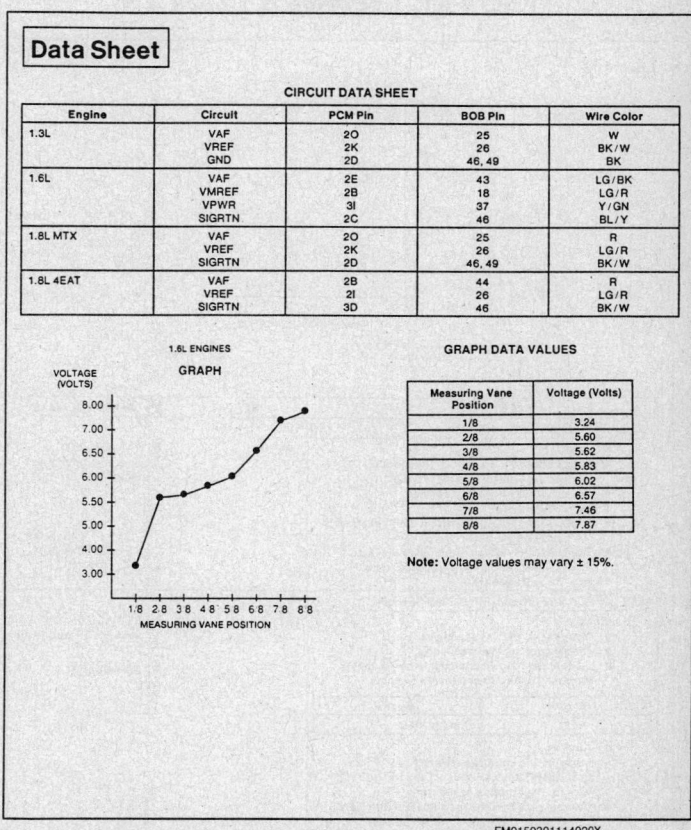

FM0159301114020X

Fig. 119   Pinpoint test VAF, vane air flow
(Part 2 of 5). 1993–95 1.3L/4-81,
1.6L/4-98 & 1.8L/4-112

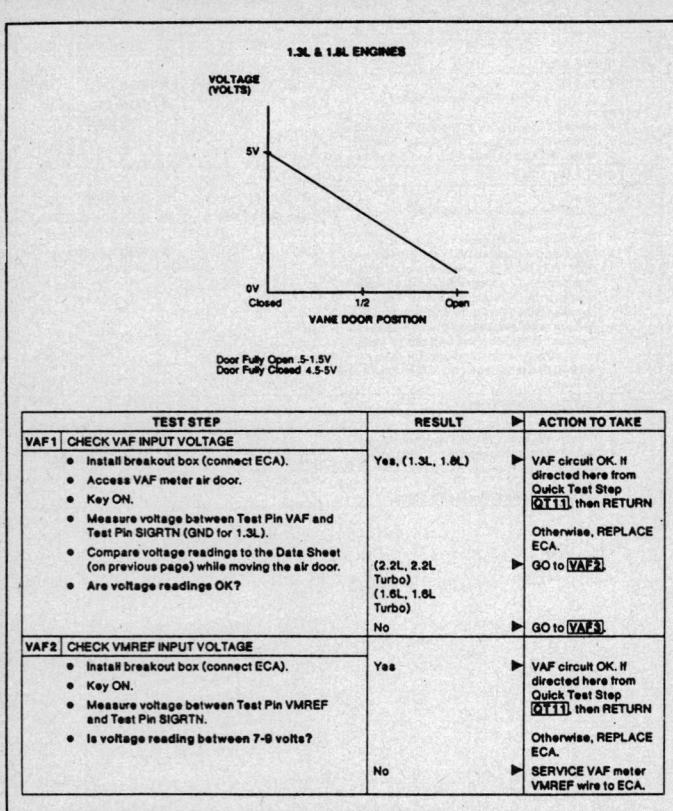

1.3L & 1.8L ENGINES

Door Fully Open .5-1.5V
Door Fully Closed 4.5-5V

TEST STEP		RESULT	▶	ACTION TO TAKE
VAF1 CHECK VAF INPUT VOLTAGE				
• Install breakout box (connect ECA).		Yes, (1.3L, 1.8L)	▶	VAF circuit OK. If directed here from Quick Test Step **QT11**, then RETURN
• Access VAF meter air door.				
• Key ON.				
• Measure voltage between Test Pin VAF and Test Pin SIGRTN (GND for 1.3L).				Otherwise, REPLACE ECA.
• Compare voltage readings to the Data Sheet (on previous page) while moving the air door.		(2.2L, 2.2L Turbo) (1.6L, 1.6L Turbo)	▶	GO to **VAF2**
• Are voltage readings OK?		No	▶	GO to **VAF3**
VAF2 CHECK VMREF INPUT VOLTAGE				
• Install breakout box (connect ECA).		Yes	▶	VAF circuit OK. If directed here from Quick Test Step **QT11**, then RETURN
• Key ON.				
• Measure voltage between Test Pin VMREF and Test Pin SIGRTN.				Otherwise, REPLACE ECA.
• Is voltage reading between 7-9 volts?		No	▶	SERVICE VAF meter VMREF wire to ECA.

Fig. 119   Pinpoint test VAF, vane air flow (Part 3 of 5). 1993–94 1.3L/4-81, 1.6L/4-98 & 1.8L/4-112

TEST STEP		RESULT	▶	ACTION TO TAKE
VAF3 CHECK VAF SIGNAL FROM VAF METER				
• Access VAF meter air door.		Yes	▶	SERVICE VAF meter VAF wire to ECA.
• Disconnect VAF meter connector.		No (1.3L, 1.8L)	▶	GO to **VAF4**.
• Jumper the following terminals between the harness connector and the VAF meter.		(2.2L, 2.2L Turbo) (1.6L, 1.6L Turbo)	▶	GO to **VAF5**.

Application	Terminal
1.3L, 1.8L	VREF, SIGRTN (GND for 1.3L)
1.6L, 1.6L Turbo 2.2L, 2.2L Turbo	VMREF, SIGRTN VPWR

• Key ON.			
• Measure voltage between the VAF terminal (at the VAF meter) and the SIGRTN wire (at the harness connector).			
• Compare voltage readings with the Data Sheet while moving the air door.			
• Are voltage readings OK?			

TEST STEP	RESULT	▶	ACTION TO TAKE
VAF4 CHECK VREF AT VAF METER			
• Disconnect VAF meter connector.	Yes	▶	REPLACE VAF meter.
• Key ON.	No	▶	GO to EEC Pinpoint Test **VREF**.
• Measure voltage between VAF meter VREF wire and VAF meter SIGRTN wire.			
• Is voltage reading between 4.5-5.5 volts?			
VAF5 CHECK VAF SIGNAL WITHOUT VMREF			
• Access VAF meter air door.	Yes	▶	SERVICE VAF meter VMREF wire to ECA.
• Disconnect VAF meter connector.	No	▶	GO to **VAF8**.
• Using jumper wires, connect the VPWR and SIGRTN terminals between the harness connector and the VAF meter. Leave VMREF and VAF disconnected.			
• Key ON.			
• Measure voltage between VAF terminal (at the VAF meter) and SIGRTN wire (at the harness connector).			
• Compare voltage reading to the Data Sheet while moving air door.			
• Are voltage readings OK?			

Fig. 119   Pinpoint test VAF, vane air flow (Part 4 of 5). 1993–94 1.3L/4-81, 1.6L/4-98 & 1.8L/4-112

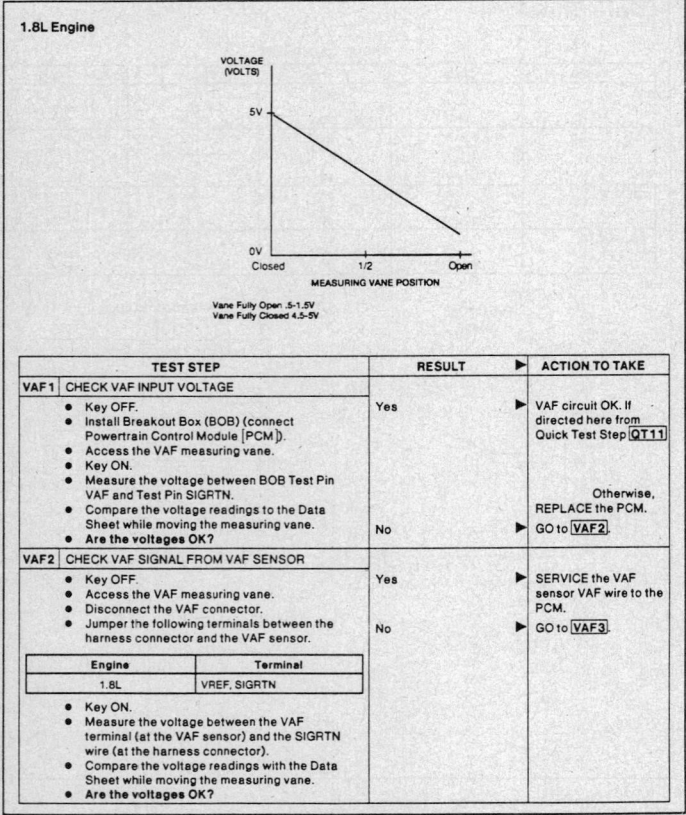

1.8L Engine

Vane Fully Open .5-1.5V
Vane Fully Closed 4.5-5V

TEST STEP		RESULT	▶	ACTION TO TAKE
VAF1 CHECK VAF INPUT VOLTAGE				
• Key OFF.		Yes	▶	VAF circuit OK. If directed here from Quick Test Step **QT11**
• Install Breakout Box (BOB) (connect Powertrain Control Module [PCM]).				
• Access the VAF measuring vane.				
• Key ON.				
• Measure the voltage between BOB Test Pin VAF and Test Pin SIGRTN.				Otherwise, REPLACE the PCM.
• Compare the voltage readings to the Data Sheet while moving the measuring vane.		No	▶	GO to **VAF2**.
• Are the voltages OK?				
VAF2 CHECK VAF SIGNAL FROM VAF SENSOR				
• Key OFF.		Yes	▶	SERVICE the VAF sensor VAF wire to the PCM.
• Access the VAF measuring vane.				
• Disconnect the VAF connector.		No	▶	GO to **VAF3**.
• Jumper the following terminals between the harness connector and the VAF sensor.				

Engine	Terminal
1.8L	VREF, SIGRTN

• Key ON.			
• Measure the voltage between the VAF terminal (at the VAF sensor) and the SIGRTN wire (at the harness connector).			
• Compare the voltage readings with the Data Sheet while moving the measuring vane.			
• Are the voltages OK?			

Fig. 119   Pinpoint test VAF, vane air flow (Part 3 of 5). 1995 1.8L/4-112

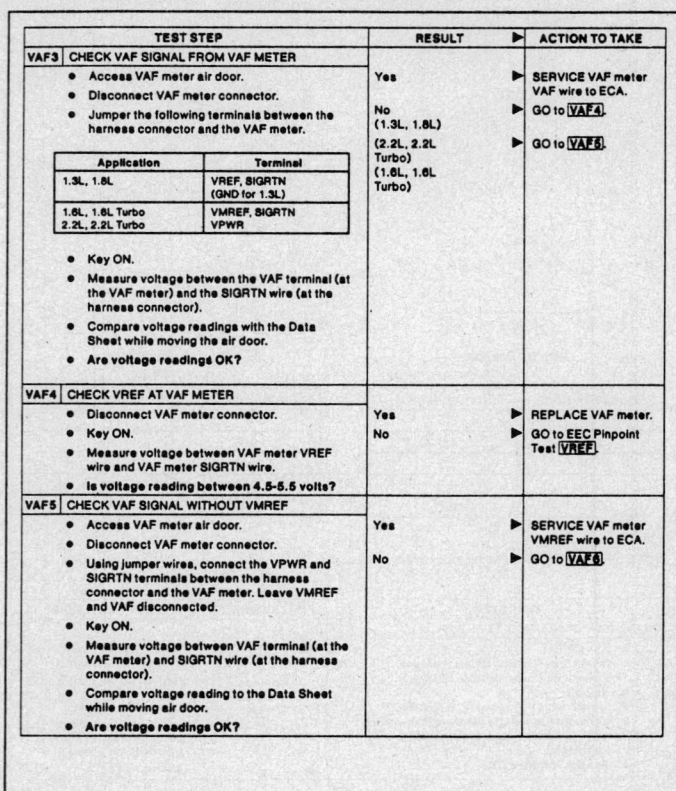

TEST STEP		RESULT	▶	ACTION TO TAKE
VAF3 CHECK VAF SIGNAL FROM VAF METER				
• Key OFF.		Yes	▶	SERVICE the VAF meter VAF wire to the PCM.
• Access the VAF measuring vane.				
• Disconnect the VAF connector.		No (1.3L, 1.8L)	▶	GO to **VAF4**.
• Jumper the following terminals between the harness connector and the VAF meter.		No (1.6L)	▶	GO to **VAF5**.

Engine	Terminal
1.3L, 1.8L	VREF, SIGRTN (GND for 1.3L)
1.6L	VMREF, SIGRTN, VPWR

• Key ON.			
• Measure the voltage between the VAF terminal (at the VAF meter) and the SIGRTN wire (at the harness connector).			
• Compare the voltage readings with the Data Sheet while moving the measuring vane.			
• Are the voltages OK?			

TEST STEP	RESULT	▶	ACTION TO TAKE
VAF4 CHECK VREF AT VAF METER			
• Key OFF.	Yes	▶	REPLACE the VAF meter.
• Disconnect the VAF meter connector.	No	▶	GO to EEC Pinpoint Test **VREF**.
• Key ON.			
• Measure the voltage between VAF meter VREF wire and VAF meter SIGRTN wire.			
• Is the voltage between 4.5-5.5 volts?			
VAF5 CHECK VAF SIGNAL WITHOUT VMREF			
• Key OFF.	Yes	▶	SERVICE the VAF meter VMREF wire to the PCM.
• Access VAF measuring vane.	No	▶	GO to **VAF6**.
• Disconnect the VAF meter connector.			
• Use jumper wires to connect the VPWR and SIGRTN terminals between the harness connector and the VAF meter. Leave VMREF and VAF disconnected.			
• Key ON.			
• Measure the voltage between VAF terminal (at the VAF meter) and SIGRTN wire (at the harness connector).			
• Compare the voltage reading to the Data Sheet while moving measuring vane.			
• Are the voltages OK?			
VAF6 CHECK VPWR / SIGRTN AT VAF METER			
• Key OFF.	Yes	▶	REPLACE the VAF meter.
• Disconnect the VAF meter connector.	No	▶	GO to **VAF7**.
• Key ON.			
• Measure the voltage between VAF meter VPWR wire and the VAF meter SIGRTN wire.			
• Is the voltage greater than 10 volts?			

Fig. 119   Pinpoint test VAF, vane air flow (Part 4 of 5). 1995 1.8L/4-112

TEST STEP		RESULT	▶	ACTION TO TAKE
VAF6	CHECK VPWR/SIGRTN AT VAF METER			
• Disconnect VAF meter connector. • Key ON. • Measure voltage between VAF meter VPWR wire and VAF meter SIGRTN wire. • Is voltage reading above 10 volts?		Yes No	▶ ▶	REPLACE VAF meter. GO to VAF7
VAF7	CHECK VPWR AT VAF METER			
• Disconnect VAF meter connector. • Key ON. • Measure voltage between VAF meter VPWR wire and ground. • Is voltage reading above 10 volts?		Yes No	▶ ▶	SERVICE VAF meter SIGRTN wire to ECA. GO to EEC Pinpoint Test VPWR.

FM0159301114050X

Fig. 119 Pinpoint test VAF, vane air flow (Part 5 of 5). 1993–95 1.3L/4-81, 1.6L/4-98 & 1.8L/4-112

Application	Circuit	ECA Pin	BOB Pin	ECA Wire Color
1.3L	VPWR GND GND GND	1B 2A 2B 2C	37,57 39,40,44,60 20 16	Y/BK BK BK BK
1.6L, 1.6L Turbo	VPWR GND GND GND	3I 2R 3A 3G	37 49 20 40	Y/GN BK BK BK
1.8L MTX	VPWR GND GND GND	1B 2A 2B 2C	37,57 39,40,44,60 20 16	W/R BK/O BK/O BK/LG
1.8L 4EAT	VPWR GND GND GND	2J, 1B 2A 2B 2C	37,57 39,40,44,60 20 16	W/R BK/O BK/O BK/LG
2.2L Non-Turbo MTX	VPWR GND GND GND	1B 2A 2B 2C	37,57 39,40,44,60 20 16	R/BK BK BK BK/LG
2.2L Non-Turbo 4EAT	VPWR GND GND GND	1B 3A 3B 3C	37,57 39,40,44,60 20 16	R/BK BK BK BK/LG
2.2L Turbo	VPWR GND GND GND	1B 3A 3B 3C	37,57 39,40,44,60 20 16	R/BK BK BK BK/LG

TEST STEP		RESULT	▶	ACTION TO TAKE
VPWR1	CHECK VPWR TO ECA			
• Install breakout box to harness connectors (leave ECA disconnected). • Key ON. • Measure voltage between Test Pin VPWR and battery ground. • Is voltage above 10 volts?		Yes No	▶ ▶	GO to VPWR2. GO to VPWR3.
VPWR2	CHECK GROUND AT ECA			
• Install breakout box to harness connectors (leave ECA disconnected). • Key ON. • Measure voltage between Test Pin VPWR and Test Pin GND. • Repeat for each ECA GND wire. • Is voltage above 10 volts for each circuit?		Yes No	▶ ▶	GO to EEC Pinpoint Test VREF. SERVICE ECA GND wire(s).

Fig. 120 Pinpoint test VPWR, vehicle power (Part 1 of 3)

Vehicle Power (VPWR)

Note

You should enter this Pinpoint Test only when directed here by other Pinpoint Tests.

Remember

This Pinpoint Test is intended to diagnose only the following:

• Circuits: VPWR, GND

Pinpoint Test Schematic

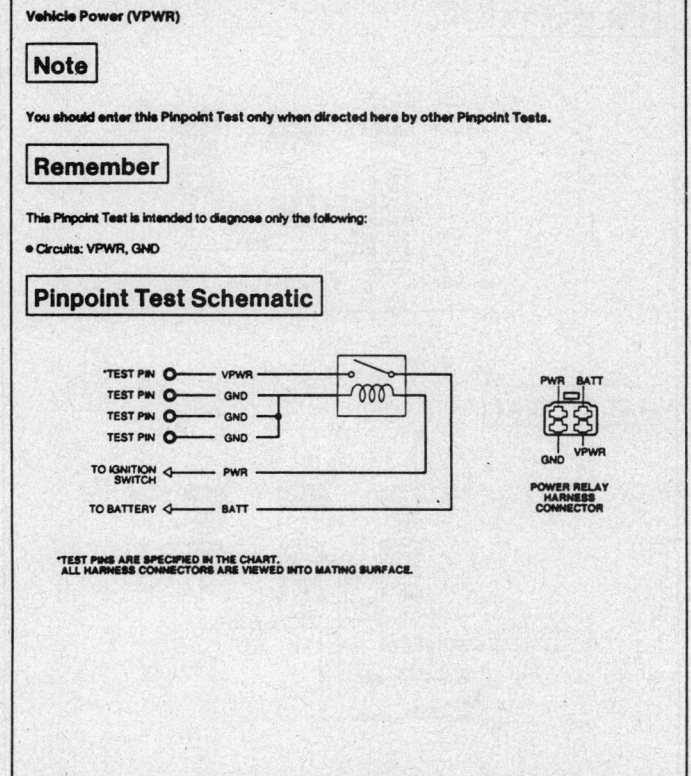

*TEST PINS ARE SPECIFIED IN THE CHART.
ALL HARNESS CONNECTORS ARE VIEWED INTO MATING SURFACE.

Fig. 120 Pinpoint test VPWR, vehicle power (Part 2 of 3)

TEST STEP		RESULT	▶	ACTION TO TAKE
VPWR3	CHECK VPWR FROM MAIN RELAY			
NOTE: For 1.8L, the main relay is located in the engine compartment fuse box. • Disconnect main relay connector. • Jumper BATT, PWR and GND wires back into mating connector (leave VPWR wire disconnected). • Key ON. • Measure voltage between main relay VPWR terminal (where VPWR wire was) and ground. • Is voltage above 10 volts?		Yes No	▶ ▶	SERVICE main relay VPWR wire to ECA, or to component in Pinpoint Test which sent you here. GO to VPWR4.
VPWR4	CHECK BATTERY TO MAIN RELAY			
• Disconnect main relay connector. • Measure voltage between main relay BATT wire and ground. • Is voltage above 10 volts?		Yes No	▶ ▶	GO to VPWR5. SERVICE main relay BATT wire to battery.
VPWR5	CHECK IGNITION POWER TO MAIN RELAY			
• Disconnect main relay connector. • Key ON. • Measure voltage between main relay PWR wire and ground. • Is voltage above 10 volts?		Yes No	▶ ▶	GO to VPWR6. SERVICE main relay PWR wire to ignition switch.
VPWR6	CHECK GROUND AT MAIN RELAY			
• Disconnect main relay connector. • Measure voltage between main relay BATT wire and main relay GND wire. • Is voltage above 10 volts?		Yes No	▶ ▶	REPLACE main relay. SERVICE main relay GND wire.

Fig. 120 Pinpoint test VPWR, vehicle power (Part 3 of 3)

You should enter this Pinpoint Test only when Quick Test Step 11 directs you here.

Reference Voltage (VREF)

Note

You should enter this Pinpoint Test only when Quick Test Step 11 directs you here.

Remember

This Pinpoint Test is intended to diagnose only the following:

● Circuits: VREF, SIGRTN

1.3L EFI

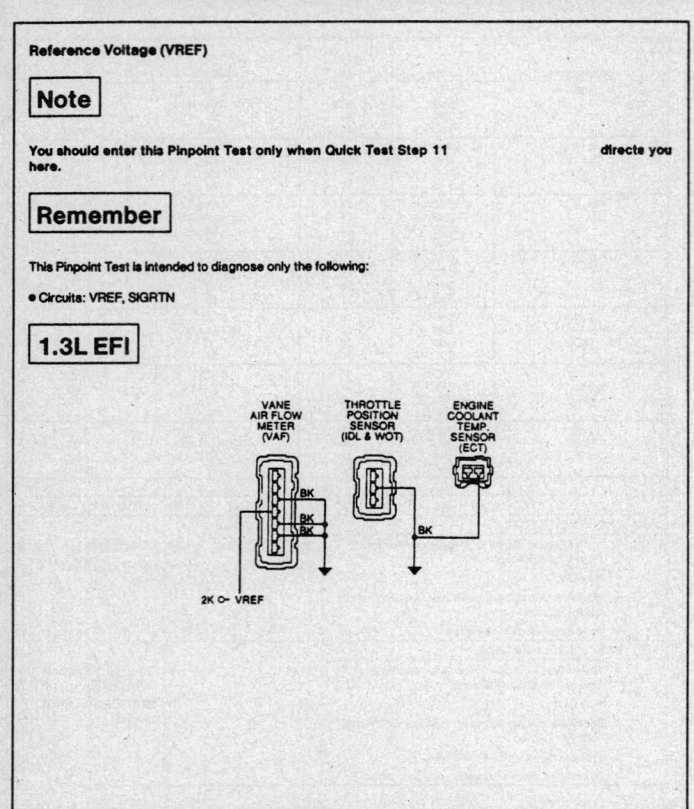

Fig. 121   Pinoint test VREF, reference voltage (Part 1 of 6). 1993-94

Reference Voltage (VREF)

Note

You should enter this Pinpoint Test only when Quick Test Step 11, other Pinpoint Tests, or the Diagnostic Routines direct you here.

Remember

This Pinpoint Test is intended to diagnose only the following:

● Circuits: VREF, SIGRTN

Pinpoint Test Schematic

1.3L

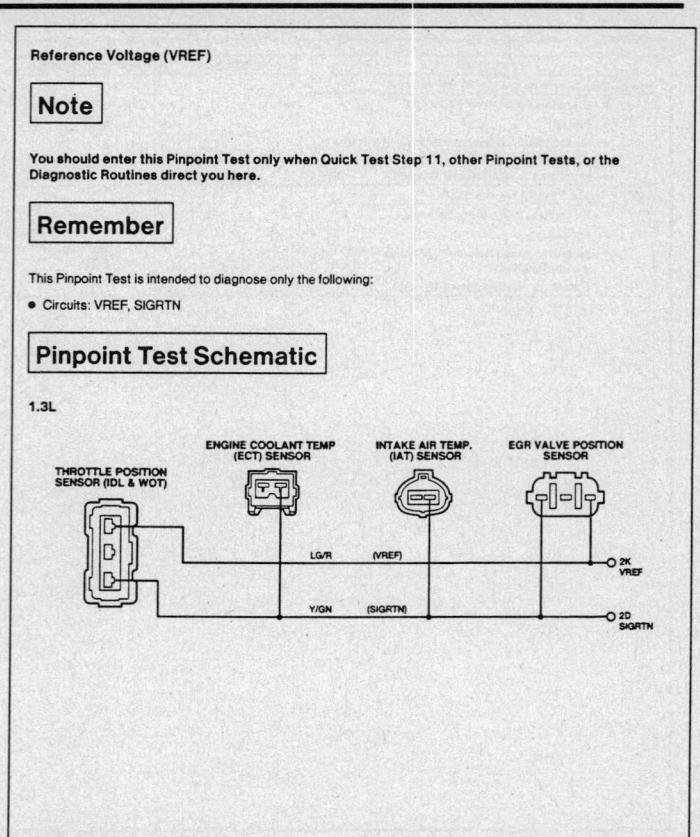

Fig. 121   Pinpoint test VREF, reference voltage (Part 1 of 6). 1995

1.6L ALL

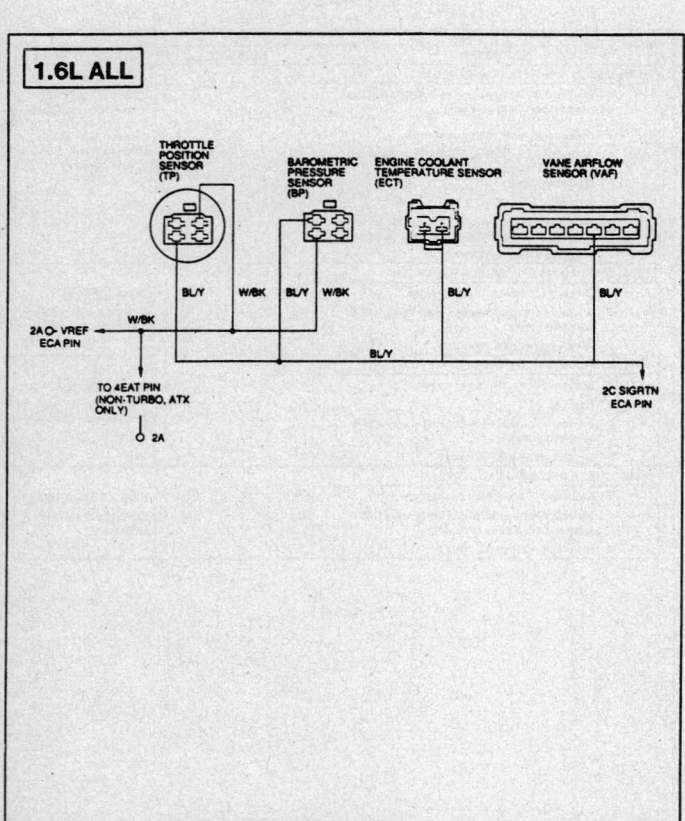

Fig. 121   Pinoint test VREF, reference voltage (Part 2 of 6). 1993-94

1.8L EFI MTX

1.8L EFI 4EAT

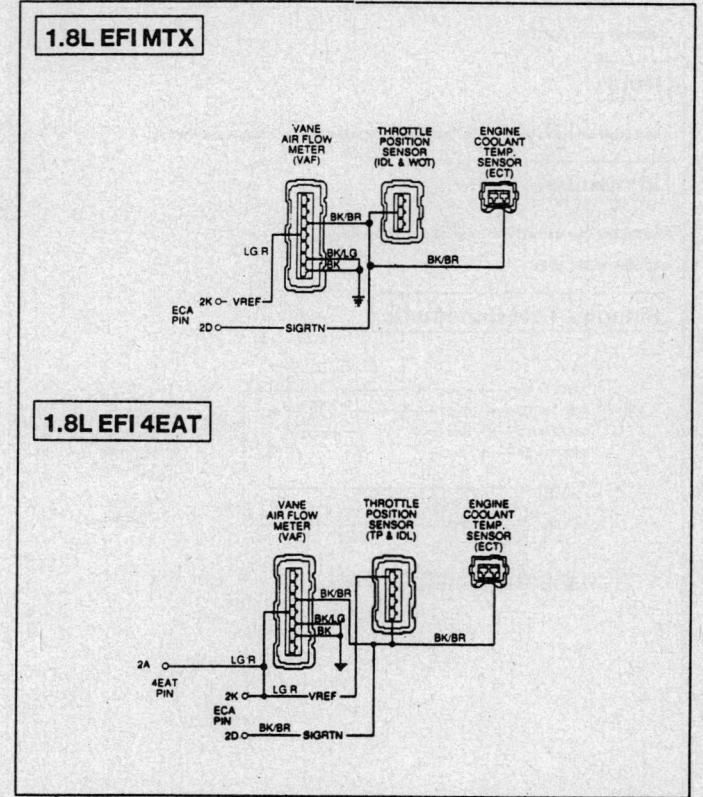

Fig. 121   Pinoint test VREF, reference voltage (Part 3 of 6). 1993-94

2.2L (ALL)

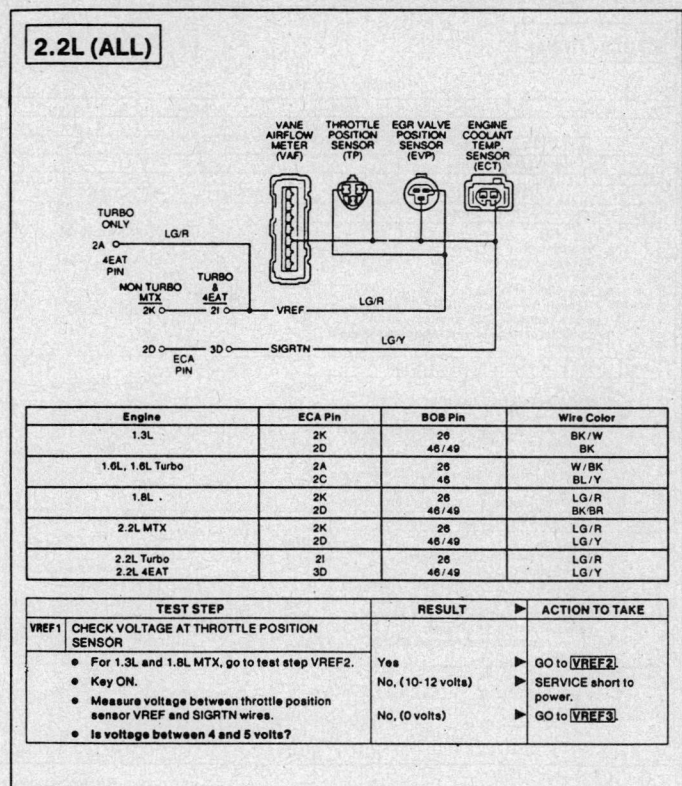

Engine	ECA Pin	BOB Pin	Wire Color
1.3L	2K	26	BK/W
	2D	48/49	BK
1.6L, 1.6L Turbo	2A	26	W/BK
	2C	46	BL/Y
1.8L .	2K	26	LG/R
	2D	48/49	BK/BR
2.2L MTX	2K	26	LG/R
	2D	48/49	LG/Y
2.2L Turbo	2I	26	LG/R
2.2L 4EAT	3D	48/49	LG/Y

	TEST STEP	RESULT	▶	ACTION TO TAKE
VREF1	CHECK VOLTAGE AT THROTTLE POSITION SENSOR			
	• For 1.3L and 1.8L MTX, go to test step VREF2.	Yes	▶	GO to VREF2.
	• Key ON.	No, (10-12 volts)	▶	SERVICE short to power.
	• Measure voltage between throttle position sensor VREF and SIGRTN wires.	No, (0 volts)	▶	GO to VREF3.
	• Is voltage between 4 and 5 volts?			

	TEST STEP	RESULT	▶	ACTION TO TAKE
VREF2	CHECK FOR VOLTAGE AT SENSOR			
	• Key ON.	Yes	▶	RETURN
	• Check voltage between wires at sensor as indicated below.	No, (0 volts)	▶	GO to VREF3.
		No, (10-12 volts)	▶	SERVICE short to power.

ENGINE	SENSOR	WIRES	VOLTAGE
1.3L	VAF	BK/W-BK	4-5
1.6L	BP	W/BK-BL/Y	4-5
1.8L	VAF	LG/R-BK/BR	4-5
2.2L	EVP	LG/R-LG/Y	4-5

	TEST STEP	RESULT	▶	ACTION TO TAKE
	• Are voltages OK?			
VREF3	CHECK FOR OPENS			
	• Key OFF.	Yes	▶	GO to VREF4.
	• Install breakout box (leave ECA disconnected).	No	▶	SERVICE wire in question.
	• Install 4EAT tester if applicable to vehicle (leave 4EAT module disconnected).			
	• Disconnect TP, VAF, BP, and EVP as applicable to vehicle.			
	• Measure resistance between ECA and 4EAT module VREF terminals, and between ECA VREF terminal and TP, BP, EVP and VAF VREF terminals.			
	• Are all resistances less than 5 ohms?			
VREF4	CHECK FOR SHORTS			
	• Key OFF.	Yes	▶	GO to VREF5.
	• Install breakout box (leave ECA disconnected).	No	▶	SERVICE short in VREF circuit.
	• Disconnect 4EAT module if applicable to vehicle.			
	• Disconnect TP, BP, VAF, and EVP sensors as applicable.			
	• Measure resistance between ECA VREF BOB Pin and ground.			
	• Is resistance greater than 10,000 ohms?			

Fig. 121 Pinoint test VREF, reference voltage (Part 4 of 6). 1993-94

Fig. 121 Pinoint test VREF, reference voltage (Part 5 of 6). 1993-94

	TEST STEP	RESULT	▶	ACTION TO TAKE
VREF5	CHECK SIGNAL RETURN			
	• Key OFF.	Yes	▶	GO to VREF6.
	• Disconnect ECA.	No	▶	SERVICE wire in question for opens.
	• Disconnect 4EAT module if applicable to vehicle.			
	• Disconnect ECT, VAF, TP, EVP and BP sensors as applicable.			
	• Measure resistance between ECA SIGRTN BOB Pin and 4EAT SIGRTN Pin and all sensor SIGRTN Pin(s).			
	• Are all resistances less than 5 ohms?			
VREF6	CHECK FOR SHORT TO POWER			
	• Key OFF.	Yes	▶	GO to EEC Pinpoint Test PGC1.
	• Install breakout box.	No	▶	SERVICE SIGRTN circuit for short to power.
	• Leave ECA connected.			
	• Connect 4EAT module if applicable to vehicle.			
	• Key ON.			
	• Measure voltage at ECA SIGRTN BOB Pin.			
	• Is voltage reading 0-1 volts?			

Fig. 121 Pinoint test VREF, reference voltage (Part 6 of 6). 1993-94

COMPUTERIZED ENGINE CONTROLS (ASPIRE, CAPRI, ESCORT & TRACER (1.8L/4-112), FESTIVA & PROBE (2.0L/4-121 w/4EAT & 2.5L/V6-152) ELECTRONIC ENGINE CONTROL (EEC) SYSTEM

10-71

Note

For 1.8L 4EAT vehicle speed sensor test, go to 4EAT Pinpoint Test VSS.

You should enter this Pinpoint Test only when Quick Test Step 11 directs you here.

Remember

This Pinpoint Test is intended to diagnose only the following:

- Circuit: VSS

Pinpoint Test Schematic

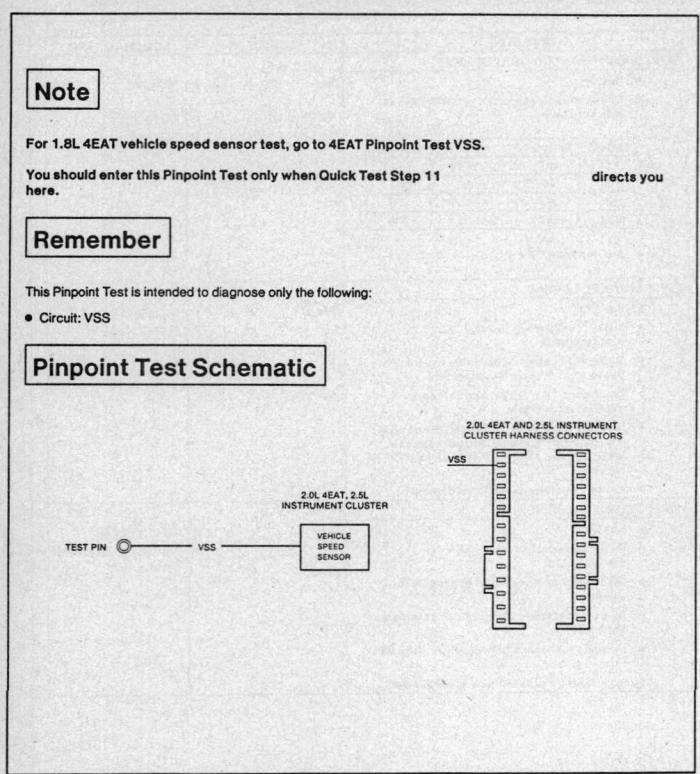

Fig. 122 Pinpoint test VSS, vehicle speed sensor (Part 1 of 2). 1993 2.0L/4-121 w/4EAT & 1993-94 1.8L/4-112 w/4EAT & 2.5L/V6-152

FM0159301117010X

Data Sheet

CIRCUIT DATA SHEET

Engine	Circuit	PCM Pin	BOB Pin	Wire Color
1.8L 4EAT	VSS	1M	3	GN
2.0L 4EAT	VSS	1M	3	GN/R
2.5L	VSS	1M	3	GN/R

TEST STEP	RESULT	▶	ACTION TO TAKE
VSS1 CHECK VSS SIGNAL TO PCM • Key OFF. • Install breakout box (leave PCM disconnected). • Key ON. • Raise vehicle on hoist. • Measure the voltage at Test Pin VSS with a digital voltmeter while spinning front tire. • **Does the voltage alternate between 0 and 5 volts?**	Yes	▶	VSS circuit OK.
	No	▶	GO to VSS2.
VSS2 CHECK VSS WIRE TO PCM FOR OPEN • Key OFF. • Install breakout box (leave PCM disconnected). • Disconnect the 14-pin instrument cluster connector. • Measure the resistance of the VSS wire between Test Pin VSS and the VSS wire at the 14-pin instrument cluster harness connector. • **Is the resistance less than 5 ohms?**	Yes	▶	GO to VSS3.
	No	▶	SERVICE the VSS wire for open.
VSS3 CHECK VSS WIRE TO PCM FOR SHORT • Key OFF. • Install breakout box (leave PCM disconnected). • Disconnect the 14-pin instrument cluster connector. • Measure the resistance of the VSS wire between Test Pin VSS and ground. • **Is the resistance greater than 10,000 ohms?**	Yes	▶	diagnose the vehicle speed sensor.
	No	▶	SERVICE the VSS wire for short.

FM0159301117020X

Fig. 122 Pinpoint test VSS, vehicle speed sensor (Part 2 of 2). 1993 2.0L/4-121 w/4EAT & 1993-94 1.8L/4-112 w/4EAT & 2.5L/V6-152

Pinpoint Test Schematic

1.3L INSTRUMENT CLUSTER HARNESS CONNECTOR
2.5L INSTRUMENT CLUSTER HARNESS CONNECTORS
1.3, 2.5L INSTRUMENT CLUSTER
TEST PIN — VSS — VEHICLE SPEED SENSOR
VSS

Data Sheet

CIRCUIT DATA SHEET

Engine	Circuit	PCM Pin	BOB Pin	Wire Color
1.3L	VSS	1M	21	GN/R
2.5L	VSS	1M	3	GN/R

TEST STEP	RESULT	▶	ACTION TO TAKE
VSS1 CHECK VSS SIGNAL TO PCM • Key OFF. • Install Breakout Box (BOB). • Key ON. • For 1.3L: — Remove the speedometer driven gear from the transaxle. Leave cable connected to driven gear. — Measure the DC voltage at BOB Test Pin VSS while rotating the speedometer cable. • For 2.5L: — Raise the vehicle on hoist. — Measure the DC voltage at BOB Test Pin VSS while spinning the front tires with the vehicle in D range. • **Does the voltage alternate between 0 and 5 volts?**	Yes	▶	VSS circuit OK. If sent to this test by Quick Test Step QT11
	No	▶	GO to VSS2.

FM0159501238010X

Fig. 123 Pinpoint test VSS, vehicle speed sensor (Part 1 of 2). 1995 1.3L/4-81 & 2.5L/V6-152

TEST STEP	RESULT	▶	ACTION TO TAKE
VSS2 CHECK VSS WIRE TO PCM FOR OPEN • Key OFF. • Install Breakout Box (leave Powertrain Control Module [PCM] disconnected). • Disconnect the 14-pin instrument cluster connector. • Measure the resistance of the VSS wire between BOB Test Pin VSS and the VSS wire at the 14-pin instrument cluster harness connector. • **Is the resistance less than 5 ohms?**	Yes	▶	GO to VSS3.
	No	▶	SERVICE the VSS wire for open.
VSS3 CHECK VSS WIRE TO PCM FOR SHORT • Key OFF. • Install Breakout Box (leave PCM disconnected). • Disconnect the 14-pin instrument cluster connector. • Measure the resistance of the VSS wire between BOB Test Pin VSS and ground (resistance should be greater than 10,000 ohms). • Key ON. • Measure the voltage on BOB Test Pin VSS (voltage should be 0V). • **Are the measurements OK?**	Yes	▶	
	No	▶	SERVICE the VSS wire for short.

FM0159501238020X

Fig. 123 Pinpoint test VSS, vehicle speed sensor (Part 2 of 2). 1995 1.3L/4-81 & 2.5L/V6-152

EMISSION CONTROL SYSTEM APPLICATION CHARTS

TABLE OF CONTENTS

	Page No.		Page No.
1993	11-1	1995	11-3
1994	11-2	1996	11-5

1993

NOTE: Refer To Page 11-6 For Description Of Abbreviations Used In This Chart.

Engine Liters/ CID/ Type	Certification Type C	A	FED	Trans. Type AT	MT	Computerized Engine Management	Fuel Induction System Type	Ignition Timing, Deg. BTDC @RPM	PCV	ACL	AIS	EGR	EVAP	CAT	SPK	FR	O2S
1.3L/81/L4	X	X	X	—	YES[29]	MFI	10@850[2]	X	—	—	—	X	X[3]	X[31]	X	X[5]
1.3L/81/L4	X	X	—	X	YES[29]	MFI	10@700[2]	X	—	—	—	X	X[3]	X[31]	X	X[5]
1.6L/98/L4	X	X	X	X	YES[29]	MFI	2@850[7]	X	—	—	—	X	X[3]	X[32]	X	X[5]
1.6L/98/L4 Turbo	X	X	X	X	YES[29]	MFI	12@850[7]	X	—	—	—	X	X[3]	X[32]	X	X[5]
1.8L/112/L4	X	X	X	X	YES[29]	MFI	10@750[8]	X	—	—	—	X	X[3]	X[31]	X	X[5]
1.9L/116/L4	X	X	X	X	YES[30]	SFI	10@750[6]	X	—	—	X[10]	X	X[3]	X[34]	X	X[35]
2.0L/121/L4	X	X	X	—	YES[29]	MFI	12@700[11]	X	—	—	X[12]	X	X[3]	X[33]	X	X[35]
2.0L/121/L4	X	X	—	X	YES[30]	MFI	10@700[11]	X	—	—	X[12]	X	X[3]	X[4]	X	X[35]
2.3L/140/L4 HSC	—	X	X	X	YES[30]	SFI	10[9]	X	—	X[13]	X[10]	X	X[14]	X[33]	X	X[35]
2.3L/140/L4 HSC	X	—	X	X	YES[30]	SFI	10[9]	X	—	X[13]	X[10]	X	X[3]	X[33]	X	X[35]
2.3L/140/L4 OHC	X	X	X	X	YES[30]	MFI	10[6]	X	X	—	X[15]	X	X[24]	X[1]	X	X[35]
2.5L/152/V6	X	X	X	X	YES[29]	MFI	10@650[16]	X	—	—	X[17]	X	X[3]	X[33]	X	X[20]
3.0L/182/V6 [18] [19]	X	X	X	X	YES[30]	SFI	10[9]	X	—	—	X[10]	X	X[3]	X[4]	X	X[20]
3.0L/182/V6 [18] [21]	X	—	—	X	YES[30]	SFI	10[9]	X	—	—	X[22]	X	X[3]	X[4]	X	X[20]
3.0L/182/V6 [18] [21]	—	X	X	X	YES[30]	SFI	10[9]	X	—	—	X[22]	X	X[3]	X[33]	X	X[20]
3.0L/182/V6 [23]	X	X	X	X	YES[30]	SFI	10[9]	X	—	—	X[22]	X	X[3]	X[34]	X	X[20]
3.0L/182/V6 SHO	—	X	—	X	YES[30]	SFI	10[6]	X	—	—	—	X	X[3]	X[1]	X	X[20]
3.0L/182/V6 SHO	X	—	—	X	YES[30]	SFI	10[6]	X	—	—	X[10]	X	X[3]	X[1]	X	X[20]
3.2L/195/V6 SHO	X	X	X	—	YES[30]	SFI	10[6]	X	—	—	X[22]	X	X[3]	X[1]	X	X[20]
3.8L/238/V6	X	X	X	X	YES[30]	SFI	10[9]	X	—	—	X[10]	X	X[27]	X[4]	X	X[20]
3.8L/238/V6 SC	X	X	X	X	YES[30]	SFI	[6]	X	—	—	X[10]	X	X[27]	X[1]	X	X[20]
4.6L/281/V8	X	X	X	X	YES[30]	SFI	10[6]	X	—	—	X[22]	X	X[28]	X[34]	X	X[20]
4.6L/281/V8[25]	X	X	X	X	YES[30]	SFI	10[6]	X	—	—	X[22]	X	X[3]	X[34]	X	X[20]
5.0L/302/V8	X	X	X	X	YES[30]	SFI	10[9]	X	—	X[36]	X[15]	X	X[26]	X[33]	X	X[20]

X—Equipped
—Not Equipped
[1]—EI/low data rate.
[2]—With STI connector grounded. On AT models, 850 RPM ±20 RPM. On MT models, at 700 RPM ±20 RPM.
[3]—Type, TWC; number of catalytic converters, 1.
[4]—D/ Thick Film Ignition-IV/Computer Controlled Dwell.
[5]—One O2S.
[6]—With single wire inline spout

Continued

1993-Continued

connector disconnected. Not adjustable.

⑦—With STI connector grounded & distributor vacuum hose disconnected & plugged. At 850 RPM ±50 RPM.

⑧—With STI connector grounded. At 750 RPM ±50 RPM.

⑨—With single wire in-line spout connector disconnected or shorting bar from double wire spout connector removed.

⑩—Pressure feedback electronic.

⑪—With STI connector grounded. At 700 RPM ±50 RPM.

⑫—Modulator valve EGR.

⑬—PAIR. Pulse type.

⑭—Type, TWC + OC; number of catalytic converters, 1.

⑮—EGR valve position.

⑯—With STI connector grounded. At 650 RPM ±50 RPM.

⑰—Control/vent solenoids.

⑱—Except flexible fuel.

⑲—Tempo & Topaz.

⑳—Two HO2S.

㉑—Sable & Taurus.

㉒—Delta pressure feedback.

㉓—Flexible fuel.

㉔—Type, TWC; number of catalytic converters, 2.

㉕—4 Valve engine.

㉖—Type, TWC & OC; number of catalytic converters, 4.

㉗—Type, TWC; number of catalytic converters, 3.

㉘—Type, TWC; number of catalytic converters, 4.

㉙—EEC.

㉚—EEC-IV.

㉛—DI/Transistorized Ignition 3-Pin.

㉜—DI/Distributor Mounted Ignition Vacuum Advance.

㉝—DI.

㉞—EI/high data rate.

㉟—One HO2S.

㊱—Pump type.

1994

NOTE: Refer To Page 11-6 For Description Of Abbreviations Used In This Chart

Engine Liters/ CID/ Type	C	A	F	E	D	AT	MT	Computerized Engine Management	Fuel Induction System Type	Ignition Timing, Deg. BTDC @RPM	PCV	ACL	AI	S	EGR	EVAP	CAT	SPK	FR	O2S
1.3L/81/L4	X	X	X	—		X	—	YES㉝	SFI	10@750㉚	X	—	—		X㉛	X	X③	X④	X	X⑤
1.3L/81/L4	X	X	X	—		—	X	YES㉝	SFI	10@700㉚	X	—	—		X㉛	X	X③	X④	X	X⑤
1.6L/98/L4	X	X	X	X		X	X	YES㉝	MFI	2@850⑦	X	—	—		—	X	X③	X㉟	X	X⑤
1.6L/98/L4 Turbo	X	X	X	X		X	X	YES㉝	MFI	12@850⑦	X	—	—		—	X	X③	X㉟	X	X⑤
1.8L/112/L4	X	X	X	X		X	X	YES㉝	MFI	10@750⑦	X	—	—		—	X	X③	X㉞	X	X⑤
1.9L/116/L4	X	X	X	X		X	X	YES㉜	SFI	10@750⑥	X	—	—		X⑩	X	X③	X①	X	X⑰
2.0L/121/L4	X	—				X	X	YES㉜	SFI	12@700⑪	X	—	—		X⑫	X	X③	X④	X	X⑰
2.0L/121/L4	—	X				X	X	YES㉜	SFI	12@700⑪	X	—	—		X㉙	X	X③	X④	X	X⑰
2.3L/140/L4 HSC	—	X				X	X	YES㉜	SFI	10⑨	X	—	X⑬		X⑩	X	X⑭	X④	X	X⑰
2.3L/140/L4 HSC	X	—				X	X	YES㉜	SFI	10⑨	X	—	X⑬		X⑩	X	X㉗	X④	X	X⑰
2.5L/152/V6	X	X	X	X		X	X	YES㉝	SFI	10@650⑯	X	—	—		X⑮	X	X③	X④	X	X⑳
3.0L/182/V6 ⑱⑲	X	X	X	—		X	X	YES㉜	SFI	10⑨	X	—	—		X⑩	X	X③	X④	X	X⑳
3.0L/182/V6 ⑱㉑	X	—				X	—	YES㉜	SFI	10⑨	X	—	—		X㉒	X	X③	X④	X	X⑳
3.0L/182/V6 ⑱㉑	—	X				X	—	YES㉜	SFI	10⑨	X	—	—		X㉒	X	X③	X㊷	X	X⑳
3.0L/182/V6 ㉓	X	X	X			X	—	YES㉜	SFI	10⑥	X	—	—		X㉒	X	X③	X①	X	X⑳
3.0L/182/V6 SHO	—	X				—	X	YES㉜	SFI	10⑥	X	—	—		—	X	X③	X②	X	X⑳
3.0L/182/V6 SHO	X	—				—	X	YES㉜	SFI	10⑥	X	—	—		X⑩	X	X③	X②	X	X⑳
3.2L/195/V6 SHO	X	X	X			X	—	YES㉜	SFI	10⑥	X	—	—		X㉒	X	X③	X②	X	X⑳
3.8L/238/V6 ㊱	X	X	X			X	—	YES㉜	SFI	10⑨	X	—	—		X⑩	X	X㉔	X④	X	X⑳
3.8L/238/V6 ㊲	X	X	X			X	—	YES㊳	SFI	10⑨	X	—	—		X㉒	X	X③	X①	X	X㊳
3.8L/238/V6 SC	X	X	X	X		X	X	YES㉜	SFI	⑥	X	—	—		X⑩	X	X㉔	X②	X	X⑳
4.6L/281/V8 ㊵	X					X	—	YES㉜	SFI	10⑥	X	—	—		X㉒	X	X㉘	X①	X	X⑳
4.6L/281/V8 ㊵	—					X	—	YES㉜	SFI	10⑤	X	—	—		X⑩	X	X㉘	X①	X	X⑳
4.6L/281/V8 ㉕㊵	X	X	X			X	—	YES㉜	SFI	10⑥	X	—	—		X㉒	X	X③	X①	X	X⑳
4.6L/281/V8 ㊶	X	X	X			X	—	YES㊳	SFI	10⑥	X	—	—		X㉒	X	X㉔	X①	X	X㊳
5.0L/302/V8	X	X	X	X		X	X	YES㉜	SFI	10⑨	X	—	X⑧		X⑮	X	X㉖	X㊷	X	X⑳

X—Equipped

—Not Equipped

①—EI/high data rate.

②—EI/low data rate.

③—Type, TWC; number of catalytic converters, 1.

④—DI/Thick Film Ignition-IV/Computer Controlled Dwell.

⑤—One O2S.

⑥—With single wire inline spout connector disconnected. Not adjustable.

⑦—With STI connector grounded & distributor vacuum hose disconnected & plugged. At 850 RPM ±50 RPM.

⑧—Pump type.

⑨—With single wire in-line spout

Continued

1994-Continued

connector disconnected or shorting bar from double wire spout connector removed.
⑩ —Pressure feedback electronic.
⑪ —With STI connector grounded. At 700 RPM ±50 RPM.
⑫ —Electronic EGR valve (Sonic).
⑬ —PAIR. Pulse type.
⑭ —Type, TWC + OC; number of catalytic converters, 1.
⑮ —EGR valve position.
⑯ —With STI connector grounded. At 650 RPM ±50 RPM.
⑰ —One O2S.
⑱ —Except flexible fuel.
⑲ —Tempo & Topaz.

⑳ —Two HO2S.
㉑ —Sable & Taurus.
㉒ —Differential pressure feedback.
㉓ —Flexible fuel.
㉔ —Type, TWC; number of catalytic converters, 3.
㉕ —4 Valve engine.
㉖ —Type, TWC & OC; number of catalytic converters, 4.
㉗ —Type, TWC + TWC; number of catalytic converters, 1.
㉘ —Type, TWC; number of catalytic converters, 4.
㉙ —EGR pressure transducer.
㉚ —With STI connector grounded. On AT models, 750 RPM ±50 RPM. On

MT models, 700 RPM ±50 RPM.
㉛ —Control/vent solenoids.
㉜ —EEC-IV.
㉝ —EEC.
㉞ —DI/Transistorized Ignition 3-Pin.
㉟ —DI/Distributor Mounted Ignition Vacuum Advance.
㊱ —Except Mustang.
㊲ —Mustang.
㊳ —Two engine control HO2S & two catalyst monitoring HO2S.
㊴ —EEC-V.
㊵ —Except Cougar & Thunderbird.
㊶ —Cougar & Thunderbird.
㊷ —DI.

1995

NOTE: Refer To Page 11-6 For Description Of Abbreviations Used In This Chart

Engine Liters/ CID/ Type	Certification Type		Trans. Type		Computerized Engine Management	Fuel Induction System Type	Ignition Timing, Deg. BTDC @RPM	Emission Control Systems								
	C A	F E D	A T	M T				P C V	A C L	A I S	E G R	E V A P	C A T	S P K	F R	O 2 S
1.3L/81/L4	X	X	X	X	YES①	SFI	10@750②	X	—	—	X③	X	X④	X⑤	X	X⑥
1.8L/112/L4	X	X	X	X	YES①	MFI	10@750⑦	X	—	—	X	X④	X⑤	X	X⑧
1.9L/116/L4	X	X	X	X	YES⑩	SFI	10@600⑨	X	—	—	X⑪	X	X④	X⑫	X	X⑧
2.0L/121/L4⑲	X	—	X	X	YES⑩	SFI	10@700⑮	X	—	—	X⑬	X	X④	X⑭	X	X⑱
2.0L/121/L4⑲	—	X	X	X	YES⑩	SFI	10@700⑮	X	—	—	X⑯	X	X④	X⑭	X	X⑱
2.0L/122/L4⑳	X	X	X	X	YES⑩	SFI	10⑨	X	—	—	X㉑	X	X㉒	X⑫	X	X⑧
2.5L/152/V6⑲	X	X	X	X	YES①	SFI	10@650⑦	X	—	—	X⑰	X	X④	X⑤	X	X⑱
2.5L/153/V6⑳	X	X	X	X	YES⑩	SFI	10⑨	X	—	—	X㉑	X	X㉓	X⑫	X	X⑱
3.0L/182/V6㉔	X	—	X	—	YES⑩	SFI	10㉖	X	—	—	X㉑	X	X④	X⑭	X	X⑱
3.0L/182/V6㉔	—	X	X	—	YES⑩	SFI	10㉖	X	—	—	X㉑	X	X④	X⑤	X	X⑱
3.0L/182/V6㉗	X	X	X	—	YES⑩	SFI	10⑨	X	—	—	X㉑	X	X④	X⑫	X	X⑱
3.0L/182/V6 SHO	—	X	—	X	YES⑩	SFI	10⑨	X	—	—	—	X	X④	X㉕	X	X⑱
3.0L/182/V6 SHO	X	—	—	X	YES⑩	SFI	10⑨	X	—	—	X⑪	X	X④	X㉕	X	X⑱
3.2L/195/V6 SHO	X	X	—	X	YES⑩	SFI	10⑨	X	—	—	X㉑	X	X④	X㉕	X	X⑱
3.8L/238/V6㉙	X	X	X	—	YES⑩	SFI	10㉖	X	—	—	X⑪	X	X㉚	X⑭	X	X⑱
3.8L/238/V6㉛	X	X	X	—	YES⑩	SFI	10㉖	X	—	—	X㉑	X	X㉚	X⑭	X	X⑱
3.8L/238/V6㉜	X	X	X	—	YES㉝	SFI	10⑨	X	—	—	X㉑	X	X④	X⑫	X	X㉘
3.8L/238/V6 SC	X	X	X	—	YES⑩	SFI	10⑨	X	—	—	X㉑	X	X㉚	X㉕	X	X⑱
4.6L/281/V8㉞	X	X	X	—	YES㉝	SFI	10⑨	X	—	—	X㉑	X	X㉚	X⑫	X	X㉘
4.6L/281/V8㉟	X	X	X	—	YES㉝	SFI	10⑨	X	—	X㊱	X㉑	X	X④	X⑫	X	X㉘
4.6L/281/V8㊲	X	X	X	—	YES⑩	SFI	10⑨	X	—	—	X㉑	X	X④	X⑫	X	X⑱
5.0L/302/V8 HO	X	X	X	X	YES⑩	SFI	10㉖	X	—	X㊳	X⑰	X	X㊴	X⑤	X	X⑱

Continued

1995-Continued

X—Equipped

—Not Equipped

①—EEC.

②—With STI connector grounded. On AT models, 750 RPM ±50 RPM. On MT models, 700 RPM ±50 RPM.

③—EGR/CVS.

④—Type, TWC; number of catalytic converters, 1.

⑤—DI.

⑥—One O2S.

⑦—With STI input connector (ten terminal) grounded.

⑧—One HO2S.

⑨—With single wire inline spout connector disconnected. Not adjustable.

⑩—EEC-IV.

⑪—Pressure feedback electronic.

⑫—EI/high data rate.

⑬—Electronic EGR valve (sonic).

⑭—DI/Thick Film Ignition-IV/Computer Controlled Dwell.

⑮—With single wire inline spout connector disconnected. Spout connector located front of engine compartment near battery.

⑯—EGR pressure transducer.

⑰—EGR valve position.

⑱—Two HO2S.

⑲—Probe.

⑳—Contour & Mystique.

㉑—Differential pressure feedback.

㉒—Type, TWC; number of catalytic converters, 2.

㉓—Type, TWC; number of catalytic converters, 4.

㉔—Except flexible fuel.

㉕—EI/low data rate.

㉖—With single wire in-line spout connector disconnected or shorting bar from double wire spout

connector removed.

㉗—Flexible fuel.

㉘—Two engine control HO2S & two catalyst monitoring HO2S.

㉙—Sable & Taurus.

㉚—Type, TWC; number of catalytic converters, 2.

㉛—Cougar & Thunderbird.

㉜—Mustang.

㉝—EEC-V.

㉞—Cougar, Crown Victoria, Grand Marquis, Thunderbird & Town Car.

㉟—Continental.

㊱—EAIR. Electric pump type.

㊲—Mark VIII.

㊳—Pump type.

㊴—Type, TWC & OC; number of catalytic converters, 4.

1996

NOTE: Refer To Page 11-6 For Description Of Abbreviations Used In This Chart

Engine Liters/ CID/ Type	Certification Type		Trans. Type		Computerized Engine Management	Fuel Induction System Type	Ignition Timing, Deg. BTDC @RPM	Emission Control Systems								
	C A	F E D	A T	M T				P C V	A C L	A I S	E G R	E V A P	C A T	S P K	F R	O 2 S
1.3L/81/L4	X	X	X	X	YES[1]	MFI	10@750[2]	X	—	—	X[3]	X	X[4]	X[5]	X	X[23]
1.8L/112/L4	X	X	X	X	YES[1]	MFI	10@750[7]	X	—	—	—	X	X[4]	X[5]	X	X[8]
1.9L/116/L4	X	X	X	—	YES[33]	SFI	10@780[9]	X	—	—	X[11]	X	X[4]	X[12]	X	X[8]
1.9L/116/L4	X	X	—	X	YES[33]	SFI	10@725[9]	X	—	—	X[11]	X	X[4]	X[12]	X	X[8]
2.0L/121/L4[19]	X	X	X	—	YES[33]	SFI	10@880[15]	X	—	—	X[13]	X	X[37]	X[14]	X	X[18]
2.0L/121/L4[19]	X	—	—	X	YES[33]	SFI	10@744[15]	X	—	—	X[13]	X	X[37]	X[14]	X	X[18]
2.0L/121/L4[19]	—	X	—	X	YES[33]	SFI	10@744[15]	X	—	—	X[16]	X	X[37]	X[14]	X	X[18]
2.0L/122/L4[20]	X	X	X	—	YES[33]	SFI	10@800[9]	X	—	—	X[21]	X	X[4]	X[12]	X	X[18]
2.0L/122/L4[20]	X	X	—	X	YES[33]	SFI	10@880[9]	X	—	—	X[21]	X	X[4]	X[12]	X	X[18]
2.5L/152/V6[19]	X	X	X	X	YES[1]	SFI	10@650[7]	X	—	—	X[17]	X	X[29]	X[5]	X	X[38]
2.5L/153/V6[20]	X	X	X	X	YES[33]	SFI	10@744[9]	X	—	—	X[21]	X	X[4]	X[12]	X	X[38]
2.5L/153/V6[20]	X	X	—	X	YES[33]	SFI	10@725[9]	X	—	—	X[21]	X	X[4]	X[12]	X	X[38]
3.0L/182/V6 SOHC[24]	X	X	X	X	YES[33]	SFI	10@900[9]	X	—	X[38]	X[21]	X	X[22]	X[14]	X	X[38]
3.0L/182/V6 SOHC[27]	X	—	X	—	YES[33]	SFI	10@900[9]	X	—	X[38]	X[21]	X	X[10]	X[12]	X	X[38]
3.0L/182/V6 SOHC[27]	—	X	X	—	YES[33]	SFI	10@900[9]	X	—	X[38]	X[21]	X	X[22]	X[12]	X	X[38]
3.0L/182/V6 DOHC	X	X	X	X	YES[33]	SFI	10@900[9]	X	—	X[38]	X[21]	X	X[22]	X[12]	X	X[38]
3.4L/207/V8	X	X	X	—	YES[33]	SFI	10@900	X	—	X[38]	X[21]	X	X[22]	X[12]	X	X[38]
3.8L/238/V6[31]	X	—	X	—	YES[33]	SFI	10@704[9]	X	—	—	X[21]	X	X[25]	X[12]	X	X[38]
3.8L/238/V6[31]	—	X	X	—	YES[33]	SFI	10@704[9]	X	—	—	X[21]	X	X[22]	X[12]	X	X[38]
3.8L/238/V6[32]	X	X	X	—	YES[33]	SFI	10@700[9]	X	—	—	X[21]	X	X[22]	X[12]	X	X[38]
3.8L/238/V6[32]	X	X	—	X	YES[33]	SFI	10@720[9]	X	—	—	X[21]	X	X[22]	X[12]	X	X[38]
4.6L/281/V8[31]	X	X	X	—	YES[33]	SFI	10@768[9]	X	—	—	X[21]	X	X[25]	X[12]	X	X[38]
4.6L/281/V8[34]	X	X	X	—	YES[33]	SFI	10@800[9]	X	—	—	X[21]	X	X[30]	X[12]	X	X[38]
4.6L/281/V8[35]	X	X	X	—	YES[33]	SFI	10@800[9]	X	—	X[38]	X[21]	X	X[22]	X[12]	X	X[38]
4.6L/281/V8[6]	X	X	X	—	YES[33]	SFI	10@900[9]	X	—	X[38]	X[21]	X	X[25]	X[12]	X	X[30]
4.6L/281/V8[28]	X	X	X	X	YES[33]	SFI	10@656[9]	X	—	—	X[21]	X	X[12]	X[12]	X	X[38]
4.6L/281/V8[26]	X	X	—	X	YES[33]	SFI	10@656[9]	X	—	X[38]	X[21]	X	X[22]	X[12]	X	X[38]

X—Equipped
—Not Equipped

[1]—EEC.
[2]—With STI connector grounded. On AT models, 750 RPM ±50 RPM. On MT models, 700 RPM ±50 RPM.
[3]—EGR/CVS.
[4]—Type, TWC; number of catalytic converters, 1.
[5]—DI.
[6]—Mark VIII.
[7]—With STI input connector (ten terminal) grounded.
[8]—One HO2S.
[9]—With single wire inline spout connector disconnected. Not adjustable.
[10]—Type, TWC; number of catalytic converters, 2. Also equipped w/converter light-off.
[11]—Pressure feedback electronic.
[12]—EI/high data rate.
[13]—Electronic EGR valve (sonic).
[14]—DI/Thick Film Ignition-IV/Computer Controlled Dwell.
[15]—With single wire inline spout connector disconnected. Spout connector located front of engine compartment near battery.
[16]—EGR pressure transducer.
[17]—EGR valve position.
[18]—Two HO2S.
[19]—Probe.
[20]—Contour & Mystique.
[21]—Differential pressure feedback.
[22]—Type, TWC; number of catalytic converters, 2.
[23]—One HO2S (downstream) & one O2S (upstream).
[24]—Except flexible fuel.
[25]—Type TWC; number of catalytic converters, 3.
[26]—Mustang Cobra.
[27]—Flexible fuel.
[28]—Mustang GT.
[43]—Type, WU-TWC & TWC; number of catalytic converters, 3.
[29]—Sable & Taurus.
[30]—Type, TWC; number of catalytic converters, 2.
[31]—Cougar & Thunderbird.

1996-Continued

㉜—Mustang.

㉝—EEC-V.

㉞—Crown Victoria, Grand Marquis & Town Car.

㉟—Continental.

㊱—Electric pump type.

㊲—Type, WU-TWC & TWC; number of catalytic converters, 2.

㊳—Four HO2S.

ACL—Air Cleaner (Thermostatic Air Cleaner)

AIS—Secondary Air Injection

AT—Automatic Transmission/Transaxle

BTDC—Before Top Dead Center

CA—California

CAT—Catalytic Converter

DI—Distributor Ignition

DIS—Distributorless Ignition System

DLC—Data Link Connector

DMIVA—Distributor Mounted Ignition Vacuum Advance

DOHC—Dual Overhead Cam

DS-II—Duraspark-II Ignition System

DS-III—Duraspark-III Ignition System

EDIS—Electronic Distributorless Ignition System

EEC—Electronic Engine Control

EEC-I—Electronic Engine Control (System I)

EEC-II—Electronic Engine Control (System II)

EEC-III—Electronic Engine Control (System III)

EEC-IV—Electronic Engine Control (System IV)

EEC-V—Electronic Engine Control (System V)

EGR—Exhaust Gas Recirculation

EVAP—Evaporative Emission Control System

FBC—Feedback Carburetor

FED—Federal

FR—Fillpipe Restrictor

HO—High Output

HSC—High Swirl Combustion

MCU—Microprocessor Control Unit

MFI—Multiport Fuel Injection

MT—Manual Transmission

OC—Oxidation Catalytic Converter

OHC—Overhead Camshaft

O2S—Oxygen Sensor

PAIR—Pulsed Secondary Air Injection.

PCM—Powertrain Control Module

PCV—Positive Crankcase Ventilation

RPM—Revolutions Per Minute

SC—Supercharged

SFI—Sequential Multiport Fuel Injection

SHO—Super High Output

SOHC—Single Overhead Cam

SPK—Spark Control

SRI—Service Reminder Indicator

SSI—Solid State Ignition

TBI—Throttle Body Fuel Injection

TFI-I—Thick Film Ignition-I

TFI-IV—Thick Film Ignition-IV

TI3—Transistorized Ignition 3-Pin

TI5—Transistorized Ignition 5-Pin

TRS—Transmission Regulated Spark

TSB—Technical Service Bulletin

TWC—Three Way Catalytic Converter

UIC—Universal Integrated Circuit Ignition System.

WU-TWC—Warm Up Three Way Catalytic Converter

VACUUM HOSE ROUTINGS

NOTE: If Unsure Of The System Used On The Vehicle Being Serviced, Refer To The "Engine Systems Identification Chart." Further Assistance For The Proper Use Of Information Contained In This Section Can Also Be Found In The Front Of This Tabbed Section Under "How To Use This Manual."

TABLE OF CONTENTS

	Page No.		Page No.
1993-94	12-1	1995	12-6

1993–94

INDEX

	Page No. 12-	Fig. No.		Page No. 12-	Fig. No.
1.3L/4-81 Engine	2	1	3.2L/V6-195 MFI SHO Engine	4	11
1.8L/4-112 Engine	2	2	3.8L/V6-232 Engine:		
1.9L/4-114 Engine:			Cougar	5	15
California Emissions	2	4	Except Cougar, Thunderbird &		
Federal Emissions	2	3	Police Models	5	14
2.3L/4-140 EFI Engine:			Police Models	5	13
Except HSC-EFI	3	5	Thunderbird:		
HSC-EFI:			Non-Supercharged	5	15
California Emissions	3	7	Supercharged	4	12
Federal Emissions	3	6	4.6L/V8-281 Engine	5	16
3.0L/V6-183 EFI Engine:			5.0L/V8-302 Engine:		
Except SHO	4	9	Except HO	6	17
SHO	3	8	HO	6	18
3.0L/V6-183 EFI/MFI Engine:					
Except SHO & Flexible Fuel	4	10			

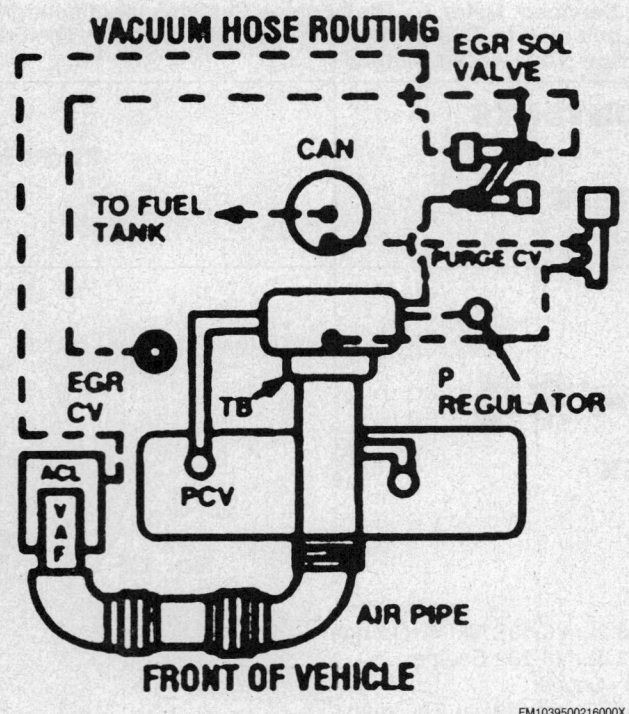

Fig. 1   Emission control vacuum hose routing.
1.3L/4-81 engine

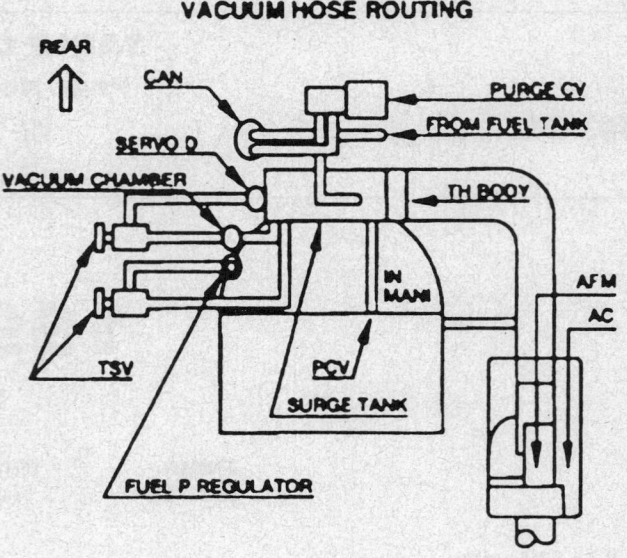

Fig. 2   Emission control vacuum hose routing.
1.8L/4-112 engine

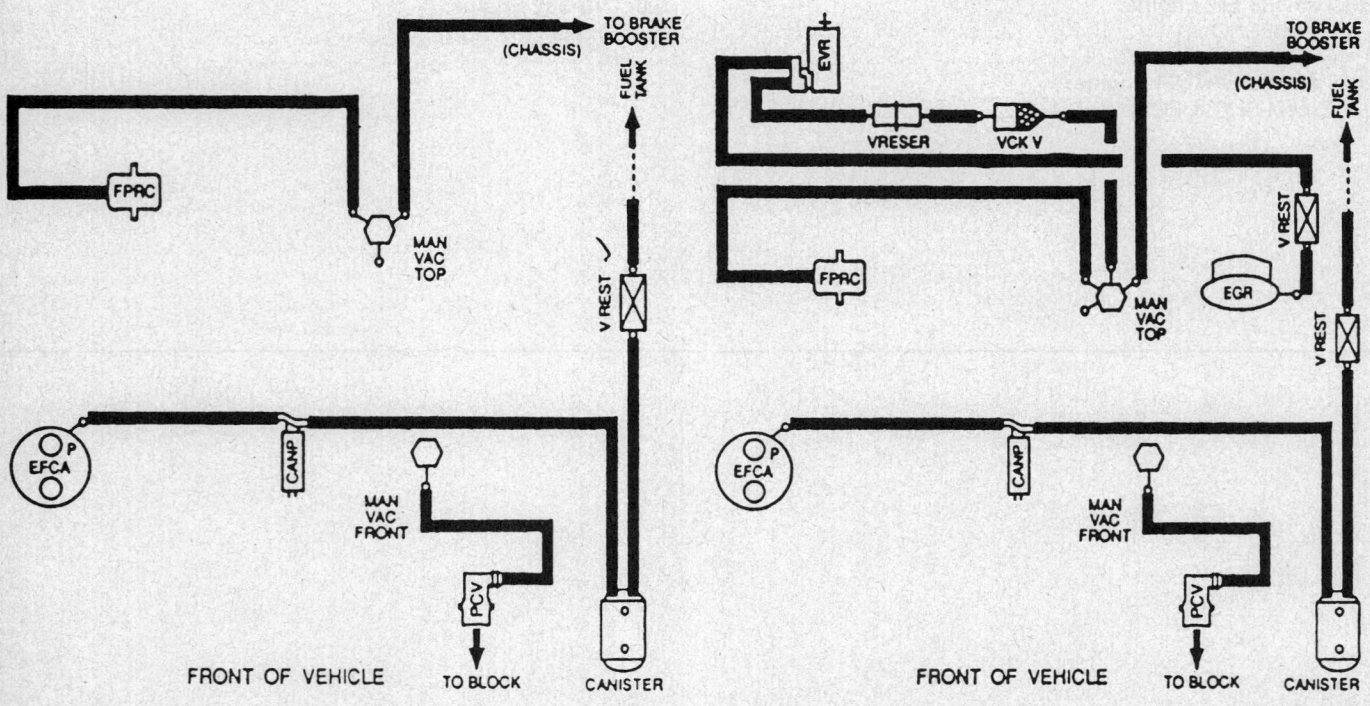

Fig. 3   Emission control vacuum hose routing.
1.9L/4-114 engine w/Federal emissions

Fig. 4   Emission control vacuum hose routing.
1.9L/4-114 engine w/California emissions

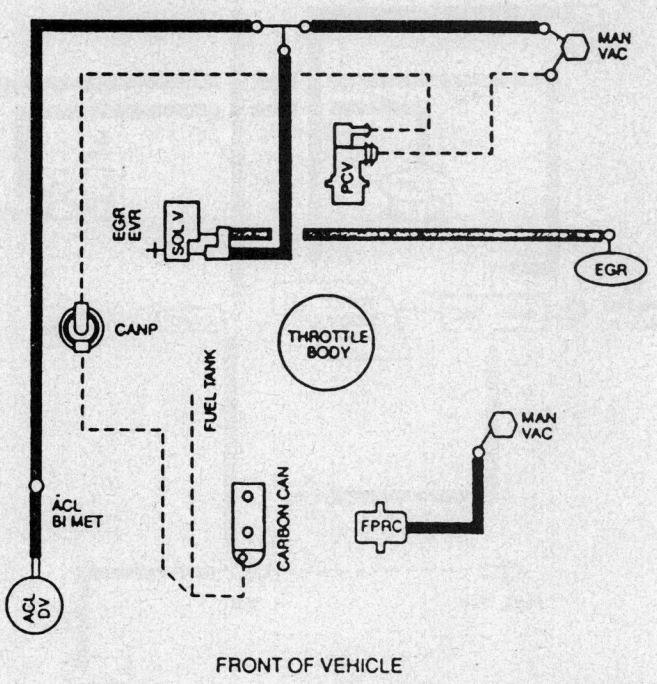

Fig. 5 Emission control vacuum hose routing.
2.3L/4-140 EFI engine except HSC-EFI

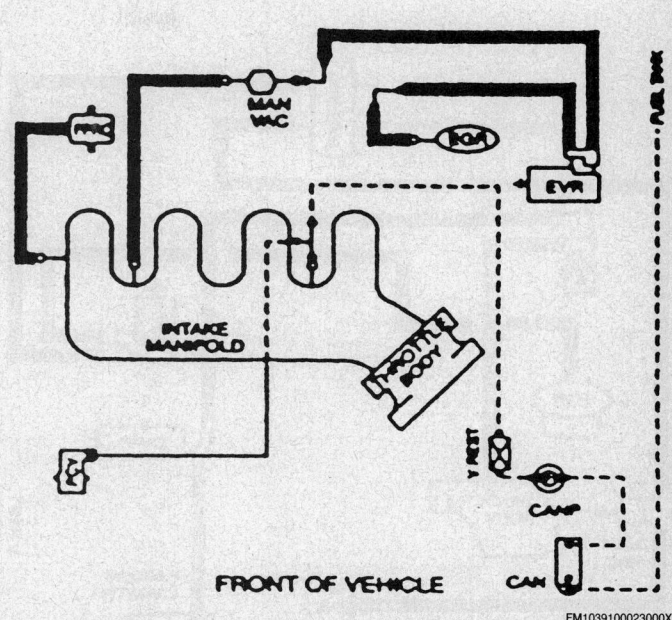

Fig. 6 Emission control vacuum hose routing.
2.3L/4-140 HSC-EFI engine w/ Federal emissions

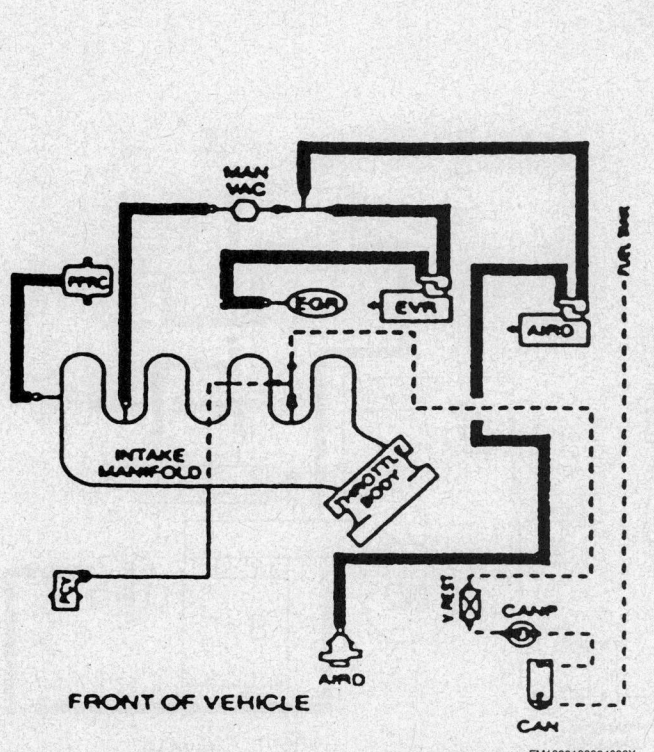

Fig. 7 Emission control vacuum hose routing.
2.3L/4-140 HSC-EFI engine w/California emissions

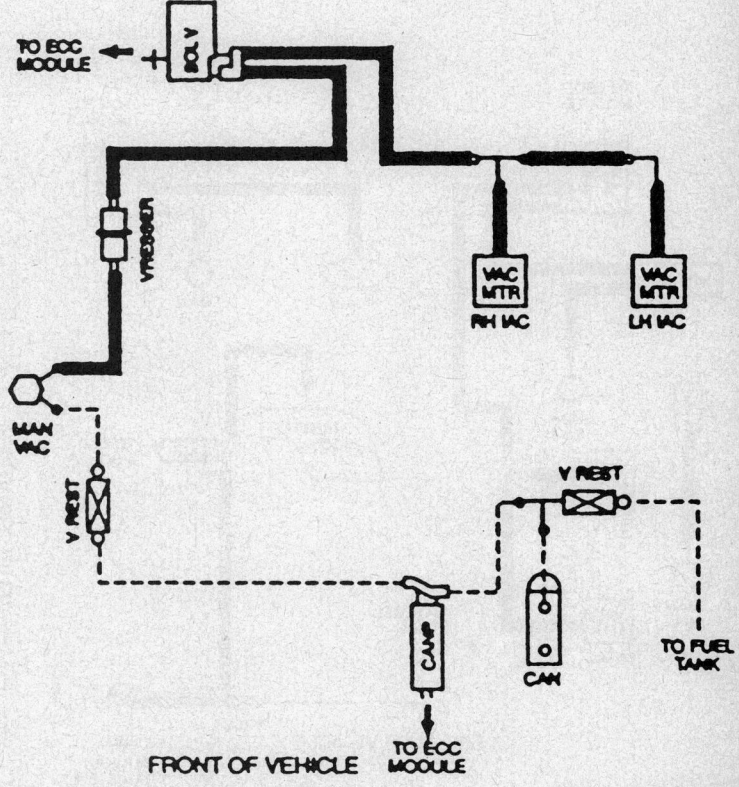

Fig. 8 Emission control vacuum hose routing. 3.0L/V6-183
EFI SHO engine

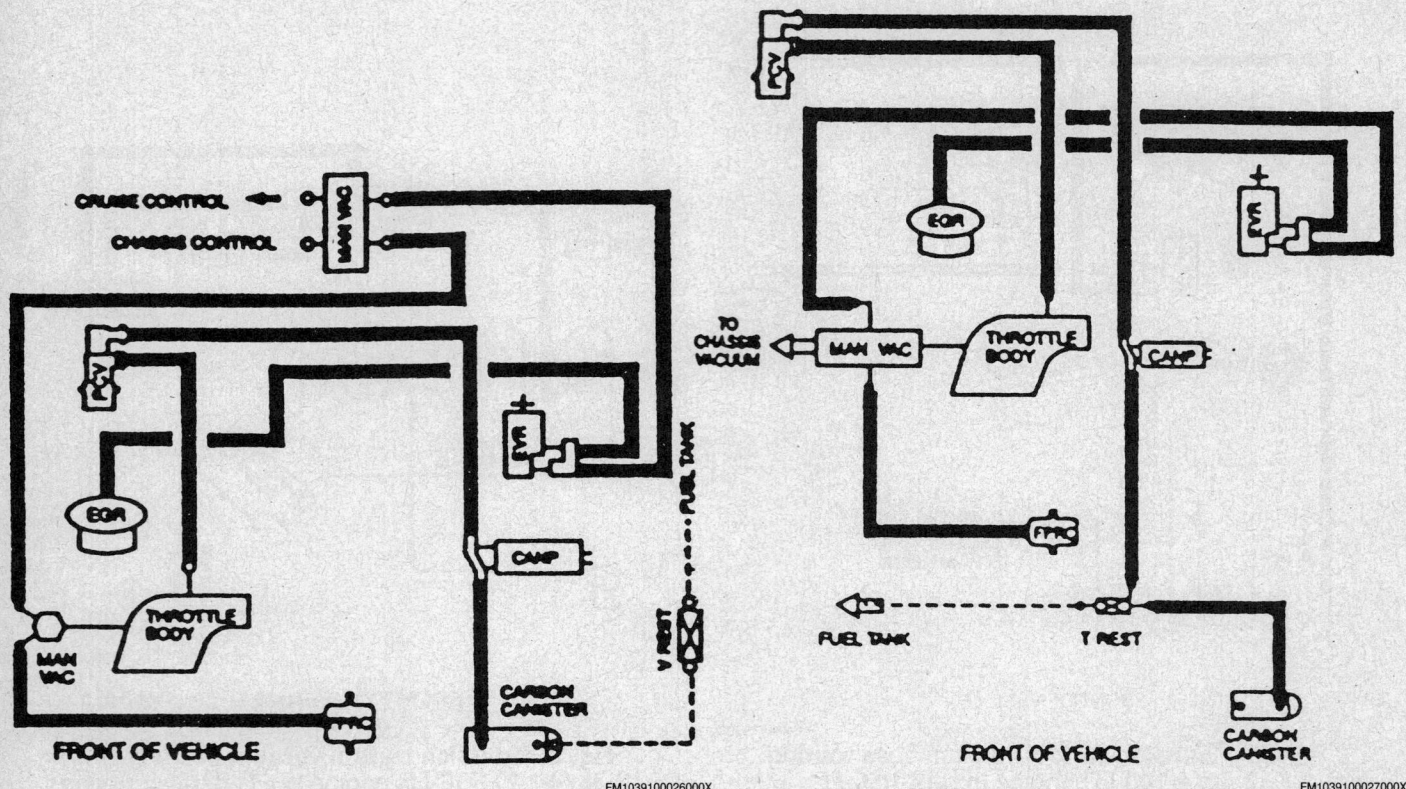

Fig. 9 Emission control vacuum hose routing. 3.0L/V6-183 EFI engine except SHO

FM1039100026000X

Fig. 10 Emission control vacuum hose routing. 3.0L/V6-183 EFI/MFI engine except SHO & flexible fuel

FM1039100027000X

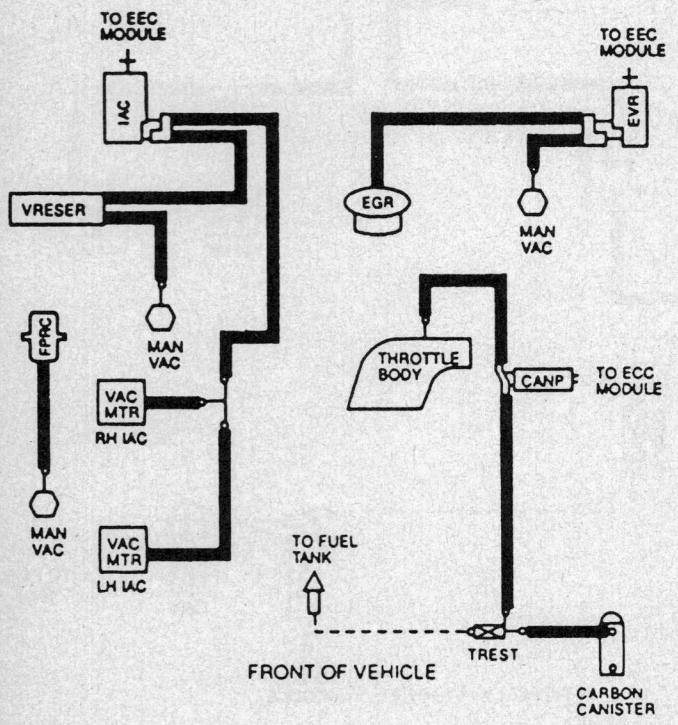

Fig. 11 Emission control vacuum hose routing. 3.2L/V6-195 MFI SHO engine

FM1039100028000X

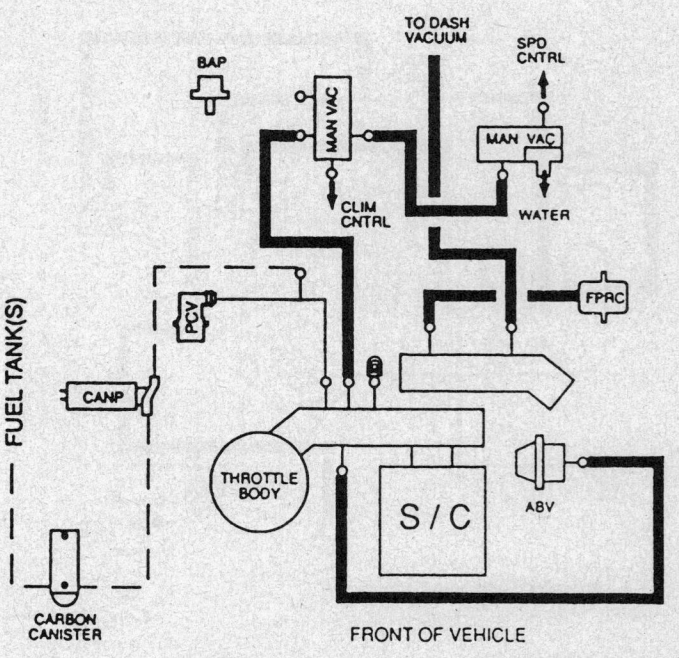

Fig. 12 Emission control vacuum hose routing. Thunderbird w/3.8L/V6-232 supercharged engine

FM1039100029000X

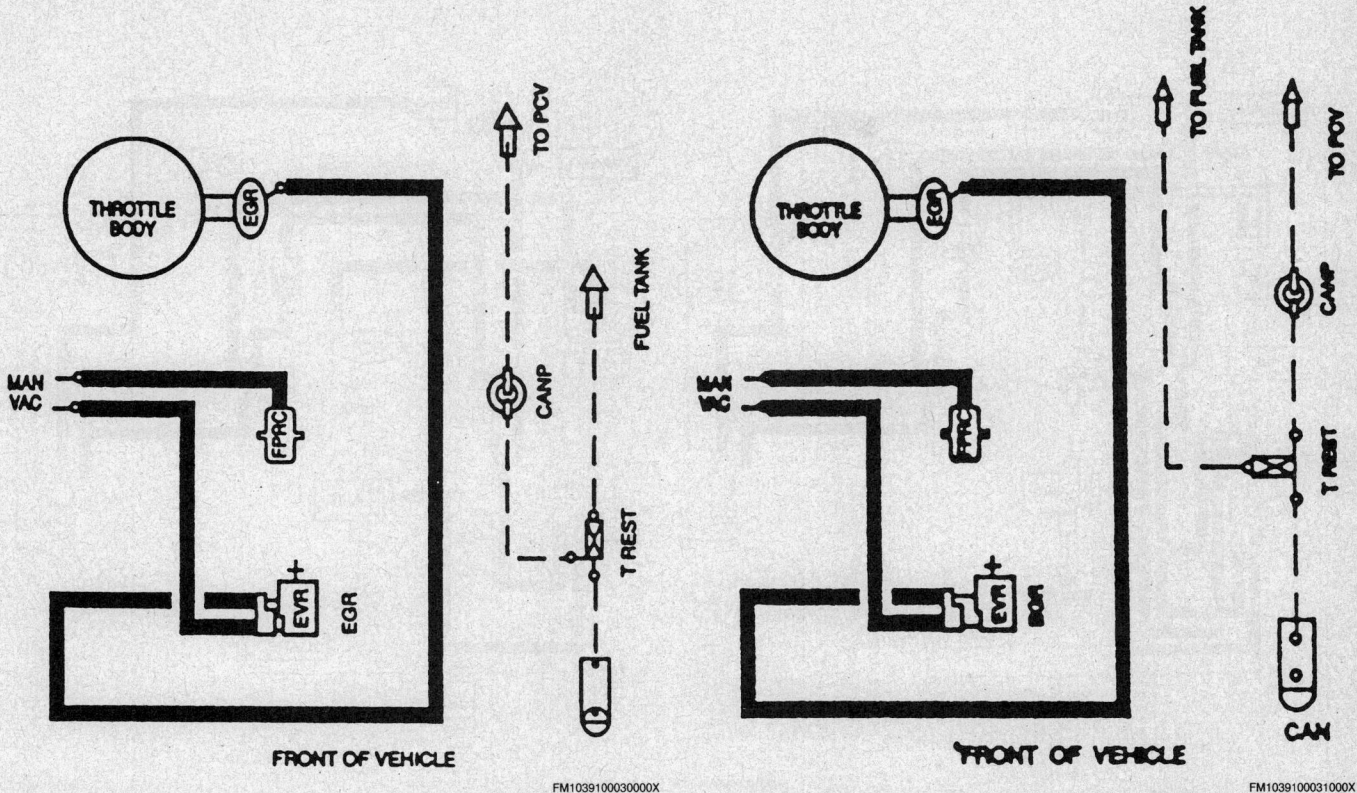

Fig. 13 Emission control vacuum hose routing. Police models w/3.8L/V6-232 engine

Fig. 14 Emission control vacuum hose routing. 3.8L/V6-232 engine except Thunderbird & police models

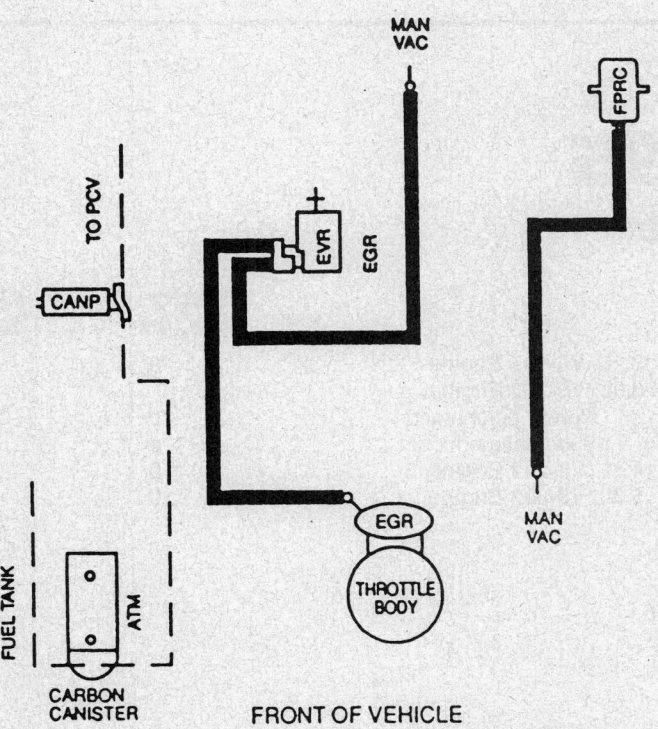

Fig. 15 Emission control vacuum hose routing. Cougar & Thunderbird w/3.8L/V6-232 engine

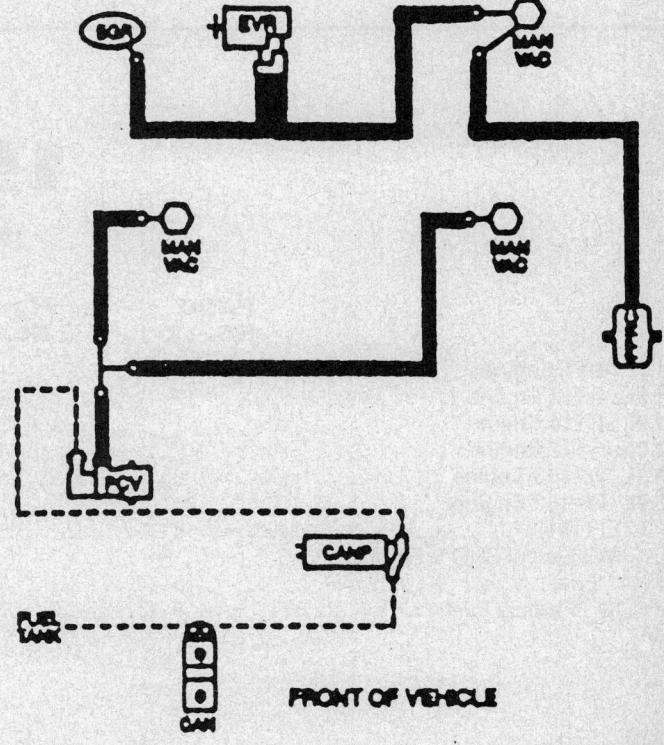

Fig. 16 Emission control vacuum hose routing. 4.6L/V8-281 engine

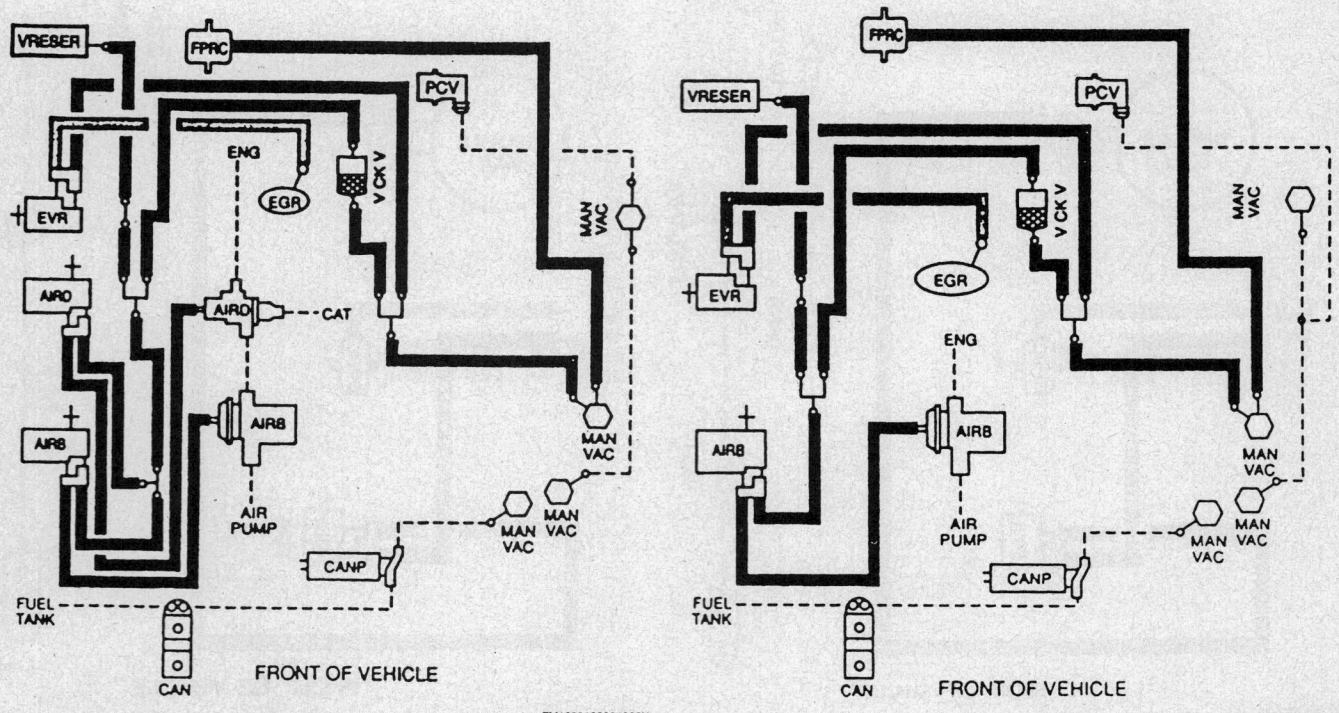

Fig. 17   Emission control vacuum hose routing.
5.0L/V8-302 engine except HO

Fig. 18   Emission control vacuum hose routing.
5.0L/V8-302 HO engine

FM1039100034000X

FM1039100035000X

1995

INDEX

	Page No. 12-	Fig. No.		Page No. 12-	Fig. No.
1.3L/4-81 Engine	7	1	3.2L/V6-195 Engine	9	9
1.8L/4-112 Engine	7	2	3.8L/V6-232 Engine:		
1.9L/4-114 Engine	7	3	Non-Supercharged	10	11
2.0L/4-122 Engine	7	4	Supercharged	9	10
2.5L/V6-153 Engine	8	5	4.6L/V8-281 Engine	10	12
3.0L/V6-183 Engine:			5.0L/V8-302 Engine	10	13
EFI SHO	8	6			
MFI Except SHO & Flexible Fuel	8	8			
MFI Flexible Fuel	8	7			

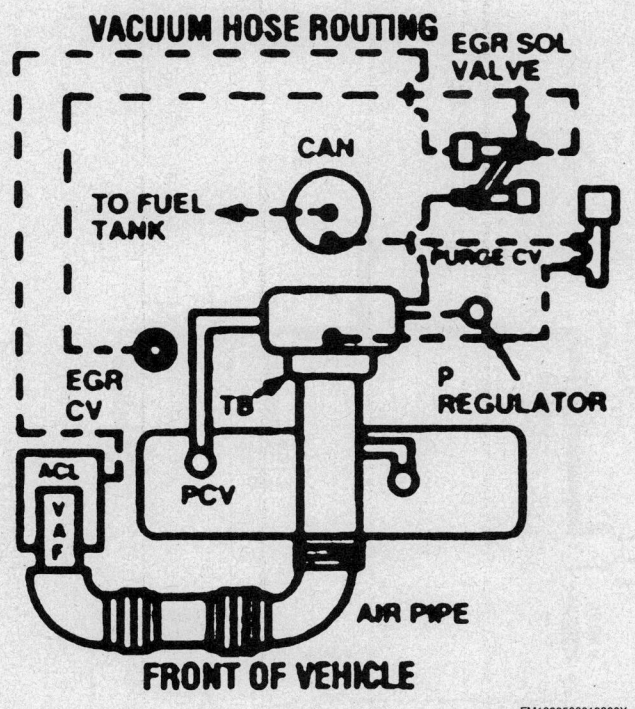

Fig. 1 Emission control vacuum hose routing.
1.3L/4-81 engine

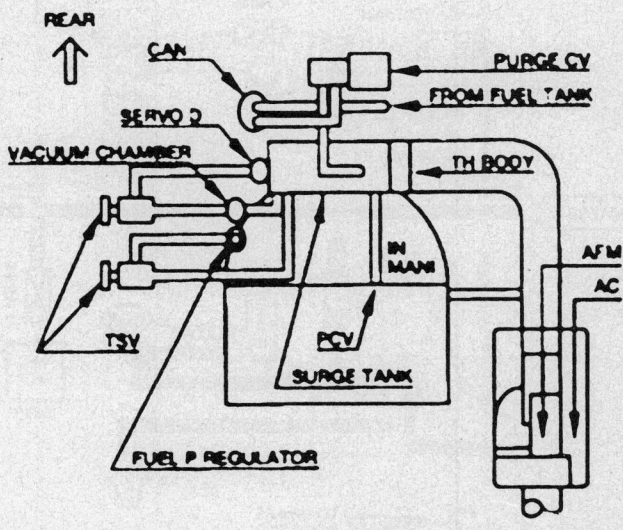

Fig. 2 Emission control vacuum hose routing.
1.8L/4-112 engine

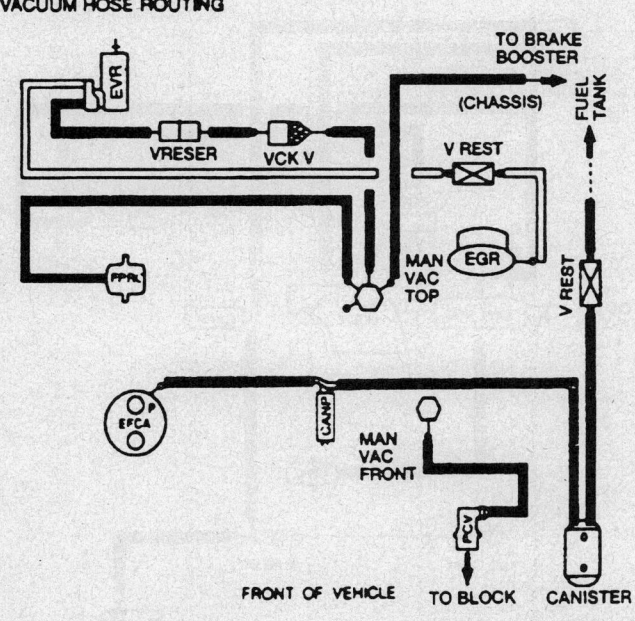

Fig. 3 Emission control vacuum hose routing.
1.9L/4-114 engine

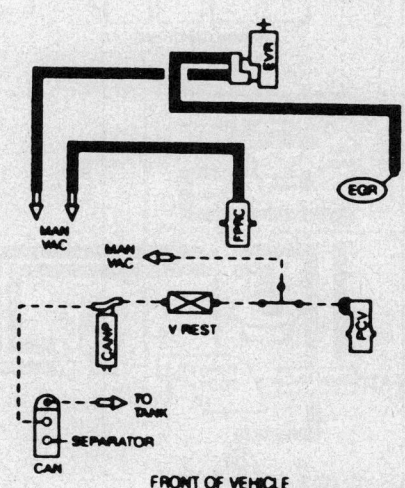

Fig. 4 Emission control vacuum hose routings. 2.0L/4-122 engine

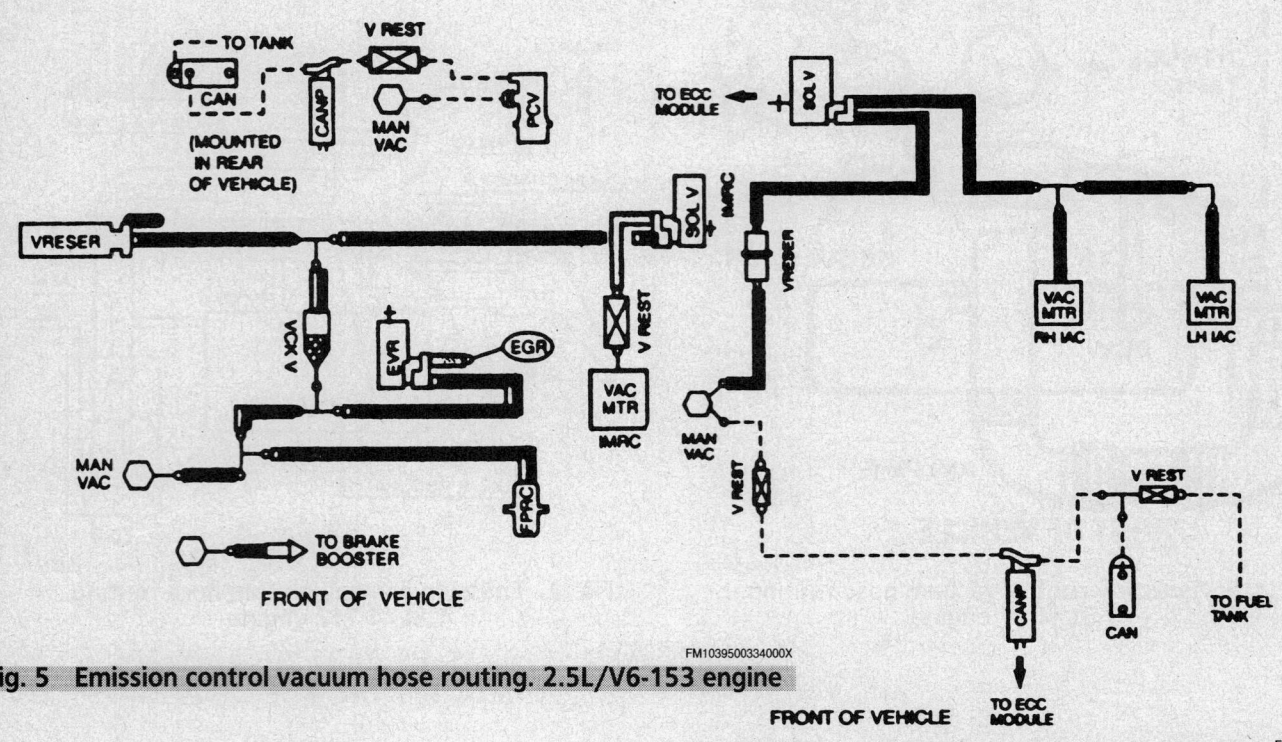

Fig. 5   Emission control vacuum hose routing. 2.5L/V6-153 engine

Fig. 6   Emission control vacuum hose routing. 3.0L/V6-183 EFI SHO engine

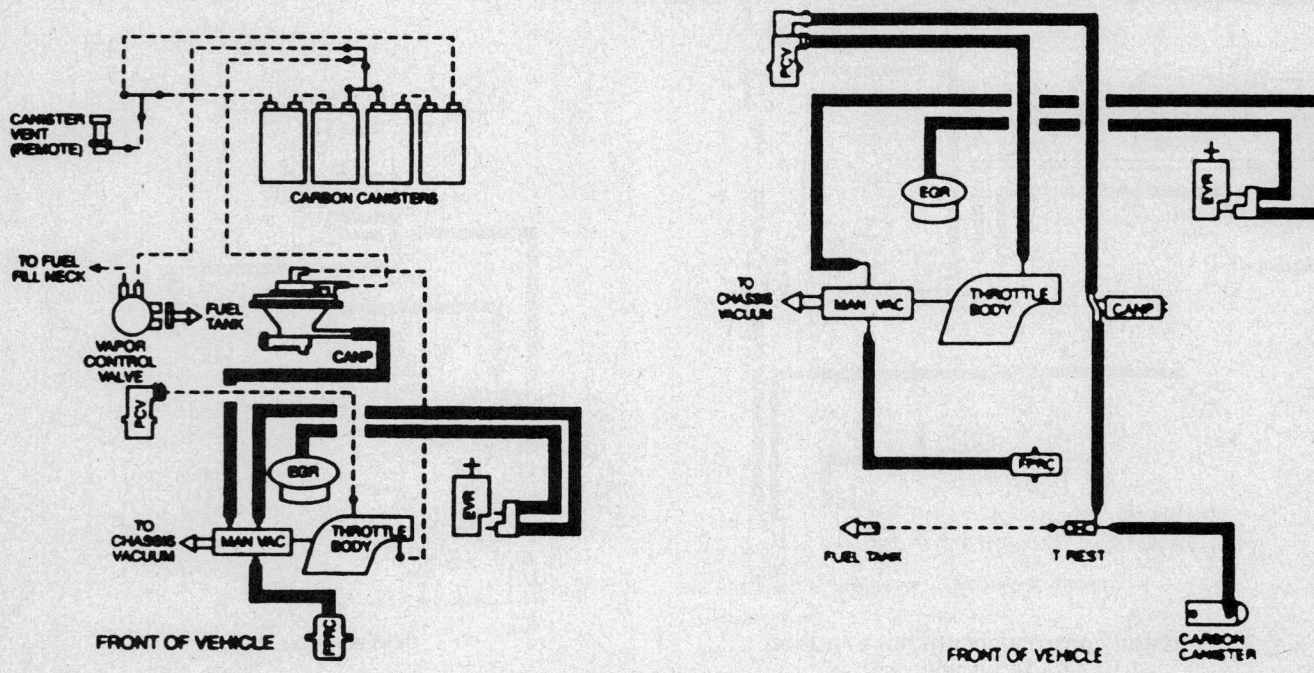

Fig. 7   Emission control vacuum hose routing. 3.0L/V6-183 MFI flexible fuel engine

Fig. 8   Emission control vacuum hose routing. 3.0L/V6-183 MFI engine except SHO & flexible fuel

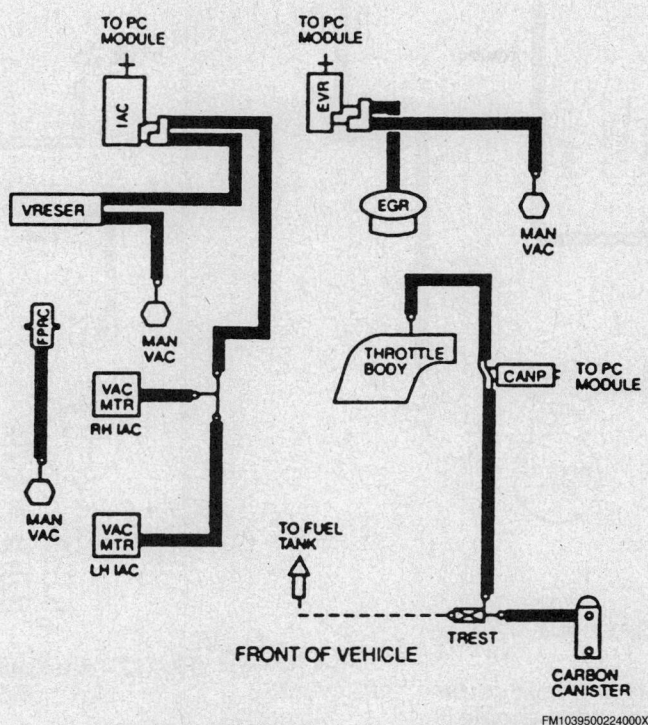

Fig. 9 Emission control vacuum hose routing.
3.2L/V6-195 engine

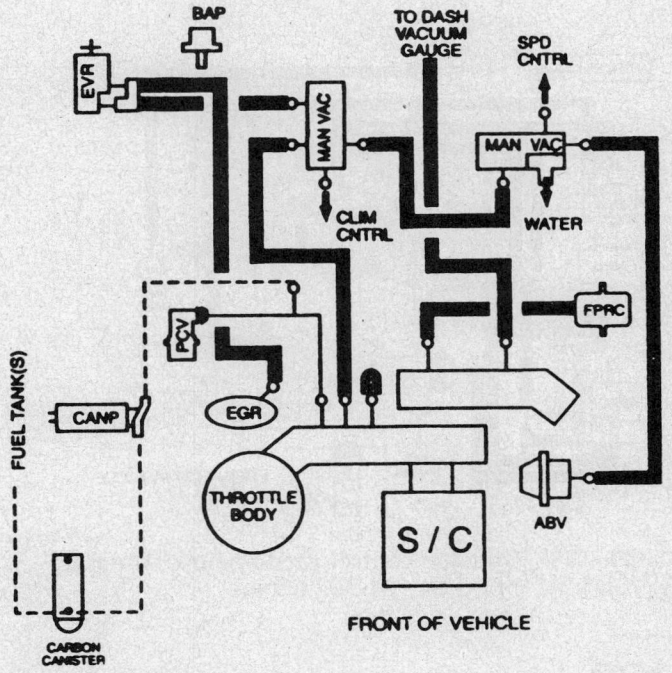

Fig. 10 Emission control vacuum hose routing.
3.8L/V6-232 supercharged engine

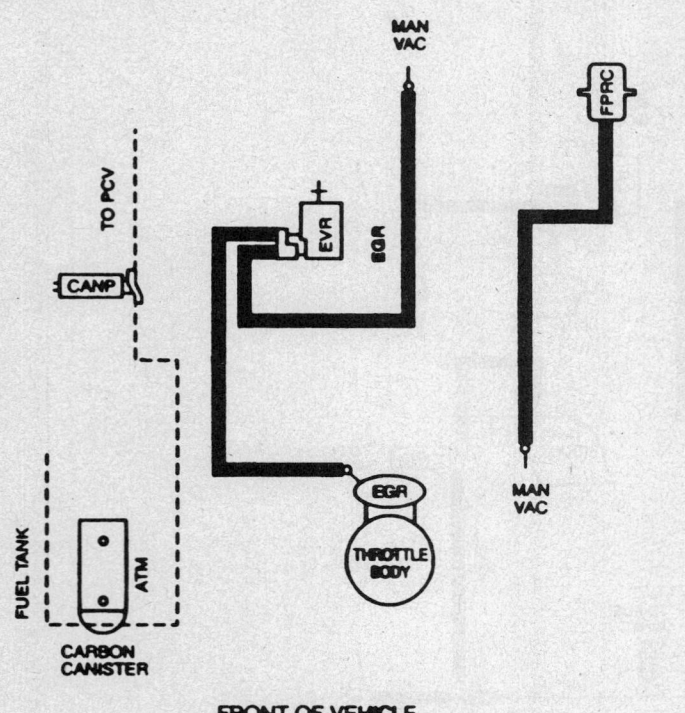

Fig. 11   Emission control vacuum hose routing. 3.8L/V6-232 non-supercharged engine

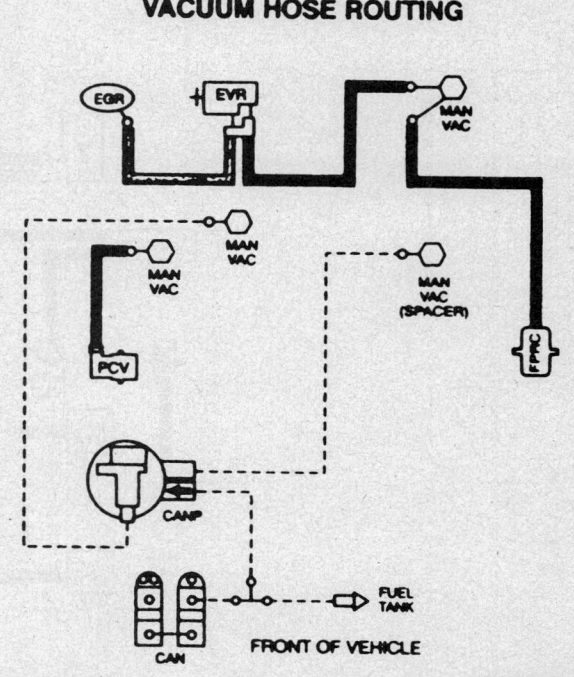

VACUUM HOSE ROUTING

Fig. 12   Emission control vacuum hose routing. 4.6L/V8-281 engine

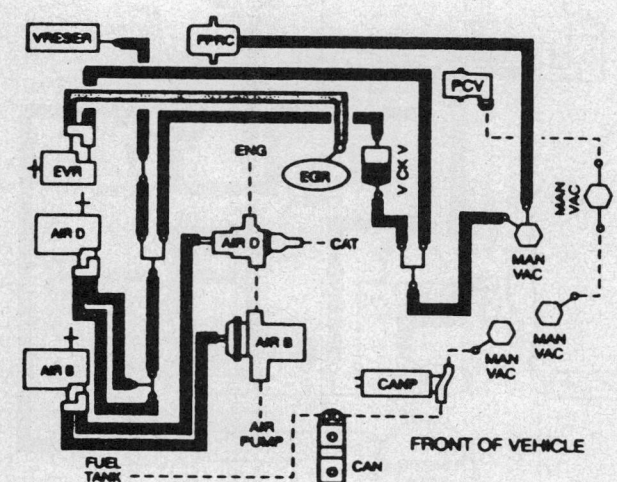

Fig. 13   Emission control vacuum hose routing. 5.0L/V8-302 engine

ENGINE COMPARTMENT REFERENCE DIAGRAMS

If Unsure Of The System Used On The Vehicle Being Serviced, Refer To The "Engine Systems Identification Chart." Further Assistance For The Proper Use Of Information Contained In This Section Can Also Be Found In The Front Of This Tabbed Section Under "How To Use This Manual."

INDEX

	Page No. 13-	Fig. No.
Aspire	1	2
Capri	3	2
Continental:		
3.8L/V6-232	4	3
4.6L/V8-281	5	4
Contour:		
2.0L/4-122 Engine	7	5
2.5L/V6-153 Engine	8	6
Cougar:		
1993:		
3.8L/V6-232	10	7
5.0L/V8-302	13	9
1994-95:		
3.8L/V6-232	15	10
4.6L/V8-281	20	13
1996:		
3.8L/V6-232	18	12
4.6L/V8-281	22	14
Crown Victoria	23	15
Escort:		
1993-94:		
1.8L/4-109	26	17
1.9L/4-116	25	16
1995-96:		
1.8L/4-109	28	19
1.9L/4-116	27	18
Festiva	29	20
Grand Marquis	23	15
Mark VIII	30	21
Mustang:		
1993:		
2.3L/4-140 Engine	32	22
5.0L/V8-302 Engine	33	23
1994-95:		
3.8L/V6-232 Engine	34	24
5.0L/V8-302 Engine	37	26
1996:		
3.8L/V6-232 Engine	37	25
4.6L/V8-281 DOHC Engine	39	27
4.6L/V8-281 SOHC Engine	40	28
Mystique:		
2.0L/4-122 Engine	7	5
2.5L/V6-153 Engine	8	6
Probe:		
1993-95:		
2.0L/4-121	42	29
2.5L/V6-152	45	31

	Page No. 13-	Fig. No.
1996:		
2.0L/4-121	43	30
2.5L/V6-152	46	32
Sable:		
1993-95:		
3.0L/V6-182	48	33
3.8L/V6-232	54	37
1996:	56	38
3.0L/V6-181 DOHC	57	39
3.0L/V6-182 OHV	58	40
Taurus:		
1993-95:		
3.0L/V6-182	48	33
3.0L/V6-182 FFV	51	35
3.0L/V6-182 SHO	50	34
3.2L/V6-195 SHO	53	36
3.8L/V6-232	54	37
1996:	56	38
3.0L/V6-181 DOHC	57	39
3.0L/V6-182 FFV	51	35
3.0L/V6-182 OHV	58	40
Tempo:		
2.3L/4-140	58	41
3.0L/V6-182	59	42
Topaz:		
2.3L/4-140	58	41
3.0L/V6-182	59	42
Thunderbird:		
1993:		
3.8L/V6-232 Except SC	10	7
3.8L/V6-232 SC	12	8
5.0L/V8-302	13	9
1994-95:		
3.8L/V6-232 Except SC	15	10
3.8L/V6-232 SC	17	11
4.6L/V8-281	20	13
1996:		
3.8L/V6-232	18	12
4.6L/V8-281	22	14
Town Car	23	15
Tracer:		
1993-94:		
1.8L/4-109	26	17
1.9L/4-116	25	16
1995-96:		
1.8L/4-109	28	19
1.9L/4-116	27	18

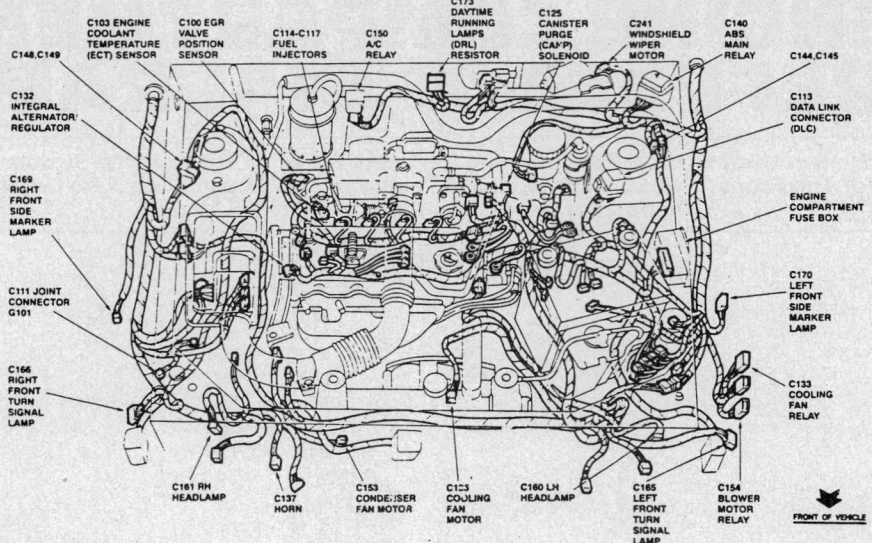

FM1019500058010X

Fig. 1   Engine compartment reference diagram (Part 1 of 3). Aspire

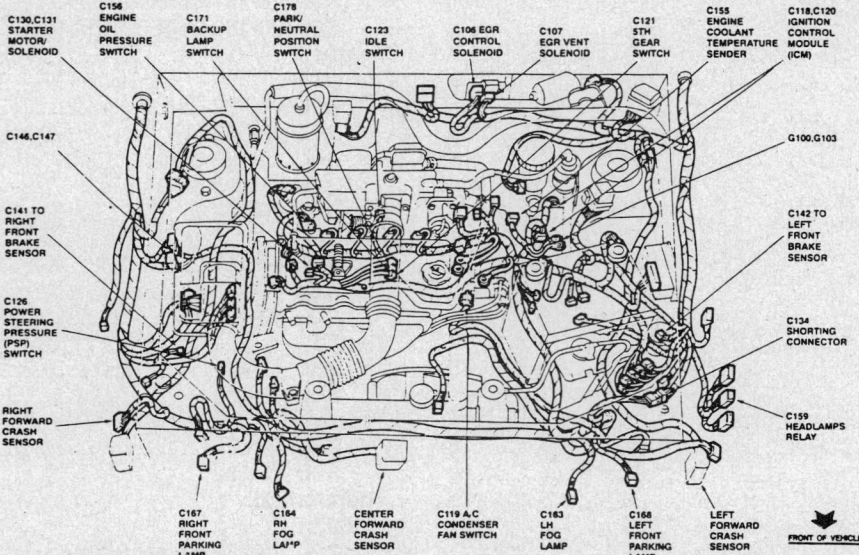

FM1019500058020X

Fig. 1   Engine compartment reference diagram (Part 2 of 3). Aspire

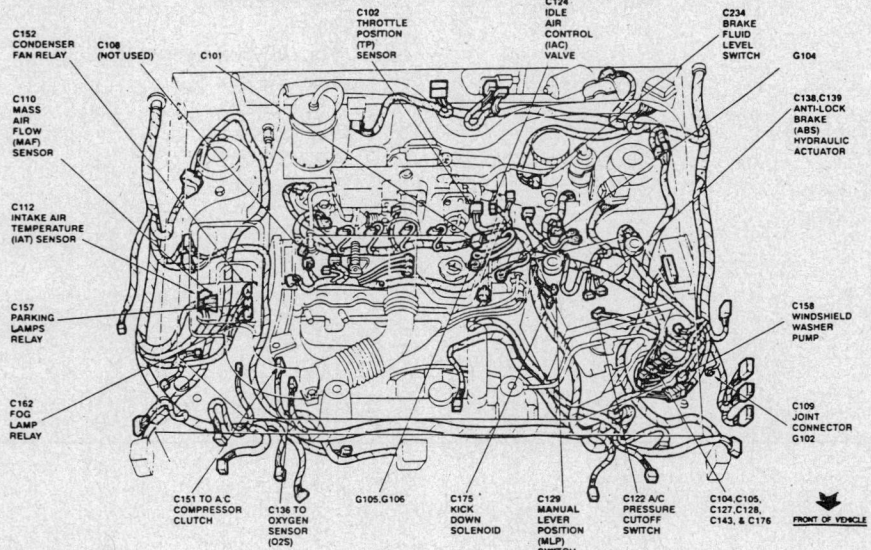

FM1019500058030X

Fig. 1   Engine compartment reference diagram (Part 3 of 3). Aspire

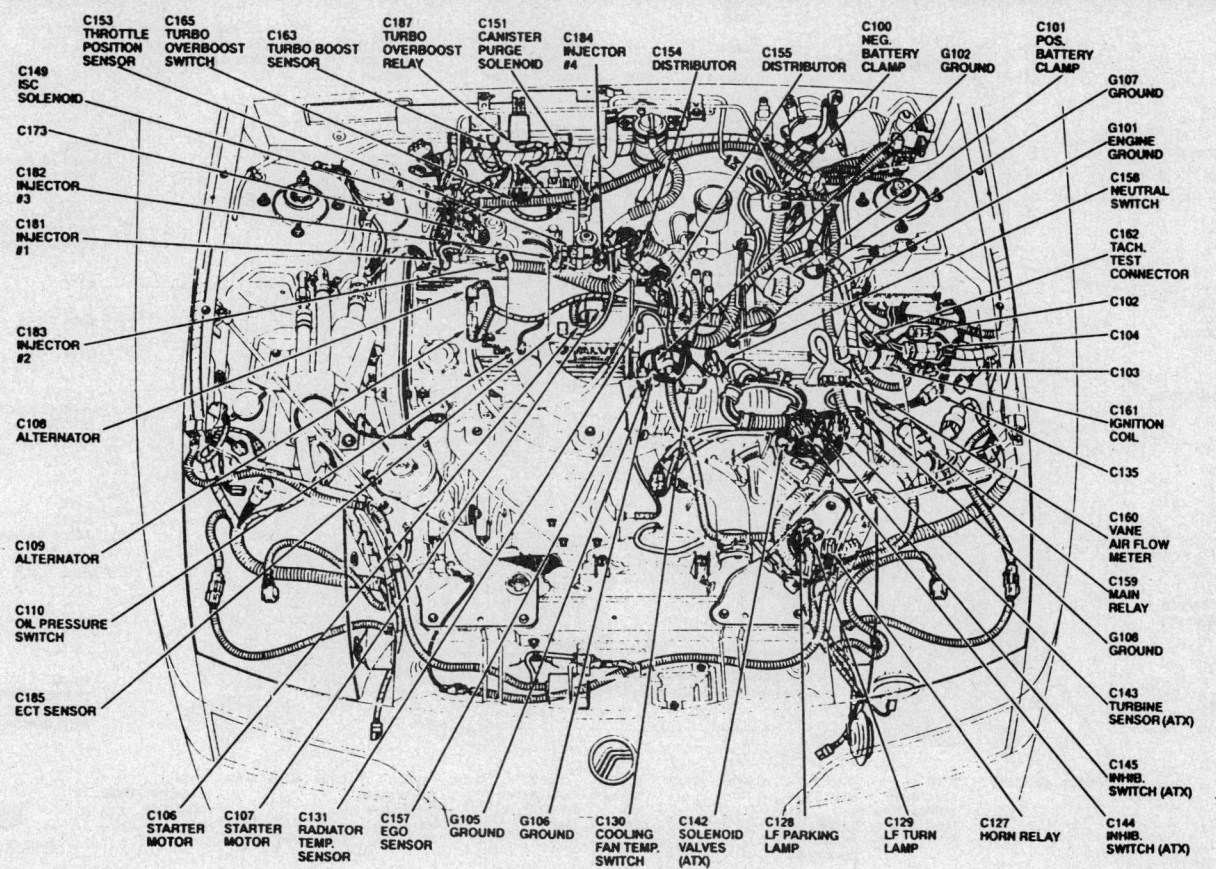

Fig. 2   Engine compartment reference diagram (Part 1 of 2). Capri

FM1019100001010X

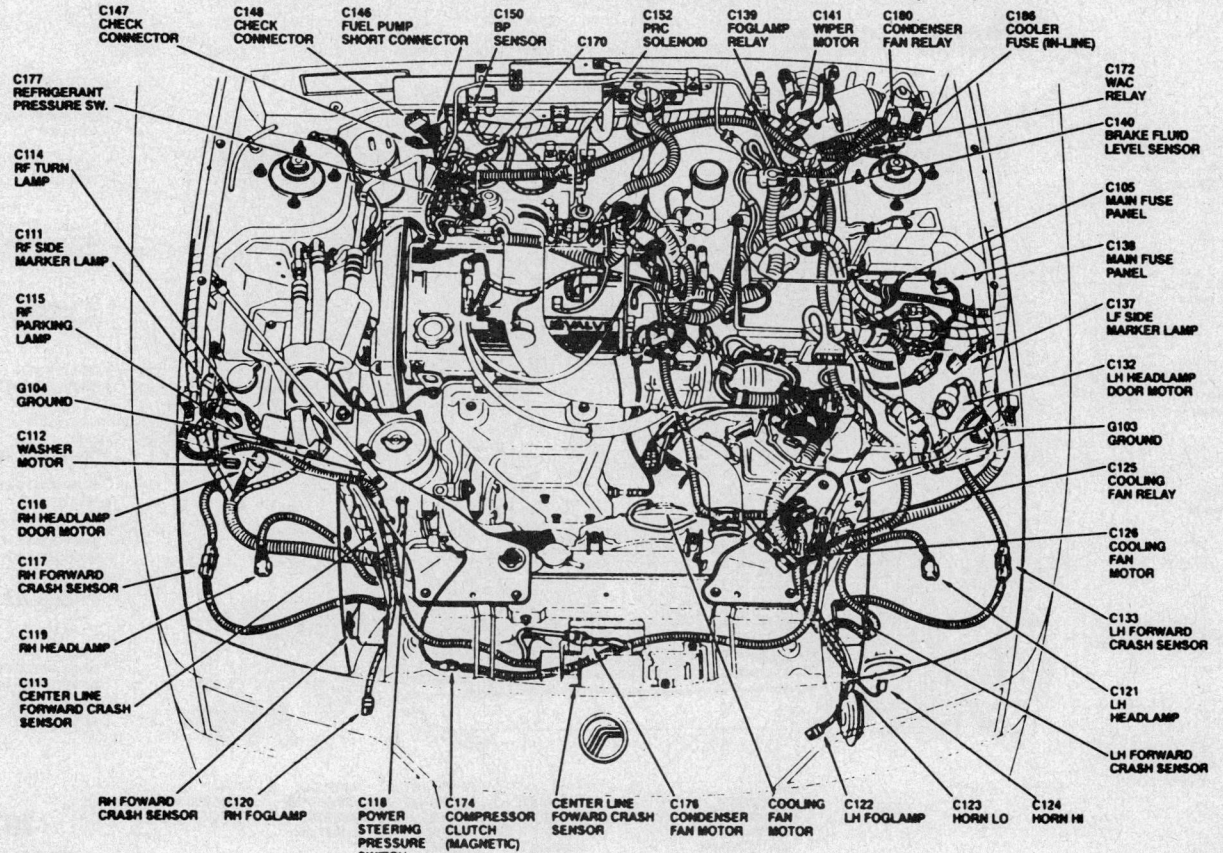

Fig. 2   Engine compartment reference diagram (Part 2 of 2). Capri

FM1019100001020X

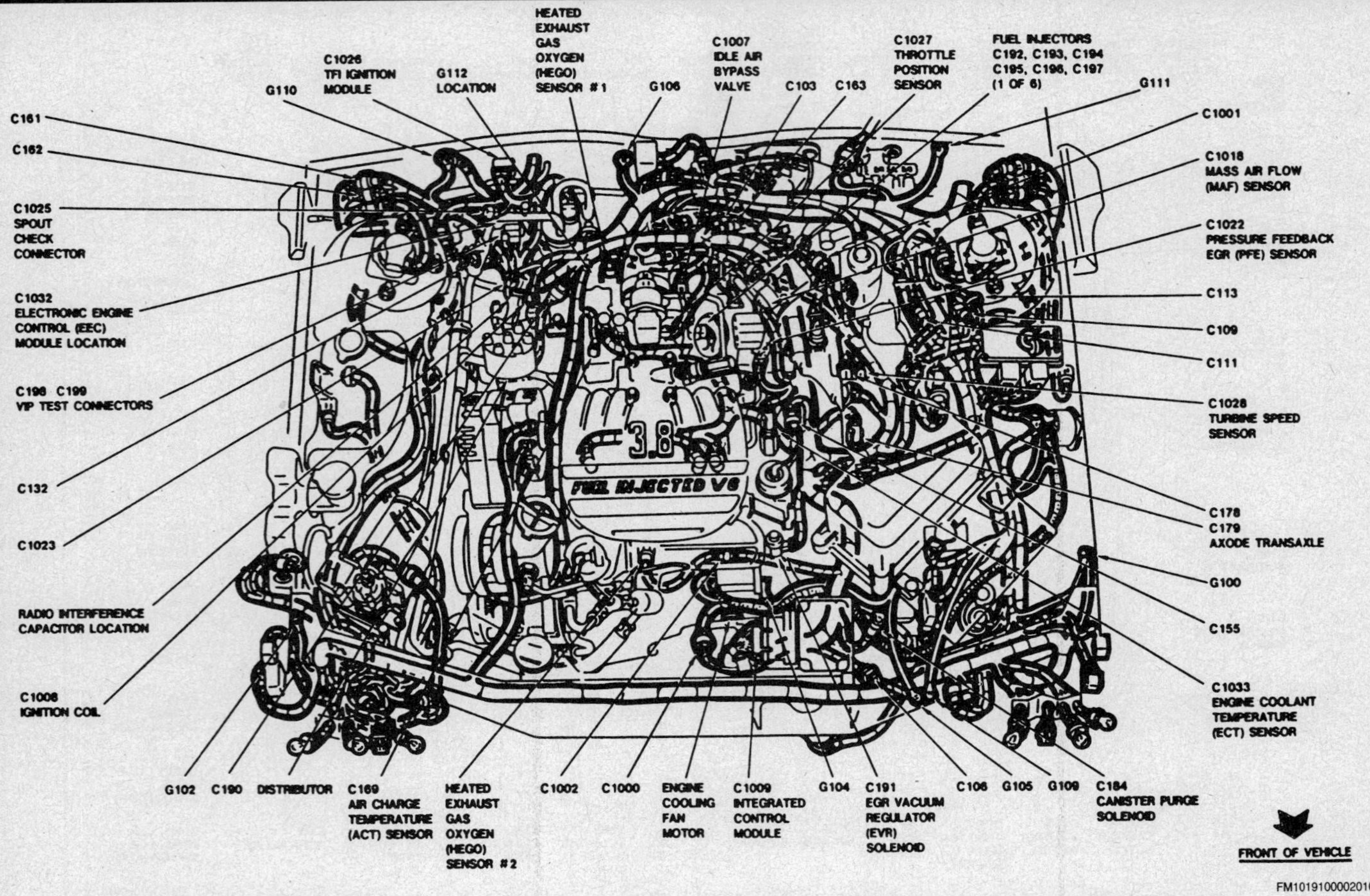

C161
C162

C1026 TFI IGNITION MODULE
G110
G112 LOCATION

HEATED EXHAUST GAS OXYGEN (HEGO) SENSOR #1
G106

C1007 IDLE AIR BYPASS VALVE
C103
C163

C1027 THROTTLE POSITION SENSOR

FUEL INJECTORS C192, C193, C194 C195, C196, C197 (1 OF 6)
G111

C1001

C1025 SPOUT CHECK CONNECTOR

C1018 MASS AIR FLOW (MAF) SENSOR

C1032 ELECTRONIC ENGINE CONTROL (EEC) MODULE LOCATION

C1022 PRESSURE FEEDBACK EGR (PFE) SENSOR

C113
C109
C111

C198 C199 VIP TEST CONNECTORS

C1028 TURBINE SPEED SENSOR

C132

C178 C179 AXODE TRANSAXLE

C1023

G100
C155

RADIO INTERFERENCE CAPACITOR LOCATION

C1008 IGNITION COIL

C1033 ENGINE COOLANT TEMPERATURE (ECT) SENSOR

G102 C190 DISTRIBUTOR

C169 AIR CHARGE TEMPERATURE (ACT) SENSOR

HEATED EXHAUST GAS OXYGEN (HEGO) SENSOR #2

C1002 C1000

ENGINE COOLING FAN MOTOR

C1009 INTEGRATED CONTROL MODULE

C104

C191 EGR VACUUM REGULATOR (EVR) SOLENOID

C106 G105 G109

C184 CANISTER PURGE SOLENOID

FRONT OF VEHICLE

FM1019100002010X

Fig. 3   Engine compartment reference diagram (Part 1 of 3). Continental w/3.8L/V6-232

C1017

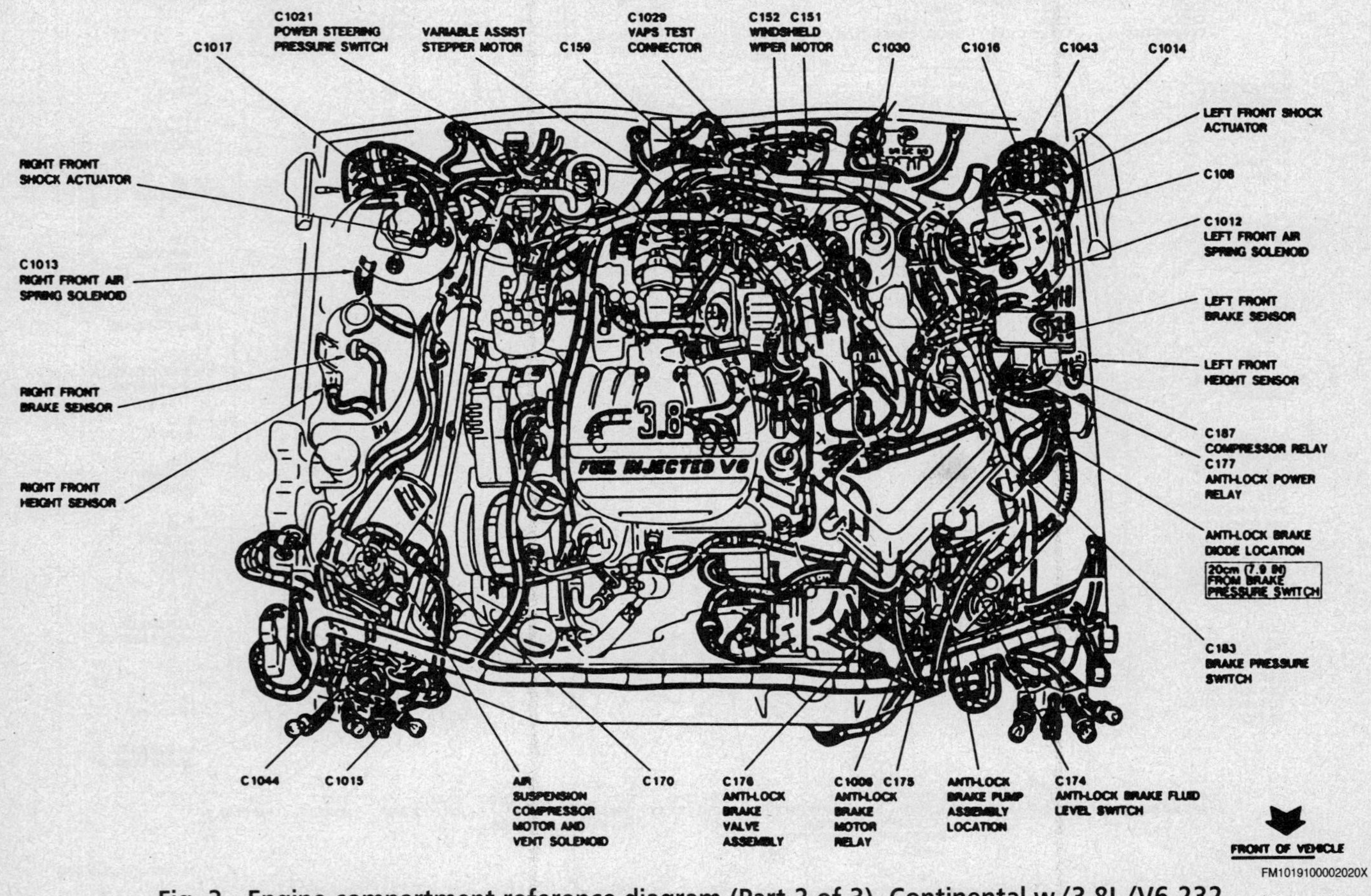

C1021 POWER STEERING PRESSURE SWITCH

VARIABLE ASSIST STEPPER MOTOR

C159

C1029 VAPS TEST CONNECTOR

C152 C151 WINDSHIELD WIPER MOTOR

C1030
C1016
C1043
C1014

RIGHT FRONT SHOCK ACTUATOR

LEFT FRONT SHOCK ACTUATOR

C108

C1013 RIGHT FRONT AIR SPRING SOLENOID

C1012 LEFT FRONT AIR SPRING SOLENOID

LEFT FRONT BRAKE SENSOR

RIGHT FRONT BRAKE SENSOR

LEFT FRONT HEIGHT SENSOR

RIGHT FRONT HEIGHT SENSOR

C187 COMPRESSOR RELAY
C177 ANTI-LOCK POWER RELAY

ANTI-LOCK BRAKE DIODE LOCATION

20cm (7.9 IN) FROM BRAKE PRESSURE SWITCH

C183 BRAKE PRESSURE SWITCH

C1044   C1015

AIR SUSPENSION COMPRESSOR MOTOR AND VENT SOLENOID

C170

C176 ANTI-LOCK BRAKE VALVE ASSEMBLY

C1006 C175 ANTI-LOCK BRAKE MOTOR RELAY

ANTI-LOCK BRAKE PUMP ASSEMBLY LOCATION

C174 ANTI-LOCK BRAKE FLUID LEVEL SWITCH

FRONT OF VEHICLE

FM1019100002020X

Fig. 3   Engine compartment reference diagram (Part 2 of 3). Continental w/3.8L/V6-232

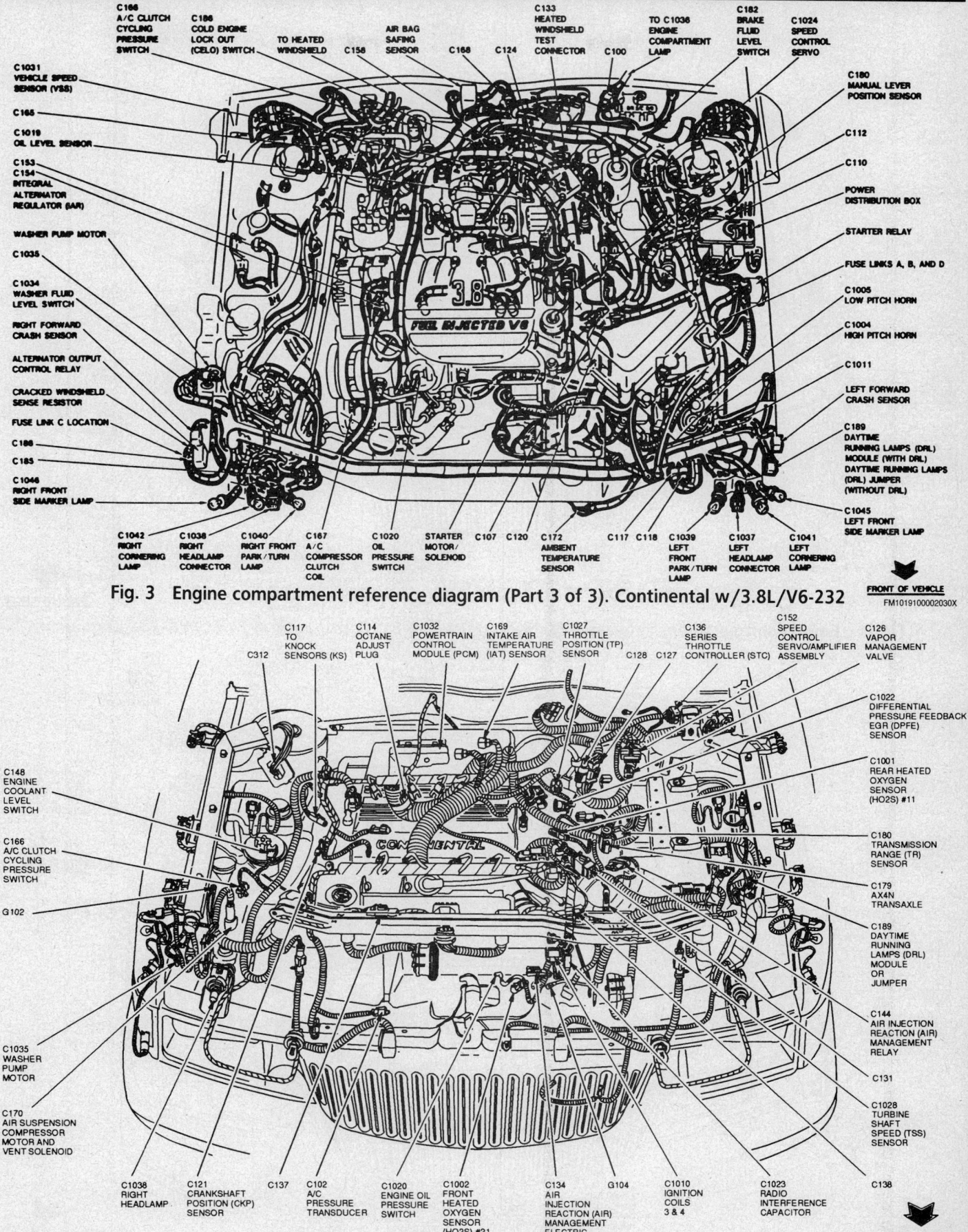

Fig. 3   Engine compartment reference diagram (Part 3 of 3). Continental w/3.8L/V6-232

FM1019100002030X

FRONT OF VEHICLE

Fig. 4   Engine compartment reference diagram (Part 1 of 3). Continental w/4.6L/V8-281 engine

ENGINE COMPARTMENT REFERENCE DIAGRAMS

13-5

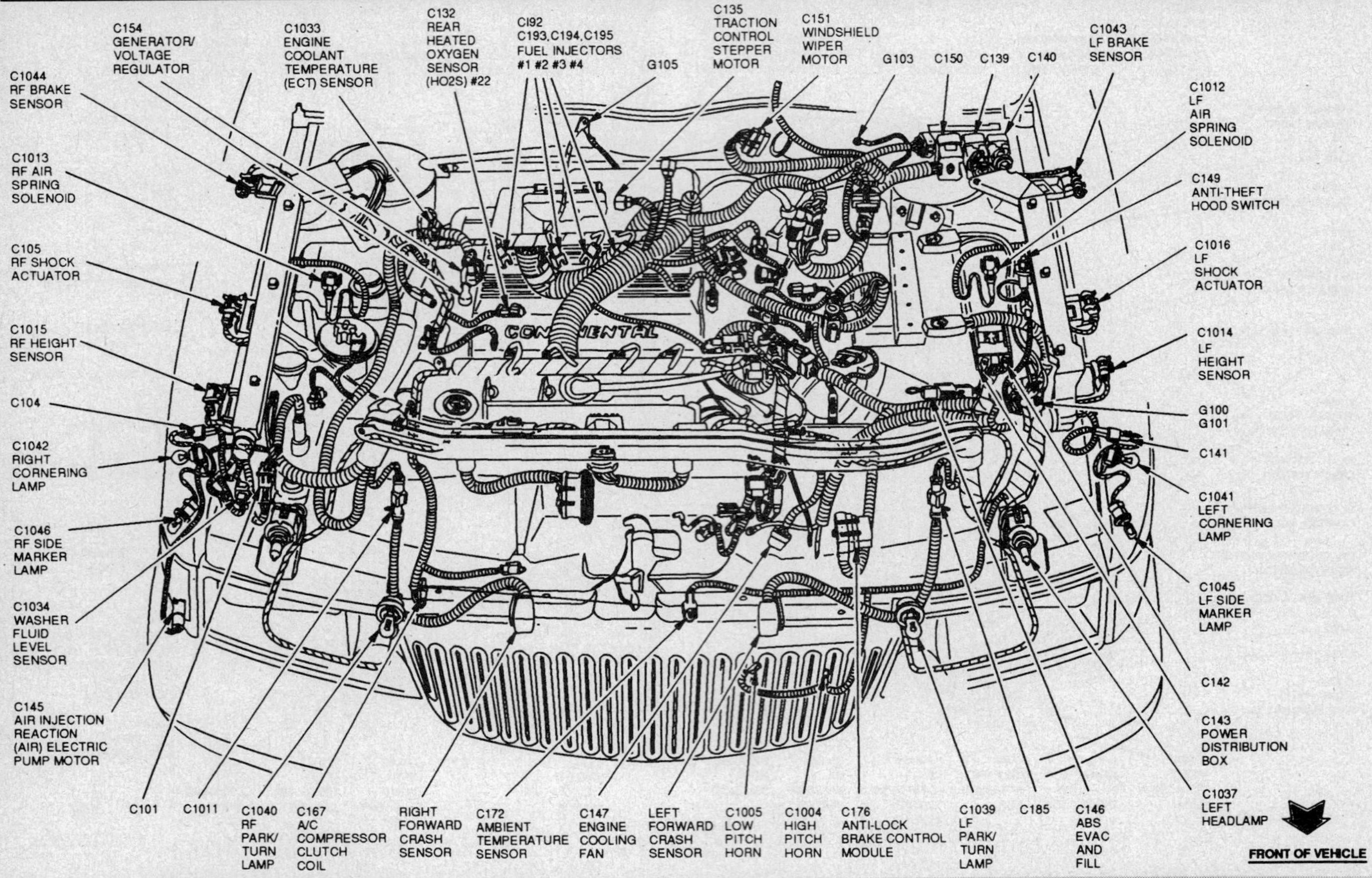

C1044
RF BRAKE
SENSOR

C154
GENERATOR/
VOLTAGE
REGULATOR

C1033
ENGINE
COOLANT
TEMPERATURE
(ECT) SENSOR

C132
REAR
HEATED
OXYGEN
SENSOR
(HO2S) #22

C192
C193,C194,C195
FUEL INJECTORS
#1 #2 #3 #4

G105

C135
TRACTION
CONTROL
STEPPER
MOTOR

C151
WINDSHIELD
WIPER
MOTOR

G103

C150

C139

C140

C1043
LF BRAKE
SENSOR

C1012
LF
AIR
SPRING
SOLENOID

C149
ANTI-THEFT
HOOD SWITCH

C1013
RF AIR
SPRING
SOLENOID

C1016
LF
SHOCK
ACTUATOR

C105
RF SHOCK
ACTUATOR

C1014
LF
HEIGHT
SENSOR

C1015
RF HEIGHT
SENSOR

G100
G101

C104

C141

C1042
RIGHT
CORNERING
LAMP

C1041
LEFT
CORNERING
LAMP

C1046
RF SIDE
MARKER
LAMP

C1045
LF SIDE
MARKER
LAMP

C1034
WASHER
FLUID
LEVEL
SENSOR

C142

C143
POWER
DISTRIBUTION
BOX

C145
AIR INJECTION
REACTION
(AIR) ELECTRIC
PUMP MOTOR

C1037
LEFT
HEADLAMP

FRONT OF VEHICLE

C101   C1011   C1040   C167   RIGHT   C172   C147   LEFT   C1005   C1004   C176   C1039   C185   C146
                 RF   A/C   FORWARD   AMBIENT   ENGINE   FORWARD   LOW   HIGH   ANTI-LOCK   LF   ABS
                 PARK/   COMPRESSOR CRASH   TEMPERATURE COOLING   CRASH   PITCH   PITCH   BRAKE CONTROL   PARK/   EVAC
                 TURN   CLUTCH   SENSOR   SENSOR   FAN   SENSOR   HORN   HORN   MODULE   TURN   AND
                 LAMP   COIL   LAMP   FILL

Fig. 4   Engine compartment reference diagram (Part 2 of 3). Continental w/4.6L/V8-281 engine

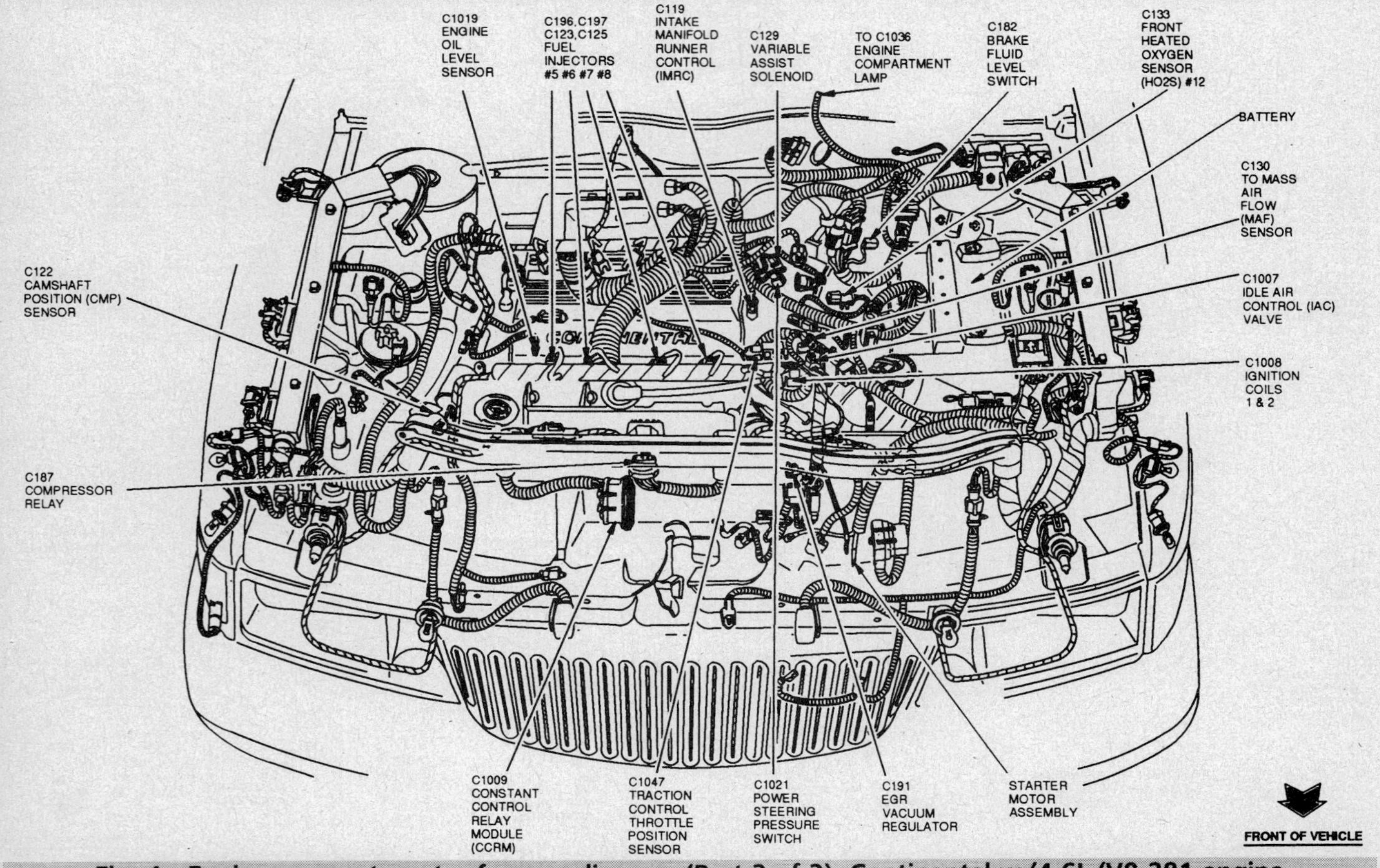

C1019
ENGINE
OIL
LEVEL
SENSOR

C196,C197
C123,C125
FUEL
INJECTORS
#5 #6 #7 #8

C119
INTAKE
MANIFOLD
RUNNER
CONTROL
(IMRC)

C129
VARIABLE
ASSIST
SOLENOID

TO C1036
ENGINE
COMPARTMENT
LAMP

C182
BRAKE
FLUID
LEVEL
SWITCH

C133
FRONT
HEATED
OXYGEN
SENSOR
(HO2S) #12

BATTERY

C130
TO MASS
AIR
FLOW
(MAF)
SENSOR

C122
CAMSHAFT
POSITION (CMP)
SENSOR

C1007
IDLE AIR
CONTROL (IAC)
VALVE

C1008
IGNITION
COILS
1 & 2

C187
COMPRESSOR
RELAY

C1009   C1047   C1021   C191   STARTER
CONSTANT   TRACTION   POWER   EGR   MOTOR
CONTROL   CONTROL   STEERING   VACUUM   ASSEMBLY
RELAY   THROTTLE   PRESSURE   REGULATOR
MODULE   POSITION   SWITCH
(CCRM)   SENSOR

FRONT OF VEHICLE

Fig. 4   Engine compartment reference diagram (Part 3 of 3). Continental w/4.6L/V8-281 engine

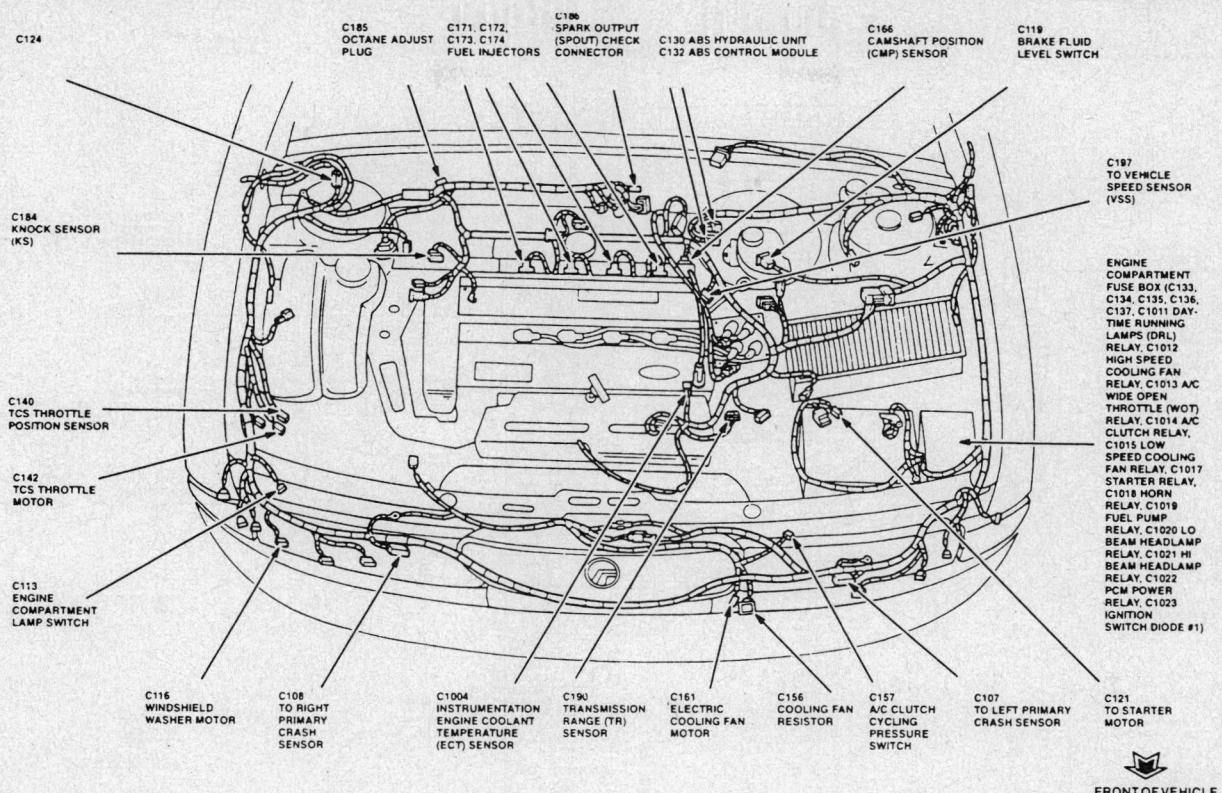

Fig. 5 Engine compartment reference diagram (Part 1 of 3). Contour & Mystique w/2.0L/4-122 engine

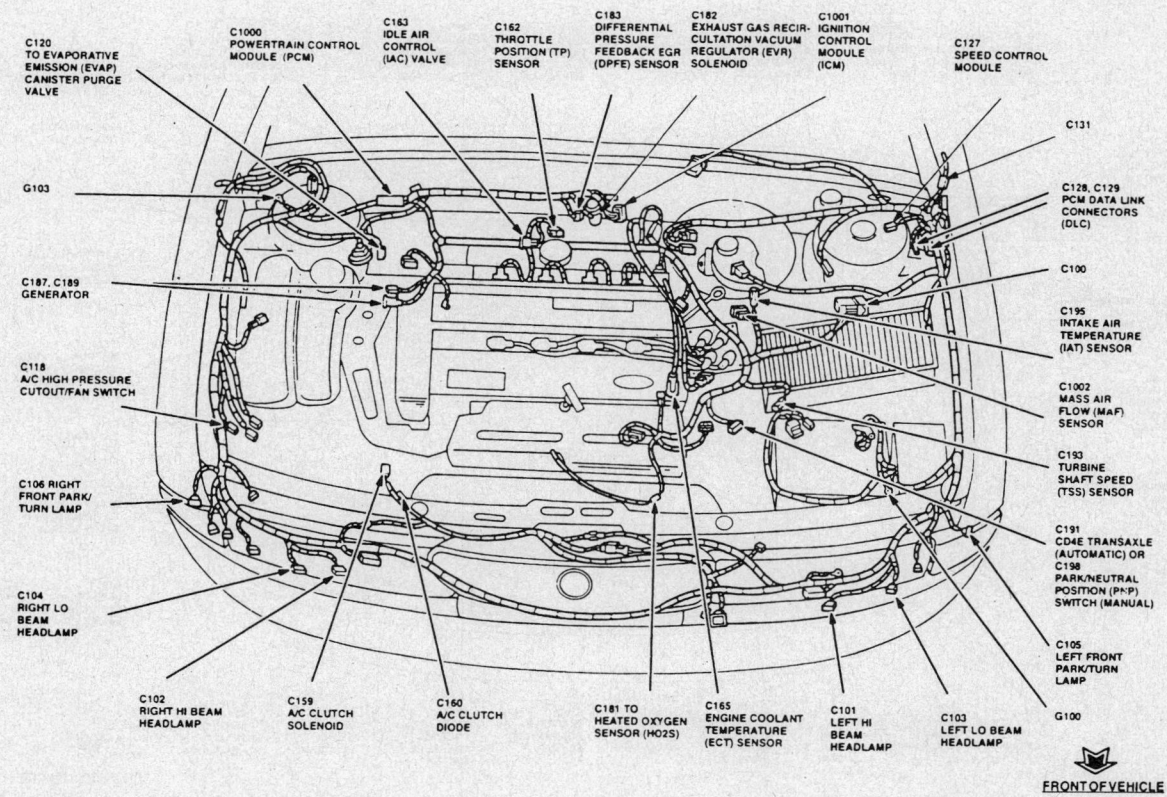

Fig. 5 Engine compartment reference diagram (Part 2 of 3). Contour & Mystique w/2.0L/4-122 engine

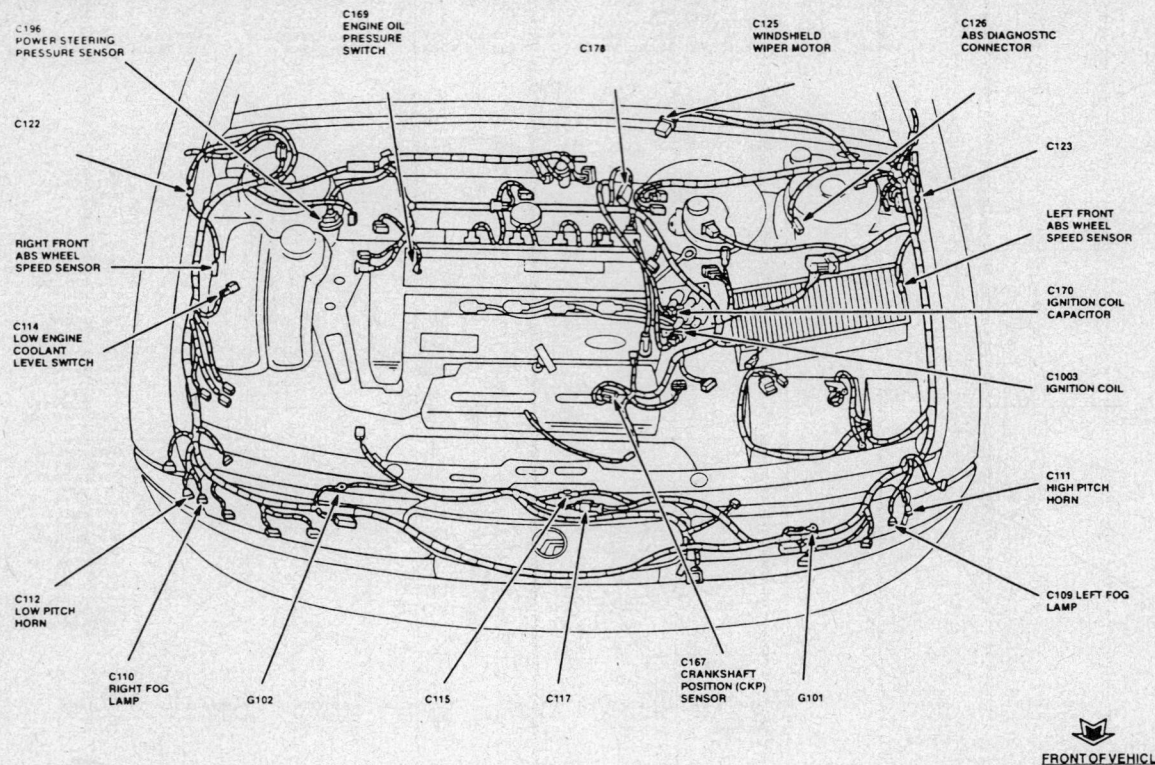

Fig. 5   Engine compartment reference diagram (Part 3 of 3). Contour & Mystique w/2.0L/4-122 engine

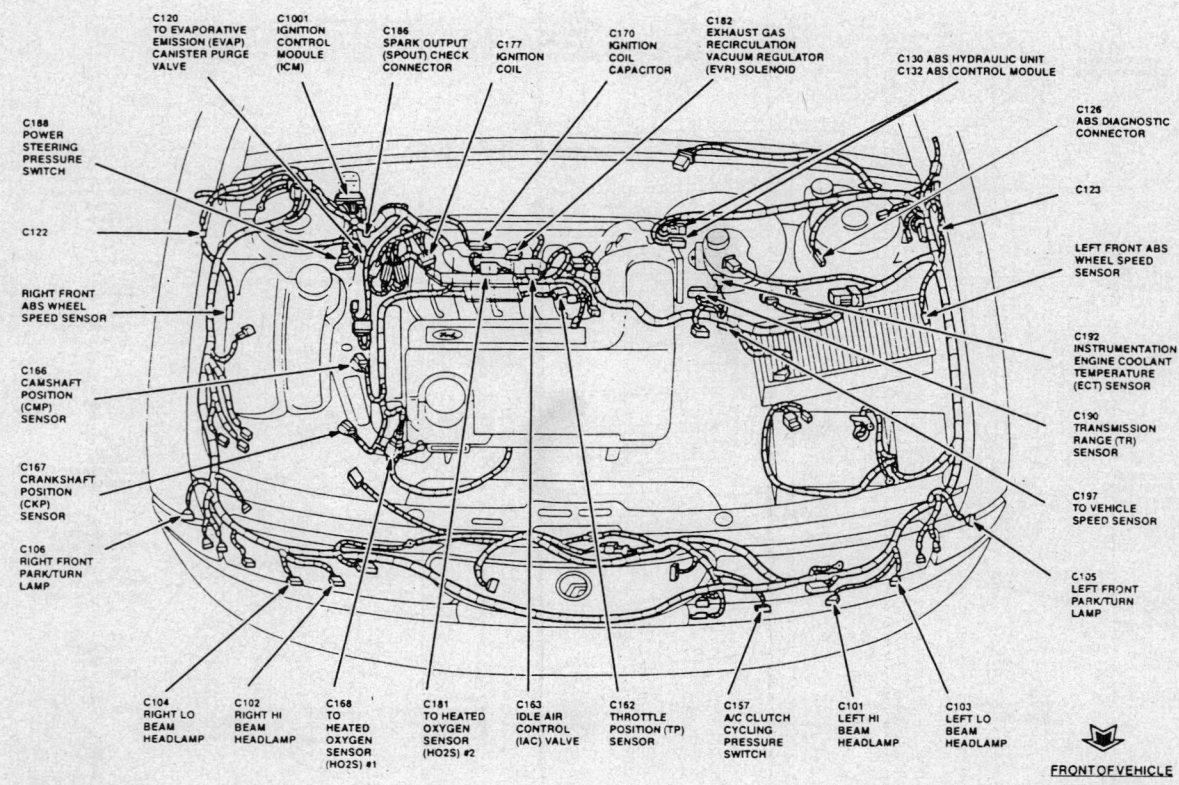

Fig. 6   Engine compartment reference diagram (Part 1 of 3). Contour & Mystique w/2.5L/V6-153 engine

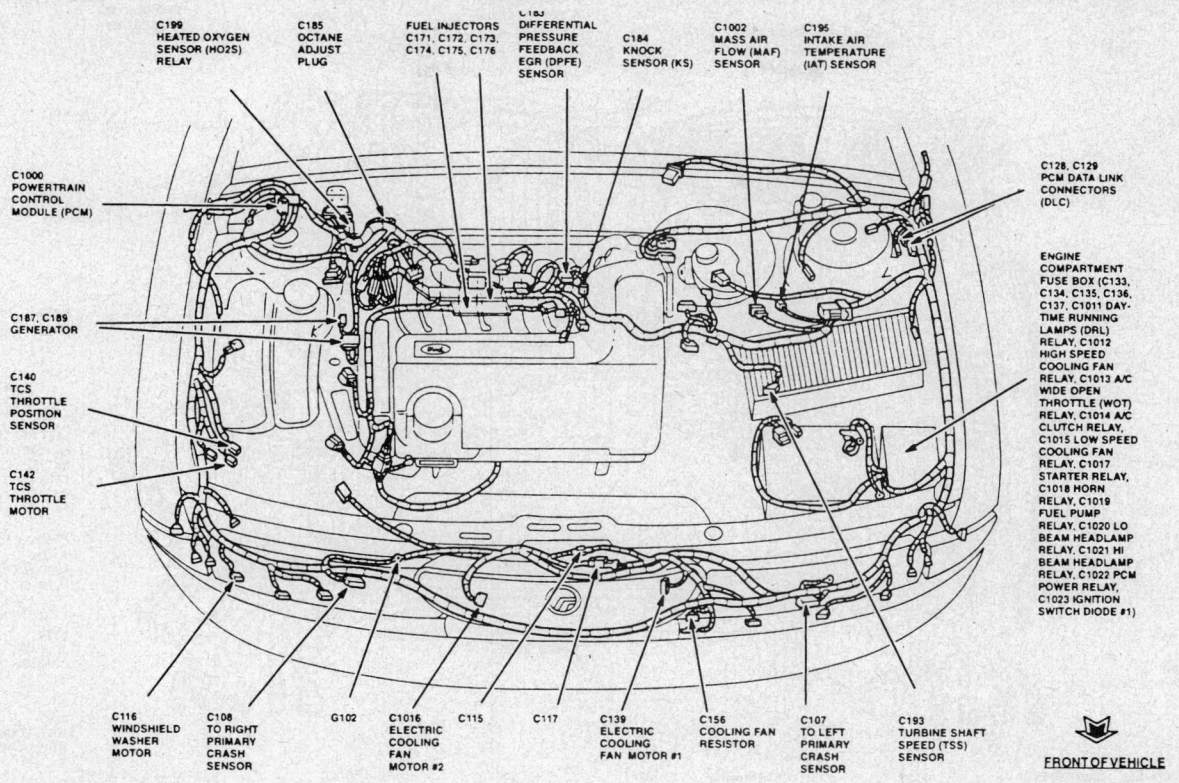

Fig. 6 Engine compartment reference diagram (Part 2 of 3). Contour & Mystique w/2.5L/V6-153 engine

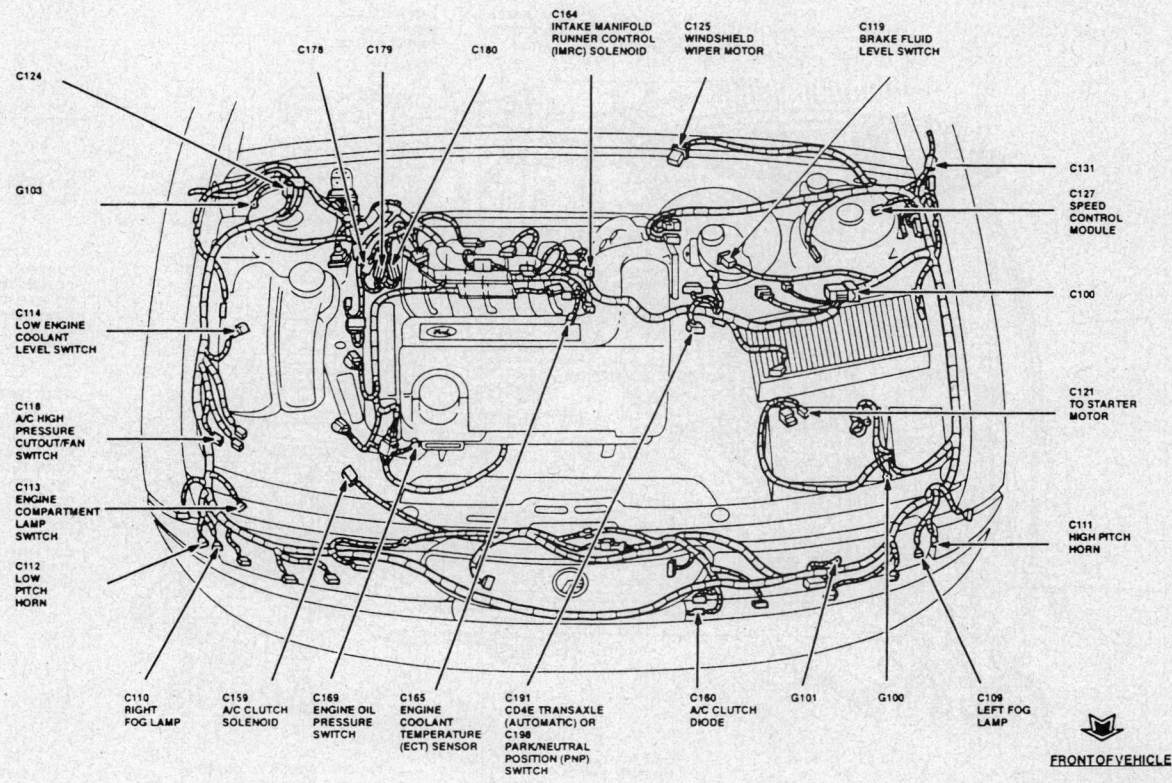

Fig. 6 Engine compartment reference diagram (Part 3 of 3). Contour & Mystique w/2.5L/V6-153 engine

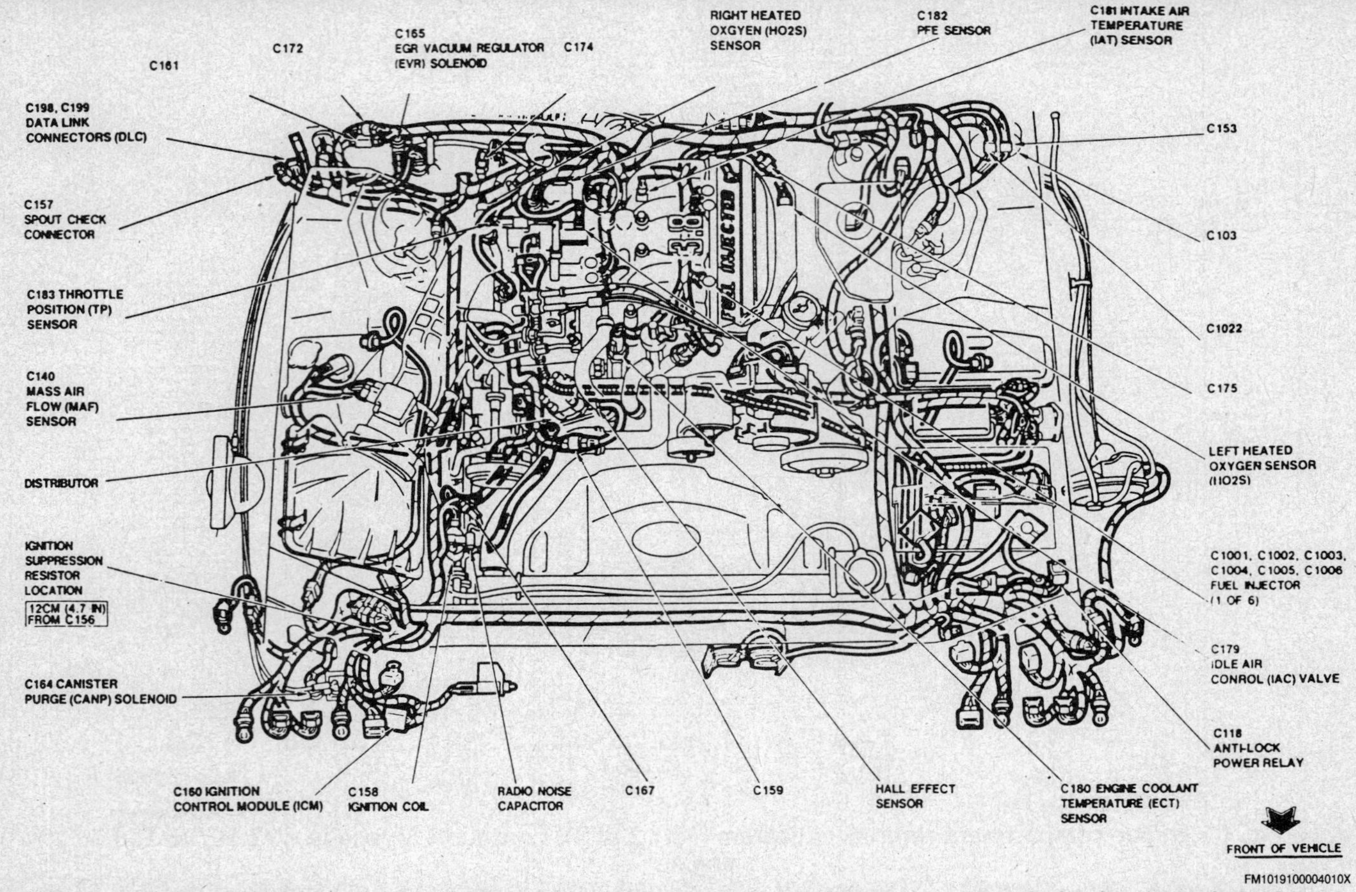

C161

C172

C165
EGR VACUUM REGULATOR
(EVR) SOLENOID

C174

RIGHT HEATED
OXGYEN (HO2S)
SENSOR

C182
PFE SENSOR

C181 INTAKE AIR
TEMPERATURE
(IAT) SENSOR

C198, C199
DATA LINK
CONNECTORS (DLC)

C153

C157
SPOUT CHECK
CONNECTOR

C103

C183 THROTTLE
POSITION (TP)
SENSOR

C1022

C140
MASS AIR
FLOW (MAF)
SENSOR

C175

LEFT HEATED
OXYGEN SENSOR
(HO2S)

DISTRIBUTOR

C1001, C1002, C1003,
C1004, C1005, C1006
FUEL INJECTOR
(1 OF 6)

IGNITION
SUPPRESSION
RESISTOR
LOCATION
12CM (4.7 IN)
FROM C156

C179
IDLE AIR
CONROL (IAC) VALVE

C164 CANISTER
PURGE (CANP) SOLENOID

C118
ANTI-LOCK
POWER RELAY

C150 IGNITION
CONTROL MODULE (ICM)

C158
IGNITION COIL

RADIO NOISE
CAPACITOR

C167

C159

HALL EFFECT
SENSOR

C180 ENGINE COOLANT
TEMPERATURE (ECT)
SENSOR

FRONT OF VEHICLE

FM1019100004010X

Fig. 7   Engine compartment reference diagram (Part 1 of 4). 1993 Cougar & Thunderbird w/3.8L/V6-232

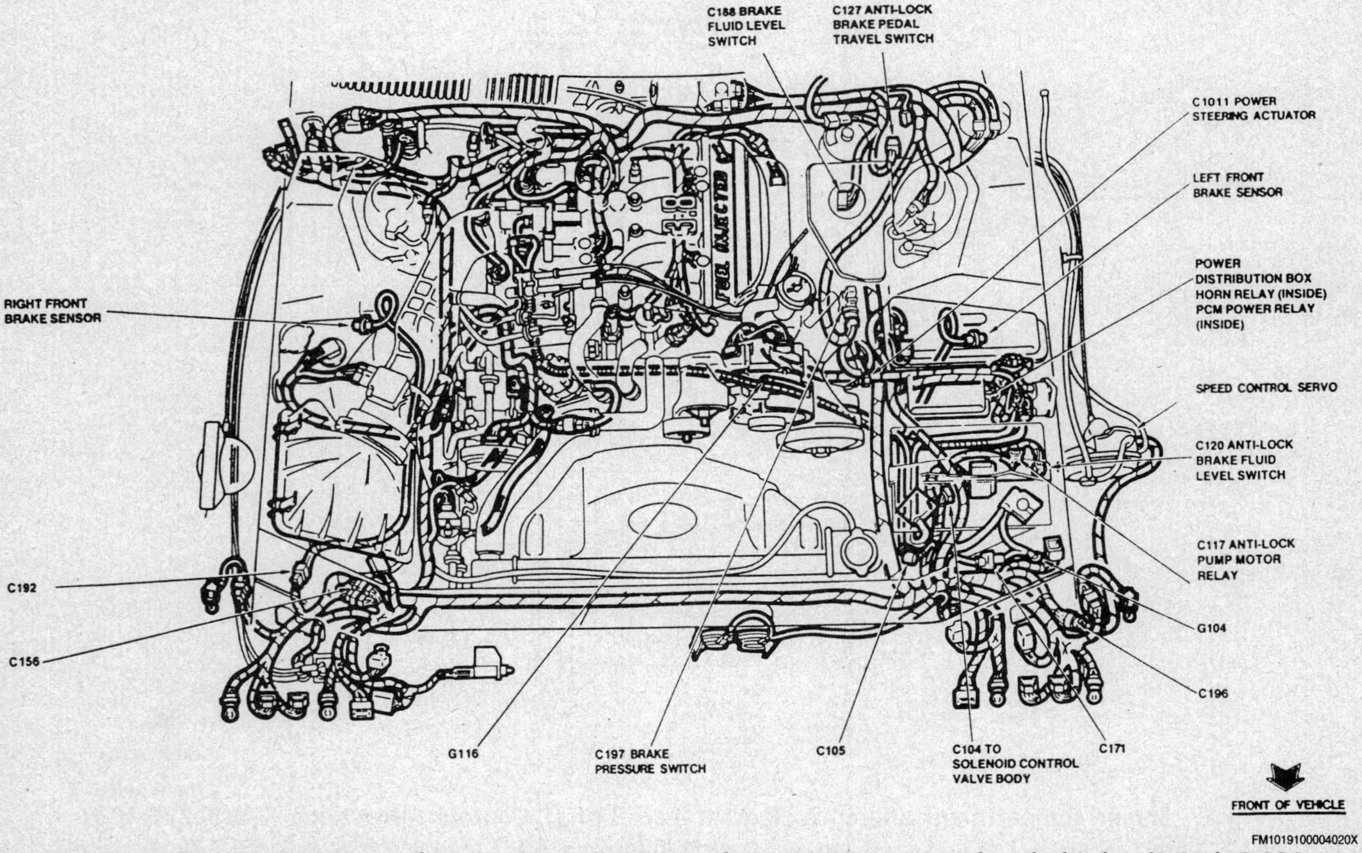

C188 BRAKE
FLUID LEVEL
SWITCH

C127 ANTI-LOCK
BRAKE PEDAL
TRAVEL SWITCH

C1011 POWER
STEERING ACTUATOR

LEFT FRONT
BRAKE SENSOR

RIGHT FRONT
BRAKE SENSOR

POWER
DISTRIBUTION BOX
HORN RELAY (INSIDE)
PCM POWER RELAY
(INSIDE)

SPEED CONTROL SERVO

C120 ANTI-LOCK
BRAKE FLUID
LEVEL SWITCH

C117 ANTI-LOCK
PUMP MOTOR
RELAY

C192

G104

C156

C196

G116

C197 BRAKE
PRESSURE SWITCH

C105

C104 TO
SOLENOID CONTROL
VALVE BODY

C171

FRONT OF VEHICLE

FM1019100004020X

Fig. 7   Engine compartment reference diagram (Part 2 of 4). 1993 Cougar & Thunderbird w/3.8L/V6-232

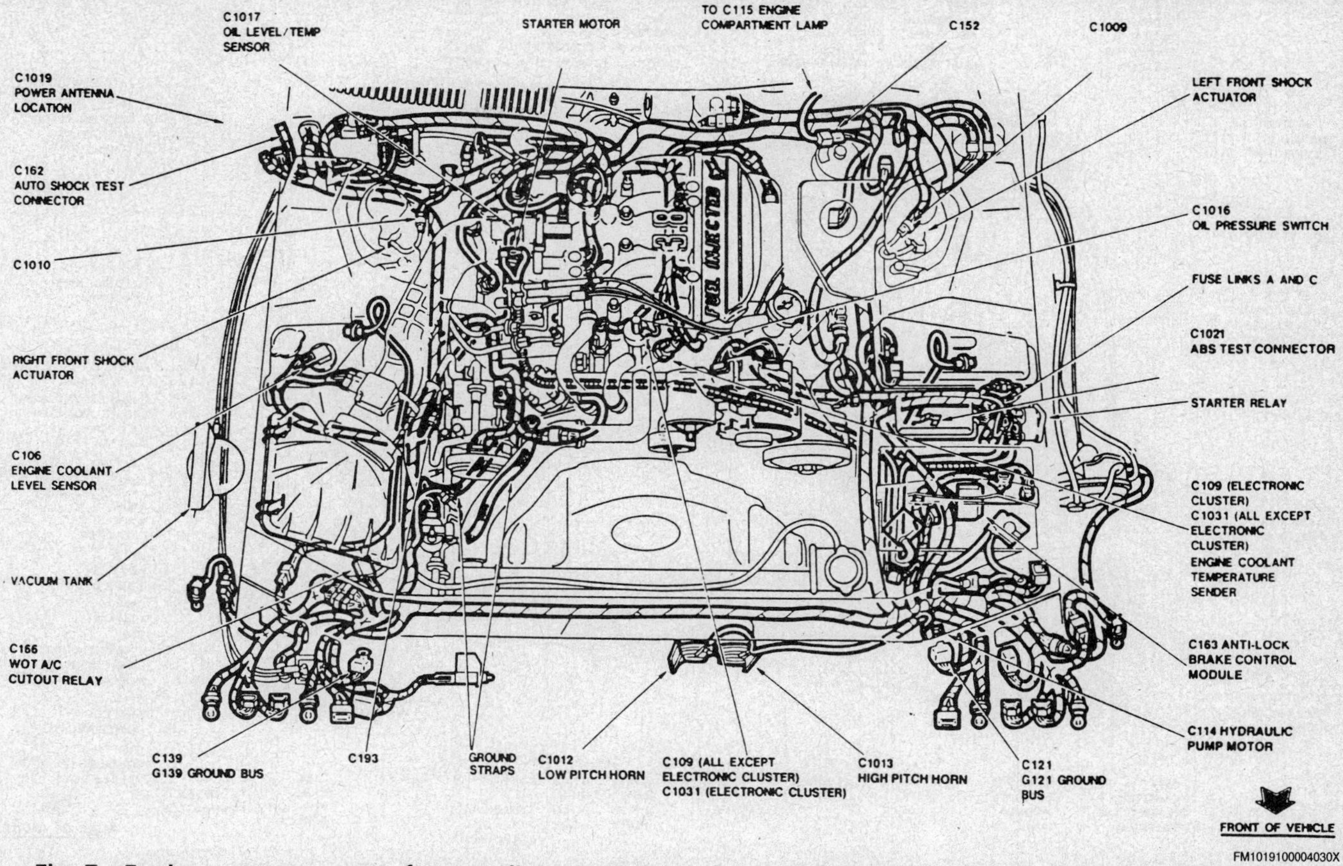

C1019
POWER ANTENNA
LOCATION

C162
AUTO SHOCK TEST
CONNECTOR

C1010

RIGHT FRONT SHOCK
ACTUATOR

C106
ENGINE COOLANT
LEVEL SENSOR

VACUUM TANK

C166
WOT A/C
CUTOUT RELAY

C1017
OIL LEVEL/TEMP
SENSOR

STARTER MOTOR

TO C115 ENGINE
COMPARTMENT LAMP

C152

C1009

LEFT FRONT SHOCK
ACTUATOR

C1016
OIL PRESSURE SWITCH

FUSE LINKS A AND C

C1021
ABS TEST CONNECTOR

STARTER RELAY

C109 (ELECTRONIC
CLUSTER)
C1031 (ALL EXCEPT
ELECTRONIC
CLUSTER)
ENGINE COOLANT
TEMPERATURE
SENDER

C163 ANTI-LOCK
BRAKE CONTROL
MODULE

C114 HYDRAULIC
PUMP MOTOR

C139
G139 GROUND BUS

C193

GROUND
STRAPS

C1012
LOW PITCH HORN

C109 (ALL EXCEPT
ELECTRONIC CLUSTER)
C1031 (ELECTRONIC CLUSTER)

C1013
HIGH PITCH HORN

C121
G121 GROUND
BUS

FRONT OF VEHICLE

FM1019100004030X

Fig. 7   Engine compartment reference diagram (Part 3 of 4). 1993 Cougar & Thunderbird w/3.8L/V6-232

A C CLUTCH
DIODE LOCATION
9CM (3.5 IN) FROM
A C CLUTCH COIL

C107
A C CLUTCH COIL

C1030
ATC AMBIENT
TEMPERATURE
SENSOR

C154

C136
RIGHT CORNERING
LAMP

C126
RIGHT LO BEAM
HEADLAMP
(T-BIRD ONLY)

C134
RIGHT FRONT
PARK/TURN LAMP

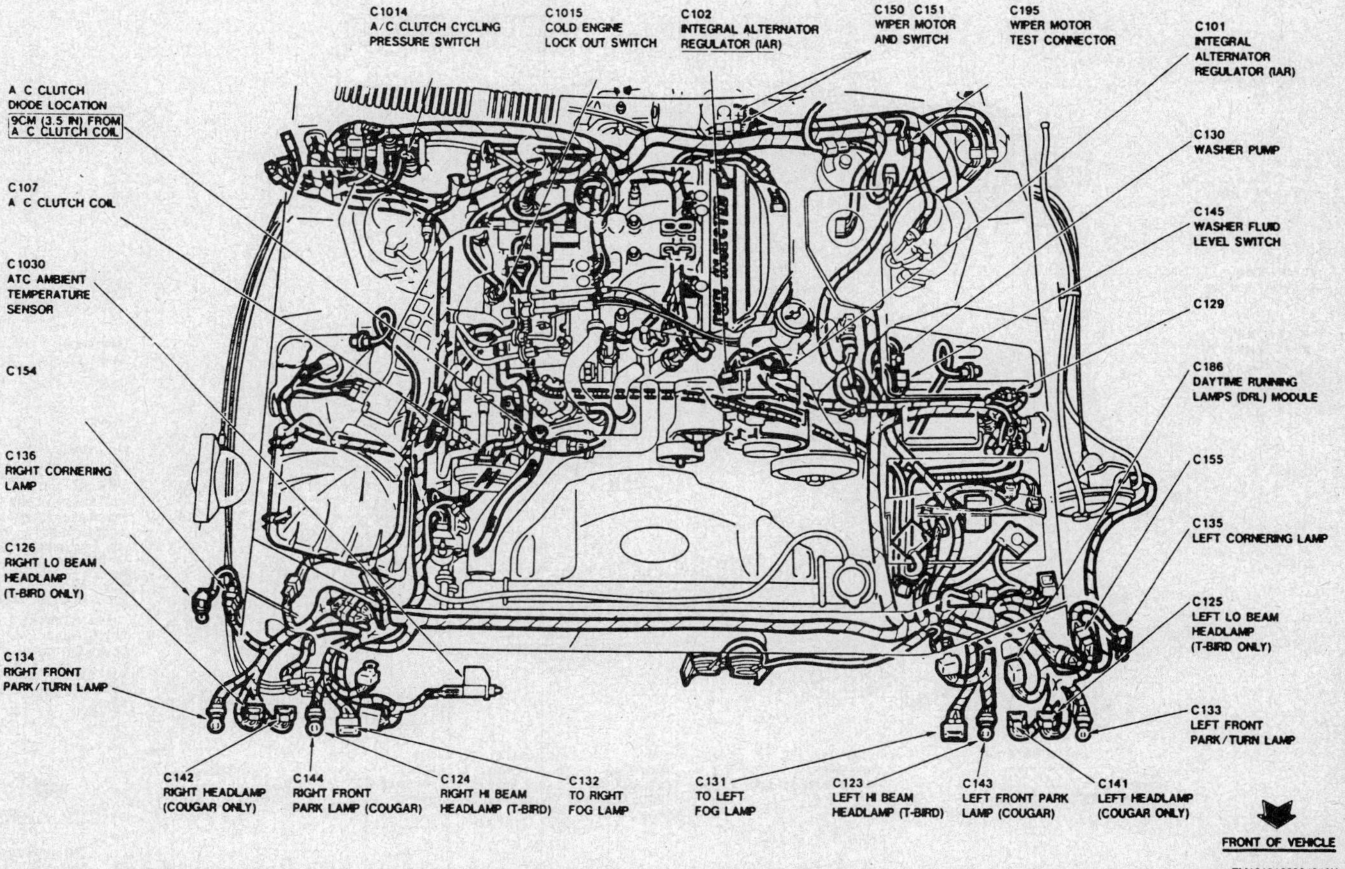

C1014
A/C CLUTCH CYCLING
PRESSURE SWITCH

C1015
COLD ENGINE
LOCK OUT SWITCH

C102
INTEGRAL ALTERNATOR
REGULATOR (IAR)

C150 C151
WIPER MOTOR
AND SWITCH

C195
WIPER MOTOR
TEST CONNECTOR

C101
INTEGRAL
ALTERNATOR
REGULATOR (IAR)

C130
WASHER PUMP

C145
WASHER FLUID
LEVEL SWITCH

C129

C186
DAYTIME RUNNING
LAMPS (DRL) MODULE

C155

C135
LEFT CORNERING LAMP

C125
LEFT LO BEAM
HEADLAMP
(T-BIRD ONLY)

C133
LEFT FRONT
PARK/TURN LAMP

C142
RIGHT HEADLAMP
(COUGAR ONLY)

C144
RIGHT FRONT
PARK LAMP (COUGAR)

C124
RIGHT HI BEAM
HEADLAMP (T-BIRD)

C132
TO RIGHT
FOG LAMP

C131
TO LEFT
FOG LAMP

C123
LEFT HI BEAM
HEADLAMP (T-BIRD)

C143
LEFT FRONT PARK
LAMP (COUGAR)

C141
LEFT HEADLAMP
(COUGAR ONLY)

FRONT OF VEHICLE

FM1019100004040X

Fig. 7   Engine compartment reference diagram (Part 4 of 4). 1993 Cougar & Thunderbird w/3.8L/V6-232

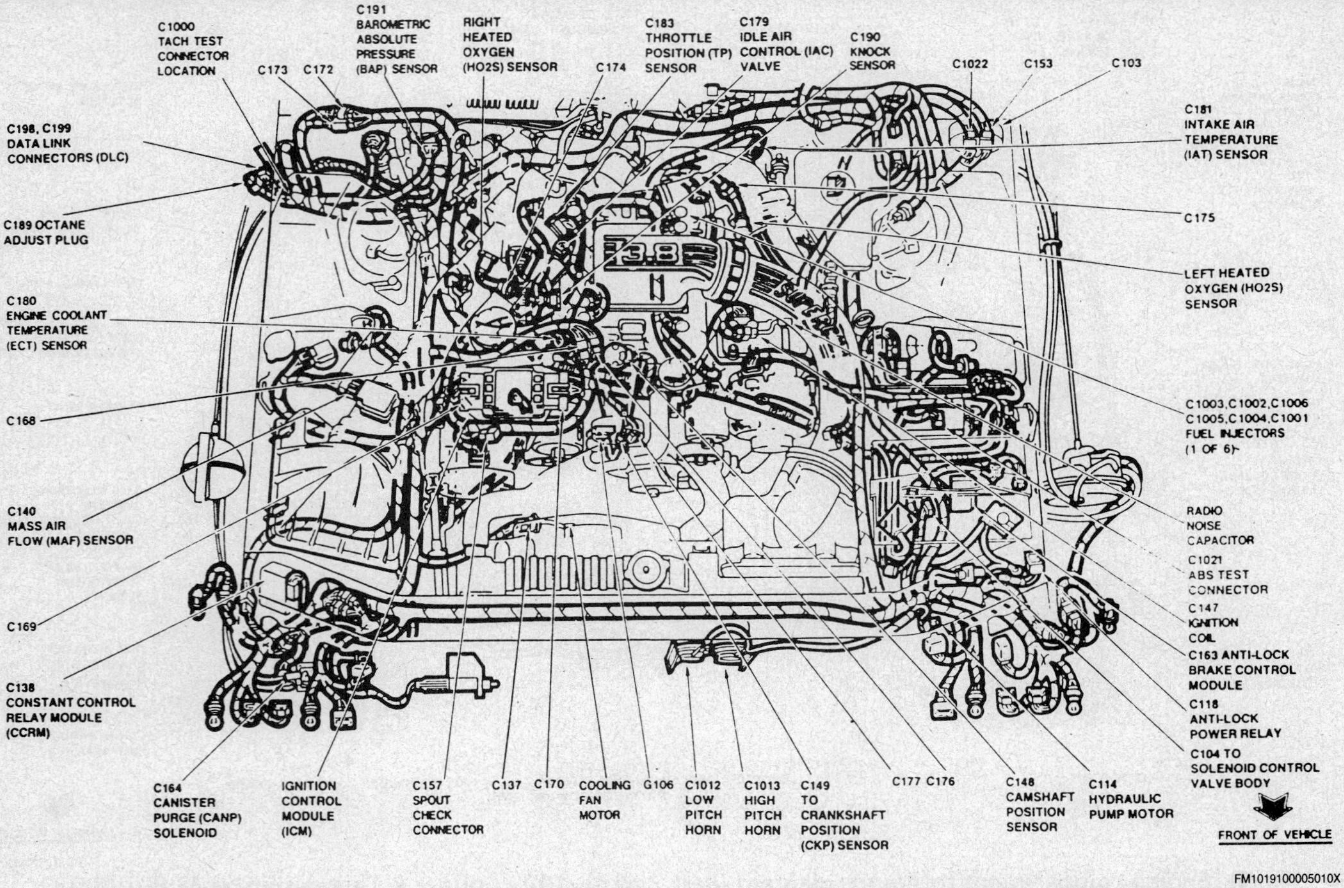

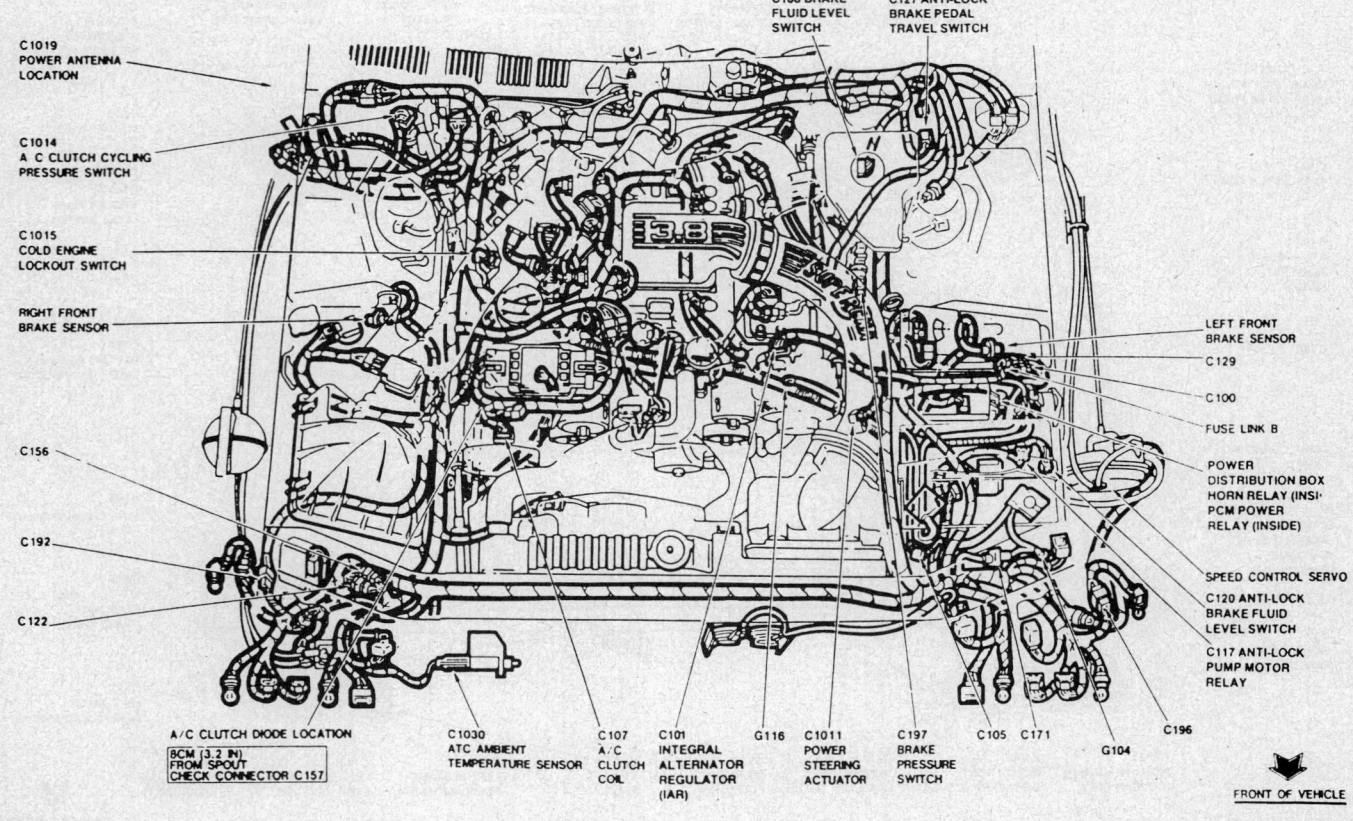

Fig. 8   Engine compartment reference diagram (Part 1 of 3). 1993 Thunderbird w/3.8L/V6-232 SC

Fig. 8   Engine compartment reference diagram (Part 2 of 3). 1993 Thunderbird w/3.8L/V6-232 SC

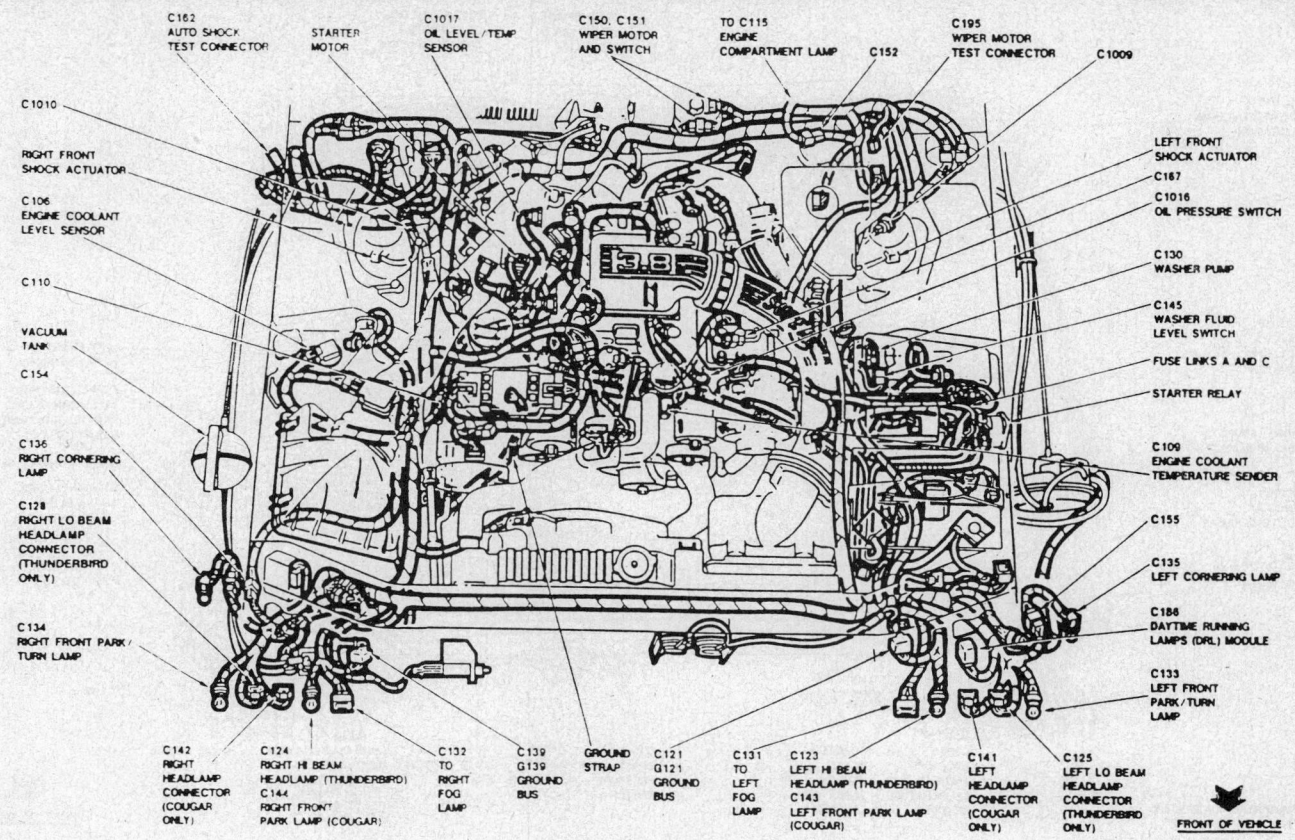

Fig. 8 Engine compartment reference diagram (Part 3 of 3). 1993 Thunderbird w/3.8L/V6-232 SC

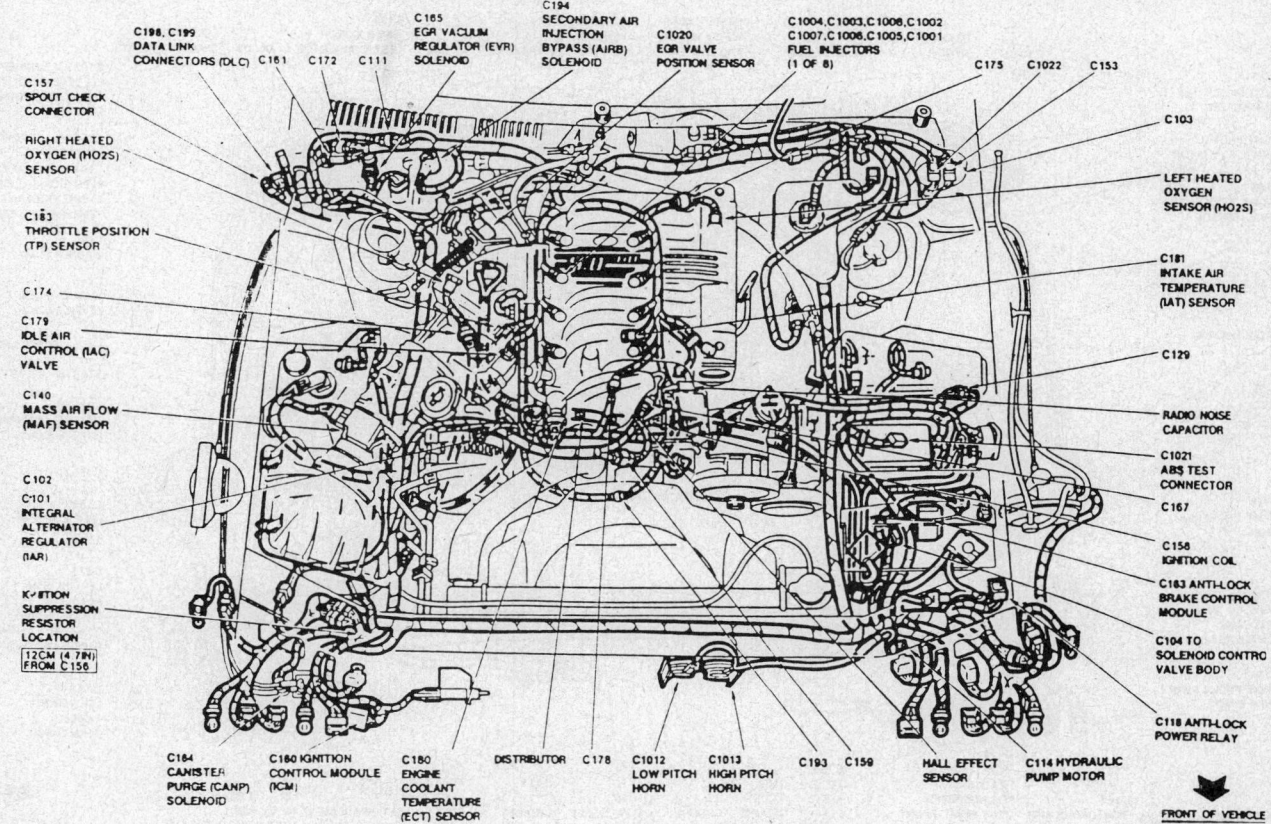

Fig. 9 Engine compartment reference diagram (Part 1 of 3). 1993 Cougar & Thunderbird w/5.0L/V8-302

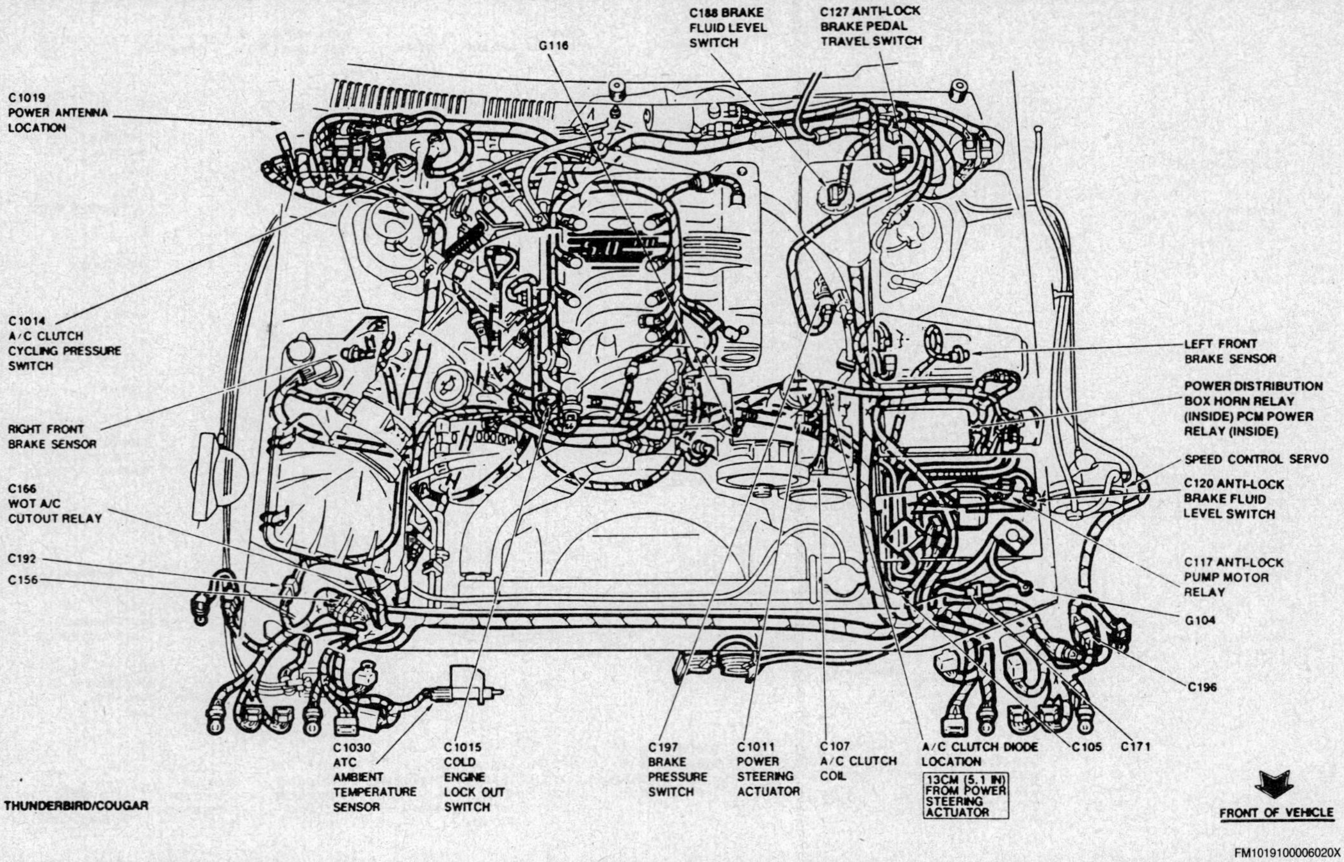

Fig. 9 Engine compartment reference diagram (Part 2 of 3). 1993 Cougar & Thunderbird w/5.0L/V8-302

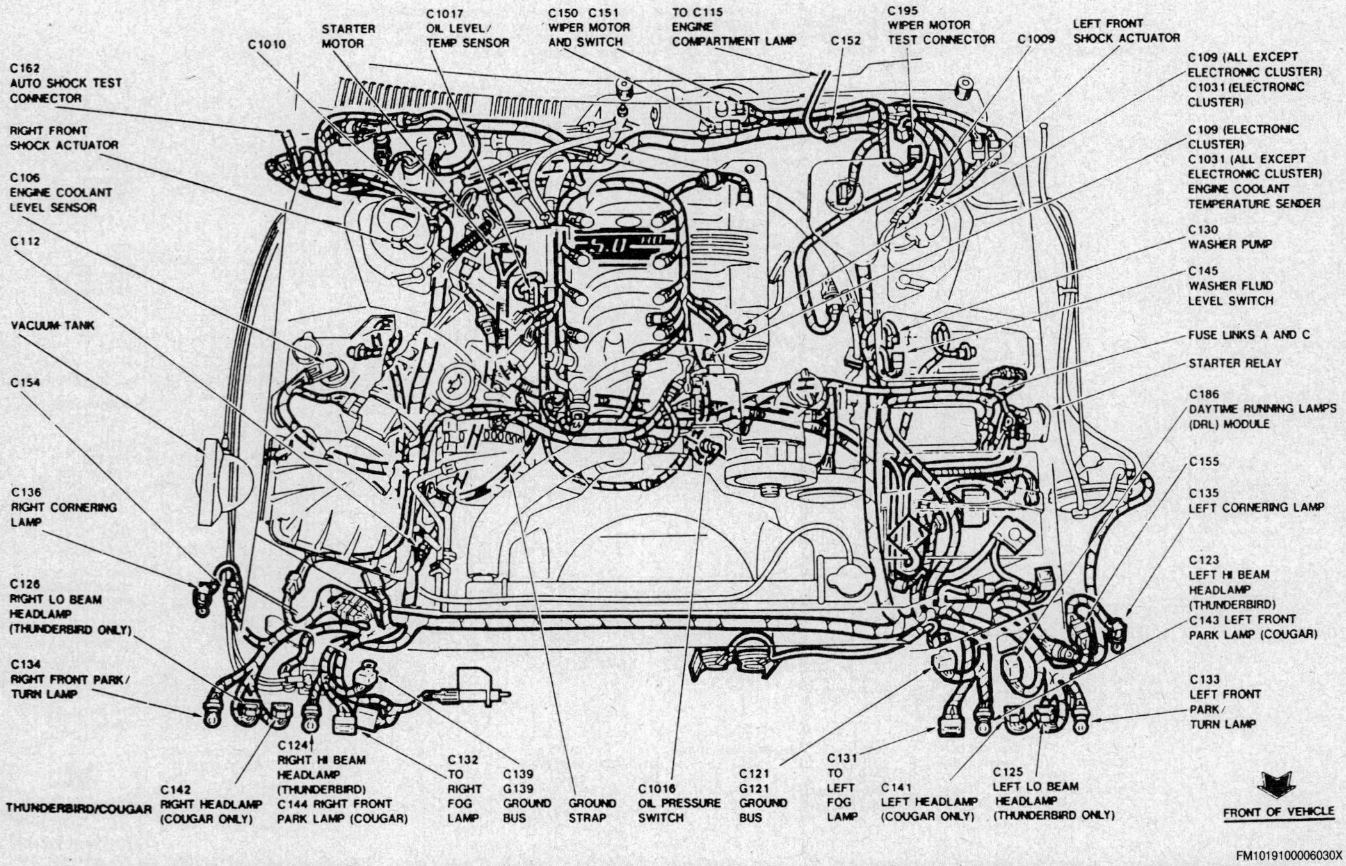

Fig. 9 Engine compartment reference diagram (Part 3 of 3). 1993 Cougar & Thunderbird w/5.0L/V8-302

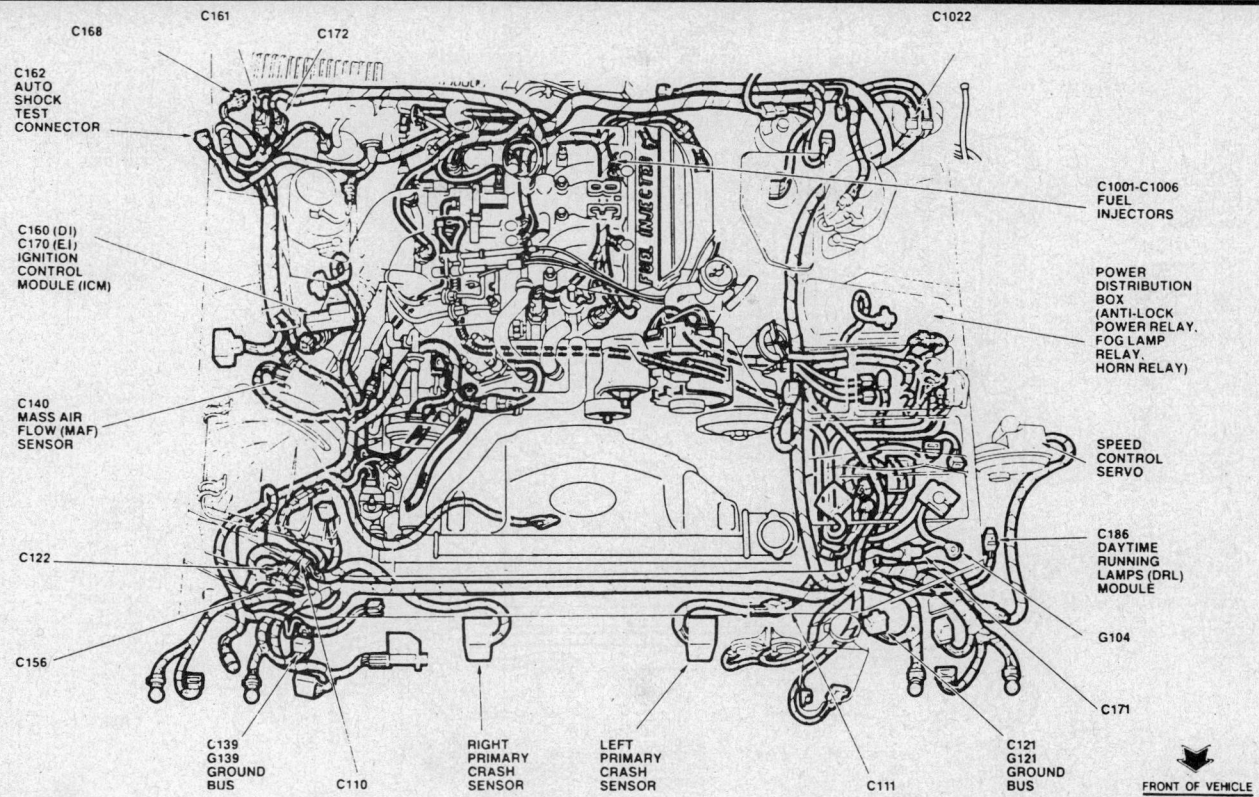

Fig. 10   Engine compartment reference diagram (Part 1 of 4). 1994–95 Cougar & Thunderbird w/3.8L/V6-232

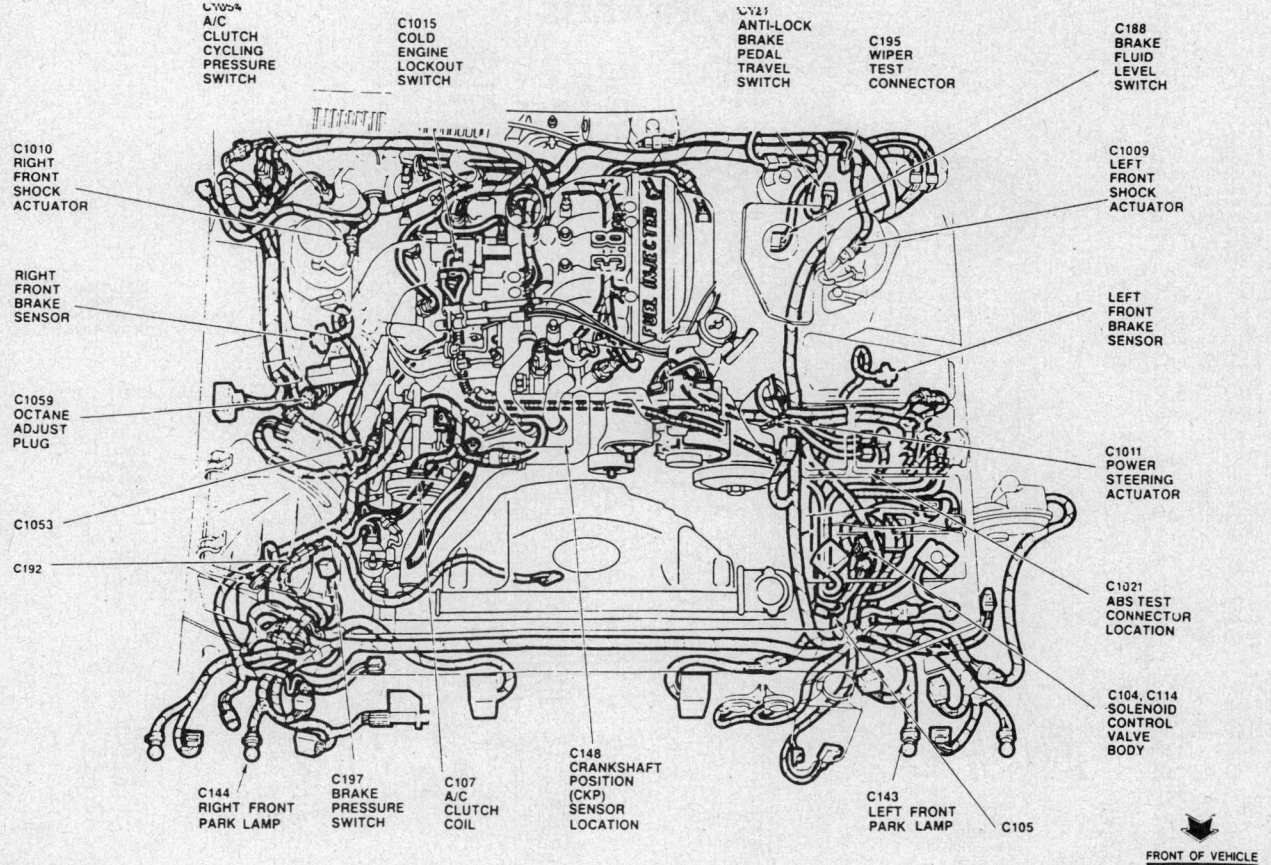

Fig. 10   Engine compartment reference diagram (Part 2 of 4). 1994–95 Cougar & Thunderbird w/3.8L/V6-232

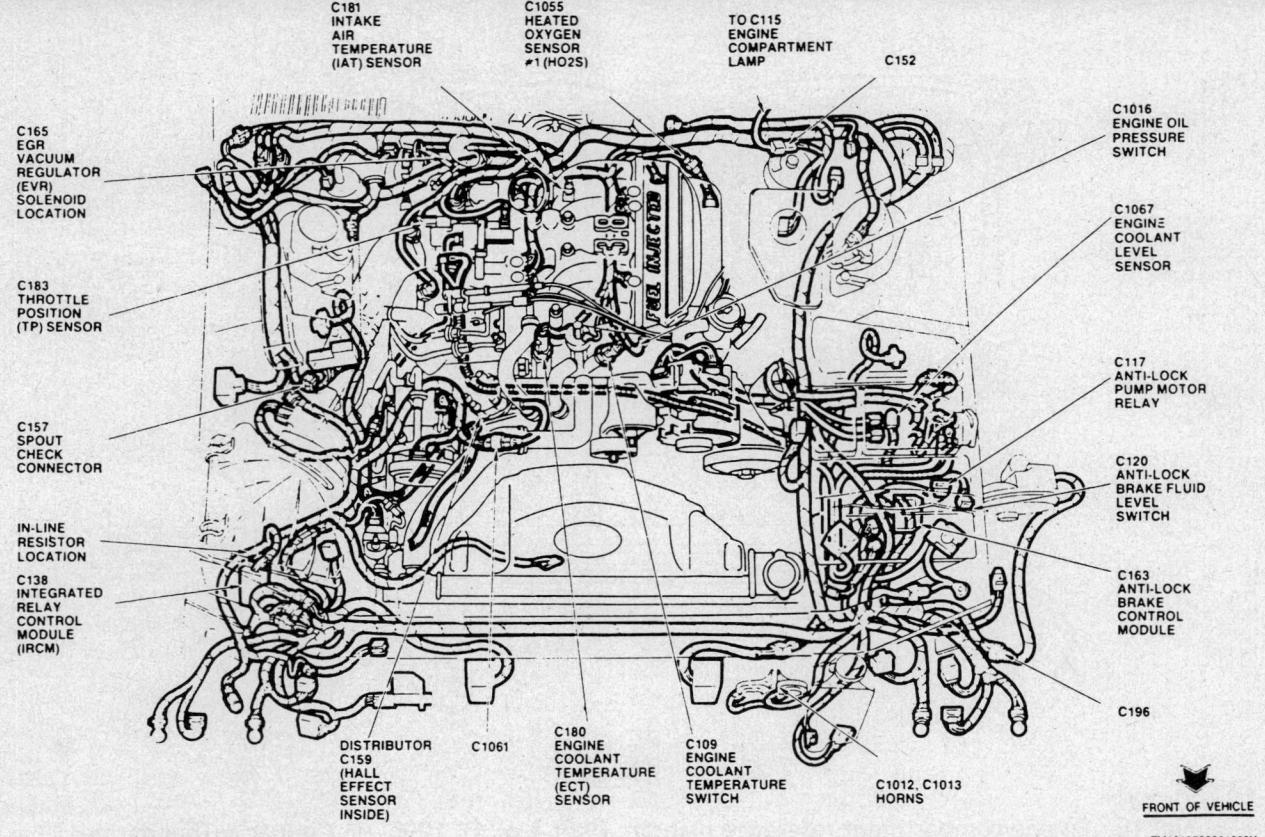

Fig. 10 Engine compartment reference diagram (Part 3 of 4). 1994–95 Cougar & Thunderbird w/3.8L/V6-232

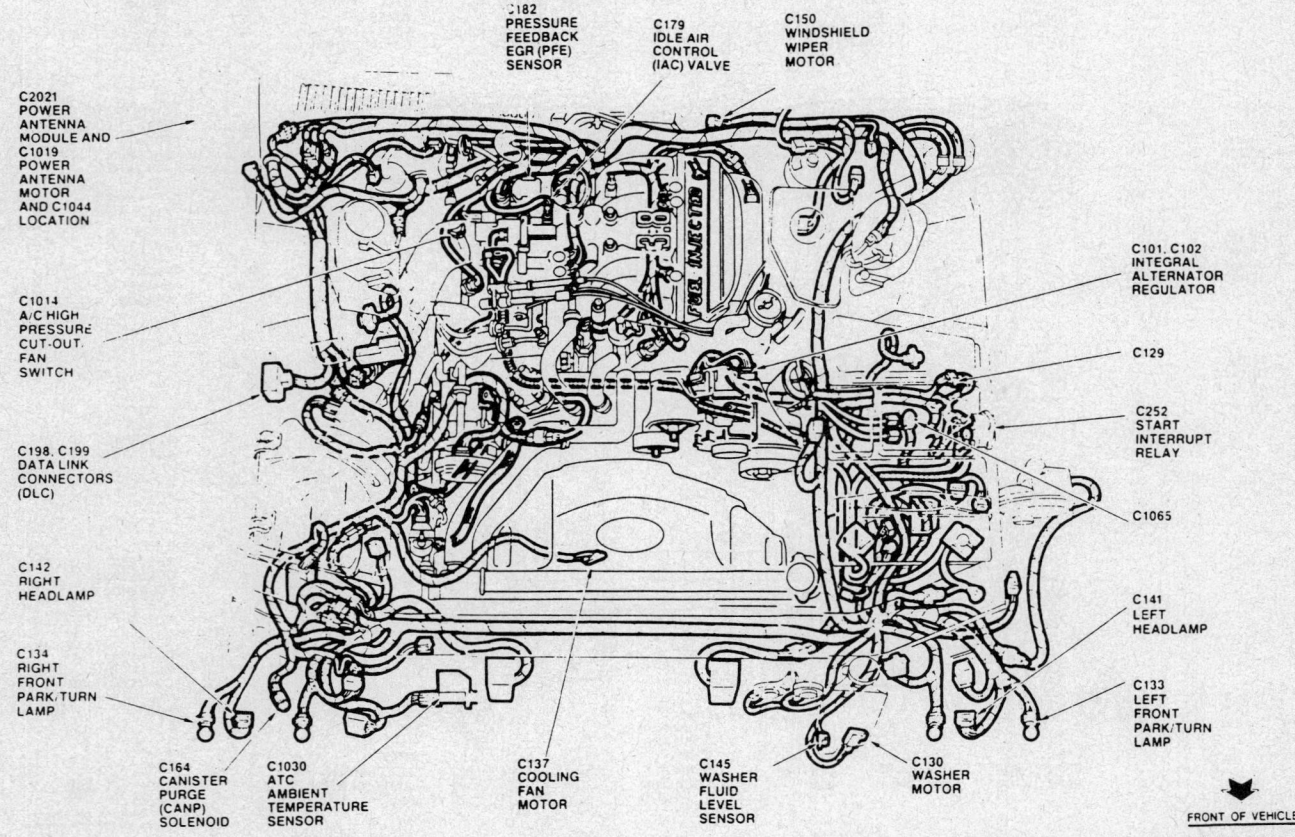

Fig. 10 Engine compartment reference diagram (Part 4 of 4). 1994–95 Cougar & Thunderbird w/3.8L/V6-232

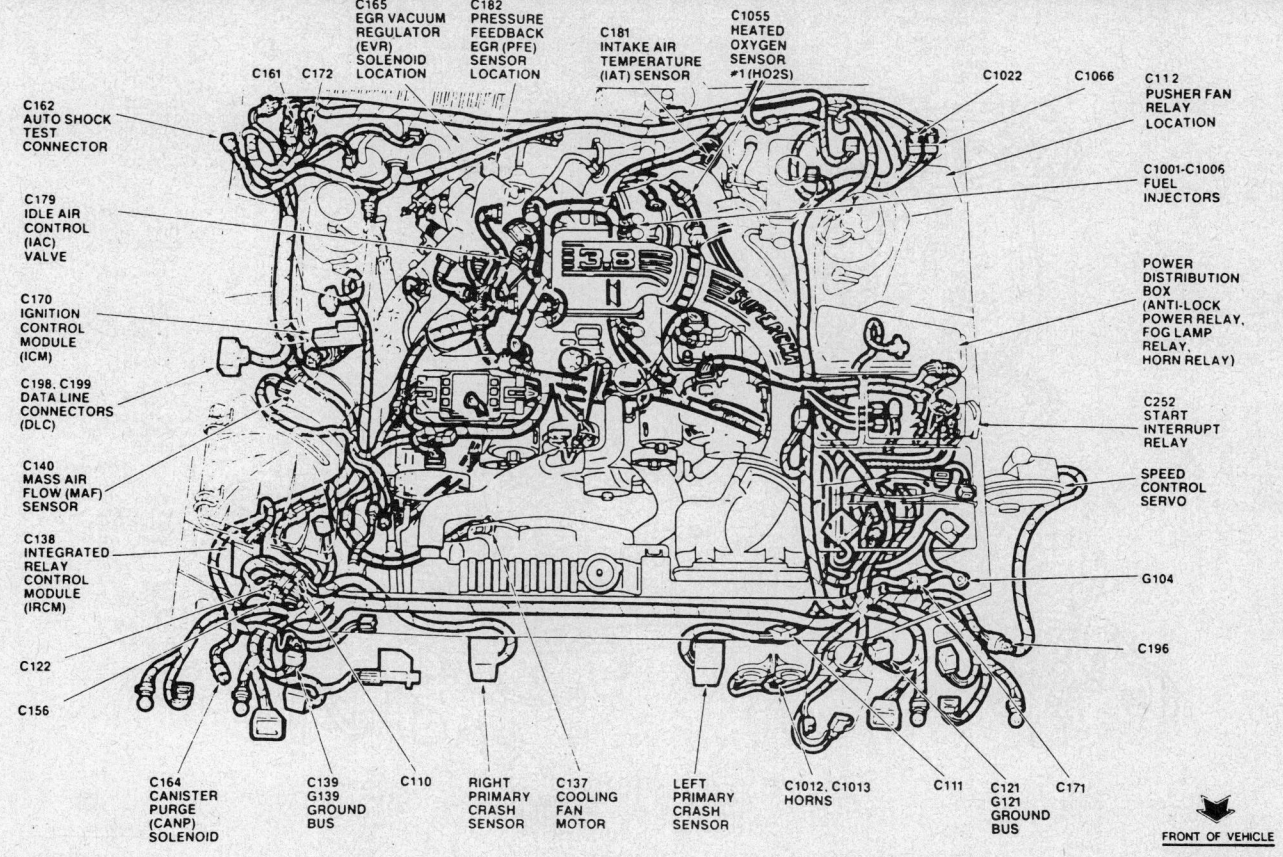

Fig. 11   Engine compartment reference diagram (Part 1 of 3). 1994–95 Thunderbird w/3.8L/V6-232 SC

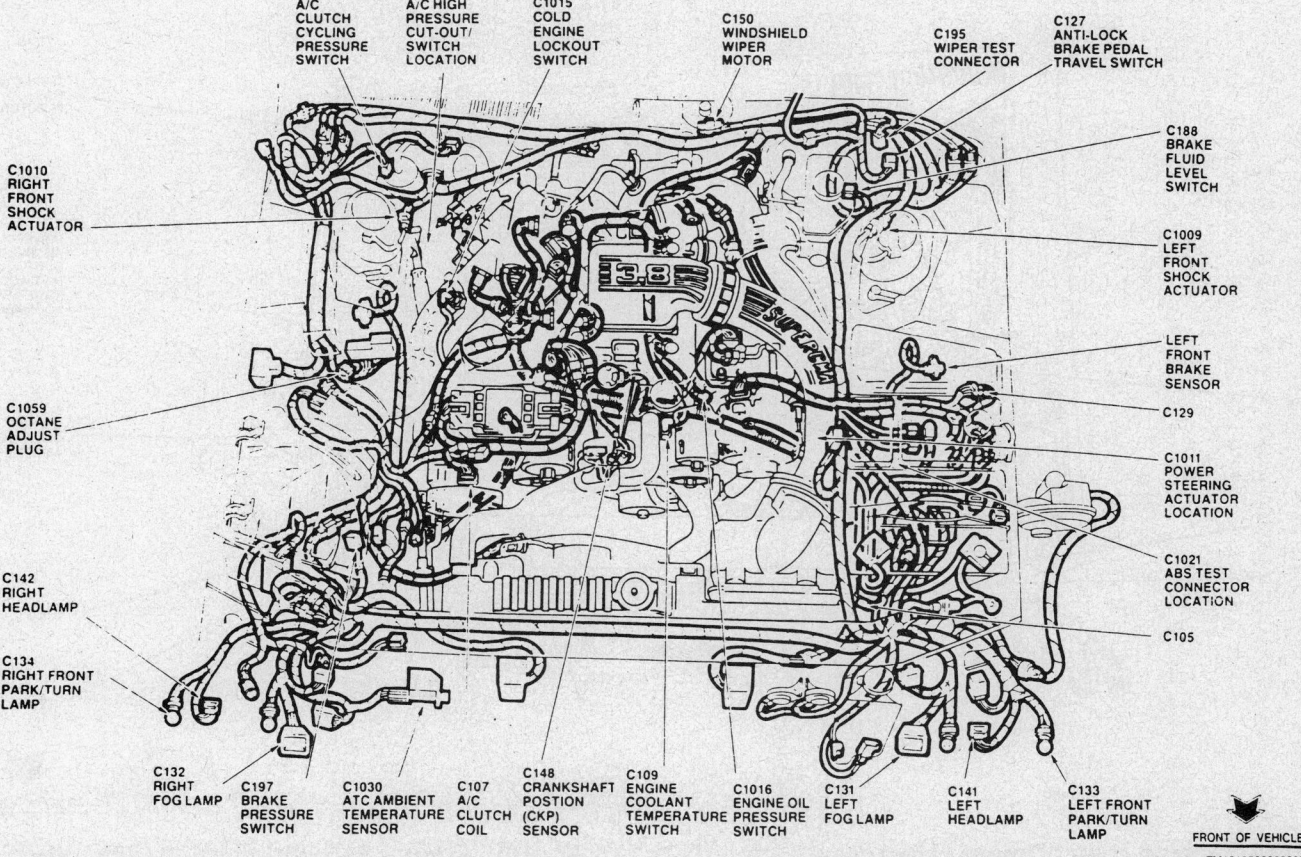

Fig. 11   Engine compartment reference diagram (Part 2 of 3). 1994–95 Thunderbird w/3.8L/V6-232 SC

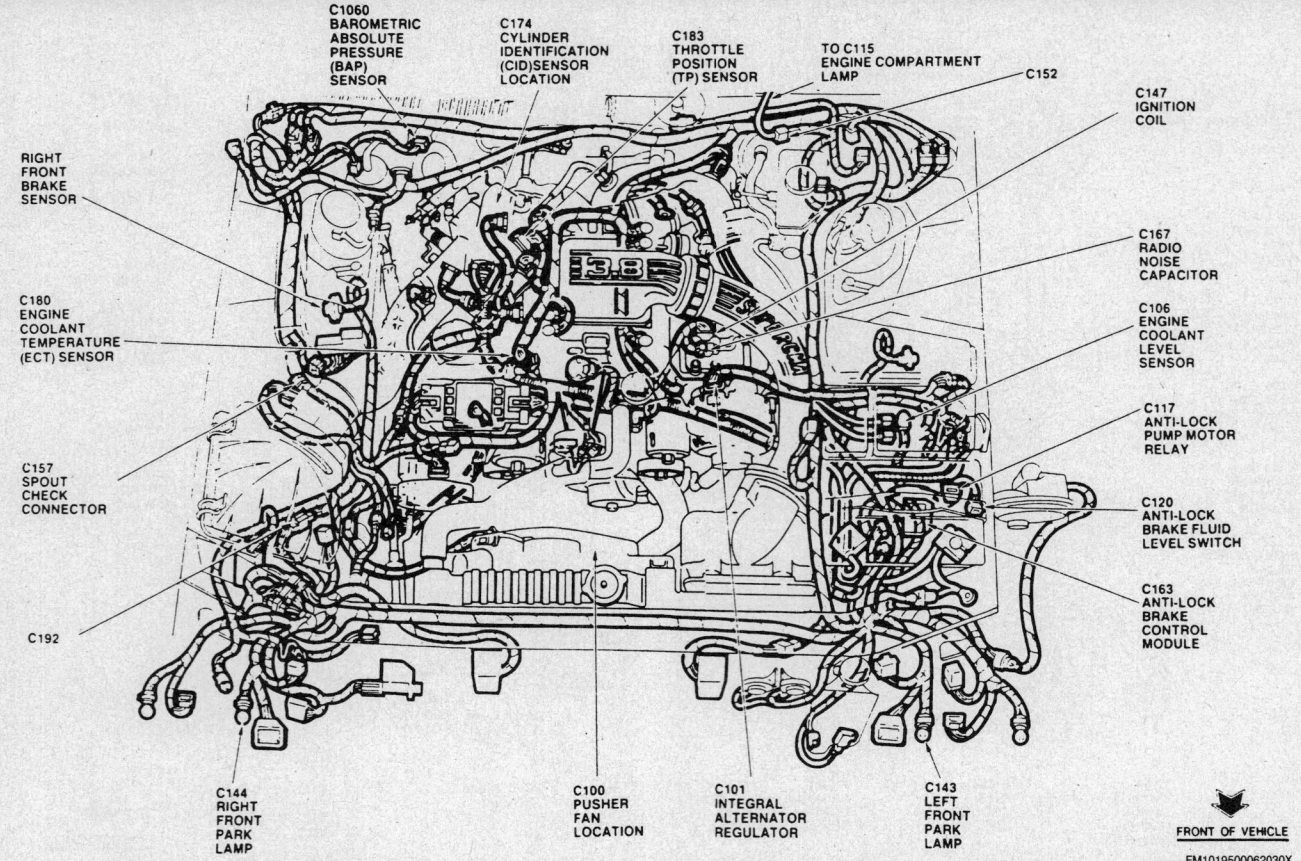

C1060
BAROMETRIC
ABSOLUTE
PRESSURE
(BAP)
SENSOR

C174
CYLINDER
IDENTIFICATION
(CID)SENSOR
LOCATION

C183
THROTTLE
POSITION
(TP) SENSOR

TO C115
ENGINE COMPARTMENT
LAMP

C152

C147
IGNITION
COIL

RIGHT
FRONT
BRAKE
SENSOR

C167
RADIO
NOISE
CAPACITOR

C106
ENGINE
COOLANT
LEVEL
SENSOR

C180
ENGINE
COOLANT
TEMPERATURE
(ECT) SENSOR

C117
ANTI-LOCK
PUMP MOTOR
RELAY

C157
SPOUT
CHECK
CONNECTOR

C120
ANTI-LOCK
BRAKE FLUID
LEVEL SWITCH

C163
ANTI-LOCK
BRAKE
CONTROL
MODULE

C192

C144
RIGHT
FRONT
PARK
LAMP

C100
PUSHER
FAN
LOCATION

C101
INTEGRAL
ALTERNATOR
REGULATOR

C143
LEFT
FRONT
PARK
LAMP

FRONT OF VEHICLE

FM1019500062030X

Fig. 11   Engine compartment reference diagram (Part 3 of 3). 1994–95 Thunderbird w/3.8L/V6-232 SC

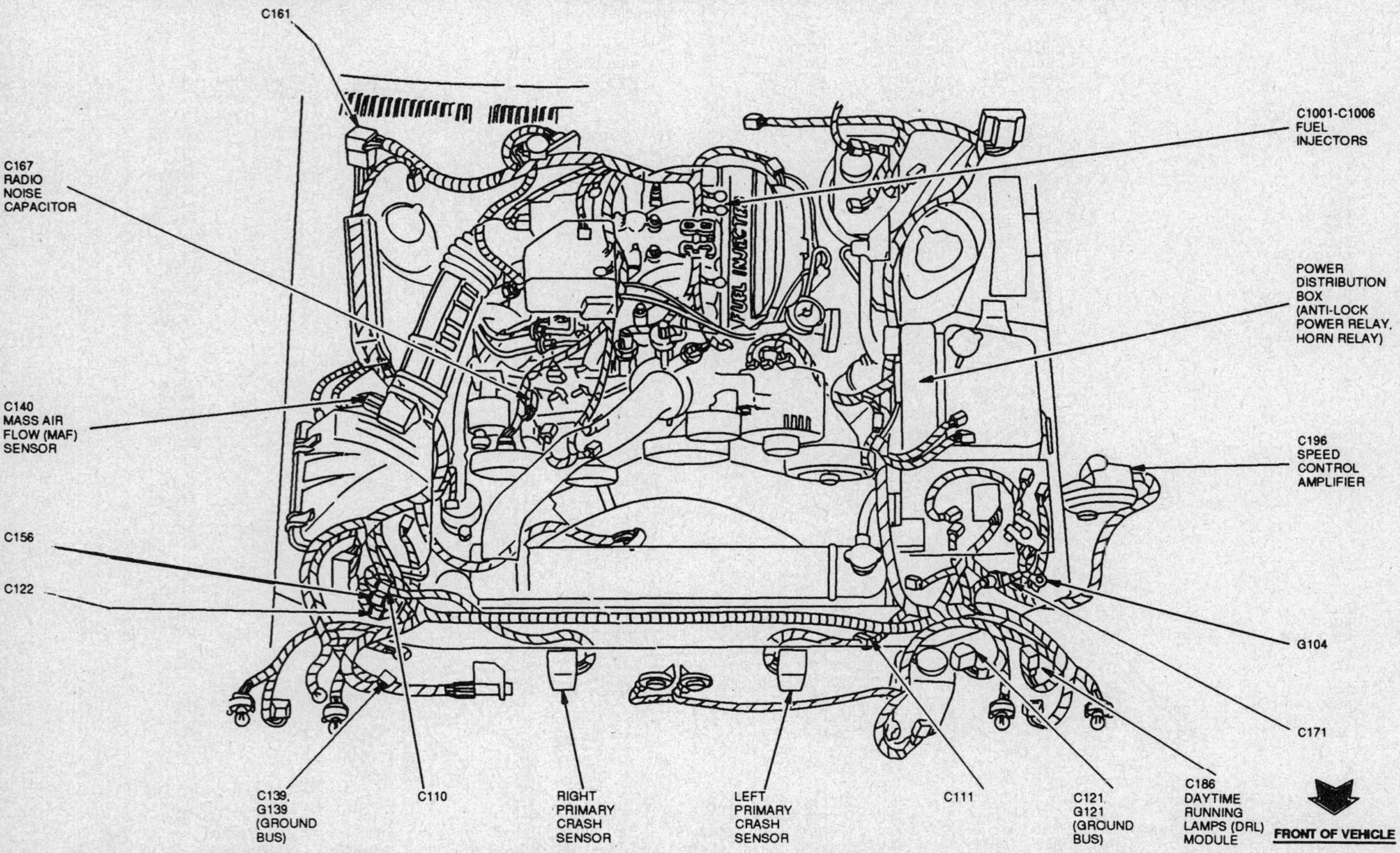

C161

C167
RADIO
NOISE
CAPACITOR

C1001-C1006
FUEL
INJECTORS

POWER
DISTRIBUTION
BOX
(ANTI-LOCK
POWER RELAY,
HORN RELAY)

C140
MASS AIR
FLOW (MAF)
SENSOR

C196
SPEED
CONTROL
AMPLIFIER

C156

C122

G104

C171

C139,
G139
(GROUND
BUS)

C110

RIGHT
PRIMARY
CRASH
SENSOR

LEFT
PRIMARY
CRASH
SENSOR

C111

C121,
G121
(GROUND
BUS)

C186
DAYTIME
RUNNING
LAMPS (DRL)
MODULE

FRONT OF VEHICLE

**Fig. 12   Engine compartment reference diagram (Part 1 of 4). 1996 Cougar & Thunderbird w/3.8L/V6-232
engine**

C147 IGNITION COIL

C148 CRANKSHAFT POSITION SENSOR (CKP)

C1059 OCTANE ADJUST PLUG

C192 TO RIGHT FRONT BRAKE SENSOR

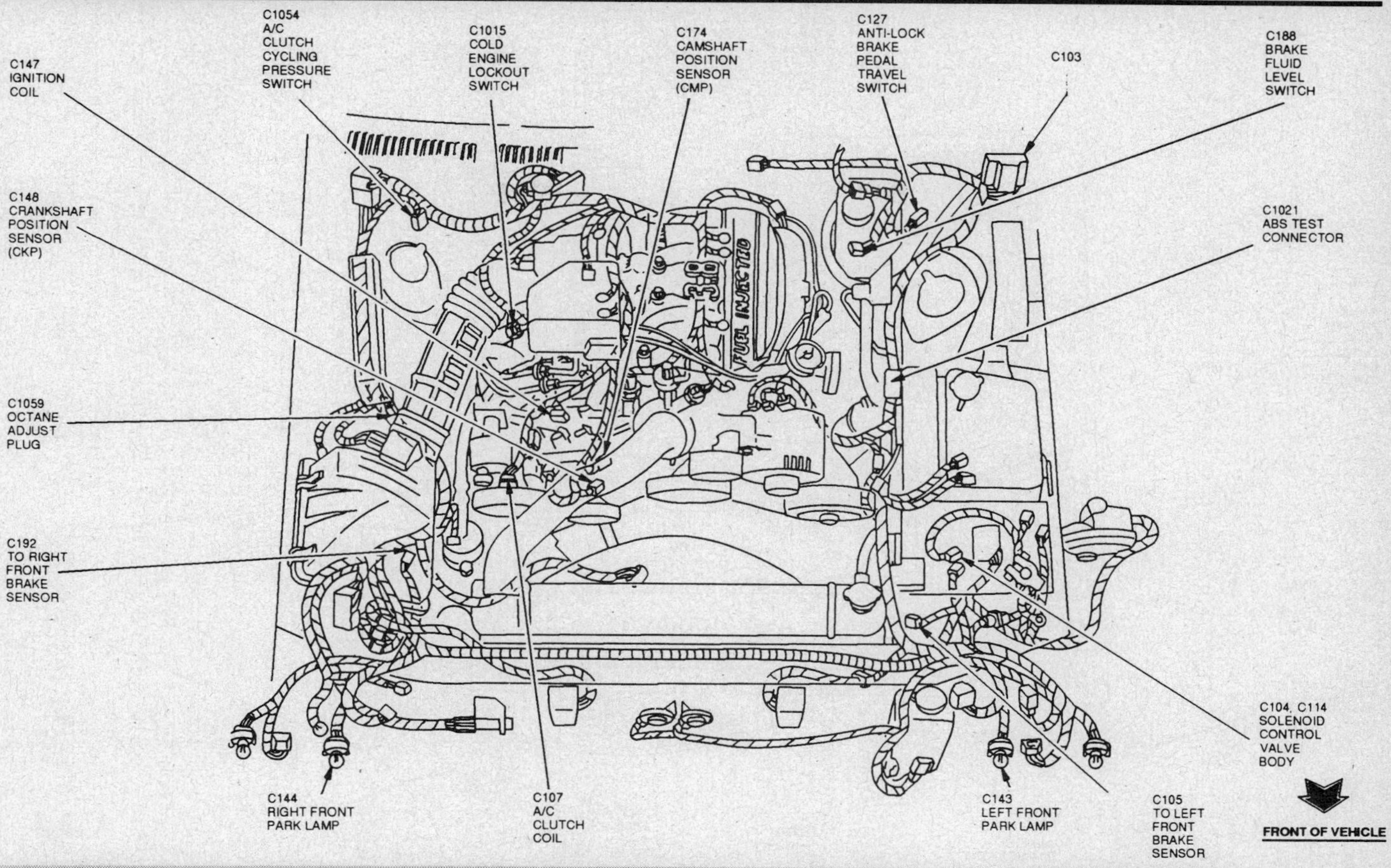

C1054 A/C CLUTCH CYCLING PRESSURE SWITCH

C1015 COLD ENGINE LOCKOUT SWITCH

C174 CAMSHAFT POSITION SENSOR (CMP)

C127 ANTI-LOCK BRAKE PEDAL TRAVEL SWITCH

C103

C188 BRAKE FLUID LEVEL SWITCH

C1021 ABS TEST CONNECTOR

C104, C114 SOLENOID CONTROL VALVE BODY

C144 RIGHT FRONT PARK LAMP

C107 A/C CLUTCH COIL

C143 LEFT FRONT PARK LAMP

C105 TO LEFT FRONT BRAKE SENSOR

FRONT OF VEHICLE

Fig. 12 Engine compartment reference diagram (Part 2 of 4). 1996 Cougar & Thunderbird w/3.8L/V6-232 engine

C165 EGR VACUUM REGULATOR (EVR) SOLENOID

C183 THROTTLE POSITION (TP) SENSOR

C116 INTAKE AIR TEMPERATURE (IAT) SENSOR

C128 TO HEATED OXYGEN SENSOR #1 (HO2S)

C138 CONSTANT CONTROL RELAY MODULE (CCRM)

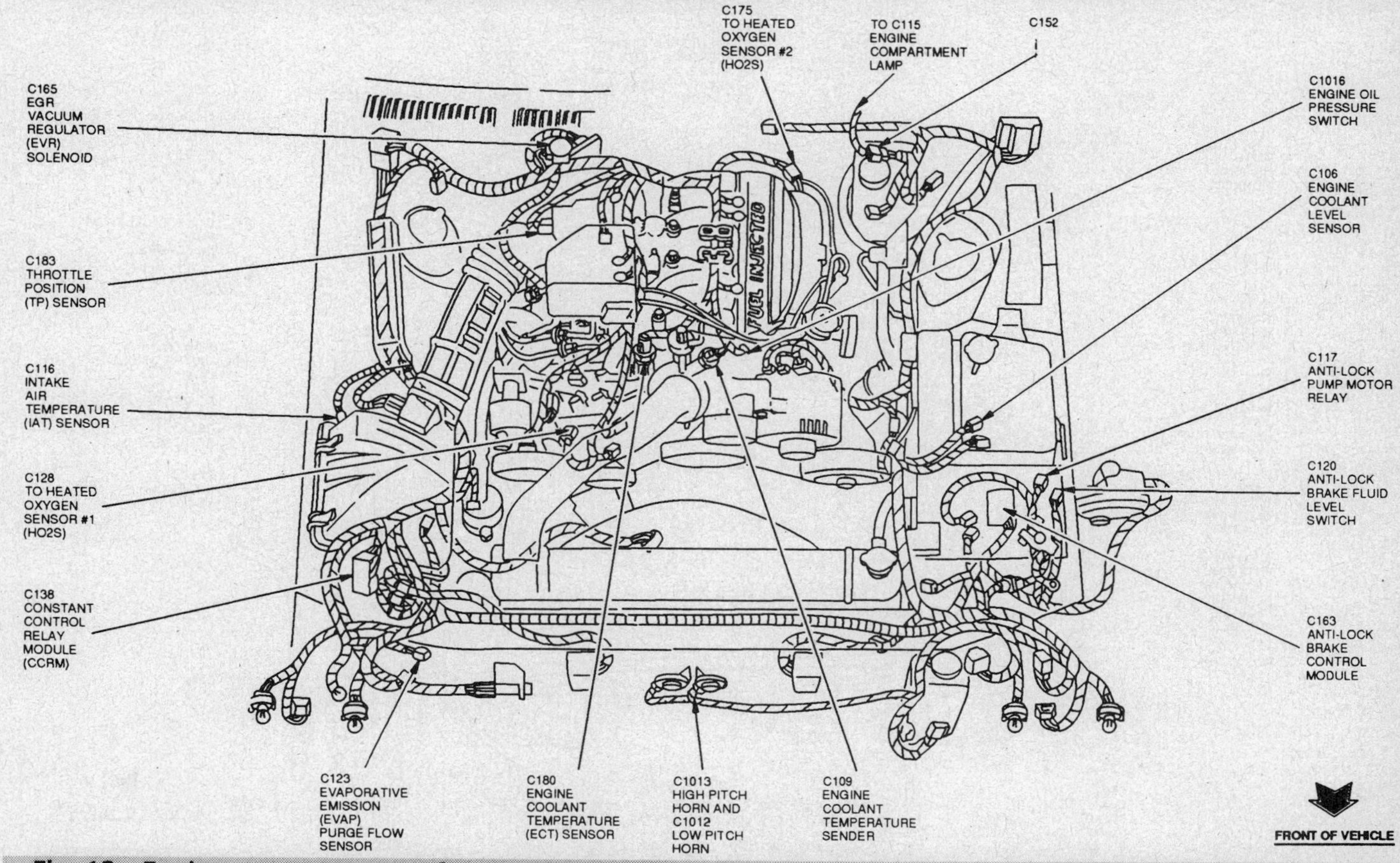

C175 TO HEATED OXYGEN SENSOR #2 (HO2S)

TO C115 ENGINE COMPARTMENT LAMP

C152

C1016 ENGINE OIL PRESSURE SWITCH

C106 ENGINE COOLANT LEVEL SENSOR

C117 ANTI-LOCK PUMP MOTOR RELAY

C120 ANTI-LOCK BRAKE FLUID LEVEL SWITCH

C163 ANTI-LOCK BRAKE CONTROL MODULE

C123 EVAPORATIVE EMISSION (EVAP) PURGE FLOW SENSOR

C180 ENGINE COOLANT TEMPERATURE (ECT) SENSOR

C1013 HIGH PITCH HORN AND **C1012** LOW PITCH HORN

C109 ENGINE COOLANT TEMPERATURE SENDER

FRONT OF VEHICLE

Fig. 12 Engine compartment reference diagram (Part 3 of 4). 1996 Cougar & Thunderbird w/3.8L/V6-232 engine

ENGINE COMPARTMENT REFERENCE DIAGRAMS

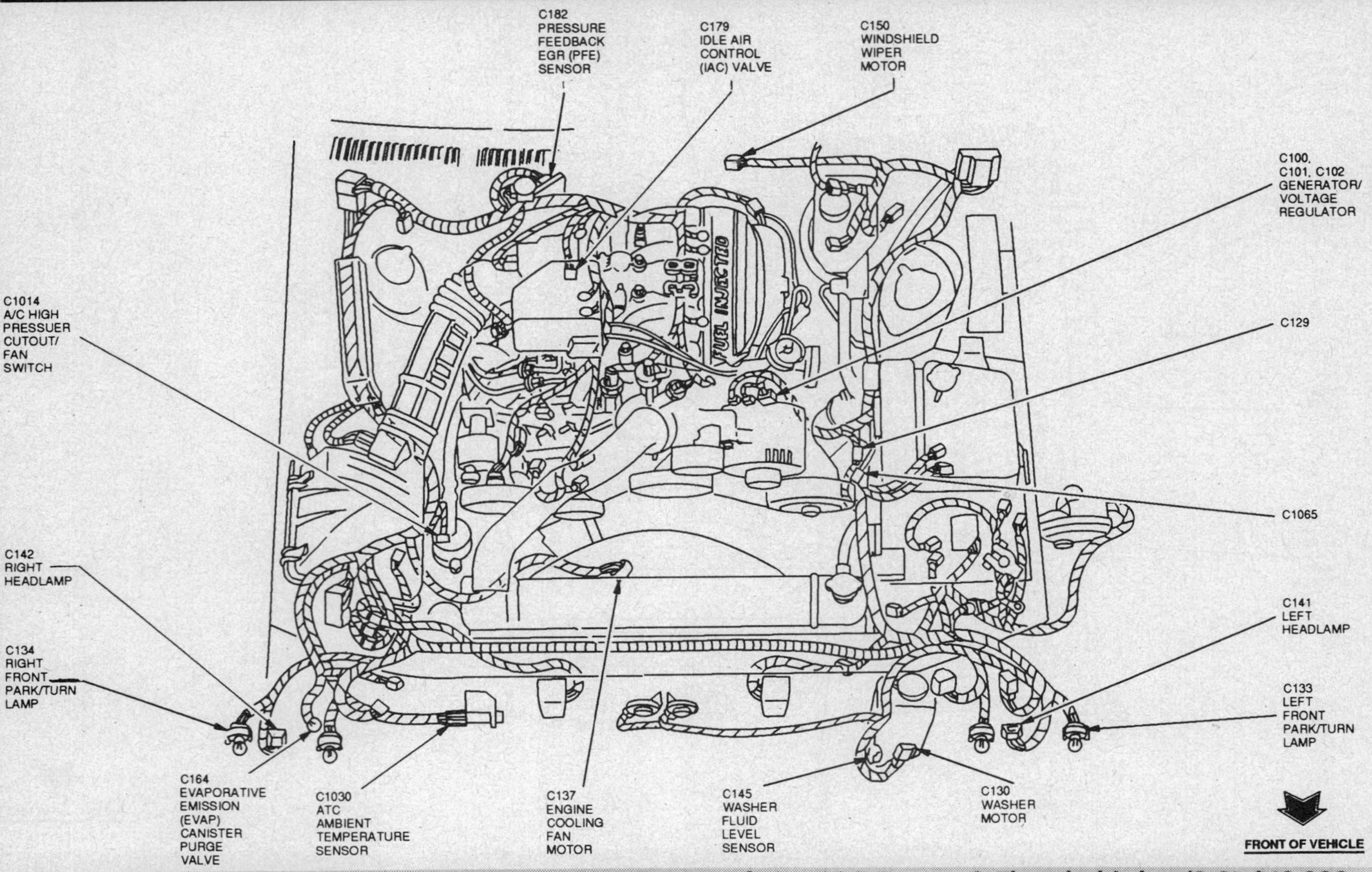

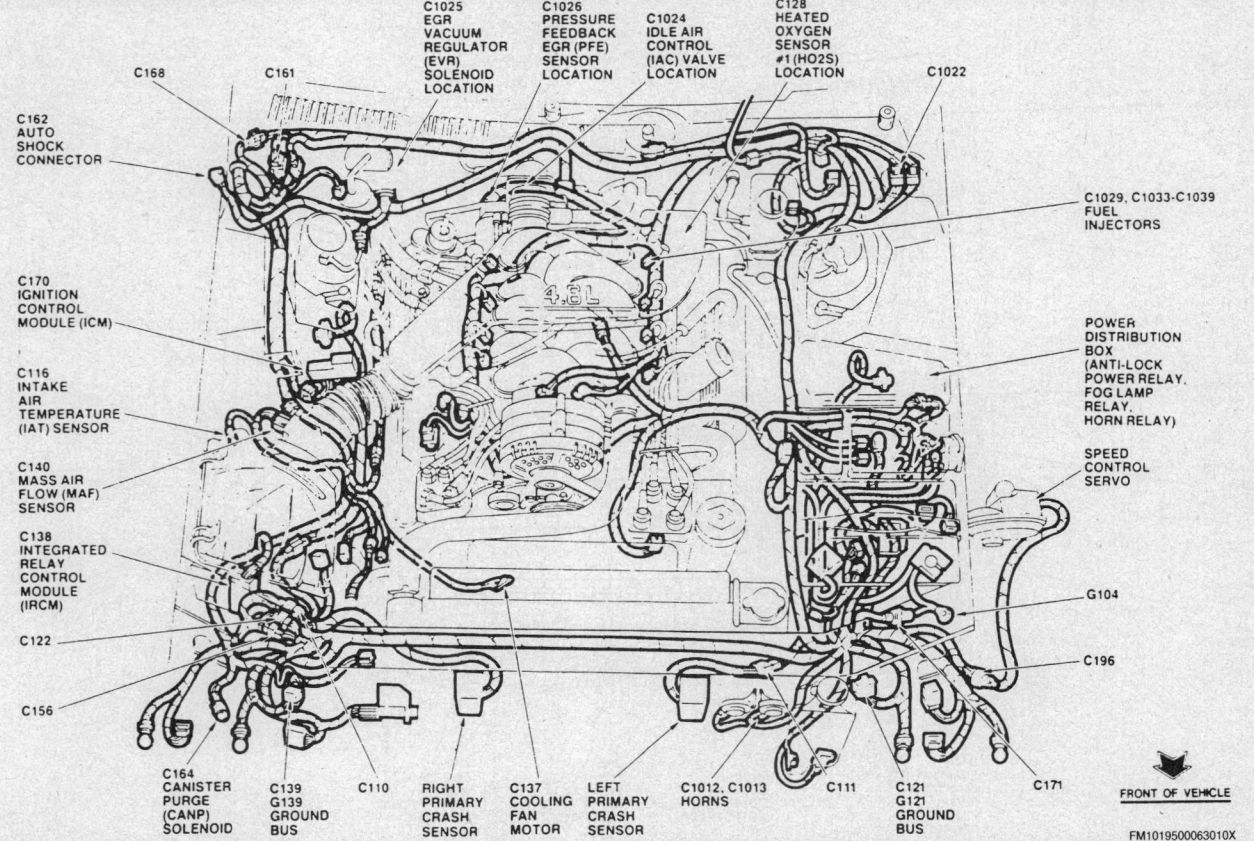

C182
PRESSURE
FEEDBACK
EGR (PFE)
SENSOR

C179
IDLE AIR
CONTROL
(IAC) VALVE

C150
WINDSHIELD
WIPER
MOTOR

C100,
C101, C102
GENERATOR/
VOLTAGE
REGULATOR

C1014
A/C HIGH
PRESSUER
CUTOUT/
FAN
SWITCH

C129

C1065

C142
RIGHT
HEADLAMP

C141
LEFT
HEADLAMP

C134
RIGHT
FRONT
PARK/TURN
LAMP

C133
LEFT
FRONT
PARK/TURN
LAMP

C164
EVAPORATIVE
EMISSION
(EVAP)
CANISTER
PURGE
VALVE

C1030
ATC
AMBIENT
TEMPERATURE
SENSOR

C137
ENGINE
COOLING
FAN
MOTOR

C145
WASHER
FLUID
LEVEL
SENSOR

C130
WASHER
MOTOR

FRONT OF VEHICLE

Fig. 12   Engine compartment reference diagram (Part 4 of 4). 1996 Cougar & Thunderbird w/3.8L/V6-232 engine

C1025
EGR
VACUUM
REGULATOR
(EVR)
SOLENOID
LOCATION

C1026
PRESSURE
FEEDBACK
EGR (PFE)
SENSOR
LOCATION

C1024
IDLE AIR
CONTROL
(IAC) VALVE
LOCATION

C128
HEATED
OXYGEN
SENSOR
#1 (HO2S)
LOCATION

C168   C161   C1022

C162
AUTO
SHOCK
CONNECTOR

C1029, C1033-C1039
FUEL
INJECTORS

C170
IGNITION
CONTROL
MODULE (ICM)

C116
INTAKE
AIR
TEMPERATURE
(IAT) SENSOR

POWER
DISTRIBUTION
BOX
(ANTI-LOCK
POWER RELAY,
FOG LAMP
RELAY,
HORN RELAY)

C140
MASS AIR
FLOW (MAF)
SENSOR

SPEED
CONTROL
SERVO

C138
INTEGRATED
RELAY
CONTROL
MODULE
(IRCM)

G104

C122

C196

C156

C164
CANISTER
PURGE
(CANP)
SOLENOID

C139
G139
GROUND
BUS

C110

RIGHT
PRIMARY
CRASH
SENSOR

C137
COOLING
FAN
MOTOR

LEFT
PRIMARY
CRASH
SENSOR

C1012, C1013
HORNS

C111

C121
G121
GROUND
BUS

C171

FRONT OF VEHICLE

FM1019500063010X

Fig. 13   Engine compartment reference diagram (Part 1 of 3). 1994–95 Cougar & Thunderbird w/4.6L/V8-281

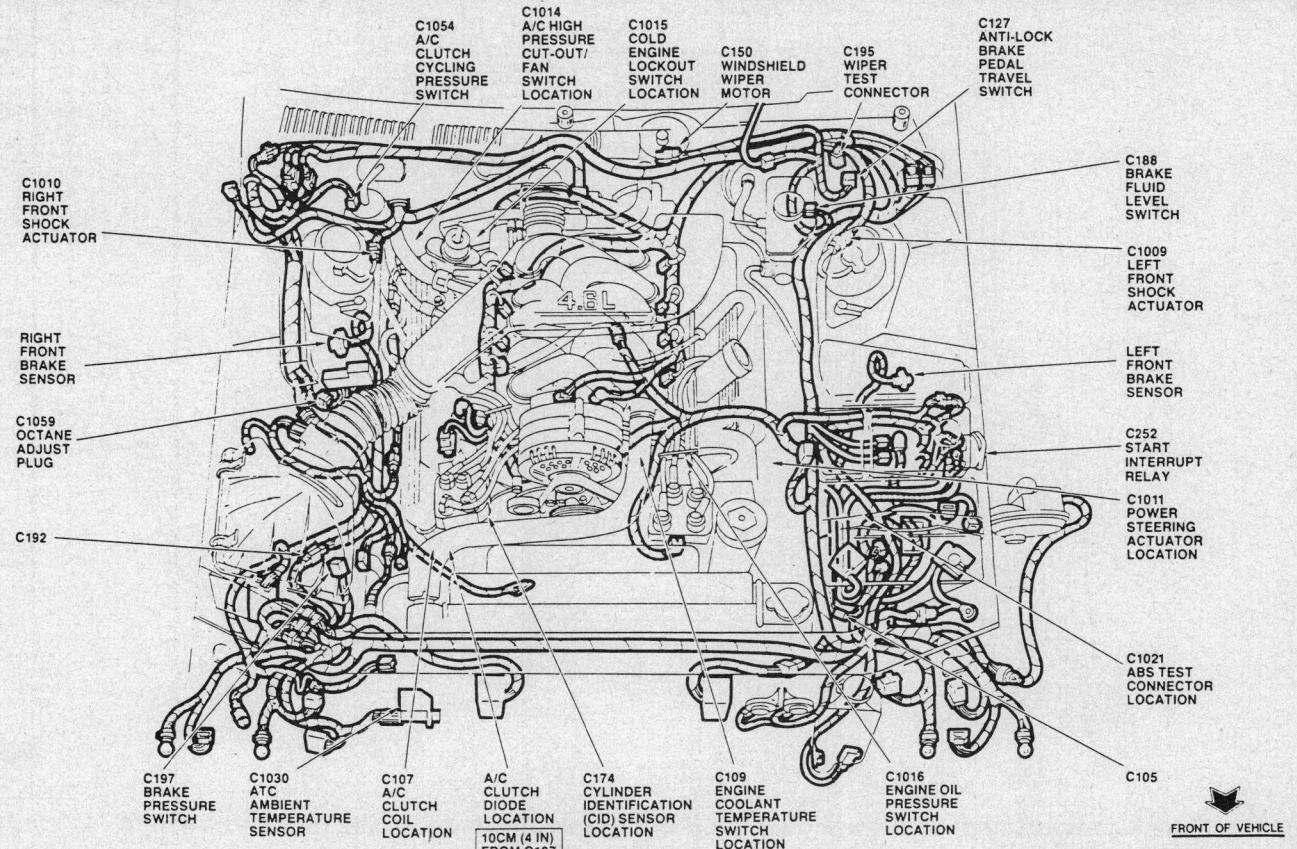

Fig. 13   Engine compartment reference diagram (Part 2 of 3). 1994–95 Cougar & Thunderbird w/4.6L/V8-281

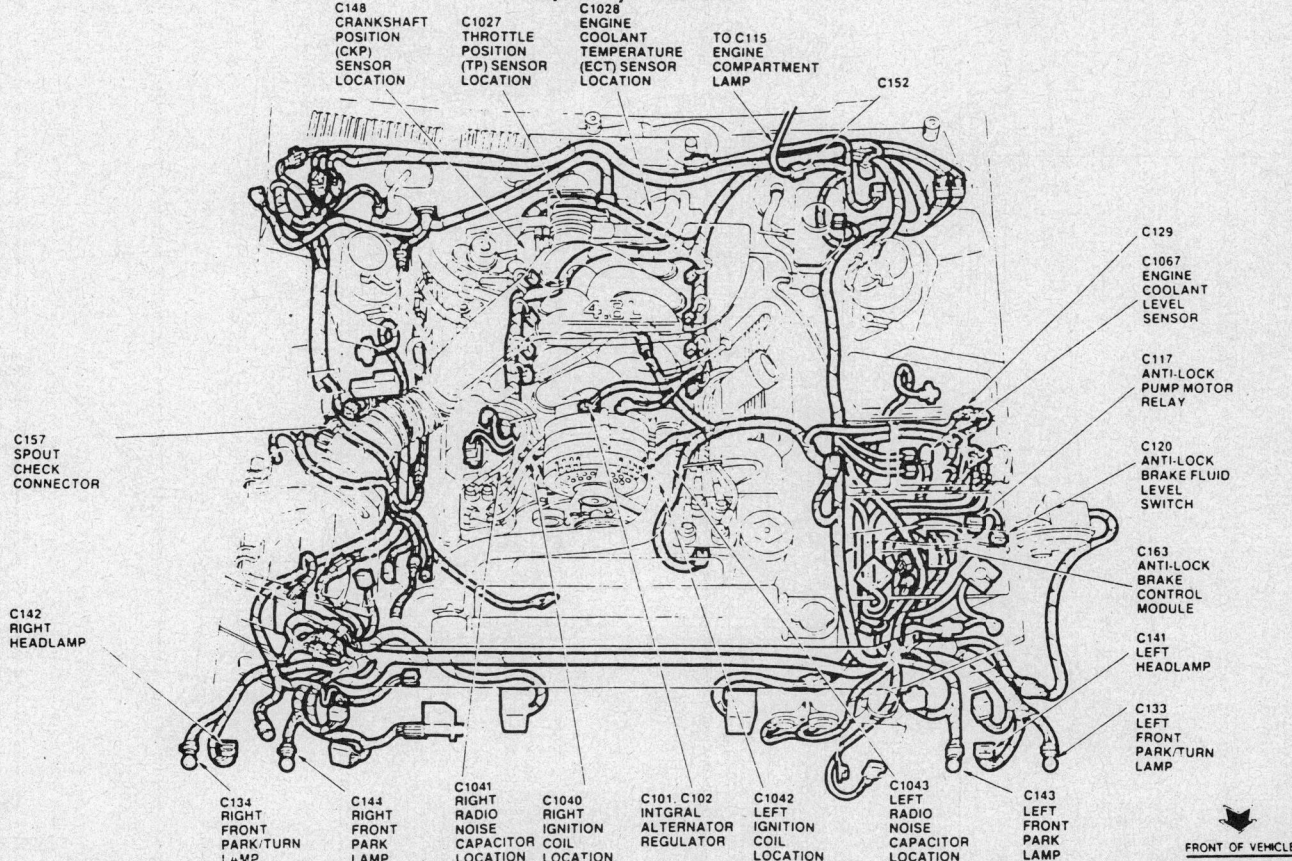

Fig. 13   Engine Compartment reference diagram (Part 3 of 3). 1994-95 Cougar & Thunderbird w/4.6L/V8-281 engine

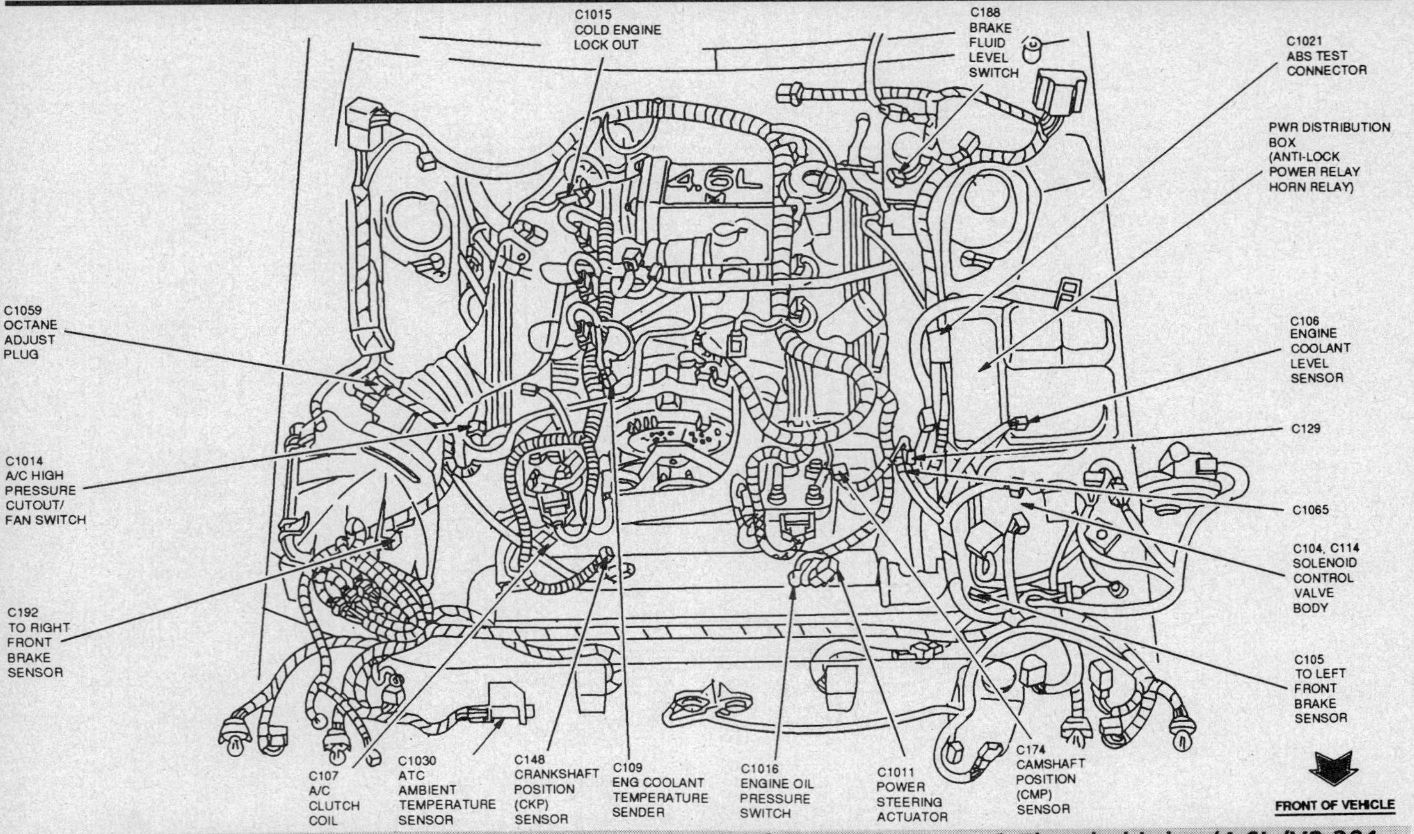

C1015
COLD ENGINE
LOCK OUT

C188
BRAKE
FLUID
LEVEL
SWITCH

C1021
ABS TEST
CONNECTOR

PWR DISTRIBUTION
BOX
(ANTI-LOCK
POWER RELAY
HORN RELAY)

C1059
OCTANE
ADJUST
PLUG

C106
ENGINE
COOLANT
LEVEL
SENSOR

C129

C1014
A/C HIGH
PRESSURE
CUTOUT/
FAN SWITCH

C1065

C104, C114
SOLENOID
CONTROL
VALVE
BODY

C192
TO RIGHT
FRONT
BRAKE
SENSOR

C105
TO LEFT
FRONT
BRAKE
SENSOR

4.6L

C107
A/C
CLUTCH
COIL

C1030
ATC
AMBIENT
TEMPERATURE
SENSOR

C148
CRANKSHAFT
POSITION
(CKP)
SENSOR

C109
ENG COOLANT
TEMPERATURE
SENDER

C1016
ENGINE OIL
PRESSURE
SWITCH

C1011
POWER
STEERING
ACTUATOR

C174
CAMSHAFT
POSITION
(CMP)
SENSOR

FRONT OF VEHICLE

Fig. 14 Engine compartment reference diagram (Part 1 of 3). 1996 Cougar & Thunderbird w/4.6L/V8-281 engine

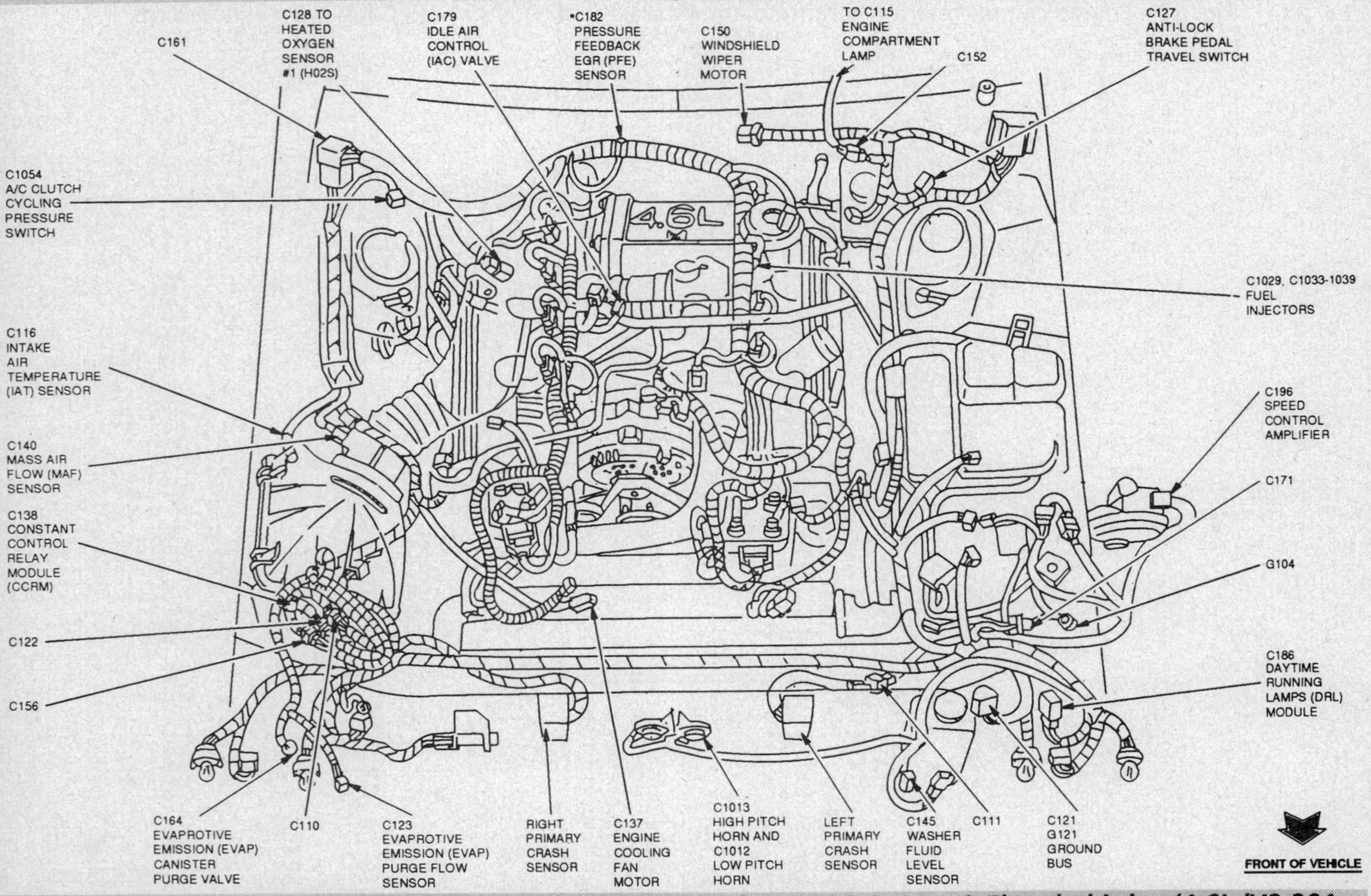

C161

C128 TO
HEATED
OXYGEN
SENSOR
#1 (HO2S)

C179
IDLE AIR
CONTROL
(IAC) VALVE

•C182
PRESSURE
FEEDBACK
EGR (PFE)
SENSOR

C150
WINDSHIELD
WIPER
MOTOR

TO C115
ENGINE
COMPARTMENT
LAMP

C152

C127
ANTI-LOCK
BRAKE PEDAL
TRAVEL SWITCH

C1054
A/C CLUTCH
CYCLING
PRESSURE
SWITCH

4.6L

C1029, C1033-1039
FUEL
INJECTORS

C116
INTAKE
AIR
TEMPERATURE
(IAT) SENSOR

C196
SPEED
CONTROL
AMPLIFIER

C140
MASS AIR
FLOW (MAF)
SENSOR

C171

C138
CONSTANT
CONTROL
RELAY
MODULE
(CCRM)

G104

C122

C186
DAYTIME
RUNNING
LAMPS (DRL)
MODULE

C156

C164
EVAPROTIVE
EMISSION (EVAP)
CANISTER
PURGE VALVE

C110

C123
EVAPROTIVE
EMISSION (EVAP)
PURGE FLOW
SENSOR

RIGHT
PRIMARY
CRASH
SENSOR

C137
ENGINE
COOLING
FAN
MOTOR

C1013
HIGH PITCH
HORN AND
C1012
LOW PITCH
HORN

LEFT
PRIMARY
CRASH
SENSOR

C145
WASHER
FLUID
LEVEL
SENSOR

C111

C121
G121
GROUND
BUS

FRONT OF VEHICLE

Fig. 14 Engine compartment refence diagram (Part 2 of 3). 1996 Cougar & Thunderbird w/4.6L/V8-281 engine

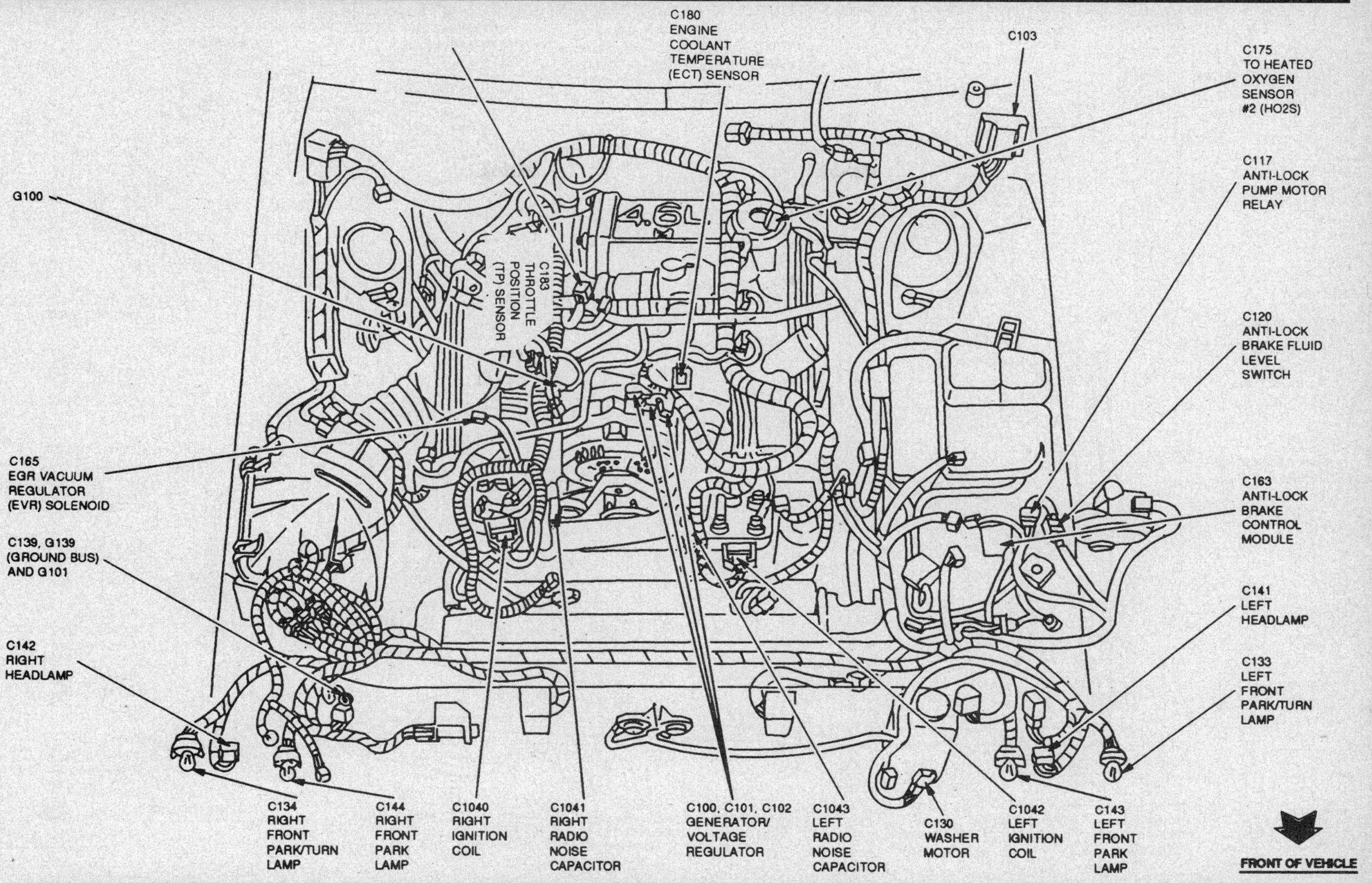

C180
ENGINE
COOLANT
TEMPERATURE
(ECT) SENSOR

C103

C175
TO HEATED
OXYGEN
SENSOR
#2 (HO2S)

C117
ANTI-LOCK
PUMP MOTOR
RELAY

G100

C183
THROTTLE
POSITION
(TP) SENSOR

C120
ANTI-LOCK
BRAKE FLUID
LEVEL
SWITCH

C165
EGR VACUUM
REGULATOR
(EVR) SOLENOID

C163
ANTI-LOCK
BRAKE
CONTROL
MODULE

C139, G139
(GROUND BUS)
AND G101

C141
LEFT
HEADLAMP

C142
RIGHT
HEADLAMP

C133
LEFT
FRONT
PARK/TURN
LAMP

C134
RIGHT
FRONT
PARK/TURN
LAMP

C144
RIGHT
FRONT
PARK
LAMP

C1040
RIGHT
IGNITION
COIL

C1041
RIGHT
RADIO
NOISE
CAPACITOR

C100, C101, C102
GENERATOR/
VOLTAGE
REGULATOR

C1043
LEFT
RADIO
NOISE
CAPACITOR

C130
WASHER
MOTOR

C1042
LEFT
IGNITION
COIL

C143
LEFT
FRONT
PARK
LAMP

FRONT OF VEHICLE

Fig. 14 Engine compartment reference diagram (Part 3 of 3). 1996 Cougar & Thunderbird w/4.6L/V8-281 engine

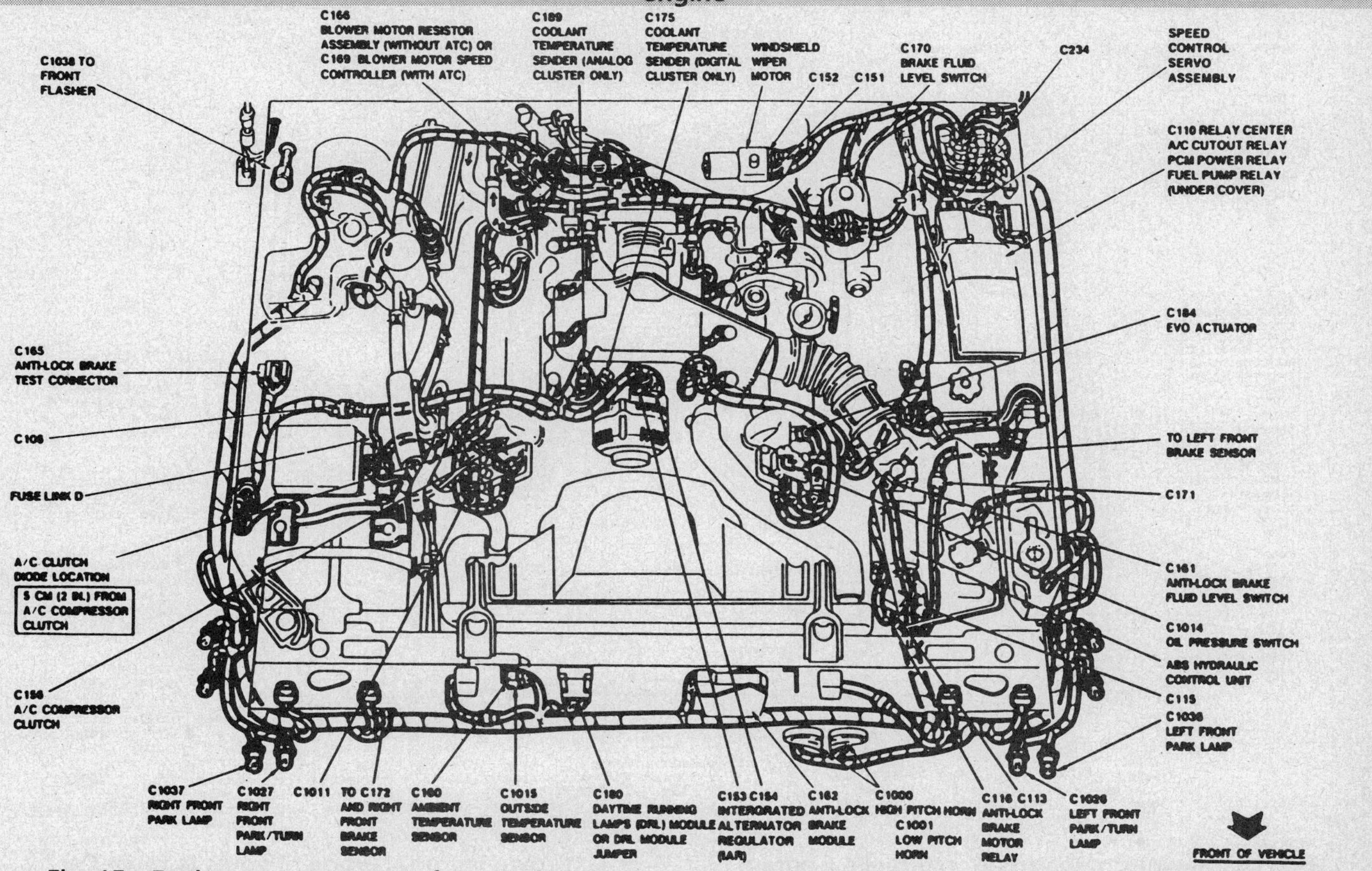

C1038 TO
FRONT
FLASHER

C166
BLOWER MOTOR RESISTOR
ASSEMBLY (WITHOUT ATC) OR
C169 BLOWER MOTOR SPEED
CONTROLLER (WITH ATC)

C189
COOLANT
TEMPERATURE
SENDER (ANALOG
CLUSTER ONLY)

C175
COOLANT
TEMPERATURE
SENDER (DIGITAL
CLUSTER ONLY)

WINDSHIELD
WIPER
MOTOR

C152

C151

C170
BRAKE FLUID
LEVEL SWITCH

C234

SPEED
CONTROL
SERVO
ASSEMBLY

C110 RELAY CENTER
A/C CUTOUT RELAY
PCM POWER RELAY
FUEL PUMP RELAY
(UNDER COVER)

C184
EVO ACTUATOR

C165
ANTI-LOCK BRAKE
TEST CONNECTOR

C106

FUSE LINK D

A/C CLUTCH
DIODE LOCATION

5 CM (2 IN.) FROM
A/C COMPRESSOR
CLUTCH

C156
A/C COMPRESSOR
CLUTCH

TO LEFT FRONT
BRAKE SENSOR

C171

C161
ANTI-LOCK BRAKE
FLUID LEVEL SWITCH

C1014
OIL PRESSURE SWITCH

ABS HYDRAULIC
CONTROL UNIT

C115

C1036
LEFT FRONT
PARK LAMP

C1037
RIGHT FRONT
PARK LAMP

C1027
RIGHT
FRONT
PARK/TURN
LAMP

C1011
RIGHT
FRONT
BRAKE
SENSOR

TO C172
AND RIGHT
FRONT
BRAKE
SENSOR

C160
AMBIENT
TEMPERATURE
SENSOR

C1015
OUTSIDE
TEMPERATURE
SENSOR

C180
DAYTIME RUNNING
LAMPS (DRL) MODULE
OR DRL MODULE
JUMPER

C153 C154
INTEGRATED ANTI-LOCK
ALTERNATOR BRAKE
REGULATOR MODULE
(IAR)

C162

C1000
HIGH PITCH HORN

C1001
LOW PITCH
HORN

C116 C113
ANTI-LOCK
BRAKE
MOTOR
RELAY

C1026
LEFT FRONT
PARK LAMP

FRONT OF VEHICLE

Fig. 15 Engine compartment reference diagram (Part 1 of 3). Crown Victoria, Grand Marquis & Town Car

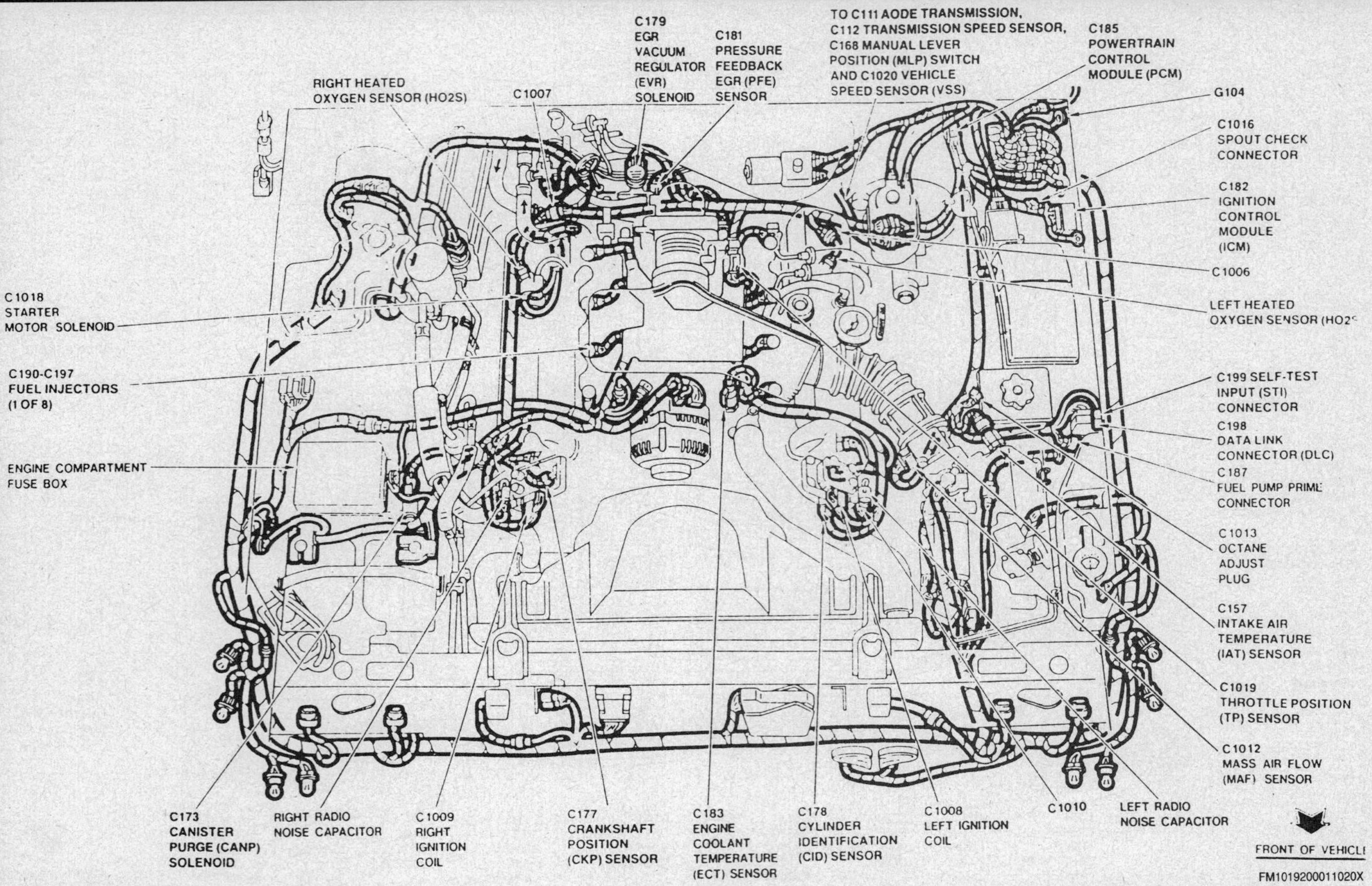

C179
EGR
VACUUM
REGULATOR
(EVR)
SOLENOID

C181
PRESSURE
FEEDBACK
EGR (PFE)
SENSOR

TO C111 AODE TRANSMISSION,
C112 TRANSMISSION SPEED SENSOR,
C168 MANUAL LEVER
POSITION (MLP) SWITCH
AND C1020 VEHICLE
SPEED SENSOR (VSS)

C185
POWERTRAIN
CONTROL
MODULE (PCM)

RIGHT HEATED
OXYGEN SENSOR (HO2S)

C1007

G104

C1016
SPOUT CHECK
CONNECTOR

C182
IGNITION
CONTROL
MODULE
(ICM)

C1006

LEFT HEATED
OXYGEN SENSOR (HO2S)

C1018
STARTER
MOTOR SOLENOID

C190-C197
FUEL INJECTORS
(1 OF 8)

ENGINE COMPARTMENT
FUSE BOX

C199 SELF-TEST
INPUT (STI)
CONNECTOR

C198
DATA LINK
CONNECTOR (DLC)

C187
FUEL PUMP PRIME
CONNECTOR

C1013
OCTANE
ADJUST
PLUG

C157
INTAKE AIR
TEMPERATURE
(IAT) SENSOR

C1019
THROTTLE POSITION
(TP) SENSOR

C1012
MASS AIR FLOW
(MAF) SENSOR

C173
CANISTER
PURGE (CANP)
SOLENOID

RIGHT RADIO
NOISE CAPACITOR

C1009
RIGHT
IGNITION
COIL

C177
CRANKSHAFT
POSITION
(CKP) SENSOR

C183
ENGINE
COOLANT
TEMPERATURE
(ECT) SENSOR

C178
CYLINDER
IDENTIFICATION
(CID) SENSOR

C1008
LEFT IGNITION
COIL

C1010

LEFT RADIO
NOISE CAPACITOR

FRONT OF VEHICLE

FM101920011020X

Fig. 15 Engine compartment reference diagram (Part 2 of 3). Crown Victoria, Grand Marquis & Town Car

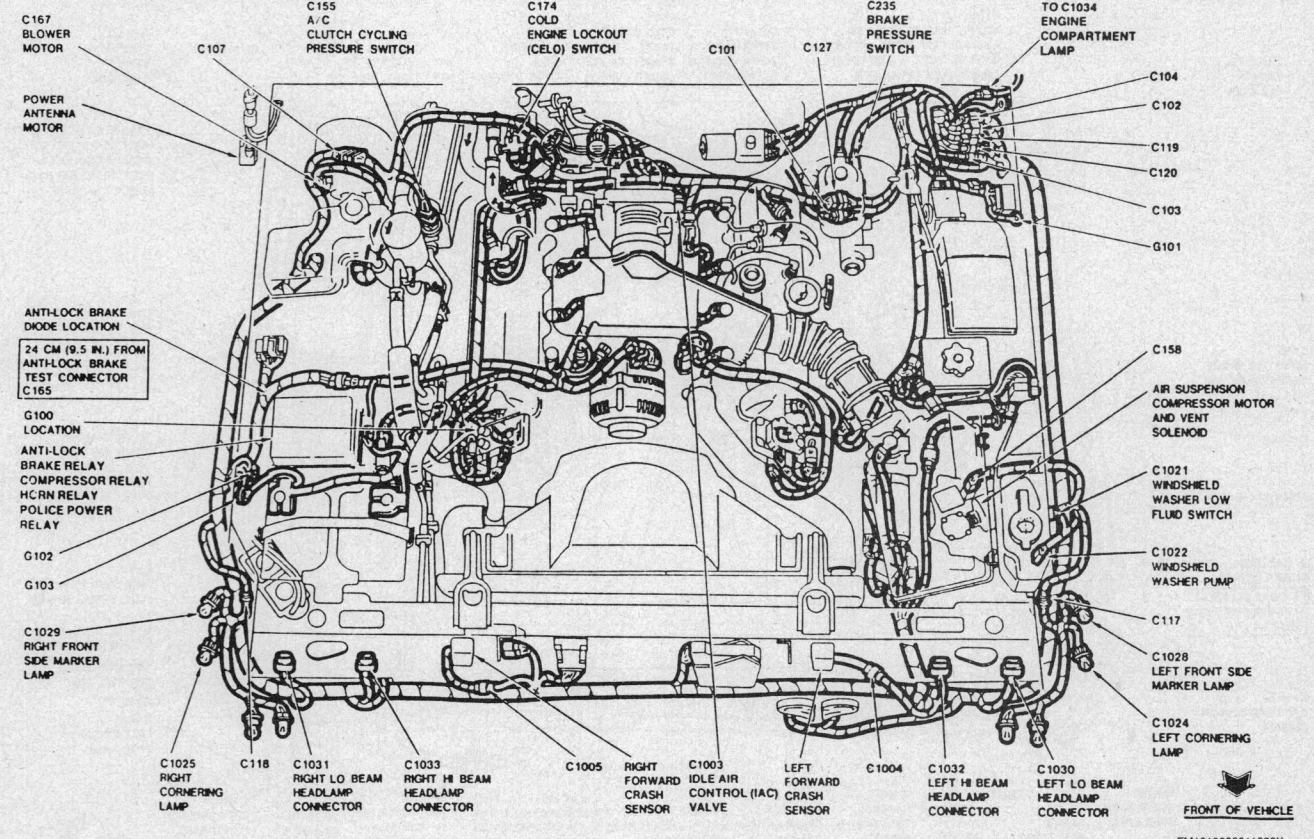

C167
BLOWER
MOTOR

C107

C155
A/C
CLUTCH CYCLING
PRESSURE SWITCH

C174
COLD
ENGINE LOCKOUT
(CELO) SWITCH

C101

C127

C235
BRAKE
PRESSURE
SWITCH

TO C1034
ENGINE
COMPARTMENT
LAMP

POWER
ANTENNA
MOTOR

C104
C102
C119
C120
C103
G101

ANTI-LOCK BRAKE
DIODE LOCATION

24 CM (9.5 IN.) FROM
ANTI-LOCK BRAKE
TEST CONNECTOR
C165

G100
LOCATION

ANTI-LOCK
BRAKE RELAY
COMPRESSOR RELAY
HORN RELAY
POLICE POWER
RELAY

G102

G103

C1029
RIGHT FRONT
SIDE MARKER
LAMP

C158

AIR SUSPENSION
COMPRESSOR MOTOR
AND VENT
SOLENOID

C1021
WINDSHIELD
WASHER LOW
FLUID SWITCH

C1022
WINDSHIELD
WASHER PUMP

C117

C1028
LEFT FRONT SIDE
MARKER LAMP

C1024
LEFT CORNERING
LAMP

C1025
RIGHT
CORNERING
LAMP

C118

C1031
RIGHT LO BEAM
HEADLAMP
CONNECTOR

C1033
RIGHT HI BEAM
HEADLAMP
CONNECTOR

C1005

C1003
RIGHT
FORWARD
CRASH
SENSOR

IDLE AIR
CONTROL (IAC)
VALVE

LEFT
FORWARD
CRASH
SENSOR

C1004

C1032
LEFT HI BEAM
HEADLAMP
CONNECTOR

C1030
LEFT LO BEAM
HEADLAMP
CONNECTOR

FRONT OF VEHICLE

FM101920011030X

Fig. 15 Engine compartment reference diagram (Part 3 of 3). Crown Victoria, Grand Marquis & Town Car

ENGINE COMPARTMENT REFERENCE DIAGRAMS

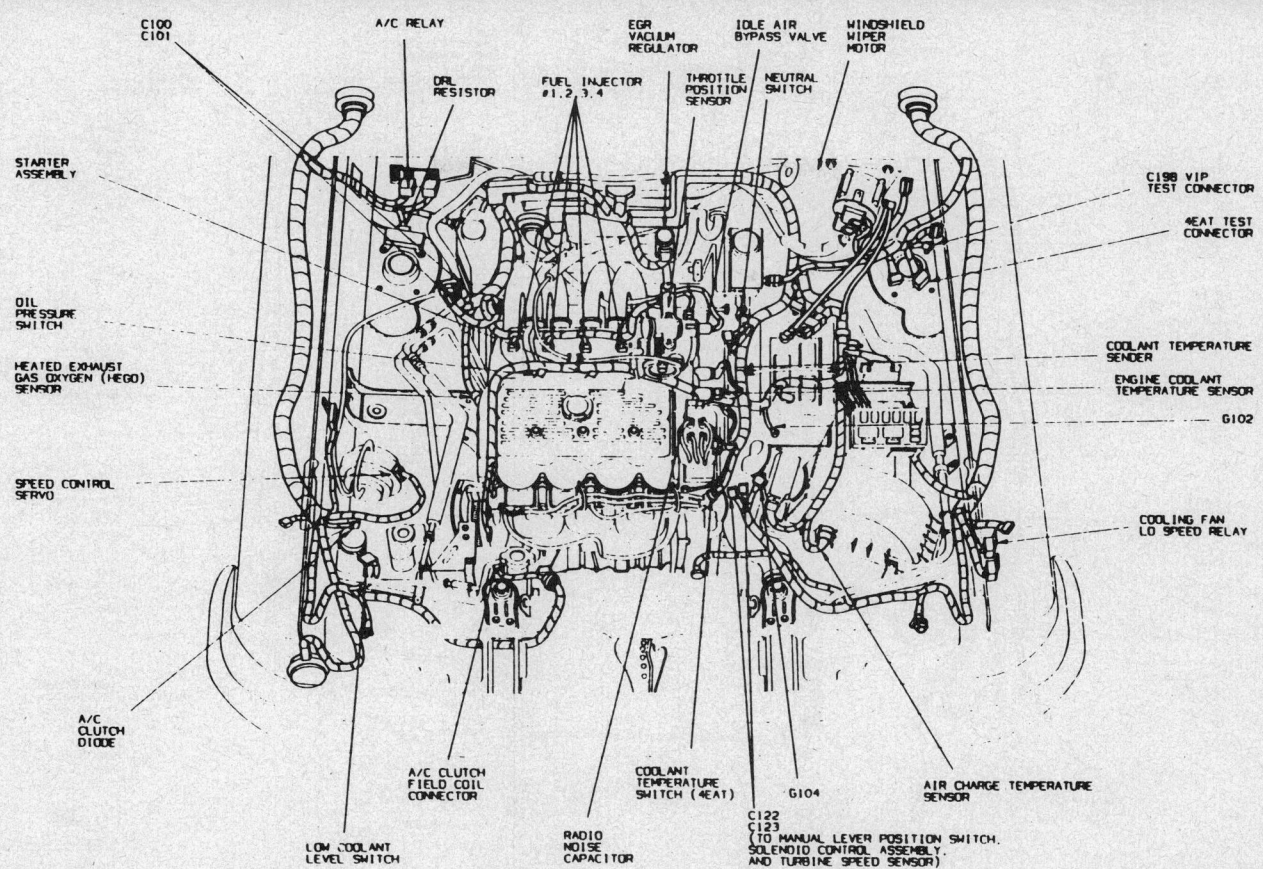

Fig. 16 Engine compartment reference diagram (Part 1 of 2). 1993–94 Escort & Tracer w/1.9L/4-116

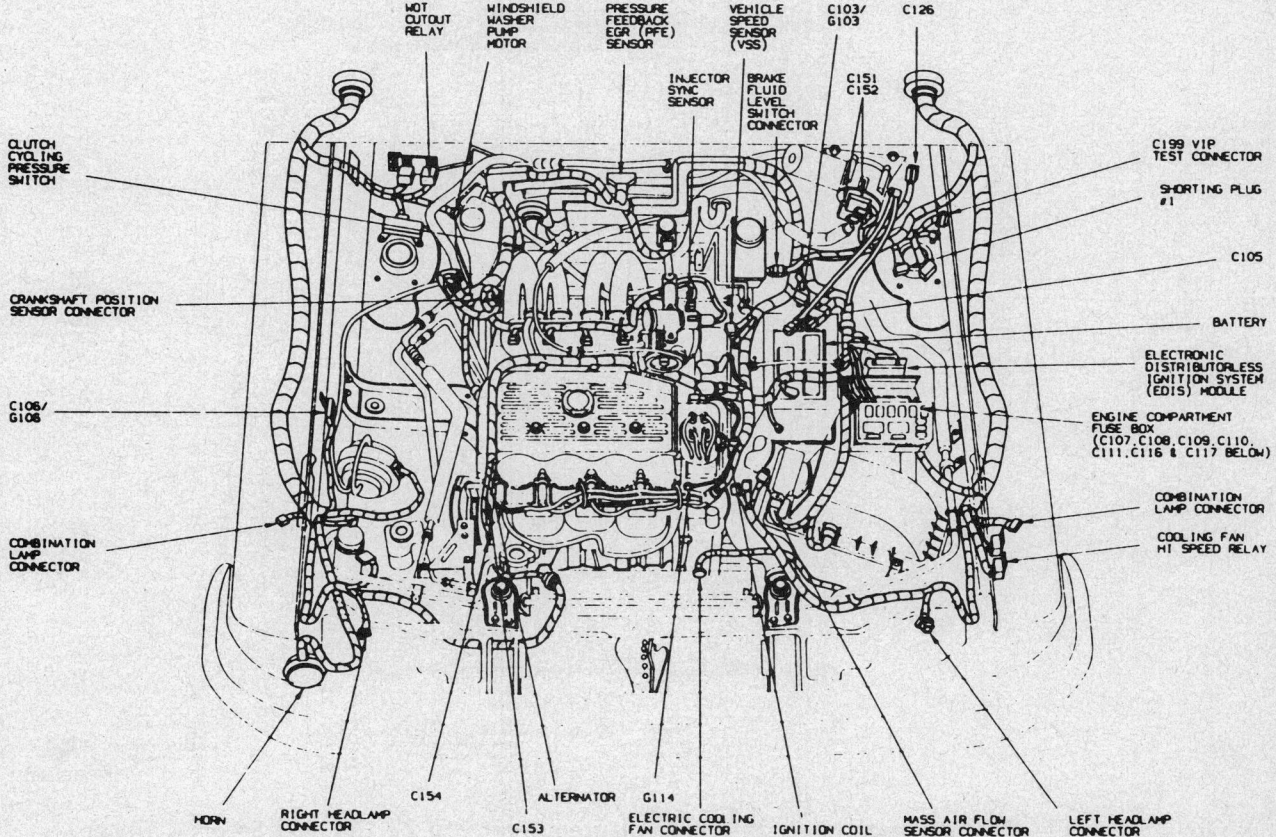

Fig. 16 Engine compartment reference diagram (Part 2 of 2). 1993–94 Escort & Tracer w/1.9L/4-116

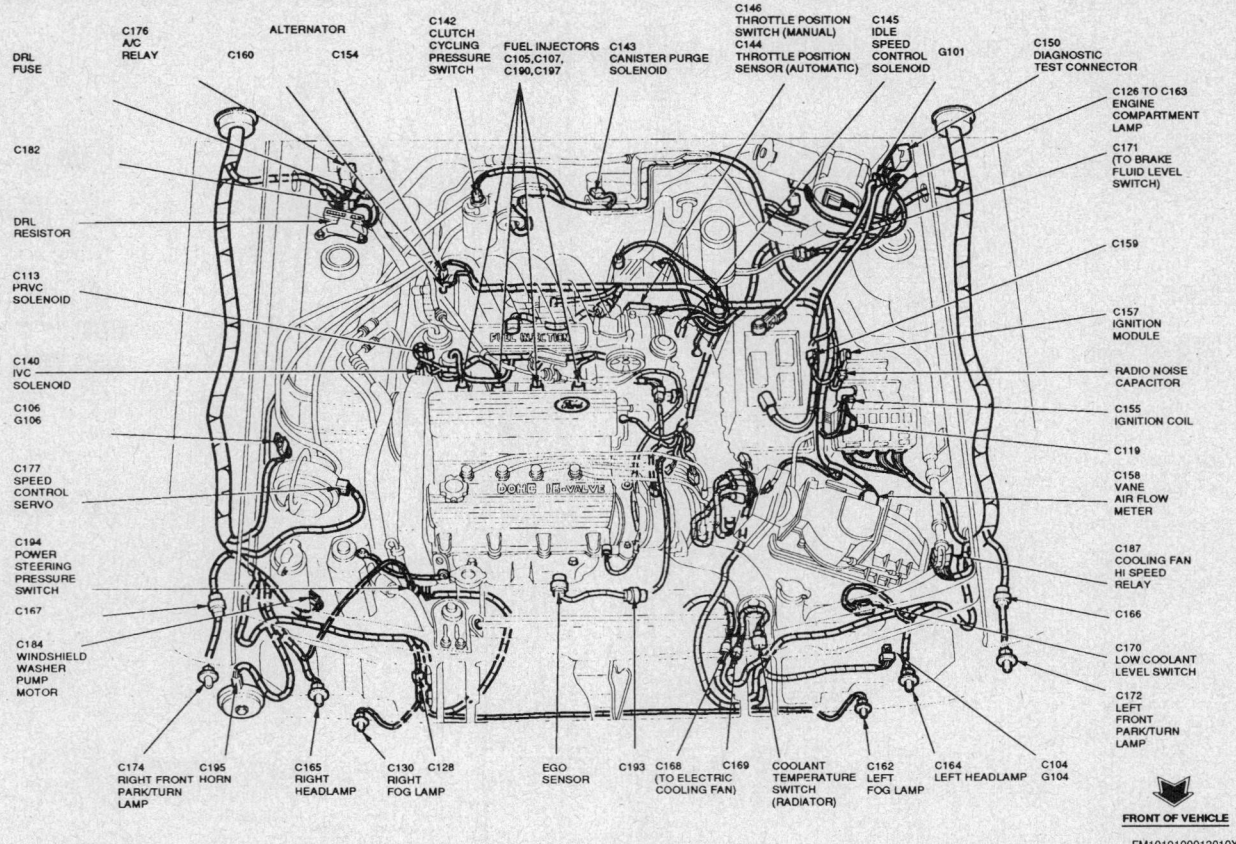

Fig. 17   Engine compartment reference diagram (Part 1 of 2). 1993–94 Escort & Tracer w/1.8L/4-109

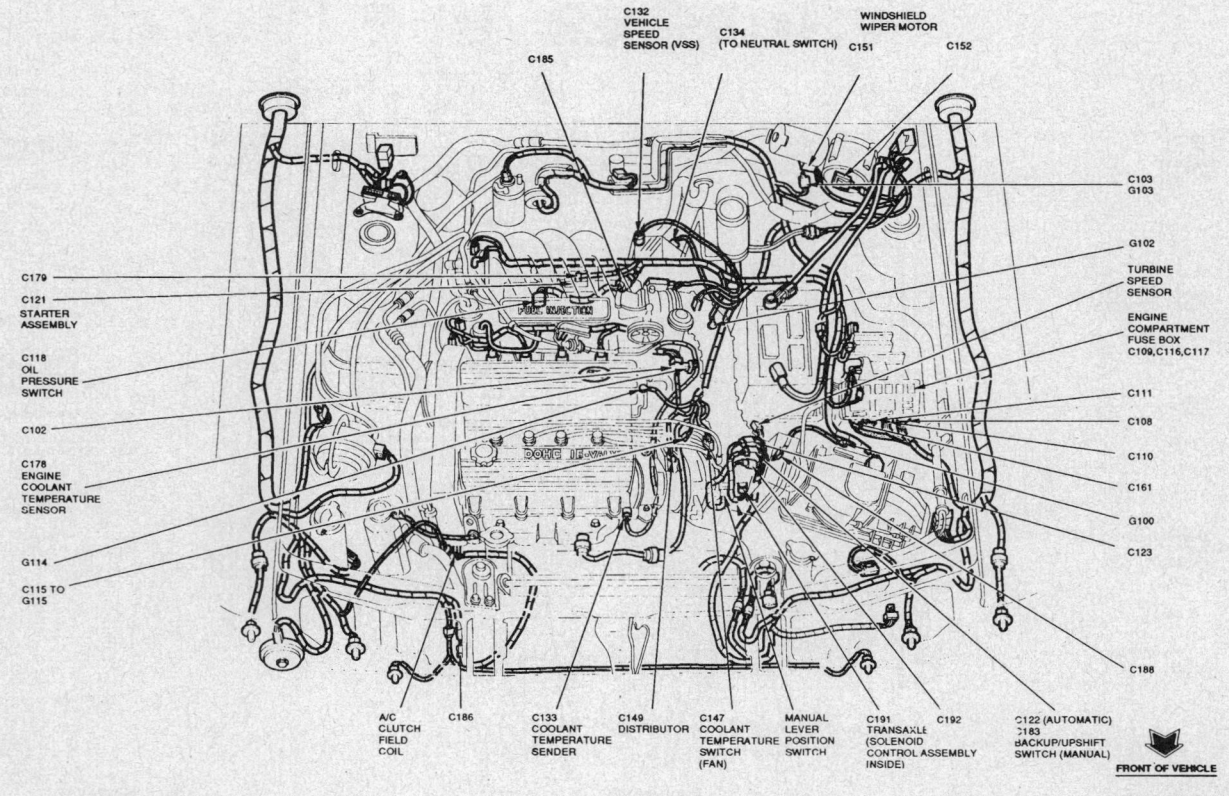

Fig. 17   Engine compartment reference diagram (Part 2 of 2). 1993–94 Escort & Tracer w/1.8L/4-109

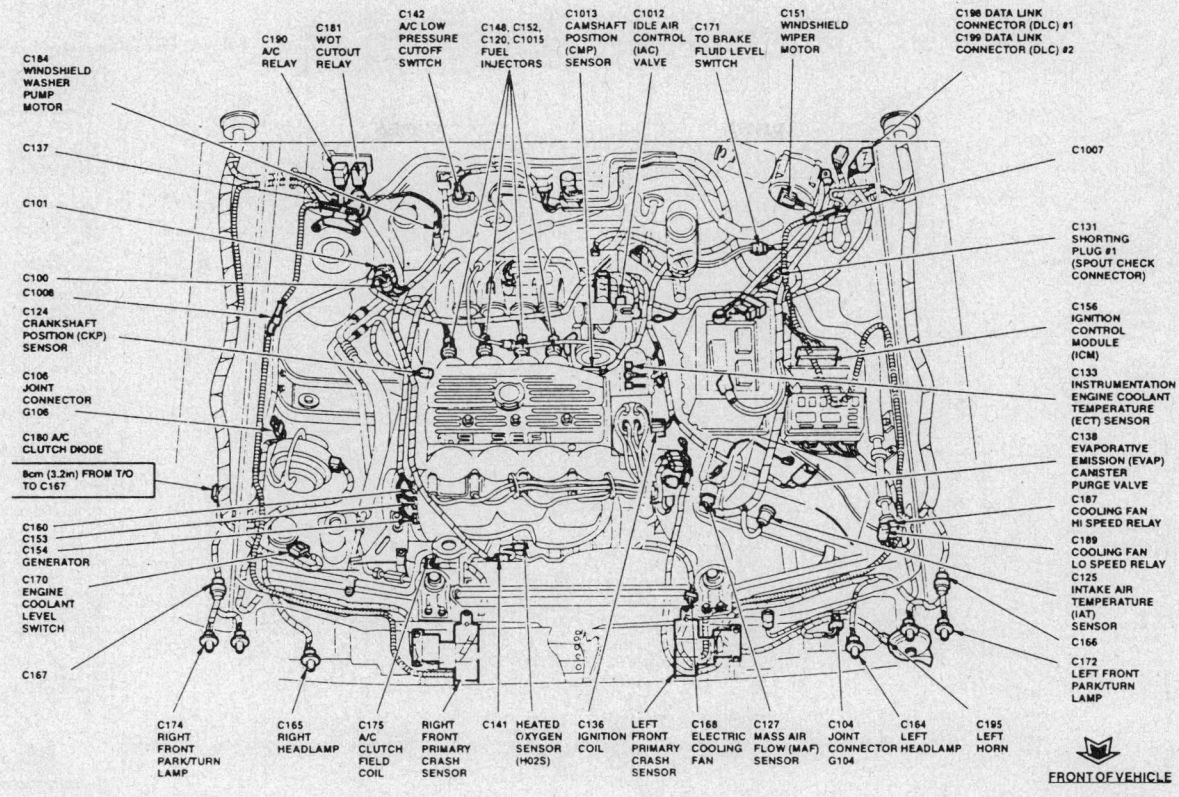

Fig. 18 Engine compartment reference diagram (Part 1 of 2). 1995–96 Escort & Tracer w/1.9L/4-116

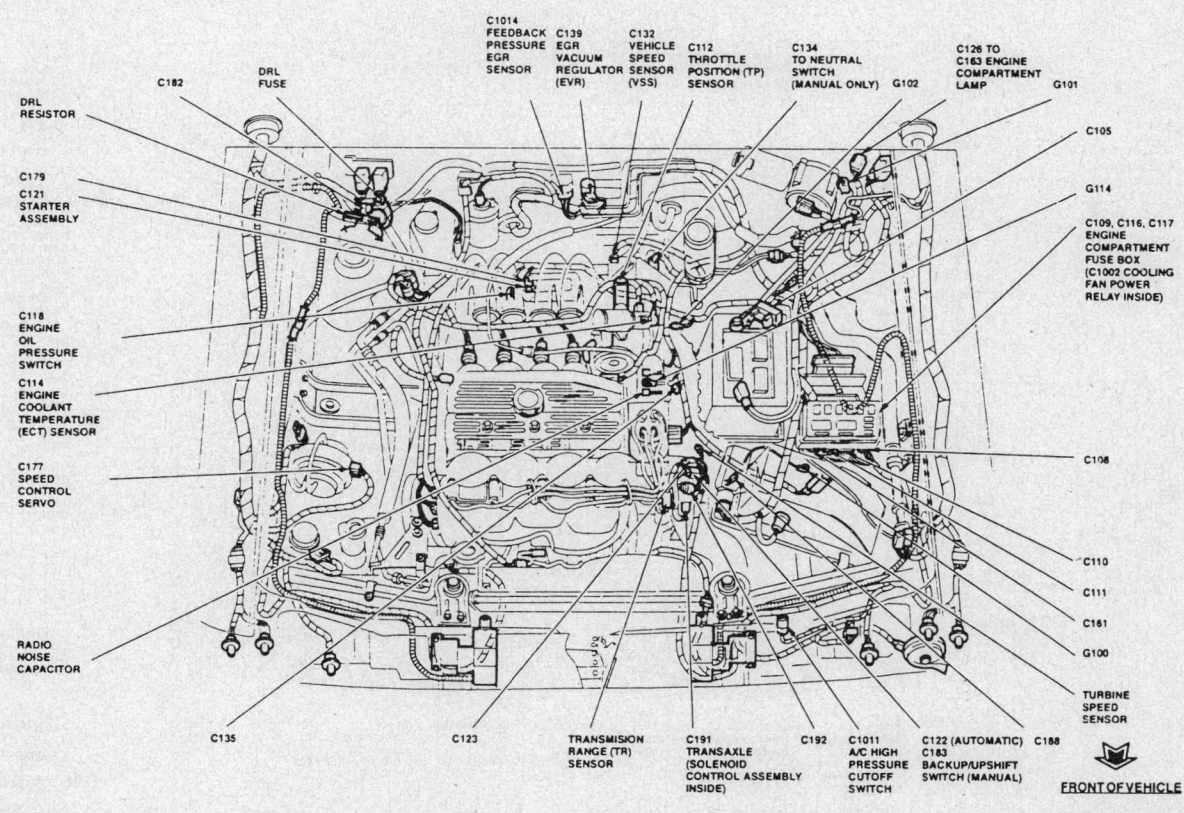

Fig. 18 Engine compartment reference diagram (Part 2 of 2). 1995–96 Escort & Tracer w/1.9L/4-116

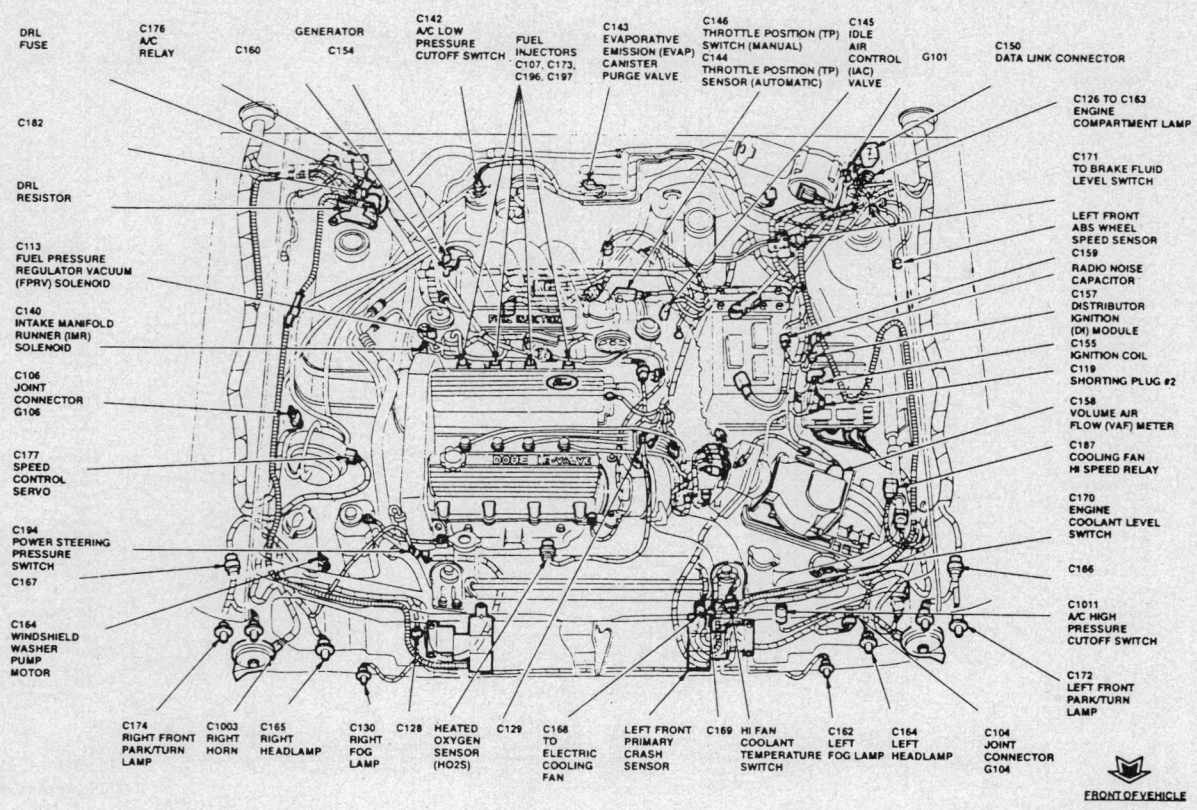

Fig. 19   Engine compartment reference diagram (Part 1 of 2). 1995–96 Escort & Tracer
w/1.8L/4-109

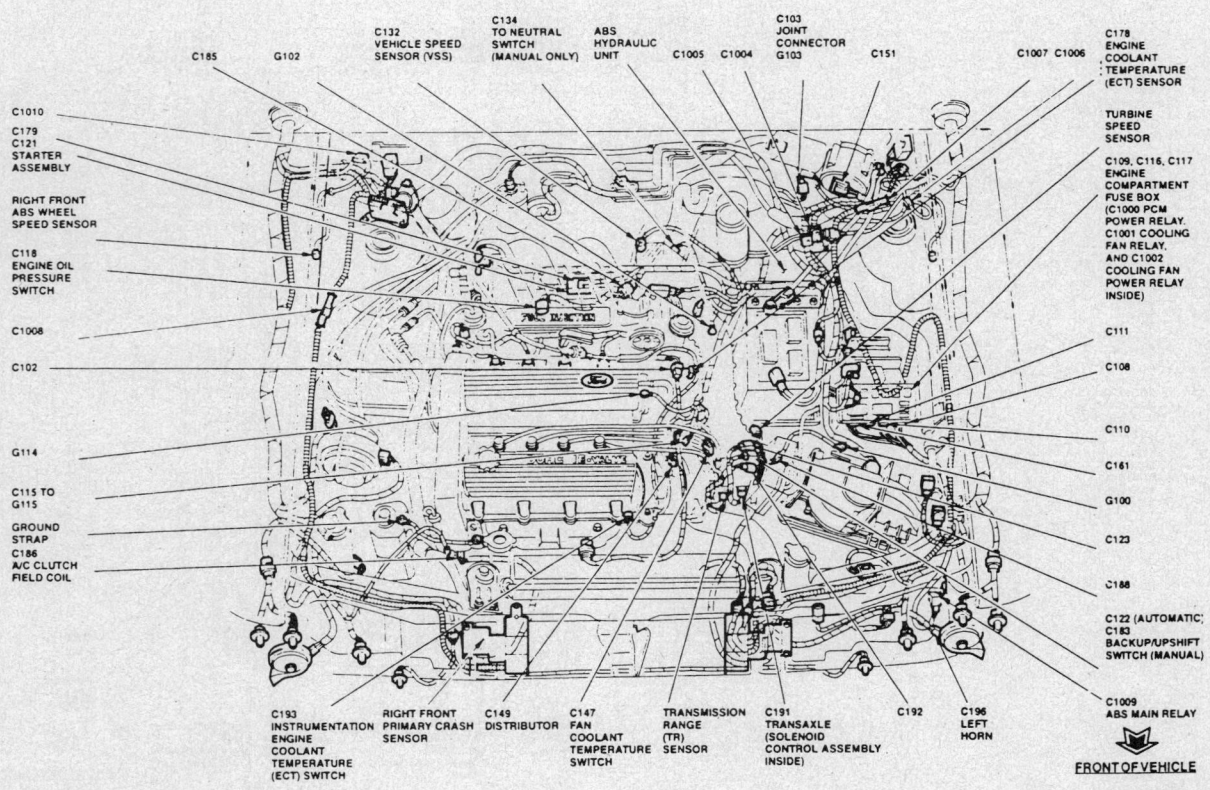

Fig. 19   Engine compartment reference diagram (Part 2 of 2). 1995–96 Escort & Tracer
w/1.8L/4-109

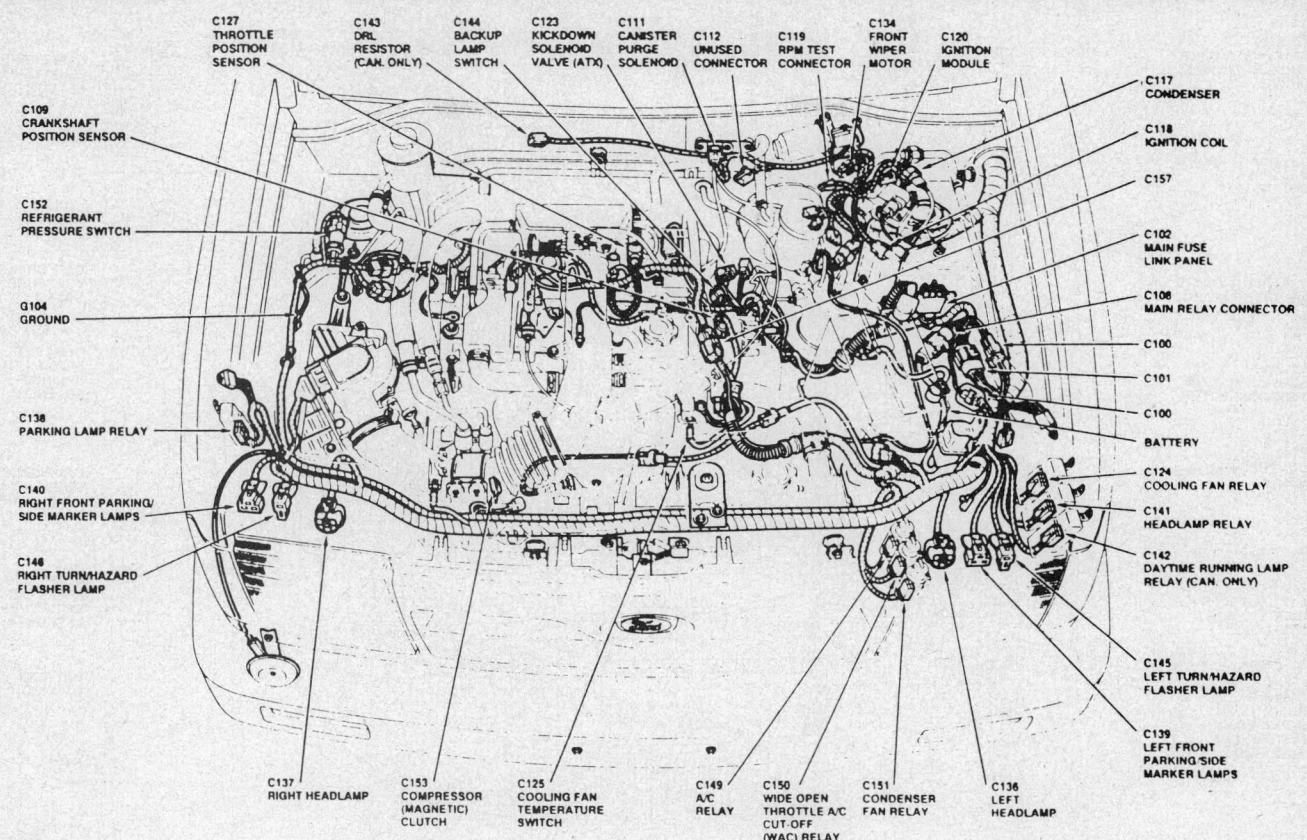

Fig. 20   Engine compartment reference diagram (Part 1 of 2). Festiva

FM1019100014010X

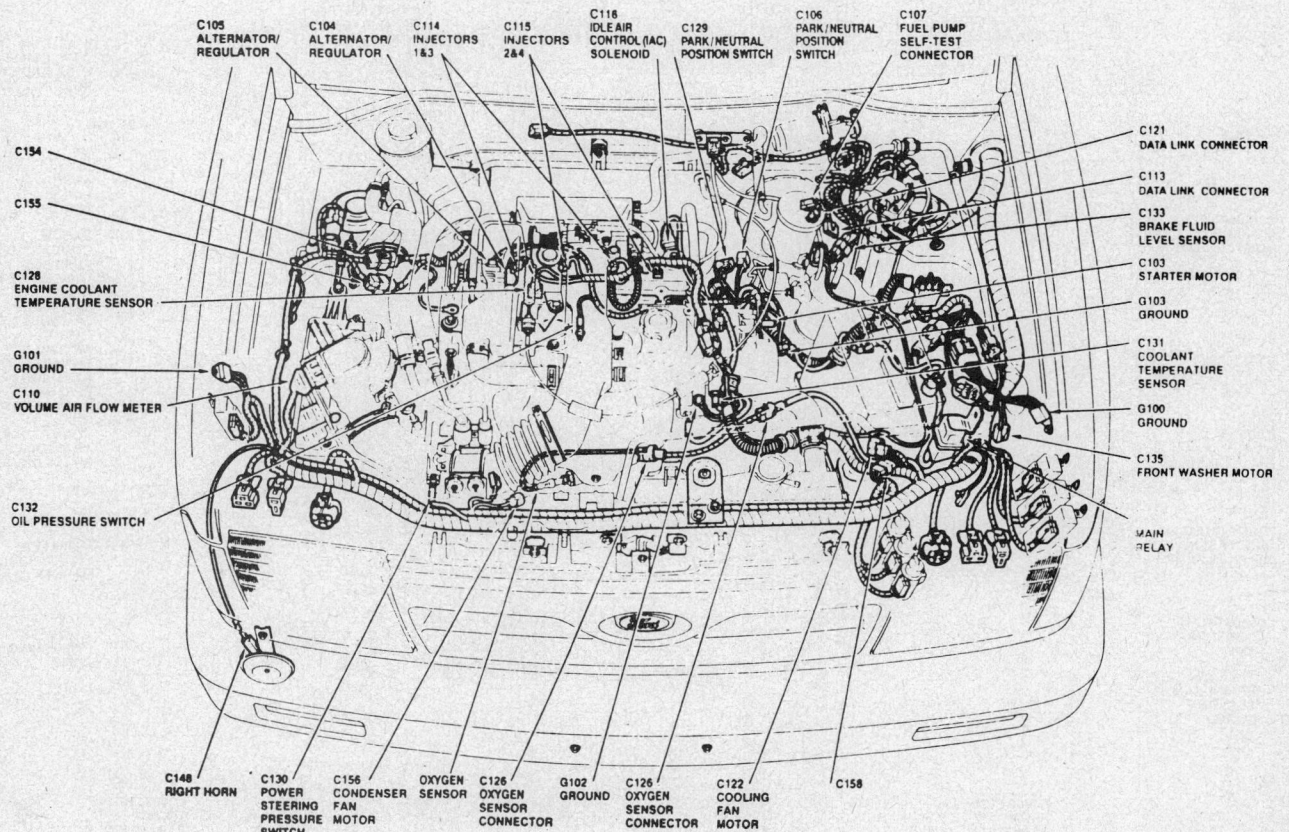

Fig. 20   Engine compartment reference diagram (Part 2 of 2). Festiva

FM1019100014020X

FORD–Engine Compartment Reference Diagrams

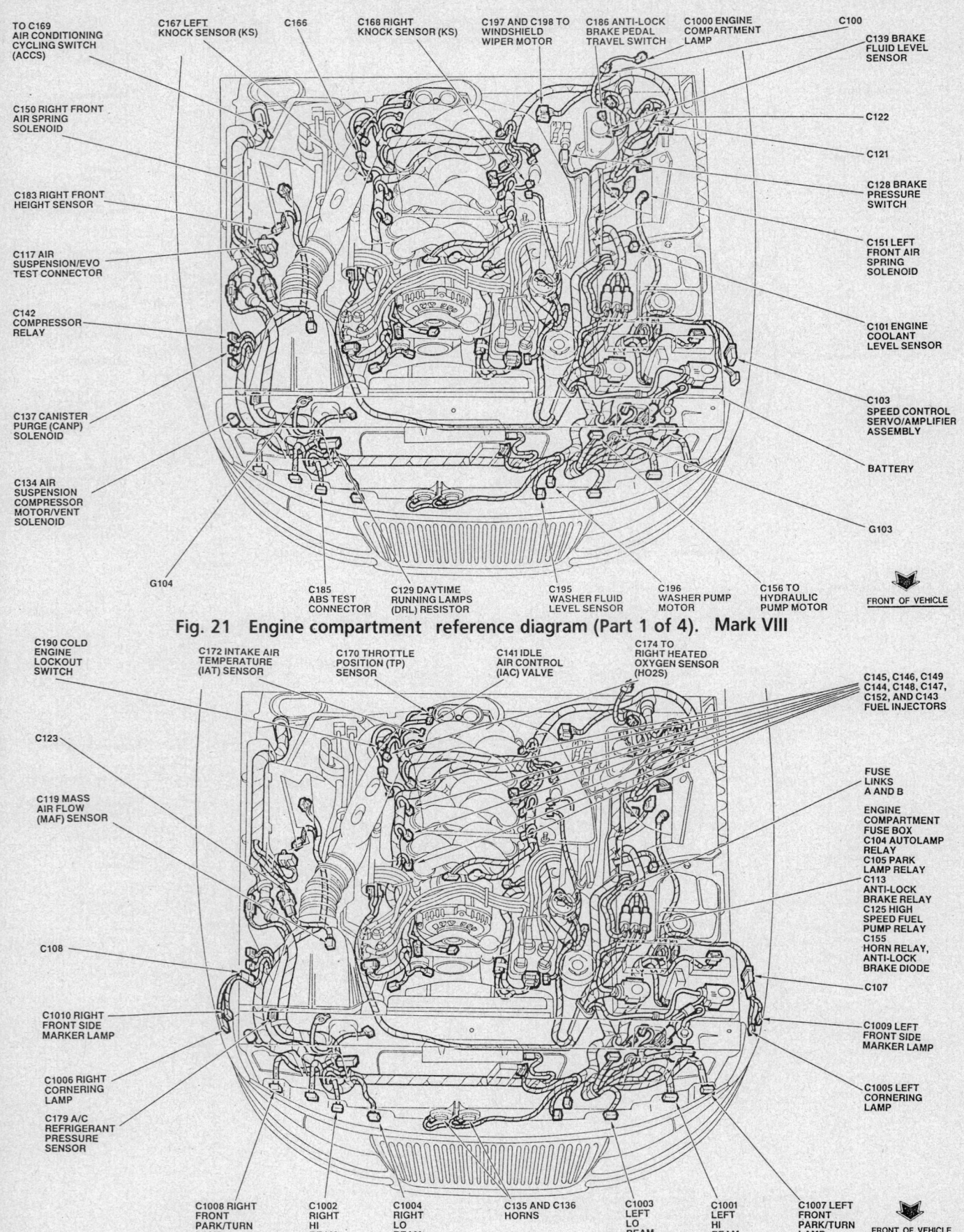

TO C169
AIR CONDITIONING
CYCLING SWITCH
(ACCS)

C167 LEFT
KNOCK SENSOR (KS)

C166

C168 RIGHT
KNOCK SENSOR (KS)

C197 AND C198 TO
WINDSHIELD
WIPER MOTOR

C186 ANTI-LOCK
BRAKE PEDAL
TRAVEL SWITCH

C1000 ENGINE
COMPARTMENT
LAMP

C100

C139 BRAKE
FLUID LEVEL
SENSOR

C150 RIGHT FRONT
AIR SPRING
SOLENOID

C122

C121

C183 RIGHT FRONT
HEIGHT SENSOR

C128 BRAKE
PRESSURE
SWITCH

C117 AIR
SUSPENSION/EVO
TEST CONNECTOR

C151 LEFT
FRONT AIR
SPRING
SOLENOID

C142
COMPRESSOR
RELAY

C101 ENGINE
COOLANT
LEVEL SENSOR

C137 CANISTER
PURGE (CANP)
SOLENOID

C103
SPEED CONTROL
SERVO/AMPLIFIER
ASSEMBLY

C134 AIR
SUSPENSION
COMPRESSOR
MOTOR/VENT
SOLENOID

BATTERY

G103

G104

C185
ABS TEST
CONNECTOR

C129 DAYTIME
RUNNING LAMPS
(DRL) RESISTOR

C195
WASHER FLUID
LEVEL SENSOR

C196
WASHER PUMP
MOTOR

C156 TO
HYDRAULIC
PUMP MOTOR

FRONT OF VEHICLE

Fig. 21   Engine compartment reference diagram (Part 1 of 4).   Mark VIII

C190 COLD
ENGINE
LOCKOUT
SWITCH

C172 INTAKE AIR
TEMPERATURE
(IAT) SENSOR

C170 THROTTLE
POSITION (TP)
SENSOR

C141 IDLE
AIR CONTROL
(IAC) VALVE

C174 TO
RIGHT HEATED
OXYGEN SENSOR
(HO2S)

C145, C146, C149
C144, C148, C147,
C152, AND C143
FUEL INJECTORS

C123

FUSE
LINKS
A AND B

ENGINE
COMPARTMENT
FUSE BOX
C104 AUTOLAMP
RELAY
C105 PARK
LAMP RELAY
C113
ANTI-LOCK
BRAKE RELAY
C125 HIGH
SPEED FUEL
PUMP RELAY
C155
HORN RELAY,
ANTI-LOCK
BRAKE DIODE

C119 MASS
AIR FLOW
(MAF) SENSOR

C107

C108

C1010 RIGHT
FRONT SIDE
MARKER LAMP

C1009 LEFT
FRONT SIDE
MARKER LAMP

C1006 RIGHT
CORNERING
LAMP

C1005 LEFT
CORNERING
LAMP

C179 A/C
REFRIGERANT
PRESSURE
SENSOR

C1008 RIGHT
FRONT
PARK/TURN
LAMP

C1002
RIGHT
HI
BEAM

C1004
RIGHT
LO
BEAM

C135 AND C136
HORNS

C1003
LEFT
LO
BEAM

C1001
LEFT
HI
BEAM

C1007 LEFT
FRONT
PARK/TURN
LAMP

FRONT OF VEHICLE

Fig. 21   Engine compartment reference diagram (Part 2 of 4).   Mark VIII

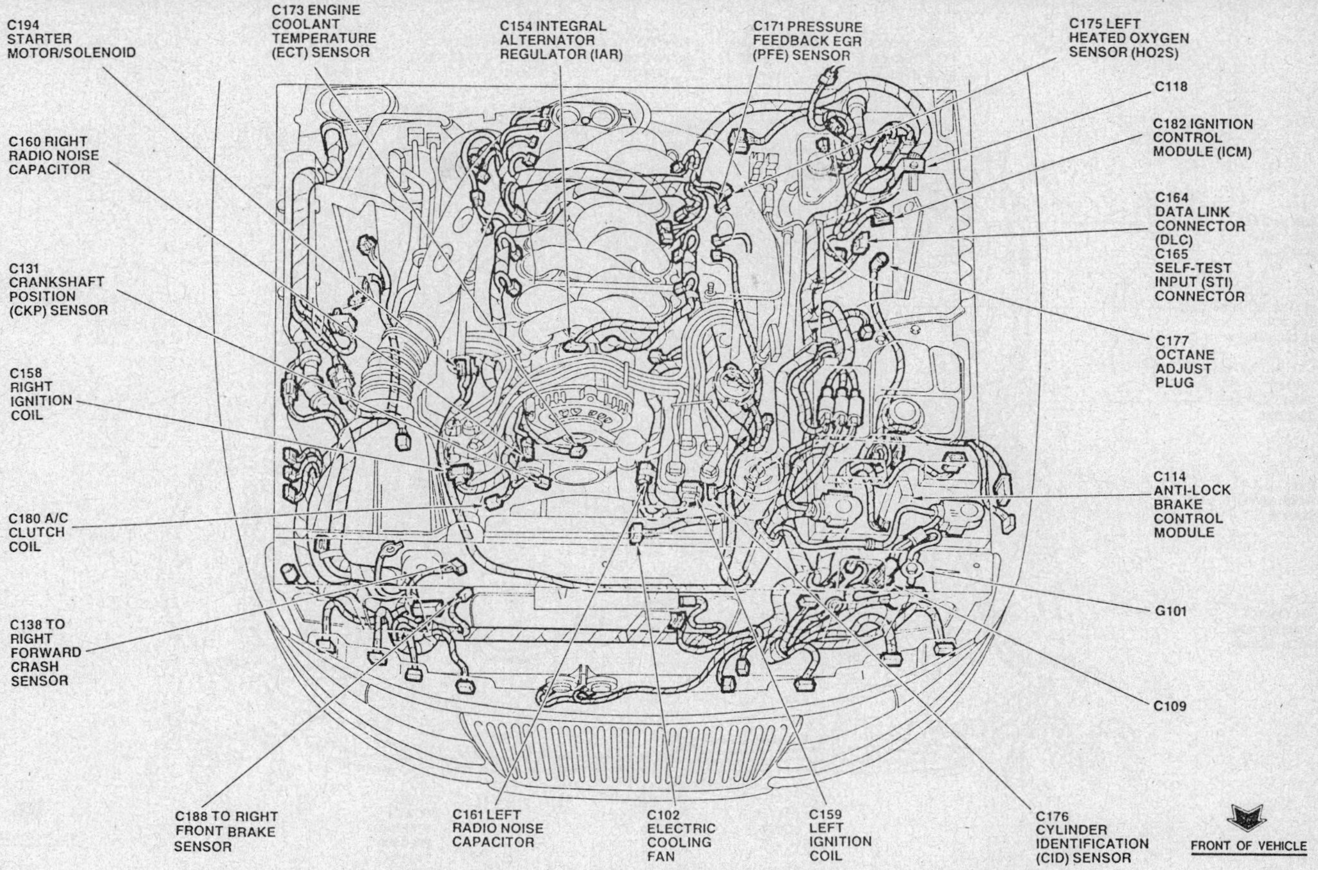

C194
STARTER
MOTOR/SOLENOID

C173 ENGINE
COOLANT
TEMPERATURE
(ECT) SENSOR

C154 INTEGRAL
ALTERNATOR
REGULATOR (IAR)

C171 PRESSURE
FEEDBACK EGR
(PFE) SENSOR

C175 LEFT
HEATED OXYGEN
SENSOR (HO2S)

C118

C182 IGNITION
CONTROL
MODULE (ICM)

C160 RIGHT
RADIO NOISE
CAPACITOR

C164
DATA LINK
CONNECTOR
(DLC)
C165
SELF-TEST
INPUT (STI)
CONNECTOR

C131
CRANKSHAFT
POSITION
(CKP) SENSOR

C177
OCTANE
ADJUST
PLUG

C158
RIGHT
IGNITION
COIL

C180 A/C
CLUTCH
COIL

C114
ANTI-LOCK
BRAKE
CONTROL
MODULE

G101

C138 TO
RIGHT
FORWARD
CRASH
SENSOR

C109

C188 TO RIGHT
FRONT BRAKE
SENSOR

C161 LEFT
RADIO NOISE
CAPACITOR

C102
ELECTRIC
COOLING
FAN

C159
LEFT
IGNITION
COIL

C176
CYLINDER
IDENTIFICATION
(CID) SENSOR

FRONT OF VEHICLE

Fig. 21 Engine compartment reference diagram (Part 3 of 4). Mark VIII

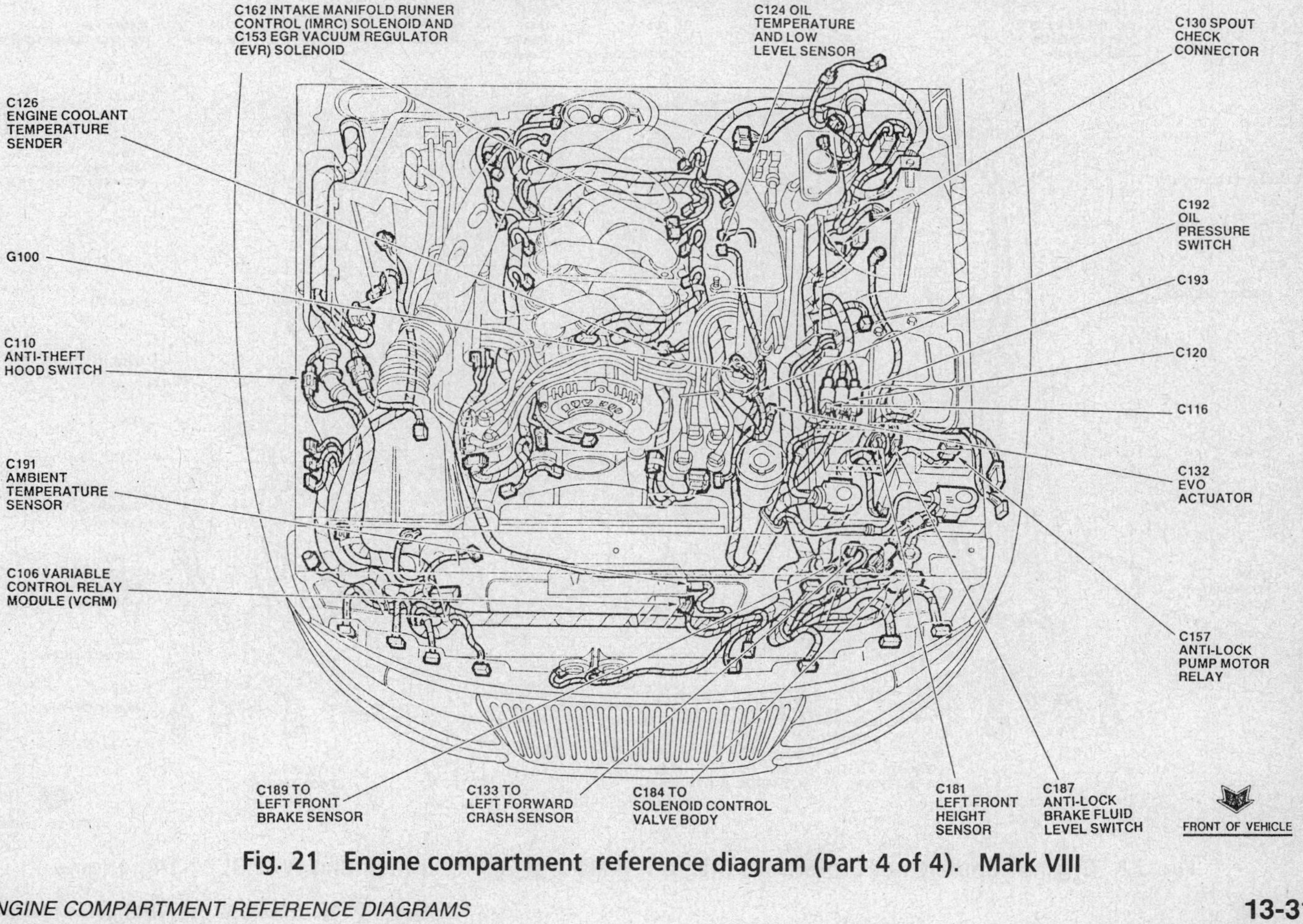

C162 INTAKE MANIFOLD RUNNER
CONTROL (IMRC) SOLENOID AND
C153 EGR VACUUM REGULATOR
(EVR) SOLENOID

C124 OIL
TEMPERATURE
AND LOW
LEVEL SENSOR

C130 SPOUT
CHECK
CONNECTOR

C126
ENGINE COOLANT
TEMPERATURE
SENDER

C192
OIL
PRESSURE
SWITCH

G100

C193

C110
ANTI-THEFT
HOOD SWITCH

C120

C116

C191
AMBIENT
TEMPERATURE
SENSOR

C132
EVO
ACTUATOR

C106 VARIABLE
CONTROL RELAY
MODULE (VCRM)

C157
ANTI-LOCK
PUMP MOTOR
RELAY

C189 TO
LEFT FRONT
BRAKE SENSOR

C133 TO
LEFT FORWARD
CRASH SENSOR

C184 TO
SOLENOID CONTROL
VALVE BODY

C181
LEFT FRONT
HEIGHT
SENSOR

C187
ANTI-LOCK
BRAKE FLUID
LEVEL SWITCH

FRONT OF VEHICLE

Fig. 21 Engine compartment reference diagram (Part 4 of 4). Mark VIII

ENGINE COMPARTMENT REFERENCE DIAGRAMS

13-31

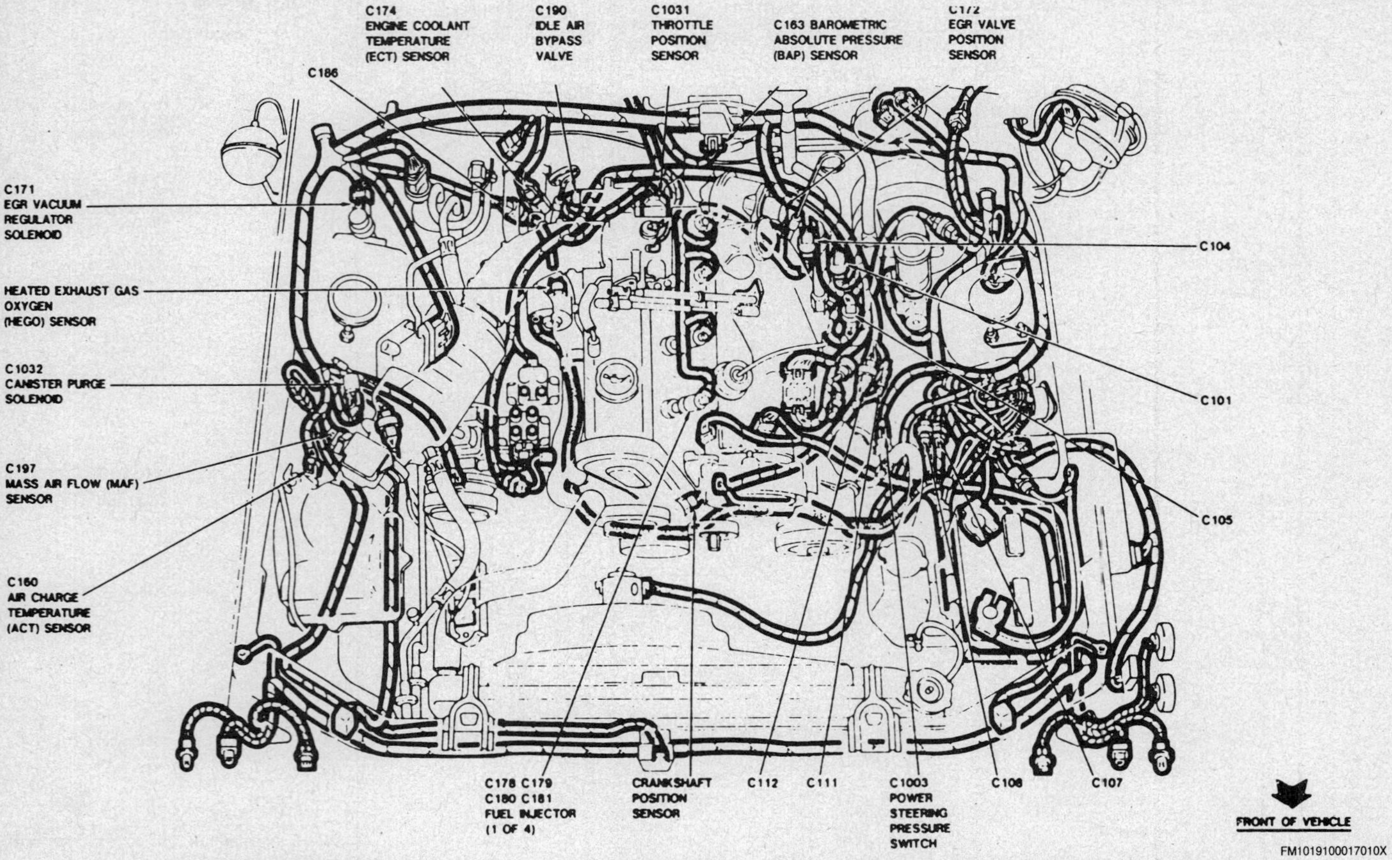

C174
ENGINE COOLANT
TEMPERATURE
(ECT) SENSOR

C190
IDLE AIR
BYPASS
VALVE

C1031
THROTTLE
POSITION
SENSOR

C163 BAROMETRIC
ABSOLUTE PRESSURE
(BAP) SENSOR

C172
EGR VALVE
POSITION
SENSOR

C186

C171
EGR VACUUM
REGULATOR
SOLENOID

HEATED EXHAUST GAS
OXYGEN
(HEGO) SENSOR

C1032
CANSTER PURGE
SOLENOID

C197
MASS AIR FLOW (MAF)
SENSOR

C160
AIR CHARGE
TEMPERATURE
(ACT) SENSOR

C104

C101

C105

C178 C179
C180 C181
FUEL INJECTOR
(1 OF 4)

CRANKSHAFT
POSITION
SENSOR

C112 C111

C1003
POWER
STEERING
PRESSURE
SWITCH

C108   C107

FRONT OF VEHICLE

FM1019100017010X

Fig. 22   Engine compartment reference diagram (Part 1 of 3). 1993 Mustang w/2.3L/4-140 engine

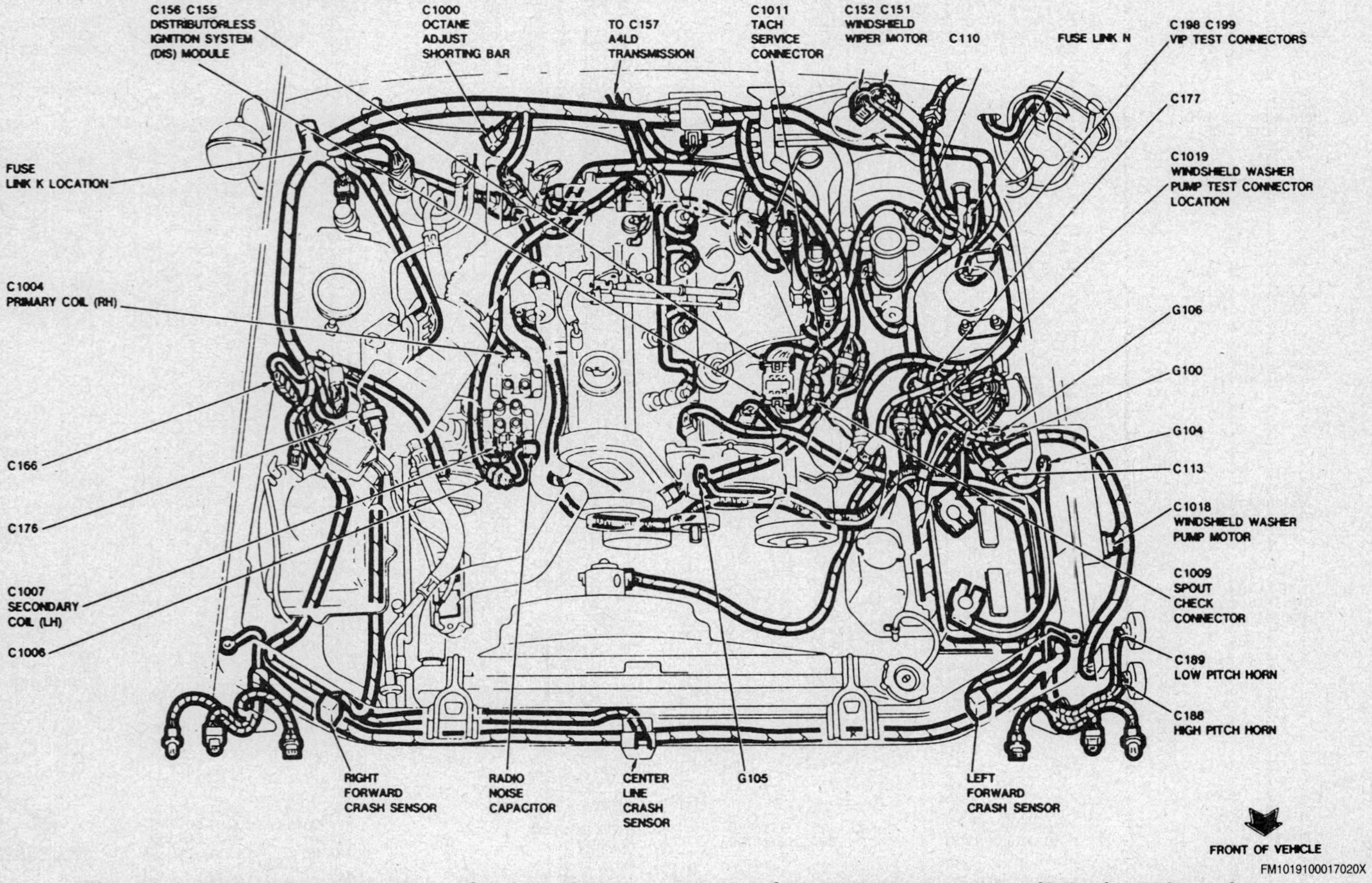

C156 C155
DISTRIBUTORLESS
IGNITION SYSTEM
(DIS) MODULE

C1000
OCTANE
ADJUST
SHORTING BAR

TO C157
A4LD
TRANSMISSION

C1011
TACH
SERVICE
CONNECTOR

C152 C151
WINDSHIELD
WIPER MOTOR

C110

FUSE LINK N

C198 C199
VIP TEST CONNECTORS

C177

FUSE
LINK K LOCATION

C1004
PRIMARY COIL (RH)

C166

C176

C1007
SECONDARY
COIL (LH)

C1006

C1019
WINDSHIELD WASHER
PUMP TEST CONNECTOR
LOCATION

G106

G100

G104

C113

C1018
WINDSHIELD WASHER
PUMP MOTOR

C1009
SPOUT
CHECK
CONNECTOR

C189
LOW PITCH HORN

C188
HIGH PITCH HORN

RIGHT
FORWARD
CRASH SENSOR

RADIO
NOISE
CAPACITOR

CENTER
LINE
CRASH
SENSOR

G105

LEFT
FORWARD
CRASH SENSOR

FRONT OF VEHICLE

FM1019100017020X

Fig. 22   Engine compartment cent reference diagram (Part 2 of 3). 1993 Mustang w/2.3L/4-140 engine

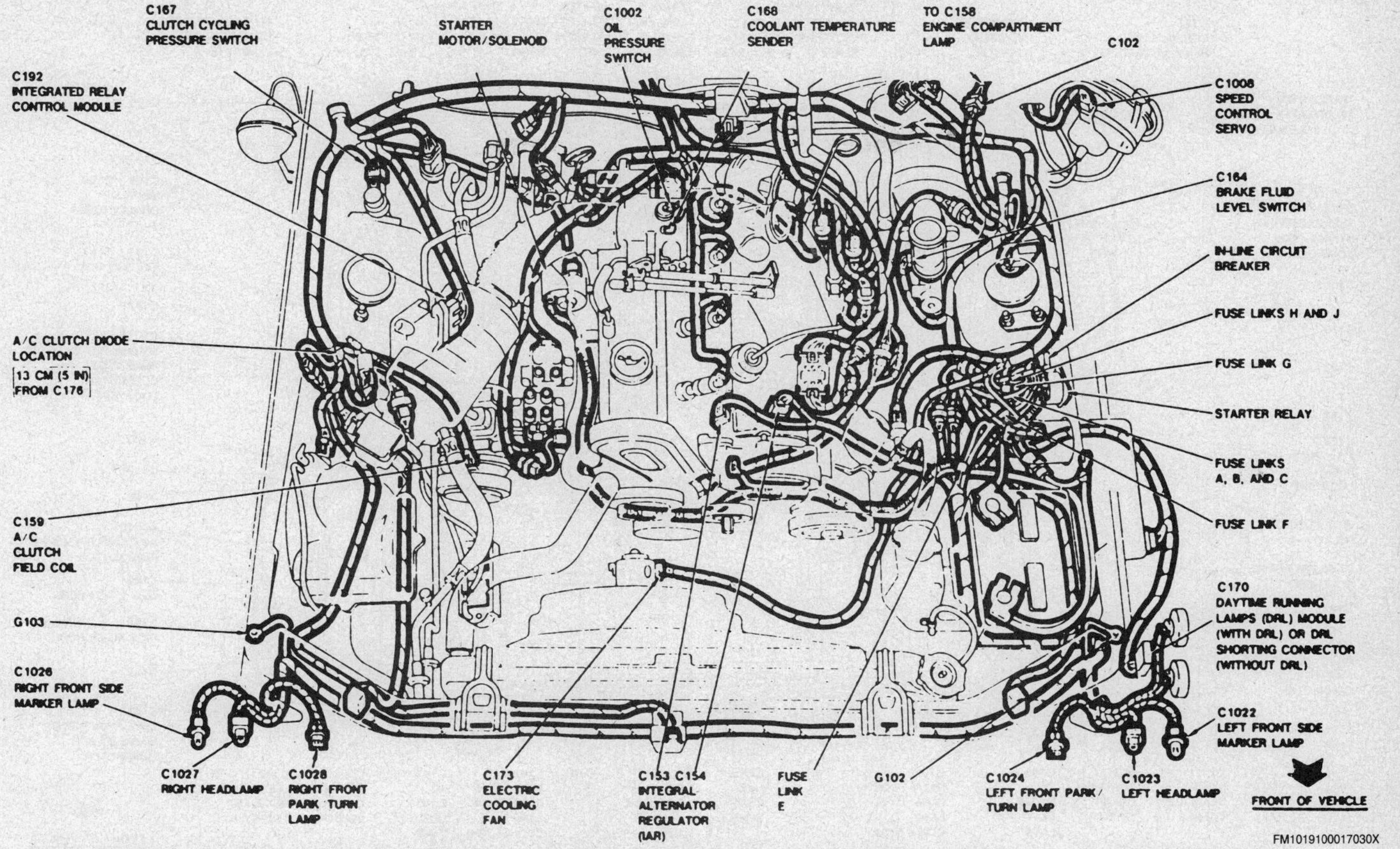

C192 INTEGRATED RELAY CONTROL MODULE

C167 CLUTCH CYCLING PRESSURE SWITCH

STARTER MOTOR/SOLENOID

C1002 OIL PRESSURE SWITCH

C168 COOLANT TEMPERATURE SENDER

TO C158 ENGINE COMPARTMENT LAMP

C102

C1008 SPEED CONTROL SERVO

C164 BRAKE FLUID LEVEL SWITCH

IN-LINE CIRCUIT BREAKER

FUSE LINKS H AND J

FUSE LINK G

STARTER RELAY

FUSE LINKS A, B, AND C

FUSE LINK F

A/C CLUTCH DIODE LOCATION 13 CM (5 IN) FROM C176

C159 A/C CLUTCH FIELD COIL

G103

C1026 RIGHT FRONT SIDE MARKER LAMP

C170 DAYTIME RUNNING LAMPS (DRL) MODULE (WITH DRL) OR DRL SHORTING CONNECTOR (WITHOUT DRL)

C1022 LEFT FRONT SIDE MARKER LAMP

C1027 RIGHT HEADLAMP

C1028 RIGHT FRONT PARK TURN LAMP

C173 ELECTRIC COOLING FAN

C153 C154 INTEGRAL ALTERNATOR REGULATOR (IAR)

FUSE LINK E

G102

C1024 LEFT FRONT PARK/ TURN LAMP

C1023 LEFT HEADLAMP

FRONT OF VEHICLE

FM1019100017030X

Fig. 22   Engine compartment reference diagram (Part 3 of 3). 1993 Mustang w/2.3L/4-140 engine

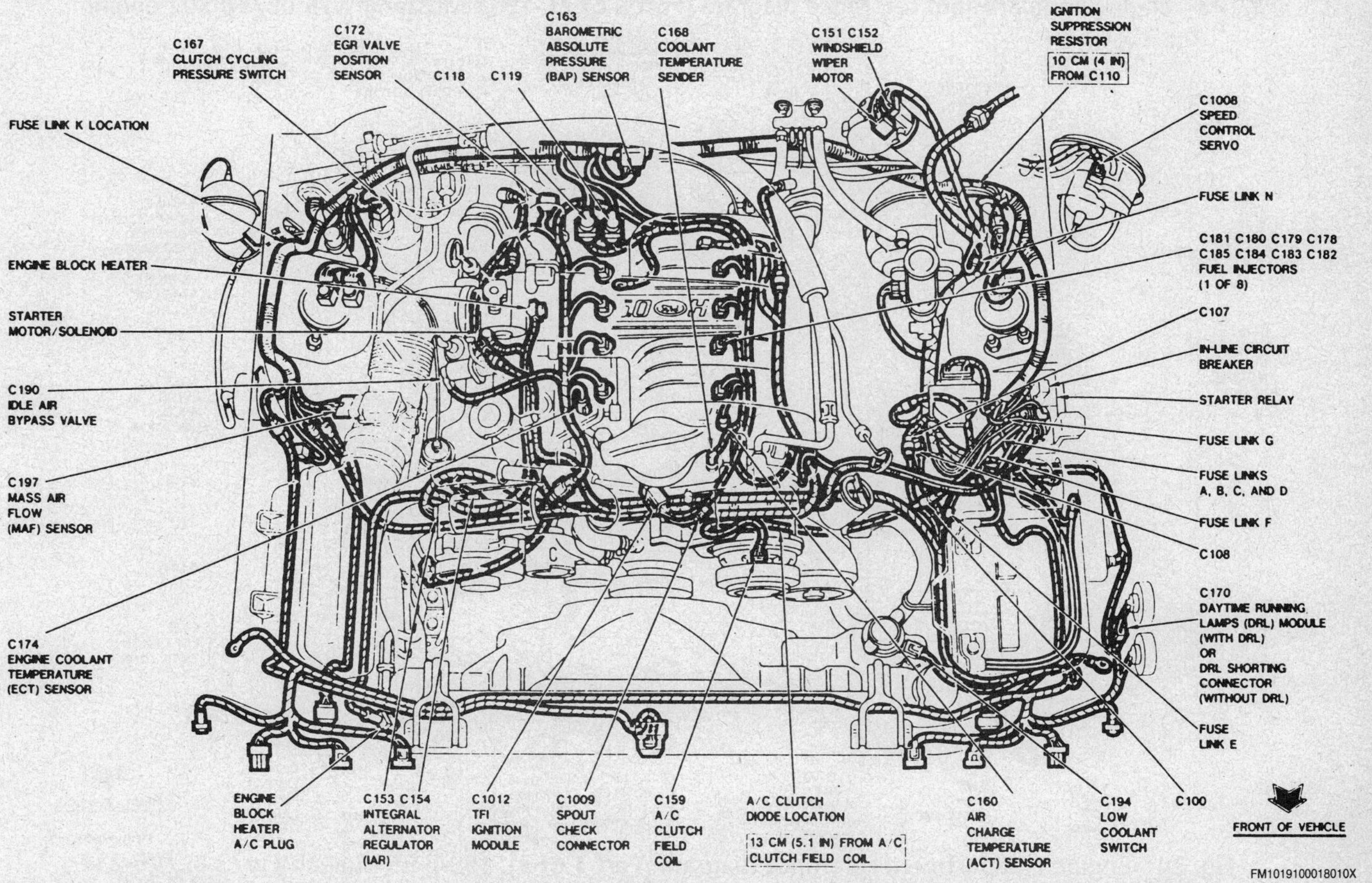

C167 CLUTCH CYCLING PRESSURE SWITCH

C172 EGR VALVE POSITION SENSOR

C118   C119

C163 BAROMETRIC ABSOLUTE PRESSURE (BAP) SENSOR

C168 COOLANT TEMPERATURE SENDER

C151 C152 WINDSHIELD WIPER MOTOR

IGNITION SUPPRESSION RESISTOR 10 CM (4 IN) FROM C110

FUSE LINK K LOCATION

ENGINE BLOCK HEATER

STARTER MOTOR/SOLENOID

C190 IDLE AIR BYPASS VALVE

C197 MASS AIR FLOW (MAF) SENSOR

C174 ENGINE COOLANT TEMPERATURE (ECT) SENSOR

C1008 SPEED CONTROL SERVO

FUSE LINK N

C181 C180 C179 C178 C185 C184 C183 C182 FUEL INJECTORS (1 OF 8)

C107

IN-LINE CIRCUIT BREAKER

STARTER RELAY

FUSE LINK G

FUSE LINKS A, B, C, AND D

FUSE LINK F

C108

C170 DAYTIME RUNNING LAMPS (DRL) MODULE (WITH DRL) OR DRL SHORTING CONNECTOR (WITHOUT DRL)

FUSE LINK E

ENGINE BLOCK HEATER A/C PLUG

C153 C154 INTEGRAL ALTERNATOR REGULATOR (IAR)

C1012 TFI IGNITION MODULE

C1009 SPOUT CHECK CONNECTOR

C159 A/C CLUTCH FIELD COIL

A/C CLUTCH DIODE LOCATION 13 CM (5.1 IN) FROM A/C CLUTCH FIELD COIL

C160 AIR CHARGE TEMPERATURE (ACT) SENSOR

C194 LOW COOLANT SWITCH

C100

FRONT OF VEHICLE

FM1019100018010X

Fig. 23   Engine compartment reference diagram (Part 1 of 2). 1993 Mustang w/5.0L/V8-302 engine

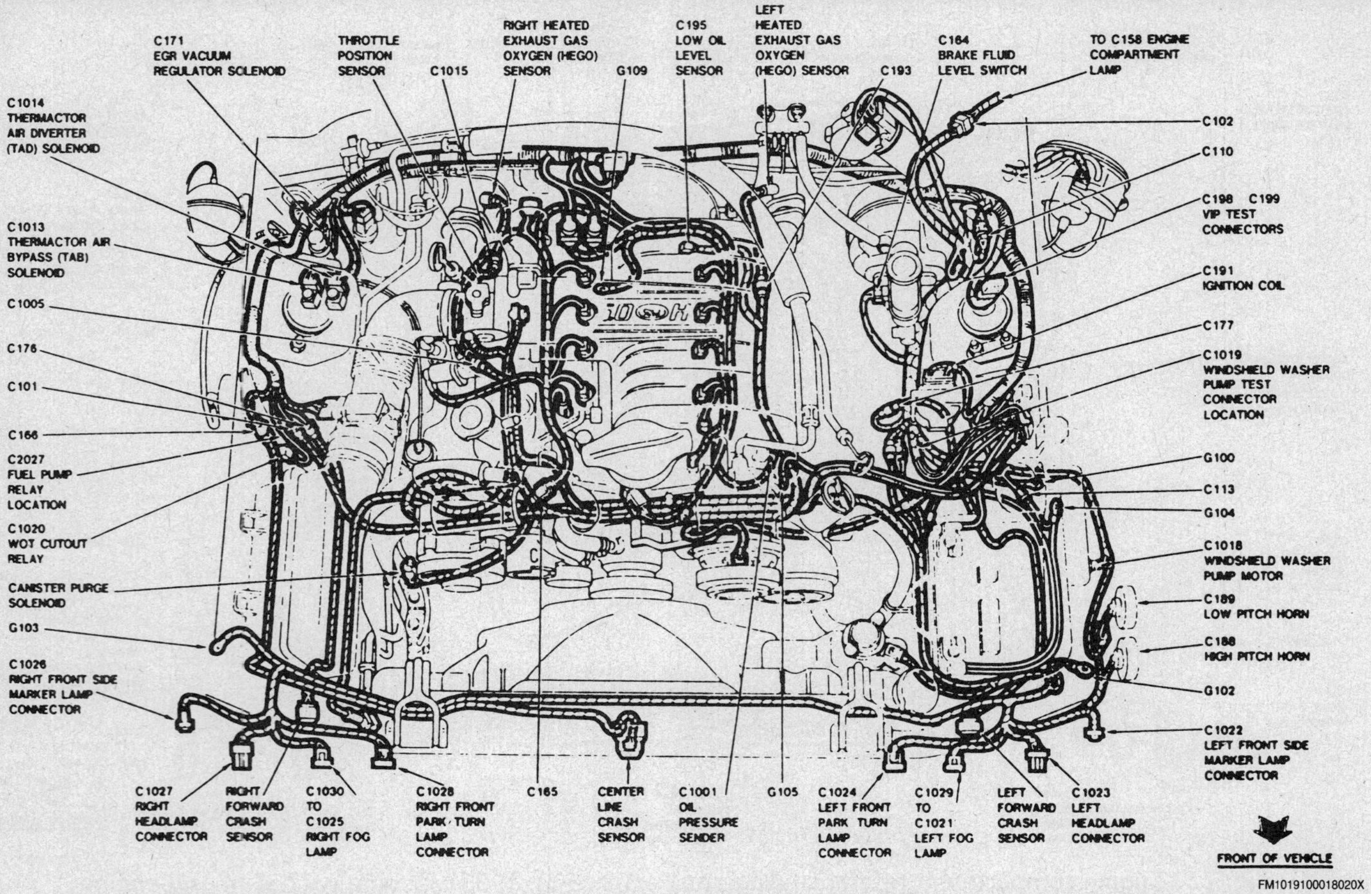

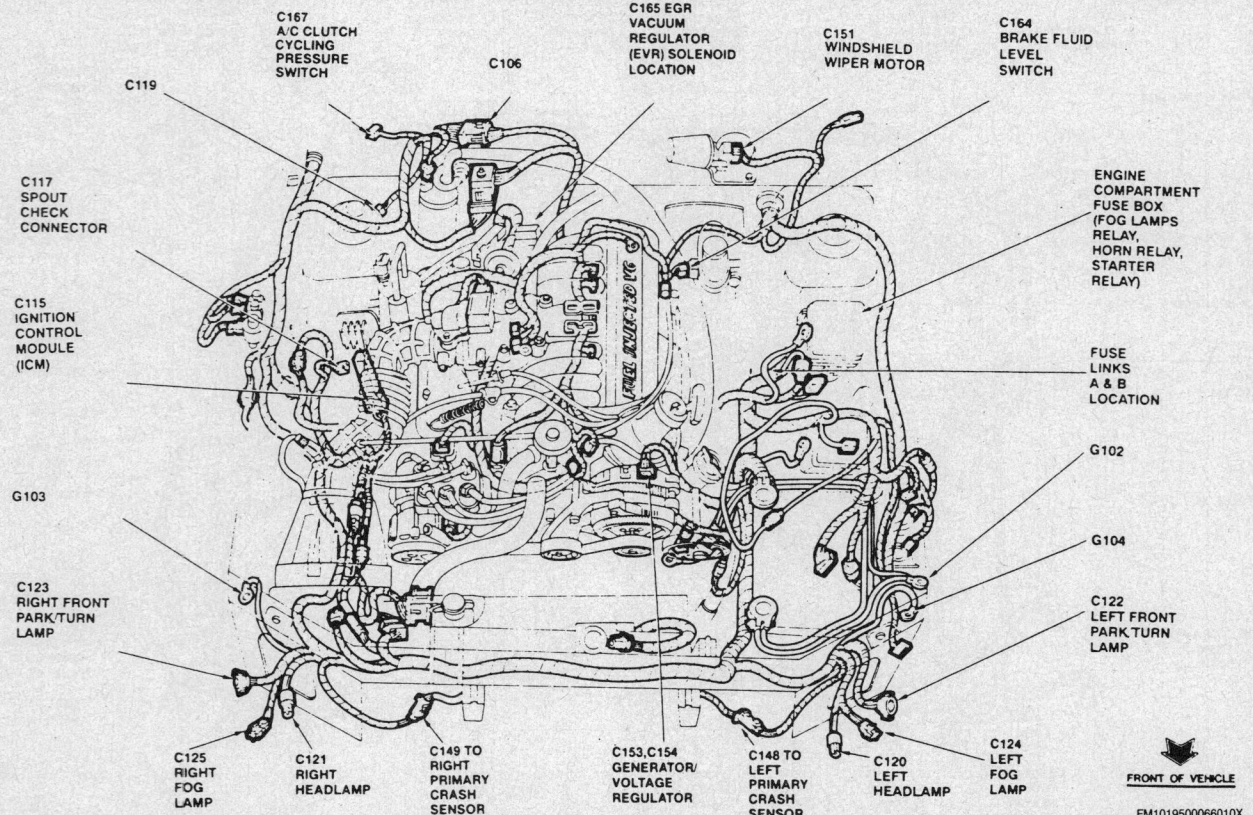

C171 EGR VACUUM REGULATOR SOLENOID

THROTTLE POSITION SENSOR

C1015

RIGHT HEATED EXHAUST GAS OXYGEN (HEGO) SENSOR

C195 LOW OIL LEVEL SENSOR

G109

LEFT HEATED EXHAUST GAS OXYGEN (HEGO) SENSOR

C193

C164 BRAKE FLUID LEVEL SWITCH

TO C158 ENGINE COMPARTMENT LAMP

C1014 THERMACTOR AIR DIVERTER (TAD) SOLENOID

C102

C110

C198 C199 VIP TEST CONNECTORS

C1013 THERMACTOR AIR BYPASS (TAB) SOLENOID

C191 IGNITION COIL

C1005

C177

C176

C1019 WINDSHIELD WASHER PUMP TEST CONNECTOR LOCATION

C101

C166

G100

C2027 FUEL PUMP RELAY LOCATION

C113

G104

C1020 WOT CUTOUT RELAY

C1018 WINDSHIELD WASHER PUMP MOTOR

CANISTER PURGE SOLENOID

C189 LOW PITCH HORN

C188 HIGH PITCH HORN

G103

G102

C1026 RIGHT FRONT SIDE MARKER LAMP CONNECTOR

C1022 LEFT FRONT SIDE MARKER LAMP CONNECTOR

C1027 RIGHT HEADLAMP CONNECTOR

RIGHT FORWARD CRASH SENSOR

C1030 TO C1025 RIGHT FOG LAMP

C1028 RIGHT FRONT PARK·TURN LAMP CONNECTOR

C165

CENTER LINE CRASH SENSOR

C1001 OIL PRESSURE SENDER

G105

C1024 LEFT FRONT PARK TURN LAMP CONNECTOR

C1029 TO C1021 LEFT FOG LAMP

LEFT FORWARD CRASH SENSOR

C1023 LEFT HEADLAMP CONNECTOR

FRONT OF VEHICLE

FM1019100018020X

Fig. 23   Engine compartment reference diagram (Part 2 of 2). 1993 Mustang w/5.0L/V8-302 engine

C167 A/C CLUTCH CYCLING PRESSURE SWITCH

C165 EGR VACUUM REGULATOR (EVR) SOLENOID LOCATION

C151 WINDSHIELD WIPER MOTOR

C164 BRAKE FLUID LEVEL SWITCH

C119

C106

C117 SPOUT CHECK CONNECTOR

ENGINE COMPARTMENT FUSE BOX (FOG LAMPS RELAY, HORN RELAY, STARTER RELAY)

C115 IGNITION CONTROL MODULE (ICM)

FUSE LINKS A & B LOCATION

G102

G103

G104

C123 RIGHT FRONT PARK/TURN LAMP

C122 LEFT FRONT PARK.TURN LAMP

C125 RIGHT FOG LAMP

C121 RIGHT HEADLAMP

C149 TO RIGHT PRIMARY CRASH SENSOR

C153,C154 GENERATOR/ VOLTAGE REGULATOR

C148 TO LEFT PRIMARY CRASH SENSOR

C120 LEFT HEADLAMP

C124 LEFT FOG LAMP

FRONT OF VEHICLE

FM1019500066010X

Fig. 24   Engine compartment reference diagram (Part 1 of 3). 1994–95 Mustang w/3.8L/V6-232 engine

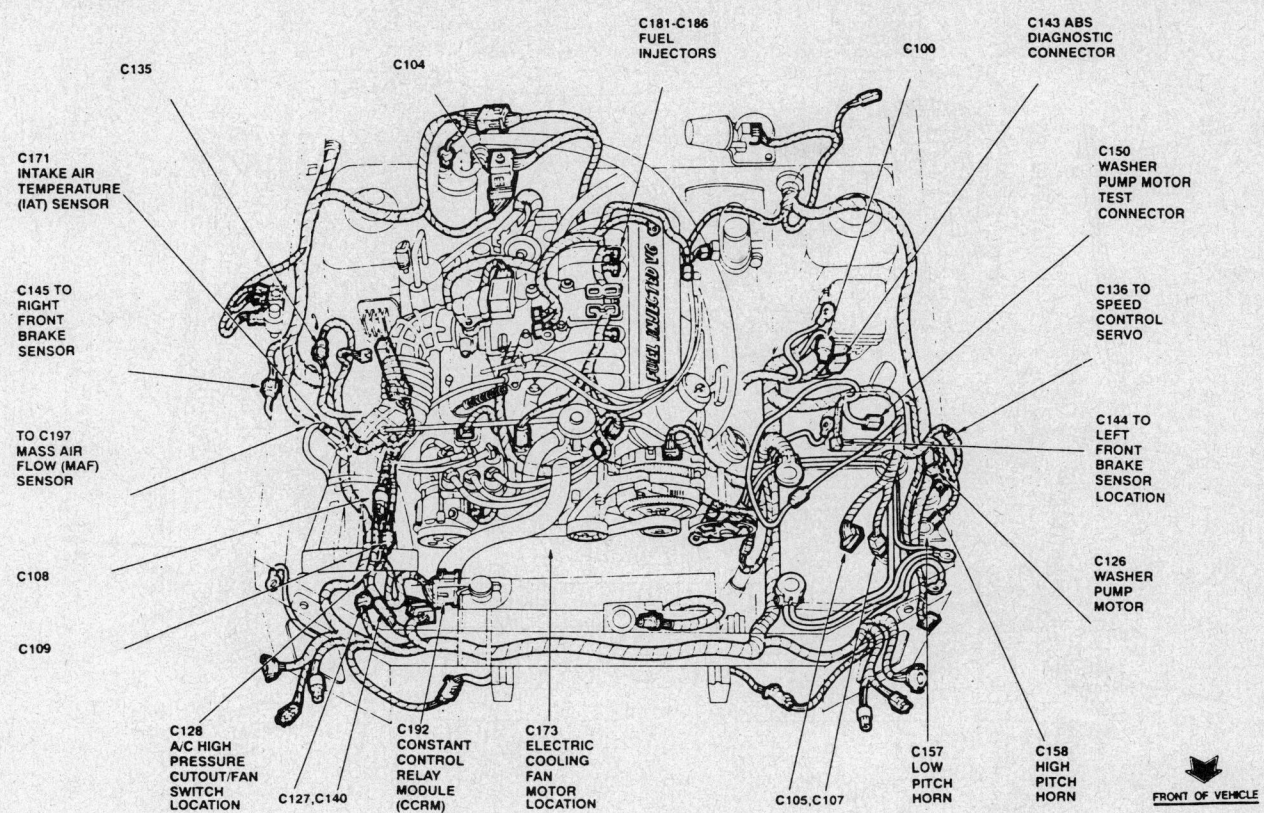

Fig. 24   Engine compartment reference diagram (Part 2 of 3). 1994-95 Mustang w/3.8L/V6-232 engine

FM1019500066020X

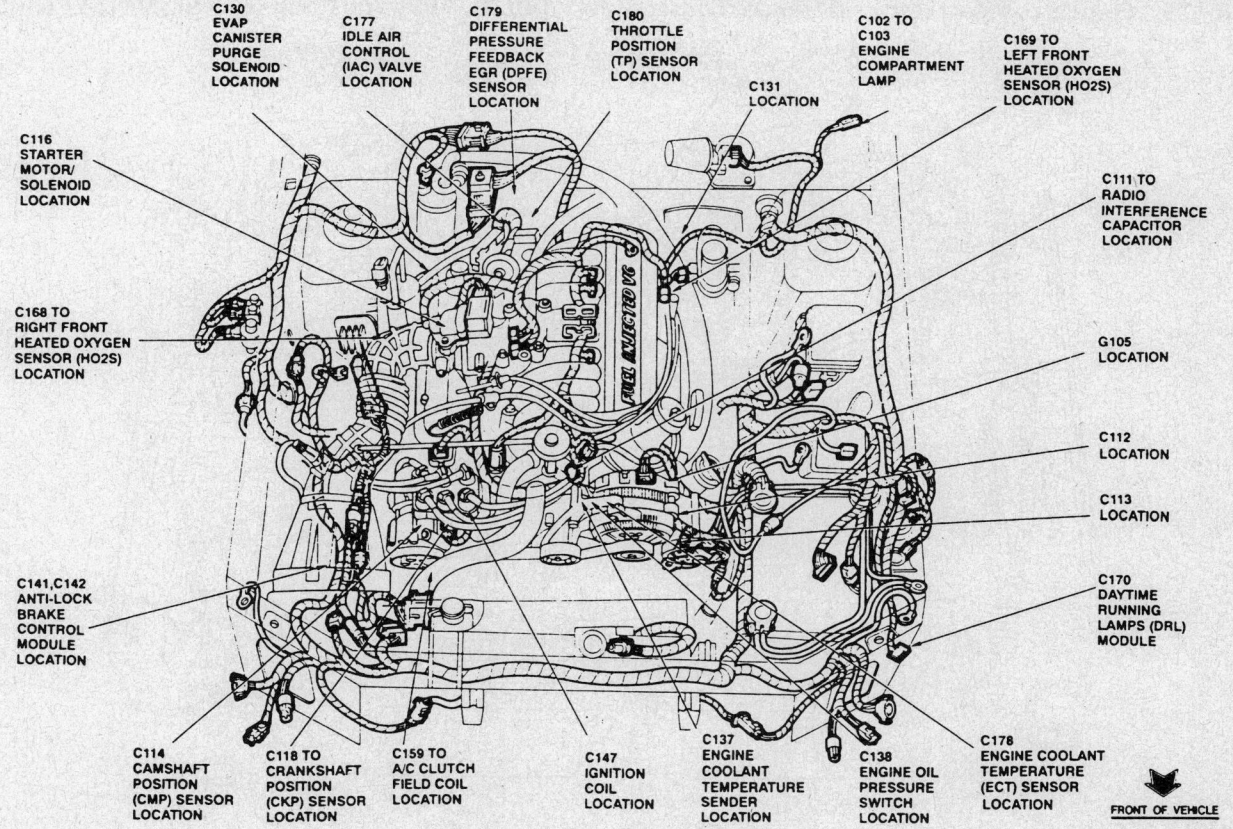

Fig. 24   Engine compartment reference diagram (Part 3 of 3). 1994-95 Mustang w/3.8L/V6-232 engine

FM1019500066030X

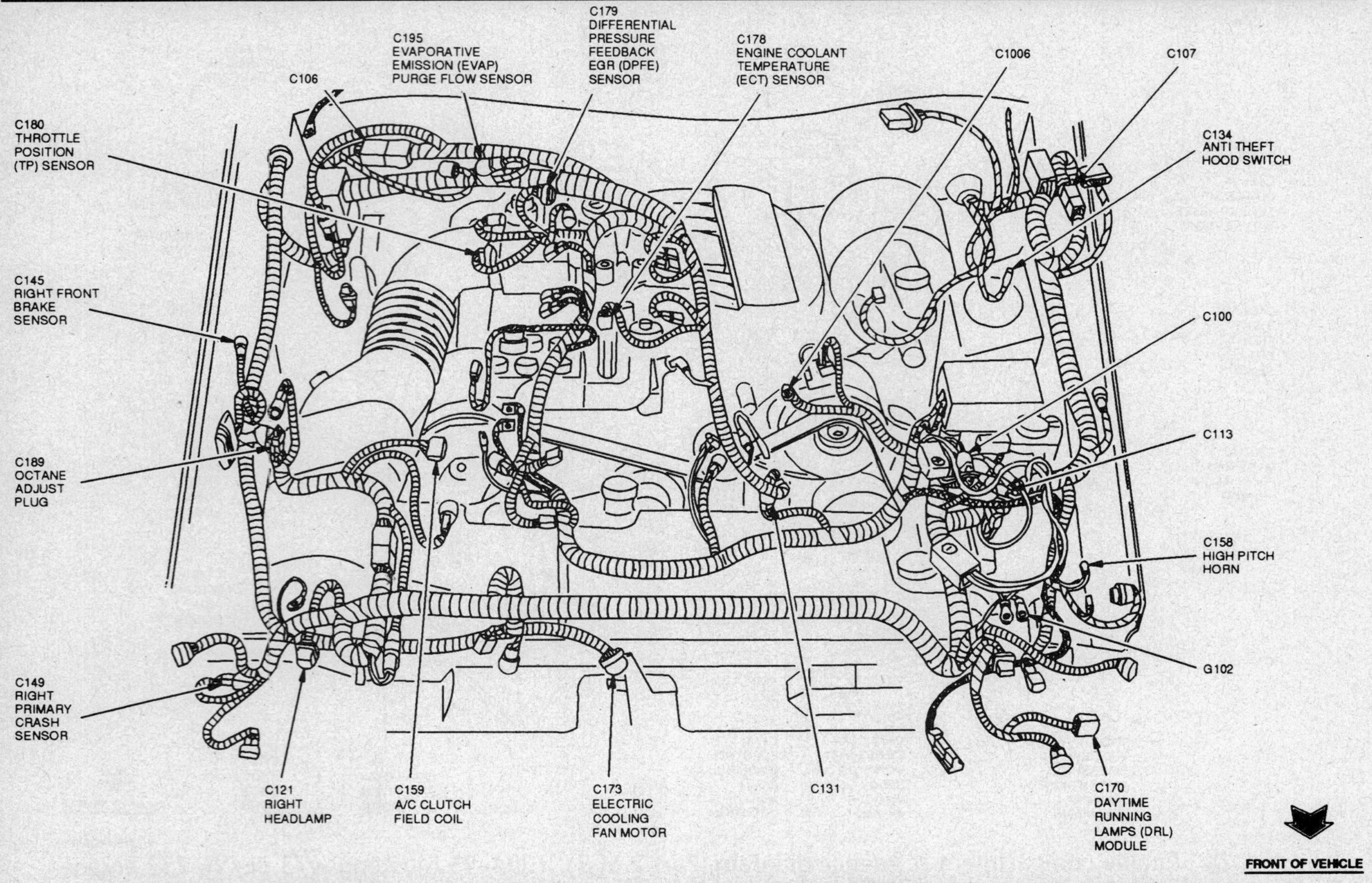

FORD–Engine Compartment Reference Diagrams

C180
THROTTLE
POSITION
(TP) SENSOR

C145
RIGHT FRONT
BRAKE
SENSOR

C189
OCTANE
ADJUST
PLUG

C149
RIGHT
PRIMARY
CRASH
SENSOR

C106

C195
EVAPORATIVE
EMISSION (EVAP)
PURGE FLOW SENSOR

C179
DIFFERENTIAL
PRESSURE
FEEDBACK
EGR (DPFE)
SENSOR

C178
ENGINE COOLANT
TEMPERATURE
(ECT) SENSOR

C1006

C107

C134
ANTI THEFT
HOOD SWITCH

C100

C113

C158
HIGH PITCH
HORN

G102

C121
RIGHT
HEADLAMP

C159
A/C CLUTCH
FIELD COIL

C173
ELECTRIC
COOLING
FAN MOTOR

C131

C170
DAYTIME
RUNNING
LAMPS (DRL)
MODULE

FRONT OF VEHICLE

Fig. 25   Engine compartment reference diagram (Part 1 of 3). 1996 Mustang w/3.8L/V6-232 engine

C119

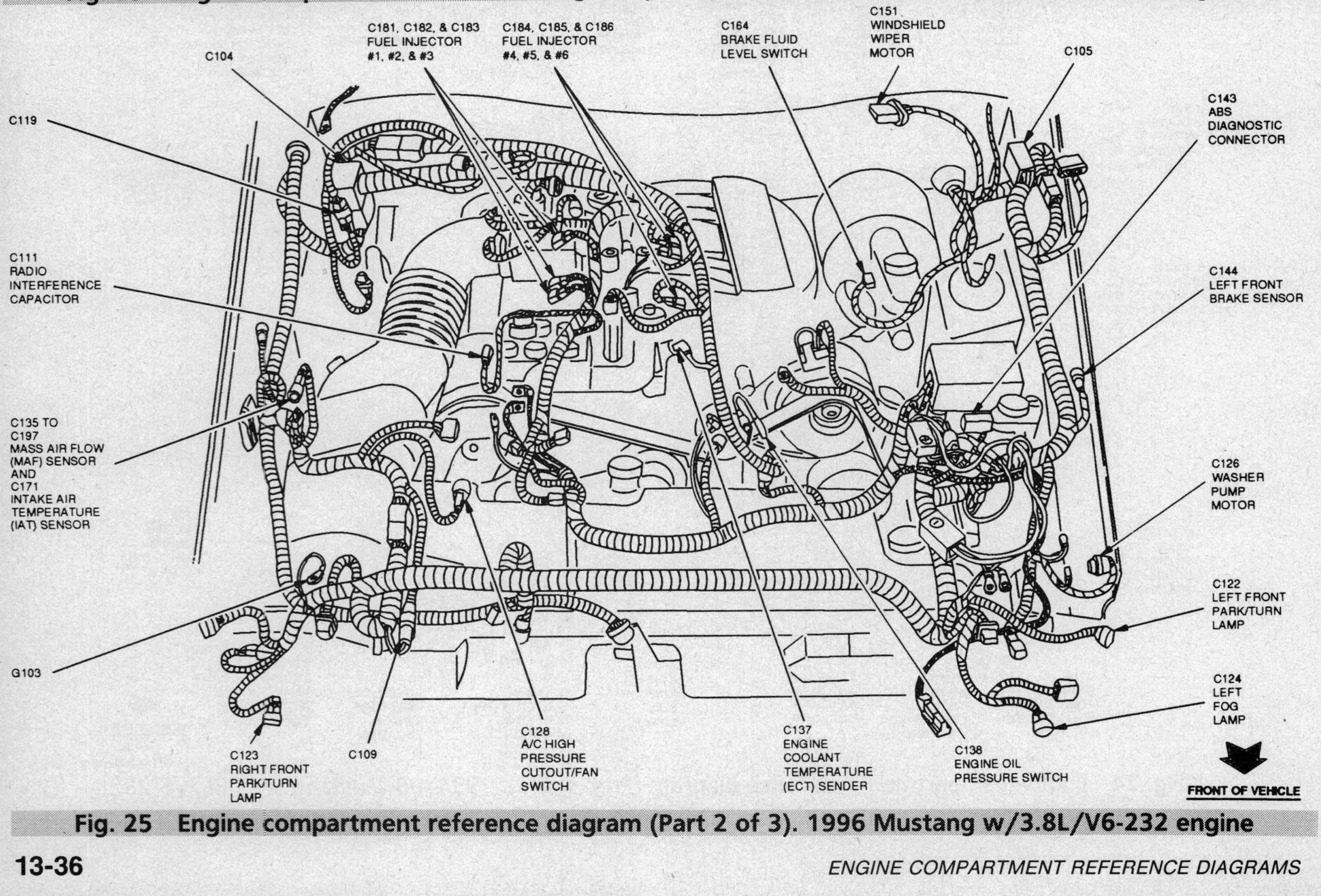

C104

C181, C182, & C183
FUEL INJECTOR
#1, #2, & #3

C184, C185, & C186
FUEL INJECTOR
#4, #5, & #6

C164
BRAKE FLUID
LEVEL SWITCH

C151
WINDSHIELD
WIPER
MOTOR

C105

C143
ABS
DIAGNOSTIC
CONNECTOR

C111
RADIO
INTERFERENCE
CAPACITOR

C144
LEFT FRONT
BRAKE SENSOR

C135 TO
C197
MASS AIR FLOW
(MAF) SENSOR
AND
C171
INTAKE AIR
TEMPERATURE
(IAT) SENSOR

C126
WASHER
PUMP
MOTOR

C122
LEFT FRONT
PARK/TURN
LAMP

G103

C124
LEFT
FOG
LAMP

C123
RIGHT FRONT
PARK/TURN
LAMP

C109

C128
A/C HIGH
PRESSURE
CUTOUT/FAN
SWITCH

C137
ENGINE
COOLANT
TEMPERATURE
(ECT) SENDER

C138
ENGINE OIL
PRESSURE SWITCH

FRONT OF VEHICLE

Fig. 25   Engine compartment reference diagram (Part 2 of 3). 1996 Mustang w/3.8L/V6-232 engine

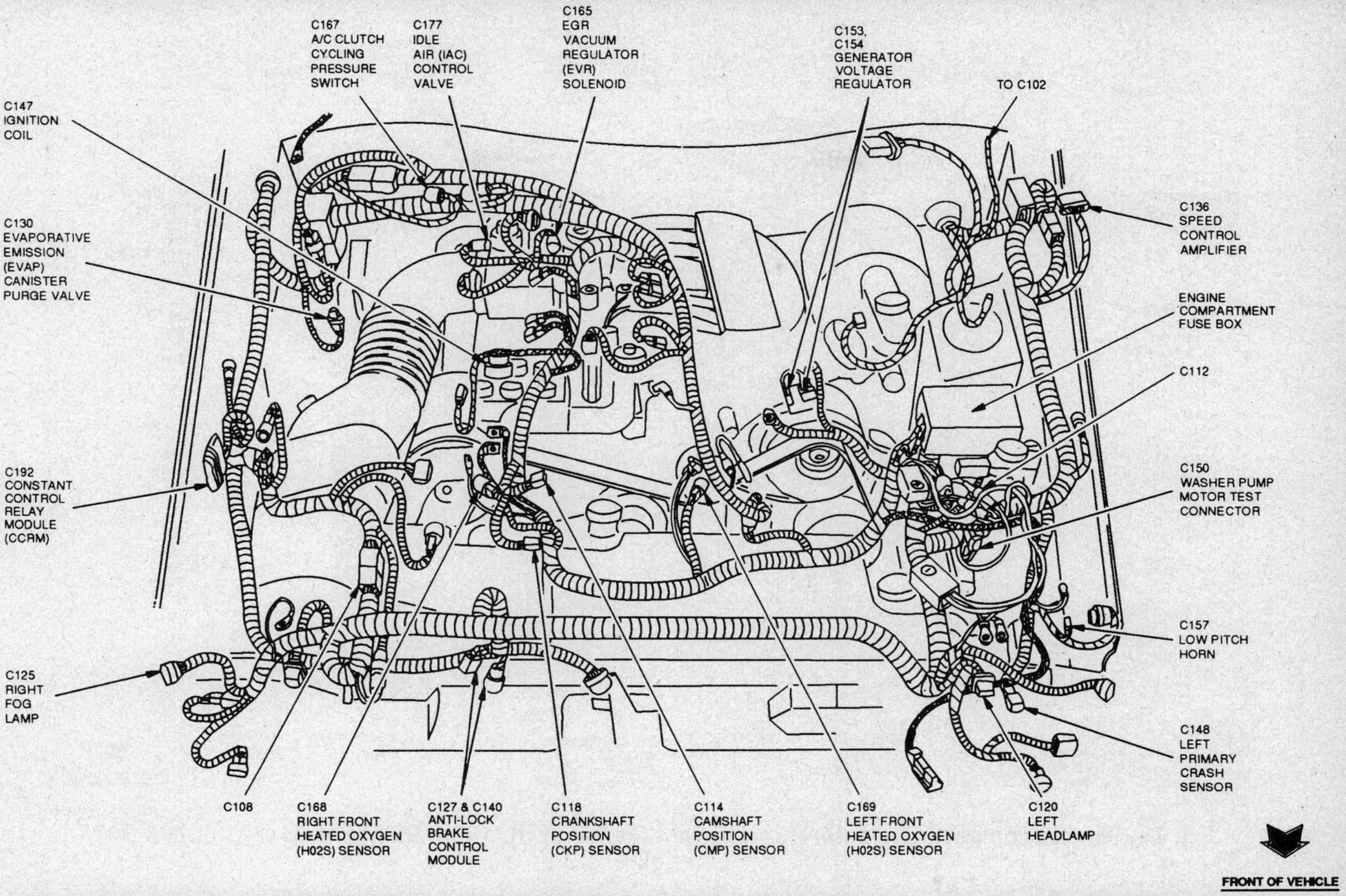

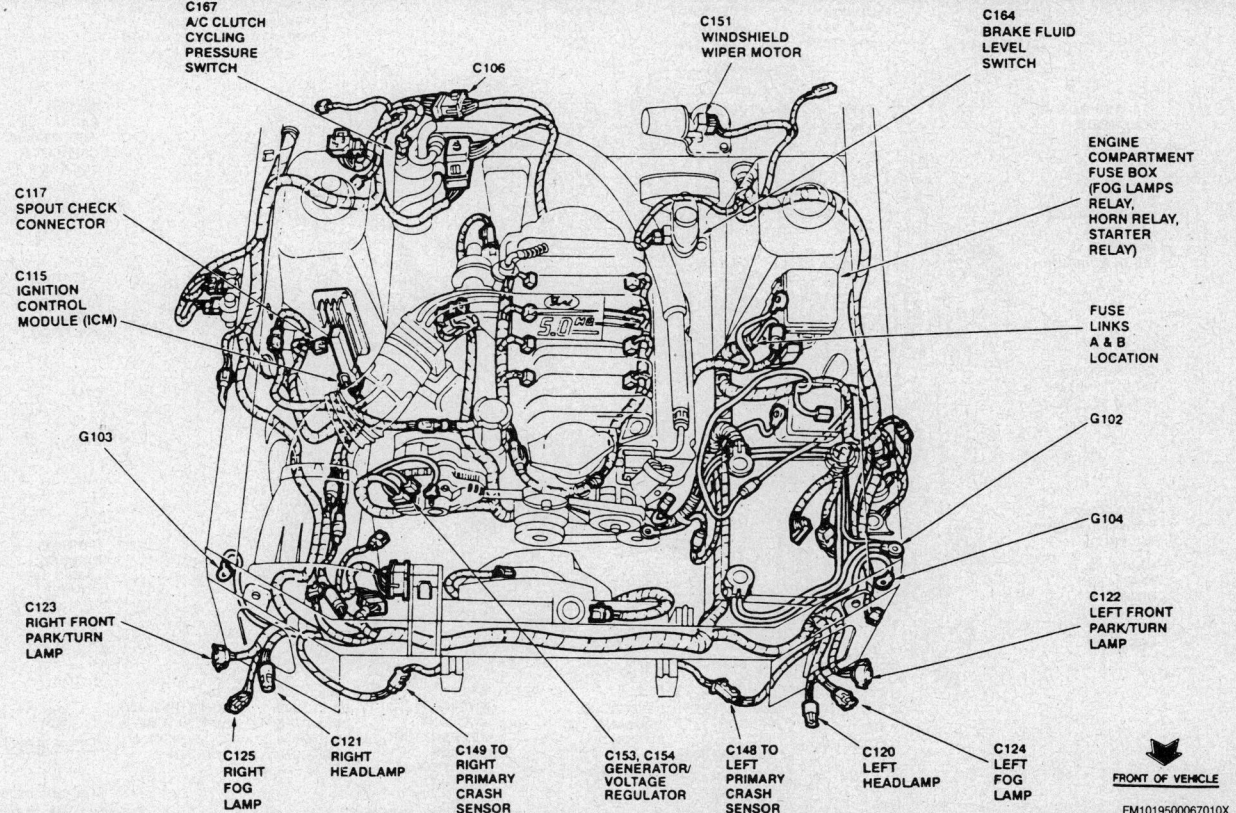

C167
A/C CLUTCH
CYCLING
PRESSURE
SWITCH

C177
IDLE
AIR (IAC)
CONTROL
VALVE

C165
EGR
VACUUM
REGULATOR
(EVR)
SOLENOID

C153,
C154
GENERATOR
VOLTAGE
REGULATOR

TO C102

C147
IGNITION
COIL

C136
SPEED
CONTROL
AMPLIFIER

C130
EVAPORATIVE
EMISSION
(EVAP)
CANISTER
PURGE VALVE

ENGINE
COMPARTMENT
FUSE BOX

C112

C192
CONSTANT
CONTROL
RELAY
MODULE
(CCRM)

C150
WASHER PUMP
MOTOR TEST
CONNECTOR

C157
LOW PITCH
HORN

C125
RIGHT
FOG
LAMP

C148
LEFT
PRIMARY
CRASH
SENSOR

C108

C168
RIGHT FRONT
HEATED OXYGEN
(H02S) SENSOR

C127 & C140
ANTI-LOCK
BRAKE
CONTROL
MODULE

C118
CRANKSHAFT
POSITION
(CKP) SENSOR

C114
CAMSHAFT
POSITION
(CMP) SENSOR

C169
LEFT FRONT
HEATED OXYGEN
(H02S) SENSOR

C120
LEFT
HEADLAMP

FRONT OF VEHICLE

Fig. 25   Engine compartment reference diagram (Part 3 of 3). 1996 Mustang w/3.8L/V6-232 engine

C167
A/C CLUTCH
CYCLING
PRESSURE
SWITCH

C106

C151
WINDSHIELD
WIPER MOTOR

C164
BRAKE FLUID
LEVEL
SWITCH

C117
SPOUT CHECK
CONNECTOR

ENGINE
COMPARTMENT
FUSE BOX
(FOG LAMPS
RELAY,
HORN RELAY,
STARTER
RELAY)

C115
IGNITION
CONTROL
MODULE (ICM)

FUSE
LINKS
A & B
LOCATION

G103

G102

G104

C123
RIGHT FRONT
PARK/TURN
LAMP

C122
LEFT FRONT
PARK/TURN
LAMP

C125
RIGHT
FOG
LAMP

C121
RIGHT
HEADLAMP

C149 TO
RIGHT
PRIMARY
CRASH
SENSOR

C153, C154
GENERATOR/
VOLTAGE
REGULATOR

C148 TO
LEFT
PRIMARY
CRASH
SENSOR

C120
LEFT
HEADLAMP

C124
LEFT
FOG
LAMP

FRONT OF VEHICLE

FM1019500067010X

Fig. 26   Engine compartment reference diagram (Part 1 of 3). 1994–95 Mustang w/5.0L/V8-302 engine

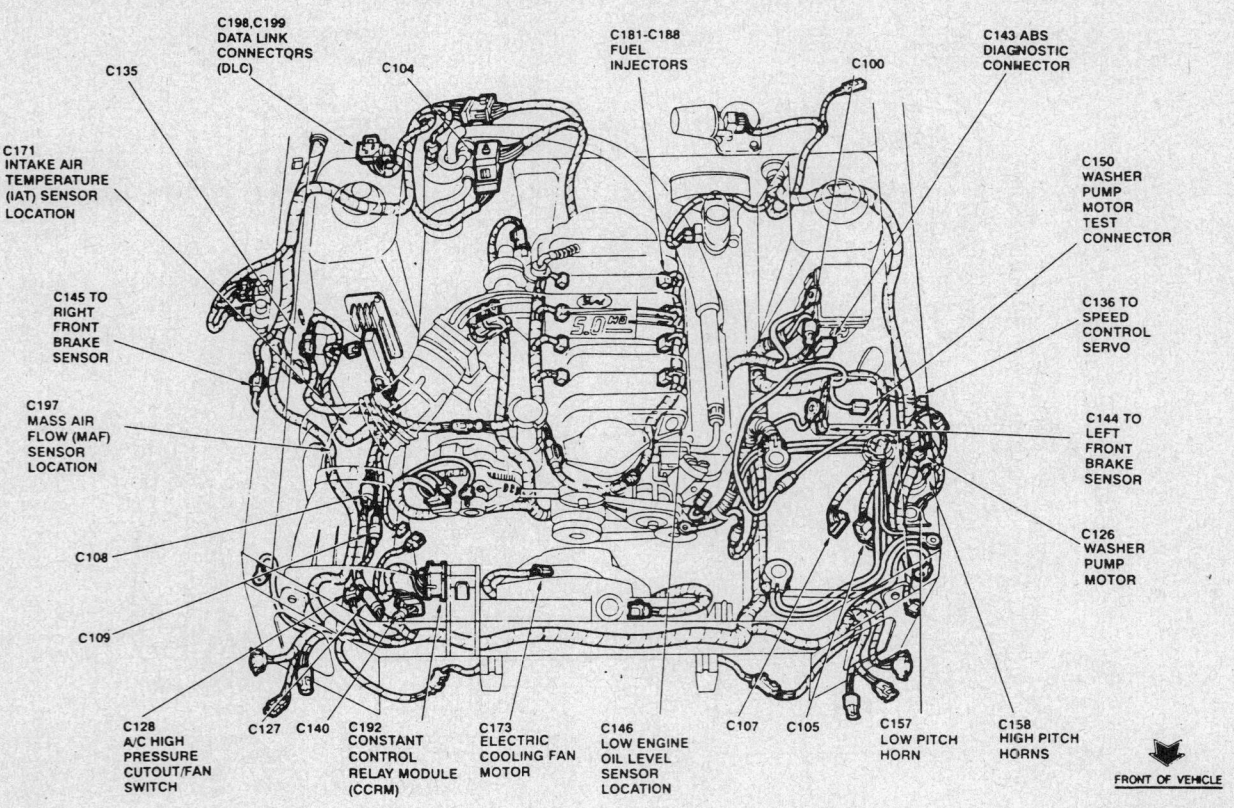

Fig. 26 Engine compartment reference diagram (Part 2 of 3). 1994–95 Mustang w/5.0L/V8-302 engine

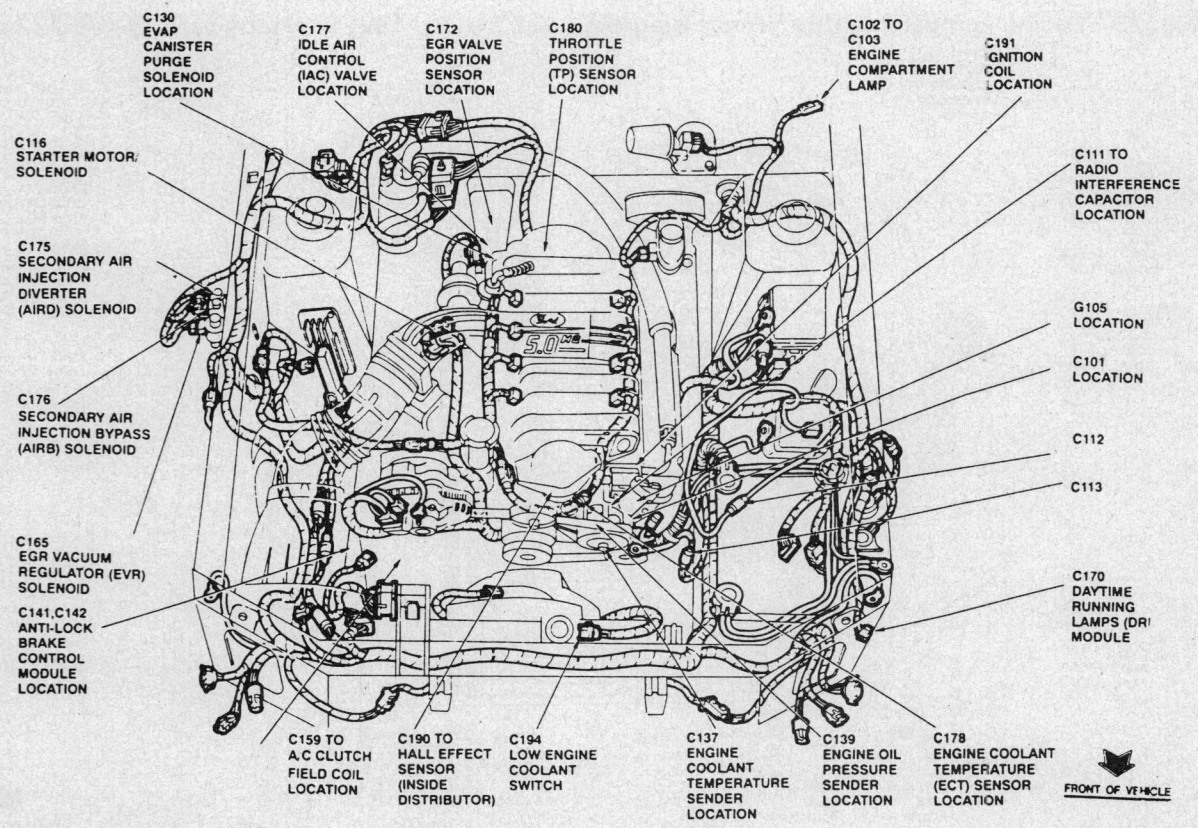

Fig. 26 Engine compartment reference diagram (Part 3 of 3). 1994–95 Mustang w/5.0L/V8-302 engine

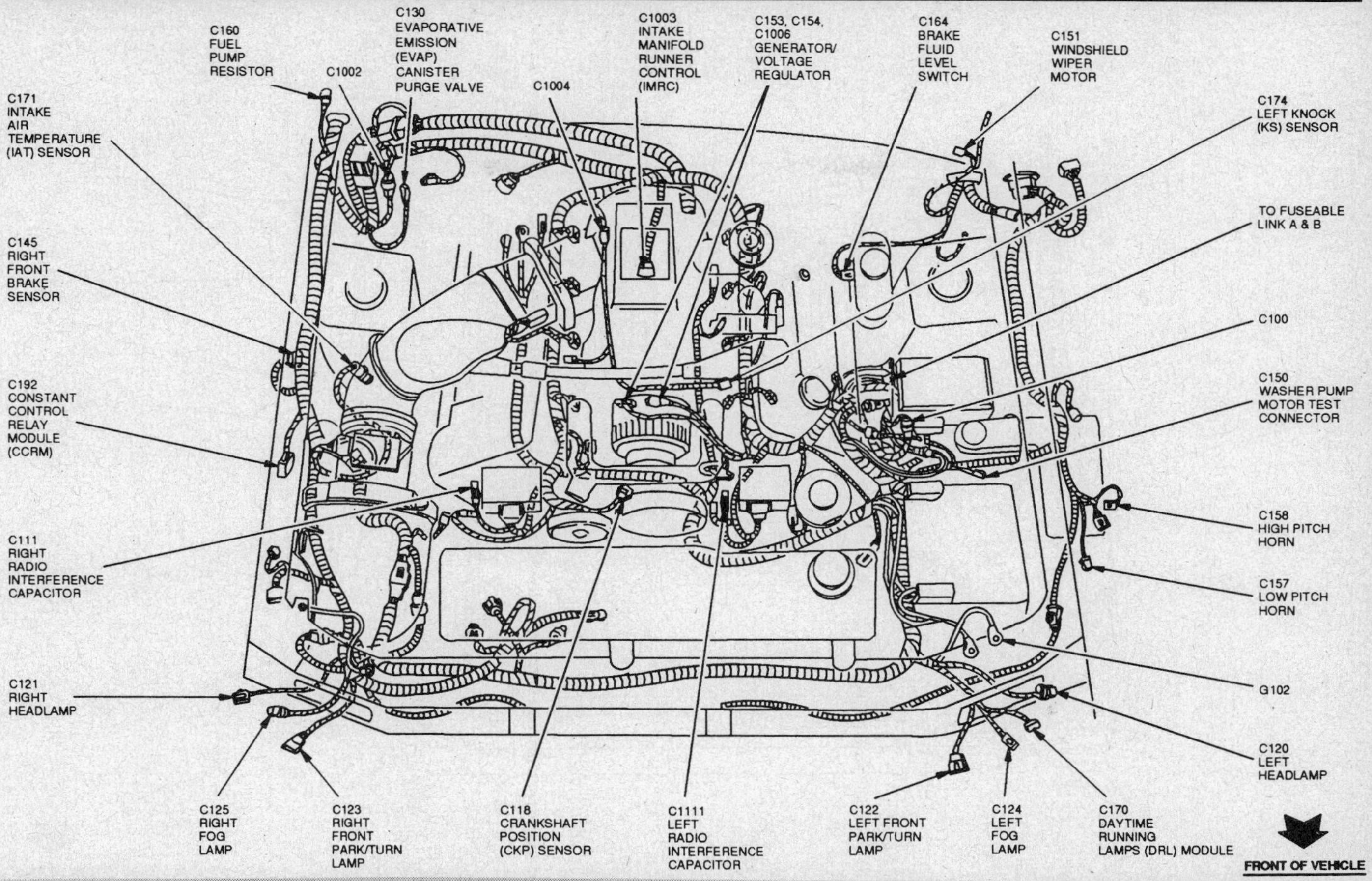

C160
FUEL
PUMP
RESISTOR

C130
EVAPORATIVE
EMISSION
(EVAP)
CANISTER
PURGE VALVE

C1003
INTAKE
MANIFOLD
RUNNER
CONTROL
(IMRC)

C153, C154,
C1006
GENERATOR/
VOLTAGE
REGULATOR

C164
BRAKE
FLUID
LEVEL
SWITCH

C151
WINDSHIELD
WIPER
MOTOR

C1002

C1004

C171
INTAKE
AIR
TEMPERATURE
(IAT) SENSOR

C174
LEFT KNOCK
(KS) SENSOR

C145
RIGHT
FRONT
BRAKE
SENSOR

TO FUSEABLE
LINK A & B

C100

C192
CONSTANT
CONTROL
RELAY
MODULE
(CCRM)

C150
WASHER PUMP
MOTOR TEST
CONNECTOR

C158
HIGH PITCH
HORN

C111
RIGHT
RADIO
INTERFERENCE
CAPACITOR

C157
LOW PITCH
HORN

G102

C121
RIGHT
HEADLAMP

C120
LEFT
HEADLAMP

C125
RIGHT
FOG
LAMP

C123
RIGHT
FRONT
PARK/TURN
LAMP

C118
CRANKSHAFT
POSITION
(CKP) SENSOR

C1111
LEFT
RADIO
INTERFERENCE
CAPACITOR

C122
LEFT FRONT
PARK/TURN
LAMP

C124
LEFT
FOG
LAMP

C170
DAYTIME
RUNNING
LAMPS (DRL) MODULE

FRONT OF VEHICLE

Fig. 27   Engine compartment reference diagram (Part 1 of 3). 1996 Mustang w/4.6L/V8-281 DOHC engine

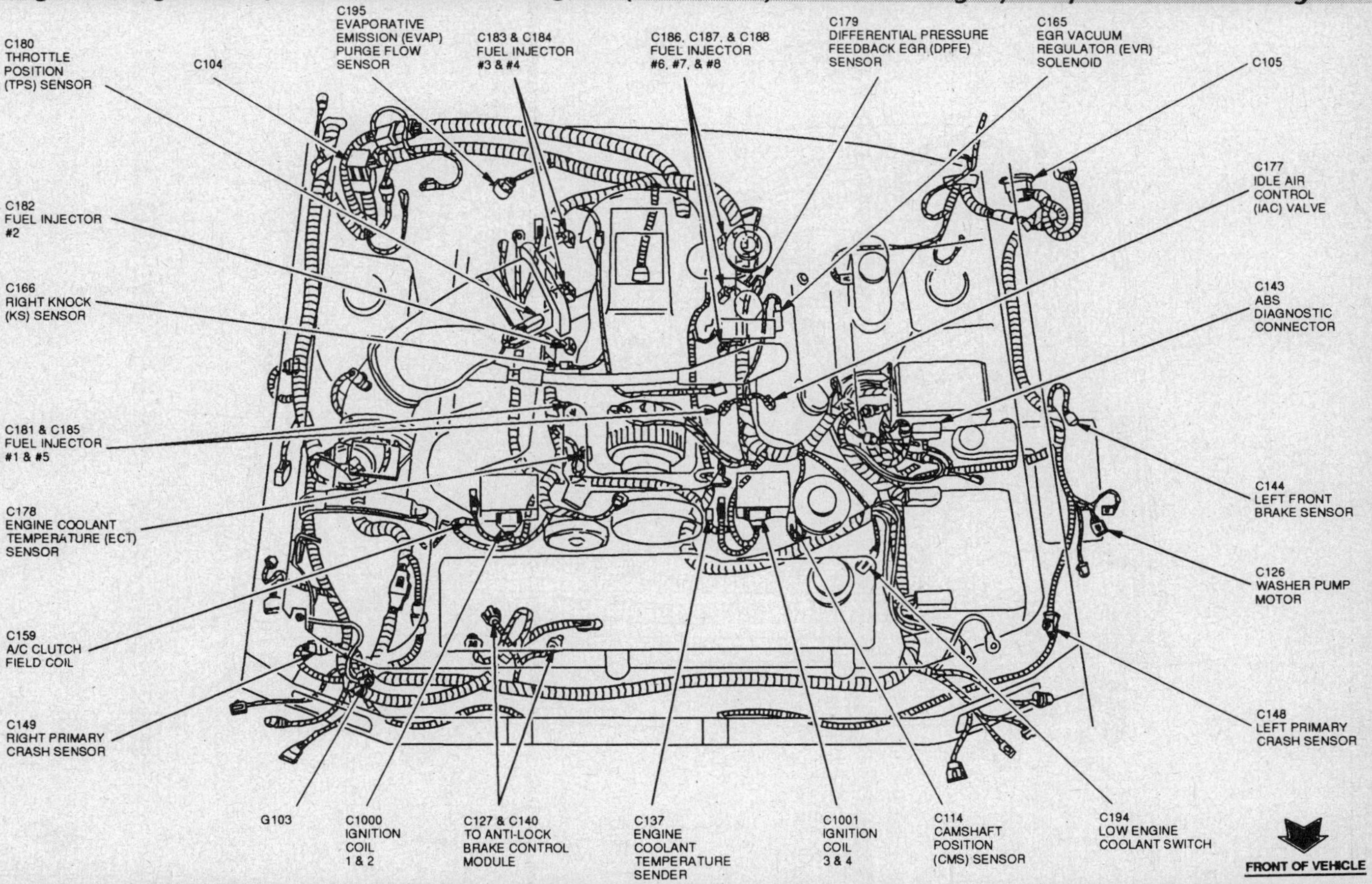

C180
THROTTLE
POSITION
(TPS) SENSOR

C104

C195
EVAPORATIVE
EMISSION (EVAP)
PURGE FLOW
SENSOR

C183 & C184
FUEL INJECTOR
#3 & #4

C186, C187, & C188
FUEL INJECTOR
#6, #7, & #8

C179
DIFFERENTIAL PRESSURE
FEEDBACK EGR (DPFE)
SENSOR

C165
EGR VACUUM
REGULATOR (EVR)
SOLENOID

C105

C177
IDLE AIR
CONTROL
(IAC) VALVE

C182
FUEL INJECTOR
#2

C166
RIGHT KNOCK
(KS) SENSOR

C143
ABS
DIAGNOSTIC
CONNECTOR

C181 & C185
FUEL INJECTOR
#1 & #5

C178
ENGINE COOLANT
TEMPERATURE (ECT)
SENSOR

C144
LEFT FRONT
BRAKE SENSOR

C126
WASHER PUMP
MOTOR

C159
A/C CLUTCH
FIELD COIL

C149
RIGHT PRIMARY
CRASH SENSOR

C148
LEFT PRIMARY
CRASH SENSOR

G103

C1000
IGNITION
COIL
1 & 2

C127 & C140
TO ANTI-LOCK
BRAKE CONTROL
MODULE

C137
ENGINE
COOLANT
TEMPERATURE
SENDER

C1001
IGNITION
COIL
3 & 4

C114
CAMSHAFT
POSITION
(CMS) SENSOR

C194
LOW ENGINE
COOLANT SWITCH

FRONT OF VEHICLE

Fig. 27   Engine compartment reference diagram (Part 2 of 3). 1996 Mustang w/4.6L/V8-281 DOHC engine

ENGINE COMPARTMENT REFERENCE DIAGRAMS

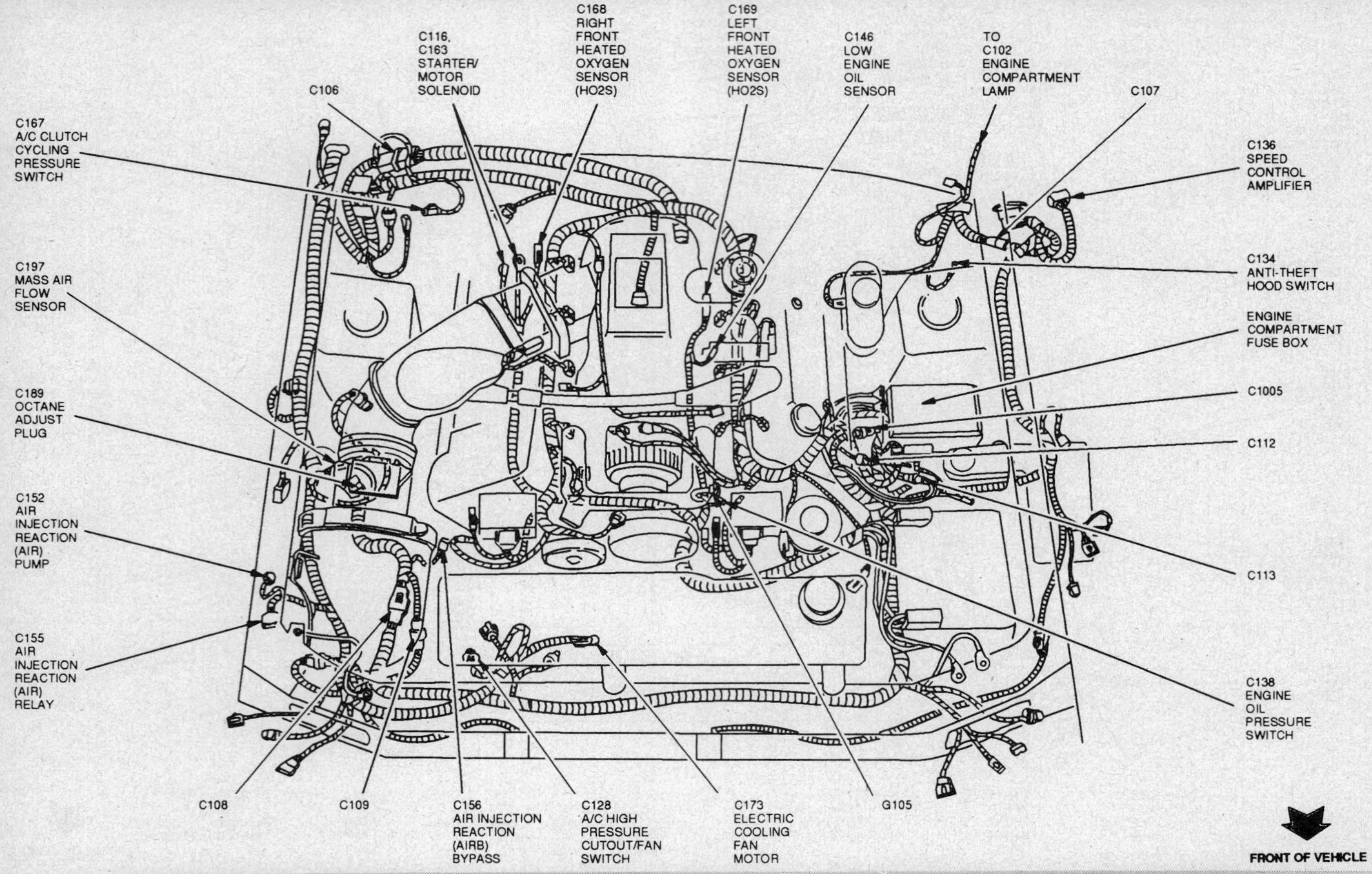

C116,
C163
STARTER/
MOTOR
SOLENOID

C168
RIGHT
FRONT
HEATED
OXYGEN
SENSOR
(HO2S)

C169
LEFT
FRONT
HEATED
OXYGEN
SENSOR
(HO2S)

C146
LOW
ENGINE
OIL
SENSOR

TO
C102
ENGINE
COMPARTMENT
LAMP

C106

C107

C167
A/C CLUTCH
CYCLING
PRESSURE
SWITCH

C136
SPEED
CONTROL
AMPLIFIER

C197
MASS AIR
FLOW
SENSOR

C134
ANTI-THEFT
HOOD SWITCH

ENGINE
COMPARTMENT
FUSE BOX

C189
OCTANE
ADJUST
PLUG

C1005

C112

C152
AIR
INJECTION
REACTION
(AIR)
PUMP

C113

C155
AIR
INJECTION
REACTION
(AIR)
RELAY

C138
ENGINE
OIL
PRESSURE
SWITCH

C108

C109

C156
AIR INJECTION
REACTION
(AIRB)
BYPASS

C128
A/C HIGH
PRESSURE
CUTOUT/FAN
SWITCH

C173
ELECTRIC
COOLING
FAN
MOTOR

G105

FRONT OF VEHICLE

Fig. 27   Engine compartment reference diagram (Part 3 of 3). 1996 Mustang w/4.6L/V8-281 DOHC engine

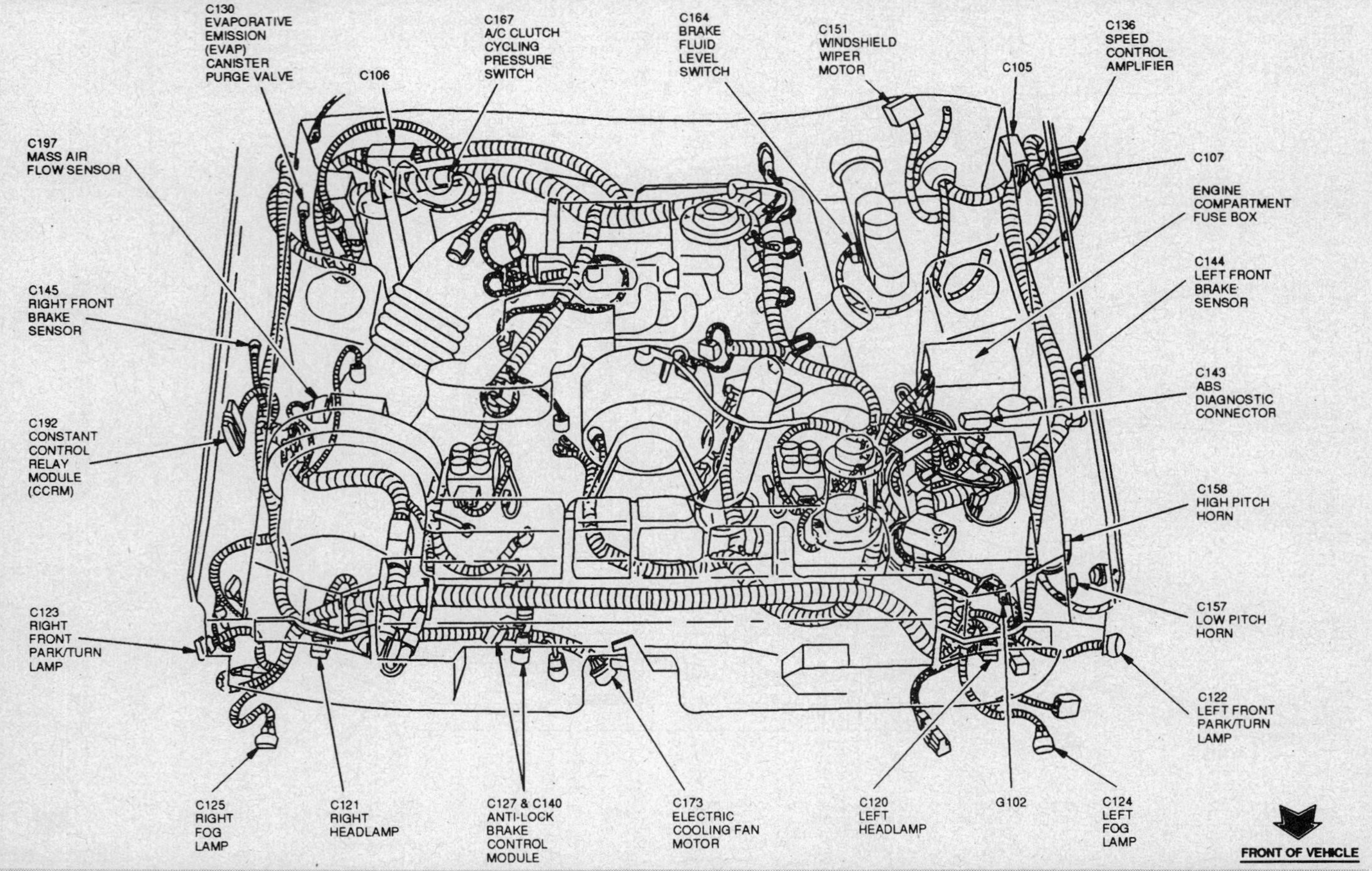

C130
EVAPORATIVE
EMISSION
(EVAP)
CANISTER
PURGE VALVE

C106

C167
A/C CLUTCH
CYCLING
PRESSURE
SWITCH

C164
BRAKE
FLUID
LEVEL
SWITCH

C151
WINDSHIELD
WIPER
MOTOR

C105

C136
SPEED
CONTROL
AMPLIFIER

C197
MASS AIR
FLOW SENSOR

C107

ENGINE
COMPARTMENT
FUSE BOX

C145
RIGHT FRONT
BRAKE
SENSOR

C144
LEFT FRONT
BRAKE
SENSOR

C143
ABS
DIAGNOSTIC
CONNECTOR

C192
CONSTANT
CONTROL
RELAY
MODULE
(CCRM)

C158
HIGH PITCH
HORN

C123
RIGHT
FRONT
PARK/TURN
LAMP

C157
LOW PITCH
HORN

C122
LEFT FRONT
PARK/TURN
LAMP

C125
RIGHT
FOG
LAMP

C121
RIGHT
HEADLAMP

C127 & C140
ANTI-LOCK
BRAKE
CONTROL
MODULE

C173
ELECTRIC
COOLING FAN
MOTOR

C120
LEFT
HEADLAMP

G102

C124
LEFT
FOG
LAMP

FRONT OF VEHICLE

Fig. 28   Engine compartment reference diagram (Part 1 of 3). 1996 Mustang w/4.6L/V8-281 SOHC engine

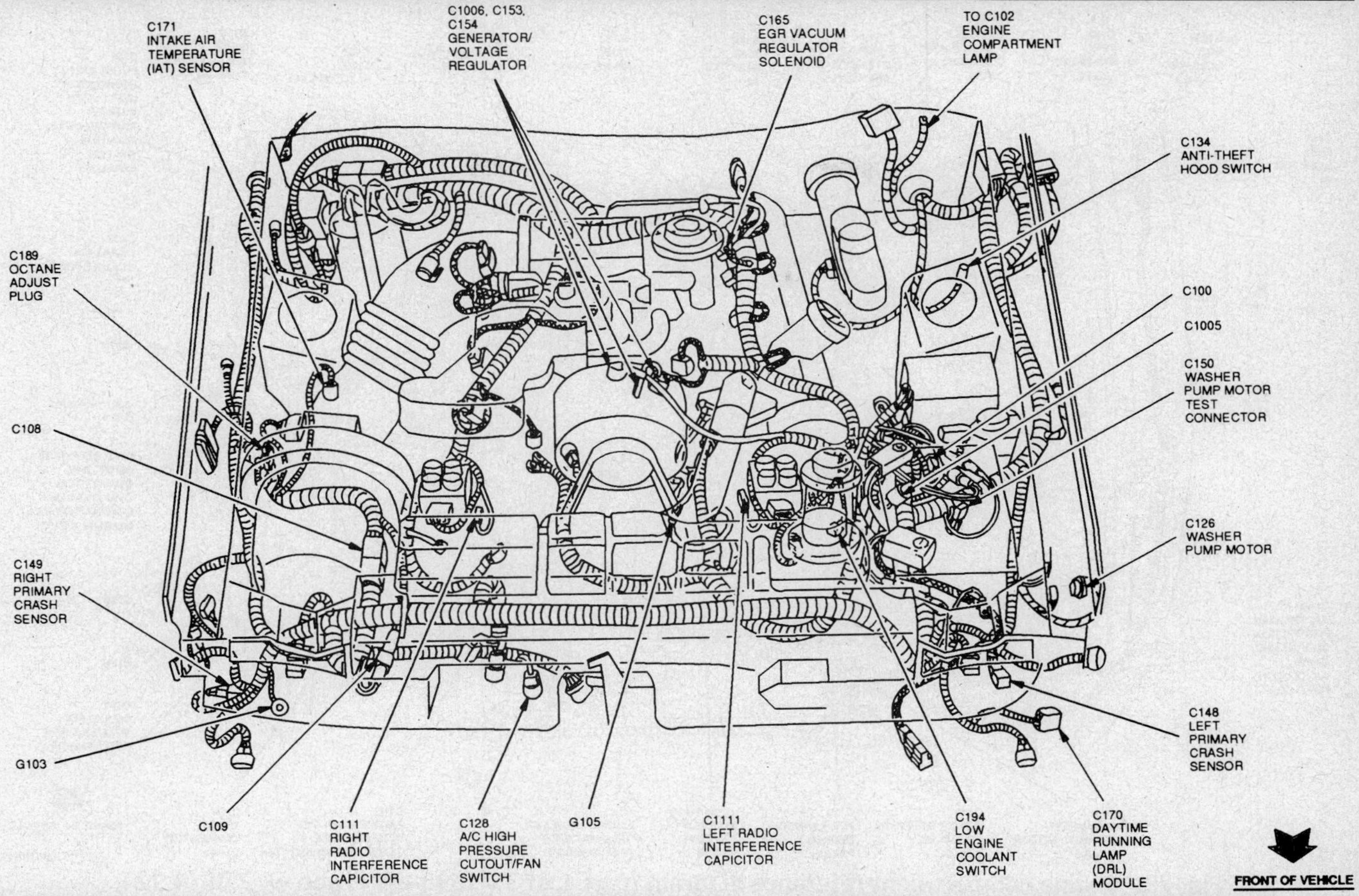

C171
INTAKE AIR
TEMPERATURE
(IAT) SENSOR

C1006, C153,
C154
GENERATOR/
VOLTAGE
REGULATOR

C165
EGR VACUUM
REGULATOR
SOLENOID

TO C102
ENGINE
COMPARTMENT
LAMP

C134
ANTI-THEFT
HOOD SWITCH

C189
OCTANE
ADJUST
PLUG

C100

C1005

C150
WASHER
PUMP MOTOR
TEST
CONNECTOR

C108

C126
WASHER
PUMP MOTOR

C149
RIGHT
PRIMARY
CRASH
SENSOR

C148
LEFT
PRIMARY
CRASH
SENSOR

G103

C109

C111
RIGHT
RADIO
INTERFERENCE
CAPICITOR

C128
A/C HIGH
PRESSURE
CUTOUT/FAN
SWITCH

G105

C1111
LEFT RADIO
INTERFERENCE
CAPICITOR

C194
LOW
ENGINE
COOLANT
SWITCH

C170
DAYTIME
RUNNING
LAMP
(DRL)
MODULE

FRONT OF VEHICLE

Fig. 28   Engine compartment reference diagram (Part 2 of 3). 1996 Mustang w/4.6L/V8-281 SOHC engine

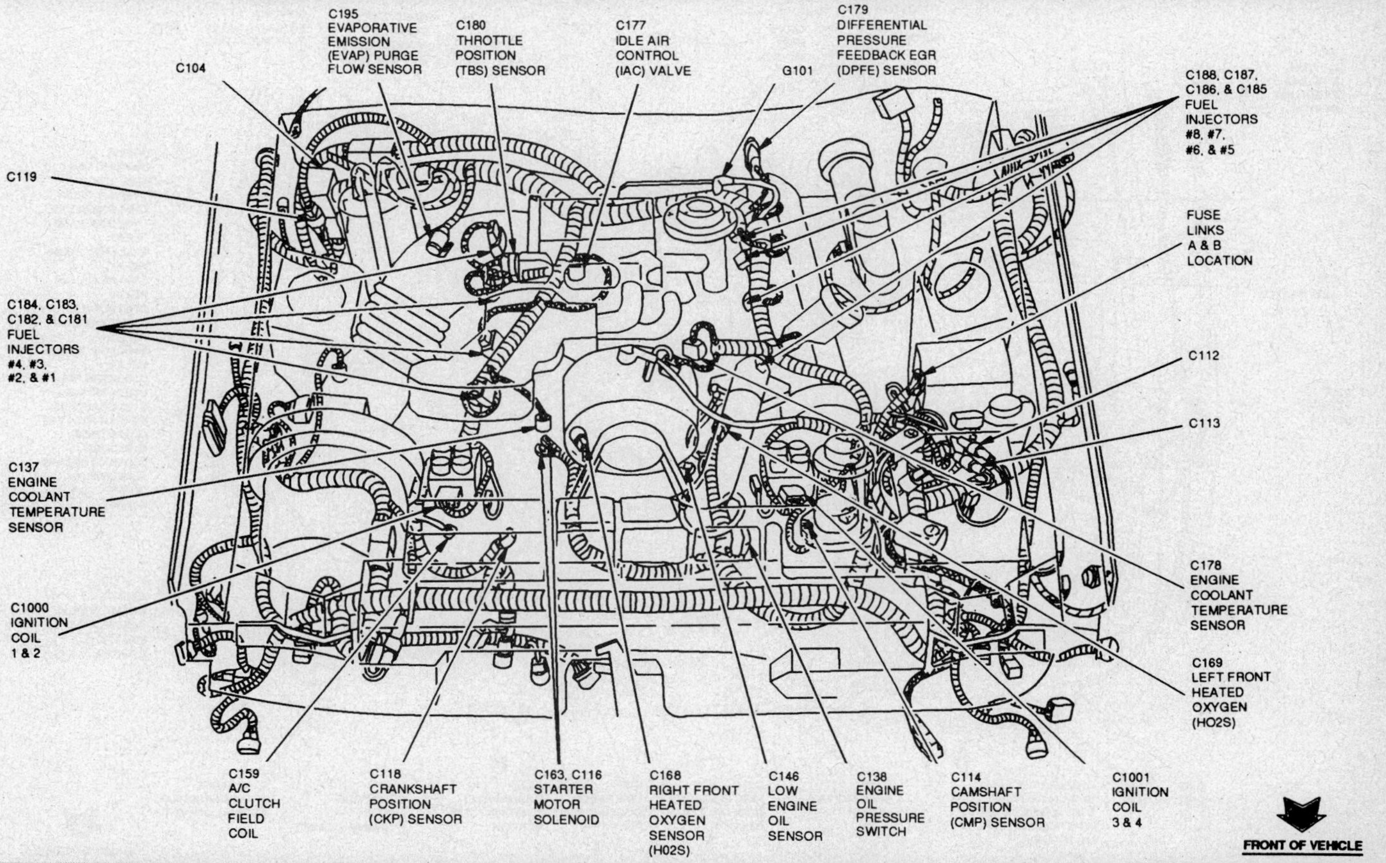

C104

C195
EVAPORATIVE
EMISSION
(EVAP) PURGE
FLOW SENSOR

C180
THROTTLE
POSITION
(TBS) SENSOR

C177
IDLE AIR
CONTROL
(IAC) VALVE

G101

C179
DIFFERENTIAL
PRESSURE
FEEDBACK EGR
(DPFE) SENSOR

C188, C187,
C186, & C185
FUEL
INJECTORS
#8, #7,
#6, & #5

C119

FUSE
LINKS
A & B
LOCATION

C184, C183,
C182, & C181
FUEL
INJECTORS
#4, #3,
#2, & #1

C112

C113

C137
ENGINE
COOLANT
TEMPERATURE
SENSOR

C178
ENGINE
COOLANT
TEMPERATURE
SENSOR

C1000
IGNITION
COIL
1 & 2

C169
LEFT FRONT
HEATED
OXYGEN
(HO2S)

C159
A/C
CLUTCH
FIELD
COIL

C118
CRANKSHAFT
POSITION
(CKP) SENSOR

C163, C116
STARTER
MOTOR
SOLENOID

C168
RIGHT FRONT
HEATED
OXYGEN
SENSOR
(HO2S)

C146
LOW
ENGINE
OIL
SENSOR

C138
ENGINE
OIL
PRESSURE
SWITCH

C114
CAMSHAFT
POSITION
(CMP) SENSOR

C1001
IGNITION
COIL
3 & 4

FRONT OF VEHICLE

Fig. 28   Engine compartment reference diagram (Part 3 of 3). 1996 Mustang w/4.6L/V8-281 SOHC engine

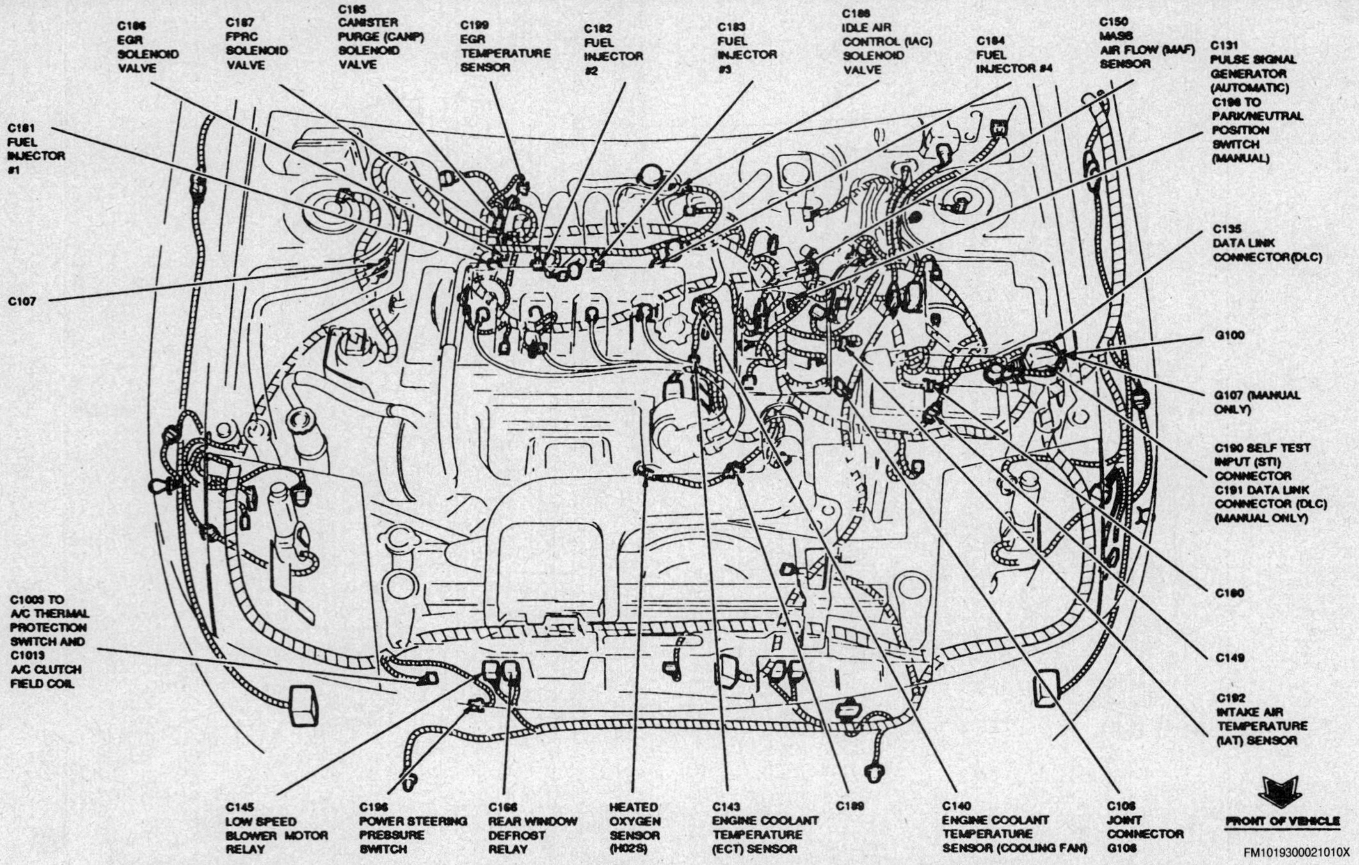

C186 EGR SOLENOID VALVE
C187 FPRC SOLENOID VALVE
C185 CANISTER PURGE (CANP) SOLENOID VALVE
C199 EGR TEMPERATURE SENSOR
C182 FUEL INJECTOR #2
C183 FUEL INJECTOR #3
C188 IDLE AIR CONTROL (IAC) SOLENOID VALVE
C184 FUEL INJECTOR #4
C150 MASS AIR FLOW (MAF) SENSOR
C131 PULSE SIGNAL GENERATOR (AUTOMATIC)
C196 TO PARK/NEUTRAL POSITION SWITCH (MANUAL)
C181 FUEL INJECTOR #1
C107
C135 DATA LINK CONNECTOR (DLC)
G100
G107 (MANUAL ONLY)
C190 SELF TEST INPUT (STI) CONNECTOR
C191 DATA LINK CONNECTOR (DLC) (MANUAL ONLY)
C190
C149
C192 INTAKE AIR TEMPERATURE (IAT) SENSOR
C1005 TO A/C THERMAL PROTECTION SWITCH AND C1013 A/C CLUTCH FIELD COIL
C145 LOW SPEED BLOWER MOTOR RELAY
C195 POWER STEERING PRESSURE SWITCH
C166 REAR WINDOW DEFROST RELAY
HEATED OXYGEN SENSOR (HO2S)
C143 ENGINE COOLANT TEMPERATURE (ECT) SENSOR
C189
C140 ENGINE COOLANT TEMPERATURE SENSOR (COOLING FAN)
C106 JOINT CONNECTOR G106
FRONT OF VEHICLE
FM1019300021010X

Fig. 29   Engine compartment reference diagram (Part 1 of 3). 1993–95 Probe w/2.0L/4-121

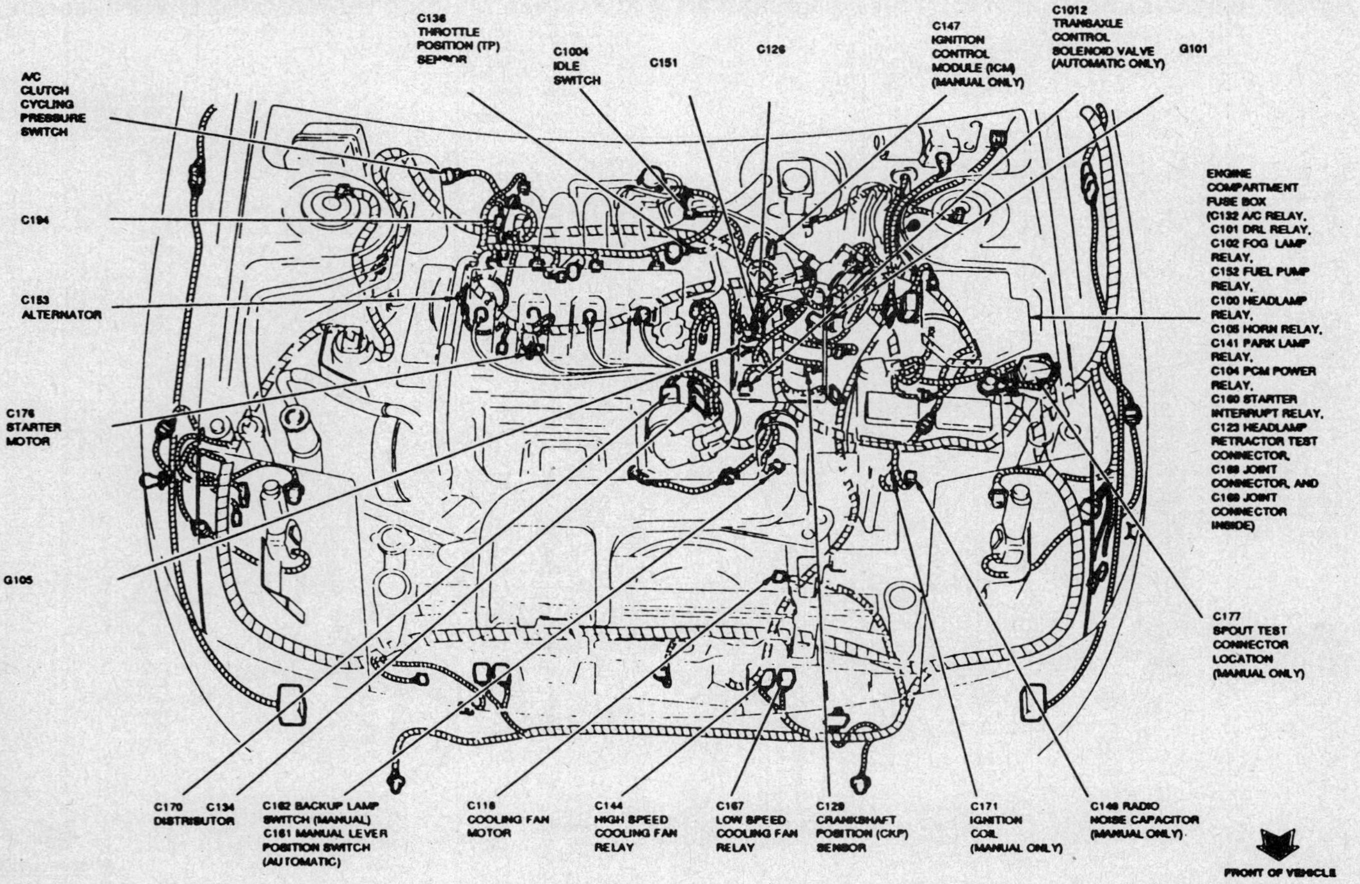

C136 THROTTLE POSITION (TP) SENSOR
C1004 IDLE SWITCH
C151
C126
C147 IGNITION CONTROL MODULE (ICM) (MANUAL ONLY)
C1012 TRANSAXLE CONTROL SOLENOID VALVE (AUTOMATIC ONLY)
G101
A/C CLUTCH CYCLING PRESSURE SWITCH
C194
C153 ALTERNATOR
C176 STARTER MOTOR
G105
ENGINE COMPARTMENT FUSE BOX (C132 A/C RELAY, C101 DRL RELAY, C102 FOG LAMP RELAY, C152 FUEL PUMP RELAY, C100 HEADLAMP RELAY, C105 HORN RELAY, C141 PARK LAMP RELAY, C104 PCM POWER RELAY, C160 STARTER INTERRUPT RELAY, C123 HEADLAMP RETRACTOR TEST CONNECTOR, C108 JOINT CONNECTOR, AND C109 JOINT CONNECTOR INSIDE)
C177 SPOUT TEST CONNECTOR LOCATION (MANUAL ONLY)
C170 DISTRIBUTOR
C134
C162 BACKUP LAMP SWITCH (MANUAL) C161 MANUAL LEVER POSITION SWITCH (AUTOMATIC)
C118 COOLING FAN MOTOR
C144 HIGH SPEED COOLING FAN RELAY
C167 LOW SPEED COOLING FAN RELAY
C129 CRANKSHAFT POSITION (CKP) SENSOR
C171 IGNITION COIL (MANUAL ONLY)
C148 RADIO NOISE CAPACITOR (MANUAL ONLY)
FRONT OF VEHICLE

Fig. 29   Engine compartment cont reference diagram (Part 2 of 3). 1993–95 Probe w/2.0L/4-121

FM1019300021020X

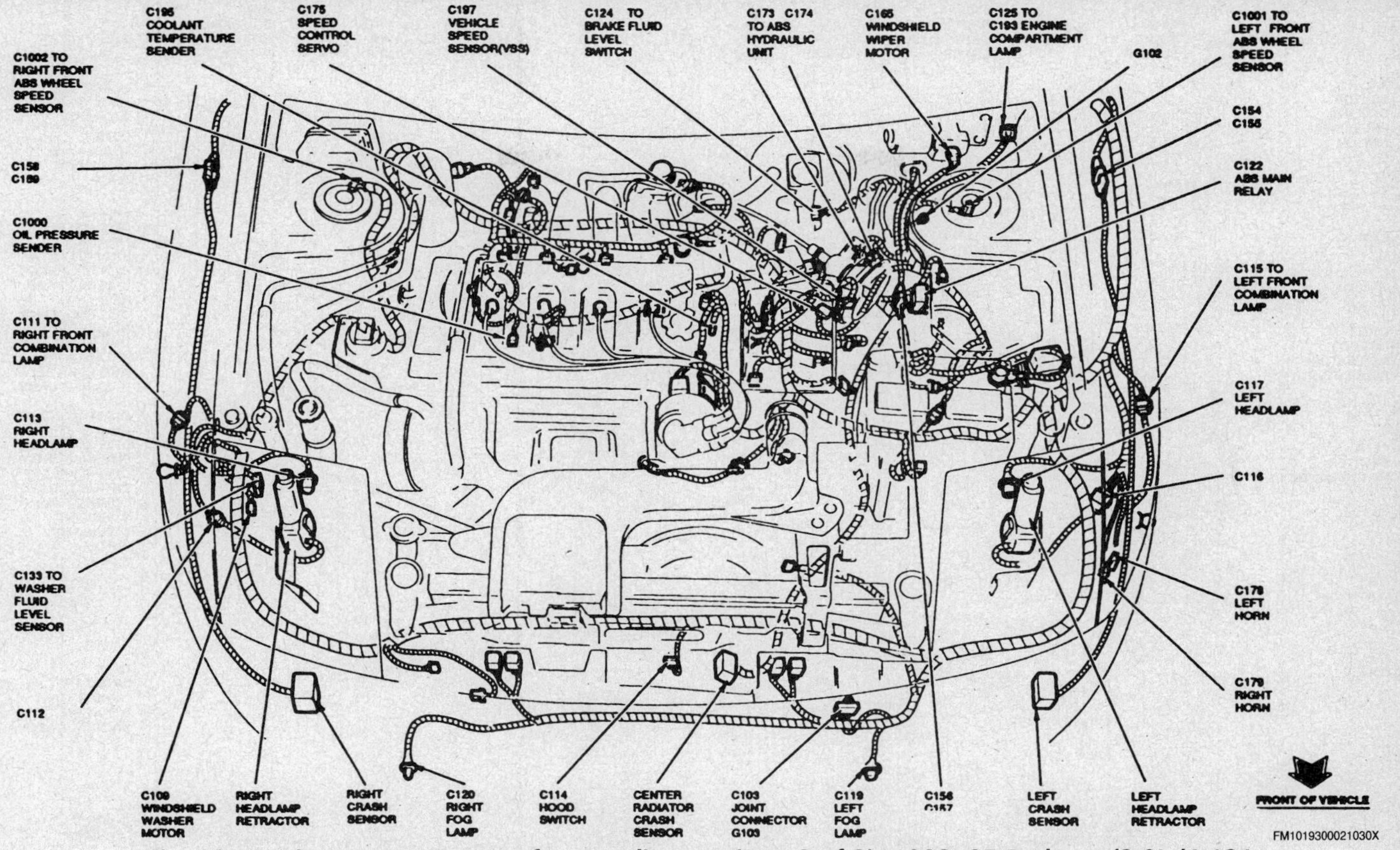

C196 COOLANT TEMPERATURE SENDER

C175 SPEED CONTROL SERVO

C197 VEHICLE SPEED SENSOR(VSS)

C124 TO BRAKE FLUID LEVEL SWITCH

C173 C174 TO ABS HYDRAULIC UNIT

C165 WINDSHIELD WIPER MOTOR

C125 TO C193 ENGINE COMPARTMENT LAMP

G102

C1001 TO LEFT FRONT ABS WHEEL SPEED SENSOR

C1002 TO RIGHT FRONT ABS WHEEL SPEED SENSOR

C158 C159

C1000 OIL PRESSURE SENDER

C111 TO RIGHT FRONT COMBINATION LAMP

C113 RIGHT HEADLAMP

C133 TO WASHER FLUID LEVEL SENSOR

C112

C154 C155

C122 ABS MAIN RELAY

C115 TO LEFT FRONT COMBINATION LAMP

C117 LEFT HEADLAMP

C116

C178 LEFT HORN

C179 RIGHT HORN

C109 WINDSHIELD WASHER MOTOR

RIGHT HEADLAMP RETRACTOR

RIGHT CRASH SENSOR

C120 RIGHT FOG LAMP

C114 HOOD SWITCH

CENTER RADIATOR CRASH SENSOR

C103 JOINT CONNECTOR G103

C119 LEFT FOG LAMP

C156 C157

LEFT CRASH SENSOR

LEFT HEADLAMP RETRACTOR

FRONT OF VEHICLE

FM1019300021030X

Fig. 29 Engine compartment reference diagram (Part 3 of 3). 1993–95 Probe w/2.0L/4-121

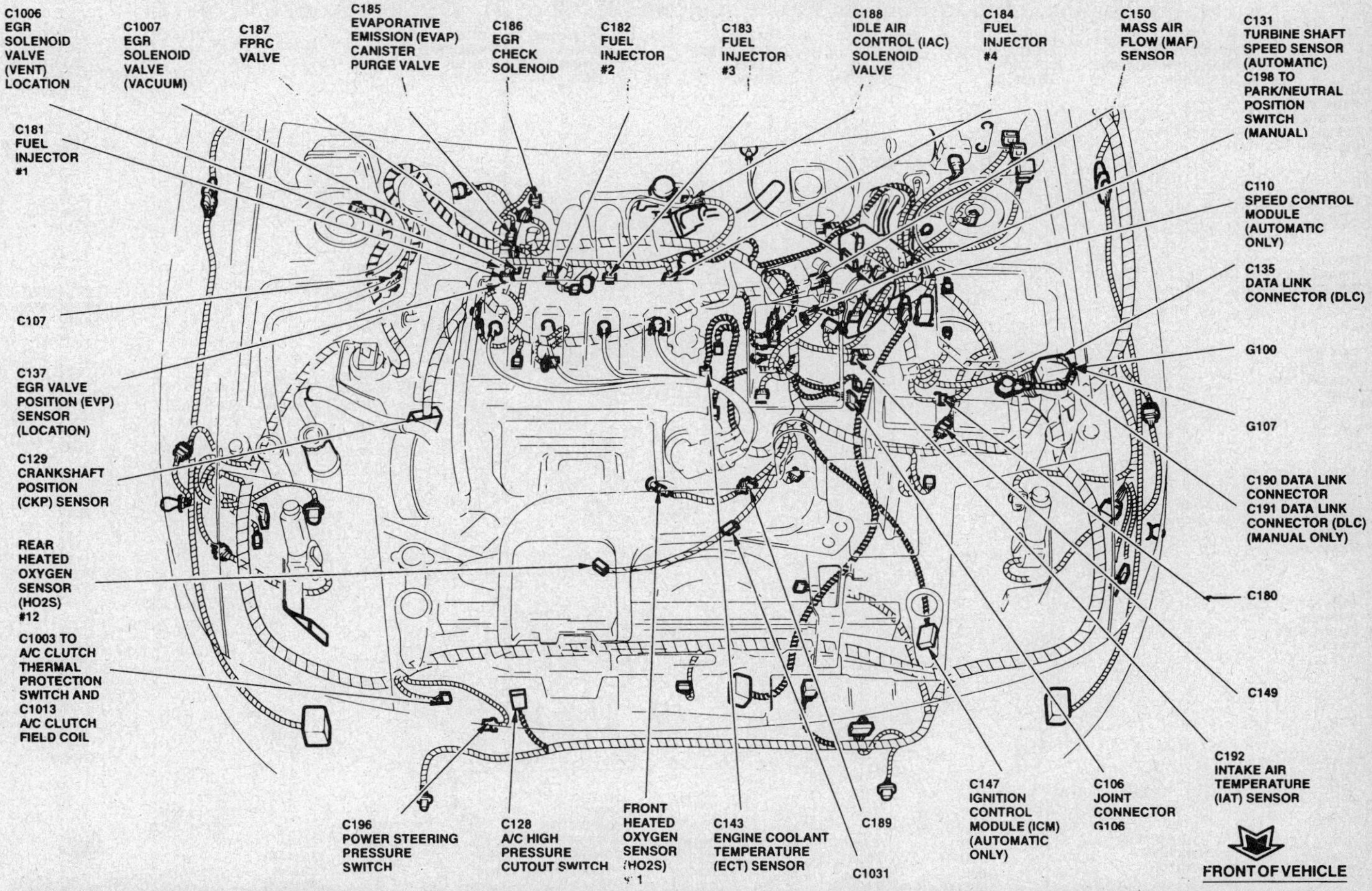

C1006 EGR SOLENOID VALVE (VENT) LOCATION

C1007 EGR SOLENOID VALVE (VACUUM)

C187 FPRC VALVE

C185 EVAPORATIVE EMISSION (EVAP) CANISTER PURGE VALVE

C186 EGR CHECK SOLENOID

C182 FUEL INJECTOR #2

C183 FUEL INJECTOR #3

C188 IDLE AIR CONTROL (IAC) SOLENOID VALVE

C184 FUEL INJECTOR #4

C150 MASS AIR FLOW (MAF) SENSOR

C131 TURBINE SHAFT SPEED SENSOR (AUTOMATIC)
C198 TO PARK/NEUTRAL POSITION SWITCH (MANUAL)

C181 FUEL INJECTOR #1

C107

C137 EGR VALVE POSITION (EVP) SENSOR (LOCATION)

C129 CRANKSHAFT POSITION (CKP) SENSOR

REAR HEATED OXYGEN SENSOR (HO2S) #12

C1003 TO A/C CLUTCH THERMAL PROTECTION SWITCH AND C1013 A/C CLUTCH FIELD COIL

C110 SPEED CONTROL MODULE (AUTOMATIC ONLY)

C135 DATA LINK CONNECTOR (DLC)

G100

G107

C190 DATA LINK CONNECTOR
C191 DATA LINK CONNECTOR (DLC) (MANUAL ONLY)

C180

C149

C192 INTAKE AIR TEMPERATURE (IAT) SENSOR

C196 POWER STEERING PRESSURE SWITCH

C128 A/C HIGH PRESSURE CUTOUT SWITCH

FRONT HEATED OXYGEN SENSOR (HO2S) #1

C143 ENGINE COOLANT TEMPERATURE (ECT) SENSOR

C189

C1031

C147 IGNITION CONTROL MODULE (ICM) (AUTOMATIC ONLY)

C106 JOINT CONNECTOR G106

FRONT OF VEHICLE

Fig. 30 Engine compartment reference diagram (Part 1 of 3). 1996 Probe w/2.0L/4-121

ENGINE COMPARTMENT REFERENCE DIAGRAMS

13-43

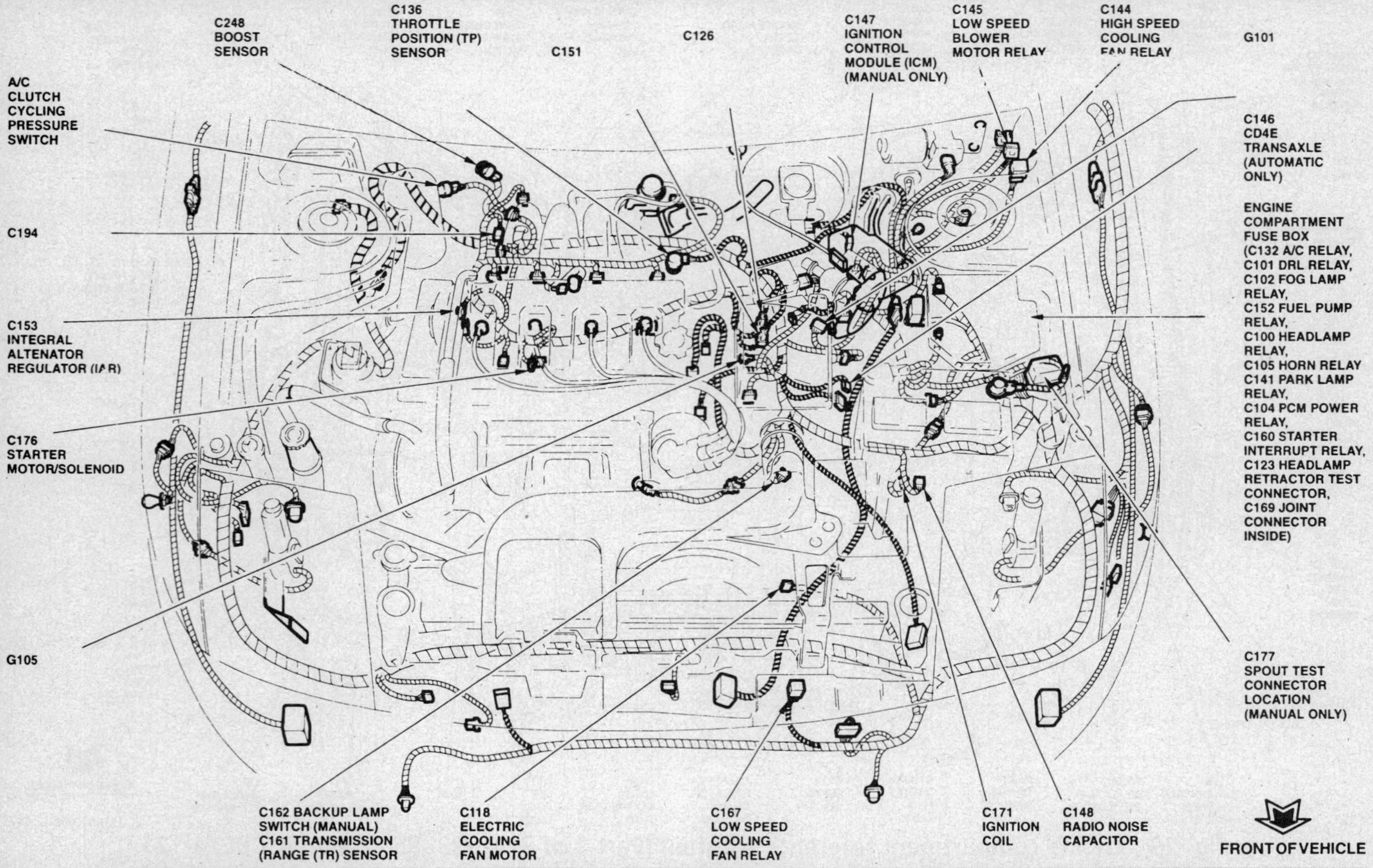

C248 BOOST SENSOR

C136 THROTTLE POSITION (TP) SENSOR

C151

C126

C147 IGNITION CONTROL MODULE (ICM) (MANUAL ONLY)

C145 LOW SPEED BLOWER MOTOR RELAY

C144 HIGH SPEED COOLING FAN RELAY

G101

A/C CLUTCH CYCLING PRESSURE SWITCH

C194

C153 INTEGRAL ALTENATOR REGULATOR (IAR)

C176 STARTER MOTOR/SOLENOID

G105

C146 CD4E TRANSAXLE (AUTOMATIC ONLY)

ENGINE COMPARTMENT FUSE BOX (C132 A/C RELAY, C101 DRL RELAY, C102 FOG LAMP RELAY, C152 FUEL PUMP RELAY, C100 HEADLAMP RELAY, C105 HORN RELAY C141 PARK LAMP RELAY, C104 PCM POWER RELAY, C160 STARTER INTERRUPT RELAY, C123 HEADLAMP RETRACTOR TEST CONNECTOR, C169 JOINT CONNECTOR INSIDE)

C177 SPOUT TEST CONNECTOR LOCATION (MANUAL ONLY)

C162 BACKUP LAMP SWITCH (MANUAL) C161 TRANSMISSION (RANGE (TR) SENSOR

C118 ELECTRIC COOLING FAN MOTOR

C167 LOW SPEED COOLING FAN RELAY

C171 IGNITION COIL

C148 RADIO NOISE CAPACITOR

FRONT OF VEHICLE

Fig. 30   Engine compartment reference diagram (Part 2 of 3). 1996 Probe w/2.0L/4-121

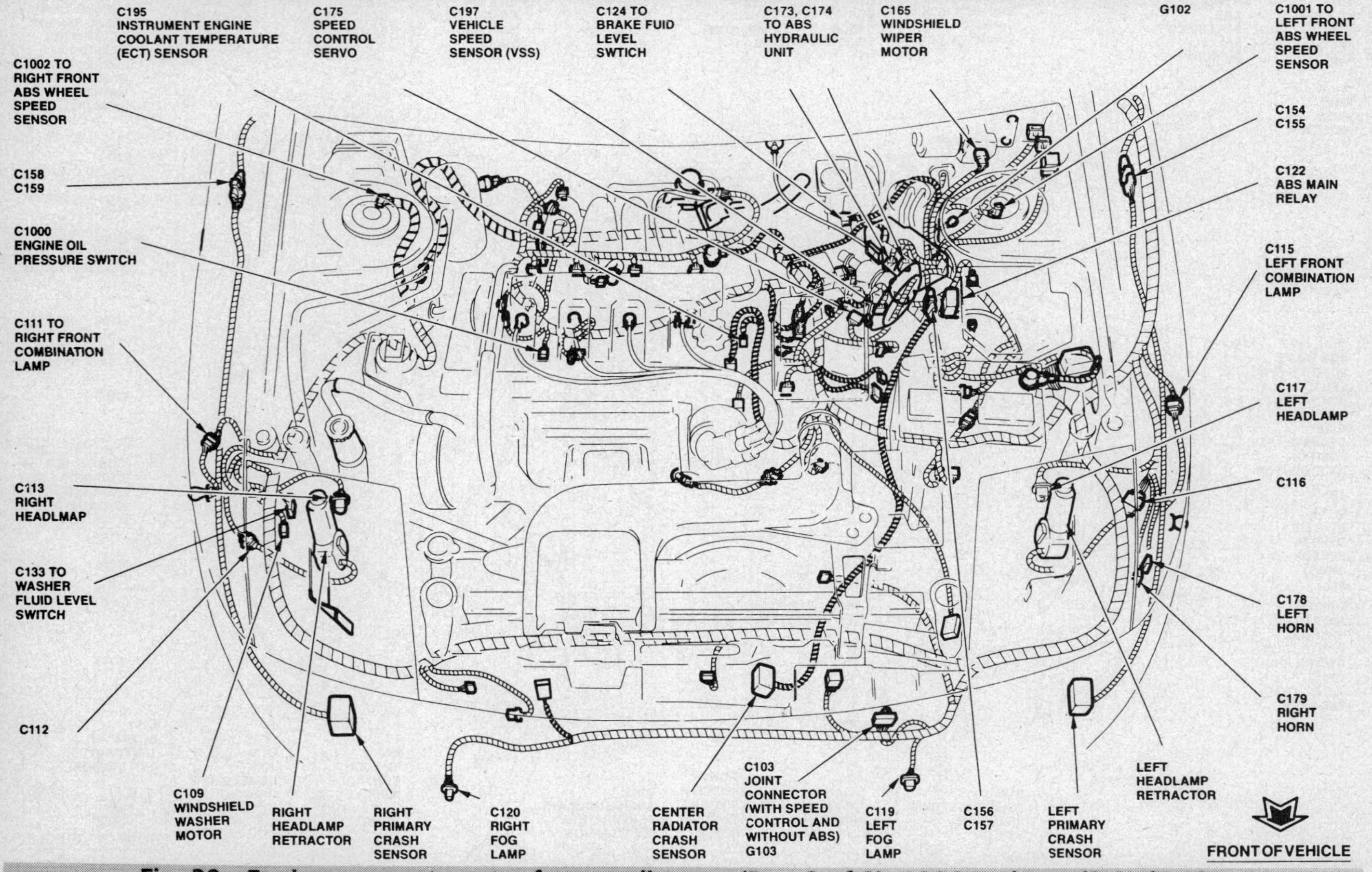

C195 INSTRUMENT ENGINE COOLANT TEMPERATURE (ECT) SENSOR

C175 SPEED CONTROL SERVO

C197 VEHICLE SPEED SENSOR (VSS)

C124 TO BRAKE FUID LEVEL SWTICH

C173, C174 TO ABS HYDRAULIC UNIT

C165 WINDSHIELD WIPER MOTOR

G102

C1001 TO LEFT FRONT ABS WHEEL SPEED SENSOR

C1002 TO RIGHT FRONT ABS WHEEL SPEED SENSOR

C158 C159

C1000 ENGINE OIL PRESSURE SWITCH

C111 TO RIGHT FRONT COMBINATION LAMP

C113 RIGHT HEADLMAP

C133 TO WASHER FLUID LEVEL SWITCH

C112

C154 C155

C122 ABS MAIN RELAY

C115 LEFT FRONT COMBINATION LAMP

C117 LEFT HEADLAMP

C116

C178 LEFT HORN

C179 RIGHT HORN

C109 WINDSHIELD WASHER MOTOR

RIGHT HEADLAMP RETRACTOR

RIGHT PRIMARY CRASH SENSOR

C120 RIGHT FOG LAMP

CENTER RADIATOR CRASH SENSOR

C103 JOINT CONNECTOR (WITH SPEED CONTROL AND WITHOUT ABS) G103

C119 LEFT FOG LAMP

C156 C157

LEFT PRIMARY CRASH SENSOR

LEFT HEADLAMP RETRACTOR

FRONT OF VEHICLE

Fig. 30   Engine compartment reference diagram (Part 3 of 3). 1996 Probe w/2.0L/4-121

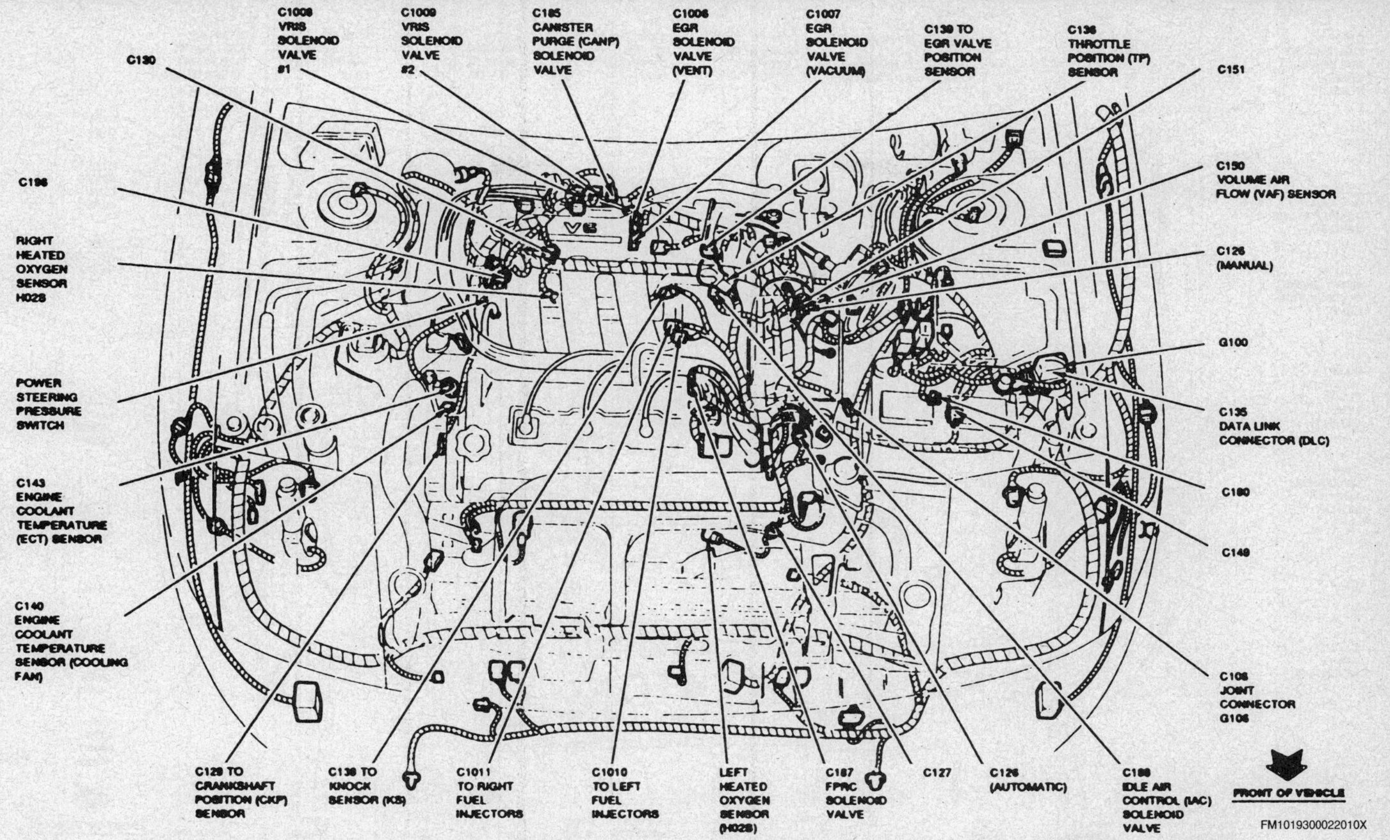

Part 1 of 3 diagram labels:

C130

C1008 VRIS SOLENOID VALVE #1

C1009 VRIS SOLENOID VALVE #2

C185 CANISTER PURGE (CANP) SOLENOID VALVE

C1008 EGR SOLENOID VALVE (VENT)

C1007 EGR SOLENOID VALVE (VACUUM)

C139 TO EGR VALVE POSITION SENSOR

C138 THROTTLE POSITION (TP) SENSOR

C151

C196

RIGHT HEATED OXYGEN SENSOR H02S

POWER STEERING PRESSURE SWITCH

C143 ENGINE COOLANT TEMPERATURE (ECT) SENSOR

C140 ENGINE COOLANT TEMPERATURE SENSOR (COOLING FAN)

C150 VOLUME AIR FLOW (VAF) SENSOR

C126 (MANUAL)

G100

C135 DATA LINK CONNECTOR (DLC)

C180

C149

C108 JOINT CONNECTOR G106

C129 TO CRANKSHAFT POSITION (CKP) SENSOR

C138 TO KNOCK SENSOR (KS)

C1011 TO RIGHT FUEL INJECTORS

C1010 TO LEFT FUEL INJECTORS

LEFT HEATED OXYGEN SENSOR (H02S)

C187 FPRC SOLENOID VALVE

C127

C126 (AUTOMATIC)

C188 IDLE AIR CONTROL (IAC) SOLENOID VALVE

FRONT OF VEHICLE

FM1019300022010X

Fig. 31 Engine compartment reference diagram (Part 1 of 3). 1993–95 Probe w/2.5L/V6-152

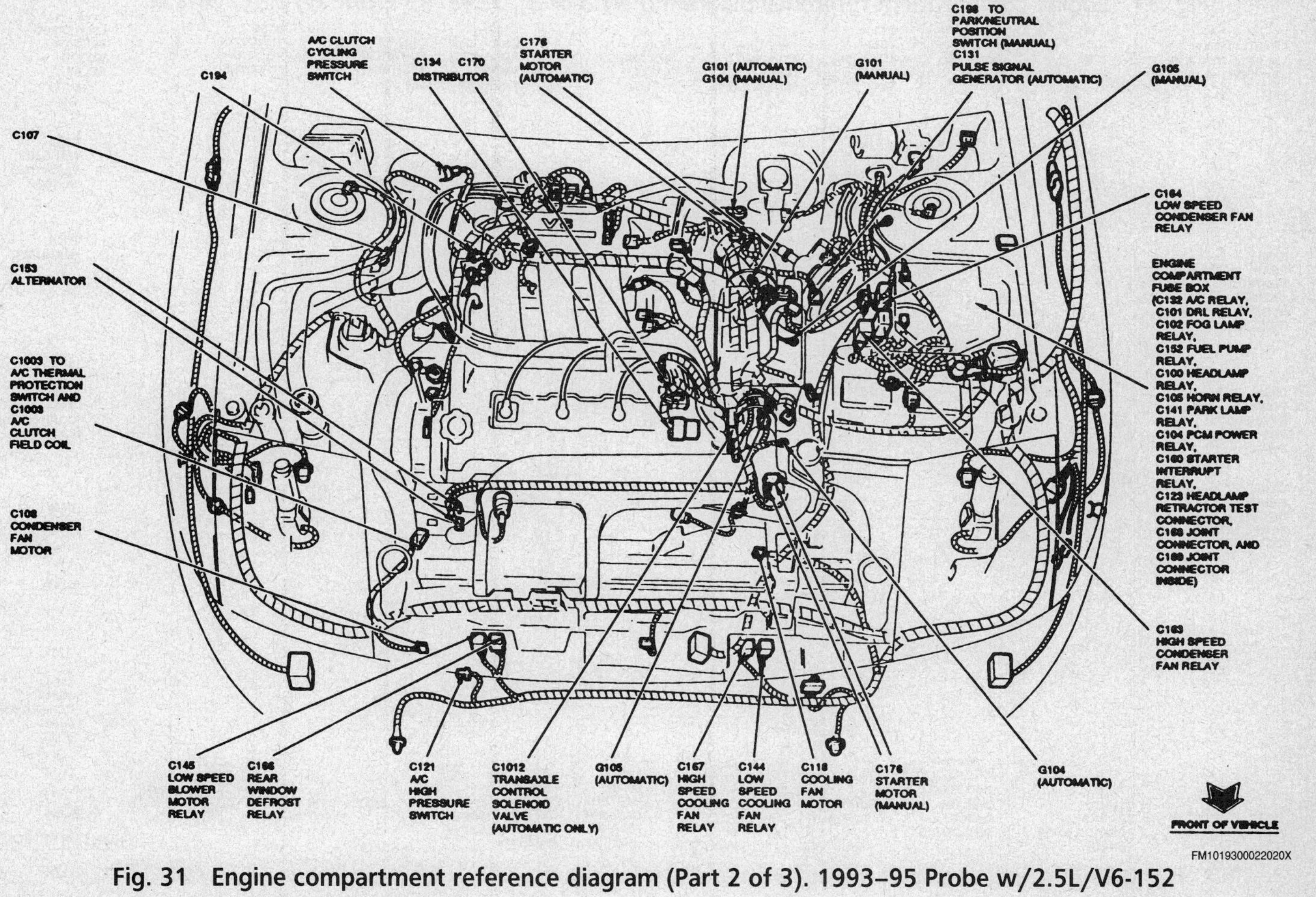

Part 2 of 3 diagram labels:

A/C CLUTCH CYCLING PRESSURE SWITCH

C134 C170 DISTRIBUTOR

C176 STARTER MOTOR (AUTOMATIC)

G101 (AUTOMATIC) G104 (MANUAL)

G101 (MANUAL)

C196 TO PARK/NEUTRAL POSITION SWITCH (MANUAL)

C131 PULSE SIGNAL GENERATOR (AUTOMATIC)

G105 (MANUAL)

C194

C107

C153 ALTERNATOR

C1009 TO A/C THERMAL PROTECTION SWITCH AND C1003 A/C CLUTCH FIELD COIL

C108 CONDENSER FAN MOTOR

C164 LOW SPEED CONDENSER FAN RELAY

ENGINE COMPARTMENT FUSE BOX (C132 A/C RELAY, C101 DRL RELAY, C102 FOG LAMP RELAY, C152 FUEL PUMP RELAY, C100 HEADLAMP RELAY, C105 HORN RELAY, C141 PARK LAMP RELAY, C104 PCM POWER RELAY, C160 STARTER INTERRUPT RELAY, C123 HEADLAMP RETRACTOR TEST CONNECTOR, C168 JOINT CONNECTOR, AND C108 JOINT CONNECTOR INSIDE)

C163 HIGH SPEED CONDENSER FAN RELAY

C145 LOW SPEED BLOWER MOTOR RELAY

C196 REAR WINDOW DEFROST RELAY

C121 A/C HIGH PRESSURE SWITCH

C1012 TRANSAXLE CONTROL SOLENOID VALVE (AUTOMATIC ONLY)

G105 (AUTOMATIC)

C167 HIGH SPEED COOLING FAN RELAY

C144 LOW SPEED COOLING FAN RELAY

C118 COOLING FAN MOTOR

C176 STARTER MOTOR (MANUAL)

G104 (AUTOMATIC)

FRONT OF VEHICLE

FM1019300022020X

Fig. 31 Engine compartment reference diagram (Part 2 of 3). 1993–95 Probe w/2.5L/V6-152

FORD–Engine Compartment Reference Diagrams

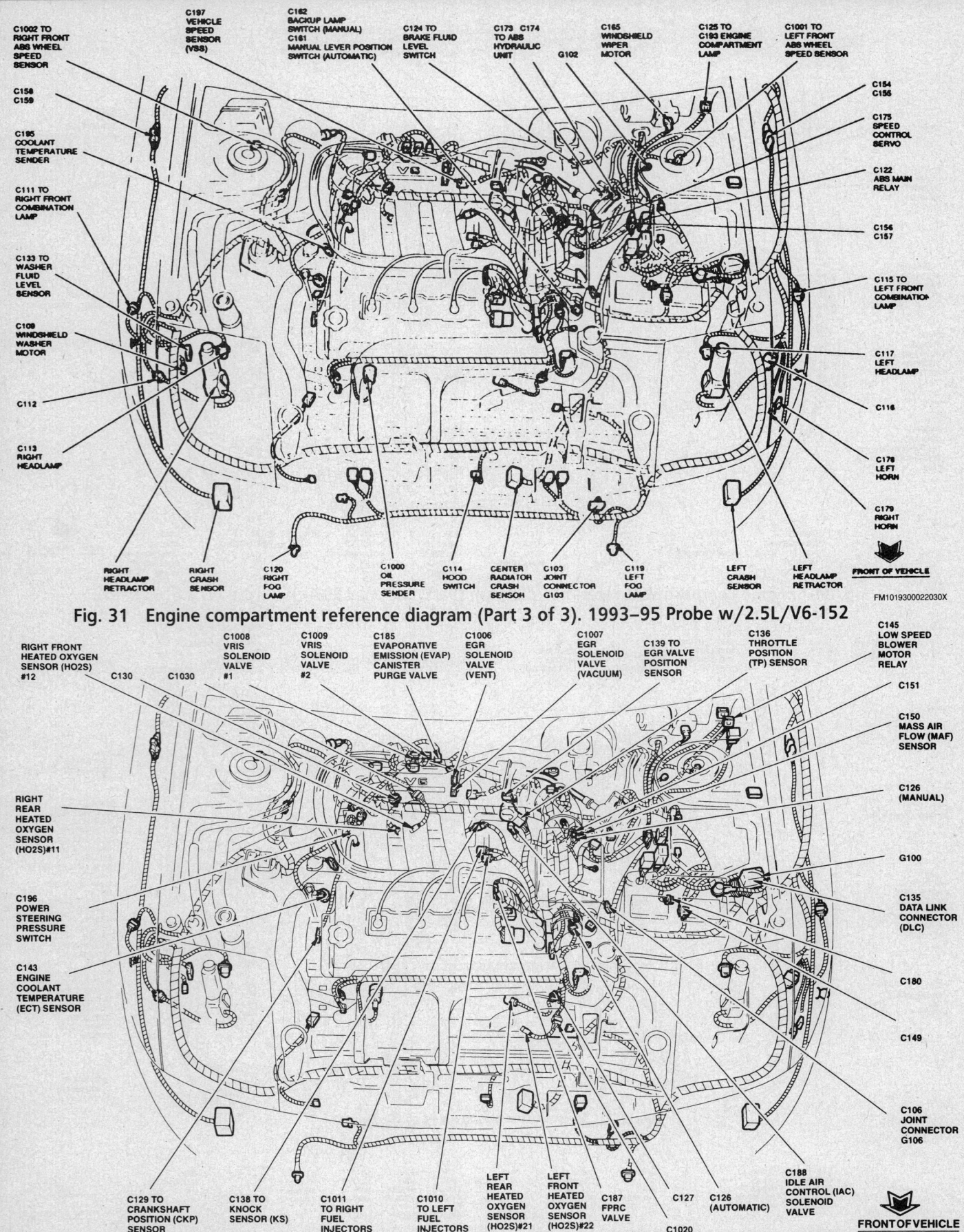

Fig. 31 Engine compartment reference diagram (Part 3 of 3). 1993–95 Probe w/2.5L/V6-152

Fig. 32 Engine compartment reference diagram (Part 1 of 3). 1996 Probe w/2.5L/V6-152

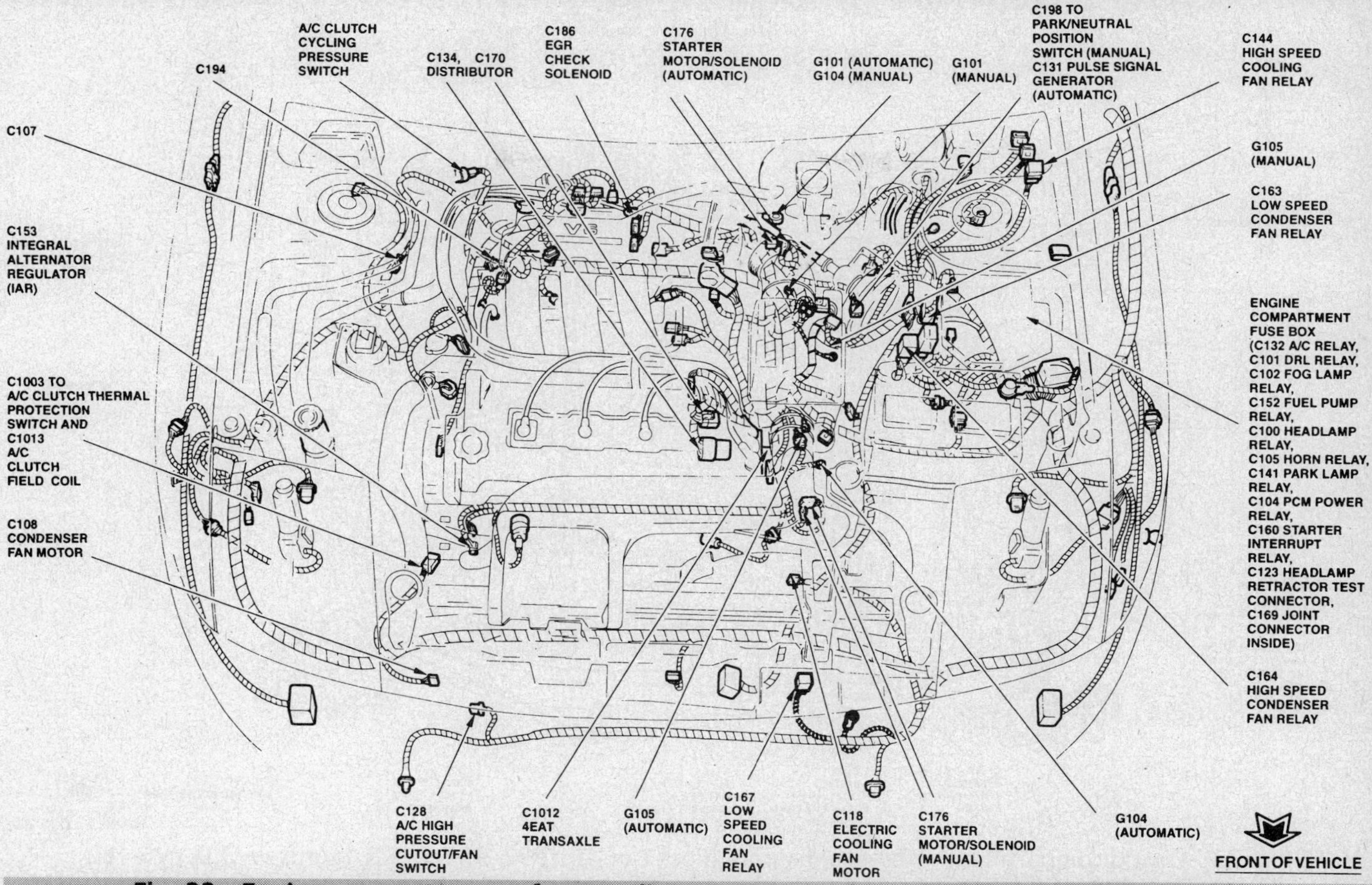

C194

A/C CLUTCH CYCLING PRESSURE SWITCH

C134, C170 DISTRIBUTOR

C186 EGR CHECK SOLENOID

C176 STARTER MOTOR/SOLENOID (AUTOMATIC)

G101 (AUTOMATIC) G104 (MANUAL)

G101 (MANUAL)

C198 TO PARK/NEUTRAL POSITION SWITCH (MANUAL) C131 PULSE SIGNAL GENERATOR (AUTOMATIC)

C144 HIGH SPEED COOLING FAN RELAY

C107

C153 INTEGRAL ALTERNATOR REGULATOR (IAR)

C1003 TO A/C CLUTCH THERMAL PROTECTION SWITCH AND C1013 A/C CLUTCH FIELD COIL

C108 CONDENSER FAN MOTOR

G105 (MANUAL)

C163 LOW SPEED CONDENSER FAN RELAY

ENGINE COMPARTMENT FUSE BOX (C132 A/C RELAY, C101 DRL RELAY, C102 FOG LAMP RELAY, C152 FUEL PUMP RELAY, C100 HEADLAMP RELAY, C105 HORN RELAY, C141 PARK LAMP RELAY, C104 PCM POWER RELAY, C160 STARTER INTERRUPT RELAY, C123 HEADLAMP RETRACTOR TEST CONNECTOR, C169 JOINT CONNECTOR INSIDE)

C164 HIGH SPEED CONDENSER FAN RELAY

C128 A/C HIGH PRESSURE CUTOUT/FAN SWITCH

C1012 4EAT TRANSAXLE

G105 (AUTOMATIC)

C167 LOW SPEED COOLING FAN RELAY

C118 ELECTRIC COOLING FAN MOTOR

C176 STARTER MOTOR/SOLENOID (MANUAL)

G104 (AUTOMATIC)

FRONT OF VEHICLE

Fig. 32   Engine compartment reference diagram (Part 2 of 3). 1996 Probe w/2.5L/V6-152

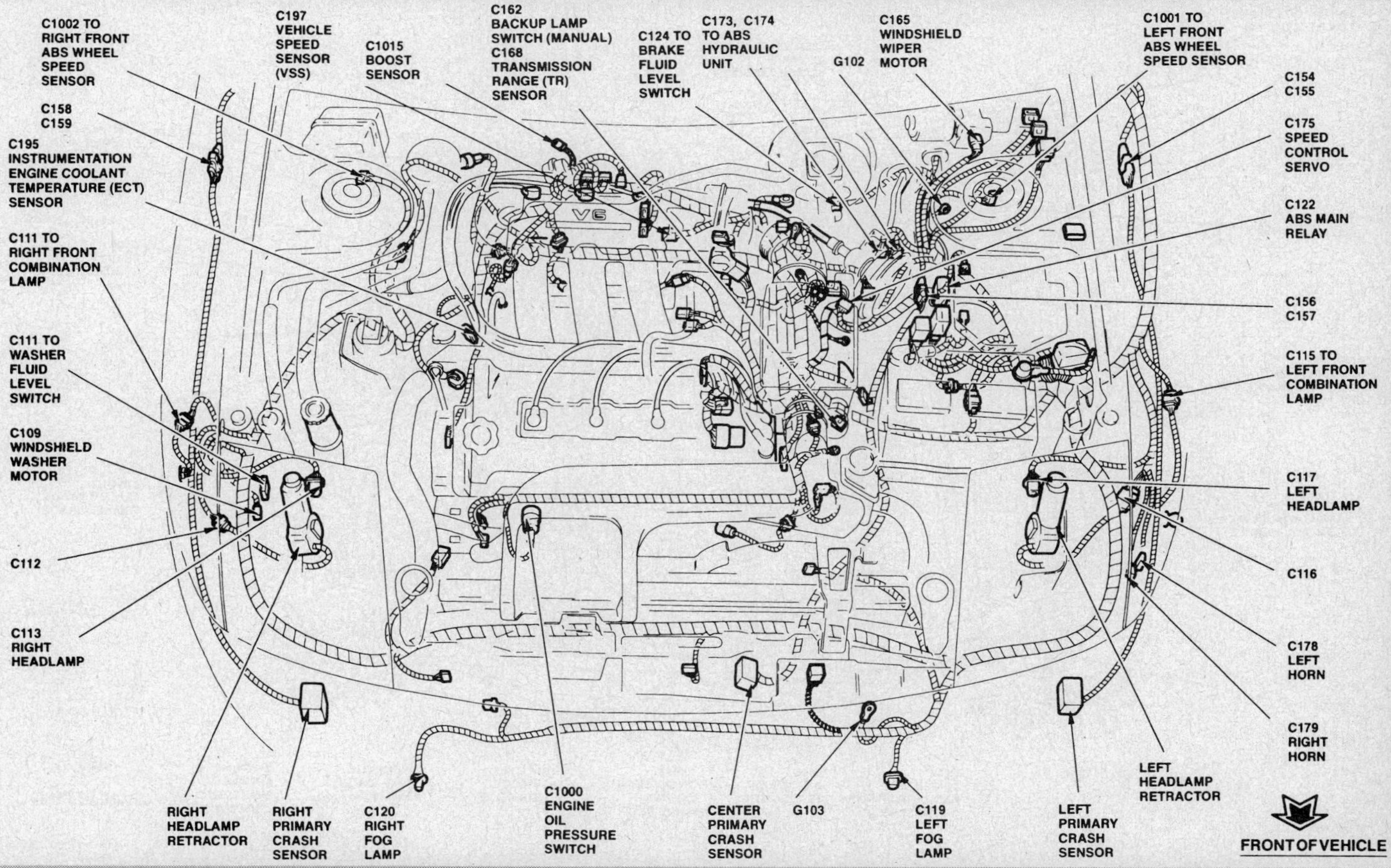

C1002 TO RIGHT FRONT ABS WHEEL SPEED SENSOR

C197 VEHICLE SPEED SENSOR (VSS)

C1015 BOOST SENSOR

C162 BACKUP LAMP SWITCH (MANUAL) C168 TRANSMISSION RANGE (TR) SENSOR

C124 TO BRAKE FLUID LEVEL SWITCH

C173, C174 TO ABS HYDRAULIC UNIT

C165 WINDSHIELD WIPER MOTOR G102

C1001 TO LEFT FRONT ABS WHEEL SPEED SENSOR

C158 C159

C195 INSTRUMENTATION ENGINE COOLANT TEMPERATURE (ECT) SENSOR

C111 TO RIGHT FRONT COMBINATION LAMP

C111 TO WASHER FLUID LEVEL SWITCH

C109 WINDSHIELD WASHER MOTOR

C112

C113 RIGHT HEADLAMP

C154 C155

C175 SPEED CONTROL SERVO

C122 ABS MAIN RELAY

C156 C157

C115 TO LEFT FRONT COMBINATION LAMP

C117 LEFT HEADLAMP

C116

C178 LEFT HORN

C179 RIGHT HORN

RIGHT HEADLAMP RETRACTOR

RIGHT PRIMARY CRASH SENSOR

C120 RIGHT FOG LAMP

C1000 ENGINE OIL PRESSURE SWITCH

CENTER PRIMARY CRASH SENSOR

G103

C119 LEFT FOG LAMP

LEFT PRIMARY CRASH SENSOR

LEFT HEADLAMP RETRACTOR

FRONT OF VEHICLE

Fig. 32   Engine compartment reference diagram (Part 3 of 3). 1996 Probe w/2.5L/V6-152

ENGINE COMPARTMENT REFERENCE DIAGRAMS

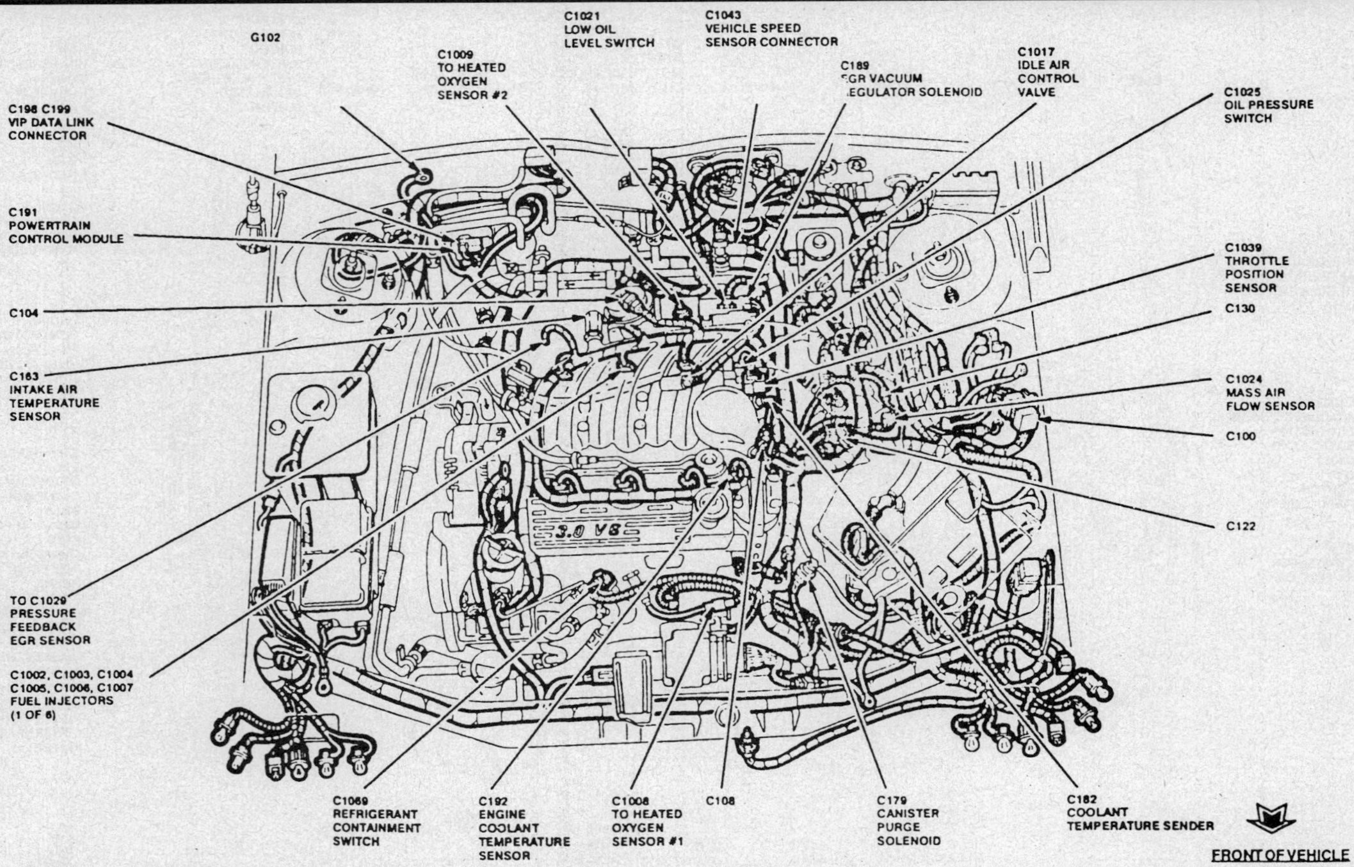

Fig. 33 Engine compartment reference diagram (Part 1 of 4). 1993–95 Sable & Taurus w/3.0L/V6-182

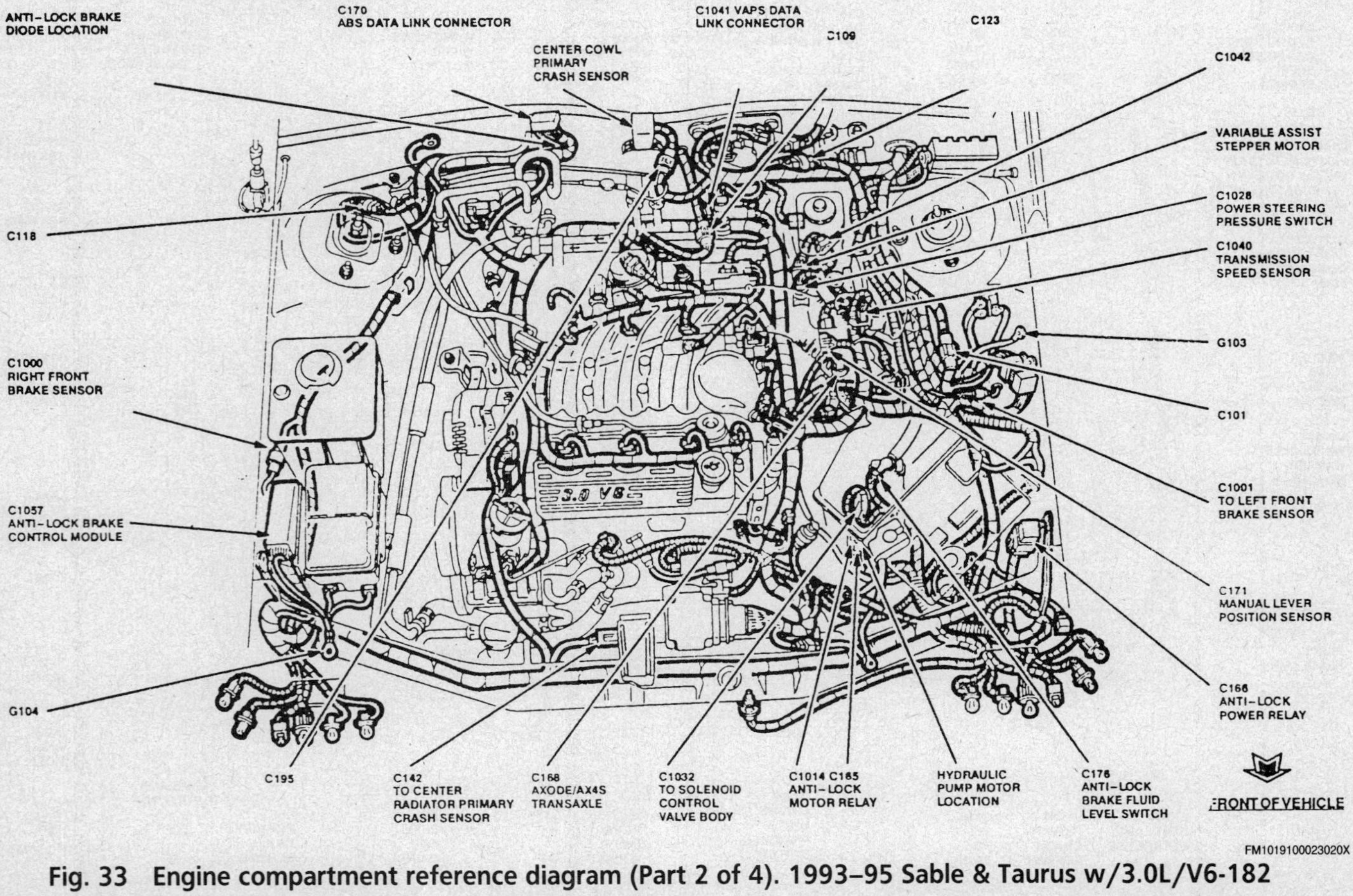

Fig. 33 Engine compartment reference diagram (Part 2 of 4). 1993–95 Sable & Taurus w/3.0L/V6-182

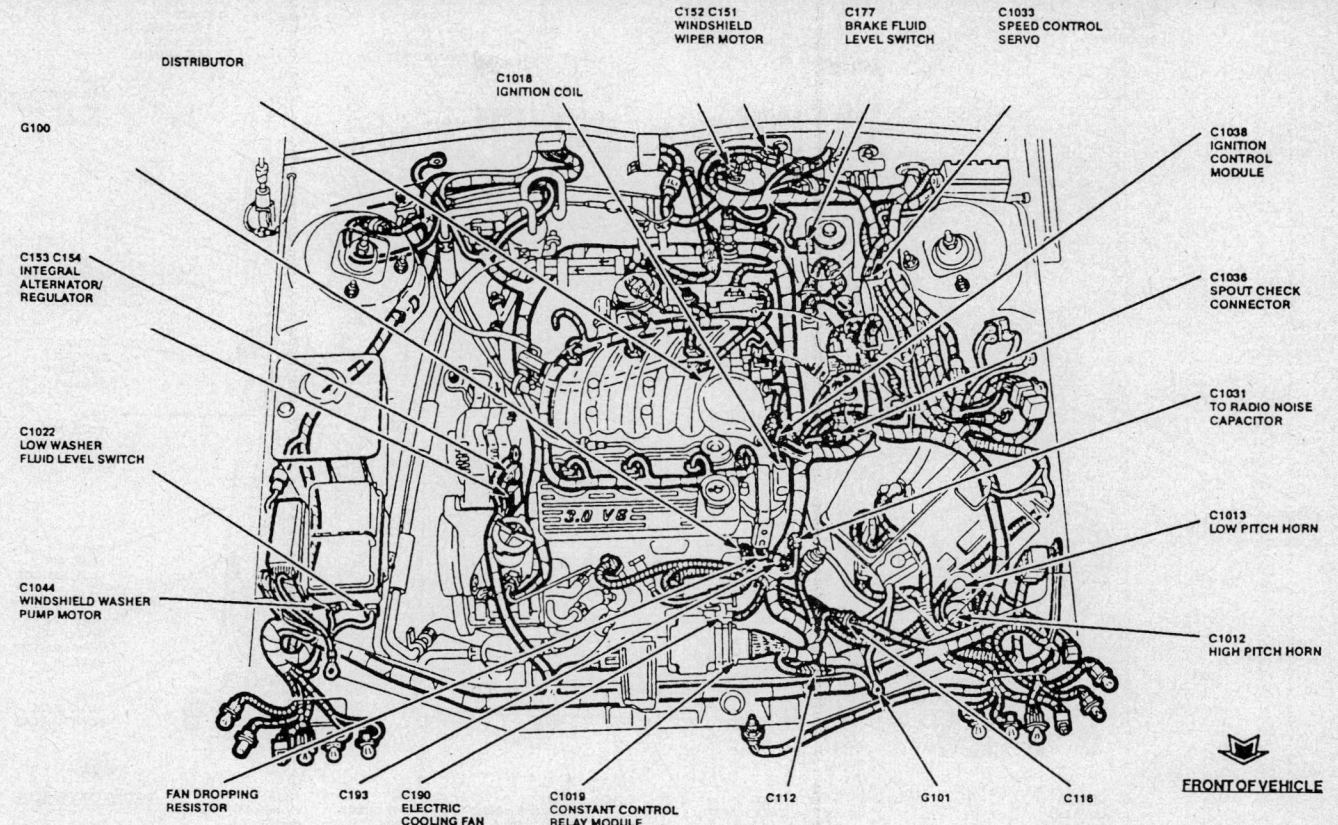

Fig. 33 Engine compartment reference diagram (Part 3 of 4). 1993–95 Sable & Taurus w/3.0L/V6-182

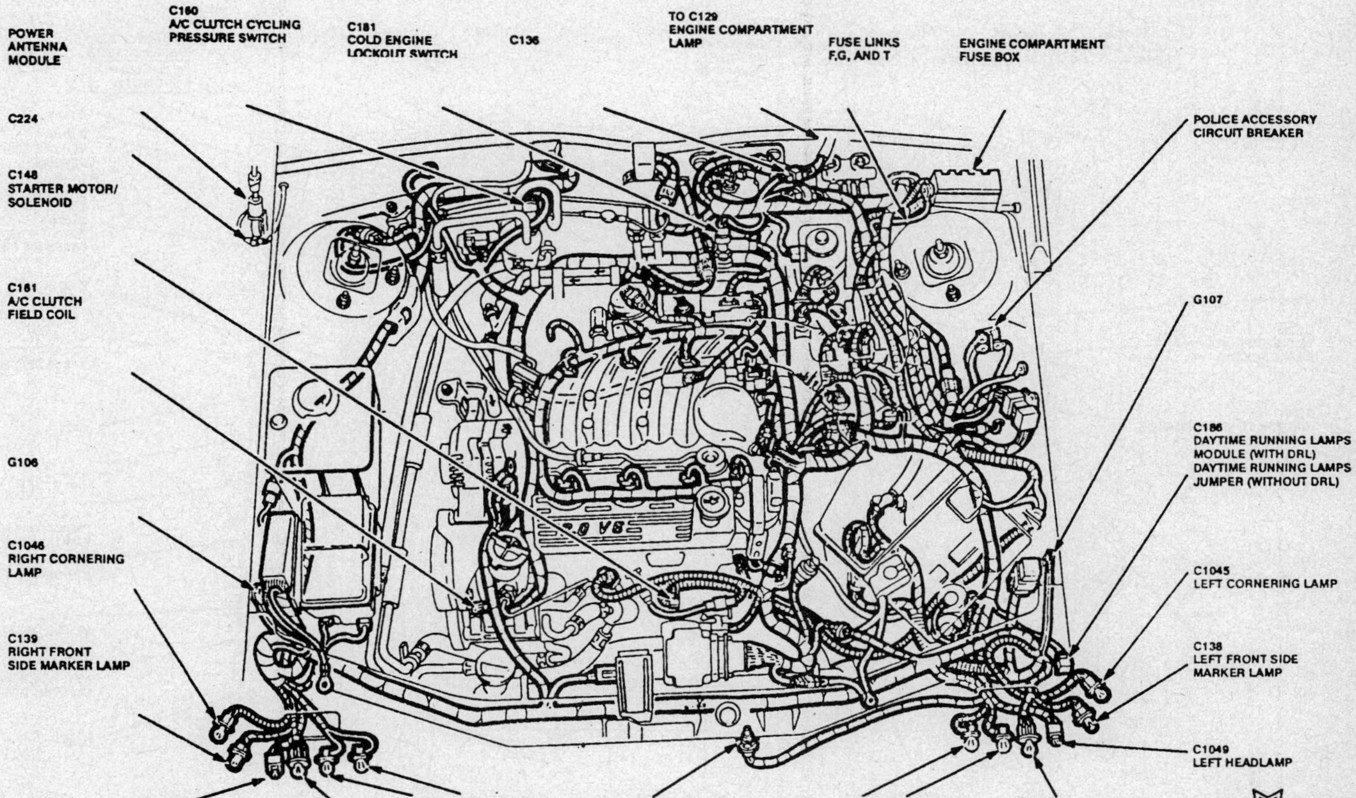

FM1019100023030X

Fig. 33 Engine compartment reference diagram (Part 4 of 4). 1993–95 Sable & Taurus w/3.0L/V6-182

FM1019100023040X

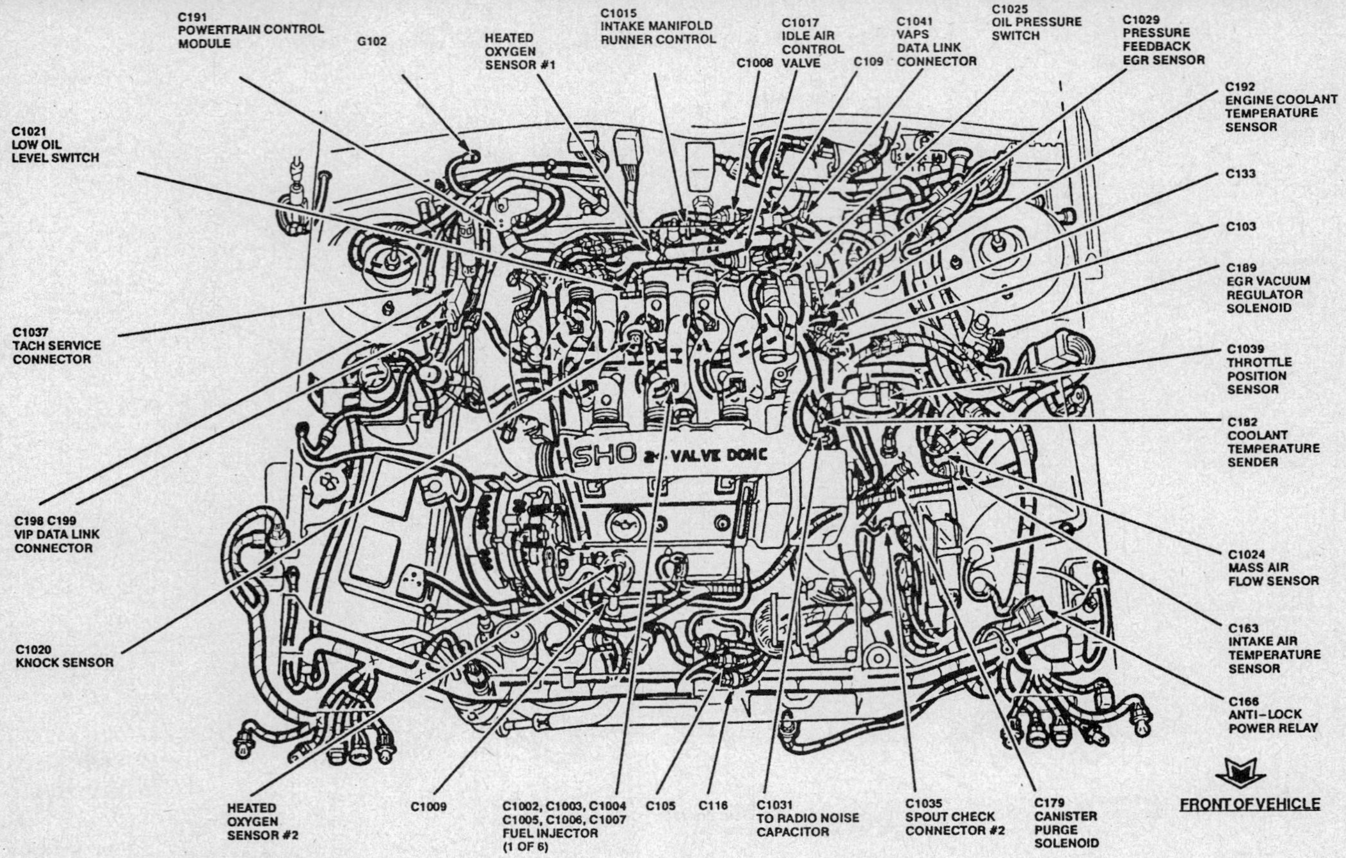

Part 1 diagram labels:

C191 POWERTRAIN CONTROL MODULE
G102
HEATED OXYGEN SENSOR #1
C1015 INTAKE MANIFOLD RUNNER CONTROL
C1017 IDLE AIR CONTROL VALVE
C1006 C109
C1041 VAPS DATA LINK CONNECTOR
C1025 OIL PRESSURE SWITCH
C1029 PRESSURE FEEDBACK EGR SENSOR
C192 ENGINE COOLANT TEMPERATURE SENSOR
C133
C103
C189 EGR VACUUM REGULATOR SOLENOID
C1039 THROTTLE POSITION SENSOR
C182 COOLANT TEMPERATURE SENDER
C1024 MASS AIR FLOW SENSOR
C163 INTAKE AIR TEMPERATURE SENSOR
C166 ANTI-LOCK POWER RELAY

C1021 LOW OIL LEVEL SWITCH
C1037 TACH SERVICE CONNECTOR
C198 C199 VIP DATA LINK CONNECTOR
C1020 KNOCK SENSOR

HEATED OXYGEN SENSOR #2
C1009
C1002, C1003, C1004, C1005, C1006, C1007 FUEL INJECTOR (1 OF 6)
C105 C116
C1031 TO RADIO NOISE CAPACITOR
C1035 SPOUT CHECK CONNECTOR #2
C179 CANISTER PURGE SOLENOID

SHO 24 VALVE DOHC

FRONT OF VEHICLE

Fig. 34 Engine compartment reference diagram (Part 1 of 3). 1993–95 Taurus w/3.0L/V6-182 SHO

Part 2 diagram labels:

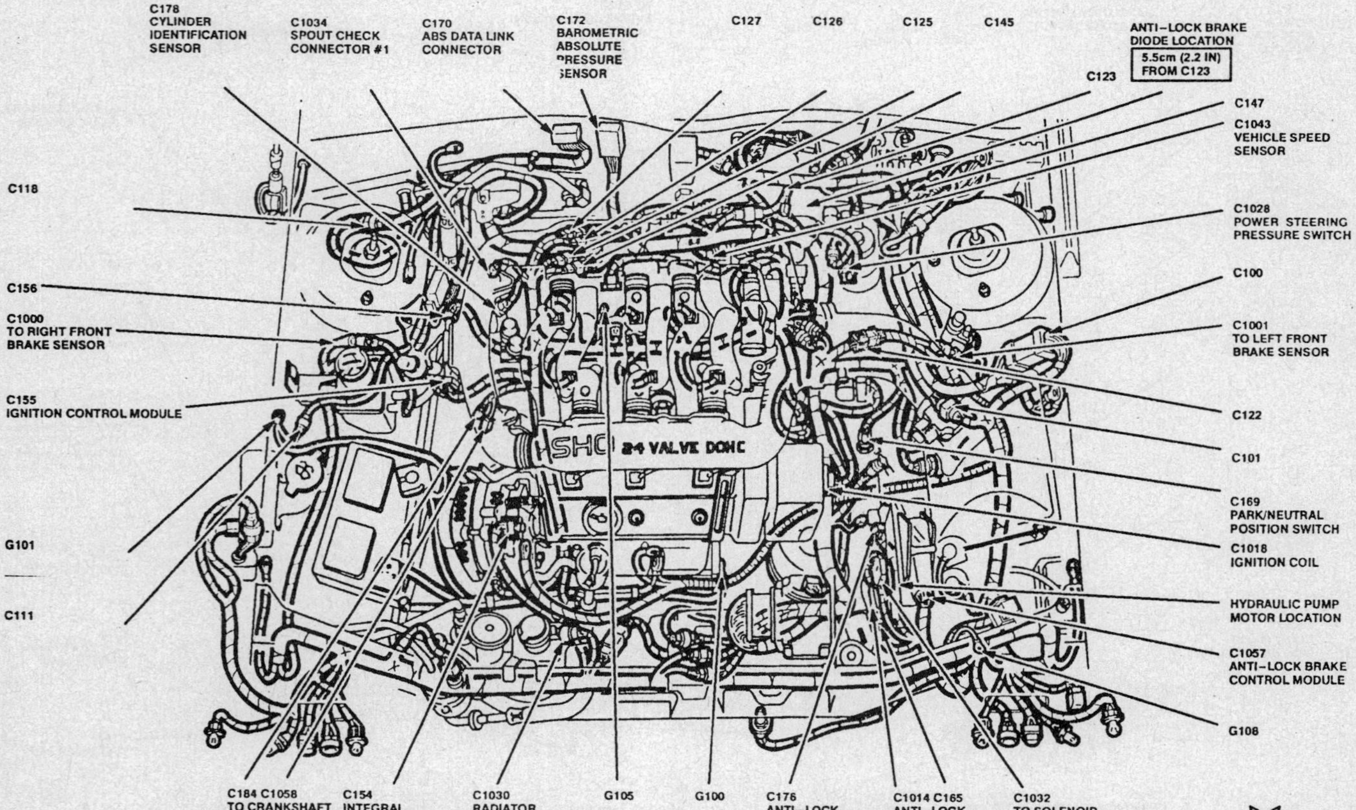

C178 CYLINDER IDENTIFICATION SENSOR
C1034 SPOUT CHECK CONNECTOR #1
C170 ABS DATA LINK CONNECTOR
C172 BAROMETRIC ABSOLUTE PRESSURE SENSOR
C127 C126 C125 C145
ANTI-LOCK BRAKE DIODE LOCATION
5.5cm (2.2 IN) FROM C123
C123

C147
C1043 VEHICLE SPEED SENSOR
C1028 POWER STEERING PRESSURE SWITCH
C100
C1001 TO LEFT FRONT BRAKE SENSOR
C122
C101
C169 PARK/NEUTRAL POSITION SWITCH
C1018 IGNITION COIL
HYDRAULIC PUMP MOTOR LOCATION
C1057 ANTI-LOCK BRAKE CONTROL MODULE
G108

C118
C156
C1000 TO RIGHT FRONT BRAKE SENSOR
C155 IGNITION CONTROL MODULE
G101
C111

SHO 24 VALVE DOHC

C184 C1058 TO CRANKSHAFT POSITION SENSOR
C154 INTEGRAL ALTERNATOR/REGULATOR
C1030 RADIATOR COOLANT SENSOR
G105 G100
C176 ANTI-LOCK BRAKE FLUID LEVEL SWITCH
C1014 C165 ANTI-LOCK MOTOR RELAY
C1032 TO SOLENOID CONTROL VALVE BODY

FRONT OF VEHICLE

Fig. 34 Engine compartment reference diagram (Part 2 of 3). 1993–95 Taurus w/3.0L/V6-182 SHO

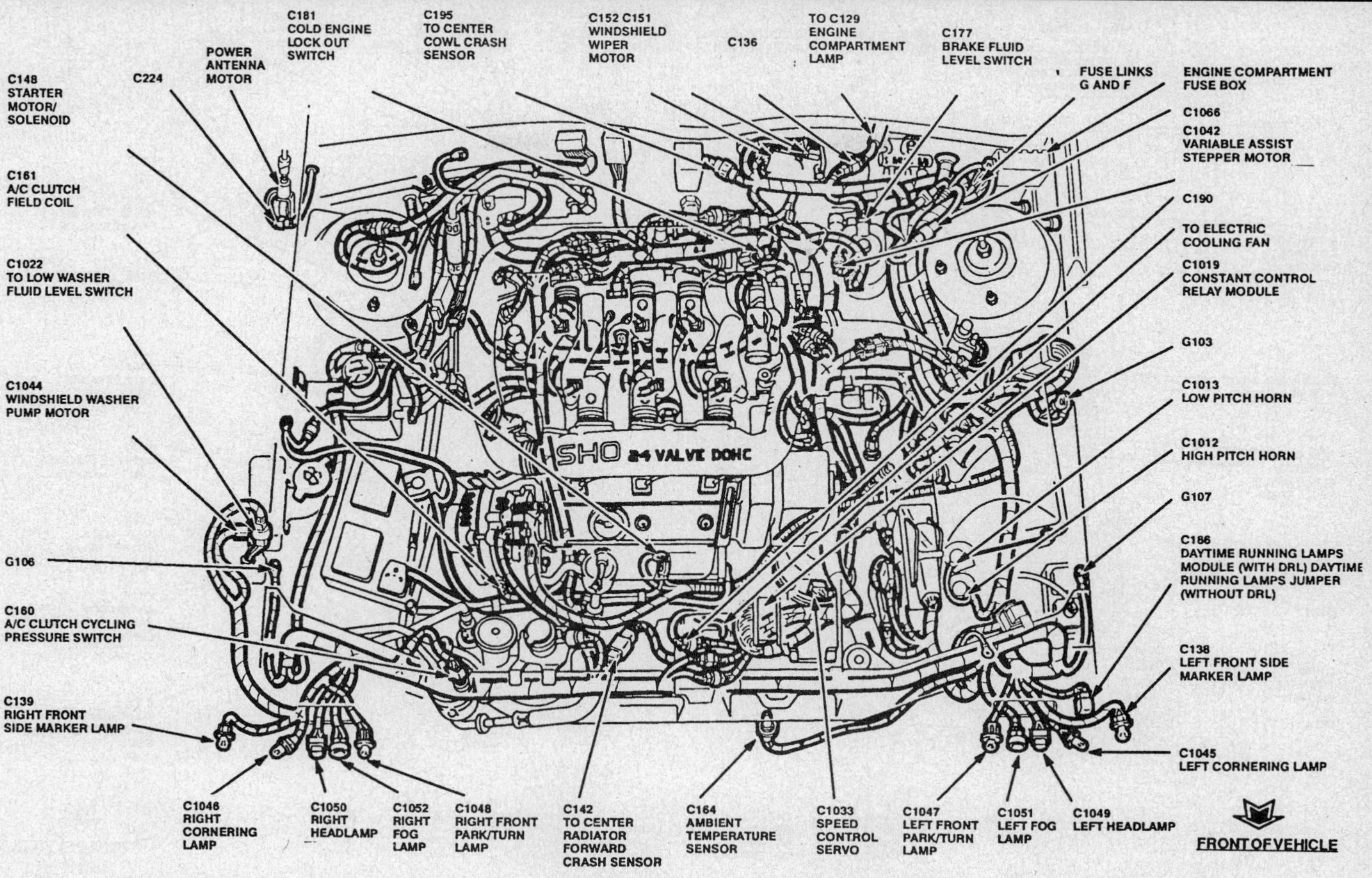

C181 COLD ENGINE LOCK OUT SWITCH
C195 TO CENTER COWL CRASH SENSOR
C152 C151 WINDSHIELD WIPER MOTOR
C136
TO C129 ENGINE COMPARTMENT LAMP
C177 BRAKE FLUID LEVEL SWITCH
FUSE LINKS G AND F
ENGINE COMPARTMENT FUSE BOX
POWER ANTENNA MOTOR
C148 STARTER MOTOR/ SOLENOID
C224
C161 A/C CLUTCH FIELD COIL
C1022 TO LOW WASHER FLUID LEVEL SWITCH
C1044 WINDSHIELD WASHER PUMP MOTOR
G106
C160 A/C CLUTCH CYCLING PRESSURE SWITCH
C139 RIGHT FRONT SIDE MARKER LAMP
C1066
C1042 VARIABLE ASSIST STEPPER MOTOR
C190 TO ELECTRIC COOLING FAN
C1019 CONSTANT CONTROL RELAY MODULE
G103
C1013 LOW PITCH HORN
C1012 HIGH PITCH HORN
G107
C186 DAYTIME RUNNING LAMPS MODULE (WITH DRL) DAYTIME RUNNING LAMPS JUMPER (WITHOUT DRL)
C138 LEFT FRONT SIDE MARKER LAMP
C1045 LEFT CORNERING LAMP
C1046 RIGHT CORNERING LAMP
C1050 RIGHT HEADLAMP
C1052 RIGHT FOG LAMP
C1048 RIGHT FRONT PARK/TURN LAMP
C142 TO CENTER RADIATOR FORWARD CRASH SENSOR
C164 AMBIENT TEMPERATURE SENSOR
C1033 SPEED CONTROL SERVO
C1047 LEFT FRONT PARK/TURN LAMP
C1051 LEFT FOG LAMP
C1049 LEFT HEADLAMP
SHO 24 VALVE DOHC
FRONT OF VEHICLE

Fig. 34 Engine compartment reference diagram (Part 3 of 3). 1993–95 Taurus w/3.0L/V6-182 SHO

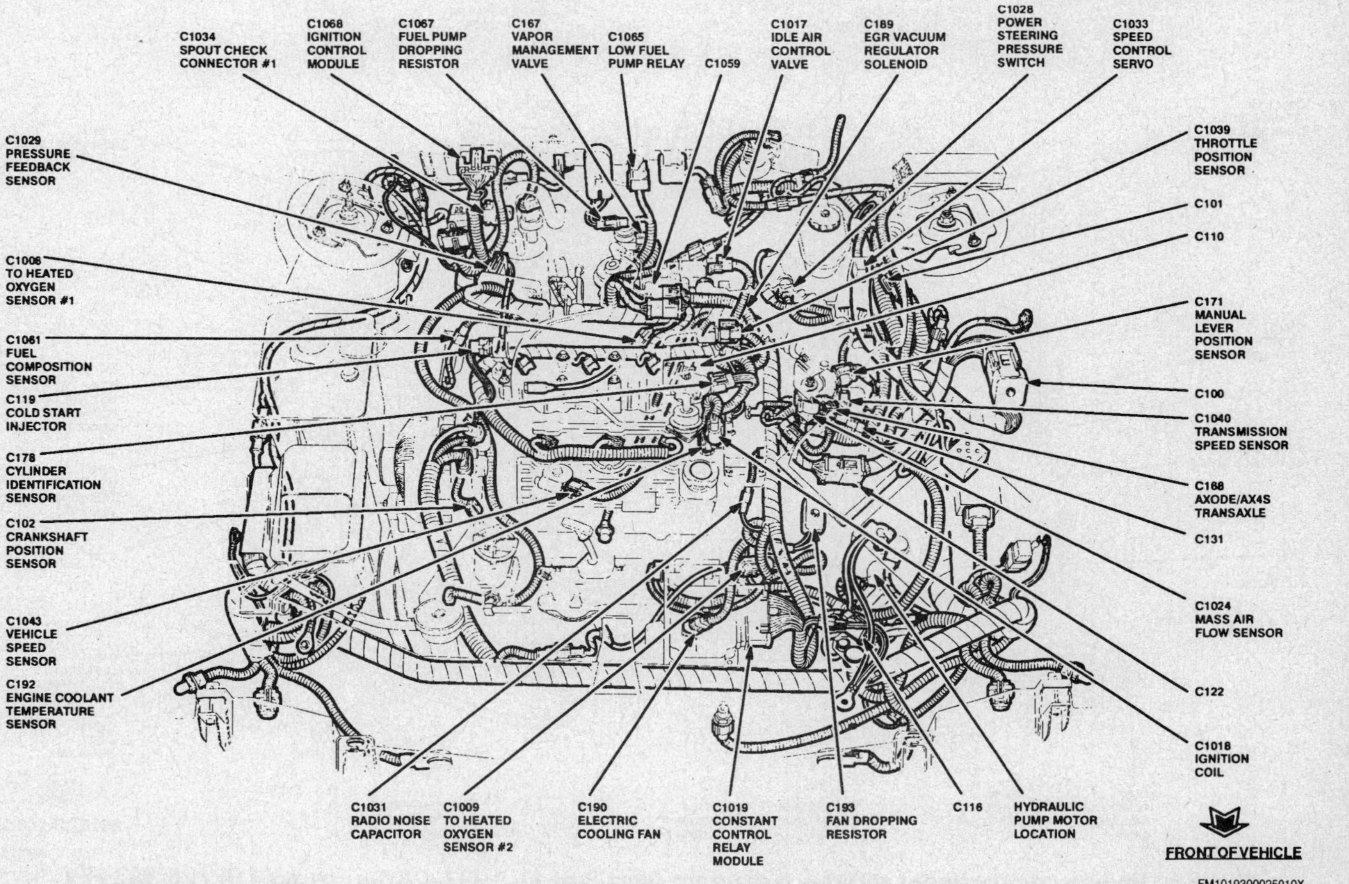

C1034 SPOUT CHECK CONNECTOR #1
C1068 IGNITION CONTROL MODULE
C1067 FUEL PUMP DROPPING RESISTOR
C167 VAPOR MANAGEMENT VALVE
C1065 LOW FUEL PUMP RELAY
C1059
C1017 IDLE AIR CONTROL VALVE
C189 EGR VACUUM REGULATOR SOLENOID
C1028 POWER STEERING PRESSURE SWITCH
C1033 SPEED CONTROL SERVO
C1029 PRESSURE FEEDBACK SENSOR
C1006 TO HEATED OXYGEN SENSOR #1
C1061 FUEL COMPOSITION SENSOR
C119 COLD START INJECTOR
C178 CYLINDER IDENTIFICATION SENSOR
C102 CRANKSHAFT POSITION SENSOR
C1043 VEHICLE SPEED SENSOR
C192 ENGINE COOLANT TEMPERATURE SENSOR
C1039 THROTTLE POSITION SENSOR
C101
C110
C171 MANUAL LEVER POSITION SENSOR
C100
C1040 TRANSMISSION SPEED SENSOR
C168 AXODE/AX4S TRANSAXLE
C131
C1024 MASS AIR FLOW SENSOR
C122
C1018 IGNITION COIL
C1031 RADIO NOISE CAPACITOR
C1009 TO HEATED OXYGEN SENSOR #2
C190 ELECTRIC COOLING FAN
C1019 CONSTANT CONTROL RELAY MODULE
C193 FAN DROPPING RESISTOR
C116
HYDRAULIC PUMP MOTOR LOCATION
FRONT OF VEHICLE

FM1019300025010X

Fig. 35 Engine compartment reference diagram (Part 1 of 3). 1993–96 Taurus w/3.0L/V6-182 FFV

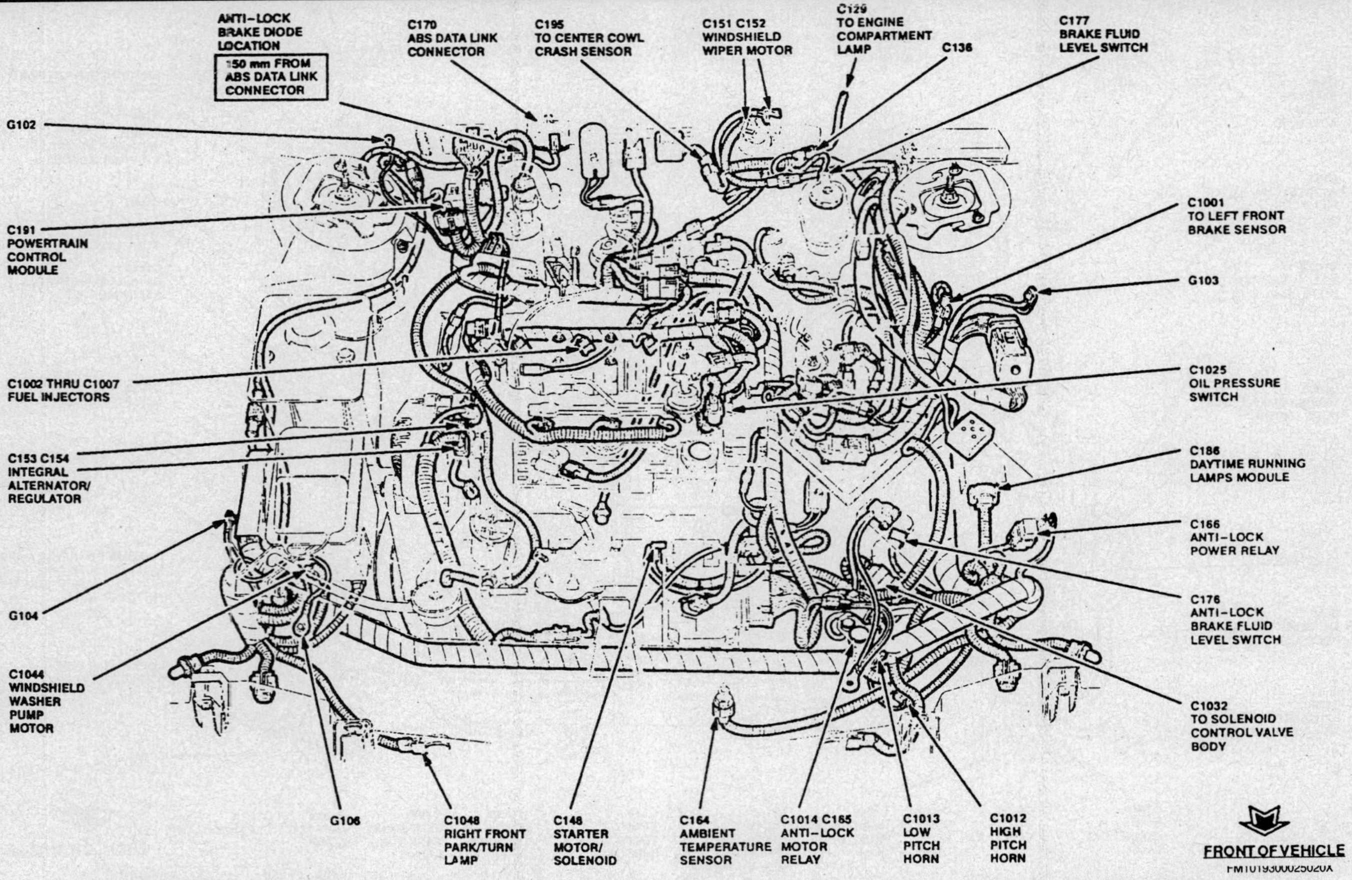

ANTI-LOCK BRAKE DIODE LOCATION
150 mm FROM ABS DATA LINK CONNECTOR

C170 ABS DATA LINK CONNECTOR

C195 TO CENTER COWL CRASH SENSOR

C151 C152 WINDSHIELD WIPER MOTOR

C129 TO ENGINE COMPARTMENT LAMP

C136

C177 BRAKE FLUID LEVEL SWITCH

G102

C191 POWERTRAIN CONTROL MODULE

C1001 TO LEFT FRONT BRAKE SENSOR

G103

C1002 THRU C1007 FUEL INJECTORS

C1025 OIL PRESSURE SWITCH

C153 C154 INTEGRAL ALTERNATOR/ REGULATOR

C186 DAYTIME RUNNING LAMPS MODULE

C166 ANTI-LOCK POWER RELAY

C176 ANTI-LOCK BRAKE FLUID LEVEL SWITCH

G104

C1044 WINDSHIELD WASHER PUMP MOTOR

C1032 TO SOLENOID CONTROL VALVE BODY

G106

C1048 RIGHT FRONT PARK/TURN LAMP

C148 STARTER MOTOR/ SOLENOID

C164 AMBIENT TEMPERATURE SENSOR

C1014 C185 ANTI-LOCK MOTOR RELAY

C1013 LOW PITCH HORN

C1012 HIGH PITCH HORN

FRONT OF VEHICLE

FM1019300025020X

Fig. 35 Engine compartment reference diagram (Part 2 of 3). 1993–96 Taurus w/3.0L/V6-182 FFV

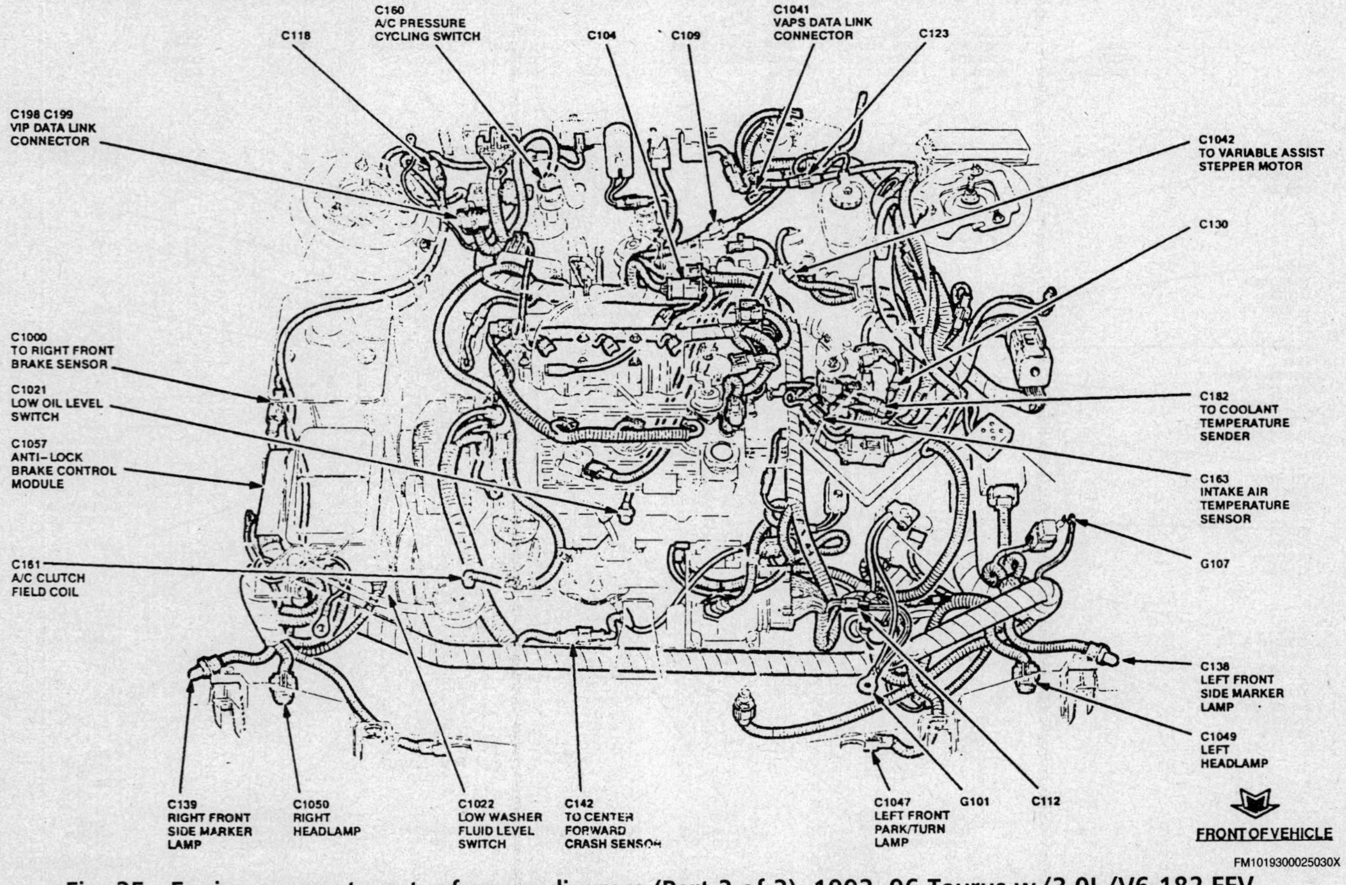

C118

C160 A/C PRESSURE CYCLING SWITCH

C104   C109

C1041 VAPS DATA LINK CONNECTOR

C123

C198 C199 VIP DATA LINK CONNECTOR

C1042 TO VARIABLE ASSIST STEPPER MOTOR

C130

C1000 TO RIGHT FRONT BRAKE SENSOR

C1021 LOW OIL LEVEL SWITCH

C182 TO COOLANT TEMPERATURE SENDER

C1057 ANTI-LOCK BRAKE CONTROL MODULE

C163 INTAKE AIR TEMPERATURE SENSOR

G107

C161 A/C CLUTCH FIELD COIL

C136 LEFT FRONT SIDE MARKER LAMP

C1049 LEFT HEADLAMP

C139 RIGHT FRONT SIDE MARKER LAMP

C1050 RIGHT HEADLAMP

C1022 LOW WASHER FLUID LEVEL SWITCH

C142 TO CENTER FORWARD CRASH SENSOR

C1047 LEFT FRONT PARK/TURN LAMP

G101   C112

FRONT OF VEHICLE

FM1019300025030X

Fig. 35 Engine compartment reference diagram (Part 3 of 3). 1993–96 Taurus w/3.0L/V6-182 FFV

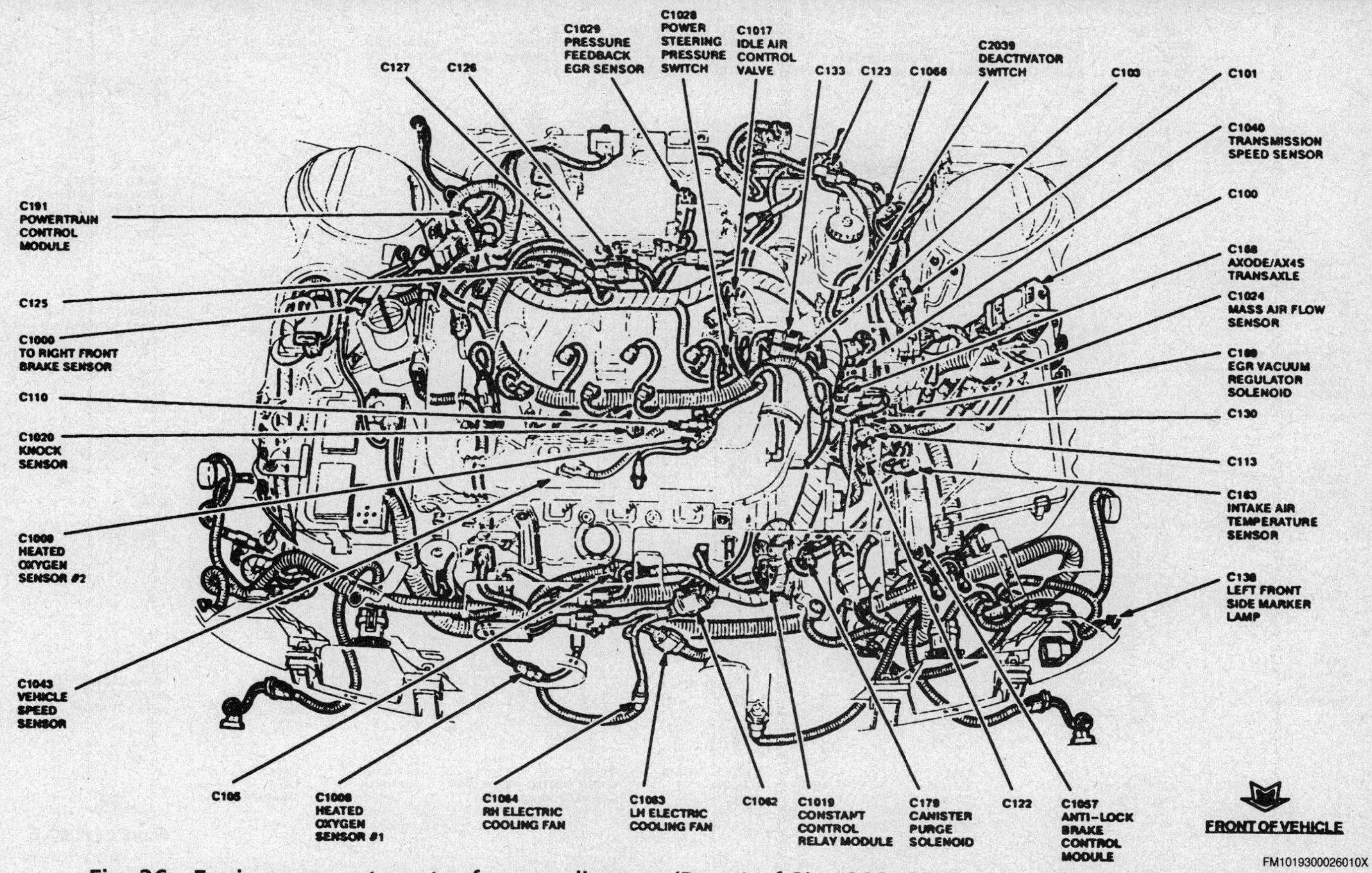

Fig. 36   Engine compartment reference diagram (Part 1 of 3). 1993–95 Taurus w/3.2L/V6-195 SHO

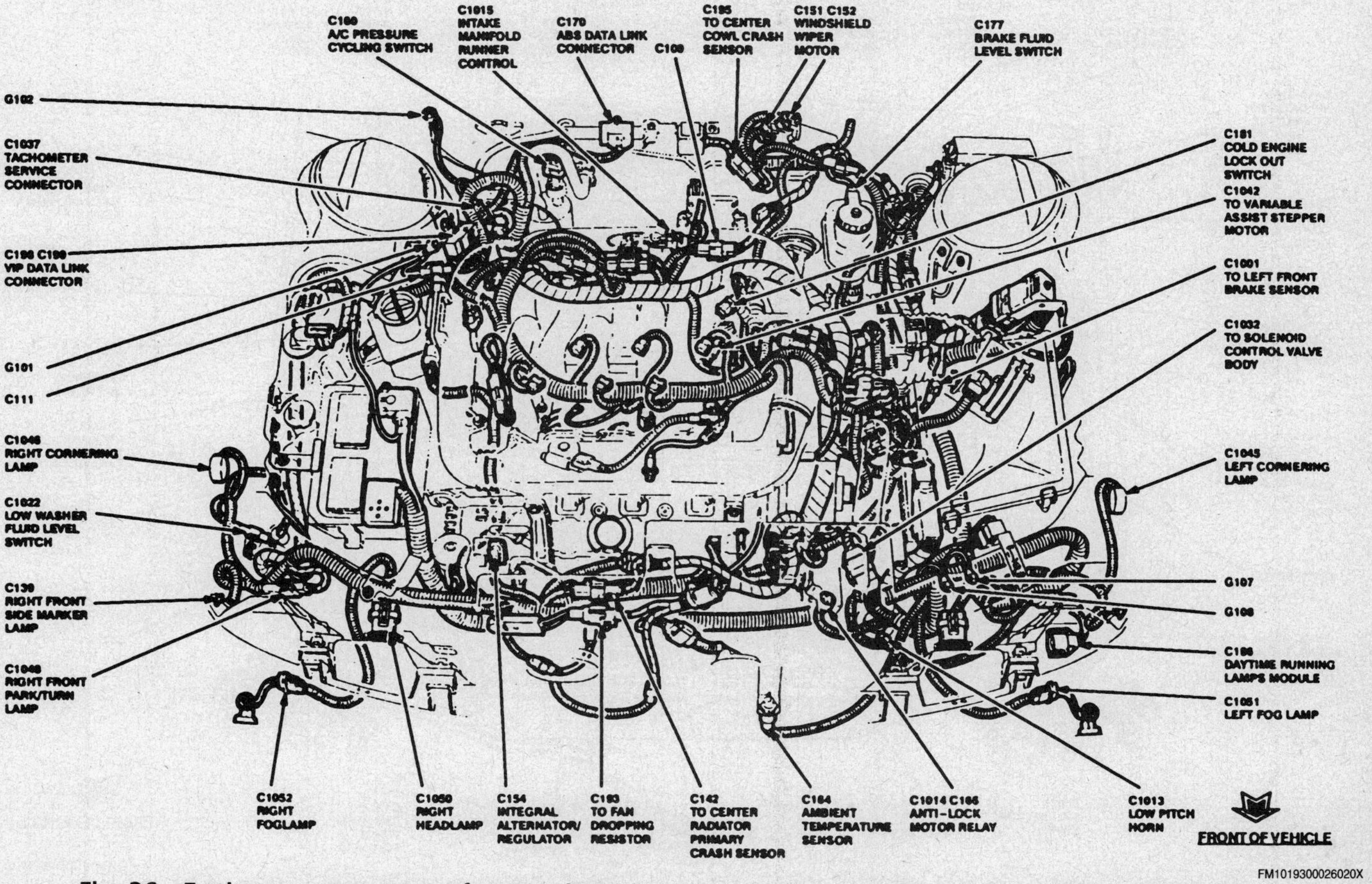

Fig. 36   Engine compartment reference diagram (Part 2 of 3). 1993–95 Taurus w/3.2L/V6-195 SHO

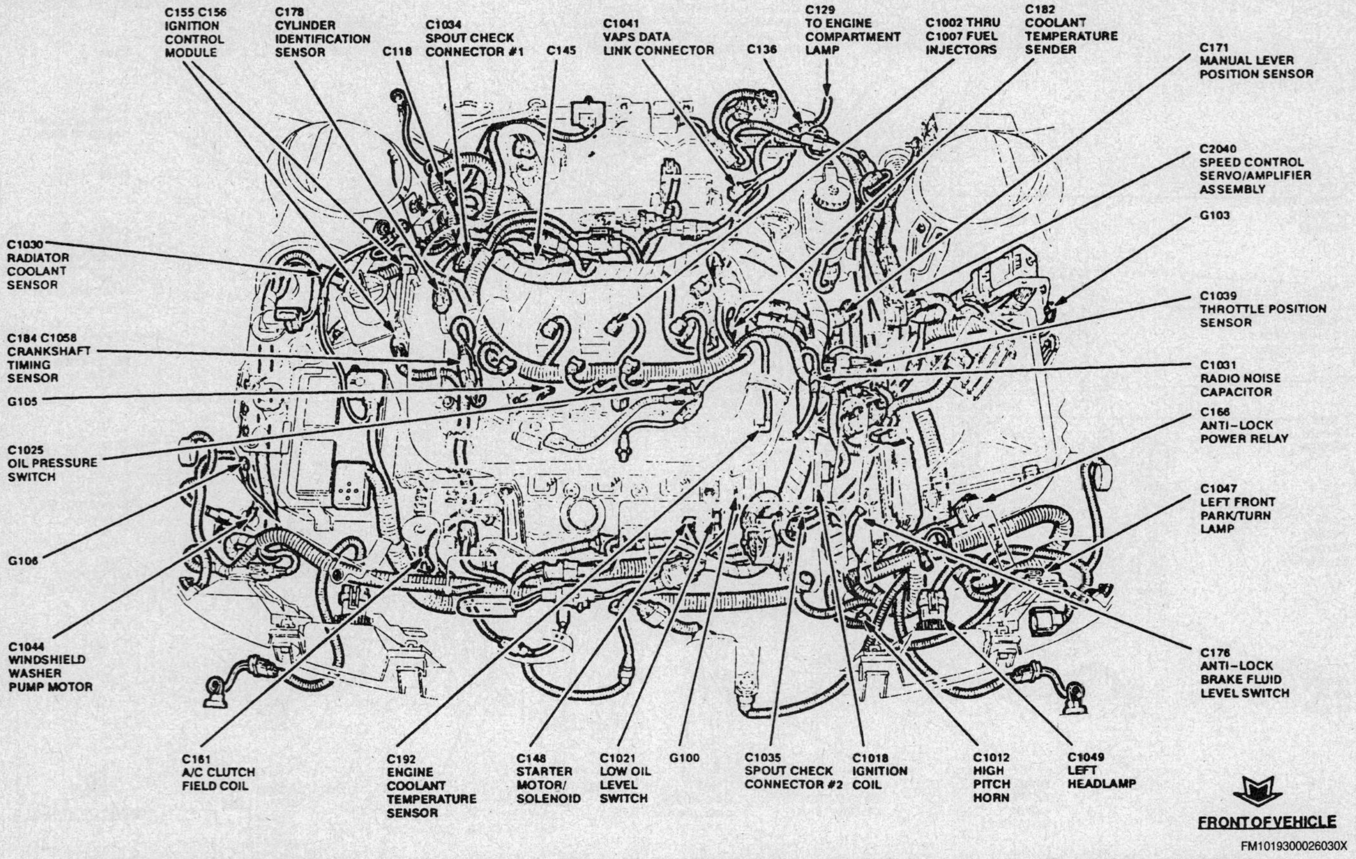

C155 C156 IGNITION CONTROL MODULE
C178 CYLINDER IDENTIFICATION SENSOR
C118
C1034 SPOUT CHECK CONNECTOR #1
C145
C1041 VAPS DATA LINK CONNECTOR
C136
C129 TO ENGINE COMPARTMENT LAMP
C1002 THRU C1007 FUEL INJECTORS
C182 COOLANT TEMPERATURE SENDER
C171 MANUAL LEVER POSITION SENSOR

C2040 SPEED CONTROL SERVO/AMPLIFIER ASSEMBLY
G103

C1030 RADIATOR COOLANT SENSOR

C1039 THROTTLE POSITION SENSOR

C184 C1058 CRANKSHAFT TIMING SENSOR
G105

C1031 RADIO NOISE CAPACITOR

C166 ANTI–LOCK POWER RELAY

C1025 OIL PRESSURE SWITCH

C1047 LEFT FRONT PARK/TURN LAMP

G106

C176 ANTI–LOCK BRAKE FLUID LEVEL SWITCH

C1044 WINDSHIELD WASHER PUMP MOTOR

C161 A/C CLUTCH FIELD COIL
C192 ENGINE COOLANT TEMPERATURE SENSOR
C148 STARTER MOTOR/ SOLENOID
C1021 LOW OIL LEVEL SWITCH
G100
C1035 SPOUT CHECK CONNECTOR #2
C1018 IGNITION COIL
C1012 HIGH PITCH HORN
C1049 LEFT HEADLAMP

FRONT OF VEHICLE

FM1019300026030X

Fig. 36 Engine compartment reference diagram (Part 3 of 3). 1993–95 Taurus w/3.2L/V6-195 SHO

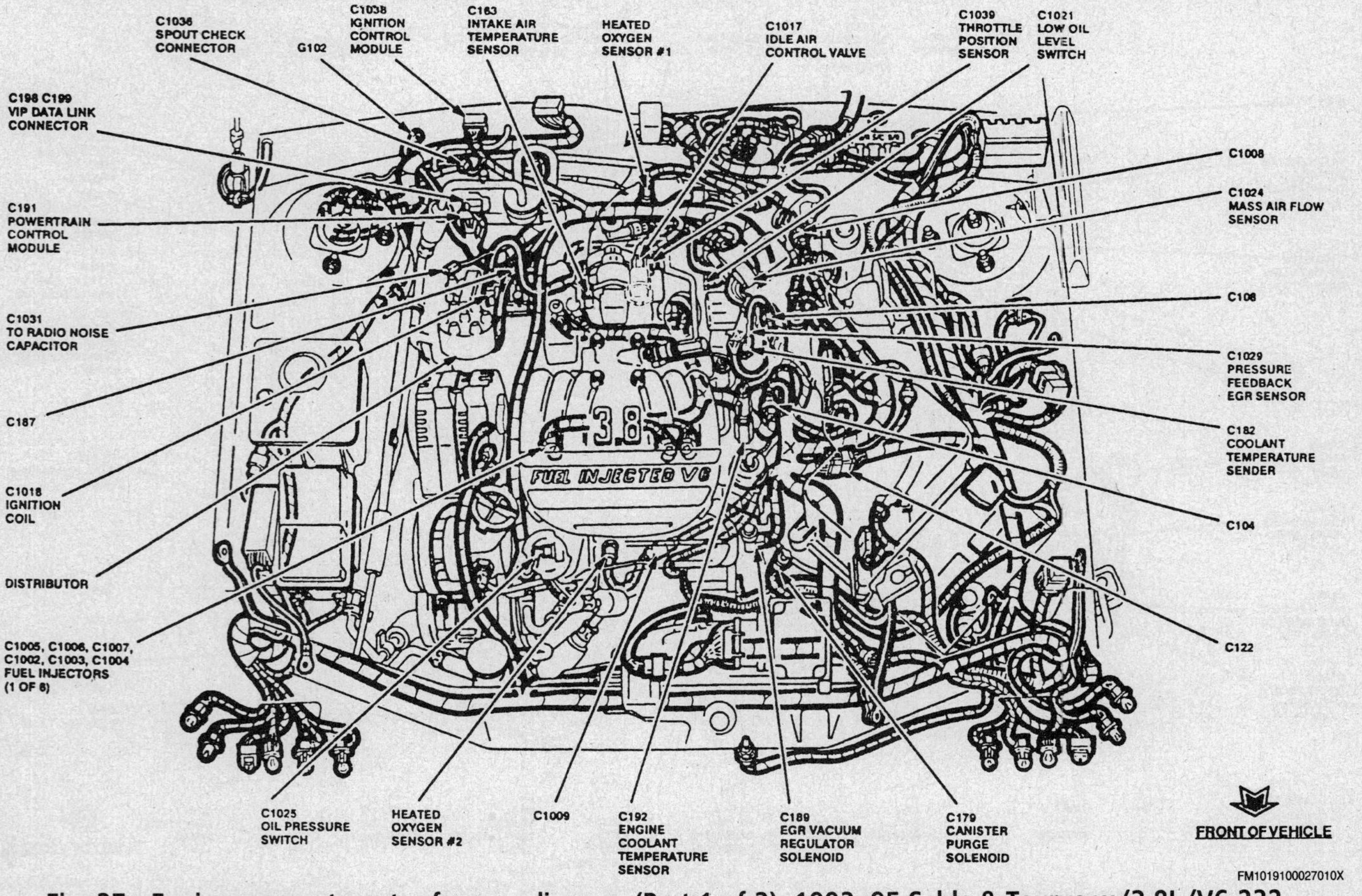

C1036 SPOUT CHECK CONNECTOR
G102
C1058 IGNITION CONTROL MODULE
C163 INTAKE AIR TEMPERATURE SENSOR
HEATED OXYGEN SENSOR #1
C1017 IDLE AIR CONTROL VALVE
C1039 THROTTLE POSITION SENSOR
C1021 LOW OIL LEVEL SWITCH

C198 C199 VIP DATA LINK CONNECTOR

C1008

C191 POWERTRAIN CONTROL MODULE

C1024 MASS AIR FLOW SENSOR

C1031 TO RADIO NOISE CAPACITOR

C106

C187

C1029 PRESSURE FEEDBACK EGR SENSOR

C182 COOLANT TEMPERATURE SENDER

C1018 IGNITION COIL

C104

DISTRIBUTOR

C122

C1005, C1006, C1007, C1002, C1003, C1004 FUEL INJECTORS (1 OF 6)

C1025 OIL PRESSURE SWITCH
HEATED OXYGEN SENSOR #2
C1009
C192 ENGINE COOLANT TEMPERATURE SENSOR
C189 EGR VACUUM REGULATOR SOLENOID
C179 CANISTER PURGE SOLENOID

FUEL INJECTED V6 3.8

FRONT OF VEHICLE

FM1019100027010X

Fig. 37 Engine compartment reference diagram (Part 1 of 3). 1993–95 Sable & Taurus w/3.8L/V6-232

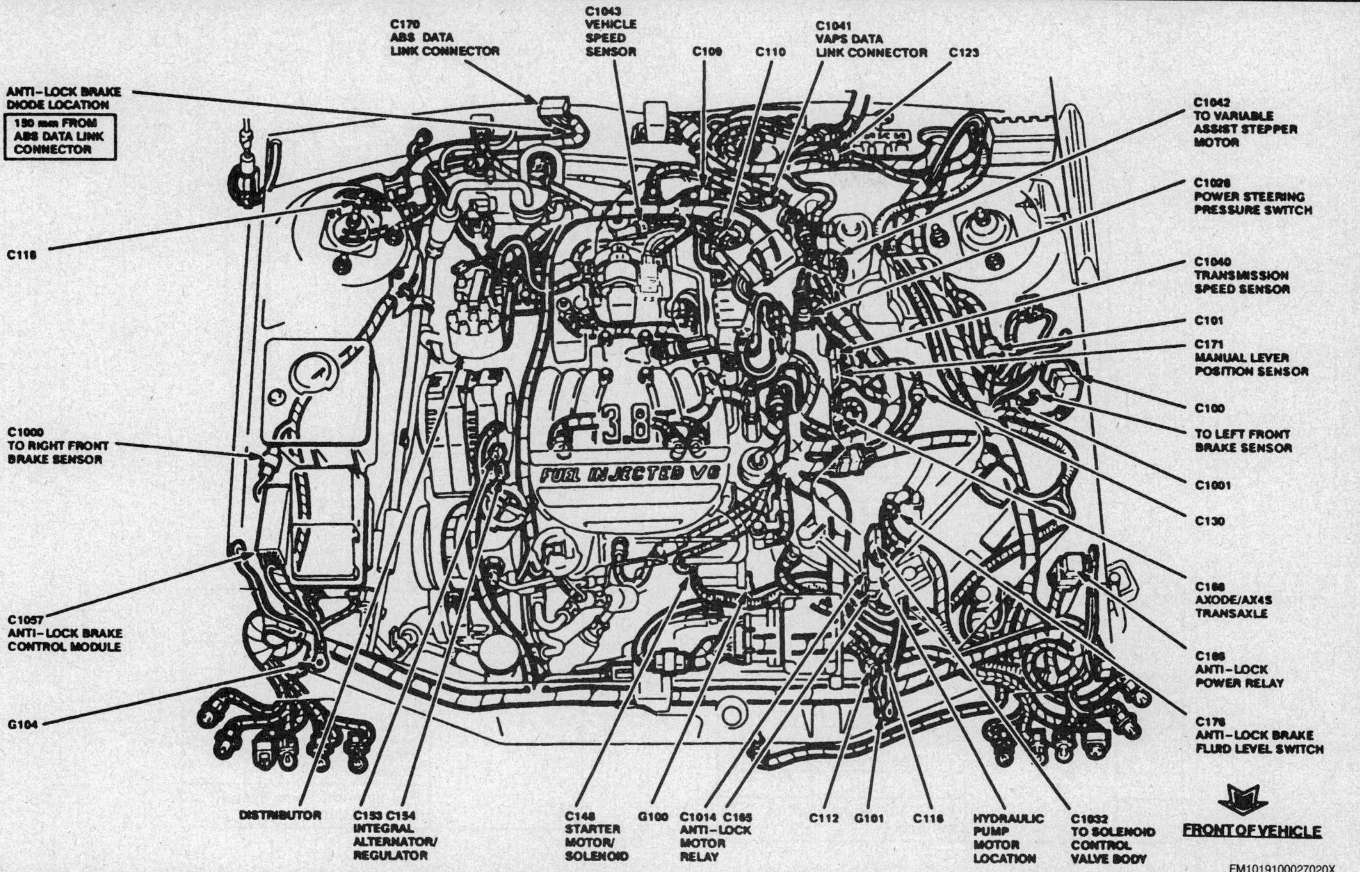

Fig. 37 Engine compartment reference diagram (Part 2 of 3). 1993–95 Sable & Taurus w/3.8L/V6-232

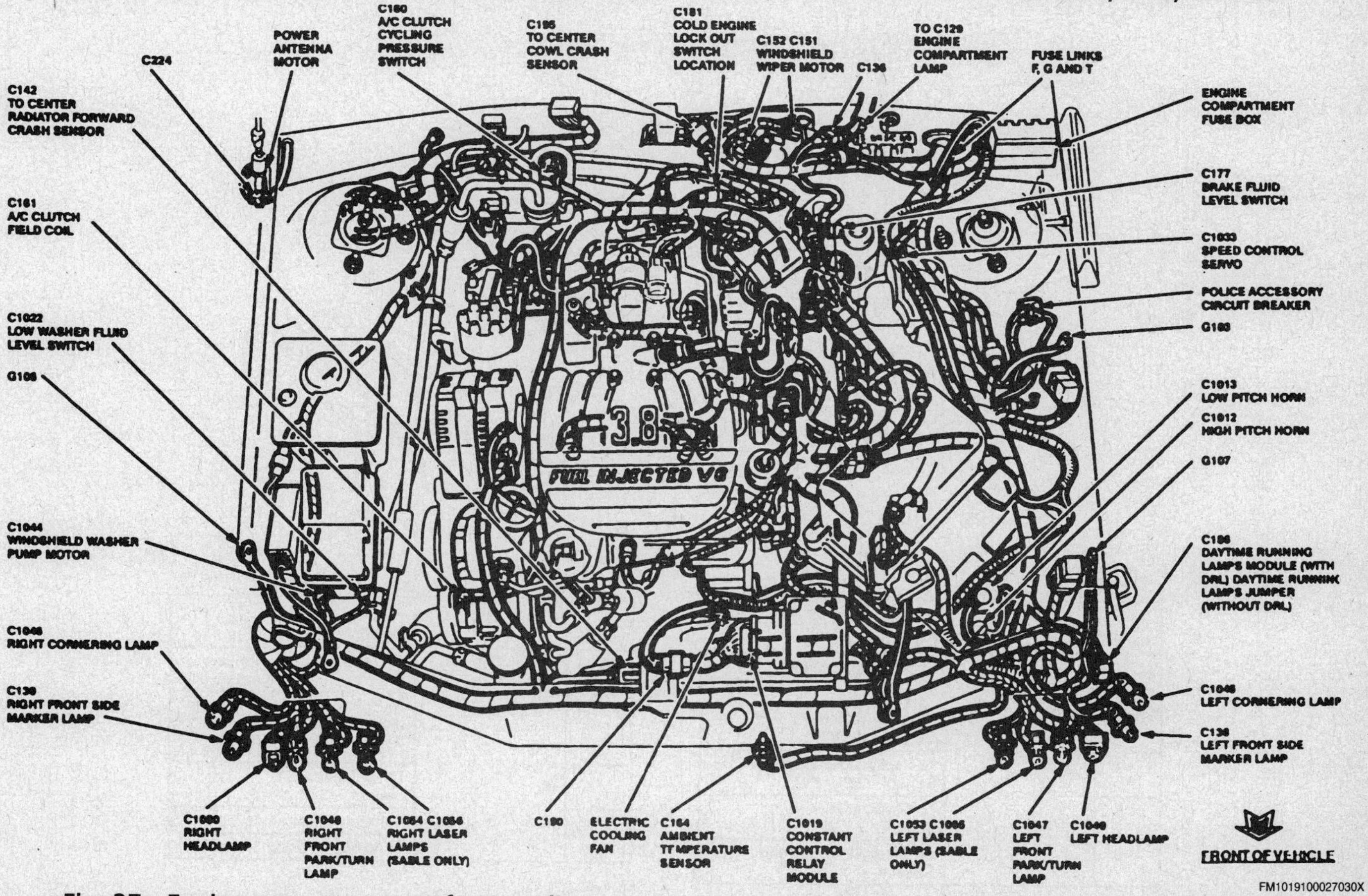

Fig. 37 Engine compartment reference diagram (Part 3 of 3). 1993–95 Sable & Taurus w/3.8L/V6-232

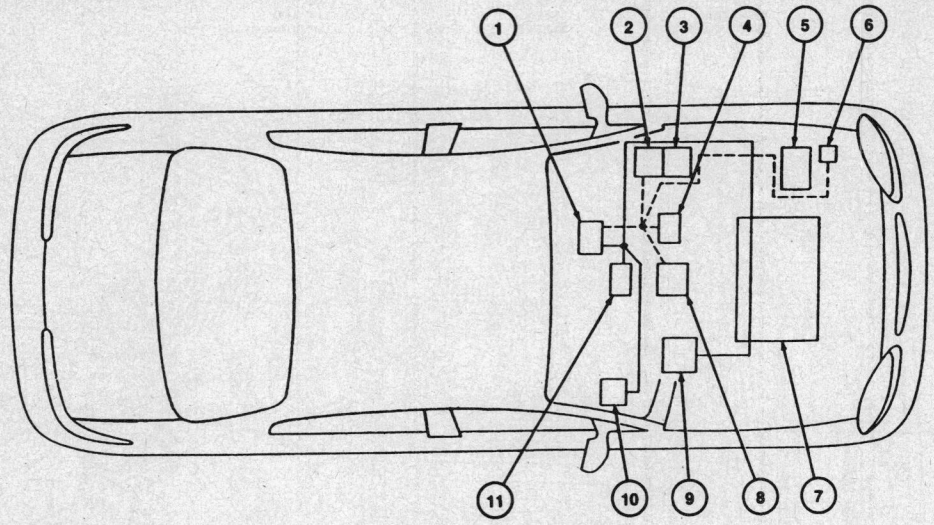

Item		Description
1		Data Link Connector
2		Fuse Junction Panel
3		Generic Electronic Module
4		Remote Anti-Theft Personality Module
5		Battery
6		Anti-Lock Brake Control Module

Item		Description
7		Engine Assembly
8		Integrated Air Bag Assembly Monitor
9		Powertrain Control Module
10		Remote Climate Control Module
11		Passive Anti-Theft System Control Module

Fig. 38   Engine compartment reference diagram (Part 1 of 3). 1996 Sable & Taurus

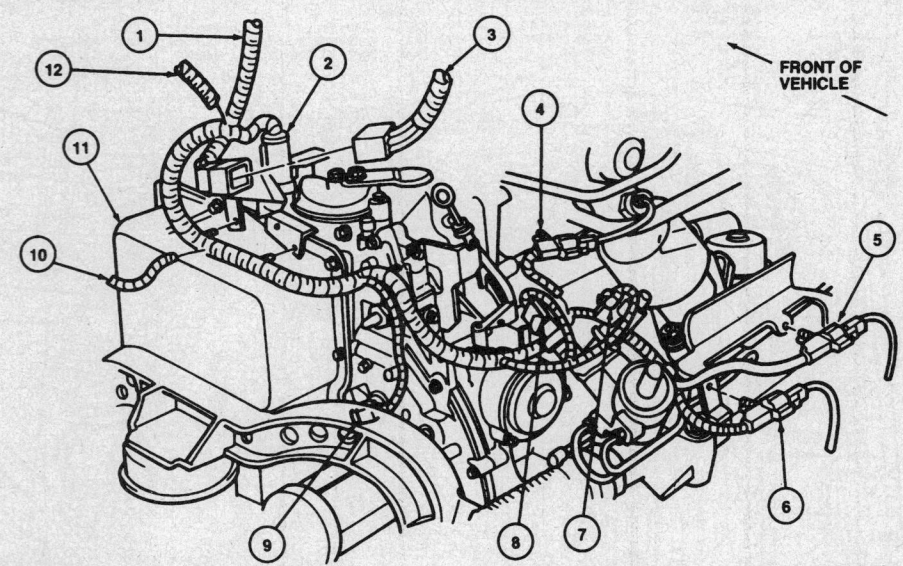

Item		Description
1		Fuel Charging Wiring
2		To Transaxle
3		Headlamp Dash Panel Junction Wire
4		To Heated Exhaust Gas Sensor - 3.0L (2V)
5		To Catalyst Monitoring Sensor
6		To Catalyst Monitoring Sensor

Item		Description
7		To Variable Assist Power Steering (VAPS) II Actuator
8		To Power Steering Pressure (PSP) Switch
9		To Turbine Speed Sensor
10		To MAF and ACT Sensor—3.0L (4V)
11		Automatic Transaxle
12		To 12B637 Wiring 3.0L (4V)

Fig. 38   Engine compartment reference diagram (Part 2 of 3). 1996 Sable & Taurus

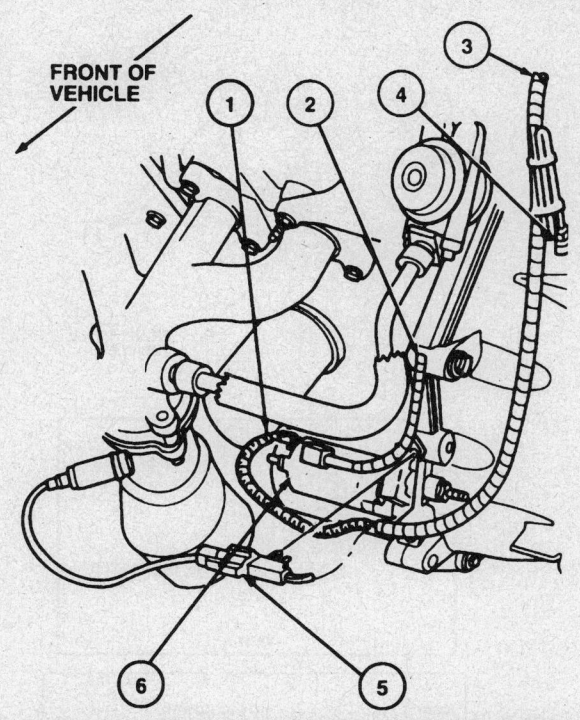

Item		Description
1		Starter Motor
2		Battery to Starter Relay Cable
3		Fuel Charging Wiring
4		To Misfire Sensor
5		To HEGO Sensor
6		To Starter Solenoid

Fig. 38 Engine compartment reference diagram (Part 3 of 3). 1996 Sable & Taurus

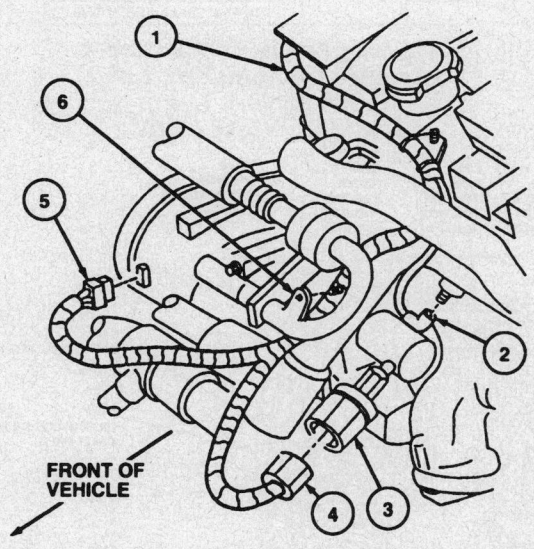

Item		Description
1		Wiring Assy
2		To Oil Pressure Switch
3		A/C Pressure Cut-Off Switch
4		To A/C High Pressure Switch
5		To A/C Compressor Clutch (2885)
6		Retainer (Part of 12B637)

Fig. 39 Engine compartment reference diagram (Part 1 of 2). 1996 Sable & Taurus w/3.0L/V6-181 DOHC

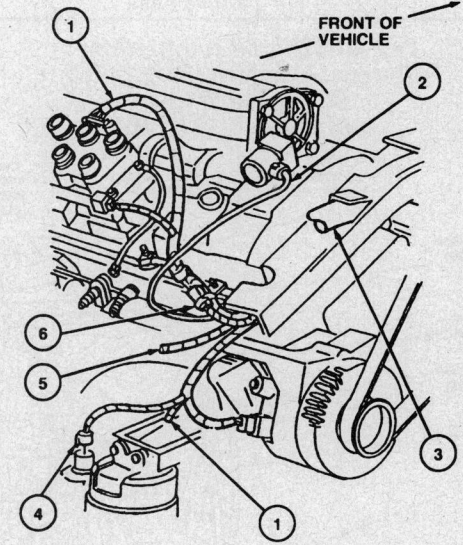

Item		Description
1		Wiring Assy
2		To Evaporator
3		To Powertrain Control Module
4		To Vehicle Speed Sensor (VSS)
5		To Vapor Management Valve
6		To Heated Exhaust Oxygen Sensor

Fig. 39 Engine compartment reference diagram (Part 2 of 2). 1996 Sable & Taurus w/3.0L/V6-181 DOHC

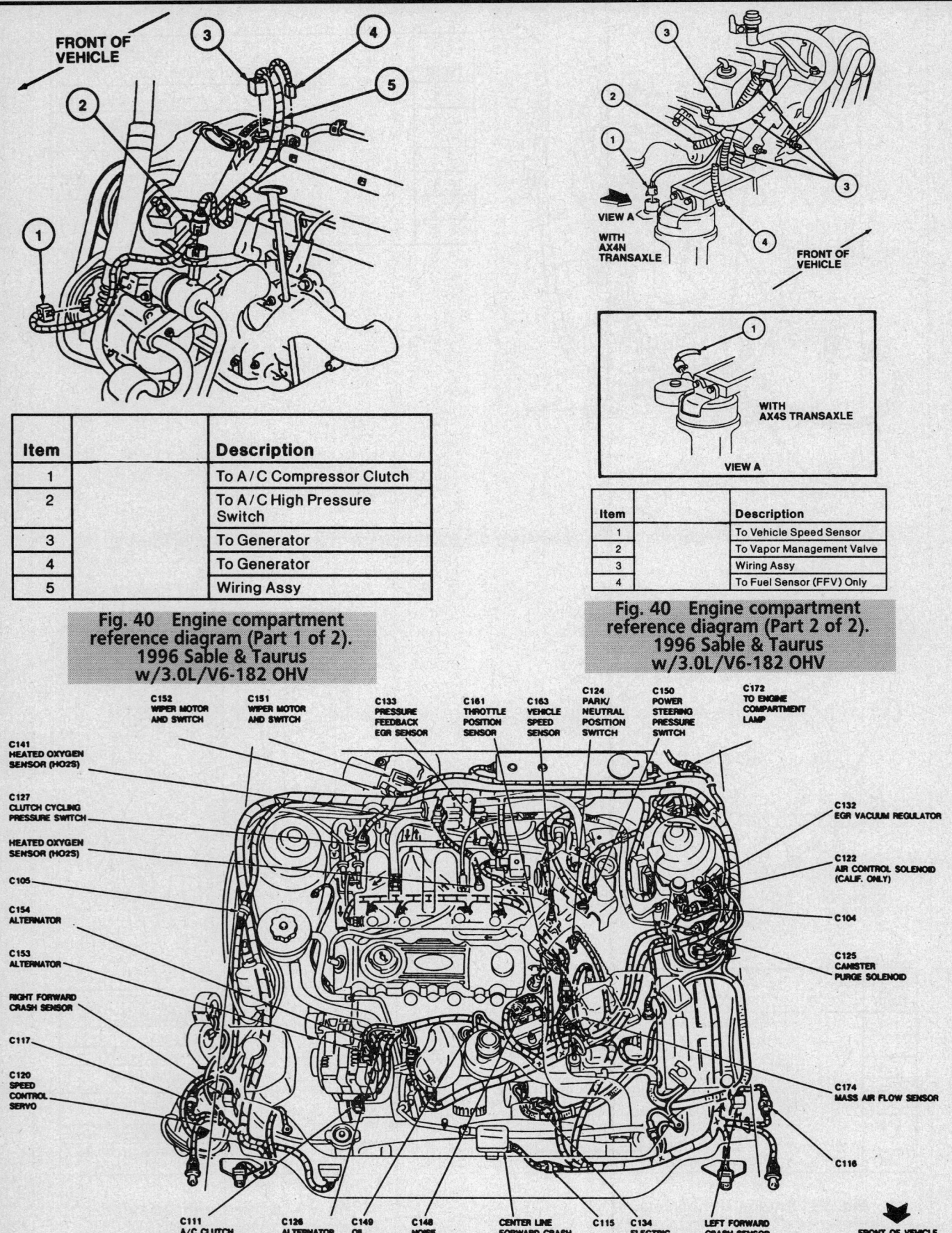

FRONT OF VEHICLE

VIEW A
WITH AX4N TRANSAXLE

FRONT OF VEHICLE

WITH AX4S TRANSAXLE

VIEW A

Item		Description
1		To A / C Compressor Clutch
2		To A / C High Pressure Switch
3		To Generator
4		To Generator
5		Wiring Assy

Fig. 40 Engine compartment reference diagram (Part 1 of 2). 1996 Sable & Taurus w/3.0L/V6-182 OHV

Item		Description
1		To Vehicle Speed Sensor
2		To Vapor Management Valve
3		Wiring Assy
4		To Fuel Sensor (FFV) Only

Fig. 40 Engine compartment reference diagram (Part 2 of 2). 1996 Sable & Taurus w/3.0L/V6-182 OHV

C152 WIPER MOTOR AND SWITCH
C151 WIPER MOTOR AND SWITCH
C133 PRESSURE FEEDBACK EGR SENSOR
C161 THROTTLE POSITION SENSOR
C163 VEHICLE SPEED SENSOR
C124 PARK/ NEUTRAL POSITION SWITCH
C150 POWER STEERING PRESSURE SWITCH
C172 TO ENGINE COMPARTMENT LAMP

C141 HEATED OXYGEN SENSOR (HO2S)
C127 CLUTCH CYCLING PRESSURE SWITCH
HEATED OXYGEN SENSOR (HO2S)
C105
C154 ALTERNATOR
C153 ALTERNATOR
RIGHT FORWARD CRASH SENSOR
C117
C120 SPEED CONTROL SERVO

C132 EGR VACUUM REGULATOR
C122 AIR CONTROL SOLENOID (CALIF. ONLY)
C104
C125 CANISTER PURGE SOLENOID
C174 MASS AIR FLOW SENSOR
C116

C111 A/C CLUTCH FIELD COIL
C126 ALTERNATOR
C149 OIL PRESSURE SWITCH
C148 NOISE SUPPRESSION CAPACITOR
CENTER LINE FORWARD CRASH SENSOR
C115
C134 ELECTRIC COOLING FAN
LEFT FORWARD CRASH SENSOR
FRONT OF VEHICLE

FM1019100028010X

Fig. 41 Engine compartment reference diagram (Part 1 of 2). Tempo & Topaz w/2.3L/4-140

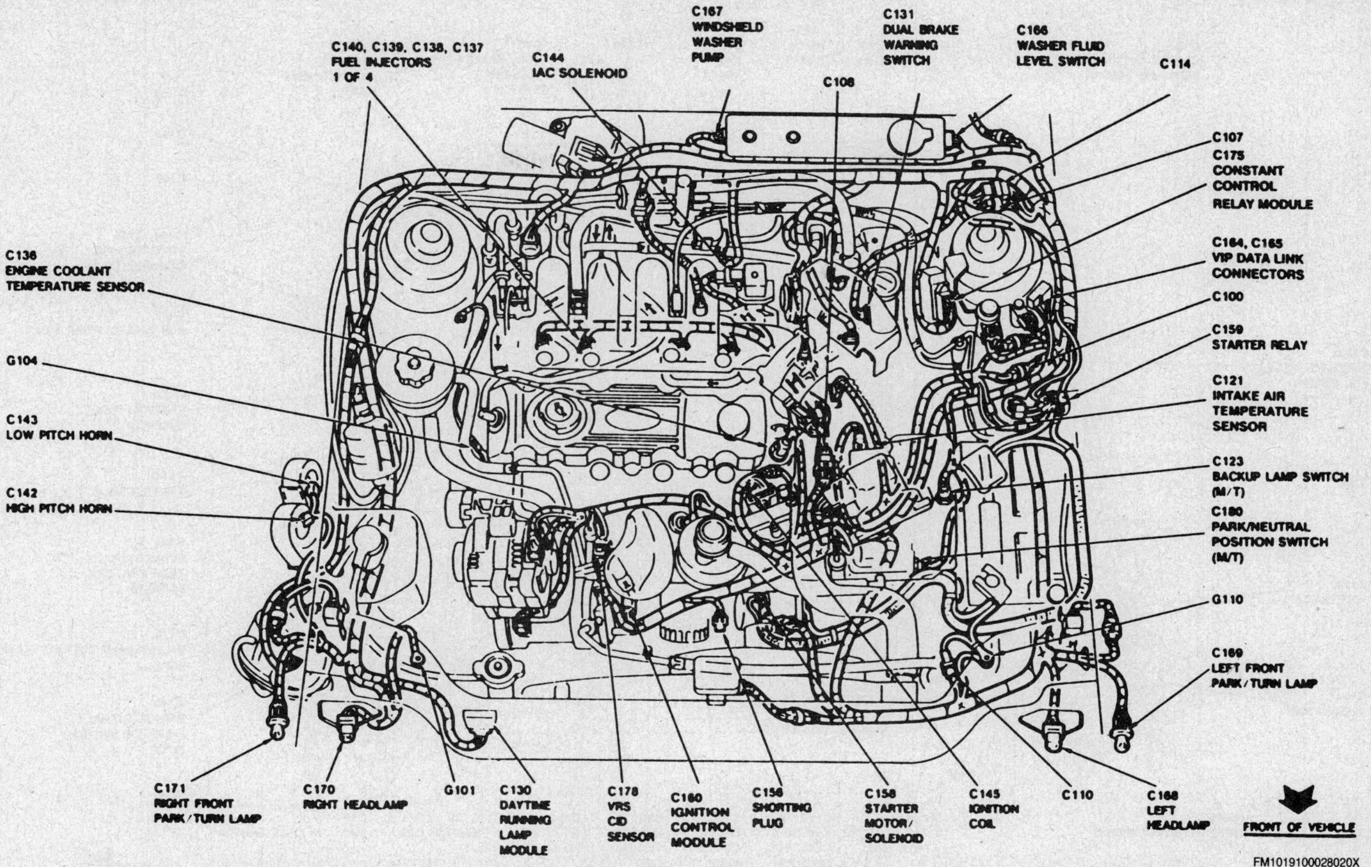

C140, C139, C138, C137
FUEL INJECTORS
1 OF 4

C144
IAC SOLENOID

C167
WINDSHIELD
WASHER
PUMP

C131
DUAL BRAKE
WARNING
SWITCH

C108

C166
WASHER FLUID
LEVEL SWITCH

C114

C136
ENGINE COOLANT
TEMPERATURE SENSOR

G104

C143
LOW PITCH HORN

C142
HIGH PITCH HORN

C107
C175
CONSTANT
CONTROL
RELAY MODULE

C164, C165
VIP DATA LINK
CONNECTORS

C100

C159
STARTER RELAY

C121
INTAKE AIR
TEMPERATURE
SENSOR

C123
BACKUP LAMP SWITCH
(M/T)

C180
PARK/NEUTRAL
POSITION SWITCH
(M/T)

G110

C169
LEFT FRONT
PARK/TURN LAMP

C171
RIGHT FRONT
PARK/TURN LAMP

C170
RIGHT HEADLAMP

G101

C130
DAYTIME
RUNNING
LAMP
MODULE

C178
VRS
CID
SENSOR

C160
IGNITION
CONTROL
MODULE

C156
SHORTING
PLUG

C158
STARTER
MOTOR/
SOLENOID

C145
IGNITION
COIL

C110

C168
LEFT
HEADLAMP

FRONT OF VEHICLE

FM1019100028020X

Fig. 41   Engine compartment reference diagram (Part 2 of 2). Tempo & Topaz w/2.3L/4-140

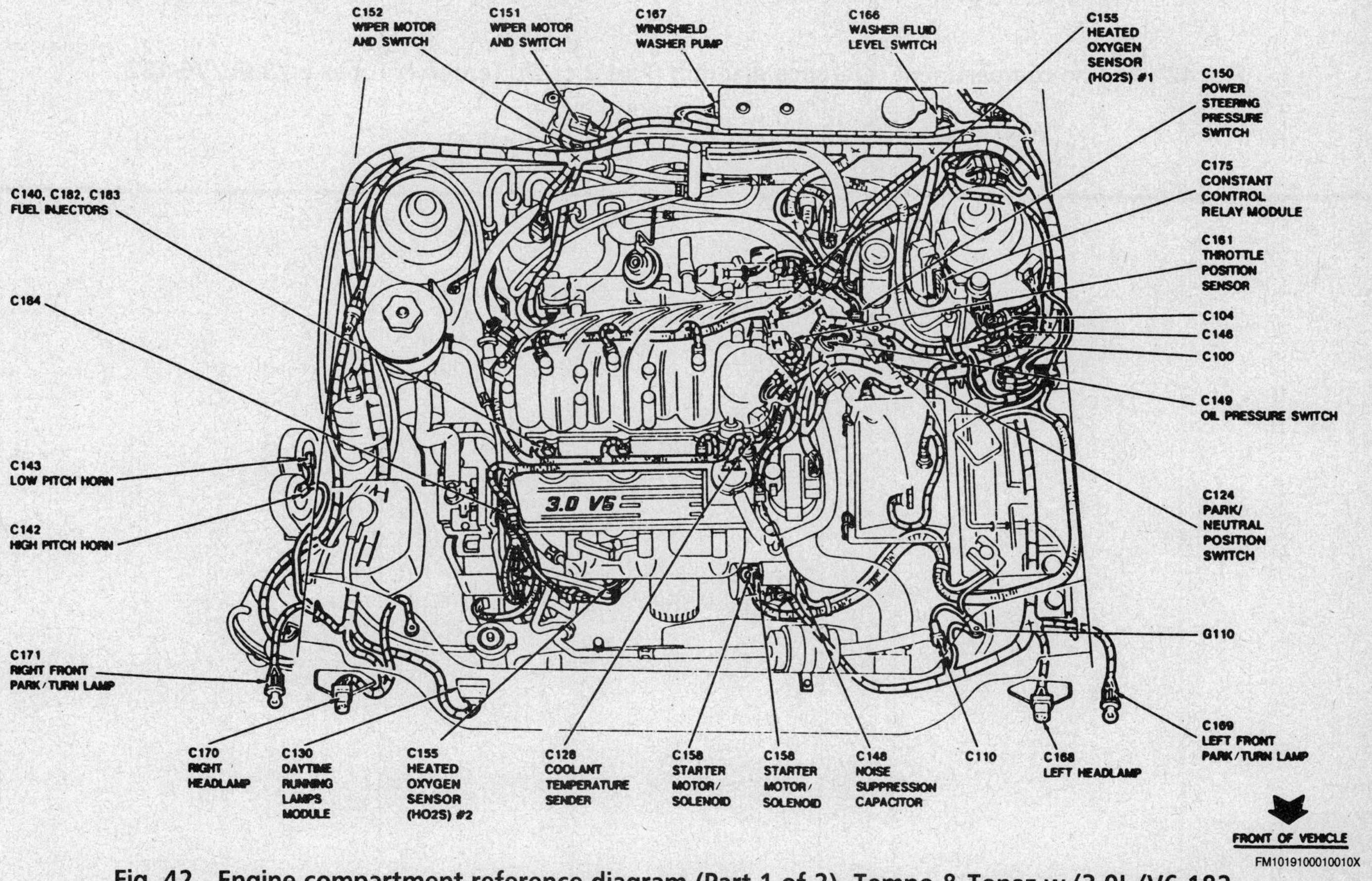

C152
WIPER MOTOR
AND SWITCH

C151
WIPER MOTOR
AND SWITCH

C167
WINDSHIELD
WASHER PUMP

C166
WASHER FLUID
LEVEL SWITCH

C155
HEATED
OXYGEN
SENSOR
(HO2S) #1

C150
POWER
STEERING
PRESSURE
SWITCH

C140, C182, C183
FUEL INJECTORS

C184

C143
LOW PITCH HORN

C142
HIGH PITCH HORN

C175
CONSTANT
CONTROL
RELAY MODULE

C161
THROTTLE
POSITION
SENSOR

C104

C146

C100

C149
OIL PRESSURE SWITCH

C124
PARK/
NEUTRAL
POSITION
SWITCH

G110

3.0 V6

C171
RIGHT FRONT
PARK/TURN LAMP

C170
RIGHT
HEADLAMP

C130
DAYTIME
RUNNING
LAMPS
MODULE

C155
HEATED
OXYGEN
SENSOR
(HO2S) #2

C128
COOLANT
TEMPERATURE
SENDER

C158
STARTER
MOTOR/
SOLENOID

C158
STARTER
MOTOR/
SOLENOID

C148
NOISE
SUPPRESSION
CAPACITOR

C110

C168
LEFT HEADLAMP

C169
LEFT FRONT
PARK/TURN LAMP

FRONT OF VEHICLE

FM1019100010010X

Fig. 42   Engine compartment reference diagram (Part 1 of 2). Tempo & Topaz w/3.0L/V6-182

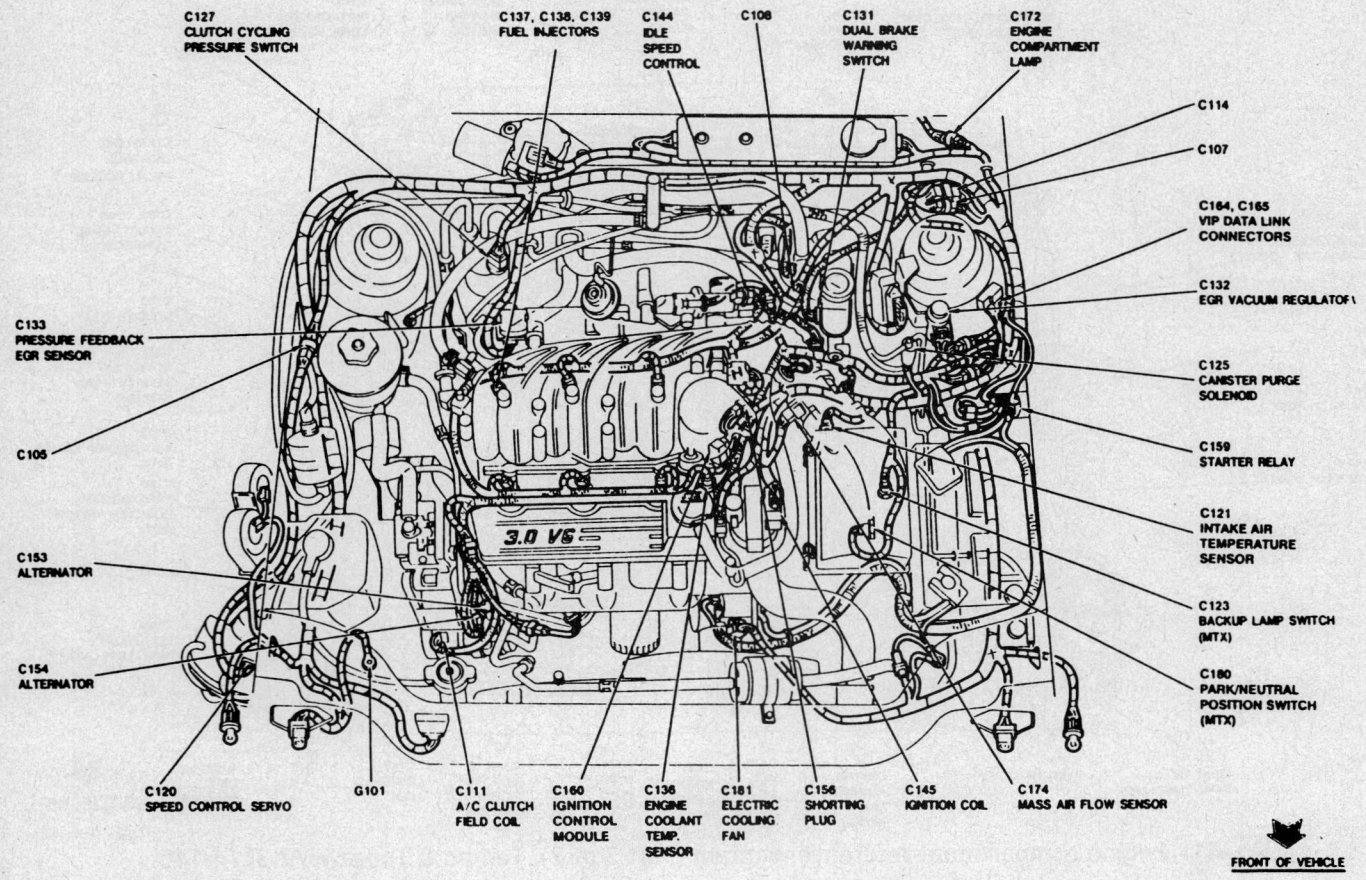

Fig. 42   Engine compartment reference diagram (Part 2 of 2). Tempo & Topaz w/3.0L/V6-182

FM1019100010020X

MISSION CONTROLS

If Uncertain About The Proper Use Of Information Contained In This Section, Please Refer To "How To Use This Manual" Located In The Front Of This Manual.

Prior To Performing Any Service Operations Listed In This Section, Consult The "Technical Service Bulletins" Section For Related Information.

TABLE OF CONTENTS

Page No.

ASPIRE, CAPRI, ESCORT & TRACER w/1.8L/4-112 ENGINE, FESTIVA & PROBE 14-22

Page No.

EXCEPT ASPIRE, CAPRI, ESCORT & TRACER w/1.8L/4-112 ENGINE, FESTIVA & PROBE 14-1

Except Aspire, Capri, Escort & Tracer w/1.8L/4-112 Engine, Festiva & Probe

INDEX

Page No.

Air Intake Systems: 14-2
Description 14-2
Diagnosis & Testing: 14-2
1993-95 14-2
1996 14-2
Catalytic Converters: 14-2
Description 14-2
Diagnosis & Testing: 14-2
Exhaust Manifold Restricted 14-2
Vacuum Test 14-2
Vacuum Test-Catalytic
Converter(s) On/Muffler(s) Off . 14-2
Vacuum Test-Exhaust
Disconnected 14-2
Vacuum Test-Rate Of Vacuum
Gauge Needle Return
Movement 14-2
Visual Inspection 14-2
Emission Related Components: . . . 14-17
Description: 14-17
Ignition Barometric Pressure
Switch 14-17
Ignition Timing Vacuum Switch . . 14-17
Inertia Switch 14-17
Ported Vacuum Switches (PVS) . 14-17
Temperature Vacuum Switch
(TVS) 14-17
Throttle Solenoid Positioner
(TSP) 14-17
Vacuum Delay Valve (VDV) 14-18
Vacuum Regulator 14-18

Page No.

Vacuum Reservoir 14-18
Vacuum Restrictor 14-18
Vacuum Vent Valves 14-19
Wide Open Throttle Control
Valve 14-19
Diagnosis & Testing: 14-19
Ignition Barometric Pressure
Switch 14-19
Ignition Timing Vacuum Switch . . 14-20
Inertia Switch 14-20
Ported Vacuum Switch 14-20
Spark Delay Valve (SDV) 14-21
Temperature Vacuum Switch
(TVS) 14-21
Throttle Solenoid Positioner
(TSP) 14-20
Vacuum Delay Valve (VDV) 14-20
Vacuum Operated Throttle
Modulator (VOTM) 14-21
Vacuum Regulator 14-21
**Evaporative Emission (EVAP)
Systems:** 14-10
Description: 14-10
Canister Purging 14-10
EEC IV 14-10
EEC V & Flexible Fuel 14-10
Fuel Tank Venting 14-10
Diagnosis & Testing: 14-10
Diagnosis By Symptom 14-10
Exhaust Gas Recirculation (EGR): . . 14-2
Description 14-2

Page No.

Diagnosis & Testing: 14-3
Diagnosis By Symptom 14-3
Functional Diagnosis 14-3
Testing 14-3
**Positive Crankcase Ventilation
(PCV) System:** 14-10
Description: 14-10
Except 3.0L/V6-182 &
3.2L/V6-195 SHO Engines . . . 14-10
3.0L/V6-182 & 3.2L/V6-195
SHO Engines 14-10
Diagnosis & Testing: 14-11
1993-95 14-11
1996 14-11
**Thermactor Systems (Secondary
Air Injection):** 14-13
Description: 14-13
Pulsed Secondary Air Injection
(PAIR) (Pulse Air System
(Thermactor II)) 14-13
Secondary Air Injection (AIR)
(Managed Air Thermactor)
System 14-13
System Components 14-14
Thermactor Air Injection System . 14-13
Diagnosis & Testing: 14-15
1993-95 14-15
1996 14-17

AIR INTAKE SYSTEMS

Description

All engines are equipped with dry-type air cleaners using a replaceable filter element. Some of these systems use air cleaner assemblies with various sensors, switches and vacuum motors to control inlet air temperature. Also, other sensors are sometimes present for different engine control systems.

Some of these systems draw air in from a cool air source only, while the others regulate air inlet temperature by drawing air from a cool sources as well as heated air from a heat shroud mounted on the exhaust manifold. The duct and valve systems which regulate air flow from these two sources is located either inside the air cleaner, mounted on the air cleaner or in one of the remote mounted inlet tubes. Flow is regulated by a door operated by a vacuum motor. Operation of the motor is controlled by delay valves, temperature sensors or other vacuum control systems and vary between application and engine calibration.

Diagnosis & Testing

1993–95

Refer to charts in **Figs. 1 through 3** for diagnosis and testing of systems.

1996

Refer to EEC-V section, under "Computerized Engine Controls" for diagnosis and testing.

CATALYTIC CONVERTERS

Description

The catalytic converter, **Fig. 4,** is an emission control device added to the exhaust system to effectively reduce the levels of Carbon Monoxide (CO), Hydrocarbons (HC), and Oxides of Nitrogen (NOx) from entering the atmosphere. The converter works as a gas reactor to speed up the heat producing chemical reaction between exhaust gas components to reduce air pollutants in the engine exhaust. The catalyst material contained inside the converter, is made of a ceramic substance that is coated with a high surface area alumina and impregnated with precious metals.

There are two basic types of catalysts: the Conventional Oxidation Catalyst (COC), containing Platinum (PL) and Palladium (Pd), effective for catalyzing oxidation reactions of HC and CO, and the Three-Way Catalyst (TWC), containing Platinum (PL) and Rhodium (RH) or Palladium (Pd) and Rhodium (RH), effective for catalyzing oxidation reactions of HC, CO and NOx.

The catalytic converter assembly consists of a structured shell containing a ceramic, honeycomb construction. In order to maintain the converters oxygen content at a high level to obtain maximum oxidation

for producing the heated chemical reaction, the oxidation catalyst requires the use of a secondary air source provided by the Pulse Air (PA) or Thermactor Air (TA) injection systems. The catalytic converter system is protected by several devices that block out the secondary air supply from the thermactor air injection system when the engine is laboring under any abnormal hot or cold operating situation. Depending on engine calibration, these block-out devices operate under one or more conditions such as, cold engine operation with rich choke mixture, abnormally high engine coolant temperatures above 225°F, wide open throttle or extended idle operation.

Diagnosis & Testing

VISUAL INSPECTION

1. Visually inspect exhaust system.
2. If exhaust system is visually satisfactory, proceed to "Vacuum Test."
3. If exhaust system is visually defective, replace any collapsed or damaged components. If problem still exists, proceed to "Vacuum Test."

VACUUM TEST

1. Attach a suitable vacuum gauge to intake manifold vacuum source, then connect a suitable tachometer.
2. Start engine and gradually increase engine speed to 2000 RPM with transmission in neutral, then decrease engine speed to base idle RPM. **Vacuum gauge reading may be normal when engine is first started and idled, however, excessive restriction in exhaust system will cause vacuum gauge needle to drop to a low point even while engine is idling.**
3. If manifold vacuum reaches above 16 inches Hg with RPM at 2000, exhaust system is functioning properly. If not, proceed to "Vacuum Test-Rate Of Vacuum Gauge Needle Return Movement."

VACUUM TEST-RATE OF VACUUM GAUGE NEEDLE RETURN MOVEMENT

1. Attach a suitable vacuum gauge to intake manifold vacuum source, then connect a suitable tachometer.
2. Start engine and gradually increase engine speed to 2000 RPM with transmission in neutral, observe rate of speed of vacuum gauge needle as it falls and rises, while maintaining 2000 RPM, then decrease engine speed to base idle RPM. **On a non-restricted system, vacuum gauge needle will drop to zero, then quickly return to normal setting without delay. On a restricted system, as engine speed is increased to 2000 RPM, vacuum gauge needle will slowly drop to zero, then as 2000 RPM is maintained, needle will slowly rise to normal. Rate of speed at which vacuum gauge**

needle returns to normal setting is much slower on a restricted system than a non-restricted system.
3. If rate of speed that vacuum gauge needle returns to normal setting is much slower than that of a non-restricted system, proceed to "Vacuum Test-Exhaust Disconnected." If not, exhaust system is functioning properly.

VACUUM TEST-EXHAUST DISCONNECTED

1. Turn engine Off, then disconnect exhaust system at exhaust manifold(s).
2. Perform "Vacuum Test" as previously described.
3. If manifold vacuum reaches above 16 inches Hg, proceed to "Vacuum Test-Catalytic Converter(s) On/Muffler(s) Off." If not, proceed to "Exhaust Manifold Restricted."

VACUUM TEST-CATALYTIC CONVERTER(S) ON/MUFFLER(S) OFF

1. Turn engine Off, reconnect exhaust system at exhaust manifold(s), then disconnect muffler(s).
2. Perform "Vacuum Test" as previously described.
3. If manifold vacuum reaches above 16 inches Hg, replace muffler(s). If not, replace catalytic converter(s) and inspect muffler(s) to ensure converter debris has not entered muffler(s).

EXHAUST MANIFOLD RESTRICTED

1. Remove exhaust manifold(s) and inspect ports for casting flash by dropping a length of chain into each port. **Do not use a wire or lamp to check ports. The restriction may be small enough for them to pass through but large enough to cause excessive backpressure at high engine RPM.**
2. If a restriction is present, remove casting flash. If casting flash cannot be removed, replace exhaust manifold(s). If a restriction is not present, exhaust system is functioning properly.

EXHAUST GAS RECIRCULATION (EGR)

Description

The Exhaust Gas Recirculation (EGR) system is designed to reintroduce exhaust gases into the combustion cycle, lowering combustion temperatures and reducing the formation of Nitrogen Oxides (NOx). There are four basic types of EGR systems used, the Differential Pressure Feedback EGR (DPFE), the EGR Valve Position (EVP) (Electronic EGR Valve (EEGR)), the Integral Backpressure Transducer EGR Valve (IBP) and the Pressure Feedback Electronic (PFE) type.

The Pressure Feedback Electronic (PFE) system, **Fig. 5,** is a subsonic closed loop EGR system that controls EGR flow rate by monitoring the pressure drop across a remotely located sharp-edged orifice. The system uses a pressure transducer as the feedback device and controlled pressure is varied by valve modulation using vacuum output of the EGR-Vacuum Regulator (EVR) solenoid. The EGR valve serves only as a pressure regulator rather than a flow metering device.

The Differential Pressure Feedback Electronic (DPFE) system, **Fig. 6**, operates in the same manner as the Pressure Feedback Electronic (PFE), except that it also monitors exhaust pressure in the exhaust system, allowing for a more accurate assessment of EGR flow requirements.

The EGR Valve Position (EVP) (Electronic EGR Valve (EEGR)) system, **Fig. 7**, is required in EEC systems where EGR flow is controlled according to Powertrain Control Module (PCM) (EEC-IV processor) demands by a EGR Valve Position (EVP) sensor attached to the valve. The valve is operated by a vacuum signal from the EGR Vacuum Regulator (EVR) solenoid which actuates the valve diaphragm. As supply vacuum overcomes spring load, the diaphragm is actuated and lifts the pintle off its seat allowing exhaust gas to recirculate. Amount of flow is proportional to pintle position. The EVP sensor sends an electrical signal of its position to the PCM (EEC-IV processor).

Diagnosis & Testing

DIAGNOSIS BY SYMPTOM

1993–95

Refer to charts in **Fig. 8** for diagnosis by symptom.

1996

Refer to EEC-V section, under "Computerized Engine Controls" for diagnosis and testing.

FUNCTIONAL DIAGNOSIS

Integral Backpressure Transducer EGR Valve (IBP) System

Do not use Rotunda EGR valve cleaner 021-80056 or any equivalent on this valve.

1. Ensure all vacuum hoses are properly routed and securely connected, replace any cracked, crimped or broken hoses.
2. Ensure there is no vacuum to EGR valve at idle with engine at normal operating temperature.
3. Connect a suitable tachometer, then plug tailpipe(s) to increase exhaust system backpressure, leaving a 1/2 inch diameter opening to allow exhaust gases to escape.
4. Disconnect vacuum supply hose from EGR valve and plug hose.
5. Start engine and run at idle with transmission in neutral, observe engine idle speed. If necessary, adjust idle speed to specifications.
6. Slowly apply 5-10 inches Hg vacuum to EGR valve using a suitable hand vacuum pump.
7. When vacuum is fully applied to EGR valve and any of the following occur, replace EGR valve:
   a. Engine does not stall.
   b. Idle speed does not drop more than 100 RPM.
   c. Idle speed does not return to normal, within 25 RPM, after vacuum is removed.
8. If EGR valve was not contaminated or in need of replacement, system is operating properly.
9. Unplug and reconnect EGR vacuum supply hose, then remove tailpipe plug(s).

Electronic EGR Valve (EEGR) System

1. Ensure all vacuum hoses are properly routed and securely connected, replace any cracked, crimped or broken hoses.
2. Ensure there is less than 2.5 inches Hg vacuum to EGR valve at idle with engine at normal operating temperature. **EVR solenoid has a constant internal leak. You will notice a small vacuum signal. Signal should be less than 1.0 inch Hg at idle.**
3. Connect a suitable tachometer, then disconnect vacuum supply hose from EGR valve and plug hose.
4. Start engine and run at idle with transmission in neutral, observe engine idle speed. If necessary, adjust idle speed to specifications.
5. Slowly apply 5-10 inches Hg vacuum to EGR valve using a suitable hand vacuum pump.
6. When vacuum is fully applied to EGR valve and engine does not stall, idle speed does not drop more than 100 RPM, or idle speed does not return to normal, within 25 RPM, after vacuum is removed, proceed as follows:
   a. Check for vacuum leak at EGR valve, if necessary, replace valve.
   b. Check for contamination in EGR valve, and if necessary, clean valve using Rotunda EGR valve cleaner 021-80056 or a suitable equivalent. Ensure there is no sand in valve.
7. If EGR valve was not contaminated or in need of replacement, system is operating properly.
8. Unplug and reconnect EGR vacuum supply hose.

Pressure Feedback Electronic (PFE) & Differential Pressure Feedback Electronic (DPFE) Systems

1. Ensure all vacuum hoses are properly routed and securely connected, replace any cracked, crimped or broken hoses.
2. Ensure there is no vacuum to EGR valve at idle with engine at normal operating temperature.
3. Connect a suitable tachometer, then plug tailpipe(s) to increase exhaust system backpressure, leaving a 1/2 inch diameter opening to allow exhaust gases to escape.
4. Disconnect vacuum supply hose from backpressure transducer and plug hose. **Do not disconnect transducer from EGR valve.**
5. Start engine and run at idle with transmission in neutral, observe engine idle speed. If necessary, adjust idle speed to specifications.
6. Slowly apply 5-10 inches Hg vacuum to backpressure transducer using a suitable hand vacuum pump.
7. When vacuum is fully applied to backpressure transducer and engine does not stall, idle speed does not drop more than 100 RPM, or idle speed does not return to normal, within 25 RPM, after vacuum is removed, proceed as follows:
   a. Check for contamination, and if necessary, disconnect transducer from pick-up tube and clean EGR valve using Rotunda EGR valve cleaner 021-80056 or a suitable equivalent. Ensure there is no sand in valve or pick-up tube.
   b. If symptom still exists, replace EGR valve.
   c. Check for vacuum leak at EGR valve, if necessary, replace valve.
8. If EGR valve was not contaminated or in need of replacement, system is operating properly.
9. Unplug and reconnect backpressure transducer vacuum supply hose, then remove tailpipe plug(s).

TESTING

EGR Load Control (Wide Open Throttle, WOT) Valve

The EGR load control (WOT) valve dumps vacuum at or near wide open throttle (WOT). The normal path between ports A and B, **Fig. 9**, is vented to atmosphere when sufficient vacuum is applied to port C.

1. With engine running at normal operating temperature, set throttle on kickdown step.
2. Connect a suitable vacuum gauge to EGR side of valve and note reading.
3. Apply at least six inches Hg vacuum to venturi port (C) of valve using a suitable hand held vacuum pump. If gauge does not drop to zero, replace valve.

EGR Valve Position Sensor (EVP) & EGR Valve Regulator Solenoid (EVR)

Refer to EEC-IV Quick Tests in "EEC-IV section for testing.

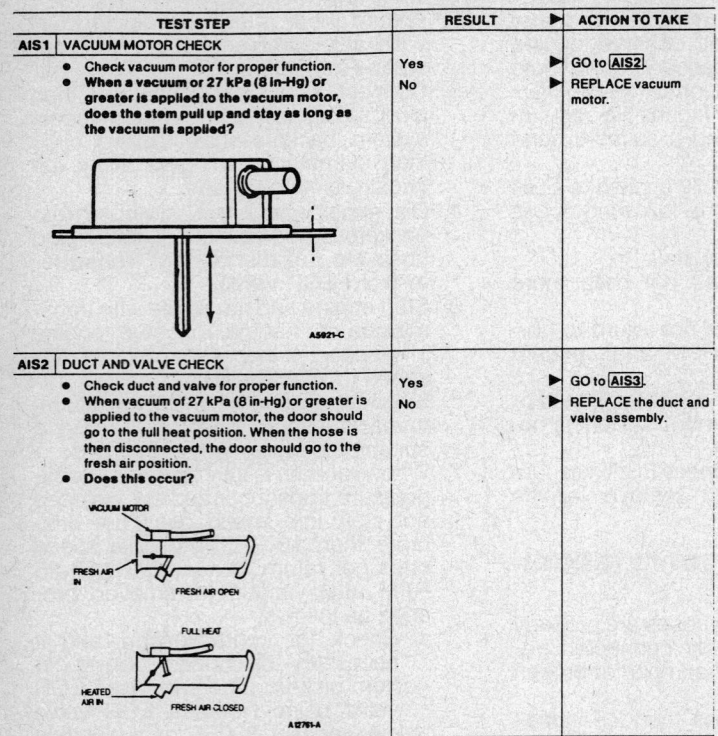

Part 1

TEST STEP	RESULT	▶	ACTION TO TAKE
AIS1 VACUUM MOTOR CHECK			
• Check vacuum motor for proper function. • When a vacuum of 27 kPa (8 in-Hg) or greater is applied to the vacuum motor, does the stem pull up and stay as long as the vacuum is applied?	Yes	▶	GO to **AIS2**.
	No	▶	REPLACE vacuum motor.
AIS2 DUCT AND VALVE CHECK			
• Check duct and valve for proper function. • When vacuum of 27 kPa (8 in-Hg) or greater is applied to the vacuum motor, the door should go to the full heat position. When the hose is then disconnected, the door should go to the fresh air position. • Does this occur?	Yes	▶	GO to **AIS3**.
	No	▶	REPLACE the duct and valve assembly.

Fig. 1   Air inlet system diagnostic tests (Part 1 of 6). 1993
FM1039300038010X

Part 2

TEST STEP	RESULT	▶	ACTION TO TAKE
AIS3 BIMETAL SENSOR CHECK			
• Check the bimetal sensor. • Bring the temperature of the bimetal sensor (9E607) below 24°C (75°F) and apply 54 kPa (16 in-Hg) vacuum. • Does the door close (go to the hot air position)?	Yes	▶	GO to **AIS4**.
	No	▶	REPLACE bimetal sensor.
AIS4 AIR FILTER CHECK			
• Check the air filter. • Is the air filter excessively dirty?	Yes	▶	REPLACE air filter.
	No	▶	Air Induction system is operating properly. RETURN to Diagnostic Routine Flow Chart
AIS5 SEALING INTEGRITY			
• Check hoses that connect air cleaner to engine. • Are there cracks or leaks? • Are there any cracks in the air cleaner assembly? • Check the air filter for proper sealing. • Are there any leaks around the air filter seal?	Yes	▶	REPLACE parts as required.
	No	▶	GO to **AIS6**.

Fig. 1   Air inlet system diagnostic tests (Part 2 of 6). 1993
FM1039300038020X

Part 3

TEST STEP	RESULT	▶	ACTION TO TAKE
AIS6 CHECK TORQUE			
• Check clamps and air cleaner screws (if equipped) for proper torque. • Is torque correct?	Yes	▶	Air Intake System is functioning properly. RETURN to Diagnostic Routine Flow Chart
	No	▶	TIGHTEN to specification.
AIS7 CHECK BOTH LEFT AND RIGHT BANK IMRC HOUSING ASSEMBLY SYSTEM FUNCTION AT IDLE (4.6L-4V)			
• Place vehicle in PARK with wheels blocked and parking brake engaged. • With engine off, remove beautification cover to expose intake manifold assembly. • Inspect IMRC vacuum actuator linkage at the back end of both left and right bank IMRC housing assemblies (Figure 11). Note the position of actuator linkage and lever mechanism with the engine off. • While observing the linkage/lever mechanism start the engine and allow it to idle. • Did the linkage/lever on both left and right bank assemblies move from engine off to engine running at idle?	Yes	▶	LEAVE engine running. GO to **AIS8**.
	No	▶	LEAVE engine running. GO to **AIS11**.
AIS8 CHECK BOTH LEFT AND RIGHT BANK IMRC HOUSING ASSEMBLY SYSTEM FUNCTION AT HIGH RPM (4.6L-4V)			
• Note the position of both IMRC vacuum actuators linkage and lever mechanism with the engine at idle. • Increase engine speed to 3500 rpm while observing linkage/lever. • Did the linkage/lever on both left and right bank assemblies move as engine speed was increased from low rpm to high rpm?	Yes	▶	IMRC system is functioning properly. Turn engine off and REPLACE beautification cover. RETURN to Diagnostic Routines
	No	▶	LEAVE engine running. GO to **AIS9**.

Fig. 1   Air inlet system diagnostic tests (Part 3 of 6). 1993
FM1039300038030X

Part 4

TEST STEP	RESULT	▶	ACTION TO TAKE
AIS9 CHECK FOR CORRECT VACUUM SIGNAL AT IMRC SOLENOID OUTLET PORT (4.6L-4V)			
• Disconnect IMRC solenoid outlet vacuum hose (top port) only. • Connect a vacuum gauge to the solenoid outlet port. • Note vacuum gauge reading as engine speed is increased to 3500 rpm. • Did gauge show vacuum at low rpm and no vacuum at high rpm.	Yes	▶	TURN engine off and RECONNECT IMRC solenoid outlet vacuum hose. GO to **AIS10**.
	No	▶	TURN engine off. GO to **AIS14**.
AIS10 CHECK FOR CORRECT VACUUM SIGNAL AT IMRC ACTUATOR INLET PORT (4.6L-4V)			
• Disconnect IMRC vacuum harness at both IMRC actuator inlet ports. NOTE: It may be necessary to remove the clean air tube from the throttle body to access the left bank IMRC actuator harness connector. Replace clean air tube before starting engine. • Install a vacuum gauge at one of the IMRC actuator vacuum harness connectors, plug the other vacuum harness connector. • Start the engine and note vacuum gauge reading as engine speed is increased to 3500 rpm. • Repeat with vacuum gauge installed on the other IMRC actuator vacuum harness connector, plug the other. • Did the gauge show vacuum at low rpm and no vacuum at high rpm?	Yes	▶	IMRC vacuum and electrical system is functioning correctly, but IMRC housing assembly does not respond correctly to applied vacuum signal. TURN engine off. GO to **AIS15** for IMRC housing assembly bench testing.
	No	▶	SERVICE vacuum harness between IMRC solenoid and IMRC actuators. RETURN to **AIS7** after service to confirm proper system function.
AIS11 CHECK FOR VACUUM AT IMRC SOLENOID OUTLET PORT (4.6L-4V)			
• Disconnect the IMRC solenoid vacuum hose (top port) only. • Connect a vacuum gauge to the solenoid outlet port. • Is manifold vacuum present with the engine at idle?	Yes	▶	TURN engine off and RECONNECT IMRC solenoid outlet vacuum hose. GO to **AIS12**.
	No	▶	LEAVE engine running. GO to **AIS13**.

Fig. 1   Air inlet system diagnostic tests (Part 4 of 6). 1993
FM1039300038040X

TEST STEP		RESULT	▶	ACTION TO TAKE
AIS12	CHECK FOR VACUUM AT IMRC ACTUATOR INLET PORT (4.6L-4V)			
	• Disconnect vacuum harness at both IMRC actuator inlet ports. NOTE: It may be necessary to remove the clean air tube from the throttle body to access the left bank IMRC actuator harness connector. Replace clean air tube before starting engine.	Yes	▶	IMRC housing assembly does not respond to applied vacuum signal. TURN engine off. GO to AIS15 for IMRC housing assembly bench testing.
	• Install a vacuum gauge at one of the IMRC actuator vacuum harness connectors, plug the other vacuum harness connector. • Start the engine and note vacuum gauge reading with the engine at idle. • Repeat with vacuum gauge installed on the other IMRC actuator vacuum harness connector, plug the other. • **Is manifold vacuum present?**	No	▶	SERVICE vacuum harness between IMRC solenoid and IMRC actuators. RETURN to AIS7 after service to confirm proper system function.
AIS13	CHECK FOR VACUUM AT IMRC SOLENOID INLET PORT (4.6L-4V)			
	• Disconnect IMRC solenoid inlet vacuum hose (bottom port). • Install a vacuum gauge at the IMRC solenoid vacuum harness inlet connector. • **Is manifold vacuum present with the engine at idle?**	Yes	▶	TURN engine off. GO to AIS14.
		No	▶	INSPECT vacuum supply hose to IMRC solenoid. SERVICE as necessary. RETURN to AIS7 after service to confirm proper system function.
AIS14	IMRC SOLENOID FUNCTIONAL CHECK (4.6L-4V)			
	• Disconnect both vacuum hoses to the IMRC solenoid, unplug electrical connector. • With solenoid de-energized, confirm that the solenoid inlet (bottom) port holds vacuum and the outlet (top) port vents vacuum (use hand vacuum pump/gauge or equivalent). • Energize solenoid (use battery voltage and note wire harness connector polarity) and confirm that an applied vacuum signal passes from the inlet to the outlet port. • **Does the solenoid pass both functional tests?**	Yes	▶	CHECK PCM and wiring system, GO to Pinpoint Test KT1. RETURN to AIS7 after service is made in Pinpoint Test Section to confirm system function.
		No	▶	REPLACE solenoid. RETURN to AIS7 after service to confirm proper system function.

FM1039300038050X

Fig. 1   Air inlet system diagnostic tests (Part 5 of 6). 1993

TEST STEP		RESULT	▶	ACTION TO TAKE
AIS15	IMRC HOUSING ASSEMBLY BENCH TEST—ACTUATOR CHECK (4.6L-4V)			
	• Remove both IMRC housing assemblies from engine, refer to Group 03 in Service Manual for IMRC Housing Assembly Removal Procedure. • With IMRC housing assemblies on bench top, apply 12 to 20 in-Hg to the IMRC actuator inlet port. • **Do both actuators hold vacuum?**	Yes	▶	GO to AIS16.
		No	▶	REPLACE leaking IMRC actuator RETURN to AIS15 to confirm IMRC housing assembly bench functional test.
AIS16	IMRC HOUSING ASSEMBLY BENCH TEST—FREEDOM OF MOVEMENT CHECK (4.6L-4V)			
	• Position IMRC housing assemblies on bench such that valve plates are free to rotate. • Apply 10 in-Hg vacuum to the IMRC actuator inlet port. Valve plates should rotate to the closed position (actuator lever mechanism contacts stop screw). • Release vacuum, valve plates should rotate quickly and freely to the open position (actuator lever mechanism contacts return stop). • Repeat applying vacuum and releasing several times to confirm freedom of movement. • **Do the valve plates rotate without stick/bind/grab in response to vacuum signal?**	Yes	▶	IMRC housing assembly is functioning correctly. RETURN to AIS7 to confirm system function.
		No	▶	IMRC Housing Assembly Cleaning Procedure. RETURN to AIS15 after cleaning procedure is complete.

FM1039300038060X

Fig. 1   Air inlet system diagnostic tests (Part 6 of 6). 1993

TEST STEP		RESULT	▶	ACTION TO TAKE
AIS1	PRELIMINARY CHECKS FOR HESITATES OR STALLS ON ACCELERATION			
	• Key off, engine off. • Check that throttle lever is resting on throttle plate stop screw. • Key on, engine running. • Check engine operating temperature and coolant level in overflow reservoir. • Check for vacuum leak (manifold, etc.) and hose routings. • Check for proper operation of EGR valve. • Check for ignition or exhaust malfunction (refer to maintenance schedule). • Check fuel quality (contamination). • **Are any problems found?**	Yes	▶	SERVICE or ADJUST as necessary. REPLACE parts as necessary.
		No	▶	GO to AIS4.
AIS2	PRELIMINARY CHECKS FOR LACK OF POWER			
	• Key on, engine off. • Check proper belt tension. • Check for throttle linkage binding. • Key on, engine running. • Check engine operating temperature and coolant level in overflow reservoir. • Check for vacuum leak (manifold, etc.) and hose routings. • Check for proper operation of EGR valve. • Check for ignition or exhaust malfunction (refer to maintenance schedule). • Check for brake drag. • Check transmission shift schedule. • **Are any problems found?**	Yes	▶	SERVICE or ADJUST as necessary. REPLACE parts as necessary.
		No	▶	GO to AIS4.
AIS3	PRELIMINARY CHECKS FOR POOR FUEL ECONOMY			
	• Key off, engine off. • Check for contaminated Idle Air Control (IAC) valve or proper sealing around valve. • Check PCV system (incorrect specifications or clogged). • Key on, engine running. • Check engine operating temperature and coolant level in overflow reservoir. • Check for ignition or exhaust malfunction (refer to maintenance schedule). • **Are any problems found?**	Yes	▶	SERVICE or ADJUST as necessary. REPLACE parts as necessary.
		No	▶	GO to AIS4.

FM1039400039010X

Fig. 2   Air inlet system diagnostic tests (Part 1 of 7). 1994

TEST STEP		RESULT	▶	ACTION TO TAKE
AIS4	VACUUM MOTOR CHECK			
	• Check vacuum motor for proper function. • When a vacuum of 27 kPa (8 in-Hg) or greater is applied to the vacuum motor, does the stem pull up and stay as long as the vacuum is applied?	Yes	▶	GO to AIS5.
		No	▶	REPLACE vacuum motor.
AIS5	DUCT AND VALVE CHECK			
	• Check duct and valve for proper function. • When vacuum of 27 kPa (8 in-Hg) or greater is applied to the vacuum motor, the door should go to the full heat position. When the hose is then disconnected, the door should go to the fresh air position. • **Does this occur?**	Yes	▶	GO to AIS6.
		No	▶	REPLACE the duct and valve assembly.

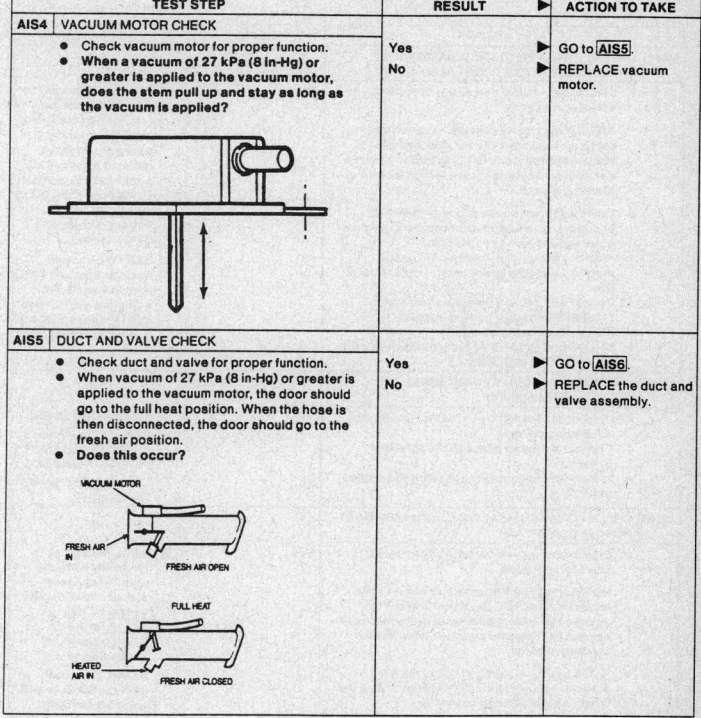

FM1039400039020X

Fig. 2   Air inlet system diagnostic tests (Part 2 of 7). 1994

TEST STEP	RESULT	▶	ACTION TO TAKE
AIS6 BIMETAL SENSOR CHECK • Check the bimetal sensor. • Bring the temperature of the bimetal sensor (9E607) below 24°C (75°F) and apply 54 kPa (16 in-Hg) vacuum. • Does the door close (go to the hot air position)?	Yes No	▶ ▶	GO to **AIS7** REPLACE bimetal sensor.
AIS7 AIR FILTER CHECK • Check the air filter. • Is the air filter excessively dirty?	Yes No	▶ ▶	REPLACE air filter. GO to **AIS8**.
AIS8 SEALING INTEGRITY • Check hoses that connect air cleaner to engine. • Are there cracks or leaks? • Are there any cracks in the air cleaner assembly? • Check the air filter for proper sealing. • Are there any leaks around the air filter seal?	Yes No	▶ ▶	REPLACE parts as required. GO to **AIS9**.
AIS9 CHECK TORQUE • Check clamps and air cleaner screws (if equipped) for proper torque. • Is torque correct?	Yes No	▶ ▶	GO to **AIS10**. TIGHTEN to specification.

FM1039400039030X

Fig. 2   Air inlet system diagnostic tests (Part 3 of 7).
1994

TEST STEP	RESULT	▶	ACTION TO TAKE
AIS10 CHECK IDLE SPEED • Check idle speed procedures at the end of this section. • Is idle speed correct?	Yes No	▶ ▶	Air intake system is functioning properly. RETURN to Symptom Flow Charts ADJUST idle speed.
AIS11 CHECK BOTH LEFT AND RIGHT BANK IMRC HOUSING ASSEMBLY SYSTEM FUNCTION AT IDLE (4.6L-4V) • Place vehicle in PARK with wheels blocked and parking brake engaged. • With engine off, remove beautification cover to expose intake manifold assembly. • Inspect IMRC vacuum actuator linkage at the back end of both left and right bank IMRC housing assemblies (Figure 10). Note the position of actuator linkage and lever mechanism with the engine off. • While observing the linkage/lever mechanism start the engine and allow it to idle. • Did the linkage/lever on both left and right bank assemblies move from engine off to engine running at idle?	Yes No	▶ ▶	LEAVE engine running. GO to **AIS12**. LEAVE engine running. GO to **AIS15**.
AIS12 CHECK BOTH LEFT AND RIGHT BANK IMRC HOUSING ASSEMBLY SYSTEM FUNCTION AT HIGH RPM (4.6L-4V) • Note the position of both IMRC vacuum actuators linkage and lever mechanism with the engine at idle. • Increase engine speed to 3500 rpm while observing linkage/lever. • Did the linkage/lever on both left and right bank assemblies move as engine speed was increased from low rpm to high rpm?	Yes No	▶ ▶	IMRC system is functioning properly. Turn engine off and REPLACE beautification cover. RETURN to Symptom Flow Charts for other possible causes. LEAVE engine running. GO to **AIS13**.
AIS13 CHECK FOR CORRECT VACUUM SIGNAL AT IMRC SOLENOID OUTLET PORT (4.6L-4V) • Disconnect IMRC solenoid outlet vacuum hose (top port) only. • Connect a vacuum gauge to the solenoid outlet port. • Note vacuum gauge reading as engine speed is increased to 3500 rpm. • Did gauge show vacuum at low rpm and no vacuum at high rpm.	Yes No	▶ ▶	TURN engine off and RECONNECT IMRC solenoid outlet vacuum hose. GO to **AIS14**. TURN engine off. GO to **AIS16**.

FM1039400039040X

Fig. 2   Air inlet system diagnostic tests (Part 4 of 7).
1994

TEST STEP	RESULT	▶	ACTION TO TAKE
AIS14 CHECK FOR CORRECT VACUUM SIGNAL AT IMRC ACTUATOR INLET PORT (4.6L-4V) • Disconnect vacuum harness at both IMRC actuator inlet ports. NOTE: It may be necessary to remove the clean air tube from the throttle body to access the left bank IMRC actuator harness connector. Replace clean air tube before starting engine. • Install a vacuum gauge at one of the IMRC actuator vacuum harness connectors, plug the other vacuum harness connector • Start the engine and note vacuum gauge reading as engine speed is increased to 3500 rpm. • Repeat with vacuum gauge installed on the other IMRC actuator vacuum harness connector, plug the other • Did the gauge show vacuum at low rpm and no vacuum at high rpm?	Yes No	▶ ▶	IMRC vacuum and electrical system is functioning correctly, but IMRC housing assembly does not respond correctly to applied vacuum signal. TURN engine off. GO to **AIS19** for IMRC housing assembly bench testing. SERVICE vacuum harness between IMRC solenoid and IMRC actuators. RETURN to **AIS11** after service to confirm proper system function.
AIS15 CHECK FOR VACUUM AT IMRC SOLENOID OUTLET PORT (4.6L-4V) • Disconnect the IMRC solenoid outlet vacuum hose (top port) only • Connect a vacuum gauge to the solenoid outlet port. • Is manifold vacuum present with the engine at idle?	Yes No	▶ ▶	TURN engine off and RECONNECT IMRC solenoid outlet vacuum hose. GO to **AIS16**. LEAVE engine running. GO to **AIS17**.
AIS16 CHECK FOR VACUUM AT IMRC ACTUATOR INLET PORT (4.6L-4V) • Disconnect vacuum harness at both IMRC actuator inlet ports. NOTE: It may be necessary to remove the clean air tube from the throttle body to access the left bank IMRC actuator harness connector. Replace clean air tube before starting engine. • Install a vacuum gauge at one of the IMRC actuator vacuum harness connectors, plug the other vacuum harness connector. • Start the engine and note vacuum gauge reading with the engine at idle • Repeat with vacuum gauge installed on the other IMRC actuator vacuum harness connector, plug the other • Is manifold vacuum present?	Yes No	▶ ▶	IMRC housing assembly does not respond to applied vacuum signal. TURN engine off. GO to **AIS19** for IMRC housing assembly bench testing. SERVICE vacuum harness between IMRC solenoid and IMRC actuators RETURN to **AIS11** after service to confirm proper system function.

FM1039400039050X

Fig. 2   Air inlet system diagnostic tests (Part 5 of 7).
1994

TEST STEP	RESULT	▶	ACTION TO TAKE
AIS17 CHECK FOR VACUUM AT IMRC SOLENOID INLET PORT (4.6L-4V) • Disconnect IMRC solenoid inlet vacuum hose (bottom port). • Install a vacuum gauge at the IMRC solenoid vacuum harness inlet connector. • Is manifold vacuum present with the engine at idle?	Yes No	▶ ▶	TURN engine off. GO to **AIS18**. INSPECT vacuum supply hose to IMRC solenoid. SERVICE as necessary. RETURN to **AIS11** after service to confirm proper system function
AIS18 IMRC SOLENOID FUNCTIONAL CHECK (4.6L-4V) • Disconnect both vacuum hoses to the IMRC solenoid, unplug electrical connector. • With solenoid de-energized, confirm that the solenoid inlet (bottom) port holds vacuum and the outlet (top) port vents vacuum (use hand vacuum pump/gauge or equivalent). • Energize solenoid (use battery voltage and note wire harness connector polarity) and confirm that an applied vacuum signal passes from the inlet to the outlet port. • Does the solenoid pass both functional tests?	Yes No	▶ ▶	CHECK PCM and wiring system. GO to Pinpoint Test KT1 RETURN to **AIS11** after service is made in Pinpoint Test Section to confirm system function. REPLACE solenoid RETURN to **AIS11** after service to confirm proper system function.
AIS19 IMRC HOUSING ASSEMBLY BENCH TEST—ACTUATOR CHECK (4.6L-4V) • Remove both IMRC housing assemblies from engine. IMRC Housing Assembly Removal Procedure • With IMRC housing assemblies on bench top, apply 12 to 20 in-Hg to the IMRC actuator inlet port. • Do both actuators hold vacuum?	Yes No	▶ ▶	GO to **AIS20**. REPLACE leaking IMRC actuator. REFER to IMRC Vacuum Actuator Removal, Replacement and Adjustment Procedure. RETURN to **AIS19** to confirm IMRC housing assembly bench functional test

FM1039400039060X

Fig. 2   Air inlet system diagnostic tests (Part 6 of 7).
1994

TEST STEP		RESULT	▶	ACTION TO TAKE
AIS20	IMRC HOUSING ASSEMBLY BENCH TEST—FREEDOM OF MOVEMENT CHECK (4.6L-4V)			
	• Position IMRC housing assemblies on bench such that valve plates are free to rotate. • Apply 10 in-Hg vacuum to the IMRC actuator inlet port. Valve plates should rotate to the closed position (actuator lever mechanism contacts stop screw). • Release vacuum, valve plates should rotate quickly and freely to the open position (actuator lever mechanism contacts return stop). • Repeat applying vacuum and releasing several times to confirm freedom of movement. • Do the valve plates rotate without stick/bind/grab in response to vacuum signal?	Yes	▶	IMRC housing assembly is functioning correctly. REPLACE on engine. REFER to IMRC Housing Assembly Replacement Procedure. RETURN to AIS11 to confirm proper system function.
		No	▶	REFER to IMRC Housing Assembly Cleaning Procedure. RETURN to AIS19 after cleaning procedure is complete.

FM1039400039070X

Fig. 2   Air inlet system diagnostic tests (Part 7 of 7). 1994

TEST STEP		RESULT	▶	ACTION TO TAKE
AIS1	CHECK ACCELERATOR CABLE FREEDOM OF TRAVEL			
	• Key off. • Disconnect accelerator cable and speed control cable from throttle body linkage. • Inspect cables for freedom of travel from accelerator pedal and speed control assembly to throttle body linkage cable connector. • Does cable travel freely?	Yes	▶	GO to AIS2.
		No	▶	SERVICE accelerator cable or speed control cable as necessary.
AIS2	VERIFY THROTTLE PLATE SCREW SETTING			
	• Key off. • Cables removed from throttle body linkage per AIS1. • Remove the clean air tube from the throttle body and verify that there is no foreign material or debris preventing the throttle plate from rotating to the fully closed position. • Verify that the Throttle Plate Stop Screw is in contact with the throttle linkage lever arm when the throttle is in the closed plate (idle) position. • Does the throttle plate stop screw contact lever arm?	Yes	▶	GO to AIS4.
		No	▶	For 1.9L: If the throttle plate stop stop screw does not contact the throttle lever airm in closed plate idle position, REPLACE throttle body assembly. For All Others: Do the following adjustment if the throttle plate stop screw does not contact the throttle lever arm: 1.) PLACE a 0.002 inch feeler gauge between the throttle plate stop screw and lever arm. ADJUST throttle plate stop screw until it just contacts the feeler gauge. 2.) REMOVE feeler gauge and turn the screw clockwise a half turn. 3.) GO to AIS3.

FM1039500212010X

Fig. 3   Air inlet system diagnostic tests (Part 1 of 9). 1995

TEST STEP		RESULT	▶	ACTION TO TAKE
AIS3	VERIFY TP SENSOR IN RANGE			
	• Key off. • Disconnect PCM. Inspect for damaged or pushed out pins, corrosion, loose wires, etc. Service as necessary. • Install breakout box and connect PCM to breakout box. • Key on, engine off. • Measure the voltage between Test Pin 47 and Test Pin 46 at the breakout box. • Slowly move throttle from closed to wide open throttle position and observe the voltage for smooth reading change. • Release throttle and allow to return to fully closed position. NOTE: On some smaller engines, the TP reading at closed throttle can be lower: 1.9L Escort/Tracer is 0.28 volts, 2.0L Probe is 0.39 volts, 2.5L Contour/Mystique is 0.45 volts. • Is the average TP reading between 0.65 and 1.25 volts at closed throttle position?	Yes	▶	REMOVE breakout box. RECONNECT all components. GO to AIS4.
		No	▶	REMOVE breakout box. RECONNECT all components. REPLACE throttle body or TP sensor as necessary.
AIS4	CHECK FOR THROTTLE BODY STICKING, BINDING, GRABBING			
	• Key off. • Accelerator cable removed from throttle body linkage per AIS1. • Clean air tube removed from throttle body per AIS2. • Snap throttle from open to closed position several times. • Gently cycle throttle by hand from closed to wide open position. Inspect for freedom of travel particularly during the initial throttle opening. • Check for foreign material or debris in the throttle bore and plate area that can cause sticking or binding. NOTE: The throttle body uses a special coating/sealant on the throttle bore and plate area to make them tolerant to engine sludge accumulation. Sludge or oil film deposits in this area do not cause a sticking or binding condition and do not require servicing. DO NOT CLEAN THE THROTTLE BORE AND PLATE AREA. CLEANING WILL DAMAGE THE THROTTLE BODY ASSEMBLY. • Does the throttle rotate freely without sticking, binding or grabbing?	Yes	▶	RECONNECT accelerator cable and clean air tube to the throttle body assembly.
		No	▶	REPLACE throttle body assembly. RECONNECT all components.

FM1039500212020X

Fig. 3   Air inlet system diagnostic tests (Part 2 of 9). 1995

TEST STEP		RESULT	▶	ACTION TO TAKE
AIS5	PRELIMINARY CHECKS FOR LACK OF POWER			
	• Key on, engine off. • Check proper belt tension. • Check for throttle linkage binding. • Key on, engine running. • Check engine operating temperature and coolant level in overflow reservoir. • Check for vacuum leak (manifold, etc.) and hose routings. • Check for proper operation of EGR valve. • Check for ignition or exhaust malfunction (refer to maintenance schedule). • Check for brake drag. • Check transaxle shift schedule. • Are any problems found?	Yes	▶	SERVICE or ADJUST as necessary. REPLACE parts as necessary.
		No	▶	GO to AIS6.
AIS6	AIR FILTER CHECK			
	• Check the air filter. • Check intake resonator (3.0L SHO and 3.2L SHO only). • Is the air filter excessively dirty or resonator damaged?	Yes	▶	REPLACE air filter or damaged resonator.
		No	▶	Air intake system is functioning properly.
AIS7	CHECK FOR PROPER OPERATION OF RELATED ENGINE SYSTEMS			
	• Verify that the following engine systems have been properly diagnosed and corrected before proceeding with the Air Intake system diagnostics: — Positive Crankcase Ventilation (PCV) System. — Exhaust System. — Ignition System (Refer to maintenance schedule). — Engine Cooling System (engine coolant temperature is above 160 degrees F). — Incorrect fuel pressure, plugged fuel filter, fuel quality (contamination). • Have the above systems been properly checked and are they functioning correctly?	Yes	▶	GO to AIS8.
		No		

FM1039500212030X

Fig. 3   Air inlet system diagnostic tests (Part 3 of 9). 1995

TEST STEP	RESULT	▶	ACTION TO TAKE
AIS8 CHECK FOR VACUUM LEAKS • Key on, engine running. • With engine at idle, listen for vacuum leaks. • Inspect the entire inlet air system from the Mass Air Flow (MAF) sensor to the intake manifold for leaks such as: — Cracked or punctured outlet air tube or air cleaner housing assembly. — Loose connections on the inlet air tube at the air cleaner housing or throttle body. — Idle Air Control (IAC) valve assembly or gasket seal. — Intake manifold assembly or gasket seal. — EGR valve diaphragm or control solenoid. — EGR valve gasket seal leak to intake manifold. — Vacuum supply connectors and hose. — PCV connectors and hose. • **Are any leaks detected in the above areas?**	Yes No	▶ ▶	SERVICE as necessary. GO to **AIS9**.
AIS9 CHECK IDLE RPM NOTE: Engine idle RPM is controlled by the PCM and cannot be adjusted. This test will verify the idle rpm is within the specification. If the engine is allowed to idle for an extended period of time, or if the engine temperature is hot enough to require cooling fan operation, it may be necessary to turn the engine off and repeat this test procedure. • Transmission in Park (wheels blocked and parking brake engaged). • A/C, heater and all accessories are off. • Key on, engine running. • Engine at normal operating temperature and cooling fan off. **WARNING: DO NOT UNPLUG COOLING FAN. IT MAY CAUSE ENGINE OVERHEATING.** • Check idle rpm as specified for the particular vehicle and engine application. (Refer to procedures detailed at the end of Section 12A.) • **Is the base idle RPM within range?**	Yes No	▶ ▶	GO to **AIS10**. GO to **AIS11**.

Fig. 3 Air inlet system diagnostic tests (Part 4 of 9). 1995

TEST STEP	RESULT	▶	ACTION TO TAKE
AIS10 CHECK IDLE CONTROL RESPONSE • Transmission still in Park. • A/C, heater and all accessories off. • Engine at normal operating temperature and cooling fan off, but not unplugged. **WARNING: DO NOT UNPLUG COOLING FAN. IT MAY CAUSE ENGINE OVERHEATING.** • Key on, engine running. • Goose throttle and let it return to the idle position. • Does the engine stall or does the RPM fluctuate excessively before returning to the base idle rpm?	Yes No	▶ ▶	GO to **AIS11**. Air Intake system is OK. to check other possible causes of the drive symptoms.
AIS11 CHECK IAC SOLENOID FOR PROPER FUNCTION • Transmission still in Park. • A/C, heater and all accessories off. • Engine at normal operating temperature and cooling fan off, but not unplugged. **WARNING: DO NOT UNPLUG COOLING FAN. IT MAY CAUSE ENGINE OVERHEATING.** • Key on, engine running. • Disconnect IAC solenoid vehicle harness connector. • Does the RPM drop or engine stall?	Yes No	▶ ▶	For Fast Idle Symptom: GO to **AIS12**. For All Other Symptoms: Throttle body is defective, REPLACE the entire throttle body assembly. CLEAR Keep Alive Memory. NOTE: Do not attempt to clean throttle bore or throttle plate area. Do not adjust air flow. IAC solenoid is defective, REPLACE IAC solenoid only. CLEAR Keep Alive Memory. NOTE: Do not attempt to clean the IAC solenoid.

Fig. 3 Air inlet system diagnostic tests (Part 5 of 9). 1995

TEST STEP	RESULT	▶	ACTION TO TAKE
AIS12 CHECK IAC CIRCUIT FOR SHORT TO GROUND • Key off. • IAC solenoid disconnected. • Disconnect PCM. Inspect for damaged or pushed out pins, corrosion, loose wires, etc. Service as necessary. • Install breakout box, leave PCM disconnected. • Measure resistance between Test Pin 21 (IAC) and Test Pins 40/60 (PWR GND) at the breakout box and chassis ground. • Is each resistance greater than 10,000 ohms?	Yes No	▶ ▶	REPLACE damaged PCM. REMOVE breakout box. RECONNECT all components. RERUN Quick Test. SERVICE short circuit. RECONNECT all components. RERUN Quick Test.
AIS13 CHECK BOTH LEFT AND RIGHT BANK IMRC HOUSING ASSEMBLY SYSTEM FUNCTION AT IDLE • Place vehicle in PARK with wheels blocked and parking brake engaged. • With engine off, remove beautification cover to expose intake manifold assembly (4.6L -4V only). • Inspect IMRC vacuum actuator linkage at the back end of both left and right bank IMRC housing assemblies (Figure 2 for 2.5L, Figure 8 for 3.0L SHO and 3.2L SHO, Figure 12 for 4.6L). Note the position of actuator linkage and lever mechanism with the engine off. • While observing the linkage/lever mechanism start the engine and allow it to idle. • Did the linkage/lever on both left and right bank move from engine off to engine running at idle?	Yes No	▶ ▶	LEAVE engine running. GO to **AIS14**. LEAVE engine running. GO to **AIS17**.
AIS14 CHECK BOTH LEFT AND RIGHT BANK IMRC HOUSING ASSEMBLY SYSTEM FUNCTION AT HIGH RPM • Note the position of the IMRC vacuum actuator(s) linkage and lever mechanism with the engine at idle. • Increase engine to 3500 rpm (4000 rpm on 3.0L SHO and 3600 rpm on 3.2L SHO) while observing linkage/lever. • Did the linkage/lever on both left and right bank move as engine rpm was increased from low rpm to high rpm?	Yes No	▶ ▶	IMRC system is functioning properly. Turn engine off. RETURN to Symptom Index or Symptom Flow Charts for other possible causes. LEAVE engine running. GO to **AIS15**.

Fig. 3 Air inlet system diagnostic tests (Part 6 of 9). 1995

TEST STEP	RESULT	▶	ACTION TO TAKE
AIS15 CHECK FOR CORRECT VACUUM SIGNAL AT IMRC SOLENOID OUTLET PORT • Disconnect IMRC solenoid outlet vacuum hose (top port) only. • Connect a vacuum gauge to the solenoid outlet port. • Note vacuum gauge reading as engine rpm is increased to 3500 rpm (4000 rpm on 3.0L SHO and 3600 rpm on 3.2L SHO). • Did gauge show vacuum at low rpm and no vacuum at high rpm?	Yes No	▶ ▶	TURN engine off and RECONNECT solenoid outlet vacuum hose. GO to **AIS16**. TURN engine off. GO to **AIS20**.
AIS16 CHECK FOR CORRECT VACUUM SIGNAL AT IMRC ACTUATOR INLET PORT • Disconnect vacuum harness at both Intake Manifold Runner Control (IMRC) actuator inlet ports. NOTE: It may be necessary on 4.6L -4V only to remove the clean air tube from the throttle body to access the left bank IMRC actuator harness connector. Replace clean air tube before starting engine. • Install a vacuum gauge at one of the IMRC actuator vacuum harness connectors, plug the other vacuum harness connector (4.6L -4V only). • Start the engine and note vacuum gauge reading as engine rpm is increased to 3500 rpm (4000 rpm on 3.0L SHO and 3600 rpm on 3.2L SHO). • Repeat with vacuum gauge installed on the other IMRC actuator vacuum harness connector, plug the other (4.6L -4V only). • Did the gauge show vacuum at low rpm and no vacuum at high rpm?	Yes No	▶ ▶	IMRC vacuum and electrical system is functioning correctly, but IMRC housing assembly does not respond correctly to applied vacuum signal. TURN engine off. GO to **AIS21** for IMRC housing assembly bench testing. SERVICE vacuum harness between IMRC solenoid and IMRC actuator. RETURN to **AIS13** after service to confirm proper system function.
AIS17 CHECK FOR VACUUM AT IMRC SOLENOID OUTLET PORT • Disconnect the IMRC solenoid outlet vacuum hose (top port) only. • Connect a vacuum gauge to the solenoid outlet port. • Is manifold vacuum present with the engine at idle?	Yes No	▶ ▶	TURN engine off and RECONNECT IMRC solenoid outlet vacuum hose. GO to **AIS18**. LEAVE engine running. GO to **AIS19**.

Fig. 3 Air inlet system diagnostic tests (Part 7 of 9). 1995

TEST STEP	RESULT	▶	ACTION TO TAKE
AIS18 CHECK FOR VACUUM AT IMRC ACTUATOR INLET PORT			
• Disconnect vacuum harness at both IMRC actuator inlet port(s). NOTE: It may be necessary on 4.6L-4V only to remove the clean air tube from the throttle body to access the left bank IMRC actuator harness connector. Replace clean air tube before starting engine. • Install a vacuum gauge at one of the IMRC actuator vacuum harness connectors (plug the other vacuum harness connector on 4.6L-4V only). • Start the engine and note vacuum gauge reading with the engine at idle. • Repeat with vacuum gauge installed on the other IMRC actuator vacuum harness connector, plug the other on 4.6L-4V only. • **Is manifold vacuum present?**	Yes No	▶ ▶	IMRC housing assembly does not respond to applied vacuum signal. TURN engine off. GO to **AIS21** for IMRC housing assembly bench testing. SERVICE vacuum harness between IMRC solenoid and IMRC actuators. RETURN to **AIS13** after service to confirm proper system function.
AIS19 CHECK FOR VACUUM AT IMRC SOLENOID INLET PORT			
• Disconnect IMRC solenoid inlet vacuum hose (bottom port). • Install a vacuum gauge at the IMRC solenoid vacuum harness inlet connector. • **Is manifold vacuum present with the engine at idle?**	Yes No	▶ ▶	TURN engine off. GO to **AIS20**. INSPECT vacuum supply hose to IMRC solenoid. SERVICE as necessary. RETURN to **AIS13** after service to confirm proper system function.
AIS20 IMRC SOLENOID FUNCTIONAL CHECK			
• Disconnect vacuum hose to the IMRC solenoid and unplug electrical connector. • With solenoid de-energized, confirm that the solenoid inlet (bottom) port holds vacuum and the outlet (top) port vents vacuum (use hand vacuum pump / gauge or equivalent). • Energize solenoid (use battery voltage and note wire harness connector polarity) and confirm that an applied vacuum signal passes from the inlet to the outlet port. • **Does the solenoid pass both functional tests?**	Yes No	▶ ▶	CHECK PCM and wiring system, GO to Pinpoint Test **KT1**. RETURN to **AIS13** after service is made in Pinpoint Test Section to confirm system function. REPLACE solenoid. RETURN to **AIS13** after service to confirm proper system function.

FM1039500212080X

Fig. 3 Air inlet system diagnostic tests (Part 8 of 9). 1995

TEST STEP	RESULT	▶	ACTION TO TAKE
AIS21 IMRC HOUSING ASSEMBLY BENCH TEST — ACTUATOR CHECK			
• Remove both IMRC housing assemblies from engine, refer to Group 03 in Service Manual for IMRC Housing Assembly Removal Procedure. • With IMRC housing assemblies on bench top, apply 40.8-68 kPa (12-20 in-Hg) to the IMRC actuator inlet port. • **Do both the actuators hold vacuum?**	Yes No	▶ ▶	GO to **AIS22**. REPLACE leaking IMRC actuator. REFER to IMRC Vacuum Actuator Removal / Replacement and Adjustment Procedure. RETURN to **AIS21** to confirm IMRC housing assembly bench functional test.
AIS22 IMRC HOUSING ASSEMBLY BENCH TEST — FREEDOM OF MOVEMENT CHECK			
• Position IMRC housing assemblies on bench such that valve plates are free to rotate. • Apply 34 kPa (10 in-Hg) vacuum to the IMRC actuator inlet port. Valve plates should rotate to the closed position (actuator lever mechanism contacts stop screw). • Release vacuum, valve plates should rotate quickly and freely to the open position (actuator lever mechanism contacts return stop). • Repeat applying vacuum and releasing several times to confirm freedom of movement. • **Do the valve plates rotate without stick / bind / grab in response to vacuum signal?**	Yes No	▶ ▶	IMRC housing assembly is functioning correctly. RETURN to engine, REFER to IMRC Housing Assembly Replacement Procedure. RETURN to **AIS13** to confirm proper system function. REFER to IMRC Housing Assembly Cleaning Procedure. RETURN to **AIS21** after cleaning procedure is complete.

FM1039500212090X

Fig. 3 Air inlet system diagnostic tests (Part 9 of 9). 1995

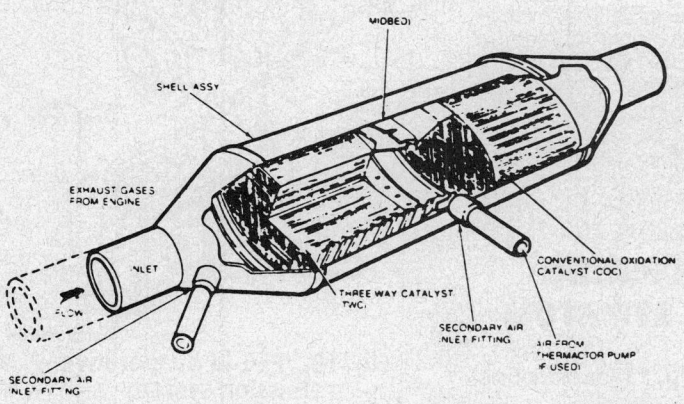

Fig. 4 Dual catalytic converter

FM1039100040000X

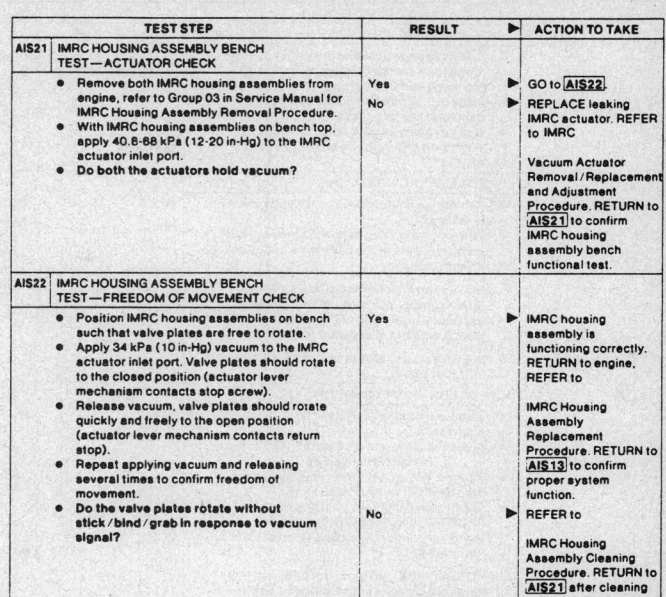

FM1039100225000X

Fig. 5 Pressure Feedback Electronic (PFE) EGR system

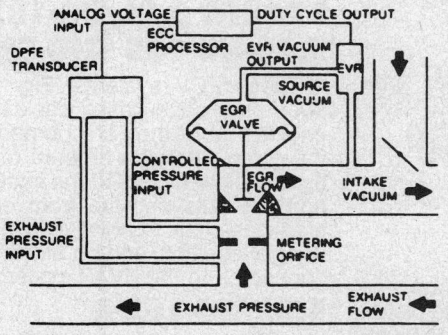

FM1039100041000X

Fig. 6 Differential Pressure Feedback Electronic (DPFE) EGR system

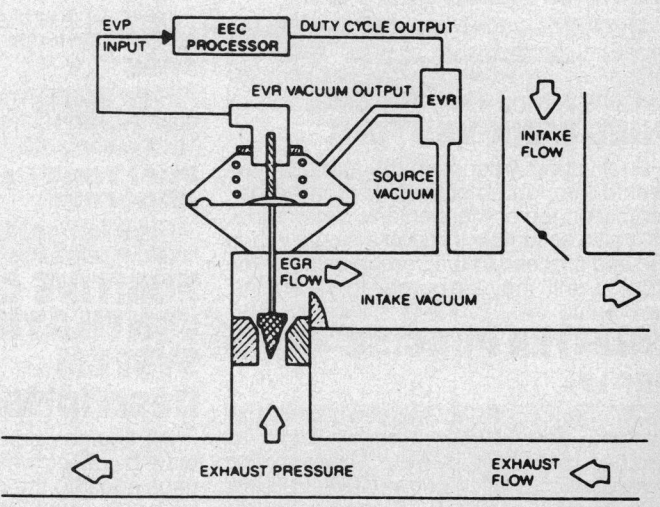

FM1039100042000X

Fig. 7 EGR Valve Position (EVP) (Electronic EGR Valve (EEGR)) system

	TEST STEP	RESULT	▶ ACTION TO TAKE
EGR1	CHECK SYSTEM INTEGRITY		
	• Check vacuum hoses and connections for looseness, pinching, leakage, splitting, blockage and proper routing. • Inspect EGR valve for loose attaching bolts or damaged flange gasket. • Does system appear to be in good condition and vacuum hoses properly routed?	Yes No	▶ GO to EGR2. ▶ SERVICE EGR system as required. RE-EVALUATE symptom.
EGR2	CHECK EGR VACUUM AT IDLE		
	• Run engine until normal operating temperature is reached. • With engine running at idle, disconnect EGR vacuum supply at the EGR valve and check for a vacuum signal. NOTE: The EVR solenoid has a constant internal leak. You may notice a small vacuum signal. This signal should be less than 3.4 kPa (1.0 In-Hg) at idle. • Is EGR vacuum signal less than 3.4 kPa (1.0 In-Hg) at idle?	Yes No	▶ GO to EGR3. ▶ RECONNECT EGR vacuum hose. INSPECT EVR solenoid for leakage. RUN EEC-IV Quick Test
EGR3	CHECK EGR VALVE FUNCTION		
	• Install a tachometer, Rotunda 059-00010 or equivalent. • Disconnect the Idle Air Control (IAC) solenoid electrical connector. • Remove and plug the vacuum supply hose from the EGR valve nipple. • Start engine, idle with transmission in NEUTRAL, and observe idle speed. If necessary, adjust idle speed according to Section 9A. NOTE: If the engine will not idle with IAC solenoid disconnected, provide an air bypass to the engine by slightly opening the throttle plate or by creating an intake vacuum leak. Do not exceed a typical idle rpm. • Slowly apply 5-10 inches of vacuum to the EGR valve nipple using a hand vacuum pump, Rotunda 021-00014 or equivalent. • Does idle speed drop more than 100 rpm with vacuum applied and return to normal (± 25 rpm) after the vacuum is removed?	Yes No	▶ The EGR valve is OK. UNPLUG and RECONNECT the EGR valve vacuum supply hose. RECONNECT the IAC solenoid connector. ▶ INSPECT the EGR valve for blockage or contamination. CLEAN the valve using Rotunda 021-80056 EGR valve cleaner. INSPECT valve for vacuum leakage. REPLACE if necessary.

FM1039300045000X

Fig. 8 EGR system diagnosis. 1993–95

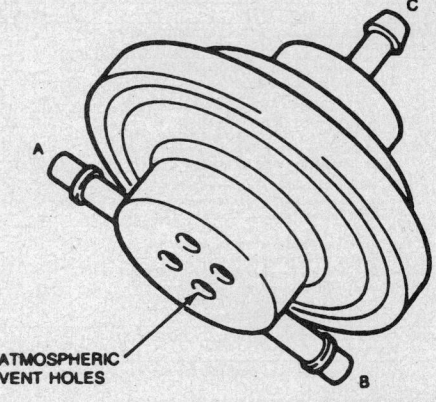

FM1039100046000X

Fig. 9 EGR load control (WOT) valve

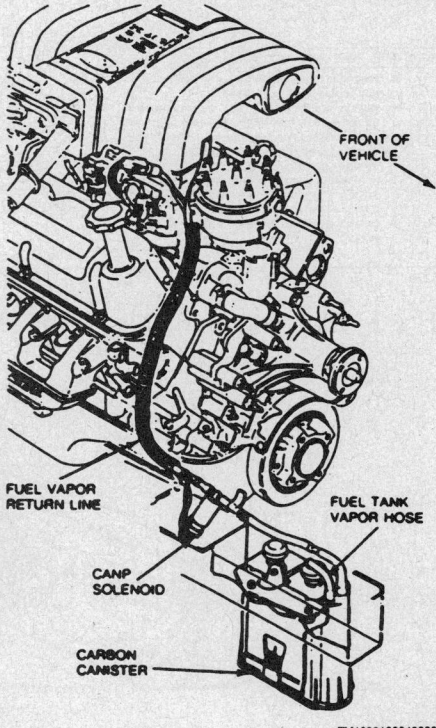

FM1039100048000X

Fig. 10 EEC-IV evaporative emission system

EVAPORATIVE EMISSION (EVAP) SYSTEMS Description
EEC IV

There are two types of systems used, **Figs 10 and 11**, the EEC-IV Evaporative Emission System and the Combined Purge Port and EEC-IV Evaporative Emission System. These systems are vacuum controlled. All systems provide fuel tank venting and canister purging.

EEC V & FLEXIBLE FUEL

The Flexible Fuel **Fig. 12**, and EEC V evaporative emission system are controlled by the PCM. All systems provide fuel tank venting and canister purging.

FUEL TANK VENTING

Fuel vapors trapped in the fuel tank are vented through an orifice vapor valve assembly on top of the fuel tank. Vapors exit the valve assembly through a single vapor line and proceed to the carbon canister for storage, until they are purged to the engine for burning.

CANISTER PURGING
EEC IV

On the EEC-IV Evaporative Emission Systems, flow of vapors from canister to engine is controlled by a purge solenoid or a vacuum controlled purge valve. Purging occurs when engine is at operating temperature and off idle.

Purging the carbon canister removes fuel vapor stored in the canister.

EEC V & Flexible Fuel

On the EEC V and Flexible Fuel evaporative emission system, flow of vapors from canister to engine is controlled by the Powertrain Control Module (PCM) and Canister Purge (CANP) valve. Purging occurs when engine is at operating temperature and at specific engine speed and load conditions.

Purging the carbon canister removes fuel vapor stored in the canister.

Diagnosis & Testing
DIAGNOSIS BY SYMPTOM
1993–95

Refer to charts in **Fig. 13** for diagnosis of EVAP systems.

1996

Refer to EEC-V section, under "Computerized Engine Controls" for symptoms other than abnormal fuel tank pressure.

Fuel Tank Pressure Abnormal

Refer to **Figs. 14 through 16** for diagnostic procedures.

POSITIVE CRANKCASE VENTILATION (PCV) SYSTEM Description

All engines produce small amounts of blow-by gases which seep past the piston rings and into the crankcase. These blow-by gases are the result of the high pressures developed within the combustion chamber during the combustion process, and contain undesirable pollutants. To pre-vent blow-by gases from entering the atmosphere while allowing proper crankcase ventilation, all engines use a PCV system.

EXCEPT 3.0L/V6-182 & 3.2L/V6-195 SHO ENGINES

These PCV systems, **Fig. 17** reintroduce crankcase gases back through the engine where they are burned. The PCV valve regulates the amount of ventilating air and blow-by gas to the intake manifold and prevents backfire from entering the crankcase. The PCV valve is mounted in a vertical position, and on some systems is connected to the EVAP system.

3.0L/V6-182 & 3.2L/V6-195 SHO ENGINES

The PCV system on the 3.0L/V6-182 and 3.2L/V6-195 SHO engines is unique because it does not use a PCV valve. The

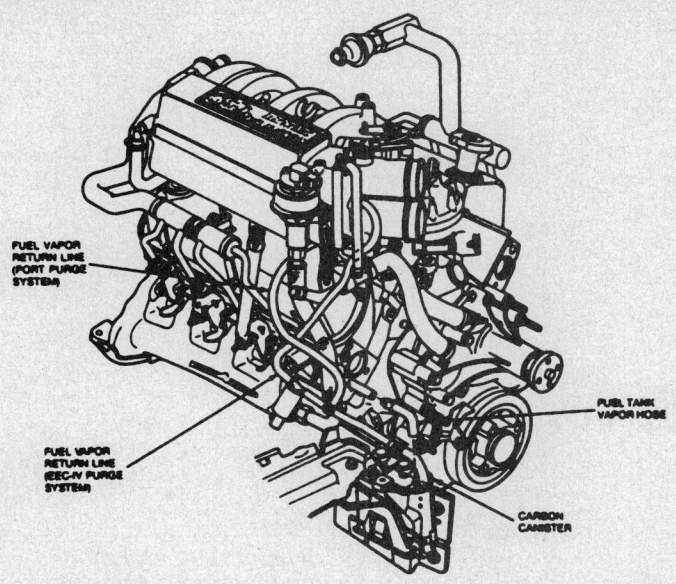

Fig. 11 Purge port & EEC-IV evaporative emission system

FM1039100049000X

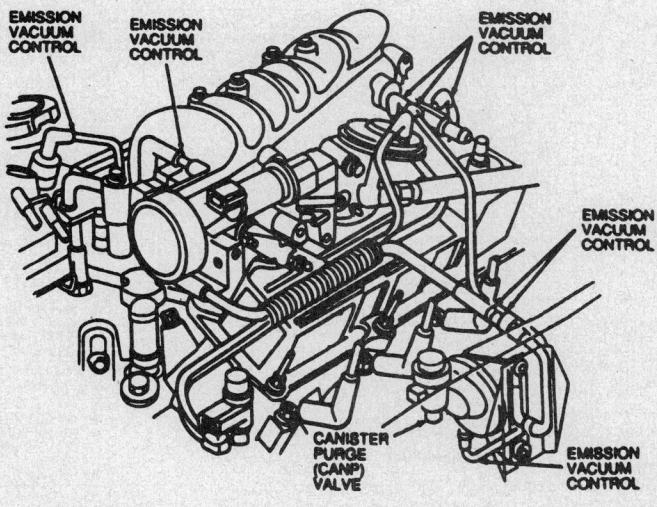

Fig. 12 Flexible fuel evaporative emission system (Part 1 of 2)

FM1039100050010X

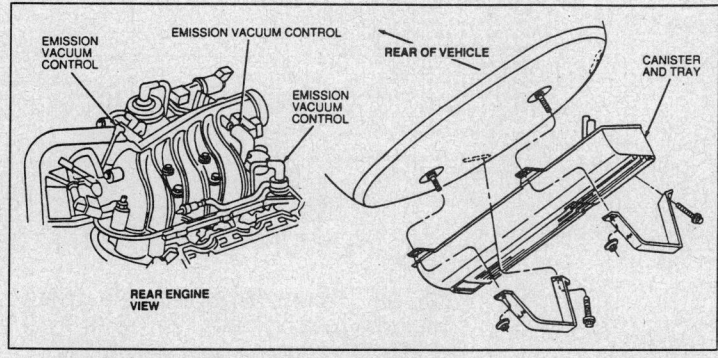

Fig. 12 Flexible fuel evaporative emission system (Part 2 of 2)

FM1039100050020X

crankcase gases flow through an oil separator to three ports in the throttle body, **Fig. 18.** Fresh air is supplied from another port on the throttle body to the cylinder head cover. Under various throttle conditions, the air and crankcase gases flow differently through the ports in the throttle body.

Diagnosis & Testing

1993–95

EXCEPT 3.0L/V6-182 & 3.2L/V6-195 SHO ENGINES

Stuck PCV Valve Check

1. Remove PCV valve from valve cover grommet. If valve rattles when shaken, proceed to "PCV System Check." If not, valve is sticking, replace valve.

PCV System Check

1. Start engine and allow to reach normal operating temperature.
2. **On 2.3L/4-120 HSC and 2.5L/V6-152 engines,** remove corrugated hose from oil separator nipple, then place a stiff piece of paper over nipple end and wait one minute.
3. **On engines except 2.3L/4-120 HSC and 2.5L/V6-152,** disconnect hose from remote air cleaner or air outlet tube (tube connecting mass air meter and throttle body), then place a stiff piece of paper over hose end and wait one minute.
4. **On all engines,** if vacuum holds paper in place, system is operating properly. If not, system is plugged or Evaporative Emission Valve is leaking, if equipped, proceed to "Evaporative Emission System Check," below.

Evaporative Emission System Check

1. Disconnect evaporative hose, if equipped, then cap connector.
2. Perform "PCV System Check" as previously described.
3. If vacuum holds paper in place, refer to "Evaporative Emission (EVAP) System" for diagnosis and testing of system. If not, check for vacuum leaks and/or obstructions in PCV system.

3.0L/V6-182 & 3.2L/V6-195 SHO ENGINES

PCV System Check

1. Check blow-by gases hoses from oil separator to throttle body for blockage, cracks or leaks.
2. Check oil separator for blockage, cracks or leaks.
3. Check fresh air hose from throttle body to cylinder head cover grommet for blockage, cracks or leaks.
4. If all above checks are satisfactory, system is operating properly. If any of the above checks display blockage, cracks or leaks, repair or replace as necessary.

1996

Refer to EEC-V section, under "Computerized Engine Controls" for diagnosis and testing.

TEST STEP	RESULT	►	ACTION TO TAKE
EVAP1 CHECK CARBON CANISTER			
• Check carbon canister for fuel saturation. • **Is excess amount of liquid fuel present in canister?**	Yes No	► ►	REPLACE carbon canister. CHECK fuel tank vent system for malfunction.
EVAP2 PRESSURE TEST FUEL/EVAP SYSTEM			
• Remove a plug line to carbon canister. • Remove gas cap and install a vacuum pump/gauge gas cap. • Apply 3/4 psi maximum air pressure. • **Is either a vacuum or fuel leak detected?**	Yes No	► ►	SERVICE as necessary either the fuel leak or EVAP vacuum leak. REMOVE fuel gas cap pressure gauge. RECONNECT carbon canister. GO to EVAP3.
EVAP3 CHECK VACUUM IN EVAP SYSTEM			
• Check for blockage/restrictions or opens (hoses) between engine vacuum port and carbon canister. • Check for blockage in fuel tank vent system. • **Is a fault indicated?**	Yes No	► ►	REPLACE damaged vacuum hoses (holes or cuts). REMOVE blockages or restrictions. For 3.0L Flexible Fuel: GO to EVAP5. All Others: GO to EVAP4

Fig. 13 Evaporative emission (EVAP) system diagnostic tests (Part 1 of 3). 1993–95

TEST STEP	RESULT	►	ACTION TO TAKE
EVAP5 CHECK CANISTER PURGE VALVE ELECTRICALLY			
• Disconnect the Canister Purge (CANP) valve. • Use a DVOM for ohmmeter test. • Measure resistance between positive and negative terminals on the CANP valve electrical connector (refer to illustration). *Canister Purge Valve Connector* • **Is resistance between 30 and 36 ohms?**	Yes No	► ►	GO to EVAP6 REPLACE Canister Purge valve.
EVAP6 CHECK CANISTER PURGE VALVE MECHANICALLY			
• Apply 5 to 10 in-Hg to the VAC port (3/8 inch) and regulator port (5/32 inch) of the valve and hold. • Apply 12 volts to the coil assembly as shown in Test Step EVAP5. • Measure air flow at the CAN port (7/16 inch). NOTE: Flow should be about 1.4 cubic feet per minute. *Canister Purge Valve (9C915)* • De-energize the coil assembly. • **Does the flow shut off?**	Yes No	► ►	Evaporative Emission System is functioning properly REPLACE Canister Purge valve.

Fig. 13 Evaporative emission (EVAP) system diagnostic tests (Part 3 of 3). 1993–95

Test Step	Result	►	Action to Take
A1 CANISTER HOSE AND INLET TUBE BLOCKAGE TEST			
• Inspect canister evaporative emission hoses and inlet nipple for blockage. • **Are evaporative emission hoses or inlet blocked?**	Yes No	► ►	REMOVE blockage or REPLACE component. RESTORE vehicle. RETEST system. GO to A2.
A2 FLOW TEST (FUEL TANK FILLER CAP REMOVED)			
• CAUTION: Failure to remove fuel tank filler cap may result in damage to fuel tank. Remove fuel tank filler cap from fuel tank filler pipe. • CAUTION: Do not use other high-pressure air supplies. Damage to fuel tank may result. Install Rotunda Vacuum Tester 014-R1054 or equivalent onto tee or evaporative emission nipple at test point B2. • Hand pump to a maximum of 17.2 kPa (2.5 psi). • **Does pressure drop to zero immediately?**	Yes No	► ►	GO to A5. PERFORM Pinpoint Test Step A3.

TEST POINT B2 WITH TEE / TEST POINT B1 WITH TEE / TEST POINT B2 WITHOUT TEE / EVAPORATIVE EMISSION HOSE / CLOSE OFF LINE / TO FUEL TANK / TEST POINT B1 WITHOUT TEE / EVAPORATIVE EMISSION CANISTER / EVAPORATIVE EMISSION HOSE

Fig. 14 Abnormal pressure in fuel tank diagnostic tests (Part 1 of 2). 1996 Contour, Cougar, Mark VIII, Mystique & Thunderbird

TEST STEP	RESULT	►	ACTION TO TAKE
EVAP4 CHECK CANISTER PURGE SOLENOID			
• Disconnect the Canister Purge (CANP) solenoid. • Apply 9 to 14 volts DC from a voltage source to the CANP solenoid. • While applying the above voltage, apply 53 kPa (16 in-Hg) of vacuum to the manifold side of the CANP solenoid with vacuum pump.	Yes No	► ►	Evaporative Emission System is functioning properly. REPLACE Canister Purge (CANP) solenoid.

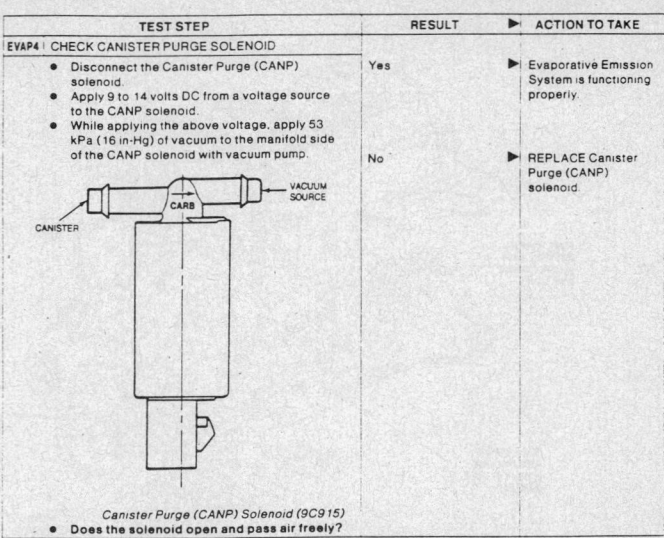

Canister Purge (CANP) Solenoid (9C915)
• **Does the solenoid open and pass air freely?**

Fig. 13 Evaporative emission (EVAP) system diagnostic tests (Part 2 of 3). 1993–95

	Test Step	Result	►	Action to Take
A3	INSPECT EVAPORATIVE EMISSION HOSE			
	• Inspect evaporative emission hose routing between fuel tank and body for pinch. • **Is evaporative emission hose pinched?**	Yes No	► ►	LOOSEN fuel tank and reroute evaporative emission hose. VERIFY service. GO to A4.
A4	INSPECT EVAPORATIVE EMISSION VALVE			
	• Remove fuel tank. • Remove evaporative emission valve. • Inspect evaporative emission valve for open air passage through orifice. • **Is air passage open?**	Yes No	► ►	INSTALL evaporative emission valve in fuel tank. INSTALL fuel tank. System test complete. REPLACE evaporative emission valve. VERIFY service.
A5	INSPECT EVAPORATIVE EMISSION TUBE			
	• Inspect evaporative emission tube and evaporative emission hoses for kinks or pinched areas. • **Are tube or evaporative emission hoses kinked or pinched?**	Yes No	► ►	SERVICE or REPLACE tube or evaporative emission hoses. VERIFY service. GO to A6.
A6	FLOW TEST (FUEL TANK FILLER CAP INSTALLED)			
	CAUTION: Do not use other high-pressure air supplies. Damage to canister may result. • Install Rotunda Vacuum Tester 014-R1054 or equivalent in evaporative emission hose at test point B1. • Hand pump to a maximum of 17.2 kPa (2.5 psi). • **Does pressure drop to zero immediately?**	Yes No	► ►	EVAP canister system flow OK. GO to A7. REPLACE evaporative emissions canister. RESTORE vehicle. RETEST system.
A7	CHECK VACUUM HOSE LEAK BETWEEN EVAPORATIVE EMISSION CANISTER PURGE VALVE AND CARBON CANISTER			
	• Check for cracks, splits and holes in the vacuum hose between the CANP solenoid and the carbon canister. • **Is a fault indicated?**	Yes No	► ►	REPLACE damaged vacuum hose (cracks, splits and holes). RESTORE vehicle. RETEST system. GO to A8.
A8	CHECK EVAPORATIVE EMISSION CANISTER RANGE VALVE SOLENOID FOR VACUUM LEAKS - CLOSED VACUUM POSITION			
	• Turn ignition switch to OFF position. • Disconnect the vacuum hose at both ends of the evaporative emission canister purge valve. • Install a hand vacuum pump to the intake manifold vacuum side of the evaporative emission canister purge valve. • Disconnect the evaporative emission canister purge valve electrically. • Apply 16 in-Hg (53 kPa) of vacuum to the evaporative emission canister purge valve. • **Does the evaporative emission canister purge valve hold vacuum for 20 seconds?**	Yes No	► ►	GO to A9. REMOVE vacuum pump. REPLACE evaporative emission canister purge valve. RESTORE vehicle. RETEST system.
A9	CHECK FOR MANIFOLD VACUUM TO CANP SOLENOID			
	• Turn ignition switch to OFF position. • Vacuum hose disconnected from manifold vacuum side of CANP solenoid. • Start engine. • Place thumb on open end of vacuum hose at CANP solenoid. • **Is vacuum present at the engine vacuum hose to CANP solenoid?**	Yes No	► ►	Evaporative Emission System is OK. RECONNECT all components. DRIVE vehicle. CHECK vacuum hose to engine from evaporative emission canister purge valve for proper routing, kinks, leaks or blockage.

Fig. 14 Abnormal pressure in fuel tank diagnostic tests (Part 2 of 2). 1996 Contour, Cougar, Mark VIII, Mystique & Thunderbird

Test Step		Result	▶	Action to Take
A1	CANISTER HOSE AND INLET NIPPLE BLOCKAGE TEST			
	• Test canister evaporative emission hose and inlet nipple for blockage. • Are evaporative emission hoses or inlet nipple blocked?	Yes No	▶ ▶	GO to A2. GO to A6.
A2	FUEL EVAPORATIVE EMISSION SYSTEM BLOCKAGE TEST			
	• Test fuel tank evaporative emission system for blockage. • Are all system passages open?	Yes No	▶ ▶	REMOVE blockage or REPLACE component. GO to A7.
A3	EVAPORATIVE EMISSION TUBE INSPECTION			
	• Inspect evaporative emission tubes and evaporative emission hoses for kinks or pinched areas. Include the excess evaporative emission venting system tubes and hoses. • Are tubes or fuel vapor hoses kinked or pinched?	Yes No	▶ ▶	SERVICE or REPLACE evaporative emission tube or evaporative emission hoses. VERIFY service. GO to A4.
A4	EVAPORATIVE EMISSION INSPECTION NEAR FUEL TANK			
	• Inspect evaporative emission hose routing between fuel tank and body for pinch. • Is evaporative emission hose pinched?	Yes No	▶ ▶	LOOSEN fuel tank and reroute evaporative emission hose. VERIFY service. GO to A5.
A5	EVAPORATIVE EMISSION VALVE INSPECTION			
	• Remove fuel tank. • Remove evaporative emission valve. • Inspect evaporative emission valve for open air passage through orifice. • Is air passage open?	Yes No	▶ ▶	INSTALL evaporative emission valve in fuel tank. INSTALL fuel tank. System test complete. REPLACE evaporative emission valve. VERIFY service.

Fig. 15 Abnormal pressure in fuel tank diagnostic tests (Part 1 of 2). 1996 Mustang, Sable & Taurus

Test Step		Result	▶	Action to Take
A6	FLOW TEST (FUEL TANK FILLER CAP INSTALLED)			
	CAUTION: Do not use other high pressure air supplies. This will result in damage to evaporative emission canister. • Install Rotunda 014-R1054 Vacuum Tester or equivalent in evaporative emission hose at test point B1. • Hand pump to a maximum of 17.2 kPa (2.5 psi). • Does pressure drop to zero immediately?	Yes No	▶ ▶	Canister system flow OK. GO to A2. PERFORM Pinpoint Test Step A3.
A7	FLOW TEST (FUEL TANK FILLER CAP REMOVED)			
	CAUTION: Failure to remove fuel tank filler cap may result in damage to evaporative emission tube. • Remove fuel tank filler cap from fuel tank filler pipe. **CAUTION: Do not use other high-pressure air supplies. Damage to fuel tank may result.** • Install Rotunda Vacuum Tester 014-R1054 or equivalent onto tee or evaporative emission canister nipple at test point B2. • Hand pump to a maximum of 17.2 kPa (2.5 psi). • Does pressure drop to zero immediately?	Yes No	▶ ▶	System OK, no service required. PERFORM Pinpoint Test Step A4.

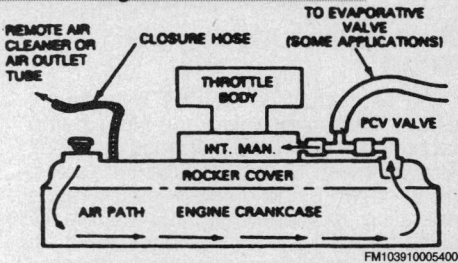

Fig. 15 Abnormal pressure in fuel tank diagnostic tests (Part 2 of 2). 1996 Mustang, Sable & Taurus

Test Step		Result	▶	Action to Take
A1	FUNCTIONAL TEST—VAPOR SUPPLY LINE DISCONNECTED			
	• With the fuel level below 1/2, disconnect evaporative emission and brake tube at fuel vapor canister. • Plug the evaporative emission and brake tube. • Using Rotunda Leak Tester 134-00003 or equivalent, pressurize the fuel system through the test fuel tank filler cap. • Remove plug from the evaporative emission and brake tube. • Did the fuel system pressure decay?	Yes No	▶ ▶	GO to A3. GO to A2.
A2	CANISTER INLET AND VAPOR TUBE BLOCKAGE TEST			
	• Inspect canister inlet nipple and evaporative emission and brake tube for blockage. • Are inlet or evaporative emission and brake tube blocked?	Yes No	▶ ▶	REMOVE blockage or REPLACE component. VERIFY service. GO to A3.
A3	FUNCTIONAL TEST—EVAPORATIVE EMISSION CONTROL VALVE SIGNAL LINE DISCONNECTED			
	• Disconnect the evaporative emission control valve signal line from the fuel tank filler pipe. • Plug the signal line at the fuel tank filler pipe. • Plug the evaporative emission supply line at fuel vapor canister. • Pressurize the fuel system. • Remove plug from the evaporative emission supply line. • Did the fuel system pressure decay?	Yes No	▶ ▶	REPLACE the evaporative emission tube shut off valve. VERIFY service. GO to A4.
A4	FUNCTIONAL TEST—EVAPORATIVE EMISSION TUBE DISCONNECTED			
	• Remove evaporative emission tube from fuel vapor valve at evaporative emission tube shut off valve. • Did the fuel tank system pressure decay?	Yes No	▶ ▶	System OK, no servicing required. REPLACE fuel vapor valve and grommet. VERIFY service.

Fig. 16 Abnormal pressure in fuel tank diagnostic tests. 1996 Continental, Crown Victoria, Grand Marquis & Town Car

THERMACTOR SYSTEMS (SECONDARY AIR INJECTION) Description

The Thermactor Systems are used to reduce Carbon Monoxide (CO) and Hydrocarbon (HC) content of exhaust gases by continuing the combustion of unburned gases after they have left the combustion chamber by injecting or pulling fresh air into the exhaust stream leaving the exhaust ports or into the catalyst. Fresh air mixes with exhaust gases to induce further oxidation of both HC and CO, reducing their concentration and converting some of them into harmless Carbon Dioxide and water.

The typical air injection system consists of: air supply pump and centrifugal filter or remote filter, air bypass valve, check valves, air manifold, air hoses and air control valve.

THERMACTOR AIR INJECTION SYSTEM

The Thermactor Air Injection System, is used to inject fresh air into the exhaust

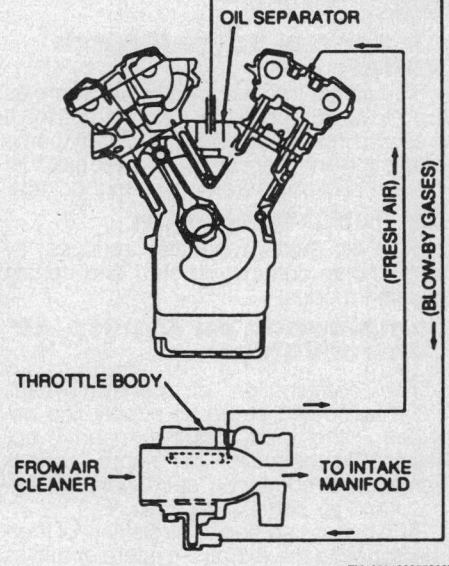

Fig. 18 PCV system. 3.0L/V6-182 & 3.2L/V6-195 SHO engines

stream leaving the exhaust ports or into the catalyst.

During highway cruise and wide open throttle operation, thermactor air is dumped to atmosphere to prevent overheating of exhaust system.

SECONDARY AIR INJECTION (AIR) (MANAGED AIR THERMACTOR) SYSTEM

The Secondary Air Injection (AIR) (Managed Air Thermactor) System, **Fig. 19**, is used in electronic control systems to divert thermactor air either upstream to the exhaust manifold check valve or downstream to the rear section check valve and dual bed catalyst. It will also dump thermactor air to atmosphere during certain modes of operation.

An air control valve is used to direct air either upstream or downstream. An air bypass valve is used to dump air to atmosphere.

PULSED SECONDARY AIR INJECTION (PAIR) (PULSE AIR SYSTEM (THERMACTOR II))

The Pulsed Secondary Air Injection (PAIR) (Pulse Air or Thermactor II) System, does not use an air pump. This system uses natural pulses present in the exhaust system to pull air into the catalyst through pulse air valves. The pulse air valve is con-

Fig. 17 PCV system. Except 3.0L/V6-182 & 3.2L/V6-195 SHO engines

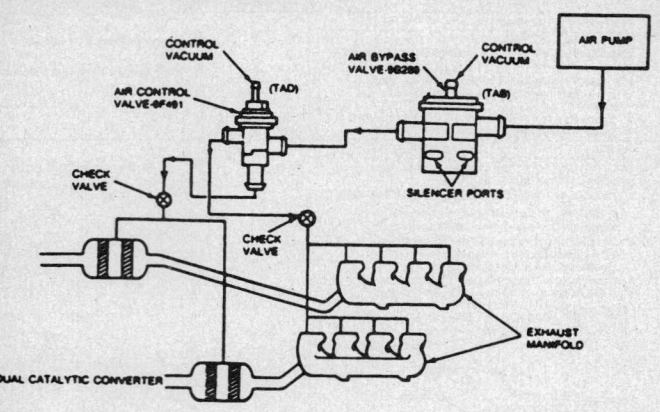

Fig. 19 Managed air thermactor system

nected to the catalyst using a long tube, and to the air cleaner and silencer using hoses.

SYSTEM COMPONENTS

Mechanical Air Supply Pump

The air supply pump is a belt driven, positive displacement, vane-type pump that provides air for the thermactor system. It is available in 19 and 22 cubic inch sizes, and is driven using different pulley ratios depending upon application. The pump receives air from a remote silencer filter on rear side of engine air cleaner connected to pumps air inlet nipple or through an impeller-type centrifugal filter fan.

Electrical Air Supply Pump

The air supply pump is an electric motor driven, vane-type pump that provides air for the thermactor system. It is controlled by the PCM to supply air to the catalytic converter when certain engine and load conditions are met.

Air Silencer/Filter

The air silencer is a combination silencer and filter used with pumps that are not equipped with an impeller-type centrifugal air filter fan or on pulse air systems. It is mounted in the engine compartment and is connected to the pump or pulse air valve inlet by a flexible hose.

Air Bypass Valves

There are two general groups of bypass valves, normally open and normally closed. Both groups are available in both remote and pump-mounted versions.

Normally closed valves, supply air to the exhaust system with medium and high applied vacuum signals during normal modes (engine operating at normal operating temperature), short idles, and some accelerations. With low or no vacuum applied to pump, air is dumped through silencer ports of valve.

Normally open valves with a vacuum vent, provide a timed air dump during decelerations and also dump when a vacuum pressure difference is maintained between the signal port and the vent port. The signal port must have three inches Hg more vacuum than the vent port to hold the dump. This mode is used to protect the catalyst from overheating.

Air Check Valve

The air check valve is a one-way valve that allows thermactor air to pass into exhaust system while preventing exhaust gases from passing in opposite direction.

Air Supply Control Valve

The air supply control valve is used in the thermactor system to direct air pump output to the exhaust manifold or downstream to the catalyst system depending on the engine control modes. It may also be used to dump air to air cleaner or dump silencer.

Air Control Valve (Switch Relief)

The air control valve works the same as the air supply control valve, except for a pressure relief valve to provide air pump protection in case of excessive exhaust system backpressure or system blockage.

Air Pump Resonator

The air pump resonator reduces air pump noise during cold start and certain cruising modes.

Combination Air Bypass/Air Control Valve

The combination air control/bypass valve is located in the air supply line between the air pump and upstream/downstream air supply check valves and combines secondary air bypass and air control functions.

The bypass portion controls flow of thermactor air to the exhaust system or allows thermactor air to be bypassed to atmosphere. When the air is not being bypassed, the air control portion of the valve

switches the air injection point to either an upstream or downstream location.

Dual Thermactor Air Control Solenoid Valve

The dual thermactor air control solenoid valve assembly consists of two normally closed solenoid valves, one controlling the Thermactor Air Bypass (TAB) valve and the other controlling the Thermactor Air Diverter (TAD) valve. Both are vented when de-energized, fed by the intake manifold vacuum reservoir and controlled by an EEC system. They may also be used for EGR shutoff.

Solenoid Vacuum Valve Assembly

The normally closed solenoid valve assembly, consists of two vacuum ports with an atmospheric vent and may or may not have a control bleed function. The outlet port of the valve is open to atmospheric vent and closed to the inlet port when de-energized. When energized, the outlet port is opened to the inlet port and closed to atmospheric vent. Control bleed is provided to prevent contamination from the intake manifold.

Thermactor Idle Vacuum (TIV) Valve

The TIV valve vents the vacuum signal to atmosphere when preset manifold vacuum or pressure is exceeded. It is used to divert thermactor airflow during cold starts to control exhaust backfire.

Vacuum Control Valve (VCV)

The VCV controls vacuum to emission control devices during engine warm-up. 2-port types, open when engine coolant reaches a predetermined temperature. 4-

SYMPTOM	POSSIBLE SOURCE	ACTION
• Backfire (Exhaust)	• Air bypass valve malfunction • Air control valve malfunction • Combination air bypass/control valve malfunction • Thermactor solenoid valve malfunction • Thermactor idle vacuum valve malfunction • Exhaust manifolds or pipes loose	• Perform bypass valve diagnosis • Perform air control valve diagnosis • Perform combination valve diagnosis • Perform solenoid diagnosis • Perform TIV diagnosis • Inspect and tighten nuts or bolts to specification.
• Surge at Steady Speed	• Air control valve malfunction • Combination air bypass/control valve malfunction • Thermactor solenoid malfunction	• Perform control valve diagnosis • Perform combination valve diagnosis • Perform solenoid diagnosis
• Engine Noise - (Hiss) • Engine Noise - (Rap, Roar)	• Thermactor hose leaks or disconnects • Thermactor hose or valves leak exhaust	• Visual inspection of hoses and connections • Visual inspection of hoses and valves. Perform air check valve diagnosis
• Poor Fuel Economy	• Air control valve malfunction • Combination air bypass/control valve malfunction • Thermactor solenoid valve malfunction • Disconnected vacuum or electrical connections for thermactor components	• Perform air control valve diagnosis • Perform combination valve diagnosis • Perform solenoid diagnosis • Visual inspection
• Exhaust Smoke - (White)	• Disconnected vacuum or electrical connections for thermactor components • Air bypass valve malfunction • Air control valve malfunction • Combination air bypass/control valve malfunction • Thermactor solenoid valve malfunction	• Visual inspection • Perform bypass valve diagnosis • Perform air control valve diagnosis • Perform combination valve diagnosis • Perform solenoid diagnosis
• State Emission Test Failure	• Disconnected vacuum or electrical connections for thermactor components • Air bypass valve malfunction • Air control valve malfunction • Combination air bypass/control valve malfunction • Thermactor solenoid valve malfunction	• Visual inspection • Perform bypass valve diagnosis • Perform air control valve diagnosis • Perform combination valve diagnosis • Perform solenoid diagnosis
• Rolling Idle	• Thermactor solenoid valve malfunction • Disconnected vacuum or electrical connections for thermactor components • Air bypass valve malfunction • Air control valve malfunction • Combination air bypass/control valve malfunction	• Perform solenoid diagnosis • Visual inspection • Perform bypass valve diagnosis • Perform air control valve diagnosis • Perform combination valve diagnosis

FM1039100057010X

Fig. 20 Thermactor system diagnosis (Part 1 of 2)

SYMPTOM	POSSIBLE SOURCE	ACTION
• Excessive Thermactor System Noise (Putt-Putt, Whirling or Hissing)	• Leak in hose.	• Locate source of leak using soap solution and replace hoses as necessary.
	• Loose, pinched or kinked hose.	• Reassemble, straighten or replace hose and clamps as required.
	• Hose touching other engine parts.	• Adjust hose to prevent contact with other engine parts.
	• Bypass valve inoperative.	• Test the valve.
	• Check valve inoperative.	• Test the valve.
	• Restricted or bent pump outlet fitting.	• Inspect fitting and remove any flash blocking the air passage way. Replace bent fittings.
	• Air dumping through bypass valve (at idle only).	• On many vehicles, the thermactor system has been designed to dump air at idle to prevent overheating the catalyst. This condition is normal. Determine that the noise persists at higher speeds before proceeding.
	• Air dump through bypass valve (decel and cruise).	• On many vehicles, the thermactor air is dumped in the air cleaner or in remote silencer. Make sure hoses are connected and not cracked.
	• Air pump resonator leaking or blocked.	• Check resonator for hole or restricted inlet/outlet tubes.
• Excessive Pump Noise - (Chirps, Squeaks and Ticks)	• Worn or damaged pump.	• Check the thermactor system for wear or damage and make necessary corrections.
• Engine noise - (Rap or Roar)	• Hose disconnected.	• Audible and visual inspection to assure all hoses are connected.
• State Emissions Test Failure	• Restricted hose.	• Inspect hoses for crimped and/or kinked hoses.
	• Plugged pulse air silencer.	• Remove inlet hose and inspect silencer inlet for dirt and foreign material. Clean or replace silencer as appropriate.
	• Pulse air valve malfunction, leaking or restricted.	• Perform pulse air check valve diagnosis.
	• Pulse air control valve malfunction.	• Perform pulse air control valve diagnosis.

FM1039100057020X

Fig. 20 Thermactor system diagnosis (Part 2 of 2)

CONDITION	POSSIBLE SOURCE	ACTION
• Excessive Belt Noise	• Loose belt.	• Tighten to specification using Tool T75L-9480-A or equivalent to hold belt tension and Belt Tension Gauge T63L-8620-A or equivalent. CAUTION: Do not use a pry bar to move air pump.
	• Seized pump.	• Replace pump.
	• Loose pulley.	• Replace pulley and/or pump if damaged. Tighten bolts to 13.6-17.0 N·m (120-150 lb-in).
	• Loose or broken mounting brackets or bolts.	• Replace parts as required and tighten bolts to specification.
• Excessive Mechanical Noise, Chirps, Squeaks, Clicks or Ticks	• Overtightened mounting bolt.	• Tighten to 34 N·m (25 lb-ft).
	• Overtightened drive belt.	• Same as loose belt.
	• Excessive flash on the air pump adjusting arm boss.	• Remove flash from the boss.
	• Distorted adjusting arm.	• Replace adjusting arm.
	• Pump or pulley mounting fasteners loose.	• Tighten fasteners to specification.

FM1039100058000X

Fig. 21 Thermactor system noise test

port types, are simply two 2-port types in one housing and operate the same as 2-port types. 3-port types, switch vacuum source to the center port from the top or bottom ports.

Electrical Vacuum Switch (EVS)

The EVS is either opened or closed at room temperature and reverse with engine at normal operating temperature.

Vacuum Check Valve

The vacuum check valve blocks airflow in one direction and allows free airflow in the other direction.

Vacuum Reservoir

The vacuum reservoir stores vacuum and provides "muscle" vacuum. It prevents rapid fluctuations or sudden drops in a vacuum signal during acceleration periods.

Pulse Air Valve

The pulse air valve is normally closed. Without vacuum signal from the solenoid, the flow of air is blocked.

Diagnosis & Testing

Engine tune up should be checked whenever the air pump system seems to be malfunctioning, especially items affecting air/fuel ratio.

1993-95
DIAGNOSIS BY SYMPTOM

Refer to charts in **Figs. 20** and **21** for symptom diagnosis.

FUNCTIONAL DIAGNOSIS
AIR Supply Pump Test

1. Check belt tension and adjust if necessary.
2. Disconnect air supply hose from bypass control valve.
3. Pump is operating satisfactorily if airflow is felt at pump outlet and flow increases as engine speed is increased.

AIR Silencer/Filter Test

1. Inspect silencer and hoses for leaks.
2. Disconnect hose from silencer outlet, remove silencer and visually inspect for plugging.
3. Air silencer is operating properly if no plugging or leaks are observed.

Normally Closed Type AIR Bypass Valve Tests

1. Disconnect air supply hose at valve outlet, then remove vacuum line and ensure a vacuum signal is present at vacuum nipple. There must be vacuum present prior to proceeding.
2. With engine at 1500 RPM and vacuum line connected to vacuum nipple, air pump supply air should be heard and felt at air bypass valve outlet.
3. With engine at 1500 RPM and vacuum line disconnected, air at air outlet should be significantly decreased or shutoff. Air pump supply air should be heard and felt at silencer or dump port.
4. If air bypass valve does not pass above tests, check air pump. If air pump is operating properly, replace air bypass valve.

Normally Open Type w/Vacuum Vents AIR Bypass Valve Tests

1. Disconnect air pump supply line at outlet, then vacuum lines from vacuum nipple and vacuum vent.
2. Accelerate engine to 1500 RPM, air pump supply air should be present at outlet.
3. Using suitable vacuum hose, connect vacuum nipple to intake manifold vacuum. No air should be present at valve outlet, all air should bypass through silencer ports.
4. Using the same vacuum hose as above step, cap vacuum vent and accelerate engine to 2000 RPM. Air pump supply air should be interrupted when throttle is released.
5. If above steps prove incorrect, check air pump, then bypass valve.

AIR Check Valve Test

1. Visually inspect thermactor system hoses, tubes, control valves and check valves for leaks that may be due to backflow of exhaust gas. If holes are found and/or traces of exhaust gas are present, check valve may be defective.
2. Valve should allow free flow of air in one direction only and should block free flow of exhaust gas in opposite direction.
3. Replace valve if air does not flow as specified.

AIR Supply Control Valve Test

1. Verify airflow is being supplied to valve inlet by disconnecting air supply hose at inlet and verifying presence of airflow with engine at 1500 RPM, then reconnect air supply hose.
2. Disconnect air supply hoses at outlets A and B, **Fig. 22**.
3. Remove vacuum line at vacuum nipple, then accelerate engine to 1500 RPM. Airflow should be felt at outlet B with little or no airflow at outlet A.
4. With engine at 1500 RPM, connect a direct vacuum line from any manifold vacuum source to air control valve vacuum nipple. Airflow should be heard or felt at outlet A with little or no airflow at outlet B.

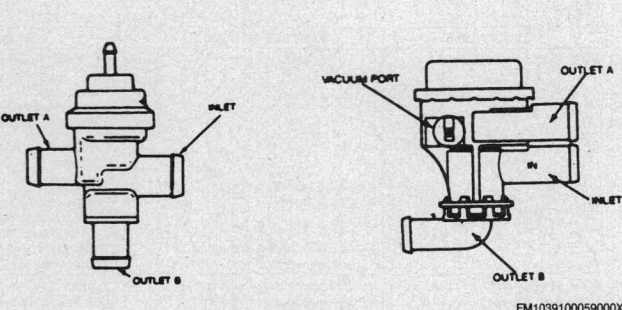

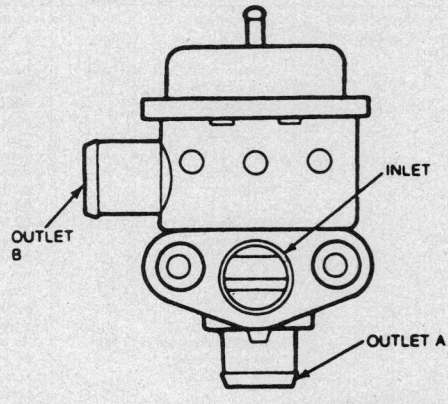

Fig. 22   Air supply control valve

FM1039100059000X

FM1039100060000X

Fig. 23   Early production air control valve (switch relief)

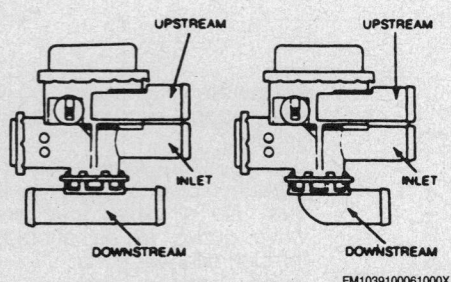

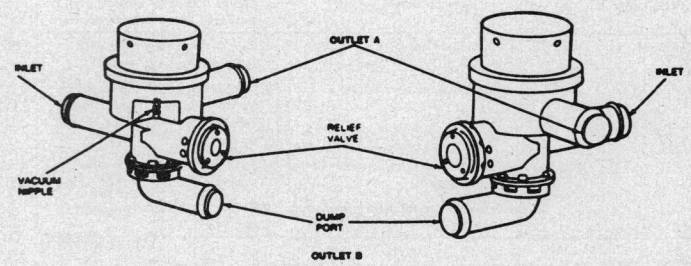

FM1039100061000X

Fig. 24   Late production air control valve (switch relief)

FM1039100062000X

Fig. 25   Air control valve (thermactor bypass type)

5. If valve does not pass steps three or 4, replace valve.

AIR Control Valve (Switch Relief) Test

Refer to "Air Supply Control Valve Test" as previously described, using **Figs. 23 through 25** for outlet locations.

AIR Pump Resonator Test

1. Visually inspect for holes, then remove hoses and check for blocked or restricted ports.
2. Replace resonator if holes, blocked or restricted ports are observed.

Combination AIR Bypass/AIR Control Valve Test

1. Disconnect hoses from outlets A and B, **Figs. 26 and 27**.
2. Disconnect and plug vacuum line to port D.
3. Run engine at 1500 RPM. There should be air flow at bypass vents.
4. Reconnect vacuum line to port D and disconnect and plug vacuum line to port S, then ensure vacuum is present inline to vacuum port D.
5. Run engine at 1500 RPM. There

should be air flow at outlet B but no air flow at outlet A.
6. Apply 8-10 inches Hg vacuum to port S and run engine at 1500 RPM. There should be air flow at outlet A.
7. **On bleed type valve,** some lesser amount of air will flow from outlet A or B and the main discharge will change when vacuum is applied to port S.

Dual Thermactor AIR Control Solenoid Valve Test

Refer to EEC-IV Quick Test in "EEC-IV" section for diagnostic test.

Solenoid Vacuum Valve Assembly Test

Refer to EEC-IV Quick Test in "EEC-IV" section for diagnostic test.

Thermactor Idle Vacuum (TIV) Valve Test

TIV Valves with code words ASH Or RED on decal.
1. With engine at idle in neutral, apply vacuum to small nipple and place fingers over TIV valve atmospheric vent holes. If no vacuum is sensed, TIV is damaged and must be replaced.

2. With engine at idle in neutral, apply 1.5-3.0 inches Hg vacuum to ASH valve or 3.5-4.5 inches of vacuum to RED valve large nipple and place fingers over TIV valve atmospheric vent holes. If no vacuum is sensed, TIV is damaged and must be replaced.
3. If TIV valve passed tests in steps one and two, valve is operating properly.

Vacuum Control Valve (VCV) Test

1. With engine cold, passage A to B should be closed and passage A to C should be open, **Fig. 28**.
2. With Engine at normal operating temperature, VCV should be open between A and B and closed between A and C.
3. **On four-port valve,** check A1 to B1 and A2 to B2 separately.
4. **On all valves,** replace VCV if above conditions are not obtained.

Vacuum Check Valve Test

Apply 16 inches Hg to "check" side of valve and trap. If vacuum remains above 15 inches Hg for 10 seconds, valve is acceptable.

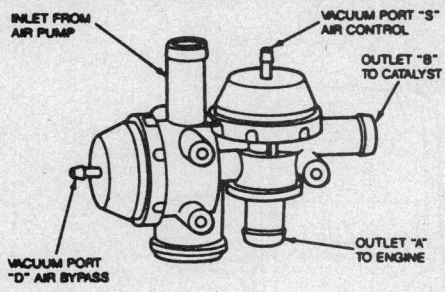

Fig. 26 Combination air control/bypass valve

Vacuum Reservoir Test

Apply 15-20 inches Hg vacuum to reservoir. If vacuum loss does not exceed 0.5 inch Hg in 60 seconds, reservoir is acceptable.

Pulse Air Valve Test

1. Visually inspect thermactor system hoses, tubes, control valves and check valves for leaks that may be due to backflow of exhaust gas. If holes are found and/or traces of exhaust gas are present, check valve may be defective.
2. Valve should allow free flow of air in one direction only and should block free flow of exhaust gas in opposite direction.
3. Replace valve if air does not flow as specified.
4. Remove inlet hose, with engine at normal operating temperature and at idle in neutral, air should be drawn into valve. Remove vacuum line and air should stop.
5. If conditions in step four are obtained, valve is operating properly.
6. If conditions are not obtained, verify vacuum is present at valve.
7. If vacuum is not present, check solenoid valve.
8. If vacuum is present, but no air flows, inspect check valve, silencer filter and air cleaner for blocked or restricted passages.
9. If vacuum is present and no blocked or restricted passages are found, replace valve.

1996

Refer to EEC-V section, under "Computerized Engine Controls" for diagnosis and testing.

EMISSION RELATED COMPONENTS
Description

IGNITION BAROMETRIC PRESSURE SWITCH

This switch, **Fig. 29** controls spark timing and/or other electrical devices according to altitude. Calibration resistors in the switch assembly cause the ignition module to vary the spark timing. Spark timing is advanced for vehicle operation above a predetermined altitude and retarded for vehicle operation below a predetermined

altitude. Some switch assemblies control both spark timing and another device while other switch assemblies control only one or the other.

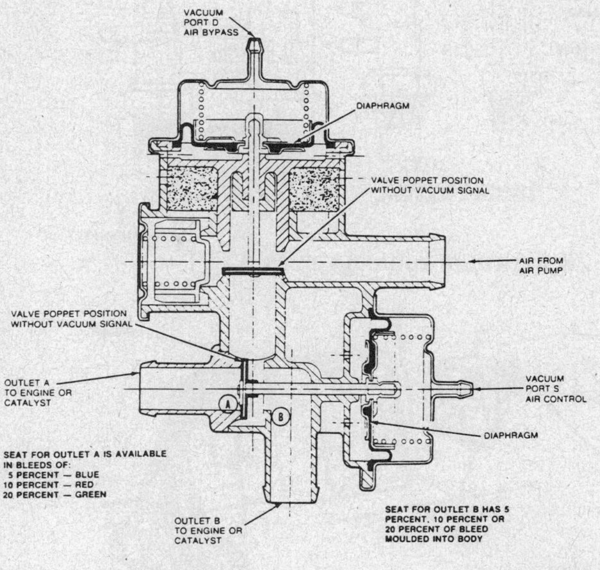

IGNITION TIMING VACUUM SWITCH

Below vacuum setting, this switch, **Fig. 30,** is open and signals the ignition module to retard spark timing. The switch is closed above the vacuum setting and the ignition module is in the non-retard spark timing mode. Calibration resistors inside the switch control the amount of retard.

INERTIA SWITCH

This switch, **Fig. 31,** is used on all vehicles with electric fuel pumps. This switch shuts off the fuel pump in the event of an accident. The switch consists of a steel ball held in place by a magnet. Upon sharp impact, the ball breaks loose from the magnet, rolls up a conical ramp, and strikes a target plate that opens the switch electrical contacts and shuts off the fuel pump. Once the switch is open, it must be manually reset before starting the vehicle.

PORTED VACUUM SWITCHES (PVS)

These switches, **Fig. 32,** control vacuum to emission components during engine warm-up. The 2-port and 4-port types open when coolant temperature reaches a predetermined value. The 3-port type switches vacuum from the center to the top or bottom ports. Electrical switches can be opened or closed until the PVS is fully cycled. All PVS units are temperature-activated and have a specific opening and closing temperature.

TEMPERATURE VACUUM SWITCH (TVS)

This switch, **Fig. 33,** has a bi-metal disc which locates itself in one of two positions,

depending on its temperature. One position allows free air flow in the vacuum line; and the other blocks air flow by sealing itself against the O-ring. The switching temperature is below the range of normal engine operating temperature.

The TVS may be used to control the vacuum signal to the thermactor dump valve, to reduce emissions.

The normally open TVS may block the purge vacuum signal to provide satisfactory cold driveability and reduce cold engine emissions. It may also be used to hold off EGR operation during cold engine operation.

The normally closed TVS may allow cold spark advance to provide satisfactory cold engine driveability.

THROTTLE SOLENOID POSITIONER (TSP)

With Dashpot

The TSP with dashpot, **Fig. 34,** acts as a variable throttle stop by extending its plunger when the solenoid is activated and retracting the plunger when the solenoid is de-energized. When energized, the TSP holds the throttle at an idle position. When de-energized, the TSP functions as an anti-dieseling device by retracting its plunger and fully closing the throttle. A TSP may also be used to increase throttle opening when the A/C is in operation.

Two types of TSPs with dashpot are used: the adjustable plunger rod length type and the fixed plunger rod length type. The TSP with dashpot does not exert sufficient force to open the throttle, however, it will hold throttle open after it has been mechanically opened.

With Vacuum Operated Throttle Modulator (VOTM)

The solenoid portion of the TSP with VOTM, **Fig. 35,** may be used as an anti-dieseling TSP or an A/C TSP. The vacuum portion can be used for maintaining a cold idle RPM or as an A/C VOTM. The VOTM,

Fig. 27 Exhaust air supply control valve w/bleed

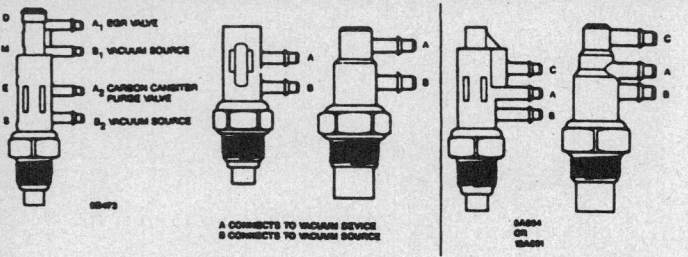

Fig. 28   Vacuum control valves (VCV)

FM1039100065000X

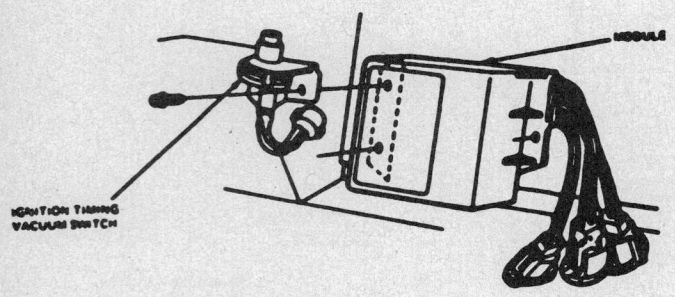

Fig. 30   Ignition timing vacuum switch

FM1039100070000X

Fig. 29   Ignition barometric pressure switch. 1993–95

VENT

operating the throttle through a connecting lever, may be activated by an electric vacuum solenoid or other vacuum control device.

VACUUM DELAY VALVE (VDV)

This valve, **Fig. 36,** further reduces emissions by delaying the spark advance during rapid acceleration and by cutting off advance immediately upon deceleration. This is a one-way valve and will not operate if installed backwards. On all systems which employ the dual diaphragm distributor, the line which has high vacuum at idle (normal operating temperature) is connected to the secondary (retard) side of the distributor vacuum advance unit. This is the connection closest to the distributor cap.

VACUUM REGULATOR

Two port regulators, **Fig. 37,** provide a constant output signal when input signal is greater than a preset level. When there is lower input vacuum, the output equals input.

Three and four port regulators, **Figs. 38 and 39,** are used to control the vacuum advance to the distributor. During engine idle conditions, the manifold vacuum signal is reduced to a constant output signal. Off idle, the output signal equals the spark port.

VACUUM RESERVOIR

The vacuum reservoir, **Fig. 40,** acts as an accumulator and prevents sudden drops or rapid fluctuations in a vacuum signal during acceleration. If vacuum in the reservoir leaks more than 1/2 inch Hg in one minute, the reservoir is defective and must be replaced.

VACUUM RESTRICTOR

The orifice type flow restrictor, **Fig. 41,** is used on some systems to control the

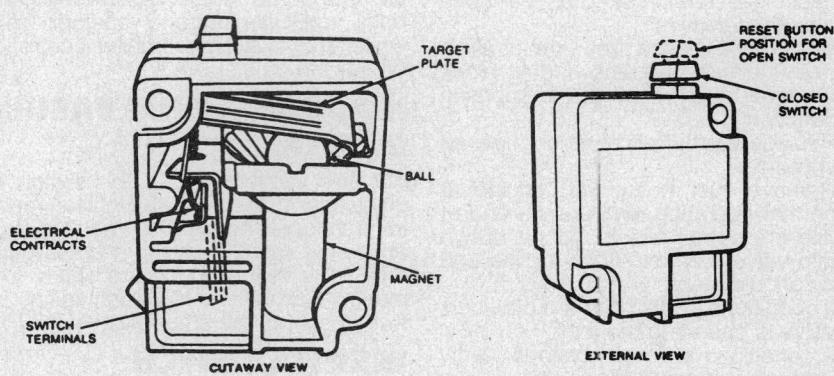

Fig. 31   Inertia switch

FM1039100071000X

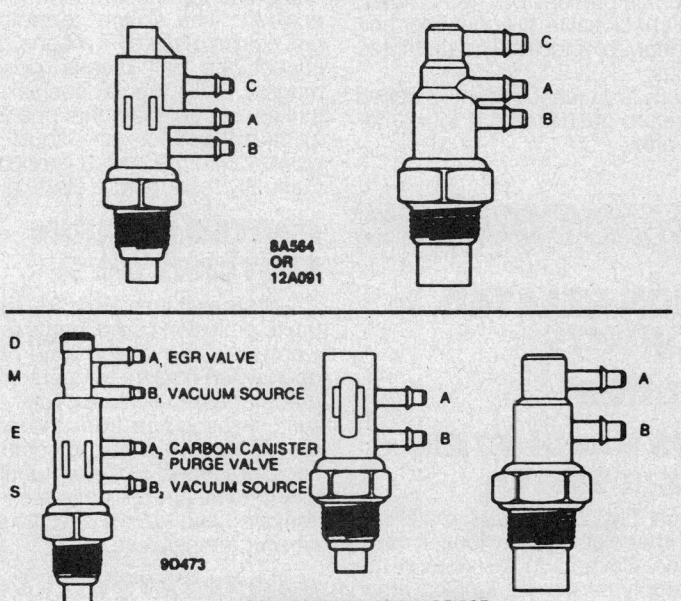

Fig. 32   Ported vacuum switches (PVS)

FM1039100072000X

EXCEPT ASPIRE, CAPRI, ESCORT & TRACER w/1.8L/4-112 ENGINE, FESTIVA & PROBE

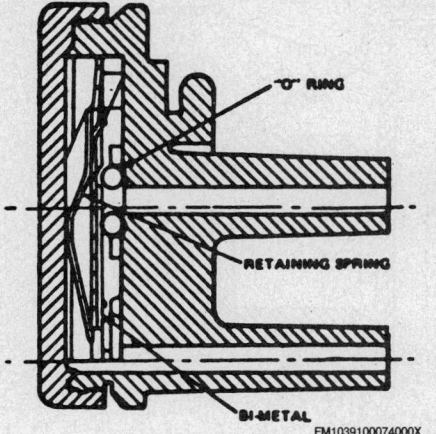

Fig. 33 Temperature vacuum switch (TVS)

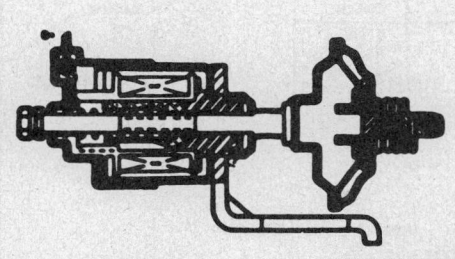

Fig. 34 Throttle solenoid positioner (TSP) w/dashpot

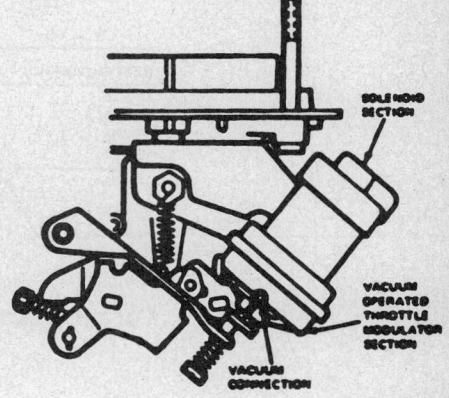

Fig. 35 Throttle solenoid positioner (TSP) w/vacuum operated throttle modulator (VOTM)

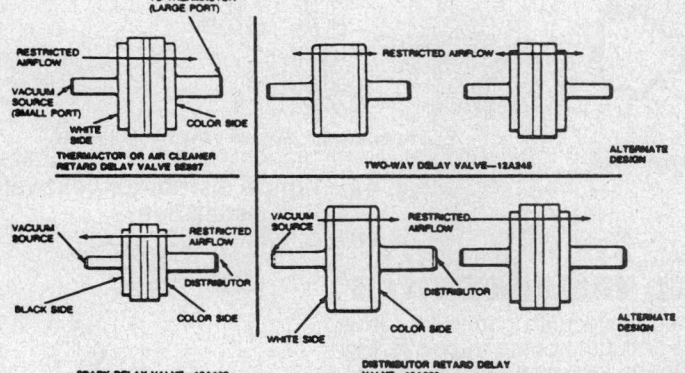

Fig. 36 Vacuum delay valves

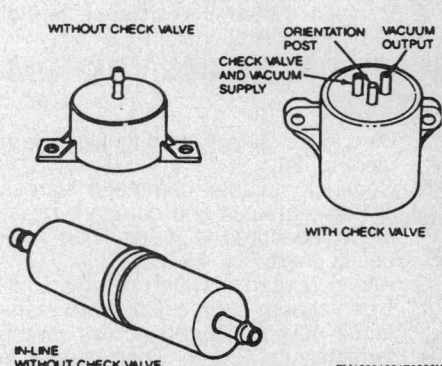

Fig. 37 Two port vacuum regulator

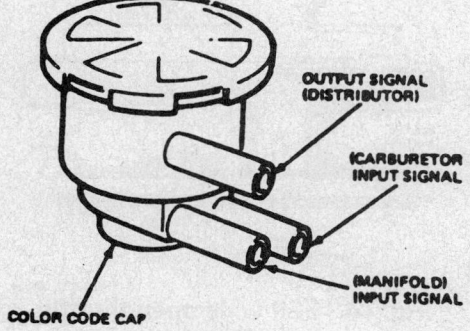

Fig. 38 Three port vacuum regulator

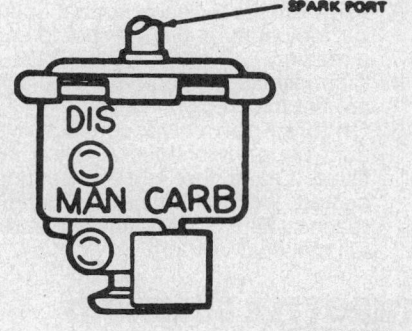

Fig. 39 Four port vacuum regulator

Fig. 40 Vacuum reservoirs

flow rate and or timing characteristics to the following systems:

1. EGR valve timing (opening and closing).
2. Part throttle spark advance.
3. Purge system.
4. Thermactor system.

The flow rate through the restrictor is the same in both directions. If blocked, it should be replaced.

VACUUM VENT VALVES

Vacuum vent valves, **Figs. 42 and 43,** control the induction of fresh air into a vacuum system to prevent chemical decay of vacuum diaphragms that can occur on contact with fuel vapors. Two types of valves are used. The black color coded valve is a vent valve only, while the natural color coded valve is a combination vent and delay valve. These valves should be installed with ports pointing downward. The vacuum source should be connected to the cap port, and the system or device operated by the valve to the body port.

WIDE OPEN THROTTLE CONTROL VALVE

This valve, **Fig. 44,** which is used on some vehicles, closes the EGR valve when the engine requires maximum power at or near wide open throttle. This valve is installed in the vacuum line between the ported vacuum connection on the carbu-

retor and EGR valve. A vacuum line from the carburetor venturi vacuum tap is connected to the top port on the valve and provides control for the valve. When venturi vacuum signal is at a predetermined level near wide open throttle, it is strong enough to overcome the calibration spring pressure and unseat the diaphragm valve, diverting EGR source vacuum to the atmosphere and causing the EGR valve to close. Normal EGR flow is resumed when there is a reduction in engine load from the wide open throttle position.

Diagnosis & Testing

IGNITION BAROMETRIC PRESSURE SWITCH

1. Disconnect switch from ignition module.

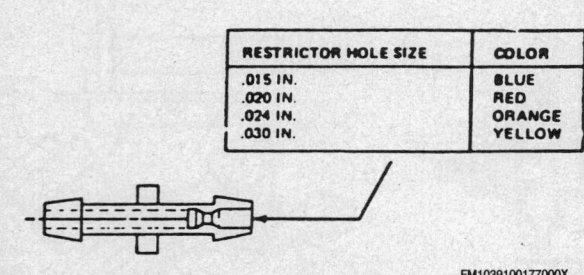

RESTRICTOR HOLE SIZE	COLOR
.015 IN.	BLUE
.020 IN.	RED
.024 IN.	ORANGE
.030 IN.	YELLOW

FM1039100177000X

Fig. 41   Vacuum restrictor

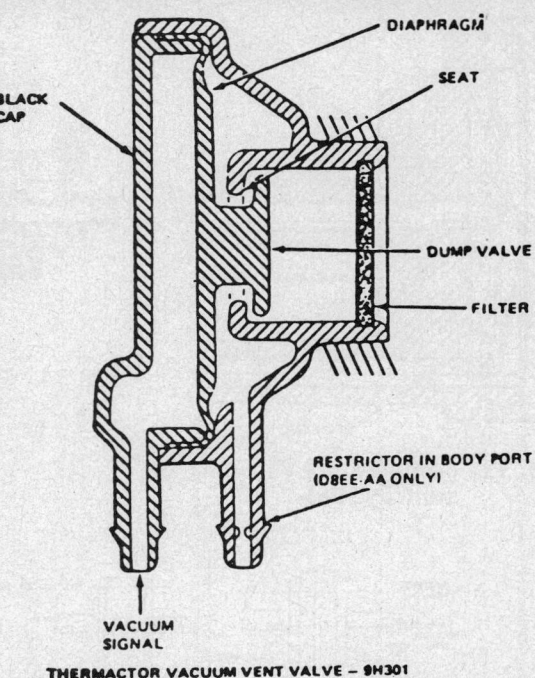

THERMACTOR VACUUM VENT VALVE – 9H301

FM1039100178000X

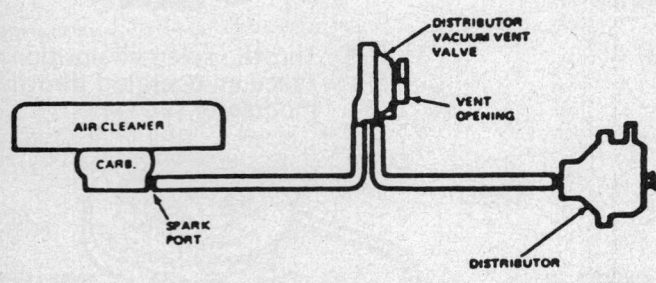

FM1039100179000X

Fig. 43   Typical vent valve installation

Fig. 42   Typical distributor vent valve installation

2. Connect suitable ohmmeter across switch terminals and compare resistance measured to values in chart, **Fig. 45.**
3. Replace switch if resistance is not within specifications.

IGNITION TIMING VACUUM SWITCH

1. Disconnect switch from ignition module, **Fig. 30.**
2. Connect suitable ohmmeter across switch terminals and compare resistance measured to "Less Than" values in chart, **Fig. 46.**
3. Apply vacuum to switch, using an outside vacuum source. Compare resistance now measured across switch terminals to "Greater Than" values in chart, **Fig. 46.**
4. Replace switch if resistance is not within specifications.

INERTIA SWITCH

Special testing equipment is required to test the inertia switch. Follow manufacturer's instructions.

Reset Instructions

1. Turn ignition switch to OFF.
2. Check for leaking fuel in engine compartment, fuel lines, and tank(s).
3. If no fuel leak is apparent, reset switch by pushing reset button on top of switch. Switch is located behind instrument panel.
4. Turn ignition switch to START momentarily, then back to OFF.
5. Check for leaking fuel in engine compartment, fuel lines, and tank(s). If gasoline can be seen or smelled other than during refueling, do not reset switch.

PORTED VACUUM SWITCH

1. Connect a vacuum gauge to port A and a vacuum source to port B, **Fig. 32.** On the four-port valve, check A1, B1 and A2, B2 separately.
2. With engine cold, ensure no vacuum flows from port A to port B.
3. Allow engine to reach normal operating temperature. Gauge should show a reading.
4. If conditions in steps two and three are not met, replace valve.
5. **On three-port valve,** connect a vacuum gauge into hose A using a T-fitting. Leave the other hoses connected. When engine temperature reaches 235°F, the gauge must read full manifold vacuum.

THROTTLE SOLENOID POSITIONER (TSP)

With Dashpot

1. Ensure plunger extends with throttle open and solenoid energized.
2. Depress plunger in toward collapsed position and ensure resistance is felt but not enough to make it difficult to bottom the plunger.

With Vacuum Operated Throttle Modulator (VOTM)

1. Ensure plunger extends and holds when solenoid is energized.
2. Apply 20 inches Hg vacuum to VOTM section using a hand vacuum pump and check that plunger extends and holds. Vacuum must not decrease to ten inches Hg in less than ten seconds.

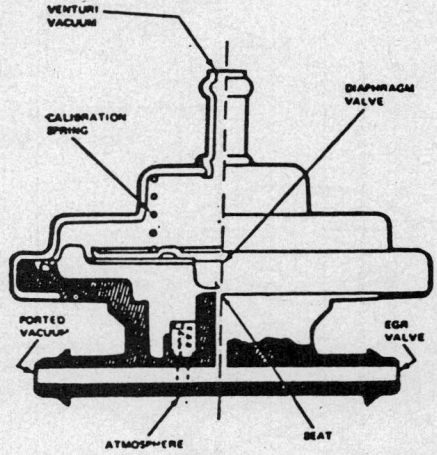

FM1039100180000X

Fig. 44   EGR wide open throttle control valve

VACUUM DELAY VALVE (VDV)

Refer to **Fig. 47,** for number value by color code. To perform the following procedure, an external vacuum source capable of maintaining a minimum constant ten inches Hg is required.

Mono Delay Valve

1. Set external vacuum source to ten inches Hg and connect black side of delay valve to vacuum source.
2. Connect a vacuum gauge with a 24 inch hose to colored side of delay valve.
3. Apply ten inches Hg vacuum and observe time in seconds for gauge to read 0-8 inches Hg. The minimum

Part Number	Resistance (Ohms) Below 3,000 Feet	Resistance (Ohms) Above 4,000 Feet
E2AE-12A243-AA	Greater Than 200,000	0
E2SE-12A243-AA	3,350 - 3,990	1,750 - 1,850
E2TE-12A243-AA	2,560 - 2,660	1,750 - 1,850
E2TE-12A243-BA	2,820 - 2,920	1,750 - 1,850
E2TE-12A243-CA	3,250 - 3,390	1,750 - 1,850

Fig. 45 Ignition barometric pressure switch resistance chart

Part Number	Vacuum Setting ± 1.7 kPa (Inches Hg ± 0.5 In.)	Resistance Value (Ohms)
E1AE-12A265-BA	Less than 11.8 (3.5)	3,200 - 3,350
	Greater than 11.8 (3.5)	2,150 - 2,250
E1SE-12A265-BA	Less than 30 (9)	3,250 - 3,370
	Greater than 30 (9)	2,150 - 2,250
E1TE-12A265-CA	Less than 10 (3)	2,800 - 2,870
	Greater than 10 (3)	2,150 - 2,250
E25E-12A265-AA	Less than 13.5 (4)	2,800 - 2,870
	Greater than 13.5 (4)	2,150 - 2,250

Fig. 46 Ignition timing vacuum switch test chart

Color	Number Value
White	5
Yellow	10
Blue	15
Green	20
Red	30

Fig. 47 SDV & VDV valve color coding

Color	I.D. No.	Time in Seconds Min.	Time in Seconds Max.
Black/Gray	1	.6	1.6
Black/Brown	2	1	3
Black/White	5	2.7	9.3
Black/Yellow	10	4.5	13.2
Black/Blue	15	6.8	18.8
Black/Green	20	8	26
Black/Orange	30	11.6	38
Black/Red	40	14	47.2
White/Pink①	5	2.7	9.3
White/Brown①	2	1	3
White/Green①	20	8	26
White/Yellow①	10	4.5	13.2
White/Gray①	1	.6	1.6
White/Blue①	20	8	26
White/Red①	40	14	47.2

①—Retard Delay Valve Only

Fig. 48 Vacuum & spark delay valve specifications chart

and maximum time for gauge to read eight inches Hg should be as shown in **Fig. 48.**

VACUUM OPERATED THROTTLE MODULATOR (VOTM)

1. Apply 20 inches Hg vacuum to VOTM using a hand vacuum pump and check that plunger extends and holds.
2. Vacuum must not decrease to ten inches Hg in less than ten seconds.

SPARK DELAY VALVE (SDV)

Refer to **Fig. 47,** for number value by color code. To perform the following procedure, an external vacuum source capable of maintaining a minimum constant ten inches Hg is required.

Mono Delay Valve

1. Set external vacuum source to ten inches Hg and connect black side of delay valve to vacuum source.
2. Connect a vacuum gauge with a 24 inch hose to colored side of delay valve.

3. Apply ten inches Hg vacuum and observe time in seconds for gauge to read 0-8 inches Hg. The minimum and maximum time for gauge to read eight inches Hg should be as shown in **Fig. 48.**

Retard Delay Valve

1. Set external vacuum source to ten inches Hg and connect colored side of delay valve to vacuum source.
2. Connect a vacuum gauge with a 24 inch hose to white side of delay valve.
3. Apply ten inches Hg of vacuum and observe time in seconds for gauge to read from 0-8 inches Hg. The minimum and maximum time for gauge to read eight inches Hg should be as shown in **Fig. 48.**

TEMPERATURE VACUUM SWITCH (TVS)

1. Apply 16 inches Hg vacuum to motor side of valve and trap. Cool to test temperature. Switch should hold vacuum as follows:
   a. **White TVS**—normally open. At

50°F must hold five inches Hg vacuum for 30 seconds. Should not hold vacuum above 76°F.
   b. **Brown TVS**—normally open. At 15°F must hold five inches Hg vacuum for 30 seconds. Should not hold vacuum above 30°F.
   c. **Purple TVS**—normally open. At 40°F must hold five inches Hg vacuum for 30 seconds. Should not hold vacuum above 55°F.
   d. **Red TVS**—normally closed. At 60°F must hold five inches Hg vacuum for 30 seconds. Should not hold vacuum at or below 50°F.

VACUUM REGULATOR

1. Disconnect vacuum line from distributor port and connect a vacuum gauge.
2. With engine at idle, the vacuum gauge reading should be within one inch Hg vacuum of the calibration point. The calibration point of each valve can be identified according to color code as follows: Black, six inches Hg; green, seven inches Hg; red, eight inches Hg.
3. Replace valve if not within specifications.

Aspire, Capri, Escort & Tracer w/1.8L/4-112 Engine, Festiva & Probe

INDEX

	Page No.		Page No.		Page No.
Air Intake Systems:	14-22	Description	14-22	Description	14-22
Description:	14-22	Diagnosis & Testing:	14-22	Diagnosis & Testing:	14-22
Air Intake (Inlet Air Control (IAC))		1993-95	14-22	1993-95	14-22
Systems	14-22	**Evaporative Emission (EVAP)**		**Positive Crankcase Ventilation**	
Bypass Air (BPA) Control		**Systems:**	14-22	**(PCV) Systems:**	14-22
Systems	14-22	Description	14-22	Description	14-22
Diagnosis & Testing:	14-22	Diagnosis & Testing:	14-22	Diagnosis & Testing:	14-22
1993-95	14-22	1993-95	14-22	1993-95	14-22
Catalytic Converters:	14-22	**Exhaust Gas Recirculation (EGR)**			
		Systems:	14-22		

EVAPORATIVE EMISSION (EVAP) SYSTEMS

Description

The Evaporative Emission Control (EVAP) system, prevents the escape of fuel vapors to the atmosphere under hot soak and engine off conditions by storing the vapors in a carbon canister. With the engine warm and running, the system purges stored vapors from the canister to the engine where they are burned.

Diagnosis & Testing

1993–95

Refer to **Figs. 1 and 2** to inspect and diagnose the evaporative emission system.

POSITIVE CRANKCASE VENTILATION (PCV) SYSTEMS

Description

The PCV system cycles crankcase emissions created by combustion blow-by into the intake manifold, where they are burned with the air/fuel mixture. The PCV valve prevents backfire into the crankcase by regulating the amount of ventilation.

Diagnosis & Testing

1993–95

Refer to **Figs. 3 and 4** to inspect and diagnosis the PCV system.

AIR INTAKE SYSTEMS

Description

AIR INTAKE (INLET AIR CONTROL (IAC)) SYSTEMS

The Air Intake (Inlet Air Control (IAC)) system delivers filtered and controlled air flow to engine. The system is comprised of three groups of components: air handling, sensors and control devices.

BYPASS AIR (BPA) CONTROL SYSTEMS

The Bypass Air (BPA) control system maintains engine idle speed throughout engine operating modes using a bypass air control valve, which responds to changes in engine coolant temperature.

Diagnosis & Testing

1993–95

Refer to **Figs. 5 and 6** to inspect and diagnose the air intake (inlet air control) system and **Figs. 7 through 9** to inspect and diagnose the bypass air control system.

EXHAUST GAS RECIRCULATION (EGR) SYSTEMS

Description

The EGR system recirculates exhaust gas to the engine air intake under normal driving conditions to reduce combustion temperatures and Oxides of Nitrogen (NOx) in the exhaust.

Diagnosis & Testing

1993–95

Refer to **Figs. 10 through 15** to inspect and diagnose the EGR system.

CATALYTIC CONVERTERS

Description

The catalytic converter is an emission control device added to the exhaust system to effectively reduce the levels of Carbon Monoxide (CO), Hydrocarbons (HC), and Oxides of Nitrogen (NOx) from entering the atmosphere. The converter works as a gas reactor to speed up the heat producing chemical reaction between exhaust gas components to reduce air pollutants in the engine exhaust. The catalyst material contained inside the converter, is made of a ceramic substance that is coated with a high surface area alumina and impregnated with precious metals.

Diagnosis & Testing

1993–95

Refer to **Fig. 16** to inspect and diagnose catalytic converters.

SYSTEM INSPECTION

1. Visually inspect the components of the Evaporative Emission System:

   Look for

ELECTRICAL	MECHANICAL
• Discharged Battery	• Fuel Odor or Leakage
• Damaged Connectors	• Damaged Vacuum or Fuel Vapor Lines
• Damaged Insulation	• Loose or Poor Line Connections
• Malfunctioning ECA	• Poor Driveability During Engine Warm-up
• Damaged Air Flow Meter	
• Inoperative Solenoids (No Clicking Sound)	

2. Exercise the wiring and connectors for the solenoids, vane air flow meter, speed sensor, and the ECA for looseness, corrosion, damage or other problems. This must be done with the engine fully warmed so as to activate the purging controls.

3. Check the fuel tanks, fuel vapor lines, vacuum lines, and connections for looseness, pinching, leakage, damage, or other obvious cause for malfunction.

4. If fuel line, vacuum line, or orifice blockage is suspected as the obvious cause of an observed malfunction, correct the cause before proceeding to the next step.

5. If all checks are OK, proceed to Pinpoint Tests.

FM1039100185000X

Fig. 1 Evaporative emission (EVAP) system inspection

TEST STEP		RESULT	▶	ACTION TO TAKE
EV1	CHECK CANISTER PURGE SOLENOID VALVE FUNCTION			
	• Disconnect the vacuum hoses A and B, and the electrical connector from the solenoid valve.	Yes	▶	GO to EV2.
	• Blow air through port A and verify that no air exits from port B.	No	▶	REPLACE the canister purge solenoid.
	• Apply 12 volts and ground as shown.			
	• Blow air through port A and verify that air flows from port B.			
	• **Does the valve function properly?**			

12V
GND
CANP SOLENOID
TO CARBON CANISTER PORT A
TO VACUUM SOURCE PORT B

FM1039300187010X

Fig. 2 Evaporative emission (EVAP) system diagnosis & testing (Part 1 of 5). 1993–95

TEST STEP		RESULT	▶	ACTION TO TAKE
EV2	CHECK FOR LIQUID FUEL IN CARBON CANISTER			
	• Run engine until warm to purge any fuel from the carbon canister.	Yes	▶	GO to EV3.
	• Turn off the engine and remove the carbon canister.	No	▶	REPLACE the carbon canister.
	• Inspect the carbon canister for liquid fuel (strong odor or excessive weight).			
	• Blow into the air vent (port C) and verify that air flows from the fuel vapor inlet (port B).			
	• Is the carbon canister free of liquid fuel, and does it function properly?			

FROM FUEL TANK
A
TO CANP SOLENOID
B
CARBON CANISTER
C
VENT TO ATMOSPHERE

TEST STEP		RESULT	▶	ACTION TO TAKE
EV3	CHECK PURGE LINES FOR BLOCKAGE			
	• Remove the purge lines leading from the canister to the engine air intake.	Yes	▶	GO to EV4
	• Check the lines for blockage by blowing through them.	No	▶	REPLACE the purge line(s), or any check valves or restrictors that may be partially plugged.
	• **Does air flow freely through the lines?**			

FM1039300187020X

Fig. 2 Evaporative emission (EVAP) system diagnosis & testing (Part 2 of 5). 1993–95

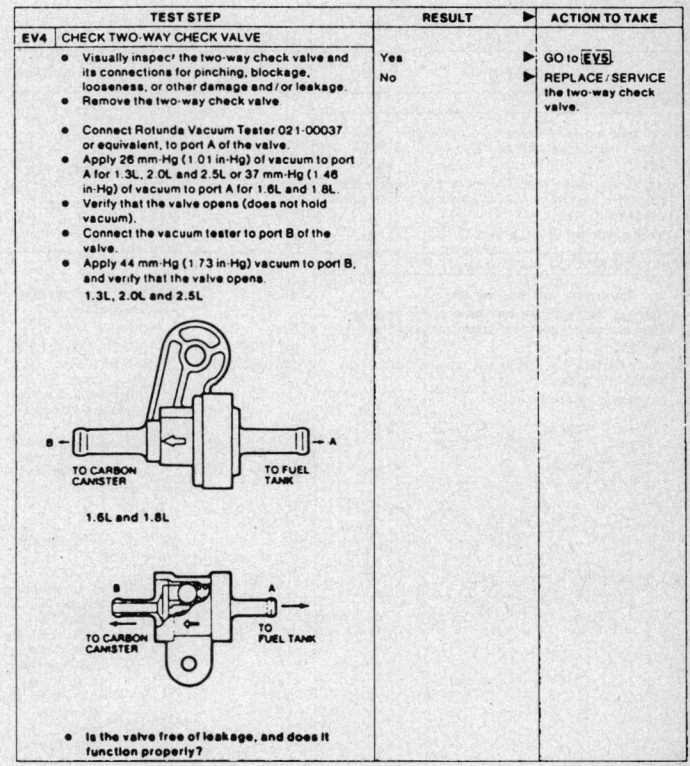

TEST STEP		RESULT	▶	ACTION TO TAKE
EV4	CHECK TWO-WAY CHECK VALVE			
	• Visually inspect the two-way check valve and its connections for pinching, blockage, looseness, or other damage and/or leakage.	Yes	▶	GO to EV5.
	• Remove the two-way check valve.	No	▶	REPLACE / SERVICE the two-way check valve.
	• Connect Rotunda Vacuum Tester 021-00037 or equivalent, to port A of the valve.			
	• Apply 26 mm-Hg (1.01 in-Hg) of vacuum to port A for 1.3L, 2.0L and 2.5L or 37 mm-Hg (1.46 in-Hg) of vacuum to port A for 1.6L and 1.8L.			
	• Verify that the valve opens (does not hold vacuum).			
	• Connect the vacuum tester to port B of the valve.			
	• Apply 44 mm-Hg (1.73 in-Hg) vacuum to port B, and verify that the valve opens.			

1.3L, 2.0L and 2.5L

B
TO CARBON CANISTER
A
TO FUEL TANK

1.6L and 1.8L

B
TO CARBON CANISTER
A
TO FUEL TANK

• Is the valve free of leakage, and does it function properly?

FM1039300187030X

Fig. 2 Evaporative emission (EVAP) system diagnosis & testing (Part 3 of 5). 1993–95

TEST STEP		RESULT	▶	ACTION TO TAKE
EV6	CHECK ROLLOVER/VENT VALVE(S) FUNCTION			
• Check the rollover/vent valves for evidence of leakage. • Remove the rollover/vent valves. Refer to Service Manual Section 10-01. • 1.8L, 2.0L and 2.5L procedure: — Hold the valves as shown in Figure A. — Blow into port A and verify that air flows through the rollover/vent valves. — Invert the valves as shown in Figure B. — Blow into port A and verify that air does not flow through the rollover/vent valves. • 1.3L and 1.6L procedure: — Connect Rotunda Vacuum/Pressure Tester 059-00008 or equivalent, to the rollover/vent valve as shown for Test 1. — Hold the valve horizontal. — Blow into Port A and verify the valve opens at 7.0 kPa (1.0 psi) maximum. — Connect the tester as shown for Test 2. — Blow into Port B and verify the valve opens at 4.9 kPa (0.7 psi) maximum. — Hold the valve upside down. — Blow into Port A and verify that pressure is held. • Does the valve(s) function properly?		Yes (1.3L and 1.8L) Yes (All Others) No	▶ ▶ ▶	GO to EV7. RETURN to the Diagnostic Routines REPLACE the rollover/vent valve(s).

1.8L, 2.0L and 2.5L 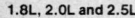 **1.3L and 1.6L**

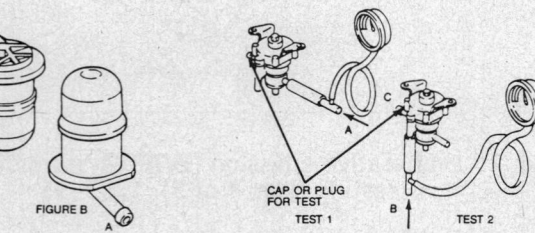

FIGURE A

FIGURE B

CAP OR PLUG FOR TEST

TEST 1   TEST 2

Fig. 2   Evaporative emission (EVAP) system diagnosis & testing (Part 4 of 5). 1993–95

TEST STEP		RESULT	▶	ACTION TO TAKE
EV7	CHECK VAPOR SEPARATOR INTEGRITY			
• Visually inspect the vapor separator and its connections with the fuel tank for hose pinching, blockage, looseness, or other mechanical damage. • Is the vapor separator and its connections free of damage?		Yes No	▶ ▶	RETURN to the Diagnostic Routines REPLACE the vapor separator or REPAIR the connecting hoses as required.

Fig. 2   Evaporative emission (EVAP) system diagnosis & testing (Part 5 of 5). 1993–95

System Inspection

1. Visually inspect the components of the PCV system.

VISUAL INSPECTION CHART

Mechanical	Electrical
• Rough idle • Slow starting • High oil consumption • Loose, leaking, clogged, or damaged hoses	• None

2. Check the fresh air supply hose and the PCV hose for air leakage or flow restriction due to loose engagement, hose splitting, cracking, or kinking, nipple damage, rubber grommet fit and elasticity or any other damage.

3. If a component is suspected as the obvious cause of a malfunction, correct the cause before proceeding to the next step.

4. If all checks are OK, proceed to the Pinpoint Tests.

FM1039100188000X

Fig. 3   Positive Crankcase Ventilation (PCV) system inspection

TEST STEP		RESULT	▶	ACTION TO TAKE
PCV1	PCV VALVE SHAKE TEST			
• Remove the PCV Valve from the engine valve cover and disconnect the valve from the PCV hose. • Vigorously shake the PCV Valve and confirm that the valve plunger is free to move and rattle within the valve body. • Is the plunger free to move?		Yes No	▶ ▶	GO to PCV2. REPLACE the PCV Valve.
PCV2	PCV SYSTEM FUNCTION			
• Idle the engine until warmed up. • Remove the fresh air inlet hose at the air inlet end, and plug the nipple immediately to prevent stalling. • Verify by feel that vacuum is present at the inlet end of the hose. • Is vacuum present?		Yes No (No Vacuum) No (Oil or sludge present)	▶ ▶ ▶	Return to Diagnostic Routines. CHECK both fresh air and PCV hoses for leaks, loose connections, blockage, or loose oil dipstick. CORRECT as required until vacuum can be felt at the inlet end of the fresh air supply hose. Return to Diagnostic Routines. NOTE: If air pressure, oil, or oily sludge is present at the intake end of the fresh air supply hose, the engine has excessive blowby, caused by cylinder bore, piston ring, or valve stem wear.

A13998-A

FM1039100189000X

Fig. 4   Positive Crankcase Ventilation (PCV) system diagnosis & testing

SYSTEM INSPECTION

1. Visually inspect the components of the Inlet Air System.

Look for:

ELECTRICAL	MECHANICAL
• Discharged Battery • Damaged, Loose Connections • Damaged Insulation • Malfunctioning ECA • Damaged Air Flow Meter	• Loose, Kinked, Pinched or Damaged Air or Vacuum Lines • Loose, Damaged Vacuum Line Connections • Poor Driveability Symptoms (Ref. Diagnostic Routines)

CA13983-B

2. Exercise the wiring and connection for the VAF Meter, Speed Sensor, TP Sensor, VAT Sensor, ECT Sensor, ISC Valve and the ECA for obvious problems due to looseness, corrosion, damage, or other causes of malfunction. This must be done with the engine operating.

3. Check the air hoses, vacuum lines and connections for looseness, pinching, kinking, or other obvious damage or cause of malfunction.

4. If any component is suspected as the obvious cause of malfunction, correct the cause before proceeding to the next step.

5. If all checks are OK, proceed to Pinpoint Tests.

FM1039100190000X

Fig. 5   Inlet air control (IAC) system inspection

TEST STEP		RESULT	▶	ACTION TO TAKE
IA1	CHECK AIR CLEANER HOUSING AND ELEMENT CONDITION			
	• Inspect the air cleaner housing, inlet air hoses and connecting components for damage, blockage, looseness, or missing fasteners. • Inspect air cleaner element for dirt. • **Are the air cleaner housing and element free of damage and dirt blockage?** CAUTION: Do not use compressed air to clean the air cleaner element.	Yes (1.3L, 1.6L and 1.8L)	▶	GO to IA2.
		Yes (2.0L)	▶	GO to IA3.
		Yes (2.5L)	▶	GO to IA4.
		No	▶	REPLACE the component in question.
IA2	CHECK VOLUME AIR FLOW (VAF) METER FUNCTION (1.3L, 1.6L AND 1.8L ONLY)			
	• Visually check the Volume Air Flow (VAF) meter for cracks, loose mounting and damage to the electrical connector or the sealed plastic cover. • Remove the VAF meter and inspect the bottom plate for cracks or loose fasteners. • Verify that the measuring vane moves smoothly and the springs shut when pushed forward and then released. • **Is the VAF meter free of cracks, damage, restrictions, and measuring vane binding?** NOTE: Electronic component troubleshooting is covered in the Pinpoint Tests.	Yes	▶	GO to IA5.
		No	▶	REPLACE the Volume Air Flow (VAF) meter.

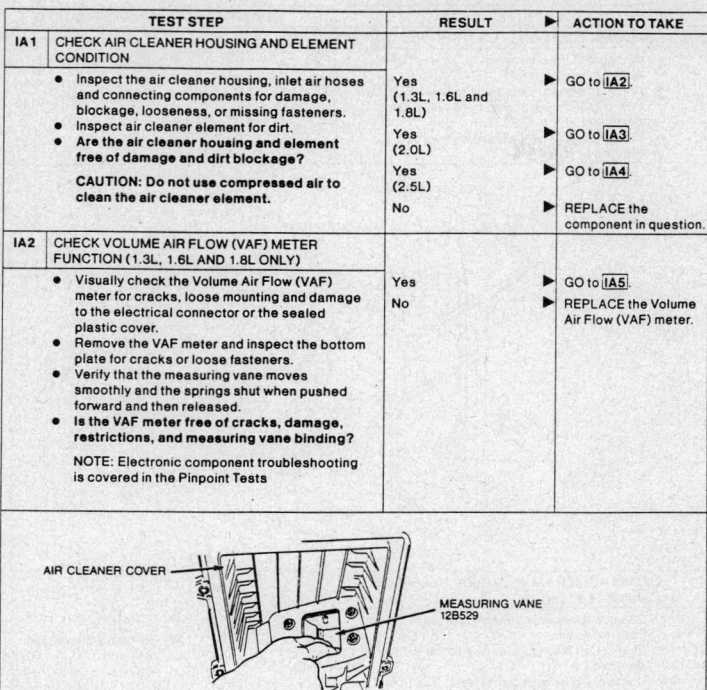

Fig. 6 Inlet air control (IAC) system diagnosis & testing (Part 1 of 10). 1993–95

TEST STEP		RESULT	▶	ACTION TO TAKE
IA3	CHECK MASS AIR FLOW (MAF) SENSOR (2.0L ONLY)			
	• Visually check the Mass Air Flow (MAF) sensor for cracks, loose mounting, damaged electrical connector, broken or contaminated heated resistor, and torn or restricted protective screen.	Yes	▶	GO to IA5.
		No	▶	REPLACE the Mass Air Flow (MAF) sensor.

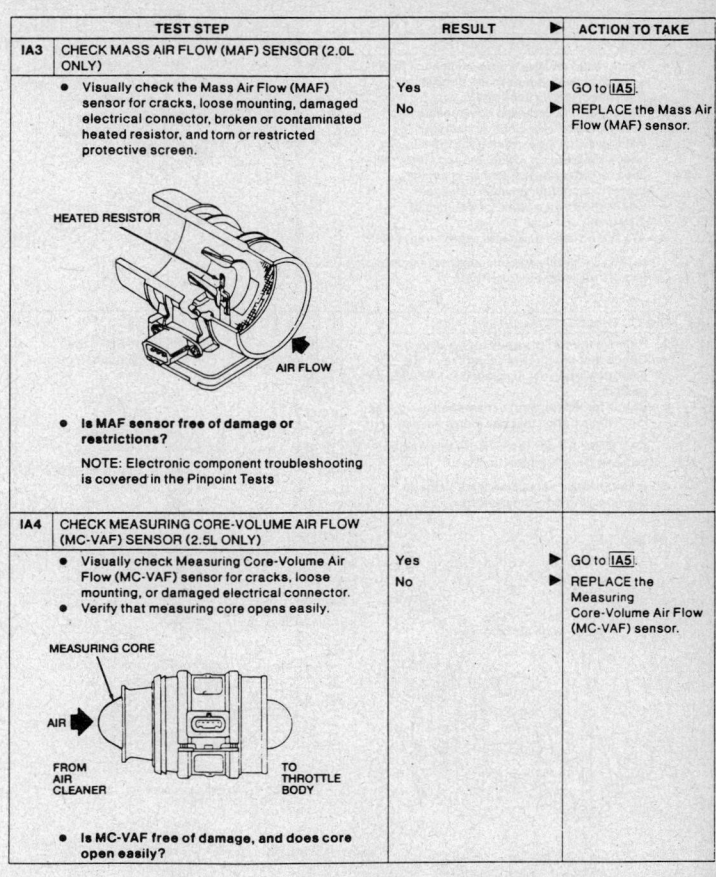

	• **Is MAF sensor free of damage or restrictions?** NOTE: Electronic component troubleshooting is covered in the Pinpoint Tests			
IA4	CHECK MEASURING CORE-VOLUME AIR FLOW (MC-VAF) SENSOR (2.5L ONLY)			
	• Visually check Measuring Core-Volume Air Flow (MC-VAF) sensor for cracks, loose mounting, or damaged electrical connector. • Verify that measuring core opens easily.	Yes	▶	GO to IA5.
		No	▶	REPLACE the Measuring Core-Volume Air Flow (MC-VAF) sensor.

	• **Is MC-VAF free of damage, and does core open easily?**			

Fig. 6 Inlet air control (IAC) system diagnosis & testing (Part 2 of 10). 1993–95

TEST STEP		RESULT	▶	ACTION TO TAKE
IA5	CHECK RESONANCE CHAMBER(S) CONDITION			
	• Visually check resonance chamber(s) for a pinched hose connection, or for cracks that allow unfiltered air and moisture to enter the system. • Check resonance chamber(s) for other damage. • **Is the resonance chamber(s) free of damage or poor connections?**	Yes (1.6L Turbo)	▶	GO to IA6.
		Yes (All others)	▶	GO to IA7.
		No	▶	SERVICE or REPLACE the resonance chamber(s).
IA6	CHECK CHARGE AIR COOLER CONDITION AND LEAKAGE (1.6L TURBO ONLY)			
	• Visually inspect the charge air cooler for cracks, corrosion, restrictions, or other damage. • Disconnect the charge air cooler inlet and outlet hoses, plug the inlet hose, and seal securely. • Connect Rotunda Radiator Pressure/Heater Core Tester 021-00012 and Rotunda Cooling System Adapter 021-00053 or equivalents to the charge air cooler outlet. • Apply 82.7-103.4 kPa (12 to 15 psi) of pressure. • **Does the charge air cooler maintain pressure?**	Yes	▶	GO to IA7.
		No	▶	LOCATE and REPAIR the leak or REPLACE the charge air cooler.

TEST STEP		RESULT	▶	ACTION TO TAKE
IA7	CHECK THROTTLE LINKAGE			
	• Check the throttle linkage for damage, proper installation, and freedom of movement when accelerator pedal is depressed. • **Is the linkage correctly installed, and does it operate properly?**	Yes	▶	GO to IA8.
		No	▶	SERVICE, CLEAN or REPLACE the linkage or part in question. ADJUST cable deflection.

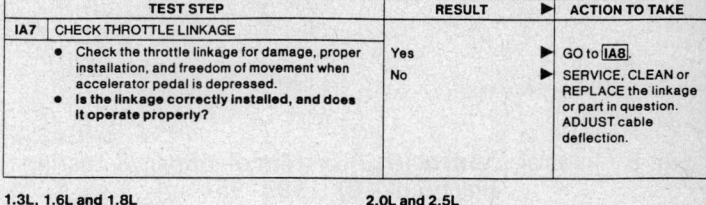

1.3L, 1.6L and 1.8L

2.0L and 2.5L

A. CABLE DEFLECTION ADJUSTMENT.
B. WIDE OPEN THROTTLE ADJUSTMENT.
C. CABLE DEFLECTION.

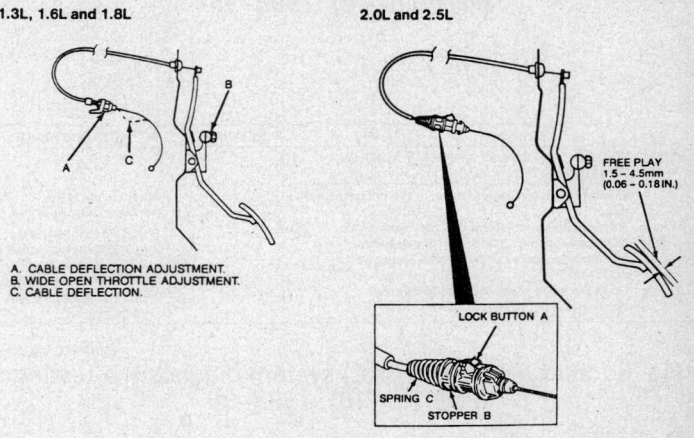

FM1039300192040X

Fig. 6 Inlet air control (IAC) system diagnosis & testing (Part 4 of 10). 1993–95

FM1039300192030X

Fig. 6 Inlet air control (IAC) system diagnosis & testing (Part 3 of 10). 1993–95

TEST STEP	RESULT	▶	ACTION TO TAKE
IA8 CHECK THROTTLE BODY CONDITION • Remove the air intake hose and check for oil smudging or oil vapors in the throttle body. • Reconnect the air intake hose. • Check throttle body and components for cracks, looseness, or other damage. • Without removing throttle body from engine, check the integrity of vacuum and electrical lines for looseness, pinching, misrouting, corrosion, or other obvious damage. • Check the throttle lever for freedom of movement. • **Are the throttle body and attachments OK?** NOTE: Electronic component troubleshooting is covered in the Pinpoint Tests.	Yes No	▶ ▶	GO to **IA9**. SERVICE or REPLACE the throttle body and/or related components as required.
IA9 CHECK THROTTLE VALVE(S) • Remove the throttle body from the engine. • Check that the throttle valve(s) move(s) smoothly from the fully closed to the fully open position. • Check for loose, bent, or damaged valves, and for contamination that can cause binding. **CAUTION: Do not remove the thin sealant coating from the throttle bore.** • **Is the throttle valve free from damage, binding, and contamination?**	Yes (1.3L, 1.6L and 2.0L) Yes (1.8L) Yes (2.5L) No	▶ ▶ ▶ ▶	RETURN to the Diagnostic Routines. GO to **IA10**. GO to **IA13**. SERVICE or REPLACE the throttle body.

1.3L, 1.6L and 1.8L

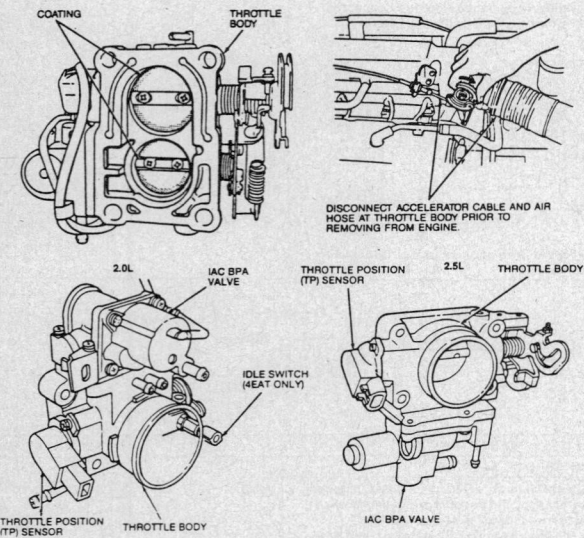

FM1039300192050X

Fig. 6   Inlet air control (IAC) system diagnosis & testing (Part 5 of 10). 1993–95

TEST STEP	RESULT	▶	ACTION TO TAKE
IA12 CHECK HIGH SPEED INLET AIR (HSIA) CONTROL SOLENOID FUNCTION (1.8L ONLY) • Connect a tachometer to measure the engine speed. • Run the engine until it is thoroughly warmed up. • Noting the position of the shutter valve lever and actuator, increase the engine speed to 5000 rpm. • **Does the shutter valve begin to open at approximately 5000 rpm?**	Yes No	▶ ▶	RETURN to the Diagnostic Routines. GO to Pinpoint Test **SCG** which covers the high speed inlet air control solenoid for further diagnosis and testing.

FM1039300192070X

Fig. 6   Inlet air control (IAC) system diagnosis & testing (Part 7 of 10). 1993–95

TEST STEP	RESULT	▶	ACTION TO TAKE
IA10 CHECK SHUTTER VALVE FUNCTION (1.8L ONLY) • Disconnect the shutter valve actuator linkage from the shutter valve. • Check that the shutter valve moves smoothly from a fully closed position to a fully open position. • **Is the shutter valve assembly free of binding or damage?**	Yes No	▶ ▶	GO to **IA11**. REPLACE the shutter valve assembly.

VACUUM RESERVOIR
SHUTTER VALVE ACTUATOR
SHUTTER VALVE
INTAKE MANIFOLD
HIGH SPEED INLET AIR CONTROL SOLENOID

TEST STEP	RESULT	▶	ACTION TO TAKE
IA11 CHECK SHUTTER VALVE VACUUM RESERVOIR LEAKAGE (1.8L ONLY) • Remove the shutter valve vacuum reservoir from the engine. • Plug or cap the nipple leading to the intake manifold. • Connect Rotunda Vacuum Tester 021-00037 or equivalent to the nipple leading to the High Speed Inlet Air (HSIA) control solenoid. Apply 508 mm-Hg (20 in-Hg) of vacuum to the reservoir. • Verify whether the reservoir and its check valve hold vacuum. • **Does the vacuum reservoir and the check valve hold vacuum?**	Yes No	▶ ▶	GO to **IA12**. REPLACE the vacuum reservoir.

FM1039300192060X

Fig. 6   Inlet air control (IAC) system diagnosis & testing (Part 6 of 10). 1993–95

TEST STEP	RESULT	▶	ACTION TO TAKE
IA13 CHECK VRIS SHUTTER VALVES (2.5L ONLY) • Disconnect the shutter valve actuator linkages from the shutter valves. • Check that the shutter valves move smoothly from the fully closed to the fully open position. • **Are the shutter valves free of binding or damage?**	Yes No	▶ ▶	GO to **IA14**. SERVICE or REPLACE the shutter valve assemblies.

INTAKE MANIFOLD
LINKAGE
FRONT
SHUTTER VALVE ACTUATORS
LINKAGE

TEST STEP	RESULT	▶	ACTION TO TAKE
IA14 CHECK VRIS SHUTTER VALVE ACTUATORS (2.5L ONLY) • Disconnect the vacuum hoses from the shutter valve actuators. • Connect a vacuum pump to the actuators. • Apply vacuum and verify that the actuator linkages are drawn into the actuators. • **Do the shutter valve actuators function properly?**	Yes No	▶ ▶	GO to **IA15**. REPLACE the shutter valve actuator in question.

VACUUM PUMP
V6
SHUTTER VALVE ACTUATOR

FM1039300192080X

Fig. 6   Inlet air control (IAC) system diagnosis & testing (Part 8 of 10). 1993–95

TEST STEP		RESULT	▶	ACTION TO TAKE
IA15	**CHECK VRIS SOLENOID VALVES (2.5L ONLY)**			
• Disconnect the solenoid valve vacuum and electrical lines. • Verify air flow between ports as shown.		Yes No	▶ ▶	GO to **IA16**. REPLACE the VRIS sol=noid valve in question.

Port	Air flow
A - B	No
A - C	No
B - C	Yes

• Apply battery voltage and ground to the terminals of the VRIS solenoid as shown below.
• Verify air flow between ports as shown.

Port	Air flow
A - B	Yes
A - C	No
B - C	No

• **Do solenoid valves function properly?**

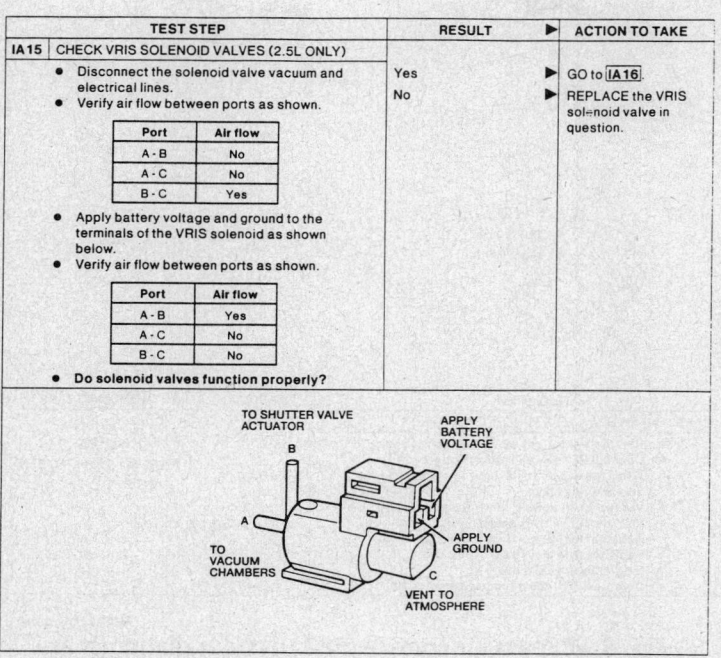

FM1039300192090X

Fig. 6 Inlet air control (IAC) system diagnosis & testing (Part 9 of 10). 1993–95

TEST STEP		RESULT	▶	ACTION TO TAKE
IA16	**CHECK ONE-WAY CHECK VALVE FUNCTION (2.5L ONLY)**			
• Disconnect and remove the check valve located under the intake manifold. • Blow through port A and verify that air flows from port B. • Blow through port B and verify that air does not flow from port A.		Yes No	▶ ▶	GO to **IA17**. REPLACE the one-way check valve.

WHITE   GREEN

A   B

• **Does one-way check valve function properly?**

TEST STEP		RESULT	▶	ACTION TO TAKE
IA17	**CHECK VACUUM CHAMBERS (2.5L ONLY)**			
• Access the vacuum chambers located under the intake manifold. • Visually check the vacuum chambers for cracks, blockage, or other damage.		Yes No	▶ ▶	RETURN to the Diagnostic Routines. REPLACE the vacuum chamber(s).

TO SOLENOID VALVE

• **Are vacuum chambers OK?**

FM1039300192100X

Fig. 6 Inlet air control (IAC) system diagnosis & testing (Part 10 of 10). 1993–95

Bypass Air (BPA) Control System (Idle Speed Adjustment)

System Inspection

1. Visually inspect the BPA valve assembly and associated components.

VISUAL INSPECTION CHART

Mechanical	Electrical
• Loose, leaking, pinching, kinked, or otherwise damaged coolant or air hoses and connections • Loose fasteners, hose clamps • White smoke from tail pipe	• Damaged or loose connections

2. If visual checks are OK, proceed to the Pinpoint Tests.

FM1039300194000X

Fig. 7 Bypass air control (BPA) system inspection. 1993–95

TEST STEP		RESULT	▶	ACTION TO TAKE
BPA1	**CHECK IDLE SPEED ADJUSTMENT**			

• Warm up the engine to normal operating temperature.
• Engine off.
• Place the selector lever in park (ATX) or neutral (MTX).
• Turn all accessories to off.
• Connect a Rotunda Digital Tachometer 055-00101 or equivalent.
• For 2.0L MTX:
  — Disconnect the idle air control solenoid connector.
  — Start engine and run at 2500 rpm for 30 seconds.
  — Note the idle speed.
  — Adjust the idle speed adjustment screw for the correct idle speed (see the General Specifications table in this section).
  — Shut engine off and rerun test.
  — Reconnect the idle air control solenoid connector.
• For all others:
  — Ground the PCM STI (TEN) pin at the Data Link Connector on 1.8L, 2.0L 4EAT and 2.5 L or at the Self-Test Input (STI) connector on 1.3L and 1.6L.
  — Start engine.
  — Note the idle speed.
  — Check the initial ignition timing using Rotunda Timing Analyzer 059-00014 or equivalent. Adjust if necessary.
  — Adjust the idle speed adjustment screw for the correct idle speed (see General Specifications table in this section).
• Turn the engine off, and allow to cool.
• After the engine has cooled, restart and note idle speed.
• **Does the engine speed up during warm-up when started cold?**
		Yes
		
		No
			▶
			
			▶
				RETURN to the Diagnostic Routines.
				GO to **BPA2**.

FM1039300196010X

Fig. 8 Bypass air control (BPA) system diagnosis & testing (Part 1 of 5). 1993

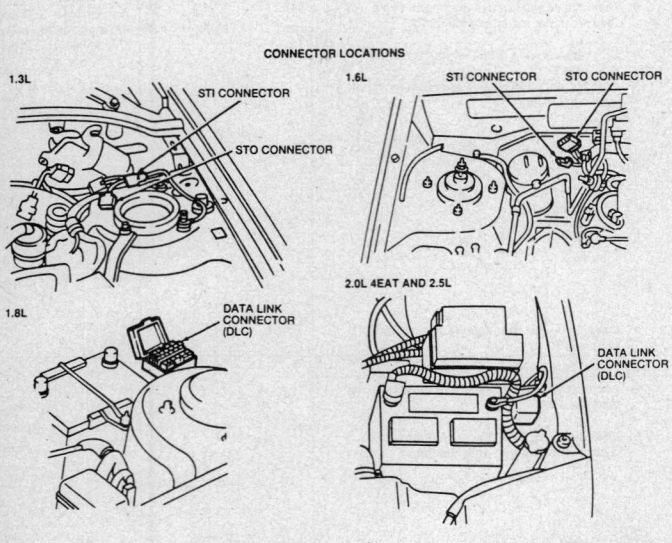

CONNECTOR LOCATIONS

Fig. 8 Bypass air control (BPA) system diagnosis & testing (Part 2 of 5). 1993

FM1039300196020X

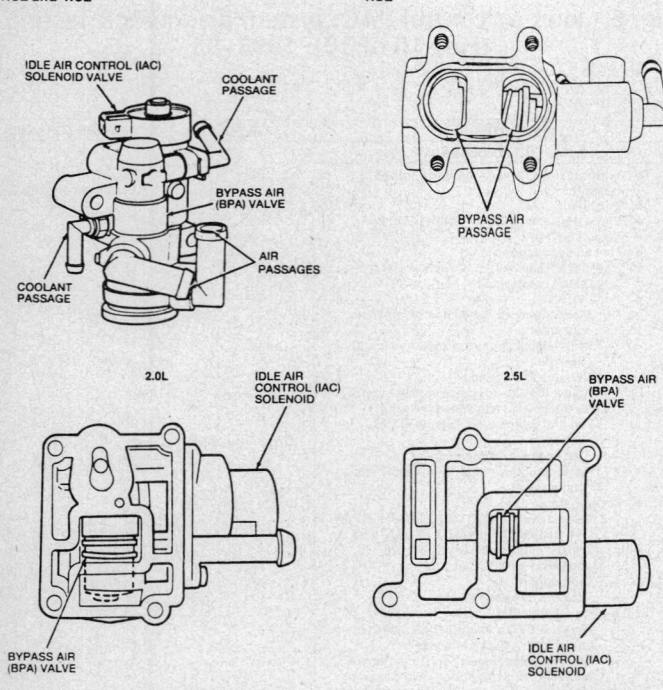

Fig. 8 Bypass air control (BPA) system diagnosis & testing (Part 4 of 5). 1993

FM1039300196040X

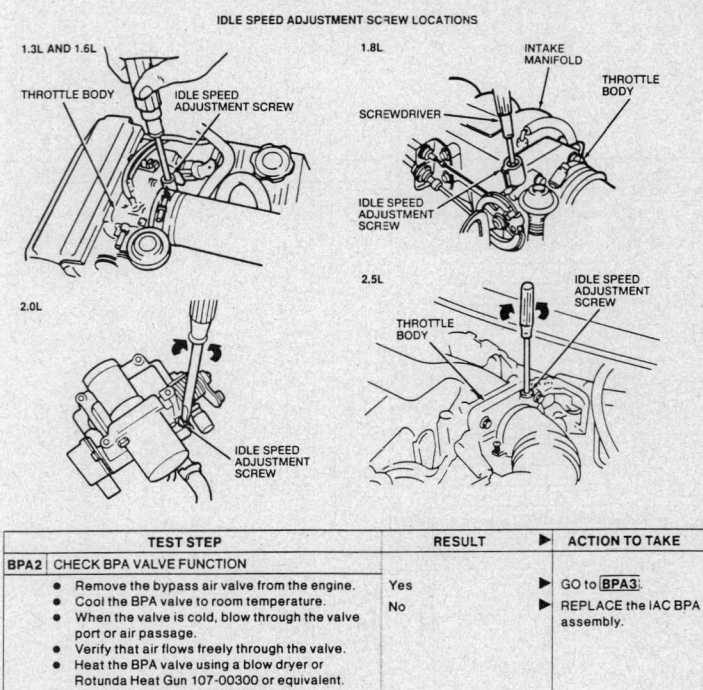

IDLE SPEED ADJUSTMENT SCREW LOCATIONS

TEST STEP		RESULT	▶	ACTION TO TAKE
BPA2	CHECK BPA VALVE FUNCTION			
	• Remove the bypass air valve from the engine. • Cool the BPA valve to room temperature. • When the valve is cold, blow through the valve port or air passage. • Verify that air flows freely through the valve. • Heat the BPA valve using a blow dryer or Rotunda Heat Gun 107-00300 or equivalent. • Verify that the air valve moves outward to restrict bypass air flow. • **Does the BPA valve function properly?**	Yes No	▶ ▶	GO to **BPA3**. REPLACE the IAC BPA assembly.

FM1039300196030X

Fig. 8 Bypass air control (BPA) system diagnosis & testing (Part 3 of 5). 1993

TEST STEP		RESULT	▶	ACTION TO TAKE
BPA3	CHECK IAC VALVE RESISTANCE			
	• Disconnect the IAC valve connector. • Connect Rotunda Digital Volt-Ohmmeter 105-00051 or equivalent to the terminals of the IAC valve and check the resistance. • **Is the resistance within the specified range (see General Specifications table in this section)?**	Yes No	▶ ▶	RETURN to the Diagnostic Routines. REPLACE the IAC BPA assembly or IAC valve.

FM1039300196050X

Fig. 8 Bypass air control (BPA) system diagnosis & testing (Part 5 of 5). 1993

TEST STEP		RESULT	▶	ACTION TO TAKE
BPA1	CHECK IAC VALVE RESISTANCE			
	• Disconnect the Idle Air Control (IAC) valve connector. • Connect Rotunda 73 Digital Multimeter 105-00051 or equivalent to the terminals of the IAC valve and check the resistance. • **Is the resistance within the specified range (see General Specifications table in this section)?**	Yes No	▶ ▶	GO to **BPA2**. REPLACE the IAC BPA assembly or IAC valve.
BPA2	CHECK BPA VALVE FUNCTION			
	• Remove the BPA valve from the engine. • Cool the BPA valve to room temperature. • When the valve is cold, blow through the valve port or air passage. Refer to illustrations after Test Steps. • Verify that air flows freely through the valve. • Heat the BPA valve using a blow dryer or Rotunda Heat Gun 107-R0300 or equivalent. • Verify that the air valve moves outward to restrict bypass air flow. • **Does the BPA valve function properly?**	Yes No	▶ ▶	RETURN to the Diagnostic Routines. REPLACE the IAC BPA assembly.

FM1039400197010X

Fig. 9 Bypass air control (BPA) system diagnosis & testing (Part 1 of 5). 1994–95

Data Link and STI Connector Locations

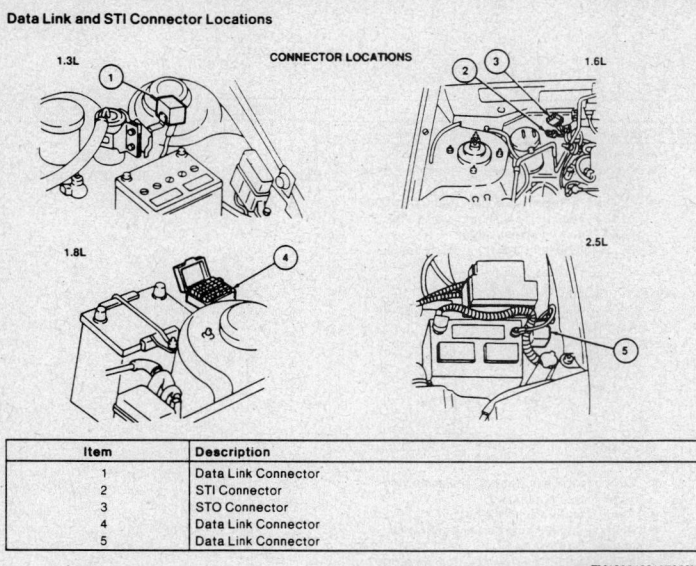

Item	Description
1	Data Link Connector
2	STI Connector
3	STO Connector
4	Data Link Connector
5	Data Link Connector

FM1039400197020X

Fig. 9 Bypass air control (BPA) system diagnosis & testing (Part 2 of 5). 1994–95

BPA Valve

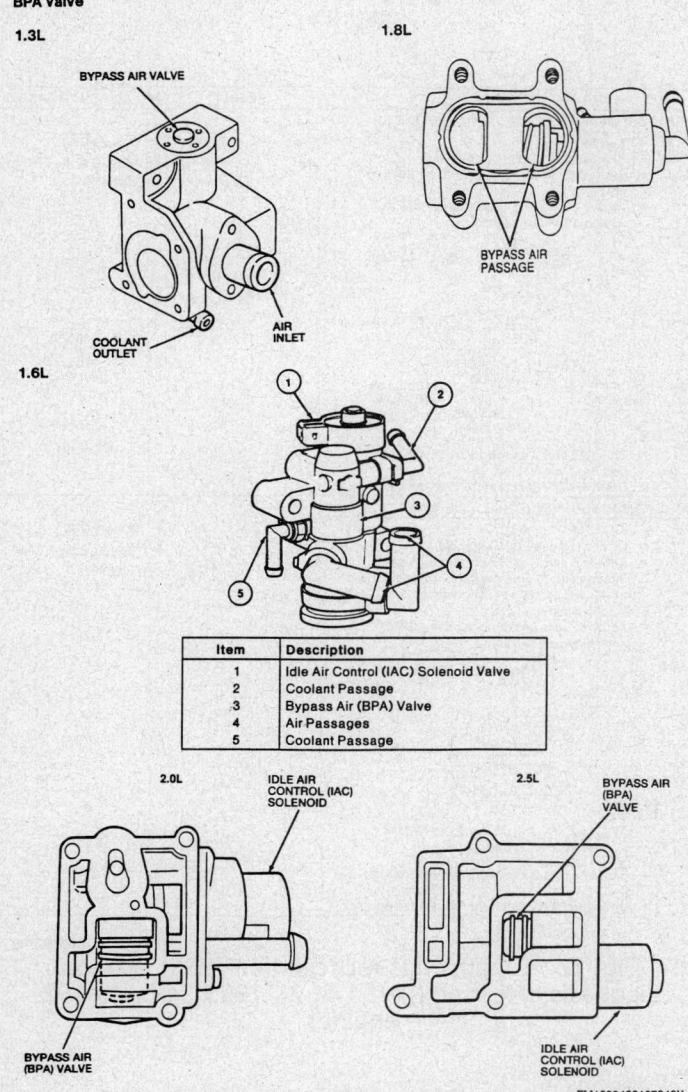

Item	Description
1	Idle Air Control (IAC) Solenoid Valve
2	Coolant Passage
3	Bypass Air (BPA) Valve
4	Air Passages
5	Coolant Passage

FM1039400197040X

Fig. 9 Bypass air control (BPA) system diagnosis & testing (Part 4 of 5). 1994–95

Idle Speed Adjustment Screw Locations

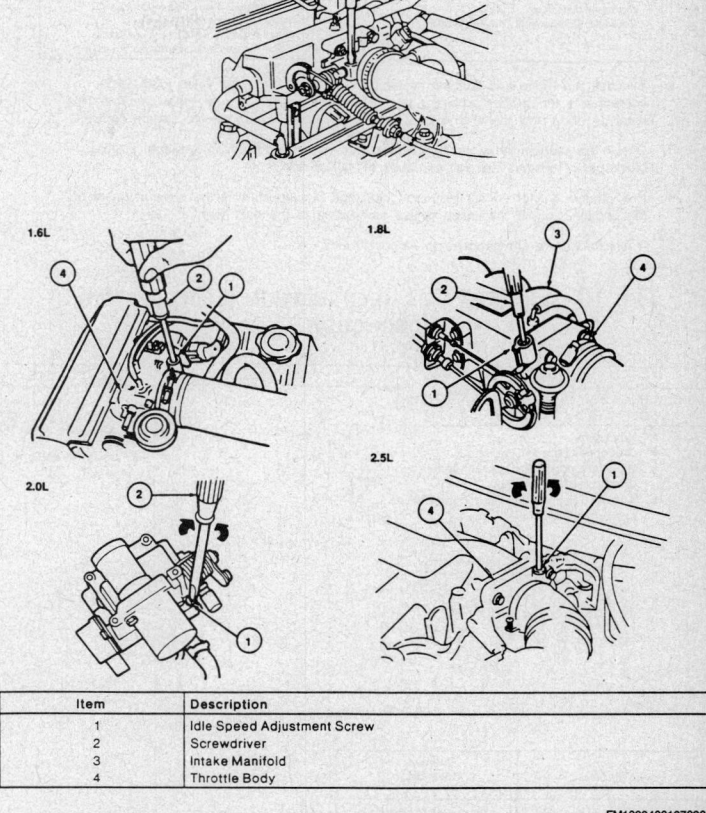

Item	Description
1	Idle Speed Adjustment Screw
2	Screwdriver
3	Intake Manifold
4	Throttle Body

FM1039400197030X

Fig. 9 Bypass air control (BPA) system diagnosis & testing (Part 3 of 5). 1994–95

Description	Specifications
PCM controlled idle speed:	
• Vehicle in PARK (ATX) or NEUTRAL (MTX)	
• All accessories off	
• Cooling fan off	
• Ignition timing OK	
• 1.3L MTX	• 650 - 750 rpm
• 1.3L ATX	• 700 - 800 rpm
• 1.6L	• 700 - 800 rpm
• 1.8L	• 700 - 800 rpm (with parking brake applied)
• 2.0L	• 650-750 rpm
• 2.5L	• 600 - 700 rpm
IAC valve resistance:	
• 1.3L	• 7.7 - 9.3 ohms
• 1.6L	• 6.0 - 14.0 ohms
• 1.8L	• 6.0 - 14.0 ohms
• 2.0L	• 7.7 - 9.3 ohms at 23°C (73°F)
• 2.5L	• 10.7 - 12.3 ohms at 20°C (68°F)

FM1039400197050X

Fig. 9 Bypass air control (BPA) system diagnosis & testing (Part 5 of 5). 1994–95

SYSTEM INSPECTION

1. Visually inspect the components of the EGR System.

Look for:

ELECTRICAL	MECHANICAL
• Damaged Connectors • Damaged Insulation • Damaged Components That Affect EGR	• Loose, Leaking, or Damaged Vacuum Lines • Poor Driveability During Engine Warm-up • EGR Valve Stuck Open • EGR Valve Attaching Bolts Loose or Missing • EGR Valve Flange Gasket Damaged or Leaking

2. Exercise the wiring and connectors for the solenoids and other listed EGR System components for obvious problems due to looseness, corrosion, or other damage. This must be done until the engine is fully warmed so as to activate the system controls.

3. Check the vacuum lines and connections for looseness, pinching, leakage, splitting, blockage, or obvious damage or cause of malfunction.

4. If a vacuum line or orifice (restrictor) blockage is suspected as the obvious cause of malfunction, correct the cause before proceeding to the next step.

5. If all checks are OK, proceed to Pinpoint Tests.

FM1039100198000X

Fig. 10 Exhaust Gas Recirculation (EGR) system inspection

TEST STEP	RESULT	▶ ACTION TO TAKE
EGR2 CHECK EGR VACUUM REGULATOR (EVR) SOLENOID • Key OFF. • Disconnect the EVR solenoid. • Blow into port B and verify that air flows through port C only. • Apply 12 volts and ground to the EVR as shown below. [diagram] 	Port	Vacuum Hose Color
A	Black with blue stripe
B	Black with orange stripe | • Blow into port A and verify that air flows through port B only. • **Does the EVR solenoid function correctly?**	Yes No	▶ GO to **EGR3**. ▶ REPLACE the EVR solenoid.

FM1039300201020X

Fig. 11 Exhaust gas recirculation (EGR) system diagnosis & testing (Part 2 of 3). 1993 2.0L/4-121 engines

TEST STEP	RESULT	▶ ACTION TO TAKE
EGR3 CHECK EGR VALVE • Run the engine until normal operating temperature is reached. • Key OFF. • Connect a Rotunda Vacuum Tester 021-00037 or equivalent to the EGR valve as shown below. [diagram] • Key ON, engine running. • Idle the engine. • Verify the engine runs rough when applied vacuum reaches the specified value of 150 mm-Hg (5.91 in-Hg), or the engine stalls at a higher vacuum. • **Does the EGR valve function correctly?** NOTE: For vehicles equipped with an EGR Temperature (EGRT) sensor (California Only), refer to the Pinpoint Test Procedures.	Yes No	▶ RETURN to Diagnostic Routines ▶ REPLACE the EGR valve.

FM1039300201030X

Fig. 11 Exhaust gas recirculation (EGR) system diagnosis & testing (Part 3 of 3). 1993 2.0L/4-121 engines

TEST STEP	RESULT	▶ ACTION TO TAKE
EGR1 CHECK EGR MODULATOR (EGRM) VALVE • Key OFF. • Disconnect the vacuum lines from the EGRM valve. • Connect a Rotunda Vacuum Tester 021-00037 or equivalent to the Number 1 port on the EGRM valve as shown below. • Block the Number 3 port as shown below. [diagram: PORT #3, PORT #1, PORT #2, BLOW AIR] • Blow into the exhaust port while applying vacuum with the tester. • Verify that the vacuum is held. • Release the exhaust port and verify that vacuum is released. • **Does the EGRM valve function correctly?**	Yes No	▶ GO to **EGR2**. ▶ REPLACE the EGRM valve.

FM1039300201010X

Fig. 11 Exhaust gas recirculation (EGR) system diagnosis & testing (Part 1 of 3). 1993 2.0L/4-121 engines

TEST STEP	RESULT	▶ ACTION TO TAKE
EGR1 CHECK EGR CONTROL (EGRC) SOLENOID • Key OFF. • Disconnect the EGRC solenoid. • Blow into port A and verify that air does not flow. • Apply 12 volts and ground to the EGRC solenoid as shown below. [diagram: VACUUM SUPPLY, EGR CONTROL SOLENOID, APPLY GROUND, APPLY 12V, TO AIR CLEANER, EGR VENT SOLENOID, VACUUM TO EGR VALVE] • Blow into port A and verify air flows through port B. • **Does the EGRC solenoid function properly?**	Yes No	▶ GO to **EGR2**. ▶ REPLACE the EGRC solenoid.
EGR2 CHECK EGR VENT (EGRV) SOLENOID • Key OFF. • Disconnect the EGRV solenoid. • Blow into port C and verify that air flows through port A. (Interconnecting hose between port B and port D is not shown in art for solenoid clarification.) • Apply 12 volts and ground to the EGRV solenoid as shown below. [diagram: VACUUM SUPPLY, EGR CONTROL SOLENOID, APPLY 12V, TO AIR CLEANER, APPLY GROUND, EGR VENT SOLENOID, VACUUM TO EGR VALVE] • Blow into port C and verify that air does not flow. • **Does the EGRV solenoid function properly?**	Yes No	▶ GO to **EGR3**. ▶ REPLACE the EGRV solenoid.

FM1039300202010X

Fig. 12 Exhaust gas recirculation (EGR) system diagnosis & testing (Part 1 of 2). 1993 2.5L/V6-152 engines

TEST STEP	RESULT	▶ ACTION TO TAKE
EGR3 CHECK EGR VALVE		
• Run the engine until normal operating temperature is reached. • Key OFF. • Connect a Rotunda Vacuum Tester 021-00037 or equivalent to the EGR valve as shown below.	Yes No	▶ RETURN to the Diagnostic Routines, Section 2B. ▶ REPLACE the EGR valve.

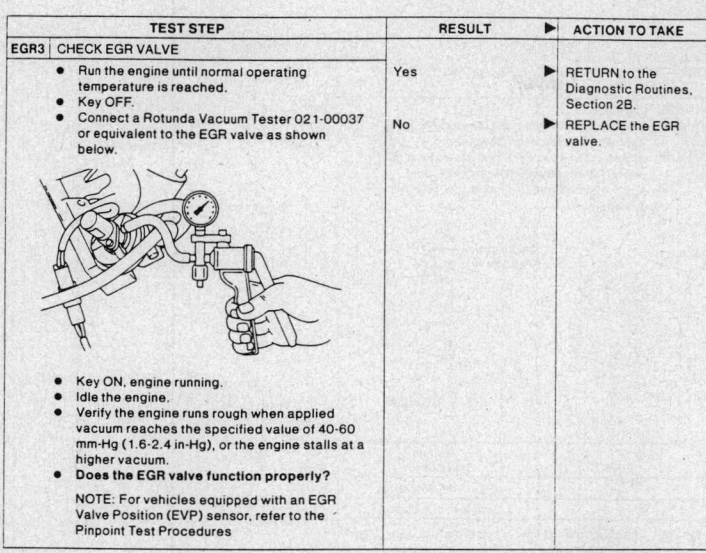

• Key ON, engine running. • Idle the engine. • Verify the engine runs rough when applied vacuum reaches the specified value of 40-60 mm-Hg (1.6-2.4 in-Hg), or the engine stalls at a higher vacuum. • **Does the EGR valve function properly?** NOTE: For vehicles equipped with an EGR Valve Position (EVP) sensor, refer to the Pinpoint Test Procedures		

FM1039300202020X

Fig. 12 Exhaust gas recirculation (EGR) system diagnosis & testing (Part 2 of 2). 1993 2.5L/V6-152 engines

TEST STEP	RESULT	▶ ACTION TO TAKE
EGR2 CHECK EGR VENT SOLENOID		
• Key OFF. • Disconnect the Exhaust Gas Recirculation Vent (EGRV) solenoid. • Disconnect the vacuum hoses. • Block port D. • Blow into port C and verify that air flows through port E (interconnecting hose between port B and port D is not shown in art for solenoid clarification). • Apply 12 volts and ground to the EGRV solenoid as shown below.	Yes No	▶ GO to **EGR3**. ▶ REPLACE the EGRV solenoid.

2.0L, 2.5L

1.3L

• Blow into port C and verify that air does not flow through port E. • **Does the EGRV solenoid function properly?**		

FM1039400203020X

Fig. 13 Exhaust gas recirculation (EGR) system diagnosis & testing (Part 2 of 3). 1994–95 1.3L/4-81, 2.0L/4-121 MTX California, 2.0L/4-121 CD4E & 2.5L/V6-152 engines

TEST STEP	RESULT	▶ ACTION TO TAKE
EGR1 CHECK EGR CONTROL SOLENOID		
• Key OFF. • Disconnect the Exhaust Gas Recirculation Control (EGRC) solenoid. • Disconnect the vacuum hoses. • Attach a hose to port A and blow into it to verify that air does not flow through port B. • Apply 12 volts and ground to the EGRC solenoid as shown below.	Yes No	▶ GO to **EGR2**. ▶ REPLACE the EGRC solenoid.

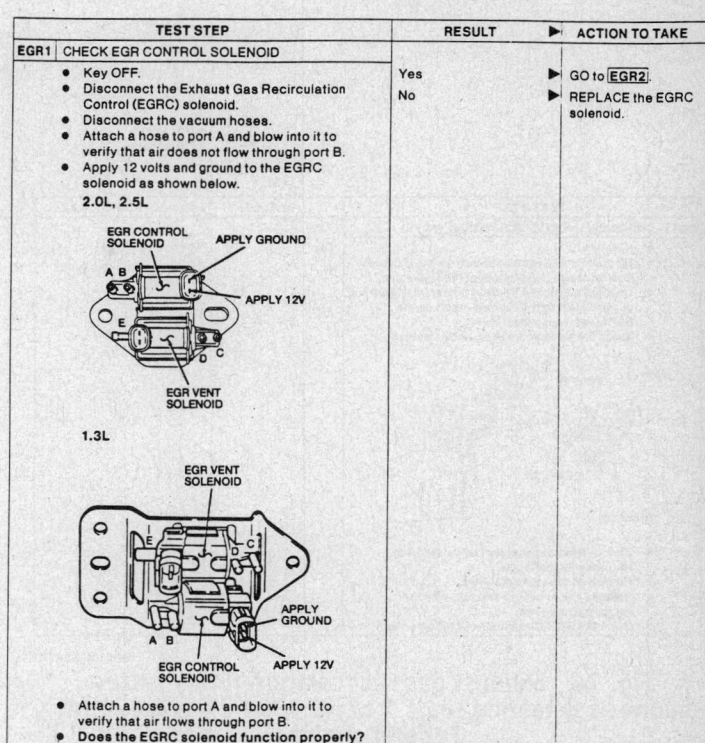

2.0L, 2.5L

1.3L

• Attach a hose to port A and blow into it to verify that air flows through port B. • **Does the EGRC solenoid function properly?**		

FM1039400203010X

Fig. 13 Exhaust gas recirculation (EGR) system diagnosis & testing (Part 1 of 3). 1994–95 1.3L/4-81, 2.0L/4-121 MTX California, 2.0L/4-121 CD4E & 2.5L/V6-152 engines

TEST STEP	RESULT	▶ ACTION TO TAKE
EGR3 CHECK EGR VALVE		
• Run the engine until normal operating temperature is reached. • Key OFF. • Connect a Rotunda Vacuum Tester 021-00037 or equivalent to the Exhaust Gas Recirculation (EGR) valve vacuum source port as shown below.	Yes No	▶ RETURN to the Diagnostic Routines ▶ REPLACE the EGR valve.

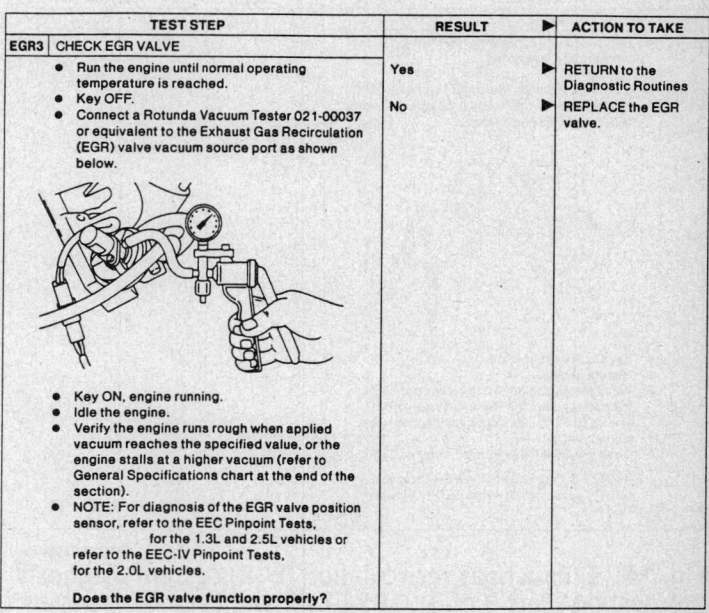

• Key ON, engine running. • Idle the engine. • Verify the engine runs rough when applied vacuum reaches the specified value, or the engine stalls at a higher vacuum (refer to General Specifications chart at the end of the section). • NOTE: For diagnosis of the EGR valve position sensor, refer to the EEC Pinpoint Tests, for the 1.3L and 2.5L vehicles or refer to the EEC-IV Pinpoint Tests, for the 2.0L vehicles. • **Does the EGR valve function properly?**		

FM1039400203030X

Fig. 13 Exhaust gas recirculation (EGR) system diagnosis & testing (Part 3 of 3). 1994–95 1.3L/4-81, 2.0L/4-121 MTX California, 2.0L/4-121 CD4E & 2.5L/V6-152 engines

TEST STEP		RESULT	▶	ACTION TO TAKE
EGR1	CHECK EGR MODULATOR (EGRM) VALVE	Yes	▶	GO to EGR2.
	• Key OFF. • Disconnect the vacuum lines from the Exhaust Gas Recirculation Modulator (EGRM) valve. • Connect a Rotunda Vacuum Tester 021-00037 or equivalent to the Number 1 port on the EGRM valve as shown below. • Block the Number 3 port as shown below.	No	▶	REPLACE the EGRM valve.

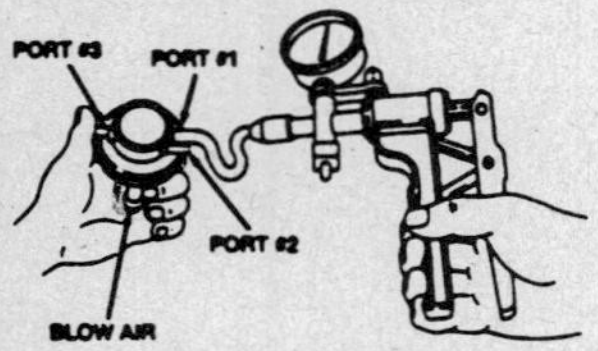

• Blow into the exhaust port while applying vacuum with the tester.
• Verify that the vacuum is held.
• Release the exhaust port and verify that vacuum is released.
• Does the EGRM valve function correctly?

FM1039400204010X

Fig. 14 Exhaust gas recirculation (EGR) system diagnosis & testing (Part 1 of 3). 1994 2.0L/4-121 MTX Federal engines

TEST STEP		RESULT	▶	ACTION TO TAKE
EGR2	CHECK EGR VACUUM REGULATOR (EVR) SOLENOID	Yes	▶	GO to EGR3.
	• Key OFF. • Disconnect the Exhaust Gas Recirculation Vacuum Regulator (EVR) solenoid. • Attach a hose to port B and blow into it to verify that air flows through port C only. • Apply 12 volts and ground to the EVR as shown below.	No	▶	REPLACE the EVR solenoid.

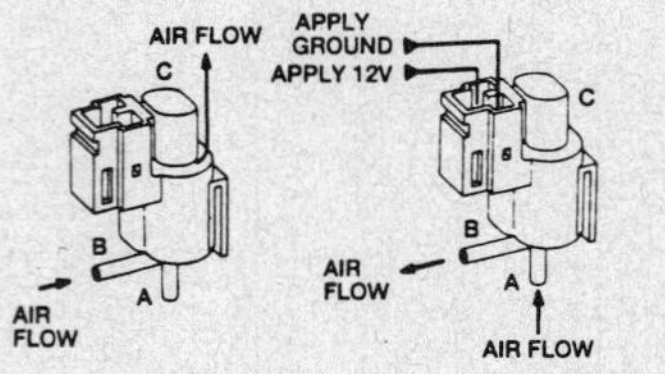

Port	Vacuum Hose Color
A	Black with blue stripe
B	Black with orange stripe

• Attach a hose to port A and blow into it to verify that air flows through port B only.
• Does the EVR solenoid function correctly?

FM1039400204020X

Fig. 14 Exhaust gas recirculation (EGR) system diagnosis & testing (Part 2 of 3). 1994 2.0L/4-121 MTX Federal engines

TEST STEP		RESULT	▶	ACTION TO TAKE
EGR3	CHECK EGR VALVE	Yes	▶	RETURN to Diagnostic Routines.
	• Run the engine until normal operating temperature is reached. • Key OFF. • Connect a Rotunda Vacuum Tester 021-00037 or equivalent to the Exhaust Gas Recirculation (EGR) valve as shown below.	No	▶	REPLACE the EGR valve.

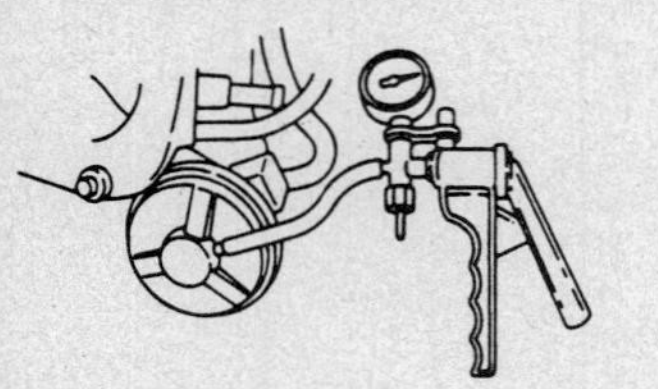

• Key ON, engine running.
• Idle the engine.
• Verify the engine runs rough when applied vacuum reaches the specified value of 150 mm-Hg (5.91 in-Hg), or the engine stalls at a higher vacuum.
• Does the EGR valve function correctly?

NOTE: For diagnosis of the EGR Temperature (EGRT) sensor, refer to the EEC-IV Pinpoint Tests

FM1039400204030X

Fig. 14 Exhaust gas recirculation (EGR) system diagnosis & testing (Part 3 of 3). 1994 2.0L/4-121 MTX Federal engines

CONDITION	POSSIBLE SOURCE	ACTION
• Rough Idle Cold	• EGR valve malfunction. • EGR flange gasket leaking. • EGR valve attaching nuts or bolts loose or missing. • Vacuum leak at EVP sensor. • EVR solenoid malfunction. • EGR valve contamination.	• REPLACE flange gasket and TIGHTEN valve attaching nuts or bolts to specification. • REPLACE flange gasket and TIGHTEN valve attaching nuts or bolts to specification. • REPLACE O-ring seal and TIGHTEN EVP sensor attaching nuts to specification. • CLEAN EGR valve.
• Rough Idle Hot	• EGR valve malfunction. • EGR flange gasket leaking. • EGR valve attaching nuts or bolts loose or missing. • Vacuum leak at EVP sensor. • EVR solenoid malfunction. • EGR valve contamination.	• REPLACE flange gasket and TIGHTEN valve attaching nuts or bolts to specification. • REPLACE flange gasket and TIGHTEN valve attaching nuts or bolts to specification. • REPLACE O-ring seal and TIGHTEN EVP sensor attaching nuts to specification. • CLEAN EGR valve.
• Rough Running, Surge, Hesitation, Poor Part Throttle Performance—Hot	• EGR valve malfunction / erratic operation. • EGR valve contamination. • EVR solenoid malfunction. • Pressure / Vacuum signal hose(s) leak (PFE DPFE).	• CLEAN EGR valve and if necessary, replace EGR valve. • REPLACE hose(s).
• Engine Stalls On Deceleration—Hot	• EGR valve malfunction. • EVR solenoid malfunction. • EGR valve contamination.	• CLEAN EGR valve and if necessary, replace EGR valve.
• Engine Spark Knock or Ping	• EGR valve malfunction. • EGR valve attaching nuts or bolts loose or missing. • Blocked or restricted passages in valve or spacer (EVP).	• REPLACE flange gasket and TIGHTEN valve attaching nuts or bolts to specification. • CLEAN passages in EGR spacer and EGR valve.

FM1039500211010X

Fig. 15 Exhaust gas recirculation (EGR) system diagnosis & testing (Part 1 of 3). 1995

CONDITION	POSSIBLE SOURCE	ACTION
• Engine Stalls At Idle—Cold	• EGR valve malfunction.	
	• EGR flange gasket leaking.	• REPLACE flange gasket and TIGHTEN valve attaching nuts or bolts to specification.
	• EGR valve attaching nuts or bolts loose or missing.	• REPLACE flange gasket and TIGHTEN valve attaching nuts or bolts to specification.
	• EVR solenoid malfunction. • EGR valve contamination.	• CLEAN EGR valve.
• Engine Stalls At Idle—Hot	• EGR valve malfunction.	
	• EGR flange gasket leaking.	• REPLACE flange gasket and TIGHTEN valve attaching nuts or bolts to specification.
	• EGR valve attaching nuts or bolts loose or missing.	• REPLACE flange gasket and TIGHTEN valve attaching nuts or bolts to specification.
	• EGR valve contamination.	• CLEAN EGR valve and if necessary, replace EGR valve.
	• Vacuum leak at EVP sensor.	• REPLACE O-ring seal and TIGHTEN EVP sensor attaching nuts to specification.
	• EVR solenoid malfunction.	
• Engine Starts But Will Not Run—Engine Hard To Start Or Will Not Start	• EGR valve malfunction.	
	• EGR flange gasket leaking.	• REPLACE flange gasket and TIGHTEN valve attaching nuts or bolts to specification.
	• EGR valve attaching nuts or bolts loose or missing.	• REPLACE flange gasket and TIGHTEN valve attaching nuts or bolts to specification.
	• EVR solenoid malfunction. • EGR valve contamination.	• CLEAN EGR valve.

FM1039500211020X

Fig. 15 Exhaust gas recirculation (EGR) system diagnosis & testing (Part 2 of 3). 1995

	TEST STEP	RESULT	► ACTION TO TAKE
EGR1	CHECK SYSTEM INTEGRITY		
	• Check vacuum hoses and connections for looseness, pinching, leakage, splitting, blockage and proper routing • Inspect EGR valve for loose attaching bolts or damaged flange gasket • Does system appear to be in good condition and vacuum hoses properly routed?	Yes No	► GO to EGR2. ► SERVICE EGR system as required RE-EVALUATE symptom.
EGR2	CHECK EGR VACUUM AT IDLE		
	• Run engine until normal operating temperature is reached. • With engine running at idle, disconnect EGR vacuum supply at the EGR valve and check for a vacuum signal. NOTE: The EVR solenoid has a constant internal leak. You may notice a small vacuum signal. This signal should be less than 3.4 kPa (1.0 in-Hg) at idle. • Is EGR vacuum signal less than 3.4 kPa (1.0 in-Hg) at idle?	Yes No	► GO to EGR3. ► RECONNECT EGR vacuum hose. INSPECT EVR solenoid for leakage
EGR3	CHECK EGR VALVE FUNCTION		
	• Install a tachometer, Rotunda 059-00010 or equivalent. • Disconnect the Idle Air Control (IAC) solenoid electrical connector. • Remove and plug the vacuum supply hose from the EGR valve nipple. • Start engine, idle with transmission in NEUTRAL, and observe idle speed. If necessary, adjust idle speed NOTE: If the engine will not idle with IAC solenoid disconnected, provide an air bypass to the engine by slightly opening the throttle plate or by creating an intake vacuum leak. Do not exceed a typical idle rpm. • Slowly apply 5-10 inches of vacuum to the EGR valve nipple using a hand vacuum pump, Rotunda 021-00014 or equivalent. • Does idle speed drop more than 100 rpm with vacuum applied and return to normal (± 25 rpm) after the vacuum is removed?	Yes No	► The EGR valve is OK. UNPLUG and RECONNECT the EGR valve vacuum supply hose. RECONNECT the IAC solenoid connector. ► INSPECT the EGR valve for blockage or contamination. CLEAN the valve using Rotunda 021-80056 EGR valve cleaner. INSPECT valve for vacuum leakage. REPLACE if necessary. If EGR valve is OK, inspect the EGR flow path in the intake manifold for blockage.

FM1039500211030X

Fig. 15 Exhaust gas recirculation (EGR) system diagnosis & testing (Part 3 of 3). 1995

	TEST STEP	RESULT	► ACTION TO TAKE
B1	INSPECT EXHAUST SYSTEM		
	• Visually inspect exhaust system. • Is exhaust system visually OK?	Yes No	► GO to B2. ► REPLACE any collapsed exhaust components. VERIFY elimination of symptom. If problem is not corrected, GO to B2.
B2	VACUUM TEST		
	• Attach vacuum gauge to intake manifold vacuum source. • Hook up tachometer. • Observe the vacuum gauge needle while performing the following: — Start engine and gradually increase the engine rpm to 2000 with the transmission in NEUTRAL. NOTE: The vacuum gauge reading may be normal when the engine is first started and idled. However, excessive restriction in the exhaust system will cause the vacuum gauge needle to drop to a low point even while the engine is idled. • Decrease engine speed to base idle rpm. • Did manifold vacuum reach above 16 inches of mercury with the engine rpm at 2000?	Yes No	► No restriction in the exhaust system. ► GO to B3.

FM1039500215010X

Fig. 16 Catalytic converter system diagnosis & testing (Part 1 of 3)

	TEST STEP	RESULT	► ACTION TO TAKE
B3	VACUUM TEST—RATE OF VACUUM GAUGE NEEDLE RETURN MOVEMENT		
	• Vacuum gauge attached to intake manifold vacuum source. • Tachometer installed. • Increase the engine speed gradually from base idle rpm to 2000 rpm with the transmission in NEUTRAL. • Observe the rate of speed of the vacuum gauge needle as it falls and rises while maintaining the increased engine rpm. NOTE: — On a non-restricted system, the vacuum gauge needle will drop to zero and then quickly return to the normal setting without delay. — On a restricted system, as the engine rpm is increased to 2000, the vacuum gauge needle will slowly drop to zero. As the increased rpm is maintained, the needle will slowly rise to normal. — The rate of speed at which the vacuum gauge needle returns to the normal setting is much slower on a restricted system than on a non-restricted system. • Decrease engine speed to base idle rpm. • Is rate of speed that the vacuum gauge needle returns to the normal setting much slower than that of a non-restricted system?	Yes No	► GO to B4. ► No restriction in the exhaust system.
B4	VACUUM TEST—EXHAUST DISCONNECTED		
	• Turn engine off. • Disconnect exhaust system at exhaust manifold(s). • Repeat vacuum test found in Step B2. • Is manifold vacuum above 16 inches of mercury?	Yes No	► GO to B5. ► GO to B6.
B5	VACUUM TEST—CATALYTIC CONVERTER(S) ON · MUFFLER(S) OFF		
	• Turn engine off. • Reconnect exhaust system at exhaust manifold(s). • Disconnect muffler(s). • Repeat vacuum test found in Step B2. • Is the manifold vacuum above 16 inches of mercury?	Yes No	► REPLACE muffler(s). ► REPLACE catalytic converter and inspect muffler to be sure converter debris has not entered muffler.

FM1039500215020X

Fig. 16 Catalytic converter system diagnosis & testing (Part 2 of 3)

TEST STEP	RESULT	►	ACTION TO TAKE
B6 EXHAUST MANIFOLD RESTRICTED			
• Remove the exhaust manifold(s). Inspect the ports for casting flash by dropping a length of chain into each port. NOTE: Do not use a wire or lamp to check ports. The restriction may be large enough for them to pass through but small enough to cause excessive back pressure at high engine rpm. • Is a restriction present?	Yes	►	REMOVE casting flash. If flash cannot be removed, REPLACE exhaust manifold(s).

FM1039500215030X

Fig. 16 Catalytic converter system diagnosis & testing (Part 3 of 3)

L CT O IC IN T U I TATION

NOTE: If Uncertain About The Proper Use Of Information Contained In This Section, Please Refer To "How To Use This Manual" Located In The Front Of This Tabbed Section.

NOTE: On Air Bag Equipped Models, Refer To "Air Bag System Precautions" Located In The Front Of This Manual For System Disarming & Arming Procedures.

NOTE: Refer to the Symptom Index in this section before performing any Pinpoint Tests.

TABLE OF CONTENTS

Page No.   **Page No.**

CONTINENTAL: **SABLE & TAURUS:**

1993............................. 15-1   1993............................. 15-19

1994............................. 15-9   1994............................. 15-24

CROWN VICTORIA, GRAND MARQUIS &   1995............................. 15-31

TOWN CAR:

1993............................. 15-40

1994............................. 15-47

1995............................. 15-56

1996............................. 15-65

1993 Continental

INDEX

	Page No. 15-	Fig. No.		Page No. 15-	Fig. No.
PINPOINT TESTS:			Pinpoint Test AR	6	17
Pinpoint Test AA	2	2	Pinpoint Test AS	6	18
Pinpoint Test AB	2	3	Pinpoint Test FA	6	19
Pinpoint Test AC	3	4	Pinpoint Test FB	6	20
Pinpoint Test AD	3	5	Pinpoint Test FC	6	21
Pinpoint Test AE	3	6	Pinpoint Test FE	6	22
Pinpoint Test AF	3	7	Pinpoint Test FF	7	23
Pinpoint Test AG	3	8	Pinpoint Test FH	7	24
Pinpoint Test AH	3	9	Pinpoint Test FJ	7	25
Pinpoint Test AJ	4	10	Pinpoint Test FL	7	26
Pinpoint Test AK	4	11	Pinpoint Test FM	8	27
Pinpoint Test AL	4	12	Pinpoint Test FN	8	28
Pinpoint Test AM	5	13	Pinpoint Test FP	8	29
Pinpoint Test AN	5	14	Pinpoint Test FQ	9	30
Pinpoint Test AP	5	15	**SYMPTOM INDEX**	2	1
Pinpoint Test AQ	6	16			

CLUSTER CONTROL ASSEMBLY MODULE DIAGNOSIS		
1	Display totally black	GO to Pinpoint Test AA
2	Display backlighted but blank	GO to Pinpoint Test AA
3	Display not illuminated	GO to Pinpoint Test AA
4	Display lit but too dim	GO to Pinpoint Test AA
5	Display scrambled, segments half lit (ghost segments), segments blink or missing, display incorrect all the time	GO to Pinpoint Test AB
6	Display stuck with all segments on	GO to Pinpoint Test AB
7	No beep when buttons pushed or driver alert given	GO to Pinpoint Test AC
8	Module does not respond to buttons	GO to Pinpoint Test AC
FUEL GAUGE DIAGNOSIS		
9	Fuel gauge will not switch between English and metric	GO to Pinpoint Test AC
10	CO displayed, bar fuel gauge cannot be called up	GO to Pinpoint Test AD
11	CS displayed, bar fuel gauge cannot be called up	GO to Pinpoint Test AE
12	Does not display F when fuel tank is full	GO to Pinpoint Test AE
13	Does not display E when fuel tank is empty	GO to Pinpoint Test AD
TEMPERATURE GAUGE DIAGNOSIS		
14	Multigauge displays top two and bottom two bars of multigauge	GO to Pinpoint Test AF
15	Temperature gauge always indicates cold temperature	GO to Pinpoint Test AG
OIL PRESSURE GAUGE DIAGNOSIS		
16	Multigauge displays top two and bottom two bars of multigauge	GO to Pinpoint Test AH
17	Oil pressure gauge always indicates low pressure and gives driver alert	GO to Pinpoint Test AJ
18	Oil pressure indication erratic	GO to Pinpoint Test AJ
19	Oil pressure warning never comes on	GO to Pinpoint Test AK
VOLTS GAUGE DIAGNOSIS		
20	Does not give no charge alert (blinking battery symbol)	GO to Pinpoint Test AL
21	Always gives charging system alert (battery symbol)	GO to Pinpoint Test AM
SPEEDOMETER DIAGNOSIS		
22	Speedometer reads constantly too high or too low	GO to Pinpoint Test AP
23	Speed indication jumps up and down erratically	GO to Pinpoint Test AQ
ODOMETER DIAGNOSIS		
24	Display reads "Error"	GO to Pinpoint Test AR
25	Display has "S" illuminated	GO to Pinpoint Test AS
26	Mileage constantly reads too high or too low	GO to Pinpoint Test AP
SPEED ALERT DIAGNOSIS		
27	Speed alert cannot be set, does not respond to speed button	GO to Pinpoint Test AC
28	No beeping when "speed" symbol flashing	GO to Pinpoint Test AC

Fig. 1   Symptom index (Part 1 of 2)   FM9099300031010X

MESSAGE CENTER MODULE DIAGNOSIS		
29	Display totally black	GO to Pinpoint Test FA
30	Display backlighted but blank	GO to Pinpoint Test FA
31	Display not illuminated	GO to Pinpoint Test FA
32	Display lit but too dim	GO to Pinpoint Test FA
33	Display scrambled, segments half lit (ghost segments), segments blink or missing, display incorrect all the time	GO to Pinpoint Test AB
34	Display stuck with all segments on	GO to Pinpoint Test FA
35	Message center module will not switch between English and metric	GO to Pinpoint Test AC
36	Module does not respond to buttons	GO to Pinpoint Test AC
37	Instantaneous fuel economy always reads zero miles/gal or 99 L/100 km	GO to Pinpoint Test FB
38	Distance does not accumulate	GO to Pinpoint Test FC
39	Instantaneous fuel economy always reads 99 miles/gal or 0 L/100 km	GO to Pinpoint Test FB
40	DTE always reads zero miles or never changes	GO to Pinpoint Test FC
41	Average speed reads zero or never changes	GO to Pinpoint Test FC
42	Door ajar warning never/always comes on	GO to Pinpoint Test FE
43	Trunk ajar warning never/always comes on	GO to Pinpoint Test FF
44	Charging system warning is always on	GO to Pinpoint Test FH
45	Air suspension warning is always on	GO to Pinpoint Test FL
46	Headlamp, tail lamp and brakelamp warning is always on	GO to Pinpoint Test FM
47	Low oil level warning is always on	GO to Pinpoint Test FN
48	Windshield washer fluid warning is always on	GO to Pinpoint Test FP
49	CHECK ENGINE warning is always on	GO to Pinpoint Test FQ
50	CHECK DCL warning is always on	GO to Pinpoint Test FQ

Fig. 1   Symptom index (Part 2 of 2)   FM9099300031020X

TEST STEP		RESULT	ACTION TO TAKE
AA0	**VERIFY CONDITION**		
			GO to AA1.
AA1	**CHECK OTHER DISPLAYS**		
	• Turn ignition switch to RUN position. • Turn headlamps off. • Check for backlighting of Message Center module.	Other modules working properly	GO to AA6.
		Other modules too dim or black	GO to AA2.
AA2	**VERIFY MODULE OPERATION**		
	• Turn ignition switch to RUN position. • Press any button on the CCA switch assembly. • Listen for beep from tone module when button is pressed. • Look closely at the speedometer and gauges. Check if normal patterns are present. Need a strong light shining into the cluster if backlighting is completely dark.	Normal patterns present	GO to AA7.
		Normal patterns not present	GO to AA3.
AA3	**CHECK FUSE**		
	• Check for blown fuse at fuse No. 16.	Fuse not blown	GO to AA5.
		Fuse blown	GO to AA4.
AA4	**CHECK FOR SHORT IN CIRCUIT 797**		
	• Before replacing fuse: • Turn ignition key to OFF. • Disconnect battery ground cable. • Connect ohmmeter from Circuit No. 797 side of fuse to ground.	No short in circuit	REPLACE fuse.
		Short found in circuit	SERVICE circuit for shorts.
AA5	**CHECK FOR POWER AT FUSE**		
	• Reconnect battery. • Measure voltage from Circuit No. 797 side of fuse No. 16 to ground.	Greater than 10V	GO to AA6.
		Less than 10V	SERVICE open in fuse holder, Circuit 38.

Fig. 2   Pinpoint test AA (Part 1 of 3)   FM9099300032010X

TEST STEP		RESULT	ACTION TO TAKE
AA6	**CHECK FOR POWER AT SPEEDOMETER**		
	• Turn ignition switch to OFF. • Remove EIC as outlined. • Turn ignition switch to RUN. • Measure voltages at the harness connector of the EIC. • Voltages should be: PIN — FUNCTION — VOLTAGE C3 — BATT — Battery Voltage C5 — RUN — Battery Voltage • Check continuity of ground circuit pin C2-4 to battery ground.	Voltage present and continuity present	REPLACE EIC.
		No voltage or continuity present	SERVICE Circuit BATT #797 RUN #687 GROUND #676
AA7	**CHECK BULBS**		
	• Remove electronic instrument cluster. • Remove speedometer light bar. • Check light bulbs.	Light bulbs not burned out	GO to AA8.
		Light bulbs burned out	REPLACE with correct bulb.
AA8	**VERIFY HARNESS CONTINUITY**		
	• Check continuity between Pin C3-13 (Circuit 464 BK/P) and 32 (Circuit 464 BK/PK)	Continuity	GO to AA9.
		No Continuity	SERVICE Circuit No. 464 for open.

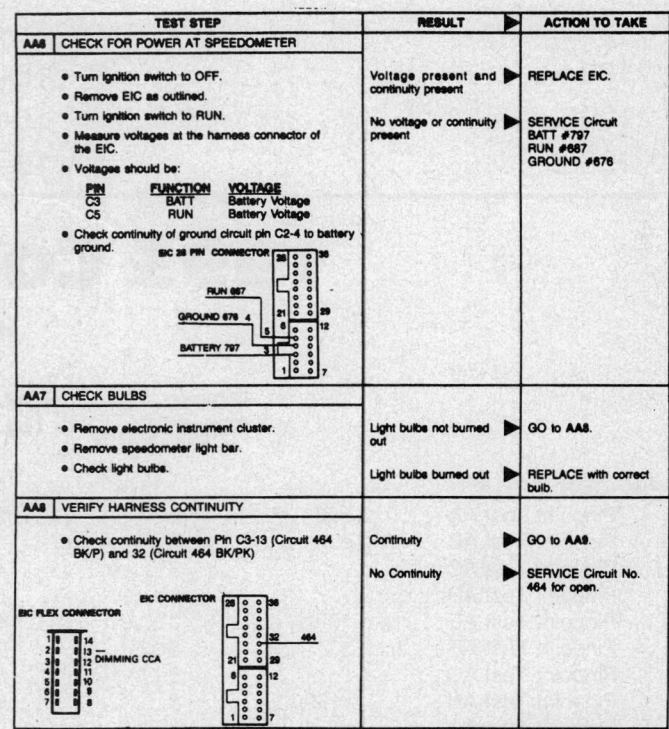

Fig. 2   Pinpoint test AA (Part 2 of 3)   FM9099300032020X

TEST STEP		RESULT	ACTION TO TAKE
AA9	**CHECK POWER TO BULBS**		
	• Turn ignition to RUN. • Measure voltage from C3-14 (Circuit 295 Lt Blue/Pk) to C2-8 (Circuit 563 O/Y) (ground).	Greater than 10V	REPLACE EIC.
		Less than 10V	SERVICE TMACC Circuit No. 295 for open.

Fig. 2   Pinpoint test AA (Part 3 of 3)   FM9099300032030X

TEST STEP		RESULT	ACTION TO TAKE
AB1	**VERIFY CONDITION**		
	NOTE: The LCD displays used in the EIC respond slowly in cold temperatures. Verify concern after the interior of the vehicle is warmed up. • Operate vehicle to determine if the display is normal. • Check display by turning ignition to RUN with headlamps OFF and observe prove-out. All segments ON for 1 second. All segments off for 1 second. • Is display normal?	Yes	System OK.
		No	REPLACE EIC. If EIC is replaced, AFFIX odometer sticker to door pillar

Fig. 3   Pinpoint test AB

TEST STEP		RESULT	▶	ACTION TO TAKE
AC0	**VERIFY CONDITION**			
	• GAUGE SELECT functions only in RUN. • MPH - Km/h functions in RUN. • SPEED ALARM functions with speed greater than 20 mph or 20 km/h.	Module does not respond to buttons	▶	GO to **AC1**.
AC1	**CHECK WARNING CHIME MODULE**			
	• Check for fasten safety belt reminder chime or key left in ignition reminder chime.	Chime sounds	▶	GO to **AC2**.
		No chime sounds	▶	SERVICE warning chime module.
AC2	**CHECK FOR BUTTON BEEP**			
	• Turn ignition to RUN position. • Press problem button and listen for beep.	Button beeps	▶	REPLACE EIC.
		Button does not beep	▶	GO to **AC3**.
AC3	**CHECK SWITCH WIRING CONNECTIONS**			
	• Remove trim applique to expose cluster. • Verify that connections from CCA switch assembly to electronic instrument cluster are securely connected.	Connections secure	▶	GO to **AC4**.
		Connections not secure	▶	Secure connections and RECHECK.
AC4	**CHECK SWITCH ASSEMBLY — (NO SWITCH PRESSED)**			
	• Unplug CCA switch assembly from electronic instrument cluster. • Measure the resistance between the orange and yellow wire of the connector. • Resistance with no switch pressed should be 4000 to 5000 ohms.	Resistance between 4000 and 5000 ohms	▶	GO to **AC5**.
		Resistance is below 4000 or above 5000 ohms	▶	REPLACE switch assembly.
AC5	**CHECK SWITCH ASSEMBLY (BUTTON PRESSED)**			
	• Unplug switch assembly from electronic instrument cluster. • Measure the resistance between the orange and yellow wire of the connector, while pressing the problem button. • The resistance should be:	Resistance within specified range	▶	GO to **AC6**.
		Resistance outside of specified range	▶	REPLACE CCA switch assembly.

BUTTON	RESISTANCE (in ohms)
GAUGE SELECT	1700-2200
MPH — Km/h	800-990
SPEED ALARM	350-480

NOTE: Press only one button

FM9099300034010X

Fig. 4   Pinpoint test AC (Part 1 of 2)

TEST STEP		RESULT	▶	ACTION TO TAKE
AE1	**VERIFY CONDITION**			
	• Turn ignition switch to RUN position. NOTE: CS indicates circuit shorted. CO indicates circuit open. • Is CS displayed?	Yes	▶	GO to **AE2**.
AE2	**CHECK 14A488 HARNESS**			
	• Turn ignition switch to OFF position. • Unplug connector between 14401 and 14A488 harness. • Reconnect battery. • Turn ignition switch to RUN. • Check digital fuel display for CO or CS. NOTE: It may take several minutes for the gauge to respond.	CS displayed	▶	GO to **AE3**.
		CO displayed	▶	SERVICE harness 14A488, connectors or fuel sender for shorts. Fuel sender should be: • 14 to 18 ohms at empty stop. • 157 to 163 ohms at full stop. • 14 to 163 ohms during operation.

FM9099300036010X

Fig. 6   Pinpoint test AE (Part 1 of 2)

TEST STEP		RESULT	▶	ACTION TO TAKE
AF1	**VERIFY CONDITION**			
	• Turn ignition key to RUN. • Display temperature on the multigauge. • Observe gauge for top two and bottom two bars.	Bars present	▶	
		Normal display	▶	System operating properly.

FM9099300037000X

Fig. 7   Pinpoint test AF

TEST STEP		RESULT	▶	ACTION TO TAKE
AC6	**CHECK TONE CIRCUIT**			
	• Remove cluster. • Turn ignition switch to RUN and wait for the fasten safety belt reminder chime to end. • Place jumper wire between harness connector Pin C2-19 and ground. Listen for chime.	Chime sounds	▶	REPLACE EIC.
		Chime does not sound	▶	SERVICE wiring Circuit No. 183 for open. CHECK for correct warning chime module part number or operation.

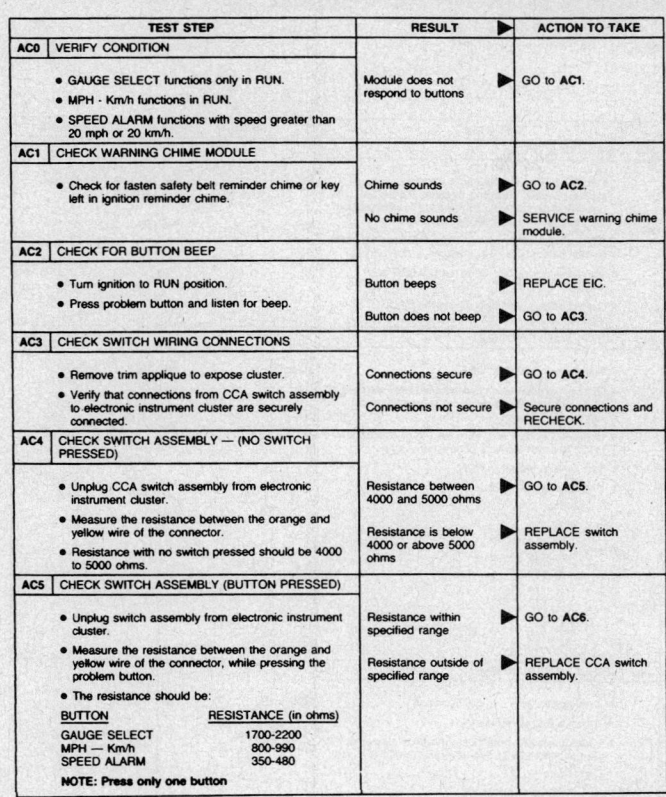

CCA CONNECTOR PLUG C2 ON EIC

EIC TONE - 19   8 – GROUND

Fig. 4   Pinpoint test AC (Part 2 of 2)

TEST STEP		RESULT	▶	ACTION TO TAKE
AD1	**VERIFY CONDITION**			
	• Turn ignition switch to RUN. • Is CO displayed?	Yes	▶	GO to **AD3**.
AD2	**CHECK 14A488 HARNESS**			
	• Turn ignition switch to OFF. • Unplug connector between 14401 and 14A488 harness that contains Circuit 29 (Y / W). • Connect a jumper wire from Circuit 29 (Y / W) at 14401 harness to ground. • Turn ignition switch to RUN. • Check digital fuel display for CO or CS. NOTE: It may take several minutes for the gauge to respond.	CO displayed	▶	GO to **AD3**. Leave jumper connected.
		CS displayed	▶	SERVICE harness 14A488, connectors or fuel sender for open. Fuel sender resistance should be: 14 to 18 ohms at empty stop, 157 to 163 ohms at full, stop operation should be between 14 to 163 ohms.

FM9099300035010X

Fig. 5   Pinpoint test AD (Part 1 of 2)

TEST STEP		RESULT	▶	ACTION TO TAKE
AD3	**CHECK 14401 HARNESS**			
	• Turn ignition switch to OFF. • Remove EIC as outlined. • Measure resistance with ohmmeter between Pin C2 and C4. • Resistance should be less than 5 ohms.	Yes	▶	REPLACE EIC.
		No	▶	SERVICE harness 14401 for open circuit.
	• Is resistance less than 5 ohms?			

EIC CONNECTOR PLUG C2

GROUND 676 — 4

FUEL LEVEL 29 — 2

FM9099300035020X

Fig. 5   Pinpoint test AD (Part 2 of 2)

TEST STEP		RESULT	▶	ACTION TO TAKE
AE3	**CHECK 14401 HARNESS**			
	• Turn ignition switch to OFF position. • Remove electronic instrument cluster as outlined. • Check continuity between Pin C2 (Circuit 29 Y / WH) and C4 (Circuit 676 PK / O). Should be an open circuit.	Yes	▶	SERVICE harness 14401 for short circuit.
		No	▶	REPLACE EIC.
	• Is there continuity?			

EIC CONNECTOR PLUG C2

GROUND 676 — 4

FUEL LEVEL 29 — 2

FM9099300036020X

Fig. 6   Pinpoint test AE (Part 2 of 2)

TEST STEP		RESULT	▶	ACTION TO TAKE
AG1	**VERIFY CONDITION**			
	CAUTION: This is used as a warning for a malfunctioning cooling system. Possible engine damage could happen if not serviced. NOTE: The gauge works off the Powertrain Control Module Data Communication Link.		▶	

FM9099300038000X

Fig. 8   Pinpoint test AG

TEST STEP		RESULT	▶	ACTION TO TAKE
AH0	**VERIFY CONDITION**			
	NOTE: The diagnostic bars are an indication of a short circuit.		▶	REPLACE EIC.

Fig. 9   Pinpoint test AH

Fig. 10   Pinpoint test AJ

TEST STEP		RESULT	▶	ACTION TO TAKE
AJ0	**VERIFY CONDITION**			
	• Verify that engine is not low on oil and that oil pressure is OK.		▶	GO to **AJ1**.
AJ1	**CHECK OIL PRESSURE GAUGE WIRING**			
	• Unplug wire to oil pressure sender and connect a jumper from wire to battery ground.	Pressure reads normal	▶	REPLACE oil pressure sender.
	• Turn ignition switch to RUN.	Pressure reads low	▶	GO to **AJ2**. REMOVE jumper.
	• Oil pressure gauge should indicate normal pressure.			
AJ2	**CHECK WIRING AT CLUSTER**			
	• Disconnect ground cable to battery.	No problem in circuit	▶	GO to **AJ3**.
	• Remove electronic instrument cluster.	Circuit open	▶	SERVICE wiring Circuit 31 for open circuit.
	• Verify continuity between Pin C2-5 (Circuit 31 Wht/Red) and wire to oil pressure sender.			
AJ3	**CHECK SENDER**			
	• Secure any unplugged connectors from shorting.	Resistance less than 25 ohms	▶	GO to **AJ4**.
	• Unplug wire to oil pressure sender.	Resistance greater than 25 ohms	▶	REPLACE oil pressure sender.
	• Reconnect battery and start vehicle without revving engine.			
	• Measure resistance of oil pressure sender using an engine ground.			
	• Next, monitor the oil pressure sender resistance as the engine is gradually revved up and down.			
	• The resistance should always be less then 55 ohms.			
AJ4	**CHECK ENGINE GROUND**			
	• Disconnect ground cable to battery.	Continuity	▶	REPLACE EIC.
	• Check for continuity between oil pressure sender case and ground cable to battery.	No continuity	▶	SERVICE engine ground for loose or corroded connections.

CCA CONNECTOR PLUG C2 ON EIC — OIL PRESSURE

FM9099300040010X

Fig. 11   Pinpoint test AK (Part 1 of 2)

TEST STEP		RESULT	▶	ACTION TO TAKE
AK0	**VERIFY CONDITION**			
	CAUTION: This is used as a warning for a malfunctioning engine lubrication system. Proper operation is needed to prevent possible engine damage.	Warning	▶	System operating properly.
	• Turn ignition switch to RUN but DO NOT start engine.	No warning	▶	GO to **AK1**.
	• Call up oil pressure gauge and observe warning.			
AK1	**CHECK SENDER**			
	• Turn ignition switch to OFF.	Warning	▶	REPLACE or SERVICE oil pressure sender.
	• Unplug wire to oil pressure sender.	No warning	▶	GO to **AK2**.
	• Turn ignition switch to RUN.			
	• Call up oil pressure gauge and observe warning.			
AK2	**CHECK SENDER WIRE**			
	• Reconnect wire to oil pressure sender.	Greater than 55 ohms	▶	REPLACE EIC.
	• Remove electronic instrument cluster.	Less than 55 ohms	▶	SERVICE Circuit 31 Wht/Red.
	• Measure resistance for sender wire Pin C2-5 (Circuit 31 Wht/Red) to C2-8 (Circuit 563 O/Y) of the electronic instrument cluster harness connector.			
	• Resistance should be greater than 55 ohms.			

CCA CONNECTOR PLUG C2 ON EIC — GROUND — OIL PRESSURE

FM9099300041010X

Fig. 11   Pinpoint test AK (Part 2 of 2)

TEST STEP		RESULT	▶	ACTION TO TAKE
AK2	**CHECK SENDER**			
	• Turn ignition switch to OFF.	Yes	▶	REPLACE or SERVICE oil pressure sender.
	• Unplug wire to oil pressure sender.	No	▶	GO to **AK3**.
	• Turn ignition switch to RUN.			
	• Call up oil pressure gauge and observe warning.			
	• Is warning present?			
AK3	**CHECK SENDER WIRE**			
	• Reconnect wire to oil pressure sender.	Yes	▶	REPLACE EIC.
	• Remove electronic instrument cluster.	No	▶	SERVICE Circuit 31 (W/R).
	• Measure resistance for sender wire Pin 1 (Circuit 31 W/R) to 4 (Circuit 676 PK/O) of the electronic instrument cluster harness connector.			
	• Resistance should be greater than 55 ohms.			

EIC CONNECTOR — GROUND 676 — OIL PRESSURE
• Is resistance greater than 55 ohms?

FM9099300041020X

Fig. 12   Pinpoint test AL (Part 1 of 2)

TEST STEP		RESULT	▶	ACTION TO TAKE
AL0	**VERIFY CONDITION**			
	CAUTION: This is used as a warning for a malfunctioning charging system. It must be operating property so the battery is charged up for starting and vehicle operations.	Blinking	▶	System is operating properly.
	NOTE: The battery symbol always flashes when the ignition switch is in RUN if engine is not running.	Not blinking	▶	GO to **AL1**.
	• Turn ignition switch to RUN but DO NOT start engine.			
	• Call up volts gauge by pressing the GAUGE SELECT button until battery symbol is lit.			
AL1	**CHECK 14290 HARNESS**			
	• Turn ignition switch to OFF.	Blinking	▶	SERVICE voltage regulator. REFER to Section 31-15.
	• Unplug 4 pin harness connector between harness 14401 and 14290. Connector is located near the voltage regulator.	Constantly on	▶	GO to **AL2**. Leave jumper connected.
	• Connect a jumper wire from the Pin of (Circuit 904 LG/R) at 14401 harness connector ground.			
	• Turn ignition switch to RUN.			
	• Check battery symbol.			

CCA CONNECTOR PLUG C2 ON EIC — GROUND — FROM WARNING RESISTOR

TEST STEP		RESULT	▶	ACTION TO TAKE
AL2	**CHECK 14401 HARNESS**			
	• Turn ignition switch to OFF position.	Continuity	▶	REPLACE EIC.
	• Remove EIC as outlined.	No Continuity	▶	SERVICE wiring Circuit 904 Lt Gm/Red.
	• Check continuity from cluster harness connector Pin C2-3 (Circuit 904 Lt Gm/Red) and Pin C2-8 (Circuit 563 O/Y).			

CCA CONNECTOR PLUG C2 ON EIC — GROUND — FROM WARNING RESISTOR

FM9099300042010X

Fig. 12   Pinpoint test AL (Part 2 of 2)

TEST STEP		RESULT	▶	ACTION TO TAKE
AL3	**CHECK 14401 HARNESS**			
	• Turn ignition switch to OFF position.	Yes	▶	GO to **AM7**.
	• Remove EIC as outlined.	No	▶	SERVICE wiring Circuit 904 (LG/R).
	• Check continuity from cluster harness connector Pin 34 (Circuit 904 LG/R) and Pin 4 (Circuit 676 PK/O).			

EIC CONNECTOR PLUG C2 — 904 IAR INPUT — GROUND 676

FM9099300042020X

TEST STEP	RESULT	▶	ACTION TO TAKE
AM0 VERIFY CONDITION			
• The battery symbol always flashes with ignition switch in RUN if the engine is not running. • Start engine. • Turn off electrical accessories. • Call up voltage gauge. • Slightly depress accelerator to increase engine speed. • Look for: • Flashing battery symbol • CHARGING SYSTEM warning on Message Center • Indicator bars on Multi-gauge	Warnings, flashing symbol and out of range readings on the gauge	▶	GO to **AM1**.
	No warnings, no flashing battery symbol, and normal reading on gauge	▶	System is operating properly.
AM1 SERVICE CHARGING SYSTEM			
	System operating properly	▶	GO to **AM2**.
AM2 CHECK CHARGE INDICATOR			
• Message center displays CHARGE SYSTEM warning.	CHARGE SYSTEM displayed	▶	GO to **AM3**.
	No CHARGE SYSTEM warning	▶	GO to **AM6**.
AM3 CHECK 14401 HARNESS			
• Turn ignition switch to OFF. • Unplug eight-pin connector between harness 14401 and 14290 located near voltage regulator. • Turn ignition switch to RUN. • Measure voltage at the 14401 harness connector (Circuit 904 Lt Grn/Red). Voltage should be present. Disconnect meter.	Voltage present	▶	GO to **AM4**. Leave connector disconnected.
	Voltage not present	▶	SERVICE Circuit 904 (Lt Grn/Red).

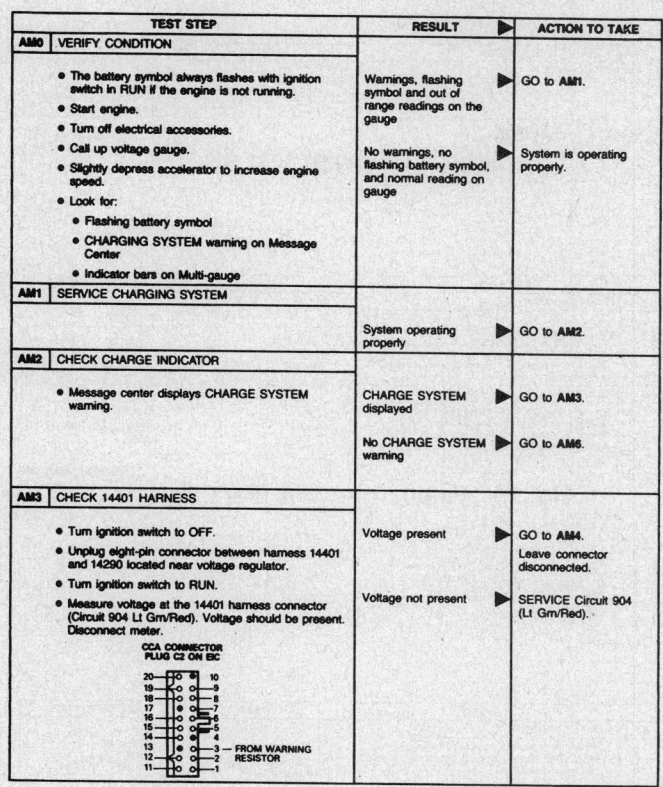

FM9099300043010X

Fig. 13   Pinpoint test AM (Part 1 of 2)

TEST STEP	RESULT	▶	ACTION TO TAKE
AM4 CHECK CIRCUIT 904 LT GRN/RED TO MODULE			
• Turn ignition switch to OFF. • Turn ignition switch to RUN position. • Check for warning.	Warning	▶	GO to **AM5**.
	No Warning	▶	SERVICE harness 14290, windshield module refer to Section 43-20, or voltage regulator refer to Section 31-15.
AM5 CHECK CONTINUITY			
• Turn ignition switch to OFF. • Remove electronic instrument cluster. • Check continuity between Pin C2-3 (Circuit 904 Lt Grn/Red) and C3-1 (Circuit 904 Grn/Red) of electronic instrument cluster (EIC to Resistor circuit).	Continuity	▶	GO to **AM6**.
	No Continuity	▶	SERVICE Circuit 904 (Lt Grn/Red) for open.
AM6 CHECK VOLTAGE			
• Turn ignition switch to RUN position. • Measure voltage of Circuit 797 LT GRN/P at fuse 16. • Measure voltage between C2-8 Circuit 563 O/Yel and C2-7 Circuit 797 Lt Grn/P of electronic instrument cluster (EIC). • Voltage should read the same.	Voltage the same	▶	REPLACE EIC.
	Cluster voltage low	▶	SERVICE Circuits 797 Lt Grn/P fuse or Circuit 38 Bk/O for voltage drop.

FM9099300043020X

Fig. 13   Pinpoint test AM (Part 2 of 2)

TEST STEP	RESULT	▶	ACTION TO TAKE
AN1 VERIFY CONDITION			
• Test drive vehicle above 8 km/h (5 mph) and look for: — Speedometer reading — Odometer changing		▶	GO to **AN2**.
AN2 CHECK ODOMETER			
• Verify that odometer advances when vehicle is driven forward. • Does odometer advance with no speed indication?	Yes	▶	REPLACE EIC.
	No	▶	GO to **AN3**.
AN3 CHECK SPEED CONTROL			
• Test drive vehicle above 30 MPH, check cruise control operation. • Did speed control operate properly during test drive above 30 MPH?	Yes	▶	GO to **AN4**.
	No	▶	SERVICE vehicle speed sensor (9E731) circuit or vehicle speed sensor.
AN4 CHECK RESISTANCE			
• Turn ignition to OFF. • Unplug 60-pin connectors from the powertrain control module and the air suspension module. • Remove EIC as outlined. • Using an ohmmeter, measure resistance between 31 (Circuit 679 GY/BL) and 4 (Circuit 676 PK/O) of the harness connector. • Resistance should be 160 to 320 ohms.	Yes	▶	REPLACE EIC.
	No	▶	SERVICE connectors, wiring Circuit 679.
• Is resistance within range?			

FM9099300044000X

Fig. 14   Pinpoint test AN

PINPOINT TEST AP: SPEEDOMETER/MILEAGE CONSTANTLY READS TOO HIGH OR LOW

TEST STEP	RESULT	▶	ACTION TO TAKE
AP1 VERIFY THE CONDITION			
		▶	GO to **AP2**.
AP2 CHECK ODOMETER ACCURACY			
• Over a known distance, compare the odometer reading with the distance traveled. • Is odometer correct?	Yes	▶	System OK.
	No	▶	GO to **AP3**.

FM9099300045010X

Fig. 15   Pinpoint test AP (Part 1 of 2)

TEST STEP	RESULT	▶	ACTION TO TAKE
AP3 CHECK VEHICLE SPEED SENSOR DRIVE GEAR			
• Remove vehicle speed sensor from transaxle and verify that correct drive gear is installed for vehicle transaxle/tire combination. • Is combination correct?	Yes	▶	GO to **AP4**.
	No	▶	INSTALL correct gear with retaining clip.
AP4 CHECK DRIVE GEAR ON TRANSAXLE OUTPUT SHAFT			
• Check that correct drive gear is installed on transaxle output shaft. • Is drive gear correct?	Yes	▶	REPLACE EIC[5].
	No	▶	INSTALL correct shaft gear.

FM9099300045020X

Fig. 15   Pinpoint test AP (Part 2 of 2)

TEST STEP		RESULT	▶	ACTION TO TAKE
AQ1	VERIFY THE CONDITION			
	● Check by test driving vehicle above 8 km/h (5 mph)	Erratic speedometer above 8 km/h (5 mph)	▶	GO to Pinpoint Test AN.
		Speedometer steady	▶	System OK.

FM9099300046000X

Fig. 16   Pinpoint test AQ

TEST STEP		RESULT	▶	ACTION TO TAKE
AR1	VERIFY CONDITION			
			▶	REPLACE EIC. AFFIX odometer sticker to door pillar.

FM9099300047000X

Fig. 17   Pinpoint test AR

TEST STEP		RESULT	▶	ACTION TO TAKE
AS1	VERIFY THE CONDITION			
			▶	GO to AS2.
AS2	DETERMINE IF SPEEDOMETER MODULE IS ORIGINAL			
	● Check for mileage sticker on door pillar. ● Is EIC (speedometer) original?	Yes	▶	REPLACE electronic instrument cluster. AFFIX sticker with original mileage to door pillar. 'S' should be illuminated and odometer should indicate 4.5 miles or less.
		No		No concern in system.

FM9099300048000X

Fig. 18   Pinpoint test AS

TEST STEP		RESULT	▶	ACTION TO TAKE
FA1	VERIFY CONDITION			
			▶	GO to FA2.
FA2	CHECK OTHER DISPLAYS			
	● Turn ignition switch to RUN. ● Check for operation of speedometer module. ● Is module lit?	Yes	▶	GO to FA3.
		No	▶	GO to Pinpoint Test AA.
FA3	CHECK BULBS AND LIGHT BAR			
	● Remove electronic instrument cluster. ● Remove message center light bar. ● Check light bulbs and light bar circuit. ● Are light bulbs burned out?	No	▶	GO to FA4.
		Yes	▶	REPLACE with correct bulbs.

FM9099300049010X

Fig. 19   Pinpoint test FA (Part 1 of 2)

TEST STEP		RESULT	▶	ACTION TO TAKE
FA4	VERIFY HARNESS CONTINUITY			
	● Check continuity between Pin C3-11 (Circuit 464 BK/PK) and 32 (Circuit 464 BK/PK).	Yes	▶	GO to FA5.
		No	▶	SERVICE Circuit 464 (BK/PK) for open.
	● Is there continuity?			
FA5	CHECK POWER TO BULBS			
	● Turn ignition switch to RUN. ● Measure voltage from C3-12 (Circuit 298 P/O) to 4 (Circuit 673 PK/Y).	Yes	▶	REPLACE EIC.
		No	▶	SERVICE run Circuit 298 (P/O) for open.
	● Is voltage greater than 10 volts?			

FM9099300049020X

Fig. 19   Pinpoint test FA (Part 2 of 2)

TEST STEP		RESULT	▶	ACTION TO TAKE
FB1	VERIFY CONDITION			
	● Test drive vehicle and verify condition. ● Verify miles accumulated on odometer. Speed indication is normal.	Condition exists	▶	GO to FB2.
		Odometer jumps inoperative or erratic	▶	GO to AN1.
FB2	CHECK SOURCE			
	NOTE: The fuel usage information comes from the powertrain control module using the Data Communication Link (DCL). ● Turn ignition switch to RUN. ● Check for CHECK ENGINE (MIL) or CHECK DCL warning on message center.	CHECK ENGINE (MIL) or CHECK DCL	▶	GO to Pinpoint Test FQ
		Warnings not present	▶	

FM9099300050000X

Fig. 20   Pinpoint test FB

TEST STEP		RESULT	▶	ACTION TO TAKE
FC1	VERIFY CONDITION			
	NOTE: The EIC receives information for these features: ● Distance to empty ● Trip distance	Yes	▶	GO to FC2.
		No	▶	GO to Pinpoint Test AN.
	NOTE: from the Data Communication Link (DCL). ● Drive vehicle and thoroughly test the symptom feature. Average may take several minutes to change. ● Observe speedometer and see if it is working properly. ● Does speedometer operate properly?			
FC2	CHECK WARNINGS			
	● Turn ignition switch to RUN. ● Check for CHECK ENGINE (MIL) or CHECK DCL warning on the message center.	CHECK ENGINE (MIL) or CHECK DCL warning	▶	
		Warnings not present	▶	REPLACE EIC.

FM9099300051000X

Fig. 21   Pinpoint test FC

TEST STEP		RESULT	▶	ACTION TO TAKE
FE1	VERIFY CONDITION			
	● DOOR AJAR warning concern.	Always on	▶	GO to FE2.
		Never on	▶	GO to FE4.
FE2	CHECK SWITCHES			
	● The following steps are to be repeated for each door ajar switch. Start with the driver's door, then front passenger, then rear passengers'. ● Turn ignition switch to OFF. This resets the warning. ● Pull connector off of the door ajar switch. ● Turn ignition switch to RUN. ● Check message center for warning. ● Repeat until no warning is displayed or all door switches are disconnected. ● Is warning still displayed?	Yes	▶	GO to FE3.
		No	▶	SERVICE the last switch tested.
FE3	CHECK CIRCUIT 627 (BK/O)			
	● Turn ignition switch to OFF. ● Remove electronic instrument cluster. ● Check continuity between Pin C2-24 (Circuit 627 BK/O) and C2-4 (Circuit 676 PK/O). Should be open.	Yes	▶	REPLACE EIC.
		No	▶	SERVICE Circuit 627 (BK/O) for short.
	● Is circuit open?			

FM9099300052010X

Fig. 22   Pinpoint test FE (Part 1 of 2)

TEST STEP		RESULT	►	ACTION TO TAKE
FE4	CHECK SWITCH			
• Turn ignition switch to OFF. • Pull connector off of the problem door ajar switch. • Connect a jumper wire from Circuit 627 (BK/O) at the harness connector to ground. • Turn ignition switch to RUN. • Check message center for warning. • **Is warning displayed?**		Yes No	► ►	SERVICE door ajar switch. GO to FE5.
FE5	CHECK WIRING			
• Leave jumper wire connected as in FE4. • Turn ignition switch to OFF. • Remove electronic instrument cluster. • Check continuity between Pin C1-24 (Circuit 627 BK/O) and C1-4 (circuit 676 PK/O). Should be shorted.		Circuit shorted Circuit open	► ►	REPLACE EIC. SERVICE Circuit 627 (BK/O) for open.

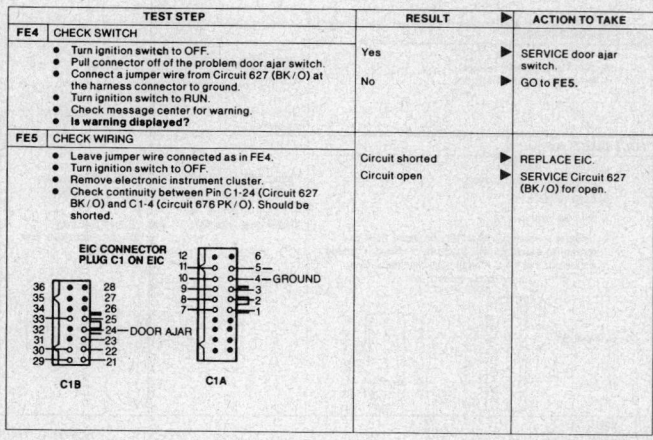

FM9099300052020X

Fig. 22   Pinpoint test FE (Part 2 of 2)

TEST STEP		RESULT	►	ACTION TO TAKE
FF3	CHECK CIRCUIT 486 BRN/W			
• Turn ignition switch to OFF. • Remove electronic instrument cluster. • Check continuity between Pin C2-33 (Circuit 486 BR/W) and Pin 4 (Circuit 676 PK/O). Circuit should be open.		Yes No	► ►	SERVICE Circuit 486 (BR/W) for short. REPLACE EIC.
EIC CONNECTOR PLUG C2				
• Is there continuity?				
FF4	CHECK SWITCH			
• Turn ignition switch to OFF. • Pull connector off of the luggage compartment ajar switch. • Connect a jumper wire from Circuit 486 (BR/W) at the harness connector to ground. • Turn ignition switch to RUN. • Check message center for warning. • **Is warning displayed?**		Yes No	► ►	SERVICE luggage compartment ajar switch. GO to FF5.
FF5	CHECK WIRING			
• Leave jumper wire connected as in FF3. • Turn ignition switch to OFF. • Remove electronic instrument cluster. • Check continuity between Pin C2-33 (Circuit 486 (BR/W) and C1-4 (Circuit 676 PK/O). Circuit should be shorted.		Yes No	► ►	REPLACE message center module. SERVICE Circuit 486 (BR/W) for open.
EIC CONNECTOR PLUG C2				
• Is there continuity?				

FM9099300053020X

Fig. 23   Pinpoint test FF (Part 2 of 2)

TEST STEP		RESULT	►	ACTION TO TAKE
FF1	VERIFY CONDITION			
		Always on Never on	► ►	GO to FF2. GO to FF4.
FF2	CHECK SWITCH			
• Turn ignition switch to OFF. This resets the warning. • Pull connector off of the luggage compartment ajar switch. • Turn ignition switch to RUN. • Check message center for warning. • **Is warning displayed?**		Yes No	► ►	GO to FF3. SERVICE latch switch.

FM9099300053010X

Fig. 23   Pinpoint test FF (Part 1 of 2)

TEST STEP		RESULT	►	ACTION TO TAKE
FH0	VERIFY CONDITION			
• Start engine and check for warning. Watch for several minutes.			►	GO to FH1.
FH1	CHECK MULTIGAUGE			
• Start engine and check warning symbol on speedometer module. Verify that multigauge has same warning.		Same warning on multigauge Different or no warning on multigauge	► ►	GO to FH2. REPLACE Message Center module.
FH2	PINPOINT TESTS			
• Refer to Pinpoint Test.		Charging system	►	GO to Pinpoint Test AM.

FM9099300054020X

Fig. 24   Pinpoint test FH

TEST STEP		RESULT	►	ACTION TO TAKE
FJ1	VERIFY CONDITION			
• Turn ignition switch to RUN. • Press MCCA buttons. • Observe message center.			►	GO to FJ2.
FJ2	CHECK WARNING CHIME MODULE			
• Check for "fasten safety belt" reminder chime or the "key left in the ignition" reminder chime. • **Does chime sound?**		Yes No	► ►	GO to FJ3. SERVICE warning chime module.
FJ3	CHECK FOR BUTTON BEEP			
• Turn ignition switch to RUN. • Press problem button and listen for beep. • **Does button beep?**		Yes No	► ►	System OK. GO to FJ4.
FJ4	CHECK SWITCH WIRING CONNECTION			
• Unsnap message center switch assembly from instrument panel using proper removal procedure. • Verify the harness connection onto the switch circuit board. • **Is connection OK?**		Yes No	► ►	GO to FJ5. SERVICE harness connector.
FJ5	CHECK SWITCH ASSEMBLY (NO BUTTON PRESSED)			

• Unplug switch module.
• Remove EIC.
• Measure resistance between the following switch harness pins and corresponding cluster harness connector pins:
  — Switch module harness Pin 1 and connector Pin 29.
  — Switch harness Pin 4 and harness Pin 4.
		Yes
		No
			►
			►
				GO to FJ6.
				SERVICE open circuit between EIC and switch harness connector.

• Is there continuity?				

FM9099300055010X

Fig. 25   Pinpoint test FJ (Part 1 of 2)

TEST STEP		RESULT	►	ACTION TO TAKE
FJ6	CHECK SWITCH ASSEMBLY (BUTTON PRESSED)			
	• Measure switch resistance between Pin 1 and Pin 4 of the connector, while pressing the symptom button. • Resistance should be:	Yes No	► ►	REPLACE EIC. REPLACE MCCA switch assembly.

Button	Resistance
SELECT	1700-2200 ohms
RESET	800-990 ohms
SYSTEM CHECK	350-480 ohms

NOTE: Press only one button.

• Is resistance within range?

FM9099300055020X

Fig. 25   Pinpoint test FJ (Part 2 of 2)

TEST STEP		RESULT	►	ACTION TO TAKE
FL0	VERIFY CONDITION			
			►	GO to FL1.
FL1	CHECK MODULE			
	• for diagnosis and service of the Air Suspension system.	System operating properly	►	GO to FL2.
		System not operating properly	►	SERVICE system.
FL2	CHECK SIGNAL			
	• Remove EIC as outlined. • Start engine. • Run for one minute. • Using a test lamp, check for continuity from the battery to the electronic instrument cluster harness connector Pin C1-9 (Circuit 419 Dk Gm/Lt Gm).	Tester lights Tester does not light	► ►	REPLACE Message Center module. SERVICE Circuit 419 Dk Gm/Lt Gm for open.

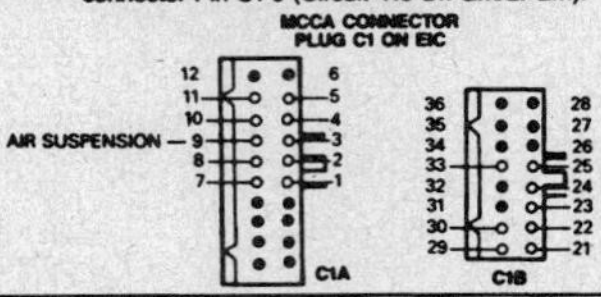

FM9099300056000X

Fig. 26   Pinpoint test FL

TEST STEP		RESULT	►	ACTION TO TAKE
FM1	VERIFY CONDITION			
			►	GO to FM2.
FM2	CHECK EXTERIOR BULBS			
	• Check low beam headlamp bulbs. • Check brake lamp bulbs. • Check rear park lamp bulbs. • Are bulbs OK?	Yes No	► ►	GO to FM3. SERVICE bulbs.
FM3	CHECK LAMP OUTAGE MODULE INPUT TO ELECTRONIC INSTRUMENT CLUSTER			
	• Disconnect Lamp Outage Module from wiring harness. (Refer to Section 13-09 for location and removal procedure.) • Turn ignition switch to RUN. • Does warning message remain on?	Yes No	► ►	GO to FM4. GO to Section 13-09 to troubleshoot lamp outage module.
FM4	CHECK FOR SHORT TO GROUND IN ELECTRONIC CLUSTER HARNESS			
	• With lamp outage module disconnected, disconnect electronic cluster. • Turn ignition switch to RUN. • For each problem lamp warning, perform the Action listed in the table below. • On the electronic cluster harness connectors, check for continuity between Ground (Pin 4) and the corresponding problem lamp pin / circuit.	Yes No	► ►	SERVICE circuit shorted to ground. REPLACE electronic instrument cluster.

Problem Lamp	Action	Check Pin / Circuit / Color
HEADLAMP	TURN ON HEADLAMPS	C1-29 / 130 / R / LG
TAIL LAMP	TURN ON HEADLAMPS	C1-23 / 132 / O / BK
BRAKELAMP	STEP ON BRAKE PEDAL	C1-25 / 135 / Y / R

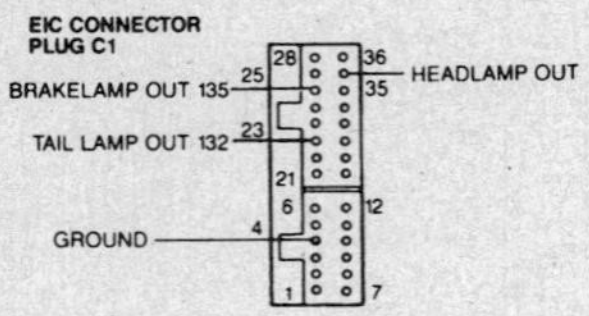

• Is there continuity?

FM9099300057000X

Fig. 27   Pinpoint test FM

TEST STEP		RESULT	►	ACTION TO TAKE
FN1	VERIFY CONDITION			
			►	GO to FN2.
FN2	CHECK TIME-OUT			
	• Park vehicle on level surface. • Check engine oil level with dipstick. Fill to FULL mark with proper motor oil. • Turn ignition switch to OFF. • Wait for more than 2 minutes. • Turn ignition switch to RUN. • Check messages for oil level warning. • Does warning display?	Yes No	► ►	GO to FN3. System operating properly.
FN3	CHECK SENSOR			
	• Turn ignition switch to OFF. • Disconnect wire from oil level sensor. • Wait for more than 2 minutes. • Turn ignition switch to RUN. • Check messages for oil level warning. • Does warning display?	Yes No	► ►	GO to FN4. SERVICE oil level sensor.
FN4	CHECK WIRING			
	• Remove electronic instrument cluster. • Disconnect wire from oil level sensor. • Measure resistance from electronic instrument cluster harness connector C2-Pin 21, Circuit 258 (W / PK) to C2-Pin 4, Circuit 676 (PK / O). • Should measure open circuit.	Yes No	► ►	REPLACE EIC. SERVICE Circuit 258 (W / PK) for short.

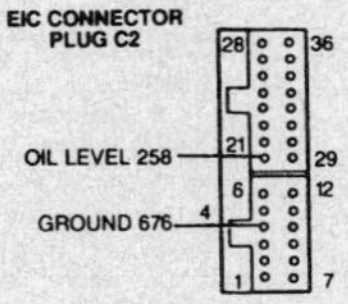

• Is circuit open?

FM9099300058000X

Fig. 28   Pinpoint test FN

TEST STEP		RESULT	►	ACTION TO TAKE
FP1	VERIFY CONDITION			
	• Drain fluid from reservoir for "warning never on". • Add fluid to reservoir for "warning always on". • Turn ignition switch to RUN. • Check message center for LOW WASHER FLUID warnings.	Warning always on Warning never on	► ►	GO to FP2. GO to FP5.
FP2	CHECK SENSOR			
	• Turn ignition switch to OFF. • Disconnect harness connector from windshield washer fluid sensor. • Turn ignition switch to RUN. • Check messages for windshield washer warning. • Is warning displayed?	Yes No	► ►	GO to FP3. SERVICE windshield washer sensor.

FM9099300059010X

Fig. 29   Pinpoint test FP (Part 1 of 3)

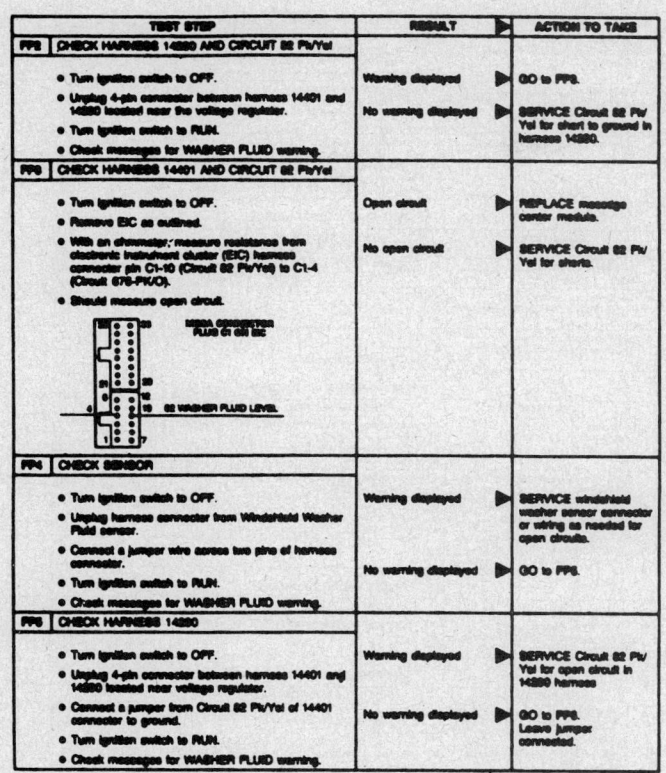

Fig. 29   Pinpoint test FP (Part 2 of 3)

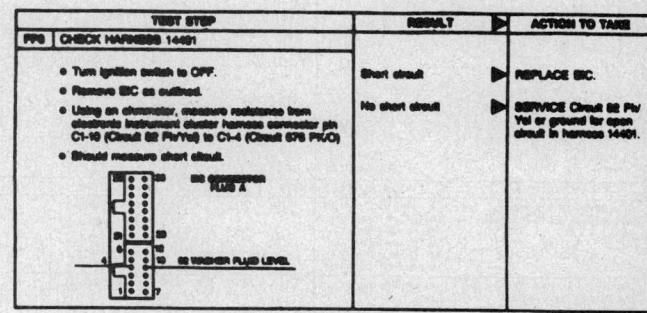

Fig. 29   Pinpoint test FP (Part 3 of 3)

Fig. 30   Pinpoint test FQ

1994 Continental

NOTE: Refer to the Symptom Index in this section before performing any Pinpoint Tests.

INDEX

PINPOINT TESTS:

	Page No. 15-	Fig. No.
Pinpoint Test AA	10	2
Pinpoint Test AB	11	3
Pinpoint Test AC	11	4
Pinpoint Test AD	12	5
Pinpoint Test AE	12	6
Pinpoint Test BA	12	7
Pinpoint Test BB	13	8
Pinpoint Test BC	13	9
Pinpoint Test CA	13	10
Pinpoint Test CB	13	11
Pinpoint Test CC	13	12
Pinpoint Test DA	13	13
Pinpoint Test DB	13	14
Pinpoint Test DC	14	15
Pinpoint Test DD	14	16
Pinpoint Test EA	14	17
Pinpoint Test FA	14	18

	Page No. 15-	Fig. No.
Pinpoint Test FB	15	19
Pinpoint Test FC	15	20
Pinpoint Test GA	15	21
Pinpoint Test GB	15	22
Pinpoint Test GC	15	23
Pinpoint Test HA	15	24
Pinpoint Test HB	15	25
Pinpoint Test JA	15	26
Pinpoint Test JB	16	27
Pinpoint Test JC	16	28
Pinpoint Test JD	17	29
Pinpoint Test JE	17	30
Pinpoint Test JF	17	31
Pinpoint Test JG	18	32
Pinpoint Test JH	18	33
Pinpoint Test JJ	18	34
SYMPTOM INDEX	10	1

EIC DISPLAY DIAGNOSIS

CONDITION	POSSIBLE SOURCE	ACTION
• CCA Display Not Illuminated, Too Dim or Blank But Backlighted	• Short in Circuit 797. • Blown fuse. • Inoperative EIC. • Blown bulb. • Open in Circuit 464. • Open in Circuit 687.	• Go to Pinpoint Test AA.
• Display Scrambled, Incorrect All the Time or Stuck with All Segments On. Segments Half Lit, Blinking or Missing	• Inoperative EIC.	• Go to Pinpoint Test AB.
• CCA Module Does Not Respond To Buttons or No Beep When Buttons Pushed or No Driver Alert Given	• Inoperative safety belt warning chime. • Inoperative EIC. • Loose connections. • Inoperative CCA switch assembly. • Open in Circuit 183.	• Go to Pinpoint Test AC.
• MCCA Display Not Illuminated Too Dim or Blank But Backlighted	• Blown bulb. • Open in Circuit 464 • Inoperative EIC. • Open in Circuit 298.	• Go to Pinpoint Test AD.
• MCCA Module Does Not Respond to Buttons or No Beep When Buttons Pushed	• Circuitry. • Warning chime. • Inoperative EIC. • Inoperative MCCA switch module.	• Go to Pinpoint Test AE.

FM9099400061010X

Fig. 1   Symptom index (Part 1 of 4)

CONDITION	POSSIBLE SOURCE	ACTION
• Display Reads "Error"	• Inoperative EIC.	• Replace EIC. Affix odometer sticker to door pillar.
• Display Has "S" Illuminated	• Inoperative EIC.	• Go to Pinpoint Test GA.
• Mileage Constantly Reads Too High Or Too Low	• Incorrect drive gear. • Inoperative EIC.	• Go to Pinpoint Test GB.
• Odometer Does Not Accumulate Mileage or Counts 1.6 km (1.0 mile) and Jumps Back 1.6 km (1.0 mile)	• Inoperative EIC. • VSS.	• Go to Pinpoint Test GC.

SPEED ALARM DIAGNOSIS

CONDITION	POSSIBLE SOURCE	ACTION
• Speed Alarm Cannot Be Set, Does Not Respond To SPEED Button	• Inoperative safety belt warning chime. • Inoperative EIC. • Loose connections. • Inoperative CCA switch assembly. • Open in Circuit 183.	• Go to Pinpoint Test AC.
• No Beeping When SPEED Symbol Flashing	• Inoperative warning chime module. • Inoperative EIC. • Loose connections. • Inoperative CCA switch assembly. • Open in Circuit 183.	• Go to Pinpoint Test AC.

MESSAGE CENTER DISPLAY DIAGNOSIS

CONDITION	POSSIBLE SOURCE	ACTION
• Instantaneous or Average Fuel Economy Always Reads 0 Miles / Gal Or 99 L / 100 km or 99 Miles / Gal or 0 L / 100 km	• EIC. • Circuitry.	• Go to Pinpoint Test HA.
• Trip Distance Does Not Accumulate or Changes, DTE Always Reads Zero or Never Changes	• EIC. • Circuitry.	• Go to Pinpoint Test HB.

WARNING INDICATORS DIAGNOSIS

CONDITION	POSSIBLE SOURCE	ACTION
• DOOR AJAR Warning Never / Always Comes On	• Inoperative door open warning lamp switch. • Inoperative EIC. • Short in Circuit 627. • Inoperative message center module. • Open in Circuit 627.	• Go to Pinpoint Test JA.
• TRUNK AJAR Warning Never / Always Comes On	• Inoperative luggage compartment door open warning lamp switch. • Short in Circuit 486. • Inoperative EIC. • Inoperative message center module. • Open in Circuit 486.	• Go to Pinpoint Test JB.
• CHARGE SYSTEM Warning Always On	• Inoperative EIC. • Shorted harness.	• Go to Pinpoint Test JC.
• RIDE CONTROL Warning Always On	• Open in Circuit 419. • Inoperative EIC.	• Go to Pinpoint Test JD.
• LOW OIL LEVEL Warning Always On	• Inoperative low oil level sensor. • Inoperative EIC. • Short in Circuit 258.	• Go to Pinpoint Test JE.

FM9099400061030X

Fig. 1   Symptom index (Part 3 of 4)

CONDITION	POSSIBLE SOURCE	ACTION
• CO Displayed, Top Two and Bottom Two Diagnostic Bars Displayed	• Open in harness 14A488 connectors or fuel pump. • Inoperative EIC. • Open in harness 14401.	• Go to Pinpoint Test BA.
• CS Displayed, Top Two and Bottom Two Diagnostic Bars Displayed	• Short in harness 14A488, connectors or fuel pump. • Short in harness 14401 • Inoperative EIC.	• Go to Pinpoint Test BB.
• Inaccurate Fuel Gauge Indication	• Inoperative fuel pump. • Valve, tube or fuel vapor canister plugged. • Fuel tank damaged. • Inoperative EIC.	• Go to Pinpoint Test BC.

TEMPERATURE GAUGE DIAGNOSIS

CONDITION	POSSIBLE SOURCE	ACTION
• Temperature Gauge Displays Top Two And Bottom Two Diagnostic Bars	• EIC. • Circuitry.	• Go to Pinpoint Test CA.
• Temperature Gauge Always Indicates Hot Or Cold Temperature	• EIC. • Circuitry. • ECT.	• Go to Pinpoint Test CB.
• No Warning Tone When Thermometer Symbol is Blinking	• EIC. • Circuitry. • Safety belt warning chime.	• Go to Pinpoint Test CC.

OIL PRESSURE GAUGE DIAGNOSIS

CONDITION	POSSIBLE SOURCE	ACTION
• Oil Pressure Gauge Always Indicates Low Pressure or Indication Erratic	• Inoperative oil pressure sender. • Open in Circuit 31. • Inoperative engine ground. • Inoperative EIC.	• Go to Pinpoint Test DA.
• Oil Pressure Warning Never Comes On	• Inoperative oil pressure sender. • Inoperative EIC.	• Go to Pinpoint Test DB.
• Oil Pressure Gauge Indicates Normal Pressure in KOEO	• Open in Circuit 31. • Inoperative oil pressure sender. • Inoperative EIC.	• Go to Pinpoint Test DC.
• No Warning Tone When Oil Can Symbol is Blinking		• Go to Pinpoint Test DD.

VOLTS GAUGE DIAGNOSIS

CONDITION	POSSIBLE SOURCE	ACTION
• Volts Gauge Always Gives Charging System Alert (Flashing Battery Symbol)	• Inoperative generator regulator.	• Go to Pinpoint Test EA.

SPEEDOMETER DIAGNOSIS

CONDITION	POSSIBLE SOURCE	ACTION
• Speedometer Reads 0 km / h (mph) At All Speeds	• Inoperative EIC. • Circuitry. • VSS	• Go to Pinpoint Test FA
• Speedometer Constantly Reads Too High Or Too Low	• Incorrect drive gear. • Inoperative EIC.	• Go to Pinpoint Test FB
• Speed Indication Jumps Up And Down Erratically	• Inoperative EIC • VSS	• Go to Pinpoint Test FC

FM9099400061020X

Fig. 1   Symptom index (Part 2 of 4)

WARNING INDICATORS DIAGNOSIS (Continued)

CONDITION	POSSIBLE SOURCE	ACTION
• Low WASHER FLUID Warning Always On	• Inoperative windshield washer reservoir fluid level sensor. • Short to ground in Circuit 82. • Inoperative message center module. • Open in windshield washer reservoir fluid level sensor connector. • Open in Circuit 82. • Inoperative EIC. • Open in ground circuit.	• Go to Pinpoint Test JF.
• CHECK ENGINE (MIL) Warning Always On	• EIC. • Circuitry.	• Go to Pinpoint Test JG.
• CHECK DCL Warning Always On	• EIC. • Circuitry.	• Go to Pinpoint Test JG.
• BRAKE Warning Never / Always On	• EIC. • Brake fluid level switch.	• Go to Pinpoint Test JH.
• High Beam Warning Never / Always On	• EIC. • Main light switch. • Circuitry.	• Go to Pinpoint Test JJ.

FM9099400061040X

Fig. 1   Symptom index (Part 4 of 4)

	TEST STEP	RESULT	▶	ACTION TO TAKE
AA1	**CHECK OTHER DISPLAYS** • Turn ignition switch to RUN position. • Turn headlamps OFF. • Check for backlighting of message center module. • Do other modules work properly?	Yes No	▶ ▶	GO to AA6. GO to AA2.
AA2	**VERIFY MODULE OPERATION** • Turn ignition switch to RUN position. • Press any button on the CCA switch module. • Listen for beep when button is pressed. • Look closely at the speedometer and gauges. Check if normal patterns are present. Need a strong light shining into the cluster if completely dark. • Are patterns normal?	Yes No	▶ ▶	GO to AA7. GO to AA3.
AA3	**CHECK FUSE** • Check for blown fuse at fuse 16. • Is fuse blown?	Yes No	▶ ▶	GO to AA4. GO to AA5.
AA4	**CHECK FOR SHORT IN CIRCUIT 797** Before replacing fuse: • Turn ignition switch to OFF. • Disconnect battery ground cable. • Connect ohmmeter from Circuit 797 side of fuse to ground. • Is circuit shorted?	Yes No	▶ ▶	SERVICE circuit for shorts. REPLACE fuse.
AA5	**CHECK FOR POWER AT FUSE** • Reconnect battery. • Measure voltage from Circuit 797 side of fuse 16 to ground. • Is voltage greater than 10 volts?	Yes No	▶ ▶	GO to AA6. SERVICE open in fuse holder, Circuit 38.

FM9099400062010X

Fig. 2   Pinpoint test AA (Part 1 of 4)

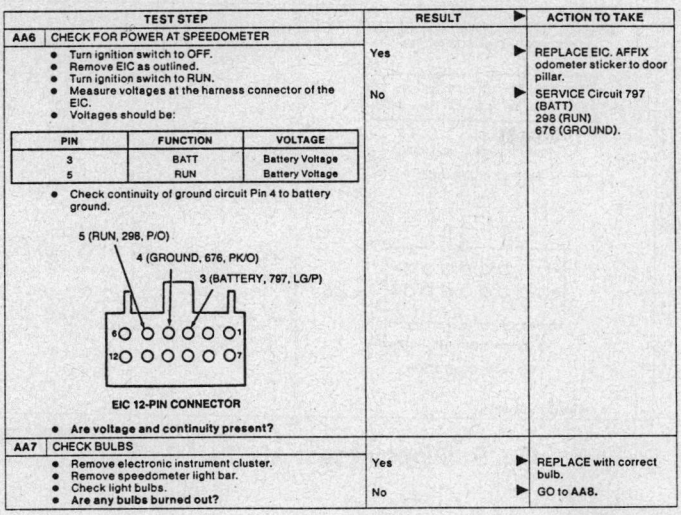

TEST STEP			RESULT	▶	ACTION TO TAKE
AA6	CHECK FOR POWER AT SPEEDOMETER				
• Turn ignition switch to OFF. • Remove EIC as outlined. • Turn ignition switch to RUN. • Measure voltages at the harness connector of the EIC. • Voltages should be:			Yes No	▶ ▶	REPLACE EIC. AFFIX odometer sticker to door pillar. SERVICE Circuit 797 (BATT) 298 (RUN) 676 (GROUND).

PIN	FUNCTION	VOLTAGE
3	BATT	Battery Voltage
5	RUN	Battery Voltage

TEST STEP			RESULT	▶	ACTION TO TAKE
	• Check continuity of ground circuit Pin 4 to battery ground.				
	5 (RUN, 298, P/O) 4 (GROUND, 676, PK/O) 3 (BATTERY, 797, LG/P) EIC 12-PIN CONNECTOR				
	• Are voltage and continuity present?				
AA7	CHECK BULBS				
	• Remove electronic instrument cluster. • Remove speedometer light bar. • Check light bulbs. • Are any bulbs burned out?		Yes No	▶ ▶	REPLACE with correct bulb. GO to AA8.

FM9099400062020X

Fig. 2   Pinpoint test AA (Part 2 of 4)

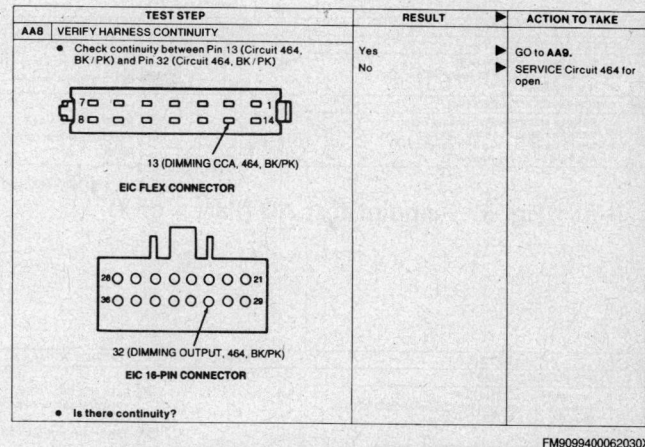

TEST STEP		RESULT	▶	ACTION TO TAKE
AA8	VERIFY HARNESS CONTINUITY			
	• Check continuity between Pin 13 (Circuit 464, BK/PK) and Pin 32 (Circuit 464, BK/PK)	Yes No	▶ ▶	GO to AA9. SERVICE Circuit 464 for open.
	13 (DIMMING CCA, 464, BK/PK) EIC FLEX CONNECTOR 32 (DIMMING OUTPUT, 464, BK/PK) EIC 16-PIN CONNECTOR			
	• Is there continuity?			

FM9099400062030X

Fig. 2   Pinpoint test AA (Part 3 of 4)

TEST STEP		RESULT	▶	ACTION TO TAKE
AA9	CHECK POWER TO BULBS			
	• Turn ignition switch to RUN. • Measure voltage from Pin 14 (Circuit 298, P.O) to Pin 4 (Circuit 676, PK/O) (ground).	Yes No	▶ ▶	REPLACE EIC. AFFIX odometer sticker to door pillar. SERVICE run Circuit 687 for open.
	14 (CCA, 298, P/O) EIC FLEX CONNECTOR 4 (GROUND, 676, PK/O) EIC 12-PIN CONNECTOR			
	• Is voltage greater than 10 volts?			

FM9099400062040X

Fig. 2   Pinpoint test AA (Part 4 of 4)

TEST STEP		RESULT	▶	ACTION TO TAKE
AB1	VERIFY CONDITION			
	NOTE: The LCD displays used in the EIC respond slowly in cold temperatures. Verify concern after the interior of the vehicle is warmed. • Operate vehicle to determine if the display is normal. • Check display by turning ignition switch to RUN with headlamps OFF and observe prove-out. All segments ON for 1 second. All segments off for 1 second. • Is display normal?	Yes No	▶ ▶	System OK. REPLACE EIC. AFFIX odometer sticker to door pillar.

FM9099400063000X

Fig. 3   Pinpoint test AB

TEST STEP		RESULT	▶	ACTION TO TAKE
AC1	VERIFY CONDITION			
	• GAUGE SELECT functions only in RUN. • English/Metric functions in RUN. • SPEED ALARM functions with speed greater than 13 mph or 20 km/h. • Check for fasten safety belt reminder chime or key left in ignition reminder chime. • Does safety belt warning chime sound?	Yes No	▶ ▶	GO to AC2. SERVICE safety belt warning chime.
AC2	CHECK FOR BUTTON BEEP			
	• Turn ignition switch to RUN position. • Press problem button and listen for beep. • Does button beep?	Yes No	▶ ▶	REPLACE EIC. AFFIX odometer sticker to door pillar. GO to AC3.
AC3	CHECK SWITCH WIRING CONNECTIONS			
	• Remove trim applique to expose cluster. • Verify that connections from CCA switch assembly to electronic instrument cluster are securely connected. • Are connections secure?	Yes No	▶ ▶	GO to AC4. SECURE connections and RECHECK.
AC4	CHECK SWITCH ASSEMBLY—(NO SWITCH PRESSED)			
	• Unplug CCA switch assembly from electronic instrument cluster. • Measure the resistance between the orange and yellow wire of the connector. • Resistance with no switch pressed should be 4000 to 5000 ohms. • Is resistance within range?	Yes No	▶ ▶	GO to AC5. REPLACE switch assembly.
AC5	CHECK SWITCH ASSEMBLY (BUTTON PRESSED)			
	• Unplug switch assembly from electronic instrument cluster. • Measure the resistance between the orange and yellow wire of the connector, while pressing the problem button. • The resistance should be:	Yes No	▶ ▶	GO to AC6. REPLACE CCA switch assembly.

BUTTON	RESISTANCE (in ohms)
GAUGE SELECT	1700-2200
English/Metric	800-1000
SPEED ALARM	350-480

NOTE: Press only one button.

• Is resistance within range?

FM9099400064010X

Fig. 4   Pinpoint test AC (Part 1 of 2)

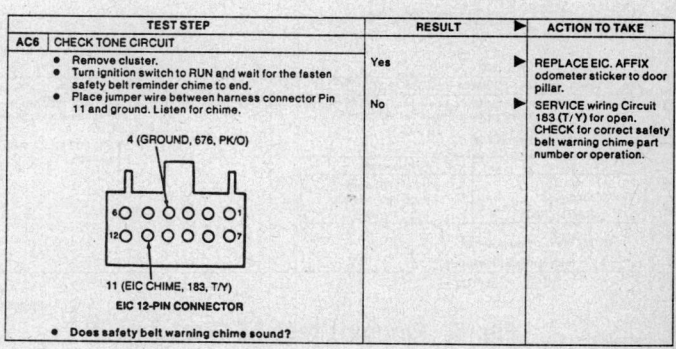

TEST STEP		RESULT	▶	ACTION TO TAKE
AC6	CHECK TONE CIRCUIT			
	• Remove cluster. • Turn ignition switch to RUN and wait for the fasten safety belt reminder chime to end. • Place jumper wire between harness connector Pin 11 and ground. Listen for chime. 4 (GROUND, 676, PK/O) 11 (EIC CHIME, 183, T/Y) EIC 12-PIN CONNECTOR • Does safety belt warning chime sound?	Yes No	▶ ▶	REPLACE EIC. AFFIX odometer sticker to door pillar. SERVICE wiring Circuit 183 (T/Y) for open. CHECK for correct safety belt warning chime part number or operation.

FM9099400064020X

Fig. 4   Pinpoint test AC (Part 2 of 2)

TEST STEP		RESULT	▶	ACTION TO TAKE
AD1	CHECK OTHER DISPLAYS			
	• Turn ignition switch to RUN. • Check for operation of speedometer module. • Is module lit?	Yes No	▶ ▶	GO to AD2. GO to Pinpoint Test AA.
AD2	CHECK BULBS AND LIGHT BAR			
	• Remove electronic instrument cluster. • Remove message center light bar. • Check light bulbs and light bar circuit. • Are light bulbs burned out?	No Yes	▶ ▶	GO to AD3. REPLACE with correct bulbs.

Fig. 5   Pinpoint test AD (Part 1 of 3)

FM9099400065010X

TEST STEP		RESULT	▶	ACTION TO TAKE
AD4	CHECK POWER TO BULBS			
	• Turn ignition switch to RUN. • Measure voltage from Pig 12 (Circuit 298, P/O) to Pin 4 (Circuit 676, PK/O-GND).	Yes No	▶ ▶	REPLACE EIC. AFFIX odometer sticker to door pillar. SERVICE run Circuit 298 (P/O) for open.

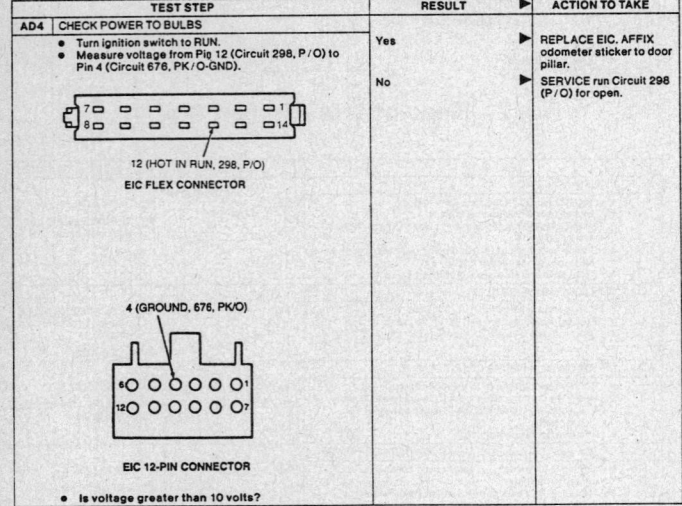

12 (HOT IN RUN, 298, P/O)

EIC FLEX CONNECTOR

4 (GROUND, 676, PK/O)

EIC 12-PIN CONNECTOR

• Is voltage greater than 10 volts?

FM9099400065030X

Fig. 5   Pinpoint test AD (Part 3 of 3)

TEST STEP		RESULT	▶	ACTION TO TAKE
AE4	CHECK SWITCH ASSEMBLY (NO BUTTON PRESSED)			
	• Disconnect switch module. • Remove EIC. • Measure resistance between the following switch harness pins and corresponding cluster harness connector pins: — Switch module harness Pin 1 and connector Pin 29. — Switch harness Pin 4 and harness Pin 4.	Yes No	▶ ▶	GO to AE5. SERVICE open circuit between EIC and switch harness connector.
	8 — 4 SIGNAL GROUND 7 — 3 6 — 2 5 — 1 INPUT SIGNAL			
	• Is there continuity?			
AE5	CHECK SWITCH ASSEMBLY (BUTTON PRESSED)			
	• Measure switch resistance between Pin 1 and Pin 4 of the connector, while pressing the symptom button. • Resistance should be:	Yes No	▶ ▶	REPLACE EIC. AFFIX odometer sticker to door pillar. REPLACE MCCA switch assembly.

Button	Resistance
SELECT	1700-2200 ohms
RESET	800-990 ohms
SYSTEM CHECK	350-480 ohms

NOTE: Press only one button.
• Is resistance within range?

FM9099400066020X

Fig. 6   Pinpoint test AE (Part 2 of 2)

TEST STEP		RESULT	▶	ACTION TO TAKE
AD3	VERIFY HARNESS CONTINUITY			
	• Check continuity between Pin 11 (Circuit 464 BK/PK) and 32 (Circuit 464 BK/PK).	Yes No	▶ ▶	GO to AD4. SERVICE Circuit 464 (BK/PK) for open.

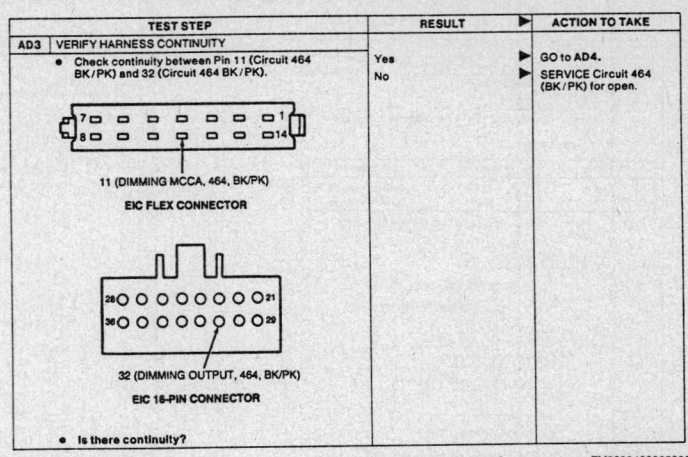

11 (DIMMING MCCA, 464, BK/PK)

EIC FLEX CONNECTOR

32 (DIMMING OUTPUT, 464, BK/PK)

EIC 16-PIN CONNECTOR

• Is there continuity?

FM9099400065020X

Fig. 5   Pinpoint test AD (Part 2 of 3)

TEST STEP		RESULT	▶	ACTION TO TAKE
AE1	VERIFY CONDITION			
	• Turn ignition switch to RUN. • Press MCCA buttons. • Observe message center. • Check for "fasten safety belt" reminder chime or the "key in ignition" reminder chime. • Does safety belt warning chime sound?	Yes No	▶ ▶	GO to AE2. REPLACE warning chime module.
AE2	CHECK FOR BUTTON BEEP			
	• Turn ignition switch to RUN. • Press problem button and listen for beep. • Does button beep?	Yes No	▶ ▶	System OK. GO to AE3.
AE3	CHECK SWITCH WIRING CONNECTION			
	• Unsnap message center switch assembly from instrument panel • Verify the harness connection onto the switch circuit board. • Is connection OK?	Yes No	▶ ▶	GO to AE4. SERVICE harness connector.

FM9099400066010X

Fig. 6   Pinpoint test AE (Part 1 of 2)

TEST STEP		RESULT	▶	ACTION TO TAKE
BA1	CHECK 14A488 HARNESS			
	• Turn ignition switch to OFF. • Unplug connector between 14401 and 14A488 harness that contains Circuit 29 (Y/W). • Connect a jumper wire from Circuit 29 (Y/W) at 14401 harness to ground. • Turn ignition switch to RUN. • Check digital fuel display for CO or CS. NOTE: It may take several minutes for the gauge to respond. • Is CO displayed?	CO displayed CS displayed	▶ ▶	GO to BA2. Leave jumper connected. SERVICE harness 14A488, connectors or fuel sender for open. Fuel sender resistance should be: 14 to 18 ohms at empty stop. 157 to 163 ohms at full, stop operation should be between 14 to 163 ohms.

FM9099400067010X

Fig. 7   Pinpoint test BA (Part 1 of 2)

TEST STEP	RESULT	▶	ACTION TO TAKE
BA2 CHECK 14401 HARNESS • Turn ignition switch to OFF. • Remove EIC as outlined. • Measure resistance with ohmmeter between Pin 2 and Pin 4. • Resistance should be less than 5 ohms.	Yes No	▶ ▶	REPLACE EIC. AFFIX odometer sticker to door pillar. SERVICE harness 14401 for open circuit.

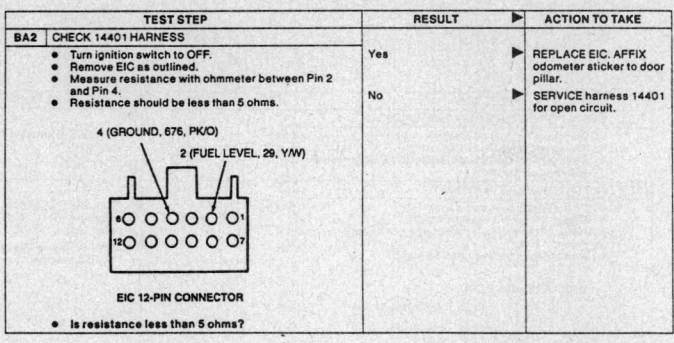

4 (GROUND, 676, PK/O)
2 (FUEL LEVEL, 29, Y/W)

EIC 12-PIN CONNECTOR

• Is resistance less than 5 ohms?

FM9099400067020X

Fig. 7   Pinpoint test BA (Part 2 of 2)

TEST STEP	RESULT	▶	ACTION TO TAKE
BC1 CHECK FUEL PUMP • Disconnect ground cable to battery. • Check fuel pump for binding, sticking, misalignment, etc. • Is fuel pump OK?	Yes No	▶ ▶	GO to BC5. SERVICE or REPLACE fuel pump as required.
BC2 CHECK FUEL TANK • Check fuel tank for dents, bulges or other damage. • Check for proper installation of fuel filler pipe tube. • Verify fill capacity of fuel tank. • Check for blockage of fuel tank vapor valve, tubing and fuel vapor canister. • Are fuel tank and supply and return tubes OK?	Yes No	▶ ▶	System OK. Concern caused by other vehicle system(s). REPLACE as required.

FM9099400069000X

Fig. 9   Pinpoint test BC

TEST STEP	RESULT	▶	ACTION TO TAKE
CB1 VERIFY CONDITION CAUTION: This is used as a warning for a malfunctioning cooling system. Possible engine damage could happen if not serviced. NOTE: The gauge works off the Powertrain Control Module Data Communication Link. • Does the temperature gauge always indicate hot or cold temperature?	Yes No	▶ ▶	PERFORM EEC-IV Diagnostic Self Test. GO to Symptom Chart.

FM9099400071000X

Fig. 11   Pinpoint test CB

TEST STEP	RESULT	▶	ACTION TO TAKE
DA1 CHECK OIL PRESSURE GAUGE WIRING • Verify that engine is not low on oil and that oil pressure is OK. • Unplug wire to oil pressure sender and connect a jumper from wire to battery ground. • Turn ignition switch to RUN. • Oil pressure gauge should indicate normal pressure. • Is pressure reading normal?	Pressure reads normal Pressure reads low	▶ ▶	GO to DA3. GO to DA2. REMOVE jumper.

FM9099400073010X

Fig. 13   Pinpoint test DA (Part 1 of 2)

TEST STEP	RESULT	▶	ACTION TO TAKE
DA2 CHECK WIRING AT CLUSTER • Disconnect ground cable to battery. • Remove electronic instrument cluster. • Verify continuity between Pin 1, Circuit 31 (W/R) and wire to oil pressure sender.	Yes No	▶ ▶	REPLACE EIC. AFFIX odometer sticker to door pillar. SERVICE wiring Circuit 31 for open circuit.

4 (GROUND, 676, PK/O)
1 (OIL PRESSURE, 31, W/R)

EIC 12-PIN CONNECTOR

• Is there continuity?

DA3 CHECK ENGINE GROUND • Disconnect ground cable to battery. • Check for continuity between oil pressure sender case and ground cable to battery. • Is there continuity?	Yes No	▶ ▶	REPLACE oil pressure sender. SERVICE engine ground for loose or corroded connections.

FM9099400073020X

Fig. 13   Pinpoint test DA (Part 2 of 2)

TEST STEP	RESULT	▶	ACTION TO TAKE
BB1 CHECK 14A488 HARNESS • Turn ignition switch to OFF position. • Unplug connector between 14401 and 14A488 harness. • Reconnect battery. • Turn ignition switch to RUN. • Check digital fuel display for CO or CS. NOTE: It may take several minutes for the gauge to respond. • Is CS displayed?	CS displayed CO displayed	▶ ▶	GO to BB2. SERVICE harness 14A488, connectors or fuel pump for shorts. Fuel pump should be: • 14 to 18 ohms at empty stop. • 157 to 163 ohms at full stop. • 14 to 163 ohms during operation.
BB2 CHECK 14401 HARNESS • Turn ignition switch to OFF position. • Remove electronic instrument cluster as outlined. • Check continuity between Pin 2 (Circuit 29, Y/W) and Pin 4 (Circuit 676, PK/O). Should be an open circuit.	Yes No	▶ ▶	SERVICE harness 14401 for short circuit. REPLACE EIC. AFFIX odometer sticker to door pillar.

4 (GROUND, 676, PK/O)
2 (FUEL LEVEL, 29, Y/W)

EIC 12-PIN CONNECTOR

• Is there continuity?

FM9099400068000X

Fig. 8   Pinpoint test BB

TEST STEP	RESULT	▶	ACTION TO TAKE
CA1 VERIFY CONDITION • Turn ignition switch to RUN. • Display temperature on the multigauge. • Observe gauge for top two and bottom two bars. • Are diagnostic bars present?	Yes No	▶ ▶	PERFORM EEC-IV Diagnostic Self Test. System operating properly.

FM9099400070000X

Fig. 10   Pinpoint test CA

TEST STEP	RESULT	▶	ACTION TO TAKE
CC1 REVIEW OPERATION/VERIFY CONDITION • Warning chime module will not beep if another sound is being produced. • Driver alert only given for temperatures above normal band. • Turn ignition switch to RUN. • Press any cluster control button and listen for beep. • Does beep sound?	Yes No	▶ ▶	System OK. GO to Pinpoint Test AC.

FM9099400072000X

Fig. 12   Pinpoint test CC

TEST STEP	RESULT	▶	ACTION TO TAKE
DB1 VERIFY CONDITION CAUTION: This is used as a warning for a malfunctioning engine lubrication system. Proper operation is needed to prevent possible engine damage. • Turn ignition switch to RUN but DO NOT start engine. • Display oil pressure gauge and observe warning. • Is warning present?	Yes No	▶ ▶	System operating properly. GO to DB2.
DB2 CHECK OIL PRESSURE SENDER • Turn ignition switch to OFF. • Disconnect wire to oil pressure sender. • Turn ignition switch to RUN. • Call up oil pressure gauge and observe warning. • Is warning present?	Yes No	▶ ▶	REPLACE or SERVICE oil pressure sender. GO to DB3.

FM9099400074010X

Fig. 14   Pinpoint test DB (Part 1 of 2)

TEST STEP		RESULT	▶	ACTION TO TAKE
DB3	CHECK OIL PRESSURE SENDER WIRE			
	• Reconnect wire to oil pressure sender. • Remove electronic instrument cluster. • Measure resistance for oil pressure sender wire to battery ground. • Resistance should be greater than 55 ohms.	Yes	▶	REPLACE EIC. AFFIX odometer sticker to door pillar.
		No	▶	SERVICE Circuit 31 (W/R).

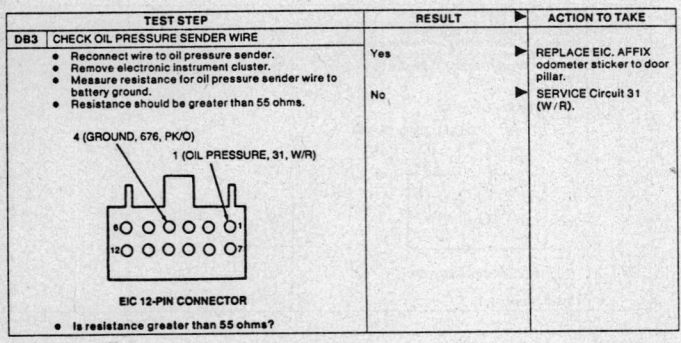

4 (GROUND, 676, PK/O)

1 (OIL PRESSURE, 31, W/R)

EIC 12-PIN CONNECTOR

• Is resistance greater than 55 ohms?

FM9099400074020X

Fig. 14   Pinpoint test DB (Part 2 of 2)

TEST STEP		RESULT	▶	ACTION TO TAKE
DC1	CHECK FOR OIL PRESSURE SENDER SHORT			
	• Disconnect wire to oil pressure switch. • Turn ignition switch to RUN position. • Does oil pressure gauge indicate low oil pressure with bottom bar lit?	Yes	▶	REPLACE oil pressure sender.
		No	▶	GO to DC2.
DC2	CHECK FOR SHORT IN WIRING			
	• Disconnect ground cable to battery. • Unplug wire to oil pressure sender. • Measure resistance between wire and battery ground cable. • Is resistance greater than 55 ohms?	Yes	▶	REPLACE EIC. AFFIX odometer sticker to door pillar.
		No	▶	SERVICE wiring Circuit 31 (W/R) for shorts.

4 (GROUND, 676, PK/O)

1 (OIL PRESSURE, 31, W/R)

EIC 12-PIN CONNECTOR

FM9099400075000X

Fig. 15   Pinpoint test DC

TEST STEP		RESULT	▶	ACTION TO TAKE
DD1	REVIEW OPERATION / VERIFY CONDITION			
	• The gauge driver alert tone is not active until at least 300 rpm or valid oil pressure has been detected (i.e. vehicle was started). • Safety belt warning chime will not beep if another sound is being produced. • Turn ignition switch to RUN. • Press GAUGE SELECT button and listen for beep. • Does beep sound?	Yes	▶	System OK.
		No	▶	GO to Pinpoint Test AC.

FM9099400076000X

Fig. 16   Pinpoint test DD

TEST STEP		RESULT	▶	ACTION TO TAKE
EA1	VERIFY CONDITION			
	CAUTION: This is used as a warning for a malfunctioning charging system. It must be operating properly so the battery is charged up for starting and vehicle operations. NOTE: The battery symbol and CHARGE SYSTEM warning always flashes when the ignition switch is in RUN if engine is not running. • Start engine. • Turn OFF electrical accessories. • Call up voltage gauge. • Slightly press accelerator pedal to increase rpm. • Look for: — Flashing battery symbol — CHARGE SYSTEM warning on message center — Indicator bars on multi-gauge • Are any warnings present?	Warnings, flashing symbol and out of range readings on the gauge	▶	GO to EA2.
		No warnings, no flashing battery symbol, and normal reading on gauge	▶	System is operating properly.
EA2	SERVICE CHARGING SYSTEM			
	• Check charging voltage. • Is system operating properly (voltage between 9.5-16.5V)?	Yes	▶	REPLACE EIC. AFFIX odometer sticker to door pillar.
		No	▶	SERVICE as required.

FM9099400077000X

Fig. 17   Pinpoint test EA

TEST STEP		RESULT	▶	ACTION TO TAKE
FA1	VERIFY CONDITION			
	• Test drive vehicle above 8 km/h (5 mph) and look for: — Speedometer reading — Odometer changing • Verify that odometer advances when vehicle is driven forward. • Does odometer advance with no speed indication?	Yes	▶	REPLACE EIC. AFFIX odometer sticker to door pillar.
		No	▶	GO to FA2.
FA2	CHECK SPEED CONTROL			
	• Test drive vehicle above 30 MPH, check speed control operation. • Did speed control operate properly during test drive above 30 MPH?	Yes	▶	GO to FA3.
		No	▶	SERVICE vehicle speed sensor (9E731) circuit or vehicle speed sensor.

FM9099400078010X

Fig. 18   Pinpoint test FA (Part 1 of 2)

TEST STEP		RESULT	▶	ACTION TO TAKE
FA3	CHECK RESISTANCE			
	• Turn ignition switch to OFF. • Unplug 60-pin connectors from the powertrain control module and the air suspension control module. • Remove EIC as outlined. • Using an ohmmeter, measure resistance between 31 (Circuit 679, GY/BK) and Pin 4 (Circuit 676, PK/O) of the EIC harness connector. • Resistance should be 160 to 320 ohms.	Yes	▶	REPLACE EIC. AFFIX odometer sticker to door pillar.
		No	▶	SERVICE connectors, wiring Circuit 679.

31 (SPEEDOMETER, 679, GY/BK)

EIC 16-PIN CONNECTOR

4 (GROUND, 676, PK/O)

EIC 12-PIN CONNECTOR

• Is resistance within range?

FM9099400078020X

Fig. 18   Pinpoint test FA (Part 2 of 2)

TEST STEP		RESULT	▶	ACTION TO TAKE
FB1	CHECK ODOMETER ACCURACY			
	• Over a known distance, compare the odometer reading with the distance traveled.	Yes	▶	System OK.
	• Is odometer correct?	No	▶	GO to FB2.
FB2	CHECK VSS DRIVE GEAR			
	• Remove vehicle speed sensor from transaxle and verify that correct drive gear is installed for vehicle transaxle/tire combination.	Yes	▶	GO to FB3.
	• Is combination correct?	No	▶	INSTALL correct gear with retaining clip.
FB3	CHECK DRIVE GEAR ON TRANSAXLE OUTPUT SHAFT			
	• Check that correct drive gear is installed on transaxle output shaft.	Yes	▶	REPLACE EIC. AFFIX odometer sticker to door pillar.
	• Is drive gear correct?	No	▶	INSTALL correct drive gear.

FM9099400079000X

Fig. 19   Pinpoint test FB

TEST STEP		RESULT	▶	ACTION TO TAKE
FC1	VERIFY THE CONDITION			
	• Check by test driving vehicle above 8 km/h (5 mph).	Erratic speedometer above 8 km/h (5 mph)	▶	GO to Pinpoint Test FA.
	• Is speedometer indication proper?	Speedometer steady	▶	System OK.

FM9099400080000X

Fig. 20   Pinpoint test FC

TEST STEP		RESULT	▶	ACTION TO TAKE
GA1	DETERMINE IF SPEEDOMETER MODULE IS ORIGINAL			
	• Check for mileage sticker on door pillar.	Yes	▶	REPLACE EIC. AFFIX sticker with original mileage to door pillar. 'S' should be illuminated and odometer should indicate 4.5 miles or less.
	• Is EIC (speedometer) original?	No	▶	No concern in system.

FM9099400081000X

Fig. 21   Pinpoint test GA

TEST STEP		RESULT	▶	ACTION TO TAKE
GB1	CHECK SPEEDOMETER			
	• Perform Pinpoint Test FB.	Yes	▶	REPLACE EIC. AFFIX odometer sticker to door pillar.
	• Verify that speedometer is operating properly.			
	• **Does speedometer operate properly?**	No	▶	GO to Pinpoint Test **FB**.

FM9099400082000X

Fig. 22   Pinpoint test GB

TEST STEP		RESULT	▶	ACTION TO TAKE
GC1	VERIFY CONDITION			
	• Check odometer operation by road testing the vehicle.	Odometer will not accumulate	▶	GO to GC2.
	• Is odometer operation proper?	Odometer accumulates 1.6 Km (1.0 mile), then loses 1.6 Km (1.0 mile)	▶	REPLACE EIC. AFFIX odometer sticker to door pillar.
GC2	VERIFY SPEEDOMETER			
	• Verify that speedometer works properly.	Yes	▶	REPLACE EIC. AFFIX odometer sticker to door pillar.
	• Does speedometer operate properly?	No	▶	GO to Pinpoint Test FA.

FM9099400083000X

Fig. 23   Pinpoint test GC

TEST STEP		RESULT	▶	ACTION TO TAKE
HA1	VERIFY CONDITION			
	• Test drive vehicle and verify condition.	Condition exists	▶	GO to HA2.
	• Verify miles accumulated on odometer. Speed indication is normal.	Odometer jumps—inoperative or erratic	▶	GO to Pinpoint Test FA.
	• Is odometer operation proper?			

FM9099400084010A

Fig. 24   Pinpoint test HA (Part 1 of 2)

TEST STEP		RESULT	▶	ACTION TO TAKE
HA2	CHECK SOURCE			
	NOTE: The fuel usage information comes from the powertrain control module using the Data Communication Link (DCL).	CHECK ENGINE (MIL) or CHECK DCL.	▶	GO to Pinpoint Test JG.
	• Turn ignition switch to RUN.	Warnings not present	▶	
	• Check for CHECK ENGINE (MIL) or CHECK DCL warning on message center.			
	• **Are any warnings present?**			PERFORM EEC-IV Diagnostic Self Tests.

FM9099400084020X

Fig. 24   Pinpoint test HA (Part 2 of 2)

TEST STEP		RESULT	▶	ACTION TO TAKE
HB1	VERIFY CONDITION			
	NOTE: The EIC receives information for these features from the Data Communication Link (DCL):	Yes	▶	GO to HB2.
	• Distance to empty	No	▶	GO to Pinpoint Test FA.
	• Trip distance			
	• Drive vehicle and thoroughly test the symptom feature. Average may take several minutes to change.			
	• Observe speedometer and see if it is working properly.			
	• **Does speedometer operate properly?**			
HB2	CHECK WARNINGS			
	• Turn ignition switch to RUN.	CHECK ENGINE (MIL) or CHECK DCL warning	▶	
	• Check for CHECK ENGINE (MIL) or CHECK DCL warning on the message center.			PERFORM EEC-IV Diagnostic Self Tests.
	• **Are any warnings present?**	Warnings not present	▶	REPLACE EIC. AFFIX odometer sticker to door pillar.

FM9099400085000X

Fig. 25   Pinpoint test HB

TEST STEP		RESULT	▶	ACTION TO TAKE
JA1	VERIFY CONDITION			
	• DOOR AJAR warning concern.	Always on	▶	GO to JA2.
	• Is door ajar warning illuminated?	Never on	▶	GO to JA4.
JA2	CHECK DOOR OPEN WARNING LAMP SWITCHES			
	• The following steps are to be repeated for each door open warning lamp switch. Start with the driver's door, then front passenger, then rear passengers'.	Yes	▶	GO to JA3.
	• Turn ignition switch to OFF. This resets the warning.	No	▶	SERVICE the last switch tested.
	• Pull connector off of the door open warning lamp switch.			
	• Turn ignition switch to RUN.			
	• Check message center for warning.			
	• Repeat until no warning is displayed or all door open warning lamp switches are disconnected.			
	• **Is warning still displayed?**			

FM9099400086010X

Fig. 26   Pinpoint test JA (Part 1 of 3)

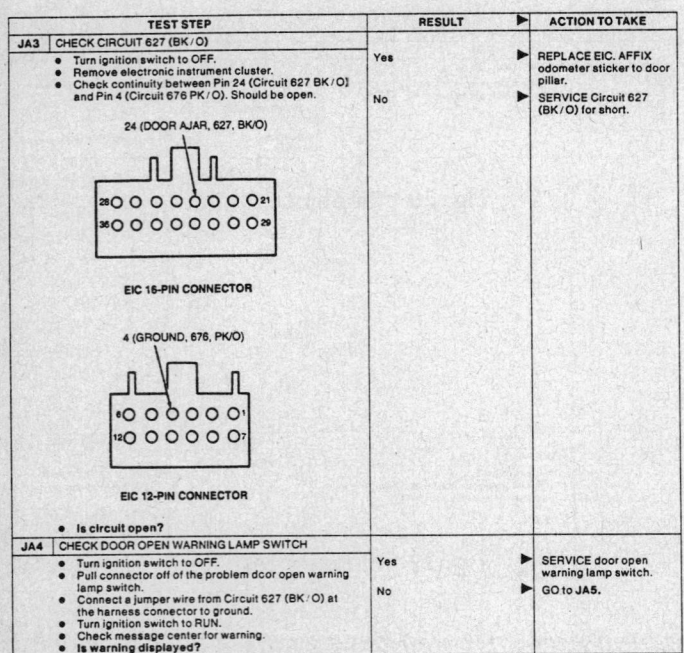

TEST STEP	RESULT	▶	ACTION TO TAKE
JA3 CHECK CIRCUIT 627 (BK/O)			
• Turn ignition switch to OFF. • Remove electronic instrument cluster. • Check continuity between Pin 24 (Circuit 627 BK/O) and Pin 4 (Circuit 676 PK/O). Should be open.	Yes	▶	REPLACE EIC. AFFIX odometer sticker to door pillar.
	No	▶	SERVICE Circuit 627 (BK/O) for short.
• Is circuit open?			
JA4 CHECK DOOR OPEN WARNING LAMP SWITCH			
• Turn ignition switch to OFF. • Pull connector off of the problem door open warning lamp switch. • Connect a jumper wire from Circuit 627 (BK/O) at the harness connector to ground. • Turn ignition switch to RUN. • Check message center for warning. • Is warning displayed?	Yes	▶	SERVICE door open warning lamp switch.
	No	▶	GO to JA5.

FM9099400086020X

Fig. 26 Pinpoint test JA (Part 2 of 3)

TEST STEP	RESULT	▶	ACTION TO TAKE
JB1 VERIFY CONDITION			
• Check EIC for warning. • Is TRUNK AJAR warning displayed?	Always on	▶	GO to JB2.
	Never on	▶	GO to JB4.
JB2 CHECK SWITCH			
• Turn ignition switch to OFF. This resets the warning. • Pull connector off of luggage compartment door open warning lamp switch. • Turn ignition switch to RUN. • Check message center for warning. • Is warning displayed?	Yes	▶	GO to JB3.
	No	▶	SERVICE door open warning lamp switch.

FM9099400087010X

Fig. 27 Pinpoint test JB (Part 1 of 3)

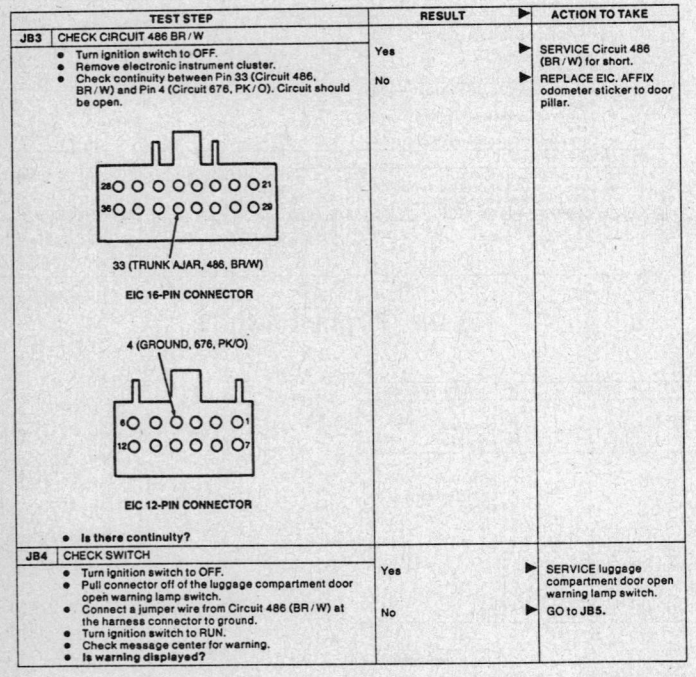

TEST STEP	RESULT	▶	ACTION TO TAKE
JB3 CHECK CIRCUIT 486 BR/W			
• Turn ignition switch to OFF. • Remove electronic instrument cluster. • Check continuity between Pin 33 (Circuit 486, BR/W) and Pin 4 (Circuit 676, PK/O). Circuit should be open.	Yes	▶	SERVICE Circuit 486 (BR/W) for short.
	No	▶	REPLACE EIC. AFFIX odometer sticker to door pillar.
• Is there continuity?			
JB4 CHECK SWITCH			
• Turn ignition switch to OFF. • Pull connector off of the luggage compartment door open warning lamp switch. • Connect a jumper wire from Circuit 486 (BR/W) at the harness connector to ground. • Turn ignition switch to RUN. • Check message center for warning. • Is warning displayed?	Yes	▶	SERVICE luggage compartment door open warning lamp switch.
	No	▶	GO to JB5.

FM9099400087020X

Fig. 27 Pinpoint test JB (Part 2 of 3)

TEST STEP	RESULT	▶	ACTION TO TAKE
JA5 CHECK WIRING			
• Leave jumper wire connected as in JA4. • Turn ignition switch to OFF. • Remove electronic instrument cluster. • Check continuity between Pin 24 (Circuit 627, BK/O) and Pin 4 (Circuit 676, PK/O). Should be shorted.	Circuit shorted	▶	REPLACE EIC. AFFIX odometer sticker to door pillar.
	Circuit open	▶	SERVICE Circuit 627 (BK/O) for open.

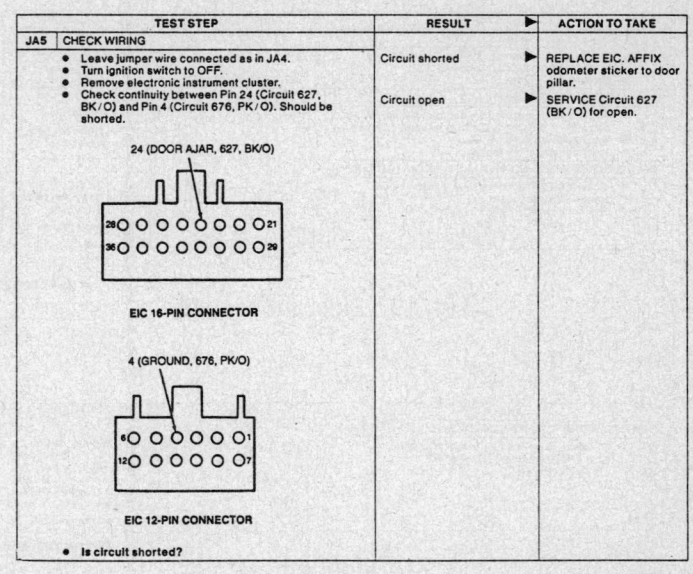

• Is circuit shorted?			

FM9099400086030X

Fig. 26 Pinpoint test JA (Part 3 of 3)

TEST STEP	RESULT	▶	ACTION TO TAKE
JB5 CHECK WIRING			
• Leave jumper wire connected as in JB3. • Turn ignition switch to OFF. • Remove electronic instrument cluster. • Check continuity between Pin 33 (Circuit 486 (BR/W) and Pin 4 (Circuit 676 PK/O). Circuit should be shorted.	Yes	▶	REPLACE message center module.
	No	▶	SERVICE Circuit 486 (BR/W) for open.

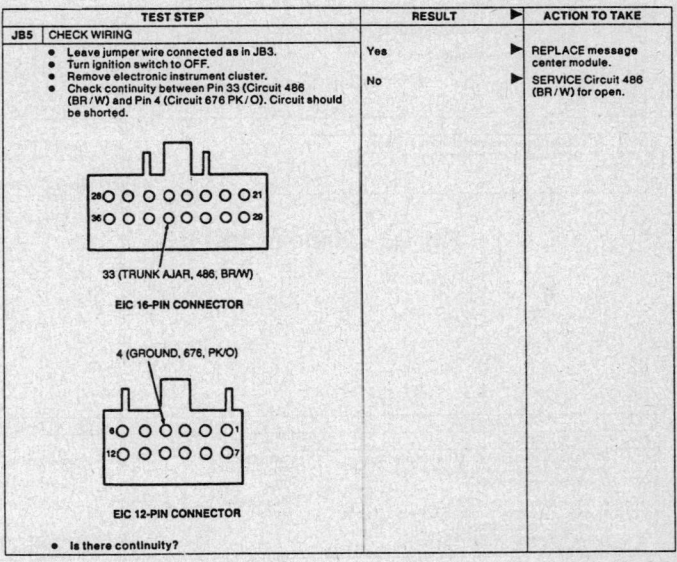

• Is there continuity?			

FM9099400087030X

Fig. 27 Pinpoint test JB (Part 3 of 3)

TEST STEP	RESULT	▶	ACTION TO TAKE
JC1 VERIFY CONDITION			
• Start engine and check for warning. Watch for several minutes. • Check battery voltage. • Is the voltage normal (above 14 volts) for engine at fast idle?	Yes	▶	GO to JC2.
	No	▶	SERVICE generator/regulator.
JC2 CHECK HARNESS TO REGULATOR			
• Disconnect 8 pin connector between E/C harness 14401 and harness 14290 near the generator regulator. • Does charge warning go away?	Yes	▶	SERVICE the generator/regulator.
	No	▶	GO to JC3.
JC3 CHECK HARNESS TO EIC			
• Turn ignition switch to OFF. • Turn ignition switch to RUN but do not start engine. • Remove jumper. Disconnect the 8-pin connector. • Measure voltage at the 8-pin connector from Circuit 904 (LG/R) to ground. • Is it greater than 4 volts?	Yes	▶	GO to JC5.
	No	▶	GO to JC4.

FM9099400088010X

Fig. 28 Pinpoint test JC (Part 1 of 2)

TEST STEP		RESULT	▶	ACTION TO TAKE
JC4	CHECK EIC INTEGRAL GENERATOR REGULATOR RESISTOR AND HARNESS			
	• Turn ignition switch to OFF. • Remove cluster. • Check for loose or corroded screws on integral generator regulator resistor on rear of EIC. • Check that resistor is 400-600 ohms. • Check continuity from resistor screws to Circuit 904 (LG/R) at 8 pin connector. • Check for short to ground on Circuit 904. • Has any check failed?	Yes	▶	SERVICE as required to obtain over 4 volts.
		No	▶	SERVICE Circuit 687 (Hot At All Times, GY/Y) to Pin 5 of EIC flex connector.
JC5	CHECK EIC WIRING FOR OPEN CIRCUIT			
	• Turn ignition switch to OFF. • Remove cluster. • Check for continuity from EIC connector Pin 34, Circuit 904, (LG/R) to EIC flex connector Pin 1, Circuit 904 (LG/R). • Is there continuity?	Yes	▶	REPLACE EIC. AFFIX odometer sticker to door pillar.
		No	▶	SERVICE Circuit 904.

FM9099400088020X

Fig. 28   Pinpoint test JC (Part 2 of 2)

TEST STEP		RESULT	▶	ACTION TO TAKE
JD1	CHECK AIR SUSPENSION SYSTEM			
	• diagnosis of the air suspension system. • Does system operate properly?	Yes	▶	GO to JD2.
		No	▶	SERVICE system.
JD2	CHECK SIGNAL			
	• Remove wiring harness connector to air suspension control module. • Connect Jumper wire between Pin 15, Circuit 419 (DG/LG) and Pin 20, Circuit 57 (BK). • Turn ignition switch to RUN. • Observe cluster. • Does warning indicator come on?	Yes	▶	SERVICE Circuit 419 (DG/LG) for open.
		No	▶	REPLACE EIC. AFFIX odometer sticker to door pillar.

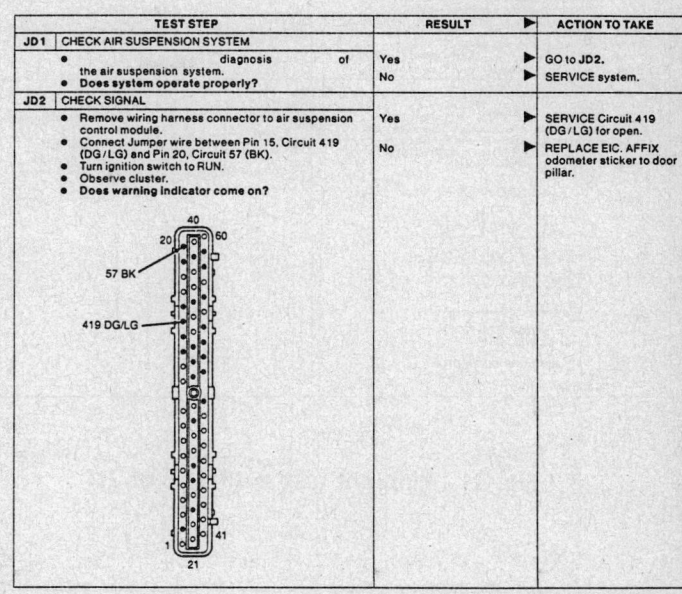

FM9099400089000X

Fig. 29   Pinpoint test JD

TEST STEP		RESULT	▶	ACTION TO TAKE
JE1	CHECK TIME-OUT			
	• Park vehicle on level surface. • Check engine oil level with oil level indicator. Fill to FULL mark with proper engine oil. • Turn ignition switch to OFF. • Wait for more than 2 minutes. • Turn ignition switch to RUN. • Check messages for oil level warning. • Does warning display?	Yes	▶	GO to JE2.
		No	▶	System operating properly.
JE2	CHECK SENSOR			
	• Turn ignition switch to OFF. • Disconnect wire from low oil level sensor. • Wait for more than 2 minutes. • Turn ignition switch to RUN. • Check messages for oil level warning. • Does warning display?	Yes	▶	GO to JE3.
		No	▶	SERVICE low oil level sensor.
JE3	CHECK WIRING			
	• Remove electronic instrument cluster. • Disconnect wire from low oil level sensor. • Measure resistance from electronic instrument cluster harness connector Pin 21, Circuit 258 (W/PK) to Pin 4, Circuit 676 (PK/O). • Should measure open circuit.	Yes	▶	REPLACE EIC. AFFIX odometer sticker to door pillar.
		No	▶	SERVICE Circuit 258 (W/PK) for short.

21 (OIL LEVEL, 258, W/PK)

28 ○○○○○○○ 21
34 ○○○○○○○ 29

EIC 16-PIN CONNECTOR

4 (GROUND, 676, PK/O)

6 ○○○○○ 1
12 ○○○○○ 7

EIC 12-PIN CONNECTOR

• is circuit open?

FM9099400090000X

Fig. 30   Pinpoint test JE

TEST STEP		RESULT	▶	ACTION TO TAKE
JF1	VERIFY CONDITION			
	• Drain fluid from washer fluid reservoir for "warning never on". • Add fluid to washer fluid reservoir for "warning always on". • Turn ignition switch to RUN. • Check message center for low WASHER FLUID warnings. • Is warning displayed?	Warning always on	▶	GO to JF2.
		Warning never on	▶	GO to JF5.
JF2	CHECK SENSOR			
	• Turn ignition switch to OFF. • Disconnect harness connector from windshield washer reservoir fluid level sensor. • Turn ignition switch to RUN. • Check messages for windshield washer fluid warning. • Is warning displayed?	Yes	▶	GO to JF3.
		No	▶	SERVICE windshield washer reservoir fluid level sensor.
JF3	CHECK HARNESS 14290 AND CIRCUIT 82 (PK/Y)			
	• Turn ignition switch to OFF. • Unplug 4-pin connector between harness 14401 and 14290 located near the generator regulator. • Turn ignition switch to RUN. • Check messages for low WASHER FLUID warning. • Is warning displayed?	Yes	▶	GO to JF4.
		No	▶	SERVICE Circuit 82 (PK/Y) for short to ground in harness 14290.
JF4	CHECK HARNESS 14401 AND CIRCUIT 82 (PK/Y)			
	• Turn ignition switch to OFF. • Remove EIC as outlined. • With an ohmmeter, measure resistance from electronic instrument cluster (EIC) harness Pin 10, Circuit 82 (PK/Y) to Pin 4, Circuit 676 (PK/O). • Should measure open circuit.	Yes	▶	REPLACE message center module.
		No	▶	SERVICE Circuit 82 (PK/Y) for shorts.
JF5	CHECK SENSOR			
	• Turn ignition switch to OFF. • Unplug harness connector from windshield washer reservoir fluid level sensor. • Connect a jumper wire across 2 pins of harness connector. • Turn ignition switch to RUN. • Check messages for low WASHER FLUID warning. • Is warning displayed?	Yes	▶	SERVICE windshield washer reservoir fluid level sensor connector or wiring as needed for open circuits.
		No	▶	GO to JF6.

4 (GROUND, 676, PK/O)

6 ○○○○○ 1
12 ○○○○○ 7

10 (WASHER FLUID LEVEL, 82, PK/Y)

EIC 12-PIN CONNECTOR

FM9099400091010X

Fig. 31   Pinpoint test JF (Part 1 of 2)

TEST STEP		RESULT	▶	ACTION TO TAKE
JF6	CHECK HARNESS 14290			
	• Turn ignition switch to OFF. • Unplug 4-pin connector between harness 14401 and 14290 located near generator regulator. • Connect a jumper from Circuit 82 (PK/Y) of 14401 connector to ground. • Turn ignition switch to RUN. • Check messages for low WASHER FLUID warning. • Is warning displayed?	Yes	▶	SERVICE Circuit 82 (PK/Y) for open circuit in 14290 harness.
		No	▶	GO to JF7. LEAVE jumper connected.
JF7	CHECK HARNESS 14401			
	• Turn ignition switch to OFF. • Remove EIC as outlined. • Using an ohmmeter, measure resistance from electronic instrument cluster harness connector Pin 10, Circuit 82 (PK/Y) to Pin 4, Circuit 676 (PK/O). • Should measure short circuit.	Yes	▶	REPLACE EIC. AFFIX odometer sticker to door pillar.
		No	▶	SERVICE Circuit 82 (PK/Y) or ground for open circuit in harness 14401.

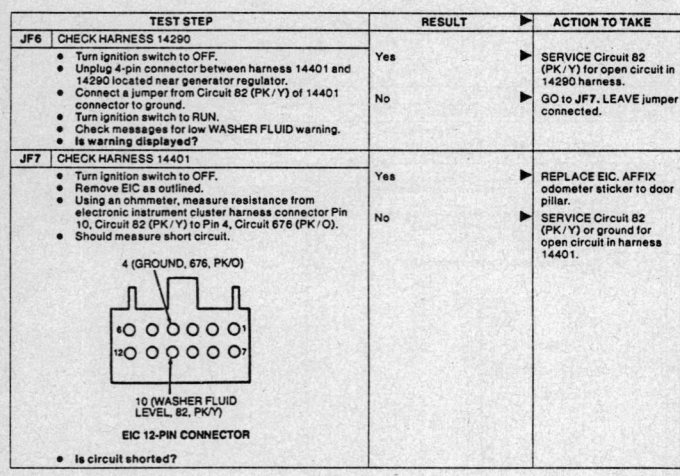

4 (GROUND, 676, PK/O)

6 O O O O O 1
12 O O O O O 7

10 (WASHER FLUID LEVEL, 82, PK/Y)

EIC 12-PIN CONNECTOR

• Is circuit shorted?

FM9099400091020X

Fig. 31   Pinpoint test JF (Part 2 of 2)

TEST STEP		RESULT	▶	ACTION TO TAKE
JG1	VERIFY CONDITION			
	• Check for warning messages. • Is any warning displayed?	CHECK ENGINE. CHECK DCL	▶	PERFORM EEC-IV Diagnostic Self Test.
		CHECK DCL only	▶	GO to Data Communications Link diagnostics. REFER to DCL Quick Check.

FM9099400092000X

Fig. 32   Pinpoint test JG

TEST STEP		RESULT	▶	ACTION TO TAKE
JH1	VERIFY CONDITION			
	NOTE: Make sure brake fluid at specified level. • Check EIC for warnings. • Is warning displayed?	Warning never on Warning always on	▶ ▶	GO to JH2. GO to JH5.
JH2	CHECK BRAKE FLUID LEVEL SWITCH			
	• Turn ignition switch to OFF. • Disconnect connector at brake fluid level switch. • Connect a jumper wire from Circuit 977 (P/W) at the brake fluid level switch connector to ground. • Turn ignition switch to RUN. • Is BRAKE SYSTEM WARNING displayed on EIC?	Yes No	▶ ▶	GO to JH3. GO to JH4.

FM9099400093010X

Fig. 33   Pinpoint test JH (Part 1 of 2)

TEST STEP		RESULT	▶	ACTION TO TAKE
JH3	CHECK FOR OPEN CIRCUIT			
	• Check continuity Circuit 530 (LG/Y) and 57 (BK) from brake fluid level switch to ground and Circuit 162 (LG/R) to ignition switch and to parking brake. • Is continuity present?	Yes	▶	REPLACE brake fluid level switch.
		No	▶	SERVICE open in circuit 530 (LG/Y), 57 (BK) or 162 (LG/R).
JH4	CHECK FOR OPEN CIRCUIT/OPEN BULB			
	• Turn ignition switch to OFF. • Disconnect jumper wire. • Disconnect EIC. • Check continuity in Circuit 977 (P/W) between EIC and brake fluid level switch. • Is continuity present?	Yes	▶	CHECK voltage at flex connector Pin 4 in RUN. CHECK brake warning bulb in EIC.
		No	▶	SERVICE Circuit 977 (P/W) for open.
JH5	CHECK HARNESS			
	• Put transaxle in PARK. • Release parking brake. • Turn ignition switch to OFF. • Disconnect connector at the brake fluid level switch. • Turn ignition switch to RUN. • Is BRAKE SYSTEM WARNING displayed on EIC?	Yes	▶	CHECK Circuit 977 (P/W) for shorts.
		No	▶	GO to JH6.
JH6	CHECK BRAKE FLUID LEVEL SWITCH			
	Make sure that: • Parking brake is OFF, DRL module is good, ignition switch is in OFF, brake fluid level is proper. • Check for ground on Circuit 162 (LG/R) in fluid level switch connector. • Is there an open circuit?	Yes	▶	REPLACE brake fluid level switch.
		No	▶	SERVICE Circuit 162 (LG/R) for shorts or faulty switches.

FM9099400093020X

Fig. 33   Pinpoint test JH (Part 2 of 2)

TEST STEP		RESULT	▶	ACTION TO TAKE
JJ1	VERIFY CONDITION			
	• Check EIC display. • Is HIGH BEAM indicator displayed?	Indicator never on Indicator always on	▶ ▶	GO to JJ2. GO to JJ3.
JJ2	CHECK BULBS			
	• Turn ignition switch to OFF. • Disconnect EIC. • Check continuity from flex connector Pin 7 to ground, Pin 3. • Is there continuity?	Yes	▶	SERVICE Circuit 932 (GY/W) to DRL jumper and Circuit 12 (LG/BK) to headlamps.
		No	▶	REPLACE bulb.
JJ3	CHECK MAIN LIGHTING SWITCH			
	• Turn main lighting switch to OFF and to low beam. • Are high beams on?	Yes	▶	SERVICE main lighting switch or turn signal and windshield wiper switch.
		No	▶	CHECK for miswiring of Circuit 932 (GY/W) to a battery circuit. On vehicles with DRL, REPLACE DRL module.

FM9099400094000X

Fig. 34   Pinpoint test JJ

1993 Sable & Taurus

INDEX

	Page No. 15-	Fig. No.		Page No. 15-	Fig. No.
Symptom index	19	1	Pinpoint test SD	22	15
Pinpoint test FA	19	2	Pinpoint test SE	22	16
Pinpoint test FB	20	3	Pinpoint test SF	22	17
Pinpoint test FC	20	4	Pinpoint test SG	22	18
Pinpoint test FD	20	5	Pinpoint test SH	22	19
Pinpoint test FE	20	6	Pinpoint test SJ	22	20
Pinpoint test FF	20	7	Pinpoint test SK	22	21
Pinpoint test FG	20	8	Pinpoint test TA	22	22
Pinpoint test FI	21	9	Pinpoint test TB	23	23
Pinpoint test FJ	21	10	Pinpoint test TC	23	24
Pinpoint test FP	21	11	Pinpoint test TD	23	25
Pinpoint test SA	21	12	Pinpoint test TE	23	26
Pinpoint test SB	21	13	Pinpoint test TF	23	27
Pinpoint test SC	22	14	Pinpoint test TX	23	28

NOTE: Refer to the Symptom Index in this section before performing any Pinpoint Tests.

DISPLAY DIAGNOSIS

1	Display totally black	GO to Pinpoint Test **TA**
2	Display back lighted but blank	GO to Pinpoint Test **TA**
3	Cluster will not dim	GO to Pinpoint Test **TD**
4	Display lit but too dim	GO to Pinpoint Test **TB**
5	Display scrambled, segments half lit (ghost segments), segments blinking or missing, display incorrect all the time	GO to Pinpoint Test **TC**
6	Display stuck with all segments on	GO to Pinpoint Test **TC**
7	No beep when buttons pushed or driver alert given	GO to Pinpoint Test **SA**
8	Cluster does not respond to buttons	GO to Pinpoint Test **SA**

TEMPERATURE GAUGE DIAGNOSIS

9	Temp gauge display blanks out thermometer symbol and lights top two and bottom two bars of multigauge	GO to Pinpoint Test **TE**
10	No warning tone when thermometer symbol is blinking	GO to Pinpoint Test **TX**
11	Temperature gauge always indicates cold temperature	GO to Pinpoint Test **TF**

SPEEDOMETER DIAGNOSIS

12	Reads 0 mph (km/h) at all speeds when vehicle in motion	GO to Pinpoint Test **SB**
13	Speedometer reads constantly too high or too low	GO to Pinpoint Test **SC**
14	Speed indication jumps up and down erratically	GO to Pinpoint Test **SD**

ODOMETER DIAGNOSIS

15	Display reads "Error" and service symbol on	GO to Pinpoint Test **SE**
16	Display has "S" illuminated	GO to Pinpoint Test **SF**
17	Odometer does not accumulate mileage, or counts 1.6 km (1.0 miles) and jumps back 1.6 km (1.0 miles)	GO to Pinpoint Test **SG**
18	Odometer reading incorrect	GO to Pinpoint Test **SH**
19	Mileage constantly reads too high or too low	GO to Pinpoint Test **SJ**

TACHOMETER DIAGNOSIS

20	Tach always indicates too high or low	GO to Pinpoint Test **SK**
21	No Tach indication	GO to Pinpoint Test **SG**
22	Tach indication erratic	GO to Pinpoint Test **SG**
23	Instantaneous fuel economy always reads zero miles/gal or 99 L/100 km	GO to Pinpoint Test **FA**
24	Trip distance does not accumulate	GO to Pinpoint Test **FB**
25	Instantaneous fuel economy always reads 99 miles/gal or 0 L/100 km	GO to Pinpoint Test **FA**
26	DTE does not go below 322 km (200 miles) with fuel tank empty	GO to Pinpoint Test **FC**
27	DTE always reads zero miles	GO to Pinpoint Test **FC**

Fig. 1   Symptom index (Part 1 of 2)

FUEL GAUGE DIAGNOSIS

28	CO displayed, when fuel remaining or DTE selected on fuel computer	GO to Pinpoint Test **FD**
29	CS displayed, when fuel remaining or DTE selected on fuel computer	GO to Pinpoint Test **FE**
30	Does not display F when fuel tank is full	GO to Pinpoint Test **FE**
31	Does not display E when fuel tank is empty	GO to Pinpoint Test **FD**
32	Inaccurate fuel indication	GO to Pinpoint Test **FF**
33	Door ajar on at all times or never illuminates when doors are open	GO to Pinpoint Test **FG**
34	Washer fluid illuminated at all times or never illuminates	GO to Pinpoint Test **FP**
35	Lamp out warnings do not function properly	GO to Pinpoint Test **FI**
36	Check oil does not function properly	GO to Pinpoint Test **FJ**

FM9099300095020X

Fig. 1   Symptom index (Part 2 of 2)

TEST STEP		RESULT	ACTION TO TAKE
FA0	**VERIFY CONDITION**		GO to FA1.
FA1	**CHECK SPEEDOMETER OPERATION**		
	• Verify that speedometer is operating properly.	Speedometer operates properly	GO to FA2.
		Speedometer does not operate properly	GO to Pinpoint Test **SF**.
FA2	**CHECK CONTINUITY OF CIRCUIT 305 (FUEL FLOW)**		
	• Verify continuity and absence of shorts in Circuit 305.	Continuity and no shorts	GO to Pinpoint Test **FD3**.
		No Continuity and/or shorts	SERVICE wiring Circuit 305 as required.
FA3	**CHECK FOR FUEL FLOW PULSES**		
	• Verify proper operation of fuel flow function in EEC.	Operates properly	REPLACE EIC (fuel computer module).*
		Does not operate properly	SERVICE or REPLACE EEC or fuel flow sensor system as required.

FM9099300096000X

Fig. 2   Pinpoint test FA

TEST STEP		RESULT	▶	ACTION TO TAKE
FB1	VERIFY CONDITION			
			▶	GO to FB2.
FB2	CHECK SPEEDOMETER OPERATION			
	• Verify that speedometer is operating properly.	Yes	▶	REPLACE cluster.
	• Does speedometer operate properly?	No	▶	GO to Pinpoint Test SF.

FM9099300097000X

Fig. 3   Pinpoint test FB

TEST STEP		RESULT	▶	ACTION TO TAKE
FC1	VERIFY CONDITION			
			▶	GO to FC2.
FC2	CHECK FUEL GAUGE			
	• Verify that fuel gauge is operating properly.	Yes	▶	GO to FC3.
	• Does fuel gauge operate properly?	No	▶	GO to Pinpoint Test FD or FE.
FC3	CHECK SPEEDOMETER			
	• Verify that speedometer is operating properly.	Yes	▶	GO to FC4.
	• Does speedometer operate properly?	No	▶	GO to Pinpoint Test SB.
FC4	CHECK FOR FUEL FLOW PULSES			
	• Verify proper operation of fuel flow function in PCM. Refer to Powertrain Control/Emissions Diagnosis Manual.*	Yes	▶	REPLACE EIC.
		No	▶	SERVICE or REPLACE PCM or fuel flow sensor system as required.

FM9099300098000X

Fig. 4   Pinpoint test FC

TEST STEP		RESULT	▶	ACTION TO TAKE
FD1	VERIFY CONDITION			
	• Does CO display?	Yes	▶	GO to FD2.
FD2	CHECK FUEL TANK SENDING UNIT AND PUMP WIRING AT FUEL TANK SENDING UNIT AND PUMP			
	• Disconnect ground cable to battery.	CO displayed	▶	GO to FD4.
	• Lower fuel tank to gain access to fuel tank sending unit and pump connector.	CS displayed	▶	GO to FD3. REMOVE jumper.
	• Unplug fuel sender connector.			
	• Jumper variable resistance terminal and ground terminal of harness together.			
	• Reconnect battery.			
	• Turn ignition switch from OFF to RUN.			
	• Check digital fuel remaining display for CO or CS.			
	NOTE: It may take several minutes for the fuel gauge to respond.			
FD3	CHECK FUEL TANK SENDING UNIT AND PUMP			
	• Turn ignition switch to OFF.	Resistance between 11 and 168 ohms	▶	INSPECT fuel tank sending unit and pump wiring connector female terminals for flash or loose fit. SERVICE as required.
	• Measure the resistance of the fuel tank sending unit and pump at the sender terminals.			
	• Verify that the resistance is between 11 and 168 ohms.	Resistance not as specified	▶	REPLACE fuel tank sending unit and pump.

FM9099300099010X

Fig. 5   Pinpoint test FD (Part 1 of 2)

TEST STEP		RESULT	▶	ACTION TO TAKE
FD4	CHECK FUEL TANK SENDING UNIT AND PUMP WIRING AT CLUSTER			
	• Disconnect ground cable to battery.	Yes	▶	REPLACE cluster. AFFIX odometer sticker to door pillar.
	• Remove cluster and secure connectors from shorting.			
	• Jumper variable resistance terminal and ground terminal of harness together at sender.	No	▶	SERVICE fuel tank sending unit and pump wiring for open circuit.
	• Verify condition between Pins 6 and 8 (ground) of cluster Connector A.			

FM9099300099020X

Fig. 5   Pinpoint test FD (Part 2 of 2)

TEST STEP		RESULT	▶	ACTION TO TAKE
FF1	VERIFY CONDITION			
			▶	GO to FF2.
FF2	CHECK FUEL GAUGE RESPONSE			
	• Disconnect ground cable to battery.	Yes	▶	GO to FF4. TURN ignition OFF.
	• Lower fuel tank (if necessary) to gain access to fuel tank sending unit and pump connections.	No	▶	GO to FF3. TURN ignition OFF.
	• Connect a 43 ohm (± 1 percent) resistor in place of fuel tank sending unit and pump. Verify resistance of resistor prior to test.			
	• Reconnect battery.			
	• Turn ignition key to RUN.			
	• Fuel gauge should illuminate 2 to 3 bars.			
	• Fuel remaining should read 13 to 15L (3 to 4 gal).			
	• Does gauge read properly?			

FM9099300101010X

Fig. 7   Pinpoint test FF (Part 1 of 2)

TEST STEP		RESULT	▶	ACTION TO TAKE
FE1	VERIFY CONDITION			
	• Does CS display?	Yes	▶	GO to FE2.
FE2	CHECK FUEL TANK SENDING UNIT AND PUMP WIRING AT CLUSTER			
	• Disconnect ground cable to battery.	Resistance between 11 and 168 ohms	▶	REPLACE cluster.5
	• Remove cluster and secure connectors from shorting.			
	• With an ohmmeter, measure resistance between Pins 6A and 8A (SIG GND) of harness.	Resistance not as specified	▶	Short exists in harness or fuel tank sending unit and pump. GO to FE3.
	• Verify that the resistance is 11 ohms or greater (normally 11 to 168 ohms).			
	• Is resistance at least 11 ohms?			
FE3	CHECK FUEL TANK SENDING UNIT AND PUMP WIRING			
	• Disconnect ground cable to battery.	Resistance between 11 and 168 ohms	▶	REPLACE fuel tank sending unit and pump.
	• Lower fuel tank to gain access to fuel tank sending unit and pump connector.			
	• Unplug connector to fuel tank sending unit and pump.	Resistance not as specified	▶	SERVICE fuel tank sending unit and pump wiring for short circuit.
	• Measure resistance between Pins 6 and 8 (GND) of harness Connector A.			
	• Verify that resistance is greater than 10,000 ohms.			

FM9099300100000X

Fig. 6   Pinpoint test FE

TEST STEP		RESULT ▶	ACTION TO TAKE
FF3	CHECK HARNESS RESISTANCE		
	• Disconnect ground cable to battery.	42-45 ohms	REPLACE cluster.
	• Remove cluster and secure connectors from shorting.	Not between 42 and 45 ohms	SERVICE Circuit 29 as required.
	• With a 43 ohm resistor in place of fuel sender, measure resistance between Pins 6 and 8 of Connector A		
FF4	CHECK FUEL TANK SENDING UNIT AND PUMP		
	• Disconnect ground cable to battery.	Yes	GO to FF5.
	• Check fuel tank sending unit and pump for binding, sticking, misalignment, etc.	No	SERVICE or REPLACE fuel tank sending unit and pump as required.
	• Is sender OK?		
FF5	CHECK FUEL TANK		
	• Check fuel tank for dents, bulges or other damage.	Yes	GO to FF6.
	• Check for proper installation of fuel tube.	No	REPLACE fuel tank or fuel tube.
	• Are fuel tank or fuel tube OK?		
FF6	CHECK FUEL VAPOR SYSTEM		
	• Check for blockage of fuel tank vapor valve, tubing or carbon canister. Refer to Section 10-00.	Yes	System OK. Fault caused by other vehicle system.
	• Is system OK?	No	SERVICE or REPLACE as required.

FM9099300101020X

Fig. 7   Pinpoint test FF (Part 2 of 2)

TEST STEP		RESULT	▶	ACTION TO TAKE
FG0	VERIFY CONDITION			
		Always on	▶	GO to FG1.
		Never on	▶	GO to FG3.
FG1	CHECK SWITCHES			
	• The following steps are to be repeated for each door ajar switch. Start with the drivers door, then front passenger, then rear passengers.	Warning still displayed	▶	GO to FG2.
	• Turn ignition switch to OFF. This resets the warning.	No warning displayed	▶	SERVICE the last switch tested.
	• Pull connector off of the door ajar switch.			
	• Turn ignition switch to RUN.			
	• Check Message Center for warning.			
	• Repeat until no warning is displayed or all door switches are disconnected.			
FG2	CHECK CIRCUIT 627 BK/O			
	• Turn ignition switch to OFF.	Circuit open	▶	REPLACE cluster.
	• Remove electronic instrument cluster.	Circuit shorted	▶	SERVICE Circuit 627 Bk/O for short.
	• Check continuity between Pins 17 and 18 of Connector A.			
FG3	CHECK SWITCH			
	Turn ignition switch to OFF.	Warning displayed	▶	SERVICE door ajar switch.
	• Pull connector off of the problem door ajar switch.	No warning displayed	▶	GO to FG4.
	• Connect a jumper wire from Circuit 627 Bk/O at the harness connector to ground.			
	• Turn ignition switch to RUN.			
	• Check Message Center for warning.			
FG4	CHECK WIRING			
	• Leave jumper wire connected as in FG3.	Circuit shorted	▶	REPLACE Message Center module.
	• Turn ignition switch to OFF.	Circuit open	▶	SERVICE Circuit 627 BK/O for open.
	• Remove electronic instrument cluster.			
	• Check continuity between Pins 17 and 8 of Connector A.			

FM9099300102010X

Fig. 8   Pinpoint test FG (Part 1 of 2)

TEST STEP		RESULT	▶	ACTION TO TAKE
FG5	CHECK WIRING			
	• Leave jumper wire connected as in FG3.	Yes	▶	REPLACE EIC.
	• Turn ignition switch to OFF.	No	▶	SERVICE Circuit 627 (BK/O) for open.
	• Remove electronic instrument cluster.			
	• Check continuity between Pins 17 and 8 of Connector A.			
	• Is there continuity?			

FM9099300102020X

Fig. 8   Pinpoint test FG (Part 2 of 2)

TEST STEP		RESULT	▶	ACTION TO TAKE
FI1	VERIFY CONDITION		▶	GO to FI2.
FI2	CHECK EXTERIOR BULBS • Check low beam headlamp bulbs. • Check brake lamp bulbs. • Check rear park lamp bulbs. • **Are bulbs OK?**	Yes No	▶ ▶	GO to FI3. SERVICE bulbs.
FI3	CHECK LAMP OUTAGE MODULE INPUT TO ELECTRONIC INSTRUMENT CLUSTER • Disconnect lamp outage module from wiring harness. • Turn ignition switch to RUN. • **Does warning message remain on?**	Yes No	▶ ▶	GO to FI4. GO to troubleshoot lamp outage module.
FI4	CHECK FOR SHORT TO GROUND IN ELECTRONIC CLUSTER HARNESS • With lamp outage module disconnected, disconnect electronic instrument cluster. • Turn ignition switch to RUN. • Check continuity between Ground, Pin 8, Circuit 563 (O/Y) and the "Headlamp Out" warning, Pin 3 (130 R/LG) on the cluster harness connector. • Check continuity between Ground, Pin 8 (563 O/Y) and the "Rear Lamp Out" warning, Pin 5 (125 Y/R) • Check continuity between Ground, Pin 8 (563 O/W) and the "Rear Lamp Out" warning, Pin 5 (135 Y/R). **Electronic Instrument Cluster Harness Connector** • **Is there continuity?**	Yes No	▶ ▶	SERVICE circuit shorted to ground. REPLACE electronic instrument cluster.

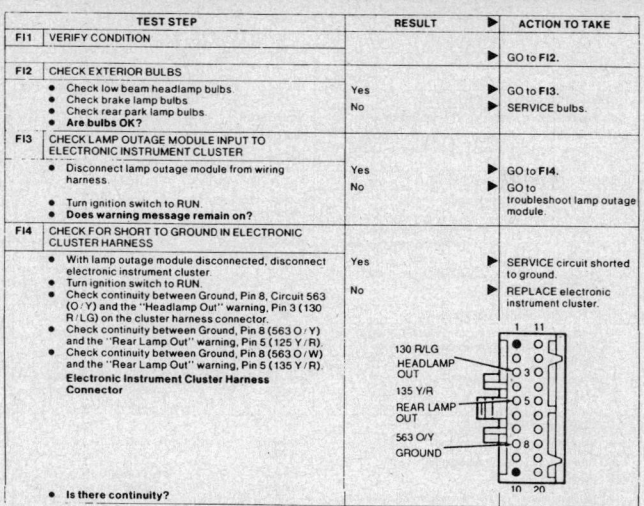

Fig. 9 Pinpoint test FI FM9099300103000X

TEST STEP		RESULT	▶	ACTION TO TAKE
FJ1	CHECK TIME-OUT • Park vehicle on level surface. • Check engine oil level with dipstick. Fill to FULL mark with proper motor oil. • Turn ignition switch to OFF. • Wait for more than two minutes. • Turn ignition switch to RUN. • Check messages for Oil Level Warning.	Warning displayed No warning displayed	▶ ▶	GO to FJ2. System operating properly.
FJ2	CHECK SENSOR • Turn ignition switch to OFF. • Disconnect wire from oil level sensor. • Wait for more than two minutes. • Turn ignition switch to RUN. • Check messages for Oil Level Warning.	Warning displayed No warning displayed	▶ ▶	GO to FJ3 SERVICE oil level sensor.

Fig. 10 Pinpoint test FJ (Part 1 of 2) FM9099300104010X

TEST STEP		RESULT	▶	ACTION TO TAKE
FJ3	CHECK SENSOR • Turn ignition switch to OFF. • Disconnect wire from oil level sensor. • Wait for more than two minutes. • Turn ignition switch to RUN. • Check messages for oil level warning. • **Is warning displayed?**	Yes No	▶ ▶	GO to FJ4. SERVICE oil level sensor.
FJ4	CHECK WIRING • Remove electronic instrument cluster. • Disconnect wire from oil level sensor. • Measure resistance from electronic instrument cluster harness Connector A, Pin 14 to Connector A, Pin 8 or ground. • Circuit should be open. • **Is circuit open?**	Yes No	▶ ▶	REPLACE cluster. SERVICE Circuit 258 (W/PK) for short.

Fig. 10 Pinpoint test FJ (Part 2 of 2) FM9099300104020X

TEST STEP		RESULT	▶	ACTION TO TAKE
FP1	VERIFY CONDITION • Warning never on. Drain fluid from reservoir. • Warning on at all times. Fill reservoir. • Turn ignition to RUN and actuate wiper/washer switch. • Check system scanner for washer fluid warnings.	Warning never on Warning on at all times Warning always illuminates when washer fluid is used	▶ ▶ ▶	GO to FP2. GO to FP6. GO to FP7.
FP2	CHECK SENSOR • Ensure washer fluid is drained from reservoir. • Disconnect electrical connector from windshield washer fluid sensor. • Check sensor for continuity. • **Is there continuity?**	No Yes	▶ ▶	REPLACE sensor. GO to FP3.
FP3	SENSOR VOLTAGE CHECK • Reconnect sensor. • Turn ignition to RUN and actuate wiper/washer switch. • Measure voltage (with respect to ground) at wiper washer fluid sensor. • **Is voltage greater than 9 volts?**	No Yes	▶ ▶	TEST wiper/washer switch. CHECK for an open between sensor and switch. GO to FP4.
FP4	CHECK FOR INTERMITTENT CONNECTION AT CLUSTER • Remove cluster from dash. Do not disconnect. • Turn ignition to RUN and actuate wiper switch. • With wiper switch activated, wiggle Connector B and check connection. • **Is connection intermittent?**	Yes No	▶ ▶	SERVICE Connector B or flexible circuit on cluster. GO to FP5.
FP5	CHECK VOLTAGE AT CLUSTER • Remove cluster as outlined. • Turn ignition to RUN. • Actuate washer fluid switch and measure voltage at Connector B, Pin 15 to ground. • **Is voltage greater than 9 volts?**	No Yes	▶ ▶	CHECK Circuit 298 for an open or short. REPLACE cluster.
FP6	 • Remove cluster as outlined. • Turn ignition to RUN and measure voltage at connector B, Pin 15 to ground. • **Is voltage greater than 3 volts?**	No Yes	▶ ▶	REPLACE cluster. CHECK Circuit 298 for a short to battery or run circuits.
FP7	CHECK SENSOR • Ensure reservoir is full. • Disconnect electrical connector and windshield washer fluid reservoir. • Check continuity across sensor. • **Is there continuity?**	No Yes	▶ ▶	CHECK for an open or short in Circuit 941. REPLACE sensor.

Fig. 11 Pinpoint test FP FM9099300105000X

TEST STEP		RESULT	▶	ACTION TO TAKE
SA1	VERIFY CONDITION • Cluster only responds to buttons when ignition is in RUN. • Warning chime module will not beep if another sound is being produced.	Display does not respond to buttons No beep sounds but display response to buttons/warnings	▶ ▶	GO to SA3. GO to SA2.
SA2	CHECK WARNING CHIME MODULE • Check for fasten safety belt reminder chime or key left in ignition reminder chime. • **Does chime sound?**	Yes No	▶ ▶	GO to SA6. SERVICE warning chime module.

Fig. 12 Pinpoint test SA (Part 1 of 2) FM9099300106010X

TEST STEP		RESULT	▶	ACTION TO TAKE
SA3	CHECK SWITCH WIRING CONNECTIONS • Remove finish panel to expose cluster. • Verify that connections at switch assembly are securely connected. • **Are connections secure?**	Yes No	▶ ▶	GO to SA4. Secure connections and RECHECK
SA4	CHECK SWITCH ASSEMBLY (BUTTON PRESSED) • Unplug switch assembly from electronic instrument cluster (6-pin connector is located at front face of cluster to the far right). • Measure resistance between Pin 2 (Y) and Pin 4 (O) of connector unplugged. • The resistance should be:	Yes No	▶ ▶	GO to SA5. REPLACE switch assembly.

BUTTON	RESISTANCE (in ohms)
E/M	4900-5400
SELECT	2200-2400
SPEED	320-360
RESET	980-985
NO BUTTON PRESSED	17000-17800

NOTE: Press only one button at a time. Wiggle wire at 6-pin switch connector and at switch module and check for loose connections.

• **Is resistance within range?**

TEST STEP		RESULT	▶	ACTION TO TAKE
SA5	CHECK CLUSTER WIRING CONNECTIONS • Visually inspect 6-pin switch connector for poor/damaged or missing connections.	Cluster pin damaged/missing Switch module pins damaged/missing All pins OK	▶ ▶ ▶	REPLACE cluster. REPLACE switch module. REPLACE cluster.
SA6	CHECK TONE CIRCUIT • Disconnect battery ground cable. • Remove cluster. • Turn ignition switch to RUN and wait for the fasten safety belt reminder chime. • Place jumper wire between harness Connector A, Pin 19 and ground. Listen for chime. • **Does chime sound?**	Yes No	▶ ▶	REPLACE cluster. SERVICE wiring Circuit 183 for open. CHECK for correct warning chime module part number or operation.

Fig. 12 Pinpoint test SA (Part 2 of 2) FM9099300106020X

TEST STEP		RESULT	▶	ACTION TO TAKE
SB1	VERIFY CONDITION		▶	GO to SB2.
SB2	VERIFY DISPLAY PROVE OUT • Turn ignition switch to RUN. • Observe display (all segments ON, then OFF, and then normal display). • **Does display prove out properly?**	Yes No	▶ ▶	GO to SB3. REPLACE cluster.¹
SB3	CHECK ODOMETER • Verify that odometer advances when vehicle is driven forward. • **Does odometer advance?**	No Yes	▶ ▶	GO to SB4. REPLACE cluster.¹
SB4	CHECK FUEL COMPUTER • Test drive vehicle. • Select TRIP DISTANCE on fuel computer. • Distance should advance as vehicle is driven. • **Does distance advance?**	Yes No	▶ ▶	REPLACE cluster.¹ GO to SB5.
SB5	CHECK SPEED CONTROL • Test drive vehicle and check operation of speed control, if so equipped. • **Does speed control operate properly?**	Yes No	▶ ▶	GO to SB10. GO to SB6.
SB6	CHECK WIRING TO SPEED SENSOR • Disconnect connector to vehicle speed sensor. • Using Rotunda Digital Volt-Ohmmeter 014-00407 or equivalent, measure the resistance between the two wires in the harness to the vehicle speed sensor. • Resistance should be greater than 500 ohms. • **Is resistance greater than 500 ohms?**	Yes No	▶ ▶	GO to SB7. SERVICE wiring Circuit 150, speed control, cluster for shorts.
SB7	CHECK VEHICLE SPEED SENSOR RESISTANCE • Using Rotunda Digital Volt-Ohmmeter 014-00407 or equivalent, measure the resistance between the two wires in the harness to the vehicle speed sensor. • Resistance should be 200 - 230 ohms. • **Is resistance within range?**	Yes No	▶ ▶	GO to SB8. REPLACE vehicle speed sensor. CHECK speedometer operation.
SB8	CHECK DRIVEN GEAR AND RETAINER CLIP • Disconnect vehicle speed sensor from transmission. Verify presence of driven gear with all teeth in good condition and the presence of retainer clip. • **Are driven gear and retainer clip OK?**	Drive gear/clip OK Drive gear/clip not OK	▶ ▶	GO to SB9. REPLACE with proper gear and/or clip.
SB9	CHECK DRIVE GEAR ON TRANSMISSION • Verify presence of drive gear on transaxle output shaft. • **Is drive gear OK?**	Drive gear present Drive gear not present	▶ ▶	GO to SB10. SERVICE gear.
SB10	CHECK WIRING TO CLUSTER • Reconnect vehicle speed sensor wiring. • Disconnect battery ground cable. • Remove cluster as outlined. • Using Rotunda Digital Volt-Ohmmeter 014-00407 or equivalent, measure the resistance between Pins 12 and 8 (ground) of Connector A. • Resistance should be 160 - 230 ohms. • **Is resistance within range?**	Resistance between 160 and 230 ohms Resistance not as specified	▶ ▶	REPLACE cluster.¹ SERVICE connectors, wiring from cluster to vehicle speed sensor Circuit 150. CHECK speedometer operation.

Fig. 13 Pinpoint test SB (Part 1 of 2) FM9099300107000X

TEST STEP		RESULT	▶	ACTION TO TAKE
SC1	VERIFY CONDITION			
			▶	GO to SC2.
SC2	CHECK ODOMETER ACCURACY			
	• Over a known distance, compare the odometer reading with the distance traveled.	Odometer accurate	▶	System OK.
		Odometer not accurate	▶	GO to SC3.
SC3	CHECK SPEED SENSOR DRIVE GEAR			
	• Remove speed sensor from transmission and verify that correct drive gear is installed for vehicle transmission / axle / tire combination.	Correct gear installed	▶	GO to SC4.
		Incorrect gear installed	▶	INSTALL correct gear with retaining clip.
SC4	CHECK DRIVE GEAR ON TRANSMISSION OUTPUT SHAFT			
	• Check that correct drive gear is installed on transaxle output shaft.	Correct gear installed	▶	REPLACE cluster module.
		Incorrect gear installed	▶	INSTALL correct shaft / gear.

FM9099300108000X

Fig. 14   Pinpoint test SC

TEST STEP		RESULT	▶	ACTION TO TAKE
SE1	VERIFY CONDITION			
	$\boldsymbol{0}$ MPH ERROR		▶	REPLACE cluster.

FM9099300110000X

Fig. 16   Pinpoint test SE

TEST STEP		RESULT	▶	ACTION TO TAKE
SG1	VERIFY CONDITION			
		Odometer will not accumulate	▶	Go to SG2.
		Odometer accumulates 16 Km (10 miles), then loses 16 Km (10 miles)	▶	REPLACE cluster
SG2	VERIFY SPEEDOMETER			
	• Verify that speedometer works properly.	Yes	▶	REPLACE cluster
	• **Does speedometer operate properly?**	No	▶	GO to Pinpoint Test SB.

FM9099300112000X

Fig. 18   Pinpoint test SG

TEST STEP		RESULT	▶	ACTION TO TAKE
SJ1	VERIFY CONDITION			
			▶	GO to SJ2.
SJ2	CHECK SPEEDOMETER			
	• Perform Pinpoint Test SC.	Yes	▶	GO to SJ3.
	• **Is system OK?**	No	▶	GO to Pinpoint Test SC.
SJ3	CHECK DISPLAY			
	• Perform Pinpoint Test TB.	Yes	▶	GO to SJ4.
	• **Is system OK?**	No	▶	GO to Pinpoint Test TB.
SJ4	CHECK ODOMETER MEMORY			
	• Perform Pinpoint Test SH.	Yes	▶	System OK
	• **Is system OK?**	No	▶	GO to Pinpoint Test SH.

FM9099300114000X

Fig. 20   Pinpoint test SJ

TEST STEP		RESULT	▶	ACTION TO TAKE
SD1	VERIFY CONDITION			
			▶	GO to SD2.
SD2	CHECK SPEED SENSOR DRIVE GEAR			
	• Remove speed sensor from transmission.	Gear / clip OK	▶	GO to SD3.
	• Check that all gear teeth are in good condition, retainer clip is installed and gear does not slip on shaft.	Gear / clip not OK	▶	REPLACE drive gear and / or retaining clip.
SD3	CHECK WIRING TO SPEED SENSOR			
	• Disconnect connector to speed sensor.	Resistance greater than 500 ohms	▶	GO to SD4.
	• Using Rotunda Digital Volt Ohmmeter 014-00407 or equivalent, check for intermittent resistance between the two wires in the harness to the speed sensor.	Resistance less than 500 ohms	▶	SERVICE wiring Circuit 150, speed control for intermittent shorts or opens. CHECK speedometer operation.
	• Resistance should be greater than 500 ohms.			
SD4	CHECK SPEED SENSOR RESISTANCE			
	• Using Rotunda Digital Volt Ohmmeter 014-00407 or equivalent, check for intermittent resistance at speed sensor.	Resistance between 200 and 230 ohms	▶	GO to SD5.
	• Resistance should be 200-230 ohms.	Resistance not as specified	▶	REPLACE speed sensor. CHECK speedometer operation.
SD5	CHECK WIRING TO CLUSTER			
	• Reconnect speed sensor wiring.	Resistance constant	▶	REPLACE cluster.
	• Disconnect battery ground cable.	Resistance intermittent	▶	SERVICE connectors / wiring from cluster to speed sensor Circuit 150. CHECK speedometer operation.
	• Remove cluster.			
	• Using Rotunda Digital Volt-Ohmmeter 014-00407 or equivalent, measure the resistance between Pin 12 and 8 (ground) of connector A.			
	• Resistance should be between 200 and 300 ohms.			

FM9099300109000X

Fig. 15   Pinpoint test SD

TEST STEP		RESULT	▶	ACTION TO TAKE
SF1	VERIFY CONDITION			
			▶	GO to SF2.
	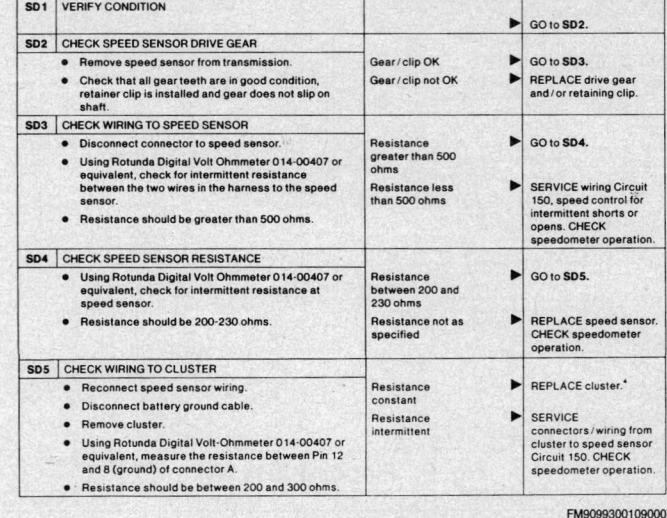			
SF2	DETERMINE IF SPEEDO / ODO MODULE IS ORIGINAL			
	• Check for mileage sticker on door pillar.	Original	▶	Display damaged. REPLACE cluster. S should be illuminated and odometer should indicate zero miles.
	• **Is module original?**	Replacement	▶	System OK. Label on door pillar should indicate mileage at which the replacement cluster was installed.

FM9099300111000X

Fig. 17   Pinpoint test SF

TEST STEP		RESULT	▶	ACTION TO TAKE
SH1	VERIFY CONDITION			
	• Enter self-diagnosis as outlined.	No	▶	REPLACE cluster.
	• **Does cluster flash?**	Yes	▶	GO to Pinpoint Test SB1.

FM9099300113000X

Fig. 19   Pinpoint test SH

TEST STEP		RESULT	▶	ACTION TO TAKE
SK1	VERIFY CONDITION			
	• Make sure engine is operating properly and is not misfiring.		▶	GO to SK2.
SK2	CHECK WIRING			
	• Disconnect battery ground cable.	Yes	▶	REPLACE cluster. RECHECK operation.
	• Remove cluster as outlined.	No	▶	SERVICE wiring Circuit 11 for open circuit.
	• Measure resistance between Connector A, Pin 20 and coil.			
	• Wiggle connections and wiring near coil to check for intermittent connection.			
	• **Is resistance less than 100 ohms?**			

FM9099300115000X

Fig. 21   Pinpoint test SK

TEST STEP		RESULT	▶	ACTION TO TAKE
TA1	VERIFY CONDITION			
	• Turn ignition to the RUN position.	Cluster partially illuminated	▶	GO to TA2.
		All displays black	▶	GO to TA3.
TA2	VERIFY ABNORMAL CONDITION			
	• Check to see if all choices (segments) except the one selected go black.	All segments except one selected go black	▶	System OK.
		Cluster partially black	▶	REPLACE cluster
TA3	CHECK FUSES			
	• Check Circuits 797 and 298 for blown fuses (battery and run voltage to cluster)	No	▶	GO to TA4.
	• **Is fuse OK?**	Yes	▶	GO to TA5.

FM9099300116010X

Fig. 22   Pinpoint test TA (Part 1 of 2)

TEST STEP		RESULT	▶	ACTION TO TAKE
TA4	CHECK FOR SHORTS			
	• Turn ignition to OFF. • Disconnect battery ground cable. • Connect an ohmmeter from circuit with blown fuse to ground. • **Is there continuity?**	No Yes	▶ ▶	REPLACE fuse. SERVICE circuit as required.
TA5	CHECK FOR POWER TO FUSE			
	• Connect battery. • Turn ignition to RUN. • Measure voltage from Circuits 797 and 298 to ground. • **Is voltage greater than 9 volts?**	Yes No	▶ ▶	GO to TA6. SERVICE open in fuse holder.
TA6	CHECK FOR LOOSE CONNECTIONS			
	• Remove cluster (leave connected). • Connect battery. • Turn ignition to RUN. • Wiggle A and B connectors on rear of cluster. • **Are connectors OK?**	No Yes	▶ ▶	SERVICE as required. GO to TA7.
TA7	CHECK POWER AND GROUND			
	• Turn ignition to OFF. • Remove cluster as outlined. • Turn ignition to RUN. • Measure voltage at the harness connector A and B of the cluster. • Voltage should be:	Yes No	▶ ▶	REPLACE cluster. SERVICE Circuit BATT 797 RUN 298 GROUND 359.

PIN	FUNCTION	VOLTAGE
7A	BATT	Battery Voltage
9A	RUN	Battery Voltage
14B	RUN	Battery Voltage

	• Check continuity of ground circuit Pins 8A and 13B to battery ground. • **Are voltage and continuity present?**			
TA8	CHECK FLEX CIRCUIT BOARD			
	• Disconnect battery ground cable. • Remove cluster as outlined. • Inspect flexible circuit traces (traces are double thick) connected to Circuits 13B and 14B (ground and run circuits). • **Are traces OK?**	Yes No	▶ ▶	REPLACE cluster. REPLACE Flexible circuit.

FM9099300116020X

Fig. 22   Pinpoint test TA (Part 2 of 2)

TEST STEP		RESULT	▶	ACTION TO TAKE
TC1	VERIFY CONDITION			
	• Turn ignition switch from OFF to RUN and observe the display prove out. All segments on one second, all segments off one second followed by a normal display.	Prove out operates Prove out does not operate properly	▶ ▶	System OK. REPLACE cluster.

FM9099300118000X

Fig. 24   Pinpoint test TC

TEST STEP		RESULT	▶	ACTION TO TAKE
TE1	VERIFY CONDITION			
			▶	GO to TE2.
TE2	CHECK FOR TEMPERATURE SENDER SHORT			
	• Unplug wire temperature sender. • Turn ignition to RUN. • Temperature gauge should indicate COLD with bottom bar illuminated.	Temperature gauge indicates as specified Temperature gauge does not indicate as specified	▶ ▶	REPLACE temperature sender. GO to TE3.
TE3	CHECK FOR SHORT IN WIRING			
	• Disconnect battery ground cable. • Unplug wire temperature sender. • Remove cluster. • Measure resistance between Pin 4A and Pin 8A (GND).	Resistance greater than 15,000 ohms Resistance less than 15,000 ohms	▶ ▶	REPLACE cluster. SERVICE wiring Circuit 39 for shorts.

FM9099300120000X

Fig. 26   Pinpoint test TE

TEST STEP		RESULT	▶	ACTION TO TAKE
TB1	VERIFY CONDITION			
	• Check to see if part of cluster is dim or all displays are dim	Part of cluster dim and part of cluster illumination OK All displays too dim	▶ ▶	REPLACE cluster. GO to TB2.
TB2	ENSURE HEADLAMPS ARE OFF			
	• Cluster will dim from 65 percent to almost off with headlamps on. • **Are headlamps off?**	No Yes	▶ ▶	TURN headlamps OFF. GO to TB3.

FM9099300117010X

Fig. 23   Pinpoint test TB (Part 1 of 2)

TEST STEP		RESULT	▶	ACTION TO TAKE
TB3	CHECK DIMMER VOLTAGE			
	• Disconnect battery ground cable. • Remove cluster as outlined and disconnect Connectors A and B. • Connect battery ground and turn ignition to RUN. • Ensure headlamps are off. Measure dimmer voltage to ground (Connector A, Pin 19). • **Is voltage greater than 3 volts?**	No Yes	▶ ▶	REPLACE cluster. SERVICE Circuit 19 and dimmer for short to battery or run circuits.

FM9099300117020X

Fig. 23   Pinpoint test TB (Part 2 of 2)

TEST STEP		RESULT	▶	ACTION TO TAKE
TD1	VERIFY CONDITION			
	• Turn ignition to RUN. • Turn headlamps on. • Dimmer should control cluster illumination from 65 percent to almost off. • **Does cluster dim properly?**	Yes No	▶ ▶	System OK. GO to TD2.
TD2	CHECK DIMMER VOLTAGE			
	• Disconnect battery ground cable. • Remove cluster as outlined. • Connect battery ground cable. • Turn ignition to RUN. • Turn headlamps on. • Voltage at Connector A, Pin 13 should vary from 5 volts to battery voltage while operating dimmer. • **Does voltage vary within range?**	Yes No	▶ ▶	System OK. REPLACE cluster.

FM9099300119000X

Fig. 25   Pinpoint test TD

TEST STEP		RESULT	▶	ACTION TO TAKE
TF1	CHECK TEMPERATURE GAUGE WIRING			
	• Unplug connector to temperature sender and connect a jumper to ground in place of sender. • Turn ignition to RUN. • Gauge should give a short circuit indication. Top two and bottom two bars of gauge illuminated.	Top two and bottom two bars illuminate Bars do not illuminate as specified	▶ ▶	GO to TF3. REMOVE jumper. GO to TF2.
TF2	CHECK WIRING AT CLUSTER			
	• Disconnect ground cable to battery. • Remove cluster. • Connect jumper in place of temperature sender. • Verify continuity between Pins 4A and 8A of harness. • **Is there continuity?**	Yes No	▶ ▶	REPLACE cluster. SERVICE wiring Circuit 39 and / or temperature sender ground line for open circuit.
TF3	CHECK SENDER			
	• Warm up engine to normal operating temperature. • Measure resistance of temperature sender.	Resistance less than 8,000 ohms Resistance greater than 8,000 ohms	▶ ▶	REPLACE cluster. GO to TF4.
TF4	CHECK COOLING SYSTEM			
	• Check thermostat, coolant level, etc. for proper operation.	Cooling system OK Cooling system not OK	▶ ▶	REPLACE temperature sender. SERVICE cooling system as required.

FM9099300121000X

Fig. 27   Pinpoint test TF

PINPOINT TEST TX: NO WARNING TONE WHEN THERMOMETER SYMBOL IS BLINKING				
TEST STEP		RESULT	▶	ACTION TO TAKE
TX1	REVIEW OPERATION / VERIFY CONDITION			
	• The gauge driver alert tone is not active until at least 300 rpm or valid oil pressure has been detected, (i.e. vehicle was started). • Warning chime module will not beep if another sound is being produced. • Driver alert only given for temperatures above normal band.		▶	GO to TX2.
TX2	CHECK WARNING CHIME			
	• Turn ignition to RUN. • Press any cluster control button and listen for beep. • **Does chime beep?**	Yes No	▶ ▶	System OK. GO to Pinpoint Test SA.

FM9099300122000X

Fig. 28   Pinpoint test TX

NOTE: Refer to the Symptom Index in this section before performing any Pinpoint Tests.

INDEX

	Page No. 15-	Fig. No.		Page No. 15-	Fig. No.
PINPOINT TESTS:			Pinpoint Test FB	27	16
Pinpoint Test AA	25	2	Pinpoint Test FC	27	17
Pinpoint Test AB	25	3	Pinpoint Test GA	28	18
Pinpoint Test AC	25	4	Pinpoint Test HA	28	19
Pinpoint Test BA	26	5	Pinpoint Test HB	28	20
Pinpoint Test BB	26	6	Pinpoint Test HC	28	21
Pinpoint Test BC	26	7	Pinpoint Test JA	28	22
Pinpoint Test CA	26	8	Pinpoint Test JB	28	23
Pinpoint Test CB	26	9	Pinpoint Test JC	29	24
Pinpoint Test CC	27	10	Pinpoint Test JD	29	25
Pinpoint Test DA	27	11	Pinpoint Test JE	29	26
Pinpoint Test EA	27	12	Pinpoint Test JF	29	27
Pinpoint Test EB	27	13	Pinpoint Test JG	30	28
Pinpoint Test EC	27	14	Pinpoint Test JH	30	29
Pinpoint Test FA	27	15	**SYMPTOM INDEX**	24	1

CONDITION	POSSIBLE SOURCE	ACTION
• Display Not Illuminated, Too Dim or Blank But Backlighted	• Instrument cluster. • Circuitry. • Instrument cluster printed circuit.	• Go to Pinpoint Test AA.
• Display Scrambled, Incorrect All the Time or Stuck With All Segments on Segments Half Lit, Blinking or Missing	• Instrument cluster.	• Go to Pinpoint Test AB.
• Display Does Not Respond To Buttons or No Beep When Buttons Pushed or Driver Alert Given	• Safety belt warning chime. • Instrument indicator switch. • Instrument cluster. • Circuitry.	• Go to Pinpoint Test AC.

FM9099400123010X

Fig. 1 Symptom index (Part 1 of 3)

CONDITION	POSSIBLE SOURCE	ACTION
• CO Displayed, Top Two and Bottom Two Diagnostic Bars Displayed	• Open in harness 14A488 connectors or fuel pump. • Inoperative EIC. • Open in harness 14401.	• Go to Pinpoint Test BA.
• CS Displayed, Top Two and Bottom Two Diagnostic Bars Displayed	• Short in harness 14A488, connectors or fuel pump. • Short in harness 14401. • Inoperative EIC.	• Go to Pinpoint Test BB.
• Inaccurate Fuel Gauge Indication	• Inoperative fuel pump. • Valve, tube or fuel vapor canister plugged. • Fuel tank damaged. • Inoperative EIC.	• Go to Pinpoint Test BC.

TEMPERATURE GAUGE DIAGNOSIS

CONDITION	POSSIBLE SOURCE	ACTION
• Temperature Gauge Displays Top Two And Bottom Two Diagnostic Bars	• EIC. • Circuitry.	• Go to Pinpoint Test CA.
• Temperature Gauge Always Indicates Hot Or Cold Temperature	• EIC. • Circuitry. • Water temperature indicator sender unit.	• Go to Pinpoint Test CB.
• No Warning Tone When Thermometer Symbol is Blinking	• EIC. • Circuitry. • Safety belt warning chime.	• Go to Pinpoint Test CC.

VOLTS GAUGE DIAGNOSIS

CONDITION	POSSIBLE SOURCE	ACTION
• Volts Gauge Always Gives Charging System Alert (Flashing Battery Symbol)	• Inoperative generator regulator.	• Go to Pinpoint Test DA.

SPEEDOMETER DIAGNOSIS

CONDITION	POSSIBLE SOURCE	ACTION
• Speedometer Reads 0 km/h (mph) At All Speeds	• Inoperative EIC. • Circuitry. • Vehicle speed sensor.	• Go to Pinpoint Test EA.
• Speedometer Constantly Reads Too High Or Too Low	• Incorrect drive gear. • Inoperative EIC.	• Go to Pinpoint Test EB.
• Speed Indication Jumps Up And Down Erratically	• Inoperative EIC. • Vehicle speed sensor.	• Go to Pinpoint Test EC.

ODOMETER DIAGNOSIS

CONDITION	POSSIBLE SOURCE	ACTION
• Display Reads "Error"	• Inoperative EIC.	• Replace EIC. Affix odometer sticker to door pillar.
• Display Has "S" Illuminated	• Inoperative EIC.	• Go to Pinpoint Test FA.
• Mileage Constantly Reads Too High Or Too Low	• Incorrect drive gear. • Inoperative EIC.	• Go to Pinpoint Test FB.
• Odometer Does Not Accumulate Mileage or Counts 1.6 km (1.0 mile) and Jumps Back 1.6 km (1.0 mile)	• Inoperative EIC. • Vehicle speed sensor.	• Go to Pinpoint Test FC.

FM9099400123020X

Fig. 1 Symptom index (Part 2 of 3)

TACHOMETER DIAGNOSIS

CONDITION	POSSIBLE SOURCE	ACTION
• Tachometer Always Indicates Too High or Too Low, No Tach Indication or Tach Indication Erratic	• EIC. • Circuitry. • Faulty ignition coil	Go to Pinpoint Test GA.

MESSAGE CENTER DISPLAY DIAGNOSIS

CONDITION	POSSIBLE SOURCE	ACTION
• Instantaneous or Average Fuel Economy Always Reads 0 Miles / Gal Or 99 L / 100 km or 99 Miles / Gal or 0 L / 100 km	• EIC. • Circuitry.	• Go to Pinpoint Test HA.
• Trip Distance Does Not Accumulate.	• EIC. • Circuitry.	• Go to Pinpoint Test HB.
• DTE Does Not Go Below 322 km (200 Miles) With Fuel Tank Empty or DTE Always Reads Zero	• EIC. • Circuitry.	• Go to Pinpoint Test HC.

WARNING INDICATORS DIAGNOSIS

CONDITION	POSSIBLE SOURCE	ACTION
• DOOR AJAR Warning Never / Always Comes On	• Inoperative door open warning lamp switch. • Inoperative EIC. • Circuitry.	• Go to Pinpoint Test JA.
• Low WASHER FLUID Warning Always On	• Inoperative windshield washer reservoir fluid level sensor. • Circuitry. • Open in windshield washer reservoir fluid level sensor connector. • Inoperative EIC.	• Go to Pinpoint Test JB.
• CHECK ENGINE (MIL) Warning Always On	• EIC. • Circuitry. • Damaged powertrain control module.	• Go to Pinpoint Test JC.
• BRAKE Warning Never / Always On	• EIC. • Brake fluid level switch.	• Go to Pinpoint Test JD.
• High Beam Warning Never / Always On	• EIC. • Headlamp switch. • Circuitry.	• Go to Pinpoint Test JE.
• Anti-Lock Warning Never / Always On	• EIC. • Circuitry. • Anti-lock brake control module.	• Go to Pinpoint Test JF.
• Low Oil Pressure Warning Never / Always On	• EIC. • Circuitry. • Oil pressure sender.	• Go to Pinpoint Test JG.
• Air Bag Warning Never / Always On	• EIC. • Circuitry. • Air bag diagnostic monitor.	• Go to Pinpoint Test JH.

Fig. 1   Symptom index (Part 3 of 3)

TEST STEP		RESULT	▶	ACTION TO TAKE
AA1	CHECK EIC DIMMING • Turn ignition switch to RUN. • Turn headlamps on. • Dimmer should control cluster illumination from 65 percent to almost off. • **Does instrument cluster dim properly?**	Yes No	▶ ▶	GO to AA5. GO to AA2.
AA2	CHECK DIMMER VOLTAGE • Disconnect battery ground cable. • Remove instrument cluster as outlined. • Connect battery ground cable. • Turn ignition switch to RUN. • Turn headlamps on. • Voltage at 20-pin connector, Pin 13 should vary from 5 volts to battery voltage while operating dimmer. • **Does voltage vary within range?**	Yes No	▶ ▶	GO to AA3. SERVICE dimmer.
AA3	CHECK INSTRUMENT CLUSTER DIMMING • Check to see if part of instrument cluster is dim or all displays are dim. • **Are all displays dim?**	Yes No	▶ ▶	GO to AA4. REPLACE instrument cluster. AFFIX odometer sticker to door pillar.
AA4	ENSURE HEADLAMPS ARE OFF • Instrument cluster will dim from 65 percent to almost off with headlamps on. • Turn headlamp bulb OFF. • Disconnect battery ground cable. • Remove instrument cluster as outlined and disconnect connectors. • Connect battery ground cable and turn ignition switch to RUN. • Ensure headlamps are off. Measure dimmer voltage to ground (20-pin connector, Pin 19). • **Is voltage greater than 3 volts?**	Yes No	▶ ▶	SERVICE Circuit 19 and dimmer short to BATTERY or RUN circuits. REPLACE instrument cluster. AFFIX odometer sticker to door pillar.
AA5	CHECK EIC ILLUMINATION • Turn ignition switch to the RUN position. • **Is instrument cluster partially illuminated?**	Yes No	▶ ▶	GO to AA6. GO to AA7.
AA6	VERIFY ABNORMAL CONDITION • Check to see if all choices (segments), except the one selected, go black. • **Do all segments except one selected go black?**	Yes No	▶ ▶	System OK. REPLACE instrument cluster. Affix odometer sticker to door pillar.
AA7	CHECK FUSES • Check Circuits 797 and 298 for blown fuses (battery and run voltage to instrument cluster). • **Is fuse OK?**	Yes No	▶ ▶	GO to AA9. GO to AA8.
AA8	CHECK FOR SHORTS • Turn ignition switch to OFF. • Disconnect battery ground cable. • Connect an ohmmeter from circuit with blown fuse to ground. • **Is there continuity?**	Yes No	▶ ▶	SERVICE circuit as required. REPLACE fuse.
AA9	CHECK FOR POWER TO FUSE • Connect battery ground cable. • Turn ignition switch to RUN. • Measure voltage from Circuits 797 and 298 to ground. • **Is voltage greater than 9 volts?**	Yes No	▶ ▶	GO to AA10. SERVICE as required.

FM9099400124010X

Fig. 2   Pinpoint test AA (Part 1 of 2)

TEST STEP		RESULT	▶	ACTION TO TAKE
AA10	CHECK FOR LOOSE CONNECTIONS • Remove instrument cluster (leave connected). • Connect battery ground cable. • Turn ignition switch to RUN. • Wiggle connectors on rear of instrument cluster. • **Are connectors OK?**	Yes No	▶ ▶	SERVICE as required. GO to AA11.
AA11	CHECK POWER AND GROUND • Turn ignition switch to OFF. • Remove instrument cluster as outlined. • Turn ignition switch to RUN. • Measure voltage at the harness connectors of the instrument cluster. • Voltage should be:	Yes No	▶ ▶	GO to AA12. SERVICE BATT Circuit 797 RUN 298 GROUND 359.

PIN	FUNCTION	VOLTAGE
7 (of 20)	BATT	Battery Voltage
9 (of 20)	RUN	Battery Voltage
14 (of 18)	RUN	Battery Voltage

TEST STEP		RESULT	▶	ACTION TO TAKE
	• Check continuity of ground Circuit Pins 8 (of 20) and 13 (of 18) to battery ground. • **Are voltage and continuity present?**			
AA12	CHECK FLEX CIRCUIT BOARD • Disconnect battery ground cable. • Remove instrument cluster as outlined. • Inspect flexible circuit traces (traces are double thick) connected to Circuits 13 (of 18) and 14 (of 18) • **Are traces OK?**	Yes No	▶ ▶	REPLACE instrument cluster. AFFIX odometer sticker to door pillar. REPLACE instrument cluster printed circuit.

FM9099400124020X

Fig. 2   Pinpoint test AA (Part 2 of 2)

TEST STEP		RESULT	▶	ACTION TO TAKE
AB1	CHECK PROVE-OUT • Turn ignition switch from OFF to RUN. • Observe the EIC display prove-out (All segments on for one second, all segments off for one second followed by a normal display). • **Does EIC prove-out properly?**	Yes No	▶ ▶	System OK. REPLACE instrument cluster. AFFIX odometer sticker to door pillar.

FM9099400125000X

Fig. 3   Pinpoint test AB

TEST STEP		RESULT	▶	ACTION TO TAKE
AC4	CHECK SWITCH ASSEMBLY (BUTTON PRESSED) • Unplug instrument indicator switch from electronic instrument cluster (6-pin connector is located at front face of instrument cluster to the far right). • Measure resistance between Pin 2 (Y) and Pin 4 (O) of connector unplugged. • The resistance should be:	Yes No	▶ ▶	GO to AC5. REPLACE instrument indicator switch.

BUTTON	RESISTANCE (in ohms)
E / M	4900-5400
SELECT	2200-2400
SPEED	320-360
RESET	980-985
NO BUTTON PRESSED	17000-17800

TEST STEP		RESULT	▶	ACTION TO TAKE
	NOTE: Press only one button at a time. Wiggle wire at 6-pin switch connector and at instrument indicator switch and check for loose connections. • **Is resistance within range?**			
AC5	CHECK CLUSTER WIRING CONNECTIONS • Visually inspect 6-pin switch connector for poor / damaged or missing connections. • **Are all pins OK?**	Yes No	▶ ▶	REPLACE instrument cluster. AFFIX odometer sticker to door pillar. REPLACE instrument indicator switch.
AC6	CHECK TONE CIRCUIT • Disconnect battery ground cable. • Remove instrument cluster. • Turn ignition switch to RUN and wait for the fasten safety belt reminder chime to end. • Place jumper wire between harness 20-pin Connector, Pin 19 and ground. Listen for chime. • **Does chime sound?**	Yes No	▶ ▶	REPLACE instrument cluster. SERVICE wiring Circuit 183 for open. CHECK for correct warning chime module part number or operation.

FM9099400126020X

Fig. 4   Pinpoint test AC (Part 2 of 2)

TEST STEP		RESULT	▶	ACTION TO TAKE
AC1	CHECK RESPONSE TO BUTTONS • Cluster only responds to buttons when ignition switch is in RUN. • Safety belt warning chime module will not beep if another sound is being produced. • **Does display respond to buttons?**	Yes No	▶ ▶	GO to AC2. GO to AC3.
AC2	CHECK WARNING CHIME MODULE • Check for fasten safety belt reminder chime or key left in ignition reminder chime. • **Does chime sound?**	Yes No	▶ ▶	GO to AC6. SERVICE safety belt warning chime.
AC3	CHECK SWITCH WIRING CONNECTIONS • Remove finish panel to expose instrument cluster. • Verify that connections at switch assembly are securely connected. • **Are connections secure?**	Yes No	▶ ▶	GO to AC4. Secure connections and RECHECK.

FM9099400126010X

Fig. 4   Pinpoint test AC (Part 1 of 2)

TEST STEP	RESULT	▶	ACTION TO TAKE
BA1 CHECK FUEL TANK SENDING UNIT AND PUMP WIRING AT FUEL TANK SENDING UNIT AND PUMP • Disconnect battery ground cable. • Lower fuel tank to gain access to fuel tank sending unit and pump connector. • Unplug fuel sender connector. • Jumper variable resistance terminal and ground terminal of harness together. • Reconnect battery. • Turn ignition switch from OFF to RUN. • Check digital fuel remaining display for CO or CS NOTE: It may take several minutes for the fuel gauge to respond. • **Is CO displayed?**	Yes No	▶ ▶	GO to **BA3**. GO to **BA2** if CS displayed. REMOVE jumper.

FM9099400127010X

Fig. 5   Pinpoint test BA (Part 1 of 2)

TEST STEP	RESULT	▶	ACTION TO TAKE
BA2 CHECK FUEL TANK SENDING UNIT AND PUMP • Turn ignition switch to OFF. • Measure the resistance of the fuel tank sending unit and pump at the sender terminals. • Verify that the resistance is between 11 and 168 ohms. • **Is resistance between 11 and 168 ohms?**	Yes No	▶ ▶	INSPECT fuel tank sending unit and pump wiring connector female terminals for flash or loose fit. SERVICE as required. REPLACE fuel tank sending unit and pump.
BA3 CHECK FUEL TANK SENDING UNIT AND PUMP WIRING AT CLUSTER • Disconnect battery ground cable. • Remove instrument cluster and secure connectors from shorting. • Jumper variable resistance terminal and ground terminal of harness together at fuel tank sending unit. • Verify condition between Pins 6 and 8 (ground) of cluster 20-pin connector. • **Is fuel tank sending unit and pump wiring OK?**	Yes No	▶ ▶	REPLACE instrument cluster. AFFIX odometer sticker to door pillar. SERVICE fuel tank sending unit and pump wiring for open circuit.

FM9099400127020X

Fig. 5   Pinpoint test BA (Part 2 of 2)

TEST STEP	RESULT	▶	ACTION TO TAKE
BB1 CHECK FUEL TANK SENDING UNIT AND PUMP WIRING AT CLUSTER • Disconnect battery ground cable. • Remove instrument cluster and secure connectors from shorting. • With an ohmmeter, measure resistance between Pins 6A and 8A (SIG GND) of harness. • Verify that the resistance is 11 ohms or greater (normally 11 to 168 ohms). • **Is resistance at least 11 ohms?**	Yes No	▶ ▶	REPLACE instrument cluster. AFFIX odometer sticker to door pillar. Short exists in harness or fuel tank sending unit and pump. GO to **BB2**.
BB2 CHECK FUEL TANK SENDING UNIT AND PUMP WIRING • Disconnect battery ground cable. • Lower fuel tank to gain access to fuel tank sending unit and pump connector. • Unplug connector to fuel tank sending unit and pump. • Measure resistance between Pins 6 and 8 (GND) of harness Connector A. • Verify that resistance is greater than 10,000 ohms. • **Is resistance greater than 10,000 ohms?**	Yes No	▶ ▶	REPLACE fuel tank sending unit and pump. SERVICE fuel tank sending unit and pump wiring for short circuit.

FM9099400128000X

Fig. 6   Pinpoint test BB

TEST STEP	RESULT	▶	ACTION TO TAKE
BC1 CHECK FUEL GAUGE RESPONSE • Disconnect battery ground cable. • Lower fuel tank (if necessary) to gain access to fuel tank sending unit and pump connections. • Connect a 43 ohm (± 1 percent) resistor in place of fuel tank sending unit and pump. Verify resistance of resistor prior to test. • Reconnect battery ground cable. • Turn ignition switch to RUN. • Fuel gauge should illuminate two to three bars. • Fuel remaining should read 13 to 15L (3 to 4 gal). • **Does fuel gauge read properly?**	Yes No	▶ ▶	GO to **BC3**. TURN ignition switch OFF. GO to **BC2**. TURN ignition switch OFF.

FM9099400129010X

Fig. 7   Pinpoint test BC (Part 1 of 2)

TEST STEP	RESULT	▶	ACTION TO TAKE
BC2 CHECK HARNESS RESISTANCE • Disconnect battery ground cable. • Remove instrument cluster and secure connectors from shorting. • With a 43-ohm resistor in place of fuel tank sending unit, measure resistance between Pins 6 and 8 of 20-pin Connector. • **Is resistance between 42-45 ohms?**	Yes No	▶ ▶	REPLACE instrument cluster. AFFIX odometer sticker to door pillar. SERVICE Circuit 29 as required.
BC3 CHECK FUEL TANK SENDING UNIT AND PUMP • Disconnect battery ground cable. • Check fuel tank sending unit and pump for binding, sticking, misalignment, etc. • **Is sender OK?**	Yes No	▶ ▶	GO to **BC4**. SERVICE or REPLACE fuel tank sending unit and pump as required.
BC4 CHECK FUEL TANK • Check fuel tank for dents, bulges or other damage. • Check for proper installation of fuel tube. • **Are fuel tank and fuel tube OK?**	Yes No	▶ ▶	GO to **BC5**. REPLACE fuel tank or fuel tube.
BC5 CHECK FUEL VAPOR SYSTEM • Check for blockage of fuel vapor valve, tubing or fuel vapor canister. • **Is system OK?**	Yes No	▶ ▶	System OK. Fault caused by other vehicle system. SERVICE or REPLACE as required.

FM9099400129020X

Fig. 7   Pinpoint test BC (Part 2 of 2)

TEST STEP	RESULT	▶	ACTION TO TAKE
CA1 CHECK FOR TEMPERATURE SENDER SHORT • Unplug water temperature indicator sender unit. • Turn ignition switch to RUN. • Instrument cluster temperature gauge should indicate COLD with bottom bar illuminated. • **Does instrument cluster temperature gauge indicate as specified?**	Yes No	▶ ▶	REPLACE water temperature indicator sender unit. GO to **CA2**.
CA2 CHECK FOR SHORT IN WIRING • Disconnect battery ground cable. • Unplug water temperature indicator sender unit. • Remove instrument cluster. • Measure resistance between Pin 4 (of 20) and Pin 8 (of 20) (GND). • **Is resistance greater than 15,000 ohms?**	Yes No	▶ ▶	REPLACE instrument cluster. AFFIX odometer sticker to door pillar. SERVICE wiring Circuit 39 for shorts.

FM9099400130000X

Fig. 8   Pinpoint test CA

TEST STEP	RESULT	▶	ACTION TO TAKE
CB1 CHECK TEMPERATURE GAUGE WIRING • Unplug connector to water temperature indicator sender unit and connect a jumper to ground in place of water temperature indicator sender unit. • Turn ignition switch to RUN. • Gauge should give a short circuit indication. Top two and bottom bars of gauge illuminated. • **Do bars illuminate as specified?**	Yes No	▶ ▶	GO to **CB3**. REMOVE jumper. GO to **CB2**.

FM9099400131010X

Fig. 9   Pinpoint test CB (Part 1 of 2)

TEST STEP	RESULT	▶	ACTION TO TAKE
CB2 CHECK WIRING AT CLUSTER • Disconnect battery ground cable to battery. • Remove instrument cluster. • Connect jumper in place of water temperature indicator sender unit. • Verify continuity between Pins 4 (of 20) and 8 (of 20) of harness. • **Is there continuity?**	Yes No	▶ ▶	REPLACE instrument cluster. Affix odometer sticker to door pillar. SERVICE wiring Circuit 39 and - or temperature sender ground line for open circuit.
CB3 CHECK SENDER • Warm up engine to normal operating temperature. • Measure resistance of temperature sender. • **Is resistance less than 8,000 ohms?**	Yes No	▶ ▶	REPLACE instrument cluster. Affix odometer sticker to door pillar GO to **CB4**.
CB4 CHECK COOLING SYSTEM • Check thermostat, coolant level, etc., for proper operation. • **Is cooling system OK?**	Yes No	▶ ▶	REPLACE water temperature indicator sender unit. SERVICE cooling system as required.

FM9099400131020X

Fig. 9   Pinpoint test CB (Part 2 of 2)

Fig. 10 Pinpoint test CC

TEST STEP	RESULT	▶	ACTION TO TAKE
CC1 CHECK WARNING CHIME			
NOTE: The gauge driver alert tone is not active until at least 300 rpm or valid oil pressure has been detected (i.e. vehicle was started). Safety belt warning chime will not beep if another sound is being produced. Driver alert only given for temperatures above normal band. • Turn ignition switch to RUN. • Press any instrument cluster control button and listen for beep. • **Does chime beep?**	Yes	▶	System OK.
	No	▶	GO to Pinpoint Test AC.

FM9099400132000X

Fig. 11 Pinpoint test DA (Part 2 of 2)

TEST STEP	RESULT	▶	ACTION TO TAKE
DA2 SERVICE CHARGING SYSTEM			
• Check charging voltage. • **Is system operating properly (voltage between 9.5-16.5V)?**	Yes	▶	REPLACE EIC. AFFIX odometer sticker to door pillar.
	No	▶	DIAGNOSE CHARGING SYSTEM and SERVICE as required.

FM9099400133020X

Fig. 12 Pinpoint test EA (Part 2 of 2)

TEST STEP	RESULT	▶	ACTION TO TAKE
EA9 CHECK WIRING TO CLUSTER			
• Reconnect vehicle speed sensor wiring. • Disconnect battery ground cable. • Remove instrument cluster as outlined. • Using Rotunda Digital Volt-Ohmmeter 014-00407 or equivalent, measure the resistance between Pins 12 and 8 (ground) of connector A. • Resistance should be 160 - 230 ohms. • **Is resistance within range?**	Yes	▶	REPLACE instrument cluster. Affix odometer sticker to door pillar.
	No	▶	SERVICE connectors / wiring from cluster to Circuit 150. CHECK speedometer operation.

FM9099400134020X

Fig. 13 Pinpoint test EB

TEST STEP	RESULT	▶	ACTION TO TAKE
EB1 CHECK ODOMETER ACCURACY			
• Over a known distance, compare the odometer reading with the distance traveled. • **Is odometer accurate?**	Yes	▶	System OK.
	No	▶	GO to EB2.
EB2 CHECK VEHICLE SPEED SENSOR DRIVE GEAR			
• Remove vehicle speed sensor and verify that correct speedometer drive gear is installed for vehicle transaxle / tire combination. • **Is correct gear installed?**	Yes	▶	GO to EB3.
	No	▶	INSTALL correct gear with retaining clip.
EB3 CHECK DRIVE GEAR ON TRANSAXLE OUTPUT SHAFT			
• Check that correct drive gear is installed on transaxle output shaft. • **Is correct gear installed?**	Yes	▶	REPLACE instrument cluster. AFFIX odometer sticker to door pillar.
	No	▶	INSTALL correct output shaft / gear.

FM9099400135000X

Fig. 14 Pinpoint test EC (Part 1 of 2)

TEST STEP	RESULT	▶	ACTION TO TAKE
EC1 CHECK VEHICLE SPEED SENSOR DRIVE GEAR			
• Remove vehicle speed sensor from transaxle. • Check that all gear teeth are in good condition, retainer clip is installed and gear does not slip on shaft. • **Is gear / clip OK?**	Yes	▶	GO to EC2.
	No	▶	REPLACE drive gear and / or retaining clip.
EC2 CHECK WIRING TO VEHICLE SPEED SENSOR			
• Disconnect connector to vehicle speed sensor. • Using Rotunda Digital Volt Ohmmeter 014-00407 or equivalent, check for intermittent resistance between the two wires in the harness to the vehicle speed sensor. • Resistance should be greater than 500 ohms. • **Is resistance greater than 500 ohms?**	Yes	▶	GO to EC3.
	No	▶	SERVICE wiring Circuit 150, speed control for intermittent shorts or opens. CHECK speedometer operation.
EC3 CHECK VEHICLE SPEED SENSOR RESISTANCE			
• Using Rotunda Digital Volt Ohmmeter 014-00407 or equivalent, check for intermittent resistance at vehicle speed sensor. • Resistance should be 200-230 ohms. • **Is resistance between 200-230 ohms?**	Yes	▶	GO to EC4.
	No	▶	REPLACE vehicle speed sensor. CHECK speedometer operation.

FM9099400136010X

Fig. 15 Pinpoint test FA

TEST STEP	RESULT	▶	ACTION TO TAKE
FA1 DETERMINE IF SPEEDO / ODO MODULE IS ORIGINAL			
• Check for mileage sticker on door pillar. • **Is module original?**	Yes	▶	Display damaged. REPLACE instrument cluster. S should be illuminated and odometer should indicate zero miles.
	No	▶	System OK. Label on door pillar should indicate mileage at which the replacement instrument cluster was installed.

FM9099400137000X

Fig. 11 Pinpoint test DA (Part 1 of 2)

	TEST STEP	RESULT	▶	ACTION TO TAKE
DA1	CHECK FOR WARNINGS			
	CAUTION: This is used as a warning for a malfunctioning charging system. It must be operating properly so the battery is charged up for starting and vehicle operations. NOTE: The battery symbol and CHARGE SYSTEM warning always flashes when the ignition switch is in RUN if engine is not running. • Start engine. • Turn OFF electrical accessories. • Call up voltage gauge. • Slightly press accelerator pedal to increase rpm. • Look for — Flashing battery symbol — CHARGE SYSTEM warning on message center — Indicator bars on multi-gauge • **Are any warnings present?**	Yes	▶	GO to DA2.
		No	▶	System is operating properly

FM9099400133010X

Fig. 12 Pinpoint test EA (Part 1 of 2)

TEST STEP	RESULT	▶	ACTION TO TAKE
EA1 CHECK DISPLAY PROVE OUT			
• Turn ignition switch to RUN. • Observe display (all segments ON, then OFF and then normal display). • **Does display prove out properly?**	Yes	▶	GO to EA2.
	No	▶	REPLACE instrument cluster. AFFIX odometer sticker to door pillar.
EA2 CHECK ODOMETER			
• Verify that odometer advances when vehicle is driven forward. • **Does odometer advance?**	No	▶	GO to EA3.
	Yes	▶	REPLACE instrument cluster. AFFIX odometer sticker to door pillar.
EA3 CHECK FUEL COMPUTER			
• Test-drive vehicle. • Select TRIP DISTANCE on fuel computer. • Distance should advance as vehicle is driven. • **Does distance advance?**	Yes	▶	REPLACE instrument cluster. Affix odometer sticker to door pillar.
	No	▶	GO to EA4.
EA4 CHECK SPEED CONTROL			
• Test-drive vehicle and check operation of speed control, if so equipped. • **Does speed control operate properly?**	Yes	▶	GO to EA9.
	No	▶	GO to EA5.
EA5 CHECK WIRING TO SPEED SENSOR			
• Disconnect connector to vehicle speed sensor. • Using Rotunda Digital Volt-Ohmmeter 014-00407 or equivalent, measure the resistance between the two wires in the harness to the vehicle speed sensor. • Resistance should be greater than 500 ohms. • **Is resistance greater than 500 ohms?**	Yes	▶	GO to EA6.
	No	▶	SERVICE wiring Circuit 150, speed control, instrument cluster for shorts.
EA6 CHECK VEHICLE SPEED SENSOR RESISTANCE			
• Using Rotunda Digital Volt-Ohmmeter 014-00407 or equivalent, measure the resistance between the two wires in the harness to the vehicle speed sensor. • Resistance should be 200 - 230 ohms. • **Is resistance within range?**	Yes	▶	GO to EA7.
	No	▶	REPLACE vehicle speed sensor. CHECK speedometer operation.
EA7 CHECK DRIVEN GEAR AND RETAINER CLIP			
• Disconnect vehicle speed sensor from transaxle. Verify presence of driven gear with all teeth in good condition and the presence of retainer clip. • **Are driven gear and retainer clip OK?**	Yes	▶	GO to EA8.
	No	▶	REPLACE with proper gear and / or clip.
EA8 CHECK DRIVE GEAR ON TRANSAXLE			
• Verify presence of drive gear on output shaft. • **Is drive gear present?**	Yes	▶	GO to EA9.
	No	▶	SERVICE gear.

FM9099400134010X

Fig. 14 Pinpoint test EC (Part 2 of 2)

TEST STEP	RESULT	▶	ACTION TO TAKE
EC4 CHECK WIRING TO CLUSTER			
• Reconnect vehicle speed sensor wiring. • Disconnect battery ground cable. • Remove instrument cluster. • Using Rotunda Digital Volt-Ohmmeter 014-00407 or equivalent, measure the resistance between Pin 12 and 8 (ground) of connector A. • Resistance should be between 200 and 300 ohms. • **Is resistance between 200-300 ohms?**	Yes	▶	REPLACE instrument cluster. AFFIX odometer sticker to door pillar.
	No	▶	SERVICE connectors / wiring from instrument cluster to vehicle speed sensor Circuit 150. CHECK speedometer operation.

FM9099400136020X

Fig. 16 Pinpoint test FB

TEST STEP	RESULT	▶	ACTION TO TAKE
FB1 CHECK SPEEDOMETER			
• Perform Pinpoint Test EB. • Verify that speedometer is operating properly. • **Does speedometer operate properly?**	Yes	▶	REPLACE EIC. AFFIX odometer sticker to door pillar.
	No	▶	GO to Pinpoint Test EB.

FM9099400138000X

Fig. 17 Pinpoint test FC

TEST STEP	RESULT	▶	ACTION TO TAKE
FC1 CHECK ODOMETER OPERATION			
• Check odometer operation by road testing the vehicle. • **Does odometer accumulate 1.6 km (1.0 mile) then lose 1.6 km (1.0 mile)?**	Yes	▶	REPLACE EIC. AFFIX odometer sticker to door pillar.
	No	▶	GO to FC2
FC2 VERIFY SPEEDOMETER			
• Verify that speedometer works properly. • **Does speedometer operate properly?**	Yes	▶	REPLACE EIC. AFFIX odometer sticker to door pillar.
	No	▶	GO to Pinpoint Test EA.

FM9099400139000X

TEST STEP		RESULT	▶	ACTION TO TAKE
GA1	CHECK WIRING			
	• Disconnect battery ground cable • Remove instrument cluster as outlined • Measure resistance between 20-pin connector, Pin 20 and coil. • Wiggle connections and wiring near coil to check for intermittent connection. • **Is resistance less than 100 ohms?**	Yes	▶	REPLACE instrument cluster. RECHECK operation.
		No	▶	SERVICE wiring Circuit 11 for open circuit.

FM9099400140000X

Fig. 18   Pinpoint test GA

TEST STEP		RESULT	▶	ACTION TO TAKE
HB1	CHECK SPEEDOMETER OPERATION			
	• Verify that speedometer is operating properly • **Does speedometer operate properly?**	Yes	▶	REPLACE instrument cluster. AFFIX odometer sticker to door pillar.
		No	▶	GO to Pinpoint Test FA.

FM9099400142000X

Fig. 20   Pinpoint test HB

TEST STEP		RESULT	▶	ACTION TO TAKE
HA1	CHECK SPEEDOMETER OPERATION			
	• Verify that speedometer is operating properly. • **Does speedometer operate properly?**	Yes	▶	GO to HA2.
		No	▶	GO to Pinpoint Test FA.
HA2	CHECK CONTINUITY OF CIRCUIT 305 (FUEL FLOW)			
	• Verify continuity and absence of shorts in Circuit 305 • **Is there continuity and no shorts?**	Yes	▶	GO to Pinpoint Test BA3.
		No	▶	SERVICE wiring Circuit 305 as required. GO to HA3
HA3	CHECK FOR FUEL FLOW PULSES			
	• Verify proper operation of fuel flow function in powertrain control module. Refer to Powertrain Control Emissions Diagnosis Manual. • **Does fuel flow operate properly?**	Yes	▶	REPLACE EIC. AFFIX odometer sticker to door pillar.
		No	▶	SERVICE or REPLACE powertrain control module.

FM9099400141000X

Fig. 19   Pinpoint test HA

PINPOINT TEST HC:
DTE DOES NOT GO BELOW 322 KM (200 MILES) WITH FUEL TANK EMPTY OR
DTE ALWAYS READS ZERO (Continued)

TEST STEP		RESULT	▶	ACTION TO TAKE
HC3	CHECK FOR FUEL FLOW PULSES			
	• Verify proper operation of fuel flow function in powertrain control module • **Is PCM operation proper?**	Yes	▶	REPLACE EIC. AFFIX odometer sticker to door pillar.
		No	▶	SERVICE or REPLACE powertrain control module.

FM9099400143020X

Fig. 21   Pinpoint test HC (Part 2 of 2)

TEST STEP		RESULT	▶	ACTION TO TAKE
HC1	CHECK FUEL GAUGE			
	• Verify that fuel gauge is operating properly. • **Does fuel gauge operate properly?**	Yes	▶	GO to HC2.
		No	▶	GO to Pinpoint Test BA or BB.
HC2	CHECK SPEEDOMETER			
	• Verify that speedometer is operating properly. • **Does speedometer operate properly?**	Yes	▶	GO to HC3.
		No	▶	GO to Pinpoint Test EA.

FM9099400143010X

Fig. 21   Pinpoint test HC (Part 1 of 2)

TEST STEP		RESULT	▶	ACTION TO TAKE
JA1	CHECK EIC FOR WARNING			
	• Check EIC to determine if the warning is always on or never on. • **Is warning always on?**	Yes	▶	GO to JA2.
		No	▶	GO to JA4.
JA2	CHECK SWITCHES			
	• The following steps are to be repeated for each door open warning lamp switch. Start with the driver's door, then front passenger, then rear passengers. • Turn ignition switch to OFF. This resets the warning. • Pull connector off of the door open warning lamp switch. • Turn ignition switch to RUN. • Check message center for warning. • Repeat until no warning is displayed or all door open warning lamp switches are disconnected. • **Is warning still displayed?**	Yes	▶	GO to JA3.
		No	▶	SERVICE the last door open warning lamp switch tested.
JA3	CHECK CIRCUIT 627 (BK/O)			
	• Turn ignition switch to OFF. • Remove electronic instrument cluster. • Check continuity between Pins 17 and 8 of Connector A. • **Is there continuity?**	Yes	▶	SERVICE Circuit 627 (BK/O) for short.
		No	▶	REPLACE instrument cluster. Affix odometer sticker to door pillar.
JA4	CHECK SWITCH			
	• Turn ignition switch to OFF. • Pull connector off of the problem door open warning lamp switch. • Connect a jumper wire from Circuit 627 (BK/O) at the harness connector to ground. • Turn ignition switch to RUN • Check message center for warning. • **Is warning displayed?**	Yes	▶	SERVICE door open warning lamp switch.
		No	▶	GO to JA5.
JA5	CHECK WIRING			
	• Leave jumper wire connected as in FG3. • Turn ignition switch to OFF • Remove electronic instrument cluster. • Check continuity between Pins 17 and 8 of Connector A • **Is there continuity?**	Yes	▶	REPLACE EIC. AFFIX odometer sticker to door pillar.
		No	▶	SERVICE Circuit 627 (BK/O) for open

FM9099400144000X

Fig. 22   Pinpoint test JA

TEST STEP		RESULT	▶	ACTION TO TAKE
JB1	CHECK EIC FOR WARNING			
	• If warning never on, drain fluid from windshield washer reservoir. • If warning on at all times, fill windshield washer reservoir. • Turn ignition switch to RUN and actuate windshield wiper/washer switch. • Check system scanner for washer fluid warnings to determine if warning is always on or never on. • **Is the warning always on?**	Yes	▶	GO to JB6.
		No	▶	GO to JB2.
JB2	CHECK SENSOR			
	• Ensure washer fluid is drained from windshield washer reservoir. • Disconnect electrical connector from windshield washer reservoir fluid level sensor. • Check windshield washer reservoir fluid level sensor for continuity. • **Is there continuity?**	Yes	▶	GO to JB3
		No	▶	REPLACE windshield washer reservoir fluid level sensor.
JB3	SENSOR VOLTAGE CHECK			
	• Reconnect windshield washer reservoir fluid level sensor. • Turn ignition switch to RUN and actuate windshield wiper/washer switch. • Measure voltage (with respect to ground) at windshield washer reservoir fluid level sensor. • **Is voltage greater than 9 volts?**	Yes	▶	GO to JB4.
		No	▶	TEST windshield wiper/washer switch. CHECK for an open between windshield washer reservoir fluid level sensor and windshield wiper/washer switch.
JB4	CHECK FOR INTERMITTENT CONNECTION AT CLUSTER			
	• Remove instrument cluster. Do not disconnect. • Turn ignition switch to RUN and actuate windshield wiper/washer switch. • With windshield wiper/washer switch activated, wiggle 18-pin Connector and check connection. • **Is connection intermittent?**	Yes	▶	SERVICE 18-pin Connector or instrument cluster.
		No	▶	GO to JB5.
JB5	CHECK VOLTAGE AT CLUSTER			
	• Remove instrument cluster as outlined. • Turn ignition switch to RUN • Actuate windshield wiper/washer switch and measure voltage at 18-pin Connector, Pin 15 to ground. • **Is voltage greater than 9 volts?**	Yes	▶	REPLACE instrument cluster. AFFIX odometer sticker to door pillar.
		No	▶	CHECK Circuit 298 for an open or short
JB6	CHECK VOLTAGE AT CLUSTER			
	• Remove instrument cluster as outlined. • Turn ignition switch to RUN and measure voltage at 18-pin connector, Pin 15 to ground • **Is voltage greater than 3 volts?**	Yes	▶	CHECK Circuit 298 for a short to BATTERY or run circuits. GO to JB7
		No	▶	REPLACE instrument cluster. AFFIX odometer sticker to door pillar
JB7	CHECK SENSOR			
	• Ensure windshield washer reservoir is full. • Disconnect electrical connector and windshield washer reservoir. • Check continuity across windshield washer reservoir fluid level sensor. • **Is there continuity?**	Yes	▶	REPLACE windshield washer reservoir fluid level sensor.
		No	▶	CHECK for an open or short in Circuit 941

FM9099400145000X

Fig. 23   Pinpoint test JB

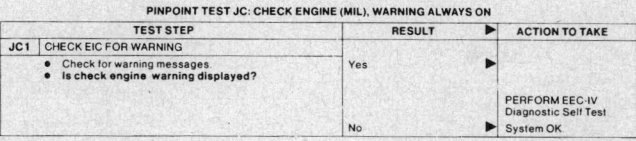

PINPOINT TEST JC: CHECK ENGINE (MIL), WARNING ALWAYS ON

TEST STEP	RESULT	▶	ACTION TO TAKE
JC1 CHECK EIC FOR WARNING			
• Check for warning messages. • **Is check engine warning displayed?**	Yes	▶	
	No		PERFORM EEC-IV Diagnostic Self Test System OK

FM9099400146000X

Fig. 24 Pinpoint test JC

TEST STEP	RESULT	▶	ACTION TO TAKE
JD1 CHECK EIC FOR WARNING			
NOTE: Make sure brake fluid at specified level.	Yes	▶	GO to JD5
• Check EIC for warnings to determine if the warning is always on or never on. • **Is warning always on?**	No	▶	GO to JD2
JD2 CHECK BRAKE FLUID LEVEL SWITCH			
• Turn ignition switch to OFF. • Disconnect connector at brake fluid level switch. • Connect a jumper wire from Circuit 977 (P/W) at the brake fluid level switch connector to ground. • Turn ignition switch to RUN. • **Is BRAKE SYSTEM WARNING displayed on EIC?**	Yes No	▶ ▶	GO to JD3. GO to JD4
JD3 CHECK FOR OPEN CIRCUIT			
• Check continuity in Circuit 57 (BK) from brake fluid level switch to ground and Circuit 977 (P/W) to ignition switch and Circuit 22 (LB/BK) to parking brake. • **Is continuity present?**	Yes No	▶ ▶	REPLACE brake fluid level switch. SERVICE open in circuit 977 (P/W), 57 (BK) or 22 (LB/BK).
JD4 CHECK FOR OPEN CIRCUIT, OPEN BULB			
• Turn ignition switch to OFF. • Disconnect jumper wire. • Disconnect EIC. • Check continuity in Circuit 977 (P/W) between EIC and brake fluid level switch. • **Is continuity present?**	Yes No	▶ ▶	CHECK voltage at 18-pin connector Pin 2 in RUN. CHECK brake warning bulb in EIC. SERVICE Circuit 977 (P/W) for open.
JD5 CHECK HARNESS			
• Put transaxle in PARK. • Release parking brake. • Turn ignition switch to OFF. • Disconnect connector at the brake fluid level switch. • Turn ignition switch to RUN. • **Is BRAKE SYSTEM WARNING displayed on EIC?**	Yes No	▶ ▶	CHECK Circuit 977 (P/W) for shorts. GO to JD6
JD6 CHECK BRAKE FLUID LEVEL SWITCH			
Make sure that: • Parking brake is OFF, DRL module is good, ignition switch is OFF, brake fluid level is proper. • Check for ground on Circuit 57 (BK) in fluid level switch connector. • **Is there an open circuit?**	Yes No	▶ ▶	REPLACE brake fluid level switch. SERVICE Circuit 57 (BK) for shorts or faulty switches.

FM9099400147000X

Fig. 25 Pinpoint test JD

TEST STEP	RESULT	▶	ACTION TO TAKE
JE1 CHECK EIC FOR WARNING			
• Check EIC display to determine if the warning is always on or never on. • **Is HIGH BEAM warning always on?**	Yes No	▶ ▶	GO to JE3 GO to JE2

FM9099400148010X

Fig. 26 Pinpoint test JE (Part 1 of 2)

TEST STEP	RESULT	▶	ACTION TO TAKE
JE2 CHECK BULBS			
• Turn ignition switch to OFF. • Disconnect EIC. • Check continuity from Pin 4 (of 20) to ground. • **Is there continuity?**	Yes No	▶ ▶	SERVICE Circuit 932 (GY/W) to DRL jumper and Circuit 12 (LG/BK) to headlamp bulbs. REPLACE bulb.
JE3 CHECK HEADLAMP SWITCH			
• Turn headlamp switch to OFF and to low beam. • **Are high beams on?**	Yes No	▶ ▶	SERVICE headlamp switch or turn signal and windshield wiper switch. CHECK for miswiring of Circuit 932 (GY/W) to a battery circuit. On vehicles with DRL, REPLACE daytime running lights control.

FM9099400148020X

Fig. 26 Pinpoint test JE (Part 2 of 2)

TEST STEP	RESULT	▶	ACTION TO TAKE
JF1 CHECK EIC FOR WARNINGS			
• Turn ignition switch to RUN. • Check EIC displays. Wait past prove-out time. • Determine if the warning is always on or never on. • **Is anti-lock warning always on?**	Yes No	▶ ▶	GO to JF2 GO to JF4.
JF2 CHECK ANTI-LOCK BRAKE MODULE			
• Disconnect anti-lock brake control module. • Check EIC for warning. • **Is anti-lock warning illuminated?**	Yes No	▶ ▶	GO to JF3. SERVICE anti-lock brake control module.
JF3 CHECK CONTINUITY			
• Turn ignition switch to OFF. • Disconnect EIC. • Check continuity in Circuit 606 (W/LB). • **Is continuity present?**	Yes No	▶ ▶	REPLACE EIC. AFFIX odometer sticker to door pillar. SERVICE Circuit 606 (W/LB).
JF4 CHECK POWER AND GROUNDS			
• Measure voltage at EIC Pins.	Yes No	▶ ▶	GO to JF5 SERVICE as required

PIN	FUNCTION	VOLTAGE
2 (OF 18)	RUN or START	Battery voltage
7 (of 20)	BATTERY	Battery voltage
9 (of 20)	RUN	Battery voltage
14 (of 18)	RUN	Battery voltage
17 (of 18)	BATTERY	Battery voltage

• Check continuity to ground at EIC Pins.

PIN	FUNCTION	VOLTAGE
2 (of 20)	GROUND	ZERO
7 (of 18)	GROUND	ZERO
8 (of 20)	GROUND	ZERO
13 (of 18)	GROUND	ZERO

• **Are all voltages as specified?**

FM9099400149010X

Fig. 27 Pinpoint test JF (Part 1 of 2)

TEST STEP	RESULT	▶	ACTION TO TAKE
JF5 CHECK ANTI-LOCK BRAKE MODULE			
• Turn ignition switch to OFF. • Disconnect connector at anti-lock brake control module. • Connect a jumper wire from Circuit 606 (W/LB) at harness connector to ground. • Turn ignition switch to RUN. • Check EIC for warning. • **Is ANTI-LOCK warning illuminated?**	Yes No	▶ ▶	SERVICE anti-lock brake control module. Go to JF6
JF6 CHECK CONTINUITY			
• Remove jumper. • Disconnect EIC. • Check continuity in Circuit 31 (W/R). • **Is continuity present?**	Yes No	▶ ▶	Replace EIC. AFFIX odometer sticker to door pillar. SERVICE circuit 31 (W/R).

FM9099400149020X

Fig. 27 Pinpoint test JF (Part 2 of 2)

TEST STEP		RESULT	▶	ACTION TO TAKE
JG1	**CHECK EIC FOR WARNINGS**			
	• Turn ignition switch to RUN.	Yes	▶	GO to JG2.
	• Check EIC displays. Wait past prove-out time.	No	▶	GO to JG4.
	• Determine if the warning is always on or never on.			
	• Is low oil pressure warning always on?			
JG2	**CHECK OIL PRESSURE SENDER**			
	• Disconnect oil pressure sender.	Yes	▶	GO to JG3.
	• Check EIC for warning.	No	▶	REPLACE oil pressure
	• Is low oil pressure warning illuminated?			sender. Refer to Section 03-01.
JG3	**CHECK CONTINUITY**			
	• Turn ignition switch to OFF.	Yes	▶	REPLACE EIC. AFFIX
	• Disconnect EIC.			odometer sticker to door
	• Check continuity in Circuit 31 (W/R).			pillar.
	• Is continuity present?	No	▶	SERVICE Circuit 31 (W/R).
JG4	**CHECK FOR POWER AND GROUNDS**			
	• Measure voltage at EIC Pins:	Yes	▶	GO to JG5.
		No	▶	SERVICE as required.

PIN	FUNCTION	VOLTAGE
2 (OF 18)	RUN or START	Battery voltage
7 (of 20)	BATTERY	Battery voltage
9 (of 20)	RUN	Battery voltage
14 (of 18)	RUN	Battery voltage
17 (of 18)	BATTERY	Battery voltage

• Check for continuity to ground at EIC Pins:

PIN	FUNCTION	VOLTAGE
2 (of 20)	GROUND	ZERO
7 (of 18)	GROUND	ZERO
8 (of 20)	GROUND	ZERO
13 (of 18)	GROUND	ZERO

• Are all voltages as specified?

FM9099400150010X

Fig. 28   Pinpoint test JG (Part 1 of 2)

TEST STEP		RESULT	▶	ACTION TO TAKE
JG5	**CHECK OIL PRESSURE SENDER**			
	• Turn ignition switch to OFF.	Yes	▶	REPLACE oil pressure
	• Disconnect connector at oil pressure sender.			sender.
	• Connect a jumper wire from Circuit 31 (W/R) at harness connector to ground.	No	▶	GO to JG6.
	• Turn ignition switch to RUN.			
	• Check EIC for warning.			
	• Is low oil pressure warning illuminated?			
JG6	**CHECK CONTINUITY**			
	• Remove jumper.	Yes	▶	REPLACE EIC. AFFIX
	• Disconnect EIC.			odometer sticker to door
	• Check continuity in Circuit 31 (W/R).			pillar.
	• Is continuity present?	No	▶	SERVICE Circuit 31 (W/R).

FM9099400150020X

Fig. 28   Pinpoint test JG (Part 2 of 2)

TEST STEP		RESULT	▶	ACTION TO TAKE
JH1	**CHECK EIC FOR WARNINGS**			
	• Turn ignition switch to RUN.	Yes	▶	GO to JH2
	• Check EIC displays. Wait past prove-out time.	No	▶	GO to JH4.
	• Determine if the warning is always or never on.			
	• Is air bag warning always on?			
JH2	**CHECK AIR BAG DIAGNOSTIC MONITOR**			
	NOTE: If the air bag warning indicator flashes on and off continuously, it means that it is showing a diagnostic trouble code. It does not mean that the air bag warning indicator needs to be serviced.	Yes	▶	GO to JH3.
		No	▶	REPLACE air bag diagnostic monitor.
	WARNING: THE BACK UP POWER SUPPLY ENERGY MUST BE DEPLETED BEFORE ANY AIR BAG COMPONENT SERVICE IS PERFORMED. TO DEPLETE BACKUP POWER SUPPLY ENERGY, DISCONNECT THE POSITIVE BATTERY CABLE AND WAIT ONE MINUTE.			
	• Disconnect battery ground cable.			
	• Disconnect positive battery cable and wait one minute.			
	• Disconnect air bag diagnostic monitor.			
	• Check EIC for warning			
	• Is air bag warning illuminated continuously?			
JH3	**CHECK CONTINUITY**			
	• Turn ignition switch to OFF.	Yes	▶	REPLACE EIC. AFFIX
	• Disconnect EIC.			odometer sticker to door
	• Check continuity in Circuit 608 (BK/Y)			pillar.
	• Is continuity present?	No	▶	SERVICE Circuit 608 (BK/Y)

FM9099400151010X

Fig. 29   Pinpoint test JH (Part 1 of 2)

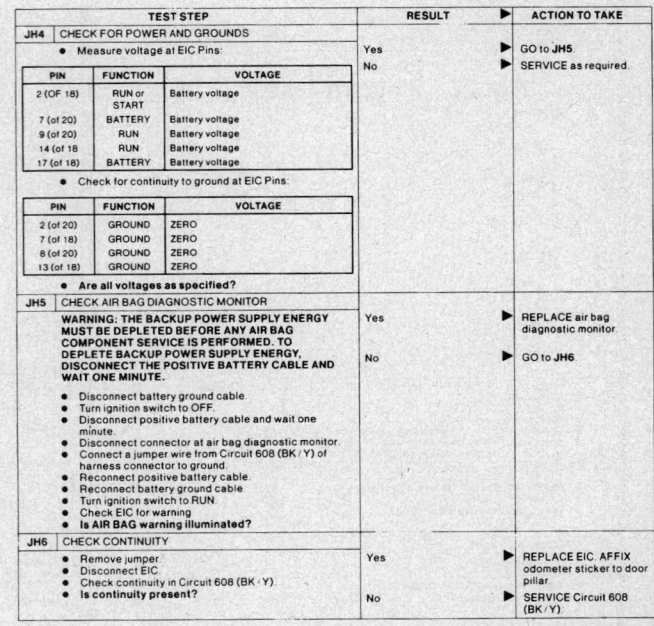

TEST STEP		RESULT	▶	ACTION TO TAKE
JH4	**CHECK FOR POWER AND GROUNDS**			
	• Measure voltage at EIC Pins:	Yes	▶	GO to JH5.
		No	▶	SERVICE as required.

PIN	FUNCTION	VOLTAGE
2 (OF 18)	RUN or START	Battery voltage
7 (of 20)	BATTERY	Battery voltage
9 (of 20)	RUN	Battery voltage
14 (of 18)	RUN	Battery voltage
17 (of 18)	BATTERY	Battery voltage

• Check for continuity to ground at EIC Pins:

PIN	FUNCTION	VOLTAGE
2 (of 20)	GROUND	ZERO
7 (of 18)	GROUND	ZERO
8 (of 20)	GROUND	ZERO
13 (of 18)	GROUND	ZERO

• Are all voltages as specified?

TEST STEP		RESULT	▶	ACTION TO TAKE
JH5	**CHECK AIR BAG DIAGNOSTIC MONITOR**			
	WARNING: THE BACKUP POWER SUPPLY ENERGY MUST BE DEPLETED BEFORE ANY AIR BAG COMPONENT SERVICE IS PERFORMED. TO DEPLETE BACKUP POWER SUPPLY ENERGY, DISCONNECT THE POSITIVE BATTERY CABLE AND WAIT ONE MINUTE.	Yes	▶	REPLACE air bag diagnostic monitor.
	• Disconnect battery ground cable.	No	▶	GO to JH6.
	• Turn ignition switch to OFF.			
	• Disconnect positive battery cable and wait one minute.			
	• Disconnect connector at air bag diagnostic monitor.			
	• Connect a jumper wire from Circuit 608 (BK/Y) of harness connector to ground.			
	• Reconnect positive battery cable.			
	• Reconnect battery ground cable.			
	• Turn ignition switch to RUN.			
	• Check EIC for warning.			
	• Is AIR BAG warning illuminated?			
JH6	**CHECK CONTINUITY**			
	• Remove jumper.	Yes	▶	REPLACE EIC. AFFIX
	• Disconnect EIC.			odometer sticker to door
	• Check continuity in Circuit 608 (BK/Y).			pillar.
	• Is continuity present?	No	▶	SERVICE Circuit 608 (BK/Y)

FM9099400151020X

Fig. 29   Pinpoint test JH (Part 2 of 2)

NOTE: Refer to the Symptom Index in this section before performing any Pinpoint Tests.

INDEX

	Page No. 15-	Fig. No.		Page No. 15-	Fig. No.
PINPOINT TESTS:			Pinpoint Test T.	35	19
Pinpoint Test A.	32	2	Pinpoint Test U.	35	20
Pinpoint Test B.	33	3	Pinpoint Test V.	36	21
Pinpoint Test C.	33	4	Pinpoint Test X.	36	22
Pinpoint Test D	33	5	Pinpoint Test Y.	36	23
Pinpoint Test E.	33	6	Pinpoint Test Z.	36	24
Pinpoint Test F.	33	7	Pinpoint Test AA	37	25
Pinpoint Test G.	34	8	Pinpoint Test BB	37	26
Pinpoint Test H.	34	9	Pinpoint Test CC	37	27
Pinpoint Test J.	34	10	Pinpoint Test DD	37	28
Pinpoint Test K.	34	11	Pinpoint Test EE	37	29
Pinpoint Test L.	34	12	Pinpoint Test FF.	38	30
Pinpoint Test M	35	13	Pinpoint Test GG	38	31
Pinpoint Test N	35	14	Pinpoint Test HH	38	32
Pinpoint Test P.	35	15	Pinpoint Test JJ	39	33
Pinpoint Test Q.	35	16	Pinpoint Test KK	39	34
Pinpoint Test R.	35	17	**SYMPTOM INDEX**	31	1
Pinpoint Test S.	35	18			

EIC DISPLAY DIAGNOSIS

CONDITION	POSSIBLE SOURCE	ACTION
• Display Not Illuminated, Too Dim or Blank But Backlighted	• Instrument cluster. • Circuitry. • Instrument cluster printed circuit.	• GO to Pinpoint Test A.
• Display Scrambled, Incorrect All the Time or Stuck With All Segments on, Segments Half Lit, Blinking or Missing	• Instrument cluster.	• GO to Pinpoint Test B.

FM9099500331010X

Fig. 1   Symptom index (Part 1 of 4)

EIC DISPLAY DIAGNOSIS (Continued)

CONDITION	POSSIBLE SOURCE	ACTION
• Display Does Not Respond To Buttons or No Beep When Buttons Pushed or Driver Alert Given	• Safety belt warning chime. • Message center switch module. • Instrument cluster. • Circuitry.	• GO to Pinpoint Test C.

FUEL GAUGE DIAGNOSIS

CONDITION	POSSIBLE SOURCE	ACTION
• CO Displayed, Top Two and Bottom Two Diagnostic Bars Displayed	• Open in harness 14A488 connectors or fuel pump (FP) module. • Inoperative EIC. • Open in harness 14401.	• GO to Pinpoint Test D.
• CS Displayed, Top Two and Bottom Two Diagnostic Bars Displayed	• Short in harness 14A488, connectors or fuel pump (FP) module. • Short in harness 14401. • Inoperative EIC.	• GO to Pinpoint Test E.
• Inaccurate Fuel Gauge Indication	• Inoperative fuel pump (FP) module. • Valve, tube or evaporative emission canister plugged. • Fuel tank damaged. • Inoperative EIC.	• GO to Pinpoint Test F.

TEMPERATURE GAUGE DIAGNOSIS

CONDITION	POSSIBLE SOURCE	ACTION
• Temperature Gauge Displays Top Two and Bottom Two Diagnostic Bars	• EIC. • Circuitry.	• GO to Pinpoint Test G.
• Temperature Gauge Always Indicates Hot or Cold Temperature	• EIC. • Circuitry. • Engine coolant temperature (ECT) sensor.	• GO to Pinpoint Test H.
• No Warning Tone When Thermometer Symbol is Blinking	• EIC. • Circuitry. • Safety belt warning chime.	• GO to Pinpoint Test J.

VOLTS GAUGE DIAGNOSIS

CONDITION	POSSIBLE SOURCE	ACTION
• Volts Gauge Does Not Give Charging System Alert (Flashing Battery Symbol)	• Inoperative generator regulator.	• GO to Pinpoint Test K.

SPEEDOMETER DIAGNOSIS

CONDITION	POSSIBLE SOURCE	ACTION
• Speedometer Reads 0 km/h (mph) At All Speeds	• Inoperative EIC. • Circuitry. • Vehicle speed sensor (VSS).	• GO to Pinpoint Test L.
• Speedometer Constantly Reads Too High or Too Low	• Incorrect drive gear. • Inoperative EIC.	• GO to Pinpoint Test M.
• Speed Indication Jumps Up and Down Erratically	• Inoperative EIC. • Vehicle speed sensor (VSS).	• GO to Pinpoint Test N.

FM9099500331020X

Fig. 1   Symptom index (Part 2 of 4)

ODOMETER DIAGNOSIS

CONDITION	POSSIBLE SOURCE	ACTION
• Display Reads "Error"	• Inoperative EIC.	• REPLACE EIC. AFFIX odometer sticker to door pillar. RESTORE vehicle. RETEST system.
• Display Has "S" Illuminated	• Inoperative EIC.	• GO to Pinpoint Test P.
• Mileage Constantly Reads Too High or Too Low	• Incorrect drive gear. • Inoperative EIC.	• GO to Pinpoint Test Q.
• Odometer Does Not Accumulate Mileage or Counts 1.6 km (1.0 mile) and Jumps Back 1.6 km (1.0 mile)	• Inoperative EIC. • Vehicle speed sensor (VSS).	• GO to Pinpoint Test R.

TACHOMETER DIAGNOSIS

CONDITION	POSSIBLE SOURCE	ACTION
• Tachometer Always Indicates Too High or Too Low, No Tach Indication or Tach Indication Erratic	• EIC. • Circuitry. • Faulty ignition coil.	• GO to Pinpoint Test S. • REFER to Powertrain Control/Emissions Diagnosis Manual[1].

MESSAGE CENTER DISPLAY DIAGNOSIS

CONDITION	POSSIBLE SOURCE	ACTION
• Instantaneous or Average Fuel Economy Always Reads 0 Miles/Gal Or 99 L/100 km or 99 Miles/Gal or 0 L/100 km	• EIC. • Circuitry.	• GO to Pinpoint Test T.
• Trip Distance Does Not Accumulate	• EIC. • Circuitry.	• GO to Pinpoint Test U.
• DTE Does Not Go Below 322 km (200 Miles) With Fuel Tank Empty or DTE Always Reads Zero	• EIC. • Circuitry.	• GO to Pinpoint Test V.

WARNING INDICATORS DIAGNOSIS

CONDITION	POSSIBLE SOURCE	ACTION
• DOOR AJAR Warning Never/Always Comes On • TRUNK AJAR Warning Never/Always Comes On	• Inoperative door open warning lamp switch. • Inoperative EIC. • Circuitry.	• GO to Pinpoint Test X.
• Charge System Warning Never/Always On	• Blown indicator lamp. • Shorts or open circuitry.	• GO to Pinpoint Test Y.
• Low WASHER FLUID Warning Never/Always On	• Inoperative windshield washer reservoir fluid level sensor. • Circuitry. • Open in windshield washer reservoir fluid level sensor connector. • Inoperative EIC.	• GO to Pinpoint Test Z.
• Check Engine Malfunction Indicator Lamp (MIL) Warning Always On	• EIC. • Circuitry. • Damaged powertrain control module (PCM).	• GO to Pinpoint Test AA.
• Brake Warning Never/Always On	• EIC. • Brake fluid level switch.	• GO to Pinpoint Test BB.
• LH Turn Indicator Never/Always On	• Shorted or open circuitry. • Malfunctioning multi-function switch.	• GO to Pinpoint Test CC.
• RH Turn Indicator Never/Always On	• Shorted or open circuitry. • Malfunctioning multi-function switch.	• GO to Pinpoint Test DD.

FM9099500331030X

Fig. 1 Symptom index (Part 3 of 4)

WARNING INDICATORS DIAGNOSIS (Continued)

CONDITION	POSSIBLE SOURCE	ACTION
• High Beam Warning Never/Always On	• EIC. • Headlamp switch. • Circuitry.	• GO to Pinpoint Test EE.
• Safety Belt Warning Never/Always On	• Blown fuse. • Malfunctioning chime module. • Inoperative safety belt switch. • Open/shorted circuitry.	• GO to Pinpoint Test FF.
• Anti-Lock Warning Never/Always On	• EIC. • Circuitry. • Anti-lock brake control module.	• GO to Pinpoint Test GG.
• Low Oil Pressure Warning Never/Always On	• EIC. • Circuitry. • Oil pressure sensor.	• GO to Pinpoint Test HH.
• Low Oil Level Indicator Never/Always On	• Low oil level. • Faulty low oil level sensor. • Malfunctioning EIC. • Shorted/open circuitry.	• ADD oil to the full line on the dipstick. • GO to Pinpoint Test JJ.
• Air Bag Warning Never/Always On	• EIC. • Circuitry. • Air bag diagnostic monitor.	• GO to Pinpoint Test KK.

FM9099500331040X

Fig. 1 Symptom index (Part 4 of 4)

TEST STEP		RESULT	▶	ACTION TO TAKE
A1	**CHECK EIC DIMMING** • Turn ignition switch to RUN. • Turn headlamps on. • Dimmer should control cluster illumination from 80 percent to almost off. • **Does instrument cluster dim properly?**	Yes ▶ No ▶		GO to **A5**. GO to **A2**.
A2	**CHECK DIMMER VOLTAGE WITH HEADLAMPS ON** • Disconnect battery ground cable. • Remove instrument cluster as outlined. • Connect battery ground cable. • Turn ignition switch to RUN. • Turn headlamps on. • Using a multimeter, voltage at 20-pin connector, Pin 13 should vary from 5 volts to battery voltage while operating dimmer switch. • **Does voltage vary within range?**	Yes ▶ No ▶		GO to **A3**. SERVICE dimmer switch. RESTORE vehicle. RETEST system.
A3	**CHECK INSTRUMENT CLUSTER DIMMING** • Check to see if part of the instrument cluster is dim or all displays are dim. • **Are all displays dim?**	Yes ▶ No ▶		GO to **A4**. REPLACE instrument cluster. AFFIX odometer sticker to door pillar. RESTORE vehicle. RETEST system.

Fig. 2 Pinpoint test A (Part 1 of 3)

TEST STEP		RESULT	▶	ACTION TO TAKE
A4	**CHECK DIMMER VOLTAGE WITH HEADLAMPS OFF** NOTE: Instrument cluster will dim from 80 percent to almost off with headlamps on. • Turn headlamp bulb OFF. • Disconnect battery ground cable. • Remove instrument cluster as outlined and disconnect connectors. • Connect battery ground cable and turn ignition switch to RUN. • Ensure headlamps are off. Using a multimeter, measure dimmer voltage to ground (20-pin connector, Pin 13). • **Is voltage greater than 3 volts?**	Yes ▶ No ▶		SERVICE Circuit 19 (LB/R) and dimmer for short to BATTERY or RUN circuits. GO to **A5**. REPLACE instrument cluster. AFFIX odometer sticker to door pillar. RESTORE vehicle. RETEST system.
A5	**CHECK ELECTRONIC INSTRUMENT CLUSTER (EIC) ILLUMINATION** • Turn ignition switch to the RUN position. • **Is instrument cluster partially illuminated?**	Yes ▶ No ▶		GO to **A6**. GO to **A7**.
A6	**VERIFY ALL SEGMENTS** • Check to see if all choices (segments), except the one selected, go black. • **Do all segments, except one selected, go black?**	Yes ▶ No ▶		System OK. RESTORE vehicle. REPLACE instrument cluster. Affix odometer sticker to door pillar. RESTORE vehicle. RETEST system.
A7	**CHECK FUSES** • Check Circuits 797 (LG/P) and 298 (P/O) for blown fuses (battery and run voltage to instrument cluster). • **Are fuses OK?**	Yes ▶ No ▶		GO to **A9**. GO to **A8**.
A8	**CHECK FOR SHORTS** • Turn ignition switch to OFF. • Disconnect battery ground cable. • Connect an ohmmeter from circuit with blown fuse to ground. • **Is there continuity?**	Yes ▶ No ▶		SERVICE circuit as required. RESTORE vehicle. RETEST system. REPLACE fuse. RESTORE vehicle. RETEST system.
A9	**CHECK FOR POWER TO FUSE** • Connect battery ground cable. • Turn ignition switch to RUN. • Using a multimeter, measure voltage from Circuits 797 (LG/P) and 298 (P/O) to ground. • **Is voltage greater than 9 volts on both circuits?**	Yes ▶ No ▶		GO to **A10**. SERVICE as required. RESTORE system. RETEST system.
A10	**CHECK FOR LOOSE CONNECTIONS** • Remove instrument cluster (leave connected). • Connect battery ground cable. • Turn ignition switch to RUN. • Wiggle connectors on rear of instrument cluster. • **Are connectors OK?**	Yes ▶ No ▶		SERVICE as required. RESTORE vehicle. RETEST system. GO to **A11**.

Fig. 2 Pinpoint test A (Part 2 of 3)

TEST STEP		RESULT	▶	ACTION TO TAKE
A11	**CHECK POWER AND GROUND VOLTAGES AND CONTINUITY** • Turn ignition switch to OFF. • Remove instrument cluster as outlined. • Turn ignition switch to RUN. • Measure voltage at the harness connectors of the instrument cluster. • Voltage should be:	Yes ▶ No ▶		GO to **A12**. SERVICE BATT Circuit 797 (LG/P) and/or RUN — Circuit 298 (P/O) and/or GROUND Circuit 563 (O/Y) for open or short circuits as necessary. RESTORE vehicle. RETEST system.

PIN	FUNCTION	VOLTAGE
7 (of connector C2)	BATT	Battery Voltage
9 (of connector C2)	RUN	Battery Voltage
14 (of connector C1)	RUN	Battery Voltage

TEST STEP		RESULT	▶	ACTION TO TAKE
	• Check continuity of ground Circuit Pins 8 (of 20) and 13 (of 18) to battery ground. • **Are voltages and continuity present?**			
A12	**CHECK FLEX CIRCUIT BOARD** • Disconnect battery ground cable. • Remove instrument cluster as outlined. • Inspect flexible circuit traces (traces are double thick) connected to Pins 13 (of 18) and 14 (of 18) on instrument cluster printed circuit. • **Are traces OK?**	Yes ▶ No ▶		REPLACE instrument cluster. AFFIX odometer sticker to door pillar. RESTORE vehicle. RETEST system. REPLACE instrument cluster printed circuit. RESTORE vehicle. RETEST system.

Fig. 2 Pinpoint test A (Part 3 of 3)

TEST STEP		RESULT	▶	ACTION TO TAKE
B1	CHECK EIC PROVE-OUT DISPLAY			
	• Turn ignition switch from OFF to RUN. • Observe the EIC display prove out (All segments on for one second, all segments off for one second followed by a normal display). • Does EIC proveout properly?	Yes No	▶ ▶	System OK. RESTORE vehicle. REPLACE instrument cluster. AFFIX odometer sticker to door pillar. RESTORE vehicle. RETEST system.

Fig. 3   Pinpoint test B

TEST STEP		RESULT	▶	ACTION TO TAKE
C1	CHECK RESPONSE TO BUTTONS			
	• Cluster only responds to buttons when ignition switch is in RUN. • Safety belt warning chime module will not beep if another sound is being produced. • Does display respond to buttons?	Yes No	▶ ▶	GO to C2. GO to C3.
C2	CHECK WARNING CHIME MODULE			
	• Check for fasten safety belt reminder chime or key left in ignition reminder chime. • Does chime sound?	Yes No	▶ ▶	GO to C6. SERVICE safety belt warning chime and / or circuit wiring. RESTORE vehicle. RETEST system.

Fig. 4   Pinpoint test C (Part 1 of 2)

TEST STEP		RESULT	▶	ACTION TO TAKE
C3	CHECK MESSAGE CENTER SWITCH WIRING CONNECTIONS			
	• Remove finish panel to expose instrument cluster. • Verify that connections at message center switch assembly are securely connected. • Are connections secure?	Yes No	▶ ▶	GO to C4. Secure connections and RECHECK. GO to C1.
C4	CHECK MESSAGE CENTER SWITCH ASSEMBLY (BUTTON PRESSED)			
	• Unplug message center switch module from electronic instrument cluster (6-pin connector is located at front face of instrument cluster to the far right). • Measure resistance between Pin 2 (Y) and Pin 4 (O) of connector unplugged. • The resistance should be: NOTE: Press only one button at a time. Wiggle wire at 6-pin switch connector and at message center switch module and check for loose connections.	Yes No	▶ ▶	GO to C5. REPLACE message center switch module. RESTORE vehicle. RETEST system.

BUTTON	RESISTANCE (in ohms)
E / M	4900-5400
SELECT	2200-2400
SPEED	320-360
RESET	980-985
NO BUTTON PRESSED	17000-17800

	• Are resistances within range?			
C5	CHECK CLUSTER WIRING CONNECTIONS			
	• Visually inspect 6-pin switch connector for poor / damaged or missing connections. • Are all pins OK?	Yes No	▶ ▶	REPLACE instrument cluster. AFFIX odometer sticker to door pillar. RESTORE vehicle. RETEST system. REPLACE message center switch module. RESTORE vehicle. RETEST system.
C6	CHECK TONE CIRCUIT			
	• Disconnect battery ground cable. • Remove instrument cluster. • Turn ignition switch to RUN and wait for the fasten safety belt reminder chime to end. • Place jumper wire between harness 20-pin Connector, Pin 19 and ground. Listen for chime. • Does chime sound?	Yes No	▶ ▶	REPLACE instrument cluster. RESTORE vehicle. RETEST system. SERVICE wiring Circuit 183 (T/Y) for open circuit. CHECK for correct warning chime module part number or operation. RESTORE vehicle. RETEST system.

Fig. 4   Pinpoint test C (Part 2 of 2)

PINPOINT TEST D: CO DISPLAYED, TOP TWO AND BOTTOM TWO DIAGNOSTIC BARS DISPLAYED

TEST STEP		RESULT	▶	ACTION TO TAKE
D1	CHECK FUEL PUMP (FP) MODULE WIRING AT FUEL TANK			
	• Disconnect battery ground cable. • Lower fuel tank to gain access to fuel pump (FP) module connector. • Unplug fuel pump (FP) module connector. • Jumper variable resistance terminal and ground terminal of harness together • Reconnect battery • Turn ignition switch from OFF to RUN. NOTE: It may take several minutes for the fuel gauge to respond. • Check digital fuel remaining display for CO or CS. • Is CO displayed?	Yes No	▶ ▶	GO to D3. GO to D2 if CS is displayed. REMOVE jumper.
D2	CHECK FUEL PUMP (FP) MODULE			
	• Turn ignition switch to OFF. • Measure the resistance of the fuel pump (FP) module at the terminals. • Verify that the resistance is between 11 and 168 ohms. • Is resistance between 11 and 168 ohms?	Yes No	▶ ▶	INSPECT fuel pump (FP) module wiring connector female terminals for flash or loose fit. SERVICE as required. RESTORE vehicle. RETEST system. REPLACE fuel pump (FP) module.
D3	CHECK FUEL PUMP (FP) MODULE WIRING AT CLUSTER			
	• Disconnect battery ground cable. • Remove instrument cluster and secure connectors from shorting. • Jumper variable resistance terminal and ground terminal of fuel pump (FP) module harness. • Verify condition between Pins 6 and 8 (ground) of cluster 20-pin connector. • Is fuel pump (FP) module wiring OK?	Yes No	▶ ▶	REPLACE fuel pump (FP) module. AFFIX odometer sticker to door pillar. RESTORE vehicle. RETEST system. SERVICE fuel pump (FP) module wiring for open circuit. RESTORE vehicle. RETEST system.

FM9099500334000X

Fig. 5   Pinpoint test D

PINPOINT TEST E: CS DISPLAYED, TOP TWO AND BOTTOM TWO DIAGNOSTIC BARS DISPLAYED

TEST STEP		RESULT	▶	ACTION TO TAKE
E1	CHECK FUEL PUMP (FP) MODULE WIRING AT CLUSTER			
	• Disconnect battery ground cable. • Remove instrument cluster and secure connectors from shorting. • With an ohmmeter, measure resistance between Pins 6 and 8 (SIG GND) of harness. • Verify that the resistance is 11 ohms or greater (normally 11 to 168 ohms). • Is resistance at least 11 ohms?	Yes No	▶ ▶	REPLACE instrument cluster. AFFIX odometer sticker to door pillar. RESTORE vehicle. RETEST system. Short exists in harness or fuel pump (FP) module. GO to E2.
E2	CHECK FUEL PUMP (FP) MODULE WIRING			
	• Disconnect battery ground cable. • Lower fuel tank to gain access to fuel tank sending unit and pump connector. • Unplug connector to the fuel pump (FP) module. • Measure resistance between Pins 6 and 8 (GND) of harness Connector A. • Verify that resistance is greater than 10,000 ohms. • Is resistance greater than 10,000 ohms?	Yes No	▶ ▶	REPLACE fuel pump (FP) module. RESTORE vehicle. RETEST system. SERVICE fuel tank sending unit and pump wiring for short circuit. RESTORE vehicle. RETEST system.

FM9099500335000X

Fig. 6   Pinpoint test E

PINPOINT TEST F: INACCURATE FUEL GAUGE INDICATION

TEST STEP		RESULT	▶	ACTION TO TAKE
F1	CHECK FUEL GAUGE RESPONSE			
	• Disconnect battery ground cable. • Lower fuel tank (if necessary) to gain access to fuel pump (FP) module connections. NOTE: Verify resistance of resistor prior to test. • Connect a 43 ohm (± 1 percent) resistor in place of the fuel pump (FP) module. • Reconnect battery ground cable. • Turn ignition switch to RUN. • Fuel gauge should illuminate two to three bars. • Fuel remaining should read 13 to 15L (3 to 4 gal). • Does fuel gauge read properly?	Yes No	▶ ▶	GO to F3. TURN ignition switch OFF. GO to F2. TURN ignition switch OFF.
F2	CHECK HARNESS RESISTANCE			
	• Disconnect battery ground cable. • Remove instrument cluster and secure connectors from shorting. • With a 43-ohm resistor in place of fuel pump (FP) module, measure resistance between Pins 6 and 8 of 20-pin connector. • Is resistance between 42-45 ohms?	Yes No	▶ ▶	REPLACE instrument cluster. AFFIX odometer sticker to door pillar. SERVICE Circuit 29 (Y / W) as required. RESTORE vehicle. RETEST system.
F3	CHECK FUEL PUMP (FP) MODULE			
	• Disconnect battery ground cable. • Check fuel pump (FP) module for binding, sticking, misalignment, etc. • Is fuel pump (FP) module OK?	Yes No	▶ ▶	GO to F4. SERVICE or REPLACE fuel pump (FP) module as required. RESTORE vehicle. RETEST system.
F4	CHECK FUEL TANK			
	• Check fuel tank for dents, bulges or other damage. • Check for proper installation of fuel tube. • Are fuel tank and fuel tube OK?	Yes No	▶ ▶	GO to F5. REPLACE fuel tank or fuel tube. RESTORE vehicle. RETEST system.
F5	CHECK EVAPORATIVE EMISSION (EVAP) SYSTEM			
	• Check for blockage of fuel vapor rollover tube, tubing or evaporative emission canister. Refer to Section 10-00. • Is system OK?	Yes No	▶ ▶	System OK. RESTORE vehicle. RETEST system. SERVICE or REPLACE as required. RESTORE vehicle. RETEST system

FM9099500336000X

Fig. 7   Pinpoint test F

PINPOINT TEST G: TEMPERATURE GAUGE DISPLAYS TOP TWO AND BOTTOM TWO DIAGNOSTIC BARS

TEST STEP		RESULT	▶	ACTION TO TAKE
G1	CHECK FOR ENGINE WATER TEMPERATURE SENDER SHORT			
	• Unplug engine water temperature sender. • Turn ignition switch to RUN. • Instrument cluster temperature gauge should indicate COLD with bottom bar illuminated. • **Does instrument cluster temperature gauge indicate as specified?**	Yes	▶	REPLACE engine water temperature sender. RESTORE vehicle. RETEST system.
		No	▶	GO to G2.
G2	CHECK FOR SHORT IN WIRING			
	• Disconnect battery ground cable. • Unplug engine water temperature sender. • Remove instrument cluster. • Measure resistance between Pin 4 (of 20) and Pin 8 (of 20) (GND) on the wiring connector. • **Is resistance greater than 15,000 ohms?**	Yes	▶	REPLACE instrument cluster. AFFIX odometer sticker to door pillar. RESTORE vehicle. RETEST system.
		No	▶	SERVICE wiring Circuit 39 (R/W) for shorts. RESTORE vehicle. RETEST system.

FM9099500337000X

Fig. 8   Pinpoint test G

TEST STEP		RESULT	▶	ACTION TO TAKE
H1	CHECK TEMPERATURE GAUGE WIRING			
	• Unplug connector to engine water temperature sender and connect a jumper between the two terminals. • Turn ignition switch to RUN. • Gauge should give a short circuit indication. Top two and bottom two bars of gauge illuminated. • **Do bars illuminate as specified?**	Yes	▶	GO to H3. REMOVE jumper.
		No	▶	GO to H2.
H2	CHECK WIRING AT CLUSTER			
	• Disconnect battery ground cable to battery. • Remove instrument cluster. • Connect jumper in place of engine water temperature sender. • Verify continuity between Pin 4 and Pin 8 of harness. • **Is there continuity?**	Yes	▶	REPLACE instrument cluster. Affix odometer sticker to door pillar. RESTORE vehicle. RETEST system.
		No	▶	SERVICE wiring Circuit 39 (R/W) and/or engine water temperature sender ground line for open circuit. RESTORE vehicle. RETEST system.
H3	CHECK ECT SENSOR RESISTANCE			
	• Warm up engine to normal operating temperature. • Measure resistance of sender. • **Is resistance less than 8,000 ohms?**	Yes	▶	REPLACE instrument cluster. Affix odometer sticker to door pillar. RESTORE vehicle. RETEST system.
		No	▶	GO to H4.
H4	CHECK COOLING SYSTEM			
	• Check thermostat, coolant level, etc., for proper operation. • **Is cooling system OK?**	Yes	▶	REPLACE engine coolant temperature (ECT) sensor. RESTORE vehicle. RETEST system.
		No	▶	SERVICE cooling system as required. RESTORE vehicle. RETEST system.

FM9099500338000X

Fig. 9   Pinpoint test H

TEST STEP		RESULT	▶	ACTION TO TAKE
J1	CHECK WARNING CHIME			
	NOTE: The gauge driver alert tone is not active until at least 300 rpm has been detected (i.e. vehicle was started). Safety belt warning chime will not beep if another sound is being produced. Driver alert only given for temperatures above normal band. • Turn ignition switch to RUN. • Press any instrument cluster control button and listen for beep. • **Does chime beep?**	Yes	▶	System OK. RESTORE vehicle.
		No	▶	GO to Pinpoint Test C.

Fig. 10   Pinpoint test J

TEST STEP		RESULT	▶	ACTION TO TAKE
K1	CHECK FOR WARNINGS			

	CAUTION: This is used as a warning for a malfunctioning charging system. It must be operating properly so the battery is charged up for starting and vehicle operations.
	
	NOTE: The battery symbol and CHARGE SYSTEM warning always flashes when the ignition switch is in RUN if engine is not running.
	
	• Start engine.
	• Turn OFF electrical accessories.
	• Call up voltage gauge.
	• Slightly press accelerator pedal to increase rpm.
	• Look for:
	  — Flashing battery symbol
	  — CHARGE SYSTEM warning on message center
	  — Indicator bars on multi-gauge
	• **Are any warnings present?**
		Yes	▶	GO to K2.

		No	▶	System is operating properly. RESTORE vehicle.
K2	SERVICE CHARGING SYSTEM			
	• Check charging voltage. • **Is system operating properly (voltage between 9.5-16.5V)?**	Yes	▶	REPLACE EIC. AFFIX odometer sticker to door pillar. RESTORE vehicle. RETEST system.
		No	▶	charging system service. RESTORE vehicle. RETEST system.

Fig. 11   Pinpoint test K

TEST STEP		RESULT	▶	ACTION TO TAKE
L1	CHECK EIC PROVE OUT DISPLAY			
	• Turn ignition switch to RUN. • Observe display (all segments on for one second, then off for one second followed by a normal display). • **Does display prove out properly?**	Yes	▶	GO to L2.
		No	▶	REPLACE instrument cluster. AFFIX odometer sticker to door pillar. RESTORE vehicle. RETEST system.
L2	CHECK ODOMETER			
	• Verify that odometer advances when vehicle is driven forward. • **Does odometer advance?**	Yes	▶	REPLACE instrument cluster. AFFIX odometer sticker to door pillar. RESTORE vehicle. RETEST system.
		No	▶	GO to L3.
L3	CHECK FUEL COMPUTER DISTANCE DISPLAY			
	• Test-drive vehicle. • Select TRIP DISTANCE on fuel computer. • Distance should advance as vehicle is driven. • **Does distance advance?**	Yes	▶	REPLACE instrument cluster. Affix odometer sticker to door pillar. RESTORE vehicle. RETEST system.
		No	▶	GO to L4.
L4	CHECK SPEED CONTROL OPERATION			
	• Test-drive vehicle and check operation of speed control, if so equipped. • **Does speed control operate properly?**	Yes	▶	GO to L9
		No	▶	GO to L5.

Fig. 12   Pinpoint test L (Part 1 of 2)

TEST STEP		RESULT	▶	ACTION TO TAKE
L5	CHECK WIRING TO SPEED SENSOR			
	• Disconnect connector to vehicle speed sensor. • Using a multimeter, measure the resistance between the two wires in the harness to the vehicle speed sensor. • Resistance should be greater than 500 ohms. • **Is resistance greater than 500 ohms?**	Yes	▶	GO to L6.
		No	▶	SERVICE wiring Circuit 150 (DG/W), speed control, instrument cluster for shorts. RESTORE vehicle. RETEST system.
L6	CHECK VEHICLE SPEED SENSOR RESISTANCE			
	• Using a DVOM, measure the resistance between the two wires in the harness to the vehicle speed sensor. • Resistance should be 200 - 230 ohms. • **Is resistance within range?**	Yes	▶	GO to L7.
		No	▶	REPLACE vehicle speed sensor. CHECK speedometer operation.
L7	CHECK DRIVEN GEAR AND RETAINER CLIP CONDITION			
	• Disconnect vehicle speed sensor from transaxle. • Verify presence of driven gear with all teeth in good condition and the presence of retainer clip. • **Are driven gear and retainer clip OK?**	Yes	▶	GO to L8.
		No	▶	REFER to (AX4S) or (AX4N) for driven gear and/or retainer clip service. RESTORE vehicle. RETEST system.
L8	CHECK DRIVE GEAR ON TRANSAXLE			
	• Verify presence of drive gear on output shaft. • **Is drive gear present?**	Yes	▶	GO to L9.
		No	▶	REFER to (AX4S) or (AX4N) for output shaft drive gear service. RESTORE vehicle. RETEST system.
L9	CHECK WIRING TO CLUSTER			
	• Reconnect vehicle speed sensor wiring. • Disconnect battery ground cable. • Remove instrument cluster as outlined. • Using a multimeter, measure the resistance between Pins 12 and 8 (ground) of connector C2. • Resistance should be 160 - 230 ohms. • **Is resistance within range?**	Yes	▶	REPLACE instrument cluster. Affix odometer sticker to door pillar. RESTORE vehicle. RETEST system.
		No	▶	SERVICE connectors/wiring from cluster to Circuit 150 (DG/W). CHECK speedometer operation.

Fig. 12   Pinpoint test L (Part 2 of 2)

TEST STEP		RESULT	▶	ACTION TO TAKE
M1	CHECK ODOMETER ACCURACY			
	• Over a known distance, compare the odometer reading with the distance traveled. • Is odometer accurate?	Yes No	▶ ▶	System OK. RESTORE vehicle. GO to M2.
M2	CHECK VEHICLE SPEED SENSOR DRIVE GEAR			
	• Remove vehicle speed sensor from transaxle and verify that correct speedometer drive gear is installed for vehicle transaxle / tire combination. • Is correct gear installed?	Yes No	▶ ▶	GO to M3. INSTALL correct gear with retaining clip. RESTORE vehicle. RETEST system.

FM9099500342010X

Fig. 13   Pinpoint test M (Part 1 of 2)

TEST STEP		RESULT	▶	ACTION TO TAKE
M3	CHECK DRIVE GEAR ON TRANSAXLE OUTPUT SHAFT			
	• Check that correct drive gear is installed on transaxle output shaft. • Is correct gear installed?	Yes No	▶ ▶	REPLACE instrument cluster. AFFIX odometer sticker to fuel filler door pillar. RESTORE vehicle. RETEST system. REFER to (AX4S) or (AX4N) for output shaft drive gear service. RESTORE vehicle. RETEST system.

FM9099500342020X

Fig. 13   Pinpoint test M (Part 2 of 2)

TEST STEP		RESULT	▶	ACTION TO TAKE
N1	CHECK VEHICLE SPEED SENSOR DRIVE GEAR			
	• Remove vehicle speed sensor from transaxle. • Check that all gear teeth are in good condition, retainer clip is installed and gear does not slip on shaft. • Is gear / clip OK?	Yes No	▶ ▶	GO to N2. REFER to (AX4S) or (AX4N) for drive gear and / or retainer clip service.
N2	CHECK WIRING TO VEHICLE SPEED SENSOR			
	• Disconnect connector to vehicle speed sensor. • Using a multimeter, check for intermittent resistance between the two wires in the harness to the vehicle speed sensor. • Resistance should be greater than 500 ohms. • Is resistance greater than 500 ohms?	Yes No	▶ ▶	GO to N3. SERVICE wiring Circuit 150 (DG / W), speed control for intermittent shorts or opens. CHECK speedometer operation.
N3	CHECK VEHICLE SPEED SENSOR RESISTANCE			
	• Using a multimeter, check for intermittent resistance at vehicle speed sensor. • Resistance should be 200-230 ohms. • Is resistance between 200-230 ohms?	Yes No	▶ ▶	GO to N4. REPLACE vehicle speed sensor. CHECK speedometer operation.
N4	CHECK WIRING TO CLUSTER			
	• Reconnect vehicle speed sensor wiring. • Disconnect battery ground cable. • Remove instrument cluster. • Using a multimeter, measure the resistance between Pin 12 and 8 (ground) of connector C2. • Resistance should be between 200 and 300 ohms. • Is resistance between 200-300 ohms?	Yes No	▶ ▶	REPLACE instrument cluster. AFFIX odometer sticker to door pillar. RESTORE vehicle. RETEST system. SERVICE connectors / wiring from instrument cluster to vehicle speed sensor Circuit 150 (DG / W). CHECK speedometer operation.

Fig. 14   Pinpoint test N

TEST STEP		RESULT	▶	ACTION TO TAKE
P1	DETERMINE IF SPEEDOMETER / ODOMETER MODULE IS ORIGINAL			
	• Check for mileage sticker on fuel filler door pillar. • Is module original?	Yes No	▶ ▶	NOTE: "S" should be illuminated and odometer should indicate zero miles indicating a damaged display. REPLACE instrument cluster. RESTORE vehicle. RETEST system. System OK. Label on door pillar should indicate mileage at which the replacement instrument cluster was installed.

FM9099500344000X

Fig. 15   Pinpoint test P

TEST STEP		RESULT	▶	ACTION TO TAKE
Q1	CHECK SPEEDOMETER OPERATION			
	• Perform Pinpoint Test M. • Verify that speedometer is operating properly. • Does speedometer operate properly?	Yes No	▶ ▶	REPLACE EIC. AFFIX odometer sticker to door pillar. RESTORE vehicle. RETEST system. GO to Pinpoint Test M.

FM9099500345000X

Fig. 16   Pinpoint test Q

TEST STEP		RESULT	▶	ACTION TO TAKE
R1	CHECK ODOMETER OPERATION			
	• Check odometer operation by road testing the vehicle. • Does odometer accumulate 1.6 km (1.0 mile) then lose 1.6 km (1.0 mile)?	Yes No	▶ ▶	REPLACE EIC. AFFIX odometer sticker to door pillar. RESTORE vehicle. RETEST system. GO to R2.
R2	VERIFY SPEEDOMETER OPERATION			
	• Verify that speedometer works properly. • Does speedometer operate properly?	Yes No	▶ ▶	REPLACE EIC. AFFIX odometer sticker to door pillar. RESTORE vehicle. RETEST system. GO to Pinpoint Test L.

FM9099500346000X

Fig. 17   Pinpoint test R

TEST STEP		RESULT	▶	ACTION TO TAKE
S1	CHECK CONTROL CIRCUIT CONTINUITY			
	• Disconnect battery ground cable. • Remove instrument cluster as outlined. • Measure resistance between 20-pin connector, Pin 20 and ignition coil. • Wiggle connections and wiring near ignition coil to check for intermittent connection. • Is resistance less than 100 ohms?	Yes No	▶ ▶	REPLACE instrument cluster. RECHECK operation. SERVICE wiring Circuit 11 (T / Y) for open circuit. RESTORE vehicle. RETEST system.

FM9099500347000X

Fig. 18   Pinpoint test S

TEST STEP		RESULT	▶	ACTION TO TAKE
T1	CHECK SPEEDOMETER OPERATION			
	• Verify that speedometer is operating properly. • Does speedometer operate properly?	Yes No	▶ ▶	GO to T2. GO to Pinpoint Test P.
T2	CHECK CONTINUITY OF CIRCUIT 305 (LB / BK) (FUEL FLOW)			
	• Verify continuity and absence of shorts in Circuit 305 (LB / BK). • Is there continuity and no shorts?	Yes No	▶ ▶	GO to Pinpoint Test D3. SERVICE wiring Circuit 305 (LB / BK) as required. GO to T3
T3	CHECK FOR FUEL FLOW PULSES			
	• Verify proper operation of fuel flow function in powertrain control module (PCM). Refer to Powertrain Control / Emissions Diagnosis Manual. [2] • Does fuel flow operate properly?	Yes No	▶ ▶	REPLACE EIC. AFFIX odometer sticker to door pillar. RETEST system. SERVICE or REPLACE powertrain control module. RESTORE vehicle. RETEST system.

FM9099500348000X

Fig. 19   Pinpoint test T

TEST STEP		RESULT	▶	ACTION TO TAKE
U1	CHECK SPEEDOMETER OPERATION			
	• Verify that speedometer is operating properly. • Does speedometer operate properly?	Yes No	▶ ▶	REPLACE instrument cluster. AFFIX odometer sticker to door pillar. RESTORE vehicle. RETEST system. GO to Pinpoint Test P.

FM9099500349000X

Fig. 20   Pinpoint test U

TEST STEP		RESULT	▶	ACTION TO TAKE
V1	CHECK FUEL GAUGE OPERATION			
	• Verify that fuel gauge is operating properly.	Yes	▶	GO to V2.
	• Does fuel gauge operate properly?	No	▶	GO to Pinpoint Test D or E.
V2	CHECK SPEEDOMETER OPERATION			
	• Verify that speedometer is operating properly.	Yes	▶	GO to V3.
	• Does speedometer operate properly?	No	▶	GO to Pinpoint Test L.
V3	CHECK FOR FUEL FLOW PULSES			
	• Verify proper operation of fuel flow function in powertrain control module (PCM).	Yes	▶	REPLACE EIC. AFFIX odometer sticker to door pillar. RESTORE vehicle. RETEST system.
	• Does PCM operate properly?	No	▶	SERVICE or REPLACE powertrain control module (PCM). RESTORE vehicle. RETEST system.

FM9099500350000X

Fig. 21   Pinpoint test V

TEST STEP		RESULT	▶	ACTION TO TAKE
X2	CHECK DOOR AJAR WARNING LAMP SWITCHES			
	• The following steps are to be repeated for each door open warning lamp switch. Start with the driver door, then front passenger, then rear passengers. • Turn ignition switch to OFF. This resets the warning. • Pull connector off of the door open warning lamp switch. • Turn ignition switch to RUN. • Check message center for warning. • Repeat until no warning is displayed or all door open warning lamp switches are disconnected. • Is warning still displayed?	Yes No	▶ ▶	GO to X3. SERVICE the last door open warning lamp switch tested. RESTORE vehicle. RETEST system.
X3	CHECK CONTINUITY OF CIRCUIT 627 (BK/O)			
	• Turn ignition switch to OFF. • Remove electronic instrument cluster. • Check continuity between Pins 17 and 8 of Connector C2. • Is there continuity?	Yes No	▶ ▶	SERVICE Circuit 627 (BK/O) for short circuit. RESTORE vehicle. RETEST system. REPLACE instrument cluster. Affix odometer sticker to door pillar. RESTORE vehicle. RETEST system.
X4	ISOLATE CAUSE OF DOOR AJAR WARNING LAMP CONCERN			
	• Turn ignition switch to OFF. • Pull connector off of the problem door open warning lamp switch. • Connect a jumper wire from Circuit 627 (BK/O) at the harness connector to ground. • Turn ignition switch to RUN. • Check message center for warning. • Is warning displayed?	Yes No	▶ ▶	SERVICE door open warning lamp switch. RESTORE vehicle. RETEST system. GO to X5.
X5	CHECK CONTROL CIRCUIT CONTINUITY			
	• Leave jumper wire connected as in Test Step X4. • Turn ignition switch to OFF. • Remove electronic instrument cluster. • Check continuity of circuit wiring for circuit 627 (BK/O). • Is there continuity?	Yes No	▶ ▶	REPLACE EIC. AFFIX odometer sticker to door pillar. RESTORE vehicle. RETEST system. SERVICE Circuit 627 (BK/O) for open circuit. RESTORE vehicle. RETEST system.

FM9099500351020X

Fig. 22   Pinpoint test X (Part 2 of 2)

TEST STEP		RESULT	▶	ACTION TO TAKE
X1	CHECK EIC FOR WARNING			
	• Check EIC to determine if the warning is always on or never on. • Is warning always on?	Yes No	▶ ▶	GO to X2. GO to X4.

FM9099500351010X

Fig. 22   Pinpoint test X (Part 1 of 2)

TEST STEP		RESULT	▶	ACTION TO TAKE
Y1	CHECK EIC FOR WARNING			
	• Check EIC for warnings to determine if the warning is always on or never on. • Is warning always on?	Yes No	▶ ▶	GO to Y2. GO to Y3.
Y2	ISOLATE WARNING SIGNAL SOURCE			
	• Remove EIC as outlined. • Disconnect connector C1 from EIC. • Is warning lamp still on?	Yes No	▶ ▶	REPLACE electronic instrument cluster. RESTORE vehicle. RETEST system. CHECK Circuit 904 (LG/R) for short to ground. REFER to battery and charging system diagnosis.

FM9099500352010X

Fig. 23   Pinpoint test Y (Part 1 of 2)

TEST STEP		RESULT	▶	ACTION TO TAKE
Y3	CHECK FOR IGNITION SWITCH POWER INPUT			
	• Remove EIC as outlined. • Using a multimeter, measure voltage at connector Pin C1-17, Circuit 16 (R/LG). • Is voltage greater than 9 volts?	Yes No	▶ ▶	GO to Y4. SERVICE Circuit 16 (R/LG) for open circuit. REFER to for Ignition Switch Continuity Test. RESTORE vehicle. RETEST system.
Y4	CHECK FOR OPEN CIRCUIT			
	• Using an ohmmeter, check continuity of Circuit 904 (LG/R). • Does Circuit 904 (LG/R) have continuity?	Yes No	▶ ▶	CHECK for blown generator warning indicator lamp. REFER to for battery and charging system diagnosis. SERVICE Circuit 904 (LG/R) for open circuit. RESTORE vehicle. RETEST system.

FM9099500352020X

Fig. 23   Pinpoint test Y (Part 2 of 2)

TEST STEP		RESULT	▶	ACTION TO TAKE
Z1	CHECK EIC FOR WARNING			
	• If warning never on, drain fluid from windshield washer reservoir. • If warning on at all times, fill windshield washer reservoir. • Turn ignition switch to RUN and actuate windshield wiper/washer switch. • Check EIC display for washer fluid warnings to determine if warning is always on or never on. • Is the warning always on?	Yes No	▶ ▶	GO to Z6. GO to Z2.
Z2	CHECK SENSOR CONTINUITY			
	• Ensure washer fluid is drained from windshield washer reservoir. • Disconnect electrical connector from windshield washer reservoir fluid level sensor. • Using a multimeter, check windshield washer reservoir fluid level sensor for continuity. • Is there continuity?	Yes No	▶ ▶	GO to Z3 REPLACE windshield washer reservoir fluid level sensor. RESTORE vehicle. RETEST system.
Z3	CHECK CIRCUIT 941 (BK/W) FOR VOLTAGE			
	• Reconnect windshield washer reservoir fluid level sensor. • Turn ignition switch to RUN and actuate windshield wiper/washer switch. • Using a multimeter, measure voltage (with respect to ground) at windshield washer reservoir fluid level sensor. • Is voltage greater than 9 volts?	Yes No	▶ ▶	GO to Z4. CHECK Circuit 941 (BK/W) for an open circuit between windshield washer reservoir fluid level sensor and windshield wiper/washer switch. TEST windshield wiper/washer switch.
Z4	CHECK FOR INTERMITTENT CONNECTION AT CLUSTER			
	• Remove instrument cluster. Do not disconnect. • Turn ignition switch to RUN and actuate windshield wiper/washer switch. • With windshield wiper/washer switch activated, wiggle 18-pin connector (C1) and check connection. • Is connection intermittent?	Yes No	▶ ▶	SERVICE 18-pin connector or instrument cluster printed circuit. GO to Z5.

FM9099500353010X

Fig. 24   Pinpoint test Z (Part 1 of 2)

TEST STEP		RESULT	▶	ACTION TO TAKE
Z5	CHECK VOLTAGE TO EIC			
	• Remove instrument cluster as outlined. • Turn ignition switch to RUN. • Actuate windshield wiper/washer switch and using a multimeter, measure RUN voltage at 18-pin connector (C1), Pin 14 to ground. • Is voltage greater than 9 volts?	Yes No	▶ ▶	REPLACE instrument cluster. AFFIX odometer sticker to door pillar. RESTORE vehicle. RETEST system. CHECK Circuit 298 (P/O) for an open or short circuit. RESTORE vehicle. RETEST system.
Z6	CHECK CIRCUIT 298 (P/O) FOR SHORT CIRCUIT			
	• Remove instrument cluster as outlined. • Turn ignition switch to RUN and using a multimeter, measure voltage at 18-pin connector (C1), Pin 14 to ground. • Is voltage greater than 3 volts?	Yes No	▶ ▶	CHECK Circuit 298 (P/O) for a short to BATTERY or run circuits. GO to Z7. REPLACE instrument cluster. AFFIX odometer sticker to door pillar. RESTORE vehicle. RETEST system.
Z7	CHECK CONTINUITY			
	• Ensure windshield washer reservoir is full. • Disconnect electrical connector and windshield washer reservoir. • Using a multimeter, check continuity across windshield washer reservoir fluid level sensor. • Is there continuity?	Yes No	▶ ▶	REPLACE windshield washer reservoir fluid level sensor. RESTORE vehicle. RETEST system. CHECK for an open or short in Circuit 941 (BK/W). RESTORE vehicle. RETEST system.

FM9099500353020X

Fig. 24   Pinpoint test Z (Part 2 of 2)

TEST STEP		RESULT	▶	ACTION TO TAKE
AA1	CHECK EIC FOR WARNING			
	• Check for warning messages. • Is check engine warning displayed?	Yes	▶	
		No	▶	PERFORM EEC-IV Diagnostic Self Test. System OK.

FM9099500354000X

Fig. 25   Pinpoint test AA

TEST STEP		RESULT	▶	ACTION TO TAKE
BB1	CHECK EIC FOR WARNING			
	NOTE: Make sure brake fluid is at specified level.	Yes	▶	GO to BB5.
	• Check EIC for warnings to determine if the warning is always on or never on • Is warning always on?	No	▶	GO to BB2.
BB2	CHECK BRAKE FLUID LEVEL SWITCH VOLTAGE SUPPLY			
	• Turn ignition switch to OFF. • Disconnect connector at brake fluid level switch. • Connect a jumper wire from Circuit 977 (P/W) at the brake fluid level switch connector to ground. • Turn ignition switch to RUN. • Is brake system warning lamp illuminated on EIC?	Yes	▶	GO to BB3.
		No	▶	GO to BB4.

FM9099500355010X

Fig. 26   Pinpoint test BB (Part 1 of 2)

TEST STEP		RESULT	▶	ACTION TO TAKE
BB3	CHECK FOR OPEN CIRCUIT			
	• Using a multimeter, check continuity in Circuit 57 (BK) from brake fluid level switch to ground and Circuit 977 (P/W) to ignition switch and Circuit 22 (LB/BK) to parking brake. • Is continuity present?	Yes	▶	REPLACE brake fluid level switch. RESTORE vehicle. RETEST system.
		No	▶	SERVICE open in circuit 977 (P/W), 57 (BK) or 22 (LB/BK). RESTORE vehicle. RETEST system.
BB4	CHECK FOR OPEN CIRCUIT/OPEN BULB			
	• Turn ignition switch to OFF. • Disconnect jumper wire. • Disconnect EIC. • Using a multimeter, check continuity in Circuit 977 (P/W) between EIC and brake fluid level switch. • Is continuity present?	Yes	▶	CHECK voltage at 18-pin connector (C1) Pin 2 in RUN. CHECK brake warning bulb in EIC. RESTORE vehicle. RETEST system.
		No	▶	SERVICE Circuit 977 (P/W) for open. RESTORE vehicle. RETEST system.
BB5	CHECK HARNESS FOR SHORT CIRCUIT			
	• Put transaxle in PARK. • Release parking brake. • Turn ignition switch to OFF. • Disconnect connector at the brake fluid level switch. • Turn ignition switch to RUN. • Is brake system warning lamp illuminated on EIC?	Yes	▶	CHECK Circuit 977 (P/W) for shorts. RESTORE vehicle. RETEST system.
		No	▶	GO to BB6.
BB6	CHECK BRAKE FLUID LEVEL SWITCH GROUND			
	Make sure that: • Parking brake is OFF, DRL module is good, ignition switch is in OFF, brake fluid level is proper. • Using a multimeter, check for ground on Circuit 57 (BK) in fluid level switch connector. • Is there an open circuit?	Yes	▶	REPLACE brake fluid level switch. RESTORE vehicle. RETEST system.
		No	▶	SERVICE Circuit 57 (BK) for shorts or faulty switches. RESTORE vehicle. RETEST system.

FM9099500355020X

Fig. 26   Pinpoint test BB (Part 2 of 2)

TEST STEP		RESULT	▶	ACTION TO TAKE
CC1	CHECK EIC FOR WARNING			
	• Check EIC for LH turn indicator to determine if the LH turn indicator is always on or never on. • Is LH turn indicator always on?	Yes	▶	GO to CC2.
		No	▶	GO to CC3.
CC2	ISOLATE LH TURN INDICATOR SOURCE			
	• Remove EIC as outlined. • Disconnect connector C1 from EIC. • Is LH turn indicator lamp still on?	Yes	▶	REPLACE electronic instrument cluster. RESTORE vehicle. RETEST system.
		No	▶	CHECK Circuit 3 (LG/W) for short to ground. REFER to steering column switches diagnosis.

FM9099500356010X

Fig. 27   Pinpoint test CC (Part 1 of 2)

TEST STEP		RESULT	▶	ACTION TO TAKE
CC3	CHECK FOR TURN SIGNAL SWITCH POWER INPUT			
	• Remove EIC as outlined. • Using the turn signal lever, signal for a LH turn. • Using a multimeter, measure voltage at connector pin C1-5, Circuit 3 (LG/W). • Is voltage greater than 9 volts?	Yes	▶	REPLACE electronic instrument cluster. RESTORE vehicle. RETEST system.
		No	▶	SERVICE Circuit 3 (LG/W) for open circuit. REFER to multi-function switch continuity test. RESTORE vehicle. RETEST system.

FM9099500356020X

Fig. 27   Pinpoint test CC (Part 2 of 2)

TEST STEP		RESULT	▶	ACTION TO TAKE
DD1	CHECK EIC FOR WARNING			
	• Check EIC for RH turn indicator to determine if the RH turn indicator is always on or never on. • Is RH turn indicator always on?	Yes	▶	GO to DD2.
		No	▶	GO to DD3.
DD2	ISOLATE RH TURN INDICATOR SOURCE			
	• Remove EIC as outlined. • Disconnect connector C1 from EIC. • Is RH turn indicator lamp still on?	Yes	▶	REPLACE electronic instrument cluster. RESTORE vehicle. RETEST system.
		No	▶	CHECK Circuit 2 (W/LB) for short to ground. REFER to steering column switches diagnosis.
DD3	CHECK FOR TURN SIGNAL SWITCH POWER INPUT			
	• Remove EIC as outlined. • Using the turn signal lever, signal for a RH turn. • Using a multimeter, measure voltage at connector pin C1-8, Circuit 2 (W/LB). • Is voltage greater than 9 volts?	Yes	▶	REPLACE electronic instrument cluster. RESTORE vehicle. RETEST system.
		No	▶	SERVICE Circuit 2 (W/LB) for open circuit. REFER to multi-function switch continuity test. RESTORE vehicle. RETEST system.

FM9099500357000X

Fig. 28   Pinpoint test DD

TEST STEP		RESULT	▶	ACTION TO TAKE
EE1	CHECK EIC FOR WARNING			
	• Check EIC display to determine if the warning is always on or never on. • Is HIGH BEAM warning always on?	Yes	▶	GO to EE3.
		No	▶	GO to EE2.
EE2	CHECK BULBS			
	• Turn ignition switch to OFF. • Disconnect EIC. • Using a multimeter, check continuity from Pin 4 (of connector C2) to ground. • Is there continuity?	Yes	▶	SERVICE Circuit 932 (GY/W) to DRL jumper and Circuit 12 (LG/BK) to headlamp bulbs. RESTORE vehicle. RETEST system.
		No	▶	REPLACE bulb. RESTORE vehicle. RETEST system.

FM9099500358010X

Fig. 29   Pinpoint test EE (Part 1 of 2)

TEST STEP		RESULT	▶	ACTION TO TAKE
EE3	CHECK HEADLAMP SWITCH			
	• Turn headlamp switch to OFF and to low beam. • Are high beams on?	Yes	▶	SERVICE headlamp switch or multi-function switch.
		No	▶	CHECK for miswiring of Circuit 932 (GY/W) to a battery circuit. On vehicles with DRL, REPLACE daytime running lamps control. RESTORE vehicle. RETEST system.

FM9099500358020X

Fig. 29   Pinpoint test EE (Part 2 of 2)

TEST STEP	RESULT	▶	ACTION TO TAKE
FF1 CHECK FOR VOLTAGE AT CIRCUIT 640 (R/Y)			
• Disconnect safety belt warning chime. • Connect a 12-volt test lamp between Circuit 640 (R/Y) in warning chime connector and ground. • Turn ignition switch to RUN. • **Does test lamp light?**	Yes No	▶ ▶	GO to FF2. CHECK Circuit 640 (R/Y) back to ignition switch. SERVICE as required. RESTORE vehicle. RETEST system.
FF2 CHECK FOR GROUND AT CIRCUIT 57 (BK)			
• Connect a 12-volt test lamp between Circuit 640 (R/Y) and 57 (BK) in warning chime connector. • Turn ignition switch to RUN. • **Does test lamp light?**	Yes No	▶ ▶	GO to FF3. CHECK Circuit 57 (BK) back to body ground. SERVICE as required. RESTORE vehicle. RETEST system.
FF3 CHECK CIRCUIT 450 (DG/LG) AND SAFETY BELT WARNING LAMP BULB			
• Connect jumper between Circuit 450 (DG/LG) and Circuit 640 (R/Y) in warning chime module connector. • Turn ignition switch to RUN. • **Does safety belt warning indicator light?**	Yes No	▶ ▶	GO to FF4. CHECK Circuit 450 (DG/LG) back to safety belt warning indicator bulb. CHECK bulb. SERVICE as required. RESTORE vehicle. RETEST system.
FF4 CHECK FOR GROUND AT CIRCUIT 85 (BR/LB)			
• Unbuckle driver side safety belt. • Connect a 12-volt test lamp between Circuit 85 (BR/LB) and Circuit 640 (R/Y) in warning chime connector. • Turn ignition switch to RUN. • **Does test lamp light?**	Yes No	▶ ▶	GO to FF5. CHECK Circuit 85 (BR/LB) back to safety belt switch. SERVICE as required. RESTORE vehicle. RETEST system.
FF5 CHECK FOR GROUND AT CIRCUIT 158 (BK/PK)			
• Insert key in ignition. • Connect a 12-volt test lamp between Circuit 158 (BK/PK) and Circuit 640 (R/Y) in warning chime connector. • Turn ignition switch to RUN. • **Does test lamp light?**	Yes No	▶ ▶	GO to FF6. CHECK Circuit 158 (BK/PK) back to ignition switch. SERVICE as required. RESTORE vehicle. RETEST system.

FM9099500359010X

Fig. 30   Pinpoint test FF (Part 1 of 2)

TEST STEP	RESULT	▶	ACTION TO TAKE
FF6 CHECK FOR VOLTAGE AT CIRCUIT 159 (R/PK)			
• Connect a 12-volt test lamp between Circuit 159 (R/PK) in warning chime connector and known good ground. • Open driver door. • **Does test lamp light?**	Yes No	▶ ▶	GO to FF7. CHECK Circuit 159 (R/PK) back to door open warning switch. SERVICE as required. RESTORE vehicle. RETEST system.
FF7 CHECK FOR VOLTAGE AT CIRCUIT 257 (W/R)			
• Connect a 12-volt test lamp between Circuit 257 (W/R) and a known good ground. • Pull headlamp switch to the ON position. • **Does test lamp light?**	Yes No	▶ ▶	GO to FF8. CHECK Circuit 257 (W/R) back to headlamp switch. SERVICE as required. RESTORE vehicle. RETEST system.
FF8 CHECK FOR VOLTAGE AT CIRCUIT 296 (W/P)			
• Connect a 12-volt test lamp between Circuit 296 (W/P) in warning chime connector and ground. • Turn ignition switch to the ACC position. • **Does test lamp light?**	Yes No	▶ ▶	GO to FF9. CHECK Circuit 296 (W/P) back to ignition switch. SERVICE as required. RESTORE vehicle. RETEST system.
FF9 CHECK FOR GROUND AT CIRCUIT 183 (T/Y)			
• Connect a 12-volt test lamp between Circuit 183 (T/Y) and Circuit 296 (W/P) of warning chime connector. • Turn ignition switch to RUN position as press a button on the electronic instrument cluster. • **Does test lamp light momentarily?**	Yes No	▶ ▶	GO to FF10. REPLACE electronic instrument cluster. RESTORE vehicle. RETEST system.
FF10 CHECK WARNING CHIME MODULE OPERATION			

• Connect warning chime module.
• Check for proper operation of:
  – Safety belt warning chime.
  – Key-in-ignition warning.
  – Headlamp switch on warning.
  – Audible beep.
• **Do all warnings operate properly?**
	Yes
	
	No
		▶
		
		▶
			System operating properly.
			
			REPLACE safety belt warning chime. RESTORE vehicle. RETEST system.

FM9099500359020X

Fig. 30   Pinpoint test FF (Part 2 of 2)

TEST STEP	RESULT	▶	ACTION TO TAKE
GG1 CHECK EIC FOR WARNINGS			
• Turn ignition switch to RUN. • Check EIC displays. Wait past prove-out time. • Determine if the warning is always on or never on. • **Is anti-lock warning always on?**	Yes No	▶ ▶	GO to GG2. GO to GG4.
GG2 CHECK ANTI-LOCK BRAKE WARNING LAMP			
• Disconnect anti-lock brake control module. • Check EIC for warning. • **Is anti-lock warning illuminated?**	Yes No	▶ ▶	GO to GG3. SERVICE anti-lock brake control module. RESTORE vehicle. RETEST system.

FM9099500360010X

Fig. 31   Pinpoint test GG (Part 1 of 2)

TEST STEP	RESULT	▶	ACTION TO TAKE
HH1 CHECK EIC FOR WARNINGS			
• Turn ignition switch to RUN. • Check EIC displays. Wait past prove-out time. • Determine if the warning is always on or never on. • **Is low oil pressure warning always on?**	Yes No	▶ ▶	GO to HH2. GO to HH4.

FM9099500361010X

Fig. 32   Pinpoint test HH (Part 1 of 2)

TEST STEP	RESULT	▶	ACTION TO TAKE
GG3 CHECK CIRCUIT 806 CONTINUITY			
• Turn ignition switch to OFF. • Disconnect EIC. • Using a multimeter, check continuity in Circuit 606 (W/LB). • **Is continuity present?**	Yes No	▶ ▶	REPLACE EIC. AFFIX odometer sticker to door pillar. RESTORE vehicle. RETEST system. SERVICE Circuit 606 (W/LB) for open circuit. RESTORE vehicle. RETEST system.
GG4 CHECK POWER AND GROUNDS			
• Using a multimeter, measure voltage at EIC Pins:	Yes No	▶ ▶	GO to GG5. SERVICE as required. RESTORE vehicle. RETEST system.

PIN	FUNCTION	VOLTAGE
2 (C1)	RUN or START	Battery voltage
7 (C2)	BATTERY	Battery voltage
9 (C2)	RUN	Battery voltage
14 (C1)	RUN	Battery voltage
17 (C1)	BATTERY	Battery voltage

• Check continuity to ground at EIC Pins:

PIN	FUNCTION	VOLTAGE
2 (C2)	GROUND	ZERO
7 (C1)	GROUND	ZERO
8 (C2)	GROUND	ZERO
13 (C1)	GROUND	ZERO

• **Are all voltages as specified?**

TEST STEP	RESULT	▶	ACTION TO TAKE
GG5 CHECK ANTI-LOCK BRAKE MODULE			
• Turn ignition switch to OFF. • Disconnect connector at anti-lock brake control module. • Connect a jumper wire from Circuit 606 (W/LB) at harness connector to ground. • Turn ignition switch to RUN. • Check EIC for warning. • **Is ANTI-LOCK warning illuminated?**	Yes No	▶ ▶	SERVICE anti-lock brake control module. RESTORE vehicle. RETEST system. Go to GG6.
GG6 CHECK CIRCUIT 31 CONTINUITY			
• Remove jumper. • Disconnect EIC. • Using a multimeter, check continuity in Circuit 31 (W/R). • **Is continuity present?**	Yes No	▶ ▶	Replace EIC. AFFIX odometer sticker to fuel filler door pillar. RESTORE vehicle. RETEST system. SERVICE circuit 31 (W/R) for open circuit. RESTORE vehicle. RETEST system.

FM9099500360020X

Fig. 31   Pinpoint test GG (Part 2 of 2)

TEST STEP	RESULT	▶	ACTION TO TAKE
HH2 CHECK OIL PRESSURE SENSOR WARNING LAMP			
• Disconnect oil pressure sensor. • Check EIC for warning. • **Is low oil pressure warning illuminated?**	Yes No	▶ ▶	GO to HH3. oil pressure sensor replacement. RESTORE vehicle. RETEST system.
HH3 CHECK CONTINUITY			
• Turn ignition switch to OFF. • Disconnect EIC. • Using a multimeter, check continuity in Circuit 31 (W/R). • **Is continuity present?**	Yes No	▶ ▶	REPLACE EIC. AFFIX odometer sticker to fuel filler door pillar. RESTORE vehicle. RETEST system. SERVICE Circuit 31 (W/R) for open circuit. RESTORE vehicle. RETEST system.
HH4 CHECK FOR POWER AND GROUNDS			
• Using a multimeter, measure voltage at EIC Pins:	Yes No	▶ ▶	GO to HH5. SERVICE as required. RESTORE vehicle. RETEST system.

PIN	FUNCTION	VOLTAGE
2 (C1)	RUN or START	Battery voltage
7 (C2)	BATTERY	Battery voltage
9 (C2)	RUN	Battery voltage
14 (C1)	RUN	Battery voltage
17 (C1)	BATTERY	Battery voltage

• Check for continuity to ground at EIC Pins:

PIN	FUNCTION	VOLTAGE
2 (C2)	GROUND	ZERO
7 (C1)	GROUND	ZERO
8 (C2)	GROUND	ZERO
13 (C1)	GROUND	ZERO

• **Are all voltages as specified?**

TEST STEP	RESULT	▶	ACTION TO TAKE
HH5 CHECK OIL PRESSURE SENSOR SUPPLY CIRCUIT			
• Turn ignition switch to OFF. • Disconnect connector at oil pressure sensor. • Connect a jumper wire from Circuit 31 (W/R) at harness connector to ground. • Turn ignition switch to RUN. • Check EIC for warning. • **Is low oil pressure warning illuminated?**	Yes No	▶ ▶	oil pressure sensor replacement. RESTORE vehicle. RETEST system. GO to HH6.
HH6 CHECK CONTINUITY OF CIRCUIT 31 (W/R)			
• Remove jumper. • Disconnect EIC. • Using a multimeter, check continuity in Circuit 31 (W/R). • **Is continuity present?**	Yes No	▶ ▶	REPLACE EIC. AFFIX odometer sticker to door pillar. RESTORE vehicle. RETEST system. SERVICE Circuit 31 (W/R) for open circuit. RESTORE vehicle. RETEST system.

FM9099500361020X

Fig. 32   Pinpoint test HH (Part 2 of 2)

TEST STEP		RESULT	▶	ACTION TO TAKE
JJ1	**CHECK OIL LEVEL WITH DIPSTICK**			
	• Park on level area, wait 15 minutes and check oil level with dipstick.	Yes	▶	ADD oil to the FULL line on the dipstick. START engine and VERIFY that EIC does not display LOW OIL LEVEL message. If EIC display is lit, GO to JJ5.
	• Is oil level low?	No	▶	GO to JJ2.
JJ2	**CHECK POWER OF EIC**			
	• Disconnect electrical connector EIC.	Yes	▶	RECONNECT electrical connector to EIC. GO to JJ3.
	• Check for battery voltage at Pin 9 (Circuit 298, P/O).			
	• Is battery voltage present?	No	▶	CHECK Fuse 5 Circuit 298 (P/O). SERVICE if necessary. RESTORE vehicle. RETEST system.
JJ3	**CHECK EIC**			
	• Short Pin 14 of EIC to ground.	Yes	▶	GO to JJ4.
	• Start engine.	No	▶	REPLACE EIC. ATTACH odometer sticker to door pillar. RESTORE vehicle. RETEST system.
	• Is low oil level warning displayed?			
JJ4	**CHECK LOW OIL LEVEL SENSOR RESISTANCE**			
	• Disconnect low oil level sensor and measure resistance between sensor terminal and ground.	Yes	▶	REPLACE low oil level sensor.
	• Is resistance greater than 100 K ohms?	No	▶	CHECK Circuit 258 (W/PK) or connector to sensor for open circuit. RESTORE vehicle. RETEST system.
JJ5	**CHECK FOR SHORT TO GROUND**			
	• Disconnect low oil level sensor.	Yes	▶	GO to JJ6.
	• Start engine.	No	▶	REPLACE low oil level sensor. RESTORE vehicle. RETEST system.
	• Is low oil level warning displayed?			
JJ6	**CHECK EIC**			
	• Turn ignition switch OFF.	Yes	▶	REPLACE EIC. ATTACH odometer sticker to door pillar. RESTORE vehicle. RETEST system.
	• Disconnect electrical connector at Pin 14 of EIC.			
	• Is low oil level warning displayed?	No	▶	SERVICE short to ground in Circuit 258 (W/PK). RESTORE vehicle. RETEST system.

FM9099500362000X

Fig. 33   Pinpoint test JJ

TEST STEP		RESULT	▶	ACTION TO TAKE
KK1	**CHECK EIC FOR WARNINGS**			
	• Turn ignition switch to RUN.	Yes	▶	GO to KK2.
	• Check EIC displays. Wait past prove-out time.	No	▶	GO to KK4.
	• Determine if the warning is always or never on.			
	• Is AIR BAG warning always on?			

FM9099500363010X

Fig. 34   Pinpoint test KK (Part 1 of 3)

TEST STEP		RESULT	▶	ACTION TO TAKE
KK2	**CHECK AIR BAG DIAGNOSTIC MONITOR OPERATION**			
	NOTE: If the air bag warning indicator flashes on and off continuously, it means that it is showing a diagnostic trouble code. It does not mean that the air bag warning indicator needs to be serviced.	Yes	▶	GO to KK3.
		No	▶	REPLACE air bag diagnostic monitor. Refer to for air bag diagnostic monitor diagnosis and replacement. RESTORE vehicle. RETEST system.
	WARNING: THE BACK UP POWER SUPPLY ENERGY MUST BE DEPLETED BEFORE ANY AIR BAG COMPONENT SERVICE IS PERFORMED OR PERSONAL INJURY MAY RESULT. TO DEPLETE BACKUP POWER SUPPLY ENERGY, DISCONNECT THE POSITIVE BATTERY CABLE AND WAIT ONE MINUTE.			
	• Disconnect battery ground cable.			
	• Disconnect positive battery cable and wait one minute.			
	• Disconnect air bag diagnostic monitor.			
	• Check EIC for warning			
	• Is air bag warning illuminated continuously?			
KK3	**CHECK CONTINUITY OF CIRCUIT 608 (BK/Y)**			
	• Turn ignition switch to OFF.	Yes	▶	REPLACE EIC. AFFIX odometer sticker to door pillar. RESTORE vehicle. RETEST system.
	• Disconnect EIC.			
	• Using a multimeter, check continuity in Circuit 608 (BK/Y).	No	▶	SERVICE Circuit 608 (BK/Y) for open circuit. RESTORE vehicle. RETEST system.
	• Is continuity present?			
KK4	**CHECK FOR POWER AND GROUNDS**			
	• Using a multimeter, measure voltage at EIC Pins:	Yes	▶	GO to KK5.
		No	▶	SERVICE as required. RESTORE vehicle. RETEST system.

PIN	FUNCTION	VOLTAGE
2 (OF C1)	RUN or START	Battery voltage
7 (of C2)	BATTERY	Battery voltage
9 (of C2)	RUN	Battery voltage
14 (of C1)	RUN	Battery voltage
17 (of C1)	BATTERY	Battery voltage

• Check for continuity to ground at EIC Pins:

PIN	FUNCTION	VOLTAGE
2 (of C2)	GROUND	ZERO
7 (of C1)	GROUND	ZERO
8 (of C2)	GROUND	ZERO
13 (of C1)	GROUND	ZERO

• Are all voltages as specified?

FM9099500363020X

Fig. 34   Pinpoint test KK (Part 2 of 3)

TEST STEP		RESULT	▶	ACTION TO TAKE
KK5	**CHECK AIR BAG DIAGNOSTIC MONITOR SUPPLY CIRCUIT**			
	WARNING: THE BACKUP POWER SUPPLY ENERGY MUST BE DEPLETED BEFORE ANY AIR BAG COMPONENT SERVICE IS PERFORMED OR PERSONAL INJURY MAY RESULT. TO DEPLETE BACKUP POWER SUPPLY ENERGY, DISCONNECT THE POSITIVE BATTERY CABLE AND WAIT ONE MINUTE.	Yes	▶	Refer to for Air Bag Diagnostic Monitor diagnosis and replacement. RESTORE vehicle. RETEST system.
	• Disconnect battery ground cable.	No	▶	GO to KK6.
	• Turn ignition switch to OFF.			
	• Disconnect positive battery cable and wait one minute.			
	• Disconnect connector at air bag diagnostic monitor.			
	• Connect a jumper wire from Circuit 608 (BK/Y) of harness connector to ground.			
	• Reconnect positive battery cable.			
	• Reconnect battery ground cable.			
	• Turn ignition switch to RUN.			
	• Check EIC for warning			
	• Is AIR BAG warning illuminated?			
KK6	**CHECK CONTINUITY OF SUPPLY CIRCUIT**			
	• Remove jumper.	Yes	▶	REPLACE EIC. AFFIX odometer sticker to fuel filler door pillar. RESTORE vehicle. RETEST system.
	• Disconnect EIC.			
	• Using a multimeter, check continuity in Circuit 608 (BK/Y).	No	▶	SERVICE Circuit 608 (BK/Y) for open circuit. RESTORE vehicle. RETEST system.
	• Is continuity present?			

FM9099500363030X

Fig. 34   Pinpoint test KK (Part 3 of 3)

1993 Crown Victoria, Grand Marquis & Town Car

NOTE: Refer to the Symptom Index in this section before performing any Pinpoint Tests.

INDEX

	Page No. 15-	Fig. No.
PINPOINT TESTS:		
Pinpoint Test AH	41	2
Pinpoint Test AL	41	3
Pinpoint Test AS	41	4
Pinpoint Test FA	42	5
Pinpoint Test FB	42	6
Pinpoint Test FC	42	7
Pinpoint Test FD	42	8
Pinpoint Test FE	42	9
Pinpoint Test FF	43	10
Pinpoint Test FG	43	11
Pinpoint Test SA	43	12
Pinpoint Test SB	43	13
Pinpoint Test SC	44	14
Pinpoint Test SD	44	15
Pinpoint Test SE	44	16

	Page No. 15-	Fig. No.
Pinpoint Test SF	44	17
Pinpoint Test SG	44	18
Pinpoint Test SH	45	19
Pinpoint Test SJ	45	20
Pinpoint Test SK	45	21
Pinpoint Test TA	45	22
Pinpoint Test TB	45	23
Pinpoint Test TC	45	24
Pinpoint Test TD	46	25
Pinpoint Test TX	46	26
Pinpoint Test WA	46	27
Pinpoint Test WB	46	28
Pinpoint Test WC	47	29
Pinpoint Test WD	47	30
SYMPTOM INDEX	40	1

	Symptom	GO to
	CLUSTER DISPLAY DIAGNOSIS	
1	Display Not Illuminated	Pinpoint Test TA
2	Display Lit But Too Dim	Pinpoint Test TA
3	Display Scrambled, Segments Half Lit (Ghost Segments), Segments Blinking or Missing, Display Incorrect All The Time	Pinpoint Test TB
4	Display Stuck With All Segments On	Pinpoint Test TB
5	No Beep When Buttons Pushed or Driver Alert Given	Pinpoint Test SA
6	Module Does Not Respond to Buttons	Pinpoint Test SA
	TEMPERATURE GAUGE DIAGNOSIS	
7	Temperature Gauge Display Blanks Out Thermometer Symbol and Lights Top Two and Bottom Two Bars of Gauge	Pinpoint Test TC
8	No Warning Tone When Thermometer Symbol Is Blinking	Pinpoint Test TX
9	Temperature Gauge Always Indicates Cold Temperature	Pinpoint Test TD
	SPEEDOMETER DIAGNOSIS	
10	Reads 0 MPH (KM/H) At All Speeds When Vehicle In Motion	Pinpoint Test SB
11	Speedometer Reads Constantly Too High or Too Low	Pinpoint Test SC
12A	Speed Indication Jumps Up and Down Erratically	Pinpoint Test SD
12B	Speed Control Indicator Always On	Pinpoint Test SJ
12C	Speed Control Indicator Does Not Come On When Speed Control Switched On	Pinpoint Test SK

FM9099300152010X

Fig. 1 Symptom index (Part 1 of 2)

	Symptom	GO to
	ODOMETER DIAGNOSIS	
13	Display Reads "Error"	Pinpoint Test SE
14	Display Has "S" Illuminated	Pinpoint Test SF
15	Odometer Does Not Accumulate Mileage, or Counts 1.6 KM (1.0 Miles) and Jumps Back 1.6 KM (1.0 Miles)	Pinpoint Test SG
16	Mileage Constantly Reads Too High or Too Low	Pinpoint Test SH
	MESSAGE CENTER DISPLAY DIAGNOSIS	
17	Instantaneous Fuel Economy or Average Fuel Economy Always Reads Zero Miles/Gal or 99 L/100	Pinpoint Test FA
18	Trip Distance Does Not Accumulate	Pinpoint Test FB
19	Instantaneous Fuel Economy or Average Fuel Economy Always Reads 99 Miles/Gal or 0 L/100	Pinpoint Test FA
20	DTE Does Not Go Below 322 KM (200 Miles) With Fuel Tank Empty	Pinpoint Test FC
21	DTE Always Reads Zero Miles	Pinpoint Test FC
22	CO DTE and Fuel Remaining Display	Pinpoint Test FD
23	CS DTE and Fuel Remaining Display	Pinpoint Test FE
24	Fuel Remaining Does Not Display F When Fuel Tank Is Full	Pinpoint Test FF
	WARNING INDICATOR DIAGNOSIS	
26A	Outside Air Temperature Wrong (But Not As In 26B or 26C)	Pinpoint Test AS
26B	Outside Air Temperature Always Reads -40°C (-40°F)	Pinpoint Test AL
26C	Outside Air Temperature Always Read 57°-60°C (135-140°F)	Pinpoint Test AH
27	Grounded Warning Indicators Always Illuminated or Always Off Are As Follows: AIR BAG, BRAKES, CHARGING SYSTEM, CHECK AIR SUSPENSION, CHECK ENGINE, DOOR AJAR, WASHER FLUID and OVERDRIVE OFF	Pinpoint Test WA
28	Pull Up Warning Indicators Always Illuminated or Always Off Are As Follows: HIGH BEAMS, SAFETY BELT, and TURN SIGNALS	Pinpoint Test WB
	FUEL GAUGE DIAGNOSIS	
29	Fuel Gauge Only Displays Top Two and Bottom Two Bars	Pinpoint Test FG
30	Fuel Gauge Does Not Illuminate All Bars With Fuel Gauge Full	Pinpoint Test FF
31	Fuel Gauge Illuminates One Or More Bars With Fuel Gauge Empty	Pinpoint Test FF
32	Inaccurate Fuel Indication	Pinpoint Test FF
33	EATC Stuck In English Mode	Pinpoint Test WC
33A	EATC Stuck In Metric Mode	Pinpoint Test WD

FM9099300152020X

Fig. 1 Symptom index (Part 2 of 2)

TEST STEP		RESULT	▶	ACTION TO TAKE
AH1	VERIFY CONDITION			
	• Turn ignition to RUN position and read outside air temperature.	Yes	▶	GO to Pinpoint Index.
	• Remove fuse 1 for 30 seconds and re-install.	No	▶	GO to AH2.
	• Read outside air temperature.			
	• **Is second reading correct?**			
AH2	CHECK CONNECTOR C101			
	• Disconnect 16-pin connector C101.	No	▶	GO to AH3.
	• Turn ignition switch to ON position.	Yes	▶	GO to AH4.
	• Remove fuse 1 for 30 seconds and re-install.			
	• Read outside air temperature.			
	• **Does temperature read -40°C (-40°F)?**			
AH3	CHECK ELECTRONIC CLUSTER			
	• Remove cluster finish panel.	No	▶	REPLACE cluster
	• Disconnect rear cluster connector C101 and using a small screwdriver remove Pin 1 from connector and reconnect connector.	Yes	▶	SERVICE wiring between cluster and connector C101.
	• Turn ignition switch to RUN position.			
	• Remove fuse 1 for 30 seconds and re-install.			
	• Read outside air temperature.			
	• **Does temperature read -40°C (-40°F)?**			

FM9099300153010X

Fig. 2   Pinpoint test AH (Part 1 of 2)

TEST STEP		RESULT	▶	ACTION TO TAKE
AH4	CHECK SENSOR CONNECTOR			
	• Reinstall Pin 1 in connector C101.	No	▶	SERVICE wiring between connector C101 and air temperature sensor.
	• Connect connector C101.			
	• Disconnect air temperature sensor at radiator support.	Yes	▶	GO to AH5.
	• Turn ignition to RUN position.			
	• Remove fuse 1 for 30 seconds and re-install.			
	• Read outside air temperature.			
	• **Does temperature read -40°C (-40°F)?**			
AH5	CHECK AIR TEMPERATURE SENSOR			
	• Using an ohmmeter, measure resistance across sensor terminals at 15-21°C (60-70°F).	Yes	▶	GO to AH1 and RETEST system.
	• **Is resistance between 33-47 ohms?**	No	▶	REPLACE sensor.

FM9099300153020X

Fig. 2   Pinpoint test AH (Part 2 of 2)

TEST STEP		RESULT	▶	ACTION TO TAKE
AL1	VERIFY CONDITION			
	• Turn ignition switch to RUN position.	Yes	▶	GO to Pinpoint Index.
	• Read outside air temperature.	No	▶	GO to AL2.
	• Remove fuse 1 for 30 seconds and re-install.			
	• **Is second reading correct?**			
AL2	CHECK SENSOR CONNECTOR			
	• Disconnect air temperature sensor.	Yes	▶	GO to AL3.
	• Jump Circuit 233 (DB/Y) to Circuit (875 BK/LB) at harness connector.	No	▶	GO to AL5.
	• Turn ignition switch to RUN position.			
	• Remove fuse 1 for 30 seconds and re-install.			
	• Read outside air temperature.			
	• **Does temperature read -40°C (-40°F)?**			
AL3	CHECK 16 PIN CONNECTOR C101			
	• Disconnect 16 pin connector C101.	No	▶	SERVICE wiring to C101 or sensor.
	• Turn ignition switch to RUN position.	Yes	▶	GO to AL4.
	• Remove fuse 1 for 30 seconds.			
	• Reinstall fuse and read outside air temperature.			
	• **Does temperature read -40°C (-40°F)?**			

FM9099300154000X

Fig. 3   Pinpoint test AL

TEST STEP		RESULT	▶	ACTION TO TAKE
AS1	VERIFY CONDITION			
	• Turn ignition to RUN position.	Yes	▶	GO to Pinpoint Index.
	• Read outside air temperature.	No	▶	GO to AS2.
	• Pull Fuse 1 (cluster should go blank).			
	• After 30 seconds, replace fuse and read outside air temperature.			
	• **Is second reading correct?**			
AS2	RESET AIR TEMPERATURE			
	• Disconnect air temperature sensor at radiator support.	Yes	▶	GO to AS3.
	• Turn ignition to RUN position.	No	▶	GO to AS4.
	• Remove Fuse 1 and install after 30 seconds. Read outside air temperature.			
	• **Does temperature read -40°C (-40°F)?**			
AS3	CHECK AIR TEMPERATURE SENSOR			
	• Using an ohmmeter, measure sensor resistance at 15-21°C (60-70°F).	Yes	▶	GO to AS1 and RETEST system.
	• **Is resistance between 33-47 ohms?**	No	▶	REPLACE sensor.

FM9099300155010X

Fig. 4   Pinpoint test AS (Part 1 of 2)

TEST STEP		RESULT	▶	ACTION TO TAKE
AS4	CHECK 16 PIN CONNECTOR C101			
	• Disconnect 16 pin connector C101.	Yes	▶	SERVICE wiring to C101 or sensor.
	• Turn ignition to RUN position.			
	• Remove Fuse 1 and install after 30 seconds. Read outside temperature.	No	▶	GO to AS5.
	• **Does temperature read -40°C (-40°F)?**			
AS5	CHECK ELECTRONIC CLUSTER			
	• Remove cluster finish panel.	Yes	▶	SERVICE wiring between cluster and connector C101.
	• Disconnect connector C101.			
	• Using small screwdriver, release Pin 1 in connector and connect connector C101 to cluster.	No	▶	REPLACE cluster
	• Turn ignition switch to RUN position.			
	• Remove Fuse 1 for 30 seconds and re-install. Read outside air temperature.			
	• **Does temperature read -40°C (-40°F)?**			

FM9099300155020X

Fig. 4   Pinpoint test AS (Part 2 of 2)

TEST STEP		RESULT	▶	ACTION TO TAKE
FA1	VERIFY CONDITION			
			▶	GO to FA2.
FA2	CHECK SPEEDOMETER OPERATION			
	• Verify that speedometer is operating properly.	Yes	▶	GO to FA3.
	• Does speedometer operate properly?	No	▶	GO to Pinpoint Test SF.
FA3	CHECK CONTINUITY OF CIRCUIT 205 (FUEL FLOW)			
	• Verify continuity and absence of shorts in Circuit 205.	Yes	▶	GO to FA4.
	• Is wiring OK?	No	▶	SERVICE wiring Circuit 205 as required.
FA4	CHECK FOR PRESENCE OF FUEL PULSES FROM PCM			
	• Turn ignition on to start vehicle with vehicle in PARK.	Yes	▶	GO to FA5.
	• Check powertrain control module, pin 34 output. Use Digital Volt Ohmmeter T80L-50-DVOM.	No	▶	REPLACE the powertrain control module.
	• Does the meter reading fluctuate?			
FA5	CHECK FOR PRESENCE OF FUEL PULSES TO CLUSTER			
	• Ignition on.	Yes	▶	REPLACE cluster.
	• Check fuel flow input to cluster. Check C255 Pin 22. Use Digital Volt Ohmmeter T80L-50-DVOM.	No	▶	SERVICE wiring between cluster and PCM. The wire is probably open. Check for intermittent contact.
	• Does the meter reading fluctuate?			

FM9099300156000X

Fig. 5 Pinpoint test FA

TEST STEP		RESULT	▶	ACTION TO TAKE
FB1	VERIFY CONDITION			
	• Verify that trip distance accumulates.	Yes	▶	System OK.
	• Does trip distance accumulate?	No	▶	GO to Pinpoint Test SG.

FM9099300157000X

Fig. 6 Pinpoint test FB

TEST STEP		RESULT	▶	ACTION TO TAKE
FC1	VERIFY CONDITION			
			▶	GO to FC2.
FC2	CHECK FUEL GAUGE			
	• Verify that fuel gauge is operating properly.	Yes	▶	GO to FC3.
	• Does gauge operate properly?	No	▶	GO to Pinpoint test FD or FE.

FM9099300158010X

Fig. 7 Pinpoint test FC (Part 1 of 2)

TEST STEP		RESULT	▶	ACTION TO TAKE
FC3	CHECK SPEEDOMETER			
	• Verify that speedometer is operating properly.	Yes	▶	GO to Pinpoint Test FA.
	• Does speedometer operate properly?	No	▶	GO to Pinpoint Test SB.

Fig. 7 Pinpoint test FC (Part 2 of 2)

TEST STEP		RESULT	▶	ACTION TO TAKE
FD1	VERIFY CONDITION			
		CO displayed	▶	GO to FD2.
FD2	CHECK FUEL SENDER WIRING AT SENDER			
	• Disconnect ground cable to battery.	CO displayed	▶	GO to FD4.
	• Lower fuel tank to gain access to fuel sender connector.	CS displayed	▶	GO to FD3.
	• Unplug fuel sender connector.			
	• Jumper variable resistance terminal and ground terminal of sender connector.			
	• Reconnect battery.			
	• Turn ignition switch from OFF to RUN.			
	• Check digital fuel remaining display for CO or CS.			
	NOTE: It may take several minutes for the gauge to respond.			
FD3	CHECK SENDER			
	• Turn ignition switch to OFF.	Yes	▶	INSPECT fuel sender wiring connector female terminals for flash or loose fit. SERVICE as required.
	• Measure the resistance of the fuel sender at the sender terminals.			
	• Verify that the resistance is less than 181 ohms (normally between 11 and 168 ohms).	No	▶	REPLACE sender.
	• Is resistance less than 181 ohms?			
FD4	CHECK FUEL SENDER WIRING AT CLUSTER			
	• Disconnect ground cable to battery.	Yes	▶	REPLACE cluster.[11]
	• Remove C254 from cluster and secure connectors from shorting.	No	▶	SERVICE fuel sender wiring for open circuit.
	• Jumper variable resistance terminal and ground terminal of harness together at sender.			
	• Verify continuity between C254 Pin 2 and C254 Pin 4 ground of cluster connector.			
	• Is resistance close to zero ohms?			

FM9099300159000X

Fig. 8 Pinpoint test FD

TEST STEP		RESULT	▶	ACTION TO TAKE
FE1	VERIFY CONDITION			
		CS displayed	▶	GO to FE2.

FM9099300160010X

Fig. 9 Pinpoint test FE (Part 1 of 2)

TEST STEP		RESULT	▶	ACTION TO TAKE
FE2	CHECK FUEL SENDER WIRING AT CLUSTER			
	• Disconnect ground cable to battery.	Yes	▶	REPLACE cluster.[12]
	• Remove cluster and secure connectors from shorting.	No	▶	Short exists in harness or sender. GO to FE3.
	• With an ohmmeter, measure resistance between C254 Pin 2 and C254 Pin 4 (SIG GND) of harness.			
	• Verify that the resistance is 5 ohms or greater (normally 11 to 168 ohms).			
	• Is resistance at least 5 ohms?			
FE3	CHECK FUEL SENDER WIRING			
	• Disconnect ground cable to battery.	Yes	▶	REPLACE fuel sender.
	• Lower fuel tank to gain access to fuel sender connector.	No	▶	SERVICE fuel sender wiring for short circuit.
	• Unplug connector fuel sender.			
	• Measure the resistance between C254 Pin 2 and C254 Pin 4 (GND) of harness.			
	• Verify that resistance is greater than 10 K ohms.			
	• Is resistance at least 10 K ohms?			

FM9099300160020X

Fig. 9 Pinpoint test FE (Part 2 of 2)

TEST STEP		RESULT	►	ACTION TO TAKE
FF1	VERIFY CONDITION			
			►	GO to FF2.
FF2	CHECK FUEL GAUGE RESPONSE			
	• Disconnect ground cable to battery.	Yes	►	GO to FF4. TURN ignition off.
	• Lower fuel tank and gain access to sender connections.	No	►	GO to FF3. TURN ignition off. LEAVE 43 ohm resistor connected.
	• Connect a 43 ohm (± 1 percent) resistor in place of fuel tank sending unit and pump. Verify value with ohm meter.			
	• Reconnect battery.			
	• Turn ignition key to RUN.			
	• Fuel gauge should read 3 to 4 bars illuminated.			
	• FUEL REMAIN should read 3 to 4 GAL (13 to 15 LTR)>			
	• Is fuel gauge correct?			
FF3	CHECK HARNESS RESISTANCE			
	• Disconnect ground cable to battery.	Yes	►	REPLACE cluster.[12]
	• Remove cluster and secure connectors from shorting.	No	►	SERVICE Circuit 29 as required.
	• Jumper sender connector.			
	• Measure resistance between C254 Pin 2 and C254 Pin 4 (GND) with 43 ohm resistor in place.			
	• Is resistance within range?			
FF4	CHECK FUEL TANK SENDING UNIT AND PUMP			
	• Disconnect ground cable to battery.	Yes	►	GO to FF5.
	• Check fuel tank sending unit and pump for binding, sticking, misalignment, etc.	No	►	SERVICE or REPLACE fuel tank sending unit and pump as required.
	• Is fuel tank sending unit and pump OK?			
FF5	CHECK FUEL TANK			
	• Check fuel tank for dents, bulges or other damage.	Yes	►	System OK. Fault caused by other vehicle system(s).
	• Check for proper installation of fuel tube.			
	• Is fuel tank OK?			
		No	►	REPLACE fuel tank, or fuel tube.

FM9099300186000X

Fig. 10   Pinpoint test FF (Part 1 of 2)

TEST STEP		RESULT	►	ACTION TO TAKE
FG1	VERIFY CONDITION			
			►	GO to FG2.
FG2	CHECK FUEL REMAINING DISPLAY			
		CO displayed	►	GO to Pinpoint Test FD.
		CS displayed	►	GO to Pinpoint test FE.

Fig. 11   Pinpoint test FG

TEST STEP		RESULT	►	ACTION TO TAKE
SA1	VERIFY CONDITION TEST EACH BUTTON			
	• Buttons function only in RUN mode.	Display does not respond to buttons	►	GO to SA3.
	• Warning chime module will not beep if another sound is being produced.	Display responds to buttons, but no chime sounds	►	GO to SA2.
SA2	CHECK WARNING CHIME MODULE			
	• Check for fasten safety belt reminder chime or key left in ignition reminder chime.	Yes	►	GO to SA8.
	• Does chime sound?	No	►	SERVICE warning chime module.
SA3	CHECK SWITCH WIRING CONNECTIONS			
	• Remove finish panel to expose cluster.	Yes	►	GO to SA4.
	• Verify that connections at switch assembly are securely connected.	No	►	Secure connections and RECHECK.
	• Are connections secure?			

FM9099300188010X

Fig. 12   Pinpoint test SA (Part 1 of 2)

TEST STEP		RESULT	►	ACTION TO TAKE
SA4	CHECK SWITCH ASSEMBLY (NO SWITCH PRESSED)			
	• Unplug switch assembly.	Yes	►	GO to SA5.
	• Measure the resistance between Pin 1 (Circuit 143, LB/Y) and Pin 8 (Circuit 875, BK/LB) of the switch assembly.	No	►	REPLACE switch assembly.
	• Resistance with no switch pressed should be 17,300 to 17,600 ohms.			
	• Is resistance within range?			
SA5	CHECK SWITCH ASSEMBLY (BUTTONS PRESSED)			
	• Unplug switch assembly from electronic instrument cluster.	Yes	►	GO to SA6.
	• Measure the resistance between Pin 1 (Circuit 143, LB/Y) and Pin 8 (Circuit 875, BK/LB) of the switch assembly while pressing the problem button.	No	►	REPLACE switch assembly.
	• The resistance should be:			

BUTTON	RESISTANCE (in ohms)
EM	5100-5200
SELECT (forward)	330-350
SELECT (reverse)	2250-2350
RESET	1000-1100

	NOTE: Press only one button.			
	• Is resistance within range?			
SA6	CHECK CLUSTER WIRING CONNECTIONS			
	• Disconnect battery ground cable.	Yes	►	GO to SA7.
	• Remove cluster.	No	►	RECONNECT connector and RECHECK.
	• Verify that connectors C255 (16-pin) is secure and properly aligned.			
	• Replug switch assembly connector.			
	• Is cluster OK?			
SA7	VERIFY HARNESS CONTINUITY			
	• Disconnect battery ground cable.	Yes	►	REPLACE cluster.[6]
	• Remove cluster and switch assembly.	No	►	SERVICE Circuit 143 or 875 or 676 for open.
	• Check continuity between Pin 1 (Circuit 143, LB/Y) of switch assembly connector and C255 Circuit 30.			
	• Check continuity between Pin 8 (Circuit 875, BK/LB) of switch assembly connector and C254 Pin 4.			
	• Is there continuity?			
SA8	CHECK TONE CIRCUIT			
	• Disconnect battery ground cable.	Yes	►	REPLACE cluster.[6]
	• Remove cluster.	No	►	SERVICE wiring Circuit 183 for open. CHECK for correct warning chime module part number or operation.
	• Turn ignition switch to RUN and wait for the fasten safety belt reminder chime to end.			
	• Place jumper wire between harness connector C254 Pin 11 and ground. Listen for chime.			
	• Does chime sound?			

FM9099300188020X

Fig. 12   Pinpoint test SA (Part 2 of 2)

TEST STEP		RESULT	►	ACTION TO TAKE
SB1	VERIFY CONDITION			
			►	GO to SB2.
SB2	VERIFY DISPLAY PROVE OUT			
	• Turn ignition switch to RUN.	Yes	►	GO to SA3.
	• Observe display (all segments ON, then OFF, and then normal display).	No	►	REPLACE cluster.
	• Does display prove out properly?			
SB3	CHECK ODOMETER			
	• Verify that odometer advances when vehicle is driven forward.	No	►	GO to SB4.
	• Does odometer advance?	Yes	►	REPLACE cluster.
SB4	CHECK SPEED CONTROL			
	• Test drive vehicle and check operation of speed control, if equipped.	Yes	►	GO to SB9.
	• Does speed control operate properly?	No	►	GO to SB5.
SB5	CHECK WIRING SPEED TO SPEED SENSOR			
	• Disconnect connector to speed sensor.	Yes	►	GO to SB6.
	• Using Rotunda Digital Volt-Ohmmeter 014-00407 or equivalent, measure the resistance between the two wires in the harness to the speed sensor.	No	►	SERVICE wiring Circuit 136, speed control, air suspension, or cluster for shorts.
	• Resistance should be greater than 500 ohms.			
	• Is resistance greater than 500 ohms?			

FM9099300189010X

Fig. 13   Pinpoint test SB (Part 1 of 2)

TEST STEP		RESULT	▶	ACTION TO TAKE
SB6	CHECK SPEED SENSOR RESISTANCE			
	• Using Rotunda Digital Volt-Ohmmeter 014-00407 or equivalent, check resistance at speed sensor.	Yes	▶	GO to SB7.
	• Resistance should be 200 to 230 ohms.	No	▶	REPLACE speed sensor. CHECK speedometer operation.
	• Is resistance within range?			
SB7	CHECK DRIVEN GEAR AND RETAINER CLIP			
	• Disconnect speed sensor from transmission. Verify presence of driven gear with all teeth in good condition and the presence of retainer clip.	Yes	▶	GO to SB8.
		No	▶	REPLACE with proper gear and / or clip.
	• Are driven gear and retainer clip OK?			
SB8	CHECK DRIVE GEAR ON TRANSMISSION			
	• Verify presence of drive gear on transmission output shaft.	Yes	▶	GO to SB9.
		No	▶	SERVICE transmission gear.
	• Is drive gear OK?			
SB9	CHECK WIRING TO CLUSTER			
	• Reconnect speed sensor wiring.	Yes	▶	REPLACE cluster.
	• Disconnect ground cable to battery.	No	▶	SERVICE connectors / wiring from cluster to speed sensor Circuit 136. CHECK speedometer operation.
	• Remove cluster.			
	• Using Rotunda Digital Volt-Ohmmeter 014-00407 or equivalent, check resistance between C2-2 Pin 31 and C2-1 Pin 4 (ground) of connector.			
	• Resistance should be 160 to 230 ohms.			
	• Is resistance within range?			

FM9099300189020X

Fig. 13 Pinpoint test SB (Part 2 of 2)

TEST STEP		RESULT	▶	ACTION TO TAKE
SD1	VERIFY CONDITION			
			▶	GO to SD2.
SD2	CHECK SPEED SENSOR DRIVE GEAR			
	• Remove speed sensor from transmission.	Yes	▶	GO to SD3.
	• Check that all gear teeth are in good condition, retainer clip is installed and gear does not slip on shaft.	No	▶	REPLACE drive gear and / or retaining clip.
	• Is speed sensor OK?			
SD3	CHECK WIRING TO SPEED SENSOR			
	• Disconnect connector to speed sensor.	Yes	▶	GO to SD4.
	• Using Rotunda Digital Volt Ohmmeter 014-00407 or equivalent, check for intermittent resistance between the two wires in the harness to the speed sensor	No	▶	SERVICE wiring Circuit 136, speed control, cluster for intermittent shorts or opens. CHECK speedometer operation.
	• Resistance should be greater than 500 ohms.			
	• Is resistance greater than 500 ohms?			
SD4	CHECK SPEED SENSOR RESISTANCE			
	• Using Rotunda Digital Volt-Ohmmeter 014-00407 or equivalent, check for intermittent resistance between the two wires in the harness to the speed sensor	Yes	▶	GO to SD5.
		No	▶	REPLACE speed sensor CHECK speedometer operation.
	• Resistance should be 200 to 230 ohms.			
	• Is resistance greater than 500 ohms?			
SD5	CHECK WIRING TO CLUSTER			
	• Reconnect speed sensor wiring.	Yes	▶	REPLACE cluster."
	• Disconnect ground cable to battery.	No	▶	SERVICE connectors wiring from cluster to speed sensor. Circuit 136 CHECK speedometer operation
	• Disconnect C254, C255 from cluster			
	• Using Rotunda Digital Volt Ohmmeter 014-00407 or equivalent, check for intermittent resistance between the C255 Pin 31 and C254 Pin 4 (ground) of connector			
	• Is wiring OK?			

FM9099300191000X

Fig. 15 Pinpoint test SD

TEST STEP		RESULT	▶	ACTION TO TAKE
SF1	VERIFY CONDITION			
			▶	GO to SF2.
	⑤000000.1 K 16691-A			
SF2	DETERMINE IF SPEEDO · ODO MODULE IS ORIGINAL			
	• Check for mileage sticker on door pillar.	Yes	▶	REPLACE cluster. If odometer reading is known, service center will program it into new cluster. If odometer reading is unknown, service center will program in "S" 00000 5 with the circled S and zero miles in the odometer
	• Is mileage sticker original?			
		No	▶	System OK.

FM9099300193000X

Fig. 17 Pinpoint test SF

TEST STEP		RESULT	▶	ACTION TO TAKE
SC1	VERIFY THE CONDITION			
			▶	GO to SC2.
SC2	CHECK ODOMETER ACCURACY			
	• Over a known distance, compare the odometer reading with the distance traveled.	Yes	▶	System OK.
		No	▶	GO to SC3.
	• Is odometer accurate?			
SC3	CHECK SPEED SENSOR DRIVE GEAR			
	• Remove speed sensor from transmission and verify that correct drive gear is installed for vehicle transmission / axle / tire combination.	Yes	▶	GO to SC4.
		No	▶	INSTALL correct gear with retaining clip.
	• Is drive gear correct?			
SC4	CHECK DRIVE GEAR ON TRANSMISSION OUTPUT SHAFT			
	• Check that correct drive gear is installed on transmission output shaft.	Yes	▶	REPLACE cluster
		No	▶	INSTALL correct shaft and / or gear.
	• Is drive gear correct?			

FM9099300190010X

Fig. 14 Pinpoint test SC

TEST STEP		RESULT	▶	ACTION TO TAKE
SE1	VERIFY CONDITION			
			▶	REPLACE cluster. AFFIX odometer sticker to door pillar.
	Error **55** MPH			

FM9099300192000X

Fig. 16 Pinpoint test SE

TEST STEP		RESULT	▶	ACTION TO TAKE
SG1	VERIFY CONDITION			
		Odometer will not accumulate	▶	GO to SG2.
		Odometer accumulates 1.6 Km (1.0 miles), then loses 1.6 Km (1.0 miles)	▶	REPLACE cluster. AFFIX odometer sticker to door pillar.

FM9099300194000X

Fig. 18 Pinpoint test SG (Part 1 of 2)

TEST STEP		RESULT	▶	ACTION TO TAKE
SG2	VERIFY SPEEDOMETER			
	• Verify that speedometer works properly.	Yes	▶	REPLACE cluster. AFFIX odometer sticker to door pillar.
	• Does speedometer operate properly?			
		No	▶	GO to Pinpoint Test SB.

Fig. 18 Pinpoint test SG (Part 2 of 2)

TEST STEP		RESULT	▶	ACTION TO TAKE
SH1	VERIFY CONDITION			
			▶	GO to SH2.
SH2	CHECK SPEEDOMETER			
	• Perform Pinpoint Test SC.	Yes	▶	REPLACE cluster.
	• Verify that speedometer is operating properly.	No	▶	GO to Pinpoint Test SC.
	• Does speedometer operate properly?			

FM9099300195000X

Fig. 19   Pinpoint test SH

TEST STEP		RESULT	▶	ACTION TO TAKE
SJ1	VERIFY CONDITION			
	• Is condition present?	Yes	▶	GO to SJ2.
SJ2	CHECK SPEED CONTROL AMPLIFIER			
	• Disconnect 8-pin connector from speed control amplifier.	Yes	▶	REPLACE amplifier. VERIFY proper operation.
	• Does Indicator go off?	No	▶	GO to SJ3.
SJ3	CHECK WIRING			
	• Check for crossed, misrouted or damaged wiring.	Yes	▶	GO to SJ4.
	• Is wiring OK?	No	▶	SERVICE wiring as required.

Fig. 20   Pinpoint test SJ

TEST STEP		RESULT	▶	ACTION TO TAKE
SK1	VERIFY CONDITION			
	• Is condition present?	Yes	▶	GO to SK2.
SK2	CHECK SPEED CONTROL AMPLIFIER			
	• Verify that vehicle has brown color speed control amplifier for use with electronic clusters.	Yes	▶	GO to SK3.
	• Is amplifier brown?	No	▶	REPLACE with correct amplifier. VERIFY proper operation.
SK3	CHECK VOLTAGE AT AMPLIFIER			
	• Remove 8-pin and 6-pin connectors from amplifier.	Yes	▶	GO to SK5.
	• Turn ignition to RUN position.	No	▶	GO to SK4.
	• Using Rotunda Digital Volt Ohmmeter 014-00407 or equivalent, connect positive lead to Circuit 203 (O/LB) of 8-pin connector and negative lead to the BK Pin of the 6-pin connector (ground).			
	• Is voltage approximately 5 volts?			
SK4	CHECK CONTINUITY OF CIRCUIT 203			
	• Using ohmmeter check continuity of Circuit 203 (O/LB) of 8-pin connector at amplifier to Pin 26 of the cluster connector C2-2.	Yes	▶	GO to SK6.
	• Is there continuity?	No	▶	SERVICE open circuit.
SK5	DISPLAY TEST			
	• Turn ignition to ON position.	Yes	▶	REPLACE amplifier. VERIFY proper operation.
	• Connect Circuit 203 (O/LB) in 8-pin connector to ground (BK) in 6-pin connector.	No	▶	GO to SK6.
	• Observe speed control indicator.			
	• Does Indicator come on?			
SK6	DISPLAY TEST			
	• Turn ignition to RUN position.	Yes	▶	GO to SK4.
	• Connect Circuit 203 (/LB) at Pin 26 of cluster connector C2-2 to ground.	No	▶	REPLACE cluster.
	• Observe speed control display.			
	• Does display turn on?			

FM9099300197010X

Fig. 21   Pinpoint test SK

TEST STEP		RESULT	▶	ACTION TO TAKE
TA1	VERIFY CONDITION			
	• Turn ignition switch to RUN position.	Only one or two displays working properly	▶	REPLACE cluster.
	• Turn headlamps off.	All displays too dim	▶	GO to TA8.
	• Check for illumination of displays.	All displays blank	▶	GO to TA2.
TA2	VERIFY MODULE OPERATION			
	• Turn ignition switch to RUN position.	Yes	▶	GO to TA7.
	• Press any button on the cluster control.	No	▶	GO to TA3.
	• Listen for beep from tone module when button is pressed.			
	• Does button beep?			
TA3	CHECK FUSE			
	• Check for blown fuses— fuse 1 (Circuit 797) or 4 (Circuit 295).	Yes	▶	GO to TA5.
	• Is fuse OK?	No	▶	GO to TA4.
TA4	CHECK FOR SHORT IN CIRCUIT 797 OR CIRCUIT 295			
	• Turn ignition key to OFF.	No	▶	GO to TA9.
	• Disconnect battery ground cable.	Yes	▶	SERVICE circuit for shorts.
	• Connect ohmmeter from Circuit 797 or Circuit 295 side of fuse to ground.			
	• Is circuit shorted?			

FM9099300198010X

Fig. 22   Pinpoint test TA (Part 1 of 2)

TEST STEP		RESULT	▶	ACTION TO TAKE
TA5	CHECK FOR POWER AT FUSE			
	• Reconnect battery.	Yes	▶	GO to TA6.
	• Measure voltage from Circuit 797 or Circuit 295 side of FUSE to ground.	No	▶	SERVICE open in fuse holder.
	• Is voltage greater than 9 volts?			
TA6	CHECK FOR POWER AT CLUSTER			
	• Turn ignition to OFF.	Yes	▶	REPLACE cluster.
	• Remove cluster as outlined.	No	▶	SERVICE Circuit 797 (BATT) 295 (RUN) 8875 (GROUND)
	• Turn ignition to RUN.			
	• Measure voltages at the harness connectors of the cluster.			
	• Voltage should be:			

PIN	FUNCTION	VOLTAGE
C2-13	BATT	Battery Voltage
C2-15	RUN	Battery Voltage
C2-12	RUN	Battery Voltage

	• Check continuity of ground circuit Pins C1-1 and C2-14 to battery ground.			
	• Are voltage and continuity present?			
TA7	CHECK FRONT CONNECTOR			
	• Verify that front cluster connector is locked in and that all pins and terminals are intact.	Connector good	▶	GO to TA6.
		Connector not locked	▶	LOCK connector and RECHECK.
		Pins or terminals not intact	▶	REPLACE connector or cluster as required.
TA8	CHECK RHEOSTAT OUTPUT			
	• Remove cluster.	Yes	▶	REPLACE cluster
	• Turn ignition to the RUN position.	No	▶	SERVICE rheostat.
	• Check rheostat output at cluster (Circuit 19) with headlamps off.			
	• Is output less than 3 volts?			
TA9	CHECK FOR SHORT IN CLUSTER			
	• Turn ignition to the OFF position.	Yes	▶	REPLACE cluster and fuse.
	• Remove cluster.	No	▶	REPLACE fuse, and INSTALL cluster.
	• Check continuity of C1 Pin 2, C2-1 Pin 5, and C2-1 Pin 3 to C1 Pin 1 or C2-1 Pin 4.			
	• Is there continuity?			

FM9099300198020X

Fig. 22   Pinpoint test TA (Part 2 of 2)

TEST STEP		RESULT	▶	ACTION TO TAKE
TB1	SELF TEST			
	• Turn ignition to OFF position.	Odometer reads: steady 32 32	▶	GO to TB2.
	• Push in the E·M and REVERSE buttons and hold.	Odometer flashes	▶	REPLACE cluster.
	• Turn ignition to ON position while holding buttons.	Speedometer reads: 02, 03 or 04	▶	REPEAT Self Test.
	• Release buttons when cluster lights.			
TB2	DISPLAY TEST			
	• Push SELECT buttons once, to enter display test.	Yes	▶	GO to Pinpoint Test Index.
	• Use E·M button to advance through steps of display test.	No	▶	REPLACE cluster.
	• Compare with known good cluster if possible.			
	• Is test successful?			

FM9099300199000X

Fig. 23   Pinpoint test TB

TEST STEP		RESULT	▶	ACTION TO TAKE
TC1	VERIFY CONDITION			
			▶	GO to TC1.
TC2	CHECK FOR TEMPERATURE SENDER SHORT			
	• Unplug wire to temperature sender at sender.	Yes	▶	REPLACE temperature sender.
	• Turn ignition key to RUN.	No	▶	GO to TC3.
	• Does temperature gauge Indicate COLD with bottom bar lit?			
TC3	CHECK FOR SHORT IN WIRING			
	• Disconnect ground cable to battery.	Yes	▶	REPLACE cluster
	• Unplug wire to temperature sender at sender.	No	▶	SERVICE wiring Circuit 39 for shorts.
	• Remove cluster.			
	• Measure resistance between C2-2 Pin 21 and C2-1 Pin 4 (GND).			
	• Is resistance greater than 15 K ohms?			

FM9099300200000X

Fig. 24   Pinpoint test TC

TEST STEP		RESULT	▶	ACTION TO TAKE
TD1	CHECK TEMPERATURE GAUGE WIRING			
	• Unplug connector to temperature sender and connect a jumper in place of sender. • Turn ignition switch to RUN. • Gauge should give a short circuit indication. (Blinking thermometer symbol and top two and bottom two bars of gauge lit.) • **Does gauge indicate short circuit?**	Yes No	▶ ▶	GO to **TD3**. REMOVE jumper. INSTALL sender. GO to **TD2**.
TD2	CHECK WIRING AT CLUSTER			
	• Disconnect ground cable to battery. • Disconnect C254 and C255 from cluster. • Connect jumper in place of temperature sender. • Verify continuity between C255 Pin 21 and C254 Pin 4 of harness. • **Is there continuity?**	Yes No	▶ ▶	REPLACE cluster[5]. SERVICE wiring Circuit 39 and/or temperature sender ground line for open circuit.
TD3	CHECK SENDER			
	• Warm up engine to normal operating temperature. • Measure resistance of temperature sender. • **Is resistance greater than 8 K ohms?**	Yes No	▶ ▶	GO to **TD4**. REPLACE cluster.
TD4	CHECK COOLING SYSTEM			
	• Check thermostat, coolant level, etc. for proper operation. • **Is cooling system OK?**	Yes No	▶ ▶	REPLACE temperature sender. SERVICE cooling system as required.

FM9099300201000X

Fig. 25   Pinpoint test TD

TEST STEP		RESULT	▶	ACTION TO TAKE
TX1	REVIEW OPERATION VERIFY CONDITION			
	• Warning chime module will not beep if another sound is being produced. • Driver alert only given for temperatures above normal band		▶	GO to **TX2**.

FM9099300202010X

Fig. 26   Pinpoint test TX (Part 1 of 2)

TEST STEP		RESULT	▶	ACTION TO TAKE
WA1	VERIFY CONDITION			
	• Refer to the appropriate Section for diagnosis and service of the affected system. NOTE: CHARGE warning is always on with the ignition in RUN and the engine off.	CHECK ENGINE or AIR BAG warning System operating properly System not operating properly	▶ ▶ ▶	GO to **WA3**. GO to **WA2**. SERVICE system.
WA2	OBSERVE PROVE-OUT			
	• Turn ignition switch to the RUN position and observe operation of warning in question. • **Does prove out operate properly?**	Yes No	▶ ▶	GO to **WA3**. REPLACE cluster.[13]
WA3	OBSERVE CONDITION			
	• Turn ignition switch to the RUN position and observe warning. • **Is warning always on?**	Yes No	▶ ▶	GO to **WA4**. GO to **WA6**.
WA4	CHECK SWITCH - WARNING ALWAYS ON			
	• Turn ignition switch to OFF. This resets the warning. • Pull connector off the switch/sensor. • Turn ignition switch to RUN. • Check cluster for warning. • **Is warning displayed?**	Yes No	▶ ▶	GO to **WA5**. SERVICE switch and/or sensor.
WA5	CHECK WIRING - WARNING ALWAYS ON			
	• Turn ignition switch to OFF. • Disconnect electronic instrument cluster. • Check continuity between the appropriate circuit (refer to Ground Inputs Warning table) and C254 Pin 4 (Circuit 875 BK/LB ground) at cluster harness connector. Circuit should be open. • **Is circuit open?**	Yes No	▶ ▶	REPLACE cluster[13]. SERVICE circuit for short.
WA6	CHECK SWITCH - WARNING NEVER COMES ON			
	• Turn ignition switch to OFF. • Pull connector off of the switch/sensor. • Connect a jumper wire from circuit at the switch/sensor connector to ground. • Turn ignition switch to RUN. • Check cluster for warning. • **Is warning displayed?**	Yes No	▶ ▶	SERVICE switch and/or sensor. GO to **WA7**.
WA7	CHECK WIRING - WARNING NEVER COMES ON			
	• Leave jumper wire connected as in WA5. • Turn ignition switch to OFF. • Remove electronic instrument cluster. • Check continuity between the appropriate circuit (refer to Ground Inputs Warning table) and C254 Pin 4 (Circuit 875 BK/LB ground) at cluster harness connector. Circuit should be shorted. • **Is circuit shorted?**	Yes No	▶ ▶	REPLACE cluster.[13] SERVICE circuit for open.

Fig. 27   Pinpoint test WA

TEST STEP		RESULT	▶	ACTION TO TAKE
TX2	CHECK WARNING CHIME			
	• Turn ignition switch to RUN. • Press any cluster control button and listen for beep. • **Does beep sound?**	Yes No	▶ ▶	System OK. GO to Pinpoint Test **SA**.

FM9099300202020X

Fig. 26   Pinpoint test TX (Part 2 of 2)

TEST STEP		RESULT	▶	ACTION TO TAKE
WB1	VERIFY CONDITION			
	• Refer to the appropriate Section for diagnosis and service of the affected system. • **Does system operate properly?**	Yes No	▶ ▶	GO to **WB2**. SERVICE system.
WB2	OBSERVE CONDITION			
	• Turn ignition switch to the RUN position and observe warning. • **Is warning always on?**	Yes No	▶ ▶	GO to **WB3**. GO to **WB5**.

FM9099300204010X

Fig. 28   Pinpoint test WB (Part 1 of 2)

TEST STEP		RESULT	▶	ACTION TO TAKE
WB3	CHECK SWITCH			
	• Turn ignition switch to OFF. This resets the warning. • Pull connector off the switch/sensor. • Turn ignition switch to RUN. • Check cluster for warning. • **Is warning displayed?**	Yes No	▶ ▶	GO to **WB4**. SERVICE switch module.
WB4	CHECK WIRING			
	• Turn ignition switch to OFF. • Remove electronic instrument cluster. • Check continuity between the appropriate circuit at cluster. Circuit should be open. • **Is circuit open?**	Yes No	▶ ▶	REPLACE cluster.[14] SERVICE circuit for short.
WB5	CHECK SWITCH			
	• Turn ignition switch to OFF. • Pull connector off the switch/sensor. • Connect a jumper wire from Circuit at the switch/module connector to positive battery. • Turn ignition switch to RUN. • Check cluster for warning. • **Is warning displayed?**	Yes No	▶ ▶	SERVICE switch and/or module. GO to **WB6**.
WB6	CHECK WIRING			
	• Remove jumper wire connected. • Turn ignition switch to OFF. • Remove electronic instrument cluster. • Check continuity between the appropriate Circuit at the cluster and connector at the switch/module. Circuit should be shorted. • **Is circuit shorted?**	Yes No	▶ ▶	REPLACE cluster.[14] SERVICE circuit for open.

FM9099300204020X

Fig. 28   Pinpoint test WB (Part 2 of 2)

WC1	CHECK EIC OUTPUT TO EATC	RESULT	▶	ACTION TO TAKE
	• Turn ignition to RUN position. • Remove the connector from the EATC. • Press the E / M button so that the cluster is in ENGLISH mode. • Check EATC mating connector Pin 20 (not on the EATC) • **Is Pin 20 at 5 volts DC?**	Yes No	▶ ▶	REPLACE EATC. GO to **WC2**
WC2	CHECK EIC OUTPUT TO EATC			
	• Leave ignition at RUN position. • Connector is removed from the EATC. • Press the E / M button so that the cluster is in ENGLISH mode. • Remove C255 from cluster. • Check Pin 32 of the cluster (not the harness). • **Is cluster Pin 32 at 5 volts DC?**	Yes No	▶ ▶	SERVICE wiring between cluster and EATC. The wire is shorted to ground or to another wire. REPLACE cluster.

FM9099300205000X

Fig. 29   Pinpoint test WC

WD1	CHECK EIC OUTPUT TO EATC	RESULT	▶	ACTION TO TAKE
	• Turn ignition to RUN position. • Remove the connector from the EATC. • Press the E / M button so that the cluster is in METRIC mode. • Check EATC mating connector Pin 20 (not on the EATC) • **Is Pin 20 at 0 volts DC?**	Yes No	▶ ▶	REPLACE EATC. GO to **WD2**.
WD2	CHECK EIC OUTPUT TO EATC			
	• Leave ignition at RUN position. • Connector still removed from the EATC. • Press the E / M button so that the cluster is in METRIC mode. • Remove C255 from cluster. • Check Pin 32 of the cluster (not the harness). • **Is cluster Pin 32 at 0 volts DC?**	Yes No	▶ ▶	SERVICE wiring between cluster and EATC. The wire is probably open. CHECK for intermittent contact. REPLACE cluster.

Fig. 30   Pinpoint test WD

1994 Crown Victoria, Grand Marquis & Town Car

NOTE: Refer to the Symptom Index in this section before performing any Pinpoint Tests.

INDEX

	Page No. 15-	Fig. No.
Symptom index	48	1
Pinpoint test AA	48	2
Pinpoint test AB	49	3
Pinpoint test AC	49	4
Pinpoint test BA	49	5
Pinpoint test BB	50	6
Pinpoint test BC	50	7
Pinpoint test CA	50	8
Pinpoint test CB	50	9
Pinpoint test CC	50	10
Pinpoint test DA	50	11
Pinpoint test DB	51	12
Pinpoint test DC	51	13
Pinpoint test DD	51	14
Pinpoint test DE	51	15
Pinpoint test EA	51	16
Pinpoint test EB	51	17
Pinpoint test EC	51	18
Pinpoint test FA	51	19
Pinpoint test FB	52	20
Pinpoint test GA	52	21
Pinpoint test HA	52	22
Pinpoint test HB	52	23
Pinpoint test HC	53	24
Pinpoint test HD	53	25
Pinpoint test HE	53	26
Pinpoint test HF	54	27
Pinpoint test HG	54	28
Pinpoint test HH	54	29
Pinpoint test HJ	55	30
Pinpoint test HK	55	31
Pinpoint test HL	56	32
Pinpoint test HM	56	33

EIC DISPLAY DIAGNOSIS

CONDITION	POSSIBLE SOURCE	ACTION
• Display Not Illuminated, Too Dim or Blank But Backlighted	• Bulb. • EIC. • Circuitry.	• Go to Pinpoint Test AA.
• Display Scrambled, Incorrect All the Time or Stuck with All Segments On. Segments Half Lit, Blinking or Missing	• EIC.	• Go to Pinpoint Test AB.
• Display Does Not Respond to Buttons or No Beep When Buttons Pushed	• Circuitry. • Safety belt warning chime. • EIC. • MCCA instrument indicator switch module. • Headlamp switch.	• Go to Pinpoint Test AC.

FUEL GAUGE DIAGNOSIS

CONDITION	POSSIBLE SOURCE	ACTION
• CO Displayed, Top Two and Bottom Two Diagnostic Bars Displayed	• Fuel tank sending unit. • EIC. • Circuitry.	• Go to Pinpoint Test BA.
• CS Displayed, Top Two and Bottom Two Diagnostic Bars Displayed	• Fuel tank sending unit. • Circuitry. • EIC.	• Go to Pinpoint Test BB.
• Inaccurate Fuel Gauge Indication	• Fuel tank sending unit. • Valve, tube or fuel vapor canister. • Fuel tank. • EIC.	• Go to Pinpoint Test BC.

TEMPERATURE GAUGE DIAGNOSIS

CONDITION	POSSIBLE SOURCE	ACTION
• Temperature Gauge Displays Top Two And Bottom Two Diagnostic Bars	• Water temperature indicator sender unit. • EIC. • Circuitry.	• Go to Pinpoint Test CA.
• Temperature Gauge Always Indicates Hot Or Cold Temperature	• Water temperature indicator sender unit. • EIC. • Circuitry.	• Go to Pinpoint Test CB.
• No Warning Tone When Thermometer Symbol is Blinking	• EIC. • Safety belt warning chime.	• Go to Pinpoint Test CC.

SPEEDOMETER DIAGNOSIS

CONDITION	POSSIBLE SOURCE	ACTION
• Speedometer Reads 0 km/h (mph) At All Speeds	• EIC. • Circuitry. • Vehicle speed sensor.	• Go to Pinpoint Test DA.
• Speedometer Constantly Reads Too High Or Too Low	• Vehicle speed sensor. • Drive gear. • EIC. • Circuitry.	• Go to Pinpoint Test DB.
• Speed Indication Jumps Up And Down Erratically	• EIC. • Vehicle speed sensor. • Circuitry.	• Go to Pinpoint Test DC.
• Speed Control Indicator Always On	• Speed control servo. • Circuitry. • EIC.	• Go to Pinpoint Test DD.
• Speed Control Indicator Does Not Come On When Speed Control Engaged	• EIC. • Circuitry. • Powertrain control module.	• Go to Pinpoint Test DE.

FM9099400207010X

Fig. 1   Symptom index (Part 1 of 3)

ODOMETER DIAGNOSIS

CONDITION	POSSIBLE SOURCE	ACTION
• Display Reads "Error"	• EIC.	• Replace EIC. Affix odometer sticker to door pillar.
• Display Has "S" Illuminated	• EIC.	• Go to Pinpoint Test EA.
• Mileage Constantly Reads Too High Or Too Low	• Drive gear.	• Go to Pinpoint Test EB.
• Odometer Does Not Accumulate Mileage or Counts 1.6 km (1.0 mile) and Jumps Back 1.6 km (1.0 mile)	• EIC. • VSS.	• Go to Pinpoint Test EC.

MESSAGE CENTER DISPLAY DIAGNOSIS

CONDITION	POSSIBLE SOURCE	ACTION
• Trip Distance Does Not Accumulate	• EIC.	• Go to Pinpoint Test EC.
• Instantaneous or Average Fuel Economy Always Reads 0 Miles/Gal Or 9 L/100 km or 99 Miles/Gal or 0 L/100 km	• EIC. • Circuitry. • Powertrain control module.	• Go to Pinpoint Test FA.
• DTE Does Not Go Below 322 km (200 Miles) With Fuel Tank Empty or DTE Always Reads Zero	• EIC. • Circuitry. • Powertrain control module.	• Go to Pinpoint Test FB.

AMBIENT TEMPERATURE SENSOR DIAGNOSIS

CONDITION	POSSIBLE SOURCE	ACTION
• Outside Air Temperature Wrong (But not As In 26B or 26C)	• Outside air temperature sensor. • Circuitry. • EIC.	• Go to Pinpoint Test GA.
• Outside Air Temperature Always Reads -40°C (-40°F)	• Outside air temperature sensor. • Circuitry. • EIC.	• Go to Pinpoint Test GA.
• Outside Air Temperature Always Reads 57°C-60°C (135°F-140°F)	• Outside air temperature sensor. • Circuitry. • EIC.	• Go to Pinpoint Test GA.

WARNING INDICATOR DIAGNOSIS

CONDITION	POSSIBLE SOURCE	ACTION
• DOOR AJAR Warning Never/Always Comes On	• Door open warning lamp switch. • EIC. • Circuitry.	• Go to Pinpoint Test HA.
• TRUNK AJAR Warning Never/Always Comes On	• Luggage compartment door open warning lamp switch. • Circuitry. • EIC.	• Go to Pinpoint Test HB.
• CHARGE SYSTEM Warning Always On	• EIC. • Circuitry.	• Go to Pinpoint Test HC.
• AIR SUSPENSION Warning Always On	• Circuitry. • EIC.	• Go to Pinpoint Test HD.
• Low WASHER FLUID Warning Never/Always On	• Windshield washer reservoir fluid level sensor. • Circuitry. • EIC.	• Go to Pinpoint Test HE.
• CHECK ENGINE (MIL) Warning Always On	• EIC. • PCM.	

FM9099400207020X

Fig. 1   Symptom index (Part 2 of 3)

WARNING INDICATOR DIAGNOSIS (Continued)

CONDITION	POSSIBLE SOURCE	ACTION
• BRAKE Warning Never/Always On	• EIC. • Circuitry. • Brake master cylinder reservoir. • Daytime running lights control.	• Go to Pinpoint Test HF.
• High Beam Warning Never/Always On	• EIC. • Circuitry. • Headlamp switch.	• Go to Pinpoint Test HG.
• Anti-Lock Warning Never/Always On (Crown Victoria/Grand Marquis only)	• EIC. • Anti-lock brake control module. • Circuitry.	• Go to Pinpoint Test HH.
• Low Oil Pressure Warning Never/Always On	• EIC. • Oil pressure sender. • Circuitry.	• Go to Pinpoint Test HJ.
• Air Bag Warning Never/Always On	• EIC. • Air bag diagnostic monitor. • Circuitry.	• Go to Pinpoint Test HK.
• Overdrive OFF Indicator Never/Always On	• EIC. • Powertrain control module. • Circuitry.	• Go to Pinpoint Test HL.
• Transmission Control Selector Indicator Never/Always On	• Bulb. • Circuitry.	• Go to Pinpoint Test HM.

FM9099400207030X

Fig. 1   Symptom index (Part 3 of 3)

	TEST STEP	RESULT	▶	ACTION TO TAKE
AA1	**CHECK DISPLAYS** • Turn ignition switch to OFF. • Turn parking lamps on. • While varying dimming level check other displays: radio, clock, transmission control selector indicator. • Do other displays illuminate properly?	Yes No	▶ ▶	GO to AA2. GO to AA3.
AA2	**CHECK FOR RHEOSTAT OUTPUT** • Turn parking lamp off. • Disconnect EIC. • Turn parking lamps on. • While varying dimming level, check voltage in Circuit 19(LB/R) at Pin 3 of MCCA instrument indicator switch module connector. • **Does voltage vary between 0 and 12V?**	Yes No	▶ ▶	REPLACE EIC. AFFIX odometer sticker to door pillar. SERVICE Circuit 19(LB/R).
AA3	**CHECK FOR RHEOSTAT OUTPUT** • Check I/P fuses 11 and 7 (Town Car) 9 and 11 (Crown Victoria/Grand Marquis). Replace if necessary. Proceed if displays still do not illuminate properly. • While varying dimming level, check voltage of fuse 7 (Town Car), fuse 11 (Crown Victoria/Grand Marquis). • **Does voltage vary between 0 and 12V?**	Yes No	▶ ▶	SERVICE Circuit 19 (LB/R). GO to AA4.
AA4	**CHECK FOR RHEOSTAT OUTPUT** • Using a 12V test lamp, check for voltage of Pin 1 of headlamp switch. Do not disconnect headlamp switch. Vary dimming level. • **Does voltage vary between 0 and 12V?**	Yes No	▶ ▶	SERVICE Circuit 88(BK/W)(Town Car), 19(LB/R)(Crown Victoria/Grand Marquis). GO to AA5.

FM9099400208010X

Fig. 2   Pinpoint test AA (Part 1 of 2)

TEST STEP		RESULT	▶	ACTION TO TAKE
AA5	CHECK FOR BATTERY VOLTAGE			
	• Disconnect headlamp switch. • Check for battery voltage in Circuit 195(T/W). • **Is there battery voltage?**	Yes	▶	REPLACE headlamp switch.
		No	▶	SERVICE fuse 11 (Town Car), fuse 9 (Crown Victoria/Grand Marquis) or Circuit 195 (T/W).

FM9099400208020X

Fig. 2   Pinpoint test AA (Part 2 of 2)

TEST STEP		RESULT	▶	ACTION TO TAKE
AC1	CHECK FOR WARNING CHIME			
	NOTE: Buttons function only with ignition switch in RUN. • Check for fasten safety belt reminder chime or key left in ignition reminder chime. • **Does safety belt warning chime sound?**	Yes	▶	GO to AC2 for Town Car. GO to AC4 for Crown Victoria/Grand Marquis.
		No	▶	DIAGNOSE safety belt warning chime
AC2	CHECK EATC OUTPUT (TOWN CAR)			
	• Check E/M button operation. • **Is EATC stuck at metric mode?**	Yes	▶	GO to AC6.
		No	▶	GO to AC3.
AC3	CHECK EATC OUTPUT (TOWN CAR) CONT.			
	• Check E/M button operation. • **Is EATC stuck at English mode?**	Yes	▶	GO to AC8.
		No	▶	GO to AC4.
AC4	CHECK SWITCH WIRING CONNECTIONS			
	• Remove finish panel to expose instrument cluster. • Verify that connections at instrument indicator switch assembly are securely connected. • **Are connections secure?**	Yes	▶	GO to AC5.
		No	▶	Secure connections and RECHECK.

FM9099400210010X

Fig. 4   Pinpoint test AC (Part 1 of 3)

TEST STEP		RESULT	▶	ACTION TO TAKE
AC10	CHECK EIC OUTPUT TO EATC			
	• Turn ignition switch to RUN. • Remove the connector from the EATC. • Press the E/M button so that the instrument cluster is in METRIC mode. • Check EATC mating connector Pin 20 (not on the EATC). • **Is Pin 20 at 0 volts DC?**	Yes	▶	REPLACE EATC.
		No	▶	GO to AC11.
AC11	CHECK EIC OUTPUT TO EATC			
	• Leave ignition switch at RUN. • Connector still removed from the EATC. • Press the E/M button so that the instrument cluster is in METRIC mode. • Remove Connector J2 from instrument cluster. • Check Pin 32 of the instrument cluster (not the harness). • **Is instrument cluster Pin 32 at 0 volts DC?**		▶	SERVICE Circuit 506(R) for open. CHECK for intermittent contact. REPLACE EIC. AFFIX odometer sticker to door pillar.

FM9099400210030X

Fig. 4   Pinpoint test AC (Part 3 of 3)

TEST STEP		RESULT	▶	ACTION TO TAKE
AB1	PERFORM SELF TEST			
	• Turn ignition to OFF position. • Push in the E/M and select (left) buttons and hold. • Turn ignition to ON position while holding buttons. • Release buttons when cluster lights. • **Does odometer flash?**	Yes	▶	REPLACE EIC, affix odometer sticker to door pillar.
		No	▶	GO to AB2.
AB2	CHECK ODOMETER DISPLAY			
	• Check odometer display. • **Does odometer read steady 32, 32?**	Yes	▶	GO to AB3.
		No	▶	GO to AB1.
AB3	DISPLAY TEST			
	• Push SELECT> button once to enter display test. • Push E/M button to step through display test inspection and verification. • Compare each step of display test to the illustrations in inspection and verification. NOTE: There are 17 segment displays. • **Are all displays as illustrated?**	Yes	▶	EIC OK.
		No	▶	REPLACE EIC. AFFIX odometer sticker to door pillar.

FM9099400209000X

Fig. 3   Pinpoint test AB

TEST STEP		RESULT	▶	ACTION TO TAKE
AC5	CHECK MCCA SWITCH ASSEMBLY (NO SWITCH PRESSED)			
	• Unplug MCCA instrument indicator switch assembly. • Measure the resistance between Pin 1 and Pin 8 (Circuit 572, O/BK and Circuit 676, PK/O, Town Car)(Circuit 143, LB/Y and Circuit 875 BK/LB, Crown Victoria/Grand Marquis) of the instrument indicator switch assembly. • Resistance with no switch pressed should be 17,300 to 17,600 ohms. • **Is resistance within range?**	Yes	▶	GO to AC4.
		No	▶	REPLACE MCCA instrument indicator switch assembly.
AC6	CHECK SWITCH ASSEMBLY (BUTTONS PRESSED)			
	• Unplug instrument indicator switch assembly from electronic instrument cluster. • Measure the resistance between Pin 1 (Circuit 572, O/BK, Town Car), (Circuit 143, LB/Y, Crown Victoria/Grand Marquis) and Pin 8 (Circuit 676, PK/O, Town Car), (Circuit 875, BK/LB, Crown Victoria/Grand Marquis) of the MCCA switch assembly while pressing the problem button. • The resistance should be:	Yes	▶	GO to AC7.
		No	▶	REPLACE MCCA instrument indicator switch assembly.

BUTTON	RESISTANCE (in ohms)
EM	5100-5200
SELECT (forward)	330-350
SELECT (reverse)	2250-2350
RESET	1000-1100

NOTE: Press only one button.
• **Is resistance within range?**

TEST STEP		RESULT	▶	ACTION TO TAKE
AC7	VERIFY HARNESS CONTINUITY			
	• Disconnect battery ground cable. • Remove EIC. • Check continuity in Circuit (572, O/BK Town Car), (143, LB/Y, Crown Victoria/Grand Marquis). • Check continuity to ground in Circuit (676, PK/O, Town Car), (875, BK/LB, Crown Victoria/Grand Marquis). • **Is there continuity?**	Yes	▶	REPLACE EIC. AFFIX odometer sticker to door pillar. SERVICE respective circuit.
		No	▶	
AC8	CHECK EIC OUTPUT TO EATC			
	• Turn ignition switch to RUN. • Remove the connector from the EATC. • Press the E/M button so that the instrument cluster is in ENGLISH mode. • Check EATC mating connector Pin 20 (not on the EATC). • **Is Pin 20 at 5 volts DC?**	Yes	▶	REPLACE EATC.
		No	▶	GO to AC9.
AC9	CHECK EIC OUTPUT TO EATC			
	• Leave ignition switch at RUN. • Connector is removed from the EATC. • Press the E/M button so that the instrument cluster is in ENGLISH mode. • Remove connector J2 from instrument cluster. • Check Pin 32 of the instrument cluster (not the harness). • **Is instrument cluster Pin 32 at 5 volts DC?**	Yes	▶	SERVICE Circuit 506 (R) for short to ground or to another wire.
		No	▶	REPLACE EIC. AFFIX odometer sticker to door pillar.

FM9099400210020X

Fig. 4   Pinpoint test AC (Part 2 of 3)

TEST STEP		RESULT	▶	ACTION TO TAKE
BA1	CHECK FUEL PUMP WIRING AT FUEL PUMP			
	• Disconnect battery ground cable. • Lower fuel tank to gain access to fuel pump connector. • Unplug fuel pump connector. • Jumper variable resistance terminal and ground terminal of fuel pump connector. • Reconnect battery. • Turn ignition switch from OFF to RUN. • Check digital fuel remaining display to determine whether it shows CO or CS. NOTE: It may take several minutes for the fuel gauge to respond. • **Does fuel gauge display show CO?**	Yes	▶	GO to BA3.
		No	▶	REMOVE jumper. GO to BA2.
BA2	CHECK FUEL PUMP			
	• Turn ignition switch to OFF. • Measure the resistance of the fuel tank sending unit at the fuel pump terminals. • Verify that the resistance is less than 181 ohms (normally between 11 and 168 ohms). • **Is resistance less than 181 ohms?**	Yes	▶	INSPECT fuel pump wiring connector female terminals for flash or loose fit. SERVICE as required.
		No	▶	REPLACE fuel pump.
BA3	CHECK FUEL PUMP WIRING AT EIC			
	• Disconnect battery ground cable. • Remove connector J1 from EIC and secure connectors from shorting. • Jumper variable resistance terminal and ground terminal of harness together at fuel pump. • Verify continuity between Pin J1-2 and Pin J1-4 ground of EIC connector. • **Is resistance close to zero ohms?**	Yes	▶	REPLACE EIC. AFFIX odometer sticker to door pillar.
		No	▶	SERVICE fuel pump wiring for open circuit.

FM9099400211000X

Fig. 5   Pinpoint test BA

TEST STEP		RESULT	▶	ACTION TO TAKE
BB1	CHECK FUEL PUMP WIRING AT EIC			
	• Disconnect battery ground cable. • Remove instrument cluster and secure connectors from shorting. • With an ohmmeter, measure resistance between Pin J1-2 and Pin J1-4 (SIG GND) of harness. • Verify that the resistance is 5 ohms or greater (normally 11 to 168 ohms). • Is resistance at least 5 ohms?	Yes	▶	REPLACE EIC. AFFIX odometer sticker to door pillar.
		No	▶	GO to BB2.
BB2	CHECK FUEL PUMP WIRING			
	• Lower fuel tank to gain access to fuel pump connector. • Unplug connector at fuel pump. • Measure the resistance between Pin J1-2 and Pin J1-4 (GND) of harness. • Verify that resistance is greater than 10 K ohms. • Is resistance at least 10 K ohms?	Yes	▶	REPLACE fuel pump.
		No	▶	SERVICE fuel pump wiring for short circuit.

FM9099400212000X

Fig. 6   Pinpoint test BB

TEST STEP		RESULT	▶	ACTION TO TAKE
BC1	CHECK FUEL GAUGE RESPONSE			
	• Disconnect battery ground cable. • Lower fuel tank and gain access to fuel pump connections. • Connect a 43 ohm (± 1 percent) resistor in place of fuel tank sending unit and pump. Verify value with ohm meter. • Reconnect battery. • Turn ignition switch to RUN. • Fuel gauge should read 3 to 4 bars illuminated. • FUEL REMAIN should read 3 to 4 GAL (13 to 15 LTR). • Is fuel gauge correct?	Yes	▶	TURN ignition switch to OFF. GO to BC3.
		No	▶	TURN ignition switch to OFF. Leave 43 ohm resistor connected. GO to BC2.
BC2	CHECK HARNESS RESISTANCE			
	• Disconnect battery ground cable. • Remove EIC and secure connectors from shorting. • Measure resistance between Pin J1-2 and Pin J1-4 (GND) with 43 ohm resistor in place. • Is resistance within range?	Yes	▶	REPLACE EIC. AFFIX odometer sticker to door pillar.
		No	▶	SERVICE Circuit 29 (Y/W).
BC3	CHECK FUEL TANK SENDING UNIT AND PUMP			
	• Disconnect battery ground cable. • Check fuel tank sending unit and pump for binding, sticking, misalignment, etc. • Check fuel sender resistance. Resistance should be 165 to 181 ohms at full stop and 5 to 14 ohms at empty stop. • Are fuel tank sending unit and pump OK?	Yes	▶	GO to BC4.
		No	▶	SERVICE or REPLACE fuel tank sending unit and pump.
BC4	CHECK FUEL TANK			
	• Check fuel tank for dents, bulges or other damage. • Check for proper installation of fuel tube. • Is fuel tank OK?	Yes	▶	System OK. Fault caused by other vehicle system(s).
		No	▶	REPLACE fuel tank or fuel tube.

FM9099400213000X

Fig. 7   Pinpoint test BC

TEST STEP		RESULT	▶	ACTION TO TAKE
CA1	CHECK FOR TEMPERATURE SENDER SHORT			
	• Unplug wire to water temperature indicator sender unit at water temperature indicator sender unit. • Turn ignition switch to RUN. • Does temperature gauge indicate COLD with bottom bar lit?	Yes	▶	REPLACE water temperature indicator sender unit.
		No	▶	GO to CA2.
CA2	CHECK FOR SHORT IN WIRING			
	• Disconnect battery ground cable. • Unplug wire to water temperature indicator sender unit at water temperature indicator sender unit. • Disconnect connector J1 and connector J2 from EIC. • Measure resistance between connector J2 Pin 21 and Pin J1-4 (GND). • Is resistance greater than 15 K ohms?	Yes	▶	REPLACE EIC. AFFIX odometer sticker to door pillar.
		No	▶	SERVICE Circuit 39 (R/W), 676(PK/O, Town Car), 875 (BK/LB, Crown Victoria/Grand Marquis) as required.

FM9099400214000X

Fig. 8   Pinpoint test CA

TEST STEP		RESULT	▶	ACTION TO TAKE
CC1	REVIEW OPERATION/CONDITION			
	NOTE. Safety belt warning chime will not beep if another sound is being produced. Driver alert only given for temperatures above normal band. • Turn ignition switch to RUN. • Press any MCCA instrument indicator switch assembly button and listen for beep. • Does beep sound?	Yes	▶	System OK.
		No	▶	GO to Pinpoint Test AC.

FM9099400216000X

Fig. 10   Pinpoint test CC

TEST STEP		RESULT	▶	ACTION TO TAKE
CB1	CHECK TEMPERATURE GAUGE WIRING			
	• Unplug connector to water temperature indicator sender unit and connect a jumper in place of water temperature indicator sender unit. • Turn ignition switch to RUN. • Gauge should give a short circuit indication. (Blinking thermometer symbol and top two and bottom two bars of gauge lit.) • Does gauge indicate short circuit?	Yes	▶	GO to CB3. REMOVE jumper. INSTALL water temperature indicator sender unit.
		No	▶	GO to CB2.
CB2	CHECK WIRING AT CLUSTER			
	• Disconnect battery ground cable. • Disconnect J1 and J2 connectors from EIC. • Connect jumper in place of water temperature indicator sender unit. • Verify continuity between Pin J2-21 and Pin J1-4 of harness. • Is there continuity?	Yes	▶	REPLACE EIC. AFFIX odometer sticker to door pillar.
		No	▶	SERVICE wiring Circuit 39 (R/W) and/or 676(PK/O, Town Car), 875 (BK/LB, Crown Victoria/Grand Marquis).
CB3	CHECK WATER TEMPERATURE INDICATOR SENDER UNIT			
	• Warm up engine to normal operating temperature. • Measure resistance of water temperature indicator sender unit. • Is resistance greater than 8 K ohms?	Yes	▶	GO to CB4.
		No	▶	REPLACE EIC. AFFIX odometer sticker to door pillar.
CB4	CHECK COOLING SYSTEM			
	• Check thermostat, coolant level, etc., for proper operation. • Is cooling system OK?	Yes	▶	REPLACE water temperature indicator sender unit.
		No	▶	SERVICE cooling system as required.

FM9099400215010X

Fig. 9   Pinpoint test CB

TEST STEP		RESULT	▶	ACTION TO TAKE
DA1	CHECK SPEEDOMETER READING			
	• Test drive vehicle above 8 km/h (5 mph) and look for: — Speedometer reading — Odometer changing • Verify that odometer advances when vehicle is driven forward. • Does odometer advance with no speed indication?	Yes	▶	REPLACE EIC. AFFIX odometer sticker to door pillar.
		No	▶	GO to DA2.
DA2	CHECK SPEED CONTROL			
	• Test drive vehicle above 30 MPH, check speed control operation. • Did speed control operate properly?	Yes	▶	GO to DA3.
		No	▶	GO to DA4.
DA3	CHECK CONTINUITY			
	• Disconnect battery ground cable. • Disconnect connectors J1 and J2 at EIC. • Disconnect vehicle speed sensor. • Check continuity in Circuit 679 (GY/BK) and continuity to ground in Circuit 676 (PK/O). • Is continuity present?	Yes	▶	REPLACE EIC. AFFIX odometer sticker to door pillar.
		No	▶	SERVICE respective circuit.
DA4	CHECK VSS			
	• Disconnect vehicle speed sensor. • Measure resistance across vehicle speed sensor. • Is resistance between 200-300 ohms?	Yes	▶	CHECK Circuits 679(GY/BK) and 676(PK/O) for continuity. If circuits OK, CHECK driven gear and retainer clip. REPLACE if necessary.
		No	▶	REPLACE vehicle speed sensor.

FM9099400217000X

Fig. 11   Pinpoint test DA

TEST STEP		RESULT	▶	ACTION TO TAKE
DB1	CHECK VEHICLE SPEED SENSOR DRIVE GEAR			
	• Remove vehicle speed sensor from transmission and verify that correct drive gear is installed for vehicle transmission / axle / tire combination. • Is drive gear correct?	Yes	▶	GO to DB2.
		No	▶	INSTALL correct gear with retaining clip.
DB2	CHECK DRIVE GEAR ON TRANSMISSION OUTPUT SHAFT			
	• Check that correct drive gear is installed on transmission output shaft. • Is drive gear correct?	Yes	▶	GO to DB3.
		No	▶	INSTALL correct output shaft and / or gear.

FM9099400218010X

Fig. 12   Pinpoint test DB (Part 1 of 2)

TEST STEP		RESULT	▶	ACTION TO TAKE
DB3	CHECK CONTINUITY			
	• Disconnect battery ground cable. • Disconnect connectors J1 and J2 at EIC. • Check continuity in Circuit 679 (GY / BK) and continuity to ground in Circuit 676 (PK / O). • Is continuity present?	Yes	▶	GO to DB4.
		No	▶	SERVICE respective circuit.
DB4	CHECK VSS			
	• Disconnect vehicle speed sensor. • Measure resistance across vehicle speed sensor. • Is resistance between 200-300 ohms?	Yes	▶	REPLACE EIC. AFFIX odometer sticker to door pillar.
		No	▶	REPLACE vehicle speed sensor.

FM9099400218020X

Fig. 12   Pinpoint test DB (Part 2 of 2)

TEST STEP		RESULT	▶	ACTION TO TAKE
DC1	CHECK SPEED SENSOR DRIVE GEAR			
	• Remove vehicle speed sensor from transmission. • Check that all gear teeth are in good condition, retainer clip is installed and gear does not slip on shaft. • Is vehicle speed sensor in good condition?	Yes	▶	GO to DB3.
		No	▶	REPLACE drive gear and / or retaining clip.

FM9099400219000X

Fig. 13   Pinpoint test DC

TEST STEP		RESULT	▶	ACTION TO TAKE
DD1	CHECK SPEED CONTROL SERVO			
	• Disconnect connector from speed control servo. • Does speed control indicator go off?	Yes	▶	REPLACE speed control servo. VERIFY proper operation.
		No	▶	GO to DD2.
DD2	CHECK EIC			
	• Disconnect cluster connector C255. • Does speed control indicator go off?	Yes	▶	CHECK Circuit 203(O / LB). SERVICE as required.
		No	▶	REPLACE EIC. AFFIX odometer sticker to door pillar.

Fig. 14   Pinpoint test DD

TEST STEP		RESULT	▶	ACTION TO TAKE
DE1	CHECK VOLTAGE AT SPEED CONTROL SERVO			
	• Disconnect connector from speed control servo. • Turn ignition switch to RUN. • Measure voltage between Circuit 203(O / LB) and Circuit 676(PK / O, Town Car), 57(BK, Crown Victoria / Grand Marquis). • Is voltage approximately 5V?	Yes	▶	GO to DE2.
		No	▶	GO to DE3.
DE2	CHECK CONTINUITY			
	• Disconnect EIC. • Check continuity in Circuit 203(O / LB). • Is continuity present?	Yes	▶	REPLACE EIC. AFFIX odometer sticker to door pillar.
		No	▶	SERVICE Circuit 203(O / LB).

FM9099400258010X

Fig. 15   Pinpoint test DE (Part 1 of 2)

TEST STEP		RESULT	▶	ACTION TO TAKE
DE3	VERIFY POWER AT SPEED CONTROL SERVO			
	• Check for battery voltage at the speed control servo connector in Circuit 295(LB / PK, Town Car), 296 (W / P, Crown Victoria / Grand Marquis). • Is battery voltage present?	Yes	▶	REPLACE speed control servo.
		No	▶	SERVICE Circuit 295(LB / PK) and / or fuse 4—Town Car. SERVICE Circuit 296(LB / PK) and / or fuse 6—Crown Victoria / Grand Marquis.

FM9099400258020X

Fig. 15   Pinpoint test DE (Part 2 of 2)

TEST STEP		RESULT	▶	ACTION TO TAKE
EA1	DETERMINE IF SPEEDOMETER / ODOMETER MODULE IS ORIGINAL			
	• Check for mileage sticker on door pillar. • Is mileage sticker original?	Yes	▶	REPLACE EIC. If odometer reading is known, program it into new EIC. If odometer reading is unknown, program in "S" 00000.5 with the circled S and zero miles in the odometer.
		No	▶	System OK.

FM9099400259000X

Fig. 16   Pinpoint test EA

TEST STEP		RESULT	▶	ACTION TO TAKE
EB1	CHECK SPEEDOMETER			
	• Verify that speedometer is operating properly. • Does speedometer operate properly?	Yes	▶	REPLACE EIC. Affix odometer sticker to door pillar.
		No	▶	GO to Pinpoint Test DB.

FM9099400260000X

Fig. 17   Pinpoint test EB

TEST STEP		RESULT	▶	ACTION TO TAKE
EC1	CHECK ODOMETER OPERATION			
	• Check odometer to determine whether it accumulates and then loses 1.6 km (1.0 mile) or it will not accumulate mileage at all. • Does odometer accumulate and then lose 1.6 km (1.0 mile)?	Yes	▶	REPLACE EIC. AFFIX odometer sticker to door pillar.
		No	▶	GO to EC2.
EC2	VERIFY SPEEDOMETER			
	• Verify that speedometer works properly. • Does speedometer operate properly?	Yes	▶	REPLACE EIC. AFFIX odometer sticker to door pillar.
		No	▶	GO to Pinpoint Test DA.

Fig. 18   Pinpoint test EC

TEST STEP		RESULT	▶	ACTION TO TAKE
FA1	CHECK MESSAGE CENTER DISPLAY			
	• Check message center display to determine whether it is showing 0 MPG, 99L / 100 KM or 99 MPG, 0L / 100 KM. • Is message center display showing 0 MPG, 99 L / 100 Km?	Yes	▶	GO to FA2.
		No	▶	GO to FA3.

FM9099400263010X

Fig. 19   Pinpoint test FA (Part 1 of 2)

TEST STEP	RESULT	▶	ACTION TO TAKE
FA2 CHECK SPEEDOMETER OPERATION • Verify that speedometer is operating properly. • **Does speedometer operate properly?**	Yes	▶	REPLACE EIC. AFFIX odometer sticker to door pillar.
	No	▶	GO to Pinpoint Test DA.
FA3 CHECK CONTINUITY OF CIRCUIT 205 (FUEL FLOW) • Verify continuity and absence of shorts in Circuit 205 (DB/LG). • **Is wiring OK?**	Yes	▶	GO to FA4.
	No	▶	SERVICE wiring Circuit 205 (DB/LG) as required.
FA4 ENTER SELF TEST MODE • Turn ignition switch to OFF. • Push and hold E/M and <SELECT (left) buttons together. • Turn ignition switch to START while holding buttons. • Release buttons when cluster lights. • Allow engine to run during remainder of test. • Observe odometer. • **Does odometer flash?**	Yes	▶	REPLACE EIC. AFFIX odometer sticker to door pillar.
	No	▶	GO to FA5.
FA5 OBSERVE ODOMETER • Continue in the self test mode. • Observe odometer. • **Does odometer read 33, 33 or 34, 34 or 35, 35?**	Yes	▶	GO to FA6.
	No	▶	GO to FA4.
FA6 ENTER DISPLAY TEST MODE • Push Select> (right) button once and observe display. • **Is the display the same as in Step 1 of segment displays in inspection and verification?**	Yes	▶	GO to FA7.
	No	▶	GO to FA4.
FA7 ENTER A/D, DIGITAL PORT TEST MODE • Push E/M and <SELECT (left) buttons together once. Observe odometer display, left two digits. • **Does odometer's left two digits read "0A"?**	Yes	▶	GO to FA8.
	No	▶	GO to FA4.
FA8 ENTER FUEL FLOW INPUT TEST MODE • Push SELECT> (right) button twice quickly. • Observe left two odometer digits change to "1b." • Repeat this step four times until odometer left two digits read "5F." (Left two digits of odometer will advance: 0A, 1B, 2C, 3D, 4E, 5F, 60, 71, 0A... etc.). • Observe the right four digits of the odometer display. The frequency of the fuel flow pulses from the PCM is shown. (Step on accelerator.) • "0000" indicates no fuel flow pulses received from the PCM. • Any other number indicates fuel flow pulses are being received from the PCM. • **Do right four digits read "0000" (no fuel pulses)?**	Yes	▶	TURN ignition switch to OFF to exit test modes. System OK. RECHECK Circuit 205; if OK then REPLACE powertrain control module.
	No	▶	REPLACE EIC. AFFIX odometer sticker to door pillar.

FM9099400263020X

Fig. 19   Pinpoint test FA (Part 2 of 2)

TEST STEP	RESULT	▶	ACTION TO TAKE
FB1 CHECK FUEL GAUGE • Verify that fuel gauge is operating properly. • **Does gauge operate properly?**	Yes	▶	GO to FB2.
	No	▶	REFER to Fuel Gauge Diagnosis in Symptom Chart.

FM9099400264010X

Fig. 20   Pinpoint test FB (Part 1 of 2)

TEST STEP	RESULT	▶	ACTION TO TAKE
FB2 CHECK SPEEDOMETER • Verify that speedometer is operating properly. • **Does speedometer operate properly?**	Yes	▶	GO to Pinpoint Test FA.
	No	▶	REFER to Speedometer Diagnosis in Symptom Chart.

FM9099400264020X

Fig. 20   Pinpoint test FB (Part 2 of 2)

TEST STEP	RESULT	▶	ACTION TO TAKE
GA1 CHECK FOR BATTERY VOLTAGE • Disconnect connector J1 at EIC. • Check for battery voltage in Circuit 296(W/P, Town Car) 54(LG/Y, Crown Victoria/Grand Marquis). • **Is there battery voltage?**	Yes	▶	GO to GA2.
	No	▶	SERVICE fuse 1, or Circuit 296(W/P, Town Car). SERVICE fuse 4 or Circuit 54(LG/Y, Crown Victoria/Grand Marquis).
GA2 CHECK AMBIENT TEMPERATURE SENSOR • Turn ignition switch to RUN. • Wait 30 seconds. • Proceed if temperature reading still incorrect. • Disconnect A/C ambient air temperature sensor and bracket. • Measure outside air temperature sensor resistance at 15-21°C (60-70°F). • **Is resistance between 33-47 K ohms?**	Yes	▶	GO to GA3.
	No	▶	REPLACE A/C ambient air temperature sensor and bracket.
GA3 CHECK CONTINUITY • Inspect in-line connectors. Service if necessary. Make sure in-line connectors are tightly engaged. • Check continuity in Circuit 233(DB/Y) and continuity to ground in Circuit 676 (PK/O, Town Car), 359(GY/R, Crown Victoria/Grand Marquis). • **Is continuity present?**	Yes	▶	REPLACE EIC. AFFIX odometer sticker to door pillar.
	No	▶	SERVICE respective circuit.

FM9099400265000X

Fig. 21   Pinpoint test GA

TEST STEP	RESULT	▶	ACTION TO TAKE
HA1 CHECK EIC FOR WARNINGS • Turn ignition switch to RUN. • Wait past prove-out time. • Check EIC for DOOR AJAR warning to determine whether warning is always on or never on. • **Is door ajar warning always on?**	Yes	▶	GO to HA2.
	No	▶	GO to HA4.
HA2 CHECK DOOR OPEN WARNING LAMP SWITCHES • The following steps are to be repeated for each door open warning lamp switch. Start with the driver's door, then front passenger's, then rear passenger's door. • Turn ignition switch to OFF. This resets the warning. • Disconnect door open warning lamp switch connector at door open warning lamp switch. • Turn ignition switch to RUN. • Check message center for warning. • Repeat until no warning is displayed or all door open lamp switches are disconnected. • **Is warning still displayed?**	Yes	▶	GO to HA3.
	No	▶	SERVICE the last switch tested.

FM9099400266010X

Fig. 22   Pinpoint test HA (Part 1 of 2)

TEST STEP	RESULT	▶	ACTION TO TAKE
HA3 CHECK CIRCUIT 627 (BK/O) • Turn ignition switch to OFF. • Disconnect electronic instrument cluster. • Check continuity to ground in Circuit 627 (BK/O). • **Is continuity to ground present?**	Yes	▶	SERVICE Circuit 627 (BK/O) for short to ground.
	No	▶	REPLACE EIC. AFFIX odometer sticker to door pillar.
HA4 CHECK POWER AND GROUNDS • Check voltage on the following pins:	Yes	▶	GO to HA5
	No	▶	SERVICE as required.

Pin	Circuit Number	Voltage
J1-3	296 (W/P)	12V (Hot At All Times)
J1-5	295 (LB/PK)	12V (Hot In Run)
J1-12	489 (PK/BK)	12V (Hot In Run)
J3-2	295 (LB/PK)	12V (Hot In Run)
J1-4	676 (PK/O)	0V
J3-1	676 (PK/O)	0V

TEST STEP	RESULT	▶	ACTION TO TAKE
• **Are all voltages as specified?**			
HA5 CHECK DOOR OPEN WARNING LAMP SWITCH • Turn ignition switch to OFF. • Pull connector off of the problem door open warning lamp switch. • Connect a jumper wire from Circuit 627 (BK/O) at the harness connector to ground. • Turn ignition switch to RUN. • Check message center for warning. • **Is warning displayed?**	Yes	▶	SERVICE door open warning lamp switch.
	No	▶	REMOVE jumper. GO to HA6.
HA6 CHECK WIRING • Turn ignition switch to OFF. • Disconnect electronic instrument cluster. • Check continuity in Circuit 627 (BK/O). • **Is continuity present?**	Yes	▶	REPLACE EIC. AFFIX odometer sticker to door pillar.
	No	▶	SERVICE Circuit 627 (BK/O) for open.

FM9099400266020X

Fig. 22   Pinpoint test HA (Part 2 of 2)

TEST STEP	RESULT	▶	ACTION TO TAKE
HB1 CHECK EIC FOR WARNINGS • Turn ignition switch to RUN. • Wait past prove-out time. • Check EIC for TRUNK AJAR warning to determine whether warning is always on or never on. • **Is trunk ajar warning always on?**	Yes	▶	GO to HB2.
	No	▶	GO to HB4.
HB2 CHECK LUGGAGE COMPARTMENT DOOR OPEN WARNING LAMP SWITCH • Turn ignition switch to OFF. This resets the warning. • Pull connector off of luggage compartment door open warning lamp switch. • Turn ignition switch to RUN. • Check EIC for warning. • **Is warning displayed?**	Yes	▶	GO to HB3.
	No	▶	SERVICE luggage compartment door open warning lamp switch.
HB3 CHECK CIRCUIT 486 (BR/W) • Turn ignition switch to OFF. • Disconnect electronic instrument cluster. • Check continuity to ground in Circuit 486 (BR/W). • **Is there continuity to ground?**	Yes	▶	SERVICE Circuit 486 (BR/W) for short.
	No	▶	REPLACE EIC. AFFIX odometer sticker to door pillar.

FM9099400267010X

Fig. 23   Pinpoint test HB (Part 1 of 2)

TEST STEP			RESULT	▶	ACTION TO TAKE
HB4	**CHECK POWER AND GROUNDS**				
• Check voltage on the following pins:			Yes	▶	GO to HB5
			No	▶	SERVICE as required.

Pin	Circuit Number	Voltage
J1-3	296 (W/P)	12V (Hot At All Times)
J1-5	295 (LB/PK)	12V (Hot In Run)
J1-12	489 (PK/BK)	12V (Hot In Run)
J3-2	295 (LB/PK)	12V (Hot In Run)
J1-4	676 (PK/O)	0V
J3-1	676 (PK/O)	0V

TEST STEP	RESULT	▶	ACTION TO TAKE
• Are all voltages as specified?			
HB5 CHECK LUGGAGE COMPARTMENT DOOR OPEN WARNING LAMP SWITCH			
• Turn ignition switch to OFF.	Yes	▶	SERVICE luggage compartment door open warning lamp switch.
• Pull connector off of the luggage compartment door open warning lamp switch.			
• Connect a jumper wire from Circuit 486 (BR/W) at the harness connector to ground.	No	▶	REMOVE jumper. GO to HB6.
• Turn ignition switch to RUN.			
• Check EIC for warning.			
• Is warning displayed?			
HB6 CHECK WIRING			
• Turn ignition switch to OFF.	Yes	▶	REPLACE EIC. AFFIX odometer sticker to door pillar.
• Disconnect electronic instrument cluster.			
• Check continuity in Circuit 486 (BR/W).			
• Is there continuity present?	No	▶	SERVICE Circuit 486 (BR/W) for open.

FM9099400267020X

Fig. 23   Pinpoint test HB (Part 2 of 2)

TEST STEP	RESULT	▶	ACTION TO TAKE
HC1 CHECK CHARGING SYSTEM VOLTAGE			
• Start engine and check for warning. Watch for several minutes.	Yes	▶	GO to HC2
• Check battery voltage.	No	▶	SERVICE generator.
• Is the voltage normal (above 14 volts) for engine at fast idle?			
HC2 CHECK HARNESS TO GENERATOR			
• Disconnect generator.	Yes	▶	SERVICE the generator.
• Connect a jumper to ground from Circuit 904 (LG/R) near the generator.	No	▶	GO to HC3.
• Does charge warning go away?			
HC3 CHECK HARNESS TO EIC			
• Turn ignition switch to OFF.	Yes	▶	GO to HC5.
• Turn ignition switch to RUN but do not start engine.	No	▶	GO to HC4.
• Remove jumper.			
• Measure voltage at generator from Circuit 904 (LG/R) to ground.			
• Is it greater than 4 volts?			

FM9099400268010X

Fig. 24   Pinpoint test HC (Part 1 of 2)

TEST STEP	RESULT	▶	ACTION TO TAKE
HC4 CHECK EIC INTEGRAL ALTERNATOR REGULATOR RESISTOR AND HARNESS			
• Turn ignition switch to OFF.	Yes	▶	SERVICE as required to obtain over 4 volts.
• Remove EIC.			
• Check for loose or corroded screws on generator warning lamp shunt resistor on rear of EIC.	No	▶	SERVICE Circuit 489 (PK/BK, Town Car), 88 (BK/W, Crown Victoria/Grand Marquis) of connector C254.
• Check that resistor is 400-600 ohms.			
• Check continuity from resistor screws to Circuit 904 (LG/R) at connector.			
• Check for short to ground on Circuit 904.			
• Has any check failed?			
HC5 CHECK EIC WIRING FOR OPEN CIRCUIT			
• Turn ignition switch to OFF.	Yes	▶	REPLACE EIC. AFFIX odometer sticker to door pillar.
• Disconnect instrument cluster.			
• Check for continuity in Circuit 904, (LG/R).	No	▶	SERVICE Circuit 904 (LG/R).
• Is there continuity?			

FM9099400268020X

Fig. 24   Pinpoint test HC (Part 2 of 2)

TEST STEP	RESULT	▶	ACTION TO TAKE
HD1 CHECK EIC FOR WARNINGS			
• Turn ignition switch to RUN.	Yes	▶	GO to HD2.
• Wait past prove-out time.	No	▶	GO to HD4.
• Check EIC for AIR SUSPENSION warning to determine whether the warning is always on or never on.			
• Is AIR SUSPENSION warning always on?			
HD2 CHECK AIR SUSPENSION CONTROL MODULE			
• Disconnect air suspension control module.	Yes	▶	GO to HD3.
• Turn ignition switch to RUN.	No	▶	SERVICE air suspension control module.
• Check EIC for warning.			
• Is warning displayed?			
HD3 CHECK CONTINUITY			
• Turn ignition switch to OFF.	Yes	▶	REPLACE EIC. AFFIX odometer sticker to door pillar.
• Disconnect EIC.			
• Check continuity in Circuit 419 (DG/LG).	No	▶	SERVICE Circuit 419 (DG/LG).
• Is continuity present?			
HD4 CHECK FOR POWER AND GROUNDS			
• Check voltage on the following pins:	Yes	▶	GO to HD5.
	No	▶	SERVICE as required.

Pin	Circuit Number	Voltage
J1-3	296 (W/P)	12V (Hot At All Times)
J1-5	295 (LB/PK)	12V (Hot In Run)
J1-12	489 (PK/BK)	12V (Hot In Run)
J3-2	295 (LB/PK)	12V (Hot In Run)
J1-4	676 (PK/O)	0V
J3-1	676 (PK/O)	0V

• Are all voltages as specified?

FM9099400269010X

Fig. 25   Pinpoint test HD (Part 1 of 2)

PINPOINT TEST HD: RIDE CONTROL/AIR SUSPENSION WARNING ALWAYS ON (Continued)

TEST STEP	RESULT	▶	ACTION TO TAKE
HD5 CHECK AIR SUSPENSION MODULE			
• Turn ignition switch to OFF.	Yes	▶	SERVICE air suspension control module.
• Disconnect connector at air suspension control module.			
• Connect a jumper wire from Circuit 419 (DG/LG) at harness connector to ground.	No	▶	GO to HD6.
• Turn ignition switch to RUN.			
• Check EIC for warning.			
• Is warning displayed?			
HD6 CHECK CONTINUITY			
• Remove jumper.	Yes	▶	REPLACE EIC. AFFIX odometer sticker to door pillar.
• Disconnect EIC.			
• Check continuity in Circuit 419 (DG/LG).	No	▶	SERVICE Circuit 419 (DG/LG).
• Is continuity present?			

FM9099400269020X

Fig. 25   Pinpoint test HD (Part 2 of 2)

TEST STEP	RESULT	▶	ACTION TO TAKE
HE1 CHECK SYSTEM AND WARNING			
• Drain fluid from windshield washer reservoir for "warning never on."	Yes	▶	GO to HE2.
• Add fluid to windshield washer reservoir for "warning always on."	No	▶	GO to HE4.
• Turn ignition switch to RUN.			
• Wait past prove-out time.			
• Check message center for low WASHER FLUID warnings to determine whether the warning is always on or never on.			
• Is warning always on?			
HE2 CHECK WINDSHIELD WASHER RESERVOIR FLUID LEVEL SENSOR			
• Turn ignition switch to OFF.	Yes	▶	GO to HE3.
• Disconnect harness connector from windshield washer reservoir fluid level sensor.	No	▶	SERVICE windshield washer reservoir fluid level sensor.
• Turn ignition switch to RUN.			
• Check EIC for windshield washer fluid warning.			
• Is warning displayed?			
HE3 CHECK CONTINUITY			
• Turn ignition switch to OFF.	Yes	▶	REPLACE EIC. AFFIX odometer sticker to door pillar.
• Disconnect EIC.			
• Check continuity in Circuit 82 (PK/Y).	No	▶	SERVICE Circuit 82 (PK/Y) for short to ground.
• Is continuity present?			
HE4 CHECK FOR POWER AND GROUNDS			
• Check voltage on the following pins:	Yes	▶	GO to HE5.
	No	▶	SERVICE as required.

Pin	Circuit Number	Voltage
J1-3	296 (W/P)	12V (Hot At All Times)
J1-5	295 (LB/PK)	12V (Hot In Run)
J1-12	489 (PK/BK)	12V (Hot In Run)
J3-2	295 (LB/PK)	12V (Hot In Run)
J1-4	676 (PK/O)	0V
J3-1	676 (PK/O)	0V

• Are all voltages as specified?

FM9099400270010X

Fig. 26   Pinpoint test HE (Part 1 of 2)

TEST STEP		RESULT	▶	ACTION TO TAKE
HE5	CHECK WINDSHIELD WASHER RESERVOIR FLUID LEVEL SENSOR			
	• Turn ignition switch to OFF. • Unplug harness connector from windshield washer reservoir fluid level sensor. • Connect a jumper wire across 2 pins of harness connector. • Turn ignition switch to RUN. • Check messages for low WASHER FLUID warning. • **Is warning displayed?**	Yes No	▶ ▶	SERVICE windshield washer reservoir fluid level sensor. GO to HE6.
HE6	CHECK CONTINUITY			
	• Turn ignition switch to OFF. • Disconnect EIC. • Check continuity in Circuit 82 (PK/Y) and continuity to ground in Circuit (950, W/BK, Town Car), (57, BK, Crown Victoria/Grand Marquis). • **Is continuity present?**	Yes No	▶ ▶	REPLACE EIC. AFFIX odometer sticker to door pillar. SERVICE respective circuit.

FM9099400270020X

Fig. 26 Pinpoint test HE (Part 2 of 2)

TEST STEP		RESULT	▶	ACTION TO TAKE
HF1	CHECK FOR EIC WARNING			
	• Put transmission in PARK. • Release parking brake. • Make sure brake fluid is at specified level. • Turn ignition switch to RUN. • Wait past prove-out time. • Check instrument cluster display to determine whether the warning is always on or never on. • **Is brake warning always on?**	Yes No	▶ ▶	GO to HF2. GO to HF8.
HF2	CHECK FOR SHORT TO GROUND			
	• Disconnect connector at brake fluid level switch. • **Is brake warning illuminated?**	Yes No	▶ ▶	GO to HF3. REPLACE brake master cylinder reservoir
HF3	CHECK FOR SHORT TO GROUND			
	• Disconnect parking brake signal switch and bracket. • **Is brake warning illuminated?**	Yes No	▶ ▶	If vehicle equipped with daytime running lights control module, GO to HF5. Otherwise GO to HF4. REPLACE parking brake signal switch and bracket.
HF4	CHECK FOR SHORT TO GROUND			
	• Disconnect EIC. • **Is brake warning illuminated?**	Yes No	▶ ▶	REPLACE EIC. AFFIX odometer sticker to pillar. SERVICE Circuit 977 (P·W) and/or Circuit 512 (T/LG, Crown Victoria/Grand Marquis).
HF5	DISCONNECT DRL MODULE			
	• Disconnect daytime running lights control module. • **Is brake warning illuminated?**	Yes No	▶ ▶	GO to HF6. GO to HF7.
HF6	CHECK FOR SHORT TO GROUND			
	• Disconnect EIC. • **Is brake warning illuminated?**	Yes No	▶ ▶	REPLACE EIC. AFFIX odometer sticker to door pillar SERVICE Circuit 977 (P·W)

FM9099400271010X

Fig. 27 Pinpoint test HF (Part 1 of 2)

PINPOINT TEST HF: BRAKE WARNING NEVER/ALWAYS ON (Continued)

TEST STEP		RESULT	▶	ACTION TO TAKE
HF7	CHECK CONTINUITY			
	• Check continuity in Circuit (977 P/W, Town Car), (512, T/LG, Crown Victoria/Grand Marquis) between daytime running lights control module and parking brake signal switch and bracket. • **Is continuity present?**	Yes No	▶ ▶	REPLACE daytime running lights control module. SERVICE respective circuit.
HF8	CHECK FOR POWER AND GROUNDS			
	• Check voltage on the following pins:	Yes No	▶ ▶	GO to HF9. SERVICE as required.

Pin	Circuit Number	Voltage
J1-3	296 (W/P)	12V (Hot At All Times)
J1-5	295 (LB/PK)	12V (Hot In Run)
J1-12	489 (PK/BK)	12V (Hot In Run)
J3-2	295 (LB/PK)	12V (Hot In Run)
J1-4	676 (PK/O)	0V
J3-1	676 (PK/O)	0V

TEST STEP		RESULT	▶	ACTION TO TAKE
	• **Are all voltages as specified?**			
HF9	CHECK EIC			
	• Turn ignition switch to OFF. • Disconnect EIC. • Ground Pin 7 of EIC (connector C256). • Turn ignition switch to RUN. • **Does brake warning illuminate?**	Yes No	▶ ▶	GO to HF10 for Crown Victoria/Grand Marquis. REPLACE EIC. AFFIX odometer sticker to door pillar.
HF10	CHECK PARKING BRAKE AND CIRCUITRY			
	• Engage parking brake. • Turn ignition switch to RUN. • Engage parking brake. • **Does brake warning illuminate?**	Yes No	▶ ▶	GO to HF12. GO to HF11.
HF11	CHECK PARKING BRAKE SWITCH			
	• Disconnect parking brake signal switch. • Ground Circuit 512 (T/LG) at parking brake signal switch connector. • **Does brake warning illuminate?**	Yes No	▶ ▶	REPLACE parking brake signal switch and bracket. SERVICE Circuit 977 (P/W), 512 (T/LG), daytime running lights control module (if equipped) as required.
HF12	CHECK BRAKE FLUID LEVEL SWITCH			
	• Turn ignition switch to OFF. • Disconnect brake fluid level switch. • Put a jumper wire across the circuits OTHER THAN 57 (BK) at the brake fluid level switch connector. • Turn ignition switch to RUN. • Check EIC for warning. • **Is brake warning illuminated?**	Yes No	▶ ▶	REPLACE brake master cylinder reservoir GO to HF13.
HF13	CHECK CONTINUITY			
	• Turn ignition switch to OFF. • Disconnect EIC. • Disconnect ignition switch. • Check continuity in Circuit 977 (P/W) between brake fluid level switch and both ignition switch and EIC. • **Is continuity present?**	Yes No	▶ ▶	SERVICE ignition switch. SERVICE respective circuit.

FM9099400271020X

Fig. 27 Pinpoint test HF (Part 2 of 2)

PINPOINT TEST HG: HIGH BEAM WARNING NEVER/ALWAYS ON

TEST STEP		RESULT	▶	ACTION TO TAKE
HG1	VERIFY CONDITION			
	NOTE: Make sure the light switches are in proper positions when checking circuit operation. • Turn ignition switch to RUN. • Wait past prove-out time. • Check EIC displays to determine whether the indicator is always on or never on. • **Is HIGH BEAM indicator always on?**	Yes No	▶ ▶	GO to HG2. GO to HG4.
HG2	CHECK EIC			
	• Disconnect connector C256 at EIC. • **Is HIGH BEAM indicator illuminated?**	Yes No	▶ ▶	REPLACE EIC. AFFIX odometer sticker to pillar. GO to HG3.
HG3	CHECK FOR SHORT TO BATTERY			
	• Reconnect EIC. • Disconnect HI-LO Beam Relay—Town Car, turn signal and windshield wiper switch—Crown Victoria/Grand Marquis. • **Is HIGH BEAM indicator illuminated?**	Yes No	▶ ▶	SERVICE short to battery in Circuit 12 (LG/BK) and/or Circuit 932 (GY/W). CHECK daytime running lights control module (if equipped) for short to battery. SERVICE as required. REPLACE HI-LO beam relay—Town Car, turn signal and windshield wiper switch—Crown Victoria/Grand Marquis.
HG4	CHECK EIC			
	• Turn ignition switch to OFF. • Disconnect EIC. • Connect a jumper wire from high beam input pin of EIC (Pin 4 of C256 connector) to positive battery terminal. Supply ground to ground pin of EIC (Pin 1 of C256 connector). • **Is HIGH BEAM indicator illuminated?**	Yes No	▶ ▶	GO to HG5. REPLACE EIC. AFFIX odometer sticker to door pillar.
HG5	CHECK CIRCUITRY			
	• Reconnect EIC. • Disconnect HI-LO beam replay—Town Car, turn signal and windshield wiper switch—Crown Victoria/Grand Marquis. • Jump Circuit 12 (LG/BK) at the HI-LO beam relay (Town Car) turn signal and windshield wiper switch (Crown Victoria/Grand Marquis) connector to positive battery terminal. • **Is HIGH BEAM indicator illuminated?**	Yes No	▶ ▶	GO to HG6. SERVICE Circuit 12 (LG/BK), Circuit 932 (GY/W), daytime running lights control module (if equipped) as required.
HG6	CHECK CONTINUITY			
	• Disconnect headlamp switch. • Check continuity in Circuit 502 (GY, Town Car) (15 R·Y, Crown Victoria·Grand Marquis). • Check continuity to power in Circuit 38 (BK/O). • **Is continuity present?**	Yes No	▶ ▶	REPLACE headlamp switch. SERVICE respective circuit.

FM9099400272000X

Fig. 28 Pinpoint test HG

TEST STEP		RESULT	▶	ACTION TO TAKE
HH1	CHECK EIC FOR WARNINGS			
	• Turn ignition switch to RUN. • Wait past prove out time. • Check EIC display to determine whether the warning is always on or never on. • **is ANTI-LOCK warning always on?**	Yes No	▶ ▶	GO to HH2. GO to HH4

FM9099400273010X

Fig. 29 Pinpoint test HH (Part 1 of 2)

TEST STEP		RESULT	▶	ACTION TO TAKE
HH2	CHECK ANTI-LOCK BRAKE MODULE			
	• Disconnect anti-lock brake control module. • Check EIC for warning. • **Is ANTI-LOCK warning illuminated?**	Yes	▶	GO to HH3.
		No	▶	SERVICE anti-lock brake control module.
HH3	CHECK CONTINUITY			
	• Turn ignition switch to OFF. • Disconnect EIC. • Check continuity in Circuit 603 (DG). • **Is continuity present?**	Yes	▶	REPLACE EIC. AFFIX odometer sticker to door pillar.
		No	▶	SERVICE Circuit 603 (DG).
HH4	CHECK POWER AND GROUNDS			
	• Check voltage on the following pins:	Yes	▶	GO to HH5.
		No	▶	SERVICE as required.

Pin	Circuit Number	Voltage
J1-3	296 (W/P)	12V (Hot At All Times)
J1-5	295 (LB/PK)	12V (Hot In Run)
J1-12	489 (PK/BK)	12V (Hot In Run)
J3-2	295 (LB/PK)	12V (Hot In Run)
J1-4	676 (PK/O)	0V
J3-1	676 (PK/O)	0V

TEST STEP		RESULT	▶	ACTION TO TAKE
	• **Are all voltages as specified?**			
HH5	CHECK ANTI-LOCK BRAKE MODULE			
	• Turn ignition switch to OFF. • Disconnect connector at anti-lock brake control module. • Connect a jumper wire from Circuit 609 (DG) at harness connector to ground. • Turn ignition switch to RUN. • Check EIC for warning. • **Is ANTI-LOCK warning illuminated?**	Yes	▶	SERVICE anti-lock brake control module.
		No		GO to HH6.
HH6	CHECK CONTINUITY			
	• Remove jumper. • Disconnect EIC. • Check continuity in Circuit 603 (DG). • **Is continuity present?**	Yes	▶	REPLACE EIC. AFFIX odometer sticker to door pillar.
		No	▶	SERVICE Circuit 603 (DG).

FM9099400273020X

Fig. 29   Pinpoint test HH (Part 2 of 2)

TEST STEP		RESULT	▶	ACTION TO TAKE
HJ1	CHECK EIC FOR WARNINGS			
	• Turn ignition switch to RUN. • Wait past prove-out time. • Check EIC display to determine whether the warning is always on or never on. • **Is LOW OIL PRESSURE warning always on?**	Yes	▶	GO to HJ2.
		No	▶	GO to HJ4.
HJ2	CHECK OIL PRESSURE SENDER			
	• Disconnect oil pressure sender. • Check EIC for warning. • **Is LOW OIL PRESSURE warning illuminated?**	Yes	▶	GO to HJ3.
		No	▶	REPLACE oil pressure sender.

FM9099400314010X

Fig. 30   Pinpoint test HJ (Part 1 of 2)

TEST STEP		RESULT	▶	ACTION TO TAKE
HJ3	CHECK CONTINUITY			
	• Turn ignition switch to OFF. • Disconnect EIC. • Check continuity in Circuit 31 (W/R). • **Is continuity present?**	Yes	▶	REPLACE EIC. AFFIX odometer sticker to door pillar.
		No	▶	SERVICE Circuit 31 (W/R).
HJ4	CHECK FOR POWER AND GROUNDS			
	• Check voltage on the following pins:	Yes	▶	GO to HJ5.
		No	▶	SERVICE as required.

Pin	Circuit Number	Voltage
J1-3	296 (W/P)	12V (Hot At All Times)
J1-5	295 (LB/PK)	12V (Hot In Run)
J1-12	489 (PK/BK)	12V (Hot In Run)
J3-2	295 (LB/PK)	12V (Hot In Run)
J1-4	676 (PK/O)	0V
J3-1	676 (PK/O)	0V

TEST STEP		RESULT	▶	ACTION TO TAKE
	• **Are all voltages as specified?**			
HJ5	CHECK OIL PRESSURE SENDER			
	• Turn ignition switch to OFF. • Disconnect connector at oil pressure sender. • Connect a jumper wire from Circuit 31 (W/R) at harness connector to ground. • Turn ignition switch to RUN. • Check EIC for warning. • **Is LOW OIL PRESSURE warning illuminated?**	Yes	▶	REPLACE oil pressure sender.
		No	▶	GO to HJ6.
HJ6	CHECK CONTINUITY			
	• Remove jumper. • Disconnect EIC. • Check continuity in Circuit 31 (W/R). • **Is continuity present?**	Yes	▶	REPLACE EIC. AFFIX odometer sticker to door pillar.
		No	▶	SERVICE Circuit 3 (W/R).

FM9099400314020X

Fig. 30   Pinpoint test HJ (Part 2 of 2)

TEST STEP		RESULT	▶	ACTION TO TAKE
HK2	CHECK AIR BAG DIAGNOSTIC MONITOR			
	NOTE: If the air bag warning indicator flashes on and off continuously it means that it is showing a diagnostic code. It does not mean that the air bag warning indicator needs to be serviced.	Yes	▶	GO to HK3.
		No	▶	REPLACE air bag diagnostic monitor.
	WARNING: THE BACKUP POWER SUPPLY ENERGY MUST BE DEPLETED BEFORE ANY AIR BAG COMPONENT SERVICE IS PERFORMED. TO DEPLETE BACKUP POWER SUPPLY ENERGY, DISCONNECT THE POSITIVE BATTERY CABLE AND WAIT ONE MINUTE. • Disconnect battery ground cable. • Disconnect positive battery cable and wait one minute. • Disconnect air bag diagnostic monitor. • Check EIC for warning. • **Is AIR BAG warning illuminated?**			
HK3	CHECK CONTINUITY			
	• Turn ignition switch to OFF. • Disconnect EIC. • Check continuity in Circuit 608 (BK/Y). • **Is continuity present?**	Yes	▶	REPLACE EIC. AFFIX odometer sticker to door pillar.
		No	▶	SERVICE Circuit 608 (BK/Y).
HK4	CHECK FOR POWER AND GROUNDS			
	• Check voltage on the following pins:	Yes	▶	GO to HK5.
		No	▶	SERVICE as required.

Pin	Circuit Number	Voltage
J1-3	296 (W/P)	12V (Hot At All Times)
J1-5	295 (LB/PK)	12V (Hot In Run)
J1-12	489 (PK/BK)	12V (Hot In Run)
J3-2	295 (LB/PK)	12V (Hot In Run)
J1-4	676 (PK/O)	0V
J3-1	676 (PK/O)	0V

TEST STEP		RESULT	▶	ACTION TO TAKE
	• **Are all voltages as specified?**			
HK5	CHECK AIR BAG DIAGNOSTIC MONITOR			
	WARNING: THE BACKUP POWER SUPPLY ENERGY MUST BE DEPLETED BEFORE ANY AIR BAG COMPONENT SERVICE IS PERFORMED. TO DEPLETE BACKUP POWER SUPPLY ENERGY, DISCONNECT THE POSITIVE BATTERY CABLE AND WAIT ONE MINUTE.	Yes	▶	REPLACE air bag diagnostic monitor.
		No	▶	GO to HK6.
	• Turn ignition switch to OFF. • Disconnect battery ground cable. • Disconnect positive battery cable and wait one minute. • Disconnect connector at air bag diagnostic monitor. • Connect a jumper wire from Circuit 608 (BK/Y) at harness connector to ground. • Reconnect positive battery cable. • Turn ignition switch to RUN. • Check EIC for warning. • **Is AIR BAG warning illuminated?**			

Fig. 31   Pinpoint test HK (Part 2 of 3)

TEST STEP		RESULT	▶	ACTION TO TAKE
HK1	CHECK EIC FOR WARNINGS			
	• Turn ignition switch to RUN. • Wait past prove-out time. • Check EIC display to determine whether the warning is always on or never on. • **Is AIR BAG warning always on?**	Yes	▶	GO to HK2.
		No	▶	GO to HK4.

Fig. 31   Pinpoint test HK (Part 1 of 3)

TEST STEP		RESULT	▶	ACTION TO TAKE
HK6	CHECK CONTINUITY			
	• Remove jumper. • Disconnect EIC. • Check continuity in Circuit 608 (BK/Y). • **Is continuity present?**	Yes	▶	REPLACE EIC. AFFIX odometer sticker to door pillar.
		No	▶	SERVICE Circuit 608 (BK/Y).

Fig. 31   Pinpoint test HK (Part 3 of 3)

TEST STEP			RESULT	▶	ACTION TO TAKE
HL1	**CHECK EIC FOR INDICATOR**				
	• Turn ignition switch to RUN.		Yes	▶	GO to HL2.
	• Wait past prove-out time.		No	▶	GO to HL4.
	• Check EIC display to determine whether the indicator is always on or never on.				
	• Is OVERDRIVE OFF indicator always on?				
HL2	**CHECK PCM**				
	• Disconnect powertrain control module.		Yes	▶	GO to HL3.
	• Check EIC for indicator.		No	▶	REPLACE powertrain control module.
	• Is OVERDRIVE OFF indicator illuminated?				
HL3	**CHECK CONTINUITY**				
	• Turn ignition switch to OFF.		Yes	▶	REPLACE bulb in EIC.
	• Disconnect EIC.		No	▶	SERVICE Circuit 911 (W/LG).
	• Check continuity in Circuit 911 (W/LG).				
	• Is continuity present?				
HL4	**CHECK FOR POWER AND GROUNDS**				
	• Check voltage on the following pins:		Yes	▶	GO to HL5.
			No	▶	SERVICE as required.

Pin	Circuit Number	Voltage
J1-3	296 (W/P)	12V (Hot At All Times)
J1-5	296 (LB/PK)	12V (Hot In Run)
J1-12	480 (PK/BK)	12V (Hot In Run)
J3-2	296 (LB/PK)	12V (Hot In Run)
J1-4	676 (PK/O)	0V
J3-1	676 (PK/O)	0V

TEST STEP			RESULT	▶	ACTION TO TAKE
	• Are all voltages as specified?				
HL5	**CHECK PCM**				
	• Turn ignition switch to OFF.		Yes	▶	REPLACE powertrain control module
	• Disconnect connector at powertrain control module.				
	• Connect a jumper wire from Circuit 911(W/LG) at harness connector to ground.				
	• Turn ignition switch to RUN.				
	• Check EIC for warning.		No	▶	GO to HL6.
	• Is OVERDRIVE OFF indicator illuminated?				
HL6	**CHECK CONTINUITY**				
	• Remove jumper.		Yes	▶	REPLACE bulb in EIC.
	• Disconnect EIC.		No	▶	SERVICE Circuit 911 (W/LG).
	• Check continuity in Circuit 911 (W/LG).				
	• Is continuity present?				

FM9099400315000X

Fig. 32   Pinpoint test HL

TEST STEP			RESULT	▶	ACTION TO TAKE
HM1	**CHECK DISPLAYS**				
	• Turn ignition switch to OFF.		Yes	▶	GO to HM2.
	• Turn parking lamps on.		No	▶	GO to AA3.
	• Check other displays: radio, MCCA instrument indicator switch module.				
	• Do other displays illuminate properly?				
HM2	**CHECK EIC BULB**				
	• Check the bulb in the EIC.		Yes	▶	SERVICE Circuit 19 (LB/R)
	• Is bulb OK?		No	▶	REPLACE bulb

FM9099400316000X

Fig. 33   Pinpoint test HM

1995 Crown Victoria, Grand Marquis & Town Car

NOTE: Refer to the Symptom Index in this section before performing any Pinpoint Tests.

INDEX

	Page No. 15-	Fig. No.
PINPOINT TESTS:		
Pinpoint Test A	57	2
Pinpoint Test B	58	3
Pinpoint Test C	58	4
Pinpoint Test D	58	5
Pinpoint Test E	59	6
Pinpoint Test F	59	7
Pinpoint Test G	59	8
Pinpoint Test H	59	9
Pinpoint Test J	59	10
Pinpoint Test K	60	11
Pinpoint Test L	60	12
Pinpoint Test M	60	13
Pinpoint Test N	60	14
Pinpoint Test P	60	15
Pinpoint Test Q	60	16
Pinpoint Test R	60	17
Pinpoint Test S	60	18
Pinpoint Test T	61	19
Pinpoint Test U	61	20
Pinpoint Test V	61	21
Pinpoint Test W	61	22
Pinpoint Test X	62	23
Pinpoint Test Y	62	24
Pinpoint Test AA	62	25
Pinpoint Test BB	63	26
Pinpoint Test CC	63	27
Pinpoint Test DD	63	28
Pinpoint Test EE	63	29
Pinpoint Test FF	64	30
Pinpoint Test GG	64	31
Pinpoint Test HH	64	32
Pinpoint Test JJ	64	33
Pinpoint Test KK	65	34
SYMPTOM INDEX	57	1

CONDITION	POSSIBLE SOURCE	ACTION
• Display Does Not Respond to Buttons or No Beep When Buttons Pushed or Driver Alert Given	• Circuitry. • Safety belt warning chime. • EIC. • Message center switch module. • Headlamp switch.	• GO to Pinpoint Test C.

FUEL GAUGE DIAGNOSIS

CONDITION	POSSIBLE SOURCE	ACTION
• CO Displayed, Top Two and Bottom Two Diagnostic Bars Displayed	• Fuel pump (FP) module. • EIC. • Circuitry.	• GO to Pinpoint Test D.
• CS Displayed, Top Two and Bottom Two Diagnostic Bars Displayed	• Fuel pump (FP) module. • Circuitry. • EIC.	• GO to Pinpoint Test E.
• Inaccurate Fuel Gauge Indication	• Fuel pump (FP) module. • Valve, tube or evaporative emission canister. • Fuel tank. • EIC.	• GO to Pinpoint Test F.

TEMPERATURE GAUGE DIAGNOSIS

CONDITION	POSSIBLE SOURCE	ACTION
• Temperature Gauge Displays Top And Bottom Two Diagnostic Bars	• Engine coolant temperature (ETC) sensor. • EIC. • Circuitry.	• GO to Pinpoint Test G.
• Temperature Gauge Always Indicates Hot Or Cold Temperature	• Engine coolant temperature (ETC) sensor. • EIC. • Circuitry.	• GO to Pinpoint Test H.
• No Warning Tone When Thermometer Symbol is Blinking	• EIC. • Safety belt warning chime.	• GO to Pinpoint Test J.

SPEEDOMETER DIAGNOSIS

CONDITION	POSSIBLE SOURCE	ACTION
• Speedometer Reads 0 km/h (mph) At All Speeds	• EIC. • Circuitry. • Vehicle speed sensor.	• GO to Pinpoint Test K.
• Speedometer Constantly Reads Too High Or Too Low	• Vehicle speed sensor. • Drive gear. • EIC. • Circuitry.	• GO to Pinpoint Test L.
• Speed Indication Jumps Up And Down Erratically	• EIC. • Vehicle speed sensor. • Circuitry.	• GO to Pinpoint Test M.
• Speed Control Indicator Always On	• Speed control servo. • Circuitry. • EIC.	• GO to Pinpoint Test N.
• Speed Control Indicator Does Not Come On When Speed Control Engaged	• EIC. • Circuitry. • Powertrain control module.	• GO to Pinpoint Test P.

ODOMETER DIAGNOSIS

CONDITION	POSSIBLE SOURCE	ACTION
• Display Reads "Error"	• EIC.	• REPLACE EIC. AFFIX odometer sticker to door pillar.
• Display Has "S" Illuminated	• EIC.	• GO to Pinpoint Test Q.
• Mileage Constantly Reads Too High Or Too Low	• Drive gear. • EIC.	• GO to Pinpoint Test R.

FM9099500364020X

Fig. 1 Symptom index (Part 2 of 4)

CONDITION	POSSIBLE SOURCE	ACTION
• Display Not Illuminated, Too Dim or Blank But Backlighted	• Dimmed to barely discernable, could be at MAX with headlamps ON. • EIC. • Circuitry.	• GO to Pinpoint Test A.
• Display Scrambled, Incorrect All the Time or Stuck with All Segments On, Segments Half Lit, Blinking or Missing	• EIC.	• GO to Pinpoint Test B.

FM9099500364010X

Fig. 1 Symptom index (Part 1 of 4)

CONDITION	POSSIBLE SOURCE	ACTION
• Overdrive OFF Indicator Never/Always On	• EIC. • Powertrain control module. • Circuitry.	• GO to Pinpoint Test JJ.
• Transmission Control Selector Indicator Never/Always On	• Bulb. • Circuitry.	• GO to Pinpoint Test KK.

FM9099500364040X

Fig. 1 Symptom index (Part 4 of 4)

CONDITION	POSSIBLE SOURCE	ACTION
• Odometer Does Not Accumulate Mileage or Counts 1.6 km (1.0 mile) and Jumps Back 1.6 km (1.0 mile)	• EIC. • Vehicle speed sensor.	• GO to Pinpoint Test S.

MESSAGE CENTER DISPLAY DIAGNOSIS

CONDITION	POSSIBLE SOURCE	ACTION
• Instantaneous or Average Fuel Economy Always Reads 0 Miles/Gal Or 99 L/100 km or 99 Miles/Gal or 0 L/100 km	• EIC. • Circuitry. • Powertrain control module.	• GO to Pinpoint Test T.
• Trip Distance Does Not Accumulate	• EIC.	• GO to Pinpoint Test S.
• DTE Does Not Go Below 322 km (200 Miles) With Fuel Tank Empty or DTE Always Reads Zero	• EIC. • Circuitry. • Powertrain control module.	• GO to Pinpoint Test U.

WARNING INDICATOR DIAGNOSIS

CONDITION	POSSIBLE SOURCE	ACTION
• DOOR AJAR Warning Never/Always Comes On	• Door open warning lamp switch. • EIC. • Circuitry. • Lighting control module.	• GO to Pinpoint Test V.
• TRUNK AJAR Warning Never/Always Comes On	• Luggage compartment door open warning lamp switch. • Circuitry. • EIC. • Lighting control module.	• GO to Pinpoint Test W.
• CHARGE SYSTEM Warning Always/Never Comes On	• EIC. • Circuitry.	• GO to Pinpoint Test X.
• RIDE CONTROL/AIR SUSPENSION Warning Always On	• Circuitry. • EIC.	• GO to Pinpoint Test Y.
• Low WASHER FLUID Warning Never/Always On	• Windshield washer reservoir fluid level sensor. • Circuitry. • EIC.	• GO to Pinpoint Test AA.
• CHECK ENGINE (MIL) Warning Always On	• EIC. • PCM.	• GO to Pinpoint Test BB. • PERFORM Diagnostic Self Test.
• LH Turn Indicator Never/Always ON (Crown Victoria, Grand Marquis)	• Shorted or open circuitry. • Malfunctioning turn signal and windshield wiper switch.	• GO to Pinpoint Test CC.
• RH Turn Indicator Never/Always On	• Shorted or open circuitry. • Malfunctioning turn signal and windshield wiper switch.	• GO to Pinpoint Test DD.
• High Beam Warning Never/Always On	• EIC. • Circuitry. • Headlamp switch.	• GO to Pinpoint Test EE.
• Safety Belt Warning Never/Always On (Crown Victoria, Grand Marquis Only)	• Blown fuse. • Malfunctioning chime module. • Inoperative safety belt switch. • Open/shorted circuitry.	• GO to Pinpoint Test FF.
• Low Oil Pressure Warning Never/Always On (Crown Victoria, Grand Marquis)	• EIC. • Oil pressure sensor. • Circuitry.	• GO to Pinpoint Test GG.
• Air Bag Warning Never/Always On (Crown Victoria, Grand Marquis)	• EIC. • Air bag diagnostic monitor. • Circuitry.	• GO to Pinpoint Test HH.

FM9099500364030X

Fig. 1 Symptom index (Part 3 of 4)

	TEST STEP	RESULT	►	ACTION TO TAKE
A1	**CHECK DISPLAYS - HEADLAMPS OFF** • Turn ignition switch to RUN. • Turn headlamps OFF. • Verify illumination of EIC, clock and radio. • **Is electronic cluster display off with other displays on?**	Yes No	► ►	GO to A2. GO to A3.
A2	**CHECK INSTRUMENT CLUSTER POWER** • Verify power at EIC Pins C1-7, C1-9, C3-2 with ignition switch in RUN position. • **Is power present?**	Yes No	► ►	REPLACE electric cluster. SERVICE Circuits 295 (LB/PK), 964 (DB/LG), 797 (LG/P) and 54 (LG/Y).
A3	**CHECK DISPLAYS - HEADLAMPS ON** • Turn ignition switch to ON. • Turn parking lamps on. • While varying dimming level check other displays: radio, clock, transmission control selector indicator. • **Do other displays illuminate properly?**	Yes No	► ►	GO to A4. GO to A5.
A4	**CHECK FOR CIRCUIT 19 (LB/R) VOLTAGE** • Turn parking lamp off. • Disconnect EIC. • Turn parking lamps on. • While varying dimming level, check voltage in Circuit 19 (LB/R) at Pin 13 of electronic instrument cluster. • **Does voltage vary between 4 and 15V?**	Yes No	► ►	REPLACE EIC. AFFIX odometer sticker to door pillar. RESTORE vehicle. RETEST system. SERVICE Circuit 19 (LB/R). RESTORE vehicle. RETEST system.
A5	**CHECK FOR LIGHTING CONTROL MODULE** • Check I/P fuses 11 and 7 (Town Car) 9 and 11 (Crown Victoria, Grand Marquis). Replace if necessary. Proceed if displays still do not illuminate properly. • While varying dimming level, verify voltage output at lighting control module. • **Does dimming input voltage vary between 4 and 15V?**	Yes No	► ►	SERVICE Circuit 19 (LB/R). RESTORE vehicle. RETEST system. GO to lighting control module diagnosis.

FM9099500365000X

Fig. 2 Pinpoint test A

TEST STEP		RESULT	▶	ACTION TO TAKE
B2	DISPLAY TEST			
	NOTE: There are 17 segment displays.	Yes	▶	REPLACE EIC. Affix odometer sticker to door pillar. RESTORE vehicle. RETEST system.
	• Push SELECT> button once to enter display test.	No	▶	EIC OK. RESTORE vehicle.
	• Push E/M button to step through display test inspection and verification.			
	• Display test start with all blue/green segments off. Test then cycles through following test to turn on each segment or indicator ISO one time only, then begins to full display after each segment has been tested individually until all blue/green segments are on. Next switch press start cycle all over again.			
	• Do any segments stay on always or never come on?			

FM9099500366020X

Fig. 3   Pinpoint test B (Part 2 of 2)

TEST STEP		RESULT	▶	ACTION TO TAKE
B1	PERFORM SELF TEST			
	• Turn ignition to OFF position.	Yes	▶	REPLACE EIC, AFFIX odometer sticker to door pillar. RESTORE vehicle. RETEST system.
	• Push in the E/M and select (left) buttons and hold.			
	• Turn ignition to ON position while holding buttons.			
	• Release buttons when cluster lights.	No	▶	GO to B2.
	• Does odometer flash?			

FM9099500366010X

Fig. 3   Pinpoint test B (Part 1 of 2)

TEST STEP		RESULT	▶	ACTION TO TAKE
C6	CHECK SWITCH ASSEMBLY (BUTTONS PRESSED)			
	• Unplug message center module from electronic instrument cluster.	Yes	▶	GO to C7.
	• Measure the resistance between Pin 1 (Circuit 572, O/BK, Town Car), (Circuit 143, LB/Y, Crown Victoria/Grand Marquis) and Pin 8 (Circuit 676, PK/O, Town Car), (Circuit 875, BK/LB, Crown Victoria/Grand Marquis) (NOTE: Press only one button of the message center switch module while pressing the problem button.)	No	▶	REPLACE message center switch module. RESTORE vehicle. RETEST system.
	• The resistance should be:			
	NOTE: Measure resistance between Pins 1 and 8 for SELECT forward and REVERSE, between Pins 2 and 8 for E/ME Reset.			

PINS	BUTTON	RESISTANCE (In ohms)
2-8	EM	5100-5200
1-8	SELECT (forward)	5100-5200
1-8	SELECT (reverse)	2250-2350
2-8	RESET	2250-2350

TEST STEP		RESULT	▶	ACTION TO TAKE
	• Is resistance within range?			
C7	VERIFY HARNESS CONTINUITY			
	• Disconnect battery ground cable.	Yes	▶	REPLACE EIC. AFFIX odometer sticker to door pillar. RESTORE vehicle. RETEST system.
	• Remove EIC.			
	• Check continuity in Circuit 143 and 152 (Town Car) 142 (Crown Victoria, Grand Marquis)			
	• Check continuity to ground in Circuit (676, PK/O and Pin 8 of switch module C1-8 of EIC, Town Car), (875, BK/LB, Crown Victoria/Grand Marquis).	No	▶	SERVICE respective circuit. RESTORE vehicle. RETEST system.
	• Is there continuity?			
C8	CHECK EATC INPUT FROM EIC IN ENGLISH MODE			
	• Turn ignition switch to RUN.	Yes	▶	REFER tc EATC Diagnostics.
	• Remove the connector from the EATC.			
	• Press the E/M button so that the instrument cluster is in ENGLISH mode.	No	▶	GO to C9.
	• Check EATC connector Pin 20 (not on the EATC)			
	• Is Pin 20 at 5 volts DC?			
C9	CHECK EIC OUTPUT TO EATC IN ENGLISH MODE			
	• Leave ignition switch at RUN.	Yes	▶	SERVICE Circuit 506 (R) for short to ground or to another wire. RESTORE vehicle. RETEST system.
	• Connector is removed from the EATC.			
	• Press the E/M button so that the instrument cluster is in ENGLISH mode.			
	• Remove connector C2 from instrument cluster.	No	▶	REPLACE EIC. affix odometer sticker to door pillar. RESTORE vehicle. RETEST system.
	• Check Pin 32 of the instrument cluster (not the harness connector).			
	• Is instrument cluster Pin 32 at 5 volts DC?			
C10	CHECK EATC INPUT FROM EIC IN METRIC MODE			
	• Turn ignition switch to RUN.	Yes	▶	REFER to EATC Diagnostics.
	• Remove the connector from the EATC.			
	• Press the E/M button so that the instrument cluster is in METRIC mode.	No	▶	GO to C11.
	• Check EATC connector Pin 20 (not on the EATC)			
	• Is Pin 20 at 0 volts DC?			

FM9099500367020X

Fig. 4   Pinpoint test C (Part 2 of 3)

TEST STEP		RESULT	▶	ACTION TO TAKE
C1	CHECK FOR WARNING CHIME			
	NOTE: Buttons function only with ignition switch in RUN.	Yes	▶	GO to C2 for Town Car. GO to C4 for Crown Victoria/Grand Marquis.
	• Check for fasten safety belt reminder chime or key left in ignition reminder chime.			
	• Does safety belt warning chime sound?	No	▶	REFER to for safety belt warning chime diagnosis.
C2	CHECK EATC METRIC MODE OUTPUT (TOWN CAR)			
	• Check E/M button operation.	Yes	▶	GO to C10.
	• Is EATC stuck at metric mode?	No	▶	GO to C3.
C3	CHECK EATC ENGLISH MODE OUTPUT (TOWN CAR)			
	• Check E/M button operation.	Yes	▶	GO to C8.
	• Is EATC stuck at English mode?	No	▶	GO to C4.
C4	CHECK SWITCH WIRING CONNECTIONS			
	• Remove finish panel to expose instrument cluster.	Yes	▶	GO to C5.
	• Verify that connections at message center switch module assembly are securely connected.	No	▶	Secure connections and RECHECK.
	• Are connections secure?			
C5	CHECK MCCA SWITCH ASSEMBLY (NO SWITCH PRESSED)			
	• Unplug message center module.	Yes	▶	GO to C6.
	• Measure the resistance between Pin 2 and Pin 8 (Circuit 572, O/BK and Circuit 676, PK/O, Town Car)(Circuit 143, LB/Y and Circuit 875 BK/LB, Crown Victoria/Grand Marquis) of the message center switch module.	No	▶	REPLACE message center switch module. RESTORE vehicle. RETEST system.
	• Resistance with no switch pressed should be 17,300 to 17,600 ohms.			
	• Is resistance within range?			

FM9099500367010X

Fig. 4   Pinpoint test C (Part 1 of 3)

TEST STEP		RESULT	▶	ACTION TO TAKE
C11	CHECK EIC OUTPUT TO EATC IN METRIC MODE			
	• Leave ignition switch at RUN.	Yes	▶	SERVICE Circuit 506(R) for open. CHECK for intermittent contact. RESTORE vehicle. RETEST system.
	• Connector still removed from the EATC.			
	• Press the E/M button so that the instrument cluster is in METRIC mode.			
	• Remove Connector C2 from instrument cluster.	No	▶	REPLACE EIC. AFFIX odometer sticker to door pillar. RESTORE vehicle. RETEST system.
	• Check Pin 32 of the instrument cluster (not the harness connector).			
	• Is instrument cluster Pin 32 at 0 volts DC?			

FM9099500367030X

Fig. 4   Pinpoint test C (Part 3 of 3)

TEST STEP		RESULT	▶	ACTION TO TAKE
D1	CHECK FUEL PUMP WIRING AT FUEL PUMP			
	• Disconnect battery ground cable.	Yes	▶	GO to D3.
	• Lower fuel tank to gain access to fuel pump (FP) module connector.	No	▶	REMOVE jumper. GO to D2.
	• Unplug fuel pump (FP) module connector.			
	• Jumper variable resistance terminal Circuit 29 (Y/W) and ground terminal Circuit 676 (PK/O) (Town Car) or Circuit 359 (GY/R) (Crown Victoria, Grand Marquis) of fuel pump (FP) module connector.			
	• Reconnect battery.			
	• Turn ignition switch from OFF to RUN.			
	NOTE: It may take several minutes for the fuel gauge to respond.			
	• Check digital fuel remaining display to determine whether it shows CO or CS.			
	• Does fuel gauge display show CO?			
D2	CHECK FUEL PUMP RESISTANCE			
	• Turn ignition switch to OFF.	Yes	▶	GO to D4.
	• Measure the resistance of the fuel pump (FP) module at Circuits 787 (PK/BK) and 57 (BK).	No	▶	REPLACE fuel pump. RESTORE vehicle. RETEST system.
	• Verify that the resistance is less than 181 ohms (normally between 15 and 160 ohms).			
	• Is resistance less than 181 ohms?			
D3	CHECK FUEL PUMP WIRING AT EIC			
	• Disconnect battery ground cable.	Yes	▶	REPLACE EIC. AFFIX odometer sticker to door pillar. RESTORE vehicle. RETEST system.
	• Remove connector C1 from EIC and secure connectors from shorting.			
	• Jumper variable resistance terminal Circuit 29 (Y/W) and ground terminal Circuit 676 (PK/O) (Town Car) or Circuit 359 (GY/R) (Crown Victoria, Grand Marquis) of harness together at fuel pump (FP) module.	No	▶	SERVICE fuel pump wiring for open circuit. RESTORE vehicle. RETEST system.
	• Verify continuity between Pin C1-2 and Pin C1-4 ground of EIC connector.			
	• Is resistance close to zero ohms?			
D4	VERIFY FUEL PUMP SENDER RESISTANCE OVER RANGE			
	• Remove fuel pump (fuel level sensor and pump).	Yes	▶	REPLACE fuel pump.
	• Measure resistance while moving float rod arm slowly from empty to full.	No	▶	INSPECT fuel pump wiring connector female terminals to flash or loose fit. SERVICE as required. RESTORE vehicle. RETEST system.
	• Does resistance exceed 181 ohms at any time?			

FM9099500368000X

Fig. 5   Pinpoint test D

TEST STEP		RESULT	▶	ACTION TO TAKE
E1	CHECK FUEL PUMP WIRING RESISTANCE AT EIC			
	• Disconnect battery ground cable. • Remove instrument cluster and secure connectors from shorting. • With an ohmmeter, measure resistance between Pin C1-6 and Pin C1-8 (SIG GND) of harness. • Verify that the resistance is 14 ohms or greater (normally 15 to 160 ohms). • Is resistance at least 14 ohms?	Yes	▶	REPLACE EIC. AFFIX odometer sticker to door pillar. RESTORE vehicle. RETEST system.
		No	▶	GO to E2.
E2	CHECK FUEL PUMP WIRING			
	• Lower fuel tank to gain access to fuel pump (FP) module connector. • Unplug connector at fuel pump (FP) module. • Measure the resistance between Pin C1-6 and Pin C1-8 (GND) of harness. • Verify that resistance is greater than 10 K ohms. • Is resistance at least 10 K ohms?	Yes	▶	REPLACE fuel pump. RESTORE vehicle. RETEST system.
		No	▶	SERVICE fuel pump wiring for short circuit. RESTORE vehicle. RETEST system.

FM9099500369000X

Fig. 6   Pinpoint test E

TEST STEP		RESULT	▶	ACTION TO TAKE
F1	CHECK FUEL GAUGE RESPONSE			
	• Disconnect battery ground cable. • Lower fuel tank and gain access to fuel pump (FP) module connections. • Connect a resistor value of between 170-100 ohms. • Reconnect battery. • Turn ignition switch to the RUN position. Display 1/2 tank or above fuel level. • Turn ignition switch to OFF. Disconnect battery. • Remove 170-100 ohms resistor. • Connect a 43 ohm (± 1 percent) resistor in place of fuel pump (FP)module. Verify value with ohm meter. • Reconnect battery. NOTE: Allow at least 30 seconds for cluster to read level. • Turn ignition switch to RUN. • FUEL REMAIN should read 3 to 4 GAL (13 to 15 LTR). • Is fuel gauge correct?	Yes	▶	TURN ignition switch to OFF. GO to F3.
		No	▶	TURN ignition switch to OFF. Leave 43 ohm resistor connected. GO to F2.
F2	CHECK HARNESS RESISTANCE			
	• Disconnect battery ground cable. • Remove EIC and secure connectors from shorting. • Measure resistance between Pin C1-6 and Pin C1-8 (GND) with 43 ohm resistor in place. • Is resistance within range?	Yes	▶	REPLACE EIC. AFFIX odometer sticker to door pillar. RESTORE vehicle. RETEST system.
		No	▶	SERVICE Circuit 29 (Y/W). RESTORE vehicle. RETEST system.
F3	CHECK FUEL TANK SENDING UNIT AND PUMP			
	• Disconnect battery ground cable. • Check fuel pump (FP) module for binding, sticking, misalignment, etc. • Check sender resistance not to exceed 181 ohms while moving arm slowly from fuel to empty. • Check fuel sender resistance. Resistance should be 135 to 165 ohms of full stop and 14 to 18 ohms at empty stop. • Is fuel pump (FP) module resistance within limits specified?	Yes	▶	GO to F4.
		No	▶	SERVICE or REPLACE fuel pump (FP) module. RESTORE vehicle. RETEST system.

FM9099500370010X

Fig. 7   Pinpoint test F (Part 1 of 2)

TEST STEP		RESULT	▶	ACTION TO TAKE
F4	CHECK FUEL TANK			
	• Check fuel tank for dents, bulges or other damage. • Check for proper installation of fuel tube. • Is fuel tank OK?	Yes	▶	System OK. Fault caused by other vehicle system(s). RESTORE vehicle.
		No	▶	REPLACE fuel tank or fuel tube. RESTORE vehicle. RETEST system.

FM9099500370020X

Fig. 7   Pinpoint test F (Part 2 of 2)

TEST STEP		RESULT	▶	ACTION TO TAKE
G1	CHECK FOR TEMPERATURE SENDER SHORT			
	• Unplug engine coolant temperature (ECT) sensor connector. • Turn ignition switch to RUN. • Does temperature gauge indicate COLD with bottom bar lit?	Yes	▶	REPLACE ECT sensor. RESTORE vehicle. RETEST system.
		No	▶	GO to G2.
G2	CHECK FOR SHORT IN WIRING			
	• Disconnect battery ground cable. • Unplug engine coolant temperature (ECT) sensor connector. • Disconnect connector C1 and connector C2 from EIC. • Measure resistance between connector C1 Pin 4 and Pin C1-8 (GND). • Is resistance greater than 15 K ohms?	Yes	▶	REPLACE EIC. AFFIX odometer sticker to door pillar. RESTORE vehicle. RETEST system.
		No	▶	SERVICE both Circuit 39 (R/W) and 875 (BK/LB, Crown Victoria/Grand Marquis) as required. RESTORE vehicle. RETEST system.

Fig. 8   Pinpoint test G

TEST STEP		RESULT	▶	ACTION TO TAKE
H1	CHECK TEMPERATURE GAUGE WIRING			
	• Unplug connector to engine coolant temperature (ECT) sensor and connect a jumper in place of ECT sensor. • Turn ignition switch to RUN. • Gauge should give a short circuit indication. (Blinking thermometer symbol and top two and bottom two bars of gauge lit.) • Does gauge indicate short circuit?	Yes	▶	GO to H3. REMOVE jumper. REPLACE ECT sensor RETEST system.
		No	▶	GO to H2.
H2	CHECK WIRING AT CLUSTER			
	• Disconnect battery ground cable. • Disconnect C1 and C2 connectors from EIC. • Connect jumper in place of engine coolant temperature (ECT) sensor. • Verify continuity between Pin C2-21 and Pin C1-4 of harness. • Is there continuity?	Yes	▶	REPLACE EIC. AFFIX odometer sticker to door pillar. RESTORE vehicle. RETEST system.
		No	▶	SERVICE wiring Circuit 39 (R/W) and/or 876 (PK/O, Town Car), 875 (BK/LB, Crown Victoria/Grand Marquis). RESTORE vehicle. RETEST system.
H3	CHECK ENGINE COOLANT TEMPERATURE (ECT) SENSOR			
	• Warm up engine to normal operating temperature. • Measure resistance of engine coolant temperature (ECT) sensor. • Is resistance greater than 8 K ohms?	Yes	▶	GO to H4.
		No	▶	REPLACE EIC. AFFIX odometer sticker to door pillar. RESTORE vehicle. RETEST system.

FM9099500371010X

Fig. 9   Pinpoint test H (Part 1 of 2)

TEST STEP		RESULT	▶	ACTION TO TAKE
H4	CHECK COOLING SYSTEM			
	• Check thermostat, coolant level, etc., for proper operation. • Is cooling system OK?	Yes	▶	REPLACE ECT sensor. RESTORE vehicle. RETEST system.
		No	▶	SERVICE cooling system as required RESTORE vehicle. RETEST system.

FM9099500371020X

Fig. 9   Pinpoint test H (Part 2 of 2)

TEST STEP		RESULT	▶	ACTION TO TAKE
J1	REVIEW OPERATION/CONDITION			
	NOTE: Safety belt warning chime will not beep if another sound is being produced. Driver alert only given for temperatures above normal band. • Turn ignition switch to RUN. • Press any message center switch module button and listen for beep. • Does beep sound?	Yes	▶	System OK.
		No	▶	GO to Pinpoint Test C.

Fig. 10   Pinpoint test J

Fig. 11 Pinpoint test K

TEST STEP	RESULT		ACTION TO TAKE
K1 CHECK SPEEDOMETER READING • Test drive vehicle above 8 km/h (5 mph) and look for: — Speedometer reading — Odometer changing • Verify that odometer advances when vehicle is driven forward. • **Does odometer advance with no speed indication?**	Yes	▶	REPLACE EIC. AFFIX odometer sticker to door pillar. RESTORE vehicle. RETEST system.
	No	▶	GO to K2.
K2 CHECK SPEED CONTROL • Test drive vehicle above 30 MPH, check speed control operation. • **Did speed control operate properly?**	Yes	▶	GO to K3.
	No	▶	GO to K4.
K3 CHECK CONTINUITY • Disconnect battery ground cable. • Disconnect connectors C1 and C2 at EIC. • Disconnect vehicle speed sensor. • Check continuity in Circuit 679 (GY/BK) and continuity to ground in Circuit 676 (PK/O). • **Is continuity present?**	Yes	▶	REPLACE EIC. AFFIX odometer sticker to door pillar. RESTORE vehicle. RETEST system.
	No	▶	SERVICE respective circuit. RESTORE vehicle. RETEST system.
K4 CHECK VSS • Disconnect vehicle speed sensor. • Measure resistance across vehicle speed sensor. • **Is resistance between 200-300 ohms?**	Yes	▶	CHECK Circuits 679(GY/BK) and 676(PK/O) for continuity. If circuits OK, CHECK driven gear and retainer clip. REPLACE if necessary. RESTORE vehicle. RETEST system.
	No	▶	REPLACE vehicle speed sensor. REFER to RESTORE vehicle. RETEST system.

FM9099500372000X

Fig. 12 Pinpoint test L

TEST STEP	RESULT		ACTION TO TAKE
L1 CHECK VEHICLE SPEED SENSOR DRIVE GEAR • Remove vehicle speed sensor from transmission and verify that correct drive gear is installed for vehicle transmission/axle/tire combination. • **Is drive gear correct?**	Yes	▶	GO to L2.
	No	▶	INSTALL correct gear with retaining clip. RESTORE vehicle. RETEST system.
L2 CHECK DRIVE GEAR ON TRANSMISSION OUTPUT SHAFT • Check that correct drive gear is installed on transmission output shaft. • **Is drive gear correct?**	Yes	▶	GO to L3.
	No	▶	INSTALL correct output shaft and/or gear. RESTORE vehicle. RETEST system.
L3 CHECK CONTINUITY • Disconnect battery ground cable. • Disconnect connectors C1 and C2 at EIC. • Check continuity in Circuit 679 (GY/BK) and 679 (C1-12, 136) continuity to ground in Circuit 875 (C1-8)(PK/O). • **Is continuity present?**	Yes	▶	GO to L4.
	No	▶	SERVICE respective circuit. RESTORE vehicle. RETEST system.
L4 CHECK VSS • Disconnect vehicle speed sensor. • Measure resistance across vehicle speed sensor. • **Is resistance between 200-300 ohms?**	Yes	▶	REPLACE EIC. AFFIX odometer sticker to door pillar. RESTORE vehicle. RETEST system.
	No	▶	REPLACE vehicle speed sensor. RESTORE vehicle. RETEST system.

FM9099500373000X

Fig. 13 Pinpoint test M

TEST STEP	RESULT		ACTION TO TAKE
M1 CHECK SPEED SENSOR DRIVE GEAR • Remove vehicle speed sensor from transmission. • Check that all gear teeth are in good condition, retainer clip is installed and gear does not slip on shaft. • **Is vehicle speed sensor in good condition?**	Yes	▶	GO to L3.
	No	▶	REPLACE drive gear and/or retaining clip. RESTORE vehicle. RETEST system.

FM9099500374000X

Fig. 14 Pinpoint test N (Part 1 of 2)

TEST STEP	RESULT		ACTION TO TAKE
N1 CHECK SPEED CONTROL SERVO • Disconnect connector from speed control servo. • **Does speed control indicator go off?**	Yes	▶	REPLACE speed control servo. VERIFY proper operation. RESTORE vehicle. RETEST system.
	No	▶	GO to N2.

FM9099500375010X

Fig. 14 Pinpoint test N (Part 2 of 2)

TEST STEP	RESULT		ACTION TO TAKE
N2 CHECK EIC • Disconnect cluster connector C2. • **Does speed control indicator go off?**	Yes	▶	CHECK Circuit 203(O/LB). SERVICE as required. RESTORE vehicle. RETEST system.
	No	▶	REPLACE EIC. AFFIX odometer sticker to door pillar. RESTORE vehicle. RETEST system.

FM9099500375020X

Fig. 15 Pinpoint test P

TEST STEP	RESULT		ACTION TO TAKE
P1 CHECK VOLTAGE AT SPEED CONTROL SERVO • Disconnect connector from speed control servo. • Turn ignition switch to RUN. • Measure voltage between Circuit 203(O/LB) and Circuit 676(PK/O, Town Car), 57(BK, Crown Victoria/Grand Marquis). • **Is voltage approximately 5V?**	Yes	▶	GO to P2.
	No	▶	GO to P3.
P2 CHECK CONTINUITY • Disconnect EIC. • Check continuity in Circuit 203(O/LB). • **Is continuity present?**	Yes	▶	REPLACE EIC. AFFIX odometer sticker to door pillar. RESTORE vehicle. RETEST system.
	No	▶	SERVICE Circuit 203(O/LB). RESTORE vehicle. RETEST system.
P3 VERIFY POWER AT SPEED CONTROL SERVO • Check for battery voltage at the speed control servo connector in Circuit 295(LB/PK, Town Car), 296 (W/P, Crown Victoria/Grand Marquis). • **Is battery voltage present?**	Yes	▶	REPLACE speed control servo. REFER to Section 10-03. RESTORE vehicle. RETEST system.
	No	▶	SERVICE Circuit 295(LB/PK) and/or fuse 4—Town Car. SERVICE Circuit 296(LB/PK) and/or fuse 8—Crown Victoria, Grand Marquis. RESTORE vehicle. RETEST system.

FM9099500376000X

Fig. 16 Pinpoint test Q

TEST STEP	RESULT		ACTION TO TAKE
Q1 DETERMINE IF SPEEDOMETER/ODOMETER MODULE IS ORIGINAL • Check for mileage sticker on door pillar. • **Is mileage sticker original?**	Yes	▶	REPLACE EIC. If odometer reading is known, program it into new EIC. If odometer reading is unknown, program in "S" 00000.5 with the circled S and zero miles in the odometer. RESTORE vehicle. RETEST system.
	No	▶	System OK. RESTORE vehicle.

FM9099500377000X

Fig. 17 Pinpoint test R

TEST STEP	RESULT		ACTION TO TAKE
R1 CHECK SPEEDOMETER • Verify that speedometer is operating properly. • **Does speedometer operate properly?**	Yes	▶	REPLACE EIC. Affix odometer sticker to door pillar. RESTORE vehicle. RETEST system.
	No	▶	GO to Pinpoint Test L.

FM9099500378000X

Fig. 18 Pinpoint test S

TEST STEP	RESULT		ACTION TO TAKE
S1 CHECK ODOMETER OPERATION • Check odometer to determine whether it accumulates and then loses 1.6 km (1.0 mile) or it will not accumulate mileage at all. • **Does odometer accumulate and then lose 1.6 km (1.0 mile)?**	Yes	▶	REPLACE EIC. AFFIX odometer sticker to door pillar. RESTORE vehicle. RETEST system.
	No	▶	GO to S2.
S2 VERIFY SPEEDOMETER • Verify that speedometer works properly. • **Does speedometer operate properly?**	Yes	▶	REPLACE EIC. AFFIX odometer sticker to door pillar. RESTORE vehicle. RETEST system.
	No	▶	GO to Pinpoint Test K.

FM9099500379000X

TEST STEP		RESULT	▶	ACTION TO TAKE
T1	CHECK MESSAGE CENTER DISPLAY			
	• Check message center display to determine whether it is showing 0 MPG, 99L / 100 KM or 99 MPG, 0L / 100 KM. • Is message center display showing 0 MPG, 99 L/ 100 Km?	Yes No	▶ ▶	GO to T2. GO to T3.
T2	CHECK SPEEDOMETER OPERATION			
	• Verify that speedometer is operating properly. • Does speedometer operate properly?	Yes No	▶ ▶	REPLACE EIC. AFFIX odometer sticker to door pillar. RESTORE vehicle. RETEST system. GO to Pinpoint Test K.
T3	OBSERVE O/D OFF INDICATOR			
	• Test drive vehicle with O/D off selected. • Does O/D off indicator flash?	Yes No	▶ ▶	(flow output interrupted by EEC system failure). GO to T4.
T4	CHECK CONTINUITY OF CIRCUIT 205 (FUEL FLOW)			
	• Verify continuity and absence of shorts in Circuit 205 (DB/LG). • Is wiring OK?	Yes No	▶ ▶	GO to T4. SERVICE wiring Circuit 205 (DB/LG) as required. RESTORE vehicle. RETEST system.

Fig. 19   Pinpoint test T (Part 1 of 2)

FM9099500380010X

TEST STEP		RESULT	▶	ACTION TO TAKE
T5	ENTER SELF TEST MODE			
	• Turn ignition switch to OFF. • Push and hold E/M and <SELECT (left) buttons together. • Turn ignition switch to START while holding buttons. • Release buttons when cluster lights. • Allow engine to run during remainder of test. • Observe odometer. • Does odometer flash?	Yes No	▶ ▶	REPLACE EIC. AFFIX odometer sticker to door pillar. RESTORE vehicle. RETEST system. GO to T5.
T6	ENTER DISPLAY TEST MODE			
	• Push Select> (right) button once and observe display. • Is the display the same as in Step 1 of segment displays in inspection and verification?	Yes No	▶ ▶	GO to T7. GO to T5.
T7	ENTER A/D, DIGITAL PORT TEST MODE			
	• Push E/M and <SELECT (left) buttons together once. Observe odometer display, left two digits. • Does odometer's left two digits read "0A"?	Yes No	▶ ▶	GO to T8. GO to T5.
T8	ENTER FUEL FLOW INPUT TEST MODE			
	• Push SELECT> (right) button twice quickly. • Observe left two odometer digits change to "1b." • Repeat this step four times until odometer left two digits read "5F." (Left two digits of odometer will advance: 0A, 1B, 2C, 3D, 4E, 5F, 60, 71, 0A... etc.) • Select 5F Observe the right four digits of the odometer select 5F then observe display. The frequency of the fuel flow pulses from the PCM is shown. (Step on accelerator.) • "0000" indicates no fuel flow pulses received from the PCM. • Any other number indicates fuel flow pulses are being received from the PCM. • Do right four digits read "0000" (no fuel pulses)?	Yes No	▶ ▶	TURN ignition switch to OFF to exit test modes. System OK. RECHECK Circuit 205; if OK then REPLACE powertrain control module. RESTORE vehicle. RETEST system. REPLACE EIC. AFFIX odometer sticker to door pillar. RESTORE vehicle. RETEST system.

Fig. 19   Pinpoint test T (Part 2 of 2)

FM9099500380020X

TEST STEP		RESULT	▶	ACTION TO TAKE
U1	CHECK FUEL GAUGE			
	• Verify that fuel gauge is operating properly. • Does gauge operate properly?	Yes No	▶ ▶	GO to U2. REFER to Fuel Gauge Diagnosis in Symptom Chart.
U2	CHECK SPEEDOMETER			
	• Verify that speedometer is operating properly. • Does speedometer operate properly?	Yes No	▶ ▶	GO to Pinpoint Test T. REFER to Speedometer Diagnosis in Symptom Chart.

Fig. 20   Pinpoint test U

FM9099500381000X

TEST STEP		RESULT	▶	ACTION TO TAKE
V1	CHECK EIC FOR WARNINGS			
	• Turn ignition switch to RUN. • Wait past prove-out time. • Check EIC for DOOR AJAR warning to determine whether warning is always on or never on. • Is door ajar warning always on?	Yes No	▶ ▶	GO to V2. GO to V4.

Fig. 21   Pinpoint test V (Part 1 of 2)

FM9099500382010X

TEST STEP		RESULT	▶	ACTION TO TAKE
V2	CHECK DOOR OPEN WARNING LAMP SWITCHES			
	• The following steps are to be repeated for each door open warning lamp switch. Start with the driver's door, then front passenger's, then rear passenger's door. • Turn ignition switch to OFF. This resets the warning. • Disconnect door open warning lamp switch connector at door open warning lamp switch. • Turn ignition switch to RUN. • Check message center for warning. • Repeat until no warning is displayed or all door open warning lamp switches are disconnected. • Is warning still displayed?	Yes No	▶ ▶	GO to V4. GO to V3.
V3	LIGHTING CONTROL MODULE CHECK			
	• Unplug lighting control module. • Is warning still present?	Yes No	▶ ▶	GO to V4. SERVICE lighting control module.
V4	CHECK CIRCUIT 627 (BK/O)			
	• Turn ignition switch to OFF. • Disconnect electronic instrument cluster. • Check continuity to ground in Circuit 627 (BK/O). • Is continuity to ground present?	Yes No	▶ ▶	SERVICE Circuit 627 (BK/O) for short to ground. RESTORE vehicle. RETEST system. GO to V5.
V5	CHECK POWER AND GROUNDS			
	• Check voltage on the following pins:	Yes No	▶ ▶	GO to V6. SERVICE as required. RESTORE vehicle. RETEST system.

Pin	Circuit Number	Voltage
C1-7	296 (W/P)	12V (Hot At All Times)
C1-9	295 (LB/PK)	12V (Hot In RUN)
C3-7	489 (PK/BK)	12V (Hot In RUN)
C3-2	295 (LB/PK)	12V (Hot In RUN)
C1-8	875 (PK/O)	0V
C3-1	875 (PK/O)	0V

	• Are all voltages as specified?			
V6	CHECK DOOR OPEN WARNING LAMP SWITCH			
	• Turn ignition switch to OFF. • Pull connector off of the problem door open warning lamp switch. • Connect a jumper wire from Circuit 627 (BK/O) at the harness connector to ground. • Turn ignition switch to RUN. • Check message center for warning. • Is warning displayed?	Yes No	▶ ▶	SERVICE door open warning lamp switch. RESTORE vehicle. RETEST system. REMOVE jumper. GO to V7. RESTORE vehicle. RETEST system.
V7	CHECK WIRING			
	• Turn ignition switch to OFF. • Disconnect electronic instrument cluster. • Check continuity in Circuit 627 (BK/O). • Is continuity present?	Yes No	▶ ▶	REPLACE EIC. AFFIX odometer sticker to door pillar. RESTORE vehicle. RETEST system. SERVICE Circuit 627 (BK/O) for open. RESTORE vehicle. RETEST system.

Fig. 21   Pinpoint test V (Part 2 of 2)

FM9099500382020X

TEST STEP		RESULT	▶	ACTION TO TAKE
W1	CHECK EIC FOR WARNINGS			
	• Turn ignition switch to RUN. • Wait past prove-out time. • Check EIC for TRUNK AJAR warning to determine whether the warning is always on or never on. • Is trunk ajar warning always on?	Yes No	▶ ▶	GO to W2. GO to W5.
W2	CHECK LUGGAGE COMPARTMENT DOOR OPEN WARNING LAMP SWITCH			
	• Turn ignition switch to OFF. This resets the warning. • Pull connector off of luggage compartment door open warning lamp switch. • Turn ignition switch to RUN. • Check EIC for warning. • Is warning displayed?	Yes No	▶ ▶	GO to W3. SERVICE luggage compartment door open warning lamp switch. RESTORE vehicle. RETEST system.
W3	LIGHTING CONTROL MODULE CHECK			
	NOTE: LCM provides pull-up to battery for EIC to keep warning off. If LCM is inoperative or removed, EIC trunk ajar warning stays on. • Disconnect trunk ajar switch. • Remove EIC. • With ignition switch in RUN position, check for battery voltage at Pin C2-27, Circuit 486. • Is battery voltage present?	Yes No	▶ ▶	GO to W4. SERVICE LCM.
W4	CHECK CIRCUIT 486 (BR/W)			
	• Turn ignition switch to OFF. • Disconnect electronic instrument cluster. • Check continuity to ground in Circuit 486 (BR/W). • Is there continuity to ground?	Yes No	▶ ▶	SERVICE Circuit 486 (BR/W) for short. RESTORE vehicle. RETEST system. REPLACE EIC. AFFIX odometer sticker to door pillar. RESTORE vehicle. RETEST system.
W5	CHECK POWER AND GROUNDS			
	• Check voltage on the following pins:	Yes No	▶ ▶	GO to W6. SERVICE as required. RESTORE vehicle. RETEST system.

Pin	Circuit Number	Voltage
C1-7	797/54 (W/P)	12V (Hot At All Times)
C1-9	295 (LB/PK)	12V (Hot In RUN)
C3-7	489 (PK/BK)	12V (Hot In RUN)
C3-2	295 (LB/PK)	12V (Hot In RUN)
C1-8	875 (PK/O)	0V
C3-1	875 (PK/O)	0V

	• Are all voltages as specified?			
W6	CHECK LUGGAGE COMPARTMENT DOOR OPEN WARNING LAMP SWITCH			
	• Turn ignition switch to OFF. • Pull connector off of the luggage compartment door open warning lamp switch. • Connect a jumper wire from Circuit 486 (BR/W) at the harness connector to ground. • Turn ignition switch to RUN. • Check EIC for warning. • Is warning displayed?	Yes No	▶ ▶	SERVICE luggage compartment door open warning lamp switch. RESTORE vehicle. RETEST system. REMOVE jumper. GO to W7.

Fig. 22   Pinpoint test W (Part 1 of 2)

FM9099500383010X

TEST STEP		RESULT	▶	ACTION TO TAKE
W7	CHECK WIRING			
	• Turn ignition switch to OFF. • Disconnect electronic instrument cluster. • Check continuity in Circuit 486 (BR/W). • **Is there continuity present?**	Yes	▶	REPLACE EIC. AFFIX odometer sticker to door pillar. RESTORE vehicle. RETEST system.
		No	▶	SERVICE Circuit 486 (BR/W) for open. RESTORE vehicle. RETEST system.

FM9099500383020X

Fig. 22   Pinpoint test W (Part 2 of 2)

TEST STEP		RESULT	▶	ACTION TO TAKE
X1	CHECK CHARGING SYSTEM VOLTAGE			
	• Start engine and check for warning. Watch for several minutes. • Check battery voltage. • **Is the voltage normal (above 14 volts) for engine at fast idle?**	Yes	▶	GO to X2.
		No	▶	SERVICE generator. RESTORE vehicle. RETEST system.
X2	CHECK HARNESS TO GENERATOR			
	• Disconnect generator. • Connect a jumper to ground from Circuit 904 (LG/R) near the generator. • **Does charge warning go away?**	Yes	▶	SERVICE the generator. RESTORE vehicle. RETEST system.
		No	▶	GO to X3.
X3	CHECK HARNESS TO EIC			
	• Turn ignition switch to OFF. • Turn ignition switch to RUN but do not start engine. • Remove jumper. • Measure voltage at generator from Circuit 904 (LG/R) to ground. • **Is it greater than 4 volts?**	Yes	▶	GO to X5.
		No	▶	GO to X4.
X4	CHECK EIC INTEGRAL ALTERNATOR REGULATOR RESISTOR AND HARNESS			
	• Turn ignition switch to OFF. • Remove EIC. • Check for loose or corroded screws on generator warning lamp shunt resistor on rear of EIC. • Check that resistor is 400-600 ohms. • Check continuity from resistor screws to Circuit 904 (LG/R) at connector. • Check for short to ground on Circuit 904. • **Has any check failed?**	Yes	▶	SERVICE as required to obtain over 4 volts. RESTORE vehicle. RETEST system.
		No	▶	SERVICE Circuit 489 (PK/BK, Town Car), 88 (BK/W, Crown Victoria/Grand Marquis) of connector C3. RESTORE vehicle. RETEST system.
X5	CHECK EIC WIRING FOR OPEN CIRCUIT			
	• Turn ignition switch to OFF. • Disconnect instrument cluster. • Check for continuity in Circuit 904, (LG/R). • **Is there continuity?**	Yes	▶	REPLACE EIC. AFFIX odometer sticker to door pillar. RESTORE vehicle. RETEST system.
		No	▶	SERVICE Circuit 904 (LG/R). RESTORE vehicle. RETEST system.

FM9099500384000X

Fig. 23   Pinpoint test X

TEST STEP		RESULT	▶	ACTION TO TAKE
Y1	CHECK EIC FOR WARNINGS			
	• Turn ignition switch to RUN. • Wait past prove-out time. • Check EIC for AIR SUSPENSION warning to determine whether the warning is always on or never on. • **Is AIR SUSPENSION warning always on?**	Yes	▶	GO to Y2.
		No	▶	GO to Y4.
Y2	CHECK AIR SUSPENSION CONTROL MODULE			
	• Disconnect air suspension control module. • Turn ignition switch to RUN. • Check EIC for warning. • **Is warning displayed?**	Yes	▶	GO to Y3.
		No	▶	SERVICE air suspension control module. RESTORE vehicle. RETEST system.
Y3	CHECK CONTINUITY			
	• Turn ignition switch to OFF. • Disconnect EIC. • Check continuity in Circuit 419 (DG/LG). • **Is continuity present?**	Yes	▶	REPLACE EIC. AFFIX odometer sticker to door pillar. RESTORE vehicle. RETEST system.
		No	▶	SERVICE Circuit 419 (DG/LG). RESTORE vehicle. RETEST system.
Y4	CHECK FOR POWER AND GROUNDS			
	• Check voltage on the following pins:	Yes	▶	GO to Y5.
		No	▶	SERVICE as required. RESTORE vehicle. RETEST system.

Pin	Circuit Number	Voltage
C1-7	797 (W/P)	12V (Hot At All Times)
C1-9	295 (LB/PK)	12V (Hot In RUN)
C3-7	489 (PK/BK)	12V (Hot In RUN)
C3-2	295 (LB/PK)	12V (Hot In RUN)
C1-8	875 (PK/O)	0V
C3-1	875 (PK/O)	0V

	• **Are all voltages as specified?**			
Y5	CHECK AIR SUSPENSION MODULE			
	• Turn ignition switch to OFF. • Disconnect connector at air suspension control module. • Connect a jumper wire from Circuit 419 (DG/LG) at harness connector to ground. • Turn ignition switch to RUN. • Check EIC for warning. • **Is warning displayed?**	Yes	▶	SERVICE air suspension control module. RESTORE vehicle. RETEST system.
		No	▶	GO to Y6.
Y6	CHECK CONTINUITY			
	• Remove jumper. • Disconnect EIC. • Check continuity in Circuit 419 (DG/LG). • **Is continuity present?**	Yes	▶	REPLACE EIC. AFFIX odometer sticker to door pillar. RESTORE vehicle. RETEST system.
		No	▶	SERVICE Circuit 419 (DG/LG). RESTORE vehicle. RETEST system.

FM9099500385000X

Fig. 24   Pinpoint test Y

TEST STEP		RESULT	▶	ACTION TO TAKE
AA1	CHECK SYSTEM AND WARNING			
	• Drain fluid from windshield washer reservoir for "warning never on." • Add fluid to windshield washer reservoir for "warning always on." • Turn ignition switch to RUN. • Wait past prove-out time. • Check message center for low WASHER FLUID warnings to determine whether the warning is always on or never on. • **Is warning always on?**	Yes	▶	GO to AA2.
		No	▶	GO to AA4.
AA2	CHECK WINDSHIELD WASHER RESERVOIR FLUID LEVEL SENSOR			
	• Turn ignition switch to OFF. • Disconnect harness connector from windshield washer reservoir fluid level sensor. • Turn ignition switch to RUN. • Check EIC for windshield washer fluid warning. • **Is warning displayed?**	Yes	▶	GO to AA3.
		No	▶	SERVICE windshield washer reservoir fluid level sensor. RESTORE vehicle. RETEST system.
AA3	CHECK CONTINUITY			
	• Turn ignition switch to OFF. • Disconnect EIC. • Check continuity in Circuit 82 (PK/Y). • **Is continuity present?**	Yes	▶	REPLACE EIC. AFFIX odometer sticker to door pillar. RESTORE vehicle. RETEST system.
		No	▶	SERVICE Circuit 82 (PK/Y) for short to ground. RESTORE vehicle. RETEST system.
AA4	CHECK FOR POWER AND GROUNDS			
	• Check voltage on the following pins:	Yes	▶	GO to AA5.
		No	▶	SERVICE as required. RESTORE vehicle. RETEST system.

Pin	Circuit Number	Voltage
C1-7	797 (W/P)	12V (Hot At All Times)
C1-9	295 (LB/PK)	12V (Hot In RUN)
C3-7	489 (PK/BK)	12V (Hot In RUN)
C3-2	295 (LB/PK)	12V (Hot In RUN)
C1-8	875 (PK/O)	0V
C3-1	875 (PK/O)	0V

	• **Are all voltages as specified?**			
AA5	CHECK WINDSHIELD WASHER RESERVOIR FLUID LEVEL SENSOR			
	• Turn ignition switch to OFF. • Unplug harness connector from windshield washer reservoir fluid level sensor. • Connect a jumper wire across the 2 pins of harness connector. • Turn ignition switch to RUN. • Check messages for low WASHER FLUID warning. • **Is warning displayed?**	Yes	▶	SERVICE windshield washer reservoir fluid level sensor. RESTORE vehicle. RETEST system.
		No	▶	GO to AA6.
AA6	CHECK CONTINUITY			
	• Turn ignition switch to OFF. • Disconnect EIC. • Check continuity in Circuit 82 (PK/Y) and continuity to ground in Circuit 875 (PK/O) Crown Victoria, Grand Marquis. • **Is continuity present?**	Yes	▶	REPLACE EIC. AFFIX odometer sticker to door pillar. RESTORE vehicle. RETEST system.
		No	▶	SERVICE respective circuit. RESTORE vehicle. RETEST system.

FM9099500386000X

Fig. 25   Pinpoint test AA

Fig. 26 Pinpoint test BB

TEST STEP	RESULT	▶	ACTION TO TAKE
BB1 CHECK EIC FOR MIL WARNING			
• Check for warning messages. • **Is CHECK ENGINE warning displayed?**	Yes	▶	
	No	▶	PERFORM Diagnostic Self Test. System OK.

Fig. 26   Pinpoint test BB   FM9099500387000X

Fig. 27 Pinpoint test CC

TEST STEP	RESULT	▶	ACTION TO TAKE
CC1 CHECK EIC FOR WARNING			
• Check EIC for LH turn indicator to determine if the LH turn indicator is always on or never on. • **Is LH turn indicator always on?**	Yes No	▶ ▶	GO to CC2. GO to CC3.
CC2 ISOLATE LH TURN INDICATOR SOURCE			
• Remove EIC as outlined. • Disconnect connector C3 from EIC. • Measure voltage Circuit 3 without turn signal activated. • **Is voltage 0V?**	Yes No	▶ ▶	REPLACE electronic instrument cluster. RESTORE vehicle. RETEST system. SERVICE Circuit 3 (LG/W). Steering Column Switches diagnosis.
CC3 CHECK FOR TURN SIGNAL SWITCH POWER INPUT			
• Remove EIC as outlined. • Using the turn signal lever, signal for a LH turn. • Using a multimeter, measure voltage at connector Pin C3-6, Circuit 3 (LG/W). • **Is voltage greater than 9 volts?**	Yes No	▶ ▶	REPLACE EIC. SERVICE Circuit 3 (LG/W) for open circuit. for turn signal and windshield wiper switch continuity test. RESTORE vehicle. RETEST system.

Fig. 27   Pinpoint test CC   FM9099500388000X

Fig. 28 Pinpoint test DD

TEST STEP	RESULT	▶	ACTION TO TAKE
DD1 CHECK EIC FOR WARNING			
• Check EIC for RH turn indicator to determine if the RH turn indicator is always on or never on. • **Is RH turn indicator always on?**	Yes No	▶ ▶	GO to DD2. GO to DD3.
DD2 ISOLATE RH TURN INDICATOR SOURCE			
• Remove EIC as outlined. • Disconnect connector C3 from EIC. • Measure voltage at Circuit 3 without turn signal activated. • **Is voltage 0V?**	Yes No	▶ ▶	REPLACE electronic instrument cluster. RESTORE vehicle. RETEST system. SERVICE Circuit 3.
DD3 CHECK FOR TURN SIGNAL SWITCH POWER INPUT			
• Remove EIC as outlined. • Using the turn signal lever, signal for a RH turn. • Using a multimeter, measure voltage at connector Pin C3-5, Circuit 2 (W/LB). • **Is voltage greater than 9 volts?**	Yes No	▶ ▶	REPLACE EIC. SERVICE Circuit 2 (W/LB) for open circuit. for turn signal and windshield wiper switch continuity test. RESTORE vehicle. RETEST system.

Fig. 28   Pinpoint test DD   FM9099500389000X

Fig. 29 Pinpoint test EE

TEST STEP	RESULT	▶	ACTION TO TAKE
EE1 VERIFY CONDITION			
NOTE: Make sure the light switches are in proper positions when checking circuit operation. • Turn ignition switch to RUN. • Wait past prove-out time. • Check EIC displays to determine whether the indicator is always on or never on. • **Is HIGH BEAM indicator always on?**	Yes No	▶ ▶	GO to EE2. GO to EE4.
EE2 CHECK EIC FOR SHORT CIRCUIT			
• Disconnect connector C3 at EIC. • Measure voltage at C3-4. • **Is voltage 0V with ignition ON, headlamps ON, highbeams OFF?**	Yes No	▶ ▶	REPLACE EIC. AFFIX odometer sticker to door pillar. RESTORE vehicle. RETEST system. GO to EE3.
EE3 CHECK FOR SHORT TO BATTERY			
• Reconnect EIC. • Disconnect HI-LO Beam Relay—Town Car, multi-function switch—Crown Victoria/Grand Marquis. • **Is HIGH BEAM indicator illuminated?**	Yes No	▶ ▶	SERVICE short to battery in Circuit 12 (LG/BK) and/or Circuit 932 (GY/W). CHECK daytime running lamps control module (if equipped) for short to battery. SERVICE as required. RESTORE vehicle. RETEST system. REPLACE HI-LO beam relay—Town Car, multi-function switch—Crown Victoria/Grand Marquis. RESTORE vehicle. RETEST system.
EE4 CHECK EIC FOR OPEN CIRCUIT			
• Turn ignition switch to OFF. • Disconnect EIC. • Connect a jumper wire from high beam input pin of EIC (Pin 4 of C3 connector) to positive battery terminal. Supply ground to ground pin of EIC (Pin 1 of C3 connector). • Measure voltage at C4. • **Is battery voltage present?**	Yes No	▶ ▶	GO to EE5. REPLACE EIC. AFFIX odometer sticker to door pillar. RESTORE vehicle. RETEST system.
EE5 CHECK CIRCUITRY			
• Reconnect EIC. • Disconnect HI-LO beam replay—Town Car, multi-function switch—Crown Victoria/Grand Marquis. • Jump Circuit 12 (LG/BK) at the HI-LO beam relay (Town Car) multi-function switch (Crown Victoria/Grand Marquis) connector to positive battery terminal. • **Is HIGH BEAM indicator illuminated?**	Yes No	▶ ▶	GO to EE6. SERVICE Circuit 12 (LG/BK), Circuit 932 (GY/W), daytime running lamps control module (if equipped) as required. RESTORE vehicle. RETEST system.
EE6 CHECK CONTINUITY			
• Disconnect headlamp switch. • Check continuity in Circuit 502 (GY, Town Car) (15 R/Y, Crown Victoria/Grand Marquis). • Check continuity to power in Circuit 38 (BK/O). • **Is continuity present?**	Yes No	▶ ▶	REPLACE headlamp switch. RESTORE vehicle. RETEST system. SERVICE respective circuit. RESTORE vehicle. RETEST system.

Fig. 29   Pinpoint test EE   FM9099500390000X

Fig. 30 Pinpoint test FF (Part 1 of 2)

TEST STEP	RESULT	▶	ACTION TO TAKE
FF1 CHECK FOR VOLTAGE AT SAFETY BELT WARNING CHIME			
• Disconnect safety belt warning chime. • Connect a 12-volt test lamp between Circuit 295 (LB/PK, Town Car), 640 (R/Y, Crown Victoria/Grand Marquis) in warning chime connector and ground. • Turn ignition switch to RUN. • **Does test lamp light?**	Yes No	▶ ▶	GO to FF2. CHECK Circuit 295 (LB/PK, Town Car), 640 (R/Y, Crown Victoria/Grand Marquis) back to ignition switch. SERVICE as required. RESTORE vehicle. RETEST system.
FF2 CHECK FOR GROUND			
• Connect a 12-volt test lamp between Circuit 295 (LB/PK, Town Car), 640 (R/Y, Crown Victoria/Grand Marquis) and 57 (BK) in warning chime connector. • Turn ignition switch to RUN. • **Does test lamp light?**	Yes No	▶ ▶	GO to FF3. CHECK Circuit 57 (BK) back to ground. SERVICE as required. RESTORE vehicle. RETEST system.
FF3 CHECK CIRCUIT 450 (DG/LG) AND SAFETY BELT WARNING INDICATOR BULB			
• Connect jumper between Circuit 450 (DG/LG) and Circuit 295 (LB/PK, Town Car), 640 (R/Y, Crown Victoria/Grand Marquis) in warning chime connector. • Turn ignition switch to RUN. • **Does safety belt warning indicator light?**	Yes No	▶ ▶	GO to FF4. CHECK Circuit 450 (DG/LG) back to safety belt warning indicator bulb. CHECK bulb. SERVICE as required. RESTORE vehicle. RETEST system.
FF4 CHECK FOR GROUND AT CIRCUIT 85 (BR/LB)			
• Unbuckle driver side safety belt. • Connect a 12-volt test lamp between Circuit 85 (BR/LB) and Circuit 295 (LB/PK, Town Car), 640 (R/Y, Crown Victoria/Grand Marquis) in warning chime connector. • Turn ignition switch to RUN. • **Does test lamp light?**	Yes No	▶ ▶	GO to FF5. CHECK Circuits 85 (BR/LB) back to safety belt switch. SERVICE as required. RESTORE vehicle. RETEST system.
FF5 CHECK FOR GROUND AT CIRCUIT 158 (BK/PK)			
• Connect a 12-volt test lamp between Circuit 158 (BK/PK) and Circuit 295 (LB/PK, Town Car), 640 (R/Y, Crown Victoria/Grand Marquis) in warning chime connector. • Turn ignition switch to RUN. • **Does test lamp light?**	Yes No	▶ ▶	GO to FF6. CHECK Circuit 158 (BK/PK) back to ignition switch. SERVICE as required. RESTORE vehicle. RETEST system.
FF6 CHECK FOR VOLTAGE AT CIRCUIT 159 (R/PK)			
• Connect a 12-volt test lamp between Circuit 159 (R/PK) in warning chime connector and ground. • Open driver door. • **Does test lamp light?**	Yes No	▶ ▶	GO to FF7. CHECK Circuit 159 (R/PK) back to door open warning lamp switch. SERVICE as required. RESTORE vehicle. RETEST system.
FF7 CHECK FOR GROUND BETWEEN CIRCUIT 158 (BK/PK) AND 159 (R/PK)			
• Open driver door. • Connect a 12-volt test lamp between Circuit 158 (BK/PK) and 159 (R/PK) in warning chime connector. • Turn headlamp switch ON. • **Does test lamp light?**	Yes No	▶ ▶	GO to FF8. CHECK Circuit 158 (BK/PK), 112 (BK/Y) back to headlamp switch. SERVICE as required. RESTORE vehicle. RETEST system.

Fig. 30   Pinpoint test FF (Part 1 of 2)   FM9099500391010X

TEST STEP		RESULT	▶	ACTION TO TAKE
FF8	**CHECK FOR VOLTAGE**			
	• Connect a 12-volt test lamp between Circuit 294 (W/LB, Town Car), 296 (W/P, Crown Victoria/Grand Marquis) in warning chime connector and ground. • Turn ignition switch to ACC. • **Does test lamp light?**	Yes	▶	GO to FF9, if equipped with electronic instrument cluster. GO to FF10, if equipped with analog instrument cluster.
		No	▶	CHECK Circuit 294 (W/LB, Town Car), 296 (W/P, Crown Victoria/Grand Marquis) back to ignition switch. SERVICE as required. RESTORE vehicle. RETEST system.
FF9	**CHECK FOR GROUND AT CIRCUIT 183 (T/Y)**			
	• Connect a 12-volt test lamp between Circuit 183 (T/Y) and Circuit 294 (W/P, Crown Victoria/Grand Marquis) of warning chime connector. • Turn ignition switch to RUN position and press a button on the electronic instrument cluster. • **Does test lamp light momentarily?**	Yes	▶	GO to FF10.
		No	▶	REFER to Message Center diagnostics. SERVICE as required. RESTORE vehicle. RETEST system.
FF10	**CHECK WARNING CHIME MODULE OPERATION**			

	• Connect warning chime module.
	• Check for proper operation of:
	   — Safety belt warning
	   — Key-in-ignition warning
	   — Headlamp switch on warning
	   — Audible beep tone
	• **Do all warnings operate properly?**
		Yes	▶	System operating properly. RESTORE vehicle.

		No	▶	REPLACE safety belt warning chime. RESTORE vehicle. RETEST system.

FM9099500391020X

Fig. 30 Pinpoint test FF (Part 2 of 2)

TEST STEP		RESULT	▶	ACTION TO TAKE
GG4	**CHECK FOR POWER AND GROUNDS**			
	• Check voltage on the following pins:	Yes	▶	GO to GG5.
		No	▶	SERVICE as required. RESTORE vehicle. RETEST system.

Pin	Circuit Number	Voltage
C1-7	797 (W/P)	12V (Hot At All Times)
C1-9	295 (LB/PK)	12V (Hot In RUN)
C3-7	489 (PK/BK)	12V (Hot In RUN)
C3-2	295 (LB/PK)	12V (Hot In RUN)
C1-8	875 (PK/O)	0V
C3-1	875 (PK/O)	0V

TEST STEP		RESULT	▶	ACTION TO TAKE
	• **Are all voltages as specified?**			
GG5	**CHECK EIC FOR OPEN CIRCUIT**			
	• Turn ignition switch to OFF. • Disconnect connector at oil pressure sensor. • Connect a jumper wire from Circuit 31 (W/R) at harness connector to ground. • Turn ignition switch to RUN. • Check EIC for warning. • **Is LOW OIL PRESSURE warning illuminated?**	Yes	▶	REPLACE oil pressure sensor. RESTORE vehicle. RETEST system.
		No	▶	GO to GG6.
GG6	**CHECK CONTINUITY**			
	• Remove jumper. • Disconnect EIC. • Check continuity in Circuit 31 (W/R). • **Is continuity present?**	Yes	▶	REPLACE EIC. AFFIX odometer sticker to door pillar. RESTORE vehicle. RETEST system.
		No	▶	SERVICE Circuit 3 (W/R). RESTORE vehicle. RETEST system.

FM9099500392020X

Fig. 31 Pinpoint test GG (Part 2 of 2)

TEST STEP		RESULT	▶	ACTION TO TAKE
HH3	**CHECK CONTINUITY OF CIRCUIT 608 (BK/Y)**			
	• Turn ignition switch to OFF. • Disconnect EIC. • Check continuity in Circuit 608 (BK/Y). • **Is continuity present?**	Yes	▶	REPLACE EIC. AFFIX odometer sticker to door pillar. RESTORE vehicle. RETEST system.
		No	▶	SERVICE Circuit 608 (BK/Y). RESTORE vehicle. RETEST system.
HH4	**CHECK FOR POWER AND GROUNDS**			
	• Check voltage on the following pins:	Yes	▶	GO to HH5.
		No	▶	SERVICE as required. RESTORE vehicle. RETEST system.

Pin	Circuit Number	Voltage
C1-7	797 (W/P)	12V (Hot At All Times)
C1-9	295 (LB/PK)	12V (Hot In RUN)
C3-7	489 (PK/BK)	12V (Hot In RUN)
C3-2	295 (LB/PK)	12V (Hot In RUN)
C1-8	875 (PK/O)	0V
C3-1	875 (PK/O)	0V

TEST STEP		RESULT	▶	ACTION TO TAKE
	• **Are all voltages as specified?**			
HH5	**CHECK AIR BAG DIAGNOSTIC MONITOR**			
	WARNING: THE BACKUP POWER SUPPLY ENERGY MUST BE DEPLETED BEFORE ANY AIR BAG COMPONENT SERVICE IS PERFORMED AS PERSONAL INJURY MAY RESULT. TO DEPLETE BACKUP POWER SUPPLY ENERGY, DISCONNECT THE POSITIVE BATTERY CABLE AND WAIT ONE MINUTE. • Turn ignition switch to OFF. • Disconnect battery ground cable. • Disconnect positive battery cable and wait one minute. • Disconnect connector at air bag diagnostic monitor. • Connect a jumper wire from Circuit 608 (BK/Y) at harness connector to ground. • Reconnect positive battery cable. • Turn ignition switch to RUN. • Check EIC for warning. • **Is AIR BAG warning illuminated?**	Yes	▶	REPLACE air bag diagnostic monitor. RESTORE vehicle. RETEST system.
		No	▶	GO to HH6.
HH6	**CHECK AIR BAG INPUT CIRCUIT CONTINUITY**			
	• Remove jumper. • Disconnect EIC. • Check continuity in Circuit 608 (BK/Y). • **Is continuity present?**	Yes	▶	REPLACE EIC. AFFIX odometer sticker to door pillar. RESTORE vehicle. RETEST system.
		No	▶	SERVICE Circuit 608 (BK/Y). RESTORE vehicle. RETEST system.

FM9099500393020X

Fig. 32 Pinpoint test HH (Part 2 of 2)

TEST STEP		RESULT	▶	ACTION TO TAKE
GG1	**CHECK EIC FOR WARNINGS**			
	• Turn ignition switch to RUN. • Wait past prove-out time. • Check EIC display to determine whether the warning is always on or never on. • **Is LOW OIL PRESSURE warning always on?**	Yes	▶	GO to GG2.
		No	▶	GO to GG4.
GG2	**CHECK EIC FOR SHORT CIRCUIT**			
	• Disconnect oil pressure sensor. • Check EIC for warning. • **Is LOW OIL PRESSURE warning illuminated?**	Yes	▶	GO to GG3.
		No	▶	REPLACE oil pressure sensor. REFER to Section 03-00. RESTORE vehicle. RETEST system.
GG3	**CHECK CONTINUITY IN CIRCUIT 31 (W/R)**			
	• Turn ignition switch to OFF. • Disconnect EIC. • Check continuity in Circuit 31 (W/R). • **Is continuity present?**	Yes	▶	REPLACE EIC. AFFIX odometer sticker to door pillar. RESTORE vehicle. RETEST system.
		No	▶	SERVICE Circuit 31 (W/R). RESTORE vehicle. RETEST system.

FM9099500392010X

Fig. 31 Pinpoint test GG (Part 1 of 2)

TEST STEP		RESULT	▶	ACTION TO TAKE
HH1	**CHECK EIC FOR WARNINGS**			
	• Turn ignition switch to RUN. • Wait past prove-out time. • Check EIC display to determine whether the warning is always on or never on. • **Is AIR BAG warning always on?**	Yes	▶	GO to HH2.
		No	▶	GO to HH4.
HH2	**CHECK AIR BAG DIAGNOSTIC MONITOR**			
	NOTE: If the air bag warning indicator flashes on and off continuously it means that it is showing a diagnostic code. It does not mean that the air bag warning indicator needs to be serviced. **WARNING: THE BACKUP POWER SUPPLY ENERGY MUST BE DEPLETED BEFORE ANY AIR BAG COMPONENT SERVICE IS PERFORMED AS PERSONAL INJURY MAY RESULT. TO DEPLETE BACKUP POWER SUPPLY ENERGY, DISCONNECT THE POSITIVE BATTERY CABLE AND WAIT ONE MINUTE.** • Disconnect battery ground cable. • Disconnect positive battery cable and wait one minute. • Disconnect air bag diagnostic monitor. • Check EIC for warning. • **Is AIR BAG warning illuminated?**	Yes	▶	GO to HH3.
		No	▶	REPLACE air bag diagnostic monitor. RESTORE vehicle. RETEST system.

FM9099500393010X

Fig. 32 Pinpoint test HH (Part 1 of 2)

TEST STEP		RESULT	▶	ACTION TO TAKE
JJ1	**CHECK EIC FOR INDICATOR**			
	• Turn ignition switch to RUN. • Wait past prove-out time. • Check EIC display to determine whether the indicator is always on or never on. • **Is OVERDRIVE OFF indicator always on?**	Yes	▶	GO to JJ2.
		No	▶	GO to JJ4.

FM9099500394010X

Fig. 33 Pinpoint test JJ (Part 1 of 2)

TEST STEP		RESULT	▶	ACTION TO TAKE
JJ2	**CHECK PCM FOR SHORTED CIRCUIT**			
	• Disconnect powertrain control module. • Check EIC for indicator. • **Is OVERDRIVE OFF indicator illuminated?**	Yes	▶	GO to JJ3.
		No	▶	REPLACE powertrain control module.
JJ3	**CHECK CONTINUITY OF CIRCUIT 911 (W/LG)**			
	• Turn ignition switch to OFF. • Disconnect EIC. • Check continuity in Circuit 911 (W/LG). • **Is continuity present?**	Yes	▶	REPLACE EIC. RESTORE vehicle. RETEST system.
		No	▶	SERVICE Circuit 911 (W/LG). RESTORE vehicle. RETEST system.
JJ4	**CHECK FOR POWER AND GROUNDS**			
	• Check voltage on the following pins:	Yes	▶	GO to JJ5.
		No	▶	SERVICE as required. RESTORE vehicle. RETEST system.

Pin	Circuit Number	Voltage
C1-7	797 (W/P)	12V (Hot At All Times)
C1-9	295 (LB/PK)	12V (Hot In RUN)
C3-7	489 (PK/BK)	12V (Hot In RUN)
C3-2	295 (LB/PK)	12V (Hot In RUN)
C1-8	875 (PK/O)	0V
C3-1	875 (PK/O)	0V

TEST STEP		RESULT	▶	ACTION TO TAKE
	• **Are all voltages as specified?**			
JJ5	**CHECK PCM FOR OPEN CIRCUIT**			
	• Turn ignition switch to OFF. • Disconnect connector at powertrain control module. • Connect a jumper wire from Circuit 911 (W/LG) at harness connector to ground. • Turn ignition switch to RUN. • Check EIC for warning. • **Is OVERDRIVE OFF indicator illuminated?**	Yes	▶	REPLACE powertrain control module.
		No	▶	GO to JJ6.
JJ6	**CHECK INDICATOR SUPPLY CIRCUIT CONTINUITY**			
	• Remove jumper. • Disconnect EIC. • Check continuity in Circuit 911 (W/LG). • **Is continuity present?**	Yes	▶	REPLACE bulb in EIC. RESTORE vehicle. RETEST system.
		No	▶	SERVICE Circuit 911 (W/LG). RESTORE vehicle. RETEST system.

FM9099500394020X

Fig. 33 Pinpoint test JJ (Part 2 of 2)

TEST STEP	RESULT	▶	ACTION TO TAKE
KK1 CHECK DISPLAYS			
• Turn ignition switch to OFF. • Turn parking lamps on. • Check other displays: radio, message center switch module. • Do other displays illuminate properly?	Yes No	▶ ▶	GO to KK2. GO to Pinpoint Test Step A3.

FM9099500395010X

Fig. 34 Pinpoint test KK (Part 1 of 2)

TEST STEP	RESULT	▶	ACTION TO TAKE
KK2 CHECK EIC BULB			
• Check the bulb in the EIC. • Is bulb OK?	Yes No	▶ ▶	SERVICE Circuit 19 (LB/R). RESTORE vehicle. RETEST system. REPLACE bulb. RESTORE vehicle. RETEST system.

FM9099500395020X

Fig. 34 Pinpoint test KK (Part 2 of 2)

1996 Crown Victoria, Grand Marquis & Town Car

NOTE: Refer To Symptom Index In This Section Before Performing Any Pinpoint Tests.

INDEX

	Page No. 15-	Fig. No.
PINPOINT TESTS:		
Crown Victoria & Grand Marquis:		
Pinpoint Test A	67	3
Pinpoint Test B	67	4
Pinpoint Test C	67	5
Pinpoint Test D	68	6
Pinpoint Test E	68	7
Pinpoint Test F	68	8
Pinpoint Test G	68	9
Pinpoint Test H	69	10
Pinpoint Test J	69	11
Pinpoint Test K	69	12
Pinpoint Test L	69	13
Pinpoint Test M	69	14
Pinpoint Test N	69	15
Pinpoint Test P	69	16
Pinpoint Test Q	70	17
Pinpoint Test R	70	18
Pinpoint Test S	70	19
Pinpoint Test T	70	20
Pinpoint Test U	70	21
Pinpoint Test V	70	22
Pinpoint Test W	71	23
Pinpoint Test X	71	24
Pinpoint Test Y	71	25
Pinpoint Test AA	71	26
Pinpoint Test BB	72	27
Pinpoint Test CC	72	28
Pinpoint Test DD	72	29
Pinpoint Test EE	72	30
Pinpoint Test FF	72	31
Pinpoint Test GG	72	32
Pinpoint Test HH	73	33
Pinpoint Test JJ	73	34
Pinpoint Test KK	73	35
Town Car:		
Pinpoint Test A	73	36
Pinpoint Test B	74	37
Pinpoint Test C	74	38
Pinpoint Test D	74	39
Pinpoint Test E	74	40
Pinpoint Test F	75	41
Pinpoint Test G	75	42
Pinpoint Test H	75	43
Pinpoint Test J	75	44
Pinpoint Test K	75	45
Pinpoint Test L	75	46
Pinpoint Test M	76	47
Pinpoint Test N	76	48
Pinpoint Test P	76	49
Pinpoint Test Q	76	50
Pinpoint Test R	76	51
Pinpoint Test S	76	52
Pinpoint Test T	76	53
Pinpoint Test U	77	54
Pinpoint Test V	77	55
Pinpoint Test W	77	56
Pinpoint Test X	77	57
Pinpoint Test Y	78	58
Pinpoint Test AA	78	59
Pinpoint Test BB	78	60
Pinpoint Test CC	78	61
Pinpoint Test DD	78	62
Pinpoint Test EE	78	63
SYMPTOM INDEX:		
Crown Victoria & Grand Marquis	66	1
Town Car	66	2

ELECTRONIC INSTRUMENT CLUSTER DISPLAY DIAGNOSIS

Condition	Possible Source	Action
• Display Not Illuminated, Too Dim or Blank But Backlighted	• Dimmed to barely visible, could be at MAX with headlamp switch in HEAD position. • Electronic instrument cluster. • Circuitry.	• GO to Pinpoint Test A.
• Display Scrambled, Incorrect All the Time or Stuck with All Segments On, Segments Half Lit, Blinking or Missing	• Electronic instrument cluster.	• GO to Pinpoint Test B.
• Display Does Not Respond to Buttons or No Beep When Buttons Pushed or Driver Alert Given	• Circuitry. • Safety belt warning chime. • Electronic instrument cluster. • Message center switch module. • Headlamp switch.	• GO to Pinpoint Test C.

FM9099600561010X

Fig. 1 Symptom index (Part 1 of 3). Crown Victoria & Grand Marquis

MESSAGE CENTER DISPLAY DIAGNOSIS

Condition	Possible Source	Action
• Instantaneous or Average Fuel Economy Always Reads 0 Miles/Gal Or 99 L/100 km or 99 Miles/Gal or 0 L/100 km	• Electronic instrument cluster. • Circuitry. • Powertrain control module.	• GO to Pinpoint Test T.
• Trip Distance Does Not Accumulate	• Electronic instrument cluster.	• GO to Pinpoint Test S.
• DTE Does Not Go Below 322 km (200 Miles) With Fuel Tank Empty or DTE Always Reads Zero	• Electronic instrument cluster. • Circuitry. • Powertrain control module.	• GO to Pinpoint Test U.

WARNING INDICATOR DIAGNOSIS

Condition	Possible Source	Action
• DOOR AJAR Warning Never/Always On	• Door open warning lamp switch. • Electronic instrument cluster. • Circuitry. • Lighting control module.	• GO to Pinpoint Test V.
• TRUNK AJAR Warning Never/Always On	• Luggage compartment door open warning lamp switch. • Circuitry. • Electronic instrument cluster. • Lighting control module.	• GO to Pinpoint Test W.
• CHARGE SYSTEM Warning Always/Never On	• Electronic instrument cluster. • Circuitry.	• GO to Pinpoint Test X.
• AIR SUSPENSION Warning Always On	• Circuitry. • Electronic instrument cluster.	• GO to Pinpoint Test Y.
• LOW WASHER FLUID Warning Never/Always On	• Windshield washer reservoir fluid level sensor. • Circuitry. • Electronic instrument cluster.	• GO to Pinpoint Test AA.
• CHECK ENGINE (MIL) Warning Always On	• Electronic instrument cluster. • Powertrain control module.	
• LH Turn Indicator Never/Always ON	• Shorted or open circuitry. • Damaged multi-function switch.	• GO to Pinpoint Test CC.
• RH Turn Indicator Never/Always On	• Shorted or open circuitry. • Damaged multi-function switch.	• GO to Pinpoint Test DD.
• High Beam Warning Never/Always On	• Electronic instrument cluster. • Circuitry. • Headlamp switch.	• GO to Pinpoint Test EE.
• Safety Belt Warning Never/Always On	• Blown fuse. • Damaged lighting control module. • Damaged safety belt buckle switch. • Open/shorted circuitry.	• GO to Pinpoint Test FF.
• Low Oil Pressure Warning Never/Always On	• Electronic instrument cluster. • Oil pressure sensor. • Circuitry.	• GO to Pinpoint Test GG.
• Air Bag Warning Never/Always On	• Electronic instrument cluster. • Air bag diagnostic monitor. • Circuitry.	• GO to Pinpoint Test HH.
• Overdrive OFF Indicator Never/Always On	• Electronic instrument cluster. • Powertrain control module. • Circuitry.	• GO to Pinpoint Test JJ.
• Transmission Control Indicator Never/Always On	• Bulb. • Circuitry.	• GO to Pinpoint Test KK.

FM9099600561030X

Fig. 1 Symptom index (Part 3 of 3). Crown Victoria & Grand Marquis

Condition	Possible Source	Action
• Display Not Illuminated, Too Dim or Blank But Backlighted	• Dimmed to barely visible, could be at MAX with headlamps ON. • Electronic instrument cluster. • Circuitry.	• GO to Pinpoint Test A.
• Display Scrambled, Incorrect All the Time or Stuck with All Segments On, Segments Half Lit, Blinking or Missing	• Electronic instrument cluster.	• GO to Pinpoint Test B.
• Display Does Not Respond to Buttons or No Beep When Buttons Pushed or Driver Alert Given	• Circuitry. • Safety belt warning chime. • Electronic instrument cluster. • Message center switch module. • Headlamp switch.	• GO to Pinpoint Test C.

FM9099600594010X

Fig. 2 Symptom index (Part 1 of 3). Town Car

FUEL GAUGE DIAGNOSIS

Condition	Possible Source	Action
• CO Displayed, Top Two and Bottom Two Diagnostic Bars Displayed	• Fuel pump module. • Electronic instrument cluster. • Circuitry.	• GO to Pinpoint Test D.
• CS Displayed, Top Two and Bottom Two Diagnostic Bars Displayed	• Fuel pump module. • Circuitry. • Electronic instrument cluster.	• GO to Pinpoint Test E.
• Inaccurate Fuel Gauge Indication	• Fuel pump module. • Evaporative emission valve, tube or canister. • Fuel tank. • Electronic instrument cluster.	• GO to Pinpoint Test F.

TEMPERATURE GAUGE DIAGNOSIS

Condition	Possible Source	Action
• Temperature Gauge Displays Top Two And Bottom Two Diagnostic Bars	• Engine coolant temperature (ETC) sensor. • Electronic instrument cluster. • Circuitry.	• GO to Pinpoint Test G.
• Temperature Gauge Always Reads Hot Or Cold Temperature	• Engine coolant temperature (ETC) sensor. • Electronic instrument cluster. • Circuitry.	• GO to Pinpoint Test H.
• No Warning Tone When Thermometer Symbol is Blinking	• Electronic instrument cluster. • Safety belt warning chime.	• GO to Pinpoint Test J.

SPEEDOMETER DIAGNOSIS

Condition	Possible Source	Action
• Speedometer Reads 0 km/h (mph) At All Speeds	• Electronic instrument cluster. • Circuitry. • Vehicle speed sensor.	• GO to Pinpoint Test K.
• Speedometer Constantly Reads Too High Or Too Low	• Vehicle speed sensor. • Drive gear. • Electronic instrument cluster. • Circuitry.	• GO to Pinpoint Test L.
• Speed Indication Jumps Up And Down Erratically	• Electronic instrument cluster. • Vehicle speed sensor. • Circuitry.	• GO to Pinpoint Test M.
• Speed Control Indicator Always On	• Speed control servo. • Circuitry. • Electronic instrument cluster.	• GO to Pinpoint Test N.
• Speed Control Indicator Does Not Come On When Speed Control Engaged	• Electronic instrument cluster. • Circuitry. • Powertrain control module.	• GO to Pinpoint Test P.

ODOMETER DIAGNOSIS

Condition	Possible Source	Action
• Display Has "S" Illuminated	• Electronic instrument cluster.	• GO to Pinpoint Test Q.
• Mileage Constantly Reads Too High Or Too Low	• Drive gear. • Electronic instrument cluster.	• GO to Pinpoint Test R.
• Odometer Does Not Accumulate Mileage or Counts 1.6 km (1.0 mile) and Jumps Back 1.6 km (1.0 mile)	• Electronic instrument cluster. • Vehicle speed sensor.	• GO to Pinpoint Test S.

FM9099600561020X

Fig. 1 Symptom index (Part 2 of 3). Crown Victoria & Grand Marquis

FUEL GAUGE DIAGNOSIS

Condition	Possible Source	Action
• CO Displayed, Top Two and Bottom Two Diagnostic Bars Displayed	• Fuel pump module. • Electronic instrument cluster. • Circuitry.	• GO to Pinpoint Test D.
• CS Displayed, Top Two and Bottom Two Diagnostic Bars Displayed	• Fuel pump module. • Circuitry. • Electronic instrument cluster.	• GO to Pinpoint Test E.
• Inaccurate Fuel Gauge Indication	• Fuel pump module. • Evaporative emission valve, tube or canister. • Fuel tank. • Electronic instrument cluster.	• GO to Pinpoint Test F.

TEMPERATURE GAUGE DIAGNOSIS

Condition	Possible Source	Action
• Temperature Gauge Displays Top Two And Bottom Two Diagnostic Bars	• Engine coolant temperature (ETC) sensor. • Electronic instrument cluster. • Circuitry.	• GO to Pinpoint Test G.
• Temperature Gauge Always Reads Hot Or Cold Temperature	• Engine coolant temperature (ETC) sensor. • Electronic instrument cluster. • Circuitry.	• GO to Pinpoint Test H.
• No Warning Tone When Thermometer Symbol is Blinking	• Electronic instrument cluster. • Safety belt warning chime.	• GO to Pinpoint Test J.

SPEEDOMETER DIAGNOSIS

Condition	Possible Source	Action
• Speedometer Reads 0 km/h (mph) At All Speeds	• Electronic instrument cluster. • Circuitry. • Vehicle speed sensor.	• GO to Pinpoint Test K.
• Speedometer Constantly Reads Too High Or Too Low	• Vehicle speed sensor. • Drive gear. • Electronic instrument cluster. • Circuitry.	• GO to Pinpoint Test L.
• Speed Indication Jumps Up And Down Erratically	• Electronic instrument cluster. • Vehicle speed sensor. • Circuitry.	• GO to Pinpoint Test M.
• Speed Control Indicator Always On	• Speed control servo. • Circuitry. • Electronic instrument cluster.	• GO to Pinpoint Test N.
• Speed Control Indicator Does Not Come On When Speed Control Engaged	• Electronic instrument cluster. • Circuitry. • Powertrain control module.	• GO to Pinpoint Test P.

ODOMETER DIAGNOSIS

Condition	Possible Source	Action
• Display Has "S" Illuminated	• Electronic instrument cluster.	• GO to Pinpoint Test Q.
• Mileage Constantly Reads Too High Or Too Low	• Drive gear. • Electronic instrument cluster.	• GO to Pinpoint Test R.
• Odometer Does Not Accumulate Mileage or Counts 1.6 km (1.0 mile) and Jumps Back 1.6 km (1.0 mile)	• Electronic instrument cluster. • Vehicle speed sensor.	• GO to Pinpoint Test S.

FM9099600594020X

Fig. 2 Symptom index (Part 2 of 3). Town Car

MESSAGE CENTER DISPLAY DIAGNOSIS

Condition	Possible Source	Action
• Instantaneous or Average Fuel Economy Always Reads 0 Miles / Gal Or 99 L / 100 km or 99 Miles / Gal or 0 L / 100 km	• Electronic instrument cluster. • Circuitry. • Powertrain control module.	• GO to Pinpoint Test T.
• Trip Distance Does Not Accumulate	• Electronic instrument cluster.	• GO to Pinpoint Test S.
• DTE Does Not Go Below 322 km (200 Miles) With Fuel Tank Empty or DTE Always Reads Zero	• Electronic instrument cluster. • Circuitry. • Powertrain control module.	• GO to Pinpoint Test U.

WARNING INDICATOR DIAGNOSIS

Condition	Possible Source	Action
• DOOR AJAR Warning Never / Always On	• Door open warning lamp switch. • Electronic instrument cluster. • Circuitry. • Lighting control module.	• GO to Pinpoint Test V.
• TRUNK AJAR Warning Never / Always On	• Luggage compartment door open warning lamp switch. • Circuitry. • Electronic instrument cluster. • Lighting control module.	• GO to Pinpoint Test W.
• CHARGE SYSTEM Warning Never / Always On	• Electronic instrument cluster.	• GO to Pinpoint Test X.
• AIR SUSPENSION Warning Always On	• Circuitry. • Electronic instrument cluster.	• GO to Pinpoint Test Y.
• Low WASHER FLUID Warning Never / Always On	• Windshield washer reservoir fluid level sensor. • Circuitry. • Electronic instrument cluster.	• GO to Pinpoint Test AA.
• CHECK ENGINE (MIL) Warning Always On	• Electronic instrument cluster. • Powertrain control module.	• GO to Pinpoint Test BB.
• LH Turn Indicator Never / Always On	• Shorted or open circuitry. • Damaged multi-function switch.	
• RH Turn Indicator Never / Always On	• Shorted or open circuitry. • Damaged malfunction switch.	
• High Beam Warning Never / Always On	• Electronic instrument cluster. • Circuitry. • Headlamp switch.	• GO to Pinpoint Test CC.
• Safety Belt Warning Never / Always On	• Blown fuse. • Damaged lighting. • Inoperative safety belt buckle switch. • Open / shorted circuitry.	
• Low Oil Pressure Warning Never / Always On	• Electronic instrument cluster. • Oil pressure sensor. • Circuitry.	
• Air Bag Warning Never / Always On	• Electronic instrument cluster. • Air bag diagnostic monitor. • Circuitry.	
• O / D OFF Indicator Never / Always On	• Electronic instrument cluster. • Powertrain control module. • Circuitry.	• GO to Pinpoint Test DD.
• Transmission Control Indicator Never / Always On	• Bulb. • Circuitry.	• GO to Pinpoint Test EE.

FM9099600594030X

Fig. 2   Symptom index (Part 3 of 3). Town Car

	Test Step	Result	▶	Action to Take
A1	CHECK DISPLAYS - HEADLAMPS OFF • Turn ignition switch to RUN. • Turn headlamp switch to OFF. • Verify illumination of electronic instrument cluster, clock and radio. • Is electronic cluster display off with other displays on?	Yes No	▶ ▶	GO to A2. GO to A3.
A2	CHECK INSTRUMENT CLUSTER POWER • Verify power at electronic instrument cluster Pins C1-7 Circuit 54 (LG / Y), C1-9 Circuit 964 (DB / LG), C3-2 Circuit 964 (DB / LG) with ignition switch in RUN position. • Is B+ present?	Yes No	▶ ▶	REPLACE electronic instrument cluster. AFFIX odometer sticker to door pillar. SERVICE Circuits 964 (DB / LG) and 54 (LG / Y).
A3	CHECK DISPLAYS - HEADLAMPS ON • Turn ignition switch to RUN. • Turn headlamp switch to PARK position. • While varying dimming level check other displays: radio, clock, transmission range indicator. • Do other displays illuminate properly?	Yes No	▶ ▶	GO to A4. GO to A5.
A4	CHECK FOR CIRCUIT 19 (LB / R) VOLTAGE • Turn headlamp switch to OFF position. • Disconnect electronic instrument cluster connector. • Turn headlamp switch to PARK position. on. • While varying dimming level, check voltage in Circuit 19 (LB / R) at connector Pin C1-13 of electronic instrument cluster. • Does voltage vary between 4 and 15V?	Yes No	▶ ▶	REPLACE electronic instrument cluster. AFFIX odometer sticker to door pillar. RESTORE vehicle. SERVICE Circuit 19 (LB / R). RESTORE vehicle. RETEST system.
A5	CHECK FOR LIGHTING CONTROL MODULE • Check fuse junction panel Fuses 8 (15A) and 18 (15A). Replace if necessary. Proceed if displays still do not illuminate properly. • While varying dimming level, verify voltage output at lighting control module. • Does dimming input voltage vary between 4 and 15V?	Yes No	▶ ▶	SERVICE Circuit 19 (LB / R). RESTORE vehicle. RETEST system. GO to lighting control module diagnosis.

FM9099600562000X

Fig. 3   Pinpoint test A. Crown Victoria & Grand Marquis

	Test Step	Result	▶	Action to Take
B1	PERFORM SELF TEST • Turn ignition switch to OFF position. • Push in the E / M and <SELECT (left) buttons and hold. • Turn ignition switch to RUN position while holding buttons. • Release buttons when cluster lights. • Does odometer flash?	Yes No	▶ ▶	REPLACE electronic instrument cluster. AFFIX odometer sticker to door pillar. RESTORE vehicle. RETEST system. GO to B2.
B2	DISPLAY TEST NOTE: There are 17 segment displays. • Push SELECT> button once to enter display test. • Push E / M button to step through display test inspection and verification. • Display test start with all blue / green segments off. Test then cycles through following test to turn on each segment or indicator ISO one time only, then begins to full display after each segment has been tested individually until all blue / green segments are on. Next switch press start cycle all over again. • Do any segments stay on always or never come on?	Yes No	▶ ▶	REPLACE electronic instrument cluster. AFFIX odometer sticker to door pillar. RESTORE vehicle. RETEST system. Electronic instrument cluster OK. RESTORE vehicle.

FM9099600563000X

Fig. 4   Pinpoint test B. Crown Victoria & Grand Marquis

	Test Step	Result	▶	Action to Take
C1	CHECK FOR WARNING CHIME NOTE: Buttons function only with ignition switch in RUN. • Check for fasten safety belt reminder chime or key in ignition reminder chime. • Does chime sound?	Yes No	▶ ▶	GO to C2. REFER to for chime diagnosis.
C2	CHECK SWITCH WIRING CONNECTIONS • Remove finish panel to expose instrument cluster. • Verify that connections at message center switch module assembly are securely connected. • Are connections secure?	Yes No	▶ ▶	GO to C3. Secure connections and RECHECK.
C3	CHECK MESSAGE CENTER SWITCH ASSEMBLY (NO SWITCH PRESSED) • Disconnect message center module. • Measure the resistance between Pin 5 and Pin 4 Circuit 143, (LB / Y) and Circuit 676 (PK / O) of the message center switch module. • Resistance with no switch pressed should be 17,300 to 17,600 ohms. • Is resistance within range?	Yes No	▶ ▶	GO to C4. REPLACE message center switch module. RESTORE vehicle. RETEST system.
C4	CHECK SWITCH ASSEMBLY (BUTTONS PRESSED) • Disconnect message center module from electronic instrument cluster. • NOTE: Press only one button of the message center switch module while measuring the resistance. Measure the resistance between Pin 5, Circuit 143, (LB / Y) and Pin 4 Circuit 676, (PK / O). • NOTE: Measure resistance between Pins 5 and 4 for SELECT > and <, between Pins 2 and 4 for E / M Reset. The resistance should be: 	PINS	BUTTON	RESISTANCE (in ohms)
---	---	---
5-4	E / M	5100-5200
6-4	SELECT >	5100-5200
6-4	SELECT <	2250-2350
5-4	RESET	2250-2350 | • Is resistance within range?	Yes No	▶ ▶	GO to C5. REPLACE message center switch module. RESTORE vehicle. RETEST system.
C5	VERIFY HARNESS CONTINUITY • Disconnect battery ground cable. • Remove electronic instrument cluster. • Check continuity in Circuit 143 (LB / Y), cluster connector Pin C1-3 and 152 (LB / W), connector C2-23. • Check continuity to ground in Circuit 676 (PK / O) and Pin 4 of switch module C1-8 of electronic instrument cluster. • Is there continuity?	Yes No	▶ ▶	GO to C6. SERVICE respective circuit. RESTORE vehicle. RETEST system.
C6	CHECK EATC INPUT FROM CLUSTER IN ENGLISH MODE • Turn ignition switch to RUN. • Remove the connector from the electronic automatic temperature control. • Press the E / M button so that the instrument cluster is in ENGLISH mode. • Check electronic automatic temperature control connector Pin C1-20. • Is Pin 20 at 5 volts dc?	Yes No	▶ ▶	GO to C8. GO to C7.

FM9099600564010X

Fig. 5   Pinpoint test C (Part 1 of 2). Crown Victoria & Grand Marquis

Test Step	Result	▶	Action to Take
C7 CHECK ELECTRONIC INSTRUMENT CLUSTER OUTPUT TO ELECTRONIC AUTOMATIC TEMPERATURE CONTROL IN ENGLISH MODE • Leave ignition switch at RUN. • Connector is removed from the electronic automatic temperature control. • Press the E/M button so that the instrument cluster is in ENGLISH mode. • Remove connector C2 from instrument cluster. • Check Pin 32 of the instrument cluster (not the harness connector). • **Is instrument cluster Pin 32 at 5 volts dc?**	Yes No	▶ ▶	SERVICE Circuit 506 (R) for short to ground or to another wire. RESTORE vehicle. RETEST system. REPLACE electronic instrument cluster. AFFIX odometer sticker to door pillar. RESTORE vehicle. RETEST system.
C8 CHECK EATC INPUT FROM ELECTRONIC INSTRUMENT CLUSTER IN METRIC MODE • Turn ignition switch to RUN. • Remove the connector from the electronic automatic temperature control. • Press the E/M button so that the instrument cluster is in METRIC mode. • Check electronic automatic temperature control connector Pin C1-20. • **Is Pin 20 at 0 volts dc?**	Yes No	▶ ▶	REFER to Electronic Automatic Temperature Control Diagnostics. GO to C9.
C9 CHECK ELECTRONIC INSTRUMENT CLUSTER OUTPUT TO ELECTRONIC AUTOMATIC TEMPERATURE CONTROL IN METRIC MODE • Leave ignition switch at RUN. • Connector still removed from the electronic automatic temperature control. • Press the E/M button so that the instrument cluster is in METRIC mode. • Remove Connector C2 from instrument cluster. • Check Pin 32 of the instrument cluster (not the harness connector). • **Is instrument cluster Pin 32 at 0 volts dc?**	Yes No	▶ ▶	SERVICE Circuit 506 (R) for open. CHECK for intermittent contact. RESTORE vehicle. RETEST system. REPLACE electronic instrument cluster. AFFIX odometer sticker to door pillar. RESTORE vehicle. RETEST system.

FM9099600564020X

Fig. 5   Pinpoint test C (Part 2 of 2). Crown Victoria & Grand Marquis

Test Step	Result	▶	Action to Take
D3 CHECK FUEL PUMP WIRING AT ELECTRONIC INSTRUMENT CLUSTER • Disconnect battery ground cable. • Remove connector C1 from electronic instrument cluster and secure connectors from shorting. • Jumper variable resistance Pin 5, Circuit 29 (Y/W) and ground Pin 8, Circuit 676 (PK/O) of harness together at fuel pump module. • **Is resistance close to zero ohms?**	Yes No	▶ ▶	REPLACE electronic instrument cluster. AFFIX odometer sticker to door pillar. RESTORE vehicle. RETEST system. SERVICE fuel pump wiring for open circuit. RESTORE vehicle. RETEST system.
D4 VERIFY FUEL PUMP MODULE RESISTANCE OVER RANGE • Remove fuel pump module. • Measure resistance while moving float rod arm slowly from empty to full. • **Does resistance exceed 181 ohms at any time?**	Yes No	▶ ▶	REPLACE fuel pump module. INSPECT fuel pump wiring connector female terminals for flash or loose fit. SERVICE as required. RESTORE vehicle. RETEST system.

FM9099600566020X

Fig. 6   Pinpoint test D (Part 2 of 2). Crown Victoria & Grand Marquis

Test Step	Result	▶	Action to Take
F1 CHECK FUEL GAUGE RESPONSE • Disconnect battery ground cable. • Lower fuel tank and gain access to fuel pump module connections. • Connect a resistor value of between 170-100 ohms. • Reconnect battery. • Turn ignition switch to the RUN position. Display 1/2 tank or above fuel level. • Turn ignition switch to OFF. Disconnect battery. • Remove 170-100 ohms resistor. • Connect a 43 ohm (± 1 percent) resistor in place of fuel pump module. Verify value with ohmmeter. • Reconnect battery. • Turn ignition switch to RUN. • NOTE: Allow at least 30 seconds for cluster to read level. FUEL REMAIN should read 3 to 4 GAL (13 to 15 LTR). • **Is fuel gauge correct?**	Yes No	▶ ▶	TURN ignition switch to OFF. GO to F3. TURN ignition switch to OFF. Leave 43 ohm resistor connected. GO to F2.
F2 CHECK HARNESS RESISTANCE • Disconnect battery ground cable. • Remove electronic instrument cluster and secure connectors from shorting. • Measure resistance between Connector Pin C1-6, Circuit 29 (Y/W) and Pin C1-8, Circuit 676 (PK/O) with 43 ohm resistor in place. • **Is resistance within range?**	Yes No	▶ ▶	REPLACE electronic instrument cluster. AFFIX odometer sticker to door pillar. RESTORE vehicle. RETEST system. SERVICE Circuit 29 (Y/W). RESTORE vehicle. RETEST system.
F3 CHECK FUEL PUMP MODULE • Disconnect battery ground cable. • Check fuel pump module for binding, sticking, misalignment, etc. • Check sender resistance not to exceed 181 ohms while moving float arm slowly from fuel to empty. • Check fuel pump resistance. Resistance should be 135 to 165 ohms of full stop and 14 to 18 ohms at empty stop. • **Is fuel pump module resistance within limits specified?**	Yes No	▶ ▶	GO to F4. SERVICE or REPLACE fuel pump module.
F4 CHECK FUEL TANK • Check fuel tank for dents, bulges or other damage. • Check for proper installation of fuel tube. • **Is fuel tank OK?**	Yes No	▶ ▶	System OK. Condition caused by other vehicle system(s). RESTORE vehicle. REPLACE fuel tank or fuel tube.

FM9099600568000X

Fig. 8   Pinpoint test F. Crown Victoria & Grand Marquis

Test Step	Result	▶	Action to Take
D1 CHECK FUEL PUMP WIRING AT FUEL PUMP MODULE • Disconnect battery ground cable. • Lower fuel tank to gain access to fuel pump module connector. • Disconnect fuel pump module connector. • Jumper variable resistance terminal Circuit 29 (Y/W) and ground terminal Circuit 676 (PK/O) of fuel pump module connector. • Reconnect battery. • Turn ignition switch from OFF to RUN. • NOTE: It may take several minutes for the fuel gauge to respond. Check digital fuel remaining display to determine whether it shows CO or CS. • **Does fuel gauge display show CO?**	Yes No	▶ ▶	GO to D3. REMOVE jumper. GO to D2.
D2 CHECK FUEL PUMP RESISTANCE • Turn ignition switch to OFF. • Measure the resistance of the fuel pump module at Pin 7, Circuit 787 (PK/BK) and Pin 6, Circuit 57 (BK). • Verify that the resistance is less than 181 ohms (normally between 15 and 160 ohms). • **Is resistance less than 181 ohms?**	Yes No	▶ ▶	GO to D4. REPLACE fuel pump.

FM9099600566010X

Fig. 6   Pinpoint test D (Part 1 of 2). Crown Victoria & Grand Marquis

Test Step	Result	▶	Action to Take
E1 CHECK FUEL PUMP WIRING RESISTANCE AT ELECTRONIC INSTRUMENT CLUSTER • Disconnect battery ground cable. • Remove instrument cluster and secure connectors from shorting. • With an ohmmeter, measure resistance between Connector Pin C1-6, Circuit 29 (Y/W) and Pin C1-8, Circuit 676 (PK/O). • Verify that the resistance is 14 ohms or greater (normally 15 to 160 ohms). • **Is resistance at least 14 ohms?**	Yes No	▶ ▶	REPLACE electronic instrument cluster. AFFIX odometer sticker to door pillar. RESTORE vehicle. RETEST system. GO to E2.
E2 CHECK FUEL PUMP WIRING • Lower fuel tank to gain access to fuel pump module connector. • Disconnect connector at fuel pump module. • Measure the resistance between Connector Pin C1-6, Circuit 29 (Y/W) and Pin C1-8, Circuit 676 (PK/O). • Verify that resistance is greater than 10 K ohms. • **Is resistance at least 10 K ohms?**	Yes No	▶ ▶	REPLACE fuel pump. SERVICE fuel pump wiring for short circuit. RESTORE vehicle. RETEST system.

FM9099600567000X

Fig. 7   Pinpoint test E. Crown Victoria & Grand Marquis

Test Step	Result	▶	Action to Take
G1 CHECK FOR TEMPERATURE SENDER SHORT • Disconnect engine coolant temperature sensor connector. • Turn ignition switch to RUN. • **Does temperature gauge indicate COLD with bottom bar lit?**	Yes No	▶ ▶	REPLACE engine coolant temperature sensor. GO to G2.

FM9099600569010X

Fig. 9   Pinpoint test G (Part 1 of 2). Crown Victoria & Grand Marquis

Test Step	Result	▶	Action to Take
G2 CHECK FOR SHORT IN WIRING • Disconnect battery ground cable. • Unplug engine coolant temperature sensor connector. • Disconnect Connector C1 and Connector C2 from electronic instrument cluster. • Measure resistance between connector C1 Pin 4, Circuit 39 (R/W) and Pin C1-8, Circuit 676 (PK/O). • **Is resistance greater than 15 K ohms?**	Yes No	▶ ▶	REPLACE electronic instrument cluster. AFFIX odometer sticker to door pillar. RESTORE vehicle. RETEST system. SERVICE Circuit 39 (R/W) as required. RESTORE vehicle. RETEST system.

FM9099600569020X

Fig. 9   Pinpoint test G (Part 2 of 2). Crown Victoria & Grand Marquis

Test Step		Result	▶	Action to Take
H1	CHECK TEMPERATURE GAUGE WIRING			
	• Unplug connector to engine coolant temperature sensor and connect a jumper in place of the sensor. • Turn ignition switch to RUN. • Gauge should give a short circuit indication. (Blinking thermometer symbol and top two and bottom two bars of gauge lit.) • Does gauge indicate short circuit?	Yes	▶	GO to H3. REMOVE jumper. REPLACE engine coolant temperature sensor.
		No	▶	GO to H2.
H2	CHECK WIRING AT CLUSTER			
	• Disconnect battery ground cable. • Disconnect C1 and C2 connectors from electronic instrument cluster. • Connect jumper in place of engine coolant temperature sensor. • Verify continuity between Pin C1-8, Circuit 676 (PK/O) and Pin C1-4, Circuit 39 (R/W). • Is there continuity?	Yes	▶	REPLACE electronic instrument cluster. AFFIX odometer sticker to door pillar. RESTORE vehicle. RETEST system.
		No	▶	SERVICE wiring Circuit 39 (R/W) and 676 (PK/O). RESTORE vehicle. RETEST system.
H3	CHECK ENGINE COOLANT TEMPERATURE SENSOR			
	• Warm up engine to normal operating temperature. • Measure resistance of engine coolant temperature sensor. • Is resistance greater than 8 K ohms?	Yes	▶	GO to H4.
		No	▶	REPLACE electronic instrument cluster. AFFIX odometer sticker to door pillar. RESTORE vehicle. RETEST system.
H4	CHECK COOLING SYSTEM			
	• Check thermostat, coolant level and other cooling system components for proper operation. • Is cooling system OK?	Yes	▶	REPLACE engine coolant temperature sensor.
		No	▶	SERVICE cooling system as required.

FM9099600570000X

Fig. 10   Pinpoint test H. Crown Victoria & Grand Marquis

Test Step		Result	▶	Action to Take
K1	CHECK SPEEDOMETER READING			
	• Test drive vehicle above 8 km/h (5 mph) and look for: — Speedometer reading — Odometer changing • Verify that odometer advances when vehicle is driven forward. • Does odometer advance with no speed indication?	Yes	▶	REPLACE electronic instrument cluster. AFFIX odometer sticker to door pillar. RESTORE vehicle. RETEST system.
		No	▶	GO to K2.
K2	CHECK SPEED CONTROL			
	• Test drive vehicle above 48 km/h (30 mph), check speed control operation. • Did speed control operate properly?	Yes	▶	GO to K3.
		No	▶	GO to K4.
K3	CHECK CONTINUITY			
	• Disconnect battery ground cable. • Disconnect connectors C1 and C2 at electronic instrument cluster. • Disconnect vehicle speed sensor. • Check continuity in connector Pin C1-12, Circuit 679 (GY/BK) and continuity to ground in connector Pin C1-8, Circuit 676 (PK/O). • Is continuity present?	Yes	▶	REPLACE electronic instrument cluster. AFFIX odometer sticker to door pillar. RESTORE vehicle. RETEST system.
		No	▶	SERVICE respective circuit. RESTORE vehicle. RETEST system.
K4	CHECK VEHICLE SPEED SENSOR			
	• Disconnect vehicle speed sensor. • Measure resistance across vehicle speed sensor. • Is resistance between 200-300 ohms?	Yes	▶	CHECK Circuits 679 (GY/BK) and 676 (PK/O) for continuity. If circuits OK, CHECK driven gear and retainer clip. REPLACE if necessary.
		No	▶	REPLACE vehicle speed sensor.

FM9099600572000X

Fig. 12   Pinpoint test K. Crown Victoria & Grand Marquis

Test Step		Result	▶	Action to Take
L4	CHECK VEHICLE SPEED SENSOR			
	• Disconnect vehicle speed sensor. • Measure resistance across vehicle speed sensor. • Is resistance between 200-300 ohms?	Yes	▶	REPLACE electronic instrument cluster. AFFIX odometer sticker to door pillar. RESTORE vehicle. RETEST system.
		No	▶	REPLACE vehicle speed sensor.

FM9099600573020X

Fig. 13   Pinpoint test L (Part 2 of 2). Crown Victoria & Grand Marquis

Test Step		Result	▶	Action to Take
N1	CHECK SPEED CONTROL SERVO			
	• Disconnect connector from speed control servo. • Does speed control indicator go out?	Yes	▶	REPLACE speed control servo. VERIFY proper operation.
		No	▶	GO to N2.
N2	CHECK ELECTRONIC INSTRUMENT CLUSTER			
	• Disconnect instrument cluster connector C2. • Does speed control indicator go off?	Yes	▶	CHECK Circuit 203 (O/LB) at Connector Pin C2-26 for short to ground. SERVICE as required. RESTORE vehicle. RETEST system.
		No	▶	REPLACE electronic instrument cluster. AFFIX odometer sticker to door pillar. RESTORE vehicle. RETEST system.

FM9099600575000X

Fig. 15   Pinpoint test N. Crown Victoria & Grand Marquis

Test Step		Result	▶	Action to Take
J1	REVIEW OPERATION/CONDITION			
	NOTE: Chime will not beep if another sound is being produced. Driver alert only given for temperatures above normal band. • Turn ignition switch to RUN. • Press any message center switch module button and listen for beep. • Does beep sound?	Yes	▶	System OK.
		No	▶	GO to Pinpoint Test C.

FM9099600571000X

Fig. 11   Pinpoint test J. Crown Victoria & Grand Marquis

Test Step		Result	▶	Action to Take
L1	CHECK VEHICLE SPEED SENSOR DRIVE GEAR			
	• Remove vehicle speed sensor from transmission and verify that correct drive gear is installed for vehicle transmission/axle/tire combination. • Is drive gear correct?	Yes	▶	GO to L2.
		No	▶	INSTALL correct gear with retaining clip.
L2	CHECK DRIVE GEAR ON TRANSMISSION OUTPUT SHAFT			
	• Check that correct drive gear is installed on transmission output shaft. • Is drive gear correct?	Yes	▶	GO to L3.
		No	▶	INSTALL correct output shaft and/or gear.
L3	CHECK CONTINUITY			
	• Disconnect battery ground cable. • Disconnect connectors C1 and C2 at electronic instrument cluster. • Check continuity in Connector Pin C1-12, Circuit 679 (GY/BK) and Pin C1-8, Circuit 676 (PK/O). • Is continuity present?	Yes	▶	GO to L4.
		No	▶	SERVICE respective circuit. RESTORE vehicle. RETEST system.

FM9099600573010X

Fig. 13   Pinpoint test L (Part 1 of 2). Crown Victoria & Grand Marquis

Test Step		Result	▶	Action to Take
M1	CHECK SPEED SENSOR DRIVE GEAR			
	• Remove vehicle speed sensor from transmission. • Check that all gear teeth are in good condition, retainer clip is installed and gear does not slip on shaft. • Is vehicle speed sensor in good condition?	Yes	▶	GO to L3.
		No	▶	REPLACE drive gear and/or retaining clip.

FM9099600574000X

Fig. 14   Pinpoint test M. Crown Victoria & Grand Marquis

Test Step		Result	▶	Action to Take
P1	CHECK VOLTAGE AT SPEED CONTROL SERVO			
	• Disconnect connector from speed control servo. • Turn ignition switch to RUN. • Measure voltage between electronic instrument cluster connector Pin C2-26, Circuit 203 (O/LB) and 57 (BK). • Is voltage approximately 5V?	Yes	▶	GO to P2.
		No	▶	GO to P3.
P2	CHECK CONTINUITY CIRCUIT 203 (O/LB)			
	• Disconnect electronic instrument cluster. • Check continuity in Circuit 203 (O/LB). • Is continuity present?	Yes	▶	REPLACE electronic instrument cluster. AFFIX odometer sticker to door pillar. RESTORE vehicle. RETEST system.
		No	▶	SERVICE Circuit 203 (O/LB). RESTORE vehicle. RETEST system.

FM9099600576010X

Fig. 16   Pinpoint test P (Part 1 of 2). Crown Victoria & Grand Marquis

Test Step		Result	▶	Action to Take
P3	VERIFY B+ AT SPEED CONTROL SERVO			
	• Check for B+ at the speed control servo connector in Pin 7, Circuit 296 (W/P). • Is battery voltage present?	Yes	▶	REPLACE speed control servo.
		No	▶	SERVICE Circuit 296 (LB/PK). RESTORE vehicle. RETEST system.

FM9099600576020X

Fig. 16   Pinpoint test P (Part 2 of 2). Crown Victoria & Grand Marquis

Test Step	Result	▶	Action to Take
Q1 DETERMINE IF SPEEDOMETER / ODOMETER MODULE IS ORIGINAL ● Check for mileage sticker on door pillar. ● **Is mileage sticker original?**	Yes	▶	REPLACE electronic instrument cluster. If odometer reading is known, program it into new electronic instrument cluster. If odometer reading is unknown, program in "S" 00000.5 with the circled S and zero miles in the odometer. RESTORE vehicle. RETEST system.
	No	▶	System OK. RESTORE vehicle.

FM9099600577000X

Fig. 17   Pinpoint test Q. Crown Victoria & Grand Marquis

Test Step	Result	▶	Action to Take
R1 CHECK SPEEDOMETER ● Verify that speedometer is operating properly. ● **Does speedometer operate properly?**	Yes	▶	REPLACE electronic instrument cluster. Affix odometer sticker to door pillar. RESTORE vehicle. RETEST system.
	No	▶	GO to Pinpoint Test L.

FM9099600578000X

Fig. 18   Pinpoint test R. Crown Victoria & Grand Marquis

Test Step	Result	▶	Action to Take
S1 CHECK ODOMETER OPERATION ● Check odometer to determine whether it accumulates and then loses 1.6 km (1.0 mile) or it will not accumulate mileage at all. ● **Does odometer accumulate and then lose 1.6 km (1.0 mile)?**	Yes	▶	REPLACE electronic instrument cluster. AFFIX odometer sticker to door pillar. RESTORE vehicle. RETEST system.
	No	▶	GO to S2.
S2 VERIFY SPEEDOMETER ● Verify that speedometer works properly. ● **Does speedometer operate properly?**	Yes	▶	REPLACE electronic instrument cluster. AFFIX odometer sticker to door pillar. RESTORE vehicle. RETEST system.
	No	▶	GO to Pinpoint Test K.

FM9099600579000X

Fig. 19   Pinpoint test S. Crown Victoria & Grand Marquis

Test Step	Result	▶	Action to Take
T1 CHECK MESSAGE CENTER DISPLAY ● Check message center display to determine whether it is showing 0 MPG, 99L / 100 KM or 99 MPG, 0L / 100 KM. ● **Is message center display showing 0 MPG, 99 L / 100 Km?**	Yes	▶	GO to T2.
	No	▶	GO to T3.

FM9099600580010X

Fig. 20   Pinpoint test T (Part 1 of 2). Crown Victoria & Grand Marquis

Test Step	Result	▶	Action to Take
U1 CHECK FUEL GAUGE ● Verify that fuel gauge is operating properly. ● **Does gauge operate properly?**	Yes	▶	GO to U2.
	No	▶	REFER to Fuel Gauge Diagnosis in Symptom Chart.
U2 CHECK SPEEDOMETER ● Verify that speedometer is operating properly. ● **Does speedometer operate properly?**	Yes	▶	GO to Pinpoint Test T.
	No	▶	REFER to Speedometer Diagnosis in Symptom Chart.

FM9099600581000X

Fig. 21   Pinpoint test U. Crown Victoria & Grand Marquis

Test Step	Result	▶	Action to Take
T2 CHECK SPEEDOMETER OPERATION ● Verify that speedometer is operating properly. ● **Does speedometer operate properly?**	Yes	▶	REPLACE electronic instrument cluster. AFFIX odometer sticker to door pillar. RESTORE vehicle. RETEST system.
	No	▶	GO to Pinpoint Test K.
T3 OBSERVE TRANSMISSION CONTROL OFF INDICATOR LAMP ● Test drive vehicle with transmission control switch pressed (overdrive locked-out). ● **Does transmission control indicator lamp indicator flash?**	Yes	▶	
	No	▶	GO to T4.
T4 CHECK CONTINUITY OF CIRCUIT 205 (FUEL FLOW) ● Verify continuity and absence of shorts in Circuit 205 (DB/LG). ● **Is wiring OK?**	Yes	▶	GO to T5.
	No	▶	SERVICE wiring Circuit 205 (DB/LG) as required. RESTORE vehicle. RETEST system.
T5 ENTER SELF TEST MODE ● Turn ignition switch to OFF. ● Push and hold E/M and <SELECT buttons together. ● Turn ignition switch to START while holding buttons. ● Release buttons when cluster lights. ● Allow engine to run during remainder of test. ● Observe odometer. ● **Does odometer flash?**	Yes	▶	REPLACE electronic instrument cluster. AFFIX odometer sticker to door pillar. RESTORE vehicle. RETEST system.
	No	▶	GO to T6.
T6 ENTER DISPLAY TEST MODE ● Push SELECT> (right) button once and observe display. ● **Is the display the same as in Step 1 of segment displays in inspection and verification?**	Yes	▶	GO to T7.
	No	▶	REPLACE electronic instrument cluster. AFFIX odometer sticker to door pillar. RESTORE vehicle. RETEST system.
T7 ENTER A/D, DIGITAL PORT TEST MODE ● Push E/M and <SELECT buttons together once. Observe odometer display, left two digits. ● **Does odometer's left two digits read "0A"?**	Yes	▶	GO to T8.
	No	▶	REPLACE electronic instrument cluster. AFFIX odometer sticker to door pillar. RESTORE vehicle. RETEST system.
T8 ENTER FUEL FLOW INPUT TEST MODE ● Push SELECT> button twice quickly. ● Observe left two odometer digits change to "1B." ● Repeat this step four times until odometer left two digits read "5F." (Left two digits of odometer will advance: 0A, 1B, 2C, 3D, 4E, 5F, 60, 71, 0A.. etc.) ● Select 5F. Observe the right four digits of the odometer select 5F then observe the display. The frequency of the fuel flow pulses from the powertrain control module is shown. (Step on accelerator pedal.) ● "0000" indicates no fuel flow pulses received from the powertrain control module. ● Any other number indicates fuel flow pulses are being received from the powertrain control module. ● **Do right four digits read "0000" (no fuel pulses)?**	Yes	▶	TURN ignition switch to OFF to exit test modes. RECHECK Circuit 205 (DB/LG); if OK then REPLACE powertrain control module.
	No	▶	REPLACE electronic instrument cluster. AFFIX odometer sticker to door pillar. RESTORE vehicle. RETEST system.

FM9099600580020X

Fig. 20   Pinpoint test T (Part 2 of 2). Crown Victoria & Grand Marquis

Test Step	Result	▶	Action to Take
V1 CHECK ELECTRONIC INSTRUMENT CLUSTER FOR WARNINGS ● Turn ignition switch to RUN. ● Wait past prove-out time. ● Check electronic instrument cluster for DOOR AJAR warning to determine whether warning is always on or never on. ● **Is door ajar warning always on?**	Yes	▶	GO to V2.
	No	▶	GO to V5.
V2 CHECK DOOR OPEN WARNING LAMP SWITCHES FOR SHORT ● The following steps are to be repeated for each door open warning lamp switch. Start with the driver's door, then front passenger's, then rear passenger's door. ● Turn ignition switch to OFF. This resets the warning. ● Disconnect door open warning lamp switch connector at door open warning lamp switch. ● Turn ignition switch to RUN. ● Check message center for warning. ● Repeat until no warning is displayed or all door open warning lamp switches are disconnected. ● **Is warning still displayed?**	Yes	▶	GO to V3.
	No	▶	REPLACE damaged door open warning lamp switch. RETEST system.
V3 LIGHTING CONTROL MODULE CHECK FOR SHORT ● Disconnect lighting control module. ● **Is warning still present?**	Yes	▶	GO to V4.
	No	▶	REPLACE lighting control module. RETEST system.
V4 CHECK CIRCUIT 344 (BK/Y) FOR SHORT ● Turn ignition switch to OFF. ● Disconnect electronic instrument cluster. ● Check continuity to ground from Connector Pin C1-17, Circuit 344 (BK/Y) and Pin C1-6, Circuit 676 (PK/O). ● **Is continuity to ground present?**	Yes	▶	SERVICE Circuit 627 (BK/O) for short to ground. RESTORE vehicle. RETEST system.
	No	▶	REPLACE electronic instrument cluster. AFFIX odometer sticker to door pillar. RESTORE vehicle. RETEST system.
V5 CHECK CIRCUIT 344 (BK/Y) FOR OPEN ● Turn ignition switch to OFF. ● Disconnect electronic instrument cluster. ● Check continuity in Circuit 344 (BK/Y) from instrument cluster Connector Pin C1-17 to driver door module Connector Pin C2-9. ● **Is continuity present?**	Yes	▶	REPLACE electronic instrument cluster. AFFIX odometer sticker to door pillar. RESTORE vehicle. RETEST system.
	No	▶	SERVICE Circuit 344 (BK/Y) for open. RESTORE vehicle. RETEST system.

FM9099600582000X

Fig. 22   Pinpoint test V. Crown Victoria & Grand Marquis

Test Step	Result	►	Action to Take
W1 CHECK ELECTRONIC INSTRUMENT CLUSTER FOR WARNINGS • Turn ignition switch to RUN. • Wait past prove out time. • Check electronic instrument cluster for TRUNK AJAR warning to determine whether the warning is always on or never on. • **Is TRUNK AJAR warning always on?**	Yes No	► ►	GO to **W2**. GO to **W5**.
W2 CHECK LUGGAGE COMPARTMENT DOOR OPEN WARNING LAMP SWITCH CIRCUIT 486 (BR/W) • Turn ignition switch to OFF. This resets the warning. • Pull connector off of luggage compartment door open warning lamp switch. • Turn ignition switch to RUN. • Check electronic instrument cluster for warning. • **Is warning displayed?**	Yes No	► ►	GO to **W3**. SERVICE luggage compartment door open warning lamp switch.
W3 LIGHTING CONTROL MODULE CHECK NOTE: Lighting control module provides pull-up to battery for electronic instrument cluster to keep warning off. If lighting control module is inoperative or removed, electronic instrument cluster luggage compartment door ajar warning stays on. • Disconnect luggage compartment door switch. • Remove electronic instrument cluster. • With ignition switch in RUN position, check for B+ at Pin C2-27, Circuit 486 (BR/W). • **Is B+ present?**	Yes No	► ►	GO to **W4**. REPLACE lighting control module. RESTORE vehicle. RETEST system.
W4 CHECK CIRCUIT 486 (BR/W) • Turn ignition switch to OFF. • Disconnect electronic instrument cluster. • Check continuity to ground in Circuit 486 (BR/W). • **Is there continuity to ground?**	Yes No	► ►	SERVICE Circuit 486 (BR/W) for short. RESTORE vehicle. RETEST system. REPLACE electronic instrument cluster. AFFIX odometer sticker to door pillar. RESTORE vehicle. RETEST system.
W5 CHECK POWER AND GROUNDS • Check voltage on the following instrument cluster connector pins:	Yes No	► ►	GO to **W6**. SERVICE as required. RESTORE vehicle. RETEST system.

Pin	Circuit Number	Voltage
C1-7	54 (LG/Y)	12V (Hot At All Times)
C1-9	964 (DB/LG)	12V (Hot In RUN)
C3-7	88 (BK/W)	12V (Hot In RUN)
C3-2	964 (DB/LG)	12V (Hot In RUN)
C1-8	676 (PK/O)	0V
C3-1	676 (PK/O)	0V

• **Are all voltages as specified?**

FM9099600583010X

Fig. 23 Pinpoint test W (Part 1 of 2). Crown Victoria & Grand Marquis

Test Step	Result	►	Action to Take
X1 CHECK CHARGING SYSTEM VOLTAGE • Start engine and check for warning. Watch for several minutes. • Check battery voltage. • **Is the voltage normal (above 14 volts) for engine at fast idle?**	Yes No	► ►	GO to **X2**. SERVICE generator.
X2 CHECK HARNESS TO GENERATOR • Disconnect generator. • Connect a jumper to ground from Circuit 904 (LG/R) near the generator. • **Does charge warning go away?**	Yes No	► ►	SERVICE the generator. GO to **X3**.
X3 CHECK HARNESS TO ELECTRONIC INSTRUMENT CLUSTER • Turn ignition switch to OFF. • Turn ignition switch to RUN but do not start engine. • Remove jumper. • Measure voltage at generator from Circuit 904 (LG/R) to ground. • **Is it greater than 4 volts?**	Yes No	► ►	GO to **X5**. GO to **X4**.
X4 CHECK ELECTRONIC INSTRUMENT CLUSTER INTEGRAL VOLTAGE REGULATOR RESISTOR AND HARNESS • Turn ignition switch to OFF. • Remove electronic instrument cluster. • Check for loose or corroded screws on generator warning lamp shunt resistor on rear of electronic instrument cluster. • Check that resistor is 400-600 ohms. • Check continuity from resistor screws to Circuit 904 (LG/R) at connector. • Check for short to ground on Circuit 904 (LG/R). • **Has any check failed?**	Yes No	► ►	SERVICE as required to obtain over 4 volts. RESTORE vehicle. RETEST system. SERVICE Circuit 904 (LG/R) for short to ground. RESTORE vehicle. RETEST system.

FM9099600584010X

Fig. 24 Pinpoint test X (Part 1 of 2). Crown Victoria & Grand Marquis

Test Step	Result	►	Action to Take
X5 CHECK ELECTRONIC INSTRUMENT CLUSTER WIRING FOR OPEN CIRCUIT • Turn ignition switch to OFF. • Disconnect instrument cluster. • Check for continuity in Circuit 904 (LG/R). • **Is there continuity?**	Yes No	► ►	REPLACE electronic instrument cluster. AFFIX odometer sticker to door pillar. RESTORE vehicle. RETEST system. SERVICE Circuit 904 (LG/R). RESTORE vehicle. RETEST system.

FM9099600584020X

Fig. 24 Pinpoint test X (Part 2 of 2). Crown Victoria & Grand Marquis

Test Step	Result	►	Action to Take
W6 CHECK LUGGAGE COMPARTMENT DOOR OPEN WARNING LAMP SWITCH FOR INTERNAL OPEN CIRCUIT • Turn ignition switch to OFF. • Pull connector off of the luggage compartment door open warning lamp switch. • Connect a jumper wire from Circuit 486 (BR/W) at the harness connector to ground. • Turn ignition switch to RUN. • Check electronic instrument cluster for warning. • **Is warning displayed?**	Yes No	► ►	SERVICE luggage compartment door open warning lamp switch. REMOVE jumper. GO to **W7**.
W7 CHECK WIRING • Turn ignition switch to OFF. • Disconnect electronic instrument cluster. • Check continuity in Circuit 486 (BR/W). • **Is there continuity present?**	Yes No	► ►	REPLACE electronic instrument cluster. AFFIX odometer sticker to door pillar. RESTORE vehicle. RETEST system. SERVICE Circuit 486 (BR/W) for open. RESTORE vehicle. RETEST system.

FM9099600583020X

Fig. 23 Pinpoint test W (Part 2 of 2). Crown Victoria & Grand Marquis

Test Step	Result	►	Action to Take
Y1 CHECK ELECTRONIC INSTRUMENT CLUSTER FOR WARNINGS • Turn ignition switch to RUN. • Wait past prove-out time. • Check electronic instrument cluster for AIR SUSPENSION warning to determine whether the warning is always on or never on. • **Is AIR SUSPENSION warning always on?**	Yes No	► ►	GO to **Y2**. GO to **Y4**.
Y2 CHECK AIR SUSPENSION CONTROL MODULE • Disconnect air suspension control module. • Turn ignition switch to RUN. • Check electronic instrument cluster for warning. • **Is warning displayed?**	Yes No	► ►	GO to **Y3**. REPLACE air suspension system.
Y3 CHECK CIRCUIT 419 (DG/LG) FOR SHORT TO GROUND • Turn ignition switch to OFF. • Disconnect electronic instrument cluster. • Check resistance to ground of Connector Pin C2-25, Circuit 419 (DG/LG). • **Is resistance less than 10 K ohms?**	Yes No	► ►	SERVICE Circuit 419 (DG/LG). RESTORE vehicle. RETEST system. REPLACE electronic instrument cluster. AFFIX odometer sticker to door pillar. RESTORE vehicle. RETEST system.
Y4 CHECK AIR SUSPENSION MODULE • Turn ignition switch to OFF. • Disconnect connector at air suspension control module. • Connect a jumper wire from Circuit 419 (DG/LG) at harness connector to ground. • Turn ignition switch to RUN. • Check electronic instrument cluster for warning. • **Is warning displayed?**	Yes No	► ►	REPLACE air suspension control module. GO to **Y5**.
Y5 CHECK CIRCUIT 419 (DG/LG) CONTINUITY • Remove jumper. • Disconnect electronic instrument cluster. • Check continuity in Circuit 419 (DG/LG) from instrument cluster Connector C2-25 to air suspension module Connector Pin C2-11. • **Is continuity present?**	Yes No	► ►	REPLACE electronic instrument cluster. AFFIX odometer sticker to door pillar. RESTORE vehicle. RETEST system. SERVICE Circuit 419 (DG/LG). RESTORE vehicle. RETEST system.

FM9099600623000X

Fig. 25 Pinpoint test Y. Crown Victoria & Grand Marquis

Test Step	Result	►	Action to Take
AA1 CHECK SYSTEM AND WARNING • Drain fluid from windshield washer reservoir for "warning never on." • Add fluid to windshield washer reservoir for "warning always on." • Turn ignition switch to RUN. • Wait past prove-out time. • Check message center for LOW WASHER FLUID warnings to determine whether the warning is always on or never on. • **Is warning always on?**	Yes No	► ►	GO to **AA2**. GO to **AA4**.
AA2 CHECK WINDSHIELD WASHER RESERVOIR FLUID LEVEL SENSOR • Turn ignition switch to OFF. • Disconnect harness connector from windshield washer reservoir fluid level sensor. • Turn ignition switch to RUN. • Check electronic instrument cluster for windshield washer fluid warning. • **Is warning displayed?**	Yes No	► ►	GO to **AA3**. SERVICE windshield washer reservoir fluid level sensor.
AA3 CHECK CIRCUIT 82 (PK/Y) FOR SHORT TO GROUND • Turn ignition switch to OFF. • Disconnect electronic instrument cluster. • Check resistance to ground of Connector Pin C1-10, Circuit 82 (PK/Y). • **Is resistance less than 10 K ohms?**	Yes No	► ►	SERVICE Circuit 82 (PK/Y) for short to ground. RESTORE vehicle. RETEST system. REPLACE electronic instrument cluster. AFFIX odometer sticker to door pillar. RESTORE vehicle. RETEST system.
AA4 JUMP WINDSHIELD WASHER RESERVOIR FLUID LEVEL SENSOR • Turn ignition switch to OFF. • Unplug harness connector from windshield washer reservoir fluid level sensor. • Connect a jumper wire across the 2 pins of harness connector. • Turn ignition switch to RUN. • Check messages for LOW WASHER FLUID warning. • **Is warning displayed?**	Yes No	► ►	SERVICE windshield washer reservoir fluid level sensor. GO to **AA5**.
AA5 CHECK CIRCUIT 82 (PK/Y) CONTINUITY • Turn to OFF. • Disconnect electronic instrument cluster. • Check continuity in Circuit 82 (PK/Y). • **Is continuity present?**	Yes No	► ►	REPLACE electronic instrument cluster. AFFIX odometer sticker to door pillar. RESTORE vehicle. RETEST system. SERVICE Circuit 82 (PK/Y) for open circuit. RESTORE vehicle. RETEST system.

FM9099600585000X

Fig. 26 Pinpoint test AA. Crown Victoria & Grand Marquis

Test Step	Result	▶	Action to Take
BB1 CHECK ELECTRONIC INSTRUMENT CLUSTER FOR MIL WARNING			
• Check for warning messages. • **Is CHECK ENGINE warning displayed?**			
	No	▶	System OK.

FM9099600586000X

Fig. 27 Pinpoint test BB. Crown Victoria & Grand Marquis

Test Step	Result	▶	Action to Take
DD1 CHECK ELECTRONIC INSTRUMENT CLUSTER FOR WARNING			
• Check electronic instrument cluster for RH turn indicator to determine if the RH turn indicator is always on or never on. • **Is RH turn indicator always on?**	Yes No	▶ ▶	GO to DD2. GO to DD3.
DD2 ISOLATE RH TURN INDICATOR SOURCE			
• Remove electronic instrument cluster as outlined. • Disconnect connector C3 from electronic instrument cluster. • Measure voltage at connector Pin C3-5 Circuit 2 (W/LB) without turn signal activated. • **Is voltage 0V?**	Yes No	▶ ▶	REPLACE electronic instrument cluster. AFFIX odometer sticker to door pillar. RESTORE vehicle. RETEST system. SERVICE Circuit 2 (W/LB) for short circuit.
DD3 CHECK FOR TURN SIGNAL SWITCH POWER INPUT			
• Remove electronic instrument cluster as outlined. • Using the turn signal lever, signal for a right turn. • Using a multimeter, measure voltage at connector Pin C3-5, Circuit 2 (W/LB). • **Is voltage greater than 9 volts?**	Yes No	▶ ▶	REPLACE electronic instrument cluster. AFFIX odometer sticker to door pillar. RESTORE vehicle. RETEST system. SERVICE Circuit 2 (W/LB) for open circuit.

FM9099600624000X

Fig. 29 Pinpoint test DD. Crown Victoria & Grand Marquis

Test Step	Result	▶	Action to Take
FF1 CHECK SAFETY BELT SWITCH INPUT			
• Unbuckle driver safety belt. • Using an ohmmeter connected to a known good ground, connect second lead to Pin C2-17, Circuit 85 (BR/LB) at lighting control module. • Measure resistance. • **Is resistance 5 ohms or less?**	Yes No	▶ ▶	GO to FF2. SERVICE Circuit 85 (BR/LB) for open circuit. RESTORE vehicle. RETEST system.

FM9099600589010X

Fig. 31 Pinpoint test FF (Part 1 of 2). Crown Victoria & Grand Marquis

Test Step	Result	▶	Action to Take
FF2 CHECK CIRCUIT 450 (BK/LG) OUTPUT AT LIGHTING CONTROL MODULE			
• Using a voltmeter connected to a known good ground, connect second lead to Pin C3-8, Circuit 450 (BK/LG) at lighting control module. • Turn ignition switch to the RUN position. • **Is voltage B+?**	Yes No	▶ ▶	GO to FF3. REPLACE lighting control module. RESTORE vehicle. RETEST system.
FF3 CHECK CIRCUIT 450 (BK/LG) INPUT AT INSTRUMENT CLUSTER			
• Turn ignition switch OFF. • Connect voltmeter to Pin C3-11, Circuit 450 (BK/LG) at instrument cluster connector. • Turn ignition switch to the RUN position. • **Is voltage B+?**	Yes No	▶ ▶	REPLACE electronic instrument cluster. AFFIX odometer sticker to door pillar. RESTORE vehicle. RETEST system. GO to FF4.
FF4 CHECK CIRCUIT 450 (BK/LG) FOR OPEN			
• Turn ignition switch OFF. • Disconnect lighting control module. • Using an ohmmeter, connect one lead to Pin C3-8, Circuit 450 (BK/LG) at module connector. Connect second lead to Pin C3-11, Circuit 450 (BK/LG) at instrument cluster connector. • Check continuity. • **Is resistance 5 ohms or less?**	Yes No	▶ ▶	REPLACE electronic instrument cluster. AFFIX odometer sticker to door pillar. RESTORE vehicle. RETEST system. SERVICE Circuit 450 (BK/LG) for open circuit. RESTORE vehicle. RETEST system.

FM9099600589020X

Fig. 31 Pinpoint test FF (Part 2 of 2). Crown Victoria & Grand Marquis

Test Step	Result	▶	Action to Take
CC1 CHECK ELECTRONIC INSTRUMENT CLUSTER FOR WARNING			
• Check electronic instrument cluster for LH turn indicator to determine if the LH turn indicator is always on or never on. • **Is LH turn indicator always on?**	Yes No	▶ ▶	GO to CC2. GO to CC3.
CC2 ISOLATE LH TURN INDICATOR SOURCE			
• Remove electronic instrument cluster as outlined. • Disconnect connector C3 from electronic instrument cluster. • Measure voltage on Pin C3-6 Circuit 3 (LG/W) without turn signal activated. • **Is voltage 0V?**	Yes No	▶ ▶	REPLACE electronic instrument cluster. AFFIX odometer sticker to door pillar. RESTORE vehicle. RETEST system. SERVICE Circuit 3 (LG/W).
CC3 CHECK FOR TURN SIGNAL SWITCH POWER INPUT			
• Remove electronic instrument cluster as outlined. • Using the turn signal lever, signal for a left turn. • Using a multimeter, measure voltage at connector Pin C3-6 Circuit 3 (LG/W). • **Is voltage greater than 9 volts?**	Yes No	▶ ▶	REPLACE electronic instrument cluster. AFFIX odometer sticker to door pillar. RESTORE vehicle. RETEST system. SERVICE Circuit 3 (LG/W) for open circuit. RETEST system.

FM9099600587000X

Fig. 28 Pinpoint test CC. Crown Victoria & Grand Marquis

Test Step	Result	▶	Action to Take
EE1 CHECK HIGH BEAM INDICATOR OPERATION			
• NOTE: Make sure the light switches are in proper positions when checking circuit operation. • Turn ignition switch to RUN. • Wait past prove-out. • Check electronic instrument cluster displays to determine whether the indicator is always on or never on. • **Is high beam indicator always on?**	Yes No	▶ ▶	GO to EE2. GO to EE4.
EE2 CHECK ELECTRONIC INSTRUMENT CLUSTER FOR SHORT CIRCUIT 932 (GY/W)			
• Disconnect connector C3 at electronic instrument cluster. • Measure voltage at connector Pin C3-4, Circuit 932 (GY/W). • **Is voltage 0V with ignition switch in RUN, headlamps on, high beams off?**	Yes No	▶ ▶	REPLACE electronic instrument cluster. AFFIX odometer sticker to door pillar. RETEST system. GO to EE3.
EE3 CHECK FOR SHORT TO B+			
• Reconnect electronic instrument cluster. • Disconnect multi-function switch. • **Is high beam indicator illuminated?**	Yes No	▶ ▶	SERVICE short to B+ in Circuit 932 (GY/W). SERVICE as required. RESTORE vehicle. RETEST system. REPLACE multi-function switch.
EE4 CHECK ELECTRONIC INSTRUMENT CLUSTER FOR OPEN CIRCUIT			
• Turn ignition switch to OFF. • Disconnect electronic instrument cluster. • Connect a jumper wire from high beam input pin of electronic instrument cluster connector Pin C3-4 to positive battery terminal. Supply ground to ground pin of electronic instrument cluster connector Pin C3-1. • **Does high beam indicator illuminate?**	Yes No	▶ ▶	GO to EE5. REPLACE electronic instrument cluster. AFFIX odometer sticker to door pillar. RESTORE vehicle. RETEST system.
EE5 CHECK CIRCUITRY			
• Reconnect electronic instrument cluster. • Disconnect multi-function switch. • Jump Circuit 932 (GY/W) multi-function switch connector Pin C2-5 to positive battery terminal. • **Is high beam indicator illuminated?**	Yes No	▶ ▶	GO to EE6. SERVICE Circuit 932 (GY/W) for open circuit. RESTORE vehicle. RETEST system.
EE6 CHECK CONTINUITY			
• Disconnect headlamp switch. • Check continuity in Circuit 15 (R/Y). • Check continuity to power in Circuit 38 (BK/O). • **Is continuity present?**	Yes No	▶ ▶	REPLACE headlamp switch. RESTORE vehicle. RETEST system. SERVICE respective circuit. RESTORE vehicle. RETEST system.

FM9099600588000X

Fig. 30 Pinpoint test EE. Crown Victoria & Grand Marquis

Test Step	Result	▶	Action to Take
GG1 CHECK ELECTRONIC INSTRUMENT CLUSTER FOR WARNINGS			
• Turn ignition switch to RUN. • Wait past prove-out time. • Check electronic instrument cluster display to determine whether the warning is always on or never on. • **Is LOW OIL PRESSURE warning always on?**	Yes No	▶ ▶	GO to GG2. GO to GG4.
GG2 CHECK ELECTRONIC INSTRUMENT CLUSTER FOR SHORT CIRCUIT			
• Disconnect oil pressure sensor. • Check electronic instrument cluster for warning. • **Is LOW OIL PRESSURE warning illuminated?**	Yes No	▶ ▶	GO to GG3. REPLACE oil pressure sensor.
GG3 CHECK CONTINUITY IN CIRCUIT 31 (W/R)			
• Turn ignition switch to OFF. • Disconnect electronic instrument cluster. • Check continuity in Circuit 31 (W/R). • **Is continuity present?**	Yes No	▶ ▶	REPLACE electronic instrument cluster. AFFIX odometer sticker to door pillar. RESTORE vehicle. RETEST system. SERVICE Circuit 31 (W/R). RESTORE vehicle. RETEST system.

FM9099600590010X

Fig. 32 Pinpoint test GG (Part 1 of 2). Crown Victoria & Grand Marquis

Test Step	Result	▶	Action to Take
GG4 CHECK FOR POWER AND GROUNDS • Check voltage on the following instrument cluster harness connector pins:	Yes No	▶ ▶	GO to GG5. SERVICE as required. RESTORE vehicle. RETEST system.

Pin	Circuit Number	Voltage
C1-7	54 (LG/Y)	12V (Hot At All Times)
C1-9	964 (DB/LG)	12V (Hot in RUN)
C3-7	88 (BK/W)	12V (Hot in RUN)
C3-2	964 (DB/LG)	12V (Hot in RUN)
C1-8	676 (GY/BK)	0V
C3-1	676 (PK/O)	0V

Test Step	Result	▶	Action to Take
• Are all voltages as specified?			
GG5 CHECK ELECTRONIC INSTRUMENT CLUSTER FOR OPEN CIRCUIT • Turn ignition switch to OFF. • Disconnect connector at oil pressure sensor. • Connect a jumper wire from Circuit 31 (W/R) to ground. • Turn ignition switch to RUN. • Check electronic instrument cluster for warning. • Is LOW OIL PRESSURE warning illuminated?	Yes No	▶ ▶	REPLACE oil pressure sensor. GO to GG6.
GG6 CHECK CONTINUITY • Remove jumper. • Disconnect electronic instrument cluster. • Check continuity in Circuit 31 (W/R). • Is continuity present?	Yes No	▶ ▶	REPLACE electronic instrument cluster. AFFIX odometer sticker to door pillar. RESTORE vehicle. RETEST system. SERVICE Circuit 3 (W/R). RESTORE vehicle. RETEST system.

FM9099600590020X

Fig. 32 Pinpoint test GG (Part 2 of 2). Crown Victoria & Grand Marquis

Test Step	Result	▶	Action to Take
JJ1 CHECK ELECTRONIC INSTRUMENT CLUSTER FOR INDICATOR • Turn ignition switch to RUN. • Wait past prove out time. • Check electronic instrument cluster display to determine whether the indicator is always on or never on. • Is OVERDRIVE OFF indicator always on?	Yes No	▶ ▶	GO to JJ2. GO to JJ4.
JJ2 CHECK POWERTRAIN CONTROL MODULE FOR SHORTED CIRCUIT • Disconnect powertrain control module. • Check electronic instrument cluster for indicator. • Is OVERDRIVE OFF indicator illuminated?	Yes No	▶ ▶	GO to JJ3. REPLACE powertrain control module.
JJ3 CHECK CONTINUITY OF CIRCUIT 911 (W/LG) • Turn ignition switch to OFF. • Disconnect electronic instrument cluster. • Check continuity in connector Pin C1-14, Circuit 911 (W/LG). • Is continuity present?	Yes No	▶ ▶	REPLACE electronic instrument cluster. RESTORE vehicle. RETEST system. SERVICE Circuit 911 (W/LG). RESTORE vehicle. RETEST system.
JJ4 CHECK POWERTRAIN CONTROL MODULE FOR OPEN CIRCUIT • Turn ignition switch to OFF. • Disconnect connector at powertrain control module. • Connect a jumper wire from Pin 79, Circuit 911 (W/LG) at harness connector to ground. • Turn ignition switch to RUN. • Check electronic instrument cluster for warning. • Is OVERDRIVE OFF indicator illuminated?	Yes No	▶ ▶	REPLACE powertrain control module. GO to JJ5.
JJ5 CHECK INDICATOR SUPPLY CIRCUIT CONTINUITY • Remove jumper. • Disconnect electronic instrument cluster. • Check continuity in connector Pin C1-14, Circuit 911 (W/LG). • Is continuity present?	Yes No	▶ ▶	REPLACE electronic instrument cluster. RESTORE vehicle. RETEST system. SERVICE Circuit 911 (W/LG). RESTORE vehicle. RETEST system.

FM9099600592000X

Fig. 34 Pinpoint test JJ. Crown Victoria & Grand Marquis

Test Step	Result	▶	Action to Take
KK1 CHECK DISPLAYS • Turn ignition switch to OFF. • Turn headlamp switch to PARK position. • Check other displays: radio, message center switch module. • Do other displays illuminate properly?	Yes No	▶ ▶	GO to KK2. GO to Pinpoint Test Step A3.
KK2 CHECK ELECTRONIC INSTRUMENT CLUSTER BULB • Check the bulb in the electronic instrument cluster. • Is bulb OK?	Yes No	▶ ▶	SERVICE Circuit 19 (LB/R). RESTORE vehicle. RETEST system. REPLACE bulb. RESTORE vehicle. RETEST system.

FM9099600593000X

Fig. 35 Pinpoint test KK. Crown Victoria & Grand Marquis

Test Step	Result	▶	Action to Take
HH1 CHECK ELECTRONIC INSTRUMENT CLUSTER FOR WARNINGS • Turn ignition switch to RUN. • Wait past prove-out time. • Check electronic instrument cluster display to determine whether the warning is always on or never on. • Is AIR BAG warning always on?	Yes No	▶ ▶	GO to HH2. GO to HH4.

FM9099600591010X

Fig. 33 Pinpoint test HH (Part 1 of 2). Crown Victoria & Grand Marquis

Test Step	Result	▶	Action to Take
HH2 CHECK AIR BAG DIAGNOSTIC MONITOR FOR INTERNAL SHORT TO GROUND NOTE: If the air bag warning indicator flashes on and off continuously it means that it is showing a diagnostic code. It does not mean that the air bag warning indicator needs to be serviced. **WARNING: THE BACKUP POWER SUPPLY ENERGY MUST BE DEPLETED BEFORE ANY AIR BAG COMPONENT SERVICE IS PERFORMED AS PERSONAL INJURY MAY RESULT. TO DEPLETE BACKUP POWER SUPPLY ENERGY, DISCONNECT THE POSITIVE BATTERY CABLE AND WAIT ONE MINUTE.** • Disconnect battery ground cable. • Disconnect positive battery cable and wait one minute. • Disconnect air bag diagnostic monitor. • Reconnect positive battery cable. • Reconnect battery ground cable. • Check electronic instrument cluster for warning. • Is AIR BAG warning illuminated?	Yes No	▶ ▶	GO to HH3. REPLACE air bag diagnostic monitor.
HH3 CHECK CONTINUITY OF CIRCUIT 608 (BK/Y) • Turn ignition switch to OFF. • Disconnect electronic instrument cluster. • Check continuity in Circuit 608 (BK/Y). • Is continuity present?	Yes No	▶ ▶	REPLACE electronic instrument cluster. AFFIX odometer sticker to door pillar. RESTORE vehicle. RETEST system. SERVICE Circuit 608 (BK/Y). RESTORE vehicle. RETEST system.
HH4 CHECK AIR BAG DIAGNOSTIC MONITOR FOR INTERNAL OPEN CIRCUIT **WARNING: THE BACKUP POWER SUPPLY ENERGY MUST BE DEPLETED BEFORE ANY AIR BAG COMPONENT SERVICE IS PERFORMED AS PERSONAL INJURY MAY RESULT. TO DEPLETE BACKUP POWER SUPPLY ENERGY, DISCONNECT THE POSITIVE BATTERY CABLE AND WAIT ONE MINUTE.** • Turn ignition switch to OFF. • Disconnect battery ground cable. • Disconnect positive battery cable and wait one minute. • Disconnect connector at air bag diagnostic monitor. • Connect a jumper wire from Circuit 608 (BK/Y) at harness connector to ground. • Reconnect positive battery cable. • Reconnect battery ground cable. • Turn ignition switch to RUN. • Check electronic instrument cluster for warning. • Is AIR BAG warning illuminated?	Yes No	▶ ▶	REPLACE air bag diagnostic monitor. GO to HH5.
HH5 CHECK AIR BAG INPUT CIRCUIT CONTINUITY • Remove jumper. • Disconnect electronic instrument cluster. • Check continuity in Circuit 608 (BK/Y). • Is continuity present?	Yes No	▶ ▶	REPLACE electronic instrument cluster. AFFIX odometer sticker to door pillar. RESTORE vehicle. RETEST system. SERVICE Circuit 608 (BK/Y). RESTORE vehicle. RETEST system.

FM9099600591020X

Fig. 33 Pinpoint test HH (Part 2 of 2). Crown Victoria & Grand Marquis

Test Step	Result	▶	Action to Take
A1 CHECK DISPLAYS - HEADLAMPS OFF • Turn ignition switch to RUN. • Turn headlamps OFF. • Verify illumination of electronic instrument cluster, clock and radio. • Is electronic cluster display off with other displays on?	Yes No	▶ ▶	GO to A2. GO to A3.
A2 CHECK INSTRUMENT CLUSTER POWER • Verify power at electronic instrument cluster Pins C1-7, Circuit 797 (LG/O), C1-9, Circuit 295 (LB/PK), C3-2, Circuit 295 (LB/PK) with ignition switch in RUN position. • Is power present?	Yes No	▶ ▶	REPLACE electronic instrument cluster. SERVICE Circuits 295 (LB/PK) or 797 (LG/P).
A3 CHECK DISPLAYS - HEADLAMPS ON • Turn ignition switch to RUN. • Turn parking lamps on. • While varying dimming level check other displays: radio, clock, transmission range indicator. • Do other displays illuminate properly?	Yes No	▶ ▶	GO to A4. GO to A5.
A4 CHECK FOR CIRCUIT 19 (LB/R) VOLTAGE • Turn parking lamps off. • Disconnect electronic instrument cluster. • Turn parking lamps on. • While varying dimming level, check voltage in Circuit 19 (LB/R) at Connector Pin C1-13 of electronic instrument cluster. • Does voltage vary between 4 and 15V?	Yes No	▶ ▶	REPLACE electronic instrument cluster. AFFIX odometer sticker to door pillar. RESTORE vehicle. RETEST system. SERVICE Circuit 19 (LB/R). RESTORE vehicle. RETEST system.
A5 CHECK FOR LIGHTING CONTROL MODULE • Check fuse junction panel fuses 18 (10A) and 7 (10A). Replace if necessary. Proceed if displays still do not illuminate properly. • While varying dimming level, verify voltage output at lighting control module. • Does dimming input voltage vary between 4 and 15V?	Yes No	▶ ▶	SERVICE Circuit 19 (LB/R). RESTORE vehicle. RETEST system. GO to lighting control module diagnosis.

FM9099600595000X

Fig. 36 Pinpoint test A. Town Car

Fig. 37 Pinpoint test B. Town Car

Test Step	Result	▶	Action to Take
B1 PERFORM SELF TEST			
• Turn ignition switch to OFF position. • Push in the E/M and <SELECT (left) buttons and hold. • Turn ignition switch to RUN position while holding buttons. • Release buttons when cluster lights. • **Does odometer flash?**	Yes No	▶ ▶	REPLACE electronic instrument cluster. AFFIX odometer sticker to door pillar. RESTORE vehicle. RETEST system. GO to B2.
B2 DISPLAY TEST			
NOTE: There are 17 segment displays. • Push SELECT> button once to enter display test. • Push E/M button to step through display test inspection and verification. • Display test start with all blue/green segments off. Test then cycles through following test to turn on each segment or indicator ISO one time only, then begins to full display after each segment has been tested individually until all blue/green segments are on. Next switch press start cycle all over again. • **Do any segments stay on always or never come on?**	Yes No	▶ ▶	REPLACE electronic instrument cluster. AFFIX odometer sticker to door pillar. RESTORE vehicle. RETEST system. Electronic instrument cluster OK. RESTORE vehicle.

FM9099600596000X

Fig. 38 Pinpoint test C (Part 2 of 2). Town Car

Test Step	Result	▶	Action to Take
C8 CHECK EATC INPUT FROM CLUSTER IN ENGLISH MODE			
• Turn ignition switch to RUN. • Remove the connector from the electronic automatic temperature control. • Press the E/M button so that the instrument cluster is in ENGLISH mode. • Check electronic automatic temperature control connector Pin C2-20, Circuit 506 (R). • **Is Pin 20 at 5 volts DC?**	Yes No	▶ ▶	REFER to Electronic Automatic Temperature Control Diagnostics. GO to C9.
C9 CHECK ELECTRONIC INSTRUMENT CLUSTER OUTPUT TO ELECTRONIC AUTOMATIC TEMPERATURE CONTROL IN ENGLISH MODE			
• Leave ignition switch at RUN. • Connector is removed from the electronic automatic temperature control. • Press the E/M button so that the instrument cluster is in ENGLISH mode. • Remove connector C2 from instrument cluster. • Check Pin 32 of the instrument cluster (not the harness connector). • **Is instrument cluster Pin 32 at 5 volts DC?**	Yes No	▶ ▶	SERVICE Circuit 506 (R) for short to ground or to another wire. RESTORE vehicle. RETEST system. REPLACE electronic instrument cluster. AFFIX odometer sticker to door pillar. RESTORE vehicle. RETEST system.
C10 CHECK EATC INPUT FROM ELECTRONIC INSTRUMENT CLUSTER IN METRIC MODE			
• Turn ignition switch to RUN. • Remove the connector from the electronic automatic temperature control. • Press the E/M button so that the instrument cluster is in METRIC mode. • Check electronic automatic temperature control connector Pin C2-20, Circuit 506 (R). • **Is Pin 20 at 0 volts DC?**	Yes No	▶ ▶	REFER to electronic automatic temperature control Diagnostics. GO to C11.
C11 CHECK ELECTRONIC INSTRUMENT CLUSTER OUTPUT TO ELECTRONIC AUTOMATIC TEMPERATURE CONTROL IN METRIC MODE			
• Leave ignition switch at RUN. • Connector still removed from the electronic automatic temperature control. • Press the E/M button so that the instrument cluster is in METRIC mode. • Remove Connector C2 from instrument cluster. • Check Pin 32 of the instrument cluster (not the harness connector). • **Is instrument cluster Pin 32 at 0 volts DC?**	Yes No	▶ ▶	SERVICE Circuit 506(R) for open. CHECK for intermittent contact. RESTORE vehicle. RETEST system. REPLACE electronic instrument cluster. AFFIX odometer sticker to door pillar. RESTORE vehicle. RETEST system.

FM9099600597020X

Fig. 39 Pinpoint test D (Part 1 of 2). Town Car

Test Step	Result	▶	Action to Take
D1 CHECK FUEL PUMP WIRING AT FUEL PUMP MODULE			
• Disconnect battery ground cable. Refer to Section 14-01. • Lower fuel tank to gain access to fuel pump module connector. • Unplug fuel pump (FP) module connector. • Jumper variable resistance terminal Circuit 29 (Y/W) and ground terminal Circuit 676 (PK/O) of fuel pump module connector. • Reconnect battery. • Turn ignition switch from OFF to RUN. • NOTE: It may take several minutes for the fuel gauge to respond. Check digital fuel remaining display to determine whether it shows CO or CS. • **Does fuel gauge display show CO?**	Yes No	▶ ▶	GO to D3. REMOVE jumper. GO to D2.

FM9099600598010X

Fig. 38 Pinpoint test C (Part 1 of 2). Town Car

Test Step	Result	▶	Action to Take
C1 CHECK FOR WARNING CHIME			
NOTE: Buttons function only with ignition switch in RUN. • Check for fasten safety belt reminder chime or key in ignition reminder chime. • **Does chime sound?**	Yes No	▶ ▶	GO to C2. REFER to chime diagnosis.
C2 CHECK ELECTRONIC AUTOMATIC TEMPERATURE CONTROL METRIC MODE OUTPUT			
• Check E/M button operation. • **Is electronic automatic temperature control stuck at metric mode?**	Yes No	▶ ▶	GO to C10. GO to C3.
C3 CHECK ELECTRONIC AUTOMATIC TEMPERATURE CONTROL ENGLISH MODE OUTPUT			
• Check E/M button operation. • **Is electronic automatic temperature control stuck at English mode?**	Yes No	▶ ▶	GO to C8. GO to C4.
C4 CHECK SWITCH WIRING CONNECTIONS			
• Remove finish panel to expose instrument cluster. • Verify that connections at message center switch module assembly are securely connected. • **Are connections secure?**	Yes No	▶ ▶	GO to C5. Secure connections and RECHECK.
C5 CHECK MESSAGE CENTER SWITCH ASSEMBLY (NO SWITCH PRESSED)			
• Disconnect message center module. • Measure the resistance between Pin 5, Circuit 143 (LB/Y) and Pin 4, Circuit 676 (PK/O) of the message center switch module. • Resistance with no switch pressed should be 17,300 to 17,600 ohms. • **Is resistance within range?**	Yes No	▶ ▶	GO to C6. REPLACE message center switch module. RESTORE vehicle. RETEST system.
C6 CHECK SWITCH ASSEMBLY (BUTTONS PRESSED)			
• Disconnect message center module from electronic instrument cluster. • NOTE: Press only one button of the message center switch module while pressing the problem button. Measure the resistance between Pin 5, Circuit 143 (LB/Y) and Pin 4, Circuit 676 (PK/O). • NOTE: Measure resistance for Pins 6 and 4 for SELECT forward and REVERSE, between Pins 5 and 4 for E/M Reset.	Yes No	▶ ▶	GO to C7. REPLACE message center switch module. RESTORE vehicle. RETEST system.

The resistance should be:

Pins	Button	Resistance (in ohms)
5-4	E/M	5100-5200
6-4	SELECT (forward)	5100-5200
6-4	SELECT (reverse)	2250-2350
5-4	RESET	2250-2350

Test Step	Result	▶	Action to Take
• **Is resistance within range?**			
C7 VERIFY HARNESS CONTINUITY			
• Disconnect battery ground cable. • Remove electronic instrument cluster. • Check continuity in Circuit 143 (LB/Y), Connector Pin C1-3 and 152 (LB/W), Connector Pin C2-23. • Using an ohmmeter, check resistance to ground in Circuit 676 (PK/O) and Pin 8 of switch module, C1-8 of electronic instrument cluster (BK/LB). • **Is resistance 10K ohms or less?**	Yes No	▶ ▶	REPLACE electronic instrument cluster. AFFIX odometer sticker to door pillar. RESTORE vehicle. RETEST system. SERVICE respective circuit. RESTORE vehicle. RETEST system.

FM9099600597010X

Fig. 39 Pinpoint test D (Part 2 of 2). Town Car

Test Step	Result	▶	Action to Take
D2 CHECK FUEL PUMP RESISTANCE			
• Turn ignition switch to OFF. • Measure the resistance of the fuel pump module at Circuits 787 (PK/BK) and 57 (BK). • Verify that the resistance is less than 181 ohms (normally between 15 and 160 ohms). • **Is resistance less than 181 ohms?**	Yes No	▶ ▶	GO to D4. REPLACE fuel pump. RESTORE vehicle. RETEST system.
D3 CHECK FUEL PUMP WIRING AT ELECTRONIC INSTRUMENT CLUSTER			
• Disconnect battery ground cable. • Remove connector C1 from electronic instrument cluster and secure connectors from shorting. • Jumper variable resistance terminal Circuit 29 (Y/W) and ground terminal Circuit 676 (PK/O) of harness together at fuel pump module. • **Is resistance close to zero ohms?**	Yes No	▶ ▶	REPLACE electronic instrument cluster. AFFIX odometer sticker to door pillar. RESTORE vehicle. RETEST system. SERVICE fuel pump wiring for open circuit. RESTORE vehicle. RETEST system.
D4 VERIFY FUEL PUMP MODULE RESISTANCE OVER RANGE			
• Remove fuel pump. • Measure resistance while moving float rod arm slowly from empty to full. • **Does resistance exceed 181 ohms at any time?**	Yes No	▶ ▶	REPLACE fuel pump module. INSPECT fuel pump wiring connector female terminals to flash or loose fit. SERVICE as required. RESTORE vehicle. RETEST system.

FM9099600598020X

Fig. 40 Pinpoint test E. Town Car

Test Step	Result	▶	Action to Take
E1 CHECK FUEL PUMP WIRING RESISTANCE AT ELECTRONIC INSTRUMENT CLUSTER			
• Disconnect battery ground cable. • Remove instrument cluster and secure connectors from shorting. • With an ohmmeter, measure resistance between Pin C1-6, Circuit 29 (Y/W) and Pin C1-8, Circuit 676 (PK/O). • Verify that the resistance is 14 ohms or greater (normally 15 to 160 ohms). • **Is resistance at least 14 ohms?**	Yes No	▶ ▶	REPLACE electronic instrument cluster. AFFIX odometer sticker to door pillar. RESTORE vehicle. RETEST system. GO to E2.
E2 CHECK FUEL PUMP WIRING			
• Lower fuel tank to gain access to fuel pump module connector. • Unplug connector at fuel pump module. • Measure the resistance between Connector Pin C1-6, Circuit 29 (Y/W) and Pin C1-8, Circuit 676 (PK/O). • Verify that resistance is greater than 10 K ohms. • **Is resistance at least 10 K ohms?**	Yes No	▶ ▶	REPLACE fuel pump. RESTORE vehicle. RETEST system. SERVICE fuel pump wiring for short circuit. RESTORE vehicle. RETEST system.

FM9099600599000X

Test Step	Result	▶	Action to Take
F1 CHECK FUEL GAUGE RESPONSE			
• Disconnect battery ground cable.	Yes	▶	TURN ignition switch to OFF. GO to F3.
• Lower fuel tank and gain access to fuel pump module connections.	No	▶	TURN ignition switch to OFF. Leave 43 ohm resistor connected. GO to F2.
• Connect a resistor value of between 170-100 ohms.			
• Reconnect battery.			
• Turn ignition switch to the RUN position. Display 1/2 tank or above fuel level.			
• Turn ignition switch to OFF. Disconnect battery.			
• Remove 170-100 ohms resistor.			
• Connect a 43 ohm (± 1 percent) resistor in place of fuel pump module. Verify value with ohmmeter.			
• Reconnect battery.			
• Turn ignition switch to RUN.			
• NOTE: Allow at least 30 seconds for cluster to read level. FUEL REMAIN should read 3 to 4 GAL (13 to 15 LTR).			
• Is fuel gauge correct?			
F2 CHECK HARNESS RESISTANCE			
• Disconnect battery ground cable.	Yes	▶	REPLACE electronic instrument cluster. AFFIX odometer sticker to door pillar. RESTORE vehicle. RETEST system.
• Remove electronic instrument cluster and secure connectors from shorting.	No	▶	SERVICE Circuit 29 (Y/W). RESTORE vehicle. RETEST system.
• Measure resistance between Connector Pin C1-6, Circuit 29 (Y/W) and Pin C1-8, Circuit 676 (PK/O) with 43 ohm resistor in place.			
• Is resistance within range?			
F3 CHECK FUEL PUMP MODULE			
• Disconnect battery ground cable.	Yes	▶	GO to F4.
• Check fuel pump module for binding, sticking, misalignment, etc.	No	▶	SERVICE or REPLACE fuel pump module.
• Check sender resistance not to exceed 181 ohms while moving arm slowly from full to empty.			
• Check fuel pump resistance. Resistance should be 135 to 165 ohms of full stop and 14 to 18 ohms at empty stop.			
• Is fuel pump module resistance within limits specified?			
F4 CHECK FUEL TANK			
• Check fuel tank for dents, bulges or other damage.	Yes	▶	System OK. Condition caused by other vehicle system(s). RESTORE vehicle.
• Check for proper installation of fuel tube.			
• Is fuel tank OK?	No	▶	REPLACE fuel tank or fuel tube.

FM9099600600000X

Fig. 41   Pinpoint test F. Town Car

Test Step	Result	▶	Action to Take
G1 CHECK FOR TEMPERATURE SENDER SHORT			
• Disconnect engine coolant temperature sensor connector.	Yes	▶	REPLACE engine coolant temperature sensor.
• Turn ignition switch to RUN.			
• **Does temperature gauge indicate COLD with bottom bar lit?**	No	▶	GO to G2.

FM9099600601010X

Fig. 42   Pinpoint test G (Part 1 of 2). Town Car

Test Step	Result	▶	Action to Take
G2 CHECK FOR SHORT IN WIRING			
• Disconnect battery ground cable.	Yes	▶	REPLACE electronic instrument cluster. AFFIX odometer sticker to door pillar. RESTORE vehicle. RETEST system.
• Unplug engine coolant temperature sensor connector.	No	▶	SERVICE Circuit 39 (R/W) as required. RESTORE vehicle. RETEST system.
• Disconnect connector C1 and connector C2 from electronic instrument cluster.			
• Measure resistance between connector Pin C1-4, Circuit 39 (R/W) and Pin C1-8, Circuit 676 (PK/O).			
• **Is resistance greater than 15 K ohms?**			

FM9099600601020X

Fig. 42   Pinpoint test G (Part 2 of 2). Town Car

Test Step	Result	▶	Action to Take
H1 CHECK TEMPERATURE GAUGE WIRING			
• Unplug connector to engine coolant temperature sensor and connect a jumper in place of the sensor.	Yes	▶	GO to H3. REMOVE jumper. REPLACE engine coolant temperature sensor. RESTORE vehicle. RETEST system.
• Turn ignition switch to RUN.	No	▶	GO to H2.
• Gauge should give a short circuit indication. (Blinking thermometer symbol and top two and bottom two bars of gauge lit.)			
• **Does gauge indicate short circuit?**			
H2 CHECK WIRING AT CLUSTER			
• Disconnect battery ground cable.	Yes	▶	REPLACE electronic instrument cluster. AFFIX odometer sticker to door pillar. RESTORE vehicle. RETEST system.
• Disconnect C1 and C2 connectors from electronic instrument cluster.	No	▶	SERVICE wiring Circuit 39 (R/W) and 676 (PK/O). RESTORE vehicle. RETEST system.
• Connect jumper in place of engine coolant temperature sensor.			
• Using an ohmmeter, measure resistance between Pin C1-8, Circuit 676 (PK/O) and Pin C1-4, Circuit 39 (R/W).			
• **Is resistance 5 ohms or less?**			
H3 CHECK ENGINE COOLANT TEMPERATURE SENSOR			
• Warm up engine to normal operating temperature.	Yes	▶	GO to H4.
• Measure resistance of engine coolant temperature sensor.	No	▶	REPLACE electronic instrument cluster. AFFIX odometer sticker to door pillar. RESTORE vehicle. RETEST system.
• **Is resistance greater than 8 K ohms?**			
H4 CHECK COOLING SYSTEM			
• Check thermostat, coolant level and other cooling system components for proper operation.	Yes	▶	REPLACE electronic automatic temperature control sensor. REFER to
• **Is cooling system OK?**	No	▶	SERVICE cooling system as required.

FM9099600602000X

Fig. 43   Pinpoint test H. Town Car

Test Step	Result	▶	Action to Take
J1 REVIEW OPERATION/CONDITION			
NOTE: Chime will not beep if another sound is being produced. Driver alert only given for temperatures above normal band.	Yes	▶	System OK.
• Turn ignition switch to RUN.	No	▶	GO to Pinpoint Test C.
• Press any message center switch module button and listen for beep.			
• **Does beep sound?**			

FM9099600603000X

Fig. 44   Pinpoint test J. Town Car

Test Step	Result	▶	Action to Take
K1 CHECK SPEEDOMETER READING			
• Test drive vehicle above 8 km/h (5 mph) and look for:	Yes	▶	REPLACE electronic instrument cluster. AFFIX odometer sticker to door pillar. RESTORE vehicle. RETEST system.
— speedometer reading	No	▶	GO to K2.
— odometer changing			
• Verify that odometer advances when vehicle is driven forward.			
• **Does odometer advance with no speed indication?**			
K2 CHECK SPEED CONTROL			
• Test drive vehicle above 48 km/h (30 mph), check speed control operation.	Yes	▶	GO to K3.
• **Did speed control operate properly?**	No	▶	GO to K4.
K3 CHECK CONTINUITY			
• Disconnect battery ground cable.	Yes	▶	REPLACE electronic instrument cluster. AFFIX odometer sticker to door pillar. RESTORE vehicle. RETEST system.
• Disconnect connectors C1 and C2 at electronic instrument cluster.	No	▶	SERVICE respective circuit. RESTORE vehicle. RETEST system.
• Disconnect vehicle speed sensor.			
• Check continuity in Connector Pin C1-12, Circuit 679 (GY/BK) and continuity to ground in Connector Pin C1-8, Circuit 676 (PK/O).			
• **Is continuity present?**			
K4 CHECK VEHICLE SPEED SENSOR			
• Disconnect vehicle speed sensor.	Yes	▶	CHECK Circuits 679 (GY/BK) and 676 (PK/O) for continuity. If circuits OK, CHECK driven gear and retainer clip. REPLACE if necessary.
• Measure resistance across vehicle speed sensor.			
• **Is resistance between 200-300 ohms?**	No	▶	REPLACE vehicle speed sensor.

FM9099600604000X

Fig. 45   Pinpoint test K. Town Car

Test Step	Result	▶	Action to Take
L1 CHECK VEHICLE SPEED SENSOR DRIVE GEAR			
• Remove vehicle speed sensor from transmission and verify that correct drive gear is installed for vehicle transmission/axle/tire combination.	Yes	▶	GO to L2.
• **Is drive gear correct?**	No	▶	INSTALL correct gear with retaining clip.
L2 CHECK DRIVE GEAR ON TRANSMISSION OUTPUT SHAFT			
• Check that correct drive gear is installed on transmission output shaft.	Yes	▶	GO to L3.
• **Is drive gear correct?**	No	▶	INSTALL correct output shaft and/or gear.
L3 CHECK CONTINUITY			
• Disconnect battery ground cable.	Yes	▶	GO to L4.
• Disconnect connectors C1 and C2 at electronic instrument cluster.	No	▶	SERVICE respective circuit. RESTORE vehicle. RETEST system.
• Check continuity in Connector Pin C1-12, Circuit 679 (GY/BK) and Pin C1-8, Circuit 676 (PK/O).			
• **Is continuity present?**			

FM9099600605010X

Fig. 46   Pinpoint test L (Part 1 of 2). Town Car

Test Step	Result	▶	Action to Take
L4 CHECK VEHICLE SPEED SENSOR			
• Disconnect vehicle speed sensor. • Measure resistance across vehicle speed sensor. • **Is resistance between 200-300 ohms?**	Yes	▶	REPLACE instrument cluster. AFFIX odometer sticker to door pillar. RESTORE vehicle. RETEST system.
	No	▶	REPLACE vehicle speed sensor.

FM9099600605020X

Fig. 46 Pinpoint test L (Part 2 of 2). Town Car

Test Step	Result	▶	Action to Take
M1 CHECK SPEED SENSOR DRIVE GEAR			
• Remove vehicle speed sensor from transmission. • Check that all gear teeth are in good condition, retainer clip is installed and gear does not slip on shaft. • **Is vehicle speed sensor in good condition?**	Yes	▶	GO to L3.
	No	▶	REPLACE drive gear and/or retaining clip.

FM9099600606000X

Fig. 47 Pinpoint test M. Town Car

Test Step	Result	▶	Action to Take
N1 CHECK SPEED CONTROL SERVO			
• Disconnect connector from speed control servo. • **Does speed control indicator go out?**	Yes	▶	REPLACE speed control servo. VERIFY proper operation.
	No	▶	GO to N2.
N2 CHECK ELECTRONIC INSTRUMENT CLUSTER			
• Disconnect instrument cluster connector C2. • **Does speed control indicator go off?**	Yes	▶	CHECK Circuit 203 (O/LB) at Connector Pin C2-26 for short to ground. SERVICE as required. RESTORE vehicle. RETEST system.
	No	▶	REPLACE electronic instrument cluster. AFFIX odometer sticker to door pillar. RESTORE vehicle. RETEST system.

FM9099600607000X

Fig. 48 Pinpoint test N. Town Car

Test Step	Result	▶	Action to Take
P1 CHECK VOLTAGE AT SPEED CONTROL SERVO			
• Disconnect connector from speed control servo. • Turn ignition switch to RUN. • Measure voltage between Connector Pin C2-26, Circuit 203 (O/LB) and Pin C1-8, Circuit 676 (PK/O). • **Is voltage approximately 5V?**	Yes	▶	GO to P2.
	No	▶	GO to P3.
P2 CHECK CONTINUITY CIRCUIT 203 (O/LB)			
• Disconnect electronic instrument cluster. • Check continuity in Circuit 203 (O/LB). • **Is continuity present?**	Yes	▶	REPLACE electronic instrument cluster. AFFIX odometer sticker to door pillar. RESTORE vehicle. RETEST system.
	No	▶	SERVICE Circuit 203 (O/LB). RESTORE vehicle. RETEST system.

FM9099600608010X

Fig. 49 Pinpoint test P (Part 1 of 2). Town Car

Test Step	Result	▶	Action to Take
P3 VERIFY B+ AT SPEED CONTROL SERVO			
• Check for B+ at the speed control servo connector in Circuit 295 (LB/PK). • **Is B+ present?**	Yes	▶	REPLACE speed control servo.
	No	▶	SERVICE Circuit 295 (LB/PK). RESTORE vehicle. RETEST system.

FM9099600608020X

Fig. 49 Pinpoint test P (Part 2 of 2). Town Car

Test Step	Result	▶	Action to Take
Q1 DETERMINE IF SPEEDOMETER/ODOMETER MODULE IS ORIGINAL			
• Check for mileage sticker on door pillar. • **Is mileage sticker original?**	Yes	▶	REPLACE electronic instrument cluster. If odometer reading is known, program it into new electronic instrument cluster. If odometer reading is unknown, program in "S" 00000.5 with the circled S and zero miles in the odometer. RESTORE vehicle. RETEST system.
	No	▶	System OK. RESTORE vehicle.

FM9099600609000X

Fig. 50 Pinpoint test Q. Town Car

Test Step	Result	▶	Action to Take
R1 CHECK SPEEDOMETER			
• Verify that speedometer is operating properly. • **Does speedometer operate properly?**	Yes	▶	REPLACE electronic instrument cluster. Affix odometer sticker to door pillar. RESTORE vehicle. RETEST system.
	No	▶	GO to Pinpoint Test L.

FM9099600610000X

Fig. 51 Pinpoint test R. Town Car

Test Step	Result	▶	Action to Take
S1 CHECK ODOMETER OPERATION			
• Check odometer to determine whether it accumulates and then loses 1.6 km (1.0 mile) or it will not accumulate mileage at all. • **Does odometer accumulate and then lose 1.6 km (1.0 mile)?**	Yes	▶	REPLACE electronic instrument cluster. AFFIX odometer sticker to door pillar. RESTORE vehicle. RETEST system.
	No	▶	GO to S2.
S2 VERIFY SPEEDOMETER			
• Verify that speedometer works properly. • **Does speedometer operate properly?**	Yes	▶	REPLACE electronic instrument cluster. AFFIX odometer sticker to door pillar. RESTORE vehicle. RETEST system.
	No	▶	GO to Pinpoint Test K.

FM9099600611000X

Fig. 52 Pinpoint test S. Town Car

Test Step	Result	▶	Action to Take
T1 CHECK MESSAGE CENTER DISPLAY			
• Check message center display to determine whether it is showing 0 MPG, 99L/100 KM or 99 MPG, 0L/100 KM. • **Is message center display showing 0 MPG, 99 L/100 Km?**	Yes	▶	GO to T2.
	No	▶	GO to T3.

FM9099600612010X

Fig. 53 Pinpoint test T (Part 1 of 2). Town Car

Test Step	Result	▶	Action to Take
T2 CHECK SPEEDOMETER OPERATION			
• Verify that speedometer is operating properly. • **Does speedometer operate properly?**	Yes	▶	REPLACE electronic instrument cluster. AFFIX odometer sticker to door pillar. RESTORE vehicle. RETEST system.
	No	▶	GO to Pinpoint Test K.
T3 OBSERVE TRANSMISSION CONTROL OFF INDICATOR LAMP			
• Test drive vehicle with transmission control switch pressed (overdrive locked-out) selected. • **Does transmission control indicator lamp off indicator flash?**			
	No	▶	GO to T4.
T4 CHECK CONTINUITY OF CIRCUIT 205 (FUEL FLOW)			
• Verify continuity and absence of shorts in Circuit 205 (DB/LG). • **Is wiring OK?**	Yes	▶	GO to T5.
	No	▶	SERVICE wiring Circuit 205 (DB/LG) as required. RESTORE vehicle. RETEST system.
T5 ENTER SELF TEST MODE			
• Turn ignition switch to OFF. • Push and hold E/M and <SELECT buttons together. • Turn ignition switch to START while holding buttons. • Release buttons when cluster lights. • Allow engine to run during remainder of test. • Observe odometer. • **Does odometer flash?**	Yes	▶	REPLACE electronic instrument cluster. AFFIX odometer sticker to door pillar. RESTORE vehicle. RETEST system.
	No	▶	GO to T6.
T6 ENTER DISPLAY TEST MODE			
• Push SELECT> (right) button once and observe display. • **Is the display the same as in Step 1 of segment displays in inspection and verification?**	Yes	▶	GO to T7.
	No	▶	REPLACE electronic instrument cluster. AFFIX odometer sticker to door pillar. RESTORE vehicle. RETEST system.
T7 ENTER A/D, DIGITAL PORT TEST MODE			
• Push E/M and <SELECT buttons together once. Observe odometer display, left two digits. • **Does odometer's left two digits read "0A"?**	Yes	▶	GO to T8.
	No	▶	REPLACE electronic instrument cluster. AFFIX odometer sticker to door pillar. RESTORE vehicle. RETEST system.
T8 ENTER FUEL FLOW INPUT TEST MODE			
• Push SELECT> button twice quickly. • Observe left two odometer digits change to "1B". • Repeat this step four times until odometer left two digits read "5F." (Left two digits of odometer will advance: 0A, 1B, 2C, 3D, 4E, 5F, 60, 71, 0A... etc.) • Select 5F. Observe the right four digits of the odometer select 5F then observe display. The frequency of the fuel flow pulses from the powertrain control module is shown. (Step on accelerator pedal.) • "0000" indicates no fuel flow pulses received from the powertrain control module. • Any other number indicates fuel flow pulses are being received from the powertrain control module. • **Do right four digits read "0000" (no fuel pulses)?**	Yes	▶	TURN ignition switch to OFF to exit test modes. System OK. RECHECK Circuit 205 (B/LG); if OK then REPLACE powertrain control module.
	No	▶	REPLACE electronic instrument cluster. AFFIX odometer sticker to door pillar. RESTORE vehicle. RETEST system.

FM9099600612020X

Fig. 53 Pinpoint test T (Part 2 of 2). Town Car

Test Step		Result	▶	Action to Take
U1	CHECK FUEL GAUGE			
	• Verify that fuel gauge is operating properly.	Yes	▶	GO to U2.
	• Does gauge operate properly?	No	▶	REFER to Fuel Gauge Diagnosis in Symptom Chart.
U2	CHECK SPEEDOMETER			
	• Verify that speedometer is operating properly.	Yes	▶	GO to Pinpoint Test T.
	• Does speedometer operate properly?	No	▶	REFER to Speedometer Diagnosis in Symptom Chart.

FM9099600613000X

Fig. 54 Pinpoint test U. Town Car

Test Step		Result	▶	Action to Take
W1	CHECK ELECTRONIC INSTRUMENT CLUSTER FOR WARNINGS			
	• Turn ignition switch to RUN.	Yes	▶	GO to W2.
	• Wait past prove-out time.	No	▶	GO to W5.
	• Check electronic instrument cluster for TRUNK AJAR warning to determine whether the warning is always on or never on.			
	• Is TRUNK AJAR warning always on?			
W2	CHECK LUGGAGE COMPARTMENT DOOR OPEN WARNING LAMP SWITCH CIRCUIT 486 (BR/W)			
	• Turn ignition switch to OFF. This resets the warning.	Yes	▶	GO to W3.
	• Pull connector off of luggage compartment door open warning lamp switch.	No	▶	SERVICE luggage compartment door open warning lamp switch.
	• Turn ignition switch to RUN.			
	• Check electronic instrument cluster for warning.			
	• Is warning displayed?			
W3	LIGHTING CONTROL MODULE CHECK			
	NOTE: Lighting control module provides pull-up to battery for electronic instrument cluster to keep warning off. If lighting control module is inoperative or removed, electronic instrument cluster luggage compartment door warning stays on.	Yes	▶	GO to W4.
		No	▶	REPLACE lighting control module. RESTORE vehicle. RETEST system.
	• Disconnect luggage compartment door switch.			
	• Remove electronic instrument cluster.			
	• With ignition switch in RUN position, check for B+ at Pin C2-27, Circuit 486 (BR/W).			
	• Is B+ present?			
W4	CHECK CIRCUIT 486 (BR/W)			
	• Turn ignition switch to OFF.	Yes	▶	SERVICE Circuit 486 (BR/W) for short. RESTORE vehicle. RETEST system.
	• Disconnect electronic instrument cluster.	No	▶	REPLACE electronic instrument cluster. AFFIX odometer sticker to door pillar. RESTORE vehicle. RETEST system.
	• Check continuity to ground in Circuit 486 (BR/W).			
	• Is there continuity to ground?			
W5	CHECK POWER AND GROUNDS			
	• Check voltage on the following instrument cluster connector pins:	Yes	▶	GO to W6.
		No	▶	SERVICE as required. RESTORE vehicle. RETEST system.

Pin	Circuit Number	Voltage
C1-7	797/54 (W/P)	12V (Hot At All Times)
C1-9	295 (LB/PK)	12V (Hot In RUN)
C3-7	654 (Y/LG)	12V (Hot In RUN)
C3-2	295 (LB/PK)	12V (Hot In RUN)
C1-8	676 (PK/O)	0V
C3-1	676 (PK/O)	0V

• Are all voltages as specified?

FM9099600615010X

Fig. 56 Pinpoint test W (Part 1 of 2). Town Car

Test Step		Result	▶	Action to Take
W6	CHECK LUGGAGE COMPARTMENT DOOR OPEN WARNING LAMP SWITCH FOR INTERNAL OPEN CIRCUIT			
	• Turn ignition switch to OFF.	Yes	▶	SERVICE luggage compartment door open warning lamp switch.
	• Pull connector off of the luggage compartment door open warning lamp switch.			
	• Connect a jumper wire from Circuit 486 (BR/W) at the harness connector to ground.	No	▶	REMOVE jumper. GO to W7.
	• Turn ignition switch to RUN.			
	• Check electronic instrument cluster for warning.			
	• Is warning displayed?			
W7	CHECK WIRING			
	• Turn ignition switch to OFF.	Yes	▶	REPLACE electronic instrument cluster. AFFIX odometer sticker to door pillar. RESTORE vehicle. RETEST system.
	• Disconnect electronic instrument cluster.			
	• Check continuity in Circuit 486 (BR/W).	No	▶	SERVICE Circuit 486 (BR/W) for open. RESTORE vehicle. RETEST system.
	• Is there continuity present?			

FM9099600615020X

Fig. 56 Pinpoint test W (Part 2 of 2). Town Car

Test Step		Result	▶	Action to Take
V1	CHECK ELECTRONIC INSTRUMENT CLUSTER FOR WARNINGS			
	• Turn ignition switch to RUN.	Yes	▶	GO to V2.
	• Wait past prove-out time.	No	▶	GO to V4.
	• Check electronic instrument cluster for DOOR AJAR warning to determine whether warning is always on or never on.			
	• Is door ajar warning always on?			
V2	CHECK DOOR OPEN WARNING LAMP SWITCHES			
	• The following steps are to be repeated for each door open warning lamp switch. Start with the driver's door, then front passenger's, then rear passenger's door.	Yes	▶	GO to V4.
	• Turn ignition switch to OFF. This resets the warning.	No	▶	GO to V3.
	• Disconnect door open warning lamp switch connector at door open warning lamp switch.			
	• Turn ignition switch to RUN.			
	• Check message center for warning.			
	• Repeat until no warning is displayed or all door open warning lamp switches are disconnected.			
	• Is warning still displayed?			
V3	LIGHTING CONTROL MODULE CHECK			
	• Disconnect lighting control module.	Yes	▶	GO to V4.
	• Is warning still present?	No	▶	REPLACE lighting control module.
V4	CHECK CIRCUIT 344 (BK/Y)			
	• Turn ignition switch to OFF.	Yes	▶	SERVICE Circuit 627 (BK/O) for short to ground. RESTORE vehicle. RETEST system.
	• Disconnect electronic instrument cluster.			
	• Check continuity to ground from Connector Pin C1-17, Circuit 344 (BK/Y) and Pin C1-8, Circuit 676 (PK/O).	No	▶	GO to V5.
	• Is continuity to ground present?			
V5	CHECK CIRCUIT 344 (BK/Y) FOR OPEN			
	• Turn ignition switch to OFF.	Yes	▶	REPLACE electronic instrument cluster. AFFIX odometer sticker to door pillar. RESTORE vehicle. RETEST system.
	• Disconnect electronic instrument cluster.			
	• Check continuity in Circuit 344 (BK/Y) from instrument cluster Connector Pin C1-17 to driver door module Connector Pin C2-9.	No	▶	SERVICE Circuit 627 (BK/O) for open. RESTORE vehicle. RETEST system.
	• Is continuity present?			

FM9099600614000X

Fig. 55 Pinpoint test V. Town Car

Test Step		Result	▶	Action to Take
X1	CHECK CHARGING SYSTEM VOLTAGE			
	• Start engine and check for warning. Watch for several minutes.	Yes	▶	GO to X2.
	• Check battery voltage.	No	▶	SERVICE generator.
	• Is the voltage normal (above 14 volts) for engine at fast idle?			
X2	CHECK HARNESS TO GENERATOR			
	• Disconnect generator.	Yes	▶	SERVICE the generator
	• Connect a jumper to ground from Circuit 904 (LG/R) near the generator.			
	• Does charge warning go away?	No	▶	GO to X3.
X3	CHECK HARNESS TO ELECTRONIC INSTRUMENT CLUSTER			
	• Turn ignition switch to OFF.	Yes	▶	GO to X5.
	• Turn ignition switch to RUN but do not start engine.	No	▶	GO to X4.
	• Remove jumper.			
	• Measure voltage at generator from Circuit 904 (LG/R) to ground.			
	• Is it greater than 4 volts?			
X4	CHECK ELECTRONIC INSTRUMENT CLUSTER INTEGRAL VOLTAGE REGULATOR RESISTOR AND HARNESS			
	• Turn ignition switch to OFF.	Yes	▶	SERVICE as required to obtain over 4 volts. RESTORE vehicle. RETEST system.
	• Remove electronic instrument cluster.			
	• Check for loose or corroded screws on generator warning lamp shunt resistor on rear of electronic instrument cluster.	No	▶	SERVICE Circuit 904 (LG/R) for short to ground. RESTORE vehicle. RETEST system.
	• Check that resistor is 400-600 ohms.			
	• Check continuity from resistor screws to Circuit 904 (LG/R) at connector.			
	• Check for short to ground on Circuit 904 (LG/R).			
	• Has any check failed?			

FM9099600616010X

Fig. 57 Pinpoint test X (Part 1 of 2). Town Car

Test Step		Result	▶	Action to Take
X5	CHECK ELECTRONIC INSTRUMENT CLUSTER WIRING FOR OPEN CIRCUIT			
	• Turn ignition switch to OFF.	Yes	▶	REPLACE electronic instrument cluster. AFFIX odometer sticker to door pillar. RESTORE vehicle. RETEST system.
	• Disconnect instrument cluster.			
	• Check for continuity in Circuit 904 (LG/R).	No	▶	SERVICE Circuit 904 (LG/R). RESTORE vehicle. RETEST system.
	• Is there continuity?			

FM9099600616020X

Fig. 57 Pinpoint test X (Part 2 of 2). Town Car

Fig. 58 Pinpoint test Y. Town Car

Test Step	Result	▶	Action to Take
Y1 CHECK ELECTRONIC INSTRUMENT CLUSTER FOR WARNINGS			
• Turn ignition switch to RUN.	Yes	▶	GO to Y2.
• Wait past prove-out time.	No	▶	GO to Y4.
• Check electronic instrument cluster for AIR SUSPENSION warning to determine whether the warning is always on or never on.			
• **Is AIR SUSPENSION warning always on?**			
Y2 CHECK AIR SUSPENSION CONTROL MODULE			
• Disconnect air suspension contro module.	Yes	▶	GO to Y3.
• Turn ignition switch to RUN.	No	▶	SERVICE air suspension control module.
• Check electronic instrument cluster for warning.			
• **Is warning displayed?**			
Y3 CHECK CIRCUIT 419 (DG/LG) FOR SHORT TO GROUND			
• Turn ignition switch to OFF.	Yes	▶	SERVICE Circuit 419 (DG/LG). RESTORE vehicle. RETEST system.
• Disconnect electronic instrument cluster.	No	▶	REPLACE electronic instrument cluster. AFFIX odometer sticker to door pillar. RESTORE vehicle. RETEST system.
• Check resistance to ground of Connector Pin C2-25, Circuit 419 (DG/LG).			
• **Is resistance less than 10 K ohms?**			
Y4 CHECK AIR SUSPENSION MODULE			
• Turn ignition switch to OFF.	Yes	▶	SERVICE air suspension control module.
• Disconnect connector at air suspension control module.	No	▶	GO to Y5.
• Connect a jumper wire from Circuit 419 (DG/LG) at harness connector to ground.			
• Turn ignition switch to RUN.			
• Check electronic instrument cluster for warning.			
• **Is warning displayed?**			
Y5 CHECK CIRCUIT 419 (DG/LG) CONTINUITY			
• Remove jumper.	Yes	▶	REPLACE electronic instrument cluster. AFFIX odometer sticker to door pillar. RESTORE vehicle. RETEST system.
• Disconnect electronic instrument cluster.	No	▶	SERVICE Circuit 419 (DG/LG). RESTORE vehicle. RETEST system.
• Check continuity in Circuit 419 (DG/LG) from instrument cluster Connector C2-25 to air suspension module Connector Pin C2-11.			
• **Is continuity present?**			

FM9099600617000X

Fig. 58 Pinpoint test Y. Town Car

Fig. 59 Pinpoint test AA. Town Car

Test Step	Result	▶	Action to Take
AA1 CHECK SYSTEM AND WARNING			
• Drain fluid from windshield washer reservoir for warning never on.	Yes	▶	GO to AA2.
• Add fluid to windshield washer reservoir for warning always on.	No	▶	GO to AA4.
• Turn ignition switch to RUN.			
• Wait past prove-out time.			
• Check message center for low WASHER FLUID warnings to determine whether the warning is always on or never on.			
• **Is warning always on?**			
AA2 CHECK WINDSHIELD WASHER RESERVOIR FLUID LEVEL WARNING WITH SENSOR DISCONNECTED			
• Turn ignition switch to OFF.	Yes	▶	GO to AA3.
• Disconnect harness connector from windshield washer reservoir fluid level sensor.	No	▶	SERVICE windshield washer reservoir fluid level sensor.
• Turn ignition switch to RUN.			
• Check electronic instrument cluster for windshield washer fluid warning.			
• **Is warning displayed?**			
AA3 CHECK CIRCUIT 82 (PK/Y) FOR SHORT TO GROUND			
• Turn ignition switch to OFF.	Yes	▶	SERVICE Circuit 82 (PK/Y) for short to ground. RESTORE vehicle. RETEST system.
• Disconnect electronic instrument cluster.	No	▶	REPLACE electronic instrument cluster. AFFIX odometer sticker to door pillar. RESTORE vehicle. RETEST system.
• Check resistance to ground of Connector Pin C1-10, Circuit 82 (PK/Y).			
• **Is resistance less than 10 K ohms?**			
AA4 CHECK WINDSHIELD WASHER RESERVOIR FLUID LEVEL WARNING WITH SENSOR SHORTED			
• Turn ignition switch to OFF.	Yes	▶	SERVICE windshield washer reservoir fluid level sensor.
• Unplug harness connector from windshield washer reservoir fluid level sensor.	No	▶	GO to AA5.
• Connect a jumper wire across the 2 pins of harness connector.			
• Turn ignition switch to RUN.			
• Check messages for low WASHER FLUID warning.			
• **Is warning displayed?**			
AA5 CHECK CIRCUIT 82 (PK/Y) CONTINUITY			
• Turn ignition switch to OFF.	Yes	▶	REPLACE electronic instrument cluster. AFFIX odometer sticker to door pillar. RESTORE vehicle. RETEST system.
• Disconnect electronic instrument cluster.	No	▶	SERVICE Circuit 82 (PK/Y) for open circuit. RESTORE vehicle. RETEST system.
• Check continuity in Circuit 82 (PK/Y).			
• **Is continuity present?**			

FM9099600618000X

Fig. 59 Pinpoint test AA. Town Car

Fig. 60 Pinpoint test BB. Town Car

Test Step	Result	▶	Action to Take
BB1 CHECK ELECTRONIC INSTRUMENT CLUSTER FOR MIL WARNING			
• Check for warning messages.			
• **Is CHECK ENGINE warning displayed?**			
	No	▶	System OK.

FM9099600619000X

Fig. 60 Pinpoint test BB. Town Car

Fig. 62 Pinpoint test DD (Part 1 of 2). Town Car

Test Step	Result	▶	Action to Take
DD1 CHECK ELECTRONIC INSTRUMENT CLUSTER FOR INDICATOR			
• Turn ignition switch to RUN.	Yes	▶	GO to DD2.
• Wait past prove out time.	No	▶	GO to DD4.
• Check electronic instrument cluster display to determine whether the indicator is always on or never on.			
• **Is OVERDRIVE OFF indicator always on?**			

FM9099600621010X

Fig. 62 Pinpoint test DD (Part 1 of 2). Town Car

Fig. 61 Pinpoint test CC. Town Car

Test Step	Result	▶	Action to Take
CC1 CHECK HIGH BEAM INDICATOR OPERATION			
• NOTE: Make sure the light switches are in proper positions when checking circuit operation.	Yes	▶	GO to CC2.
• Turn ignition switch to RUN.	No	▶	GO to CC4.
• Wait past prove-out time.			
• Check electronic instrument cluster displays to determine whether the indicator is always on or never on.			
• **Is high beam indicator always on?**			
CC2 CHECK EIC FOR SHORT CIRCUIT 932 (LG/W)			
• Disconnect connector C3 at electronic instrument cluster.	Yes	▶	REPLACE electronic instrument cluster. AFFIX odometer sticker to door pillar. RESTORE vehicle. RETEST system.
• Measure voltage at connector Pin C3-4, Circuit 932 (GY/W).	No	▶	GO to CC3.
• **Is voltage 0V with ignition switch in RUN, headlamps on, high beams off?**			
CC3 CHECK FOR SHORT TO BATTERY			
• Reconnect electronic instrument cluster.	Yes	▶	SERVICE short to B+ in Circuit 12 (LG/BK). SERVICE as required. RESTORE vehicle. RETEST system.
• Disconnect multi-function switch connector.	No	▶	REPLACE multi-function switch.
• **Is high beam indicator illuminated?**			
CC4 CHECK ELECTRONIC INSTRUMENT CLUSTER FOR OPEN CIRCUIT			
• Turn ignition switch to OFF.	Yes	▶	GO to CC5.
• Disconnect electronic instrument cluster.	No	▶	REPLACE electronic instrument cluster. AFFIX odometer sticker to door pillar. RESTORE vehicle. RETEST system.
• Connect a jumper wire from high beam input pin of electronic instrument cluster connector Pin C3-4 to positive battery terminal. Supply ground to ground pin of electronic instrument cluster connector Pin C3-1.			
• **Does high beam indicator illuminate?**			
CC5 CHECK CIRCUITRY			
• Reconnect electronic instrument cluster.	Yes	▶	GO to CC6.
• Disconnect multi-function switch connector.	No	▶	SERVICE Circuit 12 (LG/BK) for open circuit. RESTORE vehicle. RETEST system.
• Jump Circuit 12 (LG/BK) at the multi-function switch connector to positive battery terminal.			
• **Is high beam indicator illuminated?**			
CC6 CHECK CONTINUITY			
• Disconnect headlamp switch.	Yes	▶	REPLACE headlamp switch. RESTORE vehicle. RETEST system.
• Check continuity in Circuit 502 (GY).	No	▶	SERVICE respective circuit. RESTORE vehicle. RETEST system.
• Check continuity to power in Circuit 38 (BK/O).			
• **Is continuity present?**			

FM9099600620000X

Fig. 61 Pinpoint test CC. Town Car

Fig. 62 Pinpoint test DD (Part 2 of 2). Town Car

Test Step	Result	▶	Action to Take
DD2 CHECK POWERTRAIN CONTROL MODULE FOR SHORTED CIRCUIT			
• Disconnect powertrain control module.	Yes	▶	GO to DD3.
• Check electronic instrument cluster for indicator.	No	▶	REPLACE powertrain control module.
• **Is OVERDRIVE OFF indicator illuminated?**			
DD3 CHECK CONTINUITY OF CIRCUIT 911 (W/LG)			
• Turn ignition switch to OFF.	Yes	▶	REPLACE electronic instrument cluster. RESTORE vehicle. RETEST system.
• Disconnect electronic instrument cluster.	No	▶	SERVICE Circuit 911 (W/LG). RESTORE vehicle. RETEST system.
• Check continuity in connector Pin C1-4, Circuit 911 (W/LG).			
• **Is continuity present?**			
DD4 CHECK POWERTRAIN CONTROL MODULE FOR OPEN CIRCUIT			
• Turn ignition switch to OFF.	Yes	▶	REPLACE powertrain control module.
• Disconnect connector at powertrain control module.	No	▶	GO to DD5.
• Connect a jumper wire from Circuit 911 (W/LG) at harness connector to ground.			
• Turn ignition switch to RUN.			
• Check electronic instrument cluster for warning.			
• **Is OVERDRIVE OFF indicator illuminated?**			
DD5 CHECK INDICATOR SUPPLY CIRCUIT CONTINUITY			
• Remove jumper.	Yes	▶	REPLACE electronic instrument cluster. RESTORE vehicle. RETEST system.
• Disconnect electronic instrument cluster.	No	▶	SERVICE Circuit 911 (W/LG). RESTORE vehicle. RETEST system.
• Check continuity in connector Pin C1-14, Circuit 911 (W/LG).			
• **Is continuity present?**			

FM9099600621020X

Fig. 62 Pinpoint test DD (Part 2 of 2). Town Car

Fig. 63 Pinpoint test EE. Town Car

Test Step	Result	▶	Action to Take
EE1 CHECK DISPLAYS			
• Turn ignition switch to RUN.	Yes	▶	GO to EE2.
• Turn parking lamps on.	No	▶	GO to Pinpoint Test Step A3.
• Check other displays: radio front control unit, message center switch module.			
• **Do other displays illuminate properly?**			
EE2 CHECK ELECTRONIC INSTRUMENT CLUSTER BULB			
• Check the bulb in the electronic instrument cluster.	Yes	▶	SERVICE Circuit 19 (LB/R). RESTORE vehicle. RETEST system.
• **Is bulb OK?**	No	▶	REPLACE bulb. RESTORE vehicle. RETEST system.

FM9099600622000X

Fig. 63 Pinpoint test EE. Town Car

TECHNICAL SERVICE BULLETINS

When The Following Modifications, Alterations And/Or Adjustments Have Already Been Performed, An "Authorized Modifications" Decal Is Affixed Alongside The Vehicle Emission Control Decal. The Authorized Modifications Decal Includes Information On The Type Of Service Performed, The Change Authority Number, Dealer Number And Date Performed.

If Unsure Of The System Used On The Vehicle Being Serviced, Refer To The "Engine Systems Identification Chart." Further Assistance For The Proper Use Of Information Contained In This Section Can Also Be Found In The Front Of This Tabbed Section Under "How To Use This Manual."

INDEX

Page No.

Bucking & Jerking During Coastdown Deceleration Lasting Longer Than 5 Seconds: 16-2
  1994 Cougar & Thunderbird w/3.8L/V6-232 Engine........ 16-2

Bucking Or Jerking During Coast-Down: 16-7
  1993 Cougar & Thunderbird w/5.0L/V8-302 Engine...... 16-7

Check Engine (MIL) Light On; DTCs 327 & 332 At Temperatures Of 32°F Or Below-No Drive Concerns:........................ 16-3
  1993-94 Sable, Taurus, Tempo & Topaz w/2.3L/4-140 HSC & 3.0L/V6-182 Engines 16-3

Clunk On Acceleration: 16-4
  1993 Sable & Taurus Except SHO 16-4

Deposit Resistant Injectors......... 16-2

Detonation, MIL On, DTC 332:...... 16-7
  1993-95 4.6L/V8-281 Engine 16-7

Engine Knock:..................... 16-3
  1993 Escort & Tracer w/1.8L/4-112 Engine 16-3

Engine Misfire w/Diagnostic Trouble Codes P030X Or P1443: . 16-5
  1995 Continental 16-5

Engine Moan Or Hooting: 16-5
  1993-94 Cougar, Crown Victoria, Grand Marquis, Thunderbird & Town Car w/4.6L/V8-281 Engine........................ 16-5

Engine Rattle: 16-5
  1993 Mark VIII. 16-5

Fuel Injector Tick At Idle:........... 16-5
  1994 Cougar & Thunderbird w/4.6L/V8-281 Engine........ 16-5

Fuel Pump "Whine/Buzz" Noise Comes Through Radio Speaker:.. 16-2
  Except 1994-95 Aspire & 1995 Contour & Mystique........... 16-2

Hard Start, No Start Or Fuel Shutoff Lamp Lit:........................ 16-5
  1993-94 Probe w/2.0L/4-121 Engine & Speed Control, Less ABS........................... 16-5

Page No.

Hard Start, No Start, Rough Idle Or Malfunction Indicator Lamp (MIL) Check Engine Light Illuminated:... 16-5
  1993-94 Models w/EEC-IV 16-5

Hesitation/Stall, Rough Idle, Poor Heater Output; Engine Coolant Does Not Reach Normal Operating Temperature 16-2

Hesitation & Stumble During Acceleration:.................... 16-2
  1993 Cougar & Thunderbird w/5.0L/V8-302 Engine........ 16-2

High Idle RPM After Highway Cruise:......................... 16-2
  1993 Continental, Escort, Sable, Taurus & Tracer............. 16-2

High Idle RPM After Road Load:.... 16-2
  1993 Escort & Tracer 16-2

Lack Of Power; Engine Performing In Limited Operating Strategy:.... 16-2
  1993 Mark VIII. 16-2

Lack Of Power, Hesitation Or Stalls When Driving In High Ambient Temperatures Or High Altitudes: . 16-2
  1993-94 Continental, Sable & Taurus 16-2

Lack Of Power In LOS:............. 16-7
  1993 Mark VIII w/4.6L/V8-281 Engine & 4R70W Automatic Transmission 16-7

Long Crank, No Start; Insufficient Cranking Speed Creates Rich Fuel Condition:...................... 16-2
  1993 Taurus SHO 16-2

MIL Illuminated, DTC 332:......... 16-6
  1994 Probe w/2.0L/4-122 Engine 16-6

MIL Intermittently Flashing During Warm-Up w/DTC 17 & 24:........ 16-6
  1993 Probe 16-6

MIL On With DTC 327 & 332 Below 32°F:............................ 16-6
  1993-94 Sable & Taurus w/2.3L/4-140 & 3.0L/V6-182 Engine...................... 16-6

Page No.

No Crank: 16-5
  1993-94 Continental, Crown Victoria, Grand Marquis & Town Car w/4.6L/V8-281 Engine & 1993-95 Cougar, Sable, Taurus & Thunderbird w/3.0L/V6-182 & 3.8L/V6-232 Engines 16-5

No Crank/No Start; Circuit 33 Shorted At Transaxle Case:...... 16-2
  1993 Sable & Taurus............ 16-2

No Start: 16-5
  1993-94 Taurus SHO w/3.2L/V6-232 Engine........ 16-5

No Start, Hard Start, High Idle, MIL On, Early Or Late Shifting: 16-7
  1993 Mark VIII w/4.6L/V8-281 Engine........................ 16-7

Rough Idle:........................ 16-3
  1994 Probe 16-3

Rough Idle, Bucking Or Jerking While Coasting Or Decelerating, Or Hesitation & Stumbling During Operation:...................... 16-6
  1994 Sable & Taurus w/3.0L/V6-182 Engine Except SHO 16-6

Rough Idle, Hesitation Or Stumble On Acceleration:................. 16-6
  1994 Cougar & Thunderbird w/3.8L/V6-232 Engine........ 16-6

Silicone Contamination Of Exhaust Gas Oxygen (EGO) Sensors:..... 16-2
  Except 1994-95 Aspire & 1995 Contour & Mystique........... 16-2

Spark Knock:...................... 16-2
  1993 Escort & Tracer 16-2

Spark Knock Or Injector Tick/Valve Train Hash Transferred From Engine To Passenger Compartment:................... 16-3
  1993 Crown Victoria, Grand Marquis & Town Car w/4.6L/V8-281 Engine........ 16-3

DEPOSIT RESISTANT INJECTORS

California Tempo and Topaz with 2.3L HSC engine, Continental, Cougar, Mustang with 2.3L engine, Sable, Taurus and Thunderbird, 1993 California Tempo and Topaz with 2.3L HSC engines, 1993-94 Crown Victoria, Grand Marquis and Mustang with 5.0L HO engines and 1993-94 Escort and Tracer now use deposit resistant injectors. These injectors have two unique properties tolerant to deposit formation and do not require cleaning.

HIGH IDLE RPM AFTER ROAD LOAD

1993 ESCORT & TRACER

On models w/1.9L/4-116 engines, a high idle RPM may occur after a road load cruise. This may be caused by the idle air control valve.

To correct this problem, check throttle cable and linkage and if necessary, replace idle air control valve.

SPARK KNOCK

1993 ESCORT & TRACER

On these models, spark knock may occur on acceleration or during cruise because of the ignition timing.

To correct this problem, retard ignition timing 3-4° BTDC by removing octane adjust shorting bar.

LONG CRANK, NO START; INSUFFICIENT CRANKING SPEED CREATES RICH FUEL CONDITION

1993 TAURUS SHO

On models with 3.0L engine and manual transmission, intermittent long crank or no start may be experienced with no diagnostic trouble codes are indicated and fuel pressure within specifications. The cause of this problem may be the result of inadequate starter motor cranking speed allowing fuel flooding.

To correct this problem, check for long crank and no start conditions, and if necessary, replace starter motor with new 12 tooth starter motor part No. F3DZ-11002-B.

HIGH IDLE RPM AFTER HIGHWAY CRUISE

1993 CONTINENTAL, ESCORT, SABLE, TAURUS & TRACER

On Escort/Tracer models built before 12/1/92 equipped w/1.9L/4-116 engines and Taurus/Sable and Continental models built before 11/1/92 equipped w/3.8L/V6-232 engines, a high idle RPM may occur after a highway cruise. This problem may be caused by the idle air control valve.

To correct this problem, check throttle cable and linkage and, if necessary, replace idle air control valve.

LACK OF POWER; ENGINE PERFORMING IN LIMITED OPERATING STRATEGY

1993 MARK VIII

On Federal models built before 2/16/93 with calibration No. 3-38L-R00 or California models built before 3/3/93 with calibration No. 3-38Q-R00, a lack of power when engine is performing in a Limited Operating Strategy (LOS) may be exhibited. The engine will operate in a half fuel, reduced spark condition, caused by the program in the Powertrain Control Module (PCM).

To correct this problem, replace PCM with part No. F3LY-12A650-AD for Federal models or F3LY-12A650-CD for California models.

NO CRANK/NO START; CIRCUIT 33 SHORTED AT TRANSAXLE CASE

1993 SABLE & TAURUS

On these models, the engine may not crank or start because of the No. 33 circuit on the wiring harnesses being shorted at the transaxle case.

To correct this problem, add convoluted tubing to the No. 33 circuit on the wiring harnesses to prevent wiring shorts. Cut the tubing as necessary and secure to harnesses with black electrical tape.

HESITATION/STALL, ROUGH IDLE, POOR HEATER OUTPUT; ENGINE COOLANT DOES NOT REACH NORMAL OPERATING TEMPERATURE

Hesitation/stall, rough idle and poor heater output may be caused by a thermostat that is stuck in the open position or opening at a temperature lower than specified.

SILICONE CONTAMINATION OF EXHAUST GAS OXYGEN (EGO) SENSORS

EXCEPT 1994–95 ASPIRE & 1995 CONTOUR & MYSTIQUE

The EGO sensor may be contaminated if volatile types of silicone sealant are used when servicing the engine.

To correct or prevent this problem, use low silicone volatility sealant E8AZ-19562-A, specification ESE-M4G195-B. Replace EGO sensor if necessary.

HESITATION & STUMBLE DURING ACCELERATION

1993 COUGAR & THUNDERBIRD w/5.0L/V8-302 ENGINE

Some vehicles may exhibit a rough idle and hesitation on acceleration. This may be caused by poor fuel quality.

Replace the powertrain control module (PCM) with a new calibration PCM which allows for poor fuel quality part No. F4SZ-12A650-BB for Federal models, and part No. F4SZ-12A650-CB for California models.

BUCKING & JERKING DURING COASTDOWN DECELERATION LASTING LONGER THAN 5 SECONDS

1994 COUGAR & THUNDERBIRD w/3.8L/V6-232 ENGINE

Some vehicles may exhibit a bucking and jerking condition during deceleration. This is caused by the operating strategy of the powertrain control module (PCM).

Replace the PCM with a new calibration PCM, part No. F3PZ-12A650-CA for Federal models, and part No. F3PZ-12A650-DA for California models.

LACK OF POWER, HESITATION OR STALLS WHEN DRIVING IN HIGH AMBIENT TEMPERATURES OR HIGH ALTITUDES

1993–94 CONTINENTAL, SABLE & TAURUS

On models with fuel tanks built between 12-1-92 through 10-8-93, these symptoms may be caused by contamination in the fuel tank due to an excess amount of metallic weld splatters. Perform normal inspections and diagnostic procedures. If no electrical concerns are found, flush the fuel tank and replace the fuel pump assembly.

FUEL PUMP "WHINE/BUZZ" NOISE COMES THROUGH RADIO SPEAKER

EXCEPT 1994–95 ASPIRE & 1995 CONTOUR & MYSTIQUE

A "whining/buzzing" noise in the speak-

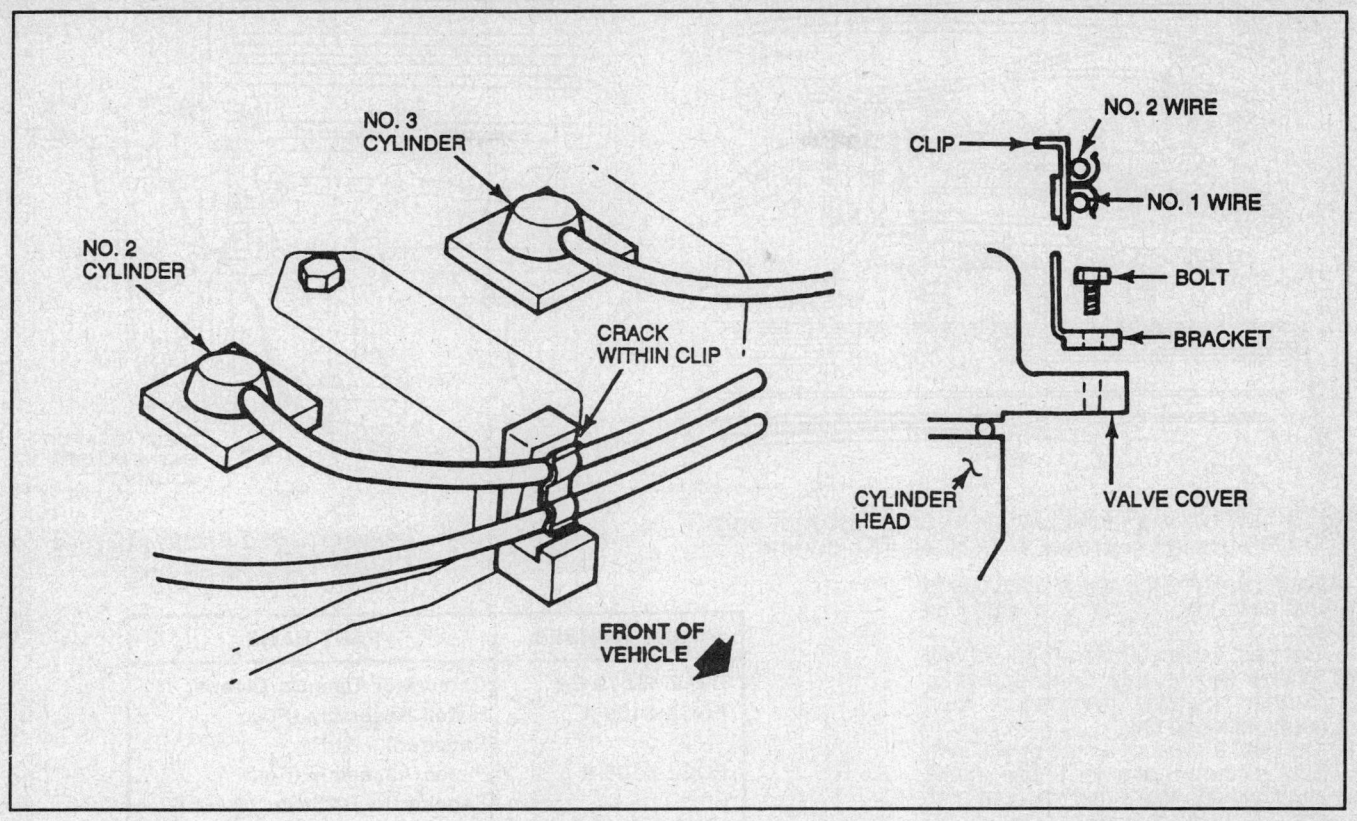

Fig. 1   Spark plug wire & clip. 1994 Probe

ers on vehicles with an in-tank electric fuel pump may be caused by the fuel pump.

To correct this condition, install electronic noise RFI filter, part No. F1PZ-18B925-A on in-tank fuel pump.

SPARK KNOCK OR INJECTOR TICK/VALVE TRAIN HASH TRANSFERRED FROM ENGINE TO PASSENGER COMPARTMENT

1993 CROWN VICTORIA, GRAND MARQUIS & TOWN CAR w/4.6L/V8-281 ENGINE

Normal engine sounds, injector tick/valve train hash or spark knock may be transferred from the engine to the passenger compartment through the radio frequency interference (RFI) cable. The RFI cable is located on the rear of the engine to the bulkhead side.

Remove RFI cable. If the engine noise goes away, replace the RFI cable.

CHECK ENGINE (MIL) LIGHT ON; DTC'S 327 & 332 AT TEMPERATURES OF 32° F OR BELOW-NO DRIVE CONCERNS

1993–94 SABLE, TAURUS, TEMPO & TOPAZ w/2.3L/4-140 HSC & 3.0L/V6-182 ENGINES

The malfunction indicator lamp (MIL) may be on intermittently at ambient temperatures of 32° F or below. DTC's 327 and 332 will be stored in continuous memory without noticeable drive symptoms. The MIL activation may be caused by water freezing in the pressure feedback EGR (PFE) sensor hose.

Use the following service procedure to determine if the PFE system is at fault (hard failure) or water is freezing in the PFE hose and sensor:

1. Perform normal diagnosis to be sure that no hard fault is present.
2. Check DTC 327 or 332 in "Key On, Engine Off" and "Key On, Engine Running" self test modes.
3. If the DTC's appear only in continuous memory mode, install the appropriate PFE service sensor, bracket and hose with part No. F43Z-9J433-A for 2.3L/4-140 HSC engine, and part No. F3DZ-9J433-A for 3.0L/V6-182 engine.

ROUGH IDLE

1994 PROBE

On models built between 3-10-94 through 3-31-94, a rough idle condition may exist. This could be caused by spark leakage in No. 1 or No. 2 spark plug wire due to damage that may have occurred during vehicle assembly, **Fig. 1**. Spark leakage can also cause the spark plug wire clip/separator to overheat and deform at the point of the cut.

Inspect No. 1 and No. 2 spark plug wire for scrapes or cuts within the area of spark plug wire clip. If spark plug wire clip/separator is scraped or cut, replace the damaged wire(s) and spark plug wire clip/separator.

ENGINE KNOCK

1993 ESCORT & TRACER w/1.8L/4-112 ENGINE

On these models, with engine numbers before 794954, a knock may be heard after an initial cold start, which may remain constant or disappear upon reaching operating temperature. This may be caused by carbon buildup on the piston face squish area or cylinder head which is removable with carburetor cleaning solvent . Should this procedure fail to eliminate the noise, all four pistons must be replaced.

Inform owners that use of fuels with octane ratings higher than 87 is not recommended for these engines as they may contribute to rapid carbon buildup.

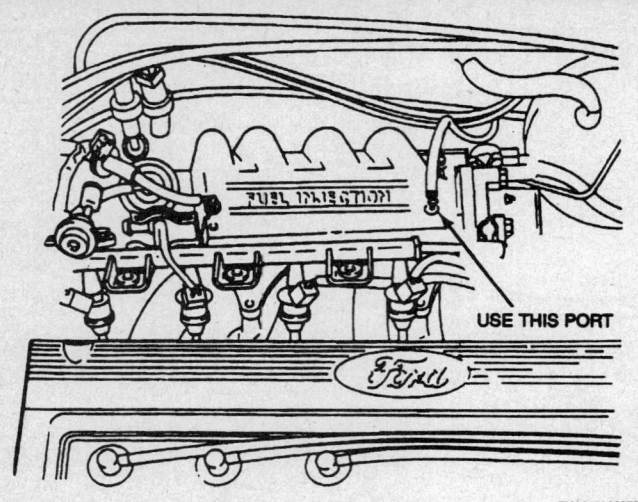

FMA019500070000X

Fig. 2 Intake manifold canister purge vacuum port. 1993 Escort & Tracer w/1.8L/4-112 engine

USE THIS PORT

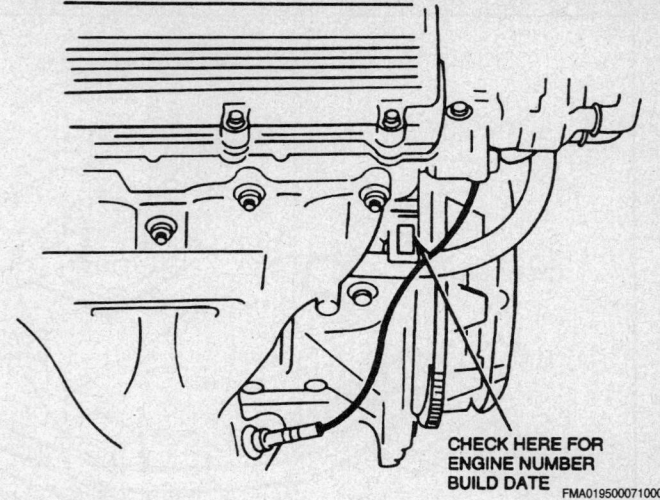

CHECK HERE FOR ENGINE NUMBER BUILD DATE

FMA019500071000X

Fig. 3 Engine number. 1993 Escort & Tracer w/1.8L/4-112 engine

After determining the knock is not due to the hydraulic lash adjusters, proceed as follows:

1. Connect exhaust hose or park vehicle in well vented area, bring engine to normal operating temperature then turn ignition to Off.
2. Connect a two foot length of 1/8 inch I.D. vacuum hose to upper intake manifold canister purge vacuum port, **Fig. 2**, place other end in can of carburetor cleaning solvent (part No. D9AZ-19579-BA) or equivalent, and pinch with clamping pliers to prevent suction during start-up. Do not use any hoses permanently installed on vehicle as deterioration may result.
3. Restart engine, allow idle to stabilize, then feed solvent by releasing pliers while maintaining engine speed between 1500 to 3000 rpm until 1/2 of solvent is consumed. Regulate solvent feed rate by partially kinking the hose.
4. Allow idle speed to drop and engine should stall. If it does not, turn ignition to Off.
5. Allow vehicle to sit for at least six and as much as 24 hours while solvent attacks carbon buildup.
6. Flush remaining carbon by repeating previous steps with remaining solvent. **Do not allow engine to stall.**
7. Remove feed hose, reconnect purge hose, then drive car three to four miles using full rpm range to eliminate any remaining carbon or solvent.
8. If previous procedure fails to eliminate knock, inspect engine number, **Fig. 3**. If number is before 794954 this engine has old level pistons which must be replaced, **Fig. 4. Refer to MOTOR'S AUTO REPAIR MANUAL for procedure.**
9. If cylinders are within specifications and oversize pistons are not required, **Fig. 5**. Do not break glaze or hone bores. This will disturb production finish and may increase oil consumption.
10. New cylinder head bolts are not required unless originals are visibly damaged.

PART NUMBER	PART NAME
D9AZ-19579-BA	Carburetor Tune-Up Cleaner
FOCZ-6108-A	Piston Assembly (Four Required) - Std.
FOCZ-6108-B	Piston Assembly (Four Required) - 0.25mm (0.10") Oversize
FOCZ-6108-C	Piston Assembly (Four Required) - 0.50mm (0.20") Oversize
F2CZ-6008-A	Gasket Set
FOCZ-6149-A	Piston Ring Set - Std.
FOCZ-6149-B	Piston Ring Set - 0.25mm (0.10") Oversize
FOCZ-6149-C	Piston Ring Set - 0.50mm (0.20") Oversize

FMA019500072000X

Fig. 4 Piston replacement. 1993 Escort & Tracer w/1.8L/4-112 engine

1.8L CYLINDER BORE SPECIFICATIONS	
ITEM	DIMENSION
Cylinder Bore (Std.)	83.006-83.013mm (3.2679-3.2682")
Cylinder Bore (.25mm (0.10" Oversize))	83.256-83.263mm (3.2778-3.2781")
Cylinder Bore (.50mm (0.20" Oversize))	83.506-83.513mm (3.2876-3.2879")
Cylinder Bore Taper	0.019mm (0.0007") Max.
Cylinder Out-Of-Round	0.019mm (0.0007") Max.

FMA019500073000X

Fig. 5 Cylinder specifications. 1993 Escort & Tracer w/1.8L/4-112 engine

CLUNK ON ACCELERATION
1993 SABLE & TAURUS EXCEPT SHO

On these models, with 3.0L/V6-182, this condition may be caused by a loose or missing righthand front engine mount upper attaching bolt.

To correct this condition, inspect for a loose or missing bolt in the righthand front mount at the A/C bracket, torn rubber or fluid leak-out at this mount and also at the righthand rear mount. If any of these fail-

PART NUMBER	PART NAME
F1DZ-6038-D	Insulator Assembly - Engine Front Support (1991/92)
F3DZ-6038-C	Insulator Assembly - Engine Front Support (1993)
F4DZ-6068-C	Insulator Assembly - Engine Rear Support (1991/93)
F3DZ-6047-A	Bolt - Engine Mount-To-Bracket (1991/93)

FMA019500092000X

Fig. 6   Mount & bolt replacement. 1993 Sable & Taurus except SHO

ures are present, replace both mounts and the bolt as follows:

1. Remove righthand front and rear engine mounts. **Refer to MOTOR'S AUTO REPAIR MANUAL for procedure.**
2. Install correct replacement mounts and new bolt and washer assembly, **Fig. 6,** to attach front mount to A/C bracket.
3. **Torque** new bolt to 115 ft. lbs. with non-ratcheting wrench. Re-inspect torque, and if it has fallen below specification, **torque** again to 120 ft. lbs.

ENGINE RATTLE
1993 MARK VIII

On these models, with engine calibrations of 3-38L-R10 (Federal), and 3-38Q-R10 (California), this condition may be heard when driving at engine speeds of 3000 to 5000 rpm. This may be caused by the EEC-IV powertrain control module (PCM) calibration.

To correct this condition, proceed as follows:

1. Remove ignition system spout connector and road test vehicle.
2. If noise disappears, reinstall connector and install revised PCM (part No. F3LY-12A650-AF for Federal, part No. F3LY-12A650-CF for California).

ENGINE MISFIRE W/DIAGNOSTIC TROUBLE CODES P030X OR P1443
1995 CONTINENTAL

On these models, engine may misfire and/or Malfunction Indicator Lamp (MIL) illuminator with diagnostic trouble codes (DTCs) P030X and/or P1443.

This condition may be caused by intermittent purge monitor information and/or too sensitive misfire monitor calibration. To correct this condition, reprogram or replace powertrain control module (PCM) as follows:

1. **On Federal models,** recalibrate PCM (part No. F5OF-12A650-AB) from 5-38D-R05 to 5-38D-R10; or install new PCM (part No. F5OZ-12A650-AC).
2. **On California models,** recalibrate PCM (part No. F5OF-12A650-BB) from 5-38D-R05 to 5-38D-R10; or install new PCM (part No. F5OZ-12A650-BC).

HARD START, NO START, ROUGH IDLE OR MALFUNCTION INDICATOR LAMP (MIL) CHECK ENGINE LIGHT ILLUMINATED
1993-94 MODELS W/EEC-IV

On 1993-94 Town Car equipped with 4.6L/V8-281 engine, 1993-94 Escort and Tracer with 1.9L/4-166 engine, 1993-94 Crown Victoria and Grand Marquis with 4.6L/V8-281 engine, 1993-94 Mark VIII with 4.6L/V8-281 engine, 1993-94 Taurus with 3.0L/V6-182 California Flex Fuel engine, 1994 Mustang with 3.8L/V6-232, and 1994 Thunderbird and Cougar with 3.8L/V6-232 supercharged engine, 3.8L/V6-232 California engine and 4.6L/V8-281 engine models, may be hard to start, not start, idle rough or have MIL illuminated.

This condition may be caused by disconnect in Ignition Control Module (ICM) or moisture in ICM. To correct this condition install new ICM connector harness wire service kit (part No. F5CZ-14A411-AA) according to instructions included in kit.

HARD START, NO START OR FUEL SHUTOFF LAMP LIT
1993-94 PROBE W/2.0L/4-121 ENGINE & SPEED CONTROL, LESS ABS

These models built between 1993 and Aug. 25, 1994, may be hard to start, not start or have fuel shutoff lamp illuminate.

This condition may be caused by corrosion or short to ground at splice 102 in circuit 9. To correct this condition proceed as follows:

1. Perform voltage drop test across circuit 9 from 30-amp fuel pump INJ fuse to alternator "S" terminal.
2. If voltage drops .2 volts or more, splice 102 needs repair.
3. Remove lefthand headlamp to gain access to main harness containing splice 102.

4. If corroded, cut out splice and re-solder.
5. Apply adhesive-lined heat-shrinkable tubing to seal splice.

NO CRANK
1993-94 CONTINENTAL, CROWN VICTORIA, GRAND MARQUIS & TOWN CAR W/4.6L/V8-281 ENGINE & 1993-95 COUGAR, SABLE, TAURUS & THUNDERBIRD W/3.0L/V6-182 & 3.8L/V6-232 ENGINES,

On these models, starter may not crank.

This condition may be caused by starter solenoid connector corrosion. To correct this condition install wiring and connector assembly (part No. F4VY-14A411-A) and apply di-electric grease to terminal connector.

FUEL INJECTOR TICK AT IDLE
1994 COUGAR & THUNDERBIRD W/4.6L/V8-281 ENGINE

These models may have fuel injector tick at idle.

This condition may be caused by fuel line transmitting injector noise. To correct this condition install new fuel line (part No. F5SZ-9S286-A) made of new noise dampening material.

ENGINE MOAN OR HOOTING
1993-94 COUGAR, CROWN VICTORIA, GRAND MARQUIS, THUNDERBIRD & TOWN CAR W/4.6L/V8-281 ENGINE

These models may moan or hoot while operating under normal conditions.

This condition may be caused by idle air bypass valve. To correct this condition, install new air bypass tube and resonator assembly (part No. F5AZ-9H308-A).

NO START
1993-94 TAURUS SHO W/3.2L/V6-232 ENGINE

These models may not start because battery is not properly recharged.

This condition may be caused when alternator wiring is trapped between righthand radiator brace and alternator pulley. As shifts, terminal connectors are loosened by tugging wiring. To correction this condition, inspect and secure wiring, replacing as necessary.

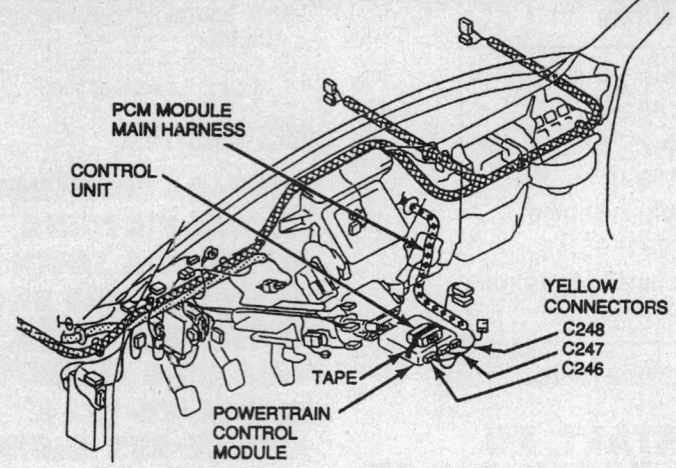

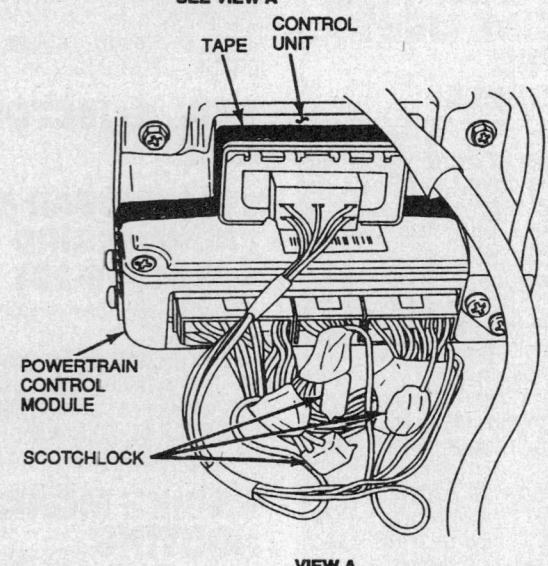

Fig. 7 PCM main harness. 1993 Probe

FMA009400009000X

ROUGH IDLE, BUCKING OR JERKING WHILE COASTING OR DECELERATING, OR HESITATION & STUMBLING DURING OPERATION

1994 SABLE & TAURUS w/3.0L/V6-182 ENGINE EXCEPT SHO

These models may have rough idle, buck or jerk while coasting or decelerating and/or hesitate and stumble during hot or cold operation.

This condition may be caused by high resistance across Mass Air Flow (MAS) sensor connector. To correct this condition install improved connector and pigtail assembly MAF sensor replacement service kit (part No. F4DZ-14A411-A).

MIL ILLUMINATED, DTC 332

1994 PROBE w/2.0L/4-122 ENGINE

On these models built from start of production through July 14, 1994, Malfunction Indicator Light (MIL) may illuminate with diagnostic trouble code (DTC) 332.

This condition may be caused by fuel pressure regulator control (FPRC) and exhaust gas recirculation (EGR) solenoid valves being incorrectly connected. To correct this condition, ensure black connector is attached to FPRC solenoid (upper) and orange to EGR solenoid (lower) at righthand rear of engine.

ROUGH IDLE, HESITATION OR STUMBLE ON ACCELERATION

1994 COUGAR & THUNDERBIRD w/3.8L/V6-232 ENGINE

These models may idle rough, or hesitate or stumble on acceleration.

This condition may be caused by poor fuel quality. To correct this condition, install new revised operating strategy powertrain control module (PCM), (Federal, part No. F4SZ-12A650-BB; California, part No. F4SZ-12A650-CB).

MIL ON WITH DTC 327 & 332 BELOW 32°F

1993–94 SABLE & TAURUS w/2.3L/4-140 & 3.0L/V6-182 ENGINE

On these models, malfunction indicator light (MIL) may be on at temperatures below 32°F with diagnostic trouble codes (DTCs) 327 and 332.

This condition may be caused by water freezing in pressure feedback EGR (PFE) sensor hose. To correct this condition, install new PFE sensor (2.3L/4-140 engine, part No. F43Z-9J433-A; 3.0L/V6-182 engine, part No. F3DZ-9J433-A), bracket and hose.

MIL INTERMITTENTLY FLASHING DURING WARM-UP W/DTC 17 & 24

1993 PROBE

On these models, malfunction indicator lamp (MIL) may intermittently flash during warm-up after cold soak with diagnostic trouble codes (DTCs) 17 and 24 displayed.

This condition may be caused by powertrain control module (PCM) logic allowing system to go into closed loop. To correct this condition, install control unit kit (part No. F32Z-12B528-A) as follows:

1. Disconnect battery ground cable, then remove center console.
2. Disconnect PCM connectors C248, C247 and C246, then remove black winding tape from PCM main harness, **Fig. 7**.
3. When connecting kit harness' six wires use Scotchlocks and refer to **Figs. 8 and 9**.
4. Connect 4-1 blue/yellow control unit wire in series as follows:
   a. Cut blue PCM wire about 2.76 inches from C248 connector 1E terminal.
   b. Connect blue/yellow control unit wire to main harness side of cut blue PCM wire.
   c. Connect blue control unit wire to connector side of cut blue PCM wire.

PIN REFERENCE CHART			
Kit Wire Color	PIN (Connector #)	PCM Module Wire Color	Function
Blue	1E (C248) at PCM module side	Circuit 746 (Blue)	MIL Output
Blue/Yellow	1E (C248) at main harness side	Circuit 746 (Blue)	MIL Output
Black	3B (C246)	Circuit 59 (Black)	Module Ground
Red/Black	1B (C248)	Circuit 702 (Red/Black)	PCM Power
Red/White	1I (C248)	Circuit 715 (Red/White)	Data Link Connector
Blue/White	2O (C247)	Circuit 717 (Blue/Black)	Canister Purge Solenoid Output

FMA009400010000X

Fig. 8   Control unit kit installation. 1993 Probe

5. Connect 4-2 black control unit wire in parallel to black PCM wire from C246 connector 3B terminal.
6. Connect 4-3 red/black control unit wire in parallel to red/black PCM wire from connector C248 terminal 1B.
7. Connect 4-4 red/white control unit wire in parallel to red/white PCM wire from connector C248 terminal 1I.
8. Connect 4-5 blue/white control unit wire in parallel to blue/black PCM wire from connector C247 terminal 2O.
9. Connect control unit wire connector to control unit, then PCM connector to PCM.
10. Mount control unit on top PCM with electrical tape.
11. Reroute control unit connector wiring to prevent interference with or from other components.
12. Install center console.

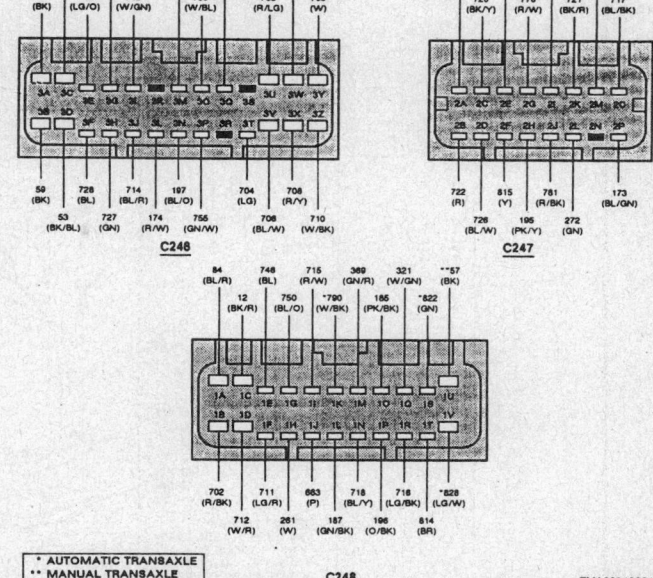

Fig. 9   Kit harness wire connection. 1993 Probe

BUCKING OR JERKING DURING COAST-DOWN
1993 COUGAR & THUNDERBIRD
w/5.0L/V8-302 ENGINE

These models built between Aug. 1, 1993, and Sept. 6, 1993, may buck and jerk during declaration coast down lasting more than five seconds from 50 mph.

This condition may be caused by powertrain control module (PCM) operating strategy. To correct this condition, install revised calibration PCM (Federal models, part No. F3PZ-12A650-CA; California models, part No. F3PZ-12A650-DA).

NO START, HARD START, HIGH IDLE, MIL ON, EARLY OR LATE SHIFTING
1993 MARK VIII
w/4.6L/V8-281 ENGINE

These models may have hard to start or no start condition, malfunction indicator light (MIL) may be on, transmission shifting may be erratic or idle may be high.

This condition may be caused by water entering throttle position sensor. To correct this condition install new sensor (part No. F2AZ-9B989-A) and water shield (part No. F3LY-9S557-A) as follows:
1. Remove engine appearance cover, then disconnect intake air tempera-

ture sensor and PCV closure hose.
2. Remove air inlet assembly from throttle body, then disconnect throttle and speed control cables.
3. Disconnect vacuum fitting and remove throttle body bolts, then disconnect throttle position sensor electrical connection and remove throttle body.
4. Remove and discard throttle position sensor gasket.
5. Install new throttle position sensor, then slide throttle position sensor bottom end into water shield and pull top over sensor.
6. Apply small liquid adhesive amount to each corner of new throttle body gasket and lay align on intake manifold.
7. Connect throttle position sensor electrical connector.
8. Install throttle body onto intake manifold and **torque** bolts to 6.0–8.8 ft. lbs.
9. Connect speed control, throttle cables and install vacuum fitting(s).
10. Install air inlet assembly, then reconnect intake air temperature sensor and PCV closure hose.
11. Install engine appearance cover.

LACK OF POWER IN LOS
1993 MARK VIII
w/4.6L/V8-281 ENGINE & 4R70W AUTOMATIC TRANSMISSION

On these Federal models built before February 16, 1993, and California models built before March 3, 1993, engine may lack power when performing in limited operating strategy (LOS). Engine will operate in LOS when vehicle wiring harness is disconnected from transmission, if powertrain control model (PCM) detects open or short in electronic pressure control (EPC) circuit or electronically controlled transmission tester is used to diagnose transmission condition.

This condition may be caused by PCM

program. To correct this condition, install revised PCM (Federal model, part No. F3LY-12A650-AD; California model, part No. F3LY-12A650-CD).

DETONATION, MIL ON, DTC 332
1993-95 4.6L/V8-281 ENGINE

On 1993-95 Town Car, 1993-95 Crown Victoria and Grand Marquis, and 1994-95 Cougar and Thunderbird models, there may be detonation and/or Malfunction Indicator Lamp (MIL) may be on during normal driving with diagnostic trouble code (DTC) 332 stored.

This condition may be caused by carbon buildup in exhaust gas recirculation (EGR) intake manifold (throttle body base) groove. To correct this condition, proceed as follows:
1. Perform "DL" pinpoint test. **Refer to "Computerized Engine Controls" for diagnosis and testing.**
2. If condition still exists, perform EGR system diagnosis. **Refer to "Computerized Engine Controls" for diagnosis and testing.**
3. If engine RPM does not change during "EGR 3" in above procedure and EGR valve checks OK, check EGR passage between intake manifold and throttle body for carbon build up.
4. If carbon build up is evident, proceed as follows:
   a. Remove throttle adapter from intake manifold and cover opening, **Fig. 10.**
   b. Remove carbon form intake manifold EGR groove and sealing surfaces with chisel.
   c. Brush carbon away, then wash EGR groove and adapter surface with suitable solvent.
   d. Replace intake manifold-to-throttle body adapter gasket, then install throttle body and adapter.

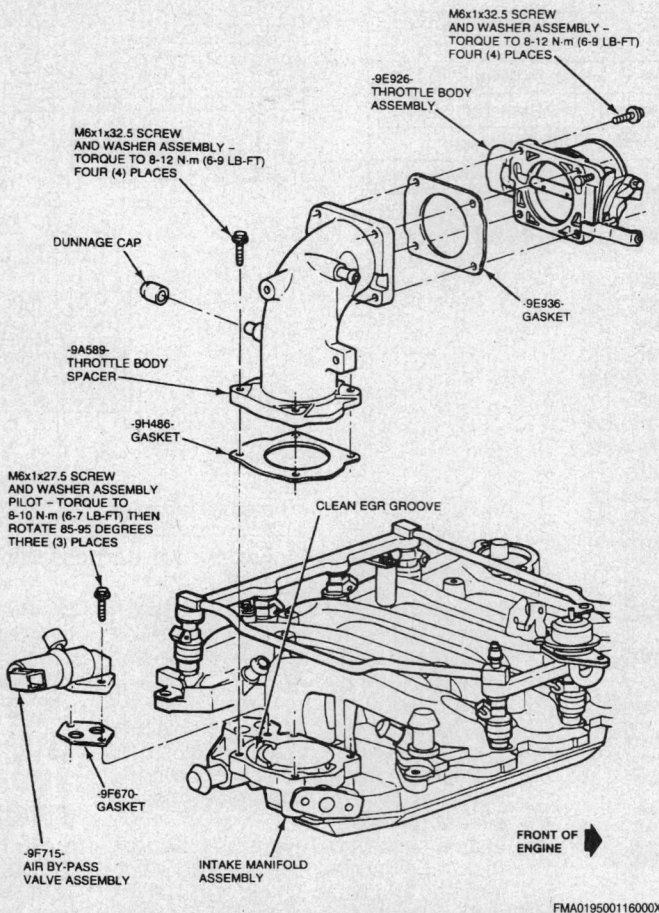

M6x1x32.5 SCREW
AND WASHER ASSEMBLY –
TORQUE TO 8-12 N·m (6-9 LB-FT)
FOUR (4) PLACES

-9E926-
THROTTLE BODY
ASSEMBLY

M6x1x32.5 SCREW
AND WASHER ASSEMBLY –
TORQUE TO 8-12 N·m (6-9 LB-FT)
FOUR (4) PLACES

DUNNAGE CAP

-9E936-
GASKET

-9A589-
THROTTLE BODY
SPACER

-9H486-
GASKET

M6x1x27.5 SCREW
AND WASHER ASSEMBLY
PILOT – TORQUE TO
8-10 N·m (6-7 LB-FT) THEN
ROTATE 85-95 DEGREES
THREE (3) PLACES

CLEAN EGR GROOVE

-9F670-
GASKET

FRONT OF
ENGINE

-9F715-
AIR BY-PASS
VALVE ASSEMBLY

INTAKE MANIFOLD
ASSEMBLY

FMA019500116000X

**Fig. 10   Throttle adapter removal. 1994–95
4.6L/V8-281 engine**

ABBREVIATIONS & ACRONYMS

A/C: Air Conditioning
A/T: Automatic Transaxle/Transmission
ACC: Air Conditioning Clutch
ACCS: Air Conditioning Cyclic Switch
ACD: Air Conditioning Demand
ACON: Air Conditioning On
ACP: Air Conditioning Pressure
ACPSW: Air Conditioning Pressure Switch
ACR: A/C Relay
ACT: Air Charge Temperature
ACV: (Thermactor) Air Control Valve
AIR BPV: (Thermactor) Air Bypass Valve
AIR: Secondary Air Injection
AIRB: Secondary Air Injection Bypass
AIRD: Secondary Air Injection Diverter
AM1: Thermactor Air Management 1 (TAB)
AM2: Thermactor Air Management 2 (TAB Or TAD)
AOD: Automatic Overdrive Transmission
AODE-W: Automatic Overdrive Electronic Wide Ratio Transmission
AODE: Automatic Overdrive Electronic Transmisson
ARC: Automatic Ride Control
ATD: After Top Dead Center
AVOM: Analog Volt-Ohm Meter
AXODE: Automatic Overdrive Electronic Transaxle
B + : Battery Postive Voltage
BARO: Barometric Pressure
BLMT: Blower Motor Switch
BLR: Blower
BOB: Breakout Box
BOO: Brake On/Off
BP: Barometric Pessure Sensor
BPA: Bypass Air
BTDC: Before Top Dead Center
CAC: Charge Air Cooler
CANP: Canister Purge
CBD: Closed Bowl Distributor
CCC: Converter Clutch Control Solenoid
CCD: Computer Controlled Dwell
CCO: Converter Clutch Overdrive lenoid
CCPS: Clutch Cycling Switch
CCRM: Constant Control Relay Module
CCS: Coast Clutch Solenoid
CD4E: Chain Driven Four-Speed Electronic Transaxle
CES: Clutch Engage Switch
CID: Cubic Inch Displacement
CID: Cylinder Identification
CKP: Crankshaft Position
CKP1: Crankshaft Position Sensor No. 1
CKP2: Crankshaft Position Sensor No. 2
CKPRTN: Crankshaft Position Sensor Signal Return
CLC: Converter Lock-Up Clutch
CMP: Camshaft Position
CO2: Carbon Dioxide
CO: Carbon Monoxide

COC: Conv_____ Or_____ lyst
CONV: Co_____
CPP: Clutch Pedal P_____
CSE GND: Case Groun_
CV: Canister Vent
CVS: Control/Vent Solenoids
DATA + : Data Positive
DATA-: Data Negative
DCL: Data Communications Link
DEF: Defroster
DI: Distributor Ignition
DIS: Distributorless Ignition
DLC: Data Link Connector
DMIVA: Distributor Mounted Vacuum Advance
DOHC: Dual Overhead Cam
DOL: Data Output Line
DPDIS: Dual Plug Distributorless Ignition
DPFE: Differential Pressure Feedback EGR
DPI: Dual Plug Inhibit
DRL: Daytime Running Lamps
DSC: Duty Cycle Solenoid
DSS: Downshift Solenoid
DTC: Diagnostic Trouble Code
DTM: Diagnostic Test Mode
DV TW: Delay Valve Two-Way
DV: Delay Valve
DVOM: Digital Volt-Ohm Meter
E4OD: Electronic 4-Speed Overdrive Transmission
EAIR: Electronic Secondary Air Injection
EAP: Electric Air Pump
ECA: Electronic Control Assembly
ECT: Engine Coolant Temperature
EDF: Electro Drive Fan
EDIS: Electronic Distributorless Ignition
EEC-IV: Fourth Generation EEC System
EEC-V: Fifth Generation EEC System
EEC: Electronic Engine Control
EEGR: Electronic EGR Valve
EFT: Fuel Temperature In Fuel Rail
EGO: Exhaust Gas Oxygen Sensor
EGR: Exhaust Gas Recirculation
EGRC: Exhaust Gas Recirculation Control Solenoid
EGRM: Exhaust Gas Recirculation Modulator Sensor Signal
EGRT: EGR Temperature
EGRV: Exhaust Gas Recirculation Vent Solenoid
EI: Electronic Ignition
EPC: Electronic Pressure Control
EPT: EGR Pressure Transducer
EVAP: Evaporative Emission
EVP: EGR Valve Position
EVR: EGR Vacuum Regulator
FC: Fan Control
FF: Flexible Fuel
FMEM: Failure Mode Effects Management
FP: Fuel Pump
FPDM: Fuel Pump Driver Module
FPM: Fuel Pump Monitor
FPRC: Fuel Pressure Regulator Control
FTP: Fuel Tank Pressure

_____nt Wheel Drive
_____overnor Control Module
_____Generator
_____Ground
GVW: Gross Vehicle Weight
HC: Hydrocarbon
HDL: Headlamp
HEDF: High Electro Drive Fan
HEGO: Heated Exhaust Gas Oxygen Sensor
HFC: High Fan Control
HFP: High Fuel Pump
HLOS: Hardware Limited Operating Strategy
HO2S: Heated Oxygen Sensor
HO: High Output
HSC: High Swirl Combustion
HSIA: High Speed Inlet Air
IAC: Idle Air Control
IAT: Intake Air Temperature
ICM: Ignition Control Module
IDM: Ignition Diagnostic Monitor
IFS: Inertia Fuel Shutoff
IGN GND: Ignition Ground
IMRC: Intake Manifold Runner Control
IMT: Intake Manifold Tuning
INJ: Injector
IP: Pressure Of Fuel In Fuel Rail
IRCM: Integrated Relay Control Module
ISC: Idle Speed Control
ITS: Idle Tracking Switch
KAM: Keep Alive Memory
KAPWR: Keep Alive Power
KC: Knock Control
KOEO: Key On Engine Off
KOER: Key On Engine Running
KS: Knock Sensor
L: Liters
LFC: Low Fan Control
LFP: Low Fuel Pump
LPS: Line Pressure Solenoid
LUS: Lock-Up Solenoid
M/T: Manual Transaxle/Transmission
MC-VAF: Measuring Core-Volume Air Flow Sensor
MAF RTN: Mass Air Flow Return
MAF: Mass Air Flow
MAP: Manifold Absolute Pressure
MAPPA: Manifold Absolute Pressure Per Altitude
MCU: Microprocessor Control Unit
MD: Misfire Detection
MFI: Multiport Fuel Injection
MIL: Malfunction Indicator Lamp
MLP: Manual Lever Position
NAAO: North American Automotive Operations
NC: Normally Closed
NDS: Neutral Drive Switch
NG: Natural Gas
NGS: New Generation Star Tester
NO: Normally Open
NOX: Nitrous Oxides
O2S: Oxygen Sensor
OASIS: Online Automotive Service Information System
OBD: On-Board Diagnostic
OBD II: Second Generation On-Board Diagnostic

Ford - Abbreviations & Acronyms

OC: Oxidation Catalytic Converter
OCT ADJ: Octane Adjust
OHC: Overhead Cam
PAIR: Pulsed Secondary Air Injection
PCM: Powertrain Control Module
PCV: Positive Crankcase Ventilation
PGC: Power & Ground Connection
PFE: Pressure Feedback EGR
PID: Parameter Identification
PF: Purge Flow
PIP: Profile Ignition Pickup
PNP: Park/Neutral Position
PSOM: Programmable Speedometer/Odometer Module
PSP: Power Steering Pressure
PSPS: Power Steering Pressure Switch
PWRGND: Power Ground
RABS: Rear Anti-Lock Brake System
REDOX: Reduction Oxidation Catalytic Converter
RM: Relay Module
ROM: Read Only Memory
RPM: Engine RPM
RTN: Return
RTS1: Reduce Torque Signal No. 1
RTS2: Reduce Torque Signal No. 2
RWD: Rear Wheel Drive
SC: Supercharged
SCG: Solenoid Controlled By Ground
SCP: Solenoid Controlled By Power
SCPP: Statert Clutch Pedal Position
SCVAC: Speed Control Vacuum Solenoid
SD: Speed Density

SDV: Spark Delay Valve
SFI: Sequential Multiport Fuel Injection
SHO: Super High Output
SIG RTN: Signal Return
SIL: Shift Indicator Lamp
SML: Switch Monitor Lamp
SPOUT: Spark Output
SS: Shift Solenoid
SS1: Shift Solenoid No. 1
SS2: Shift Solenoid No. 2
SS3: Shift Solenoid No. 3
ST: Scan Tool
STI: Self-Test Input
STO: Self-Test Output
STP: Switch To Power
TA: Traction Assist
TAB: Thermactor Air Bypass Vacuum Solenoid Valve
TACH: Tachometer
TAD: Thermactor Air Diverter Vacuum Solenoid Valve
TB: Throttle Body
TC: Traction Control
TCC: Torque Converter Clutch
TCM: Transaxle Control Module
TCIL: Transmission Control Indicator Lamp
TCS: Transmission Control Switch
TFI-IV: Thick Film Integrated IV Ignition
TI3: Transistorized Ignition 3-Pin
TI5: Transistorized Ignition 5-Pin
TOT: Transmission Oil Temperature
TP: Throttle Position
TPS: Throttle Position Sensor

TPOUT: Throttle Position Output
TR: Transmission Range
TRD: Transmission Range Drive
TRL: Transmission Range Low
TROD: Transmission Range Overdrive
TRR: Transmission Range Reverse
TSB: Technical Service Bulletin
TSS: Transmission Speed Sensor
TWC + OC: Three-Way + Oxidation Catalytic Converter
TWC: Three-Way Catalytic Converter
VAF: Vane Air Flow
VAT: Vane Air Temperature
VCRM: Variable Control Relay Module
VECI Label: Vehicle Emission Control Information Label
VLCM: Variable Load Control Module
VOM: Volt-Ohm Meter
VPWR: Vehicle Power
VREF: Reference Voltage
VRIS1: Variable Resonance Induction System No. 1 Solenoid
VRIS2: Variable Resonance Induction System No. 2 Solenoid
VSS: Vehicle Speed Sensor
VST: Vehicle Start
WAC: Wide Open Throttle A/C Cutoff
WOT: Wide Open Throttle
WU-OC: Warm-Up Oxidation Catalytic Converter
WU-TWC: Warm-Up Thee-Way Catalytic Converter
4EAT: 4-Speed Electronic Automatic Transaxle

Manual Information Locator

WITHDRAWN

Operation/Subject/Topic	Auto Repair Manual	Auto Engine Performance & Driveability (Tune Up & Electronics) Manual	Operation/Subject/Topic	Auto Repair Manual	Auto Engine Performance & Driveability (Tune Up & Electronics) Manual
Air Bags	X	—	Drive Belt Tension Data	X	—
Air Conditioning	X	—	Drum Brake Service	X	—
AIR Systems	—	X	EGR System	—	X
All-Wheel Drive Systems	X	—	Electric Engine Cooling Fans	X	—
Alternator Specifications	X	—	Electric Fuel Pumps	X	X
Alternator Systems	X	—	Electrical Symbol Identification	X	X
Anti-Lock Brake Systems	X	—	Electronic Fuel Injection	—	X
Automatic Transaxle In-Vehicle Service	X	—	Electronic Ignition	—	X
Automatic Transmission In-Vehicle Service	X	—	Electronic Instrumentation	—	X
Axle Shaft Service	X	—	Electronic Level Controls	X	—
Back-Up Light Switch, Replace	X	—	Emission Control Application Charts	—	X
Balance Shaft Service	X	—	Emission Controls	—	X
Ball Joint Service	X	—	Emission Vacuum Hose Routings	—	X
Belt Tension Data	X	—	Engine Compartment Reference Diagrams	—	X
Blower Motor, Replace	X	—	Engine Cooling Fans	X	—
Brake Booster Service	X	—	Engine Control Module, Replace	—	X
Brake Service	X	—	Engine Control Unit, Replace	—	X
Camber Adjustment	X	—	Engine Front Cover Service	X	—
Camshaft Service	X	—	Engine Mounts, Replace	X	—
Capacity Data	X	—	Engine Oil Seal Service	X	—
Carburetors	—	X	Engine Rebuilding Specifications	X	—
Caster Adjustment	X	—	Engine Repairs	X	—
Catalytic Converters	—	X	Engine Sensor Location	—	X
Clutch Service	X	—	Engine Sensor Replacement	—	X
Clutch Start Switch, Replace	X	—	Engine Sensor Specifications	—	X
Coil Pack, Replace	X	X	Engine Specifications	X	—
Coil Spring, Replace	X	—	Engine System Identification Charts	—	X
Compression Check	X	X	Engine Tightening Specifications	X	—
Compression Pressures	X	X	Engine, Replace	X	—
Computer Relearn Procedures	—	X	Evaporator Core, Replace	X	—
Computer System Diagnostics	—	X	Exhaust Gas Recirculation (EGR) Systems	—	X
Computer System Identification	—	X	Exhaust Manifold, Replace	X	—
Computer Terminal Connector Identification	—	X	Fast Idle Speed Adjustment	—	X
Computerized Engine Control Systems	—	X	Feedback Carburetors	—	X
Control Arm Service	X	—	Flasher Location	X	—
Cooling System Bleed	X	—	Front Drive Axle Service	X	—
Cooling System Data	X	—	Front Wheel Alignment	X	—
Crankshaft Pulley, Replace	X	—	Fuel Control System Identification	—	X
Crankshaft Rear Oil Seal Service	X	—	Fuel Filter, Replace	X	—
Cruise Control Systems	X	—	Fuel Injection Systems	—	X
Cylinder Block Specifications	X	—	Fuel Injector Cleaning Procedures	—	X
Cylinder Head Service	X	—	Fuel Injector, Replace	—	X
Cylinder Head Specifications	X	—	Fuel Pump Pressure Specifications	X	X
Cylinder Head, Replace	X	—	Fuel Pump Pressure Test	—	X
Cylinder Liner, Replace	X	—	Fuel Pump Relay Location	X	X
Dash Panel Service	X	—	Fuel Pump Replacement	X	X
Differential Service	X	—	Fuse Panel Location	X	—
Dimmer Switch, Replace	X	—	General Engine Specifications	X	—
Disc Brake Service	X	—	Headlight Switch, Replace	X	—
Distributor Service	—	X	Heated Air Cleaners	—	X
Distributor, Replace	X	X			
Distributorless Ignition Systems	—	X			
Drive Axle Service	X	—			

DECIMAL & MILLIMETER EQUIVALENTS

INCH	INCH	MM	INCH	INCH	MM	INCH	INCH	MM
1/64	.015625	.397	23/64	.359375	9.128	11/16	.6875	17.462
1/32	.03125	.794	3/8	.375	9.525	45/64	.703125	17.859
3/64	.046875	1.191	25/64	.390625	9.922	23/32	.71875	18.265
1/16	.0625	1.587	13/32	.40625	10.319	47/64	.734375	18.653
5/64	.078125	1.984	27/64	.421875	10.716	3/4	.75	19.050
3/32	.09375	2.381	7/16	.4375	11.113	49/64	.765625	19.447
7/64	.109375	2.778	29/64	.453125	11.509	25/32	.78125	19.884
1/8	.125	3.175	15/32	.46875	11.906	51/64	.796875	20.240
9/64	.140625	3.572	31/64	.484375	12.303	13/16	.8125	20.637
5/32	.15625	3.969	1/2	.5	12.700	53/64	.828125	21.034
11/64	.171875	4.366	33/64	.515625	13.097	27/32	.84375	21.431
3/16	.1875	4.762	17/32	.53125	13.494	55/64	.859375	21.828
13/64	.203125	5.159	35/64	.546875	13.890	7/8	.875	22.225
7/32	.21875	5.556	9/16	.5625	14.287	57/64	.890625	22.622
15/64	.234375	5.953	37/64	.578125	14.684	29.32	.90625	23.019
1/4	.25	6.350	19/32	.59375	15.081	59/64	.921875	23.415
17/64	.265625	6.747	39/64	.609375	15.478	15/16	.9375	23.812
9/32	.28125	7.144	5/8	.625	15.875	61/64	.953125	24.209
19/64	.296875	7.541	41/64	.640625	16.272	31/32	.96875	24.606
5/16	.3125	7.937	21/32	.65625	16.669	63/64	.984375	25.003
21/64	.328125	8.334	43/64	.671875	17.065	1		25.400
11/32	.34375	8.731						

Special Service Tools

Throughout this manual references are made to and illustrations may depict the use of special tools required to perform certain jobs. These special tools can generally be ordered through the dealers of the make vehicle being serviced. It is also suggested that you check with local automotive supply firms as they also supply tools manufactured by other firms that will assist in the performance of these jobs. The vehicle manufacturers special tools are supplied by:

Chrysler Corporation .... Miller Special Tools
SPX Corporation
12842 Farmington Rd.
Livonia, Michigan 48150

Ford Motor Company .... Owatonna Tool Company
Owatonna, Minnesota 55060

General Motors .... Kent-Moore
SPX Corporation
29784 Little Mack
Roseville. Michigan 48066